TABLE OF CONTENTS

This edition of the MOTOR Imported Car Repair & Engine Performance Manual, covers specifications and service procedures on 1998-2001 Audi, BMW, Jaguar, Land Rover, Mercedes-Benz, Porsche, Saab, Volkswagen and Volvo models available at time of publication. For service information on Acura, Daewoo, Honda, Hyundai, Infiniti, Isuzu, Kia, Lexus and Mazda, refer to MOTOR Imported Car Repair Manual Vol 1 or Imported Engine Performance & Driveability Manual Vol 1. For service information on Mitsubishi, Nissan, Subaru, Suzuki and Toyota models, refer to MOTOR Imported Car Repair Manual Vol 2 or Imported Engine Performance & Driveability Manual Vol 2. Data is subject to change.

This manual is divided into three sections by two tabs. The section before Tab 1 covers How To Use This Manual, Vehicle Identification, Computer Relearn Procedures, Air Bag System Precautions, Service Reminder & Warning Lamp Reset Procedures, Air Quality Standards, Vehicle Lift Points, Electrical Symbol & Wire Color Code Identification and Vehicle Maintenance Schedules. Tab 1 covers service information on Chassis & Mechanical Systems. Tab 2 covers service information on Engine Performance & Driveability.

Page No.

DECIMAL & MILLIMETER EQUIVALENTS, Inside Rear Cover

MANUAL INFORMATION LOCATOR, Inside Rear Cover

HOW TO USE THIS MANUAL 0-1

VEHICLE IDENTIFICATION 0-3

COMPUTER RELEARN PROCEDURES 0-10

AIR BAG SYSTEM PRECAUTIONS 0-12

SERVICE REMINDER & WARNING LAMP RESET PROCEDURES 0-14

AIR QUALITY STANDARDS 0-23

VEHICLE LIFT POINTS 0-24

ELECTRICAL SYMBOL & WIRE COLOR CODE IDENTIFICATION 0-33

VEHICLE MAINTENANCE SCHEDULES 0-45

CHASSIS & MECHANICAL SYSTEMS:

	Tab	Page No.
Audi	1	1-1
BMW	1	2-1
Jaguar	1	3-1
Land Rover	1	4-1
Mercedes-Benz	1	5-1
Porsche	1	6-1
Saab	1	7-1
Volkswagen	1	8-1
Volvo	1	9-1

ENGINE PERFORMANCE & DRIVEABILITY:

	Tab	Page No.
Audi	2	10-1
BMW	2	11-1
Jaguar...	[illegible]	[illegible]2-1
Land Rov[illegible]	[illegible]	[illegible]3-1
Mercede[illegible]	[illegible]	[illegible]-1
Porsche ...	[illegible]	[illegible]5-1
Saab	2	16-1
Volkswagen	2	17-1
Volvo	2	18-1

MOTOR
INFORMATION SYSTEMS

IMPORTED CAR REPAIR & ENGINE PERFORMANCE MANUAL

2nd Edition

First Printing

MOTOR
INFORMATION SYSTEMS

MOTOR is a trademark of Hearst Business Publishing, Inc.

Published by Motor Information Systems, a division of Hearst Business Publishing, Inc. A Unit Of The Hearst Corporation

5600 Crooks Road, Troy, MI 48098
Printed in the U.S.A.

ISBN 1-58251-098-9

HOW TO USE THIS MANUAL

Be aware of the possibility that replacement underhood labels may be incorrect for the application. Replacement labels may be more current than this publication. Check for existing Technical Service Bulletins (TSBs) and emission recall notices. Some states may fasten an official "Engine Identification" label to the vehicle if it has had an engine change, if it is a kit-car, or gray-market car, or for other reasons. If so, observe the ECS information on the state-installed label.

It is the technician's responsibility to cross-check available information sources. If a discrepancy exists between label information on the vehicle and this publication, the vehicle appears to be as originally equipped, and you are unable to make a positive determination or are unfamiliar with the vehicle to be tested, refer the motorist to a dealership or other inspection facility specializing in that make of vehicle. If a conflict still exists in determining the required ECS, refer the motorist to the state's referee facility for verification.

You may contact MOTOR at 1-800-4A MOTOR to report errors or missing information.

WHAT IS CONTAINED IN THIS MANUAL

This manual is separated into two categories, Mechanical & Chassis Service and Engine Performance & Driveability. The Mechanical & Chassis Service information contains mechanical specifications, engine, brakes, drive axles, transmission and many other categories. The Engine Performance & Driveability portion contains specifications, diagnostic and service procedures related to fuel, ignition, emissions, engine control and other electronic automotive systems. A listing of individual systems and procedures can be found in the index on the first page of each chapter.

The following information covers the Engine Performance & Driveability portion of this manual.

GETTING STARTED

All testing should begin with verification of the customer complaint and a basic visual inspection. Successful isolation of a specific problem in a suspected system must follow a thorough and logical approach.

Before performing any detailed system diagnostics, review the various manufacturer's Technical Service Bulletin (TSB) information found in that chapter. The TSBs are listed according to symptom and vehicle application. Many times, you will find that driveability complaints can be readily identified and easily repaired using information contained in this section.

If a basic vehicle inspection and a check of the TSBs leaves the problem unresolved, further testing will be necessary.

The following outline divides this manual into three categories; Engine Control Systems, Related Information and Additional Features.

For immediate access to frequently-used information, each manufacturer chapter includes a Quick reference chart. These charts, located on the first page of each chapter allow easy access to information, such as accessing diagnostic trouble codes, diagnostic chart index, fuel pressure and compression pressure, ignition coil and sensor specifications.

ENGINE CONTROL SYSTEMS

ENGINE SYSTEMS IDENTIFICATION

Before beginning any diagnostic work on a vehicle, the vehicle as well as its engine and related systems must be properly identified. This step is **the key to successful diagnosis and repair.**

Presented in chart form, the Engine Systems Identification will identify the Fuel, Ignition and Computer system used on the vehicle an direct you to the specific page that information on each system can be found.

To verify the engine used in the vehicle, check the Engine Code in the Vehicle Identification Number (VIN). If you are unfamiliar with the VIN system, consult the Vehicle Identification section found in the front of the manual.

COMPUTERIZED ENGINE CONTROLS

On some models, information found in this section will include fuel and ignition system testing not found in those sections. Use the information in this section if the fuel or ignition system is suspect and you have been directed here from the Engine Systems Identification Chart of referred from another section.

IGNITION SYSTEMS

Information found in this section includes testing and servicing of the ignition system and its components. Use the information in this section if the ignition system is suspect and you have been directed here from the Engine Systems Identification Chart of referred from another section.

CARBURETED FUEL SYSTEMS

If a fuel problem has been suspected on a carburetor-equipped vehicle, this section provides the necessary testing and repair information. Here you will find diagnosis and testing for the Control System (if applicable) and service procedures for the carburetor.

FUEL INJECTION

Information found in the section includes, troubleshooting, testing and servicing of the fuel system and its components. Use the information in this section if the fuel system is suspect and you have been directed here from the Engine Systems Identification Chart or referred from another section.

RELATED INFORMATION

TUNE UP SPECIFICATIONS

These charts provide basic tune up specifications including spark plug gap, ignition timing, idle speeds and fuel pump pressure. Illustrations of firing orders and timing marks are also included.

ENGINE PERFORMANCE & TUNE UP

These sections are grouped by engine configuration. Gasoline engine sections offer procedures for such maintenance routines as measuring compression pressures, spark plug replacement and fuel injector cleaning. Also included in these sections are valve, throttle position sensor, idle speed and mixture adjustments.

Diesel engine sections offer procedures for such maintenance routines as measuring compression pressures and injection nozzle pressures. Also included in these sections are valve, injection pump timing and idle speed mixture adjustments.

ELECTRIC FUEL PUMP

Diagnosis, testing and servicing procedures for the electric fuel pump system can be found in this section. Also included are specifications and fuel system pressure relief procedures.

TURBOCHARGERS & SUPERCHARGERS

Descriptions, troubleshooting and service procedures for turbochargers and superchargers can be found in this section.

EMISSION CONTROL SYSTEM APPLICATIONS CHARTS & VACUUM HOSE ROUTINGS

Application charts provide a quick reference for identifying the emission control systems and devices used on a vehicle. The accompanying vacuum hose routings provide a visual references to these devices and systems and their installation on the vehicle. Together, this information may be used for inspection, vacuum line rerouting or tracing components that may not be readily visible.

ENGINE COMPARTMENT REFERENCE DIAGRAMS

This section will help to readily identify various fuel, ignition and emission-related components on the vehicle. These illustrations are intended to avoid wasted time when searching for components that require servicing.

EMISSION CONTROLS

After consulting the Emission Control Systems Application Chart, detailed system information can be found in this section. Information includes descriptions, testing and servicing procedures.

ADDITIONAL FEATURES

VEHICLE IDENTIFICATION

Located in the front of this manual, Vehicle Identification provides a handy reference for identifying specific characteristics of the vehicle.

COMPUTER RELEARN PROCEDURES

Computer relearn procedures can be found in this section, located in the front of the manual.

AIR BAG SYSTEM PRECAUTIONS

Air bag system arming and disarming procedures can be found in this section, located in the front of the manual.

AIR QUALITY STANDARDS

This section, located in the front of this manual, includes the latest available standards for vehicle emission testing.

VEHICLE LIFT POINTS

This section, located in the front of this manual, contains information on vehicle lift point illustrations.

VEHICLE MAINTENANCE SCHEDULES

Located in the front of this manual, Vehicle Maintenance Schedules provides a handy reference of identifying factory-recommended maintenance operations and service intervals.

ELECTRICAL SYMBOL & WIRE COLOR CODE IDENTIFICATION

Throughout this manual, many wiring diagrams and schematics are used. The Electrical Symbol Identification & Wiring Color Code information, found in the front of this book provides explanations of the various symbols and wire color abbreviations used in the diagrams.

SERVICE REMINDER & WARNING LAMP RESET PROCEDURES

This section, located in the front of the manual, includes illustrated procedures for resetting the various service reminder and warning lamps.

ELECTRONIC INSTRUMENTATION

This section provides diagnosis and testing for electronic instrumentation.

VEHICLE IDENTIFICATION

INDEX

	PAGE NO.	FIG. NO.
AUDI	0-3	1
BMW	0-4	2
JAGUAR	0-5	3
LAND ROVER	0-6	4
MERCEDES-BENZ	0-6	5
PORSCHE	0-7	6
SAAB	0-8	7
VOLKSWAGEN	0-8	8
VOLVO	0-9	9

1st Thru 3rd POSITION
MANUFACTURER CODE
WAU = Europe Passenger Car
TRU = Hungary Passenger Car

4th POSITION
BODY TYPE
A = 100 Base (92-94)
A = Cabriolet (95-98)
A = A8 (97-98)
A = A4 (2000)
A = A8 3.7 (1999)
A = A6 (1998-99)
B = 100 Custom (1991)
B = 100 S (92-94)
B = V8 Quattro (92-94)
B = 90 S (93-95)
B = Cabriolet (94-95)
B = A4 (97-99)
B = A6 (00)
B = A6 Quattro (1998-99)
B = A8 (1997)
B = A8 Quattro (1998-99)
C = 100 Quattro (1991)
C = 100 S Wagon (1994)
C = 90 Quattro (1995)
C = A4 Quattro (97-99)
D = A4 (96-99)
D = A4 Quattro (2000)
D = A6 Avant Quattro
D = 100 CS (92-94)
D = 90 CS (93-94)
D = 90 Sport (1995)
E = A4 Quatto (96-99)
E = A6 Quattro (00)
E = 80 Custom (1991)
E = 80 Base (1992)
E = 90 Quattro (93-94)
E = 90 Sport Quattro (1995)
E = 100 Quattro (92-94)
F = 80 Quattro (91-92)
F = 100 Wagon (92-94)
F = 200 Custom (1991)
F = A4 Avant (1999)
F = A6 (95-97)
F = A8 4.2 Quattro (00)
G = 90 Custom (1991)
G = 200 Quattro (1991)
G = Coupe Quattro (1991)
A = A4 Avant Quattro (99)
G = A6 Quattro (95-97)
H = 90 Quattro (1991)
H = 200 Wagon (1991)
H = S4 Quattro (92-94)
H = A6 Wagon (95-97)
H = A4 Avant (00) US Only
J = A6 Wagon Quattro (95-98)
K = V8 Quattro (1991)
K = S6 (1995)
K = S6 (1997) Canada Only
K = A4 Avant Quattro US Only (00)
L = S6 Wagon (1995)
L = A6 Avant Quattro (00)
R= S4 Quattro (00)
T = TT Coupe (2000)
U = TT Quattro (2000)
Z = A6 4.2 (00)

5th POSITION
ENGINE CODE
CABRIOLET
A = 2771cc 172hp 6 Cyl
L = 2771cc 172hp 6 Cyl
COUPE QUATTRO
E = 2309cc 164hp 5 Cyl, Federal
F = 2309cc 164hp 5 Cyl, California
A4
A = 2771cc 172hp 6 Cyl
B = 1781cc 150hp 4 Cyl
C = 1781cc 150hp 4Cyl
D = 2771cc 190hp 6 Cyl
H = 2771cc 193hp 6 Cyl
A6
A = 2771cc 172hp 6 Cyl
A = 2771cc 200hp 6 Cyl
B = 2771cc 172hp 6 Cyl
C = 2771cc 172hp 6 Cyl, California
D = 2671cc 250hp 6 cyl
H = 2771cc 200hp 6 Cyl
L = 4172cc 310hp 8 Cyl
A8
F = 3697cc 230hp 8 Cyl
G = 4172cc 300hp 8 Cyl
L = 4172cc 310hp 8 Cyl
S4
D = 267cc 250hp 6 Cyl
S4 QUATTRO
P = 2226cc 227hp 5 Cyl, Federal
Q = 2226cc 227hp 5 Cyl, California
R = 2226cc 227hp 5 Cyl
S6
A = 2226cc 227hp 5 Cyl
TT
C/S = 1781cc 180hp 4 Cyl
V8 QUATTRO
E = 3562cc 240hp 8 Cyl
V = 4200cc 276hp 8 Cyl, Federal
W = 4200cc 276hp 8 Cyl
80 & 90
A = 2771cc 172hp 6 Cyl
C = 2309cc 130hp 5 Cyl, Federal
D = 2309cc 130hp 5 Cyl, California
E = 2309cc 164hp 5 Cyl, Federal
F = 2309cc 164hp 5 Cyl, California
J = 2771cc 172hp 6 Cyl, Federal
K = 2771cc 172hp 6 Cyl, California
100
C = 2309cc 130hp 5 Cyl
J = 2771cc 172hp 6 Cyl, Federal
K = 2771cc 172hp 6 Cyl, California
K = 2771cc 172hp 6 Cyl (1994)
200
D = 2226cc 162hp 5 Cyl
E = 2226cc 217hp 5 Cyl

6th POSITION
RESTRAINT SYSTEM
0 = Active
1 = Dr/Pass&Side bags w/FrHead bags (1999)
2 = Passive W/Manual Lap
2 = Dr/Pass&SideAirBagsDepwrd98-00
3 = Dr/pass AirBag + Fr&Rr Side AirBg
3 = Dr/pas AirBag + Fr&RrSideAirBag& Rr Side AirBag Dr/pass (00)Depwrd (1998)
4 = ELRA W/Manual Lap
4 = Driver & Pass AirBag Depwrd 1998
5 = Drivers Side Air Bag
5 = Dr/passAirBag+Fr/Sde bags&Fr Head AirBags
5 = Dr/Pass Front/Side& Rear AirBags Depwrd & Fr Dr/Pass Head Air Bag
6 = Dr/Pass&SideAirBagsDepwrd1998
7 = Dr/pass AirBag+Fr&Rr SideAir Bag Depowered (1998)
8 = Driver & Pass Air Bag
8 = Driver&Pass AirBag Depwrd 1998

7th & 8th POSITION
MODEL LINE
4A = 100 & S4
4A = A6 / S6
4A = A6 Wagon 1998
4B = A6 (00)
4C = V8
4D = A8(00)
8A = 80 & 90
8B = Coupe
8C = 90
8D = A4/S4 (00)
8G = Cabriolet
8N = TT (00)
44 = 100 & 200

9th POSITION
CHECK DIGIT

10th POSITION
MODEL YEAR
M = 1991
N = 1992
P = 1993
R = 1994
S = 1995
T = 1996
V = 1997
W = 1998
X = 1999
Y = 2000

11th POSITION
ASSEMBLY PLANT
A = Ingolstadt
E = Emden
G = Graz
H = Hanover
K = Osnabrueck
M = Mexico
N = Neckarsulm
P = Brazil
W = Wolfsburg

12th Thru 17th POSITION
PRODUCTION SEQUENCE NUMBER

AD1130100092000X

Fig. 1 Audi (Part 1 of 2)

1st Thru 3rd POSITION
MANUFACTURER CODE
WAU = Germany Passenger Car
TRU = Hungary Passenger Car

4th POSITION
BODY TYPE
A = A4
B = A6
D = A4 Quattro
E = A6 Quattro
F = A8 4.2 Quattro
G = S8
H = A4 Avant
K = A4 Avant Quattro
L = A6 Avant Quattro
M = A8 L 4.2 Quattro
R = S4
S = TT Coupe
T = TT Roadster
U = TT Roadster Quattro
W = TT Coupe Quattro
X = S4 Avant
Y = Allroad
Z = A6 4.2

5th POSITION
ENGINE CODE
Allroad
P = 2671cc 250hp 6 Cyl
A4
C = 1781cc 170hp 4Cyl
H = 2771cc 190hp 6 Cyl
A6
D = 2671cc 250hp 6 cyl
H = 2771cc 200hp 6 Cyl
L = 4172cc 300hp 8 Cyl
A8
L = 4172cc 310hp 8 Cyl
S4
D = 2671cc 250hp 6 Cyl
S8
U = 4172cc 360hp 8 Cyl
TT
C = 1781cc 180hp 4 Cyl
X = 1781cc 180hp 4 Cyl
TT QUATTRO
C = 1781cc 180hp 4Cyl
T = 1781cc 225hp 4 Cyl
X = 1781cc 180hp 4 Cyl

6th POSITION
RESTRAINT SYSTEM
2 = Active – Dr/Pass AirBag, Front & Side
5 = Active – Dr/Pass AirBag, Front & Rear, Side Guard Air Curtain
6 = Active – Dr/Pass AirBag, Front & Side, Side Guard Air Curtain

7th & 8th POSITION
MODEL LINE
4B = A6/Allroad
4D = A8/S8
8D = A4/S4
8N = TT

9th POSITION
CHECK DIGIT

10th POSITION
MODEL YEAR
1 = 2001

11th POSITION
ASSEMBLY PLANT
A = Ingolstadt
N = Neckarsulm
1 = Gyor

12th Thru 17th POSITION
PRODUCTION SEQUENCE NUMBER

AD1130100093000X

Fig. 1 Audi (Part 2 of 2)

1st POSITION
NATION OF ORIGIN
W = Munich, Germany
4 = U.S.A.

2nd POSITION
MANUFACTURER
B = BMW-AG
U = BMW Manufacturing Corp.

3rd POSITION
VEHICLE TYPE
A = Passenger Car
S = BMW Motorsport, GMBH
S = Passenger Car, U.S.A.

4th Thru 7th POSITION
VEHICLE DESCRIPTION
AM33 = 323i, 4 Door Sedan, 2.5L 6 Cyl (199900)
AM43 = 323i, 4 Door Sedan, 2.5L 6 Cyl (1999)
AM53 = 328i, 4 Door Sedan, 2.8L 6 Cyl (199900)
AM63 = 328i, 4 Door Sedan, 2.8L 6 Cyl (1999)
BE73 = 318is, 2 Door Coupe, 1.9L 4 Cyl (96-97)
BE83 = 318is, 2 Door Coupe, 1.9L 4 Cyl (96-97)
BF73 = 323is, 2 Door Coupe, 2.5L 6 Cyl (199899)
BF83 = 323is, 2 Door Coupe, 2.5L 6 Cyl (199899)
BG13 = 328is, 2 Door Coupe, 2.8L 6 Cyl (96-99)
BG23 = 328is, 2 Door Coupe, 2.8L 6 Cyl (96-99)
BG93 = M3, 2 Door Coupe, 2.8L 6 Cyl, (199697)
BG93 = M3, 2 Door Coupe, 3.2L 6 Cyl (1998-99)
BH73 = 318iC, 2 Door Conv., 1.9L 4 Cyl (96-97)
BH83 = 318iC, 2 Door Conv, 1.9L 4 Cyl (96-97)
BJ73 = 323iC, 2 Door Conv, 2.5L 6 Cyl (1998-99)
BJ83 = 323iC, 2 Door Conv, 2.5L (199899)
BK73 = 328iC, 2 Door Conv, 2.8L 6 Cyl (96-99)
BK83 = 328iC, 2 Door Conv, 2.8L 6 Cyl (96-99)
BK93 = M3, 2 Door Conv, 3.2L 6 Cyl (1998-99)
BK03 = M3, 2 Door Conv, 3.2L 6 Cyl (1998-99)
BM33 = 323CI,2 Door Coupe, 2.5L 6 Cyl (2000)
BM53 = 328Ci,2 Door Coupe,2.8L 6 Cyl (2000)
CC03 = 318i, 4 Door Sedan, 1.9L 4 Cyl (97-98)
CC93 = 318i, 4 Door Sedan, 1.9L 4 Cyl (97-98)
CD03 = M3, 4 Door Sedan, 2.8L 6 Cyl (96-97)
CD13 = 328i, 4 Door Sedan, 2.8L 6 Cyl (1996)
CD23 = 328i, 4 Door Sedan, 2.8L 6 Cyl (1996)
CD33 = 328i, 4 Door Sedan, 2.8L 6 Cyl (96-98)
CD43 = 328i, 4 Door Sedan, 2.8L 6 Cyl (96-98)
CD73 = 318i, 4 Door Sedan, 1.9L 4 Cyl (1996)
CD83 = 318i, 4 Door Sedan, 1.9L 4 Cyl (1996)
CD93 = M3, 4 Door Sedan, 2.8L 6 Cyl (96-97)
CD93 = M3, 4 Door Sedan, 3.2L 6Cyl (1998)
CD03 = M3, 4 Door Sedan, 3.2L 6 Cyl (1998)
CG73 = 318ti, 2 Door Hatchback, 1.9L 4 Cyl (96-99)
CG83 = 318ti, 2 Door Hatchback, 1.9L 4 Cyl (96-99)
CH73 = Z3 Roadster, 2 Dr. Conv, 1.9L 4 Cyl (96-98)
CH93 = Z3 Roadster, 2 Dr. Conv, 2.5L 6 Cyl (199900)
CH33 = Z3 Roadster, 2 Dr. Conv, 2.8L 6 Cyl (1999)
CH33 = Z3 Roadster 2.8, 2 DR Conv., 2.8L, 6 Cyl (2000)

4th Thru 7th POSITION (cont'd)
VEHICLE DESCRIPTION
CJ33 = Z3 Roadster, 2 Dr. Conv, 2.8L 6 Cyl (97-98)
CK53 = Z3 2 Door Hatchback, 2.8L 6 Cyl (199900)
CK93 = M Roadster, 2 Dr. Conv, 3.2L 6 Cyl (199900)
CM93 = M Coupe, 2 Dr. Hatchback, 3.2L 6 Cyl (1999-00)
DD53 = 528i , 4 Door Sedan, 2.8L 6 Cyl (97-9800)
DD63 = 528i , 4 Door Sedan, 2.8L 6 Cyl (97-9800)
DE53 = 540i, 4 Door Sedan, 4.4L 8 Cyl (97-98)
DE63 = 540i, 4 Door Sedan, 4.4L 8 Cyl (97-98)
DM53 = 528i, 4 Door Sedan, 2.8L 6 Cyl (1999)
DM63 = 528i, 4 Door Sedan, 2.8L 6 Cyl (1999)
DN53 = 540i, 4 Door Sedan, 4.4L 8 Cyl (199900)
DN63 = 540I, 4 DR Sedan, 4.4L 8 Cyl (2000)
DN83 = 540i Protection, 4 Dr. Sedan, 4.4L 8 Cyl (1999)
DP53 = 540i Touring, 4 Dr. Sedan, 2.8L 6 Cyl (1999)
DP53 = 540I Touring, 4 DR Wagon, 2.8L 6 Cyl (2000)
DP63 = 540i Touring, 4 Dr. Sedan, 2.8L 6 Cyl (1999)
DR63 = 540i Touring, 4 Dr. Wagon, 4.4L 8 Cyl (199900)
EF83 = 840Ci, 2 Door Coupe, 4.4L 8 Cyl (96-97)
EG43 = 850Ci, 2 Door Coupe, 5.4L 12 Cyl (96-97)
GF83 = 740i, 4 Door Sedan, 4.4L 8 Cyl (96-98)
GG83 = 740i, 4 Door Sedan, 4.4L 8 Cyl (199900)
GH83 = 740iL, 4 Door Sedan, 4.4L 8 Cyl (1999-00)
GH03 = 740iL Protection, 4 DR Sedan, 4.4L, 8 Cyl (2000)
GJ03 = 740iL, 4 Door Sedan, 5.4L 12 Cyl (199900)
GJ83 = 740iL, 4 Door Sedan, 4.4lL 8 Cyl (96-98)
GK23 = 750iL, 4 Door Sedan, 5.4L 12 Cyl (96-98)
GK93 = 750iL, 4DR Sedan, 5.4L 12 Cyl (2000)

8th POSITION
RESTRAINT SYSTEM
2 = Manual Belts w/ Dual Air Bags
3 = Manual Belts Driver & Passenger Air Bags Depowered Supplemental Restraint System (SRS)
4 = Manual Belts w/ Driver and Passenger Dual-Stage Restranint System

9th POSITION
CHECK DIGIT

10th POSITION
MODEL YEAR
T = 1996
V = 1997
W = 1998
X = 1999
Y = 2000

11th POSITION
ASSEMBLY PLANT
A = Munich
B = Dingolfing
C = Dingolfing
D = Dingolfing
E = Regensburg
F = Munich
L = Greer, S. Carolina
K = Munich
Z = Pretoria

12th Thru 17th POSITION
PRODUCTION SEQUENCE NUMBER

BM1130100054000X

Fig. 2 BMW

1st Thru 3rd POSITION
MANUFACTURERS CODE
SAJ = Jaguar, United Kingdom

4th POSITION
MODEL LINE
A = XJ6
A = Vanden Plas
C = Sovereign
F = XJ6
G = X100
G = XK8
H = XJ6, Sovereign
K = Vanden Plas
M = Majestic
M = XJ12
N = XJS/XJSC
P = XJR/Sport
S = Jagsport
T = Rouge/Classic

5th POSITION
CLASS/RESTRAINT
A = Passive Seat Belt (87-89)
D = Depowered Airbags & Side A/B
E = Depowered Airbags No Side A/B
N = Driver & Pass Air Bag
T = Driver Air Bag w/Passive Belt
V = N. American Spec. (83-87)
V = Active Seat Belt
W = Driver Air Bag (90-95)
X = Driver & Pass Air Bag
X = Full Power A/B's 1999
Y = N. American Spec. (83-87)
Y = Passive Seat Belt (89-93)

6th POSITION
BODY STYLE
1 = 4 Door Sedan
2 = 2+2 Convertible
3 = 2 Door Cabriolet
4 = Convertible
5 = 2 Door Coupe
5 = 2 Door 2+2 Coupe (96-97)
6 = 4 Door LWB 5 Seat
7 = 4 Door LWB 4 Seat

7th POSITION
ENGINE CODE
0 = 5.3L 12 Cyl, Calif
0 = 4.0L 6 Cyl, Emission L
1 = 4.0L 6 Cyl, Supercharged
2 = 4.0L 6 Cyl, Calif
2 = 4.2L 6 Cyl, Calif
3 = 4.2L 6 Cyl
3 = 6.0L
5 = 3.6L 6 Cyl Low Compression
5 = 4.0L 6 Cyl, Emission C
6 = 3.6L 6 Cyl High Compression
7 = 4.0L 6 Cyl
8 = 4.0L 6 Cyl, Supercharged
8 = 5.3L 12 Cyl
9 = 4.0L 6 Cyl

8th POSITION
TRANSMISSION & STEERING
4 = Automatic (LHS)
8 = Manual (LHS)

9th POSITION
CHECK DIGIT

10th POSITION
MODEL YEAR
D = 1983
E = 1984
F = 1985
G = 1986
H = 1987
J = 1988
K = 1989
L = 1990
M = 1991
N = 1992
P = 1993
R = 1994
S = 1995
T = 1996
V = 1997
W = 1998
X = 1999

11th POSITION
ASSEMBLY PLANT
C = Browns Lane, England

12th Thru 17th POSITION
PRODUCTION SEQUENCE NUMBER

JC1130100040000X

Fig. 3 Jaguar (Part 1 of 2)

1st Thru 3rd POSITION
MANUFACTURERS CODE
SAJ = Jaguar, United Kingdom

4th POSITION
MARKET/AIRBAGS*
F,B = Canada
P,R = Mexico
D,J = USA
*All Sedans = Driver & Passenger Front and Side Airbags

5th POSITION
TRANSMISSION/STEERING
A = Automatic LHS

6th THRU 7TH POSITIONS
VEHICLE LINE/BODY TYPE
01 = S-Type 4 Door Sedan
14 = XJ8
15 = XJR
23 = XJ8L
24 = VDP
25 = VDP Supercharged
41 = XK8/XKR Coupe
42 = XK8/XKR Convertible

8th POSITION
EMISSION CONTROL SYSTEM
B = XKR, XJR/VDP S/C
C = P/A S-Type V6, XJ8, XJ8, L, VDP, XK8
D = P/A S-Type V8
F = Mexico V6
G = Mexico V8 Normally Aspirated
K = Mexico V8 S/C
N = US/Canada S-Type 3.0
P = US/Canada S-Type 4.0
R = Mexico 3.0 S-Type
S = Mexico 4.0 S-Type

9th POSITION
CHECK DIGIT

10th POSITION
MODEL YEAR
Y = 2000
1 = 2001

11th POSITION
MODEL LINE/ASSEMBLY PLANT
F = 3.0L S-Type V6; Castle Bromwich
G = 4.0L S-Type V8; Castle Bromwich
L = 4.0L Sedan; Browns Lane
M = 4.0L S/C; Browns Lane
N = 4.0L XK8; Browns Lane
P = XKR S/C; Browns Lane

12th POSITION
MODEL
A,B,C = XK8
F,G,H = XJ Sedan
L,M,N = S-Type

13th Thru 17th POSITION
PRODUCTION SEQUENCE NUMBER

JC1130100041000X

Fig. 3 Jaguar (Part 2 of 2)

1st Thru 3rd POSITION
MANUFACTURER CODE
SAL = Europe, United Kingdom

4th & 5th POSITION, 1987-00
LINE/SERIES
DV = Defender 90" W.B., Fed.
DX = Defender 90" W.B., Calif.
HC = Range Rover 108" W.B., Fed.
HE = Range Rover 100" W.B., Calif.
HF = Range Rover 108" W.B., Calif.
HV = Range Rover 100" W.B., Fed.
JN = Discovery, Calif.
JY = Discovery, Fed
PA = Range Rover
PC = Range Rover, Callaway Engine
PE = New Range Rover, Calif.
PF = Range Rover, Class E (late build)
PV = New Range Rover, Fed.,Class E (early build)
TY = Discovery Series II, Class E (00)

4th & 5th POSITION, 2001
LINE/CLASS
PL = Range Rover SE, Trim Level 3
PM = Range Rover HSE, Trim Level 4
TY = Discovery II SE, 5 Seats Leather Trim
TW = Discovery II SE7, 7 Seats Leather Trim
TL = Discovery II SD, 5 Seats Leatherette Trim
TK = Discovery II SD7, 7 Seats Leatherette Trim
TH = Discovery II, Adventurer LE, 5 Seats
TJ = Discovery II, Adventurer LE7, 7 Seats

6th POSITION
BODY STYLE
1 = 4 Door Station Wagon
2 = 2 Door
3 = 3 Door

7th POSITION
ENGINE CODE
1 = 3.5L Fuel Injection
2 = 3.9L / 4.0L Fuel Injection, V8 EFI
2 = 4.0L V8 HC Cat (Petrol)
3 = 4.2L V8, Fuel Injection
4 = 4.6L V8, Fuel Injection
5 = 4.0L, V8, EFI-LEV, HC Cat (Petrol)
6 = 4.6L, V8 EFI - LEV

8th POSITION
TRANSMISSION
4 = 4 Speed Automatic
8 = 5 Speed Manual

9th POSITION
CHECK DIGIT

10th POSITION
MODEL YEAR
H = 1987
J = 1988
K = 1989
L = 1990
M = 1991
N = 1992
P = 1993
R = 1994
S = 1995
T = 1996
V = 1997
W = 1998
X = 1999
Y = 2000
1 = 2001

11th POSITION
ASSEMBLY PLANT
A = Solihull

12th Thru 17th POSITION
PRODUCTION SEQUENCE NUMBER

RV1130100022000X

Fig. 4 Land Rover

1st Thru 3rd POSITION
MANUFACTURER
WDB = Daimler-Benz, Germany

4th Thru 7th POSITION
MODEL
1982-85
AB23 = 240D 4 Door Sedan
AB33 = 300DT 4 Door Sedan
AB53 = 300CDT 2 Door Coupe
AB93 = 300TDT 4 Door Wagon
BA45 = 380Sl 2 Door Coupe
CA32 = 380SE 4 Door Sedan
CA33 = 380SEL 4 Door Sedan
CA37 = 500SEL 4 Door Sedan
CA43 = 380SEC 2 Door Coupe
CA44 = 500SEC 2 Door Coupe
CB20 = 300SD 4 Door Sedan
DA24 = 190E 4 Door Sedan
DB22 = 190D 4 Door Sedan

1986-99
BA48 = 560SL 2 Door Coupe
CA24 = 300SE 4 Door Sedan
CA25 = 300SEL 4 Door Sedan
CA35 = 420SEL 4 Door Sedan
CA39 = 560SEL 4 Door Sedan
CA45 = 560SEC 2 Door Coupe
CB25 = 300DL 4 Door Sedan Turbo
CB34 = 350SD 4 Door Sedan Turbo
CB35 = 350SDL 4 Door Sedan Turbo
DA24 = 190E 4 Door Sedan (1986)
DA28 = 190E 4 Door Sedan, 2.3L
DA29 = 190E 4 Door Sedan, 2.6L
DA34 = 190E 4 Dr Sed, 2.3L 16 Value
DB26 = 190D 4 Door Sedan, 2.5L
DB28 = 190D 4 Dr Sed, 2.5L 16 Valve
EA26 = 260E 4 Door Sedan
EA26 = 300E 4 Door Sedan, 2.6L
EA28 = 300E 4 Door Sedan, 2.8L
EA30 = 300E 4 Door Sedan
EA32 = 300E 4 Door Sedan
EA32 = E320 4 Dr Sed, 3.2L (94-95)
EA33 = 300DT 4 Door Sedan
EA34 = 400E 4 Door Sedan
EA34 = E420 4 Dr Sed, 4.2L (94-95)
EA36 = 500E 4 Door Sedan
EA36 = E500 4 Dr Sed, 5.0L (94-95)
EA50 = 300CE 2 Door Coupe
EA51 = 300CE 2 Door Coupe
EA52 = 300CE 2 Door Coupe
EA52 = E320 2 Dr Cpe, 3.2L (94-95)
EA66 = 300CE Convertible
EA66 = E320 Conv., 3.2L (94-95)
EA90 = 300TE 4 Door Wagon
EA92 = 300TE 4 Door Wagon
EA92 = E320 4 Dr Wag, 3.2L (94-95)
EB28 = 300D 4 Dr Sed, 2.5L Turbo
EB31 = E300 4 Dr Sed, Diesel (1995)
EB33 = 300DT 4 Door Sedan
EB93 = 300TDT 4 Door Wagon
ED30 = 300E 4 Door Sedan, 4-Matic
ED90 = 300TE 4 Door Wagon, 4-Matic
FA61 = 300SL 2 Door Roadster
FA63 = SL320 2Dr Rdster,3.2L (94-97)
FA66 = 500SL 2 Door Roadster
FA67 = 500SL 2 Door Roadster
FA67 = SL500 2Dr Rdster,5.0L (94-98)
FA68 = SL500 2 Dr Rdster, 5.0L (1999)
FA76 = 600SL 2 Door Roadster
FA76 = SL600 2Dr Rdster, 6.0L(94-99)
GA32 = 300SE

4th Thru 7th POSITION (Cont'd)
GA32 = S320 4 Door Sedan (94-99)
GA33 = S320 4 Dr Sedan, 3.2L (95-99)
GA42 = 400SE 4 Door Sedan
GA43 = 400SEL
GA43 = S420 4 Dr Sed, 4.2L (94-99)
GA51 = 500SEL
GA51 = S500 4 Dr Sedan, 5.0L (94-99)
GA57 = 600SEL
GA57 = S600 4 Dr Sedan, 6.0L (94-99)
GA70 = 500SEC
GA70 = CL500 2 Door Coupe (98-99)
GA70 = S500 4 Dr Sedan, 5.0L (94-98)
GA76 = 600SEC
GA76 = CL600 2 Door Coupe (98 99)
GA76 = S600 Coupe, 6.0L (94-95)
GA51 = 500SEL 4 Door Sedan
GA57 = 600SEL 4 Door Sedan
GB34 = 300SD 4 Door Sedan, Turbo
GB34 = S350TurboDiesel,3.5L (94-95)
HA22 = C220 4 Dr Sedan, 2.2L (94-96)
HA23 = C230 4 Dr Sedan, 2.3L (97-98)
HA28 = C280 4 Dr Sedan, 2.8L (94-97)
HA29 = C280 4 Dr Sedan, 2.8L (1998)
HA33 = C43 4 Door Sedan
JF20 = E300D 4 Dr Sed, 3.0L (96-97)
JF25 = E300DT 4 Dr Sed, 3.0L (98-99)
JF55 = E320 4 Dr Sedan, 3.2L (96-97)
JF65 = E320W 4 Dr Sed, AWD (98-99)
JF65 = E320S 4 Dr Sta Wag (98-99)
JF70 = E430 4 Door Sedan (98-99)
JF82 = E320S4,4 Dr Sed,AWD (98-99)
KK47 = SLK230 2Dr Cpe, Rdster 1999
LJ65 = CLK320 2 Dr Cpe,3.2L (98-99)
LJ70 = CLK430 2 Door Coupe (1999)

8th POSITION
RESTRAINT SYSTEM
A = Active
B = Active w/Air Bag
C = Passive
D = 3 Point Belt w/Driver Side Air Bag
E = 3 Point Belt w/Dual Air Bags
F = 3 Point Belt w/ Dual Air Bags & Side Impact Air Bags
G = Same as "F" with rear lap belt.
H = Same as "F" with curtain Airbages

9th POSITION
CHECK DIGIT

10th POSITION
MODEL YEAR
C = 1982
D = 1983
E = 1984
F = 1985
G = 1986
H = 1987
J = 1988
K = 1989
L = 1990
M = 1991
N = 1992
P = 1993
R = 1994
S = 1995
T = 1996
V = 1997
W = 1998
X = 1999

11th POSITION
ASSEMBLY PLANT
A-E = Sindelfingen
F-H = Bremen
J = Rastatt

12th Thru 17th POSITION
PRODUCTION SEQUENCE NUMBER

MB1130100084000X

Fig. 5 Mercedes-Benz (Part 1 of 2)

1st Thru 3rd POSITION
MANUFACTURER

WDB = Daimler-Benz, Germany
4JG = Daimler-Benz, Germany

4th Thru 7th POSITION
MODEL

AB54 = ML320, 4Dr MPV
AB72 = ML430, 4Dr MPV
AB74 = ML55, 4Dr MPV
FA68 = SL500R 2Dr Coupe Roadster 2 Passenger
FA76 = SL600R 2Dr Coupe Roadster 2 Passenger
HA24 = C230ML 4 Dr Sedan 5 Passenger Sport
HA29 = C280W 4 Dr Sedan 5 Passenger Sport
HA33 = C43 4 Dr Sedan 4 Passenger
JF65 = E320W 4 Dr Sedan 5 Passenger
JF82 = E320W AWD 4Dr Sedan 5 Passenger
JH65 = E320(S) 4Dr Wagon 7 Passenger
JH82 = E320(S) AWD 4Dr Wagon 7 Passenger
JF70 = E430W 4Dr Sedan 5 Passenger
JF83 = E430W AWD 4Dr Sedan 5 Passenger
JF74 = E55 AMG 4 Dr Sedan 5 Passenger
KK47 = SKJ230 Kompressor 2Dr Cpe. 2 Passenger Sport
KK49 = SLK230 Kompressor 2Dr Cpe. Roadster 2 Passenger Sport
KK65 = SLK320 2Dr Cpe
LJ65 = CLK320 2Dr Cpe. 4 Passenger
LJ70 = CLK430 2Dr Cpe. 4 Passenger
LJ74 = CLK55 2Dr Cpe. 4 Passenger
LK65 = CLK320 Cabrio 2Dr, 4 Passenger
LK70 = CLK430 Cabrio 2Dr, 4 Passenger
NG73 = S55, 4 Dr Sedan
NG70 = S430V 4Dr Sedan 5 Passenger
NG75 = S500V 4Dr Sedan 5 Passenger
NG78 = S600 4Dr Sedan 4 & 5 Passenger
PJ73 = CL55, 2Dr Coupe 4 Passenger
PJ75 = CL500 2Dr Cpe. 4 Passenger
PJ78 = CL600 2Dr Cpe. 4 Passenger
RF61 = C240 (2.6) 4Dr Sedan 5 Passenger
RF64 = C320 4Dr Sedan 5 Passenger Sport

8th POSITION
RESTRAINT SYSTEM / WEIGHT CLASS

E = GVWR 6001-7000lbs
F = 3 Point Belt w/ Dual Air Bags & Side Impact Air Bags
G = Same as "F" with rear lap belt.
H = Same as "F" with curtain Airbags
J = Same as "F" with Outboard Rear Air Bag in Door

9th POSITION
CHECK DIGIT

10th POSITION
MODEL YEAR

Y = 2000
1 = 2001

11th POSITION
ASSEMBLY PLANT

A = Vance, Alabama
A-E = Sindelfingen
F-H = Bremen
T = Osnabrueck
X = Garz

12th Thru 17th POSITION
PRODUCTION SEQUENCE NUMBER

MB1130100085000X

Fig. 5 Mercedes-Benz (Part 2 of 2)

1st Thru 3rd POSITION
MANUFACTURER

WPO = Porsche, West Germany

4th POSITION
SERIES

A = 911 & 924S Coupe
A = 911 Carrera, 2 & 4WD Coupe
A = 911 RS America
A = 911 Turbo
A = 928 S4 Coupe
A = 928 GTS
A = 944, 944S & 944 Turbo Coupe
A = 968 Coupe
B = 911 Carrera, 2 & 4WD Targa
C = 911 Carrera, 2 & 4WD Cabriolet
C = 911 Carrera Speedster
C = 911 America Roadster
C = 911 Carrerra, 2 door Convertible (96-99)
C = 944 S2 Cabriolet
C = 968 Cabriolet
C = Boxster, 2 Door Convertible
D = 911 Carrera, 2 Door Targa (96-98)
E = 911 Targa & Cabriolet
E = 911 Turbo Targa & Cabriolet
J = 928 S4 Coupe
J = 911 Turbo Coupe

5th POSITION
ENGINE TYPE

1983
A = 928S Model-4664cc, 234hp-8 Cyl
A = 911SC Model-2994cc, 172hp6 Cyl
A = 944 Model-2479cc, 4 Cyl

1984-86
A = 944 Model-2479cc, 4 Cyl
A = 944 Model-3164cc, 6 Cyl Turbo
B = 911 Model-3164cc, 6 Cyl
B = 928 Model-4664cc, 8 Cyl

1987
A = 911-3164cc, 6 Cyl-300hp, Turbo
A = 944 Model-2479cc, 4 Cyl-190/220hp
B = 911-3164cc, 6 Cyl-217hp
B = 944 & 924 Model-2479cc, 4 Cyl-150hp

1988-95
A = Varies w/Models - 968, 928, 911
B = Varies w/Models - 911 Carrera 2 & 4
B = Varies w/Models - RS America & Speedster
C = 911 Turbo

1996-99
A = 2.5L 6 Cyl, 201 hp
A = 3.6L 6 Cyl, 282hp
A = 3.4L, 6 Cyl, 296hp
C = 3.6L 6 Cyl Turbo, 400hp

2000-01
A = Normally Aspirated
B = Normally Aspirated
C = Turbo

6th POSITION
RESTRAINT SYSTEM

0 = Active
2 = Passive
9 = Passive

7th & 8th POSITION
MODEL LINE

91 = 911, 924 & 928
92 = 924, 924S, 928, & 928S
92 = 928 GTS
93 = 911 Turbo
94 = 944, 944S & 944 Turbo
95 = 944 Turbo
96 = 968, 911 Carrera 2 & 4WD
96 = 911 RS America & America Roadster
96 = 911 Turbo
98 = Boxster, Cabrio
99 = 911 Carrera
99 = 911 Carrera Convertible
99 = 911 Turbo

9th POSITION
CHECK DIGIT

10th POSITION
MODEL YEAR

D = 1983
E = 1984
F = 1985
G = 1986
H = 1987
J = 1988
K = 1989
L = 1990
M = 1991
N = 1992
P = 1993
R = 1994
S = 1995
T = 1996
V = 1997
W = 1998
X = 1999
Y = 2000
1 = 2001

11th POSITION
ASSEMBLY PLANT

N = Neckarsulm
S = Stuttgart

12th Thru 17th POSITION
PRODUCTION SEQUENCE NUMBER

PR1130100031000X

Fig. 6 Porsche

1st Thru 3rd POSITION
MANUFACTURER CODE
YK1 = Saab of Finland
YS3 = Saab of Sweden

4th POSITION
PRODUCTION LINE CODE
A = 900
C = 9000
D = 900 (94-98)
D = 9-3
E = 9-5

5th POSITION, 1983-86
SERIES CODE
B = Base Series
C = S Series
D = Turbo Series
E = S Series (4 Door)
G = Base Series
H = S Series
M = Base Series
S = S Series (3 Door)
T = Turbo Series

5TH POSITION, 1987-01
SERIES/RESTRAINT
D = S, CD/CS w/Dual Air Bags (9-3, 9-5)
F = SE, CDE/CSE w/Dual Air Bags
H = Aero w/Dual Air Bags (9-5)
J = Base/Passive
K = Base, S/Driver Air Bag
L = Turbo/Driver Air Bag
M = Non Turbo/Dual Air Bag
N = Turbo/Dual Air Bag
P = Viggen (9-3)
R = Base/Active
S = S/Active
T = Turbo/Active

6th POSITION
BODY TYPE
2 = 2 Door Notchback
3 = 3 Door Hatchback (900)(9-3)
4 = 4 Door Sedan (9-5)
5 = 5 Door Hatchback (900)(9-3), Wagon (9-5)
6 = 5 Door Hatchback (9000)
7 = Convertible (900), (9-3)

7th POSITION, 1983
ENGINE CODE
3 = 2.0L Fuel Injection
4 = 2.0L Turbo

7th POSITION, 1984-01
TRANSMISSION TYPE
5 = 5 Speed Manual
6 = 3 Speed Automatic (900)
8 = 4 Speed Automatic

8th POSITION, 1983
RESTRAINT SYSTEM
A = Air Bag
P = Passive Belt
S = Active Belt

8th POSITION, 1984-01
ENGINE CODE
B = 2.3L Fuel Inj., 16 Valve
D = 2.0L Fuel Inj., 16 Valve
E = 2.1L Fuel Inj., 16 Valve
E = 2.3L, Turbo LPT (9-5)
G = 2.3L, High Output Turbo (9-3 Viggen, 9-5 Aero)
H = 2.0L, Turbo 9-3 (Std. Output)
J = 2.0L Fuel Inj., 8 Valve
K = 2.0L, Turbo 9-3 (High Output)
L = 2.0L Turbo, 16 Valve
M = 2.3L Turbo, 16 Valve, Intercooled
N = 2.0L Turbo, Intercooled
N = 2.0L, Turbo (9-3)
P = 2.0L, Turbo High Output (9-3)
R = 2.3L Turbo, Intercooled
S = 2.0L Turbo
T = 2.0L Turbo, Intercooled
U = 2.3L Turbo
V = 2.5L Fuel Inj., V6
W = 3.0L Fuel Inj., V6
Z = 3.0L, Turbo, V6 (9-5)

9th POSITION
CHECK DIGIT

10th POSITION
MODEL YEAR
D = 1983
E = 1984
F = 1985
G = 1986
H = 1987
J = 1988
K = 1989
L = 1990
M = 1991
N = 1992
P = 1993
R = 1994
S = 1995
T = 1996
V = 1997
W = 1998
X = 1999
Y = 2000
1 = 2001

11th POSITION
ASSEMBLY PLANT
1 = Trollhatten, Sweden
2 = Trollhatten, Sweden, Line A (9-3)
3 = Arlov, Sweden
3 = Trollhattan, Sweden, Line B (9-5)
4 = Malmo, Sweden
5 = Malmo, Sweden
6 = Nystad, Finland
7 = Nystad, Finland, (9-3 Convtbl, 9-3 Viggen)
8 = Nystad, Finland
9 = Trollhattan, Sweden

12th Thru 17th POSITION
PRODUCTION SEQUENCE NUMBER

SA1130100043000X

Fig. 7 Saab

1st Thru 3rd POSITION
MANUFACTURERS CODE
WVW = Europe, Passenger Car
WV1 = Europe, Truck
WV2 = Europe, MPV
WV3 = Europe, Incomplete Vehicle
3VW = Mexico, Passenger Car
9BW = Brazil, Passenger Car

4th POSITION
BODY TYPE
A = Cabriolet Base
A = Cabrio gl, 2 Door
B = Fox Economy, 2 Door (91)
B = Fox Base, 2 Door (92-93)
B = Golf GL, 2 Door
B = Cabriolet Classic
B = Cabrio, 2 Door (95-96)
B = Cabrio GLS, 2 Door (98-99)
B = Golf Sport, 2 Door (1995)
B = Beetle GL, (1999)
C = Cabriolet Custom (91)
C = Cabriolet Base (92)
C = Passat GLS, 4 Door (1995)
C = Beetle GLS, (1999)
D = New Cabrio, GLS 2Dr (1999)
D = Cabriolet Carat
D = Corrado Sport/G60
D = Golf GTI-8V, 2 Door
D = GTI VR6, 2 Door (1994)
D = GTI, 2 Door (1998-99)
D = Passat GLS, Wagon (1995)
D = Beetle GLX, (1999)
E = Cabriolet Etienne Aigner
E = Corrado SLC
E = Passat GLX, 4 Door (95-97)
E = Eurovan, Panel Van (1995)
F = Golf GL, 4 Door
F = Golf GL/TDI , 4Door (98-99)
F = Passat GL, 4 Door (91-93)
F = Passat CL (92)
F = Passat GLX, Wagon (95-97)
G = New Golf GL
G = Fox GL, 4 Door
G = Passat GL Wagon, 4 Door
G = Passat GLS, 4 Door
H = Golf GTI-16V, 2 Door
H = Passat GLS / Wagon
H = Eurovan CL
H = Eurovan GL, 3 Door (94-95)
H = GTI VR6, 2 Door (95-99)
J = Golf City, 4 Door (1995)
J = Golf Wolfsburg Edition (1999)
J = Passat GLS Wagon
J = Passat GLX
J = Eurovan GL, 4 Door (1995)
K = Golf, 4 Door (1995)
K = Golf K2, 4Door (98)
K = Eurovan GL
K = Eurovan GLS, 3 Door (94-95, 97)
L = Eurovan GLS, 4 Door (1995)
L = Golf Celebration Ed., 4 Door
M = Jetta Custom, 2 Door (91)
M = Eurovan MV Camper
M = Eurovan Multivan (1995, 97)
M = Passat GLS/TDI (1998-99)
N = Passat GLX Wagon
P = Jetta 4 Door (1995)
P = Passat GLX
P = Jetta 4Dr. Wolfsburg Ed. (1999)
R = Jetta Custom, 4 Door (91)
R = Jetta GL/TDI (92-99)
R = Passat GLS Syncro Wagon
S = Jetta Carat (92)
S = Jetta GLS (93-99)
T = Jetta GLI-16V (91-92)
T = Jetta GLX (93-99)
T = Vanagon Multi-Van (91)
T = Jetta GT (1998)
T = Passat GLS Syncro Wagon
V = Jetta City, 4 Door (1995)

4th POSITION (Cont'd)
U= Passat GLX Syncro Wagon
W = Jetta Celebration Ed., 4 Door
W = Passat GLX Syncro Wagon
T = Passat GLS Syncro Wagon
Y = Vanagon Bus (91)
Y = Jetta K2 (1998)
Z = Vanagon Camper (91)

5th POSITION
ENGINE CODE
CABRIO
A = 1984cc 115hp 4 Cyl
B = 1984cc 115hp 4 Cyl
C = 1984cc 115hp 4 Cyl
CABRIOLET
B = 1780cc 94hp 4 Cyl, Fed
C = 1780cc 94hp 4 Cyl, Calif
CORRADO
B = 1780cc 158hp 4 Cyl, Fed
C = 1780cc 158hp 4 Cyl, Calif
D = 2792cc 178hp 6 Cyl, Calif
E = 2792cc 178hp 6 Cyl, Fed
F = 2792cc 178hp 6 Cyl
EUROVAN
C = 2461cc 109hp 5 Cyl, Fed
D = 2461cc 109hp 5 Cyl, Calif
D = 2461cc 109hp 5 Cyl (1994)
E = 2461cc 109hp 5 Cyl (1995)
H = 2792cc 140hp 6 Cyl
FOX
A = 1780cc 81hp 4 Cyl, Fed
B = 1780cc 81hp 4 Cyl, Calif
GTI
A = 1984cc 115hp 4 Cyl, Fed
C = 1984cc 115hp 4Cyl
D = 2792cc 172hp 6 Cyl
E = 2792cc 174hp 6 Cyl
F = 1896cc 90hp 4 Cyl, Diesel
G = 1896cc 90hp 4 Cyl, Diesel
S = 2792cc 172hp 6 Cyl
GOLF
A = 1780cc 100hp 4 Cyl, Fed
A = 1984cc 115hp 4 Cyl, Fed
B = 1780cc 105hp 4 Cyl, Fed
B = 1984cc 115hp 4 Cyl, Calif
C = 1984cc 115hp 4 Cyl
D = 2771cc 172hp 6 Cyl, Fed
D = 2792cc 172hp 6 Cyl, Fed
E = 1984cc 134hp 4 Cyl, Fed
E = 2771cc 172hp 6 Cyl, Calif
F = 1896cc 90hp 4 Cyl, Diesel
G = 1896cc 90hp 4 Cyl, Diesel
H = 1896cc 90hp 4 Cyl, Diesel
J = 1984cc 134hp 4 Cyl, Calif
K = 1780cc 100hp 4 Cyl, Calif
L = 1984cc 115hp 4 Cyl, Fed
R = 1984cc 115hp 4 Cyl, Calif
JETTA
A = 1780cc 100hp 4 Cyl, Fed
A = 1984cc 115hp 4 Cyl, Fed
B = 1780cc 105hp 4 Cyl, Fed
B = 1984cc 115hp 4 Cyl, Calif
C = 1984cc 115hp 4 Cyl
D = 2771cc 172hp 6 Cyl, Fed
D = 2792cc 172hp 6 Cyl, Fed
E = 1984cc 134hp 4 Cyl, Calif
E = 2771cc 172hp 6 Cyl, Calif
F = 1588cc 59hp 4 Cyl, Fed
F = 1896cc 90 hp 4 Cyl, Diesel
G =1896cc 90 hp 4 Cyl, Diesel
G =1588cc 52hp 4 Cyl, Fed
H =1896cc 90hp 4 Cyl, Diesel
J =1984cc 134hp 4 Cyl, Fed
K =1780cc 100hp 4 Cyl, Calif
L = 1984cc 115hp 4 Cyl, Fe
M = 2792cc 172hp 6 Cyl, Fed
R = 1984cc 115hp 4 Cyl, Calif
S = 2792cc 172hp 6 Cyl, Calif
S = 2792cc 172hp 6 Cyl (1994)

5th POSITION (Cont'd)
PASSAT
A = 1781cc 150hp 4 Cyl
B = 1984cc 134hp 4 Cyl, Fed
C = 1984cc 134hp 4 Cyl, Calif
D = 2792cc 172hp 6 Cyl, Fed
D = 2771cc 190hp 6 Cyl
E = 2792cc 172hp 6 Cyl,
E = 2771cc 172hp 6 Cyl
F = 2792cc 172hp 6 Cyl
G = 1896cc 90hp 4 Cyl, Diesel
VANAGON
B = 2109cc 90hp 4 Cyl
BEETLE
A = 1984cc 115hp 4 Cyl
C = 1984cc 115hp 4 Cyl
E = 2792cc 174hp 6 Cyl
F = 1896cc 96hp 4 Cyl Diesel

6th POSITION
RESTRAINT SYSTEM
0 = Active
2 = Passive W/Manual Lap
4 = ELRA W/Manual Lap
5 = Driver Air Bag
6 = Dr/Pass + Side Air Bags
8 = Driver & Pass Air Bag

7th & 8th POSITION
MODEL LINE
1C = New Beetle
1E = Cabrio/New Cabrio
1G = Golf/Jetta
1H = Golf III, GTI VR6
1H = Jetta III
1J = New Golf / New Jetta/GTI
15 = Cabriolet
25 = Vanagon
3A = Passat
3B = Passat
30 = Fox
31 = Passat
50 = Corrado
70 = Eurovan

9th POSITION
CHECK DIGIT

10th POSITION
MODEL YEAR
M =1991
N =1992
P = 1993
R = 1994
S = 1995
T = 1996
V = 1997
W = 1998
X = 1999

11th POSITION
ASSEMBLY PLANT
A = Ingolstadt
B = Brussels
E = Emden
G = Graz
H = Hanover
K = Osnabrueck
M = Mexico
N = Necharsulm
P = Brazil
W = Wolfsburg

12th Thru 17th POSITION
PRODUCTION SEQUENCE NUMBER

VW1130100076000X

Fig. 8 Volkswagen (Part 1 of 2)

1st Thru 3rd POSITION
MANUFACTURERS CODE
WVW = Europe, Passenger Car
WV2 = Europe, MPV
3VW = Mexico, Passenger Car
WV3 = Europe Incomplete
9BW = Brazil Passenger Car

4th POSITION
BODY TYPE
A = Passat GLS
B = Golf GL, 2 Door
B = Beetle GL,
B = Cabrio GL, 2Dr
B = Passat GLX
C = Cabrio Gl 2 Dr
C = Cabrio GLS 2 Dr
C = Beetle GLS
D = Cabrio, GLS 2Dr
D = Cabrio GLX
D = GTI, 2 Door, GLS
D = Beetle GLX
D = Passat GLS 4 Motion
E = Eurovan Camper
E = Passat GLX 4 Motion
G = Golf GLS 4 Dr
H = Passat GLS Wagon
J = Passat GLX Wagon
K = Passat GLS Wagon 4 Motion
K = Eurovan GLS, 3 Door
L = Passat GLX Wagon $ Motion
M = Eurovan MV 3 Dr
M = Passat GLS/TDI (98-00)
N = Passat GLX Wagon
N = Eurovan MV Weekender
P = Passat GLX
P = GTI GLX, 2 Dr
P = Jetta, Wolfsburg Ed., 4 Dr
R = Jetta GL 4 Dr
S = Jetta GLS 4 Dr
T = Jetta GLX 4 Dr
V = Passat GLX Wagon 4 Dr

5th POSITION
ENGINE CODE

CABRIO
C = 1984cc 115hp 4 Cyl

EUROVAN
B = 2792cc 201hp 6 Cyl
H = 2792cc 140hp 6 Cyl

GTI
A = 1984cc 115hp 4 Cyl, Fed
B = 1984cc 115hp 4Cyl
C = 1781cc 150hp 4Cyl
C = 1984cc 115hp 4Cyl
D = 1781cc 150hp 4Cyl
E = 2792cc 174hp 6 Cyl
F = 1896cc 90hp 4 Cyl, Diesel
G = 2792cc 174hp 6Cyl
K = 1984cc 115hp 4Cyl
P = 1896cc 90hp 4Cyl
S = 1984cc 115hp 4Cyl
T = 1984cc 115hp 4Cyl

5th POSITION (Cont'd)
ENGINE CODE

GOLF
A = 1984cc 115hp 4 Cyl, Fed
B = 1984cc 115hp 4 Cyl
C = 1781cc 150hp 4 Cyl
C = 1984cc 115hp 4 Cyl
D = 1781cc 150hp 4 Cyl
E = 2792cc 174hp 6 Cyl Can.
F = 1896cc 90hp 4 Cyl, Diesel
G = 2792cc 174hp 6 Cyl
K = 1984cc 115hp 4 Cyl
L = 1984cc 115hp 4 Cyl, Fed
P = 1896cc 90hp 4 Cyl
R = 1984cc 115hp 4 Cyl, Calif
S = 1984xx 115hp 4 Cyl
T = 1984cc 115hp 4 Cyl

JETTA
A = 1984cc 115hp 4 Cyl, Fed
B = 1984cc 115hp 4 Cyl
C = 1984cc 115hp 4 Cyl
C = 1781cc 150hp 4 Cyl
D = 1781cc 150hp 4 Cyl
E = 2792cc 174hp 6 Cyl Can.
F = 1896cc 90 hp 4 Cyl, Diesel
G = 2792cc 174hp 6 Cyl
K = 1984cc 115hp 4 Cyl
P = 1896cc 90hp 4 Cyl
S = 1984cc 115hp 4 Cyl
T = 1984cc 115hp 4 Cyl

PASSAT
A = 1781cc 150hp 4 Cyl
C = 1781cc 150hp 4 Cyl
D = 2771cc 190hp 6 Cyl
H = 2771cc 190hp 6 Cyl

BEETLE
A = 1984cc 115hp 4 Cyl
B = 1984cc 115hp 4 Cyl
C = 1781cc 150hp 4 Cyl
C = 1984cc 115hp 4 Cyl
D = 1781cc 148hp 4 Cyl
D = 1781cc 150hp 4 Cyl
F = 1896cc 96hp 4 Cyl Diesel
G = 2792cc 174hp 6 Cyl
K = 1984cc 115hp 4 Cyl
P = 1896cc 90hp 4 Cyl
S = 1984cc 115hp 4 Cyl
T = 1984cc 115hp 4 Cyl

6th POSITION
RESTRAINT SYSTEM
2 = Dr/Pass Airbag & active Frnt Dr/Pass side Airbag
4 = Dr/Pass Active & Airbag
6 = Dr/Pass Active & Airbag Front & Rear Side Airbag Side Curtain Airbag

7th & 8th POSITION
MODEL LINE
1C = New Beetle
1E = Cabrio/New Cabrio
1J = New Golf / GTI
1V = Cabrio
3B = Passat
70 = Eurovan
9M = Jetta

9th POSITION
CHECK DIGIT

10th POSITION
MODEL YEAR
Y = 2000
1 = 2001

11th POSITION
ASSEMBLY PLANT
4 = Curitiba
E = Emden
H = Hanover
M = Mexico
P = Mosel
W = Wolfsburg

12th Thru 17th POSITION
PRODUCTION SEQUENCE NUMBER

VW1130100077000X

Fig. 8 Volkswagen (Part 2 of 2)

1st Thru 3rd POSITION
MANUFACTURER CODE
YV1 = Volvo

4th POSITION
SERIES
A = 240 Series
B = 260 Series
D = 700 Series (83-85)
F = 740 Series
G = 760 Series
H = 780 Series
J = 940 Series
K = 940 SE / 960 Series
K = S90 / V90
L = 850 Series
L = S70 / V70
N = C70
R = S60
S = V70
T = S80
V = S40 / V40 Series

5th POSITION, 1980-91
RESTRAINT SYSTEM
A = 3 Point Seat Belt & Air Bag
X = 3 Point Seat Belt

5th POSITION, 1992-01
BODY TYPE / RESTRAINT SYSTEM
C = 2 Door Convertible, Dual Air Bags+Pretensioners
J = 5 Door AWD, Dual Air Bags+ Pretensioners
K = 2 Door Coupe, Dual Air Bags+Pretensioners
S = 4 Door, Driver Air Bag (92-93)
S = 4 Door, Dual Air Bags+Pretensioners (93-01)
T = 4 Door w Mechanical Pretensioners
T = 4 Door AWD & Dual Airbags & Pretensioners
V = 5 Door AWD, Dual Air Bags + Pretensioners
W = 5 Door, Driver Air Bag (92-93)
W = 5 Door, Dual Air Bags+pretensioners (93-01)
X = 5 Door w Mechanical Pre-Tensioner
Z = 5 Door V70XC AWD Dual Air Bags+ pretensioners

6th & 7th POSITION
ENGINE CODE
25 = B4204T2
29 = B4204T3
41 = B21A
45 = B21F Non-MPG
47 = B21FT
48 = B21F LH
49 = B21F MPG
50 = B5234T4
51 = B5252S
52 = B5234T6
53 = B5234T3
55 = B5254F, B5254S
56 = B5254T, B5244
56 = B5244T
57 = B5234FT, B5234T
58 = B5234T5
58 = B5244T3
58 = B5244T3 AWD/XC
60 = B5244T2
61 = B5244S
62 = B5234T8
69 = B28F, 280F
76 = D24T
77 = D24
82 = B230F
83 = B230FD
84 = B23E
86 = B230FT w/EGR Pulsair
87 = B230FT, B23FT

6th & 7th POSITION (Cont'd)
ENGINE CODE
88 = B230F, B23F
89 = B234F
90 = B6284T6
90 = B6284T
93 = B6254S
94 = B6294S
95 = B6304FS
96 = B63042S
96 = B6304S
97 = B6304S

8th POSITION, 1980-91
BODY TYPE
2 = 2 Door
4 = 4 Door
5 = 5 Door Wagon

8th POSITION, 1992-01
EMISSIONS CODE
0 = 49 State w/o EGR, Bosch (92-94)
0 = 50 State w/o EGR (95-97)
0 = w/o EGR, w/air pump (1998)
0 = w/o EGR,w/air pump (1998) engine (96)
1 = 50 State w/EGR, Bosch
3 = 49 State w/o EGR, Bendix (92-93)
3 = 49 State w/o EGR, Siemons (1994)
3 = 50 State w/EGR
3 = w/o EGR, w/o air pump (1998)
4 = w/o EGR, w/air pump (1998)
7 = w/o EGR, w/air pump (1998)
8 = w/o EGR, w/o air pump (1998)

S70, V70, C70 (Engines 53,55,56,58, 60,61,62)
A = w/o EGR, w/o air pump, w/OBDII, w/air-assisted fuel injectors, Denso, w/ RuLo,w/ORVR (55)
D = w/o EGR, w/o air pump, w/OBDII, w/variable valve timing, Bosch ME 7.0, w/RuLo, w/ORVR (53, 56, 62) Auto&Mnul (53),Auto,AWD (56,60-V70 R)
J = Auto & Mnul Trans
N = w/o EGR, w/o air pump, OBDIL, Variable valve timing, manifold Closed catalyst, Denso, Rulo, ORVR

S80 (Engines 90,94,97)
D = w/o EGR, w/o air pump, w/OBDII, w/variable valve timing, Bosch ME 7.0, w/RuLo, w/ORVR (90, 97) Auto Trans (90,94)

S40, V40 (Engine 25, 29)
5 = w/o EGR, w/o air pump, w/OBDII, w/variable valve timing, w/close-coupled catalyst, Siemens, w/RuLo, w/ORVR (25)(29) Auto Trans, USA

9th POSITION
CHECK DIGIT

10th POSITION
MODEL YEAR
A = 1980
B = 1981
C = 1982
D = 1983
E = 1984
F = 1985
G = 1986
H = 1987
J = 1988
K = 1989
L = 1990
M = 1991
N = 1992
P = 1993
R = 1994
S = 1995
T = 1996
V = 1997
W = 1998
X = 1999
Y = 2000
1 = 2001

11th POSITION
ASSEMBLY PLANT
A = Uddevalla, Sweden
F = Born, Netherlands
J = Uddevalla, Sweden
0 = Kalmar, Sweden
1 = Torslanda, Sweden
1 = Gothenburg, Sweden
2 = Ghent, Belgium
2 = Volvo Europe
3 = Halifax, Canada

12th Thru 17th POSITION
PRODUCTION SEQUENCE NUMBER

VV1130100059000X

Fig. 9 Volvo

COMPUTER RELEARN PROCEDURES

INDEX

	Page No.
Audi	0-10
Air Bag Control Module	0-10
ECM	0-10
Throttle Valve Control Module	0-10
BMW	0-10
Description	0-10
Porsche	0-11
Saab	0-10
Volkswagen	0-11
Air Bag Control Module	0-11
ECM	0-11

DESCRIPTION

A computer relearn procedure may be required on any vehicle equipped with body, engine or transmission control computers whenever battery power to the computer is interrupted. These computers gather and store information on vehicle operation. They use this information to provide maximum driveability and vehicle performance.

AUDI

AIR BAG CONTROL MODULE

Whenever the air bag control module is replaced, the new control module must be coded as follows:

1. Connect VAG 1551, or equivalent scan tool, to diagnostic connector
2. Press buttons 0 and 7 to select "Code Control Module" function 07.
3. Press Q button to confirm input.
4. "Rapid Data Transfer" will be displayed. Press Q button to confirm input.
5. "Code Control Module" will be displayed.
6. **On A6 models,** enter code number 00001, noting the following:
   a. Character positions one and two, 00, filler characters with no significance.
   b. Character position three, 0, A6 series.
   c. Character position four, 0, arming code, static.
   d. Character position five, 1, sedan or 2, wagon.
7. **On A8 models,** enter code 00224.
8. **On all models,** press Q button to confirm input.
9. "Interior Monitor" will be displayed. Press right arrow button.
10. "Rapid Data Transfer" will be displayed.
11. Press buttons 0 and 6 to select "End Output" function 06.
12. "Rapid Data Transfer" will be displayed.
13. Press Q button to confirm input.

ECM

Whenever the ECM is replaced, the new ECM will need to be "Coded." Use the following procedure to "Code" the ECM. Motronic ECM-J220 only uses the code that has been entered after the ignition has been switched Off once.

Country/Emissions	Drivetrain/Options	Transmission	Vehicle type
00 = ———	0 = Front-wheel drive without traction control (ASR)	0 = 5-speed manual	0 = ———
01 = ———	1 = Front-wheel drive with traction control (ASR)	1 = ———	1 = ———
02 = ———	2 = All-wheel drive without traction control (ASR)	2 = ———	2 = A6
03 = ———	3 = All-wheel drive with traction control (ASR)	3 = ———	3 = ———
04 = ———	4 = ———	4 = ———	4 = ———
05 = ———	5 = ———	5 = Automatic trans. 01V	5 = ———
06 = USA, equipped with EVAP system Leak Detection Pump (LDP)	6 = ———	6 = ———	6 = ———

AD1029800140000X

Fig. 1 ECM coding variations. Audi

1. Connect VAG 1551 scan tool and VAG 1551/3 adapter cable, or equivalents, to diagnostic connector.
2. Press buttons 0 and 1 to insert "Engine Electronics" address word 01 (Ignition Switched On).
3. "Rapid Data Transfer" will be displayed.
4. Press buttons 0 and 7 to select "Code Control Module" function 07, then press Q button to confirm input.
5. Input applicable code number for vehicle, **Fig. 1,** noting the following:
   a. Press Q button to confirm input.
   b. If function is unknown or cannot be carried out, incorrect code number has been entered.
6. ECM identification and coding will be displayed.
7. Press right arrow button to advance through program sequence.
8. Press buttons 0 and 6 to select "End Output" function 06, then press Q button to confirm input.

THROTTLE VALVE CONTROL MODULE

A6

When the throttle valve control module is removed and installed or replaced, adaptation of the throttle valve control module to the Motronic ECM is required. Refer to the following procedure.

1. Prepare vehicle as follows:
   a. Ensure no malfunctions are stored in memory.
   b. Ensure throttle valve is in closed throttle position.
   c. Ensure cruise control adjustment and power supply for throttle valve control module are as specified.
2. Connect VAG 1551 scan tool and VAG 1551/3 adapter cable, or equivalents, to diagnostic connector.
3. Press buttons 0 and 1 to insert "Engine Electronics" address word 01 (Ignition Switched On).
4. "Rapid Data Transfer" will be displayed.
5. Press buttons 0 and 4 to select "Basic Setting" function 04, then press Q button to confirm input.
6. System in "Basic Setting" will be displayed.
7. Press buttons 0, 6 and 0 to input display group 060, then press Q button to confirm input.

BMW

Disconnect or replace DME control unit only when ignition switch is off. After renewed operation, neutral basic values are set in the control unit for idle and emission control. Any irregularities in engine operation can be directed by means of renewed adaptations (new learned values) during a test drive, in which and engine temperature of 80°C or greater is reached.

SAAB

If the battery has been disconnected or the ECM/PCM replaced, test drive the vehicle for adaptation of new ECM/PCM.

Catalytic converter version	Vehicle Ident. Number	Catalytic converter item number
OBD II control module	WP0xx**2**xxx**W**xxxxxxx	996.113.021.53 996.113.022.53
RoW control module	WPO**ZZZ**xxx**W**xxxxxxx	996.113.021.52 996.113.022.52
German control module (tri-metal catalytic converter)	WPO**ZZZ**xxx**W**xxxxxxx	996.113.021.54 996.113.022.54
OBD II control module	WP0xx**2**xxx**X**xxxxxxx	996.113.021.53 996.113.022.53
RoW control module	WPO**ZZZ**xxx**X**xxxxxxx	996.113.021.52 996.113.022.52
German control module (tri-metal catalytic converter)	WPO**ZZZ**xxx**X**xxxxxxx	996.113.021.54 996.113.022.54

PR1139900028000X

Fig. 2 DME programming codes. 911 Carrera

Catalytic converter version	Vehicle Ident. Number	Catalytic converter item number
OBD II control module (**V**-range)	WP0xx**2**xxx**V**xxxxxxx	996.113.031.06 996.113.032.06
RoW control module (bi-metal catalytic converter)	WPO**ZZZ**xxx**V**xxxxxxx	996.113.021.06 996.113.022.06 996.113.921.01 996.113.922.01
RoW control module (bi-metal catalytic converter)	WPO**ZZZ**xxx**W**xxxxxxx	996.113.021.08 996.113.022.08 996.113.021.09 996.113.022.09 996.113.921.01 996.113.922.01
OBD II control module (**W**-range)	WP0xx**2**xxx**W**xxxxxxx	996.113.021.05 996.113.022.05 996.113.021.06 996.113.022.06 996.113.021.08 996.113.022.08 996.113.021.09 996.113.022.09
RoW control module (tri-metal catalytic converter, **X**-range)	WPO**ZZZ**xxx**X**xxxxxxx	996.113.021.10 996.113.022.10
OBD II control module (tri-metal catalytic converter, **X**-range)	WP0xx**2**xxx**X**xxxxxxx	996.113.021.10 996.113.022.10 996.113.931.00 996.113.932.00

PR1139900029000X

Fig. 3 DME programming codes. Boxster

PORSCHE

When a Digital Monitor Electronics (DME) control module is replaced, it must be reprogrammed. The vehicle identification number, catalytic converter number corresponding to the catalytic converter version used and DME and immobilizer programming codes must be provided before programming DME.

1. Connect Porsche system tester 2, or vehicle, to vehicle.
2. Place ignition in On position.
3. Select vehicle type.
4. Select DME in control unit menu, then press double arrow key.
5. Select PROGRAM CONTROL UNIT, then press double arrow key.
6. Select READ CONTROL UNITS, then press double arrow key.
7. Install new DME.
8. Select PROGRAM CONTROL UNIT, then press double arrow key.
9. Display reads INPUT VEHICLE IDENT. NUMBER. Press double arrow key to accept number.
10. Press F7 key to confirm input.
11. Display reads INPUT OLD DME PROGRAMMING CODE.
12. Input old DME programming code, then press double arrow key.
13. Press F7 key to confirm input.
14. Display reads INPUT NEW DME PROGRAMMING CODE.
15. Input new DME programming code, then press double arrow key.
16. Press F7 key to confirm input.
17. Display reads INPUT NEW IMMOBILIZER CODE.
18. Input immobilizer code, then press double arrow key.
19. Press F7 key to confirm input.
20. Display reads SELECT DATA RECORD.
21. Select data record, **Figs. 2 and 3,** then press double arrow key.
22. Control module will take five minutes to program. **Do not interrupt programming process.**

VOLKSWAGEN

AIR BAG CONTROL MODULE

Whenever the air bag control module is replaced, the new module will need to be "Coded." Use the following procedure to "Code" the ECM.

1. Connect VAG 1551, or equivalent scan tool, to diagnostic connector.
2. Place ignition in On position.
3. Press button 1 to select "Rapid Data Transfer" mode.
4. Press buttons 1 and 5 to select "Airbag" address word 15, then press Q button to confirm entry.
5. Press right arrow button.
6. Press buttons 0 and 7 to select "Code Control Module" function 07, then press Q button to confirm entry.
7. Enter appropriate code, noting the following:
   a. For driver/passenger air bag, enter code 00067.
   b. For driver/passenger and side air bag, enter code 00066.
   c. Press Q button to confirm entry.
8. Press right arrow button.
9. Press buttons 0 and 6 to end output, then press Q button to confirm entry. Ensure air bag malfunction indicator lamp turns off after four seconds.

ECM

Whenever the ECM is replaced, the new ECM will need to be "Coded." Use the following procedure to "Code" the ECM.

1. Connect VAG 1551/1552, or equivalent scan tool to diagnostic connector.
2. Select "Engine Electronics" address word "01", then press "Q" button to confirm input.
3. Press "right arrow" button, "Rapid Data Transfer" and "Select function XX" should appear on the display.
4. Press "1" button two times, "Log-in Procedure" and "Input Code Number" should appear on the display.
5. Press "0, 1, 2, 8 and 3" to input log-in code, then press "Q" button to confirm input.
6. "Rapid Data Transfer" and "Select function XX" should appear on the display.
7. Press "0" and "7" buttons to access "Code Control Module" function, then press "Q" to confirm input.
8. "Code Control Module" and "Input Code Number" should appear on the display.
9. Input five digit code number as follows:
   a. **On Golf and Jetta models with manual transaxles,** code number is "00000."
   b. **On Golf and Jetta models with automatic transaxles,** code number is "00001."
   c. **On Cabrio models with manual transaxle,** code number is "00002."
   d. **On Cabrio models with automatic transaxle,** code number is "00003."
   e. **On Passat models with manual transaxle,** code number is "00006."
   f. **On Passat models with automatic transaxle,** code number is "00007."
10. ECM identification with coding input should be displayed on scan tool.
11. Press right arrow button "Rapid Data Transfer" and "Select function" should appear on the display.
12. Press "0" and "6" buttons of the scan tool "Rapid Data Transfer" and "06 End Output should now be displayed."
13. Press "Q" button to confirm input, then disconnect scan tool.
14. ECM will use the correct coding after the ignition has been switched off once.

AIR BAG SYSTEM PRECAUTIONS

INDEX

	Page No.
Audi	0-12
Arming	0-12
Disarming	0-12
BMW	0-12
Arming	0-12
Disarming	0-12
Jaguar	0-12
Arming	0-12
Disarming	0-12
Land Rover	0-12
Arming	0-12
Disarming	0-12
Mercedes-Benz	0-13
Arming	0-13
Disarming	0-13
Porsche	0-13
Arming	0-13
Disarming	0-13
Saab	0-13
Arming	0-13
Disarming	0-13
Volkswagen	0-13
Arming	0-13
Disarming	0-13
Volvo	0-13
Arming	0-13
Disarming	0-13

AUDI

DISARMING

Front

Prior to disconnecting any air bag system electrical connectors, servicing system components or servicing other components located near an air bag system electrical connector, the system must be disarmed. Also, prior to disconnecting the battery ground cable, it is necessary to obtain the radio security code. It may also be necessary to reestablish the engine control module and automatic transmission control module basic settings using scan tool No. VAG 1551, or equivalent.

1. Disconnect battery ground cable.
2. Cover battery negative terminal.

Side

The rear driver side and rear passenger side air bags can only be switched off together. The harness connectors are located on the left and right sides of the vehicle C-pillar.

1. Remove rear seat bench.
2. Disconnect air bag connector.
3. Change coding of air bag control module from 00204 to 00104 or 00206 to 00106 as described under "Computer Relearn Procedures."

ARMING

Front

1. Connect battery ground cable. **When connecting battery ground cable, ensure no one is inside vehicle.**
2. Place ignition switch in On position, the air bag indicator lamp should be illuminated for approximately 10 seconds. After approximately 10 seconds, the air bag indicator lamp should go off.
3. If air bag indicator lamp does not illuminate or remains On after approximately 10 seconds, a condition in the air bag system is present.

Side

1. Remove rear seat bench.
2. Connect harness connector for side air bags.
3. Insert connector in rear seat bench cushion opening, then install rear seat bench.
4. Change coding of air bag control module from 00104 to 00204 or 00106 to 00206 as described under "Computer Relearn Procedures."

BMW

DISARMING

Prior to disconnecting any air bag/ Supplemental Restraint System (SRS) electrical connectors, servicing any system components or other components located near an SRS electrical connector, the system must be disarmed. The connectors and components are identified by their orange color.

1. Disconnect and isolate battery ground cable.
2. Remove steering column lower cover, then disconnect orange air bag connector located on the column below the steering wheel, **Fig. 1.**
3. Wait at least ten minutes prior to performing any service. **If the air bag warning lamp is lit on models equipped with Air Bag II system, a ten minute waiting period must be observed. The SRS is designed to retain enough deployment voltage for a short time even after the ground cable has been disconnected. Performing service before the minimum time elapses may cause unexpected deployment and possible injury.**

ARMING

1. Connect orange air bag connector located below the steering wheel on the column, **Fig. 1.**
2. Install steering column lower cover.
3. Ensure no one is inside vehicle, then connect the battery ground cable.
4. Turn ignition switch to On position and observe air bag indicator lamp. Lamp should light for approximately six seconds, then go off. If lamp flashes and remains lit after six seconds or does not light at all, an SRS problem is indicated.

JAGUAR

DISARMING

1. Record clock, radio, seats, mirrors, steering column and other memory components settings.
2. Turn ignition switch to Lock position and remove key.
3. Disconnect battery ground cable.
4. Wait at least one minute for back-up power supply to discharge.
5. **On XJ models,** if disarming system for diagnostic testing, proceed as follows:
   a. Remove both air bag modules.
   b. Connect air bag simulator tools No. JAG 7956, or equivalent, into system.
   c. Connect battery ground cable.

ARMING

1. **On XJ models,** if arming system following diagnostic testing, proceed as follows:
   a. Disconnect battery ground cable.
   b. Remove air bag simulators.
   c. Install both air bag modules.
2. **On all models,** connect battery ground cable.
3. Turn ignition switch to On position and ensure air bag MIL lamp turns off after approximately six seconds.
4. Reset clock, radio, seats, mirrors, steering column and other memory components.

LAND ROVER

DISARMING

1. Turn ignition switch to Lock position and remove key.
2. Disconnect battery ground cable, then the positive cable.
3. The air bag/Supplemental Restraint System (SRS) will store sufficient deployment voltage for up to 20 minutes after battery has been disconnected. To perform immediate service, disconnect both driver's and passenger's air bag module electrical connectors.

ARMING

1. **Ensure no one is inside vehicle.**
2. Connect battery positive cable, then the ground cable.

3. Turn ignition switch to On position and note air bag lamp operation. Lamp should light for approximately seven seconds, then go off. **If lamp does not light or flashes, an SRS malfunction is indicated.**

MERCEDES-BENZ

DISARMING

When battery is disconnected, vehicle electronic memory will be lost. Make notes of radio stations and other codes. Never use a back-up power source to retain memory.

1. Place ignition switch in Off position, then remove ignition key.
2. Disconnect all air bag squib SRS (red) electrical connectors.
3. Wait 10 minutes before starting any repairs to allow the back-up power supply to discharge.
4. If welding is to be performed on vehicle, disconnect and isolate battery ground cable, then disconnect control module connector.

ARMING

1. Ensure ignition is turned Off and nobody is inside vehicle.
2. Connect SRS red electrical connectors.
3. If disconnected, connect battery ground cable.
4. Turn ignition to On position. Air bag warning lamp, which should light for approximately four seconds, then go off. If lamp fails to light or remains illuminated after 10 seconds, there is a system malfunction.

PORSCHE

DISARMING

1. Turn ignition switch to off position.
2. Disconnect and isolate battery ground cable.
3. Wait at least 1 minute before beginning diagnosis or repairs. This is necessary to allow the air bag's back-up power supply to discharge.

ARMING

1. Turn ignition switch to off position.
2. Connect battery ground cable.

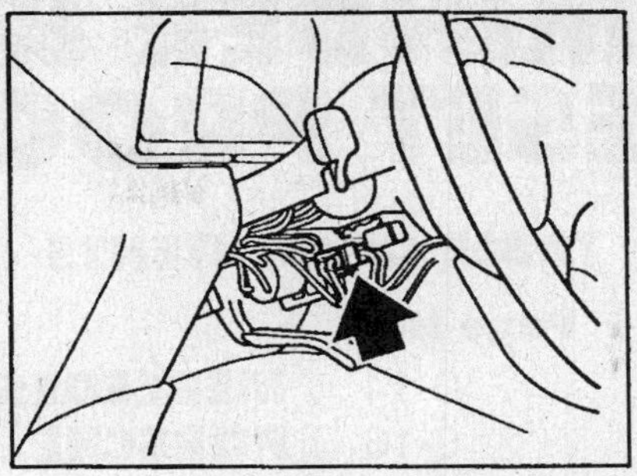

BM8019400100000X

Fig. 1 Air bag orange electrical connector location. BMW

3. Turn ignition switch to On position and note air bag warning lamp operation.
4. Lamp should light for approximately three seconds, then go off.
5. If lamp fails to light or remains illuminated, an air bag system malfunction is indicated. Diagnose and repair as necessary.

SAAB

DISARMING

1. Disconnect battery ground cable.
2. Prior to performing any service or diagnostic procedure, wait at least 20 seconds for back up power supply to deplete.

ARMING

1. Connect battery ground cable. **Ensure no one is inside vehicle when connecting battery ground cable.**
2. Turn ignition switch to On position and note SRS warning lamp operation. The SRS warning lamp should light for approximately six seconds, then go off. If lamp remains illuminated or fails to light, an SRS malfunction is indicated. Diagnose and repair as necessary.

VOLKSWAGEN

DISARMING

Do not use the computer memory saver tool on air bag equipped models. Using this tool will keep the system charged and may cause unexpected air bag unit activation. Obtain the radio security code prior to disconnecting the battery ground cable. After service has been completed and the cable connected, use this code to activate the radio.

1. Disconnect battery ground cable.
2. **Wait 20 minutes to allow air bag/ Supplemental Restraint System (SRS) capacitor to discharge prior to performing any service procedures.**

ARMING

1. **Ensure no one is in vehicle, then connect battery ground cable.**
2. Turn ignition switch to On position and note air bag warning lamp operation. Lamp should light for three to eight seconds, then go off. If lamp fails to light or remains lit after eight seconds, an SRS malfunction is indicated. Diagnose and repair as necessary.

VOLVO

DISARMING

Obtain radio anti-theft code prior to disconnecting the battery ground cable. On models equipped with a microprocessor radio, always turn the radio off before disconnecting or connecting the battery ground cable to prevent radio damage.

To disarm air bag/Supplemental Restraint System (SRS), turn the ignition switch to the off position, then disconnect the battery ground cable. Wait at least ten seconds after disconnection to perform any service procedures. The SRS is designed to retain deployment voltage for a short time even after the battery ground cable has been disconnected. Performing service before the minimum ten second wait may cause unexpected deployment and possible injury.

ARMING

To arm the SRS, turn the ignition switch to the off position, then connect the battery ground cable. Wait at least ten seconds, then turn the ignition switch to the On position. The SRS warning lamp should light for approximately ten seconds, then go off. If the lamp does not light or remains lit after the ten second interval, an SRS malfunction is indicated. Diagnose and repair as necessary.

SERVICE REMINDER & WARNING LAMP RESET PROCEDURES

TABLE OF CONTENTS

	Page No.		Page No.
AUDI	0-14	MERCEDES-BENZ	0-19
BMW	0-16	PORSCHE	0-19
JAGUAR	0-18	SAAB	0-20
LAND ROVER	0-18	VOLKSWAGEN	0-21
		VOLVO	0-22

Audi

INDEX

	Page No.
Auto-Check Indicator System	0-14
Brake Pad Wear Indicator	0-14
Electronic Ignition Warning Lamp	0-14
"Check Engine" Lamp	0-14
Service Reminder Indicator	0-14
Less Scan Tool	0-14
With Scan Tool	0-14

AUTO-CHECK INDICATOR SYSTEM

The auto-check system will monitor certain vehicle systems when the ignition switch is placed in the On position and vehicle is operated. When all monitored systems are functioning properly, the system display will indicate "OK" for a few seconds after the ignition switch is placed in the On position.

This system monitors brake fluid level and hydraulic pressure, engine oil pressure, coolant temperature and level, brake pad wear, headlamps and tail lamps, battery voltage, washer fluid level and fuel level.

When the auto-check yellow or red indicator lamp is lit, the corresponding instrument cluster warning lamp will also be illuminated and a warning tone will sound. If multiple components are not functioning properly, the indicated component warning lamps will blink in one second intervals.

When the yellow auto-check lamp is lit, the indicated component should be serviced as soon as possible. When the red auto-check lamp is lit, the indicated component must be serviced immediately. **After necessary repairs have been performed, the auto-check lamp will automatically reset.**

BRAKE PAD WEAR INDICATOR

The brake pad wear warning lamp will be illuminated when disc brake pads wear down beyond a specified limit. **Brake pad replacement will reset the warning lamp.**

"CHECK ENGINE" LAMP

The "Check Engine" lamp will be illuminated when the ignition switch is placed in the On position. After the engine is started, the lamp should go off. If the lamp remains lit, a diagnostic trouble code has been stored in the Electronic Control Unit (ECU) memory. **If the diagnostic trouble code is stored in temporary memory, the lamp will go off after the necessary repairs have been completed and the ignition switch is cycled between Off and On positions. If a diagnostic trouble code has been stored in permanent memory, complete repairs and proceed as follows:**

1. With ignition switch in Off position, insert fuse into top of fuel pump relay.
2. Place ignition switch in On position and, after approximately four seconds, remove fuse from top of fuel pump relay.
3. Insert fuse again into top of fuel pump relay for approximately ten seconds, then remove.
4. Cycle ignition switch between On and Off positions to reset "Check Engine" lamp, if necessary.

ELECTRONIC IGNITION WARNING LAMP

The electronic ignition system warning lamp will be illuminated when the ignition switch is placed in the On position. After the engine is started, the lamp should go off. **If the lamp lights during engine operation, a knocking condition is indicated or a problem has arisen in the ignition system. If lit due to a knock, the lamp will go off when engine speed is reduced; ensure the fuel has an anti-knock index of at least 87 octane. If lamp remains lit and no knocking is indicated, the ignition system should be inspected; the lamp will go off when the system is functioning properly.**

SERVICE REMINDER INDICATOR

WITH SCAN TOOL

1. Connect VAG 1551 scan tool and VAG 1551/3 adapter cable, or equivalents, to diagnostic connector.
2. "Rapid Data Transfer" will be displayed.
3. Initiate adaptation function 10 as follows:
   a. Press buttons 1 and 0 to select adaptation function 10.
   b. Press Q button to confirm input.
4. Press buttons 0 and 2 to insert channel number 02.
5. Press Q button to confirm input.

LESS SCAN TOOL

1. Place ignition to Off position.
2. Press reset button for trip recorder in instrument cluster and place ignition switch in On position, both at the same time.

3. “Service Oil” will appear on trip recorder display.
4. Pull out clock adjuster knob in instrument cluster and hold in position until message “Service Oil” is cancelled.
5. Trip recorder should now display “Service - - -.”
6. Press trip recorder reset button again to call up next service message, “Service INSP.”
7. Pull out clock adjuster knob in instrument cluster and hold in position until message “Service INSP” is cancelled.
8. Trip recorder will now display “Service - - -.”
9. Place ignition in Off position.

BMW

INDEX

	Page No.
Catalytic Converter & EGR Maintenance Reminder Lamp	0-16
"Check Engine" Lamp	0-16
Service Indicator Cluster	0-16
Service Interval Indicator	0-17
Interval Indicator	0-17
Oil Service	0-17

CATALYTIC CONVERTER & EGR MAINTENANCE REMINDER LAMP

The instrument panel catalyst (CAT) and EGR lamps will be illuminated every 25,000 miles as a reminder for service. **After the appropriate service has been completed, reset elapsed mileage switch.** The elapsed mileage switch is located under instrument panel, depress the white buttons marked CAT and EGR, **Fig. 1.** The catalytic converter and EGR lamp will go off when these buttons are depressed.

SERVICE INDICATOR CLUSTER

The service indicator cluster is used indicate when periodic maintenance is required. The service indicator consists of one yellow, five green and three red Light Emitting Diodes (LEDs), with the inscriptions "Oil Service" and "Inspection." When the ignition switch is turned to the On position, as many as five green LEDs will be illuminated.

The green LEDs will go out when the engine is started. If the yellow LED and one of the inscriptions illuminates with the ignition switch in the On position, and remain On after the engine has started, service the maintenance inscription indicated immediately. When a periodic maintenance interval has been exceeded by 1000 miles or more, the red LED will light as well as the yellow LED as a reminder for service.

After completing the required service, the service indicator can be reset as follows:

1. Turn off all accessories and place ignition switch in On position with engine stopped.
2. Position reset tool No. 62-1-100 and, if necessary, adapter 62-1-142, or equivalents, into diagnostic connector, **Figs. 2 and 3.**
3. Diagnostic connector locations vary as follows:
   a. **On 3 Series models,** the diagnostic connector is located at the front lefthand side of the engine.
   b. **On 5 Series models,** the diagnostic connector is located on brace at front of the engine.

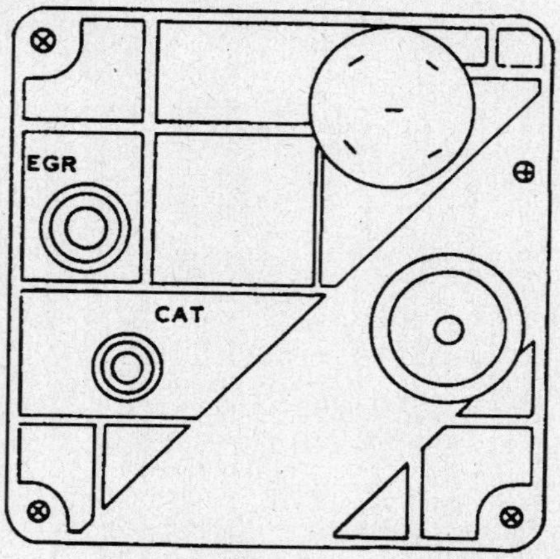

BM1139000001000X

Fig. 1 Catalyst & EGR maintenance reminder lamp reset switch identification. Early models

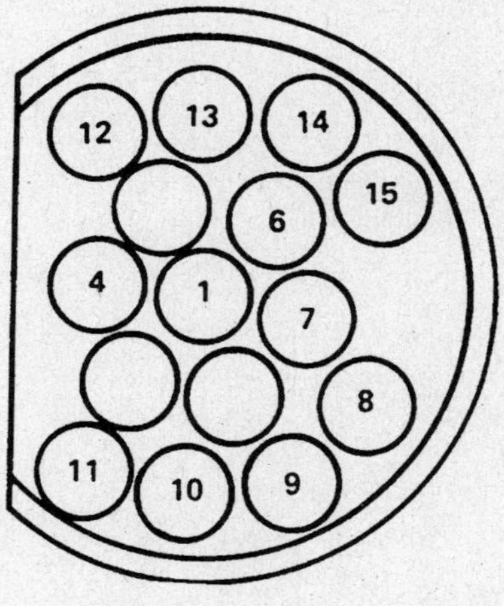

BM1139000003000X

Fig. 2 15-pin diagnostic connector pin identification

   c. **On 7 Series models,** the diagnosis connector is located in the engine compartment on the righthand strut tower.
4. **On all models,** to reset indicators after performing an engine oil and filter change, depress and hold yellow "OIL SERVICE" button of reset tool. Green function control lamp should be illuminated. After approximately ten seconds, the yellow lamp should illuminate for approximately three seconds, then turn off. Release tool oil service button, then check instrument panel LEDs. At least one additional green LED should be illuminated and the yellow or red LED and "OIL SERVICE" indicator should be off.
5. To reset indicators after performing an inspection procedure, depress and hold red inspection button of reset tool. Green function control lamp should be illuminated. After approximately three seconds, the red lamp should illuminate for approximately 12 seconds, then turn Off. Release tool inspection button, then check instrument panel LEDs. All five green LEDs should be lit and red and yellow LEDs and inspection indicator should be off.
6. If reset tool is not available, the service indicator LEDs maybe reset using a suitable digital voltmeter. **It should be noted that the service interval sequence accuracy may be disturbed by this procedure. Therefore, it is recommended that the reset tool be used, and that this procedure should only be followed when the reset tool is unattainable.** To reset indicator, turn off all accessories, then place ignition switch in the On position, engine not operating. Connect negative lead of digital voltmeter to ground, then contact positive lead of meter to pin 7 of the diagnostic connector for 10 to 12 seconds. After reset has been completed, LEDs should behave as described in preceding steps.

"CHECK ENGINE" LAMP

The "Check Engine" lamp will be illuminated when the ignition switch is in the On position and the engine is stopped. If the engine is started, the lamp should go out. If the lamp remains lit, a diagnostic trouble code has been stored. **After diagnosis and repair are complete, place the ignition switch in the Off position, then clear stored diagnostic trouble codes by disconnecting the battery ground cable for at least ten seconds.**

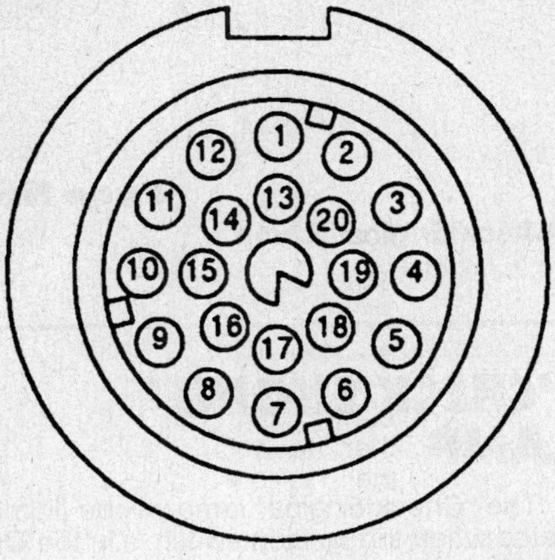

Fig. 3 20-pin diagnostic connector pin identification

SERVICE INTERVAL INDICATOR

OIL SERVICE

1. Turn ignition On, then attach resetter tool No. 61 1 110 to diagnosis plug in engine compartment.

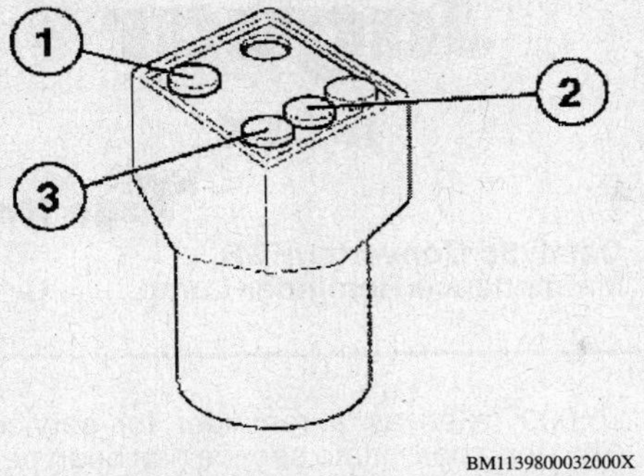

Fig. 4 Service interval indicator tool. BMW

2. Press yellow button (1) for oil service, **Fig. 4.**
3. Green lamp (2) lights up.
4. Wait until yellow lamp (3) lights and then goes out again.

INTERVAL INDICATOR

1. Turn ignition On, then attach resetter tool No. 61 1 110 to diagnosis plug in engine compartment.
2. Press red button (1) for service, **Fig. 5.**

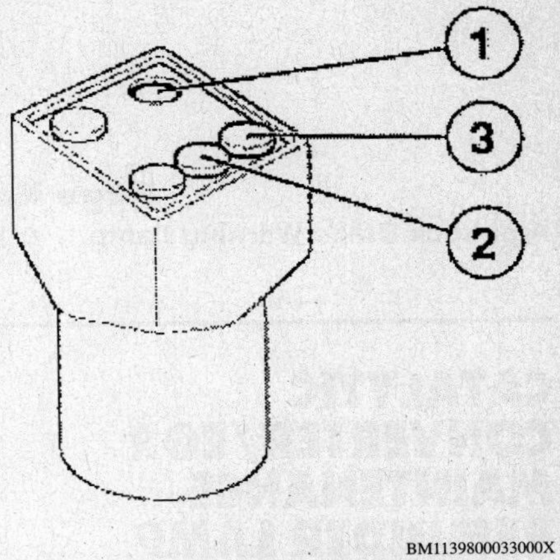

Fig. 5 Interval indicator tool. BMW

3. Press red button (1) for service.
4. Green lamp (2) lights up.
5. Wait until red lamp (3) lights up and then goes out again.
6. Turn Off ignition, wait 20 seconds and repeat procedure to adapt the interval for annual inspection to service.

Jaguar

INDEX

	Page No.
Anti-Lock Brake Warning Lamp	0-18
Catalytic Converter/EGR Maintenance Reminder Lamp	0-18
"Check Engine" Lamp	0-18

CATALYTIC CONVERTER/EGR MAINTENANCE REMINDER LAMP

The catalytic converter/EGR maintenance reminder indicator light is installed on the instrument panel. The mileage switch mechanism is built into the speedometer flexible drive line. The unit is a gear driven mechanical reduction device and is fitted with a magnetically operated reed switch. The catalytic converter/EGR maintenance reminder light will come on at 25,000 miles as a reminder for service. After the appropriate service has been performed, reset the mileage switch by inserting a reset key into the reset switch (through glove compartment). Turn key clockwise until "0" is obtained.

ANTI-LOCK BRAKE WARNING LAMP

This lamp is used to warn of a malfunction in the anti-lock brake system. **After system diagnosis and repair are complete, reset the lamp by driving the vehicle at a speed of 19 mph or more.**

"CHECK ENGINE" LAMP

The "Check Engine" lamp will be illuminated when the ignition switch is in the On position and the engine is not running. When the engine is started, the lamp should go out. If it remains lit, a diagnostic trouble code has been stored. **After diagnosis and repair are complete, place the ignition switch in the Off position, then clear stored diagnostic trouble codes by disconnecting the battery ground cable for at least ten seconds.**

Land Rover

INDEX

	Page No.
ABS Warning Lamp	0-18
Emission Maintenance Reminder ("Service Engine" Lamp)	0-18

ABS WARNING LAMP

The ABS warning lamp should light when the ignition switch is placed in the On position and go out when the vehicle speed exceeds 5 mph. This indicates that the ABS self-monitoring check was successful and no faults are present.

EMISSION MAINTENANCE REMINDER ("SERVICE ENGINE" LAMP)

The emission maintenance reminder is designed to activate at 52,500 miles and 105,000 miles and will illuminate a "Service Engine" warning lamp on the instrument cluster.

The emission maintenance reminder must be reset after the required service has been performed and a new tamper-proof label should be installed by a Land Rover of North America dealer. The reminder reset procedure is as follows:

1. **On Discovery models,** locate control unit in passenger footwell.
2. **On Range Rover models,** locate control unit below righthand front seat.
3. **On all models,** remove connector from control unit.
4. Remove tamper-proof label to reveal reset access hole.
5. Place a thin metallic probe into access hole and momentarily short between reset pins inside unit.

Mercedes-Benz

INDEX

	Page No.		Page No.
Catalytic Converter Maintenance Reminder Lamp	0-19	Oxygen Sensor Maintenance Reminder Lamp	0-19

CATALYTIC CONVERTER MAINTENANCE REMINDER LAMP

The catalytic converter maintenance reminder lamp, located on the instrument panel, will come on at 37,500 miles, indicating that the catalytic converter should be serviced. A mileage switch is installed behind the instrument panel and is driven by the speedometer cable. **After the necessary service is completed, depress the button marked "CAT" on mileage switch to reset lamp, Fig. 1.**

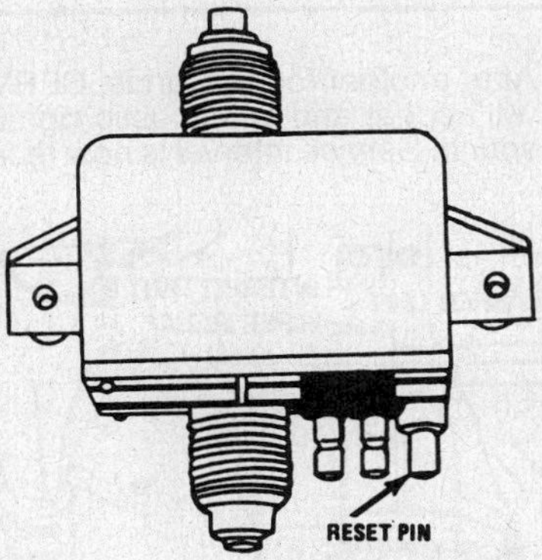

Fig. 1 Catalytic converter lamp reset pin location

OXYGEN SENSOR MAINTENANCE REMINDER LAMP

The oxygen sensor lamp is used as an oxygen sensor system circuit malfunction indicator. If the lamp illuminates, this indicates that system service should be conducted. **After the necessary service is completed, remove the oxygen sensor lamp bulb.**

Porsche

INDEX

	Page No.
EGR Indicator Lamp	
924 & 944 Turbo	0-19
Oxygen Sensor Lamp	0-19
911	0-19
924 & 944	0-19
928	0-19
"Check Engine" Lamp	0-19
DME & LH-Jetronic Fuel Systems	0-19

EGR INDICATOR LAMP

924 & 944 TURBO

After completing EGR system service, reset lamp by pushing in pin on elapsed mileage odometer. The elapsed mileage odometer is located behind the instrument cluster.

OXYGEN SENSOR LAMP

924 & 944

On 924 models, an OXS lamp will light at 30,000 mile intervals as a reminder to replace the oxygen sensor. **The 944 models do not use a warning lamp. On these models, however, it is recommended that the oxygen sensor be replaced every 60,000 miles.**

On 924 models, after replacing oxygen sensor and with vehicle still raised, locate mileage counter on left engine mount, then use a thick wire or thin metal rod to push in reset button. Ensure to push button in all the way to stop and that OXS lamp goes out.

911

An OXS lamp will light at 30,000 mile intervals as a reminder to replace the oxygen sensor. **After replacing the oxygen sensor, disconnect battery ground cable and remove speedometer. The mileage counter will be visible through speedometer mounting hole. Use a thick piece of wire or a thin rod to press white reset button on counter. Push button all the way in against stop.** Ensure warning lamp goes off.

928

The 928S (with LH Jetronic system) does not use a warning lamp. On these models, however, it is recommended that the oxygen sensor be replaced every 60,000 miles. On 928 and 928S (with CIS system) models, after replacing the oxygen sensor, reset the mileage counter which is located to the right of the passenger seat floor. Remove counter cover retaining screw and cover. Press reset button all the way in to against stop. Ensure warning lamp goes off.

"CHECK ENGINE" LAMP

DME & LH-JETRONIC FUEL SYSTEMS

The "Check Engine" lamp will be illuminated when the ignition switch is in the On position with engine not running. When the engine is started, the lamp should go out. If the lamp remains lit, a diagnostic trouble code has been stored by the Electronic Control Unit (ECU). **After diagnosis and repair are complete, place ignition switch in On position without starting engine, then depress accelerator pedal fully for more than 11 seconds. ECU memory should be cleared and the "Check Engine" lamp should be reset.**

Saab

INDEX

	Page No.
ABS Warning Lamp	0-20
Air Bag Warning Lamp	0-20
Central Warning Lamp	0-20
Charging Warning Lamp	0-20
Low Fuel Level Warning Lamp	0-20
Oil Pressure Warning Lamp	0-20
Oxygen Sensor Maintenance Reminder Lamp	0-20
"Check Engine" Lamp	0-20
Service Indicator	0-20
Automatic Reset	0-20
Manual Reset	0-20

"CHECK ENGINE" LAMP

The "Check Engine" lamp illuminates to indicate an electronic system malfunction and can also be used to display diagnostic trouble codes. **Following diagnosis and repair of a malfunction, the lamp will no longer illuminate if the system is operating properly.**

OXYGEN SENSOR MAINTENANCE REMINDER LAMP

The oxygen sensor warning lamp, marked EXH, is located on the instrument panel and will illuminate, at 30,000 mile intervals as a service reminder. **After the appropriate service has been performed, reset counter unit as shown in Figs. 1 and 2,** using the following procedure:

1. Remove padding from under instrument panel.
2. Remove counter unit cover retaining screws, then the cover.
3. Depress counter unit reset pin. Depressing reset pin will turn the EXH warning lamp off and reset the counter to zero.
4. Install counter unit cover, then install and tighten retaining screws.
5. Install padding under instrument panel.

SERVICE INDICATOR

MANUAL RESET

The Saab Information Display (SID) is equipped with a service indicator which shows the message TIME FOR SERVICE on the SID unit when it is time to service the vehicle.

The service message is shown when the day counter reaches 365 days or when 600 miles are left until next service. Refer to the following procedure to reset service indicator.

1. Hold down clear button for at least eight seconds.
2. CLEARED will appear on display after four seconds and an acoustic signal will sound.
3. After another four seconds, SERVICE will appear and an acoustic signal will sound. Service interval is now recalculated and day counter is zeroed.

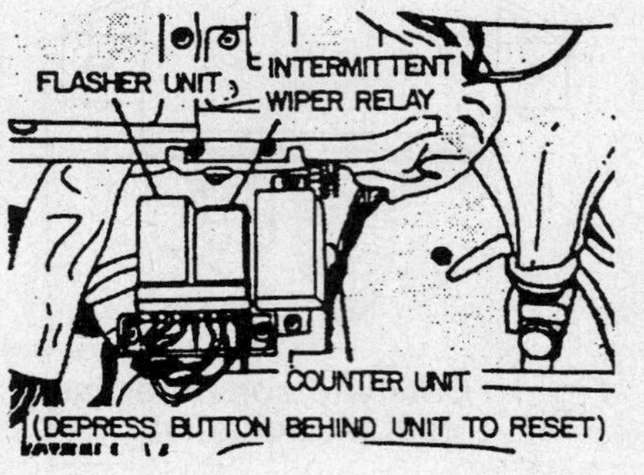

SA1139000001000X

Fig. 1 Counter unit location

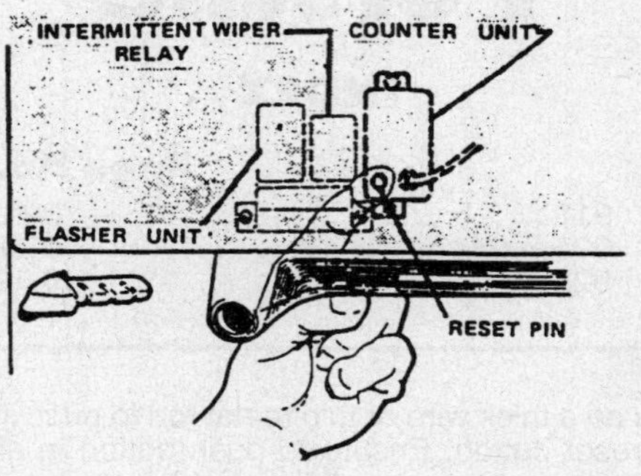

SA1139000002000X

Fig. 2 Resetting counter unit

AUTOMATIC RESET

The service message is reset automatically when it has been activated (shown) 20 times on the display. The service message can also be reset using a scan tool.

LOW FUEL LEVEL WARNING LAMP

When fuel tank fuel level falls below 2.64 gallons, the low fuel level warning lamp illuminates. The lamp will shut off once fuel level inside fuel tank is greater than 2.64 gallons.

CENTRAL WARNING LAMP

The central warning lamp illuminates when a fault occurs, if a warning lamp is illuminated in a system having to do with the vehicles safety (Air bag, oil pressure, brake fluid or ABS lamps) or engine coolant temperature exceeds 264° F. The lamp will reset once the malfunction is corrected.

OIL PRESSURE WARNING LAMP

If oil pressure falls below 4-7.25 psi, the oil pressure warning lamp will illuminate. The oil pressure warning lamp will shut off when oil pressure is above specified level.

CHARGING WARNING LAMP

When the alternator is not charging or rotating for any reason, the charging warning lamp will be illuminated. The charging warning lamp will shut off when the charging system malfunction is corrected.

AIR BAG WARNING LAMP

The air bag warning lamp informs the driver when a fault occurs in the air bag system. If a fault is detected, then air bag warning lamp and the central warning lamp will both illuminate. The warning lamps will shut off when the air bag system malfunction is corrected.

ABS WARNING LAMP

The ABS control module monitors the function of the ABS system and if a malfunction occurs, it illuminates the ABS warning lamp. The brake fluid warning lamp and central warning lamps will also illuminate when the ABS warning lamp is On.

When the ABS lamp illuminates, the ABS system is disabled and the brakes will function like conventional brakes. The ABS warning lamp will shut off when the ABS malfunction is corrected.

Volkswagen

INDEX

	Page No.
EGR Warning Lamp	0-21
Emission Control System (ESC) Lamp	0-21
Malfunction Indicator Lamp	0-21
OBD II	0-21
Oxygen Sensor Warning Lamp	0-21
Service Reminder Indicator Lamp	0-21

EGR WARNING LAMP

After performing the required service, turn off warning lamp, by pushing in reset button. On Jetta, GTI, Rabbit, Cabriolet, Golf and Scirocco models, remove instrument panel cover plate and insert a piece of wire, with a hooked end, through opening at top left corner of speedometer and pull left counter release arm. On Vanagon models, push in on raised area of reset module, which is located in line with speedometer cable.

EMISSION CONTROL SYSTEM (ESC) LAMP

This lamp should be illuminated when the ignition switch is placed in the On position. After engine is started the lamp should go off, unless a problem has been detected by the emission control system self-diagnostic computer. **After diagnosis and repair, the lamp will automatically reset when stored diagnostic trouble codes are cleared from the system memory.**

OXYGEN SENSOR WARNING LAMP

After performing the required service, turn off warning lamp by pushing in reset button. On Fox, Jetta, GTI, Rabbit, Cabriolet, Golf and Scirocco models, remove instrument panel cover plate and insert a piece of wire, with a hooked end, through opening at top left corner of speedometer and pull right counter release arm. On Vanagon models, push in on raised area of reset module, located in line with speedometer cable.

SERVICE REMINDER INDICATOR LAMP

This reminder appears in the odometer display window. When the ignition is turned On, the following displays will appear for about three seconds: IN 00, no service required; OEL, 7500 miles/6 month engine oil change; IN 01, 15,000 miles/12 month maintenance and inspection; IN 02, 30,000 miles/24 month maintenance and inspection.

After required procedures are completed, reset the SRI displays to:

1. 7500 Mile/6 Month, OEL
2. 15,000 Mile/12 Month, OEL, IN 01
3. 22,500 Mile/18 Months, OEL
4. 30,000 Mile/24 Months, OEL, IN 01, IN 02
5. 37,500 Mile/30 Months, OEL
6. 45,000 Mile/36 Months, OEL, IN 01
7. 52,500 Mile/42 Months, OEL
8. 60,000 Mile/48 Months, OEL, IN 01, IN 02

MALFUNCTION INDICATOR LAMP

OBD II

If malfunctions are recognized and verified by the engine control module, they will be indicated by switching on the MIL. Perform the functional check as follows: Turn the ignition switch to the ON position. The MIL must light up if the MIL does not light with the ignition switch on, check the bulb and/or locate and eliminate short or open in wiring circuit from the engine control module to MIL using a proper wiring diagram. If no malfunction can be detected in the wiring the ECM may be faulty. If the MIL lights with the ignition switch on, start engine and run at idle speed the MIL must go out after a few seconds. If the MIL does not go out Check the DTC memory.

Volvo

INDEX

	Page No.
Air Bag Warning Lamp	0-22
"Check Engine" Lamp...........	0-22
Service Indicator Lamp..........	0-22

AIR BAG WARNING LAMP

If the Air Bag warning lamp lights and stays on, diagnosis and repair of the air bag system will be necessary to reset the lamp.

"CHECK ENGINE" LAMP

This lamp should be illuminated when the ignition switch is placed in the On position. After the engine has been started, the lamp should go out. If it remains lit, a problem has been detected by the engine's self-diagnostic system. **After diagnosis and repair are complete and any stored diagnostic trouble codes are cleared, the lamp will reset automatically.**

SERVICE INDICATOR LAMP

Refer to **Fig. 1** for resetting the service reminder light.

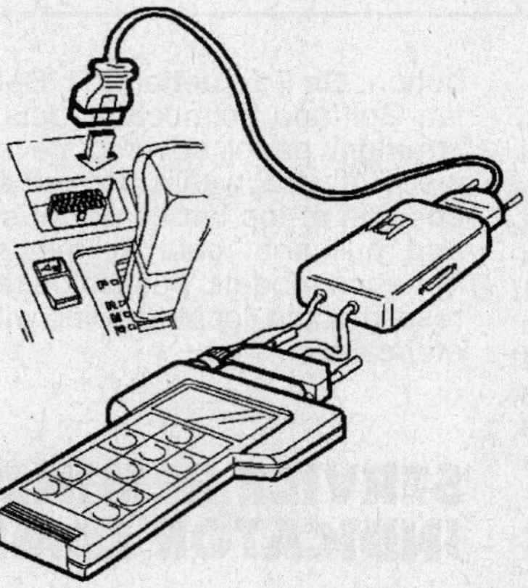

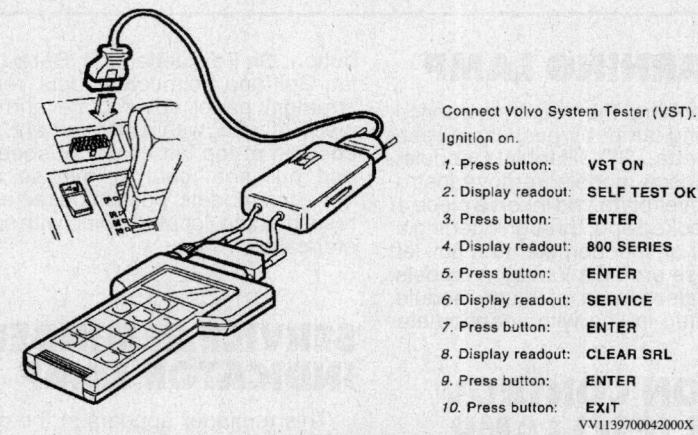

Connect Volvo System Tester (VST).
Ignition on.

1.	Press button:	VST ON
2.	Display readout:	SELF TEST OK
3.	Press button:	ENTER
4.	Display readout:	800 SERIES
5.	Press button:	ENTER
6.	Display readout:	SERVICE
7.	Press button:	ENTER
8.	Display readout:	CLEAR SRL
9.	Press button:	ENTER
10.	Press button:	EXIT

VV1139700042000X

Fig. 1 Service reminder indicator

AIR QUALITY STANDARDS

NOTE: Refer To The Most Current Edition of MOTOR's "Emission Control Systems Application" Guide For Federal & State Mandated Air Quality Standards.

VEHICLE LIFT POINTS

TABLE OF CONTENTS

	Page No.		Page No.
AUDI	0-24	**PORSCHE**	0-30
BMW	0-26	**SAAB**	0-31
JAGUAR	0-27	**VOLKSWAGEN**	0-32
LAND ROVER	0-29		

Audi

INDEX

	PAGE NO.	FIG. NO.
A4 SERIES	0-24	1
A6 SERIES	0-24	2
A8 SERIES	0-25	3
TT		
Front	0-25	4
Rear	0-25	5

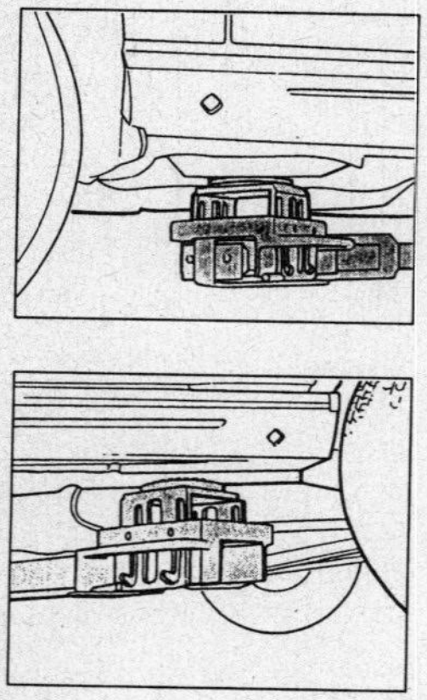

◄ Front
At side reinforcing plate of floor panel in area of stamped marking.
◄ Rear
Caution!
♦ Jack must not contact securing plate of semi-trailing arm otherwise serious damage could occur.
At reinforcing plate of lower sill in area of stamped marking.
AD1139600055000X

Fig. 1 A4 Series

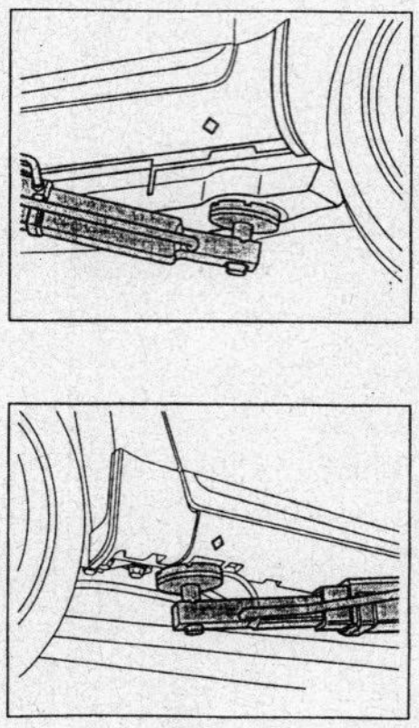

CAUTION!
To prevent damage, it is essential to use only lift pads, extensions or other accessories approved by the vehicle lift manufacturer.
Lifting points for vehicle lift and shop jack
◄ Front: at the longitudinal reinforcement of the floor pan at the area of the marking for the vehicle jack.
CAUTION!
Do not raise the vehicle at the vertical support on the rocker panel at the front of the vehicle.
◄ Rear: at the vertical reinforcement of the lower sill in the area of the marking for the vehicle jack.
AD1139800065000X

Fig. 2 A6 Series

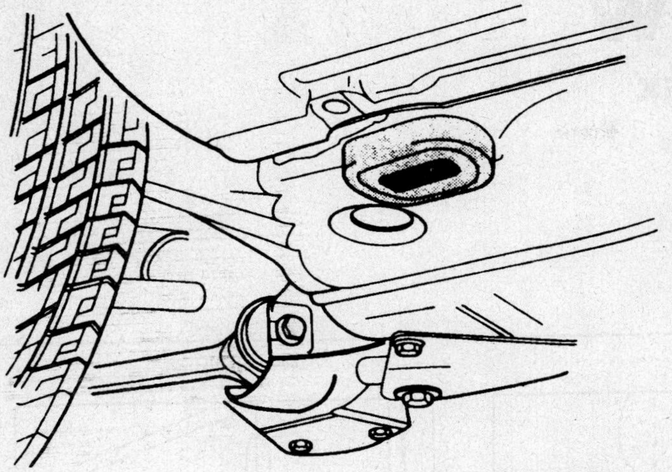
AD1139800086000X

Fig. 3 A8 Series

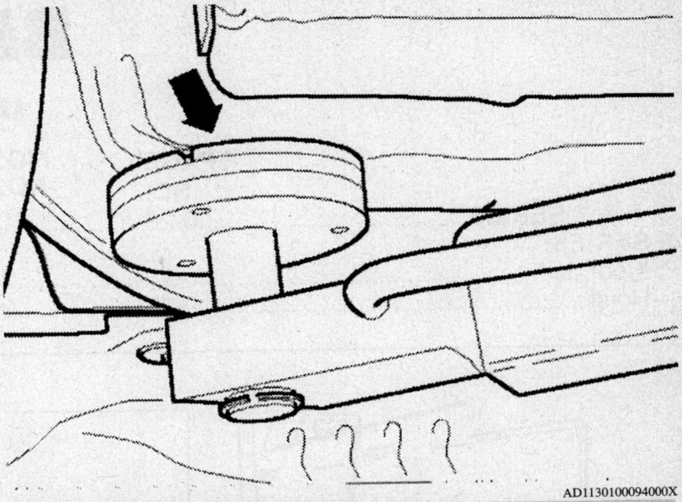
AD1130100094000X

Fig. 4 TT (Front)

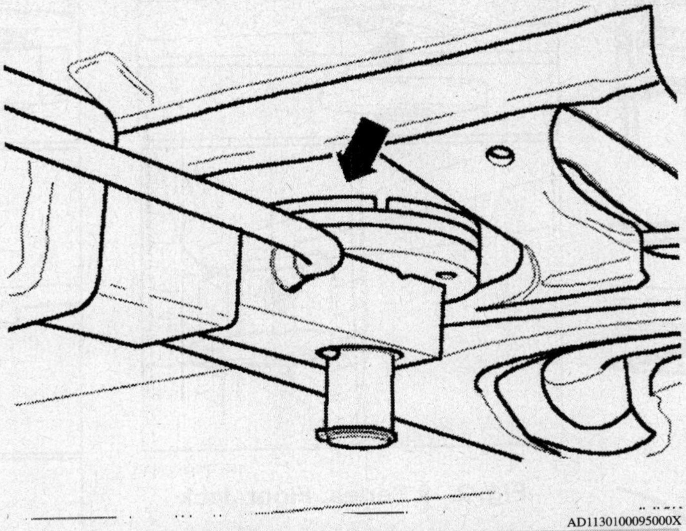
AD1130100095000X

Fig. 5 TT (Rear)

BMW

INDEX

	PAGE NO.	FIG. NO.
3, 5 & 7 SERIES	0-26	1
8 SERIES:		
Floor Jack	0-26	2
Hoist	0-26	3

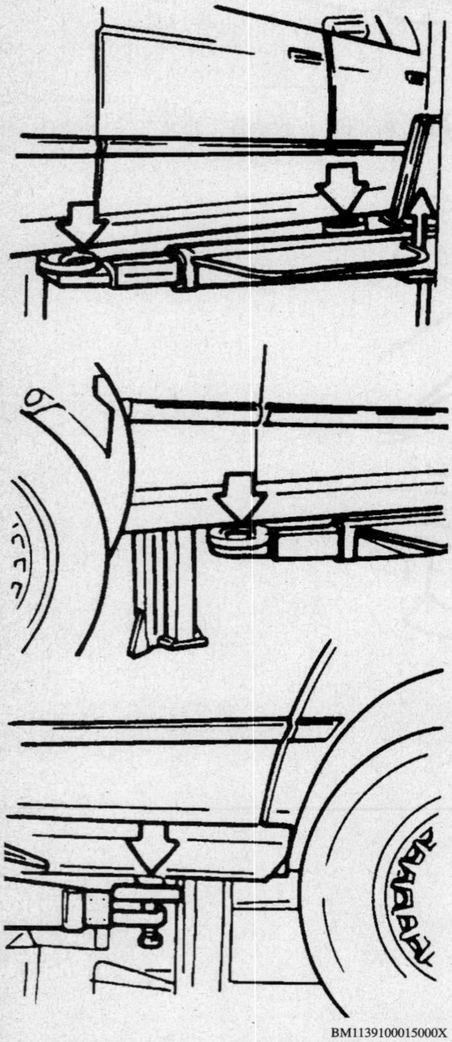

BM1139100015000X

Fig. 1 3, 5 & 7 Series

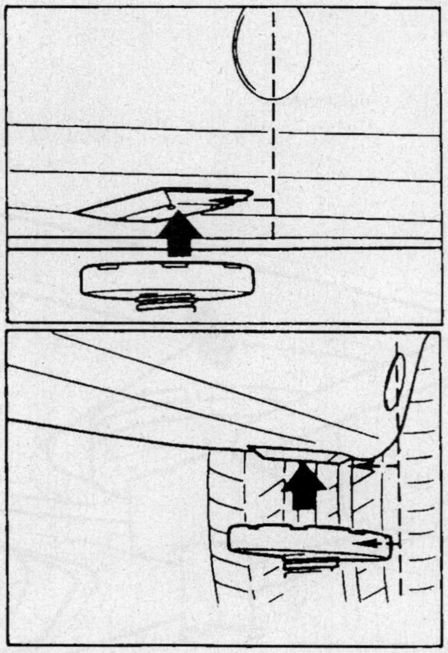

BM1139100017000X

Fig. 2 8 Series. Floor Jack

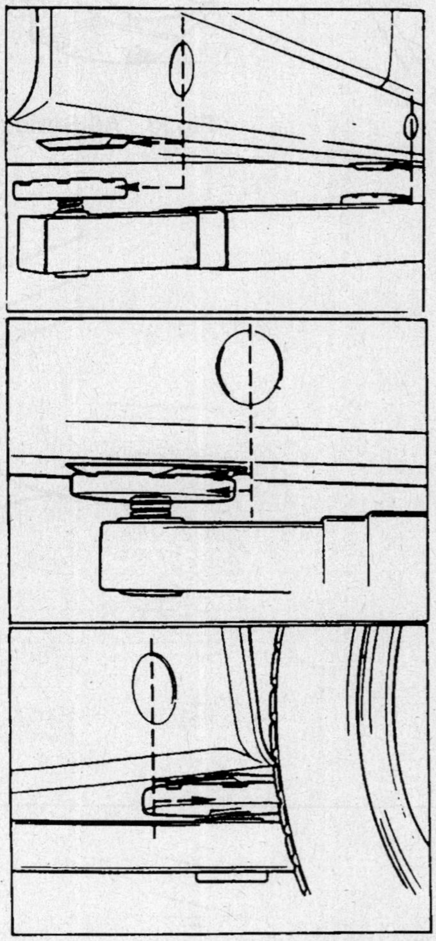

BM1139100024000X

Fig. 3 8 Series. Hoist

Jaguar

INDEX

	PAGE NO.	FIG. NO.
S-TYPE	0-27	1
XK8:		
Floor Jack:		
Front	0-27	2
Rear	0-27	3
XJ8	0-27	4

	PAGE NO.	FIG. NO.
XJS & XJ12:		
Floor Jack:		
Front	0-28	5
Rear	0-28	6
XJ6:		
Floor Jack:		
Front	0-28	7
Floor Jack	0-28	8

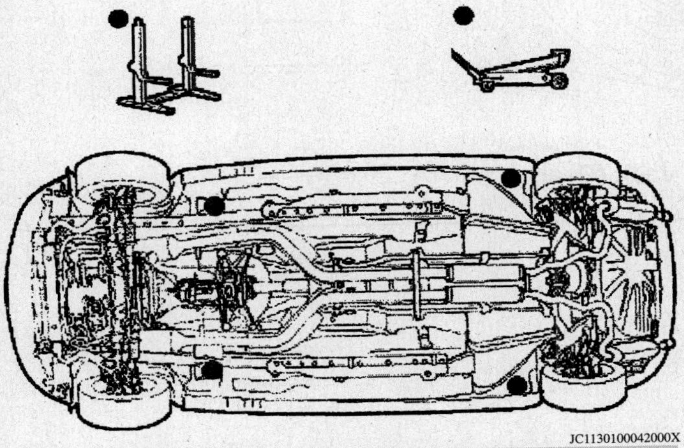

Fig. 1 S-Type

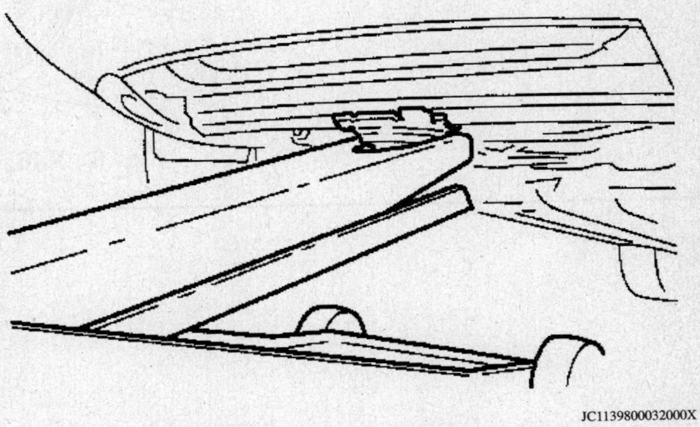

Fig. 2 XK8. Floor Jack (Front)

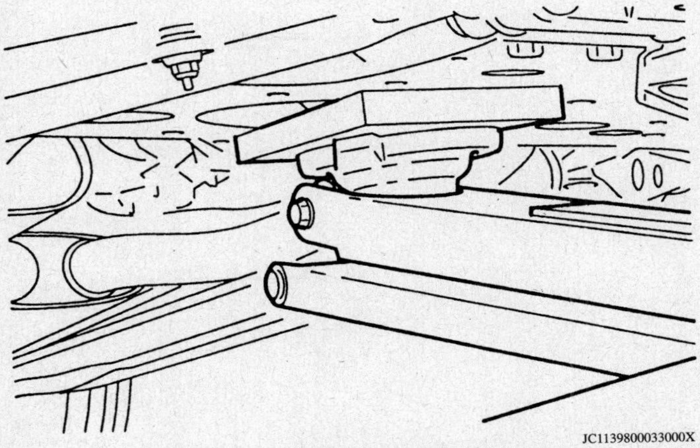

Fig. 3 XK8. Floor Jack (Rear)

Fig. 4 XJ8

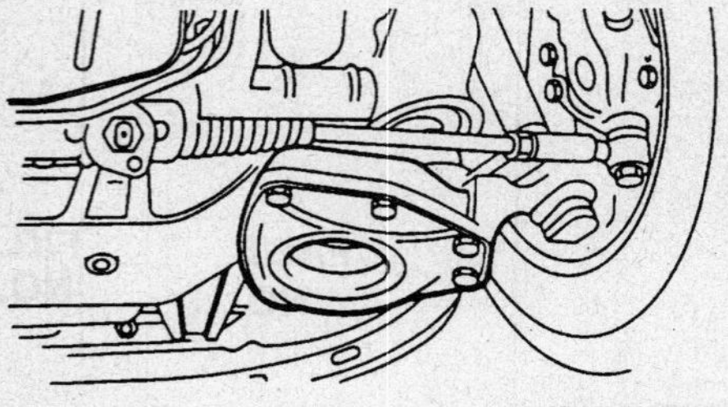

Fig. 5   XJS & XJ12. Floor Jack (Front)

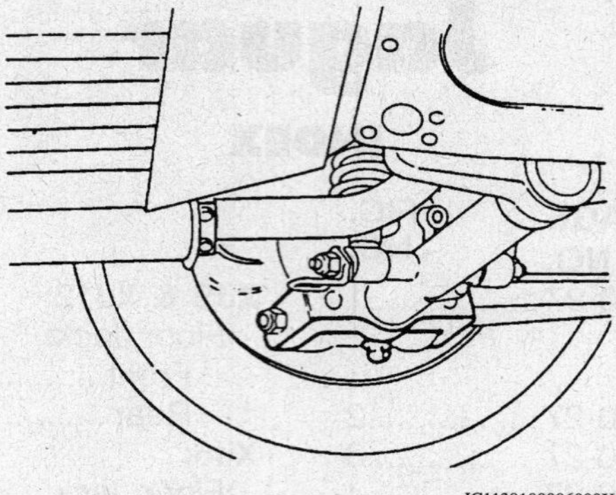

Fig. 6   XJS & XJ12. Floor Jack (Rear)

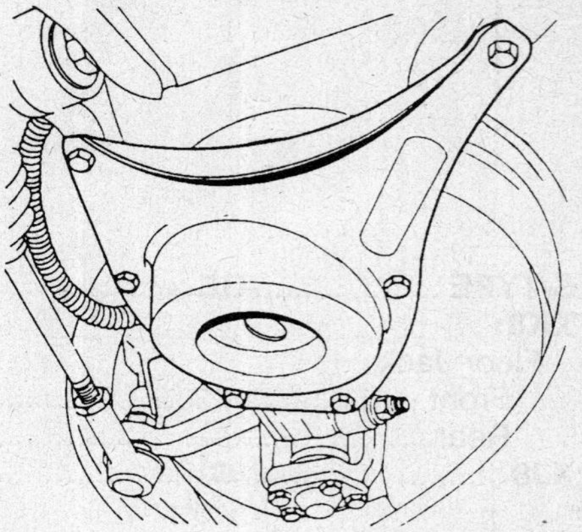

Fig. 7   XJ6. Floor Jack (Front)

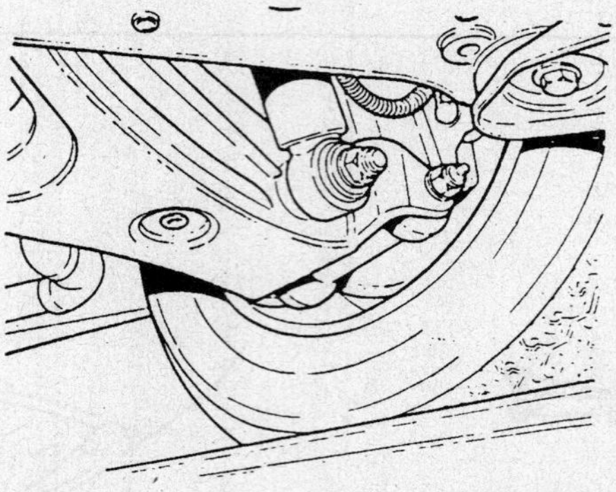

Fig. 8   XJ6. Floor Jack (Rear)

Land Rover

INDEX

	PAGE NO.	FIG. NO.
DISCOVERY & RANGE ROVER	0-29	1

NOTE: The Manufacturer Does Not Recommend Using A "Two Post" Hoist Employing Four Adjustable Support Arms. If A Vehicle Is Raised On A Two Post Hoist Responsibility Lies With The Service Provider.

NOTE: Use Only A "Drive On" Type Hoist Which Supports Vehicle On Its Own Wheels. If A "Wheel Free" Condition Is Required Use A Drive On Hoist Incorporating a Wheel Free System Or Place Vehicle On A Firm, Flat Floor And Support On Axle Stands.

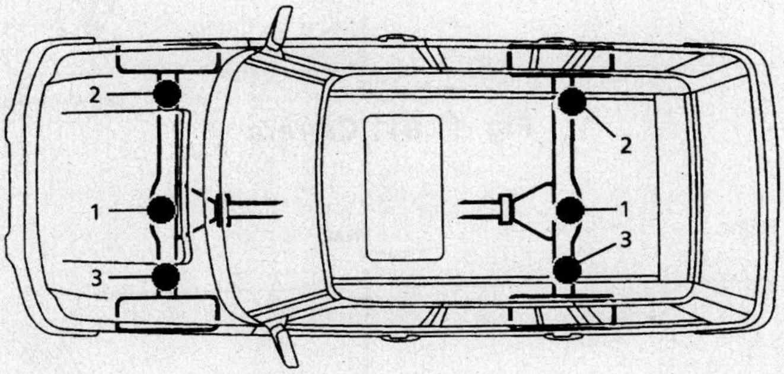

1: Central Lifting Points
2: Righthand Lift & Support Points
3: Lefthand Lift & Support Points

RV1139500001000A

Fig. 1 Discovery & Range Rover

Porsche

INDEX

	PAGE NO.	FIG. NO.		PAGE NO.	FIG. NO.
BOXSTER	0-30	2	911 CARRERA	0-30	1

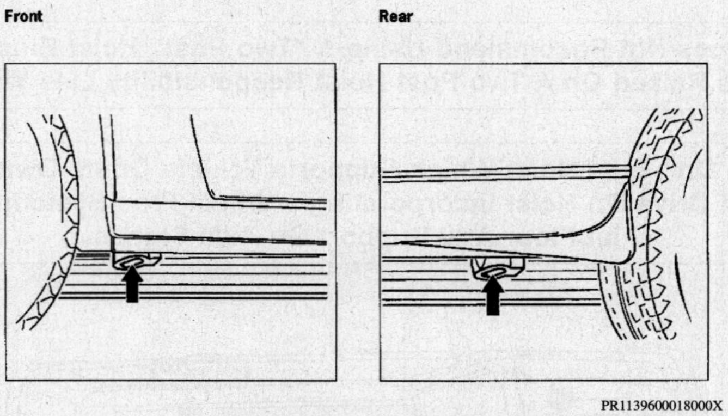

Fig. 1 911 Carrera

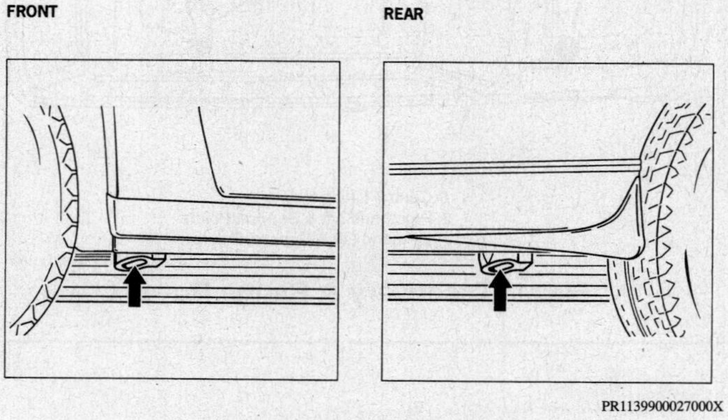

Fig. 2 Boxster

Saab

INDEX

	PAGE NO.	FIG. NO.		PAGE NO.	FIG. NO.
900	0-31	1	9000, 9-3 & 9-5	0-31	2

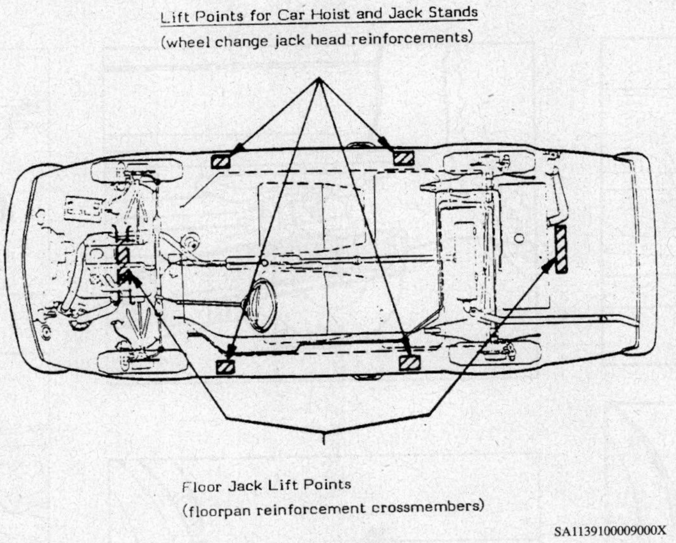

Fig. 1 900

A Front jack attachments and application points for hoist

B and C Alternate front application points for hoist

D Rear jack attachments and appliction points for hoist

E Front application point for floor jack

F Rear application point for floor jack

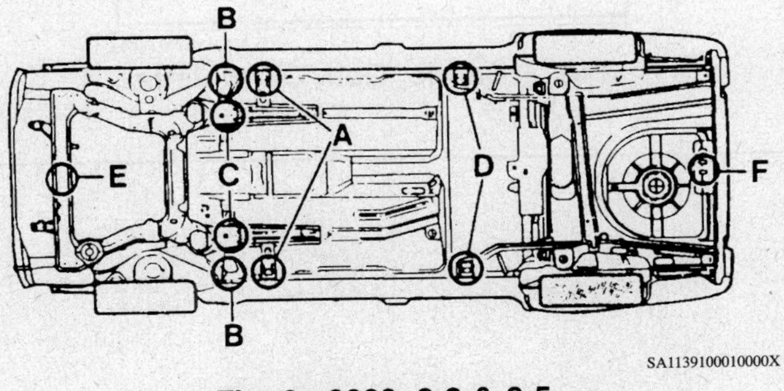

Fig. 2 9000, 9-3 & 9-5

Volkswagen

INDEX

	PAGE NO.	FIG. NO.
BEETLE	0-32	3
CABRIO, GOLF, GTI & JETTA	0-32	2
PASSAT	0-32	1

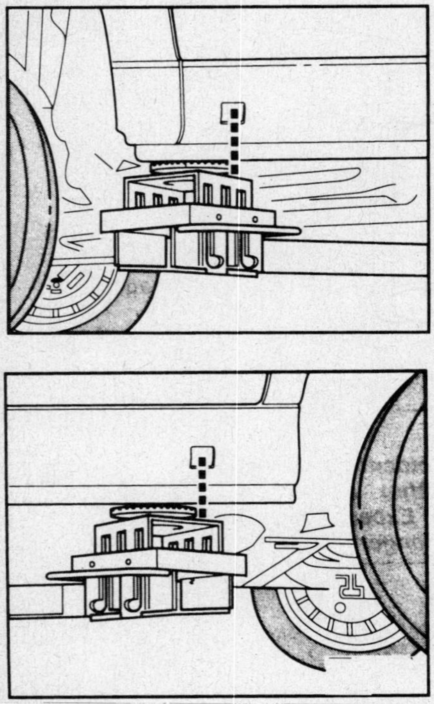

VW1139100013000A

Fig. 1 Passat

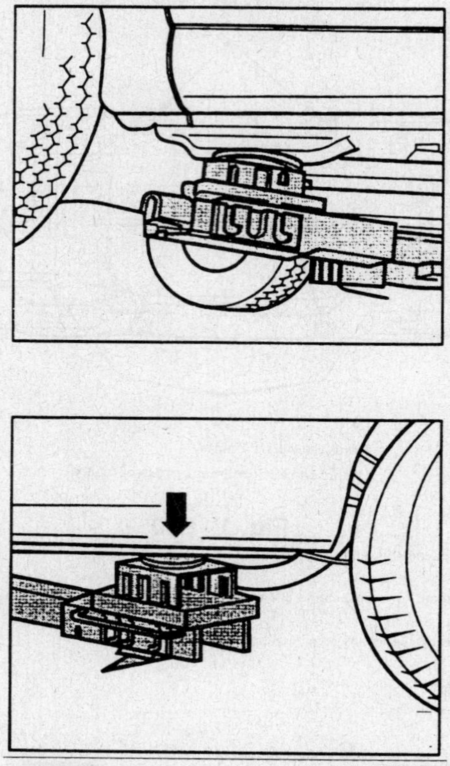

VW1139100015000A

Fig. 2 Cabrio, Golf, GTI & Jetta

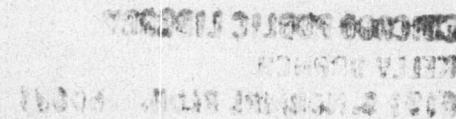

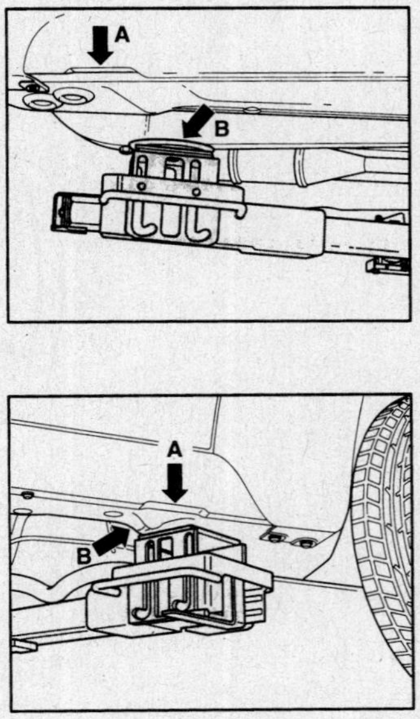

Lifting po

Front

◄ Floor jack:

Hoist: on le

Rear

◄ Jack: at inc

Hoist: at cr

VW1139900072000X

Fig. 3 Beetle

ELECTRICAL SYMBOL & WIRE COLOR CODE IDENTIFICATION

TABLE OF CONTENTS

	Page No.
ELECTRICAL SYMBOL IDENTIFICATION	0-34
WIRE COLOR CODE IDENTIFICATION	0-44

Electrical Symbol Identification

INDEX

	PAGE NO.	FIG. NO.
AUDI	0-34	1
BMW	0-35	2
JAGUAR	0-37	3
LAND ROVER	0-37	4
MERCEDES-BENZ	0-40	5
PORSCHE	0-41	6
SAAB	0-41	7
VOLKSWAGEN	0-42	8
VOLVO	0-43	9

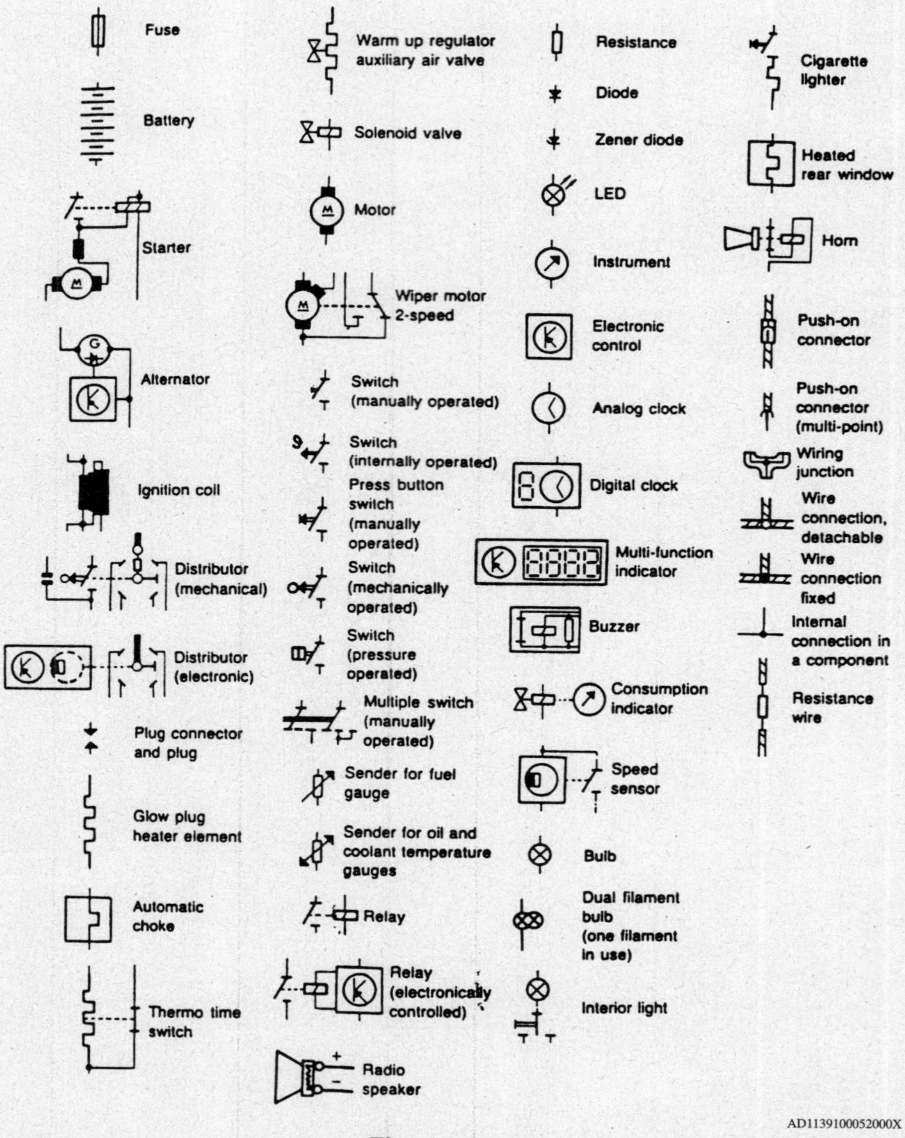

Fig. 1 Audi

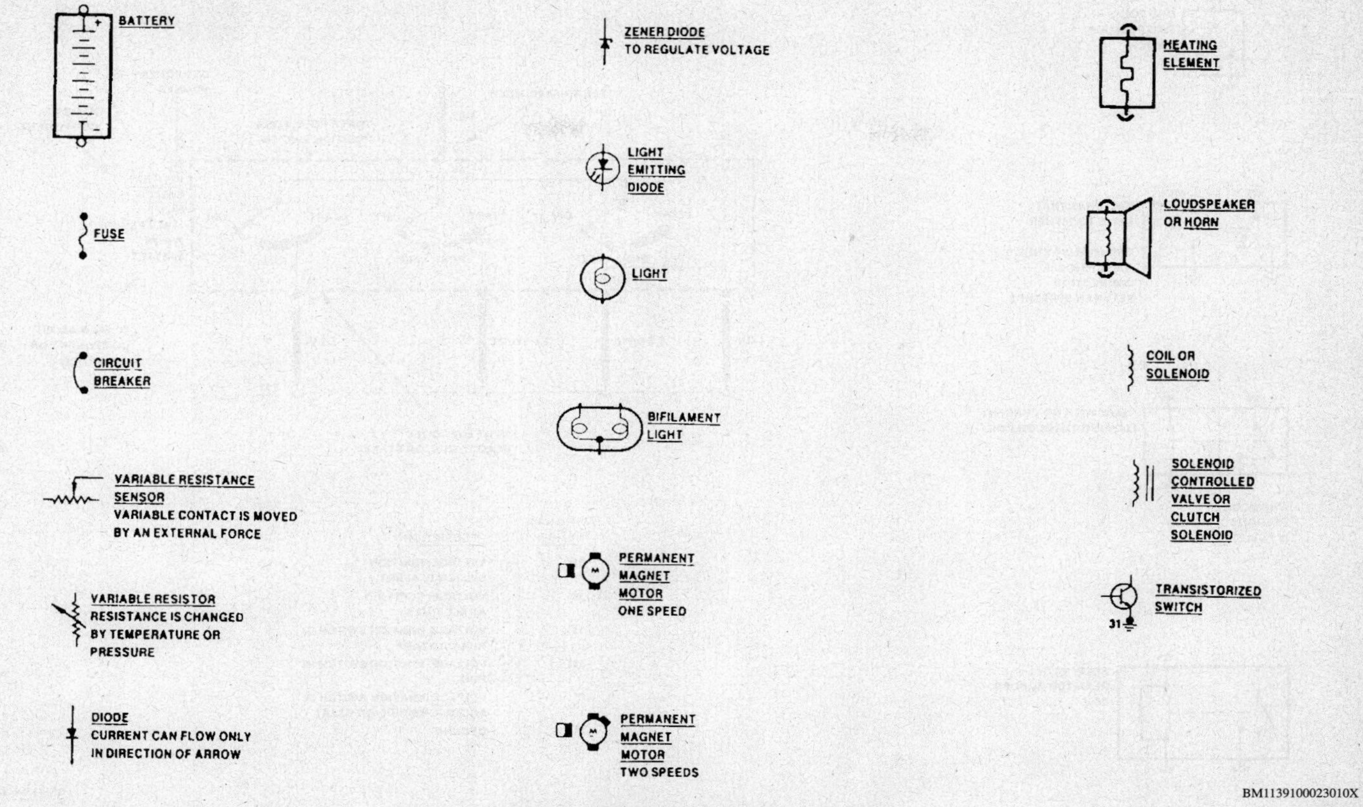
BATTERY
FUSE
CIRCUIT BREAKER
VARIABLE RESISTANCE SENSOR
VARIABLE CONTACT IS MOVED BY AN EXTERNAL FORCE
VARIABLE RESISTOR
RESISTANCE IS CHANGED BY TEMPERATURE OR PRESSURE
DIODE
CURRENT CAN FLOW ONLY IN DIRECTION OF ARROW
ZENER DIODE
TO REGULATE VOLTAGE
LIGHT EMITTING DIODE
LIGHT
BIFILAMENT LIGHT
PERMANENT MAGNET MOTOR
ONE SPEED
PERMANENT MAGNET MOTOR
TWO SPEEDS
HEATING ELEMENT
LOUDSPEAKER OR HORN
COIL OR SOLENOID
SOLENOID CONTROLLED VALVE OR CLUTCH SOLENOID
TRANSISTORIZED SWITCH
31
BM1139100023010X

Fig. 2 BMW (Part 1 of 4)

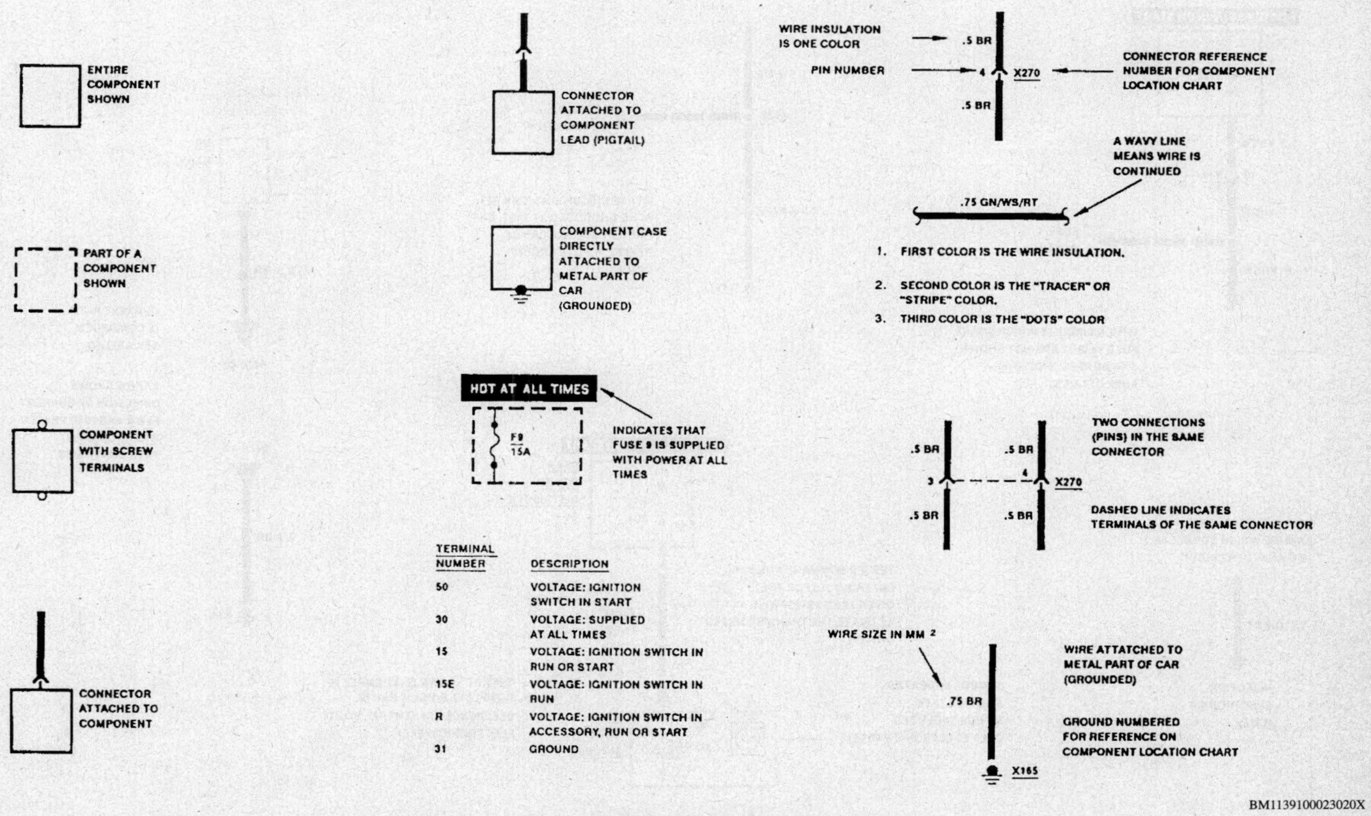
ENTIRE COMPONENT SHOWN
PART OF A COMPONENT SHOWN
COMPONENT WITH SCREW TERMINALS
CONNECTOR ATTACHED TO COMPONENT
CONNECTOR ATTACHED TO COMPONENT LEAD (PIGTAIL)
COMPONENT CASE DIRECTLY ATTACHED TO METAL PART OF CAR (GROUNDED)
HOT AT ALL TIMES
F9
15A
INDICATES THAT FUSE 9 IS SUPPLIED WITH POWER AT ALL TIMES
TERMINAL NUMBER
DESCRIPTION
50
VOLTAGE: IGNITION SWITCH IN START
30
VOLTAGE: SUPPLIED AT ALL TIMES
15
VOLTAGE: IGNITION SWITCH IN RUN OR START
15E
VOLTAGE: IGNITION SWITCH IN RUN
R
VOLTAGE: IGNITION SWITCH IN ACCESSORY, RUN OR START
31
GROUND
WIRE INSULATION IS ONE COLOR
PIN NUMBER
.5 BR
4
X270
.5 BR
CONNECTOR REFERENCE NUMBER FOR COMPONENT LOCATION CHART
A WAVY LINE MEANS WIRE IS CONTINUED
.75 GN/WS/RT
1. FIRST COLOR IS THE WIRE INSULATION.
2. SECOND COLOR IS THE "TRACER" OR "STRIPE" COLOR.
3. THIRD COLOR IS THE "DOTS" COLOR
.5 BR
.5 BR
3
4
X270
.5 BR
.5 BR
TWO CONNECTIONS (PINS) IN THE SAME CONNECTOR
DASHED LINE INDICATES TERMINALS OF THE SAME CONNECTOR
WIRE SIZE IN MM 2
.75 BR
X165
WIRE ATTATCHED TO METAL PART OF CAR (GROUNDED)
GROUND NUMBERED FOR REFERENCE ON COMPONENT LOCATION CHART
BM1139100023020X

Fig. 2 BMW (Part 2 of 4)

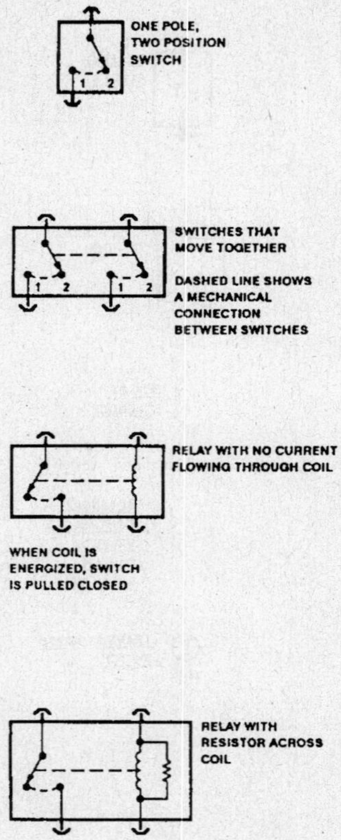

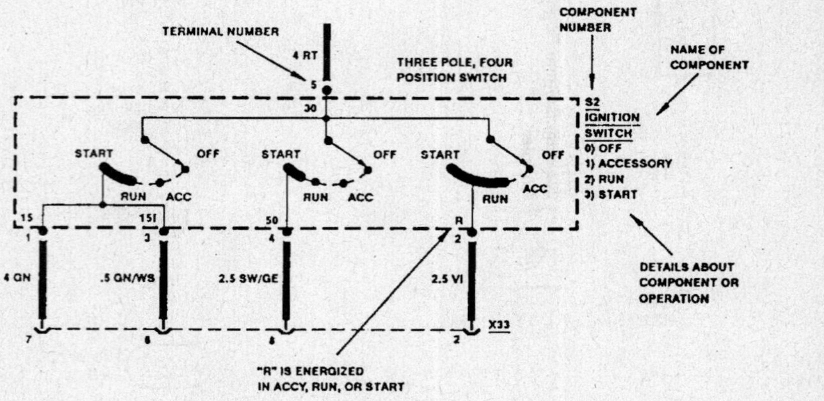

TERMINAL NUMBER	DESCRIPTION
50	VOLTAGE: IGNITION SWITCH IN START
30	VOLTAGE: SUPPLIED AT ALL TIMES
15	VOLTAGE: IGNITION SWITCH IN RUN OR START
15I	VOLTAGE: IGNITION SWITCH IN RUN
R	VOLTAGE: IGNITION SWITCH IN ACCESSORY, RUN, OR START
31	GROUND

BM1139100023030X

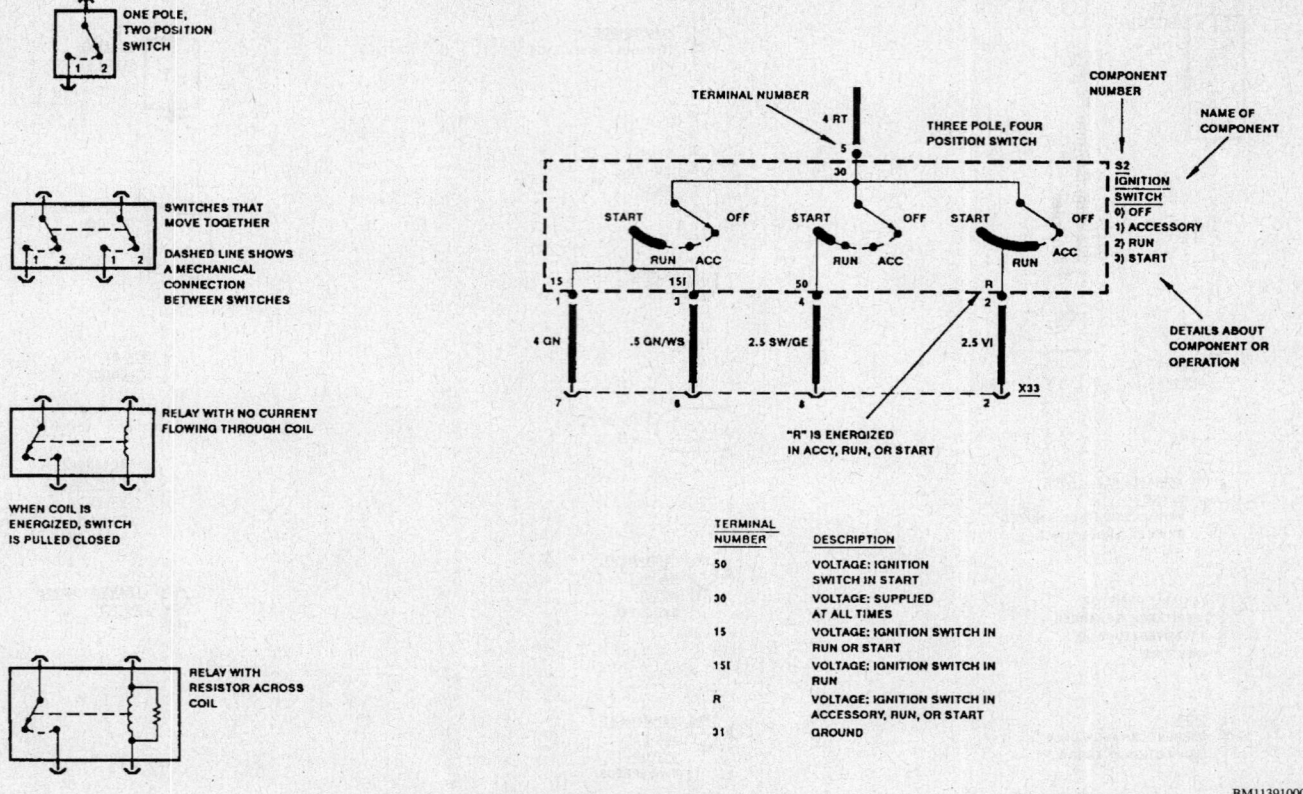

Fig. 2 BMW (Part 3 of 4)

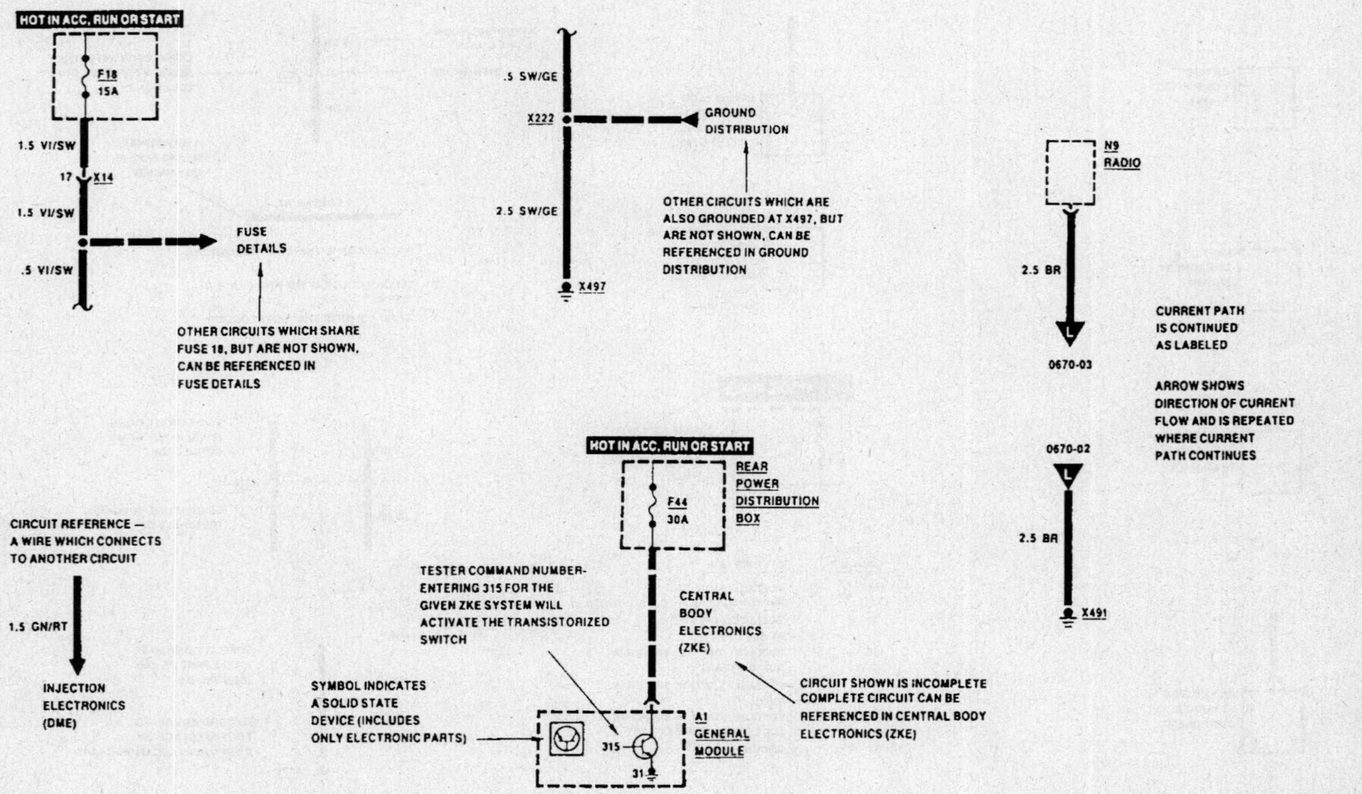

BM1139100023040X

Fig. 2 BMW (Part 4 of 4)

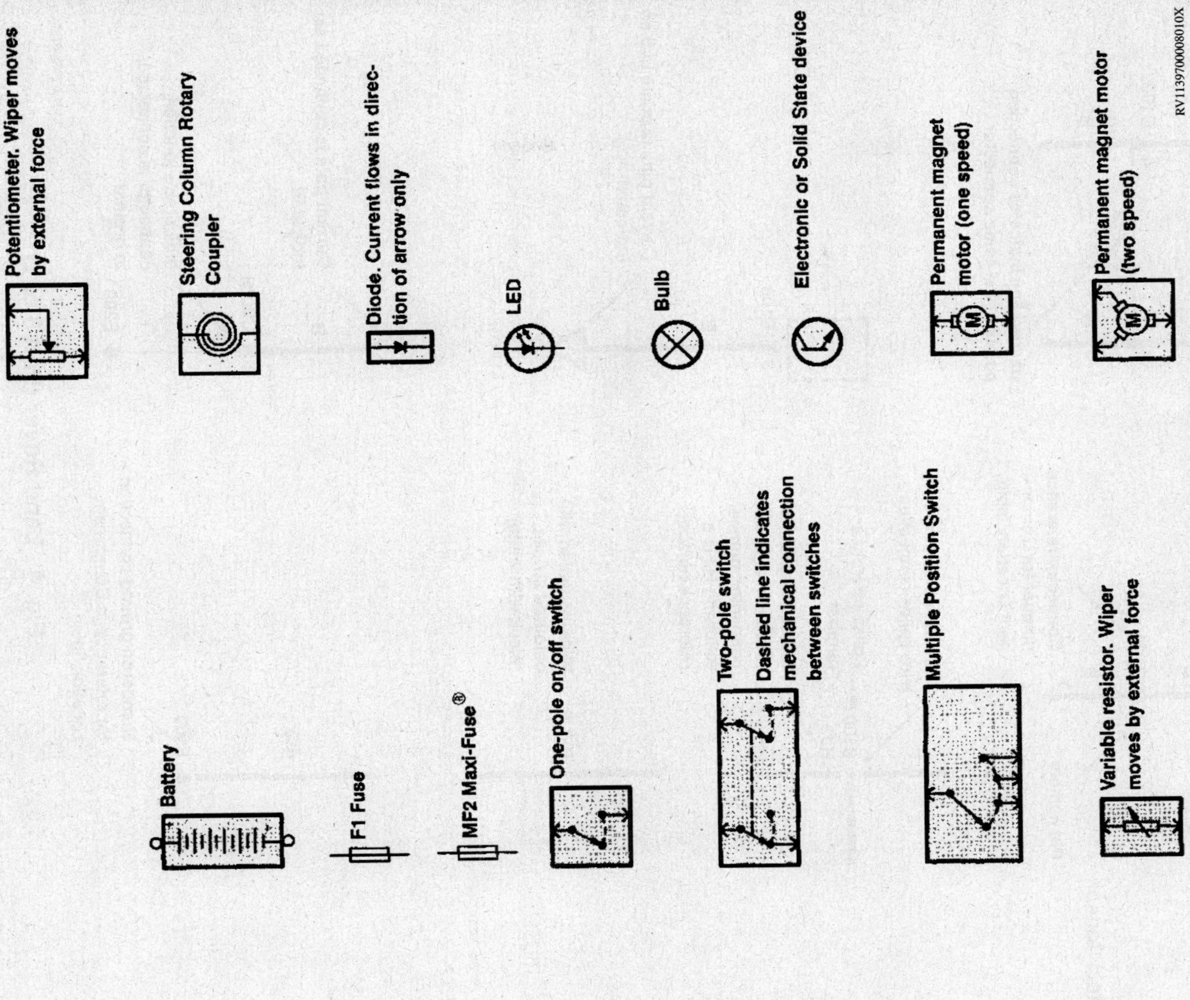
Battery
F1 Fuse
MF2 Maxi-Fuse®
One-pole on/off switch
Two-pole switch
Dashed line indicates mechanical connection between switches
Multiple Position Switch
Variable resistor. Wiper moves by external force
Potentiometer. Wiper moves by external force
Steering Column Rotary Coupler
Diode. Current flows in direction of arrow only
LED
Bulb
Electronic or Solid State device
Permanent magnet motor (one speed)
Permanent magnet motor (two speed)
RV1139700008010X
JC1139400024000X

Fig. 4 Land Rover (Part 1 of 7)

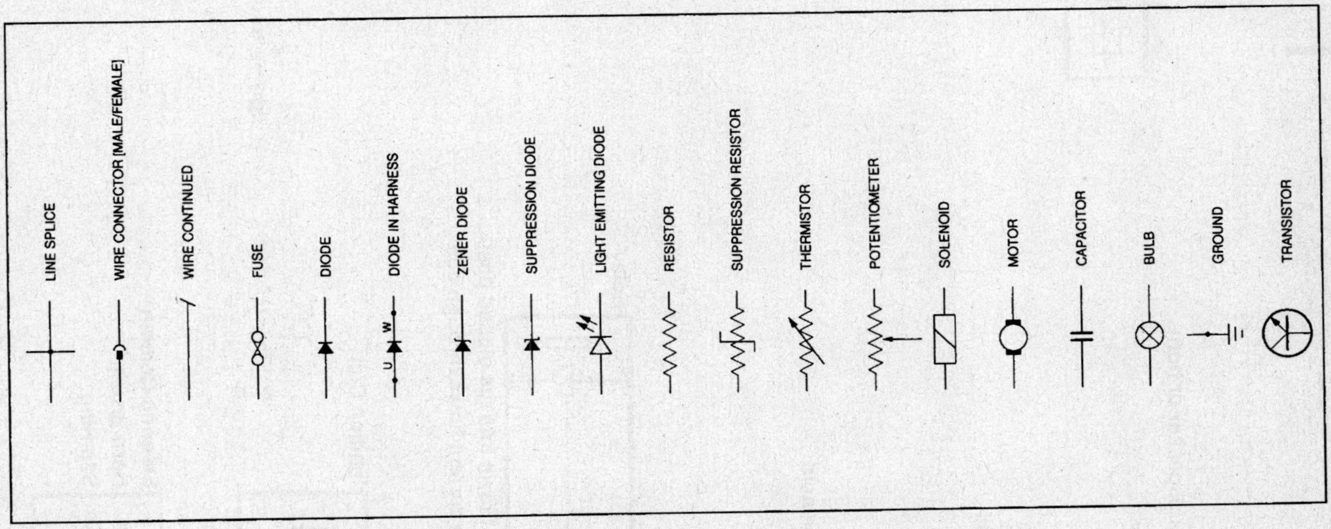
LINE SPLICE
WIRE CONNECTOR [MALE/FEMALE]
WIRE CONTINUED
FUSE
DIODE
DIODE IN HARNESS
ZENER DIODE
SUPPRESSION DIODE
LIGHT EMITTING DIODE
RESISTOR
SUPPRESSION RESISTOR
THERMISTOR
POTENTIOMETER
SOLENOID
MOTOR
CAPACITOR
BULB
GROUND
TRANSISTOR

Fig. 3 Jaguar

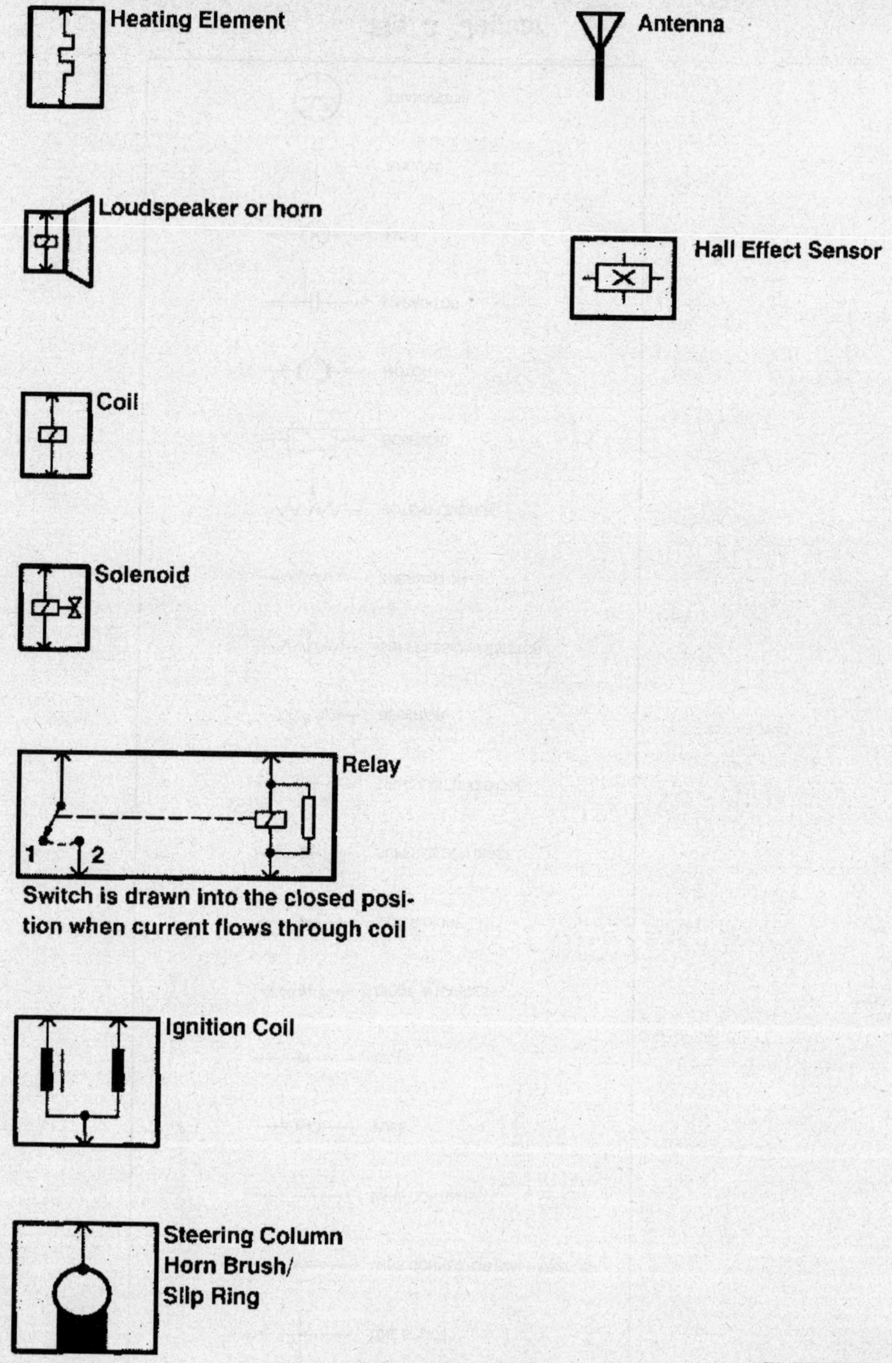
Heating Element
Antenna
Loudspeaker or horn
Hall Effect Sensor
Coil
Solenoid
Relay
1
2
Switch is drawn into the closed position when current flows through coil
Ignition Coil
Steering Column Horn Brush/ Slip Ring
RV1139700008020X

Fig. 4 Land Rover (Part 2 of 7)

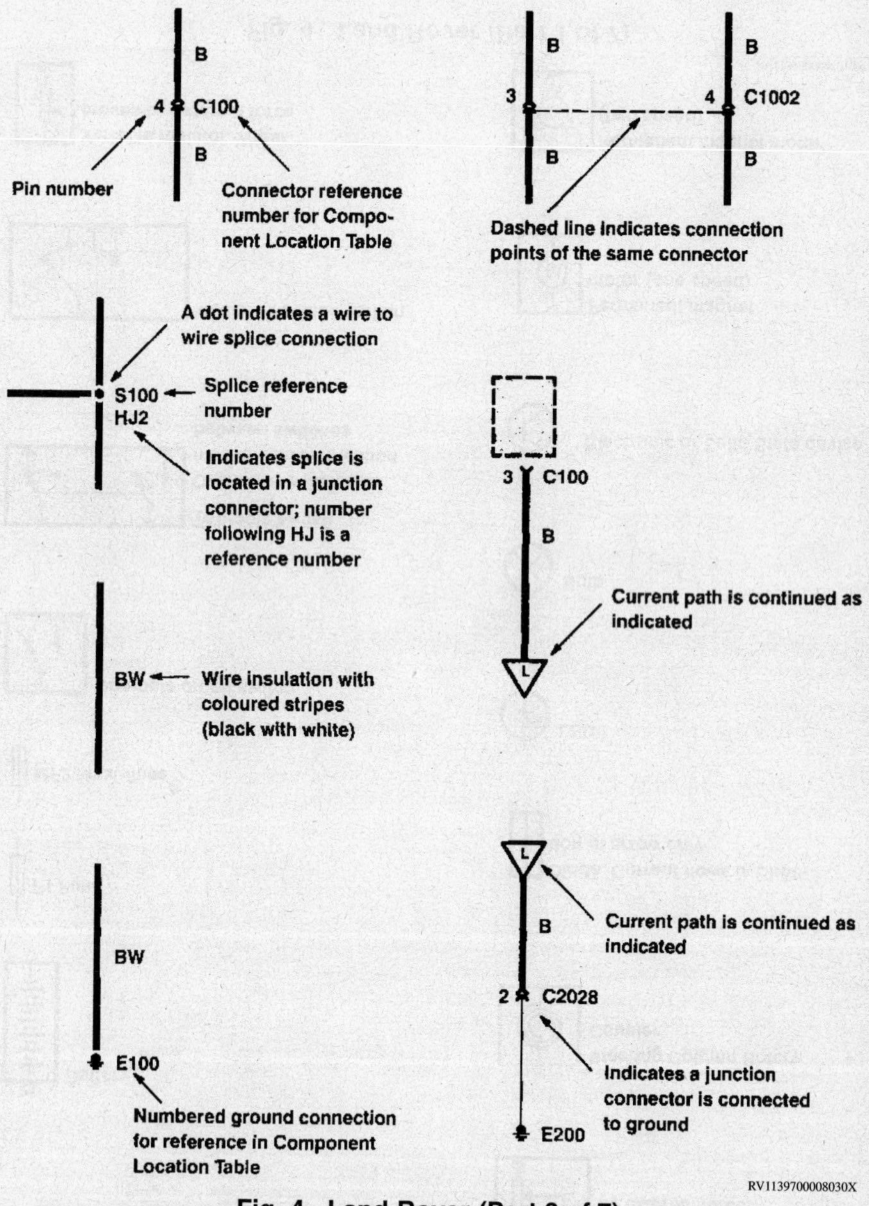
B
4
C100
B
Pin number
Connector reference number for Component Location Table
B
3
B
B
4
C1002
B
Dashed line indicates connection points of the same connector
A dot indicates a wire to wire splice connection
S100
HJ2
Splice reference number
Indicates splice is located in a junction connector; number following HJ is a reference number
3
C100
B
L
Current path is continued as indicated
BW
Wire insulation with coloured stripes (black with white)
L
B
Current path is continued as indicated
BW
2
C2028
E100
Numbered ground connection for reference in Component Location Table
Indicates a junction connector is connected to ground
E200
RV1139700008030X

Fig. 4 Land Rover (Part 3 of 7)

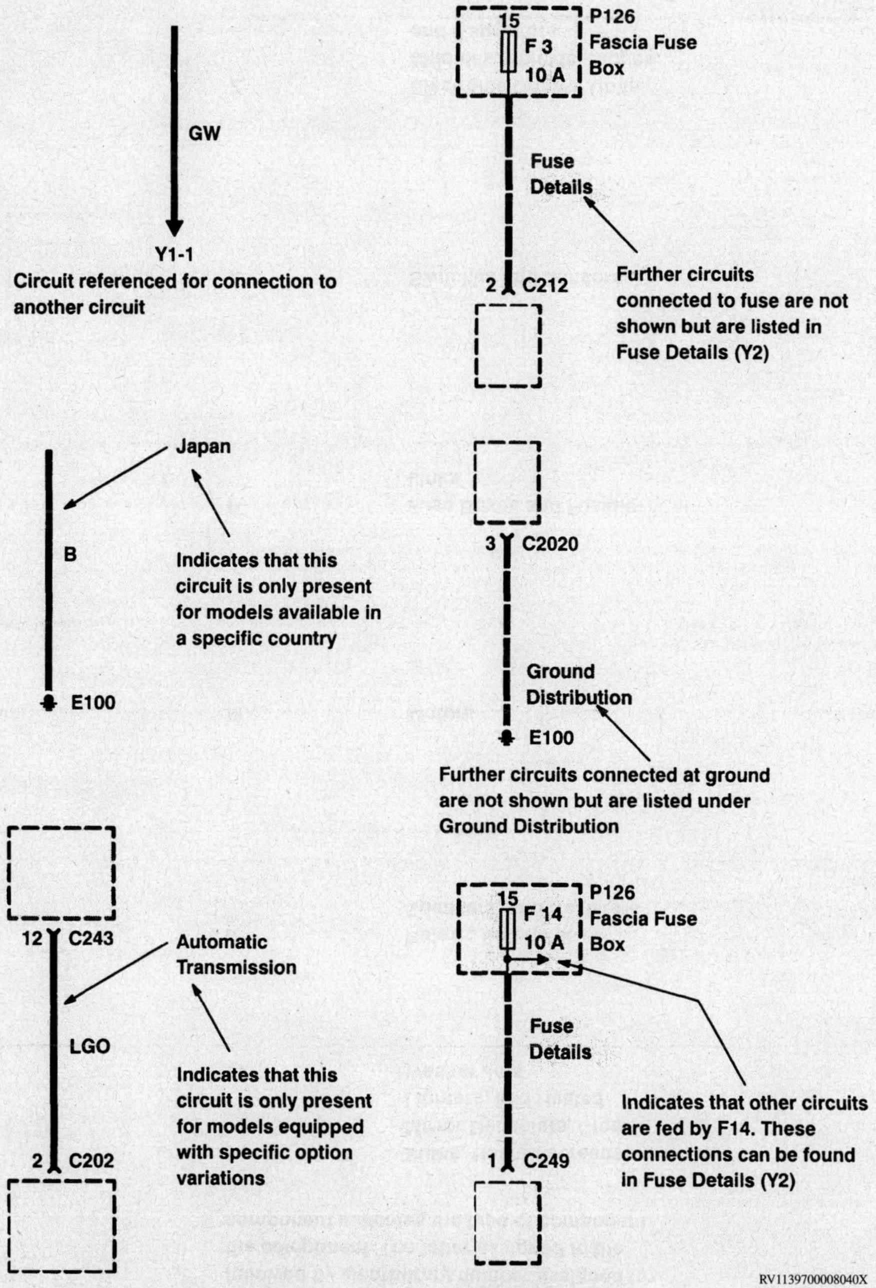

Fig. 4 Land Rover (Part 4 of 7)

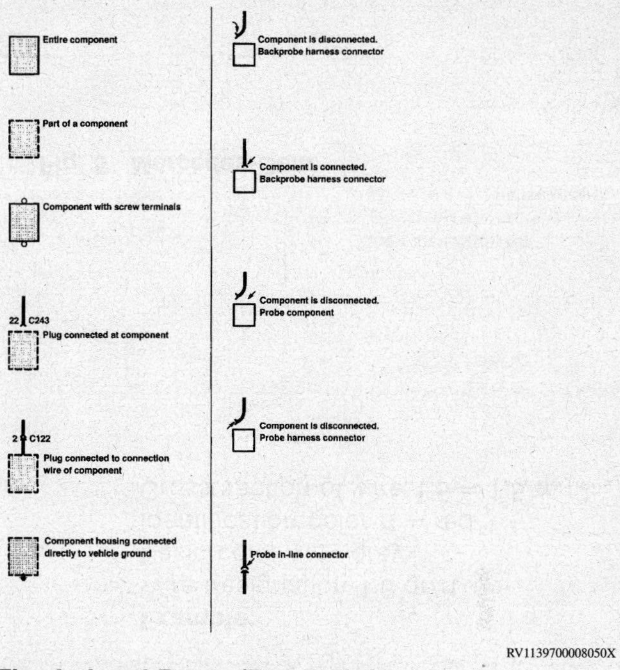

Fig. 4 Land Rover (Part 5 of 7)

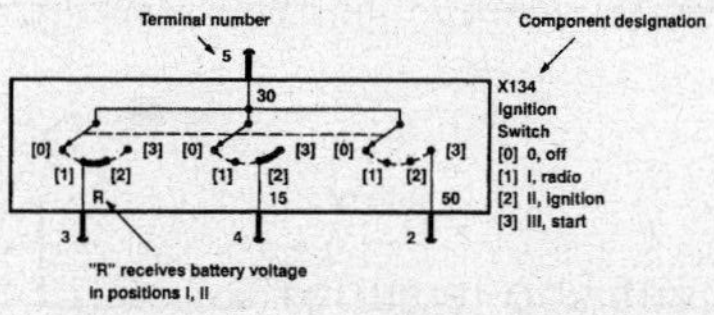

Terminal number	Designation	Terminal number	Designation
50	Battery voltage: Ignition Switch in position III	X	Switched battery voltage through the ignition load relay; ignition switch is in position II or III.
30	Battery voltage: supplied constantly	49	Flasher unit input
		49a	Flasher unit output
15	Battery voltage: Ignition Switch in position II or III	56a	High beam
		56b	Low beam
R	Battery voltage: Ignition Switch in positions I, II	85	End of relay coil
		86	Start of relay coil
31	Ground	87	Relay contact
		87a	Relay contact

RV1139700008060X

Fig. 4 Land Rover (Part 6 of 7)

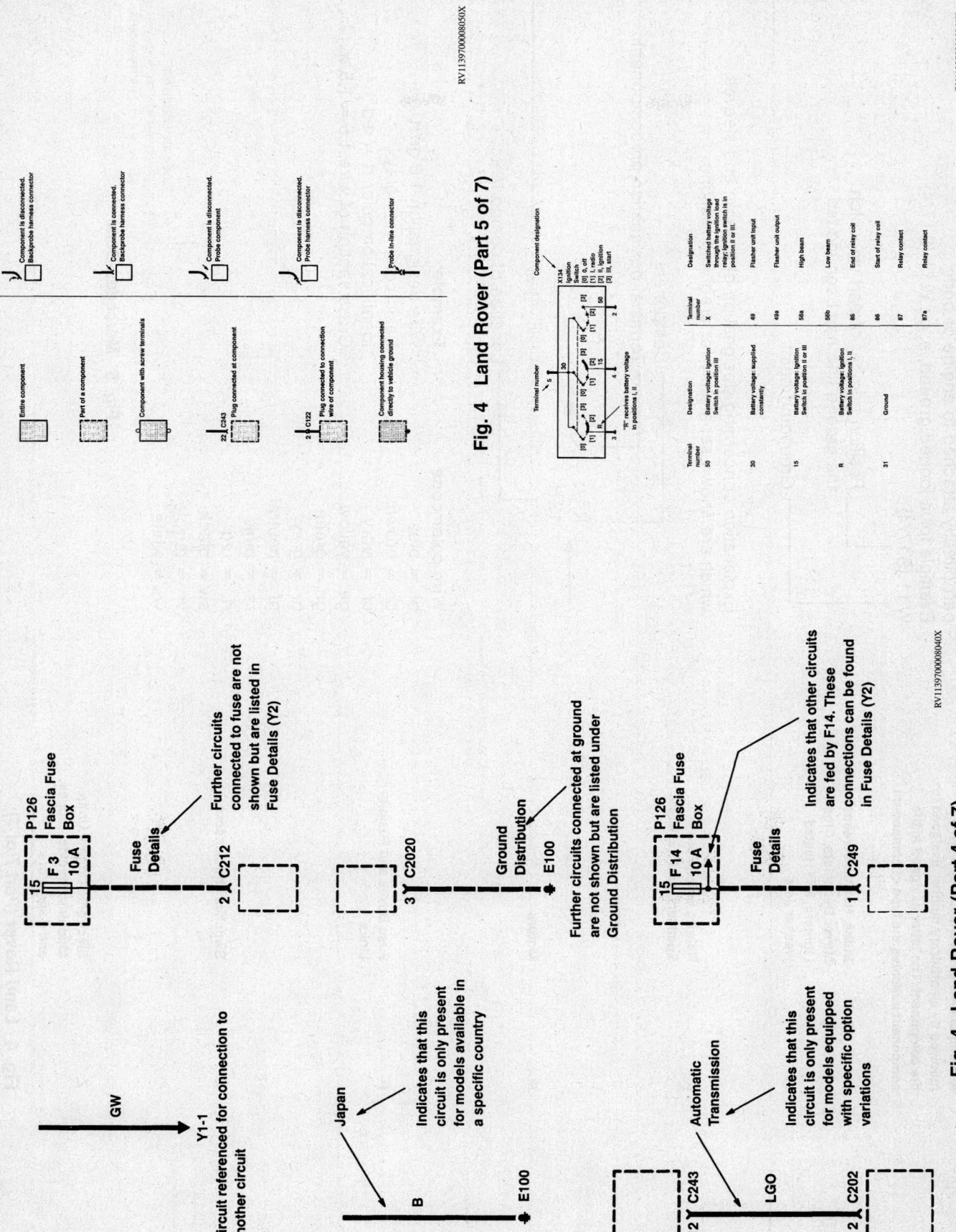

Definition of Vehicle Component Codes

All components are identified by a letter followed by an arbitrary number assigned to the component. The letter assigned to the component indicates the type of component.

B	**Bulbs, Heated Screens, Mirror Demisters, Cigar Lighters, and Heated Washer Jets**
K	**Relays, Solenoids, Speakers, and Resistors**
M	**Motors**
P	**Fuse Boxes and Fusible Links**
X	**Switches and Sensors**
Z	**Electronic Control Units, Modules, Shields, Diodes, and Capacitors**

RV1139700008070X

Fig. 4 Land Rover (Part 7 of 7)

Grounding point without designation,
part directly attached to engine or body
Example for a looped ground, e. g.: W11 (S17/4)

W11 (S17/4)
- Position number of part via which the ground line has been looped
- Grounding point

Explanation concerning designation of lines on end sleeves, which are shown separately for graphical reasons.

→ K1/1 (4) ←
12H
- Component
- Terminal designation on component
- Location of component

Wire color code
bl = blue
br = brown
el = ivory
ge = yellow
gn = green
gr = grey
nf = neutral
rs = pink
rt = red
sw = black
vi = purple
ws = white

Example:
Wire designation 1.5 gr/rt
Basic color gr = grey
Identification color rt = red
Cross section of wire 1.5 = 1.5 mm^2

MB1139100025010X

Fig. 5 Mercedes-Benz

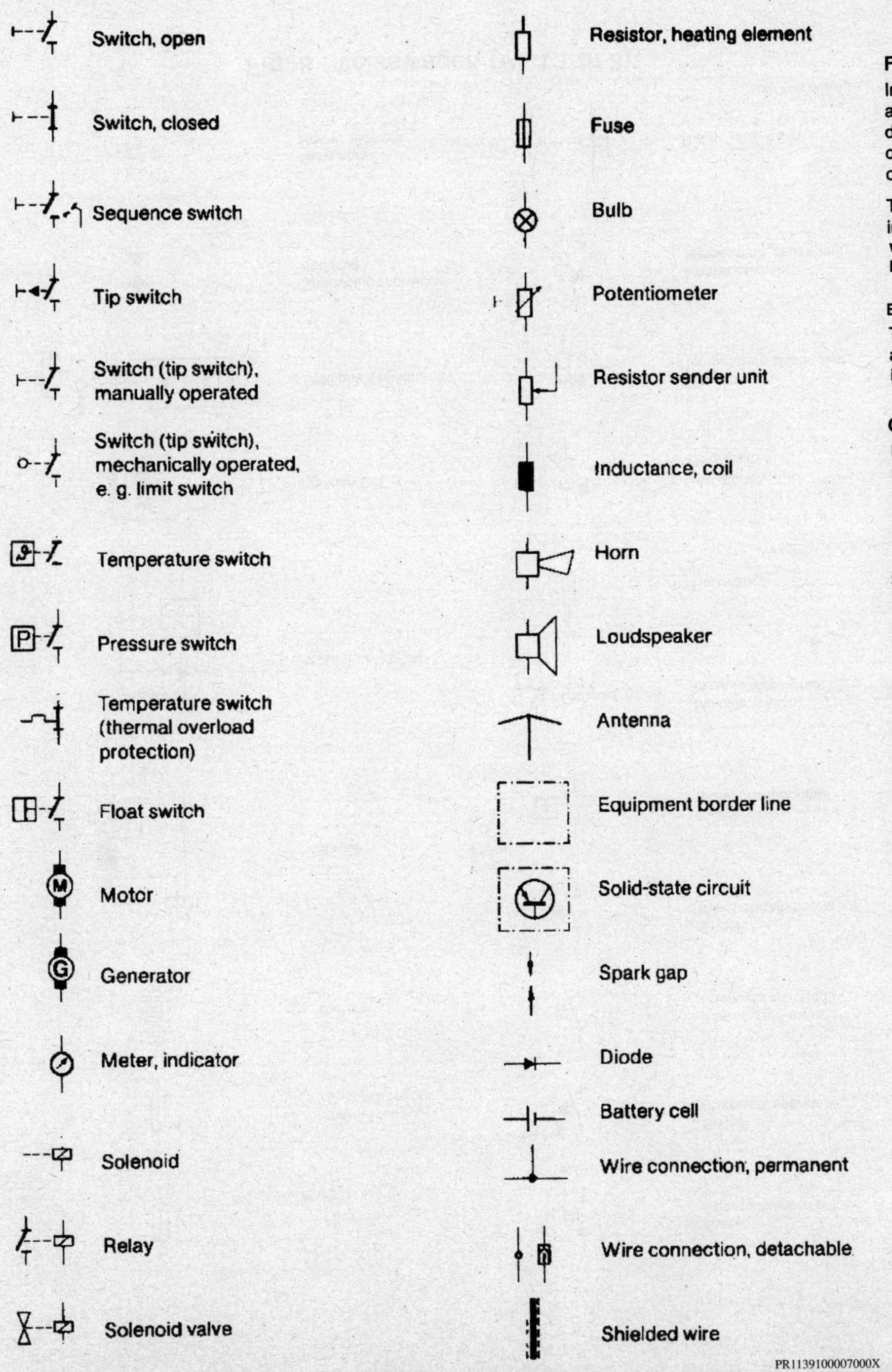

Fig. 6 Porsche

Fuses

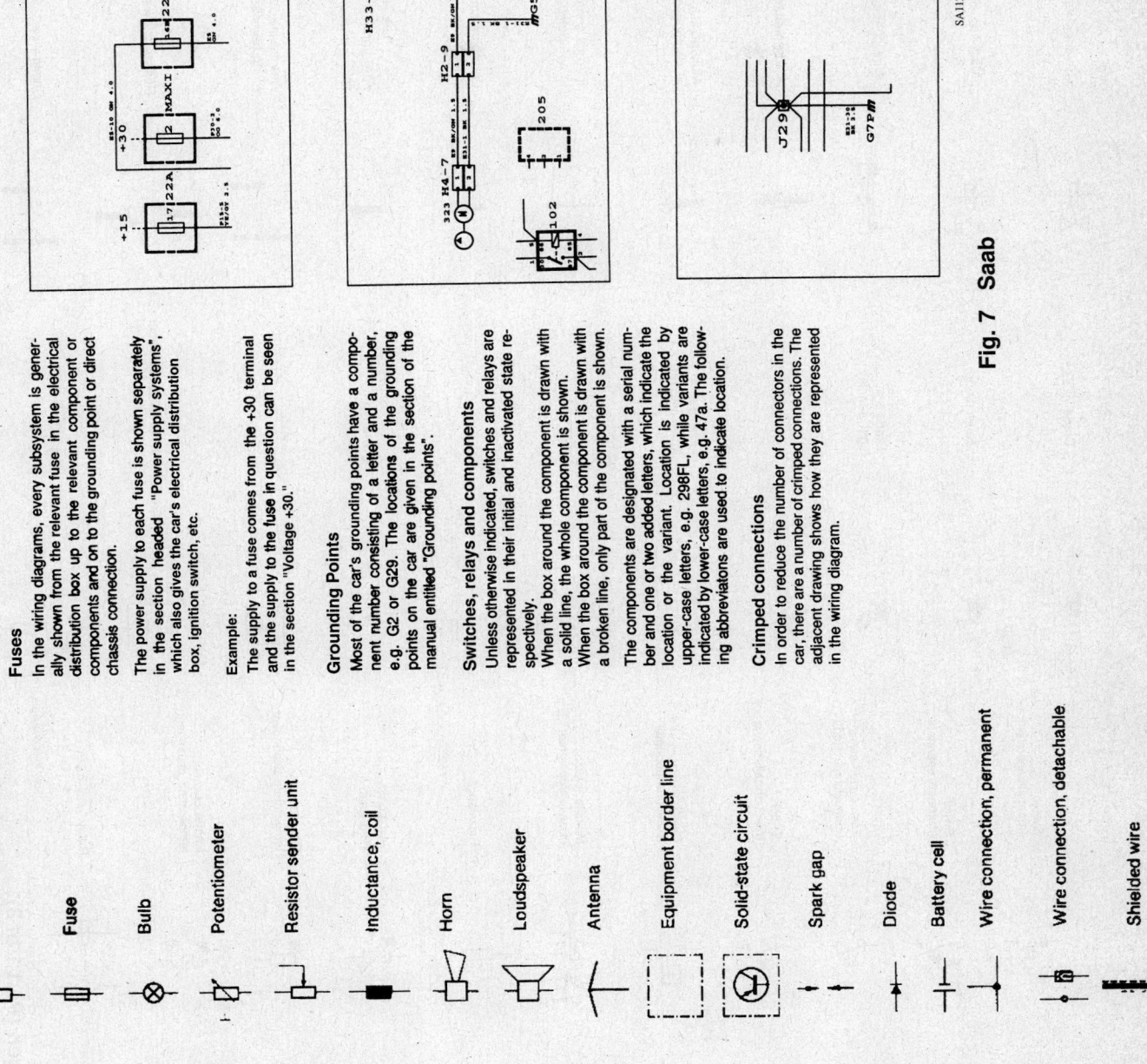

In the wiring diagrams, every subsystem is generally shown from the relevant fuse in the electrical distribution box up to the relevant component or components and on to the grounding point or direct chassis connection.

The power supply to each fuse is shown separately in the section headed "Power supply systems", which also gives the car's electrical distribution box, ignition switch, etc.

Example:

The supply to a fuse comes from the +30 terminal and the supply to the fuse in question can be seen in the section "Voltage +30."

Grounding Points

Most of the car's grounding points have a component number consisting of a letter and a number, e.g. G2 or G29. The locations of the grounding points on the car are given in the section of the manual entitled "Grounding points".

Switches, relays and components

Unless otherwise indicated, switches and relays are represented in their initial and inactivated state respectively.

When the box around the component is drawn with a solid line, the whole component is shown.

When the box around the component is drawn with a broken line, only part of the component is shown.

The components are designated with a serial number and one or two added letters, which indicate the location or the variant. Location is indicated by upper-case letters, e.g. 298FL, while variants are indicated by lower-case letters, e.g. 47a. The following abbreviatons are used to indicate location.

Crimped connections

In order to reduce the number of connectors in the car, there are a number of crimped connections. The adjacent drawing shows how they are represented in the wiring diagram.

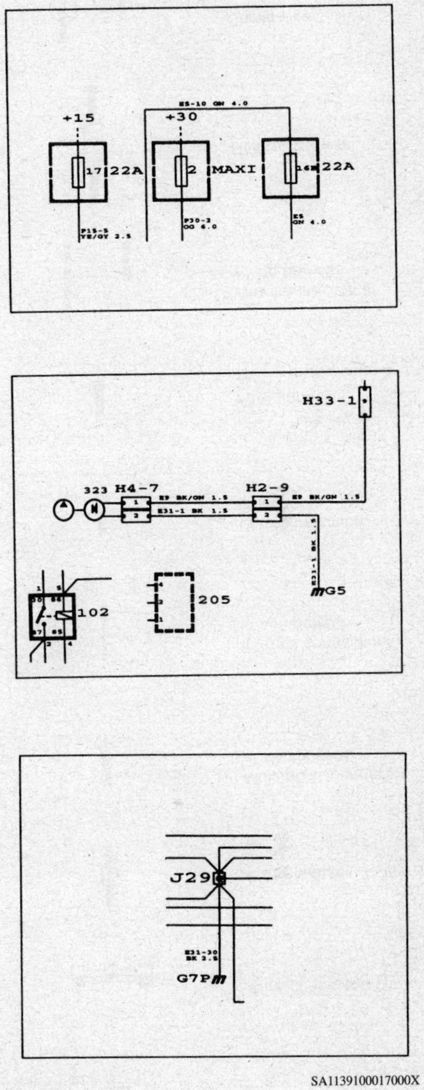

Fig. 7 Saab

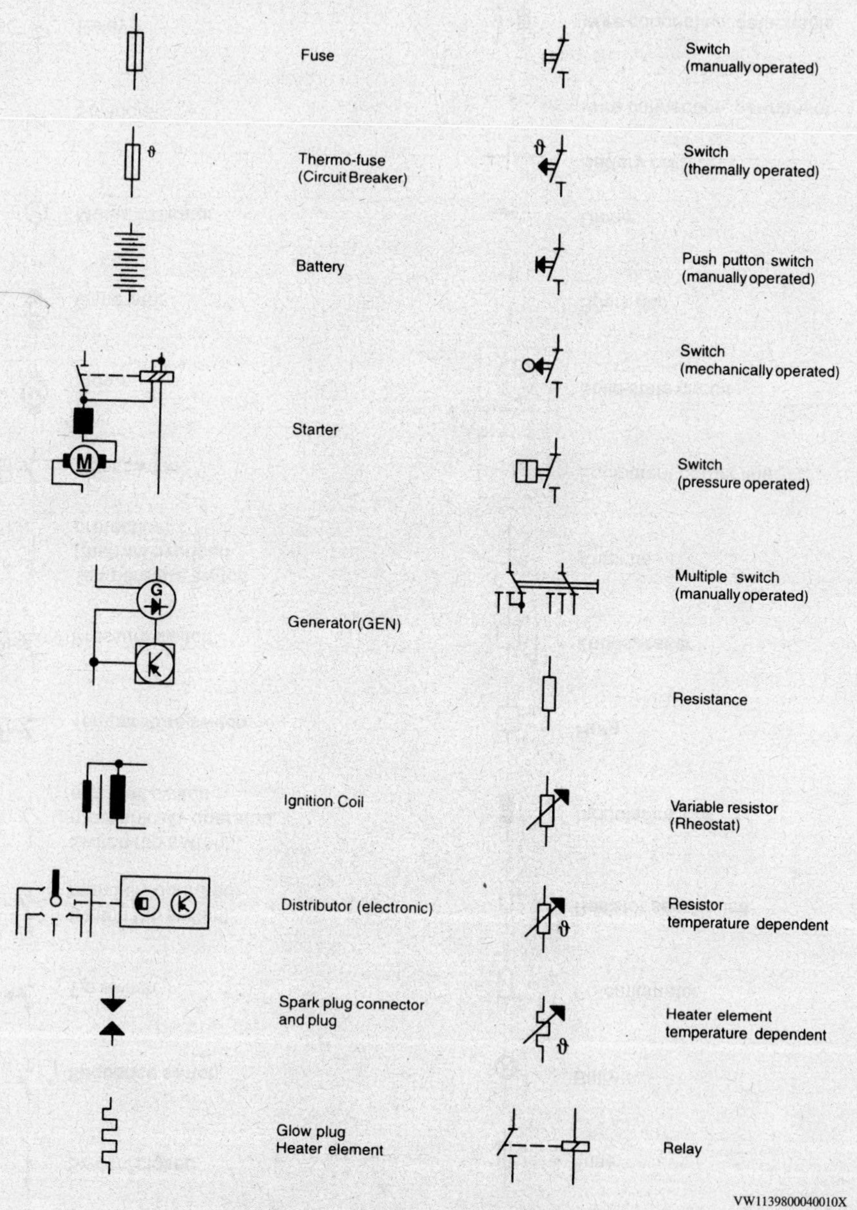
Fuse
Thermo-fuse
(Circuit Breaker)
Battery
Starter
Generator(GEN)
Ignition Coil
Distributor (electronic)
Spark plug connector
and plug
Glow plug
Heater element
Switch
(manually operated)
Switch
(thermally operated)
Push putton switch
(manually operated)
Switch
(mechanically operated)
Switch
(pressure operated)
Multiple switch
(manually operated)
Resistance
Variable resistor
(Rheostat)
Resistor
temperature dependent
Heater element
temperature dependent
Relay
VW1139800040010X

Fig. 8 Volkswagen (Part 1 of 3)

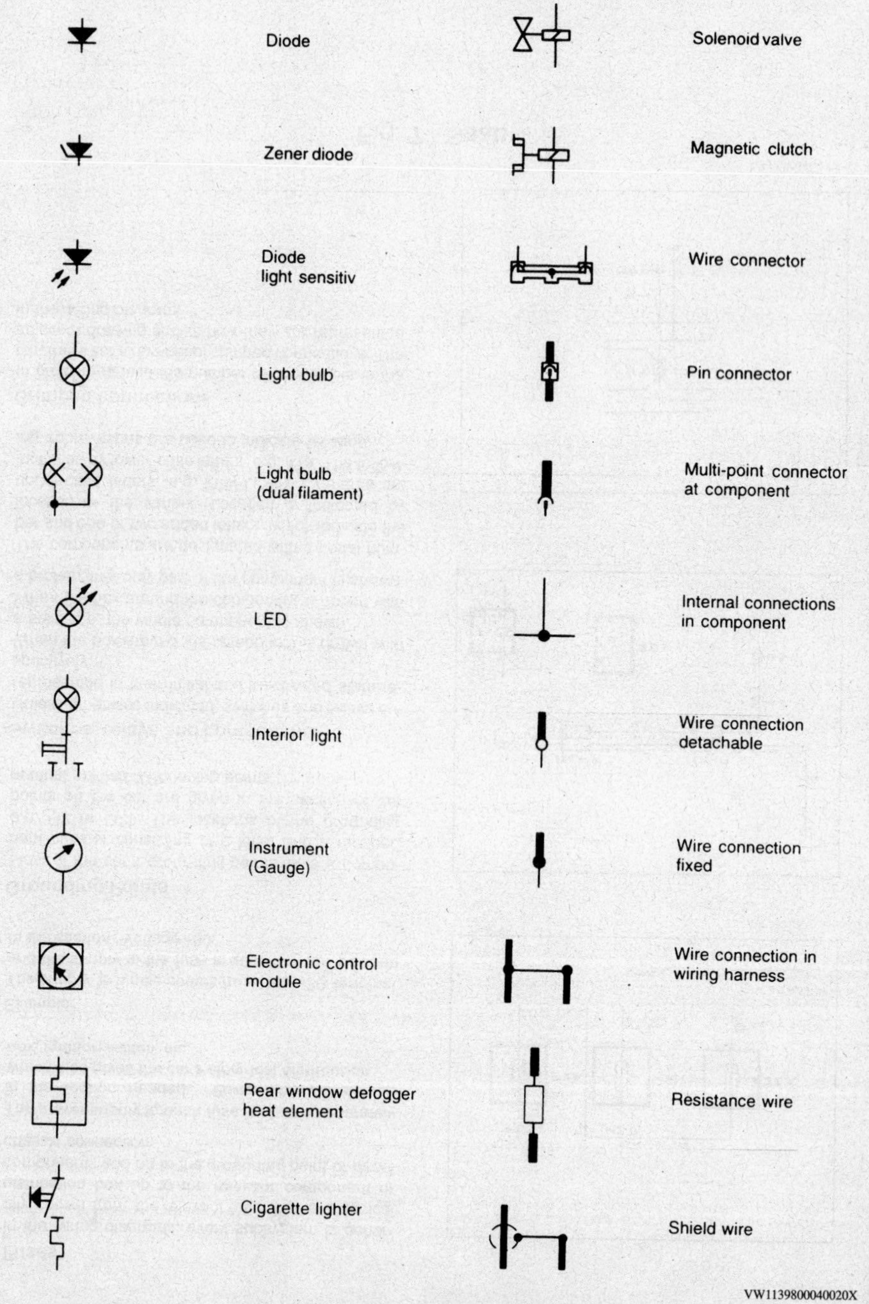
Diode
Zener diode
Diode
light sensitiv
Light bulb
Light bulb
(dual filament)
LED
Interior light
Instrument
(Gauge)
Electronic control
module
Rear window defogger
heat element
Cigarette lighter
Solenoid valve
Magnetic clutch
Wire connector
Pin connector
Multi-point connector
at component
Internal connections
in component
Wire connection
detachable
Wire connection
fixed
Wire connection in
wiring harness
Resistance wire
Shield wire
VW1139800040020X

Fig. 8 Volkswagen (Part 2 of 3)

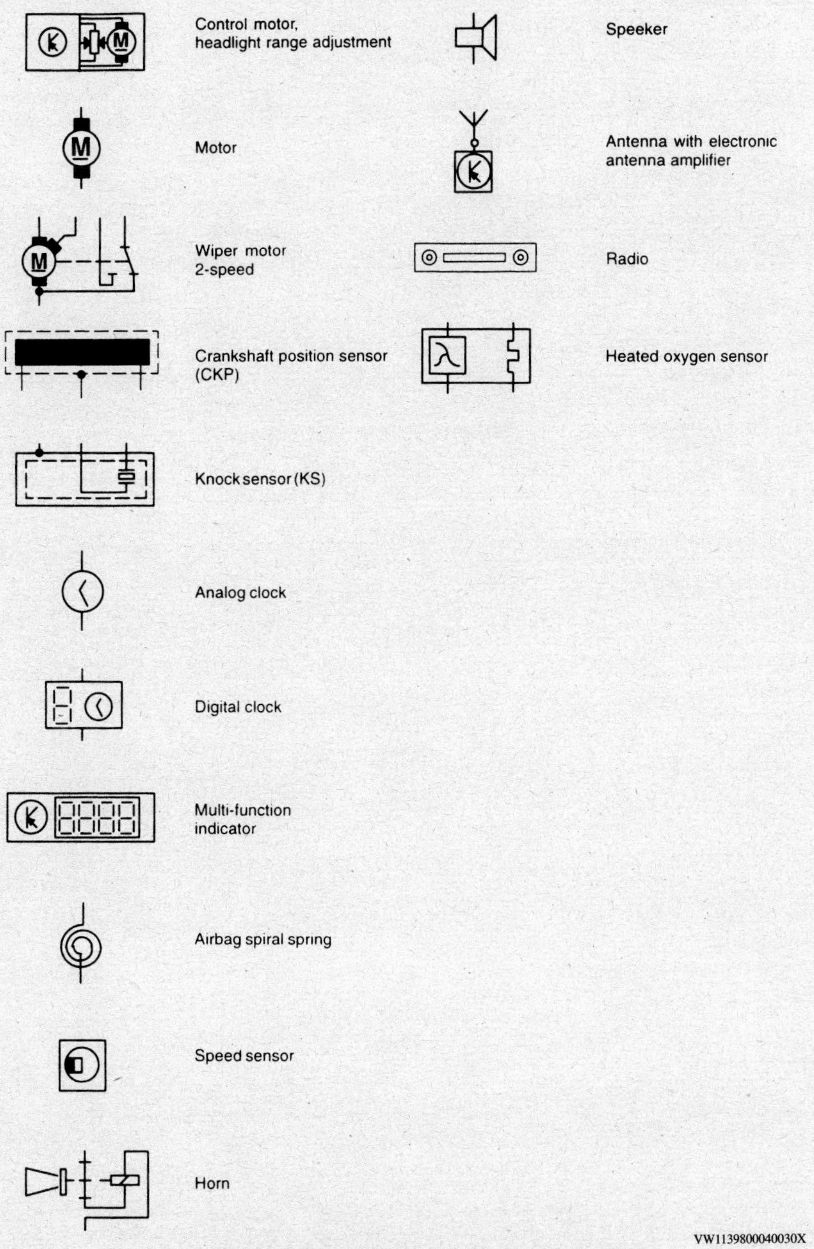

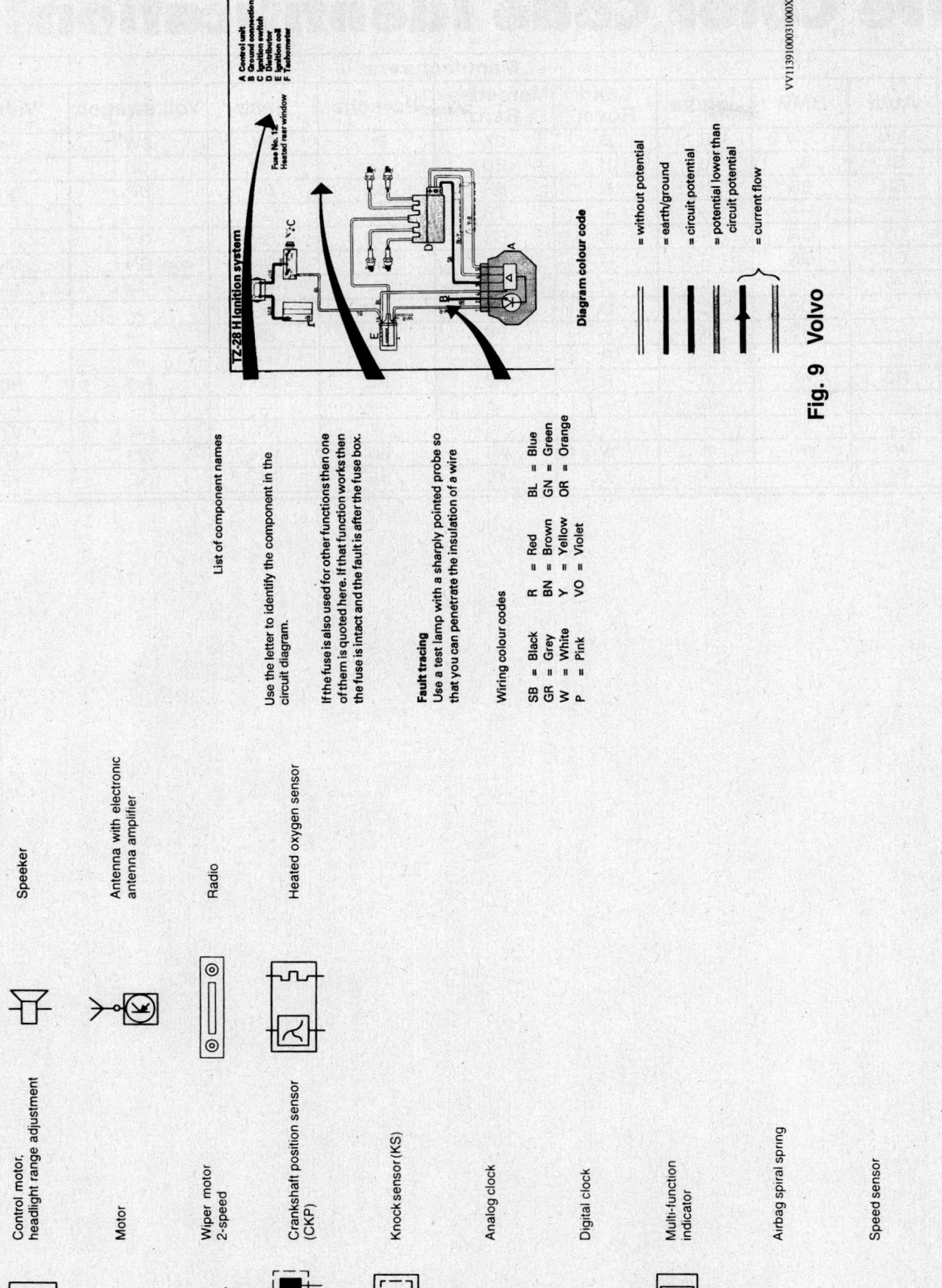

Fig. 8 Volkswagen (Part 3 of 3)

List of component names

Use the letter to identify the component in the circuit diagram.

If the fuse is also used for other functions then one of them is quoted here. If that function works then the fuse is intact and the fault is after the fuse box.

Fault tracing
Use a test lamp with a sharply pointed probe so that you can penetrate the insulation of a wire

Wiring colour codes

SB = Black	R = Red	BL = Blue
GR = Grey	BN = Brown	GN = Green
W = White	Y = Yellow	OR = Orange
P = Pink	VO = Violet	

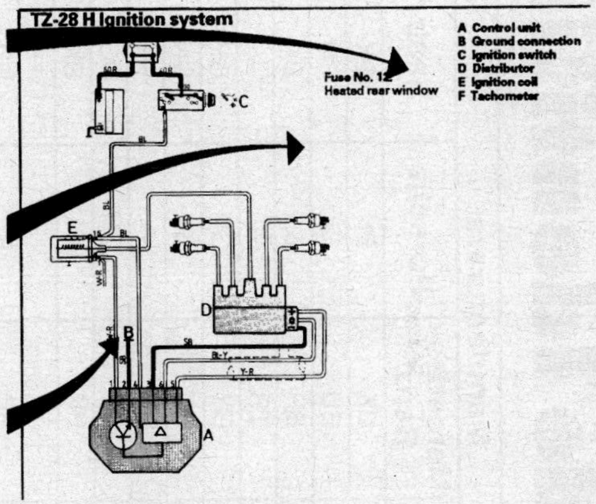

Diagram colour code

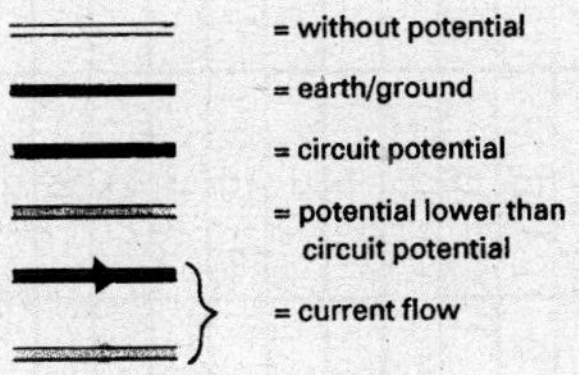

VV1139100031000X

Fig. 9 Volvo

Wire Color Code Identification

Color	Manufacturers								
	Audi	BMW	Jaguar	Land Rover	Mercedes-Benz	Porsche	Saab	Volkswagen	Volvo
Black	SW	SW	B	B	BK	BK	BK	SW	BK
Blue	BL	BL	U	U	BU	BL	BU	BL	BU
Brown	BR	BR	N	N	BR	BR	BN	BR	BN
Clear (Neutral)	—	—	—	—	TR	—	—	—	—
Gray	GY	GR	—	S	GY	GR	GY	GY	GY
Green	GN	GN	G	G	GN	GN	GN	GN	GN
Light	—	—	L	L	—	—	—	—	—
Orange	—	OR	O	O	OR	OR	OG	—	OG
Pink	—	RS	K	K	PK	PI	PK	—	PK
Purple	—	—	P	P	Vi	—	—	—	—
Red	RO	RT	R	R	RD	RE	RD	RO	RD
Slate	—	—	S	—	—	—	—	—	—
Violet	LI	VI	—	—	—	VI	VT	—	VT
White	WS	WS	W	W	WT	WT	WH	WS	WH
Yellow	GE	GE	Y	Y	YL	YE	YE	GE	YE

VEHICLE MAINTENANCE SCHEDULES

TABLE OF CONTENTS

	Page No.
AUDI	0-45
BMW	0-48
JAGUAR S-TYPE, XJ8 & XK8	0-49
JAGUAR XJ6, XJ12, XJR & XJS	0-48
LAND ROVER DISCOVERY & RANGE ROVER	0-51
MERCEDES-BENZ	0-53
PORSCHE	0-55
VOLKSWAGEN	0-63
1998 SAAB	0-57
1998 VOLVO	0-67
1999-2001 SAAB	0-60
1999-2001 VOLVO	0-70

Audi

Recommended Service	Service Interval In Miles①																															
	5000	7500	10000	15000	20000	22500	25000	30000	35000	37500	40000	45000	50000	52500	55000	60000	65000	67500	70000	75000	80000	82500	85000	90000	95000	97500	100000	105000	110000	112500	115000	120000
BODY																																
Clean & Lubricate Sunroof Guide Rails				X				X				X				X				X				X				X				X
Inspect Controls, Lamps & Electrical Devices For Proper Operation				X				X				X				X				X				X				X				X
Inspect Headlamp Alignment				X				X				X				X				X				X				X				X
Inspect Vehicle Undercoating Condition, Less Turbo				X				X				X				X				X				X				X				X
Inspect Vehicle Undercoating Condition, w/Turbo			X		X			X			X		X			X			X		X			X			X		X			X
Inspect & Clean Plenum Chamber & Water Drain Valve				X				X				X				X				X				X				X				X
Lubricate Body Hardware, Door Check Straps & Lock Cylinders, Less Turbo				X				X				X				X				X				X				X				X
Lubricate Body Hardware, Door Check Straps & Lock Cylinders, w/Turbo			X		X			X			X		X			X			X		X			X			X		X			X
Lubricate Roof Frame Guides & Locking Mechanism, Cabriolet				X				X				X				X				X				X				X				X
Replace Passenger Compartment Pollen Filter, Less Turbo				X				X				X				X				X				X				X				X
Replace Passenger Compartment Pollen Filter, w/Turbo			X		X			X			X		X			X			X		X			X			X		X			X
BRAKES																																
Change Brake Fluid	Every 24 Months, Regardless Of Mileage																															

Recommended Service	Service Interval In Miles①																															
	5000	7500	10000	15000	20000	22500	25000	30000	35000	37500	40000	45000	50000	52500	55000	60000	65000	67500	70000	75000	80000	82500	85000	90000	95000	97500	100000	105000	110000	112500	115000	120000
BRAKES																																
Inspect Brake System Connections, Hoses, Lines & Pad Thickness, Less Turbo				X				X				X				X				X				X				X				X
Inspect Brake System Connections, Hoses, Lines & Pad Thickness w/Turbo			X		X			X			X		X			X			X		X			X			X		X			X
CLUTCH & TRANSMISSION																																
Change Automatic Transaxle Fluid & Filter,1998-99 A6 Wagon												X												X								
Inspect Automatic Transaxle Fluid & Filter, 1998–2000 All	Every 10,000 Miles																															
Inspect Automatic Transaxle Fluid & Filter, 2001 A4, A6 & A8	Every 40,000 Miles																															
Inspect Manual Transaxle Fluid & Filter, 1998–2000 All	Every 10,000 Miles																															
Inspect Manual Transaxle Fluid & Filter, 2001 A4, A6 & TT	Every 40,000 Miles																															
Change Clutch Fluid	Every 24 Months, Regardless Of Mileage																															
Inspect Shift Lock, Clutch Interlock & Park/Neutral Safety Switch Operation, Less Turbo				X				X				X				X				X				X				X				X
Inspect Shift Lock, Clutch Interlock & Park/Neutral Safety Switch Operation, w/Turbo			X		X			X			X		X			X			X		X			X			X		X			X
DRIVESHAFT																																
Inspect CV Joint, Less Turbo				X				X				X				X				X				X				X				X
Inspect CV Joint, w/Turbo			X		X			X			X		X			X			X		X			X			X		X			X
ENGINE																																
Change Engine Coolant	Filled For Life																															
Change Engine Oil, 1998– 2000 Less Turbo		X		X		X		X		X		X		X		X		X		X		X		X		X		X		X		X
Change Engine Oil, 1998- 2000 w/Turbo	X		X	X	X		X	X	X		X	X	X		X	X	X		X	X	X		X	X	X		X	X	X		X	X
Change Engine Oil Filter, 1998–2000 w/Turbo	X		X		X			X			X		X			X			X		X			X			X		X			X
Change Engine Oil Filter, 2001 All	X		X		X			X			X		X			X			X		X			X			X		X			X
Clean Engine Air Filter Housing & Replace Element								X								X								X								X
Inspect Battery Electrolyte Level, Less Turbo				X				X				X				X				X				X				X				X
Inspect Battery Electrolyte Level, w/Turbo			X		X			X			X		X			X			X		X			X			X		X			X
Inspect Cooling System & Protection Level, Less Turbo				X				X				X				X				X				X				X				X
Inspect Cooling System & Protection Level, w/Turbo			X		X			X			X		X			X			X		X			X			X		X			X
Inspect Exhaust System				X				X				X				X				X				X				X				X
Inspect OBD System For DTCs, Less Turbo				X				X				X				X				X				X				X				X
Inspect OBD System For DTCs, w/Turbo			X		X			X			X		X			X			X		X			X			X		X			X
Replace Serpentine Belt																								X								
Replace Spark Plugs	Every 36 Months Or 30,000 Miles																															
Replace Timing Belt & Tensioner, A4 & A8, 1998-99																								X								

Recommended Service	Service Interval In Miles①																														
	5000	7500	10000	15000	20000	22500	25000	30000	35000	37500	40000	45000	50000	52500	55000	60000	65000	67500	70000	75000	80000	82500	85000	90000	95000	97500	100000	105000	110000	112500	115000	120000
ENGINE																																
Replace Timing Belt & Tensioner, A4, A6 & A8, 2000–01 2.7L V6 5V & 4.2L V8 Engines Only	Every 105,000 Miles																															
Replace Timing Belt & Tensioner, A4 & A6, 2000–01 2.8L V6 5V Engines Only	Every 105,000 Miles																															
Replace Timing Belt, A4 & TT, 2000 1.8L 5V Turbo Engines Only	Every 105,000 Miles																															
Replace Timing Belt, A4 & TT, 2001 1.8L 5V Turbo Engines Only	Every 120,000 Miles																															
Replace Ribbed Belt , A4, A6 & A8, 2000																												X				
Replace Ribbed Belt , 2001																					X							X				
STEERING, SUSPENSION & TIRES																																
Inspect Ball Joint & Tie Rod End Boots, Less Turbo				X				X				X				X				X				X				X				X
Inspect Ball Joint & Tie Rod End Boots, w/Turbo			X		X			X			X		X			X			X		X			X			X		X			X
Inspect Power Steering System								X								X								X								X
Inspect Tire Conditions & Pressures, Including Spare, Less Turbo				X				X				X				X				X				X				X				X
Inspect Tire Conditions & Pressures, Including Spare, w/Turbo			X		X			X			X		X			X			X		X			X			X		X			X
Rotate Tires, 2001	Every 5000 Miles																															
Rotate Tires, V6 & V8 Engines, 1998–2000		X		X		X		X		X		X		X		X		X		X		X		X		X		X		X		X
Rotate Tires, 1.8T Engine, 1998–2000	X		X		X		X		X		X		X		X		X		X		X		X		X		X		X		X	

N — Normal Service
S — Severe Service
X — Normal Or Severe Service
① — After vehicles passes 120,000 mile mark return to beginning of mileage table & start cycle over again.

BMW

NOTE: Inspection Interval Is Determined By Service Inspection Indicator.

Jaguar XJ6, XJ12, XJR & XJS

Recommended Service	Service Interval In Miles①																							
	7500	10000	15000	20000	22500	30000	37500	40000	45000	50000	52500	60000	67500	70000	75000	80000	82500	90000	97500	100000	105000	110000	112500	120000
BODY																								
Clean Power Antenna Mast & Inspect All Fluid & Lubricant Levels	At Every Engine Oil Change																							
Inspect A/C System			X			X			X			X			X			X			X			X
Inspect Convertible Top Reservoir Fluid Level & System Operation	X		X		X	X	X		X		X	X	X		X		X	X	X		X		X	X
Inspect Electrical Components, Lamps & Warning Systems For Proper Operation	X		X		X	X	X		X		X	X	X		X		X	X	X		X		X	X
Inspect Headlamp Alignment & Seat Belts & Door Ajar Warning Systems	X		X		X	X	X		X		X	X	X		X		X	X	X		X		X	X
Inspect Passive Restraint System Inertia Switch & Reverse Inhibit Switch Operation			X			X			X			X			X			X			X			X
Lubricate Hinges, Locks & Door Check Straps	X		X		X	X	X		X		X	X	X		X		X	X	X		X		X	X
Replace Windshield Wiper Inserts	X		X		X	X	X		X		X	X	X		X		X	X	X		X		X	X
BRAKES																								
Change Brake Fluid	Every 24 Months																							
Inspect Brake System Hydraulic Components, XJS									X									X						
Inspect Brake System & Parking Brake Operation	X		X		X	X	X		X		X	X	X		X		X	X	X		X		X	X
CLUTCH & TRANSMISSION																								
Change Automatic Transmission Fluid & Filter						X						X						X						X
Lubricate Exposed Automatic Transmission Selector Linkage, XJS 5.3L	X		X		X	X	X		X		X	X	X		X		X	X	X		X		X	X
DRIVE AXLE & DRIVESHAFT																								
Change Differential Lubricant,XJS						X						X						X						X
Lubricate Axle Shaft U-Joints	X		X		X	X	X		X		X	X	X		X		X	X	X		X		X	X
Lubricate Driveshaft U-Joint Grease Fittings & Tighten Driveshaft Coupling Bolts			X			X			X			X			X			X			X			X
ENGINE																								
Change Engine Coolant, XJR, XJ6 & XJ12	Every 60 Months Or 150,000 Miles																							
Change Engine Oil, Filter & Replace Drain Plug Gasket	X		X		X	X	X		X		X	X	X		X		X	X	X		X		X	X
Clean Radiator Core						X						X						X						X
Clean Engine Air Filter, XJS			X						X						X						X			
Clean Engine Breather Filter, 5.3L			X			X			X			X			X			X			X			X
Inspect Battery & Cooling System & Protection Level	X		X		X	X	X		X		X	X	X		X		X	X	X		X		X	X
Inspect Crankcase Breather & EVAP Systems						X						X						X						X
Inspect Exhaust System & Supercharger Drive Belt Tension	X		X		X	X	X		X		X	X	X		X		X	X	X		X		X	X
Replace Engine Air Filter, Less Supercharger						X						X						X						X

Recommended Service	7500	10000	15000	20000	22500	30000	37500	40000	45000	50000	52500	60000	67500	70000	75000	80000	82500	90000	97500	100000	105000	110000	112500	120000
	Service Interval In Miles①																							
ENGINE																								
Replace Engine Air Filter, w/Supercharger				X				X				X				X				X				X
Replace Spark Plugs						X						X						X						X
Replace Supercharger Drive Belt						X						X						X						X
STEERING, SUSPENSION & TIRES																								
Change Power Steering & Rear Levelling System Fluid, XJ6	Every 60 Months, Regardless Of Mileage																							
Inspect Power Steering & Steering & Suspension Systems	X		X		X	X	X		X		X	X	X		X		X	X	X		X		X	X
Inspect Steering Unit Joints & Boots, Except XJ6	X		X		X	X	X		X		X	X	X		X		X	X	X		X		X	X
Inspect Steering Unit Joints & Boots, XJ6			X			X			X			X			X			X			X			X
Inspect Wheel Alignment & Tires For Condition & Pressures	X		X		X	X	X		X		X	X	X		X		X	X	X		X		X	X
Lubricate Grease Fittings	X		X		X	X	X		X		X	X	X		X		X	X	X		X		X	X

N — Normal Service
S — Severe Service
X — Normal Or Severe Service
① — After vehicles passes 120,000 mile mark return to beginning of mileage table & start cycle over again.

Jaguar S-Type, XJ8 & XK8

Recommended Service	7500	10000	15000	20000	22500	30000	37500	40000	45000	50000	52500	60000	67500	70000	75000	80000	82500	90000	97500	100000	105000	110000	112500	120000
	Service Interval In Miles①																							
BODY																								
Clean Power Antenna Mast & Inspect All Fluid & Lubricant Levels	At Every Engine Oil Change																							
Inspect Body Perforation & Undercar Rustproofing Condition	Every 12 Months																							
Inspect Convertible Top Reservoir Fluid Level & System Operation	X		X		X	X	X		X		X	X	X		X		X	X	X		X		X	X
Replace Passenger Compartment Particle/Pollen Filter	Every 36 Months Or 70,000 Miles; More Frequently In Severe Dust Or Pollution Zones																							
Replace Windshield Wiper Inserts		X		X		X		X		X		X		X		X		X		X		X		X
Replace Wiper Blades								X								X								X
BRAKES																								
Change Brake Fluid	Every 24 Months																							
Inspect Brake Lines & Hoses		X		X		X		X		X		X		X		X		X		X		X		X

Recommended Service	Service Interval In Miles①																						
	7500	10000	15000	20000	22500	30000	37500	40000	45000	50000	52500	60000	67500	70000	75000	80000	82500	90000	97500	100000	105000	110000	112500	120000
BRAKES																								
Inspect Brake Main & Parking Pads & Rotors		X		X		X		X		X		X		X		X		X		X		X		X
DRIVESHAFT																								
Lubricate Axle Shaft U-Joints		X		X		X		X		X		X		X		X		X		X		X		X
ENGINE																								
Change Engine Coolant,	Every 60 Months Or 150,000 Miles																							
Change Engine Oil, Filter & Replace Drain Plug Gasket		X		X		X		X		X		X		X		X		X		X		X		X
Inspect Battery Electrolyte Level		X		X		X		X		X		X		X		X		X		X		X		X
Inspect Cooling System & Protection Level		X		X		X		X		X		X		X		X		X		X		X		X
Inspect Crankcase Breather & EVAP Systems						X						X						X						X
Inspect Drive Belt Tension		X		X		X		X		X		X		X		X		X		X		X		X
Inspect Drive Belt Tension Wear Indicator		X		X		X		X		X		X		X		X		X		X		X		X
Inspect Supercharger Drive Belt Tension	X		X		X		X		X		X		X		X		X		X		X		X	
Replace Drive Belt	Every 100,000 Miles																							
Replace Engine Air Filter, Less Supercharger						X						X						X						X
Replace Engine Air Filter, w/Supercharger				X				X				X				X				X				X
Replace Fuel Filter												X												X
Replace Spark Plugs	Models Less Supercharger Every 100,000 Miles; w/Supercharger Every 60,000 Miles																							
Replace Supercharger Drive Belt						X						X						X						X
STEERING, SUSPENSION & TIRES																								
Lubricate Chassis		X		X		X		X		X		X		X		X		X		X		X		X
Rotate Tires & Inspect For Wear	Every 10,000 Miles																							

N — Normal Service
S — Severe Service
X — Normal Or Severe Service
① — After vehicles passes 120,000 mile mark return to beginning of mileage table & start cycle over again.

Land Rover Discovery & Range Rover

Recommended Service	Service Interval In Miles①															
	7500	15000	22500	30000	37500	45000	52500	60000	67500	75000	82500	90000	97500	105000	112500	120000
BODY																
Inspect Electrical Components, Gauges, Instruments, Lamps & Warning Devices For Proper Operation	X	X	X	X	X	X	X	X	X	X	X	X	X	X	X	X
Inspect A/C Condenser		X		X		X		X		X		X		X		X
Inspect Seat Belts & Mountings		X		X		X		X		X		X		X		X
Inspect Wiper Blades	X	X	X	X	X	X	X	X	X	X	X	X	X	X	X	X
Lubricate Door Checks, Catches, Hinges, Latches & Locks, Except Ignition Cylinder		X		X		X		X		X		X		X		X
Replace Passenger Compartment Pollen Filters, Range Rover		X		X		X		X		X		X		X		X
Replace Supplemental Restraint System	Every 10 Years															
BRAKES																
Change Brake Fluid	Every 24 Months Or 30,000 Miles															
Inspect Brake Calipers, Drums, Pads, Rotors & Wheel Cylinders	X	X	X	X	X	X	X	X	X	X	X	X	X	X	X	X
Inspect Brake System	X	X	X	X	X	X	X	X	X	X	X	X	X	X	X	X
CLUTCH & TRANSMISSION																
Change Automatic Transmission Fluid & Filter				X				X				X				X
Change Manual Transmission Lubricant				X				X				X				X
Change Transfer Case Lubricant				X				X				X				X
Inspect Clutch Operation	X	X	X	X	X	X	X	X	X	X	X	X	X	X	X	X
Inspect Clutch System Connections, Hoses & Lines	X	X	X	X	X	X	X	X	X	X	X	X	X	X	X	X
Inspect Transmission Mounts						X						X				
DRIVE AXLE & DRIVESHAFT																
Change Differential Lubricants				X				X				X				X
Lubricate Driveshaft Grease Fittings		X		X		X		X		X		X		X		X
ENGINE																
Change Engine Coolant	Every 24 Months Or 30,000 Miles															
Change Engine Oil & Filter	X	X	X	X	X	X	X	X	X	X	X	X	X	X	X	X
Inspect Auxiliary Emission Control Devices For Proper Operation							X							X		
Inspect Battery				X				X				X				X
Inspect Fuel System Connections, Hoses & Lines	X	X	X	X	X	X	X	X	X	X	X	X	X	X	X	X
Inspect Cooling System	X	X	X	X	X	X	X	X	X	X	X	X	X	X	X	X
Inspect Distributor Cap & Rotor							X							X		
Inspect Drive Belt				X				X				X				X
Inspect Engine Mounts, Discovery						X						X				
Inspect EVAP System Integrity							X							X		
Inspect Exhaust Heat Shields & System Integrity	X	X	X	X	X	X	X	X	X	X	X	X	X	X	X	X

Recommended Service	Service Interval In Miles①															
	7500	15000	22500	30000	37500	45000	52500	60000	67500	75000	82500	90000	97500	105000	112500	120000
ENGINE																
Inspect Ignition Wiring & Spark Plug Wires							X							X		
Inspect Radiator		X		X		X		X		X		X		X		X
Inspect & Service EVAP Loss System, Range Rover														X		
Replace Drive Belt										X						
Replace Engine Air Filter Element				X				X				X				X
Replace EVAP Canister, Discovery														X		
Replace Fuel Filter, Range Rover								X								X
Replace Fuel Filter, Discovery						X						X				
Replace O2 Sensors,											X					
Replace Spark Plugs				X				X				X				X
STEERING, SUSPENSION & TIRES																
Inspect Ball Joints		X		X		X		X		X		X		X		X
Inspect Electronic Air Suspension System, Range Rover		X		X		X		X		X		X		X		X
Inspect Power Steering System		X		X		X		X		X		X		X		X
Inspect Shock Absorbers, Suspension Links & Mountings		X		X		X		X		X		X		X		X
Inspect Steering Intermediate Shaft, Range Rover				X				X				X				X
Inspect Steering System & Boot Condition		X		X		X		X		X		X		X		X
Inspect & Adjust Steering Gearbox Freeplay						X						X				
Lubricate Chassis		X		X		X		X		X		X		X		X
Service Electronic Air Suspension System, Range Rover				X				X				X				X

N — Normal Service
S — Severe Service
SRI — Service Reminder Indicator
X — Normal Or Severe Service
① — After vehicles passes 120,000 mile mark return to beginning of mileage table & start cycle over again.

Mercedes-Benz

NOTE: Some Models Are Equipped With Service Indicator Lamp

Recommended Service	Service Interval In Miles①															
	7500	15000	22500	30000	37500	45000	52500	60000	67500	75000	82500	90000	97500	105000	112500	120000
BODY																
Clean Antenna Mast w/Special Cleaning Cloth & Cassette Deck Tape Head		X		X		X		X		X		X		X		X
Clean & Lightly Lubricate Sliding Roof Rails	Every 36 Months															
Inspect A/C Refrigerant Charge, Except Model 210		X		X		X		X		X		X		X		X
Inspect Roadster Soft Top Locking Lug, SL300, SL320, SL500 & SL600		X		X		X		X		X		X		X		X
Inspect Seat Belt & Backrest Lock Integrity & Operation & Horns, Lamps & All Warning Devices		X		X		X		X		X		X		X		X
Inspect Soft Top & Roll Bar Hydraulic System, Model 129		X		X		X		X		X		X		X		X
Inspect Body Structure & Body For Paint Damage	Every 24 Months															
Lubricate Hood Hinges		X		X		X		X		X		X		X		X
Replace Passenger Compartment Pollen Filter & Windshield Wiper Inserts, Inspect Headlamp Wiper Blade Condition		X		X		X		X		X		X		X		X
BRAKES																
Adjust Parking Brake, Model 129	Once At 15,000 Miles															
Change Brake Fluid	Every 24 Months															
Inspect Brake System Connections, Hoses & Lines		X		X		X		X		X		X		X		X
Inspect Parking Brake Cables, Model 129				X				X				X				X
CLUTCH & TRANSMISSION																
Change Automatic Transmission Fluid & Filter, Except S420, S500, S600, SL500 & SL600				X				X				X				X
Change Automatic Transmission Fluid & Filter, S420, S500, S600, SL500 & SL600	Filled For Life, No Maintenance Required															
DRIVE AXLE																
Inspect Driveshaft Flex Discs				X				X				X				X
ENGINE																
Change Engine Coolant	Every 36 Months															
Change Engine Oil & Filter, Except 300D②	N	N	N	N	N	N	N	N	N	N	N	N	N	N	N	N
Change Engine Oil & Filter, 300D	Normal Service Every 5000 Miles; Severe Service Every 2500 Miles															
Inspect Cooling System Integrity & Protection Level		X		X		X		X		X		X		X		X
Inspect Diesel Engine Injection Timing	Once At 30,000 Miles															
Inspect Drive Belts, Spark Plugs, Replace If Necessary & Underhood Hoses & Lines For Chafing, Damage, Leaks, Mis-routing & Missing Parts		X		X		X		X		X		X		X		X
Inspect & Lubricate Throttle Linkage		X		X		X		X		X		X		X		X
Replace Activated Charcoal Pre-filter Or Recirculated Air Filter, Models 140 & 210						X						X				

Recommended Service	Service Interval In Miles①															
	7500	15000	22500	30000	37500	45000	52500	60000	67500	75000	82500	90000	97500	105000	112500	120000
ENGINE																
Replace Dust Filter, Model 140 w/Activated Charcoal Filter						X						X				
Replace Engine Air Filter, 1998–99 Models								X								X
Replace Fuel Filters & Diesel Pre-Filter								X								X
Replace Spark Plugs, SLK230				X				X				X				X
Replace Spark Plugs, C320 & S320						X						X				
Replace Spark Plugs, CL500, S420, S500 & SL500								X								X
Replace Spark Plugs, C280, CLK320, E320 & E430	Every 100,000 Miles															
STEERING, SUSPENSION & TIRES																
Dismount Tires From Rims, Clean & Rotate, Except S500, S600 & C36 AMG		X		X		X		X		X		X		X		X
Inspect Front Suspension Ball Joints & Steering Freeplay		X		X		X		X		X		X		X		X
Inspect Front Suspension Ball Joint Freeplay & Boot Condition								X								X
Inspect Suspension	Every 24 Months Or 15,000 Miles															
Inspect Tires & Undercar Hoses & Lines For Chafing, Damage, Leaks, Misrouting & Missing Parts		X		X		X		X		X		X		X		X
Tighten Steering Gear Bolts, Except Models 140 & 210				X				X				X				X

N — Normal Service
S — Severe Service
X — Normal Or Severe Service
① — After vehicles passes 120,000 mile mark return to beginning of mileage table & start cycle over again.
② — Change every 3750 miles in severe service or extreme operating conditions.

Porsche

Recommended Service	Service Interval In Miles①②															
	12000	15000	24000	30000	36000	45000	48000	60000	72000	75000	84000	90000	96000	105000	108000	120000
Inspect Ancillary Unit Mounts & Running Gear	At 48, 96 & 10 Years After Vehicle Build Date, Then Every 24 Months Thereafter															
BODY																
Inspect Child Seat Occupancy Coding, Boxster	At 48 & 96 Months After Vehicle Build Date, Then Every 24 Months Thereafter															
Inspect Headlamp Alignment & Headlamp & Windshield Washer System Operation		X		X		X		X		X		X		X		X
Inspect Lamps, Electrical & Warning Devices For Proper Operation		X		X		X		X		X		X		X		X
Inspect Seat Belt Condition & Operation, 911	X		X		X		X		X		X		X		X	X
Inspect Seat Belt Condition & Operation, Boxster		X		X		X		X		X		X		X		X
Inspect Supplemental Restraint System	At 48, 96 & 10 Years After Vehicle Build Date, Then Every 24 Months Thereafter															
Inspect & Lubricate Catches, Hinges, Locks & Latches & Body Rubber Seals w/Suitable Lubricant		X		X		X		X		X		X		X		X
Replace Passenger Compartment Pollen Filter		X		X		X		X		X		X		X		X
BRAKES																
Change Brake Fluid	Every 24 Months															
Inspect Brake System & Parking Brakes		X		X		X		X		X		X		X		X
CLUTCH & TRANSMISSION																
Change Automatic Transmission Fluid & Filter, 911	Every 100,000 Miles															
Change Automatic Transmission Fluid & Filter, Boxster												X				
Change Automatic Transmission Final Drive Lubricant, Boxster												X				
Change Automatic Transmission Final Drive Lubricant, 911	Every 100,000 Miles															
Change Clutch Fluid	Every 24 Months															
Change Manual Transmission Lubricant, Boxster												X				
Change Manual Transmission Lubricant, 911	Every 100,000 Miles															
Inspect Clutch Pedal Freeplay & End Position		X		X		X		X		X		X		X		X
DRIVE AXLE & DRIVESHAFT																
Inspect Axle Joint, 911		X		X		X		X		X		X		X		X
Inspect CV & Driveshaft Boots		X		X		X		X		X		X		X		X
ENGINE																
Change Engine Coolant, Boxster	Filled For Life															
Change Engine Oil & Filter		X		X		X		X		X		X		X		X
Inspect Battery Electrolyte Level & Capacity	At Least Every 12 Months Or At Every Engine Oil Change															
Inspect Cooling System, Drive Belts & Tensioner Oil Level, Engine Air Filter & Exhaust System		X		X		X		X		X		X		X		X
Inspect Crankcase Ventilation System Hose Connections, 911		X		X		X		X		X		X		X		X

Recommended Service	Service Interval In Miles①②															
	12000	15000	24000	30000	36000	45000	48000	60000	72000	75000	84000	90000	96000	105000	108000	120000
ENGINE																
Inspect Fuel System Connections, Hoses & Lines		X		X		X		X		X		X		X		X
Inspect Intake Air System & OBD System For DTCs		X		X		X		X		X		X		X		X
Inspect Throttle Actuation & Smooth Operation		X		X		X		X		X		X		X		X
Inspect Engine Compartment For Fluid Leaks, Chafing & Damaged Lines		X		X		X		X		X		X		X		X
Replace Engine Air Filter				X				X				X				X
Replace Fuel Filter								X								X
Replace Spark Plugs				X				X				X				X
Replace Serpentine Belts, 911	Every 50,000 Miles															
Replace Serpentine Belts, Boxster								X								X
Replace Timing Belt, 2.0L, 2.5L, 2.7L & 3.0L③																
STEERING, SUSPENSION & TIRES																
Inspect Ball Joint Dust Caps & Suspension Adjustment Connections Security Play, 911		X		X		X		X		X		X		X		X
Inspect Tie Rod End & Steering Gear Boots & Freeplay		X		X		X		X		X		X		X		X
Inspect Tire Conditions & Pressures, Including Spare		X		X		X		X		X		X		X		X
Inspect Track Rod Link Dust Caps & End Play, 911		X		X		X		X		X		X		X		X
Inspect Vehicle Underside For Fluid Leaks, Chafing & Damaged Lines		X		X		X		X		X		X		X		X

N — Normal Service
S — Severe Service
X — Normal Or Severe Service
① — After vehicle passes 120,000 mile mark return to beginning of mileage table & start cycle over again.
② — All 928 & 968 models, Boxster & 1998–99 911 models covering less than 15,000 miles per year should have all maintenance items listed at those mileage intervals performed once per year.
③ — Normal service replace every 45,000 miles. Inspect tension at 2,000 miles, then every 15,000 miles.

1998 Saab

Recommended Service & Service Interval (Months)	Service Interval In Miles																						
	5000	10000	15000	20000	25000	30000	35000	40000	45000	50000	55000	60000	65000	70000	75000	80000	85000	90000	95000	100000	105000	110000	115000	120000
BODY																								
Inspect Air Bag System Warning Lamp	X		X		X		X		X		X		X		X		X		X		X		X	
Inspect Headlamp & Fog Lamp Alignment	X		X		X		X		X		X		X		X		X		X		X		X	
Inspect Headlamp, Fog, Brake, Tail, Turn Signal, Backup & Mark Lamps	X		X		X		X		X		X		X		X		X		X		X		X	
Inspect Seat Belts	X		X		X		X		X		X		X		X		X		X		X		X	
Inspect Windshield Wiper & Washer System	X		X		X		X		X		X		X		X		X		X		X		X	
Lubricate Convertible Top Latches				X			X			X			X											X
Lubricate Door Hinges, Stops & Locks, 9000							X						X						X					
Lubricate Door Hinges, Stops & Locks, 900	X		X		X		X		X		X		X		X		X		X		X		X	
Replace Ventilation Air Filter, 900			X		X		X		X		X		X		X		X		X		X		X	
Replace Ventilation Air Filter , 9000							X						X						X					
BRAKES																								
Change Brake Fluid (Every 24 Mos.)							X						X						X					
Adjust Parking Brake Cable, 900	X																							
Inspect Brake Hoses & Lines	X		X		X		X		X		X		X		X		X		X		X		X	
Inspect Brake Pads & Discs	X		X		X		X		X		X		X		X		X		X		X		X	
Inspect Parking Brake System Function	X		X		X		X		X		X		X		X		X		X		X		X	
CLUTCH & TRANSMISSION																								
Change Automatic Transmission Fluid, 900				S				S				S	N			S				S				S
Change Automatic Transmission Fluid, 9000	N			S			N	S				S	N			S			N	S				S
Inspect Automatic Transmission Fluid Level			X				X				X				X				X				X	
Inspect Manual Transmission Oil Level	X		X		X		X		X		X		X		X		X		X		X		X	
DRIVE AXLE																								
Inspect Inner & Outer Drive Joint Boots			X		X		X		X		X		X		X		X		X		X		X	
ENGINE																								
Change Engine Coolant (Every 36 Mos.)							X						X						X					
Change Engine Oil & Filter	First Interval, Normal Service 5,000 Miles/Severe Service 2,500 Miles; Subsequent Intervals, Normal Service 12 Months Or 10,000 Miles/Severe Service 6 Months Or 5,000 Miles																							
Inspect Battery & Connections	X		X		X		X		X		X		X		X		X		X		X		X	
Inspect Drive Belt & Tensioner	X		X		X		X		X		X		X		X		X		X		X		X	
Inspect Engine Cooling System, Hoses & Cap, 900	X		X		X		X		X		X		X		X		X		X		X		X	
Inspect Engine Cooling System, Hoses & Cap, 9000	X				X		X		X		X		X		X		X		X		X		X	
Inspect Engine Coolant Level & Protection	X		X		X				X		X				X		X				X		X	

Recommended Service & Service Interval (Months)	Service Interval In Miles																							
	5000	10000	15000	20000	25000	30000	35000	40000	45000	50000	55000	60000	65000	70000	75000	80000	85000	90000	95000	100000	105000	110000	115000	120000
ENGINE																								
Inspect Evaporative Emission Control System (Including Filler Cap, Vapor Lines, Canister & Purge), 900													X						X					
Inspect Evaporative Emission Control System (Including Filler Cap, Vapor Lines, Canister & Purge), 9000													X											
Inspect Exhaust System & Mounting	X		X		X		X		X		X		X		X		X		X		X		X	
Inspect Fuel Lines & Connections, 900							X						X						X					
Inspect Fuel System, 9000			X		X		X		X		X		X		X		X		X		X		X	
Inspect Positive Crankcase Ventilation (PCV) & Vacuum Hoses													X						X					
Replace Air Filter							X						X						X					
Replace Camshaft Timing Belt													X											
Replace Drive Belt (9000)													X											
Replace Fuel Filter													X											
Replace Spark Plugs	At 35,00 Miles, Then Every 30,000 Miles																							

Recommended Service & Service Interval (Months)	Service Interval In Miles																							
	5000	10000	15000	20000	25000	30000	35000	40000	45000	50000	55000	60000	65000	70000	75000	80000	85000	90000	95000	100000	105000	110000	115000	120000
STEERING, SUSPENSION & TIRES																								
Inspect Ball Joints, Inner & Outer Steering Joints & Rubber Boots, 900					X		X		X		X		X		X		X		X		X		X	
Inspect Ball Joints, Inner & Outer Steering Joints & Rubber Boots, 9000			X		X		X		X		X		X		X		X		X		X		X	
Inspect Front Wheel Alignment (Toe)							X						X						X					
Inspect Power Steering Fluid Level	X		X		X		X		X		X		X		X		X		X		X		X	
Inspect Shock Absorber							X						X		X		X		X		X		X	
Inspect Tire Pressure & Thread Depth	X		X		X		X		X		X		X		X		X		X		X		X	
Retighten Front Suspension & Rear Axle Mountings	X																							
Rotate Tires	X		X		X		X		X		X		X		X		X		X		X		X	

N — Normal Service
S — Severe Service
X — Normal or Severe Service
Mos. — Months

1999–2001 Saab

Recommended Service & Service Interval (Months)	Service Interval In Miles										
	1000	10000	20000	30000	40000	50000	60000	70000	80000	90000	100000
BODY											
Adjust Headlamp & Foglamp Alignment		X	X	X	X	X	X	X	X	X	X
Inspect Air Bag System & SRS Warning Lamps	X	X	X	X	X	X	X	X	X	X	X
Inspect head, Fog, Brake, Tail, Turn Signal, Backup & Marker Lamps	X	X	X	X	X	X	X	X	X	X	X
Inspect Seat Belt Operation & Perform Visual Inspection Of Belts For Tears & Fraying	X	X	X	X	X	X	X	X	X	X	X
Lubricate Door Hinges, Stops & Locks				X			X			X	
Replace Cabin Air Filter, 2001 9–3	Every 30,000 Miles										
Replace Cabin Air Filter, 2001 9–5	Every 20,000 Miles										
BRAKES											
Inspect Brake Fluid	X	X	X		X	X		X	X		X
Inspect Brake Lines & Hoses	X	X	X	X	X	X	X	X	X	X	X
Inspect Brake Pads & Discs		X	X	X	X	X	X	X	X	X	X
Inspect Handbrake Operation	X	X	X	X	X	X	X	X	X	X	X
Replace Brake Fluid, 1999–2000				X			X			X	
Replace Brake Fluid, 2001					X				X		

Recommended Service & Service Interval (Months)	Service Interval In Miles										
	1000	10000	20000	30000	40000	50000	60000	70000	80000	90000	100000
CLUTCH & TRANSMISSION											
Change Automatic Transmission Fluid & Filter, 9-5 Series, 1999–2000	X		S	X		S	X		S	X	
Change Automatic Transmission Fluid & Filter, 9-5 Series, 2001			S			S	X		S		
Change Automatic Transmission Fluid & Filter, 9-3 Series				S			X			S	
Inspect Automatic Transmission Fluid	X	X	X	X	X	X	X	X	X	X	X
Inspect Manual Transmission Fluid				X			X			X	
DRIVE AXLE											
Inspect Inner & Outer Driveshaft Boots		X	X	X	X	X	X	X	X	X	X
ENGINE											
Change Engine Coolant, 1999–2000				X			X			X	
Change Engine Coolant, 2001					X				X		
Change Engine Oil & Filter	X	X	X	X	X	X	X	X	X	X	X
Check Battery Electrolyte Level & Clean & Grease Terminals	X	X	X	X	X	X	X	X	X	X	X
Check Engine Coolant Freezing Point & Level	X	X	X		X	X		X	X		
Inspect Drive Belt Tension, Poly-Vee Tensioner Operation & Belt Condition		X	X	X	X	X	X	X	X	X	X
Inspect Engine Coolant System, Hoses & Cap	X		X	X	X	X	X	X	X	X	X
Inspect EVAP Emission System Filler Cap, Vapor Lines, EVAP Canister & Canister Purge Valve							X				
Inspect Exhaust System & Mountings		X	X	X	X	X	X	X	X	X	X

Recommended Service & Service Interval (Months)	Service Interval In Miles										
	1000	10000	20000	30000	40000	50000	60000	70000	80000	90000	100000
ENGINE											
Inspect Fuel System Components For Leaks & Damage, 9-5 Series		X	X	X	X	X	X	X	X	X	X
Inspect Fuel System Components For Leaks & Damage, 9-3 Series				X			X			X	
Replace Air Filter				X			X			X	
Replace Camshaft Drive Belt (V6)①, 9-5 series							X				
Replace Fuel Filter							X				
Replace Spark Plugs				X			X			X	
STEERING, SUSPENSION & TIRES											
Check Power Steering Level	X	X	X	X	X	X	X	X	X	X	X
Inspect Ball Joint Clearance & Inner & Outer Steering Joints & Rubber Boots		X	X	X	X	X	X	X	X	X	X
Inspect Front Suspension & Rear Axle Mountings & Retighten Bolts	X										
Inspect Shock Absorbers & Bushes				X			X	X	X	X	X
Inspect Tire Pressure, Tread Depth & Wear	X	X	X	X	X	X	X	X	X	X	X
Rotate Tires		X	X	X	X	X	X	X	X	X	X

S — Severe Service
X — Normal or Severe Service
Mos. — Months
① — Camshaft drive belt replacements (V6) prior to 100,000 miles will be performed at no charge by an authorized Saab dealer.

Volkswagen

Recommended Service	Service Interval In Miles①																															
	5000	7500	10000	15000	20000	22500	25000	30000	35000	37500	40000	45000	50000	52500	55000	60000	65000	67500	70000	75000	80000	82500	85000	90000	95000	97500	100000	105000	110000	112500	115000	120000
BODY																																
Inspect Automatic Shoulder Belt System Operation, Seat Adjustment Lever & Acceleration Sensor				X				X				X				X				X				X				X				X
Inspect Seat Belt Pretensioners & Supplemental Restraint System	At 48 Months & 96 Months From Vehicle Build Date, Then Every 24 Months Thereafter																															
Replace Passenger Compartment Pollen Filter			X		X			X			X		X			X			X		X			X			X		X			X
BRAKES																																
Change Brake Fluid	Every 24 Months, Regardless Of Mileage																															
Inspect Brake System			X		X			X			X		X			X			X		X			X			X		X			X
CLUTCH & TRANSMISSION																																
Change Automatic Transaxle Fluid & Filter, Except Passat & New Beetle								S								S								S								S
Change Automatic Transaxle Fluid & Filter, Passat								X								X								X								X
Change Automatic Transaxle Fluid & Filter, New Beetle																X																X
Change Clutch Fluid	Every 24 Months, Regardless Of Mileage																															
Inspect Auto Shift Lock & Park/Neutral Safety Switch Operation			X		X			X			X		X			X			X		X			X			X		X			X
Inspect Automatic Transaxle Final Drive Fluid Level					X						X					X					X						X					X

Recommended Service	Service Interval In Miles①																														
	5000	7500	10000	15000	20000	22500	25000	30000	35000	37500	40000	45000	50000	52500	55000	60000	65000	67500	70000	75000	80000	82500	85000	90000	95000	97500	100000	105000	110000	112500	115000	120000
DRIVESHAFT																																
Inspect CV Joint					X						X					X					X						X					X
ENGINE																																
Change Engine Coolant 1998-99	Fill For Life																															
Change Engine Coolant 2000	Every 40,000 Miles																															
Change Engine Coolant 2001	Every 20,000 Miles																															
Change Engine Oil & Filter, Except 1.8L Turbo & 2.8L 5-Valve	X		X		X			X			X		X			X			X		X			X			X		X			X
Change Engine Oil & Filter, 1.8L Turbo & 2.8L 5-Valve	X		X	X	X		X	X	X		X	X	X		X	X	X		X	X	X		X	X	X		X	X	X		X	X
Drain Water From Separator,1.9L TDI, 1998-99	X		X		X			X			X		X			X			X		X			X			X		X			X
Drain Water From Separator,1.9L TDI, 2000	Every 40,000 MIles																															
Drain Water From Separator,1.9L TDI, 2001	Drain At 5000 MIles, Then Every 10,000 Miles Thereafter																															
Inspect Battery & Cooling System, 1998-99					X						X					X					X						X					X
Inspect Battery & Cooling System, 2000	Every 40,000 MIles																															
Inspect Battery & Cooling System, 2001	Every 20,000 MIles																															
Inspect Distributor Cap, Rotor & Spark Plug Wires								X								X								X								X
Inspect Belt & Adjust Tension & Inspect Exhaust System					X						X					X					X						X					X

Recommended Service	Service Interval In Miles①																														
	5000	7500	10000	15000	20000	22500	25000	30000	35000	37500	40000	45000	50000	52500	55000	60000	65000	67500	70000	75000	80000	82500	85000	90000	95000	97500	100000	105000	110000	112500	115000	120000
ENGINE																																
Inspect Timing Belt Condition, Cabrio, Golf, Jetta & Passat 1.9L TDI	X		X		X			X					X			X			X					X			X		X			
Inspect Timing Belt, New Beetle 1.9L TDI			X		X			X					X			X			X					X			X		X			
Replace Drive Belt, Turbo V6 Engine																											X					
Replace Air Filter, Cabrio, Golf, Jetta & Passat					X						X					X					X						X					X
Replace Air Filter, New Beetle											X										X											X
Replace Air Filter, 2001 Cabrio, Passat & Eurovan	Every 2 Years Or 40,000 Miles																															
Replace Air Filter, 2001 Golf, Jetta & New Beetle	Every 4 Years Or 40,000 Miles																															
Replace Fuel Filter, Gasoline Engines w/Replaceable Element								X								X								X								X
Replace Fuel Filter, 1.9L TDI Except 2000–01 New Beetle & Jetta					X						X					X					X						X					X
Replace Fuel Filter, 1.9L TDI, 2000 New Beetle & Jetta	Every 40,000 Miles																															
Replace Spark Plugs , 1998-99								X								X								X								X
Replace Spark Plugs , 2000–01 Except Cabrio	Every 40,000 Miles																															

Recommended Service	Service Interval In Miles①																														
	5000	7500	10000	15000	20000	22500	25000	30000	35000	37500	40000	45000	50000	52500	55000	60000	65000	67500	70000	75000	80000	82500	85000	90000	95000	97500	100000	105000	110000	112500	115000	120000
ENGINE																																
Replace Spark Plugs , 2001 Cabrio	Every 20,000 Miles																															
Replace Timing Belt, 2.0L	Every 105,000 Miles																															
Replace Timing Belt & Tensioner, Cabrio, Golf, Jetta & Passat 1.9L TDI																X																X
Replace Timing Belt & Tensioner,1.9L TDI, 1998-2001 Automatic Transmission											X										X											X
Replace Timing Belt & Tensioner, 1.9L TDI, 1998-2000 Manual Transmission	Every 55,000 Miles																															
Replace Timing Belt & Tensioner, 1.9L TDI, 2001 Manual Transmission	Every 60,000 Miles																															
Replace Timing Belt & Tensioner, 1.8L Turbo & 2.8L																								X								
STEERING, SUSPENSION & TIRES																																
Inspect Power Steering System For Fluid Leakage					X						X					X					X						X					X
Inspect Tire Conditions & Pressure In Spare & Suspension					X						X					X					X						X					X
Rotate Tires			X		X			X			X		X			X			X		X			X			X		X			X

N — Normal Service
S — Severe Service
X — Normal Or Severe Service
① — After vehicles passes 120,000 mile mark return to beginning of mileage table & start cycle over again.

1998 Volvo

Recommended Service	Service Interval In Miles①																							
	10000	20000	30000	40000	50000	60000	70000	80000	90000	100000	110000	120000	130000	140000	150000	160000	170000	180000	190000	200000	210000	220000	230000	240000
BODY																								
Inspect Headlamp & Windshield Wiper Arms & Blades & Electrical Components, Lamps & Warning Devices	X	X	X	X	X	X	X	X	X	X	X	X	X	X	X	X	X	X	X	X	X	X	X	X
Lubricate All Hinges, Latches, Sliding Mechanisms & Strikers	X	X	X	X	X	X	X	X	X	X	X	X	X	X	X	X	X	X	X	X	X	X	X	X
BRAKES																								
Change Brake Fluid	Normal Service Every 24 Months Or 30,000 Miles; In Humid Climates Or Mountains Every 12 Months Or 10,000 Miles																							
Inspect Brake System & Parking Brake	X	X	X	X	X	X	X	X	X	X	X	X	X	X	X	X	X	X	X	X	X	X	X	X
CLUTCH & TRANSMISSION																								
Change Automatic Transmission Fluid & Filter,	Not Required In Normal Service; Severe Service Or Trailer Towing Every 50,000 Miles																							
Inspect Neutral Safety Switch & Shift Interlock Operation & Transmission For Fluid Leakage	X	X	X	X	X	X	X	X	X	X	X	X	X	X	X	X	X	X	X	X	X	X	X	X
DRIVE AXLE & DRIVESHAFT																								
Inspect Driveshaft, Pilot Bearing & U-Joints, S90 & V90				X	X	X	X	X	X	X	X	X	X	X	X	X	X	X	X	X	X	X	X	X
Inspect Final Drive Unit Lubricant Level,	If Leakage Is Discovered																							

Recommended Service	Service Interval In Miles①																							
	10000	20000	30000	40000	50000	60000	70000	80000	90000	100000	110000	120000	130000	140000	150000	160000	170000	180000	190000	200000	210000	220000	230000	240000
ENGINE																								
Change Engine Oil & Filter	Normal Service Every 10,000 Miles; Severe Service & Models w/Turbocharger Every 5,000 Miles																							
Clean Engine Air Cleaner Housing & Replace Filter Element	Normal Service Every 30,000 Miles; More Frequently In Severe Service Or Dusty Conditions																							
Clean PCV System, C70, S70 & V70						X			X			X			X			X			X			X
Clean PCV System & Replace Flame Trap, S90 & V90						X		X		X		X		X		X		X		X		X		X
Inspect & Adjust V-Belt Tension			X			X			X			X			X			X			X			X
Inspect Exhaust Heat Shields & System Integrity, C70, S70 & V70						X	X	X	X	X	X	X	X	X	X	X	X	X	X	X	X	X	X	X
Inspect Exhaust Heat Shields & System Integrity, S90 & V90				X	X	X	X	X	X	X	X	X	X	X	X	X	X	X	X	X	X	X	X	X
Replace Drive Belts						X						X						X						X
Replace Fuel Filter										X					X					X				
Replace Spark Plugs			X			X			X			X			X			X			X			X
Replace Timing Belt							X							X							X			
Tighten Exhaust Pipe To Turbocharger Mounting Nuts	X	X	X	X	X	X	X	X	X	X	X	X	X	X	X	X	X	X	X	X	X	X	X	X
Reset Service Reminder Indicator	After Every Engine Oil Change																							
STEERING, SUSPENSION & TIRES																								
Inspect Shock Absorbers, Struts & Suspension & Steering Integrity, C70, S70 & V70						X	X	X	X	X	X	X	X	X	X	X	X	X	X	X	X	X	X	X
Inspect Shock Absorbers, Struts & Suspension & Steering Integrity, S90 & V90				X	X	X	X	X	X	X	X	X	X	X	X	X	X	X	X	X	X	X	X	X

Recommended Service	Service Interval In Miles①																							
	10000	20000	30000	40000	50000	60000	70000	80000	90000	100000	110000	120000	130000	140000	150000	160000	170000	180000	190000	200000	210000	220000	230000	240000
STEERING, SUSPENSION & TIRES																								
Rotate Tires, Inspect All Tires & Wheels For Conditions & Pressures	X	X	X	X	X	X	X	X	X	X	X	X	X	X	X	X	X	X	X	X	X	X	X	X

N — Normal Service
S — Severe Service
X — Normal Or Severe Service
① — After vehicle passes 240,000 mile mark return to beginning of mileage table & start cycle over again.

1999–2001 Volvo

Recommended Service	Service Interval In Miles①																			
	7500	15000	22500	30000	37500	45000	52500	60000	67500	75000	82500	90000	97500	105000	112500	120000	127500	135000	142500	150000
BODY																				
Inspect Exterior Lighting Controls		X		X		X		X		X		X		X		X		X		X
Inspect Headlamp Wiper Washer System		X		X		X		X		X		X		X		X		X		X
Inspect Washer Fluid Level	X	X	X	X	X	X	X	X	X	X	X	X	X	X	X	X	X	X	X	X
Inspect Windshield Wiper/Washer System Operation & Components		X		X		X		X		X		X		X		X		X		X
Lubricate All Hinges, Latches & Sliding Parts				X				X				X				X				X
Lubricate Power Antenna		X		X		X		X		X		X		X		X		X		X
Replace Cabin Air Filter②		X		X		X		X		X		X		X		X		X		X
BRAKES																				
Change Brake Fluid	Normal Service, Every Two Years Or 30,000 Miles. Severe Service, Once A Year																			
Check Brake Fluid Level		X		X		X		X		X		X		X		X		X		X
Inspect Brake Hoses & Lines				X				X				X				X				X
Inspect Brake Pads		X	X	X	X	X	X	X	X	X	X	X	X	X	X	X	X	X	X	X
Inspect Parking Brake		X		X		X		X		X		X		X		X		X		X
CLUTCH & TRANSMISSION																				
Inspect Automatic Transmission Fluid		X		X		X		X		X		X		X		X		X		X

Recommended Service	Service Interval In Miles①																			
	7500	15000	22500	30000	37500	45000	52500	60000	67500	75000	82500	90000	97500	105000	112500	120000	127500	135000	142500	150000
DRIVESHAFT																				
Inspect Bevel Gear (AWD Only)		X		X		X		X		X		X		X		X		X		X
Inspect Driveshaft Boots								X	X	X	X	X	X	X	X	X	X	X	X	X
Inspect Driveshaft Joints								X	X	X	X	X	X	X	X	X	X	X	X	X
Inspect Propeller Shaft, Pilot Bearing & Universal Joints								X	X	X	X	X	X	X	X	X	X	X	X	X
ENGINE																				
Change Engine Oil & Filter	X	X	X	X	X	X	X	X	X	X	X	X	X	X	X	X	X	X	X	X
Inspect Battery Condition & Components	X	X	X	X	X	X	X	X	X	X	X	X	X	X	X	X	X	X	X	X
Inspect Coolant Level	X	X	X	X	X	X	X	X	X	X	X	X	X	X	X	X	X	X	X	X
Inspect Exhaust System For Leaks/Damage								X	X	X	X	X	X	X	X	X	X	X	X	X
Inspect Fuel Lines For Leaks/Damage				X		X		X		X		X		X		X		X		X
Inspect PCV System Components								X				X				X				X
Replace Air Cleaner Filter②				X				X				X				X				X
Replace Drive Belt								X								X				
Replace Fuel Filter														X						
Replace Spark Plugs				X				X				X				X				X
Replace Timing Belt & Tensioner③														X						

Recommended Service	Service Interval In Miles①																			
	7500	15000	22500	30000	37500	45000	52500	60000	67500	75000	82500	90000	97500	105000	112500	120000	127500	135000	142500	150000
STEERING, SUSPENSION & TIRES																				
Check Power Steering Fluid Level, 1999–2000, Except 2000 S40/V40				X		X		X		X		X		X		X		X		X
Check Power Steering Fluid Level, 2000 S40/V40 & 2001 All	Inspect Every 15,000 Miles																			
Inspect Rear Suspension								X	X	X	X	X	X	X	X	X	X	X	X	X
Inspect Steering/Front Suspension								X	X	X	X	X	X	X	X	X	X	X	X	X
Inspect Tire Pressure, Wear & Condition	X	X	X	X	X	X	X	X	X	X	X	X	X	X	X	X	X	X	X	X

① — After vehicle passes 150,000 mile mark, return to beginning of mileage table & start cycle over again.
② — It may be necessary to change more frequently if driving in dusty/dirty areas.
③ — Tensioner replacement is for models equipped w/five cylinder engine only.

AUDI

INDEX OF SERVICE OPERATIONS

	Page No.
AIR BAG SYSTEM PRECAUTIONS	0-12
BRAKES	
Anti-Lock Brakes	1-180
Disc Brakes	1-162
Hydraulic Brake Systems	1-175
Power Brake Units	1-178
AIR QUALITY STANDARDS	0-23
ALL-WHEEL DRIVE SYSTEMS	1-222
AUTOMATIC TRANSAXLES	1-164
CLUTCH & MANUAL TRANSAXLE	
Adjustments	1-54
Clutch, Replace	1-55
Hydraulic System Service	1-54
Precautions	1-54
Tightening Specifications	1-62
Transaxle, Replace	1-55
COMPUTER RELEARN PROCEDURE	0-10
ELECTRICAL	
Air Bags	1-129
Air Conditioning	1-109
Alternator, Replace	1-11
Alternators	1-121
Blower Motor, Replace	1-18
Coil Pack, Replace	1-13
Combination Switch, Replace	1-14
Cooling Fans	1-112
Cruise Controls	1-123
Dash Gauges	1-115
Dash Panels	1-146
Evaporator Core, Replace	1-21
Fuel Pump Relay Location	1-10
Fuse Panel & Flasher Location	1-9
Heater Core, Replace	1-18
Ignition Lock, Replace	1-13
Ignition Switch, Replace	1-14
Instrument Cluster, Replace	1-15
Passive Restraints	1-129
Precautions	1-9
Radio, Replace	1-16
Relay Center Location	1-10
Speed Controls	1-123
Starter Motors	1-120
Starter, Replace	1-10
Steering Columns	1-149
Steering Wheel, Replace	1-14
Wiper Motor, Replace	1-17
Wiper Systems	1-125
ELECTRICAL SYMBOL IDENTIFICATION	0-33
FRONT SUSPENSION & STEERING	
Ball Joint, Replace	1-88
Ball Joint Inspection	1-88
Coil Spring, Replace	1-89
Control Arm, Replace	1-90
Power Steering	1-154
Power Steering Gear, Replace	1-94
Power Steering Pump, Replace	1-97
Power Steering System Bleed	1-99
Precautions	1-86
Steering Knuckle, Replace	1-92
Strut, Replace	1-89
Strut Service	1-90
Subframe, Replace	1-91
Technical Service Bulletins	1-101
Tie Rod End, Replace	1-94
Tightening Specifications	1-102
Wheel Bearing, Adjust	1-86
Wheel Bearing, Replace	1-86
FRONT WHEEL DRIVE AXLES	1-219
REAR AXLE & SUSPENSION	
Coil Spring, Replace	1-72
Control Arm, Replace	1-72
Hub & Bearing Service	1-68
Rear Axle, Replace	1-65
Rear Axle Shaft, Replace	1-66
Stabilizer Bar, Replace	1-73
Strut, Replace	1-69
Strut Service	1-70
Tightening Specifications	1-80
Wheel Bearing, Adjust	1-69
SPECIFICATIONS	
Application Chart	1-2
Fluid Capacities & Cooling System Data	1-7
Front Wheel Alignment Specifications	1-5
General Engine Specifications	1-3
Lubricant Data	1-8
Rear Wheel Alignment Specifications	1-6
Tune Up Specifications	1-3
TRANSFER CASE	
Description	1-83
Fluid Change	1-83
Precautions	1-83
Tightening Specifications	1-85
Transfer Case, Replace	1-83
VEHICLE IDENTIFICATION	0-3
VEHICLE LIFT POINTS	0-24
VEHICLE MAINTENANCE SCHEDULES	0-45
WHEEL ALIGNMENT	
Front Wheel Alignment	1-105
Preliminary Inspection	1-105
Rear Wheel Alignment	1-106
Vehicle Ride Height	1-108
Wheel Alignment Specifications	1-5
WIRE COLOR CODE IDENTIFICATION	0-33
1.8L ENGINE	
Compression Pressure	1-23
Cooling System Bleed	1-24
Engine Rebuilding Specifications	1-231
Engine, Replace	1-23
Oil Pan, Replace	1-24
Precautions	1-23
Radiator, Replace	1-24
Tightening Specifications	1-25
2.7L ENGINE	
Camshaft, Replace	1-31
Camshaft Seals, Replace	1-32
Compression Pressure	1-26
Cooling System Bleed	1-34
Crankshaft Rear Oil Seal, Replace	1-33
Crankshaft Seal, Replace	1-32
Cylinder Head, Replace	1-28
Engine Rebuilding Specifications	1-231
Engine, Replace	1-26
Fuel Pump, Replace	1-34
Intake Manifold, Replace	1-28
Oil Pump, Replace	1-33
Precautions	1-26
Radiator, Replace	1-34
Thermostat, Replace	1-34
Tightening Specifications	1-36
Timing Belt, Replace	1-29
Valve Adjustment	1-29
Valve Clearance Specifications	1-29
Water Pump, Replace	1-34
2.8L ENGINE	
Camshaft, Replace	1-40
Camshaft Seals, Replace	1-41
Compression Pressure	1-37
Cooling System Bleed	1-42
Crankshaft Seal, Replace	1-42
Cylinder Head, Replace	1-39
Engine Rebuilding Specifications	1-231
Engine, Replace	1-37
Fuel Pump, Replace	1-43
Intake Manifold, Replace	1-39
Oil Pump, Replace	1-42
Precautions	1-37
Radiator, Replace	1-43
Thermostat, Replace	1-43
Tightening Specifications	1-46
Timing Belt, Replace	1-40
Valve Adjustment	1-40
Valve Clearance Specifications	1-40
Water Pump, Replace	1-43
3.7L & 4.2L ENGINES	
Camshaft, Replace	1-50
Compression Pressure	1-47
Cooling System Bleed	1-51
Crankshaft Seal, Replace	1-50
Cylinder Head, Replace	1-49
Engine Rebuilding Specifications	1-231
Engine, Replace	1-47
Exhaust Manifold, Replace	1-48
Fuel Filter, Replace	1-51
Fuel Pump, Replace	1-51
Intake Manifold, Replace	1-48
Oil Pan, Replace	1-51
Oil Pump, Replace	1-51
Precautions	1-47
Radiator, Replace	1-51
Serpentine Drive Belt	1-51
Thermostat, Replace	1-51
Tightening Specifications	1-52
Timing Belt, Replace	1-49

	Page No.
Valve Adjustment	1-49
Valve Clearance	
Specifications	1-49
Valve Guides	1-49
Water Pump, Replace	1-51

Specifications

APPLICATION CHART

Engine	Engine Code	Model
1998–99		
1.8L	AEB	A4 & A4 Quattro
2.8L	AFC	A4, A4 Quattro, A6, A6 Quattro & Cabriolet
3.7L	AEW	A8
4.2L	ABZ	A8 Quattro
2000		
1.8L	ATC	TT
	ATW	A4
2.7L	APB	A6 & S4
2.8L	AHA	A4
	ATQ	A6
4.2L	AKB	A8
	ART	A6
2001		
1.8L	AMU	TT
	ATC	TT
	ATW	A4
2.7L	APB	A6 & Allroad
2.8L	AHA	A4
	ATQ	A6
4.2L	AKB	A8
	ART	A6

GENERAL ENGINE SPECIFICATIONS

Engine	Engine Code	Fuel System	Bore & Stroke, mm	Compres-sion Ratio	Net Brake HP @ RPM	Maximum Torque, Ft. Lbs. @ RPM	Oil Pressure, psi①
1998–99							
1.8L	AEB	MFI	81.0 × 86.4	9.5	150 @ 5700	155 @ 1750	—
2.8L	AFC	MFI	82.5 × 86.4	10.0	174 @ 5500	180 @ 3000	14–37
3.7L	AEW	MFI	84.5 × 82.4	10.8	230 @ 5800	229 @ 2300	—
4.2L	ABZ	MFI	84.5 × 93.0	10.8	300 @ 6000	295 @ 3300	—
2000							
1.8L	ATC	MFI	81.0 × 86.4	9.5	180 @ 5500	173 @ 1950	19
	ATW	MFI	81.0 × 86.4	9.5	150 @ 5700	155 @ 1750	15–36
2.7L	APB	MFI	81.0 × 86.4	9.3	250 @ 5800	258 @ 1850	—
2.8L	AHA	MFI	82.5 × 86.4	10.3	190 @ 6000	207 @ 3200	15–36
	ATQ	MFI	82.5 × 86.4	10.3	200 @ 6000	207 @ 3200	—
4.2L	AKB	MFI	84.5 × 93.0	10.8	310 @ 6200	302 @ 3000	—
	ART	MFI	84.5 × 93.0	10.8	300 @ 6200	295 @ 3000	—
2001							
1.8L	AMU	MFI	81.0 × 86.4	9.0	225 @ 5900	207 @ 2200	—
	ATC	MFI	81.0 × 86.4	9.5	180 @ 5500	173 @ 1950	19
	ATW	MFI	81.0 × 86.4	9.5	150 @ 5700	155 @ 1750	15–36
2.7L	APB	MFI	81.0 × 86.4	9.3	250 @ 5800	258 @ 1850	—
2.8L	AHA	MFI	82.5 × 86.4	10.3	190 @ 6000	207 @ 3200	15–36
	ATQ	MFI	82.5 × 86.4	10.3	200 @ 6000	207 @ 3200	—
4.2L	AKB	MFI	84.5 × 93.0	10.8	310 @ 6200	302 @ 3000	—
	ART	MFI	84.5 × 93.0	10.8	300 @ 6200	295 @ 3000	—

① — At idle speed.

TUNE UP SPECIFICATIONS

Engine/ Code	Spark Plug Gap Inch	Ignition Timing		Curb Idle Speed		Fast Idle Speed		Valve Lash, Inch		Fuel Press-ure, psi
		Firing Order ①	Timing ° BTDC②	Man. Trans.	Auto. Trans.	Man. Trans.	Auto. Trans.	Intake	Ex-haust	
1998–99										
1.8L/AEB	.032	⑨	④	④	④	④	④	⑤	⑤	58⑩
2.8L/AFC	.039	⑥	12④	650–750④	650–750④	④	④	⑤	⑤	55–70⑧
3.7L/AEW	.032	⑦	—	—	④	—	④	⑤	⑤	—
4.2L/ABH	.032	⑦	—	—	④	—	④	⑤	⑤	—
2000										
1.8L/ATC⑪	.032	⑨	④	800–920④	640–760④	④	④	⑤	⑤	58⑩
1.8L/ATC⑫	.032	⑨	④	720–840④	—	④	④	⑤	⑤	58⑩
1.8L/ATW	.032	⑨	④	750–850④	750–850④	④	④	⑤	⑤	50
2.7L/APB	—	⑬	④	750–850④	750–850④	④	④	⑤	⑤	58⑧
2.8L/AHA⑪	.064	⑨	④	740–860④	740–860④	④	④	⑤	⑤	55–61⑩
2.8L/AHA⑫	.064	⑨	④	620–740④	620–740④	④	④	⑤	⑤	55–61⑩
2.8L/ATQ	.038	⑥	TDC	—	650–750N④	④	④	⑤	⑤	55–61⑩
4.2L/AKB	.028–.035	③	④	—	—	—	④	⑤	⑤	—
4.2L/ART	.028–.035	③	④	—	—	—	④	⑤	⑤	—
2001										
1.8L/AMU	.032	⑨	④	④	④	④	④	⑤	⑤	—
1.8L/ATC⑪	.032	⑨	④	800–920④	640–760④	④	④	⑤	⑤	58⑩
1.8L/ATC⑫	.032	⑨	④	720–840④	—	④	④	⑤	⑤	58⑩
1.8L/ATW	.032	⑨	④	750–850④	750–850④	④	④	⑤	⑤	50
2.7L/APB	—	⑬	④	750–850④	750–850④	④	④	⑤	⑤	58⑧

Continued

TUNE UP SPECIFICATIONS—Continued

Engine/ Code	Spark Plug Gap Inch	Ignition Timing		Curb Idle Speed		Fast Idle Speed		Valve Lash, Inch		Fuel Press-ure, psi
		Firing Order ①	Timing ° BTDC②	Man. Trans.	Auto. Trans.	Man. Trans.	Auto. Trans.	Intake	Ex-haust	
2001										
2.8L/AHA⑪	.064	⑨	④	740–860④	740–860④	④	④	⑤	⑤	55–61⑩
2.8L/AHA⑫	.064	⑨	④	620–740④	620–740④	④	④	⑤	⑤	55–61⑩
2.8L/ATQ	.038	⑥	TDC	—	650–750N④	④	④	⑤	⑤	55–61⑩
4.2L/AKB	.028–.035	③	④	—	—	—	④	⑤	⑤	—
4.2L/ART	.028–.035	③	④	—	—	—	④	⑤	⑤	—

① — Determine location of number 1 wire before disconnecting spark plug wires.

② — BTDC: Before Top Dead Center.

③ — Firing order 1–5–4–8–6–3–7–2.

④ — Not adjustable. Controlled by electronic control unit.

⑤ — Equipped with hydraulic valve lash adjusters.

⑥ — Firing order 1–4–3–6–2–5. Refer to **Fig. A** for spark plug wire connections.

⑦ — Firing order 1–5–4–8–6–3–7–2. Refer to **Fig. B** for spark plug wire connections.

⑧ — With pressure regulator vacuum hose disconnected & plugged.

⑨ — Firing order 1–3–4–2.

⑩ — Connect suitable fuel pressure gauge between fuel supply & fuel return lines. Disconnect & plug vacuum line from fuel pressure regulator to intake manifold, then use suitable scan tool to trigger fuel pump relay.

⑪ — Front wheel drive.

⑫ — Quattro.

⑬ — Firing order 1–4–3–6–2–5.

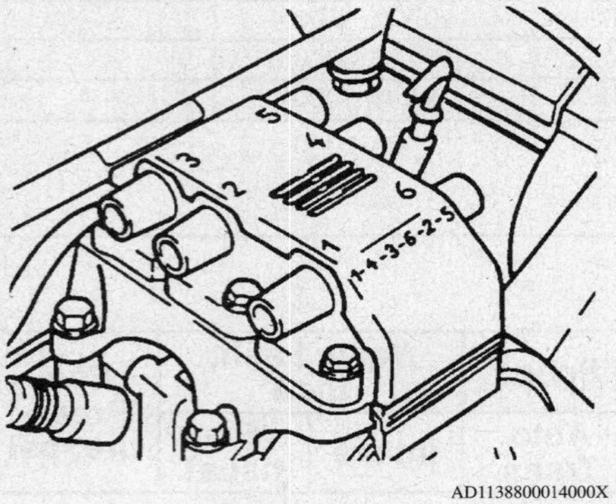

Fig. A

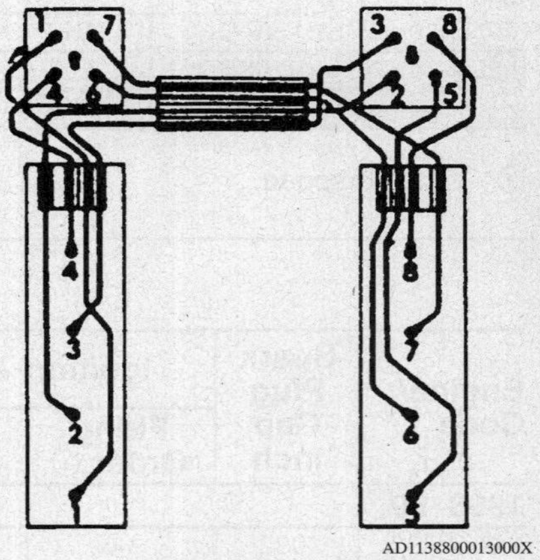

Fig. B

FRONT WHEEL ALIGNMENT SPECIFICATIONS

Model	Caster Angle, Deg.①		Camber Angle Deg.		Total Toe, Deg.②	Ball Joint Wear
	Limits	Desired	Limits	Desired		
1998–99						
A4 & A4 Quattro	—	—	−5/12 to +5/12	0	+2/15 to +1/8	③
A4 & A4 Quattro (Sport)	—	—	−2/3 to +5/12	−2/15	+2/15 to +1/8	③
A6	+1/2 to +1 5/6	+1 1/6	−1 1/4 to −1/4	−3/4	+1/12 to +1/3	③
A6 Quattro	+1/4 to +1 7/12	+11/12	−1 1/12 to −1/12	−2/3	+1/12 to +1/3	③
A8 & A8 Quattro	–	–	−1 to 0	−1/2	+3/10 to +11/30	③
Cabriolet	+1 2/3 to +2 2/3	+2 1/6	−1 1/4 to −1/4	−3/4	+1/2 to +1 1/2	③
2000						
A4 & A4 Quattro	—	—	−5/12 to +5/12	0	+2/15 to +1/8	③
A4 & A4 Quattro (Sport)	—	—	−2/3 to +5/12	−2/15	+2/15 to +1/8	③
A6	+1/2 to +1 5/6	+1 1/6	−1 1/4 to −1/4	−3/4	+1/12 to +1/3	③
A6 Quattro	+1/4 to +1 7/12	+11/12	−1 1/12 to −1/12	−2/3	+1/12 to +1/3	③
A8 & A8 Quattro	–	–	−1 to 0	−1/2	+3/10 to +11/30	③
TT	+7 1/2 to +8 1/2	+8	−1 1/4 to −1/4	−3/4	0 to +3/10	③
2001						
A4 & A4 Quattro	—	—	−5/12 to +5/12	0	+2/15 to +1/8	③
A4 & A4 Quattro (Sport)	—	—	−2/3 to +5/12	−2/15	+2/15 to +1/8	③
A6	+1/2 to +1 5/6	+1 1/6	−1 1/4 to −1/4	−3/4	+1/12 to +1/3	③
A6 Quattro	+1/4 to +1 7/12	+11/12	−1 1/12 to −1/12	−2/3	+1/12 to +1/3	③
A8 & A8 Quattro	–	–	−1 to 0	−1/2	+3/10 to +11/30	③
TT	+7 1/2 to +8 1/2	+8	−1 1/4 to −1/4	−3/4	0 to +3/10	③

① — Reference angle only. Not adjustable.
② — Toe-in (+); toe-out (–).
③ — Replace ball joint & control arm if there is any vertical end play, excessive axial play or turning resistance, boot is torn, or stud is worn.

REAR WHEEL ALIGNMENT SPECIFICATIONS

Model	Camber Angle Deg.		Toe, Deg.①	
	Limits	Desired	Per Wheel	Total
1998–99				
A4	$-1\frac{5}{6}$ to $-1\frac{1}{6}$	$-1\frac{1}{2}$	—	$+\frac{1}{12}$ to $+\frac{1}{4}$
A4 (Sport)	$-1\frac{5}{6}$ to $-1\frac{1}{6}$	$-1\frac{1}{2}$	—	$+\frac{1}{6}$ to $+\frac{1}{3}$
A4 Quattro	$-1\frac{1}{6}$ to $-\frac{1}{6}$	$-\frac{2}{3}$	—	$+\frac{1}{12}$ to $+\frac{1}{4}$
A6	$-1\frac{1}{3}$ to $1\frac{1}{3}$	$-\frac{5}{6}$	—	$+\frac{1}{12}$ to $+\frac{7}{12}$
A6 Quattro	$-\frac{1}{2}$ to 0	$-\frac{1}{4}$	—	0 to $+\frac{1}{3}$
A8 & A8 Quattro	$-1\frac{1}{6}$ to $-\frac{1}{3}$	$-\frac{2}{3}$	$+\frac{1}{60}$ to $+\frac{11}{60}$	–
Cabriolet	$-\frac{1}{6}$ to $+\frac{1}{2}$	$-\frac{2}{3}$	—	$-\frac{1}{12}$ to $+\frac{1}{4}$
2000				
A4	$-1\frac{5}{6}$ to $-1\frac{1}{6}$	$-1\frac{1}{2}$	—	$+\frac{1}{12}$ to $+\frac{1}{4}$
A4 (Sport)	$-1\frac{5}{6}$ to $-1\frac{1}{6}$	$-1\frac{1}{2}$	—	$+\frac{1}{6}$ to $+\frac{1}{3}$
A4 Quattro	$-1\frac{1}{6}$ to $-\frac{1}{6}$	$-\frac{2}{3}$	—	$+\frac{1}{12}$ to $+\frac{1}{4}$
A6	$-1\frac{1}{3}$ to $1\frac{1}{3}$	$-\frac{5}{6}$	—	$+\frac{1}{12}$ to $+\frac{7}{12}$
A6 Quattro	$-\frac{1}{2}$ to 0	$-\frac{1}{4}$	—	0 to $+\frac{1}{3}$
A8 & A8 Quattro	$-1\frac{1}{6}$ to $-\frac{1}{3}$	$-\frac{2}{3}$	$+\frac{1}{60}$ to $+\frac{11}{60}$	–
TT	$-2\frac{1}{3}$ to $-1\frac{2}{3}$	-2	—	$+\frac{3}{10}$ to $+\frac{31}{50}$
TT Quattro	$-1\frac{83}{100}$ to $-1\frac{17}{100}$	$-1\frac{1}{2}$	—	$+\frac{9}{100}$ to $+\frac{41}{100}$
2001				
A4	$-1\frac{5}{6}$ to $-1\frac{1}{6}$	$-1\frac{1}{2}$	—	$+\frac{1}{12}$ to $+\frac{1}{4}$
A4 (Sport)	$-1\frac{5}{6}$ to $-1\frac{1}{6}$	$-1\frac{1}{2}$	—	$+\frac{1}{6}$ to $+\frac{1}{3}$
A4 Quattro	$-1\frac{1}{6}$ to $-\frac{1}{6}$	$-\frac{2}{3}$	—	$+\frac{1}{12}$ to $+\frac{1}{4}$
A6	$-1\frac{1}{3}$ to $1\frac{1}{3}$	$-\frac{5}{6}$	—	$+\frac{1}{12}$ to $+\frac{7}{12}$
A6 Quattro	$-\frac{1}{2}$ to 0	$-\frac{1}{4}$	—	0 to $+\frac{1}{3}$
A8 & A8 Quattro	$-1\frac{1}{6}$ to $-\frac{1}{3}$	$-\frac{2}{3}$	$+\frac{1}{60}$ to $+\frac{11}{60}$	–
TT	$-2\frac{1}{3}$ to $-1\frac{2}{3}$	-2	—	$+\frac{3}{10}$ to $+\frac{31}{50}$
TT Quattro	$-1\frac{83}{100}$ to $-1\frac{17}{100}$	$-1\frac{1}{2}$	—	$+\frac{9}{100}$ to $+\frac{41}{100}$

① — Toe-in (+); toe-out (–).

FLUID CAPACITIES & COOLING SYSTEM DATA

Year	Model	Coolant Capacity Qts.	Coolant Type	Radiator Cap Relief Pressure Lbs.	Thermo. Opening Temp. Deg. F.	Fuel Tank Gals.	Engine Oil Refill Qts.①	Transaxle		Differential Pts.
								Man. Trans. Pts.	Auto. Trans. Qts.②	
1998–99	A4⑧	6.9	⑬	17–22	189	16.4	3.7	4.8	⑩	⑪
	A4 Quattro⑧	6.9	⑬	17–22	189	15.9	3.7	5.8	⑩	⑫
	A4⑨	6.9	⑬	17–22	189	16.4	6.3	4.8	⑩	⑪
	A4 Quattro⑨	6.9	⑬	17–22	189	16.4	6.3	5.8	⑩	⑫
	A6	8.4	⑬	17–22	189	21.1	6.3	–	④	⑤
	A6 Quattro	8.4	⑬	17–22	189	21.1	6.3	–	④	⑥
	A8	11.6	⑬	17–22	189	23.7	8	–	3.7	–
	A8 Quattro	11.6	⑬	17—22	189	23.7	8	–	–	–
	Cabriolet	11.6	⑬	17–22	179	17.4	5.3	–	⑦	2.1
2000	A4⑧	8.0	⑬	14.5	189	16.4	3.7	4.9	③	—
	A4 Quattro⑧	8.0	⑬	14.5	189	16.4	3.7	5.9	③	4
	A4⑨	6.9	⑬	17–22	189	15.6	6.3	4.9	③	—
	A4 Quattro⑨	6.9	⑬	17–22	189	15.6	6.3	5.9	③	4
	A6⑨	6.3	⑬	—	—	18.5	6.3	—	2.7	3.2
	A6⑭	6.3	⑬	—	—	18.5	6.3	—	2.7	3.2
	A6⑮	11.6	⑬	—	—	21.7	8.0	—	2.7	3.2
	A8	11.6	⑬	—	—	23.0	8.0	—	3.7	1.6
	S4⑧	8.0	⑬	14.5	189	16.4	3.7	4.9	③	—
	S4 Quattro⑧	8.0	⑬	14.5	189	16.4	3.7	5.9	③	4
	S4⑨	6.9	⑬	17–22	189	15.6	6.3	4.9	③	—
	S4 Quattro⑨	6.9	⑬	17–22	189	15.6	6.3	5.9	③	4
	TT	7.4	⑬	14.5	189	14.5	4.8	4.2	—	—
	TT Quattro	7.4	⑬	14.5	189	16.3	4.8	5.5	—	2.1
2001	Allroad	6.3	⑬	—	—	18.5	6.3	—	—	—
	A4⑧	6.9	⑬	—	—	16.6	4.2	—	—	—
	A4 Quattro⑧	6.9	⑬	—	—	16.4	4.2	—	—	—
	A4⑨	6.9	⑬	—	—	16.6	6.3	—	—	—
	A4 Quattro⑨	6.9	⑬	—	—	16.4	6.3	—	—	—
	A6⑨	6.3	⑬	—	—	18.5	6.3	—	—	—
	A6⑭	6.3	⑬	—	—	18.5	6.3	—	—	—
	A6⑮	11.6	⑬	—	—	21.7	8.0	—	—	—
	A8	11.6	⑬	—	—	23.7	8.0	—	—	—
	S4	6.3	⑬	—	—	16.4	6.3	—	—	—
	S8	11.6	⑬	—	—	23.8	8.0	—	—	—
	TT	7.4	⑬	—	—	14.5	4.8	—	—	—
	TT Quattro	7.4	⑬	—	—	16.3	4.8	—	—	—

① — Includes filter.

② — Approximate, make final inspection w/dipstick.

③ — Drain & refill, 2.7 qts.; total capacity, 9.5 qts.

④ — Drain & refill, 2.9 qts.; total capacity, 7.4 qts.

⑤ — Filled for life, no drain & refill; total capacity, 1.5 pts.

⑥ — Front differential filled for life, no drain & refill; total capacity, 1.5 pts.; center differential, filled for life, no drain & refill; total capacity, 2.1 pts.; rear differential, filled for life, no drain & refill; total capacity, 3.6 pts.

⑦ — Filled for life, no drain & refill; total capacity, 5.7 qts.

⑧ — 1.8L engine.

⑨ — 2.8L engine.

⑩ — Drain & refill, 2.9 qts.; pan removal 3.7 qts.; total capacity, 9.5 qts.

⑪ — Drain & refill, 1.6 pts.; total capacity, 1.7 pts.

⑫ — Front differential, drain & refill, 1.6 pts.; total capacity, 1.7 pts.; center differential drain & refill, 1.6 pts.; total capacity, 1.7 pts.; rear differential, drain & refill, 3.8 pts.; total capacity, 4.0 pts.

⑬ — Use engine coolant meeting Audi specifications ZVW 237 (G12), or equivalent. Red color coolant cannot be mixed w/any other coolant type.

⑭ — 2.7L engine.

⑮ — 4.2L engine.

LUBRICANT DATA

Model	Lubricant Type						
	Transaxle		Front Differential w/Automatic Transaxle	Center Differential	Rear Axle	Power Steering	Brake System
	Manual	Automatic					
1998–99							
All	G50 75W-90 Synthetic Gear Oil①	ESSO EGL 71141①	G50 75W-90 Synthetic Gear Oil①	G50W 75-90 Synthetic Gear Oil①	API GL-5 SAE 90	②	DOT 4
2000							
All	GL-4 75W-90 Synthetic Gear Oil①	ESSO LT71141	GL-4 75W-90 Synthetic Gear Oil①	GL-4 75W-90 Synthetic Gear Oil①	API GL-5 SAE 90W	③	DOT 4
2001							
All	—	—	—	—	—	—	—

① — Filled for life.

② — Models w/central hydraulic system use Audi part No. G002 000; models less central hydraulic system use Dexron II/IIE/III.

③ — Audi part No. G002 000.

Electrical

NOTE: On Air Bag Equipped Models, Refer To "Air Bag System Precautions" Located In The Front Of This Manual For System Disarming & Arming Procedures.

NOTE: Refer To "Computer Relearn Procedures" Located In The Front Of This Manual When Battery Power To The Computer Has Been Interrupted.

INDEX

	Page No.
Air Bags	1-129
Air Conditioning	1-109
Alternator, Replace	1-11
1.8L Engine	1-11
A4	1-11
TT	1-11
2.7L Engine	1-11
S4 & 1998–99 A4	1-11
2.8L Engine	1-12
1998–99	1-12
2000	1-12
3.7L & 4.2L Engines	1-12
Alternators	1-121
Blower Motor, Replace	1-18
A4 & S4	1-18
A6	1-18
A8	1-18
Cabriolet	1-18
TT	1-18
Coil Pack, Replace	1-13
Combination Switch, Replace	1-14
A4, A6, Cabriolet & S4	1-14
TT	1-14
Cooling Fans	1-112
Cruise Controls	1-123
Dash Gauges	1-115
Dash Panels	1-146
Evaporator Core, Replace	1-21
A4 & S4	1-21
A6	1-21
A8	1-22
Cabriolet	1-22
TT	1-22
Fuel Pump Relay Location	1-10
A4, A6, A8 & S4	1-10
Cabriolet	1-10
TT	1-10
Fuse Panel & Flasher Location	1-9
A4, A6 & S4	1-9
A8	1-9
Cabriolet	1-9
TT	1-9
Heater Core, Replace	1-18
A4 & S4	1-18
A6	1-19
A8	1-19
Driver Side	1-19
Passenger Side	1-19
Cabriolet	1-19
TT	1-20
Ignition Lock, Replace	1-13
A4 & S4	1-13
A6 & Cabriolet	1-13
A8	1-13
TT	1-14
Ignition Switch, Replace	1-14
Instrument Cluster, Replace	1-15
Instrument Cluster Coding	1-16
Replacement	1-15
A4 & S4	1-15
A6	1-15
A8	1-15
Cabriolet	1-15
TT	1-16
Passive Restraints	1-129
Precautions	1-9
Air Bag Systems	1-9
Battery Ground Cable	1-9
Radio Coded Anti-Theft System	1-9
Radio, Replace	1-16
Relay Center Location	1-10
A4 & S4	1-10
A6	1-10
A8	1-10
Cabriolet	1-10
TT	1-10
Speed Controls	1-123
Starter Motors	1-120
Starter, Replace	1-10
1.8L Engine	1-10
2.7L Engine	1-10
S4	1-10
2.8L Engine	1-10
3.7L & 4.2L Engines	1-11
Steering Columns	1-149
Steering Wheel, Replace	1-14
Wiper Motor, Replace	1-17
A4 & S4	1-17
A6	1-17
Front	1-17
Rear	1-17
A8	1-17
Cabriolet	1-17
TT	1-17
Wiper Systems	1-125

PRECAUTIONS

AIR BAG SYSTEMS

Refer to "Air Bag System Precautions" in the front of this manual for system disarming and arming procedures.

BATTERY GROUND CABLE

Prior to service, disconnect battery ground cable and isolate as required.

RADIO CODED ANTI-THEFT SYSTEM

Obtain the security code from the vehicle operator prior to disconnecting the battery or removing the radio. Refer to the owner's manual for security code disarming and arming procedures.

FUSE PANEL & FLASHER LOCATION

A4, A6 & S4

The fuse panel is located behind the lefthand end of the instrument panel. The central electric and fuse/relay panel is located under the lefthand side of the instrument panel. The emergency flasher relay is integrated into the emergency hazard switch.

A8

The main fuse panel is located on the passenger side A-pillar. An additional fuse/relay panel is located behind the righthand side kick panel, in the electronics compartment.

Cabriolet

The fuse/relay panel is located on the lefthand side of the engine compartment, near the air plenum chamber. The turn signal relay is located under the lefthand side of the instrument panel, left of the steering column.

TT

The main fuse box is located in the engine compartment above the battery.

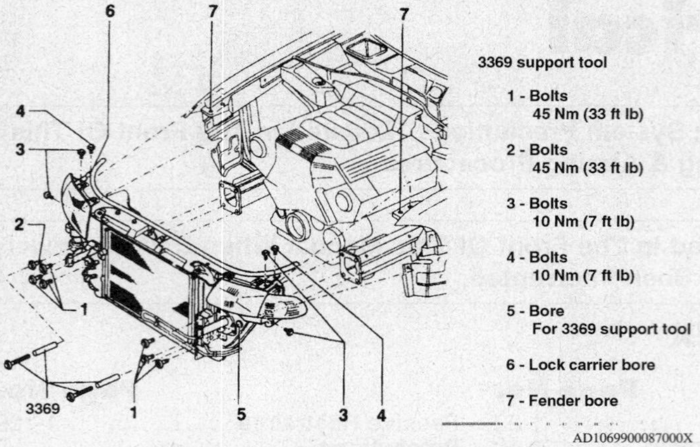

Fig. 1 Header panel mounting. 1.8L engine

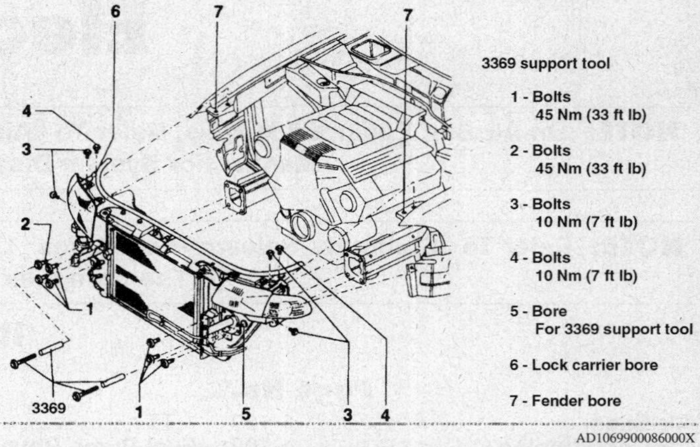

Fig. 2 Header panel mounting. S4 & 1998–99 A4 w/2.7L engine & 2000 2.8L engine

FUEL PUMP RELAY LOCATION

A4, A6, A8 & S4

The fuel pump relay is located in the central electric and control module panel.

Cabriolet

The fuel pump relay is located in the main fuse/relay panel in the air plenum chamber on the lefthand side of the engine compartment.

TT

The fuel pump relay is located at Position 4 of micro -central electrics in driver's lefthand footwell.

RELAY CENTER LOCATION

A4 & S4

The central electric and fuse/relay panel is located below the lefthand side of the instrument panel. The auxiliary relay panel is located in the electronics box found in the air plenum chamber, on the lefthand side of the engine compartment.

A6

The central electric and control module panel with relays is located under the lefthand side of the instrument panel, left of the steering column. The auxiliary relay panel No. 1 is located in the air plenum chamber on the lefthand side of the engine compartment. The auxiliary relay panel No. 2 is located in the behind the lefthand kick panel. The auxiliary relay panel No. 3 is located behind the righthand kick panel.

A8

The central electric and control module panel with relays is behind the righthand kick panel, in the electronics compartment. Additional relay centers can be found in the air plenum chamber, behind the lefthand side of the instrument panel (above the under dash trim panel) and on the righthand side of the luggage compartment, behind the trim panel.

Cabriolet

The main fuse/relay panel is located in the air plenum chamber on the lefthand side the engine compartment. The auxiliary relay panel is located under the lefthand side of the instrument panel.

TT

The relay center is located in the engine compartment above the battery.

STARTER

REPLACE

1.8L Engine

1. Obtain radio anti-theft protection code as outlined under "Precautions."
2. **On A4 and S4 models equipped with A/C,** proceed as follows:
   a. Remove front bumper.
   b. Remove three quick release screws on front of sound insulation panel.
   c. Remove air intake duct between the header panel and air cleaner.
   d. Remove wiring harness clamps located at lefthand side of radiator frame.
   e. Remove bolt (2), **Fig. 1,** and install Audi support tool No. 3369, or equivalent.
   f. Install support tool 3369 to lefthand side bore, **Fig. 1.**
   g. Remove bolts (1) and (3), then bolt (4) and pull header panel outward until the stop is reached.
   h. Install suitable M6 bolts into rear bore holes of header panel and fender.
   i. Loosen air conditioning compressor belt tensioner mounting bolts.
   j. Release belt tension using a suitable wrench on ribbed belt tensioner. A suitable hex wrench can be inserted through tensioner bores to hold tensioner in released position.
   k. Remove ribbed belt, then the hex wrench from tensioner. Mark running direction on belt for use during installation.
   l. Unbolt air conditioning compressor, then position it aside with its refrigerant lines attached
3. **On TT models,** remove battery and mounting tray.
4. **On all models,** disconnect all electrical connectors at starter.
5. Remove nuts or bolts securing starter to engine, then the starter assembly.
6. Reverse procedure to install, noting the following:
   a. **Torque** starter mounting bolts to 48 ft. lbs.
   b. **On A4 and S4 models equipped with A/C, torque** A/C compressor mounting bolt to 15 ft. lbs. and A/C belt tensioner bolt to 18 ft. lbs.

2.7L Engine

S4

1. Remove alternator as outlined under "Alternator, Replace."
2. Remove turbocharger duct as required to ease access to starter.
3. Disconnect all electrical connectors at starter.
4. **On models equipped with manual transaxle,** remove rear sound insulation panel.
5. **On all models,** remove starter mounting bolts, then the starter assembly.
6. Reverse procedure to install. **Torque** starter mounting bolts to 48 ft. lbs.

2.8L Engine

1. Remove alternator as outlined under "Alternator, Replace."
2. Disconnect starter motor electrical connectors.
3. Raise and support vehicle.
4. **On models equipped with automatic transaxle,** proceed as follows:
   a. Remove righthand front wheel as required.

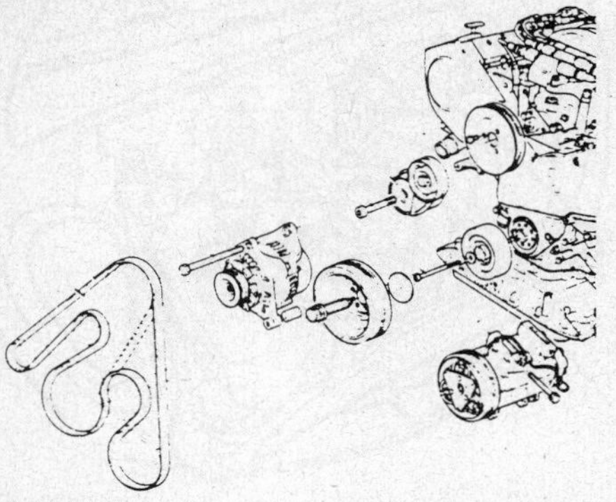

AD1129200014000X

Fig. 3 Alternator removal. 1998-99 2.8L engine

b. Remove starter motor to transaxle housing attaching bolts.
c. Remove starter from below.

5. **On models equipped with manual transaxle,** proceed as follows:
   a. Remove rear noise insulator.
   b. Remove starter motor to transaxle housing attaching bolts.
   c. Remove starter.
6. **On all models,** reverse procedure to install. **Torque** starter motor attaching bolts to 48 ft. lbs.

3.7L & 4.2L Engines

1. Remove engine cover from intake manifold.
2. Remove throttle body assembly from rear of intake manifold.
3. Attach engine support adapter tool No. 3180, or equivalent to righthand rear engine lifting lug.
4. Assemble engine support bridge with brackets tool Nos. 10-222A and 10-222A/4, or equivalents to lefthand and righthand strut towers.
5. Raise engine enough to remove weight from engine mounts.
6. Raise and support vehicle, then remove insulation panel from under engine.
7. Disconnect starter motor electrical connectors.
8. Remove starter motor attaching bolts, then the starter.
9. Reverse procedure to install.

ALTERNATOR

REPLACE

Some of the following procedures have been modified by a technical service bulletin.

1.8L Engine

A4

1. Obtain radio anti-theft protection code as outlined under "Precautions."
2. Loosen ribbed belt and remove from alternator.
3. Remove air guide at throttle body.
4. Remove upper and lower attaching nut and bolt.

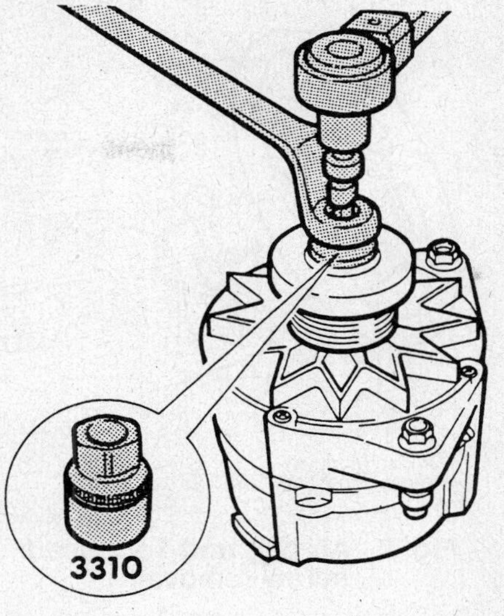

AD1129200013000X

Fig. 4 Drive belt pulley removal. 1998-99 2.8L engine

5. Move alternator slightly, then remove lower bolt.
6. Remove wiring from back of alternator, then the alternator.
7. Reverse procedure to install, noting the following:
   a. **Torque** lower attaching nut to 30 ft. lbs.
   b. **Torque** upper attaching bolt to 25 ft. lbs.

TT

1. Obtain radio anti-theft protection code as outlined under "Precautions."
2. Disconnect electrical connectors at throttle valve control module and charge pressure sender.
3. Disconnect air hose at throttle valve control module.
4. Disconnect EVAP canister vacuum hose at throttle valve control module.
5. Remove EVAP canister mounting nut, then position canister aside.
6. Mark running direction of alternator drive belt.
7. Rotate drive belt tensioner clockwise using a suitable open end wrench, then remove belt.
8. Secure belt tensioner using a suitable mandrel or pry bar.
9. Disconnect all electrical connectors from alternator.
10. Loosen alternator mounting bolts, then remove alternator.
11. Reverse procedure to install, noting the following:
    a. Drive in alternator mounting bolt bushings approximately. 039 inch before installation.
    b. Tighten all fasteners securely.

2.7L Engine

S4 & 1998-99 A4

1. Obtain radio anti-theft protection code as outlined under "Precautions."

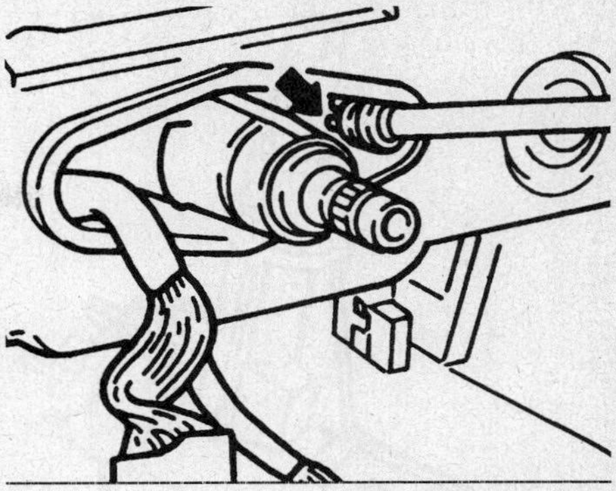

AD9129100001000X

Fig. 5 Steering lock Torx head bolt location. A6 & Cabriolet

2. Remove air intake duct bolts, then lift up rear portion of duct.
3. Remove sound insulation panel.
4. Remove front bumper.
5. Lock header panel in service position as follows:
   a. Remove three quick release screws on front of sound insulation panel.
   b. Remove air intake duct between header panel and air cleaner.
   c. Remove all wiring harness clamps located at sides of radiator frame.
   d. Remove bolt (2), **Fig. 2,** and install Audi support tool No. 3369, or equivalent.
   e. Install support tool 3369 to lefthand side bore (5), **Fig. 2.**
   f. Remove bolts (1) and (3), then bolt (4) and pull header panel outward until stop is reached.
   g. Install suitable M6 bolts into rear bore holes of header panel (6) and fender (7).
6. Remove engine appearance cover.
7. Rotate serpentine drive belt tensioner clockwise using a suitable box wrench until both holes are in alignment, then secure in place using drift tool No. 3204, or equivalent.
8. Remove serpentine belt from alternator pulley.
9. Remove refrigerant lines mounting clamp above torque arm.
10. Remove charge air cooler air duct.
11. Loosen hose connection above righthand charge air cooler, mounted on three rubber supports.
12. Remove righthand charge air cooler.
13. Cut tie wraps open, then release starter and alternator wiring snap catches.
14. Disconnect air duct from alternator fitting.
15. Disconnect all electrical connectors from alternator.
16. Remove alternator upper mounting bolt and locknut.
17. Loosen alternator lower mounting bolt.
18. Remove alternator from below vehicle. **Avoid damaging A/C refrigerant lines.**
19. Reverse procedure to install, noting the following:
    a. Drive in alternator mounting bolt bushings approximately. 039 inch before installation.

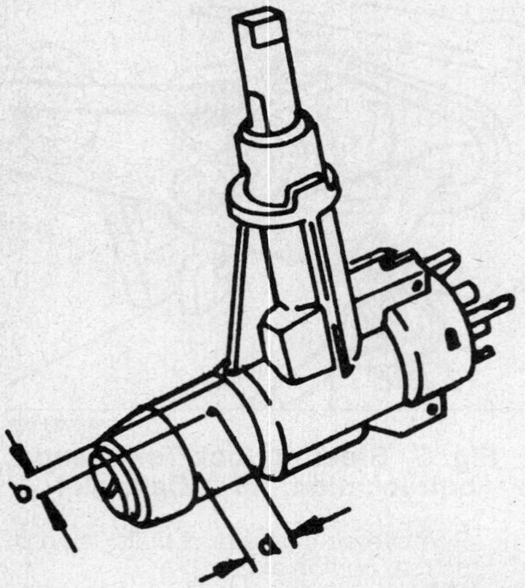

AD9129100003000X

Fig. 6 Ignition lock cylinder drilling dimensions. A6 & Cabriolet

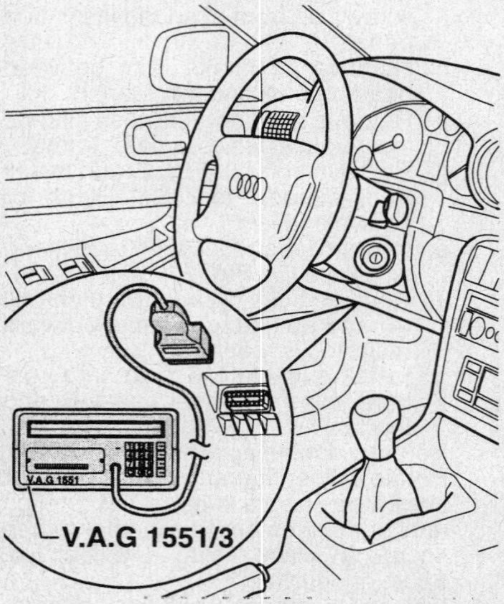

AD8019600071000X

Fig. 9 Scan tool connection to Data Link Connector (DLC)

b. **Torque** alternator lower mounting bolt to 16 ft. lbs.
c. **Torque** alternator upper mounting bolt to 33 ft. lbs.
d. **Torque** bumper horizontal mounting bolts to 33 ft. lbs.
e. **Torque** bumper vertical mounting bolts to 17 ft. lbs.

2.8L Engine

1998-99

1. Obtain radio anti-theft protection code as outlined under "Precautions."
2. Remove serpentine drive belt, **Fig. 3,** then disconnect electrical connections from alternator.
3. Remove alternator mounting bolts and brackets, then the alternator.

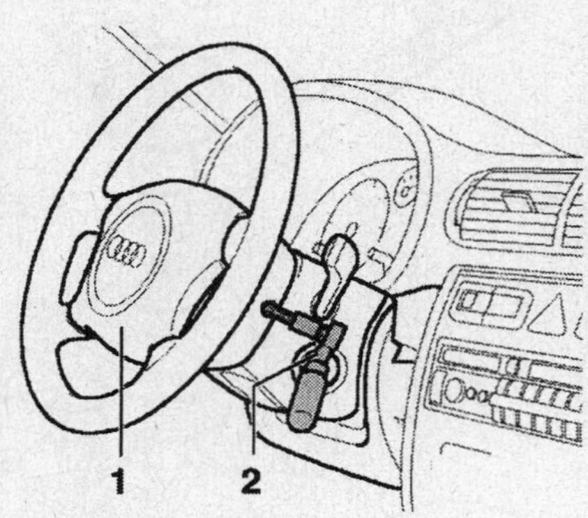

1- Air Bag Module
2- Ratchet And Tork T30 Tool

AD8010100119000X

Fig. 7 Air bag unit Torx head screw removal

4. Remove belt pulley using puller tool No. 3310, or equivalent, **Fig. 4.**
5. Reverse procedure to install. Use only OLIVE colored pulley retaining nut. Discard GOLD colored nuts.

2000

1. Obtain radio anti-theft protection code as outlined under "Precautions."
2. Remove air intake duct bolts, then lift up rear portion of duct.
3. Remove sound insulation panel.
4. Remove front bumper.
5. Lock header panel in service position as follows:
   a. Remove three quick release screws on front of sound insulation panel.
   b. Remove air intake duct between header panel and air cleaner.
   c. Remove all wiring harness clamps located at sides of radiator frame.
   d. Remove bolt (2), **Fig. 2,** and install Audi support tool No. 3369, or equivalent.
   e. Install support tool 3369 to lefthand side bore (5), **Fig. 2.**
   f. Remove bolts (1) and (3), then bolt (4) and pull header panel outward until stop is reached.
   g. Install suitable M6 bolts into rear bore holes of header panel (6) and fender (7).
6. Remove engine appearance cover.
7. Rotate serpentine drive belt tensioner clockwise using a suitable box wrench until both holes are in alignment, then secure in place using drift tool No. 3204, or equivalent.
8. Remove serpentine belt from alternator pulley.
9. Remove refrigerant lines mounting clamp above torque arm.
10. Cut tie wraps open, then release starter and alternator wiring snap catches.
11. Disconnect air duct from alternator fitting.
12. Disconnect all electrical connectors from alternator.
13. Remove alternator upper mounting bolt and locknut.
14. Loosen alternator lower mounting bolt.
15. Remove alternator from below vehicle. **Avoid damaging A/C refrigerant lines.**
16. Reverse procedure to install, noting the following:
    a. Drive in alternator mounting bolt bushings approximately. 039 inch before installation.
    b. **Torque** alternator lower mounting bolt to 16 ft. lbs.
    c. **Torque** alternator upper mounting bolt to 33 ft. lbs.
    d. **Torque** bumper horizontal mounting bolts to 33 ft. lbs.
    e. **Torque** bumper vertical mounting bolts to 17 ft. lbs.

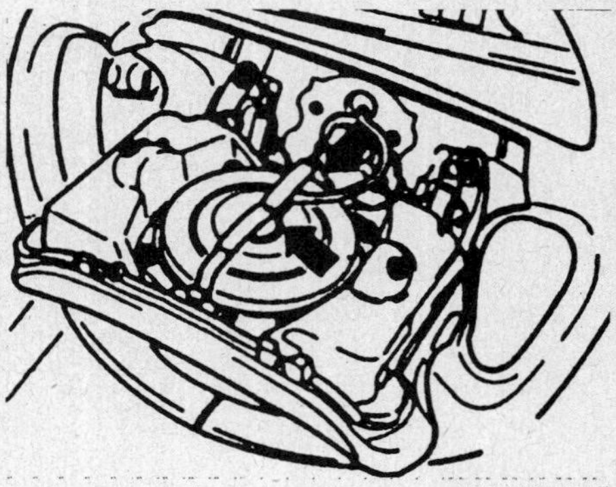

AD8019100034000X

Fig. 8 Air bag electrical connector disconnection

Code table:

Code	Meaning
XX	Empty spaces: no significance
00	Fill spaces with two zeros
X	Market versions:
2	USA (US)
3	Canada (CDN)
X	Number of cylinders:
6	6-cylinder
X	Engine versions:
2	Gasoline engine

AD9099600007000X

Fig. 10 Instrument cluster code table. Except A4, S4 & TT

3.7L & 4.2L Engines

1. Remove serpentine drive belt, then raise and support vehicle.
2. Remove sound insulation panel from under engine.
3. Disconnect alternator electrical connectors.
4. Disconnect cooling duct from rear of alternator.
5. Remove alternator attaching bolts, then the alternator.
6. Reverse procedure to install, noting the following:
   a. **Torque** alternator upper attaching bolt to 33 ft. lbs.

X	Optional equipment
00	No optional equipment
01	Brake pad wear indicator active
02	Seat belt warning system active
04	Washer fluid level indicator active
16	Navigation (not applicable for USA)
X	Market version:
0	Germany (D)
1	Europe (EU)
2	USA (US)
3	Canada (CDN)
4	Great Britain (GB)
5	Japan (JP)
6	Saudi Arabia (SA)
7	Australia (AUS)
X	Number of cylinders
4	4-cylinders
6	6-cylinders
X	Engine versions
0	TDI engine
2	Gasoline engines, 4 and 6 cylinder

AD9099900018000X

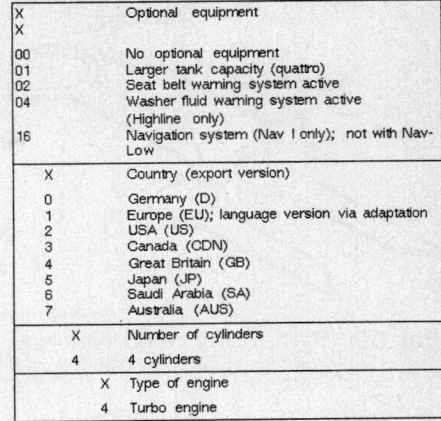

Fig. 11 Instrument cluster code table. 1998–99 A4 & S4

XX	Optional equipment/transmission version
00	No additional equipment
02	Seat belt warning active
16	Navigation I and II
X	Country version
0	Germany (D)
1	RdW Left Hand Drive
2	USA (US)
3	Canada (CDN)
4	Great Britain (GB)
5	Japan (JP)
6	Saudi Arabia (SA)
7	Australia (AUS)
8	RdW Right Hand Drive
9	JP Right Hand Drive (RHD) vehicles

AD9090000017000X

Fig. 12 Instrument cluster code table. 2000–01 A4 & S4

X X	Optional equipment
00	No optional equipment
01	Larger tank capacity (quattro)
02	Seat belt warning system active
04	Washer fluid warning system active (Highline only)
16	Navigation system (Nav I only); not with Nav-Low
X	Country (export version)
0	Germany (D)
1	Europe (EU); language version via adaptation
2	USA (US)
3	Canada (CDN)
4	Great Britain (GB)
5	Japan (JP)
6	Saudi Arabia (SA)
7	Australia (AUS)
X	Number of cylinders
4	4 cylinders
X	Type of engine
4	Turbo engine

AD9090000016000X

Fig. 13 Instrument cluster code table. TT

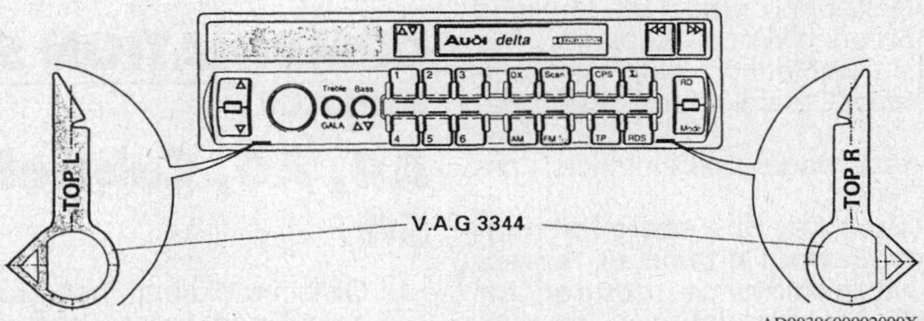

AD90396000020000X

Fig. 14 Radio unit removal. Models less Symphony radio

b. **Torque** alternator lower attaching bolt to 15 ft. lbs.

COIL PACK

REPLACE

1. Tag position of spark plug wires for installation reference.
2. Disconnect spark plug wires from coil pack.
3. Disconnect electrical connector from coil pack.
4. Remove mounting bolts, then the coil pack.
5. Reverse procedure to install.

IGNITION LOCK

REPLACE

A4 & S4

1. Obtain radio anti-theft protection code as outlined under "Precautions."
2. Remove steering wheel as outlined under "Steering Wheel, Replace."
3. Remove combination switch as outlined under "Combination Switch, Replace."
4. **A workshop key or a spare flat handled key without a lamp or remote control transmitter is required for lock cylinder removal.**
5. Insert key into lock cylinder, then turn ignition On. An access hole will appear in front of switch next to ignition key slot.
6. Insert a length of steel wire or a suitable small screwdriver approximately .0078 inch diameter into access hole until it bottoms, then extract lock cylinder from steering lock housing.
7. Reverse procedures to install, noting the following:
   a. Ensure ignition is turned to On position.
   b. Push lock cylinder with key firmly into lock housing until catch engages with an audible click.
   c. Tighten all fasteners to specifications.

A6 & Cabriolet

This procedure has been revised by a Technical Service Bulletin.

1. Obtain radio anti-theft protection code as outlined under "Precautions."
2. Remove steering wheel as outlined under "Steering Wheel, Replace."
3. Remove combination switch as outlined under "Combination Switch, Replace."
4. Remove nuts holding wiring harness clamps to steering column, then the harness.
5. Remove instrument cluster as outlined under "Instrument Cluster, Replace."
6. Disconnect ignition switch electrical connector.
7. **On models equipped with automatic transaxle,** remove Bowden cable cover for shift lock, pry off Bowden cable mounting clips using a suitable screwdriver, then disconnect Bowden cable.
8. **On all models,** remove steering lock housing Torx head bolt from righthand side of column tube, **Fig. 5.**
9. Ensure steering wheel is in straight-ahead position, then disconnect steering coupling.
10. Remove nuts and bolts securing column tube to support bracket.
11. Position steering column to allow lock removal, then remove ignition lock.
12. Remove ignition switch as outlined under "Ignition switch, Replace."
13. Drill hole in lock housing using a suitable ⅛ inch drill bit as illustrated in **Fig. 6.** Dimension A =. 50 inch, Dimension B =. 35 inch. **Do not drill too deeply into housing, which is approximately. 08 inch thick. Excessive drilling will damage lock cylinder.**
14. Using a suitable drift punch through hole previously drilled, remove lock cylinder by pressing in check spring.
15. Reverse procedures to install, noting the following:
    a. Insert lock cylinder by pushing cylinder into lock housing until check spring engages.
    b. **Torque** column mounting bolts to 26 ft. lbs.
    c. **Torque** ignition lock Torx mounting bolt to 56 inch lbs.

A8

1. Remove steering wheel as outlined under "Steering Wheel, Replace."
2. Remove steering column trim cover.
3. Loosen switch retaining clamp screw until steering column switches are loose.
4. Disconnect switch electrical connectors, then remove switch from steering column.
5. Reverse procedure to install.

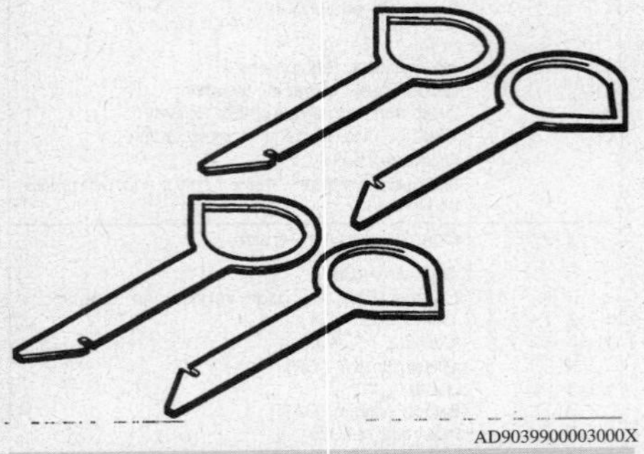

Fig. 15 Symphony radio removal key set tool No. T10057

TT

1. Obtain radio anti-theft protection code as outlined under "Precautions."
2. Remove steering wheel as outlined under "Steering Wheel, Replace."
3. Remove combination switch as outlined under "Combination Switch, Replace."
4. Disconnect reader coil electrical connector.
5. **A workshop key or a spare flat handled key without a lamp or remote control transmitter is required for lock cylinder removal.**
6. Insert key into lock cylinder and turn ignition On. An aperture will appear in front of lock next to key slot.
7. Insert a length of steel wire or a suitable pin of approximately. 060 inch diameter into aperture until it bottoms, then extract lock cylinder out of lock housing.
8. Reverse procedure to install, noting the following:
   a. Insert key into lock cylinder.
   b. Turn ignition On.
   c. Insert length of steel wire or pin into aperture and push in until it bottoms.
   d. Push lock cylinder with key firmly into steering lock housing.
   e. Withdraw wire or pin and press cylinder in until catch engages with an audible click.
   f. Tighten all fasteners to specifications.

IGNITION SWITCH

REPLACE

1. Obtain radio anti-theft protection code as outlined under "Precautions."
2. Remove steering lock assembly as outlined under "Ignition Lock, Replace."
3. Remove locking compound from ignition switch mounting screws, then the screws and switch.
4. Reverse procedure to install, noting the following:
   a. Ensure ignition lock cylinder is turned On.
   b. Coat mounting screw threads with locking compound.

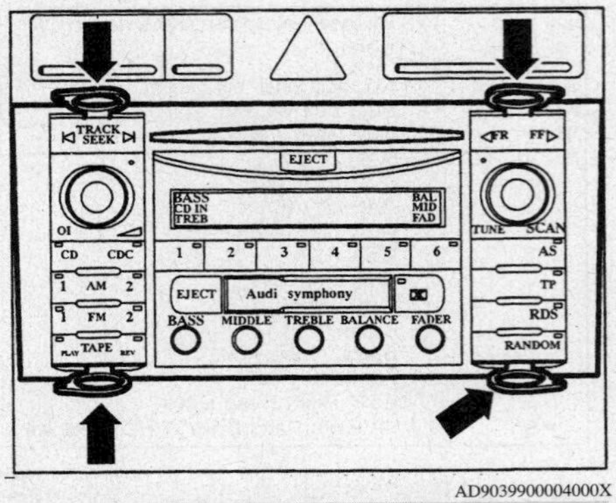

Fig. 16 Symphony radio removal

   c. Tighten all fasteners to specifications.

COMBINATION SWITCH

REPLACE

A4, A6, Cabriolet & S4

1. Obtain radio anti-theft protection code as outlined under "Precautions."
2. Remove steering wheel as outlined under "Steering Wheel, Replace."
3. Remove lefthand underdash cover and kneebar.
4. **On models equipped with telescoping steering column,** proceed as follows:
   a. Ensure column is fully extended, then press down on adjustment lever and pull lock spring off using a suitable small screwdriver.
   b. Remove telescoping adjustment lever.
5. **On models equipped with tilt steering column,** remove set screw for tilt adjustment lever, then the lever.
6. **On all models,** disconnect electrical connectors, then remove combination switch.
7. Individual switches can be removed from combination switch by removing retaining screws.
8. Reverse procedure to install.

TT

1. Obtain radio anti-theft protection code as outlined under "Precautions."
2. Pull steering column as far out as possible and tilt downward.
3. Remove steering wheel as outlined under "Steering Wheel, Replace."
4. Remove steering column upper shroud.
5. Swing down steering column lower shroud and allow it to sit on steering wheel adjuster lever.
6. Disconnect combination switch and clockspring electrical connectors.
7. Ensure front wheels are still in straight-ahead position.
8. Release locking lugs, then pull clockspring and slip ring off combination switch.
9. Remove combination switch mounting screws, then the switch.
10. Reverse procedure to install, noting the following:
    a. Ensure front wheels are still in straight-ahead position.
    b. Ensure turn signal lever is in neutral position.
    c. Ensure clockspring is properly centered.
    d. **Torque** combination switch mounting screws to 24 inch lbs.
    e. Tighten all fasteners to specifications.

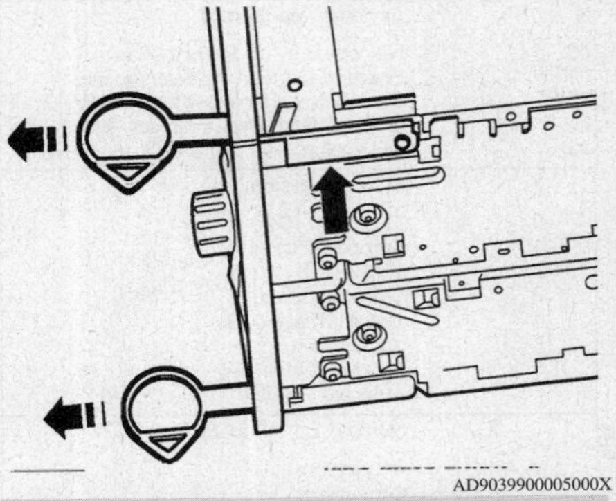

Fig. 17 Releasing removal keys from Symphony radio

STEERING WHEEL

REPLACE

1. Obtain radio anti-theft protection code as outlined under "Precautions."
2. Ensure wheels are in straight-ahead position, then remove air bag module (horn pad) Torx head bolts from lefthand and righthand side of steering wheel, **Fig. 7.**
3. Tilt air bag unit backward carefully, then lift up safety clamp and disconnect electrical connector from air bag module, **Fig. 8.**
4. Store air bag module face up (Audi rings pointing up) in a safe place. **Do not expose air bag unit to excessive heat (above 212°F) or place near anything that may puncture it.**
5. **On A4 and S4 models,** pull adjustable steering column out as far as it will go, then tilt steering wheel to lowest position.
6. **On A4, A6 and S4 models,** remove steering column trim and disconnect clockspring electrical connector.
7. **On all models,** place matchmarks on steering wheel and column if none are provided. This will ensure proper assembly.
8. Remove retaining nut and steering wheel.
9. Reverse procedure to install, noting the following:
   a. Ensure turn signal lever is in central position.
   b. Ensure clcokspring is centered.
   c. **On all models except A4, S4 and**

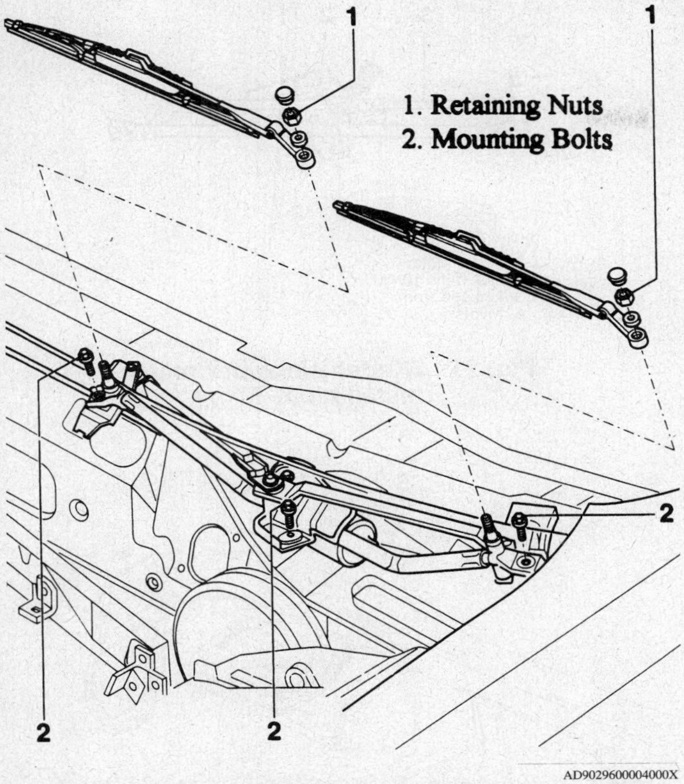

Fig. 18 Windshield wiper assembly. A4 & S4

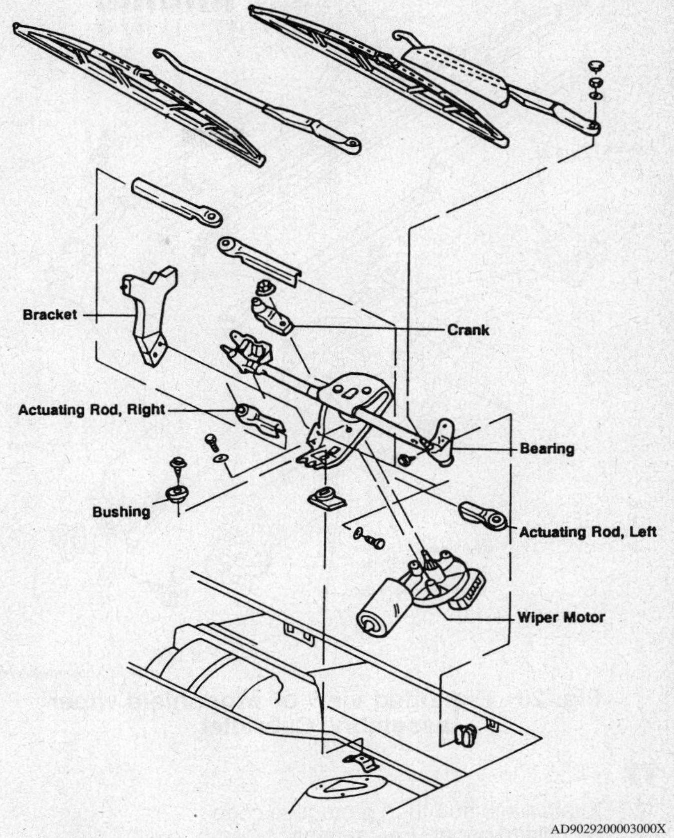

Fig. 19 Exploded view of windshield wiper assembly. A6

TT, torque steering wheel retaining nut to 30 ft. lbs.

d. **On A4, S4 and TT models, torque** steering wheel retaining nut to 44 ft. lbs.

e. **On all models,** ensure no one is inside of vehicle when connecting battery ground cable.

INSTRUMENT CLUSTER

REPLACE

Replacement

A4 & S4

1. Obtain radio anti-theft protection code as outlined under "Precautions."
2. Record values of service display and odometer reading using VAG1551 scan tool, or equivalent.
3. Pull steering column out as far as it will go using steering wheel adjustment, then tilt steering wheel to lowest position.
4. Pivot top cover of instrument cluster toward front and lift it off.
5. Pivot cover trim toward front, then remove two screws.
6. Tilt instrument cluster forward slightly, disconnect electrical connectors, then remove instrument cluster.
7. Reverse procedure to install, noting the following:
   a. Ensure no one is inside of vehicle when connecting battery ground cable.
   b. If required, code instrument cluster to the vehicle as outlined under "Instrument Cluster Coding."
   c. Set service reminders. Refer to "Service Reminder & Warning Lamp Reset Procedures" in the front section of this manual for procedures.

A6

1. Obtain radio anti-theft protection code as outlined under "Precautions."
2. Remove steering wheel as outlined under "Steering Wheel, Replace."
3. Remove combination switch as outlined under "Combination Switch, Replace."
4. Remove two screws, then the cover strip.
5. Remove instrument cluster mounting screws, then the cluster from instrument panel.
6. Disconnect instrument cluster electrical connections, then remove instrument cluster.
7. Reverse procedure to install, noting the following:
   a. Ensure no one is inside vehicle when connecting battery ground cable.
   b. If required, code instrument cluster to the vehicle as outlined under "Instrument Cluster Coding."
   c. Set service reminders, refer to "Service Reminder & Warning Lamp Reset Procedures" in the front section of this manual for procedures.

A8

1. Pull steering column out as far as it will go.
2. Lower steering column to its' lowest position.
3. Push in cover retaining clips, then remove cover from instrument cluster.
4. Remove four instrument cluster retaining screws.
5. Pull cluster rearward and disconnect electrical connectors.
6. Reverse procedure to install.

CABRIOLET

1. Obtain radio anti-theft protection code as outlined under "Precautions."
2. If required, code instrument cluster to the vehicle as outlined below.
3. Remove steering wheel as outlined under "Steering Wheel, Replace."
4. Remove combination switch as outlined under "Combination Switch, Replace."
5. Remove instrument cluster retaining screws, located at the bottom center of instrument cluster.
6. Tilt instrument cluster backward slightly, disconnect electrical connections, then remove instrument cluster.
7. Reverse procedure to install, ensure no one is inside of vehicle when connecting battery ground cable.

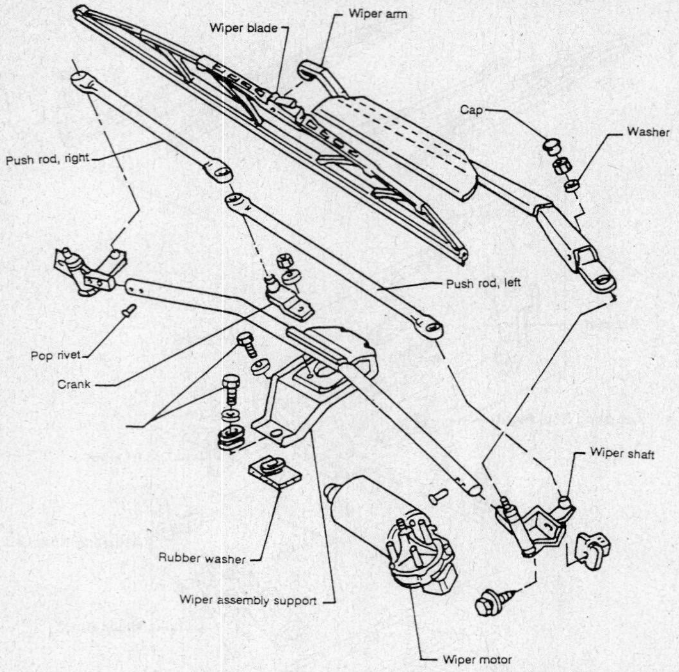

AD9029100002000X

Fig. 20 Exploded view of windshield wiper assembly. Cabriolet

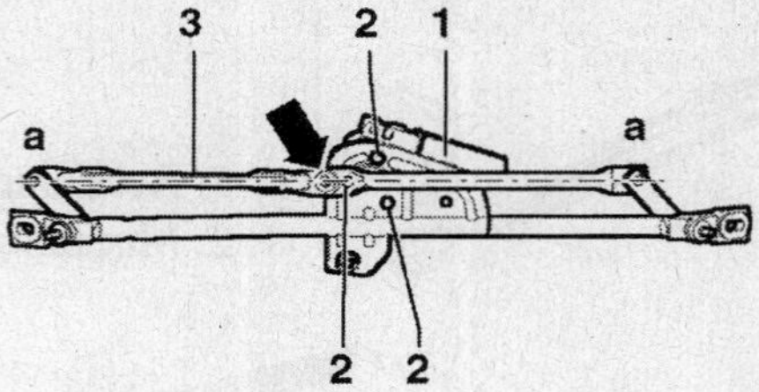

1- Wiper Motor
2- Hex Bolts 10MM
3- Linkage Rod
a- Pivots

AD9020000012000X

Fig. 21 Windshield wiper motor installation. TT

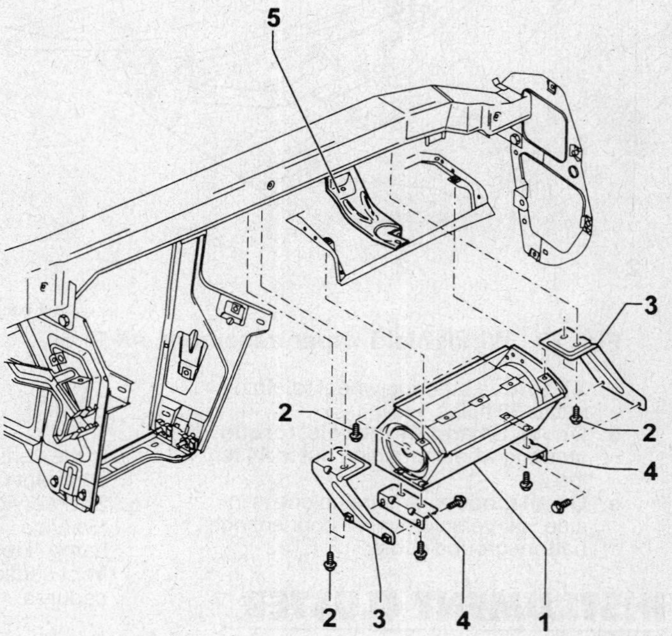

AD8019500082000X

Fig. 22 Passenger air bag unit. A4 & S4

TT

1. Obtain radio anti-theft protection code as outlined under "Precautions."
2. Record values of service display and odometer reading using VAG1551 scan tool, or equivalent.
3. Pull out steering wheel and pivot it as low as it will go.
4. Remove driver's storage compartment.
5. Loosen two Phillips head screws at bottom of cluster.
6. Pull instrument cluster out from front.
7. Slice open cable ties on rear of instrument cluster.
8. Release retainer catches, then disconnect electrical connectors.
9. Reverse procedure to install, noting the following:
   a. Ensure no one is inside of vehicle when connecting battery ground cable.
   b. If required, code instrument cluster to the vehicle as outlined under "Instrument Cluster Coding."
   c. Set service reminders. Refer to "Service Reminder & Warning Lamp Reset Procedures" in the front section of this manual for procedures.

Instrument Cluster Coding

1. Connect scan tool No. VAG 1551-3, or equivalent to Data Link Connector (DLC), **Fig. 9.**
2. Enter 17 to access instrument cluster mode.
3. Display should show current instrument cluster code.
4. Refer to tables, **Figs. 10 through 13** for code interpretation.
5. If coding is required, enter 07 to access instrument cluster coding mode.
6. Enter new code using scan tool.
7. Set service reminders. Refer to "Service Reminder & Warning Lamp Reset Procedures" in the front section of this manual for procedures.

RADIO

REPLACE

1. Obtain radio anti-theft protection code as outlined under "Precautions."
2. **On models less Symphony radio,** proceed as follows:
   a. Insert radio removal key set tool No. VAG 3344, or equivalent into righthand and lefthand face plate key holes, **Fig. 14.**
   b. Press outward while pulling radio unit from instrument panel.
   c. Disconnect antenna lead-in and electrical connectors, then remove tools from radio.
3. **On models equipped with Symphony radio,** proceed as follows:
   a. Obtain radio removal key set tool No. T10057, **Fig. 15,** or equivalent.
   b. Insert removal keys into release slots, **Fig. 16,** until they are securely engaged.
   c. Remove radio from instrument panel by pulling removal key grip rings.
   d. Disconnect antenna lead-in and electrical connectors.
   e. Press locking latch, **Fig. 17,** to remove keys from radio.
4. **On all models,** reverse procedure to install. Removal tools are not required when inserting radio into instrument panel.

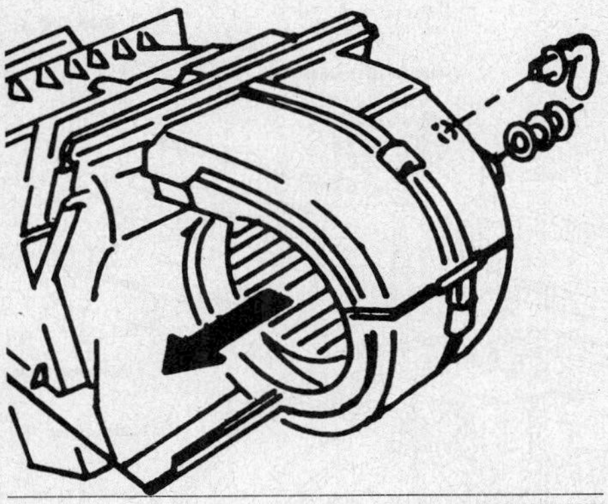

Fig. 23 Lock ring, stop washer & grommet location. A6

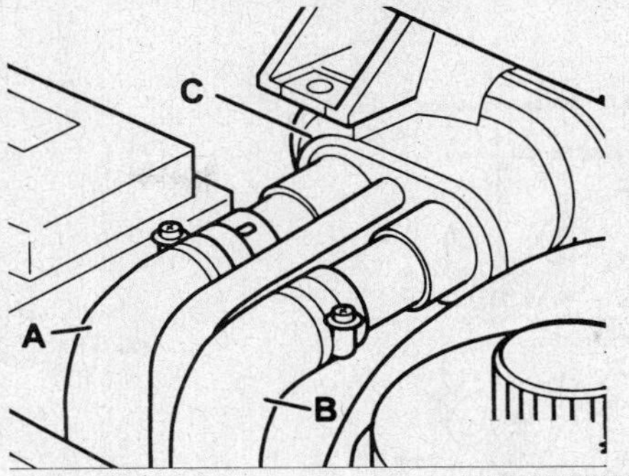

Fig. 24 Heater hose connections. A4 & S4

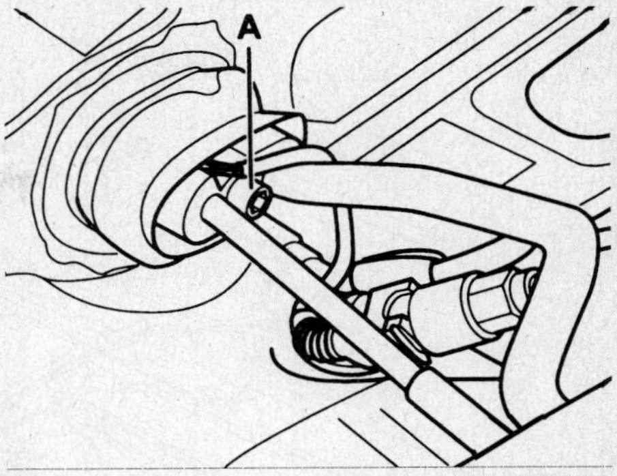

Fig. 25 Refrigerant lines removal. A4 & S4

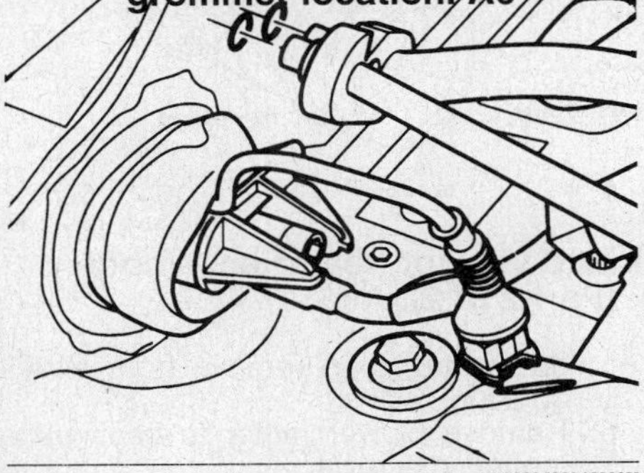

Fig. 26 Evaporator boot removal. A4 & S4

WIPER MOTOR

REPLACE

A4 & S4

The windshield wiper motor and linkage must be removed as an assembly. The crank on the wiper motor must be facing forward when removing and installing the wiper motor.

Refer to **Fig. 18** for windshield wiper motor replacement.

A6

FRONT

When replacing windshield wiper motor, refer to **Fig. 19.**

REAR

1. Remove washer nozzle.
2. Remove wiper arm to shaft retaining nut, then wiper arm from shaft.
3. Remove wiper shaft housing to window packing gland nut.
4. Remove wiper motor interior trim panel.
5. Disconnect electrical connector and washer hose.
6. Remove motor assembly mounting bolts, then pull wiper shaft from window packing.
7. Reverse procedure to install, noting the following:
   a. Ensure wiper motor is in park position prior to installing wiper arm.
   b. **Torque** wiper assembly mounting bolts to 71 inch lbs.
   c. **Torque** wiper shaft housing to window packing nut to 71 inch lbs.
   d. **Torque** wiper arm to shaft nut to 12 ft. lbs.

A8

1. Remove caps from wiper arms.
2. Loosen wiper arm retaining nuts.
3. Loosen arms from shafts by lifting gently.
4. Remove wiper arm retaining nuts, then the wiper arms from shafts.
5. Remove rubber gasket from windshield trim.
6. Remove windshield trim to bracket retaining screws.
7. Disconnect washer nozzle hoses, then remove windshield trim and cowl panel.
8. Disconnect wiper motor electrical connector.
9. Remove wiper motor and linkage assembly attaching bolts, then the wiper motor and linkage assembly.
10. Reverse procedure to install.

Cabriolet

1. Turn ignition On.
2. Run wipers until lefthand wiper arm is positioned at a 45° angle to the lefthand edge of the windshield, then turn ignition Off. Wipers must be in this position to remove motor and linkage.
3. Remove wiper arms, **Fig. 20,** then the wiper motor with linkage and support frame.
4. Disconnect wiper linkage from wiper motor, then remove wiper motor mounting bolts and wiper motor from support frame.
5. Reverse procedure to install, noting the following:
   a. Turn wipers Off.
   b. Turn ignition On until wiper motor stops running.
   c. Turn ignition Off to ensure wiper motor is in park position.
   d. Install wiper arms.

TT

1. Operate wipers, then turn Off and allow them to reach Park position.

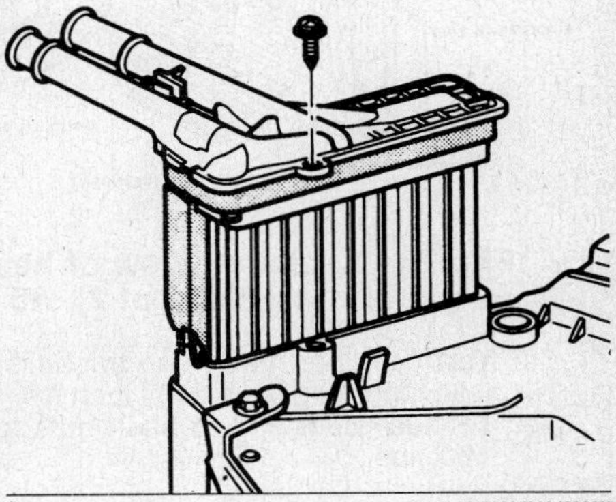

Fig. 27 Heater core removal. A4 & S4

2. Turn ignition Off.
3. Remove wiper blades.
4. Pry off wiper arm cover caps with a suitable screwdriver.
5. Loosen wiper arm to shaft hex nuts. **Do not remove at this time.**
6. Loosen wiper arms, then remove them and their mounting nuts.
7. Remove air intake screen to firewall weather seal.
8. Pry out air intake screen at edge of windshield and lift up.
9. Disconnect washer nozzle hoses, then remove air intake screen.
10. Disconnect wiper motor electrical connector.
11. Remove wiper transmission mounting bolts.
12. Tilt front of wiper transmission upward, then remove complete unit out of plenum chamber from lefthand side.
13. **Do not loosen 13 MM wiper motor crank nut.**
14. Pry linkage rod off ball joint.
15. Remove three 10 MM hex bolts on wiper motor bracket.
16. Remove wiper motor from bracket.
17. Reverse procedure to install, noting the following:
    a. Bolt wiper motor onto wiper motor bracket together with crank, **Fig. 21.**
    b. Engage linkage rod and adjust end position of linkage at pivots.
    c. Ensure wiper motor electrical connector is securely connected.

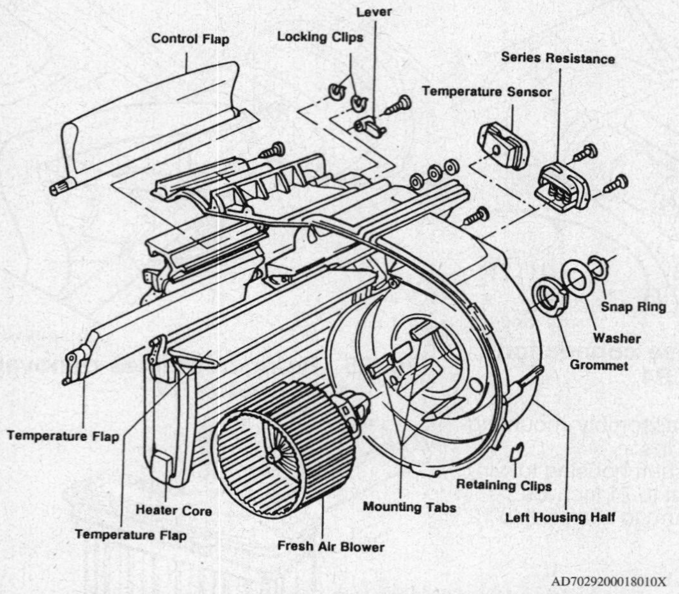

Fig. 28 Exploded view of heater assembly (Part 1 of 2). A6

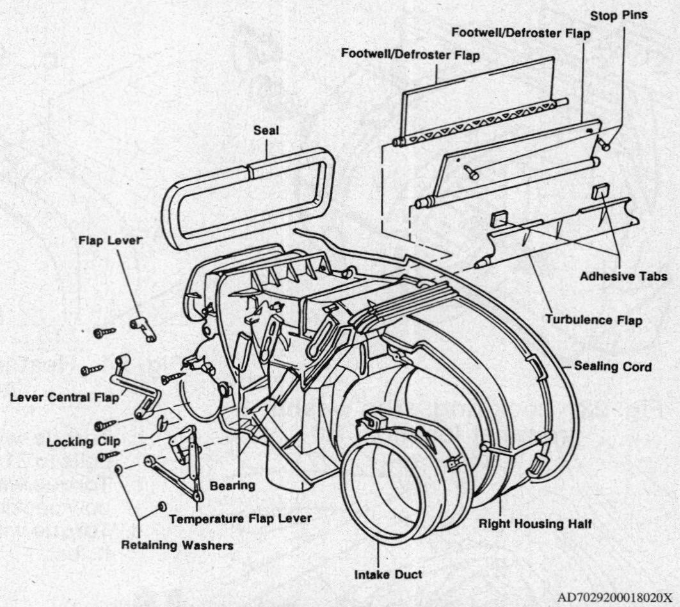

Fig. 28 Exploded view of heater assembly (Part 2 of 2). A6

d. **Torque** wiper motor and transmission mounting bolts to 44 inch lbs.
e. **Torque** wiper arm to shaft nuts to 12 ft. lbs.

BLOWER MOTOR

REPLACE

A4 & S4

1. Obtain radio anti-theft protection code as outlined under "Precautions."
2. Remove cover from under glove compartment, then the glove compartment.
3. Remove angle bracket attaching screws, then the angle brackets, **Fig. 22.**
4. Disconnect orange air bag unit electrical connector. The orange electrical connector is connected to the wiring harness and is located on the center tunnel behind the lefthand side of the air bag unit. **Do not disconnect red 2-pin connections on the air bag module. If this connection on the air bag module is loose, the air bag module must be replaced.**
5. Remove air bag unit.
6. Remove four bolts, then the blower from heater housing.
7. Reverse procedure to install.

A6

1. Obtain radio anti-theft protection code as outlined under "Precautions."
2. Remove plenum tray.
3. Remove HVAC housing as outlined under "Heater Core, Replace."
4. Remove intake duct with fresh air flap.
5. Remove lock ring, stop washer and grommet, **Fig. 23.**
6. Remove blower motor assembly.
7. Reverse procedure to install. Lubricate fresh air blower guides with petroleum jelly prior to installation.

A8

1. Remove wiper arms and cowl panel as outlined under "Wiper Motor, Replace."
2. Remove four blower motor cover attaching screws, then the cover and recirculating air flap from A/C assembly.
3. Remove both air guide rings.
4. Remove air guide attaching screws, then the air guide.
5. Loosen blower retaining clamp screw.
6. Disconnect blower electrical connector and remove blower from A/C assembly.
7. Reverse procedure to install.

Cabriolet

1. Obtain radio anti-theft protection code as outlined under "Precautions."
2. Remove cover from under glove compartment, then the glove compartment.
3. Remove six bolts, then the blower with anchor plate from the heater housing.
4. Separate fan and anchor plate, then remove motor.
5. Reverse procedure to install. Coat fitting surfaces of motor and anchor plate with silicone gasket sealer before assembling.

TT

1. Remove glove compartment.
2. Remove screw clip for foam covering, then position foam aside.
3. Remove blower motor mounting bolts.
4. Disconnect blower motor electrical connector.
5. Pull blower motor and base plate downward, then remove from HVAC housing.
6. Remove blower motor to base plate mounting screws.
7. Depress blower motor to base plate retaining lugs, then separate motor from plate.
8. Reverse procedure to install, noting the following:
   a. Ensure motor to base plate retaining lugs are properly connected.
   b. Ensure base plate is securely seated in HVAC housing.

HEATER CORE

REPLACE

A4 & S4

1. Obtain radio anti-theft protection code as outlined under "Precautions."
2. Recover refrigerant as outlined under "Air Conditioning."
3. Remove righthand air plenum cover, then the water guide.
4. Remove dust and pollen filter air plenum hosing.
5. Open cap at coolant system expansion tank.
6. Clamp coolant hoses, then remove hoses from heater core inlet/outlet, **Fig. 24.**
7. Place a suitable catch basin below heater core connection "A," then blow coolant out of heater core with compressed air through connection "B."
8. Remove A/C system vacuum supply hose from engine, then connect A/C system vacuum supply hose to heater core inlet/outlet.
9. Remove heater core inlet/outlet boot.
10. Remove bolt, then the refrigerant lines from evaporator, **Fig. 25. Plug refrigerant lines and connections at**

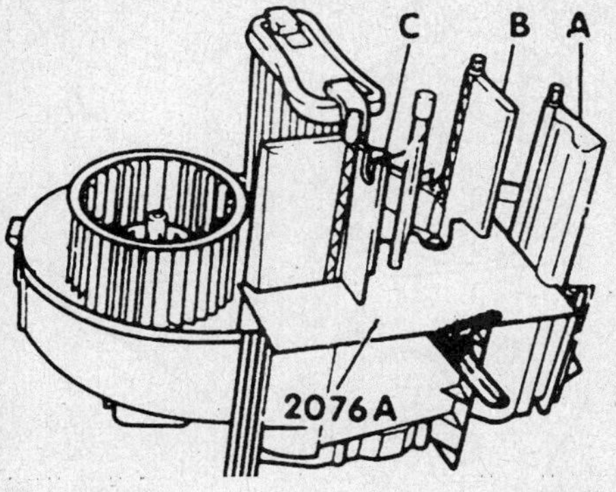

AD7029200020000X

Fig. 29 Air flaps in lefthand housing half aligning. A6

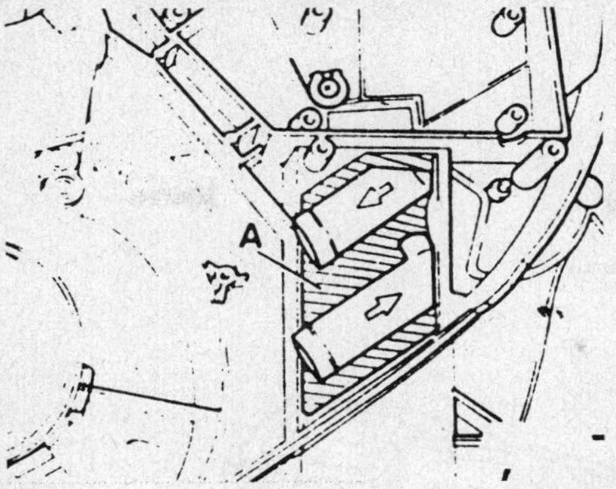

AD7029200019000X

Fig. 30 Lefthand housing half area "A." A6

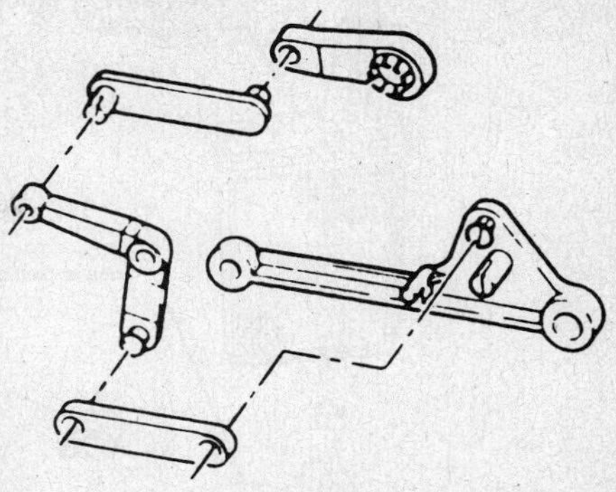

AD7029200021000X

Fig. 31 Temperature flap levers assembly. A6

evaporator to prevent dirt and moisture contamination.

11. Remove evaporator boot, **Fig. 26,** then disconnect low pressure switch electrical connector.
12. Remove instrument panel along with HVAC unit as outlined in "Dash Panel Service."
13. Place HVAC with instrument panel as a unit on a clean covered work bench to avoid damage.
14. Remove screws and press catches at heater core, then separate heater core from HVAC unit, **Fig. 27.**
15. Reverse procedure to install.

A6

1. Obtain radio anti-theft protection code as outlined under "Precautions."
2. Remove plenum tray, then the entire windshield wiper assembly.
3. Remove center console, glove compartment and driver's side tray.
4. **On models equipped with manual A/C,** remove HVAC controls.
5. **On all models,** remove footwell air outlet on driver and passenger sides, then the rubber coupling between heater box and evaporator housing.
6. Remove defroster hoses and connecting bellows to rear duct, then the connections between heater box and evaporator housing.
7. Loosen cap on coolant overflow bottle, then disconnect and remove coolant hoses from heater box.
8. Remove screw and tensioning strap, then disconnect all connections between vehicle and heater box.
9. Attach engine support bridge tool No. 10-222-A/1 and heater claw tool No. 2075, or equivalents to lip of heater box, then tighten nut on support bridge until heater box is loosened.
10. Remove support bridge and heater claw, then the heater box.
11. Remove heater core from heater box, **Fig. 28.**
12. Reverse procedure to install, noting the following:
    a. Align flaps in lefthand housing half using aligning tool No. 2076 A, or equivalent. Install flaps A, B and C, lefthand to righthand as illustrated in **Fig. 29. On models equipped with automatic climate control, install flap B turned 180° (½ turn).**
    b. Apply new self-adhesive seal to heater core so that there are no gaps around perimeter.
    c. After installing heater core, fill area "A," **Fig. 30,** at lefthand housing half with a suitable silicone rubber sealant.
    d. Assemble temperature flap levers as illustrated in **Fig. 31,** then install on heater box.

A8

PASSENGER SIDE

1. Release cooling system pressure by opening coolant expansion tank cap.
2. Drain cooling system into a suitable container.
3. Disconnect both coolant hoses from pump valve unit.
4. Disconnect pump valve unit electrical connectors.
5. Remove intake hose from air filter to engine.
6. Remove soundproofing mat from front wall of reinforcing plate (plenum).
7. Remove reinforcing plate attaching bolts, then the reinforcing plate.
8. Loosen coolant hose clamp screw.
9. Remove glove box and center console side trim panel.
10. Remove footwell air outlet.
11. Remove heater hose clip, then push both coolant hoses towards the plenum.
12. Remove heater core retaining screws, then the heater core.
13. Reverse procedure to install.

DRIVER SIDE

1. Remove passenger side heater core as outlined previously.
2. Remove windshield wiper assembly as outlined under "Wiper Motor, Replace."
3. Remove shelf from under lefthand side of instrument panel, then the trim panel from lefthand side of center console.
4. Remove footwell air outlet from under lefthand side of instrument panel.
5. Remove heater hose retaining clips, then the coolant hoses from heater core.
6. Remove heater core.
7. Reverse procedure to install.

Cabriolet

1. Obtain radio anti-theft protection code as outlined under "Precautions."
2. Recover A/C refrigerant as outlined under "Air Conditioning," then remove center vent/control panel.
3. Remove instrument panel as outlined under "Dash Panel Service."
4. Clamp heater hoses in engine compartment to prevent excessive coolant loss, then remove them from firewall. Cap hoses after removal.
5. Remove refrigerant lines from A/C evaporator.
6. Remove righthand side air plenum cover, outside air temperature sensor and mounting bolts; then remove air intake.
7. Remove two nuts from firewall. One is located directly next to heater hose fitting. The other is located several inches directly below the first.
8. Remove vacuum hose from two-way valve.
9. Remove water drain hose from HVAC housing.
10. Remove fuel injection control unit.
11. Remove heater/evaporator housing from vehicle, then separate housing and remove heater core **Fig. 32.**
12. Reverse procedure to install, noting the following:
    a. If heater core does not lock firmly in place, secure with self tapping screws.
    b. Inspect Bowden cables for kinks and ease of movement prior to reinstalling heater/evaporator assembly. Replace if required.
    c. **Torque** A/C refrigerant lines to 12 ft. lbs. Ensure there is no tension on lines during reinstallation.
    d. When installing instrument panel, push hose from defroster duct up and into blower nozzles. Ensure fit is secure.
    e. Keeping side and bottom mounting screws loose, adjust gap between instrument panel and windshield to approximately 9/32 of an inch. Close front doors and ensure retaining

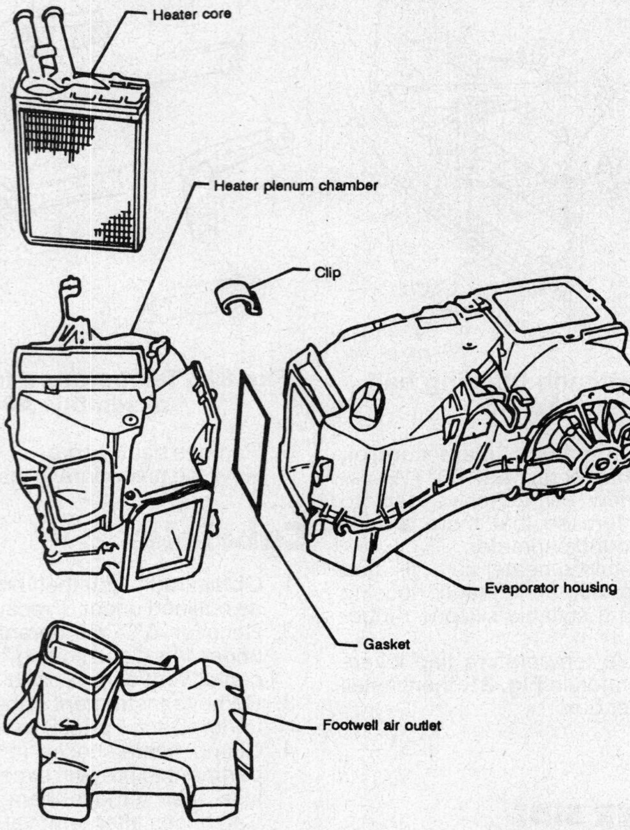

AD7029100017000X

Fig. 32 Exploded view of heater assembly. Cabriolet

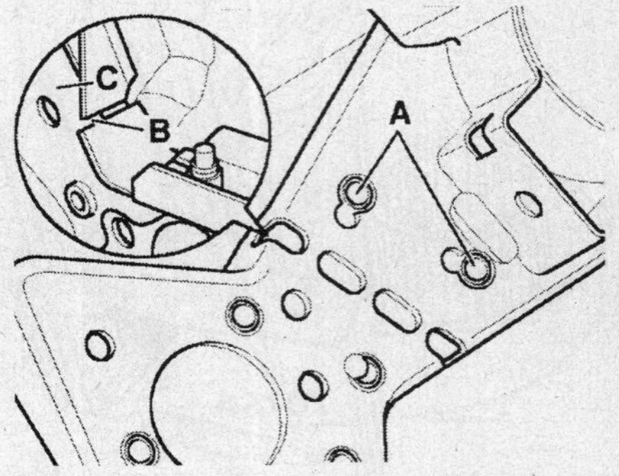

AD7020000164000X

Fig. 33 Instrument panel support drilling & sawing locations. TT

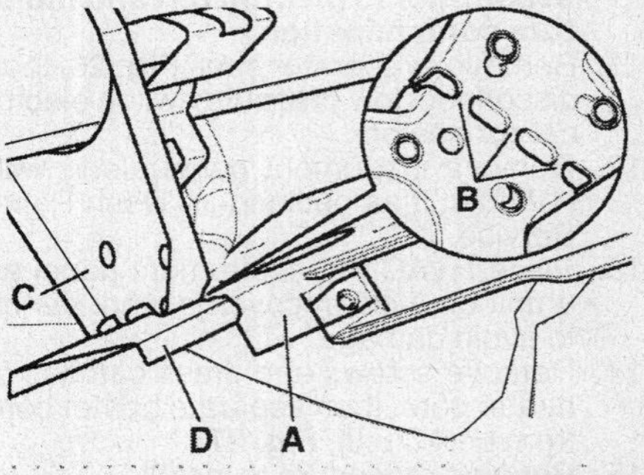

AD7020000165000X

Fig. 34 Instrument panel support bending & breaking locations. TT

tabs of trim panel fit behind edge of housing.

f. Adjust instrument panel height to match that of door trim panels, then **torque** panel mounting screws to 4 ft. lbs.

TT

1. Recover A/C refrigerant as outlined under "Air Conditioning."
2. Lift air intake plenum screen cover section, push back tabs, then remove dust and pollen filter.
3. Turn ignition On.
4. Press Recirculated air button on HVAC control head.
5. Wait until fresh/recirculated air flap moves to closed position, then turn ignition Off.
6. Relieve cooling system pressure by opening cap on coolant expansion tank.
7. Note markings and locations of heater hoses. The supply hose from cylinder head is marked with a letter "V." The return hose has a letter "R." **These hoses cannot be interchanged.**
8. Clamp off both heater hoses at a point between engine and connections using tool No. 3094, or equivalent.
9. Disconnect heater hoses at core tubes.
10. Place a suitable container under core return tube, then force remaining coolant out with compressed air through supply tube.
11. Remove insulation at evaporator expansion valve lines by unsnapping the two halves until they unlock.
12. Remove refrigerant lines at expansion valve. Discard O-rings.
13. Remove expansion valve mounting screw, then the valve and retaining plate. Discard O-rings.
14. Plug open evaporator lines to prevent dirt entry.
15. Remove HVAC housing to firewall hex nuts with washers in engine compartment. **Do not lose seals.**
16. Fold back pre-punched flaps on insulation mat, then remove HVAC housing to firewall hex nuts.
17. Remove glove compartment.
18. Remove driver's side storage compartment.
19. Remove instrument panel center panel.
20. Remove instrument panel as follows:
    a. Remove steering wheel as outlined under "Steering Wheel, Replace."
    b. Remove instrument cluster as outlined under "Instrument Cluster, Replace."
    c. Remove center console front section.
    d. Remove combination switch as outlined under "Combination Switch, Replace."
    e. Remove instrument panel end trim panels by pulling them toward rear using a suitable screwdriver.
    f. Remove instrument panel end plates that were hidden under end trim panels.
    g. Pull defroster vents upward, starting at front. **Locking lugs will break. This is normal and vents must be replaced.**
    h. Remove tweeter speaker mounting screws, then the speakers. Disconnect electrical connectors.
    i. Remove photosensor mounting screw, then the sensor. Disconnect electrical connector.
    j. Remove instrument panel right-hand brace mounting bolts, then the brace.
    k. Remove instrument panel air duct to HVAC housing screws, then the duct.
    l. Disconnect all instrument panel electrical connectors.
    m. Remove all remaining instrument panel mounting screws.
    n. Remove instrument panel toward rear.
21. Remove floor console assembly.
22. Remove footwell vent.
23. Remove air duct to defroster vent.
24. Remove front passenger's air bag

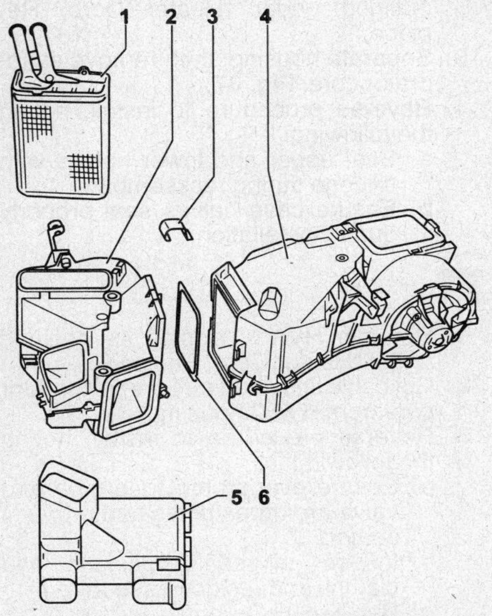

1. Heater Core
2. Heater Flap Housing
3. Retaining Clip
4. Evaporator Housing
5. Footwell Air Outlet
6. Seal

AD7029600047000X

Fig. 35 Heater & A/C assembly. A4 & S4

module as outlined under "Air Bag Systems" together with lefthand bracket for instrument panel cross member.

25. Disconnect ground connection between HVAC unit and ground connection at bottom of righthand A-pillar.
26. Cover all exposed connectors and HVAC air ducts to protect from drilling shavings.
27. Drill two 7 mm holes in instrument panel support, one at each of welding points marked "A," **Fig. 33.** Drill through both layers. Saw through support at "B" using body saw tool VAG 1523 A, or equivalent. **Do not saw through section "C" reinforcement or instrument panel support.**
28. Bend support section "A," **Fig. 34,** of support to one side or break off completely along break line "B." Remove any burrs and sharp edges from holes made in sections "C" and "D." Cover all resulting sharp edges with suitable adhesive tape.
29. Disconnect all electrical connectors at HVAC unit.
30. Remove HVAC unit towards passenger side of vehicle.
31. Remove heater core to HVAC unit mounting screws.
32. Depress heater core locking tabs, then pull core out of housing.
33. Reverse procedure to install, noting the following:
    a. When installing heater core, always secure it in flap housing with two self tapping 3.2 × 20 mm screws. This also applies even if core was originally only clipped in place.
    b. Inspect all seals, gaskets and clamps and replace as required.
    c. Replace all O-rings.
    d. Bend instrument panel support section "A," **Fig. 34,** back into position.
    e. Bolt section "B" which is welded to section "A" to section "C" of the support with two bolts such as M6 ×10 and two nuts. **Ensure bolts do not contact air bag module bracket.**
    f. Replace defroster vents.
    g. Ensure all electrical connectors are securely connected.
    h. **Torque** instrument panel righthand brace mounting bolts to 44 inch lbs.
    i. **Torque** instrument panel end mounting screws to 31 inch lbs.
    j. **Torque** HVAC housing to firewall nuts to 11 ft. lbs.
    k. Inspect insulation at evaporator expansion valve lines and replace if required.
    l. **Torque** expansion valve mounting screw to 71 inch lbs.

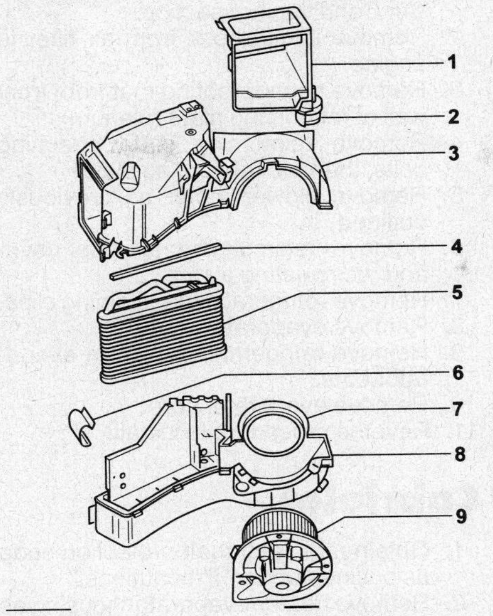

1. Intake Duct
2. Freash/Recirculating Air Flap Vacuum Unit
3. Upper Evaporator Housing
4. Gasket
5. Evaporator
6. Retaining Clip
7. Intake Ring
8. Lower Evaporator Housing
9. Freash Air Blower

AD7029600049000X

Fig. 36 Evaporator assembly. A4 & S4

EVAPORATOR CORE

REPLACE

A4 & S4

1. Obtain radio anti-theft protection code as outlined under "Precautions."
2. Recover refrigerant as outlined under "Air Conditioning" section.
3. Remove righthand air plenum cover, then the water guide.
4. Remove dust and pollen filter air plenum hosing.
5. Open cap at coolant system expansion tank.

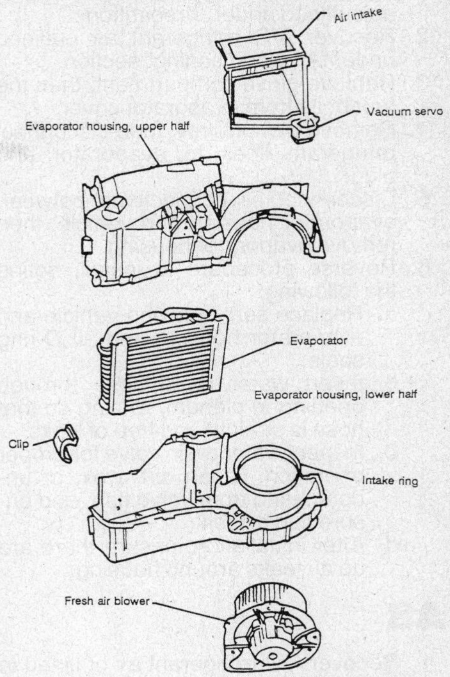

AD7029100023000X

Fig. 37 Exploded view of evaporator assembly. Cabriolet

6. Clamp coolant hoses, then remove hoses from heater core inlet/outlet, **Fig. 24.**
7. Place a suitable catch basin below heater core connection "A," then blow coolant out of heater core with compressed air through connection "B."
8. Remove A/C system vacuum supply hose from engine, then connect the A/C system vacuum supply hose to heater core inlet/outlet.
9. Remove heater core inlet/outlet boot.
10. Remove bolt, then the refrigerant lines from evaporator **Fig. 25. Plug refrigerant lines and connections at evaporator to prevent dirt and moisture contamination.**
11. Remove evaporator boot, **Fig. 26,** then disconnect low pressure switch electrical connection.
12. Remove instrument panel along with heater and A/C unit as outlined in "Dash Panel Service."
13. Place instrument panel with heater and A/C unit on a clean covered work bench to avoid damage.
14. Separate evaporator housing from heater housing, **Fig. 35**
15. Separate evaporator hosing top and bottom halves, then remove the evaporator core **Fig. 36.**
16. Reverse procedure to install.

A6

Evaporator housing cannot be disassembled. If evaporator core is faulty, the complete evaporator housing assembly must be replaced. To replace evaporator assembly proceed as follows:

1. Obtain radio anti-theft protection code

as outlined under "Precautions."
2. Recover A/C refrigerant as outlined under "Air Conditioning" section.
3. Remove glove compartment, then the four bolts from evaporator cover.
4. Remove plenum tray, then disconnect refrigerant lines to evaporator and plug.
5. Disconnect all connections between evaporator housing and vehicle, then remove evaporator housing.
6. Reverse procedure to install, noting the following:
   a. Replace seal between vehicle and evaporator housing and all O-ring seals.
   b. Insert water drain hose through opening in plenum, routing so that hose is straight and free of kinks.
   c. Inspect water drain valve for proper operation. Clean dirt, wax, or undercoating from valve flap, and ensure flap closes.
   d. After installation, ensure there are no air leaks around housing.

A8

1. Recover A/C refrigerant as outlined in "Air Conditioning" section.
2. Remove intake hose from air filter to engine.
3. Remove soundproofing mat from front wall of reinforcing plate (plenum).
4. Remove reinforcing plate attaching bolts, then the reinforcing plate.
5. Remove blower motor as previously outlined.
6. Remove recirculating air flap cover and recirculating air flap.
7. Remove refrigerant line retaining clips.
8. Remove evaporator cover.
9. Remove refrigerant lines from evaporator core.
10. Remove evaporator core.
11. Reverse procedure to install.

Cabriolet

1. Obtain radio anti-theft protection code as outlined under "Precautions."
2. Remove heater/evaporator housing as outlined under "Heater Core, Replace."
3. Separate housing, then remove evaporator core, **Fig. 37.**
4. Reverse procedure to install, noting the following:
   a. Seal upper and lower halves with silicone during reassembly.
   b. Ensure case halves seal properly during installation.

TT

1. Remove HVAC housing as outlined under "Heater Core, Replace."
2. Cut cable ties, then remove evaporator core from HVAC housing.
3. Reverse procedure to install, noting the following:
   a. Ensure evaporator drain pipe and valve are unrestricted and properly seated.
   b. Inspect all seals, gaskets and clamps and replace as required.
   c. Replace all O-rings.
   d. Tighten all fasteners to specifications.

1.8L Engine

NOTE: On Models Equipped With 1.8L Engine, Refer To "Volkswagen" Section For Repair Information Not Covered Here.

NOTE: On Air Bag Equipped Models, Refer To "Air Bag System Precautions" Located In The Front Of This Manual For System Disarming & Arming Procedures.

NOTE: Refer To "Computer Relearn Procedures" Located In The Front Of This Manual When Battery Power To The Computer Has Been Interrupted.

INDEX

	Page No.
Compression Pressure	1-23
Cooling System Bleed	1-24
Engine Rebuilding Specifications	1-231
Engine, Replace	1-23
Oil Pan, Replace	1-24
Precautions	1-23
Air Bag Systems	1-23
Battery Ground Cable	1-23
Radio Coded Anti-Theft System	1-23
Radiator, Replace	1-24
Tightening Specifications	1-25

PRECAUTIONS

Air Bag Systems

Refer to "Air Bag System Precautions" in the front of this manual for system disarming and arming procedures.

Battery Ground Cable

Prior to service, disconnect battery ground cable and isolate as required.

Radio Coded Anti-Theft System

Prior to disconnecting the battery or removing the radio, obtain the security code from the vehicle operator. Refer to the owner's manual for security code disarming and arming procedures.

COMPRESSION PRESSURE

1. Perform compression test with engine at operating temperature, spark plugs removed, oil temperature above 86°F and throttle plate completely open.
2. Disconnect coil high tension wire from distributor cap and connect to suitable ground.
3. Connect compression tester per manufacturers instructions, then crank engine until compression tester shows no further increase in pressure.
4. Compression should be 131–189 psi with a maximum difference of 44 psi. Minimum compression should be 102 psi.

ENGINE

REPLACE

1. Run wipers to vertical position and switch ignition to off, then disconnect and remove battery.
2. Open cap on coolant expansion tank to release cooling system pressure.
3. Remove front bumper.
4. Remove sound insulation panel.
5. Unbolt cooling coil power steering fluid and let hang free.
6. Loosely install outside temperature display sensor bracket.
7. Place suitable drip tray underneath engine.
8. Turn radiator drain plug counterclockwise, attach accessory hose to connection flange if needed.
9. Remove hose clamp from lower coolant hose at bottom of radiator and disconnect coolant hose.
10. Open coolant pump housing drain plug.
11. Remove coolant hose from thermostat housing.
12. Remove air ducts at lock carrier.
13. **On vehicles equipped with automatic transaxle,** proceed as follows:
    a. Place suitable drip tray underneath engine.
    b. Disconnect ATF lines at lock carrier.
    c. Disconnect harness connector for coolant fan control thermo switch at lower lefthand side of radiator and let hang free.
14. **On all models,** remove intake air duct attaching bolts and air duct.
15. Disconnect electrical harness connectors fro headlamp height adjustment.
16. Rotate turn signal lamp bulb sockets counterclockwise and remove turn signal lamp housing.
17. Remove coolant hose from radiator at upper coolant pipe.
18. Remove hood release cable at lock carrier.
19. Remove cap/dipstick from power steering fluid reservoir.
20. Disconnect electrical harness connectors at ABS hydraulic unit and let hang free.
21. Disconnect electrical harness connector for anti-theft warning system at upper lefthand lock carrier and let hang free.
22. Disconnect electrical harness connectors at both horns 1 and 2 and let hang free.
23. Remove bolts attaching air guides at radiator on lefthand and righthand sides.
24. Remove condenser attaching bolts.
25. Disconnect electrical harness connector at A/C refrigerant low pressure switch.
26. Pull condenser upward out of retaining bracket, then swing aside and hang from righthand front wheel using tie strap.
27. Disconnect green harness connector from A/C compressor magnetic clutch at lower right of lock carrier and let hang free.
28. Remove lock carrier, engine covers and air cleaner housing cover.
29. Disconnect the following electrical connectors:
    a. Wastegate bypass regulator valve.
    b. EVAP canister purge regulator valve.
    c. Power output stage
    d. MAF sensor.
30. Uncover wiring and lay on engine.
31. Pull off air duct connections and remove air cleaner housing.
32. Remove coolant hoses.
33. Remove coolant expansion tank.
34. Disconnect electrical connector from Engine Coolant Level (ECL) sensor switch and position coolant expansion tank aside.
35. **On models equipped with cruise control,** remove actuating rod from throttle valve control module, then vacuum hose from vacuum unit.
36. **On all models,** disconnect accelerator

pedal cable from throttle valve control module and mounting flange without removing positioning clip. Lay cable aside.
37. Remove air duct from throttle body.
38. Disconnect hose for Leak Detection Pump (LDP).
39. Disconnect fuel supply and return lines.
40. Disconnect vacuum hose from brake booster.
41. Remove vacuum hose from EVAP canister purge valve.
42. Remove ECM box cover.
43. Unclip Motronic Engine Control Module (ECM) retaining bracket.
44. Unhook wiring harness and set aside.
45. **On vehicles equipped with automatic transaxle,** disconnect harness connector at kickdown switch.
46. **On all models,** remove heated oxygen sensor (HO2S) electrical harness connector from bracket and set aside.
47. Remove ground connection and harness connector bracket at plenum chamber.
48. Unhook wiring harness and set aside.
49. Remove lefthand coolant hose from heater core at lower coolant pipe on engine.
50. Remove righthand coolant hose to heater core at cylinder head connector by detaching clip at connection flange.
51. Disconnect harness connector to speedometer Vehicle speed Sensor (VSS) at transaxle and set aside.
52. **On vehicles equipped with manual transaxle,** disconnect backup lamp switch electrical harness connector at transaxle and set aside.
53. **On all models,** loosen A/C compressor belt tensioner bolts and remove belt.
54. Remove A/C compressor from bracket, then hang from vehicle body using suitable wire or rope.
55. Move belt tensioner in direction of arrow to loosen belt.
56. Secure belt tensioner using drift tool No. 3204, or equivalent.
57. Secure pulley for viscous clutch using M5 × 60 MM bolt.
58. Remove pulley with viscous fan using 8 MM hex socket wrench.
59. Remove ribbed belt.
60. Remove water pump belt pulley and belt. Use drift tool No. 3204 or equivalent to counterhold at pulley.
61. Remove power steering pump belt pulley.
62. Remove power steering pump and secure aside leaving lines connected.
63. Remove turbocharger to catalytic converter attaching bolts.
64. Remove transaxle bracket for exhaust system.
65. Remove starter motor electrical connection retaining nuts and disconnect wires from starter terminals.
66. Remove starter motor electrical bracket from engine block.
67. Remove starter motor mounting bolts at transaxle and then starter motor.
68. Disconnect ground connection at righthand engine mount.
69. **On models equipped with automatic transaxle,** remove three bolts from torque converter through opening left by starter removal. Turn crankshaft ⅓ rotation ahead for each bolt.
70. **On all models,** remove upper nuts from lefthand and righthand engine mounts several turns.
71. Mark installation positions for threaded bolts and centering sleeves at bottom of lefthand and righthand engine mounts.
72. Remove retaining nuts from below lefthand and righthand engine mounts.
73. Lift engine and transaxle using workshop crane.
74. Remove bolts attaching engine to transaxle from below.
75. **On models equipped with automatic transaxle,** remove ATF line bracket on lefthand side of engine.
76. **On all models,** lower engine and install nuts loosely on threaded mounting bolts of engine mounts.
77. Remove upper nuts on engine mounts.
78. Position engine support bridge tool No. 10-222A, or equivalent on flanges of fenders with spindle face forward.
79. Attach engine support adapter tool No. 3147, or equivalent to bolt hole in transaxle bellhousing.
80. Connect engine support adapter and engine support bridge using adaptor and extension tool Nos. 2024A/1 and 2024A/2, or equivalents. Secure bolt with nut and washer.
81. Remove upper mounting bolts for engine to transaxle leaving one bolt hand tight.
82. Attach engine sling tool No. 2024, or equivalent between engine and workshop crane, then remove final engine mounting bolt.
83. Raise and guide engine out of engine compartment from front.
84. Attach engine to engine stand.
85. Reverse procedure to install, tightening to specifications.

OIL PAN

REPLACE

1. Remove sound insulation panel.
2. Drain engine oil into a suitable container.
3. Remove bolts for A/C compressor belt tensioner.
4. Release tension on belt and remove belt, then belt pulley.
5. Remove torque support stop.
6. Remove side brace from side of torque support bracket.
7. Remove torque support bracket from engine.
8. Cut tie straps from starter wire bracket, then open bracket and remove wires.
9. Remove hose from turbocharger at air guide tube in lock carrier.
10. Remove two nuts from lower engine mount.
11. Remove engine covers.
12. Set engine support bridge tool No. 10-222A, or equivalent on fender mounting edges.
13. Remove mounting eye from engine sling tool No. 2024A, or equivalent and insert bolt in center bore of engine sling then secure with cotter pin.
14. Attach engine sling bolt to engine support bridge spindle.
15. Attach engine sling to mounting eyes at front and rear of engine.
16. Using engine support bridge spindle, lift up engine as far as possible without over stretching or damaging pipes, wires or hoses.
17. Remove viscous fan and place in fan frame.
18. Use suitable engine hoist to support subframe.
19. Remove bolts from stabilizer bar and subframe. **Only loosen or lower subframe at front to avoid changing wheel alignment.**
20. Slowly lower subframe with engine hoist.
21. Pull out engine hoist and swing stabilizer down.
22. **On models equipped with manual transaxle,** loosen lefthand transaxle mount nut until it is aligned with lower edge of bolt.
23. **On models equipped with automatic transaxle,** loosen rear bolt for lefthand transaxle mount several turns. Remove front bolt for lefthand transaxle mount.
24. **On all models,** loosen rear bolt for righthand transaxle mount several turns. Remove front bolt for righthand transaxle mount.
25. Remove oil return line for turbocharger at oil pan.
26. Remove oil pan bolts.
27. Remove oil pan. Tap on pan using rubber hammer if required.
28. Reverse procedure to install, tightening to specifications.

COOLING SYSTEM BLEED

Note type of coolant. Do not allow red coolant to be mixed with any other type.

These engines do not require a specified bleed procedure. Set heater control on "Warm," then fill with coolant until expansion tank is full, run engine and continue to fill until level remains constant. Install expansion tank cap, then continue to run engine until cooling fan operates. Inspect coolant level and correct as required.

RADIATOR

REPLACE

1. Remove front bumper.
2. Unbolt cooling pipe for power steering fluid.
3. Place suitable drip pan underneath engine.
4. Open coolant open expansion tank cap.
5. Turn radiator drain plug counterclockwise, and attach accessory hose to connection flange if required.
6. Remove coolant hoses at radiator and remove clip from connecting flange.
7. **On models equipped with automatic transaxle,** remove ATF lines from radiator.

8. **On all models,** remove air guide retaining bolts at lefthand and righthand sides.
9. Remove retaining bolts from condenser.
10. Disconnect harness connector at A/C pressure switch.
11. Pull condenser upward, out of retaining bracket, swing to side and hang at righthand front wheel using wire loop.
12. Unlock both radiator retaining bolts and pull upward to remove.
13. Tilt radiator forward and remove toward top.
14. Reverse procedure to install, tightening to specifications.

TIGHTENING SPECIFICATIONS

Year	Component	Torque/Ft. Lbs.
1998–2001	A/C Compressor To Bracket	18
	Bracket For ATF Lines	84①
	Catalytic Converter To Turbocharger	22
	Condenser To Radiator	84①
	Coolant Line To Radiator	84①
	Coolant Pump Drain Plug	22
	Flexplate To Torque Converter M10 x 1	63
	Engine To Transaxle M10 x 45	33
	Engine To Transaxle M10 x 60	33
	Engine To Transaxle M12 x 67	48
	Engine To Transaxle M12 x 90	48
	Engine To Transaxle M12 x 110	48
	Engine Mount To Subframe	18
	Engine Support To Engine Mount	18
	M6 Bolts	84①
	M8 Bolts	15
	Power Steering Pump To Bracket	18
	Pulley To Coolant Pump	18
	Pulley To Power Steering Pump	18
	Stop For Torque Support At Torque Support	18
	Viscous Fan To Bearing	33

① — Inch lbs.

2.7L Engine

NOTE: On Air Bag Equipped Models, Refer To "Air Bag System Precautions" Located In The Front Of This Manual For System Disarming & Arming Procedures.

NOTE: Refer To "Computer Relearn Procedures" Located In The Front Of This Manual When Battery Power To The Computer Has Been Interrupted.

INDEX

	Page No.
Camshaft, Replace	1-31
Installation	1-32
Removal	1-31
Camshaft Seals, Replace	1-32
Compression Pressure	1-26
Cooling System Bleed	1-34
Crankshaft Rear Oil Seal, Replace	1-33
Crankshaft Seal, Replace	1-32
Cylinder Head, Replace	1-28
Engine Rebuilding Specifications	1-231
Engine, Replace	1-26
Installation	1-28
Removal	1-26
Fuel Pump, Replace	1-34
Intake Manifold, Replace	1-28
Oil Pump, Replace	1-33
Precautions	1-26
Air Bag Systems	1-26
Battery Ground Cable	1-26
Fuel System Pressure Relief	1-26
Radio Coded Anti-Theft System	1-26
Radiator, Replace	1-34
Thermostat, Replace	1-34
Tightening Specifications	1-36
Timing Belt, Replace	1-29
Valve Adjustment	1-29
Valve Clearance Specifications	1-29
Water Pump, Replace	1-34

PRECAUTIONS

Air Bag Systems

Refer to "Air Bag System Precautions" in the front of this manual for system disarming and arming procedures.

Battery Ground Cable

Prior to service, disconnect battery ground cable and isolate as required.

Radio Coded Anti-Theft System

Prior to disconnecting the battery or removing the radio, obtain the security code from the vehicle operator. Refer to the owner's manual for security code disarming and arming procedures.

Fuel System Pressure Relief

1. Remove engine cover panels.
2. Remove air ducts.
3. Remove coolant expansion tank bolts, then position aside with all hoses intact.
4. Disconnect coolant level monitor electrical connector.
5. Remove hose clamp at arrow, **Fig. 1.**
6. Remove intake pipe, then disconnect hose and water pipe. **Plug lower section of intake pipe.**
7. Disconnect fuel pressure regulator vacuum hose.
8. At this point fuel system is still under pressure. Place a suitable cloth around fuel supply line connection, **Fig. 2.**

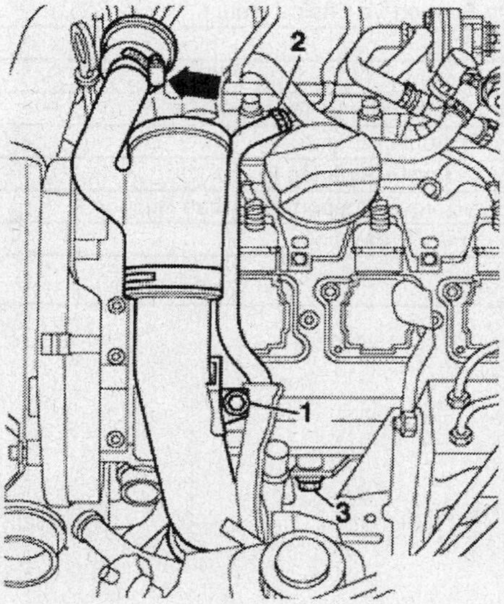

1- Intake Pipe
2- Hose
3- Water Pipe Bolt

AD1060000094000X

Fig. 1 Intake pipe removal

9. Relieve pressure by loosening fuel supply line connection.

COMPRESSION PRESSURE

1. Perform compression test with engine at operating temperature, spark plugs removed, oil temperature above 86°F and throttle propped wide open.
2. Relieve fuel system pressure as outlined under "Fuel System Pressure Relief" in "Precautions."
3. Disconnect hose at EVAP valve, **Fig. 2.**
4. Disconnect MAF sensor electrical connector.
5. Plug all open hoses and lines.
6. Remove air cleaner assembly.
7. Remove righthand cylinder bank appearance cover.
8. Disconnect hoses, then remove pressure pipe upper section. Plug lower section to prevent entry of dirt and debris.
9. Remove crankcase breathers from valve covers.
10. Disconnect ignition coil electrical connectors.
11. Remove ignition coils.
12. Disconnect 5-pin electrical connector at power output stage of ignition coils.
13. Remove spark plugs using spark plug removal tool No. 3122B, or equivalent.
14. Crank starter motor until tester shows no further pressure increase using compression tester tool No. VAG 1381 or VAG 1763, or equivalents.
15. Compression should be 131–189 psi, with a maximum difference between cylinders of 44 psi. Minimum compression should be 102 psi.

ENGINE

REPLACE

Removal

1. Remove engine cover retaining bolts, then the covers.
2. Remove cover above air filter.
3. Remove plenum cover.
4. Remove engine undercover fasteners, then the undercover and bracket.
5. Drain coolant into a suitable container as follows:
   a. If front bumper has been removed

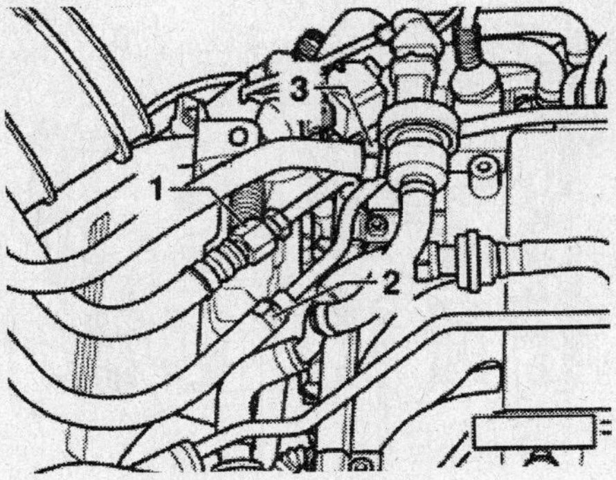

1- Intake Supply Line
2- Fuel Return Line
3- EVAP Valve

AD1060000095000X

Fig. 2 Fuel supply & return lines

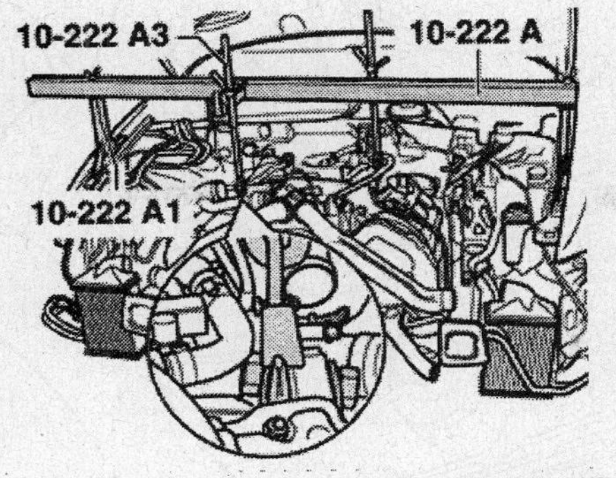

AD1060000096000X

Fig. 3 Engine support tool installation

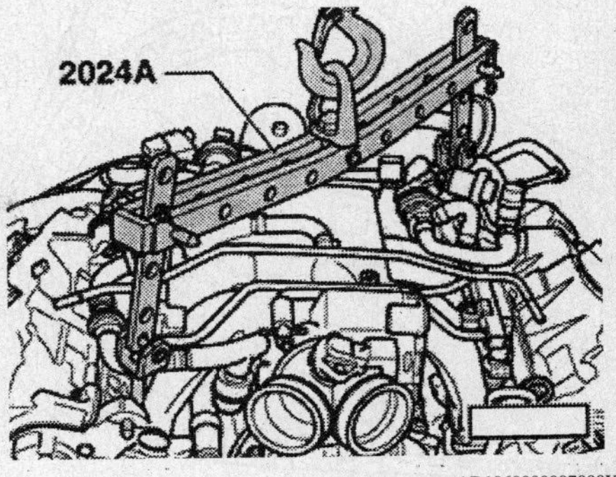

AD1060000097000X

Fig. 4 Engine sling tool installation

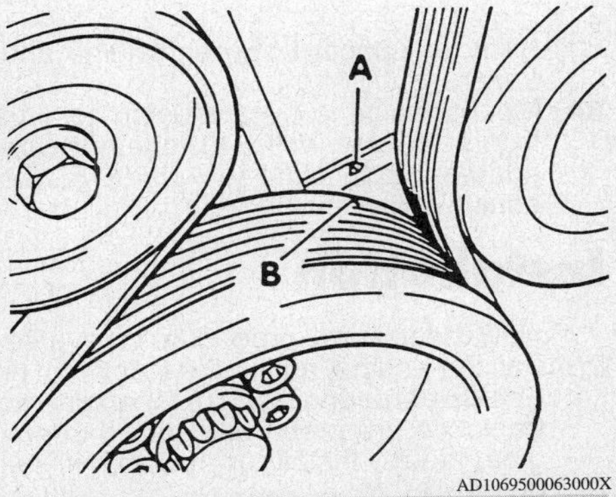

AD1069500063000X

Fig. 5 Crankshaft pulley & front case timing marks

from vehicle, open petcock on lefthand lower side of radiator. Attach drain hose on connection if required.

b. If front bumper has not been removed from vehicle, pull out retaining clip on lower hose leading from radiator to engine on righthand side, then pull hose off radiator.
c. After radiator has drained, remove engine block drain plugs and allow coolant to drain from block.

6. Remove front bumper assembly.
7. Remove lock carrier assembly.
8. Remove viscous cooling fan while counterholding with wrench tool No. 3212, or equivalent. **This is a lefthand thread.**
9. Mark running direction of serpentine belt.
10. Rotate serpentine drive belt tensioner clockwise using a suitable box wrench until both holes are in alignment, then secure in place using drift tool No. 3204, or equivalent.
11. Remove serpentine belt.
12. Disconnect coolant hoses at coolant expansion tank.
13. Remove coolant expansion tank.
14. Disconnect coolant level display sensor electrical connector.
15. Remove righthand cylinder bank valve cover.
16. Disconnect brake booster vacuum hose at intake manifold.
17. Remove air ducts.
18. Relieve fuel system pressure as outlined under "Fuel System Pressure Relief" in "Precautions."
19. Disconnect hose at EVAP valve, **Fig. 2.**
20. Disconnect MAF sensor electrical connector.
21. Disconnect electrical connectors from power output stage, then position cables aside.
22. Plug all open hoses and lines.
23. Remove air cleaner assembly.
24. Disconnect HO_2S electrical connector at firewall.
25. Disconnect knock sensor electrical connector.
26. Disconnect multi-pin harness electrical connector and move cables aside.
27. Remove pressure hoses from charge air cooler to lefthand and righthand pressure lines.
28. Disconnect battery positive cable at battery and at starter motor.
29. Disconnect all electrical connectors at starter, then position wiring aside.
30. Disconnect hose from power steering reservoir to power steering pump using tool No. 3094, or equivalent.
31. Disconnect power steering pressure hose near firewall.
32. Disconnect electrical connectors from VSS and back-up lamp switch.
33. Remove windshield wiper arms.
34. Remove water deflector retaining clips, then the deflector.
35. Remove ECM cover.
36. Unclip ECM retaining bracket.
37. Remove ECM, then disconnect electrical connectors.
38. Disconnect brake booster vacuum hose at firewall.
39. Disconnect grounds and electrical connectors at firewall, then remove lower part of connectors from bracket.
40. Pull electrical connector out of bracket, then position wiring aside. Remove bracket for harness connector.
41. Remove both heater hoses at engine by unclipping retaining clips on flange.
42. Remove hoses from turbocharger to lefthand and righthand charge air coolers.
43. Remove alternator cooling hose.
44. Disconnect ground cable at engine mount.
45. Remove coolant hose at front of engine.
46. Remove torque support.
47. Remove coolant pipe below crankshaft pulley.
48. Remove engine oil filter and oil cooler.
49. Remove heat sensor from righthand turbocharger using tool No. 3035, or equivalent.
50. Remove turbocharger heat shields.
51. Remove upper bolts to front line to turbochargers.
52. Remove heat shield above drive axles to transaxle.
53. Remove hose clamps from turbocharger outlet pipe heat shields.
54. Disconnect exhaust pipes at turbochargers.
55. Disconnect transaxle fluid cooler lines at oil pan mounts.
56. Disconnect transaxle fluid lines as required.
57. Disconnect oil line at turbocharger.
58. Remove A/C compressor mounting bolts, then note positioning of bolt guide bushings.
59. Position compressor aside with lines intact using suitable wire or rope.
60. Mark installation positions for engine mount fasteners and positioning sleeves.
61. Remove engine mount attaching nuts.
62. **On models equipped with automatic transaxle,** remove righthand charge air cooler by disconnecting upper hose connection.
63. **On all models,** disconnect air guide at alternator support.
64. Disconnect alternator electrical connectors, then remove alternator.
65. Remove air intake tube near alternator.
66. Remove oil and A/C line mounting fasteners at engine.
67. Remove righthand front wheel and tire.
68. Remove upper bellhousing to engine block bolt through wheelhousing.

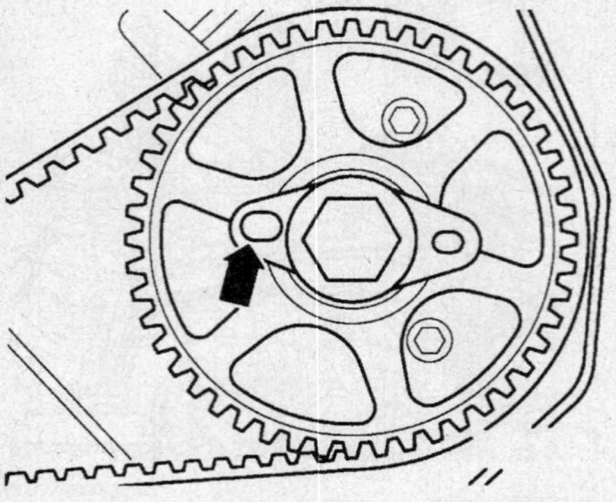

AD1069800069000X

Fig. 6 Camshaft sprocket alignment

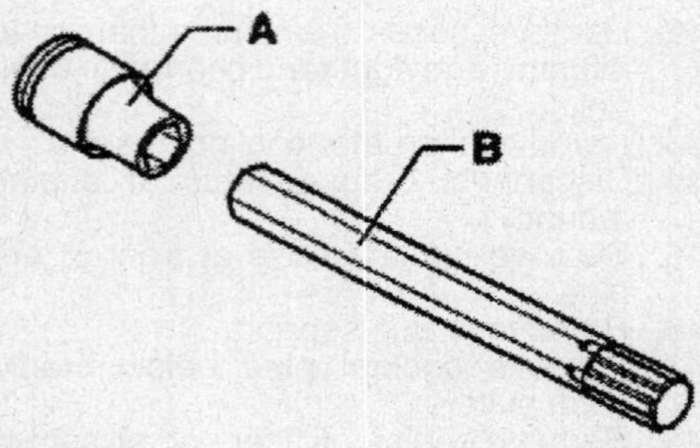

A- 10MM Socket
B- Polidrive Tool No. 3452

AD1060000099000X

Fig. 9 Cylinder head bolt removal & installation tools

69. Remove lower bellhousing to engine block bolt through engine compartment.
70. Remove starter by lifting forward and out.
71. Position engine support bridge tool No. 10-222A, or equivalent on bolted fender flanges, **Fig. 3.**
72. Raise engine using engine sling tool No. 10-222 together with engine support bridge tool No. 10-222A1 and 10-222A3, or equivalents.
73. Remove flange bolts from below.
74. Remove engine support.
75. Remove flange bolts from above.
76. Attach engine sling tool No. 2024A, or equivalent at righthand rear and lefthand front and secure, **Fig. 4. Mounting hooks must be inserted in rails as illustrated to properly balance assembly. Install mounting hooks and pins on engine sling and secure them with positioning lock.**
77. Remove lefthand front wheel and tire.
78. Support transaxle using a suitable floor jack.
79. Push engine crane into position and attach to engine sling.
80. Ensure all hoses, pipes, wiring and lines between engine and transaxle have been disconnected.
81. Slowly pull engine out toward front until free of vehicle.
82. Guide engine forward out of engine compartment.

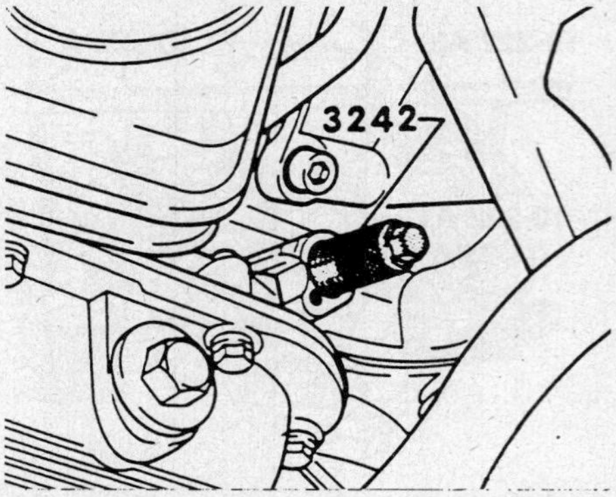

AD1069500064000X

Fig. 7 Crankshaft holding tool installation

83. Remove spacer between engine and transaxle.
84. Mount engine to a stand using holding fixture tool No. VW 540 together with adapter tool No. VW 540/1B, or equivalents.

Installation

Follow the removal procedure in reverse to install the engine, noting the following:

1. Ensure centering sleeves for engine to transaxle are properly installed in engine block. Install or replace if required.
2. Lubricate transaxle input splines shaft lightly with a thin coating of lubricant part No. G 000 100, or equivalent. **Do not lubricate release bearing guide sleeve.**
3. **On models equipped with manual transaxle,** inspect centering of clutch disc and ensure pilot bearing is in place in crankshaft.
4. **On all models,** ensure spacer between engine and transaxle is in place.
5. Tighten all fasteners to specifications.
6. Install new O-rings on engine block coolant drain plugs, then thread plugs into block. Tighten to specifications.
7. Bleed cooling system as outlined under "Cooling System Bleed."
8. Start engine and bring to operating temperature, then inspect for and correct any leaks.

INTAKE MANIFOLD

REPLACE

Refer to "Cylinder Head, Replace" for intake manifold replacement procedure.

CYLINDER HEAD

REPLACE

Avoid turning the camshaft or crankshaft when the timing belt has been removed. If movement is required, use extreme caution to avoid valve damage from piston contact.

1. Remove engine from vehicle as outlined under "Engine, Replace" in this section.

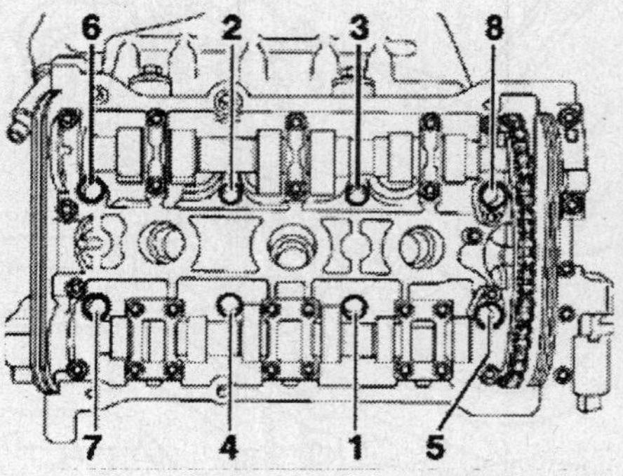

AD1060000098000X

Fig. 8 Cylinder head bolt tightening sequence

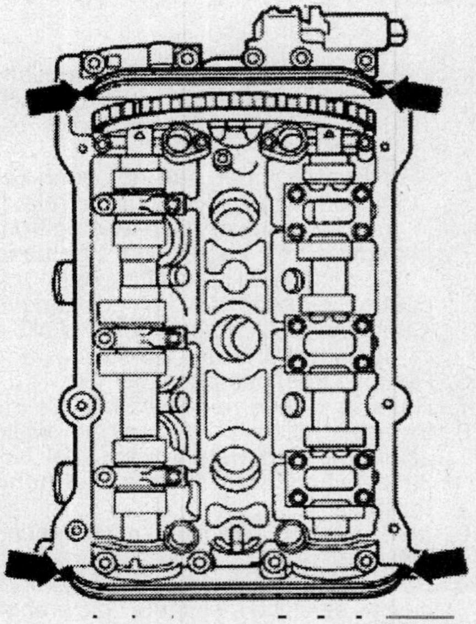

AD1060000100000X

Fig. 10 Sealant installation locations

2. Disconnect air recirculation valve connector.
3. Disconnect electrical connectors at camshaft timing control, injectors and ignition coils.
4. Disconnect crankcase breathers.
5. Unclip charge pressure control solenoid valve.
6. Disconnect EVAP valve connector.
7. Disconnect electrical connectors at TBI unit and charge air sensor.
8. Remove crankcase breather.
9. Disconnect IAT sensor electrical connector.
10. Note positioning of retaining strips, then remove turbocharger pressure pipes.
11. Remove serpentine belt tensioner.
12. Remove timing belt lefthand, righthand and center covers.
13. Rotate crankshaft by hand in running direction to TDC until timing marks are properly aligned, **Fig. 5.**
14. Ensure camshaft securing plate larger holes, **Fig. 6,** are on inside and are

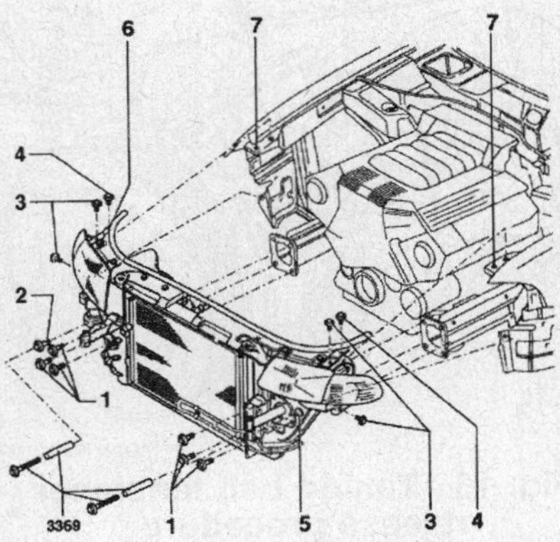

1-Bolts
- 45 Nm (33 ft lb)

2-Bolts
- 45 Nm (33 ft lb)

3-Bolts
- 10 Nm (7 ft lb)

4-Bolts
- 10 Nm (7 ft lb)

5-Bore
- For 3369 support tool

6-Lock carrier bore

7-Fender bore

Fig. 11 Header panel mounting. S4

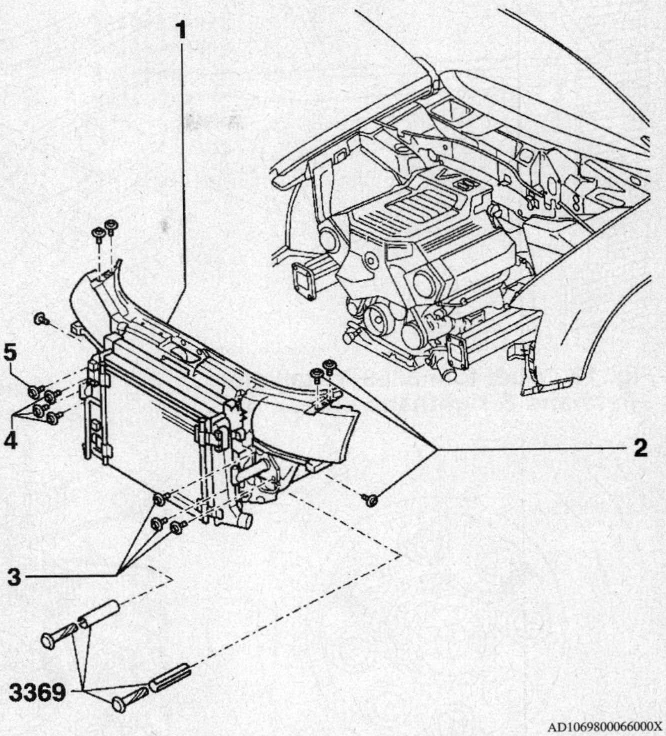

Fig. 12 Header panel mounting. A6

properly aligned. If not, rotate crankshaft one more revolution.

15. Remove sealing plug from lefthand side of engine block, **Fig. 7.**
16. The crankshaft TDC drilled point must be visible (or able to be felt) in line with sealing plug hole.
17. Install crankshaft holding tool No. 3242, or equivalent into sealing plug bore and tighten slightly.
18. Remove crankshaft pulley outer retaining bolts, then the pulley. **Do not remove crankshaft pulley center bolt.**
19. Remove serpentine belt tensioner.
20. Remove timing belt center and lefthand covers.
21. Mark timing belt running direction with chalk or felt pen before removing. A used belt can break if it rotates in improper direction.
22. Rotate timing belt tensioner roller clockwise using a suitable 8 mm hex wrench until tensioning lever compresses tensioner and Audi tool No. T 400 11, or an equivalent suitable spring pin can be inserted into plunger.
23. Insert camshaft clamp tool No. 3391, or equivalent into camshaft securing plates.
24. Loosen both camshaft bolts and unscrew approximately five turns.
25. Remove camshaft clamp tool.
26. Remove both camshaft sprockets using puller tool No. T40001, or equivalent.
27. Remove timing belt rear lefthand guard.
28. Remove intake manifold using tool No. 3249, or equivalent.
29. Remove cylinder head lifting bracket and coolant pipe from cylinder head.
30. Remove bank-to-bank coolant crossover pipe mounting bolts, then pull pipe rearward and remove.
31. Remove pipe bracket from rear bank head.
32. Remove heat sensor.
33. Remove turbocharger to exhaust manifold bolts, then the turbocharger.
34. Remove coolant pipe at front of cylinder head.
35. Remove valve cover mounting bolts, then the cover.
36. Loosen, remove and discard cylinder head bolts in opposite of tightening sequence, **Fig. 8,** using Polidrive tool No. 3452, or equivalent together with a 10 mm socket, **Fig. 9.**
37. Remove cylinder head, then discard gasket.
38. Reverse procedure to install, noting the following:
    a. If installing a new head, transfer intake manifold centering pin from old head.
    b. A new replacement head can be used on either bank. A core plug must be installed in front end of new head. Coat outside circumference of plug with sealant part No. AMV 188 001 02, or equivalent. Drive plug into position using drift tool No. VW 295, or equivalent until outside rim is flush with end of chamfer in head.
    c. Rotate crankshaft and camshafts until No. 3 cylinder reaches TDC.
    d. Install new head gasket on dowel sleeves. **"Oben" (top) marking or part number must face toward head.**
    e. Install cylinder head with new bolts and tighten finger-tight.
    f. **Torque** cylinder head bolts in sequence, **Fig. 8,** first to 44 foot lbs., rotate another 90°, then rotate an additional 90°. No further tightening will be required after repairs have been completed.
    g. Seal end points of joints between bearing caps and cylinder head.
    h. Before installing cylinder head cover and gasket, apply a small quantity of sealant part No. D 454 300 A2, or equivalent at all four end points of cylinder head sealing surfaces using a small screwdriver, **Fig. 10.**

VALVE CLEARANCE SPECIFICATIONS

This engine is equipped with hydraulic lifters. No provision for adjustment is provided.

VALVE ADJUSTMENT

This engine is equipped with hydraulic lifters which do not require adjustment.

TIMING BELT

REPLACE

Avoid turning the camshaft or crankshaft when the timing belt has been removed. If movement is required, use extreme caution to avoid valve damage from piston contact.

1. Record radio station presets.
2. Remove engine appearance cover.
3. Remove engine undercover.
4. Remove front bumper.
5. **On S4 models,** lock header panel in service position as follows:
    a. Remove three quick release screws on front of sound insulation panel.
    b. Remove air intake duct between header panel and air cleaner.
    c. Remove all wiring harness clamps located at sides of radiator frame.

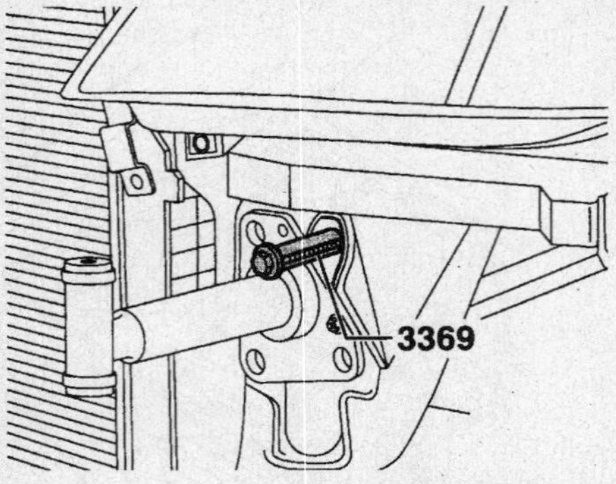

AD1069800067000X

Fig. 13 Audi tool 3369 installation (lefthand & righthand sides). A6

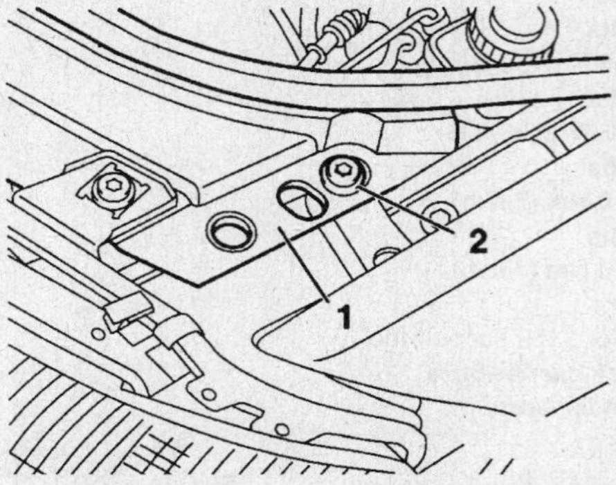

AD1069800068000X

Fig. 14 Header panel secured in service position. A6

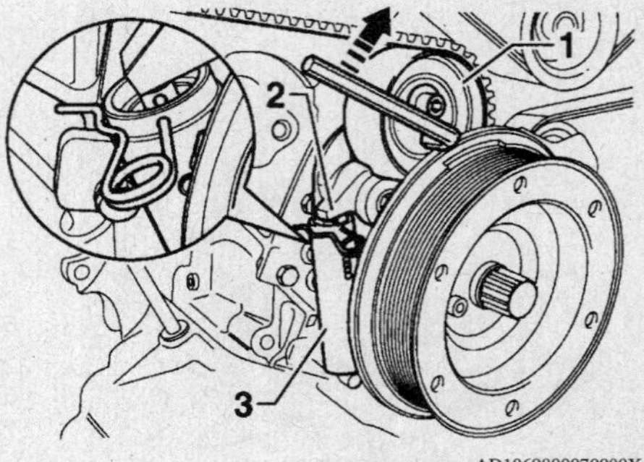

AD1069800070000X

Fig. 15 Timing belt tensioner release procedure

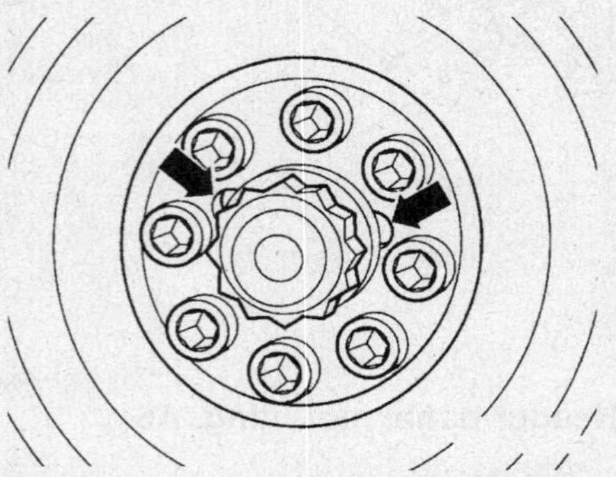

AD1069800071000X

Fig. 16 Crankshaft pulley notches

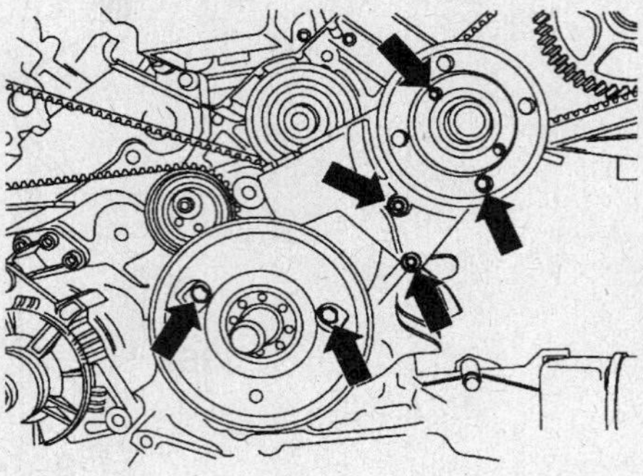

AD1069800072000X

Fig. 17 Accessory drive belt idler & guard removal

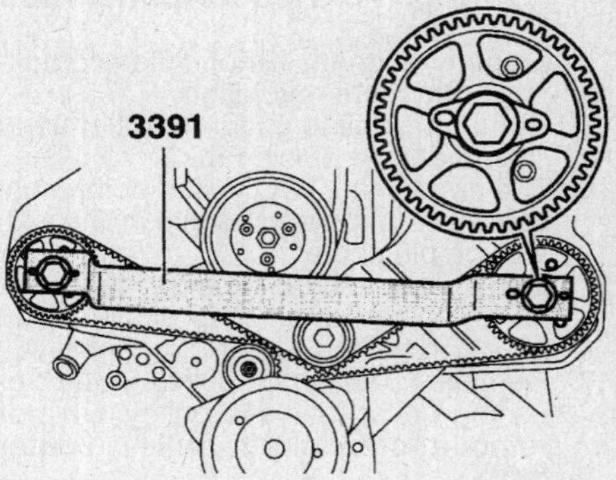

AD1069800073000X

Fig. 18 Camshaft locking bar installation

d. Remove bolt (2), **Fig. 11,** and install Audi support tool No. 3369, or equivalent.
e. Install support tool 3369 to lefthand side bore (5), **Fig. 11.**
f. Remove bolts (1) and (3), then bolt (4) and pull header panel outward until stop is reached.
g. Install suitable M6 bolts into rear bore holes of header panel (6) and fender (7).

6. **On A6 models,** lock header panel in service position as follows:
   a. Disengage hood lock release cable.
   b. Remove air duct between header panel and air cleaner.
   c. Unscrew righthand securing bolt (5), **Fig. 12,** then install Audi tool No. 3369, or equivalent.
   d. Remove securing bolts (2), **Fig. 12,** on both lefthand and righthand sides.
   e. Install Audi tool No. 3369, or equivalent into threaded holes on lefthand side, **Fig. 13.**
   f. Remove securing bolts (3 and 4), then pull header panel (1) forward. This allows for easier access to timing belt components.
   g. Secure header panel in service position, **Fig. 14.**
7. **On all models,** mark running direction, then remove serpentine belt.
8. **On 2000 S4 models,** remove any turbocharger ductwork at front of engine as required, then the serpentine belt tensioner assembly.
9. **On all models,** unclip and remove timing belt guards.
10. Rotate crankshaft until timing marks are properly aligned, **Fig. 5.**
11. Ensure camshaft securing plate larger holes, **Fig. 6,** are on inside and are properly aligned. If not, rotate crankshaft one more revolution.
12. Remove sealing plug from lefthand side of cylinder block, **Fig. 7.**
13. Install Audi crankshaft holding tool No. 3242, or equivalent into sealing plug bore and tighten slightly.
14. Remove crankshaft pulley outer retaining bolts, then the pulley. **Do not remove crankshaft pulley center bolt.**
15. Remove accessory drive belt tensioner.
16. Remove timing belt center and lefthand covers.
17. Rotate timing belt tensioner roller (1) **Fig. 15,** clockwise using an 8 MM hex wrench until tensioning lever (2) compresses tensioner (3) and Audi tool No. T 400 11, or an equivalent suitable spring pin can be inserted into plunger.
18. Remove crankshaft pulley, **Fig. 16. It is not necessary to remove center bolt, but ensure notches (arrows) are aligned with timing belt sprocket's locating lugs at installation.**
19. Remove engine accessory drive belt idler and guard under crankshaft pulley, **Fig. 17.**
20. Remove timing belt.
21. Install Audi camshaft locator bar tool No. 3391, or equivalent into camshaft sprocket locking plates, **Fig. 18.**
22. Loosen both camshaft sprocket mounting bolts approximately five turns, then remove locator bar.
23. Remove both camshaft sprockets using Audi tool No. T40001, or equivalent, **Fig. 19.**
24. Install camshaft sprockets together with locking plates and hand tighten them. **Leave them loose enough to be turned but not so loose as to be out of alignment.**
25. Install timing belt over all sprockets and pulleys, **Fig. 20.** Ensure belt is properly seated on all sprockets and pulleys.
26. Install Audi camshaft locator bar No. 3391, or equivalent into camshaft sprocket locking plates, **Fig. 18.**
27. Rotate timing belt tensioner roller using an 8 MM hex wrench, **Fig. 15,** clockwise until tensioning lever compresses tensioner and spring pin can be removed. **The tensioning roller must be pretensioned before first starting engine. Apply a suitable torque wrench to tensioning roller hex socket. On all models except 2000 S4, torque pretension roller to 11 ft. lbs. On 2000 S4, models, torque pretension roller to 33 ft. lbs.**
28. **Torque** camshaft sprocket bolts to 40 ft. lbs., then remove locator bar.
29. Install timing belt center and lefthand covers.
30. Install serpentine belt tensioner.

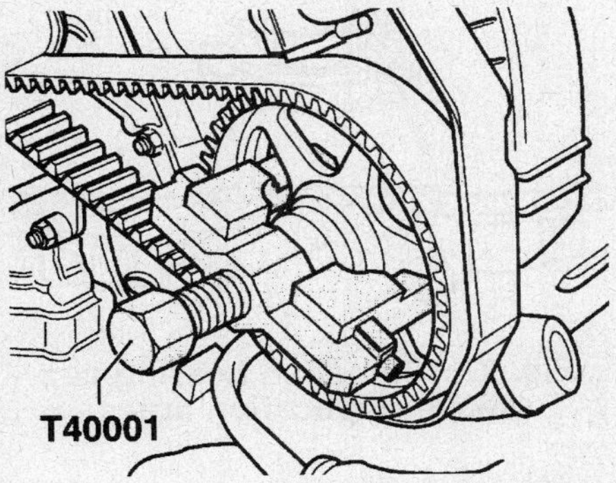

AD1069800074000X

Fig. 19 Camshaft sprocket removal

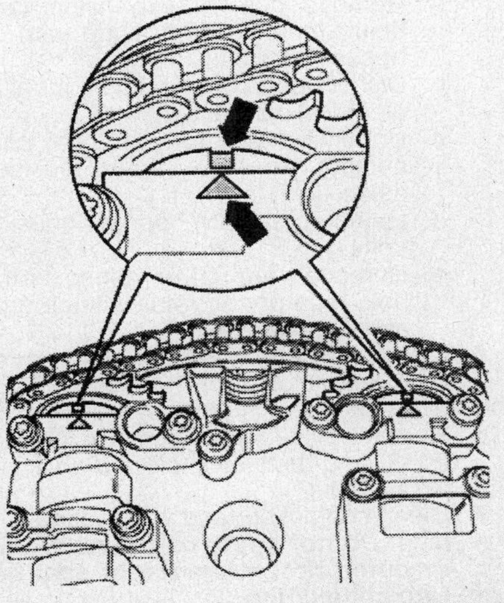

AD1060000103000X

Fig. 22 Camshaft alignment marks

31. Install crankshaft pulley. Ensure crankshaft pulley notches are aligned with timing belt sprocket's locating lugs. **Torque** attaching bolts to 15 ft. lbs. **On S4 models,** if center bolt was removed, replace it with a new double hex head 12-point grade 9.8 capscrew with oiled threads and **torque** to 148 ft. lbs., then rotate an additional 180°.
32. Remove crankshaft holding tool from lefthand side of cylinder block, then install sealing plug.
33. Install timing belt guards.
34. Install serpentine belt.
35. **On S4 models,** proceed as follows:
    a. Remove M6 bolts from header panel and fender bores, **Fig. 2.**
    b. Move header panel back into position.
    c. Remove support tools from header panel.
    d. Install and tighten header panel retaining bolts, **Fig. 2.**
36. **On A6 models,** referring to **Fig. 12,** ensure no hoses or wiring are kinked or pinched when positioning header panel to main body. **Torque** bolts (2) to

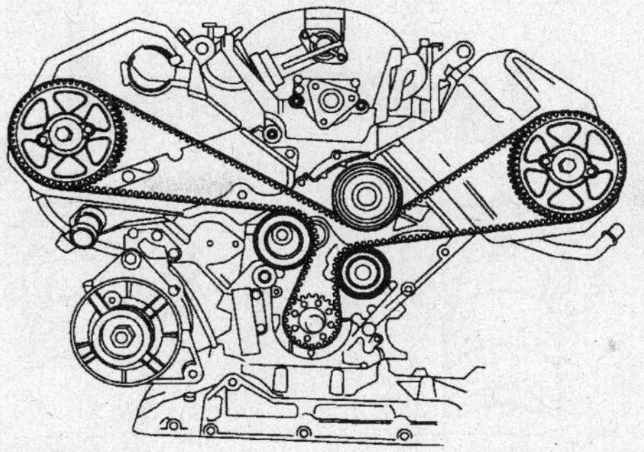

AD1069800075000X

Fig. 20 Timing belt installation

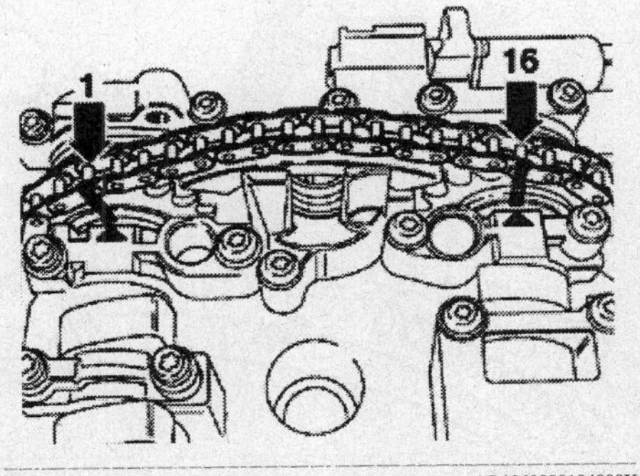

AD1060000104000X

Fig. 23 Timing chain paint mark locations

84 inch lbs. and bolts (3, 4 and 5) to 37 ft. lbs.

37. **On all models,** connect battery ground cable.
38. Start engine and ensure it operates properly.
39. Reset radio station presets and clock.

CAMSHAFT

REPLACE

Removal

1. Remove timing belt as outlined under "Timing Belt, Replace" in this section.
2. Remove valve cover.
3. Remove CMP sensor housing bolts.
4. Remove CMP sensor rotor bolt, then pry off rotor using a suitable screwdriver.
5. Insert camshaft clamp tool No. 3391, or equivalent in both camshaft securing plates.
6. Loosen both camshaft bolts, then unscrew approximately five turns.
7. Remove camshaft clamp tool.
8. Remove both camshaft sprockets using puller tool No. T40001, or equivalent.
9. Pry camshaft bearing oil feed pipes out of bearings using a suitable screwdriver. **Ensure retaining catches do not break off when prying out pipes.** Discard pipes.
10. Secure camshaft adjuster using chain

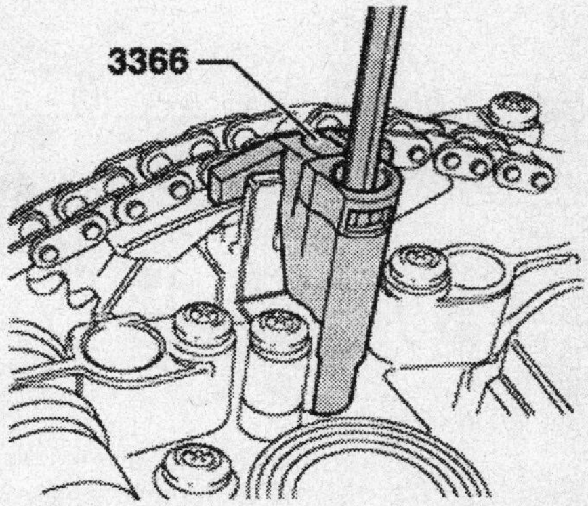

AD1060000102000X

Fig. 21 Chain tensioner retainer tool No. 3366 installation

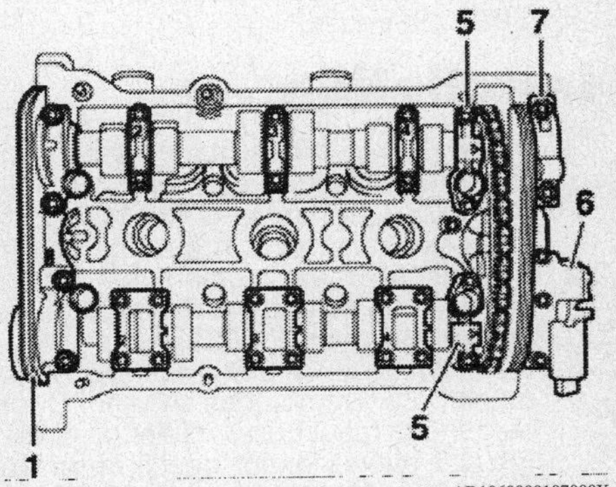

AD1060000107000X

Fig. 24 Camshaft bearing caps

tensioner retainer tool No. 3366, or equivalent, **Fig. 21. Avoid over tightening. Camshaft adjuster could be damaged.**

11. Ensure camshaft timing marks are properly aligned, **Fig. 22,** with arrows on bearing caps.
12. Clean drive chain and camshaft chain sprockets in vicinity of bearing cap arrows, then mark position of chain on sprockets with paint opposite two arrows as follows:
    a. Distance between two arrows (and between paint markings) is 16 chain rollers, **Fig. 23.**
    b. Exhaust camshaft notch is offset slightly toward the inside in relation to chain roller.
    c. **Do not mark chain with a center punch or with notches.**
13. Unscrew camshaft adjuster mounting bolts, **Fig. 24.**
14. Remove bearing cap Nos. 1, 3, 5 and 7 from intake and exhaust camshafts, then place them in proper order on a clean surface.
15. Loosen bearing cap Nos. 2 and 4 alternately and in diagonal sequence, then remove from both camshafts.
16. Remove both camshafts together with adjuster.
17. Discard rubber/metal gasket for camshaft adjuster.

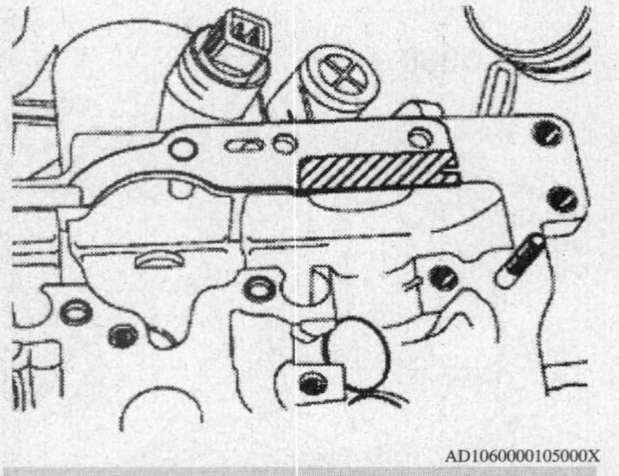

Fig. 25 Camshaft adjuster sealer application area

18. Remove and discard camshaft oil seals as outlined under "Camshaft Oil Seals, Replace."

Installation

1. Install a new rubber/metal gasket for camshaft adjuster and apply a thin coat of sealer part No. D 454 300 A2, or equivalent to shaded area, **Fig. 25.**
2. If old timing chain is being used again, install chain so that paint markings are properly aligned, **Fig. 23.**
3. If a new chain is being installed, distance between notches "A" and "B" on camshafts must be 16 rollers on chain. **Fig. 26** shows exact positions of 1st and 16th rollers on sprockets. Notch "A" is offset slightly toward inside in relation to chain roller.
4. Insert camshaft adjuster inside the chain. An assistant may be required.
5. Locate camshafts with chain and adjuster in cylinder head. Bearing cap dowel sleeves and adjuster must be in cylinder head.
6. Lubricate camshaft bearing surfaces as required.
7. Install bearing caps so that cap markings can be read from intake side of cylinder head.
8. Tighten bolts securing chain tensioner while observing position of dowel sleeves.
9. Tighten bearing caps 2 and 4 of intake and exhaust camshafts alternately and in diagonal sequence while observing position of dowel sleeves.
10. Install two bearing caps next to chain sprockets on intake and exhaust camshafts.
11. Ensure all timing chain marks are properly aligned, noting the following:
    a. Camshaft timing marks should be aligned with arrows on bearing caps, **Fig. 22.**
    b. Distance between two arrows (and between paint markings) is 16 chain rollers, **Fig. 23.**
    c. Exhaust camshaft notch is offset slightly toward the inside in relation to chain roller.
12. Apply sealer part No. D 454 300 A2, or equivalent to shaded areas of bearing caps, **Fig. 27.**

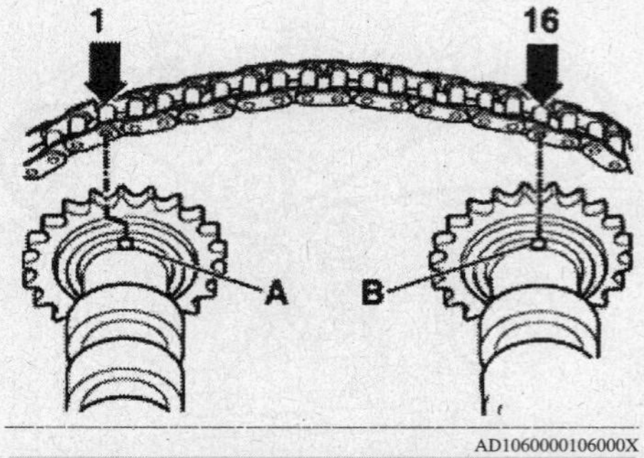

Fig. 26 Alignment marks for new timing chain installation

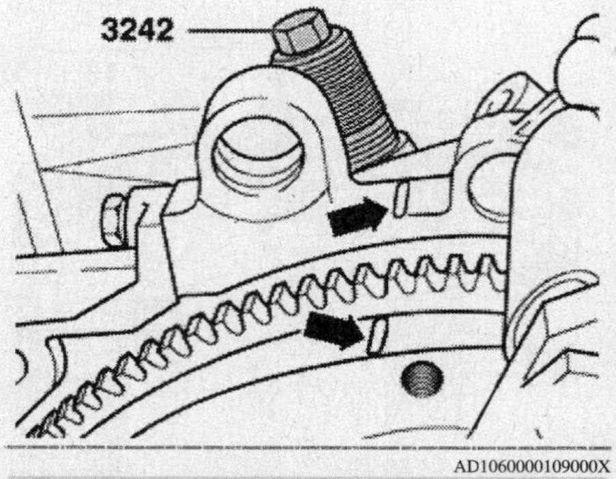

Fig. 28 Flywheel TDC mark alignment & clamping bolt tool installation. Manual Transaxle

13. Install remaining bearing caps while observing position of dowel sleeves.
14. Install new oil feed pipes for camshaft bearings.
15. Install new camshaft oil seals as outlined under "Camshaft Seals, Replace."
16. Remove chain tensioner retainer tool No. 3366.
17. Reverse remaining removal steps to complete installation.
18. **Do not start engine for approximately 30 minutes after new valve lifters have been installed. Hydraulic compensation elements must settle, otherwise valves will strike pistons. Rotate crankshaft by hand two full revolutions before starting.**

CAMSHAFT SEALS

REPLACE

1. Remove timing belt as outlined under "Timing Belt, Replace."
2. Remove timing belt rear guard.
3. **To replace front camshaft seal,** proceed as follows:
    a. Remove air cleaner intake hose.
    b. Remove engine appearance cover.
    c. Note positioning of retaining strips, then remove turbocharger front pressure pipe.
    d. Remove front CMP sensor housing bolts.
    e. Remove front CMP sensor rotor

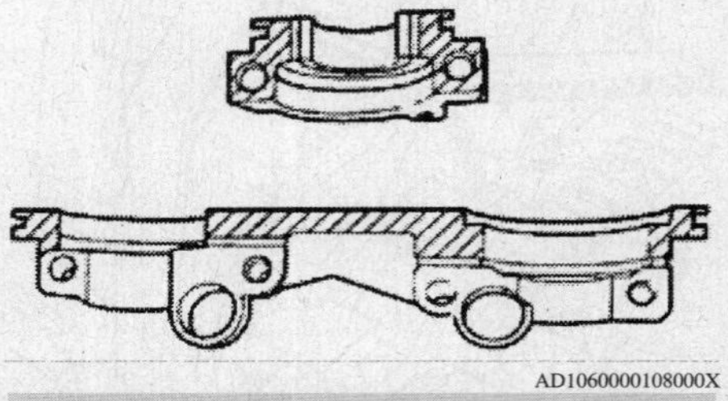

Fig. 27 Camshaft bearing cap sealer application areas

bolt, then pry off rotor using a suitable screwdriver.

4. **To replace rear camshaft seal,** proceed as follows:
    a. Remove coolant expansion tank bolts, then position aside with all hoses intact.
    b. Disconnect coolant level monitor electrical connector.
    c. Unbolt bracket for electrical connectors on firewall and position aside.
    d. Remove rear CMP sensor housing bolts.
    e. Remove rear CMP sensor rotor bolt, then pry off rotor using a suitable screwdriver.
5. **On all models,** thread in bolt from oil seal extractor tool No. 2085/1, or equivalent.
6. Remove oil seal with extractor tool No. 2085 and bolt tool No. 2085/1, or equivalents.
7. Clean contact surface and sealing surface. **Do not apply oil to sealing lip or outer circumference of seal before installation.**
8. Install guide sleeve from tool set No. 3241, or equivalent onto camshaft.
9. Press in seal until flush using press sleeve tool No. 3241/1 and bolt tool No. 3241/3, or equivalent.
10. Reverse remaining removal steps to complete installation.
11. Install timing belt as outlined under "Timing Belt, Replace."

CRANKSHAFT SEAL

REPLACE

1. Remove timing belt as outlined under "Timing Belt, Replace" in this section.
2. Remove timing belt sprocket from crankshaft.
3. Remove crankshaft seal using oil seal extractor tool No. 3203, or equivalent
4. Clean all contact and sealing surfaces.
5. **Do not apply oil to sealing lip or outer circumference of seal before installation.**
6. Install new seal using seal installation sleeve tool No. 3202/1, or equivalent.
7. Press in seal until flush using sleeve tool No. 3265, or equivalent and central bolt.
8. Install timing belt as outlined under "Timing Belt, Replace" in this section.

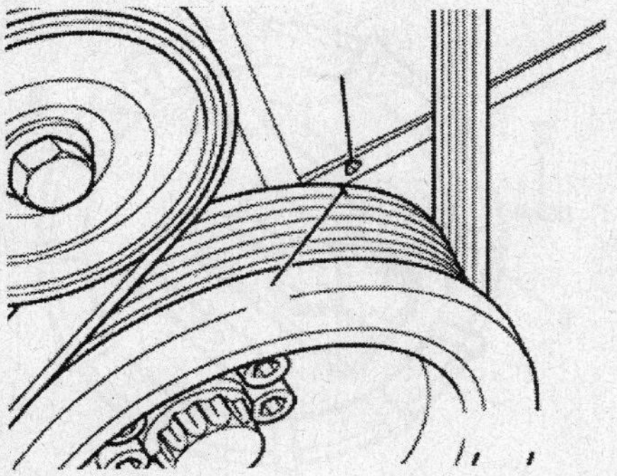

AD1060000110000X

Fig. 29 Crankshaft pulley TDC alignment marks. 2.7L engine. Automatic Transaxle

CRANKSHAFT REAR OIL SEAL

REPLACE

1. **On models equipped with manual transaxle,** proceed as follows:
   a. Drain cooling system as outlined under "Engine, Replace" in this section.
   b. Remove transaxle and clutch as outlined under "Transaxle, Replace" in "Clutch & Manual Transaxle" section.
   c. Rotate flywheel in running direction until it reaches TDC, then install clamping bolt tool No. 3242, or equivalent, **Fig. 28.**
   d. Mark position of flywheel relative to engine.
   e. Remove and discard two-step flywheel mounting bolts.
   f. Remove flywheel.
2. **On models equipped with automatic transaxle,** proceed as follows:
   a. Remove transaxle as outlined in **"Automatic Transaxles."**
   b. Drain cooling system as outlined under "Engine, Replace" in this section.
   c. Rotate crankshaft pulley center bolt in running direction using suitable tools until TDC marks are properly aligned, **Fig. 29.**
   d. Ensure camshaft securing plate larger holes, **Fig. 6,** are on inside and are properly aligned. If not, rotate crankshaft one more revolution.
   e. Remove sealing plug from lefthand side of cylinder block, **Fig. 7.**
   f. Install Audi crankshaft holding tool No. 3242, or equivalent into sealing plug bore and tighten slightly.
   g. Mark positions of holes in flexplate, shim and washer relative to crankshaft.
   h. Mark positions of shim in front of flexplate and washer behind flexplate.
   i. Remove and discard flexplate mounting bolts.
   j. Remove flexplate and shims.

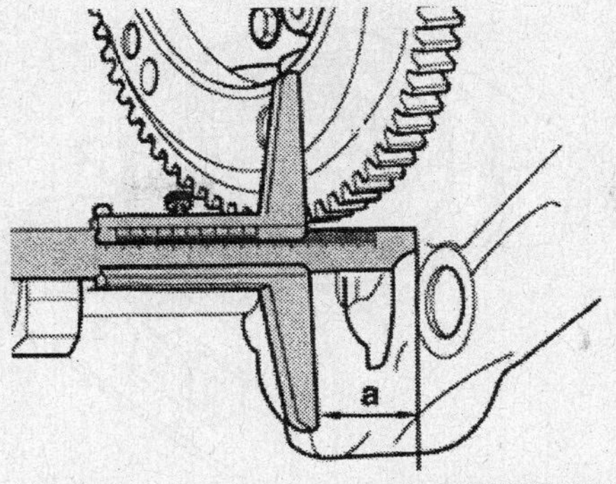

AD1060000111000X

Fig. 30 Shim warpage inspection

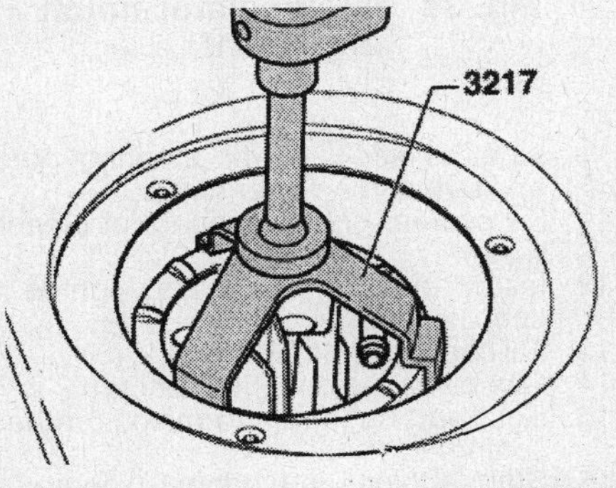

AD1020000159000X

Fig. 32 Threaded cap nut removal

3. **On all models,** remove sealing flange and oil seal.
4. Install new sealing flange and oil seal using suitable tools.
5. Reverse procedure to install, noting the following:
   a. Measure distance "a," **Fig. 30,** which is approximately 1.17 inches, at three points and calculate average value. Install a new shim if required.
   b. Ensure engine to transaxle locating dowel sleeves are in engine flange before installing transaxle.
   c. Tighten all fasteners to specifications.

OIL PUMP

REPLACE

1. Remove engine undercover.
2. Remove front bumper.
3. **On S4 models,** lock header panel in service position as follows:
   a. Remove three quick release screws on front of sound insulation panel.
   b. Remove air intake duct between header panel and air cleaner.
   c. Remove all wiring harness clamps located at sides of radiator frame.
   d. Remove bolt (2), **Fig. 11,** and install Audi support tool No. 3369, or equivalent.

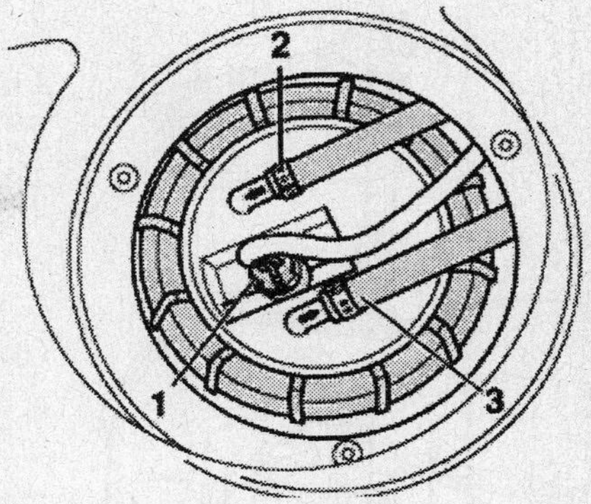

1- Electrical Connector
2- Return Line
3- Supply Line

AD1020000158000X

Fig. 31 Fuel tank flange connections

   e. Install support tool 3369 to lefthand side bore (5), **Fig. 11.**
   f. Remove bolts (1) and (3), then bolt (4) and pull header panel outward until stop is reached.
   g. Install suitable M6 bolts into rear bore holes of header panel (6) and fender (7).
4. **On A6 models,** lock header panel in service position as follows:
   a. Disengage hood lock release cable.
   b. Remove air duct between header panel and air cleaner.
   c. Unscrew righthand securing bolt (5), **Fig. 12,** then install Audi tool No. 3369, or equivalent.
   d. Remove securing bolts (2), **Fig. 12,** on both lefthand and righthand sides.
   e. Install Audi tool No. 3369, or equivalent into threaded holes on lefthand side, **Fig. 13.**
   f. Remove securing bolts (3 and 4), then pull header panel (1) forward. This allows for easier access to timing belt components.
   g. Secure header panel in service position, **Fig. 14.**
5. **On all models,** disconnect A/C refrigerant lines at oil pan.
6. Remove A/C compressor mounting bolts, then note positioning of bolt guide bushings.
7. Position compressor aside with lines intact using suitable wire or rope.
8. Drain engine oil into a suitable container.
9. Remove oil pan lower sump mounting bolts, then the lower sump.
10. Note orientation, then remove oil pump sprocket cover plate. **Counterhold at welded nut when loosening bolt.**
11. Remove brackets for oil supply pipes, then pull front longer pipe away in a downward motion. Discard O-rings.
12. Remove bolt retaining chain sprocket to oil pump using a Torx T45 tool, then the sprocket off oil pump.

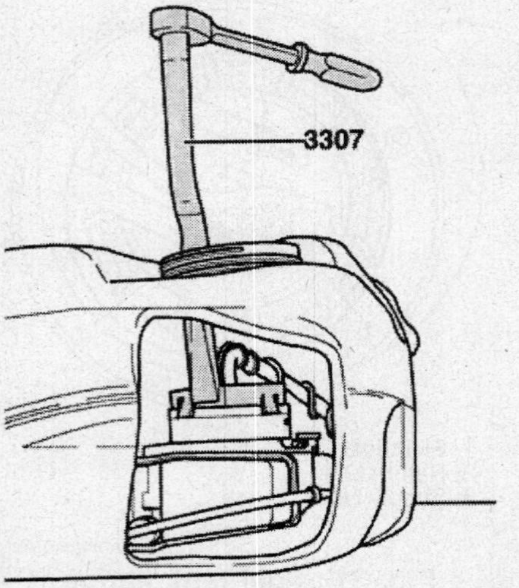

Fig. 33 Fuel pump removal from tank

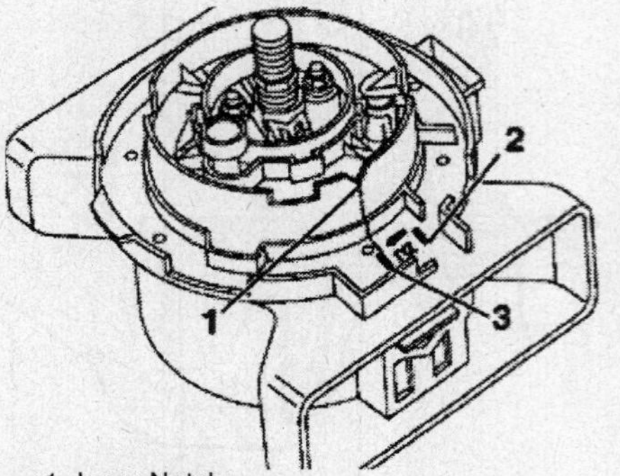

1- Inner Notch
2- Primary Outer Notch
3- Final Outer Notch

AD1020000161000X

Fig. 34 Accumulator notch alignment

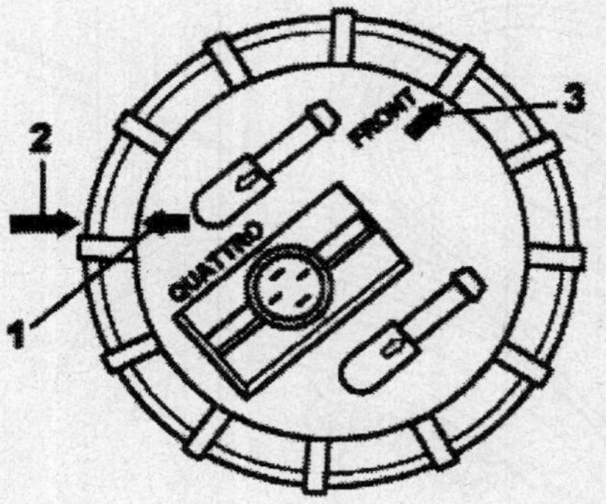

1- Quatro Arrow
2- Tank Arrow
3- Front Wheel Drive Arrow

AD1020000162000X

Fig. 35 Flange alignment details

13. Remove oil pump together with shorter oil supply pipe. Discard O-rings.
14. Reverse procedure to install, noting the following:
    a. Install shorter oil supply pipe into pump and upper section of sump with new O-rings.
    b. Install oil pump sprocket cover plate in proper orientation.
    c. Install new gasket on lower and upper sump sections with two diagonally opposite bolts. **Do not use any adhesives or sealants.**
    d. Tighten all sump mounting bolts hand-tight, then tighten to specifications, starting at center and moving outward.

COOLING SYSTEM BLEED

1. Cover expansion tank cap with a thick cloth, then slowly remove cap and allow steam to escape.
2. Install adapter tool No. VAG 1274/8, or equivalent onto expansion tank and insert extension tool No. VAG 1274/10 into adapter.
3. Loosen coolant hose on heat exchanger and pull back hose enough so bleeder hole in hose is no longer covered by the connection.
4. **Note type of coolant. Do not allow red coolant to be mixed with any other type.**
5. Fill coolant until it appears at bleeder hole in hose.
6. Push coolant hose onto connection and tighten securely.
7. Loosen bleeder screw on rear coolant pipe below expansion tank.
8. Fill coolant until it appears at bleeder screw.
9. Install bleeder screw and tighten to specifications.
10. Loosen bleeder screw on front coolant pipe between power steering pump and lefthand cylinder head.
11. Fill coolant until it appears at bleeder screw.
12. Install bleeder screw and tighten to specifications.
13. Fill coolant up to MAX mark.
14. Close expansion tank filler cap.
15. Set heater controls to maximum heat setting.
16. Start engine and bring to operating temperature, then inspect for and correct any leaks.

THERMOSTAT

REPLACE

1. Drain coolant into a suitable container.
2. Remove timing belt as outlined under "Timing Belt, Replace" in this section.
3. Remove thermostat housing mounting bolts, then the housing and thermostat. Discard O-ring.
4. Reverse procedure to install, noting the following:
    a. Ensure thermostat vent valve faces upward.
    b. Install a new thermostat O-ring.
    c. Tighten all fasteners to specifications.
    d. **Note type of coolant. Do not allow red coolant to be mixed with any other type.**
    e. Fill and bleed cooling system as outlined under "Cooling System Bleed" in this section.

WATER PUMP

REPLACE

1. Drain coolant into a suitable container.
2. Remove timing belt as outlined under "Timing Belt, Replace" in this section.
3. Remove timing belt tensioner assembly.
4. Remove timing belt idler pulley.
5. Remove water pump retaining bolts, then the water pump. Discard gasket.
6. Reverse procedure to install, noting the following:
    a. Install water pump with a new gasket.
    b. Tighten all fasteners to specifications.
    c. **Note type of coolant. Do not allow red coolant to be mixed with any other type.**
    d. Fill and bleed cooling system as outlined under "Cooling System Bleed" in this section.

RADIATOR

REPLACE

1. Remove front bumper.
2. Drain coolant into a suitable container.
3. Disconnect hoses from radiator.
4. Disconnect electrical connector from thermo switch on lower lefthand side of radiator.
5. Unbolt pressurizing fan.
6. Disconnect power steering fluid cooling lines.
7. Remove radiator shrouds.
8. Remove A/C condenser mounting bolts.
9. Disconnect A/C pressure switch electrical connector.
10. Lift condenser up out of its bracket, rotate it toward side and secure to righthand front wheel with suitable wire or rope.
11. Release two radiator retaining pins, then pull out and upward.
12. Pivot radiator toward front and lift out.
13. Reverse procedure to install, noting the following:
    a. Ensure all electrical connectors and hose clamps are securely attached.
    b. Tighten all fasteners to specifications.
    c. **Note type of coolant. Do not allow red coolant to be mixed with any other type.**
    d. Fill and bleed cooling system as outlined under "Cooling System Bleed" in this section.

FUEL PUMP

REPLACE

1. Obtain radio anti-theft protection code as outlined under "Precautions."

2. Disconnect and isolate battery ground cable.
3. Briefly open fuel filler cap, then close it again.
4. Drain fuel tank if required using fuel evacuator unit tool No. VAG1433 A, or equivalent. **Tank must be no more than ⅓ full.**
5. Remove luggage compartment liner and fuel pump flange cover.
6. **Remove everything from area that could ignite fuel or fuel vapor.**
7. Tag fuel return and supply lines, then disconnect them from flange, **Fig. 31. Fuel system is under pressure. Cover connection with suitable cloth, then release pressure by slowly opening connection.**
8. Disconnect electrical connector at flange, **Fig. 31.**
9. Remove threaded cap nut using wrench tool No. 3217, or equivalent, **Fig. 32.**
10. Remove fuel pump flange and seal from fuel tank opening. Discard seal.
11. Disconnect fuel gauge sender electrical connector on inside of flange.
12. Press release tabs to disconnect fuel return line on inside of flange.
13. Insert wrench tool No. 3307, or equivalent through fuel tank opening and place on inner part of fuel accumulator housing, **Fig. 33.**
14. Rotate wrench approximately 15° counterclockwise and remove fuel pump with inner part of fuel accumulator housing.
15. Reverse procedure to install, noting the following:
    a. Secure all hose connections with hose clamps identical to original equipment clamps. Do not install substitutes.
    b. Install outer fuel accumulator housing in tank by aligning notch on inner accumulator housing with primary notch on outer housing, **Fig. 34.**
    c. Apply wrench tool No. 3307, or equivalent, then push down and rotate inner accumulator housing with pump approximately 15° clockwise. Inner notch should align with final notch, **Fig. 34.**
    d. Lubricate O-rings with fuel, then connect fuel return line on inside of flange.
    e. Wrap fuel gauge sender wiring around fuel supply line inside tank and connect to flange.
    f. Ensure flange sealing surface and seal are clean and dry, then insert flange into tank, aligning as illustrated in **Fig. 35.**
    g. Tighten threaded cap nut to specifications using wrench tool No. 3217, or equivalent.

TIGHTENING SPECIFICATIONS

Year	Component	Torque/Ft. Lbs.
2000–01	A/C Compressor To Bracket	18
	A/C Condenser To Radiator	89①
	A/C Refrigerant Lines To Radiator	89①
	Camshaft Adjuster	89①
	Camshaft Bearing Caps	89①
	Clutch Pressure Plate To Flywheel Bolts	15
	Cylinder Head Bolts	②
	Drive Axle Heat Shields	18
	Engine Support To Engine Mount M10	33
	Engine To Transaxle, M10 Bolts	33
	Engine To Transaxle, M12 Bolts	48
	Engine Block Coolant Drain Plugs	15
	Exhaust Manifold To Cylinder Head	18
	Exhaust Pipe Clamp	30
	Exhaust Pipe To Turbocharger	18
	Flexplate To Crankshaft Bolts	44③
	Flywheel To Crankshaft Bolts (Less Two-Step)	44③
	Flywheel To Crankshaft Bolts (Two-Step)	44④
	Front Bumper Horizontal Bolts	33
	Front Bumper Vertical Bolts	17
	Front Bumper Cover Torx Screws	9①
	Fuel Tank Threaded Cap Nut	44
	Heat Shield To Turbocharger	89①
	Intake Manifold To Cylinder Head	89①
	Oil Pan Drain Plug	22
	Oil Pan Sump Bolts	89①
	Oxygen Sensor	37
	Pressurizing Fan To Radiator	89①
	Spark Plugs	18
	Thermostat Housing Bolts	89①
	Timing Belt Idler Pulley Bolt	33
	Timing Belt Tensioner Pulley Bolt	15
	Timing Sprocket To Camshaft Bolts	41
	Torque Support	33
	Valve Cover Bolts	89①
	Water Pump Bolts & Nuts	89①
	Wheel Lug Nuts	89
	All Other M6 Nuts & Bolts	89①
	All Other M8 Nuts & Bolts	15
	All Other M10 Nuts & Bolts	33
	All Other M12 Nuts & Bolts	44

① — Inch lbs.
② — Refer to “Cylinder Head, Replace” for tightening procedure.
③ — Tighten an additional 90°
④ — Tighten an additional 180°

2.8L Engine

NOTE: On Air Bag Equipped Models, Refer To "Air Bag System Precautions" Located In The Front Of This Manual For System Disarming & Arming Procedures.

NOTE: Refer To "Computer Relearn Procedures" Located In The Front Of This Manual When Battery Power To The Computer Has Been Interrupted.

INDEX

	Page No.
Camshaft, Replace	1-40
Camshaft Seals, Replace	1-41
Front	1-41
Rear	1-41
Lefthand	1-41
Righthand	1-42
Compression Pressure	1-37
Cooling System Bleed	1-42
A4 & S4	1-42
Except A4 & S4	1-43
Crankshaft Seal, Replace	1-42
Front	1-42
Rear	1-42
Cylinder Head, Replace	1-39
Engine Rebuilding Specifications	1-231
Engine, Replace	1-37
A4 & S4	1-37
Except A4 & S4	1-38
Fuel Pump, Replace	1-43
A4 & S4	1-43
A6	1-44
Cabriolet	1-44
Installation	1-45
Removal	1-44
Intake Manifold, Replace	1-39
Oil Pump, Replace	1-42
Precautions	1-37
Air Bag Systems	1-37
Battery Ground Cable	1-37
Radio Coded Anti-Theft System	1-37
Radiator, Replace	1-43
Thermostat, Replace	1-43
Tightening Specifications	1-46
Timing Belt, Replace	1-40
Valve Adjustment	1-40
Valve Clearance Specifications	1-40
Water Pump, Replace	1-43

PRECAUTIONS

Air Bag Systems

Refer to "Air Bag System Precautions" in the front of this manual for system disarming and arming procedures.

Battery Ground Cable

Prior to service, disconnect battery ground cable and isolate as required.

Radio Coded Anti-Theft System

Prior to disconnecting the battery or removing the radio, obtain the security code from the vehicle operator. Refer to the owner's manual for security code disarming and arming procedures.

COMPRESSION PRESSURE

1. Perform compression test with engine at operating temperature, spark plugs removed, oil temperature above 86°F and throttle wide open. **Disconnect both wires from final power stage and all electrical connectors from injectors.**
2. Crank starter motor until tester shows no further pressure increase using compression tester tool No. VAG 1381 and adapter tool No. 1381-A, or equivalents.
3. Compression should be 131–203 psi, with a maximum difference between cylinders of 44 psi. Minimum compression should be 109 psi.

ENGINE

REPLACE

A4 & S4

This procedure has been revised by a Technical Service Bulletin.

1. Obtain radio anti-theft protection code as outlined under "Precautions."
2. Unclip vent grille from lefthand and righthand sides and remove front bumper.
3. Remove splash shield, then disconnect cooling coil for power steering fluid at bottom lefthand side of radiator.
4. Drain coolant, then remove intake air duct to air cleaner at air scoop and lift from vehicle.
5. Disconnect electrical connectors for headlamps and turn signal lamps, then the engine coolant temperature sensor.
6. Disconnect electrical connectors for ABS hydraulic unit, then the anti-theft warning system.
7. Disconnect coolant hose at top lefthand of engine, then unclip and disconnect electrical connectors for A/C clutch.
8. Disconnect electrical connectors for horns and let cables hang free, then remove air scoop.
9. Disconnect electrical connectors at mass air flow MAF sensor and idle air control (IAC) valve, then disconnect and unclip hose from plenum chamber.
10. Disconnect hose connection at IAC, then remove air guide between air cleaner and throttle body.
11. Disconnect fuel supply and return lines, then remove coolant expansion tank.
12. Remove cover for electronics box, then unclip engine control module and disconnect electrical connectors.
13. Disconnect electrical connectors at connector station below engine control module.
14. Disconnect ground connection and remove bracket for electrical connectors at plenum chamber.
15. Disconnect both coolant lines to heater core between plenum chamber and engine.
16. Disconnect throttle cable and let cable hang free, then disconnect both electrical connectors at top of transaxle.
17. Loosen serpentine drive belt and secure with tool No. 3204, or equivalent.
18. Counterhold viscous fan belt pulley using a suitable screwdriver, then remove fan retaining bolt.
19. Remove hydraulic pump from mounting bracket. **Do not disconnect hydraulic lines.**
20. Remove A/C compressor and secure to one side with suitable wire or rope. **Do not disconnect refrigerant lines. Do not allow refrigerant lines to kink.**
21. Remove front exhaust pipe from exhaust manifold, then disconnect battery positive cable from starter.
22. Remove starter, then disconnect starter ground wire from engine support.
23. Disconnect four engine mounting bolts, then attach engine support fixture tool No. 10-222A and engine support adapter tool No. 3147, or equivalents to transaxle.
24. Attach engine sling tool No. 2024A to engine and to crane tool No. 1202A, or

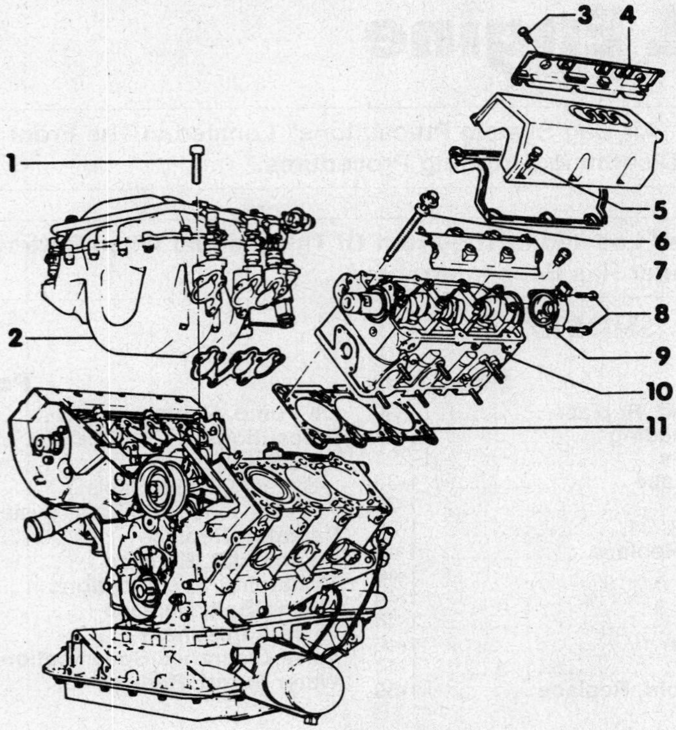

1. Bolt
2. Intake Manifold
3. Bolt
4. Cover
5. Bolt
6. Cylinder Head Bolt
7. Pressure Relief Valve
8. Bolt
9. Camshaft Position (CMP) Sensor
10. Cylinder Head
11. Cylinder Head Gasket

AD1069600030000X

Fig. 1 Exploded view of cylinder head assembly

equivalents. **Mounting hooks and pins on lifting device must be secured with locking pins.**

25. Lift engine from vehicle.
26. Reverse procedure to install, noting the following:
    a. **Note type of coolant. Do not allow red coolant to be mixed with any other type.**
    b. Install alignment sleeves to center engine assembly.
    c. Install new seals and gaskets.
    d. Inspect clutch release bearing for wear, replace if required.
    e. Clean transaxle input shaft splines. lightly lubricate clutch release bearing and input shaft splines with G 000 100 grease, or equivalent. **Do not grease guide sleeve for release bearing.**
    f. Align engine by shaking before tightening engine mounts to ensure mounts are free of stress.
    g. Adjust throttle cable.
    h. Fill cooling system and inspect oil level.
    i. Tighten all fasteners to specifications.

Except A4 & S4

This procedure has been revised by a Technical Service Bulletin.

1. Obtain radio anti-theft protection code as outlined under "Precautions."
2. Remove lower splash shield.
3. Drain coolant, then remove intake air dust between mass air flow (MAF) sensor and intake manifold.
4. Disconnect electrical connectors from MAF sensor and idle air control (IAC) valve.
5. Remove intake air preheating hose and EVAP canister purge regulator valve on MAF sensor.
6. Disconnect and remove air cleaner housing along with MAF sensor.
7. Remove cover on intake air housing, remove both screws, then push back and lift housing.
8. Remove both positive crankcase ventilation breather hoses, then disconnect vacuum hose and remove intake air housing.
9. Remove coolant hose between radiator and top of engine, then remove lefthand and righthand fuel injection line covers.

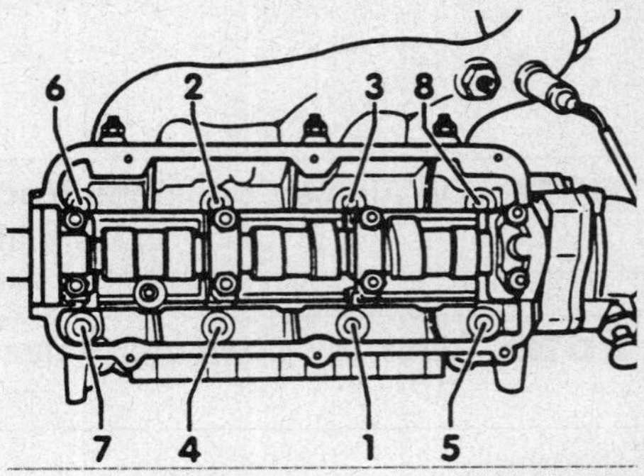

AD1069100012000X

Fig. 2 Cylinder head tightening sequence

10. Disconnect electrical connectors from fuel injectors and place aside at rear with covers.
11. Remove ignition coil assembly cover, mark position of coils to wires, then disconnect connectors from coil assembly.
12. Disconnect connectors attached to bracket on engine compartment bulkhead near plenum, then remove ignition coil assembly with holder, pulling wires of coil assembly forward through intake manifold.
13. Disconnect fuel supply and return lines, then the vacuum hose on intake manifold and remove vacuum pump.
14. Disconnect throttle cable, then the hose between EVAP canister purge regulator valve and throttle body.
15. Disconnect and uncover HO_2S electrical connector at righthand side, then the connector on plenum chamber at lefthand side.
16. Disconnect electrical connectors at oil pressure sensor and oil pressure switch, electrical wires at cruise control, blue wire at intake manifold changeover valve and brown wire at EGR valve.
17. Disconnect electrical connectors at CKP sensor at lefthand rear cylinder head, then the TP sensor.
18. Clamp off engine coolant hose using hose clamp tool No. 3094, or equivalent, then disconnect hose at pump and holder at bottom and uncover.
19. Remove cover for serpentine belt, then disconnect pressure line of power steering pump. **Place clean rags under hose to catch oil.**
20. Remove coolant hose and coolant line at righthand side, then disconnect ground wire at righthand engine support, then remove nut from support.
21. Relieve tension on serpentine drive belt using drift tool No. 3204, or equivalent, then remove serpentine drive belt.
22. Disconnect both heater hoses on engine at lefthand rear, then remove alternator air guide.
23. Disconnect clamp on oil pan, then remove alternator with wires attached and suspend on side.
24. Remove starter motor toward rear with

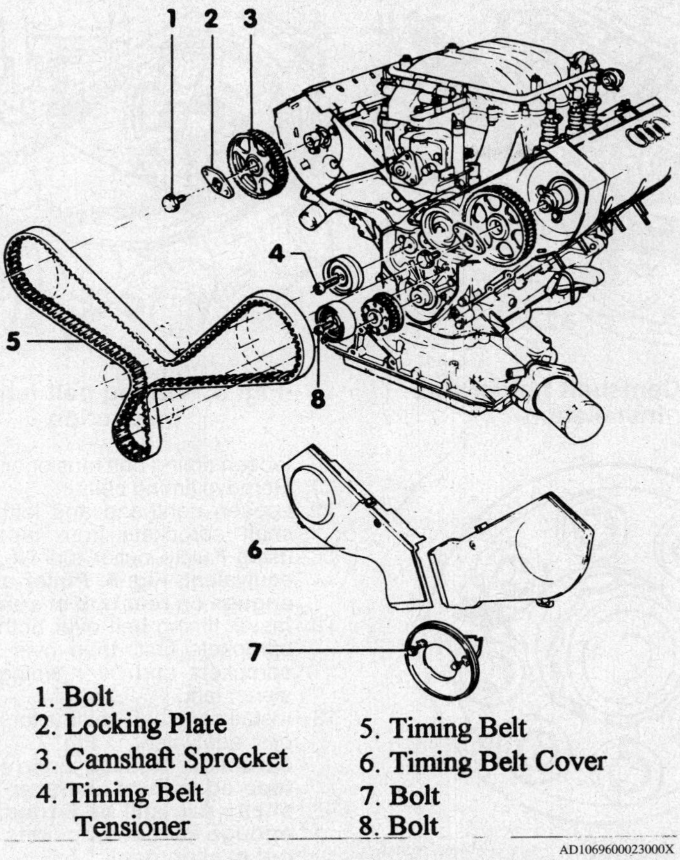

Fig. 3 Timing belt replacement

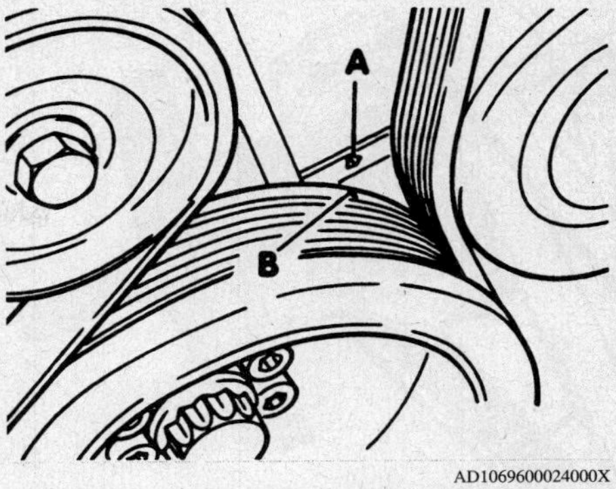

Fig. 4 Crankshaft pulley & front case timing marks

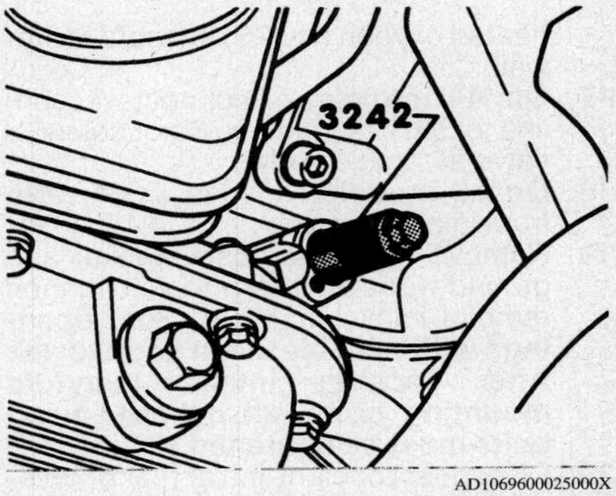

Fig. 5 Crankshaft holding tool installation

wires attached and suspend from engine at side.

25. Remove crossmember, then disconnect and remove catalytic converters.
26. Disconnect clamp for A/C compressor line on crossmember at front, then remove oil filter and oil cooler from under oil filter.
27. Disconnect A/C compressor and suspend at side, then remove engine/transaxle flange mounting bolts at top and bottom.
28. Support transaxle with engine support bridge and hook, tools No. 10-222A and 3147, or equivalents.
29. Connect engine sling tool No. 2024A, or equivalent at righthand rear and lefthand front of engine and secure as required.
30. Using a suitable hoist, lift engine slightly and disconnect front engine support from side member.
31. Lift engine carefully while turning engine support bridge tool No. 10-222A, or equivalent until clear of righthand engine mount.
32. Pull engine forward carefully until clearance is obtained, then disconnect engine from transaxle.
33. Lift out starter motor, then remove engine from vehicle.
34. Reverse procedure to install, noting the following:
    a. **Note type of coolant. Do not allow red coolant to be mixed with any other type.**
    b. Replacing all self-locking nuts.
    c. Tighten nuts and bolts to specifications.

INTAKE MANIFOLD

REPLACE

Refer to "Cylinder Head, Replace" for intake manifold replacement procedure.

CYLINDER HEAD

REPLACE

This procedure has been revised by a Technical Service Bulletin.

Avoid turning the camshaft or crankshaft when the timing belt has been removed. If movement is required, use extreme caution to avoid valve damage from piston contact.

Removal procedures given are for lefthand cylinder head, Fig. 1. Righthand cylinder head procedures are similar.

1. Obtain radio anti-theft protection code as outlined under "Precautions."
2. Remove timing belt as outlined under "Timing Belt, Replace."
3. Disconnect exhaust pipe from manifold, then exhaust hose to exhaust gas recirculation (EGR) valve at manifold.
4. Drain coolant using tool No. 3247, or equivalent, then remove air hose between MAF sensor and intake manifold.
5. Disconnect all spark plug connectors, then all electrical connectors from injectors.
6. Disconnect PCV connections on lefthand and righthand cylinder head covers, then the fuel supply and return lines.
7. Unclip cover on intake air housing, then remove both screws under cover.
8. Push back and lift intake air housing upwards, then disconnect vacuum hose from lefthand side and remove housing.
9. Remove lefthand side cover for fuel injector lines, then disconnect throttle cable
10. **On A6 models,** disconnect vacuum hose on vacuum pump and intake manifold.
11. **On all models,** disconnect hose from EVAP canister purge regulator valve to throttle body.
12. **On A4 models,** disconnect line from idle air control (IAC) valve to throttle body.
13. **On all models,** disconnect electrical connectors for idle air control (IAC) valve and throttle position (TP) sensor.
14. Disconnect vacuum hose from cruise control vacuum control unit, then electrical connectors from oil pressure sensor, oil pressure switch and camshaft position (CMP) sensor.
15. Disconnect vacuum hoses on intake manifold changeover valve (blue) and EGR valve (brown).
16. Disconnect electrical connectors for

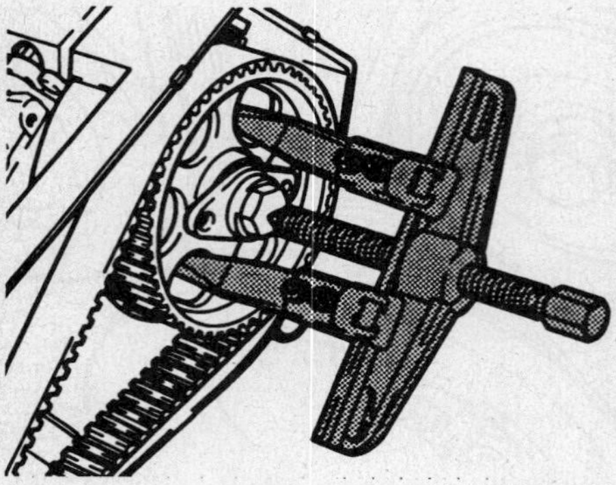

AD1069600026000X

Fig. 6 Camshaft puller tool installation

heated oxygen (HO2S) sensors at firewall.

17. **On A4 models**, disconnect vacuum line to EGR vacuum regulator solenoid valve at throttle body.
18. **On all models**, remove EGR valve from intake manifold.
19. Remove hydraulic hose bracket and ground wires on intake manifold, then remove intake manifold. **Seal openings with suitable clean shop towel. After loosing intake manifold mounting bolts, all cylinder head bolts must be tightened ¼ turn.**
20. Disconnect coolant line at rear of cylinder head.
21. **On A6 models,** remove CO sampling pipe and oxygen sensor.
22. **On A4 models,** remove HO_2S.
23. **On all models,** remove exhaust manifold heat shield.
24. Remove cylinder head cover, then the rear timing belt guard.
25. Disconnect pipe from hydraulic reservoir to pump, then remove cylinder head bolts and cylinder head.
26. Reverse procedure to install, noting the following:
    a. **Note type of coolant. Do not allow red coolant to be mixed with any other type.**
    b. Using sequence outlined in **Fig. 2, torque** cylinder head bolts in two steps: first to 44 ft. lbs., then rotate an additional ½ turn.

VALVE CLEARANCE SPECIFICATIONS

This engine is equipped with hydraulic lifters. No provision for adjustment is provided.

VALVE ADJUSTMENT

This engine is equipped with hydraulic lifters which do not require adjustment.

TIMING BELT

REPLACE

Avoid turning the camshaft or crankshaft when the timing belt has been re-

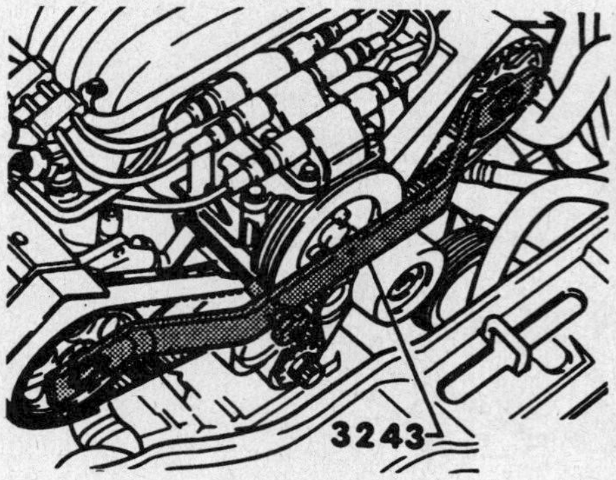

AD1069600027000X

Fig. 7 Camshaft holder tool installation

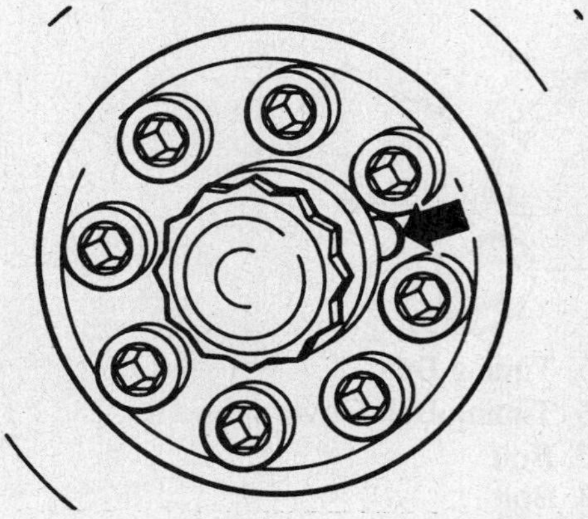

AD1069600029000X

Fig. 9 Vibration damper installation

moved. If movement is required, use extreme caution to avoid valve damage from piston contact.

Mark direction of travel on serpentine drive belt and timing belt for installation reference.

1. Obtain radio anti-theft protection code as outlined under "Precautions."
2. Remove serpentine drive belt.
3. Unclip timing belt upper covers on both sides, **Fig. 3.**
4. Position crankshaft at TDC compression stroke. Align notch on crankshaft pulley with notch on front case, **Fig. 4.**
5. Ensure large holes of locating plates on camshaft sprockets face each other. If not, rotate crankshaft one turn and reinspect position of camshaft sprocket plate large holes.
6. Remove crankshaft position sensor. Crankshaft position sensor is located on lefthand side of engine block behind oil cooler. **TDC hole in crankshaft must be seen or felt through crankshaft position sensor bore.**
7. Install crankshaft holding tool No. 3242, or equivalent into crankshaft position sensor bore and tighten slightly, **Fig. 5.**
8. Remove serpentine drive belt tensioner, lefthand and righthand upper timing belt covers, then the vibration damper. **Center bolt does not have to be loosened for damper removal.**
9. Remove lower timing belt cover, then

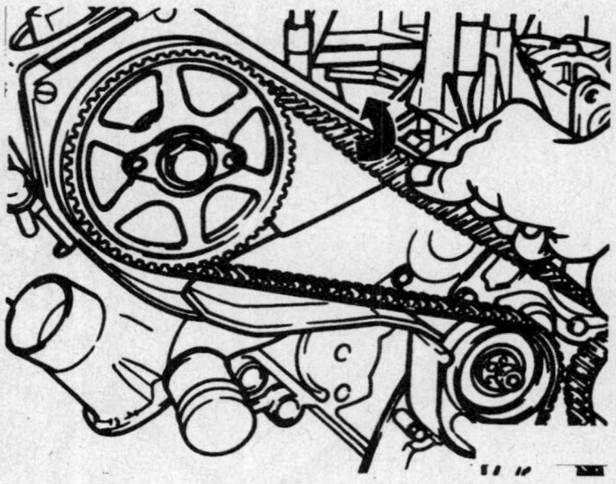

AD1069600028000X

Fig. 8 Timing belt tension inspection

loosen timing belt tensioner.

10. Remove timing belt.
11. Loosen righthand and lefthand camshaft sprockets from tapered ends using Kukko puller tool No. 20-10, or equivalent, **Fig. 6. Puller arms must engage on rear hub of sprocket.**
12. Install timing belt over both camshaft sprockets first, then over remaining sprockets and over timing belt tensioner last.
13. Install camshaft holding tool No. 3243, or equivalent, **Fig. 7. Camshaft sprockets must be loose enough on tapered ends of shafts so that camshafts can still be turned, but tight enough so that sprockets do not tilt out of alignment.**
14. Adjust timing belt tension by turning tensioner to right and holding with a suitable socket wrench, then tighten tensioner center bolt to specification. **Timing belt is properly tensioned when it can be twisted 90° at midway point between camshaft sprocket and water pump with thumb and forefinger, Fig. 8.**
15. Ensure crankshaft and camshaft timing marks are aligned, then tighten righthand and lefthand camshaft sprocket bolts to specifications.
16. Remove camshaft holding tool No. 3243, then the crankshaft holding tool No. 3242.
17. Rotate crankshaft one turn in normal direction of engine rotation, then inspect timing belt tension and timing alignment. If required, adjust timing belt tension.
18. Install timing belt lower cover.
19. Install vibration damper. **During installation notch in damper must be indexed with locking lug on crankshaft pulley, Fig. 9.**
20. Install crankshaft position sensor.
21. Install timing belt lower cover, then the righthand and lefthand upper covers.
22. Install drive belt tensioner, then the serpentine drive belt.
23. Inspect and adjust ignition timing as required.

CAMSHAFT

REPLACE

1. Remove timing belt as outlined under "Timing Belt, Replace."

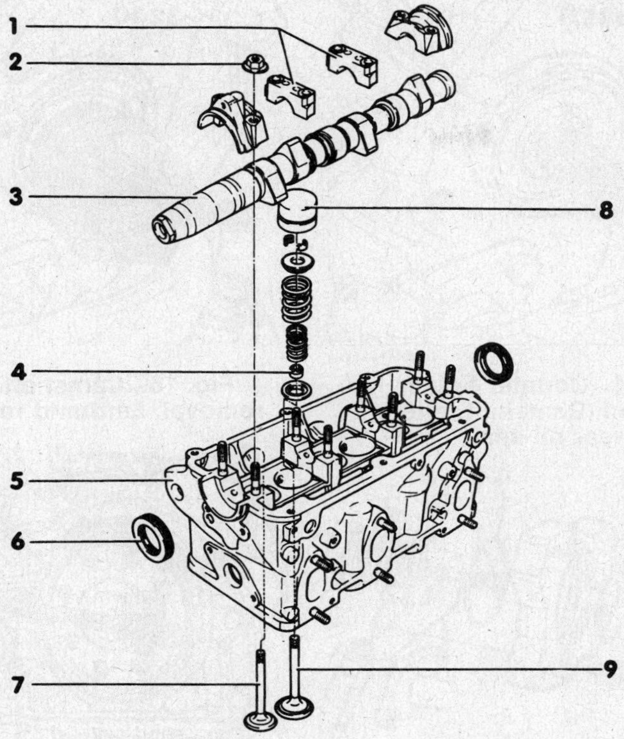

1. Bearing Cap
2. Bolt
3. Camshaft
4. Valve Stem Seal
5. Cylinder Head
6. Oil Seals
7. Exhaust Valve
8. Hydraulic Valve Lifter
9. Intake Valve

AD1069600031000X

Fig. 10 Exploded view of camshaft assembly

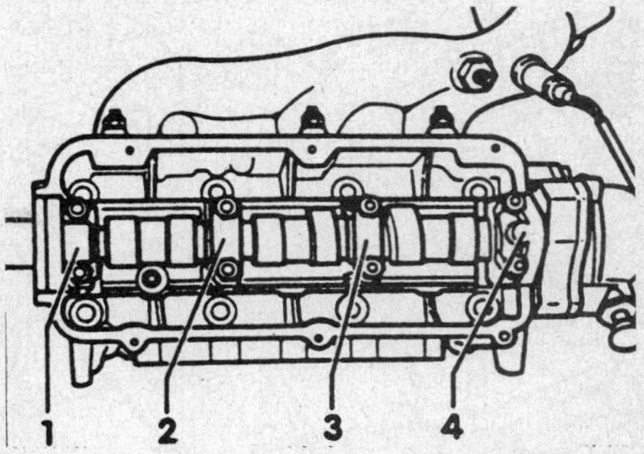

AD1069100013000X

Fig. 11 Camshaft bearing cap identification

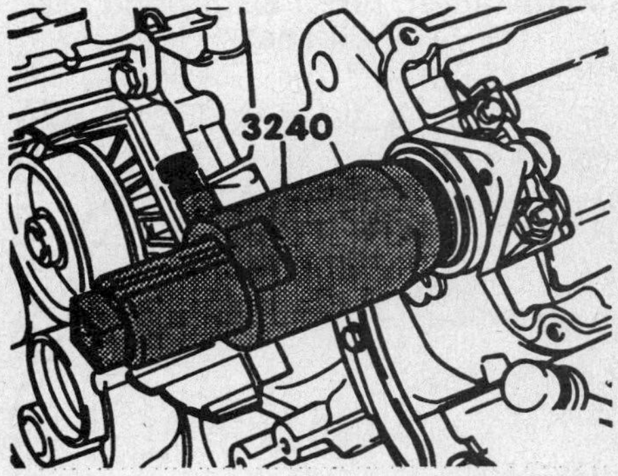

AD1069600032000X

Fig. 12 Camshaft oil seal removal. Front oil seal

2. Remove righthand or lefthand cylinder head cover, then the Camshaft Position (CMP) sensor housing on lefthand cylinder head or vacuum pump on righthand cylinder head, if equipped.
3. Remove timing belt sprocket from camshaft, then bearing caps 2 and 3, **Figs. 10 and 11. Be sure to mark bearing caps to be reinstalled in original positions.**
4. Loosen bearing caps 1 and 4 alternately in a diagonal sequence, then remove.
5. Remove camshaft.
6. Reverse procedure to install, noting the following:
   a. Tighten bearing caps 1 and 4 alternately in a diagonal sequence to specifications.
   b. Install bearing caps 2 and 3 and tighten nuts and bolts to specifications.

CAMSHAFT SEALS

REPLACE

Front

This procedure has been revised by a Technical Service Bulletin.

1. Remove timing belt as outlined under "Timing Belt, Replace."
2. Remove cylinder head cover, then the rear timing belt guard.
3. Remove seal using seal extractor tool No. 3240, or equivalent, **Fig. 12,** being careful not to score sealing surface.
4. When installing a new seal, do not lubricate seal lips with grease. Grease will fill the micro groove wipers of seal lips and leakage will result.
5. Clean bearing and sealing surfaces. **Lubricate sealing lip and oil seal with engine oil only. Do not use grease.**
6. Press lefthand front seal in as far as stop using seal installer tool No. 3241, or equivalent, **Fig. 13.**
7. Install pulling sleeve onto righthand front camshaft, then press seal in flush using seal installer tool No. 3241, or equivalent.
8. Install rear timing belt guard, then the cylinder head cover.
9. Install timing belt as outlined under "Timing Belt, Replace."

Rear

LEFTHAND

1. Remove camshaft position (CMP) sensor housing, turn bolt out of CMP plate, then pry CMP plate out of cylinder head carefully using a suitable screwdriver.
2. Screw in counter holder for seal extractor tool No. 2085-1, or equivalent, **Fig. 14,** then remove seal using seal extractor tool No. 3240 or 2085, or equivalent, **Fig. 15.**
3. When installing a new seal, do not lubricate seal lips with grease. That would fill the micro groove wipers of seal lips and leakage will result.
4. Clean bearing and sealing surfaces. **Lubricate sealing lip and oil seal with engine oil only. Do not use grease.**

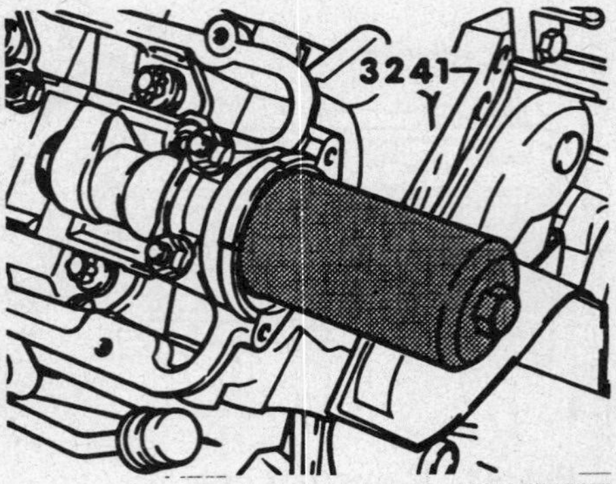

Fig. 13 Camshaft oil seal installation. Front & lefthand rear oil seal

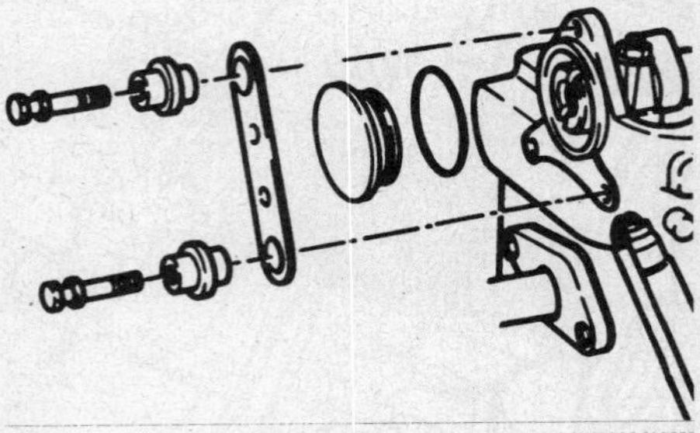

Fig. 16 Camshaft righthand rear oil seal removal. Less vacuum pump

5. Press seal in as far as stop using seal installer tool No. 3241, or equivalent, **Fig. 13.**

RIGHTHAND

1. **On models less vacuum pump,** remove bolts, spacer, cap locking device, cap and O-ring, **Fig. 16.**
2. **On models equipped with vacuum pump, Fig. 17,** remove vacuum pump or end cover, then the transfer flange.
3. **On all models,** pull piston out of camshaft, then replace O-ring seals "A," "B," "C," and "D," **Fig. 17.**
4. **On all models,** reverse procedure to install.

CRANKSHAFT SEAL

REPLACE

Rear

This procedure has been revised by a Technical Service Bulletin.

1. Remove transaxle from vehicle.
2. Remove clutch disc and flywheel or flexplate.
3. Remove seal using extractor tool No. 10-221, or equivalent, **Fig. 18.**
4. When installing a new seal, do not lubricate seal lips with grease. Grease will fill the micro groove wipers of seal lips and leakage will result.
5. Clean bearing and sealing surfaces. **Lubricate sealing lip and oil seal with engine oil only. Do not use grease.**

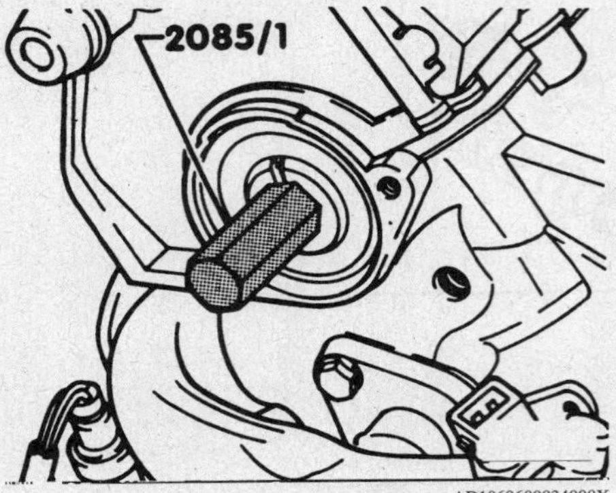

Fig. 14 Counter holder installation. Camshaft lefthand rear oil seal

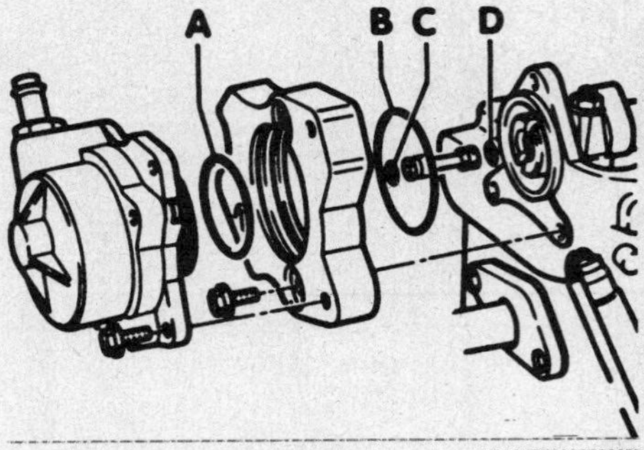

Fig. 17 Camshaft righthand rear oil seal removal. With vacuum pump

6. Press in seal as far as stop using installation tool No. 2003-3, or equivalent, and bolts of flywheel or flexplate, **Fig. 19.**
7. Install clutch disc, flywheel or flexplate and transaxle as outlined under "Transaxle, Replace" in "Clutch & Manual Transaxle" or "Automatic Transaxle."

Front

1. Remove timing belt as outlined under "Timing Belt, Replace."
2. Remove timing belt sprocket from crankshaft.
3. Remove seal using seal extractor tool No. 3203, or equivalent, **Fig. 20. Do not score sealing surface.**
4. Clean bearing and sealing surfaces. **Lubricate sealing lip and oil seal with engine oil only. Do not use grease.**
5. Slide seal over tool No. 3202-1 from retractor tool No. 3202, or equivalents, then press in seal flush using installer tool No. 3265, or equivalent, **Fig. 21,** and install center crankshaft bolt.
6. Install timing belt sprocket and timing belt as outlined under "Timing Belt, Replace."

OIL PUMP

REPLACE

1. Remove oil dipstick, then drain engine oil.

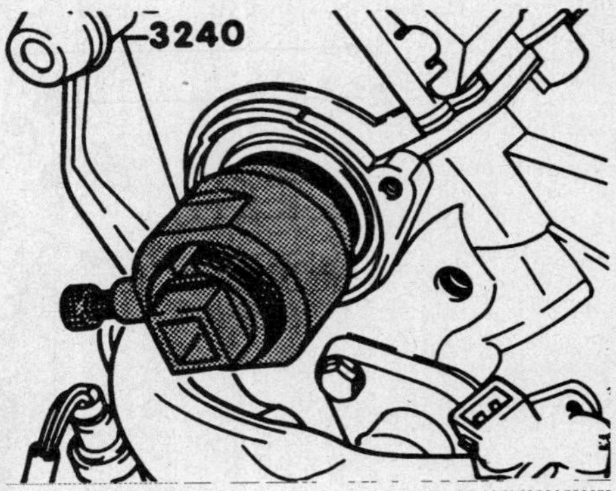

Fig. 15 Camshaft oil seal removal. Lefthand rear oil seal

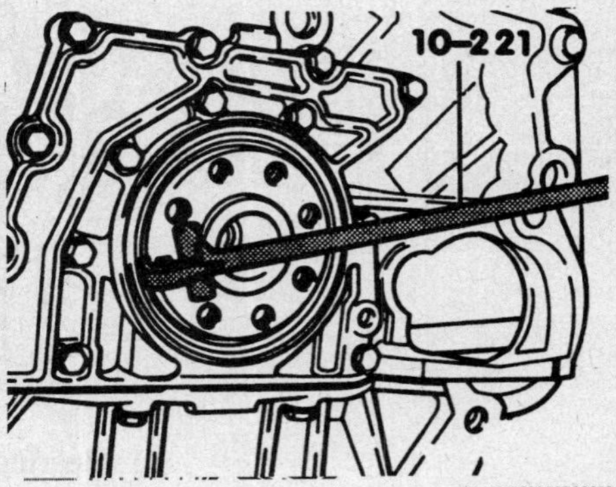

Fig. 18 Rear crankshaft seal removal

2. Remove upper and lower sections of oil pan, then remove timing belt as outlined under "Timing Belt, Replace."
3. Remove timing belt tensioning and idler from oil pump, then limiter and oil pump.
4. Reverse procedure to install. Ensure drive dog on crankshaft engages oil pump.

COOLING SYSTEM BLEED

A4 & S4

This procedure has been revised by a Technical Service Bulletin.

1. Close drain plugs at engine block and bottom lefthand side of radiator.
2. Push on connection flange of coolant hose at bottom of radiator, and install locking element for connection flange.
3. Unscrew cap on expansion tank, then screw on adapter flange tool No. VAG 1274-1, or equivalent, and extend with an auxiliary hose.
4. Open hose clamp, pull back coolant hose so vent hole is not concealed by connection.
5. Open bleed screw on coolant pipe below expansion tank
6. **Note type of coolant. Do not allow red coolant to be mixed with any other type.**
7. Pour coolant into system tank, while observing bleeder screw.

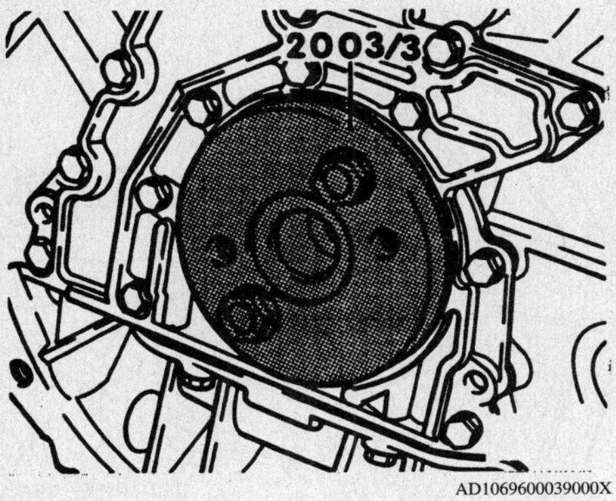

Fig. 19 Rear crankshaft seal installation

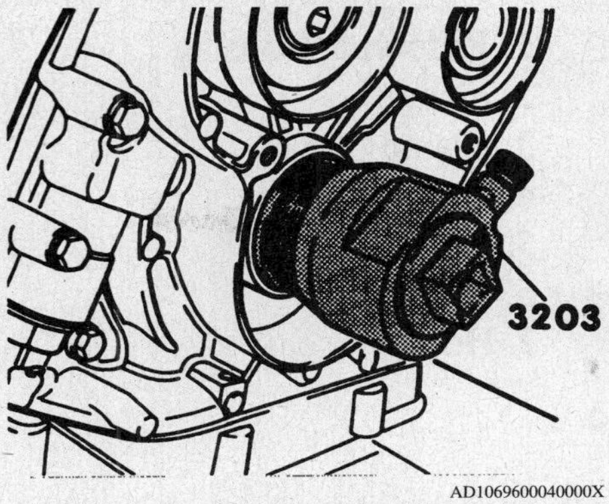

Fig. 20 Front crankshaft seal removal

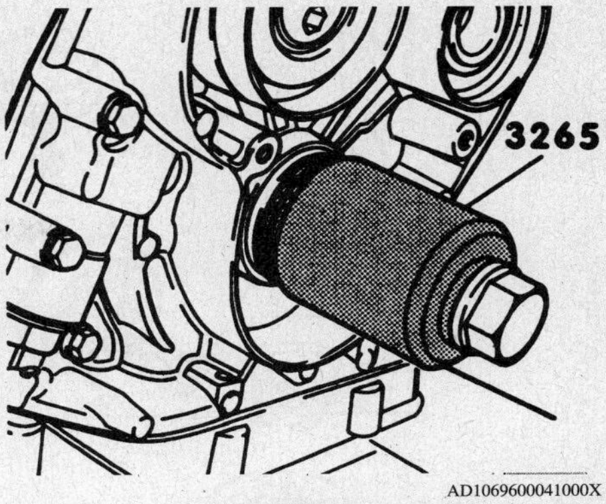

Fig. 21 Front crankshaft seal installation

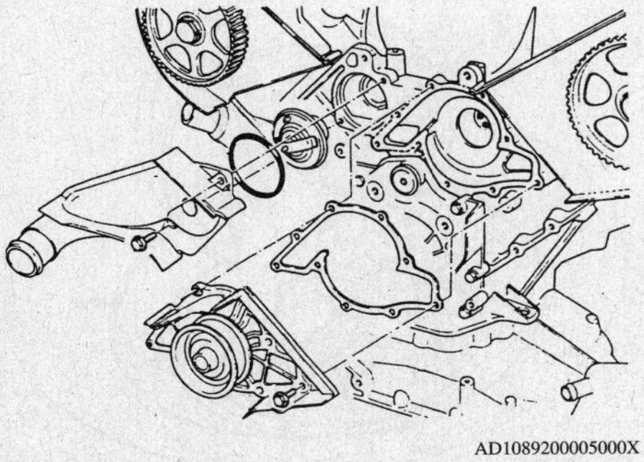

Fig. 22 Water pump replacement

8. Tighten bleeder screw as soon as coolant runs out.
9. Continue filling system until level reaches vent hole, then install coolant hose and tighten.
10. Close cap on expansion tank and set heater controls to Hot position.
11. Run engine at idle until radiator fan has come on once, then increase engine speed to 2000 RPM for about three minutes.
12. Continue running engine at idle until radiator becomes hot at bottom connection.
13. Turn engine off and inspect coolant level in expansion tank. Add coolant as required.

Except A4 & S4

This procedure has been revised by a Technical Service Bulletin.

1. Loosen bleeder screws, one under water tray cover at lefthand side next to blower and other in large water pipe at lefthand side next to temperature sensor.
2. **Note type of coolant. Do not allow red coolant to be mixed with any other type.**
3. Pour coolant into expansion tank, while observing bleeder screws.
4. Tighten bleeder screws as soon as coolant runs out.
5. Continue filling expansion tank until level reaches edge, then install cap on tank.
6. Run engine at idle until radiator fan has come on once, then increase engine speed to 2000 RPM for about 30 seconds.
7. Turn engine off, then inspect coolant level in expansion tank and top off as required.

THERMOSTAT

REPLACE

This procedure has been revised by a Technical Service Bulletin.

1. Remove timing belt as outlined under "Timing Belt, Replace."
2. Drain coolant into suitable container.
3. Remove thermostat housing, then the thermostat.
4. Reverse procedure to install, noting the following:
   a. **Note type of coolant. Do not allow red coolant to be mixed with any other type.**
   b. Ensure thermostat vent valve faces upward.

WATER PUMP

REPLACE

This procedure has been revised by a Technical Service Bulletin.

1. Drain cooling system into suitable container.
2. Remove serpentine drive belt and timing belt as outlined under "Timing Belt, Replace."
3. Remove water pump retaining bolts, then water pump and gasket **Fig. 22.**
4. Reverse procedure to install. **Note type of coolant. Do not allow red coolant to be mixed with any other type.**

RADIATOR

REPLACE

This procedure has been revised by a Technical Service Bulletin.

1. Drain cooling system.
2. Unscrew viscous fan from bearing, then pull rearward into shroud.
3. Remove shroud and viscous fan assembly.
4. Disconnect radiator hoses.
5. Remove electric cooling fan and shroud assembly.
6. Disconnect radiator air ducts.

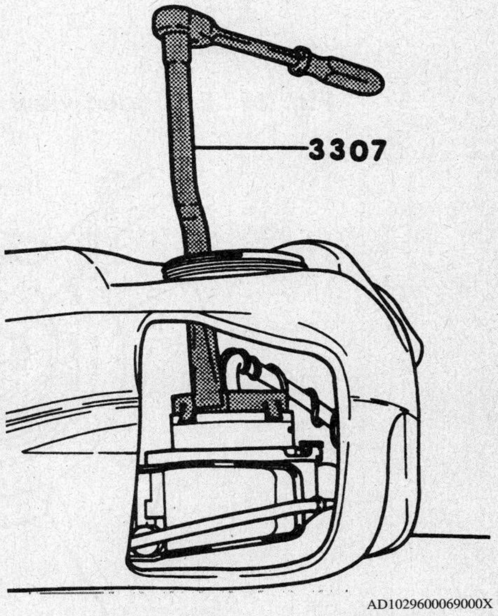

Fig. 23 Fuel pump wrench installation. A4 & S4

7. Remove radiator attaching nuts, then the radiator.
8. Reverse procedure to install. Note type of coolant. Do not allow red coolant to be mixed with any other type.

FUEL PUMP

REPLACE

A4 & S4

Fuel tank should be no more than ⅔ full when replacing pump.

1. Obtain radio anti-theft protection code as outlined under "Precautions."
2. Remove cover for fuel pump module flange located under luggage compartment trim.
3. Disconnect blue fuel supply and return lines, then loosen sealing ring using tool No. 3217, or equivalent.
4. Pull flange out and remove, then disconnect fuel level sensor and remove.
5. Install fuel pump wrench tool No. 3307, or equivalent through fuel tank opening and position at inner fuel reservoir housing, **Fig. 23.**

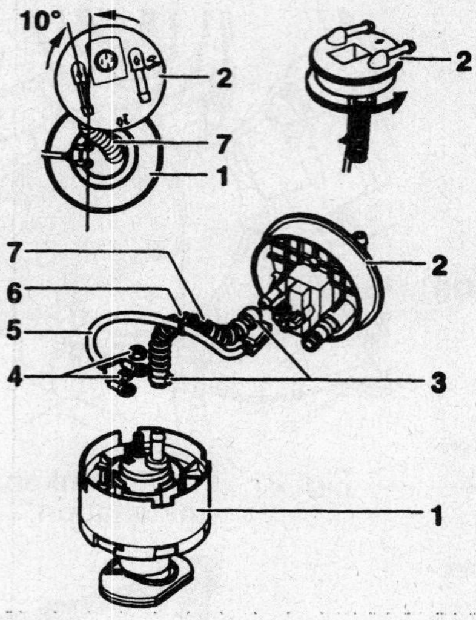

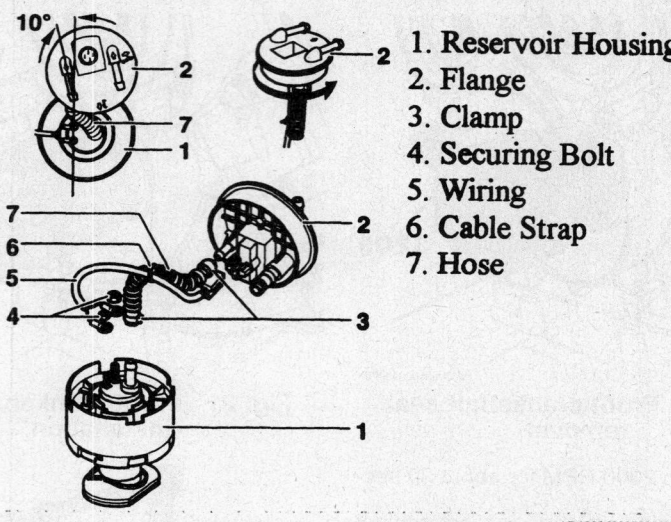

1. Reservoir Housing
2. Flange
3. Clamp
4. Securing Bolt
5. Wiring
6. Cable Strap
7. Hose

AD1029600070000X

Fig. 24 Exploded view of fuel pump assembly. A4 & S4

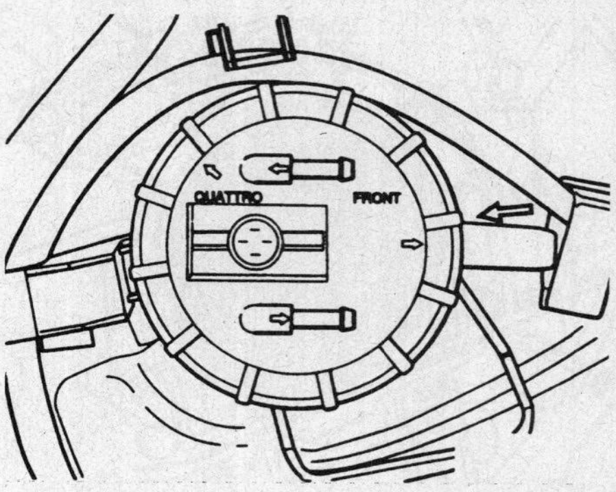

AD1029600071000X

Fig. 25 Flange installation. A4 & S4

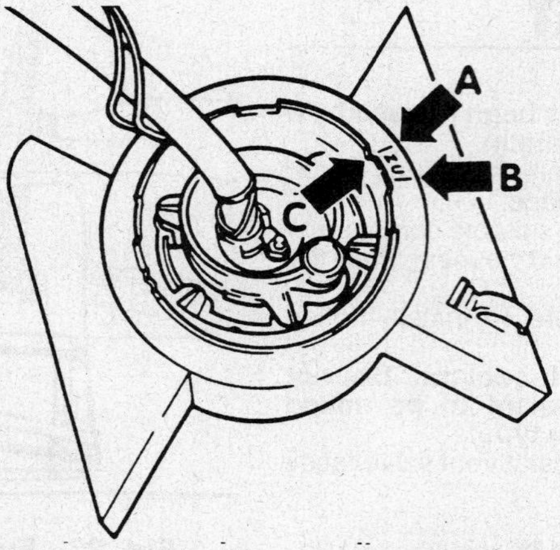

AD1029100001000X

Fig. 26 Fuel pump alignment. A6

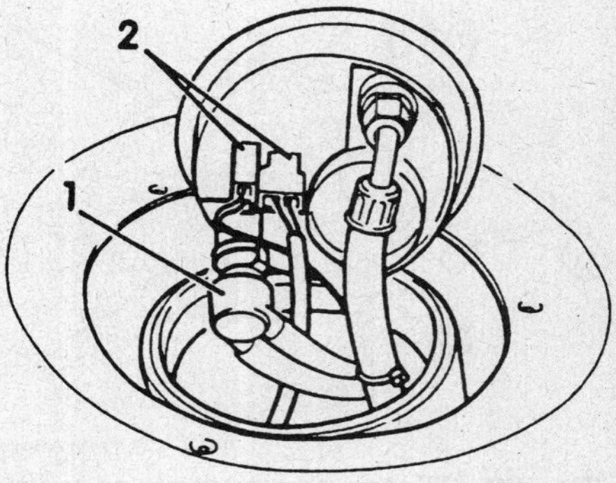

AD1029100002000X

Fig. 27 Fuel pump flange assembly. Cabriolet

6. Turn inner part of reservoir housing counterclockwise 15°, then remove fuel pump with inner part of reservoir housing.
7. Reverse procedure to install, noting the following:
   a. Install fuel pump hose and wiring into position, **Fig. 24.**
   b. When installing flange, turn in direction illustrated in **Fig. 24.**
   c. **On AWD models,** turn flange until arrows marked "QUATTRO" are aligned, **Fig. 25.**
   d. **On FWD models,** turn flange until arrows marked "FRONT" are aligned, **Fig. 25.**
   e. **On AWD models,** wiring for fuel level sensor must be routed between fuel transfer pump line and fuel tank housing.
   f. **On FWD models,** wiring for fuel level sensor must be routed between fuel return line and fuel tank housing.

A6

Fuel tank should be no more than ⅔ full when replacing pump.

1. Obtain radio anti-theft protection code as outlined under "Precautions."
2. Remove fuel gauge sender cover located under luggage compartment trim, then disconnect electrical connector for fuel gauge and fuel pump.
3. Disconnect fuel supply, return and vent hoses, then loosen retainer using tool No. 3087, or equivalent, and pull sender out of tank. **Note angle of fuel level sender for installation reference.**
4. Disconnect supply and return hoses from inside of sender housing, then the fuel pump electrical connector.
5. Turn pump housing counterclockwise approximately. 590 inch using wrench tool No. 3214, or equivalent, then pull pump out upward.
6. Reverse procedure to install, noting the following:
   a. Place fuel pump in housing so that V mark "C"is aligned with mark "A," **Fig. 26.**
   b. Rotate fuel pump clockwise using wrench tool No. 3214, or equivalent, until V mark "C" aligns with mark "B," **Fig. 26,** locked position.

Cabriolet

REMOVAL

1. Obtain radio anti-theft protection code as outlined under "Precautions."
2. Remove screws and fuel gauge sender cover located under luggage compartment trim, then disconnect fuel gauge and pump electrical connector from outer side of flange assembly.
3. Wrap fuel lines in a suitable shop towel, then slowly open fuel lines to bleed off residual pressure, then disconnect fuel lines.
4. Note position of alignment marks on tank and flange for later assembly.
5. Unscrew nut from flange assembly and fuel tank using collar nut tool No. 3217, or equivalent.
6. Disconnect fuel lines and electrical connector from inner side of flange assembly.
7. Remove fuel level sender by pressing release catch on side of sender unit, then lifting sender from tank.
8. Insert fuel pump wrench tool No. 3307,

or equivalent through tank opening and place on inner part of surge housing.

9. Rotate inner part of surge housing approximately 15° and lift out fuel pump.

INSTALLATION

1. Install fuel pump with upper section of surge housing so that notch C aligns with mark A on upper part of housing **Fig. 26.**
2. Apply fuel pump wrench tool No. 3307, or equivalent and rotate upper section of housing to righthand stop. Align marks C and B.
3. Push fuel return line (1), **Fig. 27,** onto flange assembly until clamp latches to flange pin.
4. **On FWD models,** connect fuel sending unit harness connector to inner side of flange assembly so that wiring lies over fuel supply line and does not interfere with level sensor operation, **Fig. 27.**
5. **On Quattro models,** connect fuel sending unit harness connector to flange assembly so that wiring lies over fuel return line and does not interfere with level sensor operation.
6. **On all models,** install flange assembly to tank, note alignment marks, then install collar nut and tighten using collar nut wrench tool No. 3217, or equivalent.
7. Install fuel lines and electrical connector to outer side of flange assembly.
8. Install fuel gauge sender cover located under luggage compartment trim.

TIGHTENING SPECIFICATIONS

Year	Component	Torque/Ft. Lbs.
1998–2001	A/C Compressor To Bracket	18
	Alternator To Mounting Bracket①	28
	Alternator To Mounting Bracket, M8 Bolts②	18
	Alternator To Mounting Bracket, M10 Bolts②	33
	Camshaft Bearing Cap Nut	13
	Camshaft Position Sensor Housing Bolts	84⑥
	Camshaft Sprocket Bolt①	22③
	Camshaft Sprocket Bolt②	52
	Connecting Rod Bearing Cap Bolts	22④
	Coolant Bleed Screw Mounting Bolts②	11
	Coolant Hose Mounting Bolts②	84⑥
	Crankshaft Center Bolt	148③
	Cylinder Head Bolts	⑤
	Drive Plate Bolts	44④
	Engine Coolant Temperature (ECT) Sensor Mounting Bolts②	11
	Engine Support To Engine Mount①	33
	Engine To Transaxle, M6 Bolts①	84⑥
	Engine To Transaxle, M8 Bolts①	15
	Engine To Transaxle, M8 Bolts②	18
	Engine To Transaxle, M10 Bolts	33
	Engine To Transaxle, M12 Bolts①	44
	EVAP Canister Mounting Nut	84⑥
	Exhaust Pipe To Manifold	18
	Flywheel Bolts	30③
	Fuel Supply Line To Fuel Level Sensor②	15
	Hydraulic Pump To Bracket①	18
	Idler Pulley Bolt	18
	Intake Manifold To Cylinder Head Mounting Bolts②	15
	Large Coolant Hose To Cylinder Block②	84⑥
	Lefthand Engine Support To Side Member②	33
	Lock Carrier 6 x 20 Bolts①	33⑥
	Lock Carrier 8 x 45 Bolts①	84⑥
	Main Bearing Cap Bolts	44③
	Oil Dipstick Tube Bracket Mounting Bolt	84⑥
	Oil Pan Mounting Bolts	84⑥
	Oil Pan Drain Plug	30
	Oil Pump Mounting Bolts	84⑥
	Rear Cover Mounting Bolts	84⑥
	Serpentine Drive Belt Tensioner Bolt	41
	Thermostat Housing Mounting Bolts	84⑥
	Three Way Catalytic Converter To Exhaust Manifold②	18
	Timing Belt Lower Cover Bolt	84⑥
	Timing Belt Tensioner Bolt	33
	Torque Converter To Flexplate①	26
	Torque Converter To Flexplate②	22
	Valve Cover Bolts	84⑥
	Viscous Coupling Bracket①	33
	Water Pump Mounting Bolts	84⑥

① — A4 models.
② — A6 models.
③ — Plus ½ turn.
④ — Plus ¼ turn.
⑤ — Refer to "Cylinder Head, Replace" for tightening procedure.
⑥ — Inch lbs.

3.7L & 4.2L Engines

NOTE: On Air Bag Equipped Models, Refer To "Air Bag System Precautions" Located In The Front Of This Manual For System Disarming & Arming Procedures.

NOTE: Refer To "Computer Relearn Procedures" Located In The Front Of This Manual When Battery Power To The Computer Has Been Interrupted.

INDEX

	Page No.
Camshaft, Replace	1-50
Compression Pressure	1-47
Cooling System Bleed	1-51
Crankshaft Seal, Replace	1-50
Front	1-50
Rear	1-51
Cylinder Head, Replace	1-49
Engine Rebuilding Specifications	1-231
Engine, Replace	1-47
Exhaust Manifold, Replace	1-48
Fuel Filter, Replace	1-51
Fuel Pump, Replace	1-51
Intake Manifold, Replace	1-48
Oil Pan, Replace	1-51
Oil Pump, Replace	1-51
Precautions	1-47
Air Bag Systems	1-47
Battery Ground Cable	1-47
Radio Coded Anti-Theft System	1-47
Radiator, Replace	1-51
Serpentine Drive Belt	1-51
Thermostat, Replace	1-51
Tightening Specifications	1-52
Timing Belt, Replace	1-49
Valve Adjustment	1-49
Valve Clearance Specifications	1-49
Valve Guides	1-49
Inspection	1-49
Replacement	1-49
Water Pump, Replace	1-51

PRECAUTIONS

Air Bag Systems

Refer to "Air Bag System Precautions" in the front of this manual for system disarming and arming procedures.

Battery Ground Cable

Prior to service, disconnect battery ground cable and isolate as required.

Radio Coded Anti-Theft System

Prior to disconnecting the battery or removing the radio, obtain the security code from the vehicle operator. Refer to the owner's manual for security code disarming and arming procedures.

COMPRESSION PRESSURE

1. Perform compression test with engine at operating temperature, spark plugs removed, oil temperature above 86°F and throttle wide open.
2. Remove fuse No. 1 from No. 4 fuse panel, behind righthand kick panel.
3. Compression should be 145–220 psi with a maximum difference between cylinders of 44 psi. Minimum compression should be 110 psi.

ENGINE

REPLACE

1. Disconnect and remove battery.
2. Remove intake air grill attaching screw and grill.
3. Remove sound insulation panel.
4. Remove bumper attaching bolts at lefthand and righthand sides and bumper.
5. **On models equipped with headlamp washers,** detach hose to jets on bumper in righthand side air grille.
6. **On all models,** drain coolant at bottom lefthand of radiator.
7. Remove intake air duct between air cleaner and throttle body.
8. Remove engine cover, then coolant hose clamps at righthand side belt guard.
9. Remove electronics box cover by removing seven bolts.
10. Disconnect all connectors from ECM and TCM at bulkhead.
11. Remove cruise control module with relay and fuse bracket.
12. Remove sealing strip between engine compartment and plenum chamber.
13. Cut open cable tie straps at engine wiring harness.
14. Remove wiring harness from plenum panel.
15. Remove spacer sleeves, expose wiring and place down on engine.
16. Disconnect vacuum line to brake booster unit.
17. Disconnect vacuum line at cruise control module.
18. Disconnect accelerator pedal cable and expose.
19. Disconnect coolant lines to heater core at vent valves.
20. Disconnect HO_2S connectors on lefthand and righthand sides, then push out of holder
21. Unbolt ignition power output stage.
22. Remove top part of air cleaner.
23. Disconnect harness connector at MAF sensor.
24. Expose cable to engine.
25. Remove coolant vent line to expansion tank at radiator.
26. Remove coolant supply line at expansion tank.
27. Remove hydraulic reservoir.
28. Disconnect vacuum line for intake manifold changeover valve, located at front lefthand headlamp.
29. Disconnect lefthand and righthand knock sensor connectors at fuel rail.
30. Cut open cable tie straps.
31. Disconnect harness connectors at fuel injectors.
32. Remove fuel rail together with fuel injectors and place down to side.
33. Cover openings to engine with clean cloths.
34. Remove one bolt each side from exhaust pipes to exhaust manifolds.
35. Remove crossmember attaching bolts and crossmember.
36. Loosen double clamp and remove Three Way Catalytic Converter (TWC).
37. Disconnect exhaust system at retaining loop and remove.
38. Remove exhaust pipes from exhaust manifold.
39. Remove TWC bracket along with spring.
40. Remove TWC along with front pipe.
41. Remove heat shield above three way catalytic converter.
42. Remove heat shield for selector lever cable at transaxle pan.
43. **On Quattro models,** mark alignment of driveshaft to transaxle output shaft, then disconnect driveshaft and support with wire.
44. **On all models,** disconnect and remove selector lever cable at bracket.
45. Remove lefthand and righthand drive axles.
46. Remove lefthand drive axle shield.
47. Disconnect starter cable connector at junction box on righthand side of long member.
48. Unclip and remove junction box cover.

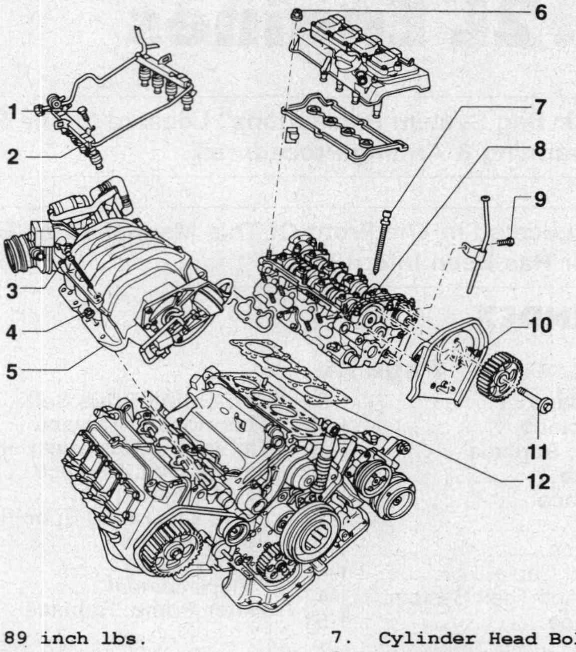

1. 89 inch lbs.
2. Fuel Rail
3. 15 ft. lbs.
4. 15 ft. lbs.
5. Two-Stage Intake Manifold
6. 89 inch lbs.
7. Cylinder Head Bolts
8. Cylinder Head
9. 89 inch lbs.
10. 89 inch lbs.
11. 41 ft. lbs.
12. Cylinder Head Gasket

AD1069900077000X

Fig. 1 Cylinder head removal

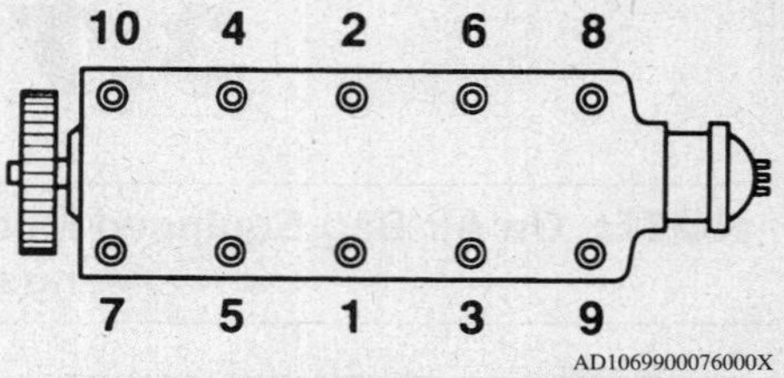

Fig. 2 Cylinder head bolt loosening sequence

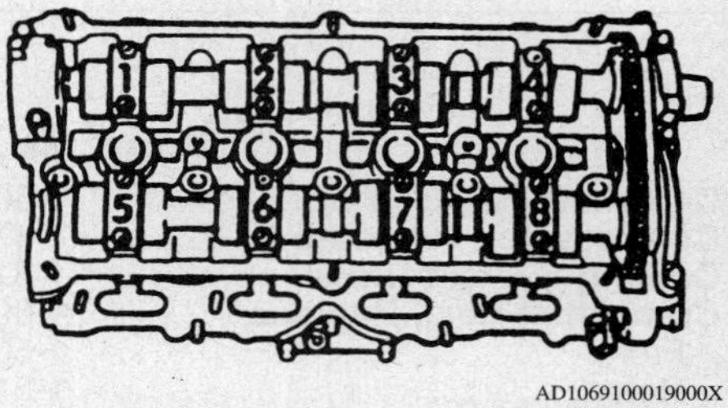

Fig. 3 Camshaft bearing caps removal

49. Disconnect electrical connectors.
50. Disconnect starter cable in junction box and at bracket.
51. Remove alternator air guide.
52. Place suitable catch pan under bottom righthand corner of radiator at transaxle cooler, then disconnect ATF lines.
53. Remove coolant hose at bottom righthand of radiator.
54. Disconnect Engine Coolant Temperature (ECT) sensor above coolant hose.
55. Remove torque support attaching bolts.
56. Remove radiator air guide bolts and guides from lefthand and righthand sides.
57. Disconnect high pressure switch electrical connector.
58. Disconnect lefthand and righthand headlamp electrical connectors.
59. Remove lefthand headlamp.
60. Unclip outside temperature sensor at bottom front of radiator, then cut open cable clip and expose cable.
61. Unbolt cooling loop for power steering fluid and place aside.
62. Detach A/C condenser and tie up to side.
63. Disconnect coolant fan electrical harness.
64. Cut open cable tie straps.
65. Remove hood supports at both front fenders.
66. Remove lock carrier bolts located below hood support.
67. Unbolt impact absorbers for bumper on lefthand and righthand sides.
68. Remove lock carrier along with radiator.
69. Loosen drive belt by pulling firmly down in middle by hand and install drift tool No. 3204, or equivalent.
70. Remove drive belt.
71. Unbolt power steering pump belt pulley.
72. Secure washers on shaft with bolt if required.
73. Remove hydraulic pump from mounting bracket and place down at side member.
74. Remove A/C compressor leaving lines connected and secure aside.
75. Remove torque support with bonded rubber bushing at lefthand front of engine.
76. Raise transaxle using suitable transaxle hoist.
77. Remove righthand and lefthand transaxle mounts.
78. Remove lefthand transaxle support.
79. Lower and remove transaxle hoist.
80. Unbolt lefthand and righthand engine mounts.
81. Disconnect both gas struts at hood, then position hood in vertical position and support with auxiliary tool.
82. Install brackets tool No. VAG 3180, or equivalent on both rear engine lifting points.
83. Attach lifting device tool No. 3033, or equivalent to both brackets evenly.
84. Slide in assembly crane tool No. VAG 1202 A and attach lifting device tool No. 3033, or equivalents.
85. Raise engine carefully and pull out toward front.
86. Remove righthand engine support.
87. Lower engine with transaxle to work surface and continue to support weight with crane.
88. Place two old tires or equivalent, if required, under engine and transaxle as an aid in separating engine from transaxle.
89. Disconnect ground wires from engine.
90. Remove starter brackets.
91. Remove starter leaving electrical wiring connected.
92. Remove alternator with electrical wiring connected.
93. Remove transaxle electrical harness bracket and disconnect all electrical harness connectors from transaxle.
94. Remove A/C compressor and hydraulic pump bracket.
95. Remove lefthand engine support.
96. **On 4.2L engine,** remove six torque converter attaching bolts from flexplate and disconnect transaxle from engine.
97. **On 3.7L engine,** remove three torque converter attaching bolts from flexplate and disconnect transaxle from engine.
98. **On all engines,** attach engine to engine stand.
99. Reverse procedure to install. Tighten all nuts and bolts to specifications.

INTAKE MANIFOLD

REPLACE

Refer to "Cylinder Head Replace" for intake manifold replacement procedures.

EXHAUST MANIFOLD

REPLACE

1. Remove exhaust manifold to exhaust pipe retaining nuts.
2. Remove exhaust manifold attaching bolts.
3. Remove exhaust manifold and gasket.
4. Reverse procedure to install noting to

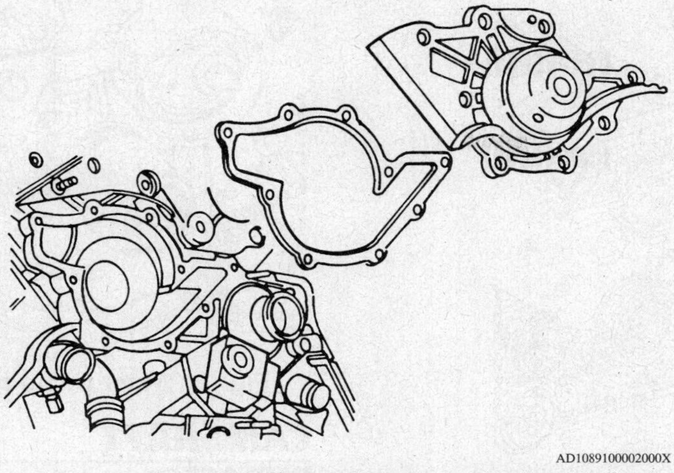

Fig. 4 Crankshaft front oil seal installation

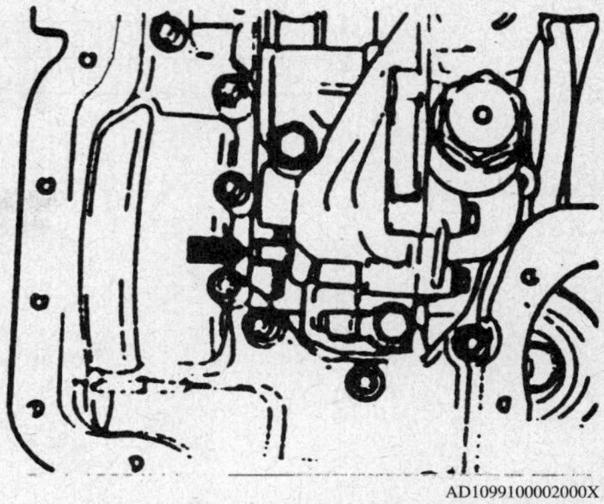

Fig. 5 Oil pump drive location

install manifold gaskets with metal side of gasket facing cylinder head.

CYLINDER HEAD

REPLACE

Avoid turning the camshaft or crankshaft when the timing belt has been removed. If movement is required, use extreme caution to avoid valve damage from piston contact.

1. Remove sound insulation panel.
2. Remove intake air grille in bumper.
3. Attach drain hose with ½ inch inside diameter to drain fitting at bottom of radiator.
4. Remove accessory drive belt.
5. Remove timing belt. Refer to "Timing Belt Replace."
6. Disconnect vacuum line to brake booster unit.
7. Disconnect vacuum line at cruise control module.
8. Disconnect accelerator pedal cable.
9. Disconnect coolant lines to heater core.
10. Disconnect lefthand and righthand knock sensor connectors at fuel rail and remove cable tie straps.
11. Disconnect fuel injector harness connectors.
12. Remove fuel rail with injectors and place aside, **Fig. 1.**
13. Remove intake manifold attaching bolts, then lift out manifold.
14. Disconnect ignition coil harness connectors.
15. Disconnect front exhaust pipe at top connection to exhaust manifold.
16. Disconnect coolant line at rear between cylinder heads and remove.
17. Remove cylinder head cover.
18. Remove oil dipstick guide tube if required.
19. Loosen cylinder head bolts in sequence, **Fig. 2,** then remove cylinder head.
20. Reverse procedure to install, noting the following:
    a. Clean all mating surfaces.
    b. Inspect cylinder head for distortion. Maximum allowable distortion is. 004 inch.
    c. Install new cylinder head gasket ensuring gasket surface marked "Top" is facing upward.
    d. Reverse loosening sequence outlined in **Fig. 2** and tighten cylinder head bolts in three steps. **Torque** bolts to 30 ft. lbs., then to 44 ft. lbs. and finally rotate an additional 180.°

VALVE CLEARANCE SPECIFICATIONS

This engine is equipped with hydraulic lifters. No provision for adjustment is provided.

VALVE ADJUSTMENT

This engine uses hydraulic valve lifters which are not adjustable. Noisy lifters may be replaced after the following inspection:

1. Run engine until radiator fan comes on at least once.
2. Raise engine speed to 2500 RPM, for two minutes.
3. If lifter(s) is still noisy, replace lifter(s) as required.

VALVE GUIDES

INSPECTION

1. Remove cylinder head as outlined under "Cylinder Head, Replace."
2. Remove hydraulic lifters, maintain order for installation reference.
3. Using a suitable valve spring compressor, remove valves from cylinder head. Maintain order for later assemble.
4. Remove all carbon deposits from valve guide.
5. Install a suitable dial indicator, set to bear against valve head on combustion chamber side of cylinder head to inspect suspected guide.
6. Insert new valve into valve guide until it is fully inserted into guide.
7. Rock valve back and forth against dial indicator.
8. Maximum clearance for intake valves is. 039 inch. Maximum clearance for exhaust valves is. 051 inch. Replace guide(s) if reading is beyond limit.

REPLACEMENT

1. Worn valve guides can be removed using rod tool No. 3121, or equivalent.
2. Press worn guides out from combustion chamber side. Use sleeve tool No. 3023, or equivalent during this procedure for proper support.
3. Coat new guides with engine oil, then press into cold cylinder head from camshaft side.
4. Press guides in until shoulder contact is made. Once valve guide is seated, do not use more than one ton of pressure, or guide shoulder may break.
5. Ream guides by hand using 7 MM reamer tool No. 3120, or equivalent and a proper cutting lubricant.

TIMING BELT

REPLACE

Avoid turning the camshaft or crankshaft when the timing belt has been removed. If movement is required, use extreme caution to avoid valve damage from piston contact.

1. Remove sound insulation panel.
2. Remove intake air grill from bumper.
3. Attach a drain hose with a ½ inch inside diameter to drain fitting at bottom lefthand side of radiator.
4. Drain engine coolant into a suitable container.
5. Loosen serpentine drive belt by placing a box end wrench on tensioner bracket and slowly push upward then remove belt. Refer to "Serpentine Drive Belt."
6. Remove engine cover.
7. Remove coolant hose clamp on righthand belt guard.
8. Remove air intake duct between air cleaner and throttle body.
9. Disconnect air shroud for viscous fan and electric coolant fan on radiator.
10. Disconnect viscous fan. Counterhold with two hold nut driver tool No. 3212, or equivalent.
11. Remove righthand front engine support mount.
12. Remove coolant hoses at engine.
13. Loosen coolant hose on upper righthand side of radiator and turn hose to right.

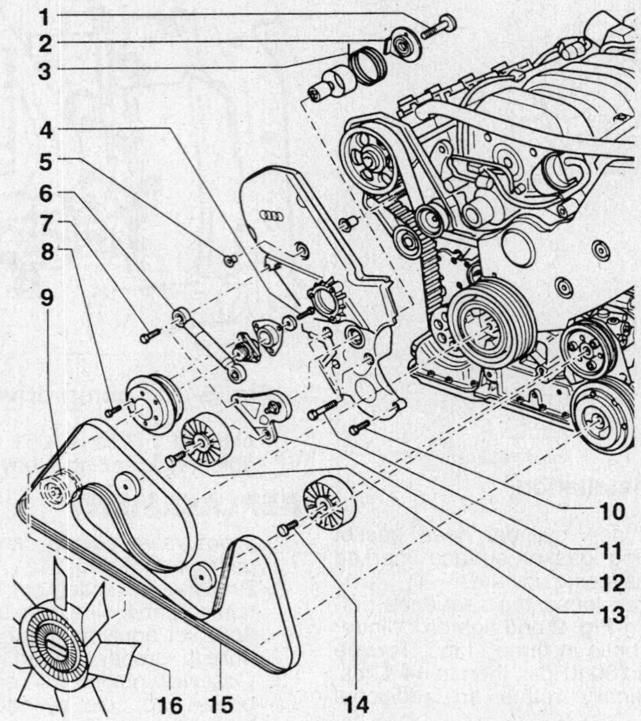

1.	26 ft lbs.	9.	Generator Pulley
2.	Retaining Plate	10.	18 ft. lbs.
3.	Torsion Spring	11.	33 ft. lbs.
4.	18 ft lbs.	12.	Hinged Mounting Bracket
5.	Flanged Nut	13.	M8x28 Bolt 18 ft. lbs.
6.	Damper	14.	M8x35 Bolt 18 ft. lbs.
7.	18 ft. lbs.	15.	Ribbed Belt
8.	18 ft. lbs.	16.	Viscous Fan

AD1069900078000X

Fig. 6 Serpentine drive belt removal

14. Loosen center bolt for vibration damper approximately one turn. Counterhold using counterhold tool No. 3197, or equivalent.
15. Rotate crankshaft to align TDC marks on vibration damper.
16. Remove camshaft position sensor housing at rear of lefthand cylinder head. **If camshaft position sensor is not positioned behind sensor plate window, rotate crankshaft 360.°**
17. Remove camshaft flange at rear of righthand cylinder head.
18. Disconnect harness connector from switch for intake manifold change over valve.
19. Remove belt guard.
20. Unclip cap at guide pulley for ribbed belt at righthand belt guard.
21. Remove top of air cleaner housing.
22. Remove righthand side belt guard mounting bolts, then lift belt guard up and out.
23. Hold camshaft sprocket with holder tool No. 3036, or equivalent.
24. Loosen camshaft sprocket bolts.
25. Remove camshaft position sensor plate and housing from lefthand head.
26. Install camshaft locking device tool No. 3341, or equivalent at rear of each cylinder head.
27. Remove cylinder head cover and turn camshaft using wrench on hex shaped end of intake camshaft.
28. Turn camshaft using holder tool No. 3036, or equivalent.
29. Using 2-hole nut turner tool No. V/159, or equivalent, loosen eccentric tensioning roller and turn to lowest point.
30. Compress drive belt damper by hand and remove tensioning roller.
31. Remove belt from camshaft sprockets.
32. Lightly strike edge of camshaft sprockets with plastic hammer to loosen from tapered ends of camshafts.
33. Remove four screws fastening vibration damper to drive belt sprocket, remove center bolt and remove vibration damper.
34. Reverse procedure to install, noting the following:
    a. To set basic adjustment of belt tensioner, turn eccentric insert of tensioning roller clockwise using two hole nut turner tool No. V/159, or equivalent.
    b. Adjust position of tensioning roller until damper length is within 5.35–5.47 inches cold and 4.96–5.08 inches warm.
    c. Tighten tension roller to specifications.

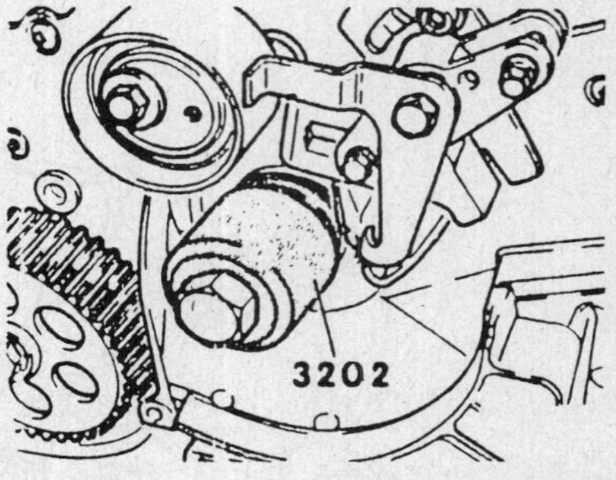

AD1099100003000X

Fig. 7 Water pump removal

CAMSHAFT

REPLACE

Avoid turning the camshaft or crankshaft when the timing belt has been removed. If movement is required, use extreme caution to avoid valve damage from piston contact.

1. Remove timing belt as outlined under "Timing Belt, Replace."
2. Remove valve cover.
3. Remove camshaft sprocket.
4. Remove exhaust camshaft as follows:
    a. Remove distributor intermediate flange and bearing cap.
    b. Remove bearing caps Nos. 2, 3 and bearing cap in front of chain, **Fig. 3.**
    c. Loosen bearing caps Nos. 1 and 4 alternately and in diagonal sequence.
5. Remove intake camshaft as follows:
    a. Remove bearing caps Nos. 6 and 7.
    b. Loosen bearing caps Nos. 5 and 8 alternately and in a diagonal sequence.
6. Install camshafts with chain so markings on chain sprockets are aligned facing center of engine.
7. Install bearing caps Nos. 5 and 8 on intake camshaft and **torque** to 11 ft. lbs. alternately and in a diagonal sequence.
8. Install bearing caps Nos. 1 and 4 on exhaust camshaft and **torque** to 11 ft. lbs. alternately and in a diagonal sequence.
9. Install remaining bearing cap and tighten to specifications.

CRANKSHAFT SEAL

REPLACE

FRONT

1. Remove timing belt as outlined under "Timing Belt, Replace."
2. Remove vibration dampener.
3. Remove oil seal using seal extractor tool No. 3203, or equivalent.
4. Lightly coat new oil seal with oil then using tool No. 3202, or equivalent, press seal ring in place, **Fig. 4.**

REAR

1. Remove engine as outlined under "Engine, Replace."
2. Remove flexplate.
3. Pry seal ring from cylinder block using extractor hook tool No. 10-221, or equivalent.
4. Completely press seal ring in place using seal installer tool No. 2003, or equivalent.

OIL PAN

REPLACE

1. Remove engine as outlined under "Engine, Replace."
2. Mount engine in a suitable holding fixture or engine stand.
3. Remove dipstick, then drain engine oil.
4. Remove oil pan retaining bolts, then oil pan.
5. Reverse procedure to install, noting the following:
   a. Ensure all sealing surfaces are clean before installing new gasket.
   b. Tighten oil pan bolts to specifications.

OIL PUMP

REPLACE

1. Remove oil pan as outlined under "Oil Pan, Replace."
2. Rotate engine in holding fixture until opening of oil pump drive points downward, **Fig. 5.**
3. Remove oil pump bolts, then oil pump pulling out downward.
4. Reverse procedure to install. Tighten bolts to specifications.

SERPENTINE DRIVE BELT

Refer to **Fig. 6,** for serpentine drive belt routing.

COOLING SYSTEM BLEED

This procedure has been revised by a Technical Service Bulletin.

Note type of coolant. Do not allow red coolant to be mixed with any other type.

These engines do not require a specified bleed procedure. After filling cooling system, run engine to operating temperature with radiator/pressure cap off. Air will then be automatically bled through cap opening.

THERMOSTAT

REPLACE

1. Drain cooling system to below thermostat level.
2. Remove coolant intake hose from engine.
3. Remove thermostat housing.
4. Remove thermostat.
5. Reverse procedure to install, noting to install thermostat with vent valve facing upward.

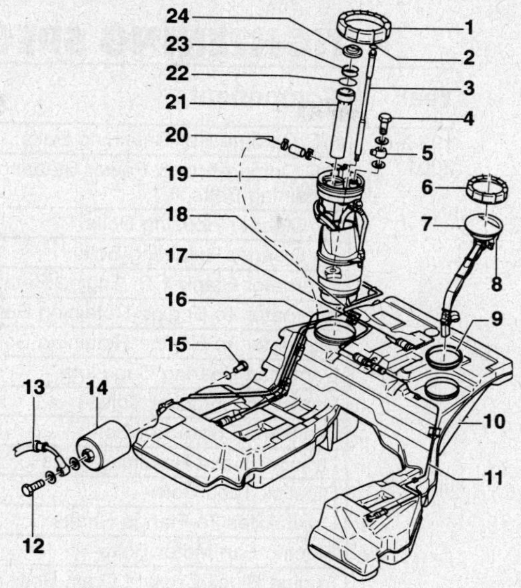

1. Lock Ring
2. O-ring
3. Mounting Tube
4. Banjo Bolt
5. Fuel Supply Line
6. Lock Ring
7. Alignment Marking
8. Lefthand Side Fuel Level Sensor
9. Seal
10. Fuel Tank
11. Vent Line
12. Banjo Bolt
13. Fuel Supply Line
14. Fuel Filter
15. Banjo Bolt
16. Vent Line
17. Vent Line
18. Vent Line For Fuel Filling
19. Fuel Pump With Integrated Reservoir & Fuel Level Sensor
20. Return Line
21. Righthand Side Fuel Gauge Sensor
22. Seal
23. Compression Spring
24. Fuel Gauge Sensor Cover

AD1069900079000X

Fig. 8 Fuel pump replacement

WATER PUMP

REPLACE

This procedure has been revised by a Technical Service Bulletin.

1. Drain coolant into suitable container.
2. Remove serpentine drive belt and serpentine drive belt tensioner.
3. Remove water pump attaching bolts, then the water pump, **Fig. 7.**
4. Reverse procedure to install. **Note type of coolant. Do not allow red coolant to be mixed with any other type.**

RADIATOR

REPLACE

Refer to "Engine Replace" for radiator replacement procedures.

FUEL PUMP

REPLACE

1. Remove luggage compartment trim.
2. Remove cover for fuel pump and fuel level sensor.
3. Disconnect electrical harness connector for fuel pump and fuel level sensor.
4. Relieve system pressure by carefully opening fuel supply line.
5. Disconnect fuel supply and fuel return lines, **Fig. 8.**
6. Open fuel level sensor cover by turning clockwise using cover removal tool No. 2012A, or equivalent, then remove compression spring.
7. Lift sensor and disconnect electrical harness connector using suitable pliers.
8. Remove fuel level sensor.
9. Remove fuel pump lock ring using locking ring removal tool No. 3342, or equivalent.
10. Loosen mounting tube and leave inserted.
11. Press on mounting tube to separate fuel pump with integrated reservoir from intake housing in fuel reservoir.
12. Remove mounting tube.
13. Remove fuel pump with integrated reservoir.
14. Pull and turn clockwise simultaneously to remove pump from fuel tank.
15. Reverse procedure to install.

FUEL FILTER

REPLACE

The fuel filter is located under the floor of the vehicle, in the righthand rear under the trim and in front of the rear axle.

1. Remove trim attaching screws and trim.
2. Disconnect fuel lines from both ends of fuel filter. Use a shop towel to avoid spillage.
3. Loosen fuel filter bracket and remove fuel filter.
4. Reverse procedure to install.

TIGHTENING SPECIFICATIONS

Year	Component	Torque/Ft. Lbs.
1998–2001	A/C Compressor Retaining Bolts	18
	A/C Compressor & Power Steering Pump Bracket Retaining Bolts	18
	Air Cleaner Housing Bolts	84⑧
	Air Cleaner Retaining Bolts	84⑧
	Alternator Bracket To Engine Retaining Bolts	84⑧
	Alternator To Engine Retaining Bolts, M8	18
	Alternator To Engine Retaining Bolts, M10	30
	Camshaft Bearing Cap Nuts	⑦
	Camshaft Sprocket Bolts	33
	Crankshaft Sprocket Bolt	59
	Cylinder Head Retaining Bolts	①
	Dipstick Tube Bolt	18
	Drive Axles To Flange Shafts	33
	Electric Fan Motor Bolts	84⑧
	Engine Block Coolant Drain Bolt	22
	Engine Support To Engine Retaining Bolts	33
	Engine Support to Body	37
	Engine To Transaxle Retaining Bolts	44
	Exhaust Manifold To Cylinder Head Retaining Bolts	18
	Exhaust Pipe To Exhaust Manifold	30
	Fan Blade Pulley Bolts	84⑧
	Fan Shroud Bolts	84⑧
	Flexplate Bolts, Automatic Transaxle	62②
	Flywheel To Crankshaft Bolts, Manual Transaxle	22③④
	Front Engine Support Bolts	30
	Hydraulic Pump Bracket To Engine	18
	Idler Pulley Eccentric Nut	18
	Injection Rail Cap Nut	84⑧
	Intake Manifold	⑤
	Lefthand Timing Cover Bolt, Lower Righthand	18
	Lefthand Timing Cover Bolts, Upper & Lower Left	33
	Lefthand Timing Cover Collar Nut	84⑧
	Lower Oil Pan To Upper Oil Pan Bolts	11–14
	Oil Cooler Mounting Nuts	18
	Oil Cooler Thermostat Housing Bolt	18
	Oil Filter To Block	11–15
	Oil Galley Plugs, Front Of Block	26
	Oil Pan Drain Plug	26
	Oil Pressure Sender	22
	Oil Pressure Switch	84⑧
	Oil Pump Drive Bolts	84⑧
	Oil Pump To Block Bolts	18
	Oil Return Line Bolts	18
	Oil Supply Line Bolts	18
	Power Steering Pump Retaining Bolts	18
	Rear Main Oil Seal Retainer Bolts	84⑧
	Rear Timing Cover Bolts	84⑧
	Retaining Plate To Swivel Bracket Bolt	26
	Righthand Timing Cover Collar Nut	84⑧
	Righthand Timing Cover Lower Bolts	33
	Serpentine Belt Pulley Bolts	18
	Stop Plate Bolt	84⑧
	Strut Rod Bolts	15
	Swivel Bracket To Lefthand Timing Cover Bolt	18
	TDC Pointer Bolt	18

Continued

TIGHTENING SPECIFICATIONS—Continued

Year	Component	Torque/Ft. Lbs.
1998–2001	Tensioner Nut	18
	Thermostat Housing Bolts	84⑧
	Timing Belt Damper Bolts	18
	Torque Converter To Flexplate Retaining Bolts (ABZ)	27
	Torque Converter To Flexplate Retaining Bolts (AEW)	63
	Upper Oil Pan To Block Bolts	18
	Upper Oil Pan To Honeycomb Insert Bolts	84⑧
	Vibration Damper To Crankshaft Attaching Bolts	332⑥
	Vibration Damper To Crankshaft Sprocket Bolts	18
	Water Pump Bolts	84⑧

① — Refer to "Cylinder Head, Replace" for tightening procedure.
② — Coat threads w/sealing compound AMV 188 001 02, or equivalent.
③ — Plus an additional ¼ (90°) turn.
④ — Coat threads w/locking compound D 000 600, or equivalent.
⑤ — Torque bolts in two steps: 11 ft. lbs., then 18 ft. lbs.
⑥ — When tool No. 2079, or equivalent is used for vibration dampener, torque is 258 ft. lbs.
⑦ — Refer to "Camshaft, Replace" for tightening procedure.
⑧ — Inch lbs.

Clutch & Manual Transaxle

NOTE: On Air Bag Equipped Models, Refer To "Air Bag System Precautions" Located In The Front Of This Manual For System Disarming & Arming Procedures.

NOTE: Refer To "Computer Relearn Procedures" Located In The Front Of This Manual When Battery Power To The Computer Has Been Interrupted.

INDEX

	Page No.
Adjustments	1-54
Clutch Pedal	1-54
Shift Lever	1-54
A4 & S4	1-54
A6 & Cabriolet	1-54
TT	1-54
Clutch, Replace	1-55
Hydraulic System Service	1-54
Clutch System Bleed	1-54
Precautions	1-54
Air Bag Systems	1-54
Battery Ground Cable	1-54
Radio Coded Anti-Theft System	1-54
Tightening Specifications	1-62
A4 & S4	1-62
A6	1-63
Cabriolet	1-63
TT	1-64
Transaxle, Replace	1-55
A4 & S4	1-55
Installation	1-56
Removal	1-55
A6 & Cabriolet	1-57
Installation	1-57
Removal	1-57
TT	1-58

PRECAUTIONS

Air Bag Systems

Refer to "Air Bag System Precautions" in the front of this manual for system disarming and arming procedures.

Battery Ground Cable

Prior to service, disconnect battery ground cable and isolate as required.

Radio Coded Anti-Theft System

Prior to disconnecting the battery or removing the radio, obtain the security code from the vehicle operator. Refer to the owner's manual for security code disarming and arming procedures.

ADJUSTMENTS

Clutch Pedal

These models have hydraulic nonadjustable type clutch release mechanisms, **Figs. 1 through 4.**

Shift Lever

A4 & S4

1. Place shift lever in Neutral.
2. Remove shift knob and boot, **Fig. 5,** then the cover.
3. Inspect clearance "A," **Fig. 6,** between shift lever assembly and body, which should be 1.45 inches on Quattro models and 1.46 inches on FWD models.
4. If clearance is not as specified, loosen adjustment bolt No. 2, **Fig. 7** and adjust pull rod for proper clearance "A" between shift lever assembly and body, **Fig. 6.**
5. Tighten adjustment bolt No. 2 to specifications, then loosen adjustment bolt Nos. 3 and 4, **Fig. 7.**
6. Position ball housing bearing horizontally in direction of travel, then tighten adjustment bolt Nos. 3 and 4 to specifications.
7. Loosen adjustment bolt No. 1, **Fig. 7,** then position shift lever angled back slightly, at right angles to direction of travel.
8. Align lever so that both lugs on ball stop are at an equal distance "A" from ball housing, **Fig. 8.**
9. Tighten adjustment bolt No. 1, then ensure lever does not move.
10. Inspect function of shifter by shifting through all gears.
11. Ensure reverse safety catch is effective. If not, loosen screws retaining ball housing, turn ball housing slightly, then tighten screws again.
12. Install cover, boot and shift knob.

A6 & CABRIOLET

1. Place shift lever in neutral.
2. Remove shift knob and boot, **Fig. 9.**
3. **On A6 models,** remove front and rear crossmembers, then catalyst heat shield.
4. **On all models,** loosen clamp bolt, then position shift lever as close to vertical as possible.
5. Align lever so that both lugs on ball stop are at an equal distance "A" from ball housing, **Fig. 8.**
6. Tighten bolt, then ensure lever does not move.
7. Inspect function of shifter by shifting through all gears.
8. Lever must be in 3rd/4th shift plane in Neutral.
9. Ensure Reverse safety catch is effective. If not, loosen screws retaining ball housing, turn ball housing slightly, then tighten screws.
10. **On A6 models,** install catalyst heat shield, then front and rear crossmembers.
11. **On all models,** install shift boot and retaining screw.

TT

1. Remove gearshift lever knob and shift boot, then place gearshift lever in Neutral.
2. Loosen bolts "A" and "B" until operating cables move freely in centering holes, **Fig. 10.**
3. Loosen bolt "C", **Fig. 11,** then install shift lever gauge tool No. 3422, or equivalent as illustrated.
4. Pivot locating pin (for attaching gauge) under bearing plate and tighten nut "D".
5. Press gearshift lever into left detent of slide.
6. Press gearshift lever with slide to left stop (direction of arrow) and tighten slide with bolt "E".
7. Move gearshift lever to righthand detent, then tighten bolt "C".
8. Install wedge and locating pin, **Fig. 12.**
9. Push wedge between gearshift lever and cover. **There must be no movement in lever.**
10. Connect operating cables in this position.
11. Remove wedge and pin, then shift lever gauge.

HYDRAULIC SYSTEM SERVICE

CLUTCH SYSTEM BLEED

Obtain a suitable brake pressure bleeder to bleed clutch hydraulic system. Follow manufacturer's instructions for bleeding

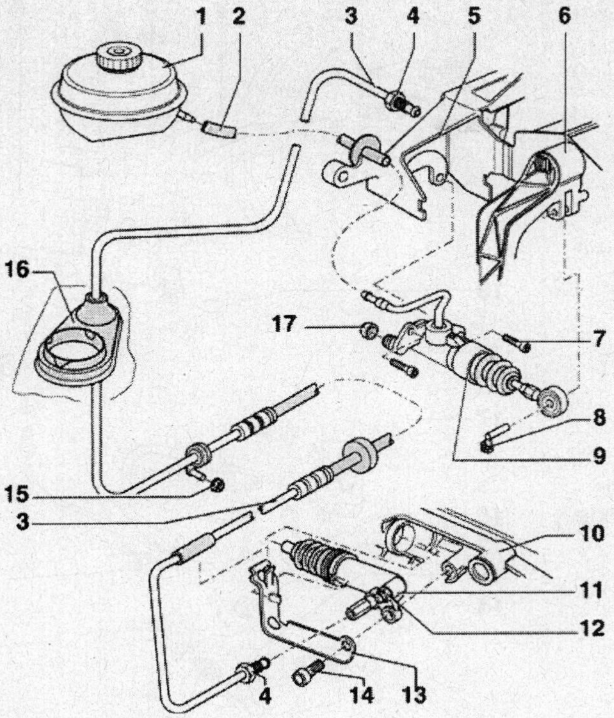

1- Brake Fluid Reservoir
2- Clutch Master Cylinder Supply Hose
3- Hose and Line Assembly
4- Line Fitting Nut
5- Mounting Bracket
6- Clutch Pedal
7- Socket Head Bolt
8- Pin & Locking Plate
9- Clutch Master Cylinder
10- Transaxle
11- Clutch Slave Cylinder
12- Bleeder Valve
13- Bracket
14- Bolt
15- Nut
16- Seal
17- Seal (Do Not Remove)

AD5040000022000X

Fig. 1 Clutch hydraulic system. A4 & S4 w/012 & 01W transaxle

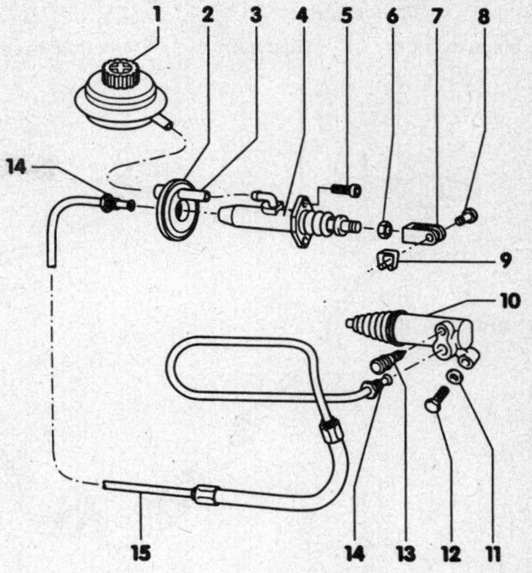

1. Brake Fluid Reservoir
2. Grommet
3. Return Hose
4. Master Cylinder
5. Bolt
6. Lock Nut
7. Clevis
8. Bolt
9. Locking Plate
10. Slave Cylinder
11. Washer
12. Bolt
13. Bleeder Valve
14. Pipe Connection Nut
15. Pressure Pipe With Pressure Hose

AD5049600018000X

Fig. 2 Clutch hydraulic system. A4 & S4 w/01A transaxle

procedures. Maximum working pressure should be 36 psi. Refer to **Figs. 1 through 4** for bleeder valve locations.

CLUTCH

REPLACE

1. Obtain radio anti-theft protection code as outlined under "Precautions."
2. Remove transaxle assembly as outlined under "Transaxle, Replace."
3. Note alignment markings and pressure plate to flywheel orientation.
4. Loosen pressure plate bolts diagonally in stages, then remove pressure plate and clutch disc. Discard bolts.
5. Inspect clutch release bearing and replace if worn or noisy.
6. Clean input shaft splines and, if installing original clutch, the hub splines.
7. Remove corrosion and apply a thin coating of lubricant part No. G 000 100, or equivalent to splines. Work clutch plate back and forth on input shaft until hub moves freely on shaft. Remove all excess grease.
8. Install clutch disc with centering tool No. 3176, or equivalent.
9. Lock flywheel into position using flywheel locking tool No. 3067, or equivalent.
10. Install pressure plate on locating pins, then tighten new bolts diagonally and in stages to specifications.
11. Remove centering and flywheel locking tools, then install transaxle assembly as outlined under "Transaxle, Replace."

TRANSAXLE

REPLACE

A4 & S4

REMOVAL

1. Obtain radio anti-theft protection code as outlined under "Precautions."
2. **On models equipped with 1.8L engine,** proceed as follows:
   a. Disconnect electrical connectors and wiring harnesses at wastegate bypass regulator solenoid valve, EVAP canister purge valve, power output stage and MAF sensor.
   b. Disconnect hoses and remove air cleaner housing.
   c. Remove coolant expansion tank from bracket, then position aside with hoses intact.
   d. Disconnect HO_2S wiring harness and position aside.
   e. Remove turbocharger to front exhaust pipe mounting nuts. **Do not bend front exhaust flex pipe more than 10°.**
3. **On models equipped with 2.8L engine,** proceed as follows:
   a. Remove intake air duct.
   b. Remove coolant expansion tank from bracket, then position aside with hoses intact.
   c. Remove HO_2S on lefthand and

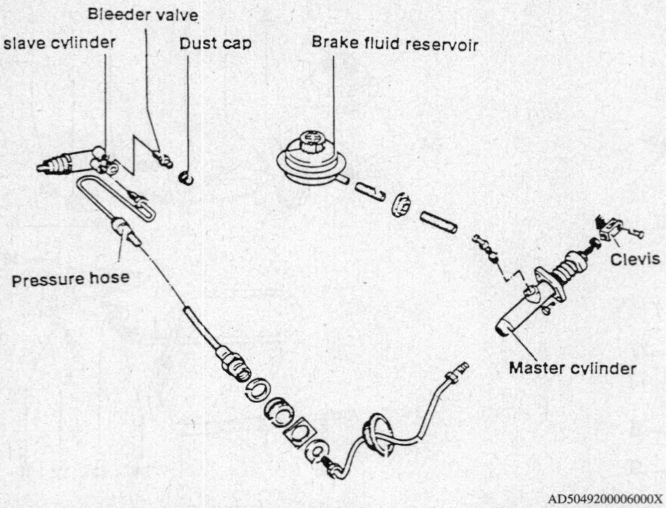

Fig. 3 Clutch hydraulic system. A6 w/01A transaxle

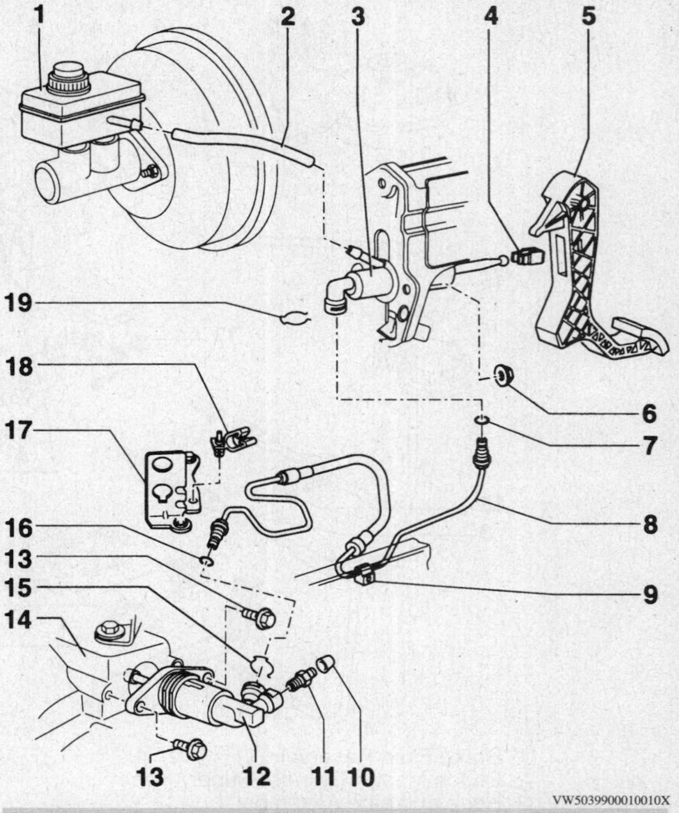

Fig. 4 Clutch hydraulic system (Part 1 of 2). TT

righthand exhaust pipes using ring wrench tool set No. 3337, or equivalent and position aside.

4. **On all models,** remove all engine to transaxle mounting bolts accessible from above.
5. Raise and support vehicle.
6. Remove sound insulation panel and bracket.
7. **On models equipped with 1.8L engine,** proceed as follows:
   a. Remove heat shield above righthand drive axle.
   b. Remove righthand transaxle support together with bonded rubber mount.
   c. Loosen exhaust clamp sleeves, then slide them toward catalytic converter.
   d. Lower and remove catalytic converter and exhaust pipe.
8. **On models equipped with 2.8L engine,** proceed as follows:
   a. Remove heat shields above lefthand and righthand drive axles.
   b. Unbolt front exhaust pipes together with catalytic converters from both exhaust manifolds.
   c. Remove engine speed (RPM) sensor on lefthand side of transaxle, then position aside.
9. **On all models,** disconnect drive axles from flange shafts, then let them rest on suspension links. **Avoid damaging axles' protective coatings.**
10. Disconnect harnesses and electrical connectors from VSS and back-up lamp switch.
11. Disconnect all other electrical connections and ground wires from transaxle and from engine and transaxle mounting bolts.
12. Remove starter mounting bolts, then position starter aside with all electrical connections intact.
13. Disconnect shift rod at transaxle.
14. Remove socket head bolt from pivot rod.
15. Remove bottom engine to transaxle mounting bolts, **except bolts A and B, Fig. 13.**
16. Assemble transaxle support tool No. 3282 and adjustment plate tool No. 3282/10, **Fig. 14,** to transaxle jack tool No. VAG1383A, or equivalents.
17. Place jack with support under transaxle, **Fig. 15.** If support tool No. 3282 is not available, use universal mount tool No. VAG1359/2, or equivalent.
18. Align adjustment plate parallel to transaxle, then lock the safety support.
19. **On models equipped with 1.8L engine,** remove lefthand transaxle support from bonded rubber mount.
20. **On models equipped with 2.8L engine,** remove righthand and lefthand supports complete with bonded rubber mounts from transaxle and subframe.
21. **On all models,** remove remaining bottom engine to transaxle mounting bolts"A" and "B," **Fig. 13.**
22. Press transaxle off dowel sleeves, then lower using transaxle jack just enough to access clutch slave cylinder.
23. Remove clutch slave cylinder, then position aside with suitable wire or rope. **Do not disconnect cylinder hydraulic lines. Do not operate clutch pedal with slave cylinder removed.**
24. Lower the transaxle completely, ensuring drive axles have sufficient clearance.
25. Mount transaxle assembly to stand using holding plate tool No. VW309 and transaxle support tool No. VW353, or equivalents.

INSTALLATION

1. Clean input shaft and clutch hub splines, then apply a thin film of grease part No. G 000 100, or equivalent. **Do not grease guide sleeve.**
2. Lubricate contact surface of clutch release lever plunger with thin layer of copper grease part No. Z 381 351 TE, or equivalent.
3. **On Quattro models,** threads in flanged shafts of transaxle and rear final drive must be cleaned of any residue from thread locking compound.
4. **On all models,** threads in clutch slave cylinder and shift lever at shift rod must be cleaned of any residue from thread locking compound.
5. Install clutch slave cylinder with bracket before centering transaxle. **Bracket must be located in slot of clutch slave cylinder.**
6. Ensure presence of engine to transaxle alignment dowel sleeves. Replace as required.
7. Raise and position transaxle to engine using support tool No. VAG1383A, or equivalent, and/or a suitable transaxle jack.
8. Insert transaxle to engine bolts using patterns and specification tables in **Figs. 16 and 17,** then tighten to specifications listed in table. Bolts must be tightened before installing clutch slave cylinder.
9. Install transaxle mounts, then tighten

1. Reservoir
2. Supply hose
3. Master cylinder
4. Retainer
5. Clutch pedal
6. Self-locking nut
7. O-ring
8. Pipe & hose assembly
9. Bracket
10. Dust cap
11. Bleeder valve
12. Actuator cylinder
13. Collared bolt
14. Transaxle
15. Clip
16. O-ring
17. Support bracket
18. Hose bracket
19. Clip

VW5039900010020X

Fig. 4 Clutch hydraulic system (Part 2 of 2). TT

bolts to specifications in tables, **Figs. 18 and 19.**

10. Connect both drive axles to transaxle, then install drive axle shield. Tighten to specification.
11. Connect electrical connections for vehicle speed sensor and back-up lamps at transaxle.
12. Connect shift control rod.
13. Install starter. Tighten to specifications.
14. **On Quattro models,** install and adjust propeller shaft as outlined under "All Wheel Drive Systems."
15. **On all models,** install exhaust pipe and catalytic converter and underbody shields.

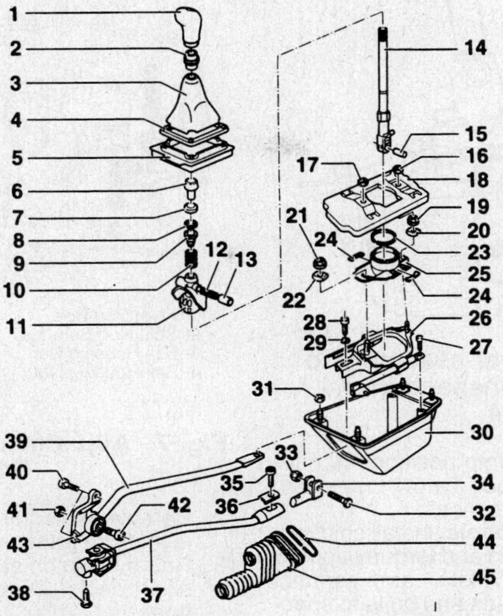

1. Gearshift Knob	16. Nut	31. Nut
2. Bushing	17. Nut	32. Bolt
3. Boot	18. Cover	33. Nut
4. Top Frame	19. Nut	34. Shift Fork
5. Bottom Frame	20. Connecting Piece	35. Bolt
6. Bushing	21. Nut	36. Clamp
7. Collar	22. Connecting Piece	37. Shift Rod
8. Circlip	23. Circlip	38. Bolt
9. Spacer Bushing	24. Pad	39. Front Shift Rod
10. Spring	25. Ball Housing	40. Bolt
11. Ball Stop	26. Rear Shift Rod	41. Nut
12. Spring	27. Bolt	42. Bolt
13. Bushing	28. Bolt	43. Shift Rod Bracket
14. Gearshift Lever	29. Washer	44. Tensioning Ring
15. Spacer Tube	30. Gearshift Housing	45. Boot

AD5049600007000X

Fig. 5 Exploded view of shift lever assembly. A4 & S4

A6 & Cabriolet

REMOVAL

1. Obtain radio anti-theft protection code as outlined under "Precautions."
2. Raise and support vehicle.
3. Remove upper engine to transaxle bolts.
4. Remove engine air intake pipe.
5. Disconnect electrical connectors from back-up lamp switch and speedometer vehicle speed sensor.
6. Disconnect any remaining electrical connectors from transaxle.
7. **On A6 and Cabriolet models,** remove bolts securing torque arm (front engine mounting).
8. **On all models,** install engine support tool No. 10-222A, or equivalent. Attach mounting hook to front engine mount, then pretension engine.
9. Remove sound insulation shield and sound insulation shield bracket.
10. Remove crossmember from below transaxle.
11. Remove complete exhaust system.
12. **On A6 and Cabriolet models,** disconnect shift rod from transaxle.
13. **On Quattro models,** remove propeller shaft as outlined under "All Wheel Drive Systems."
14. **On all models,** remove heat shields for drive axles and transaxle mount.
15. Disconnect both drive axles at transaxle and secure aside.
16. Remove righthand side heat shield for bonded rubber bushing if equipped.
17. Remove starter and secure aside.
18. Position support tool No. VAG1383A, or equivalent, and/or a suitable transaxle jack under transaxle, then pretension transaxle.
19. Remove crossmember below transaxle, then remove clutch slave cylinder and secure aside without disconnecting fluid lines.
20. Remove lower transaxle to engine mounting bolts, then lever transaxle away from engine using a suitable pry bar and lower from vehicle.

INSTALLATION

1. Ensure presence of engine to transaxle alignment dowel sleeves.
2. **On Quattro models,** threads in flanged shafts of transaxle and rear final drive must be cleaned of any residue from thread locking compound.
3. **On all models,** raise and position transaxle to engine using support tool No. VAG1383A, or equivalent, and/or a suitable transaxle jack.
4. Insert transaxle to engine bolts using patterns and specification tables in **Figs. 16 and 17,** then tighten to specifications listed in tables. Bolts must be tightened before installing clutch slave cylinder.
5. Use a suitable pry bar to press clutch slave cylinder into transaxle bore and install mounting bolt. **A special pointed mounting bolt is available as a replacement to facilitate installation of clutch slave cylinder.**

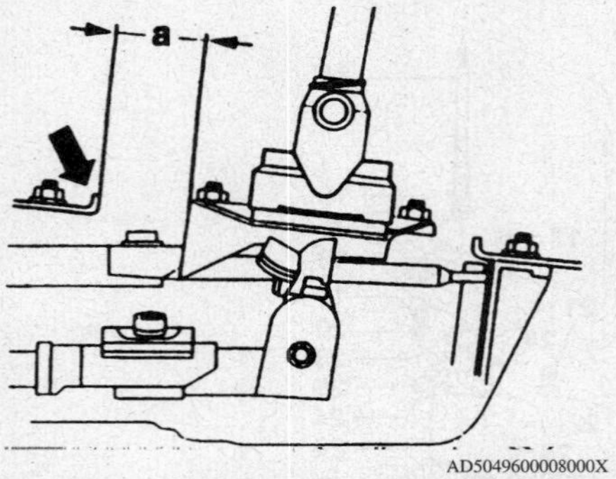

Fig. 6 Shift lever assembly to body clearance inspection. A4 & S4

6. Raise transaxle into position, then install crossmember below transaxle. Tighten to specifications.
7. **On Cabriolet models,** install shift rod, torque support rod and torque support.
8. **On all models,** install and connect starter. Tighten nuts and bolts to specifications.
9. Connect both drive axles at transaxle and tighten to specification.
10. Install heat shields for drive axles and transaxle mount.
11. **On Quattro models,** install propeller shaft as outlined under "All Wheel Drive Systems."
12. **On all models,** install crossmember below driveshaft.
13. Install complete exhaust system, use new self locking hardware.
14. **On A6 and Cabriolet models,** connect shift rod.
15. **On all models,** connect electrical connectors to transaxle.
16. Remove engine support tool, then install bolts securing torque arm (front engine mounting).
17. Install sound insulation shield, sound insulation shield bracket and engine air intake pipe.

TT

1. Obtain audio coded anti-theft code, then disconnect and isolate battery ground cable.
2. Drain transaxle fluid into a suitable container.
3. Disconnect all electrical connectors and ground straps from transaxle.
4. Remove power steering reservoir from battery bracket, but do not loosen hoses.
5. Tie reservoir up to upper radiator support.
6. Disconnect battery cable and remove battery and battery carrier.
7. Remove intake hose and connector from air mass meter.
8. Remove air cleaner housing attaching bolts and housing.
9. Disconnect all electrical connectors and wiring from transaxle.
10. Remove cable support from transaxle.
11. Remove shift cable from shift lever using Kukko tool No. 20-10, or equivalent.

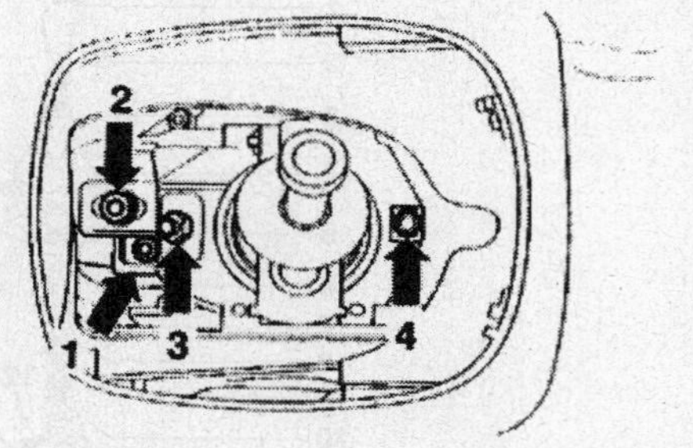

1- Pivot Rod Bolt
2- Shift Rod Bolt
3- Ball Housing Nut
4- Ball Housing Nut

AD5049600009000A

Fig. 7 Adjustment screws. A4 & S4

12. Remove selector cable with linkage lever from transaxle.
13. Remove clutch slave cylinder and position aside. **Do not open hydraulic lines.**
14. Remove cable retainer on starter.
15. Remove ground strap at engine to transaxle upper securing bolt.
16. Remove hoses and wiring connections in area of engine mount eye as required.
17. **On models equipped with dual charge air coolers,** mark running direction of serpentine belt with suitable chalk or a felt pen, then rotate belt tensioner in a clockwise direction and remove belt.
18. **On models equipped with single charge air cooler,** disconnect air duct leading to cooler at bottom of righthand crossmember.
19. **On all models,** remove front wheels and tires.
20. Remove lefthand, center and righthand sound insulation panels.
21. **On models equipped with dual charge air coolers,** proceed as follows:
    a. Remove connector pipe between the two coolers.
    b. Remove power steering pump pulley while counterholding with a suitable hex wrench.
22. **On all models,** clamp off power steering pump return and pressure hoses using hose clamps tool No. 3094, or equivalent.
23. Disconnect power steering pressure switch electrical connector.
24. Disconnect power steering pump pressure pipe.
25. Disconnect power steering pipe from transaxle, then pull speed nut off transaxle.
26. Disconnect starter electrical connectors.
27. Remove starter mounting bolts, then the starter.
28. Clamp off clutch slave cylinder pressure hose using hose clamp tool No. 3094, or equivalent.
29. Pull retainer upward, then pull pressure pipe out of hose connector.

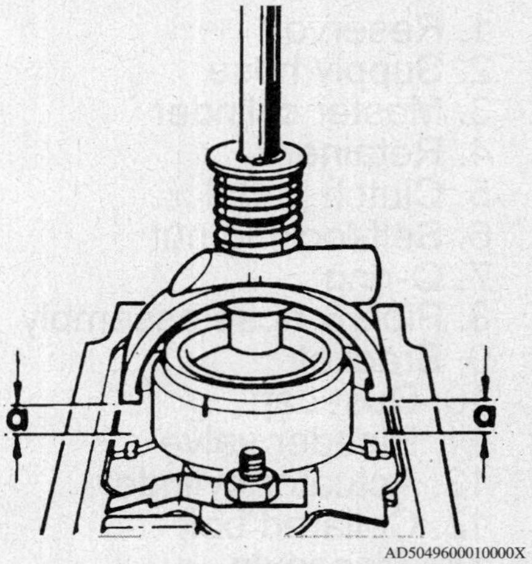

Fig. 8 Ball stop lug adjustment. A4 & S4

30. Disconnect back-up lamp switch electrical connector.
31. Disconnect exhaust pipe, then push clamp toward rear of vehicle.
32. Loosen exhaust system but keep in place by inserting hooks tool No. 3004, or equivalent on ends of chain into floor pan openings. Remove plugs if required. **Do not bend flexible joint more than 10°. Otherwise it could be damaged.**
33. Mark position of driveshaft relative to flexible coupling on transfer case.
34. Unbolt driveshaft from flexible coupling on transfer case using a suitable lever to brace triangular flange when loosening bolts.
35. Push front driveshaft tube as far rearward as possible.
36. Remove pendulum support bolts "A," **Fig. 20,** then bolts "B."**After loosening bolts "A," engine and transaxle assembly will move forward slightly. Ensure driveshaft flange oil seal is not damaged during removal and installation.**
37. Remove pendulum support, then carefully push engine and transaxle assembly forward.
38. Remove exhaust system front bracket from subframe, **Fig. 21.**
39. Pry steering rack off subframe dowel sleeve.
40. Place transaxle jack tool No. VAG1383A with universal support tool No. 1359/2, or equivalents under subframe.
41. Remove subframe bolts 1 and 3, **Fig. 21.**
42. Lower the subframe, leaving it suspended from ball joints and connecting links. Lift steering rack clear at this time, then position it aside.
43. Mark position of driveshaft relative to flexible coupling on transfer case.
44. Disconnect drive axles from flanges, guide them rearward, and rest them on subframe. **Avoid damaging axles' protective coatings.**
45. Secure subframe toward rear of vehicle with a chain by inserting hook tool

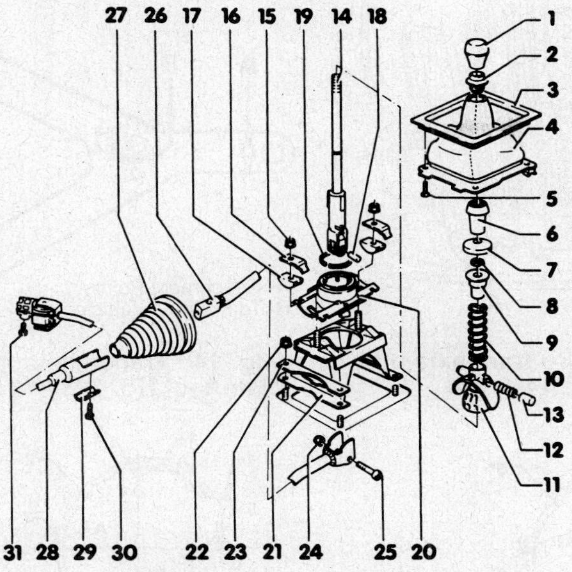

1. Shift Knob
2. Bushing
3. Retaining Frame
4. Cover
5. Bolt
6. Bushing
7. Collar
8. Circlip
9. Spacer Bushing
10. Spring
11. Ball Stop
12. Spring
13. Bushing
14. Shift Lever
15. Nut
16. Leaf Spring
17. Connecting Piece
18. Spacer Tube
19. Circlip
20. Ball Housing
21. Shift Linkage Mounting
22. Nut
23. Reinforcing Plate
24. Self Locking Nut
25. Bolt
26. Rear Shift Rod
27. Boot
28. Shift Rod With Joint
29. Clamp
30. Bolt
31. Self Locking Bolt

AD5049600011000X

Fig. 9 Exploded view of shift lever assembly. A6 & Cabriolet

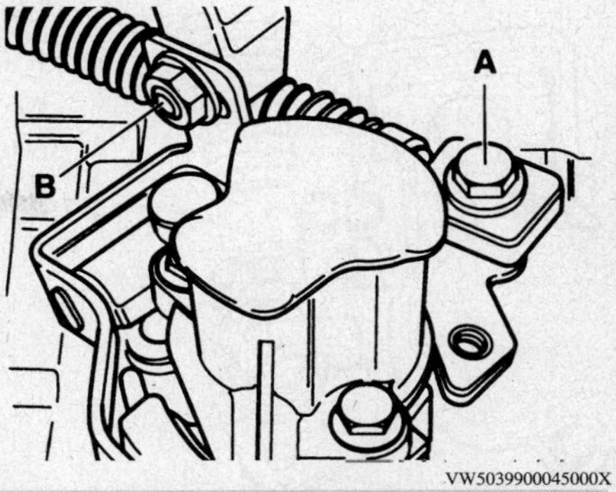

VW5039900045000X

Fig. 10 Shift lever retaining bolt locations. TT

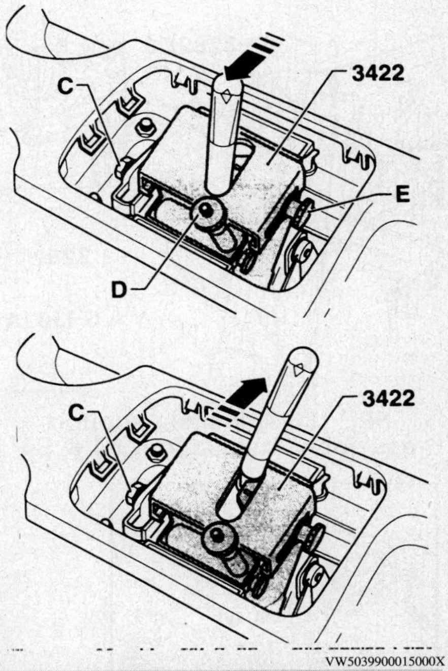

VW5039900015000X

Fig. 11 Installation of gearshift adjustment tool. TT

No. 3004, or equivalent into floor pan opening. Remove plug if required.

46. Remove righthand drive axle heat shield bolts, then the shield.
47. Remove transfer case bracket bolts 1 and 2, **Fig. 22.** Bracket cannot be removed at this stage and should be left intact.
48. Remove inspection cover mounting bolt, then the cover, **Fig. 23.**
49. Install engine support bar tool No. 10-222 A, or equivalent and bases tool No. 10-222 A/1, or equivalent, **Fig. 24.**
50. Slightly tighten engine to transaxle support to take weight off of engine and transaxle assembly.
51. Remove lefthand transaxle support bolts.
52. Lower the engine and transaxle assembly on tool spindle until distance "a," **Fig. 25,** between transaxle housing and transaxle mount is 3.9–4.3 inches.
53. Mount adjustment plate tool No. 3282/27 to transaxle support tool No. 3282, or equivalent.
54. Position transaxle support arms according to holes in adjustment plate.
55. Install mounting components "A," as illustrated, **Fig. 26. Arrow "B" must face front of vehicle.**
56. Place transaxle jack under vehicle, with arrow "B," **Fig. 26,** facing front of vehicle.
57. Align adjustment plate parallel to transaxle and secure support to transaxle with an M8 × 25 bolt.
58. Remove engine to transaxle bolts accessible from below.
59. Push transaxle off dowel sleeves, then remove transfer case bracket.
60. To separate transaxle from engine, pull it away on transfer case side first, then at front.
61. Lower the transaxle assembly.
62. Reverse procedure to install, noting the following:
    a. Secure all hose connections with hose clamps identical to original equipment clamps. Do not install substitutes.
    b. Replace all required seals, gaskets and O-rings.
    c. Push transaxle over flywheel at front side first, then at transfer case side.
    d. Install transfer case bracket with bolts finger-tight before transaxle to engine bolts.
    e. **Torque** transfer case bracket No. 1 bolts, **Fig. 22** to 27 inch lbs.
    f. **Torque** transfer case bracket No. 2 bolts to 26 ft. lbs.
    g. **Torque** transfer case bracket No. 1 bolts to 33 ft. lbs.
    h. **Torque** transaxle mount bracket to transaxle outer bolts to 30 ft. lbs, then rotate an additional 90° while pendulum support is still removed.
    i. After pendulum support has been installed, **torque** transaxle mount to transaxle inner bolts to 44 ft. lbs, then rotate an additional 90°.
    j. Adjust shift linkage as outlined under "Adjustments" in this section.
    k. Tighten all fasteners to specifications.
    l. Do not remove support bar tool until all engine and transaxle mountings have been tightened to specifications.
    m. Fill transaxle with proper fluid.
    n. Set audio coded anti-theft system and clock.

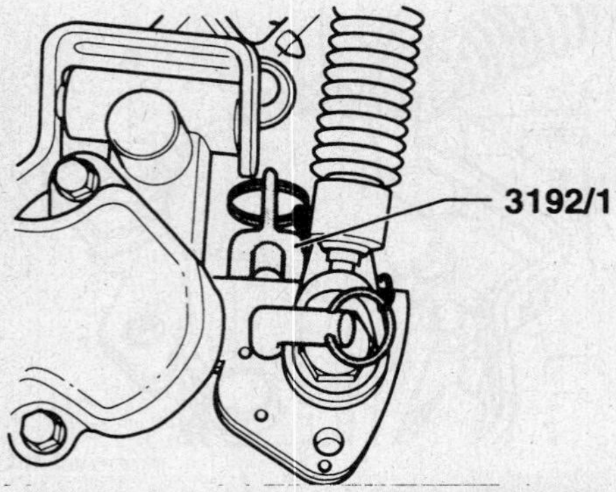

VW5039900016000X

Fig. 12 Installation of wedge & locating pin. TT

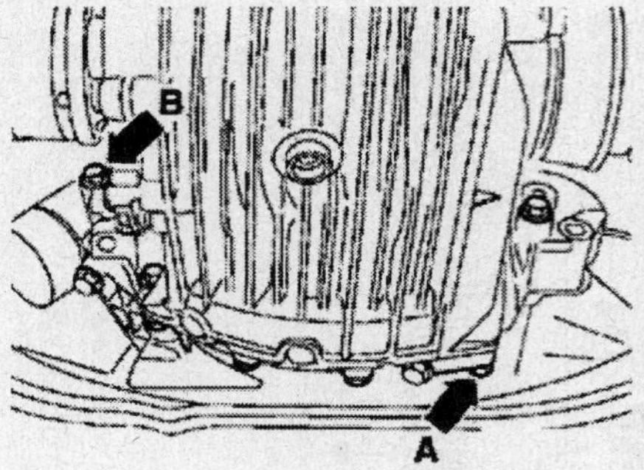

AD5030000063000X

Fig. 13 Engine to transaxle bolt removal. A4 & S4

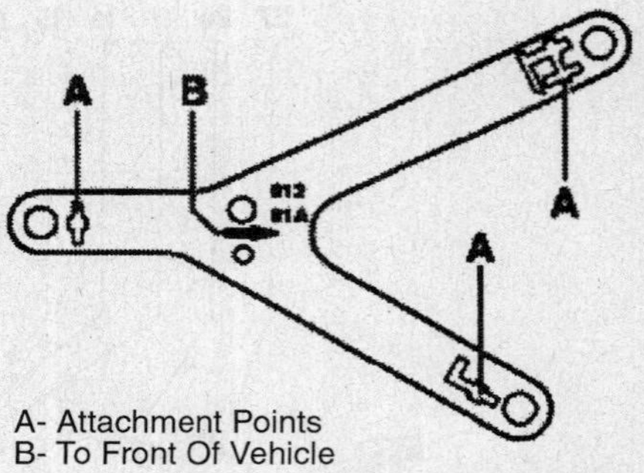

AD5030000064000X

Fig. 14 Transaxle adjustment plate tool No. 3282/10. A4 & S4

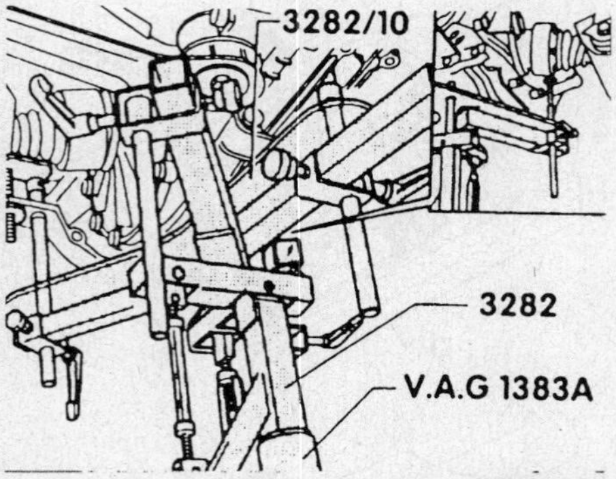

AD5039600052000X

Fig. 15 Transaxle support assembly installation. A4 & S4

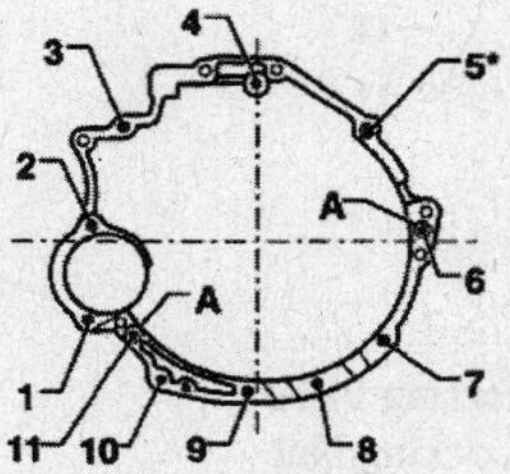

Item No.	Bolt	Tightening torque
1, 3, 4	M12 x 67	65 Nm (48 ft lb)
2, 6	M12 x 90	65 Nm (48 ft lb)
5, 11	M12 x 110	65 Nm (48 ft lb)
7 - 10	M10 x 45	45 Nm (33 ft lb)

A: Dowel sleeves

AD5030000065000X

Fig. 16 Transaxle to engine bolt installation. A4 & S4 w/1.8L engine

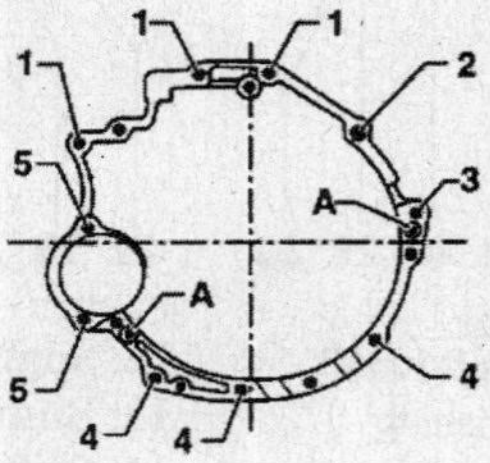

Item No.	Bolt	Qty.	Tightening torque
1	M12 x 67	3	65 Nm (48 ft lb)
2	M12 x 90	1	65 Nm (48 ft lb)
3	M12 x 80	1	65 Nm (48 ft lb)
4	M10 x 45	3	45 Nm (33 ft lb)
5	M10 x 135	1	45 Nm (33 ft lb)
5 1)	M12 x 130	1	65 Nm (48 ft lb)

1) Upper starter bolt

A: Dowel sleeves

AD5030000067000X

Fig. 17 Transaxle to engine bolt installation. A4 & S4 w/2.8L engine

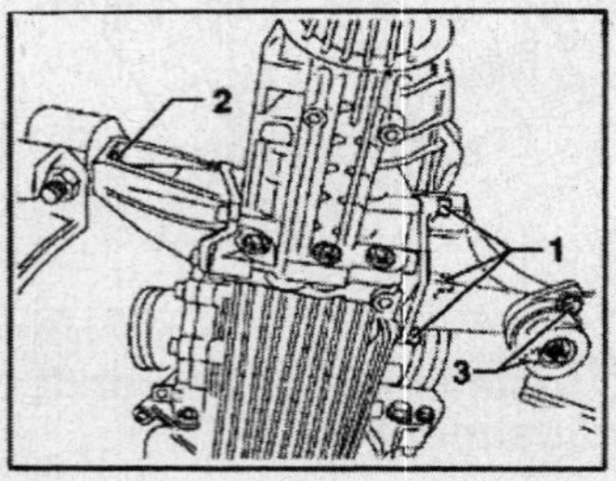

Item No.	Bolt	Qty.	Tightening torque
1	M10 x 30	3	40 Nm (30 ft lb)
2	M10 x 35	1	50 Nm (37 ft lb)
3	M8 x 20	2	23 Nm (17 ft lb)

AD5030000066000X

Fig. 18 Transaxle mount installation. A4 & S4 w/1.8L engine

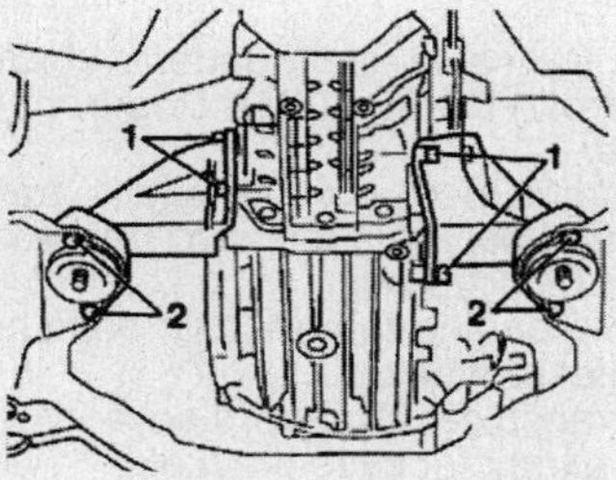

Item No.	Bolt	Qty.	Tightening torque
1	M10 x 35	3	40 Nm (30 ft lb)
2	M8 x 20	2	23 Nm (17 ft lb)

AD5030000068000X

Fig. 19 Transaxle mount installation. A4 & S4 w/2.8L engine

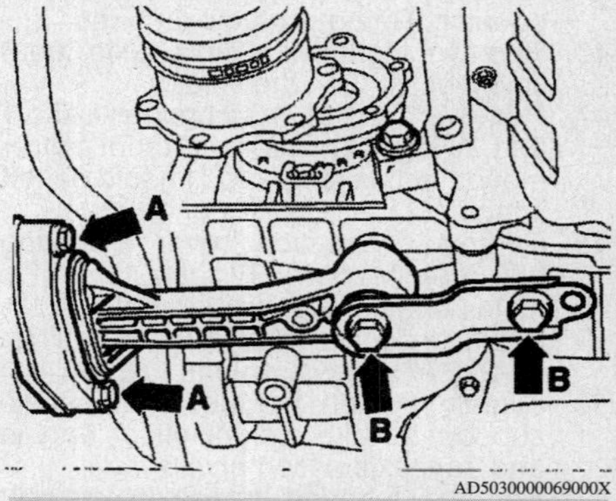

AD5030000069000X

Fig. 20 Pendulum support. TT

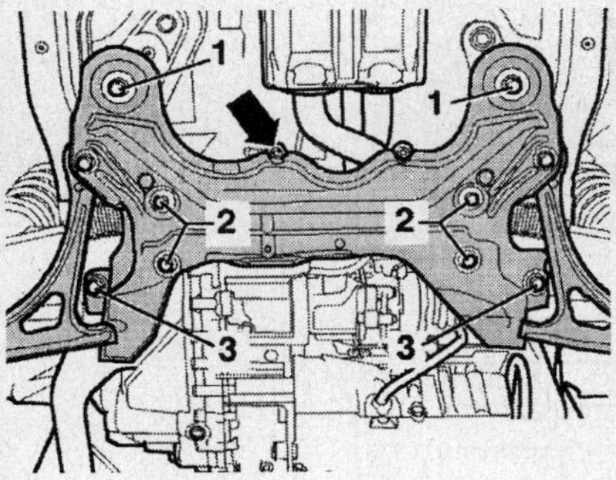

1- Subframe Bolts
2- Steering Rack Bolts
3- Subframe Bolts
arrow-exhaust System From Bracket

AD5030000070000X

Fig. 21 Subframe mounting. TT

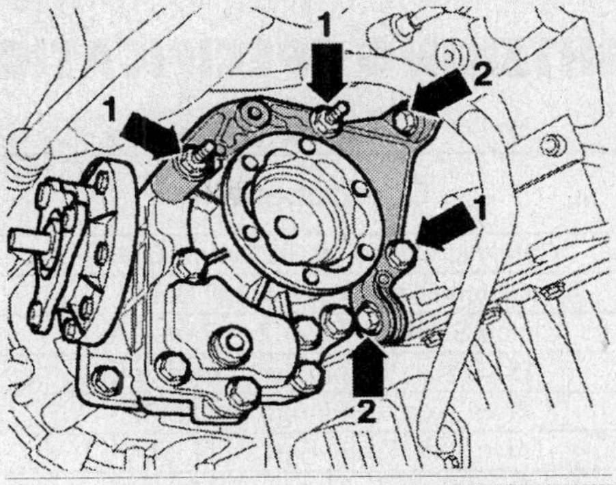

AD5030000071000X

Fig. 22 Transfer case bracket. TT

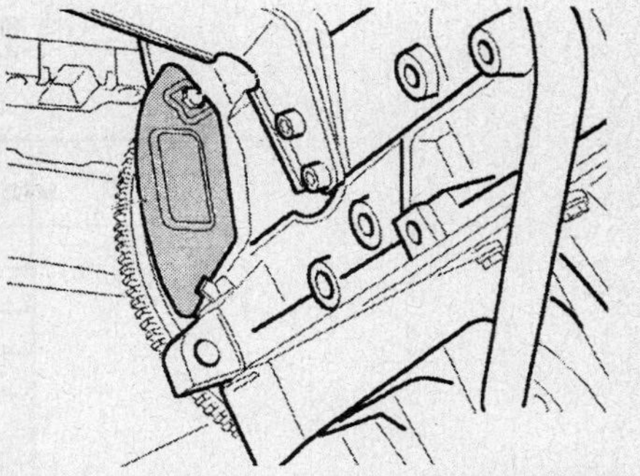

AD5030000072000X

Fig. 23 Inspection cover removal. TT

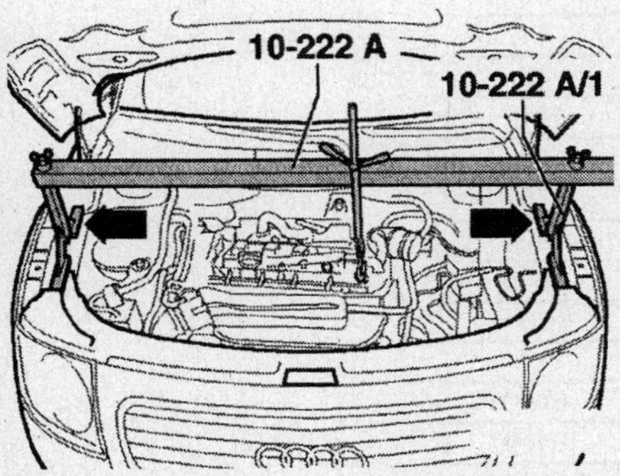

AD5030000073000X

Fig. 24 Engine support installation. TT

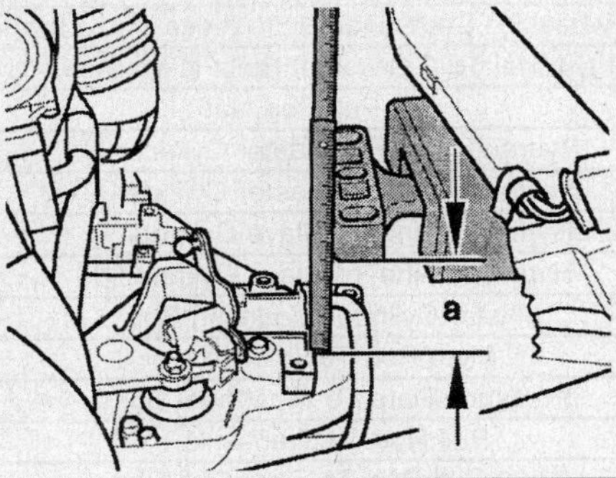

AD5030000074000X

Fig. 25 Transaxle housing to mount dimension "a." TT

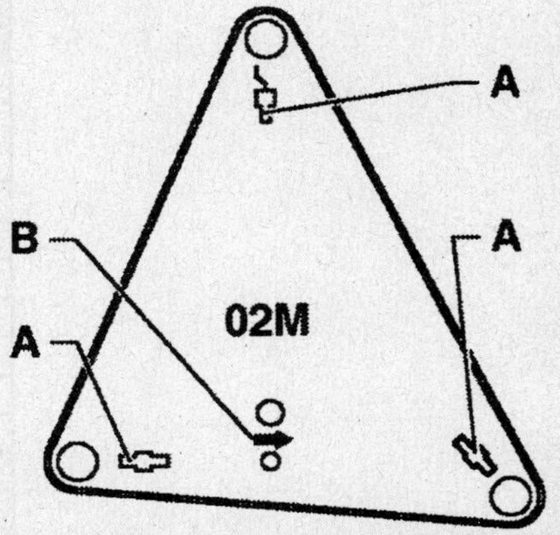

AD5030000075000X

Fig. 26 Transaxle adjustment plate tool No. tool No. 3282/27. TT

TIGHTENING SPECIFICATIONS

A4 & S4

Year	Component	Torque/Ft. Lbs.
1998–2001	Catalytic Converter To Mount Bolts	18
	Clutch Plate To Flywheel Bolts	18
	Clutch Slave Cylinder To Transaxle	18
	Drive Axle Shield To Transaxle	17
	Drive Axle To Flange Bolts, M8	30
	Drive Axle To Flange Bolts, M10	57
	Driveshaft To Output Flange①	30
	Engine Speed (RPM) Sensor Bolt	84④
	Exhaust Pipe Clamp	30
	Exhaust Pipe To Turbocharger Or Manifold	18
	Flywheel To Crankshaft Bolts (Less Two-Step)	44⑥
	Flywheel To Crankshaft Bolts (Two-Step)	44⑦
	Front Pull Rod Nut	30
	Hydraulic Line To Master Cylinder①	11
	Hydraulic Line To Master Cylinder②	18
	Hydraulic Line To Slave Cylinder①	11
	Hydraulic Line To Slave Cylinder②	18
	Master Cylinder Mounting Bolt	15
	Pivot Rod To Transaxle	30
	Pressure Plate To Fly Wheel Bolts	18③
	Pull Rod To Transaxle	30
	Rear Pull Rod To Front Pull Rod	18
	Rear Shift Rod To Shift Lever Housing	84④
	Shift Fork Nut	84④
	Shift Lever Adjustment Nut No. 1	18
	Shift Lever Adjustment Nut No. 2	18
	Shift Lever Adjustment Nut No. 3	18
	Shift Lever Adjustment Nut No. 4	84④
	Shift Lever Ball Housing Front Nut	18
	Shift Lever Ball Housing Rear Nut	84④
	Shift Lever Cover Front Mounting Nut	18
	Shift Lever Cover Rear Mounting Nut	84④
	Shift Lever Housing Nuts	84④
	Shift Rod to Shift Fork Bolt	18
	Shift Rod To Transaxle	15⑤
	Transaxle Mount To Body	30
	Transaxle Mount To Transaxle	30
	Transaxle Oil Fill Plug	18

① — AWD models.
② — FWD models.
③ — Tighten in a criss-cross pattern.
④ — Inch lbs.
⑤ — Always replace this bolt. Do not use old one.
⑥ — Tighten an additional 90°
⑦ — Tighten an additional 180°

A6

Year	Component	Torque/Ft. Lbs.
1998–2001	Clutch Slave Cylinder To Transaxle	18
	Crossmembers To Body	33
	Drive Axle To Flanged Shaft, M8	33
	Drive Axle To Flanged Shaft, M10	59
	Hydraulic Line To Clutch Slave Cylinder	11
	Hydraulic Line To Master Cylinder	11
	Master Cylinder To Pedal Bracket	15
	Pedal Bracket Mounting Nut	18
	Pressure Plate To Flywheel②	18
	Propeller Shaft To Rear Final Drive	41
	Propeller Shaft To Transaxle	41
	Rear Shift Rod To Shift Lever	84③
	Shift Lever Ball Housing Mounting Nut	18
	Shift Linkage Mounting Nut	84③
	Shift Rod With Joint to Rear Shift Rod	18
	Shift Rod With Joint To Transaxle	15
	Torque Support To Body	33
	Transaxle Support To Subframe	33
	Transaxle To Engine Bolt	①

① — Refer to "Transaxle, Replace."
② — Tighten in a criss-cross pattern.
③ — Inch lbs.

CABRIOLET

Year	Component	Torque/Ft. Lbs.
1998–2001	Axle Shaft To Drive Flange Bolts, M8	33
	Axle Shaft To Drive Flange Bolts, M10	59
	Clutch Cover Bolts	18
	Clutch Master Cylinder Bolts	14
	Driveshaft To Transaxle Bolts, Quattro Models	40
	Pedal Mounting Bracket	18
	Shift Housing To Ball Housing Nuts	18
	Shift Housing To Transaxle Nuts	84③
	Shift Lever To Rear Shift Rod Bolt	84③
	Shift Lever To Shift Fork Bolt	84③
	Shift Linkage Mount To Ball Housing Bolts	84③
	Shift Linkage Mount To Ball Housing Nuts	18
	Shift Rod Clamp Bolt	18
	Slave Cylinder Bolt	14
	Subframe Mounting Bolts	25①
	Tie Rod Coupling To Steering Rack Bolts	33
	Transaxle To Engine	②

① — Always use new bolts. Rotate an additional ¼ (90°) turn.
② — Refer to "Transaxle, Replace."
③ — Inch lbs.

TT

Year	Component	Torque/Ft. Lbs.
2000–2001	Drive Axle To Transaxle Flange Bolts	57
	Drive Axle Heat Shield Bolts	18
	Exhaust Pipe Connector Clamps	30
	Inspection Cover Bolt	89①
	Pendulum Support Bolts “A”	15②
	Pendulum Support Bolts “B”	30②
	Pendulum Support To Transaxle	30②
	Power Steering Pump Pulley Bolts	18
	Pressure Pipe To Power Steering Pump	28
	Shift Cable Support To Transaxle Bolts	17
	Shift Cable To Transaxle Shift Lever	18
	Steering Rack To Subframe Bolts	15②
	Subframe To Body Bolts	74②
	Transfer Case Bracket Bolts	③
	Transaxle Mount Bracket To Transaxle Inner Bolts	③
	Transaxle Mount Bracket To Transaxle Outer Bolts	③
	Transaxle To Engine M10 Bolts	30
	Transaxle To Engine M12 Bolts	59
	Wheel Lug Nuts	89

① — Inch lbs.
② — Always use new bolts. Rotate an additional ¼ (90°) turn.
③ — Refer to “Transaxle, Replace.”

Rear Axle & Suspension

INDEX

	Page No.
Coil Spring, Replace	1-72
Control Arm, Replace	1-72
Quattro	1-72
A4 & S4	1-72
A8	1-73
1998–99 A6	1-73
Hub & Bearing Service	1-68
Except Quattro	1-68
Quattro	1-68
Rear Axle, Replace	1-65
Except Quattro	1-65
A4 & S4	1-65
A6	1-65
A8	1-66
Cabriolet	1-65
TT	1-66
Quattro	1-66
Rear Axle Shaft, Replace	1-66
Quattro	1-66
A4 & S4	1-67
A8	1-67
TT	1-67
1998–99 A6 Quattro	1-66
Stabilizer Bar, Replace	1-73
Except Quattro	1-73
A4, S4 & Cabriolet	1-73
A6 & A8	1-73
Quattro	1-73
A4, A6, A8 & S4	1-73
Strut, Replace	1-69
Except Quattro	1-69
A4 & S4	1-69
A6, A8 & Cabriolet	1-69
TT	1-69
Quattro	1-69
A4 & S4	1-69
A6	1-70
A8	1-70
Strut Service	1-70
Except Quattro	1-70
A4 & S4	1-70
A6	1-71
A8	1-71
Cabriolet	1-71
TT	1-71
Quattro	1-72
A4	1-72
A8	1-72
1998–99 A6	1-72
Tightening Specifications	1-80
Except Quattro	1-80
Quattro	1-81
Wheel Bearing, Adjust	1-69
Except Quattro	1-69
Quattro	1-69

REAR AXLE

REPLACE

Except Quattro

A4 & S4

1. Raise and support vehicle, then remove wheel and tire assemblies.
2. Remove rear axle cover, **Fig. 1,** then unbolt heat shield cover and push forward enough to access parking brake cable adjuster.
3. Slacken both parking brake cable adjusters by removing locking element and turning adjustment nut as far as stop, then push adjuster together.
4. Remove lefthand and righthand locking plates.
5. Loosen cable retaining plate bolts and remove cables from axle.
6. Disconnect and plug brake lines at rear axle.
7. Remove ABS wheel speed sensors from mounting holes, then disconnect ABS wheel speed sensor cables at rear axle.
8. Support axle, then unbolt and remove suspension strut from axle beam, **Fig. 2.**
9. Loosen bolts in guide bushings, then lower axle from vehicle.
10. Reverse procedure to install, noting the following:
    a. Install guide bushing bolts and suspension strut bolts at axle beam finger tight. Tighten all other bolts to specifications.
    b. Adjust parking brake.
    c. Bleed brake system.
    d. Lower vehicle, then tighten guide bushing bolts and suspension strut bolts at axle beam to specification with full vehicle weight applied.

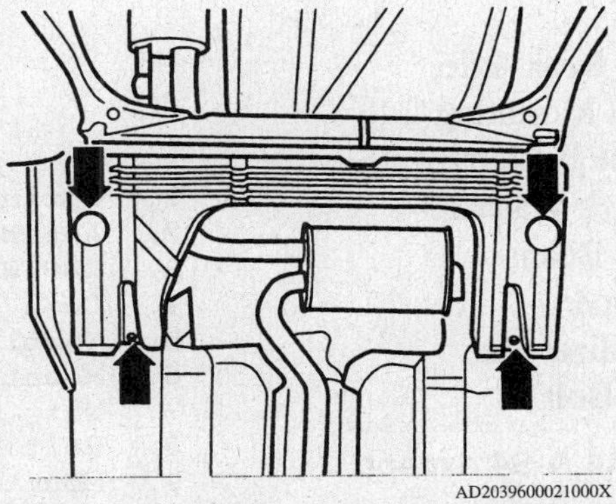

Fig. 1 Rear axle cover removal. A4 & S4 except Quattro

A6

1998–99

1. Raise and support vehicle and remove wheels.
2. Remove cover.
3. Remove mounting bracket stone deflector **Fig. 3,** if equipped.
4. Install suitable transaxle jack with axle attachment tool No. 1359/2, or equivalent under axle.
5. Remove two mounting bolts, one from lefthand and on from righthand side.
6. Move rear axle downward and remove coil spring.
7. Remove retainers for parking brake cable.
8. Remove retainer for parking brake cable.
9. Remove ABS wheel speed sensor retainer.
10. Remove ABS wheel speed sensor.
11. Disconnect ABS wheel speed sensor wiring from retainers.
12. Disconnect brake line from clips.
13. Remove brake caliper mounting bolts, then slide off caliper.
14. Remove brake pads and disc.
15. Mark outline of mounting bracket clearly on longitudinal member.
16. Remove mounting bracket bolts on both sides, then lower rear axle from vehicle.
17. Reverse procedure to install, noting the following:
    a. Align mounting brackets using markings made during removal.
    b. When installing suspension strut to rear axle mounting bolt, vehicle must be standing on its tires.
    c. Tighten nuts and bolts to specifications.

CABRIOLET

Refer to **Fig. 4** during replacement procedures.

1. Loosen lug nuts, then raise and support rear of vehicle.
2. Remove rear wheels.
3. Remove compensator bar, then the parking brake cable from clips at support bracket.
4. Pry parking brake cable guide sleeves out of support brackets.
5. Disconnect brake lines from brake hoses.
6. Remove nuts from trailing link mounting bolts. **Do not remove the bolts.**
7. Disconnect brake pressure regulator spring from rear axle.
8. Remove Panhard rod securing bolt.
9. Remove strut mounting bolts from bottom.
10. Remove trailing link mounting bolts (two mechanics required).
11. Remove rear axle.
12. Reverse procedure to install, noting the following:
    a. Bleed brake system and adjust parking brake.
    b. Tighten nuts and bolts to specifications.

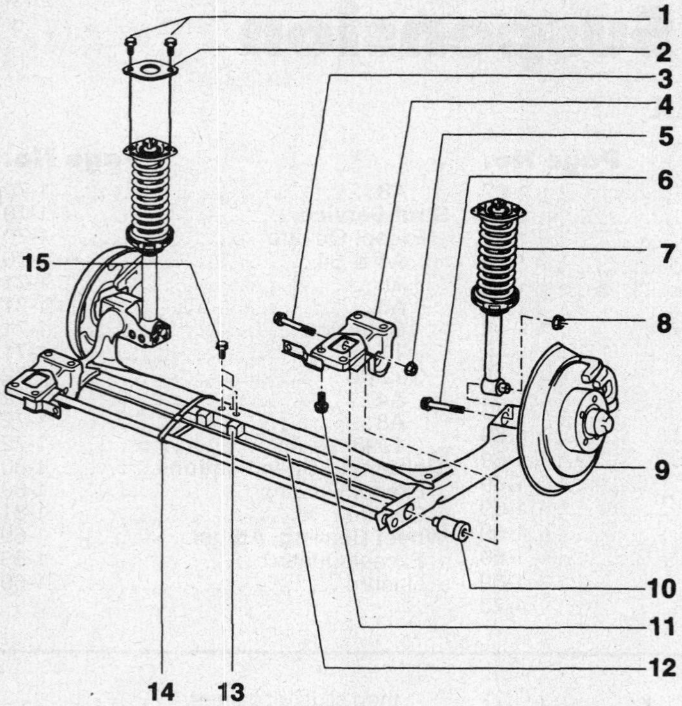

1. Hex Bolt
2. Gasket
3. Hex Bolt
4. Mounting Bracket
5. Flanged Nut
6. Hex Bolt
7. Suspension Strut
8. Hex Nut
9. Outer Rear Axle, Wheel Mounting
10. Guide Bushing
11. Bolt & Washer
12. Axle Beam
13. Damper
14. Stabilizer Bar
15. Hex Bolt

AD2039600022000X

Fig. 2 Exploded view of rear axle. A4 & S4 except Quattro

A8

On A8 models equipped with 3.7L FWD engine, refer to rear axle replacement procedure under "Quattro."

TT

1. Remove rear axle guard panel bolts, then the panel.
2. Remove rear wheels and tires.
3. Unclip brake cables.
4. Disconnect brake lines from axle beam, then plug ends to prevent entry of dirt and moisture.
5. Remove and discard brake caliper mounting bolts, then position caliper aside with suitable wire or rope.
6. Support rear axle.
7. Position transaxle jack tool No. VAG1383 with attachment tool No. 1359/2, or equivalents under axle beam.
8. Remove and discard shock absorber lower bolts at control arms.
9. Remove coil springs.
10. Remove and discard bearing bracket bolts on both sides of axle, then lower the axle.
11. Reverse procedure to install, noting the following:
    a. Lubricate kidney shaped rubber bonded bushings using grease part No. G 052 150 A2, or equivalent.
    b. Vehicle must be standing on its tires when tightening bonded rubber bushing bolts. Otherwise bushings will be placed under stress, reducing service life.
    c. Tighten all fasteners to specifications.
    d. Bleed brake system using pressure bleeder tool No. VAG1869, or equivalent.

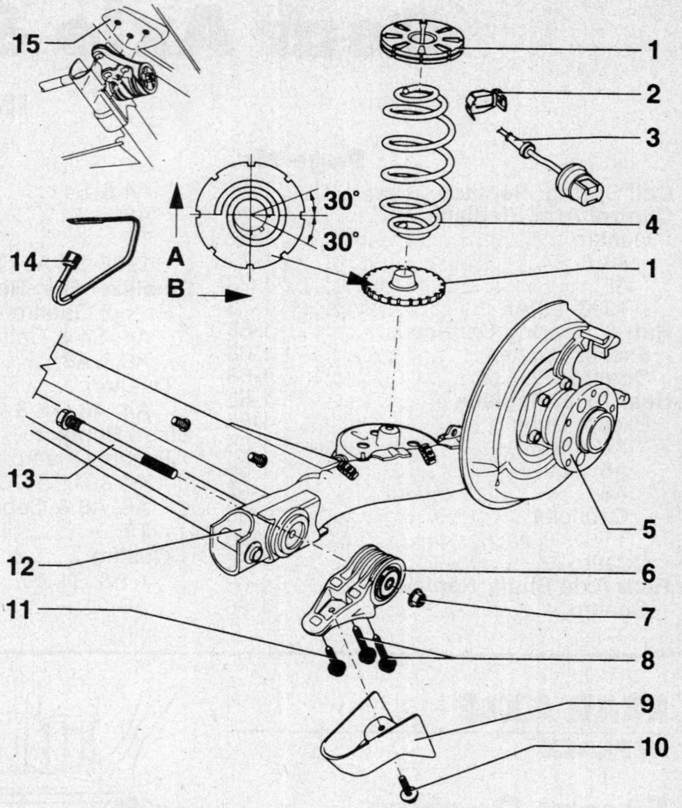

1. Spring Support
2. ABS Wheel Speed Sensor Retainer
3. ABS Wheel Speed Sensor
4. Coil Spring
5. Wheel Bearing/Hub Unit
6. Mounting Bracket
7. Nut
8. Bolt M12 x 1.5 x 90
9. Mounting Bracket Stone Deflector
10. Bolt
11. Bolt M12 x 1.5 x 60
12. Axle Beam
13. Bolt M14 x 1.5 x 190
14. Retaining Strap
15. Threads In Longitudinal Member

AD1069900080000X

Fig. 3 Rear axle assembly. 1998–99 A6 except Quattro

Quattro

Refer to "All Wheel Drive Systems" section.

REAR AXLE SHAFT

REPLACE

Quattro

1998–99 A6 QUATTRO

1. Remove wheels.
2. Disconnect connector behind three

way catalytic converter and remove rear part of exhaust system.
3. Support driveshaft using wire or similar device.
4. Mark installation position of driveshaft before removing.
5. Disconnect parking brake cable from brake calipers.
6. Disconnect parking brake cables from retaining brackets.
7. Press parking brake cable retaining clips together and push parking brake cables out from control arms.
8. Remove brake caliper retaining bolts.
9. Remove ABS wheel speed sensor wiring from axle beam and sensor from knuckle.
10. Disconnect control arm from suspension strut, **Fig. 5.**
11. Place suitable transaxle jack under final drive.
12. Remove axle beam bolts.
13. Lower rear axle using transaxle jack.
14. Reverse procedure to install noting the following:
    a. Axle beam must be aligned properly during installation.
    b. To align axle beam transversely, determine distance between axle beam and longitudinal member. Gap "A" must be same on lefthand and righthand sides, **Fig. 6.**
    c. To align axle beam longitudinally, measure dimension "A," **Fig. 7,** which should be 19.76–19.92 inches.
    d. Tighten bolts for axle beam to 81 ft. lbs., then rotate an additional ¼ turn.

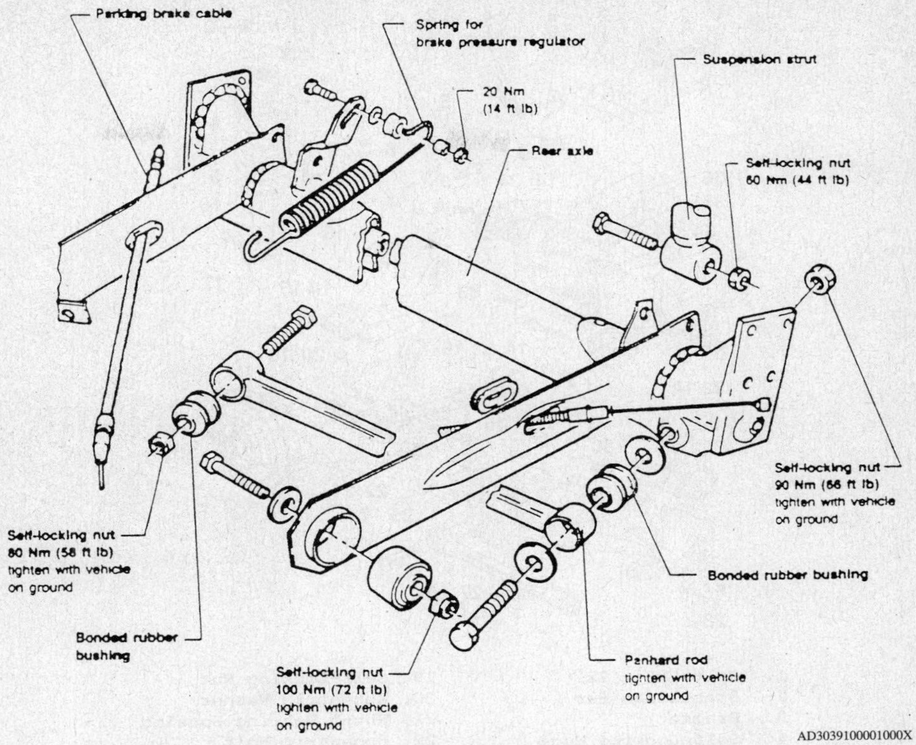

Fig. 4 Rear axle assembly. Cabriolet

A4 & S4

1. Remove cap from wheel using removal tool No. 3208, or equivalent, then loosen lug nuts.
2. Remove axle bolt and washer **Fig. 8.** Remove and install axle bolt only with tires on ground. **Do not move vehicle without driveshaft or outer constant velocity joint installed.**
3. Raise and support vehicle, then remove wheel.
4. Pull speed sensor out of axle housing slightly.
5. Loosen but do not remove lower control arm bolts at subframe.
6. Remove lower strut bolt from lower control arm.
7. Remove bolts from driveshaft flange at transaxle.
8. Remove lower mounting bolt for strut.
9. Remove bolts retaining knuckle to upper control arm and stabilizer bar link.
10. With the aid of an assistant, press down on knuckle and remove axle shaft.
11. Reverse procedure to install, noting the following:
    a. Ensure splines of driveshaft and wheel hub are free of oil, grease and old locking compound.
    b. Press speed sensor into wheel housing up to stop by hand.
    c. Replace seal between axle shaft and drive flange, self-locking nuts for transverse link and lower strut mounting and bolt securing axle shaft to wheel hub.
    d. Do not tighten to specification any bolt or nut securing a rubber bushed mounting until vehicle suspension is settled and on level ground.
    e. Tighten all other nuts and bolts to specifications.

A8

1. Pull cap off disc wheel using suction cup.
2. Loosen flanged bolt, **Fig. 9.**
3. Remove wheel and pull out wheel speed sensor.
4. Fasten brake disc to wheel hub using wheel bolt.
5. Remove bolts for brake caliper and tie caliper up to body with wire.
6. Remove brake disc.
7. Remove cover plate for brake disc by removing bolts.
8. Install spring tensioner and spring holder tool Nos. VAG 1752/1 and VAG 1752/3, or equivalents onto coil spring.
9. Remove pretensioned spring together with spring tensioner.
10. Disconnect drive axle from drive flange.
11. Remove knuckle mounting nut and bolt.
12. Remove lower control arm to link bolt.
13. Disconnect tie rod and pull out of knuckle.
14. Disconnect link rod and press out of knuckle.
15. Remove flanged bolt.
16. Pull upward on knuckle and remove drive axle.
17. Reverse procedure to install noting the following:
    a. Tighten to specifications.
    b. When installing drive axle make sure that gasket is glued onto inner CV joint.
    c. To tighten fasteners between knuckle and lower control arm, tie rod and knuckle, lift wheel carrier high enough so that shock absorber is compressed approximately 1.6–2.0 inches.

TT

1. Raise and support vehicle so load is off rear axle. Tires should still be on ground.
2. Remove drive axle flange 12-point nut, then separate drive axle from final drive flange.
3. When removing lefthand side axle shaft, push exhaust system to side using a suitable pry bar.
4. Remove drive axle using puller tool No. 3283, or equivalent.
5. Reverse procedure to install, noting the following:
    a. Remove any corrosion or paint residue from outer joint splines and threads.
    b. Insert outer joint as far as possible into hub splines.
    c. Pull outer joint into hub until joint reaches installation position in wheel bearing.
    d. Place drive axle inner joint in position, then **torque** bolts to 30 ft. lbs.
    e. Lower vehicle until tires reach ground.
    f. **Torque** 12-point hub nut to 221 ft. lbs., then back off ½ turn. **Torque**

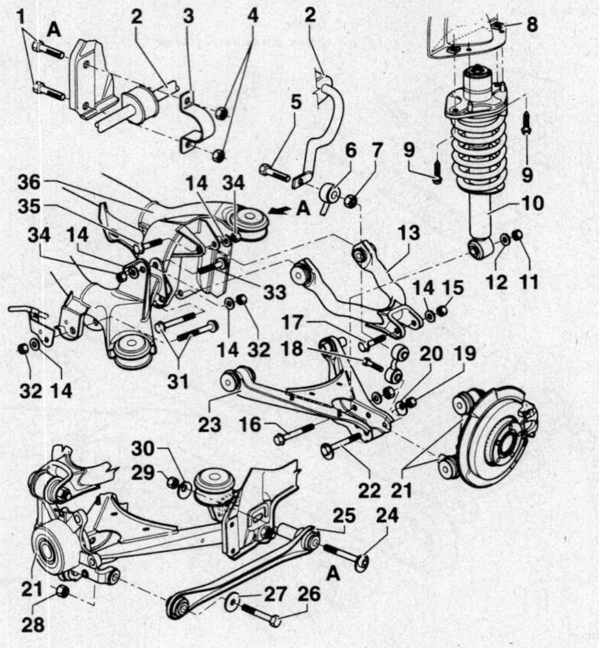

1. Bolts M8 x 22
2. Stabilizer Bar
3. Bracket
4. Self-Locking Nuts
5. Bolts M10 x 50
6. Connecting Link
7. Self-Locking Nut
8. Threads In Wheel Housing
9. Bolts
10. Suspension Strut
11. Self-Locking Nut
12. Washer
13. Upper Control Arm
14. Washer
15. Self-Locking Nut
16. Bolt M12 x 1.5 x 95
17. Bolt M12 x 1.5 x 95
18. Bolt
19. Self-Locking Nut
20. Eccentric Washer
21. Wheel Bearing Housing
22. Eccentric Bolt
23. Lower Control Arm
24. Eccentric Bolt
25. Track Rod
26. Bolt M12 x 1.5 x 85
27. Washer
28. Self-Locking Nut
29. Self-Locking Nut
30. Eccentric Washer
31. Bolt M12 x 1.5 x 100
32. Self-Locking Nut
33. Bolt M12 x 1.5
34. Self- Locking Nut
35. Bolt M12 x 1.5 x 80
36. Axle Beam

Fig. 5 Rear suspension. 1998–99 A6 Quattro

again to 37 ft. lbs.

g. Place a suitable mark at position "A" of 12-point hub nut, **Fig. 10.**
h. Place another mark at position "B" on hub above next indentation.
i. Rotate hub nut until marks align.
j. Tighten all fasteners to specifications.

HUB & BEARING SERVICE

Except Quattro

1. Remove wheel and tire, then the brake caliper as outlined under "Disc Brake Service."
2. Pry off bearing grease cap using removal tool VW 637-2, or equivalent and a suitable hammer, then remove cotter pin and hub nut, **Figs. 11 through 14.**
3. Remove wheel hub, then drive out outer wheel bearing with a suitable copper drift.
4. Drive off ABS sensor rotor evenly using a drift inserted through tapped holes in wheel hub.
5. Drive out inner wheel bearing with copper drift.
6. Reverse procedure to install, noting the following:
   a. Install inner wheel bearing using installation tool Nos. VW 295 and VW 512, or equivalents, **Fig. 15.**
   b. Press ABS sensor wheel onto wheel hub using installation tool Nos. VW 401, VW 402, VW 32-119 and VW 401, or equivalents, **Fig. 16.**
   c. Install outer wheel bearing using installation tool Nos. VW 407 and VW 30-506, or equivalents, **Fig. 17.**
   d. Adjust wheel bearing play as outlined under "Wheel Bearing, Adjust" in this section.

Quattro

1. Remove rear drive axle as outlined under "Rear Axle Shaft, Replace."

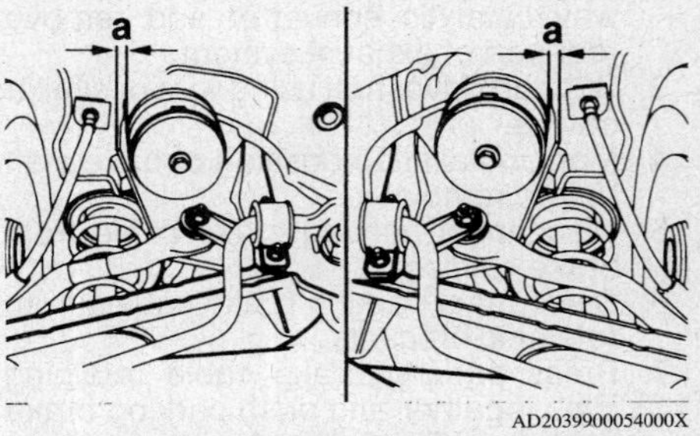

Fig. 6 Axle beam transverse alignment. 1998–99 A6 Quattro

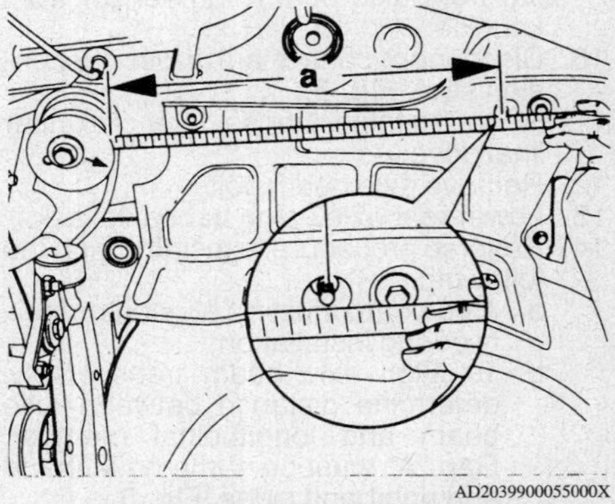

Fig. 7 Axle beam longitudinal alignment. 1998–99 A6 Quattro

2. Remove brake disc and caliper as outlined under "Disc Brake Service," then the anti-lock brake sensor and disc brake splash shield.
3. Remove bolt from lower knuckle to pivot mount, then the hub and bearing assembly, **Figs. 18 through 20.**
4. Press out wheel hub using tools illustrated in **Fig. 21.**
5. Press out wheel bearing using tools illustrated in **Fig. 22.**
6. Remove wheel bearing inner race from wheel hub using tools as illustrated in **Fig. 23.**
7. Press new wheel bearing into hub using tools illustrated in **Fig. 24,** ensuring wheel bearing is installed with large inner diameter toward wheel hub.
8. Press hub and bearing assembly onto wheel hub using tool as illustrated in **Fig. 25,** ensuring press tool bears only against inner race.
9. Reverse procedure to install, noting the following:
   a. Ensure splines of driveshaft and wheel hub are free of oil, grease and old locking compound.
   b. Press speed sensor into wheel housing up to stop by hand.
   c. Replace seal between axle shaft and drive flange, self-locking nuts for transverse link and lower strut mounting and bolt securing axle shaft to wheel hub.
   d. Tighten nuts and bolts to specifications.

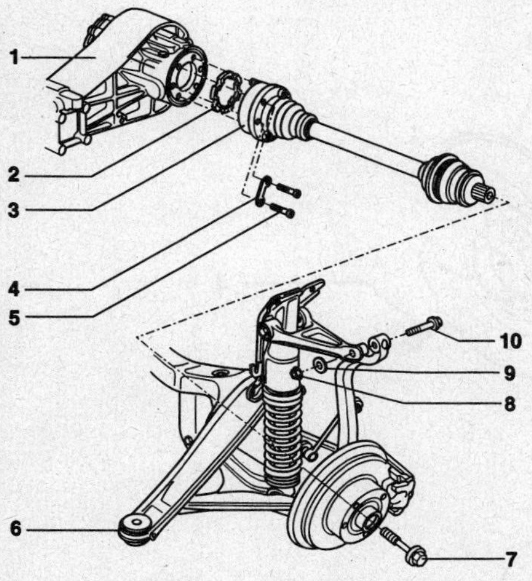

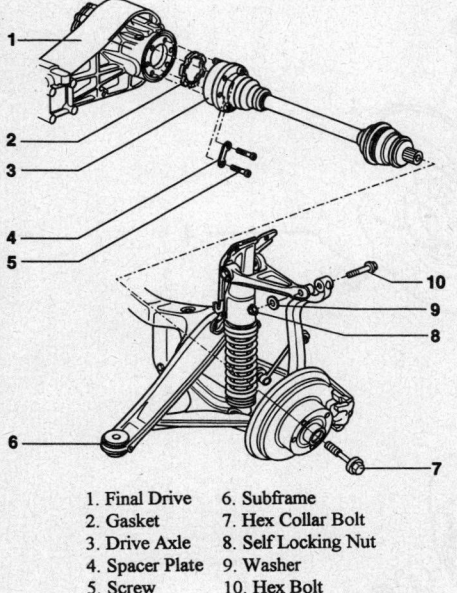

1. Final Drive
2. Gasket
3. Drive Axle
4. Spacer Plate
5. Screw
6. Subframe
7. Hex Collar Bolt
8. Self Locking Nut
9. Washer
10. Hex Bolt

AD2039600039000X

Fig. 8 Exploded view of rear axle shaft assembly. A4 & S4

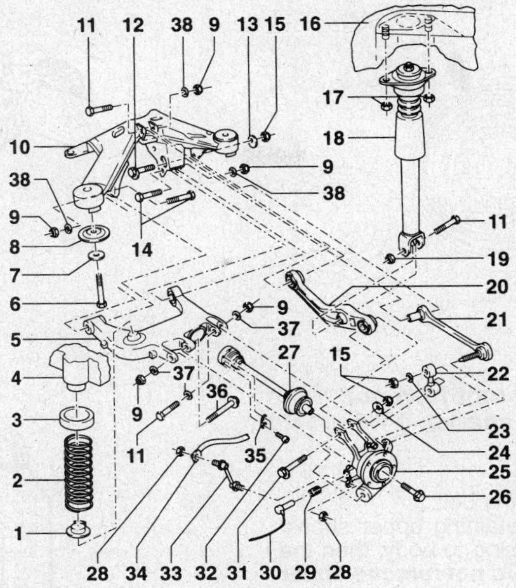

1. Spring Retainer, Lower
2. Rear Coil Spring
3. Spring Retainer, Upper
4. Spring Bracket, In Body
5. Control Arm
6. Bolt
7. Washer
8. Plate
9. Self-Locking Nut
10. Rear Subframe
11. Flanged Bolt
12. Eccentric Bolt
13. Eccentric Washer
14. Bolt With Washer
15. Self-Locking Nut
16. Shock Absorber Mount, In Body
17. Self-Locking Nut
18. Shock Absorber
19. Self-Locking Nut
20. Track Control Arm
21. Tie Rod
22. Link
23. Washer
24. Eccentric Washer
25. Wheel Bearing Housing
26. Flanged Bolt
27. Drive Axle
28. Self-Locking Nut
29. Clamping Sleeve
30. Wheel Speed Sensor
31. Eccentric Bolt
32. Drive Axle Flange Bolt
33. Link Rod
34. Stabilizer Bar
35. Backing Plate
36. Flanged Bolt
37. Washer
38. Washer

AD1069900081000X

Fig. 9 Exploded view of rear axle shaft assembly. A8 Quattro

WHEEL BEARING

ADJUST

Except Quattro

1. Raise and support rear of vehicle.
2. Remove grease cap and cotter pin and lock, then, while rotating wheel, tighten bearing adjusting nut until it is firmly seated against bearing thrust plate.
3. **On TT models,** install a new self-locking 12-point hub nut, then **torque** to 129 ft. lbs. No further adjustment is possible or required.
4. **On all models except TT,** back off adjusting nut and inspect wheel bearing clearance. Proper clearance is when bearing thrust washer can be moved slightly with a screwdriver and finger pressure.
5. **On all models,** after completing adjustment, install cotter pin and lock, grease cap and lower vehicle.

Quattro

Quattro models use a sealed one piece rear wheel bearing which is not adjustable.

STRUT

REPLACE

Except Quattro

A4 & S4

1. Raise and support vehicle, then remove wheel and tire assemblies.
2. Remove strut mounting bolts, then the strut from the axle beam, **Fig. 26.**
3. Remove rear seat back rest, then the upper strut mounting bolts, **Fig. 27.**
4. Turn strut until four catches are positioned above recesses, then pull strut down and out of fixture.
5. Reverse procedure to install.

A6, A8 & CABRIOLET

1. Raise and support vehicle, then remove wheel and tire assembly.
2. Support axle with suitable jack.
3. Remove lower strut mounting bolt.
4. Remove upper strut to vehicle mountings, then the strut assembly.
5. Reverse procedure to install. Tighten strut attaching nuts and lower strut attaching bolt to specifications with wheels resting on ground.

TT

1. Disconnect wheel speed sensor electrical connector, then the wiring from retainer on coil spring.
2. Remove and discard strut upper mount bolts with vehicle standing on its tires. Raise vehicle until bolts are accessible if required.
3. Raise vehicle to a working height to relieve load on coil spring.
4. Observe coil spring mounting orientation, then remove spring.
5. Remove and discard strut to rear axle mounting nut.
6. Remove strut assembly from vehicle.
7. Reverse procedure to install, noting the following:
   a. Ensure coil spring is installed with its end against stop on spring seat.
   b. Push rear axle upward using jack tool No. VAG1359/2, or equivalent.
   c. Vehicle must be standing on its tires when tightening bonded rubber bushing bolts. Otherwise bushings will be placed under stress, reducing service life.
   d. Tighten all nuts and bolts to specifications.

Quattro

A4 & S4

1. Raise and support vehicle, then remove wheels.
2. Place a suitable support under lower suspension arm.
3. Remove inner pivot bolt from upper suspension arm, **Fig. 28** and loosen outer bolt.
4. Pull upper arm away from upper shock mount and position aside. Do not allow excessive strain on brake fluid lines, axle boots and wiring.

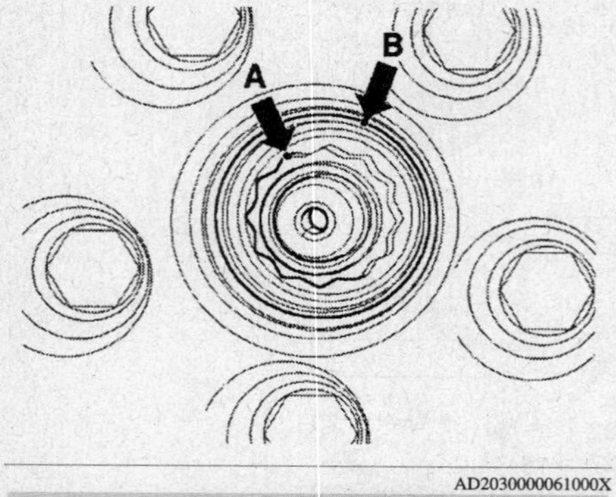

Fig. 10 12-point hub nut alignment marks. TT

5. Remove lower strut bolt.
6. Remove bolts retaining upper shock/suspension housing to body, then the strut assembly. **Do not remove upper strut bolt.**
7. Reverse procedure to install, noting the following:
   a. Loosely assemble and do not tighten to specification bolts for rubber bushed mountings until vehicle has been lowered to the ground.
   b. Tighten all fasteners to specifications.

A6

1. Raise and support vehicle, then remove wheel.
2. Place a suitable support under lower suspension arm.
3. Remove bolt from lower strut assembly mount.
4. Remove bolts at top strut mounting, then the strut assembly.
5. Reverse procedure to install, noting the following:
   a. Jack up knuckle until mounting nuts can be installed at top strut assembly mounting.
   b. Tighten nuts to specifications.

A8

1. Remove wheel.
2. Remove brake caliper retaining bolts.
3. Remove stabilizer bar brackets.
4. Remove connecting link from stabilizer bar.
5. Remove bolt for upper control arm.
6. Remove suspension strut to body bolts.
7. Remove suspension strut to control arm bolt and remove suspension strut.
8. Move knuckle slightly downward to remove suspension strut.
9. Reverse procedure to install.

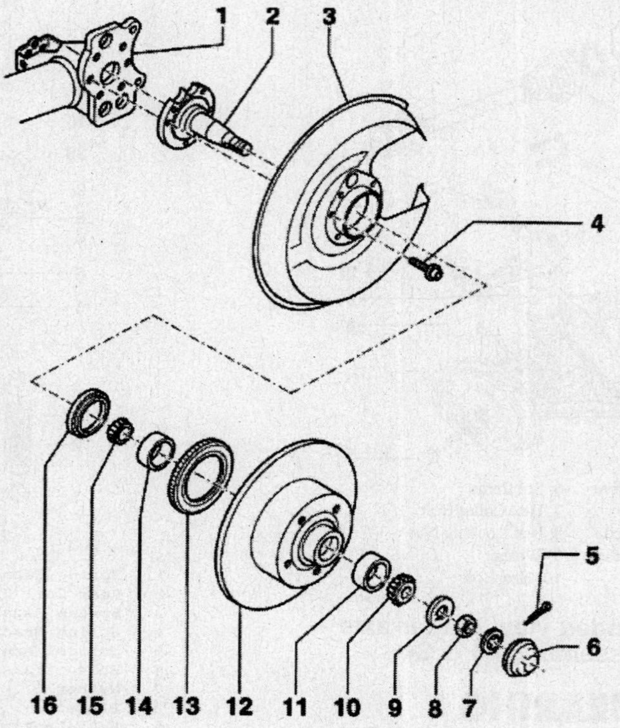

1- Axle Beam
2- Stub Axle
3- Splash Shield
4- Bolt
5- Cotter Pin
6- Grease Cap
7- Slotted Ring
8- Castle Nut
9- Thrust Washer
10- Outer Bearing
11- Outer Bearing Outer Race
12- Brake Disc And Hub
13- ABS Sensor Outer Race
14 - Inner Bearing Outer Race
15- Inner Bearing
16- Grease Seal

AD2030000062000X

Fig. 11 Exploded view of hub & bearing assembly. A4 & S4 except Quattro

STRUT SERVICE

Except Quattro

A4 & S4

DISASSEMBLE

1. Clamp strut holder tool No. VAG 1752-2, or equivalent in a suitable vise, then install strut in holder, **Fig. 29.**
2. Pry out strut cap using a suitable screwdriver, **Fig. 30,** then place tensioning tool No. 1752-1, or equivalent onto coil spring, **Fig. 31.**
3. Ensure coil spring is properly seated in tensioning device, then compress coil spring until upper spring retainer is free.
4. Remove strut top nut from piston rod, **Fig. 32,** then the washer, mounting ring, gasket and upper spring retainer.
5. Remove upper spring mount, spacer tube, mounting ring, bottom disc, ring, and auxiliary spring.
6. Remove boot mounting ring, boot, protective cap, coil spring, base and lower spring base.

ASSEMBLE

This procedure has been revised by a Technical service bulletin.

1. Clamp shock absorber in strut mount tool No. VAG 1752-2, or equivalent, then align lower spring base and base in direction of shock absorber eye, **Fig. 33.**
2. Install compressed coil spring with spring tensioner onto shock absorber. **End of coil spring must be positioned at stop on base.**
3. Install protective cap, boot, mounting ring, auxiliary spring, ring, bottom disc,

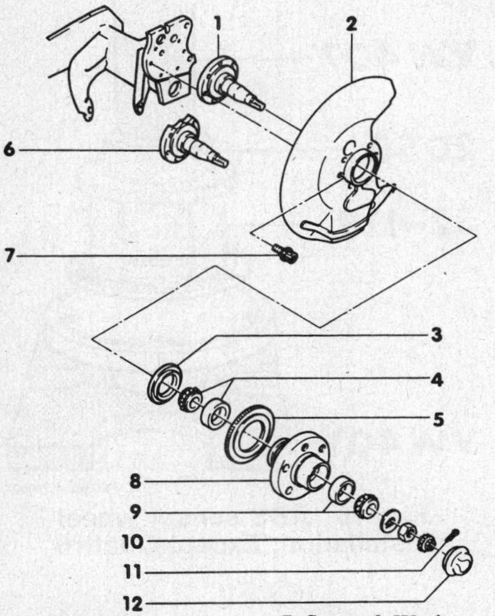

1. Stub Axle
2. Cover Plate
3. Oil Seal
4. Inner Wheel Bearing
5. ABS Wheel Speed Sensor
6. Stub Axle (Vehicles w/ABS)
7. Screw & Washer Assembly
8. Wheel Hub
9. Outer Wheel Bearing
10. Nut
11. Cotter Pin
12. Grease Cap

AD2039600016000X

Fig. 12 Exploded view of hub & bearing assembly. A6 except Quattro

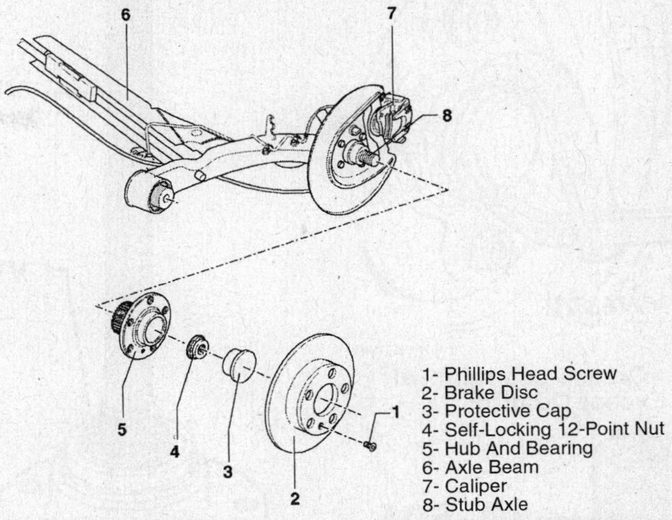

Fig. 13 Exploded view of hub & bearing assembly. TT except Quattro

mounting ring and spacer tube.

4. Install upper spring mount. **Start of spring must be positioned at recess in upper spring mount, Fig. 34.**
5. Install upper spring retainer. **Punched nuts of spring retainer must be located in recesses of upper spring mount, Fig. 35.**
6. Install gasket, mounting ring, washer and lock nut.
7. Mount gauge tool No. VAG 1752-8 onto strut mount tool No. VAG 1752-2, or equivalents, then mount gauge tool No. 1752-8, or equivalent onto upper spring retainer and tighten with hex bolts, **Fig. 36.**
8. Top locking levers of strut mount tool No. VAG 1752-2, or equivalent should be in locked position.
9. Loosen lower locking lever and turn upper spring retainer until scale of strut mount tool No. VAG 1752-2 is positioned at 0°, then place locking lever in locked position, **Fig. 37.**
10. Tighten strut top nut to specifications using tool No. 3379, or equivalent, **Fig. 38.**
11. Using a suitable punch, seat lower spring base and lower spring retainer onto spring, **Fig. 39. Punch should be positioned at raised edge of lower spring base.**
12. Release compressed coil spring. **Ensure upper and lower ends of coil spring are properly positioned.**
13. Remove strut from strut holder VAG 1752-2, or equivalent.
14. Use installation tools VW 401, 402 412 and 3118, or equivalent to press in cap, **Fig. 40. Axis "C" of cap is offset 90° from axis "A" of shock absorber eye, Fig. 41.**

A6

DISASSEMBLE

1. Clamp strut holder tool No. VAG 1752-2, or equivalent in a suitable vise, then install strut in holder, **Fig. 42.**
2. Install bolt into holes of upper spring retainer, then lock in position with clamping lever. **Note position of pointer for installation reference, Fig. 43.**
3. Compress coil spring with spring tensioner tool No. VAG 1752-1, or equivalent, then remove top locknut using removal tool No. 3017A, or equivalent, **Figs. 44 and 45.**
4. Remove rubber bushing, then loosen clamping lever (bottom arrow), **Fig. 46,** then push up height adjuster and swivel to one side.
5. Compress coil spring with spring tensioner, then remove upper spring retainer, damper ring, bump stop, protective sleeve, coil spring, protective cap and lower spring retainer.

ASSEMBLE

1. Extend shock absorber shaft fully, then install lower spring retainer onto shock absorber. **Spring retainer should be turned 90° relative to axis of shock absorber boss, Fig. 47.**
2. Install coil spring with spring tensioner onto shock absorber. **Color coding for coil spring should be facing lower spring retainer.**
3. Assemble lower spring retainer protective cap, protective sleeve, bump stop and dampener ring onto shock absorber.
4. Set height adjuster with upper spring retainer to 45° with aid of scale, then position above strut and clamp tight.
5. Install rubber bushing, then top locking nut and tighten hand tight.
6. Ensure ends of springs are properly seated relative to stops. If required, stops should be pushed up to spring ends so there is no play. **Arrow faces spring end stop on lower spring retainer.**
7. Tighten top locknut to specifications.
8. Release compressed spring, then remove spring tensioner.
9. Remove strut from strut mount.

A8

Refer to **Fig. 48** for strut service.

CABRIOLET

1. Remove strut assembly as outlined under "Strut, Replace."
2. Compress strut spring using a suitable compressor, then remove self-locking nut, washer, upper rubber mounting, damper ring and coil spring.
3. Remove lower rubber mounting, washers, bump stop, protective sleeve, cover plate and spring plate.
4. Reverse procedure to assemble. Tighten self-locking nut to specifications.

TT

1. Remove strut as outlined under "Strut, Replace" in this section.
2. Remove cap, **Fig. 49,** from top of strut.
3. Remove and discard self-locking nut using tool setup illustrated in **Fig. 50.** Tool No. 3079, or equivalent may be used if these items are not available.
4. Remove remaining components, **Fig. 49,** from strut assembly.
5. Reverse procedure to install, noting the following:
   a. Observe all regulations regarding gas-filled shock absorber disposal.

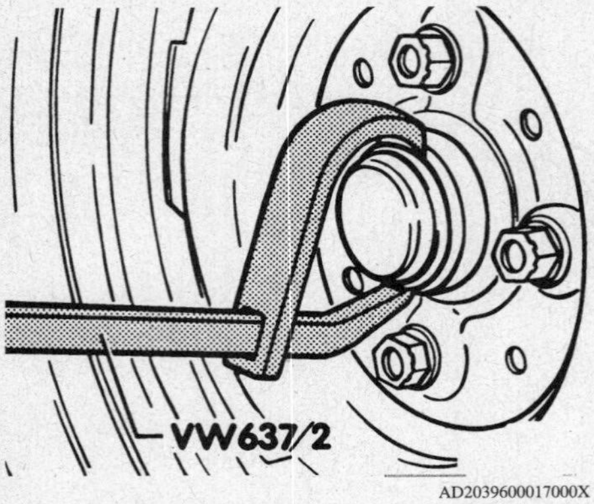

Fig. 14 Grease cap removal. Except Quattro

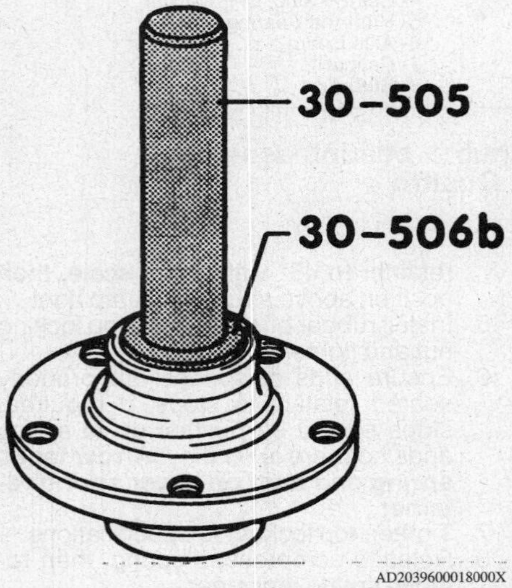

Fig. 17 Outer wheel bearing installation. Except Quattro

b. Inspect all components and replace as required.
c. Install a new self-locking shock absorber mounting nut.
d. Tighten all nuts and bolts to specifications.

Quattro

A4

DISASSEMBLE

1. Install suspension strut into spring tensioner tool No. VAG 1752, or equivalent, **Fig. 51.**
2. Compress coil spring with tensioning device tool No. VAG 1752-1, or equivalent, **Fig. 52. Ensure coil spring is properly located in adapter tool No. VAG 1752-2, or equivalent, Fig. 53.**
3. Remove adapter mounting nut and bolt, then the adapter and damper ring, **Fig. 54.**
4. Remove compressed spring together with tensioner tool No. VAG 1752-1, or equivalent.
5. Remove shock absorber from spring tensioner tool.

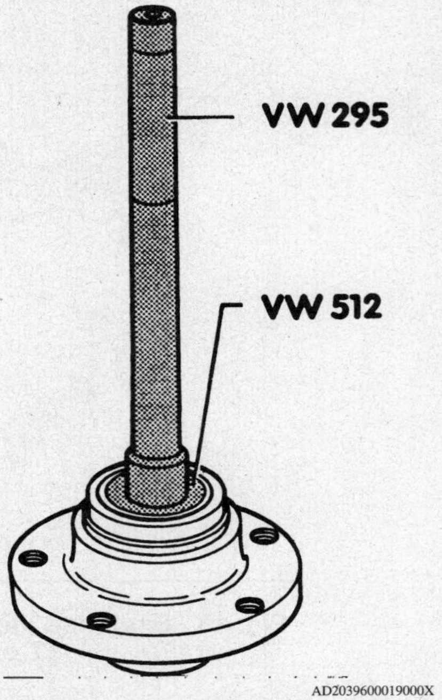

Fig. 15 Inner wheel bearing installation. Except Quattro

ASSEMBLE

1. Clamp shock absorber into tensioner tool No. VAG 1752. Position stop on lower spring retainer as illustrated in **Fig. 55.**
2. Fit compressed spring onto shock absorber. **Colored marking on coil spring must face down toward lower spring retainer. End of coil spring must rest against stop of lower spring retainer.**
3. Install damper so that end of coil spring is positioned against stop of damper ring.
4. Install adapter, then install adapter retaining bolt and tighten nut loosely. **Nut faces front of vehicle.**
5. Install locating bolt "A" into adapter and tighten nut loosely, **Fig. 56.**
6. With locking bolt "D" loose, turn adapter until pointer on degree scale is pointing to 19–23°, then move lever arm "C" with locating bolt "A" into horizontal position relative to height adjustment "B," **Fig. 56.**
7. Tighten locking bolt "D."
8. Release compressed spring and remove tensioner tool.
9. Remove locking bolt "A" from adapter at strut.
10. Tighten adapter mounting nut, then remove strut from tensioner tool.

1998–99 A6

Refer to **Fig. 57** for strut service.

A8

Refer to **Fig. 58** for strut service.

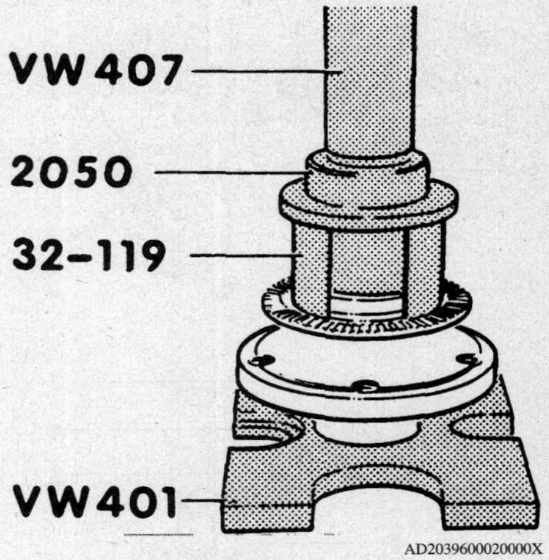

Fig. 16 ABS sensor wheel installation. Except Quattro

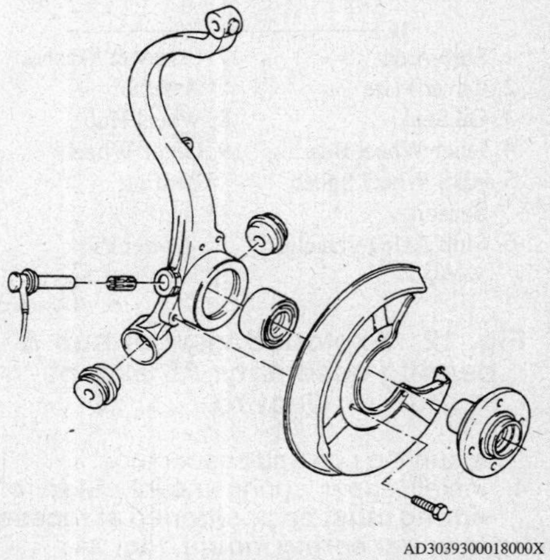

Fig. 18 Exploded view of hub & bearing assembly. A4 & S4 Quattro

COIL SPRING

REPLACE

Refer to "Strut Service" for coil spring removal procedures.

CONTROL ARM

REPLACE

Quattro

A4 & S4

UPPER

Refer to "Strut Replace" in this section.

LOWER

1. Remove cap from wheel using removal tool No. 3208, or equivalent, then loosen lug nuts.
2. Raise and support vehicle, then remove wheels and tires.

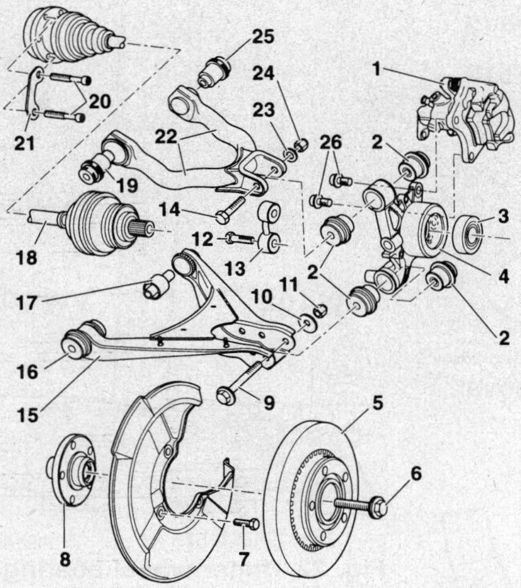

1. Brake Caliper
2. Bonded Rubber Mounts
3. Wheel Bearing
4. Wheel Bearing Housing
5. Brake Disc
6. Bolt For Drive Axle
7. Bolt
8. Hub
9. Eccentric Bolt
10. Eccentric Washer
11. Self-Locking Nut
12. Bolt
13. Connecting Link
14. Bolt M12 x 1.5 x 95
15. Lower Control Arm
16. Front Bonded Rubber Mount For Lower Control Arm
17. Rear Bonded Rubber Mount For Lower Control Arm
18. Drive Axle
19. Front Bonded Rubber Mount For Upper Control Arm
20. Multi-Point Socket Head Bolt M8 x 48
21. Plate
22. Upper Control Arm
23. Washer
24. Self-Locking Nut
25. Rear Bonded Rubber Mount For Upper Control Arm
26. Socket Head Bolt

AD2039900056000X

Fig. 19 Exploded view of hub & bearing assembly. 1998–99 A6 Quattro

3. Remove bracket for ABS wheel speed sensor cable.
4. Disconnect brake lines, **Fig. 59.**
5. Remove lower control arm to strut bolt.
6. Remove parking brake cable.
7. Remove lower control to knuckle bolt.
8. Remove lower control arm to subframe bolt, then the lower control arm.
9. Reverse procedure to install. Bleed brake system and inspect alignment.

1998–99 A6

1. Remove wheel.
2. Remove upper control arm to axle beam bolts.
3. Remove upper control arm to hub retaining bolt and nut.
4. Remove upper control arm.
5. Remove ABS wheel speed sensor wiring.
6. Remove lower control arm to body nuts and bolts.
7. Remove parking brake cable.
8. Remove suspension strut bolt.
9. Remove retaining clip for parking brake cable.
10. Press parking brake cable retaining clip locking lugs together and slide out from lower control arm.
11. Remove track rod to hub retaining bolts.
12. Mark installation position of eccentric washer on lower control arm and remove nut at bolt.
13. Remove lower control arm.
14. Reverse procedure to install

A8

1. Pull cap off disc wheel using suction cup tool No. 3208, or equivalent.
2. Loosen flanged bolt.
3. Remove wheel.
4. Pull out wheel speed sensor and remove electrical harness from brackets on control arm.
5. Remove coil spring.

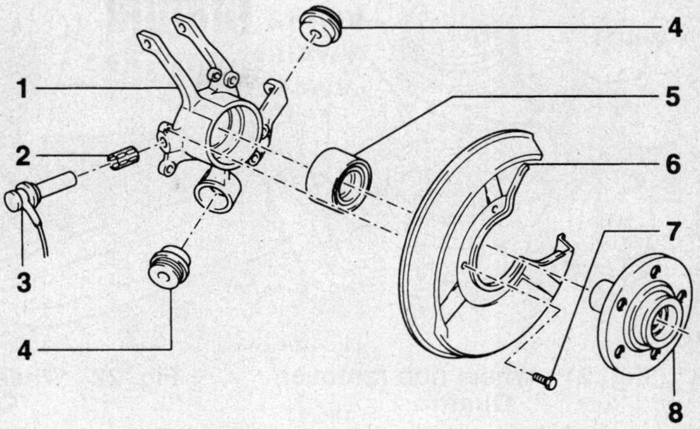

1. Wheel Bearing Housing
2. Clamping Sleeve
3. Wheel Speed Sensor
4. Bonded Rubber Bushing
5. Wheel Bearing
6. Splash Guard
7. Bolt
8. Wheel Hub

AD2039900057000X

Fig. 20 Exploded view of hub & bearing assembly. A8 Quattro

6. Remove control arm to wheel hub nuts and bolts.
7. Remove control arm to body nuts and bolts.
8. Remove lower control arm.
9. Reverse procedure to install.

STABILIZER BAR

REPLACE

Except Quattro

A4, S4 & CABRIOLET

The stabilizer bar is in unit with the rear axle.

A6 & A8

1. Raise and support vehicle.
2. Remove bolts retaining stabilizer bar to axle U beam.
3. Remove stabilizer bar.
4. Reverse procedure to install.

Quattro

A4, A6, A8 & S4

1. Remove stabilizer bar link rod from both side of stabilizer bar.
2. Remove stabilizer bar mounting clamp from both sides of crossmember.
3. Remove stabilizer bar.
4. Reverse procedure to install.

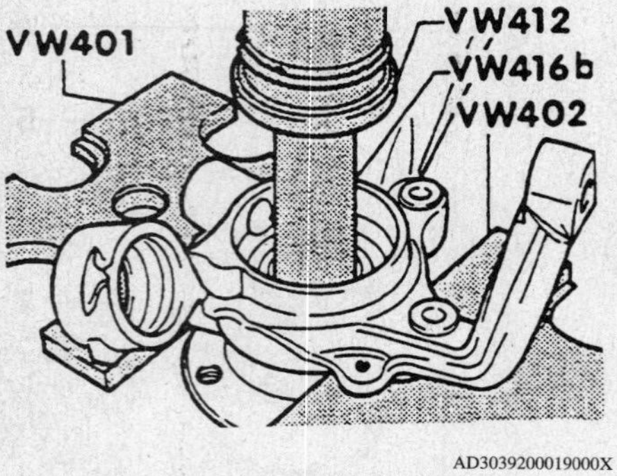

Fig. 21 Wheel hub removal. Quattro

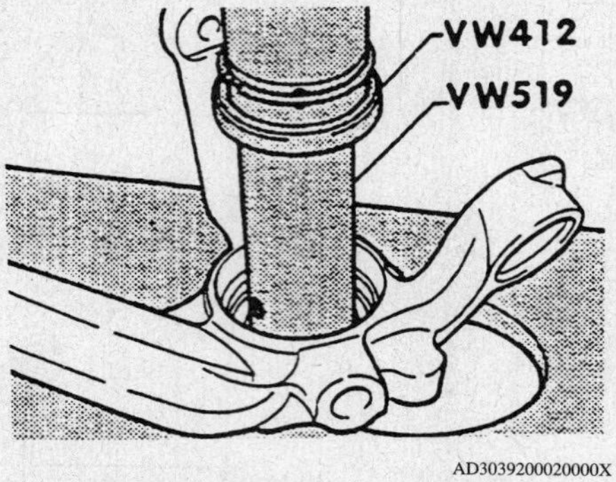

Fig. 22 Wheel bearing removal. Quattro

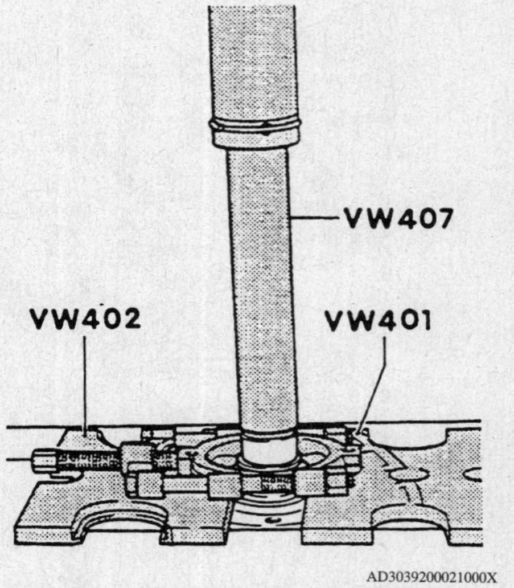

Fig. 23 Inner wheel bearing race removal. Quattro

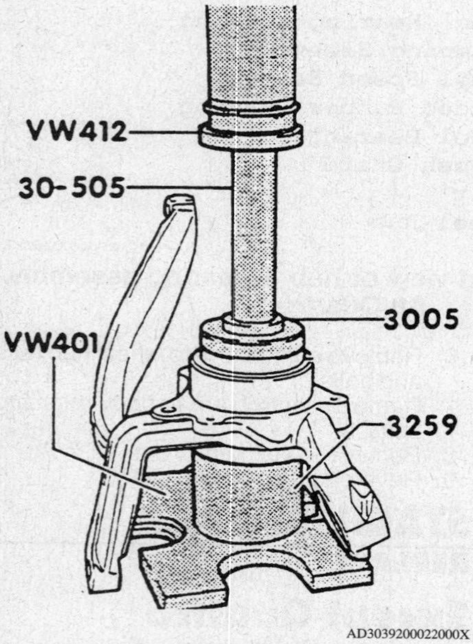

Fig. 24 Wheel bearing installation. Quattro

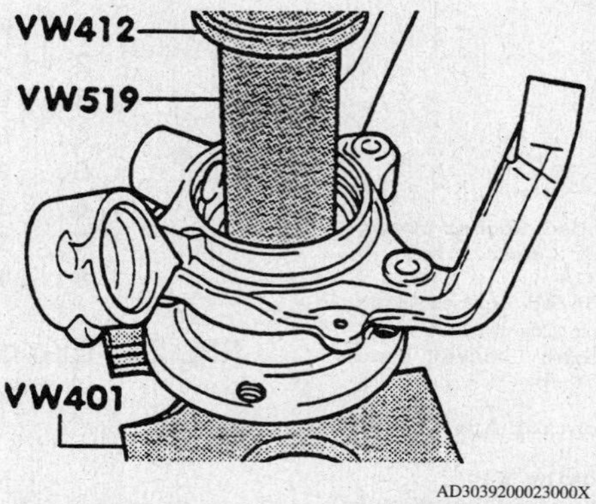

Fig. 25 Wheel hub installation. Quattro

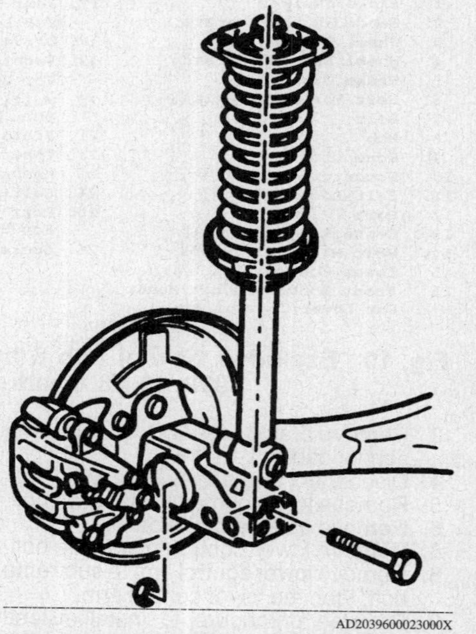

Fig. 26 Rear strut removal. A4 & S4 except Quattro

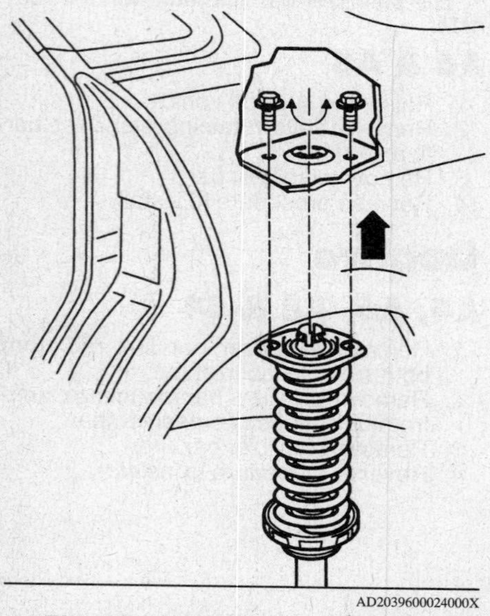

Fig. 27 Upper rear strut bolt removal. A4 & S4 except Quattro

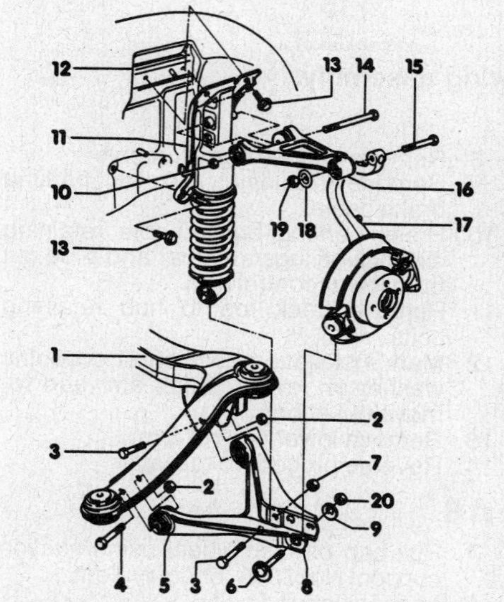

1. Rear Subframe
2. Self Locking Nut
3. Hex Bolt
4. Hex Bolt
5. Lower Control Arm
6. Eccentric Bolt
7. Self Locking Nut
8. Support For Adjusting Camber
9. Eccentric Washer
10. Self Locking Nut
11. Suspension Strut
12. Wheel Housing
13. Hex Bolt & Washer
14. Hex Bolt
15. Hex Bolt
16. Upper Control Arm
17. Wheel Bearing Housing
18. Washer
19. Self Locking Nut
20. Self Locking Nut

AD2039600040000X

Fig. 28 Rear suspension. A4 & S4

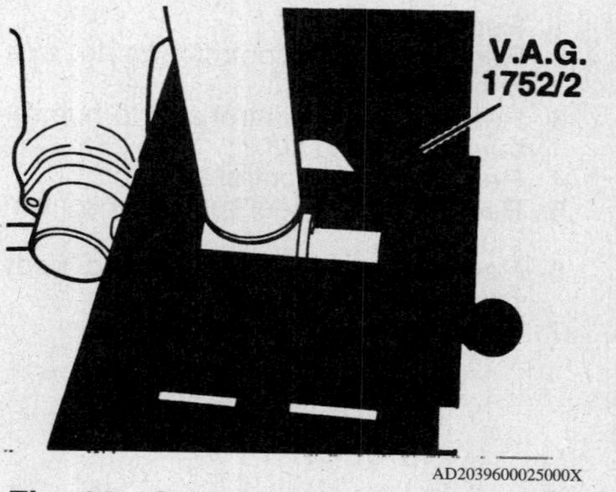

Fig. 29 Strut holder tool. A4 & S4 except Quattro

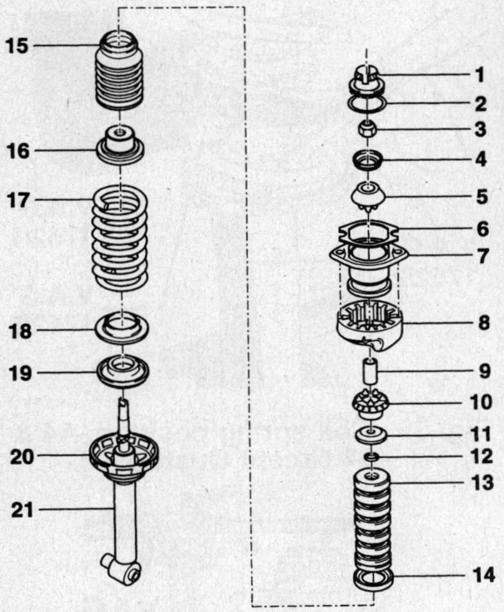

1. Cap
2. O-ring
3. Self Locking Nut
4. Dished Washer
5. Mounting Ring
6. Gasket
7. Upper Spring Retainer
8. Upper Spring Mount
9. Spacer Tube
10. Mounting Ring
11. Bottom Disc
12. Ring
13. Auxiliary Spring
14. Boot Mounting Ring
15. Boot
16. Protective Cap
17. Spring
18. Base
19. Lower Spring Base
20. Lower Spring Seat
21. Gas Shock Absorber

AD2039600026000X

Fig. 30 Exploded view of strut assembly. A4 & S4 except Quattro

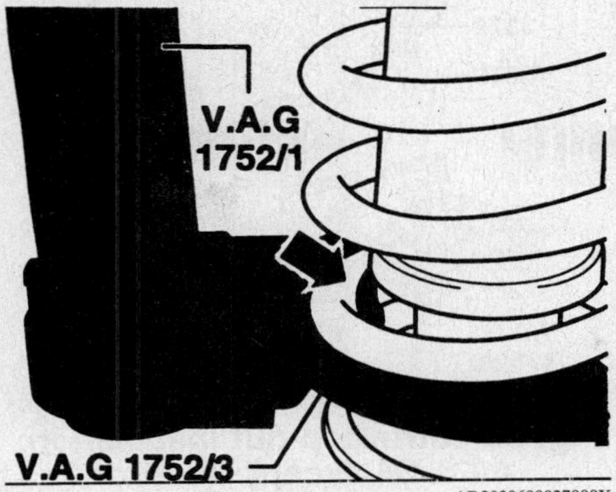

AD2039600027000X

Fig. 31 Tensioning tool installation. A4 & S4 except Quattro

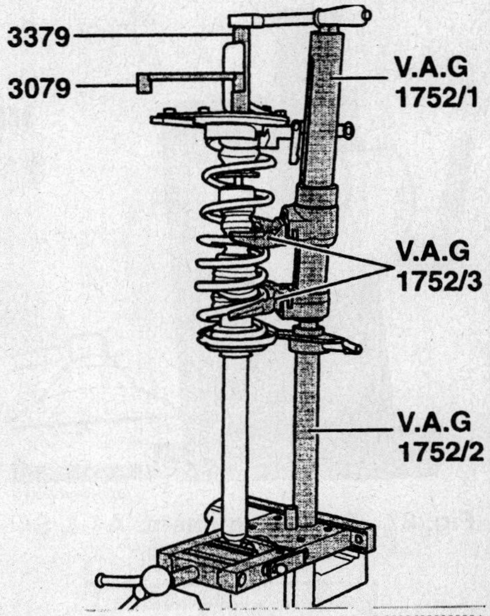

AD2039600028000A

Fig. 32 Strut top nut removal. A4 & S4 except Quattro

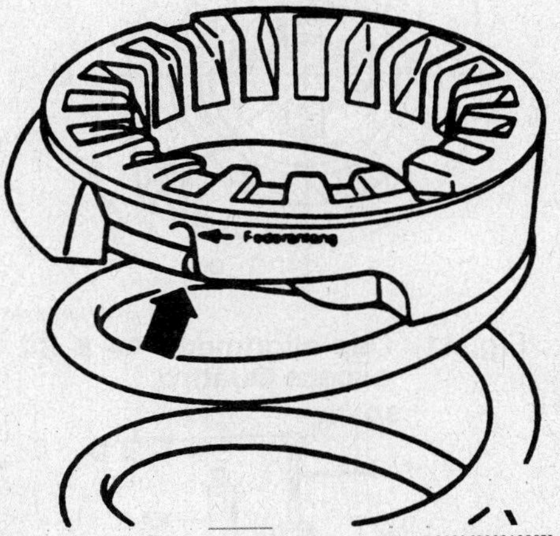

AD2039600031000X

Fig. 34 Upper spring mount installation. A4 & S4 except Quattro

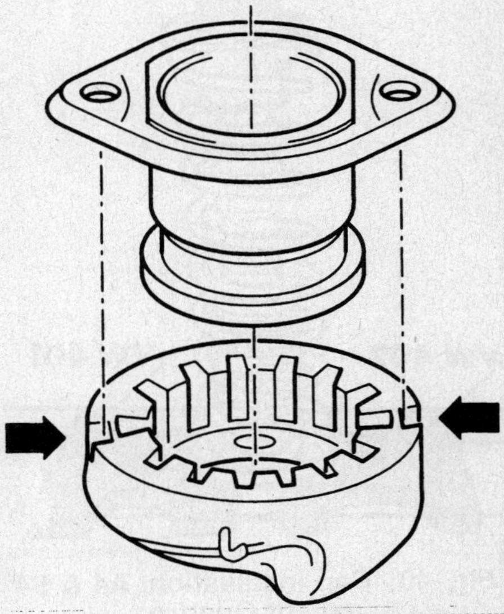

AD2039600032000X

Fig. 35 Upper spring retainer installation. A4 & S4 except Quattro

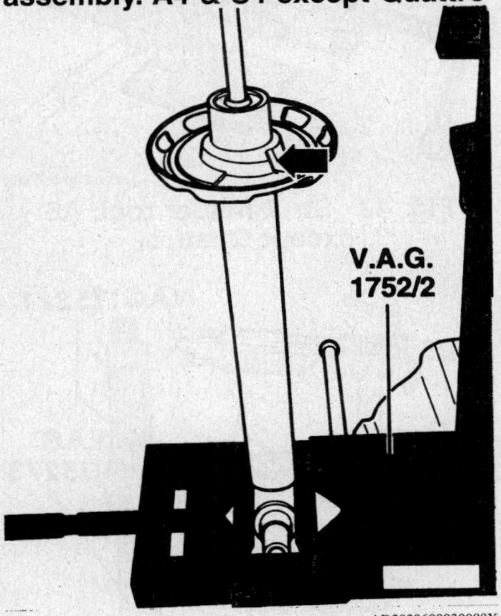

AD2039600030000X

Fig. 33 Lower spring base alignment. A4 & S4 except Quattro

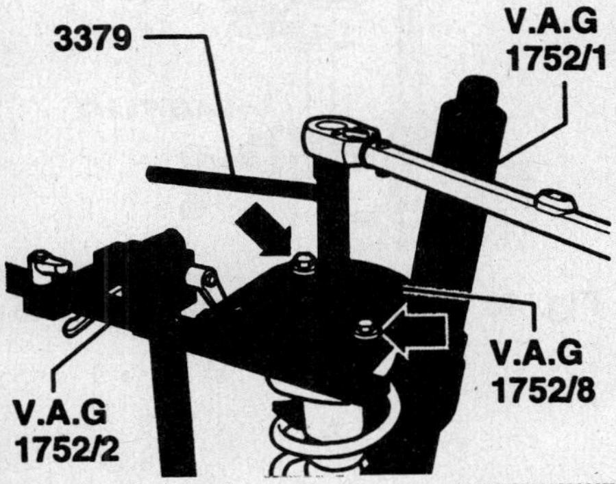

AD2039600033000X

Fig. 36 Gauge tool installation. A4 & S4 except Quattro

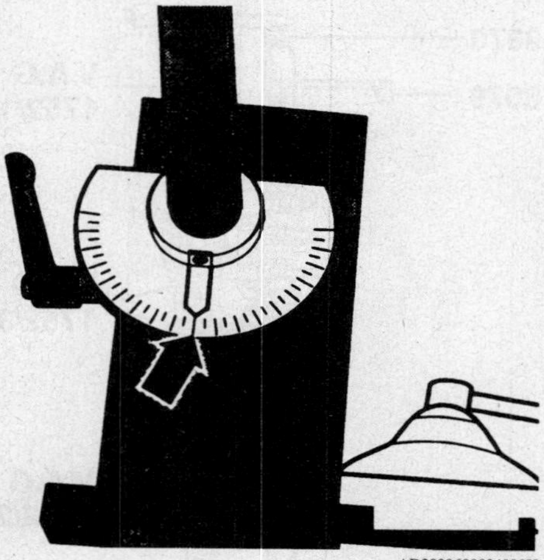

Fig. 37 Scale alignment. A4 & S4 except Quattro

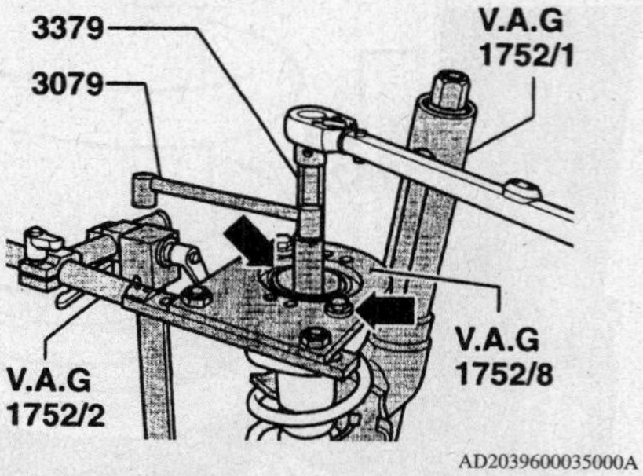

Fig. 38 Strut top nut installation. A4 & S4 except Quattro

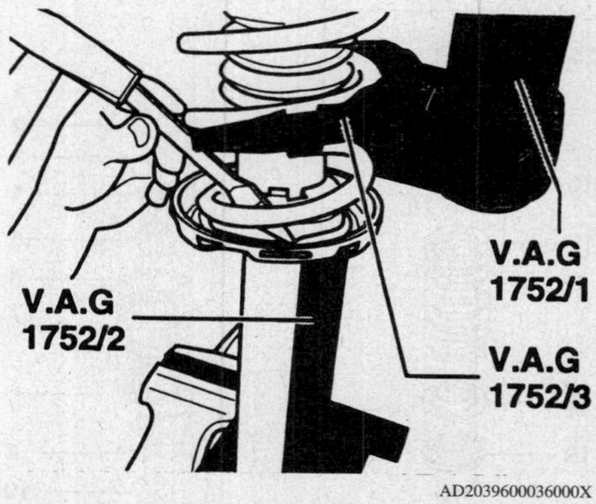

Fig. 39 Coil spring position. A4 & S4 except Quattro

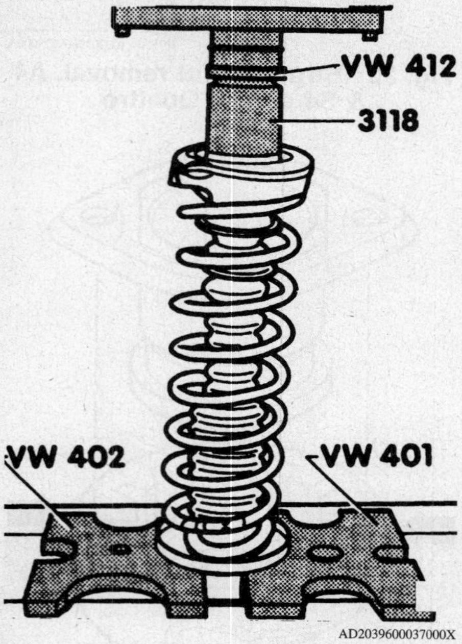

Fig. 40 Cap installation. A4 & S4 except Quattro

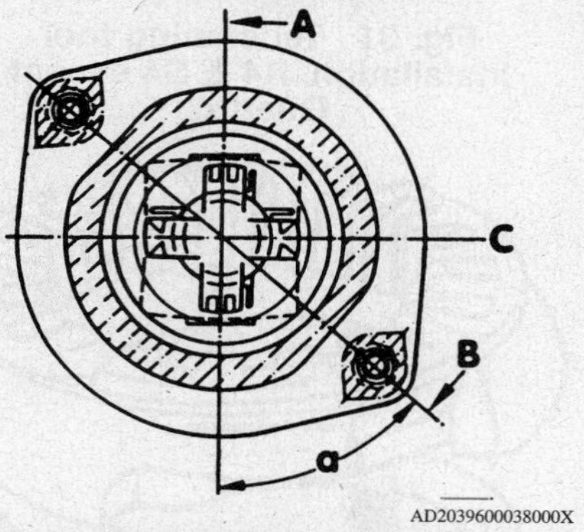

Fig. 41 Cap alignment. A4 & S4 except Quattro

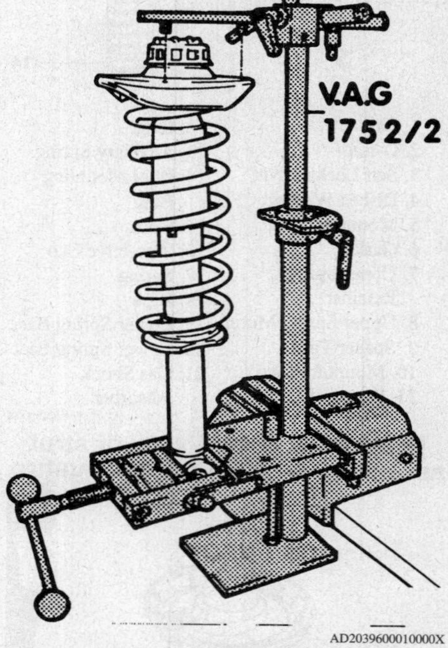

Fig. 42 Strut holder tool. A6 except Quattro

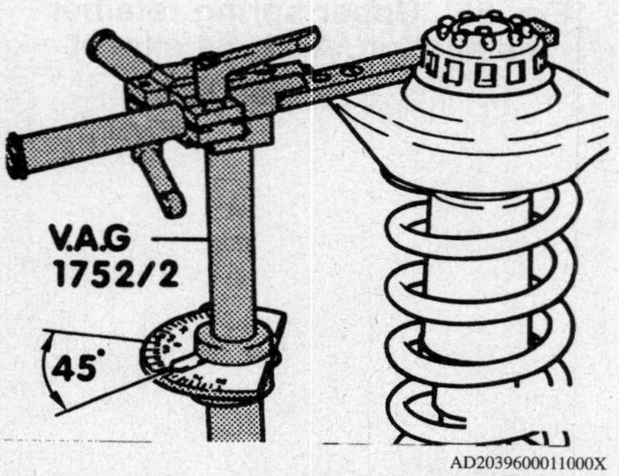

Fig. 43 Reference pointer position. A6 except Quattro

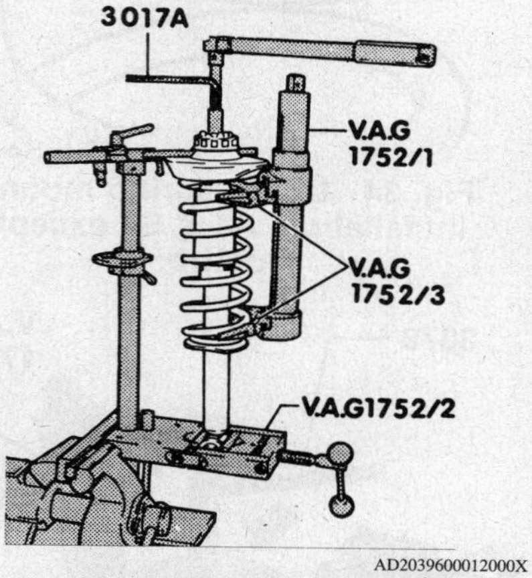

Fig. 44 Locknut removal tool. A6 except Quattro

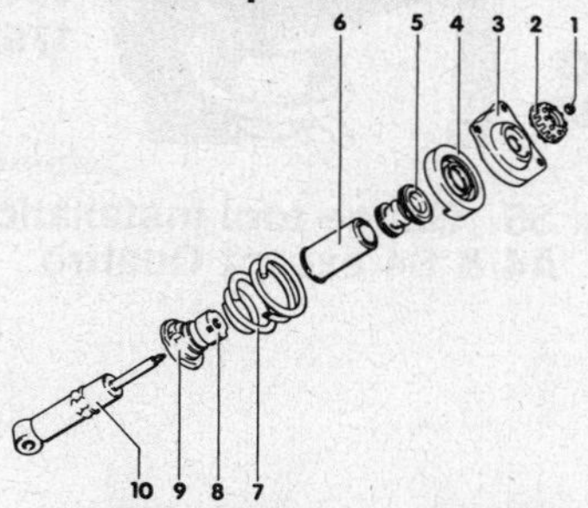

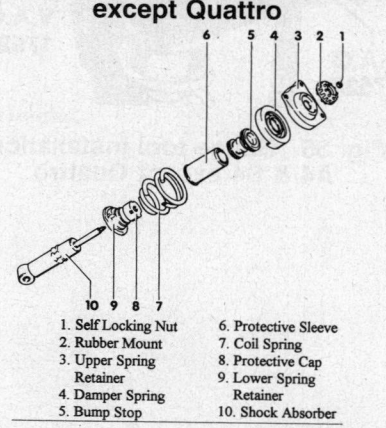

1. Self Locking Nut
2. Rubber Mount
3. Upper Spring Retainer
4. Damper Spring
5. Bump Stop
6. Protective Sleeve
7. Coil Spring
8. Protective Cap
9. Lower Spring Retainer
10. Shock Absorber

AD2039600013000X

Fig. 45 Strut assembly. A6 except Quattro

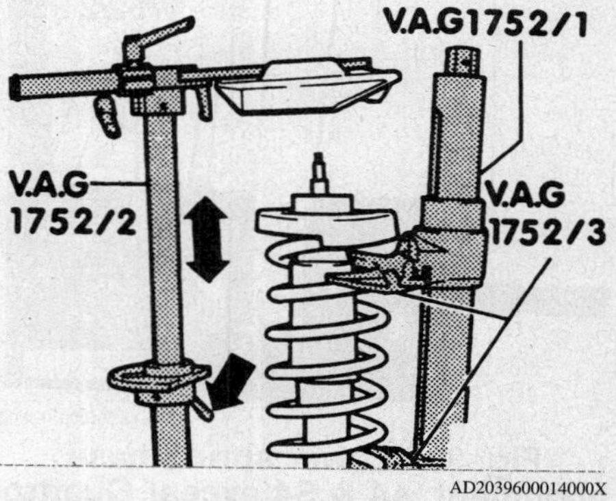

Fig. 46 Clamping lever. A6 except Quattro

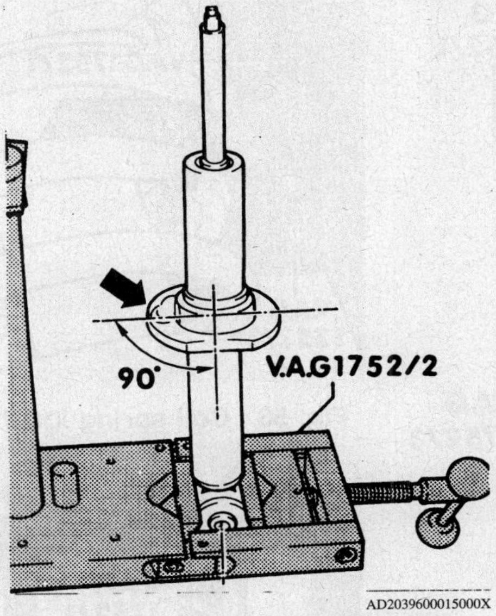

Fig. 47 Lower spring retainer installation. A6 except Quattro

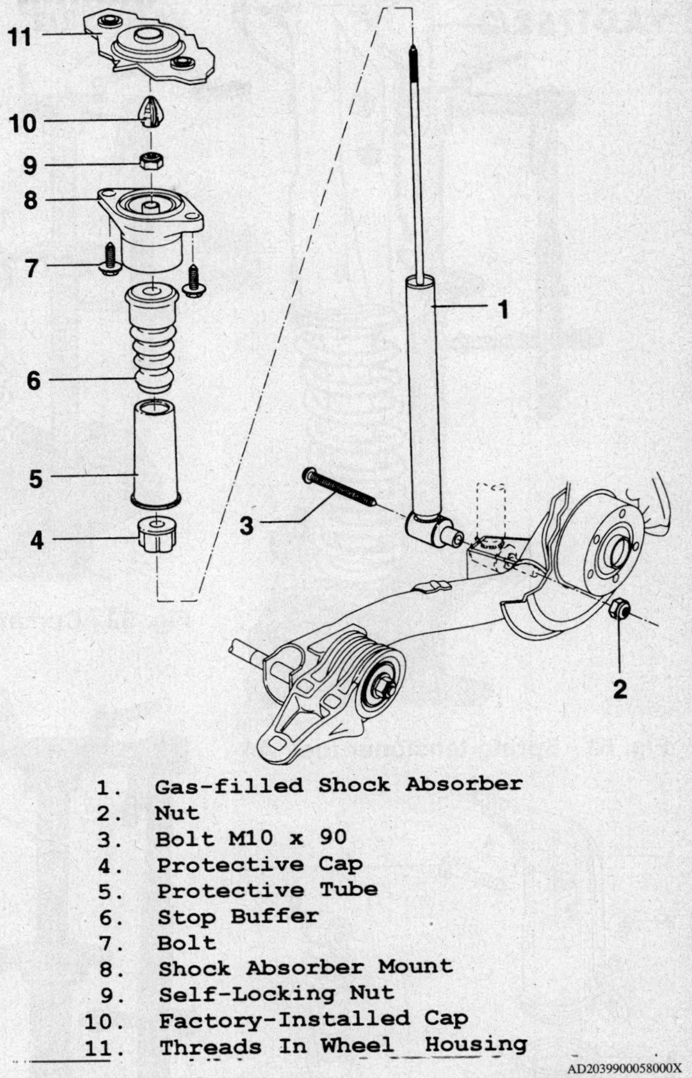

Fig. 48 Exploded view of strut. A8 except Quattro

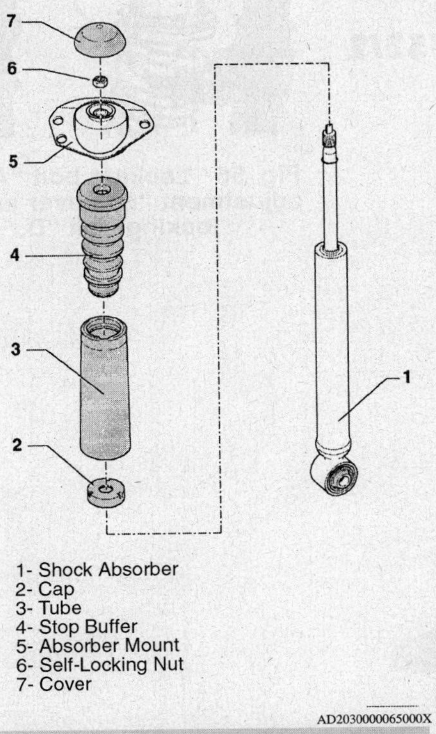

Fig. 49 Exploded view of strut. TT except Quattro

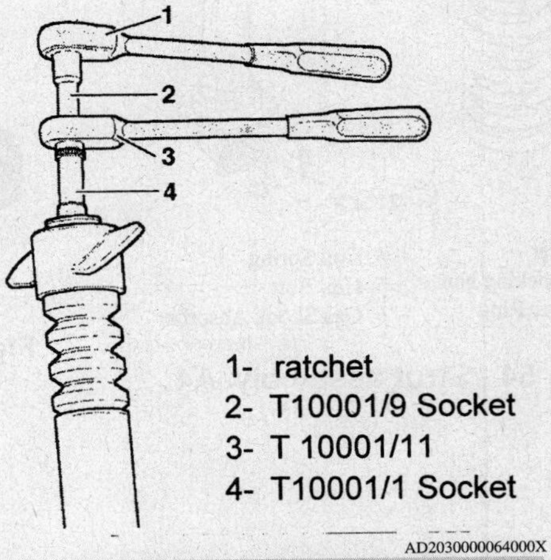

Fig. 50 Tool setup for self-locking nut removal. TT except Quattro

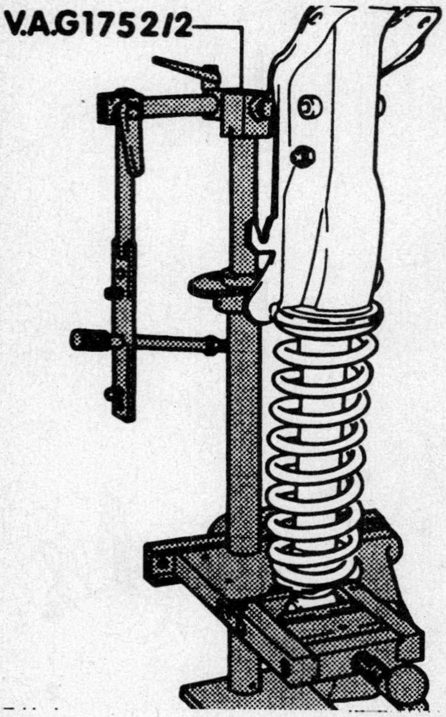

Fig. 51 Spring tensioner tool. A4

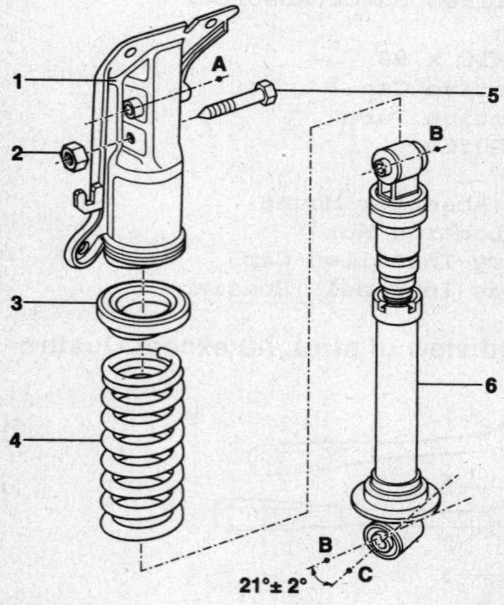

1. Adapter
2. Self Locking Nut
3. Damper Ring
4. Coil Spring
5. Hex Bolt
6. Gas Shock Absorber

Fig. 54 Strut assembly. A4

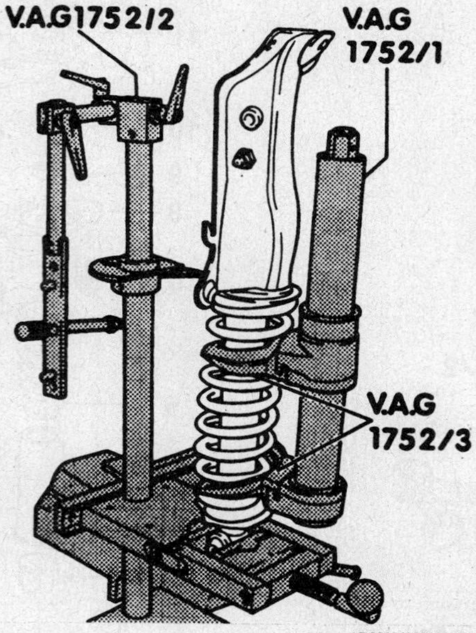

Fig. 52 Compressing coil spring. A4

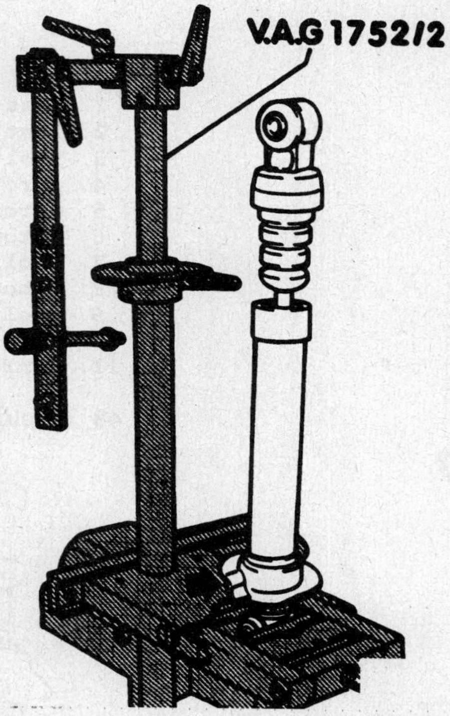

Fig. 55 Lower spring retainer position. A4

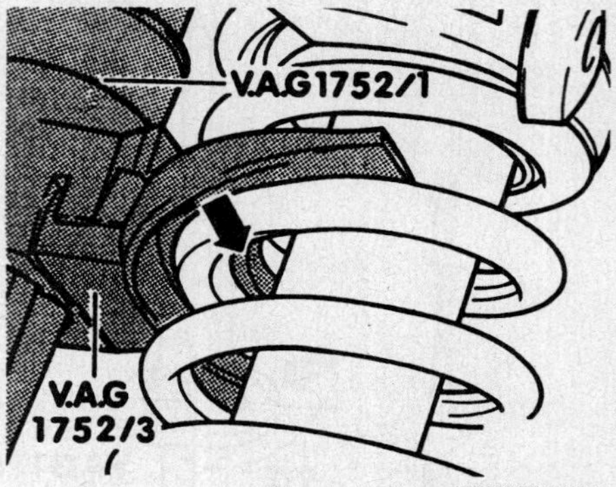

Fig. 53 Coil spring location. A4

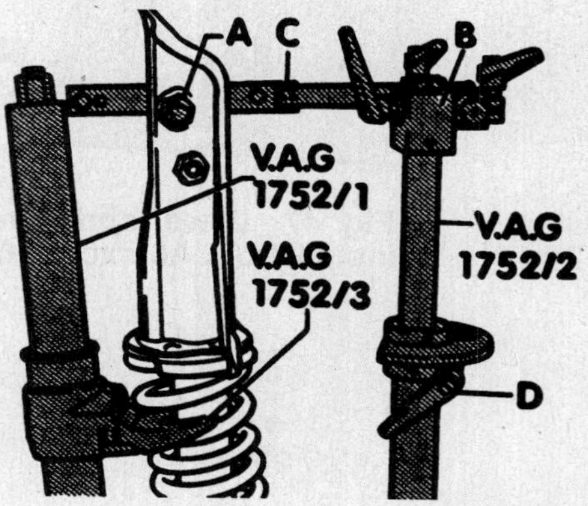

Fig. 56 Locking bolt "A," height adjustment "B," lever arm "C," & locking bolt "D." A4

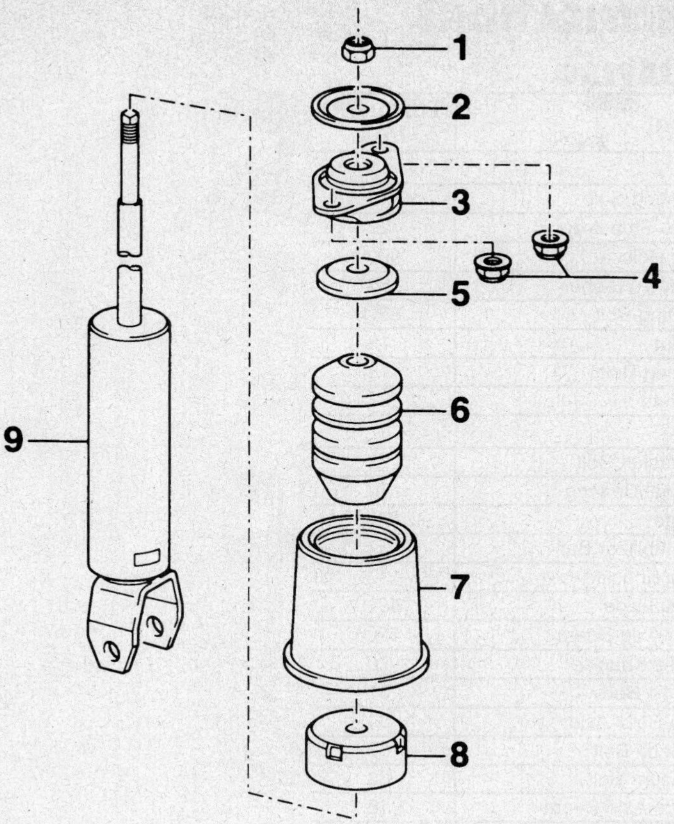

1. Nut
2. Plate
3. Shock Absorber Upper Mount
4. Nut
5. Lower Plate
6. Auxiliary Spring
7. Protective Sleeve
8. Protective Cap
9. Shock Absorber

AD2039900060000X

Fig. 57 Exploded view of strut. 1998–99 A6 Quattro

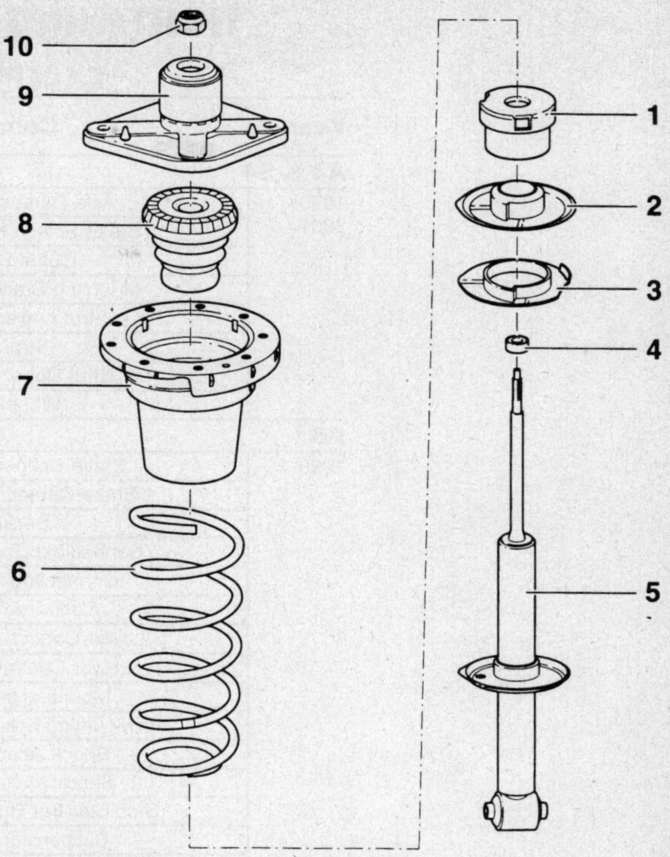

1. Protective Cap
2. Rubber Insert
3. Spring Seat
4. Spacer
5. Gas Filled Shock Absorber
6. Coil Spring
7. Spring Seat With Protective Tube
8. Buffer Stop
9. Shock Absorber Mount
10. Self-Locking Nut

AD2039900059000X

Fig. 58 Exploded view of strut. A8

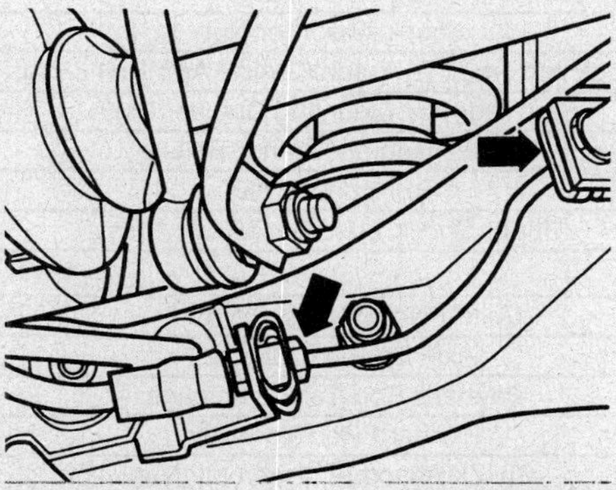

AD2039600047000X

Fig. 59 Brake line removal. A4 & S4 Quattro

TIGHTENING SPECIFICATIONS

EXCEPT QUATTRO

Year	Component	Torque/Ft. Lbs.
A4 & S4		
1998–2001	Axle Damper Mounting Bolt	15
	Brake Splash Plate To Stub Axle	22
	Guide Bushing Bolt	59①
	Mounting Bracket Bolt & Washer	55
	Strut Lower Mounting Bolt	37①
	Strut Top Nut	18
	Strut Upper Mounting Bolts	18
	Wheel Lug Nuts	81
A6		
1998–99	Brake Caliper To Bracket Bolt	22
	Brake Carrier To Wheel Bearing	70
	Backing Plate	84②
	Connecting Link To Stabilizer Bar	37
	Connecting Link To Knuckle	37
	Control Arm To Knuckle	52①
	Lower Control Arm To Axle Beam	52①
	Lower Control Arm To Knuckle	70
	Mounting Bracket To Body	81
	Mounting Bracket To Rear Axle	89
	Shock Absorber Body Bolt	37
	Shock Absorber Mount Bolt	33
	Stabilizer Bar Bracket To Axle Beam	18
	Suspension Strut To Body	33
	Suspension Strut To Control Arm	52①
	Suspension Strut To Lower Control Arm	52①
	Suspension Strut To Rear Axle	37
	Track Rod To Knuckle	70
	Upper Control Arm To Axle Beam	70
	Upper Control Arm To Knuckle	52 ①
	Wheel Bearing Hub Mounting Bolts	44
A8		
1998–2001	Brake Caliper Bolts	44
	Brake Splash Guard Bolts	84②
	Coil Spring Plate Bolt	118①
	Control Arm To Knuckle Bolts & Nuts	52①
	Knuckle Flanged Bolt	148
	Link Rob Nuts	33
	Shock Absorber Nut	18
	Shock Absorber To Track Control Arm Bolt & Nut	48
	Stabilizer Bar Mounting Bracket Bolts	22
	Subassembly Carrier Bolts	118
	Tie Rod Link Nut	70
	Upper Shock Absorber Mount Nuts	22
CABRIOLET		
1998–2001	Axle Pivot Bracket To Body	111
	Axle To Pivot Bracket	59①
	Panhard Rod To Frame Nuts	58
	Panhard Rod To Body	59
	Shock Absorber Assembly Nut	22
	Shock Absorber Assembly To Body Nuts	44
	Trailing Link To Frame Nuts	72
	Wheel Lug Nuts	81

Continued

EXCEPT QUATTRO—Continued

Year	Component	Torque/Ft. Lbs.
TT		
2000–01	Bearing Bracket To Axle	59③
	Brake Caliper Mounting Bolts	48③
	Shock Absorber To Upper Mount Nut	18③
	Strut To Rear Axle Nut	44
	Strut Upper Mount Bolts	22①
	Shock Absorber To Rear Axle Beam Bolts	44③
	Wheel Lug Nuts	89

① — Plus 1/4 (90°) turn.

② — Inch lbs.

③ — Always use new nuts & bolts. Do not install old ones.

QUATTRO

Year	Component	Torque/Ft. Lbs.
A4 & S4		
1998–2001	Axle Bolt (Collar Bolt)	85①
	Brake Splash Guard To Knuckle	84③
	Coupling Rod To Stabilizer Bar	30
	Drive Axle Bolt (Collar Bolt)	85①
	Hub Bolt (Collar Bolt)	85①
	Knuckle To Coupling Rod	37
	Knuckle To Track Rod	37
	Lower Control Arm To Rear Subframe	52①
	Lower Control Arm To Strut	52①
	Lower Control Arm To Knuckle	70
	Rear Subframe Bushing Bolts	81①
	Spacer Plate To Drive Axle	30
	Stabilizer Bar Clamp To Rear Subframe	18
	Strut Adapter To Shock Absorber	52①
	Strut Adapter To Wheel Housing	41
	Track Rod To Rear Subframe	66
	Upper Control Arm To Strut	37①
	Upper Control Arm To Knuckle	37①

Continued

QUATTRO—Continued

Year	Component	Torque/Ft. Lbs.
A6		
1998–99	Brake Caliper To Bracket Bolt	22
	Brake Carrier To Wheel Bearing	70
	Backing Plate	84③
	Connecting Link To Stabilizer Bar	37
	Connecting Link To Knuckle	37
	Control Arm To Knuckle	52①
	Drive Axle To Drive Flange	30
	Drive Axle To Hub	85②
	Lower Control Arm To Axle Beam	52①
	Lower Control Arm To Knuckle	70
	Mounting Bracket To Body	81
	Mounting Bracket To Rear Axle	89
	Shock Absorber Body Bolt	37
	Shock Absorber Mount Bolt	33
	Stabilizer Bar Bracket To Axle Beam	18
	Strut To Body	33
	Strut To Control Arm	52①
	Strut To Lower Control Arm	52①
	Strut To Rear Axle	37
	Track Rod To Knuckle	70
	Upper Control Arm To Axle Beam	70
	Upper Control Arm To Knuckle	52 ①
	Wheel Bearing Hub Mounting Bolts	44
A8		
1998–2001	Brake Caliper Bolts	44
	Brake Splash Guard Bolts	84③
	Coil Spring Plate Bolt	118①
	Control Arm To Knuckle Bolts & Nuts	52①
	Drive Axle Bolts	57
	Drive Shaft To Rear Final Drive	41
	Knuckle Flanged Bolt	148
	Link Rod Nuts	33
	Shock Absorber Nut	18
	Shock Absorber To Track Control Arm Bolt & Nut	48
	Stabilizer Bar Mounting Bracket Bolts	22
	Subassembly Carrier Bolts	118
	Tie Rod Link Nut	70
	Upper Shock Absorber Mount Nuts	22
TT		
2000–01	Axle Mount Bracket Bushing Bolts	66⑤
	Axle Mount Bracket To Body Bolts	55⑤
	Backing Plate To Control Arm Bolts	89③
	Brake Caliper Mounting Bolts	48⑤
	Brake Rotor To Hub Phillips Head Screws	35③
	12-Point Hub Nut	④⑤
	Lower Lateral Control Arm Self-Locking Nuts	52①⑤
	Shock Absorber To Rear Axle Beam Bolts	44⑤
	Stop Buffer Nuts	89③
	Wheel Lug Nuts	89

①— Plus an additional ¼ (90°) turn.
②— Plus an additional ½ (180°) turn.
③— Inch lbs.
④— Refer to "Rear Axle Shaft, Replace" for procedure.
⑤— Always use new nuts & bolts. Do not install old ones.

Transfer Case

NOTE: On Air Bag Equipped Models, Refer To "Air Bag System Precautions" Located In The Front Of This Manual For System Disarming & Arming Procedures.

INDEX

	Page No.
Description	1-83
Fluid Change	1-83
Precautions	1-83
Air Bag Systems	1-83
Battery Ground Cable	1-83
Radio Coded Anti-Theft System	1-83
Tightening Specifications	1-85
Transfer Case, Replace	1-83
Automatic Transaxle	1-84
A4, S4 & 1998–99 A6	1-84
Manual Transaxle	1-83
A4, A6 & S4	1-83
TT	1-84

PRECAUTIONS

Air Bag Systems

Refer to "Air Bag System Precautions" in the front of this manual for system disarming and arming procedures.

Battery Ground Cable

Prior to service, disconnect battery ground cable and isolate as required.

Radio Coded Anti-Theft System

Prior to disconnecting the battery or removing the radio, obtain the security code from the vehicle operator. Refer to the owner's manual for security code disarming and arming procedures.

DESCRIPTION

This Torsen type center differential is attached to the rear of the transaxle assembly. On models equipped with automatic transaxle, the differential has an independent oil reservoir.

On models equipped with manual transaxle, the differential receives torque directly from the hollow output shaft, **Fig. 1.**

Torque is split as required within the differential.

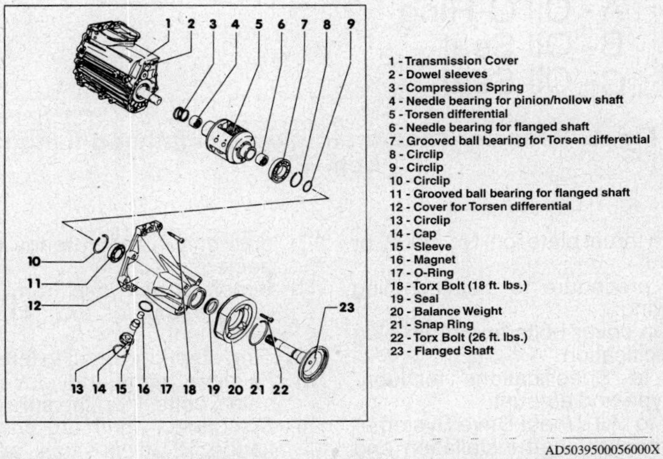

Fig. 1 Exploded view of center differential housing. A4, A6 & S4 w/manual transaxle

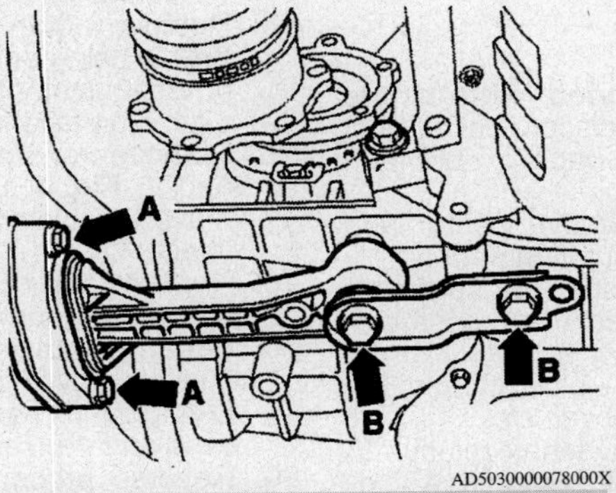

Fig. 2 Transfer case drain plug & righthand flange bolt. TT

FLUID CHANGE

These transaxles use filled-for-life fluids and do not require fluid changes.

TRANSFER CASE

REPLACE

Manual Transaxle

A4, A6 & S4

1. Obtain radio anti-theft protection code as outlined under "Precautions."
2. Raise and support vehicle.
3. Remove propeller shaft as outlined under "All Wheel Drive."
4. Remove shifter, exhaust, shielding and mount components required to allow access to center differential housing.
5. Drain transaxle oil into suitable container.
6. Remove bolts retaining center differential housing to transaxle **Fig. 1.**
7. Separate and remove housing with center differential from transaxle.
8. Remove snap ring that retains cap for output shaft access hole, then install a suitable 8 MM bolt to cap and pull from cover.
9. Remove sleeve, magnet and O-ring from cover through access hole.
10. Through the access hole, spread output shaft snap ring, then pull shaft from housing. Discard snap ring.
11. Support housing with center differential in a suitable press, then push center differential from housing using

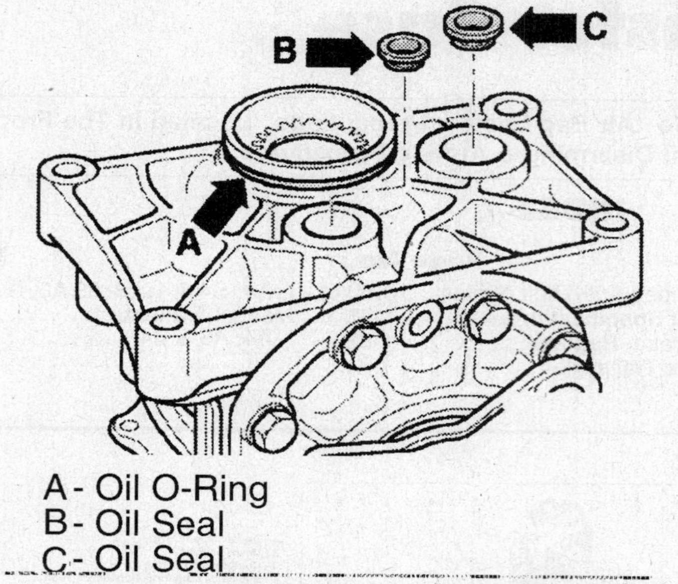

Fig. 3 Transfer case drain plug & righthand flange bolt. TT

press with thrust plate tool No. 3002, or equivalent.

12. Reverse procedure to install, noting the following:
    a. Tighten cover bolts and drain plug to specification.
    b. Refer to "Specifications" for lubricant type and amount.
    c. Refer to "All Wheel Drive Systems" for propeller shaft installation and adjustment procedures.
    d. Use a new snap ring to retain output shaft, do not over spread snap ring during installation.

TT

1. **On models equipped with single charge air cooler,** disconnect air duct leading to cooler at bottom of righthand crossmember.
2. **On all models,** remove center and righthand sound insulation panels.
3. Remove crossmember to subframe mounting bolts, then the crossmember.
4. Disconnect exhaust pipe, then push clamp toward rear of vehicle.
5. Mark position of driveshaft relative to flexible coupling on transfer case.
6. Unbolt driveshaft from flexible coupling on transfer case using a suitable lever to brace triangular flange when loosening bolts.
7. Push front driveshaft tube as far rearward as possible.
8. Remove pendulum support bolts "A," **Fig. 2,** then bolts "B."**After loosening bolts "A," engine and transaxle assembly will move forward slightly. Ensure driveshaft flange oil seal is not damaged during removal and installation.**
9. Remove righthand stabilizer bar link to stabilizer bar nut.
10. Loosen righthand ball joint upper nut until only a few threads remain connected.
11. Separate ball joint from control arm using separator tool No. 3287-A, or equivalent.
12. Turn steering wheel to left.
13. Remove righthand drive axle heat shield bolts, then the shield.
14. Disconnect righthand drive axle from flange, then position aside. **Avoid damaging axle's protective coating.**
15. Remove transfer case drain plug, **Fig. 3,** then allow lubricant to drain into a suitable container.
16. Remove righthand drive flange bolt, **Fig. 3,** using driver tool No. VAG1669, or an equivalent 6 MM hex socket and extension at least 7½ inches long.
17. Remove transfer case bracket bolts 1 and 2, **Fig. 4.** Bracket cannot be removed at this stage and should be left intact.
18. Remove and discard transfer case to transaxle mounting bolts.
19. Separate transfer case from transaxle, then remove from vehicle. Discard O-ring and seals between transfer case and transaxle, **Fig. 5.**
20. Reverse procedure to install, noting the following:
    a. Install new transfer case to transaxle O-ring and seals, **Fig. 5.** Lubricate lightly with clean oil before installation.
    b. Ensure splines are properly aligned when connecting transfer case to transaxle.
    c. **Do not draw transfer case onto transaxle by tightening mounting bolts. This may lead to damaged castings.**
    d. Install transfer case bracket before transfer case mounting bolts.
    e. Install transfer case bracket with bolts finger-tight before transaxle to engine bolts.
    f. **Torque** transfer case bracket No. 1 bolts, **Fig. 5,** to 27 inch lbs.
    g. **Torque** transfer case bracket No. 2 bolts to 26 ft. lbs.
    h. **Torque** transfer case bracket No. 1 bolts to 33 ft. lbs.
    i. **Torque** transaxle mount bracket to transaxle outer bolts to 30 ft. lbs, then rotate an additional 90° while pendulum support is still removed.
    j. After pendulum support has been installed, **torque** transaxle mount to transaxle inner bolts to 44 ft. lbs, then rotate an additional 90°.
    k. Fill transfer case with proper lubricant.

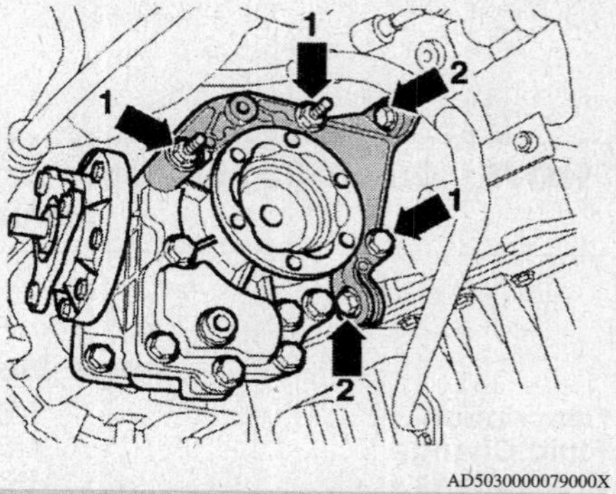

Fig. 4 Transfer case drain plug & righthand flange bolt. TT

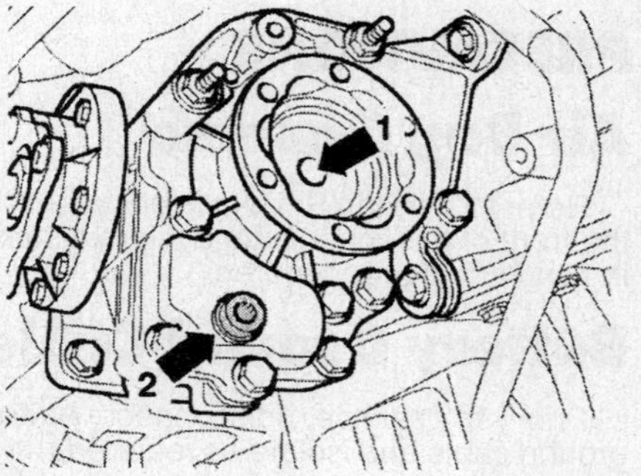

Fig. 5 Transfer case to transaxle seals. TT

Automatic Transaxle

A4, S4 & 1998-99 A6

1. Disconnect lefthand and righthand three way catalytic converters from rear exhaust system.
2. Remove heat shield above driveshaft.
3. Remove heat shield for driveshaft from cover for torsion differential.
4. Remove driveshaft from drive flange on transaxle.
5. Take up weight of transaxle from below transaxle jack and attachment plate tool Nos. VAG1383A and 1359/2, or equivalents.

6. Detach righthand transaxle heat shield mount from transaxle support.
7. Remove righthand and lefthand transaxle mounts.
8. Place a suitable drain pan under transaxle.
9. Drain lubricant from transfer gear.
10. Loosen mounting bolts for transfer housing in diagonal sequence, then remove them.
11. Push torsion differential to rear off of output pinion.
12. Reverse procedure to install. Tighten nuts and bolts to specifications.

TIGHTENING SPECIFICATIONS

Component	Torque In Ft. Lbs.
A4 & S4 & 1998–99 A6 w/AUTOMATIC TRANSAXLE	
Transfer Housing To Transaxle Housing	17
Driveshaft Heat Shield To Transaxle	17
Transaxle Support To Transaxle Mounting	30
Transaxle Mounting To Subframe	17
A4, A6 & S4 w/MANUAL TRANSAXLE	
Drain Plug	18
Filler Plug	18
Rear Cover Bolt	18
TT w/MANUAL TRANSAXLE	
Drive Axle To Transaxle Flange Bolts	57
Drive Axle Heat Shield Bolts	18
Exhaust Pipe Connector Clamps	30
Pendulum Support Bolts "A"	15①
Pendulum Support Bolts "B"	30①
Pendulum Support To Transaxle	30①
Transfer Case To Transaxle Bolts	②

① — Always use new nuts & bolts. Rotate an additional ¼ (90°) turn.

② — Refer to "Transfer Case, Replace" for procedure.

Front Suspension & Steering

NOTE: On Air Bag Equipped Models, Refer To "Air Bag System Precautions" Located In The Front Of This Manual For System Disarming & Arming Procedures.

INDEX

	Page No.
Ball Joint Inspection	1-88
Ball Joint, Replace	1-88
A4, A8, S4 & 1998–99 A6	1-88
Cabriolet	1-88
TT	1-88
Coil Spring, Replace	1-89
Control Arm, Replace	1-90
A4, A6, A8 & S4	1-90
Cabriolet	1-90
TT	1-91
Power Steering	1-154
Power Steering Gear, Replace	1-94
A4 & S4	1-94
A8 & 1998–99 A6	1-95
Cabriolet	1-95
TT	1-96
Power Steering Pump, Replace	1-97
1.8L Engine	1-97
2.7L Engine	1-98
2.8L Engine	1-98
3.7L & 4.2L Engines	1-98
Installation	1-99
Removal	1-98
Power Steering System Bleed	1-99
A4 & S4	1-99
A8 & 1998–99 A6	1-100
Cabriolet	1-101
Precautions	1-86
Air Bag Systems	1-86
Battery Ground Cable	1-86
Radio Coded Anti-Theft System	1-86
Steering Knuckle, Replace	1-92
A4 & S4	1-92
A6 & A8	1-92
Cabriolet	1-92
TT	1-93
Strut, Replace	1-89
A4, A8, S4 & 1998–99 A6	1-89
Cabriolet	1-89
TT	1-89
Strut Service	1-90
A4, A8, S4 & 1998–99 A6	1-90
Assemble	1-90
Disassemble	1-90
Cabriolet	1-90
TT	1-90
Subframe, Replace	1-91
A4 & S4	1-91
A8 & 1998–99 A6	1-91
TT	1-91
Technical Service Bulletins	1-101
Radio Whining Noise	1-101
2000 A8 w/Symphony Radio	1-101
Tie Rod End, Replace	1-94
Inner	1-94
Outer	1-94
Tightening Specifications	1-102
A4 & S4	1-102
A8 & 1998–99 A6	1-103
Cabriolet	1-103
TT	1-104
Wheel Bearing, Adjust	1-86
Wheel Bearing, Replace	1-86
A4, A8, S4 & 1998–99 A6	1-86
Cabriolet	1-87
TT	1-87
Off Vehicle	1-88
On Vehicle	1-87

PRECAUTIONS

Air Bag Systems

Refer to "Air Bag System Precautions" in the front of this manual for system disarming and arming procedures.

Battery Ground Cable

Prior to service, disconnect battery ground cable and isolate as required.

Radio Coded Anti-Theft System

Prior to disconnecting the battery or removing the radio, obtain the security code from the vehicle operator. Refer to the owner's manual for security code disarming and arming procedures.

WHEEL BEARING

ADJUST

These models use a one-piece front wheel bearing which is not adjustable.

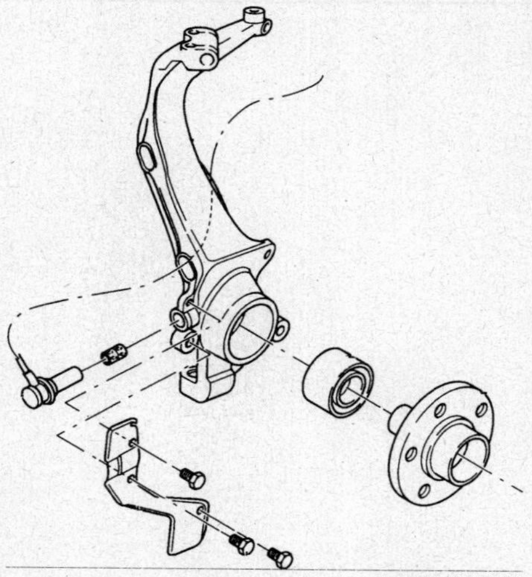

Fig. 1 Knuckle & bearing assembly. A4, A8, S4 & 1998–99 A6

WHEEL BEARING

REPLACE

A4, A8, S4 & 1998–99 A6

1. Remove steering knuckle (swing arm), **Fig. 1,** as outlined under "Steering Knuckle, Replace."
2. Press hub from bearing using tools or equivalents, **Figs. 2 and 3.**
3. Press bearing from steering knuckle using tools or equivalents, **Figs. 4 and 5.**
4. Remove bearing inner race from hub using puller tool No. 30-11, or equivalent, **Fig. 6.**
5. Press bearing into steering knuckle using tools or equivalents, **Figs. 7 and 8.**
6. Press hub into bearing using tools or equivalents, **Figs. 9 and 10.**
7. Install steering knuckle as outlined under "Steering Knuckle, Replace."

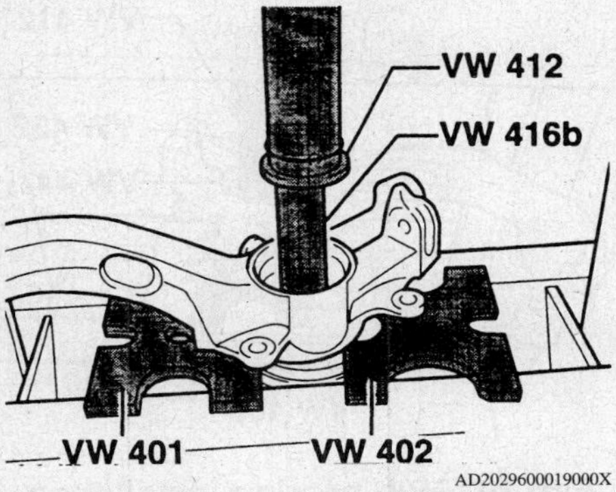

Fig. 2 Hub removal. A4 & S4 w/75 MM bearing

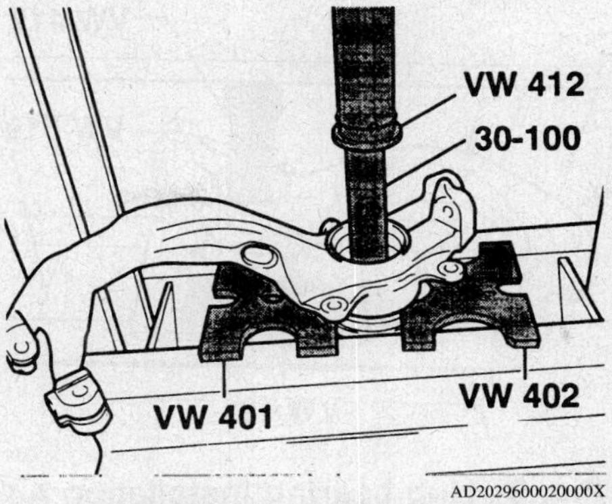

Fig. 3 Hub removal. A4, A8, S4 & 1998–99 A6 w/85 MM bearing

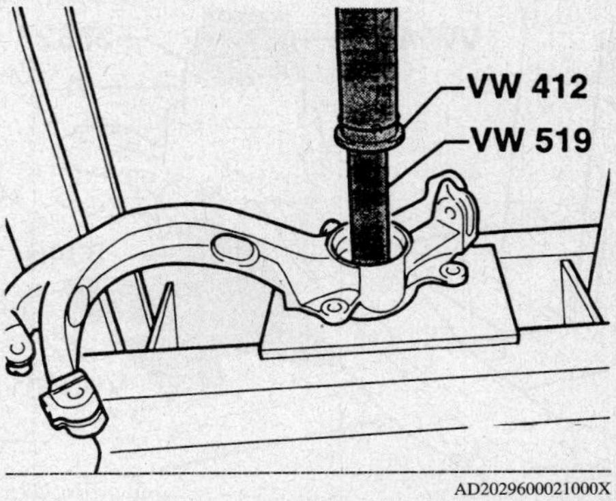

Fig. 4 Bearing removal. A4 & S4 w/75 MM bearing

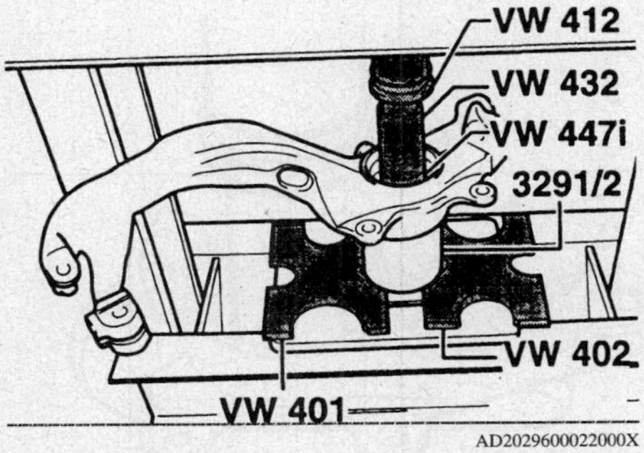

Fig. 5 Bearing removal. A4, A8, S4 & 1998–99 A6 w/85 MM bearing

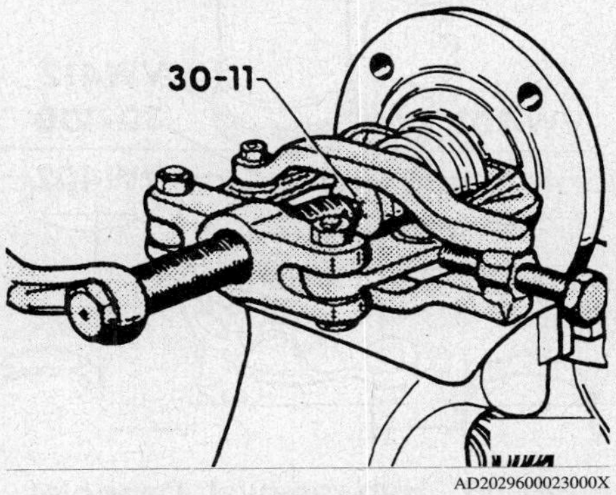

Fig. 6 Bearing inner race removal

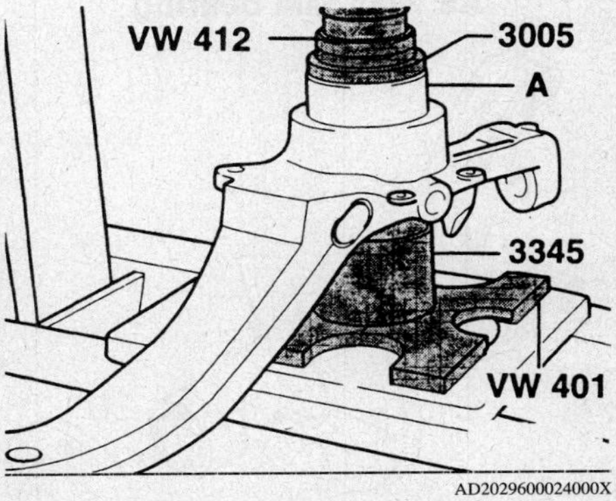

Fig. 7 Bearing knuckle installation. A4 & S4 w/75 MM bearing

Cabriolet

1. Remove knuckle assembly **Fig. 11,** as outlined under "Steering Knuckle, Replace."
2. Press hub from bearing using tools or equivalents, **Fig. 12.**
3. Press bearing from steering knuckle, using tools or equivalents, **Fig. 13.**
4. Remove bearing inner race from hub using puller tool No. 30-11, or equivalent, **Fig. 6.**
5. Press bearing into steering knuckle using tools or equivalents, **Fig. 14.**
6. Press hub into bearing, using tools or equivalents, **Fig. 15.**
7. Install steering knuckle as outlined under "Steering Knuckle, Replace."

TT

ON VEHICLE

REMOVAL

1. Remove wheel center cap.
2. Raise vehicle until load on front axle is relieved.
3. Loosen 12-point self-locking hub nut.
4. Remove tires and wheels.
5. Disconnect suspension strut coupling links on both sides of vehicle. Discard nuts.
6. Pull spring clip out of retainer, then disconnect brake hose.
7. Disconnect wheel speed sensor wiring from strut.
8. Remove brake caliper to knuckle mounting bolts, then position caliper aside using suitable wire or rope.
9. Remove brake disc backing plate.
10. Loosen ball joint upper nut until only a few threads remain connected.
11. Separate ball joint from control arm using separator tool No. 3287-A, or equivalent.
12. Support knuckle using jack tool No. VAG1383/A with universal support tool No. VAG1359/2, or equivalents.
13. Insert thrust bolts from tool No. VAG1559B, or equivalent, **Fig. 16,** into knuckle.
14. Remove circlip.
15. Install thrust piece, **Fig. 17,** with collar facing wheel bearing, press sleeve with four internal stepped diameters toward knuckle and hollow piston cylinder from tool No. VAG1459B, or equivalent with pull rod and special nut.
16. Operate foot air pump tool No. VAG1389A/1, or apply sufficient air pressure to extract wheel bearing from hub.
17. Remove inner race from hub using tool setup, **Fig. 18.**

INSTALLATION

The drive axle and wheel hub splines can either be "adhered" using locking fluid or greased for the newer version of wheel hubs, part No. 8N0 407 613 A or B. Note which type is installed on the particular vehicle.

Older wheel hubs, part No. 8N0 407 613 with hub stamped 8N0 615, can be attached for drive axles that were "adhered" but must continue to be adhered using locking fluid part No. D 185 400 A2, or equivalent.

Newer wheel hubs, part No. 8N0 407 613 A or B with hub stamped 8N0 615A or B, must never be adhered. Only use securing grease part No. G 052 142 A2, or equivalent.

A vehicle with an adhered drive axle/ wheel hub on one side and a greased version on the other is allowable because the adhered wheel hub can be replaced with a greased one. However, a greased wheel hub must never be replaced with an adhered version. Refer to **Fig. 19,** then proceed as follows:

1. Coat entire inner surface of knuckle with MoS2 grease part No. AOS 115 000 01, or equivalent.
2. Install new wheel bearing, **Fig. 20,** thrust piece and hollow piston cylinder with pull rod on knuckle. Press wheel bearing into knuckle using air pump. Insert circlip using suitable long-nosed pliers.
3. Install hub, **Fig. 21,** and hollow piston cylinder with pull rod on wheel bearing. Press hub into knuckle using air pump.
4. Clean splines and threads on drive axle and in hub.
5. Install new 12-point self-locking nut and rotate as far as possible.
6. **Torque** brake caliper to knuckle bolts to 92 ft. lbs.
7. Connect suspension strut coupling links and install new nuts.

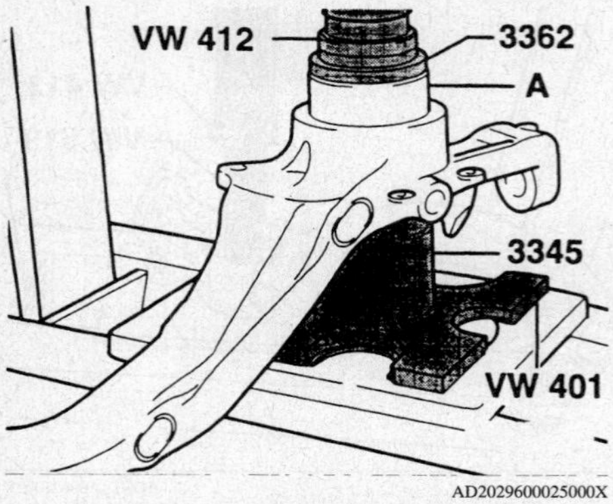

Fig. 8 Bearing knuckle installation. A4, A8, S4 & 1998–99 A6 w/85 MM bearing

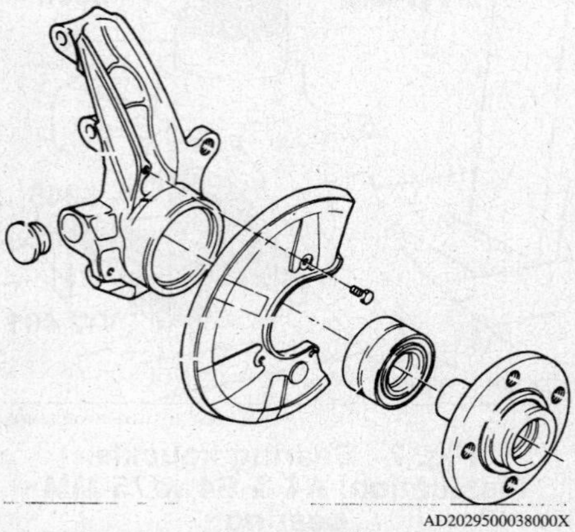

Fig. 11 Front suspension. Cabriolet

8. Lower the vehicle, but not so far that tires reach ground.
9. Tighten 12-point self-locking nut while an assistant applies brakes.

OFF VEHICLE

REMOVAL

1. Remove hub from knuckle using a suitable press and tool setup, **Fig. 22.**
2. Remove circlip using suitable snap ring pliers.
3. Remove wheel bearing from knuckle using a suitable press and tool setup, **Fig. 23.**
4. Remove inner race from hub using a suitable press and tool setup, **Fig. 18.**

INSTALLATION

The drive axle and wheel hub splines can either be "adhered" using locking fluid or greased for the newer version of wheel hubs, part No. 8N0 407 613 A or B. Note which type is installed on the particular vehicle.

Older wheel hubs, part No. 8N0 407 613 with hub stamped 8N0 615, can be attached for drive axles that were "adhered" but must continue to be adhered using locking fluid part No. D 185 400 A2, or equivalent.

Newer wheel hubs, part No. 8N0 407 613 A or B with hub stamped 8N0 615A or

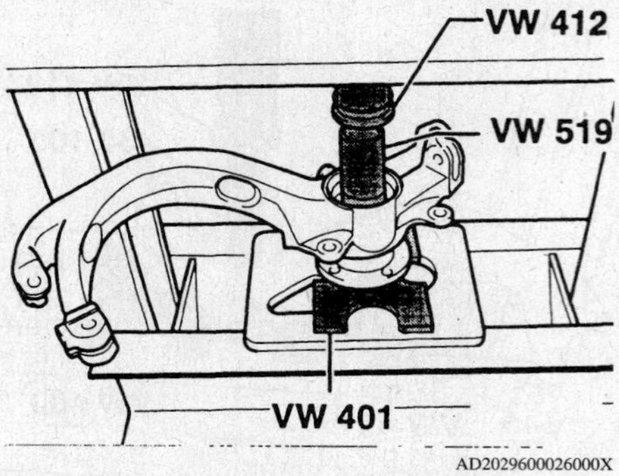

Fig. 9 Hub bearing installation A4 & S4 w/75 MM bearing

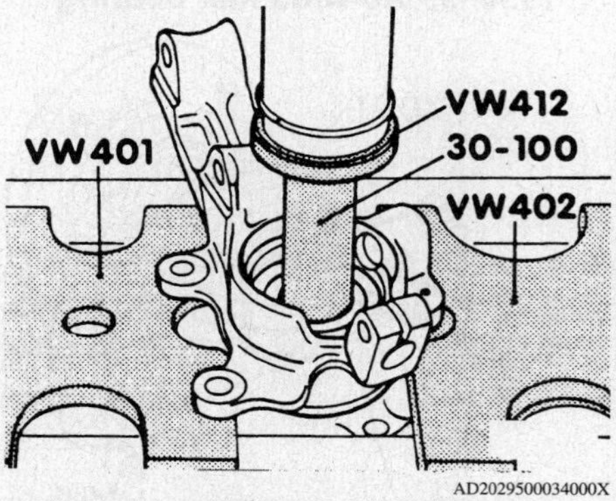

Fig. 12 Hub removal. Cabriolet

B, must never be adhered. Only use securing grease part No. G 052 142 A2, or equivalent.

A vehicle with an adhered drive axle/wheel hub on one side and a greased version on the other is allowable because the adhered wheel hub can be replaced with a greased one. However, a greased wheel hub must never be replaced with an adhered version. Refer to **Fig. 19,** then proceed as follows:

1. Install wheel bearing into knuckle using a suitable press and tool setup, **Fig. 24.**
2. Install circlip.
3. Install hub into knuckle using a suitable press and tool setup, **Fig. 25. Ensure tool makes contact with bearing inner race.**

BALL JOINT INSPECTION

Replace ball joint and control arm if there is any vertical end play, excessive axial play, excessive turning resistance, boot is torn or stud is worn.

BALL JOINT

REPLACE

A4, A8, S4 & 1998–99 A6

1. Raise and support vehicle.
2. Remove front wheels.

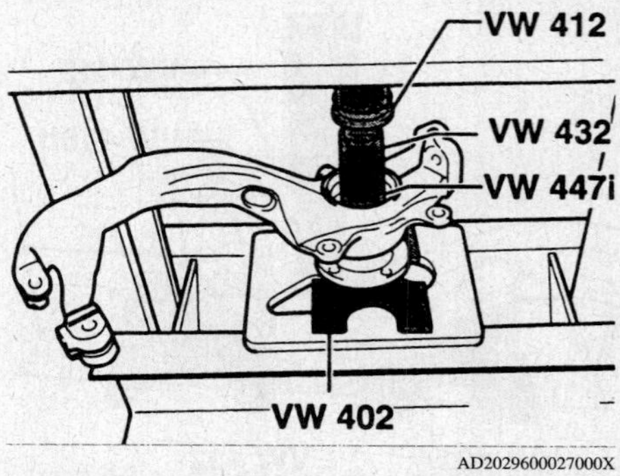

Fig. 10 Hub bearing installation A4, A8, S4 & 1998–99 A6 w/85 MM bearing

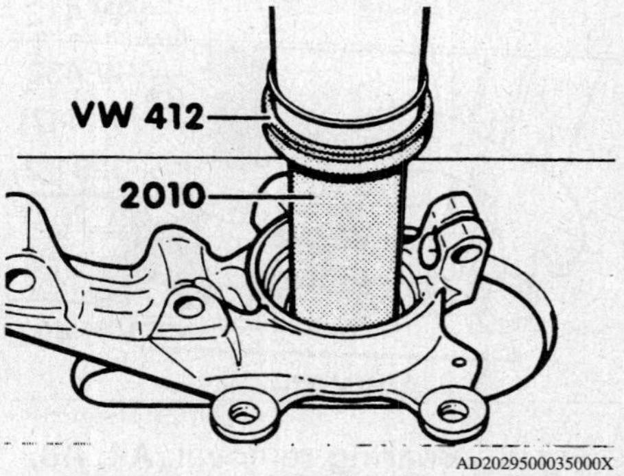

Fig. 13 Bearing removal. Cabriolet

3. Support suspension with a suitable stand if removing front lower ball joint.
4. Remove ball joint to knuckle retaining nut.
5. Separate ball joint from knuckle using a suitable ball joint separation tool.
6. **On lower ball joint,** disconnect shock absorber and stabilizer bar.
7. **On upper and lower ball joints,** remove inner control arm bolt, then the ball joint and control arm assembly.
8. Reverse procedure to install.

Cabriolet

1. Raise and support vehicle.
2. Remove front wheels.
3. Remove ball joint pinch bolt **Fig. 26.**
4. Separate ball joint from knuckle by prying down on control arm, using a suitable pry bar.
5. Remove bolts retaining ball joint to control arm, then the ball joint.
6. Reverse procedure to install, tighten nuts and bolts to specifications.

TT

1. Remove wheel and tire.
2. Mark positions of ball joint lower mounting nuts or wheel alignment will require inspection afterward.
3. Remove ball joint lower nuts.
4. Loosen ball joint upper nut until only a few threads remain connected.
5. Separate ball joint from control arm using separator tool No. 3287-A, or equivalent.

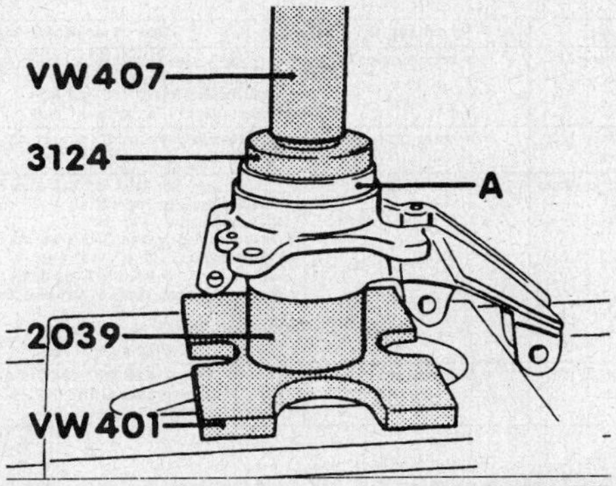

AD2029500036000X

Fig. 14 **Bearing installation. Cabriolet**

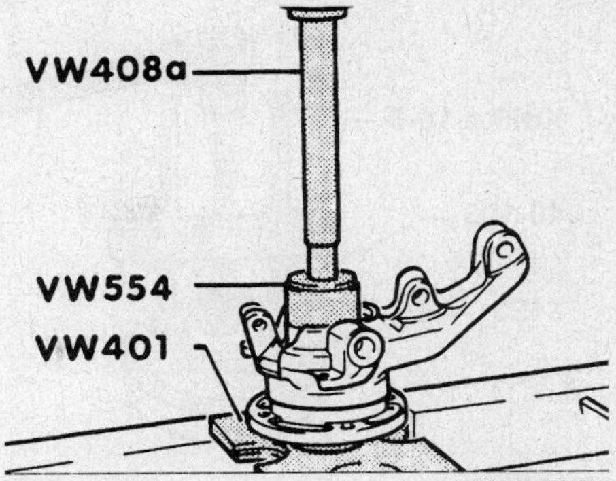

AD2029500037000X

Fig. 15 **Hub installation. Cabriolet**

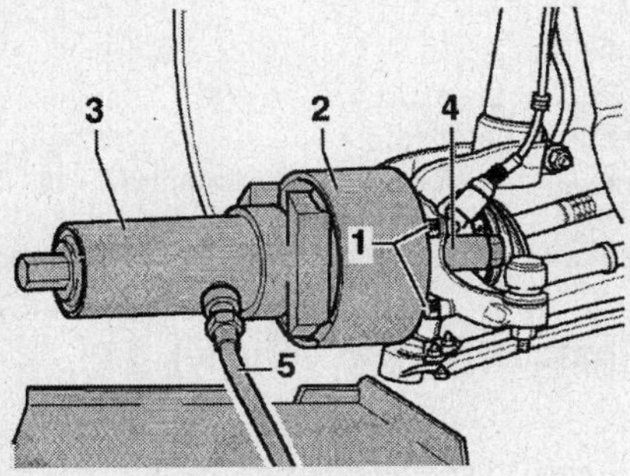

1- Thrust bolt E - 15
2- Support E - 40
3- Hollow piston cylinder HKZ - 15
4- Special nut E - 8 - 214 and pull rod
5- High pressure hose with quick release coupling

AD2020000049000X

Fig. 16 Hub removal (on vehicle). TT

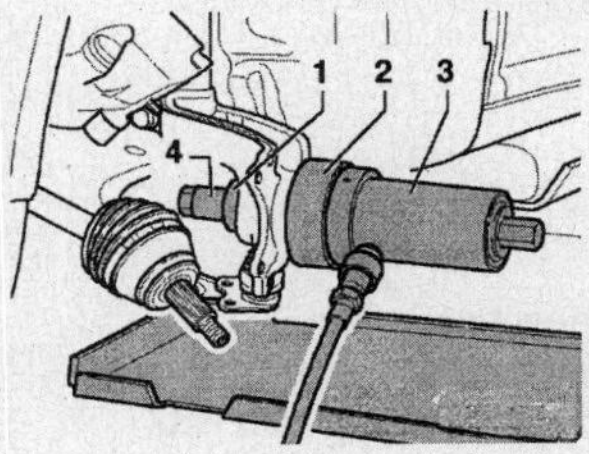

1- Thrust piece E - 5
2- Press sleeve E - 65 - 1
3- Hollow piston cylinder HKZ - 15
4- Special nut E - 8 - 214 and pull rod

AD2020000050000X

Fig. 17 Front wheel bearing removal (on vehicle). TT

6. Remove ball joint upper nut.
7. Reverse procedure to install, noting the following:
   a. Install new ball joint with new lower nuts in original positions.
   b. Tighten nuts to specifications.

COIL SPRING

REPLACE

Refer to "Strut Service" for procedure.

STRUT

REPLACE

A4, A8, S4 & 1998-99 A6

1. Raise and support vehicle.
2. Remove wheel, then the rubber grommets in plenum chamber, **Fig. 27.**
3. Remove suspension strut nut "1" as illustrated in **Fig. 28.**
4. Pull ABS wheel speed sensor cable out of bracket at brake caliper.
5. Loosen swing arm nut "1," **Fig. 29,** then remove bolt and pull both arms "2" upward and out, **Fig. 29. The slot in swing arm must not be widened. Do not loosen bolts "3" and "4," Fig. 29.** Tilt swing arm away to side in direction of arrow, **Fig. 29.**
6. Remove bolt at strut support link, then remove strut, **Figs. 30 and 31. Do not damage CV joint boot.**
7. Reverse procedure to install.

Cabriolet

1. Raise and support vehicle, then remove wheels.
2. Disconnect stabilizer bar from strut assembly, **Fig. 32.**
3. Disconnect tie rod end from strut using a suitable tie rod end puller.
4. Remove bolts holding lower end of strut to hub.
5. Remove nuts holding upper strut mounting nut cap, then remove cap.
6. While supporting strut assembly remove upper strut mounting nut, then remove strut from vehicle.
7. Do not allow brake fluid line or electrical cables to become stressed or damaged.

8. Reverse procedure to install, tighten fasteners to specifications.

TT

1. Remove tires and wheels.
2. Disconnect strut coupling links on both sides of vehicle. Discard nuts.
3. Pull spring clip out of retainer, then disconnect brake hose.
4. Disconnect wheel speed sensor wiring from strut.
5. Remove and discard strut to knuckle mounting bolt nut.
6. Insert spreader tool No. 3424, or equivalent into slot, **Fig. 33.**
7. Rotate ratchet handle through 90°, then pull ratchet handle off socket tool.
8. Push brake disc in direction of strut by hand.
9. Pull knuckle downward off strut cartridge.
10. Remove strut upper nut and mount using tool setup, **Fig. 34.** Discard nut.
11. Remove strut assembly from vehicle.
12. Reverse procedure to install, noting the following:
    a. Coat strut lower shock tower mount with lubricant part No. G 294 421 A1, or equivalent.
    b. Raise knuckle until it is possible to insert strut to knuckle bolt, then push brake disc in direction of strut by hand.
    c. Remove spreader tool.
    d. Tighten new strut upper mount nut to specifications using tool setup, **Fig. 34.**
    e. Connect coupling link to strut, then tighten new nut to specifications.

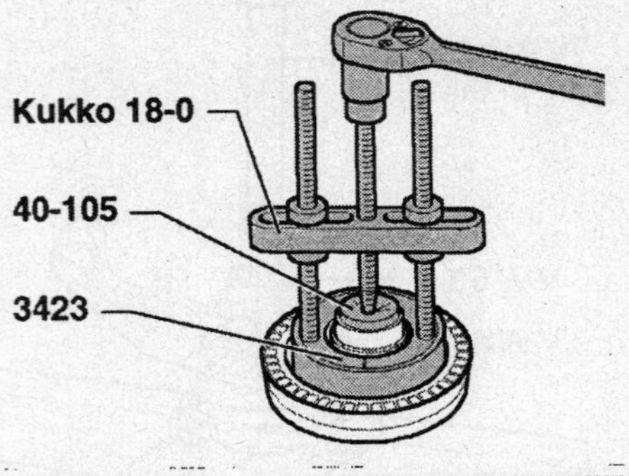

AD2020000051000X

Fig. 18 Race removal from hub. TT

Condition at vehicle	Wheel hub is	Note when assembling
Drive axle is adhered to wheel hub	not being replaced	◆ Thoroughly clean residual adhesive from splines of drive axle and wheel hub. ◆ Apply locking fluid D 185 400 A2. ◆ Tighten 12-point nut to 196 FT. LBS.
Drive axle and wheel hub are greased	not being replaced	◆ Apply securing grease G 052 142 A2. ◆ Tighten 12-point nut to 140 FT. LBS.
Drive axle is glued to wheel hub	being replaced	**For 8NO 407 613 A or B:** ◆ Thoroughly clean residual adhesive from splines of drive axle. ◆ Apply securing grease G 052 142 A2. ◆ Tighten 12-point nut to 140 FT. LBS. **For 8NO 407 613:** ◆ Thoroughly clean residual adhesive from splines of drive axle. ◆ Apply locking fluid D 185 400 A2. ◆ Tighten 12-point nut to 196 FT. LBS.
Drive axle and wheel hub are greased	being replaced	**Only install 8NO 407 613 A or B:** ◆ Apply securing grease G 052 142 A2. ◆ Tighten 12-point nut to 140 FT. LBS.

AD2020000054000X

Fig. 19 Drive axle to hub installation notes. TT

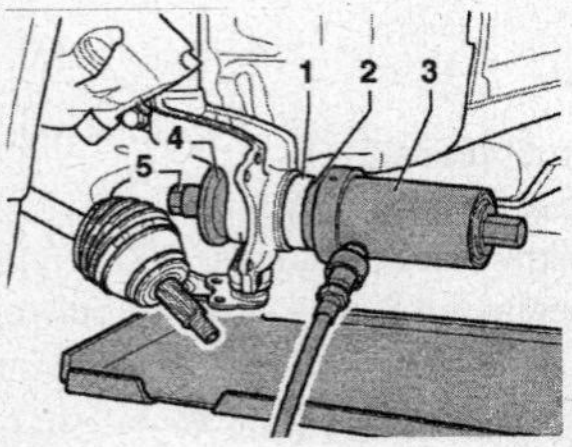

1- Wheel bearing
2- Thrust piece E - 13 - 1
3- Hollow piston cylinder HKZ - 15
4- Thrust piece E - 10
5- Special nut E - 8 - 214 and pull rod

AD2020000052000X

Fig. 20 Wheel bearing installation (on vehicle). TT

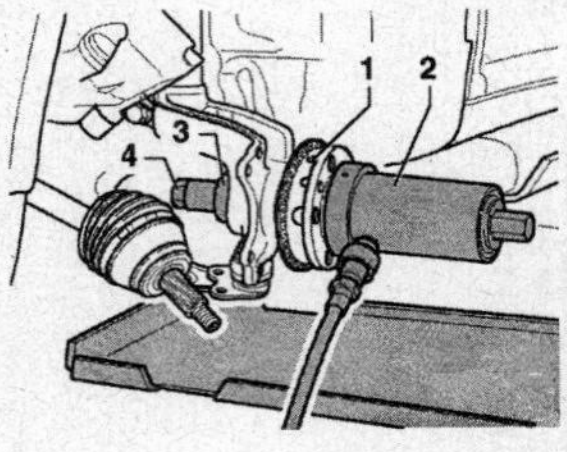

1- Hub
2- Hollow piston cylinder HKZ - 15
3- Thrust piece E - 5
4- Special nut E - 8 - 214 and pull rod

AD2020000053000X

Fig. 21 Hub installation (on vehicle). TT

STRUT SERVICE

A4, A8, S4 & 1998–99 A6

DISASSEMBLE

1. Remove strut as outlined under "Strut Replace"in this section.
2. Clamp strut mount tool No. VAG 1752-2, or equivalent into a suitable vise, then install strut into tool at clevis, **Fig. 35.**
3. Compress coil spring with tensioner tool No. VAG 1752-1 until upper spring retainer is free. **Ensure coil spring is properly located in adapter tool No. 1752-7, or equivalent, Fig. 36.**
4. Remove strut top nut using replacement tool No. 3353, or equivalent.
5. Remove shock absorber bushing, washer, upper spring retainer, auxiliary spring and protective sleeve, **Fig. 37.**
6. Remove coil spring with tensioner tool No. VAG 1752-1.
7. Remove protective cap and lower spring base.
8. Remove lower spring retainer using a suitable hammer.
9. Remove shock absorber from strut mount tool No. VAG 1752-2.

ASSEMBLE

1. Install shock absorber into strut mount tool No. VAG 1752-2.
2. Install lower spring retainer onto shock absorber. **Hole in lower spring retainer should be positioned 90° relative to bolt axis of shock absorber.**
3. Install lower spring base and protective cap, then install coil spring with tensioning device tool No. VAG 1752-1 onto shock absorber. **End of coil spring must be positioned against stop of lower spring base, Fig. 38.**
4. Set angle scale on tensioning device tool No. VAG 1752-2, or equivalent, to read 0°.
5. Install protective sleeve, auxiliary spring, upper spring retainer, washer and shock absorber bushing onto shock absorber.
6. Use gauge tool No. VAG 1752-8, or equivalent, to position upper spring retainer at 11.° **Strut must be clamped at clevis.**
7. Install strut top nut using replacement tool No. 3353, or equivalent. Tighten to specifications.
8. Release coil spring, then remove strut from strut mount tool No. VAG 1752-2. **Ensure coil spring is positioned at stop of upper spring retainer, Fig. 39.**

Cabriolet

1. Remove strut assembly as outlined under "Strut, Replace."
2. Compress coil spring with spring compressor, **Fig. 40,** until upper spring retainer is free.
3. Hold strut shaft and remove retaining nut, bearing, retainer, bump stop and sleeve, **Fig. 41.** Remove compressed coil spring carefully and lay aside.
4. Remove threaded cap from top of strut tube, then strut cartridge.
5. Reverse procedure to install, Tighten fasteners, slotted nut and threaded cap, to specifications.

TT

1. Remove strut assembly from vehicle as outlined under "Strut Replace."
2. Clamp strut into a suitable vise with tool setup, **Fig. 42.**
3. Compress coil spring with tensioning device VAG1752/1, or equivalent until upper spring plate is free.
4. Remove and discard hex nut from piston rod.
5. Remove individual strut and coil spring components with tensioning device.
6. Reverse procedure to install, noting the following:
   a. Ensure coil spring is properly seated in adapter tool No. VAG1752/7, or equivalent, **Fig. 43.**
   b. Install spring with tensioning tool onto lower spring support. Ensure end of spring is seated against its stop, **Fig. 44.**
   c. Replace all fasteners and tighten to specifications.

CONTROL ARM

REPLACE

A4, A6, A8 & S4

Refer to "Ball Joint, Replace" for procedure.

Cabriolet

1. Disconnect ball joint from control arm as outlined under "Ball Joint, Replace."
2. Remove control arm to subframe mounting bolts, then the control arm from the subframe.

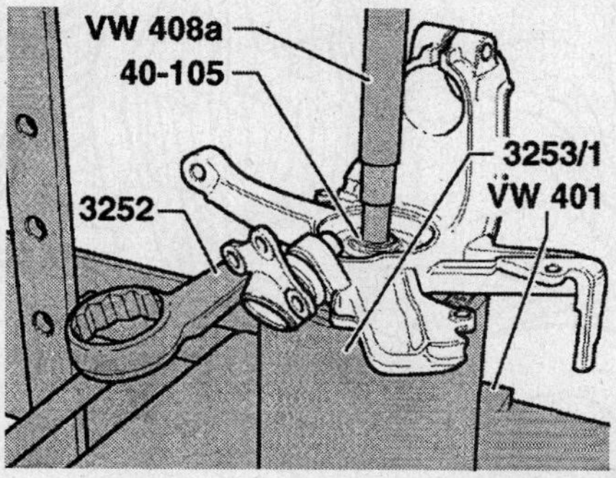

AD2020000055000X

Fig. 22 Hub removal from knuckle (off vehicle). TT

3. Reverse procedure to install, tighten nuts and bolts to specifications.

TT

1. Remove wheels and tires.
2. Remove sound insulation panels.
3. Mark positions of mounting nuts and bolts or wheel alignment will require inspection afterward.
4. Remove and discard ball joint lower mounting nuts.
5. Remove control arm mounting nuts and bolts, then the control arm. Discard nuts and bolts.
6. Reverse procedure to install, noting the following:
   a. Mount control arm in subframe and secure with new nuts and bolts.
   b. Secure ball joint to control arm with new nuts properly aligned.
   c. Tighten all nuts and bolts to specifications.

SUBFRAME

REPLACE

A4 & S4

1. Install engine support tool No. 10-222A, or equivalent, then raise and support vehicle and remove tires and wheels.
2. Remove sound insulation, then the lower strut mounting bolt.
3. Remove support link to coupling and coupling to subframe bolts, then the coupling.
4. Remove support link to subframe mounting bolt, then loosen guide link to subframe mounting bolt.
5. Remove subframe mounting bolts "1," **Fig. 45,** then the guide link to subframe mounting bolt.
6. Lower rear of subframe.
7. Pull ABS wheel speed sensor out of bracket at brake caliper, then pull support links and guide links out of subframe.
8. Remove subframe mounting nuts "3" and "4," then the bolts "5" and "6," **Fig. 45.**

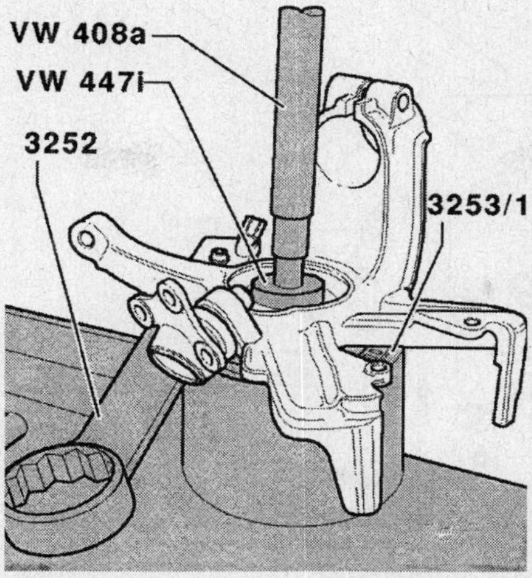

AD2020000056000X

Fig. 23 Wheel bearing removal from knuckle (off vehicle). TT

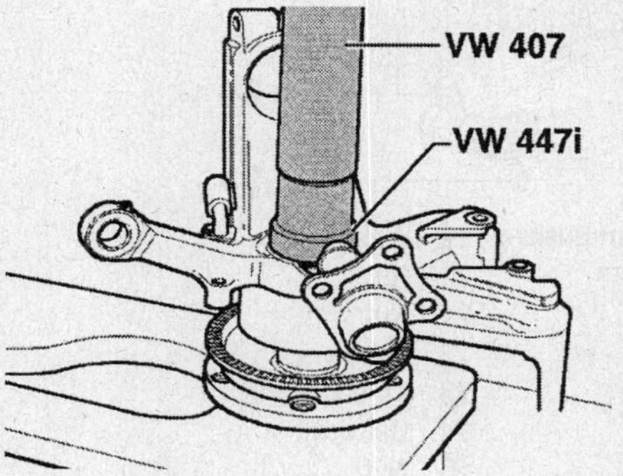

AD2020000058000X

Fig. 25 Hub to knuckle installation (off vehicle). TT

9. Remove subframe.
10. Reverse procedure to install. Align front wheels as outlined in "Wheel Alignment" section.

A8 & 1998-99 A6

1. Attach engine support to subframe.
2. Pull cap off disc wheel using suction cup tool No. 3208, or equivalent.
3. Loosen flanged bolts approximately 10 turns each.
4. Remove tires and wheels.
5. Remove underbody protection cover.
6. Remove stabilizer bar to coupling attaching nuts.
7. Remove coupling to support link attaching nuts.
8. Remove guide link bolts and washers.
9. Remove subframe support bolts and lower rear end of subframe.
10. Remove subframe mounting bolts "3, 4 and 5," **Fig. 46.**
11. Remove subframe.
12. Reverse procedure to install. Align

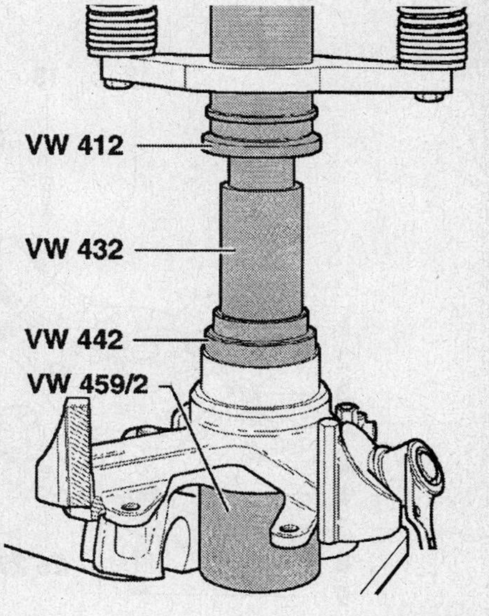

AD2020000057000X

Fig. 24 Wheel bearing to knuckle installation (off vehicle). TT

front wheels as outlined in "Wheel Alignment" section.

TT

1. Remove wheels and tires.
2. Remove sound insulation panels.
3. Remove stabilizer bar link nuts.
4. Remove sound insulation panel Torx nut.
5. Loosen ball joint upper nut until only a few threads remain connected.
6. Separate ball joint from control arm using separator tool No. 3287-A, or equivalent.
7. Remove ball joint upper nut.
8. Remove steering rack mounting bolts, **Fig. 47.**
9. Remove pendulum support mounting bolts.
10. Support subframe using transaxle jack tool No. VAG1383A and universal support tool No. 1359/2, or equivalents.
11. Remove subframe mounting bolts, then lower the subframe using transaxle jack.
12. Reverse procedure to install, noting the following:
    a. Position steering rack on subframe and insert bolts. Ensure threaded sleeve seats properly in subframe hole.
    b. Install ball joint in knuckle with a new self-locking nut, then counterhold using a suitable T40 Torx key. Ensure boot does not twist.
    c. Tighten all nuts and bolts to specifications.
    d. Inspect and adjust wheel alignment if steering wheel is not in straight-ahead position during test drive.

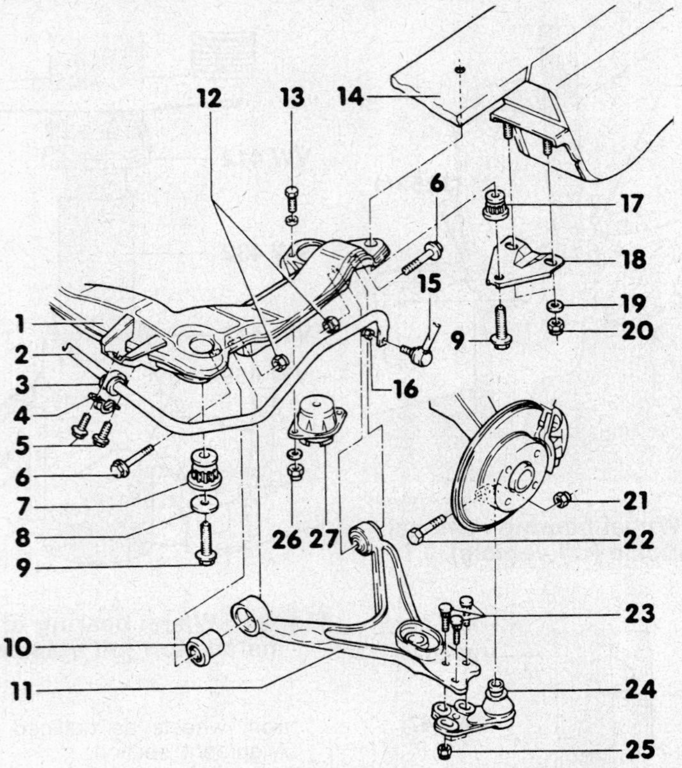

1. Subframe
2. Stabilizer Bar
3. Bushing
4. Clip
5. Bolt
6. Washer Headed Bolt
7. Subframe Bushing
8. Washer
9. Bolt
10. Control arm Bushing
11. Control Arm
12. Nut
13. Bolt
14. Chassis
15. Link Rod
16. Nut
17. Subframe Bushing
18. Support
19. Washer
20. Nut
21. Nut
22. Bolt
23. Threaded Pin
24. Ball Joint
25. Nut
26. Nut
27. Bushing

AD2029500041000X

Fig. 26 Front suspension. Cabriolet

STEERING KNUCKLE

REPLACE

A4 & S4

1. Raise and support vehicle, then remove wheels.
2. Secure brake disc using a suitable wheel bolt, then pull ABS wheel speed sensor cable out of bracket at brake caliper.
3. Remove brake caliper, then suspend from body with a suitable piece of wire. **Do not disconnect brake hose or hang caliper from brake hose.**
4. Remove brake disc, then the splash guard.
5. Pull ABS wheel speed sensor out of arm, then loosen guide link to steering knuckle (swing arm) nut **Fig. 30,** and support link to swing arm nut.
6. Pull ABS wheel speed sensor cable and rubber grommet from body, then disconnect ABS wheel speed sensor cable connector.
7. Remove ABS wheel speed sensor cable from cable brackets.
8. Remove ABS wheel speed sensor from swing arm, then the rear track rod to steering knuckle bolt.
9. Disconnect guide link ball joint and support link ball joint from steering knuckle using puller tool No. V-176, or equivalent. **Do not damage boots.**
10. Install nut to support link ball joint.
11. Remove front track rod to steering knuckle bolt, then pull both track rods upward and out.
12. Tilt steering knuckle down and away from vehicle, then pull drive axle joint from wheel hub.
13. Turn ball joint to support link nut down, then remove steering knuckle.
14. Reverse procedure to install.

A6 & A8

On these models the steering knuckle is in unit with the strut housing. Refer to "Strut, Replace" for procedure.

Cabriolet

1. Remove center hub cap.
2. Loosen axle and wheel bolts.

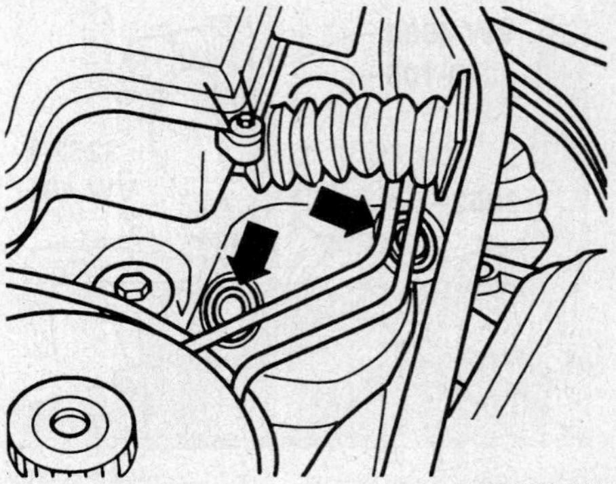

AD2029600007000X

Fig. 27 Grommet removal. A4, A8, S4 & 1998–99 A6

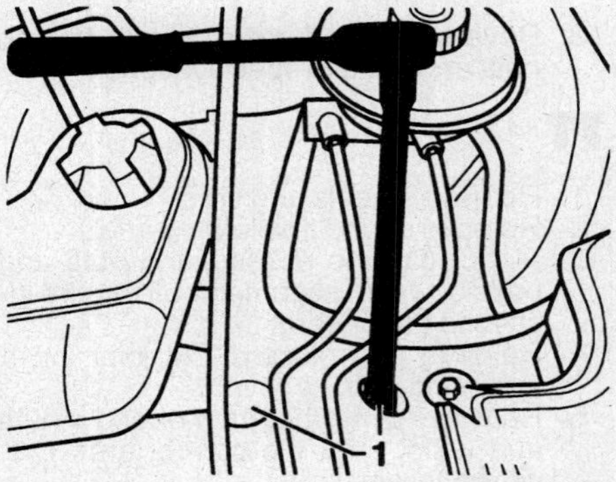

AD2029600008000X

Fig. 28 Strut nut removal. A4, A8, S4 & 1998–99 A6

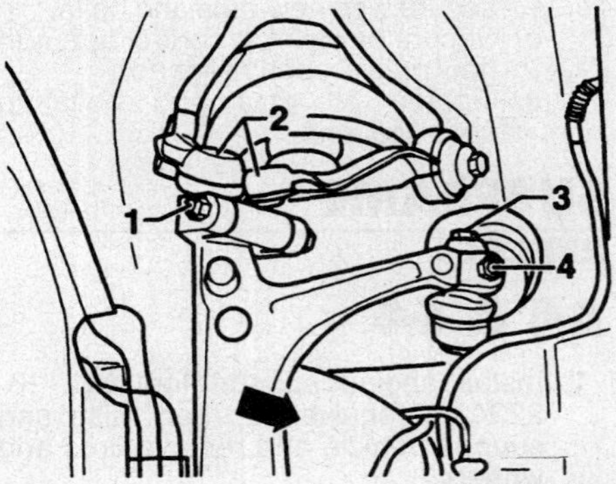

AD2029600009000X

Fig. 29 Swing arm nut removal. A4, A8, S4 & 1998–99 A6

3. Raise and support vehicle, then remove wheels.
4. Remove ABS wheel speed sensor.
5. Remove brake rotor and caliper and support aside as outlined under "Disc Brakes." **Do not disconnect brake line.**
6. Remove tie rod end, **Fig. 32,** from knuckle using a suitable tie rod end separation tool.
7. Remove ball joint pinch bolt, then separate ball joint from knuckle.
8. **On models equipped with camber adjusting knuckle to strut bolts,** mark eccentrics for installation alignment.
9. **On all models,** remove knuckle to strut bolts.

1. Mounting Bracket
2. Self Locking Nut
3. Washer
4. Self Locking Nut
5. Hex Bolt
6. Washer
7. Hex Bolt
8. Upper Track Control Arm, Rear
9. Bolt & Washer
10. Bolt
11. Hex Bolt
12. Self Locking Nut
13. Self Locking Nut
14. Swing Arm
15. Upper Track Control Arm,Front
16. Suspension Strut
17. Bolt & Washer
18. Guide Link With Hydraulic Bushing
19. Hex Collar Bolt
20. Hex Bolt
21. Brake Shield
22. Flange Nut
23. Hex Bolt
24. Washer
25. Self Locking Nut
26. Support Link
27. Ribbed Nut
28. Bolt & Washer
29. Coupling
30. Bolt & Washer
31. Hex Bolt
32. Subframe Support
33. Self Locking Nut
34. Ribbed Nut
35. Bolt & Washer
36. Subframe
37. Screw
38. Spacer Plate
39. Drive Axle w/Inner CV Joint
40. Screw
41. Drive Axle w/Inner Tripod Joint
42. Clamp

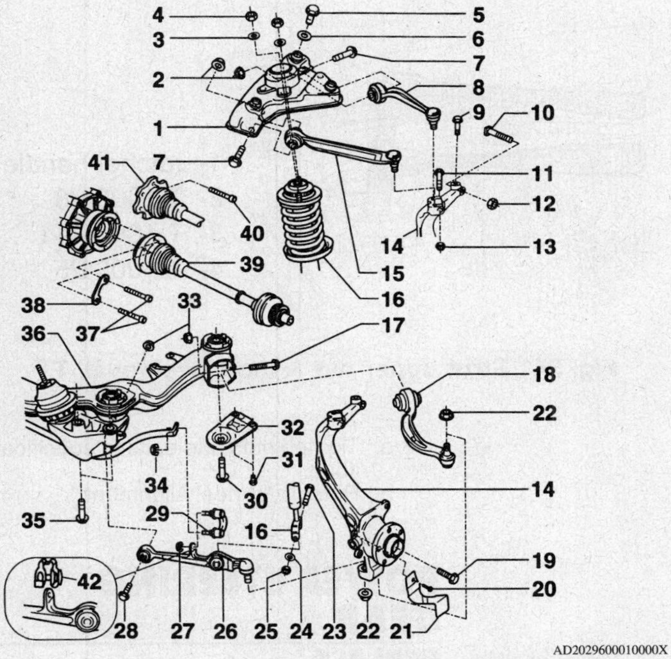

Fig. 30 Front suspension. A4 & S4

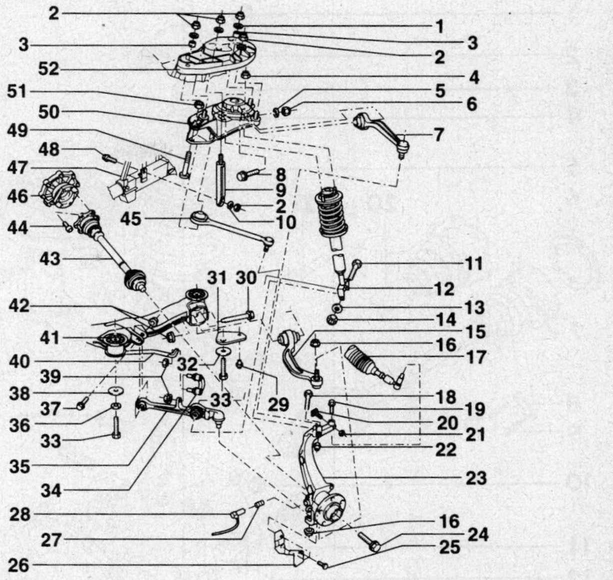

1. Washer
2. Self-Locking Nut
3. Guide Sleeve
4. Self-Locking Nut
5. Washer
6. Self-Locking Nut
7. Upper Control Arm, Rear
8. Bolt
9. Strut
10. Washer
11. Bolt
12. Suspension Strut
13. Washer
14. Self-Locking Nut
15. Guide Link
16. Flanged Nut
17. Steering Gear With Tie Rod
18. Bolt
19. Adjusting Bolt
20. Square Head Bolt
21. Self-Locking Nut
22. Self-Locking Nut
23. Swing Arm
24. Flanged Bolt
25. Bolt
26. Brake Splash Guard
27. Clamping Sleeve
28. ABS Wheel Speed Sensor
29. Bolt
30. Bolt With Washer
31. Support For Subframe
32. Washer
33. Bolt
34. Coupling
35. Support Link
36. Tensioning Washer
37. Bolt With Washer
38. Washer
39. Ribbed Nut
40. Stabilizer Bar
41. Front Subframe
42. Self-Locking Nut
43. Drive Axle
44. Bolt
45. Upper Control Arm, Front
46. Transmission
47. Side Member, In Body
48. Bolt
49. Bolt
50. Mounting Bracket
51. Circlip
52. Mounting Bracket Mount, In Body

AD2029900046000X

Fig. 31 Front suspension. A8 & 1998–99 A6

10. Separate knuckle from axle shaft.
11. Reverse procedure to install. Tighten nuts and bolts to specifications.

TT

1. Remove wheel center cap.
2. Raise vehicle until load on front axle is relieved.
3. Loosen 12-point self-locking hub nut.
4. Remove tires and wheels.
5. Disconnect suspension strut coupling links on both sides of vehicle. Discard nuts.
6. Pull spring clip out of retainer, then disconnect brake hose.
7. Disconnect wheel speed sensor wiring from strut.
8. Remove brake caliper to knuckle mounting bolts, then position caliper aside using suitable wire or rope.
9. Remove brake disc backing plate.
10. Loosen ball joint upper nut until only a few threads remain connected.
11. Separate ball joint from control arm using separator tool No. 3287-A, or equivalent.
12. Loosen tie rod end nut until only a few threads remain connected.
13. Separate tie rod end from knuckle using Kukko puller tool No. V /176, or equivalent.
14. Support knuckle using jack tool No. VAG1383/A with universal support tool No. VAG1359/2, or equivalents.
15. Disconnect ABS wheel speed sensor electrical connector.
16. Ensure sufficient clearance is available, then press drive axle out of knuckle using press tool No. 3283, or equivalent, **Fig. 48,** and position aside using suitable wire or rope.
17. Remove and discard strut to knuckle mounting bolt and nut.
18. Insert spreader tool No. 3424, or equivalent into slot, **Fig. 33.**
19. Rotate ratchet handle through 90°, then pull ratchet handle off spreader tool.
20. Push brake disc in direction of strut by hand.
21. Pull knuckle downward off strut cartridge.
22. Reverse procedure to install, noting the following:
    a. Clean splines and threads on drive axle and in hub.
    b. Install new 12-point self-locking nut and rotate as far as possible.
    c. **Torque** brake caliper to knuckle bolts to 92 ft. lbs.
    d. Connect suspension strut coupling links and install new nuts.
    e. Lower the vehicle, but not so far

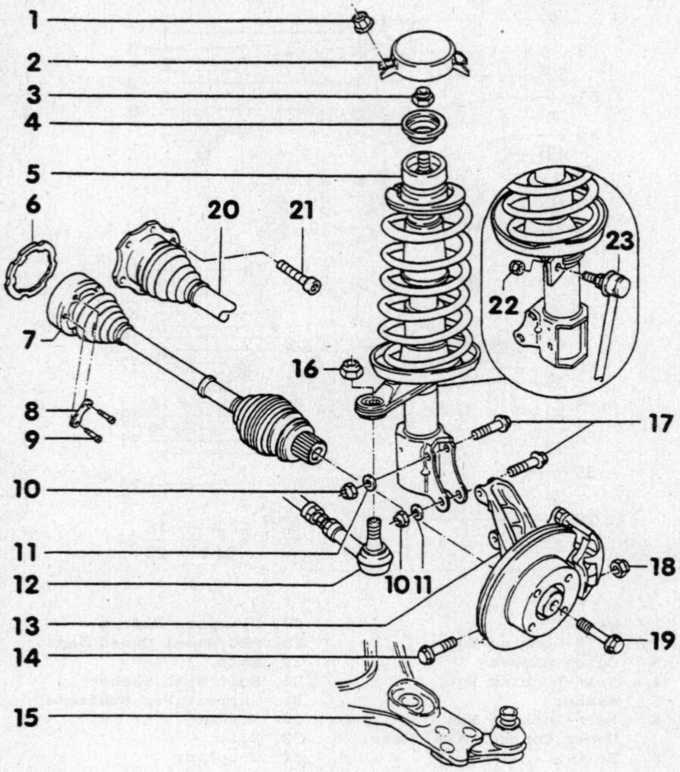

1. Nut
2. Cap
3. Nut
4. Stop
5. Strut
6. Gasket
7. Drive Axle For Manual Transaxle
8. Washer
9. Allen Bolt
10. Nut
11. Washer
12. Tie Rod
13. Steering Knuckle
14. Bolt
15. Control Arm
16. Nut
17. Bolt
18. Nut
19. Washer Headed Bolt
20. Drive Axle For Automatic Transaxle
21. Bolt
22. Nut
23. Speed Sensor

AD2029500033000X

Fig. 32 Upper front suspension. Cabriolet

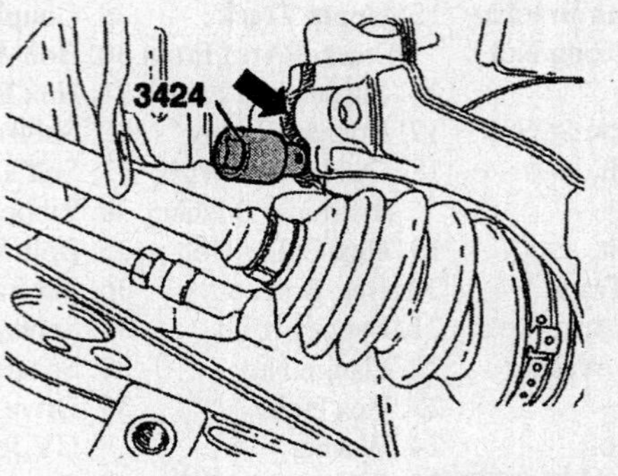

AD2020000059000X

Fig. 33 Spreader tool insertion. TT

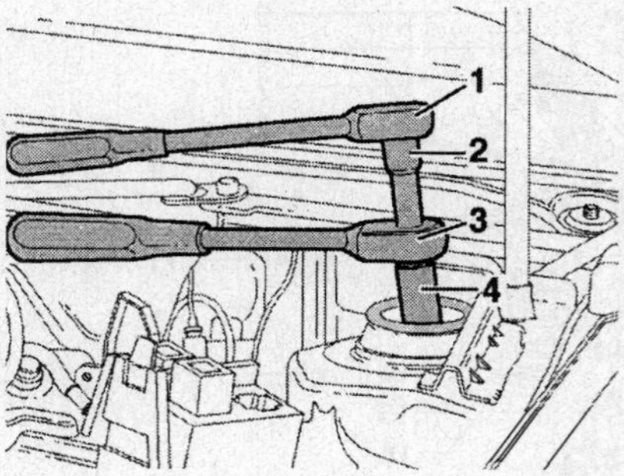

1- ratchet handle
2- T 10001/8
3- T 10001/11
4- T 10001/5

AD2020000060000X

Fig. 34 Strut upper nut & mount removal. TT

that tires reach ground.

f. Tighten 12-point self-locking nut while an assistant applies brakes.

TIE ROD END

REPLACE

Outer

1. Raise and support vehicle.
2. Remove front wheel(s).
3. Remove outer tie rod to steering knuckle nuts/bolts, **Figs. 49 through 51.**
4. Separate tie rod end from steering knuckle using a suitable tool.
5. Loosen tie rod end adjustment clamp nut or jam nut.
6. Unscrew tie rod end from tie rod, count and record number of turns required to remove.
7. Install new tie rod end using same number of turns.
8. Reverse remaining procedures to install, noting the following:
   a. Tighten nuts and bolts to specifications.
   b. Refer to "Wheel Alignment."

Inner

1. Remove outer tie rod end as outlined previously.
2. **On A4, A8, S4 and 1998–99 A6 models,** proceed as follows:
   a. Remove inner and outer steering gear boot clamps **Fig. 49.**
   b. Pull inner end of boot away from steering gear.
   c. Using a suitable crowfoot wrench, disconnect tie rod from steering gear rack.
   d. Remove boot and adjuster clamp from tie rod.
3. **On Cabriolet models,** proceed as follows:
   a. Remove inner tie rod end **Fig. 51. Remove only one tie rod at this time.**
   b. Install inner tie rod end bolt back into carrier before removing second tie rod.
   c. Remove adjuster clamp from tie rod.
4. **On all models,** reverse procedure to install, noting the following:
   a. Tighten nuts and bolts to specifications.
   b. Refer to "Wheel Alignment."

POWER STEERING GEAR

REPLACE

A4 & S4

1. Remove lefthand under dash trim panel.
2. Remove nut from eccentric pinch bolt at base of steering column, then turn eccentric bolt to relieve tension.
3. Ensure steering is straight ahead and ignition is in lock position. **Do not turn steering during remainder of procedure.**
4. Secure steering column sliding joint with wire to prevent separation.
5. Remove eccentric pinch bolt.
6. Disconnect steering column joint from steering gear.
7. Pinch off fluid lines at power steering fluid reservoir using suitable hose clamping tools.
8. Raise and support vehicle.
9. Remove front wheels.
10. Disconnect tie rods as outlined under "Tie Rod End, Replace."
11. Remove steering gear plastic shields from wheel wells.

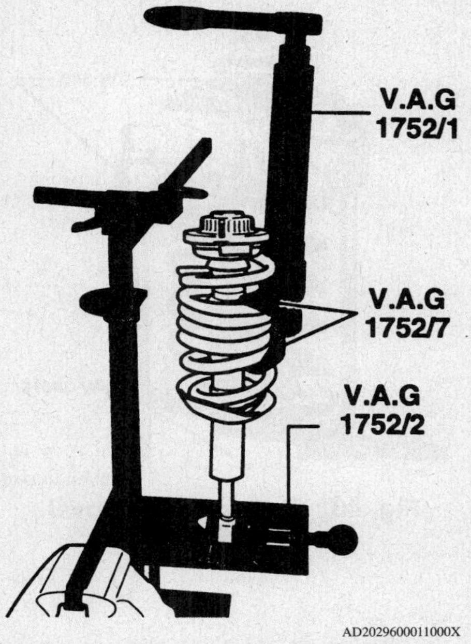

Fig. 35 Strut mount tool. A4, A8, S4 & 1998–99 A6

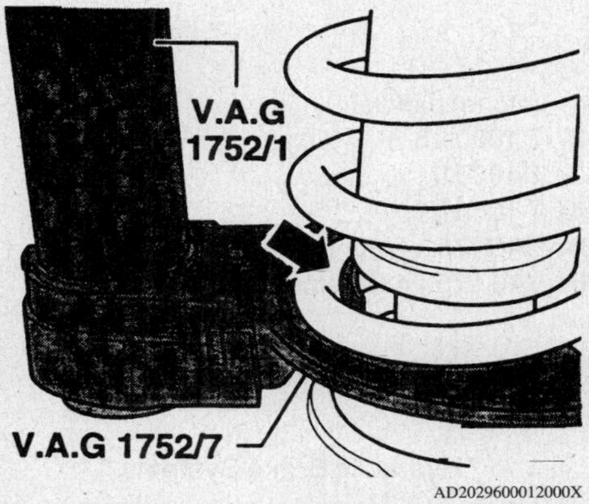

Fig. 36 Coil spring to adapter tool location. A4, A8, S4 & 1998–99 A6

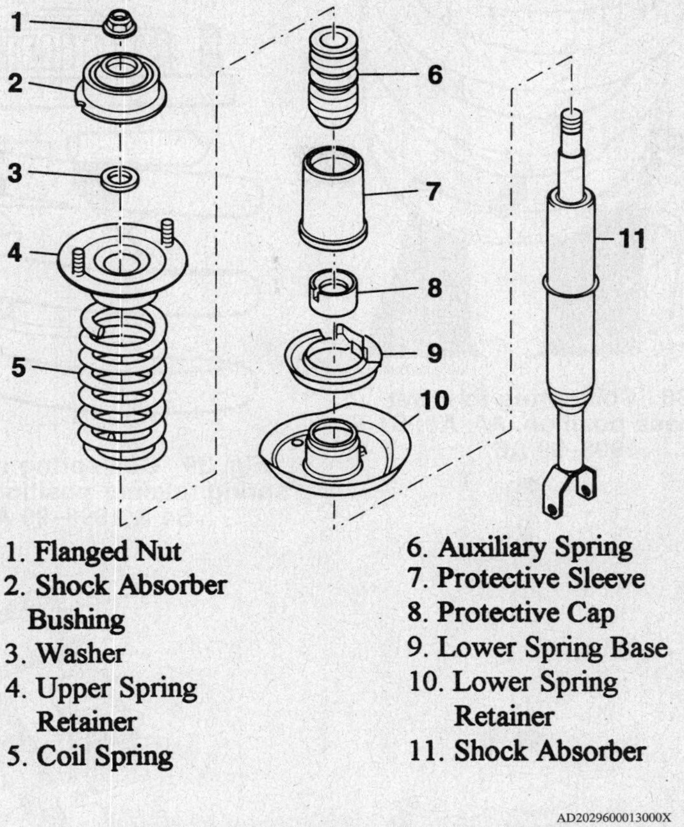

Fig. 37 Strut assembly. A4, A8, S4 & 1998–99 A6

12. Place a suitable drain pan below steering gear fluid line connections.
13. Note positions for assembly reference, then disconnect fluid lines from steering gear, **Fig. 49.** Plug and cap lines and fittings.
14. Remove three steering gear mounting bolts.
15. With the aid of an assistant, remove steering gear from lefthand side of vehicle.
16. Reverse procedure to install, noting the following:
    a. Use new seals and O-rings on all fittings.
    b. Tighten nuts, bolts and fittings to specifications.
    c. Install three steering gear mounting bolts finger tight prior to tightening to specifications.
    d. Ensure steering gear is centered prior to connecting steering column.
    e. Align fluid line fittings at steering gear as noted on disassembly.
    f. Bleed system as outlined under "Power Steering System Bleed" in this section.
    g. Inspect wheel alignment and adjust as required. Refer to "Wheel Alignment."

A8 & 1998–99 A6

1. Remove steering column lower knee bolster.
2. Disconnect steering column U-joint at firewall, **Fig. 50.**
3. Raise and support vehicle, then remove front wheels.
4. Clamp off power steering fluid reservoir supply and return lines.
5. Remove tie rod end attaching bolts, then press tie rod ends down and away.
6. On righthand side of vehicle, proceed as follows:
    a. Remove righthand steering gear mounting bolt through cutout in wheelhouse.
    b. Tie swing arm up to coil spring using cable ties.
7. On lefthand side of vehicle, proceed as follows:
    a. Remove lower half of front wheelhousing shell.
    b. Remove insulation liner in wheelhouse.
    c. Use suitable pan to catch hydraulic fluid.
    d. Remove pressure line and return line from steering gear, through wheelhousing.
    e. Disconnect harness connector from servotronic solenoid valve.
    f. Remove both mounting bolts from steering gear on lefthand side through cutout in wheelhousing.
    g. Pull steering gear to left from stop.
    h. Remove steering gear through lefthand wheel housing.
8. Reverse procedure to install.

Cabriolet

1. Remove stiffener bar from strut towers, if equipped.
2. Pry covers off air intake silencer box, then remove box.
3. Remove vacuum lines and air hoses required to allow access to steering gear.
4. Using a suitable suction device, remove fluid from brake fluid reservoir.
5. **On models equipped with manual transaxle,** disconnect and cap fluid line from brake fluid reservoir to clutch master cylinder.
6. **On all models,** pull vacuum check valve from brake booster, then disconnect line from engine.
7. Mark, then disconnect and position aside all brake fluid lines required to allow brake booster removal.
8. Disconnect electrical connectors from master cylinder.
9. Pinch off fluid lines at power steering fluid reservoir using suitable hose

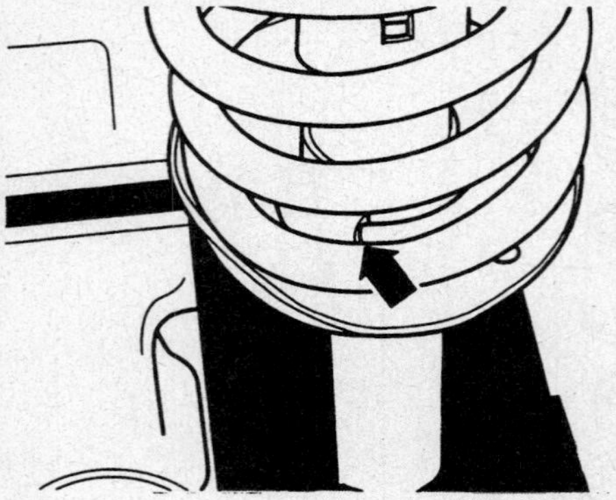

AD2029600014000X

Fig. 38 Coil spring to lower spring base position. A4, A8, S4 & 1998–99 A6

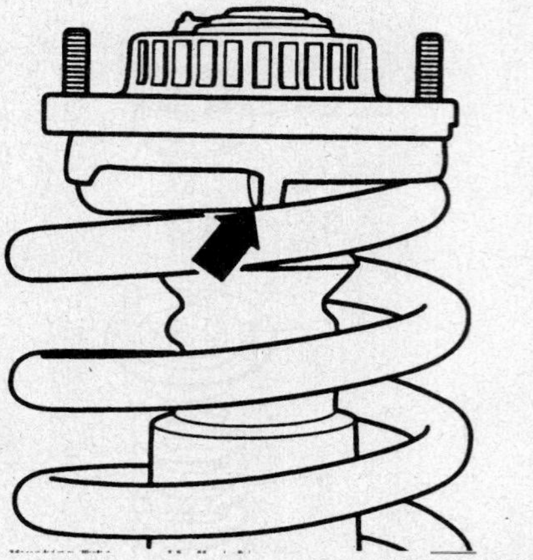

AD2029600015000X

Fig. 39 Coil spring to upper spring retainer position. A4, A8, S4 & 1998–99 A6

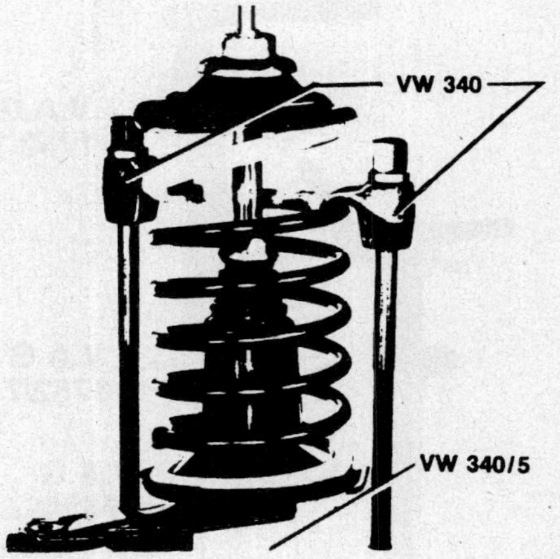

AD2029100001000X

Fig. 40 Coil spring removal. Cabriolet

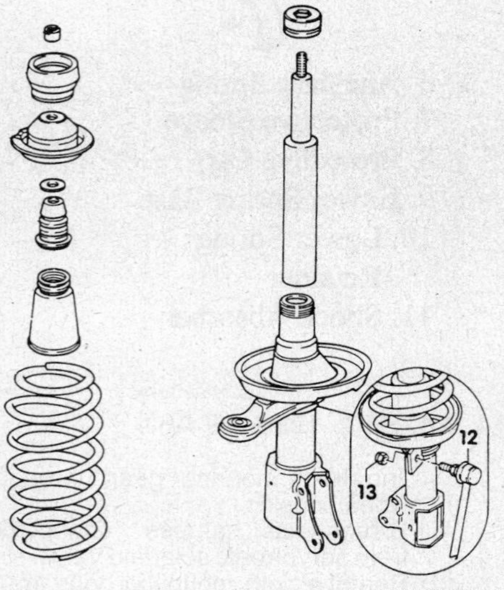

AD2029300004000X

Fig. 41 Strut assembly. Cabriolet

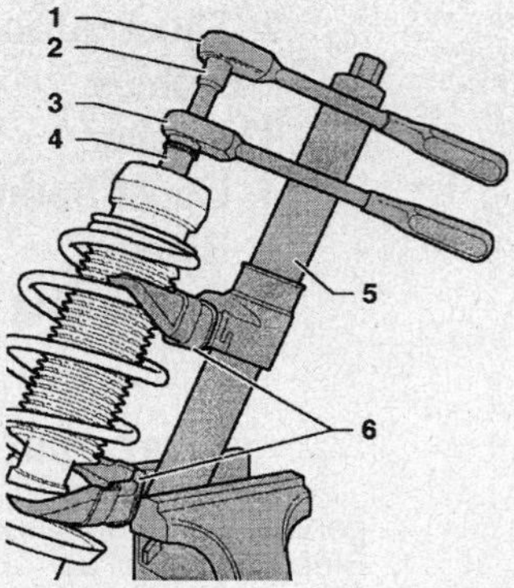

1- ratchet handle
2- T 10001/8
3- T 10001/11
4- T 10001/5
5- VAG1752/1 Spring tensioner
6- VAG1752/4 Retainer

AD2020000061000X

Fig. 42 Strut disassembly. TT

clamping tools.

10. Remove lefthand underdash trim panel and lefthand footwell air vent.
11. Ensure steering is in straight-ahead position and ignition is locked. **Do not turn steering during remainder of procedure.**
12. Secure steering column sliding joint with suitable wire or rope to prevent separation.
13. Disconnect steering coupler at steering gear.
14. Disconnect brake booster rod clevis from pedal.
15. Position firewall insulation aside to allow access to booster mounting nuts, then remove nuts.
16. Remove brake booster from engine compartment.
17. Raise and support vehicle.
18. Remove front wheels.
19. Disconnect inner and outer tie rod ends as outlined under "Tie Rod End, Replace." Place tie rods aside.
20. Place a suitable container below steering gear fluid lines connections.
21. Note positions for assembly reference, then disconnect fluid lines from steering gear **Fig. 52.** Plug and cap lines and fittings.
22. Remove steering gear mounting bolts accessed through wheelwells.
23. Remove steering damper mounting bracket bolts from wheel well.
24. Remove brake line from clamp in wheel well, position line aside for clearance.
25. Using a suitable angle wrench, remove steering gear mounting bolts.
26. Remove steering gear upward.
27. Reverse procedure to install, noting the following:
    a. Use new seals and O-rings on all fittings.
    b. Tighten nuts, bolts and fittings to specifications.
    c. Ensure steering gear is centered prior to connecting steering column.
    d. Align fluid line fittings at steering gear as noted on disassembly.
    e. Bleed system as outlined under "Power Steering System Bleed."
    f. Inspect wheel alignment and adjust as required. Refer to "Wheel Alignment."
    g. Bleed brakes as outlined under "Hydraulic Brake Systems."

TT

1. Ensure front wheels are in straight-ahead position.
2. Remove plastic cover at bottom of steering column under instrument panel.
3. Remove steering column universal joint pinch bolt, then separate joint from stub shaft. Discard pinch bolt.
4. Remove sound insulation panels under subframe.
5. Install clamp tool No. 3094, or equivalent on return hose between power steering fluid reservoir and pump.
6. Disconnect return pipe from fluid reservoir and allow fluid to drain into a suitable container.
7. Install plug in fluid reservoir return outlet.
8. Loosen tie rod end nut until only a few threads remain connected.
9. Separate tie rod end from knuckle using Kukko puller tool No. V /176, or equivalent.

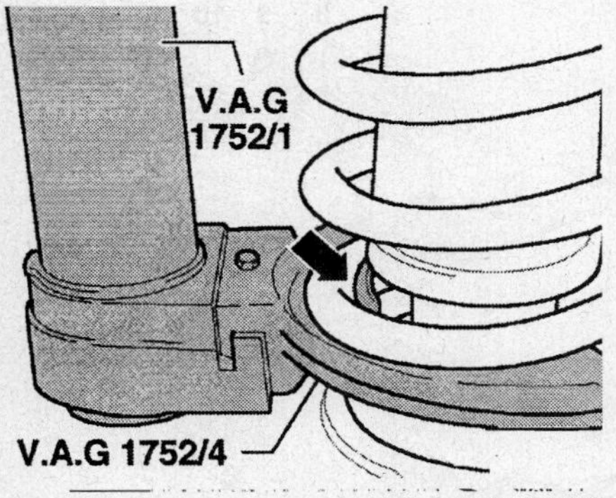

AD2020000062000X

Fig. 43 Coil spring seating. TT

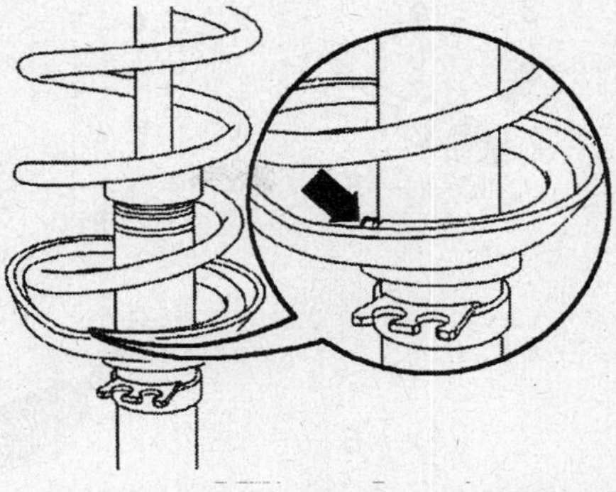

AD2020000063000X

Fig. 44 Spring seated against stop. TT

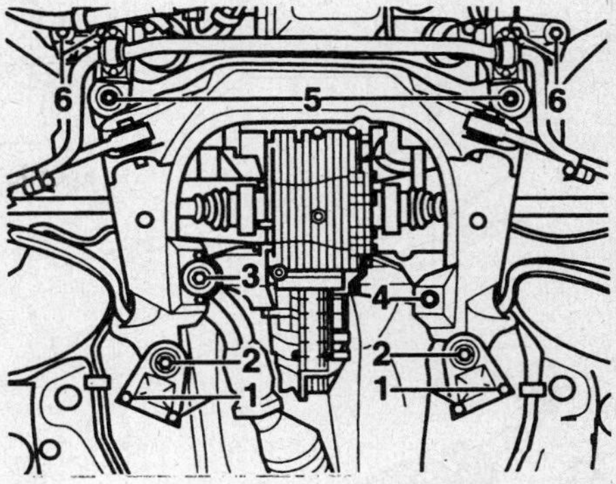

AD2029600017000X

Fig. 45 Subframe mounting bolts. A4 & S4

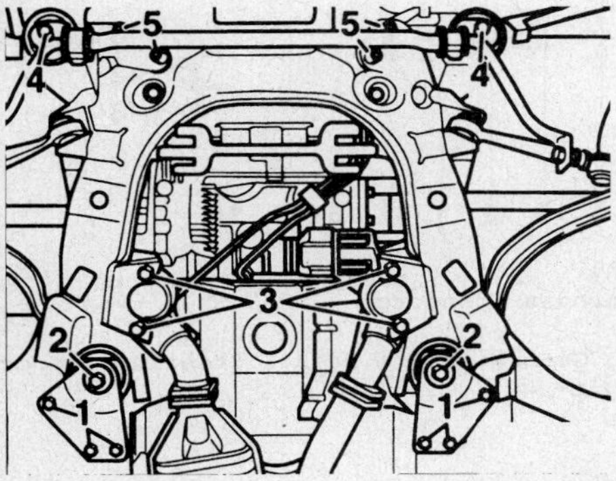

AD2029900047000X

Fig. 46 Subframe mounting bolts. A8 & 1998–99 A6

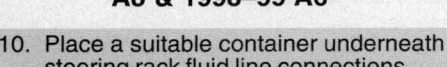

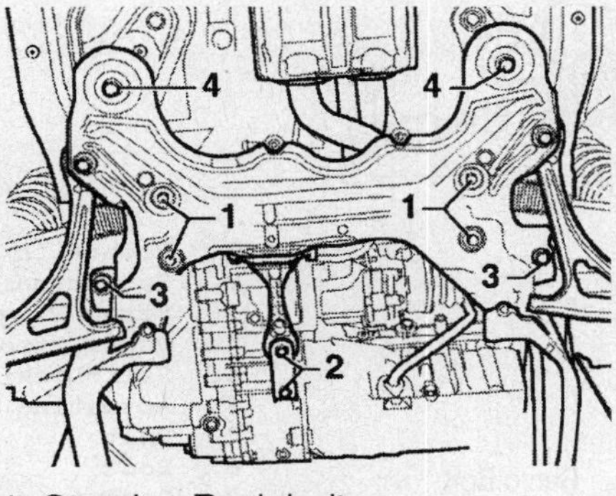

1- Steering Rack bolts
2- Pendulum Support Bolts
3- Subframe Bolts
4- Subframe Bolts

AD2020000064000X

Fig. 47 Pendulum support, steering rack & subframe mounting bolts. TT

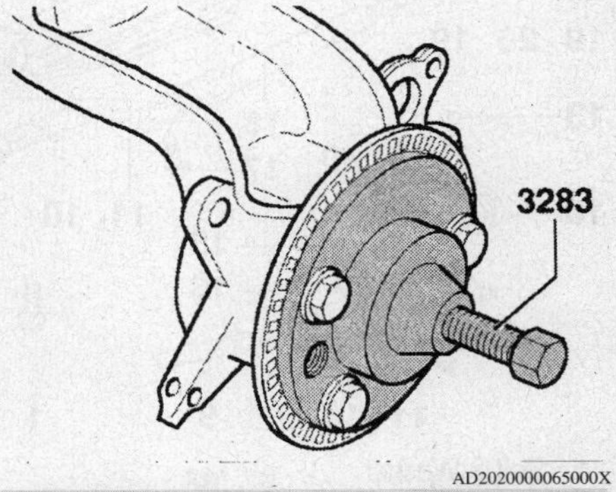

AD2020000065000X

Fig. 48 Drive axle removal from knuckle. TT

10. Place a suitable container underneath steering rack fluid line connections.
11. Disconnect expansion hose from steering rack, **Fig. 53,** then seal with plastic bag and adhesive tape.
12. Unbolt pendulum support at transaxle.
13. Remove subframe as outlined under "Subframe, Replace."
14. Disconnect fluid return pipe at retainer and rotary slide valve housing.
15. Remove steering rack mounting bolts.
16. Remove rack toward rear of vehicle.
17. Reverse procedure to install, noting the following:
    a. New steering racks are not supplied with tie rods, boots or tie rod ends.
    b. Position tie rods of new steering rack so they protrude equal lengths on both sides and will place wheels in straight-ahead position.
    c. Measure distance "a," **Fig. 54,** on lefthand side of rack, which should be 0.13 inch, to ensure rack is properly centered.
    d. Ensure all hoses and lines are clear of any objects beofre tightening connections.
    e. Do not connect steering column joint to stub shaft until vehicle is standing on its tires with front wheels in straight-ahead position. Rotate pinion as required to achieve proper adjustment.
    f. Place steering rack on subframe with guide sleeve, then tighten bolts by hand.
    g. Mount return pipe to retainer on rack, ensuring there is 0.39 inch clearance to rack.
    h. Install return pipe to rotary slide valve housing with new O-rings.
    i. Tighten all fasteners to specifications.
    j. Remove clamp tool from return hose.
    k. Inspect power steering fluid level and correct as required.
    l. Inspect and adjust wheel alignment as required. Refer to "Wheel Alignment."

POWER STEERING PUMP

REPLACE

1.8L Engine

1. Mark running direction with suitable chalk or felt pen, then remove serpentine belt.
2. **On turbocharged models,** disconnect air hose leading to charge air cooler at crossmember lower righthand section.
3. **On all models,** remove center and righthand sound insulation panels.
4. Remove power steering pump pulley nuts while counterholding with a suitable hex wrench, then the pulley.
5. Clamp off return hose between fluid reservoir and power steering pump using clamp tool No. 3094, or equivalent.
6. Place a suitable drain pan below power steering pump.
7. Open return hose spring clip, then disconnect return hose at pump.
8. Disconnect pressure hose at pump.
9. Disconnect power steering pressure switch electrical connector, then remove switch.
10. Remove power steering pump mounting bolts, then the pump.
11. Reverse procedure to install, noting the following:
    a. Replacement pumps do not arrive filled with power steering fluid. They must be filled with proper fluid and rotated by hand before installation.
    b. Remove all traces of paint on contact surfaces or threads on either side of pump.
    c. Discard all O-rings and install new ones.
    d. Ensure spring clamp and return hose are properly aligned, **Fig. 55. Mark "A" must align with pump**

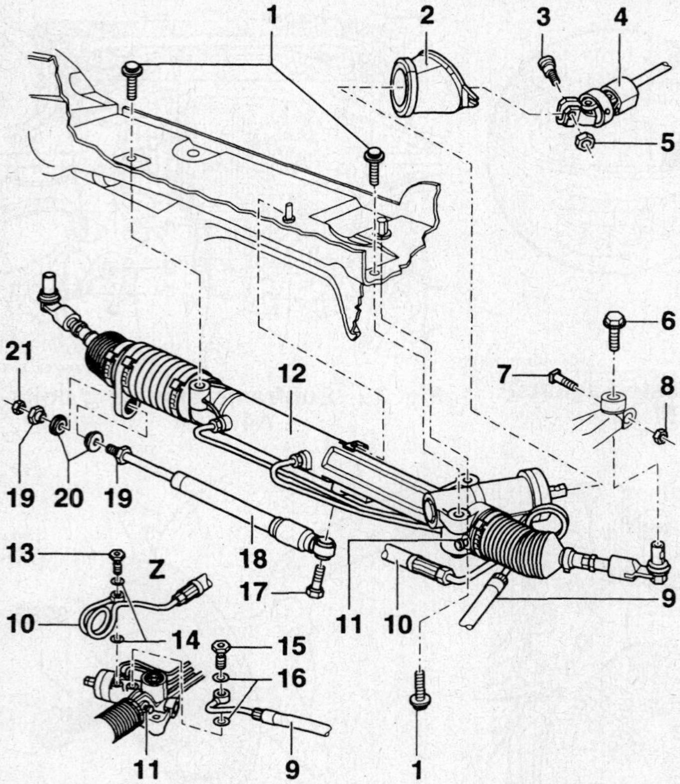

1. Bolt & Washer
2. Boot
3. Eccentric Bolt
4. Steering Coupleing
5. Nut
6. Bolt & Washer
7. Bolt
8. Nut
9. Return Hose
10. Flexible Hose
11. Centering Pin Plug
12. Steering Gear
13. Banjo Bolt
14. Seal
15. Banjo Bolt
16. Seal
17. Bolt
18. Steering Dampner
19. Bushing
20. Rubber Washers
21. Nut

AD2029500043000X

Fig. 49 Steering gear replacement. A4

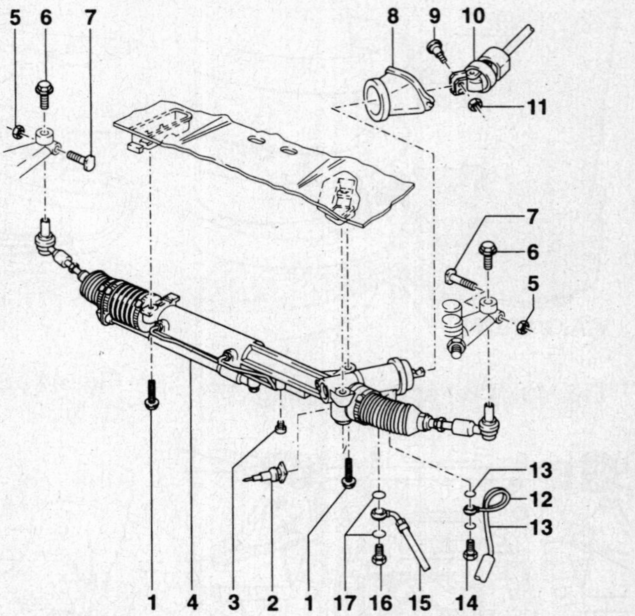

1. Both With Washer
2. Servotronic Harness Connector
3. Screw Plug
4. Power Steering Gear With Tie Rods & Steering Damper
5. Self-Locking Nut
6. Adjusting Bolt
7. Bolt
8. Boot
9. Eccentric Bolt
10. Steering Column
11. Self-Locking Nut With Washer
12. Pressure Line
13. Sealing Ring
14. Banjo Bolt
15. Return Line
16. Banjo Bolt
17. Sealing Ring

AD2029900048000X

Fig. 50 Steering gear replacement. A8 & 1999 A6

seam. Do not install clamp further than transverse mark "B."

e. Tighten all fasteners to specifications.

2.7L Engine

1. Remove engine top appearance cover.
2. Remove serpentine belt cover bolts, then the cover.
3. Mark running direction with suitable chalk or felt pen, then rotate serpentine belt tensioner clockwise and lock in place using drift tool No. 3204, or equivalent.
4. Remove serpentine belt from power steering pump pulley.
5. If required, tag their locations, then disconnect spark plug wires at ignition coils.
6. Pinch off power steering pressure and return hoses using clamp tool Nos. 3094, or equivalent.
7. Place a suitable drain pan underneath power steering pump.
8. Remove hose clamp from pressure hose.
9. Disconnect return hose, remove it from its retainer and position aside.
10. Disconnect pressure hose at pump.
11. Remove return hose clamp.
12. Disconnect return hose, then position aside.
13. Remove power steering pump mounting bolts, then the pump.
14. Reverse procedure to install, noting the following:
    a. Replacement pumps do not arrive filled with power steering fluid. They must be filled with proper fluid and rotated by hand before installation.
    b. Remove all traces of paint on contact surfaces or threads on either side of pump.
    c. Discard all O-rings and install new ones.
    d. **Torque** pump mounting bolts to 15 ft. lbs.
    e. Install pressure hose, then **torque** banjo bolt fitting to 37 ft. lbs.
    f. Install return hose with "P" mark aligned with "I" seam on pump, **Fig. 56.**
    g. Bleed fluid system as outlined under "Power Steering System Bleed" in this section.

2.8L Engine

1. **On A4 and S4 models,** remove top engine cover.
2. **On all models,** remove serpentine drive belt cover, then the drive belt.
3. Remove power steering pump pulley bolts, then the pulley, **Fig. 57.**
4. Remove power steering pump mounting bolts, then the pump.
5. Reverse procedure to install.

3.7L & 4.2L Engines

REMOVAL

1. Remove air duct bolt and air duct tube fitting.
2. Remove fan motor bolts and move motor aside, then loosen pump pulley mounting bolts.
3. Place a 13 mm wrench on tensioner bolt and turn wrench counterclockwise slowly and firmly to release belt tension.
4. Remove drive belt from idler pulley and pump pulley.

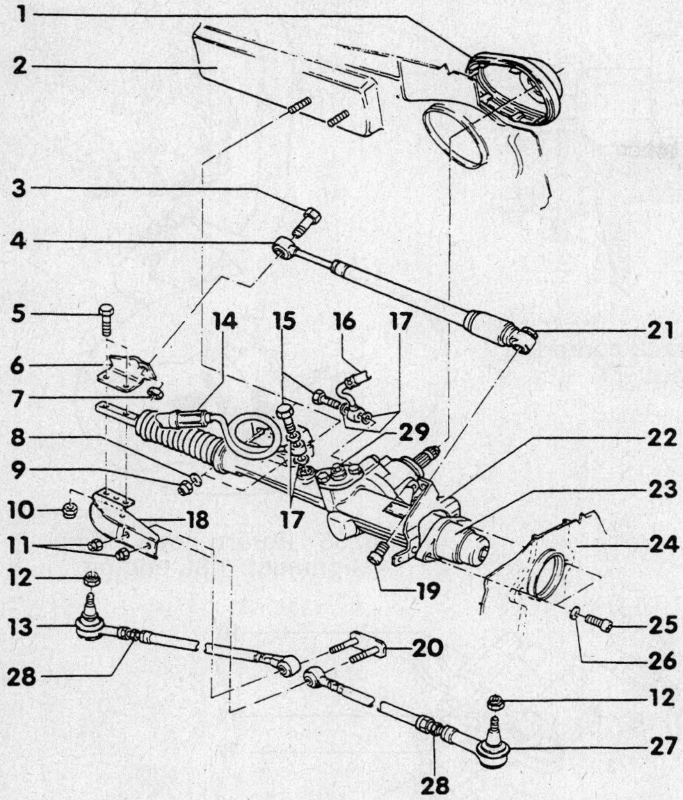

1. Firewall Seal
2. Chassis
3. Bolt
4. Steering Dampner
5. Bolt
6. Retainer
7. Nut
8. Washer
9. Nut
10. Nut
11. Nut
12. Nut
13. Tie Rod
14. Felxible Hose
15. Banjo Bolts
16. Return Hose
17. O-ring
18. Tie Rod Carrier
19. Bolt
20. Plate
21. Threaded Bushing
22. Steering Dampner Bracket
23. Steering Gear
24. Chassis
25. Bolt
26. Lock Washer
27. Tie Rod
28. Plate
29. Adjusting Bolt

AD2029500045000X

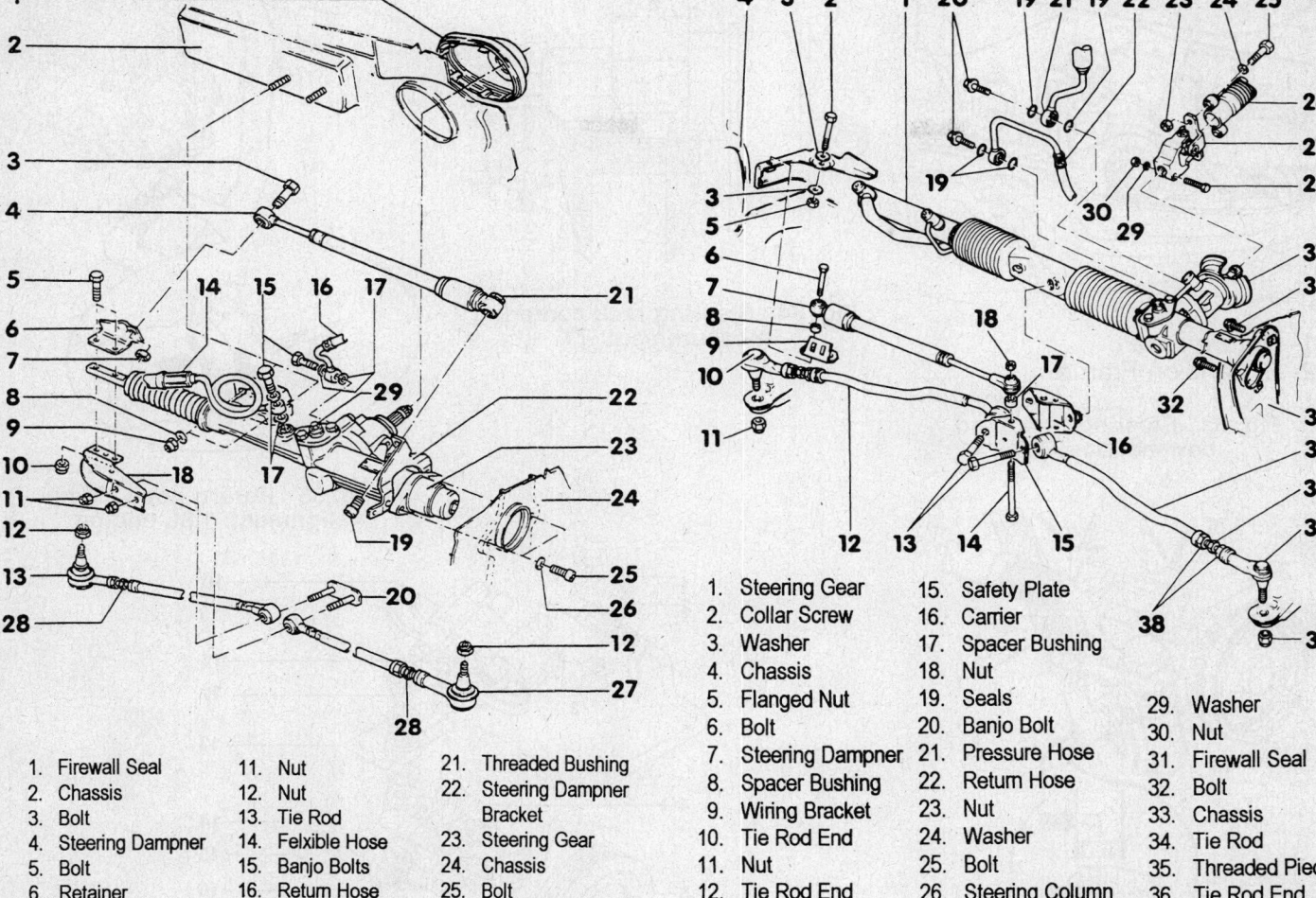

Fig. 51 Steering gear replacement. Cabriolet

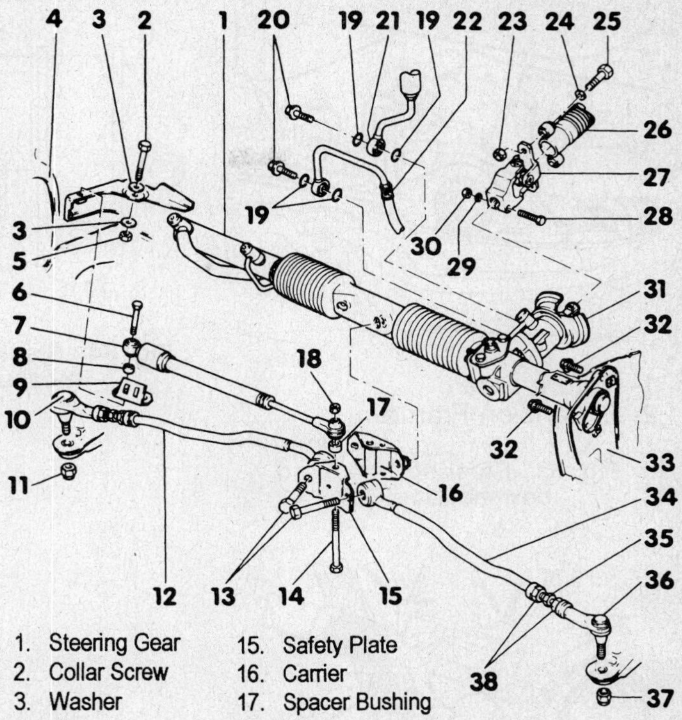

1. Steering Gear
2. Collar Screw
3. Washer
4. Chassis
5. Flanged Nut
6. Bolt
7. Steering Dampner
8. Spacer Bushing
9. Wiring Bracket
10. Tie Rod End
11. Nut
12. Tie Rod End
13. Bolt
14. Bolt
15. Safety Plate
16. Carrier
17. Spacer Bushing
18. Nut
19. Seals
20. Banjo Bolt
21. Pressure Hose
22. Return Hose
23. Nut
24. Washer
25. Bolt
26. Steering Column
27. Steering Coupleing
28. Clamp Bolt
29. Washer
30. Nut
31. Firewall Seal
32. Bolt
33. Chassis
34. Tie Rod
35. Threaded Piece
36. Tie Rod End
37. Nut
38. Lock Nut

AD2029500044000X

Fig. 52 Steering gear replacement. Cabriolet

5. Remove pulley bolts and pulley.
6. Remove shims, then clamp return and intake hoses.
7. Disconnect hydraulic hoses from pump, then seal openings in pump with plastic plugs supplied with replacement pump.
8. Remove mounting bolts with front support bracket, then rear pump mounting bolts.
9. Push pump forward from support, then twist pump, move forward and remove.

INSTALLATION

Banjo bolts with various opening sizes are provided for connecting return hose to pump. During repairs, proper banjo bolt must be selected. If code Number on label of pump is 1 and color code on face of pump is white, select bolt without a identification groove on head of bolt. If code Number on label of pump is 2 or 3 and color code on face of pump is blue or yellow, select bolt with one identification groove on head of bolt.

1. Install pump in support, then loosely install bolts on pump at rear and front.
2. Tighten screws first at rear, then at front.
3. Connect hydraulic hoses to pump. **Prior to tightening banjo bolt for expansion hose, move hose until pipe is situated exactly over corner of pump support.**
4. Install shims to pump shaft, then pulley.
5. Install bolts for pulley and tighten by hand.
6. Install drive belt, then release spring tensioner to tension drive belt.
7. Tighten Pump pulley bolts, then remove clamps from intake and return hoses.
8. Start engine and inspect hydraulic hose connections for leaks.
9. Inspect hydraulic fluid level in reservoir.

POWER STEERING SYSTEM BLEED

A4 & S4

1. Inspect power steering fluid level and correct as required.
2. Raise and support vehicle until front tires can move freely.
3. Turn steering wheel from lock to lock 10 times with ignition Off.
4. Inspect fluid level and correct as required.
5. Lower the vehicle, then start engine.
6. Turn steering wheel from lock to lock 10 times with engine running.
7. Inspect fluid level and correct as required.

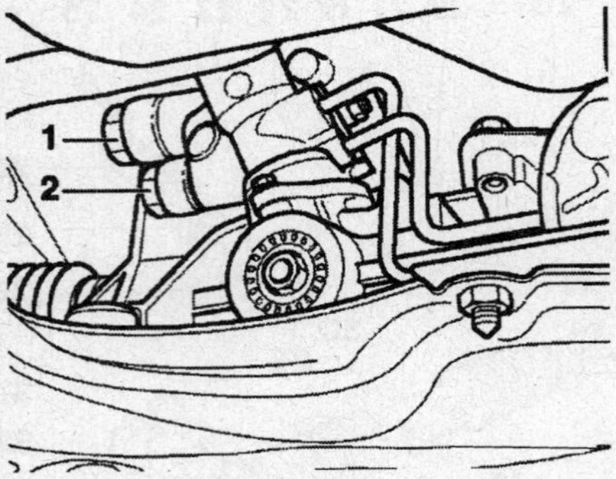

1- Return Pipe
2- Expansion Frame

AD2020000066000X

Fig. 53 Steering rack fluid connections. TT

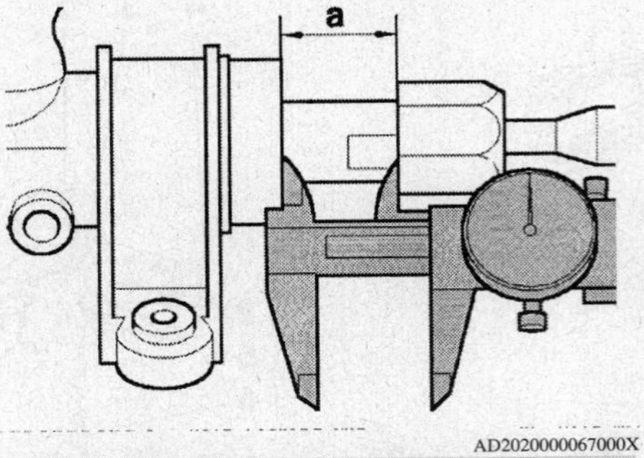

Fig. 54 Steering rack centering measurement. TT

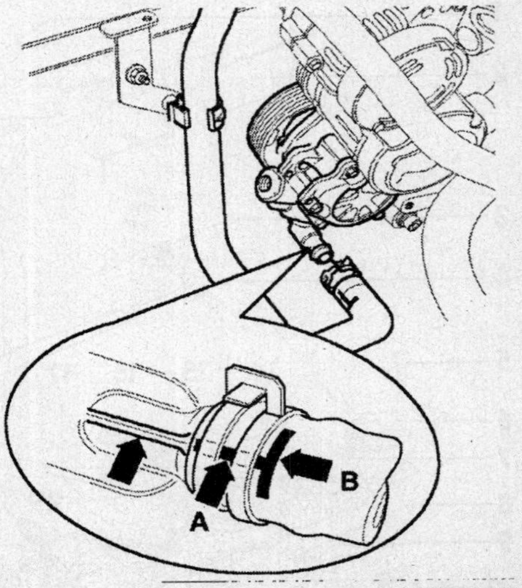

Fig. 55 Return hose clamp alignment. 1.8L engine

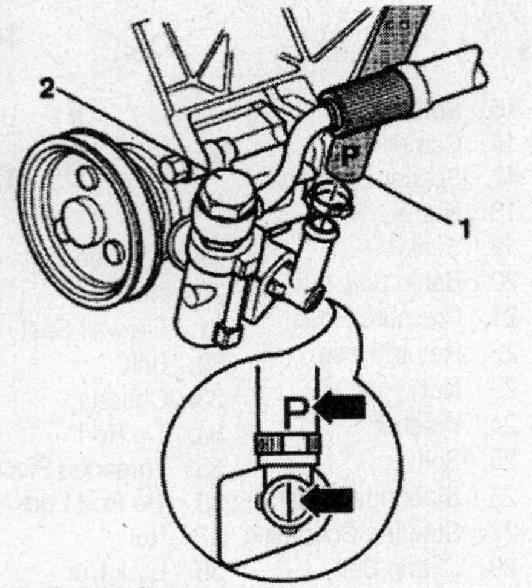

1- Return hose
2- Pressure Hose Banjo Bolt
P- Hose Mark
I- Pump Seam

AD2020000069000X

Fig. 56 Return hose alignment marks. 2.7L engine

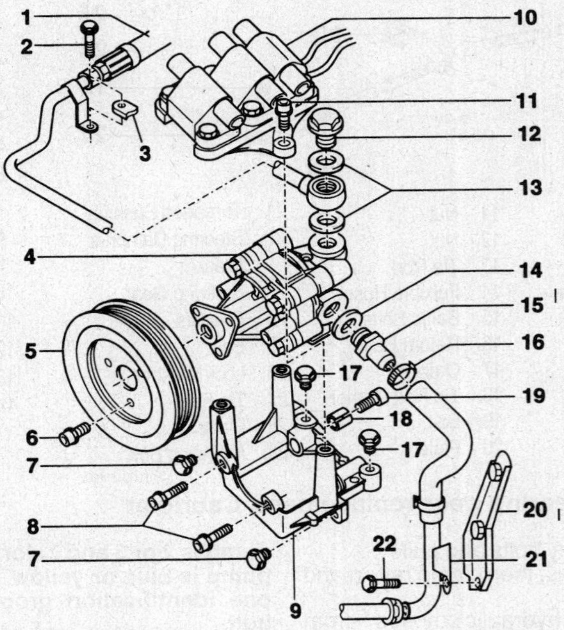

1. Flexible Hose With Delivery Line
2. Hex Bolt
3. Plate With Mounting Hole
4. Power Steering Pump
5. Belt Pulley
6. Screw
7. Bolts & Washers
8. Screw
9. Bracket For Power Steering Pump
10. Ignition Coils With Bracket
11. Screw & Washer
12. Banjo Bolt
13. Seals
14. Seal
15. Line Union
16. Crimp Type Hose Clamp
17. Bolts & Washers
18. Sliding Bushing
19. Screw
20. Bracket
21. Suction Hose
22. Bolt & Washer

AD6029600012000X

Fig. 57 Exploded view of power steering pump. 2.8L engine

8. Any remaining air in steering system will dissipate during next 6–12 miles of driving.

A8 & 1998-99 A6

1. With front wheels in straight-ahead position, run engine at idle for two minutes.
2. Turn ignition Off, then remove hydraulic fluid reservoir cap and inspect fluid level.
3. Fluid level should be at MAX mark on dipstick. Fill as required.
4. Raise and support vehicle, then turn steering wheel from full lefthand lock to full righthand lock 10 times.
5. Lower vehicle, then, with wheels on ground, turn steering wheel from full lefthand lock to full righthand lock 10 times. **Any air that may be left in system will be bled out automatically while driving.**

Cabriolet

1. Fill power steering fluid reservoir to MAX mark on dipstick.
2. Ensure front wheels are in straight-ahead position, then start and run engine at idle for two minutes.
3. Inspect fluid level.
4. As soon as no more bubbles rise in reservoir, stop engine and immediately fill reservoir to MAX mark on dipstick.

TECHNICAL SERVICE BULLETINS

Radio Whining Noise

2000 A8 w/SYMPHONY RADIO

On these models, built before VIN 4D_YN012760, there may be a slight high pitched whine in the AM mode with the engine running and headlamps or parking lamps operating. This may be caused by a generated frequency in the instrument cluster illumination circuit.

To correct this condition, obtain revised instrument cluster part No. 4D0 919 931FX with software level D29, then proceed as follows:

1. Record odometer reading.
2. Connect scan tool No. VAG 1551 or diagnostic tool No. VAS 5051, or equivalent to DLC.
3. Record SRI reading.
4. Record instrument cluster coding.
5. Remove instrument cluster as outlined in “Electrical” section.
6. Install revised instrument cluster.

TIGHTENING SPECIFICATIONS

A4 & S4

Component	Torque/Ft. Lbs.
Axle Nut M14 Bolts	85①
Axle Nut M16 Bolts	140①
Brake Caliper Mounting Bolts	85
Brake Shield To Swing Arm	84③
Drive Axle Nut, M14 Bolts	85①
Drive Axle Nut, M16 Bolts	140①
Drive Axle To Transaxle	②
Guide Link Ball Joint To Swing Arm	74
Guide Link To Subframe	66①
Hub Nut, M14 Bolts	85①
Hub Nut, M16 Bolts	140①
Ignition Coil Mounting Bolt	18
Power Steering Pump Mounting Bolts	18
Power Steering Pump Pressure Hose Bracket Mounting Bolt	71
Power Steering Pump Pulley Bolts	18
Power Steering Pump Return Hose To Pump	37
Power Steering Pump To Pressure Line	30
Strut Mounting Bracket To Body	48
Strut Mounting Bracket To Strut	15
Strut Top Nut	37
Strut To Support Link	66
Subframe Support To Body	18
Subframe Support To Subframe	81
Subframe To Body	44
Subframe To Coupling	66
Support Link To Coupling	52
Swing Arm To Track Control Arms	33
Track Control Arm To Strut Mounting Bracket	37①
Wheel Lug Bolts	81

① — Plus 1/4 (90°) turn.
② — With CV joint, M8 bolts 30 ft. lbs., w/M10 bolts 57 ft. lbs.; w/tripod joint, 57 ft. lbs.
③ — Inch lbs.

A8 & 1998-99 A6

Component	Torque/Ft. Lbs.
Brake Splash Guard Bolt	84①
Drive Axle to Transaxle Bolts	57
Front Subframe Bolt	118②
Guide Link To Subframe Bolt & Nut	66②
Guide Link Flanged Nut	74
Power Steering Gear To Body Bolts	52
Power Steering Pressure Line Banjo Bolt	30
Power Steering Return Line Banjo Bolt	37
Rear Upper control Arm To Mounting bracket Attaching Bolt & Nut	37②
Steering Column U-Joint Nut & Bolt	30
Steering Gear Drain Plug	108①
Steering Gear Tie Rod Adjusting Bolt	62
Steering Gear Tie Rod End Cross Bolt & Nut	33
Strut Lower mounting Bolt & Nut	66
Strut Mounting Bracket Nuts	74
Strut Upper Attaching Nuts	15
Subframe Support Bolt	18
Tie Rod End To Control Arm Attaching Bolt	62①
Tie Rod End To Control Arm Cross Bolt & Nut	33
Upper Control Arm To Swing Arm Nut	30
Wheel Hub Flanged Bolt	148②

① — Inch Lbs.
② — Plus ¼ (90°) turn.

CABRIOLET

Component	Torque/Ft. Lbs.
Axle Shaft To Differential Drive Flange Bolts, M8	33
Axle Shaft To Differential Drive Flange Bolts, M10	58
Ball Joint To Control Arm Nuts	48
Ball Joint To knuckle Nuts	48
Control Arm To Subframe Nuts	30①
Link Rod Nuts	33
Pump Pressure Hose Banjo Bolt	36
Pump Pulley To Pump Bolts	14
Pump Return Hose Banjo Bolt	36
Pump To Front Bracket Nuts	14
Stabilizer Bar Link Rod Nuts	14
Stabilizer Bar To Subframe Clamp Nuts	25
Strut Assembly Nuts	44
Strut Assembly Slotted Nuts	36
Strut Assembly Threaded Cap	106
Strut Assembly To knuckle Nuts	59①
Tie Rod To Strut Assembly Nuts	22
Wheel Lug Nuts	81

① — Plus an additional ½ (180°) turn.

TT

Component	Torque/Ft. Lbs.
Ball Joint To Control Arm Nuts	59
Ball Joint To Knuckle Nuts	33
Control Arm To Subframe Bolts & Nuts	52①
Coupling Link To Strut Nuts	37①
Coupling Link To Stabilizer Bar Nuts	74
Drive Axle To Transaxle Flange Bolts	57
Pendulum Support To Transaxle Bolts	30
Pendulum Support To Subframe	18
Pump Pressure Hose Banjo Bolt	28
Pump Pulley Mounting Bolts	18
Pump To Bracket Bolts	18
Stabilizer Bar To Subframe Clamp Nuts	18
Steering Column Pinch Bolt	22
Steering Rack To Subframe Bolts	15①
Strut Assembly Upper Nuts	44
Strut Assembly To Knuckle Nuts	44①
Subframe To Body Bolts	74①
Wheel Lug Nuts	89

① — Rotate an additional ¼ (90°) turn.

Wheel Alignment

INDEX

	Page No.
Front Wheel Alignment	1-105
Camber	1-105
A4 & S4	1-105
A8 & 1998–99 A6	1-105
Cabriolet	1-105
TT	1-106
Caster	1-106
Toe	1-106
A4 & S4	1-106
A8 & 1998–99 A6	1-106
Cabriolet	1-106
TT	1-106
Preliminary Inspection	1-105
Rear Wheel Alignment	1-106
Camber	1-106
A4 & S4	1-106
A8 & 1998–99 A6	1-106
TT	1-107
Toe	1-107
A4 & S4	1-107
A8 & 1998–99 A6	1-107
TT	1-107
Vehicle Ride Height	1-108
Wheel Alignment Specifications	1-5

PRELIMINARY INSPECTION

Do not attempt to inspect and adjust front wheel alignment without first conducting a preliminary inspection of the front suspension components.

When inspecting and/or adjusting front axle wheel alignment, the following conditions are important and should be adhered to:

1. Front axle wheel alignment should not be inspected until coil springs have properly settled.
2. Vehicle should be at gross vehicle weight, or curb load weight, when the inspection or adjusting procedure is made.
3. Ensure fuel tank and all fluids are filled to full levels.
4. Tire pressures should be set to specifications.
5. Test surface should be level and horizontal.
6. The steering gear should be properly adjusted.
7. Steering linkage should be free of play.

FRONT WHEEL ALIGNMENT

Camber

Camber is the amount of center line that the wheel is tilted inward or outward from true vertical, **Fig. 1.** If a wheel tilts outward, camber angle is positive. If the top of a wheel tilts inward, camber angle is negative.

A4 & S4

Front wheel camber is not adjustable at each wheel. Camber is built into the front suspension. The total built in camber may be equally split between sides by shifting the subframe as outlined below.

1. Remove sound insulation from under vehicle.
2. Remove bolts "3" and "4," **Fig. 2.** Then loosen bolts "1," "2," "5," "6," "7" and "8," **Fig. 2.**
3. Install tool No. VAG 194, or equivalent in place of bolts "3" and "4," **Fig. 3.** **Torque** tool No. VAG 1941, or equivalent, mounting bolts to 7 ft. lbs.

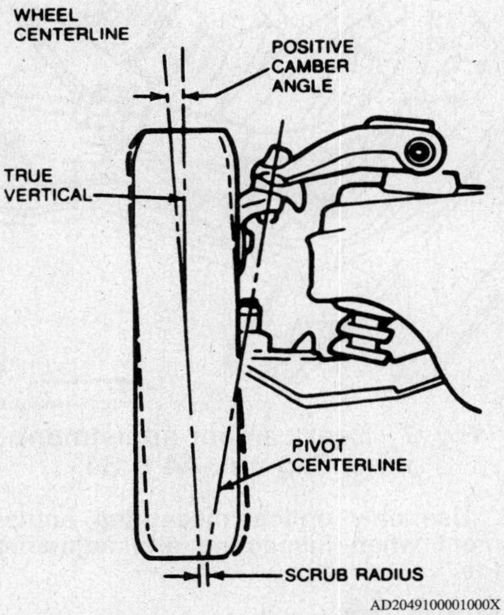

Fig. 1 Camber angle

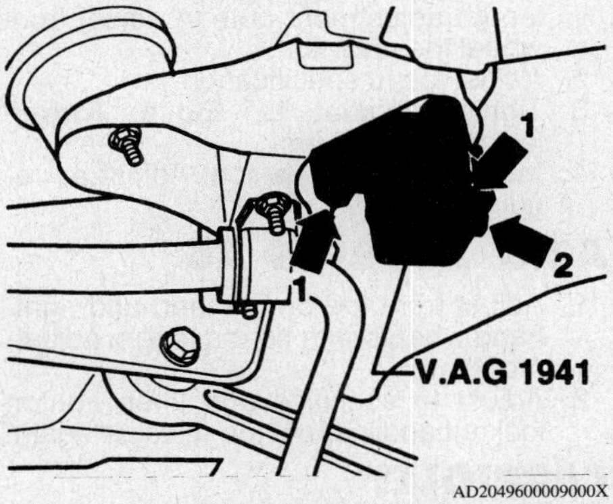

Fig. 3 Front camber adjustment tool installation. A4

4. Adjust camber to specification by turning adjusting bolt on tool No. VAG 1941.
5. Loosen adjusting bolt on tool No. VAG 1941, then inspect camber. Adjust as required.
6. Install bolts "7" and "8" and **torque** to 81 ft. lbs. plus 1/4 (90°) turn.
7. Remove tool No. VAG 1941.
8. Install bolts "5" and "6" and **torque** to 81 ft. lbs. plus 1/4 (90°) turn.

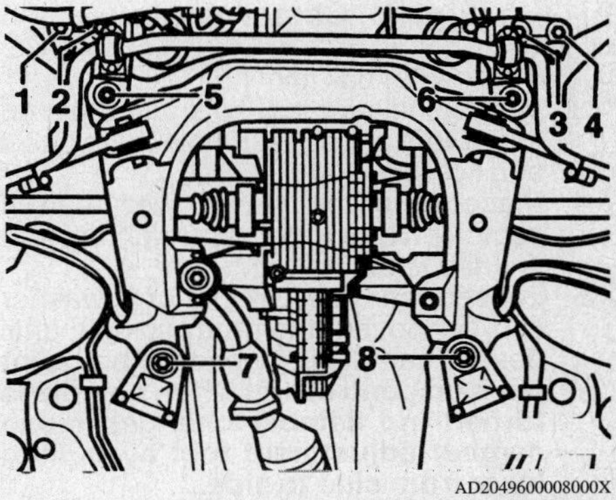

Fig. 2 Front camber adjustment bolt removal. A4

9. Install bolts "1," "2," "3" and "4," then **torque** to 44 ft. lbs.
10. Install sound insulation.

A8 & 1998-99 A6

1. Remove underbody protection pan.
2. Loosen four subframe mounting bolts.
3. Loosen two front subframe bolts just far enough so that adjustment tool No. VAG 1926, or equivalent can be placed between side member and subframe mount.
4. Install adjustment tool No. VAG 1926, or equivalent vertical to center axis of vehicle and use set screw to adjust front axle camber value to within specified range.
5. Release set screw on adjustment tool, inspect values displayed again and adjust as required.
6. Tighten both bolts at rear of front subframe to specifications and remove adjustment tool.
7. Replace both bolts with washers at front of subframe, then both bolts and washers at rear of subframe.
8. Inspect toe-in each time camber is adjusted.

CABRIOLET

1. Loosen front and center ball joint mounting nuts until washer can be moved back and forth.
2. Install camber adjustment tool No. 3196, or equivalent with hole in tool

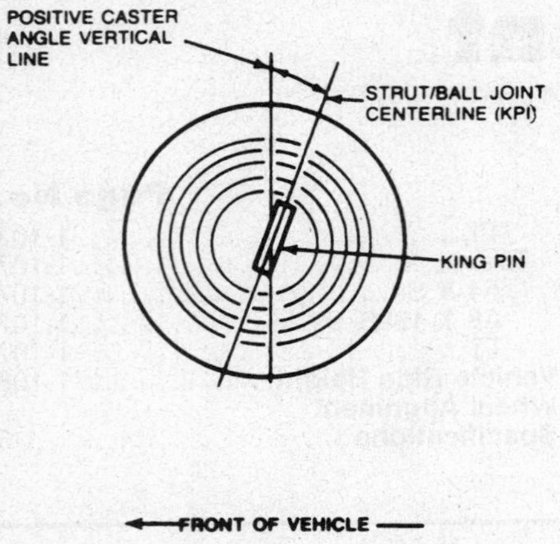

AD2049100002000X

Fig. 4 Caster angle

over center ball joint nut.

3. Turn spindle on tool so knurled pin on top of tool engages in hole in ball joint and tighten.
4. Place top of tool clamp over head of center ball joint bolt and tighten with knurled knob.
5. Loosen rear ball joint nut until washer can be moved, then turn spindle until desired camber is reached. **If ball joint jams on control arm when spindle is turned (no camber change), move camber adjustment tool by pulling lever from side to side.**
6. Pull front end of tool lever inward as far as possible while pushing rear end of lever outward with similar force and hold lever in position.
7. Have a helper tighten two outer ball joint mounting nuts.
8. Remove camber adjustment tool, then tighten center ball joint nut.
9. Tighten all ball joint nuts to specifications, then inspect toe setting and adjust if required.

TT

On these models the camber cannot be adjusted.

It is possible to center the camber uniformly within the specified tolerance range by moving the subframe.

Caster

Caster is the forward or rearward tilt of the top of the front wheel spindle, **Fig. 4.** If the top of the spindle tilts to the rear, caster is positive. If the top of the spindle tilts to the front, caster is negative.

Toe

Toe should only be inspected and adjusted after the caster and camber have been adjusted to specifications.

Inspect toe with the front wheels in the straight-ahead position. Lock steering wheel in place and measure distance between extreme front and also between the extreme rear of both front wheels. The difference between these two distances is the toe-in or toe-out dimensions, **Fig. 5.**

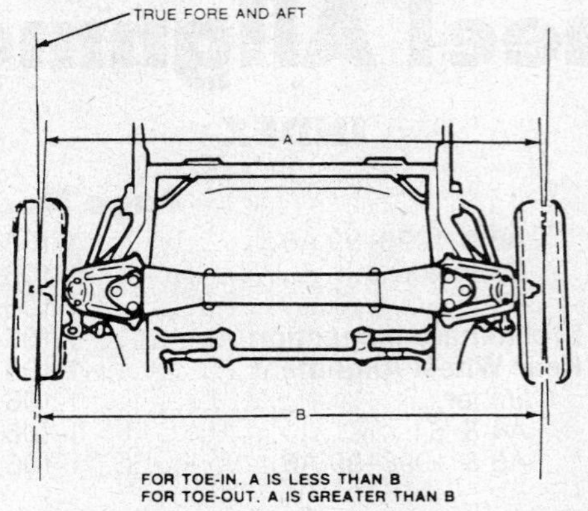

AD2049100003000X

Fig. 5 Toe dimensions

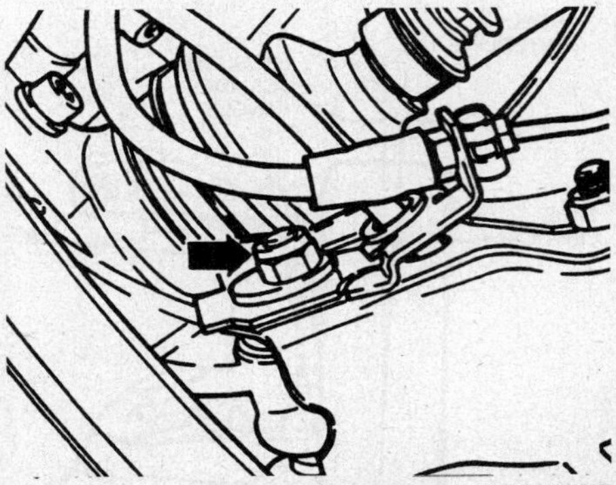

AD2049600004000X

Fig. 7 Rear camber adjustment mounting nut. A4 & S4

Use only optical measuring equipment when inspecting and adjusting toe.

A4 & S4

1. Use lefthand and righthand track rod length adjustment nuts to adjust front wheel toe, **Fig. 6.**
2. Adjust toe to specification.
3. Tighten locknut "B," **Fig. 6. Torque** locknut to 30 ft. lbs.
4. Inspect front wheel toe. Adjust as required.

A8 & 1998-99 A6

1. Adjust front toe on lefthand and righthand wheels with tie rod length adjustment nut.
2. Adjust to specifications, then tighten locknut and inspect toe-in value again.

CABRIOLET

1. Turn steering gear to center position, then remove lower transaxle cover plate attaching bolt.
2. Attach centering tool No. 3075, or equivalent with bracket over mounting nut on lefthand tie rod.
3. Remove bolt from spacer on chain of centering tool.
4. Insert bolt removed in previous step into hole marked "L" on centering tool, then tighten to steering gear.
5. Measure, then divide total toe in half.
6. Loosen clamps and outer locknut on both tie rods.

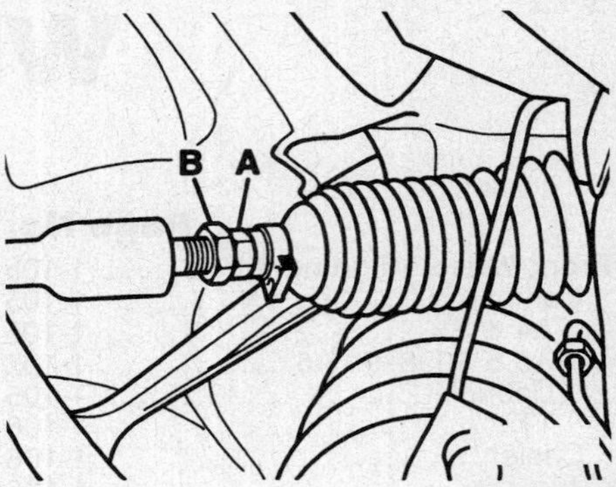

AD2049600010000X

Fig. 6 Front toe adjustment. A4 & S4

7. Turn tie rods until toe is within specifications.
8. Tighten clamps and locknuts on tie rods, then inspect and position steering wheel in center position as required.
9. Remove centering tool, then tighten lower transaxle cover plate attaching bolt to specifications.

TT

When loosening and tightening the tie rod end locknut, counterhold the tie rod end using a suitable 22 MM wrench.

Adjust toe on lefthand and righthand wheels at tie rod hexagon. **Ensure boots are not twisted after turning tie rods.**

Torque locknut to 37 ft. lbs. and inspect toe setting again. If the measured toe is still within specifications, the proper adjustment has been reached.

REAR WHEEL ALIGNMENT

Camber

Use only optical measuring equipment when inspecting and adjusting camber.

A4 & S4

On FWD models, rear wheel camber is not adjustable. **On AWD models,** use the following procedure to adjust rear camber:

1. Loosen mounting nut, **Fig. 7.**
2. Adjust camber to specifications by turning eccentric bolt, **Fig. 8. Do not turn bolt more than 90° to left or right.**
3. Tighten mounting nut and inspect camber, then adjust if required.

A8 & 1998-99 A6

1. Loosen mounting nut for knuckle and control arm.
2. Adjust camber by turning eccentric bolt.
3. Tighten mounting nut to specifications, then inspect camber value again and adjust if required.

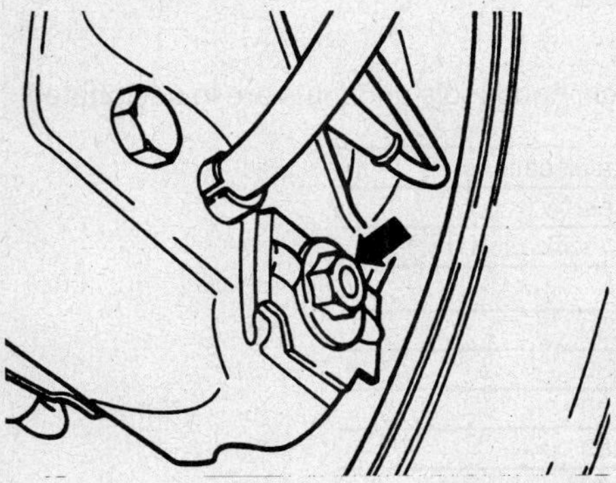

Fig. 8 Rear camber adjustment eccentric bolt. A4 & S4

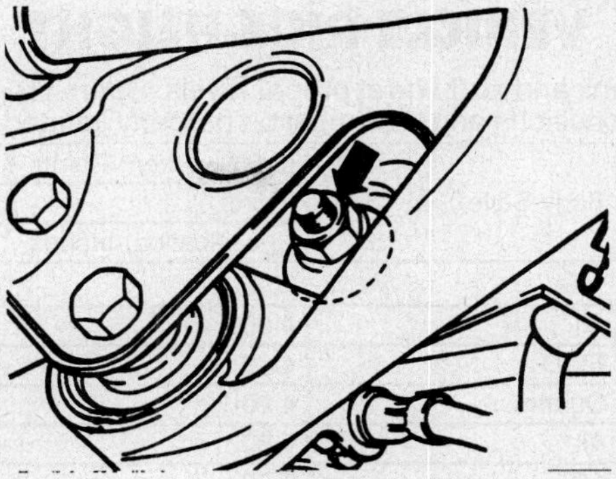

Fig. 9 Rear toe adjustment mounting nut. A4 & S4

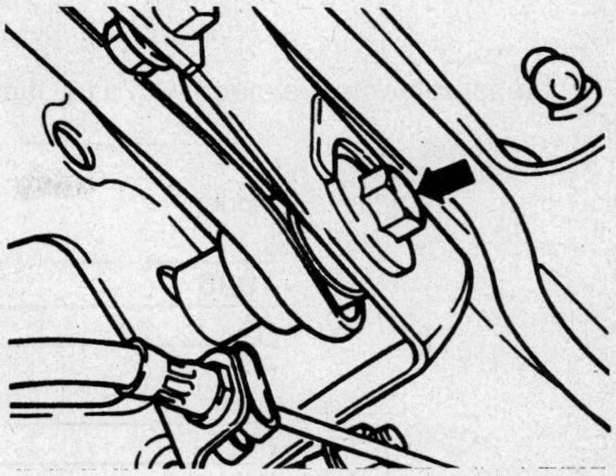

Fig. 10 Rear toe adjustment eccentric bolt. A4 & S4

TT

On these models, rear camber is not adjustable. If readings do not meet specifications, inspect axle beam for damage and replace if required.

Toe

Camber adjustment should be inspected and adjusted if required prior to adjusting toe.

Use only optical measuring equipment when inspecting and adjusting toe.

A4 & S4

Rear wheel toe on FWD models is not adjustable. On AWD models, use the following procedure to adjust rear toe.

1. Loosen mounting nut, **Fig. 9.**
2. Adjust toe to specification by turning eccentric bolt, **Fig. 10. Do not turn bolt more than 90° to left or right.**
3. Tighten mounting nut and inspect toe, then adjust if required.

A8 & 1998-99 A6

1. Loosen tie rod end eccentric bolt locknut at subframe.
2. Adjust toe as required by turning eccentric bolt, then tighten nut to specifications.

TT

EXCEPT QUATTRO

1. Remove and discard axle bracket mounting bolts.
2. Slide mounting bracket laterally as required.
3. **Torque** new mounting bracket bolts to 55 ft. lbs.

QUATTRO

On these models the overall rear axle toe setting cannot be adjusted.

By moving the rear axle it is possible to center the individual toe settings. Proceed as follows:

1. Loosen bolts on axle mounting brackets.
2. Center the individual toe settings by moving axle beam within elongated holes at mounting brackets.
3. If overall toe readings do not meet specifications, inspect axle beam for damage and replace if required.
4. It may also be required to inspect and measure body alignment in area of rear axle mounting points and repair as required.

VEHICLE RIDE HEIGHT

Measurements are made with a full fuel tank and all fluids at proper levels. Spare tire, jack, hand tools and mats are in designated positions and tires must be properly inflated.

Model	Body Style	Measurement Points & Specifications	
		Front①	Rear②
		Specification, Inches	Specification, Inches
1998			
A4	All	4.30	4.30
A6	FWD	4.30	4.30
	Quattro	4.20	4.20
A8	All	4.80	4.80
Cabriolet	All	4.20	4.20
A8	All	4.80	4.80
1999			
A4	All	4.30	4.30
A6	Avant	4.20	4.20
	FWD	4.30	4.30
	Quattro	4.20	4.20
A8	All	4.80	4.80
Cabriolet	All	4.20	4.20
2000			
A4	All	4.30	4.30
A6	Avant	4.20	4.20
	FWD	4.30	4.30
	Quattro	4.20	4.20
A8	All	5.70	5.70
Cabriolet	All	4.20	4.20
S4	Quattro	3.50	3.50
TT	Coupe	4.40	4.40

① — Ground clearance w/loaded vehicle measured from ground to lower edge of front wheelwell.

② — Ground clearance w/loaded vehicle measured from ground to lower edge of rear wheelwell.

Air Conditioning

NOTE: On Air Bag Equipped Models, Refer To "Air Bag System Precautions" Located In The Front Of This Manual For System Disarming & Arming Procedures.

NOTE: Refer To "Computer Relearn Procedures" Located In The Front Of This Manual When Battery Power To The Computer Has Been Interrupted.

INDEX

	Page No.
A/C Specifications	1-111
Charging System	1-110
Charging Valve Location	1-111
Discharging System	1-110
Refrigerant Recovery	1-110
Performance Test	1-109
Precautions	1-109
Air Bag Systems	1-109
Battery Ground Cable	1-109
Radio Coded Anti-Theft System	1-109
System Evacuation	1-110

PRECAUTIONS

AIR BAG SYSTEMS

Refer to "Air Bag System Precautions" in the front of this manual for system disarming and arming procedures.

RADIO CODED ANTI-THEFT SYSTEM

Prior to disconnecting the battery or removing the audio system, obtain the security code from the vehicle operator. Refer to the owner's manual for security code disarming and arming procedures.

BATTERY GROUND CABLE

Prior to service, disconnect battery ground cable and isolate as required.

PERFORMANCE TEST

1. Before beginning test, ensure the following conditions exist:
   a. Condenser and radiator are clean and free of obstructions.
   b. Accessory drive belt is in good condition and is properly tensioned.
   c. All air ducts, covers and seals are in good condition and properly installed.
   d. Air flow through dust and pollen filter is not obstructed by dirt and debris.
   e. Vehicle is not parked in direct sunlight.
   f. Ambient air temperature is greater than 59°F.
   g. Engine is at normal operating temperature.
   h. Coupling between evaporator housing and heater box is tight and does not draw secondary air at high fresh air blower speed.
   i. With engine running, system in "AUTO" operating mode, "LO" temperature setting selected, instrument panel air outlets open, recirculation button pressed (recirculating air symbol lights up in display) and compressor switched on (compressor symbol "Ice Crystal" lights up in display).
2. Ensure A/C system performs as follows:
   a. Cooling fan operates.
   b. Fresh air blower operates at highest speed.
   c. Recirculating/fresh air flap is in "Recirculating Air" position within one minute of starting engine.
   d. Air flows from instrument panel air outlets.
   e. Coolant cutoff valve is closed.
   f. Temperature flap is in "Cooling" position.
   g. Compressor operates (compressor clutch engaged).
3. If one or more of the above results are not satisfactory, refer to "Automatic Temperature Control, Diagnosis & Testing" in **MOTOR's Air Conditioner & Heater Manual.**
4. Close hood, measure outside (ambient) temperature, then close doors, window and sunroof.
5. Inspect A/C performance as follows:
   a. Turn ignition On and press A/C control head "AUTO" button.
   b. Press "–" (minus) temperature select button until "LO" temperature setting is displayed. **Do not select blower speed or press any air distribution buttons.**
   c. Open all instrument panel vents and start engine.
   d. With compressor on and "Ice Crystal" symbol on A/C control head lit, increase engine speed to 2000 RPM.
   e. Measure outlet air temperature from center of instrument panel vent after A/C has run for approximately five minutes. Temperature should fall within range "C," **Fig. 1.**
   f. If specified value was obtained, A/C system is satisfactory. If specified value was not obtained and compressor stopped during cooling test, proceed to step 6. If specified value was not obtained but compressor continued to run during test, proceed to step 10.

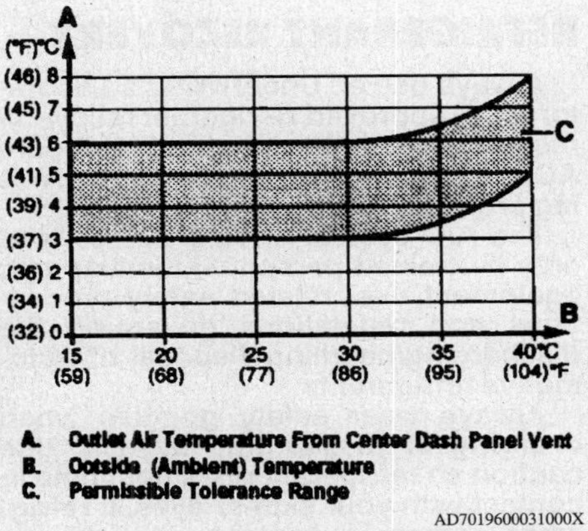

Fig. 1 Outlet air temperature chart

6. Connect scan tool No. VAG 1551, or equivalent, to DLC.
7. Immediately enter address word "08" (read measuring block value) into scan tool and press "Q" button to enter input.
8. Enter Display Group "01" (compressor switch off) conditions.
9. Read Display Group "01" channel "01" and repair cause of A/C compressor switch off.
10. Measure A/C system pressures as follows:
    a. Turn ignition Off.
    b. Remove low pressure switch connector and bridge connector terminals.
    c. Remove high pressure switch and connect connector to switch.
    d. Connect A/C manifold gauge set to service valves located below switches and read high and low pressures.
    e. Compare readings with chart, **Fig. 2.**
    f. If A/C refrigerant system pressure is less than specified, system is low on charge. Proceed to step 11. If A/C system base pressure is equal

Outside (ambient) temperature	Refrigerant system pressure
+15°C (59°F)	3.9 bar (56.5 psi)
+20°C (68°F)	4.7 bar (68.2 psi)
+25°C (77°F)	5.6 bar (81.2 psi)
+30°C (86°F)	6.7 bar (97.2 psi)
+35°C (95°F)	7.8 bar (113.1 psi)
+40°C (104°F)	9.1 bar (132.0 psi)
+45°C (113°F)	10.5 bar (152.3 psi)

AD7010100037000X

Fig. 2 A/C base pressure chart

to or more than specified, proceed to step 12.

11. Inspect and repair system as follows:
    a. Inspect for system leaks.
    b. Inspect for a faulty pressure relief valve on compressor.
    c. If pressure relief valve is faulty, inspect coolant fan operation or for a pinched/kinked refrigerant line.
    d. If system does not leak and pressure relief valve is satisfactory, recover and charge A/C system refrigerant.
12. Start engine and adjust A/C to maximum cooling. If A/C compressor clutch engages, proceed to next step. If A/C compressor clutch does not engage, inspect wiring to clutch. If wiring is satisfactory, replace compressor clutch.
13. Raise engine speed to 2000 RPM, note pressure as follows:
    a. High side pressure should increase from base pressure (ignition Off) to maximum of 290 psi.
    b. Low side pressure should decrease from base pressure (ignition Off) to pressure value, **Fig. 3.**
    c. A/C high pressure switch should turn coolant fan on to high speed when pressure is between 181–232 psi. If coolant fan does not start as specified, inspect coolant fan wiring and coolant fan operation. Repair as required.
14. If high pressure remains at base pressure or only increases slowly and low pressure drops quickly to suction pressure or lower, a low refrigerant charge is indicated. Inspect system for leaks and repair as required.
15. If high and low pressure readings are satisfactory, but proper cooling performance is not obtained, a low refrigerant charge is indicated. Inspect system for leaks and repair as required.
16. If high pressure increases only slightly over base pressure and low pressure drops only slightly from base pressure, A/C compressor is faulty. Repair or replace as required.
17. If high pressure is above specified value and low pressure drops to suction pressure or lower, A/C system line is kinked or plugged. Feel A/C system lines (high and low side) for temperature drop. Inspect lines for kinks or damage. Replace as required.
18. If high and low pressures are normal at the beginning of test, then high pressure increases above specified value and low pressure drops to suction pressure or lower after A/C operates for a period of time, this indicates that there is moisture in the system. Recover refrigerant and replace accumulator and restrictor, then charge A/C system.
19. If low pressure is low and low pressure switch turns A/C compressor off but proper cooling performance is maintained, the problem is either a faulty low pressure switch or compressor. Repair or replace as required.
20. If low pressure is too low, pressure switch turns off compressor and proper cooling is not maintained, a low refrigerant charge is indicated. Inspect system for leaks. Repair or replace components as required.
21. If low pressure is too low and A/C control head switches compressor off (air inlet temperature to fresh air blower from evaporator lower than 27°F), A/C compressor internal pressure regulation is improper. Replace compressor.

DISCHARGING SYSTEM

REFRIGERANT RECOVERY

Always use an Underwriter's Laboratory (UL) approved refrigerant recovery/recycling unit such as Kent-Moore ACR4, or equivalent, whenever recovering an A/C system.

The A/C system should be serviced only by trained personnel familiar with equipment use, related safety precautions and regulations governing the discharging/handling/disposal of automotive refrigerants.

Always wear safety goggles when charging or discharging system. Use caution so refrigerant does not come in contact with your skin or eyes. If refrigerant comes in contact with skin or eyes, do not rub. Flush immediately with cool water, then seek medical attention. Keep refrigerant away from open flames as exposure to open flame will produce poisonous gas.

A4, A6, A8, S4 & S6

Ensure initial setup has been performed on refrigerant recovery unit as per manufacturer's instructions prior to recovering refrigerant from A/C system.

1. Connect high pressure hose of refrigerant recovery unit to high pressure service valve on vehicle A/C system, then open coupler valve. **Only a high pressure service valve is used for A/C system servicing. A low pressure service valve is not installed in this system.**
2. Follow refrigerant recovery unit manufacturer's instructions and recover refrigerant from system.
3. **Disconnect A/C compressor clutch electrical connectors to prevent damage to A/C system if compressor is accidentally turned on with refrigerant system discharged.**

Cabriolet

1. Close both valves on A/C manifold gauge set, then connect hose from low pressure gauge to low pressure service valve on compressor.

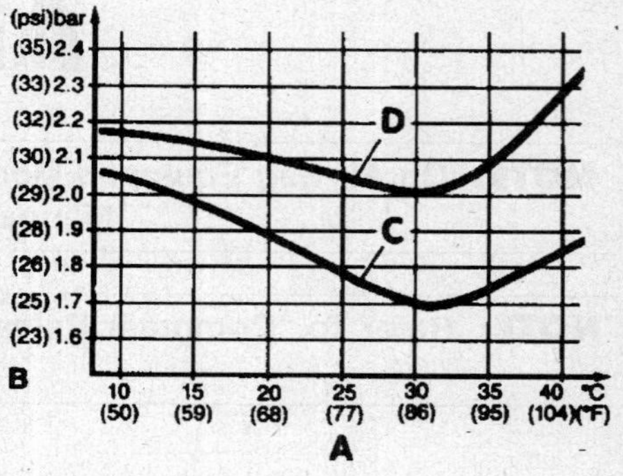

A. Outside (Ambient) Temperature
B. Low Side (Suction) Pressure
C. Low Side (Suction) Pressure Specified Value With Low Pressure Guage Connected To Service Valve On Compressor
D. Low Side (Suction) Pressure Specified Value With Low Pressure Guage Connected To Service Valve For Low Pressure Switch

AD7019600033000X

Fig. 3 Low side pressure chart

2. Remove A/C refrigerant high pressure switch (red housing) in A/C line between condenser and evaporator.
3. Connect hose from high pressure gauge to high pressure service valve located in A/C line between condenser and compressor, then the manifold gauge hose to inlet connection on refrigerant recovery/recycling unit.
4. Follow refrigerant recovery/recycling unit manufacturer's instructions to discharge A/C system into recovery/recycling unit.
5. Close manifold gauge valves when refrigerant is fully discharged.
6. Disconnect power supply from compressor clutch to prevent damage to system if compressor is accidentally switched on with refrigerant system discharged.

TT

1. Connect high pressure hose of refrigerant recovery unit to vehicle's high pressure service valve fitting, then open coupler valve.
2. Discharge refrigerant charge into refrigerant recovery unit following unit manufacturer's instructions.
3. **Disconnect A/C compressor clutch electrical connectors to prevent damage to A/C system if compressor is accidentally turned on with refrigerant system discharged.**

SYSTEM EVACUATION

Follow refrigerant recovery/recycling/recharging unit manufacturer's instructions for evacuating and recharging A/C system. Evacuate A/C system for a minimum of 30 minutes.

CHARGING SYSTEM

1. Add proper amount of refrigerant oil to system.
2. Charge system to specifications.
3. After system charge, manually rotate

A/C compressor approximately 10 turns before starting engine.

4. Start engine with A/C off, then with engine at idle, turn A/C to On position and let engine idle for a minimum of two minutes before raising engine speed.

A/C SPECIFICATIONS

Year	Model	Refrigerant		Refrigerant Oil		Compressor Clutch Air Gap, Inch
		Type	Capacity, Lbs.	Viscosity	Total System Capacity, Oz.	
1998	A4	R134a	1.44	③	8.5	②
	A6	R134a	1.75	④	8.5	.016–.024
	A8	R134a	1.32	④	8.5	.016–.024
	Cabriolet	R134a	1.44	①	7.9–9.2	②
1999	A4	R134a	1.44	③	8.5	②
	A6	R134a	1.75	①	8.5	.016–.024
	A8	R134a	1.33	⑤	8.5	.016–.024
2000	A4	R134a	1.44	③	8.5	②
	A6	R134a	1.75	①	8.5	.016–.024
	A8	R134a	1.33	⑤	8.5	.016–.024
	S4	R134a	1.54	⑥	⑦	.016–.024
	TT	R134a	1.68	⑧	5.1	.016–.024
2001	A6	R134a	1.75	①	8.5	.016–.024
	A8	R134a	1.33	⑤	8.5	.016–.024

① — Sanden Oil SD 10, or equivalent.

② — Zexel compressor,. 012–.024 inch; Denso compressor,. 014–.024 inch.

③ — Zexel compressor, Sanden SP-10, or equivalent; Denso compressor, PAG refrigerant oil Audi part No. G 052 300 A2, or equivalent.

④ — PAG refrigerant oil Audi part No. G 052 300 A2, or equivalent.

⑤ — Sanden SP-10, or equivalent.

⑥ — Zexel compressor, SP-10 PAG oil Audi part No. G 052 154 A2, or equivalent; Denso compressor, SP-10 PAG refrigerant PAG oil Audi part No. G 052 300 A2, or equivalent.

⑦ — Zexel compressor, 7.8–9.2 ounces; Denso compressor, 6.9–10.1 ounces.

⑧ — Sanden PAG oil, or equivalent.

CHARGING VALVE LOCATION

A4, A6, A8, S4, S6 and Cabriolet models are equipped with only a high pressure service valve. All testing, charging and discharging services are performed through this valve. On A4 models, this valve may be found on the inlet side of the condenser. On A6 and S6 models, this valve may be found on the outlet side of the condenser. On Cabriolet models, this valve may be found on the outlet side of the condenser or in the outlet line connected to the condenser.

TT models are equipped with both high pressure and low pressure valves. The high side valve is located in the suction line between the receiver dryer and the A/C high pressure switch. The low side valve is located in the discharge line between the evaporator and the compressor.

Cooling Fans

TABLE OF CONTENTS

	Page No.		Page No.
ELECTRIC COOLING FANS	1-112	**VARIABLE SPEED COOLING FANS**	1-114

Electric Cooling Fans

NOTE: On Air Bag Equipped Models, Refer To "Air Bag System Precautions" Located In The Front Of This Manual For System Disarming & Arming Procedures.

NOTE: Refer To "Computer Relearn Procedures" Located In The Front Of This Manual When Battery Power To The Computer Has Been Interrupted.

INDEX

	Page No.
Component Diagnosis & Testing	1-112
Coolant Temperature Sensor....	1-112
Refrigerant High Pressure Sensor	1-113
Description	1-112
A4, A6, A8 & S4	1-112
Cabriolet........................	1-112
S6	1-112
TT.............................	1-112
Precautions.......................	1-112
Air Bag Systems................	1-112
Battery Ground Cable...........	1-112
Radio Coded Anti-Theft System.	1-112

PRECAUTIONS

AIR BAG SYSTEMS

Refer to "Air Bag System Precautions" in the front of this manual for system disarming and arming procedures.

RADIO CODED ANTI-THEFT SYSTEM

Prior to disconnecting the battery or removing the audio system, obtain the security code from the vehicle operator. Refer to the owner's manual for security code disarming and arming procedures.

BATTERY GROUND CABLE

Prior to service, disconnect battery ground cable and isolate as required.

DESCRIPTION

A4, A6, A8 & S4

A4 and S4 models use a single two speed cooling fan. A6 and A8 models use dual two speed cooling fans. The cooling fan speeds are controlled by a dual element water temperature sensor and a refrigerant high pressure sensor. These sensors control relays which route electric current through resistors or directly to the fan motor to control speed.

1. Low speed is controlled by only the low temperature side of the coolant temperature sensor.
2. Second speed is controlled by either the high temperature section of the coolant temperature sensor or the refrigerant high pressure switch.

S6

This model uses dual electric three speed cooling fans. The cooling fan speeds are controlled by a water temperature sensor and a refrigerant high pressure sensor. These sensors control relays which route electric current through resistors or directly to the fan motor to control speed.

1. Low speed is controlled by a radiator fan after-run control unit. This unit is used to control underhood and water temperature while vehicle is parked.
2. Second speed is controlled by both the low temperature section of the coolant temperature sensor and the refrigerant high pressure switch.
3. Third speed is controlled by only the high temperature side of the coolant temperature sensor.

CABRIOLET

These models use a single electric three speed cooling fan. The cooling fan speeds are controlled by a water temperature sensor and a refrigerant high pressure sensor. These sensors control relays which route electric current through resistors or directly to the fan motor to control speed.

1. Low speed is only used on those models equipped with a radiator fan after-run control unit. This unit is used to control underhood and water temperature while vehicle is parked.
2. Second speed is controlled by both the low temperature section of the coolant temperature sensor and the refrigerant high pressure switch.
3. Third speed is controlled by only the high temperature side of the coolant temperature sensor.

TT

On these models there is a single electric two speed cooling fan, controlled by the Coolant Fan Control (FC) thermal switch and the A/C pressure switch. The low speed will always start whenever the A/C compressor clutch is energized. The high speed will start if the refrigerant system pressure rises above a predetermined level.

On models equipped with the 225 horsepower code AMU engine there is also an after-run coolant pump, controlled by the Coolant Fan Control module.

COMPONENT DIAGNOSIS & TESTING

COOLANT TEMPERATURE SENSOR

1. Place sensor in a suitable container of

liquid that contains a thermometer and may be heated and cooled.

2. Connect a suitable ohmmeter or continuity tester to terminals 1 and 3 of the sensor to test the second fan speed circuit.
3. Heat liquid while observing thermometer and continuity tester. Circuit should close between 198–207° F.
4. Cool liquid while observing thermometer and continuity tester. Circuit should open below 183° F.
5. Connect continuity tester to terminals 2 and 3, then repeat above procedures to test third fan speed circuit, noting the following:
   a. Third fan speed circuit should close between 210–221° F.
   b. Circuit should open below 183° F.

REFRIGERANT HIGH PRESSURE SENSOR

1. Connect a suitable refrigerant pressure gauge to high pressure port of A/C system.
2. Connect continuity tester to A/C system high pressure switch terminals.
3. Start engine and engage A/C system.
4. Observe A/C pressure gauge and continuity tester. Circuit should close when pressure rises above 205–252 psi.
5. Circuit should open when pressure drops below 170–218 psi.

Variable Speed Cooling Fans

INDEX

	Page No.
Component Replacement	1-114
Viscous Unit	1-114
Description	1-114
Troubleshooting	1-114

DESCRIPTION

Some models are equipped with a viscous clutch engine driven fan in addition to the electric cooling fan. The viscous clutch fan is a temperature sensitive unit which will increase air flow through the radiator as the temperature of the engine increases.

TROUBLESHOOTING

With ignition Off, viscous fan should rotate freely with a slight drag from the viscous fluid. There should be no sign of leakage around the body or shaft of the fan clutch. Axial play measured at the outer edge of the fan wheel should not exceed 0.59 inch.

COMPONENT REPLACEMENT

VISCOUS UNIT

1. Remove engine appearance covers as required.
2. Raise and support vehicle.
3. Remove serpentine belt by firmly pulling down at the center of the span between the alternator and A/C compressor until tensioner lock pin tool No. 3204, or an equivalent suitable drift, can be inserted into tensioner.
4. Remove serpentine belt.
5. Lock fan unit using wrench tool No. 3212, or equivalent. **This is a lefthand thread.**
6. Unscrew fan unit from shaft and place inside fan shroud. **This is a lefthand thread.**
7. Remove radiator fan shroud mounting bolts, then the fan and shroud as a unit.
8. Disconnect fan blades from viscous clutch unit.
9. Reverse procedure to install.

Dash Gauges

NOTE: On Air Bag Equipped Models, Refer To "Air Bag System Precautions" Located In The Front Of This Manual For System Disarming & Arming Procedures.

NOTE: Refer To "Computer Relearn Procedures" Located In The Front Of This Manual When Battery Power To The Computer Has Been Interrupted.

INDEX

	Page No.
Gauges	1-115
Fuel Gauge & Engine Coolant Temperature Gauge	1-115
Oil Pressure Gauge	1-116
Oil Temperature Gauge	1-116
Speedometer	1-115
Tachometer	1-115
Precautions	1-115
Air Bag Systems	1-115
Battery Ground Cable	1-115
Radio Coded Anti-Theft System	1-115

PRECAUTIONS

AIR BAG SYSTEMS

Refer to "Air Bag System Precautions" in the front of this manual for system disarming and arming procedures.

RADIO CODED ANTI-THEFT SYSTEM

Prior to disconnecting the battery or removing the audio system, obtain the security code from the vehicle operator. Refer to the owner's manual for security code disarming and arming procedures.

BATTERY GROUND CABLE

Prior to service, disconnect battery ground cable and isolate as required.

GAUGES

SPEEDOMETER

A4, S4 & TT

If the instrument cluster control module detects a DTC in its permanent memory, the letters "dEF" will appear on the trip recorder display.

Replace the instrument cluster assembly as outlined in "Electrical" section if "dEF" appears on the display.

A6 & S6

Troubleshooting

1. Connect test box tool No. VAG 1598 and associated harness, or equivalents.
2. Ensure fuses and harness connections are in good condition and are secure.
3. If speedometer does not operate, refer to **Fig. 1** for troubleshooting procedures.

Replacement

The speedometer is part of the instrument cluster and must be replaced as an assembly as outlined in this section.

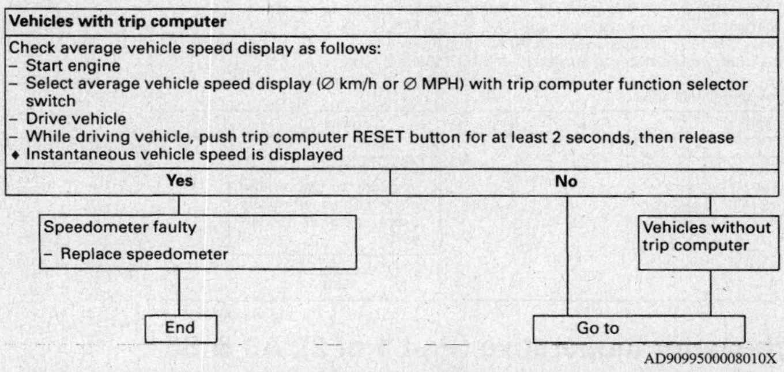

Fig. 1 Speedometer inoperative (Part 1 of 3). A6 & S6

TACHOMETER

A4, S4 & TT

If the instrument cluster control module detects a DTC in its permanent memory, the letters "dEF" will appear on the trip recorder display.

Replace the instrument cluster assembly as outlined in "Electrical" section if "dEF" appears on the display.

A6 & S6

Troubleshooting

1. Connect test box tool No. VAG 1598 and associated harness, or equivalents.
2. Ensure fuses and harness connections are in good condition and are secure.
3. If tachometer does not operate, refer to **Fig. 2** for troubleshooting procedures.

Replacement

The tachometer is part of the instrument cluster and must be replaced as an assembly as outlined in "Electrical" section.

FUEL GAUGE & ENGINE COOLANT TEMPERATURE GAUGE

A6 & S6

Troubleshooting

1. Connect test box tool Nos. VW 1301 and VAG 1598 and associated harness, or equivalents.
2. Ensure fuses and harness connections are in good condition and are secure.
3. If fuel gauge does not operate or is inaccurate, refer to **Fig. 3** for troubleshooting procedures.
4. If engine temperature gauge does not operate or is inaccurate, refer to **Fig. 4.**
5. If both fuel gauge and engine temperature gauge do not work or are inaccurate, refer to **Fig. 5.**

Replacement

The fuel and coolant temperature gauges are part of the instrument cluster and must be replaced as an assembly as outlined in "Electrical" section.

- Remove instrument cluster
- Remove red and green 26-point connectors from instrument cluster
- Check connectors for bent terminals, repair as necessary
- Connect adapter harness VAG 1598/4 to red 26-point instrument cluster connector
- Connect adapter harness to instrument cluster and VAG 1598 test box
- Reconnect green 26-point connector to instrument cluster
- Set digital multimeter (Fluke 83 or equivalent) to AC (alternating current) volt range
- Connect multimeter between sockets 8 and 14 of VAG 1598 test box
- Place transmission in neutral and apply parking brake
- Raise vehicle on hoist
- Switch ignition ON and slowly rotate wheel
- • Voltage must vary between 1.0–4.5 V (vehicle speed signal from speedometer present)

Yes → Go to A

No → Vehicle speed signal not present
- Check for open circuit in wiring to Speedometer Vehicle Speed Sensor (VSS) according to wiring diagram, repair as necessary, or
- Replace Speedometer VSS

End

AD9099500008020X

Fig. 1 Speedometer inoperative (Part 2 of 3). A6 & S6

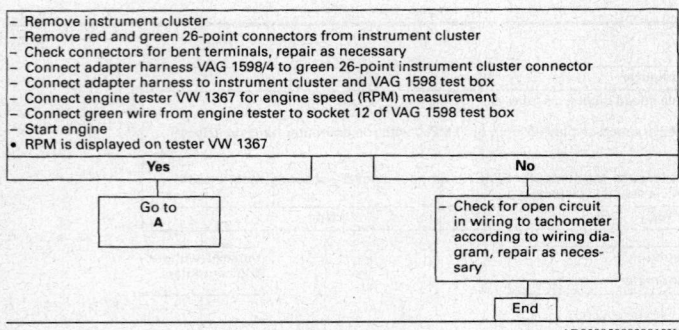

- Remove instrument cluster
- Remove red and green 26-point connectors from instrument cluster
- Check connectors for bent terminals, repair as necessary
- Connect adapter harness VAG 1598/4 to green 26-point instrument cluster connector
- Connect adapter harness to instrument cluster and VAG 1598 test box
- Connect engine tester VW 1367 for engine speed (RPM) measurement
- Connect green wire from engine tester to socket 12 of VAG 1598 test box
- Start engine
- • RPM is displayed on tester VW 1367

Yes → Go to A

No →
- Check for open circuit in wiring to tachometer according to wiring diagram, repair as necessary

End

AD9099500009010X

Fig. 2 Tachometer inoperative (Part 1 of 2). A6 & S6

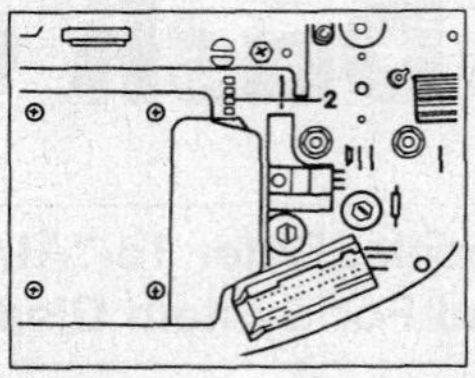

A

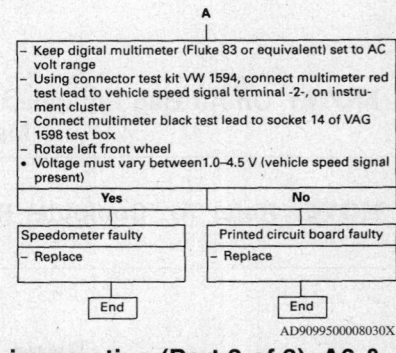

- Keep digital multimeter (Fluke 83 or equivalent) set to AC volt range
- Using connector test kit VW 1594, connect multimeter red test lead to vehicle speed signal terminal -2-, on instrument cluster
- Connect multimeter black test lead to socket 14 of VAG 1598 test box
- Rotate left front wheel
- • Voltage must vary between1.0–4.5 V (vehicle speed signal present)

Yes → Speedometer faulty
- Replace

End

No → Printed circuit board faulty
- Replace

End

AD9099500008030X

Fig. 1 Speedometer inoperative (Part 3 of 3). A6 & S6

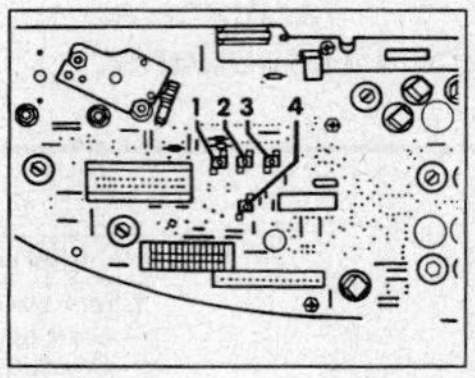

A

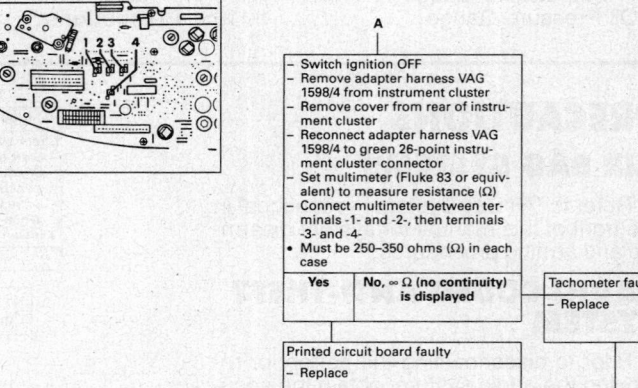

- Switch ignition OFF
- Remove adapter harness VAG 1598/4 from instrument cluster
- Remove cover from rear of instrument cluster
- Reconnect adapter harness VAG 1598/4 to green 26-point instrument cluster connector
- Set multimeter (Fluke 83 or equivalent) to measure resistance (Ω)
- Connect multimeter between terminals -1- and -2-, then terminals -3- and -4-
- • Must be 250–350 ohms (Ω) in each case

Yes → Tachometer faulty
- Replace

End

No, ∞ Ω (no continuity) is displayed → Printed circuit board faulty
- Replace

End

AD9099500009020X

Fig. 2 Tachometer inoperative (Part 2 of 2). A6 & S6

A4 & S4

Troubleshooting

1. Remove fuel sender access panel in trunk compartment.
2. Disconnect fuel sender electrical connector.
3. Connect electrical tester tool No. VAG 1301, or equivalent, on setting 470 to electrical connector, **Fig. 6.**
4. Wait four minutes, then turn ignition On.
5. Gauge needle should settle to right-hand edge of red reserve zone.

Replacement

The fuel and coolant temperature gauges are part of the instrument cluster and must be replaced as an assembly as outlined in this section.

TT

If the instrument cluster control module detects a DTC in its permanent memory, the letters "dEF" will appear on the trip recorder display.

Replace the instrument cluster assembly as outlined in "Electrical" section if "dEF" appears on the display.

OIL PRESSURE GAUGE

A4, S4 & TT

If the instrument cluster control module detects a DTC in its permanent memory, the letters "dEF" will appear on the trip recorder display.

Replace the instrument cluster assembly as outlined in "Electrical" section if "dEF" appears on the display.

A6 & S6

Troubleshooting

1. Connect test box tool No. VAG 1598 and associated harness, or equivalents.
2. Ensure fuses and harness connections are in good condition and are secure.
3. If oil pressure gauge does not operate or is inaccurate, refer to **Fig. 7** for troubleshooting procedures.

Replacement

The oil pressure gauge is part of the instrument cluster and must be replaced as an assembly as outlined in "Electrical" section.

OIL TEMPERATURE GAUGE

A4, S4 & TT

If the instrument cluster control module detects a DTC in its permanent memory, the letters "dEF" will appear on the trip recorder display.

Replace the instrument cluster assembly as outlined in "Electrical" section if "dEF" appears on the display.

A6 & S6

Troubleshooting

1. Connect test box tool No. VAG 1598 and associated harness, or equivalents.
2. Ensure fuses and harness connections are in good condition and are secure.
3. If oil temperature gauge does not operate or is inaccurate, refer to **Fig. 8** for troubleshooting procedures.

Replacement

The oil temperature gauge is part of the instrument cluster and must be replaced as an assembly as outlined in "Electrical" section.

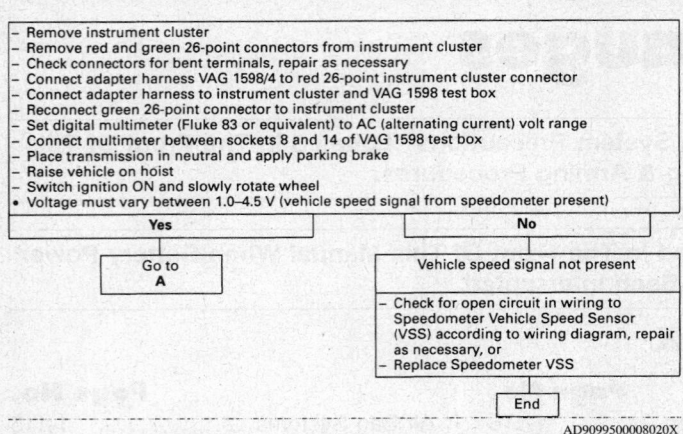

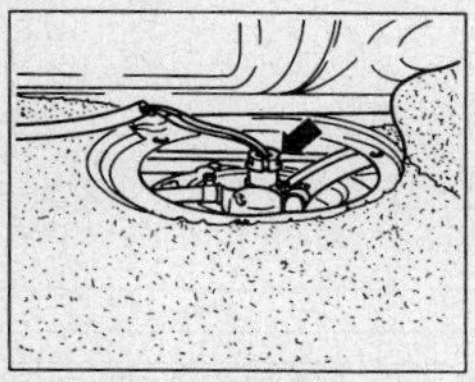

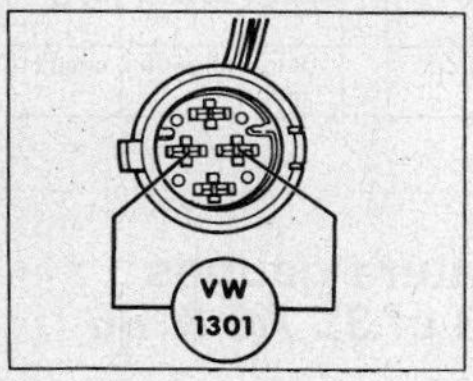

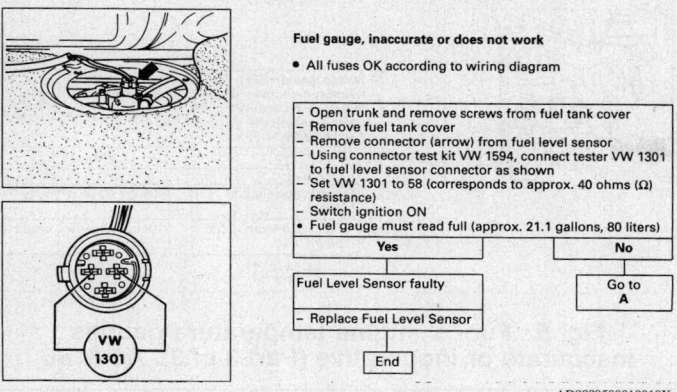

Fuel gauge, inaccurate or does not work

- All fuses OK according to wiring diagram

- Open trunk and remove screws from fuel tank cover
- Remove fuel tank cover
- Remove connector (arrow) from fuel level sensor
- Using connector test kit VW 1594, connect tester VW 1301 to fuel level sensor connector as shown
- Set VW 1301 to 58 (corresponds to approx. 40 ohms (Ω) resistance)
- Switch ignition ON
- Fuel gauge must read full (approx. 21.1 gallons, 80 liters)

Yes	No
Fuel Level Sensor faulty – Replace Fuel Level Sensor End	Go to A

AD9099500010010X

Fig. 3 Fuel gauge inaccurate or inoperative. (Part 1 of 3). A6 & S6

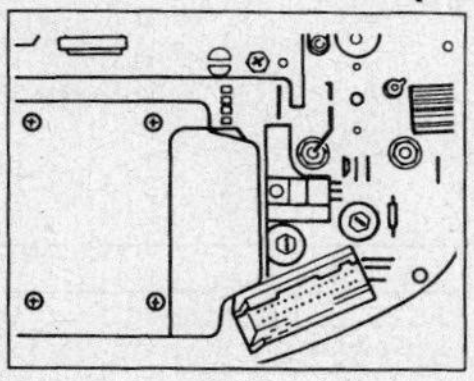

B

- Leave tester VW 1301 connected to fuel level sensor connector
- Keep VW 1301 set to 58
- Set digital multimeter (Fluke 83 or equivalent) to volt range

- Connect multimeter between socket 10 (–) of VAG 1598 test box and fuel gauge terminal -1-
- Must be 0–4.5 V

Yes	No, over 4.6V displayed
Fuel gauge faulty – Replace End	Printed circuit board faulty – Replace End

AD9099500010030X

Fig. 3 Fuel gauge inaccurate or inoperative. (Part 3 of 3). A6 & S6

- Leave VW 1301 connected between terminal T of electronic thermal switch connector and GND, keep VW 1301 set to 58
- Remove instrument cluster
- Disconnect red and green 26-point connectors from instrument cluster
- Check connectors for bent terminals, repair as necessary
- Connect adapter harness VAG 1598/4 to green 26-point instrument cluster connector
- Reconnect red 26-point connector to instrument cluster
- Set digital multimeter (Fluke 83 or equivalent) to measure resistance (Ω)
- Connect multimeter between sockets 11 and 16 of VAG 1598 test box
- Must be approx. 40 ohms (Ω)

Yes	No, ∞ Ω (no continuity) is displayed
Go to A	– Check wiring to electronic Engine Coolant Temperature (ECT) thermal switch for open circuit according to wiring diagram, repair as necessary End

AD9099500011020X

Fig. 4 Engine coolant temperature gauge inaccurate or inoperative (Part 2 of 3). A6 & S6

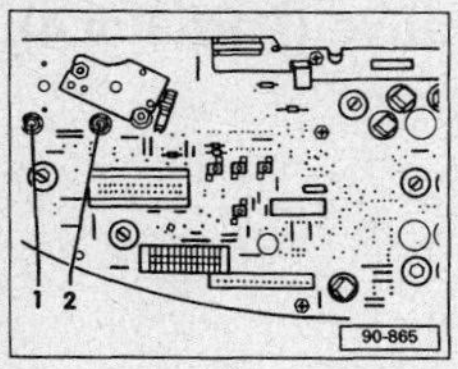

A

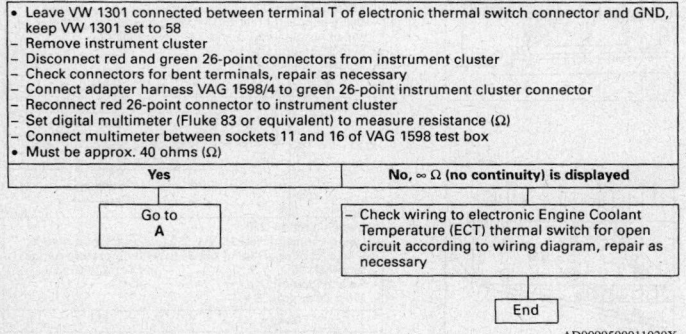

- Remove adapter harness VAG 1598/4 from instrument cluster (green connector)
- Remove cover from rear of instrument cluster
- Reconnect adapter harness VAG 1598/4 to green 26-point instrument cluster connector
- Set digital multimeter (Fluke 83 or equivalent) to measure resistance (Ω)
- Connect multimeter to Engine Coolant Temperature (ECT) gauge terminals -1- and -2-
- Must be approx. 40 ohms (Ω)

Yes	No, ∞ Ω (no continuity) is displayed
Printed circuit board faulty – Replace End	ECT gauge faulty – Replace End

AD9099500011030X

Fig. 4 Engine coolant temperature gauge inaccurate or inoperative (Part 3 of 3). A6 & S6

A

- Leave tester VW 1301 connected to fuel level sensor connector and tester value set to 58
- Remove instrument cluster
- Disconnect red and green 26-point connectors from instrument cluster
- Check connectors for bent terminals, repair as necessary
- Connect adapter harness VAG 1598/4 to red 26-point instrument cluster connector
- Reconnect green 26-point connector to instrument cluster
- Set digital multimeter (Fluke 83 or equivalent) to measure resistance (Ω)
- Connect multimeter between sockets 10 and 3 of VAG 1598 test box
- Must be 40–50 ohms (Ω)

Yes	No, ∞ Ω (no continuity) is displayed
Go to B	– Check wiring to fuel level sensor for open circuit according to wiring diagram, repair as necessary End

AD9099500010020X

Fig. 3 Fuel gauge inaccurate or inoperative. (Part 2 of 3). A6 & S6

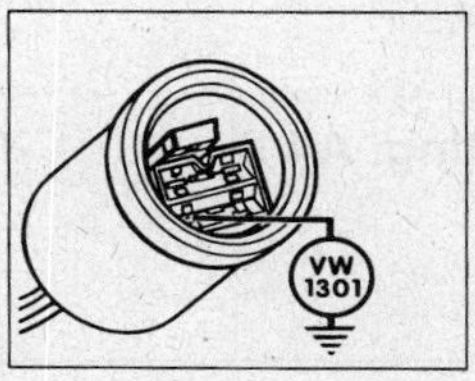

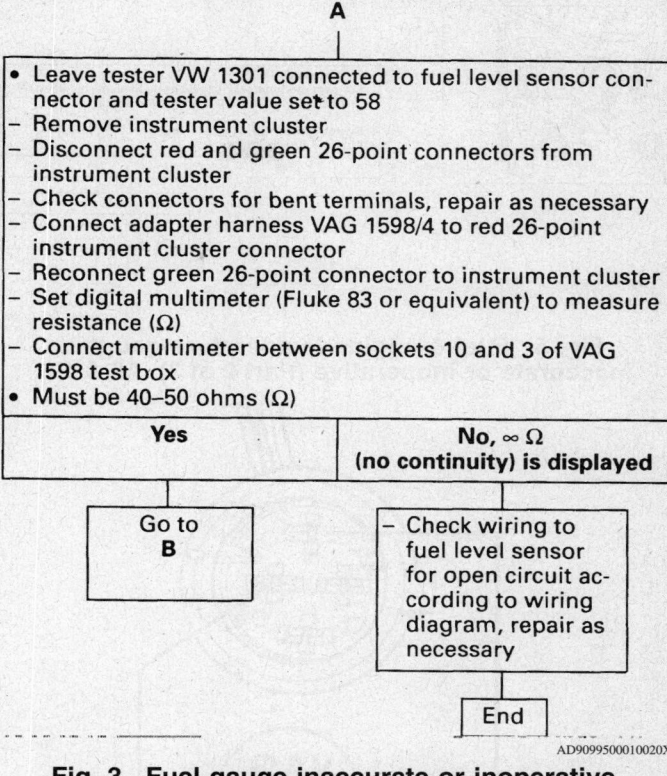

- Remove connector from electronic Engine Coolant Temperature (ECT) thermal switch
- ♦ Thermal switch located on coolant pipe behind right cylinder head
- Connect tester VW 1301 between terminal T of thermal switch connector and Ground (GND)
- Set VW 1301 to 58
- ♦ Value 58 on VW 1301 corresponds to approx. resistance 40 ohms (Ω)
- Switch ignition ON
- Engine coolant temperature gauge must display approx. 230°F (110°C)

Yes	No
Electronic Engine Coolant Temperature (ECT) thermal switch faulty – Replace electronic thermal switch End	Go to

AD9099500011010X

Fig. 4 Engine coolant temperature gauge inaccurate or inoperative (Part 1 of 3). A6 & S6

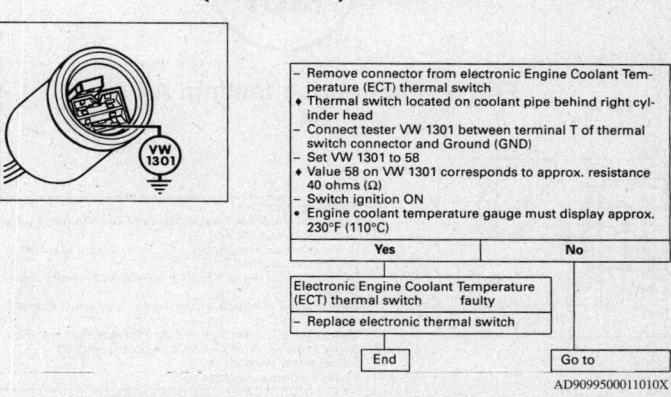

- Remove instrument cluster
- Remove red and green 26-point connectors from instrument cluster
- Check connectors for bent terminals, repair as necessary
- Connect adapter harness VAG 1598/4 to red 26-point instrument cluster connector
- Connect adapter harness to VAG 1598 test box
- Reconnect green 26-point connector to instrument cluster
- Set multimeter (Fluke 83 or equivalent) to volt range
- Connect multimeter between sockets 10 (–) and 11 (+) of VAG 1598 test box
- Switch ignition ON
- Must be approx. 12 V

Yes	No
Go to A	– Check wiring for open circuit according to wiring diagram, repair as necessary End

AD9099500012010X

Fig. 5 Fuel & engine temperature gauges inaccurate or inoperative (Part 1 of 3). A6 & S6

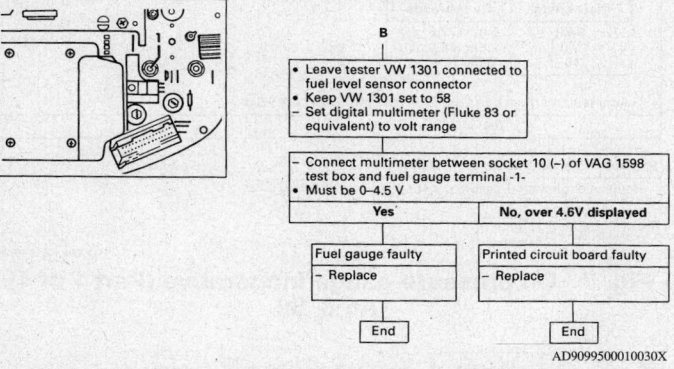

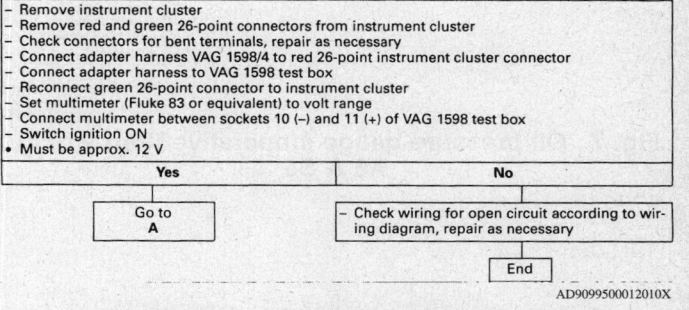

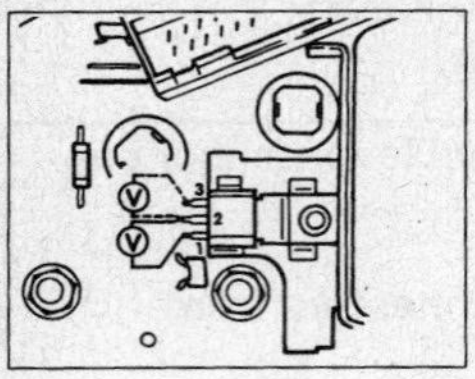

A

- Switch ignition OFF
- Connect multimeter (Fluke 83 or equivalent) between terminals -1- (+) and -2- (–) of voltage stabilizer
- Switch ignition ON
- • Must be approx. 12 V

Yes	No
Go to B	Printed circuit board faulty – Replace printed circuit board End

AD9099500012020X

Fig. 5 Fuel & engine temperature gauges inaccurate or inoperative (Part 2 of 3). A6 & S6

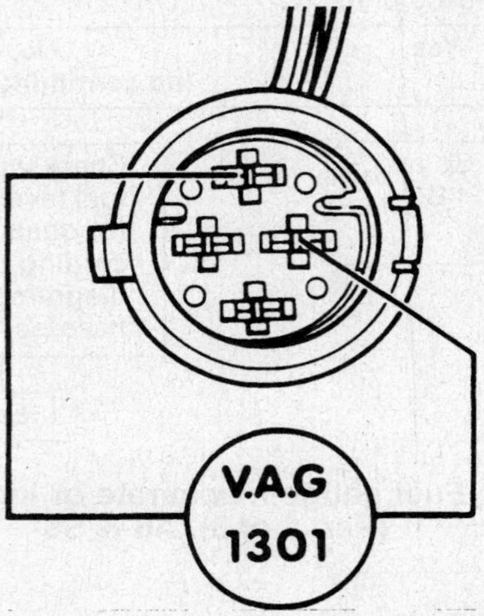

AD9099500015000X

Fig. 6 Fuel gauge testing. A4 & S4

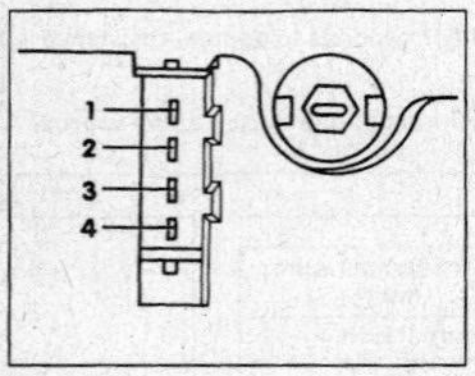

- Switch ignition OFF
- • Leave tester VW 1301 connected between engine oil pressure sensor and GND
- Remove instrument cluster but leave all connectors attached
- Set multimeter (Fluke 83 or equivalent) to measure resistance (Ω)
- Disconnect instrument cluster 4-point side panel connector
- Using connector test kit VW 1594, connect multimeter between terminal -1- of 4-point connector and GND
- Adjust tester VW 1301 to 10
- • Must be approx. 10 ohms (Ω)

Yes	No, ∞ Ω (no continuity) is displayed
Go to A	– Check wiring to engine oil pressure sensor for open circuit according to wiring diagram, repair as necessary End

AD9099500013020X

Fig. 7 Oil pressure gauge inoperative (Part 2 of 4). A6 & S6

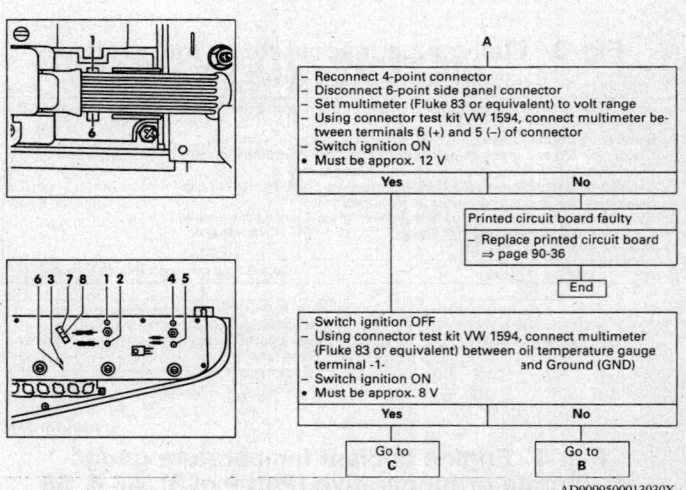

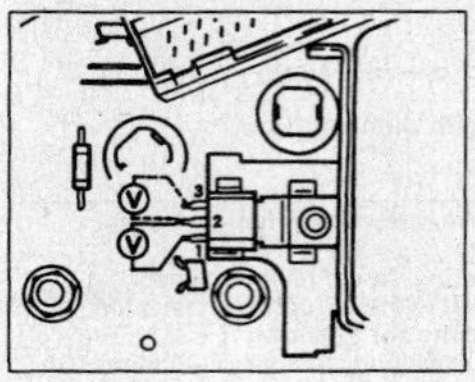

B

- Switch ignition OFF
- Connect multimeter (Fluke 83 or equivalent) between terminals -3- (+) and -2- (–)
- Switch ignition ON
- • Must be 9.15–10.25 V

Yes	No
Printed circuit board faulty – Replace printed circuit board End	Voltage stabilizer faulty – Replace printed circuit board End

AD9099500012030X

Fig. 5 Fuel & engine temperature gauges inaccurate or inoperative (Part 3 of 3). A6 & S6

- Remove connector from engine oil pressure sensor
- Connect tester VW 1301 between oil pressure sensor connector terminal G and Ground (GND)
- Switch ignition ON
- Adjust VW 1301 as follows:

Dial setting	Guage reads
340	5 bar (72.5 psi)
140	2 bar (29.0 psi)
10	0 bar (0.0 psi)

- • Gauge reading must correspond to dial setting on VW 1301

Yes	No
Engine oil pressure sensor faulty – Replace engine oil pressure sensor End	Go to next

AD9099500013010X

Fig. 7 Oil pressure gauge inoperative (Part 1 of 4). A6 & S6

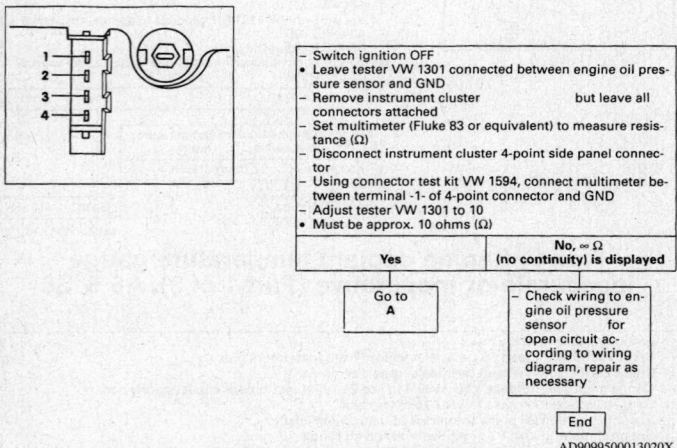

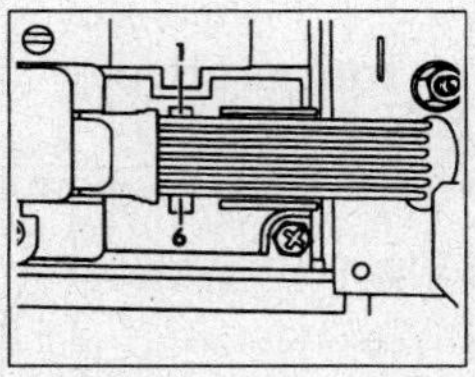

A

- Reconnect 4-point connector
- Disconnect 6-point side panel connector
- Set multimeter (Fluke 83 or equivalent) to volt range
- Using connector test kit VW 1594, connect multimeter between terminals 6 (+) and 5 (–) of connector
- Switch ignition ON
- • Must be approx. 12 V

Yes	No
(continue below)	Printed circuit board faulty – Replace printed circuit board ⇒ page 90-36 End

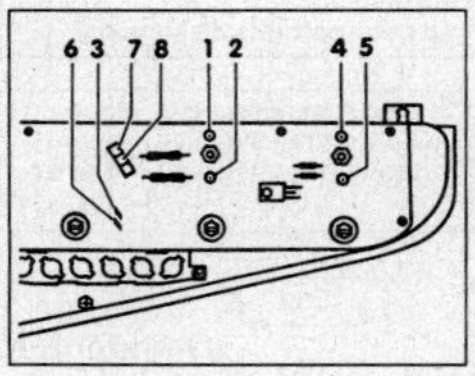

- Switch ignition OFF
- Using connector test kit VW 1594, connect multimeter (Fluke 83 or equivalent) between oil temperature gauge terminal -1- and Ground (GND)
- Switch ignition ON
- • Must be approx. 8 V

Yes	No
Go to C	Go to B

AD9099500013030X

Fig. 7 Oil pressure gauge inoperative (Part 3 of 4). A6 & S6

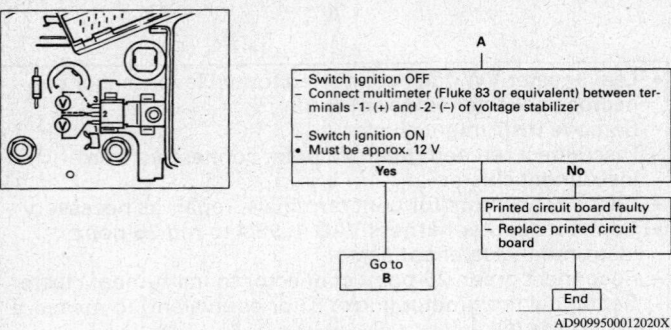

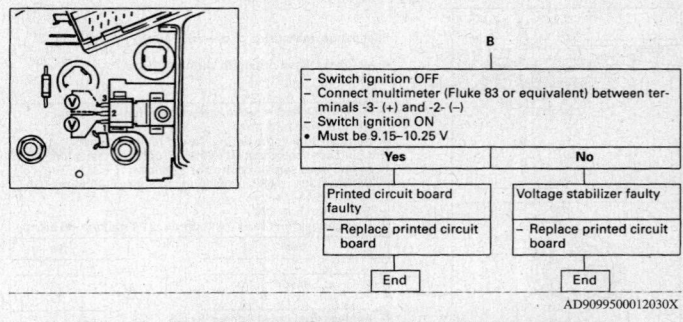

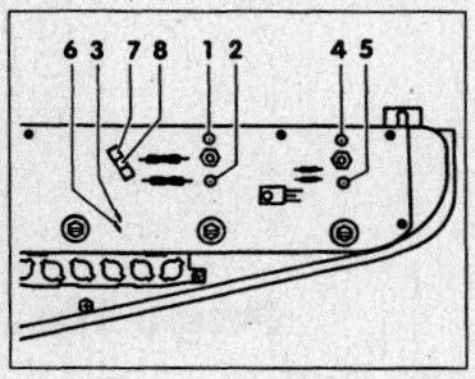

B

Printed circuit (side panel) faulty
- Replace printed circuit board (side panel)

End

C

- Switch ignition OFF
- Set multimeter (Fluke 83 or equivalent) to measure resistance (Ω)
- Using connector test kit VW 1594. connect multimeter between terminals -5- and -6-
- • Must be 0 ohms (Ω) (continuity)

Yes → Oil pressure gauge faulty – Replace → End

No, ∞ Ω (no continuity) is displayed → Printed circuit (side panel) faulty – Replace → End

AD9099500013040X

Fig. 7 Oil pressure gauge inoperative (Part 4 of 4). A6 & S6

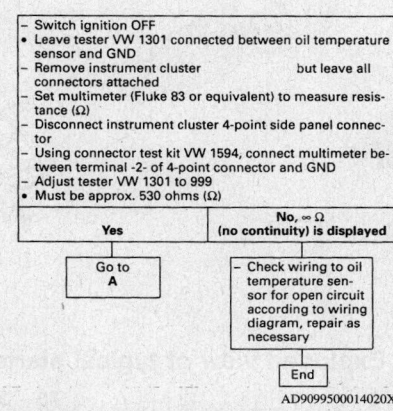

- Remove connector from engine oil temperature sensor
- Connect tester VW 1301 between oil temperature sensor connector and Ground (GND)
- Switch ignition ON
- Adjust VW 1301 as follows:

Dial setting	Guage reads
26	approx. 170°C (338°F)
110	approx. 130°C (266°F)
999	approx. 60°C (140°F)

• Gauge reading must correspond to dial setting on VW 1301

Yes → Engine oil temperature sensor faulty – Replace engine oil temperature sensor → End

No → Go to

AD9099500014010X

Fig. 8 Oil temperature gauge inoperative (Part 1 of 4). A6 & S6

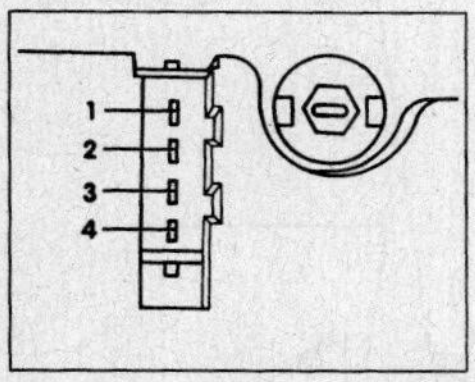

- Switch ignition OFF
- • Leave tester VW 1301 connected between oil temperature sensor and GND
- Remove instrument cluster but leave all connectors attached
- Set multimeter (Fluke 83 or equivalent) to measure resistance (Ω)
- Disconnect instrument cluster 4-point side panel connector
- Using connector test kit VW 1594, connect multimeter between terminal -2- of 4-point connector and GND
- Adjust tester VW 1301 to 999
- • Must be approx. 530 ohms (Ω)

Yes → Go to A

No, ∞ Ω (no continuity) is displayed → Check wiring to oil temperature sensor for open circuit according to wiring diagram, repair as necessary → End

AD9099500014020X

Fig. 8 Oil temperature gauge inoperative (Part 2 of 4). A6 & S6

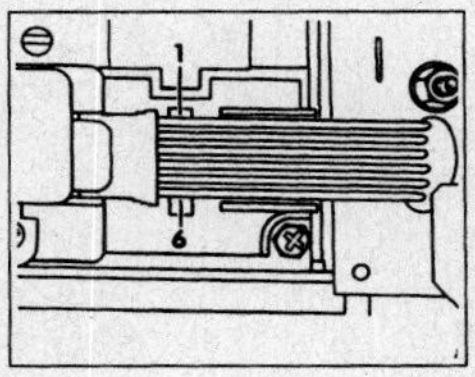

A

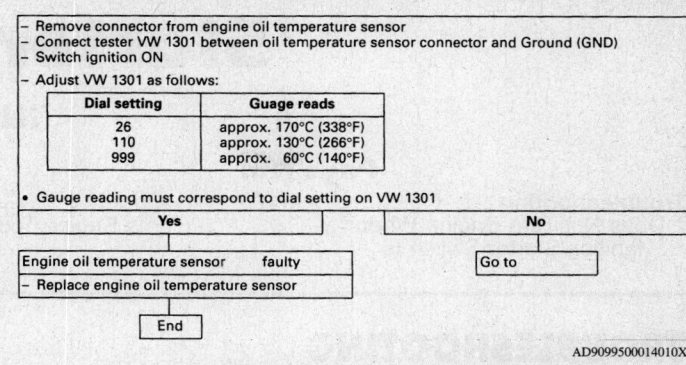

- Reconnect 4-point connector
- Disconnect 6-point side panel connector
- Set multimeter (Fluke 83 or equivalent) to volt range
- Using connector test kit VW 1594, connect multimeter between terminals 6 (+) and 5 (–) of connector
- Switch ignition ON
- • Must be approx. 12 V

No → Printed circuit board faulty – Replace → End

Yes →

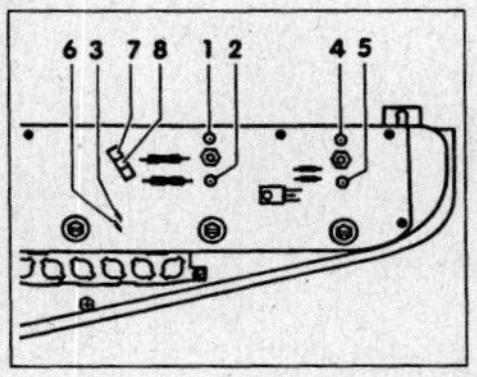

- Switch ignition OFF
- Using connector test kit VW 1594, connect multimeter (Fluke 83 or equivalent) between oil temperature gauge terminal -1- ⇒ illustration 90-866 and Ground (GND)
- Switch ignition ON
- • Must be approx. 8 V

Yes → Go to C

No → Go to B

AD9099500014030X

Fig. 8 Oil temperature gauge inoperative (Part 3 of 4). A6 & S6

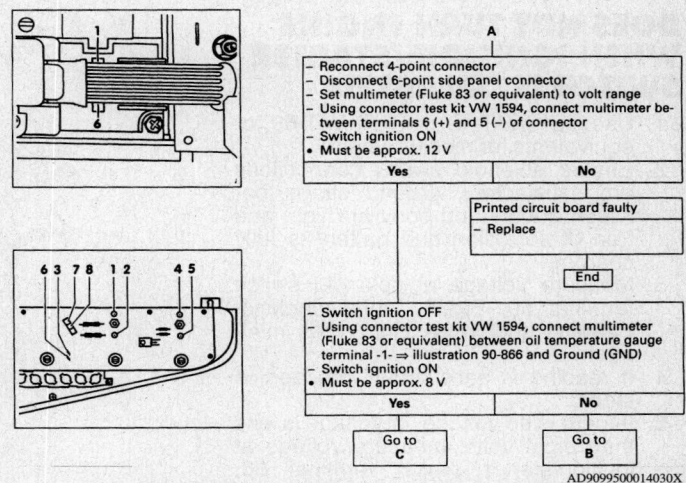

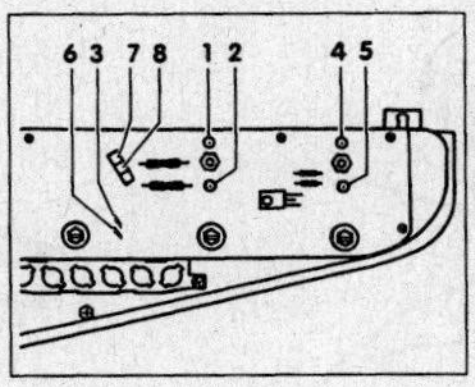

B

Printed circuit (side panel) faulty
- Replace

End

C

- Switch ignition OFF
- Set multimeter (Fluke 83 or equivalent) to measure resistance (Ω)
- Using connector test kit VW 1594, connect multimeter between terminals -2- and -3-
- • Must be 0 ohms (Ω) (continuity)

Yes → Oil temperature gauge faulty – Replace → End

No, ∞ Ω (no continuity) is displayed → Printed circuit (side panel) faulty – Replace → End

AD9099500014040X

Fig. 8 Oil temperature gauge inoperative (Part 4 of 4). A6 & S6

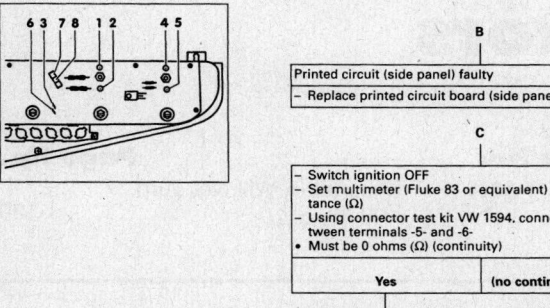

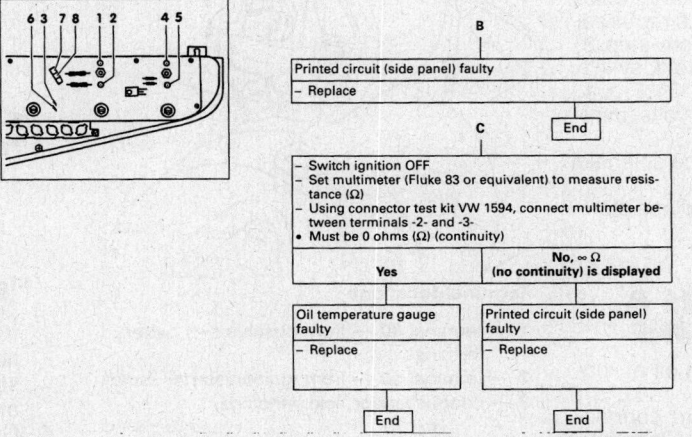

Starter Motors

INDEX

	Page No.
Troubleshooting	1-120
Does Not Turn Engine When Ignition/Starter Switch Is Operated	1-120
Turns Engine Too Slowly Or Engages & Will Not Turn Engine	1-120

TROUBLESHOOTING

Refer to **Fig. 1** when troubleshooting starter motors.

DOES NOT TURN ENGINE WHEN IGNITION/STARTER SWITCH IS OPERATED

1. Use SUN VAT-40 or SUN VAT-60, or equivalents for measurements.
2. Ensure solenoid switch connections are satisfactory, ground straps between engine and body are tight and free of corrosion and battery is fully charged.
3. Measure voltage at solenoid switch terminal 50, **Fig. 2,** while cranking. Reading should be eight volts minimum.
4. If reading is satisfactory, proceed to step 6.
5. If there is no voltage, or voltage is less than eight volts, measure voltage at ignition/starter switch terminal 50, **Fig. 3.** Reading should be eight volts minimum.
6. If there is no voltage, replace ignition/starter switch.
7. If voltage is satisfactory, inspect wiring between terminal 50 on ignition/starter switch and terminal 50 on starter solenoid and repair or replace as required.
8. If reading is satisfactory from step 3, measure voltage at solenoid switch field winding connection 3, **Fig. 1.** Reading should be eight volts minimum.
9. If there is no voltage, replace solenoid switch.
10. If voltage is satisfactory, replace starter.

TURNS ENGINE TOO SLOWLY OR ENGAGES & WILL NOT TURN ENGINE

1. Ensure engine is filled with oil of recommended viscosity.
2. Inspect V-belt tension, wire connections and battery voltage. Clean the battery terminals and charge if required.
3. Crank engine.
4. If starter turns engine, system is operating properly.
5. If starter does not turn engine, clean starter terminals and tighten connections, then clean and tighten ground strap connections between transaxle and body at transaxle.
6. Crank engine.
7. If starter turns engine, system is operating properly.
8. If starter does not turn engine, replace faulty starter.

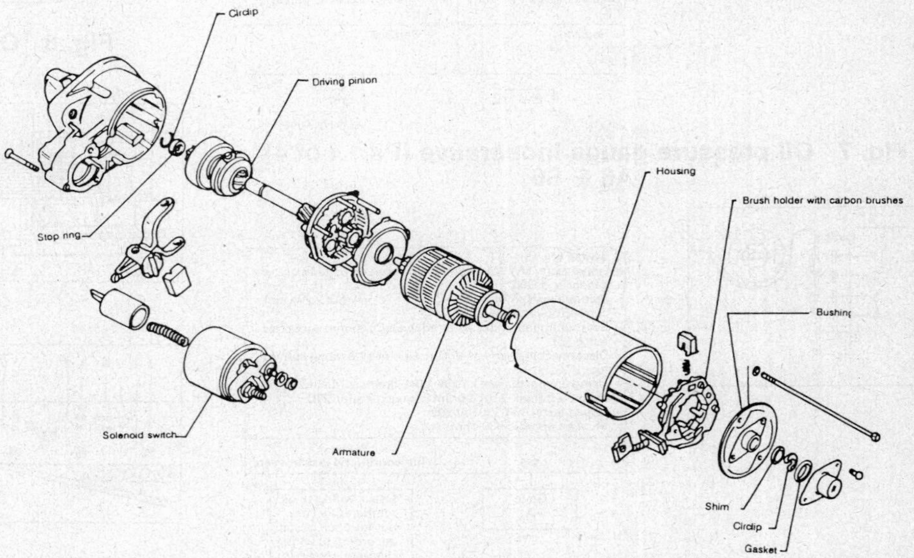

Fig. 1 Exploded view of typical starter motor

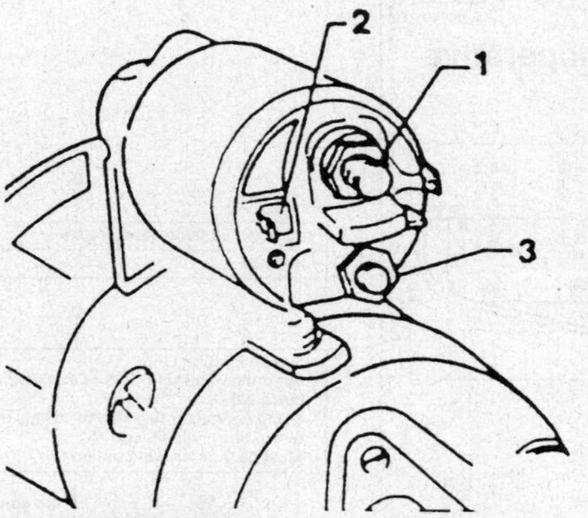

Terminal locations

1 — terminal 30 — from positive (+) battery terminal
2 — terminal 50 — from ignition/starter switch
3 — connection for field windings

AD1129100002000X

Fig. 2 Starter solenoid terminal identification

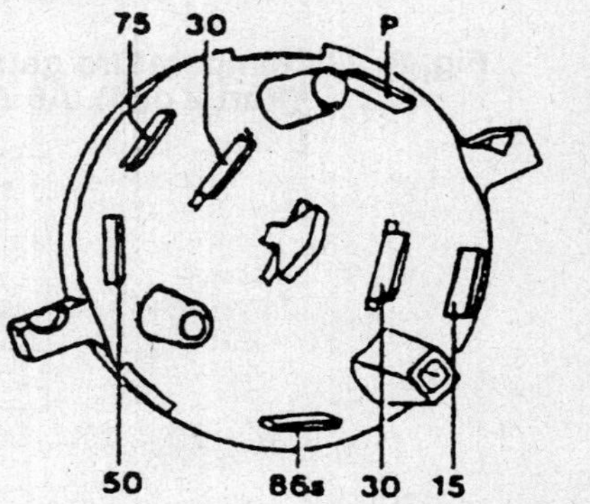

Fig. 3 Starter switch terminal identification

Alternators

INDEX

	Page No.
Alternator Specifications	1-122
Diagnosis & Testing	1-121
Exciter Circuit Inspection	1-121
Exciter Circuit Resistance Inspection	1-121
Output Test	1-121
Troubleshooting	1-121
Alternator Indicator Lamp	1-121

TROUBLESHOOTING

ALTERNATOR INDICATOR LAMP

DOES NOT LIGHT w/IGNITION ON (ENGINE NOT STARTED)

Possible open circuit between alternator D+ and indicator light.

1. Remove alternator cover, then disconnect D+ wire from alternator.
2. Connect a jumper wire between D+ and ground, then turn ignition On.
3. If indicator lamp lights, proceed as follows:
   a. Inspect for improper alternator ground, worn carbon brushes, faulty voltage regulator or rotor.
   b. If alternator grounding and brushes are faulty, make required corrections. If lamp now lights, system is operating properly.
   c. If alternator grounding and brushes are satisfactory, replace voltage regulator. If lamp still fails to light, replace alternator.
4. If indicator lamp does not light, proceed as follows:
   a. Indicator bulb is burned out.
   b. Obtain radio theft protection code as outlined under "Precautions."
   c. Replace bulb, connect ground cable and turn ignition On.
   d. If indicator lamp lights, system is operating properly.
   e. If indicator lamp does not light, wiring between alternator D+ and indicator lamp is open. Repair as required.

LAMP LIT w/IGNITION OFF

Alternator diode(s) faulty (rectifier bridge). Replace alternator.

LAMP DOES NOT GO OUT WHEN RPM INCREASES

Inspect for slipping drive belt or a short to ground between alternator D+ and indicator lamp. Otherwise alternator is faulty and requires replacement.

POSSIBLE SHORT TO GROUND BETWEEN ALTERNATOR D+ & INDICATOR LAMP

1. Disconnect alternator wiring, then turn ignition On.
2. If indicator lamp lights, there is a short to ground between alternator D+ and indicator light. Repair as required.
3. If indicator lamp does not light, test alternator output and voltage regulator. Replace faulty components as required.

DIAGNOSIS & TESTING

OUTPUT TEST

1. Use SUN VAT-40 or SUN VAT-60, or equivalents for test.
2. Connect black clamp from VAT to battery ground cable, then red clamp from VAT to battery positive cable.
3. Connect green clamp from VAT (inductive pickup) to alternator D+ either at alternator or battery.
4. Start engine, raise speed and hold at 2000 RPM.
5. Slowly adjust load control of VAT until highest possible reading is obtained. Reading must be within 10% of manufacturer's specifications. **Test must be performed and completed within 15 seconds to avoid overloading and damaging electrical system.**

EXCITER CIRCUIT INSPECTION

If complaint "battery isn't being charged" is received even though warning lamp lights when ignition is turned On and goes out when ignition is turned Off, inspect exciter circuit as follows:

1. Ensure battery voltage is approximately 12 volts minimum, then charge if required.
2. Disconnect blue wire from alternator terminal 61.
3. Turn multi-meter tool No. US 1119, or equivalent, to 200 mA range.
4. Connect multi-meter between disconnected blue wire and terminal 61.
5. Turn ignition On. Current must fall between 150 and 185 mA.
6. If reading is lower than 150 mA, inspect blue wire between alternator and instrument panel or replace instrument cluster printed circuit as required.

EXCITER CIRCUIT RESISTANCE INSPECTION

If complaint "battery isn't being charged" is received even though warning lamp lights when ignition is turned On and goes out when ignition is turned Off, measure exciter circuit resistance as follows:

1. Obtain radio theft protection code as outlined under "Precautions."
2. Disconnect blue wire (D +/61) from back of alternator.
3. Turn multi-meter tool No. US 1119, or equivalent, to 200 ohm range.
4. Connect multi-meter between disconnected blue wire and battery positive terminal.
5. Turn ignition On. Resistance should be 140–160 ohms.
6. If reading is infinite, reverse probes and inspect again.
7. If reading is still infinite, replace printed circuit.

ALTERNATOR SPECIFICATIONS

Year	Model	Alternator Type	Alternator Maximum Output Amps	Voltage
1998	A4	Bosch	120	14.0
	A6	①	①	13.5–14.3
	A8	Bosch	120	14.0
	Cabriolet	①	①	13.5–14.3
	S4	Bosch	120	14.0
1999	A4	Bosch	120	14.0
	A6	①	①	13.5–14.3
	A8	Bosch	120	14.0
	S4	Bosch	120	14.0
2000	A4 1.8L	②	90	14.0
	A4 2.8L	②	120	14.0
	A6 2.7L & 2.8L	②	120	14.0
	A6 4.2L	②	150	14.0
	A8	②	150	14.0
	S4	②	120	14.0
	TT	②	120	14.0
2001	A4 1.8L	②	90	14.0
	A4 2.8L	②	120	14.0
	A6 2.7L & 2.8L	②	120	14.0
	A6 4.2L	②	150	14.0
	A8	②	150	14.0
	S4	②	120	14.0
	S8	②	150	14.0
	TT	②	120	14.0

① — Equipped w/either 90 amp Valeo or 120 amp Bosch.
② — Predominantly equipped w/Bosch alternators, but some models may be equipped w/Valeo alternator.

Speed Control Systems

NOTE: On Air Bag Equipped Models, Refer To "Air Bag System Precautions" Located In The Front Of This Manual For System Disarming & Arming Procedures.

NOTE: Refer To "Computer Relearn Procedures" Located In The Front Of This Manual When Battery Power To The Computer Has Been Interrupted.

NOTE: Prior To Performing Any Service Operations Listed In This Section, Consult The "Technical Service Bulletins" Section For Related Information.

INDEX

	Page No.
Adjustments	1-123
Vacuum Servo Linkage	1-123
Component Replacement	1-124
Main Control Unit	1-124
Vacuum Pump	1-124
Vacuum Servo	1-124
Vacuum Vent Valves	1-124
Precautions	1-123
Air Bag Systems	1-123
Battery Ground Cable	1-123
Radio Coded Anti-Theft System	1-123
System Diagnosis & Testing	1-123
Brake Or Clutch Pedal Switch Faulty	1-123
Control Switch Inspection	1-123
Inspect Ground Circuit To Control Unit	1-123
Vacuum Pump Inspection	1-124
Vacuum Pump Vent Valve Inspection	1-124
Vacuum System Inspection	1-123

PRECAUTIONS

AIR BAG SYSTEMS

Refer to "Air Bag System Precautions" in the front of this manual for system disarming and arming procedures.

RADIO CODED ANTI-THEFT SYSTEM

Prior to disconnecting the battery or removing the audio system, obtain the security code from the vehicle operator. Refer to the owner's manual for security code disarming and arming procedures.

BATTERY GROUND CABLE

Prior to service, disconnect battery ground cable and isolate as required.

ADJUSTMENTS

VACUUM SERVO LINKAGE

A6 & S6

1. Ensure throttle is in closed position.
2. Turn adjuster nut until there is. 004–.012 inch clearance between bushing and contact plate.

A4 & S4

1. Start and idle engine.
2. Ensure throttle is in closed position.
3. Turn adjuster nut up to its stop, then turn back 360°.
4. Ensure there is. 020–.039 inch clearance between linkage and actuator.

CABRIOLET

1. Remove engine cover, then the engine compartment cross support.
2. Remove air hose between Mass Air Flow (MAF) sensor and intake manifold.
3. Remove electrical connectors from MAF sensor and idle air control (IAC) valve.
4. Unclip cover from noise damper and remove mounting screws, then press noise damper back and lift up.
5. Remove crankcase breathers and vacuum hose, then the noise damper.
6. Remove servo linkage safety clip, then pry linkage out of ball stud with a suitable screwdriver.
7. Adjust linkage until clearance is. 019–.040 inch.

SYSTEM DIAGNOSIS & TESTING

Before testing, ensure fuses for cruise control system are satisfactory and brake lamps operate properly. Inspect wiring between control unit wiring harness and component before assuming component is faulty. If electrical measurements are required, use multi-meter tool No. US 1119, or equivalent.

VACUUM SYSTEM INSPECTION

Before testing, ensure fuses for cruise control system are intact and brake lamps are operational. Inspect wiring between control unit wiring harness and component before assuming component is faulty. If electrical measurements are required, use multi-meter tool No. US 1119, or equivalent.

1. Disconnect vacuum hose from vacuum pump, then depress servo unit diaphragm.
2. Plug disconnected vacuum hose. Diaphragm must remain in depressed state without moving.
3. If diaphragm returns, inspect vent valves, servo unit or vacuum hoses for leaks, then repair or replace as needed.
4. If diaphragm remains depressed, vacuum system is satisfactory.

INSPECT GROUND CIRCUIT TO CONTROL UNIT

1. Inspect installation locations.
2. Disconnect control unit harness connector.
3. Connect multi-meter tool No. US 1119, or equivalent, between control unit harness terminal 5 and ground, **Fig. 1.**
4. If circuit is open, repair open circuit as required.
5. If continuity exists, proceed to tests outlined under "Brake Or Clutch Pedal Switch Faulty."

BRAKE OR CLUTCH PEDAL SWITCH FAULTY

1. Connect multi-meter tool No. US 1119, or equivalent, between control unit harness connector terminals 5 and 11, **Fig. 1.**
2. Depress brake or clutch pedal.
3. If continuity exists, replace faulty brake or clutch pedal switch.
4. If circuit is open on models with 8-pin type control unit connectors, proceed to tests outlined under "Vacuum Pump Inspection."

CONTROL SWITCH INSPECTION

1. Connect multi-meter tool No. US 1119, or equivalent, set to voltage scale between control unit harness electrical connector terminals 5 and 5, **Fig. 1,**

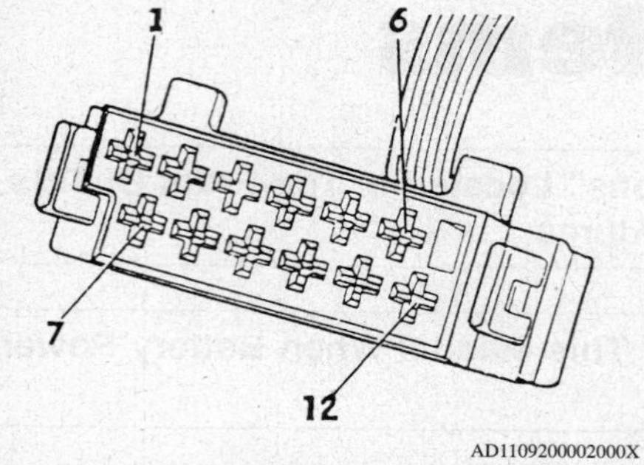

Fig. 1 Control unit harness connector terminal identification

then proceed as follows:

a. Turn cruise control switch to On position, then drive vehicle at a speed in excess of 20 mph and read voltage.
b. If voltage is zero, repair wiring and/or replace combination switch as outlined in "Electrical" section.
c. If 12 volts are found, connect multimeter set to Ohm scale to terminals 5 and 10, then push cruise control switch to Resume position.
d. If circuit is open, repair wiring and/or replace combination switch as outlined in "Electrical" section.
e. If circuit is closed, connect multimeter set to ohm scale to terminals 4 and 5, then press Fix/Set button and read meter.
f. If circuit is open, repair wiring and/or replace combination switch as outlined in "Electrical" section.
g. If circuit is closed, connect multimeter set to ohm scale to terminals 5 and 11, then press On button and read meter.
h. If circuit is open, repair wiring and/or replace combination switch as outlined in "Electrical" section.
i. If circuit is closed proceed to tests under "Brake Or Clutch Pedal Switch Faulty."

VACUUM PUMP INSPECTION

1. Turn ignition On.
2. Connect a jumper wire between control unit connector terminals 5 and 11, **Fig. 1.** Turn cruise control switch on. If vacuum pump does not run, proceed as follows:
   a. Connect terminal 6 to ground using a suitable jumper wire.
   b. Connect terminal 7 to a 12 volt source using a suitable jumper wire.
   c. If pump operates, proceed to "Vacuum Pump Vent Valve Inspection."
   d. If pump does not operate, repair open in wiring and/or replace pump.

VACUUM PUMP VENT VALVE INSPECTION

1. Turn ignition On.
2. Touch a jumper wire between control unit harness connector terminal 7 and ground, **Fig. 1.**
3. Connect a 12 volt source to terminal 7 using a suitable jumper wire, **Fig. 1.**
4. Repeatedly touch terminal 12 using a suitable jumper wire while listening for a click from vacuum pump vent valve.
5. If vent valve fails to click, replace faulty vacuum pump and/or repair wiring.
6. If valve clicks, inspect speed signal.

COMPONENT REPLACEMENT

MAIN CONTROL UNIT

A4 & S4

1. Remove glove compartment.
2. Remove control unit mounting screw.
3. Remove control unit from mounting bracket, then disconnect electrical connector.
4. Reverse procedure to install, noting the following:
   a. Ensure all electrical connectors and wiring are properly routed and connected to avoid pinching.
   b. **Torque** control unit mounting screw to 27 inch lbs.
   c. **Torque** glove compartment mounting bolts to 44 inch lbs.

A6, CABRIOLET & S6

1. Obtain radio theft protection code as outlined under "Precautions."
2. Remove glove compartment.
3. Remove Phillips head mounting screw from rear side of instrument panel.
4. Remove control unit from strap, then disconnect electrical connector.
5. Reverse procedure to install.

A8

The main control unit is located in the "E" box in the air plenum chamber.

VACUUM SERVO

1. Disconnect vacuum hose from servo.
2. Remove linkage clip or unscrew linkage.
3. Remove servo mounting nut, then the servo from bracket.
4. Reverse procedure to install. **Torque** mounting nut to 18 ft. lbs.

VACUUM VENT VALVES

1. Obtain radio theft protection code as outlined under "Precautions."
2. Remove cover and air duct from under lefthand side of instrument panel.
3. Remove electrical connectors and vacuum hoses from vacuum vent valves.
4. **On all models except A4 and S4,** push vacuum vent valve out of bushing from behind using J-shaped tool No. 2041, or equivalent, if required.
5. **On A4 and S4 models,** push or rotate vent valve out of its bracket.
6. Reverse procedure to install, noting the following:
   a. **Once valve is removed, the threads are destroyed. Do not use valve again.**
   b. Install new valve loosely by hand.
   c. Push vent valve through bushing as far as possible using a 10 MM socket. **Do not rotate it into position.**
   d. Pull brake or clutch pedal as far back as possible.
   e. **On A4 and S4 models,** ensure there is no more than. 027 inch clearance at dimension "A," **Fig. 2.**
   f. **On all models,** release pedal slowly and inspect for proper adjustment.

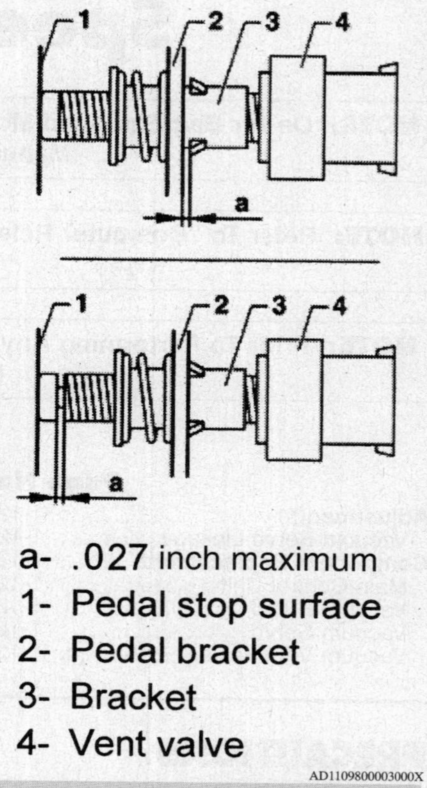

Fig. 2 Vacuum vent valve installation. A4 & S4

VACUUM PUMP

A6, CABRIOLET & S6

1. Remove vacuum pump mounting nuts.
2. Remove vacuum pump with rubber grommets.
3. Disconnect vacuum hose.
4. Reverse procedure to install.

A4 & S4

The vacuum pump is installed below the ABS unit.

1. Remove lefthand front wheelhouse panel.
2. Remove vacuum pump mounting nuts.
3. Remove vacuum pump with rubber grommets.
4. Disconnect vacuum hose.
5. Reverse procedure to install. **Torque** pump mounting nuts to 44 inch lbs.

Wiper Systems

NOTE: On Air Bag Equipped Models, Refer To "Air Bag System Precautions" Located In The Front Of This Manual For System Disarming & Arming Procedures.

NOTE: "Electrical Symbol & Wire Color Code Identification" Located In The Front Of This Manual May Be Used As An Aid When Using Wiring Circuits Found In This Section.

NOTE: Refer To "Computer Relearn Procedures" Located In The Front Of This Manual When Battery Power To The Computer Has Been Interrupted.

INDEX

	Page No.
Adjustments	1-125
Windshield Washer Nozzles	1-125
Component Replacement	1-125
Headlamp Washer Nozzle	1-126
Heated Windshield Washer Nozzles	1-125
Washer Bottle	1-125
Wiper Motor & Linkage	1-125
Precautions	1-125
Air Bag Systems	1-125
Battery Ground Cable	1-125
Radio Coded Anti-Theft System	1-125
Troubleshooting	1-125

PRECAUTIONS

AIR BAG SYSTEMS

Refer to "Air Bag System Precautions" in the front of this manual for system disarming and arming procedures.

RADIO CODED ANTI-THEFT SYSTEM

Prior to disconnecting the battery or removing the audio system, obtain the security code from the vehicle operator. Refer to the owner's manual for security code disarming and arming procedures.

Battery Ground Cable

Prior to service, disconnect battery ground cable and isolate as required.

TROUBLESHOOTING

Refer to **Figs. 1 through 6** when troubleshooting wiper system problems.

ADJUSTMENTS

WINDSHIELD WASHER NOZZLES

Use only adjusting tool No. 3125, or equivalent, to adjust washer nozzles. Do not use wires or needles or nozzle damage may result.

Refer to **Figs. 7 and 8** for location and dimensions when adjusting windshield washer spray pattern.

COMPONENT REPLACEMENT

WIPER MOTOR & LINKAGE

Refer to the "Electrical" section of the chapter for procedures.

HEATED WINDSHIELD WASHER NOZZLES

EXCEPT TT

1. Disconnect washer hose from nozzle.
2. Disconnect electrical connector from nozzle.
3. Press retaining tab from underside of nozzle using a suitable screwdriver while pushing nozzle from hood. Angled end of screwdriver should be. 8–1.2 inches.
4. Reverse procedure to install.

TT

1. Ensure windshield wipers are in park position.
2. Turn ignition Off.
3. Remove wiper blades.
4. Pry off wiper arm cover caps using a suitable screwdriver.
5. Loosen hex nuts, but do not remove completely at this time.
6. Loosen wiper arms.
7. Remove hex nuts, then the wiper arms.
8. Remove plenum chamber cover screen weatherstrip at firewall.
9. Pry out plenum chamber cover screen at edge of windshield and lift up.
10. Disconnect washer nozzle hoses on rear of plenum chamber cover screen, then remove screen.
11. Remove washer nozzle by rotating in counterclockwise direction.
12. Disconnect nozzle electrical connectors.
13. Reverse procedure to install.
    a. **Torque** wiper arm retaining nuts to 12 ft. lbs.
    b. Adjust nozzles as outlined under "Adjustments" in this section.

WASHER BOTTLE

A4 & S4

1.8L Engine

1. Raise and support vehicle.
2. Remove lefthand front wheel.
3. Remove inner fender liner.
4. Disconnect electrical connectors and fluid hoses from windshield washer bottle.
5. From engine compartment, disconnect electrical connectors and fluid hoses from headlamp washer bottle.
6. Remove headlamp washer bottle mounting bolts.
7. Remove headlamp washer bottle from vehicle, pulling crossflow hose through inner fender.
8. Remove windshield washer bottle mounting bolts.
9. Remove windshield washer bottle from vehicle.
10. Reverse procedure to install. **Torque** wheel lug nuts to 89 ft. lbs.

2.7L & 2.8L Engines

1. Raise and support vehicle.
2. Remove lefthand front wheel.
3. Remove inner fender liner.
4. Disconnect electrical connectors and fluid hoses from washer bottle.
5. Remove windshield washer bottle mounting bolts.
6. Remove washer bottle from vehicle.
7. Reverse procedure to install. **Torque** wheel lug nuts to 89 ft. lbs.

CABRIOLET

1. Remove coolant reservoir.
2. Twist reservoir filler neck to rear 90°, then pull from reservoir.
3. Raise and support vehicle.
4. Remove front tire.

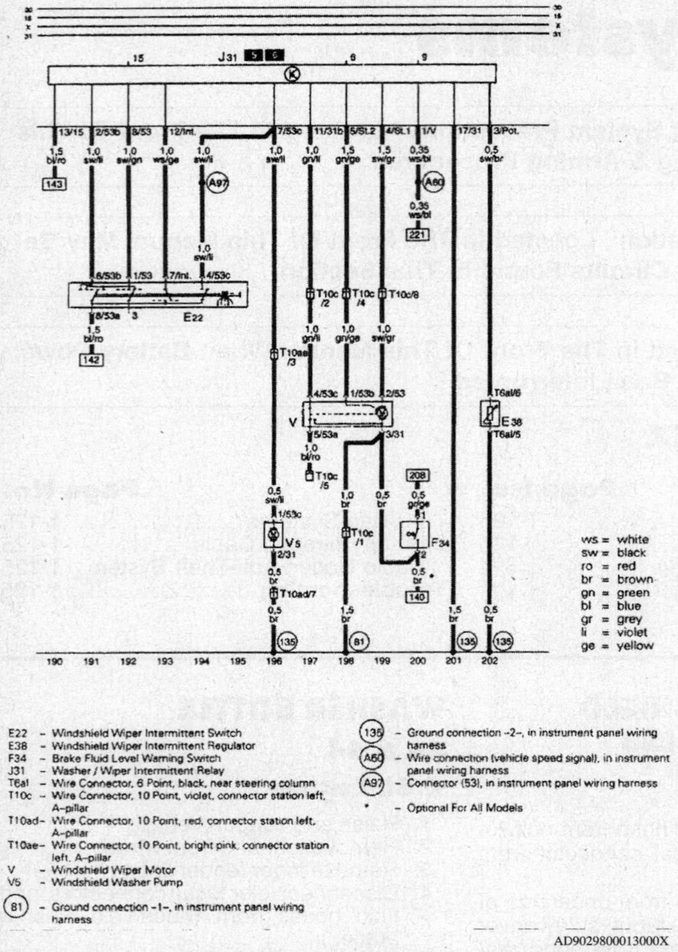

Fig. 1 Wiper system wiring diagram. 1998–99 A4 & S4

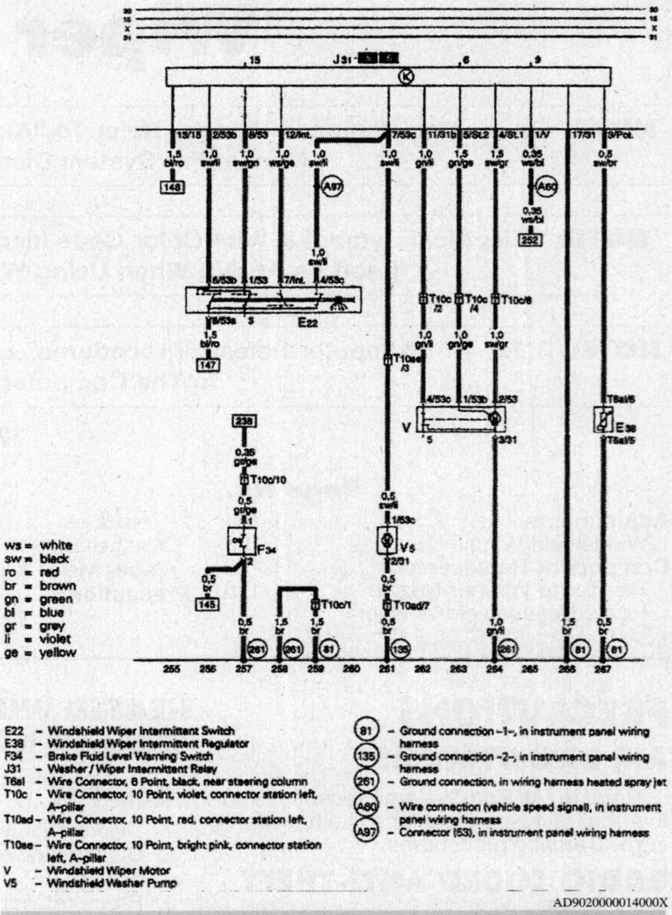

Fig. 2 Wiper system wiring diagram. 2000–01 A4 & S4

5. Remove inner fender panel and brace.
6. Disconnect electrical connector and hoses from reservoir.
7. Remove mounting bolts then reservoir.
8. Remove washer pumps and grommets from reservoir.
9. Reverse procedure to install.

TT

1. Raise and support vehicle.
2. Remove lefthand front tire.
3. Remove lefthand front wheelhouse panel.
4. Remove washer bottle mounting bolts.
5. Disconnect electrical connector and hose from washer pump.
6. Pull washer pump out of bottle.
7. Remove bottle from vehicle.
8. Reverse procedure to install. **Torque** wheel lug nuts to 89 ft. lbs.

HEADLAMP WASHER NOZZLE

A4 & S4

1. Raise and support vehicle.
2. Remove front tires.
3. Remove bumper cover screws at wheel arch.
4. Remove bumper cover to absorber mounting bolts.
5. Disconnect headlamp washer hose.
6. Slide bumper cover forward off mounts.
7. Remove bolts retaining headlamp washer units to bumper cover, then the washer units.
8. Reverse procedure to install, noting the following:
   a. **Torque** washer unit mounting bolts to 84 inch lbs.
   b. **Torque** bumper cover to absorber mounting bolts to 17 ft. lbs.
   c. **Torque** wheel lug nuts to 89 ft. lbs.

S6

1. Pull off cover of spray head.
2. Pull telescoping unit out by hand, then clamp off washer hose to keep it extended.
3. Twist and pull to remove spray nozzle from telescoping unit.
4. Remove headlamp components required to access telescoping unit.
5. Release clamp then remove hose from telescoping unit.
6. Remove nut and spacer from telescoping unit.
7. Remove mounting bolts at rear of telescoping unit, then pull telescoping unit out to rear.
8. Reverse procedure to install.

TT

1. Remove front tires.
2. Remove front bumper assembly.
3. Disconnect washer fluid supply connector at lefthand washer nozzle. This supplies both nozzles.
4. Disconnect hose at nozzle to be removed.
5. Remove bolts from nozzle, then from nozzle retainer.
6. Reverse procedure to install, noting the following:
   a. Ensure all electrical connectors, wiring and hoses are properly routed to avoid pinching.
   b. **Torque** front bumper mounting bolts to 26 ft. lbs.
   c. **Torque** wheel lug nuts to 89 ft. lbs.

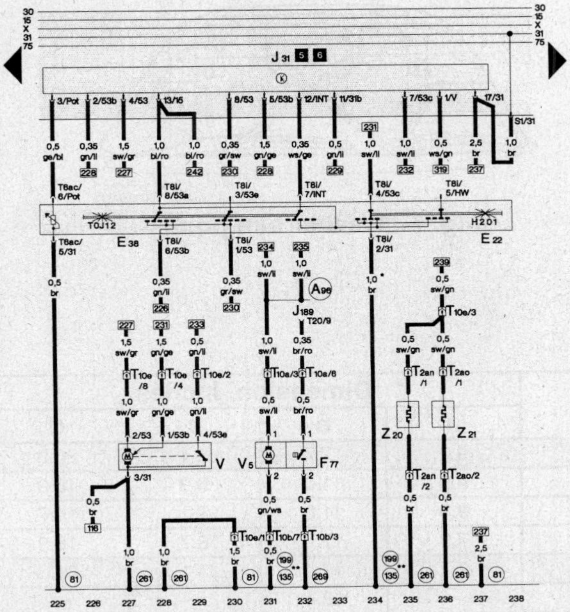

E 22 - Windshield Wiper/Washer Switch
E 38 - Windshield Wiper Intermittent Regulator
F 77 - Windshield Washer Fluid Level Warning Switch
J 31 - Wiper/Washer Intermittent Relay
J 189 - Auto Check System
T 2 an - Connector 2 pin, washer jet, left
T 2 ao - Connector 2 pin, washer jet, right
T 6 ac - Connector 6 pin, brown, on windshield wiper intermittent regulator
T 8 i - Connector 8 pin, on windshield wiper/washer switch
T 10 a - Connector 10 pin, pink, connector station A pillar, left
T 10 b - Connector 10 pin, red, connector station A pillar, left
T 10 e - Connector 10 pin, violet, connector station A pillar, left
T 20 - Connector 20 pin, red/white, on instrument cluster
V - Windshield Wiper Motor
V 5 - Windshield Washer Pump
Z 20 - Left Washer Nozzle Heater
Z 21 - Right Washer Nozzle Heater

(81) - Ground connection -1-, in instrument panel wiring harness
(135) - Ground connection -2-, in instrument panel wiring harness
(199) - Ground connection -3-, in instrument panel wiring harness
(261) - Ground connection, in wiring harness heated spray jet
(269) - Ground connector (sensor ground) -1-, in instrument panel wiring harness
(A96) - Connector (53a), in instrument panel wiring harness

* - only wagon
** - booth is possible

AD9029900009000X

Fig. 3 Wiper system wiring diagram. 1998–99 A6

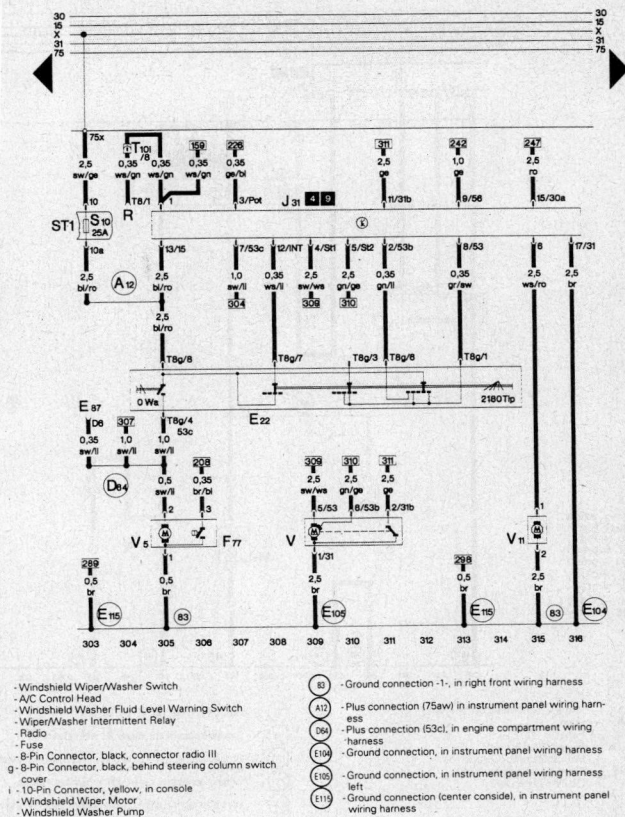

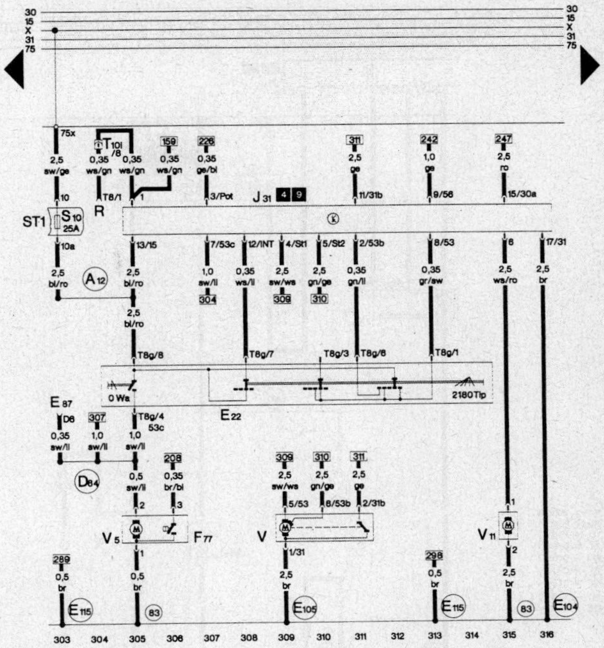

E 22 - Windshield Wiper/Washer Switch
E 87 - A/C Control Head
F 77 - Windshield Washer Fluid Level Warning Switch
J 31 - Wiper/Washer Intermittent Relay
R - Radio
S 10 - Fuse
T 8 - 8-Pin Connector, black, connector radio III
T 8 g - 8-Pin Connector, black, behind steering column switch cover
T 10 i - 10-Pin Connector, yellow, in console
V - Windshield Wiper Motor
V 5 - Windshield Washer Pump
V 11 - Headlight Washer Pump

(83) - Ground connection -1-, in right front wiring harness
(A12) - Plus connection (75aw) in instrument panel wiring harness
(D64) - Plus connection (53c), in engine compartment wiring harness
(E104) - Ground connection, in instrument panel wiring harness
(E105) - Ground connection, in instrument panel wiring harness left
(E115) - Ground connection (center console), in instrument panel wiring harness

AD9029900011000X

Fig. 4 Wiper system wiring diagram. 1998–99 A8

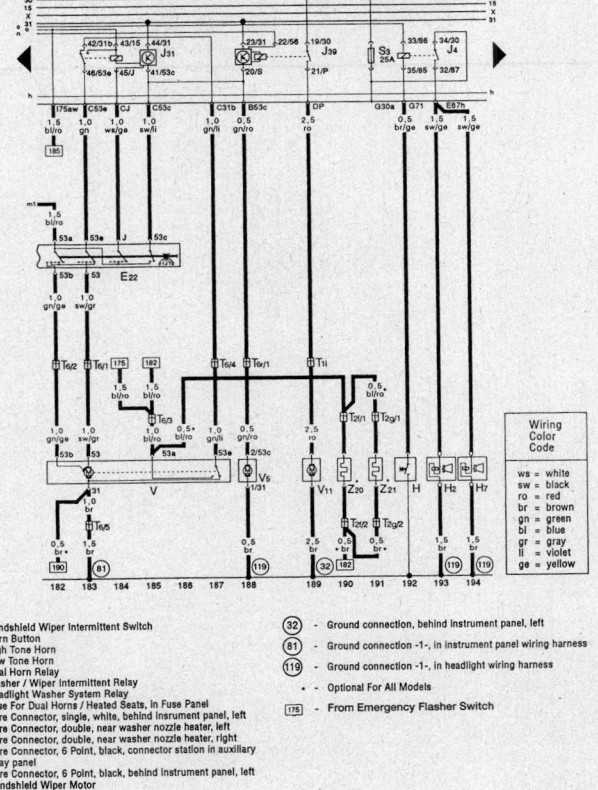

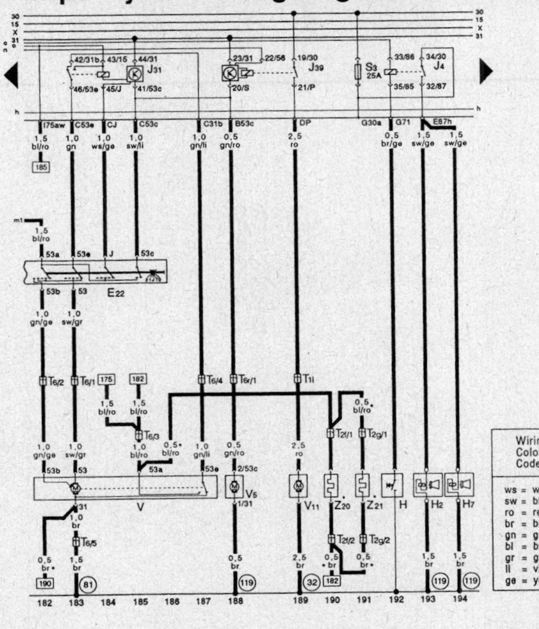

E22 = Windshield Wiper Intermittent Switch
H = Horn Button
H2 = High Tone Horn
H7 = Low Tone Horn
J4 = Dual Horn Relay
J31 = Washer / Wiper Intermittent Relay
J39 = Headlight Washer System Relay
S3 = Fuse For Dual Horns / Heated Seats, In Fuse Panel
T1i = Wire Connector, single, white, behind insrument panel, left
T2f = Wire Connector, double, near washer nozzle heater, left
T2g = Wire Connector, double, near washer nozzle heater, right
T6 = Wire Connector, 6 Point, black, connector station in auxiliary relay panel
T6r = Wire Connector, 6 Point, black, behind instrument panel, left
V = Windshield Wiper Motor
V5 = Windshield Washer Pump
V11 = Headlight Washer Pump
Z20 = Washer Nozzle Heater, Left
Z21 = Washer Nozzle Heater, Right

(32) - Ground connection, behind instrument panel, left
(81) - Ground connection -1-, in instrument panel wiring harness
(119) - Ground connection -1-, in headlight wiring harness
* - Optional For All Models
[175] - From Emergency Flasher Switch

AD9029500007000X

Fig. 5 Wiper system wiring diagram. Cabriolet

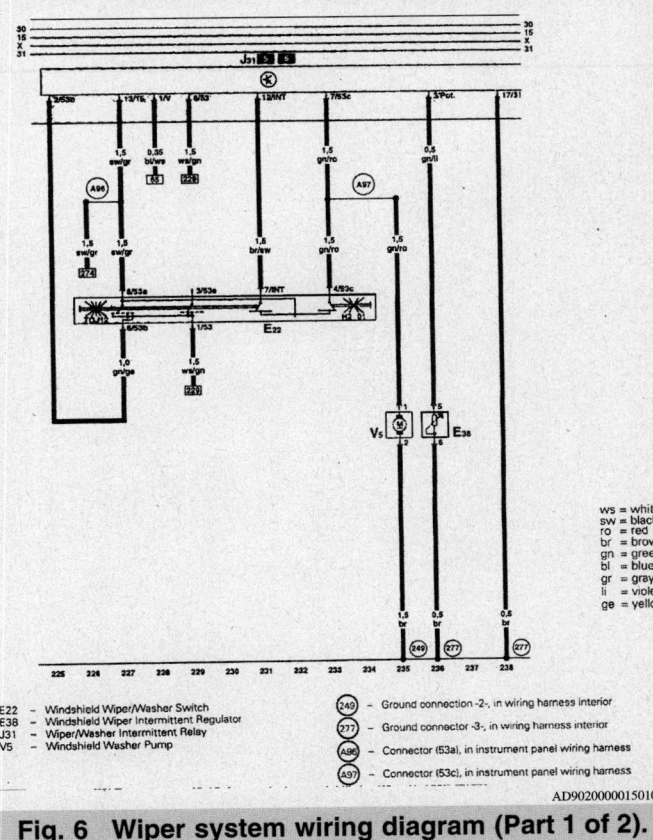

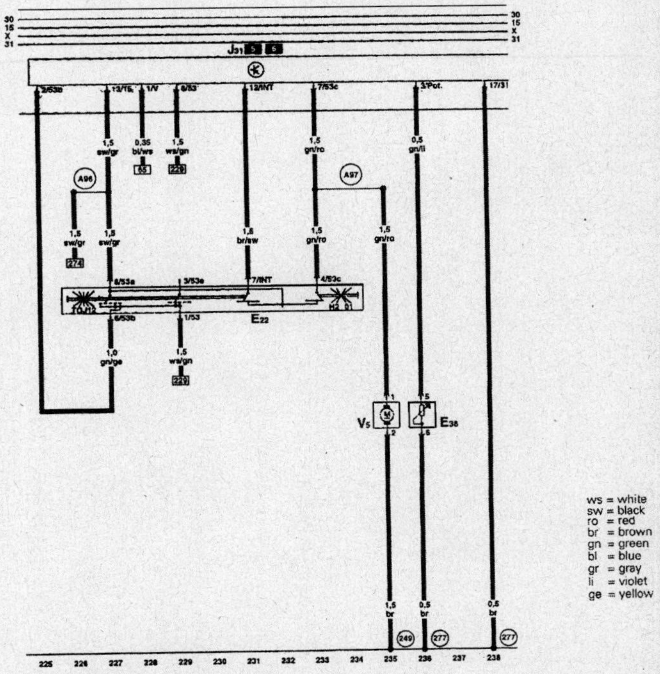

E22 – Windshield Wiper/Washer Switch
E38 – Windshield Wiper Intermittent Regulator
J31 – Wiper/Washer Intermittent Relay
V5 – Windshield Washer Pump

(249) – Ground connection -2-, in wiring harness interior
(277) – Ground connector -3-, in wiring harness interior
(A96) – Connector (53a), in instrument panel wiring harness
(A97) – Connector (53c), in instrument panel wiring harness

AD9020000015010X

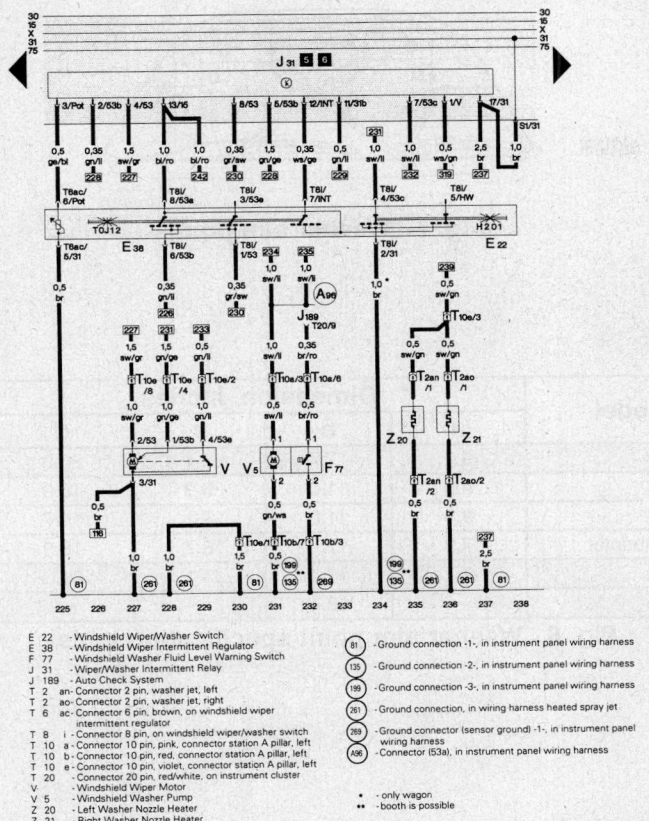

Fig. 6 Wiper system wiring diagram (Part 1 of 2). TT

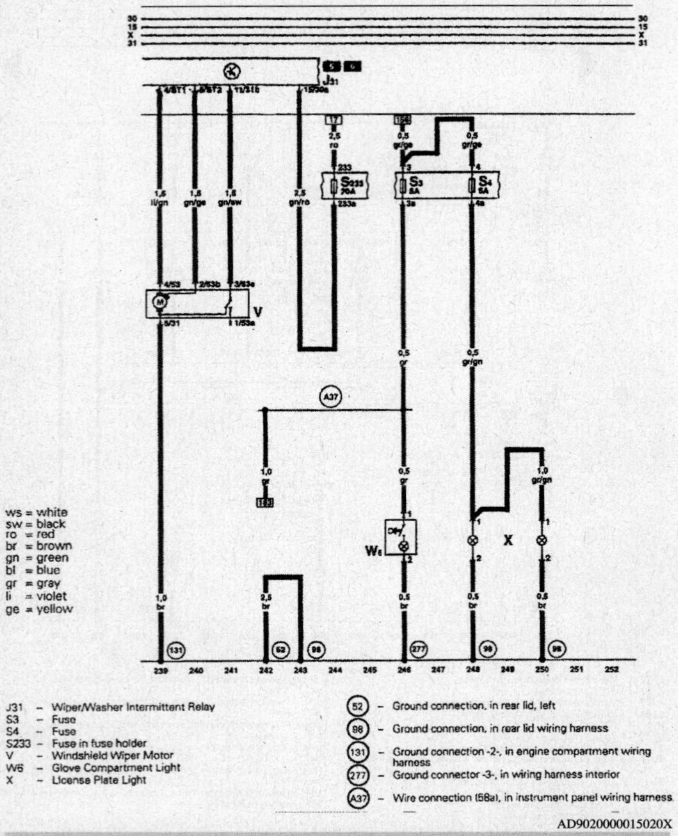

Fig. 6 Wiper system wiring diagram (Part 2 of 2). TT

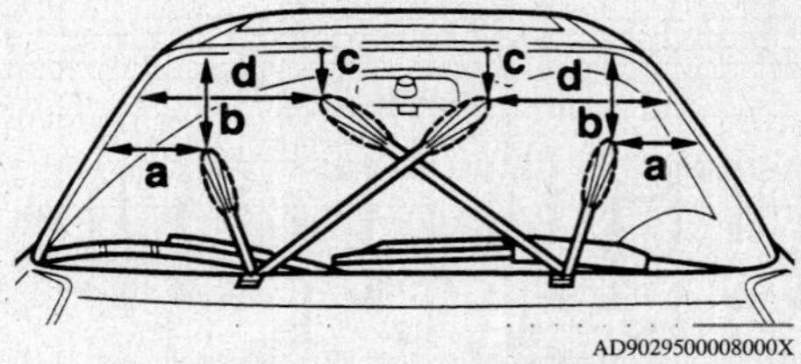

Fig. 7 Washer aim points

Model	Dimension, Inches			
	a	b	c	d
A4	9.2	17.4	3.1	20.3
A6	9.0	11.0	6.3	18.9
A8	9.8	11.0	7.1	19.7
Cabriolet	7.9	17.7	8.7	18.9
S4	9.2	17.4	3.1	20.3
TT	—	15.6	—	—

Fig. 8 Washer aim point specification table

Air Bag System

INDEX

	Page No.
Air Bag System Disarming & Arming	1-129
Arming	1-129
Disarming	1-129
Collision Inspection	1-131
Component Locations	1-131
Component Service	1-131
Air Bag & Pyrotechnical Seat Belt Tensioner Disposal	1-141
Deploying Pyrotechnical Front Seat Belt Tensioners	1-142
Air Bag Control Module, Replace	1-134
A4 & S4	1-134
A6 & S6	1-134
A8	1-135
Cabriolet	1-135
TT	1-135
Driver's Air Bag Module, Replace	1-131
A4, A8 & S4	1-131
A6 & S6	1-131
Cabriolet & TT	1-131
Passenger's Air Bag Module, Replace	1-132
A4 & S4	1-132
A6 & S6	1-132
A8	1-132
Cabriolet	1-132
TT	1-133
Pyrotechnical Seat Belt Tensioner, Replace	1-140
A4 & S4	1-140
A6 & S6	1-140
A8	1-141
TT	1-141
Seat Occupant Sensor Mat	1-139
A4 & S4	1-139
A8	1-139
Side Air Bag Crash Sensor, Replace	1-135
A4 & S4	1-135
A6 & S6	1-135
A8	1-136
TT	1-136
Side Air Bag Module, Replace	1-136
A4 & S4	1-136
A6 & S6	1-137
A8	1-138
TT	1-139
Spiral Spring, Replace	1-133
A4, A8, S4 & Cabriolet	1-133
A6 & S6	1-133
TT	1-133
Description & Operation	1-129
Diagnosis & Testing	1-131
Precautions	1-129
Scheduled Maintenance	1-130
Tightening Specifications	1-145

AIR BAG SYSTEM DISARMING & ARMING

Disarming

Prior to disconnecting any air bag system electrical connectors or servicing any system components or other components located near an air bag system electrical connector, the system must be disarmed. Also, prior to disconnecting the battery ground cable, obtain the radio anti-theft system code. It may also be required to reestablish the engine control module and automatic transaxle control module basic settings using scan tool No. VAG 1551, or equivalent.

1. Obtain radio theft protection code as outlined under "Precautions."
2. Disconnect battery ground cable.
3. Cover battery ground terminal.

Arming

1. Connect battery ground cable. **When connecting battery ground cable, ensure no one is inside vehicle.**
2. From safe position at sides of or below air bag modules, turn ignition On. Air bag indicator lamp should light for approximately 10 seconds, then go off.
3. If air bag indicator lamp does not light or remains lit after approximately 10 seconds, an air bag system fault condition is present. Refer to "Diagnosis & Testing."

DESCRIPTION & OPERATION

The air bag system is designed to supplement protection offered by seat belts in a frontal and/or side impact collisions. The air bag system incorporates an on-board diagnostic feature. Faults detected in the system are stored in the control unit memory. The fault codes can be extracted from the control unit memory using scan tool Nos. VAG 1551 or 1552, or equivalents.

The A4, A6 and S6 models are equipped with next generation driver's and passenger's air bags, front seat mounted side impact air bags and pyrotechnic front seat belt tensioners. A6 models also offer rear seat mounted aide air bag as an option on some models.

The A8 models are equipped with next generation driver's and passenger's air bags, front and rear seat side impact air bags and pyrotechnic front and rear seat belt tensioners.

On the A4, A6 and S4 models there are roof panel air bags located in the roof lining on both sides of the vehicle. They will cover the entire side window areas during an impact and protect all occupants' heads. These roof panel air bags remain inflated for approximately five seconds to provide additional protection if the vehicle rolls over.

Under certain collision conditions, the air bag control module will transmit a crash signal to the central door locking system module, releasing the door and rear lid locks. The interior lamps and emergency flashers will also be turned On and the interior switches will be blocked.

The TT models are equipped with a front passenger's front air bag deactivation switch, located in the glove compartment. It has a lock cylinder and operates with the ignition key. To deactivate the passenger's front air bag, turn the switch to the OFF position. A center console "Airbag Off →" lamp should light and remain lit as long as the air bag is deactivated. **Do not push on this lamp.** To activate the air bag again, turn the switch to the On position and the "Airbag Off →" lamp should go out.

PRECAUTIONS

Prior to disconnecting any air bag system or seat belt electrical connectors or servicing any system components or other components located near an air bag system electrical connector, the system must be disarmed. Refer to "Air Bag System Disarming & Arming." Prior to disconnecting the battery ground cable, obtain the radio security code. It may also be necessary to reestablish the engine control module and automatic transmission control module basic settings using scan tool Nos. VAG 1551 or 1552, or equivalents.

Always observe the following safety measures when working on the air bag system:

1. Testing of air bag system is never conducted with test lamp, ohmmeter or voltmeter. Use scan tool Nos. VAG 1551 or 1552, or equivalents.
2. Air bag system components or seat belt tensioner units must not be opened or repaired. Always install new components.
3. Air bag modules have an expiration date. This date can be found on sticker located on driver side B-pillar. After 14 years for A6, Cabriolet and S6 models, or 15 years for A4, A8 and S4 models, air bag modules must be replaced. For safety reasons, other air bag system components may also require replacement at this time.
4. If air bag module, seat belt tensioner unit or triggering unit has been dropped on hard surface or shows signs of damage they must not be installed on vehicle. Replace components instead.

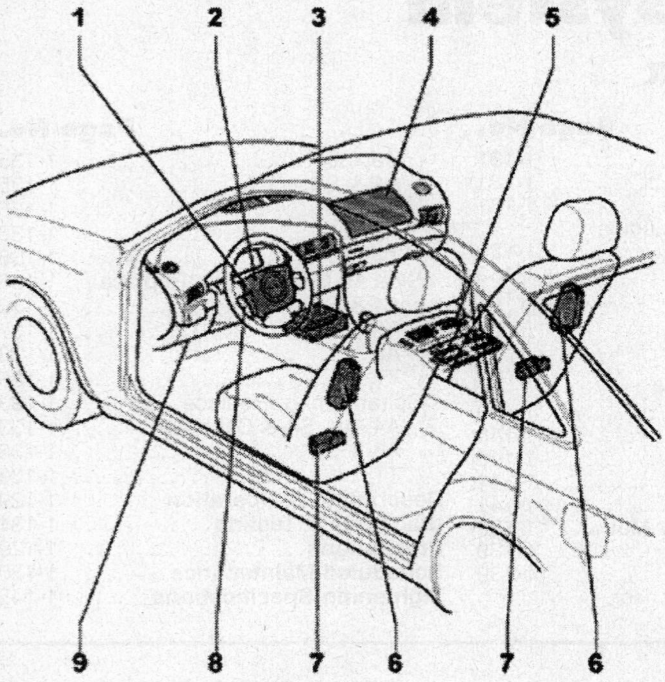

1 Driver's Air Bag Module
2 Driver's Air Bag Module
3 Air Bag Control Module
4 Front Passenger's Air Bag Module
5 Seat Occupant Sensor
6 Front Side Impact Air Bags
7 Side Imapct Air Bag Sensor
8 Spiral Spring
9 DLC

AD8010000103000X

Fig. 1 SRS component locations. A4 & S4

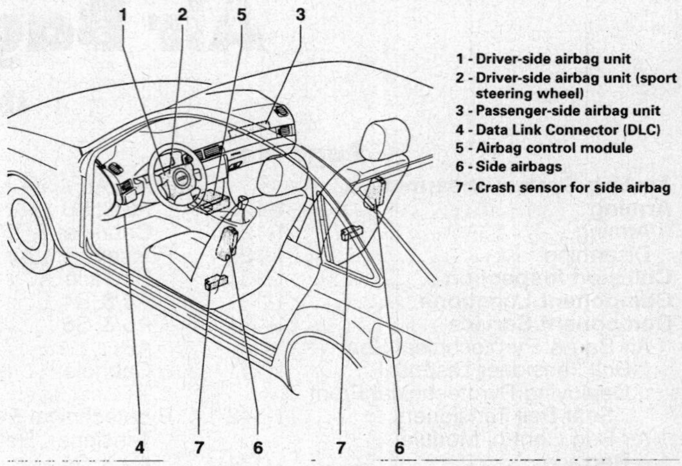

1 - Driver-side airbag unit
2 - Driver-side airbag unit (sport steering wheel)
3 - Passenger-side airbag unit
4 - Data Link Connector (DLC)
5 - Airbag control module
6 - Side airbags
7 - Crash sensor for side airbag

AD8019800087000X

Fig. 2 SRS component locations. 1998–99 A6

5. Always replace air bag system components and seat belt tensioner units which have been damaged.
6. Visually inspect vehicle's trim panels for damage before every installation.
7. **Do not attempt any repairs on any vehicle trim panels, such as top trim panels for A–D pillars.**
8. Replace passenger's air bag module lids and retaining frames after deployment.
9. Inspect instrument panel carefully in areas surrounding passenger's air bag module. Replace instrument panel if any damage is discovered.
10. Lateral acceleration sensors should be replaced if floor pan has been damaged.
11. Seatback covers and paddings should be replaced after side impact air bag module deployment.
12. Head-level air bags must only be folded at roof to A-pillar intersection.
13. Always remove entire head-level air bag unit first when carrying out repairs behind it.
14. **Do not leave undeployed air bag module or seat belt tensioner unattended if work is interrupted. Install into vehicle as soon as unit is removed from packaging.**
15. Always place removed air bag module so pad is facing upwards.
16. **Do not point open end of seat belt tensioner toward anyone.**
17. Avoid working directly in front of air bag modules. It is safer to approach them from sides or below.
18. Ensure all seat belt system mechanical components and those for 3-point seat belt are properly attached prior to connecting seat belt tensioner electrical connector.
19. Air bag module or seat belt tensioner unit must not be exposed to grease, or cleaned with any type of cleaning agent.
20. **Do not expose air bag modules or seat belt tensioner units to temperatures of 212°F or more for even brief periods while handling them during repair process. Keep units clear of heat sources.**
21. Storage, transportation and disposal of air bag modules and seat belt tensioner units are subject to laws for flammable solids.
22. Deployed air bag modules and seat belt tensioner units do not have to be disposed of as hazardous waste but can be disposed of with automotive metal scrap for recycling.
23. Some triggering units contain mercury switch and must be disposed of in approved manner. Triggering units without red part identification label contain mercury switch. Triggering units with red part identification label do not contain mercury switch and can be disposed of with automotive scrap.
24. Air bag modules should not be stored for more than three months.
25. **Do not install additional seat and back rest covers on vehicle. Use only original equipment seat and back rest covers.**
26. **Do not use seat cushions, mats or similar items, as seat occupant sensor and air bag operation may be impaired.**
27. When servicing seats, install new upholstery clips. Clips must be installed in same locations as originals.
28. Replace seat cover if damaged in area near side air module.
29. **Never use upholstery needles or other sharp objects in area of side impact air bag module.**
30. Scan tool Nos. VAG 1551 or 1552, or equivalents, will display Code 0111 or "Too Large" in case of released seat belt tensioners.
31. Prior to disconnecting the battery ground cable, obtain radio security code from vehicle operator. Refer to owner's manual for security code disarming and arming procedures.

SCHEDULED MAINTENANCE

Air bag modules have an expiration date. The date can be found on a label attached to the driver side B-pillar. If label is missing, use vehicle build date listed on label on driver's side door pillar. After 15 years for A8 and Cabriolet models, or 14 years for A4, A6, S4 and TT models, the air bag modules must be replaced. For safety reasons, other air bag system components may also require replacement at this time. Refer to "Component Service" for replacement procedures. After replacing components, install a new air bag date sticker, with expiration date punched out, to driver's side B-pillar.

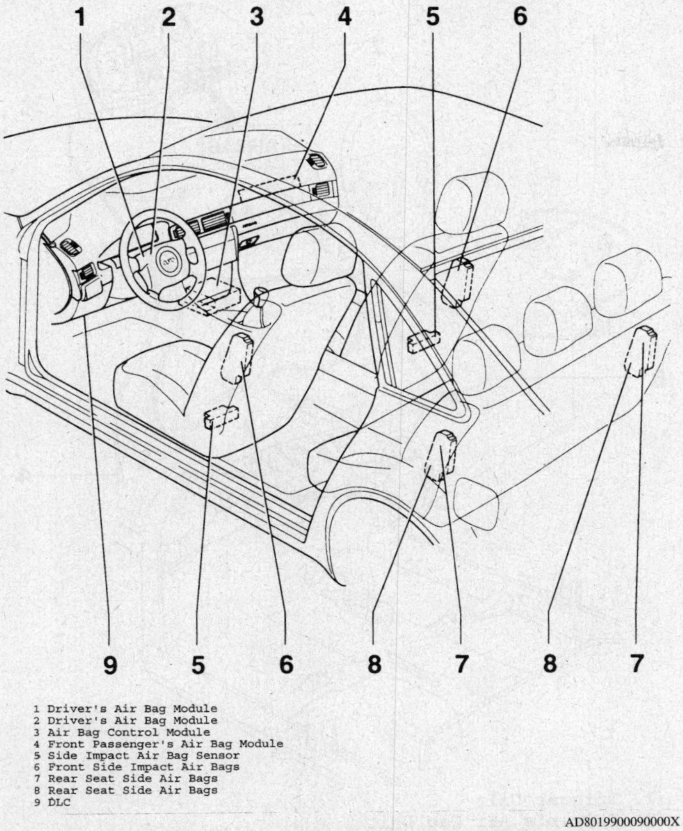

Fig. 3 SRS component locations. 2000 A6

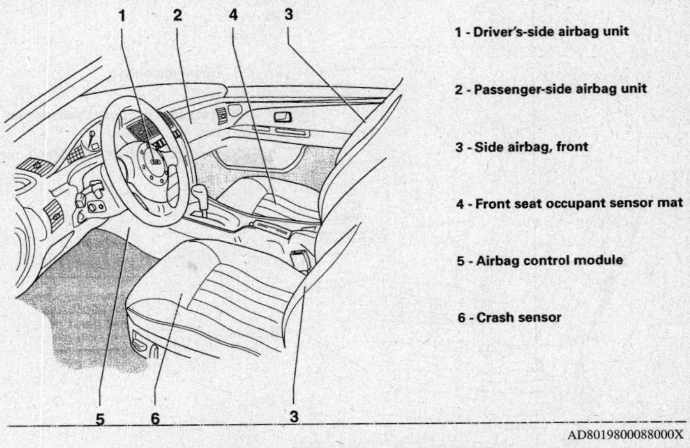

Fig. 4 Front SRS components. A8

COMPONENT LOCATIONS

Refer to **Figs. 1 through 7** for component locations.

DIAGNOSIS & TESTING

Refer to **MOTOR's "Air Bag Manual"** for complete diagnosis and testing.

COLLISION INSPECTION

On vehicles which have experienced an air bag system deployment, certain SRS components must be replaced. To determine which air bag/SRS components require replacement, refer to the "General Information" section located in MOTOR's "Air Bag Manual"

To ensure proper system operation on any vehicle involved in a collision, perform procedures outlined under "Diagnosis and Testing" in **MOTOR's "Air Bag Manual."** All system components should be inspected for dents, cracks, exposure to excessive heat and other damage. All air bag system wiring should be inspected for chafing and interference with other vehicle components. The instrument panel should also be inspected. When repairing vehicle, system should be disarmed as outlined under "Air Bag System Disarming & Arming." **Also when performing service procedures, do not expose components or wiring to heat guns, welding or spray guns.**

COMPONENT SERVICE

Prior to disconnecting any air bag system electrical connectors or servicing any system components or other components located near an air bag system electrical connector, the system must be disarmed, refer to "Air Bag System Disarming & Arming." Failure to disarm air bag system could result in system deployment and personal injury. Also refer to "Precautions" before servicing the component. After completing the service procedure, the air bag system must be armed again. Refer to "Air Bag System Disarming & Arming."

Driver's Air Bag Module, Replace

A4, A8 & S4

1. Ensure steering wheel is in straight-ahead position.
2. Disarm air bag system as outlined under "Air Bag System Disarming & Arming."
3. Remove Torx T30 head screws at sides or rear of steering wheel, **Fig. 8.**
4. Disconnect air bag module and tilt downward.
5. Disconnect air bag module electrical connector.
6. Remove air bag module.
7. Reverse procedure to install, noting the following:
   a. Ensure air bag module electrical connector clicks into place
   b. Tighten mounting bolts to specifications.
   c. Arm air bag system as outlined under "Air Bag System Disarming & Arming."

A6 & S6

1. Ensure steering wheel is in straight-ahead position.
2. Disarm air bag system as outlined under "Air Bag System Disarming & Arming."
3. Release steering column adjustment mechanism, then pull out and raise wheel as far as possible.
4. **On models less sport steering wheel,** rotate Torx T30 head screws at rear sides of steering wheel 90° clockwise (as viewed from front) to release locking lugs, **Fig. 9.**
5. **On models equipped with sport steering wheel,** remove air bag module Torx T30 mounting bolts, **Fig. 10.**
6. **On all models,** disconnect air bag module electrical connectors.
7. Remove air bag module.
8. Reverse procedure to install, noting the following:
   a. Tighten mounting bolts to specifications.
   b. Arm air bag system as outlined under "Air Bag System Disarming & Arming."

CABRIOLET & TT

1. Ensure front wheels are in straight-ahead position.
2. Disarm air bag system as outlined under "Air Bag System Disarming & Arming."
3. Remove air bag module mounting bolts from behind steering wheel, **Fig. 10.**
4. Disconnect coil electrical connector.
5. Remove air bag module.
6. Reverse procedure to install, noting the following:

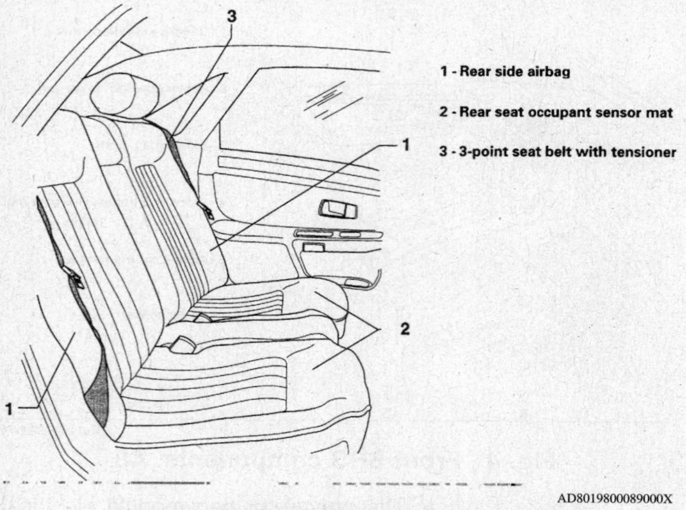

Fig. 5 Rear SRS components. A8

a. Tighten mounting bolts to specifications.
b. Arm air bag system as outlined under "Air Bag System Disarming & Arming."

Passenger's Air Bag Module, Replace

A4 & S4

1. Disarm air bag system as outlined under "Air Bag System Disarming & Arming."
2. Remove glove compartment.
3. Remove angle bracket attaching screws, then the angle brackets, **Fig. 11.**
4. Disconnect orange air bag module electrical connector. The orange air bag module electrical connector is connected to wiring harness located on center tunnel behind air bag module to the left. **Do not disconnect red 2-pin connections on air bag module. If the red 2-pin electrical connection on the air bag module is loose, the air bag module must be replaced.**
5. Remove air bag module.
6. Reverse procedure to install, noting the following:
   a. Tighten righthand air bag mounting bolt.
   b. Tighten lefthand air bag mounting bolt.
   c. Tighten air bag module attaching bolts to specifications.

A6 & S6

1. Disarm air bag system as outlined under "Air Bag System Disarming & Arming."
2. Remove glove compartment.
3. Disconnect air bag module electrical connector by lifting it over retaining tab using suitable screwdriver and disconnecting harness in direction of arrow, **Fig. 12. Do not disconnect red 2-pin harness connector.**
4. Remove and discard four front passenger's air bag module to mounting plate nuts, **Fig. 13.**
5. Remove front passenger's air bag module.
6. Reverse procedure to install, noting the following:
   a. Ensure electrical connectors are properly engaged by listening for audible click.
   b. Tighten new air bag module mounting nuts to specifications.
   c. Arm air bag system as outlined under "Air Bag System Disarming & Arming."

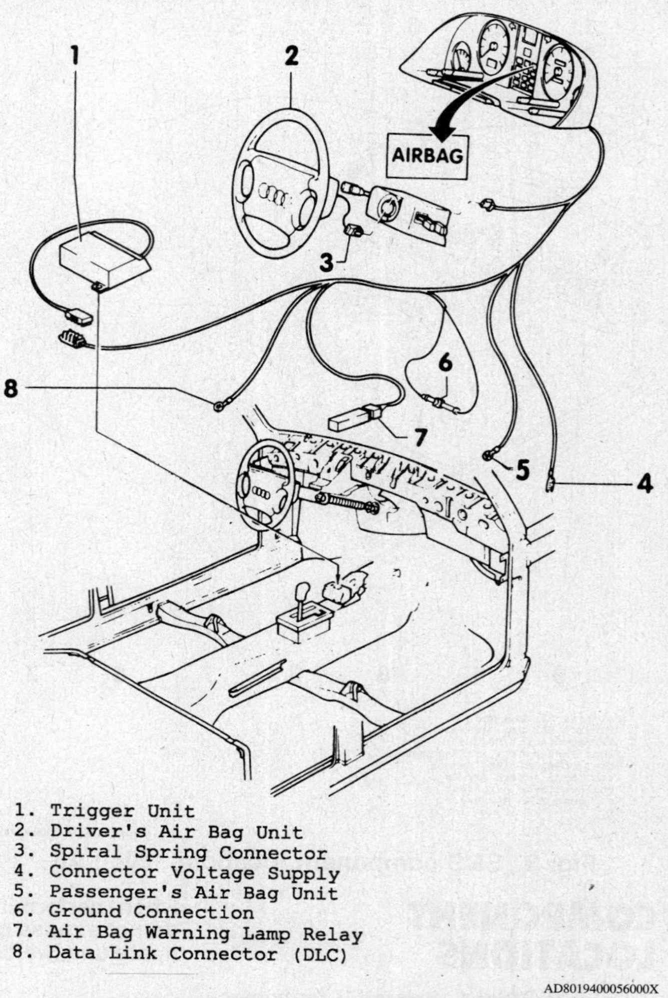

Fig. 6 SRS component locations. Cabriolet

A8

1. Disarm air bag system as outlined under "Air Bag System Disarming & Arming."
2. Remove glove compartment.
3. Remove front passenger's air bag module lefthand mounting bracket and support bracket.
4. Disconnect front passenger's air bag module orange electrical connector (2), **Fig. 14. Do not disconnect 2-pin red passenger's air bag electrical connector.**
5. Remove four air bag module attaching screws.
6. Remove front passenger's air bag module downward.
7. Reverse procedure to install, noting the following:
   a. Front passenger's air bag module retaining screws (7), **Fig. 14,** are encapsulated with a thread coating. Always use new original equipment screws. Remove residual thread coating from mounting bracket threads using a tap of the appropriate thread size.
   b. When installing air bag module, ensure electrical connectors are properly engaged.
   c. Tighten module retaining nuts to specifications.
   d. Arm air bag system as outlined under "Air Bag System Disarming & Arming."

CABRIOLET

1. Disarm air bag system as outlined under "Air Bag System Disarming & Arming."
2. Remove glove compartment.
3. Remove passenger's air bag mounting bolts.
4. Disconnect air bag module electrical connector, then remove module. Store

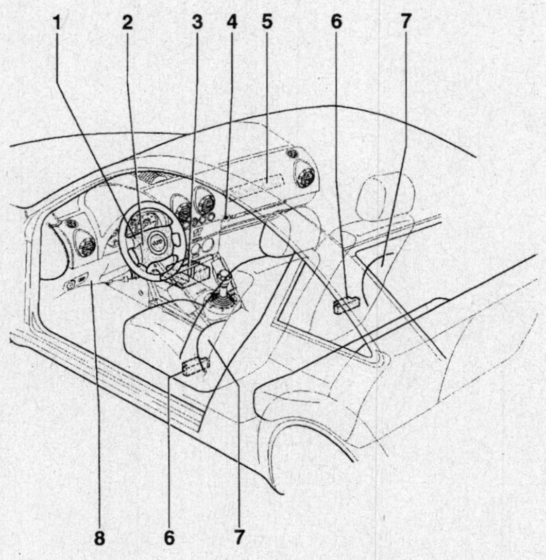

Component locations, overview

1 - Driver's airbag unit
2 - Removing and installing coil connector with slip ring
3 - Airbag control unit
4 - Deactivation switch for passenger's airbag
5 - Passenger's airbag unit
6 - Lateral acceleration sensor
7 - Side airbag
8 - Data Link Connector (DLC)

AD8010100116000X

Fig. 7 SRS component locations. TT

module in a secure place with impact cushion facing upward.

5. Reverse procedure to install. Tighten righthand air bag mounting bolt, then lefthand mounting bolt. Tighten air bag module attaching bolts to specifications.

TT

1. Disarm air bag system as outlined under "Air Bag System Disarming & Arming."
2. Remove glove compartment.
3. Disconnect electrical connector. **Do not disconnect red 2-pin connector.**
4. Remove four mounting screws, air bag module and brackets.
5. Remove two mounting screws and air bag module from brackets.
6. Reverse procedure to install, noting the following:
   a. Ensure connector engages with audible click.
   b. Tighten mounting bolts to specifications.
   c. Arm air bag system as outlined under "Air Bag System Disarming & Arming."

Spiral Spring, Replace

A4, A8, S4 & CABRIOLET

1. Place steering wheel in straight-ahead position.
2. Disarm air bag system as outlined under "Air Bag System Disarming & Arming."
3. Remove driver's air bag module as outlined under "Air Bag Module, Replace.".
4. Remove steering column adjustment lever handle.
5. Remove steering column upper and lower covers.
6. Disconnect spiral spring electrical connectors, **Fig. 15.**
7. Remove steering wheel to column shaft mounting bolt or nut.
8. Remove steering wheel using suitable puller tool.
9. Remove spiral spring mounting screws.
10. Remove spiral spring. **Do not twist spring after removal.**

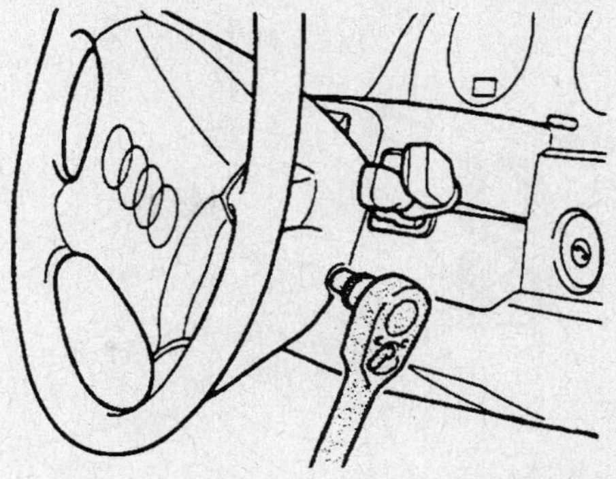

AD8019400063000X

Fig. 8 Driver's air bag module replacement. A4, A8 & S4

11. Reverse procedure to install, noting the following:
    a. Tighten spiral spring, steering wheel and air bag module mounting bolts and nut to specifications.
    b. Arm air bag system as outlined under "Air Bag System Disarming & Arming."

A6 & S6

1. Ensure steering wheel is in straight-ahead position.
2. Disarm air bag system as outlined under "Air Bag System Disarming & Arming."
3. Remove driver's air bag module as outlined under "Air Bag Module, Replace."
4. Remove steering wheel to column shaft mounting nut.
5. Remove steering wheel using suitable puller tool.
6. Remove steering column adjustment lever handle.
7. Remove steering column upper and lower covers.
8. Disconnect spiral spring electrical connectors, **Fig. 16.**
9. Release spiral spring locking lugs, then pull spiral spring and cancelling cam away from combination switch. **Do not twist spring after removal.**
10. Reverse procedure to install, noting the following:
    a. Ensure wiring and electrical connectors are properly routed to avoid pinching.
    b. Tighten steering wheel and air bag module mounting bolts and nuts to specifications.
    c. Arm air bag system as outlined under "Air Bag System Disarming & Arming."

TT

1. Remove driver's air bag as outlined under "Air Bag Module, Replace."
2. Pull out steering column and tilt downward as far as possible.
3. Remove mounting screws and steering column grip.

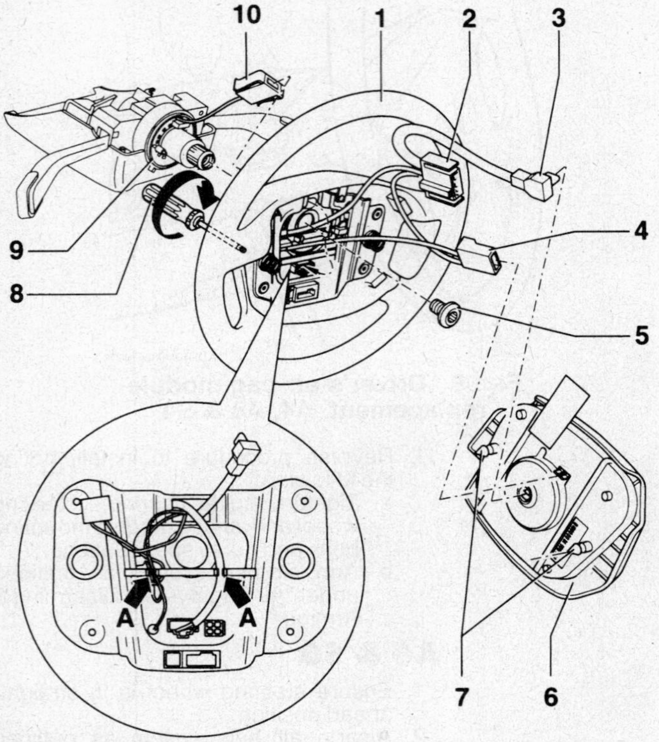

1 Steering Wheel
2 Spiral Spring Electrical Connector
3 Air Bag Electrical Connector
4 Electrostatic Discharge Electrical Connector
5 Steering Wheel Bolt
6 D river's Air Bag Module
7 Air Bag Locking Lugs
8 Torx T30 Bit Driver
9 Cancelling Cam & Spiral Spring
10 Heated Wheel Electrical Connector

AD8019900091000X

Fig. 9 Driver's air bag module replacement. A6 & S6 less sport steering wheel

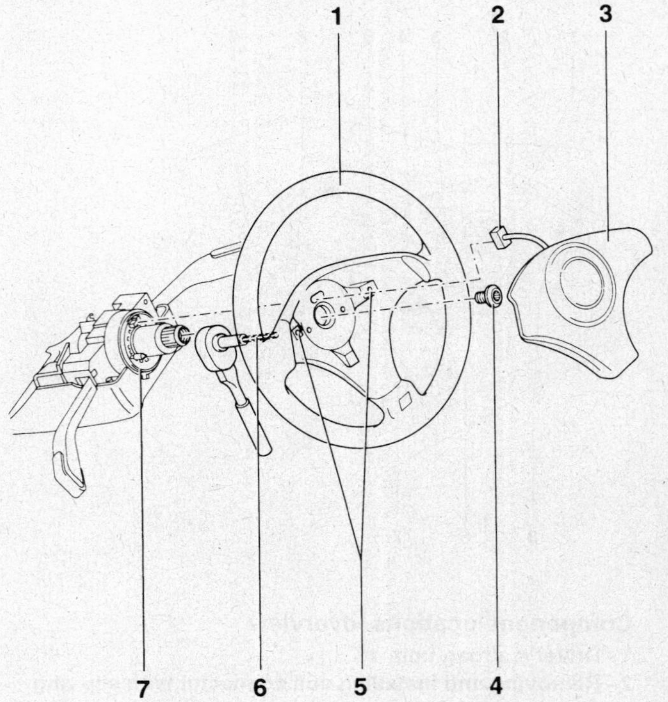

1 Steering Wheel
2 Spiral Spring Electrical Connector
3 Air Bag Module
4 Steering Wheel Bolt
5 Air Bag Mounting Screws
6 Torx T30 Bit Socket
7 Cancelling Cam & Spiral Spring

AD8019900092000X

Fig. 10 Driver's air bag module replacement. A6 & S6 w/sport steering wheel, Cabriolet & TT

4. Remove mounting screws and upper steering column switch trim.
5. Remove mounting bolt and lower steering column switch trim.
6. Disconnect connector.
7. Disconnect locking lugs and pull coil connector with slip ring off steering column switch.
8. Reverse procedure to install, noting the following:
   a. Tighten mounting bolts to specifications.
   b. Arm air bag system as outlined under "Air Bag System Disarming & Arming."

Air Bag Control Module, Replace

New air bag control modules must be coded prior to installation. Refer to "Air Bag Control Module Coding" under "Function Tests" in "Diagnosis & Testing" in MOTOR's "Air Bag Manual."

A4 & S4

1. Disarm air bag system as outlined under "Air Bag System Disarming & Arming."
2. Remove bolt covers from side of front console, **Fig. 17.**
3. Remove two bolts attaching front console to rear console from each side of front console.
4. Remove ashtray.
5. Remove nut through ashtray opening.
6. Apply hand brake, then raise rear console slightly and disengage from front console.
7. Remove rear console, then detach cable for diagnostic connector.
8. Remove four bolts attaching front console to instrument panel, **Fig. 18.**
9. Remove trim from center of instrument panel.
10. Remove heater controls from center of instrument panel.
11. Remove nut covers from each side of front console.
12. Remove nut from each side of front console.
13. Remove four bolts attaching front console to instrument panel.
14. Detach front console from instrument panel, then remove front console.
15. Disconnect electrical connector from air bag control module, **Fig. 19.**
16. Remove air bag control module attaching nuts, then remove control module.
17. Reverse procedure to install, noting the following:
   a. Install air bag control module before connecting electrical connector.
   b. Tighten air bag module attaching nuts to specifications.
   c. Arm air bag system as outlined under "Air Bag System Disarming & Arming."
   d. New air bag control must be coded prior to installation, refer to "Air bag Control Module Coding."

A6 & S6

1. Disarm air bag system as outlined under "Air Bag System Disarming & Arming."
2. Open ashtray and unclip trim, then remove radio, **Fig. 20.**
3. Remove air conditioning control head.
4. Remove front ashtray and switch panel trim.
5. Remove four front console mounting bolts.
6. Remove trim cap and mounting nut.
7. Pull center console over pin on driver's side.
8. Remove center console toward rear.
9. Remove righthand rear footwell vent air ducts' connecting pieces.
10. Disconnect air bag control module electrical connector retainer.
11. Remove three mounting nuts and air bag control module, **Fig. 21.**
12. Reverse procedure to install, noting the following:
   a. Tighten air bag module mounting nuts to specifications.
   b. Arm air bag system as outlined under "Air Bag System Disarming & Arming."

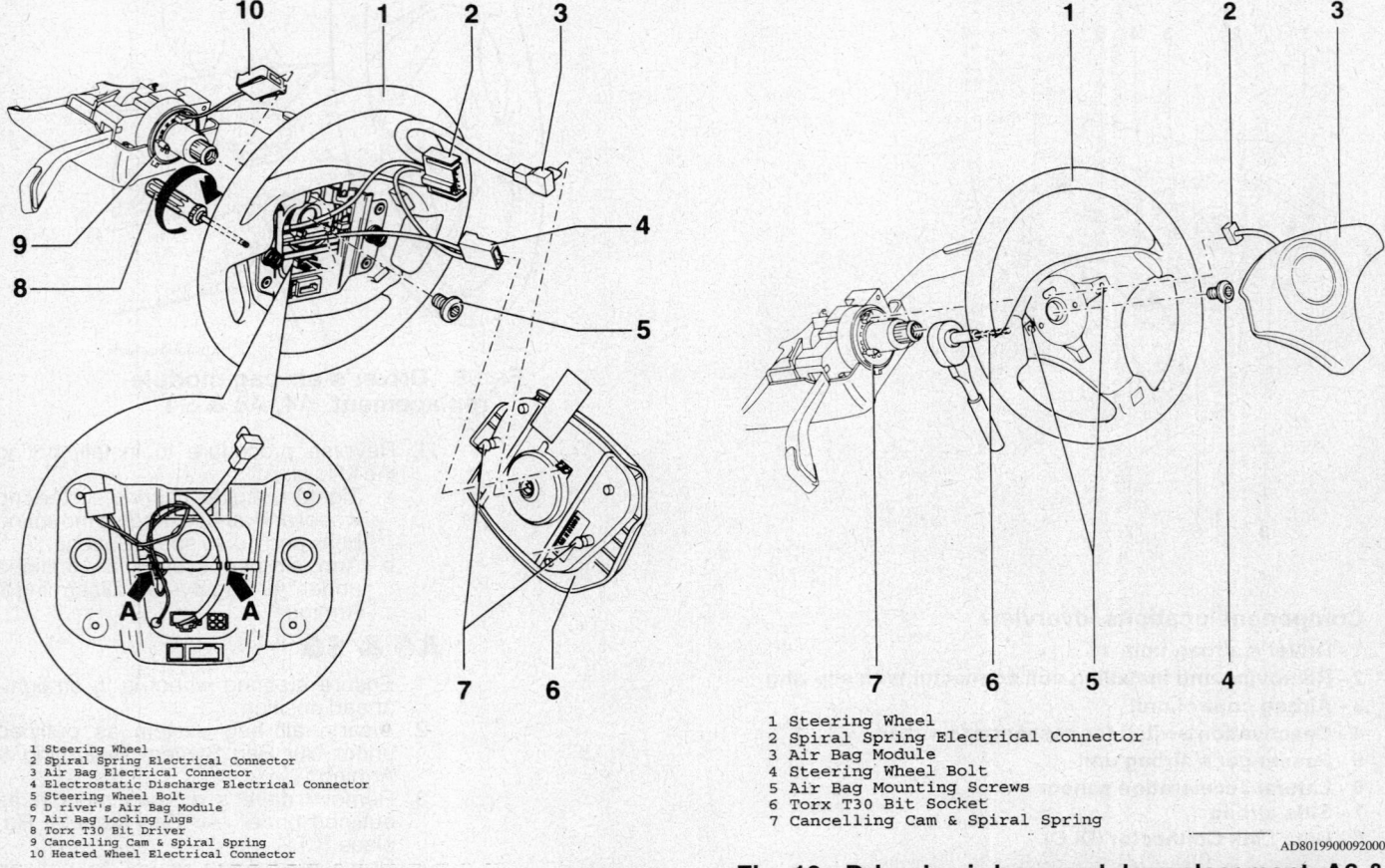

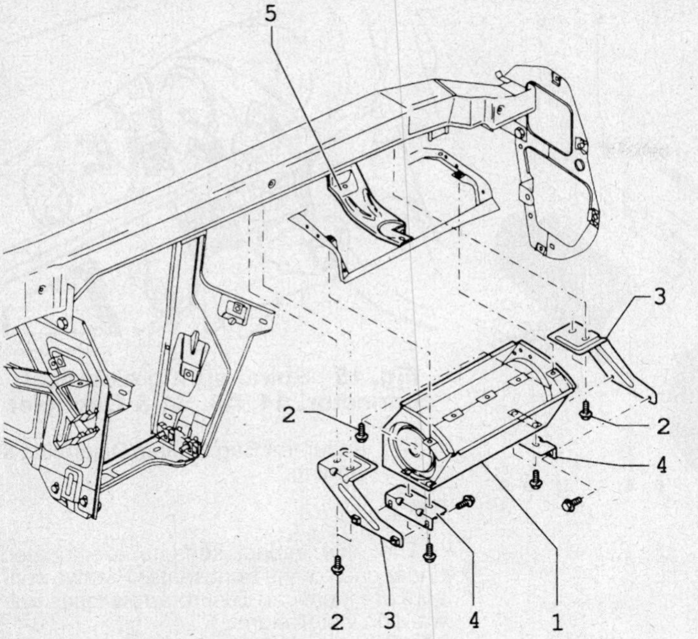

Fig. 11 Passenger's air bag module. A4 & S4

A8

1. Disarm air bag system as outlined under "Air Bag System Disarming & Arming."
2. Remove armrest and rear air outlet from center console, **Fig. 22.**
3. Remove lefthand and righthand side trim panels from center console.
4. Disconnect air outlet mounting.
5. Disconnect telephone wiring harness, as required.
6. Disconnect duct for side and rear passenger air outlet.
7. Remove center console.
8. Remove parking brake lever trim.
9. Disconnect air bag control module electrical connector.
10. Remove mounting nuts and air bag control module.
11. Reverse procedure to install, noting the following:
    a. Tighten air bag module mounting nuts to specifications.
    b. Arm air bag system as outlined under "Air Bag System Disarming & Arming."

CABRIOLET

1. Disarm air bag system as outlined under "Air Bag System Disarming & Arming."
2. Remove ashtray from rear center console, **Fig. 23.**
3. Remove rear center console mounting screws.
4. Pull rear center console upward to detach from locking lugs.
5. Disconnect electrical connectors, then remove rear center console.
6. Remove knobs from heater control panel, then the trim plate.
7. **On models equipped with automatic air conditioning,** remove HVAC control panel.
8. **On all models,** remove filler retaining screws and filler.
9. Remove gear shift lever knob.
10. Remove screw attaching gear shift lever boot to front center console, then the boot, **Fig. 24.**
11. Pull front center console toward rear to disengage from guides.
12. Disconnect front center console electrical connectors, then remove front center console.
13. Remove control module retaining nuts, **Fig. 25.**
14. Disconnect control module electrical connector, then remove triggering unit.
15. Reverse procedure to install. Tighten control module retaining nuts to specifications.

TT

1. Disarm air bag system as outlined under "Air Bag System Disarming & Arming."
2. Pry out screws caps, then remove mounting screws and footwell vent trim.
3. Pull out footwell vent.
4. Remove mounting nuts and control module.
5. Press catch, flick over retainer and disconnect connector.
6. Reverse procedure to install, noting the following:

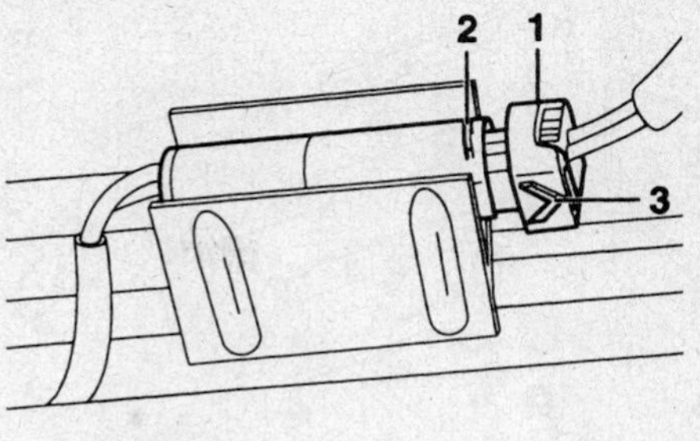

Fig. 12 Front passenger's air bag module electrical connector. A6 & S6

a. Tighten air bag module mounting nuts to specifications.
b. Arm air bag system as outlined under "Air Bag System Disarming & Arming."

Side Air Bag Crash Sensor, Replace

A4 & S4

1. Disarm air bag system as outlined under "Air Bag System Disarming & Arming."
2. Push front seat forward.
3. Remove seat track stopper screw from lefthand seat track.
4. Remove cap nut, then the fillister head screw or unclip stop spring retaining seat track to bracket. Some models may be equipped with stop spring instead of a fillister screw.
5. Pull up seat release lever, then push seat out toward rear.
6. Disconnect electrical connectors from seat and remove seat.
7. Remove lower A-pillar trim cover.
8. Detach and raise inside door sill.
9. Lift up floor mat in area of sensor.
10. Disconnect wiring harness connector from crash sensor.
11. Remove two side air bag sensor retaining screws, then the side air bag sensor.
12. Reverse procedure to install, noting the following:
    a. Install side air bag crash sensor with arrow on housing facing toward front of vehicle.
    b. Tighten side air bag sensor attaching screws to specifications.
    c. **After completing installation, turn ignition On, then close doors and connect battery ground cable. Ensure no one is inside vehicle when connecting battery ground cable.**

A6 & S6

A side impact air bag crash sensor is installed under each front seat. The sensors are identical.

1. Disarm air bag system as outlined under "Air Bag System Disarming & Arming."

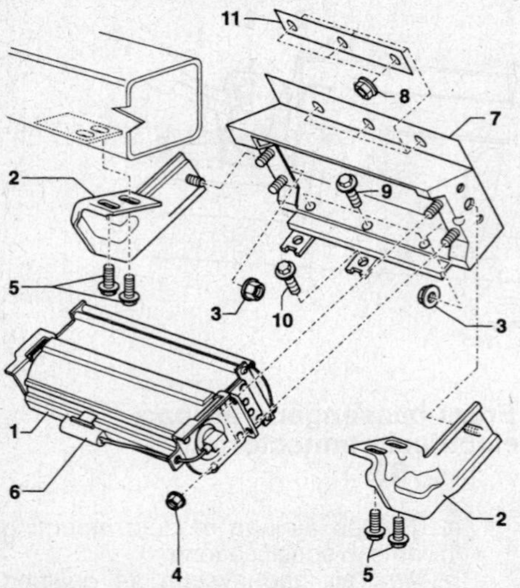

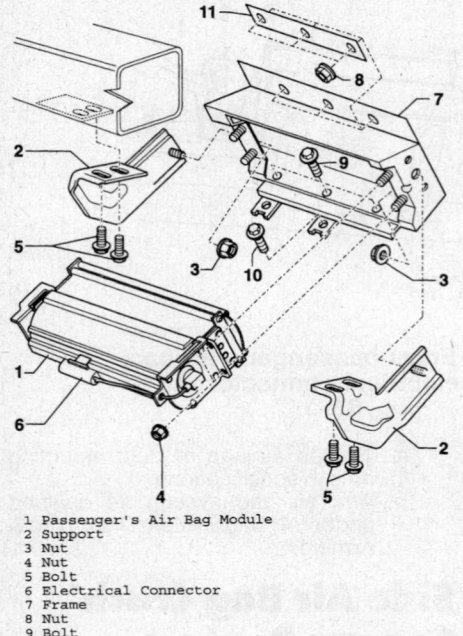

1 Passenger's Air Bag Module
2 Support
3 Nut
4 Nut
5 Bolt
6 Electrical Connector
7 Frame
8 Nut
9 Bolt
10 Bolt
11 Backing Plate

AD8019800093000X

Fig. 13 Passenger's air bag module. A6 & S6

2. Move front seat forward, then remove rail covers on rocker panel side and tunnel side.
3. Move front seat rearward and remove seat front trim piece.
4. **On models equipped with power memory seat,** proceed as follows:
   a. Remove front seat rail front cover piece.
   b. Remove two mounting bolt and unclip seat at clips.
5. **On all models,** disconnect side impact air bag electrical connector. **Technician must be grounded before touching side impact air bag ignition wire. This can be accomplished by briefly touching door striker or vehicle body.**
6. Insert air bag adapter harness tool No. VAS 5061, or equivalent, in connector station, **Fig. 26.**
7. Connect air bag ignition wire to air bag adapter harness.
8. Disconnect seat harness electrical connector.
9. Cover rear carpet in area of seat rails.
10. Slide seat rearward and out of guide.
11. Remove lower A-pillar trim.
12. Unclip sill panel trim on inside.
13. Disconnect side air crash sensor electrical connector.
14. Remove three mounting screws and side impact air bag crash sensor.
15. Reverse procedure to install, noting the following:
    a. Install side impact air bag crash sensor with arrow visible on outside of housing and facing toward front of vehicle.
    b. Tighten side impact air bag sensor mounting screws to specifications.
    c. Arm air bag system as outlined under "Air Bag System Disarming & Arming."

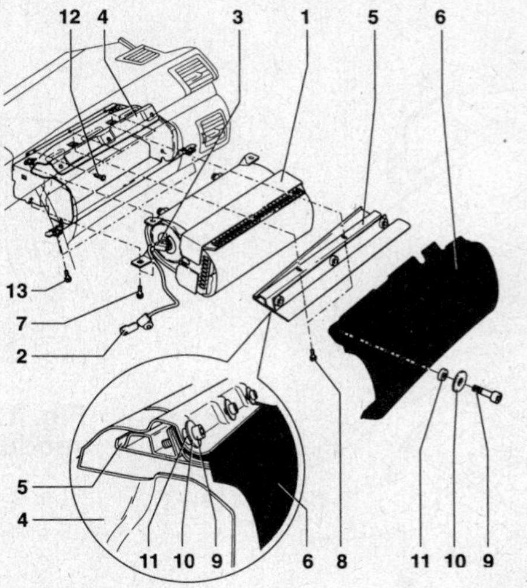

1 Air Bag Module
2 Orange Connector
3 Red Connector [Do Not Disconnect]
4 Bracket
5 Retainer
6 Cover
7 Screw
8 Screw
9 Screw
10 Washer
11 Spacer
12 Screw
13 Screw

AD8019800095000X

Fig. 14 Front passenger's air bag module. A8

A8

A side impact air bag crash sensor is installed under each front seat. The sensors are identical.

1. Disarm air bag system as outlined under "Air Bag System Disarming & Arming."
2. Raise front seat catches and remove cover strips.
3. Move front seat rearward and remove front mounting bolts.
4. Move front seat forward and remove rear mounting bolts.
5. Disconnect front seat electrical connectors.
6. Remove seat belt lower mounting bolt.
7. Remove front seat.
8. Remove inside door sill panel.
9. Remove one side impact crash sensor trim plug and two mounting nuts, **Fig. 27.**
10. Remove air vent trim.
11. Pull floor mat from B-pillar and fold upward.
12. Lift air duct.
13. Disconnect side impact air bag crash sensor electrical connector.
14. Remove mounting screws and side impact air bag crash sensor.
15. Reverse procedure to install, noting the following:
    a. Install side impact air bag crash sensor with arrow on housing facing toward front of vehicle.
    b. Tighten side impact air bag sensor mounting screws to specifications.
    c. Arm air bag system as outlined under "Air Bag System Disarming & Arming."

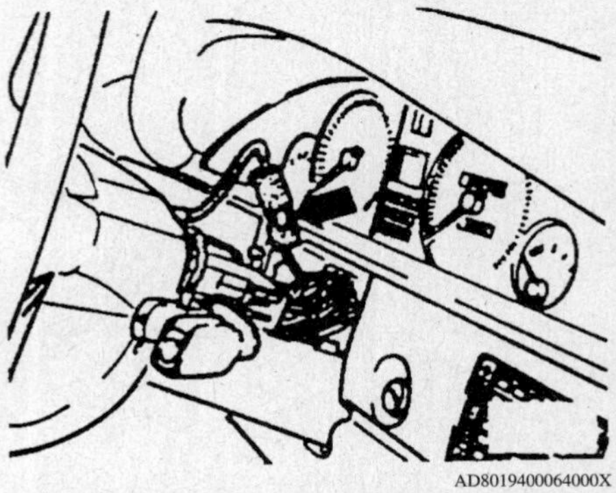

AD8019400064000X

Fig. 15 Spiral spring electrical connector. A4, A8, S4 & Cabriolet

TT

The side impact sensors are located under each of the front seats. The two sensors are identical. Ensure arrow faces outward on installation.

1. Disarm air bag system as outlined under "Air Bag System Disarming & Arming."
2. Push seat forward and remove rear mounting bolts.
3. Push seat back, then remove trim covers and mounting front mounting bolts.
4. Tilt seat back, disconnect connectors and remove seat.
5. Remove two mounting screws and set aside hood lock cable.
6. Remove mounting and disconnect A-pillar trim.
7. Unclip sill panel trim on inside and lift carpeting around sensor.
8. Cut through cable tie and disconnect sensor connector.
9. Reverse procedure to install, noting the following:
   a. Tighten mounting screws to specifications.
   b. Replace cable tie.
   c. Arm air bag system as outlined under "Air Bag System Disarming & Arming."

Side Air Bag Module, Replace

A4 & S4

1. Disarm air bag system as outlined under "Air Bag System Disarming & Arming."
2. Push front seat forward.
3. Remove seat track stopper screw from lefthand seat track.
4. Remove cap nut and fillister head screw or unclip stop spring retaining seat track to bracket. Some models may be equipped with stop spring instead of fillister screw.
5. Pull up seat release lever and push seat out toward rear.
6. Disconnect electrical connectors and remove seat.
7. Remove outer trim and side trim from seat.

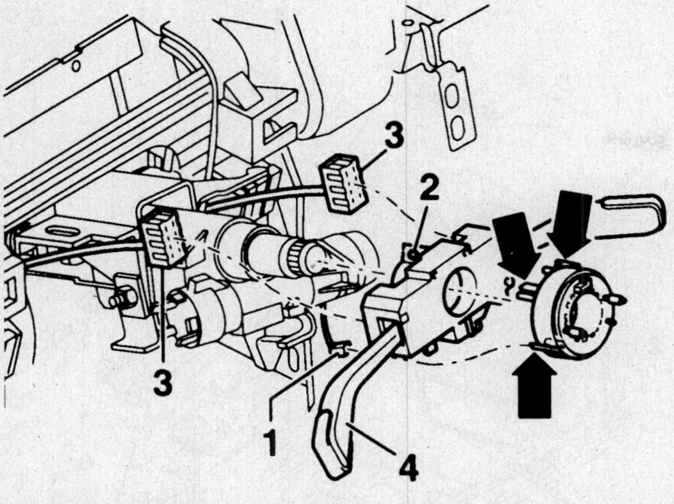

Fig. 16 Spiral spring replacement. A6 & S6

8. Disconnect harness connector, **Fig. 28.**
9. Push ground wire out of harness connector terminal No. 4.
10. Press on lug and unclip side impact air bag connector from connector strip.
11. Disconnect adapter for seat back rest heater.
12. Disconnect side impact air bag wiring from outside of seat.
13. Remove two side impact air bag module mounting screws, **Fig. 29.**
14. Disconnect side impact air bag from retaining hooks.
15. Remove side impact air bag module.
16. Reverse procedure to install:
    a. **Do not cut anti-crush fleece in area of retaining hook.**
    b. Drill out mounting holes to. 217 inch.
    c. Install new screws and nut supplied with replacement air bag module.
    d. Tighten mounting screws and nuts to specifications.
    e. Install new upholstery clips in same locations as original clips.
    f. Use only seat covers for use with side impact air bags.
    g. Arm air bag system as outlined under "Air Bag System Disarming & Arming."

A6 & S6

FRONT

1. Disarm air bag system as outlined under "Air Bag System Disarming & Arming."
2. Remove front seat backrest trim.
3. Disconnect backrest cover around side impact air bag module, **Fig. 30.**
4. Disconnect retainer and side impact air bag module electrical connector.
5. Remove and discard side impact air bag module mounting bolts. Discard mounting bolts.
6. Unclip side impact air bag module at retaining hook. **Do not cut away anti-squeak pad around retaining hooks.**
7. Remove side impact air bag module.
8. Reverse procedure to install, noting the following:
    a. Drill out mounting holes to. 217 inch, as required.
    b. Tighten news side impact air bag module mounting bolts to specifications.
    c. Use only seat covers for use with side impact air bags.
    d. Arm air bag system as outlined under "Air Bag System Disarming & Arming."

REAR w/FIXED BACKREST

1. Disarm air bag system as outlined under "Air Bag System Disarming & Arming."
2. Remove rear seat lower bench.

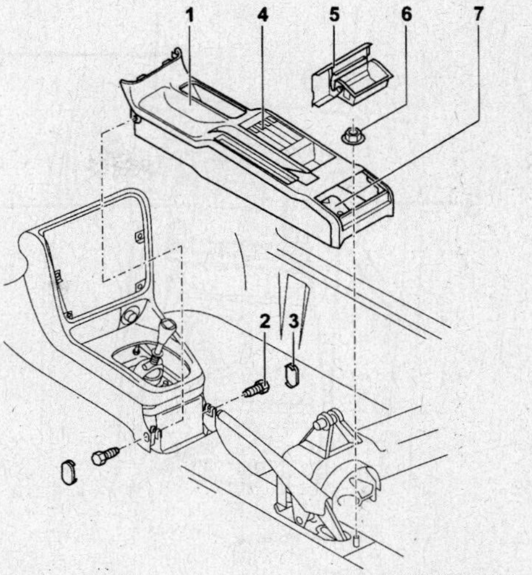

Fig. 17 Rear center console. A4 & S4

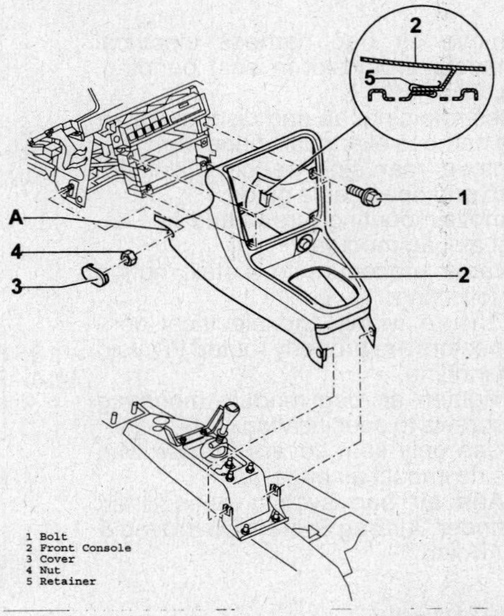

Fig. 18 Front center console. A4 & S4

3. Disconnect air bag module electrical connector, **Fig. 31.**
4. Remove mounting screws and air bag module.
5. Reverse procedure to install, noting the following:
    a. Ensure wiring and electrical connectors are properly routed to avoid pinching.
    b. Tighten air bag module mounting screws to specifications.
    c. Use only seat covers for use with side impact air bags.
    d. Arm air bag system as outlined under "Air Bag System Disarming & Arming."

REAR w/FOLDING BACKREST

1. Disarm air bag system as outlined under "Air Bag System Disarming & Arming."
2. Remove rear seat lower bench.

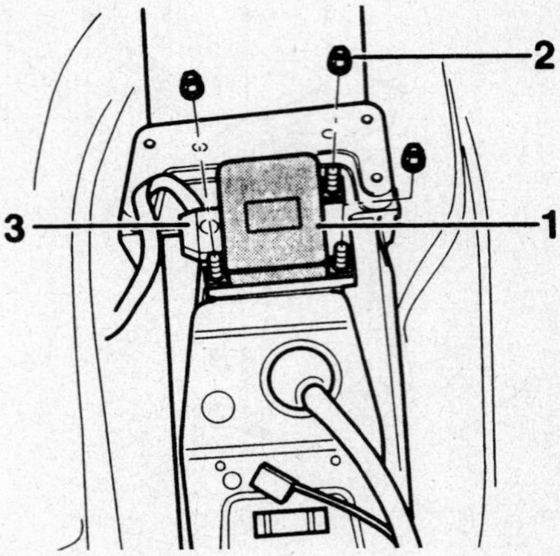

1 Control Module
2 Nut
3 Bracket

AD8019600079000X

Fig. 19 Air bag control module replacement. A4 & S4

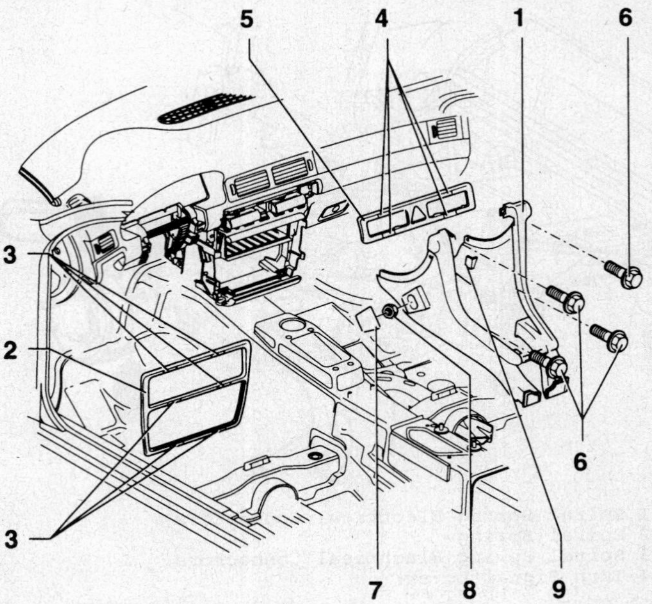

1 Center Console
2 Trim Section
3 Trim Section Fasteners
4 Switch Panel Trim Fasteners
5 Switch Panel Trim
6 Bolts
7 Trim Cap
8 Nut
9 Retainer

AD8019900094000X

Fig. 20 Front section of center console replacement. A6 & S6

3. Remove air bag harness electrical connector from slot in seat padding, **Fig. 32.**
4. Press retaining tab and disconnect air bag harness electrical connector.
5. Remove rear side padding, cut tie-wrap and open cable guide.
6. Remove mounting screws and side impact air bag module.
7. Reverse procedure to install, noting the following:
   a. Ensure wiring and electrical connectors are properly routed to avoid pinching.
   b. Tighten air bag module mounting screws to specifications.
   c. Use only seat covers for use with side impact air bags.
   d. Arm air bag system as outlined under "Air Bag System Disarming & Arming."

A8

FRONT LESS SPORT SEAT

1. Raise front seat catches and remove cover strips.
2. Move front seat rearward and remove front mounting bolts.
3. Move front seat forward and remove rear mounting bolts.
4. Disarm air bag system as outlined under "Air Bag System Disarming & Arming."
5. Disconnect front seat electrical connectors.
6. Remove seat belt lower mounting bolt at seat rail.
7. Remove front seat.
8. Remove front seat backrest cover.
9. Unclip safety catch and disconnect side impact air bag module electrical connector.
10. Remove two mounting screws and disconnect ground wire.
11. Remove two side impact air bag module mounting screws, **Fig. 33.**
12. Press side impact air bag module forward approximately ⅜ inch and separate from hangers.
13. Remove side impact air bag module.
14. Reverse procedure to install, noting the following:
    a. Tighten side impact air bag module mounting bolts to specifications.
    b. Install new upholstery clips must be installed in same locations as original clips.
    c. Use only seat covers for use with side impact air bags.
    d. Arm air bag system as outlined under "Air Bag System Disarming & Arming."

FRONT w/SPORT SEAT

1. Raise front seat catches and remove cover strips.
2. Move front seat rearward and remove front mounting bolts.
3. Move front seat forward and remove rear mounting bolts.
4. Disarm air bag system as outlined under "Air Bag System Disarming & Arming."
5. Disconnect front seat electrical connectors.
6. Remove seat belt lower mounting bolt at seat rail.
7. Remove front seat.
8. Remove side impact air bag wiring harness from clips located underneath lower seat frame.
9. Disconnect side impact air bag wiring terminal connections from harness connector.
10. Remove seat backrest cover.
11. Unclip safety latch and disconnect electrical connector from side impact air bag module.
12. Remove two nuts and disconnect ground cable.
13. Remove screw, press side impact air bag module forward approximately ⅜ inch and disconnect from hangers, **Fig. 34.**
14. Remove side impact air bag module.
15. Reverse procedure to install, noting the following:
    a. Apply locking compound part No. D 000 600 A2, or equivalent, to ground cable nuts.
    b. Tighten side impact air bag module mounting bolts to specifications.
    c. New upholstery clips must be installed in same locations as original clips.
    d. Use only seat covers for use with side impact air bags.
    e. Arm air bag system as outlined under "Air Bag System Disarming & Arming."

REAR w/SPLIT SEAT

1. Disarm air bag system as outlined under "Air Bag System Disarming & Arming."
2. Move rear seat as far forward as possible.
3. Remove center armrest padding.
4. Disconnect electrical connectors.
5. Disconnect wiring harness from wiring straps.
6. Remove armrest support screw, slide armrest support toward rear bulkhead and unclip from bracket.

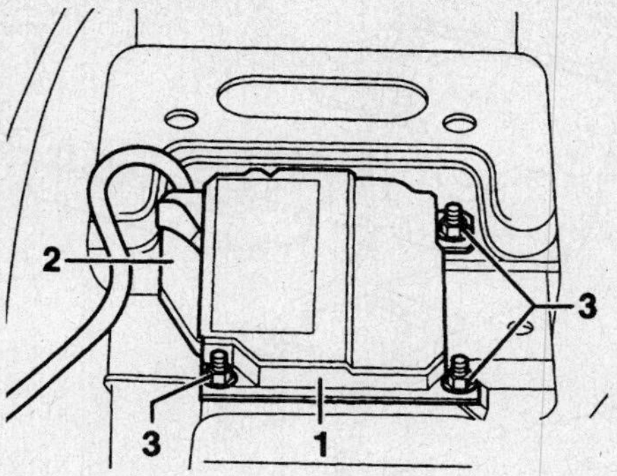

1 Control Module
2 Electrical Connector
3 Nuts

AD8019800099000X

Fig. 21 Air bag control module replacement. A6 & S6

7. Remove mounting bolt and rear seat belt.
8. Remove two seat adjuster mounting nuts.
9. Lift seat cushion so frame studs clear adjuster.
10. Slide seat cushion toward rear bulkhead and back rest upward at same time.
11. Slide seat enough to disengage seat cushion hooks from back rest hooks.
12. Remove upholstery clips in area of side impact air bag module using suitable screwdriver.
13. Remove safety clip.
14. Disconnect side impact air bag electrical connector.
15. Pull seat cover to clear side impact air bag mounting nuts.
16. Remove mounting nuts and disconnect ground wire.
17. Remove side impact air bag by pushing it approximately 3/8 inch toward padding and pulling out from top.
18. Reverse procedure to install, noting the following:
    a. Tighten side impact air bag module mounting bolts to specifications.
    b. Install new upholstery clips must be installed in same locations as original clips.
    c. Use only seat covers for use with side impact air bags.
    d. Arm air bag system as outlined under "Air Bag System Disarming & Arming."

REAR w/BENCH SEAT

1. Disarm air bag system as outlined under "Air Bag System Disarming & Arming."
2. Remove two rear seat bench mounting bolts.
3. Lift seat bench upward and disconnect electrical connectors.
4. Remove rear seat bench.
5. Rear two rear seat backrest mounting bolts.
6. Lift rear seat backrest up and out of mounting bracket.
7. Disconnect electrical connectors and remove rear seat backrest.
8. Remove upholstery hooks in area of side impact air bag module using suitable screwdriver.
9. Remove safety clip.
10. Disconnect side impact air bag electrical connector.
11. Pull seat cover to clear side impact air bag mounting nuts.
12. Remove mounting nuts and disconnect ground wire.
13. Remove side impact air bag by pushing it approximately 3/8 inch toward padding and pulling out from top.
14. Reverse procedure to install, noting the following:
    a. Tighten side impact air bag module mounting bolts to specifications.
    b. Install new upholstery clips must be installed in same locations as original clips.
    c. Use only seat covers for use with side impact air bags.
    d. Arm air bag system as outlined under "Air Bag System Disarming & Arming."

TT

1. Disarm air bag system as outlined under "Air Bag System Disarming & Arming."
2. Remove seat as outlined under "Side Impact Air Bag Crash Sensor, Replace."
3. Remove height adjustment lever by pressing retainer tab using screwdriver and at same time pulling off handle.
4. Disconnect air bag connector from connector rail.
5. Disconnect backrest heater and seat belt lock connectors.
6. Remove cable ties and cut through cables in seat bottom.
7. Release control cable from clip, then unhook cable at retaining spring.
8. Disconnect seat bottom brackets
9. Pull seat side trim in height adjustment lever area slightly outward and flip front of seat upward.
10. Remove two spring trim mounting screws and pry out clips using suitable screwdriver.
11. Pull off spring trim approximately. 787 inch and remove spring trim toward rear.
12. Cut through cable ties and hook seat cover from securing rail at rear.
13. Pull off adjuster knob and pull out release handle.
14. Push expanding rivet through and remove trim piece.
15. Unhook backrest fabric from securing channel over for approximately 7.87 inches.
16. Bend open tab and disconnect fabric.
17. Disconnect backrest fabric at side impact air bag module for approximately 3.93 inches.
18. Disconnect air bag wiring from clips.
19. Loosen bottom of side air bag module mounting screw.
20. Press side impact air bag module downward and pull it outward.
21. Reverse procedure to install, noting the following:
    a. Position side impact air bag module so locking pins engage holes.
    b. Tighten new air bag module mounting screws to specifications.
    c. Arm air bag system as outlined under "Air Bag System Disarming & Arming."

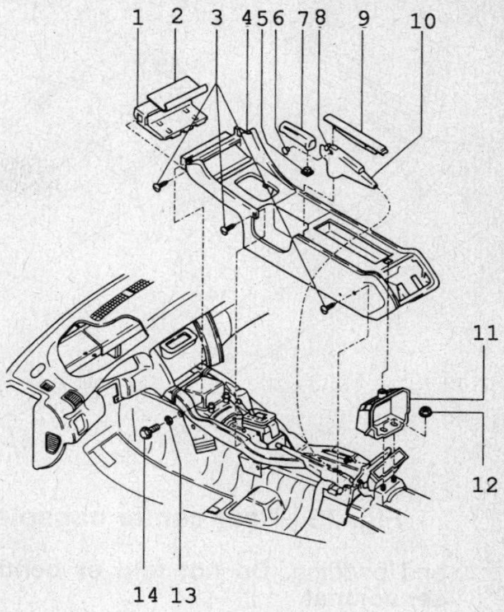

1 Ashtray
2 Trim
3 Screw
4 Center Console
5 Clip
6 Cover
7 Grip
8 Screw
9 Trim Strip
10 Parking Brake Lever Trim
11 Armrest Support
12 Nut
13 Washer
14 Bolt

AD8019800096000X

Fig. 22 Center console replacement. A8

Seat Occupant Sensor Mat

A4 & S4

The seat occupant sensor mat is available only in conjunction with the seat heater and seat cushion.

A8

FRONT

1. Disarm air bag system as outlined under "Air Bag System Disarming & Arming."
2. Raise front seat catches and remove cover strips.
3. Move front seat rearward and remove front mounting bolts.
4. Move front seat forward and remove rear mounting bolts.
5. Disconnect front seat electrical connectors.
6. Remove seat belt lower mounting bolt at seat rail.
7. Remove front seat.
8. Remove bottom seat cover.
9. Remove cable straps, then disconnect sensor mat and seat heater electrical connectors.
10. Remove sensor mat, heating element

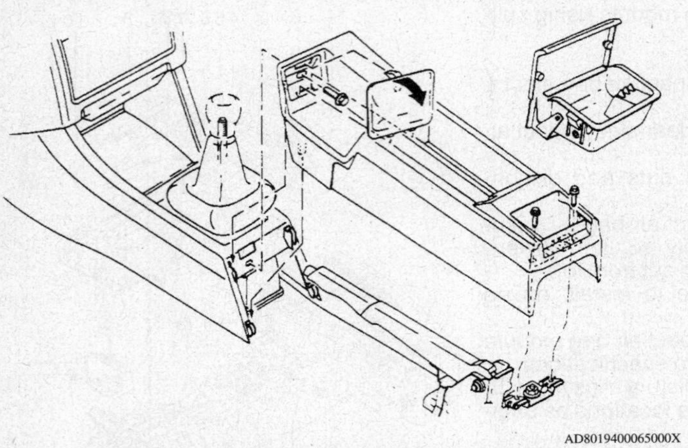

Fig. 23 Rear center console. Cabriolet

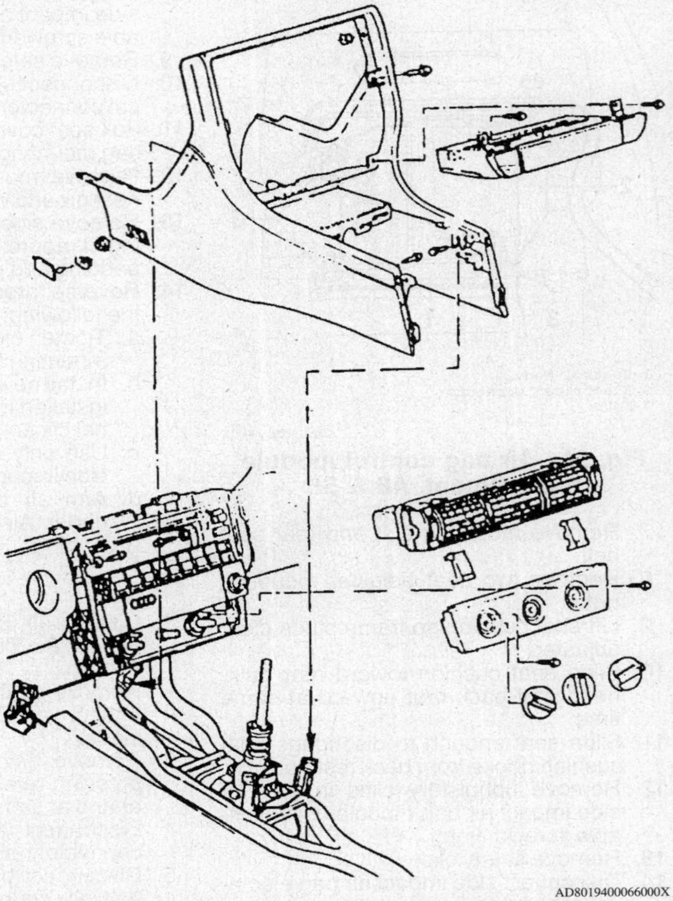

Fig. 24 Front center console. Cabriolet

and padding. **Do not fold or bend sensor mat.**

11. Reverse procedure to install. Arm air bag system as outlined under "Air Bag System Disarming & Arming."

REAR w/SPLIT SEAT

1. Disarm air bag system as outlined under "Air Bag System Disarming & Arming."
2. Move rear seat as far forward as possible.
3. Remove center armrest padding.
4. Disconnect electrical connectors.
5. Disconnect wiring harness from wiring straps.
6. Remove armrest support screw, slide armrest support toward rear bulkhead and unclip from bracket.
7. Remove mounting bolt and rear seat belt.
8. Remove two seat adjuster mounting nuts.
9. Lift seat cushion so seat frame studs clear seat adjuster.
10. Slide seat cushion toward rear bulkhead and back rest upward at same time.
11. Slide seat enough to disengage seat cushion hooks from back rest hooks.
12. Disconnect sensor mat and seat heater electrical connectors.
13. Remove sensor mat, heating element and padding. **Do not fold or bend sensor mat.**
14. Reverse procedure to install. Arm air bag system as outlined under "Air Bag System Disarming & Arming."

REAR w/BENCH SEAT

1. Disarm air bag system as outlined under "Air Bag System Disarming & Arming."
2. Remove two rear seat bench mounting bolts.
3. Lift seat bench upward and disconnect electrical connectors.
4. Remove rear seat bench.
5. Remove lower seat cover.
6. Remove cable straps securing wiring harness.
7. Remove lower seat cover to access sensor mat, **Fig. 35.**
8. Cut sensor mat from padded areas and remove wiring harness from opening. **Do not fold or bend sensor mat.**
9. Reverse procedure to install, noting the following:
   a. Glue mat at arrows, **Fig. 35.**
   b. Arm air bag system as outlined under "Air Bag System Disarming & Arming."

Pyrotechnical Seat Belt Tensioner, Replace

A4 & S4

1. Disarm air bag system as outlined under "Air Bag System Disarming & Arming."
2. Remove upper and lower B-pillar trim panel, **Fig. 36.**
3. Remove trim from inner door sill.
4. Disconnect red connector at belt tensioner.
5. Remove belt guide to B-pillar mounting screws.
6. Remove seat belt tensioner and belt end to B-pillar mounting screws.
7. Remove upper portion of shoulder belt to height adjuster on B-pillar mounting nut.
8. Guide belt out of upper B-pillar trim.
9. Reverse procedure to install, noting the following:
   a. Ensure belt tensioner anti-twist stop engages B-pillar.
   b. Install belt webbing turned 180°, **Fig. 36.**
   c. Ensure lower belt webbing is properly installed to metal stud.
   d. Arm air bag system as outlined under "Air Bag System Disarming & Arming."

A6 & S6

FRONT

1. Disarm air bag system as outlined under "Air Bag System Disarming & Arming."
2. Remove sill panel trim, **Fig. 37.**
3. Remove seat belt to sill mounting bolt.
4. Remove upper B-pillar cover.
5. Remove mounting screws and lower B-pillar cover.
6. Remove seat belt to height adjuster mounting nut.
7. Disconnect seat belt retractor electrical connector.
8. Remove seat belt retractor to B-pillar mounting bolt.
9. Remove seat belt.
10. Reverse procedure to install, noting the following:
    a. Ensure retaining tab is properly inserted.
    b. Tighten mounting bolts and nuts to specifications.
    c. Ensure seat belt is not obstructed

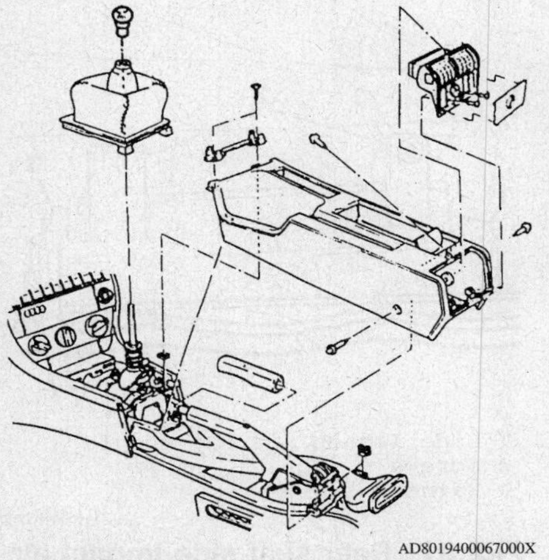

AD8019400067000X

Fig. 25 Air bag control module nut locations. Cabriolet

by wires and cables.

d. Arm air bag system as outlined under "Air Bag System Disarming & Arming."

REAR

1. Disarm air bag system as outlined under "Air Bag System Disarming & Arming."
2. Remove rear seat lower bench.
3. Remove seat belt lower mounting bolt, **Fig. 38.**
4. Remove belt guide trim.
5. Pry out belt adjuster trim at lug.
6. Remove rear shelf panel.
7. Disconnect seat belt tensioner electrical connector.
8. **On models equipped with CD player or sub-woofer,** remove luggage compartment trim as required.
9. **On all models,** remove seat belt tensioner lower bolt.
10. Remove pyrotechnical seat belt tensioner.
11. Reverse procedure to install, noting the following:
    a. Ensure wiring and electrical connectors are properly routed to avoid pinching.
    b. Tighten mounting bolts and nuts to specifications.
    c. Arm air bag system as outlined under "Air Bag System Disarming & Arming."
    d. Inspect belt fastened sensor as outlined under "Seat Belt Fastened Sensor Operation Inspection."

A8

1. Disarm air bag system as outlined under "Air Bag System Disarming & Arming."
2. Remove upper and lower B-pillar trim panels.
3. Open locking bar, **Fig. 39.**
4. Disconnect seat belt tensioner electrical connector.
5. Remove mounting bolts and seat belt tensioner.
6. Reverse procedure to install noting the following:
    a. Tensioner cable must be installed so there is approximately two inches running in parallel to seat belt runout.
    b. Arm air bag system as outlined under "Air Bag System Disarming & Arming."

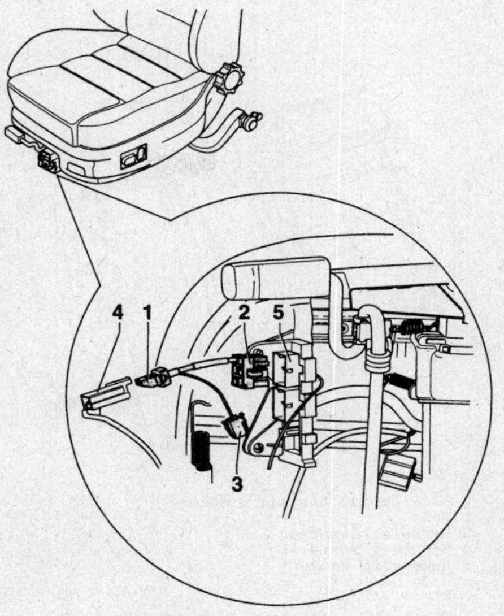

1 Air Bag Adapter Harness
2 Air Bag Adapter Harness Tool No. VAS 5061
3 Connector
4 Air Bag Ignition Wire
5 Connector

AD8019800100000X

Fig. 26 Side impact air bag adapter harness connections. A6

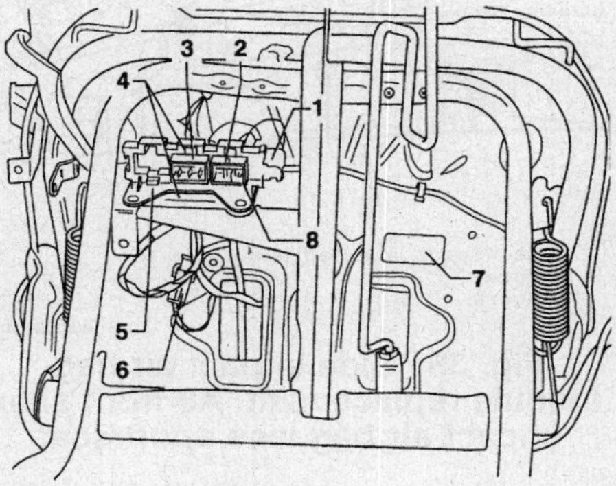

1 Side Air Bag Connector
2 Sensor Mat Harness Connector
3 Seat Heater Connector
4 Lugs
5 Connector Strip
6 Adapter Seat Backrest Heater
7 Air Bag Label
8 Bar In Connector

AD8019800108000X

Fig. 28 Side impact air bag module wiring harness & connectors. A4 & S4

TT

1. Disarm air bag system as outlined under "Air Bag System Disarming & Arming."
2. Remove rear seat bench by lifting rear seat and pulling forward.
3. Remove two center mounting screws and center seat belt buckles.
4. Remove side seat belt end fitting, then slide seat toward rear at side and center mounts.

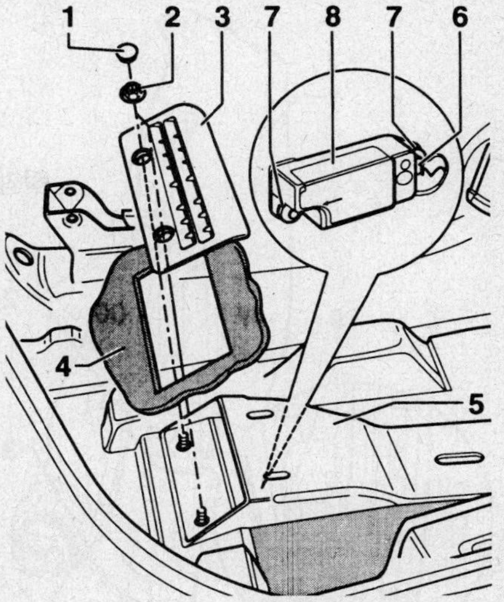

1 Trim Plug
2 Nuts
3 Plate
4 Floor Mat
5 Air Duct
6 Side Impact Air Bag Crash Sensor Electrical Connector
7 Mounting Screws
8 Side Impact Air Bag Crash Sensor

AD8019800101000X

Fig. 27 Side impact air bag crash sensor replacement. A8

5. Guide seat out through widened opening at slot.
6. Open flap and remove cover over outer floor panel anchorage point.
7. Remove outer floor panel anchorage mounting bolt and plate.
8. Remove striker pin on rear backrest, then disconnect and remove side trim.
9. Disconnect belt tensioner connector.
10. Remove mounting screw and belt tensioner with locating piece.
11. Reverse procedure to install noting the following:
    a. Tighten mounting bolts and nuts to specifications.
    b. Arm air bag system as outlined under "Air Bag System Disarming & Arming."

Air Bag & Pyrotechnical Seat Belt Tensioner Disposal

When handling a deployed air bag assembly or Pyrotechnic seat belt tensioner, a face shield and rubber gloves should be worn. Vehicle interior and A/C, vent, defroster and heater ducts should be vacuumed. If sinus or throat irritation is encountered during air bag removal, exit vehicle and breathe fresh air. If skin irritation is encountered, flush effected area with cool water. If sinus, throat, skin or any other type of irritation continues, consult a physician. After handling a deployed air bag assembly or pyrotechnic seat belt tensioner, wash hands and rinse thoroughly with water.

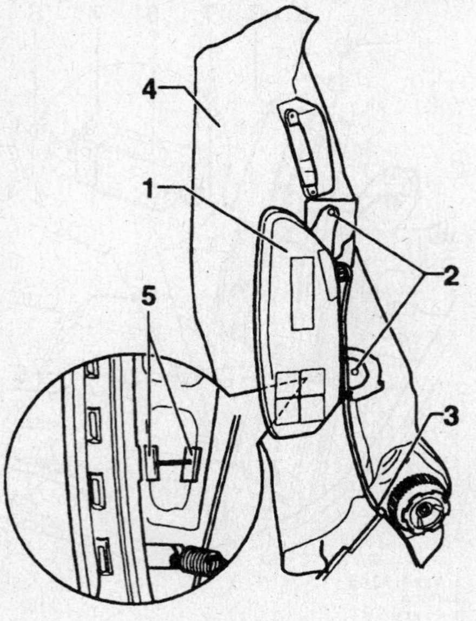

1 Side Air Bag Module
2 Screws
3 Harness
4 Seatback
5 Retaining Hooks

AD8019800109000X

Fig. 29 Side impact air bag module replacement. A4 & S4

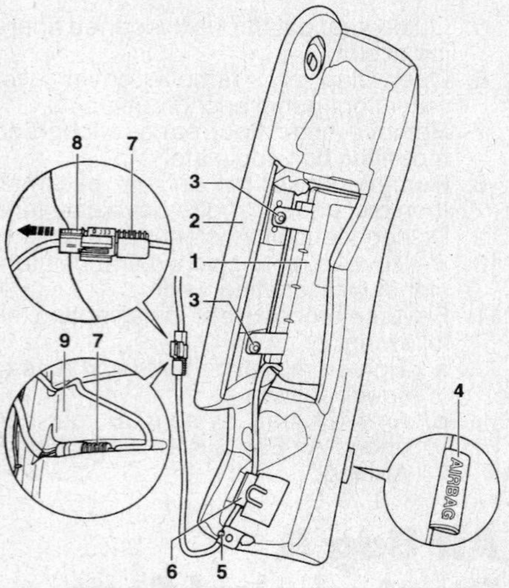

1. Side air bag unit
2. Padding
3. Screws
4. Label
5. Tie-wrap
6. Cable guide
7. Electrical connector
8. Retaining tab

AD8019900095000X

Fig. 32 Rear seat side impact air bag replacement. A6 & S6 w/ folding backrest

A unit that has been deployed should be removed as outlined under "Driver Side Air Bag Assembly, Replace," "Passenger Side Air Bag Assembly, Replace" or "Pyrotechnic Seat Belt Tensioner, Replace." Prior to removing a deployed air bag assembly, place tape over air bag exhaust vents. After unit has been removed, it should be placed

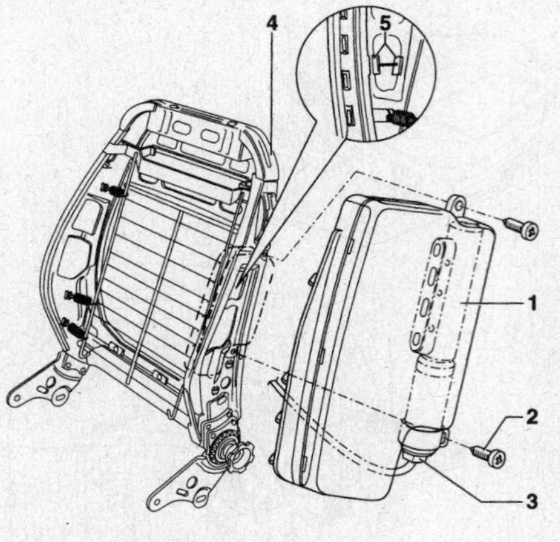

1 Side Impact Air Bag module
2 Bolt
3 Harness Connector
4 Backrest Frame
5 Retaining Hooks

AD8019800102000X

Fig. 30 Side impact air bag module replacement. A6 & S6

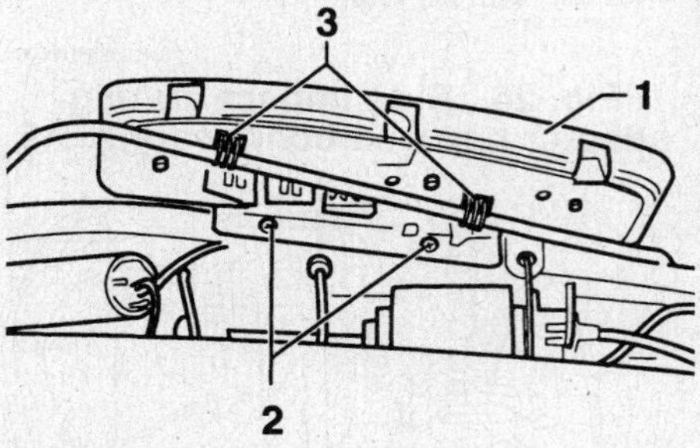

1 Side Impact Air Bag Module
2 Screws
3 Hangers

AD8019800103000X

Fig. 33 Side impact air bag module replacement. A8 front side impact air bag less sport seat

in a heavy duty plastic bag and sealed securely. The sealed plastic bag should then be placed with automotive scrap. To dispose of a unit that has not been deployed, consult Audi.

DEPLOYING PYROTECHNICAL FRONT SEAT BELT TENSIONERS

A6 & S6

Pyrotechnical seat belt tensioners must be deployed prior to disposal.

1. Disarm air bag system as outlined under "Air Bag System Disarming & Arming."
2. Remove upper and lower B-pillar trim covers.
3. Remove bolt for outer seat belt attachment.
4. Cut seat belt webbing above latch plate, approximately eight inches above belt reel.
5. Disconnect electrical connector from belt reel.
6. Connect wiring harness 8D1 971 259, or equivalent, to seat belt tensioner.

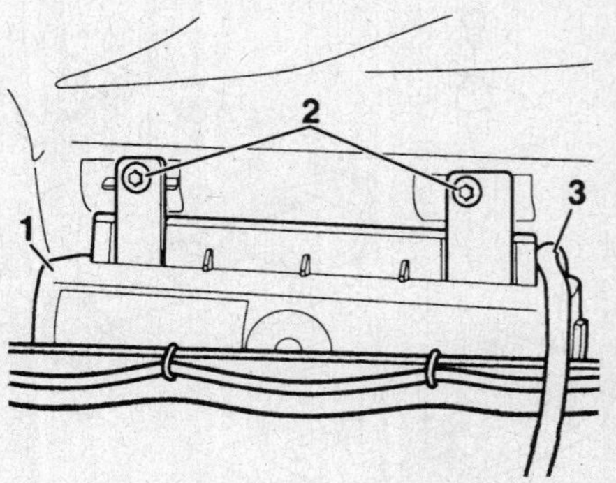

1 Side Impact Air Bag Module
2 Screws
3 Harness

AD8019900096000X

Fig. 31 Rear seat side impact air bag replacement. A6 & S6 w/fixed backrest

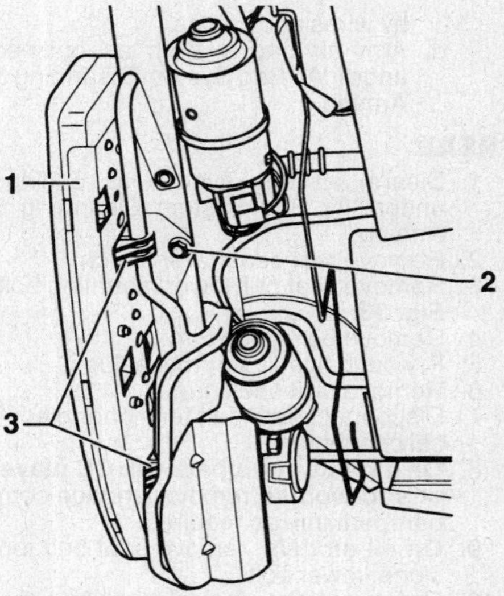

1 Side air bag module
2 Screws
3 Hangers

AD8019800104000X

Fig. 34 Side impact air bag module replacement. A8 front side impact air bag w/sport seat

Cut harness connector off other, then strip end of both wires and slit cable sheath. Ends of wire must be at least 12 inches apart.

7. Open windows and close vehicle doors.
8. Extend wiring harness 8D1 971 259, or equivalent, outside vehicle to its full extent.
9. Locate a fully charged battery outside vehicle near the extended wiring harness.
10. Ensure no one is inside or in area of vehicle.
11. Contact wiring harness stripped ends to battery posts to deploy the seat belt tensioner. If tensioner fails to deploy, contact Audi.
12. Allow seat belt tensioner to cool for at least 30 minutes.

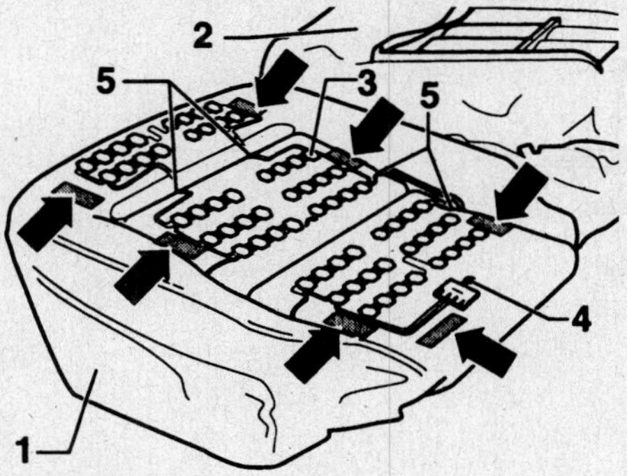

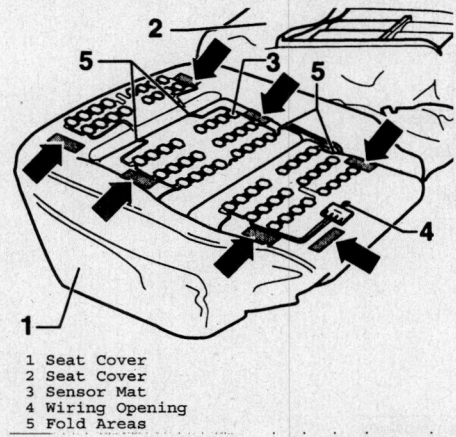

1 Seat Cover
2 Seat Cover
3 Sensor Mat
4 Wiring Opening
5 Fold Areas

AD8019800105000X

Fig. 35 Sensor mat replacement. A8 rear with bench seat

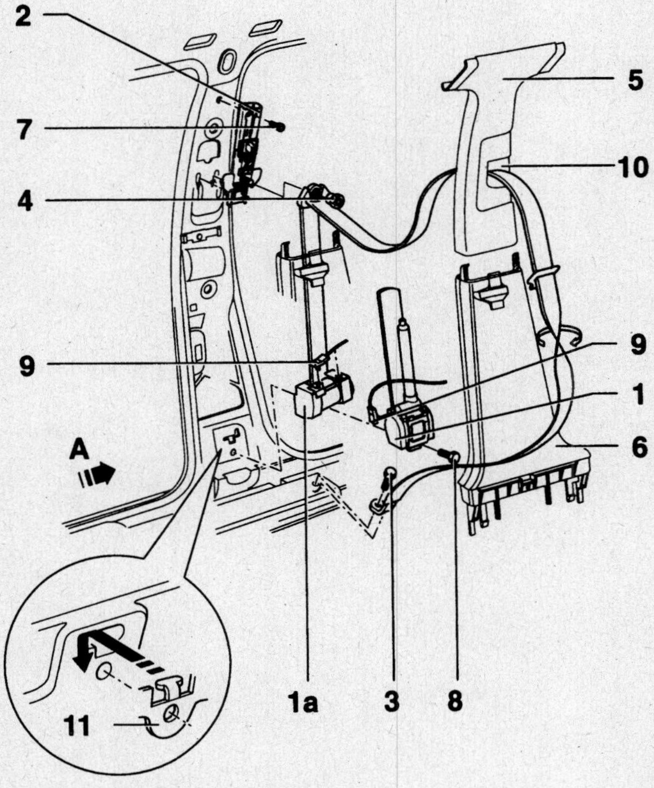

1 Seat Belt Tensioner
1a Seat Belt Tensioner
2 Belt Height Adjuster
3 Bolt
4 Nut
5 Upper B-Pillar Trim
6 Lower B-Pillar Trim
7 Bolt
8 Bolt
9 Harness Connector
10 Height Adjuster
11 Bracket

AD8019800106000X

Fig. 37 Pyrotechnic seat belt tensioner replacement. A6 & S6

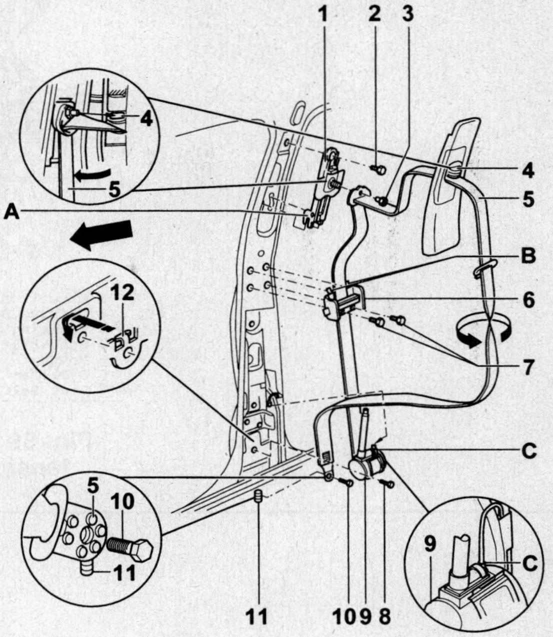

1 Height Adjuster
2 Bolt
3 Nut
4 Height Adjuster Pushbutton
5 Seat Belt
6 Belt Guide
7 Bolt
8 Bolt
9 Belt Tensioner
10 Bolt
11 Metal Stud
12 Anti-Twist Stop

AD8019600080000X

Fig. 36 Pyrotechnical seat belt tensioner replacement. A4 & S4

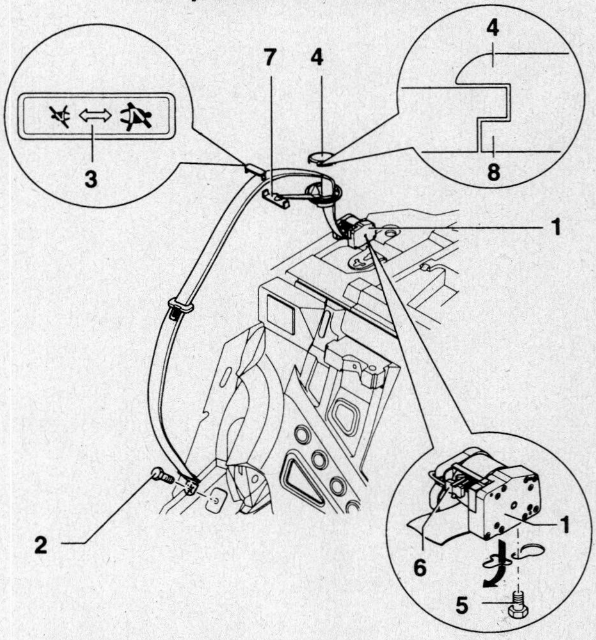

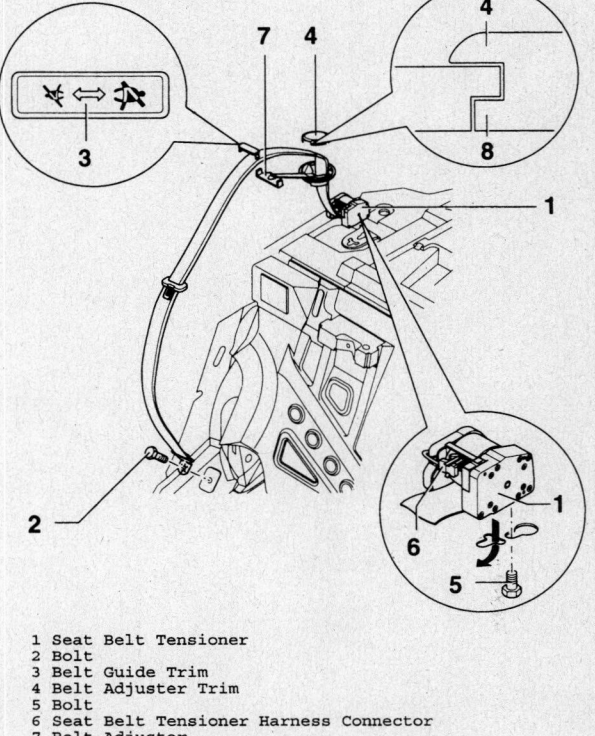

1 Seat Belt Tensioner
2 Bolt
3 Belt Guide Trim
4 Belt Adjuster Trim
5 Bolt
6 Seat Belt Tensioner Harness Connector
7 Belt Adjuster
8 Lug

AD8019900097000X

Fig. 38 Rear pyrotechnical seat belt tensioner replacement. A6 & S6

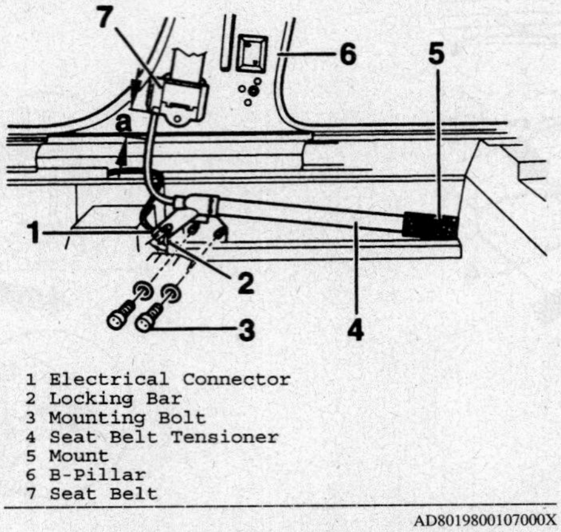

Fig. 39 Pyrotechnic seat belt tensioner replacement. A8

TIGHTENING SPECIFICATIONS

Year	Component	Torque/Ft. Lbs.
A4 & S4		
1998–2001	Air Bag Control Module	53①
	Air Bag Module, Driver's	62①
	Air Bag Module, Side Impact	48①
	Pyrotechnical Seat Belt Retractor	37
	Seat Belt End Tab To Floor Panel	37
	Seat Belt To Height Adjuster	37
	Side Impact Air Bag Sensor	53①
A6 & S6		
1998–2001	Air Bag Control Module	53①
	Air Bag Module, Driver's (w/Sport Steering Wheel)	62①
	Air Bag Module, Front Side Impact	49①
	Air Bag Module, Passenger's	80①
	Air Bag Module, Rear Seat Side Impact	71①
	Front Seat Front Mount	17
	Seat Belt Pretensioner	37
	Seat Belt To B-Pillar	37
	Seat Belt To Floor	37
	Side Impact Air Bag Crash Sensor	53①
	Steering Wheel Socket Head Bolt	44
A8		
1998–2001	Air Bag Control Module Nuts	53①
	Front Side Air Bag Module Screws (Less Sport Seat)	31①
	Front Side Air Bag Module Screws (With Sport Seat)	53①
	Passenger's Front Air Bag Module Mounting Screws	53①
	Rear Side Air Bag Module Screws	44①
	Seat Belt Pretensioner Bolts	44①
	Side Air Crash Sensor Screws	40①
CABRIOLET		
1998	Air Bag Control Module Nuts	53①
	Driver's Air Bag Module To Steering Wheel Bolts	53①
	Passenger's Air Bag Mounting Bolts	17
TT		
2000–01	Air Bag Control Module	53①
	Air Bag Module, Driver's	66①
	Air Bag Module, Passenger's	80①
	Air Bag Module, Side Impact	62①
	Air Bag Module, Side Impact Sensor	53①
	Anchorage Point, Outer	37
	B-Pillar Brace	30
	Hood Lock Cable	35①
	Lower Trim Panel, A-Pillar	13①
	Seat, Front	22
	Seat Bracket, Rear	14
	Seat Belt	41
	Seat Belt Tensioner	41
	Steering Wheel	44
	Steering Column Grip	25①
	Steering Column Switch Trim	5①

① — Inch Lbs.

Dash Panel Service

NOTE: On Air Bag Equipped Models, Refer To "Air Bag System Precautions" Located In The Front Of This Manual For System Disarming & Arming Procedures.

NOTE: Refer To "Computer Relearn Procedures" Located In The Front Of This Manual When Battery Power To The Computer Has Been Interrupted.

INDEX

	Page No.
Dash Panel, Replace	1-146
A4 & S4	1-146
A6 & S6	1-146
A8	1-147
Cabriolet	1-147
TT	1-148
Precautions	1-146
Air Bag Systems	1-146
Battery Ground Cable	1-146
Radio Coded Anti-Theft System	1-146

PRECAUTIONS

AIR BAG SYSTEMS

Refer to "Air Bag System Precautions" in the front of this manual for system disarming and arming procedures.

RADIO CODED ANTI-THEFT SYSTEM

Prior to disconnecting the battery or removing the audio system, obtain the security code from the vehicle operator. Refer to the owner's manual for security code disarming and arming procedures.

BATTERY GROUND CABLE

Prior to service, disconnect battery ground cable and isolate as required.

DASH PANEL

REPLACE

A4 & S4

1. Obtain radio theft protection code as outlined under "Precautions."
2. Remove driver side storage compartment, then the glove compartment.
3. Remove parking brake lever trim.
4. Unclip cover and remove rear center console to front center console mounting bolts.
5. Remove ash tray, then the rear center console rear mounting nut.
6. Remove rear center console, then disconnect diagnostic cable.
7. Remove dash panel center trim, then the radio and HVAC control knobs.
8. Unclip cover, then remove center front console to dash panel mounting nuts and bolts.
9. Unclip and remove center front console.
10. Remove center section of dash panel.
11. Remove steering wheel with air bag as outlined under "Steering Wheel, Replace" in the "Electrical" section.
12. Remove passenger side air bag as outlined under "Component Service" of the "Air Bag System" section.
13. Remove dash panel mounting bolts, then the dash panel, **Fig. 1.**
14. Reverse procedure to install. **Torque** instrument panel mounting bolts to 44 inch lbs.

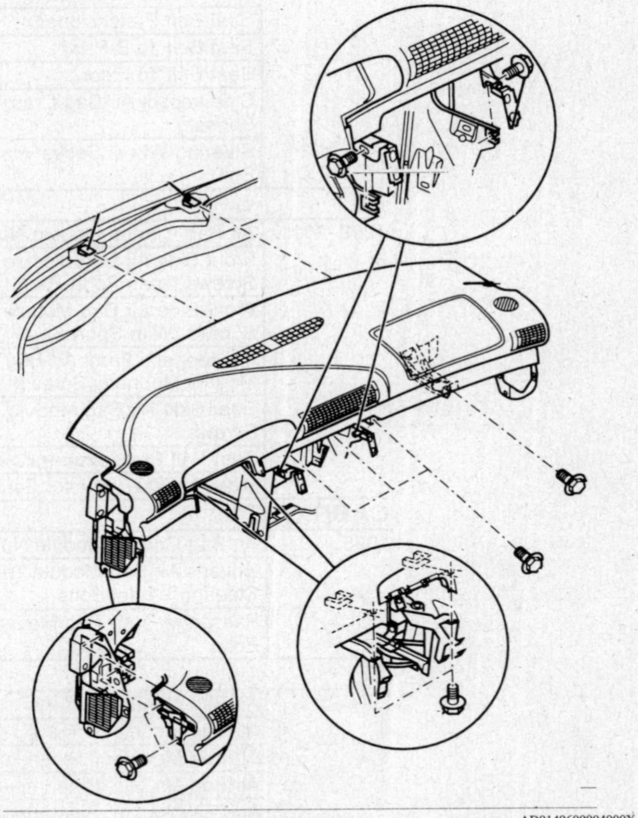

Fig. 1 Dash panel removal. A4 & S4

A6 & S6

1. Remove driver's side air bag module.
2. Remove steering wheel.
3. Pull steering column out and down as far as it will go using steering column adjusters.
4. Remove instrument cluster, **Fig. 2.**
5. Remove driver's side storage compartment.
6. Remove glove compartment.
7. Remove center console as outlined under "Floor Console."
8. Remove center section of instrument panel.
9. Remove steering column adjuster

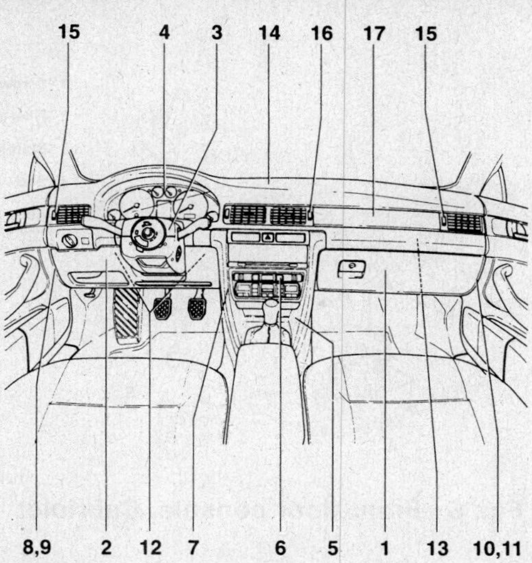

1. Glove Box
2. Driver's Side Storage Compartment
3. Steering Column Switch
4. Instrument Cluster
5. Front Section Of Center Console
6. Center Section Of Instrument Panel
7. Reinforcing Bracket For Center Section
8. Instrument Panel End Trim (Left)
9. Instrument Panel End Mounting Screws (Left)
10. Instrument Panel End Trim (Right)
11. Instrument Panel End Mounting Screws (Right)
12. Instrument Panel Mounting Screws (Driver Side)
13. Passenger Side Airbag
14. Photosensor
15. Harness Connectors For Side Vent Lighting & Temp. Sensor
16. Harness connector For Center Vent Lighting
17. Trim Strip For Instrument Panel

AD9149900011000X

Fig. 2 Instrument panel component locations. A6 & S6

handle screws and handle.

10. Remove upper and lower steering column cover attaching screws and covers.
11. Disconnect electrical connectors from steering column switch.
12. Remove steering column switch screw and switch from column.
13. Remove five instrument panel center reinforcing bracket attaching bolts and bracket.
14. Remove lefthand and righthand side instrument panel end trim using suitable screwdriver to unclip from instrument panel.
15. Remove lefthand and righthand side instrument panel end mounting bolts.
16. Remove instrument panel mounting screws from lefthand and righthand side of steering column opening.
17. Disconnect and remove passenger side air bag module.
18. Remove photosensor and secure harness connector with cord or cable tie.
19. Disconnect photosensor electrical connector.
20. Disconnect lefthand and righthand side vent lighting electrical connectors.
21. Disconnect lefthand and righthand side temperature sensor electrical connectors.
22. Disconnect harness connector for center vent lighting.
23. Pull instrument panel rearward and remove.
24. Reverse procedure to install. **Torque** instrument panel mounting bolts to 35 inch lbs.

A8

1. Move seats to rearmost position with seatbacks down.
2. Turn ignition On, then position flaps for windshield air outlets in instrument panel to closed position
3. **On models equipped with A/C,** press "Def" button and turn ignition Off.
4. **On all models,** remove driver's side storage compartment, **Fig. 3.**
5. Remove glove box.
6. Remove both inside door sill plates.
7. Remove center console and mount for center air outlet.
8. Remove steering column cover.
9. Remove steering wheel and steering column switch.
10. Remove instrument cluster.
11. Remove driver's side air duct.
12. Disconnect harness connectors at ABS control module and at connector strip.

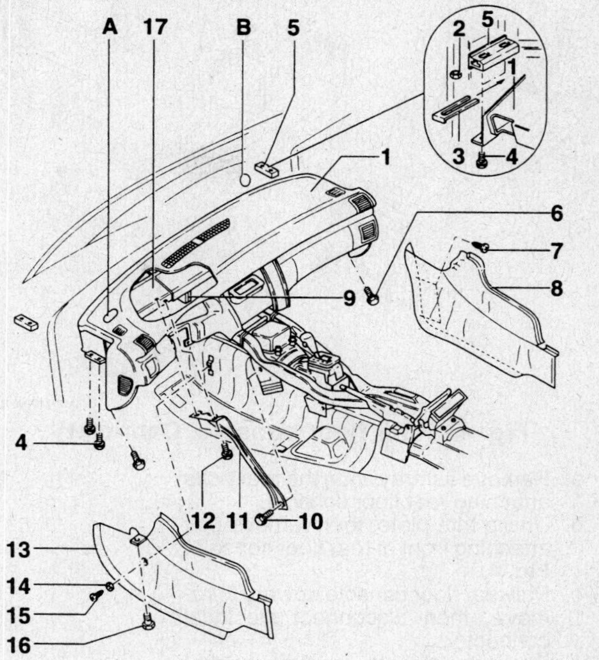

1. Instrument Panel
2. Nut
3. Spacer Piece
4. Bolt
5. Bracket For Instrument Panel
6. Bolt
7. Screws
8. Righthand Side Trim For Center Console
9. Air Guide Duct
10. Bolt
11. Supporting Bracket
12. Bolts
13. Lefthand Side Trim For Center Console
14. Washer
15. Screw
16. Bolt
17. Instrument Panel Carrier

AD9149900012000X

Fig. 3 Dash panel component locations. A8

13. Disconnect harness connector (position A) at righthand side A-pillar.
14. Disconnect harness connector (position B) at righthand side A-pillar.
15. Remove supporting bracket.
16. Pull both air guide ducts in instrument panel carrier off air conditioner.
17. Disconnect harness connector for headlamp range control.
18. Unbolt casing tube from instrument panel carrier.
19. Remove lefthand and righthand side instrument panel end mounting bolts.
20. Pull instrument panel rearward and remove.
21. Reverse procedure to install, noting the following:
    a. **Torque** instrument panel support bolts to 16 ft. lbs.
    b. **Torque** instrument panel mounting bolts to 23 ft. lbs.

CABRIOLET

1. Obtain radio theft protection code as outlined under "Precautions."
2. Remove floor console as follows:

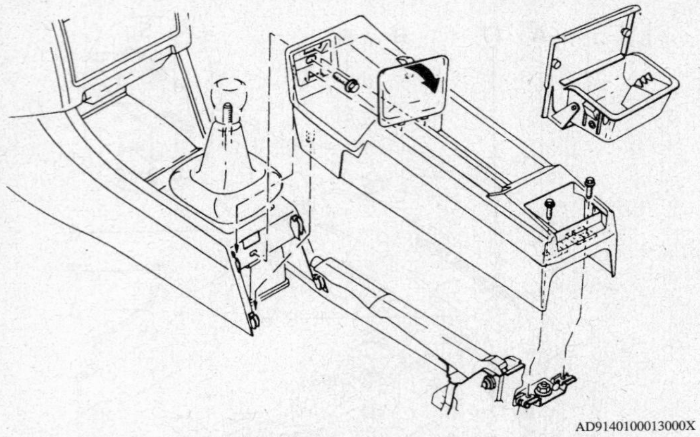

Fig. 4 Rear floor console. Cabriolet

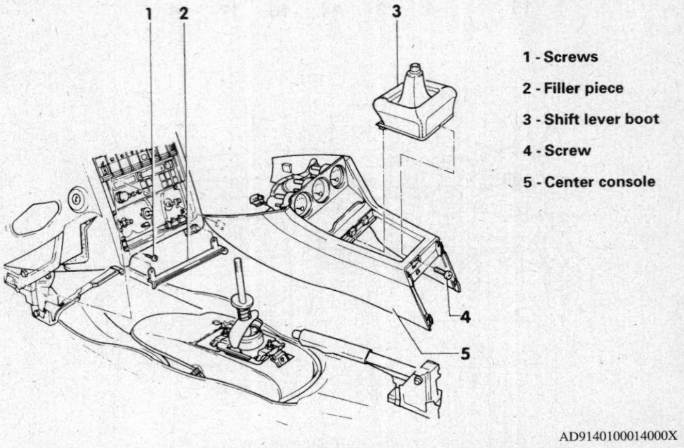

Fig. 5 Front floor console. Cabriolet

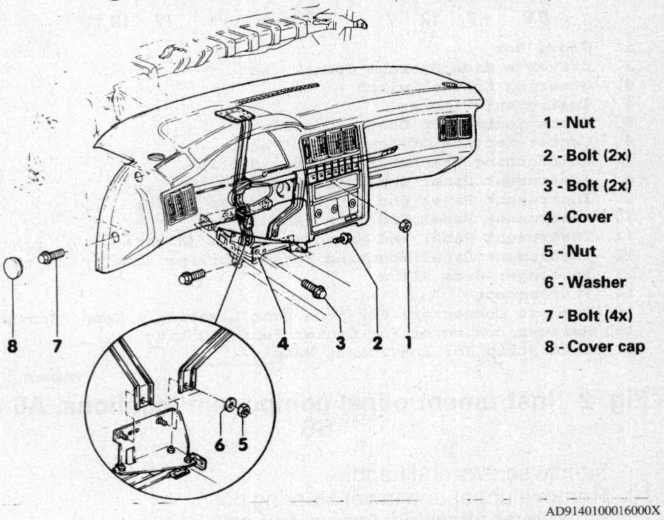

Fig. 6 Instrument panel. Cabriolet

a. Remove ashtray, then the rear bolts attaching rear floor console.
b. Unclip trim plate, then remove bolt attaching front of rear floor console, **Fig. 4.**
c. Pull rear floor console upward to remove, then disconnect electrical connectors.
d. Remove climate control knobs, then the trim plate.
e. Remove screws, then the filler piece, **Fig. 5.**
f. Remove shift knob, then pull shift boot upward.
g. Remove front floor console by pulling rearward, then disconnecting electrical connectors.

3. Remove trim plate for automatic temperature control unit, then unscrew control, pull out and disconnect multi-pin connector.
4. Remove screws for lower cover on passenger side, then pull out of bracket.
5. Remove screws for lower cover on driver's side, then pull off of retaining clip and bracket.
6. Disconnect terminal connection or pull off multi-pin connection.
7. Disconnect wiring harness from relay carrier and relay plate with fuse box.
8. Disconnect wiring harness outlet from instrument panel below steering column.
9. Disconnect terminal connections from tunnel located beneath center of instrument panel.
10. Disconnect connection from welded stud on crossmember.
11. Remove cover caps on instrument panel, then the screws, **Fig. 6.**
12. Remove nuts from heater housing, then the Phillips head screw from defroster duct.
13. Push up defroster vent duct connector slightly, then carefully pull away from instrument panel.
14. Remove instrument panel.
15. Reverse procedure to install, noting the following:
    a. Push hose from defroster duct up and into blower nozzles and ensure a secure fit.
    b. Keeping side and bottom mounting screws loose, adjust gap between instrument panel and windshield to approximately 9⁄16 inch.
    c. Close both front doors and ensure retaining tabs of trim panel fit behind edge of housing.
    d. Adjust instrument panel to same height as door trim panels.
    e. **Torque** instrument panel mounting screws to 44 inch lbs.
    f. **Torque** rear console mounting bolts to 44 inch lbs.

TT

1. Remove steering wheel as outlined under "Steering Wheel, Replace."
2. Remove instrument cluster as outlined under "Instrument Cluster, Replace."
3. Remove center console front section.
4. Remove combination switch as outlined under "Combination Switch, Replace."
5. Remove instrument panel end trim panels by pulling them toward rear using a suitable screwdriver.
6. Remove instrument panel end plates that were hidden under end trim panels.
7. Pull defroster vents upward, starting at front. **Locking lugs will break. This is normal and vents must be replaced.**
8. Remove tweeter speaker mounting screws, then the speakers. Disconnect electrical connectors.
9. Remove photosensor mounting screw, then the sensor. Disconnect electrical connector.
10. Remove instrument panel righthand brace mounting bolts, then the brace.
11. Remove instrument panel air duct to HVAC housing screws, then the duct.
12. Disconnect all instrument panel electrical connectors.
13. Remove all remaining instrument panel mounting screws.
14. Remove instrument panel toward rear.
15. Reverse procedure to install, noting the following:
    a. Replace defroster vents.
    b. Ensure all electrical connectors are securely connected.
    c. **Torque** instrument panel righthand brace mounting bolts to 44 inch lbs.
    d. **Torque** instrument panel end mounting screws to 31 inch lbs.

Steering Columns

NOTE: On Air Bag Equipped Models, Refer To "Air Bag System Precautions" Located In The Front Of This Manual For System Disarming & Arming Procedures.

NOTE: Refer To "Computer Relearn Procedures" Located In The Front Of This Manual When Battery Power To The Computer Has Been Interrupted.

INDEX

	Page No.
Adjustments	1-149
Telescoping Adjustment Cable	1-149
Precautions	1-149
Air Bag Systems	1-149
Battery Ground Cable	1-149
Radio Coded Anti-Theft System	1-149
Steering Column, Replace	1-149
A4 & S4	1-149
A6 & S6	1-150
A8	1-150
TT	1-151
Steering Column Service	1-152
Internal Components	1-152
Telescoping Adjustment Cable	1-152

PRECAUTIONS

AIR BAG SYSTEMS

Refer to "Air Bag System Precautions" in the front of this manual for system disarming and arming procedures.

RADIO CODED ANTI-THEFT SYSTEM

Prior to disconnecting the battery or removing the audio system, obtain the security code from the vehicle operator. Refer to the owner's manual for security code disarming and arming procedures.

BATTERY GROUND CABLE

Prior to service, disconnect battery ground cable and isolate as required.

ADJUSTMENTS

TELESCOPING ADJUSTMENT CABLE

1. Remove lefthand underdash cover and storage shelf.
2. Grasp cable and pull all free play from adjusting cable and latch.
3. Measure gap between cable adjusting nut and column, which should be. 12–.14 inch. Adjust if required.
4. Depress telescoping adjustment lever and slide column through full stroke of movement several times.
5. If any binding is noticed, turn adjusting nut to decrease gap, then inspect column movement.
6. When column moves freely with lever depressed, secure adjusting nut with suitable sealer paint.

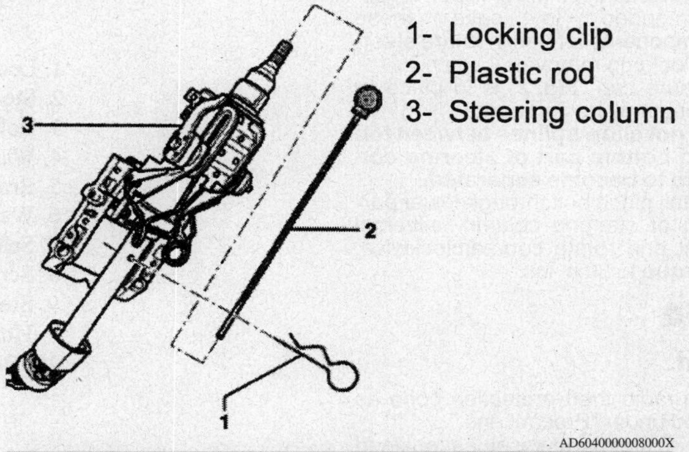

Fig. 1 Transportation safeguard device. A4 & S4

STEERING COLUMN

REPLACE

A4 & S4

1. Obtain radio theft protection code as outlined under "Precautions."
2. Remove driver's air bag module as outlined under "Component Service" in the "Air Bag System" section.
3. Remove steering wheel as outlined under "Steering Wheel, Replace" in "Electrical" section.
4. Remove storage shelf from lefthand side of instrument panel.
5. Remove combination switch as outlined under "Combination Switch, Replace" in the "Electrical" section.
6. **On models equipped with automatic transaxle,** proceed as follows:
   a. Ensure transaxle range selector lever is in Park position.
   b. Turn ignition On.
   c. Lift shift cable locking clip slightly, then disconnect cable from steering lock housing.
7. **On all models,** secure steering column with a suitable piece of wire or a transportation safeguard device, **Fig. 1,** then remove universal joint pinch bolt and separate universal joint from steering gear pinion. **Do not allow splines between top and bottom part of steering column to become separated.**
8. Remove steering column mounting bolts, then the steering lock housing.
9. Remove steering column.

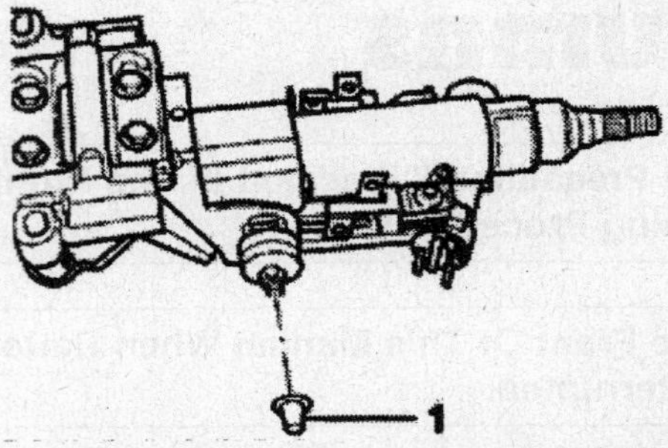

AD6040000009000X

Fig. 2 Steering column cap installation. A4 & S4

10. Reverse procedure to install, noting the following:
    a. New replacement steering columns arrive with a transportation safeguard device installed, **Fig. 1,** which must be removed after column installation in vehicle. It is recommended to save these components for use in future steering column removals.
    b. Ensure cap, **Fig. 2,** is in place or wiring may be damaged.
    c. **Do not allow splines between top and bottom part of steering column to become separated.**
    d. Install pinch bolt through lower portion of steering column universal joint and rotate counterclockwise. **Torque** to 30 ft. lbs.

A6 & S6

Removal

1. Obtain radio theft protection code as outlined under "Precautions."
2. Remove steering wheel as outlined under "Steering Wheel, Replace" in the "Electrical" section.
3. Remove combination switch as outlined under "Combination Switch, Replace" in the "Electrical" section.
4. Remove lefthand lower cover from dash panel, then lefthand footwell air duct.
5. Remove instrument cluster trim mounting screws, then the instrument cluster trim.
6. Remove instrument cluster mounting bolts, then pull instrument cluster out of dash panel and disconnect electrical connectors.
7. Remove instrument cluster.
8. Remove electrical connector housing from ignition lock, then righthand and lefthand electrical harnesses steering column.
9. Disconnect universal joint from steering column, then remove mounting bolts, **Fig. 3.**
10. Remove steering column Torx bolt using a suitable T30 insert.
11. Remove steering column mounting bolts from bracket, then the steering column from bracket.
12. Push steering column tube with steering lock down and turn to left, then pull steering lock housing out of steering column tube and remove.
13. Pull steering column up out of dash panel and remove.

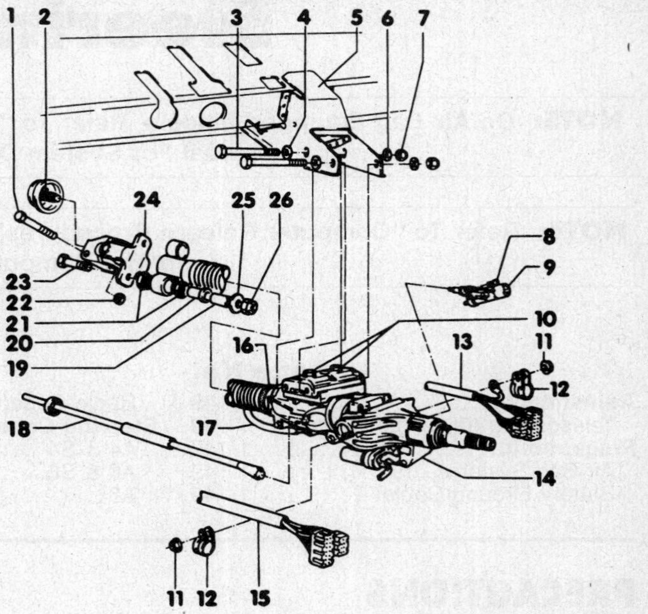

1. Locking Bolt
2. Steering Pinion
3. Bolt
4. Washer
5. Bracket
6. Washer
7. Self Locking Nut
8. Screw
9. Steering Lock Housing
10. Bolts
11. Combination Nut/Washer Assembly
12. Clamp
13. Wiring Harness
14. Steering Column w/Steering Column Tube
15. Left Steering Column Wiring Harness
16. Installation Sleeve
17. Cable For Lenght Adjustment
18. Tensioning Cable
19. Spacer Bushing
20. Bushing
21. Rubber Bushings
22. Self Locking Nut
23. Bolt
24. Universal Joint
25. Washer
26. Self Locking Nut

AD6049600005000X

Fig. 3 Steering column removal. A6 & S6

Installation

1. Install installation sleeve onto steering column corrugated tube, then slide into steering column tube to stop.
2. Slide steering column tube into position onto steering column. **Distance between steering column and base of steering column tube should be. 79 inch.**
3. Install cable to steering column tube.
4. Install steering column into dash panel, then the steering lock housing.
5. Install Torx screw and **torque** to 60 inch lbs.
6. Install electrical connector housing on ignition switch.
7. Install steering column tube in bracket and tighten mounting screws hand tight.
8. Insert key in ignition switch and unlock steering column.
9. Mount universal joint on to steering column. **Torque** bolts to 18 ft. lbs.
10. Align steering column so steering lock wheel is concentric to hole in dash panel.
11. **Torque** steering column tube to bracket bolts to 26 ft. lbs.
12. Remove installation sleeve, then install instrument cluster and trim.
13. Install air duct, then the lower cover.
14. Install combination switch and steering wheel.

A8

1. Remove driver's air bag module.
2. Remove steering column trim, **Fig. 4.**
3. Remove steering wheel.
4. Remove steering column switch.
5. Remove steering column upper slot cover attaching screw and cover from instrument panel.
6. Loosen cable tie for connectors on steering column.
7. Remove circlip for selector lever lock cable, **Fig. 5.**
8. Turn ignition key and remove cable.
9. Disconnect harness connectors from servomotors.
10. Remove nut from universal joint.
11. Release tension on eccentric by turning bolt in clockwise direction and remove bolt.

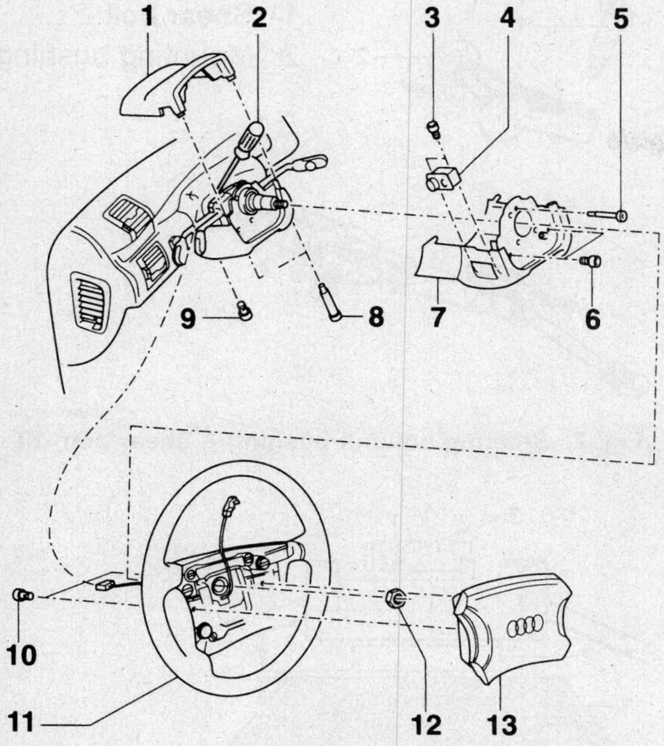

1. Upper Steering Column Trim
2. Bolt
3. Screw
4. Steering Column Adjustment Switch
5. Screw
6. Screw
7. Lower Steering Column Trim
8. Screw
9. Bolt
10. Bolt
11. Steering Wheel With Coil Spring
12. Nut
13. Airbag Unit

AD6049900006000X

Fig. 4 Steering column cover removal. A8

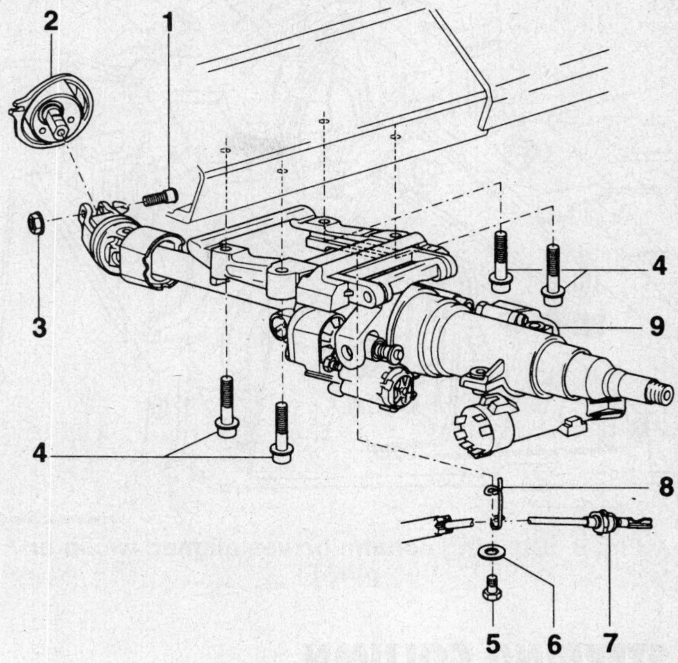

1. Eccentric Bolt
2. Steering Gear
3. Self-Locking Nut w/Washer
4. Bolt w/Washer
5. Bolt
6. Washer
7. Selector Lever Lock Cable
8. Bracket
9. Steering Column

AD6049900007000X

Fig. 5 Steering column removal. A8

12. Swing universal joint downward and away.
13. Remove bracket for selector lever lock cable.
14. Remove steering column/assembly carrier bolts and remove steering column.
15. Reverse procedure to install.

TT

1. Obtain radio theft protection code as outlined under "Precautions."
2. Remove driver's air bag module as outlined under "Component Service" in the "Air Bag System" section.
3. Remove steering wheel as outlined under "Steering Wheel, Replace" in "Electrical" section.
4. Remove column height adjustment handle mounting bolts, then the handle.
5. Remove steering column upper and lower shrouds.
6. Remove combination switch mounting screws as outlined under "Combination Switch, Replace" in "Electrical" section.
7. Disconnect turn signal and windshield wiper electrical connectors at combination switch, then position switch aside. **Ensure spiral spring coil connector is not twisted out of center position.**
8. Remove steering column universal joint cover plastic retainer nuts, then the cover.
9. **Prevent upper and lower portions of steering column from pulling apart when disconnecting column from steering gear shaft. The splines will separate if halves are pulled too far apart or pushed too close together.**
10. Push or pull steering column together or apart until alignment hole is visible, **Fig. 6,** then insert a suitable clip or alignment pin.
11. Remove universal joint pinch bolt, then disconnect joint from gear shaft.
12. Remove steering column mounting nuts and bolts, then the column from vehicle.
13. Reverse procedure to install, noting the following:
    a. New steering columns arrive with a mounting bushing and shear bolt, **Fig. 7.** Insert bushing in new column and tighten bolt until head shears off.
    b. Insert steering column in central tube together with mounting bushing.
    c. Insert mounting bushing hex bolt from righthand side.
    d. Mount steering column into position with new bolts. **Torque** to 15 ft. lbs.
    e. **Torque** mounting bushing nut to 84 inch lbs.
    f. Slide universal joint onto steering gear shaft and secure with a new bolt. **Torque** to 22 ft. lbs.
    g. Install combination switch and coil connector, ensuring there is a. 117 inch gap "a," **Fig. 8,** from steering wheel.

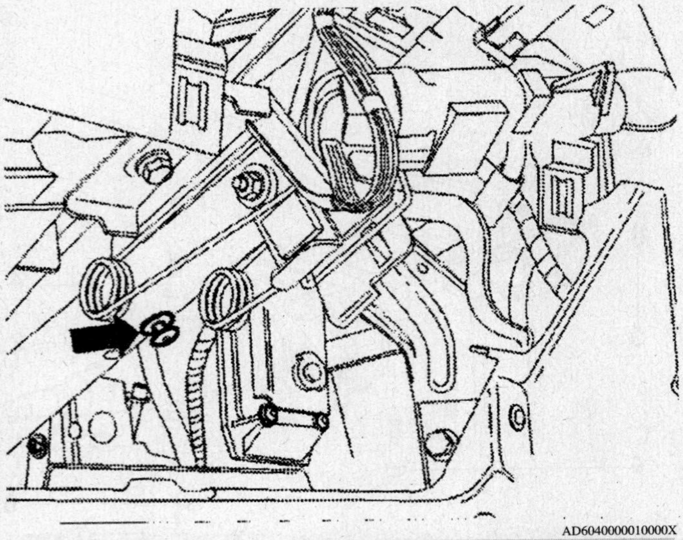

Fig. 6 Steering column halves aligned w/clip or pin. TT

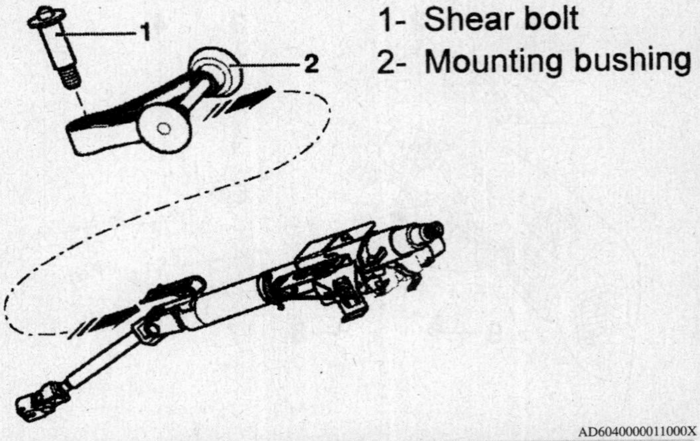

Fig. 7 Steering column bushing & shear bolt. TT

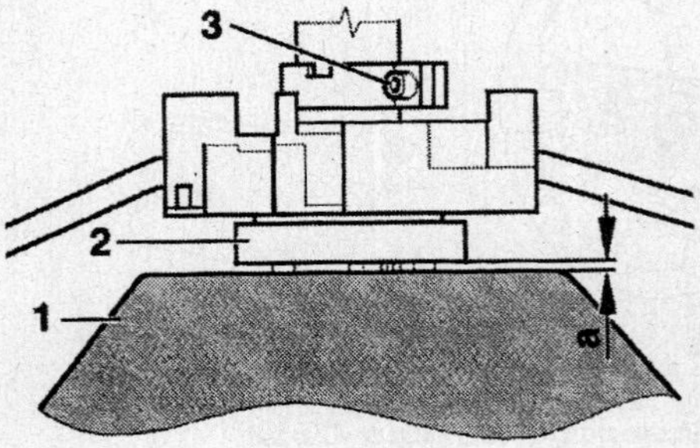

Fig. 8 Combination switch & coil connector. TT

STEERING COLUMN SERVICE

INTERNAL COMPONENTS

A4, A6, A8, S4, S6 & TT

The steering column is serviced as an assembly and cannot be disassembled.

Cabriolet

Refer to **Figs. 9 and 10** when servicing steering column.

TELESCOPING ADJUSTMENT CABLE

1. Remove steering column as outlined under "Steering Column, Replace."
2. Cut through cable at threaded adjusting nut sleeve using suitable side cutters.
3. Remove cable pieces.
4. Set basic adjustment of adjusting nut to 0.60 inch from base of threaded adjusting nut sleeve.
5. Insert cable into latch.
6. Crimp spring sleeve on end of cable to lock into latch using standard pliers.
7. Attach cable to adjustment lever mechanism.
8. Adjust cable as outlined under "Adjustments."
9. Install steering column as outlined under "Steering Column, Replace."

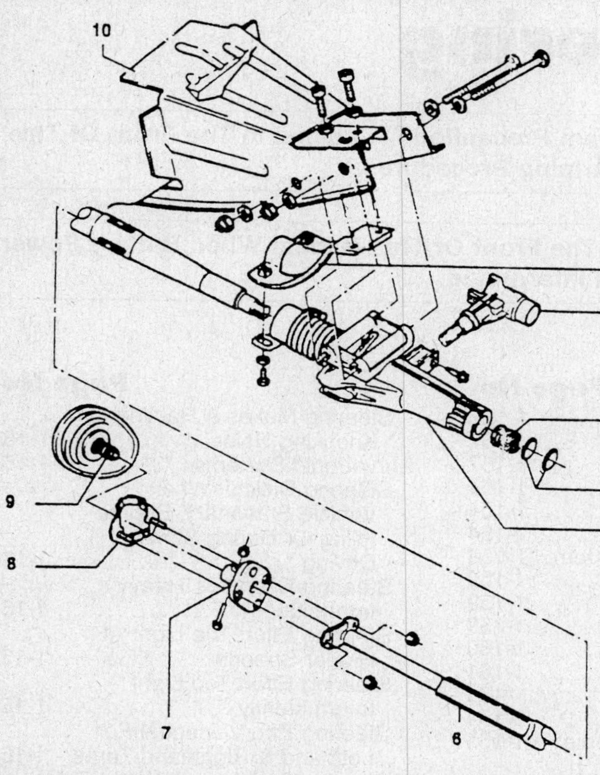

1. Mounting plate
   Install to the support bracket (top) and to steering column tube (bottom).
2. Steering lock housing
   Position at steering column tube and fasten.
   Connect to ignition wiring connector.
3. Spring
   Install on steering column.
4. Lock washers
   Removing: grind down (carefully), then pry out with screwdriver.
5. Steering column
   Consists of upper and lower section.
6. Steering column, collapsible
   Install up to stop, on column tube, install free of strain
7. Flange tube
   To install, slide into steering pinion and bolt to steering columnand restraining bracket.
   As replacement part, has coupling disc riveted on.
8. Retaining bracket
9. Steering pinion
10. Support bracket

AD6049100001000X

Fig. 9 Exploded view of steering column. Cabriolet w/collapsible column

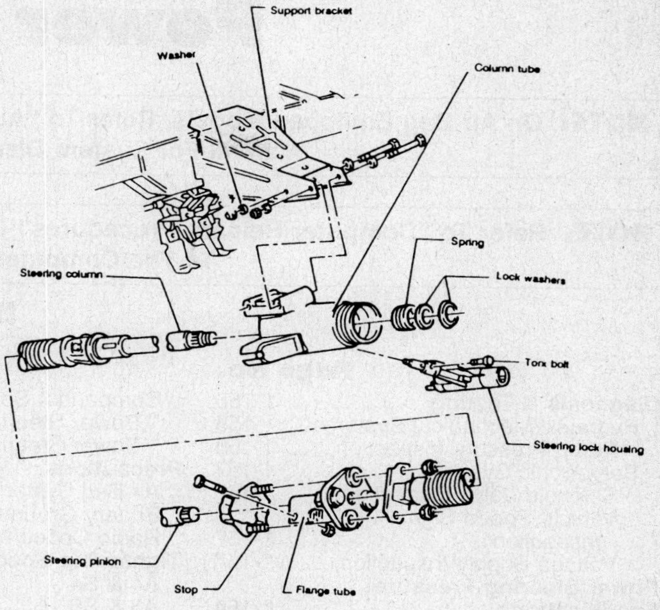

AD6049100003000X

Fig. 10 Exploded view of steering column. Cabriolet less collapsible column

Power Steering

NOTE: On Air Bag Equipped Models, Refer To "Air Bag System Precautions" Located In The Front Of This Manual For System Disarming & Arming Procedures.

NOTE: Refer To "Computer Relearn Procedures" Located In The Front Of This Manual When Battery Power To The Computer Has Been Interrupted.

INDEX

	Page No.
Diagnosis & Testing	1-155
Hydraulic/Mechanical Systems	1-155
Pump Pressure Inspection	1-155
Servotronic System	1-157
Solenoid Valve Inspection	1-157
Vehicle Speed Signal Inspection	1-157
Voltage Supply Inspection	1-157
Power Steering Pressure Specifications	1-154
Power Steering System Bleed	1-158
A4 & S4	1-158
A6, A8 & S6	1-158
Cabriolet	1-158
Power Steering System Service	1-157
Adjustments	1-157
A4, A8 & S4	1-157
A6 & S6	1-157
Cabriolet	1-157
TT	1-157
Component Service	1-157
Power Steering Gears	1-157
Power Steering Pumps	1-157
Precautions	1-154
Air Bag Systems	1-154
Battery Ground Cable	1-154
Radio Coded Anti-Theft System	1-154
Tightening Specifications	1-159
A4 & S4	1-159
A6 & S6	1-159
A8	1-160
Cabriolet	1-161
TT	1-161
Troubleshooting	1-154
Hydraulic/Mechanical Systems	1-154
Noise At Idle Or Steering Wheel Vibrates When Stopped	1-154
Reservoir Fluid Runs Over	1-154
Steering Heavy	1-154
Steering Makes A Rattling Or Knocking Noise	1-154
Servotronic Systems	1-154
Steering Difficult When Vehicle Stationary, Engine Idling Or During Slow Driving	1-154
Steering Effort Too Heavy Intermittently	1-155
Steering Effort Too Light At Higher Speeds	1-154
Steering Effort Too Light Intermittently	1-155
Steering Effort Unequal For Lefthand & Righthand Turns	1-155
Steering Satisfactory While Idling When Vehicle Stationary, But Too Heavy When Driving	1-155

POWER STEERING PRESSURE SPECIFICATIONS

Model	Pump Pressure, psi
A4 & S4	1595–1740
A6 & S6	1740–1885
A8	1596–1740
Cabriolet	1450–1595
TT	1595–1740

PRECAUTIONS

AIR BAG SYSTEMS

Refer to "Air Bag System Precautions" in the front of this manual for system disarming and arming procedures.

RADIO CODED ANTI-THEFT SYSTEM

Prior to disconnecting the battery or removing the audio system, obtain the security code from the vehicle operator. Refer to the owner's manual for security code disarming and arming procedures.

BATTERY GROUND CABLE

Prior to service, disconnect battery ground cable and isolate as required.

TROUBLESHOOTING

Hydraulic/ Mechanical Systems

RESERVOIR FLUID RUNS OVER

The seals in the hydraulic pump are leaking. Repair or replace the hydraulic pump.

STEERING HEAVY

1. V-belt loose. Tighten belt or replace if required.
2. Pump pressure too low. Measure pump pressure.

STEERING MAKES A RATTLING OR KNOCKING NOISE

Excessive play exists between the pressure plate and steering rack. Adjust the steering gear.

NOISE AT IDLE OR STEERING WHEEL VIBRATES WHEN STOPPED

1. V-belt faulty or tension improper. Tighten belt, or replace if required.
2. Hydraulic pump faulty. Replace hydraulic pump.

Servotronic Systems

On A6 and S6 models, the Servotronic control module is located in the auxiliary relay panel No. 1 in plenum, position 16.

STEERING DIFFICULT WHEN VEHICLE STATIONARY, ENGINE IDLING OR DURING SLOW DRIVING

1. No voltage supply at Servotronic control unit. Measure voltage supply as outlined under "Diagnosis & Testing."
2. Wiring from Servotronic control unit to Servotronic valve faulty. Inspect wiring as outlined under "Diagnosis & Testing."
3. Electrical fault in Servotronic valve. Inspect Servotronic valve as outlined under "Diagnosis & Testing."
4. Servotronic control unit faulty. Replace Servotronic control unit as a test. **If fault condition is not eliminated, install original control unit.**
5. Hydraulic defect in steering system. Measure pump pressure. If satisfactory, replace steering gear. If not, replace pump.

STEERING EFFORT TOO LIGHT AT HIGHER SPEEDS

1. Servotronic control unit faulty. Replace Servotronic control unit as a test. **If**

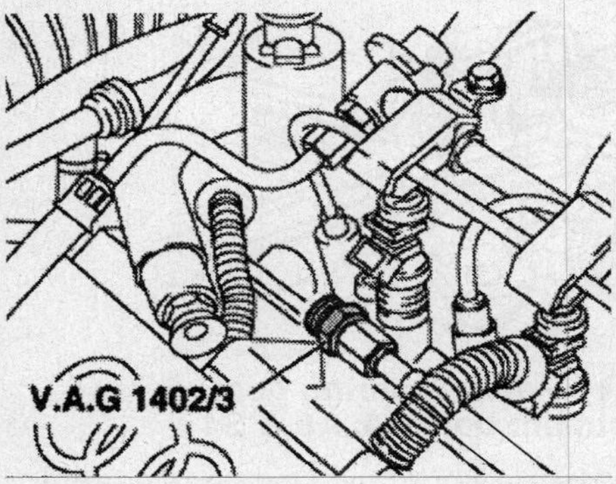

Fig. 1 VAG1402/3 adapter installation. 2-valve engine

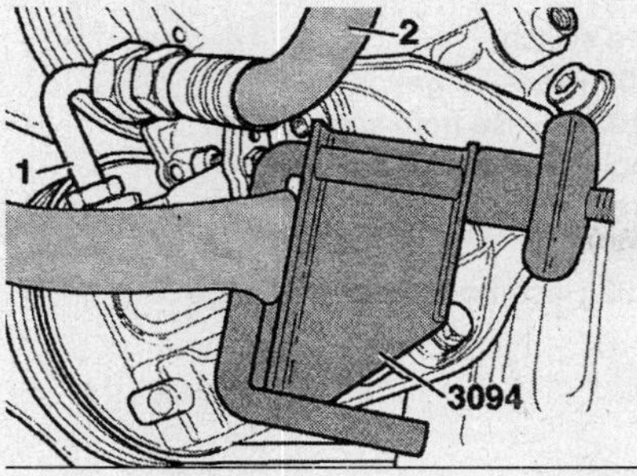

1- VAG1402/1
2- VAG 1402/6 Hose from adapter set

Fig. 2 Adapter & hose installation. TT

fault condition is not eliminated, install original control unit.

2. No speed signal at Servotronic control unit. Inspect wiring and connection. **Speed signal can also be suppressed or falsified by faults in other systems.**
3. Oil strainer or port in Servotronic valve blocked. Clean strainer, then replace Servotronic valve if required.

STEERING EFFORT TOO HEAVY INTERMITTENTLY

The Servotronic valve wiring has a short to ground. Inspect wiring and connections to valve as outlined under "Diagnosis & Testing."

STEERING EFFORT TOO LIGHT INTERMITTENTLY

The Servotronic valve wiring is shorted. Inspect wiring and connections to valve as outlined under "Diagnosis & Testing."

STEERING SATISFACTORY WHILE IDLING WHEN VEHICLE STATIONARY, BUT TOO HEAVY WHEN DRIVING

1. Servotronic control unit faulty. Replace Servotronic control unit as a test. **If fault condition is not eliminated, install original control unit.**
2. Hydraulic defect in steering system. Replace steering gear.

STEERING EFFORT UNEQUAL FOR LEFTHAND & RIGHTHAND TURNS

There is a hydraulic fault condition in the steering system. Replace the steering gear.

DIAGNOSIS & TESTING

Hydraulic/ Mechanical Systems

PUMP PRESSURE INSPECTION

A4

1. Pinch off pressure and return hoses using hose clamps tool No. 3094, or equivalent.
2. Disconnect pressure line at power steering pump.
3. Install adapter tool No. VAG 1402/3, or equivalent, into power steering pump in place of banjo bolt.
4. Close pressure gauge shutoff valve.
5. Remove clamp tools.
6. Start engine, then inspect power steering fluid reservoir level and correct as required.
7. Measure pressure reading at idle speed. **Do not measure for more than 10 seconds.**
8. Replace power steering pump if pressure does not meet specifications.
9. Inspect fluid level and correct as required.
10. Inspect hydraulic system for leakage and correct as required.
11. Bleed hydraulic system.

A6, A8 & S6

1. Remove top engine cover and serpentine drive belt cover, if required.
2. Install hose clamps tool No. 3094, or equivalent, to return and pressure hoses at reservoir and carefully close off lines. **If hose clamps 3094 are not available, use suitable clamping pliers.**
3. Press spring clamp to disconnect fuel injection valve.
4. Disconnect flexible hose from suction pipe, then connect adapter tool No. US 1074-4C, or equivalent, in place of flexible hose.
5. Connect hose of pressure gauge tool No. US 1074B, or equivalent, to adapter and close valve on pressure gauge.
6. Connect fuel injector.
7. Remove hose clamps from suction and return hoses.
8. Start engine, at idle, read pump pressure at pressure gauge, then turn Off engine. **Do not measure for longer than 10 seconds or damage may occur.**
9. If pressure is not within specifications, replace power steering pump.
10. Reverse steps 1 through 7, noting the following:
    a. Run engine at idle with wheels in straight-ahead position for approximately two minutes.
    b. Turn ignition Off and immediately inspect level of fluid in reservoir.
    c. Fill fluid in reservoir to MAX mark if required.

CABRIOLET

1. **Install hose clamps tool No. 3094, or equivalent, to return and pressure hoses, then carefully close off lines. Use suitable clamping pliers if hose clamps 3094 are not available.**
2. Disconnect pressure hose from pump, then remove copper sealing ring from banjo bolt and install onto adapter tool No. US 1074-4C, or equivalent.
3. Thread adapter into pump, then close valve of pressure gauge US 1074B, or equivalent, and route hose of pressure gauge downward to pump.
4. Thread hose of pressure gauge onto adapter, then remove hose clamp(s) from pressure hose and, if required, the return hose.
5. Start and idle engine, read pump pressure at pressure gauge, then stop engine. **Do not measure for more than 10 seconds or damage may occur.**
6. If pressure is not within specifications, inspect pressure and flow limiting valve.
7. Reverse steps 1 through 5, noting the following:
    a. Install pressure hose using new sealing rings on banjo bolt.
    b. Run engine at idle with wheels in straight-ahead position for approximately two minutes, turn ignition Off and immediately inspect level of

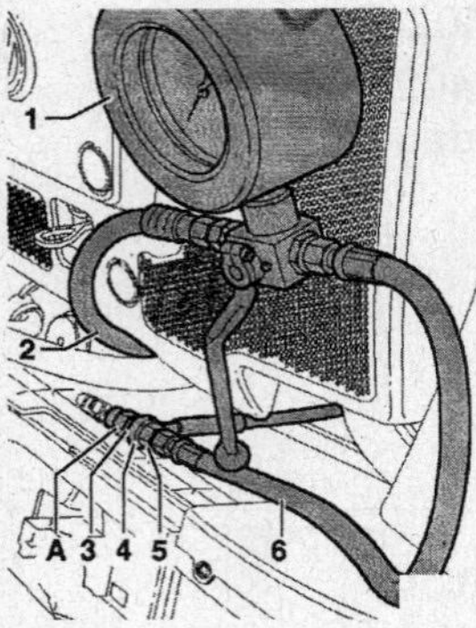

A- Pressure switch
1- VAG1402 Pressure gauge
2- VAG 1402/6 Hose from adapter set
3- Banjo bolt
4- Pressure hose banjo union
5- VAG1402/2
6- VAG1402 Hose from pressure gauge

AD6020000016000X

Fig. 3 Pressure gauge installation. TT

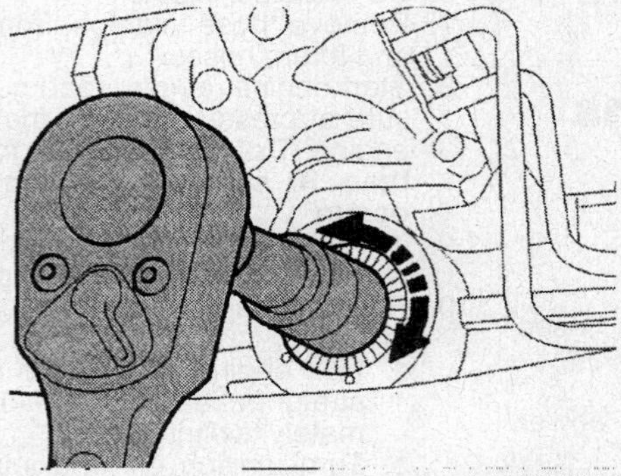

AD6020000017000X

Fig. 5 Rack adjustment screw. TT

fluid in reservoir. Fill fluid in reservoir to MAX mark if required.

S4

1. Remove engine top appearance cover.
2. Remove serpentine belt cover.
3. Pinch off pressure hose using hose clamp tool No. 3094, or equivalent.
4. Depress spring clip, then disconnect fuel injector harness electrical connector.
5. Counter-hold at hex on flexible hose, then disconnect and remove supply line from flexible hose.
6. **On models equipped with 2-valve engine,** install adapter tool No. VAG 1402/3, or equivalent, into power steering pump in place of flexible hose, **Fig. 1.**
7. **On models equipped with 5-valve engine,** install pressure gauge hose tool No. VAG 1402, or equivalent, to expansion hose.
8. **On all models,** close pressure gauge shutoff valve.
9. Connect fuel injector harness connector.
10. Remove hose clamp from suction hose.
11. Start engine, then inspect power steering fluid reservoir level and correct as required.
12. Measure pressure reading at idle speed. **Do not measure for more than 10 seconds.**
13. Replace power steering pump if pressure does not meet specifications.

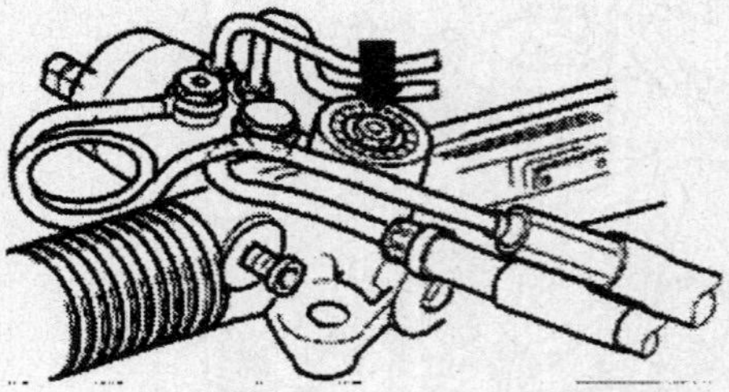

AD6029600013000X

Fig. 4 Power steering gear adjustment bolt. A4, A8 & S4

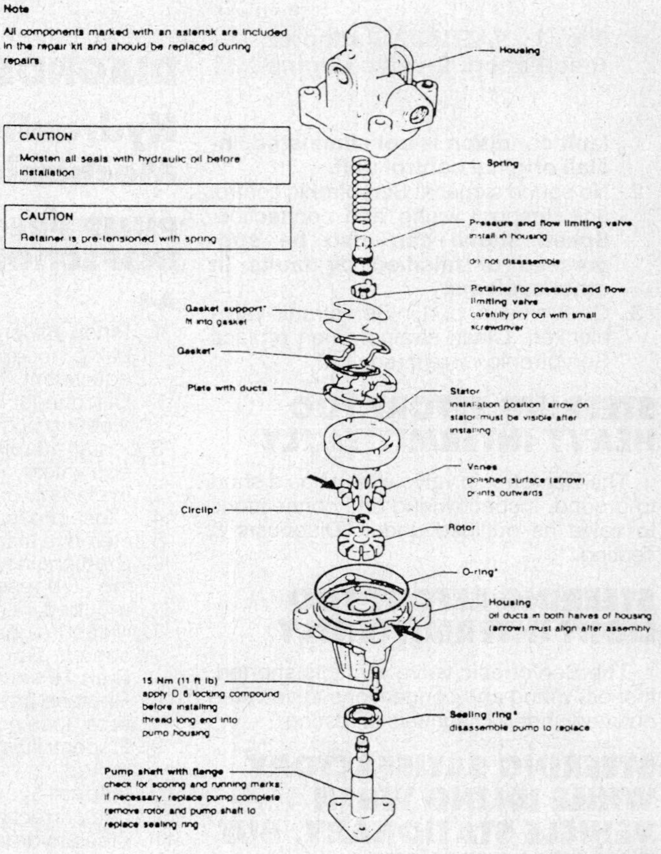

AD6029100004000X

Fig. 6 Power steering pump. Cabriolet

14. Inspect fluid level and correct as required.
15. Inspect hydraulic system for leakage and correct as required.
16. Bleed hydraulic system.

TT

1. Pinch off return hose with clamp tool No. 3094, or equivalent.
2. Remove sound insulation tray.
3. Pinch off pressure hose with clamp tool.
4. Place suitable drain pan under vehicle.
5. **On models equipped with pressure switch,** disconnect electrical connector and remove switch.
6. **On all models,** disconnect pressure pipe at pump.
7. Install adapter tool No. VAG 1402/1 and a sealing ring with hose tool No. VAG 1402/6, or equivalents, **Fig. 2.**
8. Connect pressure gauge tool No. VAG 1402 with hoses and adapters, **Fig. 3.**
9. Remove clamp tools.
10. Start engine, then inspect power steering fluid reservoir level and correct as required.
11. Rotate steering wheel approximately 10 turns from lock to lock.
12. Close cutoff valve with engine running at idle speed and record pressure reading. **Do not measure for more than five seconds.**
13. Replace power steering pump if pressure does not meet specifications.
14. Inspect fluid level and correct as required.
15. Inspect hydraulic system for leakage and correct as required.
16. Bleed hydraulic system.

Servotronic System

VOLTAGE SUPPLY INSPECTION

1. Remove cover from auxiliary relay panel No. 1 in plenum.
2. Remove Servotronic control module from auxiliary relay panel No. 1, position 16.
3. Turn ignition On.
4. Measure voltage between auxiliary relay panel terminals No. 6 and No. 8. Voltage should be 12 volts.
5. If voltage is not as specified, replace wiring for open or short.

SOLENOID VALVE INSPECTION

1. Remove cover from auxiliary relay panel No. 1 in plenum.
2. Remove Servotronic control module from auxiliary relay panel No. 1, position 16.
3. Measure resistance between auxiliary relay panel terminals No. 2 and No. 5. Resistance should be 6–12 ohms.
4. If voltage is not as specified, then disconnect electrical connector from solenoid valve and inspect wiring for open or short.
5. If wiring harness is satisfactory, replace solenoid valve.

VEHICLE SPEED SIGNAL INSPECTION

Vehicle speed signal is supplied by the speedometer.

1. If voltage supply, solenoid valve and vehicle speed display are satisfactory, replace wiring harness between auxiliary relay panel No. 1 terminal No. 4 and speedometer for open or short.
2. If wiring harness is satisfactory, replace Servotronic control module.

POWER STEERING SYSTEM SERVICE

Adjustments

A4, A8 & S4

1. Ensure front wheels are in straight-ahead position.
2. Stop engine, then raise and support vehicle with an assistant in driver's seat.
3. Rotate steering wheel back and forth approximately 30° to center axis while listening for a knocking noise. This would indicate excessive play.
4. Tighten steering gear adjusting bolt, **Fig. 4,** from lefthand wheelwell until knocking noise is no longer heard inside vehicle.
5. Road test vehicle. **If steering wheel does not return to straight-ahead position by itself, adjusting bolt should be turned back a little more.**

A6 & S6

1. Stop engine, then raise and support vehicle.

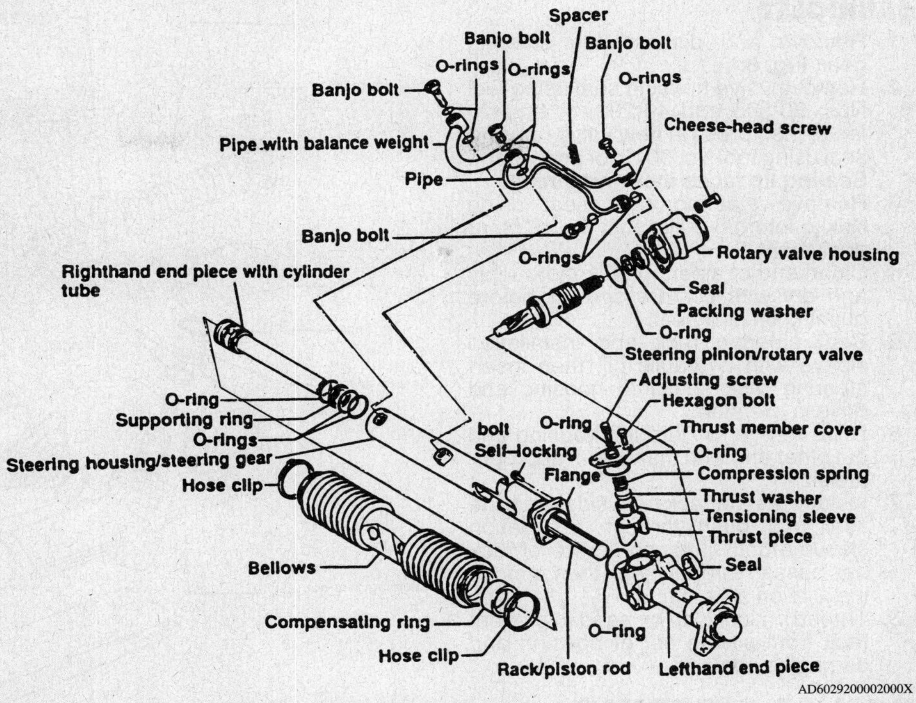

Fig. 7 Power steering gear. A6 & S6

2. Move steering wheel back and forth approximately 30° from center position and listen for rattling and popping noises from steering gear.
3. A second technician turns adjusting screw clockwise until rattling and popping noises are not heard inside vehicle, then turn in adjusting screw an additional 45°.
4. Test drive vehicle and ensure proper adjustment. Correct if required. **If steering does not return to straight-ahead on its own, loosen adjusting screw approximately 15°.**

CABRIOLET

1. Stop engine, then raise and support vehicle.
2. Move steering wheel back and forth approximately 30° from center position and listen for rattling and popping noises from steering gear.
3. A second technician turns adjusting screw clockwise until rattling and popping noises are not heard inside vehicle.
4. Test drive vehicle and ensure proper adjustment. Correct if required.

TT

1. Ensure front wheels are in straight-ahead position.
2. Stop engine, then raise and support vehicle with an assistant in driver's seat.
3. Rotate steering wheel back and forth approximately 30° to center axis while listening for a knocking noise. This would indicate excessive play.
4. Rotate rack adjustment screw into cover, **Fig. 5,** until knocking noise is no longer heard inside vehicle.
5. Road test vehicle and ensure steering self-centers without sticking.
6. Secure the adjusting nut to prevent rotation by making a center-punch mark in steering rack housing collar.

Component Service

POWER STEERING PUMPS

A4, A6, A8, S4, S6 & TT

The power steering pump is serviced only as an assembly. Refer to "Power Steering Pump, Replace" in "Front Suspension & Steering" section for procedure.

CABRIOLET

Refer to **Fig. 6** for service.

POWER STEERING GEARS

A4, A8, S4 & TT

The power steering gear is only serviced as an assembly. Refer to "Power Steering Gear, Replace" in "Front Suspension & Steering" section for procedure.

A6 & S6

1. Remove and disassemble steering gear, **Fig. 7.**
2. Drive out valve housing seal using tool No. 3013, or equivalent.
3. Press in new valve housing seal using tool Nos. 30-505 and 3161, or equivalents.
4. Remove seal in lefthand end housing by installing Kukko internal puller tool No. 21-4, or equivalent. Tighten nut until extractor jaws just grip metal shell of seal.
5. Press out seal by hand, then drive in seal using tool No. VW 416b, or equivalent.

CABRIOLET

1. Remove and disassemble steering gear, **Fig. 8.**
2. Remove valve housing seal using tool Nos. 30-505 and 40-202, or equivalents, then press in new valve housing seal using tool No. 3013, or equivalent. **Sealing lip faces steering pinion.**
3. Remove steering rack seal using Kukko internal puller tool No. 21/3, or equivalent.
4. Clean end of steering rack thoroughly and dry with compressed air before pushing on new seal.
5. Coat steering rack and installation sleeve with hydraulic oil, then insert steering rack seal into housing and drive in to a stop.
6. Drive sleeve "B" through housing and out other end with mandrel of appropriate size.
7. Install steering rack from side opposite seal and push through installation sleeve a until flattened portion of rack has passed through seal, then remove installation sleeve a.
8. Thread on lock cap by hand to prevent rack from sliding out of housing and damaging seal.

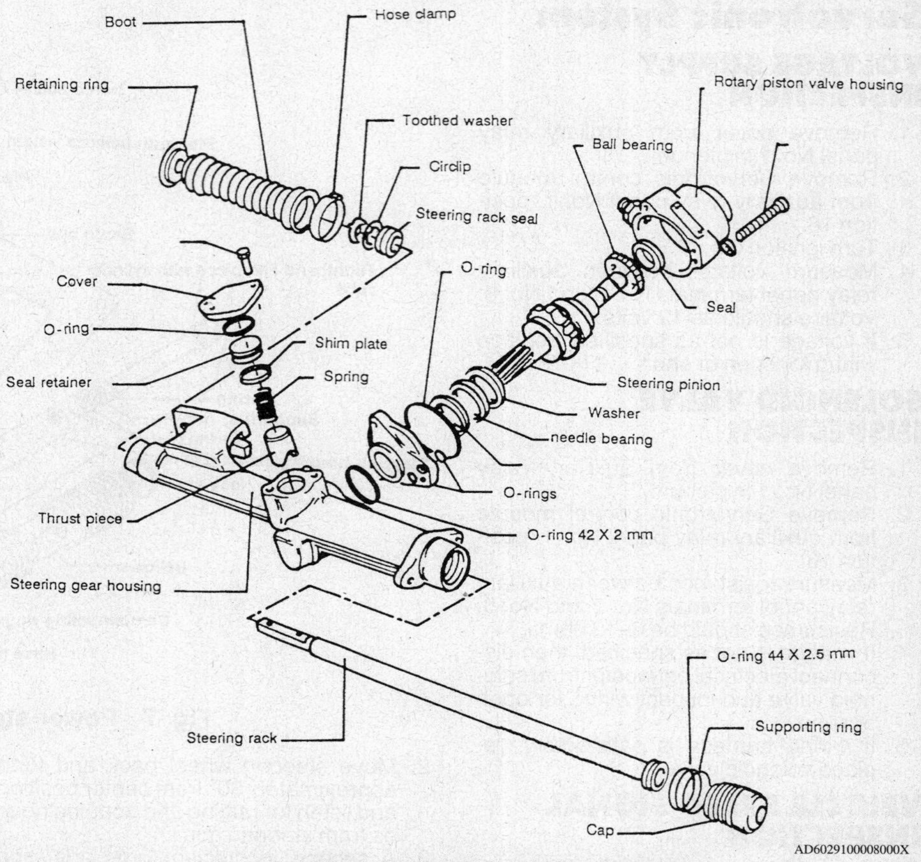

Fig. 8 Power steering gear. Cabriolet

POWER STEERING SYSTEM BLEED

A4 & S4

1. Inspect power steering fluid level and correct as required.
2. Raise and support vehicle until front tires can move freely.
3. Turn steering wheel from lock to lock 10 times with ignition Off.
4. Inspect fluid level and correct as required.
5. Lower the vehicle, then start engine.
6. Turn steering wheel from lock to lock 10 times with engine running.
7. Inspect fluid level and correct as required.
8. Any remaining air in steering system will dissipate during next 6–12 miles of driving.

A6, A8 & S6

1. With front wheels in straight-ahead position, run engine at idle for two minutes.
2. Turn ignition Off, then remove hydraulic fluid reservoir cap and inspect fluid level.
3. Fluid level should be at MAX mark on dipstick. Fill as required.
4. Raise and support vehicle, then turn steering wheel from full lefthand lock to full righthand lock 10 times.
5. Lower vehicle, then, with tires on ground, turn steering wheel from full lefthand lock to full righthand lock 10 times. **Any air that may be left in system will be bled out automatically while driving.**

CABRIOLET

1. Fill power steering fluid reservoir to MAX mark on dipstick.
2. With front wheels in straight ahead position, run engine at idle for two minutes.
3. Inspect fluid level.
4. As soon as no more bubbles rise in reservoir, stop engine and immediately fill reservoir to MAX mark on dipstick.

TIGHTENING SPECIFICATIONS

A4 & S4

Year	Component	Torque/Ft. Lbs.
1998–2001	Inner Tie Rod To Rack	74
	Oil Cooler Line Mounting Bolts	84①
	Outer To Inner Tie Rod End Jam Nuts	30
	Power Steering Pump Bracket Mounting Bolts	18
	Power Steering Pump Mounting Bolts	15
	Power Steering Pump Pulley Mounting Bolts	18
	Pressure Line To Flexible Hose	30
	Pressure Line To Pump Banjo Bolt	37
	Return Hose To Steering Gear	37
	Steering Column To Steering Gear Pinch Bolt	30
	Steering Damper To Bracket Nut	84①
	Steering Damper To Steering Gear Bolt	26
	Steering Gear Mounting Bolts	48
	Suction Hose To Pump	37
	Tie Rod To Swing Arm Horizontal Bolt	33
	Tie Rod To Swing Arm Vertical Bolt	60①

① — Inch lbs.

A6 & S6

Year	Component	Torque/Ft. Lbs.
1998–2001	Balancing Line Banjo Bolt	15
	Hydraulic Fluid Reservoir Mounting Bolts	84①
	Ignition Coil To Power Steering Pump Bracket	18
	Lefthand End Housing To Flange	84①
	Oil Cooler Line Mounting Bolts	84①
	Power Steering Pump Bracket Mounting Bolts	18
	Power Steering Pump To Power Steering Pump Bracket	18
	Power Steering Pump Pulley Mounting Bolts	18
	Pressure Hose Bracket To Power Steering Pump	84①
	Pressure Hose To Power Steering Pump	37
	Pressure Hose To Steering Gear	30
	Return Hose To Steering Gear	30
	Rotary Slide Valve Housing To Lefthand End Housing	11
	Safety Plate To Carrier	30
	Servotronic Valve To Valve Housing	27①
	Steering Damper To Carrier	30
	Steering Damper To Righthand Wheel Housing	30
	Steering Gear To Lefthand Wheel Housing	37

Continued

A6 & S6—Continued

Year	Component	Torque/Ft. Lbs.
1998–2001	Steering Gear To Righthand Wheel Housing	26
	Suction Hose Mounting Bolt	84①
	Suction Hose Mounting Clip Retaining Bolt	15
	Suction Hose To Power Steering Pump	37
	Thrust Piece Cover Mounting Bolt	15
	Tie Rod To Steering Gear	44
	Tie Rod To Strut	37
	Tie Rod Wheel Alignment Lock Nut	37
	Universal Joint To Steering Column	18
	Universal Joint To Steering Gear	18

① — Inch lbs.

A8

Year	Component	Torque/Ft. Lbs.
1998–2001	Flexible Hose Retaining Clip Mounting Nut	15
	Flexible Hose To Steering Gear	30
	Hydraulic Reservoir Mounting Bolts	80①
	Ignition Coil To Power Steering Pump Bracket	10
	Oil Cooler Line Mounting Bolts	84①
	Outer Tie Rod End To Inner Tie Rod End	30
	Power Steering Pump Bracket Mounting Bolts	18
	Power Steering Pump Mounting Bolts	15
	Power Steering Pump Pulley Mounting Bolt	18
	Pressure Line Bracket Mounting Bolt	71
	Pressure Line To Flexible Hose	30
	Pressure Line To Pump Banjo Bolt	37
	Return Hose To Steering Gear	37
	Steering Column To Steering Gear	30
	Steering Damper To Steering Gear, Bolt	26
	Steering Damper To Steering Gear, Nut	84①
	Steering Gear Centering Plug Screw	13
	Steering Gear Mounting Bolts	48
	Suction Hose To Cylinder Head	71
	Suction Hose To Pump	37
	Tie Rod To Swing Arm Horizontal Bolt	33
	Tie Rod To Swing Arm Vertical Bolt	60①

① — Inch lbs.

CABRIOLET

Year	Component	Torque/Ft. Lbs.
1998	Rotary Piston Valve Housing Bolts	14
	Steering Gear Housing Cover Bolts	14
	Steering Rack Cap	36
	Steering Pump Housing Bolts	11

TT

Year	Component	Torque/Ft. Lbs.
2000–01	Pressure Hose Banjo Bolt To Rack	28
	Pressure Pipe Banjo Bolt To Pump	28
	Pressure Switch To Banjo Bolt	11
	Return Hose Banjo Bolt To Rack	33
	Steering Column U-Joint Pinch Bolt	22
	Steering Pump Bracket To Block Mounting Bolts	33
	Steering Pump To Bracket Mounting Bolts	18
	Steering Pump Pulley Bolts	18
	Steering Gear To Subframe Bolts	15 + 90°
	Steering Gear Heat Shield Bolt	18
	Steering Gear Heat Shield Nut	16
	Tie Rod End To Knuckle Nuts	33
	Tie Rod End Jam Nuts	37

Disc Brakes

TABLE OF CONTENTS

	Page No.
APPLICATION CHART	1-162
DUAL PISTON FRONT BRAKES	1-167
ITT FN 3 SINGLE PISTON FRONT BRAKES	1-163
SINGLE PISTON REAR BRAKES	1-170
TEVES SINGLE PISTON FRONT BRAKES	1-165

Application Chart

FRONT DISC

Model	Application
A4	Lucas Single Or Dual Piston Brakes
	Teves Single Or Dual Piston Brakes
A6	Teves Single Piston Brakes
A8	Teves Single Piston Brakes
Cabriolet	Dual Piston Brakes
S4	Dual Piston Brakes
S6	Dual Piston Brakes
TT	ITT FN 3 Single Piston Brakes

REAR DISC

Model	Application
A4	Single Piston Brakes
A6	Single Piston Brakes
A8	Single Piston Brakes
Cabriolet	Single Piston Brakes
S4	Single Piston Brakes
S6	Single Piston Brakes
TT	Lucas Single Piston Brakes

ITT FN 3 Single Piston Front Brakes

NOTE: On Air Bag Equipped Models, Refer To "Air Bag System Precautions" Located In The Front Of This Manual For System Disarming & Arming Procedures.

INDEX

	Page No.
Brake Pad Service	1-163
Brake Rotor, Replace	1-164
Caliper Service	1-164
Disc Brake Specifications	1-173
Precautions	1-163
Air Bag Systems	1-163
Battery Ground Cable	1-163
Radio Coded Anti-Theft System	1-163
Tightening Specifications	1-164

PRECAUTIONS

Air Bag Systems

Refer to "Air Bag System Precautions" in the front of this manual for system disarming and arming procedures.

Radio Coded Anti-Theft System

Prior to disconnecting the battery or removing the audio system, obtain the security code from the vehicle operator. Refer to the owner's manual for security code disarming and arming procedures.

Battery Ground Cable

Prior to service, disconnect battery ground cable and isolate as required.

BRAKE PAD SERVICE

1. Raise and support vehicle, then remove front tires.
2. If brake pads are to be used again, mark installed positions for installation reference.
3. Remove caliper guide pin caps.
4. Pry brake pad retaining spring out from brake caliper housing using a suitable screwdriver.
5. Remove caliper guide pins.
6. Remove caliper housing, then position aside using suitable wire or rope.
7. Remove brake pads.
8. Clean brake caliper housing using a suitable methylated spirit. **Pay close attention to pad bonding surfaces. They must be free of all grease and adhesive residues.**
9. Siphon off a small amount of brake fluid from reservoir with a bleeder bottle or suitable tool.
10. Push piston back into bore using a suitable installation tool.
11. Ensure pads are installed in proper locations, **Fig. 1.**
12. Remove protective foil from outer brake pad as required.
13. Install caliper housing with both guide pins to brake carrier.
14. Install both guide pin caps. Tighten to specifications.

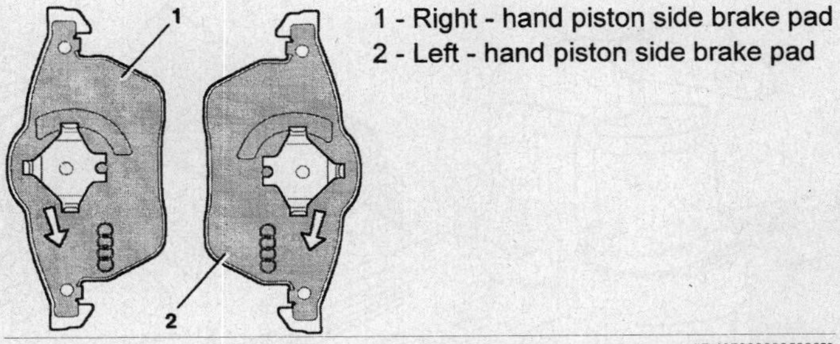

Fig. 1 Brake pad orientation. ITT FN 3 brakes

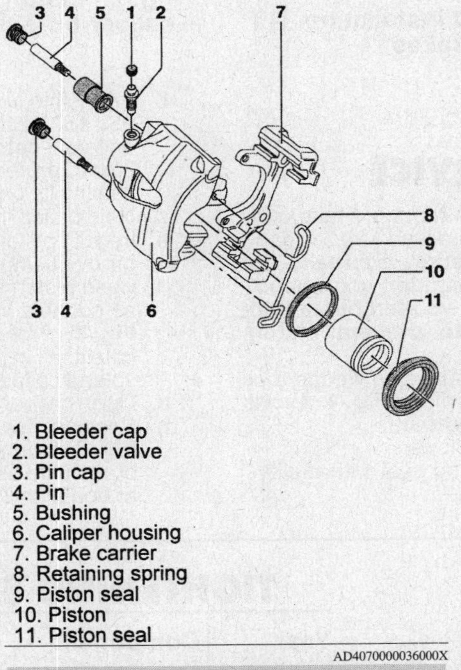

Fig. 2 Exploded view of front caliper assembly. ITT FN 3 brakes

15. Insert retaining spring into caliper housing.
16. Install tires, then lower the vehicle to the ground. Tighten wheel lug nuts to specifications.
17. Depress brake pedal firmly several times with vehicle stationary to allow pads to properly seat in normal operating positions.
18. Inspect brake fluid level and correct as

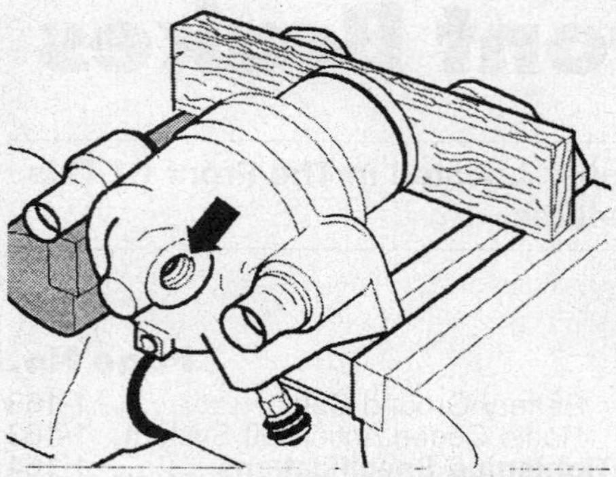

Fig. 3 Brake caliper piston removal. ITT FN 3 brakes

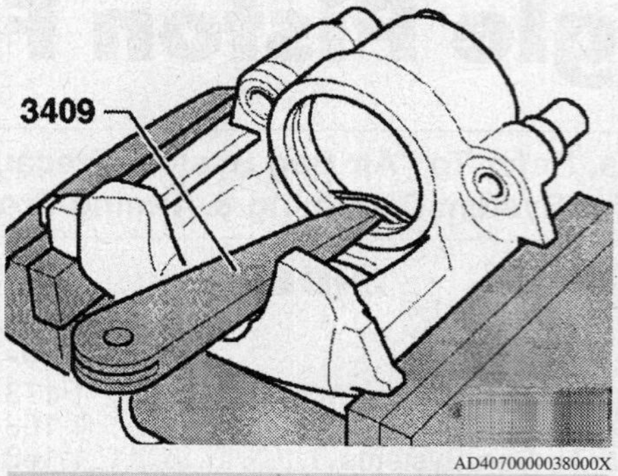

Fig. 4 Piston seal removal. ITT FN 3 brakes

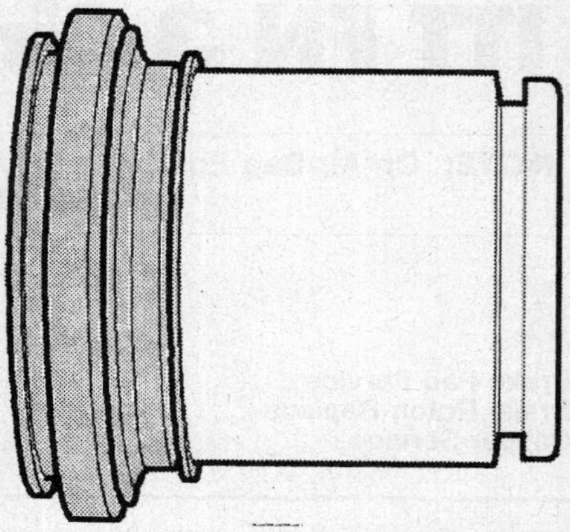

Fig. 5 Protective seal installation. ITT FN 3 brakes

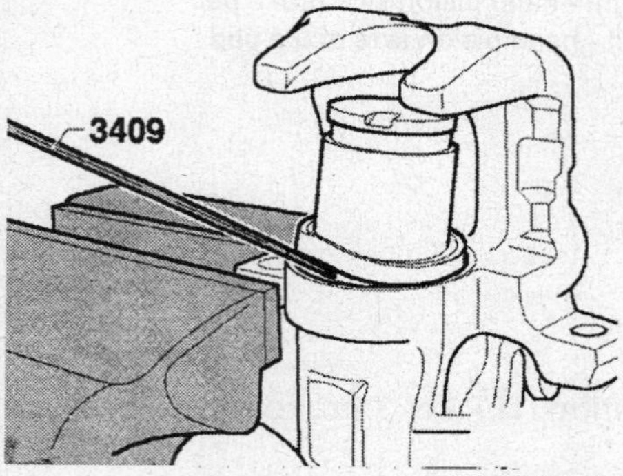

Fig. 6 Piston seal installation. ITT FN 3 brakes

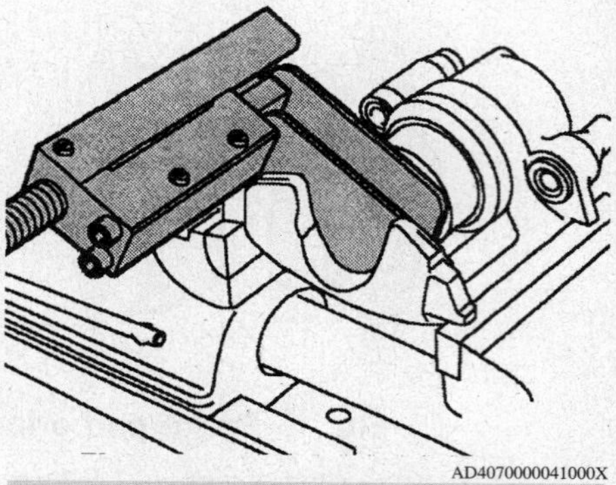

Fig. 7 Piston installation into caliper bore. ITT FN 3 brakes

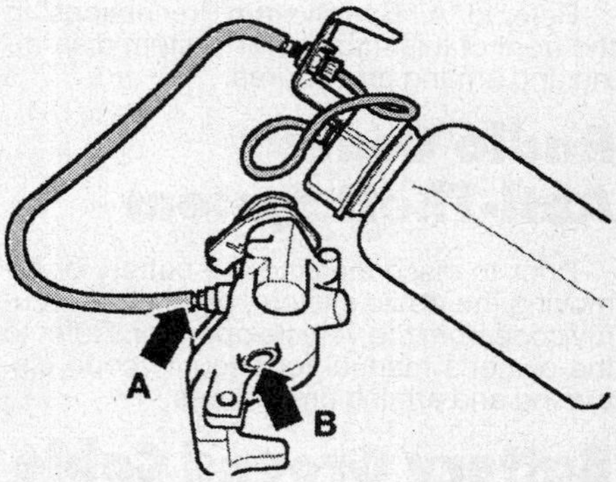

A. Bleeder valve
B. Threaded port

Fig. 8 Caliper pre-bleeding. ITT FN 3 brakes

required.

CALIPER SERVICE

1. Force piston, **Fig. 2,** out of brake caliper using compressed air, **Fig. 3. Apply air pressure gradually to guard against sudden expulsion. Place a suitable wooden block into caliper recess to prevent piston damage.**
2. Remove piston seal using wedge tool No. 3409, or equivalent, **Fig. 4. Avoid damaging bore surface.**
3. Install piston as follows:
   a. Clean piston and seal with methylated spirits.
   b. Apply thin coat of paste part No. G 052 150 A2, or equivalent, to piston and seal before installation.
   c. Place protective seal with outer sealing lip on piston, **Fig. 5.**
   d. Hold piston in front of caliper.
   e. Install piston seal lip into bore groove using wedge tool, **Fig. 6.**
   f. Push piston into caliper bore using a suitable piston installer tool, **Fig. 7.** Protective seal should locate itself in piston groove.
4. Pre-bleed caliper as follows:
   a. Open caliper bleeder valve, **Fig. 8.**
   b. Position caliper as illustrated, **Fig. 8,** then fill with fresh specified brake fluid using a standard bleeder bottle until fluid flows without any bubbles from brake hose port.
   c. Close bleeder valve.

BRAKE ROTOR

REPLACE

Refer to "Front Suspension & Steering" or "Rear Axle & Suspension" under "Strut, Replace" and "Shock Absorber, Replace," for procedures.

TIGHTENING SPECIFICATIONS

Year	Component	Torque/Ft. Lbs.
2000–01	Caliper Housing To Carrier Bolts	18
	Carrier To Knuckle Pin Bolts	92
	Hydraulic Line To Caliper Housing Banjo Bolt	26
	Wheel Lug Nuts	89

Teves Single Piston Front Brakes

NOTE: On Air Bag Equipped Models, Refer To "Air Bag System Precautions" Located In The Front Of This Manual For System Disarming & Arming Procedures.

INDEX

	Page No.
Brake Pad Service	1-165
Brake Rotor, Replace	1-166
Caliper Service	1-165
Overhaul	1-165
Disc Brake Specifications	1-173
Precautions	1-165
Air Bag Systems	1-165
Battery Ground Cable	1-165
Radio Coded Anti-Theft System	1-165
Tightening Specifications	1-166

PRECAUTIONS

Air Bag Systems

Refer to "Air Bag System Precautions" in the front of this manual for system disarming and arming procedures.

Radio Coded Anti-Theft System

Prior to disconnecting the battery or removing the audio system, obtain the security code from the vehicle operator. Refer to the owner's manual for security code disarming and arming procedures.

Battery Ground Cable

Prior to service, disconnect battery ground cable and isolate as required.

BRAKE PAD SERVICE

This procedure has been revised by a Technical Service Bulletin.

1. Raise and support vehicle, then remove wheel assemblies.
2. If brake pads are to be used again, mark installed positions for installation reference. Inner pads are different from side to side and have a specified direction of rotation.
3. Use a suitable screwdriver to pry brake pad retaining spring out of caliper housing, **Fig. 1.**
4. Remove guide pin caps, then the guide pins.
5. Remove brake caliper housing from carrier. Secure brake caliper housing to vehicle with a suitable piece of wire. **Do not allow brake caliper to hang from hydraulic lines. Do not disconnect hydraulic lines.**
6. Remove outer brake pad from carrier.
7. Pull inner brake pad with expanding spring out of piston.
8. Extract part of brake fluid from reservoir using a suitable suction device, then push piston back into caliper housing.
9. Install inner brake pad in piston. Inner pads are different from side to side and have a specified direction of rotation.

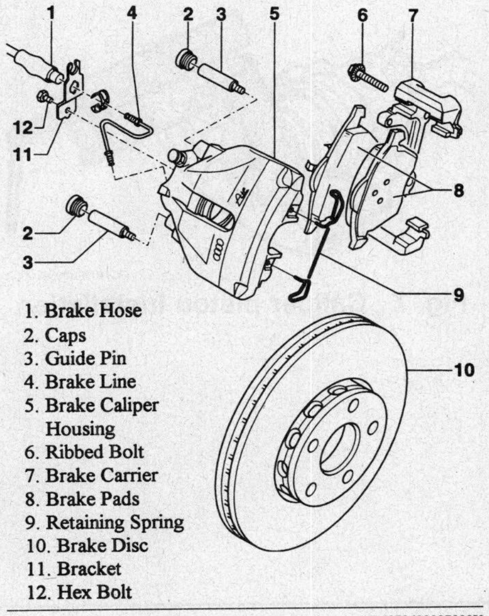

Fig. 1 Exploded view of front brakes

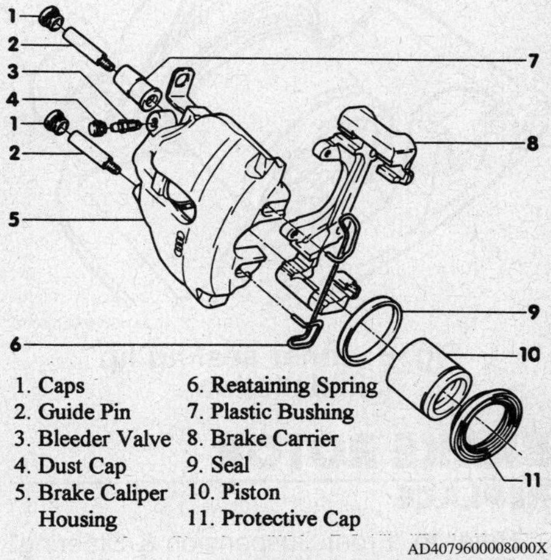

Fig. 2 Exploded view of brake caliper

10. Pull protective sheet off backing plate for outer brake pad, then fit outer brake pad onto brake carrier. **Do not damage adhesive layer on backing plate.**
11. Install brake caliper housing onto carrier.
12. Install guide pins and caps, then the brake pad retaining spring into caliper housing.
13. Install wheel assemblies, then lower vehicle. **Depress brake pedal firmly several times with vehicle stationary to adjust brake pads to their normal operating positions.**
14. Inspect brake fluid level and fill as required.

CALIPER SERVICE

Overhaul

1. Force piston, **Fig. 2,** out of brake caliper with compressed air, **Fig. 3. Apply air pressure gradually to guard against sudden piston release. Place a suitable wooden block into recess of brake caliper to prevent piston damage.**
2. Remove caliper piston seal using a suitable screwdriver, **Fig. 4.**
3. Install piston as follows:
   a. Install protective cap with sealing lip onto piston, **Fig. 5.**
   b. Insert inner sealing lip of protective cap into groove in brake caliper housing using a suitable screwdriver, **Fig. 6. Hold piston in front of caliper housing during this step.**
   c. Press piston into brake caliper housing using a suitable piston resetting tool, **Fig. 7. Outer sealing lip of protective cap fits into groove in piston.**
4. Pre-bleed caliper as follows:
   a. Open caliper bleeder valve and fill caliper with brake fluid using a suitable bleeder bottle, **Fig. 8.**
   b. Fill caliper until brake fluid flows out brake hose connection free of bubbles.
   c. Close bleeder valve.

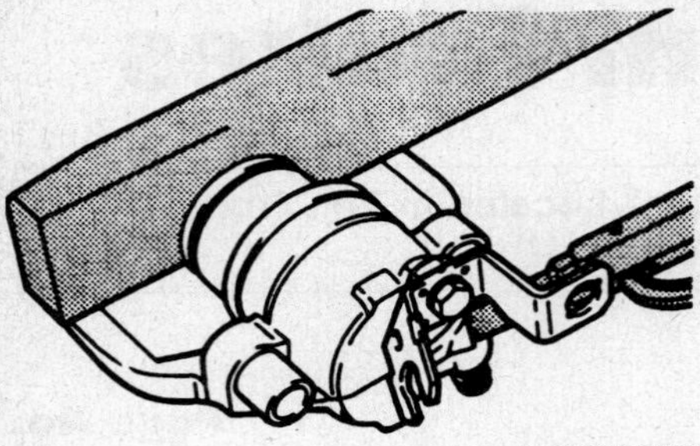

Fig. 3 Brake caliper piston removal

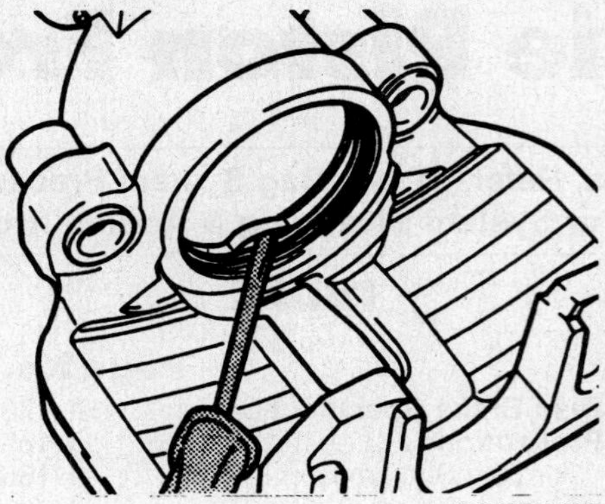

Fig. 4 Caliper piston seal removal

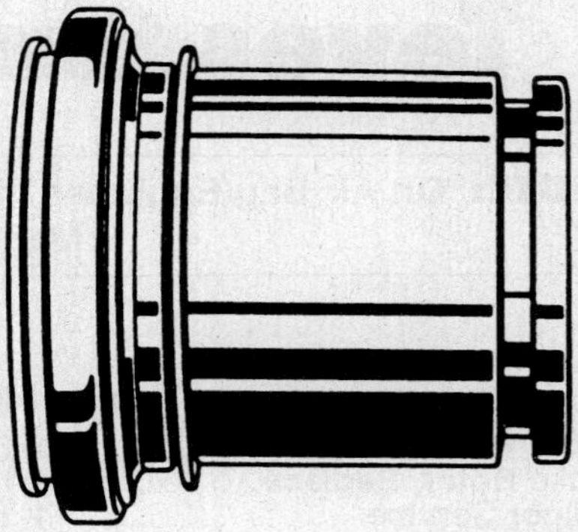

Fig. 5 Protective cap installation

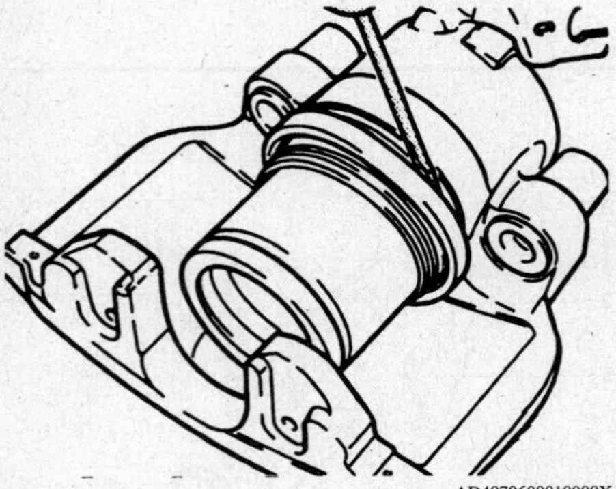

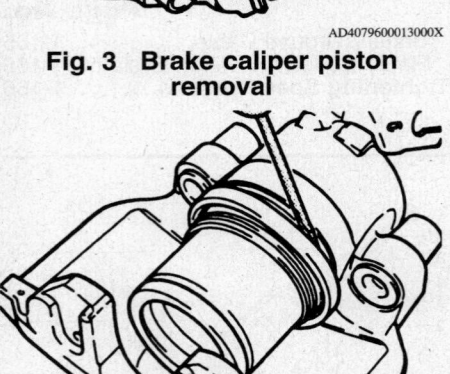

Fig. 6 Inner sealing lip installation

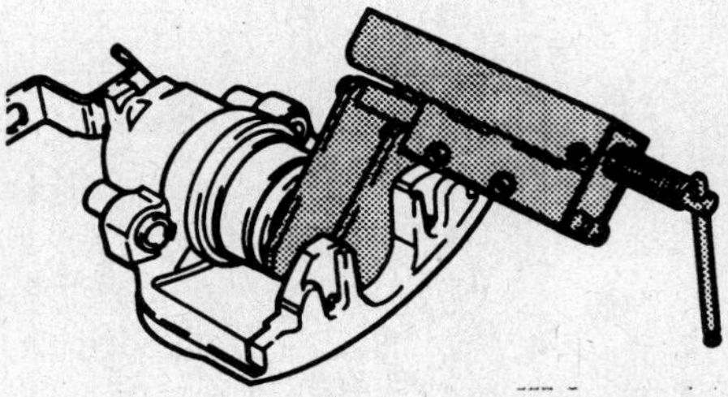

Fig. 7 Caliper piston installation

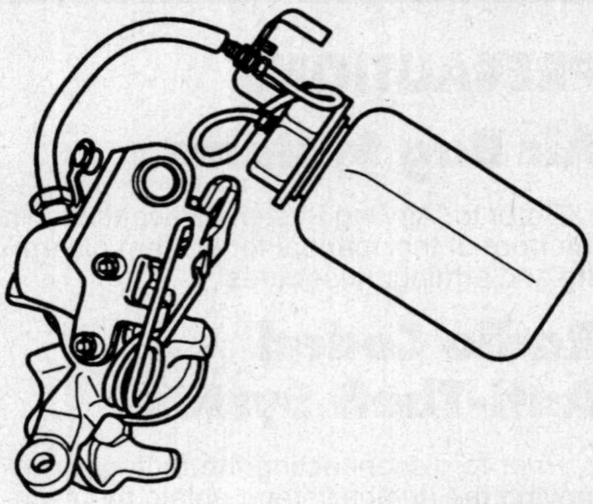

Fig. 8 Caliper pre-bleeding

BRAKE ROTOR

REPLACE

Refer to "Front Suspension & Steering" or "Rear Axle & Suspension" under "Strut, Replace" and "Shock Absorber, Replace" procedures.

TIGHTENING SPECIFICATIONS

Year	Component	Torque/Ft. Lbs.
1998–2001	Caliper Housing To Carrier	18
	Carrier To Wheel Bearing Housing	92
	Hydraulic Line To Caliper Housing	11

Dual Piston Front Brakes

NOTE: On Air Bag Equipped Models, Refer To "Air Bag System Precautions" Located In The Front Of This Manual For System Disarming & Arming Procedures.

INDEX

	Page No.
Brake Pad Service	1-167
Cabriolet	1-167
S6	1-167
Brake Rotor, Replace	1-168
Caliper Service	1-168
Overhaul	1-168
Disc Brake Specifications	1-173
Precautions	1-167
Air Bag Systems	1-167
Battery Ground Cable	1-167
Radio Coded Anti-Theft System	1-167
Tightening Specifications	1-169

PRECAUTIONS

Air Bag Systems

Refer to "Air Bag System Precautions" in the front of this manual for system disarming and arming procedures.

Radio Coded Anti-Theft System

Prior to disconnecting the battery or removing the audio system, obtain the security code from the vehicle operator. Refer to the owner's manual for security code disarming and arming procedures.

Battery Ground Cable

Prior to service, disconnect battery ground cable and isolate as required.

BRAKE PAD SERVICE

S6

Removal

1. Raise and support vehicle, then remove wheel assemblies.
2. **If brake pads are to be used again, mark installed positions for installation reference.**
3. Secure brake disc on wheel hub with a wheel lug nut.
4. Remove outer brake pad mounting bolts, **Fig. 1.**
5. Extract part of brake fluid from reservoir using a suitable bleeder bottle, then push piston back into caliper housing by inserting a suitable screwdriver into floating frame and pressing firmly to outside.
6. Disconnect wiring harness electrical connector, then remove brake pad wear indicator wiring from brake caliper bracket.
7. Press caliper floating frame forcefully inward toward vehicle, then pry brake pads out of piston with a suitable screwdriver and remove brake pads.

Installation

1. Install inner brake pad with brake pad wear indicator into upper piston. **Do not damage protective covers.**
2. Install inner brake pad into lower piston.
3. Clip wiring for brake pad wear indicator into bracket on brake caliper.
4. Install lower part of connector for brake pad wear indicator into bracket on brake caliper.
5. Press floating frame outward to stop, then install outer brake pads. **Do not damage adhesive layer on backing plate.**
6. Install outer brake pad mounting bolts and tighten to specifications.
7. Remove wheel lug nut from wheel hub, then install wheel assemblies and lower vehicle. **Depress brake pedal firmly several times with vehicle stationary to adjust brake pads to their normal operating positions.**
8. Inspect brake fluid level and fill as required.

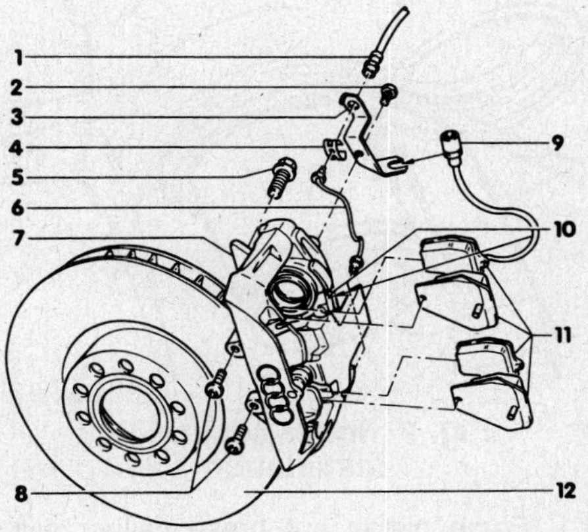

1. Brake Hose
2. Bolt
3. Bracket
4. Retaining Spring
5. Serrated Bolt
6. Brake Line
7. Brake Caliper
8. Bolt
9. Harness Connector
10. Wiring Bracket
11. Brake Pads
12. Brake Disc

AD4079600019000X

Fig. 1 Exploded view of front brakes. S6

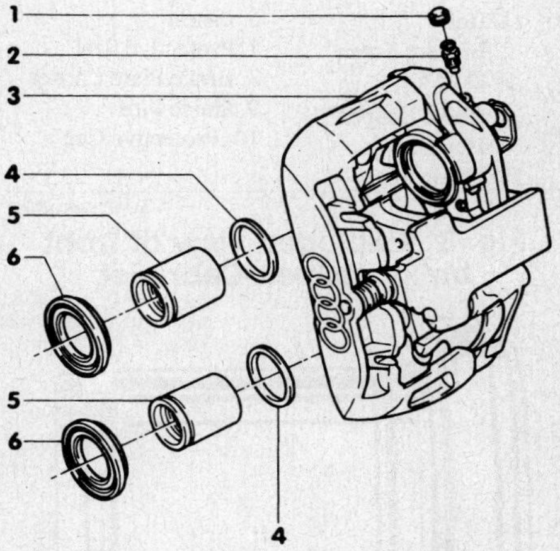

1. Dust Cap
2. Bleeder Valve
3. Brake Caliper Housing
4. Piston Seal
5. Piston
6. Piston Outer Seal

AD4079600021000X

Fig. 2 Exploded view of front brake caliper. S6

CABRIOLET

1. Raise and support vehicle, then remove front tires.
2. Pull plug connector for wear indicator out of clip, then press connector on knurled surface and pull apart.
3. Remove lower caliper mounting bolt using open end wrench to hold guide pin head.
4. Swing caliper upward, then remove brake pads.
5. Place an old brake pad into caliper and push piston back into caliper housing. **Always remove some brake fluid from master cylinder reservoir prior to installing new pads. When caliper piston is pushed back, fluid is forced out of caliper and into reservoir. After pads are installed, fill reservoir to MAX mark.**
6. Install brake pads, then swing caliper downward and install **new** lower self-locking mounting bolt. Use an open end wrench to hold guide pin in position when tightening lower mounting bolt to specifications.
7. Connect wear indicator plug and attach to retaining clip.
8. Depress brake pedal several times to

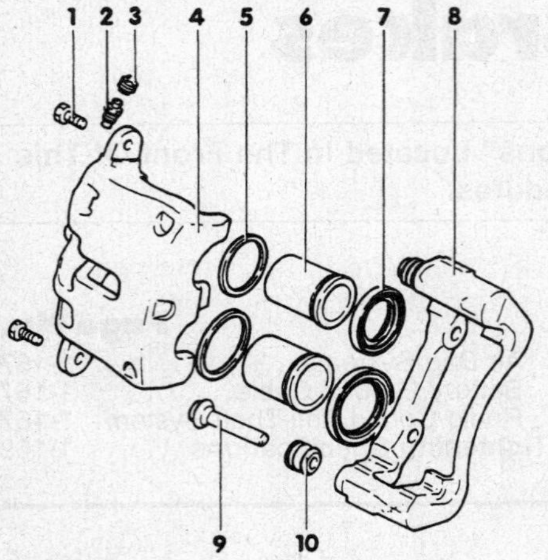

1. Bolt
2. Bleeder Screw
3. Dust Cap
4. Brake Caliper Housing
5. Piston Seal
6. Piston
7. Protective Seal
8. Brake Plate Carrier
9. Guide Pins
10. Protective Cap

AD4079600022000X

Fig. 3 Exploded view of front brake caliper. Cabriolet

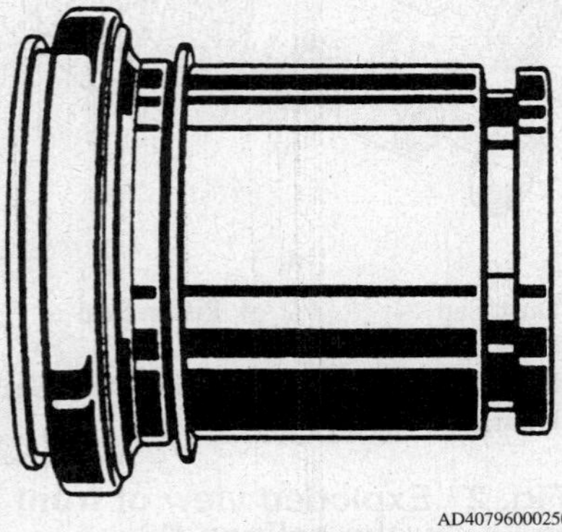

AD4079600025000X

Fig. 6 Protective cap installation

position caliper piston and seat brake pads.

CALIPER SERVICE

OVERHAUL

Refer to **Figs. 2 and 3** when servicing front disc brake calipers, noting the following:

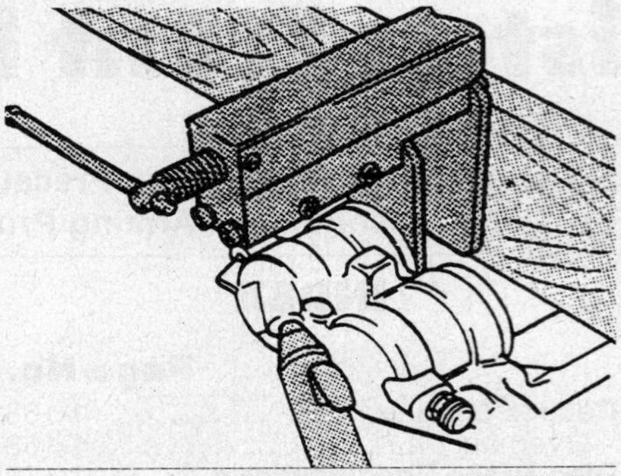

AD4079600023000X

Fig. 4 Brake caliper piston removal

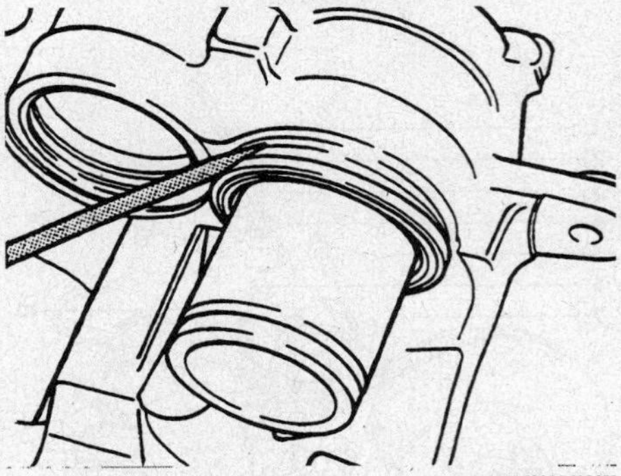

AD4079600026000X

Fig. 7 Inner sealing lip installation

1. Force piston out brake caliper with compressed air, **Fig. 4. Apply air pressure gradually to guard against sudden piston release. Place a suitable wooden block into recess of brake caliper to prevent piston damage.**
2. Remove caliper piston seal using a suitable screwdriver, **Fig. 5.**

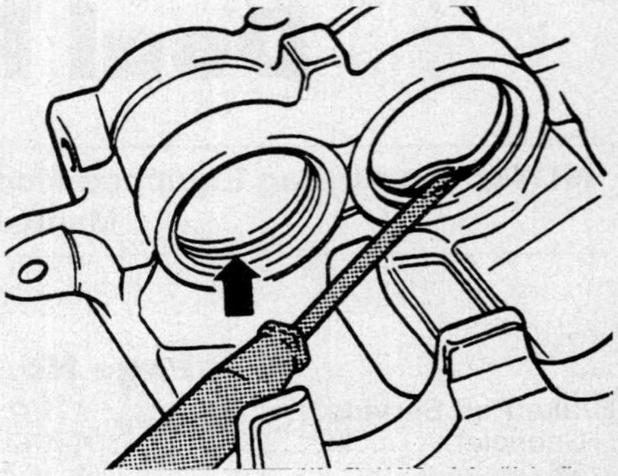

AD4079600024000X

Fig. 5 Caliper piston seal removal

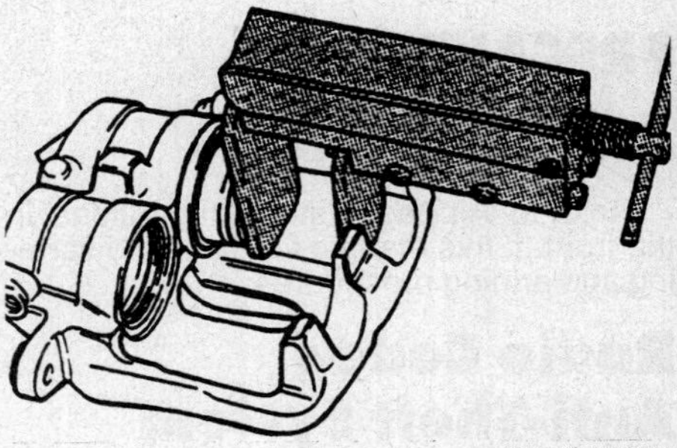

AD4079600027000X

Fig. 8 Caliper piston installation

3. Install piston as follows:
   a. Install protective cap with sealing lip onto piston, **Fig. 6.**
   b. Insert inner sealing lip of protective cap into groove in brake caliper housing using a suitable screwdriver, **Fig. 7. Hold piston in front of caliper housing during this step.**
   c. Press piston into brake caliper housing using a suitable piston resetting tool, **Fig. 8. Outer sealing lip of protective cap fits into groove in piston.**

BRAKE ROTOR

REPLACE

Refer to “Front Suspension & Steering” or “Rear Axle & Suspension” under “Strut, Replace” and “Shock Absorber, Replace” procedures.

TIGHTENING SPECIFICATIONS

Year	Component	Torque/Ft. Lbs.
CABRIOLET		
1998	Brake Caliper Housing To Carrier	26
	Carrier To Wheel Bearing Housing	92
S6		
1998–2001	Brake Caliper Housing To Floating Frame	184
	Hydraulic Line Bracket To Brake Caliper Housing	18
	Outer Brake Pad Mounting Bolts	18

Single Piston Rear Brakes

NOTE: On Air Bag Equipped Models, Refer To "Air Bag System Precautions" Located In The Front Of This Manual For System Disarming & Arming Procedures.

INDEX

	Page No.
Adjustments	1-171
Parking Brake	1-171
A4 & S4	1-171
A6, S6 & Cabriolet	1-172
A8	1-172
TT	1-172
Rear Brake Basic Setting, Inspection	1-171
Brake Pad Service	1-170
Except TT	1-170
TT	1-170
Brake Rotor, Replace	1-173
Caliper Service	1-171
Overhaul	1-171
Disc Brake Specifications	1-173
Precautions	1-170
Air Bag Systems	1-170
Battery Ground Cable	1-170
Radio Coded Anti-Theft System	1-170
Tightening Specifications	1-174

PRECAUTIONS

Air Bag Systems

Refer to "Air Bag System Precautions" in the front of this manual for system disarming and arming procedures.

Radio Coded Anti-Theft System

Prior to disconnecting the battery or removing the audio system, obtain the security code from the vehicle operator. Refer to the owner's manual for security code disarming and arming procedures.

Battery Ground Cable

Prior to service, disconnect battery ground cable and isolate as required.

BRAKE PAD SERVICE

Except TT

1. Raise and support vehicle, then remove wheel assemblies.
2. **If brake pads are to be used again, mark installed positions for installation reference.**
3. Remove caliper housing to carrier mounting bolts, then the caliper housing, **Fig. 1.**
4. Remove brake pads from carrier.
5. Extract part of brake fluid from reservoir using a suitable bleeder bottle, then install piston using installation tool No. 3272, or equivalent.
6. Install brake pads, then the caliper housing and tighten to specifications.
7. Install wheel assemblies and lower vehicle.
8. **On A4 and A8 models,** depress brake pedal firmly several times with vehicle stationary to adjust brake pads to their normal operating positions.
9. **On A6, Cabriolet and S6 models,** adjust rear brakes as outlined under "Adjustments" in this section.

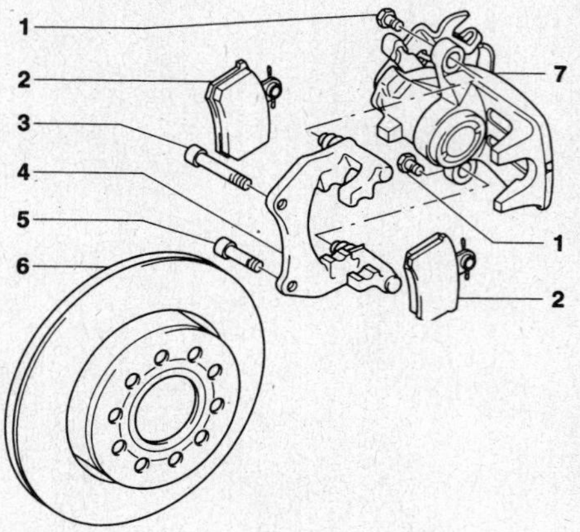

1. Self Locking Bolt
2. Brake Pads
3. Ribbed Bolt
4. Brake Carrier With Guide Pin & Protective Cap
5. Ribbed Bolt
6. Brake Disc
7. Brake Caliper Housing

AD4079600028000X

Fig. 1 Exploded view of rear brakes

10. **On all models,** inspect brake fluid level and fill as required.

TT

1. Raise and support vehicle, then remove rear tires.
2. **If brake pads are to be used again, mark installed positions for installation reference.**
3. Remove brake cable retaining clip, **Fig. 2.**
4. Push brake lever in direction of arrow, **Fig. 2,** then disconnect brake cable.
5. Counter-hold guide pins, then remove and discard caliper mounting bolts, **Fig. 3.**
6. Remove brake pads and pad retaining springs.
7. Clean brake caliper housing using a suitable methylated spirit. **Pay close attention to pad bonding surfaces. They must be free of all grease and adhesive residues.**
8. Siphon off a small amount of brake fluid from reservoir using a bleeder bottle or suitable tool.
9. Carefully seat piston using removal and installer tool No. 3272, or equivalent, as follows:
   a. Mount installer tool so its collar sits on caliper, **Fig. 4.**
   b. Rotate tool knob clockwise to seat piston. Use a 13 MM open end wrench on tool flats if piston is stubborn. **Do not exert excessive force.**
10. Install pads and retaining springs into carrier.
11. Remove protective foil from outer brake pad as required.
12. Install caliper with new self-locking bolts. Tighten to specifications.
13. Connect parking brake cable, then install retainer clip.
14. Install tires, then lower the vehicle to the ground. Tighten wheel lug nuts to specifications.
15. **Depress brake pedal firmly several times with vehicle stationary to**

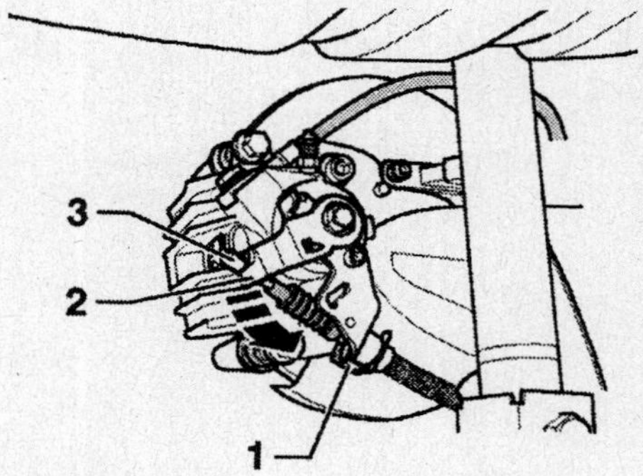

1. Clip
2. Brake lever
3. Brake cable

AD4070000043000X

Fig. 2 Brake cable removal from rear caliper. TT

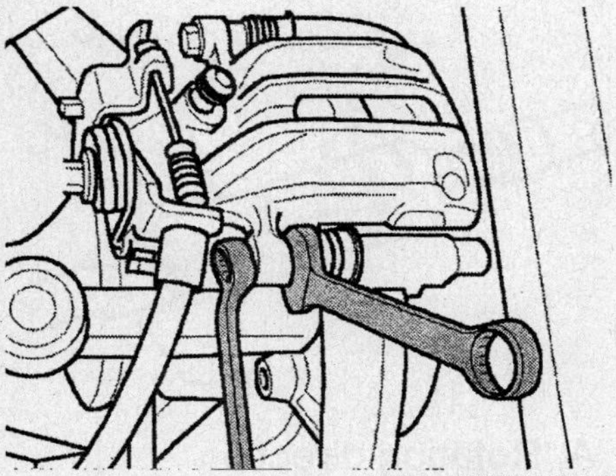

AD4070000044000X

Fig. 3 Caliper mounting bolt removal. TT

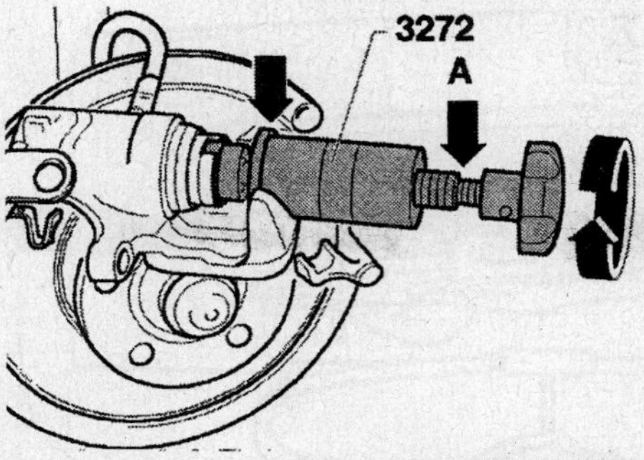

AD4070000045000X

Fig. 4 Piston seating w/tool No. 3272. TT

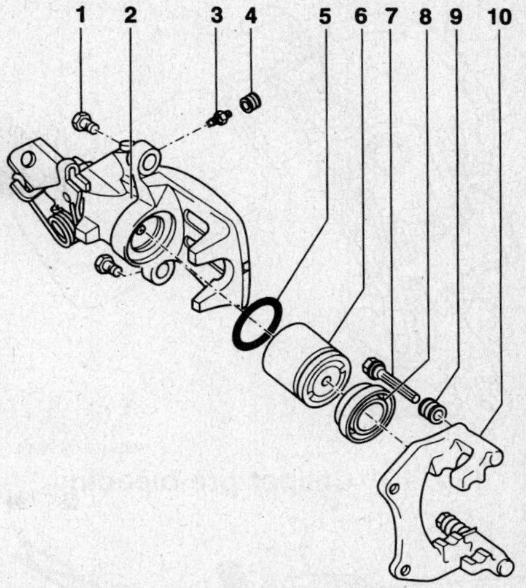

1. Self Locking Bolt
2. Brake Caliper Housing
3. Bleeder Valve
4. Dust Cap
5. Seal
6. Piston
7. Guide Pin
8. Protective Cap
9. Protective Cap
10. Brake Carrier

AD4079600029000X

Fig. 5 Exploded view of rear brake caliper

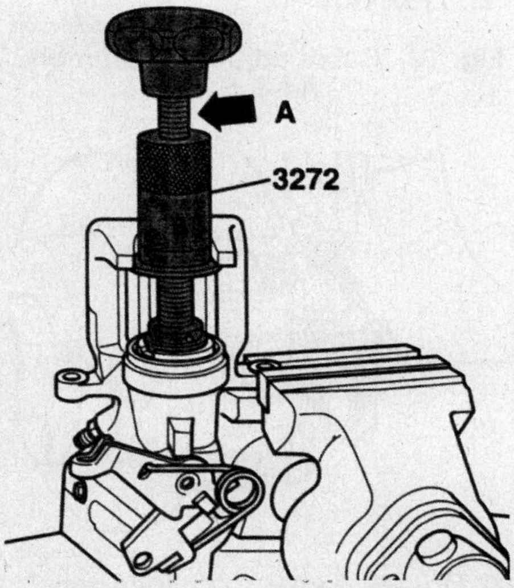

AD4079600030000X

Fig. 6 Rear caliper piston replacement

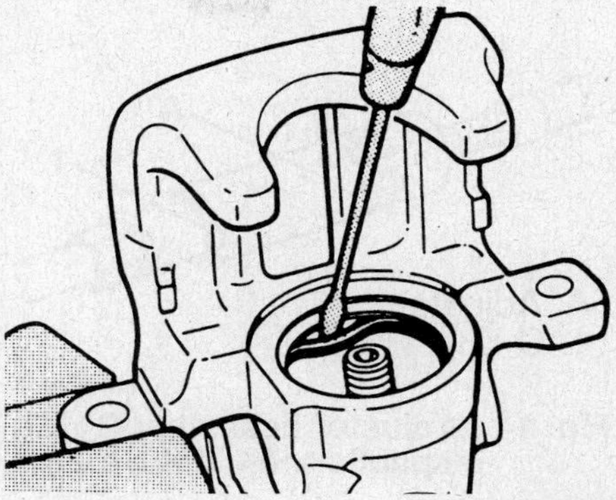

AD4079600032000X

Fig. 7 Caliper piston seal removal

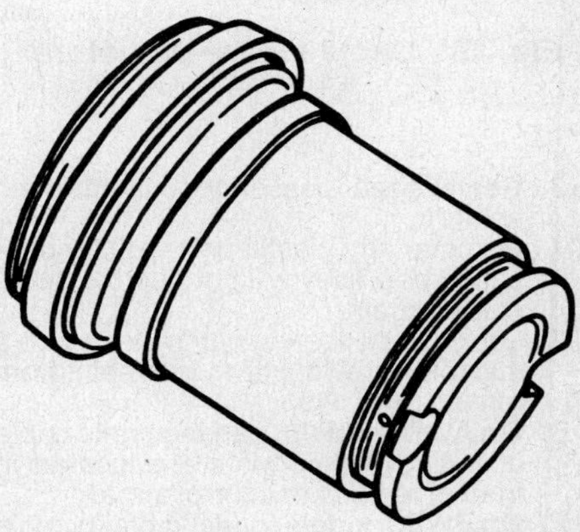

AD4079600031000X

Fig. 8 Protective cap installation

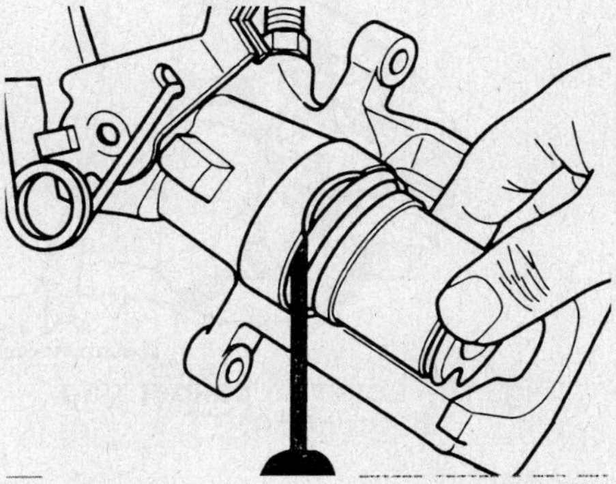

AD4079600033000X

Fig. 9 Inner sealing lip installation

allow pads to properly seat in normal operating positions.

16. Inspect brake fluid level and correct as required.

CALIPER SERVICE

OVERHAUL

Refer to **Fig. 5** when servicing front disc brake calipers, noting the following:

1. Remove piston from caliper housing using replacement tool No. 3272, or equivalent, **Fig. 6.**
2. Remove caliper piston seal using a suitable screwdriver, **Fig. 7.**
3. Install piston as follows:
   a. Install protective cap with sealing lip onto piston, **Fig. 8.**
   b. Insert inner sealing lip of protective cap into groove in brake caliper housing using a suitable screwdriver, **Fig. 9. Hold piston in front of caliper housing during this step.**
   c. Install piston into brake caliper housing using replacement tool No. 3272, or equivalent, **Fig. 6. Outer sealing lip of protective cap fits into groove in piston.**
4. Pre-bleed caliper as follows:
   a. Open caliper bleeder valve and fill caliper with brake fluid using a suitable bleeder bottle, **Fig. 10.**
   b. Fill caliper until brake fluid flows out brake hose connection free of bubbles.
   c. Close bleeder valve.

ADJUSTMENTS

Rear Brake Basic Setting, Inspection

Parking brake cable must be free of tension during basic setting inspection.

1. Push caliper lever against stop on both sides of vehicle using a suitable screwdriver. Parking brake cable is too tight if lever of opposite side caliper is pulled away from stop.
2. If required, loosen adjustment nut for parking brake cable until both levers rest against stop.
3. Push a suitable screwdriver between end of rear spring and roller.
4. Press brake pedal once, then ensure both tires rotate freely.
5. Remove screwdriver.

Parking Brake

A4 & S4

Always perform rear brake basic setting prior to adjusting parking brake cables.

1. Depress brake pedal firmly at least once.
2. Ensure parking brake lever is fully released.

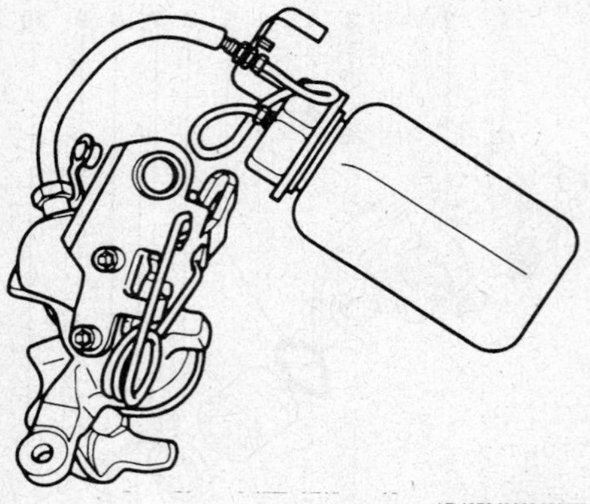

Fig. 10 Caliper pre-bleeding

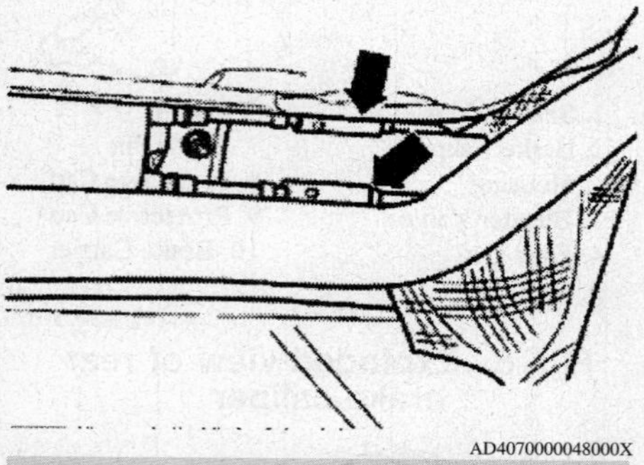

Fig. 13 Cable sleeve adjusters. A4 & S4

3. Remove rear passenger compartment ashtray.
4. Remove any plastic parts at compensating bar. They will not need to be installed again.
5. Lock compensating bar in place with a suitable screwdriver to prevent it from turning, **Fig. 11.**
6. **On AWD models,** parking brake cable adjusting components are located in front of rear lower control arms.
7. **On FWD models,** parking brake cable adjusting components are located in tunnel on underside of vehicle.
8. **On all models,** remove locking clip, **Fig. 12.**
9. Counter-hold hex nut using a suitable 13 MM open end wrench, then rotate adjusting nut in to its stop.
10. Slide cable adjuster together.
11. Back off adjusting nut until locking clip slot is visible, then install locking clip.
12. Pull both cable sleeve adjusters apart evenly until there is tension on cables, **Fig. 13. Ensure lever does not lift off at caliper.**
13. Remove screwdriver from compensator, then fully apply parking brake three times.
14. Inspect adjuster assembly and ensure O-ring is not visible, **Fig. 14.**
15. Inspect parking brake tension and adjust by rotating adjuster assembly in or out as required.
16. Ensure lever does not contact rear caliper.
17. Measure gap "a," **Fig. 15,** which should be visible, but not wider than.

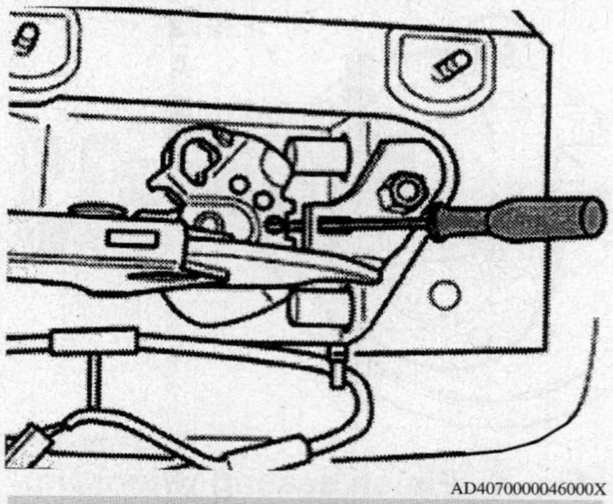

Fig. 11 Compensating bar locked w/screwdriver. A4 & S4

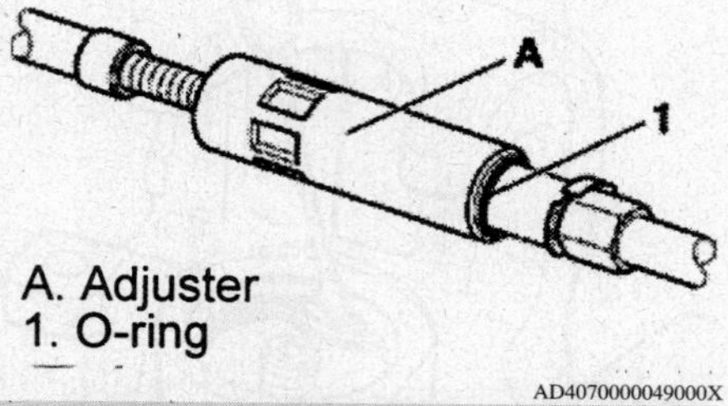

Fig. 14 Adjuster assembly O-ring inspection. A4 & S4

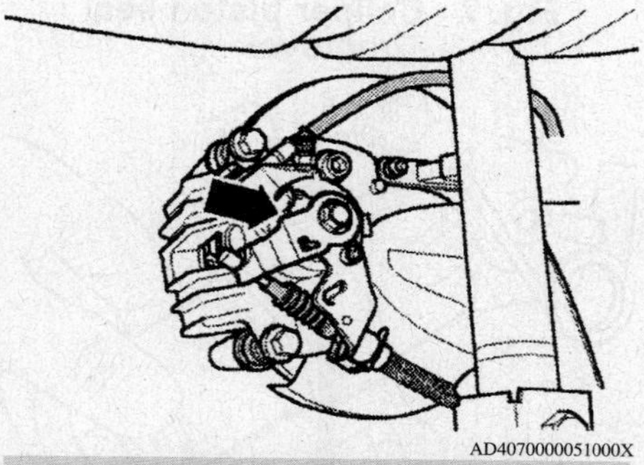

Fig. 16 Lever to caliper gap inspection. TT

059 inch.

A6, S6 & CABRIOLET

Always perform rear brake basic setting prior to adjusting parking brake cables.

1. Tighten adjusting nut for parking brake lever until both levers lift slightly off their stops.
2. Back off adjusting nut two turns, then press levers for parking brake cable alternately against stop using a suitable screwdriver.
3. Cable is too tight if lever on opposite side is pulled away from stop.
4. Loosen parking brake cable adjusting nut until both levers rest against stops.
5. Pull up on parking brake and release, then ensure both tires rotate freely.

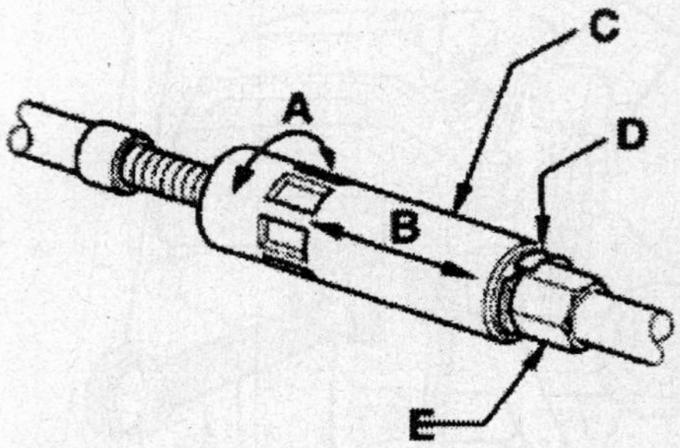

Fig. 12 Cable adjuster assembly. A4 & S4

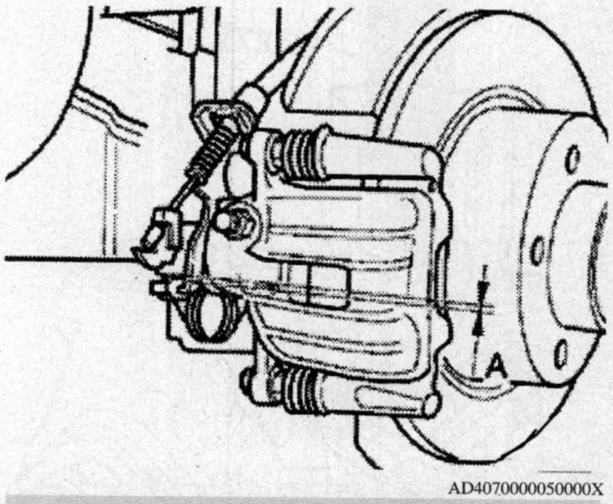

Fig. 15 Lever to caliper gap inspection. A4 & S4

A8

Always perform rear brake basic setting prior to adjusting parking brake cables.

1. Depress brake pedal firmly at least once.
2. Ensure parking brake lever is fully released.
3. Loosen cable adjusting nut using extension tool No. 3343, or equivalent, until both levers rest on caliper stops.
4. Tighten pull rod nut so both levers are seen to move.
5. Fully apply parking brake at least three times.
6. Adjust pull rod nut so just one lever lifts off its caliper stop.

TT

Always perform rear brake basic setting prior to adjusting parking brake cables.

1. Remove floor console switch panel and storage tray.
2. Remove floor console rear cover panel.
3. Tighten adjusting nut with parking brake lever in released position until

lever lifts off brake caliper stop, **Fig. 16.**

4. Measure gap, **Fig. 16,** which should be visible, but not wider than. 059 inch.
5. Back off adjusting nut two turns, then using a suitable screwdriver, press levers for parking brake cable alternately against stop.
6. Fully apply parking brake three times, then release and ensure both rear tires rotate freely.

BRAKE ROTOR

REPLACE

Refer to "Front Suspension & Steering" or "Rear Axle & Suspension" under "Strut, Replace" and "Shock Absorber, Replace" procedures.

DISC BRAKE SPECIFICATIONS

Model	Year	Front Disc Brake						Rear Disc Brake					
			Rotor						Rotor				
		Brake Lining Wear Limit, Inch②	Thickness, Inch			Thickness Variation Parallelism Inch	Lateral Run Out (T.I.R.) Inch	Brake Lining Wear Limit, Inch②	Thickness, Inch			Thickness Variation Parallelism Inch	Lateral Run-Out (T.I.R.) Inch
			Nominal	Min. Refinish	Discard Limit①				Nominal	Min. Refinish	Discard Limit①		
A4	1998–2001	⑥	④	—	⑤	—	—	.280③	.390	—	.310	—	—
A6 2.8L	1998–2001	.079	.984	—	.906	—	—	.276③	.394	—	.315	—	—
A6 2.7L & 4.2L	2000–01	.079	1.181	—	1.102	—	—	.276③	.866	—	.787	—	—
A8	1998–2001	.079	.984	—	.906	—	—	.276③	.787	—	.709	—	—
A8 & S8	2001	.079	1.181	—	1.102	—	—	.276③	.866	—	.787	—	—
Cabriolet	1998	.079	.984	—	.866	—	—	.276③	.394	—	.315	—	—
S4	2001	.079	1.181	—	1.102	—	—	.276③	.866	—	.787	—	—
TT	2000–01	.079	.984	—	.906	—	—	.079	.354	—	.275	—	—

① — Discard thickness is stamped on rotor.

② — Above rivet head or backing plate. Original equipment type brake lining.

③ — Includes backing plate.

④ — Teves/ATE vented rotor,. 984 inch; Teves/ATE solid rotor,. 590 inch; Lucas internally vented rotor,. 870 inch; Lucas solid rotor,. 510 inch; double piston front brake caliper brake, 1.180 inch.

⑤ — Teves/ATE vented rotor,. 906 inch; Teves/ATE solid rotor,. 510 inch; Lucas internally vented rotor,. 790 inch; Lucas solid rotor,. 430 inch; double piston front caliper brake, 1.100 inch.

⑥ — Except double piston caliper brake,. 080 inch; double piston caliper brake,. 120 inch.

TIGHTENING SPECIFICATIONS

Year	Component	Torque/Ft. Lbs.
A4 & S4		
1998–2001	Brake Caliper Housing To Carrier	26
	Carrier Mounting Bolts (AWD)	44
	Carrier Mounting Bolts (FWD)	70
A6		
1998–2001	Brake Caliper Housing To Carrier	20
	Carrier Mounting Bolts	48
A8		
1998–2001	Brake Caliper Housing To Carrier	22
	Carrier Mounting Bolts (AWD)	44
	Carrier Mounting Bolts (FWD)	70
CABRIOLET & S6		
1998–2001	Brake Caliper Housing To Carrier	26
	Carrier Mounting Bolts	48
TT		
2000–01	Brake Caliper Housing To Carrier	26
	Carrier Mounting Bolts	48

Hydraulic Brake Systems

NOTE: On Air Bag Equipped Models, Refer To "Air Bag System Precautions" Located In The Front Of This Manual For System Disarming & Arming Procedures.

INDEX

	Page No.
Adjustments	1-175
Brake Pressure Regulator	1-175
A6 & S6	1-175
Cabriolet	1-175
Brake System Bleed	1-177
Component Replacement	1-175
Brake Pressure Regulator	1-177
Master Cylinder	1-175
A4 & S4	1-175
A6, S6 & Cabriolet	1-176
A8	1-176
TT	1-176
Diagnosis & Testing	1-175
Brake Pressure Regulator	1-175
A4, S4 & TT	1-175
A6 & S6	1-175
Cabriolet	1-175
Precautions	1-175
Air Bag Systems	1-175
Battery Ground Cable	1-175
Radio Coded Anti-Theft System	1-175

PRECAUTIONS

Air Bag Systems

Refer to "Air Bag System Precautions" in the front of this manual for system disarming and arming procedures.

Radio Coded Anti-Theft System

Prior to disconnecting the battery or removing the audio system, obtain the security code from the vehicle operator. Refer to the owner's manual for security code disarming and arming procedures.

Battery Ground Cable

Prior to service, disconnect battery ground cable and isolate as required.

DIAGNOSIS & TESTING

Brake Pressure Regulator

A4, S4 & TT

On these models there is no mechanical brake pressure regulator. Specially matched control module software controls brake pressure regulation.

A6 & S6

Brake pressure regulator is mounted on body (lefthand rear), and operated by a spring attached to the rear axle. Prior to inspection, ensure system is properly bled and filled.

1. Firmly depress brake pedal once, with vehicle on ground.
2. Release pedal suddenly and ensure lever on pressure regulator moves.

CABRIOLET

Brake pressure regulator is mounted on righthand rear of body and operated by spring attached to rear axle.

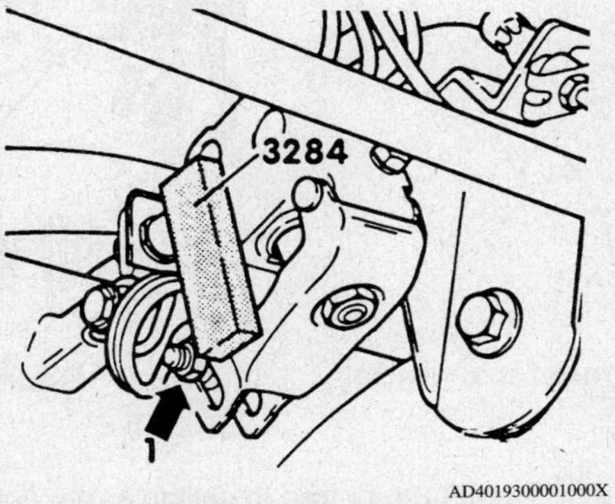

Fig. 1 Brake compensator valve adjustment. Cabriolet

1. Test must be conducted with empty vehicle on the ground, full fuel tank and driver's seat occupied.
2. Firmly depress pedal once while vehicle is still on ground.
3. Release pedal suddenly and ensure lever on pressure regulator moves.
4. Ensure brake system is properly filled and bled.
5. Connect gauge assembly tool No. US 1116, or equivalent to lefthand front and righthand rear calipers, according to manufacturer's instructions.
6. Bounce vehicle several times.
7. Bleed both hoses and gauge using bleeder valve on gauge.
8. Depress brake pedal until gauge on front axle reads 1450 psi. Hold for five seconds.
9. If rear pressure reading varies more than 145 psi within five seconds, replace pressure regulator.

ADJUSTMENTS

Brake Pressure Regulator

CABRIOLET

1. For the following procedure, the vehicle must be empty and standing level on all four tires, fuel tank must be full and jack and spare tire must be in normal locations.
2. Raise and support vehicle using a suitable wheel type lift.
3. Ensure vehicle is level and suspension is in normal position.
4. Loosen brake compensator spring adjustment bolt and nut.
5. Insert pins of adjustment tool No. 3284, or equivalent, into holes on arm and body of brake compensator, **Fig. 1.**
6. Tighten spring adjustment bolt and nut, then remove tool.
7. Measure brake system pressures as outlined under "Diagnosis & Testing."

A6 & S6

1. Ensure brake system is properly filled and bled.
2. Raise and support vehicle. Ensure there is no load on rear axle and springs are fully extended.
3. Press lever on brake pressure regulator against stop towards back of vehicle.
4. Loosen nut at axle side of spring.
5. Bend a. 28 inch rod and place between spring and bearing, then **torque**nut to 15 ft. lbs. and remove rod.
6. Hook tension spring to support.
7. Measure brake system pressures as outlined under "Diagnosis & Testing."

COMPONENT REPLACEMENT

Master Cylinder

A4 & S4

1. Remove driver's side storage compartment.
2. Separate brake pedal from master cylinder pushrod as follows:
   a. Remove stop lamp switch.
   b. Insert brake pedal release tool No. T10006, or equivalent, from below, **Fig. 2.**
   c. Hold brake pedal tightly.

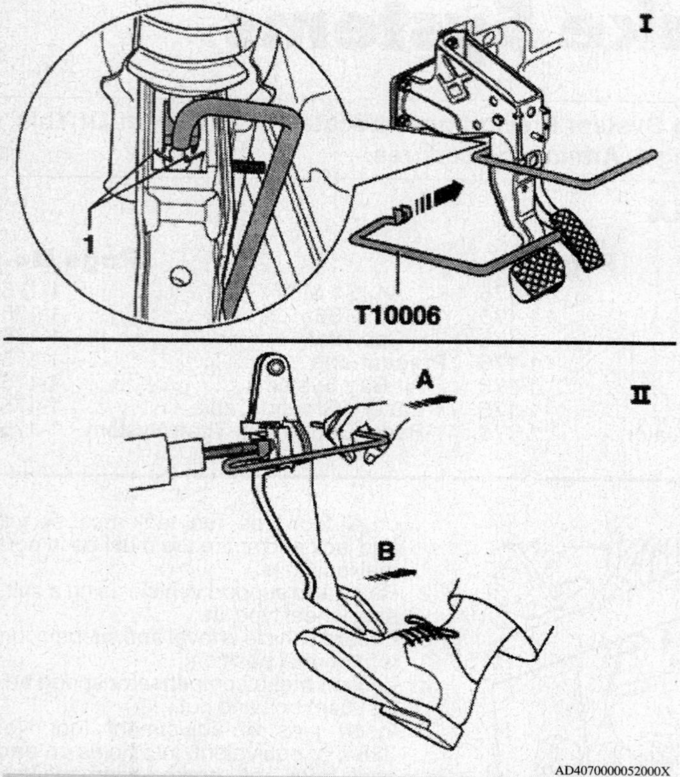

AD4070000052000X

Fig. 2 Brake pedal separation from master cylinder pushrod. A4 & S4

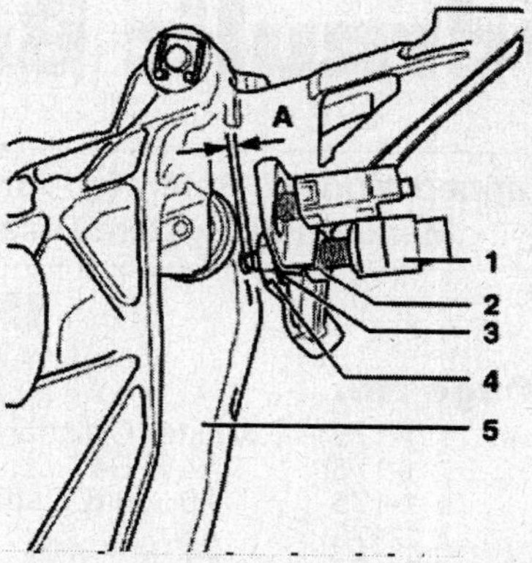

1- Brake light switch
2- Hex nut, M12 x 1.5
3- Spring washer, M12
4- Hex nut, M12 x 1.5
5- Brake pedal

AD4070000053000X

Fig. 3 Stop lamp switch pushrod protrusion gap. A4 & S4

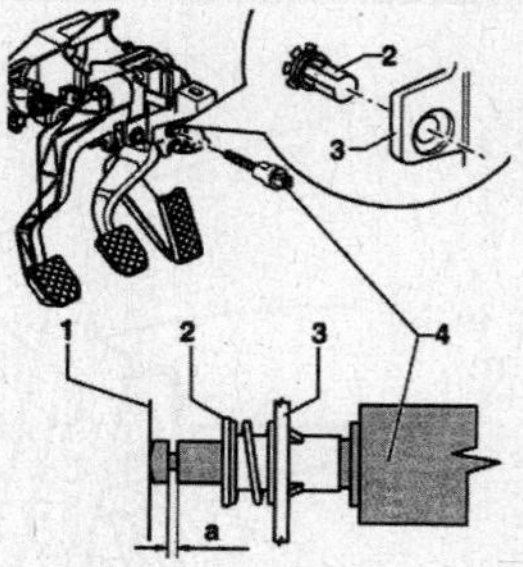

1- Stop surface of brake pedal
2- Spring clip-Press into pedal cluster from behind
3- Pedal cluster
4- Brake light switch -F-
a- Clearance: max. 0.7 mm (0.028 in.)

AD4070000054000X

Fig. 4 Speed control switch pushrod protrusion gap. A4 & S4

d. Lift catch off push rod using a slight pull on release tool "A."
e. Keep tension on tool to prevent pushrod from engaging catches.
f. Separate brake pedal from master cylinder pushrod "B."

3. Connect bleeder hose and bleeder bottle to lefthand front brake caliper bleeder valve, then open bleeder valve.
4. Operate brake pedal to pump out as much brake fluid as possible.
5. Close bleeder valve.
6. Remove brake fluid reservoir to master cylinder mounting bolt.
7. Disconnect brake fluid level warning switch electrical connector.
8. **On models equipped with manual transaxle,** disconnect clutch master cylinder supply hose, then seal with a suitable plug.
9. **On all models,** cover plenum to catch any brake fluid spillage.
10. Remove brake fluid reservoir by pressing locking catch down, then pulling reservoir out of sealing plugs.
11. Disconnect brake lines from master cylinder, then seal lines and ports using plugs from repair kit.
12. Disconnect booster vacuum hose.
13. Remove Torx T45 bolts from servo.
14. Remove brake servo together with master cylinder as a unit.
15. Remove master cylinder to servo mounting nuts.
16. Reverse procedure to install, noting the following:
    a. Clean all spilled brake fluid from plenum before installing servo and master cylinder.
    b. Ensure pushrod is properly located in master cylinder when mounting to servo.
    c. Adjust stop lamp switch pushrod protrusion gap to. 004–.020 inch, **Fig. 3.**
    d. Adjust speed control switch pushrod protrusion gap to. 028 inch, **Fig. 4.**
    e. Connect brake bleeder tool No. US1116, or equivalent.
    f. Open bleeder valve on clutch slave cylinder, then connect bleeder hose.
    g. Start bleeder unit and allow approximately six ounces of brake fluid to flow out of clutch slave cylinder, then close bleeder valve.
    h. Bleed brake system as outlined under "Brake System Bleed."

A6, S6 & CABRIOLET

Refer to **Figs. 5 and 6** when replacing master cylinder.

1. Disconnect brake lines from master cylinder.
2. Remove master cylinder to booster, or master cylinder to servo attaching bolts.
3. Remove master cylinder.
4. Reverse procedure to install, then bleed system.

A8

Refer to **Fig. 7** when replacing master cylinder.

1. Extract brake fluid, then disconnect electrical connection for brake level warning system. **Remove strainer from reservoir when extracting brake fluid.**
2. Disconnect brake lines from master cylinder.
3. Remove brake fluid reservoir.
4. Remove master cylinder to servo attaching bolts.
5. Remove master cylinder.
6. Reverse procedure to install, then bleed system.

TT

1. Siphon out as much brake fluid as possible from fluid reservoir with a suction bottle.
2. Clamp off clutch master cylinder supply hose with clamp tool No. 3094, or equivalent.
3. Disconnect clutch master cylinder supply hose.
4. Disconnect fluid level sender electrical connector.
5. Disconnect brake lines at master cylinder, then cap them with plugs from repair kit part No. 1H0 698 311 A.
6. Remove master cylinder mounting nuts, then separate master cylinder from servo unit.

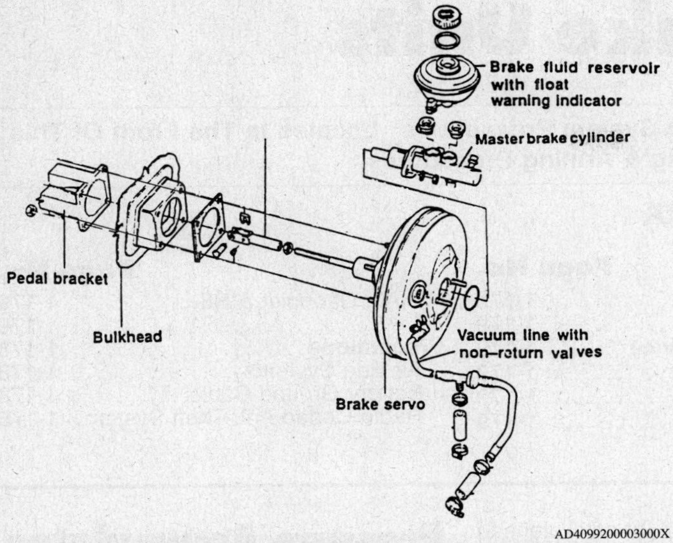

Fig. 5 Exploded view of hydraulic brake system. A6 & S6

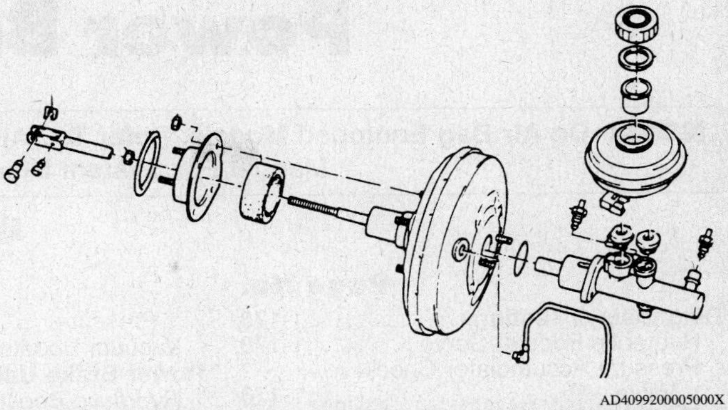

Fig. 6 Exploded view of hydraulic brake system. Cabriolet

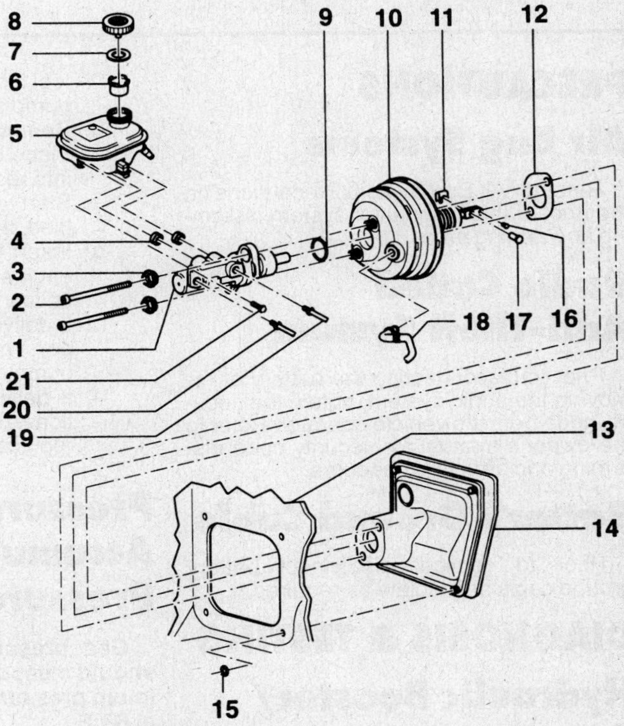

1.	Brake Master Cylinder	12.	Gasket
2.	Bolt	13.	Bulkhead
3.	Flanged Nut	14.	Pedal Cluster
4.	Seal	15.	Nut
5.	Brake Fluid Reservoir	16.	Grommet
6.	Strainer	17.	Pin
7.	Seal	18.	Vacuum Hose
8.	Cover	19.	Brake Line
9.	Seal	20.	Brake Line
10.	Vacuum Brake Booster	21.	Bolt
11.	Safety Clip		

AD4099900008000X

Fig. 7 Exploded view of hydraulic brake system. A8

7. Reverse procedure to install, noting the following:
   a. Ensure pushrod is properly located in master cylinder when mounting to servo.
   b. **Torque** master cylinder mounting nuts to 15 ft. lbs.
   c. Bleed brake hydraulic system as outlined under "Brake System Bleed."
   d. Bleed clutch hydraulic system as outlined under "Clutch system Bleed" in "Clutch & Manual transaxle" section.

Brake Pressure Regulator

1. Raise and support vehicle.
2. Disconnect regulator from operating arm.
3. Remove brake fluid lines.
4. Remove regulator mounting bolts, then regulator.
5. Reverse procedure to install, noting the following:
   a. Bleed brakes as outlined under "Brake System Bleed."
   b. Adjust regulator as outlined under "Adjustments."

BRAKE SYSTEM BLEED

The following procedure has been modified by a Technical Service Bulletin.

To bleed brake system, use a catch bottle with a transparent hose attached so brake fluid can be inspected for air bubbles.

1. Connect brake pressure bleeding tool No. VAG 1869, or equivalent, per tool manufacturer's instructions.
2. Bleed brakes in following sequence:
   a. Righthand rear caliper.
   b. Lefthand rear caliper.
   c. Righthand front caliper.
   d. Lefthand front caliper.
   e. Righthand rear caliper (once more).
   f. **On models with height sensitive brake pressure regulator,** press regulator lever firmly towards rear axle when bleeding rear calipers.
   g. **On models equipped with ABS,** road test vehicle and make at least one ABS controlled brake application.

Power Brake Units

NOTE: On Air Bag Equipped Models, Refer To "Air Bag System Precautions" Located In The Front Of This Manual For System Disarming & Arming Procedures.

INDEX

	Page No.
Diagnosis & Testing	1-178
Hydraulic Booster/Servo	1-178
Pressure Accumulator Check Valve	1-178
Pressure Accumulator Pressure Relief Valve	1-178
Pressure Accumulator-Gas Pressure	1-178
Vacuum Booster	1-179
Power Brake Unit Service	1-179
Hydraulic Booster/Servo	1-179
Vacuum Booster	1-179
A4 & S4	1-179
A6, Cabriolet & S6	1-179
A8	1-179
Precautions	1-178
Air Bag Systems	1-178
Battery Ground Cable	1-178
Radio Coded Anti-Theft System	1-178

PRECAUTIONS

Air Bag Systems

Refer to "Air Bag System Precautions" in the front of this manual for system disarming and arming procedures.

Radio Coded Anti-Theft System

Prior to disconnecting the battery or removing the audio system, obtain the security code from the vehicle operator. Refer to the owner's manual for security code disarming and arming procedures.

Battery Ground Cable

Prior to service, disconnect battery ground cable and isolate as required.

DIAGNOSIS & TESTING

Hydraulic Booster/ Servo

1. With ignition Off, depress brake pedal approximately 20 times to reduce system pressure.
2. Disconnect warning lamp switch electrical connector, then remove switch.
3. Attach pressure gauge with hollow bolt and copper washers to brake servo unit. Attach thick copper washer between brake servo unit and banjo fitting and thin copper washer between hollow bolt and banjo fitting.
4. Start engine and let idle until pressure gauge reading exceeds 2030 psi.
5. If specified pressure is not reached, measure delivery rate of central hydraulic pump as follows:
   a. **Turn ignition Off, leaving pressure gauge connected.**
   b. Disconnect pressure line from hydraulic pump.
   c. Connect hose of pressure limiter tool No. VW 1354, or equivalent, to pump using existing hollow bolt.
   d. Remove fluid reservoir from cap.
   e. Place end of pressure limiter hose into reservoir.
   f. Start engine, let idle until line is bled, then turn ignition Off.
   g. Insert hose in measuring jar, start engine, run at idle, then measure delivery rate.
   h. If delivery rate is not at least. 3 qt. per minute, replace hydraulic pump.
   i. If delivery rate is within specifications, but operating pressure is not, replace pressure accumulator.

Pressure Accumulator-Gas Pressure

Gas pressure of new accumulator should measure 1131–1189 psi and minimum pressure should measure 435 psi at 68°F.

1. With ignition Off, depress brake pedal approximately 20 times to reduce system pressure.
2. Disconnect warning lamp switch electrical connector, then remove switch.
3. Attach pressure gauge with hollow bolt and copper washers to brake servo unit. Attach thick copper washer between brake servo unit and banjo fitting, then the thin copper washer between hollow bolt and banjo fitting.
4. Start engine and let idle until pressure gauge reads approximately 2030 psi.
5. Turn ignition off.
6. Pump brake pedal until pressure drops slowly. Pressure at which gauge needle drops rapidly from, to zero is gas pressure of pressure accumulator.
7. If pressure is less than 435 psi, replace accumulator.

Pressure Accumulator Check Valve

1. With ignition Off, depress brake pedal approximately 20 times to reduce system pressure.
2. Disconnect warning lamp switch electrical connector, then remove switch.
3. Attach pressure gauge with hollow bolt and copper washers to brake servo unit. Attach thick copper washer between brake servo unit and banjo fitting, then the thin copper washer between hollow bolt and banjo fitting.
4. Start engine, let idle until pressure gauge reads approximately 2030 psi, then turn ignition Off.
5. Pump brake pedal until pressure drops to 1957 psi.
6. If operating pressure drops below 1885 psi within 5 minutes, replace pressure accumulator.

Pressure Accumulator Pressure Relief Valve

1. Ensure pump delivery rate is within specifications. Refer to "Hydraulic Booster/Servo," Step 5.
2. With ignition Off, depress brake pedal approximately 20 times to reduce system pressure.
3. Disconnect warning lamp switch electrical connector, then remove switch.
4. Attach pressure gauge with hollow bolt and copper washers to brake servo unit. Attach thick copper washer between brake servo unit and banjo fitting and the thin copper washer between hollow bolt and banjo fitting.
5. Start engine and let idle until pressure gauge reading exceeds 2030 psi.
6. If 2030 psi cannot be achieved, replace pressure accumulator, then measure system pressure.

Vacuum Booster

1. Depress brake pedal firmly approximately 20 times with ignition Off.
2. Depress brake pedal and hold.
3. Start engine, if brake booster is working properly, pedal will fall slightly and then hold.

POWER BRAKE UNIT SERVICE

Hydraulic Booster/ Servo

1. Remove master cylinder as outlined under "Hydraulic Brake System."
2. Disconnect hydraulic lines from booster/servo.
3. Remove brake booster/servo attaching bolts.
4. Disconnect booster pushrod from brake pedal.
5. Reverse procedure to install, noting the following:
   a. Adjust pushrod length to 9.04–9.08 inches from face of booster/servo unit to center of clevis hole.
   b. **Torque** booster mounting bolts to 18 ft. lbs.

Vacuum Booster

A4 & S4

1. Remove master cylinder as outlined under "Hydraulic Brake System" section.
2. Disconnect hydraulic lines from brake servo unit.

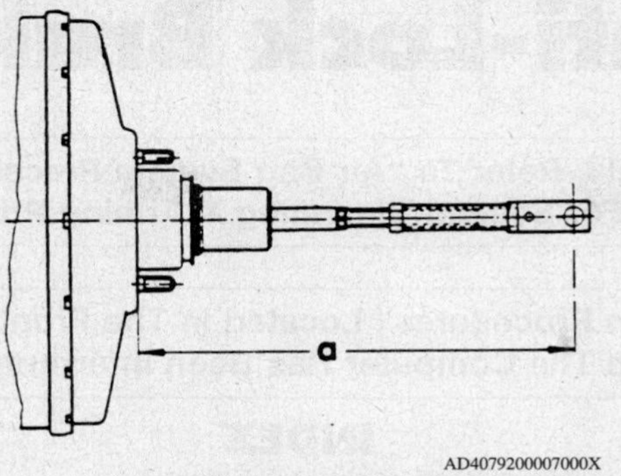

Fig. 1 Brake booster pushrod adjustment. A6, Cabriolet & S6

3. Remove stowage area from under left-hand side dash.
4. Disconnect vacuum line from booster/ servo.
5. Remove brake servo unit attaching bolts.
6. Pull back and remove brake lamp switch and cruise control vent valve from brake pedal if equipped.
7. Install removal tool No. 3289, then disconnect pushrod from brake pedal.
8. Remove brake servo unit.
9. Reverse procedure to install. Bleed brake system.

A6, CABRIOLET & S6

1. Remove master cylinder as outlined under "Hydraulic Brake System."
2. Disconnect vacuum line(s) from booster.
3. Remove brake booster attaching bolts.
4. Disconnect booster pushrod from brake pedal.
5. Reverse procedure to install, noting the following:
   a. **On Cabriolet models,** adjust pushrod length "a" to 10.66–10.70 inches, **Fig. 1.**
   b. **On A6 models,** adjust pushrod length "a" to 9.04–9.08 inches, **Fig. 1.**
   c. **On all models, torque** booster mounting bolts to 18 ft. lbs.

A8

1. Remove lower steering column slot cover.
2. Remove instrument panel lower knee bolster.
3. Remove brake master cylinder to brake pedal pin.
4. Remove plenum panel cover and start engine.
5. Place a suitable container under right-hand rear brake caliper, then open bleeder screw.
6. Pump brake pedal to pump brake fluid out of brake reservoir.
7. Remove fluid reservoir attaching bolts.
8. Disconnect harness connector from brake fluid level warning switch.
9. Remove brake fluid reservoir. **Brake fluid reservoir is engaged in brake master cylinder on underside. Press eye downward while pulling brake fluid reservoir out of seal.**
10. Disconnect brake lines and immediately seal with stoppers.
11. Pull off vacuum hose.
12. Remove mounting bolts for brake booster.
13. Remove brake booster together with brake master cylinder.
14. Reverse procedure to install.

Anti-Lock Brakes

NOTE: On Air Bag Equipped Models, Refer To "Air Bag System Precautions" Located In The Front Of This Manual For System Disarming & Arming Procedures.

NOTE: Refer To "Computer Relearn Procedures" Located In The Front Of This Manual When Battery Power To The Computer Has Been Interrupted.

INDEX

	Page No.
Diagnosis & Testing	1-180
Hydraulic Modulator High & Low Pressure Testing	1-182
With LED Type Tester	1-180
With Scan Tool	1-182
Precautions	1-180
Air Bag Systems	1-180
Battery Ground Cable	1-180
Radio Coded Anti-Theft System	1-180
System Coding	1-182
Component Replacement	1-183
Electronic Control Unit	1-183
Front Wheel Speed Sensors	1-184
Hydraulic Control Unit Mounting Bracket	1-184
Hydraulic Control Unit	1-184
Rear Wheel Speed Sensors	1-184
TT	1-182
System Service	1-182
Brake System Bleed	1-182
Technical Service Bulletins	1-184
ABS Lamp On After Battery Jump Starting Or Charging ABS Fuses Blown	1-184
Troubleshooting	1-180

PRECAUTIONS

Air Bag Systems

Refer to "Air Bag System Precautions" in the front of this manual for system disarming and arming procedures.

Radio Coded Anti-Theft System

Prior to disconnecting the battery or removing the audio system, obtain the security code from the vehicle operator. Refer to the owner's manual for security code disarming and arming procedures.

Battery Ground Cable

Prior to service, disconnect battery ground cable and isolate as required.

TROUBLESHOOTING

Refer to "Diagnosis & Testing" for ABS troubleshooting.

DIAGNOSIS & TESTING

WITH LED TYPE TESTER

LED 1 & 3 DO NOT LIGHT, TESTER IN POSITION 1

Refer to **Fig. 1,** for LED identification numbers. Weaker illumination of an LED indicates a contact resistance in respective circuit.

1. Inspect for continuity between ABS control unit connector terminal 34 and ground at battery ground cable (LED 1), **Fig. 2.**
2. Inspect for continuity between ABS control unit connector terminal 10 and ground at battery ground cable (LED 3).
3. If continuity does not exist, repair shorted or open circuit.

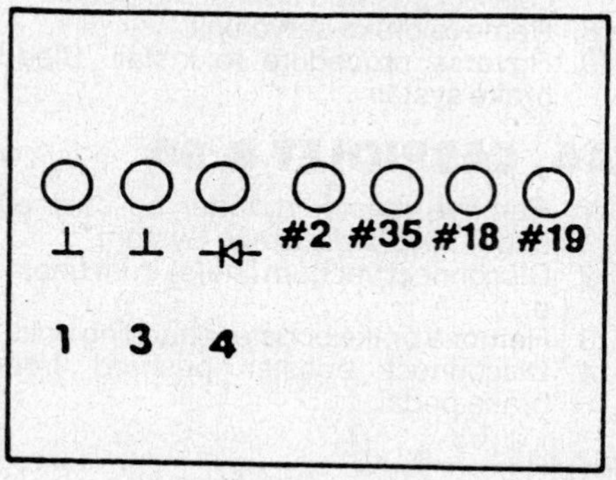

Fig. 1 LED identification

LED 4 DOES NOT LIGHT, TESTER IN POSITION 1

Refer to **Fig. 1,** for LED identification. Weaker illumination of an LED indicates a contact resistance in respective circuit.

1. Inspect for continuity between ABS control unit connector terminal 32 and black hydraulic modulator connector terminal 12 (LED 4), **Figs 2 and 3.**
2. If continuity does not exist, repair shorted or open circuit.
3. Inspect for continuity between ABS control unit connector terminal 20 and ground, at battery ground cable.
4. If continuity does not exist, repair shorted or open circuit. If terminal 20 is disconnected, battery LED will not be lit.
5. Inspect for faulty ABS On/Off switch, wiring, lamp bulb and warning lamp diode. Inspect warning lamp diode as follows:

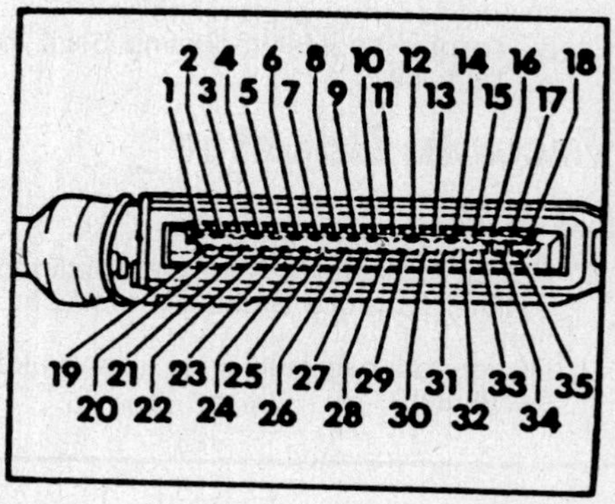

Fig. 2 ABS control unit connector terminal identification

a. Inspect for continuity between black hydraulic modulator connector terminal 10 and ABS control unit terminal 29. **Figs. 2 and 3.**
b. If continuity does not exist, repair shorted or open circuit.
c. Inspect for continuity and contact resistance, both ways, in the top socket between black hydraulic modulator terminals 10 and 12.
d. Ohmmeter must read continuity in one direction and no continuity in the other. Diode is not replaceable. Black hydraulic modulator must be replaced as a unit.

LED 4, 2, 35, 18 & 19 DO NOT LIGHT, TESTER IN POSITION 1

1. Turn ignition Off.
2. Remove solenoid valve relay from hydraulic modulator. Refer to **Fig. 4** for solenoid valve terminal locations.
3. Measure continuity between solenoid valve relay terminals 30 and 87a, which should be. 0 ohms.
4. Measure resistance between solenoid

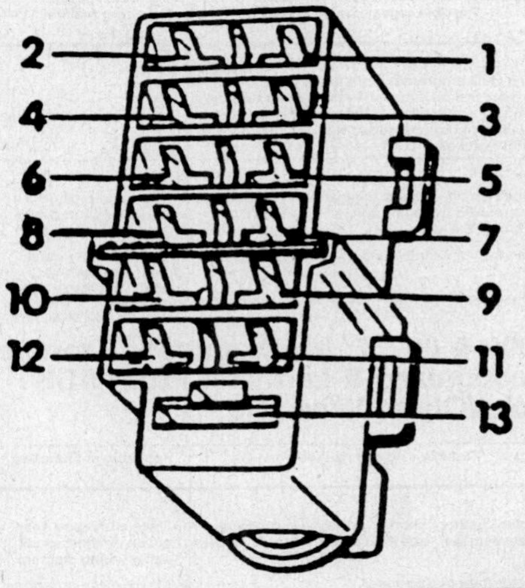

Fig. 3 Black hydraulic modulator connector terminal identification

valve relay terminals 85 and 86, which should be between 70–120 ohms.

5. Remove black connector from top of hydraulic modulator. Inspect for continuity between connector terminal 8 and ground.
6. Inspect for continuity between black hydraulic unit male terminal 8 and solenoid valve relay socket terminal 87a.
7. Inspect for continuity between black hydraulic modulator connector terminal 12 and ABS control unit connector contact 32, **Fig. 2.**
8. Repair circuits for shorts or opens if required. If continuity inspections are satisfactory but LEDs do not light, replace solenoid valve relay.

LED 35 DOES NOT LIGHT

Refer to **Figs. 2 and 3** for terminal locations.

1. Inspect for continuity between ABS control unit connector terminal 35 and black hydraulic modulator connector terminal 5.
2. If continuity does not exist, repair shorted or open circuit.

LED 18 DOES NOT LIGHT

Refer to **Figs. 2 and 3** for terminal locations.

1. Inspect for continuity between ABS control unit connector terminal 18 and black hydraulic modulator connector terminal 1.
2. If continuity does not exist, repair shorted or open circuit.

LED 19 DOES NOT LIGHT

Refer to **Figs. 2 and 3** for terminal locations.

1. Inspect for continuity between ABS control unit connector terminal 19 and black hydraulic modulator connector terminal 1.
2. If continuity does not exist, repair shorted or open circuit.

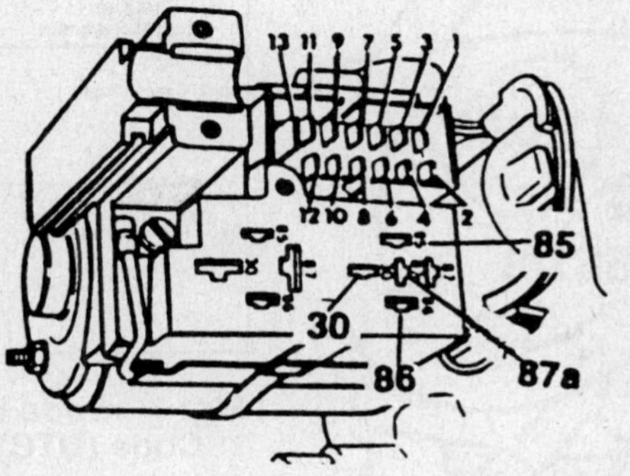

Fig. 4 Solenoid valve relay terminal identification

LED FOR ALTERNATOR DOES NOT LIGHT, TESTER IN POSITION 2

1. Inspect for continuity between alternator terminal 61 (located on back of alternator) and ABS control unit connector terminal 15, **Fig. 2.**
2. If continuity does not exist, repair shorted or open circuit.

LED FOR ALTERNATOR DOES NOT GO OUT WHEN ENGINE STARTS

Measure alternator output. Repair or replace as required.

LED FOR BRAKES DOES NOT LIGHT

1. Inspect for continuity between brake lamp switch terminal and ABS control unit connector 25, **Fig. 2.**
2. If continuity does not exist, repair brake lamp switch or ABS circuit for short or open.

LED FOR BRAKES DOES NOT GO OUT WHEN BRAKE PEDAL IS DEPRESSED

1. Inspect brake lamp switch adjustment.
2. Inspect mechanical function of brake lamp switch.
3. Repair shorted or open circuit.

ABS RETURN PUMP DOES NOT RUN, TESTER IN POSITION 3

1. Turn ignition Off.
2. Remove ABS return pump relay.
3. Inspect for continuity between black hydraulic modulator connector terminal 11 and ABS control unit connector terminal 28, **Figs. 2 and 3.**
4. Inspect for continuity between black hydraulic modulator connector terminal 9 and ABS control unit connector terminal 14.
5. Inspect for continuity between black hydraulic modulator connector terminal 2 and ABS control unit connector terminal 1.
6. Inspect for continuity between return pump motor positive terminal and top, male hydraulic modulator terminal 9.
7. Turn ignition On.
8. Inspect for battery voltage in black hydraulic modulator connector terminals 2 and 13. Reading should be approximately battery voltage.
9. If readings are not satisfactory, repair circuits for shorts or opens.
10. If readings are satisfactory, but return pump does not run, replace return pump relay.

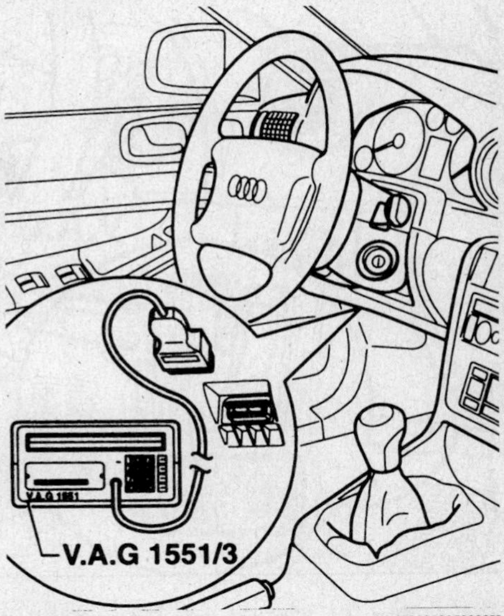

Fig. 5 Data Link Connector location. A4, A8 & S4

ABS RETURN PUMP DOES NOT RUN, RELAY GOOD, TESTER IN POSITION 3

1. Turn ignition Off.
2. Remove black hydraulic modulator connector.
3. Inspect for continuity between male terminal 11, in hydraulic modulator socket and terminal 85 in return pump relay socket. Refer to **Figs. 3 and 4.**
4. Inspect for continuity between male terminal 13 in the hydraulic modulator socket and terminal 87 in return pump relay socket.
5. Inspect for continuity between male terminal 11 in hydraulic modulator socket and terminal 28 of ABS control unit connector, **Figs. 2 and 3.**
6. If readings are not satisfactory, repair circuits for shorts or opens.
7. If readings are satisfactory but return pump does not run, replace hydraulic modulator.

WRONG SOLENOID VALVE OPERATES, TESTER IN POSITION 5

1. Inspect for proper connection of brake lines to hydraulic modulator.
2. Inspect for proper wiring between hydraulic modulator and ABS control unit.

SENSOR SIGNAL ON METER BELOW MINIMUM VALUE

1. Measure air gap between wheel speed sensor and ring gear.
2. Inspect for loose or faulty ring gear.
3. Inspect for excessive wheel bearing play.

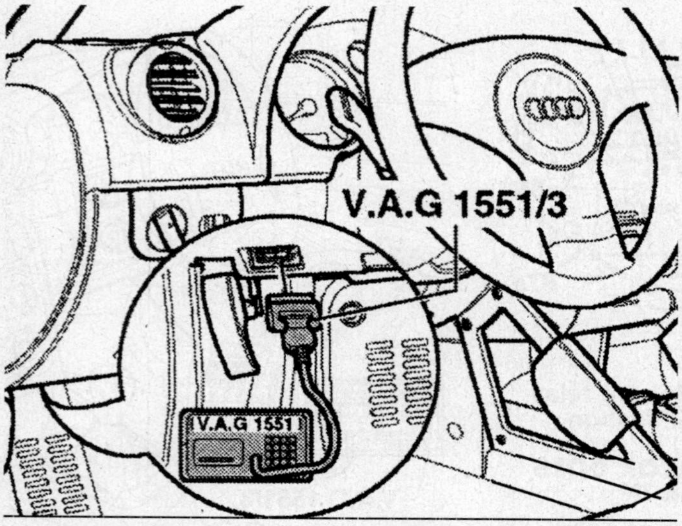

AD4020000052000X

Fig. 6 Data Link Connector location. TT

VAG 1551 Scan Tool printout	Possible cause of malfunction	Repairing malfunction
00000		
No DTC recognized	♦ The OBD program is completed. ♦ If there is a malfunction in the system, but the ABS control module -J104- does not detect any malfunctions: proceed to troubleshooting with ABS tester VAG 1710.	
00277		
ABS Inlet/Outlet Valve,LF -N137	♦ Open circuit, or short to positive or Ground between ABS hydraulic unit -N55- and ABS control module -J104-. ♦ Left front ABS inlet/outlet valve -N137- faulty.	– Trace and repair open circuit or short circuit using wiring diagram. – Check ABS hydraulic unit; test with VAG 1710 (test steps 1, 5).

AD4029600030000X

Fig. 7 Code 00000 & 00277: No Diagnostic Trouble Code (DTC) Recognized & Lefthand Front ABS Inlet/Outlet Valve. S6

VAG 1551 Scan Tool printout	Possible cause of malfunction	Repairing malfunction
00283		
ABS Wheel Speed Sensor,LF -G47[1]	♦ Open circuit or short to positive (+) in wiring between -G47- and ABS control module -J104-.	– Trace and repair open circuit or short circuit using wiring diagram
	♦ Rotor dirty or damaged.	– Check, clean or replace rotor.
	♦ Excessive wheel bearing play.	– Replace wheel bearing
	♦ -G47- not properly installed.	– Check position of -G47-
	♦ -G47- faulty.	– Check -G47-; test with VAG 1710 (test step 6).

[1] Can be erroneously indicated as a sporadic malfunction if one of the wheels is rotated at more than 6 km/h with the ignition on.

AD4029600031000X

Fig. 8 Code 00283: Lefthand Front ABS Wheel Speed Sensor. S6

NO RESPONSE FROM SELECTED SENSOR, TESTER IN POSITION 6

1. Turn ignition Off.
2. Disconnect appropriate wheel speed sensor connector. Front sensors are located near front shock towers. Rear sensors are located beneath rear seat cushion.
3. Connect ohmmeter to female terminals, then measure the resistance. Reading should be. 8–1.8K ohms.
4. If readings are not within specified range, replace wheel speed sensor.
5. If readings are within the specified range, inspect for continuity between wheel speed sensor and ABS control unit connector.
6. Bridge male terminals of wheel speed sensor connector.
7. Remove ABS control unit connector, then inspect for continuity between bridged wheel speed sensor and corresponding terminals of ABS control unit connector.
8. If continuity does not exist, repair shorted or open circuit.

WITH SCAN TOOL

ACCESSING DIAGNOSTIC TROUBLE CODES (DTC)

Connect a suitable scan tool to Data Link Connector (DLC), **Figs. 5 and 6.**

Follow scan tool manufacturer's instructions to access DTCs.

DTCs may only be accessed with vehicle stationary. Vehicle speeds above six mph with scan tool connected will cause ABS system shutdown.

DIAGNOSTIC TROUBLE CODE INTERPRETATION

Refer to "Diagnostic Chart Index" for diagnostic code and definition.

DIAGNOSTIC TESTS

S6

Refer to **Figs. 7 through 19** for DTC interpretation, possible cause of malfunction and correction procedures.

A4, A6, A8, S4 & S6

Refer to **Figs. 20 through 40** for DTC interpretation, possible cause of malfunction and correction procedures.

TT

Refer to **Figs. 41 through 52** for DTC interpretation, possible cause of malfunction and correction procedures.

CLEARING DIAGNOSTIC TROUBLE CODES

Connect a suitable scan tool using proper cable to the Data Link Connector (DLC).

Follow scan tool manufacturer's instructions to access DTCs. **DTCs must be accessed prior to clearing codes. The ECU will not allow erasure of stored DTCs until all codes have been read.**

Follow scan tool manufacturer's instructions to clear ECU memory.

READ MEASURING VALUE BLOCK

Connect a suitable scan tool using proper cable to the Data Link Connector (DLC).

Follow scan tool manufacturer's instructions to access "Read Measuring Value Block," then refer to **Fig. 53.**

ELECTRICAL TESTING

A4, A6, A8, S4 & S6

This section has been revised by a Technical Service Bulletin.

Refer to **Fig. 54** when performing electrical tests.

TT

Refer to **Fig. 55** for electrical testing table.

HYDRAULIC MODULATOR HIGH & LOW PRESSURE TESTING

1. Remove bleeder screw from one front brake caliper.
2. Connect gauge set tool No. VW 1310, or equivalent, then bleed gauges.
3. Install brake pedal depressor between brake pedal and driver's seat.
4. Load brake pedal until gauge reads 725 psi.
5. Watch gauge for 45 seconds. Pressure must not drop more than 58 psi.
6. If pressure drops more than 58 psi, replace ABS hydraulic unit.
7. Load brake pedal depressor until gauge reads 87 psi.
8. Watch gauge for three minutes. Pressure must not drop more than 14 psi.
9. If pressure drops more than 14 psi, replace ABS hydraulic unit.

SYSTEM SERVICE

Brake System Bleed

Refer to "Hydraulic Brake System" for procedures.

SYSTEM CODING

TT

Refer to **Fig. 56** for ABS Mark 20 IE system coding.

VAG 1551 Scan Tool printout	Possible cause of malfunction	Repairing malfunction
00284		
ABS Inlet/Outlet Valve,RF -N138	♦ Open circuit or short to positive (+) or Ground in wiring between ABS hydraulic unit -N55- and ABS control module -J104-.	– Trace or repair open circuit or short circuit using wiring diagram.
	♦ -N138- faulty.	– Check ABS hydraulic unit; test with VAG 1710 (test steps 1, 5).
00285		
ABS Wheel Speed Sensor,RF -G45[1]	♦ Open circuit or short to positive (+) in wiring between -G45- and ABS control module -J104-.	– Trace and repair open circuit or short circuit using wiring diagram.
	♦ Rotor dirty or damaged.	– Check, clean or replace rotor.
	♦ Wheel bearing play excessive.	– Replace wheel bearing
	♦ Speed sensor -G45- not installed correctly.	– Check position of -G45-
	♦ Speed sensor -G45- faulty.	– Check -G45-; test with VAG 1710 (test step 6)

[1] Can be erroneously indicated as a sporadic malfunction if one of the wheels is rotated at more than 6 km/h with the ignition on.

AD4029600032000X

Fig. 9 Code 00284 & 00285: Righthand Front ABS Inlet/Outlet Valve & Righthand Front ABS Wheel Speed Sensor. S6

VAG 1551 Scan Tool printout	Possible cause of malfunction	Repairing malfunction
00287		
ABS Wheel Speed Sensor,RR -G44[1]	♦ Open circuit or short to positive (+) in wiring between -G44- and ABS control module -J104-.	– Trace and repair open or short circuit using wiring diagram.
	♦ Rotor dirty or damaged.	– Check, clean or replace rotor.
	♦ Wheel bearing play excessive.	– Check and adjust wheel bearing play
	♦ -G44- not properly installed.	– Check position of -G44-
	♦ -G44- faulty.	– Check -G44-; test with VAG 1710 (test step 6).
00289		
ABS Inlet/Outlet Valve,RR -N140	♦ Open circuit or short to positive (+) or Ground in wiring between ABS hydraulic unit -N55- and ABS control module -J104-.	– Trace or repair open circuit or short circuit using wiring diagram.
	♦ -N140- faulty.	– Check ABS hydraulic unit; test with VAG 1710 (test steps 1, 5).

[1] Can be erroneously indicated as a sporadic malfunction if one of the wheels is rotated at more than 6 km/h with the ignition on.

AD4029600034000X

Fig. 11 Code 00287 & 00289: Righthand Rear ABS Wheel Speed Sensor & Righthand Rear ABS Inlet/Outlet Valve (FWD). S6

VAG 1551 Scan Tool printout	Possible cause of malfunction	Repairing malfunction
00286		
ABS Inlet/Outlet Valve,LR -N139	♦ Open circuit or short circuit to positive (+) or Ground in wiring between ABS hydraulic unit -N55- and ABS control module -J104-.	– Trace and repair open circuit or short circuit using wiring diagram.
	♦ -N139- faulty.	– Check ABS hydraulic unit; test with VAG 1710 (test steps 1, 5).

AD4029600033000X

Fig. 10 Code 00286: Lefthand Rear ABS Inlet/Outlet Valve (FWD). S6

VAG 1551 Scan Tool printout	Possible cause of malfunction	Repairing malfunction
00290		
ABS Wheel Speed Sensor,LR -G46[1]	♦ Open circuit or short to positive (+) in wiring between -G46- and ABS control module -J104-.	– Trace and repair open circuit or short circuit using wiring diagram.
	♦ Rotor dirty or damaged.	– Check, clean or replace rotor.
	♦ Wheel bearing play excessive.	– Check and adjust wheel bearing play
	♦ -G46- not properly installed.	– Check position of -G46-
	♦ -G46- faulty.	– Check -G46-; test with VAG 1710 (test step 6).

[1] Can be erroneously indicated as a sporadic malfunction if one of the wheels is rotated at more than 6 km/h with the ignition on.

AD4029600035000X

Fig. 12 Code 00290: Lefthand Rear ABS Wheel Speed Sensor. S6

Component Replacement

ELECTRONIC CONTROL UNIT

A4, A6, S4 & S6

The electronic control unit is located beneath the lefthand side of the rear seat.

1. Turn ignition Off.
2. Remove rear seat.
3. Remove spring retaining electrical connector, then disconnect electrical connector.
4. Remove screws securing control unit.
5. Reverse procedure to install.

A8

1. Remove lower slot cover from between knee bolster and lower column cover.
2. Remove knee bolster.
3. Remove ABS control module.
4. Disconnect ABS control module electrical harness connector.
5. Reverse procedure to install.

TT

The control module is mounted to the hydraulic unit, located on the lefthand side of the engine compartment.

1. Disconnect MAF sensor electrical connector from air intake duct.
2. Remove air cleaner housing bolts, then position housing aside.
3. Siphon off as much brake fluid as possible from brake fluid reservoir.
4. Connect bleeder bottle to bleeder screw on lefthand front brake caliper, then open the screw.
5. Insert brake pedal depressor tool No. VAG 1869/2, or equivalent, between brake pedal and driver's seat. **Pedal depressor must remain in position until all brake lines have been connected to hydraulic unit.**
6. Depress brake pedal by at least 2.34 inches, then close bleeder screw.
7. Disconnect control module electrical connector.
8. Cover engine compartment to prevent brake fluid splashing over any components or damaging painted surfaces.
9. Disconnect hydraulic unit to brake master cylinder brake fluid lines and position aside.
10. Disconnect remaining lines on hydraulic unit
11. Plug brake lines and threaded ports with plugs from tool No. 1H0 698 311 A, or equivalent.
12. Remove hydraulic unit mounting bracket bolts, **Fig. 57.**
13. Remove hydraulic unit with control module.
14. Disconnect hydraulic pump motor electrical connector from control module.
15. Remove and discard control module Torx bolts, then separate control module from hydraulic unit, **Fig. 58.** Ensure hydraulic unit valve dome is not canted against control module solenoid valves.
16. Cover control module magnetic coils with a clean lint free cloth.
17. Cover valve dome to prevent damage.
18. Reverse procedure to install, noting the following:
    a. Remove sealing plugs on new hydraulic unit only when a particular brake line is ready for connection.
    b. When assembling control module and hydraulic unit, ensure hydraulic unit valve dome is not canted against control module solenoid valves.
    c. Install new control module Torx bolts, then **torque** to 36 inch lbs.
    d. **Torque** hydraulic unit mounting bracket bolts to 72 inch lbs.
    e. **Torque** brake fluid line fittings to 11 ft. lbs.
    f. Bleed brakes as outlined under "Brake System Bleed" in "Hydraulic Brake Systems" chapter.
    g. Code control module as outlined under "System Coding" in "System Service" section.

VAG 1551 Scan Tool printout	Possible cause of malfunction	Repairing malfunction
00301		
ABS Return Flow Pump–V39	♦ Open circuit or contact resistance in Ground connection or power supply to -V39-.	– Trace and repair open circuit or contact resistance using wiring diagram.
	♦ Open circuit or short circuit to positive (+) in wiring between ABS return flow pump relay -J105- and ABS control module -J104-.	– Trace and repair open circuit or short circuit using wiring diagram.
	♦ ABS return flow pump relay -J105-, ABS return flow pump -V39-, or ABS hydraulic unit faulty.	– Check -J105-, -V39- and -N55-; test with VAG 1710 (test step 3).

[1)] Can be erroneously indicated as a sporadic malfunction if one of the wheels is rotated at more than 6 km/h with the ignition on.

AD4029600036000X

Fig. 13 Code 00301: ABS Return Flow Pump. S6

VAG 1551 Scan Tool printout	Possible cause of malfunction	Repairing malfunction
00302		
ABS Solenoid Valve Relay –J106	♦ Open circuit or contact resistance in Ground connection or power supply to -J106-.	– Trace and repair open circuit or connector resistance using wiring diagram.
	♦ Open circuit or short circuit to positive (+) or Ground in wiring between -J106- and ABS control module -J104-.	– Trace and repair open circuit or short circuit using wiring diagram.
	♦ ABS Solenoid Valve Relay -J106- or ABS hydraulic unit -N55- faulty.	– Check -J106- and ABS hydraulic unit; test with VAG 1710 (test step 1).

AD4029600037000X

Fig. 14 Code 00302: ABS Solenoid Valve Relay. S6

VAG 1551 Scan Tool printout	Possible cause of malfunction	Repairing malfunction
00526		
Brake Light Switch–F	♦ Open circuit or short circuit to positive (+) in wiring between Brake Light Switch, Right or Left Brake Light or ABS control module -J104-	– Trace and repair open circuit or short circuit using wiring diagram.
	♦ Right or left brake light faulty.	– Replace Right or Left Brake Light.
	♦ Brake light switch faulty.	– Read measuring value block to check brake light switch test using VAG 1710 (test step 2).

AD4029600038000X

Fig. 15 Code 00526: Brake Lamp Switch. S6

HYDRAULIC CONTROL UNIT

Refer to **Fig. 59** when replacing the ABS hydraulic control unit.

HYDRAULIC CONTROL UNIT MOUNTING BRACKET

Refer to **Figs. 60 and 61** when replacing the ABS hydraulic control unit mounting bracket.

FRONT WHEEL SPEED SENSORS

A4 & S4

1. Turn ignition Off, then raise and support vehicle and remove wheel assembly.
2. Remove boot from wheel housing, then separate harness connector for wheel speed sensor cable and pull out of brackets.
3. Remove ABS wheel speed sensor from wheel bearing housing.
4. Reverse procedure to install.

A6 & S6

1. Remove connectors from retainers.
2. Disconnect electrical connectors.
3. Reverse procedure to install.

A8

1. Turn ignition Off, then raise and support vehicle and remove wheel assembly.
2. Remove front half of wheel housing liner.
3. Disconnect ABS wheel speed sensor harness electrical connector.
4. Remove electrical harness from brackets.
5. Remove wheel speed sensor from swing arm.
6. Reverse procedure to install.

CABRIOLET

Replace PVC cap after repeated removal of sensor to ensure proper air gap.

1. Turn ignition Off.
2. Remove mounting bolts for sensors, then the sensors.
3. Replace O-ring seals on sensors.
4. Lubricate O-ring seals and sensors with brake assembly lubricant.
5. Install sensors in housings until PVC tips touch rotor on CV joints.
6. Install new retaining bolts, then **torque** to 84 inch lbs. while holding sensors against wheel bearing housings.
7. Install wiring grommet into bracket on wheel bearing/strut housing.

TT

1. Turn ignition Off.
2. Raise and support vehicle.
3. Disconnect wheel speed sensor electrical connector.
4. Remove sensor mounting bolt, then the sensor.
5. Reverse procedure to install, noting the following:
   a. Clean inner surface of sensor mounting hole and coat with paste lubricant part No. G 000 650, or equivalent.
   b. **Torque** sensor mounting bolt to 72 inch lbs.
   c. Turn steering wheel fully left and right and ensure there is adequate clearance for speed sensor wiring.

REAR WHEEL SPEED SENSORS

A4 & S4

1. Turn ignition Off, then remove rear seat.
2. Disconnect wiring harness holder and separate ABS wheel speed sensor harness connector, then press out grommet.
3. Raise and support vehicle, then remove wheel assembly.
4. Pull ABS wheel speed sensor connector cable out of brackets, then remove sensor from axle beam.
5. Reverse procedure to install.

A6, CABRIOLET & S6

Both terminal connections for rear speed sensor are located beneath rear seat. For replacement procedure, see "Front Wheel Speed Sensors."

A8

1. Turn ignition Off, then raise and support vehicle and remove wheel assembly.
2. Disconnect ABS wheel speed sensor harness electrical connector.
3. Remove electrical harness from brackets.
4. Remove wheel speed sensor from wheel bearing housing.
5. Reverse procedure to install.

TT

1. Turn ignition Off.
2. Raise and support vehicle.
3. Disconnect wheel speed sensor electrical connector.
4. Remove sensor mounting bolt, then the sensor.
5. Reverse procedure to install, noting the following:
   a. Clean inner surface of sensor mounting hole and coat with paste lubricant part No. G 000 650, or equivalent.
   b. **Torque** sensor mounting bolt to 72 inch lbs.

TECHNICAL SERVICE BULLETINS

ABS LAMP ON AFTER BATTERY JUMP STARTING OR CHARGING ABS FUSES BLOWN

On A4 and A6 models, if the ABS lamp is on after charging or jumping a completely discharged battery, the system fuses should be inspected for open circuit condition.

Replacing fuses should return vehicle to operating condition.

VAG 1551 Scan Tool printout	Possible cause of malfunction	Repairing malfunction
00532		
Supply Voltage (B+)	♦ Open circuit or connector resistance in voltage supply to ABS control module -J104- (terminal 1) or Ground connection to -J104-. ♦ Voltage drops or excess voltage in vehicle system.	– Trace and repair open circuit or contact resistance using wiring diagram; perform test with VAG 1710 (test step 1). – Check generator and voltage regulator ⇒ wiring diagram; carry out functional check with VAG 1710 (test steps 1 and 5).

Note:

- ♦ As soon as voltage of vehicle electrical system is again within permissible range, the ABS is switched on again and the ABS warning light -K47- goes out.
- ♦ This malfunction is only stored if it occurs at a vehicle speed in excess of 6 km/h (4 mph).

AD4029600039000X

Fig. 16 Code 00532: Supply Voltage (B+). S6

VAG 1551 Scan Tool printout	Possible cause of malfunction	Repairing malfunction
00649		
ABS Rear Inlet/Outlet Valve,Rear–N160	♦ Open circuit in wiring, short to positive or ground in wiring between ABS Hydraulic Unit -N55- and control module -J104-. ♦ ABS Rear Inlet/Outlet Valve -N160- malfunctioning.	– Determine open circuit in wiring or short circuit according to wiring diagram and repair. – Check hydraulic unit, carry out functional testing with VAG 1710 (test steps 1 and 5).

AD4029600041000X

Fig. 18 Code 00649: Rear Inlet/Outlet Valve (AWD). S6

VAG 1551 scan tool printout	Possible cause of malfunction	Repairing malfunction
DTC		
00000		
No DTC recognized	If this display appears, the On Board Diagnostic (OBD) program is ended. No malfunction is stored in DTC memory. If appropriate warning lights nevertheless come on, investigate the following points: ♦ Voltage supply for ABS control module -J104- less than 10.5 V at a vehicle speed of less than 6 km/h (4 mph) ♦ Open circuit in wiring between ABS control module -J104- and instrument cluster -J218- (ABS warning light -K47-) If it is not possible to pinpoint a malfunction and no further malfunction exists, there may be a mechanical problem (solenoid valve jamming). Troubleshooting should be extended to include electrical testing	– Test power supply for ABS control module -J104- – Test cable connections

AD4029600010000X

Fig. 20 Code 00000: No Diagnostic Trouble Code (DTC) Recognized. A4, A6, A8, S4 & S6

VAG 1551 scan tool printout	Possible cause of malfunction	Repairing malfunction
DTC		
00265		
ABS Outlet Valve,LF–N102	♦ Open circuit, short circuit to positive or to Ground (GND) in wiring between ABS hydraulic unit -N55- and ABS control module -J104- ♦ Left front ABS outlet valve -N102- faulty	– Carry out electrical test step 1 – If no malfunction can be pinpointed during the electrical test, check all the wiring and harness connectors for loose contact – If none of the measures stated pinpoints the malfunction, replace the ABS control module
00267		
ABS Outlet Valve,RF–N100	♦ Open circuit, short circuit to positive or to Ground (GND) in wiring between ABS hydraulic unit -N55- and ABS control module -J104- ♦ Right front ABS outlet valve -N100- faulty	– Carry out electrical test step 2 – If no malfunction can be pinpointed during the electrical test, check all the wiring and harness connectors for loose contact – If none of the measures stated pinpoints the malfunction, replace the ABS control module

AD4029600012000X

Fig. 22 Code 00265 & 00267: Lefthand Front ABS Outlet Valve & Righthand Front ABS Outlet Valve. A4, A6, A8, S4 & S6

VAG 1551 Scan Tool printout	Possible cause of malfunction	Repairing malfunction
00597		
Varying Wheel Speed Impulse[1)]	♦ One rotor with incorrect number of teeth installed. ♦ One rotor dirty or damaged. ♦ One speed sensor not properly installed. ♦ Excessive wheel bearing play at one wheel, or wheel bearing malfunctioning. ♦ One speed sensor malfunctioning.	– Check all rotors and read measuring value block – Check all rotors. Clean or replace. – Check installation positions of all wheel speed sensors – Check all wheel bearings – Check all speed sensors; test with VAG 1710 (test step 6).

[1)] Can be erroneously indicated as a sporadic malfunction if one of the wheels is rotated at more than 6 km/h with the ignition on.

AD4029600040000X

Fig. 17 Code 00597: Varying Wheel Speed Impulse. S6

VAG 1551 Scan Tool printout	Possible cause of malfunction	Repairing malfunction
65535		
Control Module Malfunctioning	♦ Open circuit or contact resistance in power supply or Ground connection to ABS control module -J104-. ♦ ABS control module -J104- malfunctioning.	– Trace and repair open circuit or connector resistance using wiring diagram. – Replace ABS control module -J104-.

Note:

If the DTC "ABS Return Flow Pump -V39-" is also displayed, first correct that malfunction.

AD4029600042000X

Fig. 19 Code 65535: Control Module Malfunctioning. S6

VAG 1551 scan tool printout	Possible cause of malfunction	Repairing malfunction
DTC		
00257		
ABS Inlet Valve,LF–N101	♦ Open circuit, short circuit to positive or to Ground (GND) in wiring between ABS hydraulic unit -N55- and ABS control module -J104- ♦ Left front ABS inlet valve -N101- faulty	– Carry out electrical test test steps 1 and 13 – If no malfunction can be pinpointed during the electrical test, check all the wiring and harness connectors for loose contact – If none of the measures stated pinpoints the malfunction, replace the ABS control module
00259		
ABS Inlet Valve,RF–N99	♦ Open circuit, short circuit to positive or to Ground (GND) in wiring between ABS hydraulic unit -N55- and ABS control module -J104- ♦ Right front ABS inlet valve -N99- faulty	– Carry out electrical test test steps 2 and 14 – If no malfunction can be pinpointed during the electrical test, check all the wiring and harness connectors for loose contact – If none of the measures stated pinpoints the malfunction, replace the ABS control module

AD4029600011000X

Fig. 21 Code 00257 & 00259: Lefthand Front ABS Inlet Valve & Righthand Front ABS Inlet Valve. A4, A6, A8, S4 & S6

VAG 1551 scan tool printout	Possible cause of malfunction	Repairing malfunction
DTC		
00273		
ABS Inlet Valve,RR–N133	♦ Open circuit, short circuit to positive or to Ground (GND) in wiring between ABS hydraulic unit -N55- and ABS control module -J104- ♦ Right rear ABS inlet valve -N133- faulty	– Carry out electrical test test steps 4 and 16 – If no malfunction can be pinpointed during the electrical test, check all the wiring and harness connectors for loose contact – If none of the measures stated pinpoints the malfunction, replace the ABS control module
00274		
ABS Inlet Valve,LR–N134	♦ Open circuit, short circuit to positive or to Ground (GND) in wiring between ABS hydraulic unit -N55- and ABS control module -J104- ♦ Left rear ABS inlet valve -N134- faulty	– Carry out electrical test ⇒ test steps 3 and 15 – If no malfunction can be pinpointed during the electrical test, check all the wiring and harness connectors for loose contact – If none of the measures stated pinpoints the malfunction, replace the ABS control module

AD4029600013000X

Fig. 23 Code 00273 & 00274: Righthand Rear ABS Inlet Valve & Lefthand Rear ABS Inlet Valve. A4, A6, A8, S4 & S6

VAG 1551 scan tool printout DTC	Possible cause of malfunction	Repairing malfunction
00275		
ABS Outlet Valve,RR–N135	♦ Open circuit, short circuit to positive or to Ground (GND) in wiring between ABS hydraulic unit -N55- and ABS control module -J104- ♦ Right rear ABS outlet valve -N135- faulty	– Carry out electrical test test step 4 – If no malfunction can be pinpointed during the electrical test, check all the wiring and harness connectors for loose contact – If none of the measures stated pinpoints the malfunction, replace the ABS control module
00276		
ABS Outlet Valve,LR–N136	♦ Open circuit, short circuit to positive or to Ground (GND) in wiring between ABS hydraulic unit -N55- and ABS control module -J104- ♦ Left rear ABS outlet valve -N136- faulty	– Carry out electrical test ⇒ test step 3 – If no malfunction can be pinpointed during the electrical test, check all the wiring and harness connectors for loose contact – If none of the measures stated pinpoints the malfunction, replace the ABS control module

AD4029600014000X

Fig. 24 Code 00275 & 00276: Righthand Rear ABS Outlet Valve & Lefthand Rear ABS Outlet Valve. A4, A6, A8, S4 & S6

VAG 1551 scan tool printout DTC	Possible cause of malfunction	Repairing malfunction
00285		
ABS Wheel Speed Sensor,RF –G45*	♦ Rotor dirty or damaged ♦ Excessive wheel bearing play ♦ Right front wheel speed sensor -G45- not properly installed ♦ Right front wheel speed sensor -G45- faulty ♦ Short circuit to Ground (GND)	– Examine rotor, clean or replace – Replace wheel bearing – Check installation position of wheel speed sensor – Read measuring value block display field 2, function test
or:		– Carry out electrical test test step 8 – If neither read measuring value block function nor electrical test reveals a malfunction, check all the wiring and harness connectors for loose contact
ABS Wheel Speed Sensor,RF –G45* Open/Short circuit to B+	♦ Wrong ABS control module identification ♦ Open circuit or short circuit to positive in the wiring between right front wheel speed sensor -G45- and ABS control module -J104-	– Check ABS control module identification – If none of the measures stated pinpoints the malfunction, replace the ABS control module

AD4029600016000X

Fig. 26 Code 00285: Righthand Front ABS Wheel Sensor. A4, A6, A8, S4 & S6

VAG 1551 scan tool printout DTC	Possible cause of malfunction	Repairing malfunction
00290		
ABS Wheel Speed Sensor,LR –G46	♦ Rotor dirty or damaged ♦ Excessive wheel bearing play ♦ Left rear wheel speed sensor -G46- not properly installed ♦ Left rear wheel speed sensor -G46- faulty ♦ Short circuit to Ground (GND)	– Examine rotor, clean or replace – Replace wheel bearing – Check installation position of wheel speed sensor – Read measuring value block display field 3, function test
Or:		– Carry out electrical test test step 9 – If neither Read measuring value block not electrical test reveals a malfunction, check all the wiring and harness connectors for loose contact
ABS Wheel Speed Sensor,LR –G46 Open/Short circuit to B+	♦ Wrong ABS control module identification ♦ Open circuit or short circuit to positive in the wiring between left rear speed sensor -G44- and ABS control module -J104-	– Check ABS control module identification – If none of the measures stated pinpoints the malfunction, replace the ABS control module

AD4029600018000X

Fig. 28 Code 00290: Lefthand Rear ABS Wheel Sensor. A4, A6, A8, S4 & S6

VAG 1551 scan tool printout DTC	Possible cause of malfunction	Repairing malfunction
00302		
ABS Solenoid Valve Relay–J106	♦ Faulty cable connection or excessive terminal resistance in Ground (GND) connection to ABS solenoid valve relay -J106- ♦ Open circuit or short circuit to positive or to Ground (GND) in wiring between relay -J106- and ABS control module -J104- ♦ ABS solenoid valve relay -J106- or ABS hydraulic unit -N55- faulty	– Examine Ground (GND) connection for terminal resistance and faulty wiring – Locate and repair open circuit in wiring or short circuit – Test ABS solenoid valve relay -J106- and ABS hydraulic unit; Carry out electrical test test steps 11 and 13; Read measuring value block display field 8

AD4029600020000X

Fig. 30 Code 00302: ABS Solenoid Valve. A4, A6, A8, S4 & S6

VAG 1551 scan tool printout DTC	Possible cause of malfunction	Repairing malfunction
00283		
ABS Wheel Speed Sensor,LF –G47*	♦ Rotor dirty or damaged ♦ Excessive wheel bearing play ♦ Left front wheel speed sensor -G47- not properly installed ♦ Left front wheel speed sensor -G47- faulty ♦ Short circuit to Ground (GND)	– Examine rotor, clean or replace – Replace wheel bearing – Check installation position of wheel speed sensor – Read measuring value block display field 1, function test
or:		– Carry out electrical test test step 7 – If neither read measuring value block function nor electrical test reveals a malfunction, check all the wiring and harness connectors for loose contact
ABS Wheel Speed Sensor,LF –G47* Open/Short circuit to B+	♦ Wrong ABS control module identification ♦ Open circuit or short circuit to positive in the wiring between left front wheel speed sensor -G47- and ABS control module -J104-	– Check ABS control module identification – If none of the measures stated pinpoints the malfunction, replace the ABS control module

AD4029600015000X

Fig. 25 Code 00283: Lefthand Front ABS Wheel Sensor. A4, A6, A8, S4 & S6

VAG 1551 scan tool printout DTC	Possible cause of malfunction	Repairing malfunction
00287		
ABS Wheel Speed Sensor,RR –G44*	♦ Rotor dirty or damaged ♦ Excessive wheel bearing play ♦ Right rear wheel speed sensor -G44- not properly installed ♦ Right rear wheel speed sensor -G44- faulty ♦ Short circuit to Ground (GND)	– Examine rotor, clean or replace – Replace wheel bearing – Check installation position of wheel speed sensor – Read measuring value block display field 4, function test
or:		– Carry out electrical test test step 10 – If neither Read measuring value block not electrical test reveals a malfunction, check all the wiring and harness connectors for loose contact
ABS Wheel Speed Sensor,RR –G44* Open/Short circuit to B+	♦ Wrong ABS control module identification ♦ Open circuit or short circuit to positive in the wiring between right rear wheel speed sensor -G44- and ABS control module -J104-	– Check ABS control module identification – If none of the measures stated pinpoints the malfunction, replace the ABS control module

AD4029600017000X

Fig. 27 Code 00287: Righthand Rear ABS Wheel Sensor. A4, A6, A8, S4 & S6

VAG 1551 scan tool printout DTC	Possible cause of malfunction	Repairing malfunction
00301		
ABS Return Flow Pump–V39	♦ Open circuit in wiring or terminal resistance in Ground (GND) connection or power supply to return flow pump -V39- ♦ Open circuit or short circuit to positive or to Ground (GND) in wiring between ABS return flow pump relay -J105- and ABS control module -J104- ♦ ABS return flow pump relay -J105-, ABS return flow pump -V39- or ABS hydraulic unit faulty	– Locate and repair open circuit in wiring or terminal resistance – Locate and repair open circuit in the wiring or short circuit – Test ABS return flow pump relay -J105-, ABS return flow pump -V39- and ABS hydraulic unit -N55-; Carry out electrical test test steps 12 and17, Read measuring value block display field 7

AD4029600019000X

Fig. 29 Code 00301: ABS Return Flow Pump. A4, A6, A8, S4 & S6

VAG 1551 scan tool printout DTC	Possible cause of malfunction	Repairing malfunction
00526		
Brake Light Switch–F		
Front-wheel-drive: Open circuit	♦ Both brake lights -M9- and -M10-or ABS control module -J104- faulty ♦ Wiring from brake lights to ABS control module faulty	– Locate and repair open circuit in wiring or short circuit – Replace bulbs – Test brake light switch ⇒ Read measuring value block
All-wheel-drive: Incorrect signal	♦ Open circuit or short circuit to positive or to Ground (GND) in wiring between brake light switch, bulbs for brake lights -M9- and -M10- or ABS control module -J104- ♦ Bulbs for brake light -M9-or -M10-faulty ♦ Brake light switch faulty	

AD4029600021000X

Fig. 31 Code 00526: Brake Lamp Switch. A4, A6, A8, S4 & S6

VAG 1551 scan tool printout DTC	Possible cause of malfunction	Repairing malfunction
00529		
RPM Information Missing *Note:* *Only for models with TCS*	♦ Open circuit or short circuit to positive or to Ground (GND) in wiring between ABS control module -J104- and Engine Control Module (ECM) ♦ ECM faulty ♦ ABS control module -J104- faulty	– Locate and repair open circuit in wiring or short circuit – If tachometer in instrument cluster is faulty and no malfunction can be found in the wiring, the engine control module is faulty – If tachometer in instrument cluster is faulty and no malfunction can be found in the wiring, the ABS control module -J104- is faulty

AD4029600022000X

Fig. 32 Code 00529: RPM Information Missing. A4, A6, A8, S4 & S6

VAG 1551 scan tool printout DTC	Possible cause of malfunction	Repairing malfunction
00597		
Varying Wheel Speed Impulse	♦ Rotor dirty or damaged ♦ Excessive wheel bearing play ♦ Wheel speed sensors -G44-, -G45-, -G46- or -G47- not properly installed ♦ Wheel speed sensors -G44-, -G45-, -G46- or -G47- faulty ♦ Different wheels and tire sizes mounted on vehicle	– Check rotor – Check wheel bearing – Check wheel speed sensors Carry out electrical test test steps 7 through 10 – Check wheels and tire sizes
00623		
ABS/Transm.Electrical Connection *Note:* *Only for models with TCS*	Manual transmission: ♦ ABS control module -J104- incorrectly coded Automatic transmission: ♦ Open circuit or short circuit to Ground (GND) between ABS control module -J104- and Transmission Control Module (TCM) -J217- ♦ ABS control module -J104- incorrectly coded	– Check coding of ABS control module -J104- – Check coding of ABS control module -J104- – Locate and repair open circuit in wiring or short circuit

AD4029600024000X

Fig. 34 Code 00597 & Code 00623: Varying Wheel Speed Impulse & ABS/Transaxle Electrical Connection. A4, A6, A8, S4 & S6

VAG 1551 scan tool printout DTC	Possible cause of malfunction	Repairing malfunction
00644		
EDL Switch-Over Valve,LF –N168 *Note:* *Only for models with ABS/EDL or ABS/EDL/TCS*	♦ Open circuit, short circuit to positive or Ground (GND) in the wiring between ABS hydraulic unit -N55- and ABS control module -J104- ♦ Left front traction control switch-over valve -N168- faulty	– Carry out electrical test test steps 5 and 17 – If no malfunction can be pinpointed with the electrical test, check all the wiring and harness connectors for loose contact – If none of the measures stated pinpoints the malfunction, replace the ABS control module
00645		
EDL Outlet Valve,LF–N169 *Note:* *Only for models with ABS/EDL or ABS/EDL/TCS*	♦ Open circuit, short circuit to positive or Ground (GND) in the wiring between ABS hydraulic unit -N55- and ABS control module -J104- ♦ Left front traction control outlet valve -N169- faulty	– Carry out electrical test test steps 6 and 17 – If no malfunction can be pinpointed with the electrical test, check all the wiring and harness connectors for loose contact – If none of the measures stated pinpoints the malfunction, replace the ABS control module

AD4029600026000X

Fig. 36 Code 00644 & 00645: Lefthand Front ELD Switch-Over Valve & Lefthand Front ELD Outlet Valve. A4, A6, A8, S4 & S6

VAG 1551 scan tool printout DTC	Possible cause of malfunction	Repairing malfunction
00532		
Supply Voltage (B+)	♦ Terminal resistance in power supply to ABS control module -J104- (terminal 1) ♦ Voltage drops in electrical system *Note:* ♦ *The ABS, ABS/EDL or ABS/EDL/TCS system is switched on again and the warning lamps go out as soon as the battery positive voltage (B+) is again within the permissible range.* ♦ *This malfunction is stored only if it occurs when the vehicle is travelling at more than 6 km/h (4 mph).*	– Locate and repair open circuit in wiring or terminal resistance – Test generator and voltage regulator – Replace faulty battery

AD4029600023000X

Fig. 33 Code 00532: Supply Voltage (B+). A4, A6, A8, S4 & S6

VAG 1551 scan tool printout DTC	Possible cause of malfunction	Repairing malfunction
00642		
EDL Switch-Over Valve,RF –N166 *Note:* *Only for models with ABS/EDL or ABS/EDL/TCS*	♦ Open circuit, short circuit to positive or Ground (GND) in the wiring between ABS hydraulic unit -N55- and ABS control module -J104- ♦ Right front traction control switch-over valve -N166- faulty	– Carry out electrical test test steps 5 and 18 – If no malfunction can be pinpointed with the electrical test, check all the wiring and harness connectors for loose contact. – If none of the measures stated pinpoints the malfunction, replace the ABS control module
00643		
EDL Outlet Valve,RF–N167 *Note:* *Only for models with ABS/EDL or ABS/EDL/TCS*	♦ Open circuit, short circuit to positive or Ground (GND) in the wiring between ABS hydraulic unit -N55- and ABS control module -J104- ♦ Right front traction control outlet valve -N167- faulty	– Carry out electrical test test steps 6 and 18 – If no malfunction can be pinpointed with the electrical test, check all the wiring and harness connectors for loose contact – If none of the measures stated pinpoints the malfunction, replace the ABS control module

AD4029600025000X

Fig. 35 Code 00642 & 00643: Righthand Front ELD Switch-Over Valve & Righthand Front ELD Outlet Valve. A4, A6, A8, S4 & S6

VAG 1551 scan tool printout DTC	Possible cause of malfunction	Repairing malfunction
00646		
ABS–ASR/Motor,Electrical Connection 1 *Note:* *Only for models with TCS (ASR)*	♦ Open circuit or short circuit to positive or to Ground (GND) in the wiring between ABS control module -J104- and Engine Control Module (ECM) ♦ ABS control module -J104- faulty ♦ ECM faulty	– Locate and repair open circuit in wiring or short circuit – Replace ABS control module -J104- – Replace ECM
00647		
ABS–ASR/Motor,Electrical Connection 2 *Note:* *Only for models with TCS (ASR)*	♦ Open circuit or short circuit to positive or to Ground (GND) in the wiring between ABS control module -J104- and Engine Control Module (ECM) ♦ ECM faulty ♦ ABS control module -J104- faulty	– Locate and repair open circuit in wiring or short circuit – Replace ECM – Replace ABS control module -J104-

AD4029600027000X

Fig. 37 Code 00646 & 00647: ABS-ASR Motor Electrical Connection No. 1 & No. 2. A4, A6, A8, S4 & S6

VAG 1551 scan tool printout DTC	Possible cause of malfunction	Repairing malfunction
00668		
Battery Positive Voltage (B+) Term.30 Open circuit *Note:* *Only for models with ABS/EDL or ABS/EDL/TCS*	♦ Open circuit in power supply to ABS control module -J104- (terminal 50) or short circuit to Ground (GND)	– Test cable connection
00761		
DTC stored in ECM *Note:* *Only for models with TCS*	♦ A malfunction is stored in the Engine Control Module (ECM). The ECM is not in a position to reduce engine torque	– Repair malfunction in engine management system – Erase ECM Diagnostic Trouble Code (DTC) memory

AD4029600028000X

Fig. 38 Code 00668 & 00761: Battery Positive Voltage (B+) Terminal No. 30 Open Circuit & Diagnostic Trouble Code (DTC) Stored In Engine Control Module (ECM). A4, A6, A8, S4 & S6

DTC VAG1551 Scan Tool display	Possible cause	Corrective action
01201 ABS Pump Voltage Supply ***Note:*** *This malfunction affects the Ground (GND) connection for the ABS return flow pump -V39-.*	♦ Open circuit or excessive resistance in Ground (GND) connection to hydraulic control unit, terminal 16	– Carry out electrical testing – Check for contact resistance in Ground (GND) connection. – Trace and repair open circuit in Ground (GND) connection.
	♦ Malfunction in hydraulic control unit	– If no malfunction can be found in Ground (GND) connection, replace hydraulic control unit.
01203 ABS/Dash Pan. Ins. Electr. Consumer Open/short circuit to Ground	♦ Open circuit in wiring between instrument cluster combination processor and hydraulic control unit, terminal 10 ♦ Malfunction in instrument cluster combination processor	– Trace and repair open circuit in wiring. – Check instrument cluster combination processor.

AD4029900010000X

Fig. 39 Code 01201 & 01203: ABS Pump Voltage Supply & ABS/Dash Panel Instrument Electrical Consumer Open/Short Circuit To Ground. 1998–2000 except A8

DTC Scan tool print-out	Possible malfunction cause	Corrective action
00285 Wheel speed sensor front right -G 45	◆ Open circuit in: - Wheel speed sensor wire - Connector - Wheel speed sensor coil ◆ Short circuit in sensor	- Check wheel speed sensor; Read measuring value block, function 08, display group 002, display field 2 - Check ground wires to control module. - Perform electrical testing test steps No. 5 and 9.
	◆ Control module faulty	- If measures mentioned do not find problem, remove hydraulic control unit and replace control module
Mechanical malfunction 1)	◆ Air gap between sensor and impulse wheel too large.	- Check installation of wheel speed sensor and impulse wheel
	◆ ABS outlet valve does not open.	- Check hydraulic control unit via OBD service unit as necessary
Signal outside of tolerance 1)	◆ Loose contact in: - Wheel speed sensor wire - Connector - Wheel speed sensor coil ◆ Damage to impulse wheel ◆ Impulse wheel axial runout too great.	- Perform electrical testing test steps No. 5 and 9. - Check installation of wheel speed sensor and impulse wheel

1) This malfunction type can only be recognized above 13 mph (conduct test drive).

AD4020000054000X

Fig. 42 Code 00285: Righthand Front Wheel Speed Sensor. TT

DTC Scan tool print-out	Possible malfunction cause	Corrective action
00290 Wheel speed sensor rear left -G46	◆ Open circuit in: - Wheel speed sensor wire - Connector - Wheel speed sensor coil ◆ Short circuit in sensor	- Check wheel speed sensor; Read measuring value block, function 08, display group 002, display field 3 - Check ground wires to control module. - Perform electrical testing test steps No. 8 and 12.
	◆ Control module faulty	- If measures mentioned do not find problem, remove hydraulic control unit and replace control module
Mechanical malfunction 1)	◆ Air gap between sensor and impulse wheel too large.	- Check installation of wheel speed sensor and impulse wheel
	◆ ABS outlet valve does not open.	- Check hydraulic control unit via OBD service unit as necessary
Signal outside of tolerance 1)	◆ Loose contact in: - Wheel speed sensor wire - Connector - Wheel speed sensor coil ◆ Damage to impulse wheel ◆ Wheel bearing play too great	- Perform electrical testing test steps No. 8 and 12. - Check installation of wheel speed sensor and impulse wheel

1) This malfunction type can only be recognized above 13 mph (conduct test drive).

AD4020000056000X

Fig. 44 Code 00290: Lefthand Rear Wheel Speed Sensor. TT

VAG 1551 scan tool printout DTC	Possible cause of malfunction	Repairing malfunction
65535 Control Module Malfunctioning	♦ ABS control module -J104- faulty	– Replace ABS control module -J104- ***Note:*** *DTC memory should not be erased in this case. The data stored in DTC memory can help to determine the damage in the ABS control module. Such information is useful for constant product improvement.*

AD4029600029000X

Fig. 40 Code 65535: Control Module Malfunctioning. A4, A6, A8, S4 & S6

DTC Scan tool print-out	Possible malfunction cause	Corrective action
00283 Wheel speed sensor front left -G 47	◆ Open circuit in: - Wheel speed sensor wire - Connector - Wheel speed sensor coil ◆ Short circuit in sensor	- Check wheel speed sensor; Read measuring value block, function 08, display group 002, display field 1 - Check ground wires to control module. - Perform electrical testing test steps No. 6 and 10.
	◆ Control module faulty	- If measures mentioned do not find problem, remove hydraulic control unit and replace control module
Mechanical malfunction 1)	◆ Air gap between sensor and impulse wheel too large.	- Check installation of wheel speed sensor and impulse wheel
	◆ ABS outlet valve does not open.	- Check hydraulic control unit via OBD service unit as necessary
Signal outside of tolerance 1)	◆ Loose contact in: - Wheel speed sensor wire - Connector - Wheel speed sensor coil ◆ Damage to impulse wheel ◆ Impulse wheel axial runout too great.	- Perform electrical testing test steps No. 6 and 10. - Install wheel speed sensor and check impulse wheel

1) This malfunction type can only be recognized above 13 mph (conduct test drive).

AD4020000053000X

Fig. 41 Code 00283: Lefthand Front Wheel Speed Sensor. TT

DTC Scan tool print-out	Possible malfunction cause	Corrective action
00287 Wheel speed sensor rear right -G 44	◆ Open circuit in: - Wheel speed sensor wire - Connector - Wheel speed sensor coil ◆ Short circuit in sensor	- Check wheel speed sensor; Read measuring value block, function 08, display group 002, display field 4 - Check ground wires to control module. - Perform electrical testing test steps No. 7 and 11.
	◆ Control module faulty	- If measures mentioned do not find problem, remove hydraulic control unit and replace control module
Mechanical malfunction 1)	◆ Air gap between sensor and impulse wheel too large.	- Check installation of wheel speed sensor and impulse wheel
	◆ ABS outlet valve does not open.	- Check hydraulic control unit via OBD Page 01-110; service unit as necessary
Signal outside of tolerance 1)	◆ Loose contact in: - Wheel speed sensor wire - Connector - Wheel speed sensor coil ◆ Damage to impulse wheel ◆ Wheel bearing play too great	- Perform electrical testing test steps No. 7 and 11. - Check installation of wheel speed sensor and impulse wheel

1) This malfunction type can only be recognized above 13 mph (conduct test drive).

AD4020000055000X

Fig. 43 Code 00287: Righthand Rear Wheel Speed Sensor. TT

DTC Scan tool print-out	Possible malfunction cause	Corrective action
00668 Supply voltage terminal 30 Signal outside of tolerance	◆ Power supply wiring, connectors or fuse for -J104 faulty	- Check fuse, wiring, connectors and voltage supply to control module. - Perform electrical testing test steps No. 1 and 2. - Eliminate any malfunction recognized and perform output DTM

AD4020000057000X

Fig. 45 Code 00668: Supply Voltage Terminal 30 Signal Outside Of Tolerance. TT

DTC / Scan tool print-out	Possible malfunction cause	Corrective action
01044 Control module incorrectly coded	◆ Incorrect code was entered via VAG1551	- Check coding of control module
	◆ Coding bridge in wiring harness from contacts 3 to 14 damaged	- Check wiring harness perform electrical testing, test step No. 13.

AD4020000058000X

Fig. 46 Code 01044: Control Module Improperly Coded. TT

DTC / Scan tool print-out	Possible malfunction cause	Corrective action
01130 ABS operation Signal outside of tolerance 1)	◆ Electrical interferences from external sources (high frequency radiation, e.g. non-insulated ignition cable)	- Check all wiring, connectors for short to positive or ground. - Erase DTC memory. - Conduct test drive, exceeding 13 mph. - Check DTC memory again.

AD4020000059000X

Fig. 47 Code 01130: ABS Operation Signal Outside Of Tolerance. TT

DTC / Scan tool print-out	Possible malfunction cause	Corrective action
01276 Hydraulic pump ABS -V64 Signal outside of tolerance 1)	◆ Pump motor faulty ◆ Control module faulty	- Perform electrical testing test step No. 16. - If pump motor runs properly when conducting test step No. 16, remove hydraulic control unit and replace control module

1) This malfunction type can only be recognized above 13 mph (conduct test drive).

AD4020000060000X

Fig. 48 Code 01276: Hydraulic Pump ABS V64 Signal Outside Of Tolerance. TT

DTC / Scan tool print-out	Possible malfunction cause	Corrective action
01312 CAN-Bus drive faulty	◆ ABS control module incorrectly coded ◆ ECM incorrectly coded ◆ TCM incorrectly coded ◆ Open or short circuit in CAN-Bus wiring	- Code ABS control module - Code ECM - Code TCM - Check wiring per wiring diagram for open or short circuit. - Check data wiring between ECM and ABS control module
01312 CAN-Bus drive faulty (sporadically occurring malfunction)	◆ Can occur when starting the engine. No Malfunction!	- Erase DTC memory

AD4020000061000X

Fig. 49 Code 01312: CAN-BUS Drive Faulty. TT

DTC / Scan tool print-out	Possible malfunction cause	Corrective action
01314 Engine control module no communication (static and sporadic malfunction)	**Data transfer between control module -J104 and ECM occurs via CAN-Bus.**	- Check coding table
◆ This malfunction occurs only with ATC **Note continuation in Part 2.**	◆ The software versions responsible for the CAN-Bus in the control module -J104 and the ECM do not match.	- Check part numbers of both control modules via function 01, "Check control module"
		- Determine correct part numbers for vehicle
	◆ Malfunction in ECM	- Check DTC memory of ECM. Eliminate any malfunction found and erase DTC memory.

AD4020000062010X

Fig. 50 Code 01314: No Communication With ECM (Part 1 of 2). TT

DTC / Scan tool print-out	Possible malfunction cause	Corrective action
01314 Engine control module no communication	**Data transfer between control module -J104 and ECM occurs via CAN-Bus.**	- Check coding table
Continuation from Part 1.	◆ CAN-Bus wiring malfunction.	- Check CAN-Bus wiring
◆ This malfunction occurs only with ATC	◆ Wires for CAN-Bus Low and CAN-Bus High have been interchanged.	- Check wiring for proper connection. If wires are interchanged, control module cannot receive and send signals.
	◆ The output of one of the control modules communicating via CAN-Bus is faulty.	

AD4020000062020X

Fig. 50 Code 01314: No Communication With ECM (Part 2 of 2). TT

DTC / Scan tool print-out	Possible malfunction cause	Corrective action
01315 Transmission control module no communication (static or sporadic malfunction)	**Data transfer between control module -J104 and TCM occurs via CAN-Bus.**	
◆ This malfunction occurs only with automatic transmission and ATC **Note continuation** in Part 2.	◆ The software versions responsible for the CAN-Bus in the control module -J104 and the TCM do not match.	- Check part numbers of both control modules via function 01, "Check control module"
		- Determine correct part numbers for vehicle
	◆ Malfunction in TCM	- Check DTC memory of TCM. Eliminate any malfunction found and erase DTC memory of TCM and ECM.

AD4020000063010X

Fig. 51 Code 01315: No Communication With TCM (Part 1 of 2). TT

DTC / Scan tool print-out	Possible malfunction cause	Corrective action
01315 Transmission control module no communication **Continuation from Part 1.**	**Data transfer between control module -J104 and TCM occurs via CAN-Bus.**	
◆ This malfunction occurs only with automatic transmission and ATC	◆ CAN-Bus wiring malfunction.	- Check CAN-Bus wiring.
	◆ Wires for CAN-Bus Low and CAN-Bus High have been interchanged.	- Check wiring for proper connection. If wires are interchanged, control module cannot receive and send signals.
	◆ The output of one of the control modules communicating via CAN-Bus is faulty.	

AD4020000063020X

Fig. 51 Code 01315: No Communication With TCM (Part 2 of 2). TT

DTC / Scan tool print-out	Possible malfunction cause	Corrective action
65535 Control module malfunction	◆ Control module faulty	- Replace control module. In this case, DTC memory should not be erased. The data stored in DTC memory help to determine damage in control module. These determinations serve to continuously improve the product.

AD4020000064000X

Fig. 52 Code 65535: Control Module Malfunction. TT

Display field	Designation	Test conditions	VAG 1551 display specification
1	Left front wheel speed (km/h)		1 (car not moving) up to 19[1]
2	Right front wheel speed (km/h)		1 (car not moving) up to 19[1]
3	Left rear wheel speed (km/h)		1 (car not moving) up to 19[1]
4	Right rear wheel speed (km/h)		1 (car not moving) up to 19[1]
5	Brake light switch	• Brake pedal not depressed	0
		• Brake pedal depressed	1
6 [2]	Brake light switch	• Brake pedal not depressed	0
		• Brake pedal depressed	1
6 (7 [2])	Voltage at ABS return flow pump -V39-	• Return flow pump not running	0
		• Not permissible, return flow pump running	1
7 (8 [2])	ABS solenoid valve relay -J106-	• Relay has picked up	1
		• Relay has not picked up	0

[1] On Board Diagnostic (OBD) is terminated by the ABS control module -J104- if the vehicle is driven at a speed greater than 19 km/h (12 mph).

[2] Only on vehicles with all-wheel-drive (quattro models). Differences in adjusting and checking brake light switch ⇒ page 46-42

AD4029600044010X

Fig. 53 Read measuring valve block test table (Part 1 of 2)

Test step	VAG 1598/20 sockets	Test of	• Test conditions – Additional operations	Specified value	Repairing malfunction
6 *Note:* *Only for models with ABS/EDL or ABS/EDL/TCS*	4 + 27	♦ Left front traction control outlet valve -N169- ♦ Right front traction control outlet valve -N167-	• Wiring between ABS control module and ABS hydraulic unit OK	12 Ω – 28 Ω	– Test electric wiring between ABS control module and ABS hydraulic unit for short circuit to Ground (GND) or positive – If the wiring harness is OK, replace the ABS hydraulic unit

AD4029600045020X

Fig. 54 Electrical testing table (Part 2 of 11). A4, A6, A8, S4 & S6

Switch on measuring range: Resistance measurement 2 kΩ and 20kΩ					
Test step	VAG 1598/20 sockets	Test of	Test conditions - Additional operations	Specification	Corrective steps
7	9 + 10[1] 35 + 10[2,3]	Left Front Wheel Speed Sensor -G47-	Wiring between control module and speed sensor OK	400 Ω – 2300 Ω	- Test wiring between control module and speed sensor for short to ground or positive - If wiring is OK, replace appropriate wheel speed sensor
8	15 + 14 42 + 14[3]	Right Front Wheel Speed Sensor -G45-			
9	13 + 12	Left rear ABS wheel speed sensor -G46-			
10	11 + 38	Right rear ABS wheel speed sensor -G44-			

Different outputs at the ABS control module -J104- are assigned depending on the system installed.

[1] Only for FWD with ABS/EDL Bosch 5

[2] Only for All Wheel Drive ABS/EDL Bosch 5, pressure-regulated

[3] Only for All Wheel Drive ABS/EDL Bosch 5, suction-regulated

AD4029600045030A

Fig. 54 Electrical testing table (Part 3 of 11). A4, A6, A8, S4 & S6

Display field	Designation	Test conditions	VAG 1551 display specification
9 [3]	Engine speed (RPM)		In 60 RPM steps, 60, 120, 180, 240, etc., from 60 to 6540 RPM
10 [3]	Actual engine torque Nm (MMI = AET)		Display range 0 to 100% 0% ~ –100 Nm (overrun) 100% ~ +410 Nm 20% to 30% idling
11 [3]	TCS push-button	TCS push-button not pressed	0
		TCS push-button pressed	1

[3] Only on models with TCS.

AD4029600044020X

Fig. 53 Read measuring valve block test table (Part 2 of 2)

Switch to voltage measuring range 200 Ω					
Test step	VAG 1598/20 sockets	Test of	• Test conditions – Additional operations	Specified value	Repairing malfunction
1	5 + 33	♦ Left front ABS inlet valve -N101- ♦ Left front ABS outlet valve -N102-	• Wiring between ABS control module and ABS hydraulic unit OK	9 Ω – 22 Ω	– Check wiring between ABS control module and ABS hydraulic unit for short circuit to Ground (GND) or positive – If the wiring harness is OK, replace the ABS hydraulic unit
2	54 + 26	♦ Right front ABS inlet valve -N99- ♦ Right front ABS outlet valve -N100-			
3	53 + 25	♦ Left rear ABS inlet valve -N134- ♦ Left rear ABS outlet valve -N136-			
4	6 + 34	♦ Right rear ABS inlet valve -N133- ♦ Right rear ABS outlet valve -N135-			
5 *Note:* *Only for models with ABS/EDL or ABS/EDL/TCS*	3 + 55	♦ Left front traction control switch-over valve -N168- ♦ Right front traction control switch-over valve -N166-	• Wiring between ABS control module and ABS hydraulic unit OK	12 Ω – 28 Ω	

AD4029600045010X

Fig. 54 Electrical testing table (Part 1 of 11). A4, A6, A8, S4 & S6

Switch to voltage measuring range 200 Ω					
Test step	VAG 1598/20 sockets	Test of	• Test conditions – Additional operations	Specified value	Repairing malfunction
11	2 + 37	ABS solenoid valve relay -J106-	• Wiring between ABS control module and ABS hydraulic unit OK	30 Ω – 80 Ω	– Test electric wiring between ABS control module and ABS hydraulic unit for short circuit to Ground (GND) or positive – If the wiring harness is OK, replace the relay
12	2 + 7	ABS return flow pump relay -J105-	• Wiring between ABS control module and ABS hydraulic unit OK	30 Ω – 80 Ω	– Test electric wiring between ABS control module and ABS hydraulic unit for short circuit to Ground (GND) or positive – If the wiring harness is OK, replace relay

AD4029600045040X

Fig. 54 Electrical testing table (Part 4 of 11). A4, A6, A8, S4 & S6

Test of operation and correct connections					
Test step	VAG 1598/20 sockets	Test of	• Test conditions – Additional operations	Specification	Repairing malfunction
13 [1]	Bridge 1 + 2, 28 + 37	Left front ABS inlet valve -N101- and brake line connection	• Ignition on – Bridge sockets 5 + 28 – Depress brake pedal and hold	• Left front wheel can be turned by hand	– If wheel locks, check whether another wheel can be turned. If yes, the hydraulic brake lines are improperly connected. Check the brake line connections and unions. Make sure that the system operates properly. Repeat test step 13 – If all wheels lock, there is a malfunction of the inlet valve ⇒ Diagnostic Trouble Code DTC 00257
			– Remove bridge	• Left front wheel locks	
			– Release brake pedal		

[1] A second technician is required to conduct this test.

AD4029600045050X

Fig. 54 Electrical testing table (Part 5 of 11). A4, A6, A8, S4 & S6

Test of operation and correct connections

Test step	VAG 1598/20 sockets	Test of	• Test conditions – Additional operations	Specification	Repairing malfunction
14 [1]	Bridge 1 + 2, 28 + 37	Right front ABS inlet valve -N100- and brake line connection	• Ignition on – Bridge sockets 54 + 28		
			– Depress brake pedal and hold	• Right front wheel can be turned by hand·	– If wheel locks, check whether another wheel can be turned. If yes, the hydraulic brake lines are improperly connected. Check the brake line connections and unions. Make sure that the system operates properly. Repeat test step 14 – If all wheels lock, there is a malfunction of the inlet valve ⇒ Diagnostic Trouble Code DTC 00259
			– Remove bridge	• Right front wheel locks	
			– Release brake pedal		

[1] A second technician is required to conduct this test.

AD4029600045060X

Fig. 54 Electrical testing table (Part 6 of 11). A4, A6, A8, S4 & S6

Test of operation and correct connections

Test step	VAG 1598/20 sockets	Test of	• Test conditions – Additional operations	Specification	Repairing malfunction
16 [1]	Bridge 1 + 2, 28 + 37	Right rear ABS inlet valve -N133- and brake line connection	• Ignition on – Bridge sockets 6 + 28		
			– Depress brake pedal and hold	• Right rear wheel can be turned by hand	– If wheel locks, check whether another wheel can be turned. If yes, the hydraulic brake lines are improperly connected. Check the brake line connections and unions. Make sure that the system operates properly. Repeat test step 16 – If all wheels lock, there is a malfunction of the inlet valve ⇒ Diagnostic Trouble Code, DTC 00273
			– Remove bridge	• Right rear wheel locks	
			– Release brake pedal		

[1] A second technician is required to conduct this test.

AD4029600045080X

Fig. 54 Electrical testing table (Part 8 of 11). A4, A6, A8, S4 & S6

Function and leak test

Test step	VAG 1598/20 sockets	Test of	Test conditions - Additional operations	Specification	Corrective steps
17	Bridge 1 + 2, 7 + 37, 37 + 28	ABS Return Flow Pump	Connect pressure gauge VAG 1310A to left front brake caliper and bleed		- Return flow pump faulty, replace ABS Hydraulic Unit
		Left Front Traction Control Switch-Over Valve	- Bridge sockets 3 + 28		
		Left Front Traction Control Outlet Valve	- Switch ignition on for not more than 10 seconds, switch off ignition	Switch-Over Valve operates Return Flow Pump runs	- Test Switch-Over Valve and Outlet Valve by measuring resistance; if malfunction found replace ABS Hydraulic Unit
		ABS Hydraulic Unit		Pressure at gauge max. 5 bar	
		Left Front ABS Outlet Valve			
		Right Rear ABS Outlet Valve	- Bridge sockets 4 + 28 - Switch on ignition for not more than 10 seconds, switch ignition off - Disconnect pressure gauge VAG 1310A and bleed brakes	Outlet Valve operates Pressure at gauge rises: FWD: 170 ± 25 bar (2465 ± 363 psi) All Wheel Drive, pressure-regulated: 90 ± 25 bar (1305 ± 363 psi) All Wheel Drive, suction-regulated: 170 ± 25 bar (2465 ± 363 psi)	- Pressure limiting valve and/or Left Front ABS Outlet Valve and/ or Right Rear ABS Outlet Valve faulty, Replace ABS Hydraulic Unit

AD4029600045090A

Fig. 54 Electrical testing table (Part 9 of 11). A4, A6, A8, S4 & S6

Test of operation and correct connections

Test step	VAG 1598/20 sockets	Test of	• Test conditions – Additional operations	Specification	Repairing malfunction
15 [1]	Bridge 1 + 2, 28 + 37	Left rear ABS inlet valve -N134- and brake line connection	• Ignition on – Bridge sockets 53 + 28		
			– Depress brake pedal and hold	• Left rear wheel can be turned by hand	– If wheel locks, check whether another wheel can be turned. If yes, the hydraulic brake lines are improperly connected. Check the brake line connections and unions. Make sure that the system operates properly. Repeat test step 15 – If all wheels lock, there is a malfunction of the inlet valve ⇒ Diagnostic Trouble Code DTC 00274
			– Remove bridge	• Left rear wheel locks	
			– Release brake pedal		

[1] A second technician is required to conduct this test.

AD4029600045070X

Fig. 54 Electrical testing table (Part 7 of 11). A4, A6, A8, S4 & S6

Function and leak test

Test step	VAG 1598/20 sockets	Test of	Test conditions - Additional operations	Specification	Corrective steps
18	Bridge 1 + 2, 7 + 37, 37 + 28	ABS Return Flow Pump	Connect pressure gauge VAG 1310A to right front brake caliper and bleed		- Return flow pump faulty, replace ABS Hydraulic Unit
		Right Front Traction Control Switch-Over Valve	- Bridge sockets 55 + 28		
		Right Front Traction Control Outlet Valve	- Switch ignition on for not more than 10 seconds, switch off ignition	Switch-Over Valve operates Return Flow Pump runs	- Test Switch-Over Valve and Outlet Valve by measuring resistance; if malfunction found replace ABS Hydraulic Unit
		Pressure limiting valve in ABS Hydraulic Unit		Pressure at gauge max. 5 bar	
		Right Front ABS Outlet Valve			
		Left Rear ABS Outlet Valve	- Bridge sockets 27 + 28 - Switch on ignition for not more than 10 seconds, switch ignition off - Disconnect pressure gauge VAG 1310A and bleed brakes	Outlet Valve operates Pressure at gauge rises: FWD: 170 ± 25 bar (2465 ± 363 psi) All Wheel Drive, pressure-regulated: 90 ± 25 bar (1305 ± 363 psi) All Wheel Drive, suction-regulated: 170 ± 25 bar (2465 ± 363 psi)	- Pressure limiting valve and/or Right Front ABS Outlet Valve and/ or Left Rear ABS Outlet Valve faulty, Replace ABS Hydraulic Unit

AD4029600045100A

Fig. 54 Electrical testing table (Part 10 of 11). A4, A6, A8, S4 & S6

If there is no malfunction when establishing communication between the VAG 1551 ST and the ABS control module, the control module identification appears in the display.

The dealership code, WSC XXXXX, indicates the dealership or workshop in which the control module was last coded.

Control module index [1]	System designation [2]
G [5]	Front Wheel Drive / ABS/EDL Bosch 5
J [4]	All Wheel Drive / ABS/EDL Bosch 5, pressure-regulated
L [4]	All Wheel Drive / ABS/EDL Bosch 5, suction-regulated

[3] This index indicates the software status.

[4] This index for control modules with speed sensor outputs for automatic transmission and "poor road" info for On Board Diagnostic (USA)

[5] This index for control module with "poor road" info for On Board Diagnostic (USA)

Notes:

- *The control module index can only be altered by replacing the control module.*
- *Application of ABS/EDL/TCS Control Module ___*

AD4029600045110X

Fig. 54 Electrical testing table (Part 11 of 11). A4, A6, A8, S4 & S6

Switch to measuring range:
Resistance measurement (2kΩ)

Step	VAG1598 sockets	To be tested	• Test conditions - Additional steps	Specified Value	Measures for deviations from specified values
5	19 + 20	Resistance wheel speed sensor front, right -G45	• Ignition switched off	1.0-1.3 kΩ	- Check connector at wheel speed sensor. - Check resistance of wheel speed sensor. - Check wiring to wheel speed sensor; during testing move wire (check for loose contact).
6	1 + 2	Resistance wheel speed sensor front, right -G47	• Ignition switched off	1.0-1.3 kΩ	- Check connector at wheel speed sensor. - Check resistance of wheel speed sensor. - Check wiring to wheel speed sensor; during testing move wire (check for loose contact).

AD4020000065030X

Fig. 55 Electrical testing table (Part 3 of 9). TT

Switch to measuring range:
Voltage measurement (2 V)

Step	VAG1598 sockets	To be tested	• Test conditions - Additional steps	Specified Value	Measures for deviations from specified values
9	19 + 20	Voltage signal wheel speed sensor front, right -G45	• Vehicle raised • Ignition switched off - Turn front right wheel approx. 1 rev./sec.	min. 65 mV alternating voltage	- Check installation of wheel speed sensor and impulse wheel - Check if wheel speed sensor is interchanged Read measuring value block
10	1 + 2	Voltage signal wheel speed sensor front, left -G47	• Vehicle raised • Ignition switched off - Turn front left wheel approx. 1 rev./sec.	min. 65 mV alternating voltage	- Check installation of wheel speed sensor and impulse wheel - Check if wheel speed sensor is interchanged Read measuring value block.

AD4020000065050X

Fig. 55 Electrical testing table (Part 5 of 9). TT

Switch to measuring range:
Voltage measurement (20 V)

Step	VAG1598 sockets	To be tested	• Test conditions - Additional steps	Specified Value	Measures for deviations from specified value
1	24 + 25	Voltage supply for hydraulic pump -V64: terminal 30 on -J104	• Ignition switched off	10.0-14.5 V	- Check wiring from contact 24 to ground. - Check wiring from contact 25 via fuse (30A) to B+.
2	8 + 9	Voltage supply for hydraulic unit -N55: terminal 30 on -J104	• Ignition switched off	10.0-14.5 V	- Check wiring from contact 8 to ground. - Check wiring from contact 9 via fuse (30A) to B+.

AD4020000065010X

Fig. 55 Electrical testing table (Part 1 of 9). TT

Switch to measuring range:
Voltage measurement (20 V)

Step	VAG1598 sockets	To be tested	• Test conditions - Additional steps	Specified Value	Measures for deviations from specified values
3	8 + 4	Voltage supply at control module through terminal 75	• Ignition switched on	10.0-14.5 V	- Check wiring from contact 8 to ground. - Check wiring from contact 4 to terminal 75.
4	8 + 18	Function of brake light switch -F	• Ignition switched off - Release brake pedal - Press brake pedal	0.0-0.5 V 10.0-14.5 V	- Check wiring from contact 8 to ground. - Check wiring from contact 18 via fuse (10A) to terminal 30. - Check brake light switch -F. - Adjust brake light switch -F

AD4020000065020X

Fig. 55 Electrical testing table (Part 2 of 9). TT

Switch to measuring range:
Resistance measurement (2kΩ)

Step	VAG1598 sockets	To be tested	• Test conditions - Additional steps	Specified Value	Measures for deviations from specified values
7	22 + 23	Resistance wheel speed sensor rear, right -G44	• Ignition switched off	1.0-1.3 kΩ	- Check connector at wheel speed sensor. - Check resistance of wheel speed sensor. - Check wiring to wheel speed sensor; during testing move wire (check for loose contact).
8	2 + 10	Resistance wheel speed sensor rear, left -G46	• Ignition switched off	1.0-1.3 kΩ	- Check connector T2e - Check resistance of wheel speed sensor. - Check wiring to wheel speed sensor; during testing move wire (check for loose contact).

AD4020000065040X

Fig. 55 Electrical testing table (Part 4 of 9). TT

Switch to measuring range:
Voltage measurement (2 V). Resistance measurement (200 Ω) in test step 13

Step	VAG1598 sockets	To be tested	• Test conditions - Additional steps	Specified Value	Measures for deviations from specified values
11	22 + 23	Voltage signal wheel speed sensor rear, right -G44	• Vehicle raised • Ignition switched off - Turn rear right wheel approx. 1 rev./sec.	190-1140 mV	- Check installation of wheel speed sensor and impulse wheel - Check if wheel speed sensor is interchanged Read measuring value block.
12	5 + 6	Voltage signal wheel speed sensor rear, left -G46	• Vehicle raised • Ignition switched off - Turn rear left wheel approx. 1 rev./sec.	190-1140 mV	- Check installation of wheel speed sensor and impulse wheel - Check if wheel speed sensor is interchanged Read measuring value block.
13	3 + 14	Coding bridge	• Ignition switched off	0.0-1.0 Ω	- Check wiring and contacts in connector. - Replace if deviating from specified value

AD4020000065060X

Fig. 55 Electrical testing table (Part 6 of 9). TT

Function check: Warning light for ABS (K47)					
Step	VAG1598 sockets	To be tested	- Test conditions - Additional steps	Specified Value	Measures for deviations from specified values
14	-	Function of warning light ABS -K47	- Ignition switched off		- Check voltage supply from terminal 75 at contact 4 of control module.
			- Switch on ignition	Warning light -K47 lights up for 2 seconds and switches off.	- Check wiring from contact 16 of control module to instrument cluster.
					- Check for malfunction in instrument cluster

AD4020000065070X

Fig. 55 Electrical testing table (Part 7 of 9). TT

Function check: Warning light for ABS (K47)					
Step	VAG1598 sockets	To be tested	- Test conditions - Additional steps	Specified Value	Measures for deviations from specified values
15	-	Function of red brake warning symbol	- Ignition switched off - Remove connector for one of the front wheel speed sensor wires.		- Check voltage supply from terminal 75 at contact 4 of control module.
			- Switch on ignition, start engine and rev up over 2000 RPM	Red brake warning symbol lights up.	- Check wiring from contact 16 of control module to instrument cluster.
			- Connect sensor wire, begin OBD, check and then erase DTC memory.		- Check for malfunction in instrument cluster

AD4020000065080X

Fig. 55 Electrical testing table (Part 8 of 9). TT

Function check: Indicator light for ABS (K47)					
Step	VAG1598 sockets	To be tested	- Test conditions - Additional steps	Specified Value	Measures for deviations from specified values
16	-	Function of hydraulic pump for ABS -V64	- Disconnect connector of pump motor from control module.		
			- Apply a voltage 10.0-14.5 V to connector of pump motor.	Pump motor runs normally. Do not let pump motor run longer than 10 seconds.	- If pump motor does not run, remove hydraulic control unit and replace pump motor and valve block

AD4020000065090X

Fig. 55 Electrical testing table (Part 9 of 9). TT

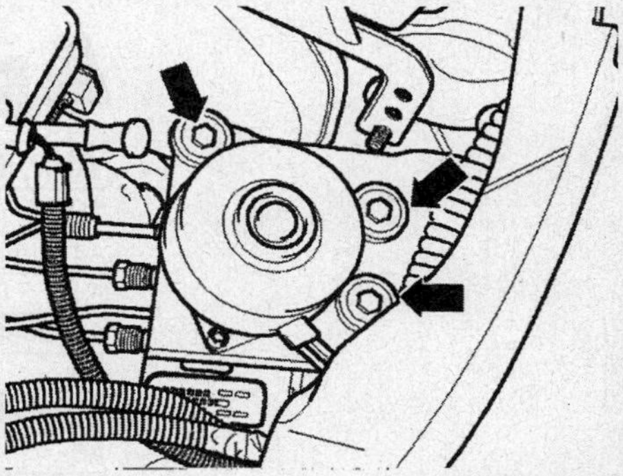

AD4020000066000X

Fig. 57 Hydraulic unit mounting bracket bolt removal. TT

Year	Drive Type	Engine & Code	Control Module	Coding	Variations
2000	FWD	1.8L ATC	8N0 907 379	13204	ABS/EDL/ATC Less MSR
	AWD	1.8L ATC	8N0 907 379 A	13504	ABS/EDL Less MSR
	AWD	1.8L AMU	8N0 907 379 A	13504	ABS/EDL Less MSR

Fig. 56 ABS Mark 20 IE coding table. TT

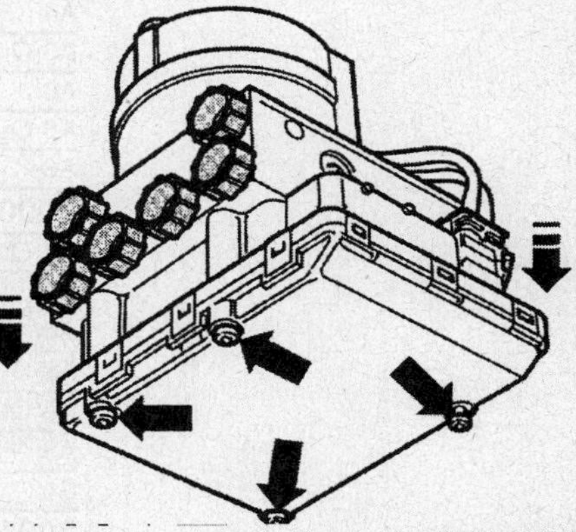

AD4020000067000X

Fig. 58 Control module removal. TT

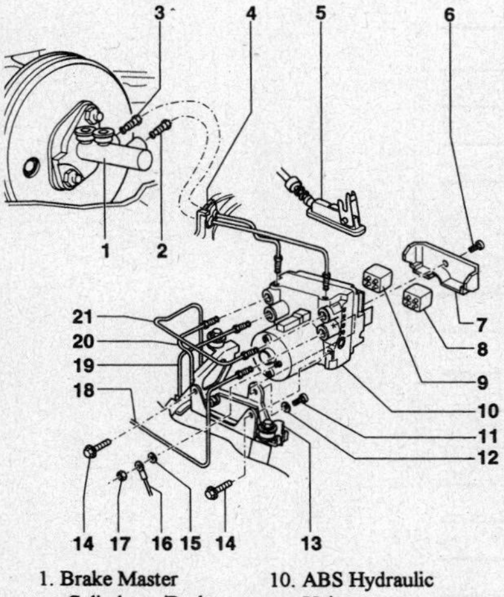

1. Brake Master Cylinder w/Brake Servo Unit
2. Brake Line
3. Brake Line
4. Boot
5. ABS Wiring Harness Connector
6. Screw
7. Cover Panel
8. ABS Solenoid Valve Relay
9. ABS Return Flow Pump Relay
10. ABS Hydraulic Unit
11. Screw
12. Washer
13. Bracket For ABS Hydraulic Unit
14. Bolt & Washer
15. Serrated Washer
16. Ground Cable
17. Hex Nut
18. Brake Line
19. Brake Line
20. Brake Line
21. Brake Line

AD4029600047000X

Fig. 59 Exploded view of ABS hydraulic control unit. A4, A6, A8, S4 & S6

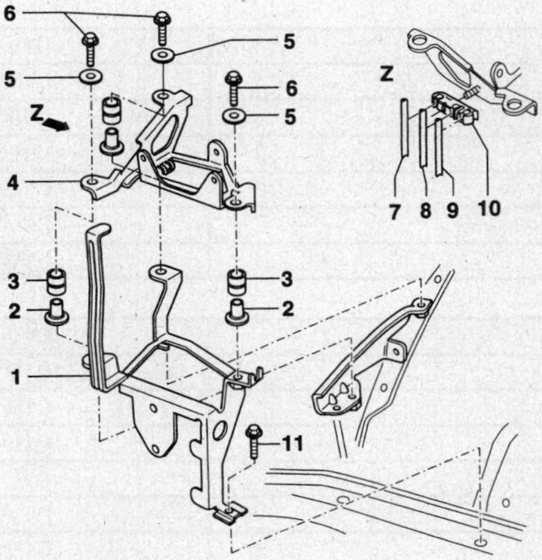

1. Angle Bracket
2. Bearing Bushing
3. Buffer
4. Mounting Bracket For ABS Hydraulic Unit
5. Washer
6. Bolt & Washer
7. Brake Line
8. Brake Line
9. Brake Line
10. Fixture
11. Bolt & Washer

AD4029600048000X

Fig. 60 Exploded view of ABS hydraulic control unit mounting bracket. A4 & S4

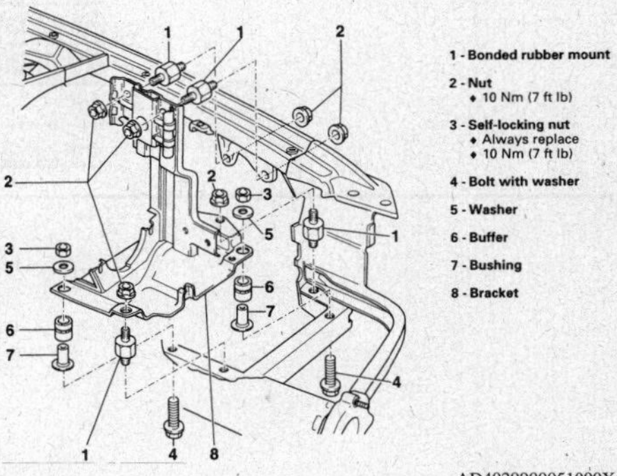

AD4029900051000X

Fig. 61 Exploded view of ABS hydraulic control unit mounting bracket. A8

Automatic Transaxles

TABLE OF CONTENTS

	Page No.
APPLICATION CHART	1-194
01F & 01K AUTOMATIC TRANSAXLES	1-195
01L & 01V AUTOMATIC TRANSAXLES	1-208
01N AUTOMATIC TRANSAXLE	1-202

Application Chart

Year, Model	Transaxle Type
1998	
A4 Quattro	01V
A4	01V
A6 Quattro	01V
A6	01V
A8 Quattro	01L
A8	01V
Cabriolet	01N
1999	
A4 Quattro	01V
A4	01V
A6 Quattro	01V
A6	01V
A8 Quattro	01L
A8	01V
2000	
A4 Quattro	01V
A4	01V
A6	01V
A8 Quattro	01L
A8 Quattro	01L
A8	01V
S4	01V
2001	
A4 Quattro	01V
A4	01V
A6	01V
A8 Quattro	01L
A8 Quattro	01L
A8	01V
S4	01V

01F & 01K Automatic Transaxles

NOTE: On Air Bag Equipped Models, Refer To "Air Bag System Precautions" Located In The Front Of This Manual For System Disarming & Arming Procedures.

NOTE: Refer To "Computer Relearn Procedures" Located In The Front Of This Manual When Battery Power To The Computer Has Been Interrupted.

INDEX

	Page No.
Adjustments	1-196
Ignition Locking Cable	1-196
Multi-Function/Transaxle Range Switch	1-197
Selector Lever Cable	1-197
Selector Lever Housing	1-197
Shift Lock Solenoid	1-197
Description	1-195
Identification	1-195
01F Transaxle	1-195
01K Transaxle	1-195
In-Vehicle Repairs	1-198
Flanged Shaft Seal, Replace	1-198
Ignition Locking Cable, Replace	1-198
Multi-Function/Transaxle Range Switch, Replace	1-198
Propeller Shaft, Replace	1-199
Transaxle Control Module (TCM), Replace	1-199
Transaxle Control Module Coding	1-198
Valve Body, Replace	1-199
Maintenance	1-196
Fluid Change	1-196
Fluid Level Inspection	1-196
Precautions	1-195
Air Bag Systems	1-195
Battery Ground Cable	1-195
Radio Coded Anti-Theft System	1-195
Technical Service Bulletins	1-200
Delayed 1–2 Upshift On Cold Start Warm-Up	1-200
Tightening Specifications	1-201
Transaxle, Replace	1-199
Troubleshooting	1-195
Brake Transaxle Shift Interlock (BTSI)	1-195
Transaxle	1-196

PRECAUTIONS

Air Bag Systems

Refer to "Air Bag System Precautions" in the front of this manual for system disarming and arming procedures.

Radio Coded Anti-Theft System

Prior to disconnecting the battery or removing the audio system, obtain the security code from the vehicle operator. Refer to the owner's manual for security code disarming and arming procedures.

Battery Ground Cable

Prior to service, disconnect battery ground cable and isolate as required.

IDENTIFICATION

01F TRANSAXLE

The identification codes are located on the data plate on the lefthand and righthand sides of the transaxle, **Fig. 1.**

The manufacturer's model number and transaxle code can be found on the vehicle data plate, **Fig. 2.**

Refer to **Fig. 3** for transaxle specifications.

01K TRANSAXLE

The identification codes are located on the data plate on the lefthand and righthand sides of the transaxle, **Fig. 4.**

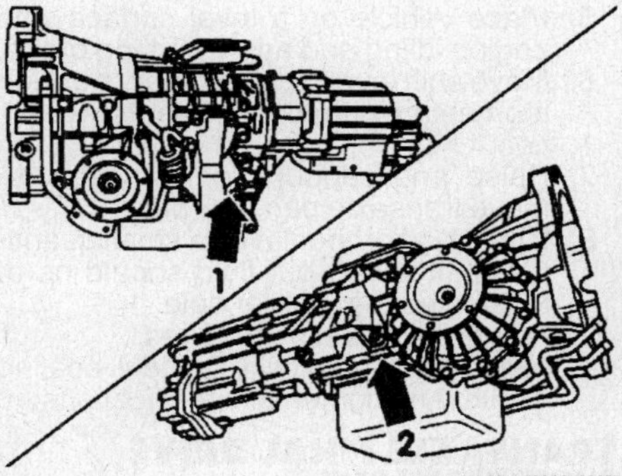

AD5019500001000X

Fig. 1 Transaxle data plate locations. 01F transaxle

The manufacturer's model number and transaxle code can be found on the vehicle data plate, **Fig. 2.**

Refer to **Fig. 5** for transaxle specifications.

DESCRIPTION

These transaxles are electronically controlled and fully automatic. They have four forward speeds and a lock-up torque converter. The 01F transaxle uses an electronically controlled clutch to offer traction control. An Emergency Running Mode (ERM) allows operation of the transaxle even when certain systems fail. When the ERM is active the shift indicator area in the instrument cluster will be lit. If ERM is activated while vehicle is running, Fourth gear will be engaged until engine is stopped. If ERM is activated and the engine started the transaxle will operate in second gear if shift

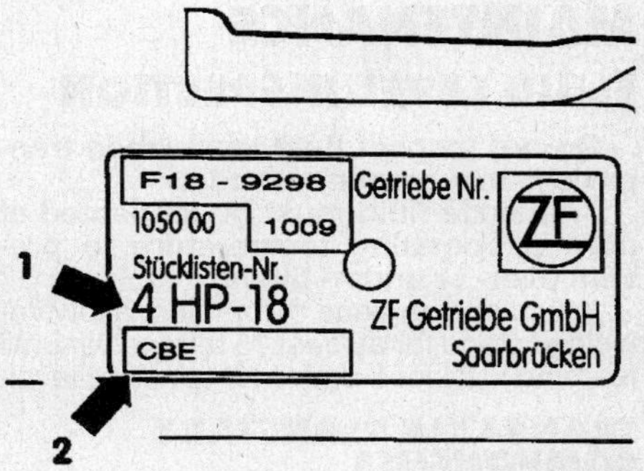

AD5019500002000X

Fig. 2 Transaxle data plate

lever is in a forward position and in reverse gear with shift lever in R position. All other transaxle electronic functions will be disabled.

A permanently engaged Torsen third differential is available on these transaxles, it is mounted to the rear of the transaxle and is used to drive a rear axle differential and give all wheel drive capabilities.

These transaxles offer an adaptive program to suit various driver habits and driving conditions. The control system also will also interact with the vehicle ABS system when the traction control system is in operation.

TROUBLESHOOTING

BRAKE TRANSAXLE SHIFT INTERLOCK (BTSI)

Refer to shifter component location diagram, **Fig. 6,** and wiring diagram, **Fig. 7,** during diagnosis and fault condition inspection in the BTSI system.

Automatic transmission			01F 4x4 quattro all-wheel-drive		
Transmission	Code letters			CRF	CJD
	Manufactured	from: to:		05.94 —	05.94 —
Torque converter	Identification			F11 /169 001	F11 /169 001
Application	Type			Audi A6 quattro	Audi A6 quattro
	Engine			2.8 liter 128 kW (174 hp)	2.8 liter 128 kW (174 hp)
Ratios	1st gear			2.580:1	2.580:1
	2nd gear			1.407:1	1.407:1
	3rd gear (3GR)			1.000:1	1.000:1
	4th gear (4GR)			0.742:1	0.742:1
	Reverse			2.882:1	2.882:1
Intermediate drive for front final drive	No. of teeth	Input gear		27	27
		Intermediate gear		33	33
		Output gear		34	36
	Ratio			1.259:1	1.333:1
Intermediate drive for rear final drive	No. of teeth	Input gear		37	37
		Output gear		39	39
	Ratio			1.054:1	1.054:1

AD5019500003000X

Fig. 3 Transaxle specification table. 01F transaxle

Refer to "Adjustments" and "In-Vehicle Repairs" for related information on shift lock solenoid and ignition lock cable.

TRANSAXLE

The 01F and 01K automatic transaxles are equipped with a transaxle control unit. This unit has a self-diagnosis capability and can store transaxle malfunctions in its memory. For further repairs and troubleshooting refer to **MOTOR's "Imported Transmission Manual."**

MAINTENANCE

FLUID LEVEL INSPECTION

Do not inspect fluid level when transaxle is in emergency mode.

Transaxle fluid must be inspected at normal operating temperature to prevent over- or under- filling.

If fluid shows signs of foaming, allow vehicle to stand for at least 15 minutes or until foaming subsides prior to inspecting level.

TRANSAXLE PLANETARY COMPONENTS

With Filler Pipe

1. Obtain dipstick part No. 01F 321 431 A and remove cap from dipstick tube.
2. Prior to warming fluid to perform level inspection, ensure level reaches at least 20°C mark on dipstick.
3. Inspect fluid for condition and contamination.
4. Connect a suitable scan tool to the Diagnostic Link Connector (DLC).
5. Access scan tool function 08, then Display Group 004 and Display Field 4 to read transaxle fluid temperature.
6. Operate vehicle to warm transaxle fluid to normal operating temperature of 140–176°F (60–80°C.).
7. Place vehicle on a level surface with engine idling and apply parking brake.
8. Move shift lever into each gear position momentarily, then place in Park position.
9. Ensure oil level is between MIN and MAX marks on dipstick.
10. Adjust fluid level as required.

Less Filler Pipe

1. Raise and support vehicle, then remove filler plug on transaxle pan to ensure sufficient fluid is in transaxle to prevent damage during inspection procedure.
2. Connect a suitable scan tool to Data Link Connector.
3. Access scan tool function 8 (transaxle electronics), then Display Group 004 and Display Field 4 to read transaxle fluid temperature.
4. Operate vehicle to warm transaxle fluid to normal operating temperature of 140–176°F (60–80°C.)
5. Place vehicle on a level surface with engine idling and apply parking brake.
6. Move shift lever into each gear position momentarily, then place in Park position.
7. Raise and support vehicle, then remove transaxle pan filler plug.
8. If fluid is at proper level, a small quantity will flow out, but fluid should be at least to bottom of filler hole.
9. Adjust fluid level as required.
10. Install filler plug with a new sealing gasket and tighten to specifications.

TRANSAXLE FINAL DRIVE DIFFERENTIALS

1. Raise and support vehicle.
2. Remove differential level inspection plug, **Fig. 8.**
3. Fluid is at proper level it is at bottom edge of filler hole.
4. Refer to "Lubricant Data Charts" for fluid amount and type, then add as required to proper level.
5. Install differential level inspection plug and tighten to specifications.

FLUID CHANGE

TRANSAXLE PLANETARY COMPONENTS

1. Raise and support vehicle.
2. Remove transaxle fluid pan drain plug, then allow fluid to drain into a suitable container. Discard seal.
3. **On models with transaxle filler tube,** disconnect filler tube from pan. Discard seal.
4. **On all models,** remove pan mounting bolts, then the pan.
5. Remove strainer mounting bolts, then the strainer. Discard strainer O-ring seal.

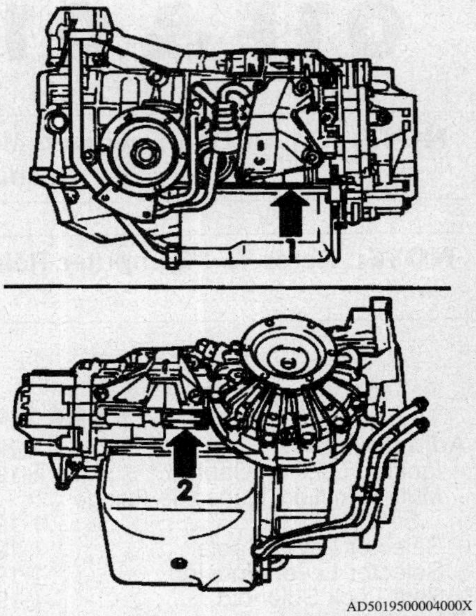

Fig. 4 Transaxle code locations. 01K transaxle

6. Clean strainer and pan with a suitable cleaning fluid, then blow dry.
7. Install strainer using a new O-ring seal. Tighten screws to specifications.
8. Install oil pan using a new gasket. Tighten mounting bolts to specifications.
9. **On models equipped with transaxle filler tube,** install tube to pan using a new gasket and tighten fitting to specifications.
10. **On all models,** install drain plug with a new gasket and tighten to specifications.
11. Fill transaxle with proper fluid. Refer to "Specifications" for fluid amounts and type, then to "Inspecting Fluid Level."

TRANSAXLE FINAL DRIVE DIFFERENTIALS

The differential fluid is of a permanent fill type and is not normally replaced. No provision has been made for draining fluid.

ADJUSTMENTS

IGNITION LOCKING CABLE

1. Apply parking brake.
2. Remove center console, then place selector lever in "N" position.
3. Remove locking cable from selector lever housing.
4. Loosen locking cable adjustment bolt.
5. Place ignition switch in "On" position.
6. Place a. 059 inch feeler gauge between locking flap and locking pin.
7. Adjust locking cable so locking pin is pushed against feeler gauge, then tighten adjustment nut.
8. After operating several times, clearance between locking pin and locking flap must be. 047–.067 inch.
9. Move selector lever to "N" position, then install locking cable to selector lever housing. **Cable must be free of kinks.**
10. Install center console.

Automatic transmission			01K Front wheel drive	
Transmission	Code letters		CRC	CJE
	Manufactured	from: to:	05.94 —	09.94 —
Torque converter	Identification		F11 /169 001	F11 /169 001
Application	Type		Audi A6	Audi A6
	Engine		2.8 liters 128 kW (174 hp)	2.8 liters 128 kW (174 hp)
Ratios	1st gear		2.580:1	2.580:1
	2nd gear		1.407:1	1.407:1
	3rd gear (3GR)		1.000:1	1.000:1
	4th gear (4GR)		0.742:1	0.742:1
	Reverse		2.882:1	2.882:1
Intermediate drive for front final drive	No. of teeth	Input gear	27	27
		Intermediate gear	33	33
		Output gear	34	36
	Ratio		1.259:1	1.333:1

AD5019500005000X

Fig. 5 Transaxle specification table. 01K transaxle

MULTI-FUNCTION/ TRANSAXLE RANGE SWITCH

1. Remove lefthand transaxle support, then unscrew selector lever cable at selector lever.
2. Turn back selector lever clamping screw fully and pull lever off selector shaft.
3. Rotate selector shaft in opposite direction of travel using a suitable 8 MM wrench as far as stop and into P position.
4. Turn selector shaft back two detents into N position.
5. Mount adjusting aid tool No. 0501 311 626, or equivalent, onto selector shaft, then loosen multi-function switch mounting screws.
6. Rotate multi-function switch until hole in adjustment aid tool No. 0501 311 626, or equivalent, is aligned with adjustment hole on switch, then install a pin into adjustment hole.
7. Tighten multi-function switch to specifications, then remove adjustment tool.
8. Install lever on selector shaft, then tighten clamping screw.
9. Install selector lever cable and tighten mounting nut.
10. Install lefthand transaxle support.

SELECTOR LEVER CABLE

At Transaxle

1. Place selector lever in "P" position, then loosen bolts at selector lever cable bracket until bracket can be moved.
2. Move selector shaft lever at transaxle rearward as far as stop to "P" position. While doing so, pull selector lever cable as illustrated in **Fig. 9.**
3. Align selector lever cable by moving bracket, then tighten bolts.
4. Turn ignition On, then depress and hold brake pedal.
5. Shift selector lever through all ranges and ensure selector lever position and indicator in instrument cluster are the same.

At Selector Lever

1. Remove center console and footwell heating duct.
2. Place selector lever in "P" position, then loosen selector lever cable nut at clamp.
3. Move selector shaft lever at transaxle rearward as far as stop to "P" position. While doing so, pull selector lever cable as illustrated in **Fig. 9.**
4. Align markings on selector lever cable bracket with center of bolts, then tighten selector lever cable nut.
5. Turn ignition On, then depress and hold brake pedal.
6. Shift selector lever through all ranges and ensure selector lever position and selector lever indicator on instrument cluster are the same.

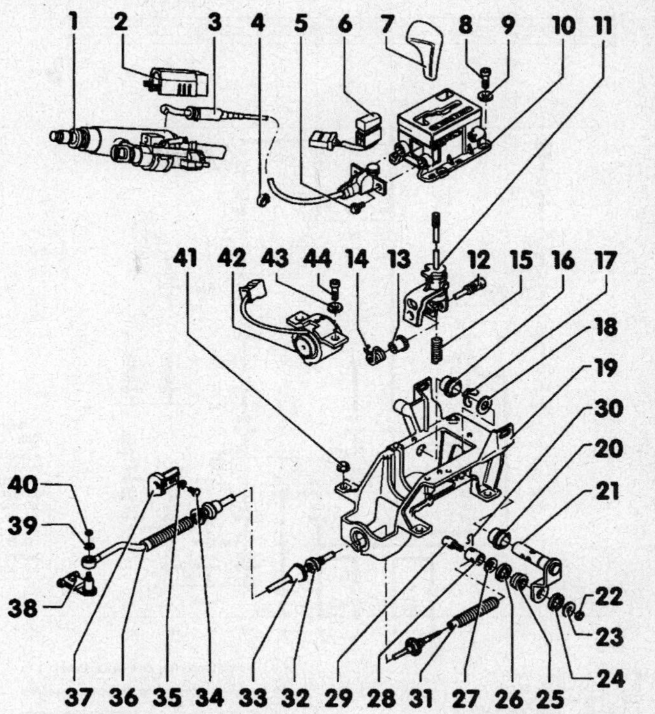

1. Ignition Starter Switch
2. Trim Cover
3. Locking Cable
4. Clip
5. Bolt
6. Transaxle Range (TR) Program Switch
7. Selector Lever Handle
8. Screw
9. Washer
10. Selector Lever Housing
11. Selector Lever
12. Guide Pin
13. Bushing
14. Torsion Spring
15. Compression Spring
16. Bushing
17. Circlip
18. Washer
19. Selector Mechanism Housing
20. Bushing
21. Selector Mechanism Lever
22. Nut
23. Washer
24. Cup
25. Bushing
26. Cup
27. Washer
28. Clamping Sleeve
29. Clamping Pin
30. Spring Clip
31. Boot
32. Selrctor Lever With Guide And Bushing
33. Grommet
34. Bolt
35. Washer
36. Boot
37. Mounting Bracket
38. Transaxle Selector Lever
39. Washer
40. Nut
41. Nut With Washer
42. Shift Lock Solenoid
43. Washer
44. Screw

AD5019500033000X

Fig. 6 Shifter component locations

SELECTOR LEVER HOUSING

1. Place selector lever in Neutral position.
2. Install selector lever housing with nuts loosely secured.
3. Position selector lever housing so that selector lever travel is equal when moving from N to D and N to R.
4. Tighten selector lever housing nuts.

SHIFT LOCK SOLENOID

1. Place selector lever in R position.
2. Measure clearance between selector lever and solenoid using feeler gauge.
3. Clearance should be. 024–.055 inch. Adjust solenoid by loosening mounting screws and positioning as required.

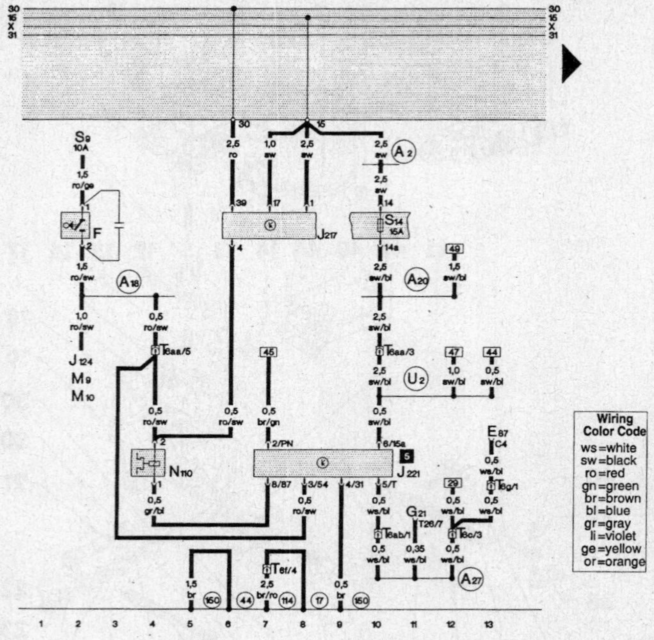

E 87 - A/C Control Head
F - Brake Light Switch
G 21 - Speedometer
J 124 - Rear Lamp Control Module
J 217 - Transmission Control Module (TCM)
J 221 - Shift Lock Control Module
M 9 - Left Brake Light
M 10 - Right Brake Light
N 110 - Shift Lock Solenoid
S 9 - Fuse
S 14 - Fuse
T 6 aa - 6-Pin Connector, red, connector station 1
T 6 ab - 6-Pin Connector, yellow, connector station 1
T 6 c - 6-Pin Connector, green, connector station 2
T 6 f - 6-Pin Connector, yellow, in footwell, front right
T 6 g - 6-Pin Connector, blue, connector station 2
T 26 - 26-Pin Connector, red, on instrument cluster

(17) - ground connection, on intake manifold
(44) - ground connection, on left A-pillar, lower part
(114) - ground connection, in automatic transmission wiring harness
(150) - ground connection, in automatic transmission wiring harness
(A2) - plus connection (15), in instrument panel wiring harness
(A18) - wire connection (54), in instrument panel wiring harness
(A20) - wire connection (15a), in instrument panel wiring harness
(A27) - wire Connection (vehicle speed signal), in instrument panel wiring harness
(U2) - wire connection -1- (15), in automatic transmission wiring harness

AD5019500027010X

Fig. 7 Brake shift interlock wiring diagrams (Part 1 of 4). FWD & Quattro

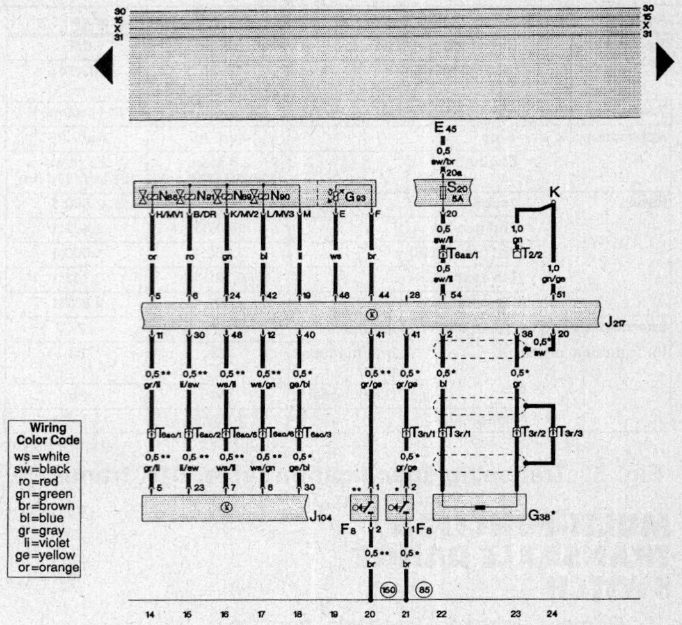

E 45 - Cruise Control Switch
F 8 - Kick Down Switch
G 38 - Transmission Vehicle Speed Sensor (VSS)
G 93 - Transmission Fluid Temperature Sensor
J 104 - ABS Control Module (w/EDL)
J 217 - Transmission Control Module (TCM)
K - DLC (Data Link Connector) Rapid Data Transfer
N 88 - Solenoid Valve 1
N 89 - Solenoid Valve 2
N 90 - Solenoid Valve 3
N 91 - Solenoid Valve 4
S 20 - Fuse
T 2 - Double Connector, white, Data Link Connector, on auxiliary relay panel I
T 3 n - 3-Pin Connector, yellow, in electronic box, in footwell, right front
T 3 r - 3-Pin Connector, black, on Transmission Control Module (TCM)
T 6 aa - 6-Pin Connector, red, connector station 1
T 6 ao - 6-Pin Connector, orange, connector station 1

(85) - ground connection -1-, in engine compartment wiring harness
(150) - ground connection, in automatic transmission wiring harness

* - vehicles with automatic transmission O1K
** - vehicles with automatic transmission O1F

AD5019500027020X

Fig. 7 Brake shift interlock wiring diagrams (Part 2 of 4). FWD & Quattro

IN-VEHICLE REPAIRS

TRANSAXLE CONTROL MODULE CODING

When coding the transaxle control module ensure gear selector lever is in P or N position and throttle pedal is in idle position.

1. Connect a suitable scan tool and access transaxle electronics.
2. Select function 07, then press Q button to enter coding functions.
3. When module code displays, refer to **Fig. 10** for proper code sequence.
4. If code is improper, enter new code using scan tool keyboard, then press arrow button.
5. Disconnect scan tool.

FLANGED SHAFT SEAL, REPLACE

Righthand Or Lefthand Side Driveshaft

1. Raise and support vehicle.
2. Remove catalytic converter.
3. Disconnect driveshaft from flange shaft.
4. Turn steering to full lock, then position and secure driveshaft aside.
5. Install two suitable bolts into flanged shaft threaded holes, then using a suitable bar, counter-hold while loosening flanged shaft center retaining bolt.
6. Remove center retaining bolt, then flanged shaft.
7. Remove seal from transaxle using a suitable pry bar.
8. Pack space between lips of new seal with a suitable multi-purpose grease.
9. Drive a new seal into transaxle case using driver tool No. 3305 for righthand side or No. 3171 for lefthand side, or equivalents.
10. Reverse remaining procedures to install. Tighten all nuts and bolts to specifications.

Propeller Shaft

1. Remove propeller shaft as outlined under "All Wheel Drive Systems."
2. Install two bolts into flanged shaft threaded holes with a suitable bar to counter-hold, then loosen flanged shaft center retaining bolt.
3. Remove center retaining bolt, then the flanged shaft.
4. Remove seal from transaxle using a suitable pry bar.
5. Pack space between lips of new seal with multipurpose grease.
6. Drive new seal into transaxle case using driver tool No. 3306, or equivalent.
7. Reverse remaining procedures to install. Tighten all bolts and nuts to specifications.

IGNITION LOCKING CABLE, REPLACE

1. Remove center console, steering wheel and instrument cluster.
2. Place selector lever in "N" position.
3. Remove locking cable from selector lever housing.
4. Remove cap from ignition switch, then the spring clip from locking cable.
5. Turn ignition On, then turn locking cable down approximately 90° to disengage cable end from ignition switch.
6. Reverse procedure to install. Refer to "Adjustments."

MULTI-FUNCTION/ TRANSAXLE RANGE SWITCH, REPLACE

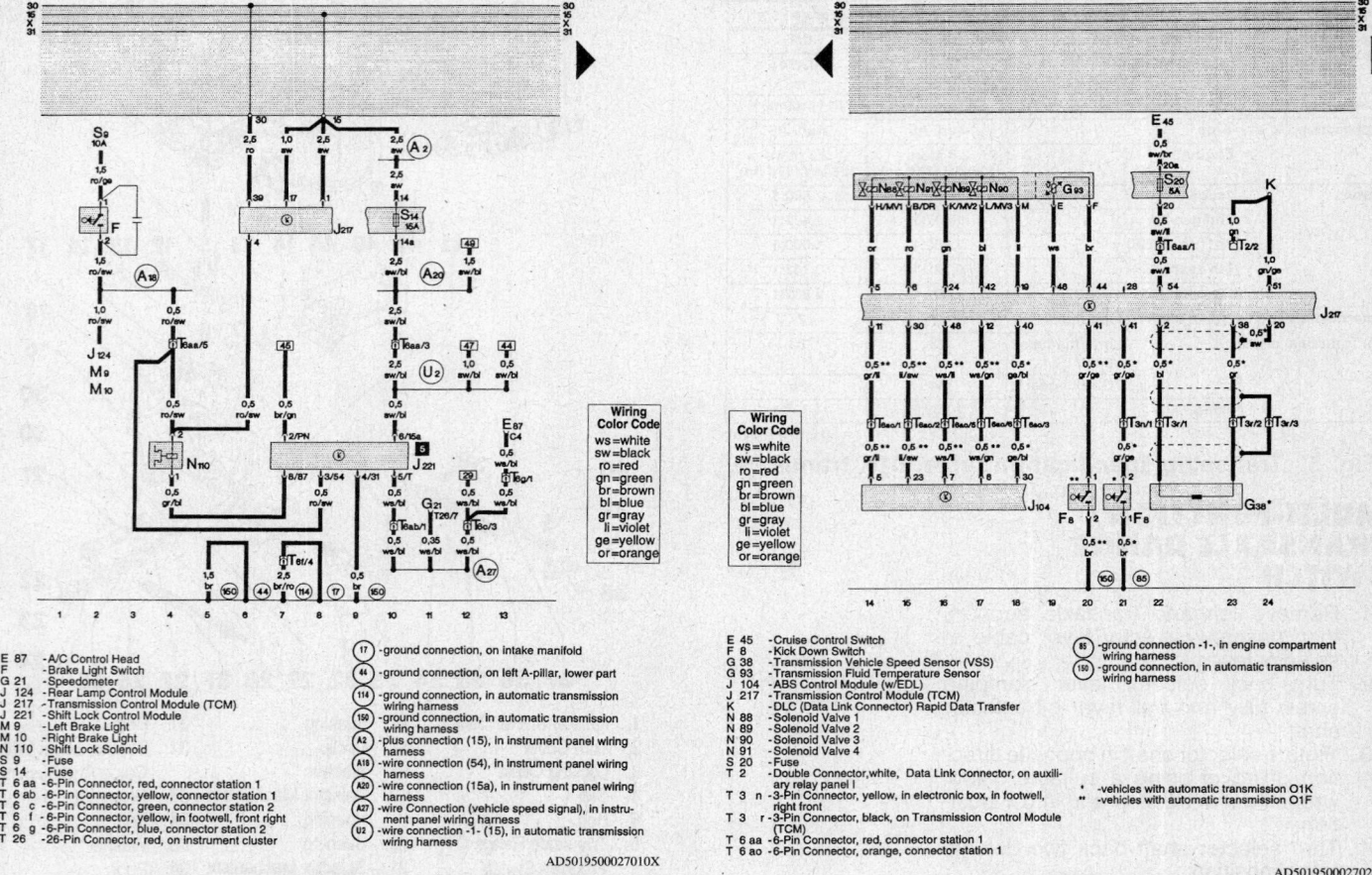

1. Remove lefthand transaxle support, then unscrew selector lever cable at selector lever.
2. Turn back selector lever clamping screw fully and pull lever off selector shaft.
3. Remove switch mounting screws, then the switch.
4. Turn selector shaft in opposite direction of travel, as far as stop, into "P" position then turn back two stops to "N"

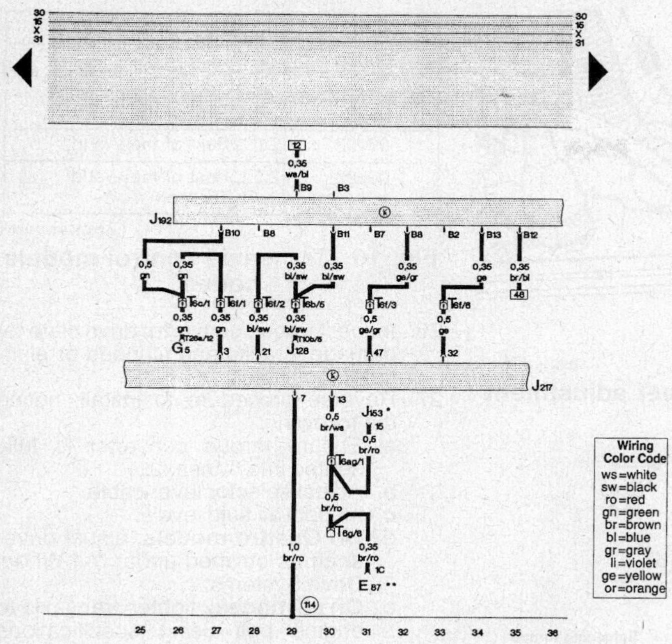

E 87 -A/C Control Head
G 5 -Tachometer
J 128 -Computer Display Unit
J 153 -A/C Clutch Control Module
J 192 -MFI Engine Control Module (ECM)
J 217 -Transmission Control Module (TCM)
T 6 ag -6-Pin Connector, orange, connector station 2
T 6 b -6-Pin Connector, red,connector station 2
T 6 c -6-Pin Connector, green, connector station 2
T 6 f -6-Pin Connector, yellow, in footwell, front right
T 6 g -6-Pin Connector, blue, connector station 2
T 10 b -10-Pin Connector, black, on instrument cluster
T 26 a -26-Pin Connector, green, on instrument cluster

(114) -ground connection, in automatic transmission wiring harness

* -vehicles with manual air conditioning
** -vehicles with automatic climate control

AD5019500027030X

Fig. 7 Brake shift interlock wiring diagrams (Part 3 of 4). FWD & Quattro

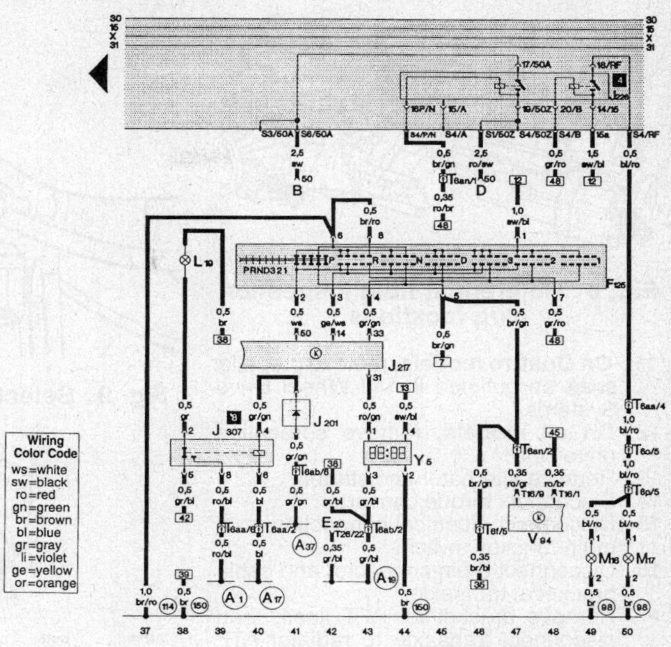

B -Starter
D -Ignition/Starter Switch
E 20 -Instrument Panel Light Dimmer Switch
F 125 -Multi-Function Transmission Range (TR) Switch
J 201 -Protection Diode
J 217 -Transmission Control Module (TCM)
J 226 -Park/Neutral Position (PNP) Relay
J 307 -Selector Lever Light Relay
L 19 -Automatic Transmission Console Light
M 16 -Left Back-Up Light
M 17 -Right Back-Up Light
T 6 aa -6-Pin Connector, red, connector station 1
T 6 ab -6-Pin Connector, yellow, connector station 1
T 6 an -6-Pin Connector, white, connector station 2
T 6 f -6-Pin Connector, yellow, in footwell, front right
T 6 o -6-Pin Connector, brown, connector station 1
T 6 p -6-Pin Connector, black, in luggage compartment, rear left
T 16 -16-Pin Connector, connector C on V94, under rear seat, right
T 26 -26-Pin Connector, red, on instrument cluster
V 94 -Central Locking/Alarm System/Interior Light Delay Control Module
Y 5 -Transmission Range (TR) Selector Lever Display

(98) -ground connection, in rear lid wiring harness
(114) -ground connection, in automatic transmission wiring harness
(150) -ground connection, in automatic transmission wiring harness
(A1) -plus connection (30a), in instrument panel wiring harness
(A17) -wire connection (61), in instrument panel wiring harness
(A19) -wire connection (58d), in instrument panel wiring harness
(A37) -wire connection (58a), in instrument panel wiring harness

AD5019500027040X

Fig. 7 Brake shift interlock wiring diagrams (Part 4 of 4). FWD & Quattro

position using a suitable 8 MM wrench.

5. Install switch and mounting screws. Tighten screws sufficiently to allow switch to be moved for adjustment.
6. Refer to "Adjustment" to complete installation.

PROPELLER SHAFT, REPLACE

Refer to "All Wheel Drive Systems" for replacement procedures.

TRANSAXLE CONTROL MODULE (TCM), REPLACE

1. Turn ignition Off and wait 30 seconds.
2. Remove righthand A-pillar trim, then pull back carpet in righthand footwell.
3. Remove electronic box cover screws, then lift off cover.
4. Remove braces required to access control module.
5. Disconnect TCM electrical connectors.
6. Remove TCM attaching bolts, then the TCM.
7. Reverse procedure to install, code TCM as outlined under "Transaxle Control Module Coding."

VALVE BODY, REPLACE

This valve body must be serviced as an assembly. No provision is made for internal service.

1. Raise and support vehicle, then disconnect transaxle 8-pin connector.
2. Loosen 8-pin connector to transaxle retaining nut.
3. Remove transaxle fluid pan drain plug, then allow fluid to drain into a suitable container. Discard seal.
4. **On models equipped with transaxle filler tube,** disconnect filler tube from pan. Discard seal.
5. **On all models,** remove pan mounting bolts, then the pan.
6. Remove transaxle fluid strainer attaching bolts, then the strainer.
7. Remove nut securing valve body wiring harness to transaxle, then push connector body through into transaxle.
8. Remove valve body attaching bolts, then the valve body.
9. Disconnect valve body harness connectors from valve body solenoids.
10. Unclip and remove harness from valve body.
11. Reverse procedure to install, noting the following:
    a. Replace seals on 8-pin connector body, drain plug, filler tube and transaxle fluid strainer.
    b. Replace gasket on oil pan. Ensure oil pan magnets are properly positioned.
    c. Ensure gear selector is in Park position and selector lever pin engages manual valve of valve body.
    d. Tighten valve body bolts to specifications in a spiral pattern from center out.
    e. Tighten to specifications.

TRANSAXLE

REPLACE

1. Obtain radio theft protection code as outlined under "Precautions."
2. Disconnect electrical connector for speedometer at transaxle.
3. Disconnect intake air duct vacuum hoses, then remove intake air duct and noise insulation.
4. **On models equipped with ATF filler pipe,** disconnect filler pipe at top and remove. Seal filler pipe with a suitable shop towel.
5. **On all models,** remove upper transaxle to engine mounting bolts.
6. Remove noise insulation from under engine, then loosen mounting bolts for engine torque support.
7. Install engine support bridge tool No. 10-222A, or equivalent, then lift engine enough to take up weight.
8. Remove front crossmember.
9. Remove exhaust system.
10. Remove lefthand drive axle heat shield, then disconnect drive axles from transaxle and tie up with suitable wire or rope.

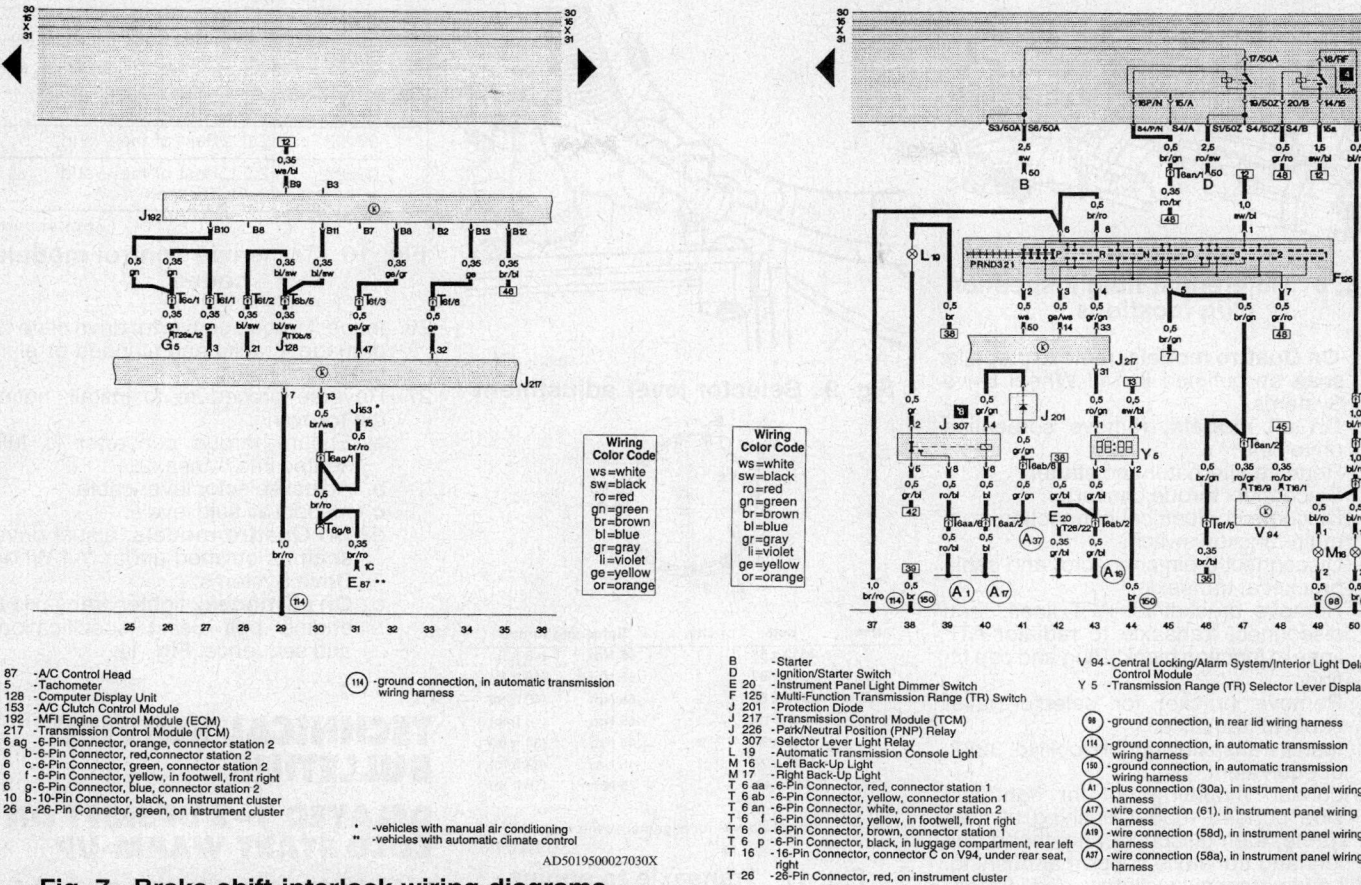

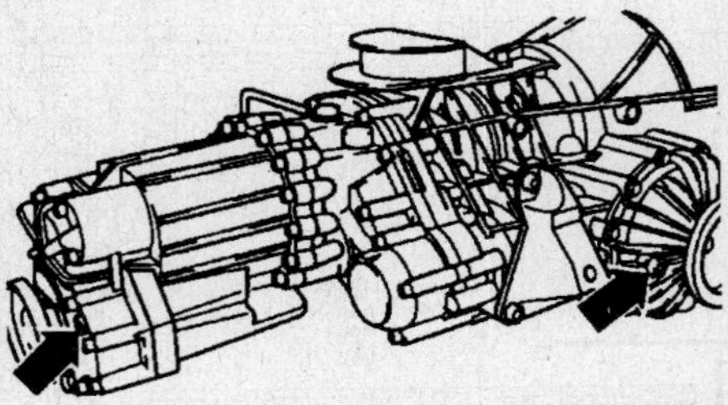

AD5019500006000X

Fig. 8 Differential fluid inspection plug locations

11. **On Quattro models,** remove propeller shaft as outlined in "All Wheel Drive Systems."
12. **On all models,** remove serpentine drive belt.
13. Remove alternator and starter.
14. Disconnect torque converter.
15. Disconnect electrical connection from multi-function switch.
16. Disconnect 8-pin connector and cable bracket at transaxle.
17. Remove bracket for AFT lines, then disconnect transaxle to radiator ATF lines at junction block. Plug and cap fittings.
18. Remove bracket for selector lever cable at transaxle.
19. Install transaxle support tool No. 3282, or equivalent.
20. Loosen mounting nut for righthand side bonded rubber bushing at subframe, then disconnect righthand and lefthand transaxle support at bushing.
21. Lower transaxle slightly and disconnect selector lever cable at selector shaft lever.
22. Remove flanged nut for cable guide, then release cable guide at transaxle and push up, along with cables.
23. Remove lower transaxle to engine mounting bolts.

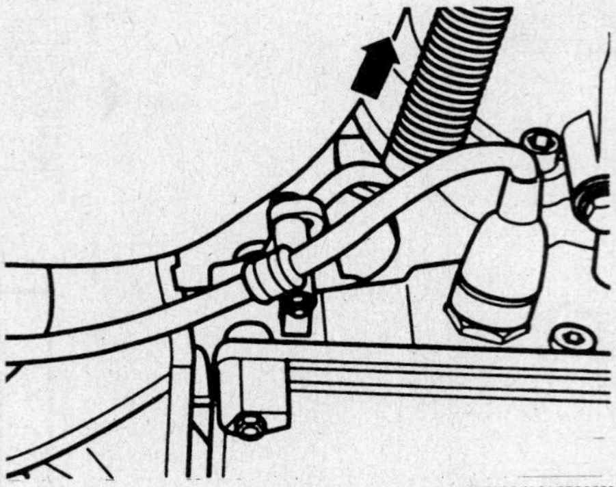

AD5029600157000X

Fig. 9 Selector lever adjustment

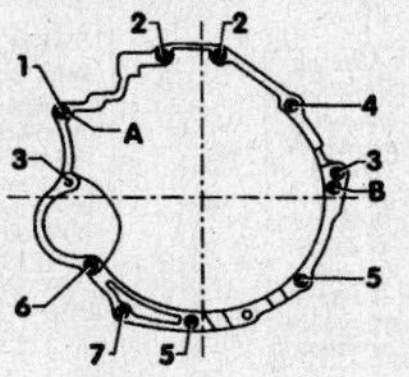

Item	Bolt	Qty.	Tightening torque	
1	M12 x 50	1	65 Nm	(48 ft lb)
2	M12 x 67	2	65 Nm	(48 ft lb)
3	M12 x 80	2	65 Nm	(48 ft lb)
4	M12 x 100	1	65 Nm	(48 ft lb)
5	M10 x 38	2	45 Nm	(33 ft lb)
6	M10 x 70	1	45 Nm	(33 ft lb)
7	M8 x 40	1	25 Nm	(18 ft lb)

A, B Dowel sleeves for alignment/centering

AD5019500036000X

Fig. 11 Transaxle to engine tightening specifications

24. Disconnect and lower transaxle from engine. **Push torque converter off of drive plate when removing transaxle.**
25. Secure torque converter in transaxle.

Coding	Country
00000	2.8 L USA 2.5 L TDI Rest of the World
00001	2.8 L Rest of the World
00002	2.6 L Rest of the World
00003	2.2 L Rest of the World 2.4 L Thailand

AD5019600075000X

Fig. 10 Transaxle control module codes

26. Inspect torque converter drive plate for damage, cracks and stripped or elongated bolt holes.
27. Reverse procedure to install, noting the following:
    a. Ensure torque converter is fully seated into transaxle.
    b. Adjust selector lever cable.
    c. Inspect all fluid levels.
    d. **On Quattro models,** adjust driveshaft as outlined under "All Wheel Drive Systems."
    e. **On all models,** tighten transaxle to engine bolt using specifications and sequence, **Fig. 11.**

TECHNICAL SERVICE BULLETINS

DELAYED 1–2 UPSHIFT ON COLD START WARM-UP

A6 models may display a delayed 1–2 gear upshift when transaxle oil temperature is below 104°F and after a fresh engine start. This is a normal condition caused by warm-up programming to help the engine more rapidly reach operating temperature. The condition will last for approximately two minutes.

TIGHTENING SPECIFICATIONS

Year	Component	Torque/Ft. Lbs.
1998–2001	ATF Filler Pipe To ATF Oil Pan	30
	ATF Line Bracket To Transaxle	72③
	ATF Lines To Junction Block	18
	ATF Lines To Transaxle	18
	Axle To Hub Bolt, 14 MM	85①
	Axle To Hub Bolt, 16 MM	140①
	Cable Guide To Transaxle	30
	Cover To Fuel Rail	84③
	Crossmember To Body	18
	Differential Filler Plug (FWD)	37
	Differential Filler Plug (Quattro)	30
	Drain Bolt (Transaxle)	30
	Drive Axle Heat Shield To Bracket	18
	Driveshaft To Drive Flange	59
	Driveshaft To Flanged Shaft	59
	Driveshaft To Hub Bolt, 14 MM	85①
	Driveshaft to Hub Bolt, 16 MM	140①
	Filler Plug (Transmission Less Filler Tube)	44
	Filler Tube Gland Nut	18
	Flanged Shaft Retaining Bolt	18
	Hub To Axle Bolt, 14 MM	85①
	Hub To Axle Bolt, 16 MM	140①
	Multi-Function Switch Bolts	72③
	Oil Pan	84③
	Oil Strainer	72③
	Selector Lever Cable Bracket To Transaxle	17
	Selector Lever Cable Clamping Nut	15
	Selector Lever Cable Mounting Nut	84③
	Selector Shaft Clamping Screw	72③
	Torque Converter To Drive Plate	63
	Torque Support To Body	33
	Transaxle Support To Bonded Rubber Bushing	30
	Transaxle Support To Transaxle	30
	Transaxle To Engine Mounting Bolts	②
	Valve Body	53③
	8-Pin Connector To Transaxle	15

① — Plus an additional 90° (¼) turn.

② — Refer to “Transaxle, Replace.”

③ — Inch lbs.

01N Automatic Transaxle

NOTE: On Air Bag Equipped Models, Refer To "Air Bag System Precautions" Located In The Front Of This Manual For System Disarming & Arming Procedures.

NOTE: Refer To "Computer Relearn Procedures" Located In The Front Of This Manual When Battery Power To The Computer Has Been Interrupted.

INDEX

	Page No.
Adjustments	1-203
Ignition Locking Cable	1-203
Selector Lever Cable	1-203
Selector Lever Housing	1-203
Shift Lock Solenoid	1-203
Description	1-202
Identification	1-202
In-Vehicle Repairs	1-203
Flanged Shaft Seal, Replace	1-203
Ignition Locking Cable, Replace	1-204
Multi-Function/Transaxle Range (TR) Switch, Replace	1-204
Shifter Components, Replace	1-204
Transaxle Control Module (TCM), Replace	1-204
Valve Body Connector Strip, Replace	1-205
Valve Body, Replace	1-205
Maintenance	1-202
Fluid Change	1-203
Fluid Inspection	1-202
Precautions	1-202
Air Bag Systems	1-202
Battery Ground Cable	1-202
Radio Coded Anti-Theft System	1-202
Technical Service Bulletins	1-206
Delayed 1–2 Upshift On Cold Start Warm Up	1-206
Tightening Specifications	1-207
Transaxle, Replace	1-205
Troubleshooting	1-202
Brake Transaxle Shift Interlock (BTSI)	1-202
Transaxle	1-202

PRECAUTIONS

Air Bag Systems

Refer to "Air Bag System Precautions" in the front of this manual for system disarming and arming procedures.

Radio Coded Anti-Theft System

Prior to disconnecting the battery or removing the audio system, obtain the security code from the vehicle operator. Refer to the owner's manual for security code disarming and arming procedures.

Battery Ground Cable

Prior to service, disconnect battery ground cable and isolate as required.

IDENTIFICATION

The manufacturer's code number (1) and transaxle number (2) are located on the top lefthand side of the transaxle, **Fig. 1.** The transaxle identification may also be found on the vehicle data plate.

Refer to **Fig. 2** for transaxle specifications.

DESCRIPTION

This fully automatic 4-speed transaxle is electronically controlled and has a lock-up torque converter. The Transaxle Control Module (TCM) monitors signals from the valve body, vehicle speed sensor, malfunction switch, throttle position potentiometer, Engine Control Module (ECM), engine speed sensor, program switch, selector lever lock solenoid, Data Link Connector (DLC), cruise control switch, brake lamp switch, kickdown switch, starter lock-out relay and transaxle range display. The TCM uses this information to determine transaxle shift points.

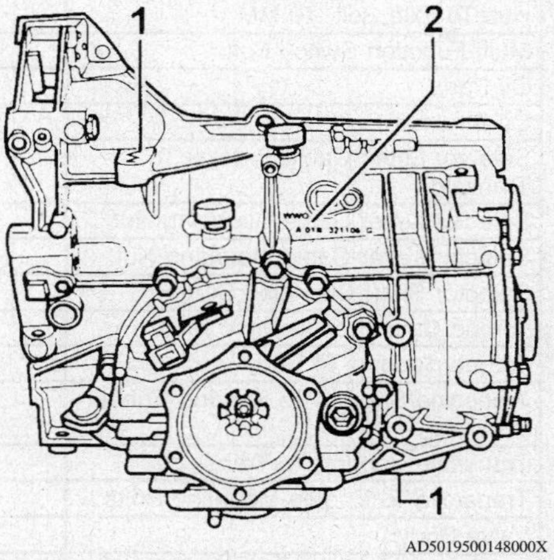

Fig. 1 Transaxle identification

An Emergency Running Mode (ERM) allows operation of the transaxle even when certain systems fail. If ERM is activated while vehicle is running with the shifter in D, 3 or 2, third gear will be hydraulically engaged until engine is stopped. If ERM is activated and the shifter is placed in position 1 or R the transaxle will operate hydraulically in that respective gear. All other transaxle related electronic functions will be disabled.

TROUBLESHOOTING

TRANSAXLE

The 01N automatic transaxle is equipped with a transaxle control unit. The control unit has a self-diagnosis capability and can store transaxle malfunctions in its memory. For further repairs and troubleshooting refer to **MOTOR's "Imported Transmission Manual."**

BRAKE TRANSAXLE SHIFT INTERLOCK (BTSI)

Refer to shifter component location diagrams, **Fig. 3,** and wiring diagrams, **Fig. 4,** when troubleshooting BTSI system fault conditions.

Refer to "Adjustments" and "In-Vehicle Repairs" for related information on shift lock solenoid and ignition lock cable.

MAINTENANCE

FLUID INSPECTION

Transaxle Planetary Components

Do not inspect fluid level when transaxle is in emergency mode.

Transaxle fluid must be inspected at normal operating temperature to prevent over- or under- filling.

If fluid shows signs of foaming, allow vehicle to stand for at least 15 minutes, or until foaming subsides, prior to inspecting level.

1. Ensure level reaches at least 20°C mark on dipstick prior to driving vehicle for warming transaxle fluid for level inspection.

Automatic transmission			01N	
Transmission	Code letters		01N.H	CLR
	Manufacture	from	1/95	
		to		
Torque convertor	Code letters		LCDB	µ:2.2
Valve body	Code letters		LCA	
	Manufacture	from	1/95	
		to		
Number of splined plates			Inner	Outer
	Clutch K1		5	4
	Clutch K2		5	5
	Clutch K3		6	5
	Brake B1		6	6
	Brake B2		6	5
Allocation	Type			
	Engine		2.8L – 129kW (172 hp)	

AD5019500149010X

Fig. 2 Transaxle specifications table (Part 1 of 2)

Transmission	Code letters		CLR
	1st gear		2.714
	2nd gear		1.551
	3rd gear		1.000
	4th gear		0.679
	Rev gear		2.111
Intermediate gear	No. of teeth		
		Drive shaft	44
		Input shaft	51
	Ratio		1.159
Intermediate gear	No. of teeth		
		Pinion	11
		Crown wheel	35
	Ratio		3.182
Drive shaft	Flange dia. (mm)		130
ATF Cooler	Equipment		integrated in engine radiator

AD5019500149020X

Fig. 2 Transaxle specification table (Part 2 of 2)

2. Inspect fluid for contamination. Correct as required.
3. Connect a suitable scan tool to Data Link Connector (DLC).
4. Access scan tool function 08, then Display Group 005 and Display Field 1 to read transaxle fluid temperature.
5. Operate vehicle to warm transaxle fluid to normal operating temperature of 140–176°F (60–80°C).
6. Place vehicle on a level surface with engine idling and apply parking brake.
7. Position shift lever in each gear position momentarily, then place in Park.
8. Ensure fluid level is between dipstick MIN and MAX marks.
9. Adjust fluid level as required. Refer to "Specifications" for amount and type.

Transaxle Final Drive Differential

1. Raise and support vehicle.
2. Remove differential level inspection plug located on lefthand side of transaxle on differential housing.
3. Proper fluid level is when fluid is at bottom edge of filler hole.
4. Refer to "Specifications" for fluid amount and type and correct as required.
5. Install differential level inspection plug and tighten to specifications.

FLUID CHANGE

Transaxle Planetary Components

1. Raise and support vehicle.
2. Disconnect filler tube from pan, then allow fluid to drain into a suitable container. Discard seal.
3. Remove pan mounting bolts, then the pan.
4. Remove strainer mounting bolts, then the strainer. Discard strainer O-ring seal.
5. Clean strainer and pan with a suitable cleaning fluid, blow dry only.
6. Install strainer using a new O-ring seal. Tighten screws to specifications.
7. Install oil pan using a new gasket. Tighten mounting bolts to specifications.
8. Install filler tube to pan using a new gasket.
9. Install drain plug with a new gasket and tighten to specifications.
10. Fill transaxle with proper fluid. Refer to "Specifications" for fluid amounts and type, then to "Inspecting Fluid Level."

Transaxle Final Drive Differential

Differential fluid is of a permanent fill type and is not normally replaced. No provision has been made for draining.

ADJUSTMENTS

IGNITION LOCKING CABLE

1. Remove center console, then place selector lever in "N" position.
2. Remove bolts retaining locking cable to selector lever housing.
3. Loosen locking cable adjustment bolt, then turn ignition On.
4. Place a. 059 inch feeler gauge between locking flap and locking pin.
5. Adjust locking cable so that locking pin is pushed against feeler gauge, then tighten adjustment nut.
6. After operating several times, clearance between locking pin and locking flap should be. 047–.067 inch.
7. Move selector lever to "N" position, then install locking cable to selector lever housing. **Cable must be free of kinks.**
8. Install center console.
9. Ensure proper operation of locking cable.

SELECTOR LEVER CABLE

1. Raise and support vehicle, then remove components required to access shift cable.
2. Place selector lever in "P" position, then loosen nut at selector lever cable clamp, **Fig. 3.**
3. Move selector shaft lever at transaxle rearward as far as stop to "P" position. Ensure park pawl is engaged.
4. Tighten selector lever cable nut.
5. Turn ignition On, then depress and hold brake pedal.
6. Shift selector lever through all ranges and ensure selector lever position agrees with selector lever indicator on instrument cluster.

SELECTOR LEVER HOUSING

1. Place selector lever in the Neutral position.
2. Install selector lever housing with nuts loosely secured.
3. Position selector lever housing so that selector lever travel is equal when moving from N to D and N to R.
4. Tighten selector lever housing nuts.

SHIFT LOCK SOLENOID

1. Place selector lever in R position.
2. Measure clearance between selector lever and solenoid with a suitable feeler gauge.
3. Clearance should be. 024–.055 inch. Adjust solenoid by loosening mounting screws and positioning for proper clearance.

IN-VEHICLE REPAIRS

FLANGED SHAFT SEAL, REPLACE

Righthand Side

1. Raise and support vehicle.
2. Disconnect driveshaft from drive flange.

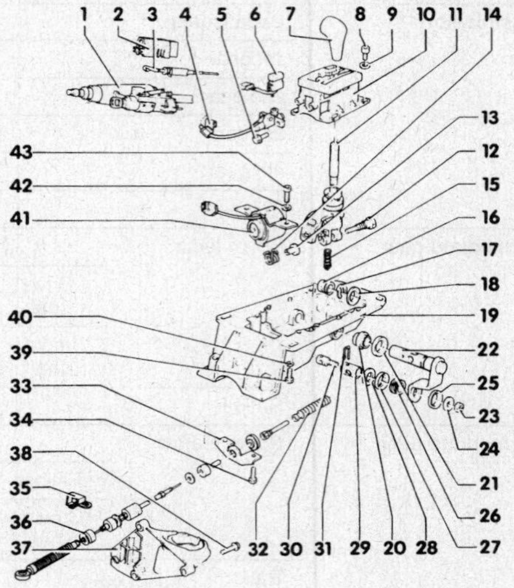

1. Ignition Starter Switch
2. Trim Cover
3. Lock Cable
4. Clip
5. Bolt (7 ft. lbs.)
6. Transaxle Range Program Switch
7. Shift Knob
8. Screw (7 ft. lbs.)
9. Washer
10. Shifter Housing
11. Selector Lever
12. Guide Pin (16 ft. lbs.)
13. Bushing
14. Spring
16. Bushing
17. Circlip[
18. Washer
19. Selector Lever Housing
20. Bushing
21. Collar
22. Shift Lever
23. Nut (15 ft. lbs.)
24. Washer
25. Collar
26. Bushing
27. Collar
28. Washer
29. Clamping Sleeve
30. Locking Pin
31. Spring Clip
32. Boot
33. Selector Lever Cable Bracket
34. Bolt (17 ft. lbs.)
35. Bracket
36. Selector Lever Cable w/Guide & Bushing
37. Transaxle Support
38. Bolt (30 ft. lbs.)
39. Bolt (30 ft. lbs.)
40. Washer
41. Shift Lock Solenoid
42. Washer Bolt (7 ft. lbs.)

AD5019500171000X

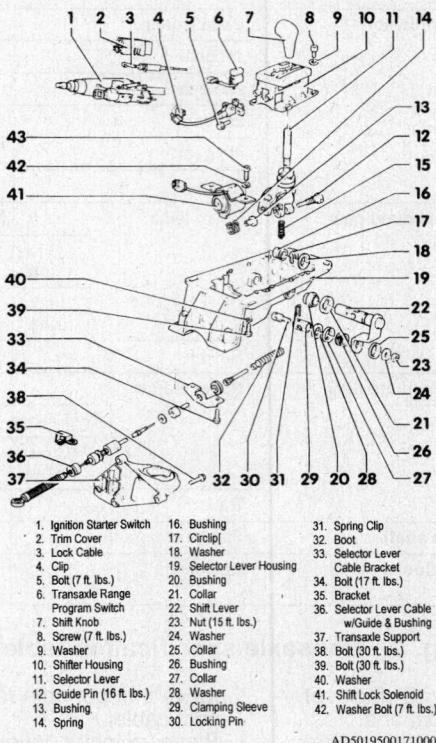

Fig. 3 Exploded view of shifter components

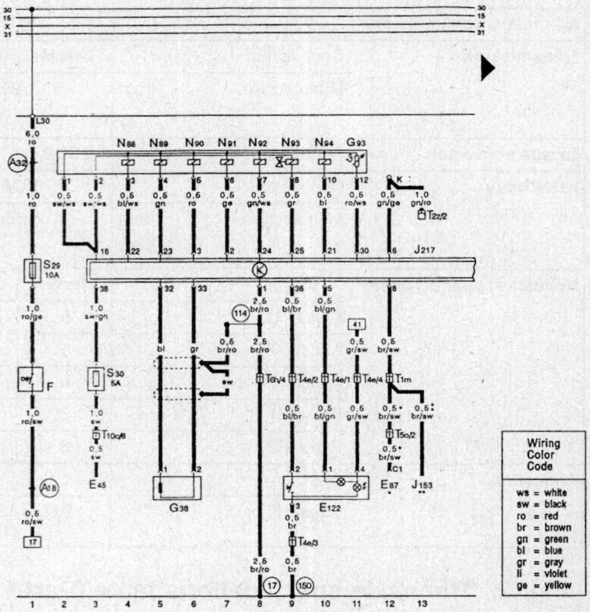

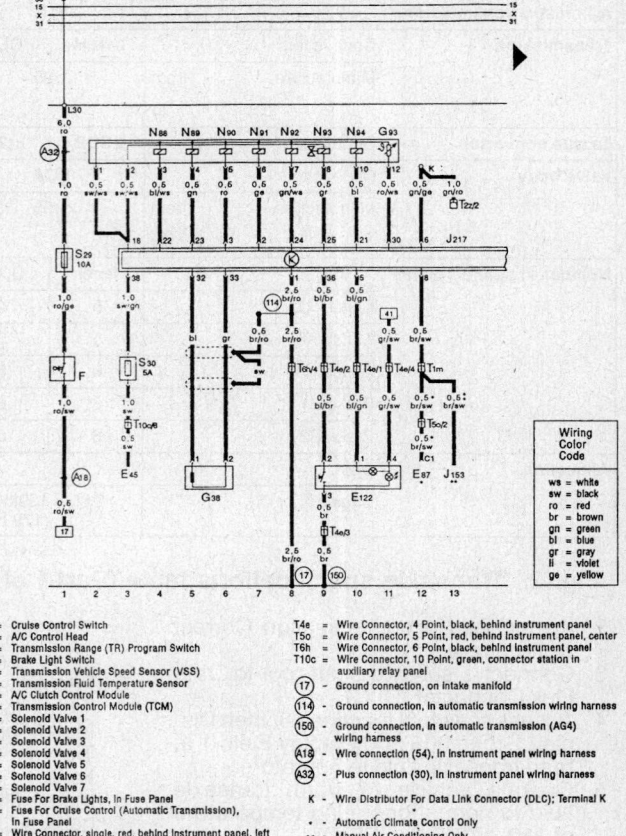

E45 = Cruise Control Switch
E87 = A/C Control Head
E122 = Transmission Range (TR) Program Switch
F = Brake Light Switch
G38 = Transmission Vehicle Speed Sensor (VSS)
G93 = Transmission Fluid Temperature Sensor
J153 = A/C Clutch Control Module
J217 = Transmission Control Module (TCM)
N88 = Solenoid Valve 1
N89 = Solenoid Valve 2
N90 = Solenoid Valve 3
N91 = Solenoid Valve 4
N92 = Solenoid Valve 5
N93 = Solenoid Valve 6
N94 = Solenoid Valve 7
S29 = Fuse For Brake Lights, In Fuse Panel
S30 = Fuse For Cruise Control (Automatic Transmission), In Fuse Panel
T1m = Wire Connector, single, red, behind instrument panel, left
T2z = Wire Connector, double, white, In Plenum Near Relay Panel (Data Link Connector)
T4e = Wire Connector, 4 Point, black, behind instrument panel
T5o = Wire Connector, 5 Point, red, behind instrument panel, center
T6h = Wire Connector, 6 Point, black, behind instrument panel
T10c = Wire Connector, 10 Point, green, connector station in auxiliary relay panel
(17) - Ground connection, on intake manifold
(114) - Ground connection, in automatic transmission wiring harness
(150) - Ground connection, in automatic transmission (AG4) wiring harness
(A18) - Wire connection (54), in instrument panel wiring harness
(A32) - Plus connection (30), in instrument panel wiring harness
K - Wire Distributor For Data Link Connector (DLC); Terminal K
* - Automatic Climate Control Only
** - Manual Air Conditioning Only

AD5019500150010X

Fig. 4 BTSI wiring diagram (Part 1 of 4)

3. Turn steering to full lock, then position driveshaft aside.
4. Pry shaft cover cap from center of flange using a suitable screwdriver, then remove circlip from shaft. Discard circlip and shaft cover cap.
5. Pull flange from shaft using Kukko puller tool No. 18-1 and sleeve No. VW 681, or equivalents.
6. Remove seal from transaxle using a suitable pry bar.
7. Pack space between lips of new seal with a suitable multi-purpose grease.
8. Drive a new seal into transaxle case using driver tool No. 3323, or equivalent.
9. Reverse remaining procedures to install, noting the following:
   a. Use new circlip to retain flange to shaft.
   b. Install a new shaft cover cap and seat it using driver tool No. 3244, or equivalent. Ensure cap is properly seated or differential fluid will leak into driveshaft joint.
   c. Tighten all bolts and nuts to specifications.
   d. Fill differential housing with lubricant as outlined under "Maintenance."

Lefthand Side

1. Raise and support vehicle.
2. Disconnect driveshaft from flange shaft.
3. Turn steering to full lock, then position and secure driveshaft aside.
4. Install two suitable bolts into flanged shaft threaded holes then, using a suitable bar, counter-hold flanged shaft while loosening center retaining bolt.
5. Remove center retaining bolt, then the flanged shaft.
6. Remove seal from transaxle using a suitable pry bar.
7. Pack space between lips of new seal with a suitable multipurpose grease.
8. Drive a new seal into transaxle case using driver tool No. 3377, or equivalent.
9. Reverse remaining procedures to install, noting the following:
   a. Tighten all bolts and nuts to specifications.
   b. Fill differential housing with lubricant as outlined under "Maintenance."

IGNITION LOCKING CABLE, REPLACE

Refer to **Fig. 3** for related information while performing this procedure.

1. Remove center console, steering wheel, and instrument cluster.
2. Place selector lever in "N" position, then turn ignition On.
3. Remove bolts retaining locking cable to selector lever housing, then the locking cable from housing.
4. Remove cap from ignition switch (1), **Fig. 5,** then the spring clip (2) from the locking cable.
5. **Note exact routing of cable for installation reference.** Rotate cable end (3) 90° to disengage from ignition lock, then remove cable from vehicle.
6. Reverse procedure to install. Adjust as outlined under "Adjustments."

MULTI-FUNCTION/ TRANSAXLE RANGE (TR) SWITCH, REPLACE

1. Disconnect TR switch electrical connector at righthand rear of transaxle.
2. Remove bolt holding TR switch clamp bracket, then the clamp bracket.
3. Pull TR switch from transaxle case, discard sealing O-ring.
4. Reverse procedure to install, use new sealing O-ring.

SHIFTER COMPONENTS, REPLACE

Refer to **Fig. 3** when replacing shift components. Refer to "Adjustments" for related shift component information.

TRANSAXLE CONTROL MODULE (TCM), REPLACE

1. Switch Off ignition and wait 30 seconds.
2. Remove lefthand side underdash components to allow access to area above pedal support.
3. Remove mounts, then disconnect TCM electrical connectors.

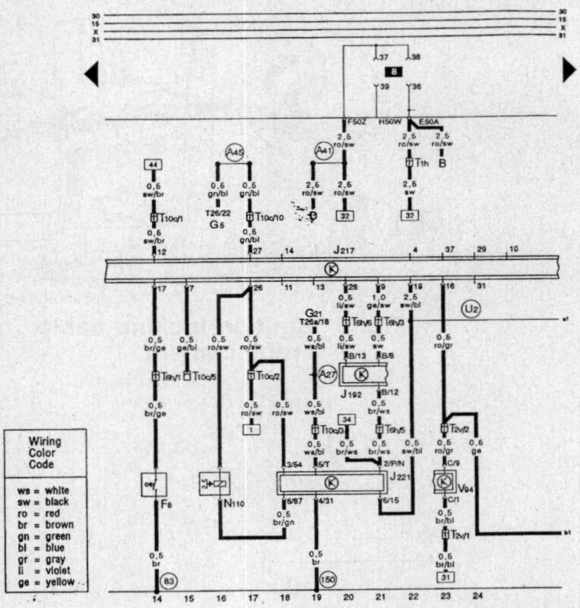

B = Battery
D = Ignition / Starter Switch
F8 = Kick Down Switch
G5 = Tachometer
G21 = Speedometer
J192 = MFI Engine Control Module (ECM)
J217 = Transmission Control Module (TCM)
J221 = Shift Lock Control Module
N110 = Shift Lock Solenoid
T1h = Wire Connector, single, red, behind instrument panel, left
T2v = Wire Connector, double, white, behind instrument panel
T6h = Wire Connector, 6 Point, black, behind instrument panel
T10c = Wire Connector, 10 Point, green, connector station in auxiliary relay panel
T26 = Wire Connector, 26 Point, yellow, on instrument cluster
T26a = Wire Connector, 26 Point, blue, on instrument cluster
V94 = Central Locking/Alarm System/Interior Light Delay Control Module

(83) - Ground connection -1-, in right front wiring harness
(150) - Ground connection -1-, in automatic transmission (AG4) wiring harness
(A27) - Wire connection (speed signal), in instrument panel wiring harness
(A41) - Plus connection (50), in instrument panel wiring harness
(A45) - Plus connection (RPM signal), in instrument panel wiring harness
(U2) - Wire connection -1- (15), in automatic tansmission wiring harness

AD5019500150020X

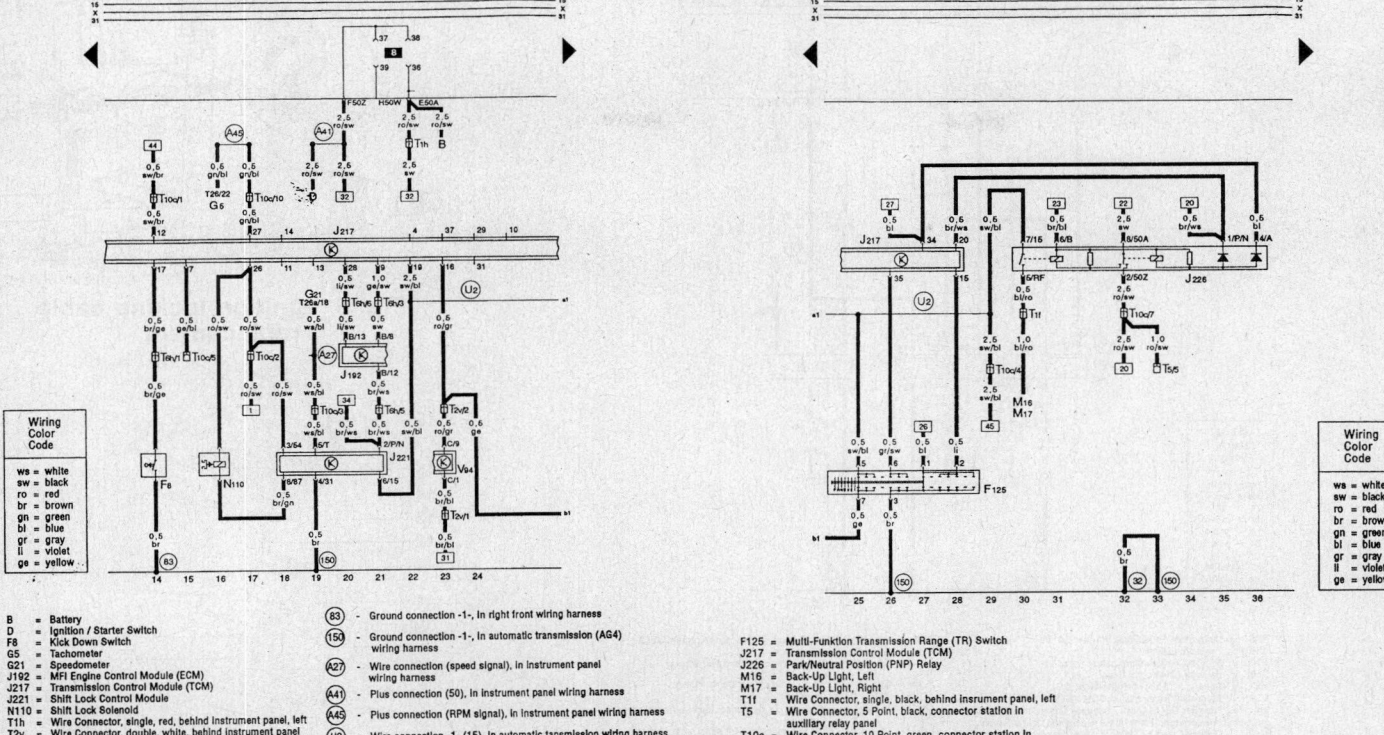

Fig. 4 BTSI wiring diagram (Part 2 of 4)

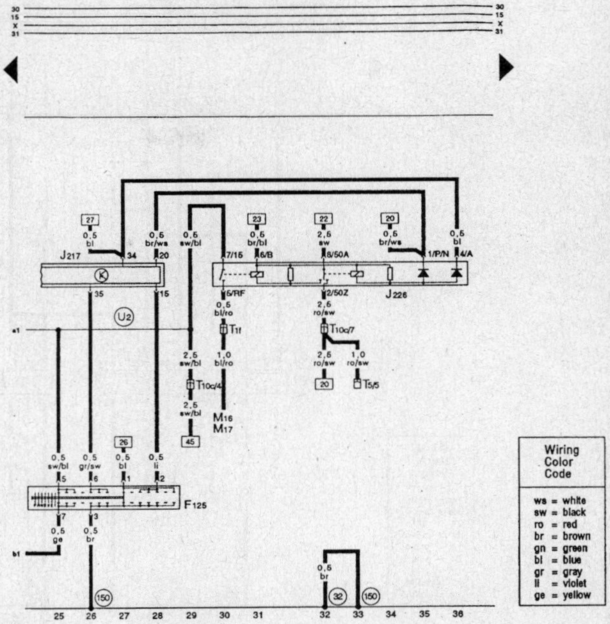

F125 = Multi-Funktion Transmission Range (TR) Switch
J217 = Transmission Control Module (TCM)
J226 = Park/Neutral Position (PNP) Relay
M16 = Back-Up Light, Left
M17 = Back-Up Light, Right
T1f = Wire Connector, single, black, behind insrument panel, left
T5 = Wire Connector, 5 Point, black, connector station in auxiliary relay panel
T10c = Wire Connector, 10 Point, green, connector station in auxiliary relay panel

(32) - Ground connection, behind instrument panel, left
(150) - Ground connection, in automatic transmission (AG4) wiring harness
(U2) - Ground connection -1- (15), in automatic transmission wiring harness

AD5019500150030X

Fig. 4 BTSI wiring diagram (Part 3 of 4)

4. Remove TCM mounting bolts, then the TCM.
5. Reverse procedure to install.

VALVE BODY, REPLACE

1. Disconnect shift solenoid harness connector from transaxle.
2. Remove fluid filler tube, then the fluid pan and gasket with spacers, **Fig. 6.** Discard gasket, but retain spacers.
3. Remove fluid strainer. Discard O-ring seal.
4. Remove electrical connector retaining bolt, pull connector from transaxle case and discard O-ring.
5. Remove valve body mounting bolts, then the valve body, while disconnecting operating rod from manual valve. **Use caution so sealing plug does not drop out.**
6. Remove sealing plug, then discard two O-rings.
7. Reverse procedure to install, noting the following:
   a. Use new O-rings and gaskets.
   b. Install new O-rings on sealing plug, then install plug so that lug seats in groove of transaxle housing.
   c. Tighten all bolts and nuts to specifications.
   d. Install manual valve body (2) fully into valve body, pushrod (1) in direction of arrow as illustrated, **Fig. 7.** Tighten stop screw (3) to specifications.
   e. When installing fluid strainer, insert tube and O-ring only. 117 inch into valve body. **Do not push fully into place (to stop). Pan installation will properly position strainer.**
   f. Insert spacers into new pan gasket.
   g. Tighten pan attaching bolts to specifications.

VALVE BODY CONNECTOR STRIP, REPLACE

The valve body must be replaced if connector strip retaining clips are damaged or broken during this procedure.

1. Disconnect shift solenoid harness connector from transaxle.
2. Remove fluid filler tube, then the fluid pan and gasket with spacers, **Fig. 6.** Discard gasket, but retain spacers.
3. Remove fluid strainer, then discard O-ring seal.
4. Remove electrical connector retaining bolt, then pull connector from transaxle case and discard O-ring.
5. Remove connector strip guide, then pry connector strip from solenoids using removal tool No. 3373, or equivalent, **Fig. 8.**
6. Reverse procedure to install, noting the following:
   a. Use new O-rings and gaskets.
   b. When installing fluid strainer, insert tube and O-ring approximately. 117 inch into valve body. **Do not push fully into place (to stop). Pan installation will properly position fluid strainer.**
   c. Insert spacers into new pan gasket.
   d. Tighten pan attaching bolts to specifications.

TRANSAXLE

REPLACE

1. Obtain radio theft protection code as outlined under "Precautions."
2. **On models equipped with noise insulation shield,** remove shield by pulling off vacuum hoses, then removing air duct and retaining bolts.
3. **On models equipped with split filler tube,** loosen ATF filler pipe at top and remove from vehicle, then cover lower pipe with a shop towel.
4. **On all models,** remove transaxle to engine upper bolts, then push up on coolant hoses.
5. Install engine support assembly tool Nos. 10-222A and 10-222A-1, or equivalents.
6. Remove engine lower cover and mounting, then the drive axle heat shields.
7. Remove body crossmember, then the exhaust system and catalytic converters.
8. Disconnect axle shafts from transaxle, then remove starter, position aside and secure with wire.
9. Place suitable drain pan below ATF line connections, then disconnect ATF

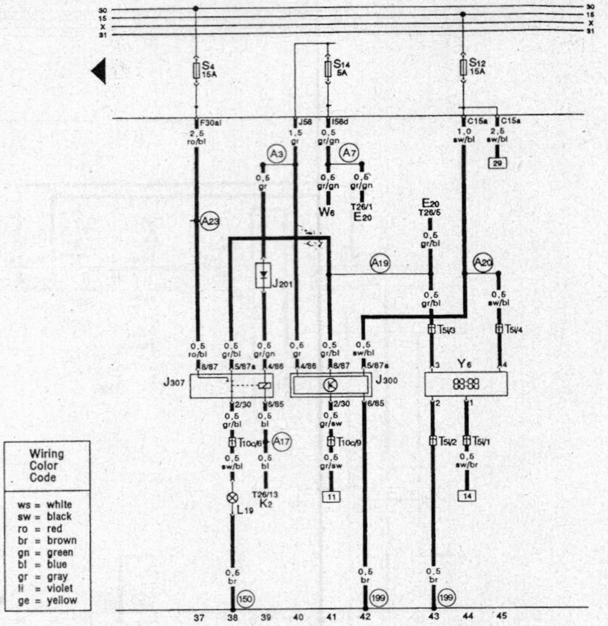

E20 = Instrument Panel Light Dimmer Switch
J201 = Protection Diode
J300 = Program Switch Illumination Relay
J307 = Selector Lever Light Relay
K2 = Generator (GEN) Warning Light
L19 = Automatic Transmission Console Light
S4 = Fuse For Digital Clock / Luggage Compartment Light/ Interior Light, Front /Make-Up Mirror Lights/ Reading Lights / Cigarette Lighters / Boardcomputer / Automatic Climate Control / Radio / Auto Check System, In Fuse Panel
S12 = Fuse For Cruise Control / Electronic Thermoswitch / Auto Check System / Instrument Cluster / Interior Light With Delay / Back-Up Lights / Servotronic / Boardcomputer / Automatic Transmission / Airbag Control Light / Coolant Fan Afterrun / Differential Lock, In Fuse Panel
S14 = Fuse For License Plate Light / Glove Compartment Light / Engine Compartment Light, In Fuse Panel
T5l = Wire Connector, 5 Point, black, behind instrument panel
T10c = Wire Connector, 10 Point, green, connector station in auxiliary relay panel
T26 = Wire Connector, 26 Point, yellow, on instrument cluster
W6 = Glove Compartment Light
Y6 = Transmission Range (TR) Selector Lever Display
(150) - Ground connection, in automatic transmission (AG4) wiring harness
(199) - Ground connection -3-, in instrument panel wiring harness
(A3) - Plus connection (58), in instrument panel wiring harness
(A7) - Plus connection (58D1), in instrument panel wiring harness
(A17) - Plus connection (61), in instrument panel wiring harness
(A19) - Plus connection (58d), in instrument panel wiring harness
(A20) - Plus connection (15a), in instrument panel wiring harness
(A23) - Plus connection (30al), in instrument panel wiring harness

AD5019500150040X

Fig. 4 BTSI wiring diagram (Part 4 of 4)

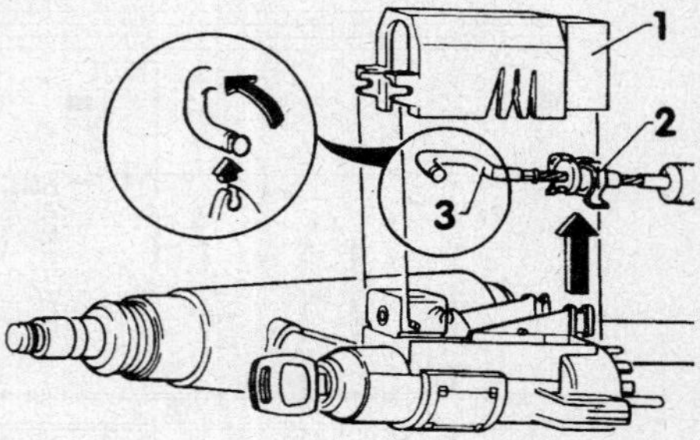
AD5019500175000X

Fig. 5 Ignition locking cable replacement

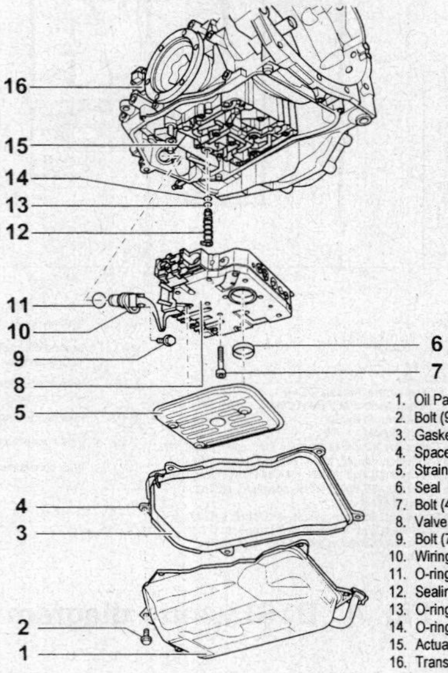

1. Oil Pan
2. Bolt (9 ft. lbs.)
3. Gasket
4. Spacer
5. Strainer
6. Seal
7. Bolt (44 inch lbs.)
8. Valve Body
9. Bolt (7 ft. lbs.)
10. Wiring Plug
11. O-ring
12. Sealing Plug
13. O-ring
14. O-ring
15. Actuating Rod
16. Transaxle Housing

AD5029500157000X

Fig. 6 Valve body replacement

lines and mounting bracket. Position ATF lines aside.

10. Remove torque converter mounting nuts. Use a suitable wrench to counterhold vibration damper center bolt.
11. Remove heat shield for multi-function switch.
12. Disconnect electrical connectors, then remove wiring harness clamp.
13. Install transaxle support tool No. 3282, or equivalent.
14. Remove bolt from transaxle rubber/metal rear mount.
15. Remove lower engine to transaxle bolts.
16. Separate transaxle from engine, then lower and remove transaxle. Push torque converter off drive plate when removing transaxle.
17. Secure torque converter in transaxle.
18. Reverse procedure to install noting the following:
    a. Inspect guide sleeves for proper alignment during installation.
    b. Inspect and adjust selector lever cable if required.
    c. Tighten to specifications.

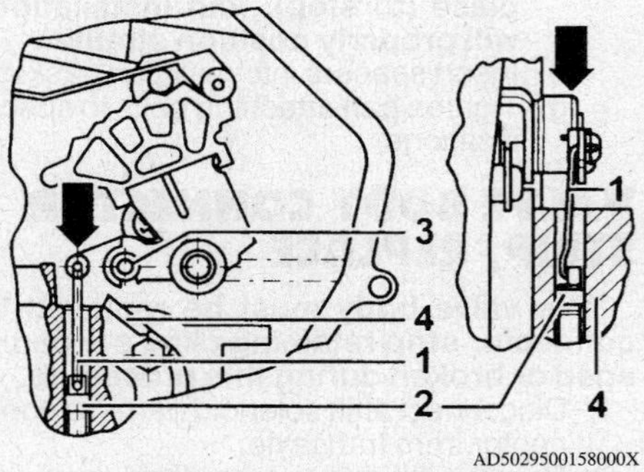
AD5029500158000X

Fig. 7 Manual valve assembly adjustment

TECHNICAL SERVICE BULLETINS

DELAYED 1–2 UPSHIFT ON COLD START WARM UP

Cabriolet models may display a delayed 1–2 gear upshift when transaxle fluid temperature is below 104°F and after a fresh engine start. This is a normal condition caused by warm-up programming to help the engine reach operating temperature sooner. The condition will last for approximately two minutes.

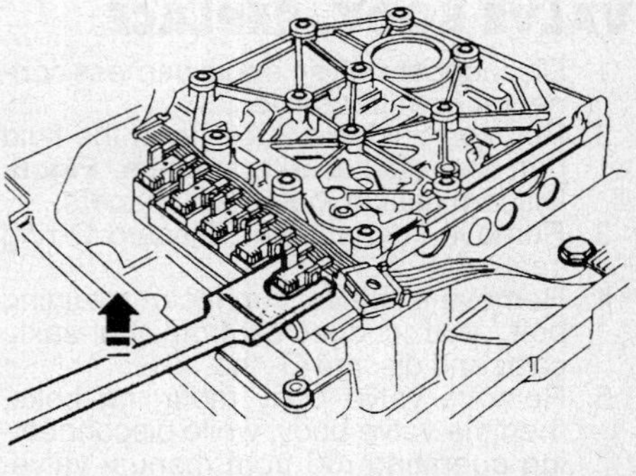
AD5029500159000X

Fig. 8 Valve body connector strip removal

TIGHTENING SPECIFICATIONS

Year	Component	Torque/Ft. Lbs.
1998	Axle Shaft To Hub Bolt, 14 MM	85①
	Axle Shaft To Hub Bolt, 16 MM	140①
	Differential Filler Plug	18
	Drive Axle To Drive Flange	59
	Drive Axle To Hub Bolt, 14 MM	85①
	Drive Axle To Hub Bolt, 16 MM	140①
	Hub To Axle Bolt, 14 MM	85①
	Hub To Axle Bolt, 16 MM	140①
	Oil Pan	72②
	Oil Strainer	72②
	Starter To Transaxle	48
	Torque Converter to Drive Plate	63
	Transaxle Mount To Body	82
	Transaxle Mount To Transaxle	30
	Transaxle To Engine Mounting Bolts, M10	33
	Transaxle To Engine Mounting Bolts, M12	48

① — Plus an additional 90° (¼) turn.
② — Inch lbs.

01L & 01V Automatic Transaxles

NOTE: On Air Bag Equipped Models, Refer To "Air Bag System Precautions" Located In The Front Of This Manual For System Disarming & Arming Procedures.

NOTE: Refer To "Computer Relearn Procedures" Located In The Front Of This Manual When Battery Power To The Computer Has Been Interrupted.

INDEX

	Page No.
Adjustments	1-210
Ignition Lock Cable	1-210
Propeller Shaft	1-210
Selector Lever Cable	1-210
Shift Lever	1-210
Description	1-208
Identification	1-208
01L Transaxle	1-208
01V Transaxle	1-208
In-Vehicle Repairs	1-210
Coding Transaxle Control Module	1-210
Final Drive, Replace	1-210
Ignition Lock Cable, Replace	1-210
Multi-Function/Transaxle Range Switch, Replace	1-211
Propeller Shaft, Replace	1-211
Selector Cable, Replace	1-212
Shifter Components, Replace	1-212
Speedometer Vehicle Speed Sensor, Replace	1-213
Transaxle Control Module (TCM), Replace	1-213
Transaxle Input Speed Sensor, Replace	1-213
Transaxle Vehicle Speed Sensor, Replace	1-213
Valve Body, Replace	1-213
Maintenance	1-209
Fluid Change	1-209
Fluid Inspection	1-209
Precautions	1-208
Air Bag Systems	1-208
Battery Ground Cable	1-208
Radio Coded Anti-Theft System	1-208
Technical Service Bulletins	1-215
Delayed 1–2 Upshift On Cold Start Warm Up	1-215
Tightening Specifications	1-218
Transaxle, Replace	1-214
Troubleshooting	1-208
Brake Transaxle Shift Interlock (BTSI)	1-209
Transaxle	1-208

PRECAUTIONS

Air Bag Systems

Refer to "Air Bag System Precautions" in the front of this manual for system disarming and arming procedures.

Radio Coded Anti-Theft System

Prior to disconnecting the battery or removing the audio system, obtain the security code from the vehicle operator. Refer to the owner's manual for security code disarming and arming procedures.

Battery Ground Cable

Prior to service, disconnect battery ground cable and isolate as required.

IDENTIFICATION

01V TRANSAXLE

The transaxle identification code (2) and serial number (1) are located on a plate attached to the lower front of the transaxle, **Figs. 1 and 2.**

The model number and transaxle code may also be found on the vehicle data plate.

Refer to **Figs. 3 and 4** for transaxle specifications.

01L TRANSAXLE

The manufacturer's code number and transaxle number are located on the bottom of the transaxle, in front of the oil pan, **Fig. 5.** The transaxle identification may also be found on the vehicle data plate.

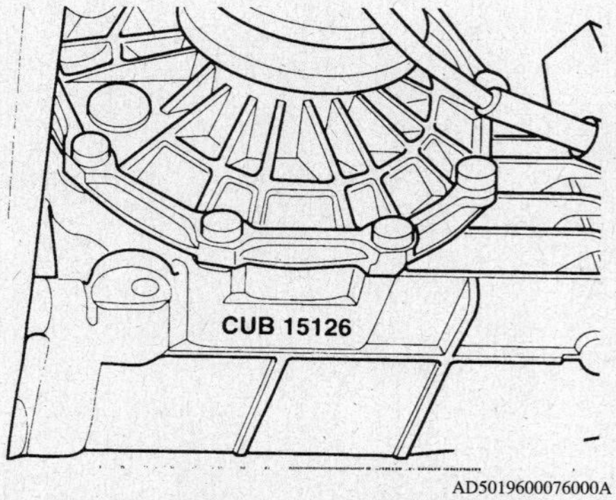

Fig. 1 Transaxle data plate location

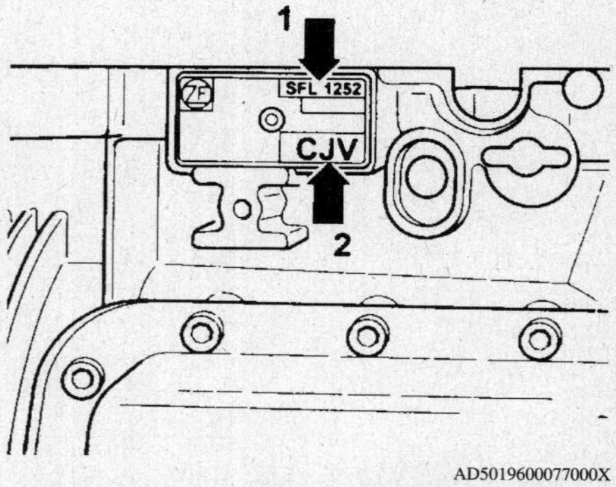

Fig. 2 Transaxle code location

DESCRIPTION

This transaxle is an electronically controlled fully automatic 5 speed with a lock-up torque converter. The differential uses an electronically controlled clutch for traction control. The transaxle control electronics offer an adaptive program to suit various driving habits and conditions. The transaxle control system also interacts with the vehicle ABS system.

On Quattro models, this transaxle has a permanently engaged Torsen third differential mounted to the rear of the transaxle in an attached housing. This differential is used to drive a rear axle differential.

An Emergency Running Mode (ERM) allows operation of the transaxle even when certain systems fail. When ERM is active the shift indicator segments in the instrument cluster will all be lit.

If ERM is activated while the vehicle is running, fourth gear will be engaged. Park and neutral positions are available and reverse gear will function. All other transaxle related electronic functions will be disabled.

TROUBLESHOOTING

TRANSAXLE

The 01V automatic transaxle is equipped with a transaxle control unit. The control unit has a self-diagnosis capability and can store transaxle malfunctions in its memory. For further repairs and troubleshooting refer to **MOTOR's "Imported Transmission Manual."**

Automatic transmission			01V.E	01V.J
Transmission	Code letters		DCS	DDT
	Manufactured	from	4.95	09.96
		to	-	-
Torque converter	Code letters		N24	R24
Application	Model		Audi A4 1996	Audi A4 1996
	Engine		2.8 L 128 kW (172 hp)	2.8 L 128 kW (172 hp)
Ratios	1st gear		3.665	3.665
	2nd gear		1.999	1.999
	3rd gear		1.407	1.407
	4th gear		1.000	1.000
	5th gear		0.742	0.742
	Reverse		4.096	4.096
	Intermediate stage		1.172	1.207
	Front final drive		2.727	3.091
	Speedometer		electronic	electronic

AD5019600078010X

Fig. 3 Transaxle specification table FWD (Part 1 of 2). A4, A8 & S4

Automatic transmission			01V.1	
Transmission	Code letters		CJP	
	Manufactured	from	10.95	
		to	-	
Torque converter	Code letters		N24	
Application	Model		Audi A4 1996	
	Engine		2.8 L 128 kW (172 hp)	
Ratios	1st gear		3.665	
	2nd gear		1.999	
	3rd gear		1.407	
	4th gear		1.000	
	5th gear		0.742	
	Reverse		4.096	
	Intermediate stage for front final drive		1.172	
	Front final drive		2.727	
	Intermediate stage for rear final drive		0.775	
Rear final drive	Code letters		ABU	
	Speedometer		electronic	

AD5019600078020X

Fig. 3 Transaxle specification table AWD (Part 2 of 2). A4, A8 & S4

Automatic transmission			01V.A
Transmission	Code letters		DPS
	Manufactured	from	07.97
		to	–
Torque converter	Code letters		F31
Application	Model		Audi A6 1998 ➤
	Engine		2.8 liter V6 5V 147 kW (200 hp)
Ratios	1st gear		3.665
	2nd gear		1.999
	3rd gear		1.407
	4th gear		1.000
	5th gear		0.742
	Reverse gear		4.096

AD5019900175010X

Fig. 4 Transaxle specification table FWD (Part 1 of 2). A6

Automatic transmission			01V.7
Transmission	Code letters		DPT
	Manufactured	from	07.97
		to	
Torque converter	Code letters		F31
application	Model		Audi A6 1998 ➤
	Engine		2.8 liter V6 5V 147 kW (200 hp)
Ratios	1st gear		3.665
	2nd gear		1.999
	3rd gear		1.407
	4th gear		1.000
	5th gear		0.742
	Reverse gear		4.096

AD5019900175020X

Fig. 4 Transaxle specification table AWD (Part 2 of 2). A6

BRAKE TRANSAXLE SHIFT INTERLOCK (BTSI)

Refer to shifter component location diagrams, **Fig. 6,** and to wiring diagrams, **Figs. 7 and 8,** when servicing or testing BTSI system fault conditions.

Refer to "Adjustments" and "In-Vehicle Repairs" for related information on shift lock solenoid and ignition lock cable.

MAINTENANCE

This transaxle uses different lubricants in the planetary and differential sections. Care should be used to prevent intermixing of lubricants

FLUID INSPECTION

Planetary

Do not inspect fluid level when transaxle is in emergency mode.

Transaxle fluid must be inspected at normal operating temperature to prevent over- or under- filling.

If fluid shows signs of foaming, allow vehicle to stand for at least 15 minutes or until foaming subsides prior to inspecting level.

1. Ensure sufficient fluid is in transaxle to prevent damage during inspection procedure.
2. Connect a suitable scan tool to the Data Link Connector.
3. Access scan tool function 08, then Display Group 04 and Display Field 1 to read transaxle fluid temperature.
4. Operate vehicle to warm transaxle fluid to normal operating temperature of 140–176°F (60–80°C).
5. Place vehicle on a level surface with engine idling and apply parking brake.
6. Position shift lever in each gear position momentarily, then place in Park position.
7. Remove transaxle pan filler plug (2), **Fig. 9.**
8. If fluid level is proper, a small quantity will flow out.
9. Adjust fluid level as required as follows:
   a. To lower fluid level, remove drain plug (1) and allow to drain until fluid no longer flows from filler hole.
   b. Install drain plug with a new sealing gasket and tighten to specifications.
   c. To add fluid, insert nozzle of a suitable fluid pump through filler hole and through port of fluid deflector cap (4).
   d. Add fluid until fluid flows from filler port.
10. Install filler plug with a new sealing gasket and tighten to specifications.

Front Differential

1. Raise and support vehicle.
2. Remove filler plug from front differential case. Discard seal.
3. Fluid level should be even with bottom of filler hole.
4. Install filler plug with a new seal ring, then tighten to specifications.

Center Differential

1. Raise and support vehicle.
2. Separate righthand catalyst from rear exhaust system and position aside. Discard self-locking bolts and nuts.
3. Remove and discard filler plug from rear differential case.
4. Fluid level should be even with bottom of filler hole.
5. Add suitable fluid as required.
6. Install new filler plug and tighten to specifications.
7. Install righthand catalyst to exhaust system using new self-locking nuts and bolts.

FLUID CHANGE

Planetary

Transaxle fluid is considered a lifetime fill under normal operating conditions. Fluid change is only recommended at 30,000 mile intervals when vehicle is operated under severe conditions such as operation under extremely high temperatures, trailer towing, continuous mountain driving or continuous stop and go driving.

Use only the recommended fluid or its equivalent.

1. Raise and support vehicle.
2. Remove transaxle fluid pan drain plug, then allow fluid to drain into a suitable container. Discard seal.
3. Remove pan mounting bolts, then the pan.
4. Remove strainer mounting bolts, then the strainer. Discard strainer O-ring seal.
5. Clean strainer and pan with a suitable cleaning fluid. **Blow dry only.**
6. Install strainer using a new O-ring seal, then tighten to specifications
7. Install pan using a new gasket, then

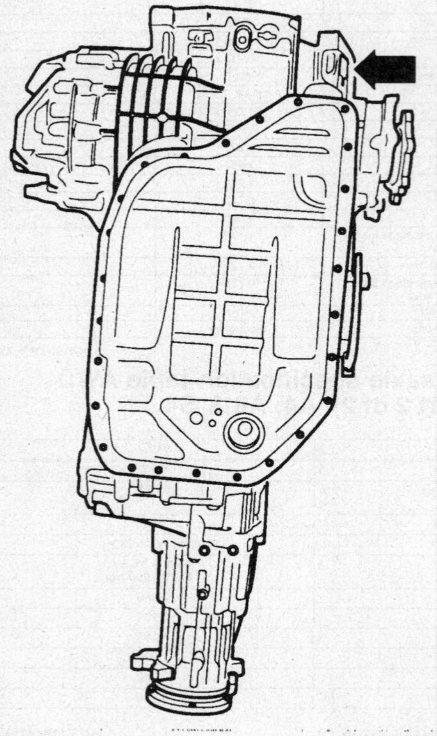

AD5029900239000X

Fig. 5 Identification plate location

tighten to specifications.

8. **On models equipped with transaxle filler tube,** install tube to pan using a new gasket and tighten to specifications.
9. **On all models,** install drain plug with a new gasket and tighten to specifications.
10. Fill transaxle with proper fluid.

Front Differential

No provision for draining front differential fluid is provided. Changing the differential fluid requires disassembly of the front differential case.

Center Differential

1. Raise and support vehicle.
2. Separate righthand catalyst from rear exhaust system and position aside. Discard self-locking bolts and nuts.
3. Remove drain plug from rear differential case and allow fluid to drain into a suitable container. Discard drain plug seal.
4. Remove filler plug, discard filler plug seal, then install new drain plug seal and tighten to specifications.
5. Fill center differential using suitable fluid until fluid is level with edge of filler hole.
6. Install new filler plug and tighten to specifications.
7. Install righthand catalyst to exhaust system using new self-locking nuts and bolts.
8. Road test vehicle to allow Torsen differential to fill, then inspect fluid level as outlined under "Fluid Inspection."

ADJUSTMENTS

IGNITION LOCK CABLE

Refer to **Fig. 6** for related information when servicing ignition lock cable.

1. Ensure cable is properly attached at both ends and is routed stress free.
2. Loosen mounting bolt, **Fig. 10,** (6) until cable clamp (3) can be moved back and forth in direction (5).
3. Install adjustment gauge tool No. 3352 (4), or equivalent, between lever and cable eye.
4. Pull cable in direction of arrow (5), then tighten bolt (6) to specifications.
5. Inspect function of locking system as follows:
   a. Turn ignition lock On. Shifter must move smoothly out of park with a force of 5.6 lbs. or less applied to gearshift button.
   b. **It must not be possible to remove ignition key unless shift lever is in P position.**
   c. With shifter in P position, ignition switch must turn freely to key withdrawal position and key must slide easily from ignition.
   d. **With ignition key withdrawn it must not be possible to shift out of P position.**

PROPELLER SHAFT

Refer to "All Wheel Drive Systems" for adjustment procedures.

SHIFT LEVER

1. Place selector in "P" position, then loosen cable clamp.
2. Set lever on transaxle to "P," up to stop.
3. With cable in tension free position, tighten cable clamp nut to specifications.

SELECTOR LEVER CABLE

Refer to **Fig. 6** for related information during the following procedure.

1. Remove retaining clip (C) from selector cable at selector shaft arm, **Fig. 11.**
2. Disconnect cable from selector shaft arm.
3. Move selector lever from P position to 2 position, then back, lever must move smoothly.
4. Ensure selector shaft of transaxle is in park position (fully rearward, park pawl engaged).
5. Shift cable socket should fit stress free onto ball of selector shaft arm.
6. Loosen cable securing plate mounting bolt at transaxle support as required.
7. Adjust cable for a stress free fit, then tighten securing plate mounting bolt to specifications.
8. Inspect gear selector system for free movement.

IN-VEHICLE REPAIRS

CODING TRANSAXLE CONTROL MODULE

When coding the Transaxle Control

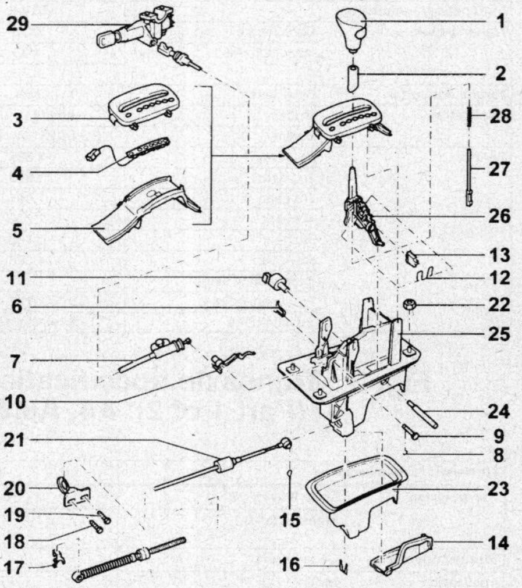

1. Selector Lever Handle
2. Sleeve
3. Cover
4. Light Guide
5. Guide
6. Securing Spring
7. Lock Cable
8. Lock Washer
9. Bolt
10. Lever Foe Lock Cable
11. Shift Lock Solenoid
12. Spring Clamp
13. Detent Segment
14. Cover
15. Locking Clip
16. Locking Plate
17. Clip
18. Hex Bolt
19. Hex Bolt
20. Mounting Plate
21. Selector Lever Cable
22. Nut
23. Rubber Housing
24. Bearing Pin
25. Mounting Bracket
26. Selector Rod
27. Pull Rod
28. Spring
29. Ignition Starter Switch

AD5019600128000X

Fig. 6 Shifter component locations

Module (TCM) ensure gear selector lever is in P or N position and throttle pedal is in idle position.

1. Connect a suitable scan tool and access transaxle electronics as outlined under "Accessing Diagnostic Trouble Codes" section of "Diagnosis & Testing."
2. Select function 07, then press Q button, or equivalent, to enter coding functions.
3. When module code displays, refer to **Fig. 12** for proper code sequence.
4. If code is improper, enter new code using scan tool keyboard, then press arrow, or equivalent button.
5. Disconnect scan tool.

FINAL DRIVE, REPLACE

Front Wheel Drive Components

Refer to **Fig. 13** when servicing final drive components of the front wheel drive systems on both FWD and Quattro models.

Quattro Components

Refer to **Fig. 14** when servicing final drive components of the center differential of Quattro models.

IGNITION LOCK CABLE, REPLACE

Refer to **Fig. 6** for related information when servicing ignition lock cable.

1. Remove console, then the lefthand lower underdash panels.
2. Place steering column in rear/down

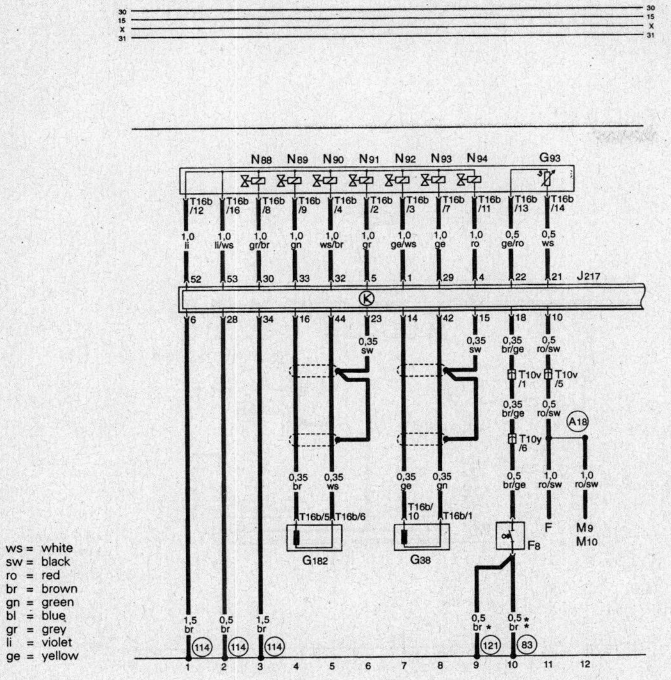

F – Brake Light Switch
F8 – Kick Down Switch
G38 – Transmission Vehicle Speed Sensor (VSS)
G93 – Transmission Fluid Temperature Sensor
G182 – Transmission Input Speed Sensor (ISS)
J217 – Transmission Control Module (TCM)
M9 – Left Brake Light
M10 – Right Brake Light
N88 – Soleniod Valve 1
N89 – Solenoid Valve 2
N90 – Soleniod Valve 3
N91 – Solenoid Valve 4
N92 – Soleniod Valve 5
N93 – Solenoid Valve 6
N94 – Soleniod Valve 7
T10v – Wire Connector, 10 Point, brown, connector station right, A–pillar
T10y – Wire Connector, 10 Point, blue, connector station, on electronics box in plenum chamber
T16b – Wire Connector, 16 Point, on transmission
(83) – Ground connection –1–, in right front wiring harness
(114) – Ground connection, in automatic transmission wiring harness
(121) – Ground connection –2–, in right front wiring harness
(A18) – Wire connection (54), in instrument panel wiring harness
* – 1.8l–Motronic Engine Only
** – 2.8l–Motronic Engine Only

AD5019800187010X

Fig. 7 BTSI wiring diagram (Part 1 of 5). 1998

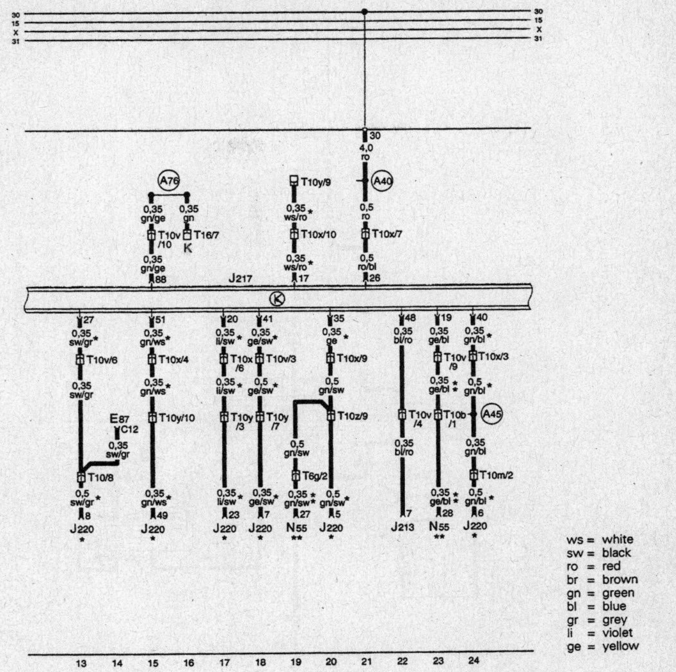

E87 – A / C Control Head
J213 – Cruise Control, Control Module
J217 – Transmission Control Module (TCM)
J220 – Motronic Engine Control Module (ECM)
N55 – ABS Hydraulic Unit
T6g – Wire Connector, 6 Point, gray, connector station right, A–pillar
T10 – Wire Connector, 10 Point, brown, connector station, electronics box in plenum chamber
T10b – Wire Connector, 10 Point, orange, connector station left, A–pillar
T10m – Wire Connector, 10 Point, black, connector station, electronics box in plenum chamber
T10v – Wire Connector, 10 Point, brown, connector station right, A–pillar
T10x – Wire Connector, 10 Point, red, connector station right, A–pillar
T10y – Wire Connector, 10 Point, blue, connector station, electronics box in plenum chamber
T10z – Wire Connector, 10 Point, yellow, connector station, electronics box in plenum chamber
T16 – Wire Connector, 16 point, center console, rear (diagnostic connection)
(A40) – Plus connection –1– (30), in instrument panel wiring harness
(A45) – Wire connection (RPM–Signal), in instrument panel wiring harness
(A76) – Plus connection (K–diagnostic wire), in instrument panel wiring harness
* – 1.8l–Motronic Engine Only
** – ASC Only

AD5019800187020X

Fig. 7 BTSI wiring diagram (Part 2 of 5). 1998

position, then remove steering wheel.

3. Remove steering column jacket, then the multi-function switch.
4. Turn ignition On and ensure shifter is in Park position.
5. Remove shift housing cover.
6. Remove lock cable, **Fig. 10,** (1) from ignition switch, then pull cable from switch.
7. Remove bolt (6) from lock cable bracket (3).
8. Unclip cable from lever and locking spring by raising locking spring slightly.
9. Untie the tie strap (2), then remove cable from shifter.
10. Reverse procedure to install. Refer to "Adjustments."

PROPELLER SHAFT, REPLACE

Removal

1. Remove exhaust system center muffler.
2. Remove heat shields, as required, to access propeller shaft.
3. Remove crossmember below propeller shaft. **Note position for later installation.**
4. Place match marks on all propeller shaft components to be separated.
5. Loosen, but do not remove propeller shaft coupling bolts at transaxle and differential.
6. Loosen, but do not remove center bearing mounting bolts.
7. Install alignment fixture tool No. 3405, or equivalent, to propeller shaft, **Fig. 15.**
8. Support propeller shaft, then remove coupling and center bearing bolts. **Note position of center bearing shims.**
9. Lower propeller shaft from vehicle.

Installation & Adjustment

1. Clean all locking compound residue from components and use new self-locking screws.
2. Install propeller shaft with alignment fixture tool No. 3405, or equivalent, **Fig. 15,** into vehicle, aligning match marks made during removal.
3. **Install coupling bolts, but not the center bearing bolts.**
4. Measure distance between mounting points and center bearing support.
5. Ensure measurements are equal for both sides, then refer to **Fig. 16** to select shims.
6. Force propeller shaft as far forward as possible and mark position of center bearing supports on body.
7. Force propeller shaft as far rearward as possible and mark position of center bearing supports on body.
8. Position center bearing supports an equal distance between marks, then install center bearing support shims and bolts.
9. Install heat shields, then the heat shield to transaxle bolts.
10. Install crossmember below propeller shaft properly positioned as noted during removal.
11. Install exhaust system, then the crossmember below exhaust.

MULTI-FUNCTION/ TRANSAXLE RANGE SWITCH, REPLACE

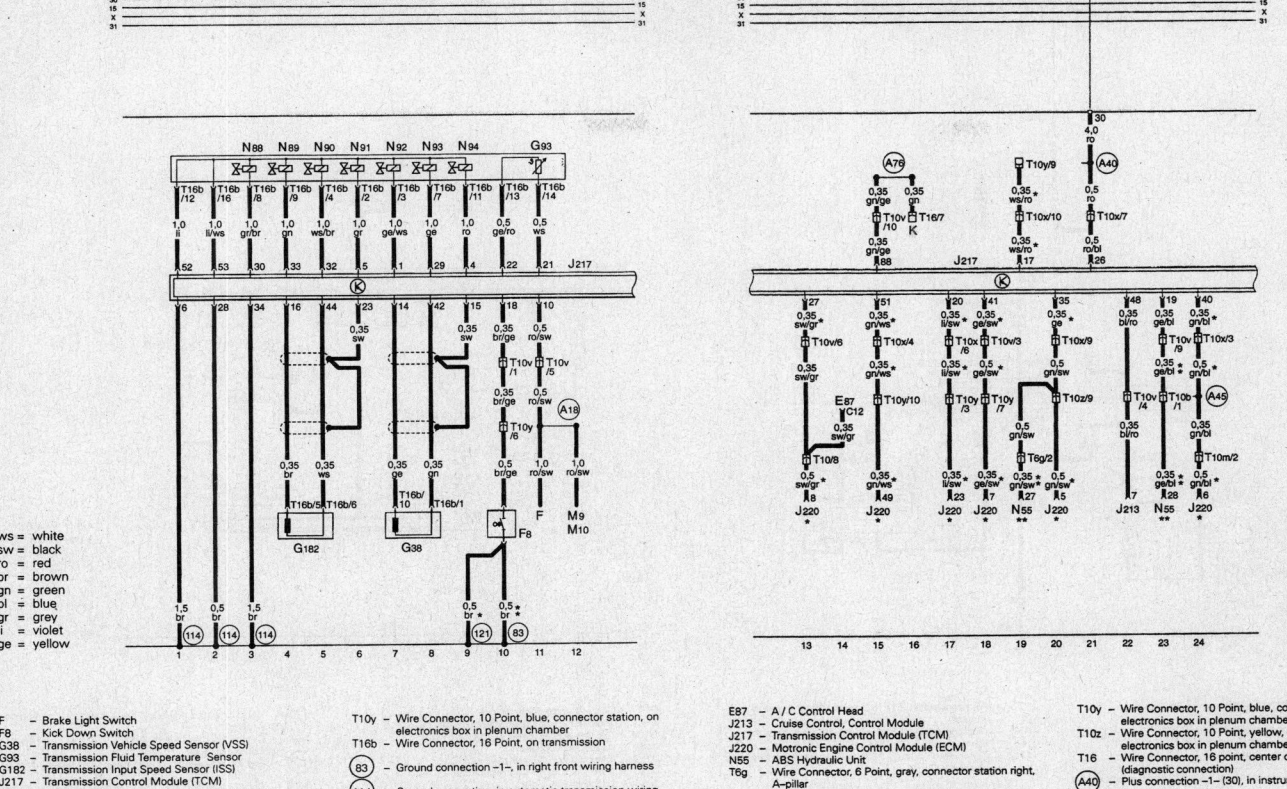

1. Remove lefthand transaxle support, then disconnect electrical connector.
2. Remove switch mounting screws, then pull switch from alignment dowel and selector shaft.
3. Slide new switch onto selector shaft, ensuring flat of selector shaft is properly aligned to switch.
4. Ensure switch is properly engaged

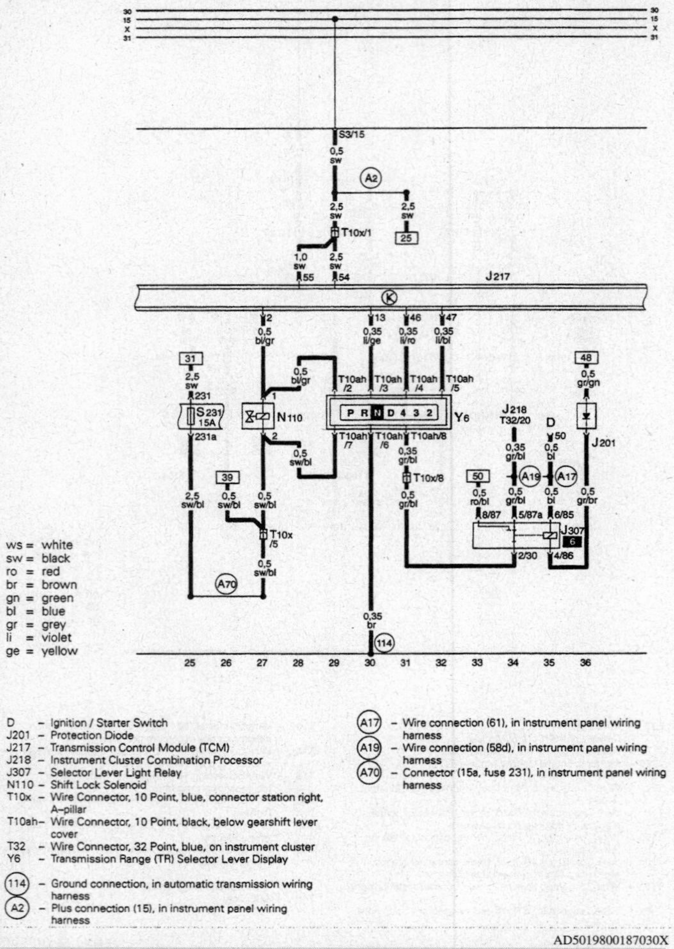

Fig. 7 BTSI wiring diagram (Part 3 of 5). 1998

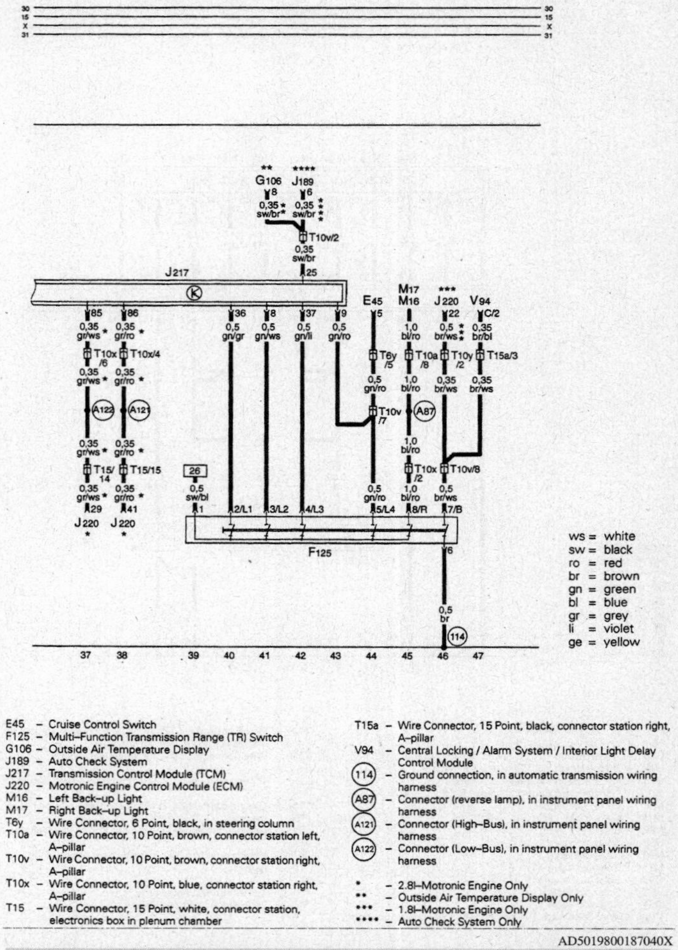

Fig. 7 BTSI wiring diagram (Part 4 of 5). 1998

onto alignment dowel, then install mounting screws. Tighten screws to specifications.

5. Install transaxle support. Tighten support to transaxle bolts and transaxle mount to subframe nuts to specifications.

SELECTOR CABLE, REPLACE

Refer to **Fig. 6** for related information when servicing selector cable.

1. Raise and support vehicle, then remove exhaust system shield below gear shift housing.
2. Remove lower cover from gear shift housing by pressing cover locking tab (A) forward, **Fig. 6.**
3. Remove cable retaining clip from cable end, then pull cable socket end off shifter lever ball.
4. Remove cable retaining clip from shifter housing, then pull cable from shifter housing.
5. Remove shield (B) from selector shaft area of transaxle.
6. Remove retaining clip from cable end at selector shaft arm, then press ball off socket of arm.
7. Remove cable mounting bracket bolts (D), then bracket (E) with cable from transaxle.
8. Remove selector cable from mounting bracket.
9. Reverse procedure to install. Refer to "Adjustments" for cable adjustment procedures.

SHIFTER COMPONENTS, REPLACE

A4 & S4

1. Remove stop buffer from cable lever.
2. Move selector lever to 3 position.
3. Slide shaft sleeve down and pull button out of selector lever handle until it clicks, then pull handle upward to remove.
4. Remove front portion of center console.
5. Disconnect electrical harness connectors.
6. Remove cover, then raise and support vehicle.
7. Remove front crossmember from below exhaust system.
8. Remove exhaust system for access to shift mechanism from below.
9. **On AWD models,** disconnect driveshaft from transaxle drive flange. Tie up driveshaft to body with suitable wire or rope.
10. **On all models,** remove heat shield from bottom of mounting bracket.
11. Remove selector lever cable sleeve from shift mechanism cover and slide back.
12. Remove cover from mounting bracket.
13. Press together ends of securing clip and remove.
14. Pull down locking plate for securing selector lever cable to mounting bracket and remove.
15. Pull selector lever cable off of selector lever.
16. Unclip lock cable from securing spring on mounting bracket by lifting securing spring slightly.
17. Remove four nuts and mounting bracket from below while pulling selector lever cable out of mounting bracket. **Do not kink cable.**
18. Move selector lever into Tiptronic gate, then remove frame.
19. Move selector lever to 2 position.
20. Lift lever from lock cable, detach from mounting and remove from mounting bracket.
21. Move selector lever to D position.
22. Carefully pry spring clip for Tiptronic position out of mounting bracket from outside.
23. Pull out locking clips for selector lever mount bushings.

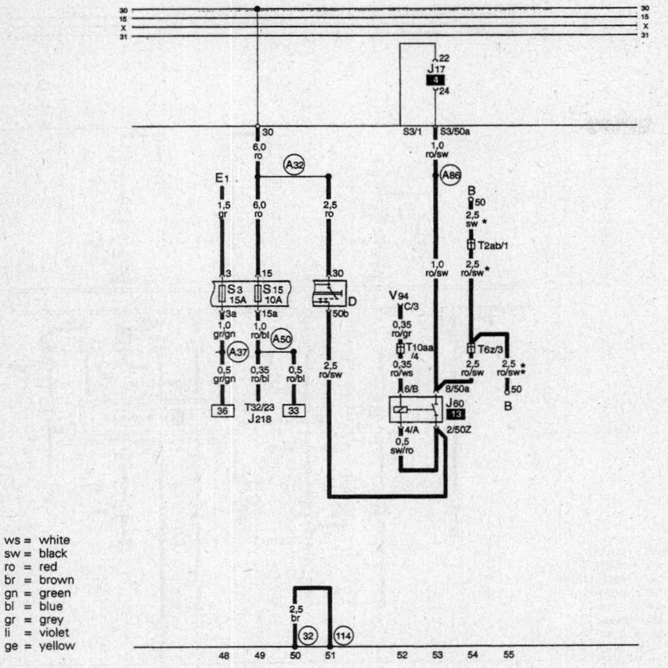

B – Starter
D – Ignition / Starter Switch
E1 – Light Switch
J17 – Fuel Pump (FP) Relay
J60 – Starter Interlock Alarm System Relay
J218 – Instrument Cluster Combination Processor
T2ab – Wire Connector, double, gray, in engine compartment, right
T6z – Wire Connector, 6 Point, red, connector station, electronics box in plenum chamber
T10aa – Wire Connector, 10 Point, orange, connector station right, A–pillar
T32 – Wire Connector, 32 Point, blue, on instrument cluster
V94 – Central Locking / Alarm System / Interior Light Delay Control Module

(32) – Ground connection, behind instrument panel, left
(114) – Ground connection, in automatic transmission wiring harness
(A32) – Plus connection (30), in instrument panel wiring harness
(A37) – Wire connection (58a), in instrument panel wiring harness
(A50) – Plus connection (30as), in instrument panel wiring harness
(A86) – Connection (50a), in instrument panel wiring harness

* – 2.8l–Motronic Engine Only
** – 1.8l–Motronic Engine Only

AD5019800187050X

Fig. 7 BTSI wiring diagram (Part 5 of 5). 1998

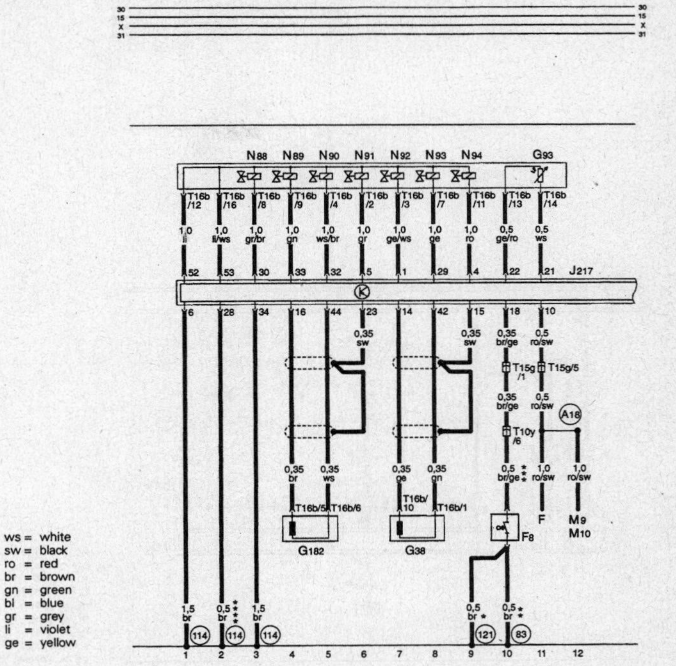

F – Brake Light Switch
F8 – Kick Down Switch
G38 – Transmission Vehicle Speed Sensor (VSS)
G93 – Transmission Fluid Temperature Sensor
G182 – Transmission Input Speed Sensor (ISS)
J217 – Transmission Control Module (TCM)
M9 – Left Brake Light
M10 – Right Brake Light
N88 – Soleniod Valve 1
N89 – Solenoid Valve 2
N90 – Soleniod Valve 3
N91 – Solenoid Valve 4
N92 – Soleniod Valve 5
N93 – Solenoid Valve 6
N94 – Soleniod Valve 7
T10y – Wire Connector, 10 Point, blue, connector station, on electronics box in plenum chamber
T15g – Wire Connector, 15 Point, brown, connector station right, A–pillar
T16b – Wire Connector, 16 Point, on transmission

(83) – Ground connection –1–, in right front wiring harness
(114) – Ground connection, in automatic transmission wiring harness
(121) – Ground connection –2–, in right front wiring harness
(A18) – Wire connection (54), in instrument panel wiring harness

* – 1.8L–Injection Engine Only, up to 8/99
** – 2.8L–Injection Engine Only, up to 8/99
*** – 1.8L– and 2.8L–Injection Engine Only, up to 8/99
**** – Up to 8/99

AD5019900188010X

Fig. 8 BTSI wiring diagram (Part 1 of 5). 1999–2001

24. Push out selector lever mounting bushings using a suitable screwdriver.
25. Remove complete selector lever unit.
26. Reverse procedure to install. Adjust selector lever cable as required.

A6 & A8

Refer to **Fig. 6** when replacing shift components. Refer to "Adjustments" for related shift component information.

SPEEDOMETER VEHICLE SPEED SENSOR, REPLACE

1. Raise and support vehicle, then remove components required to access area above lefthand inner driveshaft.
2. Disconnect electrical connector.
3. Depress lock bar on sensor, then rotate sensor body to release lock.
4. Lift out sensor, then remove and discard O-rings.
5. Reverse procedure to install. Use new sealing O-rings.

TRANSAXLE CONTROL MODULE (TCM), REPLACE

1. Switch Off ignition and wait 30 seconds.
2. Remove righthand A-pillar trim, then the righthand front door scuff plate.
3. Pull back carpet in righthand footwell, then lift electronics box off mounting clips.
4. Remove electronic box cover screws, then lift off cover.
5. Inspect electronics box for signs of water leakage. Repair as required.
6. Release TCM connector latches, then the connector.
7. Reverse procedure to install.

TRANSAXLE INPUT SPEED SENSOR, REPLACE

Never use a sensor that has been dropped. This could cause the internal ceramic magnet to crack or break.

1. Remove valve body as outlined under "Valve Body, Replace."
2. **Note position of connector,** then disconnect electrical connector.
3. Remove sensor mounting bolt and sensor with spacer sleeves.
4. Reverse procedure to install. Use two 20 MM spacer sleeves and tighten mounting bolt to specifications.

TRANSAXLE VEHICLE SPEED SENSOR, REPLACE

Never use a sensor that has been dropped. This could cause the internal ceramic magnet to crack or break.

1. Remove transaxle fluid pan as outlined under "Valve Body, Replace."
2. Remove transaxle fluid strainer, then disconnect electrical connector.
3. Remove sensor mounting bolt, then the sensor with spacer sleeves.
4. Reverse procedure to install. Use 8 MM spacer sleeves and tighten mounting bolt to specifications.

VALVE BODY, REPLACE

This valve body is serviced as an assembly. No provision is made for internal service.

1. Raise and support vehicle, then remove components required to access transaxle 16-pin connector.
2. Disconnect 16-pin connector from transaxle.
3. Pull clip retaining 16-pin connector body to transaxle.
4. Remove transaxle fluid pan drain plug, then allow fluid to drain into a suitable container. Discard seal.
5. Remove pan mounting bolts, then the pan. Discard pan gasket.
6. Remove bolts securing transaxle fluid strainer, then the strainer. Discard O-ring.
7. Disconnect electrical connector to transaxle vehicle speed sensor, then

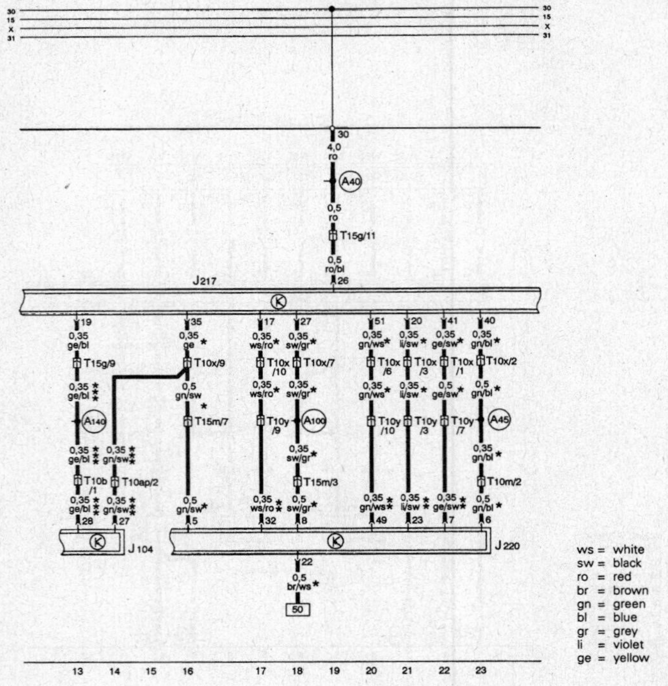

J104 - ABS Control Module (w/EDL)
J217 - Transmission Control Module (TCM)
J220 - Motronic Engine Control Module (ECM)
T10b - Wire Connector, 10 Point, orange, connector station left, A-pillar
T10m - Wire Connector, 10 Point, black, connector station, electronics box in plenum chamber
T10x - Wire Connector, 10 Point, red, connector station right, A-pillar
T10y - Wire Connector, 10 Point, blue, connector station, electronics box in plenum chamber
T10ap - Wire Connector, 10 Point, gray, connector station right, A-pillar
T15g - Wire Connector, 15 Point, brown, connector station right, A-pillar
T15m - Wire Connector, 15 Point, red, connector station, electronics box in plenum chamber

(A40) - Plus connection -1- (30), in instrument panel wiring harness
(A45) - Wire connection (RPM-Signal), in instrument panel wiring harness
(A100) - Connector -2- (87), in instrument panel wiring harness
(A140) - Connection (ASC), in instrument panel wiring harness
* - 1.8L- and 2.8L-Injection Engine Only, up to 8/99
** - 1.8L-Injection Engine Only, up to 8/99
*** - ASC Only, up to 8/99

AD5019900188020X

Fig. 8 BTSI wiring diagram (Part 2 of 5). 1999–2001

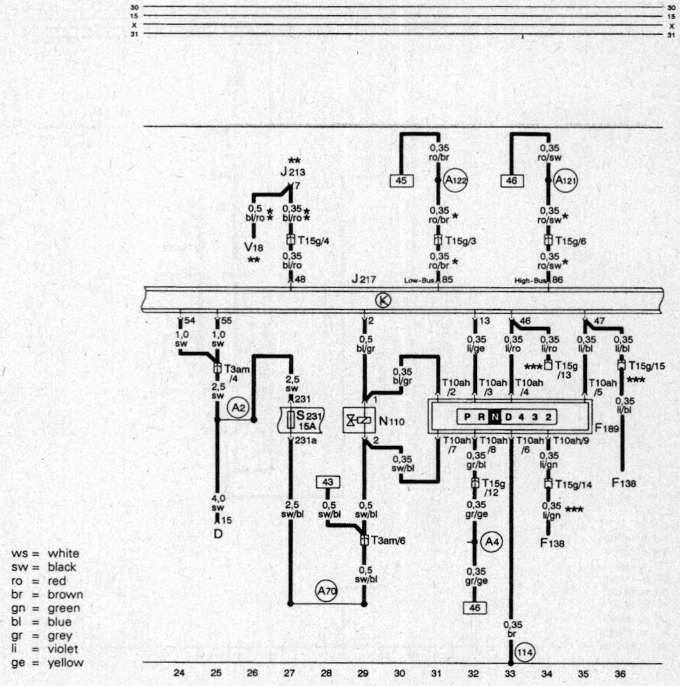

D - Ignition / Starter Switch
F138 - Airbag Spiral Spring/Return Spring with Slip Ring
F189 - Tiptronic Switch
J213 - Cruise Control, Control Module
J217 - Transmission Control Module (TCM)
N110 - Shift Lock Solenoid
T3am - Wire Connector, 3 Point, brown, connector station right, A-pillar
T10ah - Wire Connector, 10 Point, black, below gearshift lever cover
T15g - Wire Connector, 15 Point, brown, connector station right, A-pillar
V18 - Cruise Control Vacuum Pump

(114) - Ground connection, in automatic transmission wiring harness
(A2) - Plus connection (15), in instrument panel wiring harness
(A4) - Plus connection (58b), in instrument panel wiring harness
(A70) - Connector (15a, fuse 231), in instrument panel wiring harness
(A121) - Connector (High-Bus), in instrument panel wiring harness
(A122) - Connector (Low-Bus), in instrument panel wiring harness
* - From 8/99
** - 1.8L- and 2.8L-Injection Engine Only, up to 8/99
*** - Only on vehicles with Tiptronic steering wheel

AD5019900188030X

Fig. 8 BTSI wiring diagram (Part 3 of 5). 1999–2001

push 16-pin connector body through transaxle case. Discard O-ring seal.
8. Remove valve body mounting bolts, **Fig. 17,** then the valve body.
9. Disconnect valve body harness connectors from valve body solenoids and transaxle input speed sensor.
10. Unclip and remove harness from valve body.
11. Reverse procedure to install.

TRANSAXLE

REPLACE

1. Remove engine cover.
2. Remove intake air duct between air cleaner and throttle body.
3. Remove intake hoses between air cleaner housing and radiator support.
4. Loosen mounting bolts on fan shroud and cooling fan, then position cooling fan aside.
5. Disconnect electrical connectors.
6. Remove righthand and lefthand mounting nuts from front exhaust pipes.
7. Remove all engine/transaxle connecting bolts.
8. Remove covers over strut mounting and air cleaner housing.
9. Install engine support tool No. 10-222A with adapter 10-222A/4, or equivalents, on bolts of strut mounts, **Fig. 18.**
10. Disconnect fuel line from pressure regulator.
11. Install holding device tool No. 3180, or equivalent, in holding eyes from transaxle side, **Fig. 18.**
12. Take up weight of engine slightly using spindles.
13. Raise vehicle and remove front tires.
14. Remove noise insulators.
15. Remove heat shields for both front drive axles.
16. Remove righthand and lefthand drive axles.
17. Remove lower mounting nuts for front exhaust pipes.
18. Remove heated oxygen sensors.
19. Disconnect driveshaft from transaxle and position aside.
20. Remove lower mounting bolts from engine mounts.
21. Remove mounting bolts from righthand torque arm.
22. Raise engine using spindles until mount comes out of subframe.
23. Remove lower mounting bolts between oil pan and transaxle.
24. Disconnect starter electrical connectors.
25. Remove three torque converter bolts through starter opening.
26. Lower engine using spindles, then install lefthand engine mount on subframe.
27. Remove rear bracket for noise insulation.
28. Disconnect multi-function switch connector.
29. Disconnect VSS electrical connector.
30. Remove engine speed sensor from lefthand front of transaxle.
31. Remove multi-function switch.
32. Disconnect selector lever cable from transaxle.
33. Disconcert fluid lines from transaxle, then pull out and position aside.
34. Support transaxle from below using suitable transaxle jack.
35. Remove lefthand transaxle support with transaxle mount.
36. Remove righthand transaxle support with transaxle mount.
37. Remove subframe mounting bolts Nos. 1 and 2, **Fig. 19.**
38. Lower rear subframe approximately four inches from mounting point on body by releasing tension on engine support.

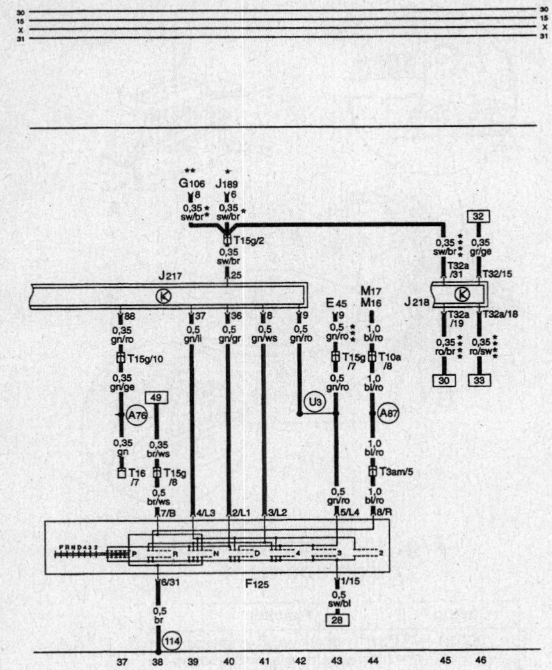

ws = white
sw = black
ro = red
br = brown
gn = green
bl = blue
gr = grey
li = violet
ge = yellow

E45 – Cruise Control Switch
F125 – Multi–Function Transmission Range (TR) Switch
G106 – Outside Air Temperature Display
J189 – Auto Check System
J217 – Transmission Control Module (TCM)
J218 – Instrument Cluster Combination Processor
M16 – Left Back–up Light
M17 – Right Back–up Light
T3am – Wire Connector, 3 Point, brown, connector station right, A–pillar
T10a – Wire Connector, 10 Point, brown, connector station left, A–pillar
T15g – Wire Connector, 15 Point, brown, connector station right, A–pillar
T16 – Wire Connector, 16 point, center console, rear (diagnostic connection)
T32 – Wire Connector, 32 Point, blue, on instrument cluster
T32a – Wire Connector, 32 Point, green, on instrument cluster
(114) – Ground connection, in automatic transmission wiring harness
(A76) – Plus connection (K–diagnostic wire), in instrument panel wiring harness
(A87) – Connector (reverse lamp), in instrument panel wiring harness
(U3) – Wire connection –1–, in automatic transmission wiring harness
* – Auto Check System Only (Up to 8/99)
** – Outside Air Temperature Display Only (Up to 8/99)
*** – 1.8L– and 2.8L–Injection Engine Only (Up to 8/99)
**** – From 8/99

AD5019900188040X

Fig. 8 BTSI wiring diagram (Part 4 of 5). 1999–2001

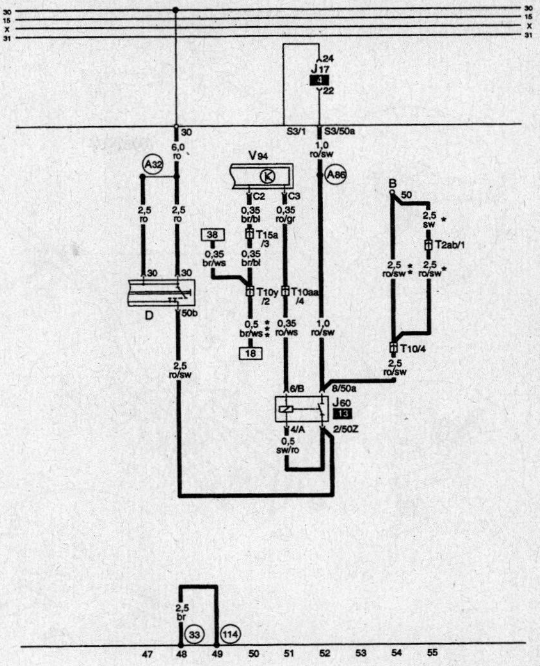

ws = white
sw = black
ro = red
br = brown
gn = green
bl = blue
gr = grey
li = violet
ge = yellow

B – Starter
D – Ignition / Starter Switch
J17 – Fuel Pump (FP) Relay
J60 – Starter Interlock Alarm System Relay
T2ab – Wire Connector, double, gray, in engine compartment, right
T10 – Wire Connector, 10 Point, brown, connector station, electronics box in plenum chamber
T10y – Wire Connector, 10 Point, blue, connector station, electronics box in plenum chamber
T10aa – Wire Connector, 10 Point, orange, connector station right, A–pillar
T15a – Wire Connector, 15 Point, black, connector station right, A–pillar
V94 – Central Locking / Alarm System / Interior Light Delay Control Module
(33) – Ground connection, behind instrument panel, right
(114) – Ground connection, in automatic transmission wiring harness
(A32) – Plus connection (30), in instrument panel wiring harness
(A86) – Connection (50a), in instrument panel wiring harness
* – 2.7L– and 2.8L–Injection Engine Only
** – 1.8L–Injection Engine Only
*** – 1.8L– and 2.8L–Injection Engine Only (Up to 8/99)

AD5019900188050X

Fig. 8 BTSI wiring diagram (Part 5 of 5). 1999–2001

39. Support engine at front using suitable stand.
40. Remove remaining engine to transaxle connecting bolts.
41. Push torque converter off flexplate using suitable pry bar.
42. Separate transaxle from engine using a suitable pry bar.
43. Lower transaxle jack and guide transaxle out diagonally downward.
44. Reverse procedure to install, noting the following:
    a. Replace all self-locking fasteners.
    b. Replace all gaskets and O-rings.
    c. Tighten transaxle to engine bolts to specifications, **Fig. 20.**
    d. Tighten all bolts and nuts to specifications.

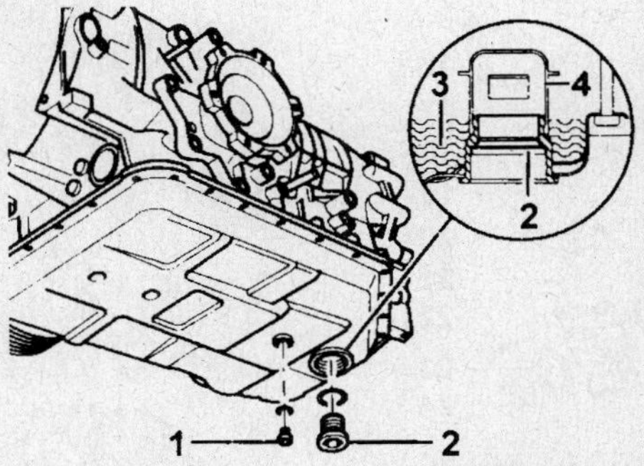

AD5019600079000X

Fig. 9 Planetary fluid level inspection

    e. Inspect wheel alignment and adjust as required.

TECHNICAL SERVICE BULLETINS

DELAYED 1–2 UPSHIFT ON COLD START WARM UP

A4 models may display a delayed 1–2 gear upshift when transaxle fluid temperature is below 104°F and after a fresh engine start. This is a normal condition caused by warm-up programming to help the engine more rapidly reach operating temperature. The condition will last for approximately two minutes.

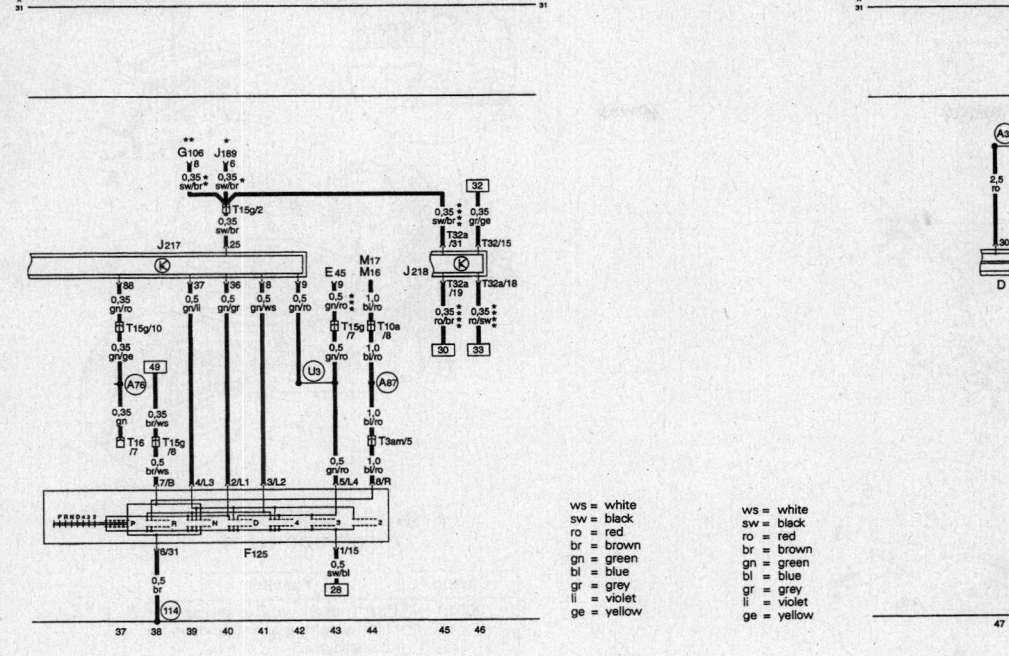

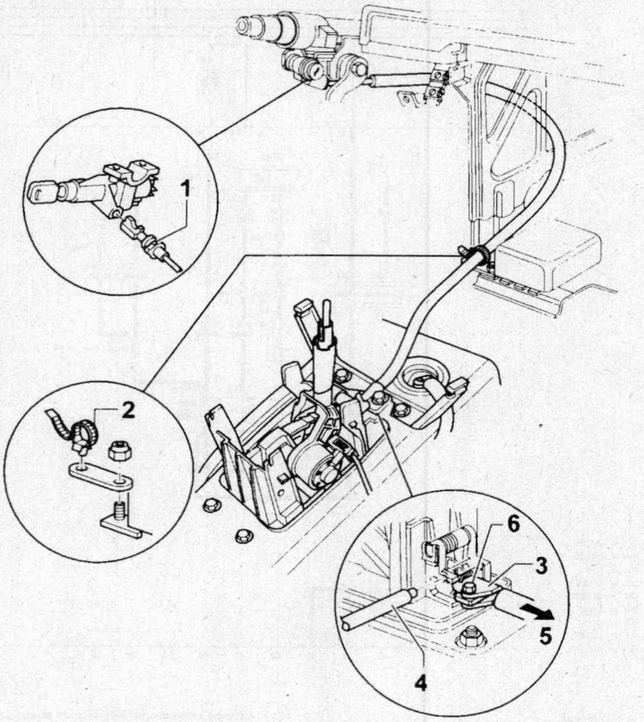

AD5019600137000X

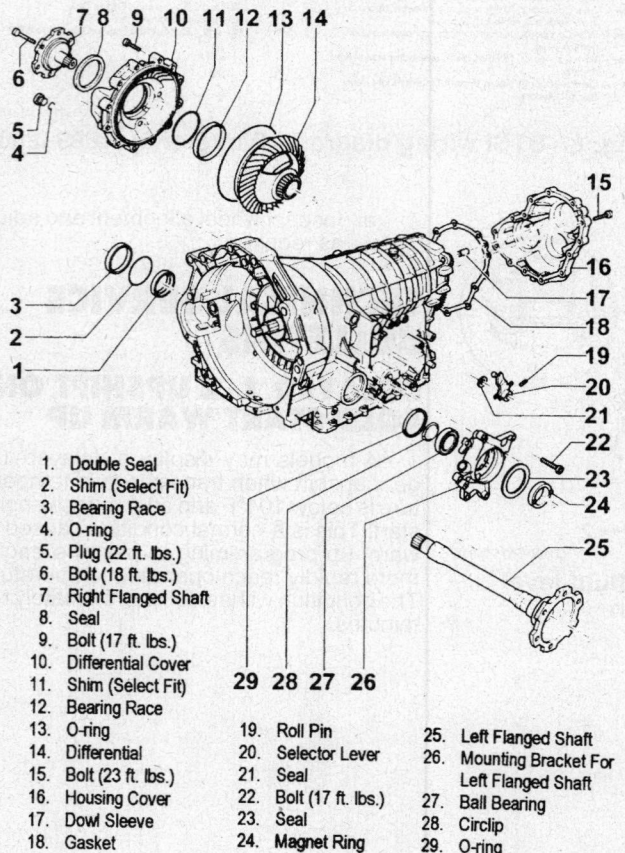

Fig. 10 Ignition lock cable removal & adjustment

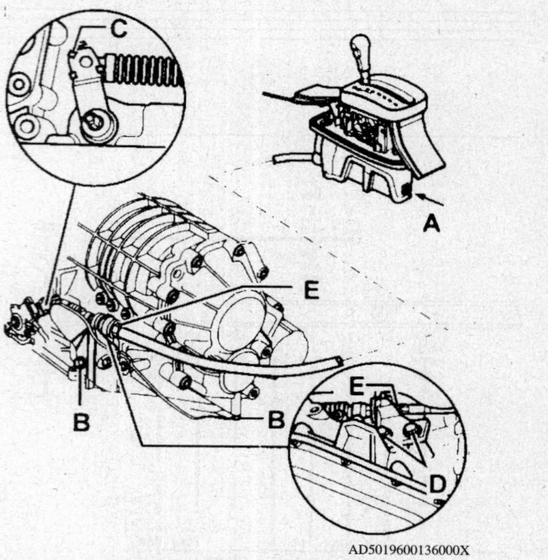

AD5019600136000X

Fig. 11 Selector cable replacement

Coding	Function
00010	DSP[1] not active; Transmission shifts according to known characteristic curve (not applicable for US or Canadian vehicles)
00000	DSP active

[1] Dynamic shift program: optimal matching of transmission shift characteristics to the respective driving conditions.

AD5019600144000X

Fig. 12 Transaxle control module codes

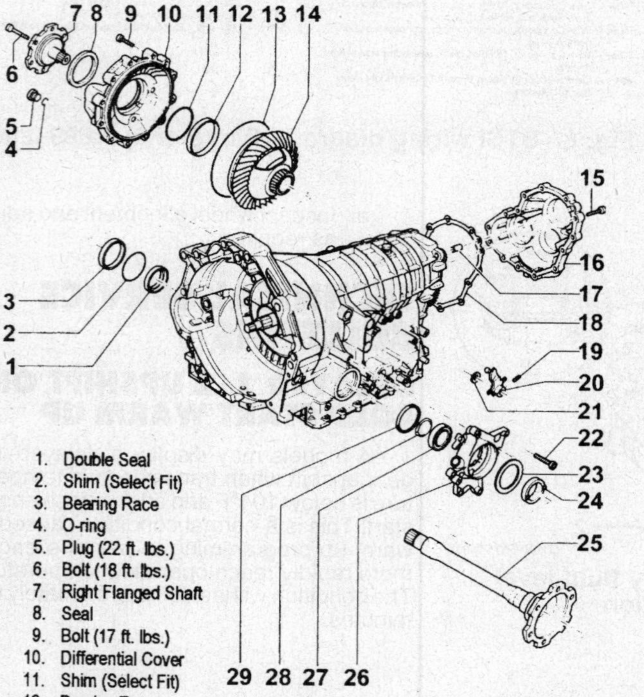

1. Double Seal
2. Shim (Select Fit)
3. Bearing Race
4. O-ring
5. Plug (22 ft. lbs.)
6. Bolt (18 ft. lbs.)
7. Right Flanged Shaft
8. Seal
9. Bolt (17 ft. lbs.)
10. Differential Cover
11. Shim (Select Fit)
12. Bearing Race
13. O-ring
14. Differential
15. Bolt (23 ft. lbs.)
16. Housing Cover
17. Dowl Sleeve
18. Gasket
19. Roll Pin
20. Selector Lever
21. Seal
22. Bolt (17 ft. lbs.)
23. Seal
24. Magnet Ring
25. Left Flanged Shaft
26. Mounting Bracket For Left Flanged Shaft
27. Ball Bearing
28. Circlip
29. O-ring

AD5019600146000X

Fig. 13 Exploded view of front wheel drive final drive components

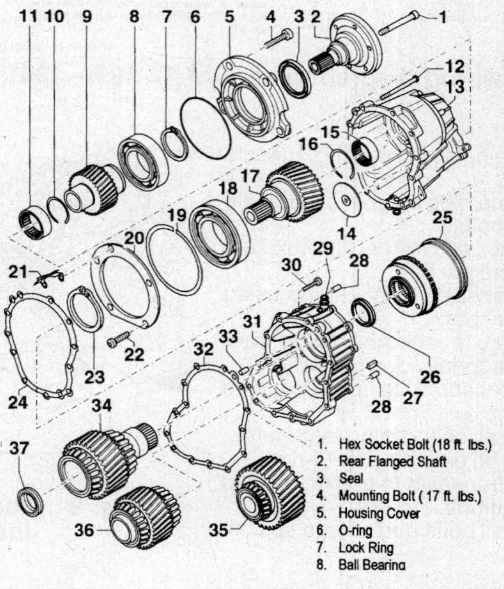

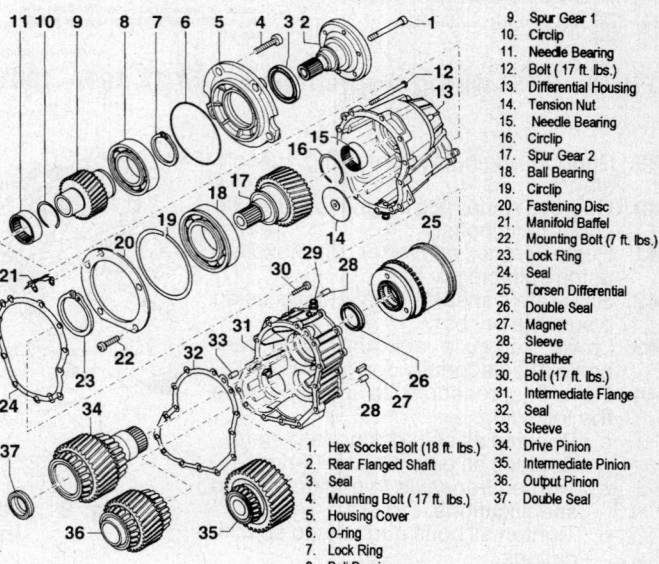

1. Hex Socket Bolt (18 ft. lbs.)
2. Rear Flanged Shaft
3. Seal
4. Mounting Bolt (17 ft. lbs.)
5. Housing Cover
6. O-ring
7. Lock Ring
8. Ball Bearing
9. Spur Gear 1
10. Circlip
11. Needle Bearing
12. Bolt (17 ft. lbs.)
13. Differential Housing
14. Tension Nut
15. Needle Bearing
16. Circlip
17. Spur Gear 2
18. Ball Bearing
19. Circlip
20. Fastening Disc
21. Manifold Baffel
22. Mounting Bolt (7 ft. lbs.)
23. Lock Ring
24. Seal
25. Torsen Differential
26. Double Seal
27. Magnet
28. Sleeve
29. Breather
30. Bolt (17 ft. lbs.)
31. Intermediate Flange
32. Seal
33. Sleeve
34. Drive Pinion
35. Intermediate Pinion
36. Output Pinion
37. Double Seal

AD5019600147000X

Fig. 14 Exploded view of center differential

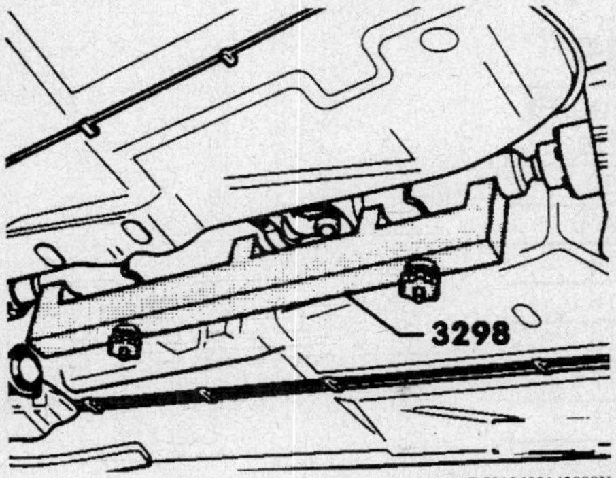

AD5019600142000X

Fig. 15 Alignment tool to propeller shaft installation

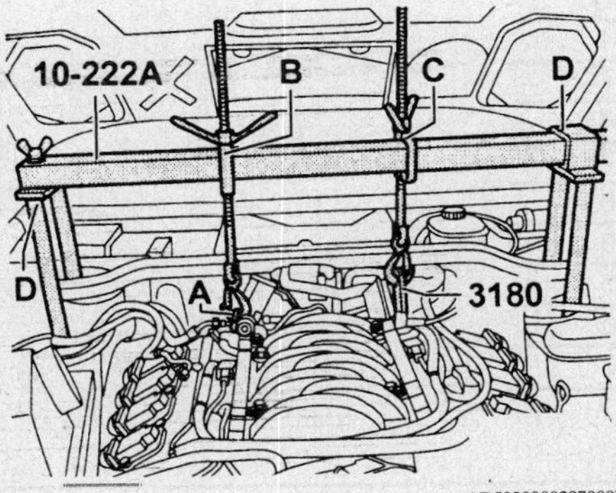

AD5029900297000X

Fig. 18 Engine support installation

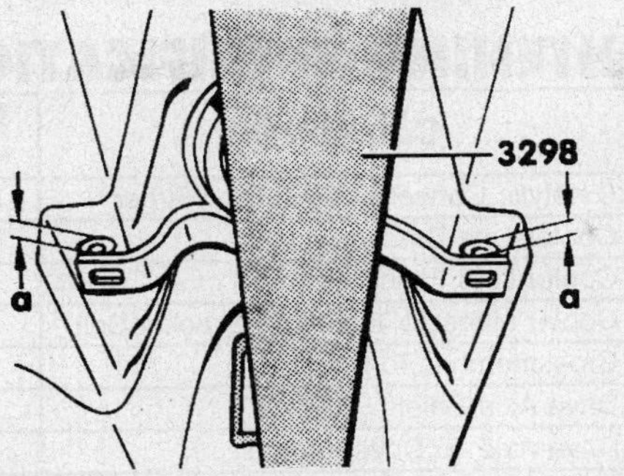

Shims	
Clearance -a- (mm)	Thickness (mm)
0 ... 3	–
3.1 ... 5	2
5.1 ... 7	4
7.1 ... 9	6
9.1 ... 11	8
11.1 ... 13	10

AD5019600143000X

Fig. 16 Propeller shaft center bearing shim selection & installation

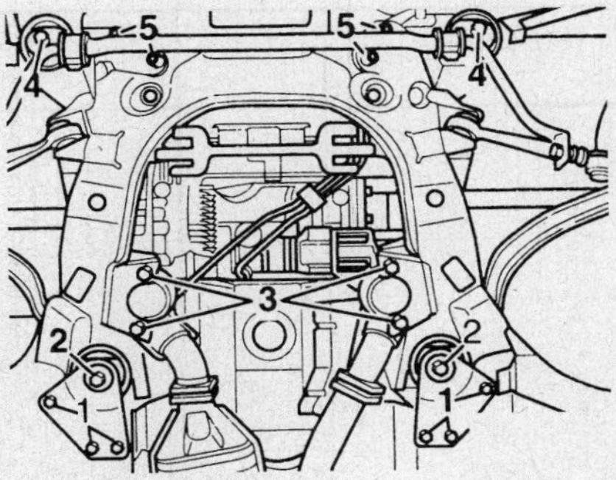

AD5029900298000X

Fig. 19 Subframe mounting bolt locations

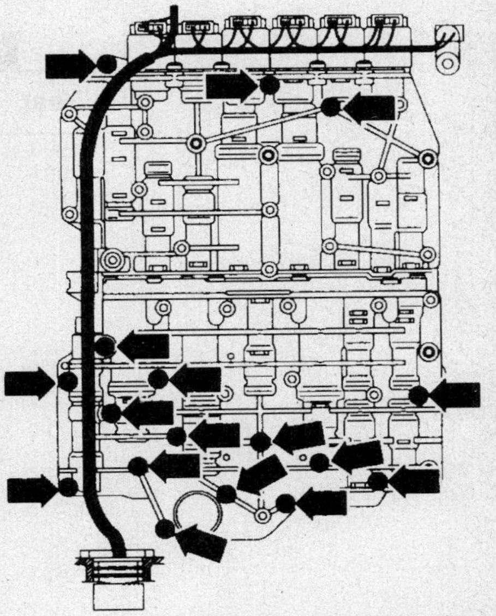

AD5019600145000X

Fig. 17 Valve body removal

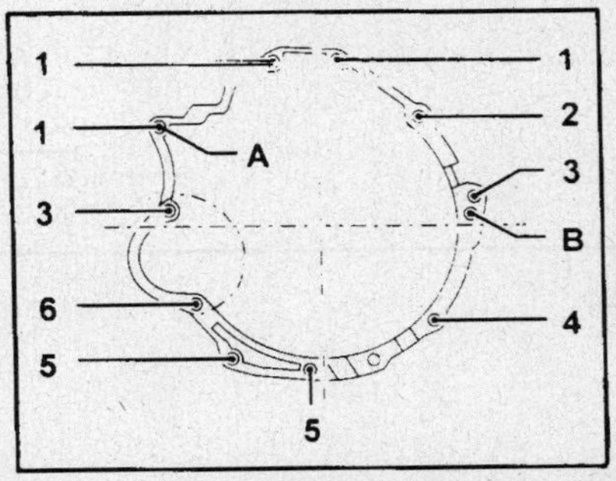

Item	Bolt	Qty.	Nm (ft lb)
1	M12 x 67	3	65 (48)
2	M12 x 90	1	65 (48)
3	M12 x 80	2	65 (48)
4	M10 x 60	1	45 (33)
5	M10 x 45	2	45 (33)
6	M10 x 75	1	45 (33)

AD5019600141000X

Fig. 20 Transaxle to engine bolts

TIGHTENING SPECIFICATIONS

Year	Component	Torque/Ft. Lbs.
1998–2001	Catalytic Converter To Turbocharger	22
	Cooler Line Bracket	84②
	Cooler Line Fittings	18
	Cooler Lines To Transaxle Bracket Bolt	15
	Crossmember To Body	18
	Drive Axle Shield	17
	Drive Axle To Drive Flange	57
	Drive Axle To Wheel Hub	148①
	Driveshaft To Transaxle	57
	Driveshaft To Transaxle Heat Shield	18
	Engine Mount To Subframe	30
	Heat Shield Under Multi-Function Switch	84②
	Multi-Function Switch	71
	Subframe To Body, Stretch M12	81①
	Subframe To Body, Front M10	44
	Subframe To Body, Rear M8	17
	Torque Arm To Long Member	30
	Torque Converter To Flex Plate	63
	Transaxle Mount To Subframe	17
	Transaxle Support To Transaxle	30
	Transaxle Support To Transaxle Mount	30

① — Plus ¼ (90°) turn.
② — Inch lbs.

Front Wheel Drive Axles

INDEX

	Page No.
Driveshaft, Replace	1-219
A4, A8 & S4	1-219
A6 & S6	1-219
Cabriolet	1-219
Driveshaft Service	1-219
A4, A6, A8, S4 & S6	1-219
Cabriolet	1-220
Tightening Specifications	1-221

DRIVESHAFT

REPLACE

A4, A8 & S4

1. Remove wheel cover, then the drive axle bolt in hub.
2. Raise and support vehicle, then remove tires.
3. Remove drive axle mounting bolts.
4. Remove cable for ABS wheel speed sensor from bracket at brake caliper, then pull ABS wheel speed sensor slightly out of swing arm.
5. Remove swing arm to track control arms mounting bolt and push both track control arms up and out, then tilt swing arm away.
6. Remove drive axle.
7. Reverse procedure to install.

A6 & S6

1. Remove wheel cover and the drive axle bolt in hub.
2. Pull speed sensor slightly out of housing, then remove drive axle flange to transaxle mounting bolts.
3. Press drive axle upward toward front of vehicle, then turn steering to full lock and remove drive axle.
4. Reverse procedure to install.

CABRIOLET

Less Attached Wheel Bearing Housing

1. Loosen wheel bolts.
2. Remove wheel hub to axle shaft bolt.
3. Raise and support vehicle, then remove washer and wheel.
4. Remove bolts attaching axle shaft to drive flange, then disconnect lower ball joint.
5. Swing wheel bearing housing outward and remove axle shaft.
6. Reverse procedure to install. Tighten nuts and bolts to specifications.

Attached Wheel Bearing Housing

1. Loosen wheel bolts.
2. Remove wheel hub to axle shaft bolt.
3. Raise and support vehicle, then remove washer and wheel.
4. Remove axle shaft flange, nut from link rod, and control arm to stabilizer bar to subframe mounting bolts.
5. Push control arm downward, then press axle shaft out of hub using puller tool No. VAG 1389, or equivalent.
6. Reverse procedure to install, noting the following:
   a. **Ensure splines on stub axle and wheel hub are free of oil, grease and old locking compound.**
   b. Apply a. 2 inch band of D6 locking compound around end of outer CV joint splines, then install axle shaft. **Allow one hour for compound to harden.**
   c. Tighten nuts and bolts to specifications.

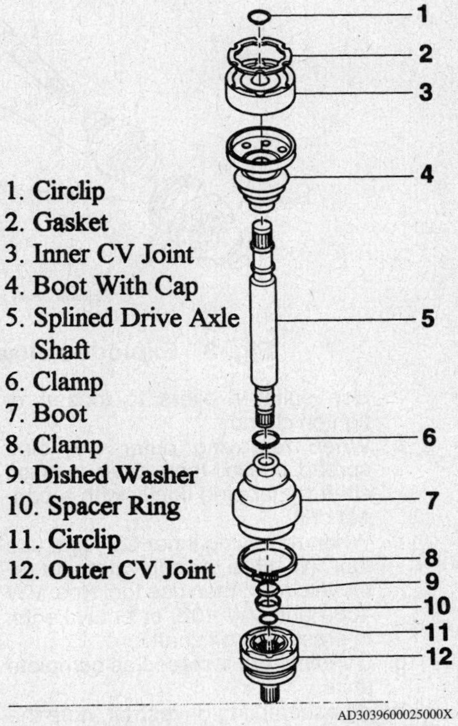

Fig. 1 Exploded view of drive axle w/inner CV joint. A4, A6, A8, S4 & S6

DRIVESHAFT SERVICE

A4, A6, A8, S4 & S6

DRIVE AXLE w/INNER CV JOINT

Refer to **Fig. 1** during service procedures.

Disassembly

1. Remove outer CV joint boot clamps.
2. Push back outer CV joint boot.
3. Thread in removal tool No. 3207, or equivalent, until CV joint is forced off splined shaft.
4. Remove dished washer, spacer ring and circlip.
5. Remove outer CV joint boot.
6. Remove inner CV joint boot clamps.
7. Remove inner CV joint boot.
8. Remove inner CV joint circlip and gasket.
9. Remove inner CV joint using removal tool Nos. VW 402 and VW 411, or equivalents. **Support ball hub during this step.**

Assembly

1. Install inner CV joint using installation tool Nos. VW 401, VW 402, VW 40-204A, VW 522 and VW 412, or equivalents. Press joint on as far as stop, then install circlip and gasket. **Chamfer on inner diameter of ball hub (splines) must face toward collar of drive axle.**
2. Install inner CV joint boot, then the boot clamps using installation tool No. VAG 1275, or equivalent.
3. Install outer CV joint boot onto axle shaft.
4. Install circlip, spacer ring and dished washer.
5. Install outer CV joint onto axle shaft, then tap into place with a suitable plastic hammer until circlip locks in place.
6. Install outer CV joint boot onto CV joint.
7. Install tripod joint boot clamps using installation tool No. VAG 1275, or equivalent.

DRIVE AXLE w/INNER TRIPOD JOINT

Refer to **Fig. 2** during service procedures.

Disassembly

1. Clamp drive axle in a suitable vise.
2. Remove CV joint boot clamps.
3. Push back CV joint boot.
4. Thread in removal tool 3207, or equivalent, until CV joint is forced off splined shaft.
5. Remove dished washer, spacer ring and circlip.
6. Remove CV joint boot.
7. Remove tripod joint boot clamps.
8. Remove tripod joint boot.

Assembly

1. Install tripod joint boot, using installation tool No. VAG 1474-5, or equivalent, to install boot over splined shaft bead.
2. Vent tripod joint boot, then install tripod joint boot clamps using installation tool

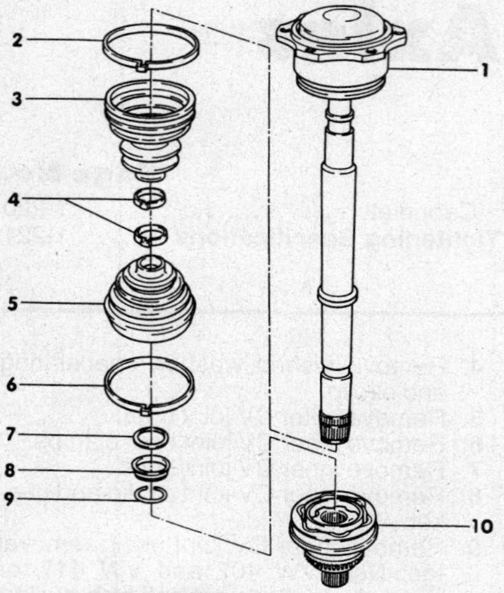

1. Drive Axle w/Inner Tripod Joint
2. Clamp
3. Inner Boot
4. Clamp
5. Outer Boot
6. Clamp
7. Dished Washer
8. Spacer Ring
9. Circlip
10. Outer CV Joint

AD3039600024000X

Fig. 2 Exploded view of drive axle w/inner tripod joint. A4, A6, A8, S4 & S6

No. VAG 1275, or equivalent.

3. Install CV joint boot using installation tool No. VAG 1474-5, or equivalent, to position boot over splined shaft bead.
4. Install circlip, spacer ring and dished washer.
5. Install CV joint onto axle shaft. Tap into place with a suitable plastic hammer unit circlip locks in place.
6. Install CV joint boot onto CV joint, then vent air from boot.
7. Install tripod joint boot clamps using installation tool No. VAG 1275, or equivalent.
8. Remove drive axle from vise.

CABRIOLET

Refer to **Fig. 3** during service procedures.

1. When disassembling driveshaft, note the following:
   a. Use suitable pliers to loosen or tighten clamps.
   b. When removing outer CV joint, spread circlip, then drive joint off shaft by tapping lightly with a copper drift.
   c. When removing inner CV joint, use tool VW 161a, or equivalent, to remove circlip, then use tool Nos. VW 408a and VW 402, or equivalents, to press joint off shaft.
   d. CV joints are replaced as complete units.
2. When assembling driveshaft, note the following:
   a. Always install new boot clamps and circlips. Inspect boots for cracks or wear. Replace if required.
   b. Drive outer CV joint onto shaft using a plastic hammer until circlip is engaged in shaft groove.
   c. Press inner CV joint onto shaft until circlips can be can be pressed into groove. **Chamfer on inside diameter of ball hub (splines) must face contact shoulder on driveshaft.**
   d. Note position of dished washer.
   e. **On models equipped with 4 cylinder engines,** 90 grams of G6 or equivalent grease are required for each CV joint when installing or replacing boot.
   f. **On models equipped with 6 and 8 cylinder engines,** 120 grams of G6 or equivalent grease are required for inner CV joint and 90 grams are required for outer CV joint.
   g. **On all models,** boots will sometimes be pressed in when installed, causing a vacuum inside the boot which in turn leads to an inward fold when vehicle is driven. To correct this condition, lift small diameter end of boot to equalize pressure, allowing boot to regain normal shape.

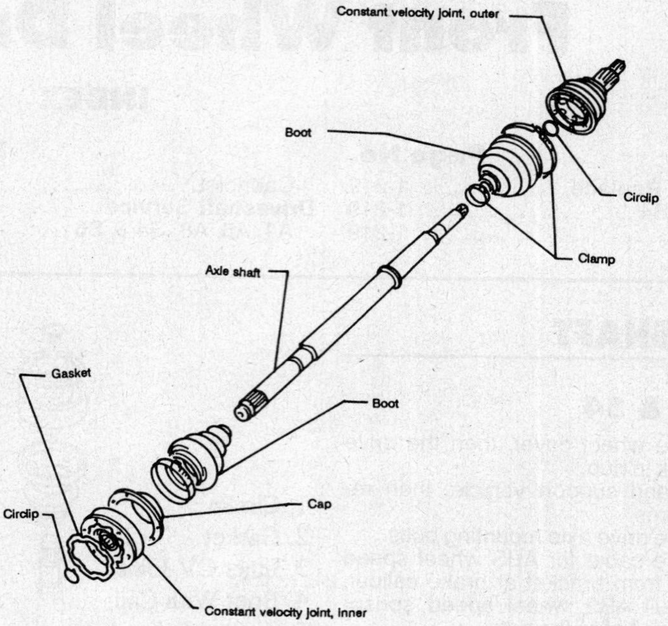

AD3039100008000X

Fig. 3 Exploded view of drive axle. Cabriolet

TIGHTENING SPECIFICATIONS

Year	Component	Torque/Ft. Lbs.
A4, A8 & S4		
1998–2001	Axle Nut	148①
	Drive Axle To Transaxle Mounting Bolts	57
	Track Control Arms To Swing Arm	30
	Wheel Lug Nuts	89
A6 & S6		
1998–2001	Axle Nut	148①
	Drive Axle To Transaxle Mounting Bolts⑤	59
	Drive Axle To Transaxle Mounting Bolts, M8⑥	33
	Drive Axle To Transaxle Mounting Bolts, M10⑥	59
	Wheel Lug Nuts	89
CABRIOLET		
1998–2001	Axle Nut③	195
	Axle Nut, 14 MM④	88①
	Axle Nut, 16 MM④	147①
	Axle Shaft To Differential Drive Flange Bolts, M8	33
	Axle Shaft To Differential Drive Flange Bolts, M10	58
	Ball Joint To Control Arm Nuts	48
	Ball Joint To Wheel Bearing Housing Nuts	48
	Driveshaft Nut③	195
	Driveshaft Nut, 14 MM④	88①
	Driveshaft Nut, 16 MM④	147①
	Hub Nut③	195
	Hub Nut, 14 MM④	88①
	Hub Nut, 16 MM④	147①
	Link Rod Nuts	33
	Stabilizer Bar Link Rod Nuts	14
	Strut Assembly To Wheel Bearing Housing Nuts	59②
	Tie Rod To Strut Assembly Nuts	22
	Wheel Lug Nuts	81

① — Tighten an additional 90° (¼) turn.

② — Tighten an additional 180° (½) turn.

③ — AWD.

④ — FWD.

⑤ — Axle with inner tripod joint

⑥ — Axle with inner CV joint.

All-Wheel Drive Systems

NOTE: On Air Bag Equipped Models, Refer To "Air Bag System Precautions" Located In The Front Of This Manual For System Disarming & Arming Procedures.

NOTE: Refer To "Computer Relearn Procedures" Located In The Front Of This Manual When Battery Power To The Computer Has Been Interrupted.

INDEX

	Page No.
Adjustments	1-222
Propeller Shaft Alignment	1-223
Propeller Shaft Center Bearing	1-222
Description	1-222
Driveshaft, Replace	1-223
A4 & S4 Quattro	1-223
A6 Quattro & S6	1-223
A8	1-223
Driveshaft Service	1-223
Precautions	1-222
Air Bag Systems	1-222
Battery Ground Cable	1-222
Radio Coded Anti-Theft System	1-222
Propeller Shaft, Replace	1-226
A4 & S4 Quattro	1-226
A6 Quattro, A8 & S6	1-227
TT	1-227
Rear Axle, Replace	1-223
A4 & S4 Quattro	1-223
A6 Quattro & S6	1-224
A8	1-224
TT	1-224
Rear Axle Service	1-225
Differential Drive Flange Oil Seal, Replace	1-226
A4 Quattro	1-226
A6 Quattro, A8 & S6	1-226
Differential Input Flange Oil Seal & Bearing, Replace	1-225
A4 & S4 Quattro	1-225
A6 Quattro, A8 & S6	1-225
TT	1-225
Differential Lock	1-226
Assembly	1-226
Disassembly	1-226
Tightening Specifications	1-228
A4 & S4 Quattro	1-228
A6 Quattro & A8	1-228
S6	1-229
TT	1-230

PRECAUTIONS

Air Bag Systems

Refer to "Air Bag System Precautions" in the front of this manual for system disarming and arming procedures.

Radio Coded Anti-Theft System

Prior to disconnecting the battery or removing the audio system, obtain the security code from the vehicle operator. Refer to the owner's manual for security code disarming and arming procedures.

Battery Ground Cable

Prior to service, disconnect battery ground cable and isolate as required.

DESCRIPTION

The Quattro all wheel drive system utilizes a center Torsen type limited slip differential to distribute torque to the front and rear differentials and provide power to the tires with the most traction.

The rear differential on some models is equipped with a locking device which disables the differential unit and allows both rear wheel to receive equal power for better traction at low speeds. The locking unit is automatically disengaged at a set vehicle speed to prevent differential damage and unsafe handling.

The front and rear differential on some models are equipped with Electronic Differential Lock (EDL) System. This system works along with the ABS system to apply torque to the tires which have the most traction.

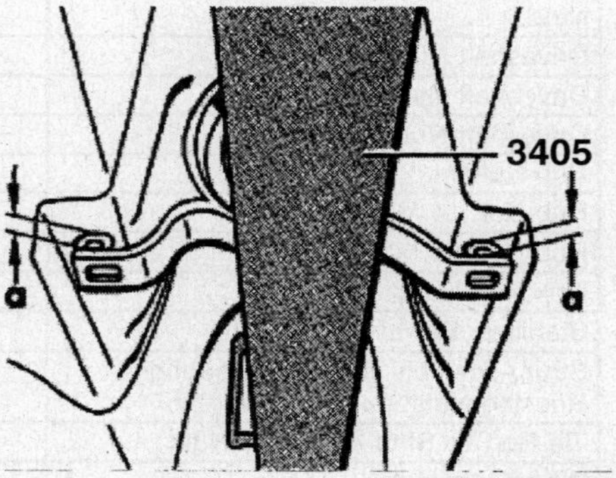

AD3039800029000X

Fig. 1 Propeller shaft adjustment dimension "a"

ADJUSTMENTS

PROPELLER SHAFT CENTER BEARING

A4 & S4 Quattro

1. Remove exhaust system, then the propeller shaft heat shield.
2. Loosen mounting bolts to body.
3. Install alignment fixture tool No. 3405, or equivalent, to propeller shaft.
4. Remove mounting bolts and shims.
5. Equalize clearance "a," **Fig. 1.**
6. Select adjustment washers from chart, **Fig. 2,** to correct clearance if required.

Washers

Distance a mm	Thickness mm	Part Number
0-3	—	—
3.1-5	2	857 521 143
5.1-7	4	857 521 143 A
7.1-9	6	857 521 143 B
9.1-11	8	857 521 143 C
11.1-13	10	857 521 143 D

AD3039100014000X

Fig. 2 Propeller shaft adjustment washers chart

7. Reverse procedure to install components loosened or removed. Tighten nuts and bolts to specifications.

A6 Quattro & S6 Quattro

1. Install alignment and removal tool to propeller shaft as outlined under "Propeller Shaft, Replace," for the respective model.
2. Remove center support mounting bolts and washers.
3. Measure distance "a" as illustrated, **Fig. 1.** Clearance must be equal on both sides.
4. Select adjustment washers from chart, **Fig. 2,** to correct clearance if required.
5. Reverse procedure to install components loosened or removed. Tighten nuts and bolts to specifications.

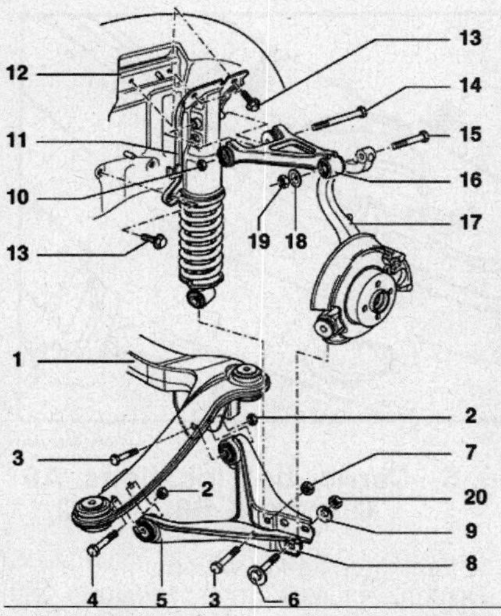

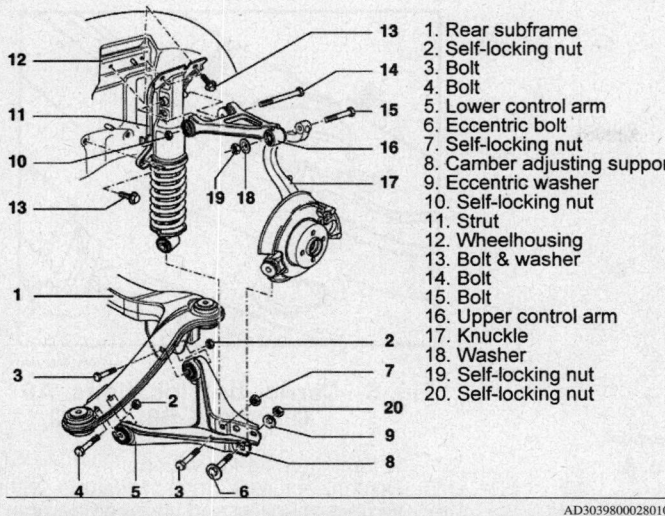

Fig. 3 Component view of rear axle (Part 1 of 2). A4 & S4 Quattro

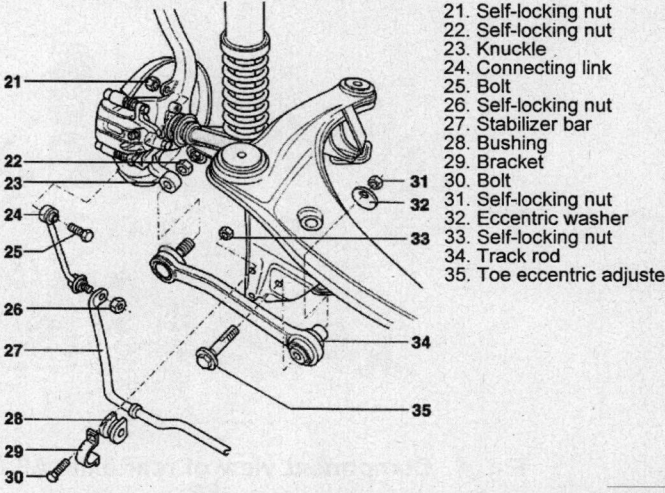

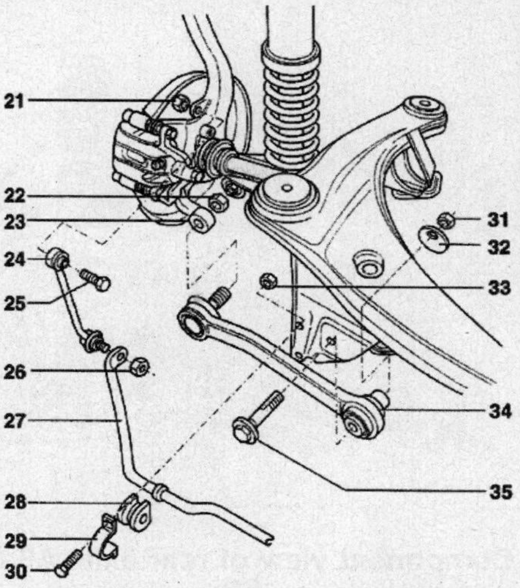

Fig. 3 Component view of rear axle (Part 2 of 2). A4 & S4 Quattro

PROPELLER SHAFT ALIGNMENT

1. Perform steps 1 through 4 as outlined under "Propeller Shaft Center Bearing" in this section.
2. Push propeller shaft fully to rear using alignment tool, then mark position of center support bearing on body.
3. Push propeller shaft fully to front using alignment tool, then mark position of center support bearing on body.
4. Position center support bearing between two marks, then install bolts, washers and spacers and tighten bolts to specifications.
5. Install all removed components, then tighten to specifications.

DRIVESHAFT

REPLACE

A4 & S4 QUATTRO

1. Remove wheel cover and loosen bolt securing axle shaft in hub.
2. Raise and support vehicle, then remove tires.
3. Pull speed sensor slightly out of housing.
4. Remove drive axle to final drive flange mounting bolts.
5. Loosen coupling rod to wheel bearing housing bolt.
6. Loosen upper control arm to wheel bearing housing bolt.
7. To remove lefthand drive axle, proceed as follows:
   a. Remove exhaust system.
   b. Remove rear and center sound insulators.
8. To remove either drive axle, proceed as follows:
   a. Remove lower drive axle on inside at final drive.
   b. Remove drive axle from wheel bearing housing.
9. Reverse procedure to install.

A6 QUATTRO & S6

1. Remove wheel cover and bolt securing axle shaft in hub.
2. Raise and support vehicle, then remove tires.
3. Remove brake caliper and secure to body with suitable wire or rope.
4. To remove righthand side drive axle, remove fuel tank cover plate.
5. To remove lefthand side drive axle, remove inner CV joint heat shield.
6. To remove either drive axle, install two wheel bolts in wheel hub and use a suitable tire iron to hold wheel and prevent rotation.
7. Remove driveshaft to flange securing bolts, then pull speed sensor slightly out of housing.
8. Remove lower suspension strut mounting bolt.
9. Remove transverse link from wheel bearing housing.
10. Swivel wheel bearing housing downward, then remove drive axle.
11. Reverse procedure to install.

A8

Refer to "Rear Axle Shaft, Replace" in "Rear Axle & Suspension" section for driveshaft replacement procedures.

DRIVESHAFT SERVICE

For service procedures, refer to "Driveshaft Service" in the "Front Wheel Drive Axles" chapter.

REAR AXLE

REPLACE

A4 & S4 Quattro

1. Raise and support vehicle.
2. Remove rear tires.
3. Disconnect exhaust system at clamp and remove rear section of exhaust system. **Do not bend exhaust pipe flex coupling more than 10° or it could be damaged.**
4. If same rear axle will be installed again, disconnect parking brake cables at parking brake lever, underbody and at fuel tank. Leave parking brake cables in position at rear axle and at brake calipers.
5. Mark position of propeller shaft to rear final drive for installation reference.
6. Loosen mounting bolts of propeller shaft at rear final drive and identify any shims.
7. Tie propeller shaft to mounting on parking brake cable, then remove propeller shaft mounting bolts. **Do not allow propeller shaft to hang unsupported. Center joint and bearing will be damaged.**
8. Remove drive axles, **Fig. 3,** from rear final drive as outlined under "Axle Shaft, Replace."
9. Disconnect brake lines at fittings at lefthand rear below vehicle.
10. Disconnect wheel speed sensor wiring as required.
11. Install spring compressor tool No. VAG 1752/1 and holder tool No. VAG 1752/3 adaptor, or equivalent, with protective linings at second and next to last spring coils.
12. **On models equipped with headlight range control,** disconnect control linkage at rear axle.
13. **On all models,** remove bolts from suspension strut mounting bracket while coil spring is still compressed.
14. Rotate strut outward at top and relieve coil spring tension.
15. Repeat spring compression and strut removal procedures on opposite side of vehicle.
16. Remove exhaust system bracket from rear final drive unit.
17. Install support tools Nos. VAG 1383A and VAG 1359-2, or equivalents, under rear final drive. Secure final

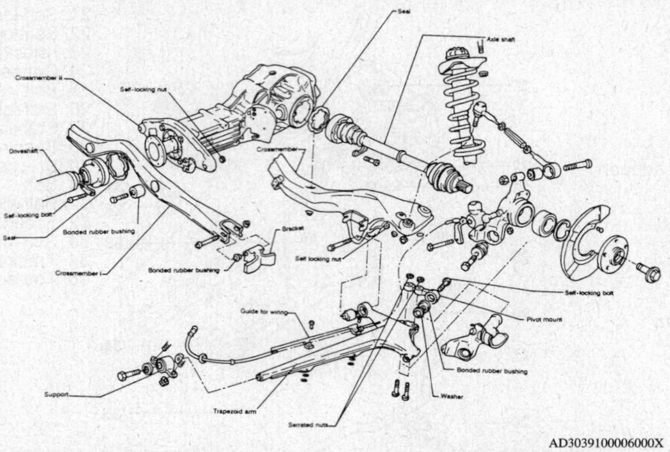

Fig. 4 Component view of rear axle. A6 Quattro & S6

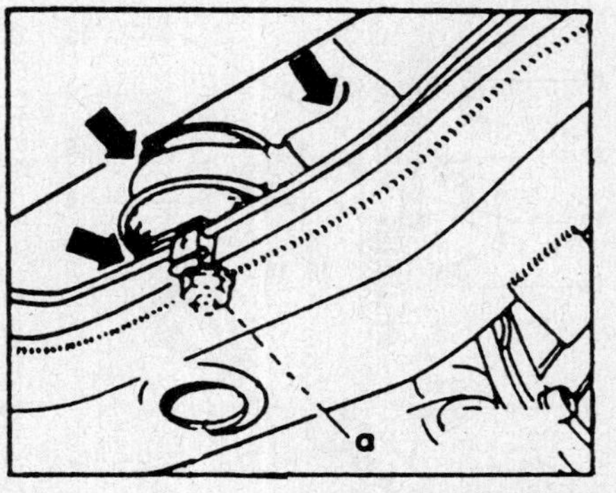

Fig. 5 Carrier bolt locations. A6 Quattro & S6

drive with strap.
18. Remove final drive front crossmember mounting bolts, then the final drive to rear crossmember mounting bolts.
19. Remove rear final drive unit.
20. Reverse procedure to install, noting the following:
    a. Install propeller shaft so markings are aligned.
    b. Replace gaskets at output and input flanges.
    c. Remove all thread locking compound residue from mounting bolts.
    d. **Replace all bolts, nuts and washers. Do not use old ones.**
    e. Tighten subframe mounting bolts in sequence: righthand rear, lefthand rear, righthand front and lefthand front.
    f. Bleed brake as outlined under "Brake System Bleed" in "Hydraulic Brake Systems" section.
    g. Inspect rear final drive oil level.
    h. Inspect wheel alignment and adjust as required.

A6 Quattro & S6

1. Remove underbody cover.
2. **On S6 models,** engage differential lock.
3. **On all models,** scribe propeller shaft and differential flange for alignment during reassembly, if not already marked.
4. Remove propeller shaft to differential flange attaching bolts, **Fig. 4,** then disconnect propeller shaft and tie out of way with suitable wire or rope. **Do not allow propeller shaft to hang unsupported. Center joint and bearing will be damaged.**
5. Remove cover from lefthand side axle shaft CV joint.
6. Remove righthand and lefthand axle shaft to differential flange attaching bolts, then disconnect axle shafts and tie out of way with suitable wire or rope.
7. Disconnect parking brake cables at calipers, then press cables out of rubber guides.
8. Disconnect parking brake cable in front, then remove cable retainer on lefthand side.
9. Loosen heat shield, then install transaxle jack tool No. VW 1383, or equivalent, to support axle.
10. Loosen nut (a), **Fig. 5,** then remove three bolts (arrows).
11. Remove bolts for crossmember, then disconnect exhaust pipe and lower axle slightly.
12. **On models equipped with differential lock,** proceed as follows:
    a. Note positioning of vacuum hoses for assembly reference.
    b. Disconnect vacuum hoses and pull out of bracket with rubber guides.
    c. Disconnect electrical connector for differential lock indicator lamp.
13. **On all models,** carefully lower the axle.
14. Reverse procedure to install, noting the following:
    a. Propeller shaft and differential flanges must be installed so painted marks or scribe marks are aligned.
    b. Adjust propeller shaft if required as outlined under "Propeller Shaft, Adjust."
    c. Tighten bolts and nuts to specifications.

A8

Refer to "Rear Axle Shaft, Replace" in "Rear Axle & Suspension" section for rear axle replacement procedures.

TT

1. Remove fuel tank righthand rear shield.
2. Disconnect exhaust system and position aside as required. **Do not bend flexible joint more than 10° or it could be damaged.**
3. Remove rear heat shield and exhaust bracket.
4. Mark alignment of rear driveshaft tube to final drive flange with paint.
5. Disconnect rear driveshaft tube with flexible coupling and vibration damper from rear final drive unit.
6. Separate righthand drive axle at flanges and position between upper and lower transverse link.
7. Separate lefthand drive axle at flanges and position between upper and lower transverse link.
8. Remove final drive to front mounting bracket bolts using driver tool No. T 10035, or equivalent.
9. Remove final drive mounting bracket to subframe bolts.
10. Support final drive by positioning transmission jack tool No. VAG 1383 A with universal mounting tool No. VAG 1359/2, or equivalents, under final drive only.
11. Remove rear subframe bolts on lefthand and righthand.
12. Remove final drive rear mounting bracket bolts on lefthand and righthand.
13. Disconnect Haldex coupling electrical connector.
14. Pull lefthand and righthand vent pipes out of underbody.
15. Lower final drive slightly using transmission jack.
16. Pull final drive away from rear subframe, holding rear end of driveshaft. Allow driveshaft to rest on heat shield. Keep driveshaft straight and always store it extended, **Fig. 6. Do not damage driveshaft flange seal during removal and installation. If this seal is damaged the driveshaft must be replaced.**
17. Lower final drive unit from vehicle, then remove mounting bracket if unit is to be replaced or mounted on repair stand.
18. Reverse procedure to install, noting the following:
    a. **Do not damage driveshaft flange seal during removal and installation, Fig. 6.** If this seal is damaged the driveshaft must be replaced.
    b. **Install new subframe to body bolts. Do not use old ones.**
    c. Tighten all bolts and nuts to specifications.

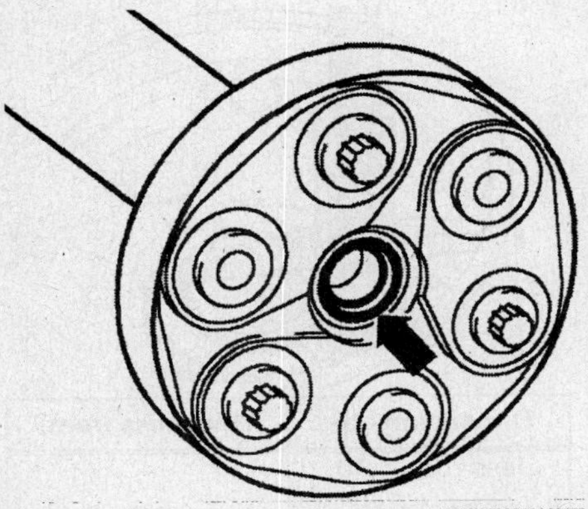

Fig. 6 Driveshaft flange seal. TT

d. Inspect final drive lubricant level and correct as required.

REAR AXLE SERVICE

Differential Input Flange Oil Seal & Bearing, Replace

A4 & S4 QUATTRO

1. Remove exhaust system, then the propeller shaft heat shield.
2. Mark position of propeller shaft to rear axle for installation reference.
3. Place a suitable oil pan below rear axle, then drain fluid.
4. Loosen mounting bolts of propeller shaft at rear axle.
5. Tie propeller shaft to mounting on parking brake cable, then remove propeller shaft mounting bolts.
6. Install support tool Nos. VAG 1383A and VAG 1359-2, or equivalents, under rear final drive.
7. Remove rear final drive front crossmember mounting bolts, then lower differential slightly.
8. Remove extension housing to rear differential mounting bolts, then remove flange shaft with extension housing.
9. Remove oil seal and bearing from extension housing as follows:
   a. Place extension housing in a suitable vise, then remove sleeve with a Kukko 3-armed extractor tool No. 45-2, or equivalent.
   b. Remove transaxle support from extension housing, then the locking ring.
   c. Thread a bolt into cap bore, then remove cap.
   d. Expand locking ring on flange shaft, then remove ring.
   e. Remove flange shaft using removal tool Nos. VW 771 and VW 771-15, or equivalent.
   f. Pry out seal using removal tool No. 2078, or equivalent.
   g. Remove locking ring, then the flange shaft bearing using removal tool Nos. VW 771 and VW 771-15, or equivalent.
   h. Press new bearing into extension housing using installation tool Nos. VW 402, VW 409 and VW 433, or equivalents.
   i. Install locking ring, then coat outer edge of seal with suitable transaxle fluid and drive seal into extension housing using installation tool No. 2062, or equivalent.
   j. Install flange shaft using installation tool Nos. VW 402, VW 409 and VW 433, or equivalents, then install locking ring. **Ensure locking ring seats in groove.**
   k. Install sleeve using installation tool Nos. VW 402, VW 409 and VW 433, or equivalents.
   l. Install cap and secure with locking ring.
   m. Install transaxle support, then remove extension housing from vise.
10. Reverse procedure to install, noting the following:
   a. Tighten all bolts and nuts to specifications.
   b. Inspect final drive lubricant level and correct as required.

A6 QUATTRO, A8 & S6

Removal

1. Place a suitable drain pan underneath differential and drain oil.
2. Scribe a mark on propeller shaft and differential flange prior to disassembly, then disconnect and tie up propeller shaft.
3. Remove cover.
4. Disconnect front parking brake cable.
5. Support differential with transaxle jack VAG 1383-A, or equivalent, then remove crossmember and carefully lower the differential.
6. Remove differential bracket from differential, then the differential cover bolts.
7. Remove differential cover using a suitable slide hammer.
8. Press sleeve off using a suitable press and holding fixture, then remove small circlip.
9. Press flange off, then pry out seal using prying tool No. VW 681, or equivalent.
10. Clean oil seal seat. **Do not use solvent.**
11. Remove large circlip, then press bearing out.

Installation

1. Press new bearing in, then install large circlip.
2. Install oil seal with washer 020 311 391 F or 016 311 391 P (.04 inch thickness) onto drift tool No. 2005, or equivalent.
3. Drive oil seal in until seated, then remove drift and washer.
4. Press flange in, then install small circlip.
5. Install sleeve by driving on with plastic hammer. Press on using punch tool No. VW 407, or equivalent if required.
6. Install cover with new O-ring, then the flange. Tighten differential cover bolts to specifications.
7. Install differential bracket.
8. Raise differential and install crossmember.
9. Connect front parking brake cable.
10. Install cover.
11. Install propeller shaft, then fill differential as required.
12. Install heat shields, then the main/rear muffler and retainers.
13. Tighten propeller shaft to flange bolts, differential to crossmember and bracket to differential bolts to specifications.

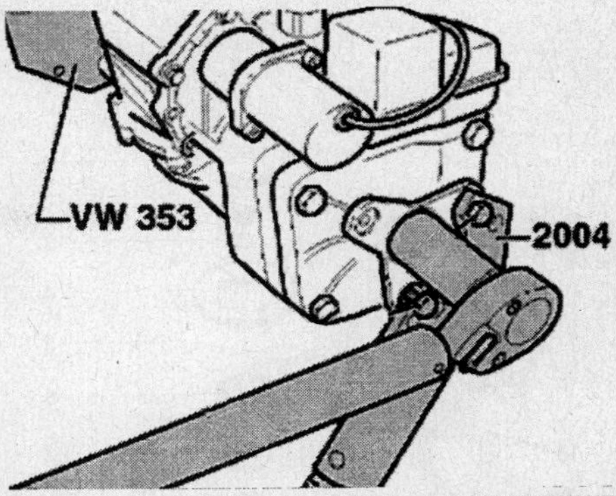

Fig. 7 Driveshaft flange nut removal. TT

TT

1. Remove rear axle as outlined under "Rear Axle, Replace."
2. Mount final drive unit to holding plate tool No. VW 309 and support plate tool No. VW 353, or equivalents.
3. Position a suitable drain pan under final drive.
4. Remove driveshaft flange hex nut using two M8 × 20 bolts and holder tool No. 2004, or equivalent, **Fig. 7.** Counter-hold with a suitable pipe. Discard hex nut.
5. Remove driveshaft flange. If flange is difficult to remove, use Kukko 3-arm puller tool No. 12-1, or equivalent.
6. Remove seal using removal tool No. VW 681, or equivalent.
7. Reverse procedure to install, noting the following:
   a. Drive new oil seal in until flush using seal installer tool No. T10019, or equivalent.
   b. Fill space between sealing lip and dust lip with multi-purpose grease part No. G052 128 A1, or equivalent.
   c. Install driveshaft flange.
   d. Apply locking fluid part No. D 000 600, or equivalent, to new hexagon nut and tighten to specifications.
   e. Tighten all bolts and nuts to specifications.

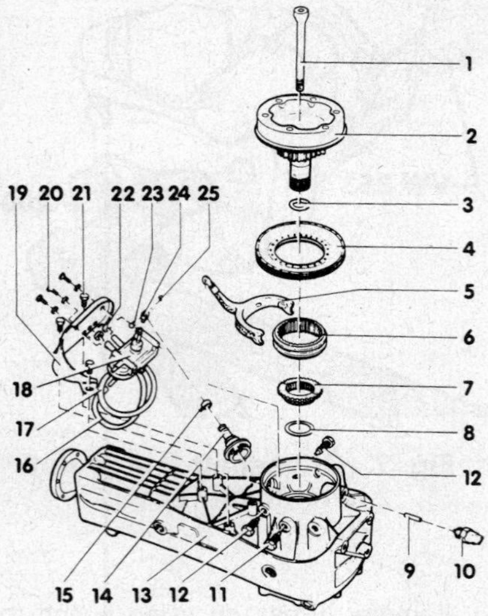

1. Bolt
2. Flanged Shaft
3. Shim
4. Oil Seal
5. Shift Fork
6. Sleeve
7. Locking Ring
8. Shim
9. Extension Pin
10. Switch
11. Shouldered Bolt (Shift Fork Stop)
12. Shouldered Bolt (Shift Fork Pivot)
13. Rear Differential
14. Boot
15. Vacuum Hose
16. Vacuum Hose
17. Actuator
18. Actuator Bracket
19. Screw
20. Screw
21. Grommet
22. Bolt
23. Clevis
24. Clevis Pin Lock

AD3039500027000X

Fig. 8 Exploded view of differential lock

f. Inspect fluid level and correct as required.

Differential Drive Flange Oil Seal, Replace

A4 QUATTRO

1. Remove exhaust system.
2. Remove drive axles from rear final drive as outlined under "Axle Shaft Replace."
3. Install two bolts into rear final drive flange shaft, then using a suitable lever to hold flange shaft in place, remove flange shaft mounting bolt.
4. Place a suitable drain pan below rear final drive, then remove flange shaft.
5. Pry out seal using removal tool No. VAG 1383, or equivalent.
6. Reverse procedure to install, noting the following:
   a. Coat outer edge of seal with suitable transaxle fluid, then install using installation tool No. 2062, or equivalent.
   b. Inspect rear final drive lubricant level and correct as required.

A6 QUATTRO, A8 & S6

RIGHTHAND SIDE

1. Remove righthand side underbody cover, then disconnect parking brake cable from righthand side caliper.
2. Disconnect and lower trapezoidal arm from crossmember, then press parking brake cable out of bracket.
3. Disconnect axle shaft from flange, then remove flange bolt.
4. Place an oil drain pan underneath and remove flange.
5. Pry out oil seal using a suitable prying tool, then drive in new oil seal to stop.
6. Install flange and axle shaft.
7. Connect trapezoidal arm, parking brake cable and underbody cover.
8. Tighten flange to differential bolts, driveshaft to flange M8 bolts, driveshaft to flange M10 bolts and trapezoidal arms to crossmember to specifications.

LEFTHAND SIDE

1. Remove lefthand side axle shaft protector, then disconnect parking brake cable from righthand side caliper.
2. Disconnect trapezoidal arm from crossmember and lower, then press parking brake cable out of bracket.
3. Disconnect axle shaft from flange, then loosen exhaust pipe.
4. Move exhaust pipe toward righthand side, trapezoidal arm to lefthand side and axle shaft downward.
5. Drain differential oil, then remove flange shaft bolt and flange. **Do not lose adjustment shim between flange shaft and differential gear.**
6. Pry out oil seal using prying tool No. 2078, or equivalent.
7. Thread in threaded rod of seal installation tool No. 3066, or equivalent, then install new oil seal onto installation tool.
8. Draw in new oil seal and tighten hex nut up to stop.
9. Install flange shaft and axle shaft, then fill differential with proper lubricant.
10. Tighten exhaust pipe, then connect trapezoidal arm and parking brake cable.
11. Install lefthand side axle shaft protector.
12. Tighten flange to differential bolts, axle shaft to flange M8 bolts, axle shaft to flange M10 bolts and trapezoidal arms to crossmember to specifications.

Differential Lock

DISASSEMBLY

1. Remove lefthand rear axle seal as outlined under "Differential Drive Flange Oil Seal, Replace."
2. Remove shift fork clevis pin, **Fig. 8,** at vacuum actuator.
3. Remove clamp from shift fork boot.
4. Remove vacuum actuator unit, holding bracket and boot.
5. Remove switch and extension pin.
6. Remove two shouldered shift fork pivot bolts and the stop bolt.
7. Guide shift fork and sleeve from case.
8. Remove locking ring and shim from differential carrier.

ASSEMBLY

1. Place locking ring onto differential carrier without shim. **Oil grooves of differential carrier and locking ring must be aligned.**
2. Measure dimension (b) from face of differential carrier to face of locking ring using a suitable depth gauge, **Fig. 9.**
3. Select a suitable shim. Install shim below locking ring.
4. Install shift fork, sleeve, pivot bolts and stop bolt.
5. Install vacuum actuator, boot and clamp. **Do not connect clevis.**
6. Install switch and extension pin.
7. Install drive flange seal as outlined under "Differential Drive Flange Oil Seal, Replace."
8. Install drive flange, then tighten center bolt to specifications.
9. Manually shift differential to stop in both direction.
10. Cycle actuator in both directions using a suitable vacuum pump.
11. Adjust actuator clevis so that shift fork will reach stop in both directions.
12. Connect actuator clevis to shift fork.

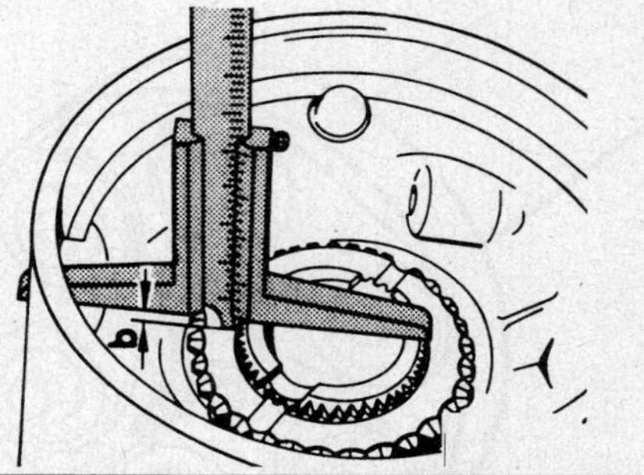

Dimension –b–	Thickness (mm)
less than 4.10	–
4.11 – 4.40	0.3
4.41 – 4.70	0.6
4.71 – 4.90	0.9

AD3039500026000X

Fig. 9 Lock ring shim measurement

PROPELLER SHAFT

REPLACE

A4 & S4 Quattro

Do not bend propeller shaft more than 25° or damage to universal joint may occur.

1. Remove center muffler, then the propeller shaft heat shield.
2. Mark position of propeller shaft to rear final drive for installation reference.
3. Loosen, but do not remove, mounting bolts of both propeller shaft flanges.
4. Install alignment fixture tool No. 3405, or equivalent, to propeller shaft. **Do not mount alignment fixture onto balancing plates.**
5. Loosen bolts of center bearing, then remove mounting bolts at flanges to transaxle and rear final drive.
6. Remove bolts of center bearing and identify shims.
7. Slide propeller shaft toward rear final drive, then remove driveshaft together with alignment fixture tool.

8. Reverse procedure to install, noting the following:
   a. Install propeller shaft so markings are aligned.
   b. Replace gaskets at output and input flanges.
   c. Remove and residue of old thread locking compound from mounting bolts.
   d. Adjust the propeller shaft as outlined under "Adjustments."

A6 Quattro, A8 & S6

Propeller shaft service must be performed with vehicle on a suitable dual support hoist.

1. Raise and support vehicle.
2. Loosen, but do not remove, propeller shaft bolts at transaxle, differential and center support.
3. Ensure white dot on rear propeller shaft flange is aligned with a black dot on differential flange. If not, scribe mark on propeller shaft and differential flanges prior to disassembly.
4. Install alignment tool No. 3139, or equivalent, **Fig. 10,** on driveshaft and tighten plastic nuts.
5. Remove propeller shaft bolts at transaxle and differential, then support propeller shaft and tool and remove center support bolts.
6. Remove propeller shaft together with alignment tool. **Do not bend propeller shaft. Store and transport together with tool.**
7. Reverse procedure to install, noting the following:
   a. Propeller shaft and differential flanges must be installed so painted marks or scribe marks are aligned.
   b. Always inspect alignment after installation.

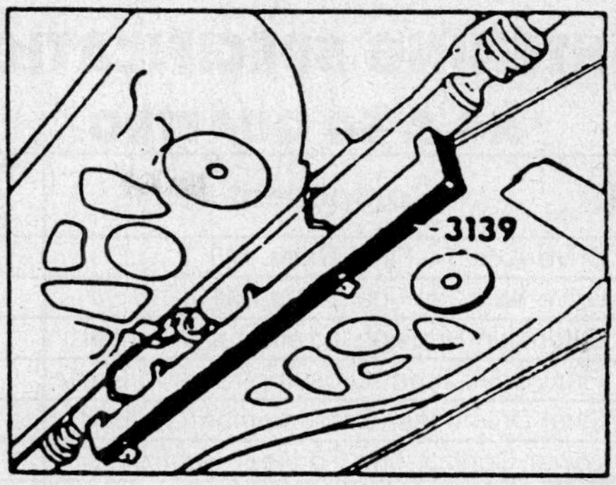

AD3039100009000X

Fig. 10 Propeller shaft alignment tool

   c. Adjust propeller shaft as outlined under "Adjustments."
   d. Tighten to specifications.

TT

1. Raise and support vehicle on a suitable twin post hoist.
2. Mark positions of all components in relation to each other for installation reference.
3. Remove center sound insulators.
4. Disconnect exhaust system as required.
5. Disconnect catalytic converters from front exhaust pipe. **Do not bend flexible joint more than 10° or it could be damaged.**
6. Remove fuel tank righthand rear shield.
7. Remove center heat shield and exhaust bracket.
8. Remove three driveshaft to transfer case coupling bolts using a suitable lever to brace triangular flange.
9. Remove pendulum support from subframe. Discard bolts.
10. Disconnect front driveshaft tube from rear driveshaft tube at flange.
11. Push front driveshaft tube forward and pivot it out of flange on rear driveshaft tube. Avoid excessive downward tilting.
12. Pull front driveshaft tube off centering pin. **Do not damage driveshaft flange seal during removal and installation, Fig. 6.** If this seal is damaged the driveshaft must be replaced. Ensure driveshaft is horizontal when taking it off guide pin.
13. Tilt front driveshaft tube down and remove from vehicle.
14. Disconnect rear driveshaft tube with flexible coupling and vibration damper from rear final drive unit.
15. Remove driveshaft center bearing mounting bolts, then the bearing. **Flexible coupling and vibration damper cannot be separated from one another.**
16. Reverse procedure to install, noting the following:
    a. Ensure all components are installed in same positions in relation to each other.
    b. Open side of heat shield should face transfer case.
    c. Ensure three projecting sleeves on transmission flange, rear final drive flange and driveshaft flanges engage in flex coupling mounting holes.
    d. Tighten center bearing to body bolts after driveshaft has been installed.
    e. Tighten all bolts and nuts to specifications.

TIGHTENING SPECIFICATIONS

A4 & S4 QUATTRO

Year	Component	Torque/Ft. Lbs.
1998–2001	Drive Axle To Final Drive, M8	41
	Drive Axle To Final Drive, M10	30
	Extension Housing To Rear Differential	26
	Final Drive Front Crossmember To Body	30
	Final Drive Rear Crossmember To Body	15
	Lower Control Arm To Rear Subframe	52①
	Lower Control Arm To Strut	52①
	Lower Control Arm To Knuckle	70
	Propeller Shaft Center Bearing To Body	17
	Propeller Shaft To Rear Final Drive	41
	Propeller Shaft To Transaxle	41
	Rear Crossmember To Rear Final Drive	41
	Rear Subframe Bushing Bolts	81①
	Stabilizer Bar Clamp To Rear Subframe	18
	Subframe To Body	81①
	Track Rod To Knuckle	37
	Track Rod To Subframe	66
	Transaxle Front Support To Final Drive	30
	Transaxle Support To Extension Housing	40
	Upper Control Arm To Strut	37①
	Upper Control Arm To Knuckle	37①

① — Plus an additional 90° (1/4) turn.

A6 QUATTRO & A8

Year	Component	Torque/Ft. Lbs.
1998–2001	Axle Nut	147①
	Axle Shaft To Drive Flange Bolts	59
	Axle To Crossmember Bolts	33
	Brake Caliper To Wheel Bearing Housing Bolts	48
	Center Support Bearing To Body Bolts	14
	Crossmember I To Crossmember II & Body Bolts	33
	Crossmember II To Axle Bolts	33
	Diagonal Arm To Axle Bolts	73
	Diagonal Arm To Frame Bolts	70
	Differential Cover Bolts	18
	Drive Flange To Differential	7①
	Driveshaft To Flange, 8 MM Bolt	33
	Driveshaft To Flange, 10 MM Bolt	60
	Driveshaft Nut	147①
	Exhaust System Support To Crossmember Bolt	40
	Hub Nut	147①
	Pivot Mount To Trapezoidal Arm Nut	81
	Propeller Shaft To Differential Flange Bolts	40
	Propeller Shaft To Transaxle Flange Bolts	40
	Rear Crossmember To Rear Suspension Bolts	37
	Strut Assembly Nut	22

Continued

A6 QUATTRO & A8—Continued

Year	Component	Torque/Ft. Lbs.
1998–2001	Strut Lower Mounting Bolts	66
	Strut To Axle Bolts	70
	Strut To Body Nuts	14
	Transverse Link To Subframe Nut	33
	Transverse Link To Wheel Bearing Housing Nut	148
	Trapezoidal Arm To Crossmember Nut	33
	Trapezoidal Arm To Subframe Nut	63
	Trapezoidal Arm To Support Bolt	125
	Trapezoidal Arm To Wheel Bearing Housing Bolt	125
	Wheel Lug Nuts	81

① — Plus an additional 90° (1/4) turn.

S6

Year	Component	Torque/Ft. Lbs.
1998–2001	Axle Shaft To Differential Drive Flange Bolts	59
	Axle Nut	147①
	Axle To Crossmember Bolts	33
	Brake Caliper To Wheel Bearing Housing Bolts	48
	Center Support Bearing To Body Bolts	14
	Crossmember I To Crossmember II & Body Bolts	33
	Crossmember II To Axle Bolts	33
	Driveshaft Nut	147①
	Drive Flange To Differential	7①
	Exhaust System Support To Crossmember Bolts	40
	Hub Nut	147①
	Pivot Mount To Trapezoidal Arm Nut	81
	Propeller Shaft To Differential Flange Bolts	40
	Propeller Shaft To Transaxle Flange Bolts	40
	Rear Crossmember To Rear Suspension Bolts	37
	Stabilizer Bar To Control Arm	88①
	Strut Assembly Nut	22
	Strut Lower Mounting Bolts	66
	Strut To Body Nuts	19
	Support To Frame Nuts	100
	Tie Rod To Strut	37
	Track Control Arm To Strut	48
	Transverse Link To Subframe Nut	33
	Transverse Link To Wheel Bearing Housing Nut	148
	Trapezoidal Arm To Crossmember Nut	33
	Trapezoidal Arm To Subframe Nut	63
	Trapezoidal Arm To Support Bolt	125
	Trapezoidal Arm To Wheel Bearing Housing Bolt	125
	Wheel Lug Nuts	81

① — Plus an additional 90° (1/4) turn.

TT

Year	Component	Torque/Ft. Lbs.
2000–01	Axle Mount Bracket Bushing Bolts	66①
	Axle Mount Bracket To Body Bolts	55①
	Backing Plate To Control Arm Bolts	89②
	Brake Caliper Mounting Bolts	48①
	Brake Rotor To Hub Phillips Head Screws	35②
	Driveshaft Center Bearing To Body Bolts	18
	Driveshaft Flange Nut	162
	Driveshaft To Flange	30
	Flex Coupling To Driveshaft	44
	Flex Coupling To Final Drive Unit	44
	Flex Coupling To Transfer Case	44
	Front Driveshaft Tube To Rear Tube	30
	Hub Nut (12-Point)	①③
	Lower Lateral Control Arm Self-Locking Nuts	52①④
	Pendulum Support Bolts	15①④
	Shock Absorber To Rear Axle Beam Bolts	44①
	Stop Buffer Nuts	89②
	Wheel Lug Nuts	89

① — Always use new nuts & bolts. Do not install old ones.
② — Inch lbs.
③ — Refer to “Rear Axle Shaft, Replace” in Chassis section for procedure.
④ — Plus an additional 90° (¼) turn.

Engine Rebuilding Specifications

INDEX

	Page No.
Camshaft	1-231
Crankshaft, Bearings & Rods	1-232
Cylinder Block	1-232
Cylinder Head, Valve Guide & Valve Seats	1-231
Pistons, Pins & Rings	1-232
Valves	1-231

CYLINDER HEAD, VALVE GUIDE & VALVE SEATS

All Measurements Given In Inches Unless Otherwise Specified.

Engine	Year	Cylinder Head		Valve Stem To Guide Clearance		Valve Seats		
		Warpage Limit	Minimum Height	Intake	Exhaust	Seat Angle Degrees	Seat Width Intake	Seat Width Exhaust
1.8L	1998–2001	.004	–	.031	.031	45	.059–.070	.070
2.7L	2000–01	.004	5.431	.031	.031	45	—	—
2.8L	1998–2001	.002	5.226	.039	.051	45	.079	.094
3.7L	1998–2001	.004	5.482	.039	.051	45	.059–.071	.059–.071
4.2L	1998–2001	.004	5.482	.039	.051	45	.059–.071	.059–.071

VALVES

All Measurements Given In Inches Unless Otherwise Specified.

Engine	Year	Valve Stem Diameter		Valve Installed Height①		Valve Face Angle, Degrees②	Valve Clearance	
		Intake	Exhaust	Intake	Exhaust		Intake	Exhaust
1.8L	1998–2001	.2339–.2350	.2339–.2343	–	–	45	③	③
2.7L	2000–01	.2324–.2328	.2317–.2321	—	—	45	③	③
2.8L (2 V)	1998–2001	.2339–.2350	.2339–.2343	1.331	1.343	45	③	③
2.8L (5V)	1998–2001	.2346–.2350	.2338–.2342	1.331	1.343	45	③	③
3.7L	1998–2001	–	–	1.433	1.433	45	③	③
4.2L	1998–2001	–	–	1.417	1.429	45	③	③

① — Measured from top of valve stem to top of cylinder head.

② — Do not reface valves. Only lapping is permitted.

③ — Equipped with hydraulic valve lash adjusters. No adjustment is required.

CAMSHAFT

All Measurements Given In Inches Unless Otherwise Specified.

Engine	Year	Camshaft Endplay	Camshaft Max Runout
1.8L	1998–2001	.0080	.0004
2.8L	1998–2001	.0020–.0059①	.0004
3.7L	1998–2001	.0059	–
4.2L	1998–2001	.0059	–

① — Wear limit,. 0079 inch.

CRANKSHAFT, BEARINGS & RODS

All Measurements Given In Inches Unless Otherwise Specified.

Engine	Year	Crankshaft			Bearing Clearance		Connecting Rods	
		Standard Journal Diameter		Endplay	Main Bearings	Connecting Rod Bearings	Piston Pin Bore Diameter	Side Clearance
		Main Bearing	Crank Pin					
1.8L	1998–2001	2.1245–2.1260	1.8803–1.8820	.0030–.0090	.0008–.0016④	.0004–.0020	—	—
2.7L	2000–01	—	—	.0035–.0097	.0007–.0017	.0005–.0024	—	—
2.8L	1998–99	2.5574–2.5599	2.1244–2.1347	.0027–.0091①	.0007–.0018②	.0006–.0024③	–	–
3.7L	1998–2001	–	–	–	–	–	–	–
4.2L	1998–2001	–	–	–	–	–	–	–

① — Wear limit. 0098 inch.
② — Wear limit. 0039 inch.
③ — Wear limit. 0047 inch.
④ — Wear limit. 0060 inch.

PISTONS, PINS & RINGS

All Measurements Given In Inches Unless Otherwise Specified.

Engine	Year	Piston Diameter, Std.	Piston Ring End Gap		Piston Ring Side Clearance	
			Comp.	Oil	Comp.	Oil
1.8L	1998–2001	3.1180	.0078–.0157	.0098–.0197	③	.0011–.0023④
2.7L	2000–01	3.2470	⑤	.0098–.0195⑥	.0007–.0031②	.0007–.0031②
2.8L	1998–2001	3.2472	①	.010–.020⑥	.0008–.0031②	.0008–.0031②
3.7L	1998–2001	–	–	–	–	–
4.2L	1998–2001	–	–	–	–	–

① — Piston ring No. 1,. 014–.020 inch, wear limit. 039 inch; piston ring No. 2,. 020–.028 inch, wear limit. 043 inch.
② — Wear limit. 004 inch.
③ — Upper compression ring,. 0023–.0035 inch, wear limit. 0078 inch; lower compression ring,. 0019–.0315 inch, wear limit. 0078 inch.
④ — Wear limit. 0059 inch.
⑤ — Upper compression ring,. 0137–.0195 inch, wear limit. 0390 inch; lower compression ring,. 0195–.0273 inch, wear limit. 0055 inch.
⑥ — Wear limit. 0312 inch.

CYLINDER BLOCK

All Measurements Given In Inches Unless Otherwise Specified.

Engine	Year	Cylinder Bore Diameter, Std.	Cylinder Bore Out Of Round Max.
1.8L	1998–2001	3.1894	—
2.7L	2000–01	3.2178	—
2.8L	1998–2001	3.2484	.0031
3.7L	1998–2001	–	–
4.2L	1998–2001	–	–

BMW

INDEX OF SERVICE OPERATIONS

Page No.

ACTIVE SUSPENSION SYSTEMS 2-240
AIR BAG SYSTEM PRECAUTIONS 0-12
AIR QUALITY STANDARDS 0-23
BRAKES
- Anti-Lock Brakes 2-184
- Disc Brakes 2-175
- Drum Brakes 2-178
- Hydraulic Brakes 2-179
- Power Brake Units 2-181

CLUTCH & MANUAL TRANSMISSION
- Adjustments 2-89
- Application Chart 2-89
- Clutch, Replace 2-90
- Hydraulic System Service 2-89
- Precautions 2-89
- Technical Service Bulletins 2-97
- Tightening Specifications 2-98
- Transmission, Replace 2-90

COMPUTER RELEARN PROCEDURES 0-10
DRIVE AXLES 2-231
ELECTRICAL
- Air Bags 2-155
- Air Conditioning 2-135
- Alternators 2-142
- Alternator, Replace 2-15
- Blower Motor, Replace 2-21
- Coil Pack, Replace 2-16
- Cooling Fans 2-139
- Cruise Controls 2-143
- Dash Panel 2-164
- Distributor, Replace 2-16
- Evaporator Core, Replace 2-23
- Fuel Pump Relay Location 2-12
- Fuse Panel & Flasher Location 2-12
- Headlamp Switch, Replace 2-17
- Heater Core, Replace 2-22
- Ignition Lock, Replace 2-17
- Ignition Switch, Replace 2-17
- Instrument Cluster, Replace 2-18
- Multi-function Switch, Replace 2-18
- Passive Restraints 2-155
- Precautions 2-12
- Radio, Replace 2-19
- Relay Center Location 2-12
- Speed Controls 2-143
- Starter Motors 2-141
- Starter, Replace 2-13
- Steering Columns 2-167
- Steering Wheel, Replace 2-18
- Stop Light Switch, Replace 2-18
- Technical Service Bulletins 2-24
- Turn Signal Switch, Replace 2-18
- Wiper Motor, Replace 2-19
- Wiper Switch, Replace 2-21
- Wiper Systems 2-149

ELECTRICAL SYMBOL IDENTIFICATION 0-33
FRONT SUSPENSION & STEERING
- Ball Joint, Replace 2-117

Page No.

- Ball Joint Inspection 2-117
- Coil Spring, Replace 2-117
- Control Arm, Replace 2-118
- Crossmember, Replace 2-120
- Description 2-116
- Hub & Bearing, Replace 2-116
- Power Steering 2-171
- Power Steering Gear, Replace 2-122
- Power Steering Pump, Replace 2-123
- Power Steering System Bleed 2-123
- Precautions 2-116
- Stabilizer Bar, Replace 2-120
- Steering Knuckle, Replace 2-119
- Strut, Replace 2-117
- Technical Service Bulletins 2-124
- Tension Strut, Replace 2-122
- Tie Rod, Replace 2-122
- Tightening Specifications 2-124
- Wheel Bearing, Adjust 2-116

FRONT WHEEL DRIVE
- Axle Shaft, Replace 2-128
- Differential Carrier, Replace 2-128
- Tightening Specifications 2-129

REAR AXLE & SUSPENSION
- Coil Spring, Replace 2-105
- Control Arm, Replace 2-106
- Description 2-99
- Hub & Bearing, Replace 2-103
- Integral Link, Replace 2-108
- Precautions 2-99
- Propeller Shaft, Replace 2-102
- Rear Axle, Replace 2-99
- Rear Halfshaft, Replace 2-101
- Shock Absorber, Replace 2-104
- Stabilizer Bar, Replace 2-108
- Strut, Replace 2-104
- Technical Service Bulletins 2-108
- Tightening Specifications 2-110
- Traction Strut, Replace 2-107
- Trailing Arm, Replace 2-107

SERVICE REMINDER & WARNING LAMP RESET PROCEDURES 0-14
SPECIFICATIONS
- Engine Identification 2-2
- Fluid Capacities & Cooling System Data 2-8
- Front Wheel Alignment Specifications 2-6
- General Engine Specifications 2-4
- Lubricant Data 2-10
- Rear Wheel Alignment Specifications 2-7
- Tune Up Specifications 2-5

TRANSFER CASE
- Tightening Specifications 2-115
- Transfer Case, Replace 2-114

Page No.

TRACTION CONTROL SYSTEMS 2-239
VEHICLE IDENTIFICATION 0-3
VEHICLE LIFT POINTS 0-24
VEHICLE MAINTENANCE SCHEDULES 0-45
WHEEL ALIGNMENT
- Front Wheel Alignment 2-130
- Preliminary Inspection 2-130
- Rear Wheel Alignment 2-130
- Vehicle Ride Height 2-130
- Wheel Alignment Specifications 2-6

WIRE COLOR CODE IDENTIFICATION 0-33
1.9L (M44) FOUR-CYLINDER ENGINE
- Camshaft, Replace 2-28
- Compression Pressure 2-25
- Cooling System Bleed 2-29
- Crankshaft Damper, Replace 2-27
- Crankshaft Rear Oil Seal, Replace 2-28
- Cylinder Head, Replace 2-26
- Engine Rebuilding Specifications 2-241
- Engine, Replace 2-25
- Exhaust Manifold, Replace 2-26
- Front Cover, Replace 2-27
- Front Cover Seal, Replace 2-27
- Fuel Filter, Replace 2-29
- Fuel Pump, Replace 2-29
- Hydraulic Lifters, Replace 2-27
- Intake Manifold, Replace 2-26
- Main & Rod Bearings 2-28
- Oil Pan, Replace 2-29
- Oil Pump, Replace 2-29
- Piston & Rod Assembly 2-28
- Precautions 2-25
- Radiator, Replace 2-29
- Rocker Arms, Replace 2-27
- Serpentine Drive Belt 2-29
- Technical Service Bulletins 2-30
- Thermostat, Replace 2-29
- Tightening Specifications 2-31
- Timing Case, Replace 2-28
- Timing Chain, Replace 2-27
- Timing Chain Tensioner, Replace 2-28
- Valve Adjustment 2-27
- Valve Cover, Replace 2-27
- Water Pump, Replace 2-29

2.5L (M52 & M54), 2.8L (M52), 3.0L (M54) & 3.2L (S52 & S54) IN-LINE SIX CYLINDER ENGINES
- Camshaft, Replace 2-43
- Compression Pressure 2-33
- Cooling System Bleed 2-50
- Crankshaft Damper, Replace 2-42
- Crankshaft Rear Oil Seal, Replace 2-48
- Cylinder Head, Replace 2-38

Page No.

Engine Rebuilding Specifications 2-241
Engine, Replace 2-33
Exhaust Manifold, Replace 2-37
Front Cover, Replace 2-43
Front Cover Seal, Replace 2-43
Fuel Filter, Replace 2-52
Fuel Pump, Replace 2-51
Hydraulic Lifters, Replace 2-42
Intake Manifold, Replace 2-34
Main & Rod Bearings 2-48
Oil Pan, Replace 2-49
Oil Pump, Replace 2-50
Piston & Rod Assembly 2-48
Precautions 2-33
Radiator, Replace 2-50
Serpentine Drive Belt 2-50
Technical Service Bulletins 2-52
Thermostat, Replace 2-50
Tightening Specifications 2-53
Timing Chain, Replace 2-43
Timing Chain Tensioner, Replace 2-43
Valve Adjustment 2-42
Valve Cover, Replace 2-41
Variable Camshaft Timing (VANOS) Adjustment Unit, Replace 2-46
Water Pump, Replace 2-50

4.4L (M62) & 5.0L (S62) V8 ENGINES

Camshaft, Replace 2-68
Compression Pressure 2-55
Cooling System Bleed 2-78
Crankshaft Damper, Replace 2-64
Crankshaft Rear Oil Seal, Replace 2-76
Cylinder Head, Replace 2-59
Engine Rebuilding Specifications 2-241
Engine, Replace 2-56
Exhaust Manifold, Replace 2-58
Front Cover, Replace 2-65
Front Cover Seal, Replace 2-66
Fuel Filter, Replace 2-79
Fuel Pump, Replace 2-79
Intake Manifold, Replace 2-57
Main & Rod Bearings 2-76
Oil Pan, Replace 2-76
Oil Pump, Replace 2-77
Precautions 2-55
Radiator, Replace 2-78
Serpentine Drive Belt 2-78
Technical Service Bulletins 2-79
Thermostat, Replace 2-78
Tightening Specifications 2-80
Timing Chain, Replace 2-66
Timing Chain Tensioner, Replace 2-68
Valve Adjustment 2-64
Valve Cover, Replace 2-64
Variable Camshaft Timing (VANOS) Adjustment Unit, Replace 2-72
Water Pump, Replace 2-78

5.4L (M73) V12 ENGINE

Camshaft, Replace 2-85
Compression Pressure 2-82
Cooling System Bleed 2-86
Crankshaft Damper, Replace 2-85
Crankshaft Rear Oil Seal, Replace 2-86
Cylinder Head, Replace 2-84
Engine Rebuilding Specifications 2-241
Engine, Replace 2-82
Exhaust Manifold, Replace 2-83
Front Cover, Replace 2-85
Front Cover Seal, Replace 2-85
Fuel Filter, Replace 2-87
Fuel Pump, Replace 2-87
Intake Manifold, Replace 2-83
Main & Rod Bearings 2-86
Oil Pan, Replace 2-86
Oil Pump, Replace 2-86
Precautions 2-82
Radiator, Replace 2-87
Rocker Arms, Replace 2-84
Serpentine Drive Belt 2-86
Technical Service Bulletins 2-87
Thermostat, Replace 2-86
Tightening Specifications 2-88
Timing Chain, Replace 2-85
Timing Chain Tensioner, Replace 2-85
Valve Adjustment 2-84
Valve Cover, Replace 2-84
Water Pump, Replace 2-87

Specifications

ENGINE IDENTIFICATION

Model	Chassis Series	Engine Series	Liter
1998			
M3	E36	S52	3.2L
Z3 M Coupe & Z3 M Roadster	E36/7	S52	3.2L
Z3 1.9	E36/7	M44	1.9L
Z3 2.8	E36/7	M52	2.8L
318i	E36	M44	1.9L
318ti	E36/5	M44	1.9L
323i, is	E36	M52	2.5L
328i, is	E36	M52	2.8L
528i	E39	M52	2.8L
540i	E39	M62	4.4L
740i, iL	E38	M62	4.4L
750iL	E38	M73	5.4L
1999			
M3	E36	S52	3.2L
Z3 M Coupe & Z3 M Roadster	E36/7	S52	3.2L
Z3 2.3	E36/7	M52 TU	2.5L
Z3 2.8	E36/7	M52 TU	2.8L
318ti	E36/5	M44	1.9L
323i, is Coupe & Convertible	E36	M52	2.5L

Continued

ENGINE IDENTIFICATION—Continued

Model	Chassis Series	Engine Series	Liter
1999			
323i Sedan	E46	M52 TU	2.5L
328i, is Coupe & Convertible	E36	M52	2.8L
328i Sedan	E46	M52 TU	2.8L
528i	E39	M52 TU	2.8L
540i	E39	M62	4.4L
740i, iL	E38	M62	4.4L
750iL	E38	M73	5.4L
2000			
M5	E39	S62	5.0L
X5	E53	M62	4.4L
Z3 M Coupe & Z3 M Roadster	E36/7	S52	3.2L
Z3 2.3	E36/7	M52 TU	2.5L
Z3 2.8	E36/7	M52 TU	2.8L
323Ci, i, xi	E46	M52 TU	2.5L
328Ci, i, xi	E46	M52 TU	2.8L
528i	E39	M52 TU	2.8L
540i	E39	M62	4.4L
740i, iL	E38	M62	4.4L
750iL	E38	M73	5.4L
2001			
M3	E46	S54	3.2L
M5	E39	S62	5.0L
X5 3.0i	E53	M54	3.0L
X5 4.4i	E53	M62	4.4L
Z3 M Coupe & Z3 M Roadster	E36/7	M54	3.2L
Z3 2.5i	E36/7	M54	2.5L
Z3 3.0i	E36/7	M54	3.0L
325Ci, i, xi	E46	M54	2.5L
330Ci, i, xi	E46	M54	3.0L
525i Sedan	E39	M54	2.5L
525i Sport Wagon	E39	M54	2.5L
530i	E39	M54	3.0L
540i	E39	M62	4.4L
740i, iL	E38	M62	4.4L
750iL	E38	M73	5.4L

GENERAL ENGINE SPECIFICATIONS

Engine, Liter	Model	Engine Series	Fuel Injection	Bore & Stroke, Inches	Compression Ratio	Maximum Brake, HP @ RPM	Maximum Torque, Ft. Lbs. @ RPM	Oil Pressure
1998								
1.9	Z3 1.9, 318i, ti	M44	MFI	3.35 x 3.29	10.0	138 @ 6000	133 @ 4300	③
2.5	323i, is	M52	MFI	3.31 x 2.95	10.5	168 @ 5500	181 @ 3950	①
2.8L	Z3	M52	MFI	3.31 x 3.31	10.0	189 @ 5300	203 @ 3950	①
	328i, is & 528i	M52	MFI	3.31 x 3.31	10.2	190 @ 5300	206 @ 2950	①
3.2L	M3 & Z3 M Coupe & Z3 M Roadster	S52	MFI	3.40 x 3.53	10.5	240 @ 6000	236 @ 3800	①
4.4L	540i & 740i, iL	M62	MFI	3.62 x 3.26	10.0	282 @ 5800	310 @ 3900	②
5.4L	750iL	M73	MFI	3.35 x 3.11	10.0	322 @ 5000	361 @ 3900	③
1999								
1.9L	318ti	M44	MFI	3.35 x 3.29	10.0	138 @ 6000	133 @ 4300	③
2.5L	Z3 2.3 & 323i Sedan	M52 TU	MFI	3.31 x 2.95	10.5	170 @ 5500	181 @ 3950	①
	323i, is Couple & Convertible	M52	MFI	3.31 x 2.95	10.5	170 @ 5500	181 @ 3950	①
2.8L	Z3 Coupe, Z3 2.8, 328i Sedan & 528i	M52 TU	MFI	3.31 x 3.31	10.2	193 @ 5500	206 @ 2950	①
	328Ci, i Coupe & Convertible	M52	MFI	3.31 x 3.31	10.2	193 @ 5500	206 @ 2950	①
3.2L	M3 & Z3 M Coupe & Z3 M Roadster	S52	MFI	3.40 x 3.53	10.5	240 @ 6000	236 @ 3800	①
4.4L	540i & 740i, iL	M62	MFI	3.62 x 3.26	10.0	282 @ 5800	324 @ 3600	②
5.4L	750iL	M73	MFI	3.35 x 3.11	10.0	326 @ 5000	361 @ 3900	③
2000								
2.5L	Z3 2.3, 323Ci/i	M52 TU	MFI	3.31 x 2.95	10.5	170 @ 5000	181 @ 3500	—
2.8L	Z3 2.8, 328Ci/i & 528i	M52 TU	MFI	3.31 x 3.31	10.2	193 @ 5500	206 @ 3500	—
3.2L	Z3 M Coupe & Z3 M Roadster	S52	MFI	3.40 x 3.53	10.5	240 @ 6000	236 @ 3800	—
4.4L	X5, 540i & 740i, iL	M62	MFI	3.62 x 3.26	10.0	282 @ 5800	324 @ 3600	—
5.0L	M5	S62	MFI	3.70 x 3.50	11.0	400 @ 600	369 @ 3800	—
5.4L	750iL	M73	MFI	3.35 x 3.11	10.0	326 @ 5000	361 @ 3900	—
2001								
2.5L	Z3 2.5i, 325Ci, i, xi & 525i	M54	MFI	3.31 x 2.95	10.5	184 @ 6000	175 @ 3500	—
3.0L	Z3 Coupe, Z3 3.0i, X5 3.0i, 330Ci, i, xi & 530i	M54	MFI	3.31 x 3.53	10.2	225 @ 5900	214 @ 3500	—
3.2L	M3	S54	MFI	3.43 x 3.58	—	333 @ 7900	262	—
	Z3 M Coupe & Z3 M Roadster	M54	MFI	3.43 x 3.58	—	315 @ 7400	251 @ 4900	—
4.4L	X5 4.4i, 540i & 740i, iL	M62	MFI	3.62 x 3.26	10.0	282 @ 5800	324 @ 3600	—
5.0L	M5	M54	MFI					—
5.4L	750iL	M73	MFI	3.35 x 3.11	10.0	326 @ 5000	361 @ 3900	—

① — Minimum @ idle speed 7.25 psi. Regulated pressure, 58.01 psi.

② — Minimum @ idle speed 7.25 psi. Regulated pressure, 65.27 psi.

③ — Minimum @ idle speed 7.25 psi. Regulated pressure, 59.47–65.27 psi.

TUNE UP SPECIFICATIONS

Model	Engine	Series	Spark Plug Gap Inch	Ignition Timing	Curb Idle Speed②	Fuel Pump Pressure, psi.①	Valve Lash, Inch		Air Conditioning	
				Firing Order	Timing BTDC		Intake	Exhaust	Off	On
1998										
M3 & Z3 M Coupe & Z3 M Roadster	3.2L	S52	.024	⑩	⑧	⑧	⑧	51–58	⑨	⑨
Z3 1.9 & 318i, is & ti	1.9L	M44	.028⑪	⑦	③	750–850③	③	51–58	⑨	⑨
Z3 2.8 & 328i, is	2.8L	M52	.028⑪	⑩	⑧	650–750⑧	⑧	51–58	⑨	⑨
323i, is	2.5L	M52	.028⑪	⑩	⑧	650–750⑧	⑧	51–58	⑨	⑨
528i	2.8L	M52	.028⑪	⑩	⑧	700–800N⑧	730–830N⑧	51	⑨	⑨
540i & 740i, iL	4.4L	M62	.028⑪	⑤	③	530–630N③	650–750N③	51	⑨	⑨
750iL	5.4L	M73	.028⑪	⑥	③	550–650N③	650–750N③	51	⑨	⑨
1999										
M3 & Z3 M Coupe & Z3 M Roadster	3.2L	S52	.024	⑩	⑧	⑧	⑧	51–58	⑨	⑨
Z3 Coupe	2.8L	M52 TU	.028⑪	⑩	⑧	700–800⑧	730–830⑧	51–58	⑨	⑨
Z3 2.3	2.5L	M52	.028⑪	⑩	⑧	700–800N⑧	730–830N⑧	51–58	⑨	⑨
Z3 2.8	2.8L	M52	.028⑪	⑩	⑧	700–800N⑧	730–830N⑧	51–58	⑨	⑨
318ti	1.9L	M44	.028⑪	⑦	③	750–850③	750–850③	51–58	⑨	⑨
323i, is Coupe & Convertible	2.5L	M52	.028⑪	⑩	⑧	650–750⑧	⑧	51–58	⑨	⑨
323i Sedan	2.5L	M52 TU	④	⑩	⑧	700–800⑧	730–830⑧	51	⑨	⑨
328i, is Coupe & Convertible	2.8L	M52	.028⑪	⑩	⑧	650–750⑧	⑧	51–58	⑨	⑨
328i Sedan	2.8L	M52 TU	④	⑩	⑧	700–800⑧	730–830⑧	51	⑨	⑨
528i	2.8L	M52 TU	.028⑪	⑩	⑧	700–800N⑧	730–830N⑧	51	⑨	⑨
540i	4.4L	M62	.028⑪	⑤	③	700–800N③	730–830N③	51	⑨	⑨
740i, iL	4.4L	M62	.028⑪	⑤	③	530–630N③	650–750N③	51	⑨	⑨
750iL	5.4L	M73	.028⑪	⑥	③	550–650N③	650–750N③	51	⑨	⑨
2000										
M5	5.0L	S62	.028⑪	⑤	⑧	⑧	⑧	73	⑨	⑨
X5	4.4L	M62	④	⑤	③	③	③	51–58	⑨	⑨
Z3 M Coupe & Z3 M Roadster	3.2L	S52	.024	⑩	⑧	⑧	⑧	51–58	⑨	⑨
Z3 Coupe	2.8L	M52 TU	.028⑪	⑩	⑧	700–800⑧	730–830⑧	51–58	⑨	⑨
Z3 2.3	2.5L	M52	.028⑪	⑩	⑧	700–800N⑧	730–830N⑧	51–58	⑨	⑨
Z3 2.8	2.8L	M52	.028⑪	⑩	⑧	700–800N⑧	730–830N⑧	51–58	⑨	⑨
323Ci, i	2.5L	M52 TU	④	⑩	⑧	700–800⑧	730–830⑧	51	⑨	⑨
328Ci, i	2.8L	M52 TU	④	⑩	⑧	700–800⑧	730–830⑧	51	⑨	⑨
528i	2.8L	M52 TU	.028⑪	⑩	⑧	700–800N⑧	730–830N⑧	51	⑨	⑨
540i	4.4L	M62	.028⑪	⑤	③	700–800N③	730–830N③	51	⑨	⑨
740i, iL	4.4L	M62	.028⑪	⑤	③	530–630N③	650–750N③	51	⑨	⑨
750iL	5.4L	M73	.028⑪	⑥	③	550–650N③	650–750N③	51	⑨	⑨

Continued

TUNE UP SPECIFICATIONS—Continued

Model	Engine	Series	Spark Plug Gap Inch	Ignition Timing	Curb Idle Speed②	Fuel Pump Pressure, psi.①	Valve Lash, Inch		Air Conditioning	
				Firing Order	Timing BTDC		Intake	Exhaust	Off	On
2001										
M3	3.2L	S54	④	⑩	⑧	⑧	⑧	73	⑨	⑨
M5	5.0L	S62	.028⑪	⑤	⑧	⑧	⑧	73	⑨	⑨
X5 3.0i	3.0L	M54	④	⑩	⑧	⑧	⑧	51–58	⑨	⑨
X5 4.4i	4.4L	M62	④	⑤	③	③	③	51–58	⑨	⑨
Z3 M Coupe & Z3 M Roadster	3.2L	S54	④	⑩	⑧	⑧	⑧	73	⑨	⑨
Z3 2.5i	2.5L	M54	.028⑪	⑩	⑧	⑧	⑧	51–58	⑨	⑨
Z3 3.0i	3.0L	M54	.028⑪	⑩	⑧	⑧	⑧	51–58	⑨	⑨
325Ci, i & xi	2.5L	M52 TU	④	⑩	⑧	⑧	⑧	51	⑨	⑨
330Ci, i & xi	2.8L	M52 TU	④	⑩	⑧	700–800⑧	730–830⑧	51	⑨	⑨
525i	5.4L	M54	.028⑪	⑩	⑧	⑧	⑧	51	⑨	⑨
530i	3.0L	M54	.028⑪	⑩	⑧	⑧	⑧	51	⑨	⑨
540i	4.4L	M62	.028⑪	⑤	③	700–800N③	730–830N③	51	⑨	⑨
740i, iL	4.4L	M62	.028⑪	⑤	③	530–630N③	650–750N③	51	⑨	⑨
750iL	5.4	M73	.028⑪	⑥	③	550–650N③	650–750N③	51	⑨	⑨

BTDC — Before Top Dead Center.
C — Cold.
N — Neutral.
① — With engine idling.
② — When adjusting idle speed, set parking brake & chock drive wheels.
③ — Controlled by Bosch Motronic system.
④ — Models w/four-mass electrodes cannot be adjusted.
⑤ — Firing order, 1-5-4-8-6-3-7-2.
⑥ — Cylinder numbering front to rear, right bank, 1-2-3-4-5-6; left bank 7-8-9-10-11-12. Firing order, 1-7-5-11-3-9-6-12-2-8-4-10.
⑦ — Firing order, 1-3-4-2.
⑧ — Controlled by Siemens MS system.
⑨ — Equipped w/hydraulic valve lash adjusters.
⑩ — Firing order, 1-5-3-6-2-4.
⑪ — W/dual mass electrode, 0.035 inch. Models w/three- and four-mass electrodes cannot be adjusted.

FRONT WHEEL ALIGNMENT SPECIFICATIONS

Model	Year	Suspension	Caster Angle, Deg.①		Camber Angle, Deg.		Total Toe-In, Degrees	Max. Wheel Lock, Deg.	
			10° Wheel Lock	20° Wheel Lock	Limits	Desired		Inside	Outside
M3	1998–99	Standard	+7 7/12	+7 5/6	–1 4/15 to 4/15	–23/30	1/3③	38	32
		Sports	+6 29/30	+7 1/5	-2 1/2 to -1 1/2	-2	1/6③	38	32
	2001	All	+7 5/12	+7 2/3	-1 1/3 to -2/3	-1	4/15④	40 9/10	33 53/60
M5	2000–01	All	+6 9/20	+6 49/60	–1 to 0	-1/2	1/6⑤	41 1/2	32
X5	2000–01	All	+6 5/6	+7 1/10	-37/60 to +13/60	-1/5	3/10⑤	37 1/10	37 1/10
Z3 Coupe	1999–2000	All	+3 5/6	+3 57/60	-1 7/20 to -7/20	-51/60	3/10③	41	34
Z3 M Coupe & Z3 M Roadster	1998–2001	All	+7 7/12	+7 5/6	-1 4/15 to -4/15	-23/30	1/3③	—	—
Z3 1.9	1998	Standard	+3 41/60	+3 4/5	-1 7/30 to -7/30	-11/15	3/10③	41	34
		Low-Slung Sports	+3 4/5	+3 14/15	–1 17/30 to –17/30	–1 1/15	3/10③	40	33
Z3 2.3	1999–2000	Standard	+3 41/60	+3 4/5	-7/30 to 1 7/30	-11/15	3/10③	41	34
		Low-Slung Sports	+3 4/5	+3 14/15	–1 17/30 to -17/30	–1 1/15	3/10③	41	34
Z3 2.5	2001	Standard	+3 41/60	+3 4/5	-7/30 to 1 7/30	-11/15	3/10③	41	34
		Low-Slung Sports	+3 4/5	+3 14/15	–1 17/30 to -17/30	–1 1/15	3/10③	41	34

Continued

FRONT WHEEL ALIGNMENT SPECIFICATIONS—Continued

Model	Year	Suspension	Caster Angle, Deg.①		Camber Angle, Deg.		Total Toe-In, Degrees	Max. Wheel Lock, Deg.	
			10° Wheel Lock	20° Wheel Lock	Limits	Desired		Inside	Outside
Z3 2.8	1998–2000	Standard	+3 41/60	+3 4/5	-7/30 to 1 7/30	-11/15	3/10③	41	34
		Low-Slung Sports	+3 4/5	+3 14/15	−1 17/30 to -17/30	−1 1/15	3/10③	41	34
Z3 3.0	2001	Standard	+3 41/60	+3 4/5	-7/30 to 1 7/30	-11/15	3/10③	41	34
		Low-Slung Sports	+3 4/5	+3 14/15	−1 17/30 to -17/30	−1 1/15	3/10③	41	34
318i	1998	Standard	+3 11/15	+3 13/15	−1 to 0	-1/2	3/10②	44	36
		Low-Slung Sports	+3 5/6	+3 57/60	−1 7/20 to −7/20	−51/60	3/10②	44	36
318ti	1998–99	Standard	+3 11/15	+3 13/15	−1 to 0	−1/2	3/10②	44	36
		Low-Slung Sports	+3 5/6	+3 57/60	−1 7/20 to −7/20	−51/60	3/10②	44	36
323i Convertible, 328i Convertible, 323is & 328is	1998–99	Standard	+3 11/15	+3 13/15	−1 to 0	-1/2	3/10②	44	36
		Low-Slung Sports	+3 5/6	+3 57/60	−1 7/20 to −7/20	−51/60	3/10②	44	36
323i & 328i	1999–2000	Standard	+5 13/30	+5 37/60	-2/3 to 0	-1/3	7/30②	43 3/5	35 3/5
		Low-Slung Sports	+5 3/5	+5 47/60	-1/20 to -23/60	-43/60	7/30②	43 3/5	35 3/5
325xi & 330xi	2001	All	+5 9/20	+5 37/60	0 to -2/3	-1/3	7/30②	39	35 1/2
525i & 530i	2001	Standard	+6 7/15	+6 7/10	−43/60 to +17/60	−13/60	1/12⑤	42	33 1/2
		Low-Slung Sports	+6 41/60	+6 11/12	−1 1/10 to −1/10	−3/5	1/12⑤	41 1/2	33
528i	1998–2000	Standard	+6 7/15	+6 7/10	−43/60 to +17/60	−13/60	1/12⑤	42	33 1/2
		Low-Slung Sports	+6 41/60	+6 11/12	−1 1/10 to −1/10	−3/5	1/12⑤	41 1/2	33
540i	1998–2000	Standard	+6 3/10	+6 3/5	−43/60 to +17/60	-13/60	7/30⑤	42	32 3/10
		Low-Slung Sports	+6 17/30	+6 5/6	−1 7/60 to -7/60	-37/60	7/30	42	32 4/5
740i, iL & 750iL	1998–2001	Standard	+5 29/30	+6 1/10	−43/60 to +17/60	−13/60	7/30⑤	43	33
		Low-Slung Sports	+6 1/5	+6 1/3	-1 1/10 to -1/10	-3/5	7/30⑤	43	33

① — Plus or minus 1/2 degree.
② — Plus or minus 2/15 degree.
③ — Plus or minus 1/12 degree.
④ — Plus or minus 7/60 degree.
⑤ — Plus or minus 1/6 degree.

REAR WHEEL ALIGNMENT SPECIFICATIONS

Model	Year	Suspension	Camber Deg.		Total Toe-In, Degree	
			Limits	Desired	Limits	Desired
M3	1998–99	All	-1 11/12 to -1 7/12	-1 3/4	1/5 to 5/12	1/3
	2001	All	-2 to -1 1/2	-1 3/4	4/15 to 7/15	11/30
M5	2000–01	All	⑦	⑧	⑨	1/6
X5	2000–01	All	-2 1/6 to -1 1/2	-1 5/6	2/15 to 7/15	3/10
Z3 Coupe	1999–2000	All	-3 1/60 to -2 1/60	-2 31/60	5/12 to 51/60	19/30
Z3 M Coupe & Z3 M Roadster	1998–2001	All	-2 1/4 to -1/4	-1 3/4	17/60 to 43/60	-1/2
Z3 1.9	1998	Standard	-2 5/6 to -1 5/6	-2 1/3	7/20 to 47/60	17/30
		Low-Slung Sports	-3 1/3 to -2 1/3	-2 5/6	31/60 to 57/60	11/15

Continued

REAR WHEEL ALIGNMENT SPECIFICATIONS—Continued

Model	Year	Suspension	Camber Deg.		Total Toe-In, Degree	
			Limits	Desired	Limits	Desired
Z3 2.3	1999–2000	Standard	-2 5/6 to -1 5/6	-2 1/3	7/60 to 11/20	1/3
		Low-Slung Sports	-3 1/3 to -2 1/3	-2 5/6	17/60 to 43/60	1/2
Z3 2.5i	2001	Standard	-2 5/6 to -1 5/6	-2 1/3	7/60 to 11/20	1/3
		Low-Slung Sports	-3 1/3 to -2 1/3	-2 5/6	17/60 to 43/60	1/2
Z3 2.8	1998–2000	Standard	-2 5/6 to -1 5/6	-2 1/3	7/60 to 11/20	1/3
		Low-Slung Sports	-3 1/3 to -2 1/3	-2 5/6	17/60 to 43/60	1/2
Z3 3.0i	2001	Standard	-2 5/6 to -1 5/6	-2 1/3	7/60 to 11/20	1/3
		Low-Slung Sports	-3 1/3 to -2 1/3	-2 5/6	17/60 to 43/60	1/2
318i	1998	Standard	–1 11/12 to –1 5/12	–1 2/3	3/10 to 1/2	6/15
		Low-Slung Sports	–2 1/4 to –1 3/4	–2	3/10 to 1/2	6/15
318ti	1998–99	Standard	-2 1/2 to -1 1/2	-2	17/60 to 43/60	1/2
		Low-Slung Sports	-3 to -2	-2 1/2	23/60 to 49/60	3/5
323i Convertible, 328i Convertible, 323is & 328is	1998–99	Standard	–1 11/12 to –1 5/12	–1 2/3	3/10 to 1/2	6/15
		Low-Slung Sports	–2 1/4 to –1 3/4	–2	3/10 to 1/2	6/15
323Ci & 328Ci	2000	Standard	-1 3/4 -1 1/4	-1 1/2	1/10 to 11/30	4/15
		Low-Slung Sports	-2 19/20 to -1 49/60	-2 1/15	1/10 to 11/30 ;	4/15
323i & 328i	1999–2000	Standard	-1 3/4 -1 1/4	-1 1/2	1/10 to 11/30	4/15
		Low-Slung Sports	-2 19/20 to -1 49/60	-2 1/15	1/10 to 11/30	4/15
325Ci, 325i, 330Ci & 330i	2001	Standard	-1 3/4 -1 1/4	-1 1/2	1/10 to 11/30	4/15
		Low-Slung Sports	-2 19/20 to -1 49/60	-2 1/15	1/10 to 11/30	4/15
325xi & 330xi	2001	All	-1 1/2 to -1	-1 1/4	1/6 to 11/30	4/15
528i	1998–2000	All	-2 1/6 to -1 1/2	-1 5/6	1/10 to 13/30	4/15
525i & 530i	2001	All	-2 1/6 to -1 1/2	-1 5/6	1/10 to 13/30	4/15
540i	1998–2001	Standard	(1)	(2)	(3)	(4)
		Low-Slung Sports	(6)	(2)	(6)	(4)
740 iL & 750iL	1998–2001	Standard	(5)	(1)	2/15 to 7/15	3/10

(1) — Check, -2 1/2° to -1 5/6°; Adjust, -2 3/20° to -1 59/60°.
(2) — Check, -2 1/6°; Adjust, -2 1/15°.
(3) — Check, +1/10° to +13/30°; Adjust, +3/10° to +13/30°.
(4) — Check, +4/15°; Adjust +11/30°.
(5) — Check, -1 5/6° to -1 1/6°; Adjust, -1 8/15° to -1 11/30°.
(6) — Check, +1/15° to +3/10°; Adjust, +3/10° to +13/30°.
(7) — Check, -2 1/2° to -1 7/12°; Adjust, -1 9/10° to -1 11/15°.
(8) — Check, -1 5/6°; Adjust -1 49/60°.
(9) — Check, 0 to +1/3°; Adjust, +1/30° to +3/10°.

FLUID CAPACITIES & COOLING SYSTEM DATA

Model	Cooling System Capacity Qts.		Radiator Cap Relief Pressure Lbs.	Coolant Type	Thermo. Opening Temp. °F	Fuel Tank Gals.	Engine Oil Refill Qts.(2)	Transmission Oil(1)		Rear Axle Oil Pts.
	Less A/C	With A/C						Auto. Trans. Qts.	Man. Trans. Pts.	
1998										
M3	—	11.4	17.6–31.9	EG	198	16.4	6.7	—	2.5	(4)
Z3 M Coupe & Z3 M Roadster	—	11.4	17.6–31.9	EG	198	13.5	6.7	—	2.5	(4)
Z3 1.9L	—	7.1	17.6–31.9	EG	203	13.5	5.3	9.3	2.1	1.9
Z3 2.8L	—	10.6	17.6–31.9	EG	198	13.5	6.9	9.3	2.5	1.9
318i, is	—	7.1	17.6–31.9	EG	203	17	5.2	9.3	2.1	(4)

Continued

FLUID CAPACITIES & COOLING SYSTEM DATA—Continued

Model	Cooling System Capacity Qts.		Radiator Cap Relief Pressure Lbs.	Coolant Type	Thermo. Opening Temp. °F	Fuel Tank Gals.	Engine Oil Refill Qts.②	Transmission Oil①		Rear Axle Oil Pts.
	Less A/C	With A/C						Auto. Trans. Qts.	Man. Trans. Pts.	
1998										
318ti	6.9	7.1	17.6–31.9	EG	203	14.5	5.3	9.3	2.1	1.9
323 & 328	—	10.6	17.6–31.9	EG	198	17	6.9	9.3	2.5	④
528i	—	11.1	17.6–31.9	EG	198	18.5	6.9	9.3	2.5	3.4
540i	—	14.3	17.6–31.9	EG	185	18.5	7.9	10.3	3.6	3.4
740i, iL	—	13.2	17.6–31.9	EG	185	22.5	7.9	10.3	—	⑤
750iL	—	13.7	17.6–31.9	EG	203	25.1	8.5	13.8	—	⑤
1999										
M3	—	11.4	17.6–31.9	EG	198	16.4	6.7	—	2.5	④
Z3 M Coupe & Z3 M Roadster	—	11.4	17.6–31.9	EG	198	13.5	6.7	—	2.5	④
Z3 2.3	—	10.6	17.6–31.9	EG	207	13.5	6.9	9.3	2.5	1.9
Z3 2.8	—	10.6	17.6–31.9	EG	207	13.5	6.9	9.3	2.5	1.9
318ti	6.9	7.1	17.6–31.9	EG	203	14.5	5.3	9.3	2.1	1.9
323 Coupe & Convertible	—	10.6	17.6–31.9	EG	198	17	6.9	9.3	2.5	④
323 Sedan	—	8.9	17.6–31.9	EG	207	16.6	6.9	9.5	2.1	②
328 Coupe & Convertible	—	10.6	17.6–31.9	EG	198	17	6.9	9.3	2.5	④
328 Sedan	—	8.9	17.6–31.9	EG	207	16.6	6.9	9.5	2.1	②
528i	—	11.1	17.6–31.9	EG	207	18.5	6.9	9.3	2.5	3.4
540i	—	14.3	17.6–31.9	EG	185	18.5	7.9	10.3	3.6	3.4
740i, iL	—	13.2	17.6–31.9	EG	185	22.5	7.9	10.3	—	⑤
750iL	—	13.7	17.6–31.9	EG	203	25.1	8.5	13.8	—	⑤
2000										
M5	—	14.3	17.6–31.9	EG	174	18.5	6.9	3.6	5.6	3.4
X5	—	13.2	17.6–31.9	EG	185	24.6	8.5	10.3③	—	⑦⑧
Z3 M Coupe & Z3 M Roadster	—	11.4	14.5	EG	198	13.5	6.7	—	2.5	④
Z3 2.3	—	10.6	17.6–31.9	EG	207	13.5	6.9	9.3	2.5	1.9
Z3 2.8	—	10.6	17.6–31.9	EG	207	13.5	6.9	9.3	2.5	1.9
328 Sedan	—	8.9	17.6–31.9	EG	207	16.6	6.9	9.5	2.1	②
323i, Ci & 328i, Ci	—	8.9	17.6–31.9	EG	207	16.6	6.9	9.5	2.1	②
528i	—	11.1	17.6–31.9	EG	207	18.5	6.9	9.3	2.5	3.4
540i	—	14.3	17.6–31.9	EG	185	18.5	7.9	10.3	3.6	3.4
740i, iL	—	13.2	17.6–31.9	EG	185	22.5	7.9	10.3	—	⑤
750iL	—	13.7	17.6–31.9	EG	203	25.1	8.5	13.8	—	⑤
2001										
M3	—	10.6	17.6–31.9	EG	176	16.6	5.8	—	—	②
M5	—	14.3	17.6–31.9	EG	174	18.5	6.9	3.6	5.6	3.4
X5 3.0L	—	10.0	17.6–31.9	EG	207	24.6	7.9	9.5③	2.5⑨	⑦⑧
X5 4.4L	—	13.2	17.6–31.9	EG	185	24.6	8.5	10.3③	—	⑦⑧
Z3 M Coupe & Z3 M Roadster	—	—	—	EG	—	—	—	—	—	—
Z3 2.5	—	10.6	17.6–31.9	EG	207	13.5	6.9	9.3	2.1	1.9
Z3 3.0	—	10.6	17.6–31.9	EG	207	13.5	6.9	9.3	2.5	1.9
325Ci, i	—	8.9	17.6–31.9	EG	207	16.6	6.9	9.5	2.1	②
325xi	—	8.9	17.6–31.9	EG	207	16.6	6.9	9.5⑥	2.5⑥	②⑦
330Ci, i	—	8.9	17.6–31.9	EG	207	16.6	6.9	9.5	2.1	②
330xi	—	8.9	17.6–31.9	EG	207	16.6	6.9	9.5⑥	2.5⑥	②⑦
525i	—	11.1	17.6–31.9	EG	207	18.5	6.9	8.2	2.5	3.4

Continued

FLUID CAPACITIES & COOLING SYSTEM DATA—Continued

Model	Cooling System Capacity Qts.		Radiator Cap Relief Pressure Lbs.	Coolant Type	Thermo. Opening Temp. °F	Fuel Tank Gals.	Engine Oil Refill Qts.②	Transmission Oil①		Rear Axle Oil Pts.
	Less A/C	With A/C						Auto. Trans. Qts.	Man. Trans. Pts.	
2001										
530i	—	11.1	17.6–31.9	EG	207	18.5	6.9	8.2	2.5	3.4
540i	—	14.3	17.6–31.9	EG	185	18.5	7.9	10.3	3.6	3.4
740i, iL	—	13.2	17.6–31.9	EG	185	22.5	7.9	10.3	—	⑤
750iL	—	13.7	17.6–31.9	EG	203	25.1	8.5	13.8	—	⑤

EG — Ethylene Glycol
① — Life-time fill.
② — 168mm, 1.9 pts.; 188mm, 3.4 pts.; 210mm, 2.5 pts.
③ — NV 125 transfer case, 1.057 pts.
④ — Four-screw side cover, 2.3 pts.; six-screw side cover, 3.6 pts.; eight-screw side cover, 2.7 pts.
⑤ — Six-screw side cover, 3.0 pts.; eight-screw side cover, 3.4 pts.
⑥ — NV 124 transfer case, 0.338 pt.
⑦ — Front axle, 1.3 pts.
⑧ — 168mm, 1.9 pts.; 188mm, 210mm & 220mm, 2.5 pts.; 215mm, 3.4 pts.

LUBRICANT DATA

Model	Year	Lubricant Type						
		Transmission		Hydraulic Clutch Fluid	Transfer Case	Drive Axle	Power Steering	Brake System
		Manual	Automatic					
All	All	MTF-LT-1	②	DOT 4	MTF-LT-1	SAF-XO	①	DOT 4

① — Power Steering Fluid Dexron III; Except models w/self leveling suspension use Pentosin CHF 11S.
Models w/hydroboost use SLF BMW Part No. 81 22 9 407 549 or equivalent.
② — THMR1, Dexron III; 5L40E, Texaco ETL 8072B; 5HP-19, 5HP-24 & 5HP-30, Esso LT 71141.

Electrical

NOTE: On Air Bag Equipped Models, Refer To "Air Bag System Precautions" Located In The Front Of This Manual For System Disarming & Arming Procedures.

NOTE: Refer To "Computer Relearn Procedures" Located In The Front Of This Manual When Battery Power To The Computer Has Been Interrupted.

NOTE: Prior To Performing Any Service Operations Listed In This Section, Consult The "Technical Service Bulletins" Section For Related Information.

INDEX

Page No.

Air Bags 2-155
Air Conditioning 2-135
Alternators 2-142
Alternator, Replace 2-15
M3 2-15
M5 2-15
X5 2-15
Z3 1.9 2-15
318 2-15
323, 325, 328, 330, 525, 528 & 530 2-15
540 & 740 2-15
750 2-15
Blower Motor, Replace 2-21
M3 2-21
M5, 525, 528, 530 & 540 2-22
X5 2-22
Z3 2-22
318 2-22
323, 325, 328 & 330 2-22
740 & 750 2-22
Coil Pack, Replace 2-16
M3 2-16
M5 2-16
X5 2-16
Z3 2-16
318 2-16
323, 325, 328, 330, 525 & 530 2-16
540 & 740 2-17
750 2-17
Cooling Fans 2-139
Cruise Controls 2-143
Distributor, Replace 2-16
750 2-16
Evaporator Core, Replace 2-23
M3 & 318 2-23
M5, 525, 528, 530 & 540 2-23
X5 2-24
Z3 2-24
323, 325, 328 & 330 2-24
740 & 750 2-24
Fuel Pump Relay Location 2-12
M3 2-12
Z3, 525, 528, 530, 540 & 740 2-12
318 2-12
323, 325, 328 & 330 2-12
323Ci, 325, 328Ci & 330 & 2000 323i & 328i & 1999 323i & 328i Sedans 2-12
750 2-12
Fuse Panel & Flasher Location 2-12
M3 2-12
M5, 525, 528, 530, 540, 740 & 750 2-12

Page No.

Z3 & 318 2-12
323, 325, 328 & 330 2-12
Headlamp Switch, Replace 2-17
M3 & 318 2-17
M5, 525, 528, 530 & 540 2-17
X5 2-18
Z3 2-18
323, 325, 328 & 330 2-18
740 & 750 2-18
Heater Core, Replace 2-22
M3 & 318 2-22
M5, 525, 528, 530 & 540 2-22
X5 2-23
Z3 2-23
323, 325, 328 & 330 2-23
740 & 750 2-23
Ignition Lock, Replace 2-17
M3 2-17
M5, X5, 528, 525, 530, 540, 740 & 750 2-17
Z3 & 318 2-17
323, 325, 328 & 330 2-17
323, 325, 328 & 330 2-17
Ignition Switch, Replace 2-17
M3, Z3, 318, 323, 325, 328 & 330 2-17
M5, 528, 530, 540, 740 & 750 2-17
X5 2-17
Instrument Cluster, Replace 2-18
M3 2-18
M5, 525, 528, 530 & 540 2-19
X5, 740 & 750 2-19
Z3 2-19
318 2-19
323, 325, 328 & 330 2-19
Multi-function Switch, Replace 2-18
M3 2-18
M5, 525, 528, 530, 540, 740 & 750 2-18
X5 2-18
Z3 & 318 2-18
323, 325, 328 & 330 2-18
Passive Restraints 2-155
Precautions 2-12
Air Bag Systems 2-12
Battery Ground Cable 2-12
Radio, Replace 2-19
M3 2-19
M5, 525, 528, 530 & 540 2-19
X5 2-19
Z3 & 318 2-19
323, 325, 328 & 330 2-19
740 & 750 2-19

Page No.

Relay Center Location 2-12
M3 2-12
Z3 2-12
318 2-12
323, 325, 328 & 330 2-12
525, 528, 530 & 540 2-12
740 & 750 2-12
Speed Controls 2-143
Starter Motors 2-141
Starter, Replace 2-13
M3 2-13
1998–99 2-13
2001 2-13
M5 2-13
X5 2-13
3.0i 2-13
4.4i 2-13
Z3 2-13
1.9 2-13
2.3 2-13
2.5 & 3.0 2-14
2.8 2-14
M 2-13
318 2-14
323 & 328 2-14
1998 2-14
1999 2-14
2000 2-14
325 & 300 2-14
525 & 530 2-14
528 2-14
1998 2-14
1999–2000 2-14
540 & 740 2-14
750 2-14
Steering Columns 2-167
Steering Wheel, Replace 2-18
Stop Light Switch, Replace 2-18
M3, M5, X5, Z3, 318, 525, 528, 530, 540, 740 & 750 2-18
323, 325, 328 & 330 2-18
Technical Service Bulletins 2-24
Steering Wheel Squeak 2-24
Turn Signal Switch, Replace 2-18
Wiper Motor, Replace 2-19
M3 & 318 2-19
M5, 525, 528, 530 & 540 2-20
X5 2-20
Z3 2-20
323 & 328 2-21
740 & 750 2-21
Wiper Switch, Replace 2-21
Wiper Systems 2-149

PRECAUTIONS

AIR BAG SYSTEMS

Refer to "Air Bag System Precautions" in the front of this manual for system disarming and arming procedures.

BATTERY GROUND CABLE

Prior to service, disconnect battery ground cable and isolate as required.

FUSE PANEL & FLASHER LOCATION

M3

1998-99

The fuse panel (power distribution panel) is located on the rear lefthand side of the engine compartment.

The flasher relay is located in the fuse panel.

2001

The fuse panel (power distribution panel) is located in the glove compartment.

The flasher relay is located in the fuse panel.

Z3 & 318

The fuse panel (power distribution panel) is located on the rear lefthand side of the engine compartment.

The flasher relay is located in the fuse panel.

323, 325, 328 & 330

323is & 328is & 1998-99 328i & 1998 323i & 1999 323i & 328i Convertibles

The fuse panel (power distribution panel) is located on the rear lefthand side of the engine compartment.

The flasher relay is located in the fuse panel.

323Ci, 325, 328Ci & 330 & 2000 323i & 328i & 1999 323i & 328i Sedans

The fuse panel (power distribution panel) is located in the glove compartment.

The flasher relay is located in the fuse panel.

M5, 525, 528, 530, 540, 740 & 750

There are two fuse panel (power distribution panel) locations. The front fuse panel is located on the rear lefthand side of the engine compartment. The rear fuse panel is located below the lefthand side of the rear seat.

The flasher relay is located in the front fuse panel.

FUEL PUMP RELAY LOCATION

M3

1998-99

The fuel pump relay is in the fuse panel, on the rear lefthand side of the engine compartment.

2001

The fuel pump relay is in the fuse panel, behind the glove compartment on the rear lefthand side of the engine compartment.

Z3, 525, 528, 530, 540 & 740

The fuel pump relay is located in the E box, located on the righthand rear of the engine compartment.

318

The fuel pump relay is in the fuse panel, on the rear lefthand side of the engine compartment.

323, 325, 328 & 330

323is & 328is & 1998-99 328i & 1998 323i & 1999 323i & 328i Convertibles

The fuel pump relay is in the fuse panel, on the rear lefthand side of the engine compartment.

323CI, 325, 328CI & 330 & 2000 323I & 328I & 1999 323I & 328I SEDANS

The fuel pump relay is in the fuse panel, behind the glove compartment on the rear lefthand side of the engine compartment.

750

Fuel pump relay Number One for cylinders 1 through 6 and Number Two for cylinders 7 through 12 are located in auxiliary relay box No. 2, located in front of righthand front shock tower.

RELAY CENTER LOCATION

M3

1998-99

The power distribution/fuse/relay panel is located on the rear lefthand side of the engine compartment.

The under dash relay panel is located under the lefthand side of the instrument panel.

The lefthand splice panel/relay panel is located under the lefthand side of the instrument panel.

The righthand splice panel/relay panel is located under the righthand side of the instrument panel.

2001

The power distribution panel is located in the glove compartment.

The E box is located on the lefthand rear of the engine compartment.

Z3

The power distribution/fuse/relay panel is located on the rear lefthand side of the engine compartment.

The E box is located on the righthand rear of the engine compartment.

The under dash relay panel is located under the lefthand side of the instrument panel.

318

The power distribution/fuse/relay panel is located on the rear lefthand side of the engine compartment.

The under dash relay panel is located under the lefthand side of the instrument panel.

The lefthand splice panel/relay panel is located under the lefthand side of the instrument panel.

The righthand splice panel/relay panel is located under the righthand side of the instrument panel.

323, 325, 328 & 330

323is & 328is & 1998-99 328i & 1998 323i & 1999 323i & 328i Convertibles

The power distribution/fuse/relay panel is located on the rear lefthand side of the engine compartment.

The under dash relay panel is located under the lefthand side of the instrument panel.

The lefthand splice panel/relay panel is located under the lefthand side of the instrument panel.

The righthand splice panel/relay panel is located under the righthand side of the instrument panel.

323Ci, 325, 328Ci & 330 & 2000 323i & 328i & 1999 323i & 328i Sedans

The power distribution panel is located in the glove compartment.

The E box is located on the lefthand rear of the engine compartment.

525, 528, 530 & 540

The front power distribution box/relay panel is located on the rear lefthand side of the engine compartment.

The rear power distribution box/relay panel is located under the lefthand side of the rear seat.

The auxiliary relay panel is located on the lefthand side of the engine compartment.

740 & 750

The front power distribution box/relay panel is located on the rear lefthand side of the engine compartment.

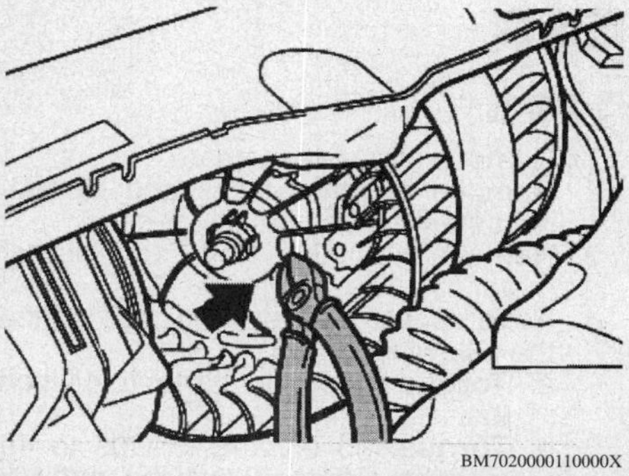

Fig. 1 Blower motor wheel brace cutting. 1998–99 M3

The rear power distribution box/relay panel is located under the lefthand side of the rear seat.

The lefthand auxiliary relay panel is located on the lefthand side of the engine compartment, forward of the shock tower.

The righthand auxiliary relay panel is located on the righthand side of the engine compartment, forward of the shock tower.

STARTER

REPLACE

M3

1998–99

1. Raise and support vehicle.
2. Remove mounting bolts and reinforcing brace.
3. Remove fuel lines' cover.
4. Disconnect fuel lines from back-up lamp bracket.
5. Remove mounting nuts and starter motor electrical connectors.
6. Remove starter motor mounting bolts.
7. Remove mounting nut, support and starter motor.
8. Reverse procedure to install, noting the following:
   a. **Torque** support to starter to 44 inch lbs.
   b. **Torque** support to crankcase to 35 ft. lbs.
   c. **Torque** starter motor mounting bolts to 35 ft. lbs.
   d. **Torque** M5 electrical leads to 49 inch lbs., M6 to 58 inch lbs. and M8 to 11 ft. lbs.

2001

1. Raise and support vehicle.
2. Remove mounting bolts and front axle support reinforcement plate.
3. Disconnect starter motor electrical connectors.
4. Remove mounting bolts and starter motor.
5. Reverse procedure to install, noting the following.
   a. **Torque** front axle support reinforcement plate mounting bolts to 44 ft. lbs., then tighten an additional 90° and final tighten an additional 15°.
   b. **Torque** support to starter to 44 inch lbs.
   c. **Torque** support to crankcase to 35 ft. lbs.
   d. **Torque** starter motor mounting bolts to 35 ft. lbs.
   e. **Torque** M5 electrical leads to 49 inch lbs., M6 to 58 inch lbs. and M8 to 11 ft. lbs.

M5

1. Raise and support vehicle.
2. Remove front and rear lower engine covers.
3. Remove mounting screws and heat shield.
4. Disconnect starter motor electrical connectors.
5. Remove mounting bolts and starter motor.
6. Reverse procedure to install, noting the following:
   a. **Torque** starter motor mounting bolts to 35 ft. lbs.
   b. **Torque** M5 electrical leads to 49 inch lbs., M6 to 58 inch lbs. and M8 to 11 ft. lbs.

X5

3.0i

1. Raise and support vehicle. **Do not remove reinforcement plate.**
2. Remove mounting nuts and disconnect starter motor battery positive electrical connectors.
3. Remove mounting bolts and starter motor.
4. Turn starter and disconnect electrical connectors.
5. Reverse procedure to install, noting the following:
   a. **Torque** starter motor mounting bolts to 35 ft. lbs.
   b. **Torque** M5 electrical leads to 49 inch lbs., M6 to 58 inch lbs. and M8 to 11 ft. lbs.

4.4i

1. Raise and support vehicle.
2. Remove mounting bolts and reinforcement plate.
3. Remove mounting nuts and disconnect starter motor electrical connectors.
4. Remove mounting bolts and starter motor.
5. Reverse procedure to install, noting the following.
   a. **Torque** front axle support reinforcement plate mounting bolts to 41 ft. lbs., then tighten an additional 90° and final tighten an additional 15°.
   b. **Torque** support to starter to 44 inch lbs.
   c. **Torque** M5 electrical leads to 49 inch lbs., M6 to 58 inch lbs. and M8 to 11 ft. lbs.

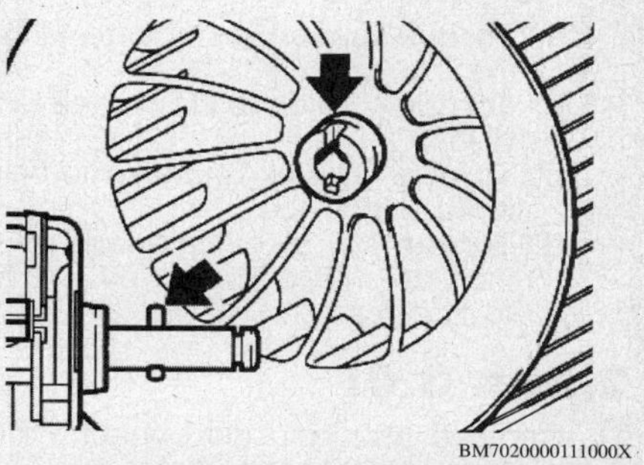

Fig. 2 Blower motor installation. 1998–99 M3

Z3

M

1998–2000

Refer to "1998–99" under "M3."

2001

Refer to "2001" under "M3."

1.9

1. Disconnect starter electrical connectors.
2. Loosen starter motor upper mounting bolt from under hood.
3. Remove oil dipstick guide tube and remove upper mounting bolt.
4. Raise and support vehicle.
5. Remove lower starter mounting bolt.
6. Pull starter motor rear down and out of bell housing.
7. Rotate starter until solenoid is at top.
8. Remove starter. **Do not damage wiring harnesses.**
9. Reverse procedure to install, noting the following:
   a. **Torque** starter motor mounting bolts to 35 ft. lbs.
   b. **Torque** M5 electrical leads to 49 inch lbs., M6 to 58 inch lbs. and M8 to 11 ft. lbs.

2.3

1. Remove air intake filter housing.
2. Disconnect Mass Air Flow (MAF) sensor connector.
3. Disconnect intake hose vacuum line and clip.
4. Disconnect throttle cable from actuator by pulling it upward out of retainer and unhooking.
5. Remove clamps, then the intake hose from throttle assembly and Idle Speed Control (ISC) valve.
6. Remove lower engine covers, as required.
7. Relieve fuel pressure as outlined in appropriate engine section.
8. Remove fuel lines to access starter.
9. Remove nuts and disconnect starter motor electrical connectors.
10. Remove mounting bolts and starter motor downward past fuel lines. **Do not damage fuel lines' sealing faces.**
11. Reverse procedure to install, noting the following.

a. **Torque** support to starter to 44 inch lbs.
b. **Torque** support to crankcase to 35 ft. lbs.
c. **Torque** starter motor mounting bolts to 35 ft. lbs.
d. **Torque** M5 electrical leads to 49 inch lbs., M6 to 58 inch lbs. and M8 to 11 ft. lbs.

2.5i & 3.0i

1. Remove nuts and disconnect starter motor electrical connectors.
2. Disconnect battery positive cable duct from firewall.
3. Disconnect heater valve from bracket to access starter motor.
4. Remove starter motor upper mounting bolt.
5. Raise and support vehicle.
6. Remove lower mounting bolt and starter motor.
7. Reverse procedure to install, noting the following.
   a. **Torque** support to starter to 44 inch lbs.
   b. **Torque** support to crankcase to 35 ft. lbs.
   c. **Torque** starter motor mounting bolts to 35 ft. lbs.
   d. **Torque** M5 electrical leads to 49 inch lbs., M6 to 58 inch lbs. and M8 to 11 ft. lbs.

2.8

1998

Automatic Transmission

1. Remove intake manifold as described in appropriate engine section.
2. Disconnect starter electrical connectors.
3. Remove starter motor brace nuts and mounting bolts.
4. Remove support mounting nut and starter motor.
5. Reverse procedure to install, noting the following.
   a. Install new O-ring seals on intake manifold.
   b. **Torque** support to starter to 44 inch lbs.
   c. **Torque** support to crankcase to 35 ft. lbs.
   d. **Torque** starter motor mounting bolts to 35 ft. lbs.
   e. **Torque** M5 electrical leads to 49 inch lbs., M6 to 58 inch lbs. and M8 to 11 ft. lbs.

Manual Transmission

Refer to "1998–99" under "M3."

1999-2000

Refer to "Z3 2.3."

318

Refer to "Z3 1.9."

323 & 328

1998

AUTOMATIC TRANSMISSION

Refer to "1998 w/Automatic Transmission" under "Z3 2.8."

MANUAL TRANSMISSION

Refer to "1998–99" under "M3."

1999

323i & 328i CONVERTIBLES & 323is & 328is

Automatic Transmission

Refer to "1998 w/Automatic Transmission" under "Z3 2.8."

Manual Transmission

Refer to "1998–99" under "M3."

323i & 328i SEDANS

Refer to "Z3 2.3."

2000

323Ci, 323i, 328Ci & 328i

Refer to "Z3 2.3."

325 & 300

1. Raise and support vehicle
2. **On 325Ci, 325i, 330Ci and 330i models,** remove mounting bolts and front axle support reinforcement plate.
3. **On 325xi and 330xi models,** remove mounting bolts and lower engine cover.
4. **On all models,** lower transmission approximately 0.2 inch as outline under "Transmission, Replace" in appropriate "Clutch & Manual Transmission" or "Automatic Transmission" section.
5. Remove vacuum tank from exhaust flap, as required.
6. Disconnect fuel line clips.
7. Disconnect Crankshaft Position (CKP) sensor.
8. Remove nuts and disconnect starter motor electrical connectors.
9. Remove mounting bolts and starter motor.
10. Reverse procedure to install, noting the following.
    a. **Torque** front axle support reinforcement plate mounting bolts to 44 ft. lbs., then tighten an additional 90°.
    b. **Torque** support to starter to 44 inch lbs.
    c. **Torque** support to crankcase to 35 ft. lbs.
    d. **Torque** starter motor mounting bolts to 35 ft. lbs.
    e. **Torque** M5 electrical leads to 49 inch lbs., M6 to 58 inch lbs. and M8 to 11 ft. lbs.

528

1998

1. Remove rear splash guard.
2. Remove mounting nuts and disconnect starter electrical connectors.
3. Remove mounting bolts and starter motor.
4. Reverse procedure to install, noting the following.
   a. **Torque** support to starter to 44 inch lbs.
   b. **Torque** M5 electrical leads to 49 inch lbs., M6 to 58 inch lbs. and M8 to 11 ft. lbs.

1999-2000

Refer to "Z3 2.3."

525 & 530

1. Disconnect Crankshaft Position (CKP) sensor electrical connector.
2. Remove nuts and disconnect starter motor electrical connectors.
3. Remove mounting bolts and starter motor.
4. Reverse procedure to install, noting the following.
   a. **Torque** support to starter to 44 inch lbs.
   b. **Torque** M5 electrical leads to 49 inch lbs., M6 to 58 inch lbs. and M8 to 11 ft. lbs.

540 & 740

1. Raise and support vehicle.
2. Remove mounting bolts and splash guards.
3. Remove mounting bolts and catalytic converter heat shields.
4. Disconnect righthand oxygen sensor connector from transmission clip.
5. Remove nuts and disconnect starter motor electrical connectors.
6. Remove mounting bolts and starter.
7. Reverse procedure to install, noting the following.
   a. **Torque** support to starter to 44 inch lbs.
   b. **Torque** M5 electrical leads to 49 inch lbs., M6 to 58 inch lbs. and M8 to 11 ft. lbs.

750

1. Raise and support vehicle.
2. Remove mounting bolts and splash guard.
3. Remove mounting bolts and front axle support retaining plate.
4. Remove heat baffle plate.
5. Disconnect battery positive cable bracket from crankcase.
6. Remove mounting nuts, bolts and righthand exhaust pipe.
7. Remove mounting nuts, bolts and heat baffle plate.
8. Disconnect starter motor electrical connectors.
9. Remove mounting nuts and support bracket.

10. Remove starter motor.
11. Reverse procedure to install, noting the following.
    a. **Torque** front axle support reinforcement plate mounting bolts to 44 ft. lbs., then tighten an additional 90°.
    b. **Torque** support to starter to 44 inch lbs.
    c. **Torque** support to crankcase to 35 ft. lbs.
    d. **Torque** starter motor mounting bolts to 35 ft. lbs.
    e. **Torque** M5 electrical leads to 49 inch lbs., M6 to 58 inch lbs. and M8 to 11 ft. lbs.
    f. Install new self-locking exhaust pipe nuts and seal ring.
    g. Coat exhaust pipe threads with suitable copper paste.

ALTERNATOR

REPLACE

M3

1998–99

1. Remove intake air filter housing.
2. Lock fan coupling pulley in place using holder tool No. 11 5 050, or equivalent. **Fan nut has lefthand threads.**
3. Remove fan and clutch assembly left-hand threaded nut using wrench tool No. 11 5 040, or equivalent. Remove fan coupling.
4. Remove drive belt.
5. Remove mounting bolts and place power steering pump fluid reservoir aside with lines connected.
6. Disconnect air hose, as required.
7. Disconnect electrical connector.
8. Remove cover cap, mounting nut and battery positive lead.
9. Grip alternator firmly and remove mounting bolts
10. Remove alternator.
11. Reverse procedure to install.

2001

1. Remove fan cowl and alternator drive belt.
2. Drain main flow oil filter into suitable container.
3. Disconnect oil cooler lines.
4. Remove mounting nut and disconnect battery lead from alternator.
5. Disconnect alternator electrical connectors.
6. Remove alternator mounting bolt.
7. Release mounting bolt and pull tensioning roller out.
8. Remove alternator.
9. Reverse procedure to install.

M5

1. Remove drive belt.
2. Disconnect battery positive lead from cable holders.
3. Remove cap, mounting screw and deflection roller.
4. Remove mounting bolts and power steering pump belt pulley.
5. Remove mounting bolts and pull alternator out.
6. Disconnect electrical connectors.

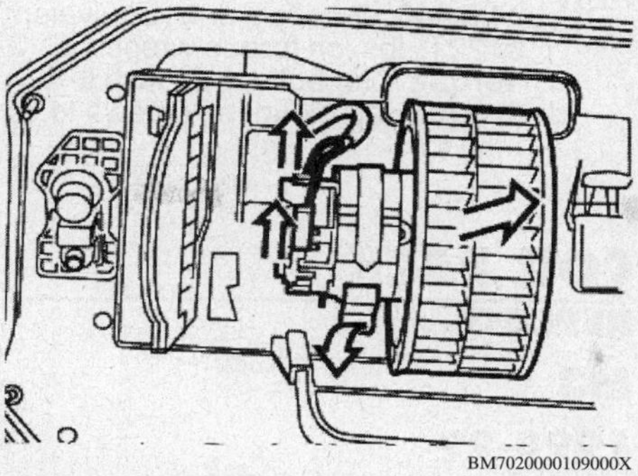

Fig. 3 Blower motor replacement. 318

Fig. 4 Blower motor replacement. 740 & 750

7. Remove mounting nut and disconnect battery positive lead.
8. Remove alternator.
9. Reverse procedure to install.

X5

3.0i

Refer to "1998–99" under "M3."

4.4i

1. Remove drive belt and fan cowl.
2. Drain engine coolant into suitable container.
3. Remove alternator mounting bolts.
4. Remove mounting nut and disconnect battery positive cable.
5. Disconnect alternator electrical connectors.
6. Remove mounting bolt and roller.
7. Remove mounting bolts and alternator.
8. Reverse procedure to install.

Z3

1.9

1. Remove upper section of air cleaner with Mass Air Flow (MAF) sensor.
2. Remove drive belt.
3. **On models equipped with hydraulic drive belt tensioners,** remove guide pulley.
4. **On models equipped with mechanic tensioner,** remove upper reversing roller mounting bolt.
5. **On all models,** remove mounting nuts, bolt and cap.
6. Remove lower mounting bolt.
7. Grip alternator firmly, then remove upper mounting bolt and alternator.
8. Reverse procedure to install.

2.3, 2.5i, 2.8 & 3.0i

Refer to "1998–99" under "M3."

M COUPE & M ROADSTER

1998–2000

Refer to "1998–99" under "M3."

2001

Refer to "2001" under "M3."

318

Refer to "1.9" under "Z3."

323, 325, 328, 330, 525, 528 & 530

Refer to "1998–99" under "M3."

540 & 740

AIR COOLED

1. Remove drive belt.
2. Remove mounting bolts and place oil filter housing aside.
3. Disconnect alternator electrical connectors.
4. Remove mounting nut and disconnect battery positive lead.
5. Disconnect cable clip and cooling air guide.
6. Remove mounting bolts and alternator.
7. Reverse procedure to install.

LIQUID COOLED

1. Lock fan coupling pulley in place using holder tool No. 11 5 050, or equivalent. **Fan nut has lefthand threads.**
2. Remove fan and clutch assembly left-hand threaded nut using wrench tool No. 11 5 040, or equivalent. Remove fan coupling.
3. Remove alternator mounting bolts.
4. Remove mounting bolt and battery positive lead.
5. Disconnect electrical connectors.
6. Remove mounting nut and place roller aside.
7. Remove mounting bolts and alternator.
8. Reverse procedure to install.

750

1. Remove drive belt, fan cowl and left-hand intake air filter housing.
2. Disconnect radiator hose bracket.
3. Loosen hose clamp and remove cooling air hose.
4. Disconnect connector.
5. Remove mounting bolt and remove tensioning roller.
6. Remove mounting bolts and pull alternator forward.
7. Disconnect electrical connectors.
8. Remove mounting nut and battery positive lead.
9. Remove alternator.

DISTRIBUTOR

REPLACE

750

The distributor on these models is used only to direct secondary spark voltage and is an integral part of the timing cover. Only the distributor cap and rotor can be serviced separately.

Lefthand

1. Lock fan coupling pulley in place using holder tool No. 11 5 050, or equivalent. **Fan nut has lefthand threads.**
2. Remove fan and clutch assembly lefthand threaded nut using wrench tool No. 11 5 040, or equivalent. Remove fan coupling.
3. Disconnect cover clips, then the air pump auxiliary hose clip.
4. Disconnect Mass Air Flow (MAF) sensor electrical connector.
5. Place suction filter housing with MAF sensor aside.
6. Disconnect cable connector.
7. Disconnect clips and remove lefthand cover.
8. Mark ignition leads for installation in proper firing order.
9. Disconnect shielded connectors.
10. Mark ignition wires for installation in proper firing order.
11. Remove mounting screws and distributor cap. **Do not damage radiator fins.**
12. Remove mounting bolts and rotor.
13. Reverse procedure to install, noting the following:

Righthand

1. Disconnect connector and air pump inlet hose clips.
2. Disconnect connector and remove intake filter housing top righthand section.
3. Remove fan coupling as described under "Lefthand."
4. Disconnect clips and remove oil drip tray.
5. Disconnect clip and remove cylinders Nos. 1–6 non-return valve pressure hose.
6. Disconnect coolant vent hose bracket.
7. Remove mounting screws and cylinders Nos. 1–6 non-return valve.
8. Disconnect clip and remove air pump pressure pipe hose.
9. Disconnect and remove pressure pipe.
10. Disconnect air pump intake hose clip and connector.
11. Disconnect clip and remove righthand cover cap.
12. Disconnect shielded connectors.
13. Mark ignition wires for installation in proper firing order.
14. Remove mounting screws and distributor cap. **Do not damage radiator fins.**
15. Remove mounting bolts and rotor.
16. Reverse procedure to install, noting the following:
    a. Install new non-return valve gasket.
    b. **Torque** fan and clutch mounting nut to 29 ft. lbs. using wrench tool No. 11 5 040, or equivalent. (Equivalent of 22 ft. lbs. on torque wrench.)
    c. **Torque** rotor bolts to 25 inch lbs.
    d. **Torque** cap mounting screws to 35 inch lbs.

COIL PACK

REPLACE

M3

1998–99

1. Disconnect clips cover remove mounting screws.
2. Remove oil filler neck cap and ignition coil cover.
3. Disconnect ignition coil electrical connectors.
4. Remove mounting screws and ignition coils.
5. Reverse procedure to install, noting the following:
    a. Screw down grounding strap to mounting and cylinders Nos. 1 and 6 ignition coils.
    b. **On models equipped with metal cover,** screw down cable duct grounding strap to mounting between cylinders Nos. 2 and 3.

2001

1. Disconnect clips and thread heater cable out of duct.
2. Turn toggle approximately 90° and remove interior ventilation microfilter to front.
3. Remove mounting screws and heater bulkhead to top.
4. Remove engine vent and valve cover mounting screws, then the oil filler cap and valve cover.
5. Disconnect and remove ignition coil.
6. Reverse procedure to install.

M5

1. Remove nuts and ignition coils' covers.
2. Remove cable holder mounting nuts.
3. Remove ignition coil's mounting screws and disconnect electrical connectors.
4. Remove ignition coils.
5. Reverse procedure to install.

X5

3.0i

Refer to "1998–99" under "M3."

4.4i

1. Turn fasteners 90° counterclockwise and remove acoustic cover.
2. Remove sealing caps, nuts and ignition coil covers.
3. Disconnect coil electrical connectors.
4. Remove mounting screws and coil. Mark coil ground strap position.
5. Reverse procedure to install, noting the following:
    a. Screw thin grounding strap to ignition coil for cylinders Nos. 2 or 7.
    b. Screw thick grounding strap to ignition coil for cylinders Nos. 3 or 7.

Z3

M, 2.3, 2.5i, 2.8 & 3.0i

1998–99

1. Disconnect clips cover remove mounting screws.
2. Remove oil filler neck cap and ignition coil cover.
3. Disconnect ignition coil electrical connectors.
4. Remove mounting screws and ignition coils.
5. Reverse procedure to install, noting the following:
    a. Screw down grounding strap to mounting and cylinders Nos. 1 and 6 ignition coils.
    b. **On models equipped with metal cover,** screw down cable duct grounding strap to mounting between cylinders Nos. 2 and 3.
    c. **On models equipped with plastic cover,** screw down ignition coils' connecting plate grounding strap to cylinder No. 1 coil retaining pin.
    d. **On models equipped with plastic cover,** screw down cable duct grounding strap to ignition coils connecting plate between cylinders Nos. 2 and 3.

2001

1. Remove engine vent and valve cover mounting screws, then the oil filler cap and valve cover.
2. Disconnect and remove ignition coil.
3. Reverse procedure to install.

1.9

1. Disconnect ignition coil primary connector.
2. Remove mounting nuts and ignition coil.
3. Disconnect corresponding ignition coil and spark plug lead.
4. Reverse procedure to install.

318

Refer to "Z3 1.9."

323, 325, 328, 330, 525 & 530

1. **On 323Ci, 325, 328Ci and 330 and 2000 323i and 328i and 1999 323i & 328i Sedan models,** remove microfilter housings.
2. **On all models,** disconnect clips cover remove mounting screws.
3. Remove oil filler neck cap and ignition coil cover.
4. Disconnect ignition coil electrical connectors.
5. Remove mounting screws and ignition coils.
6. Reverse procedure to install, noting the following:
    a. Screw down grounding strap to mounting and cylinders Nos. 1 and 6 ignition coils.
    b. **On models equipped with metal cover,** screw down cable duct grounding strap to mounting between cylinders Nos. 2 and 3.
    c. **On models equipped with plastic**

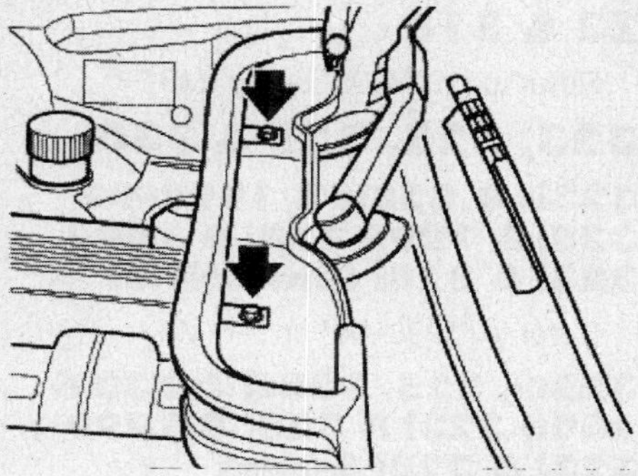
BM7020000094000X

Fig. 5 Cable channel replacement. M3, 318i, 318ti, 323is & 328is & 1998 323i & 328i & 1999 323i & 328i Convertibles

cover, screw down ignition coils' connecting plate grounding strap to cylinder No. 1 coil retaining pin.
d. **On models equipped with plastic cover,** screw down cable duct grounding strap to ignition coils connecting plate between cylinders Nos. 2 and 3.

540 & 740

1. Remove sealing caps, mounting nuts and acoustic cover, or pressure stud fasteners and remove acoustic cover.
2. Remove sealing caps, nuts and ignition coil covers.
3. Disconnect coil electrical connectors.
4. Remove mounting screws and coil. Mark coil ground strap position.
5. Reverse procedure to install. Screw grounding straps to ignition coil for cylinders Nos. 3 and 6.

750

1. Disconnect coil electrical connector.
2. Remove sealing cap.
3. Remove mounting nuts and ignition coils.
4. Reverse procedure to install.

IGNITION LOCK

REPLACE

M3

1998–99

1. Remove steering wheel as outlined under "Steering Wheel, Replace."
2. Remove lefthand under dash panels.
3. Remove steering shaft collar and snap ring.
4. Pull lower steering column cover away from upper cover.
5. **On 318ti models,** loosen steering column mounting shear-off bolts.
6. **On all models,** remove mounting screw, pull off clip, press retaining hook and remove ignition switch.
7. Disconnect ground cable, then remove mounting screws and starter switch.
8. **On models equipped with automatic transmission,** disconnect shift interlock cable.
9. **On all models,** remove snap ring and sleeve from upper column bearing, then pry out bearing.
10. Remove shear-off screws and turn steering long to R position.
11. Remove steering lock by pressing down on steering column.
12. Reverse procedure to install, noting the following.
    a. Tighten new shear-off screws until they shear. Lock screws with varnish.
    b. Install snap ring using installer tool No. 32 1 090, or equivalent.

2001

1. Remove steering wheel as outlined under "Steering Wheel, Replace."
2. Remove upper and lower steering column covers.
3. Lever out electronic immobilizer antenna ring using removal tool No. 61 3 002/020, or equivalent.
4. Unlock interlock through hole.
5. With ignition lock key, turn lock barrel to R position.
6. Press removal tool No. 32 3 110, or equivalent, into locking cylinder hole and remove lock.
7. Reverse procedure to install.

M5, X5, 528, 525, 530, 540, 740 & 750

1. Remove upper steering column bearing and cover.
2. Lever out electronic immobilizer antenna ring using removal tool No. 61 3 002/020, or equivalent.
3. Remove indicators/wipers switches' bracket.
4. Disconnect interlock cable, as required.
5. Remove shear-off screws, plate and steering lock.
6. Remove lock cylinder.
7. Reverse procedure to install.

Z3 & 318

Refer to "1998–99" under "M3."

323, 325, 328 & 330

323, 325, 328 & 330

323is & 328is & 1998-99 328i & 1998 323i & 1999 323i & 328i Convertibles

Refer to "1998–99" under "M3."

323Ci, 325, 328Ci & 330 & 2000 323i & 328i & 1999 323i & 328i Sedans

Refer to "2001" under "M3."

IGNITION SWITCH

REPLACE

M3, Z3, 318, 323, 325, 328 & 330

1. Remove mounting screws and lower lefthand side of instrument panel.
2. Remove steering column cover lower section.

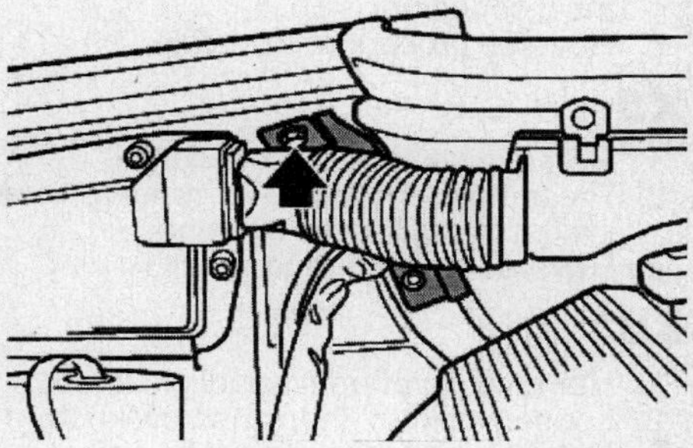
BM7020000112000X

Fig. 6 Righthand air collector bracket replacement. M3, 323is & 328is & 1998 323i & 328i & 1999 323i & 328i Convertibles

3. Disconnect ignition switch connector.
4. Remove mounting screws and switch.
5. Reverse procedure to install.

M5, 528, 530, 540, 740 & 750

1. Remove steering column cover lower section.
2. Disconnect ignition switch connector.
3. Remove mounting screws and switch.
4. Reverse procedure to install.

X5

1. Remove mounting screws, then the upper and lower steering column covers.
2. Disconnect ignition switch connector.
3. Remove mounting screws and switch.
4. Reverse procedure to install.

HEADLAMP SWITCH

REPLACE

M3 & 318

1998-99

1. Remove lower lefthand side of instrument panel trim panel.
2. Pull lower side panel off of clips.
3. Pull off light switch knob.
4. Remove mounting nut and pull switch out through the rear of panel.
5. Disconnect electrical connector.
6. Reverse procedure to install.

2001

1. Remove lefthand wooden finisher panel.
2. Remove lefthand glove compartment.
3. Remove mounting screws and remove switch through glove compartment.
4. Disconnect connectors and remove switch.
5. Reverse procedure to install.

M5, 525, 528, 530 & 540

1. Fully extend and lower steering column.
2. Remove instrument cluster trim.
3. Pull knob from headlight switch.
4. Remove headlight switch mounting nuts.

5. Remove switch, then disconnect electrical connector.
6. Reverse procedure to install.

X5

1. Remove lefthand fresh air grille.
2. Press retaining lock and remove light switch through grille opening.
3. Reverse procedure to install.

Z3

1. Remove cover from headlight knob.
2. Loosen locknut, then unscrew knob.
3. Release switch locking tabs using release tool No. 61 3 100, or equivalent, then push switch out of instrument panel.
4. Disconnect electrical connector and remove switch.
5. Reverse procedure to install.

323, 325, 328 & 330

323is & 328is & 1998-99 328i & 1998 323i & 1999 323i & 328i Convertibles

Refer to "1998–99" under "M3."

323Ci, 325, 328Ci & 330 & 2000 323i & 328i & 1999 323i & 328i Sedans

Refer to "2001" under "M3."

740 & 750

1. Wrap snap ring pliers tool No. 61 1 300, or equivalent, tips with insulating tape.
2. Place tips of pliers into slot of switch trim, expand pliers and carefully pull trim out of dash.
3. Remove switch mask and slide.
4. Compress retainer clips, then pull switch from dash.
5. Disconnect electrical connectors.
6. Reverse procedure to install.

STOP LIGHT SWITCH

REPLACE

M3, M5, X5, Z3, 318, 525, 528, 530, 540, 740 & 750

1998-2000

1. Remove lower lefthand instrument panelling.
2. Disconnect connector.
3. Press brake pedal as far as possible.
4. Pull tappet and sleeve forward, then press clips together and pull switch back.
5. Switch will automatically adjust after installation.

2001

1. Remove pedal assembly trim.
2. Disconnect electrical connector.
3. Remove switch from mount.
4. Press brake pedal until switch cab be installed against stop.

323, 325, 328 & 330

323is & 328is & 1998-99 328i & 1998 323i & 1999 323i & 328i Convertibles

Refer to "1998–2000" under "M3."

323Ci, 325, 328Ci & 330 & 2000 323i & 328i & 1999 323i & 328i Sedans

Refer to "2001" under "M3."

MULTI-FUNCTION SWITCH

REPLACE

M3

1998-99

1. Remove steering wheel as outlined under "Steering Wheel, Replace."
2. Remove lefthand lower instrument panel and lower steering column trim.
3. Remove mounting screws and frame by levering downward using suitable screwdriver.
4. Remove lever by pressing retainers.
5. Loosen cable straps and disconnect switch electrical connectors.
6. Reverse procedure to install.

2001

1. Remove steering wheel as outlined under "Steering Wheel, Replace."
2. Remove upper and lower steering column covers.
3. Disconnect ring antenna, wiper switch and turn indicator connectors.
4. Remove mounting screws and frame.
5. Remove switch by unlock retainers and pulling it toward top.
6. Reverse procedure to install.

M5, 525, 528, 530, 540, 740 & 750

1. Adjust steering column as far down and rearward as possible.
2. Remove steering column trim to column mounting screw.
3. Press inward on upper column trim panel to disengage upper trim latch tabs from lower trim panel.
4. Pivot upper and lower trim panels away from column.
5. Press in on tabs holding switch to assembly frame and remove switch.
6. Disconnect electrical connectors.
7. Reverse procedure to install.

X5

1. Remove upper and lower steering column covers.
2. Remove steering wheel as outlined under "Steering Wheel, Replace."
3. Disconnect electrical connectors.
4. Disconnect steering column adjustment connectors, as required.
5. Remove mounting screws and frame.
6. Disconnect clips and remove switch.
7. Reverse procedure to install.

Z3 & 318

Refer to "1998–99" under "M3."

323, 325, 328 & 330

323is & 328is & 1998-99 328i & 1998 323i & 1999 323i & 328i Convertibles

Refer to "1998–99" under "M3."

323Ci, 325, 328Ci & 330 & 2000 323i & 328i & 1999 323i & 328i Sedans

Refer to "2001" under "M3."

TURN SIGNAL SWITCH

REPLACE

Refer to "Multi-Function Switch, Replace" for replacement procedure.

STEERING WHEEL

REPLACE

1. Remove driver's air bag as outlined in "Air Bag System" section.
2. Ensure steering wheel is in straight-ahead position.
3. Mark steering wheel and column for installation alignment.
4. Remove mounting bolt.
5. **On models with early model air bag,** remove contact ring spring clip mounting screw.
6. **On all models,** remove steering wheel.
7. Reverse procedure to install, noting the following:
   a. Coat slip rings with suitable grease.
   b. Ensure column lockpin engages steering wheel hole.
   c. Adjust contact ring, as required.
   d. **Torque** mounting bolt to 46 ft. lbs.
   e. **Torque** mounting screw to 59 ft. lbs.

INSTRUMENT CLUSTER

REPLACE

M3

1998-99

1. Remove steering wheel as outlined under "Steering Wheel, Replace."
2. Place suitable clean rags on steering column.
3. Remove mounting screws and lift instrument cluster up slightly and pull as far as steering column.
4. Disconnect electrical connectors.
5. Remove instrument cluster.
6. Reverse procedure to install.

2001

1. Move steering column completely down and fully extended.
2. Remove mounting screws and fold instrument carrier forward.
3. Disconnect connectors and remove instrument cluster.
4. Reverse procedure to install.

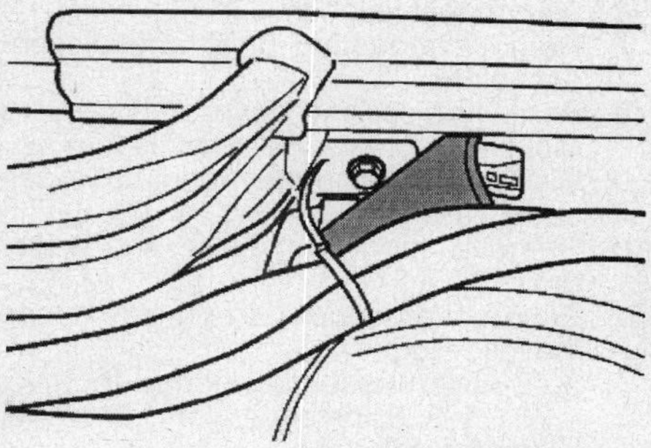

Fig. 7 Lefthand air collector bracket replacement. M3, 323is & 328is & 1998 323i & 328i & 1999 323i & 328i Convertibles

318

1. Remove steering wheel as outlined under "Steering Wheel, Replace."
2. Place suitable clean rags on steering column.
3. Remove mounting screws and lift instrument cluster up slightly and pull as far as steering column.
4. Disconnect electrical connectors.
5. **On 318ti models,** unscrew light switch button.
6. **On all models,** remove instrument cluster.
7. Reverse procedure to install.

M5, 525, 528, 530 & 540

1. Move steering column completely down and fully extended.
2. Unclip left and righthand wood instrument cluster wood trim.
3. Remove mounting screws and disconnect frame clips.
4. Remove mounting screws and fold instrument carrier forward.
5. Disconnect electrical connectors and remove instrument cluster.
6. Reverse procedure to install.

X5, 740 & 750

Refer to "2001" under "M3."

Z3

1. Remove steering wheel as previously described.
2. Turn rotary clips 90° and remove, then pull instrument panel trim down and backward.
3. Remove caps and screws, then screw trim and pull from tray.
4. Place suitable clean rags on steering column.
5. Remove mounting screws and slide instrument cluster out of trim, then fold over.
6. Remove lower lefthand instrument panel, knee proctor and lefthand lower shelf as required.
7. Disconnect electrical connectors and remove instrument cluster.
8. Reverse procedure to install.

323, 325, 328 & 330

323is & 328is & 1998-99 328i & 1998 323i & 1999 323i & 328i Convertibles

Refer to "1998–99" under "M3."

323Ci, 325, 328Ci & 330 & 2000 323i & 328i & 1999 323i & 328i Sedans

Refer to "2001" under "M3."

RADIO

REPLACE

M3

1998-99

1. Insert suitable radio unhooking hooks through left and righthand sides of face plate.
2. Pull radio from instrument panel using hooks.
3. Disconnect all connectors and remove radio
4. Reverse procedure to install.

2001

1. Remove decorative strip around radio.
2. Remove mounting screws and pull radio out.
3. Disconnect all connectors and remove radio.
4. Reverse procedure to install.

M5, 525, 528, 530 & 540

1. Remove volume control knob.
2. Insert suitable screwdriver into slot approximately 0.04 inch and it 90°.
3. Install removal tool No. 65 1 100, or equivalent, into cassette socket and pull radio out.
4. Disconnect all connectors and remove radio.
5. Reverse procedure to install.

X5

1. Remove volume control knobs.
2. Turn Torx lock screws 90° and pull multi-information display out.
3. Disconnect connectors and remove multi-information display.
4. Disconnect left and righthand cap screws, then pull radio out.
5. Disconnect connectors and remove radio.
6. Reverse procedure to install.

Z3 & 318

Refer to "1998–99" under "M3."

323, 325, 328 & 330

323is & 328is & 1998-99 328i & 1998 323i & 1999 323i & 328i Convertibles

Refer to "1998–99" under "M3."

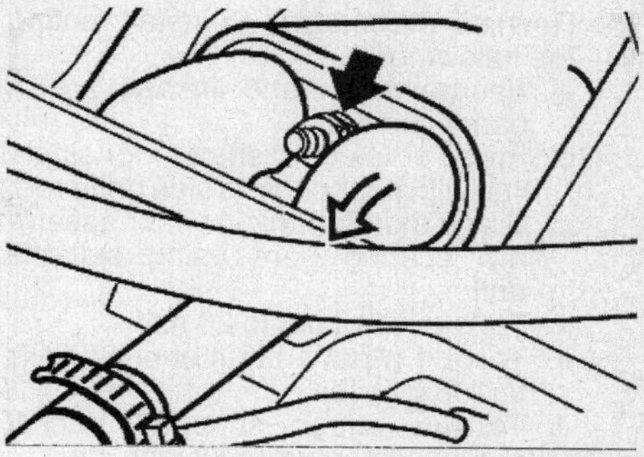

Fig. 8 Heater water inlet flange replacement. M3, 323is & 328is & 1998 323i & 328i & 1999 323i & 328i Convertibles

323Ci, 325, 328Ci & 330 & 2000 323i & 328i & 1999 323i & 328i Sedans

Refer to "2001" under "M3."

740 & 750

1. Fold left and righthand finishers over.
2. Remove mounting screws and pull radio out.
3. Disconnect connectors and remove radio.
4. Reverse procedure to install.

WIPER MOTOR

REPLACE

Do not allow wiper motor to run with wiper arms attached when hood is raised into the service position.

M3 & 318

1998-99

Four-Door

1. Ensure wiper motor is in park position, then remove wiper arms.
2. Remove mounting bolts and nuts, then disconnect static grounding wire at hood hinge.
3. Disconnect hood gas strut, raise hood to service position and lock into place. Support hood with support tool No. 51 2 140, or equivalent.
4. Remove fresh air intake cowl grill.
5. Loosen wiring harness on end wall and bend insulation sheet aside.
6. Remove cable channel mounting screws, then press wiring harness aside.
7. Remove fresh air inlet box and place aside.
8. Cover cowl panelling inside and edges with suitable plastic sheet.
9. Remove wiper assembly mounting screws and bolts.
10. Disconnect wiper motor electrical connector.
11. Wrap driver's side wiper shaft with suitable insulating tape.
12. Remove wiper assembly by working out of body.
13. Remove shaft nut and crank.
14. Remove mounting bolts and motor.

15. Reverse procedures to install, noting the following:
    a. Ensure motor and linkage are in park position.
    b. Install crank onto shaft to for single line with passenger's side drive rod.
    c. Brace motor crank in wiper assembly locating bore using suitable drift.
    d. **Torque** shaft nut to 20 ft. lbs.
    e. **Torque** wiper shaft mounting bolts to 106 inch lbs.
    f. **Torque** wiper support bracket mounting screws to 88 inch lbs.
    g. **Torque** wiper assembly mounting screws to 88 inch lbs.
    h. **Torque** wiper arm mounting nuts to 18 ft. lbs. Wait 15 minutes and tighten as previously specified.

Two-Door

1. Ensure wiper motor is in park position, then remove wiper arms.
2. Remove mounting bolts and nuts, then disconnect static grounding wire at hood hinge.
3. Disconnect hood gas strut, raise hood to service position and lock into place. Support hood with support tool No. 51 2 140, or equivalent.
4. Remove fresh air intake cowl grill mounting bolts.
5. Disconnect clips and remove radiator grill.
6. Remove cable channel mounting screws, then press wiring harness aside.
7. Remove fresh air inlet box and place aside.
8. Remove soundproofing sheet.
9. Remove mounting screws and cover, then disconnect control module connector and place wiring harness aside.
10. Remove wiper assembly mounting screws and bolts.
11. Disconnect wiper motor electrical connector.
12. Cover cowl panelling inside and edges with suitable plastic sheet.
13. Wrap driver's side wiper shaft with suitable insulating tape.
14. Remove wiper assembly by working out of body.
15. Remove shaft nut and crank.
16. Remove mounting bolts and motor.
17. Reverse procedures to install, noting the following:
    a. Ensure motor and linkage are in park position.
    b. Install crank onto shaft to for single line with passenger's side drive rod.
    c. Brace motor crank in wiper assembly locating bore using suitable drift.
    d. **Torque** shaft nut to 20 ft. lbs.
    e. **Torque** wiper shaft mounting bolts to 106 inch lbs.
    f. **Torque** wiper assembly mounting screws to 88 inch lbs.
    g. **Torque** wiper support bracket mounting screws to 88 inch lbs.
    h. **Torque** wiper arm mounting nuts to 18 ft. lbs. Wait 15 minutes and tighten as previously specified.

2001

1. Remove wiper arms.
2. Disconnect clips and thread cable out of duct.
3. Turn toggle approximately 90°, then remove cover and microfilter.
4. Remove mounting screws and heater bulkhead.
5. Disconnect connector.
6. Remove mounting nuts and remove wiper assembly through heater bulkhead opening.
7. Remove shaft nut and crank.
8. Remove mounting bolts and motor.
9. Reverse procedure to install, noting the following:
    a. **Torque** shaft crank nut to 20 ft. lbs.
    b. **Torque** wiper shaft nut to 88 inch lbs.
    c. **Torque** wiper assembly mounting nuts to 88 inch lbs.
    d. **Torque** wiper arm mounting nuts to 22 ft. lbs. Wait 15 minutes and tighten as previously specified.

M5, 525, 528, 530 & 540

FRONT

1. Remove nuts and wiper arms using wiper arm puller tool No. 61 6 060, or equivalent.
2. Remove engine hood sealing frame.
3. Disconnect clips, twist and remove left and righthand air ducts.
4. Disconnect mounting brackets, then remove covers and left and righthand microfilters.
5. Disconnect split rivets and remove cowl screen.
6. Remove mounting screws and cowl cover.
7. Twist levers approximately 90° and remove cable cover.
8. Disconnect connectors, then remove mounting bolts and wiper assembly.
9. Remove motor shaft nut and crank arm.
10. Remove mounting bolts and motor.
11. Reverse procedure to install, noting the following:
    a. Install wiper motor assembly bolts hand tight to allow stress free alignment.
    b. **Torque** wiper motor mounting bolts to 106 inch lbs.
    c. **Torque** crank mounting nut to 20 ft. lbs.
    d. **Torque** wiper assembly mounting bolts to 88 inch lbs.
    e. **Torque** wiper arm mounting nuts to 29 ft. lbs. Wait 15 minutes and tighten as previously specified.

REAR

1. Remove mounting nut and wiper arm.
2. Open lid, then lift out indicator lamp and disconnect connector. Remove lamp.
3. Disconnect rotary clip and open tool box.
4. Lift emergency unlocking finisher and push through trim.
5. Disconnect straps, then remove mounting screw and tool box.
6. Disconnect finisher.
7. Remove mounting bolts and disconnect plate.
8. Partially disconnect trim and remove mounting screws. Remove lid trim.
9. Disconnect connector and cut open cable ties.
10. Remove mounting bolts and wiper motor.
11. Reverse procedure to install, noting the following:
    a. Position assembly gauge tool No. 61 1 320, or equivalent, on wiper motor disk drive.
    b. Close rear window until drive arm with limit stop is fixed by tool.
    c. Open window and **torque** mounting bolt to 88 inch lbs.
    d. **Torque** motor mounting bolts to 88 inch lbs.
    e. **Torque** wiper arm mounting nut to 119 inch lbs. Wait 15 minutes and tighten as previously specified.

X5

FRONT

1. Remove covers, nuts and wiper arms using wiper arm puller tool No. 61 6 060, or equivalent.
2. Disconnect seals, turn bars 90° and remove cowl cover.
3. Disconnect expansion rivets and remove cowl panel cover.
4. Remove microfilter air funnel.
5. Remove mounting screws, nut and remove wiper assembly bracket.
6. Disconnect electrical connector.
7. Remove wiper assembly with motor.
8. Reverse procedure to install, noting the following:
    a. **Torque** wiper assembly bracket mounting bolts to 88 inch lbs.
    b. **Torque** wiper arm nuts to 22 ft. lbs. Wait 15 minutes and tighten as previously specified.

REAR

1. Remove cap, mounting nut and wiper arm using wiper arm puller tool No. 61 6 060, or equivalent.
2. Lever out luggage compartment lamp and disconnect connector. Remove lamp.
3. Lever out rear lid upper section side trim.
4. Remove caps and mounting screws, then lever out lower trim.
5. Disconnect motor electrical connector.
6. Remove mounting bolts and wiper motor.
7. Reverse procedure to install, noting the following:
    a. Install new rubber grommet.
    b. Hand tighten mounting bolts and center motor.
    c. **Torque** mounting bolts to 88 inch lbs.
    d. **Torque** wiper blade mounting nut to 119 inch lbs. Wait 15 minutes and tighten as previously specified.

Z3

1. Ensure wiper motor is in park position.
2. Remove cover caps, mounting nuts and wiper arms.

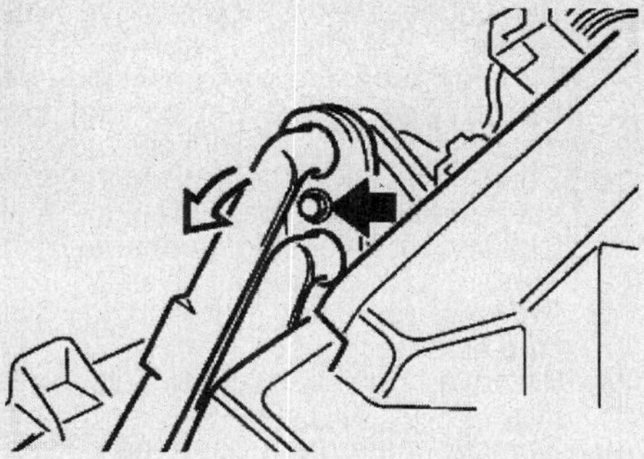
BM7020000115000X

Fig. 9 Three-way flange replacement. M3, 323is & 328is & 1998 323i & 328i & 1999 323i & 328i Convertibles

3. Remove air intake grill rubber seals.
4. Remove expanding rivets and air intake grill.
5. Remove mounting screws, then pull wiper assembly sideways out of upper guide and pull forward.
6. Disconnect electrical connector and remove wiper assembly.
7. Remove shaft nut and motor crank.
8. Remove motor mounting bolts and motor.
9. Reverse procedure to install, noting the following.
   a. Ensure motor is in park position before installing to assembly.
   b. Install crank arm so that it is parallel and in line with wiper link rods.
   c. Move motor and linkage slightly to final tighten crank arm to motor shaft.
   d. **Torque** motor mounting bolts to 88 inch lbs.
   e. **Torque** shaft nut to 20 ft. lbs.
   f. **Torque** wiper arm mounting nuts to 18 ft. lbs. Wait 15 minutes and tighten as previously specified.

323 & 328

Front

Do not allow wiper motor to run with wiper arms attached when hood is raised into the service position.

1. Remove wiper arms. Ensure wiper motor is in park position.
2. Disconnect static grounding wire at hood hinge.
3. Disconnect hood gas strut, raise hood to service position and lock into place.
4. Remove fresh air intake cowl grill and covers.
5. Remove and wiring cable channel from fresh air inlet box.
6. Remove fresh air inlet box and place aside.
7. **On four-door models,** remove trim covers from intake manifold and valve cover.
8. **On two-door models,** proceed as follows:
   a. Remove coolant and washer fluid bottles, place aside.
   b. Remove control unit cover.
   c. Disconnect control unit electrical connectors, then remove control unit.
9. **On all models,** remove wiper assembly covers, then place protective cover around cowl area.
10. Disconnect wiper motor electrical connector, then remove holder for plug. **Do not allow plug to be pushed into passengers compartment.**
11. Remove wiper pivot shaft and wiper frame assembly mounting nuts and brackets, then wrap protective tape around lefthand pivot shaft.
12. Pull lefthand shaft down into cowl area, then move wiper assembly as far to righthand side of vehicle as possible.
13. Rotate assembly towards front and remove from cowl.
14. Remove motor shaft nut, then the crank arm from shaft.
15. Remove mounting bolts and motor.
16. Reverse procedures to install, noting the following:
   a. Ensure motor and linkage are in park position before connecting crank arm to motor shaft
   b. After positioning assembly, tighten lefthand pivot shaft mounting nut first, then the remaining bolts.
   c. Connect and run wiper assembly prior to attaching wiper arms to ensure entire assembly is in park position.

323is & 328is & 1998-99 328i & 1998 323i & 1999 323i & 328i Convertibles

Refer to "1998–99" under "M3."

323Ci, 325, 328Ci & 330 & 2000 323i & 328i & 1999 323i & 328i Sedans

Refer to "2001" under "M3."

740 & 750

1. Raise and lock hood into vertical service position by disconnecting gas struts, then secure hood hinges with suitable bolts.
2. Remove nuts and wiper arms using wiper arm puller tool No. 61 6 060, or equivalent.
3. Press flaps down, loosen mounting screws and remove fresh air duct. **Do not remove screws.**
4. Remove mounting screws and cover.
5. Remove motor shaft nut and crank arm.
6. Remove mounting bolts and motor.
7. Reverse procedure to install, noting the following:
   a. **Torque** wiper motor bracket mounting bolts to 66 inch lbs.
   b. **Torque** wiper motor crank mounting nut to 15 ft. lbs.
   c. **Torque** wiper assembly mounting screws to 88 inch lbs.
   d. **Torque** wiper arm mounting nuts to 18 ft. lbs. Wait 15 minutes and tighten as previously specified.

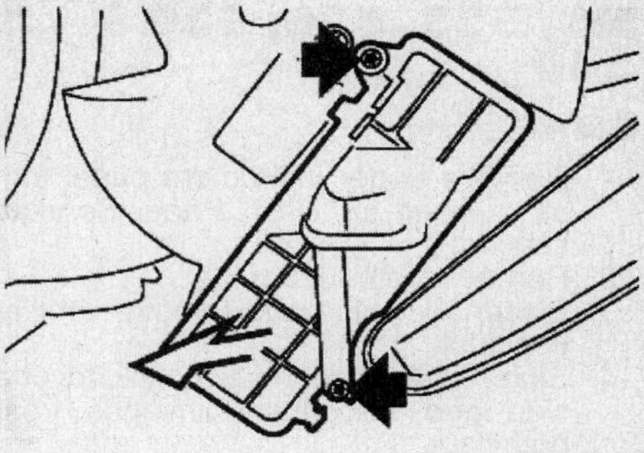
BM7020000116000X

Fig. 10 Heater core replacement. M3, 323is & 328is & 1998 323i & 328i & 1999 323i & 328i Convertibles

WIPER SWITCH

REPLACE

Refer to "Multi-Function Switch, Replace" for replacement procedure.

BLOWER MOTOR

REPLACE

M3

1998-99

1. Remove wiper motor assembly as outlined under "Wiper Motor, Replace."
2. Remove clips and blower cover.
3. Disconnect connector.
4. Remove clips and lift lefthand upper blower section out.
5. Cut blower wheels off at brace, **Fig. 1.**
6. Remove blower motor.
7. Reverse procedure to install, noting the following:
   a. Install motor and gears in manifold box individually.
   b. Assemble motor and gears in box.
   c. Install blower wheel on motor shaft so colors match.
   d. Blower arrow indicates correct wheel installation position.
   e. Blower wheels are defined by differing driver pin press-in depths, **Fig. 2.**

2001

1. Remove heater bulkhead as outlined under "Heater Core, Replace."
2. Remove filter as outlined under "Wiper Motor, Replace."
3. Partially disconnect rubber seal, then remove mounting screws and blower impeller cover.
4. Remove mounting bolts and blower motor cover.
5. Disconnect connect and mounting clip using rubber window seal fitting hook tool No. 51 3 057, or equivalent.
6. Lever blower out.
7. Remove engine protective hoods.
8. Remove blower motor with impeller toward front.
9. Reverse procedure to install.

M5, 525, 528, 530 & 540

Front

1. Remove upper instrument panel trim as outlined in "Dash Panel Service" section.
2. Remove foam rubber mat.
3. Disconnect clips and remove ventilation duct.
4. Slide air flap connecting link to one side and disconnect linkages from both flaps.
5. Remove clips and blower cover.
6. Disconnect electrical connector then remove mounting screws and blower motor.
7. Reverse procedure to install.

Rear

1. Remove rear fresh air grill.
2. Turn adapter clockwise, unlock and remove rear cover.
3. Remove mounting bolts and pull storage tray out.
4. Disconnect connector.
5. Pull carpet out of clips.
6. Disconnect trim clips.
7. Remove mounting bolts and move console up.
8. Remove mounting bolts, disconnect connector and remove blower motor.

X5

1. Remove instrument panel trim as outlined in "Dash Panel Service" section.
2. Disconnect clips and remove cover.
3. Disconnect electrical connector.
4. Remove mounting bolts and blower motor.
5. Reverse procedure to install.

Z3

1. Remove caps, mounting nuts and wiper arms.
2. Remove left and righthand air intake protective grill rubber seals.
3. Remove expanding rivets and air intake protective grill.
4. Remove mounting bolts and wiper console. Disconnect connector.
5. Disconnect clamping straps and remove fan cover.
6. Disconnect fan resistance, connector and clip, then remove blower motor.
7. Reverse procedure to install.

318

1. Remove air collector as outlined under "Heater Core, Replace."
2. Loosen clips and mounting bolts, then remove blower cover.
3. Disconnect connector and loosen clip, **Fig. 3.**
4. Pull cable up and remove blower motor.
5. Reverse procedure to install.

323, 325, 328 & 330

323is & 328is & 1998–99 328i & 1998 323i & 1999 323i & 328i Convertibles

Refer to "1998–99" under "M3."

323Ci, 325, 328Ci & 330 & 2000 323i & 328i & 1999 323i & 328i Sedans

Refer to "2001" under "M3."

740 & 750

1. Remove instrument panel as outlined in "Dash Panel Service" section.
2. Disconnect ventilation duct, then the left and righthand linkage clips.
3. Remove connector, then cut cable connector, remove mounting bolts and cover.
4. Remove mounting bolts and blower, **Fig. 4.**
5. Reverse procedure to install.

HEATER CORE

REPLACE

M3 & 318

1998–99

1. Drain cooling system into suitable container.
2. Remove rubber portion and pry air collector grill out.
3. Remove cable channel mounting bolts, **Fig. 5.**
4. Remove mounting bolts and righthand air collector bracket, **Fig. 6.**
5. Remove lefthand mounting bolts and remove air collector, **Fig. 7.**
6. Remove heater controls as outlined under "Control Module, Replace"
7. Loosen mounting nut and remove heater water inlet flange, **Fig. 8.**
8. Blow low pressure compressed air into delivery line to prevent coolant from dripping onto carpet from core.
9. Remove heater water inlet flange mounting studs
10. Remove mounting bolts and knee protection.
11. Remove steering column strip connector.
12. Remove mounting bolt and heater core three-way flange, **Fig. 9.**
13. Remove mounting bolt and heater core, **Fig. 10.**
14. Reverse procedure to install, noting the following:
    a. Install new O-rings.
    b. **Torque** heater core mounting bolt to 9 inch lbs.
    c. **Torque** heater core three-way flange mounting bolt to 27 inch lbs.
    d. **Torque** heater water inlet flange mounting studs to 18 inch lbs.
    e. **Torque** heater water inlet flange mounting nut to 31 inch lbs.

2001

1. Recover refrigerant as outlined in "Air Conditioning" section.
2. Remove filter as outlined under "Wiper Motor, Replace."
3. Remove clips and thread cable out of heater bulkhead cable duct.
4. Remove mounting bolts and filter housing.
5. Remove mounting bolts and heater bulkhead.
6. Disconnect clamps and remove water hoses.
7. Blow low pressure compressed air into delivery line to prevent coolant from dripping onto carpet from core.
8. Remove mounting bolts, then the pressure and suction pipe.
9. Disconnect unlocking mechanism and remove recirculating air flap.
10. Remove mounting nut and lay twin pipe aside.
11. Remove bulkhead mounting bolts, **Fig. 11.**
12. Remove instrument panel as outlined in "Dash Panel Service" section.
13. Remove lower steering column shear and mounting bolts.
14. Remove left and righthand A-pillar door seal and trim.
15. Remove left and righthand transverse reinforcement mounting bolts.
16. Remove left and righthand air bag transverse reinforcement mounting bolts.
17. Disconnect heater electrical connectors.
18. Remove left and righthand center console transverse reinforcement mounting bolts.
19. Disconnect cable tie, open left and righthand catches and pull fuse box down.
20. Remove left and righthand fuse box pivots.
21. Remove transverse reinforcement and heater.
22. Reverse procedure to install. Install new O-rings.

M5, 525, 528, 530 & 540

1. Drain cooling system into suitable container.
2. Disconnect clip, twist and remove lefthand engine compartment air duct.
3. Disconnect heater core water hoses.
4. Blow low pressure compressed air into delivery line to prevent coolant from dripping onto carpet from core.
5. Remove console as outlined under "Console, Replace."
6. Remove mounting bolts and lefthand footwell air outlet.
7. Remove mounting bolts, heater core pipes and bracket.
8. Disconnect rear compartment ventilation actuator motor and set aside.
9. **On models built before March 1999,** proceed as follows:
    a. Remove mounting bolts and righthand footwell air outlet.
    b. Disconnect clips and remove rear compartment ventilation duct.
10. **On models built after February 1999,** proceed as follows:
    a. Disconnect mounting lugs and move righthand footwell air outlet to right.
    b. Disconnect mounting screws and retainers, then turn rear compartment flap to right and remove heating element cover.
11. **On all models,** remove heater core.
12. Reverse procedure to install. Install new O-rings.

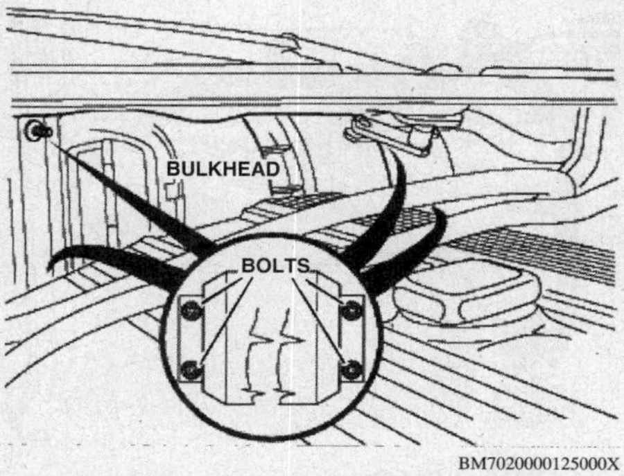

Fig. 11 Bulkhead replacement. 2001 M3

X5

1. Drain coolant into suitable container.
2. Remove heater bulkhead as outlined under "Wiper Motor, Replace."
3. Disconnect clamps and water hoses from flange. Blow remaining coolant from core.
4. Remove instrument panel trim panel as outlined in "Dash Panel Service" section.
5. Disconnect mount clips and pull lefthand footwell air duct to left.
6. Remove mounting screws and pull lefthand footwell air outlet down.
7. Remove mounting screws and remove pipes.
8. Disconnect holder and righthand footwell duct.
9. Disconnect rear footwell air duct.
10. Disconnect clip, remove mounting screws and pull cover down.
11. Remove evaporator temperature sensor and set aside.
12. Remove footwell flap and servodrive, as required.
13. Remove heater core.
14. Reverse procedure to install using new seals.

Z3

1. Drain cooling system into suitable container.
2. Disconnect clips and remove water hoses.
3. Blow low pressure compressed air into delivery line to prevent coolant from dripping onto carpet from core.
4. Remove instrument panel as outlined in "Dash Panel Service."
5. Remove knee protectors.
6. Clip together and remove lines from heater core.
7. Remove mounting bolt and footwell air outlet.
8. Remove mounting bolts and heater core.
9. Reverse procedure to install.

323, 325, 328 & 330

323is & 328is & 1998-99 328i & 1998 323i & 1999 323i & 328i Convertibles

Refer to "1998–99" under "M3."

323Ci, 325, 328Ci & 330 & 2000 323i & 328i & 1999 323i & 328i Sedans

Refer to "2001" under "M3."

740 & 750

1. Drain cooling system into suitable container.
2. Disconnect clip, then remove mounting bolts and engine cover.
3. Disconnect heater core water hoses on bulkhead, **Fig. 12.**
4. Blow low pressure compressed air into delivery line to prevent coolant from dripping onto carpet from core.
5. Remove console as outlined under "Console, Replace."
6. Remove steering wheel as outlined under "Steering Wheel, Replace.".
7. Remove lower instrument panel trim.
8. Remove steering column collar.
9. Move steering column to bottom and fully extended position.
10. Remove mounting screw and upper steering column trim by pressing in and disconnecting clip.
11. Remove interlock cable from lock.
12. Remove clamp bolt and press steering spindle down.
13. Remove shear-off screws.
14. Disconnect steering column lines from brackets.
15. Disconnect ignition switch connector and remove.
16. Remove support tube mounting bolts and steering column.
17. Remove mounting bolts, then the left and righthand footwell air ducts.
18. Remove mounting bolts, then the left and righthand rear air ducts.
19. Pry out righthand footwell flap actuator motor and disconnect linkage.
20. Lever out lefthand footwell flap actuator motor and disconnect linkage.
21. Remove mounting bolts and nut, then pry out left and righthand brackets.
22. Disconnect and remove temperature sensor.
23. Disconnect clips and remove heater core cover.
24. Remove mounting bolts and remove heater core, **Fig. 13.**
25. Reverse procedure to install, noting the following:
    a. **Torque** steering column support tube mounting nut to 71 inch lbs.
    b. Tighten shear-off screws until heads shear off.
    c. **Torque** new steering column spindle clamp self-locking nut to 14 ft. lbs.
    d. **Torque** steering wheel mounting bolt to 46 ft. lbs. or nut to 59 ft. lbs.
    e. **Torque** driver air bag type II mounting bolts to 18 inch lbs.
    f. **Torque** driver air bag type I mounting bolts to 71 inch lbs.
    g. Install new O-rings.

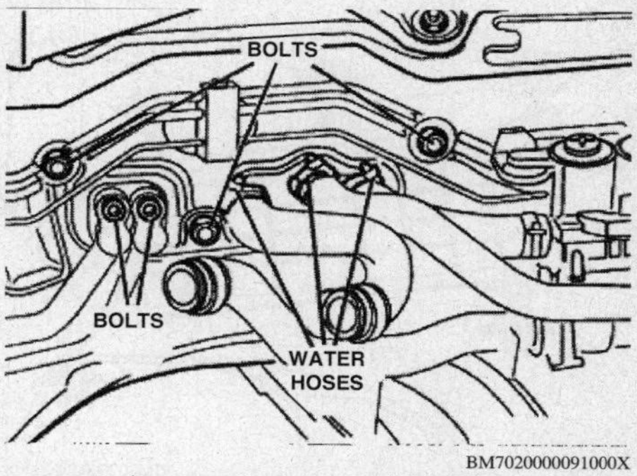

Fig. 12 Bulkhead water hose replacement. 740 & 750

EVAPORATOR CORE

REPLACE

M3 & 318

1998-99

1. Recover refrigerant as outlined in "Air Conditioning" section
2. Remove heater core as previously outlined.
3. Remove left and righthand mounting bolts, cut cable strap and remove reinforcement pipe from steering column, **Fig. 14.**
4. Remove reinforcement pipe for passenger's air bag, **Fig. 15.**
5. Disconnect connector, then remove mounting bolt and heater.
6. **On 318ti models,** loosen clamp.
7. **On all models,** remove mounting bolts and cover.
8. Remove expansion valve as previously outlined,
9. Disconnect connector and remove evaporator sensor.
10. Disconnect wiring harness from brackets and place aside.
11. Remove mounting bolt and place cover aside.
12. Disconnect clips and remove lower housing.
13. Remove evaporator core.
14. Reverse procedure to install. Install new O-rings.

2001

Refer to "Heater Core, Replace."

M5, 525, 528, 530 & 540

1. Recover refrigerant as outlined in "Air Conditioning" section
2. Remove heater core as outlined under "Heater Core, Replace."
3. Remove mounting bolts, then the left and righthand footwell air outlets.
4. Remove mounting bolts and evaporator cover.
5. Remove clips and evaporator tube cover.
6. Remove clips and footwell vent outlet.
7. Remove mounting bolts and heater core cover.

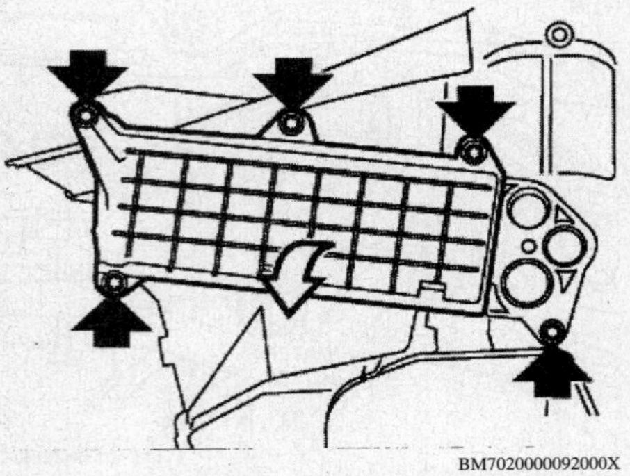

Fig. 13 Heater core replacement. 740 & 750

8. Remove mounting bolts and housing lower section.
9. Remove expansion valve as previously outlined.
10. Remove evaporator core.
11. Reverse procedure to install. Install new O-rings.

X5

1. Remove heater core as described under "Heater Core, Replace."
2. Disconnect clip and remove center defroster nozzle.
3. Disconnect electrical connector.
4. Disconnect blower limit switch and pull it down.
5. Remove mounting screws and holder, then disconnect expansion valve, pull to left and remove out of housing.
6. Remove clips, mounting screws and blower housing.
7. Remove mounting screws and housing base.
8. Remove clips, mounting bolt and retainers, then separate housing sections.
9. Press flange down and out of housing.
10. Disconnect temperature sensor hold and remove evaporator core.
11. Reverse procedure to install.

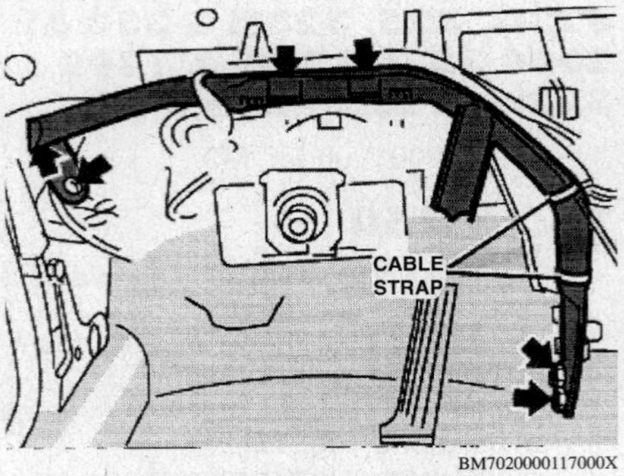

Fig. 14 Steering column reinforcement pipe replacement. 1998–99 M3 & 318i

Z3

1. Recover refrigerant as outlined in "Air Conditioning" section.
2. Remove mounting bolts and pipes.
3. Remove holder, mounting bolts and pipes with pressure plate.
4. Remove mounting bolts and cover.
5. Remove evaporator core.
6. Reverse procedure to install. Install new O-rings.

323, 325, 328 & 330

323is & 328is & 1998–99 328i & 1998 323i & 1999 323i & 328i Convertibles

Refer to "1998–99" under "M3."

323Ci, 325, 328Ci & 330 & 2000 323i & 328i & 1999 323i & 328i Sedans

Refer to "2001" under "M3."

740 & 750

1. Recover refrigerant as outlined in "Air Conditioning" section

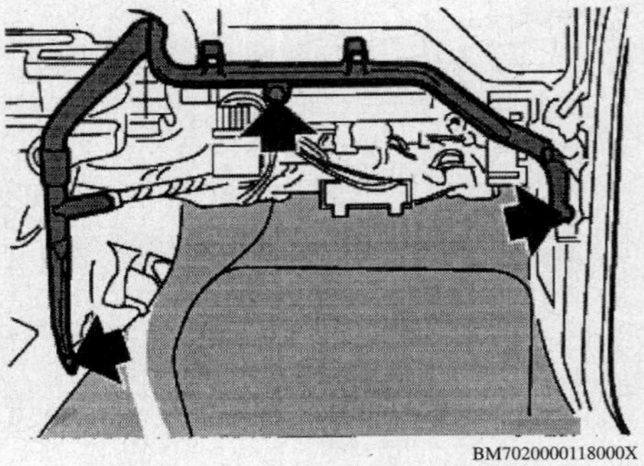

Fig. 15 Passenger air bag reinforcement pipe replacement.

2. Remove expansion valve as previously outlined.
3. Disconnect left and righthand hoses.
4. Disconnect linkages.
5. Remove mounting bolts and clips, then the lower housing.
6. Remove evaporator core.
7. Reverse procedure to install.

TECHNICAL SERVICE BULLETINS

STEERING WHEEL SQUEAK

2000 Z3

On some of these models built before July 1999 the steering wheel may squeak.

This condition may be caused by the ribbon connector plastic rub rubbing on the directional switch housing.

To correct this condition, proceed as follows:

1. Remove steering wheel as outlined under "Steering Wheel, Replace."
2. Cover openings.
3. Trim ribbon connector rub flush with housing.
4. Remove plastic trimmings and tape.
5. Install steering wheel and **torque** to 46 ft. lbs.

1.9L (M44) Four-Cylinder Engine

NOTE: On Air Bag Equipped Models, Refer To "Air Bag System Precautions" Located In The Front Of This Manual For System Disarming & Arming Procedures.

NOTE: Refer To "Computer Relearn Procedures" Located In The Front Of This Manual When Battery Power To The Computer Has Been Interrupted.

NOTE: Prior To Performing Any Service Operations Listed In This Section, Consult The "Technical Service Bulletins" Section For Related Information.

INDEX

	Page No.
Camshaft, Replace	2-28
Installation	2-28
Removal	2-28
Compression Pressure	2-25
Cooling System Bleed	2-29
Crankshaft Damper, Replace	2-27
Crankshaft Rear Oil Seal, Replace	2-28
Cylinder Head, Replace	2-26
Installation	2-26
Removal	2-26
Engine Rebuilding Specifications	2-241
Engine, Replace	2-25
Exhaust Manifold, Replace	2-26
Front Cover, Replace	2-27
Lower	2-27
Upper	2-27
Front Cover Seal, Replace	2-27
Fuel Filter, Replace	2-29
Fuel Pump, Replace	2-29
Hydraulic Lifters, Replace	2-27
Intake Manifold, Replace	2-26
Lower	2-26
Upper	2-26
Main & Rod Bearings	2-28
Main Bearings	2-28
Rod Bearings	2-28
Oil Pan, Replace	2-29
Oil Pump, Replace	2-29
Piston & Rod Assembly	2-28
Precautions	2-25
Air Bag Systems	2-25
Battery Ground Cable	2-25
Fuel System Pressure Relief	2-25
Radiator, Replace	2-29
Rocker Arms, Replace	2-27
Serpentine Drive Belt	2-29
Replacement	2-29
Technical Service Bulletins	2-30
Engine Will Not Turn Over	2-30
Rough Idle	2-30
Thermostat, Replace	2-29
Tightening Specifications	2-31
Timing Case, Replace	2-28
Installation	2-28
Removal	2-28
Timing Chain, Replace	2-27
Installation	2-27
Removal	2-27
Timing Chain Tensioner, Replace	2-28
Valve Adjustment	2-27
Valve Cover, Replace	2-27
Water Pump, Replace	2-29

PRECAUTIONS

AIR BAG SYSTEMS

Refer to "Air Bag System Precautions" in the front of this manual for system disarming and arming procedures.

BATTERY GROUND CABLE

Prior to service, disconnect battery ground cable and isolate as required.

FUEL SYSTEM PRESSURE RELIEF

Relieve fuel system pressure before disconnecting any fuel line or fuel system component.

1. Remove fuel pump relay(s).
2. Connect battery ground cable and crank engine for 10 seconds.
3. When fuel system repairs are complete, install fuel pump relays and crank engine to restore fuel pump pressure.

COMPRESSION PRESSURE

1. Relieve fuel pressure as outlined under "Precautions."
2. **On models equipped with automatic transmission,** place gear selector in P position.
3. **On models equipped with manual transmission,** place gearshift lever in neutral position.
4. **On all models,** set hand brake.
5. Turn ignition switch to Off position.
6. Disconnect Digital Motor Electronics (DME) master relay.
7. Remove spark plugs.
8. Install compression tester adapter tool No. 11 0 226, or equivalent, into spark plug bore by hand.
9. Connect compression gauge tool No. 11 0 224, or equivalent, onto adapter.
10. Fully depress accelerator pedal and operate starter motor until compression pressure reading is at maximum.
11. Normal compression pressure should measure 145–160 psi.
12. Maximum permissible difference between individual cylinders is 6 psi.

ENGINE

REPLACE

1. Remove ignition coil from sprint strut.
2. Lift hood to assembly position and lock in place.
3. **On 318 models,** remove firewall air manifold and wiper system bracket as outlined under "Wiper Motor, Replace" in "Electrical" section.
4. **On Z3 models,** turn rotary clips 90° and remove lower instrument panel trim.
5. **On all models,** disconnect cable from accelerator lever shaft.
6. Compress hook and pull cable out of engine compartment wall.
7. Remove cap, press locking hooks together and press nipple mount out of operating lever.
8. Pull cable out of rubber mount and disconnect mount from bracket.
9. Disconnect Mass Air Flow (MAF) sensor connector and remove active carbon filter lead mounting screw.
10. Loosen hose clamp and remove air intake hose from gaiter.
11. Open clamps and loosen retainers, then disconnect connector and hose clip. Remove intake filter.
12. Remove air filter housing upper section with MAF sensor and gaiter.
13. Remove mounting nuts, clip and air filter housing lower section.
14. Lock belt pulley in position using holding tool No. 11 5 050, or equivalent, then remove mounting nut using wrench tool No. 11 5 040, or equivalent. **Nut has lefthand threads.**
15. Remove fan coupling.

16. Remove radiator as outlined under "Radiator, Replace."
17. Disconnect heater hoses at heater and heating valve.
18. Remove mounting bolts and tie power steering fluid reservoir tank aside.
19. Remove power steering pump from alternator bracket and tie aside with lines connected.
20. Remove lower intake manifold as outlined under "Intake Manifold, Replace."
21. Remove battery trim panel, control module cover, cable channel on separating wall and heater separating wall.
22. Disconnect diagnosis connector, then the Camshaft Position (CMP) and Crankshaft Position (CKP) sensors.
23. Disconnect alternator cable and remove engine wiring harness connection screw.
24. Disconnect Engine Coolant Temperature (ECT) sensor and oil pressure switch connectors.
25. Disconnect fuel injectors' and knock sensors' connectors.
26. Disconnect wire harness from right and lefthand sides of engine.
27. Relieve fuel system pressure as outlined under "Precautions."
28. Disconnect fuel supply and return lines. Seal hoses with suitable clamps.
29. Attach engine lifting/support tool No. 11 0 070, or equivalent, to engine.
30. Disconnect righthand ground lead.
31. Remove left and righthand engine mount bolts.
32. **On models equipped with automatic transmission,** disconnect oil line from engine carrier and oil sump.
33. **On all models,** remove engine.
34. Reverse procedure to install. Tighten mounting bolts and nuts to specifications.

INTAKE MANIFOLD

REPLACE

UPPER

1. Remove accelerator cable as outlined under "Engine, Replace."
2. Loosen front manifold support.
3. Remove throttle valve rubber gaiter.
4. Disconnect Throttle Position Sensor (TPS) connector.
5. Disconnect tank ventilation hose.
6. Disconnect brake booster adapter.
7. Loose back manifold support.
8. Remove mounting bolts and remove upper intake manifold.
9. Reverse procedure to install using new seals.

LOWER

1. Remove upper intake manifold as outlined under "Upper."
2. Loose dipstick guide pipe.
3. Remove mounting bolts and manifold support.
4. Relieve fuel pressure as outlined under "Precautions."
5. Disconnect fuel hoses. Seal hose with suitable clamps.

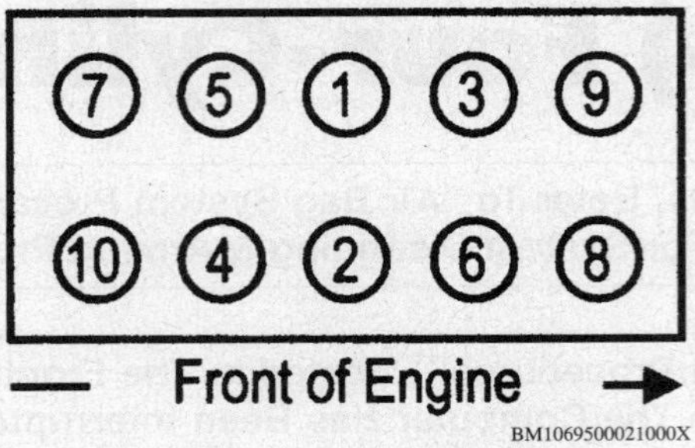

Fig. 1 Cylinder head bolt tightening sequence

6. Lower engine coolant level by draining it into suitable container.
7. Disconnect preheating hose from pressure regulating valve flange.
8. Remove pressure regulating valve flange.
9. Disconnect Camshaft Position (CMP) and Crankshaft Position (CKP) sensors.
10. Disconnect cable duct from lower intake manifold.
11. Disconnect alternator and starter electrical connectors.
12. Remove lower intake manifold mounting bolts.
13. Disconnect oil pressure switch and Engine Coolant Temperature (ECT) sensor electrical connectors.
14. Remove lower intake manifold.
15. Reverse procedure to install using new gasket and seals.

EXHAUST MANIFOLD

REPLACE

1. Remove mounting nuts and disconnect exhaust pipe from manifold.
2. Remove air injection pipe, as required.
3. Remove mounting nuts and exhaust manifold.
4. Reverse procedure to install, noting the following:
   a. Coat threads with suitable CRC copper paste.
   b. Install new gaskets.
   c. Tighten new mounting nuts to specifications.

CYLINDER HEAD

REPLACE

With the timing chain removed, avoid turning the camshaft or crankshaft. If movement is required, exercise extreme caution to avoid valve damage caused by piston contact.

REMOVAL

1. Remove air filter housing as outlined under "Engine, Replace."
2. Remove upper front cover as outlined "Front Cover, Replace."
3. Remove spark plugs.
4. Raise and support vehicle.
5. Drain engine coolant into suitable container.
6. Remove mounting bolts and disconnect exhaust pipe from manifold.
7. Remove lower intake manifold as outlined under "Intake Manifold, Replace."
8. Remove timing chain tensioner as outlined under "Timing Chain Tensioner, Replace."
9. Disconnect water hose from rear branch flange.
10. Disconnect heater feed and return hoses.
11. Rotate crankshaft in normal rotational direction until cylinder No. 1 piston is at firing TDC. Ensure camshaft rear alignment block bores are pointing up.
12. Install camshaft alignment tool No. 11 3 240, or equivalent.
13. Remove mounting bolts and camshaft sprockets.
14. Disconnect slide rail from cylinder head.
15. Turn slide rail adjusting bolt back approximately two turns.
16. Turn crankshaft approximately 45° in reverse of normal rotation.
17. Remove cylinder head bolts in reverse of tightening sequence, **Fig. 1.**
18. Remove cylinder head.

INSTALLATION

1. Ensure locating dowels on cylinder head are in good condition and correct located.
2. Ensure gasket surfaces are clean.
3. Install new gasket and profile seal, then the cylinder head.
4. Lightly oil new bolts and **torque** to 22 ft. lbs. in sequence, **Fig. 1.**
5. Tighten cylinder head bolts an additional 90° in sequence, then final tighten an additional 90° in sequence.
6. Place adjusting screw for slide rail is free of play. Tighten bolt.
7. Ensure camshafts alignment blocks bores are in up position using alignment tool No. 11 3 240, or equivalent.
8. Remove crankshaft alignment hole plug from lefthand lower rear of engine.
9. Rotate engine from 45° BTDC to TDC position.
10. Install alignment pin tool No. 11 2 300, or equivalent, through hole in block.
11. Install camshaft sprockets into timing chain and onto camshafts so that arrow marks on sprockets are pointing up. Ensure sprockets slots are centered over camshaft holes.
12. Install chain and camshaft sprockets. Ensure sprocket arrows point up and long bores align centrally.
13. Install sensor gear onto inlet sprocket. Ensure sensor gear cylinder axis arrow points up.
14. Install camshaft sprocket bolts hand tight. Ensure sprockets are free.
15. Install timing chain tensioner as outlined under "Timing Chain Tensioner, Replace."
16. Tighten camshaft sprocket bolts to specifications. Remove alignment tools.
17. Connect heater feed and return hoses.
18. Connect water hose from rear branch flange.

19. Install lower intake manifold as outlined under "Intake Manifold, Replace."
20. Remove mounting bolts and disconnect exhaust pipe from manifold. Lightly coat threads with suitable copper paste.
21. Install spark plugs.
22. Install upper front cover as outlined "Front Cover, Replace."
23. Install air filter housing as outlined under "Engine, Replace."

VALVE COVER

REPLACE

1. Remove ignition coil from spring strut dome.
2. Remove battery and bracket.
3. Slightly lift grille and loosen cable duct from firewall end.
4. Turn screws 90° and remove cover.
5. Disconnect spark plug connectors.
6.
7. Loosen ignition lead and remove it with cable duct.
8. Disconnect engine breather hose.
9. Remove mounting bolts and valve cover. **Mark position and order of valve cover bolt seal components.**
10. Reverse procedure to install, noting the following:
    a. Coat contact surfaces with Drei Bond No. 1209 sealing agent, or equivalent.
    b. Replace seals as required.
    c. Ensure seal is correctly seated at rear.
    d. Install mounting bolts hand tight.
    e. Tighten mounting bolts to specifications crosswise from inside to outside.

VALVE ADJUSTMENT

This engine is equipped with hydraulic lifters and requires no valve adjustment,

ROCKER ARMS

REPLACE

1. Remove valve cover as outlined under "Valve Cover, Replace."
2. Remove spark plugs.
3. Remove fan coupling as outlined under "Engine, Replace."
4. Rotate engine in normal rotation direction until camshaft lob above rocker points vertically up.
5. Press valve down valve compressor tool 11 5 130, or equivalent, and remove rocker arm. **Mark rocker arms for installation in original positions.**
6. Reverse procedure to install.

HYDRAULIC LIFTERS

REPLACE

1. Remove rocker arms as outlined under "Rocker Arm, Replace."
2. Pull lifter from cylinder head.
3. Reverse procedure to install.

CRANKSHAFT DAMPER

REPLACE

1. Remove air conditioning compressor drive belt and pulley, as required.
2. Remove alternator drive belt.
3. Install adapter tool No. 11 2 410 and holder tool No. 11 2 150, or equivalents.
4. Remove mounting bolt and crankshaft damper.
5. Reverse procedure to install, noting the following:
    a. Replace front cover seal as outlined under "Front Cover Seal, Replace."
    b. Tighten new mounting bolt to specifications.

FRONT COVER

REPLACE

UPPER

Removal

1. Remove valve cover as outlined under "Valve Cover, Replace."
2. Remove thermostat as outlined under "Thermostat, Replace."
3. Remove mounting bolts, cable holder and cylinder detection sensor. Disconnect connector.
4. Remove mounting bolts and upper front cover.
5. Cut and remove rubber seals.

Installation

1. Coat sealing surfaces with Drei Bond No. 1209 sealer, or equivalent.
2. Install alignment studs part No. 11 4 110, or equivalent.
3. Insert new seals into position, then coat seals top and bottom with Drei Bond No. 1209 sealer, or equivalent.
4. Apply thin, even coat of Drei Bond No. 1209 sealer, or equivalent, to groove ends.
5. Seat new rubber seal in groove.
6. Apply thin coat of suitable grease to top side of rubber profile gasket and booth ends of guide plate tool No. 11 2 330, or equivalent.
7. Install gasket and guide plate tool.
8. Install front cover and mounting bolts. Fit flush.
9. Remove guide plate tool.
10. Install valve cover less spray lead oil feed sealing ring.
11. Hand tighten mounting bolts with large washers and press front cove down until upped edge and cylinder head align.
12. Remove alignment studs and tighten mounting bolts to specifications.
13. Install valve cover as outlined under "Valve Cover, Replace."

LOWER

1. Remove upper front cover as outlined under "Upper."
2. Remove crankshaft dampener as outlined under "Crankshaft Dampener, Replace."
3. Remove mounting bolts and belt pulley.
4. Remove mounting bolts and lower front cover.
5. Reverse procedure to install, noting the following:
    a. Ensure alignment dowels are in place and are in good condition.
    b. Install new seal using alignment pin tool No. 11 4 110, or equivalent.
    c. Coat front and rear of seal thinly with Drei Bond No. 1209 sealer, or equivalent.
    d. Initially **torque** mounting bolts to 44 inch lbs.
    e. Alternately tighten mounting bolts to specifications.

FRONT COVER SEAL

REPLACE

1. Remove crankshaft damper as outlined under "Crankshaft Damper, Replace."
2. Remove radial sealing ring using extractor tool No. 11 2 310, or equivalent.
3. Reverse procedure to install, noting the following:
    a. Lightly coat new seal with oil.
    b. Install flush with cover using installer tool No. 11 4 150, or equivalent.

TIMING CHAIN

REPLACE

With the timing chain removed, avoid turning the camshaft or crankshaft. If movement is required, exercise extreme caution to avoid valve damage caused by piston contact.

REMOVAL

1. Remove upper front cover as outlined under "Front Cover, Replace."
2. Remove spark plugs.
3. Loosen but do not remove crankshaft dampener mounting bolt as outlined under "Crankshaft Dampener, Replace."
4. Rotate crankshaft in normal rotational direction until cylinder No. 1 piston is at firing TDC. Ensure camshaft rear alignment block bores are pointing up.
5. Remove crankshaft alignment hole plug from lefthand lower rear of engine.
6. Install alignment pin tool No. 11 2 300, or equivalent, through hole in block.
7. Install camshaft alignment tool No. 11 3 240, or equivalent.
8. Remove crankshaft dampener as outlined under "Crankshaft Dampener, Replace."
9. Remove lower front cover as outlined under "Front Cover, Replace."
10. Remove timing chain tensioner as outlined under "Timing Chain Tensioner, Replace."
11. Remove camshaft sprockets.
12. Remove timing chain sprocket with chain.

INSTALLATION

1. Install slide and tensioning rails.

2. Turn adjusting screw approximately two turns.
3. Place adjusting screw for slide rail is free of play. Tighten bolt.
4. Align timing chain sprocket with woodruff key and install with chain.
5. Place chain over camshaft sprockets.
6. Install chain and camshaft sprockets. Ensure sprocket arrows point up and long bores align centrally.
7. Install sensor gear onto inlet sprocket. Ensure sensor gear cylinder axis arrow points up.
8. Install camshaft sprocket bolts hand tight. Ensure sprockets are free.
9. Install timing chain tensioner as outlined under "Timing Chain Tensioner, Replace."
10. Tighten camshaft sprocket bolts to specifications. Remove alignment tools.
11. Install lower front cover as outlined under "Front Cover, Replace."
12. Install crankshaft dampener as outlined under "Crankshaft Dampener, Replace."
13. Install spark plugs.
14. Install upper front cover as outlined under "Front Cover, Replace."

TIMING CHAIN TENSIONER

REPLACE

1. Remove plug and hydraulic chain tensioner.
2. Place tensioner into vice with suitable protective jaws.
3. Slowly push tensioner together leaving lock washer visible.
4. Repeat previous step twice.
5. Install tensioner using new sealing ring.

TIMING CASE

REPLACE

REMOVAL

1. Remove timing chain as outlined under "Timing Chain, Replace," then the guide and tensioning rails.
2. Remove alternator as outlined in "Electrical" section.
3. Remove mounting bolts and alternator carrier.
4. Loosen oil filter cover and allow oil to drain into oil pan.
5. Remove mounting bolts and tie power steering pump aside with lines connected.
6. Remove mounting bolts and full-flow oil filter housing.
7. Remove oil pan as outlined under, "Oil Pan, Replace."
8. Remove mounting bolts and gear case.
9. Remove oil pump and control valve as outlined under "Oil Pump, Replace," as required.
10. Remove water pump as outlined under "Water Pump, Replace," as required.

BM1060100031000X

Fig. 2 Piston & rod assembly

INSTALLATION

1. Ensure dowel sleeves are properly located.
2. Install new seal.
3. Cost oil sump separating joint seal with Drei Bond No. 1209 sealer, or equivalent.
4. Apply sealing compound thinly and evenly to groove sends and seal new rubber seal in groove.
5. Apply thin coat of grease to top side of rubber profiler gasket and booth sides of guide plate tool No. 11 2 330, or equivalent.
6. Place guide tool on top of rubber profile gasket and install gear case.
7. Tighten mounting bolts to specifications and remove guide plate.
8. Install new front cover seal as outlined under "Front Cover Seal, Replace."
9. Install oil pan as outlined under, "Oil Pan, Replace."
10. Install full-flow oil filter housing.
11. Install power steering pump
12. Install carrier and alternator.
13. Install timing chain as outlined under "Timing Chain, Replace."

CAMSHAFT

REPLACE

REMOVAL

1. Remove spark plugs.
2. Remove rocker arms as outlined under "Rocker Arm, Replace."
3. Remove upper front cover as outlined under "Front Cover, Replace."
4. Remove timing chain tensioner as outlined under "Timing Chain Tensioner, Replace.".
5. Rotate crankshaft in normal rotational direction until cylinder No. 1 piston is at firing TDC. Ensure camshaft rear alignment block bores are pointing up.
6. Remove crankshaft alignment hole plug from lefthand lower rear of engine.
7. Install alignment pin tool No. 11 2 300, or equivalent, through hole in block.
8. Remove mounting bolts and camshaft sprockets.
9. Remove chain guide.
10. Mark camshaft and bearing components for installation alignment.
11. Remove camshaft bearings and camshafts.

INSTALLATION

1. Install camshafts and bearings.
2. Tighten mounting bolts to specifications.
3. Install chain guide.
4. Ensure camshafts alignment blocks bores are in up position using alignment tool No. 11 3 240, or equivalent.
5. Install camshaft sprockets into timing chain and onto camshafts so that arrow marks on sprockets are pointing up.
6. Install camshaft sensor wheel into intake camshaft sprocket so that arrow points up.
7. Install camshaft sprocket bolts and hand tighten. Sprockets must remain free.
8. Install chain tensioner as outlined under "Timing Chain Tensioner, Replace."
9. Tighten camshaft sprocket bolts to specification.
10. Install upper front cover as outlined under "Front Cover, Replace." Install rocker arms as outlined under "Rocker Arm, Replace."
11. Install spark plugs.

PISTON & ROD ASSEMBLY

The piston, connecting rods and bearings must be install in original positions.

Injection nozzles for cooling the pistons are installed on the underside of the cylinder between the bearing seats. **Do not damage the spray nozzles when removing the pistons.**

Pistons and pins are paired and must not be fitted individually.

Fit connecting rod with piston pin to piston in such a way that both of the visible pair numbers on the install direction arrow on the piston point to the right, **Fig. 2.**

MAIN & ROD BEARINGS

MAIN BEARINGS

1. Oil bolt threads.
2. **Torque** bolts to 15 ft. lbs.
3. Tighten bolts an additional 50°.

ROD BEARINGS

1. Oil bolt threads.
2. **Torque** to 44 inch lbs.
3. **Torque** to 15 ft. lbs.
4. Tighten an additional 70°.

CRANKSHAFT REAR OIL SEAL

REPLACE

1. Remove transmission as outlined in

"Clutch & Manual Transmission" or "Automatic Transmission" sections.
2. Raise and support vehicle.
3. Drain engine oil into suitable container.
4. Lock flywheel using holding tool No. 11 2 170, or equivalent.
5. Remove mounting bolts and flywheel.
6. Loosen but do not remove oil pan mounting bolts and carefully pull pan down while separating oil pan gasket with suitable knife.
7. Remove mounting bolts and end cover.
8. Life out sealing ring.
9. Drive in new sealing ring using driver tools Nos. 11 1 260 and 00 5 500, or equivalents.
10. Apply thing coat of Drei Bond No. 1209 sealing compound, or equivalent, to oil pan edges.
11. Install end cover with seal using support bushing as an installation tool.
12. Lubricate crankshaft contact face, then push on end cover straight and with tilting sideways.
13. Coat mounting bolts with sealing compound.
14. Tighten mounting bolts to specification.

OIL PAN

REPLACE

1. Raise and support vehicle.
2. Drain engine oil into suitable container.
3. Disconnect brake booster vacuum line.
4. Remove mounting bolt and oil dip stick tube. Discard sealing oil ring.
5. **On Z3 models,** proceed as follows:
   a. Measure and record left and righthand detent buffer protrusion for installation alignment.
   b. Remove buffers.
   c. Disconnect cable and lines, then place aside.
6. **On all models,** support engine using support fixture 00 0 200, or equivalents.
7. Raise engine approximately 0.2 inch.
8. Disconnect steering spindle from steering gear.
9. Disconnect left and righthand engine mounts.
10. Brace front axle support with fixture tool No. 31 2 220, or equivalent. and suitable transmission jack.
11. Disconnect left and righthand control arms from engine carrier.
12. Disconnect mounting bolt and lower front axle support.
13. **Do not disconnect steering gear from front axle support.**
14. Disconnect fuel lines' brackets from oil pan.
15. **On models equipped with automatic transmission,** remove oil pipes from oil pan.
16. **On all models,** remove mounting bolts and oil pan from rear.
17. Remove oil wiper and intake pipe, as required.
18. Reverse procedure to install, noting the following:
   a. Seal oil pan with Three Bond No. 1209 sealer, or equivalent.
   b. Hand tighten bolts.
   c. Tighten oil pan to engine bolts to specifications first, then oil pan to transmission bolts.

OIL PUMP

REPLACE

1. Remove lower front cover as outlined under "Front Cover."
2. Remove mounting bolts and oil pump cover.
3. Remove rotor set. **Oil pump gears are matched and must be replaced as set.**
4. Holding spacer down with suitable drift and remove circlip and control valve.
5. Reverse procedure to install. Tighten mounting bolts to specification.

SERPENTINE DRIVE BELT

Refer to **Fig. 3** for serpentine belt routing.

REPLACEMENT

1. If reusing belt, mark rotational direction for installation.
2. Remove fan coupling as outlined under "Engine, Replace."
3. Remove dust cab.
4. Push tensioning device back on bolt connect **lefthand threads.**
5. Remove belt.
6. Reverse procedure to install. Preload tensioning device as far as possible and lock using holding tool No. 11 3 340, or equivalent.

COOLING SYSTEM BLEED

1. Set heater controls to maximum temperature and fan to low speed.
2. Run engine and flush engine cooling circuit with 3–4 short bursts to 4500–5000 RPM. **Do not run engine for more than 30 seconds.**
3. Close bleed screw when escaping coolant is free from air bubbles.
4. Run engine until thermostat opens.

THERMOSTAT

REPLACE

1. Remove fan couples as outlined under "Engine, Replace."
2. Drain cooling system into suitable container.
3. Disconnect coolant hoses.
4. Remove mounting bolts and thermostat housing.
5. Thermostat is integrated part of housing and can only replaced as an assembly.
6. Reverse procedure to install using new gasket. Tighten mounting bolts to specifications.

WATER PUMP

REPLACE

1. Raise and support vehicle.
2. Remove alternator drive belt.
3. Drain coolant into suitable container.
4. Remove water pump mounting bolts.
5. Insert two M6 bolts into thread and press pump out evenly.
6. Reverse procedure to install using new gasket. Tighten mounting bolts to specifications.

RADIATOR

REPLACE

1. Raise and support vehicle.
2. Drain coolant into suitable container.
3. Remove fan cowl.
4. Disconnect air conditioning temperature switch.
5. Disconnect upper and lower water hoses, then the expansion hose.
6. **On models equipped with automatic transmission,** disconnect cooler lines
7. **On all models,** disconnect radiator mounting catches with suitable screwdriver.
8. Remove radiator.
9. Reverse procedure to install.

FUEL PUMP

REPLACE

1. Relieve fuel system pressure as outlined under "Precautions."
2. Drain enough fuel from tank to ensure pump unit can be removed without spillage.
3. **On Z3 models,** procedure as follows:
   a. Remove passenger seat.
   b. Cut and fold carpet.
   c. Remove mounting screws and cover.
4. **On all models,** disconnect fuel pump and fuel level sensor electrical connectors.
5. Disconnect fuel inlet hose.
6. Remove ring nut using ring nut wrench tool No. 16 1 020, or equivalent.
7. Mark position of unit in fuel tank for installation reference.
8. Lift and rotate unit from fuel tank.**Do not deform fuel level sensor arm or altitude sensor tube.**
9. Reverse procedure to install, noting the following.
   a. Ensure altitude sensor tube is properly positioned into fuel tank baffle.
   b. Ensure match marks of unit and tank are aligned.
   c. Replace ring nut and seal.

FUEL FILTER

REPLACE

1. Relieve fuel system pressure as outlined under "Precautions."
2. Clamp fuel feed hose on both sides of fuel filter with clamping tool No. 13 3 010, or equivalent.
3. Loosen line clamps and disconnect hoses from fuel filter.
4. Remove fuel filter.

5. Reverse procedure to install. Ensure fuel filter is installed in correct flow direction.

TECHNICAL SERVICE BULLETINS

ROUGH IDLE

On some of these models there may be rough idle at operating temperatures.

This condition may be caused by unfavorable valve timing during overlap phase.

To correct this condition, adjust camshaft timing using new intake camshaft alignment tool No. 90 88 6 119 110, or equivalent, to retard intake camshaft timing 6°.

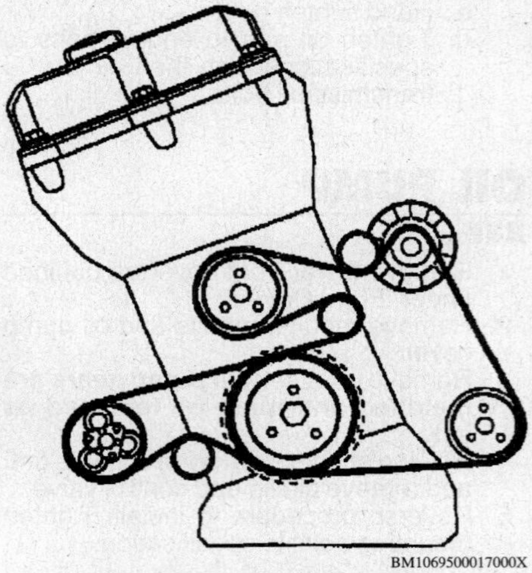

Fig. 3 Serpentine belt routing

ENGINE WILL NOT TURN OVER

On some models, the engine will not turn over.

This condition may be caused by a fuel injector stuck in open position. To correct this condition, proceed as follows:

1. Remove fuel injectors and inspect leakage rate.
2. Replace hydraulic locked injectors.
3. Inspect engine compression pressures.
4. If any cylinder's compression is less than 143 psi, piston/connecting rod may have damaged and further engine tear down is required.

TIGHTENING SPECIFICATIONS

Year	Component	Torque, Ft. Lbs.
1998–99	Block Coolant Drain Plug	18
	Camshaft Bearing	⑨
	Camshaft Sprocket	88①
	Chain Tensioner Plug	30
	Chain Tensioner Plunger	33
	Connecting Rod	④
	Crankshaft Damper	243
	Crankcase End Cover	②
	Crankshaft Increment Wheel	115①
	Cylinder Head	⑤
	Cylinder Head Cover Oil Trap	13
	Engine Mount	⑪
	Exhaust Manifold	②③
	Exhaust Pipe To Manifold	33
	Fan	29⑦
	Front Cover	②
	Flywheel	88
	Intake Manifold	②
	Main Bearing Caps	④
	Main Oil Duct Plug	25
	Oil Cooler Line	16
	Oil Drain	⑩
	Oil Filter Cover	⑬
	Oil Filter Lines	⑫
	Oil Pan	⑭
	Oil Pump	18
	Oil Pump Cover	88①
	Oil Pump Sprocket	⑮
	Oil Spray Nozzle	106①
	Oxygen Sensor	41
	Thermostat Bleeder	71①
	Thermostat Housing	88①
	Valve Cover	⑧
	Water Pump	⑥

① — Inch lbs.
② — M6, 88 inch lbs.; M7, 11 ft. lbs.; M8, 17 ft. lbs.; M10, 35 ft. lbs.
③ — Coat w/Molukote HSC paste, or equivalent.
④ — Refer to "Main & Rod Bearings" for tightening specifications.
⑤ — Refer to "Cylinder Head, Replace" for tightening specifications and sequence.
⑥ — M6, 88 inch lbs.; M8, 16 ft. lbs.
⑦ — **Torque** of 29 ft. lbs. when using wrench tool No. 11 5 040, or equivalent, is equal to 22 ft. lbs. on torque wrench.
⑧ — M6, 88 inch lbs.; M7 and 8, 11 ft. lbs.
⑨ — M6, 88 inch lbs.; M7, 10 ft. lbs.; M8, 15 ft. lbs.
⑩ — M12, 18 ft. lbs.; M22, 44 ft. lbs.
⑪ — M8, 16 ft. lbs.; M10, 35 ft. lbs.
⑫ — M8, 14 ft. lbs.; M20, 30 ft. lbs.
⑬ — M8, 16 ft. lbs.; M10 & 12, 24 ft. lbs.; Screw-On, 18 ft. lbs.
⑭ — M6 x 8.8, 88 inch lbs.; M6 x 10.9,106 inch lbs.
⑮ — M6, 88 inch lbs.; M10 35 ft. lbs.; M10 x 1, 18 ft. lbs.

2.5L (M52 & M54), 2.8L (M52), 3.0L (M54) & 3.2L (S52 & S54) Inline Six Cylinder Engines

NOTE: On Air Bag Equipped Models, Refer To "Air Bag System Precautions" Located In The Front Of This Manual For System Disarming & Arming Procedures.

NOTE: Refer To "Computer Relearn Procedures" Located In The Front Of This Manual When Battery Power To The Computer Has Been Interrupted.

NOTE: Prior To Performing Any Service Operations Listed In This Section, Consult The "Technical Service Bulletins" Section For Related Information.

INDEX

	Page No.
Camshaft, Replace	2-43
M3	2-43
X5	2-45
Z3	2-46
323 & 328	2-46
325, 330, 525 & 530	2-46
528	2-46
Compression Pressure	2-33
Cooling System Bleed	2-50
Crankshaft Damper, Replace	2-42
M3	2-42
X5	2-42
Z3	2-43
323 & 328	2-43
325, 330, 525 & 530	2-43
528	2-43
Crankshaft Rear Oil Seal, Replace	2-48
Cylinder Head, Replace	2-38
M3	2-38
1998–99	2-38
2001	2-39
X5	2-40
Installation	2-40
Removal	2-40
Z3	2-40
2.3, 2.5i & 3.0i	2-40
2.8	2-40
M Coupe & M Roadster	2-40
323 & 328	2-41
323Ci & 328Ci & 2000 323i & 328i & 1999 323i & 328i Sedans	2-41
323is & 328is & 1998–99 328i & 1998 323i & 1999 323i & 328i Convertibles	2-41
325, 330, 525 & 530	2-41
528	2-41
1998	2-41
1999–2000	2-41
Engine Rebuilding Specifications	2-241
Engine, Replace	2-33
M3	2-33
X5	2-33
Z3	2-33
323, 325, 328 & 330	2-33
525, 528 & 530	2-34
Exhaust Manifold, Replace	2-37
M3	2-37
X5 3.0i	2-37
Z3	2-38
323 & 328	2-38
325,330, 525 & 530	2-38
528	2-38
Front Cover, Replace	2-43
Front Cover Seal, Replace	2-43
Fuel Filter, Replace	2-52
M3	2-52
X3	2-52
Z3	2-52
323, 325, 328 & 330	2-52
525 & 530	2-52
528	2-52
Fuel Pump, Replace	2-51
M3	2-51
Z3	2-51
323, 325, 328 & 330	2-51
525, 528 & 530	2-51
Hydraulic Lifters, Replace	2-42
Installation	2-42
Removal	2-42
Intake Manifold, Replace	2-34
M3	2-34
X5 3.0i	2-34
Z3	2-34
323 & 328	2-36
325 & 330	2-36
525 & 530	2-36
528	2-37
Main & Rod Bearings	2-48
Main Bearings	2-48
M3	2-48
X5	2-48
Z3	2-48
323 & 328	2-48
325, 328, 525 & 530	2-48
528	2-48
Rod Bearings	2-48
Oil Pan, Replace	2-49
M3	2-49
X5	2-49
Z3	2-49
323, 325, 328 & 330	2-49
525, 528 & 530	2-50
Oil Pump, Replace	2-50
Piston & Rod Assembly	2-48
Precautions	2-33
Air Bag Systems	2-33
Battery Ground Cable	2-33
Fuel System Pressure Relief	2-33
Radiator, Replace	2-50
M3	2-50
X5	2-50
Z3	2-51
323, 325, 328 & 330	2-51
525 & 530	2-51
528	2-51
Serpentine Drive Belt	2-50
Replacement	2-50
Technical Service Bulletins	2-52
Coolant Hose Leak	2-53
Coolant Leak From Righthand Side Of Cylinder Head	2-52
Coolant Temperature Gauge Fluctuates & Heater Output Too Low	2-52
Engine Compartment Buzz Or Rattle	2-52
Engine Will Not Turn Over	2-53
Rough Idle	2-52
Thermostat, Replace	2-50
Tightening Specifications	2-53
Timing Chain, Replace	2-43
Timing Chain Tensioner, Replace	2-43
Installation	2-43
Removal	2-43
Valve Adjustment	2-42

	Page No.
Valve Cover, Replace	2-41
M3	2-41
X5	2-41
Z3	2-41
323 & 328	2-42
325 & 330	2-42
525 & 530	2-42
528	2-42
Variable Camshaft Timing (VANOS) Adjustment Unit, Replace	2-46
M3	2-46
X5	2-47
Z3	2-48
323 & 328	2-48
325, 330, 525 & 530	2-48
528	2-48
Water Pump, Replace	2-50

PRECAUTIONS

AIR BAG SYSTEMS

Refer to "Air Bag System Precautions" in the front of this manual for system disarming and arming procedures.

BATTERY GROUND CABLE

Prior to service, disconnect battery ground cable and isolate as required.

FUEL SYSTEM PRESSURE RELIEF

Relieve fuel system pressure before disconnecting any fuel line or fuel system component.

1. Remove fuel pump relay(s).
2. Connect battery ground cable and crank engine for 10 seconds.
3. When fuel system repairs are complete, install fuel pump relays and crank engine to restore fuel pump pressure.

COMPRESSION PRESSURE

1. Relieve fuel pressure as outlined under "Precautions."
2. **On models equipped with automatic transmission,** place gear selector in P position.
3. **On models equipped with manual transmission,** place gearshift lever in neutral position.
4. **On all models,** set hand brake.
5. Turn ignition switch to Off position.
6. Disconnect Digital Motor Electronics (DME) master relay.
7. Remove spark plugs.
8. Install compression tester adapter tool No. 11 0 226, or equivalent, into spark plug bore by hand.
9. Connect compression gauge tool No. 11 0 224, or equivalent, onto adapter.
10. Fully depress accelerator pedal and operate starter motor until compression pressure reading is at maximum.
11. **On all models except 2001 M3, Z3 M Coupe and Z3 M Roadster,** normal compression pressure should measure 145–160 psi.
12. **On 2001 M3, Z3 M Coupe and Z3 M Roadster models,** normal compression pressure should measure 160–174 psi.
13. **On all models,** maximum permissible difference between individual cylinders is 6 psi.

ENGINE

REPLACE

M3

1998–99

1. Lift hood to assembly position and lock in place.
2. Remove splash guard.
3. Remove transmission as outlined in "Clutch & Manual Transmission" or "Automatic Transmission" sections.
4. Drain coolant into suitable container.
5. Remove radiator as outlined under "Radiator" replace.
6. Remove engine cover.
7. Remove intake manifold as outlined under "Intake Manifold, Replace."
8. Disconnect connectors and position engine wiring harness aside with cable duct.
9. Disconnect heating valve and heater hoses.
10. Remove mounting bolts and position power steering fluid reservoir aside with lines connected.
11. Remove mounting bolts and position power steering pump aside with lines connected.
12. Connect engine lifting tool No. 11 0 020, or equivalent, to engine lifting eyes.
13. Disconnect righthand ground cable.
14. Remove left and righthand engine mount mounting bolts.
15. Remove engine.
16. Reverse procedure to install. Tighten mounting bolts and nuts to specifications.

2001

1. Lift hood to assembly position and lock in place.
2. Open cable duct on lower section of microfilter housing and feed out cables.
3. Remove mounting screws and lower section of microfilter.
4. Remove mounting screws and splash guard.
5. Remove transmission as outlined in "Clutch & Manual Transmission" or "Automatic Transmission" sections.
6. Remove air conditioning compressor drive belt.
7. Remove mounting bolts and place air condition compressor aside with lines connected.
8. Drain coolant into suitable container.
9. Disconnect water hoses.
10. Remove radiator as outlined under "Radiator" replace.
11. Remove fuel injectors' cover.
12. Mark Oxygen Sensors (O2S) and connectors for installation. **Do not mix O2Ss.**
13. Remove cable from retainer and disconnect O2S connectors.
14. Disconnect O2S cable from cable guide on rear side of engine.
15. Remove O2Ss.
16. Remove intake manifold as outlined under "Intake Manifold, Replace."
17. Disconnect water pipe and heating valve hoses.
18. Disconnect connectors and place engine wiring harness aside with cable duct.
19. Remove mounting bolts and place power steering fluid reservoir aside with lines connected.
20. Lock belt pulley in position using holding tool No. 11 5 050, or equivalent, then remove mounting nut using wrench tool No. 11 5 040, or equivalent. **Nut has lefthand threads.**
21. Remove fan clutch.
22. Remove mounting bolts and place power steering pump aside with lines connected.
23. Connect engine lifting tool No. 11 0 020, or equivalent, to engine lifting eyes.
24. Disconnect righthand ground cable.
25. Remove left and righthand engine mount mounting bolts.
26. Remove engine.
27. Reverse procedure to install, noting the following:
    a. Coat O2S threads with Never Seez. or equivalent compound.
    b. Install O2S using socket wrench tool No. 11 7 030, or equivalent.
    c. Tighten mounting bolts and nuts to specifications.

X5

Refer to "2001" under "M3."

Z3

Refer to "1998–99" under "M3."

323, 325, 328 & 330

323is & 328is & 1998–99 328i & 1998 323i & 1999 323i & 328i Convertibles

1. Lift hood to assembly position and lock in place.
2. Remove firewall air manifold and wiper system bracket as outlined under "Wiper Motor, Replace" in "Electrical" section.
3. Remove splash guard.
4. Remove transmission as outlined in "Clutch & Manual Transmission" or "Automatic Transmission" sections.
5. Drain coolant into suitable container.

6. Remove radiator as outlined under "Radiator, Replace."
7. Remove engine cover.
8. Remove intake manifold as outlined under "Intake Manifold, Replace."
9. Disconnect connectors and place engine wiring harness aside with cable duct.
10. Disconnect heating valve and heater hoses.
11. Remove mounting bolts and place power steering fluid reservoir aside with lines connected.
12. Remove mounting bolts and place power steering pump aside with lines connected.
13. Connect engine lifting tool No. 11 0 020, or equivalent, to engine lifting eyes.
14. Disconnect righthand ground cable.
15. Remove left and righthand engine mount mounting bolts.
16. Remove engine.
17. Reverse procedure to install. Tighten mounting bolts and nuts to specifications.

323Ci, 325, 328Ci & 330 & 2000 323i & 328i & 1999 323i & 328i Sedans

Refer to "2001" under "M3."

525, 528 & 530

Refer to "1998–99" under "M3."

INTAKE MANIFOLD

REPLACE

M3

1998–99

1. Disconnect Mass Air Flow (MAF) sensor connector.
2. Disconnect air intake hose from idle speed actuator rubber gaiter.
3. Remove suction filter housing with MAF sensor and rubber gaiter.
4. Remove bulkhead heater air collector as outlined under "Wiper Motor, Replace" in "Electrical" section.
5. Place cable channel aside.
6. Disconnect brake booster vacuum connector.
7. Remove fuel injectors' cover.
8. Disconnect Oxygen Sensors (O2S) connectors.
9. Disconnect VANOS solenoid valve.
10. Lift connector strip off fuel injectors and place aside.
11. Disconnect ventilation connector.
12. Relieve fuel system pressure as outlined under "Precautions."
13. Disconnect fuel delivery and return lines. Plug lines with suitable clamps.
14. Secure fuel lines to intake manifold bracket.
15. Remove mounting bolts and throttle valve. Cables and preheating unit remain connected.
16. Remove mounting bolt and dipstick guide tube.
17. Disconnect cyclone oil separator return hose.
18. Remove mounting bolts, then the front and rear intake manifold supports.
19. Remove mounting bolt and disconnect coolant line bracket.
20. Disconnect temperature sensor and Idle Speed Control (ISC) valve connectors.
21. Disconnect tank vent valve connector.
22. Remove tank vent valve from bracket and disconnect hose.
23. Remove mounting bolts, intake manifold and tank vent valve.
24. Reverse procedure to install, noting the following:
    a. Replace gasket, as required.
    b. Tighten mounting bolts and nuts to specifications.

2001

1. Open cable duct on lower section of microfilter housing and feed out cables.
2. Remove mounting screws and lower section of microfilter.
3. Remove intake filter housing mounting bolt and disconnect Mass Air Flow (MAF) sensor connector.
4. Disconnect vacuum hose, clamp and clips, then remove intake filter housing with MAF sensor.
5. Disconnect engine vent hose and battery positive lead.
6. Disconnect oil dipstick guide tube and vacuum hose.
7. Disconnect tank venting valve from intake manifold holder.
8. Remove mounting bolts, then disconnect front and rear intake manifold supports.
9. Disconnect intake manifold vacuum hose.
10. Disconnect clamps using clamp pliers tool No. 11 9 160, or equivalent.
11. Disconnect condensate return.
12. Raise intake manifold slightly and disconnect throttle assembly. Feed vacuum line and wiring harness out.
13. Remove intake manifold.
14. Reverse procedure to install. Tighten mounting bolts and nuts to specifications.

X5 3.0i

1. Remove caps, mounting bolts and fuel injectors' cover.
2. Remove cap, mounting bolt and ignition coil cover.
3. Mark Oxygen Sensors (O2S) connectors for installation. **Do not mix O2S connectors.**
4. Disconnect O2S connectors.
5. Disconnect battery positive cable from intake manifold and retainer.
6. Disconnect vent hose from valve cover.
7. Disconnect Intake Air Temperature (IAT) sensor connector.
8. Disconnect fuel injectors' terminal strip and place it aside.
9. Disconnect connector and remove tank venting valve from manifold retainer.
10. Relieve fuel system pressure as outlined under "Precautions."
11. Disconnect fuel lines. Plug fuel lines with suitable clamps.
12. Disconnect fuel return line from oil dipstick guide tube.
13. Remove intake filter housing mounting bolt and disconnect Mass Air Flow (MAF) sensor connector.
14. Disconnect vacuum hose, clamp and clips, then remove intake filter housing with MAF sensor.
15. Disconnect intake hose vacuum lines.
16. Disconnect clips and pull intake hose out of connecting piece.
17. Remove intake manifold suction jet pump.
18. Disconnect clamps, then the intake hose from throttle assembly and Idle Speed Control (ISC) valve.
19. Disconnect resonance flap and ISC valve.
20. Disconnect oil pressure and temperature switches.
21. Disconnect tank venting valve connectors.
22. Remove cable duct mounting screws.
23. Disconnect throttle assembly connector.
24. Remove mounting bolts and throttle assembly.
25. Disconnect electrical connectors and place cable duct aside.
26. Disconnect knock sensors connector.
27. Remove manifold support mounting nut.
28. Disconnect air injection vacuum line as required.
29. Remove mounting nuts and intake manifold.
30. Reverse procedure to install, noting the following:
    a. Replace intake manifold gaskets as required.
    b. Replace rubber dampers and manifold support as required.
    c. Install new throttle assembly sealing ring.
    d. Install new oil dipstick guide tube and throttle assembly sealing rings
    e. Tighten mounting bolts and nuts to specifications.

Z3

M COUPE & M ROADSTER

1998–2000

Refer to "1998–99" under "M3."

2001

1. Remove intake filter housing mounting bolt and disconnect Mass Air Flow (MAF) sensor connector.
2. Disconnect vacuum hose, clamp and clips, then remove intake filter housing with MAF sensor.
3. Disconnect engine vent hose and battery positive lead.
4. Disconnect oil dipstick guide tube and vacuum hose.
5. Disconnect tank venting valve from intake manifold holder.
6. Remove mounting bolts, then disconnect front and rear intake manifold supports.
7. Disconnect intake manifold vacuum hose.
8. Disconnect clamps using clamp pliers

tool No. 11 9 160, or equivalent.
9. Disconnect condensate return.
10. Raise intake manifold slightly and disconnect throttle assembly. Feed vacuum line and wiring harness out.
11. Remove intake manifold.
12. Reverse procedure to install. Tighten mounting bolts and nuts to specifications.

Z3 2.3

1. Remove fuel injectors' cover.
2. Mark Oxygen Sensors (O2S) and connectors for installation. **Do not mix O2Ss.**
3. Remove cable from retainer and disconnect O2S connectors.
4. Disconnect battery positive cable retainer.
5. Disconnect VANOS solenoid valve connector and valve cover vent hose.
6. Disconnect retainer and Intake Air Temperature (IAT) sensor connector.
7. Disconnect fuel injectors' terminal strip and place it aside.
8. Disconnect tank venting valve connector and holder.
9. Disconnect terminal strip fuel hoses and cable.
10. Relieve fuel system pressure as outlined under "Precautions."
11. Disconnect fuel feed and return lines. Plug fuel lines with suitable clamps.
12. Remove oil dipstick guide tube mounting bolt.
13. Disconnect return line from dipstick guide tube.
14. Disconnect engine wiring harness and retainers, then remove mounting bolts and intake filter housing.
15. Disconnect Mass Air Flow (MAF) sensor connector, intake hose vacuum line and hose clip.
16. Disconnect clamps and remove intake hose with MAF sensor.
17. Pull throttle cable up and disconnect from actuator.
18. Disconnect clamps and remove intake hose from throttle assembly and Idle Speed Control (ISC) valve.
19. Disconnect resonance flap and ISC valve connectors, the then oil pressure and temperature switches' connectors.
20. Remove cable duct mounting screws.
21. Disconnect fuel lines, oil level sensor cable and oil return line from oil dipstick guide tube.
22. Remove oil dipstick guide tube.
23. Press cable duct aside and disconnect throttle assembly connector.
24. Remove mounting bolts and throttle assembly.
25. Disconnect intake manifold connectors and lay cable duct aside.
26. Disconnect knock sensors' connectors.
27. Remove intake manifold support mounting nuts.
28. Remove mounting nuts and intake manifold.
29. Reverse procedure to install, noting the following:
    a. Replace intake manifold gaskets as required.
    b. Replace rubber dampers and manifold support as required.
    c. Install new oil dipstick guide tube and throttle assembly sealing rings
    d. Tighten mounting bolts and nuts to specifications.

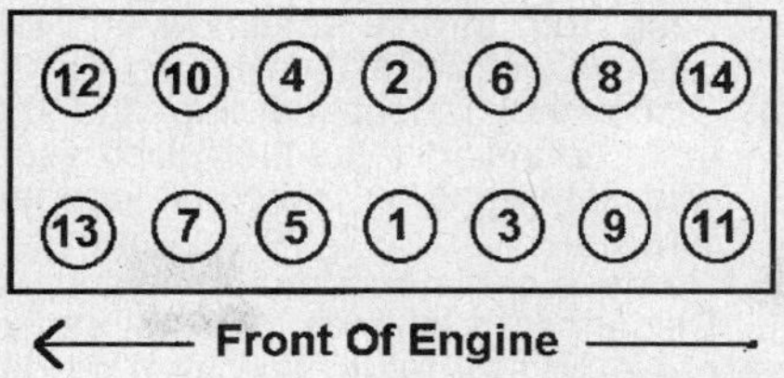

BM1069500024000X

Fig. 1 Cylinder head bolt tightening sequence

Z3 2.5i & 3.0i

1. Remove caps, mounting bolts and fuel injectors' cover.
2. Remove cap, mounting bolt and ignition coil cover.
3. Mark Oxygen Sensors (O2S) connectors for installation. **Do not mix O2S connectors.**
4. Disconnect O2S connectors.
5. Disconnect battery positive cable from intake manifold and retainer.
6. Disconnect vent hose from valve cover.
7. Disconnect Intake Air Temperature (IAT) sensor connector.
8. Disconnect fuel injectors' terminal strip and place it aside.
9. Disconnect connector and remove tank venting valve from manifold retainer.
10. Relieve fuel system pressure as outlined under "Precautions."
11. Disconnect fuel lines. Plug fuel lines with suitable clamps.
12. Disconnect fuel return line from oil dipstick guide tube.
13. Remove intake filter housing mounting bolt and disconnect Mass Air Flow (MAF) sensor connector.
14. Disconnect vacuum hose, clamp and clips, then remove intake filter housing with MAF sensor.
15. Disconnect clips and pull intake hose out of connecting piece.
16. Remove intake manifold suction jet pump.
17. Disconnect clamps, then the intake hose from throttle assembly and Idle Speed Control (ISC) valve.
18. Disconnect resonance flap and ISC valve.
19. Disconnect oil pressure and temperature switches.
20. Disconnect tank venting valve connectors.
21. Remove cable duct mounting screws.
22. Disconnect throttle assembly connector.
23. Remove mounting bolts and throttle assembly.
24. Disconnect electrical connectors and place cable duct aside.
25. Disconnect knock sensors connector.
26. Remove manifold support mounting nut.
27. Disconnect air injection vacuum line as required.
28. Remove mounting nuts and intake manifold.
29. Reverse procedure to install, noting the following:
    a. Replace intake manifold gaskets as required.
    b. Replace rubber dampers and manifold support as required.
    c. Install new throttle assembly sealing ring.
    d. Install new oil dipstick guide tube and throttle assembly sealing rings
    e. Tighten mounting bolts and nuts to specifications.

Z3 2.8

1998

Refer to "1998–99" under "M3."

1999-2000

1. Remove fuel injectors' cover.
2. Mark Oxygen Sensors (O2S) and connectors for installation. **Do not mix O2Ss.**
3. Remove cable from retainer and disconnect O2S connectors.
4. Disconnect battery positive cable retainer.
5. Disconnect VANOS solenoid valve connector and valve cover vent hose.
6. Disconnect retainer and Intake Air Temperature (IAT) sensor connector.
7. Disconnect fuel injectors' terminal strip and place it aside.
8. Disconnect tank venting valve connector and holder.
9. Disconnect terminal strip fuel hoses and cable.
10. Relieve fuel system pressure as outlined under "Precautions."
11. Disconnect fuel feed and return lines. Plug fuel lines with suitable clamps.
12. Remove oil dipstick guide tube mounting bolt.
13. Disconnect return line from dipstick guide tube.
14. Disconnect engine wiring harness and retainers, then remove mounting bolts and intake filter housing.
15. Disconnect Mass Air Flow (MAF) sensor connector, intake hose vacuum line and hose clip.
16. Disconnect clamps and remove intake hose with MAF sensor.
17. Pull throttle cable up and disconnect from actuator.
18. Disconnect clamps and remove intake hose from throttle assembly and Idle Speed Control (ISC) valve.
19. Disconnect resonance flap and ISC valve connectors, the then oil pressure and temperature switches' connectors.
20. Remove cable duct mounting screws.
21. Disconnect fuel lines, oil level sensor cable and oil return line from oil dipstick guide tube.
22. Remove oil dipstick guide tube.
23. Press cable duct aside and disconnect throttle assembly connector.
24. Remove mounting bolts and throttle assembly.
25. Disconnect intake manifold connectors and lay cable duct aside.

26. Disconnect knock sensors' connectors.
27. Remove intake manifold support mounting nuts.
28. Remove mounting nuts and intake manifold.
29. Reverse procedure to install, noting the following:
    a. Replace intake manifold gaskets as required.
    b. Replace rubber dampers and manifold support as required.
    c. Install new oil dipstick guide tube and throttle assembly sealing rings
    d. Tighten mounting bolts and nuts to specifications.

323 & 328

323is & 328is & 1998-99 328i & 1998 323i & 1999 323i & 328i CONVERTIBLES

Refer to "1998–99" under "M3."

323Ci & 328Ci & 2000 323i & 328i & 1999 323i & 328i SEDANS

1. Open cable duct on lower section of microfilter housing and feed out cables.
2. Remove mounting screws and lower section of microfilter.
3. Remove fuel injectors' cover.
4. Mark Oxygen Sensors (O2S) and connectors for installation. **Do not mix O2Ss.**
5. Remove cable from retainer and disconnect O2S connectors.
6. Disconnect battery positive cable retainer.
7. Disconnect rubber strip and solenoid valve connector.
8. Disconnect side trim panel cable penetrations.
9. Disconnect lock and pull side trim panel up.
10. Disconnect VANOS solenoid valve connector and valve cover vent hose.
11. Disconnect retainer and Intake Air Temperature (IAT) sensor connector.
12. Disconnect fuel injectors' terminal strip and place it aside.
13. Disconnect tank venting valve connector and holder.
14. Disconnect terminal strip fuel hoses and cable.
15. Relieve fuel system pressure as outlined under "Precautions."
16. Disconnect fuel feed and return lines. Plug fuel lines with suitable clamps.
17. Remove oil dipstick guide tube mounting bolt.
18. Disconnect return line from dipstick guide tube.
19. Disconnect engine wiring harness and retainers, then remove mounting bolts and intake filter housing.
20. Disconnect Mass Air Flow (MAF) sensor connector, intake hose vacuum line and hose clip.
21. Disconnect clamps and remove intake hose with MAF sensor.
22. Pull throttle cable up and disconnect from actuator.
23. Disconnect clamps and remove intake hose from throttle assembly and Idle Speed Control (ISC) valve.
24. Disconnect resonance flap and ISC valve connectors, the then oil pressure and temperature switches' connectors.
25. Remove cable duct mounting screws.
26. Disconnect fuel lines, oil level sensor cable and oil return line from oil dipstick guide tube.
27. Remove oil dipstick guide tube.
28. Press cable duct aside and disconnect throttle assembly connector.
29. Remove mounting bolts and throttle assembly.
30. Disconnect intake manifold connectors and lay cable duct aside.
31. Disconnect knock sensors' connectors.
32. Remove intake manifold support mounting nuts.
33. Remove mounting nuts and intake manifold.
34. Reverse procedure to install, noting the following:
    a. Replace intake manifold gaskets as required.
    b. Replace rubber dampers and manifold support as required.
    c. Install new oil dipstick guide tube and throttle assembly sealing rings
    d. Tighten mounting bolts and nuts to specifications.

325 & 330

1. Open cable duct on lower section of microfilter housing and feed out cables.
2. Remove mounting screws and lower section of microfilter.
3. Remove caps, mounting bolts and fuel injectors' cover.
4. Remove cap, mounting bolt and ignition coil cover.
5. Mark Oxygen Sensors (O2S) connectors for installation. **Do not mix O2S connectors.**
6. Disconnect O2S connectors.
7. Disconnect battery positive cable from intake manifold and retainer.
8. Disconnect rubber strip and solenoid valve connector.
9. Disconnect side trim panel cable penetrations.
10. Disconnect lock and pull side trim panel up.
11. Disconnect vent hose from valve cover.
12. Disconnect Intake Air Temperature (IAT) sensor connector.
13. Disconnect fuel injectors' terminal strip and place it aside.
14. Disconnect connector and remove tank venting valve from manifold retainer.
15. Relieve fuel system pressure as outlined under "Precautions."
16. Disconnect fuel lines. Plug fuel lines with suitable clamps.
17. Disconnect fuel return line from oil dipstick guide tube.
18. Remove intake filter housing mounting bolt and disconnect Mass Air Flow (MAF) sensor connector.
19. Disconnect vacuum hose, clamp and clips, then remove intake filter housing with MAF sensor.
20. Remove intake manifold suction jet pump.
21. Disconnect clamps, then the intake hose from throttle assembly and Idle Speed Control (ISC) valve.
22. Disconnect resonance flap and ISC valve.
23. Disconnect oil pressure and temperature switches.
24. Disconnect tank venting valve connectors.
25. Remove cable duct mounting screws.
26. Disconnect fuel lines and oil lever sensor cable from oil dipstick guide tube.
27. Disconnect oil return line from oil dipstick guide tube.
28. Remove mounting bolt and oil dipstick guide tube.
29. Disconnect throttle assembly connector.
30. Remove mounting bolts and throttle assembly.
31. Disconnect electrical connectors and place cable duct aside.
32. Disconnect knock sensors connector.
33. Remove manifold support mounting nut.
34. Disconnect air injection vacuum line as required.
35. Remove mounting nuts and intake manifold.
36. Reverse procedure to install, noting the following:
    a. Replace intake manifold gaskets as required.
    b. Replace rubber dampers and manifold support as required.
    c. Install new throttle assembly sealing ring.
    d. Install new oil dipstick guide tube and throttle assembly sealing rings
    e. Tighten mounting bolts and nuts to specifications.

525 & 530

1. Remove caps, mounting bolts and fuel injectors' cover.
2. Remove cap, mounting bolt and ignition coil cover.
3. Mark Oxygen Sensors (O2S) connectors for installation. **Do not mix O2S connectors.**
4. Disconnect O2S connectors.
5. Disconnect battery positive cable from intake manifold and retainer.
6. Disconnect vent hose from valve cover.
7. Disconnect Intake Air Temperature (IAT) sensor connector.
8. Disconnect fuel injectors' terminal strip and place it aside.
9. Disconnect connector and remove tank venting valve from manifold retainer.
10. Relieve fuel system pressure as outlined under "Precautions."
11. Disconnect fuel lines. Plug fuel lines with suitable clamps.
12. Disconnect fuel return line from oil dipstick guide tube.
13. Remove intake filter housing mounting bolt and disconnect Mass Air Flow (MAF) sensor connector.
14. Disconnect vacuum hose, clamp and clips, then remove intake filter housing

with MAF sensor.
15. Disconnect clips and pull intake hose out of connecting piece.
16. Remove intake manifold suction jet pump.
17. Disconnect clamps, then the intake hose from throttle assembly and Idle Speed Control (ISC) valve.
18. Disconnect resonance flap and ISC valve.
19. Disconnect oil pressure and temperature switches.
20. Disconnect tank venting valve connectors.
21. Remove cable duct mounting screws.
22. Disconnect throttle assembly connector.
23. Remove mounting bolts and throttle assembly.
24. Disconnect electrical connectors and place cable duct aside.
25. Disconnect knock sensors connector.
26. Remove manifold support mounting nut.
27. Disconnect air injection vacuum line as required.
28. Remove mounting nuts and intake manifold.
29. Reverse procedure to install, noting the following:
    a. Replace intake manifold gaskets as required.
    b. Replace rubber dampers and manifold support as required.
    c. Install new throttle assembly sealing ring.
    d. Install new oil dipstick guide tube and throttle assembly sealing rings
    e. Tighten mounting bolts and nuts to specifications.

528

1998

Refer to "1998–99" under "M3."

1999-2000

1. Remove fuel injectors' cover.
2. Mark Oxygen Sensors (O2S) and connectors for installation. **Do not mix O2Ss.**
3. Remove cable from retainer and disconnect O2S connectors.
4. Disconnect battery positive cable retainer.
5. Disconnect VANOS solenoid valve connector and valve cover vent hose.
6. Disconnect retainer and Intake Air Temperature (IAT) sensor connector.
7. Disconnect fuel injectors' terminal strip and place it aside.
8. Disconnect tank venting valve connector and holder.
9. Disconnect terminal strip fuel hoses and cable.
10. Relieve fuel system pressure as outlined under "Precautions."
11. Disconnect fuel feed and return lines. Plug fuel lines with suitable clamps.
12. Remove oil dipstick guide tube mounting bolt.
13. Disconnect return line from dipstick guide tube.
14. Disconnect engine wiring harness and retainers, then remove mounting bolts and intake filter housing.
15. Disconnect Mass Air Flow (MAF) sensor connector, intake hose vacuum line and hose clip.
16. Disconnect clamps and remove intake hose with MAF sensor.
17. Pull throttle cable up and disconnect from actuator.
18. Disconnect clamps and remove intake hose from throttle assembly and Idle Speed Control (ISC) valve.
19. Disconnect resonance flap and ISC valve connectors, the then oil pressure and temperature switches' connectors.
20. Remove cable duct mounting screws.
21. Disconnect fuel lines, oil level sensor cable and oil return line from oil dipstick guide tube.
22. Remove oil dipstick guide tube.
23. Press cable duct aside and disconnect throttle assembly connector.
24. Remove mounting bolts and throttle assembly.
25. Disconnect intake manifold connectors and lay cable duct aside.
26. Disconnect knock sensors' connectors.
27. Remove intake manifold support mounting nuts.
28. Remove mounting nuts and intake manifold.
29. Reverse procedure to install, noting the following:
    a. Replace intake manifold gaskets as required.
    b. Replace rubber dampers and manifold support as required.
    c. Install new oil dipstick guide tube and throttle assembly sealing rings
    d. Tighten mounting bolts and nuts to specifications.

EXHAUST MANIFOLD

REPLACE

M3

1998-99

1. Disconnect Oxygen Sensor (O2S) and cable.
2. Remove exhaust pipe to manifold mounting bolts.
3. **On models equipped with automatic transmission,** remove mounting bolts and transmission suspension.
4. **On all models,** loosen exhaust bracket clamps.
5. Remove secondary air induction non-return valve and pipe as required.
6. Remove mounting nuts and exhaust manifolds.
7. Reverse procedure to install, noting the following:
    a. Install new gaskets.
    b. Coat threads with CRC copper paste, or equivalent.
    c. Tighten mounting bolts and nuts to specifications.

2001

1. Open cable duct on lower section of microfilter housing and feed out cables.
2. Remove mounting screws and lower section of microfilter.
3. Remove expansion rivets and air duct.
4. Remove engine vent hose, oil cap and ignition coil cover.
5. Mark O2S monitor and connectors for installation. **Do not mix O2Ss.**
6. Remove cable from retainer and disconnect O2S connectors.
7. Drain cooling system into suitable container.
8. Remove lower radiator hose.
9. Feed O2S cables out of exhaust manifold shield.
10. Remove cylinder head check valve.
11. Remove exhaust manifold shield plate and air conditioning hoses.
12. Remove engine splash shield.
13. Remove mounting bolts and reinforcement plate.
14. Remove front exhaust pipe holder.
15. Disconnect connector.
16. Remove exhaust pipe to manifold mounting bolts.
17. Remove mounting nuts and exhaust system air deflector.
18. Support exhaust system with suitable jack and support tool No. 31 2 220, or equivalent.
19. Remove mounting bolts and exhaust system reinforcement plates. Rear plate remains connected with two rubber mounts.
20. Remove mounting bolts and body reinforcement.
21. Remove rear muffler to exhaust pipe mounting bolts, then the exhaust pipe.
22. Remove O2S from exhaust manifolds.
23. **Exhaust manifolds cannot be remove individually.**
24. Remove mounting nuts, disconnect front exhaust manifold and place on engine support arm.
25. Disconnect rear exhaust manifold from cylinder head.
26. Remove exhaust manifolds together.
27. Reverse procedure to install, noting the following:
    a. Coat threads with CRC copper paste, or equivalent.
    b. Tighten reinforcement plate rear mounting bolts first.
    c. **Torque** reinforcement plate mounting bolts to 44 ft. lbs.
    d. Tighten reinforcement plate mounting bolts an addition 90°, then an additional 30°.
    e. Install new cylinder head check valve seal and mounting nuts.

X5 3.0i

1. Remove mounting bolts and exhaust system air deflector.
2. Support exhaust system with suitable jack and support tool No. 31 2 220, or equivalent.
3. Remove mounting bolts and reinforcement plates. Rear plate remains attached to exhaust system with two rubber mounts.
4. Remove mounting screws and body reinforcement strut.
5. Remove rear muffler to intermediate pipes flange mounting bolts.
6. Remove catalytic converters to intermediate pipes mounting bolts, then the

intermediate pipes.
7. Remove mounting bolts and reinforcement plate.
8. Remove stabilizer bracket and rubber mount.
9. Disconnect left and righthand stabilizer links.
10. Disconnect Oxygen Sensors (O2S) cable retainer and connector.
11. Remove O2S using socket tool No. 11 7 020, or equivalent.
12. Remove fuel injectors' cover.
13. Mark O2S monitor and connectors for installation. **Do not mix O2Ss.**
14. Remove cable from retainer and disconnect O2S connectors.
15. Disconnect O2S cable from cable guide on rear side of engine.
16. Remove O2Ss.
17. Remove front exhaust manifold with catalytic converter, then the rear. **Rear exhaust manifold can only be removed after front.**
18. Reverse procedure to install, noting the following:
    a. **Torque** reinforcement plate mounting bolts to 41 ft. lbs.
    b. Tighten reinforcement plate mounting bolts an addition 90°, then an additional 15°.
    c. Coat threads with CRC copper paste, or equivalent.

Z3

M COUPE & M ROADSTER

1998–2000

Refer to "1998–99" under "M3."

2001

1. Remove engine vent hose, oil cap and ignition coil cover.
2. Mark O2S monitor and connectors for installation. **Do not mix O2Ss.**
3. Remove cable from retainer and disconnect O2S connectors.
4. Feed O2S cables out of exhaust manifold shield.
5. Remove cylinder head check valve.
6. Remove exhaust manifold shield plate and air conditioning hoses.
7. Remove engine splash shield.
8. Remove front exhaust pipe holder.
9. Disconnect connector.
10. Remove exhaust pipe to manifold mounting bolts.
11. Remove mounting nuts and exhaust system air deflector.
12. Support exhaust system with suitable jack and support tool No. 31 2 220, or equivalent.
13. Remove mounting bolts and exhaust system reinforcement plates. Rear plate remains connected with two rubber mounts.
14. Remove mounting bolts and body reinforcement.
15. Remove rear muffler to exhaust pipe mounting bolts, then the exhaust pipe.
16. Remove O2S from exhaust manifolds.
17. **Exhaust manifolds cannot be remove individually.**
18. Remove mounting nuts, disconnect front exhaust manifold and place on engine support arm.
19. Disconnect rear exhaust manifold from cylinder head.
20. Remove exhaust manifolds together.
21. Reverse procedure to install, noting the following:
    a. Coat threads with CRC copper paste, or equivalent.
    b. Install new cylinder head check valve seal and mounting nuts.
    c. Tighten mounting bolts and nuts to specifications.

Z3 2.3, 2.5i & 3.0i

1. Support engine with fixture tool No. 00 0 200, or equivalent. **Fixture must connect to both side walls and secure engine by front suspension eye.**
2. Raise engine approximately 0.2 inch.
3. Support exhaust system with suitable jack and support tool No. 31 2 220, or equivalent.
4. Remove mounting nuts and exhaust pipe to manifold connecting plate.
5. Remove rear exhaust pipe bracket mounting bolt.
6. Disconnect rubber mounts from bracket, then lower and remove exhaust systems.
7. Remove righthand engine support arm.
8. Disconnect Oxygen Sensors (O2S) cable retainer and connector.
9. Remove O2S using socket tool No. 11 7 020, or equivalent.
10. Remove fuel injectors' cover.
11. Mark O2S monitor and connectors for installation. **Do not mix O2Ss.**
12. Remove cable from retainer and disconnect O2S connectors.
13. Disconnect O2S cable from cable guide on rear side of engine.
14. Remove O2Ss.
15. Remove front exhaust manifold with catalytic converter, then the rear. **Rear exhaust manifold can only be removed after front.**
16. Reverse procedure to install, noting the following:
    a. Install new exhaust manifold gaskets.
    b. Coat O2S threads with Never Seez. or equivalent compound.
    c. Coat threads with CRC copper paste, or equivalent.
    d. Tighten mounting bolts and nuts to specifications.

Z3 2.8

1998

Refer to "1998–99" under "M3."

1999–2000

1. Support engine with fixture tool No. 00 0 200, or equivalent. **Fixture must connect to both side walls and secure engine by front suspension eye.**
2. Raise engine approximately 0.2 inch.
3. Remove exhaust pipe to manifold mounting nuts.
4. Remove exhaust bracket mounting bolts.
5. Support exhaust system with suitable jack and support tool No. 31 2 220, or equivalent.
6. Remove mounting bolts and disconnect reinforcement plate.
7. Remove rear muffler and rear rubber mount mounting nuts.
8. Remove exhaust system.
9. Remove righthand engine support arm.
10. Disconnect Oxygen Sensors (O2S) cable retainer and connector.
11. Remove O2S using socket tool No. 11 7 020, or equivalent.
12. Remove fuel injectors' cover.
13. Mark O2S monitor and connectors for installation. **Do not mix O2Ss.**
14. Remove cable from retainer and disconnect O2S connectors.
15. Disconnect O2S cable from cable guide on rear side of engine.
16. Remove O2Ss.
17. Remove front exhaust manifold with catalytic converter, then the rear. **Rear exhaust manifold can only be removed after front.**
18. Reverse procedure to install, noting the following:
    a. Install new exhaust manifold gaskets.
    b. Coat O2S threads with Never Seez. or equivalent compound.
    c. Coat threads with CRC copper paste, or equivalent.
    d. Tighten mounting bolts and nuts to specifications.

323 & 328

323is & 328is & 1998–99 328i & 1998 323i & 1999 323i & 328i CONVERTIBLES

Refer to "1998–99" under "M3."

323Ci & 328Ci & 2000 323i & 328i & 1999 323i & 328i SEDANS

Refer to "1999–2000 2.8" under "Z3."

325,330, 525 & 530

Refer to "2.5i & 3.0i" under "Z3."

528

1998

Refer to "1998–99" under "M3."

1999–2000

Refer to "1999–2000 2.8" under "Z3."

CYLINDER HEAD

REPLACE

M3

1998–99

REMOVAL

1. Disconnect Mass Air Flow (MAF) sensor connector.

2. Remove idle speed actuator hose.
3. Disconnect clips and remove bellow.
4. Remove mounting nuts and suction filter housing with MAF sensor and rubber gaiter.
5. Remove valve cover as outlined under "Valve Cover, Replace."
6. Remove spark plugs.
7. Remove intake manifold as outlined under "Intake Manifold, Replace."
8. Remove VANOS unit as outlined under "Variable Camshaft Timing (VANOS) Adjustment Unit, Replace."
9. Remove camshaft sensor.
10. Drain engine coolant into suitable container.
11. Disconnect exhaust pipe at manifold
12. Disconnect water hoses from cylinder head.
13. Remove exhaust camshaft sprocket mounting bolts and shims.
14. Remove mounting nuts and intake camshaft thrust washer.
15. Remove camshaft sprockets and secondary chain.
16. Remove chain tensioner.
17. Remove cylinder head chain guide.
18. Remove sprocket with primary timing chain, then sprocket from chain. **Secure chain with suitable wire.**
19. Remove timing case cover to cylinder head mounting bolts.
20. Remove cylinder head bolts using head bolt wrench tool No. 11 2 250, or equivalent, in reverse of tightening sequence, **Fig. 1.**
21. Remove cylinder head.

INSTALLATION

1. Ensure cylinder head and block surfaces are clean and in good condition
2. Ensure cylinder head locating dowels are in place and good condition.
3. Apply Dried Bond No. 1209, or equivalent, permanently elastic sealing compound, to timing case cover joint.
4. Install new cylinder head gasket. **Do not machine cylinder head.**
5. Ensure all washers are in place.
6. Place cylinder head into position. Ensure there is not oil in block and timing case cover tapped holes.
7. **On models with cast iron block,** proceed as follows:
   a. Install new M10 x 95 cylinder head bolts with lightly oiled threads hand tighten.
   b. **Torque** bolts to 22 ft. lbs. in sequence, **Fig. 1.**
   c. Tighten bolts an additional 90.°
   d. Final tighten bolts an additional 90.°
8. **On models with cast aluminum block,** proceed as follows:
   a. Install new M10 x 110 cylinder head bolts with lightly oiled threads hand tighten.
   b. **Torque** bolts to 29 ft. lbs. in sequence, **Fig. 1.**
   c. Tighten bolts an additional 90.°
   d. Final tighten bolts an additional 90.°
9. **On all models,** install timing case cover to cylinder head mounting bolts and tighten to specification.
10. Remove three cylinder head cover rear mounting bolts.
11. Align camshafts on hexagon as required.
12. Rotate camshaft until cylinder No. 1 intake and exhaust tips point towards one another.
13. Install camshaft locking tool No. 11 3 240, or equivalent. Ensure locking tool lies flush on cylinder head.
14. Lift timing chain and hold under tension.
15. Turn engine in normal rotational direction from 30° BTDC to TDC position.
16. Hold in this position by installing crank timing pin tool No. 11 2 300, or equivalent, into timing hole in block.
17. Install primary can on camshaft sprocket.
18. Install sprocket to camshaft. Align lefthand side threaded bores with deep bores.
19. Install chain tensioning tool No 11 4 220, or equivalent, into camshaft chain tensioner bore and turn tool's threaded center pin in until it contacts bow cover. **Do not tighten center pin.**
20. Ensure camshaft bolt holes are centered in sprocket slots.
21. Install chain guide and chain tensioner.
22. Install secondary chain on sprockets. Ensure flat side faces VANOS adjustment nut and collar faces camshaft.
23. Mount sprockets with chain. Ensure slots are centered.
24. Install intake camshaft thrust washer and tighten mounting nuts to specifications.
25. Install exhaust camshaft shim and mounting bolts with zero backlash.
26. Install VANOS unit as outlined under "Variable Camshaft Timing (VANOS) Adjustment Unit, Replace."
27. Install camshaft sensor.
28. Install exhaust pipe at manifold
29. Install water hoses to cylinder head.
30. Install intake manifold as outlined under "Intake Manifold, Replace."
31. Install spark plugs.
32. Install valve cover as outlined under "Valve Cover, Replace."
33. Install intake air ducting with MAF sensor.

2001

REMOVAL

1. Remove both exhaust manifolds as outlined under "Exhaust Manifold, Replace."
2. Lever out expansion rivets and remove intake hood with pipe, then disconnect hose clamp and disconnect plug.
3. Open retainer and rotate air intake filter housing upper section to left, this disconnect intake hose.
4. Remove air intake filter housing upper section.
5. Disconnect lefthand hand xenon headlamp control module connector, as required.
6. Remove mounting bolt and air intake filer housing. Remove air cleaner element.
7. Remove air intake filter housing lower section.
8. Remove valve cover as outlined under "Valve Cover, Replace."
9. Remove spark plugs.
10. Remove intake manifold as outlined under "Intake Manifold, Replace."
11. Drain engine coolant into suitable container.
12. Remove camshafts as outlined under "Camshaft, Replace."
13. Raise rocker arm.
14. Mark adjustment plates for installation in original positions.
15. Remove adjustment plates using magnetic holder tool No. 11 4 400, or equivalent.
16. Disconnect connector trip using disconnecting tool No. 121 120, or equivalent, alternating front to rear.
17. Disconnect supplementary air line.
18. Disconnect Idle Speed Control (ISC) valve bracket from return line and place aside with hoses connected.
19. Disconnect temperature sensor connector.
20. Remove thermostat housing as outlined under "Thermostat, Replace."
21. Disconnect vacuum hose and feed upper cover towards top.
22. Disconnect wiring harness lug and pull connector strip upward.
23. Disconnect intake and exhaust Camshaft Position (CMP) sensors.
24. Disconnect throttle actuator connector.
25. Place connector strip aside.
26. Remove throttle plug rod. **Do not remove pipe.**
27. Relieve fuel pressure as outlined under "Precautions."
28. Disconnect water hose and return line, then the fuel feed line.
29. Remove thrust bearing flange. **Flange and cylinder head are machined as single unit and must be replaced as unit.**
30. Remove sliding rail mounting bolt.
31. Remove timing case cover to cylinder head mounting bolts.
32. Remove cylinder head bolts in reverse of tightening sequence, **Fig. 1.**
33. Remove cylinder head.

INSTALLATION

1. Ensure cylinder head and block surfaces are clean and in good condition
2. Ensure cylinder head locating dowels are in place and good condition.
3. Apply Dried Bond No. 1209, or equivalent permanently elastic sealing compound, to timing case cover joint.
4. Install new cylinder head gasket.
5. Place cylinder head into position. Ensure there is not oil in block and timing case cover tapped holes.
6. Install new cylinder head bolts with lightly oiled threads hand tighten.
7. **Torque** bolts to 22 ft. lbs. in sequence, **Fig. 1.**
8. Tighten bolts an additional 90°.
9. Final tighten bolts an additional 90°.
10. Install chain holder and mounting bolts
11. Install new sealing washer and tighten sliding rail mounting bolt.
12. Install thrust bearing flange and tighten mounting bolts.
13. Install new O-ring, then the pipe.
14. Install thermostat housing using new O-ring.

15. Raise rocket arm.
16. Install adjustment plates in original positions using magnetic holder tool No. 11 4 400, or equivalent.
17. Install camshafts as outlined under "Camshaft, Replace."
18. Install intake manifold as outlined under "Intake Manifold, Replace."
19. Install spark plugs.
20. Install valve cover as outlined under "Valve Cover, Replace."
21. Install intake air ducting with MAF sensor.
22. Install exhaust manifolds as outlined under "Exhaust Manifold, Replace."

X5

REMOVAL

1. Remove both exhaust manifolds as outlined under "Exhaust Manifold, Replace."
2. Install engine support arm with engine mount and remove fixture tool No. 00 0 200, or equivalent.
3. Remove air intake filter housing with Mass Air Flow (MAF) sensor.
4. Remove valve cover as outlined under "Valve Cover, Replace."
5. Remove spark plugs.
6. Remove intake manifold as outlined under "Intake Manifold, Replace."
7. Drain engine coolant into suitable container.
8. Remove thermostat housing as outlined under "Thermostat, Replace."
9. Remove coolant pipe. If pipe cannot be fed out, proceed as follows:
   a. Loosen banjo bolt.
   b. Disconnect VANOS adjustment oil pressure line.
10. Remove double VANOS adjustment unit as outlined under "Variable Camshaft Timing (VANOS) Adjustment Unit, Replace."
11. Remove camshafts with bearing strips as outlined under "Camshaft, Replace."
12. Remove timing case cover to cylinder head mounting bolts.
13. Remove mounting bolts and chain guide.
14. Remove cylinder head bolts using head bolt wrench tool No. 11 2 250, or equivalent, in reverse of tightening sequence, **Fig. 1.**
15. Remove cylinder head.

INSTALLATION

1. Ensure cylinder head and block surfaces are clean and in good condition
2. Ensure cylinder head locating dowels are in place and good condition.
3. Apply Dried Bond No. 1209, or equivalent permanently elastic sealing compound, to timing case cover joint.
4. Install new cylinder head gasket. A 0.0118 inch thick cylinder head gasket is available for milled heads.
5. Place cylinder head into position. Ensure there is not oil in block and timing case cover tapped holes.
6. Install new cylinder head bolts with lightly oiled threads hand tighten.
7. **Torque** bolts to 29 ft. lbs. in sequence, **Fig. 1.**
8. Tighten bolts an additional 90°.
9. Final tighten bolts an additional 90°.
10. Install chain guide.
11. Install timing case cover to cylinder head mounting bolts and tighten to specification.
12. Install camshafts as outlined under "Camshaft, Replace."
13. Install VANOS unit as outlined under "Variable Camshaft Timing (VANOS) Adjustment Unit, Replace."
14. Install coolant pipe.
15. Install intake manifold as outlined under "Intake Manifold, Replace."
16. Install spark plugs.
17. Install valve cover as outlined under "Valve Cover, Replace."
18. Install intake air ducting with MAF sensor.
19. Install exhaust manifolds as outlined under "Exhaust Manifold, Replace."

Z3

M COUPE & M ROADSTER

1998–2000

Refer to "1998–99" under "M3."

2001

Refer to "2001" under "M3."

Z3 2.3, 2.5i & 3.0i

Refer to "X5."

Z3 2.8

1998

Removal

1. Disconnect Mass Air Flow (MAF) sensor connector.
2. Remove idle speed actuator hose.
3. Disconnect clips and remove bellow.
4. Remove mounting nuts and suction filter housing with MAF sensor and rubber gaiter.
5. Remove valve cover as outlined under "Valve Cover, Replace."
6. Remove spark plugs.
7. Remove intake manifold as outlined under "Intake Manifold, Replace."
8. Remove VANOS unit as outlined under "Variable Camshaft Timing (VANOS) Adjustment Unit, Replace."
9. Remove camshaft sensor.
10. Drain engine coolant into suitable container.
11. Disconnect exhaust pipe at manifold
12. Disconnect water hoses from cylinder head.
13. Remove exhaust camshaft sprocket mounting bolts and shims.
14. Remove mounting nuts and intake camshaft thrust washer.
15. Remove camshaft sprockets and secondary chain.
16. Remove chain tensioner.
17. Remove cylinder head chain guide.
18. Remove sprocket with primary timing chain, then sprocket from chain. **Secure chain with suitable wire.**
19. Remove timing case cover to cylinder head mounting bolts.
20. Remove cylinder head bolts using head bolt wrench tool No. 11 2 250, or equivalent, in reverse of tightening sequence, **Fig. 1.**
21. Remove cylinder head.

Installation

1. Ensure cylinder head and block surfaces are clean and in good condition
2. Ensure cylinder head locating dowels are in place and good condition.
3. Apply Dried Bond No. 1209, or equivalent permanently elastic sealing compound, to timing case cover joint.
4. Install new cylinder head gasket. A 0.0118 inch thick cylinder head gasket is available for milled heads.
5. Ensure all washers are in place.
6. Place cylinder head into position. Ensure there is not oil in block and timing case cover tapped holes.
7. **On models with cast iron block,** proceed as follows:
   a. Install new M10 x 95 cylinder head bolts with lightly oiled threads hand tighten.
   b. **Torque** bolts to 22 ft. lbs. in sequence, **Fig. 1.**
   c. Tighten bolts an additional 90°.
   d. Final tighten bolts an additional 90°.
8. **On models with cast aluminum block,** proceed as follows:
   a. Install new M10 x 110 cylinder head bolts with lightly oiled threads hand tighten.
   b. **Torque** bolts to 29 ft. lbs. in sequence, **Fig. 1.**
   c. Tighten bolts an additional 90.°
   d. Final tighten bolts an additional 90.°
9. **On all models,** install timing case cover to cylinder head mounting bolts and tighten to specification.
10. Remove three cylinder head cover rear mounting bolts.
11. Align camshafts on hexagon as required.
12. Rotate camshaft until cylinder No. 1 intake and exhaust tips point towards one another.
13. Install camshaft locking tool No. 11 3 240, or equivalent. Ensure locking tool lies flush on cylinder head.
14. Lift timing chain and hold under tension.
15. Turn engine in normal rotational direction from 30° BTDC to TDC position.
16. Hold in this position by installing crank timing pin tool No. 11 2 300, or equivalent, into timing hole in block.
17. Install primary can on camshaft sprocket.
18. Install sprocket to camshaft. Align left-hand side threaded bores with deep bores.
19. Install chain tensioning tool No 11 4 220, or equivalent, into camshaft chain tensioner bore and turn tool's threaded center pin in until it contacts bow cover. **Do not tighten center pin.**
20. Ensure camshaft bolt holes are centered in sprocket slots.
21. Install chain guide and chain tensioner.
22. Install secondary chain on sprockets.

Ensure flat side faces VANOS adjustment nut and collar faces camshaft.
23. Mount sprockets with chain. Ensure slots are centered.
24. Install intake camshaft thrust washer and tighten mounting nuts to specifications.
25. Install exhaust camshaft shim and mounting bolts with zero backlash.
26. Install VANOS unit as outlined under "Variable Camshaft Timing (VANOS) Adjustment Unit, Replace."
27. Install camshaft sensor.
28. Install exhaust pipe at manifold
29. Install water hoses to cylinder head.
30. Install intake manifold as outlined under "Intake Manifold, Replace."
31. Install spark plugs.
32. Install valve cover as outlined under "Valve Cover, Replace."
33. Install intake air ducting with MAF sensor.

1999–2000

Refer to "X5."

323 & 328

323is & 328is & 1998–99 328i & 1998 323i & 1999 323i & 328i CONVERTIBLES

Refer to "1998" under "2.8" under "Z3."

323Ci & 328Ci & 2000 323i & 328i & 1999 323i & 328i SEDANS

Refer to "X5."

325, 330, 525 & 530

Refer to "X5."

528

1998

Refer to "1998" under "2.8" under "Z3."

1999–2000

Refer to "X5."

VALVE COVER

REPLACE

M3

1998–99

1. Remove fuel injectors' cover.
2. Remove cylinder head cover.
3. Remove ignition coils as outlined in "Electrical" section.
4. Remove mounting bolts and valve cover.
5. Reverse procedure to install, noting the following:
   a. Apply Drei Bond No. 1209, or equivalent, to joint contact surfaces.
   b. Apply thin and even bead of Drei Bond No. 1209, or equivalent, to half-moon sections at rear of cylinder head.
   c. Hand tighten mounting bolts without preloads.
   d. Tighten mounting bolts to specifications is criss-cross pattern.

2001

1. Open cable duct on lower section of microfilter housing and feed out cables.
2. Remove mounting screws and lower section of microfilter.
3. Open microfilter lower section cable duct and feed out cables.
4. Remove mounting screws and microfilter housing lower section.
5. Remove expansion rivets and air duct.
6. Remove engine vent hose, sealing cap and ignition coil cover.
7. Disconnect exhaust Camshaft Position (CMP) sensor connectors, mounting bolts and fuel injectors' cover.
8. Disconnect hollow screw and remove sealing ring between cylinder head cover and return line. **Do not drop sealing ring into engine.**
9. Disconnect ignition coils' ground strap.
10. Mark O2S connectors for installation. **Do not mix O2Ss.**
11. Disconnect O2S sensors.
12. Remove cable from cable guide and place aside.
13. Remove mounting bolts and valve cover.
14. Reverse procedure to install, noting the following:
    a. Apply Drei Bond No. 1209, or equivalent, on left and righthand sides of transition between cylinder head and VANOS adjustment unit.
    b. Apply thin and even bead of Drei Bond No. 1209, or equivalent, to half-moon sections at VANOS adjustment unit and rear of cylinder head.
    c. Install new sealing rings.
    d. Assemble new gasket on cover. Guide pins may buckle slightly during installation.
    e. Ensure guide pins are exactly fed into bore holes.
    f. Hand tighten mounting bolts without preloads.
    g. Tighten mounting bolts to specifications is criss-cross pattern from inside to outside.
    h. Ensure Oxygen Sensor (O2S) cables are properly routed and clipped onto exhaust manifold shield plate.

X5

1. Remove caps, mounting bolts and fuel injectors' cover.
2. Disconnect caps, then remove mounting bolts, oil filler neck cap and ignition coil cover. Snack oil filler neck cap into cover.
3. Remove ignition coils as outlined in "Electrical" section.
4. Disconnect ignition coil wiring harness and place aside.
5. Disconnect engine breather hose.
6. Remove ground strap, mounting bolts and valve cover.
7. Reverse procedure to install, noting the following:
   a. Apply Drei Bond No. 1209, or equivalent, on left and righthand sides of transition between cylinder head and VANOS adjustment unit.
   b. Apply thin and even bead of Drei Bond No. 1209, or equivalent, to half-moon sections at VANOS adjustment unit and rear of cylinder head.
   c. Hand tighten mounting bolts without preloads.
   d. Tighten mounting bolts to specifications is criss-cross pattern from inside to outside.

Z3

M COUPE & M ROADSTER

1998–2000

Refer to "1998–99" under "M3."

2001

1. Remove cable duct from bulkhead.
2. Remove engine vent hose, sealing cap and ignition coil cover.
3. Disconnect exhaust Camshaft Position (CMP) sensor connectors, mounting bolts and fuel injectors' cover.
4. Disconnect hollow screw and remove sealing ring between cylinder head cover and return line. **Do not drop sealing ring into engine.**
5. Disconnect ignition coils' ground strap.
6. Mark O2S connectors for installation. **Do not mix O2Ss.**
7. Disconnect O2S sensors.
8. Remove cable from cable guide and place aside.
9. Remove mounting bolts and valve cover.
10. Reverse procedure to install, noting the following:
    a. Apply Drei Bond No. 1209, or equivalent, on left and righthand sides of transition between cylinder head and VANOS adjustment unit.
    b. Apply thin and even bead of Drei Bond No. 1209, or equivalent, to half-moon sections at VANOS adjustment unit and rear of cylinder head.
    c. Install new sealing rings.
    d. Assemble new gasket on cover. Guide pins may buckle slightly during installation.
    e. Ensure guide pins are exactly fed into bore holes.
    f. Hand tighten mounting bolts without preloads.
    g. Tighten mounting bolts to specifications is criss-cross pattern from inside to outside.
    h. Ensure Oxygen Sensor (O2S) cables are properly routed and clipped onto exhaust manifold

shield plate.

Z3 2.3, 2.5i & 3.0i

Refer to "X5."

Z3 2.8

1998

Refer to "1998–99" under "M3."

1999-2000

Refer to "X5."

323 & 328

323is & 328is & 1998-99 328i & 1998 323i & 1999 323i & 328i CONVERTIBLES

Refer to "1998–99" under "M3."

323Ci & 328Ci & 2000 323i & 328i & 1999 323i & 328i SEDANS

Refer to "X5."

325 & 330

1. Open cable duct on lower section of microfilter housing and feed out cables.
2. Remove mounting screws and lower section of microfilter.
3. Remove caps, mounting bolts and fuel injectors' cover.
4. Disconnect caps, then remove mounting bolts, oil filler neck cap and ignition coil cover. Snack oil filler neck cap into cover.
5. Remove ignition coils as outlined in "Electrical" section.
6. Disconnect ignition coil wiring harness and place aside.
7. Disconnect engine breather hose.
8. Remove ground strap, mounting bolts and valve cover.
9. Reverse procedure to install, noting the following:
   a. Apply Drei Bond No. 1209, or equivalent, on left and righthand sides of transition between cylinder head and VANOS adjustment unit.
   b. Apply thin and even bead of Drei Bond No. 1209, or equivalent, to half-moon sections at VANOS adjustment unit and rear of cylinder head.
   c. Hand tighten mounting bolts without preloads.
   d. Tighten mounting bolts to specifications is criss-cross pattern from inside to outside.

BM1060100032000X

Fig. 2 Piston & rod assembly

525 & 530

Refer to "X5."

528

1998

Refer to "1998–99" under "M3."

1999-2000

Refer to "X5."

VALVE ADJUSTMENT

These engines are equipped with hydraulic lifters and require no valve adjustment,

HYDRAULIC LIFTERS

REPLACE

REMOVAL

1. Remove camshaft as outlined under "Camshaft, Replace."
2. Remove bearing strip with hydraulic lifters.
3. Remove hydraulic lifters, as required, using suction cup tool No. 11 3 250, or equivalent.

INSTALLATION

1. Used lifters may only be installed in original positions.
2. Lifters expand when not under load from camshaft and require time before they can be pushed down.
3. Closed valves may still be open and contacting pistons.
4. After install camshaft wait as follows before cranking engine to TDC position:
   a. At 68°F, wait four minutes.
   b. At 50–68°F, wait 11 minutes.
   c. At 32–50°F, wait 30 minutes.

CRANKSHAFT DAMPER

REPLACE

M3

1998-99

1. Remove mounting bolts and splash guard.
2. Lock belt pulley in position using holding tool No. 11 5 050, or equivalent, then remove mounting nut using wrench tool No. 11 5 040, or equivalent. **Nut has lefthand threads.**
3. Remove fan clutch.
4. Remove alternator drive belt.
5. Remove mounting bolts and vibration damper.
6. Reverse procedure to install. Tighten mounting bolts to specifications.

2001

1. Remove mounting bolts and splash guard.
2. Remove fan cowl.
3. Remove air conditioning compressor drive belt.
4. Remove alternator drive belt.
5. Remove mounting bolts and TDC marking plate.
6. Remove mounting bolts and belt pulley.
7. Install holder tool No. 11 0 280, or equivalent, and support it using air conditioning mounting bracket.
8. Remove mounting bolts and vibration damper.
9. Reverse procedure to install. Tighten mounting bolts to specifications.

X5

1. Remove mounting bolts and splash guard.
2. Lock belt pulley in position using holding tool No. 11 5 050, or equivalent, then remove mounting nut using wrench tool No. 11 5 040, or equivalent. **Nut has lefthand threads.**
3. Remove fan clutch.
4. Remove air conditioning compressor drive belt.
5. Remove alternator drive belt.
6. **On models equipped with two-part vibration damper and hub,** remove mounting bolts and vibration damper.
7. **On models equipped with one-part vibration damper and hub,** proceed as follows:
   a. Lock damper with bracing tool No. 11 8 190/200, or equivalent.
   b. Remove mounting bolt and washer.
8. **On all models,** reverse procedure to

install. Tighten mounting bolts to specifications.

Z3

M COUPE & M ROADSTER

1998–2000

Refer to "1998–99" under "Z3."

2001

Refer to "2001" under "M3."

Z3 2.3, 2.5i & 3.0i

Refer to "X5."

Z3 2.8

1998

Refer to "1998–99" under "Z3."

1999–2000

Refer to "X5."

323 & 328

323is & 328is & 1998–99 328i & 1998 323i & 1999 323i & 328i CONVERTIBLES

Refer to "1998–99" under "M3."

323Ci & 328Ci & 2000 323i & 328i & 1999 323i & 328i SEDANS

Refer to "X5."

325, 330, 525 & 530

Refer to "X5."

528

1998

Refer to "1998–99" under "Z3."

1999–2000

Refer to "X5."

FRONT COVER

REPLACE

With the timing chain removed, avoid turning the camshaft or crankshaft. If movement is required, exercise extreme caution to avoid valve damage caused by piston contact.

1. Remove VANOS unit as outlined under "Variable Camshaft Timing (VANOS) Adjustment Unit, Replace."
2. Remove thermostat as outlined under "Thermostat, Replace."
3. Remove alternator drive belt and tensioner.
4. Brace water pump with drive belt, then remove mounting bolts.
5. **On 323is and 328is and 1998–2000 Z3 M Coupe and Z3 M Roadster and 1998–99 M3 and 328i and 1999 323i and 328i Convertibles, and 1998 Z3 2.8, 323i and 528i models,** remove engine speed sensor.
6. **On all models,** remove crankshaft vibration dampener and hub as outlined under "Crankshaft Damper, Replace."
7. Remove oil pan as outlined under "Oil Pan, Replace."
8. Drive timing case cover dowel pins out toward rear using suitable punch of less than 0.1969 inch.
9. Remove timing case cover to cylinder head mounting bolts.
10. Remove mounting bolts and timing case cover.
11. Reverse procedure to install, noting the following:
    a. Drive locating dowels out of cover until they protrude approximately 0.0787–0.1181 inch.
    b. Install new seals and O-rings.
    c. Remove all traces of old sealant from mating surfaces.
    d. Place beads of Drei Bond No. 1209, or equivalent sealing compound, to cylinder head gasket on left and righthand sides.
    e. Apply thin and even bead of Drei Bond No. 1209, or equivalent sealing compound, to entire timing case cover to cylinder head gasket surface.
    f. Initially **torque** mounting screws to 44 inch lbs.
    g. Drive in dowel pins until they are flush.
    h. Tighten mounting bolts in alternate sequence to specifications.
    i. Tighten timing case cover to cylinder head mounting bolts to specifications.
    j. Replace front cover seal as outlined under "Front Cover Seal, Replace."

FRONT COVER SEAL

REPLACE

1. Remove vibration damper as outlined under "Crankshaft Damper, Replace."
2. Remove vibration hub as required.
3. Remove seal using extractor tools No. 11 2 380, or equivalent.
4. Reverse procedure to install new seal coated with suitable engine oil using installer bushing tool No. 11 3 280, or equivalent.

TIMING CHAIN

REPLACE

Refer to "Cylinder Head, Replace."

TIMING CHAIN TENSIONER

REPLACE

REMOVAL

Remove tensioner. **Spring is under pressure.**

INSTALLATION

1. Install new sealing ring.
2. **On models equipped with hydraulic tensioner,** proceed as follows:
    a. Place tensioner on level base.
    b. Carefully compress.
    c. Repeat procedure twice.
3. **On all models,** tighten to specifications.

CAMSHAFT

REPLACE

With the timing chain removed, avoid turning the camshaft or crankshaft. If movement is required, exercise extreme caution to avoid valve damage caused by piston contact.

M3

1998–99

Removal

1. Remove VANOS adjustment unit as outlined under "Variable Camshaft Timing (VANOS) Adjustment Unit, Replace."
2. Remove exhaust sprocket mounting bolts.
3. Loosen intake sprocket mounting nuts.
4. **On models equipped less plate spring,** remove thrust washer.
5. **On models equipped with plate spring,** remove thrust washers and plate spring.
6. **On all models,** remove sprockets with chain.
7. Remove mounting bolts and thrust washer, then the sensor gear.
8. Remove secondary chain tensioner.
9. Remove chain guide.
10. Remove primary chain tensioner.
11. Remove sprocket with primary timing chain, then sprocket from chain. **Secure chain with suitable wire.**
12. Pull back setting mandrel tool No. 11 2 300, or equivalent, until flywheel is no longer located in position.
13. Lift timing chain and hold under tension.
14. Rotate engine in reverse of normal rotational direction approximately 30°. **Ensure no pistons are at TDC.**
15. Remove camshaft studs.
16. Install camshaft fixture tool No. 11 3 260, or equivalent, and **torque** mounting bolts into cylinders Nos. 1 and 4 spark plug threads to 21–24 ft. lbs.
17. Remove bearing cover No. 1.
18. Pretension bearing caps by turning eccentric shaft, then remove bearing cover mounting nuts.
19. Remove eccentric shaft tensions and fixture tool.
20. Mark bearing covers for installation in original position, then remove them.
21. Remove camshaft.

Installation

1. Oil camshafts, bearing, caps, friction washers, toothed shafts's splines and spline hubs before installation.
2. Install camshafts with intake and exhaust valves' tips pointing toward cylinder No. 1.

3. Install bearing covers in original positions. Covers are clearly marked, A for exhaust and E for intake.
4. Install camshaft fixture tool No. 11 3 260, or equivalent, and **torque** mounting bolts into cylinders Nos. 1 and 4 spark plug threads to 21–24 ft. lbs.
5. Pretension bearing caps by turning eccentric shaft, then tighten bearing cover mounting nuts to specifications.
6. Tighten bolts to specifications. Remove fixture.
7. Align camshafts using suitable open-end wrench.
8. Install camshaft locking tool No. 11 3 240, or equivalent. Ensure locking tool lies flush on cylinder head.
9. Lifting timing chain and hold under tension.
10. Rotate engine from 30° BTDC to TDC and lock with locking tool No. 11 2 300, or equivalent.
11. Install timing chain on to sprocket, then install sprocket on to exhaust camshaft with threaded bores on lefthand side aligned down deep holes.
12. Install chain tensioning tool No 11 4 220, or equivalent, into camshaft chain tensioner bore and turn tool's threaded center pin in until it contacts bow cover. **Do not tighten center pin.**
13. Ensure long sprocket slots are centered on threaded bores.
14. Install chain guide.
15. Install secondary chain tensioner.
16. Install sensor gear to intake camshaft.
17. Install thrust washer and tighten dowels to specifications.
18. Ensure flat side of chain is facing VANOS housing and collar facing camshaft.
19. Install camshaft sprockets with secondary timing chain, with slots centered.
20. **On models equipped with plate spring,** proceed as follows:
    a. Install 0.0787 inch thrust washer.
    b. Install plate spring with large support diameter facing camshaft.
    c. Install 0.1575 inch thrust washer.
    d. Tighten mounting nuts to specifications.
21. **On models equipped less plate spring,** install thrust washer on intake camshaft and tighten mounting nuts to specifications.
22. **On all models,** install exhaust camshaft shims and mounting bolts. Install bolts with zero backlash.
23. Install VANOS units as outlined under "Variable Camshaft Timing (VANOS) Adjustment Unit, Replace."

2001

Removal

1. Remove valve cover as outlined under "Valve Cover, Replace."
2. Remove spark plugs.
3. Lock belt pulley in position using holding tool No. 11 5 050, or equivalent, then remove mounting nut using wrench tool No. 11 5 040, or equivalent. **Nut has lefthand threads.**
4. Remove fan clutch.
5. Remove VANOS adjustment unit as outlined under "Variable Camshaft Timing (VANOS) Adjustment Unit, Replace."
6. Remove camshaft sprockets' mounting bolts, spline hub with plate spring and supporting ring. **Do not let supporting ring fall out.**
7. Remove timing chain tensioner.
8. Remove exhaust and intake sprockets from centering sleeve by holding timing chain under tension, feed out sprockets and secure chain against slipping down.
9. Pull back setting mandrel tool until flywheel is no longer located in position.
10. Lift timing chain and hold under tension.
11. Rotate engine in reverse of normal rotational direction approximately 30°. **Ensure no pistons are at TDC.**
12. Grip camshafts at hexagon head and remove centering sleeves's mounting bolts.
13. Remove centering sleeves with thrust washer.
14. Remove toothed sleeves.
15. Remove profile seals.
16. Remove mounting nuts and No. 1 thrust bearing flange.
17. Rotate intake camshaft until cylinder No. 1 cam tips are horizontal.
18. Install camshaft fixture tool No. 11 4 380, or equivalent, and tighten mounting bolts into cylinders Nos. 2 and 5 spark plug threads.
19. Mark bearing covers for installation in original position.
20. Pretension camshaft by turning eccentric shaft.
21. Remove mounting nuts and bearing caps.
22. Remove eccentric shaft tension and fixture tool. **Do not tilt camshaft when relieving tension.**
23. Remove intake camshaft.
24. Rotate exhaust camshaft until cylinder No. 1 cam tips are horizontal.
25. Install camshaft fixture tool No. 11 4 380, or equivalent, and tighten mounting bolts into cylinders Nos. 2 and 5 spark plug threads.
26. Mark bearing covers for installation in original position.
27. Pretension camshaft by turning eccentric shaft.
28. Remove mounting nuts and bearing caps.
29. Remove eccentric shaft tension and fixture tool. **Do not tilt camshaft when relieving tension.**
30. Remove exhaust camshaft.
31. Remove mounting bolts and signal disks as required.

Installation

1. Camshafts, caps and tools are marked E for intake and A for exhaust.
2. Intake camshaft has identifying groove behind locating bore; exhaust camshaft does not have groove.
3. Exhaust camshaft signal disk has seven blades; intake disk has six blades.
4. Install signal disks, align locating lug to groove and tighten mounting bolt to specifications.
5. Oil camshafts contact faces, rocker arms and bearing cover before installation.
6. Install intake camshaft with cylinder No. 1 cams pointed horizontally inward.
7. Install camshaft fixture tool No. 11 4 380, or equivalent, and tighten mounting bolts into cylinders Nos. 2 and 5 spark plug threads.
8. Pretension camshaft by turning eccentric shaft.
9. Align bearing caps by hand, install mounting nuts and hand tighten from inside to out in ½ turn increments.
10. Tighten bolts to specifications. Remove fixture.
11. Rotate intake camshaft at hexagon upward until locating bore is vertical.
12. Install setting gauge tool No. 11 9 130, or equivalent.
13. Adjust inlet camshaft hexagon until gauge pin tool No. 11 7 342, or equivalent, aligns setting gauge and locating bore. Setting gauge must rest flat on cylinder head.
14. Remove tools.
15. Install exhaust camshaft with cylinder No. 1 cams pointed horizontally inward.
16. Install camshaft fixture tool No. 11 4 380, or equivalent, and tighten mounting bolts into cylinders Nos. 2 and 5 spark plug threads.
17. Pretension camshaft by turning eccentric shaft.
18. Align bearing caps by hand, install mounting nuts and hand tighten from inside to out in ½ turn increments.
19. Tighten bolts to specifications. Remove fixture.
20. Rotate exhaust camshaft at hexagon upward until locating bore is vertical.
21. Install setting gauge tool No. 11 9 130, or equivalent.
22. Adjust inlet camshaft hexagon until gauge pin tool No. 11 7 342, or equivalent, aligns setting gauge and locating bore. Setting gauge must rest flat on cylinder head.
23. Remove tools.
24. Align thrust bearing flange by hand, install mounting nuts and hand tighten in

½ turn increments.
25. Coat toothed sleeves' splines with engine oil and install aligning bores to camshafts' tapped holes.
26. Install thrust washers on centering sleeves with large chamfer pointing toward camshaft rear.
27. Install centering sleeves, grip camshafts and tighten mounting bolts.
28. Install setting gauge tool No. 11 9 130, or equivalent, for intake camshaft.
29. Adjust inlet camshaft hexagon until gauge pin tool No. 11 7 342, or equivalent, aligns setting gauge and locating bore. Setting gauge must rest flat on cylinder head.
30. Remove tools.
31. Install setting gauge tool No. 11 9 130, or equivalent, for exhaust camshaft.
32. Adjust inlet camshaft hexagon until gauge pin tool No. 11 7 342, or equivalent, aligns setting gauge and locating bore. Setting gauge must rest flat on cylinder head.
33. Remove tools.
34. Lifting timing chain and hold under tension.
35. Rotate engine from 30° BTDC to TDC and lock with locking tool No. 11 2 300, or equivalent.
36. Hold timing chain under tension and install thrust washer with tapped holes horizontal.
37. Install intake sprocket on centering sleeves with elongated holes centered.
38. Hold timing chain under tension and feed on sprocket.
39. Install exhaust sprocket on centering sleeve with elongated holes centered.
40. Press tensioning rail against timing chain and inspect elongated holes' positions.
41. Install chain tensioner.
42. Install exhaust camshaft plate spring and supporting ring in spline hub with plate spring small support diameter pointing to supporting ring.
43. Remove spline hub with plate spring and supporting ring. **Do not let supporting ring fall out.**
44. Hand tighten spline hub mounting bolts removing free play.
45. Loosen mounting bolts until hub can be moved by hand.
46. Install intake camshaft plate spring and supporting ring in spline hub with plate spring small support diameter pointing to supporting ring.
47. Remove spline hub with plate spring and supporting ring. **Do not let supporting ring fall out.**
48. Hand tighten spline hub mounting bolts removing free play.
49. Loosen mounting bolts until hub can be moved by hand.
50. Install VANOS units as outlined under "Variable Camshaft Timing (VANOS) Adjustment Unit, Replace."
51. Rotate engine from 30° BTDC to TDC and lock with locking tool No. 11 2 300, or equivalent.
52. Attach gauge tool No. 11 9 140, or equivalent to intake camshaft.
53. Ensure tool rests flat on cylinder head or protrudes no more than 0.02 inch on exhaust side. Adjust as required.
54. Attach gauge tool No. 11 9 140, or equivalent to exhaust camshaft.
55. Ensure tool rests flat on cylinder head or protrudes no more than 0.02 inch on intake side. Adjust as required.

X5

REMOVAL

1. Remove VANOS adjustment unit as outlined under "Variable Camshaft Timing (VANOS) Adjustment Unit, Replace."
2. Remove timing chain tensioner.
3. Press secondary chain tensioner down and lock in place to using locking tool No. 11 3 292, or equivalent.
4. Remove mounting nuts and sensor gear.
5. Remove plate spring.
6. Remove mounting nuts and intake camshaft corrugated washer.
7. Remove sprocket mounting bolts.
8. Remove exhaust and intake sprockets with chain, friction washer and toothed shaft.
9. Mark toothed shaft for installation in original position.
10. Remove toothed shaft and sleeve.
11. Remove mounting bolts and secondary chain tensioner.
12. Remove screw-in pins.
13. Feed sprocket toward front and out of timing case. Chain remains over exhaust camshaft.
14. Remove screw-in pin on intake side, as required, then the thrust washer.
15. Remove sensor gear.
16. Remove camshaft mounting studs.
17. Pull back setting mandrel tool until flywheel is no longer located in position.
18. Lift timing chain and hold under tension.
19. Rotate engine in reverse of normal rotational direction approximately 30°. **Ensure no pistons are at TDC.**
20. Remove camshaft studs.
21. Remove bearing cover No. 1.
22. Install camshaft fixture tool No. 11 3 260, or equivalent, and **torque** mounting bolts into cylinders Nos. 1 and 4 spark plug threads to 21–24 ft. lbs.
23. Pretension bearing caps by turning eccentric shaft, then remove bearing cover mounting nuts.
24. Remove eccentric shaft tensions and fixture tool.
25. Mark bearing covers for installation in original position, then remove them.
26. Remove camshaft.

INSTALLATION

1. Oil camshafts, bearing, caps, friction washers, toothed shafts's splines and spline hubs before installation.
2. Position timing chain on exhaust camshaft.
3. Install camshafts with intake and exhaust valves' tips pointing toward cylinder No. 1.
4. Install bearing covers in original positions. Covers are clearly marked, A for exhaust and E for intake.
5. Install camshaft fixture tool No. 11 3 260, or equivalent, and **torque** mounting bolts into cylinders Nos. 1 and 4 spark plug threads to 21–24 ft. lbs.
6. Pretension bearing caps by turning eccentric shaft, then tighten bearing cover mounting nuts to specifications.
7. Tighten bolts to specifications. Remove fixture.
8. Align camshafts using suitable open-end wrench.
9. Install camshaft locking tool No. 11 3 240, or equivalent. Ensure locking tool lies flush on cylinder head.
10. Lifting timing chain and hold under tension.
11. Rotate engine from 30° BTDC to TDC and lock with locking tool No. 11 2 300, or equivalent.
12. Position sensor gear on intake camshaft.
13. Install washer and tighten dowels to specifications.
14. Feed sprocket onto timing chain so sprocket arrow faces cylinder head upper separating face.
15. Install chain tensioning tool No 11 4 220, or equivalent, into camshaft chain tensioner bore and turn tool's threaded center pin in until it contacts bow cover. **Do not tighten center pin.**
16. Ensure sprocket arrow faces cylinder head upper separating face.
17. Tighten screw-in pin to specifications.
18. Install secondary chain tensioner.
19. Install toothed sleeve and align to shaft so tooth gaps are opposed.
20. Secure toothed shaft.
21. Insert toothed shaft pin into camshaft and toothed sleeve splines tooth gaps.
22. Push toothed shaft until toothed sleeve longitudinal holes are centrally positioned with thread.
23. Place sprockets on alignment tool No, 11 6 180, or equivalent, and install chain.
24. Remove chain with sprockets from alignment tool and install so intake tooth gaps are opposed.
25. Align chain with sprockets so intake tooth gaps are exactly opposed.
26. Secure toothed shaft.
27. Install toothed shaft pin into camshaft and sprocket splines tooth gaps.
28. Push toothed shaft until approximately 0.04 inch of splines can still be seen.
29. Ensure corrugated washer FRONT lettering is visible and install. Hand tighten mounting nuts.
30. Install exhaust side mounting bolts and initially **torque** to 44 inch lbs., then release ½ turn.
31. Install thrust washer.
32. Ensure cup spring F mark is visible with small locating diameter pointing toward sensor gear.
33. Install fit cup spring.
34. Position sensor gear for arrow faces cylinder head upper separating face.
35. Install mounting nuts and hand tighten.
36. Withdraw toothed shaft to stop.
37. Press secondary chain tensioner down and remove locking pin.
38. Preload tensioning rail with chain tensioning tool No 11 4 220, or equivalent.

Torque to 6 inch lbs.
39. Preload cup spring by pressing sensor gear and hand tightening mounting nuts.
40. Remove gasket and ensure dowel sleeves are not damaged and positioned correctly,
41. Install fixture too No. 11 6 150, or equivalent, align and tighten mounting nuts until tool fully contacts cylinder.
42. **Torque** exhaust sprocket bolts to approximately 44 inch lbs.
43. **Torque** intake and exhaust sprocket mounting nuts to approximately 44 inch lbs.
44. Tighten exhaust mounting bolts to specifications.
45. Tighten exhaust and intake mounting nuts to specifications.
46. Pull locking tool No. 11 2 300, or equivalent, back until flywheel is not longer secured.
47. Remove camshaft tools Nos. 11 3 244 and 11 3 240.
48. Crank engine two in rotational direction until cam tips on cylinder No. 1 face one another.
49. Lock with locking tool No. 11 2 300, or equivalent.
50. Install camshaft locking tool No. 11 3 240, or equivalent.
51. Tool may protrude approximately 0.04 inch on intake side. If tool protrudes above exhaust side, adjust timing, again.
52. Remove alignment fixture tool No. 11 6 150.
53. Install VANOS units as outlined under "Variable Camshaft Timing (VANOS) Adjustment Unit, Replace."

Z3

M COUPE & M ROADSTER

1998–2000

Refer to "1998–99" under "M3."

2001

Refer to "2001" under "M3."

Z3 2.3, 2.5i & 3.0i

Refer to "X5."

Z3 2.8

1998

Refer to "1998–99" under "M3."

1999–2000

Refer to "X5."

323 & 328

323is & 328is & 1998–99 328i & 1998 323i & 1999 323i & 328i CONVERTIBLES

Refer to "1998–99" under "M3."

323Ci & 328Ci & 2000 323i & 328i & 1999 323i & 328i SEDANS

Refer to "X5."

325, 330, 525 & 530

Refer to "X5."

528

1998

Refer to "1998–99" under "M3."

1999–2000

Refer to "X5."

VARIABLE CAMSHAFT TIMING (VANOS) ADJUSTMENT UNIT

REPLACE

With the VANOS unit removed, avoid turning the camshaft or crankshaft. If movement is required, exercise extreme caution to avoid valve damage caused by piston contact.

M3

1998–99

Removal

1. Lock belt pulley in position using holding tool No. 11 5 050, or equivalent, then remove mounting nut using wrench tool No. 11 5 040, or equivalent. **Nut has lefthand threads.**
2. Remove fan clutch.
3. Remove valve cover as outlined under "Valve Cover, Replace."
4. Remove spark plugs.
5. Disconnect VANOS oil line and solenoid valve electrical connector.
6. Remove engine lifting eye.
7. Remove cable duct.
8. Remove intake camshaft plastic cover.
9. Rotate crankshaft in normal rotational direction until camshafts' lobes for cylinder No. 1 face one another.
10. Remove plastic plug from crankshaft timing hole in lefthand lower rear of engine.
11. Secure crankshaft in TDC position by inserting crank timing pin tool No. 11 2 300, or equivalent, into timing hole in block.
12. Remove three rear cylinder head studs and lock camshafts into position by installing camshaft timing tool No. 11 3 240, or equivalent.
13. Remove two cylinder head plugs to access exhaust camshaft sprocket mounting bolts.
14. Remove exhaust camshaft sprocket mounting bolts.
15. Press down on camshaft chain tensioner and lock using lock pin tool No. 11 3 292, or equivalent.
16. Remove front cylinder head cover mounting bolts.
17. **On models equipped with plate spring,** proceed as follows:
    a. Install turning tool No. 11 5 490, or equivalent, into camshaft sprocket.
    b. Turn sprockets and secondary chain clockwise while removing VANOS adjustment unit.
18. **On models equipped less plate spring,** remove VANOS adjustment unit.

Installation

1. **On models equipped with plate spring,** turn sprockets and secondary chain clockwise until detent position is reached using turning tool No. 11 5 490, or equivalent.
2. **On models equipped less plate spring,** turn camshaft secondary chain and sprockets clockwise by hand as far as possible.
3. **On all models,** press adjustment unit spline shaft back as far as housing detent.
4. Seal contact edges along cylinder head and VANOS unit joint using Drei Bond No. 1209, or equivalent sealing compound.
5. Install new seal.
6. Position VANOS and turn spline shaft of unit internal spline engages.
7. **On models equipped with plate spring,** proceed as follows:
    a. Install turn tool on exhaust camshaft.
    b. Turn chain and gears counterclockwise until spline shaft engages sprocket internal spline.
    c. Ensure first suitable tooth engages.
    d. Slide VANOS adjustment unit toward cylinder head.
    e. Guide helical bevel splined shaft into helical bevel splined sprocket turning sprockets with chain counterclockwise.
    f. Turn chain and gears counterclockwise using turning tool.
8. **On models equipped less plate spring,** proceed as follows:
    a. Turn chain and gears by hand counterclockwise until spline shaft locates in sprocket internal spline.
    b. Ensure first suitable tooth engages.
    c. Slide VANOS adjustment unit toward cylinder head.
    d. Guide helical bevel splined shaft into helical bevel spline sprocket turning sprockets with chain counterclockwise.
    e. Guide chain with sprockets counterclockwise by hand.
9. **On all models,** install and tighten VANOS mounting bolts.
10. Remove secondary chain tensioner lock pin tool.
11. Remove primary chain tensioner.
12. Install screw chain tensioning tool No 11 4 220, or equivalent, into camshaft chain tensioner bore and adjust to tensioning rail.
13. Preload camshaft chain tensioner using weighted wrench tool No. 00 2 050, or equivalent, or **torque** center pin to 12 inch lbs.
14. Tighten exhaust camshaft sprocket

mounting bolts to specification in two steps.
15. Remove camshaft and crankshaft locking tools.
16. Turn engine in normal rotational direction two turns.
17. Secure crankshaft in TDC position by inserting crank timing pin tool No. 11 2 300, or equivalent, into timing hole in block.
18. Installing camshaft timing tool No. 11 3 240, or equivalent. Ensure tool locates flush against cylinder head. Remove tool.
19. Remove chain tensioning tool.
20. Install camshaft chain tensioner with new sealing rings and tighten to specifications.
21. Install air fitting tool No. 11 3 450, or equivalent, to VANOS oil pressure line.
22. Apply 29–116 psi compressed air to fitting.
23. Measure and record distance between secondary chain tensioner and sensor gear edge.
24. Connect test connector tool No. 12 6 050, or equivalent, to VANOS unit solenoid valve connection.
25. Connect tool positive wire to 12-volt source and negative terminal to vehicle ground. **Do not reverse VANOS unit polarity.**
26. Measure and record gap between secondary chain tensioner and sensor gear edge.
27. If control travel distance (second measurement minus first) is less than 0.335 inch, remove and adjust VANOS unit.
28. Remove special tools.
29. Install cable duct and suspension lug.
30. Install oil pressure line using new seals and tighten to specifications.
31. Connect solenoid valve connector.
32. Remove setting mandrel.
33. Install valve cover as outlined under "Valve Cover, Replace."

2001

Removal

1. Remove valve cover as outlined under "Valve Cover, Replace."
2. Remove spark plugs.
3. Lock belt pulley in position using holding tool No. 11 5 050, or equivalent, then remove mounting nut using wrench tool No. 11 5 040, or equivalent. **Nut has lefthand threads.**
4. Remove fan clutch.
5. Install fixture tool No. 11 5 100, or equivalent, to crankshaft hub.
6. Rotate crankshaft in normal rotational direction to cylinder No. 1 firing TDC.
7. Secure crankshaft damper in position with plug mandrel tool No. 11 2 300, or equivalent.
8. Disconnect timing case cover oil line bracket.
9. Remove VANOS adjustment unit oil line.
10. Install connecting piece tool No. 11 7 130, or equivalent, to VANOS adjustment unit.
11. Connect 29–116 psi compressed air.
12. Disconnect solenoid valve connector.
13. Connect switch tool No. 12 6 050, or equivalent, to solenoid valves and battery.
14. Alternately press buttons 1 and 2 several times.
15. Hold down toggle switch button 1 and, at same time, rotate intake camshaft against rotational direction as far as possible.
16. Alternately press buttons 3 and 4 several times.
17. Hold down toggle switch button 3 and, at same time, rotate exhaust camshaft against rotational direction as far as possible.
18. Disconnect compressed air.
19. Remove mounting bolts, sliding rail and holder.
20. Remove VANOS adjustment unit mounting bolts.
21. Press buttons 2 and 4 to activate solenoid valves and vent hydraulic piston oil chamber.
22. Disconnect VANOS unit from cylinder head adapter sleeves.
23. Disconnect VANOS unit until intake and exhaust side hydraulic pistons are extended.
24. Remove toothed shaft mounting bolts support VANOS unit with hand.
25. Remove VANOS unit. Toothed shafts remain with VANOS gear on engine.

Installation

1. Install connecting piece tool No. 11 7 130, or equivalent, to VANOS adjustment unit.
2. Cover bore with suitable shop rag.
3. Connect 29–116 psi compressed air.
4. Connect switch tool No. 12 6 050, or equivalent, to solenoid valves and battery.
5. Press buttons 2 and 4 to activate solenoid valves and vent hydraulic piston oil chamber.
6. Disconnect compressed air and remove connecting piece tool.
7. If engine damage suggests swarf/chip contamination, replace control valve with integrated filter.
8. Install new sealing rings coated with suitable engine oil.
9. Assembly control valve in cylinder head.
10. Ensure dowel sleeves are in good condition and proper position.
11. Install new gasket with beading points toward VANOS unit and secure with suitable sealing compound on adapter sleeves.
12. Install VANOS unit on toothed shafts.
13. Support VANOS with hand, grip dieldrin and screw together at hexagon alternately between intake and exhaust sides in ½ turn increments. Tighten to specifications.
14. Align radial piston pump to spline hub driver.
15. Press tool buttons 1 and 3 simultaneously, activating solenoid valves and allow air to escape from hydraulic pistons.
16. Simultaneously push VANOS adjustment unit until it rests on cylinder head.
17. Tighten mounting bolts.
18. Install chain holder and mounting bolts. **Do not tighten.**
19. Install sliding rail and mounting bolts.
20. Tighten sliding rail and holder mounting bolts.
21. Disconnect switch tool.
22. Install solenoid valves' mounting bolts.
23. Install banjo bolt with new sealing rings. **Do not tighten.**
24. Install oil line bracket and tighten mounting bolt.
25. Tighten oil line banjo bolt.
26. Install valve cover as outlined under "Valve Cover, Replace."

X5

Removal

1. Remove air intake filter housing with Mass Air Flow (MAF) sensor.
2. Lock belt pulley in position using holding tool No. 11 5 050, or equivalent, then remove mounting nut using wrench tool No. 11 5 040, or equivalent. **Nut has lefthand threads.**
3. Remove fan clutch.
4. Remove valve cover as outlined under "Valve Cover, Replace."
5. Remove spark plugs.
6. Remove intake camshaft plastic cover.
7. Disconnect VANOS oil line.
8. Install air fitting tool No. 11 3 450, or equivalent, to VANOS oil pressure line.
9. Cover double VANOS adjustment unit with suitable shop rags.
10. Apply 29–116 psi compressed air to fitting.
11. Rotate engine to ensure camshafts are in initial positions.
12. Rotate engine at least two revolution in normal rotational direction until intake and exhaust camshafts' cylinder No. 1 cam tips face each other.
13. Remove plastic plug from crankshaft timing hole in lefthand lower rear of engine.
14. Secure crankshaft in TDC position by inserting crank timing pin tool No. 11 2 300, or equivalent, into timing hole in block.
15. Remove rear cylinder head studs and lock camshafts into position by installing camshaft timing tool No. 11 3 240, or equivalent.
16. Disconnect compressed air connection. Tool remains fitted.
17. Have suitable clean shop rags and container ready to collect oil when plugs are removed.
18. Remove cylinder head plugs to access camshaft sprocket mounting bolts.
19. **Ensure oil does not run onto drive belts. Remove any oil with rags.**
20. Remove sealing caps with short flat nose pliers tool No. 11 6 170, or equivalent.
21. Remove intake and exhaust setscrews. **Lefthand threads.**
22. Disconnect camshaft sensor and solenoid valves' connectors.
23. Remove engine suspension eye.
24. Remove mounting nuts and double VANOS adjustment unit.

Installation

1. Seal contact edges along cylinder head and VANOS unit joint using Drei

Bond No. 1209, or equivalent sealing compound.
2. Install new seal.
3. Install double VANOS unit and mounting bolts.
4. Connect camshaft sensor and solenoid valves' connectors.
5. Install and tighten hydraulic piston setscrews in intake and exhaust side toothed shaft.
6. Install sealing caps using short flat nose pliers tool No. 11 6 170, or equivalent.
7. Install sealing plugs with new sealing rings. Tighten to specifications.
8. Install engine suspension eye.
9. Remove primary chain tensioner.
10. Install screw chain tensioning tool No 11 4 220, or equivalent, into camshaft chain tensioner bore and adjust to tensioning rail.
11. Preload camshaft chain tensioner using weighted wrench tool No. 00 9 250, or equivalent, or **torque** center pin to 6 inch lbs.
12. Remove crank timing pin and camshaft timing tools.
13. Cover double VANOS adjustment unit with suitable shop rags.
14. Apply 29–116 psi compressed air to fitting.
15. Crank engine twice in normal rotational direction until intake and exhaust cylinder No. 1 cam tips face each other.
16. Secure crankshaft in TDC position by inserting crank timing pin tool No. 11 2 300, or equivalent, into timing hole in block.
17. Installing camshaft timing tool No. 11 3 240, or equivalent. Ensure tool locates flush against cylinder head.
18. Timing tool may protrude up to 0.04 inch above intake side.
19. Disconnect compressed air and remove connecting tool.
20. Install oil pressure line using new seals and tighten to specifications.
21. Remove chain tensioning tool.
22. Remove crank timing pin and camshaft timing tools.
23. Install valve cover as outlined under "Valve Cover, Replace."

Z3

M COUPE & M ROADSTER

1998–2000

Refer to "1998–99" under "M3."

2001

Refer to "2001" under "M3."

Z3 2.3, 2.5i & 3.0i

Refer to "X5."

Z3 2.8

1998

Refer to "1998–99" under "M3."

1999–2000

Refer to "X5."

323 & 328

323is & 328is & 1998-99 328i & 1998 323i & 1999 323i & 328i CONVERTIBLES

Refer to "1998–99" under "M3."

323Ci & 328Ci & 2000 323i & 328i & 1999 323i & 328i SEDANS

Refer to "X5."

325, 330, 525 & 530

Refer to "X5."

528

1998

Refer to "1998–99" under "M3."

1999–2000

Refer to "X5."

PISTON & ROD ASSEMBLY

The piston, connecting rods and bearings must be install in original positions.

Injection nozzles for cooling the pistons are installed on the underside of the cylinder between the bearing seats. **Do not damage the spray nozzles when removing the pistons.**

Pistons and pins are paired and must not be fitted individually.

Fit connecting rod with piston pin to piston in such a way that both of the visible pair numbers on the install direction arrow on the piston point to the right, **Fig. 2.**

MAIN & ROD BEARINGS

Main Bearings

M3

1998–99

1. Oil bolt threads.
2. **Torque** bolts to 15 ft. lbs.
3. Tighten bolts an additional 70°.

2001

1. **Torque** bolts to 18 ft. lbs.
2. Tighten bolts an additional 50°.

X5

1. Oil bolt threads.
2. **Torque** bolts to 15 ft. lbs.
3. Tighten bolts an additional 50°.

Z3

M COUPE & M ROADSTER

1998–2000

Refer to "1998–99" under "M3."

2001

Refer to "2001" under "M3."

Z3 2.3, 2.5i & 3.0i

Refer to "X5."

Z3 2.8

1998 Aluminum Block

Refer to "X5."

1998 Iron Block

Refer to "1998–99" under "M3."

1999–2000

Refer to "X5."

323 & 328

323is & 328is & 1998-99 328i & 1998 323i & 1999 323i & 328i CONVERTIBLES

Aluminum Block

Refer to "X5."

Iron Block

Refer to "1998–99" under "M3."

323Ci & 328Ci & 2000 323i & 328i & 1999 323i & 328i SEDANS

Refer to "X5."

325, 328, 525 & 530

Refer to "X5."

528

1998

Aluminum Block

Refer to "X5."

Iron Block

Refer to "1998–99" under "M3."

1999–2000

Refer to "X5."

Rod Bearings

1. Oil bolt threads.
2. **Torque** to 44 inch lbs.
3. **Torque** to 15 ft. lbs.
4. Tighten an additional 70°.

CRANKSHAFT REAR OIL SEAL

REPLACE

Refer to "1.9L M44 Four-Cylinder Engine" section.

OIL PAN

REPLACE

M3

1998–99

1. Remove air intake filter housing with Mass Air Flow (MAF) sensor.
2. Raise and support vehicle, then remove engine splash guard.
3. Drain engine oil into suitable container.
4. Loosen oil dipstick guide tube.
5. Remove cyclone oil separator oil return hose from dipstick.
6. Remove guide tube.
7. Support engine with fixture tool 00 0 200, or equivalent.
8. Disconnect power steering oil lines from engine support bracket and place to one side.
9. Raise engine approximately 0.2 inch.
10. Disconnect steering shaft from steering gear.
11. Remove mounting bolts and place power steering pump aside with lines connected.
12. Drain power steering reservoir into suitable container, remove mounting bolts and place aside with lines connected.
13. Loosen top and remove bottom left and righthand engine mount mounting bolts.
14. Disconnect left and righthand engine carrier control arms.
15. Remove mounting bolts and lower front axle support
16. **On models with automatic transmission,** remove oil pipes from oil pan.
17. **On all models,** remove mounting bolts and oil pan.
18. Reverse procedure to install, noting the following:
    a. Apply 0.118 inch wide by 0.079 inch tall bead of Drei Bond No. 1209, or equivalent sealing compound, around joint.
    b. Install new gasket.
    c. Position oil pan and install mounting bolts hand tight.
    d. Tighten mounting bolts to specifications starting from front of engine.
    e. Install new oil dipstick O-ring.

2001

1. Support engine with fixture tool 00 0 200, or equivalent.
2. Remove fan cowl.
3. Lock belt pulley in position using holding tool No. 11 5 050, or equivalent, then remove mounting nut using wrench tool No. 11 5 040, or equivalent. **Nut has lefthand threads.**
4. Remove fan clutch.
5. Raise engine approximately 0.2 inch.
6. Remove air intake filter housing.
7. Disconnect oil dipstick guide tube from intake manifold.
8. Raise and support vehicle, then remove engine splash guard.
9. Remove front end reinforcement.
10. Drain engine oil into suitable container.
11. Disconnect condensate return and open cable holder.
12. Disconnect steering shaft from steering gear.
13. Disconnect power steering pump oil lines from bracket.
14. Remove drive belt, mounting bolts and power steering pump, then place it aside with lines connected.
15. Disconnect oil lever and level sensors connectors.
16. Loosen top and remove bottom left and righthand engine mount mounting bolts.
17. Disconnect left and righthand engine carrier control arms.
18. Disconnect left and righthand stabilizer bar brackets.
19. Support front axle support with fixture tool No. 31 2 220, or equivalent, and suitable jack.
20. Remove mounting bolts and lower front axle support approximately 3.94 inches.
21. Remove cyclone oil separator oil return hose from oil pan.
22. Remove mounting bolts and sump cover.
23. Remove mounting bolts and oil pan.
24. Reverse procedure to install, noting the following:
    a. Apply 0.118 inch wide by 0.079 inch tall bead of Drei Bond No. 1209, or equivalent sealing compound, around joint.
    b. Install new gasket.
    c. Position oil pan and install mounting bolts hand tight.
    d. Tighten mounting bolts to specifications starting from front of engine.
    e. Install new oil dipstick O-ring.

X5

1. Disconnect sealing strip, turn toggles 90° and remove heater bulkhead cover.
2. Remove mounting screws and heater bulkhead.
3. Lift hood and lock into assembly position.
4. Remove fuel injectors' cover.
5. Remove air filter housing upper section with Mass Air Flow (MAF) sensor.
6. Support engine with fixture tool 00 0 200, or equivalent.
7. Loosen top and remove bottom left and righthand engine mount mounting bolts.
8. Raise engine approximately 0.2 inch.
9. Raise and support vehicle, then remove engine splash guard.
10. Remove front end reinforcement.
11. Remove left and righthand swivel bearings.
12. Remove output shafts.
13. Disconnect propeller shaft at front.
14. Remove drive belt, mounting bolts and place power steering pump aside with lines connected.
15. Drain engine oil into suitable container.
16. Remove cyclone oil separator oil return hose from dipstick.
17. Remove oil dipstick guide tube.
18. Disconnect steering shaft from steering gear.
19. Temporarily install left and righthand swivel bearings to sprint strut.
20. Temporarily install tension strut, control arm and tie rod to swivel bearing.
21. Support front axle support with fixture tool No. 31 2 220, or equivalent, and suitable jack.
22. Remove mounting bolts and lower front axle support approximately 3.54–3.94 inches.
23. Remove front axle differential.
24. Remove mounting bolts and oil pan.
25. Reverse procedure to install, noting the following:
    a. Apply 0.118 inch wide by 0.079 inch tall bead of Drei Bond No. 1209, or equivalent sealing compound, around joint.
    b. Install new gasket.
    c. Position oil pan and install mounting bolts hand tight.
    d. Tighten mounting bolts to specifications starting from front of engine.
    e. Install new oil dipstick O-ring.

Z3

Refer to "1998–99" under "M3."

323, 325, 328 & 330

323is & 328is & 1998–99 328i & 1998 323i & 1999 323i & 328i Convertibles

Refer to "1998–99" under "M3."

323Ci, 328Ci, 325 & 330 & 2000 323i & 328i & 1999 323i & 328i Sedans

1. Support engine with fixture tool 00 0 200, or equivalent.
2. Raise engine approximately 0.2 inch.
3. Remove air intake filter housing.
4. Raise and support vehicle, then remove engine splash guard.
5. Drain engine oil into suitable container.
6. **On models with automatic transmission,** remove oil lines from oil pan.
7. **On all models,** loosen oil dipstick guide tube.
8. Remove cyclone oil separator oil return hose from dipstick.
9. Remove guide tube.
10. Remove front end reinforcement.
11. Disconnect steering shaft from steering gear.
12. Remove mounting bolts and place power steering pump aside with lines connected.
13. Disconnect power steering oil lines from engine support bracket and place to one side.
14. Loosen top and remove bottom left and righthand engine mount mounting bolts.
15. **On 325xi and 330xi models,** proceed as follows:
    a. Remove left and righthand swivel bearings.
    b. Remove output shafts.
    c. Remove front propeller shaft.
    d. Remove front axle differential.
16. **On all models,** disconnect left and righthand engine carrier control arms.
17. Disconnect left and righthand stabilizer bar brackets.
18. Remove mounting bolts and lower front axle support
19. Remove mounting bolts and oil pan.

20. Reverse procedure to install, noting the following:
    a. Apply 0.118 inch wide by 0.079 inch tall bead of Drei Bond No. 1209, or equivalent sealing compound, around joint.
    b. Install new gasket.
    c. Position oil pan and install mounting bolts hand tight.
    d. Tighten mounting bolts to specifications starting from front of engine.
    e. Install new oil dipstick O-ring.

525, 528 & 530

1. Raise and support vehicle, then remove engine splash guard.
2. Drain engine oil into suitable container.
3. Loosen oil dipstick guide tube.
4. Remove cyclone oil separator oil return hose from dipstick.
5. Remove guide tube.
6. Support engine with fixture tool 00 0 200, or equivalent.
7. Raise engine approximately 0.2 inch.
8. Disconnect steering shaft from steering gear.
9. Remove mounting bolts and place power steering pump aside with lines connected.
10. Drain power steering reservoir into suitable container, remove mounting bolts and place aside with lines connected.
11. Loosen top and remove bottom left and righthand engine mount mounting bolts.
12. Remove oil pipes from oil pan, as required.
13. Support front axle support with fixture tool No. 31 2 220, or equivalent, and suitable jack.
14. Remove mounting bolts and lower front axle support
15. Remove mounting bolts and oil pan.
16. Reverse procedure to install, noting the following:
    a. Apply 0.118 inch wide by 0.079 inch tall bead of Drei Bond No. 1209, or equivalent sealing compound, around joint.
    b. Install new gasket.
    c. Position oil pan and install mounting bolts hand tight.
    d. Tighten mounting bolts to specifications starting from front of engine.
    e. Install new oil dipstick O-ring.

OIL PUMP

REPLACE

1. Remove oil pan as outlined under "Oil Pan, Replace."
2. Remove oil pump sprocket mounting nut. **Lefthand threads.**
3. Remove sprocket with chain.
4. Remove mounting bolts, oil pump and pickup.
5. Reverse procedure to install. Tighten mounting bolts and nuts to specifications.

SERPENTINE DRIVE BELT

Refer to **Fig. 3** for serpentine belt routing.

REPLACEMENT

1. If reusing belt, mark rotational direction for installation.
2. Lock belt pulley in position using holding tool No. 11 5 050, or equivalent, then remove mounting nut using wrench tool No. 11 5 040, or equivalent. **Nut has lefthand threads.**
3. Remove fan clutch.
4. Remove dust cab.
5. Push tensioning device back on bolt connect **Lefthand threads.**
6. Remove belt.
7. Reverse procedure to install. Preload tensioning device as far as possible and lock using holding tool No. 11 3 340, or equivalent.

COOLING SYSTEM BLEED

1. Set heater controls to maximum temperature and fan to low speed.
2. Run engine and flush engine cooling circuit with 3–4 short bursts to 4500–5000 RPM. **Do not run engine for more than 30 seconds.**
3. Close bleed screw when escaping coolant is free from air bubbles.
4. Run engine until thermostat opens.

THERMOSTAT

REPLACE

1. Lock belt pulley in position using holding tool No. 11 5 050, or equivalent, then remove mounting nut using wrench tool No. 11 5 040, or equivalent. **Nut has lefthand threads.**
2. Remove fan clutch.
3. Drain cooling system into suitable container.
4. Remove water hoses.
5. Remove engine suspension eye.
6. Remove cable channel.
7. Remove mounting bolts, housing and thermostat
8. Reverse procedure to install using new gasket. Tighten thermostat mounting bolts to specifications.

WATER PUMP

REPLACE

1. Remove alternator drive belt.
2. Raise and support vehicle, then drain coolant into suitable container.
3. Remove mounting bolts and water pump pulley.
4. Remove water pump mounting bolts.
5. Insert two M6 bolts into thread and press pump out evenly.
6. Reverse procedure to install using new O-ring coated with suitable coolant. Tighten mounting bolts to specifications.

RADIATOR

REPLACE

M3

1998-99

1. Raise and support vehicle, then drain coolant into suitable container.
2. Remove radiator upper cover.
3. Lock belt pulley in position using holding tool No. 11 5 050, or equivalent, then remove mounting nut using wrench tool No. 11 5 040, or equivalent. **Nut has lefthand threads.**
4. Remove fan coupling.
5. Remove expanding rivets from left and righthand cowl sides.
6. Disconnect guide tabs and remove fan cowl.
7. Disconnect air conditioning temperature switch connector.
8. Disconnect upper and lower water hoses, then the expansion hose.
9. **On models equipped with automatic transmission,** disconnect transmission fluid cooler lines.
10. **On all models,** disconnect left and righthand catches using suitable screwdriver.
11. Remove radiator.
12. Reverse procedure to install.

2001

1. Remove oil cooler underguard.
2. Remove mounting bolts and disconnect oil cooler line.
3. Remove mounting bolt and oil cooler.
4. Raise and support vehicle, then drain coolant into suitable container.
5. Remove mounting bolts and underbody protection.
6. Remove expansion rivets, intake hood and pipe.
7. Disconnect lefthand Xenon headlamp connector and cover.
8. Remove mounting bolts and lefthand Xenon headlamp control module.
9. Remove air intake filter housing.
10. Remove expansion rivets, then the left and righthand air ducts. **Do not disconnect coolant hoses.**
11. Disconnect fan cowl left and righthand lugs.
12. Disconnect fan clutch from water pump.
13. Remove mounting bolts, then disconnect sensor and electric fan connectors.
14. Remove fan cowl.
15. Disconnect plastic clips and radiator lines.
16. Remove mounting bolt and radiator.
17. Reverse procedure to install.

X5

1. Raise and support vehicle, then drain coolant into suitable container.
2. Remove expansion rivets and intake hood.
3. Lock belt pulley in position using holding tool No. 11 5 050, or equivalent, then remove mounting nut using wrench tool No. 11 5 040, or equivalent. **Nut has lefthand threads.**
4. Remove fan coupling.
5. Disconnect AUC sensor connector.
6. Remove expansion rivets and fan cowl.
7. Disconnect clamp and remove expansion tank hose.
8. Disconnect electrical connector.
9. Disconnect and remove expansion tank.

10. Disconnect upper water hose.
11. **On models equipped with automatic transmission,** disconnect lock and remove oil cooler with lines connected.
12. **On all models,** disconnect lower water hose.
13. Remove mounting bolts and bracket.
14. Disconnect sealing strip between radiator and cassette.
15. Remove cassette mounting bolts, then the radiator.
16. Reverse procedure to install.

Z3

Z3 M Coupe, M Roadster, 2.3 & 2.8

Refer to "1998–99" under "M3."

Z3 2.5i & 3.0i

1. Disconnect temperature switch connector.
2. Raise and support vehicle, then drain coolant into suitable container.
3. Disconnect fan cowl left and righthand expansion rivets.
4. Remove fan cowl and impeller.
5. Disconnect clip and vent hose.
6. Disconnect hose connector.
7. Disconnect clips and coolant hoses.
8. Disconnect radiator retainers.
9. **On models equipped with automatic transmission,** disconnect retainers and remove bottom cover.
10. **On all models,** slide radiator up and toward rear.
11. **On models equipped with automatic transmission,** remove mounting bolts and oil cooler.
12. **On all models,** remove radiator.
13. Reverse procedure to install.

323, 325, 328 & 330

323is & 328is & 1998–99 328i & 1998 323i & 1999 323i & 328i Convertibles

Refer to "1998–99" under "M3."

323Ci, 328Ci, 325 & 330 & 2000 323i & 328i & 1999 323i & 328i Sedans

1. Raise and support vehicle, then drain coolant into suitable container.
2. Disconnect engine wiring harness holder.
3. Disconnect retainers, then remove mounting bolts and air intake filter housing.
4. Disconnect expansion rivets and remove intake hood.
5. Disconnect fan clutch from water pump.
6. Disconnect electrical connectors.
7. Remove expansion rivets and fan cowl.
8. Disconnect coolant hose from expansion tank.
9. Disconnect level sensor connector.
10. Disconnect clips and coolant hoses.
11. Remove mounting bolts and radiator.
12. Reverse procedure to install.

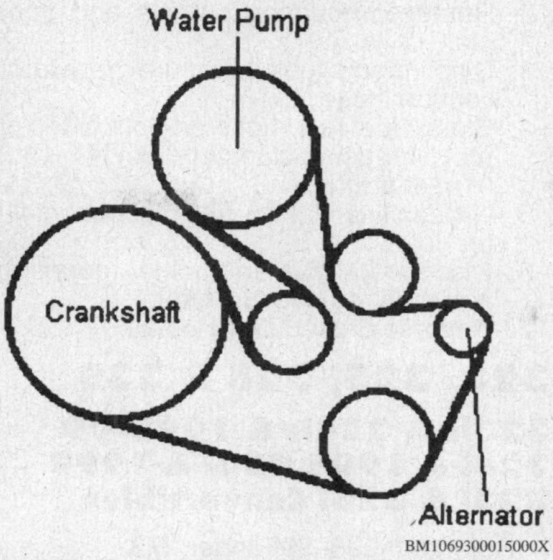

Fig. 3 Serpentine belt routing

525 & 530

1. Raise and support vehicle, then drain coolant into suitable container.
2. Lock belt pulley in position using holding tool No. 11 5 050, or equivalent, then remove mounting nut using wrench tool No. 11 5 040, or equivalent. **Nut has lefthand threads.**
3. Remove fan coupling.
4. Disconnect connector and water hoses, then remove holder and auxiliary water pump.
5. Disconnect AUC sensor connector.
6. Remove expansion rivets and fan cowl.
7. Remove spring and upper water hose.
8. Remove left and righthand mounting bolts, then the brackets.
9. Disconnect electrical connector and spring, then the lower water hose.
10. Remove radiator.
11. Reverse procedure to install.

528

1. Raise and support vehicle, then drain coolant into suitable container.
2. Remove expansion rivets and fan cowl.
3. Disconnect level sensor connector, as required.
4. Disconnect temperature sensor connector.
5. Disconnect water hoses, then the expansion hose.
6. Disconnect sealing lip and remove mounting bolts.
7. Remove radiator.
8. Reverse procedure to install.

FUEL PUMP

REPLACE

M3

1998–99

1. Relieve fuel system pressure as outlined under "Precautions."
2. Remove enough fuel from tank to ensure pump unit can be removed without spillage.
3. Remove rear seat cushion, then the righthand access cover.
4. Disconnect electrical connectors and fuel lines.
5. Remove ring nut using ring nut wrench tool No. 16 1 020, or equivalent.
6. Mark position of unit in fuel tank for installation alignment.
7. Lift and rotate unit from fuel tank. **Do not deform fuel level sensor arm or altitude sensor tube.**
8. Reverse procedure to install. Install new ring nut and seal.

2001

1. Relieve fuel system pressure as outlined under "Precautions."
2. Remove enough fuel from tank to ensure pump unit can be removed without spillage.
3. Remove rear seat cushion.
4. Fold floor trim panel forward, cut and fold insulating mat.
5. Disconnect rubber grommet.
6. Remove mounting nuts and cover.
7. Disconnect electrical connectors, clips and fuel hose.
8. Remove ring nut using ring nut wrench tool No. 16 1 020, or equivalent.
9. Mark position of unit in fuel tank for installation alignment.
10. Lift and rotate unit from fuel tank. **Do not deform fuel level sensor arm or altitude sensor tube.**
11. Reverse procedure to install. Install new ring nut and seal.

Z3

1. Relieve fuel system pressure as outlined under "Precautions."
2. Remove enough fuel from tank to ensure pump unit can be removed without spillage.
3. Remove passenger's seat.
4. Cut and fold carpet, then remove mounting screws and cover.
5. Disconnect hose clip using pliers tool No. 32 3 020, or equivalent, then the fuel lines and electrical connector.
6. Remove ring nut using ring nut wrench tool No. 16 1 020, or equivalent.
7. Mark position of unit in fuel tank for installation alignment.
8. Lift and rotate unit from fuel tank. **Do not deform fuel level sensor arm or altitude sensor tube.**
9. Reverse procedure to install. Install new ring nut and seal.

323, 325, 328 & 330

323is & 328is & 1998–99 328i & 1998 323i & 1999 323i & 328i Convertibles

Refer to "1998–99" under "M3."

323Ci, 325, 328Ci & 330 & 2000 323i & 328i & 1999 323i & 328i Sedans

Refer to "2001" under "M3."

525, 528 & 530

1. Relieve fuel system pressure as outlined under "Precautions."

2. Remove enough fuel from tank to ensure pump unit can be removed without spillage.
3. Remove rear seat cushion and rubber grommet.
4. Cut and fold insulating mat.
5. Remove mounting screws and cover.
6. Disconnect electrical connectors and fuel lines.
7. Remove ring nut using ring nut wrench tool No. 16 1 020, or equivalent.
8. Mark position of unit in fuel tank for installation alignment.
9. Lift and rotate unit from fuel tank. **Do not deform fuel level sensor arm or altitude sensor tube.**
10. Reverse procedure to install. Install new ring nut and seal.

FUEL FILTER

REPLACE

M3

1998-99

1. Relieve fuel system pressure as outlined under "Precautions."
2. Remove cover.
3. Clamp fuel feed hose on both sides of fuel filter using clamping tool No. 13 3 010, or equivalent.
4. Loosen line clamps and disconnect filter hoses.
5. Remove fuel filter.
6. Reverse procedure to install. Ensure fuel filter is installed in correct flow direction.

2001

1. Relieve fuel system pressure as outlined under "Precautions."
2. Remove mounting screws and cover.
3. Clamp fuel feed hose on both sides of fuel filter using clamping tool No. 13 3 010, or equivalent.
4. Disconnect fuel hoses.
5. Disconnect fuel pressure regulator vacuum line.
6. Remove mounting bolt and fuel filter.
7. Reverse procedure to install. Ensure fuel filter is installed in correct flow direction.

X3

Refer to "1998–99" under "M3."

Z3

1998-2000

Refer to "1998–99" under "M3."

2001

1. Relieve fuel system pressure as outlined under "Precautions."
2. Remove mounting screws and floor plate cover.
3. Disconnect fuel pressure regulator vacuum hose.
4. Clamp fuel feed hose on both sides of fuel filter using clamping tool No. 13 3 010, or equivalent.
5. Loosen line clamps and disconnect filter hoses.
6. Disconnect clips and holder mounting nut, then remove fuel filter.
7. Reverse procedure to install.

323, 325, 328 & 330

323is & 328is & 1998-99 328i & 1998 323i & 1999 323i & 328i Convertibles

Refer to "1998–99" under "M3."

323Ci, 325, 328Ci & 330 & 2000 323i & 328i & 1999 323i & 328i Sedans

1. Relieve fuel system pressure as outlined under "Precautions."
2. Remove engine underguard.
3. Clamp fuel feed hose on both sides of fuel filter using clamping tool No. 13 3 010, or equivalent.
4. Loosen line clamps and disconnect filter hoses.
5. Remove fuel filter.
6. Reverse procedure to install. Ensure fuel filter is installed in correct flow direction.

525 & 530

Refer to "2001" under "Z3."

528

Refer to "1998–99" under "M3."

TECHNICAL SERVICE BULLETINS

ROUGH IDLE

323is & 328is & 1998-99 328i & 1998 Z3 2.8, 323i & 528i & 1999 323i & 328i Convertibles

On some of these models there may be rough idle that may occur with Diagnostic Trouble Code (DTC) 212.

This condition may be cause by the VANOS control piston jamming or binding. There may be a burr on one or more of edges.

To correct this condition, install VANOS with revised, chamfered control edge control piston (part No. 11 36 1 738 495).

COOLANT TEMPERATURE GAUGE FLUCTUATES & HEATER OUTPUT TOO LOW

Z3 2.3, 323Ci & 328Ci & 1999-2000 Z3 2.8 & 528i & 2000 323i & 328i & 1999 323i & 328i Sedans

On some of these models built since September 1998, the coolant temperature gauge may fluctuate in and out of red zone and/or the heater output may be too low.

This condition may be cause by thermostat spring tension breaking the retaining lugs.

To correct this condition, install revised thermostat with 40% less spring tension (part No. 11 53 1 437 040, which identified by an orange paint spot on housing near the electrical connector).

ENGINE COMPARTMENT BUZZ OR RATTLE

Z3 2.3, 323Ci & 328Ci & 1999-2000 Z3 2.8 & 528i & 2000 323i & 328i & 1999 323i & 328i Sedans

On some of these models built between September 1998 to January 2000, there may be a buzzing or rattling noise coming from the front oil pan and filter housing support area. The noise may be most noticeable during engine warm up, at speeds between 1200–2000 RPM steady or during acceleration/deceleration through 1200–2000 RPM range.

This condition may be cause by oil pump resonance or pulsation.

To correct this condition, install revised oil pump (part No. 11 41 7 507 350) with a restricter in the pilot control orifice.

COOLANT LEAK FROM RIGHTHAND SIDE OF CYLINDER HEAD

Z3 2.3, 323Ci & 328Ci & 1999-2000 Z3 2.8 & 528i & 2000 323i & 328i & 1999 323i & 328i Sedans

On some of these models built between September to October 1999, there may be a coolant leak from the front righthand side of the cylinder head.

This condition may be cause by a machining flaw hair line crack.

To correct this condition, replace the cylinder head, gasket, valve stem seals, head bolts, heat shields with gasket, air valve gasket, self-locking nuts and gasket ring.

COOLANT HOSE LEAK

Z3

On some of these models built on July 27 and 28, 1999, there may be a coolant hose leak on lefthand side of engine between expansion tank and coolant pipe.

This condition may be caused by the hose being 3/4 inch too short.

To correct this condition install revised hose (part No. 11 53 1 716 643).

ENGINE WILL NOT TURN OVER

On some models, the engine will not turn over.

This condition may be caused by a fuel injector stuck in open position. To correct this condition, proceed as follows:

1. Remove fuel injectors and inspect leakage rate.
2. Replace hydraulic locked injectors.
3. Inspect engine compression pressures.
4. If any cylinder's compression is less than 143 psi, piston/connecting rod may have damaged and further engine tear down is required.

TIGHTENING SPECIFICATIONS

Year	Component	Torque, Ft. Lbs.
1998–2001	Block Coolant Drain Plug	18
	Camshaft Bearing	⑧
	Camshaft Pin	15
	Camshaft Pin Nut	88①
	Camshaft Signal Disk	37
	Camshaft Splined Shaft, Intake	30⑦
	Camshaft Sprocket	16
	Chain Tensioner	52
	Connecting Rod	⑥
	Crankshaft Damper	302
	Crankshaft Damper Pulley	16
	Crankcase End Cover	⑧
	Crankcase Struts/Bearing Shell	⑧
	Crankshaft Increment Wheel	115①
	Cylinder Head	⑤
	Cylinder Head Cover	⑧
	Cylinder Head Cover Oil Trap	13
	Engine Mount	⑩
	Exhaust Manifold	15
	Fan	29⑫
	Flywheel, Automatic	88
	Flywheel, Manual	77
	Front Cover	⑧
	Intake Manifold	⑧
	Main Bearing Caps	⑥
	Main Oil Duct Plug	25
	Oil Cooler Line	16
	Oil Drain	⑪
	Oil Filter Cover	⑨
	Oil Filter Lines	④
	Oil Pan	③
	Oil Pump	18
	Oil Pump Cover	88①
	Oil Pump Sprocket	②
	Oil Spray Nozzle	106①
	Oxygen Sensor	37
	Stabilizer Link	44
	Thermostat Housing	88①
	Thermostat Bleeder	71①
	Timing Case	⑧
	Timing Case To Cylinder Head	15
	Valve Cover	⑧
	VANOS Banjo Bolt	24
	VANOS Hydraulic Piston	88①
	VANOS Oil Filter	24

Continued

TIGHTENING SPECIFICATIONS—Continued

Year	Component	Torque, Ft. Lbs.
1998–2001	VANOS Oil Line	115①
	VANOS Plug	37
	VANOS Toothed Shaft	88①
	VANOS Solenoid Valve	22
	Vibration Damper	302
	Vibration Damper Pulley	16
	Water Pump	⑧

①— Inch lbs.
②— M6, 88 inch lbs.; M10, 35 ft. lbs.; M10 x 1, 18 ft. lbs.
③— M6 x 8.8, 88 inch lbs.; M6 x 10.9, 106 inch lbs.; M8 x 8.8, 16 ft. lbs.
④— M8, 16 ft. lbs.; M20, 30 ft. lbs.
⑤— Refer to "Cylinder Head, Replace" for tightening specifications and sequence.
⑥— Refer to "Main & Rod Bearings" for tightening specifications and sequence.
⑦— Final tighten an additional 60.°
⑧— M6, 88 inch lbs.; M7, 11 ft. lbs.; M8 15 ft. lbs.; M10, 32 ft. lbs.
⑨— M8, 16 ft. lbs.; M10 & 12, 24 ft. lbs.; Screw-On, 18 ft. lbs.
⑩— M8, 16 ft. lbs.; M10, 35 ft. lbs.
⑪— M12, 18 ft. lbs.; M22, 44 ft. lbs.
⑫— **Torque** of 29 ft. lbs. when using wrench tool No. 11 5 040, or equivalent, is equal to 22 ft. lbs. on torque wrench.

4.4L (M62) & 5.0L (S62) V8 Engines

NOTE: On Air Bag Equipped Models, Refer To "Air Bag System Precautions" Located In The Front Of This Manual For System Disarming & Arming Procedures.

NOTE: Refer To "Computer Relearn Procedures" Located In The Front Of This Manual When Battery Power To The Computer Has Been Interrupted.

INDEX

	Page No.
Camshaft, Replace	2-68
M5	2-68
X5, 540 & 740	2-70
1998	2-70
1999–2001	2-71
Compression Pressure	2-55
Cooling System Bleed	2-78
Crankshaft Damper, Replace	2-64
M5	2-64
X5, 540 & 740	2-65
Crankshaft Rear Oil Seal, Replace	2-76
Cylinder Head, Replace	2-59
M5	2-59
Lefthand	2-59
Righthand	2-60
X5	2-61
Lefthand	2-61
Righthand	2-61
540 & 740	2-62
1998	2-62
1999–2001	2-63
Engine Rebuilding Specifications	2-241
Engine, Replace	2-56
M5	2-56
X5	2-56
540 & 740	2-57
Exhaust Manifold, Replace	2-58
M5	2-58
X5	2-58
540 & 740	2-59
Front Cover, Replace	2-65
M5	2-65
Lower	2-65
Upper	2-65
X5, 540 & 740	2-65
1998	2-65
1999–2001	2-66
Front Cover Seal, Replace	2-66
M5	2-66
Z5, 540 & 740	2-66
Fuel Filter, Replace	2-79
M5	2-79
X5	2-79
540	2-79
740	2-79
Fuel Pump, Replace	2-79
Intake Manifold, Replace	2-57
M5	2-57
X5	2-58
540 & 740	2-58
Main & Rod Bearings	2-76
Main Bearings	2-76
Rod Bearings	2-76
M5	2-76
X5, 540 & 740	2-76
Oil Pan, Replace	2-76
M5	2-76
X5	2-77
540 & 740	2-77
Oil Pump, Replace	2-77
M5	2-77
X5	2-77
540 & 740	2-78
Precautions	2-55
Air Bag Systems	2-55
Battery Ground Cable	2-55
Fuel System Pressure Relief	2-55
Radiator, Replace	2-78
M5	2-78
X5	2-78
540	2-78
740	2-78
Serpentine Drive Belt	2-78
Replacement	2-78
Technical Service Bulletins	2-79
Coolant Temperature Gauge Indicates High	2-79
Engine Will Not Turn Over	2-79
Intermittent Rough Idle	2-79
Irregular Engine Clicking	2-79
Thermostat, Replace	2-78
M5	2-78
X5, 540 & 740	2-78
Tightening Specifications	2-80
Timing Chain, Replace	2-66
M5	2-66
X5, 540 & 740	2-67
Timing Chain Tensioner, Replace	2-68
Valve Adjustment	2-64
Valve Cover, Replace	2-64
M5	2-64
X5	2-64
540 & 740	2-64
Variable Camshaft Timing (VANOS) Adjustment Unit, Replace	2-72
M5	2-72
X5, 540 & 740	2-74
Water Pump, Replace	2-78

PRECAUTIONS

AIR BAG SYSTEMS

Refer to "Air Bag System Precautions" in the front of this manual for system disarming and arming procedures.

BATTERY GROUND CABLE

Prior to service, disconnect battery ground cable and isolate as required.

FUEL SYSTEM PRESSURE RELIEF

Relieve fuel system pressure before disconnecting any fuel line or fuel system component.

1. Remove fuel pump relay(s).
2. Connect battery ground cable and crank engine for 10 seconds.
3. When fuel system repairs are complete, install fuel pump relays and crank engine to restore fuel pump pressure.

COMPRESSION PRESSURE

1. Relieve fuel pressure as outlined under "Precautions."
2. **On models equipped with automatic transmission,** place gear selector in P position.
3. **On models equipped with manual transmission,** place gearshift lever in neutral position.
4. **On all models,** set hand brake.
5. Turn ignition switch to Off position.
6. Disconnect Digital Motor Electronics (DME) master relay.
7. Remove spark plugs.
8. Install compression tester adapter tool No. 11 0 226, or equivalent, into spark plug bore by hand.
9. Connect compression gauge tool No. 11 0 224, or equivalent, onto adapter.
10. Fully depress accelerator pedal and operate starter motor until compression pressure reading is at maximum.
11. Normal compression pressure should measure 174–203 psi.

12. Maximum permissible difference between individual cylinders is 6 psi.

ENGINE

REPLACE

M5

1. Lock hood in vertical service position.
2. Disconnect clips, then the air duct by turning upward at firewall.
3. Pull air duct forward and remove it.
4. Disconnect lefthand air intake hose clamp and Mass Air Flow (MAF) sensor connector.
5. Disconnect MAF sensor cable holders' clip, then the air intake hose from intake manifold.
6. Disconnect retainers and remove air intake filer upper housing section with MAF sensor and hose.
7. Remove air intake filter lower housing.
8. Remove lefthand wheelhousing cover and intake filter lower housing section from hose.
9. Disconnect righthand air intake hose clamp and Mass Air Flow (MAF) sensor connector.
10. Disconnect MAF sensor cable holders' clip, then the air intake hoe from intake manifold.
11. Disconnect retainers and remove air intake filer upper housing section with MAF sensor and hose.
12. Remove air intake filter lower housing.
13. Remove righthand wheelhousing cover and intake filter lower housing section from hose.
14. Remove engine acoustic cover.
15. Remove mounting screws and electronics box cover.
16. Disconnect Digital Motor Electronics (DME) control module connector.
17. Disconnect electronics box connector for temperature sensor.
18. Disconnect locks and remove strip, then disconnect nut and remove grounding cable strap.
19. Disconnect remaining electronics box engine wiring harness connectors.
20. Disconnect rubber strip, fasteners and clips, then remove heater bulkheads.
21. Place wiring harness on engine.
22. Disconnect oil pressure switch connector.
23. Remove mounting bolt and grounding cable, then the mounting bolt and main flow oil filter housing.
24. Place filter housing aside with lines connected.
25. Raise and support vehicle.
26. Remove mounting screws and lower righthand floor panel.
27. Disconnect cap, mounting nut and battery positive lead.
28. Loosen screw and remove cable holder.
29. Remove expansion rivet, pull panel down and remove battery positive lead.
30. Disconnect cable clip and remove battery positive lead from holders.
31. Remove transmission as outlined in "Clutch & Manual Transmission" or "Automatic Transmission" sections.
32. Drain cooling system into suitable container.
33. Remove radiator as outlined under "Radiator Replace."
34. Remove alternator and air conditioning drive belts.
35. Remove air conditioning compressor as outlined in "Air Conditioning" section.
36. Remove mounting bolts and place power steering pump aside with lines connected.
37. Remove lefthand micro filter housing.
38. Remove brake booster low pressure lead.
39. Disconnect locks, strip and clips, then remove hose.
40. Relieve fuel system pressure as outlined under "Precautions."
41. Disconnect fuel hose.
42. Disconnect vacuum connection.
43. Disconnect clip and heater hose, then the lock and return water hose.
44. Remove righthand exhaust manifold as outlined under "Exhaust Manifold, Replace."
45. Disconnect ground tape from righthand engine support.
46. Remove left and righthand engine mount nuts.
47. Remove mounting nuts and intake manifold cover.
48. Support engine at lifting lugs using engine lifting/support tool No. 11 0 260, or equivalent.
49. Remove engine. **Do not pinch or damage air conditioner compressor lines, lefthand exhaust manifold, valve covers or heater valve.**
50. Reverse procedures to install, noting the following:
    a. Tighten mounting bolts and nuts to specifications.
    b. Engine mounts in bracket front bore.
    c. **Torque** intake manifold cover center mounting nuts to 44 inch lbs., then the remaining nuts. Final tighten nuts to specifications.
    d. Install new MAF sensor gasket coat with suitable acid free grease.
    e. Replace air intake manifold sealing ring, as required. Apply thin coat of suitable petroleum jelly to ring.

X5

1. Disconnect sealing strip and turn toggles 90°, then remove cover, mounting bolts and heater bulkhead.
2. Lock hood in vertical service position.
3. Turn fasteners 90° and remove engine acoustic cover.
4. Disconnect throttle bellows, then remove air intake filter housing with Mass Air Flow (MAF) sensor.
5. Remove windshield washer reservoir.
6. Open clip and disconnect brake booster vacuum hose.
7. Relieve fuel system pressure as outlined under "Precautions."
8. Disconnect fuel feed line from injector pipe. Seal hose ends with clamp tools No. 13 5 281/2, or equivalent.
9. Remove front splash guard.
10. Remove mounting bolts and reinforcement plate.
11. Raise and support vehicle.
12. Drain cooling system into suitable container.
13. Remove alternator and air conditioning drive belts.
14. Remove power steering pump as outlined in "Front Suspension & Steering" section. and place aside with lines connected.
15. Recover air conditioning refrigerant as outlined in "Air Conditioning" section.
16. Disconnect compressor to condenser line, then the suction line. Tie lines aside. Compress remains with engine.
17. Remove transmission as outlined in "Automatic Transmission" section.
18. Remove heat shield and disconnect starter motor cable connectors.
19. Remove starter motor.
20. Disconnect lines and remove transmission oil cooler.
21. Remove radiator as outlined under "Radiator Replace."
22. Disconnect water hoses from alternator and thermostat housing.
23. Disconnect coolant manifold hoses.
24. Disconnect heater hoses.
25. Disconnect plug connection and remove heating valve with hoses.
26. Disconnect tank venting valve hose.
27. Disconnect control module box connectors and place wiring harness on engine.
28. Disconnect positive lead from support point and place on engine.
29. Disconnect control module box transmission wiring harness.
30. Disconnect wiring harness from transmission and Oxygen Sensors (O2S), then place it on engine.
31. Disconnect coolant expansion tank hoses and coolant level sensor connector.
32. Remove expansion tank.
33. Drain power steering reservoir into suitable container.
34. Disconnect reservoir from carrier with lines connected.
35. Disconnect grounding strap from oil filter housing.
36. Remove mounting bolts and main flow oil filter housing.
37. Attach housing to engine with lines connected.
38. Temporarily install power steering pump reservoir.
39. Support engine with suitable wooden block tied to front axle support.
40. Remove left and righthand swivel bearings.
41. Remove output shafts.
42. Disconnect propeller shaft at front.
43. Disconnect hose, cable and connector, then feed wiring harness out, and remove mounting nut, bolts and partition wall.
44. Disconnect ground tape from righthand engine support.
45. Remove left and righthand engine mount nuts.

46. Support engine at lifting lugs using engine lifting/support tool No. 11 0 000, or equivalent.
47. Remove engine. **Do not pinch or damage fuel and air conditioner compressor lines, valve cover, compressor, condenser, exhaust manifold, front axle differential or steering spindle.**
48. Reverse procedures to install, noting the following:
    a. Tighten mounting bolts and nuts to specifications.
    b. **Torque** reinforcement plate mounting bolts to 41 ft. lbs. Tighten an additional 90° , and final tighten an additional 15°.
    c. Replace bulkhead rubber seals, as required. Coat seals with suitable agent.

540 & 740

1. Lock hood in vertical service position.
2. Remove engine acoustic cover.
3. Disconnect brake booster vacuum connection.
4. Remove mounting bolts and main flow oil filter housing.
5. Disconnect oil pressure switch connector.
6. Attach housing to engine with lines connected.
7. Relieve fuel system pressure as outlined under "Precautions."
8. Disconnect fuel feed and return lines from injector tube.
9. Disconnect Mass Air Force (MAF) sensor connector.
10. Disconnect clip and remove air intake hose.
11. **On 740 models,** disconnect Intake Air Temperature (IAT) sensor.
12. **On all models,** remove MAF sensor.
13. Remove mounting bolts and air filter housing.
14. Remove throttle body hose, then disconnect clip and remove gaiter.
15. Disconnect ASC+T connector.
16. Disconnect accelerator and cruise control cables.
17. Disconnect throttle body vacuum hose.
18. Remove mounting bolts and throttle valve neck.
19. Disconnect connectors, then remove mounting bolts and throttle body.
20. Disconnect tank vent valve connector and vacuum hose.
21. Lock belt pulley in position using holding tool No. 11 5 050, or equivalent, then remove mounting nut using wrench tool No. 11 5 040, or equivalent. **Nut has lefthand threads.**
22. Remove fan coupling.
23. Remove left and righthand cover and disconnect ignition coils.
24. Disconnect alternator electrical connectors.
25. Disconnect Oxygen Sensor (O2S) connectors.
26. Record route for installation, then disconnect back-up lamp connector.
27. Disconnect starter motor wires.
28. Disconnect oil level switch connector.
29. Disconnect cylinders No. 3/4 and 1/3 knock sensors' connectors from cable duct.
30. Disconnect Crankshaft Position (CKP) sensor connector from cable duct.
31. Disconnect cylinders No. 7/8 and 5/6 knock sensors' connectors from cable duct.
32. Disconnect Camshaft Position (CMP) sensor connector from cable duct.
33. Disconnect battery positive lead from protective tube bracket.
34. Disconnect Idle Speed Adjuster (ISA) and Throttle Position Sensor (TPS) connectors.
35. Disconnect wires from oil dipstick guide tube.
36. Disconnect wire from upper front section of oil pan.
37. Disconnect water box rear connector for Engine Coolant Temperature (ECT) sensor, remote thermometer sensor and ignition coils ground.
38. Disconnect ground connections.
39. Disconnect Diagnosis Link Connector (DLC) from bracket and ignition coils connectors.
40. Remove mounting bolts and cable ducts from brackets.
41. Remove electronics box cover mounting screws.
42. Remove O2S heating and Digital Motor Electronics (DME) relays.
43. Disconnect electronics box connector for temperature sensor.
44. Disconnect connector for automatic transmission, cruise control and DME control modules.
45. Disconnect electronics box connectors.
46. Place wiring harness aside.
47. Disconnect DLC from spring strut chock absorber and place aside.
48. Raise and support vehicle.
49. Disconnect left and righthand side heat baffle plate.
50. Drain cooling system into suitable container.
51. Remove radiator as outlined under "Radiator Replace."
52. Remove transmission as outlined in "Clutch & Manual Transmission" or "Automatic Transmission" sections.
53. Disconnect battery positive lead, then remove starter motor as outlined in "Electrical" section.
54. Disconnect battery positive lead from oil pan.
55. Disconnect lefthand carrier bracket and alternator.
56. Remove alternator cooling air duct.
57. Remove alternator drive belt.
58. Remove power steering pump as outlined in "Front Suspension & Steering" section.
59. Remove drive belt, mounting bolts and air conditioning compressor. Place compressor aside with lines connector.
60. Disconnect ground tape from righthand engine support.
61. Remove left and righthand engine mount nuts.
62. Disconnect coolant manifold hoses.
63. Remove left and righthand exhaust manifolds as outlined under "Exhaust Manifold, Replace."
64. Support engine at lifting lugs using engine lifting/support tool No. 11 0 000, or equivalent.
65. Remove coolant reservoir bottle.
66. Remove heat shields on front axle carrier, then disconnect oil level switch.
67. Remove bolts and ground cable from motor mounts.
68. Release tensioner and remove serpentine drive belt.
69. Remove alternator, then the power steering pump without disconnecting hoses and place aside.
70. Remove A/C compressor without disconnecting hoses and place aside.
71. Disconnect all cables, hoses and connectors from throttle body.
72. Remove cylinder head trim covers, then disconnect ignition coils.
73. Disconnect fuel lines and coolant lines from engine.
74. Remove engine. **Do not pinch or damage ABS module and air conditioner compressor lines, valve cover, steering spindle or heater valve.**
75. Reverse procedures to install, noting the following:
    a. Tighten mounting bolts and nuts to specifications.
    b. **On 540 models,** engine mounts in bracket front bore.
    c. **On 740 models,** engine mounts in bracket rear bore.
    d. **On all models, do not cross connect left and righthand engine knock sensors or engine damage will result.**
    e. Route O2S lines under heat shield.
    f. Install new throttle valve and body gaskets.
    g. Replace throttle body O-ring, as required.
    h. Adjust accelerator pedal free play.
    i. Adjust cruise control cable with 0.039–0.079 inch play.
    j. Adjust throttle cable to zero backlash.
    k. Install new MAF sensor gasket coat with suitable acid free grease.

INTAKE MANIFOLD

REPLACE

M5

1. Disconnect clips, then the air duct by turning upward at firewall.
2. Pull air duct forward and remove it.
3. Disconnect lefthand air intake hose clamp and Mass Air Flow (MAF) sensor connector.
4. Disconnect MAF sensor cable holders' clip, then the air intake hoė from intake manifold.
5. Disconnect retainers and remove air intake filer upper housing section with MAF sensor and hose.
6. Remove air intake filter lower housing.
7. Remove lefthand wheelhousing cover and intake filter lower housing section from hose.
8. Disconnect righthand air intake hose clamp and Mass Air Flow (MAF) sensor connector.
9. Disconnect MAF sensor cable holders'

clip, then the air intake hose from intake manifold.
10. Disconnect retainers and remove air intake filer upper housing section with MAF sensor and hose.
11. Remove air intake filter lower housing.
12. Remove righthand wheelhousing cover and intake filter lower housing section from hose.
13. Remove mounting nuts and intake manifold cover.
14. Mark funnels for installation alignment. Funnels for cylinders Nos. 2–4 and 6–8 are identical. Funnels for cylinders Nos. 1 and 5 are different.
15. Remove mounting nuts and funnels.
16. Loosen outside, then inside intake manifold mounting bolts.
17. Remove outside, then inside intake manifold mounting bolts.
18. Disconnect connector from holder and oil separator mounting bolt.
19. Remove oil separator with hose connected.
20. Remove clamps, then remove hoses and intake manifold.
21. Reverse procedure to install, noting the following:
    a. Install new sealing rings and gasket.
    b. Replace seals as required.
    c. Install new funnel mounting nuts.
    d. **Torque** intake manifold cover center mounting nuts to 44 inch lbs., then the remaining nuts. Final tighten nuts to specifications.

X5

1. Disconnect sealing strip and turn toggles 90°, then remove cover, mounting bolts and heater bulkhead.
2. Turn fasteners 90° and remove engine acoustic cover.
3. Remove covers and disconnect ignition coils.
4. Disconnect throttle bellows, then remove air intake filter housing with Mass Air Flow (MAF) sensor.
5. Disconnect from firewall support, feed battery positive lead out and lay aside.
6. Disconnect wiring harness from intake manifold components and place aside with cable duct.
7. Disconnect air injection vacuum control hoses.
8. Disconnect throttle body vacuum hose.
9. Relieve fuel system pressure as outlined under "Precautions."
10. Disconnect fuel feed line from injector pipe. Seal hose ends with clamp tools No. 13 5 281/2, or equivalent.
11. Disconnect engine ventilation hose from valve cover, then from oil separator.
12. Disconnect brake booster connector.
13. Remove oil separator from rear cover.
14. Remove intake manifold mounting nuts and decoupling elements.
15. Raise intake manifold approximately 0.39 inch and tilt to one side.
16. Disconnect oil drain hose from rear cover.
17. Remove intake manifold.
18. Reverse procedures to install, noting the following:
    a. Replace oil drain hose as required.
    b. Ensure oil drain hose is routed without kinks.
    c. Install one left and righthand decoupling elements with mounting nuts. **Do not tighten.**
    d. Align manifold, then install remaining decoupling elements and mounting nuts.
    e. Tighten mounting nuts to specifications crosswise from inside to outside.

540 & 740

1. Remove mounting bolts and air filter housing with Mass Air Flow (MAF) sensor.
2. Disconnect wiring harness from intake manifold components and place aside with cable duct.
3. Disconnect ASC+T connector.
4. Remove throttle body hose, then disconnect clip and remove gaiter.
5. Disconnect accelerator and cruise control cables.
6. Disconnect throttle body vacuum hose.
7. Remove mounting bolts and throttle valve neck.
8. Disconnect connectors, then remove mounting bolts and throttle body.
9. Relieve fuel system pressure as outlined under "Precautions."
10. Disconnect fuel feed and return lines from injection pipe.
11. Remove brake booster line connector.
12. Disconnect clip and slide engine vent hose aside.
13. Remove intake manifold mounting nuts, decoupling elements and intake manifold.
14. Reverse procedure to install, noting the following:
    a. Replace seals as required.
    b. Install one left and righthand decoupling elements with mounting nuts. **Do not tighten.**
    c. Align manifold, then install remaining decoupling elements and mounting nuts.
    d. Tighten mounting nuts to specifications crosswise from inside to outside.

EXHAUST MANIFOLD

REPLACE

M5

LEFTHAND

1. Raise and support vehicle, then remove splash guard.
2. Remove exhaust system and lefthand heat shield.
3. Loosen lefthand motor mount nut approximately 0.31 inch.
4. Pull air duct forward and remove it.
5. Disconnect lefthand air intake hose clamp and Mass Air Flow (MAF) sensor connector.
6. Disconnect MAF sensor cable holders' clip, then the air intake hose from intake manifold.
7. Disconnect retainers and remove air intake filer upper housing section with MAF sensor and hose.
8. Remove air intake filter lower housing.
9. Remove lefthand wheelhousing cover and intake filter lower housing section from hose.
10. Remove mounting bolt and grounding cable, then the mounting bolt and main flow oil filter housing.
11. Place filter housing aside with lines connected.
12. Support engine with engine support tool No. 00 0 200, or equivalent.
13. Raise engine approximately 0.236–0.315 inch.
14. If transmission is removed, engine must be raise an additional 0.397 inch at flywheel end.
15. Remove mounting bolts, then the front exhaust manifold.
16. Remove rear manifold.
17. Reverse procedure to install, noting the following:
    a. Coat threads with CRC copper paste, or equivalent anti-seize compound.
    b. Install new gaskets.
    c. Seal beads face exhaust manifold.
    d. Install new mounting nuts.
    e. Tighten mounting nut and bolts to specification.

RIGHTHAND

1. Raise and support vehicle, then remove splash guard.
2. Remove exhaust system and righthand heat shield.
3. Remove mounting bolts, then the front exhaust manifold.
4. Remove rear manifold.
5. Reverse procedure to install, noting the following:
    a. Coat threads with CRC copper paste, or equivalent anti-seize compound.
    b. Install new gaskets.
    c. Seal beads face exhaust manifold.
    d. Install new mounting nuts.
    e. Tighten mounting nut and bolts to specification.

X5

LEFTHAND

1. Raise and support vehicle, then remove splash guard.
2. Remove exhaust system.
3. Remove mounting bolts and reinforcement plate.
4. Disconnect propeller shaft at front.
5. Remove exhaust manifold mounting bolts and disconnect from studs.
6. Raise front manifold as high as possible, past steering gear end and hydraulic screw connection mating surface.
7. Remove front exhaust manifold toward bottom.
8. Reverse procedure to install, noting the following:
    a. Coat threads with CRC copper paste, or equivalent anti-seize compound.
    b. Install new gaskets.
    c. Seal beads face exhaust manifold.
    d. Install new mounting nuts.

e. Tighten mounting nut and bolts to specification.
f. **Torque** reinforcement plate mounting bolts to 41 ft. lbs. Tighten an additional 90° , and final tighten an additional 15°.

RIGHTHAND

1. Raise and support vehicle, then remove splash guard.
2. Remove exhaust system.
3. Remove mounting bolts and reinforcement plate.
4. Remove mounting bolts, then the front exhaust manifold.
5. Remove rear manifold.
6. Reverse procedure to install, noting the following:
   a. Coat threads with CRC copper paste, or equivalent anti-seize compound.
   b. Install new gaskets.
   c. Seal beads face exhaust manifold.
   d. Install new mounting nuts.
   e. Tighten mounting nut and bolts to specification.

540 & 740

1998

Lefthand

1. Raise and support vehicle, then remove splash guard.
2. Remove exhaust system and lefthand heat shield.
3. Loosen lefthand motor mount nut approximately 0.31 inch.
4. Remove engine acoustic cover.
5. Support engine with engine support tool No. 00 0 200, or equivalent.
6. Raise engine approximately 0.236–0.315 inch.
7. If transmission is removed, engine must be raise an additional 0.397 inch at flywheel end.
8. Remove mounting bolts, then the front exhaust manifold.
9. Remove rear manifold.
10. Reverse procedure to install, noting the following:
    a. Coat threads with CRC copper paste, or equivalent anti-seize compound.
    b. Install new gaskets.
    c. Seal beads face exhaust manifold.
    d. Install new mounting nuts.
    e. Tighten mounting nut and bolts to specification.

Righthand

1. Raise and support vehicle, then remove splash guard.
2. Remove exhaust system and righthand heat shield.
3. Remove mounting bolts, then the front exhaust manifold.
4. Remove rear manifold.
5. Reverse procedure to install, noting the following:
   a. Coat threads with CRC copper paste, or equivalent anti-seize compound.
   b. Install new gaskets.
   c. Seal beads face exhaust manifold.
   d. Install new mounting nuts.
   e. Tighten mounting nut and bolts to specification.

1999–2001

Lefthand

1. Raise and support vehicle, then remove splash guard.
2. Remove exhaust system and lefthand heat shield.
3. Disconnect connector and remove Oxygen Sensor (O2S) using socket wrench tool No. 11 7 030, or equivalent.
4. Remove engine acoustic cover.
5. Support engine with engine support tool No. 00 0 200, or equivalent.
6. Loosen lefthand motor mount nut.
7. Disconnect steering shaft from steering gear.
8. Raise engine approximately 0.984 inch.
9. If transmission is removed, engine must be raise an additional 0.397 inch at flywheel end.
10. Remove exhaust manifold mounting bolts and disconnect from studs.
11. Raise front manifold as high as possible, past steering gear end and hydraulic screw connection mating surface.
12. Remove front exhaust manifold toward bottom.
13. Reverse procedure to install, noting the following:
    a. Coat threads with CRC copper paste, or equivalent anti-seize compound.
    b. Install new gaskets.
    c. Seal beads face exhaust manifold.
    d. Install new mounting nuts.
    e. Coat O2S threads with Never Seez, or equivalent compound.
    f. Tighten mounting nut and bolts to specification.

Righthand

1. Raise and support vehicle, then remove splash guard.
2. Remove exhaust system and righthand heat shield.
3. Disconnect connector and remove Oxygen Sensor (O2S) using socket wrench tool No. 11 7 030, or equivalent.
4. Remove mounting bolts, then the front exhaust manifold.
5. Remove rear manifold.
6. Reverse procedure to install, noting the following:
   a. Coat threads with CRC copper paste, or equivalent anti-seize compound.
   b. Install new gaskets.
   c. Seal beads face exhaust manifold.
   d. Install new mounting nuts.
   e. Coat O2S threads with Never Seez, or equivalent compound.
   f. Tighten mounting nut and bolts to specification.

CYLINDER HEAD

REPLACE

M5

LEFTHAND

REMOVAL

1. Remove lefthand exhaust manifold as outlined under "Exhaust Manifold, Replace."
2. Drain coolant into suitable container.
3. Disconnect clips, then the air duct by turning upward at firewall.
4. Pull air duct forward and remove it.
5. Disconnect lefthand air intake hose clamp and Mass Air Flow (MAF) sensor connector.
6. Disconnect MAF sensor cable holders' clip, then the air intake hose from intake manifold.
7. Disconnect retainers and remove air intake filer upper housing section with MAF sensor and hose.
8. Remove air intake filter lower housing.
9. Remove lefthand wheelhousing cover and intake filter lower housing section from hose.
10. Remove intake manifold as outlined under "Intake Manifold, Replace."
11. Remove spark plugs.
12. Remove both valve covers as outlined under "Valve Cover, Replace."
13. Lock belt pulley in position using holding tool No. 11 5 050, or equivalent, then remove mounting nut using wrench tool No. 11 5 040, or equivalent. **Nut has lefthand threads.**
14. Remove fan coupling.
15. Disconnect Camshaft Position (CMP) sensors' connectors.
16. Remove mounting screws and bracket, then disconnect connector and place cable aside.
17. Disconnect lefthand knock sensor connector.
18. Disconnect cable duct and raise approximately 0.08 inch.
19. Disconnect cable strip from fuel injectors. Pull cable up and feed out of bracket.
20. Disconnect pull rods at servomotor ball heads.
21. Remove mounting bolts and injection pipe.
22. Remove mounting bolts, disconnect connector and remove throttle actuator.
23. Remove throttle supplementary air distributor molded hose.
24. Remove knock sensor cable guide from return line.
25. Remove heating feed line from block and both return lines for heads.
26. Disconnect throttle body brake booster hose.
27. Disconnect pressure regulator vacuum hose.
28. Remove cylinder head oil lines.
29. Remove CMP sensors.
30. Grip camshaft with suitable wrench and remove banjo bolt and signal rings.
31. Crank engine from 45° before TDC in

normal rotational direction to TDC position.
32. Install timing pin tool No. 11 2 300, or equivalent, through hole and into flywheel.
33. Remove lefthand camshaft adjustment unit as outlined under "Variable Camshaft Timing (VANOS) Adjustment Unit, Replace."
34. Disconnect timing pin tool from into flywheel.
35. Turn crankshaft in reverse of normal rotational direction to 45° before TDC.
36. Remove thermostat as outlined under "Thermostat, Replace."
37. Remove left timing case cover as outlined in "Front Cover, Replace."
38. Remove chain tensioner as outlined under "Timing Chain Tensioner, Replace."
39. Remove mounting bolts and lefthand intake camshaft spacer ring.
40. Remove spline hub with plate spring and supporting ring. **Do not allow ring to fall out.**
41. Disconnect intake sprocket from centering sleeve. Support chain with suitable wire.
42. Disconnect sliding rail.
43. Remove cylinder head mounting bolts in sequence, **Fig. 1.**
44. Remove cylinder head.

INSTALLATION

1. Coat joint between block and timing case cover with Drei Bond No. 1209, or equivalent.
2. Ensure locating dowels are in good condition and positioned correctly.
3. Install new cylinder head gasket.
4. Install new head bolts. **Do not wash thread coating off.**
5. **Torque** cylinder head bolts to 22 ft. lbs. in sequence, **Fig. 1.**
6. Tighten head bolts an additional 80° in sequence.
7. Final tighten bolts an additional 80° in sequence.
8. Install and tighten side rail mounting bolt.
9. Keep timing chain tensioned and install intake sprocket on centering sleeve. **Do not install mounting bolts.**
10. Install chain tensioner as outlined under "Timing Chain Tensioner, Replace."
11. Crank engine from 45° before TDC in normal rotational direction to TDC position. **Do not allow sprocket to slip off centering sleeve.**
12. Install timing pin tool No. 11 2 300, or equivalent, through hole and into flywheel.
13. Align secondary chain drive to intake camshaft sprocket bores using hook wrench tool No. 11 7 150, or equivalent.
14. Install plate spring and supporting ring in spline shaft. Plate spring small support diameter points to supporting ring which is supported by spline hub retaining lugs.
15. Install spline hub with plate spring and supporting ring.

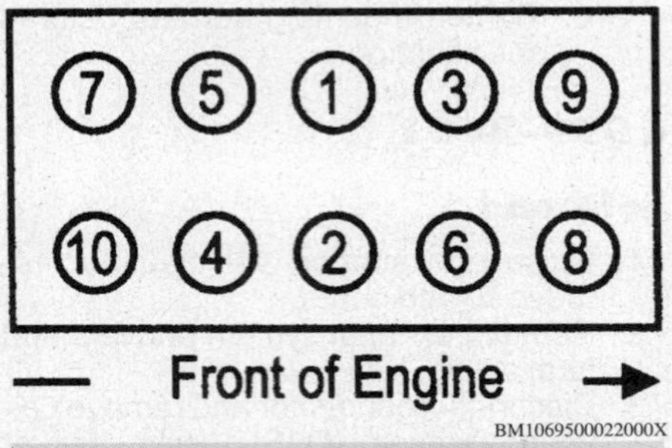

Fig. 1 Cylinder head bolt tightening sequence

16. Install intake camshaft sprocket spacer ring and hand tighten mounting bolts.
17. Loosen mounting bolts until spline hub can be moved by hand.
18. Install lefthand timing case cover as outlined under "Front Cover, Replace."
19. Install lefthand camshaft adjustment unit as outlined under "Variable Camshaft Timing (VANOS) Adjustment Unit, Replace."
20. Install CMP sensors.
21. Install cylinder head oil lines.
22. Connect pressure regulator vacuum hose.
23. Connect throttle body brake booster hose.
24. Install heating feed line from block and both return lines for heads.
25. Install knock sensor cable guide.
26. Install throttle supplementary air distributor molded hose.
27. Install throttle actuator and mounting bolts, then connect connector.
28. Install injection pipe and mounting bolts.
29. Connect pull rods at servomotor ball heads.
30. Connect fuel injectors' cable strip.
31. Connect lefthand knock sensor connector.
32. Connect CMP sensors' connectors.
33. Install fan coupling.
34. Install both valve covers as outlined under "Valve Cover, Replace."
35. Install intake manifold as outlined under "Intake Manifold, Replace."
36. Install spark plugs.
37. Install lefthand air intake and MAF sensor.
38. Install lefthand exhaust manifold as outlined under "Exhaust Manifold, Replace."

RIGHTHAND

REMOVAL

1. Remove righthand exhaust manifold as outlined under "Exhaust Manifold, Replace."
2. Drain coolant into suitable container.
3. Disconnect clips, then the air duct by turning upward at firewall.
4. Pull air duct forward and remove it.
5. Disconnect righthand air intake hose clamp and Mass Air Flow (MAF) sensor connector.
6. Disconnect MAF sensor cable holders' clip, then the air intake hose from intake manifold.
7. Disconnect retainers and remove air intake filer upper housing section with MAF sensor and hose.
8. Remove air intake filter lower housing.
9. Remove righthand wheelhousing cover and intake filter lower housing section from hose.
10. Remove intake manifold as outlined under "Intake Manifold, Replace."
11. Disconnect engine wiring harness from cylinder heads and place aside.
12. Disconnect fuel injector's fuel line and place aside.
13. Disconnect Idle Speed Control (ISC) valve connector.
14. Disconnect clamps, then remove ISC valve hose and rubber mounting.
15. Remove ISC valve.
16. Remove throttle supplementary air distributor molded hose.
17. Disconnect solenoid operated valve vacuum hoses.
18. Remove throttle body brake booster hose.
19. Remove heating feed line from block and cylinder heads' return lines.
20. Disconnect pull rods at servomotor ball heads.
21. Remove both valve covers as outlined under "Valve Cover, Replace."
22. Remove spark plugs.
23. Lock belt pulley in position using holding tool No. 11 5 050, or equivalent, then remove mounting nut using wrench tool No. 11 5 040, or equivalent. **Nut has lefthand threads.**
24. Remove fan coupling.
25. Remove thermostat as outlined under "Thermostats, Replace."
26. Remove cylinder head oil lines.
27. Remove cable channel bracket.
28. Remove Camshaft Position (CMP) sensors.
29. Crank engine in normal rotational direction to TDC position.
30. Install timing pin tool No. 11 2 300, or equivalent, through hole and into flywheel.
31. Remove righthand camshaft adjustment unit as outlined under "Variable Camshaft Timing (VANOS) Adjustment Unit, Replace."
32. Disconnect timing pin tool from into flywheel.
33. Turn crankshaft in reverse of normal rotational direction to 45° before TDC.
34. Remove chain tensioner as outlined under "Timing Chain Tensioner, Replace."
35. Remove right timing case cover as outlined in "Front Cover, Replace."
36. Remove mounting bolts and righthand intake camshaft spacer ring.
37. Remove spline hub with plate spring and supporting ring. **Do not allow ring to fall out.**
38. Disconnect intake sprocket from centering sleeve. Support chain with suitable wire.
39. Disconnect sliding rail.
40. Remove cylinder head mounting bolts in sequence, **Fig. 1.**

41. Remove cylinder head.

INSTALLATION

1. Coat joint between block and timing case cover with Drei Bond No. 1209, or equivalent.
2. Ensure locating dowels are in good condition and positioned correctly.
3. Install new cylinder head gasket.
4. Install new head bolts. **Do not wash thread coating off.**
5. **Torque** cylinder head bolts to 22 ft. lbs. in sequence, **Fig. 1.**
6. Tighten head bolts an additional 80° in sequence.
7. Final tighten bolts an additional 80° in sequence.
8. Install and tighten side rail mounting bolt.
9. Keep timing chain tensioned and install intake sprocket on centering sleeve. **Do not install mounting bolts.**
10. Crank engine from 45° before TDC in normal rotational direction to TDC position. **Do not allow sprocket to slip off centering sleeve.**
11. Install timing pin tool No. 11 2 300, or equivalent, through hole and into flywheel.
12. Align secondary chain drive to intake camshaft sprocket bores using hook wrench tool No. 11 7 150, or equivalent.
13. Install plate spring and supporting ring in spline shaft. Plate spring small support diameter points to supporting ring which is supported by spline hub retaining lugs.
14. Install spline hub with plate spring and supporting ring.
15. Install intake camshaft sprocket spacer ring and hand tighten mounting bolts.
16. Loosen mounting bolts until spline hub can be moved by hand.
17. Install righthand timing case cover as outlined under "Front Cover, Replace."
18. Install chain tensioner as outlined under "Timing Chain Tensioner, Replace."
19. Install righthand camshaft adjustment unit as outlined under "Variable Camshaft Timing (VANOS) Adjustment Unit, Replace."
20. Install CMP sensors.
21. Install cable channel bracket.
22. Install cylinder head oil lines.
23. Install thermostat as outlined under "Thermostats, Replace."
24. Install fan coupling.
25. Install spark plugs.
26. Install both valve covers as outlined under "Valve Cover, Replace."
27. Connect pull rods at servomotor ball heads.
28. Connect throttle body brake booster hose.
29. Connect solenoid operated valve vacuum hoses.
30. Install throttle supplementary air distributor molded hose.
31. Install ISC valve.
32. Connect fuel injector's fuel line.
33. Install intake manifold as outlined under "Intake Manifold, Replace."
34. Install righthand air intake and MAF sensor.
35. Install righthand exhaust manifold as outlined under "Exhaust Manifold, Replace."

X5

LEFTHAND

REMOVAL

1. Remove lefthand exhaust manifold as outlined under "Exhaust Manifold, Replace."
2. Remove mounting bolts and splash guard.
3. Drain coolant into suitable container.
4. Remove both valve covers as outlined under "Valve Cover, Replace."
5. Remove spark plugs.
6. Remove intake manifold as outlined under "Intake Manifold, Replace."
7. Removal coolant manifold hoses.
8. Remove mounting bolts and coolant manifold.
9. Remove lefthand camshaft adjustment unit as outlined under "Variable Camshaft Timing (VANOS) Adjustment Unit, Replace."
10. Disconnect timing pin tool from into flywheel.
11. Lift timing chain and hold under tension, then turn crankshaft in reverse of normal rotational direction to 45° before TDC.
12. Remove camshaft locking tools.
13. Disconnect guide rail.
14. Remove cylinder head mounting bolts in sequence, **Fig. 1.**
15. Remove cylinder head.

INSTALLATION

1. Coat joint between block and timing case cover with Drei Bond No. 1209, or equivalent.
2. Ensure locating dowels are in good condition and positioned correctly.
3. Install new cylinder head gasket.
4. Install new head bolts. **Do not wash thread coating off.**
5. **Torque** cylinder head bolts to 22 ft. lbs. in sequence, **Fig. 1.**
6. Tighten head bolts an additional 80° in sequence.
7. Final tighten bolts an additional 80° in sequence.
8. Align camshafts with marker bores point upward using suitable open end wrench.
9. Install camshaft locking tools Nos. 11 2 446 and 11 2 442, or equivalents, to camshafts on lefthand cylinder head.
10. Install camshaft locking tools Nos. 11 2 445 and 11 2 441, or equivalents, to camshafts on righthand cylinder head.
11. Ensure locking tools fit with no gaps.
12. Install lock holder tool No. 11 2 443, or equivalent, to hold camshaft lock tools in place. Secure tools with bolt tool No. 11 2 444, or equivalent, in spark plug hole.
13. Lift timing chain and hold under tension.
14. Crank engine from 45° before TDC in normal rotational direction to TDC position.
15. Install timing pin tool No. 11 5 180, or equivalent, through hole and into flywheel.
16. Install lefthand camshaft adjustment unit as outlined under "Variable Camshaft Timing (VANOS) Adjustment Unit, Replace."
17. Install coolant manifold.
18. Install intake manifold as outlined under "Intake Manifold, Replace."
19. Install spark plugs.
20. Install both valve covers as outlined under "Valve Cover, Replace."
21. Install lefthand exhaust manifold as outlined under "Exhaust Manifold, Replace."

RIGHTHAND

REMOVAL

1. Remove righthand exhaust manifold as outlined under "Exhaust Manifold, Replace."
2. Remove mounting bolts and splash guard.
3. Drain coolant into suitable container.
4. Remove both valve covers as outlined under "Valve Cover, Replace."
5. Remove spark plugs.
6. Lock belt pulley in position using holding tool No. 11 5 050, or equivalent, then remove mounting nut using wrench tool No. 11 5 040, or equivalent. **Nut has lefthand threads.**
7. Remove fan coupling.
8. Remove intake manifold as outlined under "Intake Manifold, Replace."
9. Removal coolant manifold hoses.
10. Remove mounting bolts and coolant manifold.
11. Remove righthand camshaft adjustment unit as outlined under "Variable Camshaft Timing (VANOS) Adjustment Unit, Replace."
12. Disconnect connecting piece with vent pipe from oil separator angle bracket.
13. Disconnect timing pin tool from into flywheel.
14. Lift timing chain and hold under tension, then turn crankshaft in reverse of normal rotational direction to 45° before TDC.
15. Remove camshaft locking tools.
16. Remove cylinder head mounting bolts in sequence, **Fig. 1.**
17. Remove cylinder head.

INSTALLATION

1. Coat joint between block and timing case cover with Drei Bond No. 1209, or equivalent.
2. Ensure locating dowels are in good condition and positioned correctly.
3. Install new cylinder head gasket.
4. Install new head bolts. **Do not wash thread coating off.**
5. **Torque** cylinder head bolts to 22 ft. lbs. in sequence, **Fig. 1.**
6. Tighten head bolts an additional 80° in sequence.
7. Final tighten bolts an additional 80° in sequence.
8. Align camshafts with marker bores point upward using suitable open end wrench.
9. Install camshaft locking tools Nos. 11 2

446 and 11 2 442, or equivalents, to camshafts on lefthand cylinder head.
10. Install camshaft locking tools Nos. 11 2 445 and 11 2 441, or equivalents, to camshafts on righthand cylinder head.
11. Ensure locking tools fit with no gaps.
12. Install lock holder tool No. 11 2 443, or equivalent, to hold camshaft lock tools in place. Secure tools with bolt tool No. 11 2 444, or equivalent, in spark plug hole.
13. Lift timing chain and hold under tension.
14. Crank engine from 45° before TDC in normal rotational direction to TDC position.
15. Install timing pin tool No. 11 2 300, or equivalent, through hole and into flywheel.
16. Install righthand camshaft adjustment unit as outlined under "Variable Camshaft Timing (VANOS) Adjustment Unit, Replace."
17. Install coolant manifold.
18. Install intake manifold as outlined under "Intake Manifold, Replace."
19. Install fan.
20. Install spark plugs.
21. Install both valve covers as outlined under "Valve Cover, Replace."
22. Install lefthand exhaust manifold as outlined under "Exhaust Manifold, Replace."

540 & 740

1998

LEFTHAND

Removal

1. Remove lefthand exhaust manifold as outlined under "Exhaust Manifold, Replace."
2. Remove mounting bolts and splash guard.
3. Drain coolant into suitable container.
4. Remove both valve covers as outlined under "Valve Cover, Replace."
5. Remove spark plugs.
6. **On 540 models,** lift water valve out of mounting and press aside.
7. **On all models,** removal coolant manifold hoses.
8. Remove mounting bolts and coolant manifold.
9. Remove left and righthand cylinder head oil lines.
10. Turn engine in normal rotational direction to cylinder No. 1 TDC.
11. Loosen three accessible exhaust and intake camshaft sprocket mounting bolts ½ turn.
12. Turn engine one revelation to cylinder No. 1 TDC and brace camshaft with suitable wrench.
13. Loosen remaining exhaust and intake camshaft mounting bolts ½ turn.
14. Remove chain tensioner as outlined under "Timing Chain Tensioner, Replace."
15. Remove top lefthand timing case cover as outlined under "Front Cover, Replace."
16. Remove mounting bolts and lefthand intake camshaft sprocket. Support chain with suitable wire.
17. Turn crankshaft in reverse of normal rotational direction to 45° before TDC.
18. Loosen angle bracket grub screw and remove guide rail.
19. Remove mounting bolt and oil separator from angle bracket.
20. Remove cylinder head mounting bolts in sequence, **Fig. 1.**
21. Remove cylinder head.

Installation

1. Coat joint between block and timing case cover with Drei Bond No. 1209, or equivalent.
2. Ensure locating dowels are in good condition and positioned correctly.
3. Install new cylinder head gasket.
4. Install new head bolts. **Do not wash thread coating off.**
5. **Torque** cylinder head bolts to 22 ft. lbs. in sequence, **Fig. 1.**
6. Tighten head bolts an additional 80° in sequence.
7. Final tighten bolts an additional 80° in sequence.
8. Ensure return pipe is correctly seated in oil separator.
9. Replace sealing ring as required.
10. Press oil separator into angle section.
11. Tighten guide rail and oil separator mounting bolt.
12. Install new grub screw until it makes contact with angle section with play. **Do not tighten.**
13. Align camshafts with marker bores point upward using suitable open end wrench.
14. Install camshaft locking tools Nos. 11 2 445 and 11 2 441, or equivalents, to camshafts on righthand cylinder head.
15. Install camshaft locking tools Nos. 11 2 446 and 11 2 442, or equivalents, to camshafts on lefthand cylinder head.
16. Ensure locking tools fit with no gaps.
17. Install lock holder tool No. 11 2 443, or equivalent, to hold camshaft lock tools in place. Secure tools with bolt tool No. 11 2 444, or equivalent, in spark plug hole.
18. Crank engine from 45° before TDC in normal rotational direction to TDC position.
19. Remove plug from flywheel timing plug pin hole and install timing pin tool No. 11 2 300, or equivalent, through hole and into flywheel.
20. Install sprocket with chain to intake camshaft with long bores centered.
21. Install mounting screws hand tight.
22. Install chain tensioning tool No 11 3 390, or equivalent, into camshaft chain tensioner bore.
23. Preload threaded center pin using weighted wrench tool No. 00 9 250, or equivalent, to 6 inch lbs.
24. Tighten camshaft sprocket mounting bolts to specifications in following sequence:
    a. All lefthand exhaust camshaft sprocket mounting bolts.
    b. Three righthand exhaust camshaft sprocket mounting bolts.
    c. All lefthand intake camshaft sprocket mounting bolts.
    d. Three righthand intake camshaft sprocket mounting bolts.
25. Remove camshaft and crankshaft locking tools.
26. Turn engine one revelation.
27. Tighten remaining camshaft sprocket mounting bolts to specifications.
28. Install left and righthand cylinder head oil lines.
29. Remove chain tensioning tool.
30. Install chain tensioner as outlined under "Timing Chain Tensioner, Replace."
31. Install top lefthand timing case cover as outlined under "Front Cover, Replace."
32. Connect coolant manifold hoses.
33. Install new coolant manifold seals and sealing rings.
34. Install coolant manifold.
35. Install valve covers as outlined under "Valve Cover, Replace."
36. Fill cooling system.
37. Install exhaust manifold as outlined under "Exhaust Manifold, Replace.".

RIGHTHAND

Removal

1. Remove righthand exhaust manifold as outlined under "Exhaust Manifold, Replace."
2. Remove mounting bolts and splash guard.
3. Drain coolant into suitable container.
4. Remove both valve covers as outlined under "Valve Cover, Replace."
5. Remove spark plugs.
6. Lock belt pulley in position using holding tool No. 11 5 050, or equivalent, then remove mounting nut using wrench tool No. 11 5 040, or equivalent. **Nut has lefthand threads.**
7. Remove fan coupling.
8. **On 540 models,** lift water valve out of mounting and press aside.
9. **On all models,** removal coolant manifold hoses.
10. Remove mounting bolts and coolant manifold.
11. Remove left and righthand cylinder head oil lines.
12. Turn engine in normal rotational direction to cylinder No. 1 TDC.
13. Loosen three accessible exhaust and intake camshaft sprocket mounting bolts ½ turn.
14. Turn engine one revelation to cylinder No. 1 TDC and brace camshaft with suitable wrench.
15. Loosen remaining exhaust and intake camshaft mounting bolts ½ turn.
16. Remove chain tensioner as outlined under "Timing Chain Tensioner, Replace."
17. Remove top righthand timing case cover as outlined under "Front Cover, Replace."
18. Remove mounting bolts and righthand intake camshaft sprocket. Support chain with suitable wire.
19. Turn crankshaft in reverse of normal rotational direction to 45° before TDC.
20. Remove cylinder head mounting bolts in sequence, **Fig. 1.**
21. Remove cylinder head.

Installation

1. Coat joint between block and timing case cover with Drei Bond No. 1209, or equivalent.
2. Ensure locating dowels are in good condition and positioned correctly.
3. Install new cylinder head gasket.
4. Install cylinder head.
5. Install new head bolts. **Do not wash thread coating off.**
6. **Torque** cylinder head bolts to 22 ft. lbs. in sequence, **Fig. 1.**
7. Tighten head bolts an additional 80° in sequence.
8. Final tighten bolts an additional 80° in sequence.
9. Ensure return pipe is correctly seated in oil separator.
10. Align camshafts with marker bores point upward using suitable open end wrench.
11. Install camshaft locking tools Nos. 11 2 445 and 11 2 441, or equivalents, to camshafts on righthand cylinder head.
12. Install camshaft locking tools Nos. 11 2 446 and 11 2 442, or equivalents, to camshafts on lefthand cylinder head.
13. Ensure locking tools fit with no gaps.
14. Install lock holder tool No. 11 2 443, or equivalent, to hold camshaft lock tools in place. Secure tools with bolt tool No. 11 2 444, or equivalent, in spark plug hole.
15. Crank engine from 45° before TDC in normal rotational direction to TDC position.
16. Remove plug from flywheel timing plug pin hole and install timing pin tool No. 11 2 300, or equivalent, through hole and into flywheel.
17. Install sprocket with chain to intake camshaft with long bores centered.
18. Brace sprocket and press bow cover against timing chain and inspect long bore positions.
19. Install sensor gear with mark pointing upward.
20. Install mounting bolts and hand tighten.
21. Install tensioning bracket tool No. 11 7 380, or equivalent, to righthand cylinder head.
22. Install chain tensioning tool No 11 3 390, or equivalent, into camshaft chain tensioner bore.
23. Preload threaded center pin using weighted wrench tool No. 00 9 250, or equivalent, to 6 inch lbs.
24. Tighten camshaft sprocket mounting bolts to specifications in following sequence:
    a. All lefthand exhaust camshaft sprocket mounting bolts.
    b. Three righthand exhaust camshaft sprocket mounting bolts.
    c. All lefthand intake camshaft sprocket mounting bolts.
    d. Three righthand intake camshaft sprocket mounting bolts.
25. Remove camshaft and crankshaft locking tools.
26. Turn engine one revelation.
27. Tighten remaining camshaft sprocket mounting bolts to specifications.
28. Install left and righthand cylinder head oil lines.
29. Remove chain tensioning tool.
30. Install chain tensioner as outlined under "Timing Chain Tensioner, Replace."
31. Install top lefthand timing case cover as outlined under "Front Cover, Replace."
32. Connect coolant manifold hoses.
33. Install new coolant manifold seals and sealing rings.
34. Install coolant manifold.
35. Install fan.
36. Install valve covers as outlined under "Valve Cover, Replace."
37. Fill cooling system.
38. Install exhaust manifold as outlined under "Exhaust Manifold, Replace.".

1999-2001

LEFTHAND

Removal

1. Remove lefthand exhaust manifold as outlined under "Exhaust Manifold, Replace."
2. Remove mounting bolts and splash guard.
3. Drain coolant into suitable container.
4. Remove both valve covers as outlined under "Valve Cover, Replace."
5. Remove spark plugs.
6. Remove intake manifold as outlined under "Intake Manifold, Replace."
7. **On 540 models,** lift water valve out of mounting and press aside.
8. **On all models,** removal coolant manifold hoses.
9. Remove mounting bolts and coolant manifold.
10. Remove lefthand camshaft adjustment unit as outlined under "Variable Camshaft Timing (VANOS) Adjustment Unit, Replace."
11. Disconnect connecting piece with vent pipe from oil separator angle bracket.
12. Disconnect timing pin tool from into flywheel.
13. Lift timing chain and hold under tension, then turn crankshaft in reverse of normal rotational direction to 45° before TDC.
14. Remove camshaft locking tools.
15. Loosen angle bracket grub screw and disconnect guide rail.
16. Remove cylinder head mounting bolts in sequence, **Fig. 1.**
17. Remove cylinder head.

Installation

1. Coat joint between block and timing case cover with Drei Bond No. 1209, or equivalent.
2. Ensure locating dowels are in good condition and positioned correctly.
3. Install new cylinder head gasket.
4. Install new head bolts. **Do not wash thread coating off.**
5. **Torque** cylinder head bolts to 22 ft. lbs. in sequence, **Fig. 1.**
6. Tighten head bolts an additional 80° in sequence.
7. Final tighten bolts an additional 80° in sequence.
8. Install and tighten guide rail mounting bolt.
9. Install angle bracket until it snaps in place.
10. Install new grub screw until it makes contact with angle section with play. **Do not tighten.**
11. Align camshafts with marker bores point upward using suitable open end wrench.
12. Install camshaft locking tools Nos. 11 2 446 and 11 2 442, or equivalents, to camshafts on lefthand cylinder head.
13. Install camshaft locking tools Nos. 11 2 445 and 11 2 441, or equivalents, to camshafts on righthand cylinder head.
14. Ensure locking tools fit with no gaps.
15. Install lock holder tool No. 11 2 443, or equivalent, to hold camshaft lock tools in place. Secure tools with bolt tool No. 11 2 444, or equivalent, in spark plug hole.
16. Lift timing chain and hold under tension.
17. Crank engine from 45° before TDC in normal rotational direction to TDC position.
18. Install timing pin tool No. 11 2 300, or equivalent, through hole and into flywheel.
19. Ensure hose connection between vent pipe and connecting piece does not slip or leak.
20. Install new vent pipe and angle bracket sealing rings. Apply thin coat of grease to sealing rings.
21. Install vent pipe in angle bracket.
22. Install lefthand camshaft adjustment unit as outlined under "Variable Camshaft Timing (VANOS) Adjustment Unit, Replace."
23. Install coolant manifold.
24. Install intake manifold as outlined under "Intake Manifold, Replace."
25. Install spark plugs.
26. Install both valve covers as outlined under "Valve Cover, Replace."
27. Install lefthand exhaust manifold as outlined under "Exhaust Manifold, Replace."

RIGHTHAND

Removal

1. Remove righthand exhaust manifold as outlined under "Exhaust Manifold, Replace."
2. Remove mounting bolts and splash guard.
3. Drain coolant into suitable container.
4. Remove both valve covers as outlined under "Valve Cover, Replace."
5. Remove spark plugs.
6. Lock belt pulley in position using holding tool No. 11 5 050, or equivalent, then remove mounting nut using wrench tool No. 11 5 040, or equivalent. **Nut has lefthand threads.**
7. Remove fan coupling.
8. Remove intake manifold as outlined under "Intake Manifold, Replace."
9. **On 540 models,** lift water valve out of mounting and press aside.

10. **On all models,** removal coolant manifold hoses.
11. Remove mounting bolts and coolant manifold.
12. Remove righthand camshaft adjustment unit as outlined under "Variable Camshaft Timing (VANOS) Adjustment Unit, Replace."
13. Disconnect connecting piece with vent pipe from oil separator angle bracket.
14. Disconnect timing pin tool from into flywheel.
15. Lift timing chain and hold under tension, then turn crankshaft in reverse of normal rotational direction to 45° before TDC.
16. Remove camshaft locking tools.
17. Remove cylinder head mounting bolts in sequence, **Fig. 1.**
18. Remove cylinder head.

Installation

1. Coat joint between block and timing case cover with Drei Bond No. 1209, or equivalent.
2. Ensure locating dowels are in good condition and positioned correctly.
3. Install new cylinder head gasket.
4. Install new head bolts. **Do not wash thread coating off.**
5. **Torque** cylinder head bolts to 22 ft. lbs. in sequence, **Fig. 1.**
6. Tighten head bolts an additional 80° in sequence.
7. Final tighten bolts an additional 80° in sequence.
8. Align camshafts with marker bores point upward using suitable open end wrench.
9. Install camshaft locking tools Nos. 11 2 446 and 11 2 442, or equivalents, to camshafts on lefthand cylinder head.
10. Install camshaft locking tools Nos. 11 2 445 and 11 2 441, or equivalents, to camshafts on righthand cylinder head.
11. Ensure locking tools fit with no gaps.
12. Install lock holder tool No. 11 2 443, or equivalent, to hold camshaft lock tools in place. Secure tools with bolt tool No. 11 2 444, or equivalent, in spark plug hole.
13. Lift timing chain and hold under tension.
14. Crank engine from 45° before TDC in normal rotational direction to TDC position.
15. Install timing pin tool No. 11 2 300, or equivalent, through hole and into flywheel.
16. Install righthand camshaft adjustment unit as outlined under "Variable Camshaft Timing (VANOS) Adjustment Unit, Replace."
17. Install coolant manifold.
18. Install intake manifold as outlined under "Intake Manifold, Replace."
19. Install fan.
20. Install spark plugs.
21. Install both valve covers as outlined under "Valve Cover, Replace."
22. Install lefthand exhaust manifold as outlined under "Exhaust Manifold, Replace."

VALVE COVER

REPLACE

M5

1. Remove intake manifold as outlined under "Intake Manifold, Replace."
2. Remove ignition coils as outlined in "Electrical" section.
3. Disconnect grounding strips from cylinder head cover and place wiring harness aside.
4. Disconnect battery positive terminal on support point.
5. Disconnect engine venting hose.
6. Disconnect main flow oil filter from mounting and place aside with lines connected.
7. Remove mounting nuts, washers and rubber mounts, then the valve covers.
8. Reverse procedure to install, noting the following:
   a. Replace valve cover seal, as required, coating outer and inner grooves and sealing face with suitable anti-friction glycerine coating.
   b. Press internal gasket into groove without torsional stress starting at corners.
   c. Apply coat of Drei Bond No. 1209, or equivalent, to contact surfaces.
   d. Install two mounting nut, washer and rubber mount elements without preload and align cover.
   e. Install remaining mounting elements and tighten to specifications.
   f. Replace ignition coil profile seals, as required.

X5

1. Disconnect sealing strip and turn toggles 90°, then remove cover, mounting bolts and heater bulkhead.
2. Turn fasteners 90° and remove engine acoustic cover.
3. Disconnect throttle bellows, then remove air intake filter housing with Mass Air Flow (MAF) sensor.
4. Disconnect from firewall support, feed battery positive lead out and lay aside.
5. Remove windshield washer fluid reservoir.
6. Disconnect water hoses from holder and press heater valve aside with hoses connected.
7. Remove front axle differential vent line and positive lead from under ignition coils' cover.
8. Remove ignition coils as outlined in "Electrical" section.
9. Disconnect vent hose.
10. Disconnect left and righthand cable ducts, then fold inward.
11. Disconnect battery positive terminal.
12. Remove mounting nuts, washers and rubber mounts, then the valve covers.
13. Reverse procedure to install, noting the following:
   a. Replace valve cover seal, as required, coating outer and inner grooves and sealing face with suitable anti-friction glycerine coating.
   b. Press internal gasket into groove without torsional stress starting at corners.
   c. Apply coat of Drei Bond No. 1209, or equivalent, to contact surfaces.
   d. Apply thin uniform bead of Drei Bond No. 1209, or equivalent, to transmission area half moons.
   e. Install two mounting nut, washer and rubber mount elements without preload and align cover.
   f. Install remaining mounting elements and tighten to specifications.
   g. Replace ignition coil profile seals, as required.

540 & 740

1. Remove engine acoustic covers.
2. Disconnect Mass Air Flow (MAF) sensor and hose clip, then remove hose.
3. **On 740 models,** disconnect Intake Air Temperature (IAT) sensor.
4. **On all models,** disconnect clips and remove MAF sensor.
5. Remove mounting bolt and filter housing.
6. Remove ignition coils as outlined in "Electrical" section.
7. Disconnect left and righthand cable ducts, then fold inward.
8. Disconnect battery positive terminal.
9. Remove mounting nuts, washers and rubber mounts, then the valve covers.
10. Reverse procedure to install, noting the following:
   a. Replace valve cover seal, as required, coating outer and inner grooves and sealing face with suitable anti-friction glycerine coating.
   b. Press internal gasket into groove without torsional stress starting at corners.
   c. Apply coat of Drei Bond No. 1209, or equivalent, to contact surfaces.
   d. Apply thin uniform bead of Drei Bond No. 1209, or equivalent, to transmission area half moons.
   e. Install two mounting nut, washer and rubber mount elements without preload and align cover.
   f. Install remaining mounting elements and tighten to specifications.
   g. Replace ignition coil profile seals, as required.
   h. Install new MAF sensor gasket coated with suitable acid free grease.

VALVE ADJUSTMENT

These engines are equipped with hydraulic lifters and require no valve adjustment,

CRANKSHAFT DAMPER

REPLACE

M5

1. Remove mounting bolts and splash guard.
2. Lock belt pulley in position using holding tool No. 11 5 050, or equivalent, then remove mounting nut using

wrench tool No. 11 5 040, or equivalent. **Nut has lefthand threads.**

3. Remove fan coupling.
4. Disconnect clips, then the air duct by turning upward at firewall.
5. Pull air duct forward and remove it.
6. Disconnect righthand air intake hose clamp and Mass Air Flow (MAF) sensor connector.
7. Disconnect MAF sensor cable holders' clip, then the air intake hose from intake manifold.
8. Disconnect retainers and remove air intake filer upper housing section with MAF sensor and hose.
9. Remove air intake filter lower housing.
10. Remove righthand wheelhousing cover and intake filter lower housing section from hose.
11. Remove expansion rivets, disconnect hose clamps and place coolant expansion tank aside.
12. Remove expansion rivets and disconnect fan cowl sealing strip.
13. Disconnect AUC sensor and remove fan cowl.
14. Remove alternator and air conditioning compressor drive belts.
15. Remove mounting bolts, cover and belt pulley.
16. Attach holder tool No. 11 0 270, or equivalent, to damper.
17. Remove mounting bolts and vibration damper.
18. Reverse procedure to install, noting the following:
    a. Install new mounting bolts.
    b. **Torque** vibration damper mounting bolts to 44 ft. lbs.
    c. Tighten mounting bolts an addition 50°.
    d. Final tighten bolts an additional 50°.
    e. Tighten pulley mounting bolts to specifications.

X5, 540 & 740

1. Remove mounting bolts and splash guard.
2. Remove alternator and air conditioning compressor drive belts.
3. Remove mounting bolts and vibration damper.
4. Reverse procedure to install using new mounting bolts. Tighten mounting bolts to specifications.

FRONT COVER

REPLACE

M5

UPPER

LEFTHAND

1. Disconnect check valve electrical connector and vacuum hose.
2. Disconnect secondary air line from timing case cover and holder, then remove it.
3. Remove lefthand valve cover as outlined under "Valve Cover, Replace."
4. Lock belt pulley in position using holding tool No. 11 5 050, or equivalent, then remove mounting nut using wrench tool No. 11 5 040, or equivalent. **Nut has lefthand threads.**
5. Remove fan coupling.
6. Install lefthand camshaft adjustment unit as outlined under "Variable Camshaft Timing (VANOS) Adjustment Unit, Replace."
7. Remove connectors and place pressure accumulator aside. Disconnect cable.
8. Remove pressure control valve using suitable pliers.
9. Disconnect cable holder, then remove mounting bolts and timing case cover. **Do not allow gasket to drop into engine.**
10. Reverse procedure to install, noting the following:
    a. Ensure dowel sleeves are properly located.
    b. Install new gasket.
    c. Apply coat of Deri Bond No. 1209, or equivalent, to joint between cylinder head lower timing case cover.
    d. **Torque** mounting bolts to 18 inch lbs.
    e. **Torque** mounting bolts to 88 inch lbs.
    f. Final **torque** mounting bolts to 88 inch lbs.
    g. Install new secondary air line sealing rings with thin coat of suitable grease.

RIGHTHAND

1. Disconnect oil dipstick guide tube mounting bolt.
2. Disconnect check valve electrical connector and vacuum hose.
3. Disconnect secondary air line from timing case cover and holder, then remove it.
4. Remove righthand valve cover as outlined under "Valve Cover, Replace."
5. Lock belt pulley in position using holding tool No. 11 5 050, or equivalent, then remove mounting nut using wrench tool No. 11 5 040, or equivalent. **Nut has lefthand threads.**
6. Remove fan coupling.
7. Install chain tensioner as outlined under "Timing Chain Tensioner, Replace."
8. Install lefthand camshaft adjustment unit as outlined under "Variable Camshaft Timing (VANOS) Adjustment Unit, Replace."
9. Remove pressure control valve using suitable pliers.
10. Remove oil return line.
11. Disconnect cable holder, then remove mounting bolts and timing case cover. **Do not allow gasket to drop into engine.**
12. Reverse procedure to install, noting the following:
    a. Ensure dowel sleeves are properly located.
    b. Install new gasket.
    c. Apply coat of Deri Bond No. 1209, or equivalent, to joint between cylinder head lower timing case cover.
    d. **Torque** mounting bolts to 18 inch lbs.
    e. **Torque** mounting bolts to 88 inch lbs.
    f. Final **torque** mounting bolts to 88 inch lbs.
    g. Install new secondary air line sealing rings with thin coat of suitable grease.

LOWER

1. Remove engine as outlined under "Engine, Replace."
2. Remove left and righthand cylinder heads as outlined under "Cylinder Head, Replace."
3. Remove alternator as outlined in "Electrical" section.
4. Remove vibration damper as outlined under "Crankshaft Damper, Replace."
5. Remove water pump as outlined under "Water Pump, Replace."
6. Remove lower oil sump section as outlined under "Oil Pan, Replace."
7. Remove oil circuit changeover valves.
8. Remove oil pump as outlined under "Oil Pump, Replace."
9. Remove upper oil sump section as outlined under "Oil Pan, Replace."
10. Secure tensioning rail and timing chain with suitable plastic strap.
11. Open cable tie and clamp, then feed cable out.
12. Disconnect oil return line.
13. Remove mounting bolts and lower timing case cover.
14. Reverse procedure to install, noting the following:
    a. Install new seals.
    b. Ensure dowel sleeves are in good condition and properly positioned.
    c. Apply thin coat of Drei Bond No. 1209, or equivalent to front and back of seals.
    d. Initially **torque** mounting bolts to 44 inch lbs.
    e. Tighten mounting bolts to specifications in alternating pattern.

X5, 540 & 740

1998

UPPER

Lefthand

1. Remove lefthand valve cover as outlined under "Valve Cover, Replace."
2. Lock belt pulley in position using holding tool No. 11 5 050, or equivalent, then remove mounting nut using wrench tool No. 11 5 040, or equivalent. **Nut has lefthand threads.**
3. Remove fan coupling.
4. Remove mounting bolts, cover and sealing strip.
5. Reverse procedure to install, noting the following.
    a. Install new seal.
    b. Apply coat of Deri Bond No. 1209, or equivalent, to joint between cylinder head lower timing case cover.
    c. Tighten mounting bolts to specifications.

Righthand

1. Remove righthand valve cover as outlined under "Valve Cover, Replace."

2. Remove timing chain tensioner as outlined under "Timing Chain Tensioner, Replace."
3. Remove Camshaft Position (CMP) sensor.
4. Remove oil dipstick tube top mounting bolt.
5. Remove mounting bolts, cover and sealing strip.
6. Reverse procedure to install, noting the following.
   a. Install new seal.
   b. Apply coat of Deri Bond No. 1209, or equivalent, to joint between cylinder head lower timing case cover.
   c. Tighten mounting bolts to specifications.

LOWER

1. Remove left and righthand upper timing case covers as outlined under "Upper."
2. Remove vibration damper as outlined under "Crankshaft Damper, Replace."
3. Remove water pump as outlined under "Water Pump, Replace."
4. Remove upper oil sump as outlined under "Oil Pan, Replace."
5. Remove alternator as outlined in "Electrical" section.
6. Press bow cover against timing chain and secure with suitable plastic strap.
7. Remove mounting bolts and lower front cover.
8. Reverse procedure to install, noting the following:
   a. Install new seal.
   b. Apply coat of Deri Bond No. 1209, or equivalent, to joint between cylinder head lower timing case cover.
   c. Initially **torque** mounting bolts to 44 inch lbs.
   d. Tighten mounting bolts to specifications in alternating pattern.

1999–2001

UPPER

Lefthand

1. Remove valve cover as outlined under "Valve Cover, Replace."
2. Remove air intake filter housing with Mass Air Flow (MAF) sensor.
3. Lock belt pulley in position using holding tool No. 11 5 050, or equivalent, then remove mounting nut using wrench tool No. 11 5 040, or equivalent. **Nut has lefthand threads.**
4. Remove fan coupling.
5. Drain coolant into suitable container.
6. Disconnect lock and water hose, then disconnect connector and remove mounting bolts and VANOS solenoid valve using socket tool No. 11 6 420, or equivalent.
7. Disconnect check valve connector.
8. Disconnect secondary air line from timing case and bracket, and remove it.
9. Remove mounting bolts, cover and sealing strip.
10. Reverse procedure to install, noting the following.
    a. Install new seal.
    b. Apply coat of Deri Bond No. 1209, or equivalent, to joint between cylinder head lower timing case cover.
    c. Tighten mounting bolts to specifications.

Righthand

1. Disconnect check valve connector.
2. Disconnect secondary air line from timing case and bracket, and remove it.
3. Remove oil dipstick tube top mounting bolt.
4. Remove valve cover as outlined under "Valve Cover, Replace."
5. Remove timing chain tensioner as outlined under "Timing Chain Tensioner, Replace."
6. Remove mounting bolts and solenoid valve sealing flange.
7. Remove Camshaft Position (CMP) sensor or disconnect cable duct connector, as required.
8. Remove mounting bolts, cover and sealing strip.
9. Reverse procedure to install, noting the following.
   a. Install new seal.
   b. Apply coat of Deri Bond No. 1209, or equivalent, to joint between cylinder head lower timing case cover.
   c. Tighten mounting bolts to specifications.

LOWER

1. Drain coolant into suitable container.
2. Remove left and righthand upper timing case covers as outlined under "Upper."
3. Remove vibration damper as outlined under "Crankshaft Damper, Replace."
4. Remove water pump as outlined under "Water Pump, Replace."
5. Remove alternator as outlined in "Electrical" section.
6. Remove upper oil sump as outlined under "Oil Pan, Replace."
7. Press bow cover against timing chain and secure with suitable plastic strap.
8. Remove mounting bolts and lower front cover.
9. Reverse procedure to install, noting the following:
   a. Install new seal.
   b. Apply coat of Deri Bond No. 1209, or equivalent, to joint between cylinder head lower timing case cover.
   c. Initially **torque** mounting bolts to 44 inch lbs.
   d. Tighten mounting bolts to specifications in alternating pattern.

FRONT COVER SEAL

REPLACE

M5

1. Remove vibration damper as outlined under "Crankshaft Damper, Replace."
2. Remove seal using extractor tools Nos. 11 2 386 and 11 2 380, or equivalents.
3. Reverse procedure to install new seal, noting the following:
   a. Coated with suitable engine oil.
   b. Install seal onto sprocket using installer tool No. 11 7 231, or equivalent.
   c. Install seal using bushing tools No. 11 7 210, or equivalent.
   d. Pull seal flush with case using installer tool No. 11 7 213, or equivalent.

Z5, 540 & 740

1. Remove vibration damper as outlined under "Crankshaft Damper, Replace."
2. Remove seal using extractor tools Nos. 11 2 380 and 11 2 383, or equivalents.
3. Reverse procedure to install new seal coated with suitable engine oil using installer bushing tool No. 11 3 220, or equivalent.

TIMING CHAIN

REPLACE

With the timing chain removed, avoid turning the camshaft or crankshaft. If movement is required, exercise extreme caution to avoid valve damage caused by piston contact.

M5

REMOVAL

1. Remove engine as outlined under "Engine, Replace."
2. Remove both cylinder heads as outlined under "Cylinder Head, Replace."
3. Remove alternator as outlined in "Electrical" section.
4. Remove crankshaft damper as outlined under "Crankshaft Damper, Replace."
5. Remove water pump as outlined under "Water Pump, Replace."
6. Remove lower oil sump as outlined under "Oil Pan, Replace."
7. Remove mounting bolts and oil circuit changeover valves using suitable clean shop rag.
8. Remove oil pump as outlined under "Oil Pump, Replace."
9. Remove upper oil sump as outlined under "Oil Pan, Replace."
10. Open plastic strap and remove timing chain.
11. Remove left and righthand cylinder head oil lines.
12. Remove mounting bolt and tensioning rail with oil guide, as required.
13. Disconnect lug and guide rail, as required.
14. Remove mounting bolts and reversing rail, as required.

INSTALLATION

1. Replace reversing and tensioning rails, as required.
2. Replace throttle ring as required.
3. Install throttle ring and new O-rings coated with oil in reversing rail.
4. Install reversing rail and tighten lower mounting bolts, then uppers to specifications.
5. Slide it over guide pin until lug snaps into place.

6. Install bow cover oil guide with new O-ring to pivot rail.
7. Tighten tensioning rail mounting bolt.
8. Install timing chain over crankshaft sprocket and reversing rail.
9. Align chain to guide rail.
10. Press bow cover against timing chain and secure with plastic strap.
11. Install upper oil sump as outlined under "Oil Pan, Replace."
12. Install oil pump as outlined under "Oil Pump, Replace."
13. Install mounting bolts and oil circuit changeover valves using suitable clean shop rag.
14. Install lower oil sump as outlined under "Oil Pan, Replace."
15. Install water pump as outlined under "Water Pump, Replace."
16. Install crankshaft damper as outlined under "Crankshaft Damper, Replace."
17. Install alternator as outlined in "Electrical" section.
18. Install both cylinder heads as outlined under "Cylinder Head, Replace."
19. Install engine as outlined under "Engine, Replace."

X5, 540 & 740

1998

Removal

1. Remove spark plugs.
2. Remove valve covers as outlined under "Valve Cover, Replace."
3. Remove left and righthand cylinder head oil lines.
4. Remove crankshaft damper as outlined under "Crankshaft Damper, Replace."
5. Remove alternator air cooling duct.
6. Remove left and righthand brake cooling ducts.
7. Disconnect engine support pressure line retainer.
8. Install holding tool No. 11 2 450, or equivalent.
9. Loosen vibration damper hub center bolt.
10. Turn engine until cylinder No. 1 is at firing TDC. Ensure camshafts bores point upward.
11. Lock crankshaft with timing pin tool No. 11 2 300, or equivalent.
12. Remove timing chain tensioner as outlined under "Timing Chain Tensioner, Replace."
13. Remove top left and righthand timing case covers as outlined under "Front Cover, Replace."
14. Counterhold camshaft with suitable open-end wrench and loosen righthand intake camshaft sprocket mounting bolts.
15. Lock lefthand cylinder head camshafts in position using camshaft lock tools No. 11 2 441 and 11 2 445, and secure with lock holder tool No. 11 2 443, or equivalents.
16. Loosen lefthand intake camshaft sprocket.
17. Lock righthand cylinder head camshafts in position using camshaft lock tools No. 11 2 442 and 11 2 446, and secure with lock holder tool No. 11 2 443, or equivalents.
18. Remove center bolt and crankshaft damper hub.
19. **Do not turn engine.**
20. Remove crankshaft timing pin.
21. Remove upper oil sump as outlined under "Oil Pan, Replace."
22. Remove water pump with thermostat housing as outlined under "Water Pump, Replace."
23. Remove gear case cover as outlined under "Front Cover, Replace."
24. Remove intake camshaft sprockets and timing chain.
25. Remove mounting bolt and tensioning rail with oil guide, as required.
26. Disconnect grub screw, then remove mounting bolt and reversing rail, as required.
27. Loosen oil separator mounting bolt, then disconnect mounting bolts and remove guide rail, as required.

Installation

1. Replace reversing and tensioning rails, as required.
2. Replace sprockets, as required.
3. Install guide rail, then tighten lower mounting bolts, upper bolt and oil separator bolt.
4. Install pivot rail with new O-rings and tighten mounting bolts to specifications.
5. Replace throttle ring as required.
6. Install throttle ring and new O-rings coated with oil in reversing rail.
7. Install reversing rail and tighten lower mounting bolts, then uppers to specifications.
8. Install new grub and hand tighten until it contacts angle section without play. **Do not tighten.**
9. Install bow cover oil guide with new O-ring to pivot rail and tighten
10. Install lefthand intake cam sprocket with timing chain. Ensure long bores are centered.
11. Install two mounting bolts and fit flush.
12. Install righthand intake camshaft with timing chain. Ensure long bores are centered.
13. Install two mounting bolts and fit flush.
14. Brace sprocket, pressure bow cover against chain and inspect long bores on both intake camshaft sprockets.
15. Install sensor gear with mark upward. Install mounting bolts and fit flush.
16. Install remaining lefthand intake camshaft mounting bolts and fit flush without play.
17. Press bow cover against timing chain and secure with suitable plastic strap.
18. Install timing case cover as outlined under "Front Cover, Replace."
19. Install upper oil sump section as outlined under "Oil Pan, Replace."
20. Lock crankshaft using timing pin tool.
21. Install tensioner block tool No. 11 7 380, or equivalent, against righthand chain
22. Install chain tensioning tool No 11 3 390, or equivalent, into camshaft chain tensioner bore.
23. **Torque** bow cover to 6 inch lbs.
24. Tighten intake camshaft sprockets' mounting bolts to specifications.
25. Remove special tools.
26. Install left and righthand cylinder head oil lines.
27. Install lefthand upper timing case cover as outlined under "Front Cover, Replace."
28. Install timing chain tensioner as outlined under "Timing Chain Tensioner, Replace."
29. Install righthand upper timing case cover as outlined under "Front Cover, Replace."
30. Remove crankshaft timing pin.
31. Install new vibration damper hub center bolt.
32. **Torque** vibration damper hub center bolt to 74 ft. lbs.
33. Tighten damper hub center bolt an additional 60°.
34. Tighten hub center bolt an additional 60°.
35. Tighten center bolt an additional 30°.
36. Install vibration damper as outlined under "Crankshaft Damper, Replace."
37. Install valve covers as outlined under "Valve Cover, Replace."
38. Install spark plugs.

1999–2001

Removal

1. Remove spark plugs.
2. Remove valve covers as outlined under "Valve Cover, Replace."
3. Remove left and righthand cylinder head oil lines.
4. Remove crankshaft damper as outlined under "Crankshaft Damper, Replace."
5. Install holding tool No. 11 2 450, or equivalent.
6. Loosen vibration damper hub center bolt.
7. Turn engine until cylinder No. 1 is at firing TDC. At TDC firing position camshaft markings face upward and righthand intake camshaft is twisted on splines of adjustment unit.
8. **On 540 and 740 models,** lock crankshaft with timing pin tool No. 11 2 300, or equivalent.
9. **On X5 models,** lock crankshaft with timing pin tool No. 11 5 180, or equivalent.
10. **On all models,** remove timing chain tensioner as outlined under "Timing Chain Tensioner, Replace."
11. Remove top left and righthand timing case covers as outlined under "Front Cover, Replace."
12. Remove mounting nut and righthand sensor gear. **Nut has lefthand threads.**
13. Remove mounting nut and lefthand sensor gear. **Nut has lefthand threads.**
14. Counterhold camshaft with suitable open-end wrench and loosen lefthand exhaust camshaft sprocket mounting bolts ½ turn. **Bolts have lefthand threads.**
15. Counterhold camshaft with suitable open-end wrench and loosen righthand exhaust camshaft sprocket mounting bolts ½ turn. **Bolts have lefthand threads.**

16. Counterhold camshaft with suitable open-end wrench and loosen lefthand intake camshaft sprocket mounting bolts ½ turn. **Bolts have lefthand threads.**
17. Counterhold camshaft with suitable open-end wrench and loosen righthand intake camshaft sprocket mounting bolts ½ turn. **Bolts have lefthand threads.**
18. Lock lefthand cylinder head camshafts in position using camshaft lock tools No. 11 2 441 and 11 2 445, or equivalents, then secure with lock holder tool No. 11 2 443, and mounting bolt tool No. 11 2 44, or equivalents.
19. Lock righthand cylinder head camshafts in position using camshaft lock tools No. 11 2 442 and 11 2 446, or equivalents, then secure with lock holder tool No. 11 2 443, and mounting bolt tool No. 11 2 44, or equivalents.
20. Remove center bolt and crankshaft damper hub.
21. Remove crankshaft timing pin.
22. **Do not turn engine.**
23. Remove upper oil sump as outlined under "Oil Pan, Replace."
24. Remove water pump with thermostat housing as outlined under "Water Pump, Replace."
25. Remove gear case cover as outlined under "Front Cover, Replace."
26. Remove mounting bolt and plastic strap and tensioning rail with oil guide.
27. **On 540 and 740 models,** remove oil separator mounting bolt.
28. **On X5 models,** oil separator is external.
29. **On all models** remove guide rail mounting bolt.
30. Disconnect lug and guide rail.
31. Feed timing chain out of adjustment unit and remove.
32. **On 540 and 740 models,** remove grub screw.
33. **On X5 models,** oil separator is external.
34. **On all models,** remove mounting bolts and reversing rail, as required.

Installation

1. Replace reversing and tensioning rails, as required.
2. Replace throttle ring as required.
3. Install throttle ring and new O-rings coated with oil in reversing rail.
4. Install reversing rail and tighten lower mounting bolts, then uppers to specifications.
5. **On 540 and 740 models,** install new grub and hand tighten until it contacts angle section without play. **Do not tighten.**
6. **On X5 models,** oil separator is external.
7. **On all models,** install timing chain over reversing rail (inside pins), lefthand camshaft adjustment nut and crankshaft sprocket.
8. Feed timing chain onto righthand camshaft adjustment unit.
9. Raise timing chain slightly in guide rail area, then slide it over guide pin until lug snaps into place.
10. Align timing chain to guide rail.
11. Install oil separator and tighten mounting bolts.
12. Install bow cover oil guide with new O-ring to pivot rail.
13. Press bow cover against timing chain, secure with plastic strap and tighten mounting bolt.
14. Install timing case cover as outlined under "Front Cover, Replace."
15. Install upper oil sump section as outlined under "Oil Pan, Replace."
16. Lock crankshaft using timing pin tool.
17. Install tensioner block tool No. 11 7 380, or equivalent, against righthand chain
18. Install chain tensioning tool No 11 4 230, or equivalent, into camshaft chain tensioner bore.
19. Connect suitable multimeter with acoustic continuity test to lefthand camshaft adjustment unit contact pin and oil line.
20. Attach hook wrench tool No. 11 6 440, or equivalent, to camshaft adjustment nut and move to 29 ft. lbs.
21. Ensure camshaft adjustment unit is at lefthand stop with acoustic multimeter.
22. **Torque** lefthand intake camshaft mounting bolt to 11 ft. lbs., then slacken ¼ turn. **Bolt has lefthand threads.**
23. Connect suitable multimeter with acoustic continuity test to righthand camshaft adjustment unit contact pin and oil line.
24. Attach hook wrench tool No. 11 6 440, or equivalent, to camshaft adjustment nut and move to 29 ft. lbs.
25. Ensure camshaft adjustment unit is at lefthand stop with acoustic multimeter.
26. **Torque** righthand intake camshaft mounting bolt to 11 ft. lbs., then slacken ¼ turn. **Bolt has lefthand threads.**
27. **Torque** righthand exhaust camshaft mounting bolt to 11 ft. lbs., then slacken ¼ turn. **Bolt has lefthand threads.**
28. Pretension tensioning rail to 6 inch lbs.
29. **Torque** lefthand intake camshaft mounting bolt to 11 ft. lbs., then slacken ¼ turn. **Bolt has lefthand threads.**
30. Connect suitable multimeter with acoustic continuity test to righthand camshaft adjustment unit contact pin and oil line.
31. Attach hook wrench tool No. 11 6 440, or equivalent, to camshaft adjustment nut and move to 29 ft. lbs.
32. Counterhold camshaft with suitable wrench and tighten lefthand intake camshaft sprocket mounting bolt to specifications. **Bolt has lefthand threads.**
33. Counterhold camshaft with suitable wrench and tighten lefthand exhaust camshaft sprocket mounting bolt to specifications. **Bolt has lefthand threads.**
34. Connect suitable multimeter with acoustic continuity test to righthand camshaft adjustment unit contact pin and oil line.
35. Attach hook wrench tool No. 11 6 440, or equivalent, to camshaft adjustment nut and move to 29 ft. lbs.
36. Counterhold camshaft with suitable wrench and tighten righthand intake camshaft sprocket mounting bolt to specifications. **Bolt has lefthand threads.**
37. Counterhold camshaft with suitable wrench and tighten righthand exhaust camshaft sprocket mounting bolt to specifications. **Bolt has lefthand threads.**
38. Install righthand sensor gear and hand tighten mounting nut without play. **Do not tighten.**
39. Align righthand sensor gear using locking fixture tool No. 11 6 450, or equivalent.
40. Tighten sensor gear mounting bolt to specifications. Remove locking fixture tool.
41. Install lefthand sensor gear and hand tighten mounting nut without play. **Do not tighten.**
42. Align lefthand sensor gear using locking fixture tool No. 11 6 450, or equivalent.
43. Tighten sensor gear mounting bolt to specifications. Remove locking fixture tool.
44. Remove camshafts' locking tools and tensioning block.
45. Install left and righthand cylinder head oil lines.
46. Install upper timing case covers as outlined under "Front Cover, Replace."
47. Install timing chain tensioner as outlined under "Timing Chain Tensioner, Replace."
48. Remove crankshaft timing pin.
49. Install new vibration damper hub center bolt.
50. **Torque** vibration damper hub center bolt to 74 ft. lbs.
51. Tighten damper hub center bolt an additional 60°.
52. Tighten hub center bolt an additional 60°.
53. Tighten center bolt an additional 30°.
54. Install vibration damper as outlined under "Crankshaft Damper, Replace."
55. Install valve covers as outlined under "Valve Cover, Replace."
56. Install spark plugs.

TIMING CHAIN TENSIONER

REPLACE

1. **On 540 and 740 models,** remove air intake filter housing.
2. **On M5 models,** remove righthand air intake filter housing.
3. **On all models,** remove timing chain tensioner.
4. Reverse procedure to install after draining oil chamber between sleeve and piston. Tighten to specifications.

CAMSHAFT

REPLACE

M5

LEFTHAND

Removal

1. Raise and support vehicle, then drain engine block coolant into suitable container.

2. Remove air intake filter housing upper section with Mass Air Flow (MAF) sensor.
3. Remove both valve covers as outlined under "Valve Cover, Replace."
4. Remove spark plugs.
5. Remove hose between radiator and thermostat housing.
6. Lock belt pulley in position using holding tool No. 11 5 050, or equivalent, then remove mounting nut using wrench tool No. 11 5 040, or equivalent. **Nut has lefthand threads.**
7. Remove fan coupling.
8. Remove both cylinder head oil lines.
9. Remove lefthand camshaft adjustment unit as outlined under "Variable Camshaft Timing (VANOS) Adjustment Unit, Replace."
10. Remove crankshaft timing pin tool.
11. Turn engine in reverse of normal rotation to 45° before TDC.
12. Remove lefthand upper timing case covers as outlined under "Front Cover, Replace."
13. Remove timing chain tensioner as outlined under "Timing Chain Tensioner, Replace."
14. Remove mounting bolts and lefthand intake camshaft spacer ring.
15. Remove lefthand intake camshaft spline hub, plate spring and supporting ring. **Do not allow supporting ring to fall out.**
16. Disconnect intake camshaft sprocket from centering sleeve.
17. Keep chain tensioned and feed out sprocket. Secure chain with suitable wire.
18. Remove lefthand exhaust camshaft sprocket mounting bolt
19. Remove lefthand exhaust camshaft spline hub, plate spring and supporting ring. **Do not allow supporting ring to fall out.**
20. Disconnect intake camshaft sprocket from centering sleeve.
21. Remove exhaust camshaft spacer ring.
22. Relieve chain pressure by compressing secondary chain tensioner and holding with locking clip tool No. 11 7 140, or equivalent.
23. Remove plug mandel tools from camshafts.
24. Counter hold camshafts with suitable open end wrench, then remove mounting bolts and centering sleeves.
25. Remove secondary sprockets and timing chain.
26. Remove toothed sleeves from exhaust and intake camshafts.
27. Turn exhaust camshaft using suitable open end wrench until cylinder No. 6 exhaust cam faces upward.
28. Turn intake camshaft using suitable open end wrench until cylinder No. 8 intake cam faces upward.
29. Mark bearing covers for installation in original positions.
30. Loosen bearing cover mounting nuts in ½ turn steps from outside to inside.
31. Remove bearing covers and camshafts.
32. Install camshaft into suitable vice with

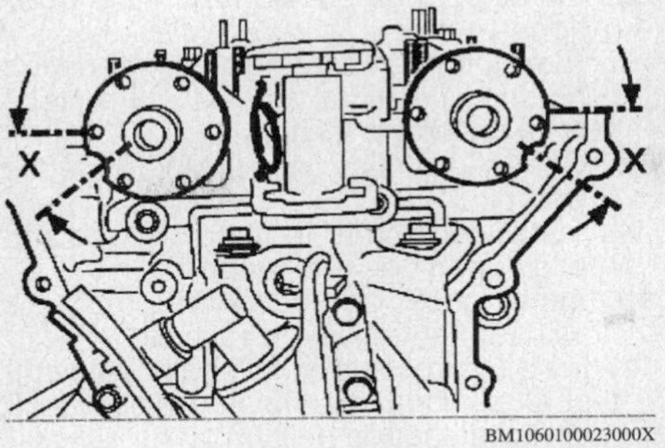

Fig. 2 Camshaft service position, Lefthand. 1998

protective jaws, then remove mounting banjo bolt and signal ring, as required.

Installation

1. Install intake camshaft signal ring with one dowel pin and exhaust camshaft signal ring with two dowel pins, then align bores. Tighten mounting bolts to specifications.
2. Oil camshaft contact face in cylinder head, bucket tappets, camshafts and bearing caps.
3. Install camshafts.
4. Turn exhaust camshaft using suitable open end wrench until cylinder No. 6 exhaust cam faces upward.
5. Turn intake camshaft using suitable open end wrench until cylinder No. 8 intake cam faces upward.
6. Install bearing covers in original positions.
7. Evenly tighten bearing cover mounting nuts to specifications in ½ turn steps from outside to inside.
8. Turn exhaust camshaft using suitable open end wrench until cylinder No. 5 exhaust cam faces upward.
9. Turn intake camshaft using suitable open end wrench until cylinder No. 7 intake cam faces upward.
10. Coat all VANOS gear sliding surfaces with oil
11. Install camshafts' toothed sleeves and align openings with tapped holes.
12. Install chain on secondary sprockets with tapped holes are vertical.
13. Install sprockets with chain on camshafts so bearing cap stud is flush with sprocket tapped hole.
14. Push exhaust and intake centering sleeves on and align bores to tapped holes.
15. Install centering sleeves mounting bolts, counter hold camshaft with suitable open end wrench and tighten.
16. Align camshafts with 1st bearing cap locating bore and lock camshafts using plug mandel tools No. 11 7 120, or equivalent.
17. Remove secondary chain tensioner locking clip.
18. Install spacer ring aligning bores to sprocket threads.
19. Install plate spring with small support diameter toward support ring and supporting ring with retaining lugs on spline hub.
20. Install spline hub with plate spring and support ring.
21. Install spacer ring and hand tighten mounting bolts without play.
22. Loosen spacer ring mounting bolts so spline hub can be moved with fingers.
23. Keep timing chain tensioned and install intake camshaft sprocket on centering sleeve. **Do not install mounting bolts.**
24. Install timing chain tensioner as outlined under "Timing Chain Tensioner, Replace."
25. Turn engine from 45° before TDC to TDC position and hold with crankshaft locking tool No. 11 2 300, or equivalent. **Do not allow intake camshaft sprocket to slip off centering sleeve.**
26. Align secondary chain drive to intake camshaft sprocket using hook wrench tool No. 11 7 150, or equivalent.
27. Install plate spring with small support diameter toward support ring and supporting ring with retaining lugs on spline hub.
28. Install spline hub with plate spring and support ring.
29. Install spacer ring and hand tighten mounting bolts without play.
30. Loosen spacer ring mounting bolts so spline hub can be moved with fingers.
31. Install upper timing case covers as outlined under "Front Cover, Replace."
32. Install lefthand camshaft adjustment unit as outlined under "Variable Camshaft Timing (VANOS) Adjustment Unit, Replace."
33. Install both cylinder head oil lines.
34. Install fan.
35. Install hose between radiator and thermostat housing.
36. Install spark plugs.
37. Install both valve covers as outlined under "Valve Cover, Replace."
38. Install air intake filter housing upper section with Mass Air Flow (MAF) sensor.

RIGHTHAND

Removal

1. Raise and support vehicle, then drain engine block coolant into suitable container.
2. Remove air intake filter housing upper section with Mass Air Flow (MAF) sensor.
3. Remove both valve covers as outlined under "Valve Cover, Replace."
4. Remove spark plugs.
5. Remove hose between radiator and thermostat housing.
6. Lock belt pulley in position using holding tool No. 11 5 050, or equivalent, then remove mounting nut using wrench tool No. 11 5 040, or equivalent. **Nut has lefthand threads.**
7. Remove fan coupling.
8. Remove both cylinder head oil lines.
9. Remove righthand camshaft adjustment unit as outlined under "Variable Camshaft Timing (VANOS) Adjustment Unit, Replace."
10. Remove crankshaft timing pin tool.

11. Turn engine in reverse of normal rotation to 45° before TDC.
12. Remove timing chain tensioner as outlined under "Timing Chain Tensioner, Replace."
13. Remove righthand upper timing case covers as outlined under "Front Cover, Replace."
14. Remove mounting bolts and righthand intake camshaft spacer ring.
15. Remove righthand intake camshaft spline hub, plate spring and supporting ring. **Do not allow supporting ring to fall out.**
16. Disconnect intake camshaft sprocket from centering sleeve.
17. Keep chain tensioned and feed out sprocket. Secure chain with suitable wire.
18. Remove righthand exhaust camshaft sprocket mounting bolt
19. Remove righthand exhaust camshaft spline hub, plate spring and supporting ring. **Do not allow supporting ring to fall out.**
20. Disconnect intake camshaft sprocket from centering sleeve.
21. Remove exhaust camshaft spacer ring.
22. Relieve chain pressure by compressing secondary chain tensioner and holding with locking clip tool No. 11 7 140, or equivalent.
23. Remove plug mandel tools from camshafts. Camshafts spring away approximately 30° in rotational direction.
24. Counter hold camshafts with suitable open end wrench, then remove mounting bolts and centering sleeves.
25. Remove secondary sprockets and timing chain.
26. Remove toothed sleeves from exhaust and intake camshafts.
27. Turn exhaust camshaft using suitable open end wrench until cylinder No. 6 exhaust cam faces upward.
28. Turn intake camshaft using suitable open end wrench until cylinder No. 8 intake cam faces upward.
29. Mark bearing covers for installation in original positions.
30. Loosen bearing cover mounting nuts in ½ turn steps from outside to inside.
31. Remove bearing covers and camshafts.
32. Install camshaft into suitable vice with protective jaws, then remove mounting banjo bolt and signal ring, as required.

Installation

1. Install intake camshaft signal ring with one dowel pin and exhaust camshaft signal ring with two dowel pins, then align bores. Tighten mounting bolts to specifications.
2. Oil camshaft contact face in cylinder head, bucket tappets, camshafts and bearing caps.
3. Install camshafts.
4. Turn exhaust camshaft using suitable open end wrench until cylinder No. 6 exhaust cam faces upward.
5. Turn intake camshaft using suitable open end wrench until cylinder No. 8 intake cam faces upward.
6. Install bearing covers in original positions.
7. Evenly tighten bearing cover mounting nuts to specifications in ½ turn steps from outside to inside.
8. Coat all VANOS gear sliding surfaces with oil
9. Install camshafts' toothed sleeves and align openings with tapped holes.
10. Install chain on secondary sprockets with tapped holes are vertical.
11. Install sprockets with chain on camshafts so bearing cap stud is flush with sprocket tapped hole.
12. Push exhaust and intake centering sleeves on and align bores to tapped holes.
13. Install centering sleeves mounting bolts, counter hold camshaft with suitable open end wrench and tighten.
14. Align camshafts with 1st bearing cap locating bore and lock camshafts using plug mandel tools No. 11 7 120, or equivalent.
15. Remove secondary chain tensioner locking clip.
16. Install spacer ring aligning bores to sprocket threads.
17. Install plate spring with small support diameter toward support ring and supporting ring with retaining lugs on spline hub.
18. Install spline hub with plate spring and support ring.
19. Install spacer ring and hand tighten mounting bolts without play.
20. Loosen spacer ring mounting bolts so spline hub can be moved with fingers.
21. Keep timing chain tensioned and install intake camshaft sprocket on centering sleeve. **Do not install mounting bolts.**
22. Install timing chain tensioner as outlined under "Timing Chain Tensioner, Replace."
23. Turn engine from 45° before TDC to TDC position and hold with crankshaft locking tool No. 11 2 300, or equivalent. **Do not allow intake camshaft sprocket to slip off centering sleeve.**
24. Align secondary chain drive to intake camshaft sprocket using hook wrench tool No. 11 7 150, or equivalent.
25. Install plate spring with small support diameter toward support ring and supporting ring with retaining lugs on spline hub.
26. Install spline hub with plate spring and support ring.
27. Install spacer ring and hand tighten mounting bolts without play.
28. Loosen spacer ring mounting bolts so spline hub can be moved with fingers.
29. Install upper timing case covers as outlined under "Front Cover, Replace."
30. Install righthand camshaft adjustment unit as outlined under "Variable Camshaft Timing (VANOS) Adjustment Unit, Replace."
31. Install both cylinder head oil lines.
32. Install fan.
33. Install hose between radiator and thermostat housing.
34. Install spark plugs.
35. Install both valve covers as outlined under "Valve Cover, Replace."
36. Install air intake filter housing upper section with Mass Air Flow (MAF) sensor.

X5, 540 & 740

1998

LEFTHAND

Removal

1. Raise and support vehicle, then remove mounting bolts and splash guard.
2. Remove both valve covers as outlined under "Valve Cover, Replace."
3. Remove spark plugs.
4. Remove left and righthand cylinder head oil lines.
5. Turning engine in normal rotational direction until cylinder No. 1 is at TDC position.
6. Counterhold camshafts with suitable wrench.
7. Loosen three accessible righthand exhaust and intake camshaft sprockets approximately ½ turn.
8. Turn engine one revolution in normal rotational direction until cylinder No. 1 is at TDC position.
9. Loosen remaining righthand exhaust and intake camshaft sprockets approximately ½ turn.
10. Remove timing chain tensioner as outlined under "Timing Chain Tensioner, Replace."
11. Remove upper lefthand timing case cover as outlined under "Front Cover, Replace."
12. Remove mounting bolts and lefthand exhaust camshaft sprocket. Secure chain with suitable wire.
13. Crank engine in reverse of normal rotation to 45° before TDC.
14. Remove secondary camshaft sprocket mounting bolts.
15. Relieve chain pressure by compressing secondary chain tensioner and holding with locking pin tool No. 11 3 310, or equivalent.
16. Remove both secondary camshaft sprockets with chain.
17. Turn lefthand camshafts to service position using install tool No. 11 3 430, or equivalent. Service position has camshafts' recesses approximately 30–40° below cylinder head surface, **Fig. 2.**
18. Mark bearing covers for installation in original positions.
19. Loosen bearing cover mounting nuts in ½ turn steps from outside to inside.
20. Remove bearing covers and camshafts.

Installation

1. Install camshafts to service position using install tool No. 11 3 430, or equivalent. Service position has camshafts' recesses approximately 30–40° below cylinder head surface, **Fig. 2.**

2. Install bearing covers in original positions.
3. Evenly tighten bearing cover mounting nuts to specifications in ½ turn steps from outside to inside.
4. Turn camshafts until marker bores point upward using install tool No. 11 3 430, or equivalent.
5. Lock lefthand cylinder head camshafts using lock tools No. 11 2 442 and 11 2 446, or equivalents.
6. Lock righthand cylinder heads camshafts using lock tools No. 11 2 441 and 11 2 445, or equivalents.
7. Align camshafts using suitable open end wrench so tools fit heads without gaps.
8. Hold camshaft lock tools in place using holder tool No. 11 2 443 with bolt tool No. 11 2 444, or equivalents.
9. Install secondary camshaft sprockets and chain. Center long bores.
10. Remove secondary chain tensioner locking pin.
11. Turn engine from 45° before TDC to TDC position and hold with crankshaft locking tool No. 11 2 300, or equivalent.
12. Install lefthand intake camshaft sprocket with chain. Center long bores.
13. Install camshaft mounting bolts and fit flush.
14. Install chain tensioning tool No 11 3 390, or equivalent, into righthand timing case cover.
15. Pretension bow cover to 6 inch lbs.
16. Tighten camshaft sprocket mounting bolts to specifications in following sequence:
    a. All lefthand exhaust camshaft sprocket mounting bolts.
    b. Three righthand exhaust camshaft sprocket mounting bolts.
    c. All lefthand intake camshaft sprocket mounting bolts.
    d. Three righthand intake camshaft sprocket mounting bolts.
17. Remove camshaft and crankshaft locking tools.
18. Install both cylinder head oil lines.
19. Remove chain tensioning tool.
20. Install upper front cover as outlined under "Front Cover, Replace.".
21. Install timing chain tensioner as outlined under "Timing Chain Tensioner, Replace."
22. Install spark plug.
23. Install both valve covers as outlined under "Valve Cover, Replace."

RIGHTHAND

Removal

1. Raise and support vehicle, then remove mounting bolts and splash guard.
2. Remove both valve covers as outlined under "Valve Cover, Replace."
3. Remove spark plugs.
4. Lock belt pulley in position using holding tool No. 11 5 050, or equivalent, then remove mounting nut using wrench tool No. 11 5 040, or equivalent. **Nut has lefthand threads.**
5. Remove fan coupling.
6. Remove left and righthand cylinder head oil lines.
7. Turning engine in normal rotational direction until cylinder No. 1 is at TDC position.
8. Counterhold camshafts with suitable wrench.
9. Loosen three accessible lefthand exhaust and intake camshaft sprockets approximately ½ turn.
10. Turn engine one revolution in normal rotational direction until cylinder No. 1 is at TDC position.
11. Loosen remaining lefthand exhaust and intake camshaft sprockets approximately ½ turn.
12. Remove timing chain tensioner as outlined under "Timing Chain Tensioner, Replace."
13. Remove upper righthand timing case cover as outlined under "Front Cover, Replace."
14. Remove mounting bolts and righthand exhaust camshaft sprocket. Secure chain with suitable wire.
15. Crank engine in reverse of normal rotation to 45° before TDC.
16. Remove secondary camshaft sprocket mounting bolts.
17. Relieve chain pressure by compressing secondary chain tensioner and holding with locking pin tool No. 11 3 310, or equivalent.
18. Remove both secondary camshaft sprockets with chain.
19. Turn lefthand camshafts to service position using install tool No. 11 3 430, or equivalent. Service position has camshafts' recesses approximately 30–40° above cylinder head surface, **Fig. 3.**
20. Mark bearing covers for installation in original positions.
21. Loosen bearing cover mounting nuts in ½ turn steps from outside to inside.
22. Remove bearing covers and camshafts.

Installation

1. Install camshafts to service position using install tool No. 11 3 430, or equivalent. Service position has camshafts' recesses approximately 30–40° above cylinder head surface, **Fig. 2.**
2. Install bearing covers in original positions.
3. Evenly tighten bearing cover mounting nuts to specifications in ½ turn steps from outside to inside.
4. Turn camshafts until marker bores point upward using install tool No. 11 3 430, or equivalent.
5. Lock righthand cylinder heads camshafts using lock tools No. 11 2 441 and 11 2 445, or equivalents.
6. Lock lefthand cylinder head camshafts using lock tools No. 11 2 442 and 11 2 446, or equivalents.
7. Align camshafts using suitable open end wrench so tools fit heads without gaps.
8. Hold camshaft lock tools in place using holder tool No. 11 2 443 with bolt tool No. 11 2 444, or equivalents.
9. Install secondary camshaft sprockets and chain. Center long bores.
10. Remove secondary chain tensioner locking pin.
11. Turn engine from 45° before TDC to TDC position and hold with crankshaft locking tool No. 11 2 300, or equivalent.
12. Install righthand intake camshaft sprocket with chain. Center long bores.
13. Install sensor gear with mark pointing upward.
14. Install tensioner block tool No. 11 7 380, or equivalent, against righthand chain
15. Install chain tensioning tool No 11 3 390, or equivalent, into righthand timing case cover.
16. Pretension bow cover to 6 inch lbs.
17. Tighten camshaft sprocket mounting bolts to specifications in following sequence:
    a. All lefthand exhaust camshaft sprocket mounting bolts.
    b. Three righthand exhaust camshaft sprocket mounting bolts.
    c. All lefthand intake camshaft sprocket mounting bolts.
    d. Three righthand intake camshaft sprocket mounting bolts.
18. Remove camshaft and crankshaft locking tools.
19. Install both cylinder head oil lines.
20. Remove chain tensioning tool.
21. Install upper front cover as outlined under "Front Cover, Replace."
22. Install fan.
23. Install spark plug.
24. Install both valve covers as outlined under "Valve Cover, Replace."

1999–2001

LEFTHAND

Removal

1. Raise and support vehicle, then remove mounting bolts and splash guard.
2. Remove both valve covers as outlined under "Valve Cover, Replace."
3. Remove spark plugs.
4. Remove timing chain tensioner as outlined under "Timing Chain Tensioner, Replace."
5. Remove both upper timing case covers as outlined under "Front Cover, Replace."
6. Remove lefthand camshaft adjustment unit as outlined under "Variable Camshaft Timing (VANOS) Adjustment Unit, Replace."
7. Feed timing chain out of camshaft adjustment unit distributor.
8. Remove camshaft adjustment unit distributor sealing ring mounting bolt.
9. Remove distributor by moving it back and forth.
10. Remove crankshaft locking tool.
11. Lift timing chain and hold under tension.
12. Turn engine is reverse of normal rotation to 45° before TDC.
13. Remove camshaft locking tools.
14. Turn exhaust camshaft using suitable open end wrench until cylinder No. 6 exhaust cam faces upward.
15. Turn intake camshaft using suitable

open end wrench until cylinder No. 8 intake cam faces upward.
16. Mark bearing covers for installation in original positions.
17. Loosen bearing cover mounting nuts in ½ turn steps from outside to inside.
18. Remove bearing covers and camshafts.

Installation

1. Install camshafts.
2. Turn exhaust camshaft using suitable open end wrench until cylinder No. 6 exhaust cam faces upward.
3. Turn intake camshaft using suitable open end wrench until cylinder No. 8 intake cam faces upward.
4. Install bearing covers in original positions.
5. Evenly tighten bearing cover mounting nuts to specifications in ½ turn steps from outside to inside.
6. Turn camshafts until marker bores point upward.
7. Lock cylinder heads camshafts using lock tools No. 11 2 441 and 11 2 445, or equivalents.
8. Align camshafts using suitable open end wrench so tools fit heads without gaps.
9. Hold camshaft lock tools in place using holder tool No. 11 2 443 with bolt tool No. 11 2 444, or equivalents.
10. Turn engine from 45° before TDC to TDC position and hold with crankshaft locking tool No. 11 2 300, or equivalent.
11. Install non-return valve using new sealing ring. Install new gasket over non-return valve.
12. Align compression ring contact points upward and apply light coat of oil to camshaft adjustment unit distributor.
13. Install distributor straight.
14. Install sealing ring and mounting bolts.
15. Install lefthand camshaft adjustment unit as outlined under "Variable Camshaft Timing (VANOS) Adjustment Unit, Replace."
16. Install timing chain tensioner as outlined under "Timing Chain Tensioner, Replace."
17. Install both upper timing case covers as outlined under "Front Cover, Replace."
18. Install timing chain tensioner as outlined under "Timing Chain Tensioner, Replace."
19. Install spark plug.

RIGHTHAND

Removal

1. Raise and support vehicle, then remove mounting bolts and splash guard.
2. Remove both valve covers as outlined under "Valve Cover, Replace."
3. Remove spark plugs.
4. Remove timing chain tensioner as outlined under "Timing Chain Tensioner, Replace."
5. Remove both upper timing case covers as outlined under "Front Cover, Replace."
6. Remove righthand camshaft adjustment unit as outlined under "Variable Camshaft Timing (VANOS) Adjustment Unit, Replace."

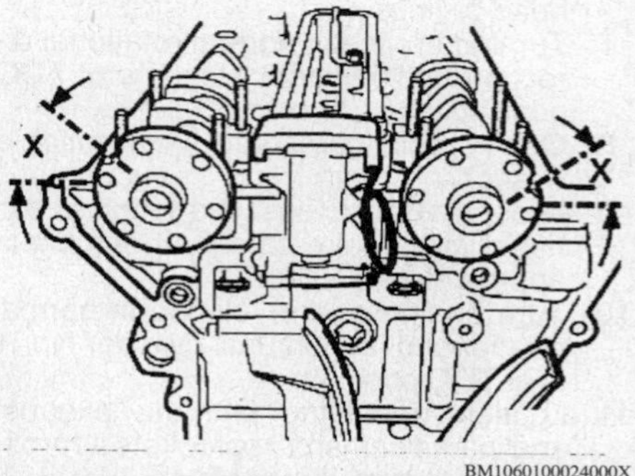

BM1060100024000X

Fig. 3 Camshaft service position, Righthand. 1998

7. Feed timing chain out of camshaft adjustment unit distributor.
8. Remove camshaft adjustment unit distributor sealing ring mounting bolt.
9. Remove distributor by moving it back and forth.
10. Remove crankshaft locking tool.
11. Lift timing chain and hold under tension.
12. Turn engine is reverse of normal rotation to 45° before TDC.
13. Remove camshaft locking tools.
14. Turn exhaust camshaft using suitable open end wrench until cylinder No. 6 exhaust cam faces upward.
15. Turn intake camshaft using suitable open end wrench until cylinder No. 8 intake cam faces upward.
16. Mark bearing covers for installation in original positions.
17. Loosen bearing cover mounting nuts in ½ turn steps from outside to inside.
18. Remove bearing covers and camshafts.

Installation

1. Install camshafts.
2. Turn exhaust camshaft using suitable open end wrench until cylinder No. 6 exhaust cam faces upward.
3. Turn intake camshaft using suitable open end wrench until cylinder No. 8 intake cam faces upward.
4. Install bearing covers in original positions.
5. Evenly tighten bearing cover mounting nuts to specifications in ½ turn steps from outside to inside.
6. Turn camshafts until marker bores point upward.
7. Lock cylinder head camshafts using lock tools No. 11 2 442 and 11 2 446, or equivalents.
8. Align camshafts using suitable open end wrench so tools fit heads without gaps.
9. Hold camshaft lock tools in place using holder tool No. 11 2 443 with bolt tool No. 11 2 444, or equivalents.
10. Turn engine from 45° before TDC to TDC position and hold with crankshaft locking tool No. 11 2 300, or equivalent.
11. Install non-return valve using new sealing ring. Install new gasket over non-return valve.
12. Align compression ring contact points upward and apply light coat of oil to camshaft adjustment unit distributor.
13. Install distributor straight.
14. Install sealing ring and mounting bolts.
15. Remove righthand camshaft adjustment unit as outlined under "Variable Camshaft Timing (VANOS) Adjustment Unit, Replace."
16. Install timing chain tensioner as outlined under "Timing Chain Tensioner, Replace."
17. Install both upper timing case covers as outlined under "Front Cover, Replace."
18. Install timing chain tensioner as outlined under "Timing Chain Tensioner, Replace."
19. Install spark plug.

VARIABLE CAMSHAFT TIMING (VANOS) ADJUSTMENT UNIT

REPLACE

M5

LEFTHAND

Removal

1. Raise and support vehicle, then drain engine block coolant into suitable container.
2. Remove air intake filter housing upper section with Mass Air Flow (MAF) sensor.
3. Remove intake manifold as outlined under "Intake Manifold, Replace."
4. Remove both valve covers as outlined under "Valve Cover, Replace."
5. Remove spark plugs.
6. Remove hose between radiator and thermostat housing.
7. Lock belt pulley in position using holding tool No. 11 5 050, or equivalent, then remove mounting nut using wrench tool No. 11 5 040, or equivalent. **Nut has lefthand threads.**
8. Remove fan coupling.
9. Remove both cylinder head oil lines.
10. Rotate crankshaft in normal rotational direction to cylinder No. 1 firing TDC.
11. Secure crankshaft damper in position with plug mandrel tool No. 11 2 300, or equivalent.
12. Remove VANOS adjustment unit oil line.
13. Install connecting piece tool No. 11 7 130, or equivalent, to VANOS adjustment unit.
14. Connect 29–116 psi compressed air.
15. Disconnect solenoid valve connector.
16. Connect switch tool No. 12 6 050, or equivalent, to solenoid valves and battery.
17. Alternately press buttons 3 and 4 several times.
18. Hold down toggle switch button 4 and, at same time, rotate intake camshaft against rotational direction as far as possible using suitable open end wrench.

19. Alternately press buttons 1 and 2 several times.
20. Hold down toggle switch button 2 and, at same time, rotate exhaust camshaft against rotational direction as far as possible using suitable open end wrench.
21. Remove plug mandrel tool from crankshaft damper.
22. Turn engine in normal rotational direction one revolution to overlap TDC position.
23. Loosen accessible camshaft sprocket mounting bolts.
24. Rotate crankshaft in normal rotational direction to cylinder No. 1 firing TDC.
25. Secure crankshaft damper in position with plug mandrel tool.
26. Loosen remaining camshaft sprocket mounting bolts.
27. Align camshafts' openings with 1st bearing cap locating bore and lock camshafts using plug mandel tools No. 11 7 120, or equivalent.
28. Remove VANOS adjustment unit mounting bolts.
29. Lever and remove VANOS adjustment unit using suitable screwdriver at left and righthand side openings.
30. Remove plug mandrel tool from crankshaft damper.
31. Turn engine is reverse of normal rotation to 45° before TDC.

Installation

1. Turn engine from 45° before TDC to TDC position and lock with plug mandrel tool No. 11 2 300, or equivalent.
2. Install intake and exhaust camshafts' toothed shafts.
3. Brace against twin surface, release hex head and **torque** to 88 inch lbs.
4. Cover bore with suitable shop rag.
5. Connect switch tool No. 12 6 050, or equivalent, to solenoid valves and battery.
6. Press button 1 and, at same time, press exhaust side toothed shaft back to stop by hand.
7. Press button 4 and, at same time, press intake side toothed shaft back to stop by hand.
8. Install new O-rings coated with oil. Secure O-ring with grease, as required.
9. Turn exhaust and intake camshafts' spline hubs to right stop.
10. Install VANOS adjustment unit with solenoid valves' cables at bottom. **Ensure VANOS splined shafts remain in initial position.**
11. Turn splined shaft until straight splines are engaged.
12. Push adjustment unit with splined shaft into gear until helical cut splines are meshing with spline hub.
13. If helical cut splines cannot be pushed into spline hub, turn spline hub in reverse of normal rotation direction until splined shaft is positioned with spline hub using hook wrench tool No. 11 7 150, or equivalent. **Ensure first fitting tooth snaps into place.**
14. Align radial piston pump to spline hub driver.
15. Push VANOS adjustment unit until O-rings rests against timing case cover.
16. Install one mounting bolt on left and righthand sides, then tighten without play. **Do not tighten bolts. Unit must not rest against timing case cover.**
17. **Torque** six accessible VANOS camshaft sprockets' mounting bolts to 88 inch lbs., then loosen bolts 1/4 turn.
18. Install VANOS adjustment unit mount bolts, then tighten alternately and evenly in 1/2 turn increments until VANOS units rests against timing case.
19. Tighten VANOS adjustment unit mounting bolts to specifications.
20. Remove plug mandrel tool from crankshaft damper.
21. Turn engine in reverse of normal rotational direction until there is noticeable resistance and spline hubs are at stop.
22. Turn engine in reverse of normal rotational direction until cylinder No. 1 is at firing TDC position and lock with plug mandrel tool.
23. **Torque** six accessible VANOS camshaft sprockets' mounting bolts to 88 inch lbs.
24. Remove plug mandel tools from camshafts.
25. Remove plug mandrel tool from crankshaft damper.
26. Turn engine in normal rotational direction one revolution to overlap TDC position.
27. **Torque** six remaining VANOS camshaft sprockets' mounting bolts to 88 inch lbs.
28. Turn engine in normal rotational direction until cylinder No. 1 is at firing TDC position and lock with plug mandrel tool.
29. Remove righthand VANOS adjustment unit oil line.
30. Install connecting piece tool No. 11 7 130, or equivalent, to righthand VANOS adjustment unit.
31. Connect 29–116 psi compressed air.
32. Disconnect solenoid valves on righthand cylinder bank.
33. Connect switch tool No. 12 6 050, or equivalent, to righthand solenoid valves and battery.
34. Alternately press buttons 1 and 2 several times.
35. Hold down toggle switch button 1 and, at same time, rotate intake camshaft against rotational direction as far as possible using suitable open end wrench.
36. Alternately press buttons 3 and 4 several times.
37. Hold down toggle switch button 3 and, at same time, rotate exhaust camshaft against rotational direction as far as possible using suitable open end wrench.
38. Ensure exhaust and intake camshafts' groove in inside 1st bearing cap groove and both left and righthand banks.
39. Install lefthand VANOS adjustment unit sealing ring and oil line, then tighten to specifications.
40. Remove special tools from righthand bank.
41. Install righthand VANOS adjustment unit sealing ring and oil line, then tighten to specifications.
42. Install fan.
43. Install hose between radiator and thermostat housing.
44. Install spark plugs.
45. Install both valve covers as outlined under "Valve Cover, Replace."
46. Install intake manifold as outlined under "Intake Manifold, Replace."
47. Install air intake filter housing upper section with Mass Air Flow (MAF) sensor.

RIGHTHAND

Removal

1. Raise and support vehicle, then drain engine block coolant into suitable container.
2. Remove air intake filter housing upper section with Mass Air Flow (MAF) sensor.
3. Remove intake manifold as outlined under "Intake Manifold, Replace."
4. Remove both valve covers as outlined under "Valve Cover, Replace."
5. Remove spark plugs.
6. Remove hose between radiator and thermostat housing.
7. Lock belt pulley in position using holding tool No. 11 5 050, or equivalent, then remove mounting nut using wrench tool No. 11 5 040, or equivalent. **Nut has lefthand threads.**
8. Remove fan coupling.
9. Remove both cylinder head oil lines.
10. Rotate crankshaft in normal rotational direction to cylinder No. 1 firing TDC.
11. Secure crankshaft damper in position with plug mandrel tool No. 11 2 300, or equivalent.
12. Remove VANOS adjustment unit oil line.
13. Install connecting piece tool No. 11 7 130, or equivalent, to VANOS adjustment unit.
14. Connect 29–116 psi compressed air.
15. Disconnect solenoid valve connector.
16. Connect switch tool No. 12 6 050, or equivalent, to solenoid valves and battery.
17. Alternately press buttons 1 and 2 several times.
18. Hold down toggle switch button 2 and, at same time, rotate exhaust camshaft against rotational direction as far as possible using suitable open end wrench.
19. Alternately press buttons 3 and 4 several times.
20. Hold down toggle switch button 4 and, at same time, rotate intake camshaft against rotational direction as far as possible using suitable open end wrench.
21. Remove plug mandrel tool from crankshaft damper.
22. Turn engine in normal rotational direction one revolution to overlap TDC position.

23. Loosen accessible camshaft sprocket mounting bolts.
24. Rotate crankshaft in normal rotational direction to cylinder No. 1 firing TDC.
25. Secure crankshaft damper in position with plug mandrel tool.
26. Loosen remaining camshaft sprocket mounting bolts.
27. Align camshafts' openings with 1st bearing cap locating bore and lock camshafts using plug mandel tools No. 11 7 120, or equivalent.
28. Remove VANOS adjustment unit mounting bolts.
29. Lever and remove VANOS adjustment unit using suitable screwdriver at left and righthand side openings.
30. Remove plug mandrel tool from crankshaft damper.
31. Turn engine is reverse of normal rotation to 45° before TDC.

Installation

1. Turn engine from 45° before TDC to TDC position and lock with plug mandrel tool No. 11 2 300, or equivalent.
2. Install intake and exhaust camshafts' toothed shafts.
3. Brace against twin surface, release hex head and **torque** to 88 inch lbs.
4. Cover bore with suitable shop rag.
5. Connect switch tool No. 12 6 050, or equivalent, to solenoid valves and battery.
6. Press button 1 and, at same time, press exhaust side toothed shaft back to stop by hand.
7. Press button 4 and, at same time, press intake side toothed shaft back to stop by hand.
8. Install new O-rings coated with oil. Secure O-ring with grease, as required.
9. Turn exhaust and intake camshafts' spline hubs to right stop.
10. Install VANOS adjustment unit with solenoid valves' cables at bottom. **Ensure VANOS splined shafts remain in initial position.**
11. Turn splined shaft until straight splines are engaged.
12. Push adjustment unit with splined shaft into gear until helical cut splines are meshing with spline hub.
13. If helical cut splines cannot be pushed into spline hub, turn spline hub in reverse of normal rotation direction until splined shaft is positioned with spline hub using hook wrench tool No. 11 7 150, or equivalent. **Ensure first fitting tooth snaps into place.**
14. Align radial piston pump to spline hub driver.
15. Push VANOS adjustment unit until O-rings rests against timing case cover.
16. Install one mounting bolt on left and righthand sides, then tighten without play. **Do not tighten bolts. Unit must not rest against timing case cover.**
17. **Torque** six accessible VANOS camshaft sprockets' mounting bolts to 88 inch lbs., then loosen bolts 1/4 turn.
18. Install VANOS adjustment unit mount bolts, then tighten alternately and evenly in 1/2 turn increments until VANOS units rests against timing case.
19. Tighten VANOS adjustment unit mounting bolts to specifications.
20. Remove plug mandrel tool from crankshaft damper.
21. Turn engine in reverse of normal rotational direction until there is noticeable resistance and spline hubs are at stop.
22. Turn engine in reverse of normal rotational direction until cylinder No. 1 is at firing TDC position and lock with plug mandrel tool.
23. **Torque** six accessible VANOS camshaft sprockets' mounting bolts to 88 inch lbs.
24. Remove plug mandel tools from camshafts.
25. Remove plug mandrel tool from crankshaft damper.
26. Turn engine in normal rotational direction one revolution to overlap TDC position.
27. **Torque** six remaining VANOS camshaft sprockets' mounting bolts to 88 inch lbs.
28. Turn engine in normal rotational direction until cylinder No. 1 is at firing TDC position and lock with plug mandrel tool.
29. Remove righthand VANOS adjustment unit oil line.
30. Install connecting piece tool No. 11 7 130, or equivalent, to righthand VANOS adjustment unit.
31. Connect 29–116 psi compressed air.
32. Disconnect solenoid valves on righthand cylinder bank.
33. Connect switch tool No. 12 6 050, or equivalent, to righthand solenoid valves and battery.
34. Alternately press buttons 3 and 4 several times.
35. Hold down toggle switch button 4 and, at same time, rotate exhaust camshaft against rotational direction as far as possible using suitable open end wrench.
36. Alternately press buttons 1 and 2 several times.
37. Hold down toggle switch button 2 and, at same time, rotate intake camshaft against rotational direction as far as possible using suitable open end wrench.
38. Ensure exhaust and intake camshafts' groove in inside 1st bearing cap groove and both left and righthand banks.
39. Install righthand VANOS adjustment unit sealing ring and oil line, then tighten to specifications.
40. Remove special tools from righthand bank.
41. Install righthand VANOS adjustment unit sealing ring and oil line, then tighten to specifications.
42. Install fan.
43. Install hose between radiator and thermostat housing.
44. Install spark plugs.
45. Install both valve covers as outlined under "Valve Cover, Replace."
46. Install intake manifold as outlined under "Intake Manifold, Replace."
47. Install air intake filter housing upper section with Mass Air Flow (MAF) sensor.

X5, 540 & 740

LEFTHAND

Removal

1. Remove air intake filter housing with Mass Air Flow (MAF) sensor.
2. Lock belt pulley in position using holding tool No. 11 5 050, or equivalent, then remove mounting nut using wrench tool No. 11 5 040, or equivalent. **Nut has lefthand threads.**
3. Remove fan clutch.
4. Remove both valve cover as outlined under "Valve Cover, Replace."
5. Remove spark plugs.
6. Remove left and righthand cylinder head oil lines.
7. Rotate engine in normal rotational direction until cylinder No. 1 is at firing TDC.
8. **On 540 and 740 models,** lock crankshaft with timing pin tool No. 11 2 300, or equivalent.
9. **On X5 models,** lock crankshaft with timing pin tool No. 11 5 180, or equivalent.
10. **On all models,** remove timing chain tensioner as outlined under "Timing Chain Tensioner, Replace."
11. Install both upper timing case covers as outlined under "Front Cover, Replace."
12. Remove mounting bolts and lefthand camshaft sensor gear. **Bolt has lefthand threads.**
13. Remove mounting bolts and righthand camshaft sensor gear. **Bolt has lefthand threads.**
14. Counterhold camshafts with suitable open end wrench.
15. Loosen lefthand exhaust camshaft sprocket mounting bolt approximately 1/2 turn. **Bolt has lefthand threads.**
16. Loosen righthand exhaust camshaft sprocket mounting bolt approximately 1/2 turn. **Bolt has lefthand threads.**
17. Loosen lefthand intake camshaft sprocket mounting bolt approximately 1/2 turn. **Bolt has lefthand threads.**
18. Loosen righthand intake camshaft sprocket mounting bolt approximately 1/2 turn. **Bolt has lefthand threads.**
19. Lock righthand camshafts using lock tools No. 11 2 441 and 11 2 445, or equivalents.
20. Hold camshaft lock tools in place using holder tool No. 11 2 443 with bolt tool No. 11 2 444, or equivalents.
21. Lock lefthand camshafts using lock tools No. 11 2 442 and 11 2 446, or equivalents.
22. Hold camshaft lock tools in place using holder tool No. 11 2 443 with bolt tool No. 11 2 444, or equivalents.
23. Relieve chain pressure by compressing secondary chain tensioner and holding with locking pin tool No. 11 3

310, or equivalent.

24. Remove mounting bolts, then pull exhaust sprocket and camshaft adjustment unit forward until no longer located on camshaft positions. **Bolts have lefthand threads.**
25. Feed timing chain forward over adjustment unit sprocket.
26. Remove exhaust sprocket with secondary chain and camshaft adjustment unit.

Installation

1. Pull timing chain up and fit over camshaft adjustment unit with exhaust sprocket.
2. Position secondary chain and feed on from front over camshaft adjustment unit sprocket.
3. Install exhaust sprocket and camshaft adjustment unit.
4. Install mounting bolts and hand tighten without play. **Do not tighten.**
5. Compress secondary chain tensioner and remove locking clip.
6. Install tensioner block tool No. 11 7 380, or equivalent, against righthand chain
7. Install chain tensioning tool No 11 3 390, or equivalent, into righthand timing case cover. **Do not tighten.**
8. Connect suitable multimeter with acoustic continuity test to lefthand camshaft adjustment unit contact pin and oil line.
9. Attach hook wrench tool No. 11 6 440, or equivalent, to camshaft adjustment nut and move to 29 ft. lbs.
10. Ensure camshaft adjustment unit is at lefthand stop with acoustic multimeter.
11. **Torque** lefthand intake camshaft sprocket mounting bolt to 11 ft. lbs., then loosen ¼ turn.
12. **Torque** lefthand exhaust camshaft sprocket mounting bolt to 11 ft. lbs., then loosen ¼ turn.
13. Connect suitable multimeter with acoustic continuity test to righthand camshaft adjustment unit contact pin and oil line.
14. Attach hook wrench tool No. 11 6 440, or equivalent, to camshaft adjustment nut and move to 29 ft. lbs.
15. Ensure camshaft adjustment unit is at lefthand stop with acoustic multimeter.
16. **Torque** righthand intake camshaft sprocket mounting bolt to 11 ft. lbs., then loosen ¼ turn.
17. **Torque** righthand exhaust camshaft sprocket mounting bolt to 11 ft. lbs., then loosen ¼ turn.
18. Pretension tensioning rail to 6 inch lbs.
19. Pretensioning timing chain will move camshaft adjustment unit. Reset to lefthand stop as previously described.
20. Counterhold camshaft with suitable wrench and tighten lefthand intake camshaft sprocket mounting bolt to specifications. **Bolt has lefthand threads.**
21. Counterhold camshaft with suitable wrench and tighten lefthand exhaust camshaft sprocket mounting bolt to specifications. **Bolt has lefthand threads.**
22. Counterhold camshaft with suitable wrench and tighten righthand intake camshaft sprocket mounting bolt to specifications. **Bolt has lefthand threads.**
23. Counterhold camshaft with suitable wrench and tighten righthand exhaust camshaft sprocket mounting bolt to specifications. **Bolt has lefthand threads.**
24. Install righthand sensor gear and hand tighten mounting nut without play. **Do not tighten.**
25. Align righthand sensor gear using locking fixture tool No. 11 6 450, or equivalent.
26. Tighten sensor gear mounting bolt to specifications. Remove locking fixture tool.
27. Install lefthand sensor gear and hand tighten mounting nut without play. **Do not tighten.**
28. Align lefthand sensor gear using locking fixture tool No. 11 6 450, or equivalent.
29. Tighten sensor gear mounting bolt to specifications. Remove locking fixture tool.
30. Remove camshaft timing tools.
31. Disconnect tension on chain tensioning tool and remove tensioner block.
32. Install left and righthand cylinder head oil lines.
33. Install upper timing case covers as outlined under “Front Cover, Replace.”
34. Install timing chain tensioner as outlined under “Timing Chain Tensioner, Replace.”
35. Remove crank timing pin tool.
36. Install valve cover as outlined under “Valve Cover, Replace.”

RIGHTHAND

Removal

1. Remove air intake filter housing with Mass Air Flow (MAF) sensor.
2. Lock belt pulley in position using holding tool No. 11 5 050, or equivalent, then remove mounting nut using wrench tool No. 11 5 040, or equivalent. **Nut has lefthand threads.**
3. Remove fan clutch.
4. Remove both valve cover as outlined under “Valve Cover, Replace.”
5. Remove spark plugs.
6. Remove left and righthand cylinder head oil lines.
7. Rotate engine in normal rotational direction until cylinder No. 1 is at firing TDC.
8. **On 540 and 740 models,** lock crankshaft with timing pin tool No. 11 2 300, or equivalent.
9. **On X5 models,** lock crankshaft with timing pin tool No. 11 5 180, or equivalent.
10. **On all models,** remove timing chain tensioner as outlined under “Timing Chain Tensioner, Replace.”
11. Install both upper timing case covers as outlined under “Front Cover, Replace.”
12. Remove mounting bolts and righthand camshaft sensor gear. **Bolt has lefthand threads.**
13. Remove mounting bolts and lefthand camshaft sensor gear. **Bolt has lefthand threads.**
14. Counterhold camshafts with suitable open end wrench.
15. Loosen lefthand exhaust camshaft sprocket mounting bolt approximately ½ turn. **Bolt has lefthand threads.**
16. Loosen righthand exhaust camshaft sprocket mounting bolt approximately ½ turn. **Bolt has lefthand threads.**
17. Loosen lefthand intake camshaft sprocket mounting bolt approximately ½ turn. **Bolt has lefthand threads.**
18. Loosen righthand intake camshaft sprocket mounting bolt approximately ½ turn. **Bolt has lefthand threads.**
19. Lock righthand camshafts using lock tools No. 11 2 441 and 11 2 445, or equivalents.
20. Hold camshaft lock tools in place using holder tool No. 11 2 443 with bolt tool No. 11 2 444, or equivalents.
21. Lock lefthand camshafts using lock tools No. 11 2 442 and 11 2 446, or equivalents.
22. Hold camshaft lock tools in place using holder tool No. 11 2 443 with bolt tool No. 11 2 444, or equivalents.
23. Relieve chain pressure by compressing secondary chain tensioner and holding with locking pin tool No. 11 3 310, or equivalent.
24. Remove mounting bolts, then pull exhaust sprocket and camshaft adjustment unit forward until no longer located on camshaft positions. **Bolts have lefthand threads.**
25. Feed timing chain forward over adjustment unit sprocket.
26. Remove exhaust sprocket with secondary chain and camshaft adjustment unit.

Installation

1. Pull timing chain up and fit over camshaft adjustment unit with exhaust sprocket.
2. Position secondary chain and feed on from front over camshaft adjustment unit sprocket.
3. Install exhaust sprocket and camshaft adjustment unit.
4. Install mounting bolts and hand tighten without play. **Do not tighten.**
5. Compress secondary chain tensioner and remove locking clip.
6. Install tensioner block tool No. 11 7 380, or equivalent, against righthand chain
7. Install chain tensioning tool No 11 3 390, or equivalent, into righthand timing case cover. **Do not tighten.**
8. Connect suitable multimeter with acoustic continuity test to lefthand camshaft adjustment unit contact pin and oil line.
9. Attach hook wrench tool No. 11 6 440, or equivalent, to camshaft adjustment nut and move to 29 ft. lbs.
10. Ensure camshaft adjustment unit is at lefthand stop with acoustic multimeter.
11. **Torque** lefthand intake camshaft sprocket mounting bolt to 11 ft. lbs., then loosen ¼ turn.
12. **Torque** lefthand exhaust camshaft sprocket mounting bolt to 11 ft. lbs.,

Fig. 4 Alternator serpentine belt routing

then loosen ¼ turn.
13. Connect suitable multimeter with acoustic continuity test to righthand camshaft adjustment unit contact pin and oil line.
14. Attach hook wrench tool No. 11 6 440, or equivalent, to camshaft adjustment nut and move to 29 ft. lbs.
15. Ensure camshaft adjustment unit is at lefthand stop with acoustic multimeter.
16. **Torque** righthand intake camshaft sprocket mounting bolt to 11 ft. lbs., then loosen ¼ turn.
17. **Torque** righthand exhaust camshaft sprocket mounting bolt to 11 ft. lbs., then loosen ¼ turn.
18. Pretension tensioning rail to 6 inch lbs.
19. Pretensioning timing chain will move camshaft adjustment unit. Reset to lefthand stop as previously described.
20. Counterhold camshaft with suitable wrench and tighten lefthand intake camshaft sprocket mounting bolt to specifications. **Bolt has lefthand threads.**
21. Counterhold camshaft with suitable wrench and tighten lefthand exhaust camshaft sprocket mounting bolt to specifications. **Bolt has lefthand threads.**
22. Counterhold camshaft with suitable wrench and tighten righthand intake camshaft sprocket mounting bolt to specifications. **Bolt has lefthand threads.**
23. Counterhold camshaft with suitable wrench and tighten righthand exhaust camshaft sprocket mounting bolt to specifications. **Bolt has lefthand threads.**
24. Install righthand sensor gear and hand tighten mounting nut without play. **Do not tighten.**
25. Align righthand sensor gear using locking fixture tool No. 11 6 450, or equivalent.
26. Tighten sensor gear mounting bolt to specifications. Remove locking fixture tool.
27. Install lefthand sensor gear and hand tighten mounting nut without play. **Do not tighten.**
28. Align lefthand sensor gear using locking fixture tool No. 11 6 450, or equivalent.
29. Tighten sensor gear mounting bolt to specifications. Remove locking fixture tool.
30. Remove camshaft timing tools.
31. Disconnect tension on chain tensioning tool and remove tensioner block.
32. Install left and righthand cylinder head oil lines.
33. Install upper timing case covers as outlined under "Front Cover, Replace."
34. Install timing chain tensioner as outlined under "Timing Chain Tensioner, Replace."
35. Remove crank timing pin tool.
36. Install valve cover as outlined under "Valve Cover, Replace."

MAIN & ROD BEARINGS

Main Bearings

1. Install new bearing cover bolts. **Do not wash coating off.**
2. **Torque** bearing cover bolts to 15 ft. lbs.
3. Tighten M10 bolts an additional 70°.
4. Tighten M11 bolts an additional 100°.
5. Install new bearing cover support bolts.
6. **Torque** cover support bolts to 15 ft. lbs.
7. Tighten an additional 45°.
8. Install new support sleeve bolts.
9. **Torque** support sleeve bolts to 88 inch lbs.

Rod Bearings

M5

1. Oil bolt threads.
2. **Torque** to 44 inch lbs.
3. **Torque** to 15 ft. lbs.
4. Tighten an additional 65°.

X5, 540 & 740

1. Oil bolt threads.
2. **Torque** to 44 inch lbs.
3. **Torque** to 15 ft. lbs.
4. Tighten an additional 80°.

CRANKSHAFT REAR OIL SEAL

REPLACE

1. Drain engine oil into suitable container.
2. Remove transmission as outlined in "Clutch & Manual Transmission" or "Automatic Transmission" section.
3. Block flywheel using locking tool No. 11 2 070, or equivalent.
4. Remove mounting bolts and flywheel.
5. Loosen lower mounting bolts.
6. Remove rear cover mounting bolts.
7. Disconnect oil sump gasket from end cover.
8. Remove end cover and radial seal.
9. Reverse procedure to install, noting the following:
   a. Drive in new seal using driver tools Nos. 11 1 230 and 00 5 500, or equivalent.
   b. Apply suitable sealer to lower mating surface areas.
   c. Coat contact points with Drei Bond No. 1209, or equivalent.
   d. Install sealing ring using installed tool No, 11 2 390, or equivalent.
   e. Install new mounting bolt washers.
   f. Tighten mounting bolts to specification. **Do not use retaining compound.**

OIL PAN

REPLACE

M5

Lower

1. Raise and support vehicle, then remove mounting bolts and splash guard.
2. Drain engine oil into suitable container.
3. Remove left and righthand covers, then the left and righthand air channel.
4. Remove mounting bolts and underbody protection bar.
5. Disconnect oil level switch connector.
6. Remove mounting bolts and oil pan.
7. Reverse procedure to install, Tighten mounting bolts to specifications.

Upper

1. Lock hood in vertical service position.
2. Remove air filter housing with Mass Air Flow (MAF) sensor.
3. Disconnect clips and turn air ducts upward to disconnect from firewall, then remove by pulling forward and out.
4. Disconnect oil dipstick guide tub from righthand timing case cover.
5. Remove left and righthand side engine mount nuts.
6. Support engine with engine support tool No. 00 0 200, or equivalent.
7. Raise engine approximately 0.236–0.315 inch.
8. Disconnect air conditioning compressor and alternator drive belts.
9. Remove mounting bolts and place power steering pump aside with lines connected.
10. Remove belt tensioner from oil sump.
11. Remove air conditioning compressor support bracket from oil sump.
12. Disconnect oil dipstick guide tube from oil pan.
13. Disconnect oil return line from pan.
14. Disconnect steering shaft from steering gear.
15. Remove lower oil sump section as outlined under "Lower."
16. Remove mounting bolts and oil circuit changeover valves using suitable clean shop rag.
17. Remove mounting bolts and oil pump as outlined under "Oil Pump, Replace."
18. Disconnect coolant line bracket from front axle support.
19. Support front axle support with fixture tool No. 31 2 220, or equivalent, and suitable jack.
20. Remove mounting bolts and lower front axle support approximately 2.36 inches.
21. Remove mounting bolts inside oil sump.
22. Remove sealing cover mounting bolts.

23. Remove upper oil sump mounting bolts,
24. Disconnect batter lead and starter motor connectors from upper oil sump.
25. Remove upper oil sump.
26. Reverse procedure to install, noting the following:
    a. Install mounting bolts into transmission end without preload.
    b. Tighten engine, then transmission end mounting bolts.
    c. Install new oil return line sealing ring.
    d. Replace oil dipstick guide tube O-ring, as required.

X5

Lower

1. Raise and support vehicle.
2. Open main flow oil filter cover and drain oil into sump.
3. Remove mounting bolts and reinforcement plate.
4. Drain engine oil into suitable container.
5. Disconnect oil level switch connector.
6. Disconnect cable guide.
7. Remove mounting bolts and oil pan.
8. Reverse procedure to install, noting the following:
    a. Tighten mounting bolts to specifications.
    b. **Torque** reinforcement plate mounting bolts to 41 ft. lbs.
    c. Tighten plate mounting bolts an additional 90°.
    d. Final tighten plate bolts an additional 15°.

Upper

1. Disconnect sealing strip and turn toggles 90°, then remove cover, mounting bolts and heater bulkhead.
2. Lock hood in vertical service position.
3. Remove engine acoustic covers.
4. Remove air filter housing upper section with Mass Air Flow (MAF) sensor.
5. Disconnect oil dipstick guide tub from righthand timing case cover.
6. Support engine with engine support tool No. 00 0 200, or equivalent.
7. Remove left and righthand side engine mount nuts.
8. Disconnect clips and turn air ducts upward to disconnect from firewall, then remove by pulling forward and out.
9. Raise engine approximately 0.394–0.472 inch.
10. Remove front splash guard and reinforcement plate.
11. Disconnect positive lead from starter motor and disconnect cable guides' clip.
12. Remove left and righthand swivel bearings.
13. Remove output shafts.
14. Remove righthand output shaft bearing pedestal from oil sump.
15. Disconnect propeller shaft at front.
16. Disconnect steering shaft from steering gear.
17. Temporarily install left and righthand swivel bearings, then connect with spring strut bolt.
18. Temporarily install tension strut, control arm and tie rod to swivel bearing.
19. Remove front axle differential.
20. Support front axle support with fixture tool No. 31 2 220, or equivalent, and suitable jack.
21. Disconnect front axle support from engine carrier and lower approximately 3.544 inches. Steering gear remains attached to front axle support. **Do not overstretch steering gear return hose.**
22. Disconnect alternator drive belt.
23. Remove mounting bolts and place power steering pump aside with lines connected.
24. Relieve air conditioning compressor drive belt tension and remove adjustable plate from oil sump.
25. Drain engine oil into suitable container.
26. Remove lower oil sump section as outlined under “Lower.”
27. Disconnect oil dipstick guide tube from oil pan.
28. Disconnect main flow oil filter oil return line.
29. Remove oil pump snorkel.
30. Remove mounting bolts inside oil sump.
31. Remove cable guide.
32. Remove sealing cover mounting bolts.
33. Remove mounting bolts and upper oil sump.
34. Reverse procedure to install, noting the following:
    a. Install mounting bolts into transmission end without preload.
    b. Tighten engine, then transmission end mounting bolts.
    c. Install new oil return line sealing ring.
    d. Replace oil dipstick guide tube O-ring, as required.

540 & 740

Lower

1. Raise and support vehicle, then remove mounting bolts and splash guard.
2. Open main flow oil filter cover and drain oil into sump.
3. Drain engine oil into suitable container.
4. Disconnect oil level switch connector.
5. Remove mounting bolts and oil pan.
6. Reverse procedure to install, noting the following:
    a. Install stud screws to secure.
    b. Clean all old sealing material from mating surfaces.
    c. Install new gasket.
    d. Tighten mounting bolts to specifications, then remove stud screws.

Upper

1. Lock hood in vertical service position.
2. Remove engine acoustic covers.
3. Remove air filter housing with Mass Air Flow (MAF) sensor.
4. Disconnect oil dipstick guide tub from righthand timing case cover.
5. Remove left and righthand side engine mount nuts.
6. Support engine with engine support tool No. 00 0 200, or equivalent.
7. Raise engine approximately 0.236–0.315 inch.
8. Remove mounting bolts and place power steering pump aside with lines connected.
9. **On 740 models,** proceed as follows:
    a. Disconnect battery positive lead protective tube between oil pan and righthand engine support.
    b. Disconnect battery positive lead from starter motor and bracket.
10. **On all models,** disconnect oil dipstick guide tube from oil pan.
11. Disconnect oil return line from pan.
12. Disconnect steering shaft from steering gear.
13. Disconnect hydraulic line bracket from front axle support.
14. Support front axle support with fixture tool No. 31 2 220, or equivalent, and suitable jack.
15. Remove mounting bolts and lower front axle support approximately 2.36 inches.
16. Remove mounting bolts and oil pump as outlined under “Oil Pump, Replace.”
17. Remove sealing cover mounting bolts.
18. Remove mounting bolts and upper oil sump.
19. Disconnect oil cooler line bracket, as required
20. Reverse procedure to install, noting the following:
    a. Coat joint edges with three Bond No. 1209, or equivalent sealing compound.
    b. Install mounting bolts into transmission end without preload.
    c. Tighten engine, then transmission end mounting bolts.
    d. Install new oil return line sealing ring.
    e. Replace oil dipstick guide tube O-ring, as required.

OIL PUMP

REPLACE

M5

1. Remove oil pan as outlined under “Oil Pan, Replace.”
2. Remove mounting bolts and oil circuit changeover valves using suitable clean shop rag.
3. Remove mounting bolt and oil return line.
4. Remove mounting bolts and impact plate.
5. Remove mounting bolts and oil pump cover.
6. Remove mounting bolts and oil pump sprocket with chain.
7. Remove mounting bolts and oil pump.
8. Reverse procedure to install. Tighten mounting bolts to specifications.

X5

1. Remove upper oil pan as outlined under “Oil Pan, Replace.”
2. Remove mounting bolts and oil pump sprocket with chain.
3. Remove mounting bolts, nuts and oil pump.
4. Reverse procedure to install, noting the following:
    a. Tighten mounting bolts to specifications.

   b. Adjust chain deflection to 0.315–0.472 inch.

540 & 740

1. Remove lower oil pan as outlined under "Oil Pan, Replace."
2. Disconnect oil return line.
3. Disconnect cover, then remove mounting bolts and oil pump sprocket with chain.
4. Remove mounting bolts and oil pump.
5. Reverse procedure to install, noting the following:
   a. Tighten mounting bolts to specifications.
   b. Adjust chain deflection to 0.315–0.472 inch.

SERPENTINE DRIVE BELT

Refer to **Figs. 4 and 5** for serpentine belt routing.

REPLACEMENT

1. If reusing belt, mark rotational direction for installation.
2. Lock belt pulley in position using holding tool No. 11 5 050, or equivalent, then remove mounting nut using wrench tool No. 11 5 040, or equivalent. **Nut has lefthand threads.**
3. Remove fan clutch.
4. Remove engine splash shield.
5. Tighten alternator tensioning wheel bolt and compress belt tensioner.
6. Hold tensioner under tension and remove drive belt.
7. Tighten air conditioning compressor tensioning wheel bolt and compress belt tensioner.
8. Hold tensioner under tension and remove drive belt.
9. Reverse procedure to install.

COOLING SYSTEM BLEED

1. Set heater controls to maximum temperature and fan to low speed.
2. Run engine and flush engine cooling circuit with 3–4 short bursts to 4500–5000 RPM. **Do not run engine for more than 30 seconds.**
3. Close bleed screw when escaping coolant is free from air bubbles.
4. Run engine until thermostat opens.

THERMOSTAT

REPLACE

M5

1. Partially drain cooling system.
2. Remove left and righthand air intake filter housing upper section with Mass Air Flow (MAF) sensor.
3. Disconnect coolant hoses and Engine Coolant Temperature (ECT) sensor connector.
4. Remove mounting bolts and connecting piece. VANOS oil lines remain connected.
5. Remove mounting bolts and thermostat cover with thermostat.
6. Reverse procedure to install using new O-rings.

X5, 540 & 740

1. Partially drain cooling system.
2. Disconnect coolant hoses and electrical connector.
3. Remove mounting bolts and thermostat cover with thermostat.
4. Reverse procedure to install using new sealing ring.

WATER PUMP

REPLACE

1. Remove vibration damper as outlined under "Crankshaft Damper, Replace."
2. Remove thermostat housing as outlined under "Thermostat, Replace."
3. Remove water pump pulley.
4. Disconnect coolant hoses.
5. Remove mounting bolts and water pump.
6. Reverse procedure to install.

RADIATOR

REPLACE

M5

1. Raise and support vehicle, then drain coolant into suitable container.
2. Remove righthand air intake filter housing.
3. Remove expansion tank rivets and disconnect hose clamps.
4. Disconnect level sensor connector.
5. Disconnect expansion tank hose.
6. Remove expansion tank.
7. Disconnect AUC sensor connector, as required.
8. Remove expanding rivets and sealing strip.
9. Remove fan cowl.
10. Disconnect water hose.
11. Disconnect Engine Coolant Temperature (ECT) sensor connector.
12. Disconnect hydraulic lines from cooling loop.
13. Remove radiator.
14. Reverse procedure to install.

X5

1. Raise and support vehicle, then drain coolant into suitable container.
2. Remove fan cowl expansion rivets and mounting bolts.
3. Disconnect lugs and remove underhood intakes.
4. Disconnect fan cowl water hose clip.
5. Lock belt pulley in position using holding tool No. 11 5 050, or equivalent, then remove mounting nut using wrench tool No. 11 5 040, or equivalent. **Nut has lefthand threads.**
6. Remove fan coupling.
7. Disconnect AUC sensor connector.
8. Remove expansion rivets and fan cowl.
9. Disconnect water hose at top and bottom of radiator.
10. Disconnect water hoses from mounting plate.
11. Disconnect electrical connector.
12. **On models equipped with automatic transmission,** disconnect lock and remove oil cooler with lines connected.
13. **On all models,** disconnect lower water hose.
14. Remove mounting bolts and bracket.
15. Disconnect sealing strip between radiator and cassette.
16. Remove cassette mounting bolts, then the radiator.
17. Reverse procedure to install.

540

1. Raise and support vehicle, then drain coolant into suitable container.
2. Remove air cleaner cover.
3. Remove expansion tank cap.
4. Remove vent screw.
5. Remove mounting bolts and splash guard.
6. Remove drain hose.
7. Disconnect coolant level sensor.
8. Disconnect expansion hose.
9. Disconnect retainer, then remove expansion tank and vent hose.
10. Disconnect AUC sensor connector, as required.
11. Remove expanding rivets and sealing strip.
12. Remove fan cowl.
13. Disconnect Engine Coolant Temperature (ECT) sensor connector.
14. Disconnect upper and lower coolant hoses.
15. Remove radiator.
16. Reverse procedure to install.

740

1. Raise and support vehicle, then drain coolant into suitable container.
2. Remove air intake filter housing.
3. Disconnect level sensor connector.
4. Disconnect clamp and remove expansion tank hose.
5. Open expansion tank cap and remove vent plug.
6. Disconnect clips and remove expansion tank.
7. Disconnect AUC sensor, as required.
8. Lock belt pulley in position using holding tool No. 11 5 050, or equivalent, then remove mounting nut using

wrench tool No. 11 5 040, or equivalent. **Nut has lefthand threads.**
9. Remove fan coupling.
10. Remove expanding rivers and sealing strip.
11. Remove fan cowl.
12. Disconnect air conditioning temperature switch connector.
13. Remove upper and lower coolant hose.
14. Disconnect radiator mounts using suitable screwdriver.
15. Remove radiator.
16. Reverse procedure to install.

FUEL PUMP

REPLACE

1. Relieve fuel system pressure as outlined under "Precautions."
2. Remove enough fuel from tank to ensure pump unit can be removed without spillage.
3. Remove rear seat cushion and rubber grommet.
4. Cut and fold insulating mat.
5. Remove mounting screws and cover.
6. Disconnect electrical connectors and fuel lines.
7. Remove ring nut using ring nut wrench tool No. 16 1 020, or equivalent.
8. Mark position of unit in fuel tank for installation alignment.
9. Lift and rotate unit from fuel tank. **Do not deform fuel level sensor arm or altitude sensor tube.**
10. Reverse procedure to install. Install new ring nut and seal.

FUEL FILTER

REPLACE

M5

1. Relieve fuel pressure as outlined under "Precautions."
2. Remove mounting bolts and floor plate.
3. Remove fuel pressure regulator vacuum hose.
4. Pull bracket out and remove fuel pressure regulator.
5. Disconnect clamps and remove fuel hoses.
6. Remove mounting bolt and fuel filter.
7. Reverse procedure to install.

X5

1. Relieve fuel pressure as outlined under "Precautions."
2. Remove lefthand side fuel tank underbody protection.
3. Remove mounting screws and bend lefthand rear wheelhousing open.
4. Remove mounting screws and nuts, then lower fuel tank underbody protection.
5. Remove fuel pressure regulator vacuum hose.
6. Pull bracket out and remove fuel pressure regulator.

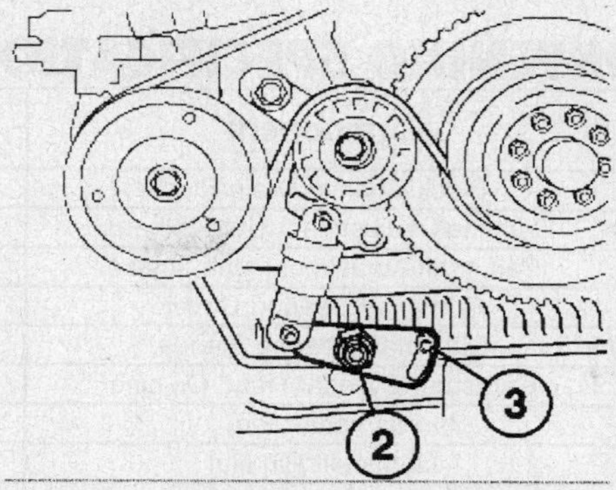

Fig. 5 Air conditioning compressor serpentine belt routing

7. Disconnect clamps and remove fuel hoses.
8. Remove mounting bolts, holder and fuel filter.
9. Reverse procedure to install.

540

Less Integrate Fuel Pressure Regulator

1. Relieve fuel pressure as outlined under "Precautions."
2. Clamp fuel feed hose on both sides of fuel filter using clamping tools No. 13 3 010, or equivalent.
3. Disconnect clips and fuel lines.
4. Remove mounting bolt and fuel filter.
5. Reverse procedure to install. Ensure correct fuel flow direction.

With Integrate Fuel Pressure Regulator

1. Relieve fuel pressure as outlined under "Precautions."
2. Remove mounting bolts and floor plate.
3. Remove fuel pressure regulator vacuum hose.
4. Pull bracket out and remove fuel pressure regulator.
5. Disconnect clamps and remove fuel hoses.
6. Remove mounting bolt and fuel filter.
7. Reverse procedure to install.

740

1. Relieve fuel pressure as outlined under "Precautions."
2. Remove mounting screws and fold lower trim aside.
3. Clamp fuel feed hose on both sides of fuel filter using clamping tools No. 13 3 010, or equivalent.
4. Disconnect clips and fuel lines.
5. Remove mounting bolt and fuel filter.
6. Reverse procedure to install. Ensure correct fuel flow direction.

TECHNICAL SERVICE BULLETINS

COOLANT TEMPERATURE GAUGE INDICATES HIGH

1998 540 & 740

On some of these models the check engine map my or may not illuminate with Diagnostic Trouble Code (DTC) 139 and/or the coolant temperature gauge may indicate higher than normal coolant temperature.

This condition may be caused by the thermostat.

To correct this condition install revised thermostat (part No. 11 53 1 437 526) with housing burrs removed, new O-ring seal material and thicker internal thermostat resistor foil.

IRREGULAR ENGINE CLICKING

X5, 540 & 740

On some of these models this may be a loud clicking coming from the lower crankcase on righthand bank. This loud, irregular tapping similar to a mechanical typewriter occurs at operating temperature between idle and approximately 2000 RPM with the engine under load, transmission in drive and air conditioning switch to On position.

This condition may be caused by crankshaft main bearings. BMW says condition in no way compromises reliability.

To correct this condition replace crankshaft main bearing shells.

INTERMITTENT ROUGH IDLE

1998 540 & 740

On some of these models there may be an intermittent rough idle at operating temperature with the air conditioning switch on and transmission in drive.

This condition may be caused by a binding water pump impeller shaft.

To correct this condition replace the water pump.

ENGINE WILL NOT TURN OVER

On some models, the engine will not turn over.

This condition may be caused by a fuel injector stuck in open position.

To correct this condition, proceed as follows:

1. Remove fuel injectors and inspect leakage rate.
2. Replace hydraulic locked injectors.
3. Inspect engine compression pressures.
4. If any cylinder's compression is less than 143 psi, piston/connecting rod may have damaged and further engine tear down is required.

TIGHTENING SPECIFICATIONS

Year	Component	Torque, Ft. Lbs.
1998–2001	Block Coolant Drain Plug	18
	Camshaft Adjustment Unit, Exhaust	92
	Camshaft Adjustment Unit, Intake	81
	Camshaft Bearing Cover	⑪
	Camshaft Bearing Flange	115①
	Camshaft Cylinder Head Oil Line	⑯
	Camshaft Pin	15
	Camshaft Pin Nut	88①
	Camshaft Signal Ring	37
	Camshaft Sprocket	11
	Chain Tensioner	29
	Connecting Rod	⑥
	Crankshaft Damper	13③
	Crankshaft Damper Center Bolt	⑦
	Crankshaft Damper Pulley	13
	Crankcase End Cover	⑪
	Crankshaft Increment Wheel	115①
	Cylinder Head	⑤
	Cylinder Head Cover	⑰
	Cylinder Head Cover Oil Trap	13
	Electronic Box Cover	39①
	Engine Mount	⑨
	Exhaust Manifold	②
	Fan	29⑧
	Flywheel, Automatic	88
	Flywheel, Manual	77
	Front Cover	⑨⑩
	Intake Manifold	⑨
	Intake Manifold Hood	71①
	Main Bearing Caps	⑥
	Main Oil Duct Plug	25
	Oil Cooler Line	16
	Oil Drain Line	22
	Oil Drain Plug	⑫
	Oil Filter Cover	⑬
	Oil Filter Lines	⑭
	Oil Pan, Lower	④
	Oil Pan, Upper	④
	Oil Pump	17
	Oil Pump Cover	88①
	Oil Pump Sprocket	⑮
	Oil Spray Nozzle	106①
	Oxygen Sensor	41
	Reinforcement Plate	⑨
	Reversing Rail	10
	Sensor Gear	29
	Signal Ring	37
	Thermostat Bleeder	71①
	Thermostat Housing	88①
	Timing Case	⑨⑩
	Timing Case To Cylinder Head	15
	VANOS Cover	14
	VANOS Hydraulic Piston Shaft	88①
	VANOS Oil Line	115①
	VANOS Sensor Sprocket	29
	VANOS Solenoid Valve	18
	VANOS Sprocket, Exhaust	92

Continued

TIGHTENING SPECIFICATIONS—Continued

Year	Component	Torque, Ft. Lbs.
1998–2001	VANOS Sprocket, Intake	81
	Vibration Damper	13③
	Vibration Damper Center Bolt	⑦
	Vibration Damper Pulley	13
	Water Pump	②

① — Inch lbs.
② — M6, 88 inch lbs.; M8, 17 ft. lbs.
③ — For M5 models, refer to "Crankshaft Damper, Replace" for tightening specifications and sequence.
④ — M6 8.8, 88 inch lbs.; M6 10.9, 106 inch lbs.; M8 8.8, 16 ft. lbs.
⑤ — Refer to "Cylinder Head, Replace" for tightening specifications and sequence.
⑥ — Refer to "Main & Rod Bearings" for tightening specifications and sequence.
⑦ — Refer to "Timing Chain, Replace" for tightening specifications and sequence.
⑧ — **Torque** of 29 ft. lbs. when using wrench tool No. 11 5 040, or equivalent, is equal to 22 ft. lbs. on torque wrench.
⑨ — M6, 88 inch lbs.; M7, 11 ft. lbs.; M8, 16 ft. lbs.; M10, 35 ft. lbs.
⑩ — For M5 models, refer to "Front Cover, Replace" for tightening specifications and sequence.
⑪ — M6, 88 inch lbs.; M7, 11 ft. lbs.; M8, 15 ft. lbs.
⑫ — M12, 18 ft. lbs.; M22, 44 ft. lbs.
⑬ — M8, 16 ft. lbs.; M10 & 12, 24 ft. lbs.; Screw-On, 18 ft. lbs.
⑭ — M8, 16 ft. lbs.; M20, 30 ft. lbs.
⑮ — M6, 88 inch lbs.; M10, 35 ft. lbs.; M10 x 1, 18 ft. lbs.
⑯ — M5, 44 inch lbs.; M8, 88 inch lbs.
⑰ — M6, 88 inch lbs.; M7 & M8 11 ft. lbs.

5.4L (M73) V12 Engine

NOTE: On Air Bag Equipped Models, Refer To "Air Bag System Precautions" Located In The Front Of This Manual For System Disarming & Arming Procedures.

NOTE: Refer To "Computer Relearn Procedures" Located In The Front Of This Manual When Battery Power To The Computer Has Been Interrupted.

NOTE: Prior To Performing Any Service Operations Listed In This Section, Consult The "Technical Service Bulletins" Section For Related Information.

INDEX

	Page No.
Camshaft, Replace	2-85
Compression Pressure	2-82
Cooling System Bleed	2-86
Crankshaft Damper, Replace	2-85
Crankshaft Rear Oil Seal, Replace	2-86
Cylinder Head, Replace	2-84
Lefthand	2-84
Righthand	2-84
Engine Rebuilding Specifications	2-241
Engine, Replace	2-82
Exhaust Manifold, Replace	2-83
Lefthand	2-83
Righthand	2-84
Front Cover, Replace	2-85
Lower	2-85
Upper	2-85
Front Cover Seal, Replace	2-85
Fuel Filter, Replace	2-87
Fuel Pump, Replace	2-87
Intake Manifold, Replace	2-83
Main & Rod Bearings	2-86
Main Bearings	2-86
Rod Bearings	2-86
Oil Pan, Replace	2-86
Lower	2-86
Upper	2-86
Oil Pump, Replace	2-86
Precautions	2-82
Air Bag Systems	2-82
Battery Ground Cable	2-82
Fuel System Pressure Relief	2-82
Radiator, Replace	2-87
Rocker Arms, Replace	2-84
Serpentine Drive Belt	2-86
Replacement	2-86
Technical Service Bulletins	2-87
Timing Chain Whining	2-87
Thermostat, Replace	2-86
Tightening Specifications	2-88
Timing Chain, Replace	2-85
Timing Chain Tensioner, Replace	2-85
Valve Adjustment	2-84
Valve Cover, Replace	2-84
Water Pump, Replace	2-87

PRECAUTIONS

AIR BAG SYSTEMS

Refer to "Air Bag System Precautions" in the front of this manual for system disarming and arming procedures.

BATTERY GROUND CABLE

Prior to service, disconnect battery ground cable and isolate as required.

FUEL SYSTEM PRESSURE RELIEF

Relieve fuel system pressure before disconnecting any fuel line or fuel system component.

1. Remove fuel pump relay(s).
2. Connect battery ground cable and crank engine for 10 seconds.
3. When fuel system repairs are complete, install fuel pump relays and crank engine to restore fuel pump pressure.

COMPRESSION PRESSURE

1. Relieve fuel pressure as outlined under "Precautions."
2. Place gear selector in P position.
3. Set hand brake.
4. Turn ignition switch to Off position.
5. Disconnect Digital Motor Electronics (DME) master relay.
6. Remove spark plugs.
7. Install compression tester adapter tool No. 11 0 226, or equivalent, into spark plug bore by hand.
8. Connect compression gauge tool No. 11 0 224, or equivalent, onto adapter.
9. Fully depress accelerator pedal and operate starter motor until compression pressure reading is at maximum.
10. Normal compression pressure should measure 145–174 psi.
11. Maximum permissible difference between individual cylinders is 6 psi.

ENGINE

REPLACE

1. Raise hood to service position and lock into place.
2. Remove front axle support left and righthand heat baffle plates.
3. Drain coolant into suitable container.
4. Remove transmission as outlined in "Automatic Transmission" section.
5. Remove radiator as outlined under "Radiator, Replace."
6. Disconnect lefthand air intake filter housing and Mass Air Flow (MAF) sensor connector.
7. Disconnect retainers, clips and connectors, then remove hose and upper air intake filter housing.
8. Remove mounting bolts and lower filter housing.
9. Disconnect righthand air intake filter housing and Mass Air Flow (MAF) sensor connector.
10. Disconnect clips and connectors, then remove hose and upper air intake filter housing.
11. Remove mounting bolts and lower filter housing.
12. Disconnect oil filter cover and allow oil to flow into pan.
13. Disconnect oil pressure switch connector.
14. Disconnect bracket and remove oil line from main flow oil filter housing.
15. Remove mounting bolts and main flow oil filter housing from bracket.
16. Disconnect mounting bolt and remove coolant hose bracket.
17. Disconnect clips and remove coolant hoses from heating unit end wall.
18. Disconnect clips and remove coolant hose from back of coolant manifold.
19. Disconnect cable tie and hose clip, then remove brake booster vacuum hose.
20. Disconnect heating valve connectors.
21. Pull heating valve out of bracket and remove with hoses.
22. Remove mounting bolts and splash guard.
23. Lock belt pulley in position using holding tool No. 11 5 050, or equivalent, then remove mounting nut using

wrench tool No. 11 5 040, or equivalent. **Nut has lefthand threads.**
24. Remove fan coupling.
25. Turn mounting screws 90° and remove cylinder head cover.
26. Disconnect connector.
27. Remove mounting bolts and cylinder head wiring harness bracket.
28. Disconnect lefthand ignition coils Nos. 1 and 2 connections.
29. Disconnect tank vent valve connector.
30. Disconnect battery positive cable.
31. Disconnect Camshaft Position (CMP) sensor connector from vacuum control unit.
32. Remove tank vent valves with bracket.
33. Disconnect alternator connectors.
34. Disconnect Diagnostic Link Connector (DLC) connector.
35. Disconnect throttle valves actuator motors' connectors.
36. Disconnect cable ducts' knock sensors connectors.
37. Disconnect rear cable duct rear mounting nut.
38. Disconnect fuel injectors' connectors.
39. Open tank vent valves connectors, press interlock down and remove hose.
40. Disconnect oil drip tray.
41. Disconnect non-return valve pressure pipe hoses.
42. Disconnect pressure hose from air pump.
43. Remove non-return valve pressure pipe hoses with brackets.
44. Disconnect Engine Coolant Temperature (ETC) sensor connector.
45. Disconnect oil level sensor connector and starter motor.
46. Slide cable duct backward and remove from front interlock.
47. Disconnect lefthand bank Digital Motor Electronics (DME) Crankshaft Position (CKP) sensor connector.
48. Disconnect lines from transmission bell housing bracket.
49. Disconnect transmission position switch connector.
50. Disconnect automatic transmission shift connector.
51. Mark for assembly, then disconnect left and righthand Oxygen Sensor (O2S) connectors.
52. Disconnect O2S wiring harness from heat shields.
53. Disconnect wiring harness from transmission brackets.
54. Remove left and righthand catalytic converters' heat baffle plates.
55. Remove engine wiring harness from underside.
56. Disconnect lefthand cylinder head wiring harness cable tie.
57. Disconnect ground wires from spring strut shock absorber.
58. Remove electronics box cover.
59. Remove DME relays and starter motor inhibitor.
60. Disconnect electronics box temperature sensor connector.
61. Disconnect DME, transmission and engine power control connectors.
62. Disconnect lefthand cylinder head wiring harness cable tie.
63. Remove engine wiring harness.
64. Remove positive battery lead from starter motor and alternator.
65. Remove rear splash guard and front axle support heat baffle plate.
66. Remove mounting bolts and exhaust pipes from manifolds.
67. Remove alternator and air conditioning compressor drive belts.
68. Remove splash guard, then disconnect clamp and remove alternator air cooling hose.
69. Remove mounting bolts and power steering pump, then place it aside with lines connected.
70. Remove mounting bolts and tie air conditioning compress aside with lines connected.
71. Attach engine hoist tool No. 11 0 000, or equivalent, to engine lifting eyes.
72. Disconnect ground tape from engine support.
73. Disconnect top left and righthand engine mount nuts.
74. Remove engine. **Do damage ABS unit, air conditioning compressor, valve covers and steering shaft.**
75. Reverse procedure to install.

INTAKE MANIFOLD

REPLACE

The left and righthand intake manifolds may be removed individually.

1. Remove mounting bolts and cylinder head wiring harness bracket.
2. Disconnect righthand ignition coils Nos. 1 and 2 connections.
3. Disconnect tank vent valve connector.
4. Disconnect battery positive cable.
5. Disconnect Camshaft Position (CMP) sensor connector from vacuum control unit.
6. Remove tank vent valves with bracket.
7. Disconnect alternator connectors.
8. Disconnect Diagnostic Link Connector (DLC) connector.
9. Disconnect throttle valves actuator motors' connectors.
10. Disconnect cable ducts' knock sensors connectors.
11. Disconnect rear cable duct rear mounting nut.
12. Disconnect fuel injectors' connectors.
13. Open tank vent valves connectors, press interlock down and remove hose.
14. Disconnect oil drip tray.
15. Disconnect non-return valve pressure pipe hoses.
16. Disconnect pressure hose from air pump.
17. Remove non-return valve pressure pipe hoses with brackets.
18. Disconnect Engine Coolant Temperature (ETC) sensor connector.
19. Disconnect oil level sensor connector and starter motor.
20. Slide cable duct backward and remove from front interlock.
21. Lift wiring harness up and secure to hood.
22. Relieve fuel pressure as outlined under "Precautions."
23. Disconnect clips and remove fuel hoses from injection valve strips.
24. Remove mounting bolts and injection valve strip with fuel injectors.
25. Disconnect connector, then remove mounting bolts and throttle body. Place throttle body aside with hoses connected.
26. Mark knock sensor lines' routing for installation.
27. Remove mounting bolts and noise insulation strip.
28. Remove mounting nut and place ignition wiring harness aside.
29. Remove mounting bolts and intake manifold.
30. Remove mounting bolts and control valve venting.
31. Remove vent pipe, as required.
32. Reverse procedure to install, noting the following:
    a. Coat fuel injectors' seals with suitable acid-free grease.
    b. Install new hose clips.
    c. Install new throttle body gasket.
    d. Tighten mounting bolts and nuts to specifications.

EXHAUST MANIFOLD

REPLACE

LEFTHAND

1. Remove rear splash guard and front axle support heat baffle plate.
2. Remove exhaust pipe to manifold mounting bolts.
3. Remove flange connection mounting bolts.
4. Remove exhaust pipes.
5. Disconnect non-return valve connector.
6. Disconnect clips and remove air pump intake hose.
7. Disconnect connector and remove air intake filter housing upper section.
8. Lock belt pulley in position using holding tool No. 11 5 050, or equivalent, then remove mounting nut using wrench tool No. 11 5 040, or equivalent. **Nut has lefthand threads.**
9. Remove fan coupling.
10. Disconnect oil drip tray.
11. Disconnect clips and remove non-return valves' pressure hoses.
12. Disconnect clip from remove air pump pressure hose.
13. Remove mounting bolts and non-return valve.
14. Remove distributor cap as outlined in "Electrical" section.
15. Disconnect spark plug connectors.
16. Remove mounting nut and ignition wiring harness aside.
17. Remove exhaust manifold heat baffle plate mounting bolt.
18. Disconnect flanges and remove secondary air induction pipe.
19. Remove mounting nuts and cylinders Nos. 7–9 exhaust manifold.
20. Disconnect heating valve connections and heating hoses' cable tie.
21. Disconnect clip and remove brake booster vacuum hose.
22. Remove heating valve from bracket and place on manifold.
23. Remove mounting nuts, heat baffle

plate and cylinders Nos. 10–12 exhaust manifold.
24. Reverse procedure to install, noting the following:
 a. Install new exhaust manifold gaskets with smooth side toward cylinder head.
 b. Install new exhaust manifold mounting nuts, coating threads with CRC copper paste, or equivalent.
 c. Install new secondary air induction pipe gasket.
 d. Install new non-return valve gaskets.
 e. Install new exhaust pipe seals.
 f. Install new exhaust pipe mounting nuts, coating threads with CRC copper paste, or equivalent.

RIGHTHAND

1. Remove rear splash guard and front axle support heat baffle plate.
2. Remove exhaust pipe to manifold mounting bolts.
3. Remove flange connection mounting bolts.
4. Remove exhaust pipes.
5. Disconnect non-return valve connector.
6. Disconnect clips and remove air pump intake hose.
7. Disconnect connector and remove air intake filter housing upper section.
8. Lock belt pulley in position using holding tool No. 11 5 050, or equivalent, then remove mounting nut using wrench tool No. 11 5 040, or equivalent. **Nut has lefthand threads.**
9. Remove fan coupling.
10. Remove mounting bolts and non-return valve.
11. Disconnect clips and remove non-return valves' pressure hoses.
12. Disconnect clip from remove air pump pressure hose.
13. Disconnect oil dipstick guide tube from oil pan.
14. Remove mounting bolt and guide tube from valve cover.
15. Remove distributor cap as outlined in "Electrical" section.
16. Disconnect spark plug connectors.
17. Remove mounting nut and ignition wiring harness aside.
18. Remove exhaust manifold heat baffle plate mounting bolt.
19. Disconnect flanges and remove secondary air induction pipe.
20. Remove mounting nuts and cylinders Nos. 1–3 exhaust manifold.
21. Remove mounting bolts and nut, then the starter motor heat baffle plate.
22. Remove mounting nuts, heat baffle plate and cylinders Nos. 4–6 exhaust manifold.
23. Reverse procedure to install, noting the following:
 a. Install new exhaust manifold gaskets with smooth side toward cylinder head.
 b. Install new exhaust manifold and pipe mounting nuts, coating threads with CRC copper paste, or equivalent.
 c. Install new secondary air induction pipe gasket.

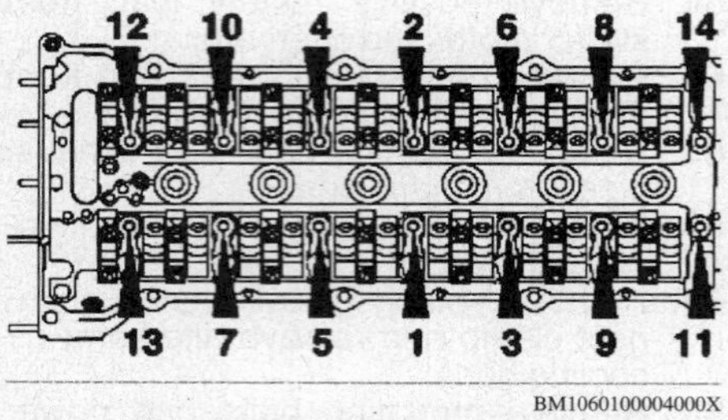

Fig. 1 Cylinder head bolt tightening sequence

 d. Install new non-return valve gaskets.
 e. Install new exhaust pipe seals.

CYLINDER HEAD

REPLACE

LEFTHAND

1. Remove upper timing case cover as outlined under "Front Cover, Replace."
2. Raise and support vehicle, then remove splash guard.
3. Remove front axle support left and righthand heat baffle plates.
4. Drain engine coolant into suitable container.
5. Remove spark plugs.
6. Remove both valve covers as outlined under "Valve Cover, Replace."
7. Mark for installation and remove Crankshaft Position (CKP) sensors' connectors.
8. Disconnect CKP sensors wiring harness from transmission and cylinder head brackets.
9. Disconnect clip and remove hose from back of coolant manifold and cylinder head.
10. Disconnect face wall heating unit hose clips.
11. Remove mounting bolts and coolant manifold.
12. Disconnect and remove non-return valves as outlined under "Exhaust Manifold, Replace."
13. Remove exhaust pipes as outlined under "Exhaust Manifold, Replace."
14. Remove cylinder head mounting bolts in reverse of tightening sequence, **Fig. 1.**
15. Remove cylinder head.
16. Reverse procedure to install, noting the following:
 a. Install new cylinder head gasket.
 b. **Torque** cylinder head bolts to 22 ft. lbs. in sequence.
 c. Tighten head bolts an additional 60° in sequence.
 d. Final tighten bolts an additional 60° in sequence.
 e. Install new coolant manifold O-ring.
 f. Install new coolant drain plug sealing ring and tighten to specifications.

RIGHTHAND

1. Remove upper timing case cover as outlined under "Front Cover, Replace."
2. Raise and support vehicle, then remove splash guard.
3. Remove front axle support left and righthand heat baffle plates.
4. Drain engine coolant into suitable container.
5. Remove spark plugs.
6. Remove both valve covers as outlined under "Valve Cover, Replace."
7. Mark for installation and remove Crankshaft Position (CKP) sensors' connectors.
8. Disconnect CKP sensors wiring harness from transmission and cylinder head brackets.
9. Disconnect clip and remove hose from back of coolant manifold and cylinder head.
10. Disconnect face wall heating unit hose clips.
11. Remove mounting bolts and coolant manifold.
12. Disconnect oil dipstick guide tube from oil pan.
13. Remove mounting bolt and guide tube from valve cover.
14. Remove exhaust pipes as outlined under "Exhaust Manifold, Replace."
15. Remove cylinder head mounting bolts in reverse of tightening sequence, **Fig. 1.**
16. Remove cylinder head.
17. Reverse procedure to install, noting the following:
 a. Install new cylinder head gasket.
 b. **Torque** cylinder head bolts to 22 ft. lbs. in sequence.
 c. Tighten head bolts an additional 60° in sequence.
 d. Final tighten bolts an additional 60° in sequence.
 e. Install new coolant manifold O-ring.
 f. Install new coolant drain plug sealing ring and tighten to specifications.

VALVE COVER

REPLACE

1. Remove intake manifolds as outlined under "Intake Manifold, Replace."
2. Remove rubber mounts, mounting nuts and valve covers.
3. Reverse procedure to install, noting the following:
 a. Install new gasket coating sealing timing case and timing case cover edges with Hylomar SQ 32M, or equivalent.
 b. Install brackets and tighten mounting nuts to specifications.

VALVE ADJUSTMENT

These engines are equipped with hydraulic lifters and require no valve adjustment,

ROCKER ARMS

REPLACE

1. Remove valve cover as outlined under "Valve Cover, Replace."
2. Remove spark plugs.
3. Remove mounting bolts and oil line.

4. Turn engine in normal rotational direction until camshaft cams point upward.
5. Press valve down using compression tool No. 11 4 130, or equivalent.
6. Remove rocket arm.
7. Reverse procedure to install, noting the following:
   a. Rocker arms must be installed in original positions.
   b. Ensure oil line injector bores face rocker arms.

CRANKSHAFT DAMPER

REPLACE

1. Lock belt pulley in position using holding tool No. 11 5 050, or equivalent, then remove mounting nut using wrench tool No. 11 5 040, or equivalent. **Nut has lefthand threads.**
2. Remove fan coupling.
3. Remove alternator and air conditioning compressor drive belts.
4. Remove left and righthand underbody protection panels.
5. Remove mounting bolts and bracket, then disconnect clips and place alternator cooling air guide aside.
6. Remove left and righthand brake air ducts.
7. Remove mounting bolts and water pump pulley.
8. Lock damper in position using holding tool No. 11 2 420, or equivalent, then remove mounting bolt.
9. Remove vibration damper.
10. Reverse procedure to install, noting the following:
    a. **Torque** vibration damper mounting bolt to 74 ft. lbs.
    b. Tighten mounting bolt an additional 60°.
    c. Tighten bolt an additional 60°.

FRONT COVER

REPLACE

LOWER

1. Drain engine coolant into suitable container.
2. Remove upper timing case as outlined under "Upper."
3. Remove upper oil pan as outlined under "Oil Pan, Replace."
4. Disconnect hose around vibration damper.
5. Remove vibration damper as outlined under "Crankshaft Damper, Replace."
6. Remove mounting bolts and lower cover.
7. Reverse procedure to install. Tighten mounting bolts to specifications.

UPPER

Removal

1. Remove both cylinder heads as outlined under "Cylinder Head, Replace."
2. Lock belt pulley in position using holding tool No. 11 5 050, or equivalent, then remove mounting nut using wrench tool No. 11 5 040, or equivalent. **Nut has lefthand threads.**
3. Remove fan coupling.
4. Remove non-return valve as outlined under "Exhaust Manifold, Replace."
5. Remove both distributor housing as outlined in "Electrical Section."
6. Remove mounting bolt and Camshaft Position (CMP) sensor, as required.
7. Remove oil drip tray guide mounting screw, then the cover and oil filler plug mounting bolt.
8. Remove secondary air induction pipe mounting bolt.
9. Remove upper timing case mounting bolts.
10. Remove timing chain guide rail.
11. Turn engine in normal rotational direction to cylinder No. 1 firing TDC position. Ensure camshaft flange is flush with oil baffle bolt connection.
12. Remove dust cover and secure crankshaft with locking tool No. 11 2 300, or equivalent.
13. Secure both camshafts with locking fixture tool No. 11 3 190, or equivalent.
14. Remove chain tensioner cap using suitable screwdriver.
15. Loose lock nut and adjusting screw a few turns.
16. Remove left and righthand sprockets's mounting bolts. **Do allow chain to drop.**
17. Remove mounting bolt and remove sliding rail by pulling it up. Remove lower retaining tab.
18. Remove mounting bolts and timing case by lifting it upward.

Installation

1. Install new seals so sealant bead faces case.
2. Install new dowel sleeve seals on both cylinder banks.
3. Install new gasket and apply thin, uniform coat of Hylomar SQ 32 M, or equivalent above and below attachment point.
4. Install timing case.
5. Install cylinder head and lower timing case mounting bolts and fit flush.
6. Tighten upper timing case mounting bolts to specifications.
7. Tighten cylinder head mounting bolts to specifications.
8. Tighten mounting bolts to specifications a second time.
9. Ensure sensor gear is secured to lefthand camshaft with lug.
10. Install left and righthand camshaft sprockets by aligning long bores, installing mounting bolts and fitting flush.
11. Assembly adjusting bolt, lock nut, plug, new sealing ring, O-ring, dowel sleeve, compression spring with cylindrical portion facing piston and chain tensioning piston.
12. Install chain tensioning piston with guide lugs in bow cover, then install compression spring and tighten plug to specifications.
13. Press bow cover briefly toward chain and measure distance to rail.
14. Press bow cover firmly and measure distance to rail.
15. Adjust difference between measurements to 0.217–0.256 inch using adjusting screw. Tighten lock nut and install new cap.
16. Tighten left then righthand camshaft mounting bolts to specifications.
17. Install timing chain guide rail and secure with tab.
18. Install rail mounting bolt and tighten.
19. Ensure dowel sleeves are properly installed, then coat upper and lower edges with Hylomar SQ 32 M, or equivalent.
20. Install new seals with bead facing case cover. Secure seals using Hylomar SQ 32 M, or equivalent.
21. Install chain cover, then the oil filler plug mounting bolt and fit flush.
22. Install oil drip tray mounting bolt and fit flush.
23. Install secondary air induction pipe bracket mounting bolt and fit flush.
24. Tighten mounting bolts to specifications.
25. Install CMP sensor and tighten mounting bolt, as required.
26. Install non-return valve as outlined under "Exhaust Manifold, Replace."
27. Install both distributor housing as outlined in "Electrical Section."
28. Install fan coupling.

FRONT COVER SEAL

REPLACE

1. Remove vibration damper as outlined under "Crankshaft Damper, Replace."
2. Remove seal using extractor tools Nos. 11 2 383 and 11 1 210, or equivalents.
3. Reverse procedure to install new seal coated with suitable engine oil using installer bushing tool No. 11 5 110, or equivalent.

TIMING CHAIN

REPLACE

Refer to "Front Cover, Replace."

TIMING CHAIN TENSIONER

REPLACE

Refer to "Front Cover, Replace."

CAMSHAFT

REPLACE

1. Remove both valve covers as outlined under "Valve Cover, Replace."
2. Remove spark plugs.
3. Remove splash guard.
4. Remove rocker arms as outlined under "Rocker Arm, Replace."
5. Remove upper timing case cover as outlined under "Front Cover, Replace."
6. Remove mounting bolts and oil injector strip.
7. Remove mounting bolts, bearing caps and camshaft.
8. Reverse procedure to install, noting the following:
   a. Bearing caps are matched to cylinder head and should be installed in original position.

b. Tighten mounting nuts to specifications.

MAIN & ROD BEARINGS

Main Bearings

1. Install new bearing cover bolts. **Do not wash coating off.**
2. **Torque** bearing cover bolts to 15 ft. lbs.
3. Tighten bolts an additional 70°.
4. Tighten M11 bolts an additional 100°.
5. Install new bearing cover support bolts.
6. **Torque** cover support bolts to 15 ft. lbs.
7. Tighten an additional 45°.
8. Install new support sleeve bolts.
9. **Torque** support sleeve bolts to 88 inch lbs.

Rod Bearings

1. Oil bolt threads.
2. **Torque** to 44 inch lbs.
3. **Torque** to 15 ft. lbs.
4. Tighten an additional 70°.

CRANKSHAFT REAR OIL SEAL

REPLACE

1. Remove transmission as outlined in "Automatic Transmission" section.
2. Drain engine oil into suitable container.
3. Block flywheel using locking tool No. 11 2 070, or equivalent.
4. Remove mounting bolts and flywheel.
5. Loosen lower mounting bolts.
6. Remove rear cover mounting bolts.
7. Disconnect oil pan gasket from end cover.
8. Remove end cover.
9. Remove seal using driver tools Nos. 11 1 230 and 00 5 500, or equivalent.
10. Reverse procedure to install, noting the following:
    a. Coat contact joint edges with thin, uniform layer of Hylomare SQ 32, or equivalent.
    b. Coat sealing ring lip with oil.
    c. Install sealing ring using installed tool No, 11 2 390, or equivalent.
    d. Install new mounting bolt washers.
    e. Tighten mounting bolts to specifications.

OIL PAN

REPLACE

LOWER

1. Remove engine splash guard.
2. Open main flow oil filter cover and allow engine oil to return to sump.
3. Drain engine oil into suitable container.
4. Disconnect engine oil level switch connector.
5. Remove mounting bolts and oil pan. Remove oil level switch
6. Reverse procedure to install. Tighten new mounting bolts to specifications.

UPPER

1. Raise hood to service position and lock into place.
2. Turn screws 90° and remove cylinder head cover.
3. Remove air filter housing with Mass Air Flow (MAF) sensor.
4. Remove left and righthand engine mount nuts.
5. Support engine with engine support tool No. 00 0 200, or equivalent.
6. Raise engine approximately 0.216–0.315 inch.
7. Disconnect oil dipstick guide tube from oil pan.
8. Remove mounting bolt and guide tube from valve cover.
9. Remove lower oil pan as outlined under "Lower."
10. Remove alternator and air conditioning compressor drive belts.
11. Remove mounting bolts and power steering pump hydraulic line bracket.
12. Remove mounting bolts and power steering pump, then place aside with lines connected. **Do not tension lines.**
13. Disconnect alternator battery positive lead.
14. Loosen engine mounting arm clip.
15. Remove mounting bolts and oil pan protective tube.
16. Remove mounting bolts and retaining plate from front axle support.
17. Remove mounting bolts and heat baffle plate.
18. Disconnect crankcase positive battery lead bracket.
19. Disconnect engine oil return line from pan.
20. Disconnect steering shaft from steering gear.
21. Disconnect oil cooler line bracket from front axle support.
22. Support front axle support with fixture tool No. 31 2 220, or equivalent, and suitable jack.
23. Remove mounting bolts and lower front axle support approximately 2.36 inches.
24. Remove mounting bolts inside oil pan.
25. Remove oil pump as outlined under "Oil Pump, Replace."
26. Remove sealing cover mounting bolts.
27. Remove mounting bolts and oil pan.
28. Reverse procedure to install, noting the following:
    a. Coat joint edges with Hylomar SQ 32 M, or equivalent sealing compound.
    b. Install new gasket.
    c. Install mounting bolts into transmission end without preload.
    d. Tighten engine, then transmission end mounting bolts.
    e. Install new oil return line sealing ring.
    f. Replace oil dipstick guide tube O-ring, as required.

OIL PUMP

REPLACE

1. Remove upper oil pan as outlined under "Oil Pan, Replace."
2. Remove mounting bolts and oil pump sprocket with chain.
3. Remove mounting bolts, nuts and oil pump.
4. Reverse procedure to install, noting the following:
    a. Tighten mounting bolts to specifications.
    b. Adjust chain deflection to 0.276 inch.

SERPENTINE DRIVE BELT

Refer to **Fig. 2** for serpentine drive belt routing.

REPLACEMENT

1. If reusing belt, mark rotational direction for installation.
2. Lock belt pulley in position using holding tool No. 11 5 050, or equivalent, then remove mounting nut using wrench tool No. 11 5 040, or equivalent. **Nut has lefthand threads.**
3. Remove fan clutch.
4. Remove engine splash shield.
5. Tighten alternator tensioning wheel bolt and compress belt tensioner.
6. Hold tensioner under tension and remove drive belt.
7. Tighten air conditioning compressor tensioning wheel bolt and compress belt tensioner.
8. Hold tensioner under tension and remove drive belt.
9. Reverse procedure to install.

COOLING SYSTEM BLEED

1. Set heater controls to maximum temperature and fan to low speed.
2. Run engine and flush engine cooling circuit with 3–4 short bursts to 4500–5000 RPM. **Do not run engine for more than 30 seconds.**
3. Close bleed screw when escaping coolant is free from air bubbles.
4. Run engine until thermostat opens.

THERMOSTAT

REPLACE

1. Partially drain cooling system.
2. Lock belt pulley in position using holding tool No. 11 5 050, or equivalent, then remove mounting nut using wrench tool No. 11 5 040, or equivalent. **Nut has lefthand threads.**
3. Remove fan clutch.
4. Remove non-return valve as outlined under "Exhaust Manifold, Replace."
5. Remove mounting bolts and thermostat cover.
6. Remove thermostat and gasket.
7. Reverse procedure to install, noting the following:
    a. Install thermostat with vent bore pointing upward.
    b. Install new gasket.
    c. Tighten mounting bolts to specifications.

WATER PUMP

REPLACE

1. Remove non-return valve as outlined under "Exhaust Manifold, Replace."
2. Raise and support vehicle, then drain cooling system into suitable container.
3. Disconnect coolant lever sensor connector.
4. Remove intake air filter housing.
5. Disconnect clamps and coolant expansion tank hose.
6. Open coolant expansion tank cap and remove vent plug.
7. Disconnect clip and remove expansion tank.
8. Disconnect AUC sensor, as required.
9. Remove expanding rivets and fan cowl.
10. Disconnect air conditioning compressor drive belt.
11. Disconnect and remove water pump coolant hoses.
12. Lock belt pulley in position using holding tool No. 11 5 050, or equivalent, then remove mounting nut using wrench tool No. 11 5 040, or equivalent. **Nut has lefthand threads.**
13. Remove fan clutch.
14. Remove mounting bolts and water pump pulley.
15. Remove vent hose from bracket and disconnect water pump clip.
16. Remove water pump mounting bolts.
17. Install three bolts in bores and evenly press water pump off engine.
18. Reverse procedure to install, noting the following:
    a. Install new O-rings coated with suitable anti-friction agent.
    b. Tighten mounting bolts to specifications.

RADIATOR

REPLACE

1. Raise and support vehicle, then drain coolant into suitable container.
2. Raise and support vehicle, then drain cooling system into suitable container.
3. Disconnect coolant lever sensor connector.
4. Remove intake air filter housing.
5. Disconnect clamps and coolant expansion tank hose.

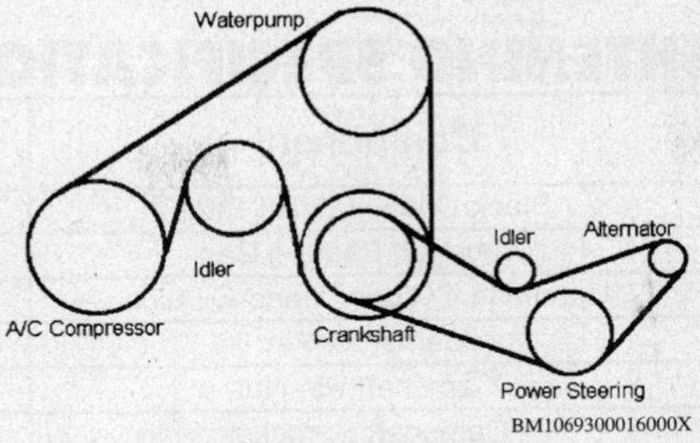

Fig. 2 Belt routing

6. Open coolant expansion tank cap and remove vent plug.
7. Disconnect clip and remove expansion tank.
8. Disconnect AUC sensor, as required.
9. Remove expanding rivets and fan cowl.
10. Disconnect air conditioning temperature switch connector.
11. Remove upper and lower coolant hose.
12. Disconnect radiator mounts using suitable screwdriver.
13. Remove radiator.
14. Reverse procedure to install.

FUEL PUMP

REPLACE

1. Relieve fuel system pressure as outlined under "Precautions."
2. Remove enough fuel from tank to ensure pump unit can be removed without spillage.
3. Remove rear seat cushion and rubber grommet.
4. Cut and fold insulating mat.
5. Remove mounting screws and cover.
6. Disconnect electrical connectors and fuel lines.
7. Remove ring nut using ring nut wrench tool No. 16 1 020, or equivalent.
8. Mark position of unit in fuel tank for installation alignment.
9. Lift and rotate unit from fuel tank. **Do not deform fuel level sensor arm or altitude sensor tube.**
10. Reverse procedure to install. Install new ring nut and seal.

FUEL FILTER

REPLACE

1. Relieve fuel pressure as outlined under "Precautions."
2. Remove mounting screws and fold lower trim aside.
3. Clamp fuel feed hose on both sides of fuel filter using clamping tools No. 13 3 010, or equivalent.
4. Disconnect clips and fuel lines.
5. Remove mounting bolt and fuel filter.
6. Reverse procedure to install. Ensure correct fuel flow direction.

TECHNICAL SERVICE BULLETINS

TIMING CHAIN WHINING

1998–99 750iL

On some of these models there may be whining at approximately 1000–1500 RPM at all engines temperatures.

This condition may be caused by normal timing chain operations.

To correct this condition install revised engine mounts and vibration dampers as follows:

1. Remove lower engine splash guards.
2. Loosen left and righthand engine mount nuts.
3. Remove exhaust system.
4. Install new center exhaust mounts (part No. 18 21 1 745).
5. Remove air filter housing upper section and engine cover.
6. Remove fan and two lower engine mount nuts.
7. Raise engine approximately 1 inch.
8. Install new engine mounts (righthand part No. 22 11 1 092 824 and lefthand part No. 22 11 1 092 823).
9. Replace engine mount hold down nuts with new engine mount vibration dampers (part No. 22 11 6 750 246) and **torque** to 31 ft. lbs.
10. Install engine cover and air filter housing.
11. Install fan.
12. Support transmission rear and instal new rear transmission mount (part No. 24 70 1 141 545).
13. Install exhaust system.
14. Install lower engine splash guard.

TIGHTENING SPECIFICATIONS

Year	Component	Torque, Ft. Lbs.
1998–2001	Block Coolant Drain Plug	18
	Camshaft Bearing Cap	⑧
	Camshaft Cylinder Head Oil Line	⑩
	Camshaft Pin	15
	Camshaft Pin Nut	88①
	Camshaft Sprocket	⑧
	Chain Tensioner Plug	30
	Chain Tensioner Plunger	52
	Connecting Rod	⑬
	Crankcase End Cover	⑧
	Crankshaft Increment Wheel	115①
	Cylinder Head	⑤
	Cylinder Head Cover	⑨
	Cylinder Head Cover Oil Trap	13
	Engine Mount	④
	Exhaust Manifold	⑧
	Fan	30
	Front Cover	⑧
	Flywheel	88
	Intake Manifold	⑧
	Main Bearing Caps	⑬
	Main Oil Duct Plug	25
	Oil Cooler Line	16
	Oil Drain Line	22
	Oil Drain Plug	⑪
	Oil Filter Cover	⑫
	Oil Filter Lines	⑥
	Oil Pan	③
	Oil Pump	18
	Oil Pump Cover	88①
	Oil Pump Sprocket	②
	Oil Spray Nozzle	106①
	Oxygen Sensor	41
	Thermostat Bleeder	71①
	Thermostat Housing	88①
	Timing Case	⑧
	Valve Cover	⑨
	Vibration Damper	⑦
	Water Pump	⑧

① — Inch lbs.
② — M6, 88 inch lbs.; M10, 35 ft. lbs.; M10 x 1, 18 ft. lbs.
③ — M6 8.8, 88 inch lbs.; M6 10.9, 106 inch lbs.; M8 8.8, 16 ft. lbs.
④ — M8, 16 ft. lbs.; M10, 35 ft. lbs.
⑤ — Refer to "Cylinder Head, Replace" for tightening specifications and sequence.
⑥ — M8, 16 ft. lbs.; M20, 30 ft. lbs.
⑦ — Refer to "Crankshaft Damper, Replace" for tighten specifications and sequence.
⑧ — M6, 88 inch lbs., M7, 11 ft. lbs.; M8, 16 ft. lbs.; M10, 35 ft. lbs.
⑨ — M6, 88 inch lbs., M7 & M8, 11 ft. lbs.
⑩ — M5, 44 inch lbs.; M8, 88 inch lbs.
⑪ — M12, 18 ft. lbs.; M22, 44 ft. lbs.
⑫ — M8, 16 ft. lbs.; M10 & 12, 24 ft. lbs.; Screw-On, 18 ft. lbs.
⑬ — Refer to "Main & Rod Bearings" for tightening specifications and sequence.

Clutch & Manual Transmission

NOTE: On Air Bag Equipped Models, Refer To "Air Bag System Precautions" Located In The Front Of This Manual For System Disarming & Arming Procedures.

NOTE: Prior To Performing Any Service Operations Listed In This Section, Consult The "Technical Service Bulletins" Section For Related Information.

INDEX

	Page No.
Adjustments	2-89
Clutch Pedal	2-89
Application Chart	2-89
Clutch, Replace	2-90
Less Self Adjusting Clutch (SAC)	2-90
With Self Adjusting Clutch (SAC)	2-90
Hydraulic System Service	2-89
Clutch Bleed	2-89
Slave Cylinder, Replace	2-89
Precautions	2-89
Air Bag Systems	2-89
Battery Ground Cable	2-89
Technical Service Bulletins	2-97
Oil Drain/Fill Plug Leak	2-97
Tightening Specifications	2-98
Transmission, Replace	2-90
318	2-94
323, 325, 328 & 330	2-94
525	2-96
528	2-96
530	2-97
540	2-97
M3	2-90
M5	2-91
X5	2-92
Z3	2-92

PRECAUTIONS

AIR BAG SYSTEMS

Refer to "Air Bag System Precautions" in the front of this manual for system disarming and arming procedures.

BATTERY GROUND CABLE

Prior to service, disconnect battery ground cable and isolate as required.

ADJUSTMENTS

CLUTCH PEDAL

All models use hydraulic clutch release mechanisms with automatic wear compensation. No clutch pedal adjustment is necessary.

HYDRAULIC SYSTEM SERVICE

CLUTCH BLEED

Check tool operating instructions. **Charging pressure must not exceed 29 psi.**

1. Raise and support vehicle.
2. Remove transmission underbody protection, as required.
3. Remove mounting nuts and clutch slave cylinder. Pressure line remains connected.
4. Install clutch bleeding tool No. 21 5 030, or equivalent, to slave cylinder.
5. Press piston rod completely into cylinder with spindle help.
6. Connect breather devise to brake fluid expansion tank.
7. Attach breather hose to breather valve.
8. Hold clutch slave cylinder in position with bleeding tool.
9. Open breather valve.
10. When brake fluid emerges without bubbles, withdraw piston rod on clutch slave cylinder with spindle help, then press back in.
11. Continue process until no air bubbles escape.
12. When no air bubbles escape, close breather valve.
13. Switch off breather devise and remove from brake fluid expansion tank.
14. Slowly retract clutch slave cylinder piston rod with bleeding tool.
15. Remove bleeding tool from clutch slave cylinder.
16. Install clutch slave cylinder on transmission.
17. Replace self-locking nuts and tighten to specifications.
18. Inspect expansion tank brake fluid level and correct.

SLAVE CYLINDER, REPLACE

1. **On 525, 528, 530 and 540 models,** remove microfilter housing.
2. **On all models,** remove transmission underbody protection.
3. Close clutch sensor supply hose using clamp tool No. 13 3 010, or equivalent.
4. Disconnect clutch slave cylinder pressure line.
5. Remove mounting nuts and slave cylinder. **Relieve clutch slave cylinder slowly, or cylinder may suck air in sealing sleeve.**
6. Reverse procedure to install, noting the following:
   a. Lightly coat pressure pin with suitable grease.
   b. Tighten mounting bolts and nuts to specifications.
   c. Bleed clutch system as described under "Hydraulic Clutch System Bleed."

CLUTCH

REPLACE

LESS SELF ADJUSTING CLUTCH (SAC)

REMOVAL

1. Remove transmission as outlined under "Transmission, Replace."
2. Hold flywheel with suitable locking holder.
3. Loosen clutch mounting bolts one turn at a time in diagonal sequence until clutch disc spring pressure is relieved.
4. Remove mounting bolts, pressure plate and disc.

INSTALLATION

Handle clutch disc carefully. Do not touch friction pad surfaces.

1. Install clutch disc. **Note "Engine Side/ Transmission Side" designations.**
2. Center disc with centering drive disc drift tool No. 21 2 130, or equivalent.
3. Fit pressure plate.
4. Install mounting bolts, then firmly tighten crosswise by hand one turn at a time.
5. Tighten mounting bolts to specifications.
6. Remove special tools.

WITH SELF ADJUSTING CLUTCH (SAC)

Self Adjusting Clutch (SAC) is identified by three recesses , each with one pressure piece on the adjustment ring and one compression spring.

REMOVAL

1. Remove transmission as outlined under "Transmission, Replace."
2. Hold flywheel with flywheel locking holder tool No. 11 2 170, or equivalent.
3. Install clamping fixture tool No. 21 2 160, or equivalent. **Only engage clutch housing in adjusting springs area.**
4. Pretension diaphragm spring to stop with clamping fixture.
5. Remove mounting bolts and SAC.
6. Remove clutch disc.

INSTALLATION

Handle clutch disc carefully. Do not touch friction pad surfaces.

New SAC

1. Install clutch disc using suitable clutch center pin tool (five-speed No. 21 2 142, or six-speed No. 21 2 141, or equivalents).
2. Push SAC onto flywheel dowel pins and tighten mounting bolts to specifications.
3. Remove locking piece using suitable Allen key turning clockwise. **There may be a slight plate spring snapping.**
4. Remove centering tools.

Used SAC

1. Mounting SAC on clamping fixture and block adjustment ring at one thrust piece using suitable screwdriver.
2. Turn adjustment ring on one thrust piece back to stop and secure with locating pin tool No. 21 2 154, or equivalent.
3. Screw spindle until diaphragm spring is pretensioned to stop.
4. Install clutch disc using suitable clutch center pin tool (five-speed No. 21 2 142, or six-speed No. 21 2 141, or equivalents).
5. Mount SAC on flywheel with alignment pins.
6. Tighten mounting bolts to specifications.
7. Release spindle until load is fully remove from diaphragm spring.
8. Remove clamping fixture and centering tools.

TRANSMISSION

REPLACE

M3

1998-99

1. Raise and support vehicle.
2. Disconnect oxygen sensor and retainer clip.
3. Remove exhaust pipe to manifold mounting nuts.
4. Remove exhaust bracket mounting bolts.
5. Disconnect exhaust system center suspension rubber rings.
6. Disconnect rear muffler left and righthand brackets.
7. Remove exhaust system.
8. Remove heat shield, then the brackets and exhaust suspension bar.
9. Remove transmission joint mounting nuts.
10. Remove propeller shaft as outlined in "Rear Axle & Suspension" section.
11. Disconnect retainer and selector rod from linkage joint. Remove shims.
12. Remove mounting nuts and clutch slave cylinder with lines connected.
13. Disconnect back-up lamp switch.
14. Remove mounting bolts and cross tube.
15. Install engine rear loading fixture tool No. 11 8 022, or equivalent, to left and righthand control arms, **Fig. 1.**
16. Ensure engine oil pan rest securely on tool.
17. Support transmission with suitable jack.
18. Remove mounting bolts and crossmember with rubber mount.
19. Lower jack.
20. Lower engine and transmission until cylinder head and manifold almost contact fire wall or heating connections.
21. Prevent engine from tilting forward by installing support fixture No. 11 8 021, or equivalent, to front axle support. Ensure engine oil pan rest securely on tool.
22. Remove housing lug spring using suitable screwdriver and swivel upward.
23. Remove transmission mounting bolts. **Ensure transmission is supported with suitable jack. Do not allow transmission to hang on input shaft.**
24. Remove transmission.
25. Reverse procedure to install, noting the following:
    a. Apply thin coat of suitable grease to transmission input shaft spline grooves and guide spigots.
    b. Remove release actuator. Then grease and install as previously described.
    c. Replace dowel sleeves, as required.
    d. Apply thin coat of suitable grease to bearing pin.
    e. Apply thin coat of suitable grease to selector rod.
    f. Preload rear muffler mount forward 0.59 inch.
    g. Align exhaust system carrier so it is free of tension.
    h. Replace exhaust pipe to manifold seals, as required.
    i. Install new exhaust pipe to manifold mounting nuts. Coat thread with CRC copper paste, or equivalent.

2001

1. Remove intake manifold as outlined in appropriate engine section.
2. Lock belt pulley in position using holding tool No. 11 5 050, or equivalent, then remove mounting nut using wrench tool No. 11 5 040, or equivalent. **Nut has lefthand threads.**
3. Remove fan clutch.
4. Remove mounting bolts and front axle support reinforcement plate.
5. Remove engine front underguard and underbody protection.
6. Remove both exhaust manifolds as outlined in appropriate engine section.
7. Remove exhaust manifold to pipe mounting nuts.
8. Support catalytic converters with suitable jack and support tool No. 31 2 220, or equivalent.
9. Remove intermediate pipes to catalytic converters mounting nuts and catalytic converters.
10. Remove mounting nuts and air deflector.
11. Support intermediate pipes with suitable jack and support tool No. 31 2 220, or equivalent.
12. Remove mounting bolts and reinforcement plates. Rear plate is connected to exhaust system with two rubber mounts.
13. Remove mounting bolts and body reinforcement strut.
14. Remove rear muffler to intermediate pipes mounting bolts and pipes.
15. Remove heat shields and rear underbody protection bracket.
16. Support transmission with suitable transmission jack.
17. Disconnect oxygen sensor cable from crossmember.
18. Remove mounting bolts and crossmember.
19. Disconnect propeller shaft from transmission output flange as outlined in "Rear Axle & Suspension" section.
20. Tie shaft aside.
21. Lower transmission until cylinder head touches bulkhead.
22. Support engine front with suitable transmission jack.
23. Remove clutch slave cylinder with pressure line connected. **Relieve clutch slave cylinder slowly, or cylinder may suck air in sealing sleeve.**
24. Disconnect locking clamp, then remove shift rod from joint. Remove disks.
25. Remove housing lug spring using suitable screwdriver and swivel upward.
26. Remove bearing pin.
27. Disconnect back-up lamp and gear detection switches' connectors.

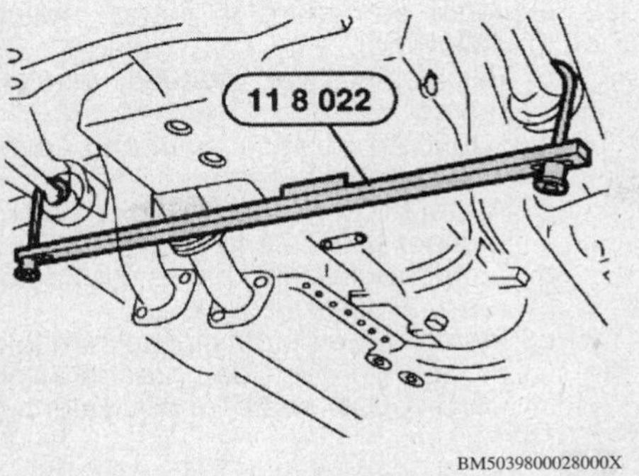

Fig. 1 Engine rear loading support

28. Support transmission with support tools Nos. 23 0 041 and 23 0 042, or equivalents, and suitable transmission jack.
29. Remove transmission mounting bolts. **Do not allow transmission to hand on input shaft.**
30. Remove transmission.
31. Reverse procedure to install, noting the following:
    a. Replace dowel sleeves, as required.
    b. Lubricate release unit and lever with suitable grease.
    c. Apply thin layer of suitable grease to taper splines and groove.
    d. Lubricate bearing pin and selector rod with suitable grease.
    e. Install new exhaust pipe to manifold mounting nuts. Coat threads using CRC copper paste, or equivalent.

M5

1. Remove rear splash guard.
2. **On models equipped with trailing hitch,** remove finisher strip.
3. **On all models,** disconnect expanding rivets, then remove left and righthand wheelhousing panels.
4. Remove mounting nuts and pull rear bumper back slightly.
5. **On models equipped with Park Distance Control (PDC),** disconnect PDC cable connectors.
6. **On all models,** remove rear bumper.
7. Raise and support vehicle.
8. Disconnect lefthand exhaust temperature sensor holder and connector.
9. Disconnect left and righthand oxygen and monitor sensors' connectors.
10. Support exhaust system with suitable jack and support tool No. 31 2 220, or equivalent.
11. Remove mounting bolts and disconnect catalytic converters' rear from body.
12. Remove catalytic converter to left and righthand exhaust manifolds mounting nuts.
13. Remove pipe clamps' mounting bolts.
14. Remove rear muffler inside left and righthand mounting nuts.
15. Remove rear mounting nuts and exhaust system.
16. Remove center, lefthand and righthand heat shields.
17. Disconnect back-up lamp and gear detection switches' connectors.
18. Remove clutch slave cylinder with pressure line connected. **Relieve clutch slave cylinder slowly, or cylinder may suck air in sealing sleeve.**
19. Remove speed sensor.
20. Support transmission with support tools Nos. 00 2 023, or equivalent, and suitable transmission jack.
21. Disconnect cable from crossmember.
22. Remove mounting bolts and crossmember.
23. Disconnect cable from transmission.
24. Remove mounting bolts and exhaust bracket.
25. Support engine using engine support spacer tool No. 11 7 360, or equivalent, between lefthand engine oil pan rib and front axle support.
26. Lower engine to rest rib on tool.
27. Disconnect propeller shaft from transmission output flange as outlined in "Rear Axle & Suspension" section.
28. Tie shaft aside.
29. Disconnect retainer, then remove selector rod from joint and washer.
30. Remove retaining clip with suitable screwdriver, then the bearing pin and selector arm.
31. Support transmission with support tools Nos. 23 0 041 and 23 0 042, or equivalents, and suitable transmission jack.
32. Lower transmission until engine oil pan is supported on spacer tool.
33. Remove transmission mounting bolts. **Do not allow transmission to hand on input shaft.**
34. Remove transmission.
35. Reverse procedure to install, noting the following:
    a. Replace dowel sleeves, as required.
    b. Lubricate release unit and lever with suitable grease.
    c. Apply thin layer of suitable grease to taper splines and groove.
    d. Lubricate bearing pin and selector rod with suitable grease.
    e. Install new exhaust pipe to manifold mounting nuts. Coat threads using CRC copper paste, or equivalent.

X5

1. Raise and support vehicle.
2. Remove mounting bolts and disconnect rear from intermediate muffler.
3. Measure pipe section length of replacement muffler, transfer measurement and cut exhaust pipes accordingly.
4. Remove rubber mounts' bolts and intermediate muffler. Remove rubber mounts and install on replacement muffler.
5. Remove front righthand and rear heat shields.
6. Remove mounting bolts and front axle support reinforcement plate.
7. Remove engine front underguard.
8. Disconnect stabilizer bar and slide it forward.
9. Remove mounting bolts and push front propeller shaft back.
10. Remove flexible disk with centering flange.
11. Disconnect propeller shaft from transfer case.
12. Remove mounting bolts and exhaust bracket.
13. Support transmission with support tools No. 23 0 130, or equivalent, and suitable transmission jack.
14. Disconnect propeller shaft as from transmission output flange outlined in "Rear Axle & Suspension" section.
15. Tie shaft aside.
16. Lower transmission. **Do not rest exhaust manifold on stabilizer bar.**
17. Remove clutch slave cylinder with pressure line connected. **Relieve clutch slave cylinder slowly, or cylinder may suck air in sealing sleeve.**
18. Disconnect back-up lamp switch connector.
19. Remove housing lug spring using suitable screwdriver and swivel upward.
20. Support engine front with suitable transmission jack.
21. Remove transmission mounting bolts. **Do not allow transmission to hand on input shaft.**
22. Remove transmission.
23. Reverse procedure to install, noting the following:
   a. Replace dowel sleeves, as required.
   b. Lubricate release unit and lever with suitable grease.
   c. Apply thin layer of suitable grease to taper splines and groove.
   d. Lubricate bearing pin and selector rod with suitable grease.
   e. Install new exhaust pipe to manifold mounting nuts. Coat threads using CRC copper paste, or equivalent.

Z3

M COUPE & ROADSTER

1998–2000

Refer to "1998–99 M3."

1.9

1. Raise and support vehicle.
2. Disconnect oxygen sensor and cable from holder.
3. Remove exhaust manifold to pipe mounting nuts.
4. Disconnect exhaust carrier clamp.
5. Disconnect rubber ring on differential carrier.
6. **On models equipped with bracket mount,** disconnect left and righthand rear muffler, then remove exhaust system.
7. **On models equipped with clamp,** loosen collar nut with clamp and remove exhaust system.
8. **On all models,** remove heat shield, then the brackets and exhaust suspension bar.
9. Remove transmission joint mounting nuts.
10. Remove propeller shaft as outlined in "Rear Axle & Suspension" section.
11. Remove retainer and selector rod from linkage joint. Remove washers.
12. Remove mounting nuts, then the clutch slave cylinder with pressure line connected. **Relieve clutch slave cylinder slowly, or cylinder may suck air in sealing sleeve.**
13. Disconnect back-up lamp switch and oxygen sensor connectors.
14. Remove cross tube.
15. Install engine rear loading fixture tool No. 11 8 022, or equivalent, to left and righthand control arms, **Fig. 1.**
16. Ensure engine oil pan rest securely on tool.
17. Support transmission with suitable jack.
18. Remove mounting bolts and crossmember with rubber mount.
19. Lower jack.
20. Lower engine and transmission until cylinder head and manifold almost contact fire wall or heating connections.
21. Remove housing lug spring using suitable screwdriver and swivel upward.
22. Remove shaft.
23. Remove transmission mounting bolts. **Ensure transmission is supported with suitable jack. Do not allow transmission to hang on input shaft.**
24. Remove transmission downward.
25. Reverse procedure to install, noting the following:
   a. Apply thin coat of suitable grease to transmission input shaft spline grooves and guide spigots.
   b. Remove release actuator. Then grease and install as previously described.
   c. Replace dowel sleeves, as required.
   d. Apply thin coat of suitable grease to bearing pin.
   e. Apply thin coat of suitable grease to selector rod.
   f. **On models with rear muffler bracket,** preload rubber mount forward 0.59 inch.
   g. **On all models,** install new exhaust system rubber rings as required.
   h. Install new exhaust manifold to pipe seal.
   i. Lightly coat exhaust manifold threads with suitable copper paste and install new self-locking nuts.

2.3

1. Raise and support vehicle.
2. Remove exhaust pipe to manifold mounting nuts.
3. Remove exhaust bracket mounting bolts.
4. Support exhaust system with suitable jack and support tool No. 31 2 220, or equivalent.
5. Remove mounting bolts and exhaust system reinforcement plates. Front plate is connected to exhaust system with rubber mounts.
6. Remove muffler front and rear rubber mount nuts.
7. Remove exhaust system.
8. Remove heat shield, then the brackets and exhaust suspension bar.
9. Remove transmission joint mounting nuts.
10. Remove propeller shaft as outlined in "Rear Axle & Suspension" section.
11. Disconnect retainer and selector rod from linkage joint. Remove shims.
12. Remove mounting nuts and clutch slave cylinder with lines connected.
13. Disconnect back-up lamp switch.
14. Remove mounting bolts and cross tube.
15. Remove heater bulkhead.
16. Remove injector pipe cover and support engine with engine support tool No. 00 0 200, or equivalent.
17. Support transmission with suitable jack.
18. Remove mounting bolts and cross-member with rubber mount.
19. Lower jack.
20. Lower engine and transmission until cylinder head and manifold almost contact fire wall or heating connections.
21. Remove housing lug spring using suitable screwdriver and swivel upward.
22. Remove transmission mounting bolts. **Ensure transmission is supported with suitable jack. Do not allow transmission to hang on input shaft.**
23. Remove transmission.
24. Reverse procedure to install, noting the following:
    a. Apply thin coat of suitable grease to transmission input shaft spline grooves and guide spigots.
    b. Remove release actuator. Then grease and install as previously described.
    c. Replace dowel sleeves, as required.
    d. Apply thin coat of suitable grease to bearing pin.
    e. Apply thin coat of suitable grease to selector rod.
    f. Align exhaust system carrier so it is free of tension.
    g. Replace exhaust pipe to manifold seals, as required.
    h. Install new exhaust pipe to manifold mounting nuts. Coat thread with CRC copper paste, or equivalent.

2.5

Refer to "325 & 330" under "323, 325, 328 & 330."

2.8

1998

1. Raise and support vehicle.
2. Disconnect oxygen sensor connector.
3. Remove exhaust pipe to manifold mounting nuts.
4. Remove exhaust bracket mounting bolts.
5. Support exhaust system with suitable jack and support tool No. 31 2 220, or equivalent.
6. Disconnect exhaust center mount.
7. Disconnect rear muffler left and right-hand brackets.
8. Disconnect vacuum put hose.
9. Remove exhaust system.
10. Remove heat shield, then the brackets and exhaust suspension bar.
11. Remove transmission joint mounting nuts.
12. Remove propeller shaft as outlined in "Rear Axle & Suspension" section.
13. Disconnect retainer and selector rod from linkage joint. Remove shims.
14. Remove mounting nuts and clutch slave cylinder with lines connected.
15. Disconnect back-up lamp switch.
16. Remove mounting bolts and cross tube.
17. Remove heater bulkhead.
18. Remove injector pipe cover and support engine with engine support tool No. 00 0 200, or equivalent.
19. Support transmission with suitable jack.
20. Remove mounting bolts and cross-member with rubber mount.
21. Lower jack.
22. Lower engine and transmission until cylinder head and manifold almost contact fire wall or heating connections.
23. Remove housing lug spring using suitable screwdriver and swivel upward.
24. Remove transmission mounting bolts. **Ensure transmission is supported with suitable jack. Do not allow transmission to hang on input shaft.**
25. Remove transmission.
26. Reverse procedure to install, noting the following:
    a. Apply thin coat of suitable grease to transmission input shaft spline grooves and guide spigots.
    b. Remove release actuator. Then grease and install as previously described.
    c. Replace dowel sleeves, as required.
    d. Apply thin coat of suitable grease to bearing pin.
    e. Apply thin coat of suitable grease to selector rod.
    f. Preload rear muffler mount forward 0.59 inch.
    g. Align exhaust system carrier so it is free of tension.
    h. Replace exhaust pipe to manifold seals, as required.
    i. Install new exhaust pipe to manifold mounting nuts. Coat thread with CRC copper paste, or equivalent.

1999–2000

Refer to "2.3."

3.0

1. Raise and support vehicle.
2. Support exhaust system with suitable jack and support tool No. 31 2 220, or equivalent.
3. Remove exhaust pipe to manifold mounting nuts.
4. Remove exhaust bracket mounting bolts.
5. Remove mounting bolts and exhaust system reinforcement plates. Front plate is connected to exhaust system with rubber mounts.
6. Disconnect vacuum hose from unit at rear of rear muffler.
7. Remove muffler left and righthand rubber mount nuts.
8. Remove exhaust system.
9. Remove heat shield, then the brackets and exhaust suspension bar.
10. Remove transmission joint mounting nuts.
11. Remove propeller shaft as outlined in "Rear Axle & Suspension" section.
12. Disconnect retainer and selector rod from linkage joint. Remove shims.
13. Remove mounting nuts and clutch slave cylinder with lines connected.
14. Disconnect back-up lamp switch.
15. Remove mounting bolts and cross tube.
16. Install engine rear loading fixture tool No. 11 8 022, or equivalent, to left and righthand control arms, **Fig. 1.**
17. Ensure engine oil pan rest securely on tool.
18. Support transmission with suitable jack.
19. Remove mounting bolts and cross-member with rubber mount.
20. Lower jack.
21. Lower engine and transmission until cylinder head and manifold almost contact fire wall or heating connections.
22. Prevent engine from tilting forward by installing support fixture No. 11 8 021, or equivalent, to front axle support. Ensure engine oil pan rest securely on tool.
23. Remove housing lug spring using suitable screwdriver and swivel upward.

24. Remove transmission mounting bolts. **Ensure transmission is supported with suitable jack. Do not allow transmission to hang on input shaft.**
25. Remove transmission.
26. Reverse procedure to install, noting the following:
    a. Apply thin coat of suitable grease to transmission input shaft spline grooves and guide spigots.
    b. Remove release actuator. Then grease and install as previously described.
    c. Replace dowel sleeves, as required.
    d. Apply thin coat of suitable grease to bearing pin.
    e. Apply thin coat of suitable grease to selector rod.
    f. Preload rear muffler mount forward 0.59 inch.
    g. Align exhaust system carrier so it is free of tension.
    h. Replace exhaust pipe to manifold seals, as required.
    i. Install new exhaust pipe to manifold mounting nuts. Coat thread with CRC copper paste, or equivalent.

318

Refer to "Z3 1.9."

323, 325, 328 & 330

323IS & 328IS & 1998-99 328I & 1998 323I & 1999 323I & 328I CONVERTIBLES

1. **On 323is and 1998 323i and 1999 323i & 328i convertibles models equipped with ASC+T,** proceed as follows:
    a. Disconnect clip and Mass Air Flow (MAF) sensor connector.
    b. Disconnect clip and remove air intake hose with MAF sensor.
    c. Disconnect throttle body cables.
    d. Remove mounting bolts and throttle body.
2. **On all models,** raise and support vehicle.
3. Disconnect oxygen sensor connector.
4. Remove exhaust pipe to manifold mounting nuts.
5. Remove exhaust bracket mounting bolts.
6. Support exhaust system with suitable jack and support tool No. 31 2 220, or equivalent.
7. Disconnect exhaust center mount.
8. Disconnect rear muffler left and righthand brackets.
9. Disconnect vacuum put hose.
10. Remove exhaust system.
11. Remove heat shield, then the brackets and exhaust suspension bar.
12. Remove transmission joint mounting nuts.
13. Remove propeller shaft as outlined in "Rear Axle & Suspension" section.
14. Disconnect retainer and selector rod from linkage joint. Remove shims.
15. Remove mounting nuts and clutch slave cylinder with lines connected.
16. Disconnect back-up lamp switch.
17. Remove mounting bolts and cross tube.
18. Remove heater bulkhead.
19. Remove injector pipe cover and support engine with engine support tool No. 00 0 200, or equivalent.
20. Support transmission with suitable jack.
21. Remove mounting bolts and crossmember with rubber mount.
22. Lower jack.
23. Lower engine and transmission until cylinder head and manifold almost contact fire wall or heating connections.
24. Remove housing lug spring using suitable screwdriver and swivel upward.
25. Remove transmission mounting bolts. **Ensure transmission is supported with suitable jack. Do not allow transmission to hang on input shaft.**
26. Remove transmission.
27. Reverse procedure to install, noting the following:
    a. Apply thin coat of suitable grease to transmission input shaft spline grooves and guide spigots.
    b. Remove release actuator. Then grease and install as previously described.
    c. Replace dowel sleeves, as required.
    d. Apply thin coat of suitable grease to bearing pin.
    e. Apply thin coat of suitable grease to selector rod.
    f. Preload rear muffler mount forward 0.59 inch.
    g. Align exhaust system carrier so it is free of tension.
    h. Replace exhaust pipe to manifold seals, as required.
    i. Install new exhaust pipe to manifold mounting nuts. Coat thread with CRC copper paste, or equivalent.

2000 323CI & 323I & 1999 323I SEDAN

1. Remove air intake hood, then the microfilter housing and heater bulkhead.
2. Raise and support vehicle, then remove reinforcement plate and engine underguard.
3. Remove mounting bolts and front axle support reinforcement.
4. Remove exhaust pipe to manifold mounting nuts.
5. Remove exhaust bracket mounting bolts.
6. Support exhaust system with suitable jack and support tool No. 31 2 220, or equivalent.
7. Remove mounting bolts and exhaust system reinforcement plates. Front plate is connected to exhaust system with rubber mounts.
8. Remove muffler front and rear rubber mount nuts.
9. Remove exhaust system.
10. Remove exhaust heat shields, then the mounting bolts and exhaust bracket.
11. Support transmission with suitable transmission jack.
12. Remove mounting bolts and crossmember.
13. Remove transmission joint mounting nuts.
14. Disconnect propeller shaft from transmission output flange as outlined in "Rear Axle & Suspension" section.
15. Tie propeller shaft aside.
16. Lower transmission until cylinder head touches firewall.
17. Install engine rear loading fixture tool No. 11 8 022, or equivalent, to left and righthand control arms, **Fig. 1.**
18. Ensure engine oil pan rest securely on tool.
19. Remove mounting nuts, then the clutch slave cylinder with pressure line connected. **Relieve clutch slave cylinder slowly, or cylinder may suck air in sealing sleeve.**
20. Disconnect locking clamp, then remove shift rod from joint. Remove disks.
21. Remove housing lug spring using suitable screwdriver and swivel upward.
22. Remove bearing pin and disconnect back-up lamp connector.
23. Remove transmission mounting bolts. **Ensure transmission is supported with suitable jack. Do not allow transmission to hang on input shaft.**
24. Pull transmission as far to rear as possible, turn 10° counterclockwise and remove it.
25. Reverse procedure to install, noting the following:
    a. Apply thin coat of suitable grease to transmission input shaft spline grooves and guide spigots.
    b. Lubricate shift rod pin with suitable grease.
    c. Align exhaust system carrier so it is free of tension.
    d. Replace exhaust pipe to manifold seals, as required.
    e. Install new exhaust pipe to manifold mounting nuts. Coat thread with CRC copper paste, or equivalent.
    f. Install new reinforcement plate mounting bolts.

325CI, 325I, 330CI & 330I

1. Remove air intake hood, then the microfilter housing and heater bulkhead.
2. Raise and support vehicle, then remove reinforcement plate and engine underguard
3. Remove mounting bolts and front axle support reinforcement.
4. Support exhaust system with suitable jack and support tool No. 31 2 220, or equivalent.
5. Remove exhaust pipe to manifold mounting nuts.
6. Remove exhaust bracket mounting bolts.
7. **On sedan and couple models,** remove mounting bolts and exhaust system reinforcement plates. Front plate is connected to exhaust system with rubber mounts.
8. **On convertible models,** remove mounting bolts and body reinforcement, then the reinforcement plate mounting bolts. Reinforcement plate is

connected to exhaust system with rubber mounts.
9. **On sedan and couple models,** disconnect vacuum hose from unit at rear of rear muffler.
10. **On all models,** remove muffler left and righthand rubber mount nuts.
11. Remove exhaust system.
12. Remove exhaust heat shields, then the mounting bolts and exhaust bracket.
13. Support transmission with suitable transmission jack.
14. Remove mounting bolts and crossmember.
15. Remove transmission joint mounting nuts.
16. Disconnect propeller shaft from transmission output flange as outlined in "Rear Axle & Suspension" section.
17. Tie propeller shaft aside.
18. Lower transmission until cylinder head touches firewall.
19. Install engine rear loading fixture tool No. 11 8 022, or equivalent, to left and righthand control arms, **Fig. 1.**
20. Ensure engine oil pan rest securely on tool.
21. Remove mounting nuts, then the clutch slave cylinder with pressure line connected. **Relieve clutch slave cylinder slowly, or cylinder may suck air in sealing sleeve.**
22. Disconnect locking clamp, then remove shift rod from joint. Remove disks.
23. Remove housing lug spring using suitable screwdriver and swivel upward.
24. Remove bearing pin and disconnect back-up lamp connector.
25. Remove transmission mounting bolts. **Ensure transmission is supported with suitable jack. Do not allow transmission to hang on input shaft.**
26. Pull transmission as far to rear as possible, turn 10° counterclockwise and remove it.
27. Reverse procedure to install, noting the following:
    a. Apply thin coat of suitable grease to transmission input shaft spline grooves and guide spigots.
    b. Lubricate shift rod pin with suitable grease.
    c. Align exhaust system carrier so it is free of tension.
    d. Replace exhaust pipe to manifold seals, as required.
    e. Install new exhaust pipe to manifold mounting nuts. Coat thread with CRC copper paste, or equivalent.
    f. Install new reinforcement plate mounting bolts.

325XI & 330XI

1. Remove air intake hood.
2. Disconnect and remove fan cowl.
3. Remove microfilter housing and heater bulkhead.
4. Support engine with engine support tool No. 00 0 200, or equivalent.
5. Remove left and righthand engine mount nuts.
6. Remove front, middle and rear engine underguards.
7. Support exhaust system with suitable jack and support tool No. 31 2 220, or equivalent.
8. Remove exhaust pipe to manifold mounting nuts.
9. Remove exhaust bracket mounting bolts.
10. **On sedan and couple models,** remove mounting bolts and exhaust system reinforcement plates. Front plate is connected to exhaust system with rubber mounts.
11. **On convertible models,** remove mounting bolts and body reinforcement, then the reinforcement plate mounting bolts. Reinforcement plate is connected to exhaust system with rubber mounts.
12. **On sedan and couple models,** disconnect vacuum hose from unit at rear of rear muffler.
13. **On all models,** remove muffler left and righthand rubber mount nuts.
14. Remove exhaust system.
15. Remove center and rear underbody protection panels.
16. Remove mounting nuts and front propeller shaft.
17. Remove mounting bolts and exhaust bracket.
18. Remove transmission joint mounting nuts.
19. Disconnect propeller shaft from transmission output flange as outlined in "Rear Axle & Suspension" section.
20. Tie propeller shaft aside.
21. Remove front axle support righthand heat shield and righthand engine underguard bracket.
22. Remove mounting nuts, then the clutch slave cylinder with pressure line connected. **Relieve clutch slave cylinder slowly, or cylinder may suck air in sealing sleeve.**
23. Remove back-up lamp switch connector.
24. Support transmission and transfer case using support tool No. 23 0 140, or equivalent, and suitable transmission jack.
25. Disconnect transmission cable.
26. Remove mounting bolts and crossmember.
27. Disconnect transfer case vent line.
28. Remove transfer case as outlined in "Transfer Case" section.
29. Lower transmission.
30. Disconnect locking clamp, then remove selector rod from joint. Remove disks.
31. Remove housing lug spring using suitable screwdriver and swivel upward.
32. Remove bearing pin.
33. Disconnect steering shaft from steering gear.
34. Raise engine and remove lefthand mount. Ensure angle provides access to top righthand engine mount.
35. Remove mounting bolt and press exhaust flap vacuum tank aside.
36. Remove transmission mounting bolts. **Ensure transmission is supported with suitable jack. Do not allow transmission to hang on input shaft.**
37. Remove transmission as far as possible to rear and turn counterclockwise.
38. Remove transmission.
39. Reverse procedure to install, noting the following:
    a. Apply thin coat of suitable grease to transmission input shaft spline grooves and guide spigots.
    b. Remove release actuator. Then grease and install as previously described.
    c. Replace dowel sleeves, as required.
    d. Apply thin coat of suitable grease to bearing pin.
    e. Apply thin coat of suitable grease to selector rod.
    f. Lubricate bearing pin and selector rod with suitable grease.

328CI & 2000 328I & 1999 328I SEDANS

1. Remove air intake hood, then the microfilter housing and heater bulkhead.
2. Raise and support vehicle, then remove reinforcement plate and engine underguard
3. Remove mounting bolts and front axle support reinforcement.
4. Remove exhaust pipe to manifold mounting nuts.
5. Remove exhaust bracket mounting bolts.
6. Support exhaust system with suitable jack and support tool No. 31 2 220, or equivalent.
7. Remove mounting bolts and exhaust system reinforcement plates. Front plate is connected to exhaust system with rubber mounts.
8. Remove muffler front and rear rubber mount nuts.
9. Remove exhaust system.
10. Remove exhaust heat shields, then the mounting bolts and exhaust bracket.
11. Support transmission with suitable transmission jack.
12. Remove mounting bolts and crossmember.
13. Remove transmission joint mounting nuts.
14. Disconnect propeller shaft from transmission output flange as outlined in "Rear Axle & Suspension" section.
15. Tie propeller shaft aside.
16. Lower transmission until cylinder head touches firewall.
17. Install engine rear loading fixture tool No. 11 8 022, or equivalent, to left and righthand control arms, **Fig. 1.**
18. Ensure engine oil pan rest securely on tool.
19. Remove mounting nuts, then the clutch slave cylinder with pressure line connected. **Relieve clutch slave cylinder slowly, or cylinder may suck air in sealing sleeve.**
20. Disconnect locking clamp, then remove shift rod from joint. Remove disks.
21. Remove housing lug spring using suitable screwdriver and swivel upward.
22. Remove bearing pin and disconnect back-up lamp connector.
23. Remove transmission mounting bolts. **Ensure transmission is supported**

with suitable jack. Do not allow transmission to hang on input shaft.

24. Pull transmission as far to rear as possible, turn 10° counterclockwise and remove it.
25. Reverse procedure to install, noting the following:
    a. Apply thin coat of suitable grease to transmission input shaft spline grooves and guide spigots.
    b. Lubricate shift rod pin with suitable grease.
    c. Align exhaust system carrier so it is free of tension.
    d. Replace exhaust pipe to manifold seals, as required.
    e. Install new exhaust pipe to manifold mounting nuts. Coat thread with CRC copper paste, or equivalent.
    f. Install new reinforcement plate mounting bolts.

525

SEDAN

1. Remove mounting bolts and splash guard.
2. Support exhaust system with suitable jack and support tool No. 31 2 220, or equivalent.
3. Remove mounting bolts and disconnect catalytic converters' rear from body.
4. Remove exhaust pipe to manifold mounting bolts.
5. Remove exhaust carrier mounting bolts and nuts.
6. Remove center muffler bracket mounting bolt.
7. Remove rear muffler bracket mounting bolt.
8. Remove exhaust system.
9. Remove front splash guard.
10. Remove mounting bolts and reinforcement carrier.
11. Remove exhaust heat shields.
12. Remove transmission joint mounting nuts.
13. Disconnect propeller shaft from transmission output flange as outlined in "Rear Axle & Suspension" section.
14. Tie propeller shaft aside.
15. Remove rear heat shield.
16. Disconnect back-up lamp connector.
17. Remove mounting nuts, then the clutch slave cylinder with pressure line connected. **Relieve clutch slave cylinder slowly, or cylinder may suck air in sealing sleeve.**
18. Disconnect links and swivel stabilizer bar upward.
19. Support transmission with suitable transmission jack.
20. Remove mounting bolts and crossmember.
21. Lower transmission.
22. Disconnect retainer, then remove selector rod from joint. Remove washers.
23. Disconnect clip using suitable screwdriver, then remove bearing pin and selector arm.
24. Remove transmission mounting bolts. **Ensure transmission is supported with suitable jack. Do not allow transmission to hang on input shaft.**
25. Remove transmission.
26. Reverse procedure to install, noting the following:
    a. Replace dowel sleeves, as required.
    b. Lubricate release unit and lever with suitable grease.
    c. Apply thin layer of suitable grease to taper splines and groove.
    d. Lubricate bearing pin and selector rod with suitable grease.
    e. Align exhaust system carrier so it is free of tension.
    f. Install new exhaust pipe to manifold gaskets.
    g. Install new exhaust mounting bolts. Coat threads with CRC copper paste, or equivalent.

WAGON

1. Remove mounting bolts and splash guard.
2. Support exhaust system with suitable jack and support tool No. 31 2 220, or equivalent.
3. Remove mounting bolts and disconnect catalytic converters' rear from body.
4. Remove exhaust pipe to manifold mounting bolts.
5. Remove exhaust carrier mounting bolts and nuts.
6. Remove center muffler bracket mounting bolt.
7. Remove rear muffler bracket mounting bolt.
8. Remove exhaust system.
9. Remove exhaust heat shields.
10. Disconnect cable from crossmember.
11. Support transmission with suitable transmission jack.
12. Remove mounting bolts and crossmember.
13. Remove propeller shaft as outlined in "Rear Axle & Suspension" section.
14. Remove transmission underbody protection bracket and heat shield.
15. Disconnect back-up lamp connector and cable retainers.
16. Remove mounting nuts, then the clutch slave cylinder with pressure line connected. **Relieve clutch slave cylinder slowly, or cylinder may suck air in sealing sleeve.**
17. Disconnect links and swivel stabilizer bar upward.
18. Support transmission with suitable transmission jack.
19. Remove mounting bolts and crossmember.
20. Support engine with support tool No. 11 7 370, or equivalent, between engine oil pan and front axle support.
21. Lower transmission.
22. Support front of engine with suitable transmission jack.
23. Disconnect retains, then remove selector rod from joint. Remove spacers.
24. Disconnect clip using suitable screwdriver, then remove bearing pin and selector arm.
25. Remove transmission mounting bolts. **Ensure transmission is supported with suitable jack. Do not allow transmission to hang on input shaft.**
26. Remove transmission.
27. Reverse procedure to install, noting the following:
    a. Replace dowel sleeves, as required.
    b. Lubricate release unit and lever with suitable grease.
    c. Apply thin layer of suitable grease to taper splines and groove.
    d. Lubricate bearing pin and selector rod with suitable grease.
    e. Align exhaust system carrier so it is free of tension.
    f. Install new exhaust pipe to manifold gaskets.
    g. Install new exhaust mounting bolts. Coat threads with CRC copper paste, or equivalent.

528

1. Remove mounting bolts and splash guard.
2. Disconnect oxygen sensor connector.
3. Remove mounting bolts and disconnect catalytic converters' rear from body.
4. Support exhaust system with suitable jack and support tool No. 31 2 220, or equivalent.
5. Remove exhaust pipe to manifold mounting bolts.
6. Remove exhaust carrier mounting bolts and nuts.
7. Remove mounting nut and exhaust system.
8. Remove exhaust heat shields.
9. Disconnect cable from crossmember.
10. Support transmission with suitable transmission jack.
11. Remove mounting bolts and crossmember.
12. Remove propeller shaft as outlined in "Rear Axle & Suspension" section.
13. Remove transmission underbody protection bracket and heat shield.
14. Disconnect back-up lamp connector and cable retainers.
15. Remove mounting nuts, then the clutch slave cylinder with pressure line connected. **Relieve clutch slave cylinder slowly, or cylinder may suck air in sealing sleeve.**
16. Disconnect links and swivel stabilizer bar upward.
17. Support transmission with suitable transmission jack.
18. Remove mounting bolts and crossmember.
19. Support engine with support tool No. 11 7 370, or equivalent, between engine oil pan and front axle support.
20. Lower transmission.
21. Support front of engine with suitable transmission jack.
22. Disconnect retains, then remove selector rod from joint. Remove spacers.
23. Disconnect clip using suitable screwdriver, then remove bearing pin and selector arm.
24. Remove transmission mounting bolts. **Ensure transmission is supported with suitable jack. Do not allow**

transmission to hang on input shaft.

25. Remove transmission.
26. Reverse procedure to install, noting the following:
    a. Replace dowel sleeves, as required.
    b. Lubricate release unit and lever with suitable grease.
    c. Apply thin layer of suitable grease to taper splines and groove.
    d. Lubricate bearing pin and selector rod with suitable grease.
    e. Align exhaust system carrier so it is free of tension.
    f. Install new exhaust pipe to manifold gaskets.
    g. Install new exhaust mounting bolts. Coat threads with CRC copper paste, or equivalent.

530

Refer to "525 Wagon."

540

1. Remove noise insulation cover by pressing interlocks down.
2. Raise and support vehicle.
3. Support exhaust system with suitable jack and support tool No. 31 2 220, or equivalent.
4. Remove mounting bolts and disconnect catalytic converters' rear from body.
5. Remove catalytic converter to left and righthand exhaust manifolds mounting nuts.
6. Remove rear mounting nut and exhaust system.
7. Remove center, lefthand and righthand heat shields.
8. Remove front axle support lefthand heat shield.
9. Disconnect oxygen sensor cables from crossmember and transmission.
10. Disconnect back-up lamp switch connector, then the cable from crossmember and transmission.
11. Disconnect connector, then remove mounting bolts and impulse sensor. Record number of shims between transmission housing and pulse sensor.
12. Support transmission with support tools Nos. 23 0 040 and 23 0 042, or equivalents, and suitable transmission jack.
13. Remove mounting bolts and crossmember.
14. Disconnect propeller shaft from transmission output flange as outlined in "Rear Axle & Suspension" section.
15. Tie propeller shaft aside.
16. Support engine using engine support spacer tool No. 11 7 310, or equivalent, between engine oil pan and front axle support.
17. Ensure center track rod is not excessively loaded when transmission is removed by turning front wheels to righthand lock.
18. Lower transmission until engine oil pan is supported on spacer tool.
19. Disconnect retainer, then remove selector rod from joint and washer.
20. Remove retaining clip with suitable screwdriver, then the bearing pin and selector arm.
21. Remove clutch slave cylinder with pressure line connected. **Relieve clutch slave cylinder slowly, or cylinder may suck air in sealing sleeve.**
22. Remove transmission mounting bolts. **Do not allow transmission to hand on input shaft.**
23. Remove transmission.
24. Reverse procedure to install, noting the following:
    a. Replace dowel sleeves, as required.
    b. Lubricate release unit and lever with suitable grease.
    c. Apply thin layer of suitable grease to taper splines and groove.
    d. Lubricate bearing pin and selector rod with suitable grease.
    e. Ensure pulse generator to flywheel gap is 0.0137–0.0295 inch
    f. Install new exhaust pipe to manifold mounting nuts. Coat threads using CRC copper paste, or equivalent.

TECHNICAL SERVICE BULLETINS

OIL DRAIN/FILL PLUG LEAK

S5D 250G & S6S 420G

On some models equipped with these transmission, there may be an oil filler/drain plug leak.

This condition may be caused by the filler plug.

To correct this condition, install revised plug (part No. 23 11 7 510 100).

TIGHTENING SPECIFICATIONS

Year	Component	Torque, Ft. Lbs.
1998–2001	Actuating Unit	88①
	Actuating Unit Switch	53①
	Clutch Housing	④
	Clutch To Flywheel	⑤
	Driveshaft To Rear Axle	⑩
	Flexible Disk On Propeller Shaft	66
	Flexible Disk On Transmission	74
	Front Axle Support Reinforcement	44⑧
	Hydraulic Line	13②
	Master Cylinder	16
	Pedal To Master Cylinder	88①
	Propeller Shaft, Front To Differential	44
	Propeller Shaft To Transmission	44
	Propeller Shaft Universal Joint	⑨
	Oil Drain Plug (Five-Speed)	37
	Oil Drain Plug (Six-Speed)	38
	Reinforcement Plate To Transmission	17
	Slave Cylinder	16③
	Transfer Case	55
	Transfer Case To Transmission	32
	Transmission Mount	⑥
	Transmission To Clutch Housing	56
	Transmission To Engine	⑦

① — Inch lbs.

② — On 323Ci, 325, 328Ci & 330 & 2000 323i & 328i & 1999 323i & 328i Sedans: torque to 15 ft. lbs. plus 44 inch lbs.

③ — 1998–99 M3, 26 ft. lbs.

④ — M8, 20 ft. lbs.; M10, 38 ft. lbs.; M12 63 ft. lbs.

⑤ — M8 8.8, 16 ft. lbs.; M8 10.9, 25 ft. lbs.

⑥ — M8, 15 ft. lbs.; M10, 31 ft. lbs.

⑦ — Hex bolts: M8, 18 ft. lbs.; M10, 36 ft. lbs., M12, 55 ft. lbs. Torx bolts: M8, 16 ft. lbs.; M10, 32 ft. lbs., M12, 53 ft. lbs.

⑧ — Tighten an additional 90°.

⑨ — M 10, 8.8, 35 ft. lbs.; M10, 10.9, 44 ft. lbs.; M12 8.8, 60 ft. lbs.; M12, 10.9 except on M3 & M5 models, 74 ft. lbs.; M12, 10.9 on M3 & M5 models, 75 ft. lbs.; M14, 103 ft. lbs.

⑩ — Universal Joint w/Compression Nut, 47 ft. lbs.; Universal Joint w/Torx Bolt, 63 ft. lbs.; Constant-Velocity Joint, Compression Nut M8, 24 & M10, 47 ft. lbs.; Finned nut, M8, 32 ft. lbs. & M10, 52 ft. lbs.

Rear Axle & Suspension

NOTE: On Air Bag Equipped Models, Refer To "Air Bag System Precautions" Located In The Front Of This Manual For System Disarming & Arming Procedures.

NOTE: Prior To Performing Any Service Operations Listed In This Section, Consult The "Technical Service Bulletins" Section For Related Information.

INDEX

	Page No.
Coil Spring, Replace	2-105
M3, Z3, 318, 323, 325, 328 & 330	2-105
525, 528, 530, 540, 740 & 750	2-105
Control Arm, Replace	2-106
Lower	2-106
Upper	2-106
Description	2-99
Hub & Bearing, Replace	2-103
M3, Z3, 318, 323, 325, 328 & 330	2-103
M5	2-104
X5	2-104
525, 528, 530 & 540	2-104
740 & 750	2-104
Integral Link, Replace	2-108
M5, 525, 528, 530, 540, 740 & 750	2-108
X5	2-108
Precautions	2-99
Air Bag Systems	2-99
Battery Ground Cable	2-99
Propeller Shaft, Replace	2-102
M3, Z3, 318, 323, 325, 328 & 330	2-102
M5, X5, 525, 528, 530, 540, 740 & 750	2-102
Rear Axle, Replace	2-99
M3, 318, 323, 325, 328 & 330	2-99
M5, 525, 528, 530 & 540	2-100
X5	2-100
Z3	2-100
740 & 750	2-101
Rear Halfshaft, Replace	2-101
M3, Z3, 318, 323, 325, 328 & 330	2-101
M5, 525, 528, 530 & 540	2-101
X5	2-101
740 & 750	2-102
Shock Absorber, Replace	2-104
M3, Z3, 318, 323, 325, 328 & 330	2-104
X5	2-105
525, 528 & 540 Sports Wagon	2-105
Stabilizer Bar, Replace	2-108
M3, Z3, 318, 323, 325, 328 & 330	2-108
M5, X5, 525, 528, 530 & 540 540, 740 & 750	2-108
Strut, Replace	2-104
M5, 525, 528, 530 & 540 Sedan	2-104
740 & 750	2-104
Technical Service Bulletins	2-108
Noisy Rear Axle Differential	2-109
Rear Axle Differential Whine	2-109
Rear Popping Or Snapping	2-109
Rear Shock Absorber Rattle	2-108
Rear Stabilizer Bar Links Pop Off	2-108
Tightening Specifications	2-110
Traction Strut, Replace	2-107
M5, 525, 528, 530, 540, 740 & 750	2-107
X5	2-107
Trailing Arm, Replace	2-107
M3, Z3, 318, 323, 325, 328 & 330	2-107

PRECAUTIONS

AIR BAG SYSTEMS

Refer to "Air Bag System Precautions" in the front of this manual for system disarming and arming procedures.

BATTERY GROUND CABLE

Prior to service, disconnect battery ground cable and isolate as required.

DESCRIPTION

Refer to **Figs. 1 through 7** for rear axle description.

REAR AXLE

REPLACE

M3, 318, 323, 325, 328 & 330

318i, 323is & 328is & 1998-99 M3 & 328i & 1998 323i & 1999 323i & 328i Convertibles

1. Disconnect handbrake cables at lever.
2. Raise and support vehicle, then remove rear tire and wheel assemblies.
3. Remove exhaust system.
4. Disconnect propeller shaft from differential carrier as outlined under "Propeller Shaft, Replace."
5. **On models equipped with disc brakes,** proceed as follows:
   a. Remove left and righthand brake line holders' mounting bolts.
   b. Remove brake calipers as outlined in "Disc Brake" section.
   c. Push calipers between output shaft and control arm.
   d. Suspend calipers aside with suitable wire.
   e. Disconnect anti-lock brake and brake pad wear indicator connectors.
6. **On models equipped with drum brakes,** disconnect left and righthand brake lines.
7. **On all models,** support trailing arm with suitable lift.
8. Remove mounting bolt and lower trailing arm.
9. Disconnect speedometer signal connector.
10. Remove mounting bolts, heat shield and bracket.
11. Remove parking brake cables from guides.
12. Remove trailing arm console mounting bolts.
13. Support rear axle assembly with fixture tools No. 00 2 030/00, 00 2 040/33 and 33 3 290, or equivalents.
14. Remove carrier mounting bolts and nuts.
15. Lower rear axle slightly and remove coil springs.
16. Lower and remove rear axle.
17. Reverse procedure to install, noting the following:
   a. Damaged body bushes may be repaired with suitable Helicoil thread inserts installed flush with original thread.
   b. Connect springs with body rubber rings.
   c. Tighten mounting bolts and nuts to specifications.
   d. Align rear suspension as outlined in "Wheel Alignment" section.
   e. **On models equipped with drum brakes,** bleed brake systems as outlined in "Hydraulic Brake System" section.

318ti

1. Raise and support vehicle, then remove rear tire and wheel assemblies.
2. Disconnect handbrake lever cables, then pull cables from guide tubes.
3. Disconnect propeller shaft from differential carrier as outlined under "Propeller Shaft, Replace."

4. Disconnect speedometer signal connector.
5. Disconnect anti-lock brake connector.
6. Disconnect brake pad wear indicator connector as required.
7. Disconnect stabilizer bar from trailing arms as required.
8. Disconnect carbon canister pipe.
9. Install suitable pedal support and actuate brake pedal.
10. Disconnect left and righthand brake lines.
11. Support rear axle with fixture tools Nos. 00 2 030/042, 33 3 271/272/273 and 33 4 274/275/303, or equivalents.
12. Support and slightly raise trailing arm with suitable lift.
13. Remove mounting bolt, disconnect shock absorber and lower trailing arm slightly.
14. Remove mounting bolts and lower rear axle under coil springs are exposed.
15. Remove coil springs.
16. Lower and remove rear axle.
17. Reverse procedure to install, noting the following:
    a. Tighten mounting bolts and nuts to specifications.
    b. Bleed brake systems as outlined in "Hydraulic Brake System" section.

323Ci, 325, 328Ci & 330 & 2000 323i & 328i & 1999 323i & 328i Sedans & 2001 M3

1. **On convertible models,** remove mounting bolts and tension strut.
2. **On 2001 M3 models,** remove mounting bolts and V-strut.
3. **On all models,** remove propeller shaft as outlined under "Propeller Shaft, Replace."
4. Remove both coil springs as outlined under "Coil Spring, Replace."
5. **On 2001 M3 models,** remove intermediate exhaust pipe with catalytic converter.
6. **On all models,** remove fuel tank panel and heat shield.
7. Remove mounting bolts and nuts, then the rear axle carrier tension strut.
8. Release handbrake lever cables and pull from differential carrier.
9. Remove left and righthand brake line holder mounting bolts.
10. Remove left and righthand shock absorbers as outlined under "Shock Absorber, Replace.".
11. Support trailing arm with suitable lift.
12. Remove mounting bolt and lower trailing arm.
13. Mark left and righthand control arms eccentric bolts for installation alignment.
14. Remove mounting nuts, then the left and righthand control arms eccentric bolts.
15. Disconnect anti-lock brake and brake lining wear indicator connectors.
16. Disconnect left and righthand as outlined in "Disc Brakes" section.
17. Push calipers through between output shaft and control arm. Tie brake calipers aside.
18. Mark left and righthand bearing pedestal to body for installation alignment.
19. Support differential carrier with suitable transmission jack and fixture tool No. 33 4 390, or equivalent. **Ensure dust protection sleeve does not touch tool flange.**
20. Remove mounting bolts and rear axle.
21. Reverse procedure to install, noting the following:
    a. Align rear suspension as outlined in "Wheel Alignment" section.
    b. Rubber mount thrust washer must point toward bolt head.
    c. Tighten mounting bolts and nuts to specifications.

M5, 525, 528, 530 & 540

1. Raise and support vehicle, then remove rear tire and wheel assemblies.
2. Disconnect propeller shaft from differential carrier as outlined under "Propeller Shaft, Replace."
3. Disconnect brake calipers as outlined in "Disc Brake" section.
4. Suspend calipers aside with suitable wire.
5. Disconnect anti-lock brake impulse sensors' connectors.
6. Disconnect handbrake lever cables.
7. Remove heat shield above propeller shaft.
8. Disconnect ride height sensor connector, as required.
9. Support differential carrier with suitable transmission jack and fixture tool No. 33 4 390, or equivalent.
10. Remove left and righthand trim panels.
11. Disconnect left and righthand shock absorbers from wheel carriers.
12. Remove left and righthand mounting bolts.
13. Lower and remove rear axle.
14. Reverse procedure to install, noting the following:
    a. Tighten mounting bolts and nuts to specifications.
    b. Rubber coated detent plate must be installed at rear in driving direction.
    c. Install bushing into wheel carrier.
    d. Align rear suspension as outlined in "Wheel Alignment" section.

X5

1. Raise and support vehicle, then remove rear tire and wheel assemblies.
2. Disconnect propeller shaft from differential carrier as outlined under "Propeller Shaft, Replace."
3. **On models equipped with air suspension,** proceed as follows:
    a. Disconnect air supply system fuse.
    b. Loosen distributor block pipes.
    c. Remove line mounting nut. **Brace nut and line.**
    d. Open line holder flaps.
    e. Loosen nut and remove plastic shim.
    f. Record line routing for installation.
    g. Remove line holder.
4. **On all models,** remove brake calipers as outlined in "Disc Brake" section.
5. Suspend calipers aside with suitable wire.
6. Disconnect handbrake lever cables.
7. Remove heat shield above propeller shaft.
8. Disconnect ride height sensor connector, as required.
9. Disconnect locking clip.
10. Disconnect differential carrier vent line.
11. Remove shock absorbers from lower control arms as outlined under "Shock Absorber, Replace."
12. Support rear axle with suitable transmission jack and fixture tool No. 33 1 221/226, or equivalent.
13. Remove left and righthand mounting bolts, then lower and remove rear axle.
14. **On models equipped with coil springs,** remove coil springs as outlined under "Coil Spring, Replace."
15. **On all models,** reverse procedure to install, noting the following:
    a. Stop plates with threaded pins must be installed in rear direction.
    b. Threaded pins must align in vehicle longitudinal direction.
    c. Position stop plates on four rubber mounts.
    d. Lug must align in wheel carrier hole recess.
    e. Replace line holder.
    f. Damaged body bushes may be repaired with suitable Helicoil thread inserts installed flush with original thread.
    g. Tighten mounting bolts and nuts to specifications.
    h. Align rear suspension as outlined in "Wheel Alignment" section.

Z3

1. Raise and support vehicle, then remove rear tire and wheel assemblies.
2. Disconnect handbrake lever cables, then pull cables from guide tubes.
3. Remove oddments tray and handbrake lever, as required.
4. Disconnect propeller shaft from differential carrier as outlined under "Propeller Shaft, Replace."
5. Disconnect speedometer signal connector.
6. Disconnect anti-lock brake connector.
7. Disconnect brake pad wear indicator connector as required.
8. Disconnect stabilizer bar from trailing arms as required.
9. Disconnect carbon canister pipe.
10. **On M Coupe and M Roadster models,** remove brake calipers as outlined in "Disc Brakes" section.
11. **On all models except M Coupe and M Roadster,** install suitable pedal support and actuate brake pedal.
12. **On all models,** disconnect left and righthand brake lines.
13. Support rear axle with fixture tools Nos. 00 2 030/042, 33 3 271/272/273 and 33 4 274/275/303, or equivalents.
14. Support and slightly raise trailing arm with suitable lift.
15. Remove mounting bolt, disconnect shock absorber and lower trailing arm slightly.
16. Remove mounting bolts and lower rear axle under coil springs are exposed.
17. Remove coil springs.

18. Lower and remove rear axle.
19. Reverse procedure to install, noting the following:
    a. Tighten mounting bolts and nuts to specifications.
    b. Bleed brake systems as outlined in "Hydraulic Brake System" section.

740 & 750

1. Raise and support vehicle, then remove rear tire and wheel assemblies.
2. Disconnect propeller shaft from differential carrier as outlined under "Propeller Shaft, Replace."
3. Drain gasoline from righthand half fuel tank into suitable container.
4. Disconnect fuel tank filler neck hose and seal.
5. Disconnect brake calipers as outlined in "Disc Brake" section.
6. Suspend calipers aside with suitable wire.
7. Disconnect anti-lock brake impulse sensors' connectors.
8. Disconnect parking brake from connection and body.
9. Remove mounting bolt and disconnect control rod.
10. Remove level control valve from differential carrier.
11. Disconnect left and righthand shock absorbers from wheel carriers.
12. Support rear axle with suitable transmission jack and fixture tool No. 33 4 220, or equivalent.
13. Remove mounting bolts, then lower and remove rear axle assembly.
14. Reverse procedure to install, noting the following:
    a. Tighten mounting bolts and nuts to specifications.
    b. Rear detent plate threaded pins must be installed along vehicles's longitudinal axis.
    c. Square shock absorber rubber mount points toward bolt head. Align rear suspension as outlined in "Wheel Alignment" section

REAR HALFSHAFT

REPLACE

M3, Z3, 318, 323, 325, 328 & 330

318i, 323is & 328is & 1998-99 M3 & 328i & 1998 323i & 1999 323i & 328i Convertibles

1. Raise and support vehicle, then remove rear tire and wheel assembly.
2. Remove rear exhaust pipe.
3. Disconnect stabilizer from rear axle carrier and tilt down.
4. Remove axle nut.
5. Remove mounting bolts and remove halfshaft from differential flange. Suspend shaft with suitable wire.
6. Press halfshaft off hub using axle removal tools Nos. 33 2 111/116/117, or equivalents. **Do not allow halfshaft to fall.**
7. Reverse procedure to install, noting the following:
    a. Install half shaft into hub using installation tools Nos. 33 2 115/116/119, or equivalents.
    b. Install new rear axle nut and tighten to specifications.

Z3 & 318ti

1. Raise and support vehicle, then remove rear tire and wheel assembly.
2. Disconnect retaining plate.
3. Remove axle nut.
4. Remove mounting bolts and remove halfshaft from differential flange. Suspend shaft with suitable wire.
5. Support suitable transmission jack, remove mounting bolt and lower trailing arm.
6. Press halfshaft off hub using axle removal tools Nos. 33 2 111/116/117, or equivalents. **Do not allow halfshaft to fall.**
7. Reverse procedure to install, noting the following:
    a. Install half shaft into hub using installation tools Nos. 33 2 115/116/119, or equivalents.
    b. Install new rear axle nut and tighten to specifications.
    c. Install new retaining plate using driver tool No. 33 1 020, or equivalent.

323Ci, 325, 328Ci & 330 & 2000 323i & 328i & 1999 323i & 328i Sedans & 2001 M3

The righthand halfshaft is longer then the lefthand shaft.

1. Raise and support vehicle, then remove rear tire and wheel assembly.
2. Lower rear exhaust pipe.
3. Disconnect stabilizer from rear axle carrier and tilt down.
4. Remove axle nut.
5. Remove mounting bolts and remove halfshaft from differential flange. Suspend shaft with suitable wire.

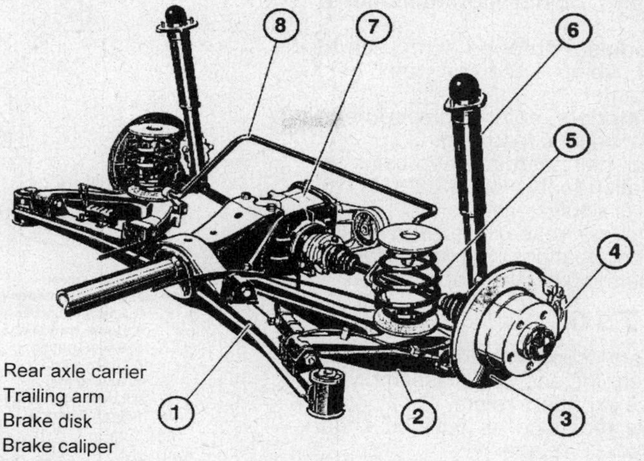

Fig. 1 Rear axle. Z3 & 318ti

6. Press halfshaft off hub using axle removal tools Nos. 33 2 111/116/117, or equivalents. **Do not allow halfshaft to fall.**
7. Reverse procedure to install, noting the following:
    a. Install half shaft into hub using installation tools Nos. 33 2 115/116/119, or equivalents.
    b. Install new rear axle nut, oil and tighten to specifications. Secure collar nut by caulking on halfshaft flat areas.

M5, 525, 528, 530 & 540

1. Raise and support vehicle, then remove rear tire and wheel assembly.
2. Remove rear axle as outlined under "Rear Axle, Replace."
3. Remove axle nut.
4. Press halfshaft off hub using axle removal tools Nos. 33 2 111/116/117, or equivalents. **Do not allow halfshaft to fall.**
5. Reverse procedure to install, noting the following:
    a. Install half shaft into hub using installation tools Nos. 33 2 115/116/118, or equivalents.
    b. Install new rear axle nut and tighten to specifications.
    c. Secure collar nut by penning at shaft flat area.

X5

1. Raise and support vehicle, then remove rear tire and wheel assembly.
2. Remove rear muffler from center.
3. Remove mounting bolts and remove halfshaft from differential flange. Suspend shaft with suitable wire.
4. Raise wheel carrier using suitable jack and wooden block.
5. Remove axle nut.
6. Press halfshaft off hub using axle removal tools Nos. 33 2 111/116/117, or

equivalents. **Do not allow halfshaft to fall.**
7. **On models equipped with height control,** remove control arm from wheel carrier.
8. **On all models,** reverse procedure to install, noting the following:
   a. Install half shaft into hub using installation tools Nos. 33 2 115/116/118, or equivalents.
   b. Install new rear axle nut and tighten to specifications. Secure collar nut by penning at shaft flat area.

740 & 750

1. Raise and support vehicle, then remove rear tire and wheel assembly.
2. Remove exhaust system.
3. Remove rear axle as outlined under "Rear Axle, Replace."
4. Remove axle nut.
5. Press halfshaft off hub using axle removal tools Nos. 33 2 111/116/117, or equivalents. **Do not allow halfshaft to fall.**
6. **On models equipped with height control,** remove control arm from wheel carrier.
7. **On all models,** remove mounting bolt and shock absorber from wheel carrier.
8. Lift wheel carrier with suitable jack and remove half shaft.
9. Reverse procedure to install, noting the following:
   a. Install half shaft into hub using installation tools Nos. 33 2 115/116/118, or equivalents.
   b. Install new rear axle nut and tighten to specifications. Secure collar nut by penning at shaft flat area.

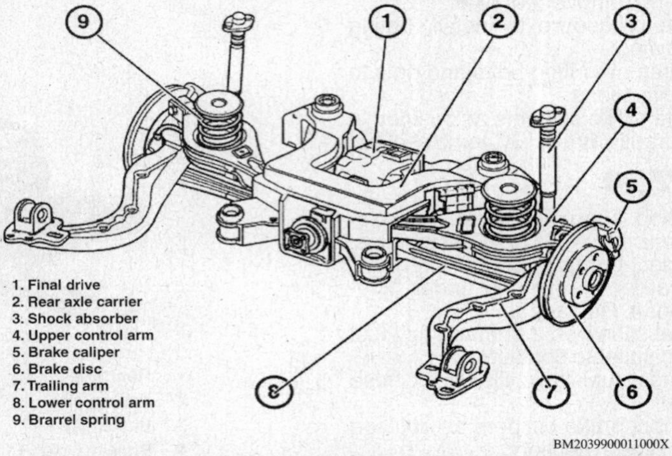

Fig. 2 Rear axle. 318i, 323is & 328is & 1998–99 M3 & 328i & 1998 323i & 1999 323i & 328i Convertibles

PROPELLER SHAFT

REPLACE

M3, Z3, 318, 323, 325, 328 & 330

w/Rear Constant-Velocity Joint

1. Remove exhaust system and heat shield.
2. Remove mounting bolts and exhaust suspension frame.
3. Remove transmission joint disk mounting nuts.
4. Remove mounting nuts and differential final drive flange constant-velocity joint.
5. Remove center bearing mounting bolts. **Do not allow propeller shaft to fall into joints.**
6. Bend propeller shaft downward at center mount and disconnect transmission or constant-velocity joint centering pin.
7. Protect constant-velocity joint with suitable transport cap.
8. Reverse procedure to install, noting the following:
   a. Pull joint to limit position, then coat constant-velocity joint and input flange with suitable grease.
   b. Install new seals and mounting nuts.
   c. **Do not compress constant-velocity joint.**
   d. Draw constant-velocity joint evenly onto drive flange by alternately tightening two opposing nuts
   e. Coat centering mount with Molykote Longterm No. 1 grease, or equivalent.
   f. Preload center mount forward 0.0787–0.1575 inch, **Fig. 8.**
   g. Tighten new transmission joint disk mounting nuts on flange side, only.
   h. Install exhaust suspension frame clamp with long collar at rear.

With Slide

1. Remove exhaust system and heat shield.
2. Remove mounting bolts and exhaust suspension frame.
3. **On models equipped with transmission flexible disk,** remove transmission joint disk mounting nuts.
4. **On models equipped with transmission universal joint,** remove mounting nuts and universal joint.
5. Loosen threaded sleeve several turns using wrench tool No. 26 1 040, or equivalent.
6. Mark universal joint to differential drive flange for installation alignment.
7. Remove mounting nuts and differential final drive flange universal joint.
8. Remove center bearing mounting bolts. **Do not allow propeller shaft to fall into joints.**
9. Bend propeller shaft downward at center mount and disconnect transmission/universal joint centering mount.
10. Reverse procedure to install, noting the following:
    a. Coat centering mount with Molykote Longterm No. 1 grease, or equivalent.
    b. Preload center mount forward 0.1575–0.2362 inch, **Fig. 8.**
    c. Install new differential universal joint mounting nuts and tighten to specifications.
    d. **On models equipped with transmission flexible disk,** tighten new transmission joint disk mounting nuts on flange side, only.
    e. **On models equipped with transmission universal joint,** tighten new transmission joint disk mounting nuts, only.
    f. **On all models,** install exhaust suspension frame clamp with long collar at front.

M5, X5, 525, 528, 530, 540, 740 & 750

1. Remove exhaust system and heat shields.
2. Disconnect cable from crossmember,
3. Support transmission with suitable jack.
4. Remove mounting bolts and crossmember.
5. Remove transmission joint disk mounting nuts.
6. Remove differential final drive flange constant-velocity joint mounting nuts.
7. Disconnect constant-velocity joint by pressing off input flange with suitable screwdriver.
8. Remove center bearing mounting bolts. **Do not allow propeller shaft to fall into joints.**
9. Bend propeller shaft downward at center mount and disconnect from transmission output flange and remove constant-velocity joint from differential input flange.
10. Protect constant-velocity joint with suitable transport cap.
11. Reverse procedure to install, noting the following:
    a. Pull joint to limit position, then coat constant-velocity joint and input flange with suitable grease.
    b. Install new seals and mounting nuts.
    c. **Do not compress constant-velocity joint.**
    d. Draw constant-velocity joint evenly onto drive flange by alternately tightening two opposing nuts
    e. Coat centering mount with Molykote Longterm No. 1 grease, or equivalent.
    f. Tighten new transmission joint disk

mounting nuts on flange side, only.

HUB & BEARING

REPLACE

M3, Z3, 318, 323, 325, 328 & 330

318i, 323is & 328is & 1998-99 328i & 1998 323i & 1999 323i & 328i Convertibles

1. Remove halfshaft as outlined under "Rear Halfshaft, Replace."
2. Remove brake disc as outlined in "Disc Brake" section.
3. Drive out drive flange using bearing removal tools Nos. 33 2 116 and 33 4 201/202/203, or equivalent.
4. Remove bearing inner race using bearing removal tool No. 00 7 500, or equivalent.
5. Remove circlip.
6. Remove angular contact ball bearing using bearing removal tools Nos. 33 4 031/041/042/043/045, or equivalent.
7. Reverse procedure to install, noting the following:
   a. Install new angular contact ball bearing using bearing installer tools Nos. 33 4 041/042/043/046/047/049, or equivalents.
   b. Install drive flange using installer tools Nos. 33 4 041/042/043/045/048, or equivalents.

Z3 1.9 & 318ti

1. Remove halfshaft as outlined under "Rear Halfshaft, Replace."
2. Remove brake disc as outlined in "Disc Brake" section.
3. Drive out drive flange using bearing removal tools Nos. 33 2 116 and 33 4 201/202/203, or equivalent.
4. Remove bearing inner race using bearing removal tools Nos. 00 7 500 and 33 1 312, or equivalents.
5. Remove circlip.
6. Remove angular contact ball bearing using bearing removal tools Nos. 33 4 041/042/043/044/045, or equivalent.
7. Reverse procedure to install, noting the following:
   a. Install new angular contact ball bearing using bearing installer tools Nos. 33 4 041/042/043/046/047, or equivalents.
   b. Install drive flange using installer tools Nos. 33 4 041/042/045/048, or equivalents.

Z3 M Coupe & M Roadster & 1998-99 M3

1. Remove halfshaft as outlined under "Rear Halfshaft, Replace."
2. Remove brake disc as outlined in "Disc Brake" section.
3. Drive out drive flange using bearing removal tools Nos. 33 2 116 and 33 4 201/202/203, or equivalent.
4. Remove bearing inner race using bearing removal tool No. 33 3 240, or equivalent.

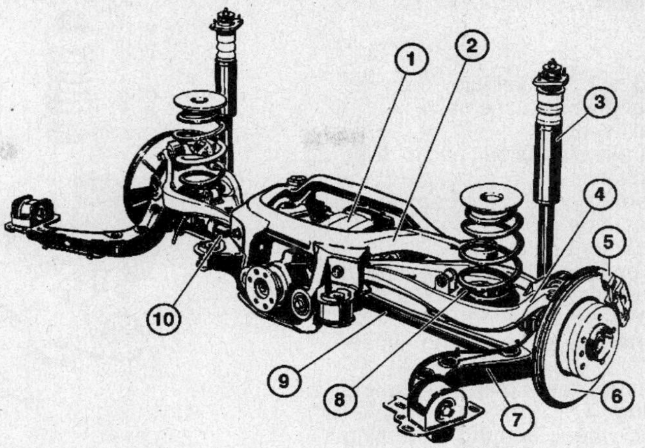

1	Final drive	6	Brake disk
2	Rear axle carrier	7	Trailing arm
3	Shock absorber	8	Barrel spring
4	Upper control arm	9	Lower control arm
5	Brake caliper	10	Stabilizer

BM2030100012000X

Fig. 3 Rear axle. 323Ci, 325, 328Ci & 330 & 2000 323i & 328i & 1999 323i & 328i Sedans & 2001 M3

5. Remove circlip.
6. Remove angular contact ball bearing using bearing removal tools Nos. 33 3 261/262/263, or equivalent.
7. Reverse procedure to install, noting the following:
   a. Install new angular contact ball bearing using bearing installer tools Nos. 33 3 261/264/265, or equivalents.
   b. Install drive flange using installer tools Nos. 33 3 261/262/263, or equivalents.

Z3 2.3, 2.5, 2.8 & 3.0

1. Remove halfshaft as outlined under "Rear Halfshaft, Replace."
2. Remove brake disc as outlined in "Disc Brake" section.
3. Drive out drive flange using bearing removal tools Nos. 33 2 116 and 33 4 201/202/203, or equivalent.
4. Remove bearing inner race using bearing removal tool No. 33 1 307 and 33 4 090, or equivalents.
5. Remove circlip.
6. Remove angular contact ball bearing using bearing removal tools Nos. 33 4 031/032/033/038/039, or equivalent.
7. Reverse procedure to install, noting the following:
   a. Install new angular contact ball bearing using bearing installer tools Nos. 33 4 032/034/035/038/039, or equivalents.
   b. Install drive flange using installer tools Nos. 33 4 041/042/045/048, or equivalents.

323Ci & 325 & 2000 323i & 1999 323i Sedan

1. Remove halfshaft as outlined under "Rear Halfshaft, Replace."
2. Remove brake disc as outlined in "Disc Brake" section.
3. Drive out drive flange using bearing removal tools Nos. 33 2 116 and 33 4 201/202/203, or equivalent.
4. Remove bearing inner race using bearing removal tool No. 33 1 306 and 33 4 090, or equivalents.
5. Remove circlip.
6. Remove angular contact ball bearing using bearing removal tools Nos. 33 4 031/041/042/043/048, or equivalent.
7. Reverse procedure to install, noting the following:
   a. Install new angular contact ball bearing using bearing installer tools Nos. 33 4 041/042/043/047/049, or equivalents.
   b. Install drive flange using installer tools Nos. 33 4 041/042/043/045/048, or equivalents.

328Ci & 330 & 2000 328i & 1999 328i Sedan & 2001 M3

1. Remove halfshaft as outlined under "Rear Halfshaft, Replace."
2. Remove brake disc as outlined in "Disc Brake" section.
3. Drive out drive flange using bearing removal tools Nos. 33 2 116 and 33 4 201/202/203, or equivalent.
4. Remove wheel bearing inner race from drive flange. **Bearing is destroyed when flange is remove.**
5. Remove circlip.
6. Remove wheel bearing using bearing removal tools Nos. 33 3 261/262/263, or equivalent.
7. Reverse procedure to install, noting the following:
   a. Install new angular contact ball bearing using bearing installer tools Nos. 33 3 261/264/265, or equivalents.
   b. Install drive flange using installer tools Nos. 33 3 261/262/263, or

equivalents.

M5

1. Raise and support vehicle, then remove tire and wheel assembly.
2. Remove axle nut.
3. Remove brake disc as outlined in "Disc Brake" section.
4. Drive out drive flange using bearing removal tools Nos. 33 2 116 and 33 4 201/202/203, or equivalent.
5. Remove bearing inner race using bearing removal tools Nos. 00 7 500 and 33 1 312, or equivalent.
6. Remove mounting bolts and wheel bearing.
7. Reverse procedure to install, noting the following:
   a. Tighten wheel bearing mounting bolts to specifications.
   b. Apply light coat of oil and install drive flange using installer tools Nos. 33 2 115/116/118, or equivalents.
   c. Install new collar nut. Secure collar nut by peening on shaft flat areas.

X5

1. Raise and support vehicle, then remove tire and wheel assembly.
2. Remove axle nut.
3. Remove brake disc as outlined in "Disc Brake" section.
4. Drive out drive flange using bearing removal tools Nos. 33 2 116 and 33 4 201/202/203, or equivalent.
5. Remove bearing inner race, as required.
6. Remove mounting bolts and wheel bearing.
7. Reverse procedure to install, noting the following:
   a. Tighten wheel bearing mounting bolts to specifications.
   b. Apply light coat of oil and install drive flange using installer tools Nos. 33 2 115/116/118, or equivalents.
   c. Install new collar nut. Secure collar nut by peening on shaft flat areas.

525, 528, 530 & 540

1. Raise and support vehicle, then remove tire and wheel assembly.
2. Remove axle nut.
3. Remove brake disc as outlined in "Disc Brake" section.
4. Drive out drive flange using bearing removal tools Nos. 33 2 116 and 33 4 201/202/203, or equivalent.
5. Remove bearing inner race using bearing removal tools Nos. 00 7 500 and 33 1 312, or equivalent.
6. Remove mounting bolts and wheel bearing.
7. Reverse procedure to install, noting the following:
   a. Tighten wheel bearing mounting bolts to specifications.
   b. Apply light coat of oil and install drive flange using installer tools Nos. 33 2 115/116/118, or equivalents.
   c. Install new collar nut. Secure collar nut by peening on shaft flat areas.

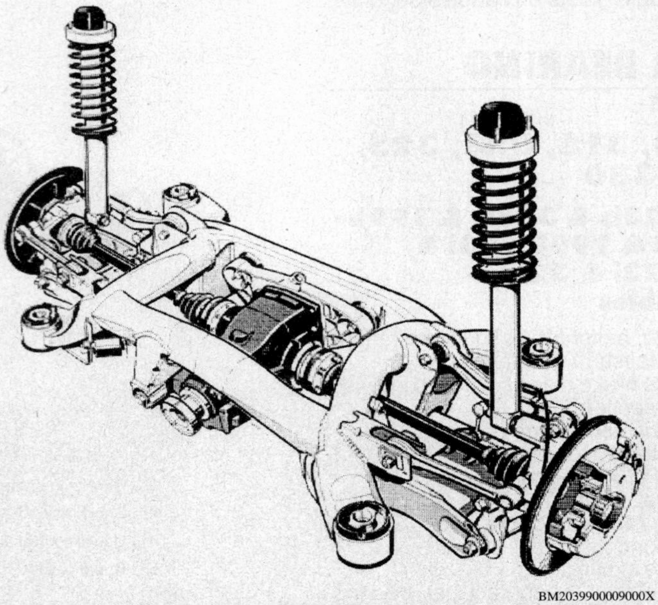

Fig. 4 Rear axle. M5, 525, 528, 530 & 540 sedans

740 & 750

1. Raise and support vehicle, then remove tire and wheel assembly.
2. Remove halfshaft as outlined under "Rear Halfshaft, Replace."
3. Remove brake disc as outlined in "Disc Brake" section.
4. Disconnect anti-lock brake pulse generator connector.
5. Drive out drive flange using bearing removal tools Nos. 33 2 116 and 33 4 201/202/203, or equivalent.
6. Remove bearing inner race, as required.
7. Remove circlip.
8. Remove bearing using removal tools Nos. 33 3 261/262/266, or equivalent.
9. Reverse procedure to install, noting the following:
   a. Red sealing ring must face outward.
   b. Install wheel bearing using bearing installer tools Nos. 33 3 261/264/268, or equivalents.
   c. Install drive flange using installer tools Nos. 33 3 261/266/267, or equivalents.

STRUT

REPLACE

M5, 525, 528, 530 & 540 SEDAN

1. Disconnect air supply unit connector.
2. Remove rear shelf trim and radio speaker.
3. Raise and support vehicle, then remove tire and wheel assembly.
4. Remove wheel housing trim.
5. Remove cover and shock absorber mounting nut.
6. Disconnect Electronic Damper Control (EDC) connector, as required.
7. Support wheel carrier with suitable jack. **Do not expose brake lines to loads.**
8. Remove shock absorber wheel carrier mounting bolts and shock absorber.
9. Reverse procedure to install. Tighten new mounting bolts and nuts to specifications.

740 & 750

1. Remove luggage compartment floor trim
2. Raise and support vehicle, then remove tire and wheel assembly.
3. Remove brake caliper as outlined in "Disc Brake" section and tie aside.
4. Remove cover and shock absorber upper mounting nuts.
5. Disconnect Electronic Damper Control (EDC) connector, as required.
6. Remove shock absorber lower mounting nut.
7. Remove shock absorber wheel carrier mounting bolts and shock absorber.
8. Reverse procedure to install, noting the following:
   a. Ensure rubber mount square head points toward screw head.
   b. Ensure tapered pin and bore are grease free.
   c. Tighten new mounting bolts and nuts to specifications.

SHOCK ABSORBER

REPLACE

M3, Z3, 318, 323, 325, 328 & 330

1. **On coupe and sedan models,** remove luggage compartment trim panel.
2. **On roadster models,** remove plastic caps and convertible top compartment panel.

3. **On all models,** raise and support rear of vehicle.
4. Support trailing arm with suitable lift and remove mounting bolt.
5. Remove cap and mounting nuts.
6. Remove reinforcement plate, as required.
7. Remove shock absorber.
8. Reverse procedure to install, noting the following:
   a. Install new seal between shock absorber and body.
   b. Install new self-locking nuts and tighten to specifications.
   c. Rubber mount thrust washer must point toward bolt head.

X5

1. Disconnect air supply fuse.
2. Remove nuts, expansion rivets and luggage compartment trim.
3. Support wheel carrier with suitable jack. **Do not expose brake lines to loads.**
4. Remove shock absorber upper mounting nuts.
5. Remove shock absorber lower control arm mounting bolt.
6. Force shock absorber off lower control arm with suitable wooden wedge.
7. Reverse procedure to install. Tighten new mounting nuts to specifications.

525, 528 & 540 SPORTS WAGON

1. Disconnect air supply unit connector.
2. Remove luggage compartment floor trim, then the mounting bolts and shock absorber cover.
3. Remove longitudinal sides' caps.
4. Support wheel carrier with suitable jack. **Do not expose brake lines to loads.**
5. Remove shock absorber upper mounting nuts.
6. Remove shock absorber wheel carrier mounting bolts and shock absorber.
7. Reverse procedure to install. Tighten new mounting bolts and nuts to specifications.

COIL SPRING

REPLACE

M3, Z3, 318, 323, 325, 328 & 330

318i, 323is & 328is & 1998-99 M3 & 328i & 1998 323i & 1999 323i & 328i Convertibles

1. Raise and support rear of vehicle, then remove rear tire and wheel assembly.
2. Disconnect halfshaft from differential as outlined under "Rear Halfshaft, Replace."
3. Disconnect brake line from trailing arm.
4. Support trailing arm with suitable jack.
5. Disconnect stabilizer from control arm and rear axle carrier.
6. Remove shock absorber mounting bolt and lower trailing arm.
7. Remove coil spring by pressing suspension down. **Do not damage brake line.**
8. Reverse procedure to install, noting the following:
   a. Coat top spring ring with suitable lubricant.
   b. Tighten mounting bolts to specifications.

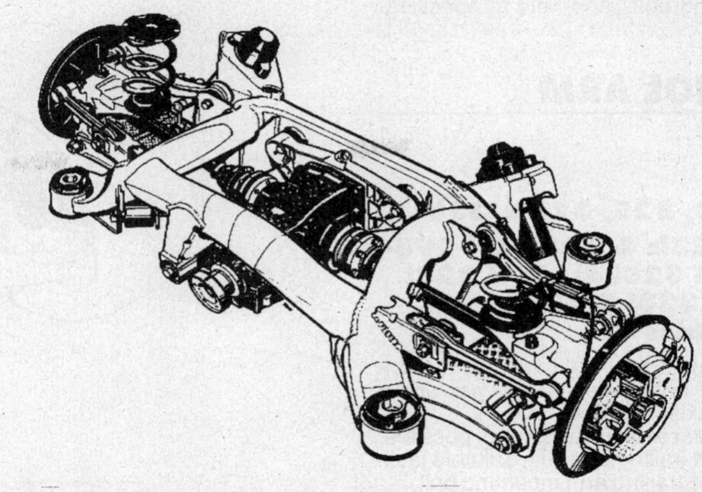

Fig. 5 Rear axle. 525, 528, 530 & 540 sports wagon

Z3 & 318ti

1. Remove halfshaft as outlined under "Rear Halfshaft, Replace."
2. Disconnect stabilizer from trailing arm.
3. Support trailing arm with suitable jack.
4. Remove shock absorber mounting bolt and lower trailing arm.
5. Remove coil spring by pressing suspension down.
6. Reverse procedure to install. Tighten mounting bolts to specifications.

323Ci, 325, 328Ci & 330 & 2000 323i & 328i & 1999 323i & 328i Sedans & 2001 M3

1. Raise and support rear of vehicle, then remove rear tire and wheel assembly.
2. Disconnect halfshaft from differential as outlined under "Rear Halfshaft, Replace."
3. Disconnect fuel tank panel.
4. Disconnect stabilizer from rear axle carrier.
5. Disconnect brake hose bracket on trailing arm.
6. Support trailing arm with suitable jack.
7. Remove shock absorber mounting bolt and lower trailing arm.
8. Remove coil spring by pressing suspension down. **Do not damage brake line.**
9. Reverse procedure to install, noting the following:
   a. Coat top spring pad with suitable tire mounting paste.
   b. Tighten mounting bolts to specifications.

525, 528, 530, 540, 740 & 750

Sedan

1. Remove strut as outlined under "Strut, Replace."
2. Clamp strut tool No. 31 3 121, or equivalent, into suitable vise.
3. Install coil spring with upper and lower coil between tool spring holder.
4. Relieve thrust bearing stress by tightening tool.
5. Remove mounting nut and spring.
6. Reverse procedure to install. Tighten new mounting bolts and nuts to specifications.

Sports Wagon

1. Raise and support vehicle, then remove rear tire and wheel assemblies.
2. Remove exhaust system.
3. Remove left and righthand brake calipers as outlined in "Disc Brake" section.
4. Remove propeller shaft as outlined under "Propeller Shaft, Replace."
5. Disconnect handbrake cables from brackets.
6. Support differential carrier with suitable transmission jack and fixture tool No. 33 4 390, or equivalent.
7. Remove rear axle carrier mounting bolts.
8. Lower rear axle carrier until springs can be removed.
9. Reverse procedure to install. Tighten

mounting bolts and nuts to specifications.

CONTROL ARM

REPLACE

LOWER

M3, 323, 325, 328 & 330

318i, 323is & 328is & 1998-99 M3 & 328i & 1998 323i & 1999 323i & 328i Convertibles

1. Disconnect rear axle without disconnecting halfshafts as outlined under "Rear Axle, Replace."
2. Move rear axle as far back as possible.
3. Support trailing arm with suitable jack.
4. Remove trailing arm mounting bolt.
5. Remove mounting bolt and lower control arm.
6. Reverse procedure to install. Tighten new mounting bolts to specifications.

323Ci, 325, 328Ci & 330 & 2000 323i & 328i & 1999 323i & 328i Sedans & 2001 M3

1. Support trailing arm with suitable jack.
2. Spread and remove control arm plastic panel.
3. Mark control arm eccentric bolt for installation alignment.
4. Remove nut and eccentric bolt.
5. Remove rear axle carrier mounting bolt and control arm.
6. Reverse procedure to install, noting the following:
   a. Control arm welded seam faces upward.
   b. Control arm plastic panel opening points upward.
   c. Tighten mounting bolts and nuts to specifications.
   d. Align rear suspension as outlined in "Wheel Alignment" section.

M5, 525, 528, 530, 540, 740 & 750

Sedan

1. Disconnect air supply unit retainer.
2. Raise and support vehicle, then remove tire and wheel assembly.
3. Disconnect anti-lock brake pulse generator connector.
4. Disconnect level control system control rod, as required.
5. Remove mounting nut and disconnect stabilizer link.
6. Mark rear axle carrier eccentric bolt for installation alignment.
7. Remove disk collar nut and eccentric bolt.
8. Remove arm mounting nut and bolt.
9. Support wheel carrier with suitable jack.
10. Remove mounting nut , bolt and lower control arm.
11. Reverse procedure to install, noting the following:
    a. Tighten new mounting bolts and nuts to specifications.
    b. Align rear suspension as outlined in "Wheel Alignment" section.

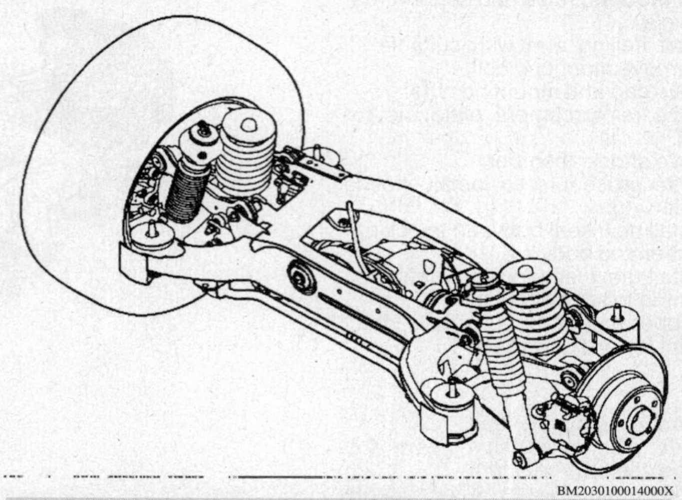

Fig. 6 Rear axle. X5

Sports Wagon

1. Raise and support vehicle, then remove tire and wheel assembly.
2. Disconnect anti-lock brake pulse generator connector.
3. Disconnect level control system control rod, as required.
4. **On models equipped with coil springs,** tension coil spring as outlined under "Coil Spring, Replace." Coil spring remains with vehicle.
5. **On models equipped with air suspension,** disconnect air supply unit retainer, then release system pressure by loosening distribution block pipes.
6. **On all models,** remove mounting bolt and disconnect shock absorber from lower control arm.
7. Remove mounting nut and disconnect stabilizer link.
8. Mark rear axle carrier eccentric bolt for installation alignment.
9. Remove disk collar nut and eccentric bolt.
10. Remove arm mounting nut and bolt.
11. Support wheel carrier with suitable jack.
12. Remove mounting nut , bolt and lower control arm.
13. Reverse procedure to install, noting the following:
    a. Tighten new mounting bolts and nuts to specifications.
    b. Ensure eccentric support spigots line in rear axle carrier holes.
    c. Align rear suspension as outlined in "Wheel Alignment" section.

X5

1. Raise and support vehicle, then remove tire and wheel assembly.
2. Disconnect level control system control rod, as required.
3. **On models equipped with air suspension,** disconnect air supply unit retainer, then release system pressure by loosening distribution block pipes.
4. **On models equipped with coil springs,** remove integral link as outlined under "Integral Link, Replace."
5. **On all models,** remove mounting bolt and disconnect shock absorber from lower control arm.
6. Mark rear axle carrier eccentric bolt for installation alignment.
7. Remove disk collar nut and eccentric bolt.
8. Remove arm mounting nut and bolt.
9. Support wheel carrier with suitable jack.
10. Remove mounting nut , bolt and lower control arm.
11. Reverse procedure to install, noting the following:
    a. Tighten new mounting bolts and nuts to specifications.
    b. Ensure eccentric support spigots line in rear axle carrier holes.
    c. Align rear suspension as outlined in "Wheel Alignment" section.

UPPER

M3, 318, 323, 325, 328 & 330

318i, 323is & 328is & 1998-99 M3 & 328i & 1998 323i & 1999 323i & 328i Convertibles

1. Remove coil spring as outlined under "Coil Spring, Replace."
2. Disconnect stabilizer support.
3. Remove upper control arm mounting bolt.
4. Disconnect differential carrier as outlined under "Rear Axle, Replace." **Do not disconnect half shafts.**
5. Move rear axle as far back as possible.
6. Disconnect brake lining wear indicator and anti-lock brake sensor connectors.
7. Remove mounting bolts and upper control arm.
8. Reverse procedure to install. Tighten new mounting bolts to specifications.

M5, 525, 528, 530, 540, 740 & 750

Sedan

1. Raise and support vehicle, then remove rear tire and wheel assembly.
2. Remove upper mounting bolt and nut.
3. Open plastic line holders.
4. Remove brace mounting nut and control arm.
5. Reverse procedure to install, noting the following:
   a. Ensure tapered pin and bore are grease free.
   b. Install new nuts and bolts, then tighten to specifications.
   c. Ensure bolt head is at front in driving direction.
   d. Align rear suspension as outlined in "Wheel Alignment" section.

Sports Wagon

1. Raise and support vehicle, then remove rear tire and wheel assembly.
2. **On models equipped with coil springs,** tension coil spring as outlined under "Coil Spring, Replace." Coil spring remains on vehicle.
3. **On models equipped with air suspension,** disconnect air supply unit retainer, then release system pressure by loosening distribution block pipes.
4. **On all models,** remove shock absorber lower control arm mounting bolt.
5. Remove control arm mounting nut and push shock absorber aside.
6. Remove control arm mounting bolt.
7. Open plastic line holders.
8. Remove brace mounting nut and control arm.
9. Reverse procedure to install, noting the following:
   a. Ensure tapered pin and bore are grease free.
   b. Install new nuts and bolts, then tighten to specifications.
   c. Ensure bolt head is at rear in driving direction.
   d. Align rear suspension as outlined in "Wheel Alignment" section.

X5

1. **On models equipped with coil springs,** proceed as follows:
   a. Remove brake caliper as outlined in "Disc Brakes" section.
   b. Tie caliper aside.
   c. Remove anti-lock brake pulse generator.
   d. Support wheel carrier with suitable jack.
   e. Remove shock absorber from lower control arm.
2. **On models equipped with air suspension,** proceed as follows:
   a. Disconnect air supply unit retainer.
   b. Release system pressure by loosening distribution block pipes.
   c. Raise and support vehicle, then remove rear tire and wheel assembly.
3. **On all models,** remove upper mounting nut.
4. Open holder flaps and disconnect lines.

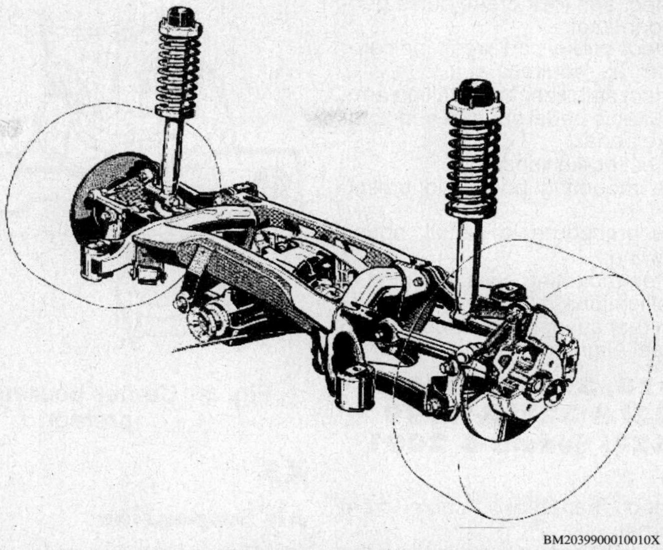

BM2039900010010X

Fig. 7 Rear axle. 740 & 750

5. Remove mounting nut and plastic shim.
6. Remove mounting nut, bolt and control arm.
7. Reverse procedure to install, noting the following:
   a. Ensure tapered pin and bore are grease free.
   b. Install new nuts and bolts, then tighten to specifications.
   c. Align rear suspension as outlined in "Wheel Alignment" section.

TRACTION STRUT

REPLACE

M5, 525, 528, 530, 540, 740 & 750

1. Raise and support vehicle, then remove tire and wheel assembly.
2. Remove mounting nut and eccentric bolt.
3. Remove mounting nut and traction strut.
4. Reverse procedure to install, noting the following:
   a. Ensure tapered pin and bore are grease free.
   b. Install new nuts and tighten to specifications.
   c. Install eccentric washer.
   d. Align rear suspension as outlined in "Wheel Alignment" section.

X5

1. **On models equipped with coil springs,** disconnect shock absorber from lower control arm.
2. **On all models,** raise and support vehicle, then remove tire and wheel assembly.
3. Remove mounting nut and eccentric bolt.
4. Remove mounting nut and traction strut.
5. Reverse procedure to install, noting the following:
   a. Ensure tapered pin and bore are grease free.
   b. Install new nuts and tighten to specifications.
   c. Install eccentric washer.
   d. Align rear suspension as outlined in "Wheel Alignment" section.

TRAILING ARM

REPLACE

M3, Z3, 318, 323, 325, 328 & 330

318i, 323is & 328is & 1998-99 M3 & 328i & 1998 323i & 1999 323i & 328i Convertibles

1. Disconnect handbrake cable from wheel brake.
2. Remove halfshaft as outlined under "Rear Halfshaft, Replace."
3. Disconnect brake line holder from trailing arm.
4. Remove brake caliper as outlined in "Disc Brake" section. Tie caliper aside with lines connected.
5. Support trailing arm with suitable jack.
6. Remove shock absorber mounting bolt.
7. Remove control arm mounting bolts.
8. Remove bearing pedestal mounting bolts and trailing arm.
9. Reverse procedure to install, noting the following:
   a. Tighten mounting bolts and nuts to specifications.
   b. Align rear suspension as outlined in "Wheel Alignment" section.

Z3 & 318ti

1. Raise and support vehicle, then remove tire and wheel assembly.
2. Disconnect handbrake lever cable.
3. Remove coil spring as outlined under "Coil Spring, Replace."

4. Disconnect anti-lock brake pulse generator connector.
5. Disconnect brake pad wear indicator connector, as required.
6. Disconnect stabilizer from trailing arm.
7. Install suitable pedal support and actuate brake pedal.
8. Disconnect brake lines.
9. Remove mounting bolts and trailing arm.
10. Reverse procedure to install, noting the following:
    a. Tighten mounting bolts and nuts to specifications.
    b. Align rear suspension as outlined in "Wheel Alignment" section.

323Ci, 325, 328Ci & 330 & 2000 323i & 328i & 1999 323i & 328i Sedans & 2001 M3

1. Disconnect handbrake cable from wheel brake.
2. Remove coil spring as outlined under "Coil Spring, Replace."
3. Remove halfshaft from drive flange as outlined under "Rear Halfshaft, Replace."
4. Remove anti-lock brake pulse generator.
5. Mark control arm eccentric bolt for installation alignment.
6. Remove mounting nut and eccentric bolt.
7. Remove trailing arm mounting nut and bolt.
8. Remove fuel tank panel.
9. Mark bearing pedestal for installation alignment.
10. Remove bearing pedals mounting bolt and trailing arm.
11. Reverse procedure to install, noting the following:
    a. Tighten mounting bolts and nuts to specifications.
    b. Align rear suspension as outlined in "Wheel Alignment" section.

INTEGRAL LINK

REPLACE

M5, 525, 528, 530, 540, 740 & 750

1. Disconnect air supply unit retainer.
2. Raise and support vehicle, then remove rear tire and wheel assembly.
3. **On sports wagon models equipped with coil spring,** tension coil spring as outlined under "Coil Spring, Replace." Coil spring remains with vehicle.
4. **On all models,** support wheel carrier with suitable jack.
5. Remove mounting nut and bolt, then press lower control arm down.
6. Remove mounting bolt and integral link.
7. Reverse procedure to install. Tighten new mounting nuts and bolts to specifications.

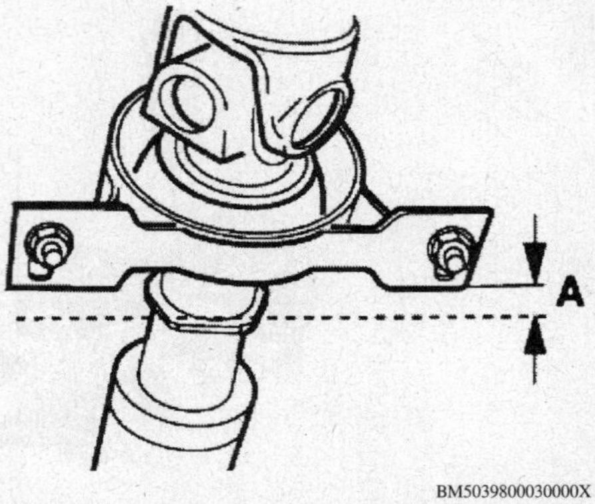

Fig. 8 Center bearing mount preload

X5

Air Suspension

1. Disconnect air supply unit fuse.
2. Raise and support vehicle, then remove rear tire and wheel assembly.
3. Support wheel carrier with suitable jack.
4. Remove mounting nut and bolt, then press lower control arm down.
5. Remove mounting bolt and integral link.
6. Reverse procedure to install. Tighten new mounting nuts and bolts to specifications.

Coil Spring Suspension

1. Remove brake caliper as outlined in "Disc Brakes" section.
2. Tie caliper aside.
3. Remove anti-lock brake pulse generator.
4. Disconnect stabilizer link from lower control arm.
5. Disconnect shock absorber from lower control arm.
6. Remove traction strut as outlined under "Traction Strut, Replace."
7. Remove lower control arm as outlined under "Control Arm, Replace."
8. Support wheel carrier with suitable jack.
9. Remove mounting nut and bolt, then press lower control arm down.
10. Remove mounting bolt and integral link.
11. Reverse procedure to install. Tighten new mounting nuts and bolts to specifications.

STABILIZER BAR

REPLACE

M3, Z3, 318, 323, 325, 328 & 330

1. Disconnect stabilizer bar from upper control arm and rear axle carrier.
2. Remove stabilizer bar.
3. Reverse procedure to install. Coast retaining bracket with Circolight, or equivalent.

M5, X5, 525, 528, 530 & 540 540, 740 & 750

1. Remove left and righthand bracket mounting nuts.
2. Mark stabilizer bar lefthand side for installation alignment.
3. Remove mounting bolts, stabilizer bar and brackets.
4. Reverse procedure to install. Tighten mounting bolts and nuts to specifications.

TECHNICAL SERVICE BULLETINS

REAR STABILIZER BAR LINKS POP OFF

Z3 & 318ti

On some of these models built before September 1999 the rear stabilizer bar links may come off.

This condition may be caused by stabilizer bars links not meeting production specifications.

To correct this condition replace stabilizer bars links with models made by BOGE (part No. 33 55 1 135 307), noting the following:

1. If stabilizer bar has nicks or missing paint, replace as required.
2. Lubricate stabilizer bar with suitable rubbing alcohol. **Do not use silicone or petroleum lubricant.**
3. Rotate and hold link to 76° angle with bar and 42° angle with bracket.
4. Before tightening lower bracket to control arm, ensure link is parallel to sway bar shoulder and not twisted.
5. Ensure bracket is fully pushed into body whole when tightening.
6. **Do not put weight on wheels until alcohol has dried (at least ½ hour**.

REAR SHOCK ABSORBER RATTLE

Z3

On some of these models built before October 1998, there may be a rattle from the vehicle back when driving on rough roads.

This condition may be caused by mounting surface not being smooth or intermittent contact between shock top and mount.

To correct this condition, proceed as follows:

1. Remove both rear shock absorbers.
2. Inspect mounting surface for punch burrs around stud holes and weld splatter on contact surface.
3. Repair imperfections and touch up with suitable rustproofing primer, as required.
4. Remove shock absorber nut, plate, mount and gasket.
5. Inspect mount for cracks or damage. Replace as required.
6. Clean shock absorber top, peel new sealing washer protective film off and adhere to shock. Ensure washer is centered.
7. Clean upper plate underside, peel new

sealing washer protective film off and adhere to plate. Ensure washer is centered.
8. Install mount, plate with sealing washer and new mounting nut. **Torque** nut to 10 ft. lbs.
9. Install new gasket and install shock absorber.
10. If vehicle was built before October 1998, install reinforcement plate (part No. 51 71 8 413 359) on body top with chambered face down, against body.
11. **Do not connect lower shock absorber to mount.**
12. **Torque** upper mounting nuts to 18 ft. lbs.
13. Connect lower shock absorber and **torque** mounting bolt to 57 ft. lbs.

REAR AXLE DIFFERENTIAL WHINE

323Ci & 2000 323i & 1999 323i Sedan

On some of these 323Ci, 2000 323i and 1999 323i Sedan models built before April 2000 and equipped with 5L40E transmission, there may be a loud while or howling at 70 mph with the engine under light load.

This condition may be caused by differential gear meshing whine being transmitted to the body via the propeller shaft center bearing.

To correct this condition install propeller shaft insulation strip, as follows:

1. Remove exhaust system and heat shields.
2. Support propeller shaft with suitable jack.
3. Remove propeller shaft to transmission output flange mounting bolts.
4. Mark center bearing position for installation in original position.
5. Remove center bearing mounting nuts and lower propeller shaft.
6. Install butyl insulation strip (part No. 26 12 7 511 140) on top of center bearing housing.
7. Apply thin coast of suitable mineral based engine oil to exposed side of insulation strip.
8. Install propeller shaft mounting bolts. **Torque** new mounting nuts to 74 ft. lbs.
9. **Torque** center bearing mounting nuts to 16 ft. lbs.
10. Ensure strip is squeeze out between housing and tunnel.
11. Install heat shields and exhaust system.

328Ci & 2000 328i & 1999 328i Sedan

On some of these 328Ci, 2000 328i and 1999 328i Sedan models built before October 2000 and equipped with 5L40E transmission, there may be a loud while or howling at 70 mph with the engine under light load.

Refer to "323Ci & 2000 323i & 1999 323i Sedan" for cause and correction.

528i

On some of these 528i models built before September 1998 equipped with THMR-1 transmission and 528i models built before September 2000 equipped with 5L40E transmission, there may be a loud while or howling at 70 mph with the engine under light load.

Refer to "323Ci & 2000 323i & 1999 323i Sedan" for cause and correction.

On 528i models, the propeller shaft does not have to be remove from the transmission output flange.

REAR POPPING OR SNAPPING

1999 323i & 328i Sedans

On some of these models built before July 1998 there may be a popping or snapping when driving over dips or hard cornering.

This condition may be caused by the coil spring sticking to the rubber upper mount.

To correct this condition coat mounting with suitable talcum powder as follows:

1. Raise and support vehicle with rear wheels hanging free.
2. Clean upper coils and mounts with suitable dry shop rag. **Do not us spray cleaners or solvents on mounts.**
3. Apply liberal coating of suitable talcum (baby) powder to mount and spring contact area.

NOISY REAR AXLE DIFFERENTIAL

1998 540, 740 & 750

On some of these models built in November 1997 the rear axle differential may be noisy

This condition may be caused by improperly hardened differential pinion shaft.

To correct this condition remove differential assembly.

TIGHTENING SPECIFICATIONS

Year	Component	Torque, Ft. Lbs.
318i, 323is & 328is & 1998–99 M3 & 328i & 1998 323i & 1999 323i & 328i Convertibles		
1998–1999	Auxiliary Control Arm	94①
	Compression Strut To Body	⑩
	Control Arm To Differential Carrier	57①
	Control Arm To Trailing Arm	81
	Drain/Fill Plug	52
	Differential Carrier, Front	70
	Differential Carrier, Rear	57
	Differential Carrier w/Rubber Mounts To Body	57
	Drive Flange To Axle Shaft	⑬⑭
	Half Shaft	⑥⑦
	Propeller Shaft Center Mount	15
	Propeller Shaft Center Pivot Journal	72㉒
	Propeller Shaft Constant-Velocity Joint To Rear Axle Drive Flange	㉑
	Propeller Shaft Universal Joint To Rear Axle Drive Flange	③
	Propeller Shaft Universal Joint To Transmission	⑱
	Shock Absorber Piston Rod Thrust Bearing	10
	Shock Absorber Support On Body/Different Carrier	18
	Shock Absorber To Trailing Arm, Wheel Carrier, Carrier Arm, Control Arm	74①
	Strut	88
	Trailing Arm Console To Body	57
	Trailing Arm To Console	81
	Trailing Arm To Differential Carrier	①⑧
	Vibration Damper	57
323Ci, 325, 328Ci & 330 & 2000 323i & 328i & 1999 323i & 328i Sedans & 2001 M3		
1999–2001	Auxiliary Control Arm	94①
	Compression Strut To Body	⑩
	Control Arm To Differential Carrier	57①
	Control Arm To Trailing Arm	81
	Differential Carrier, Front	②
	Differential Carrier, Rear	④
	Differential Carrier w/Rubber Mounts To Body	57
	Drain/Fill Plug	52
	Drive Flange To Axle Shaft	⑬⑭
	Half Shaft	⑥⑦
	Propeller Shaft Center Mount	15
	Propeller Shaft Center Pivot Journal	72㉒
	Propeller Shaft Constant-Velocity Joint To Rear Axle Drive Flange	㉑
	Propeller Shaft Universal Joint To Rear Axle Drive Flange	⑳
	Propeller Shaft Universal Joint To Transmission	⑱
	Shock Absorber Piston Rod Thrust Bearing	10
	Shock Absorber Support On Body/Different Carrier	21
	Shock Absorber To Trailing Arm, Wheel Carrier, Carrier Arm, Control Arm	74①
	Strut	66
	Tension Strut (2001 M3)	44⑫
	Trailing Arm Console To Body	57
	Trailing Arm To Console	81
	Trailing Arm To Differential Carrier	①⑧
	Vibration Damper	57

Continued

TIGHTENING SPECIFICATIONS—Continued

Year	Component	Torque, Ft. Lbs.
M5, 525, 528, 530 & 540		
1998–2001	Auxiliary Control Arm	94①
	Compression Strut To Body	⑩
	Control Arm To Differential Carrier, Upper	81①
	Control Arm To Rear Axle Support	44①
	Control Arm To Wheel Carrier, Upper	105
	Differential Carrier, Front	111
	Differential Carrier, Rear	77⑤
	Differential Carrier w/Rubber Mounts To Body	120
	Drain/Fill Plug	52
	Drive Flange To Axle Shaft	⑬⑭
	Half Shaft	⑥⑦
	Propeller Shaft Center Mount	15
	Propeller Shaft Center Pivot Journal	72㉒
	Propeller Shaft Constant-Velocity Joint To Rear Axle Drive Flange	㉑
	Propeller Shaft Flexible Disk	66
	Propeller Shaft Flexible Disk To Transmission	74
	Propeller Shaft Universal Joint To Rear Axle Drive Flange	⑳
	Propeller Shaft Universal Joint To Transmission	⑱
	Shock Absorber Piston Rod Thrust Bearing	⑮
	Shock Absorber Support On Body/Different Carrier	⑯
	Shock Absorber To Trailing Arm, Wheel Carrier, Carrier Arm, Control Arm	94①
	Stabilizer Link	48
	Swing Arm, Integral Link, Wheel Carrier	189①
	Swing Arm To Rear Axle Support, Front	43①
	Swing Arm To Rear Axle Support, Rear	①⑪
	Traction Rod To Wheel Carrier	48⑨
	Trailing Arm To Differential Carrier	①⑧
	Vibration Damper	57
	Wheel Carrier Bearing	22⑫
X5		
2000–01	Auxiliary Control Arm	94①
	Compression Strut To Body	⑩
	Control Arm To Differential Carrier, Upper	74①
	Control Arm To Rear Axle Support	44①
	Control Arm To Wheel Carrier, Upper	122
	Differential Carrier, Front	74
	Differential Carrier, Rear	122
	Differential Carrier w/Rubber Mounts To Body	120
	Drain/Fill Plug	52
	Drive Flange To Axle Shaft	310⑬
	Propeller Shaft Center Mount	15
	Propeller Shaft Center Pivot Journal	72㉒
	Propeller Shaft Constant-Velocity Joint To Rear Axle Drive Flange	㉑
	Propeller Shaft Universal Joint To Rear Axle Drive Flange	③
	Propeller Shaft Universal Joint To Transmission	⑱
	Shock Absorber Support On Body/Different Carrier	41
	Stabilizer Bar Bracket To Rear Axle Support	14

Continued

TIGHTENING SPECIFICATIONS—Continued

Year	Component	Torque, Ft. Lbs.
X5		
2000–01	Stabilizer Link	74
	Swing Arm, Integral Link, Wheel Carrier	184①
	Swing Arm To Rear Axle Support, Front	74①
	Swing Arm To Rear Axle Support, Rear	122①
	Traction Rod To Wheel Carrier	48⑨
	Trailing Arm To Differential Carrier	①⑧
	Vibration Damper	57
	Wheel Carrier Bearing	74
Z3 & 318ti		
1998–2001	Auxiliary Control Arm	94①
	Compression Strut To Body	⑩
	Control Arm To Differential Carrier	57①
	Control Arm To Trailing Arm	81
	Differential Carrier, Front	81
	Differential Carrier, Rear	57
	Differential Carrier w/Rubber Mounts To Body	57
	Drain/Fill Plug	52
	Drive Flange To Axle Shaft	⑬⑭
	Half Shaft	⑥⑦
	Propeller Shaft Center Mount	15
	Propeller Shaft Center Pivot Journal	72㉒
	Propeller Shaft Constant-Velocity Joint To Rear Axle Drive Flange	㉑
	Propeller Shaft Universal Joint To Rear Axle Drive Flange	⑲
	Propeller Shaft Universal Joint To Transmission	⑱
	Shock Absorber Piston Rod Thrust Bearing	10
	Shock Absorber Support On Body/Different Carrier	18
	Shock Absorber To Trailing Arm, Wheel Carrier, Carrier Arm, Control Arm	94①
	Stabilizer Bar To Trailing Arm	16⑰
	Strut	94
	Trailing Arm Console To Body	57
	Trailing Arm To Console	81
	Trailing Arm To Differential Carrier	①⑧
	Vibration Damper	57
740 & 750		
1998–2001	Auxiliary Control Arm	94①
	Compression Strut To Body	⑩
	Control Arm To Differential Carrier, Upper	81①
	Control Arm To Rear Axle Support	44①
	Control Arm To Wheel Carrier, Upper	118
	Differential Carrier, Front	94
	Differential Carrier, Rear	③
	Differential Carrier w/Rubber Mounts To Body	57
	Drain/Fill Plug	52
	Drive Flange To Axle Shaft	⑬⑭
	Half Shaft	⑥⑦
	Propeller Shaft Center Pivot Journal	72㉒
	Propeller Shaft Constant-Velocity Joint To Rear Axle Drive Flange	㉑
	Propeller Shaft Universal Joint To Rear Axle Drive Flange	⑳
	Propeller Shaft Universal Joint To Transmission	⑱

Continued

TIGHTENING SPECIFICATIONS—Continued

Year	Component	Torque, Ft. Lbs.
740 & 750		
1998–2001	Shock Absorber Piston Rod Thrust Bearing	⑮
	Shock Absorber Support On Body/Different Carrier	18
	Shock Absorber To Trailing Arm, Wheel Carrier, Carrier Arm, Control Arm	94①
	Stabilizer Link	31
	Swing Arm, Integral Link, Wheel Carrier	174①
	Swing Arm To Rear Axle Support, Front	44①
	Swing Arm To Rear Axle Support, Rear	96①
	Traction Rod To Wheel Carrier	48⑨
	Trailing Arm To Differential Carrier	①⑧
	Vibration Damper	57

① — Vehicle w/complete equipment in normal driving position w/full fuel tank. No weight in passenger seats.

② — 323Ci, 325, 328Ci & 330 & 2000 323i & 328i & 1999 323i & 328i Sedans, 70 ft. lbs.; 2001 M3, 147 ft. lbs.

③ — 75 ft. lbs.; Tighten also via screw head, 55 ft. lbs.

④ — 323Ci, 325, 328Ci & 330 & 2000 323i & 328i & 1999 323i & 328i Sedans, 128 ft. lbs.; 2001 M3, 54 ft. lbs.

⑤ — Tighten also via screw head.

⑥ — Fillister head bolt M10, 61 ft. lbs.; w/locking teeth M10, 71 ft. lbs; w/locking teeth M12, 81 ft. lbs.

⑦ — Torx M10, 61 ft. lbs.; w/ribbed teeth, M8, 47 ft. lbs.; w/ribbed teeth M10 black, 74 ft. lbs.; w/ribber teeth M10 silver, 59 ft. lbs.; w/ribber teeth M12, 100 ft. lbs.

⑧ — 49 ft. lbs.; 10.9, 57 ft. lbs.

⑨ — Tapered spigot & bore must be free of grease.

⑩ — M8 8.8, 15 ft. lbs.; M8 10.9, 22 ft. lbs.

⑪ — Sedan, 85 ft. lbs.; Sports Wagon, 128 ft. lbs.

⑫ — Final tighten an additional 90°.

⑬ — Collar nut lightly oiled.

⑭ — M22, 147 ft. lbs.; M24, 184 ft. lbs.; M27 221 ft. lbs.

⑮ — M10, 17 ft. lbs.; M14, 20 ft. lbs.

⑯ — Yellow chrome-plates, 18 ft. lbs; Silver-gray, 21 ft. lbs.

⑰ — Vehicle complete with normal equipment, plus 150 lbs. in front seats and 150 lbs. centered in models with rear seat, plus 31 lbs. centered in luggage compartment.

⑱ — M10 8.8, 35 ft. lbs.; M10 10.9, 44 ft. lbs.; M12 8.8, 60 ft. lbs.; M12 10.9 except M3 and M5, 74 ft. lbs.; M12 10.9, M3 & M5, 84 ft. lbs.; M14, 103 ft. lbs.

⑲ — Compression nut, 47 ft. lbs. (replace w/ribbed nut); Torx bolt, 63 ft. lbs.

⑳ — Compression nut, 47 ft. lbs. (replace w/ribbed nut); Torx bolt, 52 ft. lbs.

㉑ — Compression nut, M8, 24 ft. lbs.; M10, 47 ft. lbs. Finned nut, M8, 32 ft. lbs.; M10, 52 ft. lbs.

㉒ — Use suitable Loctite.

Transfer Case

NOTE: On Air Bag Equipped Models, Refer To "Air Bag System Precautions" Located In The Front Of This Manual For System Disarming & Arming Procedures.

INDEX

Page No.	Page No.	Page No.
Tightening Specifications 2-115	Transfer Case, Replace 2-114	X5 2-114
	325xi & 330xi 2-114	

TRANSFER CASE

REPLACE

X5

Automatic Transmission

1. Ensure shift selector is in P position.
2. Remove exhaust system.
3. Remove mounting bolts and reinforcement plate.
4. Remove heat shields.
5. Disconnect oxygen sensors' connectors.
6. Disconnect stabilizer bar as outlined in "Front Suspension & Steering" section.
7. Remove rear heat shield.
8. Remove propeller shaft to front differential mounting bolts and remove flexible disk with centering flange.
9. Disconnect propeller shaft from transfer case.
10. Loosen selector lever clamp bushing mounting nut.
11. Remove mounting nut and pull cable out of holder.
12. Support transmission with suitable jack and fixture tools.
13. Disconnect oxygen sensor cable from transmission crossmember.
14. Remove mounting bolts and crossmember.
15. Disconnect vent line.
16. Disconnect oxygen sensor cable from transfer case.
17. Remove propeller shaft as outlined in "Rear Axle & Suspension" section.
18. Support transfer case with suitable transmission jack and fixture tool No. 27 1 100, or equivalent.
19. Remove mounting bolts and transfer case.
20. Reverse procedure to install, noting the following:
    a. Replace dowel sleeves, as required.
    b. Apply thin coat of Weicon Antisize grease, or equivalent, to splines.
    c. Apply suitable grease to centering mount.
    d. Flexible disk arrows must point toward flange arms.
    e. **Torque** reinforcement plate mounting bolts to 41 ft. lbs., then tighten an additional 90° and final tighten an additional 15°.
    f. Tighten mounting bolts and nuts to specifications.

Manual Transmission

1. Remove exhaust system.
2. Remove rear and front righthand heat shields.
3. Remove mounting bolts and reinforcement plate.
4. Disconnect stabilizer bar as outlined in "Front Suspension & Steering" section.
5. Remove propeller shaft to front differential mounting bolts and remove flexible disk with centering flange.
6. Disconnect propeller shaft from transfer case.
7. Support transmission with suitable jack and fixture tool No. 23 0 130, or equivalent.
8. Remove mounting bolts and crossmember.
9. Disconnect vent line.
10. Remove propeller shaft as outlined in "Rear Axle & Suspension" section.
11. Support transfer case with suitable transmission jack and fixture tool No. 27 1 100, or equivalent.
12. Remove mounting bolts and transfer case.
13. Reverse procedure to install, noting the following:
    a. Replace dowel sleeves, as required.
    b. Install new seal ring on transfer case drive shaft.
    c. Apply thin coat of Weicon Antisize grease, or equivalent, to splines.
    d. Apply suitable grease to centering mount.
    e. Flexible disk arrows must point toward flange arms.
    f. **Torque** reinforcement plate mounting bolts to 41 ft. lbs., then tighten an additional 90° and final tighten an additional 15°.
    g. Tighten mounting bolts and nuts to specifications.

325xi & 330xi

1. Remove underbody protection and exhaust system.
2. Remove rear and righthand front heat shields.
3. Remove mounting bolts and front propeller shaft.
4. Support transmission with suitable jack and fixture.
5. Remove mounting bolts and transmission crossmember.
6. Disconnect vent line.
7. Remove propeller shaft as outlined in "Rear Axle & Suspension" section.
8. Remove mounting bolts and transfer case.
9. Reverse procedure to install, noting the following:
    a. Replace dowel sleeves, as required.
    b. Apply thin coat of Weicon Antisize grease, or equivalent, to splines.
    c. **On models equipped with manual transmission,** replace drive shaft sealing ring.
    d. **On all models,** tighten mounting bolts and nuts to specifications.

TIGHTENING SPECIFICATIONS

Year	Component	Torque, Ft. lbs.
X5		
2000–01	Case To Transmission	32
	Crossmember	①
	Drain Plug	24
	Propeller Shaft Center Pivot Journal	72⑤
	Propeller Shaft Constant-Velocity Joint To Rear Axle Drive Flange	④
	Propeller Shaft Universal Joint To Rear Axle Drive Flange	③
	Propeller Shaft Universal Joint To Transmission	②
	Reinforcement Plate	⑥
	Vibration Damper	17
325xi & 330xi		
2001	Case To Transmission	32
	Crossmember	55
	Propeller Shaft Center Pivot Journal	72⑤
	Propeller Shaft Constant-Velocity Joint To Rear Axle Drive Flange	④
	Propeller Shaft Universal Joint To Rear Axle Drive Flange	③
	Propeller Shaft Universal Joint To Transmission	②
	Drain Plug	24

① — M8, 15 ft. lbs.; M10, 30 ft. lbs.; M12, 55 ft. lbs.

② — M10 8.8, 35 ft. lbs.; M10 10.9, 44 ft. lbs.; M12 8.8, 60 ft. lbs.; M12 10.9 except M3 and M5, 74 ft. lbs.; M12 10.9, M3 & M5, 84 ft. lbs.; M14, 103 ft. lbs.

③ — Compression nut, 47 ft. lbs. (replace w/ribbed nut); Torx bolt, 52 ft. lbs.

④ — Compression nut, M8, 24 ft. lbs.; M10, 47 ft. lbs. Finned nut, M8, 32 ft. lbs.; M10, 52 ft. lbs.

⑤ — Use suitable Loctite.

⑥ — Refer to “Transfer Case, Replace” for tightening specifications and sequence.

Front Suspension & Steering

NOTE: On Air Bag Equipped Models, Refer To "Air Bag System Precautions" Located In The Front Of This Manual For System Disarming & Arming Procedures.

NOTE: Prior To Performing Any Service Operations Listed In This Section, Consult The "Technical Service Bulletins" Section For Related Information.

INDEX

	Page No.
Ball Joint, Replace	2-117
Ball Joint Inspection	2-117
Coil Spring, Replace	2-117
Control Arm, Replace	2-118
M3, Z3, 318, 323, 325, 328 & 328	2-118
M5 & 540	2-119
X5	2-119
525, 528 & 530	2-119
740 & 750	2-119
Crossmember, Replace	2-120
M3, Z3, 318, 323, 325, 328 & 330	2-120
M5 & 540	2-121
X5	2-121
525, 528 & 530	2-122
740 & 750	2-122
Description	2-116
Hub & Bearing, Replace	2-116
M3, Z3, 318, 323, 328, 740 & 750	2-116
M5, 525, 528, 530 & 540	2-116
X5	2-117
325 & 330	2-117
Power Steering	2-171
Power Steering Gear, Replace	2-122
M3, Z3, 318, 323, 325, 328 & 330	2-122
M5, 540, 740 & 750	2-123
X5	2-123
525, 528 & 530	2-123
Power Steering Pump, Replace	2-123
Power Steering System Bleed	2-123
Precautions	2-116
Air Bag Systems	2-116
Battery Ground Cable	2-116
Stabilizer Bar, Replace	2-120
M3, Z3, 318, 323, 325, 328 & 330	2-120
M5 & 540	2-120
X5	2-120
525, 528 & 530	2-120
740 & 750	2-120
Steering Knuckle, Replace	2-119
M3, Z3, 318, 323, 325 & 330	2-119
M5, 525, 528, 530 & 540	2-120
X5	2-120
740 & 750	2-120
Strut, Replace	2-117
M3, Z3, 318, 323, 325, 328 & 330	2-117
M5, 525, 528, 530 & 540	2-118
X5	2-118
740 & 750	2-118
Technical Service Bulletins	2-124
Center Tie Rod Noise	2-124
Front Suspension Creaking	2-124
Power Steering Hose Leak	2-124
Steering Wheel Vibration Or Buzz	2-124
Tension Strut, Replace	2-122
M5 & 540	2-122
X5	2-122
525, 528 & 530	2-122
740 & 750	2-122
Tie Rod, Replace	2-122
Tightening Specifications	2-124
Wheel Bearing, Adjust	2-116

PRECAUTIONS

AIR BAG SYSTEMS

Refer to "Air Bag System Precautions" in the front of this manual for system disarming and arming procedures.

BATTERY GROUND CABLE

Prior to service, disconnect battery ground cable and isolate as required.

DESCRIPTION

Refer to **Figs. 1 through 3** for front axle description.

WHEEL BEARING

ADJUST

1. Remove wheel, bearing cap and cotter pin.
2. **Torque** castle nut to 22–24 ft. lbs. while turning hub to align bearing rollers and to force away grease which can affect play. Give hub an additional two turns without disturbing castle nut.
3. Loosen castle nut until hub can move axially. **Torque** castle nut to 24 inch lbs., then turn back to nearest slot and insert a new cotter pin.
4. Ensure notched washer turns freely in both directions using suitable screwdriver.

HUB & BEARING

REPLACE

M3, Z3, 318, 323, 328, 740 & 750

1. Remove brake disc as outlined in "Disc Brakes" section.
2. Remove anti-lock brake impulse sensor.
3. Remove grease cap.
4. Unlock axle nut using suitable chisel.
5. Remove collar nut using socket tool No. 31 2 080, or equivalent.
6. Remove bearing using puller tools No. 31 2 116 and 33 4 201/202/203, or equivalents, and wheel studs.
7. Remove inner bearing race from spindle using bearing puller tools Nos. 33 4 401/402/406, or equivalents. If suitable bearing tool is not available, proceed as follows:
   a. Bend dust guard plate, as required.
   b. Bend dust guard plate back.
   c. Remove bearing inner race using puller tools Nos. 00 7 500 and 31 2 106, or equivalents.
8. Reverse procedure to install, noting the following:
   a. Install new bearing using bearing installer tool No. 31 2 110, or equivalent.
   b. Install new collar nut and tighten to specifications.
   c. Lock collar nut.
   d. Install new grease cap using suitable sealing compound.

M5, 525, 528, 530 & 540

1. Remove brake disc as outlined in "Disc Brakes" section. Brake lines remain connected.
2. Remove anti-lock brake impulse sensor.
3. Disconnect stabilizer link as outlined under "Stabilizer Bar, Replace."
4. Remove mounting nut and disconnect track rod using knuckle puller tool No. 31 2 240, or equivalent.
5. Mark strut position in swivel bearing for installation.
6. Remove mounting nut, expand and pull swivel bearing down using expansion tool No. 31 2 200, or equivalent.
7. Remove mounting bolts and wheel bearing.
8. Reverse procedure to install, noting the following:

a. Contact face of wheel bearing, swivel bearing and threaded bores must be clean and grease free.
b. Press swivel bearing upward to stop with suitable jack.
c. Tighten mounting bolts and new self-locking nuts to specifications.

X5

1. Remove swivel bearing.
2. Clamp swivel bearing in suitable aluminum jawed vice.
3. Remove drive flange using bearing removal tools Nos. 33 2 116/150 and 33 4 200, or equivalents.
4. Remove circlip and bearings using puller tools No. 31 2 113 and 33 2 261/262/263, or equivalents.
5. Reverse procedure to install, noting the following:
   a. Coat bearing seat over more that half length with Loctite No. 648, or equivalent.
   b. Wider bearing chamfer must point toward swivel base.
   c. Install new bearing using bearing installer tools No. 31 2 113 and 33 3 261//268, or equivalents.

325 & 330

325Ci, 325i, 330Ci & 330i

Refer to "M3, Z3, 318, 323, 328, 740 & 750."

325xi & 330xi

1. Remove swivel bearing.
2. Clamp swivel bearing in suitable aluminum jawed vice.
3. Remove drive flange using bearing removal tools Nos. 33 2 116 and 33 4 200, or equivalents.
4. Remove circlip and bearings using puller tools No. 31 2 113 and 33 2 261/262/266, or equivalents.
5. Reverse procedure to install, noting the following:
   a. Coat bearing seat over more that half length with Loctite No. 648, or equivalent.
   b. Wider bearing chamfer must point toward swivel base.
   c. Install new bearing using bearing installer tools No. 31 2 113 and 33 3 261/266/268, or equivalents.

BALL JOINT INSPECTION

1. Raise and support vehicle.
2. Grasp tire at top and bottom.
3. Attempt to move tire in a side to side motion while observing ball joint for visible play.
4. If any play is observed, replace ball joint as outlined under "Ball Joint, Replace."

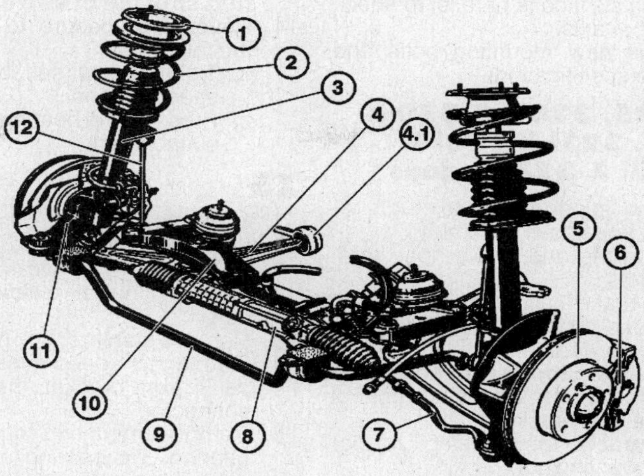

1	Thrust bearing	8	Steering gear
2	Coil spring	9	Stabilizer
3	Spring strut shock absorber	10	Front axle support
4	Control arm	11	Steering knuckle
4.1	Control arm holder	12	Stabilizer link
5	Brake disk		
6	Brake caliper		
7	Track rod		

BM2020100007000X

Fig. 1 Front suspension components. M3, Z3, 318, 323, 325, 328 & 330

BALL JOINT

REPLACE

Refer to "Control Arm, Replace" for ball joint replacement.

COIL SPRING

REPLACE

1. Remove strut as outlined under "Strut, Replace."
2. Clamp strut tool No. 31 3 141, or equivalent, into suitable vise.
3. Position protective insert tool No. 31 3 101, or equivalent, on spring plate, as required.
4. Install strut coil spring with upper and lower coil between tool spring holders.
5. Relieve thrust bearing stress by tightening tool.
6. Remove mounting nut and spring using socket tool No. 31 3 210, or equivalent. **Do not use impact tools.**
7. Reverse procedure to install, noting the following:
   a. Replace rubber damper, auxiliary spring, protective tube and spring pad, as required.
   b. Support coil spring with larger end turn diameter downward.
   c. Ensure both spring ends are outside retainers.
   d. Tighten new mounting bolts and nuts to specifications.

STRUT

REPLACE

M3, Z3, 318, 323, 325, 328 & 330

Z3, 323is & 328is & 1998-99 M3, 328i & 1998 323i & 1999 323i & 328i Convertibles

1. Raise and support vehicle, then remove tire and wheel assembly.
2. Remove wires and brake hose form strut holders.
3. Support hub and bearing with suitable wire.
4. Remove stabilizer bar ball pin mounting nut.
5. Remove steering knuckle mounting bolts and nuts.
6. Remove upper mounting nuts and strut.
7. Reverse procedure to install, noting the following:
   a. **On M3 and Z3 M Roadster models,** thrust bearing long sheet-metal flange must point forward.
   b. **On all models,** ensure ball pin

wrench surface is parallel to shock absorber axis.
   c. Tighten new mounting bolts and nuts to specifications.

323Ci, 325, 328Ci & 330 & 2000 M3, 323i & 328i & 1999 323i & 328i Sedans

1. Raise and support vehicle, then remove tire and wheel assembly.
2. Remove wires and brake hose form strut holders,
3. Remove brake caliper as outlined in "Disc Brake" section. Support aside with suitable wire.
4. **On models equipped with headlamp range adjustment,** disconnect control arm angle joint bracket.
5. **On all models,** remove stabilizer bar ball pin mounting nut.
6. Remove mounting nut and press tie rod off steering knuckle using knuckle puller tool No. 32 3 090, or equivalent.
7. Remove mounting nut and force control arm off steering knuckle using joint separation tool.
8. Suspend steering knuckle with suitable wire.
9. Mark support bearing threaded pin to wheelhousing for install alignment.
10. **On M3 models,** remove centering pin mounting nut.
11. **On all models,** remove support bearing mounting nut.
12. Remove support bearing and strut.
13. Reverse procedure to install, noting the following:
    a. Position positioning pin into gap and press steering knuckle upward onto stop.
    b. Tighten new mounting bolts and nuts to specifications.

M5, 525, 528, 530 & 540

1. Remove brake caliper as outline in "Disc Brake" section and tie to body with line connected.
2. Disconnect anti-lock brake sensor and brake wear cable from bracket and connection box.
3. Remove mounting bolt and disconnect stabilizer link.
4. Remove mounting bolt and disconnect track rod using knuckle puller tool No. 31 2 240, or equivalent.
5. Move steering to opposite lock.
6. Mark strut to swivel bearing position for installation alignment.
7. Remove mounting nut and expand swivel bearing using expansion tool No. 31 2 200, or equivalent.
8. Remove cap and disconnect Electronic Damper Control (EDC) connector.
9. Remove mounting nuts and strut thrust bearing from wheelhousing.
10. Protect wheelhousing with suitable cover.
11. Remove engine shielding, as required.
12. Press swivel bearing down with suitable lever such, as socket wrench extension, until strut can be tilted out and removed. Assistance may be required.
13. Press strut out of swivel bearing using suitable screwdriver or pry bar. **Do not turn strut out of swivel bearing.**
14. Reverse procedure to install, noting the following:
    a. Tighten new self-locking nuts to specifications.
    b. Press swivel bearing up to stop with suitable jack.

X5

1. Mark strut support bearing to wheelhousing for installation alignment.
2. Remove one or two support bearing mounting nut(s). Leave one nut secure.
3. Remove stabilizer link mounting nut.
4. Disconnect speed sensor/brake wear cable from bracket, then the housing connector.
5. Remove mounting nuts and swivel bearing. Tie bearing aside with suitable wire.
6. Remove remaining support bearing mounting nut and strut.

740 & 750

1. Remove brake caliper as outlined in "Disc Brake" section and tie to body with line connected.
2. Remove mounting bolt and disconnect track rod using knuckle puller tool No. 32 1 190, or equivalent.
3. Remove mounting nut and bolt and disconnect stabilizer push rod.
4. Disconnect cable from strut bracket.
5. , then the control arm from front axle support.
6. Remove mounting bolt and expand swivel bearing by twisting slot 90° using expansion tool No. 31 2 200, or equivalent. Leave tool in steering knuckle.
7. Remove cap and disconnect Electronic Damper Control (EDC) connector, as required.
8. Remove mounting nuts and strut thrust bearing from wheelhousing.
9. Protect wheelhousing with suitable cover.
10. Remove engine shielding, as required.
11. Press swivel bearing down with suitable lever such as socket wrench extension until strut can be tilted out and removed. Assistance may be required.
12. Press strut out of swivel bearing using suitable screwdriver or pry bar. **Do not turn strut out of swivel bearing.**
13. Reverse procedure to install, noting the following:
    a. Tighten new self-locking nuts to specifications.
    b. Press swivel bearing up to stop with suitable jack.

CONTROL ARM

REPLACE

M3, Z3, 318, 323, 325, 328 & 328

Z3, 323IS & 328IS & 1998-99 M3, 328I & 1998 323I & 1999 323I & 328I CONVERTIBLES

1. Raise and support front of vehicle, then remove tire and wheel assembly.
2. Remove mounting nut and disconnect stabilizer link.
3. Support wheel bearing and hub with suitable wire.
4. Remove strut mounting nut.
5. Remove steering knuckle mounting bolts and nuts.
6. Remove nut and ball joint using knuckle puller tool No. 31 2 160, or equivalent.
7. Remove control arm bracket mounting bolts.
8. Remove control arm to steering knuckle.
9. Remove mounting nuts and bolts.
10. Knock ball joint loose using suitable plastic mallet.
11. Remove mounting nut and knock control arm ball joint loose using suitable plastic hammer.
12. Reverse procedure to install, noting the following:
    a. **On M3, Z3 M Coupe and Z3 M Roadster models,** remove shield plates between manifold and wheelhousing, as required.
    b. **On all models,** force ball joint upward using suitable transmission jack.
    c. Tighten new mounting bolts and nuts to specifications.
    d. Align front suspension as outlined in "Wheel Alignment" section.

323CI & 328CI & 2000 M3, 323I & 328I & 1999 323I & 328I SEDANS

1. Raise and support vehicle, then remove tire and wheel assembly.
2. Remove engine underguard.
3. Remove mounting bolts and front axle reinforcement.
4. Remove mounting bolts and reinforcement plate.
5. Remove mounting nut and disconnect control arm angle joint bracket.
6. Remove mounting nut and disconnect control arm ball joint using suitable plastic hammer.
7. Remove control arm.
8. Remove mounting nut and press control arm off steering knuckle using knuckle puller tool No. 32 3 090, or equivalent.
9. Remove mounting bolts and control arm bracket from engine support.
10. Reverse procedure to install, noting the following:
    a. Force ball joint upward using suitable transmission jack and base fixture tool No. 11 7 360, or equivalent.
    b. Tighten new mounting bolts and nuts to specifications.
    c. **Torque** reinforcement plate mounting bolts to 44 ft. lbs., then tighten an additional 90°.
    d. Align front suspension as outlined in "Wheel Alignment" section

325 & 330

325Ci, 325i, 330Ci & 330i

Refer to "323Ci & 328Ci & 2000 M3, 323i & 328i & 1999 323i & 328i Sedans."

325xi & 330xi

1. Remove half shaft as outlined in "Front Wheel Drive" section.
2. Remove mounting nut and press control arm off steering knuckle using knuckle puller tool No. 32 3 090, or equivalent.
3. Remove mounting nut and control arm ball joint using ball joint puller tool No. 32 2 040, or equivalent.
4. Reverse procedure to install, noting the following:
   a. Install new control arm rubber mounts.
   b. Tighten new mounting bolts and nuts to specifications.
   c. Align front suspension as outlined in "Wheel Alignment" section.

M5 & 540

1. Raise and support vehicle, then remove tire and wheel assembly.
2. Disconnect stabilizer link.
3. Mark strut to swivel bearing for installation alignment.
4. Remove mounting bolt and expand swivel bearing by twisting slot 90° using expansion tool No. 31 2 200, or equivalent.
5. Remove front axle support/swivel bearing mounting nut.
6. Press control arm off swivel bearing using knuckle puller tool No. 31 2 240, or equivalent.
7. Reverse procedure to install, noting the following:
   a. Tighten new self-locking nuts to specifications.
   b. Align front suspension as outlined in "Wheel Alignment" section.

X5

1. Raise and support vehicle, then remove tire and wheel assembly.
2. Remove mounting nut and control arm from front axle support.
3. Loosen control arm to swivel bearing mounting nut three threads.
4. Press control arm off swivel bearing using knuckle puller tool No. 31 2 240, or equivalent.
5. Remove mounting nut and control arm.
6. Reverse procedure to install, noting the following:
   a. Tighten new self-locking nuts to specifications.
   b. Align front suspension as outlined in "Wheel Alignment" section.

525, 528 & 530

1. Remove engine splash guard.
2. Remove mounting nuts and control arm from front axle support.
3. Press control arm off swivel bearing using knuckle puller tool No. 31 2 240, or equivalent.
4. Reverse procedure to install, noting the following:
   a. Tighten new self-locking nuts to specifications.
   b. Align front suspension as outlined in "Wheel Alignment" section.

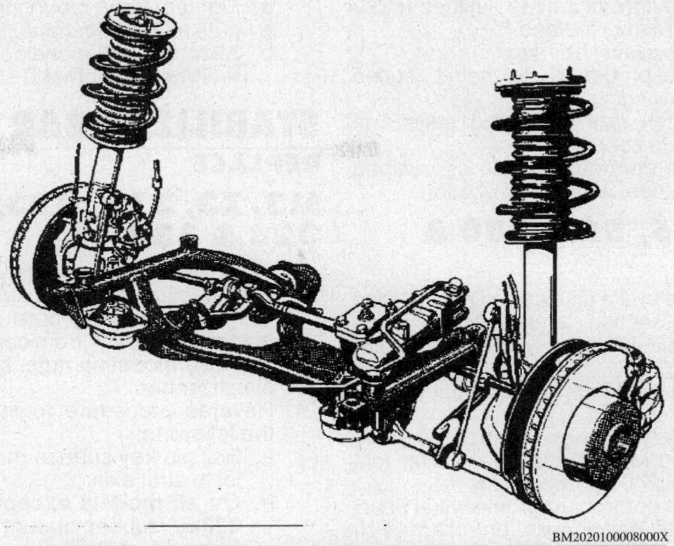

Fig. 2 Front suspension components (Part 1 of 2). M5, 525, 528, 530, 540, 740 & 750

740 & 750

1. Raise and support vehicle, then remove tire and wheel assembly.
2. Remove mounting bolt and control arm from front axle support.
3. Mark strut to swivel bearing for installation alignment.
4. Remove mounting bolt and expand swivel bearing by twisting slot 90° using expansion tool No. 31 2 200, or equivalent.
5. Remove front axle support/swivel bearing mounting nut.
6. Press control arm off swivel bearing using knuckle puller tool No. 31 2 240, or equivalent.
7. Reverse procedure to install, noting the following:
   a. Tighten new self-locking nuts to specifications.
   b. Align front suspension as outlined in "Wheel Alignment" section.

STEERING KNUCKLE

REPLACE

M3, Z3, 318, 323, 325 & 330

Z3, 323IS & 328IS & 1998-99 M3, 328I & 1998 323I & 1999 323I & 328I CONVERTIBLES

1. Remove wheel hub and bearing as outlined under "Hub & Bearing, Replace."
2. Disconnect tie rod using removal tool No. 32 2 070, or equivalent.
3. Remove mounting bolts and guard plate.
4. Remove mounting bolts, nuts and ball joint using removal tool No. 31 2 160, or equivalent.
5. Remove steering knuckle.
6. Reverse procedure to install, noting the following:
   a. Ensure proper replacement steering knuckle is install. Knuckles very according to model and steering applications.
   b. Tighten new mounting bolts and nuts to specifications.

323CI, 325, 328CI & 330 & 2000 M3, 323I & 328I & 1999 323I & 328I SEDANS

1. Remove wheel hub and bearing as outlined under "Hub & Bearing, Replace."
2. Disconnect tie rod using removal tool No. 32 2 090, or equivalent.
3. Remove mounting nut and press control arm off steering knuckle using removal tool.
4. Support steering knuckle with suitable wire.
5. Remove mounting bolt and expand swivel bearing by twisting slot 90° using expansion tool No. 31 2 200, or equivalent, as required. Leave tool in steering knuckle.
6. Remove steering knuckle.
7. Remove mounting bolts and guard plate.
8. Reverse procedure to install, noting the following:
   a. Install positioning pin into gap and press steering knuckle upward to stop.
   b. Tighten new mounting bolts and nuts to specifications.

325 & 330

325Ci, 325i, 330Ci & 330i

Refer to "323Ci & 328Ci & 2000 M3, 323i & 328i & 1999 323i & 328i Sedans."

325xi & 330xi

1. Remove drive shaft as outlined in "Front Wheel Drive" section.

2. Remove control arm as outlined under "Control Arm, Replace."
3. Remove swivel bearing.
4. Reverse procedure to install, noting the following:
   a. Tighten new mounting bolts and nuts to specifications.
   b. Align front suspension as outlined in "Wheel Alignment" section.

M5, 525, 528, 530 & 540

1. Remove brake disc as outlined in "Disc Brake" section and support aside using suitable wire with line connected.
2. Remove anti-lock brake impulse sensor.
3. Remove mounting nut and press track-track rod off using knuckle puller tool No. 31 2 240, or equivalent.
4. Remove control arm from swivel bearing as outlined under "Control Arm, Replace."
5. Remove traction or tension strut as outlined under "Tension Strut, Replace."
6. Pull swivel bearing down and remove.
7. Reverse procedure to install, noting the following:
   a. Tighten new mounting bolts and nuts to specifications.
   b. Align front suspension as outlined in "Wheel Alignment" section.

X5

1. Remove drive shaft as outlined in "Front Wheel Drive" section.
2. Remove brake disc as outlined in "Disc Brakes" section.
3. Remove anti-lock brake pulse generator.
4. Remove mounting nut and press tie rod off using knuckle puller tool No. 32 3 090, or equivalent.
5. Remove mounting nut and press control arm off swivel bearing using knuckle puller tool No. 31 2 240, or equivalent.
6. Remove swivel bearing.
7. Reverse procedure to install, noting the following:
   a. Tighten new mounting bolts and nuts to specifications.
   b. Align front suspension as outlined in "Wheel Alignment" section.

740 & 750

1. Remove wheel hub and bearing as outlined under "Hub & Bearing, Replace."
2. Remove steering knuckle protective plate.
3. Remove anti-lock brake impulse sensor.
4. Remove mounting nut and disconnect track rod using knuckle puller tool No. 31 1 190, or equivalent.
5. Remove control arm as outlined under "Control Arm, Replace."
6. Remove traction strut as outline under "Tension Strut, Replace."
7. Remove steering knuckle.
8. Reverse procedure to install, noting the following:
   a. Tighten new mounting bolts and nuts to specifications.
   b. Align front suspension as outlined in "Wheel Alignment" section.

STABILIZER BAR

REPLACE

M3, Z3, 318, 323, 325, 328 & 330

1. Remove mounting nuts and disconnect stabilizer link from strut.
2. Remove mounting nuts and disconnect stabilizer link from control arm.
3. Remove mounting nuts, brackets and stabilizer bar.
4. Reverse procedure to install, noting the following:
   a. Ball pin key surface must be parallel to strut axis.
   b. **On all models except 325xi and 330xi,** rubber mount open end faces downward.
   c. **On 325xi and 330xi models,** rubber mount open side faces forward.
   d. **On all models,** tighten new mounting nuts to specifications.

M5 & 540

1. Remove splash guard.
2. Support engine as outlined under "Oil Pan, Replace" in appropriate engine section.
3. Remove mounting nuts and disconnect track rod from pitman arm using knuckle puller tool No. 31 2 240, or equivalent.
4. Remove idler arm.
5. Remove mounting nuts and disconnect track rod from steering knuckle using knuckle puller tool No. 31 2 240, or equivalent.
6. Remove heat shield and positive cable from front axle support.
7. Disconnect steering pump oil cooler line from front axle support.
8. Disconnect wheelhousing trim from front axle support front area.
9. Remove steering gear with lines connected from front axle support.
10. Remove pressure strut mounting nuts and bolt, then turn steering onto lock.
11. Remove mounting nuts and disconnect stabilizer mount from front axle support.
12. Remove left and righthand stabilizer mounting nuts.
13. Mark strut to swivel bearing position for installation alignment.
14. Remove mounting bolt and expand swivel bearing by twisting slot 90° using expansion tool No. 31 2 200, or equivalent, as required.
15. Press control arm off swivel bearing using knuckle puller tool No. 31 2 240, or equivalent.
16. Support front axle support using suitable jack.
17. Remove mounting bolt, lower front axle support and remove stabilizer bar.
18. Reverse procedure to install. Tighten new mounting nuts to specifications.

X5

1. Remove underbody protection.
2. Remove mounting bolts and reinforcement plate.
3. Remove stabilizer pressure rod.
4. Remove stabilizer rubber mounts.
5. Disconnect lefthand swivel bearing guide joint.
6. Press strut forward.
7. Lift stabilizer bar over drive shafts and remove to rear.
8. Reverse procedure to install, noting the following:
   a. Tighten new mounting nuts to specifications.
   b. **Torque** reinforcement plate mounting bolts to 41 ft. lbs., then tighten an additional 90° and final tighten an additional 15°.

525, 528 & 530

1. Support engine as outlined under "Oil Pan, Replace" in appropriate engine section.
2. Partially loosen trim beside rear mounting bolts.
3. Support front axle support with suitable jack.
4. Remove mounting bolts.
5. Remove mounting nuts and stabilizer link.
6. Lower front axle support, then remove stabilizer bar by pulling back and downward.
7. Reverse procedure to install. Tighten new mounting nuts to specifications.

740 & 750

1. Remove front axle support as outlined under "Crossmember, Replace."
2. Remove stabilizer to strut link mounting nut.
3. Remove mounting nut and from stabilizer rod.
4. Remove mounting nuts, mounts and stabilizer bar.
5. Reverse procedure to install. Tighten new mounting nuts to specifications.

CROSSMEMBER

REPLACE

M3, Z3, 318, 323, 325, 328 & 330

Z3, 323is & 328is & 1998–99 M3, 328i & 1998 323i & 1999 323i & 328i CONVERTIBLES

1. Support engine as outlined under "Oil Pan, Replace" in appropriate engine section.
2. Remove mounting bolts and control arm brackets.
3. Remove mounting nuts, then knock left and righthand ball joints loose using suitable plastic hammer.
4. Remove steering gear mounting bolts.
5. **On convertible and roadster models,** remove mounting bolts and reinforcing cross struts.
6. **On all models,** support front axle carrier with suitable jack.

7. Remove mounting bolts and front axle carrier.
8. Reverse procedure to install, noting the following:
   a. Force ball joint upward using suitable transmission jack and fixture tool No. 11 7 360, or equivalent.
   b. Tighten new mounting bolts and nuts to specifications.
   c. Damaged engine support threads may be repaired with suitable Heli-coil inserts.
   d. Align front suspension as outlined in "Wheel Alignment" section.

323Ci & 328Ci & 2000 M3, 323i & 328i & 1999 323i & 328i SEDANS

1. Remove engine underguard.
2. Support engine as outlined under "Oil Pan, Replace" in appropriate engine section.
3. Remove mounting bolts and front axle reinforcement.
4. Remove mounting bolts and reinforcement plate.
5. Remove ride level sensors.
6. Remove mounting bolts and control arm brackets.
7. Remove mounting nuts, then knock left and righthand ball joints loose using suitable plastic hammer.
8. Remove steering gear mounting bolts.
9. Support front axle carrier with suitable jack.
10. Remove mounting bolts and front axle carrier.
11. Reverse procedure to install, noting the following:
   a. Force ball joint upward using suitable transmission jack and fixture tool No. 11 7 360, or equivalent.
   b. Tighten new mounting bolts and nuts to specifications.
   c. Damaged engine support threads may be repaired with suitable Heli-coil inserts.
   d. **Torque** reinforcement plate mounting bolts to 44 ft. lbs., then tighten an additional 90°.
   e. Align front suspension as outlined in "Wheel Alignment" section

325 & 330

325Ci, 325i, 330Ci & 330i

Refer to "323Ci & 328Ci & 2000 M3, 323i & 328i & 1999 323i & 328i Sedans."

325xi & 330xi

1. Remove engine underguard.
2. Support engine as outlined under "Oil Pan, Replace" in appropriate engine section.
3. Remove ride level sensors.
4. Remove heat shield.
5. Remove left and righthand engine mounts' nuts.
6. Disconnect pressure line holder.
7. Disconnect left and righthand stabilizer bars.
8. Remove mounting bolts and control arm brackets.
9. Remove mounting bolts and steering gear.

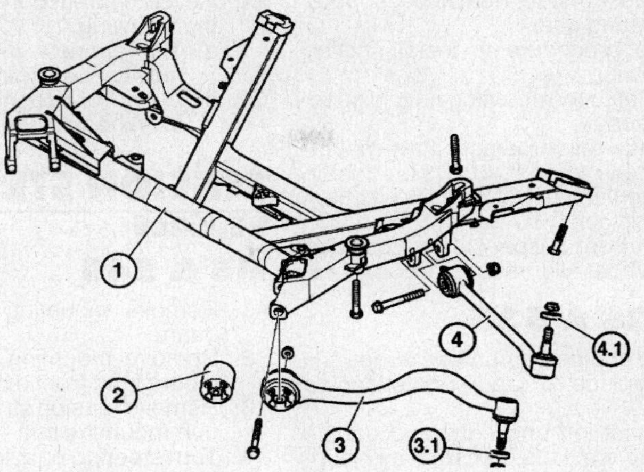

1 Front axle support
2 Rubber mount on tension strut
3 Tension strut
3.1 Washer
4 Control arm
4.1 Washer

BM2029900005000X

Fig. 2 Front suspension components (Part 2 of 2). M5, 525, 528, 530, 540, 740 & 750

10. Support front axle carrier with suitable jack.
11. Remove mounting bolts and front axle carrier.
12. Reverse procedure to install, noting the following:
   a. Tighten new mounting bolts and nuts to specifications.
   b. **Torque** reinforcement plate mounting bolts to 44 ft. lbs., then tighten an additional 90°.
   c. Align front suspension as outlined in "Wheel Alignment" section.

M5 & 540

1. Remove splash guard.
2. Support engine as outlined under "Oil Pan, Replace" in appropriate engine section.
3. Disconnect left and righthand engine mounting brackets from front axle support.
4. Raise and support vehicle, then remove tire and wheel assemblies.
5. Remove mounting nuts and disconnect track rod from pitman arm using knuckle puller tool No. 31 2 240, or equivalent.
6. Remove idler arm.
7. Disconnect stabilizer bar from front axle support.
8. Remove mounting nuts and disconnect track rod from steering knuckle using knuckle puller tool No. 31 2 240, or equivalent.
9. Remove heat shield and positive cable from front axle support.
10. Disconnect power steering oil cooler line from front axle support.
11. Disconnect wheelhousing trim.
12. Remove steering gear and support aside with lines connected.
13. Disconnect control arm from front axle support as outlined under "Control Arm, Replace."
14. Remove mounting nuts and disconnect stabilizer mount from front axle support.
15. Remove pressure strut mounting nuts and bolt, then turn steering onto lock.
16. Support front axle support with suitable jack.
17. Remove mounting bolts and front axle carrier.
18. Reverse procedure to install, noting the following
   a. Tighten new mounting bolts and nuts to specifications.
   b. Align front suspension as outlined in "Wheel Alignment" section.

X5

1. Raise and support vehicle, then remove front tire and wheel assemblies.
2. Remove mounting bolts and reinforcement plate.
3. Remove splash shield.
4. Support engine as outlined under "Oil Pan, Replace" in appropriate engine section.
5. Raise engine approximately 0.4 inch.
6. Mark steering column to gear for installation alignment, then remove clamp.
7. Remove steering tie rods using knuckle puller tool No. 32 3 090, or equivalent.
8. Remove mounting nuts, then the left and righthand control arms from front axle support.
9. Remove mounting nuts, then the left and righthand tension struts from front axle support.
10. Remove left and righthand engine mount nuts from front axle support.
11. Remove steering gear mounting bolts.
12. Support front axle support with suitable jack.
13. Remove mounting bolts and lower front axle support.
14. Disconnect power steering gear banjo

bolts and remove front axle support with steering gear.
15. Reverse procedure to install, noting the following:
    a. Tighten new mounting nuts to specifications.
    b. **Torque** reinforcement plate mounting bolts to 41 ft. lbs., then tighten an additional 90° and final tighten an additional 15°.
    c. Align front suspension as outlined in "Wheel Alignment" section.

525, 528 & 530

1. Support engine as outlined under "Oil Pan, Replace" in appropriate engine section.
2. Disconnect left and righthand engine mounting brackets from front axle support.
3. Disconnect stabilizer bar from front axle support.
4. Disconnect tension strut from front axle support as outlined under "Tension Strut, Replace."
5. Disconnect control arm from front axle support as outlined under "Control Arm, Replace."
6. Remove heat shield and bracket from engine shielding.
7. Support strut from outside.
8. Mark track rods for installation alignment.
9. Remove steering gear mounting bolts.
10. Partially loosen trim beside rear mounting bolts.
11. Remove mounting bolts and front axle carrier.
12. Reverse procedure to install, noting the following
    a. Tighten new mounting bolts and nuts to specifications.
    b. Align front suspension as outlined in "Wheel Alignment" section.

740 & 750

1. Support engine as outlined under "Oil Pan, Replace" in appropriate engine section.
2. Remove mounting bolts and splash guard.
3. Remove steering gear and support aside with lines connected.
4. Disconnect left and righthand engine mounting brackets from front axle support.
5. Remove idler arm.
6. Remove reinforcement and heat shield.
7. Disconnect power steering oil cooler line from front axle support, as required.
8. Remove traction strut as outlined under "Tension Strut, Replace."
9. Disconnect stabilizer bar from link.
10. Raise and support vehicle, then remove tire and wheel assemblies.
11. Remove mounting nuts and disconnect track rod from pitman arm and steering knuckle using knuckle puller tool No. 31 1 190, or equivalent.
12. Support front axle support with suitable jack.
13. Remove mounting bolts and front axle carrier.
14. Reverse procedure to install, noting the following
    a. Tighten new mounting bolts and nuts to specifications.
    b. Align front suspension as outlined in "Wheel Alignment" section.

TENSION STRUT

REPLACE

M5 & 540

1. Remove mounting bolts and splash guard.
2. Remove mounting nut and stabilizer mount from front axle support.
3. Remove tension strut to front axle support mounting nut.
4. Turn steering onto lock, as required.
5. Mark strut to swivel bearing position for installation alignment.
6. Remove mounting bolt and expand swivel bearing by twisting slot 90° using expansion tool No. 31 2 200, or equivalent, as required.
7. Remove mounting nut and disconnect ball joint using knuckle puller tool No. 31 2 240, or equivalent.
8. Remove traction strut.
9. Reverse procedure to install. Tighten new mounting nuts to specifications.

X5

1. Raise and support vehicle, then remove tires and wheels assemblies.
2. Loosen control arm to swivel bearing mounting nut three threads.
3. Press control arm off swivel bearing using knuckle puller tool No. 31 2 240, or equivalent.
4. Remove mounting nut and guide joint.
5. Remove mounting nut and tension strut.
6. Reverse procedure to install, noting the following:
    a. Tighten new mounting bolts and nuts to specifications.
    b. Align front suspension as outlined in "Wheel Alignment" section.

525, 528 & 530

1. Remove engine compartment insulation.
2. Raise and support vehicle, then remove tire and wheel assemblies.
3. Remove left and righthand air ducts.
4. Remove cap, then the tension strut to front axle support mounting nut and bolt.
5. Remove mounting nut and disconnect ball stud from steering knuckle using knuckle puller tool No. 31 2 240, or equivalent.
6. Mark strut to swivel bearing position for installation alignment.
7. Remove mounting bolt and expand swivel bearing by twisting slot 90° using expansion tool No. 31 2 200, or equivalent, as required.
8. Reverse procedure to install, noting the following:
    a. Tighten new mounting nuts to specifications.
    b. Align front suspension as outlined in "Wheel Alignment" section.

740 & 750

1. Remove mounting bolts and splash guard.
2. Remove tension strut to front axle support mounting nut.
3. Remove mounting nut and disconnect ball joint using knuckle puller tool No. 31 2 240, or equivalent.
4. Remove traction strut.
5. Reverse procedure to install. Tighten new mounting nuts to specifications.

TIE ROD

REPLACE

1. Raise and support vehicle, then remove front tire and wheel assemblies.
2. Loosen adjusting nut.
3. Remove mounting nuts and disconnect front steering knuckle using knuckle puller tool No. 32 2 090, or equivalent.
4. Reverse procedure to install, noting the following:
    a. Tighten new self-locking nuts to specifications.
    b. Align front suspension as outlined in "Wheel Alignment" section.

POWER STEERING GEAR

REPLACE

M3, Z3, 318, 323, 325, 328 & 330

Z3, 323is & 328is & 1998–99 M3, 328i & 1998 323i & 1999 323i & 328i CONVERTIBLES

1. Raise and support vehicle, then remove front tire and wheel assemblies.
2. Remove steering wheel as outlined in "Electrical" section.
3. Remove mounting nuts and disconnect track rods using knuckle puller tool No. 32 2 070, or equivalent.
4. Disconnect tank hose and hollow union bolt.
5. Remove mounting bolt and disconnect universal joint from steering gear.
6. Remove mounting bolts and steering gear in forward direction.
7. Reverse procedure to install, noting the following:
    a. Tighten new self-locking nuts to specifications.
    b. Bleed power steering system.
    c. Align front suspension as outlined in "Wheel Alignment" section.

323Ci & 328Ci & 2000 M3, 323i & 328i & 1999 323i & 328i SEDANS

1. Raise and support vehicle, then remove front tire and wheel assemblies.
2. Remove splash guard.
3. Remove mounting nuts and disconnect track rods using knuckle puller tool No. 32 2 090, or equivalent.
4. Disconnect banjo bolts.
5. Mark steering column and gear for installation alignment.

6. Remove clamping bolt and disconnect disk joint from steering gear.
7. Remove mounting bolts and steering gear in forward direction.
8. Reverse procedure to install, noting the following:
   a. Tighten new self-locking nuts to specifications.
   b. Bleed power steering system.
   c. Align front suspension as outlined in "Wheel Alignment" section.

325 & 330
325Ci, 325i, 330Ci & 330i

Refer to "323Ci & 328Ci & 2000 M3, 323i & 328i & 1999 323i & 328i Sedans."

325xi & 330xi

1. Raise and support vehicle, then remove front tire and wheel assemblies.
2. Remove underbody protection panels and engine carrier acoustic insulation.
3. Remove mounting nuts and disconnect track rods using knuckle puller tool No. 32 2 090, or equivalent.
4. Disconnect banjo bolts.
5. Mark steering column and gear for installation alignment.
6. Remove clamping bolt and disconnect double joint from steering gear.
7. Support front axle support with suitable jack.
8. Disconnect front axle support from engine carrier as outlined under "Crossmember, Replace."
9. Lower front axle support approximately 0.79 inch.
10. Remove mounting bolts and steering gear.
11. Reverse procedure to install, noting the following:
    a. Tighten new self-locking nuts to specifications.
    b. Bleed power steering system.
    c. Align front suspension as outlined in "Wheel Alignment" section.

M5, 540, 740 & 750

1. Raise and support vehicle, then remove front tire and wheel assemblies.
2. Remove steering wheel as outlined in "Electrical" section.
3. Remove splash guard and heat shield.
4. Drain power steering fluid into suitable container. **Do not reuse.**
5. Remove hydraulic lines and seal bores. Seal and cap lines of openings.
6. Remove mounting nuts and disconnect track rods using knuckle puller tool No. 31 1 190, or equivalent.
7. Remove pitman arm.
8. Remove mounting bolt and disconnect universal joint from steering gear.
9. Remove mounting bolts and steering gear.
10. Reverse procedure to install, noting the following:
    a. Ensure steering wheel and gear are straight ahead.
    b. Tighten new self-locking nuts to specifications.
    c. Ensure universal joint mounting bolt is located in steering gear retaining groove.
    d. Install new sealing rings.

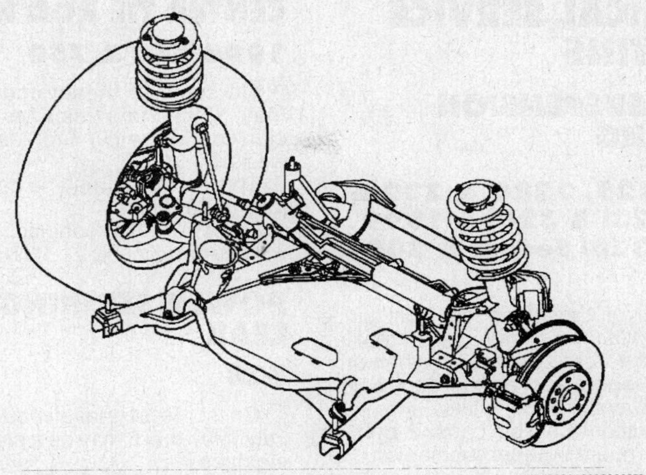

Fig. 3 Front suspension components. X5

   e. Bleed power steering system.
   f. Align front suspension as outlined in "Wheel Alignment" section.

X5

1. Raise and support vehicle, then remove front tire and wheel assemblies.
2. Remove splash shield.
3. Remove mounting bolts and reinforcement plate.
4. Remove left and righthand engine support arm nuts.
5. Remove steering tie rods using knuckle puller tool No. 32 3 090, or equivalent.
6. Support engine as outlined under "Oil Pan, Replace" in appropriate engine section.
7. Raise engine approximately 0.57 inch.
8. Mark steering column and gear for installation alignment.
9. Remove clamping bolt and disconnect joint from steering gear.
10. Remove steering tie rods using knuckle puller tool No. 32 3 090, or equivalent.
11. Support front axle support with suitable jack.
12. Remove mounting bolts and lower axle support
13. Remove banjo bolts and steering gear to lefthand side.
14. Reverse procedure to install, noting the following:
    a. **Torque** reinforcement plate mounting bolts to 41 ft. lbs., then tighten an additional 90° and final tighten an additional 15°.
    b. Tighten new self-locking nuts to specifications.
    c. Bleed power steering system.
    d. Align front suspension as outlined in "Wheel Alignment" section.

525, 528 & 530

1. Raise and support vehicle, then remove front tire and wheel assemblies.
2. Remove steering wheel as outlined in "Electrical" section.
3. Disconnect left and righthand engine mounts from front axle support, then raise engine approximately 1.57 inches.
4. Drain power steering fluid into suitable container. **Do not reuse.**
5. Remove mounting nuts and disconnect track rods using knuckle puller tool No. 31 2 240, or equivalent.
6. Remove hollow bolts and seal bores.
7. Remove mounting bolt and disconnect universal joint from steering gear.
8. Remove mounting bolts, turn and remove steering gear from lefthand side.
9. Reverse procedure to install, noting the following:
   a. Tighten new self-locking nuts to specifications.
   b. Install new sealing rings.
   c. Bleed power steering system.
   d. Align front suspension as outlined in "Wheel Alignment" section.

POWER STEERING PUMP

REPLACE

1. Drain hydraulic fluid into suitable container. **Do not reuse.**
2. Remove engine underguard.
3. Remove drive belt.
4. Disconnect suction and pressure lines from pump.
5. Remove mounting bolts and pulley.
6. Remove mounting bolts and pump.
7. Reverse procedure to install, noting the following:
   a. Tighten mounting bolts and nuts to specifications.
   b. Bleed power steering system.

POWER STEERING SYSTEM BLEED

1. Remove cap and fill power steering tank to MAX mark.
2. Start engine.
3. Turn steering wheel from left to right lock twice.
4. Stop engine and adjust fluid level as required.

TECHNICAL SERVICE BULLETINS

FRONT SUSPENSION CREAKING

323Ci, 325, 328Ci & 330 & 2000 323i & 328i & 1999 323i & 328i Sedans & 2001 M3

On some of these models built since September 1998 there may be a creaking noise from the front suspension when driving slowly over grade changes, such as entering driveways or parking lots.

This condition may be caused by rear control arm mount bumper rubbing on interior.

To correct this condition by coating contact area with 3M Spray Lube No. 08878, or equivalent lubricant as follows:

1. Front suspension must be loaded, such as on alignment rack.
2. Spray lubricant inside of the rear bushing, on inboard side so rubber bumper and inside of outer sleeve are well lubed.
3. On some models built between March 15 and April 23, 1999, control arm mounting have rubber bumper enclosed within the hydraulic chamber. On these models, replace both mounts with standard units.

CENTER TIE ROD NOISE

1998 740 & 750

On some of these models built before May 1998 there may be a groaning or clunking when turning, especially in hot weather.

This condition may be caused by tie rod joint material

To correct this condition revised center tie rod (part No. 32 21 1 096 057).

1.

POWER STEERING HOSE LEAK

528

On some of these models built during July 1997 there may be a slow power steering hose leak.

This condition may be caused by hose material

To correct this condition replace Gates hoses (marked BMW Gates CSM/CSM) with Continental hoses (marked Conti TCH-TDHY).

STEERING WHEEL VIBRATION OR BUZZ

323is & 328is & 1998-99 328i & 1998 323i & 1999 323i & 328i Convertibles

On some of these models there may be a high frequency buzz felt in the steering wheel. In some cases there may be vibration similar to tire balance problem felt in a 2–5 mph window between 50–60 mph.

This condition may be caused by power steering hydraulic pulses.

To correct this condition, proceed as follows:

1. Disconnect power steering pump hose and drain fluid into suitable container.
2. Disconnect line from rack and remove it.
3. Remove cooling tubs mounting bolt on righthand side of rack and install new line (part No. 32 41 1 094 976). **Torque** new M6 x 16 mounting bolt to 80 inch lbs.
4. Connect pressure line to pump and rack using new seal rings. **Torque** to 26 ft. lbs.
5. Ensure adequate clearance between line and components.
6. Remove two T40 mounting bolts from pump back.
7. Install new brace (part No. 32 42 1 710 015) with small portion aligned with block tapped bosses. **Torque** new M8 x 50 mounting bolts and washers to 18 ft. lbs.
8. Remove fluid reservoir mounting bracket.
9. Install rubber grommets (part No. 34 51 1 162 819) into new bracket (part No. 32 41 1 093 236) and spacers into grommets.
10. Install bracket and **torque** new mounting bolts to 18 ft. lbs.

TIGHTENING SPECIFICATIONS

Year	Component	Torque, Ft. Lbs.
318i, 323is & 328is & 1998–99 M3 & 328i & 1998 323i & 1999 323i & 328i Convertibles		
1998–1999	Control Arm To Front Axle Support	66
	Control Arm To Steering Knuckle/Swivel Bearing	48
	Front Axle Carrier	①
	Power Steering Hose	⑮
	Shock Absorber Piston Rod On Thrust Bearing	⑦
	Spring Strut Ring	96
	Spring Strut To Wheel House	⑥
	Stabilizer Bar Holder	16⑧
	Stabilizer Link	44⑩
	Stabilizer Link Bracket	31
	Steering Column To Gear Universal Joint/Coupling	14
	Steering Gear	31
	Steering Guide Arm	⑬
	Steering Knuckle To Spring Strut	79
	Steering Pump	16
	Steering Tie Rod Clamp	33
	Tie Rod/Axial Joint To Rack	52
	Tie Rod Castle Nut or Self-Locking Nut	24–29
	Tie Rod Clamp	10

Continued

TIGHTENING SPECIFICATIONS—Continued

Year	Component	Torque, Ft. Lbs.
323Ci, 325, 328Ci & 330 & 2000 323i & 328i & 1999 323i & 328i Sedans & 2001 M3		
1999–2001	Adapter To Body (325xi & 330xi)	44
	Axle Shaft Drive Flange (325xi & 330xi)	310
	Control Arm Ball Joint To Front Axle Carrier (325xi & 330xi)	59
	Control Arm Bracket To Engine Carrier	44
	Control Arm Bracket To Front Axle Carrier	44
	Control Arm To Ball Joint (325xi & 330xi)	59
	Control Arm To Front Axle Support	66
	Control Arm To Steering Knuckle/Swivel Bearing	48
	Front Axle Carrier	(1)
	Front Axle Support To Adapter (325xi & 330xi)	81
	Power Steering Hose	(15)
	Shock Absorber Piston Rod On Thrust Bearing	(7)
	Spring Strut Ring	96
	Spring Strut To Wheel House	(6)
	Stabilizer Bar Holder	16(8)
	Stabilizer Link (325xi)	44(10)
	Stabilizer Bar Link	48
	Steering Column To Gear Universal Joint/Coupling	16
	Steering Gear	22
	Steering Guide Arm	(13)
	Steering Knuckle To Spring Strut	60
	Steering Pump	16
	Steering Tie Rod Clamp	33
	Tie Rod/Axial Joint To Rack	74
	Tie Rod Castle Nut or Self-Locking Nut	48
	Tie Rod Clamp	10
M5, 525, 528, 530 & 540		
1998–2001	Control Arm To Front Axle Support	(5)
	Control Arm To Steering Knuckle/Swivel Bearing	59
	Front Axle Carrier	(1)
	Power Steering Hose	(15)
	Pressure Strut	94(3)
	Shock Absorber Piston Rod On Thrust Bearing	(7)
	Spring Strut Ring	96
	Spring Strut To Wheel House	(6)
	Stabilizer Bar Holder	16(8)
	Stabilizer Link Bracket	48
	Stabilizer Link Bracket, Swivel Bearing	44
	Steering Column To Gear Universal Joint/Coupling	14
	Steering Drop Arm	45
	Steering Gear	(12)
	Steering Guide Arm	46
	Steering Knuckle To Spring Strut	60
	Steering Pump	18
	Steering Tie Rod Clamp	38
	Swivel Bearing	81

Continued

TIGHTENING SPECIFICATIONS—Continued

Year	Component	Torque, Ft. Lbs.
M5, 525, 528, 530 & 540		
1998–2001	Tension Strut	59
	Tie Rod/Axial Joint To Rack	52
	Tie Rod Castle Nut or Self-Locking Nut	48
	Tie Rod Clamp	20
	Traction Strut	59
X5		
2000–01	Axle Shaft Drive Flange	310
	Control Arm To Front Axle Support	74③④
	Control Arm To Steering Knuckle/Swivel Bearing	59
	Front Axle Carrier	②53
	Power Steering Hose	⑮
	Shock Absorber Piston Rod On Thrust Bearing	⑦
	Spring Strut Ring	96
	Spring Strut To Pivot Mount	184
	Spring Strut To Wheel House	⑥
	Stabilizer Bar Holder	16⑧
	Stabilizer Link	48⑩
	Steering Column To Gear Universal Joint/Coupling	⑭
	Steering Gear	74
	Steering Guide Arm	⑬
	Steering Pump	16
	Steering Tie Rod Clamp	38
	Swivel Bearing	44
	Tension Strut	122③
	Tension Strut Guide	59
	Tie Rod/Axial Joint To Rack	81
	Tie Rod Castle Nut or Self-Locking Nut	59
	Tie Rod Clamp	10
Z3 & 318ti		
1998–2001	Control Arm To Front Axle Support	66
	Control Arm To Steering Knuckle/Swivel Bearing	48
	Front Axle Carrier	①
	Power Steering Hose	⑮
	Shock Absorber Piston Rod On Thrust Bearing	⑦
	Spring Strut Ring	96
	Spring Strut To Wheel House	⑥
	Stabilizer Bar Holder	16⑧
	Stabilizer Link	44⑩
	Stabilizer Link Bracket	31
	Steering Column To Gear Universal Joint/Coupling	14
	Steering Gear	31
	Steering Guide Arm	⑬
	Steering Knuckle To Spring Strut	79
	Steering Pump	16
	Steering Tie Rod Clamp	33
	Tie Rod/Axial Joint To Rack	52
	Tie Rod Castle Nut or Self-Locking Nut	24–29
	Tie Rod Clamp	10

Continued

TIGHTENING SPECIFICATIONS—Continued

Year	Component	Torque, Ft. Lbs.
740 & 750		
1998–2001	Bearing Collar Nut	214
	Control Arm To Front Axle Support	57
	Control Arm To Steering Knuckle/Swivel Bearing	69
	Front Axle Carrier	①
	Power Steering Hose	⑨
	Shock Absorber Piston Rod On Thrust Bearing	⑦
	Spring Strut Ring	96
	Spring Strut To Wheel House	⑥
	Stabilizer Bar Holder	16⑧
	Stabilizer Bar Link	48
	Steering Column To Gear Universal Joint/Coupling	14
	Steering Drop Arm	45
	Steering Gear	⑪
	Steering Guide Arm	⑬
	Steering Knuckle To Spring Strut	60
	Steering Pump	16
	Tie Rod Castle Nut or Self-Locking Nut	48
	Tie Rod Clamp	20
	Traction Strut	69

① — M10 8.8, 31 ft. lbs.; M10 9.8, 35 ft. lbs.; M12 8.8, 57 ft. lbs.; M12 10.9, 81 ft. lbs.; M12 12.9, 77 ft. lbs.

② — M10 8.8, 31 ft. lbs.; M10 9.8, 35 ft. lbs.; M12 8.8, 57 ft. lbs.; M12 10.9, 74 ft. lbs.; M12 12.9, 77 ft. lbs.

③ — Vehicle w/complete equipment in normal driving position w/full fuel tank. No weight in passenger seats.

④ — Tighten an additional 75–105°.

⑤ — 525, 528 & 530; 57 ft. lbs.; 540, 81 ft. lbs.

⑥ — 18mm, 18 ft. lbs.; 21mm, 25 ft. lbs.

⑦ — M12 external piston, 47 ft. lbs.; M12 internal piston, 32 ft. lbs.; M14 47 ft. lbs.

⑧ — Vehicle complete with normal equipment, plus 150 lbs. in front seats and 150 lbs. centered in models with rear seat, plus 31 lbs. centered in luggage compartment.

⑨ — Cap screw, 27 ft. lbs.; M10, 106 inch lbs.; M14, 26 ft. lbs.; M16, 29 ft. lbs.; M18, 33 ft. lbs.

⑩ — Wrench surface on ball head must be parallel to shock absorber axis.

⑪ — M10 8.8, 31 ft. lbs.; M10 10.9, 46 ft. lbs.

⑫ — M10 8.8, 31 ft. lbs.; Ball-and-nut M10 10.9, 46 ft. lbs.; rack & pinion, 37 ft. lbs., then tighten an additional 90°.

⑬ — M10, 31 ft. lbs.; M12, 63 ft. lbs.

⑭ — Aluminum joint, 21 ft. lbs.; steel joint 18 ft. lbs.

Front Wheel Drive

NOTE: On Air Bag Equipped Models, Refer To "Air Bag System Precautions" Located In The Front Of This Manual For System Disarming & Arming Procedures.

INDEX

	Page No.
Axle Shaft, Replace	2-128
325xi & 330xi	2-128
X5	2-128
Differential Carrier, Replace	2-128
325xi & 330xi	2-128
X5	2-128
Tightening Specifications	2-129

AXLE SHAFT

REPLACE

X5

1. Remove mounting bolts and reinforcement plate.
2. Remove front engine underguard.
3. Raise and support vehicle, then remove tire and wheel assembly.
4. Remove anti-lock brake pulse generator.
5. Remove steering tie rod from swivel bearing.
6. Remove tension strut with guide joint as outlined in "Front Suspension & Steering" section.
7. Remove control arm as outlined in "Front Suspension & Steering" section.
8. Remove output shaft collar nut.
9. Tilt swivel bearing to one side.
10. Remove output shaft from differential using puller to 31 5 110, or equivalent.
11. Reverse procedure to install, noting the following:
    a. Install new output shaft radial seal using driver tool No. 31 5 130, or equivalent.
    b. Push output shaft over snap ring resistance until it audibly snaps into place.
    c. **Torque** reinforcement plate mounting bolts to 41 ft. lbs., then tighten an additional 90° and final tighten an additional 15°.
    d. Tighten mounting bolts and nuts to specifications.

325xi & 330xi

1. Remove front, middle and rear engine underguards.
2. Remove front axle support righthand heat shield.
3. Raise and support vehicle, then remove tire and wheel assembly.
4. Remove anti-lock brake pulse generator.
5. Disconnect control arm ride level sensor.
6. Disconnect brake hose from mounting.
7. Remove brake caliper as outlined in "Disc Brake" section. Tie caliper aside with hoses connected.
8. Disconnect stabilizer link from bar.
9. Remove output shaft collar nut.
10. Press output shaft out of drive flange.
11. Disconnect front axle support control arm at front and rear.
12. Tilt swivel bearing to one side.
13. Remove output shaft from differential using puller to 31 1 170, or equivalent.
14. Remove radial seal using suitable screwdriver.
15. Reverse procedure to install, noting the following:
    a. Install new output shaft radial seal using driver tool No. 31 5 130, or equivalent.
    b. Push output shaft over snap ring resistance until it audibly snaps into place.
    c. Tighten mounting bolts and nuts to specifications.

DIFFERENTIAL CARRIER

REPLACE

X5

1. Remove heater bulkhead.
2. Raise and lock hood into assembly position.
3. Remove fuel injectors' cover.
4. **On 3.0i models,** remove air filter housing upper section with Mass Air Flow (MAF) sensor.
5. **On all models,** support engine with engine support tool No. 00 0 200, or equivalent.
6. Remove left and righthand engine mount nuts.
7. **On 3.0i models,** raise engine approximately 0.2 inch.
8. **On 4.4i models,** raise engine approximately 0.39–0.47 inch.
9. **On all models,** remove mounting bolts and reinforcement plate.
10. Remove front splash guard.
11. Remove propeller shaft to front differential mounting bolts and remove flexible disk with centering flange.
12. Disconnect propeller shaft from transfer case.
13. Disconnect steering column from steering gear is outline in "Front Suspension & Steering" section.
14. Remove left and righthand swivel bearings as outline under "Steering Knuckle, Replace"in "Front Suspension & Steering" section.
15. Support front axle support with suitable jack, fixture tool No. 31 2 220, or equivalent, and wood block.
16. Disconnect front axle support from engine carrier and lower support approximately 0.79 inch.
17. Remove lefthand engine mount.
18. Remove vent hose.
19. Remove mounting bolts and front axle differential carrier.
20. Reverse procedure to install, noting the following:
    a. Install new sealing ring and apply suitable anti-friction agent.
    b. Apply thin coat of Weicon Antisize grease to transfer case splines.
    c. **Torque** reinforcement plate mounting bolts to 41 ft. lbs., then tighten an additional 90° and final tighten an additional 15°.
    d. Tighten new bolts and nuts to specifications.

325xi & 330xi

1. Support engine with engine support tool No. 00 0 200, or equivalent.
2. Remove top righthand engine mount nut and bottom lefthand engine mount nut.
3. Raise engine approximately 0.4 inch.
4. Remove front, middle and rear engine underguards.
5. Remove rear and center underbody protection panels.
6. Remove mounting nuts and front propeller shaft.
7. Remove control arm from front axle support as outlined in "Front Suspension & Steering" section.
8. Remove left and righthand swivel bearings as outline under "Steering Knuckle, Replace" in "Front Suspension & Steering" section.
9. Remove output shafts as outlined under "Axle Shaft, Replace."

10. Disconnect steering column from steering gear as outlined in "Front Suspension & Steering" section.
11. Support front axle support using suitable jack, fixture tool No. 31 2 220, or equivalent, and wooden block.
12. Disconnect front axle support from engine carrier.
13. Remove vent hose.
14. Remove mounting bolts and front axle differential carrier.
15. Reverse procedure to install, noting the following:
    a. Install new sealing ring coated with suitable anti-friction agent.
    b. Install new output shaft radial seal.
    c. Tighten mounting bolts and nuts to specifications.

TIGHTENING SPECIFICATIONS

Year	Component	Torque/ Ft.lbs.
2000–01	Drain Plug	48
	Final Drive To Engine Oil Pan	44
	Output Shaft To Engine Oil Pan	16

Wheel Alignment

INDEX

	Page No.
Front Wheel Alignment	2-130
Camber	2-130
Caster	2-130
Toe-In	2-130
Preliminary Inspection	2-130
Rear Wheel Alignment	2-130
Camber & Toe-In	2-130
Vehicle Ride Height	2-130
Wheel Alignment Specifications	2-6

PRELIMINARY INSPECTION

1. Check tires for wear and proper inflation.
2. Check front wheel bearings, front suspension, steering linkage and ball joints for wear or looseness.
3. Ensure front shock absorbers are functioning properly.

FRONT WHEEL ALIGNMENT

CASTER

Caster values are designed into the front suspension geometry and are not adjustable. If caster is not within specification, check for worn or damaged suspension components. Replace as required.

CAMBER

M3, Z3, 318, 323, 325, 328 & 330

318i, 323is & 328is & 1998-99 M3 & 328i & 1998 323i & 1999 323i & 328i Convertibles

Camber is preset during production and is not adjustable.

323Ci, 325, 328Ci & 330 & 2000 323i & 328i & 1999 323i & 328i Sedans & 2001 M3

1. Drive centering pin out toward bottom.
2. **On M3 models,** remove center pin.
3. **On all models,** remove strut rear mounting bolt.
4. Loosen remaining mounting bolts 1½ turns.
5. Adjust camber using setting tool No. 32 3 140, or equivalent, over wheelhousing and nuts.
6. Install and tighten rear mounting nut.
7. Install new mounting nuts and tighten.

M5, 525, 528, 530, 540, 740 & 750

Camber is preset during production and is not adjustable.

X5

1. Remove windshield washer reservoir, as required.
2. Remove wheelhousing cap.
3. Remove center pin and loosen mounting nut opposite pin approximately 1½ turns.
4. Install setting tool No. 32 3 143/144, or equivalent, over opening and remaining nuts.
5. Install new remaining nuts. **Do not tighten.**
6. Adjust camber with special tool.
7. Remove tool and tighten nuts.

TOE-IN

1. Position steering gear in straight ahead position.
2. Loosen track rod lock nut.
3. Adjust toe-in by rotating steering tie rod.
4. Tighten lock nut.

REAR WHEEL ALIGNMENT

CAMBER & TOE-IN

M3, Z3, 318, 323, 325, 328 & 330

1. Install new collar nut with eccentric washer between support cams and tighten.
2. Loosen collar nut approximately ½ turn.
3. Turn eccentric bolt and adjust camber.
4. Tighten collar nut.
5. Replace collar nut that has been tightened more than 10 times.
6. Loosen bearing support bolts approximately 1½ turns.
7. Adjust toe-in using setting tool No. 32 3 080, or equivalent, between stops. On models equipped with pin/notch, using tool No. 32 3 030, or equivalent.
8. Tighten mounting bolts.

M5, 525, 528, 530, 540, 740 & 750

1. Install new collar nut with eccentric washer between support cams and tighten.
2. Loosen collar nut approximately ½ turn.
3. Turn eccentric bolt and adjust camber.
4. Tighten collar nut.
5. Replace collar nut that has been tightened more than 10 times.
6. Loosen bearing support bolts approximately 1½ turns.
7. Remove mounting bolts and trim over traction strut/rear axle carrier.
8. Install new collar nut and tighten.
9. Loosen collar nut 0.5–1 turn.
10. Adjust toe-in using eccentric bolt.
11. Tighten collar nut.
12. Replace collar nut that has been tightened more than 10 times.

X5

1. Install new nut n eccentric bolt and tighten. **Bolt must be between stops.**
2. Loosen collar nut approximately ¾ turn.
3. Turn eccentric bolt and adjust camber.
4. Tighten collar nut.
5. Replace collar nut that has been tightened more than four times.
6. Loosen bearing support bolts approximately 1½ turns.
7. Install new nut on strut/rear axle support with washer located between stops and tighten.
8. Loosen collar nut approximately ¾ turn.
9. Adjust toe-in using eccentric bolt.
10. Tighten collar nut.
11. Replace collar nut that has been tightened more than four times.

VEHICLE RIDE HEIGHT

Vehicle ride height is measured from the lower edge of the wheelhouse to the rim flange at middle of wheel. Refer to **Fig. 1** for specifications.

Year	Rim Size	Ride Height, Inch							
		Front				Rear			
		Standard	Sports	M Sports	Rough Road	Standard	Sports	M Sports	Rough Road
M3									
1998–99	17-Inch	22.640–23.446	21.656–22.443	—	—	20.868–21.656	20.868–21.656	—	—
2001	18-Inch	24.428–24.215	—	—	—	22.719–23.506	—	—	—
	19-Inch	23.979–24.766	—	—	—	22.231–24.018	—	—	—
M5									
2001	17-Inch	22.916–23.703	—	—	—	21.853–22.640	—	—	—
	18-Inch	23.428–24.2125	—	—	—	22.364–23.152	—	—	—
X5 w/AIR SPRINGS									
2000–01	17-Inch	26.577–27.365	—	—	—	26.656–27.499	—	—	—
	18-Inch	27.089–27.916	—	—	—	27.169–27.965	—	—	—
	19-Inch	27.601–28.389	—	—	—	27.680–28.467	—	—	—
	20-Inch	28.113–28.901	—	—	—	28.192–28.979	—	—	—
X5 w/STEEL SPRINGS									
2000–01	17-Inch	26.577–27.365	—	—	—	26.971–27.759	—	—	—
	18-Inch	27.089–27.916	—	—	—	27.483–28.271	—	—	—
	19-Inch	27.601–28.389	—	—	—	27.995–28.782	—	—	—
	20-Inch	28.113–28.901	—	—	—	28.507–29.294	—	—	—
Z3 COUPE①									
1998–2001	15-Inch	24.884–25.672	—	—	—	21.853–11.640	—	—	—
	16-Inch	25.396–26.183	—	—	—	22.364–23.152	—	—	—
	17-Inch	25.987–26.774	—	—	—	22.955–23.742	—	—	—
Z3 ROADSTER①									
1998–2001	15-Inch	25.081–25.869	24.491–25.278	—	—	21.853–11.640	21.261–22.049	—	—
	16-Inch	25.593–26.381	25.002–25.278	—	—	22.364–23.152	21.774–22.561	—	—
	17-Inch	26.184–16.971	25.593–26.381	—	—	22.955–23.742	22.364–23.152	—	—
Z3 M COUPE①									
1998–2001	17-Inch	25.751–26.538	—	—	—	22.955–23.742	—	—	—
Z3 M ROADSTER①									
1998–2001	17-inch	25.751–26.538	—	—	—	22.955–23.752	—	—	—

Fig. 1 Vehicle ride height specifications (Part 1 of 4)

Year	Rim Size	Ride Height, Inch							
		Front				Rear			
		Standard	Sports	M Sports	Rough Road	Standard	Sports	M Sports	Rough Road
318i									
1998	15-Inch	22.286–22.073	21.695–22.482	—	23.073–23.861	20.002–20.789	19.569–20.356	—	20.790–21.577
	16-inch	22.796–23.585	22.207–22.994	—	23.575–24.733	20.514–21.301	20.081–20.868	—	21.301–22.089
	17-inch	23.388–24.175	22.798–22.585	—	24.176–24.963	21.104–21.892	20.671–21.459	—	21.892–22.680
318ti									
1998–99	15-Inch	22.286–22.073	21.695–22.482	—	23.073–23.861	20.238–21.026	19.648–20.436	—	21.026–21.459
	16-inch	22.796–23.585	22.207–22.994	—	23.575–24.733	20.750–21.538	20.159–20.947	—	21.538–22.325
	17-inch	23.388–24.175	22.798–22.585	—	24.176–24.963	21.341–22.128	20.750–21.538	—	22.128–22.916
323i & 328i									
1998	15-Inch	22.286–22.073	21.695–22.482	—	23.073–23.861	20.002–20.789	19.569–20.356	—	20.790–21.577
	16-inch	22.796–23.585	22.207–22.994	—	23.575–24.733	20.514–21.301	20.081–20.868	—	21.301–22.089
	17-inch	23.388–24.175	22.798–22.585	—	24.176–24.963	21.104–21.892	20.671–21.459	—	21.892–22.680
2000	15-Inch	22.286–23.073	21.695–22.483	—	22.955–23.734	20.947–21.734	20.317–20.750	—	21.734–22.522
	16-Inch	22.798–23.585	22.207–22.944	—	23.467–24.254	21.459–22.246	20.829–21.616	—	22.246–23.034
	17-Inch	23.388–24.254	22.798–23.585	—	24.058–24.845	22.049–22.836	21.419–22.207	—	22.837–23.624
	18-Inch	23.900–24.687	23.309–24.097	—	24.569–25.357	22.561–23.349	21.931–22.719	—	23.349–24.136
323i & 328i CONVERTIBLES									
1999	15-Inch	22.286–22.073	21.695–22.482	—	23.073–23.861	20.002–20.789	19.569–20.356	—	20.790–21.577
	16-inch	22.796–23.585	22.207–22.994	—	23.575–24.733	20.514–21.301	20.081–20.868	—	21.301–22.089
	17-inch	23.388–24.175	22.798–22.585	—	24.176–24.963	21.104–21.892	20.671–21.459	—	21.892–22.680
323i & 328i SEDANS									
1999	15-Inch	22.286–23.073	21.695–22.483	—	22.955–23.734	20.947–21.734	20.317–20.750	—	21.734–22.522
	16-Inch	22.798–23.585	22.207–22.944	—	23.467–24.254	21.459–22.246	20.829–21.616	—	22.246–23.034
	17-Inch	23.388–24.254	22.798–23.585	—	24.058–24.845	22.049–22.836	21.419–22.207	—	22.837–23.624
	18-Inch	23.900–24.687	23.309–24.097	—	24.569–25.357	22.561–23.349	21.931–22.719	—	23.349–24.136
323is & 328is									
1998–99	15-Inch	22.286–22.073	21.695–22.482	—	23.073–23.861	20.002–20.789	19.569–20.356	—	20.790–21.577
	16-inch	22.796–23.585	22.207–22.994	—	23.575–24.733	20.514–21.301	20.081–20.868	—	21.301–22.089
	17-inch	23.388–24.175	22.798–22.585	—	24.176–24.963	21.104–21.892	20.671–21.459	—	21.892–22.680

Fig. 1 Vehicle ride height specifications (Part 2 of 4)

Year	Rim Size	Ride Height, Inch							
		Front				Rear			
		Standard	Sports	M Sports	Rough Road	Standard	Sports	M Sports	Rough Road
325Ci, 325i, 330Ci & 330i									
2001	15-Inch	22.286–23.073	21.695–22.483	—	22.955–23.734	20.947–21.734	20.317–20.750	—	21.734–22.522
	16-Inch	22.798–23.585	22.207–22.944	—	23.467–24.254	21.459–22.246	20.829–21.616	—	22.246–23.034
	17-Inch	23.388–24.254	22.798–23.585	—	24.058–24.845	22.049–22.836	21.419–22.207	—	22.837–23.624
	18-Inch	23.900–24.687	23.309–24.097	—	24.569–25.357	22.561–23.349	21.931–22.719	—	23.349–24.136
325xi & 330xi									
2001	16-Inch	27.404–25.254	—	—	—	21.128–22.916	—	—	—
	17-Inch	24.058–24.845	—	—	—	22.719–23.506	—	—	—
	18-Inch	24.569–25.357	—	—	—	22.231–24.018	—	—	—
525, 528 & 530 SEDANS									
1998–2001	15-Inch	22.404–23.191	21.616–22.404	21.616–22.409	23.191–23.979	21.144–21.931	20.553–21.341	20.553–21.341	②
	16-Inch	22.916–23.703	22.128–22.916	22.128–22.916	23.703–24.491	21.656–22.443	21.065–21.833	21.065–21.833	③
	17-Inch	23.506–24.294	22.719–23.506	22.719–23.506	24.294–25.081	22.246–23.034	21.565–22.443	21.565–22.443	④
	18-Inch	24.019–24.806	23.231–24.018	23.231–24.018	24.806–25.593	21.758–22.546	22.168–22.994	22.168–22.994	⑤
525, 528 & 540 SPORTS WAGONS									
1998–2001	15-Inch	22.404–23.191	21.616–22.404	—	23.191–23.979	21.183–22.010	21.183–21.971	—	⑥
	16-Inch	22.916–23.703	22.128–22.916	—	23.703–24.491	21.695–22.483	21.695–22.483	—	⑦
	17-Inch	23.506–24.294	22.719–23.506	—	24.294–25.081	22.286–22.719	21.892–23.113	—	⑧
	18-Inch	24.019–24.806	23.231–24.018	—	24.806–25.593	23.191–23.585	22.798–23.585	—	⑨
540 SEDAN									
1998–2001	15-Inch	22.404–23.191	21.616–22.404	21.734–22.522	23.191–23.979	21.144–21.931	20.553–21.341	20.711–21.498	②
	16-Inch	22.916–23.703	22.128–22.916	22.246–23.534	23.703–24.491	21.656–22.443	21.065–21.833	21.223–22.010	③
	17-Inch	23.506–24.294	22.719–23.506	22.837–23.624	24.294–25.081	22.246–23.034	21.565–22.443	21.813–22.601	④
	18-Inch	24.019–24.806	23.231–24.018	23.345–24.136	24.806–25.593	21.758–22.546	22.168–22.994	22.365–23.113	⑤
740 & 750 LESS RIDE LEVEL CONTROL									
1998–2001	16-Inch	23.743–24.530	22.955–23.743	—	24.609–25.396	22.010–22.789	22.010–22.789	—	22.798–23.585
	17-Inch	24.333–25.121	23.546–24.333	—	25.199–25.987	22.601–23.388	22.601–23.388	—	23.388–24.276
	18-inch	24.845–25.632	24.058–24.845	—	25.711–26.499	23.133–23.506	23.133–23.506	—	23.900–24.687

Fig. 1 Vehicle ride height specifications (Part 3 of 4)

Year	Rim Size	Ride Height, Inch							
		Front				Rear			
		Standard	Sports	M Sports	Rough Road	Standard	Sports	M Sports	Rough Road
740 & 750 w/RIDE LEVEL CONTROL									
1998–2001	16-Inch	23.743–24.530	22.955–23.743	—	24.609–25.396	22.010–22.789	22.010–22.789	—	22.010–22.789
	17-Inch	24.333–25.121	23.546–24.333	—	25.199–25.987	22.601–23.388	22.601–23.388	—	22.601–23.388
	18-inch	24.845–25.632	24.058–24.845	—	25.711–26.499	23.133–23.506	23.133–23.506	—	23.133–23.506

① — Using measuring aid tool No. 31 3 010, or equivalent.
② — Ride Level Control, Pneumatic Spring, 21.734–22.522 inches; Rough Road Package Less Ride Level Control, 21.931–22.719 inches.
③ — Ride Level Control, Pneumatic Spring, 22.246–23.634 inches; Rough Road Package Less Ride Level Control, 22.443–22.231 inches.
④ — Ride Level Control, Pneumatic Spring, 22.837–23.624 inches; Rough Road Package Less Ride Level Control, 23.034–23.821 inches.
⑤ — Ride Level Control, Pneumatic Spring, 23.349–24.136 inches; Rough Road Package Less Ride Level Control, 23.546–24.333 inches.
⑥ — Ride Level Control, Pneumatic Spring, 21.2774–22.561 inches; Rough Road Package Less Ride Level Control, 21.892–22.758 inches.
⑦ — Ride Level Control, Pneumatic Spring, 22.286–23.073 inches; Rough Road Package Less Ride Level Control, 22.483–23.270 inches.
⑧ — Ride Level Control, Pneumatic Spring, 22.876–23.664 inches; Rough Road Package Less Ride Level Control, 23.073–23.861 inches.
⑨ — Ride Level Control, Pneumatic Spring, 22.388–24.176 inches; Rough Road Package Less Ride Level Control, 23.585–24.373 inches.

Fig. 1 Vehicle ride height specifications (Part 4 of 4)

Air Conditioning

NOTE: On Air Bag Equipped Models, Refer To "Air Bag System Precautions" Located In The Front Of This Manual For System Disarming & Arming Procedures.

NOTE: Prior To Performing Any Service Operations Listed In This Section, Consult The "Technical Service Bulletins" Section For Related Information.

INDEX

	Page No.
A/C Specifications	2-137
Description	2-135
Oil Charge	2-136
Performance Test	2-136
Precautions	2-135
Air Bag Systems	2-135
Battery Ground Cable	2-135
Product Compatibility	2-135
R-134a Systems	2-135
System Evacuation	2-136
Technical Service Bulletins	2-138
Air Conditioning Cutting Off During Light Acceleration	2-138
Air Conditioning Inoperative	2-138
Auxiliary Fan Clicking	2-138
Blower Fails	2-138
Center Vent Clicking	2-138
Condenser Leaks	2-138
Evaporator Ices During Operation	2-138
Filler Neck Leak	2-138
No Air Conditioning	2-138

PRECAUTIONS

R-134A SYSTEMS

R-134a is a non-toxic, non-flammable, clear, odorless, liquefied gas.

R-134a refrigerant is not compatible with R-12 refrigerant. Even small amounts of R-12 in an R-134a system can cause lubricant contamination, improper air conditioning performance or compressor failure. Never add R-12 to an R-134a system.

New service ports have been added to compressor to prevent charging system with R-12 refrigerant. **R-134a systems require a special compressor lubricant.**

Avoid breathing R-134a refrigerant and lubricant vapor or mist. Exposure may irritate eyes, nose and throat. Use only approved service equipment to recover R-134a systems.

AIR BAG SYSTEMS

Refer to "Air Bag System Precautions" in the front of this manual for system disarming and arming procedures.

BATTERY GROUND CABLE

Prior to service, disconnect battery ground cable and isolate as required.

PRODUCT COMPATIBILITY

Before replenishing refrigerant or refrigerant oil, ensure product compatibility with the system being serviced. Refer to "Air Conditioning Specifications."

DESCRIPTION

Switching On the air conditioning system will activate the refrigerant circuit. The solenoid coil receives power, producing a magnetic field causing the armature clutch plate to be pulled, and which is fixed onto the compressor shaft next to an inner plate op-

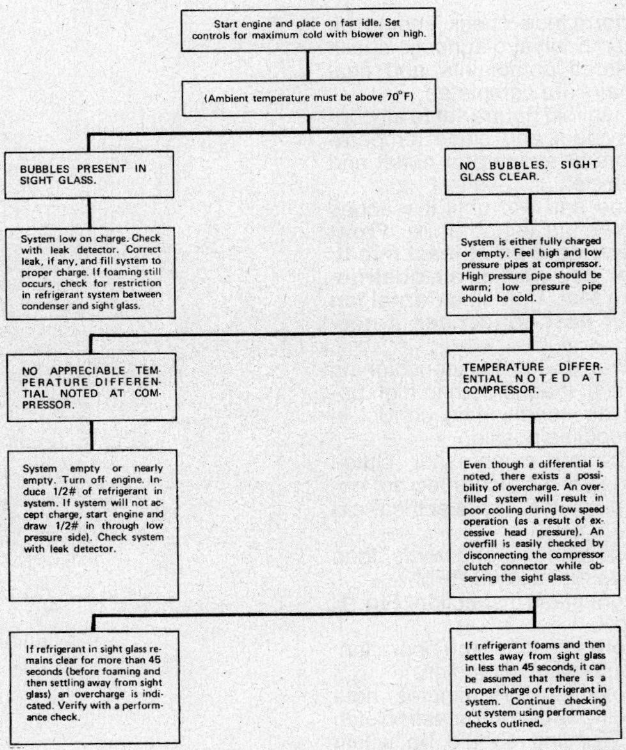

BM7019600041000X

Fig. 1 Sight glass inspection procedure chart

erating freely on the same shaft. The compressor increases refrigerant vapor pressure, which is drawn into the suction end of the compressor assembly. The refrigerant is then compressed, raising refrigerant vapor temperature. The high pressure vapors pass through a high pressure line to a condenser located inline with the engine radiator. This high pressure, hot refrigerant is cooled by air flow provided by an additional fan.

When the refrigerant vapors reach a predetermined temperature, the vapors condense, cool and are supplied to the tank/drier assembly. The refrigerant flows from the drier assembly to an expansion valve, which meters refrigerant volume. Refrigerant rate is controlled by the temperature and pressure of the evaporator outlet. The evaporator further cools the refrigerant flow, in turn cooling the blower supplied fresh air passing around the evaporator assembly and which is finally fed into the passenger compartment through air ducts.

Ambient Air Temperature	°F	68	86	104
Suction (Low Side) Pressure	PSI	17	18	24
Discharge (High Side) Pressure	PSI	170	192	256
Evaporator Outlet Temperature	°F	36-43		

BM7019600042000X

Fig. 2 Performance specification chart

Moisture from fresh or circulating air flowing past the evaporator, condenses. The condensation is discharged through a rubber hose on the transmission and could cause a puddle under the vehicle. This is a completely normal condition and does not indicate a leak.

If water should freeze on the evaporator a temperature switch with a capillary sensor stops the refrigerant circuit and the frozen water on the evaporator melts. Once water is melted the temperature switch then releases power flow and the circuit is operated again. This is done to prevent damage to the refrigerant system from icing-up conditions.

Suction Gauge (Low Pressure)	Discharge Gauge (High Pressure)	Problem
17–24 PSI Pressure will normally increase and decrease within this range	170–256 PSI At 68°–104° F Ambient Temperature	• Normal
Normal	Too High	• Restriction in line • Plugged receiver Look for Frost Ring (See Note) • Plugged condenser • Radiator overheating • Air in system • Overcharged system • Fan inoperative
Too High	Too High	• Very hot shop no auxiliary fan directed toward condenser • Restricted air flow through condenser • Radiator overheating • Fan inoperative • Overcharged system
Too High	Too Low	• Compressor head gasket blown • Compressor valve problem
Too High	Too Low	• Undercharged system • Restriction in line • Plugged receiver Look for Frost Ring (See Note) • Expansion valve inoperative
Vacuum	Low	• Expansion valve sticking closed • Plugged receiver (See Note). • Iced up (moisture in system) • Undercharged system
Too High	Normal or Too High	• Expansion valve capillary tube temperature sensing bulb exposed to engine compartment heat or poor contact with evaporator outlet tube • Expansion valve sticking open
Normal	Normal	• Moisture in system, passes critical point and clears up but freezes again.

Note: If the condenser is hot from top to bottom and the receiver is hot but the receiver outlet line is cool, the receiver is restricted. Replace the receiver.

BM7019600043000X

Fig. 3 Refrigeration system analysis chart

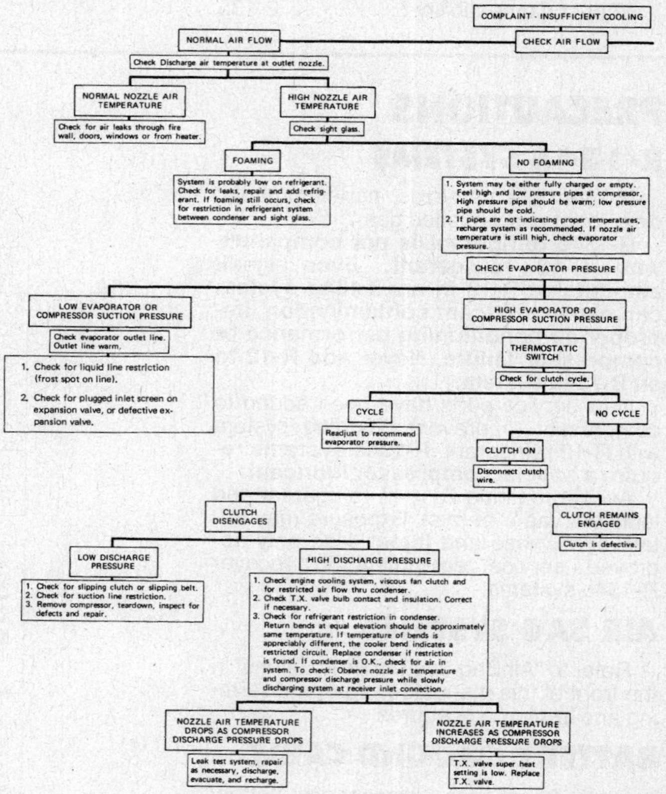

BM7019600044010X

Fig. 4 Insufficient cooling diagnosis chart (Part 1 of 2)

PERFORMANCE TEST

System performance check should be performed as both initial diagnostic check for cooling related complaints and final check after repairs are completed.

1. Connect manifold gauge set to air conditioning system and place temperature sensors at evaporator outlet and outside vehicle.
2. Start engine and run until it reaches normal operating temperature. **Front of vehicle should be at least five ft. away from any wall or air obstruction during test. Use an external fan to force air past condenser, if necessary.**
3. Place blower switch (air conditioning blower switch, if equipped) in high position and air conditioning control in maximum cooling position.
4. Air conditioning compressor clutch should engage. If clutch does not engage, check clutch and electrical circuit.
5. Close doors windows and vents, then set engine to run at 2000 RPM.
6. Perform sight glass inspection, **Fig. 1**, as required.
7. Observe compressor clutch operation. Clutch should cycle off and on.
8. After approximately 15 minutes, note gauge reading with compressor clutch engaged. Reading should be within 15% of specifications, **Fig. 2.**
9. If reading is not as specified or evaporator outlet temperature is not within specified range, refer to diagnostic charts, **Figs. 3 and 4.** TX valve-expansion valve and thermostatic switch not adjustable on all models.

SYSTEM EVACUATION

Connect suitable air conditioning service station to the vehicle service valves.

Follow equipment manufactures instructions to evacuate refrigerant from system.

OIL CHARGE

1. Drain and measure as much oil as possible from components being replaced, noting the following:
   a. Accumulate drained and extracted oil in same measuring container.
   b. When draining compressor, turn clutch plate by hand to pump out remaining oil.
2. Drain oil from new compressor. Turn clutch plate by hand to pump out remaining oil.
3. Assemble system.
4. Remove system moisture by applying deep vacuum for at least 30 minutes.
5. Inject system with fresh oil equal to amount drained from replaced components.
6. Components contain approximately:
   a. Condenser, 0.71 ounce.
   b. Drier, 0.35 ounce.
   c. Evaporator, 1.41 ounces.
   d. Line, 0.35 ounce.

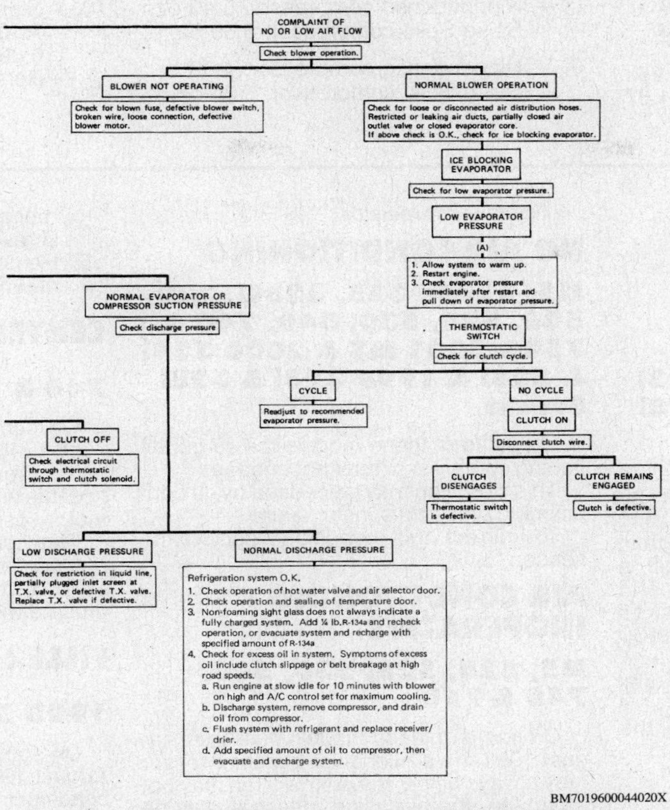

Fig. 4 Insufficient cooling diagnosis chart (Part 2 of 2)

A/C SPECIFICATIONS

Year	Refrigerant Capacity, Lbs.	Compressor Oil Viscosity	Total System Oil Capacity, Oz.	Type
M3				
1998–99	②	R-134a	①	④
2001	1.58–1.69	R-134a	①	⑥
M5				
2000–01	1.63–1.68	R-134a	①	⑥
X5				
2000–01	0.945–0.99	R-134a	①	⑥
Z3				
1998–2001	②	R-134a	①	④
318				
1998–99	②	R-134a	①	④
323is & 328is & 1998–99 328i & 1998 323i & 1999 323i & 328i Convertibles				
1998–99	②	R-134a	①	④
323Ci, 325, 328Ci & 330 & 2000 323i & 328i & 1999 323i & 328i Sedans				
1999–2001	1.58–1.69	R-134a	①	⑥
525, 528, 530 & 540				
1998	2.56–2.76	R-134a	①	③
1999–2001	1.63–1.68	R-134a	①	⑥
740 & 750				
1998	2.61–2.72	R-134a	①	⑤
1999–2001	1.48–1.52	R-134a	①	⑥

① — Special Poly Alkaline Glycol (PAG) lubricant required, BMW Part No. 81 229 407 724, or equivalent.
② — Round tube condenser, 2.15–2.26 lbs.; flat tube condenser, 1.76–1.87 lbs.
③ — Nippondenso compressor, 5.40 oz.; Seiko Seiki compressor, 6.08 oz.
④ — Nippondenso compressor, 4.05 oz.; Seiko Seiki compressor, 5.06 oz.
⑤ — Nippondenso compressor, 5.07–7.10 oz.; Seiko Seiki compressor, 6.09–6.76 oz.
⑥ — Refer to compressor rating plate.

TECHNICAL SERVICE BULLETINS

EVAPORATOR ICES DURING OPERATION

323Ci & 328Ci & 2000 323i & 328i & 1999 323i & 328i Sedans

On some of these models built before November 1999 the ventilation grills' air output may be reduced or cease after using air conditioning for a considerable length of time. After air conditioning is turned off, a large amount of water condensates and drains from vehicle. The output is restored after the system has been off for at least 30 minutes.

This condition may be caused by a faulty evaporator temperature sensor.

To correct this condition replace the sensor.

AIR CONDITIONING CUTTING OFF DURING LIGHT ACCELERATION

540 & 740

On some of these models built between September 1998 and January 2000 the air conditioning system may blow warm air during light accelerating from a stop.

This condition may be caused by DME calibration.

To correct this condition reprogram DME with latest software.

BLOWER FAILS

528 & 540

On some of these models the blower may fail intermittently.

This condition may be caused by a faulty blower output regulator final stage resistor.

To correct this condition, replace the final stage resistor with revised unit (part No. 64 11 8 385 549) as follows:

1. Remove trim panel to right of oddment tray and remove glove compartment underside cover.
2. Remove final stage resistor connector.
3. Press tab down and remove resistor. **Do not pull on protruding metal bridges.**
4. Install new resistor.

NO AIR CONDITIONING

M5, 323Ci, 325, 328Ci, 330, 525, 528, 530, 540, 740 & 750& 2001 M3 & 2000 323i & 328i & 1999 323i & 328i Sedans

On some of these models the air conditioning compressor may not engage.

This condition may be caused by air conditioning pressure sensor failure

To correct this condition replace the sensor.

AIR CONDITIONING INOPERATIVE

M5, 525, 528, 530, 540, 740 & 750

On some of these models built after August 1998 the air conditioning compressor may always be on, the auxiliary fan may not switch on, the high side pressure may be more than 300 psi and the compress pressure relief valve may be activated.

This condition may be caused by incorrectly coded control module.

To correct this condition code control module with latest software.

CONDENSER LEAKS

Z3, 318, 323is & 328is & 1998-99 328i & 1998 323i & 1999 323i & 328i Convertibles

On some of these models equipped with automatic transmissions the air conditioning may be blowing hot air.

This condition may be caused by the transmission cooler rubbing the condenser. This rubbing causes the condenser to leak.

To correct this condition increase the clearance between the condenser and transmission cooler as follows:

1. Raise and support vehicle, then remove left and righthand lower front covers.
2. Remove mounting bolts and center cover.
3. Remove fan shroud's two lower mounting screws, as required.
4. Remove condenser spacers inside rubber grommets using suitable screwdriver.
5. Remove 0.157 inch from spacers and mounting screws.

CENTER VENT CLICKING

740 & 750

On some of these models built before June 1998 there may be a clicking from the center vents during drive (especially noticeable when radio is turned off and blower motor speed is low).

This condition may be caused by incorrect control module programming.

To correct this condition replace control module with unit having latest software.

FILLER NECK LEAK

1998 528

On some of these models built between August 1997 and June 1998 may have air conditioning low pressure/intake filler neck leak.

This condition may be caused by hose vibrations.

To correct this condition, proceed as follows:

1. Recover refrigerant.
2. Install revised low pressure/intake hose (part No. 64 53 8 384 859) with reinforcement sleeve.
3. On models that are not leaking and do not have current hose, install reinforcement brace (part No. 64 53 4 100 832). **Do not install brace on revised hose.**
4. **Torque** brace mounting nut to 53 inch lbs.

AUXILIARY FAN CLICKING

1998-99 540

On some of these models built between September 1998 and April 1999 may have a clicking when the auxiliary fan is operating.

This condition may be caused by the air intake duct mounting bolt interfering with the fan blades.

To correct this condition remove 0.118 inch from bolt tip.

Cooling Fans

TABLE OF CONTENTS

	Page No.		Page No.
ELECTRIC COOLING FANS	2-139	VARIABLE SPEED COOLING FANS............................	2-140

Electric Cooling Fans

NOTE: On Air Bag Equipped Models, Refer To "Air Bag System Precautions" Located In The Front Of This Manual For System Disarming & Arming Procedures.

INDEX

	Page No.
Component Diagnosis & Testing..........................	2-140
Component Replacement	2-139
Electric Cooling Fan	2-139
Precautions.....................	2-139
Air Bag Systems...............	2-139
Battery Ground Cable...........	2-139

PRECAUTIONS

AIR BAG SYSTEMS

Refer to "Air Bag System Precautions" in the front of this manual for system disarming and arming procedures.

BATTERY GROUND CABLE

Prior to service, disconnect battery ground cable and isolate as required.

COMPONENT REPLACEMENT

ELECTRIC COOLING FAN

Z3, 318, 323is & 328is & 1998-99 M3, 328i & 1998 323i & 1999 323i & 328i Convertibles

1. Remove radiator top cover.
2. Remove front underbody protection, as required.
3. Remove front bumper.
4. Disconnect connector.
5. Remove mounting bolts and fan carrier.
6. Reverse procedure to install.

X5

1. Remove front bumper and carrier.
2. **On 3.0i models,** remove expansion rivets and air intake hood.
3. **On 4.4i models,** remove expansion rivets, mounting bolts and disconnect lugs, then remove air intake hood.
4. **On all models,** disconnect connector.
5. Disconnect cable tie, then remove left and righthand mounting bolts.

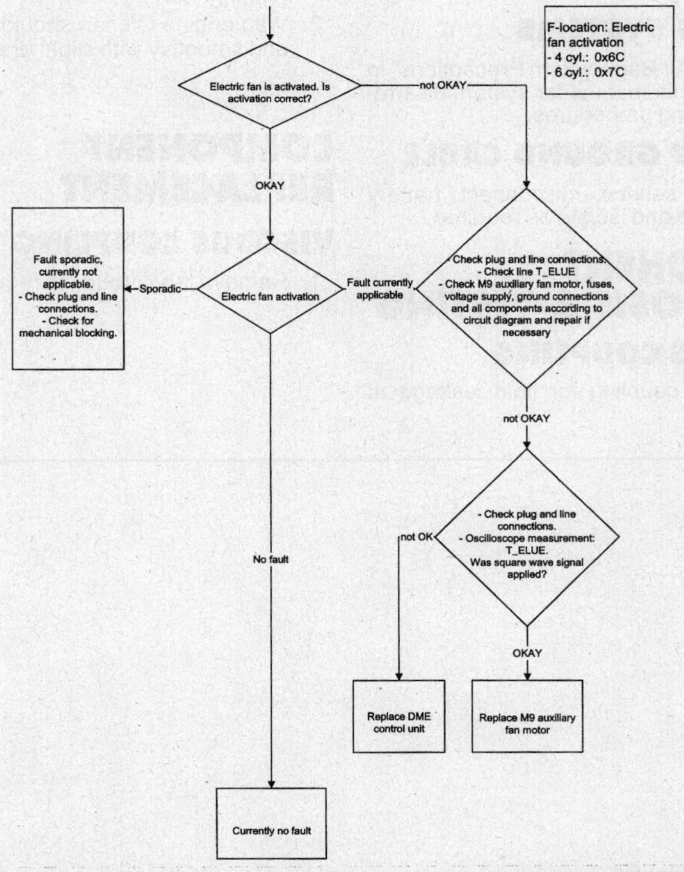

BM1040100001000X

Fig. 1 Electrical fan diagnosis

6. Remove expansion rivets and panels.
7. Remove fan with cowl toward bottom.

8. Disconnect locks and remove protective grill.
9. Remove mounting bolts and fan impeller.
10. Reverse procedure to install. Ensure cowl attaches to left and righthand holders.

325 & 330

1. Remove expansion rivets and air intake hood.
2. Remove front bumper.
3. Disconnect connector.
4. Remove expansion rivets and fan cowl.
5. Remove mounting bolts and fan impeller.
6. Reverse procedure to install.

COMPONENT DIAGNOSIS & TESTING

Refer to **Fig. 1** for electric cooling fan diagnosis.

Variable Speed Cooling Fans

NOTE: On Air Bag Equipped Models, Refer To "Air Bag System Precautions" Located In The Front Of This Manual For System Disarming & Arming Procedures.

INDEX

	Page No.
Component Diagnosis & Testing	2-140
Viscous Coupling	2-140
Component Replacement	2-140
Viscous Coupling	2-140
Precautions	2-140
Air Bag Systems	2-140
Battery Ground Cable	2-140

PRECAUTIONS

AIR BAG SYSTEMS

Refer to "Air Bag System Precautions" in the front of this manual for system disarming and arming procedures.

BATTERY GROUND CABLE

Prior to service, disconnect battery ground cable and isolate as required.

COMPONENT DIAGNOSIS & TESTING

VISCOUS COUPLING

1. Inspect coupling for fluid leakage at shaft.
2. Inspect coupling for worn or seized bearing.
3. With engine Off, fan should turn freely and smoothly with slight drag.

COMPONENT REPLACEMENT

VISCOUS COUPLING

1. Remove fan shroud, as required.
2. Lock fan coupling pulley in place using holder tool No. 11 5 050, or equivalent. **Fan nut has lefthand threads.**
3. Remove fan and clutch assembly lefthand threaded nut using wrench tool No. 11 5 040, or equivalent. Remove fan coupling.
4. Reverse procedure to install.

Starter Motors

NOTE: On Air Bag Equipped Models, Refer To "Air Bag System Precautions" Located In The Front Of This Manual For System Disarming & Arming Procedures.

INDEX

	Page No.
Precautions	2-141
Air Bag Systems	2-141
Battery Ground Cable	2-141
Starter Specifications	2-141
Troubleshooting	2-141
Starter Does Not Turn, Only Solenoid Clicks	2-141
Starter Inoperative	2-141
Starter Slips	2-141
Starter Turns Too Slowly	2-141

PRECAUTIONS

AIR BAG SYSTEMS

Refer to "Air Bag System Precautions" in the front of this manual for system disarming and arming procedures.

BATTERY GROUND CABLE

Prior to service, disconnect battery ground cable and isolate as required.

TROUBLESHOOTING

STARTER INOPERATIVE

1. Turn on headlamps, then engage starter motor.
2. If headlamps go out when starting, repair or replace starter motor.
3. If headlamps remain on, the solenoid is defective and/or carbon brushes worn.

STARTER TURNS TOO SLOWLY

1. Bearings worn or dirty.
2. Electrical defect in solenoid, armature or coils.
3. Drive pinion (free running) worn or defective.

STARTER SLIPS

1. Flywheel and/or starter teeth damaged.
2. Drive pinion defective.
3. Starter engaging mechanism defective.

STARTER DOES NOT TURN, ONLY SOLENOID CLICKS

1. Turn on headlamps, then engage starter.
2. If headlamps go out, battery is defective or there is a short circuit in the starter motor.
3. If lamps stay on, carbon brushes are worn or the solenoid switch is defective.

STARTER SPECIFICATIONS

Model	Year	Starter Motor				Solenoid Switch Winding, Amps	
		Rated Power, kW	Testing Voltage	Armature Axial Play, Inch	Minimum Brush Length, Inch	Pull-In	Hold-In
M3	1998–99	1.7	11.7–12.3	0.0039–0.0079	.512	51.0	9.5
	2001	1.4	11.7–12.3	0.0039–0.0079	.512	54.5	10.5
M5, X5, 525, 528, 530 & 540	1998–2001	1.7	11.7–12.3	0.0039–0.0079	.512	51.0	9.5
Z3 M Coupe & M Roadster	1998–2001	1.7	11.7–12.3	0.0039–0.0079	.512	51.0	9.5
	2001	1.4	11.7–12.3	0.0039–0.0079	.512	54.5	10.5
Z3 1.9	1998	1.4	11.7–12.3	0.0039–0.0079	.512	54.5	10.5
Z3 2.3	1999–2000	1.7	11.7–12.3	0.0039–0.0079	.512	51.0	9.5
Z3 2.5	2001	1.4	11.7–12.3	0.0039–0.0079	.512	54.5	10.5
Z3 2.8	1998–2000	1.7	11.7–12.3	0.0039–0.0079	.512	51.0	9.5
Z3 3.0	2001	1.4	11.7–12.3	0.0039–0.0079	.512	54.5	10.5
318	1998–99	1.4	11.7–12.3	0.0039–0.0079	.512	54.5	10.5
323 & 328	1998	1.7	11.7–12.3	0.0039–0.0079	.512	51.0	9.5
	1999①	1.7	11.7–12.3	0.0039–0.0079	.512	51.0	9.5
	1999②	1.4	11.7–12.3	0.0039–0.0079	.512	54.5	10.5
	2000	1.4	11.7–12.3	0.0039–0.0079	.512	54.5	10.5
325 & 330	2001	1.4	11.7–12.3	0.0039–0.0079	.512	54.5	10.5
740	1998–2001	1.7	11.7–12.3	0.0039–0.0079	.512	51.0	9.5
750	1998–2001	2.2	11.7–12.3	0.0039–0.0079	.512	60.0	10.0

① — Coupe & Convertible.

② — Sedan.

Alternators

NOTE: On Air Bag Equipped Models, Refer To "Air Bag System Precautions" Located In The Front Of This Manual For System Disarming & Arming Procedures.

INDEX

	Page No.
Alternator Specifications	2-142
Diagnosis & Testing	2-142
Precautions	2-142
Air Bag Systems	2-142
Battery Ground Cable	2-142
Troubleshooting	2-142
Battery Charge Insufficient	2-142
Charge Indicator Lamp Glows OR On w/Ignition Off	2-142
Charge Indicator Lamp Not On w/Ignition On	2-142
Charge Indicator Lamp On w/Ignition Off	2-142

PRECAUTIONS

AIR BAG SYSTEMS

Refer to "Air Bag System Precautions" in the front of this manual for system disarming and arming procedures.

BATTERY GROUND CABLE

Prior to service, disconnect battery ground cable and isolate as required.

TROUBLESHOOTING

Ensure battery, starter and alternator connections are correct and in good condition. Check engine to body ground strap connections. Check alternator drive belt before performing these procedures.

CHARGE INDICATOR LAMP NOT ON w/IGNITION ON

1. Disconnect alternator electrical plug connector.
2. Using suitable jumper wire, connect terminal D+/61 with ground terminal 31.
3. If charge lamp comes on:
   a. Check carbon brushes.
   b. Check slip rings for dirt or oxidation.
   c. Check voltage regulator for proper operation.
4. If lamp does not come on:
   a. Check indicator lamp bulb.
   b. Check wire harness for open or short to ground.

CHARGE INDICATOR LAMP ON w/IGNITION OFF

1. Replace diode plate.

CHARGE INDICATOR LAMP GLOWS OR ON w/IGNITION OFF

1. Check regulator voltage, replace regulator as necessary.
2. Repair or replace alternator assembly.

BATTERY CHARGE INSUFFICIENT

1. Check regulator voltage, replace voltage regulator as necessary.
2. Check battery, replace as necessary.
3. Check vehicle electrical system for power drain.
4. Test alternator output, repair or replace as necessary.

DIAGNOSIS & TESTING

1. Connect volt/ammeter, and oscilloscope if available, following manufacturer's instructions.
2. Start engine and run until it reaches normal operating temperature.
3. Switch on electrical accessories to create load and maintain engine speed of 900–1000 RPM.
4. Regulated voltage should be within specifications, charge rate should be greater than 15 amperes and scope pattern, if applicable, should show a ripple of less than 6%. **Refer to oscilloscope manufacturer's instructions to diagnose variances in scope pattern.**
5. If charge indicator lamp goes out while engine is running and scope pattern is acceptable, but regulated voltage is less than specified, or if regulated voltage is greater than specified, check for defective voltage regulator.
6. If voltage or amperage are not as specified, or if charge indicator remains illuminated, check for open or grounded D+ lead.
7. If wiring is satisfactory and charging system malfunction persists, repair or replace alternator as needed.
8. After performing test, turn off accessories and return engine to idle.

ALTERNATOR SPECIFICATIONS

Model	Amps	Watts	Volts	Regulated Voltage @ 86 to 140°F.①
All	65	910	14	13.5–14.2
	70	980	14	13.5–14.2
	80	1120	14	13.5–14.2
	90	1260	14	13.5–14.2
	105	1470	14	13.5–14.2
	115	1610	14	13.5–14.2
	140	1960	14	13.5–14.2

① — At 1500 RPM w/all lights & accessories off.

Speed Control Systems

NOTE: On Air Bag Equipped Models, Refer To "Air Bag System Precautions" Located In The Front Of This Manual For System Disarming & Arming Procedures.

NOTE: Prior To Performing Any Service Operations Listed In This Section, Consult The "Technical Service Bulletins" Section For Related Information.

INDEX

	Page No.
Adjustments	2-143
Control Cable	2-143
Component Replacement	2-143
Control Cable	2-143
Control Module	2-143
Drive Motor	2-143
Precautions	2-143
Air Bag Systems	2-143
Battery Ground Cable	2-143
System Diagnosis & Testing	2-143
Wiring Diagrams	2-143
Technical Service Bulletins	2-143
Cruise Control Intermittently Inoperative	2-143

PRECAUTIONS

AIR BAG SYSTEMS

Refer to "Air Bag System Precautions" in the front of this manual for system disarming and arming procedures.

BATTERY GROUND CABLE

Prior to service, disconnect battery ground cable and isolate as required.

ADJUSTMENTS

CONTROL CABLE

1. Start and run engine until operating temperature is reached.
2. Measure distance between control cable nipple and holder.
3. If measurement is not 0.039–0.079 inch, adjust as required using cable nut and screw.

SYSTEM DIAGNOSIS & TESTING

Wiring Diagrams

Refer to **Figs. 1 through 5** for wiring diagrams.

COMPONENT REPLACEMENT

CONTROL MODULE

1. Remove mounting screws and access cover.
2. Disconnect electrical connector, then remove mounting nuts and control module.
3. Reverse procedure to install.

DRIVE MOTOR

1. Compress retainers and disconnect control cable.
2. Disconnect electrical connector, then remove mounting nuts and drive motor.
3. Press spring clip down and pull cable sleeve from drive motor.
4. Disconnect cable from pulling strap.
5. Reverse procedure to install. Adjust control cable as outlined under "Adjustments."

CONTROL CABLE

1. Remove caps, nuts and engine appearance covers.
2. Move throttle lever to full throttle position and disconnect control cable.
3. Press top and bottom clips, then remove guide sleeve.
4. Disconnect control cable at actuator motor.
5. Compress retainers and disconnect cable.
6. Reverse procedure to install. Adjust cable as outlined under "Adjustments."

TECHNICAL SERVICE BULLETINS

CRUISE CONTROL INTERMITTENTLY INOPERATIVE

1998–99 528, 540, 740 & 750 & 1999 323i & 328i Sedans

On some of these models the cruise control may intermittently not switch to on position. This condition can occur when starting off or when the ignition switch is turn to On position twice within a 6–30 second period.

This condition may be caused by a faulty brake lamp switch.

To correct this condition replace the brake lamp switch.

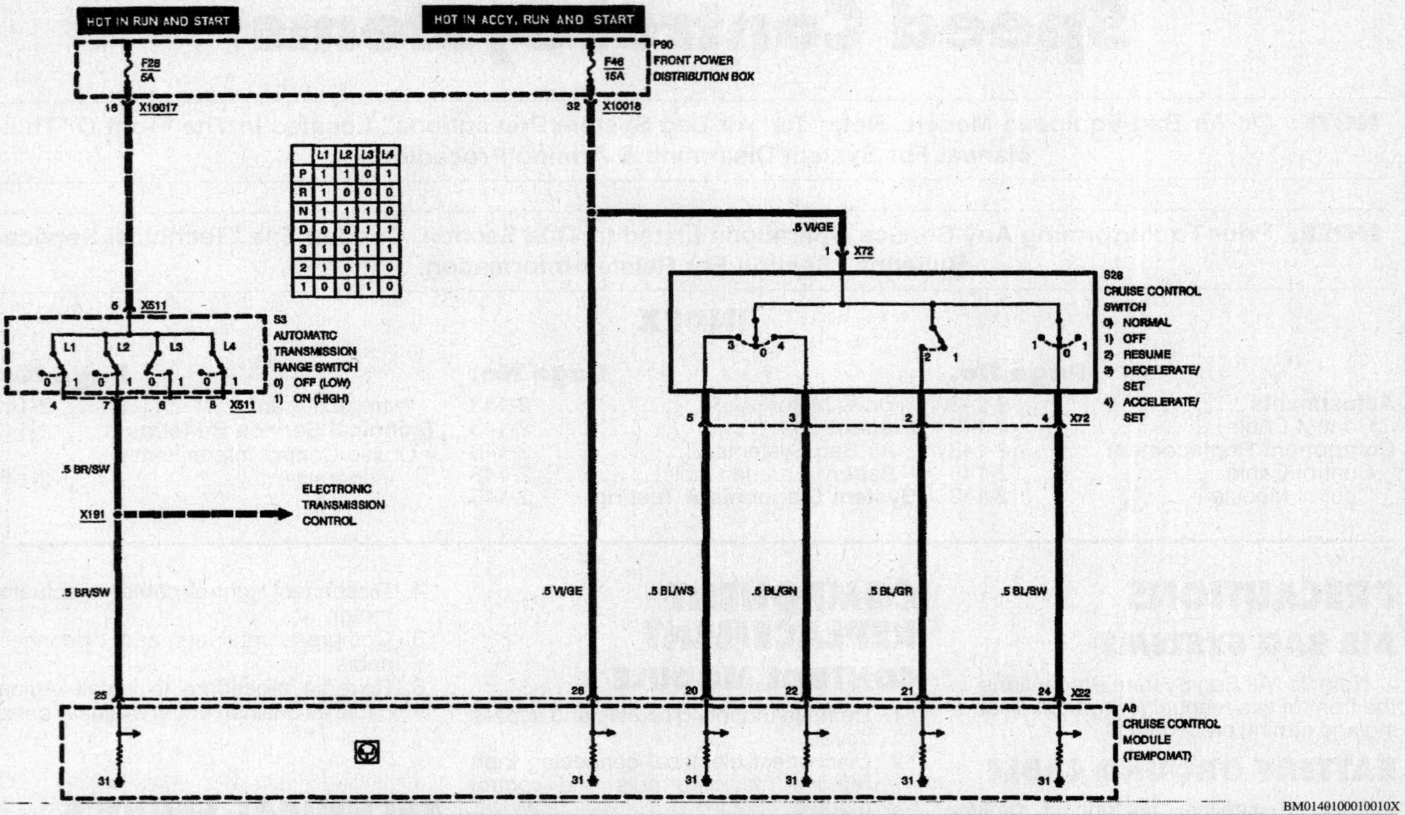

Fig. 1 Wiring diagram (Part 1 of 2). 1998 Z3

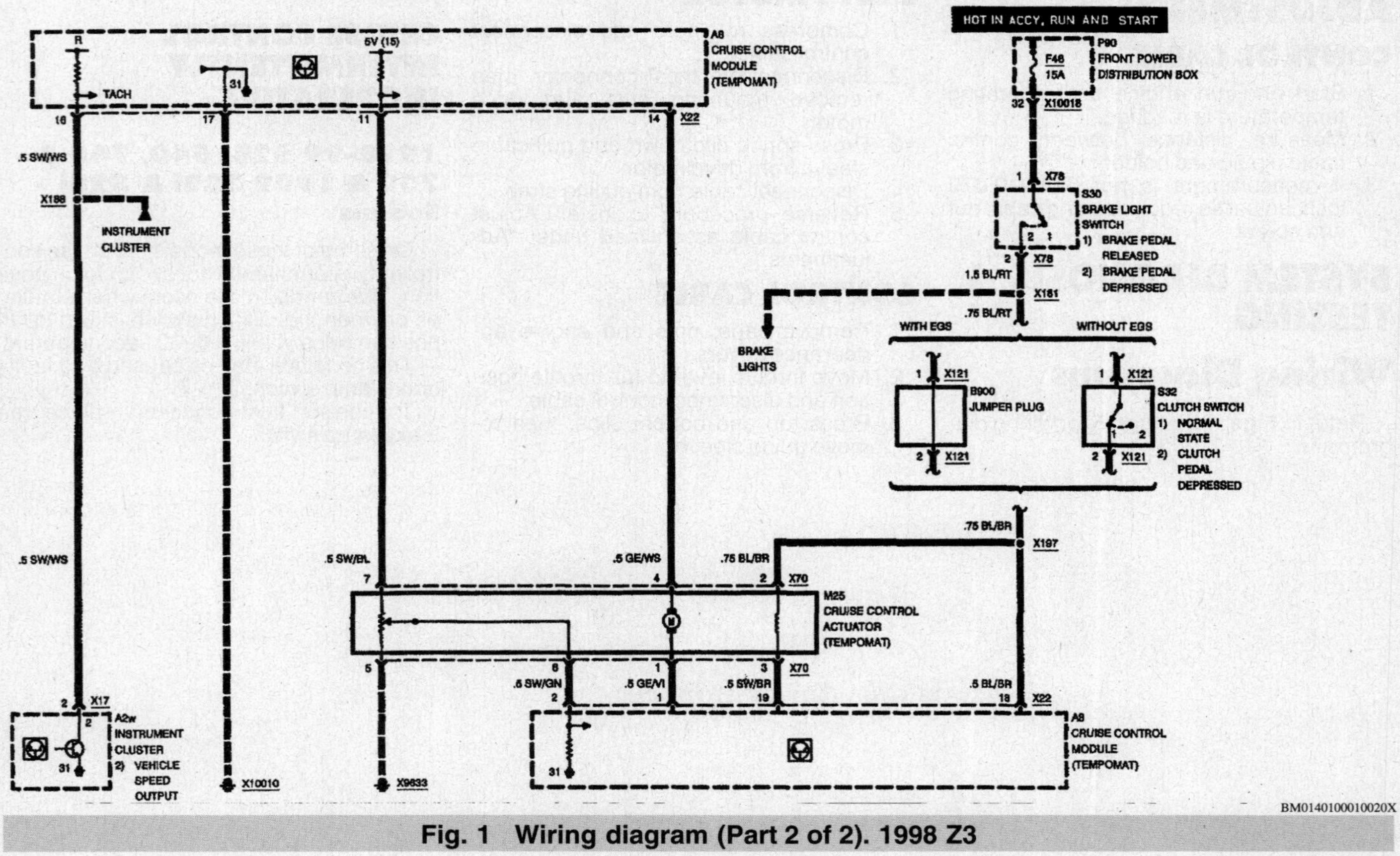

Fig. 1 Wiring diagram (Part 2 of 2). 1998 Z3

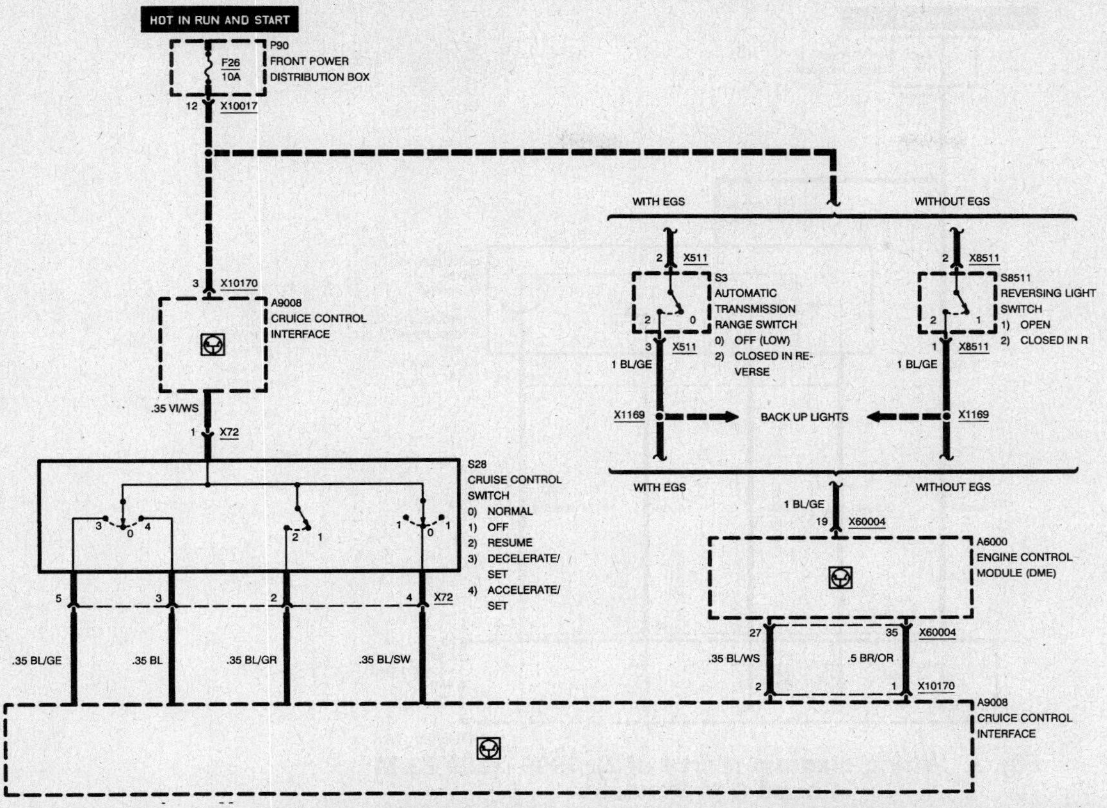

BM0140100012010X

Fig. 2 Wiring diagram (Part 1 of 2). 1999–2000 Z3 Coupe, 2.3 & 2.8

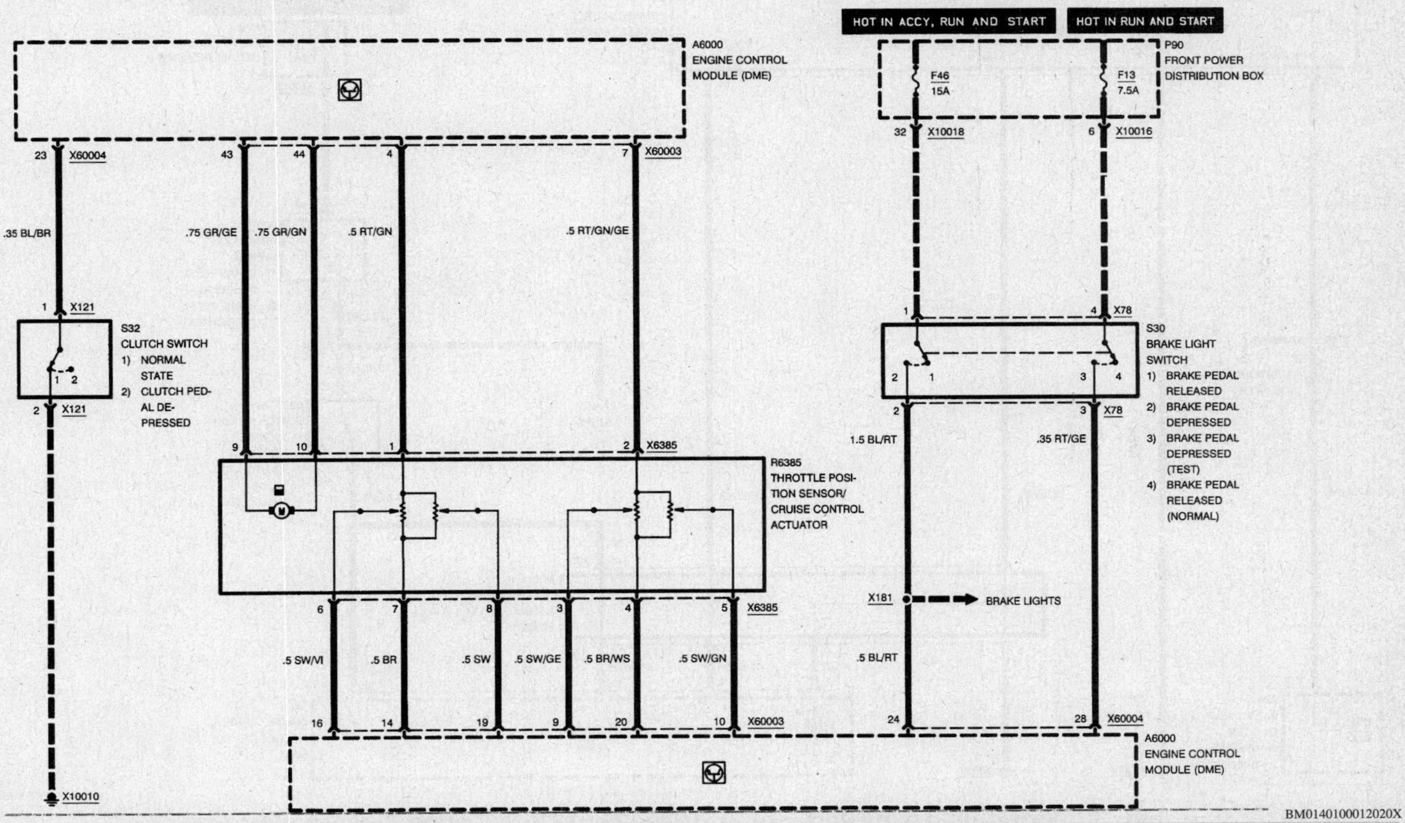

BM0140100012020X

Fig. 2 Wiring diagram (Part 2 of 2). 1999–2000 Z3 Coupe, 2.3 & 2.8

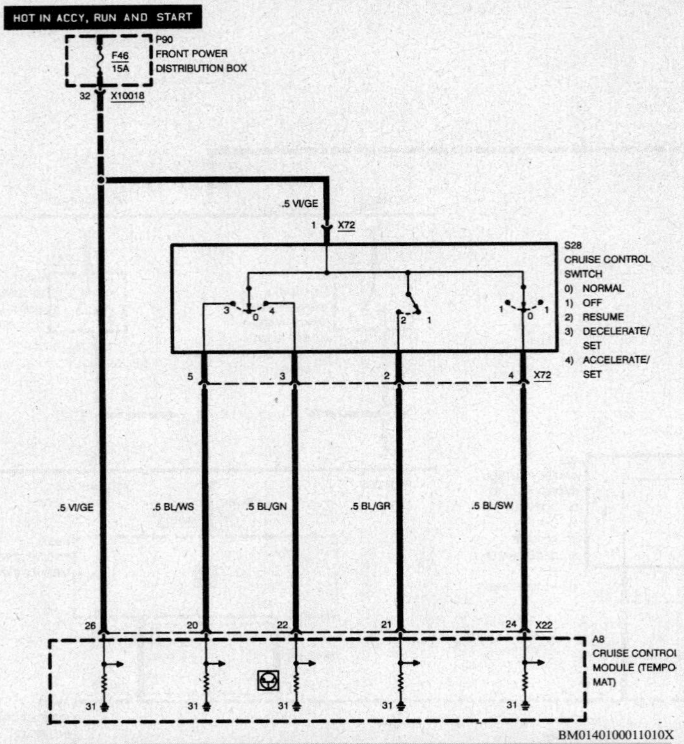

Fig. 3 Wiring diagram (Part 1 of 2). 1999–2000 Z3 M Coupe & M Roadster

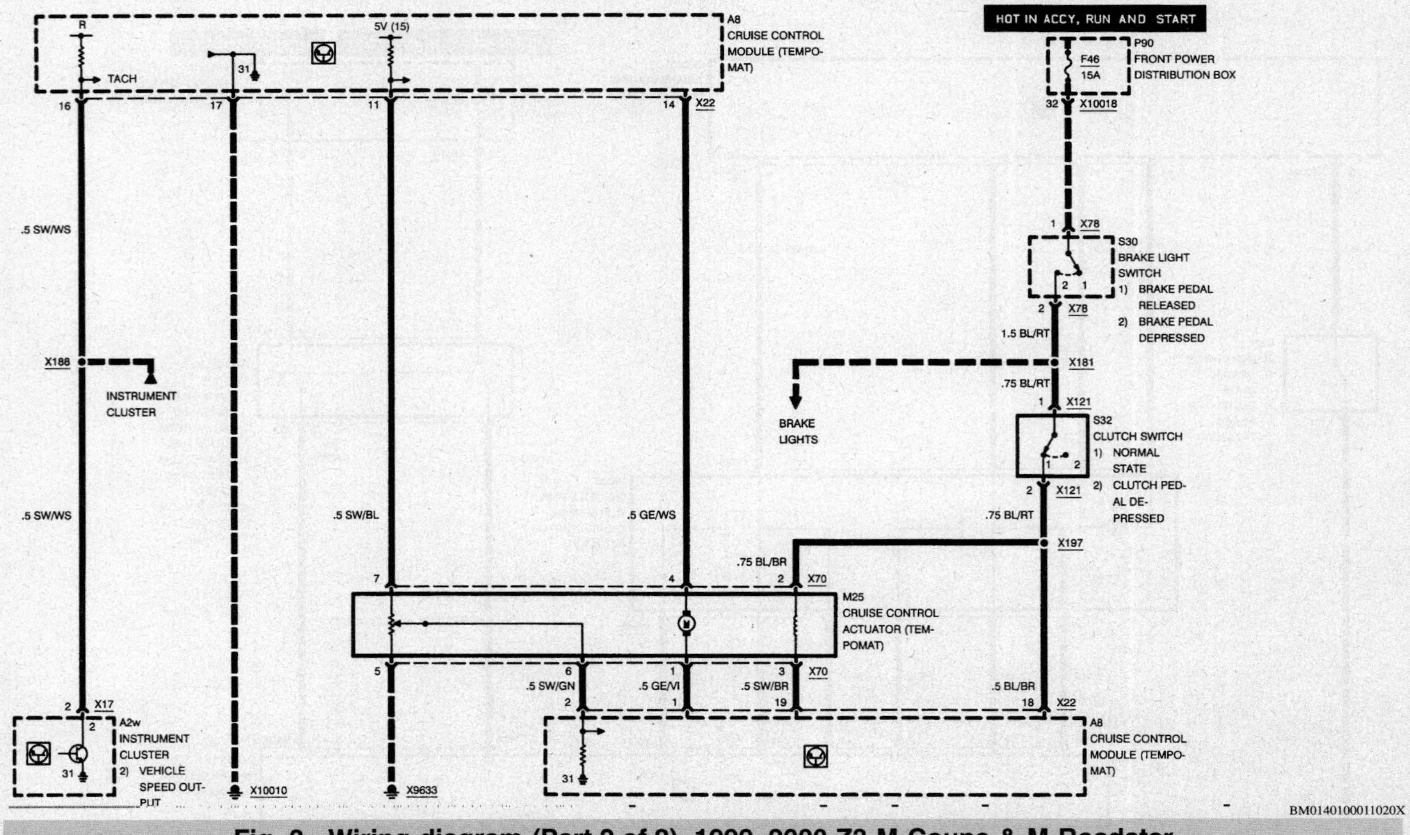

Fig. 3 Wiring diagram (Part 2 of 2). 1999–2000 Z3 M Coupe & M Roadster

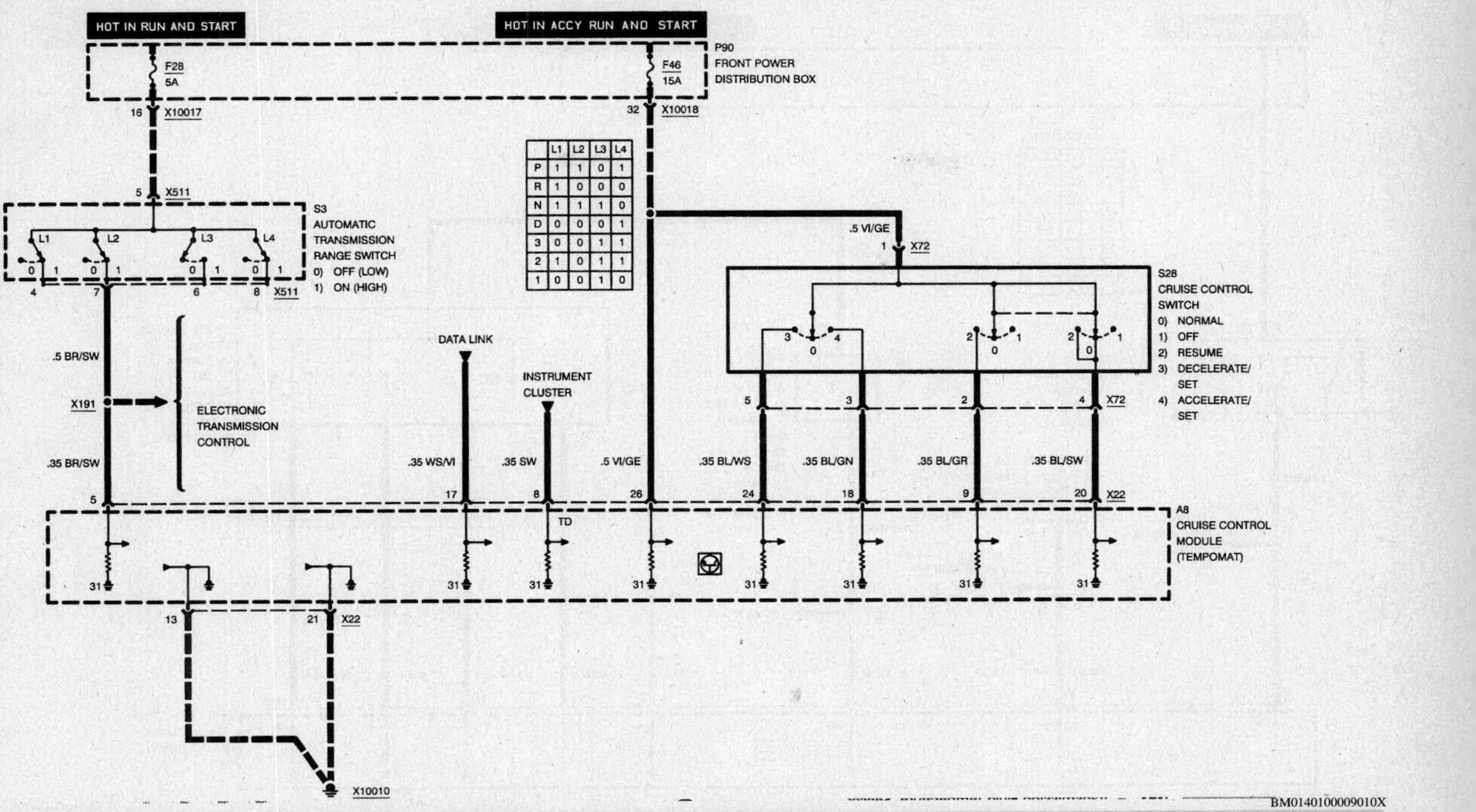

	L1	L2	L3	L4
P	1	1	0	1
R	1	0	0	0
N	1	1	1	0
D	0	0	0	1
3	0	0	1	1
2	1	0	1	1
1	0	0	1	0

Fig. 4 Wiring diagram (Part 1 of 2). 318i, 323is & 328is & 1998–99 M3, 328i & 1998 323i & 1999 323i & 328i Convertibles

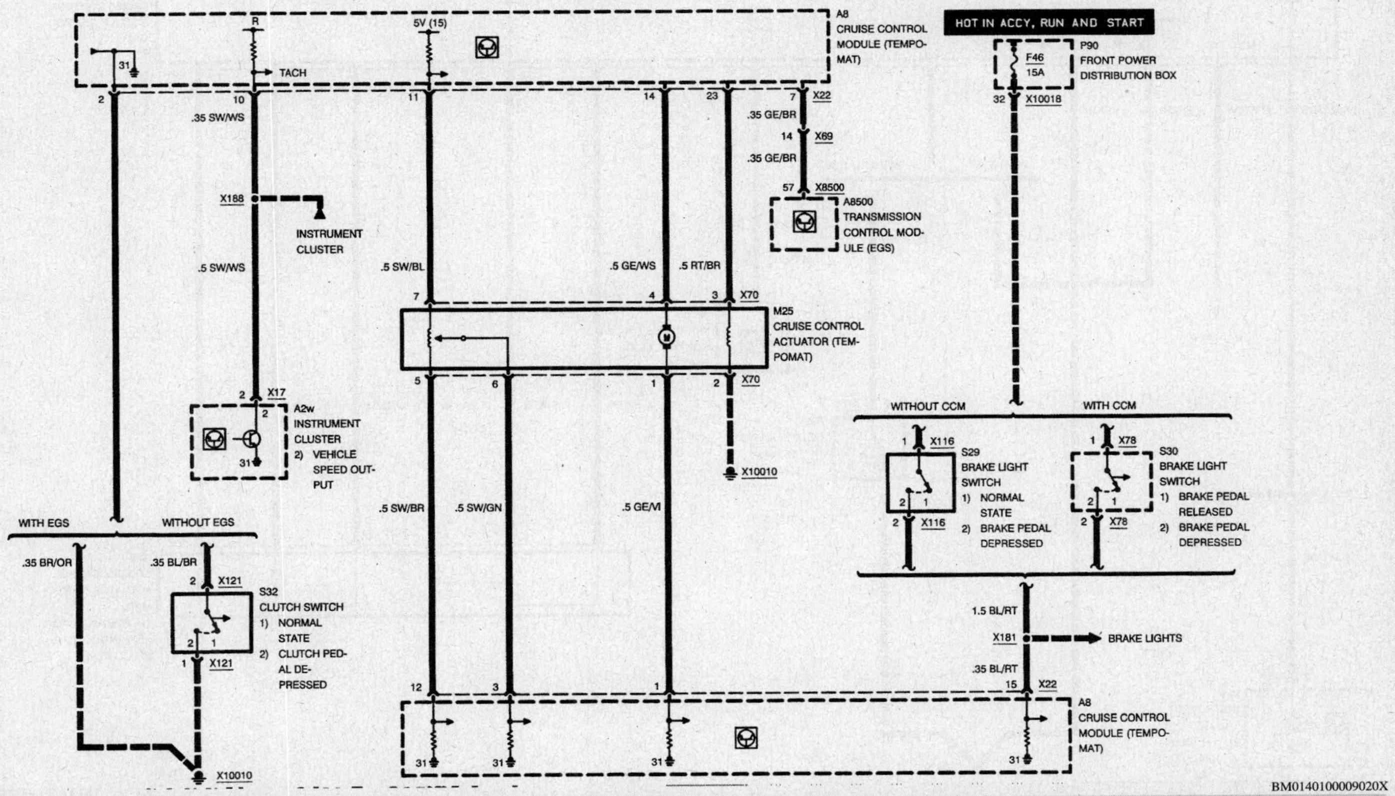

Fig. 4 Wiring diagram (Part 2 of 2). 318i, 323is & 328is & 1998–99 M3, 328i & 1998 323i & 1999 323i & 328i Convertibles

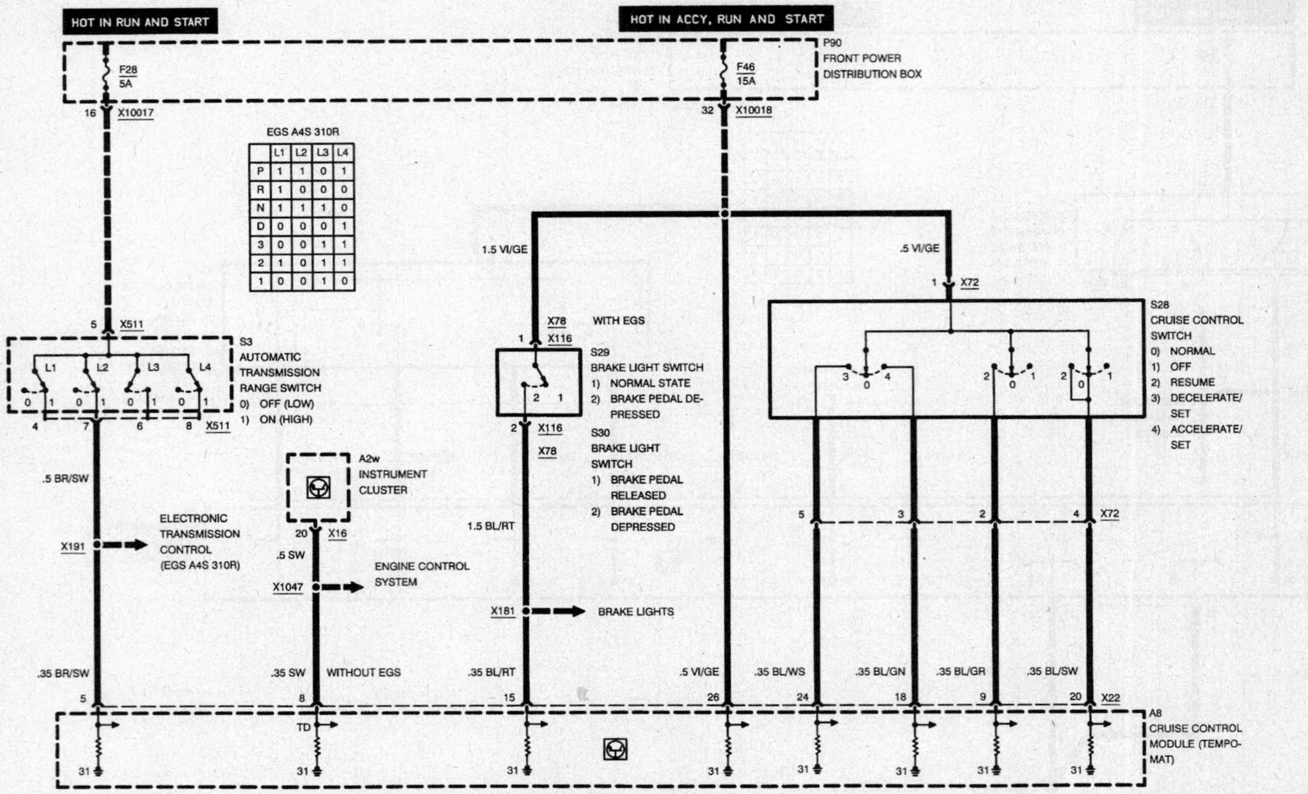

	L1	L2	L3	L4
P	1	1	0	1
R	1	0	0	0
N	1	1	1	0
D	0	0	0	1
3	0	0	1	1
2	1	0	1	1
1	0	0	1	0

BM0140100008010X

Fig. 5 Wiring diagram (Part 1 of 2). 318ti

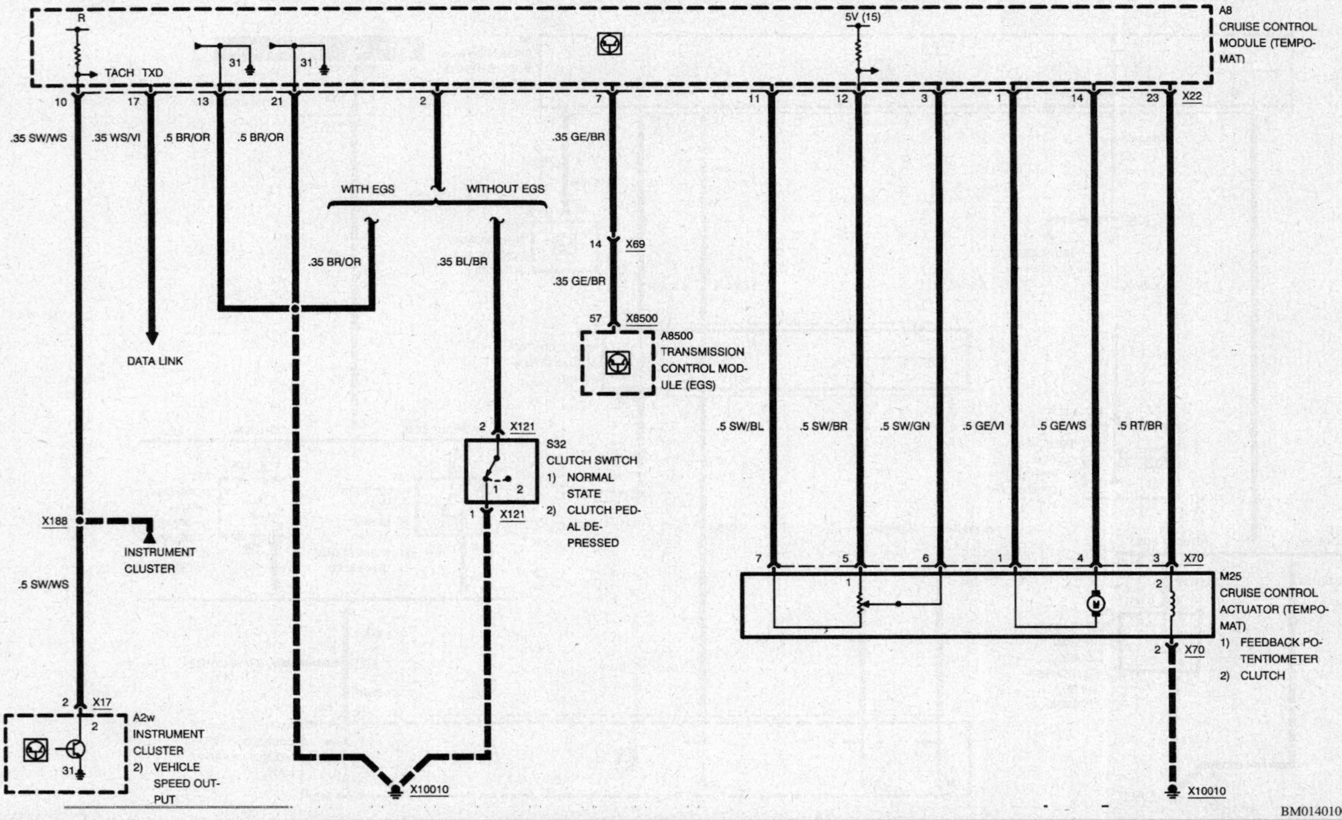

BM0140100008020X

Fig. 5 Wiring diagram (Part 2 of 2). 318ti

Wiper Systems

NOTE: On Air Bag Equipped Models, Refer To "Air Bag System Precautions" Located In The Front Of This Manual For System Disarming & Arming Procedures.

NOTE: Prior To Performing Any Service Operations Listed In This Section, Consult The "Technical Service Bulletins" Section For Related Information.

INDEX

Page No.

Component Diagnosis & Testing 2-149
Wiring Diagrams 2-149

Page No.

Precautions 2-149
Air Bag Systems 2-149
Battery Ground Cable 2-149

Page No.

Technical Service Bulletins 2-149
Windshield Wiper Inoperative ... 2-149

PRECAUTIONS

AIR BAG SYSTEMS

Refer to "Air Bag System Precautions" in the front of this manual for system disarming and arming procedures.

BATTERY GROUND CABLE

Prior to service, disconnect battery ground cable and isolate as required.

COMPONENT DIAGNOSIS & TESTING

Wiring Diagrams

Refer to **Figs. 1 through 3** for wiring diagrams.

TECHNICAL SERVICE BULLETINS

WINDSHIELD WIPER INOPERATIVE

538, 540, 740 & 750

On some of these models the windshield wipes may fail to operate.

This condition may be caused by a relay failure

To correct this condition replace relay with improve unit (538 and 540 part No. 16 36 8 364 501; 740 & 750 part No. 12 63 1 742 690).

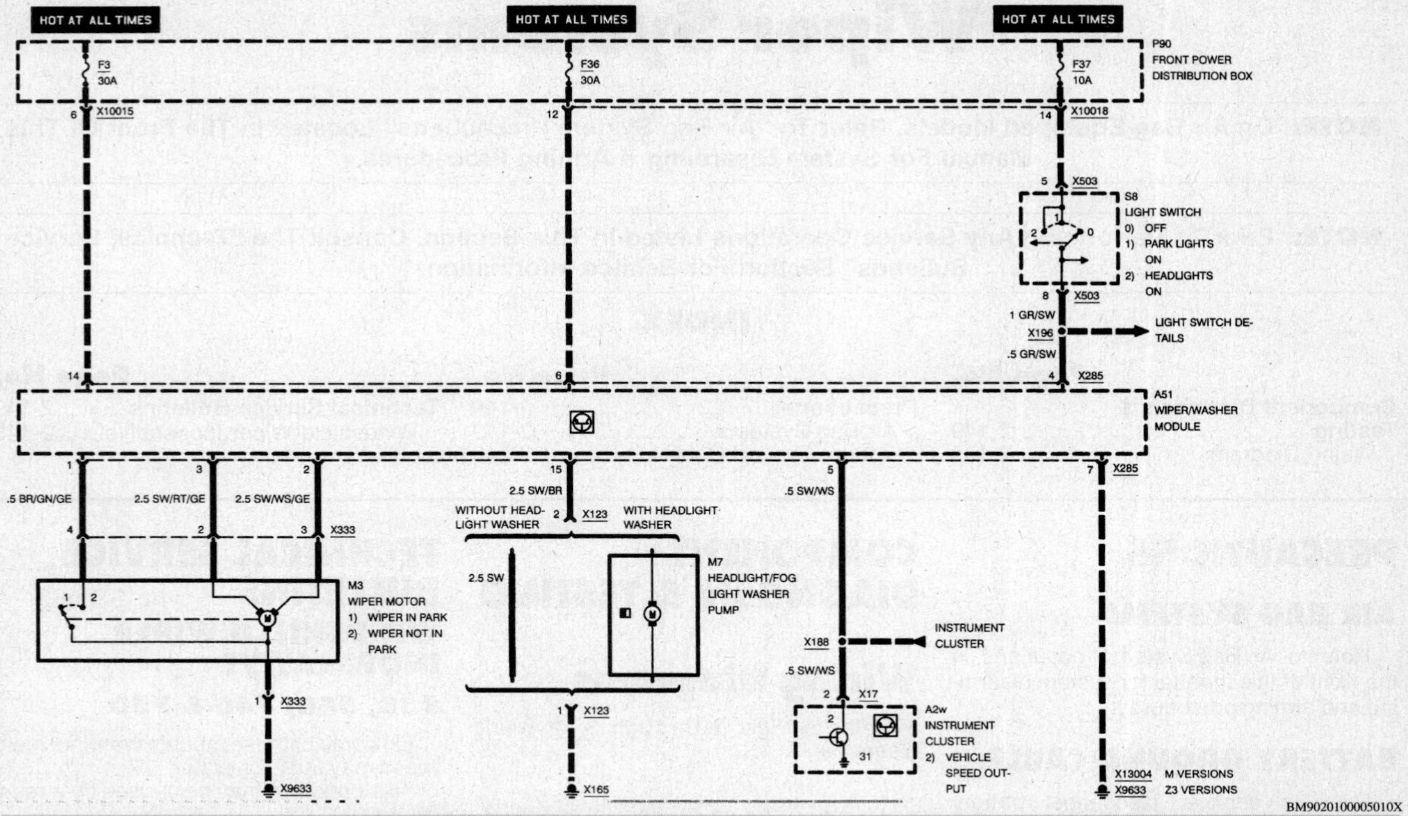

Fig. 1 Wiring diagram (Part 1 of 3). Z3

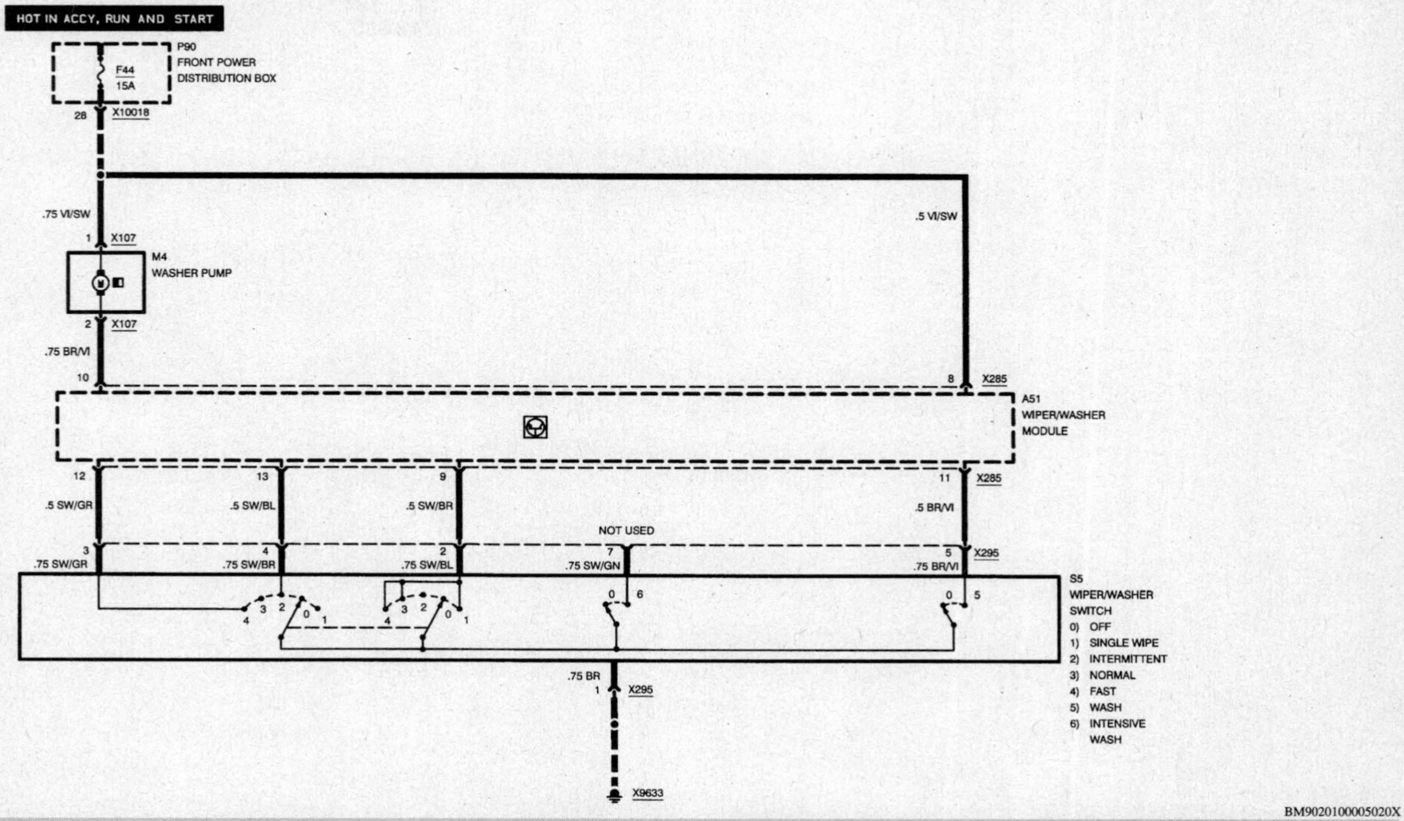

Fig. 1 Wiring diagram (Part 2 of 3). Z3

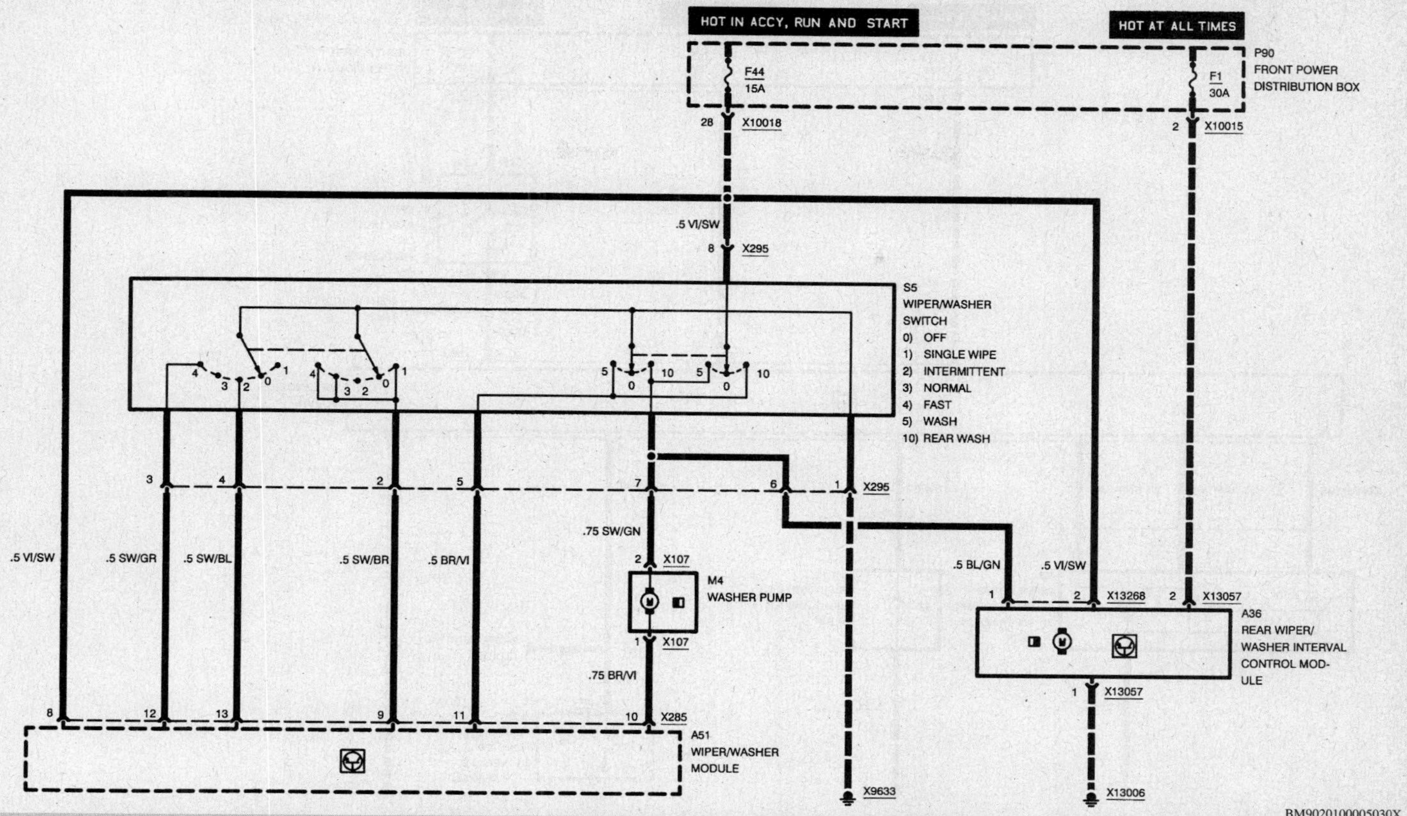

Fig. 1 Wiring diagram (Part 3 of 3). Z3

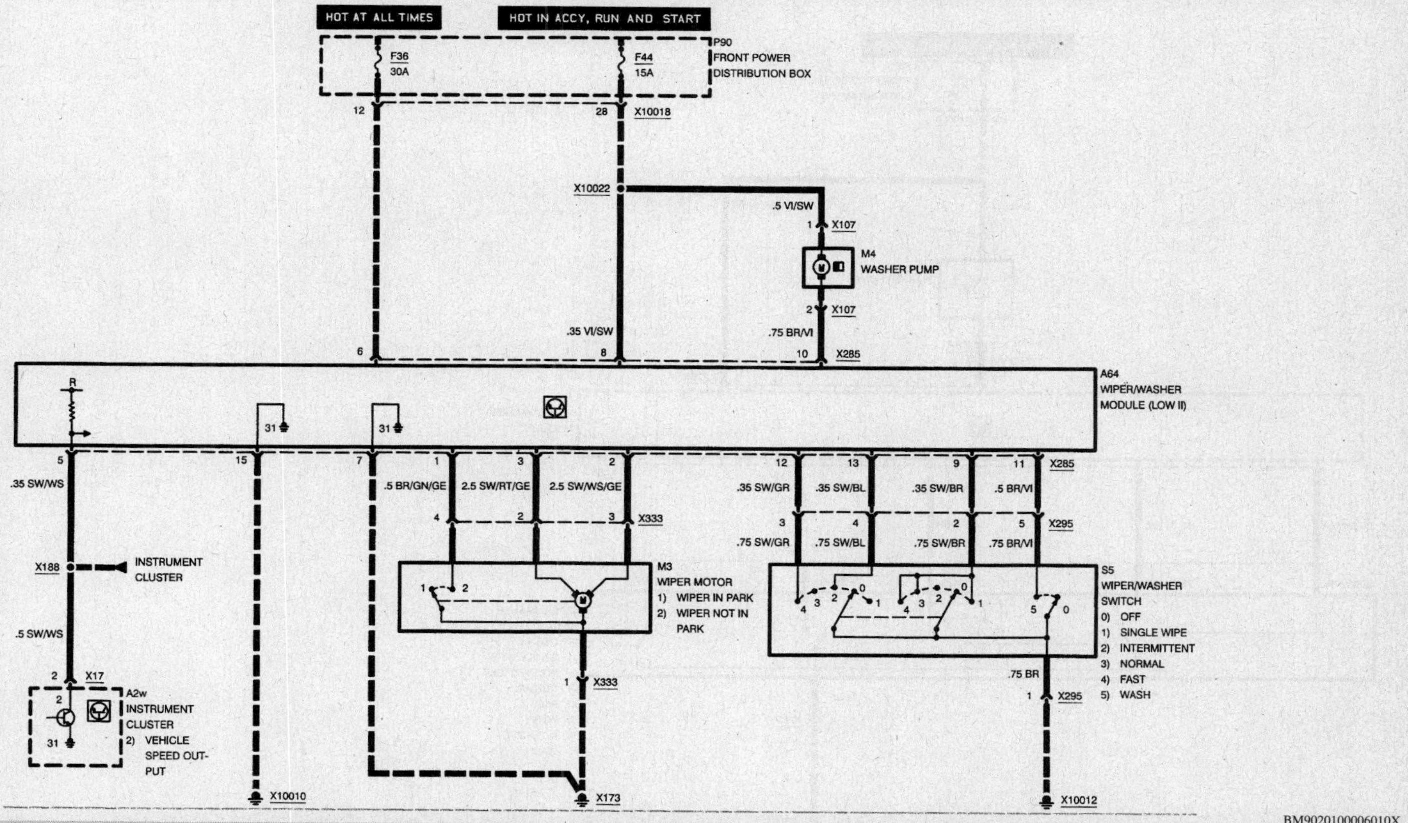

Fig. 2 Wiring diagram (Part 1 of 3). 318i, 323is & 328is & 1998–99 M3, 328i & 1998 323i & 1999 323i & 328i Convertibles

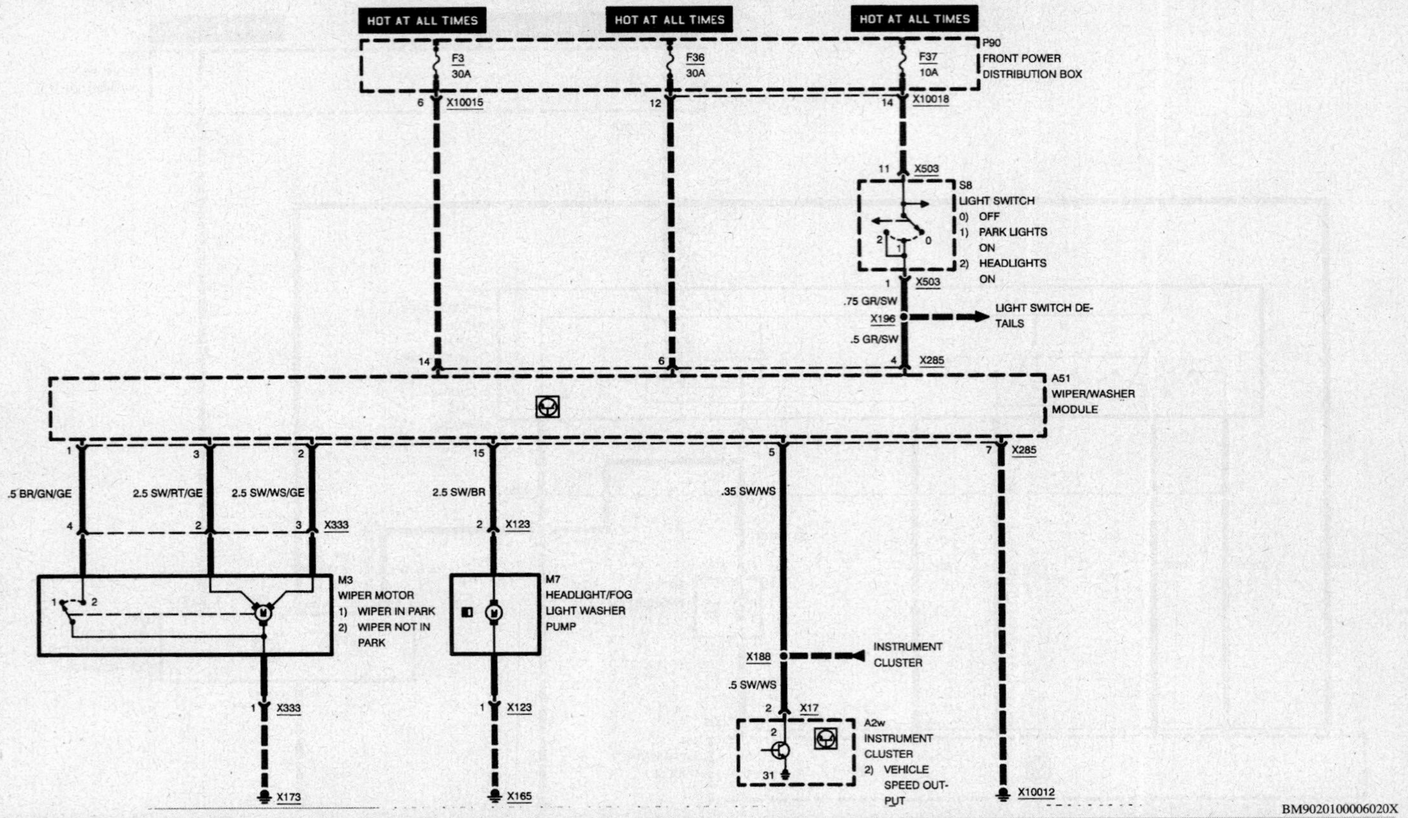

Fig. 2 Wiring diagram (Part 2 of 3). 318i, 323is & 328is & 1998–99 M3, 328i & 1998 323i & 1999 323i & 328i Convertibles

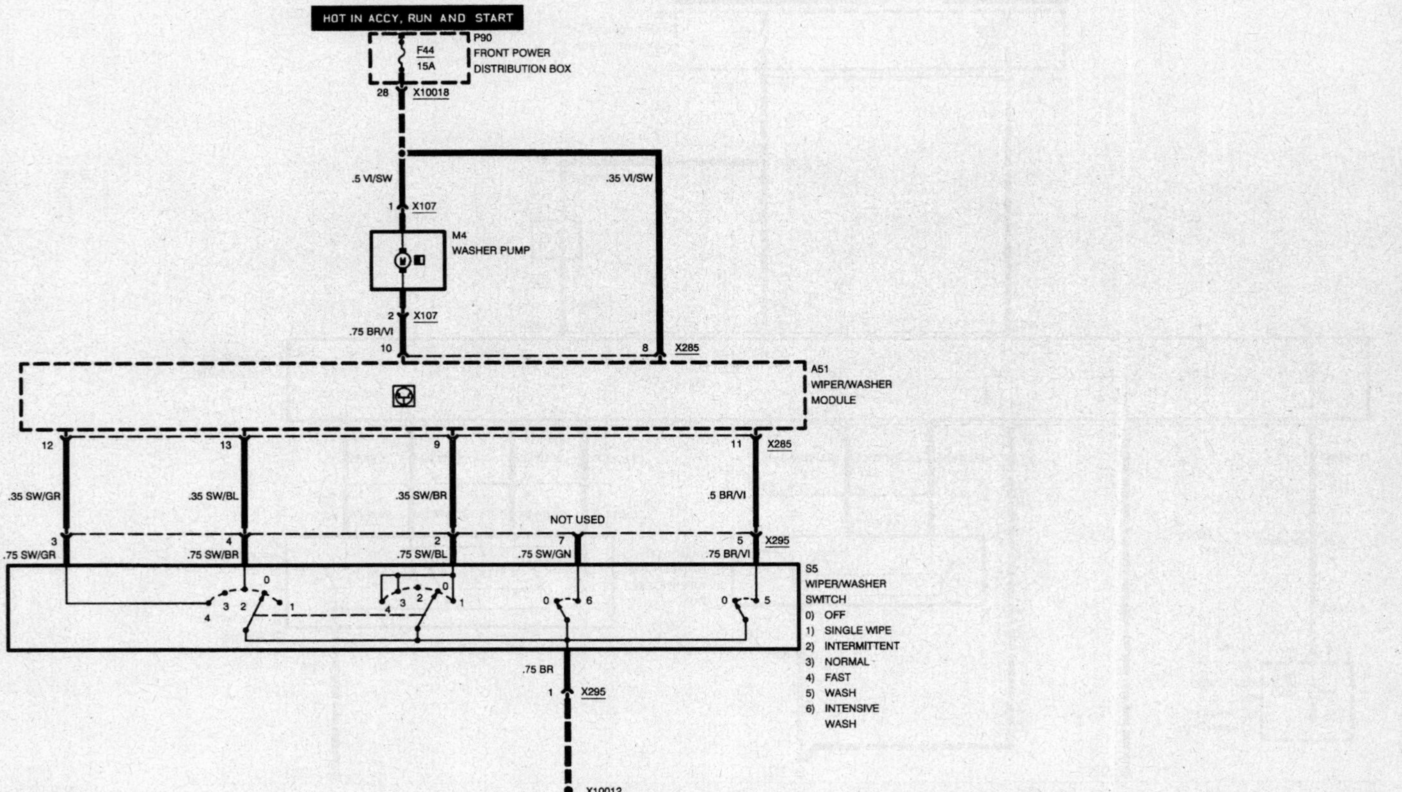

Fig. 2 Wiring diagram (Part 3 of 3). 318i, 323is & 328is & 1998–99 M3, 328i & 1998 323i & 1999 323i & 328i Convertibles

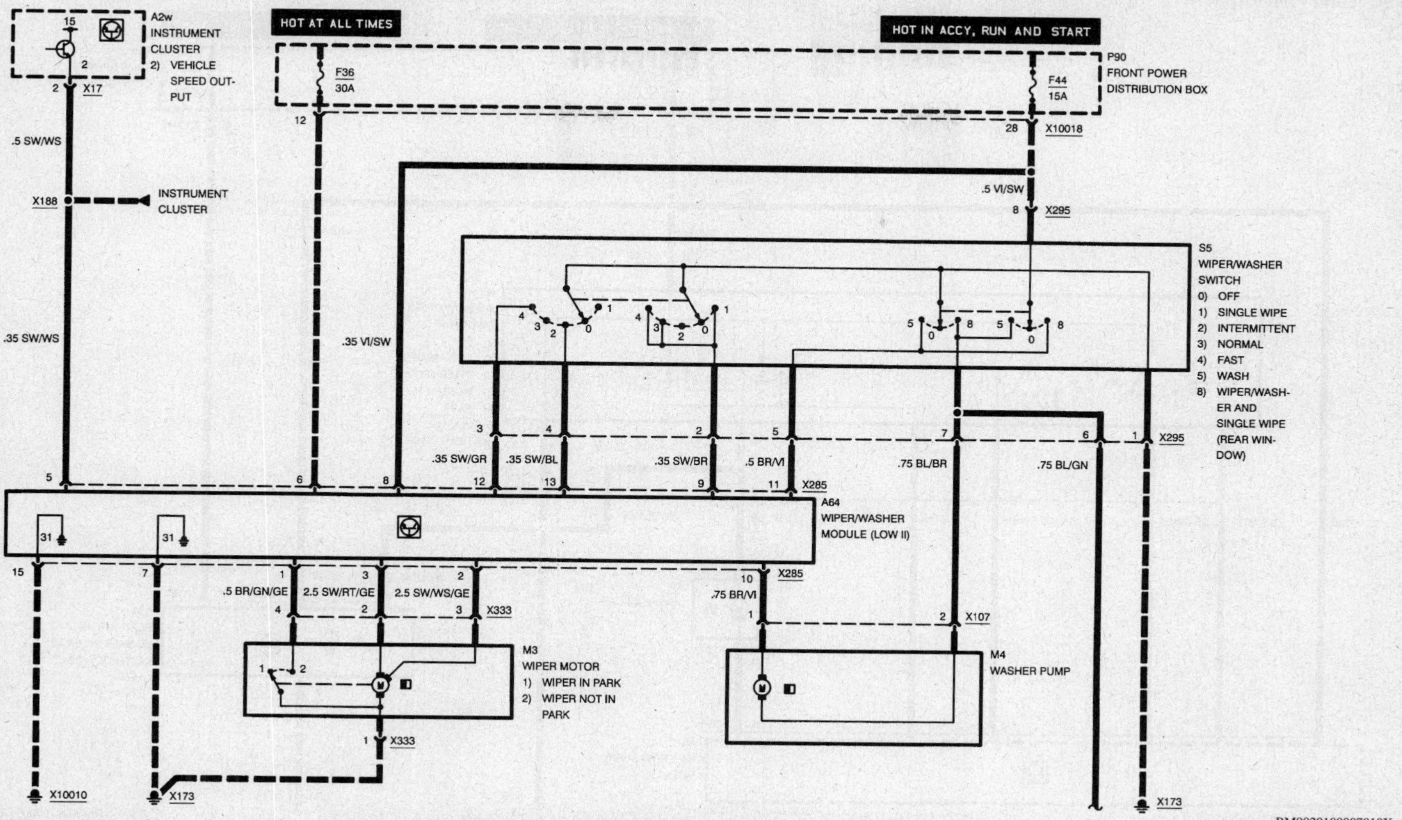

A2w
INSTRUMENT CLUSTER
2) VEHICLE SPEED OUTPUT
HOT AT ALL TIMES
HOT IN ACCY, RUN AND START
F36
30A
F44
15A
P90
FRONT POWER DISTRIBUTION BOX
X17
.5 SW/WS
X188
INSTRUMENT CLUSTER
X10018
.5 VI/SW
X295
S5
WIPER/WASHER SWITCH
0) OFF
1) SINGLE WIPE
2) INTERMITTENT
3) NORMAL
4) FAST
5) WASH
8) WIPER/WASHER AND SINGLE WIPE (REAR WINDOW)
.35 SW/WS
.35 VI/SW
.35 SW/GR
.35 SW/BL
.35 SW/BR
.5 BR/VI
.75 BL/BR
.75 BL/GN
X285
A64
WIPER/WASHER MODULE (LOW II)
.5 BR/GN/GE
2.5 SW/RT/GE
2.5 SW/WS/GE
X333
.75 BR/VI
X107
M3
WIPER MOTOR
1) WIPER IN PARK
2) WIPER NOT IN PARK
M4
WASHER PUMP
X10010
X173
BM9020100007010X

Fig. 3 Wiring diagram (Part 1 of 4). 318ti

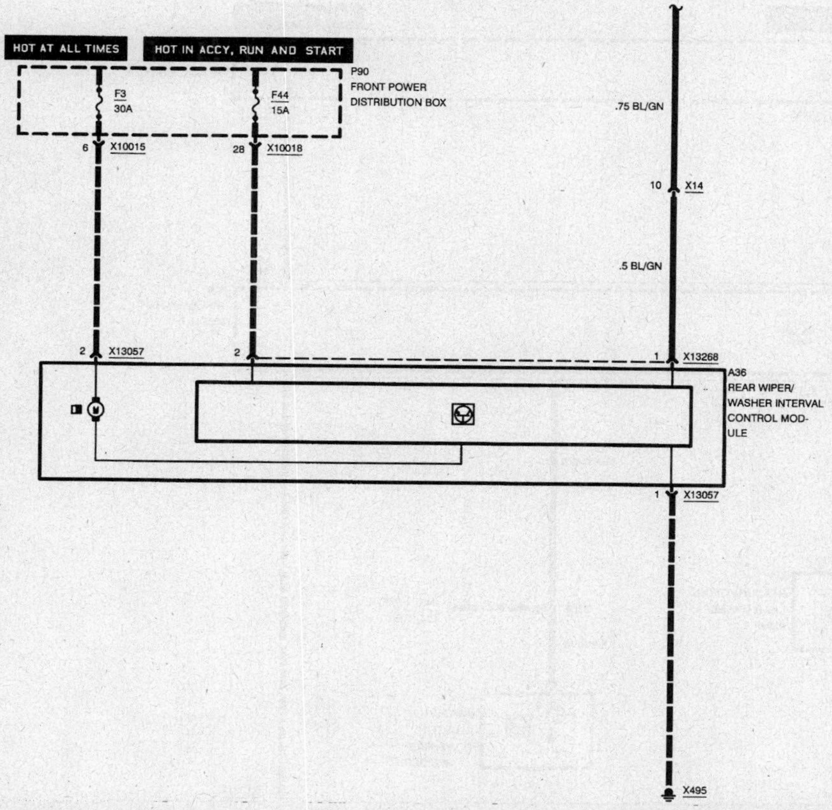

HOT AT ALL TIMES
HOT IN ACCY, RUN AND START
F3
30A
F44
15A
P90
FRONT POWER DISTRIBUTION BOX
X10015
X10018
.75 BL/GN
X14
.5 BL/GN
X13057
X13268
A36
REAR WIPER/WASHER INTERVAL CONTROL MODULE
X495
BM9020100007020X

Fig. 3 Wiring diagram (Part 2 of 4). 318ti

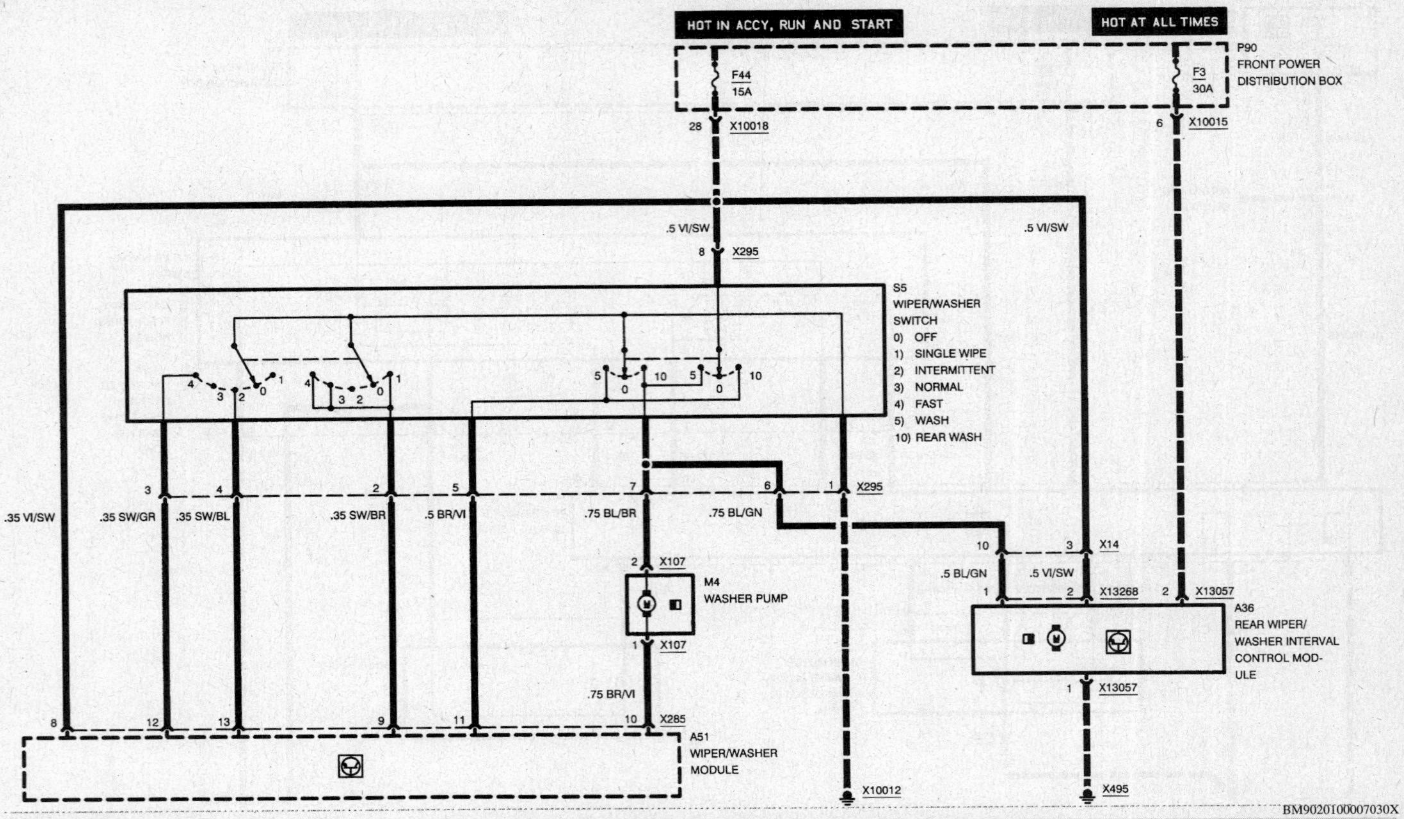
HOT IN ACCY, RUN AND START
HOT AT ALL TIMES
F44 15A
F3 30A
P90 FRONT POWER DISTRIBUTION BOX
28 X10018
6 X10015
.5 VI/SW
8 X295
.5 VI/SW
S5 WIPER/WASHER SWITCH
0) OFF
1) SINGLE WIPE
2) INTERMITTENT
3) NORMAL
4) FAST
5) WASH
10) REAR WASH
3 4 2 5 7 6 1 X295
.35 VI/SW
.35 SW/GR
.35 SW/BL
.35 SW/BR
.5 BR/VI
.75 BL/BR
.75 BL/GN
10 3 X14
.5 BL/GN
.5 VI/SW
1 2 X13268
2 X13057
2 X107
M4 WASHER PUMP
1 X107
A36 REAR WIPER/ WASHER INTERVAL CONTROL MOD- ULE
1 X13057
.75 BR/VI
8 12 13 9 11 10 X285
A51 WIPER/WASHER MODULE
X10012
X495
BM9020100007030X

Fig. 3 Wiring diagram (Part 3 of 4). 318ti

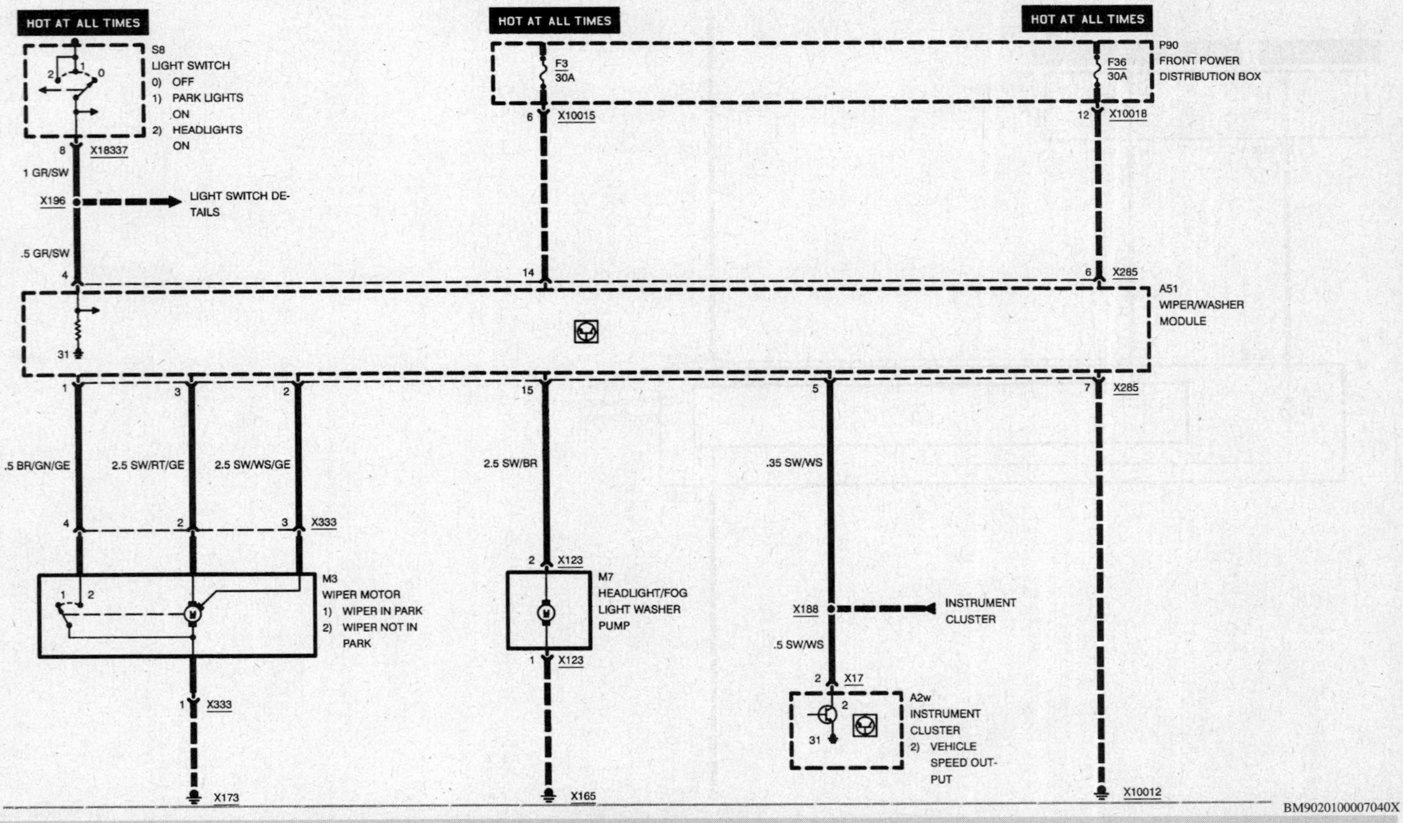
HOT AT ALL TIMES
S8 LIGHT SWITCH
0) OFF
1) PARK LIGHTS ON
2) HEADLIGHTS ON
8 X18337
1 GR/SW
X196
LIGHT SWITCH DE- TAILS
.5 GR/SW
HOT AT ALL TIMES
HOT AT ALL TIMES
F3 30A
F36 30A
P90 FRONT POWER DISTRIBUTION BOX
6 X10015
12 X10018
14
6 X285
A51 WIPER/WASHER MODULE
31
1 3 2 15 5 7 X285
.5 BR/GN/GE
2.5 SW/RT/GE
2.5 SW/WS/GE
2.5 SW/BR
.35 SW/WS
4 2 3 X333
M3 WIPER MOTOR
1) WIPER IN PARK
2) WIPER NOT IN PARK
2 X123
M7 HEADLIGHT/FOG LIGHT WASHER PUMP
1 X123
X188
INSTRUMENT CLUSTER
.5 SW/WS
2 X17
A2w INSTRUMENT CLUSTER
2) VEHICLE SPEED OUT- PUT
1 X333
X173
X165
X10012
BM9020100007040X

Fig. 3 Wiring diagram (Part 4 of 4). 318ti

Air Bag System

NOTE: Prior To Performing Any Service Operations Listed In This Section, Consult The "Technical Service Bulletins" Section For Related Information.

INDEX

	Page No.
Air Bag System Disarming & Arming	2-155
Arming	2-155
Disarming	2-155
Collision Inspection	2-156
Component Locations	2-156
Component Service	2-156
Air Bag & Pyrotechnic Seat Belt Pretensioners Disposal	2-161
Contact Ring, Replace	2-161
Driver's Air Bag Module, Replace	2-156
Head Protection Air Bag Module	2-157
Passenger's Air Bag Module, Replace	2-156
Pyrotechnic Seat Belt Pretensioners	2-162
Roll Bar Cassette & Actuator, Replacement	2-162
Roll Bar, Retracting	2-162
SRS Control Module, Replace	2-162
Side Impact Air Bag Module	2-157
Diagnosis & Testing	2-156
Precautions	2-155
Scheduled Maintenance	2-155
Tightening Specifications	2-163

AIR BAG SYSTEM DISARMING & ARMING

Disarming

Prior to disconnecting any air bag/ Supplemental Restraint System (SRS) electrical connectors, servicing any system components or other components located near an SRS electrical connector, the system must be disarmed. The connectors and components are identified by their orange color.

1. Obtain radio theft protection code prior to disconnecting the battery.
2. Disconnect ground and positive cables from battery.
3. Isolate battery ground cable and cover battery negative post or terminal.
4. Wait at least five seconds prior to performing any service. The SRS is designed to retain enough deployment voltage for a short time even after ground cable has been disconnected. Performing service before minimum time lapses may cause unwanted deployment and possible injury.

Arming

1. Ensure nobody is in vehicle.
2. Connect battery positive cable and ground cable.
3. From a safe position to the side of or below the air bag modules, turn ignition On and observe air bag indicator lamp. The should light for approximately five seconds, and then go off. If lamp flashes and remains lit after five seconds, or does not light, an SRS problem or condition is indicated. Refer to "Diagnosis & Testing."
4. Activate radio using radio theft protection code.

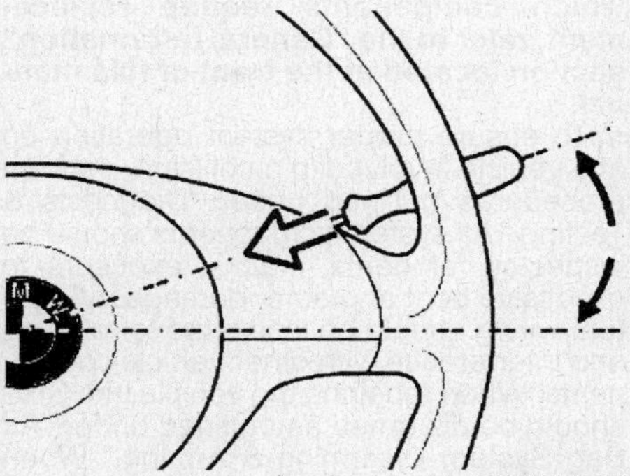

Fig. 1 Releasing driver's air bag module lock

PRECAUTIONS

Prior to disconnecting any SRS electrical connectors, servicing any system components or other components located near an air bag system connector, the SRS must be disarmed. Refer to "Air Bag System Disarming & Arming." Wait at least five seconds prior to performing any service. The SRS is designed to retain enough deployment voltage for a short time even after the battery ground cable has been disconnected. Performing service before the minimum time lapses may cause unwanted deployment and possible injury.

SRS electrical connectors and components are identified by an orange color.

Always observe the following safety measures when working on the air bag system:

1. When repairing vehicle, SRS must be disarmed as outlined under "Air Bag System Disarming & Arming."
2. SRS components must not be opened or repaired. These components must be replaced.
3. Do not use SRS components from another vehicle. Always install new components.
4. Do not paint air bag to correct cosmetic flaws. It must be replaced.
5. Inspect all components prior to installation. Do not install any components that appear to have been improperly handled or stored, or that show any signs of damage.
6. If air bag unit, SRS control unit have been dropped 18 inches or more, do not install on vehicle. These components must be replaced.
7. Always replace SRS components which have been damaged.
8. Do not leave an undeployed air bag or pyrotechnic seat belt tensioner units unattended if work is interrupted. Install into vehicle as soon as unit is removed from packaging.
9. Always place a removed air bag unit so that padded side is facing upward.
10. SRS testing is never conducted with a test lamp, ohmmeter or voltmeter. Use only an BMW SRS tester, or an suitable equivalent.
11. Air bag unit must not be exposed to grease, or cleaned with any type of cleaning agent.
12. Do not expose SRS components to temperatures above 167°F for even brief periods during a repair process. Keep units clear of all heat sources.
13. Storage, transportation and disposal of air bag units are subject to laws for explosive substances.
14. Deployed air bag units do not have to be disposed of as a hazardous waste, but may be discarded with automotive metal scrap for recycling.
15. To avoid electrostatic discharge damage to air system and other components, the technician should touch a suitable metal object prior to handing the component.

SCHEDULED MAINTENANCE

The follow components should be inspected:

1. Inspect air bag warning lamp operation as follows:
   a. Turn ignition switch to On position and observe air bag lamp.

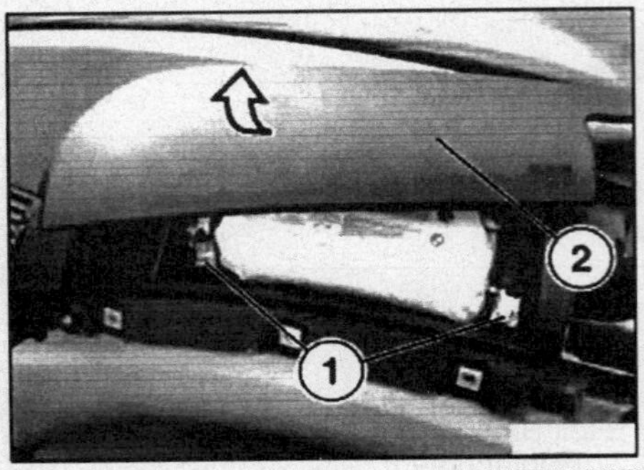

Fig. 2 Passenger's air bag module cover replacement. M3, 318, 323, 325, 318 & 330

   b. Lamp should light for approximately five seconds and go off.
   c. If lamp flashes and remains lit after five seconds, or does not light, an SRS condition is indicated. Refer to "Diagnosis & Testing."
2. Inspect condition of SRS wiring harnesses and electrical connectors. Replace any that are worn or damaged.
3. Inspect air bag cover assembly for cuts or splits or damage. Replace as required.
4. Components should be inspected for change in form and position. Replace as required.
5. Ensure sensors, cables and air bag diagnosis/control unit have not been damaged. Replace as required.
6. Do not treat air bag assembly with cleaning solutions, lubricants or protectants.
7. **Ensure no additional components or accessories have been connected to SRS wiring harnesses.**
8. Inspect RPS using DIS tester or MoDIC to trigger roll bar deployment. After 50 activations, system must be inspected for wear.

COMPONENT LOCATIONS

Components are located as follows:
SRS Module:
M3, 318, 323, 325, 328 and 330: Under rear seat in center.
M Coupe, M Roadster, Z3 and Z8: Under front of center console.
M5, X5, 525, 528, 530, 540, 740 and 750: Under center console behind parking brake lever.
Driver's Air Bag Module: On Steering Wheel.
Head Protection Air Module: Stored Behind Roof Panel Trim Over Front Doors.
Front Side Impact Air Bag Module: Inside Each Front Door.
Passenger's Air Bag Module: Righthand Side Of Instrument Panel.
Passenger Side Impact Sensor: Righthand B pillar.
Passenger's Seat Occupancy Sensor Pad: Front Passenger Seat Bottom Cushion.
Pyrotechnic Seat Belt Pretensioners: Mounted On Buckle Side Of Seat Belt.
Rear Side Impact Air Bag Module: Inside Each Rear Door.
Rollover Sensor: On Longitudinal Axis, Behind Lefthand Backrest.
Safety Belt Contacts: Seat Belt Latch Receptacles.
Side Impact Sensor: Lefthand & Righthand B Pillars.

DIAGNOSIS & TESTING

Refer to MOTOR's "Air Bag Manual" for diagnosis and testing.

COLLISION INSPECTION

On vehicles that have experienced an SRS deployment, certain system components must be replaced. To determine which components require replacement, refer to the "General Information" section located at the front of this manual.

To ensure proper system operation on any vehicle involved in a collision, perform procedures outlined under "Diagnosis & Testing." All system components should be inspected for dents, cracks, exposure to excessive heat and other damage. All system wiring should be inspected for chafing and interference with other vehicle components. When repairing the vehicle, the SRS should be disarmed as outlined under "Air Bag System Disarming & Arming." When performing service procedures, do not expose components or wiring to heat guns, welding or spray guns.

COMPONENT SERVICE

On some models it may be necessary to clear the SRS module trouble code memory after replacing the component to turn the air bag warning lamp off. Refer to "Diagnosis & Testing."

DRIVER'S AIR BAG MODULE, REPLACE

1. Disarm SRS as outlined under "Air Bag System Disarming & Arming."
2. Insert suitable screwdriver through opening in rear of steering wheel and press down on lock, **Fig. 1.**
3. If a springy resistance is noticed, press lock as far down as possible and pull air bag unit away from steering wheel. Repeat procedure for other side.
4. Disconnect air bag module electrical connectors.
5. Remove air bag module.
6. Reverse procedure to install, noting the following:
   a. Insert air bag unit with hooks into locks and press into steering wheel.
   b. Do not pinch wires.
   c. Ensure electrical connectors are properly connected.
   d. After completing installation, arm SRS as outlined under "Air Bag System Disarming & Arming."

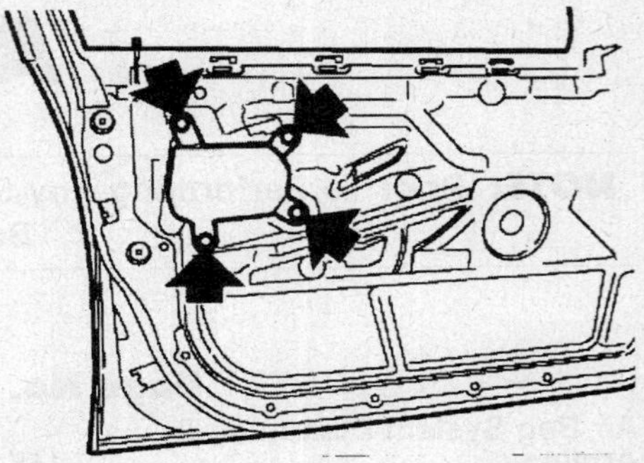

Fig. 3 Side impact air bag module replacement. M3, M5, X5, 325, 328, 330, 525, 528, 530, 540, 740 & 750

PASSENGER'S AIR BAG MODULE, REPLACE

M3, 318, 323, 325, 318 & 330

1. Disarm SRS as outlined under "Air Bag System Disarming & Arming."
2. Remove righthand wood finish panel.
3. Remove two mounting screws and righthand fresh air nozzle.
4. Lever passenger's air bag cover from instrument panel.
5. Remove mounting screws (1) and passenger's air bag cover, **Fig. 2.**
6. Remove mounting screws and passenger's air bag by lifting module up, moving to one side, opening tab and disconnect connection.
7. Reverse procedure to install, noting the following:
   a. Do not pinch wires.
   b. Ensure electrical connectors are properly connected.
   c. Ensure cover retaining lugs snap into place.
   d. Tighten mounting screws to specifications.
   e. After completing installation, arm system as outlined under "Air Bag System Disarming & Arming."

Z3

1. Disarm SRS as outlined under "Air Bag System Disarming & Arming."
2. Remove glove compartment.
3. Lift passenger's air bag cover.
4. Remove mounting bolts and disconnect electrical connector.
5. Remove passenger's air bag module.
6. Reverse procedure to install, noting the following:
   a. Do not pinch wires.
   b. Ensure electrical connectors are properly connected.
   c. Tighten mounting bolts to specifications.
   d. After completing installation, arm system as outlined under "Air Bag System Disarming & Arming."

M5, X5, 525, 528, 530 & 540

1. Disarm SRS as outlined under "Air Bag System Disarming & Arming."

2. Insert suitable plastic wedges in detents on both sides of instrument panel upper passenger's air bag cover.
3. Remove cover and place on instrument panel.
4. Remove two righthand and lefthand passenger's air bag module mounting nuts.
5. Disconnect passenger's air bag electrical connector.
6. Remove passenger's air bag module.
7. Reverse procedure to install, noting the following:
   a. Do not pinch wires.
   b. Ensure electrical connectors are properly connected.
   c. Tighten mounting nuts to specifications.
   d. If passenger's air bag cover alignment is required use suitable plastic wedges in detents on both sides of cover.
   e. After completing installation, arm system as outlined under "Air Bag System Disarming & Arming."

740 & 750

1. Disarm SRS as outlined under "Air Bag System Disarming & Arming."
2. Carefully lift off upper cover using plastic wedges, as required. Mounting clip will remain on instrument panel.
3. Remove four mounting nuts and lift passenger's air bag module from instrument panel.
4. Disconnect electrical connector.
5. Remove cover mounting clip from instrument panel.
6. Reverse procedure to install, noting the following:
   a. Do not pinch wires.
   b. Ensure electrical connectors are properly connected.
   c. Install new instrument panel passenger's air bag module upper cover mounting clip.
   d. Tighten mounting nuts to specifications.
   e. After completing installation, arm system as outlined under "Air Bag System Disarming & Arming."

SIDE IMPACT AIR BAG MODULE

M3, M5, X5, 325, 328, 330, 525, 528, 530, 540, 740 & 750

1. Disarm SRS as outlined under "Air Bag System Disarming & Arming."
2. Remove door trim panel.
3. Remove mounting screws and side impact air bag, **Fig. 3.**
4. Remove wiring from module retainer and disconnect electrical connectors.
5. Reverse procedure to install, noting the following:
   a. Do not pinch wires.
   b. Ensure electrical connectors are properly connected.
   c. Tighten new side air bag module micro-encapsulated mounting screws to specifications.
   d. After completing installation, arm system as outlined under "Air Bag System Disarming & Arming."

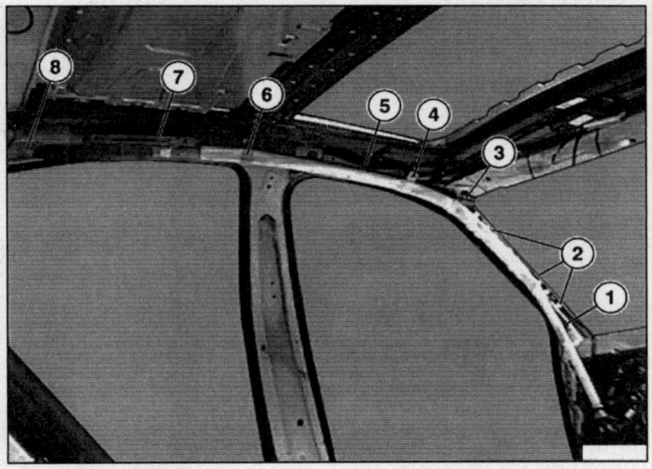

1	Retaining screw, A-pillar (front)	5	Retainer, grab handle, front
2	Retaining clips, retainer, trim panel, A-pillar	6	Retainer B-pillar
3	Retainer, A-pillar, front	7	Retainer, grab handle, rear
4	Retainer, A-pillar, rear	8	Retaining screw, rear

BM8019900171000X

Fig. 4 Head protection air bag module retainer locations. M3, 325 & 330

Z3

1. Disarm SRS as outlined under "Air Bag System Disarming & Arming."
2. Remove door trim panel.
3. Remove locking clip and disconnect connectors.
4. Remove mounting screws and side impact air bag module.
5. Reverse procedure to install, noting the following:
   a. Do not pinch wires.
   b. Ensure electrical connectors are properly connected.
   c. Ensure locking clip snaps into place.
   d. Tighten new side air bag module micro-encapsulated mounting screws to specifications.
   e. After completing installation, arm system as outlined under "Air Bag System Disarming & Arming."

HEAD PROTECTION AIR BAG MODULE

M3, 325 & 330

1. Disarm SRS as outlined under "Air Bag System Disarming & Arming."
2. Remove front and rear grab handles.
3. Remove both A-pillar front roof trim sections. Mounting screw is located under the "AIRBAG" tab.
4. Remove front seat belt mounting bolt.
5. Remove both B-pillar top of door trim panels.
6. Remove rear roof pillars' interior.
7. Remove mounting screws and both C-pillar rear roof trim sections.
8. Remove righthand front seat.
9. Lift out sun visor.
10. Lift out front reading lamps and disconnect electrical connectors.
11. Remove front center finish panel from headliner.
12. Lift out headliner interior lamp and disconnect electrical connector.
13. Adjust lefthand front seat back rest to lowest position.
14. Pull headliner upwards and out of sheet metal tabs, then pull headliner toward righthand rear door to remove.
15. Remove steering wheel.
16. Remove upper and lower steering column trim.
17. Disconnect connector from ring antenna.
18. Disconnect wiper switch electrical connector.
19. Disconnect turn signal indicator lever electrical connector.
20. Remove mounting screws and steering column switch.
21. Remove shelf or ash tray towards top by pressing center console roller cover slightly downward to push storage tray slightly upward.
22. Remove two center console bracket screws located in shelf or ash tray opening, then disconnect electrical connector, as required, and remove bracket.
23. Disconnect catches and remove front console top rear trim.
24. Remove parking brake lever and transmission shift lever boots.
25. Remove two front console mounting screws from transmission shift lever boot opening.
26. Lift front console shift lever panel and feed out storage tray. Disconnect electrical connectors.
27. Remove glove compartment.
28. Remove instrument panel decorative stripe from above glove compartment.
29. Remove radio and on light switch using folding leg tool No. 00 9 321, or equivalent.
30. Remove instrument panel lower center insert from carrier by pressing insert upward in center.

31. Remove storage tray finisher.
32. Remove four mounting screws, pull instrument panel lower center carrier outward and disconnect electrical connectors.
33. Remove lefthand instrument panel storage compartment.
34. Press light switch unit upward slightly, through lefthand storage compartment opening, then slide rearward. Disconnect light switch electrical connector.
35. Move steering column to full downward position.
36. Remove two upper mounting screws and tilt instrument cluster forward.
37. Disconnect electrical connectors and remove instrument cluster.
38. Remove mounting screws and pull radio outward. Disconnect electrical connectors and remove radio.
39. **On models equipped with radio onboard monitor,** proceed as follows:
    a. Remove center fresh air grille.
    b. Disconnect D-shaped menu button.
    c. Insert suitable screwdriver into D-shaped menu button opening, then turn catch as far to right as possible.
    d. Pull out lefthand side of monitor.
    e. Turn screwdriver to left and pull out righthand side of monitor.
    f. Disconnect electrical connectors and remove monitor.
40. **On models equipped with automatic air conditioning,** remove heater controls using locking tool No. 64 1 010, or equivalent. Disconnect electrical connectors.
41. **On models equipped with manual air conditioning,** proceed as follows:
    a. Remove control knobs.
    b. Remove finish panel.
    c. Remove four control panel screws.
    d. Unlock clips and push control panel inward.
    e. Remove frame.
    f. Disconnect control cable, microswitch and electrical connectors.
    g. Remove control panel.
42. **On all models,** remove passenger's air bag module as outlined under "Passenger's Air Bag Module, Replace."
43. Remove instrument panel mounting screw above glove compartment opening, as required.
44. Remove glove compartment lamp.
45. Remove mounting screws, release pin and glove compartment insert.
46. Remove two mounting screws and defroster nozzle.
47. Remove screw or expansion rivet from lower section from righthand side of instrument panel.
48. Remove instrument panel mounting nuts.
49. Ensure all instrument panel retainers are removed, and all electrical connectors and cables are disconnected.
50. Fully apply parking brake.
51. Move front seats to full rearward position.
52. Pull instrument panel rearward and lift out through front righthand door.

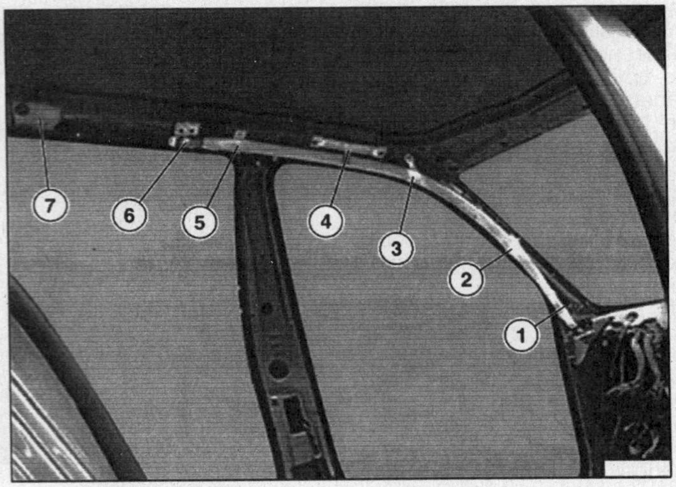

1 Retaining screw, A-pillar (front)
2 Bracket, A-pillar, bottom
3 Bracket, A-pillar, top
4 Bracket for front grab handle
5 Bracket on B-pillar
6 Bracket, grab handle, rear
7 Retaining screw, rear

BM8019900172000X

Fig. 5 Head protection air bag module retainer locations. M5, 525, 530 & 540

53. Cut cable tie and disconnect head protection air bag module gas generator connector.
54. Remove mounting nut and gas generator, **Fig. 4.**
55. Remove mounting bolt and filler hose bracket.
56. Remove head protection air bag module lower A-pillar mounting bolt. Bolt is held in end fitting by retaining disk.
57. Remove mounting bolts and A-pillar mid bracket.
58. Remove mounting bolts and A-pillar dual bracket by first pushing back, then toward front.
59. Remove mounting bolts and front grab handle bracket.
60. Remove mounting bolts and B-pillar bracket by first moving up, then toward front.
61. Remove mounting bolts and rear grab handle bracket.
62. Remove C-pillar mounting bolt and head protection air bag module. Bolt is held in end fitting by retaining disk.
63. Reverse procedure to install, noting the following:
    a. Ensure both front and rear grab handle bracket retaining clips are over air bag module.
    b. Ensure grab handle bracket clips properly seat in body.
    c. Ensure B-pillar bracket lugs properly seat in body.
    d. Ensure retaining clip grommet lip is over air bag.
    e. Ensure dual bracket lugs properly seat in body.
    f. Gas generator lug must engage A-pillar hole.
    g. Tighten new mounting bolts and nuts to specifications.

M5, 525, 530 & 540

1. Disarm SRS as outlined under "Air Bag System Disarming & Arming."
2. Remove front and rear grab handles
3. Remove both A-pillar front roof trim sections. Mounting screw is located under the "AIRBAG" tab.
4. Remove front seat belt mounting bolt.
5. Remove both B-pillar top of door trim panels.
6. Remove rear roof pillars interior.
7. Remove mounting screws and both C-pillar rear roof trim sections.
8. Remove righthand front seat.
9. Lift out sun visor.
10. Lift out front reading lamps and disconnect electrical connectors.
11. Remove front center finish panel from headliner.
12. Lift out headliner interior lamp and disconnect electrical connector.
13. Adjust lefthand front seat back rest to lowest position.
14. Pull headliner upwards out of sheet metal tabs and toward righthand rear door to remove.
15. Insert suitable radio unlatching tools through face plate.
16. Pull radio from instrument panel.
17. Disconnect all connectors. Mark connector positions for installation.
18. Remove lefthand lower instrument panel trim and steering wheel.
19. Remove mounting screws and press instrument cluster out from rear.
20. Disconnect electrical connector and remove instrument cluster.
21. Disconnect glove compartment straps.
22. Release clips and remove righthand wood trim.

23. Remove screws exposed by wood trim removal.
24. Pry out cap from righthand end of instrument panel and remove screw.
25. Remove lower instrument panel screws accessible through glove compartment opening.
26. Remove mounting screws and righthand console base trim.
27. Remove lower instrument panel screws exposed by console base trim removal.
28. Remove mounting screws and lefthand console base trim.
29. Remove lower instrument panel screws exposed by instrument cluster removal.
30. Remove lower instrument panel through righthand door opening.
31. Remove passenger's air bag module as outlined under "Passenger's Air Bag Module, Replace."
32. Remove upper instrument panel trim righthand end mounting bolts.
33. Disconnect temperature control cable.
34. Pry out cap from lefthand end of instrument panel and remove screw.
35. Remove lefthand lower instrument panel cover and compartment.
36. Disconnect steering column rubber gaiter.
37. Remove upper instrument panel trim righthand end mounting bolts.
38. Lift instrument panel trim upwards and remove through righthand door opening.
39. Cut cable tie and disconnect head protection air bag module gas generator connector.
40. Remove mounting nut and gas generator, **Fig. 5.**
41. Remove mounting bolt and filler hose bracket.
42. Remove head protection air bag module lower A-pillar mounting bolt. The bolt is held in end fitting by a retaining disk.
43. Remove mounting bolts and A-pillar mid bracket.
44. Remove mounting bolts and A-pillar dual bracket by first pushing back, then toward front.
45. Remove mounting bolts and front grab handle bracket.
46. Remove mounting bolts and B-pillar bracket by first moving up, then toward front.
47. Remove mounting bolts and rear grab handle bracket.
48. Remove C-pillar mounting bolt and head protection air bag module. Bolt is held in end fitting by retaining disk.
49. Reverse procedure to install, noting the following:
    a. Ensure both front and rear grab handle bracket retaining clips are over air bag module.
    b. Ensure grab handle bracket clips properly seat in body.
    c. Ensure B-pillar bracket lugs properly seat in body.
    d. Ensure retaining clip grommet lip is over air bag.
    e. Ensure dual bracket lugs properly seat in body.
    f. Gas generator lug must engage A-pillar hole.
    g. Tighten new mounting nuts to specifications.

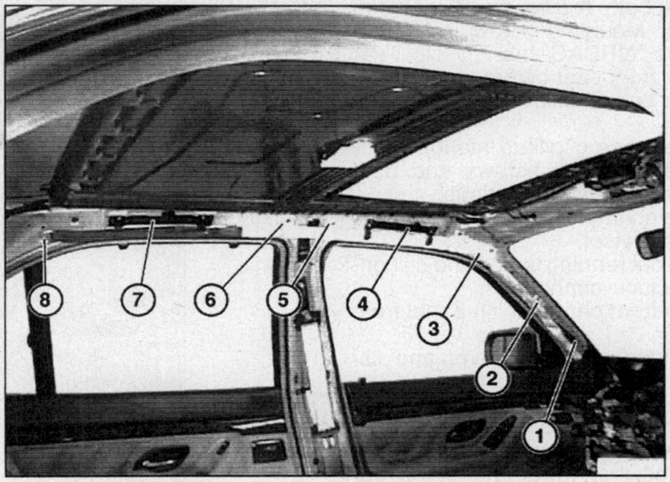

1	Mounting bolt on A-pillar	5	Bracket on B-pillar
2	Bracket on A-pillar	6	Bracket on B-pillar
3	Dual bracket on A-pillar	7	Bracket, grab handle, rear
4	Bracket for front grab handle	8	Mounting bolt on C-pillar

BM8019900173000X

Fig. 6 Front head protection air bag module retainer locations. 740 & 750

X5

Front

1. Disarm SRS as outlined under "Air Bag System Disarming & Arming."
2. Remove both sun visors and counter support.
3. Remove front and rear grab handles
4. Remove both A-pillar front roof trim sections.
5. Remove both B-pillar top of door trim panels.
6. Remove both C-pillar rear roof trim sections.
7. Remove both D-pillar rear roof trim sections.
8. Remove headline front bracket.
9. Remove front and rear head restraints.
10. Remove sunroof lid, as required.
11. Remove front and rear interior lamps and disconnect electrical connectors.
12. Remove ultrasonic module and disconnect electrical connectors.
13. Remove screws inside sunroof.
14. Disconnect trim covers, then remove mounting screws and dividing net mounts.
15. Move both seat backrests as far back as possible.
16. Remove luggage compartment roller cover.
17. Fold both rear seat backrests forward.
18. Remove front and rear door muckets.
19. Support at front and remove mounting screw under headliner.
20. Press headliner aside at rear, sliding three guides out of body clips, then turn and remove headliner.
21. Remove instrument panel as outlined in "Dash Panel Service" section.
22. **On models equipped with rear head protection air bag module,** remove it as outlined under "Rear."
23. **On all models,** disconnect air bag module gas generator connector.
24. Remove mounting bolt and gas generator.
25. Loosen A-pillar mounting bolts. **Do not remove mounting bolts.**
26. **Do not remove rear roof frame mounting bolt.**
27. Disconnect A-pillar clips and remove head protection air bag. Disconnect roof frame clips.
28. Reverse procedure to install. Tighten new mounting nuts to specifications.

Rear

1. Disarm SRS as outlined under "Air Bag System Disarming & Arming."
2. Remove headliner as outlined under "Front."
3. Disconnect air bag module gas generator connector.
4. Loosen gas generator mounting bolts at roof crossmember.
5. Remove air bag cassette mounting bolts.
6. Remove mounting bolts and slide gas generator upward, then remove air bag module toward front.
7. Reverse procedure to install, noting the following:
    a. Ensure gas generator lug engages roof crossmember.
    b. Ensure anchor retaining strap under casing ribs.
    c. Tighten new mounting nuts to specifications.

740 & 750

Front

1. Disarm SRS as outlined under "Air Bag System Disarming & Arming."
2. Remove front and rear grab handles

3. Remove both A-pillar front roof trim sections. Mounting screw is located under the "AIRBAG" tab.
4. Remove front seat belt mounting bolt.
5. Remove both B-pillar top of door trim panels.
6. Remove rear roof pillars interior.
7. Remove mounting screws and both C-pillar rear roof trim sections.
8. Remove righthand front seat.
9. Lift out sun visor.
10. Lift out front reading lamps and disconnect electrical connectors.
11. Remove front center finish panel from headliner.
12. Lift out headliner interior lamp and disconnect electrical connector.
13. Adjust lefthand front seat back rest to lowest position.
14. Pull headliner upwards out of sheet metal tabs, then toward righthand rear door to remove.
15. Place steering column in full down position. Cover steering column with suitable rags.
16. Remove two upper mounting screws and tilt instrument cluster forward.
17. Disconnect instrument cluster electrical connectors and lift cluster from carrier.
18. Disconnect headlight switch(es) by reaching through instrument cluster opening.
19. Pry out and lift off passenger's air bag cover and position aside.
20. Remove passenger's air bag module as outlined under "Passenger's Air Bag Module, Replace."
21. Remove passenger's air bag reinforcement.
22. Open glove compartment and remove upper glove compartment cover mounting screws to access righthand wood trim strip mounting nuts.
23. Remove plastic mounting nuts and pull trim to rear out of dash panel.
24. Remove glove compartment cover, then the righthand dash end panel and end panel mounting screws.
25. Remove righthand end and center of dash panel to reinforcements mounting screws.
26. Remove wood trim to left and right of steering column by lifting and pulling rearward.
27. Remove console mounting screws exposed by trim removal.
28. Remove screws for lefthand under dash shelf, disconnect parking brake release cable, and lift out shelf.
29. Remove lefthand end of dash to reinforcements mounting bolts.
30. Release latch tabs and remove vent using suitable 0.035–0.040 inch feeler gauge inserted in lower edge of upper center air vent.
31. Through air vent hole remove mounting bolts and disconnect electrical connectors. There is a spacer under most forward center screw.
32. Release latch tabs and pull vent from dash panel using suitable 0.035–0.040 inch feeler gauge inserted around edge of lower center air vent. Disconnect Bowden cable, as required.
33. Remove left and righthand air duct joint straps screws, lift dash panel up and to rear, then guide panel out of vehicle.
34. Cut cable tie and disconnect head protection air bag module gas generator connector.
35. Remove mounting nut and gas generator, **Fig. 6.**
36. Remove mounting bolt and filler hose bracket.
37. Remove head protection air bag module lower A-pillar mounting bolt. Bolt is held in end fitting by retaining disk.
38. Remove mounting bolts and A-pillar mid bracket.
39. Remove mounting bolts and A-pillar dual bracket by first pushing back, then toward front.
40. Remove mounting bolts and front grab handle bracket.
41. Remove mounting bolts and B-pillar bracket by first moving up, then toward front.
42. Remove mounting bolts and rear grab handle bracket.
43. Remove C-pillar mounting bolt and head protection air bag module. Bolt is held in end fitting by retaining disk.
44. Reverse procedure to install, noting the following:
    a. Ensure both front and rear grab handle bracket retaining clips are over air bag module.
    b. Ensure grab handle bracket clips properly seat in body.
    c. Ensure B-pillar bracket lugs properly seat in body.
    d. Ensure retaining clip grommet lip is over air bag.
    e. Ensure dual bracket lugs properly seat in body.
    f. Gas generator lug must engage A-pillar hole.
    g. Tighten new mounting nuts to specifications.

Rear

1. Disarm SRS as outlined under "Air Bag System Disarming & Arming."
2. Remove front and rear grab handles.
3. Remove both A-pillar front roof trim sections. Mounting screw is located under the "AIRBAG" tab.
4. Remove front seat belt mounting bolt.
5. Remove both B-pillar top of door trim panels.
6. Remove rear roof pillars interior.
7. Remove mounting screws and both C-pillar rear roof trim sections.
8. Remove righthand front seat.
9. Lift out sun visor.
10. Lift out front reading lamps and disconnect electrical connectors.
11. Remove front center finish panel from headliner.
12. Lift out headliner interior lamp and disconnect electrical connector.
13. Adjust lefthand front seat back rest to lowest position.
14. Pull headliner upwards out of sheet metal tabs, then toward righthand rear door to remove.
15. Remove rear package shelf trim piece.
16. Remove two rear head protection air bag cassette to rear compartment mounting screws, **Fig. 7.**
17. Remove two nuts securing rear head protection air bag gas generator to rear compartment.
18. Remove rear head protection air bag cassette with gas tube from rear compartment retaining clips. **Do not damage rear window with gas tube.**
19. Remove gas generator from retaining clips and disconnect electrical connector.
20. Reverse procedure to install, noting the following:
    a. Ensure both front and rear grab handle bracket retaining clips are over air bag module.
    b. Ensure grab handle bracket clips properly seat in body.
    c. Ensure B-pillar bracket lugs properly seat in body.
    d. Ensure retaining clip grommet lip is over air bag.
    e. Ensure dual bracket lugs properly seat in body.
    f. Gas generator lug must engage A-pillar hole.

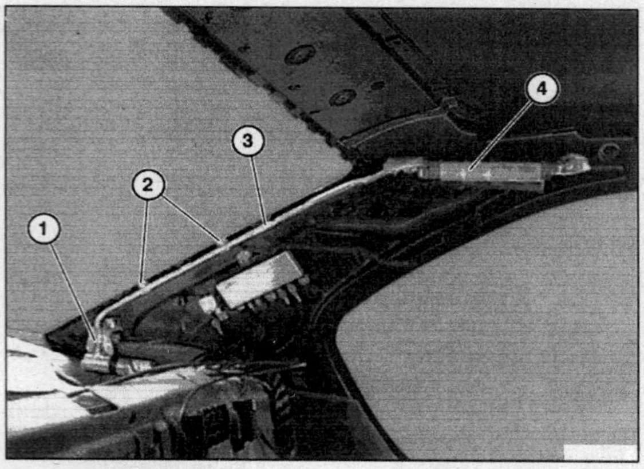

1 Gas generator
2 Retaining clips for gas lance
3 Gas lance
4 Head airbag cassette in rear compartment

BM8019900174000X

Fig. 7 Rear head protection air bag module retainer locations. 740 & 750

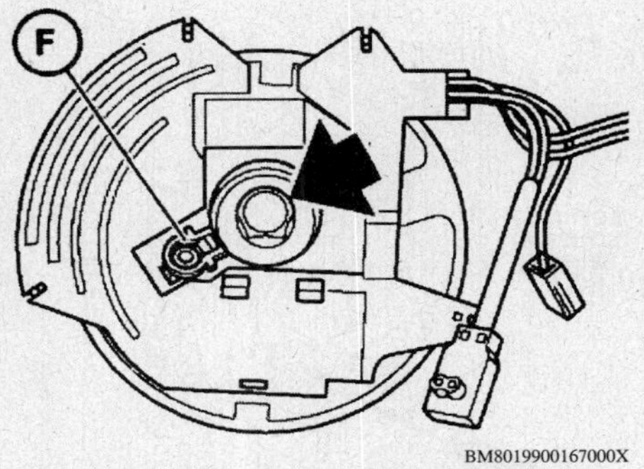

Fig. 8 Contact ring torsion spring. M5, 525, 530, 528, 540, 740 & 750

g. Tighten new mounting nuts to specifications.

CONTACT RING, REPLACE

M3, 318, 323, 325, 328 & 330

1. Remove driver's air bag as outlined under "Driver's Air Bag Module, Replace."
2. Mark installation position of steering wheel in relation to steering shaft, then remove mounting nut and steering wheel..
3. Carefully remove contact ring lock using suitable screwdriver, then disconnect electrical connector.
4. Remove mounting nuts and contact ring.
5. Reverse procedure to install, noting the following:
   a. Remove centering pin following installation of contact ring on steering wheel by pressing lockpin ends together.
   b. Ensure lockpin in column engages hole in steering wheel.
   c. Tighten mounting bolts to specifications.
   d. Arm SRS as outlined under "Air Bag System Disarming & Arming."

M5, X5, 525, 530, 528, 540, 740 & 750

1. Position front wheels in straight-ahead position.
2. Disarm SRS as outlined under "Air Bag System Disarming & Arming."
3. Remove driver's air bag assembly as outlined under "Driver's Air Bag Module, Replace."
4. Mark steering wheel to steering shaft relationship for installation.
5. Remove mounting bolt and steering wheel.
6. Remove mounting nuts and carefully pull off contact ring by torsion spring (F), **Fig. 8.**
7. Reverse procedure to install, noting the following:
   a. New contact ring is held in center position by screw, **Fig. 9.**
   b. Remove screw after installing contact ring.
   c. Adjust contact ring by pressing down on torsion spring and rotating contact ring, as required.

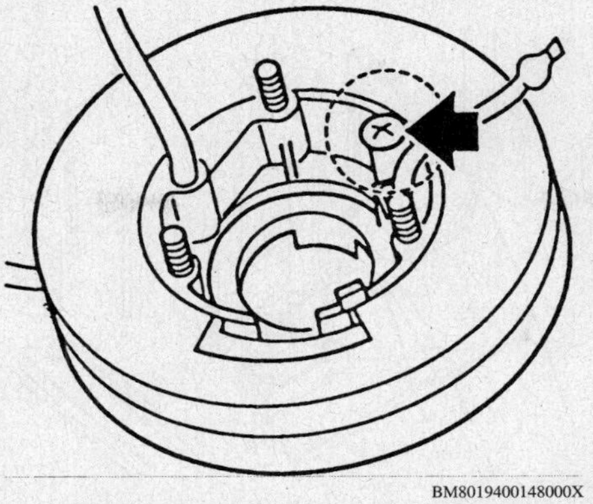

Fig. 9 New contact ring center position screw

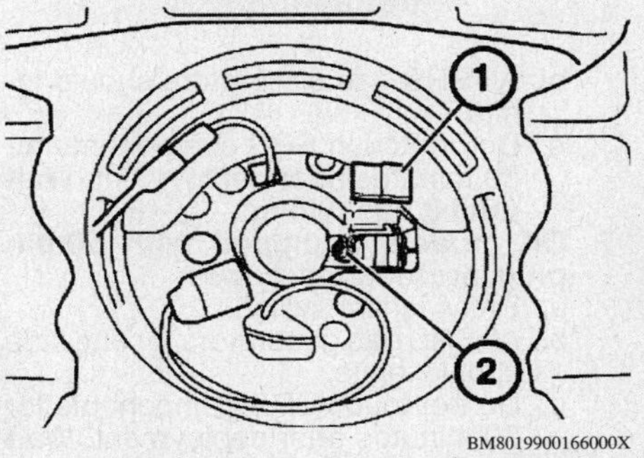

Fig. 11 Contact ring lock. Z3

   d. Center position is determined by halving total number of turns.
   e. Ensure marks (1) are aligned, then release the torsion spring, **Fig. 10.**
   f. Ensure retaining pin in column engages hole in steering wheel.
   g. After completing installation, arm system as outlined under "Air Bag System Disarming & Arming."

Z3

1. Disarm SRS as outlined under "Air Bag System Disarming & Arming."
2. Remove driver's air bag as outlined under "Driver's Air Bag Module, Replace."
3. Mark steering wheel to steering shaft relationship for installation.
4. Remove mounting nut and steering wheel.
5. Carefully lift out contact ring lock with suitable screwdriver, **Fig. 11.**
6. Disconnect contact ring electrical connector.
7. Remove cover and disconnect ground wire.
8. Remove mounting screws and contact ring.
9. Reverse procedure to install, noting the following:
   a. New contact ring is retained in center position with securing pin, **Fig. 9.**
   b. Remove pin following installation of contact ring on steering wheel.
   c. Remove contact ring lockpin by pressing lockpin ends together.
   d. Guide horn wires through square opening.
   e. Lock nuts with varnish.

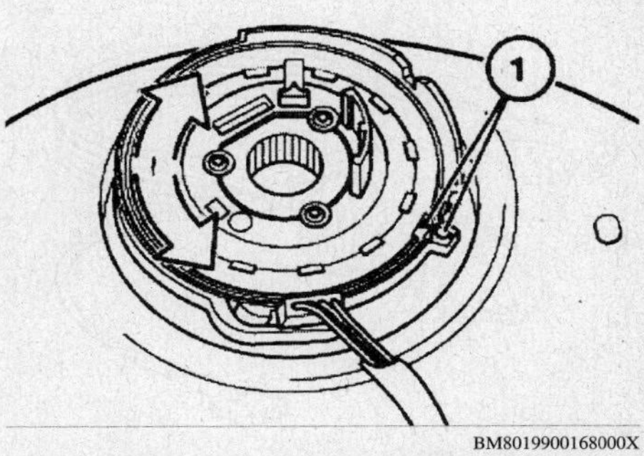

Fig. 10 Contact ring alignment marks. M5, 525, 530, 528, 540, 740 & 750

   f. Insert spring in bore and connect lock.
   g. Press down on lock until it engages.
   h. After completing installation, arm SRS as outlined under "Air Bag System Disarming & Arming."

AIR BAG & PYROTECHNIC SEAT BELT PRETENSIONERS DISPOSAL

After deployment, air bag modules and seat belt pretensioners should be placed in a plastic bag and disposed of in the same manner as any other scrap parts. Note the following:

1. **When handling deployed air bag assembly or seat belt pretensioner face shield and rubber gloves should be worn.**
2. There may be material adhered to air bag module that could irritate eyes and/or skin. **If any irritation develops, seek medical attention, noting the following:**
   a. If sinus or throat irritation is encountered during component removal, exit vehicle and breath fresh air.
   b. If material does come in contact with eyes and/or skin, immediately rinse affected area with a large amount of cool, clean water.
   c. If sinus, throat, skin or any other type of irritation continues, consult a physician.
3. After handling deployed component, wash hands and rinse thoroughly with water.
4. **Inflator will be quite hot immediately after deployment. Wait 30 minutes to allow inflator to cool.**
5. Do not put water or oil on SRS components after deployment.
6. Put deployed components in hermetically sealed container and discard.
7. Use suitable vacuum cleaner to remove any residual powder from vehicle interior as follows:
   a. Work from outside to center of vehicle.
   b. Vacuum air conditioning, vent, defroster and heater ducts.
   c. Run blower motor on low speed and vacuum any powder expelled from plenum.

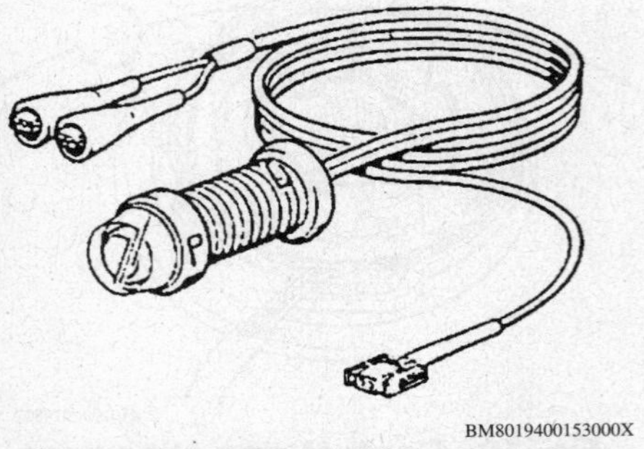

Fig. 12 Air bag deployment tool

d. It may be necessary to vacuum interior of vehicle second time to ensure all powder is recovered.

8. Prior to removing deployed air bag assembly, place tape over air bag exhaust vents.
9. Before disposing of SRS equipped vehicle, or prior to disposing of air bag module or seat belt pretensioner, component must be deployed as follows:
   a. If vehicle is to be scrapped, deploy components inside vehicle.
   b. If vehicle is to continue in service, component must be removed and deployed outside vehicle.

DEPLOYMENT INSIDE VEHICLE

This procedure should only be performed if vehicle is to be scrapped. Ensure air bag is securely mounted to vehicle prior to deployment. Use only BMW igniter tool No. 62 1 270 and test lead No. 62 1 210, or equivalents, **Fig. 12.** Perform procedure with vehicle parked outdoors. Ensure no people, animals or objects are within 32 feet of vehicle. All vehicle doors must be closed prior to deployment.

1. Disarm SRS as outlined under "Air Bag System Disarming & Arming."
2. Disconnect SRS control module connector.
3. Connect igniter tool and test lead to SRS control module, noting the following:
   a. **On models equipped with 30-pin plug,** use BMW test lead 62 1 210, or equivalent.
   b. **On models equipped with 50-pin plug,** use BMW test lead 62 1 310 or 62 1 330 (according to plug code), or equivalent.
4. **On all models,** at distance of approximately 32 feet from rear vehicle, connect igniter tool to fully charged 12-volt battery.
5. **Clear all persons, animals and objects from area within 32 feet of vehicle.**
6. **On models equipped with 20-pin plug,** proceed as follows:
   a. Press igniter switch.

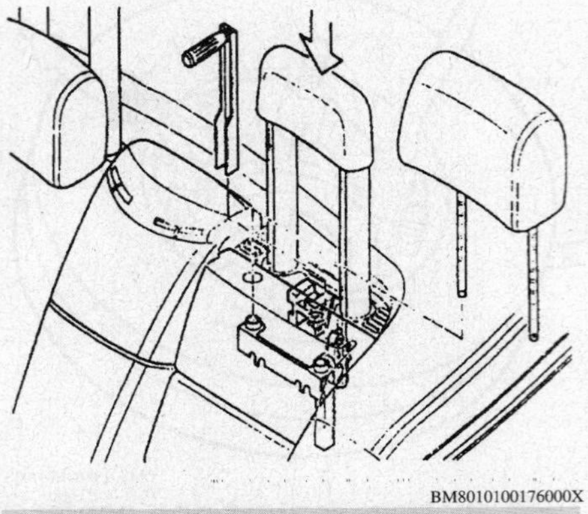

Fig. 13 Roll bar retracting tool installation

   b. All SRS gas generators should ignite.
   c. Do not touch SRS components for 30 minutes after deployment. **Wait until it has cooled.**
7. **On models equipped with 50-pin plug,** proceed as follows:
   a. Press igniter switch.
   b. All SRS gas generators for one side should ignite.
   c. Do not touch SRS components for 30 minutes after deployment. **Wait until it has cooled.**
   d. Disconnect igniter from battery.
   e. Connect igniter to free connector.
   f. Igniter and battery must located approximately 32 feet from rear of vehicle.
   g. Ensure no persons or animals are within 32 feet of the vehicle.
   h. Connect igniter to battery.
   i. Press igniter switch.
   j. All SRS gas generators for other side should ignite.
   k. Do not touch SRS components for 30 minutes after deployment. **Wait until it has cooled.**
8. **On all models, if deployment did take place,** contact BMW for disposal instructions.

DEPLOYMENT OUTSIDE OF VEHICLE

Contact BMW for disposal instructions.

ROLL BAR, RETRACTING

1. Remove rear head rest.
2. Insert retracted tool into roll bar front slot, **Fig. 13.**
3. Press tool down to release locking lever ratchet.
4. Push roll bar down to clear ratchet.
5. Remove tool and press roll bar down until it locks into actuator.

ROLL BAR CASSETTE & ACTUATOR, REPLACEMENT

Roll bar cassette and actuator cannot be adjusted or repaired. **Remove cassette in released state, only.**

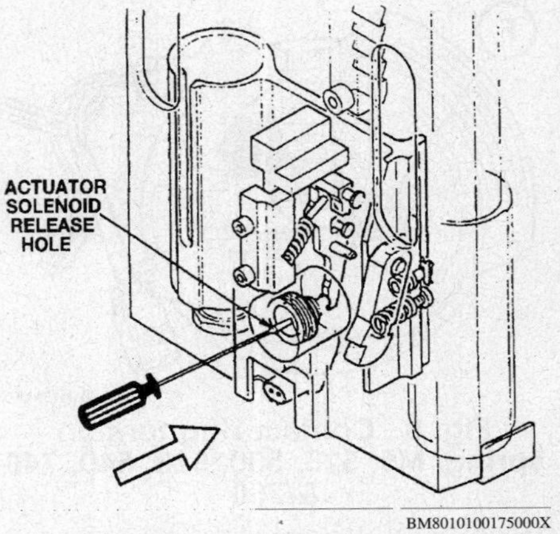

Fig. 14 Roll over bar cassette release

1. Actuator lever overlap of 0.0472 inch is critical.
2. To release cassette, insert suitable screwdriver into small actuator hole, **Fig. 14.**

SRS CONTROL MODULE, REPLACE

1. Disarm SRS as outlined under "Air Bag System Disarming & Arming."
2. Remove interior component required to access control module.
3. Remove mounting bolts and disconnect electrical connector.
4. Remove SRS control module.
5. Reverse procedure to install, noting the following:
   a. After completing control module installation, ensure electrical connector is properly connected to the module.
   b. Arm SRS as outlined under "Air Bag System Disarming & Arming."
   c. Replacement SRS control modules must be coded after installation is completed using BMW system tester and latest software.
   d. Ensure all SRS faults have been corrected before coding the SRS control module.

PYROTECHNIC SEAT BELT PRETENSIONERS

Pyrotechnic seat pretensioners are mounted on the buckle side of the seat belt. The SRS must be disarmed prior to performing any service procedures as outlined under "Air Bag System Disarming & Arming."

TIGHTENING SPECIFICATIONS

Year	Component	Torque/ Ft. Lbs.
M3, 318, 323, 325, 328 & 330		
1998–2001	Driver's Air Bag	③
	Head Protection Air Bag, Screw	22①
	Head Protection Air Bag Bracket	35①
	Head Protection Air Bag End Fitting	97①
	Head Protection Air Bag Gas Generator	35①
	Passenger's Air Bag	16
	Passenger's Air Bag Strap	80①
	Side Impact Air Bag Module	75①
	Steering Wheel	②
M5, 525, 528, 530 & 540		
1998–2001	Driver's Air Bag	③
	Head Protection Air Bag, Screw	22①
	Head Protection Air Bag End Fitting	97①
	Head Protection Air Bag Gas Generator	35①
	Passenger's Air Bag	88①
	Side Impact Air Bag Module	75①
	Steering Wheel	②
X5		
2000–01	Head Protection Air Bag, Screw	22①
	Head Protection Air Bag Cassette, Rear	27①
	Head Protection Air Bag End Fitting	97①
	Head Protection Air Bag Gas Generator	35①
	Passenger's Air Bag	16
	Side Impact Air Bag Module	75①
	Steering Wheel	②
Z3		
1998–2001	Driver's Air Bag	③
	Passenger's Air Bag	18
	Side Impact Air Bag Module	75①
	Steering Wheel	②
740 & 750		
1998–2001	Driver's Air Bag	③
	Head Protection Air Bag, Screw	22①
	Head Protection Air Bag Cassette	97①
	Head Protection Air Bag End Fitting	97①
	Head Protection Air Bag Gas Generator	35①
	Passenger's Air Bag	88①
	Side Impact Air Bag Module	75①
	Steering Wheel	②

① — Inch lbs.

② — Nut, 59 ft. lbs.; screw, 46 ft. lbs.

③ — Air Bag Module, 71 inch lbs.; Air Bag Module II, 18 inch lbs.

Dash Panel Service

NOTE: On Air Bag Equipped Models, Refer To "Air Bag System Precautions" Located In The Front Of This Manual For System Disarming & Arming Procedures.

INDEX

	Page No.
Dash Panel, Replace	2-164
318ti	2-166
740 & 750	2-166
M3, 318i/is, 323, 325, 328 & 330	2-164
M5, 525, 528, 530 & 540	2-165
X5	2-165
Z3	2-165
Precautions	2-164
Air Bag Systems	2-164
Battery Ground Cable	2-164

PRECAUTIONS

AIR BAG SYSTEMS

Refer to "Air Bag System Precautions" in the front of this manual for system disarming and arming procedures.

BATTERY GROUND CABLE

Prior to service, disconnect battery ground cable and isolate as required.

DASH PANEL

REPLACE

The instrument cluster on some models may require coding after removal.

M3, 318I/IS, 323, 325, 328 & 330

318i/is, 323is & 328is & 1998–99 M3, 328i & 1998 323i & 1999 323i & 328i Convertibles

1. **On coupe and sedan models,** remove louver grills above glove compartment, then upper mounting bolts through louver openings.
2. **On convertible models,** reach through louver grills using suitable screwdriver and remove upper mounting bolts.
3. **On all models,** open glove compartment door and remove mounting bolts.
4. Close glove compartment door and remove lower mounting bolts.
5. Pull glove compartment from dash panel and disconnect wiring connectors.
6. **On models with passenger's air bag,** remove passenger's air bag as outlined in "Air Bag System" section.
7. **On models with clock,** proceed as follows:
   a. Insert suitable 0.035–0.040 inch feeler gauge between clock and frame at bottom, then pry out and disconnect clock.
   b. Insert suitable 0.035–0.040 inch feeler gauge between frame and shelf at bottom lefthand end, then pry out frame as feeler gauge is moved to right.
8. **On models with multi information display,** proceed as follows:
   a. Insert suitable 0.035–0.040 inch feeler gauge between multi information display and shelf at bottom righthand end.
   b. Pry out multi information display as feeler gauge is moved to left disengaging clips.
9. **On all models,** pry out and disconnect shelf unit.
10. Pull knobs from air conditioning and heater control unit, then remove screws found behind knobs and pry off front panel.
11. Push back, disconnect, then remove air conditioning and heater control unit.
12. Remove steering wheel as outlined in "Electrical" section.
13. Remove instrument cluster mounting bolts, then pull rearward from dash panel.
14. Disconnect and remove instrument cluster.
15. Remove both A-pillar trims, then the trim from lower righthand dash.
16. Remove lower lefthand dash trim mounting screws and slide trim to left to release clips.
17. Remove shift knob, then shifter trim plate.
18. Lift out rear ash tray, then pry out screw trim caps from rear console.
19. Remove mounting bolts and lift out rear console.
20. Remove mounting bolts and front console.
21. Remove dash defroster vents trim frames and mounting bolts using suitable right angle drive screwdriver.
22. Remove mounting bolts from right and lefthand end of dash panel.
23. Disconnect any connectors and components routed through or mounted to dash panel.
24. Remove dash panel.
25. Reverse procedure to install. Ensure all dash panel mounting clips and pegs are in place.

323Ci, 325, 328Ci & 330 & 2001 M3 & 2000 323i & 328i & 1999 323i & 328i Sedans

1. Remove steering wheel as outlined in "Electrical" section.
2. Move steering column to bottom, extended position.
3. Remove mounting screw and remove steering column top cover by pressing both sides of inward and pulling upward.
4. Move steering column to top, extended position.
5. Remove expansion rivets and remove steering column lower cover by pressing both sides of inward and pulling downward.
6. Disconnect ring antenna, wiper switch and turn indicator lever connectors.
7. Remove mounting screws and steering column switch.
8. Press roller cover down and push tray up, then remove shelf or ashtray.
9. Remove mounting screw and shelf or tray bracket.
10. Disconnect cigarette lighter electrical connector and remove bracket.
11. Remove storage tray mounting bolts.
12. Disconnect catches and trim.
13. Disconnect boot.
14. Remove mounting bolts, raise trim and feed storage tray toward rear.
15. Disconnect hazard warning/central locking connector.
16. Disconnect car phone connector, as required.
17. Remove shift knob by tugging firmly. **Do not wrench knob.**
18. Remove center console shift lever trim with rubber gaiter.
19. Disconnect cable connectors.
20. Remove mounting bolts and selector lever finisher toward rear. Disconnect connectors.
21. Open glove compartment, then disconnect retaining strap and shock absorber pins.
22. Remove mounting bolts, bracket and glove compartment.
23. Remove clipped-in decorative strips.

24. Remove center console insert and glasses compartments.
25. Remove mounting screws, switch and center console carrier. Disconnect connectors.
26. Remove A-pillar front roof pillar mucket and plate.
27. Remove mounting screws and front left and righthand roof trim.
28. Remove wooden finisher, then remove mounting screws and lefthand glove compartment.
29. Remove mounting screws and remove lamp switch by pressing it up through glove compartment opening. Disconnect connector.
30. Pull air conditioning control panel out using locking tool No. 64 1 010, or equivalent. Disconnect electrical connectors.
31. Remove radio as outlined in "Electrical" section.
32. Remove passenger's air bag as outlined in "Air Bag System" section.
33. Remove mounting screws and glove compartment lamp. Disconnect connector.
34. Remove mounting bolts through glove compartment opening.
35. Remove instrument panel for guides by pressing to rear.
36. Disconnect connectors and remove panel.
37. Remove mounting screws and defroster nozzle.
38. Remove lower instrument panel mounting screws or expansion rivets.
39. Loosen nut and disconnect solar sensor connector.
40. Remove instrument panel mounting nuts.
41. Move front seats as far as back as possible and ensure handbrake is fully applied.
42. Remove instrument panel to rear and out righthand front door.
43. Reverse procedure to install.

M5, 525, 528, 530 & 540

1. Pull door edge protector from both A-pillar trims.
2. Pull A-pillar trims up and outward to remove.
3. Remove radio as outlined in "Electrical" section.
4. Remove instrument cluster as outlined in "Electrical" section.
5. Disconnect glove compartment straps.
6. Release clips and remove righthand wood trim.
7. Remove screws exposed by wood trim removal.
8. Pry out cap from righthand end of instrument panel and remove screw.
9. Remove lower instrument panel screws accessible through glove compartment opening.
10. Remove mounting screws and righthand console base trim.
11. Remove lower instrument panel screws exposed by console base trim removal.
12. Remove mounting screws and left console base trim.
13. Remove lower instrument panel screws exposed by instrument cluster removal.
14. Remove lower instrument panel through righthand door.
15. Remove passenger's air bag as outlined in "Air Bag System" section.
16. Remove bolts retaining righthand end of upper instrument panel trim.
17. Disconnect temperature control cable.
18. Pry out cap from lefthand end of instrument panel and remove screw.
19. Remove lefthand lower instrument panel cover and compartment.
20. Disconnect steering column rubber gaiter.
21. Remove bolts retaining righthand end of upper instrument panel trim.
22. Lift instrument panel trim upwards and remove out right door.
23. Reverse procedure to install.

X5

1. Disconnect mucket, then remove left and righthand A-pillar trim panel and screw.
2. Disconnect top clip and remove left and righthand roof pillar front trim panels.
3. Press retaining hooks in and remove lamp switch unit. Disconnect connector.
4. Remove instrument cluster as outlined in "Electrical" section.
5. Move steering column to bottom extended position.
6. Remove mounting screws, then the upper and lower steering column trim panels.
7. Remove steering wheel as outlined in "Electrical" section.
8. Disconnect turn indicator/dimmer, windshield wipers' and steering column stalks connectors.
9. Disconnect steering column adjustment stalk connectors, as required.
10. Remove mounting screws and steering column stalk fixture.
11. Disconnect clips and remove steering column stalks.
12. Unlock and remove fresh air grill using hook release tools No. 61 1 020, or equivalent.
13. Remove radio as outlined in "Electrical" section.
14. Remove passenger's air bag as outlined in "Air Bag System" section.
15. Remove mounting screws and toggle, then lower bottom righthand instrument panel.
16. Disconnect footwell lamp connector and remove bottom righthand instrument panel.
17. Unlock and remove trim to left of pedal assembly.
18. Remove toggle and lower trim above pedal assembly, then disconnect footwell lamp connector.
19. Remove preselector lever finisher and remove hazard warning flashers/ center locking switch by pressing it through opening. Disconnect connector.
20. Disconnect heating controls and remove using disassembly tool No. 00 9 340, or equivalent. Disconnect connectors.
21. Remove center console switch unit. Disconnect connector.
22. Remove storage box by levering out with disassembly tool No. 00 9 340, or equivalent.
23. Remove mounting screws and rear fresh air grill. Disconnect connectors.
24. Remove air duct, then remove center console rear mounting bolts.
25. Disconnect center console carpet clips and remove rear cup holder mounting screws.
26. Remove mounting bolts and center console rear with cup holder.
27. Remove center console left and righthand mounting screws, then disconnect carpet clips.
28. Remove center console rear mounting bolts and disconnect connectors,
29. Set handbrake to maximum setting and remove rubber gaiter.
30. Raise center console rear and lift over handbrake lever.
31. Remove center console by feeding connector out and lifting it over shift selector lever.
32. Remove bottom lefthand instrument panel mounting screws and disconnect On-Board Diagnosis (OBD) socket connector.
33. Disconnect steering wheel trim rubber gaiter and remove bottom lefthand instrument panel trim.
34. Open glove compartment and remove lamp. Disconnect connector.
35. Raise glove compartment and disconnect retaining strap pin.
36. Lever out and open glove compartment cover.
37. Remove mounting screws and fold glove compartment down.
38. Disconnect portable lamp connector, as required.
39. Remove glove compartment and feed out holder cable.
40. Remove decorative strip' clips.
41. Remove mounting bolts and instrument panel . Disconnect speakers.
42. Reverse procedure to install.

Z3

1. Remove radio as outlined in "Electrical" section.
2. Remove shifter knob.
3. Remove screws from right and lefthand side of console.
4. Remove boot from parking brake lever.
5. Pull console trim below parking brake lever rearward, then lift out.
6. Remove trims from screws at forward end of console, then the screws.
7. Remove screws through radio opening.
8. Disconnect heater control panel, then tilt and push through opening.
9. Raise rear of console and pull rearward to allow access, then disconnect electrical connectors.
10. Slide console forward to disengage from parking brake lever, then remove console from vehicle.
11. Remove passenger's air bag as outlined in "Air Bag System" section.
12. Remove instrument cluster as outlined

in "Electrical" section.
13. Remove combination switch as outlined in "Electrical" section.
14. Remove headlight switch as outlined in "Electrical" section.
15. Pry out and remove switches from instrument panel near steering column.
16. Remove mounting bolts from each end of instrument panel.
17. Remove screws below center ventilation grill.
18. Remove instrument panel trim strip at base of windshield, then remove instrument panel mounting bolts.
19. Pull instrument panel rearward, then remove from vehicle.
20. Reverse procedure to install.

318TI

1. Remove glove compartment door by pressing tabs to center, then pull rearward.
2. Remove trim caps and glove compartment mounting bolts, then the glove compartment.
3. **On models with passenger's air bag,** remove passenger's air bag as outlined in "Air Bag System" section.
4. **On all models,** remove steering wheel as outlined in "Electrical" section.
5. Remove instrument cluster mounting bolts, then pull cluster rearward from dash panel.
6. Disconnect and remove instrument cluster.
7. Remove steering column switches as outlined in"Electrical" section.
8. Remove headlight switch as outlined in "Electrical" section.
9. Remove headlight aim control, as required.
10. Remove radio as outlined in "Electrical" section.
11. Through radio opening, release clock retaining tab, then push out and disconnect clock.
12. Through radio opening, release rear defogger switch retaining tab, then push out and disconnect switch.
13. Pull knobs from heater control switch, then remove mounting screws found behind knobs.
14. Remove trim plate, then disconnect and lift out heater control.
15. Remove A-pillar trims.
16. Remove trim frames from dash defroster vents, thence mounting screws using suitable right angle drive screwdriver.
17. Remove mounting bolts from right and lefthand end of dash panel.
18. Disconnect any connectors and components routed through or mounted to dash panel.
19. Remove dash panel from vehicle.
20. Reverse procedure to install. Ensure all dash panel mounting clips and pegs are in place.

740 & 750

1. Remove left and righthand A-pillar trims.
2. Remove complete instrument cluster as outlined in "Electrical" section.
3. Disconnect headlight switch(es) by reaching through instrument cluster opening.
4. Pry out and lift off passenger's air bag cover and position aside.
5. Remove passenger's air bag as described under "Air Bag System" section.
6. Remove passenger's air bag reinforcement.
7. Open glove compartment and remove upper cover mounting.
8. Remove plastic mounting nuts and pull trim to rear out of dash panel.
9. Remove glove compartment cover, then the righthand dash end panel and end panel mounting screws.
10. Remove righthand end and center of dash panel to reinforcements mounting screws.
11. Remove wood trim to right and lefthand of steering column by lifting, then pulling rearward.
12. Remove socket head cap screws from console mounting exposed by trim removal.
13. Remove lefthand under dash shelf mounting screws, disconnect parking brake release cable and lift out shelf.
14. Remove lefthand end of dash to reinforcements mounting bolts.
15. Release latch tabs and remove upper center air vent by inserted suitable 0.035–0.040 inch feeler gauge in lower edge.
16. Through air vent hole remove mounting bolts and disconnect electrical connectors. Note spacer under most forward center screw.
17. Release latch tabs and pull lower center air vent from dash panel by inserting suitable 0.035–0.040 inch feeler gauge around edge. Disconnect Bowden cable, as required.
18. Remove right and lefthand air duct joint straps screws, lift dash panel up and to rear, then guide panel out of vehicle.
19. Reverse procedure to install. Ensure all dash panel mounting clips and pegs are in place.

Steering Columns

NOTE: On Air Bag Equipped Models, Refer To "Air Bag System Precautions" Located In The Front Of This Manual For System Disarming & Arming Procedures.

NOTE: Prior To Performing Any Service Operations Listed In This Section, Consult The "Technical Service Bulletins" Section For Related Information.

INDEX

Page No.
Precautions 2-167
Air Bag Systems 2-167
Battery Ground Cable 2-167
Steering Column, Replace 2-167
M3, Z3, 318, 323, 325, 328 & 330 2-167
M5, 525, 528, 530, 540, 740 & 750 2-167
X5 2-168
Steering Column Service 2-168
M3, Z3, 318, 323, 325, 328 & 330 2-168
M5, X5, 525, 528, 530, 540, 740 & 750 2-169
Technical Service Bulletins 2-169
Steering Column Does Move To Correct Position 2-169
Steering Column Does Not Adjust 2-169
Tightening Specifications 2-170

PRECAUTIONS

AIR BAG SYSTEMS

Refer to "Air Bag System Precautions" in the front of this manual for system disarming and arming procedures.

BATTERY GROUND CABLE

Prior to service, disconnect battery ground cable and isolate as required.

STEERING COLUMN

REPLACE

M3, Z3, 318, 323, 325, 328 & 330

Z3, 318, 323is & 328is & 1998-99 M3, 328i & 1998 323i & 1999 323i & 328i Convertibles

1. Remove steering wheel as outlined in "Electrical" section.
2. Remove lower instrument panel trim as outlined in "Dash Panel Service" section.
3. Remove column universal joint bolt, then disconnect steering column by pulling down and out of spline.
4. **On 318ti models,** remove steering column cover mounting bolts.
5. **On all models,** remove upper column retaining collar, **Fig. 1.**
6. Disconnect interlock cable, as required.
7. Unlock bayonet connector and steering column electrical connectors.
8. Remove mounting bolt and dash panel carrier.
9. Remove shear-off screws using suitable chisel or grind off.
10. Remove steering column.
11. Reverse procedure to install, noting the following:

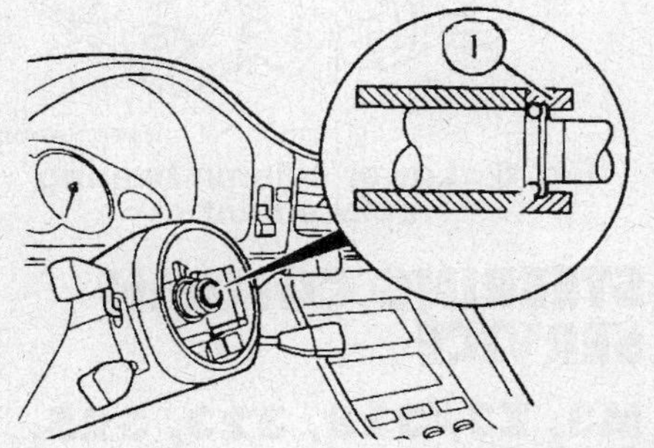
BM6049100002000X

Fig. 1 Collar replacement

a. Ensure bayonet connector is locked into correct position.
b. Ensure collar snap ring locks into recess in collar.
c. Ensure bolt locates in upper steering spindle retaining groove.
d. Tighten mounting bolts to specifications.

323Ci, 325, 328Ci & 330 & 2001 M3 & 2000 323i & 328i & 1999 323i & 328i Sedans

1. Remove steering wheel as outlined in "Electrical" section.
2. Remove upper and lower steering column trim, then the pedal assembly panel as outlined in "Dash Panel Service" section.
3. Lock steering wheel in straight ahead position.
4. Remove mounting bolts and splash guard.
5. Remove clamping bolt and force disk joint off steering gear.
6. Pull lower steering column down.
7. Remove universal joint mounting bolt, then the lower steering column.
8. Remove mounting screws and disconnect connectors, then remove switch block.
9. Disconnect ring antenna connector.
10. Pull steering column upper section toward interior.
11. Remove interlock cable, as required.
12. Disconnect steering column connector, then the cable duct wiring harness.
13. Remove shear-off screws using suitable chisel or grind off.
14. Remove upper mounting bolt and steering column.
15. Reverse procedure to install. Tighten mounting bolts to specifications.

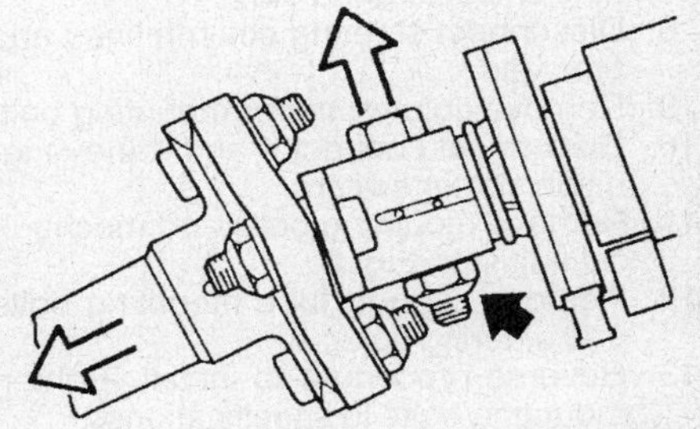
BM6049100003000X

Fig. 2 Clamping bolt replacement

M5, 525, 528, 530, 540, 740 & 750

1. Remove steering wheel as outlined in "Electrical" section.
2. Remove lower instrument panel trim as outlined in "Dash Panel Service" section.
3. Remove upper column retaining collar, **Fig. 1.**
4. Remove mounting screws, then disconnect and remove upper steering column cover.
5. Disconnect interlock cable from steering lock as required.
6. Remove clamping bolt and press steering column down, **Fig. 2.**

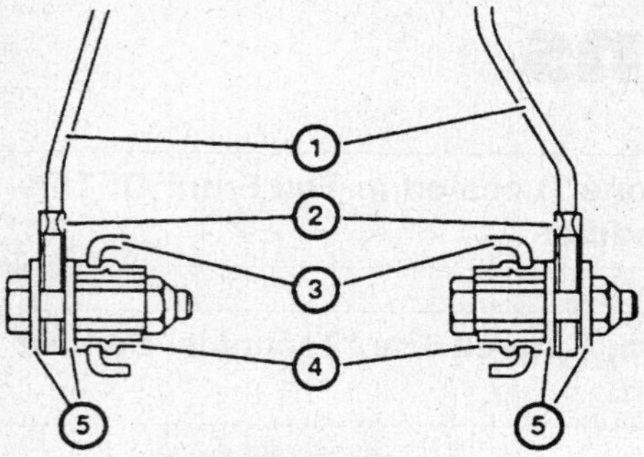

1 Lever (left, right)
2 Sliding cover
3 Steering column slide
4 Rubber mount
5 Washer
Replace self-locking nuts.

BM6049100004000X

Fig. 3 Mechanical adjuster replacement

7. Remove shear-off screws using suitable chisel or grind off.
8. Disconnect steering column lines and brackets.
9. Remove column upper mounting bolt.
10. Disconnect connector and remove ignition starter switch.
11. Remove mounting bolts and mechanical adjuster, **Fig. 3.**
12. Remove support tube mounting bolts and steering column.
13. Reverse procedure to install. Tighten mounting bolts to specifications.

X5

1. Remove lower lefthand instrument panel and disconnect On-Board Diagnosis (OBD) connector.
2. Remove lower instrument panel trim as outlined in "Dash Panel Service" section.
3. Remove steering wheel as outlined in "Electrical" section.
4. Remove mounting screws, then disconnect and remove upper and lower steering column covers.
5. Remove upper column retaining collar, **Fig. 1.**
6. Disconnect interlock cable from steering lock as required.
7. Remove mounting bolts and disconnect connector, then remove steering column stalk fixture.
8. Remove clamping bolt and press steering column down, **Fig. 2.**
9. Remove shear-off screws using suitable chisel or grind off.
10. Disconnect steering column lines and brackets.
11. Remove column upper mounting bolt.
12. Disconnect connector and remove ignition starter switch.
13. Remove mounting bolts and mechanical adjuster, **Fig. 3.**
14. Remove support tube mounting bolts and steering column.
15. Reverse procedure to install. Tighten mounting bolts to specifications.

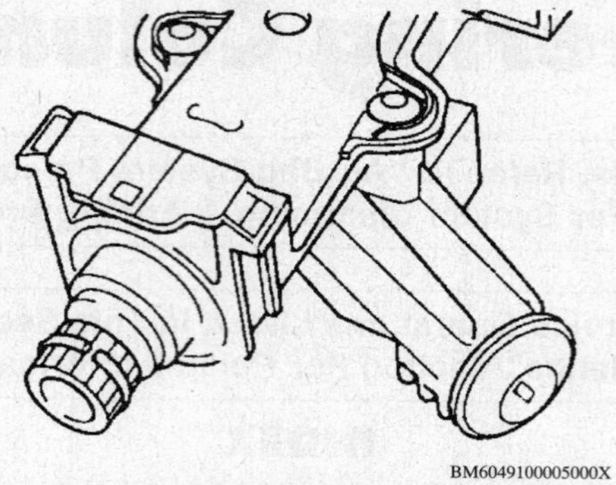

BM6049100005000X

Fig. 4 Snap ring & shaft sleeve removal

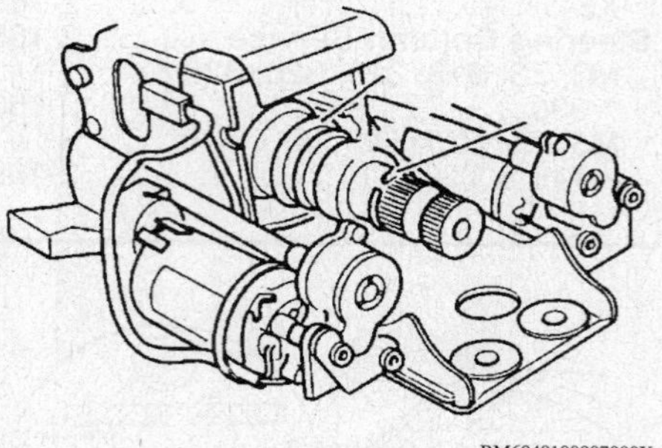

BM6049100007000X

Fig. 6 Lower column bearing replacement

STEERING COLUMN SERVICE

M3, Z3, 318, 323, 325, 328 & 330

Z3, 318, 323is & 328is & 1998-99 M3, 328i & 1998 323i & 1999 323i & 328i Convertibles

1. Remove mounting screws and clip, then the upper and lower column covers.
2. Remove mounting screws, clip, retaining hook and multi-function switch.
3. Remove ground strap mounting screws.
4. Remove headless screws and starter switch.
5. Remove snap ring and shaft sleeve, **Fig. 4.**
6. Remove steering column bearing and inner sleeve.
7. Remove shear-off screws and turn steering lock to R position.
8. Remove steering lock by pressing steering column down.
9. Remove lower steering column bearing snap ring, collar, spring and support ring.
10. Remove steering column.
11. Knock lower steering column bearing out of outer tube. Plug steering column bore with suitable plastic cap.
12. Remove mounting nuts, bolts and adjustment lever assembly.
13. Reverse procedure to assemble, noting the following:
    a. Apply light coat of suitable grease to bearing block and steering column tube.
    b. Assembly adjustment lever with dowel pin jammed to inside length of 0.827–0.854 inch.
    c. Install mounting bolt until it contacts stud, then push lever to left. Bolt square should must engage outer tube.
    d. Tighten jammed lever nut to specifications.
    e. Lubricate bearing seat with suitable grease.
    f. Recess in steering column collar must point to snap ring.
    g. Steering lock dowel pin must fit secure into bore.
    h. Install steering column inner bearing sleeve with bevelled end pointing to steering lock.
    i. Mount steering lock sleeve and push on snap ring until it engages using set piece tool No. 32 1 090, or installation tool No. 32 3 070, or equivalent, **Fig. 5.**

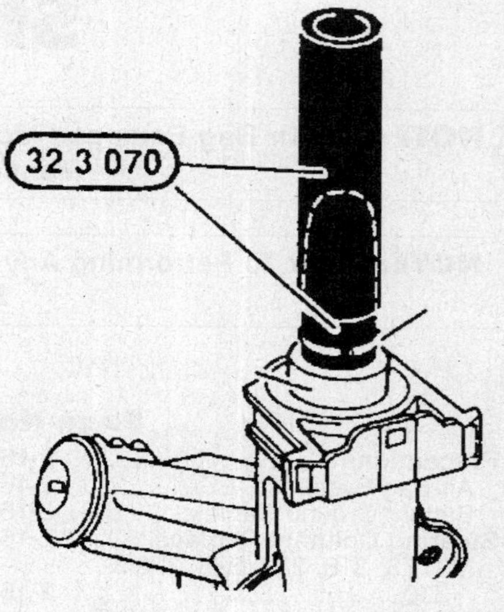

BM6049100006000X

Fig. 5 Steering lock sleeve installation

323Ci, 325, 328Ci & 330 & 2001 M3 & 2000 323i & 328i & 1999 323i & 328i Sedans

1. Remove mounting screws and cable duct.
2. Remove ring antenna using releasing tool No. 61 3 100, or equivalent.
3. Press lock barrel inward through hole and turn to R position (first click).
4. Remove locking cylinder using releasing mandrel tool No. 32 3 110, or equivalent.
5. Disconnect helical coiled spring at both ends.
6. Remove bushing and crash sleeve by pressing disk off sleeve and lifting sleeve out of steering shaft groove.

7. Remove crash disk.
8. Remove mounting nut and operating lever.
9. Remove cable holder.
10. Remove mounting nut, bolt with washer, plate and bracket.
11. Remove steering angle sensor by pressing locking hooks.
12. Remove locking element by pressing hooks.
13. Remove mounting screws and ignition starter switch.
14. Reverse procedure to assemble, noting the following:
    a. Push upper column to stop.
    b. Install steering angle sensor using bushing tool No. 32 3 040, or equivalent.
    c. Ensure locking element engages steering angle sensor and both hooks snap into place.
    d. Replace guide bushing and grease as required.
    e. Install new sliding blocks, stop element and stop buffer as required.
    f. **Do not grease friction plate.**
    g. Install plate mounting nut using suitable Loctite, or equivalent.
    h. Press clamping disk onto operating lever with marking facing lever.
    i. Snap clamping disk into elongated mounting bracket hole.
    j. Apply grease to needle rollers and ensure needle rollers are installed correctly.
    k. Lubricate operating lever axial needle bearings using Glizzando grease, or equivalent.
    l. Install wash with wide tongue aligned in wide link and install new mounting nut.
    m. Install new bushing and crash sleeve.
    n. Install ring antenna rubber ring.

M5, X5, 525, 528, 530, 540, 740 & 750

1. Remove ring antenna using releasing tool No. 61 3 300, or equivalent.
2. **On X5 models,** remove mounting bolt and damper.
3. **On all models,** remove grub screws and ignition starter switch.
4. Remove snap ring and shaft sleeve, **Fig. 4.**

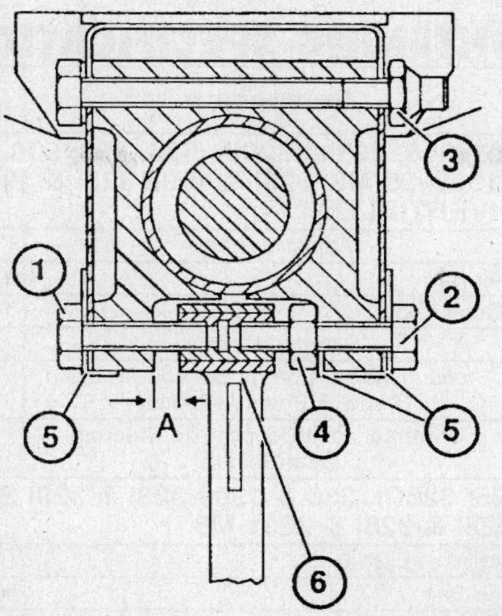

Fig. 7 Cross-sectional view of mechanic adjuster

5. Remove steering column bearing and inner sleeve.
6. Remove shear-off screws.
7. Turn lock cylinder to R position and remove using releasing mandrel tool No. 32 3 110, or equivalent.
8. Remove steering angle sensor.
9. Remove lower steering column bearing snap ring, end collar and spring, **Fig. 6.**
10. Remove steering column from tube.
11. Knock lower steering column bearing out of outer tube. Plug steering column bore with suitable plastic cap.
12. Remove mounting bolts, then remove connector by twisting bracket.
13. Remove gearbox motor and shaft.
14. Disconnect mechanical adjuster torsion springs, **Fig. 7.**
15. Remove mounting nut, axial grooved ball bearing, clamping disc and retainer.
16. Press clamping fixture out of adjusting lever using fixture tool No. 32 1 200, or equivalent, nuts, bolts and adjustment lever assembly.
17. Reverse procedure to assemble, noting the following:
    a. Install new mechanical adjuster nut.
    b. Press contact ring out of new bearing.
    c. Install new bearing using driver tools Nos. 32 1 150 and 00 5 500, or equivalents.
    d. Ensure steering angle sensor pin engages.
    e. Install steering column inner bearing sleeve with bevelled end pointing to steering lock.
    f. Mount steering lock sleeve and push on snap ring until it engages using set piece tool No. 32 1 090, or installation tool No. 32 3 070, or equivalent, **Fig. 5.**

TECHNICAL SERVICE BULLETINS

STEERING COLUMN DOES MOVE TO CORRECT POSITION

528, 540, 740 & 750

On some of these models built between Sept. 1, 1998 and May 8, 2000, the steering column either moves in or out to an undefined position or does not move at all.

This condition may be caused by Seat/Steering Module (SM/LSM) software error.

To correct this condition program module with latest software.

STEERING COLUMN DOES NOT ADJUST

528, 540, 740 & 750

On some of these models the steering column does not move from the Comfort Exit position. In addition, neither the steering column nor the driver's seat can be adjusted using their respective switches. This condition can usually be cleared by cycling the ignition switch several times, or switching the ignition off and allowing system to go to consumer shut-off.

This condition may be caused by Seat/Steering Module (SM/LSM) software error.

To correct this condition, program module with latest software.

TIGHTENING SPECIFICATIONS

Year	Component	Torque, Ft. Lbs.
M5, X5, Z3, 318, 323is, 328is, 525, 528, 530, 540, 740 & 750 & 1998–99 M3, 328i & 1998 323i & 1999 323i & 328i CONVERTIBLES		
1998–2001	Adjusting Lever	27①④
	Air Bag	13
	Outer Tube	16
	Steering Column	16
	Steering Wheel Control Console To Dash Panel & Pedal Assembly	16
	Universal Joint/Coupling To Steering Gear/Spindle	14②
323Ci, 325, 328Ci, 330 & 1999 323i & 328i SEDANS & 2000 323i & 328i & 2001 M3		
1999–2001	Adjusting Lever	③
	Air Bag	13
	Outer Tube	16
	Steering Column	16
	Steering Wheel Control Console To Dash Panel & Pedal Assembly	16
	Universal Joint/Coupling To Steering Gear/Spindle	16

① — Inch lbs.
② — X5 w/steel joint, 18 ft. lbs.; X5 w/Aluminum joint, 21 ft. lbs.
③ — Open, close & torque to 35 inch lbs.; Open, close & torque to 42 inch lbs.; Open, close & torque to 42 inch lbs.
④ — Jammed position, 61 inch lbs.

Power Steering

NOTE: On Air Bag Equipped Models, Refer To "Air Bag System Precautions" Located In The Front Of This Manual For System Disarming & Arming Procedures.

NOTE: Prior To Performing Any Service Operations Listed In This Section, Consult The "Technical Service Bulletins" Section For Related Information.

INDEX

	Page No.
Power Steering Pressure Specifications	2-171
Power Steering System Bleed	2-171
Component Service	2-172
Z3, 318, 323is & 328is & 1998–99 M3, 328i & 1998 323i & 1999 323i & 328i Convertibles	2-172
Power Steering System Service	2-171
Precautions	2-171
Air Bag Systems	2-171
Battery Ground Cable	2-171
Technical Service Bulletins	2-172
Brake Induced Steering Vibration	2-172
Steering Wheel Vibration Or Buzz	2-172
Tightening Specifications	2-174

POWER STEERING PRESSURE SPECIFICATIONS

Model	Year	Maximum Rated Pressure, PSI①	
		Impeller Pump	Piston Pump
M3	1998–99	1595–1740	—
	2001	1624–1740	—
M5	2000–01	1885–2031	—
X5	2000–01	1740–1885	—
Z3 1.9	1998	1305–1421	—
Z3 2.3, 2.5, 2.8 & 3.0	1998–2001	1595–1740	—
318	1998–99	1305–1421	—
323Ci & 328Ci	2000	1624–1740	—
323i & 328	1998	1595–1740	—
	1999	1595–1740②	—
	2000	1624–1740	—
323is & 328is	1998–99	1595–1740	—
328	1998–99	1595–1740	—
325 & 330	2001	1624–1740	—
525, 528 & 530	1998–2001	1595–1740	—
540	1998–2001	1885–2031	—
740 & 750	1998–2001	1740–2031	2901

① — Engine running at idle.
② — Coupe & Convertible, 1595–1740 psi; Sedan 1624–1740 psi.

PRECAUTIONS

AIR BAG SYSTEMS

Refer to "Air Bag System Precautions" in the front of this manual for system disarming and arming procedures.

BATTERY GROUND CABLE

Prior to service, disconnect battery ground cable and isolate as required.

POWER STEERING SYSTEM SERVICE

POWER STEERING SYSTEM BLEED

1. Remove cap and fill power steering tank to MAX mark.
2. Start engine.
3. Turn steering wheel from left to right lock twice.
4. Stop engine and adjust fluid level as required.

Component Service

Z3, 318, 323IS & 328IS & 1998–99 M3, 328I & 1998 323I & 1999 323I & 328I CONVERTIBLES

Disassemble

1. Remove oil leakage line.
2. Remove oil pressure line and O-rings.
3. Mark adjusting screw to case position for installation alignment.
4. Record depth of adjusting screw.
5. Remove adjusting screw, spring, O-ring and pressure piece.
6. Remove screw cap.
7. Center steering gear.
8. Center steering rack.
9. Record rack protrusion measurement for assembly alignment.
10. Remove dust cap and steering pinion shaft nut.
11. Remove circlip and pinion shaft
12. Remove bearing bushing.
13. Drive radial shaft seal and bearing out of bushing using driver tool Nos. 32 1 140/250, or equivalents.
14. Remove leakage oil line connection.
15. Remove case by installing retaining ring through oil leakage bore.
16. Remove pinion shaft bushing.
17. Press radial seal out of bearing bushing using driver tools Nos. 32 1 140/210 and 33 3 331, or equivalents.
18. Drive radial shaft seal out of pipe using driver tool Nos. 32 1 140 and 32 1 210, or equivalents.
19. Drive bearing out of spindle housing using suitable punch.
20. Drive radial shaft seal out of spindle housing using suitable punch. **Do not damage polished bore.**

Assemble

1. Install new O-ring, plastic bushing and thrust shim in bearing sleeve.
2. Drive shaft seal into bearing bushing using driver tool Nos. 31 1 140/220, or equivalents.
3. Install plastic bushing and thrust shim, then drive new radial shaft seal in using driver tools.
4. Pack bearing with suitable grease and press into steering spindle housing using driver tools.
5. Drive new radial shaft seal into steering spindle housing using driver tools.
6. Install new piston ring and O-ring.
7. Install rack into pipe and fit bearing bushing to rack, then slide into pipe.
8. Install circlip in open side opposite oil leakage bore.
9. Install new pinion and O-rings.
10. Install new radial shaft seal using driver tools. Install new O-ring.
11. Drive bearing with lettering upward into bushing using driver tools.
12. Slide bearing bushing onto steering spindle with radial shaft seal outermost.
13. Grease rack and pinion.
14. Pull rack out to dimension recorded during disassembly.
15. Install steering spindle and retaining ring.
16. Install protective cap.
17. Install and tighten new self-locking nut.
18. Tighten screw cap to specifications.
19. Install foil insert and new O-ring.
20. Grease and install pressure piece, spring and O-ring.
21. Tighten adjusting screw to depth measured during disassembly. Align marks.
22. Secure adjusting screw by peening.
23. Install oil leakage line.
24. Install pressure line and new O-ring.

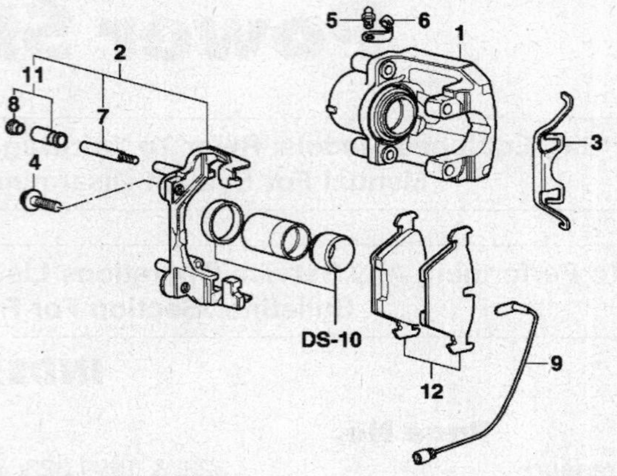

1 Brake-caliper housing
2 Brake console
3 Spring retainer
4 Bolt
5 Bleeder valve
6 Dust cap
7 Guide bolt
8 Protecting plug
9 Brake-pad-wear sensor
10 Brake caliper gasket set
11 Guide-sleeve repair kit
12 Brake linings repair set

BM4070100010000X

Fig. 1 Exploded view of front & rear brake caliper. M5, 323Ci, 325, 328Ci, 330, 525, 528, 530 & 540 & 2001 M3 & 2000 323i & 328i & 1999 323i & 328i Sedans

TECHNICAL SERVICE BULLETINS

BRAKE INDUCED STEERING VIBRATION

1999 323i & 328i Sedans

On some of these models built before October 1999 there may be a steering vibration during braking in the 60–50 mph range.

This condition may be caused by excessive sensitivity of the front axle.

To correct this condition remove front brake rotors, pads and steering coupling, then replace with revised parts (323 kit No. 34 11 0 009 774, 328 kit No. 34 11 0 009 776)

STEERING WHEEL VIBRATION OR BUZZ

323is & 328is & 1998–99 328i & 1998 323i & 1999 323i & 328i Convertibles

On some of these models there may be a high frequency buzz felt in the steering wheel. In some cases there may be vibration similar to tire balance problem felt in a 2–5 mph window between 50–60 mph.

This condition may be caused by power steering hydraulic pulses.

To correct this condition, proceed as follows:

1. Disconnect power steering pump hose and drain fluid into suitable container.
2. Disconnect line from rack and remove it.
3. Remove cooling tubes mounting bolt on righthand side of rack and install new line (part No. 32 41 1 094 976). **Torque** new M6 x 16 mounting bolt to 80 inch lbs.
4. Connect pressure line to pump and rack using new seal rings. **Torque** to 26 ft. lbs.
5. Ensure adequate clearance between line and components.
6. Remove two T40 mounting bolts from pump back.
7. Install new brace (part No. 32 42 1 710 015) with small portion aligned with block tapped bosses. **Torque** new M8 x 50 mounting bolts and washers to 18 ft. lbs.
8. Remove fluid reservoir mounting bracket.
9. Install rubber grommets (part No. 34 51 1 162 819) into new bracket (part No. 32 41 1 093 236) and spacers into grommets.
10. Install bracket and **torque** new mounting bolts to 18 ft. lbs.

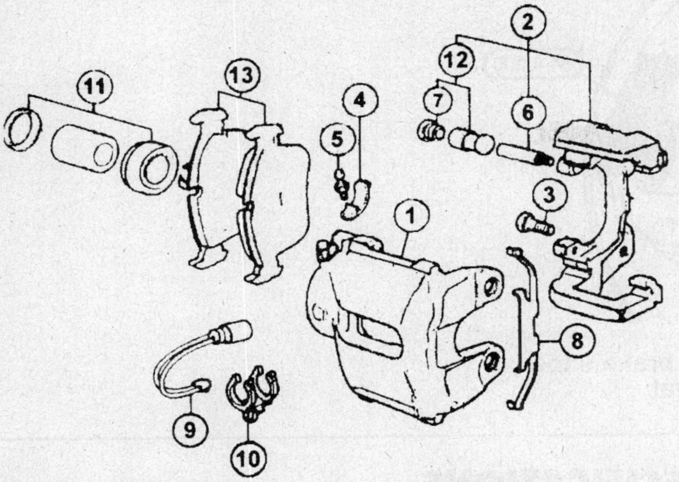

1. Brake Caliper Housing
2. Brake Console
3. Bolt
4. Dust Cap
5. Bleeder Valve
6. Guide Bolt
7. Protecting Plug
8. Spring Retainer
9. Pad Wear Sensor
10. Sensor Holder
11. Seal Set
12. Guide Sleeve Repair Kit
13. Pad Set

BM4079500008000X

Fig. 2 Exploded view of front brake caliper. Z3, 318, 323is & 328is & 1998–99 M3, 328i & 1998 323i & 1999 323i & 328i Convertibles

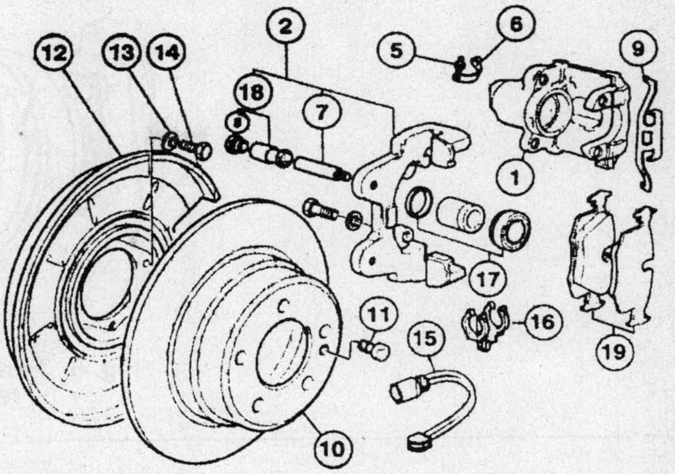

1) Brake-caliper housing
2) Brake console
3) Washer
4) Shouldered bolt
5) Bleeder valve
6) Dust cap
7) Guide bolt
8) Protecting plug
9) Spring retainer
10) Brake disc
11) Hexagon-socket-head bolt
12) Left guard plate
13) Washer
14) Bolt
15) Brake-pad-wear sensor
16) Bracket
17) Seal set for brake caliper
18) Guide bolt (complete)
19) Brake pad

BM4079500009000X

Fig. 3 Exploded view of rear brake caliper. Z3, 318, 323is & 328is & 1998–99 M3, 328i & 1998 323i & 1999 323i & 328i Convertibles

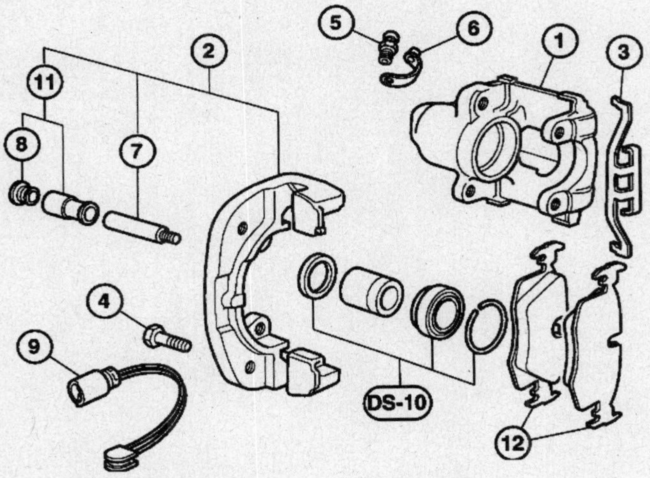

1 Brake-caliper housing
2 Brake console
3 Spring retainer
4 Hex screw
5 Bleeder valve
6 Dust cap
7 Guide bolt
8 Protecting plug
9 Brake-pad-wear sensor
10 Brake caliper gasket set
11 Guide-sleeve repair kit
12 Brake linings repair set

BM4070100011000X

Fig. 4 Exploded view of front & rear brake caliper. 740

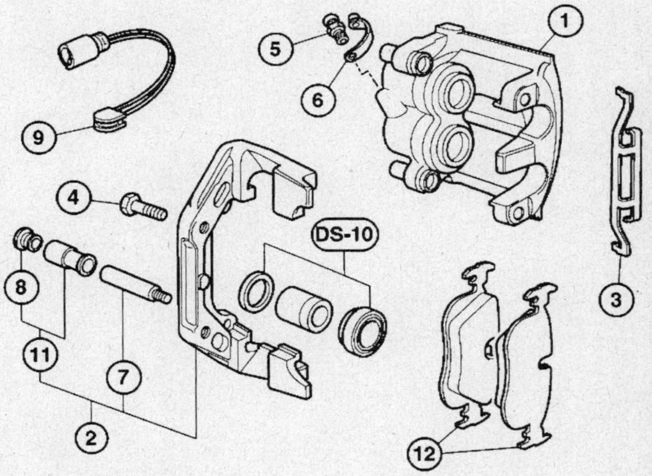

1 Brake-caliper housing
2 Brake console
3 Spring retainer
4 Bolt
5 Bleeder valve
6 Dust cap
7 Guide bolt
8 Protecting plug
9 Brake-pad-wear sensor
10 Seal set for brake caliper
11 Guide-sleeve repair kit
12 Brake-pad repair kit

BM4070100012000X

Fig. 5 Exploded view of front brake caliper. 750

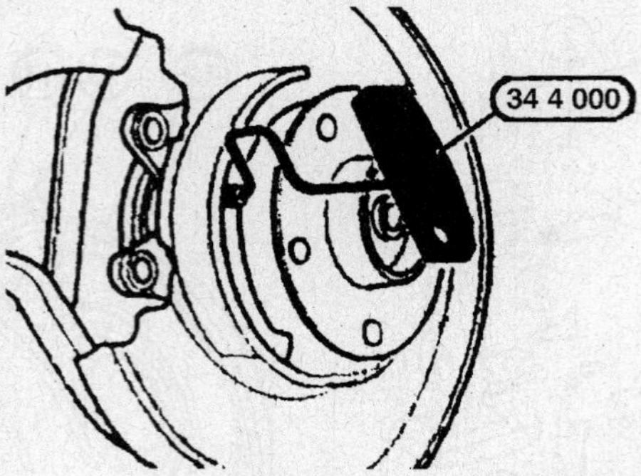

Fig. 6 Parking brake shoe removal

TIGHTENING SPECIFICATIONS

Year	Component	Torque, Ft. Lbs.
1998–2001	Adjusting Screw	20
	Drain Plug	31
	Pipe To Steering Gear	71①

① — Inch lbs.

Disc Brakes

NOTE: On Air Bag Equipped Models, Refer To "Air Bag System Precautions" Located In The Front Of This Manual For System Disarming & Arming Procedures.

NOTE: Prior To Performing Any Service Operations Listed In This Section, Consult The "Technical Service Bulletins" Section For Related Information.

INDEX

	Page No.
Adjustments	2-176
Parking Brake	2-176
Brake Pad Service	2-175
Pads, Replace	2-175
Caliper Service	2-175
Overhaul	2-175
Replace	2-175
Description	2-175
Disc Brake Specifications	2-177
Parking Brake Service	2-176
Parking Brake Specifications	2-177
Rotor, Replace	2-175
Technical Service Bulletins	2-176
Brake Induced Steering Vibration	2-176
Brake Squeal	2-176
Front Brake Noise	2-176
Steering Wheel Twitch On Rapid Braking	2-176
Tightening Specifications	2-177

DESCRIPTION

Refer to **Figs. 1 through 5** for disc brake descriptions.

BRAKE PAD SERVICE

PADS, REPLACE

Front

1. Raise and support vehicle, then remove front tire and wheel assemblies.
2. Remove retaining spring, as required.
3. Disconnect brake pad wear indicator connector from lefthand side of caliper.
4. Remove plastic plugs and remove brake hose out from bracket.
5. Remove guide bolts and lift brake caliper toward vehicle rear.
6. Remove brake pads and suspend caliper aside with suitable wire.
7. Reverse procedure to install, noting the following:
   a. Turn caliper piston back into bore using fixture tool No. 34 1 050, or equivalent.
   b. Check fluid level and bleed brake system as required.
   c. Replace dust sleeve as required.
   d. Clean contact piston surfaces and coat with suitable anti-squeak compound.
   e. Clean brake pad tee heads and thinly coat with suitable anti-squeak compound.
   f. Clean brake pad to caliper contact surface and thinly coat with suitable anti-squeak compound.
   g. Clean hammer head guides and thinly coat with suitable anti-squeak compound.
   h. Replace guide pins as required.
   i. Clean guide pins. **Do not grease.**
   j. Tighten mounting bolts to specifications.

Rear

1. Raise and support vehicle, then remove rear tire and wheel assemblies.
2. Remove retaining spring.
3. Disconnect lining wear indicator electrical connector from righthand side.
4. Remove caps and guide bolts, then lift brake caliper toward vehicle rear.
5. Remove brake pads and suspend caliper aside with suitable wire.
6. Reverse procedure to install, noting the following:
   a. Turn caliper piston back into bore using fixture tool No. 34 1 050, or equivalent.
   b. Check fluid level and bleed brake system as required.
   c. Replace dust sleeve as required.
   d. Clean contact piston surfaces and coat with suitable anti-squeak compound.
   e. Clean brake pad tee heads and thinly coat with suitable anti-squeak compound.
   f. Clean brake pad to caliper contact surface and thinly coat with suitable anti-squeak compound.
   g. Clean hammer head guides and thinly coat with suitable anti-squeak compound.
   h. Replace guide pins as required.
   i. Clean guide pins. **Do not grease.**
   j. Tighten mounting bolts to specifications.

ROTOR

REPLACE

1. Raise and support vehicle, then remove tire and wheel assembly.
2. Remove brake pads as outlined under "Pad, Replace," as required.
3. Remove caliper mounting bolts, then position caliper aside with brake hoses connected.
4. Remove mounting bolts and rotor. **Tapping rotor with rubber hammer may be required. Do not strike friction ring.**
5. **Do not remove balance clips.**
6. Reverse procedure to install, noting the following
   a. **On M3 models,** odd part number discs are for lefthand side; even for righthand.
   b. **On all models,** tighten mounting bolts to specification.

CALIPER SERVICE

REPLACE

Front

1. Raise and support vehicle, then remove front tire and wheel.
2. Press and hold brake pedal with suitable prop.
3. Disconnect brake pipe from connection with hose.
4. Remove wear indicator connector from lefthand side.
5. Remove mounting bolts and caliper.
6. Reverse procedure to install, noting the following:
   a. Tighten mounting bolts to specifications.
   b. Bleed brake system.
   c. Ensure brake pad wear sensor wire does not contact rotor or wheel.

Rear

1. Raise and support vehicle, then remove rear tire and wheel assembly.
2. Drain moderate amount of brake fluid from reservoir using suitable syringe.
3. Disconnect and plug caliper hydraulic line.
4. Disconnect brake pad wear sensor, then remove caliper.
5. Reverse procedure to install. Tighten mounting bolts to specifications and bleed brake system.

OVERHAUL

Disassemble

1. Press piston out with compressed air through connection bore.

2. Place suitable hardwood or felt liner in caliper recess.
3. Remove sealing ring with suitable plastic needle.

Inspection

1. Inspect guide sleeves and repair as required.
2. Clean caliper and piston with alcohol, blow dry with compressed air.

Assemble

1. Apply light coat of ATE brake cylinder paste, or equivalent, to cylinder bore, piston, dust cover and sealing cover.
2. Install sealing cover in rear cylinder bore groove.
3. Install dust cover to piston, the sealing bulge in from groove.
4. Press piston in under suitable hardwood board. **Do not tilt piston.**

PARKING BRAKE SERVICE

1. Remove brake disc as outlined under "Rotor, Replace."
2. Remove parking brake shoes' return spring using suitable brake spring pliers,
3. Turn retainers 90° and remove using retainer tool No. 34 4 000, or equivalent, **Fig. 6.**
4. Remove shoes by rotating outward from adjuster.
5. Reverse procedure to install, noting the following:
   a. Lubricate all brake shoe contact points and brake adjuster screws with suitable brake lubricant.
   b. Tighten mounting bolts to specification.
   c. Adjust parking brake shoes as outlined under "Adjustments."

ADJUSTMENTS

PARKING BRAKE

1. Ensure parking brake lever is fully released and cables operate freely, then raise and support vehicle.
2. Remove one wheel bolt from each wheel.
3. Rotate wheel until bolt hole is aligned with adjustment screw.
4. Turn adjusting screw until wheel can no longer turn.
5. **On 1998–99 M3, 740 and 750 models,** loosen adjusting screw eight notches.
6. **On 323Ci, 325, 328Ci and 330 and 2001 M3 and 2000 323i and 328i and 1999 323i and 328i Sedan models,** loosen adjusting screw 10 notches.
7. **On M5, X5, 525, 528, 530 and 540 models,** loosen adjusting screw 12 notches.
8. **On Z3, 318, 323is and 328is and 1998–99 328i and 1998 323i and 1999 323i and 328i Convertible models,** loosen adjusting screw 18 notches.
9. **On all models,** pull parking brake lever up five notches, then tighten adjusters until rear wheels can just barely be rotated
10. Release brake lever and ensure rear wheels rotate freely.

TECHNICAL SERVICE BULLETINS

BRAKE SQUEAL

323Ci, 325 & 328Ci & 2000 323i & 328i & 1999 323i & 328i Sedans

On some of these models there may be a front brake squeal.

This condition may be caused by Textar front brake pads.

To correct this condition install Jurid 620 compound pads (front part No. 34 11 6 752 481 & rear part No. 34 21 1 164 501). Clean and lubricate all metal to metal contact points with Bostick never-Seez, or equivalent.

BRAKE INDUCED STEERING VIBRATION

1999 323i & 328i Sedans

On some of these models built before October 1999 there may be a steering vibration during braking in the 60–50 mph range.

This condition may be caused by excessive sensitivity of the front axle.

To correct this condition remove front brake rotors, pads and steering coupling, then replace with revised parts (323 kit No. 34 11 0 009 774, 328 kit No. 34 11 0 009 776).

STEERING WHEEL TWITCH ON RAPID BRAKING

1999 323i & 328i Sedans

On some of these models there may be very slight twitch in steering wheel when brakes are applied rapidly.

This condition may be caused by unequal amounts of toe-in or slight differential in front brake caliper pressure build up.

To correct this condition if alignment is known to be correct and vehicle is not equipped with Dynamic Stability Control (DSC), install dampener (part No. 34 00 91 57 00) in master cylinder line closest to booster.

FRONT BRAKE NOISE

M3 & Z3 M Roadster

On some of these models built between January 1997 and September 1998 there may be excessive front brake noise.

This condition may be caused by brake pad material.

To correct this condition install Jurid 187 brake pads (part No. 34 11 1 162 535). Clean and lubricate all metal to metal contact points with Bostick never-Seez, or equivalent.

DISC BRAKE SPECIFICATIONS

Model	Year	Front Disc Brake						Rear Disc Brake					
			Rotor						Rotor				
			Thickness, Inch						Thickness, Inch				
		Brake Lining Wear Limit, Inch②	Nominal	Min. Refinish	Discard Limit ①	Thickness Variation Parallelism Inch	Lateral Run Out (T.I.R.) Inch	Brake Lining Wear Limit, Inch②	Nominal	Min. Refinish	Discard Limit①	Thickness Variation Parallelism Inch	Lateral Run-Out (T.I.R.) Inch
M3	1998–99	0.118	—	④	1.039④	0.0004	④⑥	0.118	—	④	.724④	0.0004	④⑥
	2001	0.118	—	④	0.803	0.0004	④⑥	0.118	—	④	⑤	0.0004	④⑥
M5	2000–01	0.118	—	④	1.118	0.0004	④⑥	0.118	—	④	⑨	0.0004	④⑥
X5	2000–01	0.118	—	⑦	1.118	0.0008	⑥	0.118	—	⑦	.724	0.0004	⑥

Continued

DISC BRAKE SPECIFICATIONS—Continued

Model	Year	Front Disc Brake						Rear Disc Brake					
			Rotor						Rotor				
		Brake Lining Wear Limit, Inch②	Thickness, Inch			Thickness Variation Parallelism Inch	Lateral Run Out (T.I.R.) Inch	Brake Lining Wear Limit, Inch②	Thickness, Inch			Thickness Variation Parallelism Inch	Lateral Run-Out (T.I.R.) Inch
			Nominal	Min. Refinish	Discard Limit ①				Nominal	Min. Refinish	Discard Limit①		
Z3	1998–99	0.118	—	⑦	③	0.0004	⑥	0.118	—	⑦	⑤	0.0004	⑥
318	1998–99	0.118	—	⑦	③	0.0004	⑥	0.118	—	⑦	⑤	0.0004	⑥
323 & 328	1998	0.118	—	⑦	③	0.0004	⑥	0.118	—	⑦	⑤	0.0004	⑥
	1999⑧	0.118	—	⑦	③	0.0004	⑥	0.118	—	⑦	⑤	0.0004	⑥
	1999⑩	0.118	—	⑦	0.803	0.0004	⑥	0.118	—	⑦	⑤	0.0004	⑥
	2000	0.118	—	⑦	0.803	0.0004	⑥	0.118	—	⑦	⑤	0.0004	⑥
525 & 530	2001	0.118	—	⑦	0.803	0.0004	⑥	0.118	—	⑦	⑨	0.0004	⑥
528	1998–2000	0.118	—	⑦	0.803	0.0004	⑥	0.118	—	⑦	⑨	0.0004	⑥
540	1998–2001	0.118	—	⑦	1.118	0.0004	⑥	0.118	—	⑦	⑨	0.0004	⑥
740	1998–2001	0.118	—	⑦	1.118	0.0004	⑥	0.118	—	⑦	0.409	0.0004	⑥
750	1998–2001	0.118	—	⑦	1.197	0.0004	⑥	0.118	—	⑦	0.724	0.0004	⑥

① — Discard thickness is stamped on rotor.
② — Above rivet head or backing plate. Original equipment type brake lining.
③ — Solid rotor 0.409 inch; vented rotor 0.803 inch.
④ — Do not machine.
⑤ — Solid rotor, 0.331 inch; vented rotor, 0.685 inch.
⑥ — Disc installed, 0.0079 inch; disc removed, 0.0016 inch.
⑦ — Maximum machine limit per friction ring side, 0.031 inch.
⑧ — Coupe & Convertible.
⑨ — Solid rotor, 0.331 inch; vented rotor, 0.724 inch.
⑩ — Sedan.

PARKING BRAKE SPECIFICATIONS

Model	Drum Diameter, Inches	Minimum Liner Thickness, Inch	Maximum Radial Runout, Inch
M3 & Z3 M Coupe & Z3 M Roadster	7.087	0.059	0.0039
M5, X5, 525, 528, 530 & 540	7.284	0.059	0.0039
Z3, 318, 323, 325, 328 & 330	6.300	0.059	0.0039
740 & 750	7.087	0.059	0.0039

TIGHTENING SPECIFICATIONS

Year	Component	Torque, Ft. Lbs.
1998–2001	Bleeder Valve	①
	Brake Disc To Hub	12
	Front Caliper To Steering Knuckle	81
	Guide Bolt	18–26
	Hose Coupling	13–14
	Rear Caliper To Trailing Arm	48

① — 7mm, 31–44 inch lbs.; 11 mm, 106–142 inch lbs.

Drum Brakes

NOTE: On Air Bag Equipped Models, Refer To "Air Bag System Precautions" Located In The Front Of This Manual For System Disarming & Arming Procedures.

INDEX

	Page No.
Adjustments	2-178
Parking Brake	2-178
Brake Service	2-178
Shoe, Replace	2-178
Drum Brake Specifications	2-178
Tightening Specifications	2-178

BRAKE SERVICE

SHOE, REPLACE

1. Raise and support vehicle, then remove tire and wheel assembly.
2. Disconnect parking brake cables.
3. Remove mounting bolt and drum. If drum is difficult to remove, proceed as follows:
   a. Turn drum until wheel stud bore is approximately 80° off vertical axis.
   b. Push parking brake lever back using suitable screwdriver.
   c. If drum is still difficult to remove, turn drum until wheel stud bore is 50° before vehicle axis.
   d. Press adjusting tool No. 34 4 010, or equivalent, down in tooth profile.
   e. Slack automatic brake control by removing tool.
   f. Repeat procedure until drum can be removed.
4. Disconnect parking brake cable.
5. Remove shoes.
6. Reverse procedure to install, noting the following:
   a. Install four new shoes.
   b. Install new return springs.
   c. Turn slack control pinion in thrust sleeve direction until shoes' diameter is 8.98 inches.

ADJUSTMENTS

PARKING BRAKE

Refer to "Disc Brake" Section.

DRUM BRAKE SPECIFICATIONS

Model	Year	Brake Lining Wear Limit, Inch②	Brake Drum Inside Diameter, Inches			Drum Runout Limit, Inch	Drum Maximum Out Of Roundness, Inch
			Nominal	Maximum Refinish	Maximum Inside Diameter (Discard Limit)①		
Z3 & 318	1998–2001	0.059	9.000	9.035	—	0.002	—

① — Maximum brake drum inside diameter (discard limit) is stamped on drum.

② — Above rivet head or shoe. Original equipment type brake linings.

TIGHTENING SPECIFICATIONS

Year	Component	Torque, Ft. Lbs.
1999–2001	Carrier To Semi-Trailing Arm/Wheel Carrier	48
	Drum To Hub	12
	Wheel Cylinder	88①

① — Inch lbs.

Hydraulic Brake Systems

NOTE: On Air Bag Equipped Models, Refer To "Air Bag System Precautions" Located In The Front Of This Manual For System Disarming & Arming Procedures.

INDEX

	Page No.
Brake System Bleed	2-180
Component Replacement	2-179
Master Cylinder, Replace	2-179
Hydraulic Brake System Specifications	2-180
Precautions	2-179
Air Bag Systems	2-179
Battery Ground Cable	2-179
Tightening Specifications	2-180

PRECAUTIONS

AIR BAG SYSTEMS

Refer to "Air Bag System Precautions" in the front of this manual for system disarming and arming procedures.

BATTERY GROUND CABLE

Prior to service, disconnect battery ground cable and isolate as required.

COMPONENT REPLACEMENT

MASTER CYLINDER, REPLACE

M3, Z3, 318, 3232, 325, 328 & 330

Z3, 318, 323is & 328is & 1998-99 M3, 328i & 1998 323i & 1999 323i & 328i Convertibles

1. Remove brake fluid from master cylinder using suitable syringe.
2. Remove mounting bolt.
3. Disconnect reservoir from master cylinder by titling to side.
4. Plug master cylinder connections.
5. Disconnect brake lines, then plug bores and lines.
6. Remove mounting nuts and master cylinder.
7. Remove plug and clutch hose, as required.
8. Reverse procedure to install, noting the following:
   a. Install new mounting nuts and seal.
   b. Coat sealing rings with suitable brake fluid. **Do not use ATE brake cylinder paste.**
   c. Tighten mounting bolts to specifications.
   d. Bleed brake system as required.

323Ci, 325, 328Ci & 330 & 2001 M3 & 2000 323i & 328i & 1999 323i & 328i Sedans

1. Remove microfilter.
2. Disconnect clips and thread bulkhead cable out of duct.
3. Remove mounting screws and microfilter housing.
4. Remove mounting screws and heater bulkhead.
5. Remove brake fluid from master cylinder using suitable syringe.
6. Disconnect master cylinder connector.
7. Disconnect clutch hydraulic system supply hose, as required.
8. **On models equipped with Dynamic Stability Control (DSC),** disconnect clip, sensor connectors and precharge supply hose. Secure hose vertically with suitable wire.
9. **On all models,** remove mounting screw and reservoir.
10. Disconnect brake lines.
11. Remove mounting nuts and master cylinder.
12. Reverse procedure to install, noting the following:
    a. Install new mounting nuts and seal.
    b. Tighten mounting bolts to specifications.
    c. Bleed brake system as required.

M5, 525, 528, 530 & 540

1. Remove mircofilter and air duct.
2. Remove brake fluid from master cylinder using suitable syringe.
3. Remove clutch master cylinder supply hose.
4. Disconnect reservoir from master cylinder by tilting to side.
5. Disconnect brake lines.
6. Remove line aperture and master cylinder covers.
7. Disconnect brake booster vacuum hose.
8. Remove brake lines, then plug bores and lines.
9. Remove brake lamp switch.
10. Disconnect retainer, recoil spring and pin.
11. Remove mounting nut and pull pedal assembly slightly away from bulkhead.
12. Pull brake unit out of bulkhead and swing it aside.
13. Remove mounting nuts and master cylinder.
14. Remove plug and clutch hose, as required.
15. Reverse procedure to install, noting the following:
    a. Install new mounting nuts and seal.
    b. Tighten mounting bolts to specifications.
    c. Bleed brake system as required.

X5

1. Remove cover and microfilter.
2. Remove brake fluid from master cylinder using suitable syringe.
3. Disconnect reservoir connector.
4. Disconnect clutch hydraulic system hose, as required.
5. **On models equipped with Dynamic Stability Control (DSC),** disconnect clip and precharge supply hose. Secure hose vertically with suitable wire.
6. **On all models,** remove reservoir by pressing left and righthand retaining lugs, then pulling tank vertically out of master cylinder.
7. Remove heater bulkhead and positive support point on lefthand partition wall.
8. Disconnect hood locking cable.
9. Pull wiring harness upward out of partition wall and remove mounting nuts.
10. Remove mounting screw and windshield washer rubber mount.
11. Disconnect brake lines.
12. Remove line aperture cover and disconnect power brake booster vacuum hose.
13. Remove mounting bolts and master cylinder.
14. Reverse procedure to install, noting the following:
    a. Install new mounting nuts and seal.
    b. Tighten mounting bolts to specifications.
    c. Bleed brake system as required.

740 & 750

1. Remove brake fluid from master cylinder using suitable syringe.
2. Disconnect reservoir from master cylinder by tilting laterally.
3. Plug master cylinder connections.
4. Disconnect brake lines, then plug bores and lines.
5. Remove mounting nuts and master cylinder.
6. Remove plug and clutch hose, as required.
7. Reverse procedure to install, noting the following:
   a. Install new mounting nuts and seal.
   b. Tighten mounting bolts to specifications.
   c. Bleed brake system as required.

BRAKE SYSTEM BLEED

The following procedure has been revised by a Technical Service Bulletin.

Ensure traction control systems are turned Off prior to bleeding brake system.

1. Connect suitable pressure bleeder to brake fluid reservoir. **Maximum charging pressure is 43.5 psi.**
2. Attach bleeder hose and container to righthand rear wheel. Bleed until no bubbles appear.
3. Repeat previous step for lefthand rear, righthand front and lefthand front wheels.
4. Support rear suspension at wheel carriers and lower car so rear suspension compresses to its normal loaded position (to prevent damage to output shaft joints). **Wheels must be able to turn freely.**
5. Attach bleeder hose and container to righthand rear bleeder and open bleeder.
6. Depress brake pedal to stop 20 times.
7. Start engine and run in first gear at approximately 3500 RPM while operating ASC button at two second intervals for one minute.
8. Close bleeder and repeat previous three steps on lefthand rear wheel.
9. Attach bleeder hose and container to righthand front wheel and open bleeder.
10. Depress brake pedal to step 12 times. Close bleeder and repeat on lefthand front wheel.
11. Disconnect pressure bleeder.

HYDRAULIC BRAKE SYSTEM SPECIFICATIONS

Model	Leak Test②		Function Test①③
	Line Pressure, PSI	Maximum Pressure Drop Within Two Minutes, %	Line Pressure, PSI
Z3 M Coupe & Z3 M Roadster & 1998–99 M3	464	8	③
Z3, 318, 323is & 328is & 1998–99 328i & 1998 323i & 1999 323i & 328i Convertibles	551	8	③
323Ci, 325, 328Ci & 330 & 2001 M3 & 2000 323i & 328i & 1999 323i & 328i Sedans	522	8	1088–1305
525, 528, 530, 540, 740 & 750	406–479	8	1088–1305
X5	479	8	1088–1305

① — With engine running. At 45 lbs. pedal force.

② — At 112 lbs. pedal force. Discharge reservoir vacuum by operating pedal firmly 10 times.

③ — Nine-inch master vacuum, Lucas 65, 725–870 psi; 10-inch master vacuum Lucas 80, 914–1059 psi.

TIGHTENING SPECIFICATIONS

Year	Component	Torque, Ft. Lbs.
1998–2001	Expansion Tank	31①
	Master Cylinder To Booster	19

① — Inch lbs.

Power Brake Units

NOTE: On Air Bag Equipped Models, Refer To "Air Bag System Precautions" Located In The Front Of This Manual For System Disarming & Arming Procedures.

INDEX

	Page No.
Description	2-181
Hydraulic Booster System	2-181
Vacuum Booster System	2-181
Diagnosis & Testing	2-181
Brake Booster Low-Pressure Test	2-181
Power Brake Unit Service	2-181
Hydraulic Power Flow Regulator, Replace	2-181
Power Brake Booster, Replace	2-182
Power Brake Unit Service	2-47
Precautions	2-181
Air Bag Systems	2-181
Battery Ground Cable	2-181
Tightening Specifications	2-183

PRECAUTIONS

AIR BAG SYSTEMS

Refer to "Air Bag System Precautions" in the front of this manual for system disarming and arming procedures.

BATTERY GROUND CABLE

Prior to service, disconnect battery ground cable and isolate as required.

DESCRIPTION

HYDRAULIC BOOSTER SYSTEM

The hydraulic system incorporates a power flow regulator which diverts a small flow of fluid from the power steering operating circuit for the power assisted brake system, **Fig. 1.** It charges the hydraulic reservoir in a high pressure range without impairing the function of power steering. The pressurized hydraulic oil volume is supplied to the booster for the sake of power assistance and is applied by operating the connected standard tandem master cylinder. Should the power steering pump fail, the hydraulic reservoir has sufficient reserve pressure to permit many full stop braking actions. After using up this pressure reserve, brake operation without power assistance is still possible, but greater force will be required on the brake pedal.

VACUUM BOOSTER SYSTEM

The vacuum assist diaphragm assembly multiplies the force exerted on the master cylinder piston in order to increase the hydraulic pressure delivered to the wheel brake hydraulic units while decreasing the effort necessary to obtain acceptable stopping performance.

Vacuum assist units get their energy by opposing engine vacuum to atmospheric pressure. A piston, cylinder and flexible diaphragm utilize this energy to provide brake assistance. The diaphragm is balanced with engine vacuum until the brake pedal is depressed, allowing atmospheric pressure to unbalance the unit and apply force to the brake system.

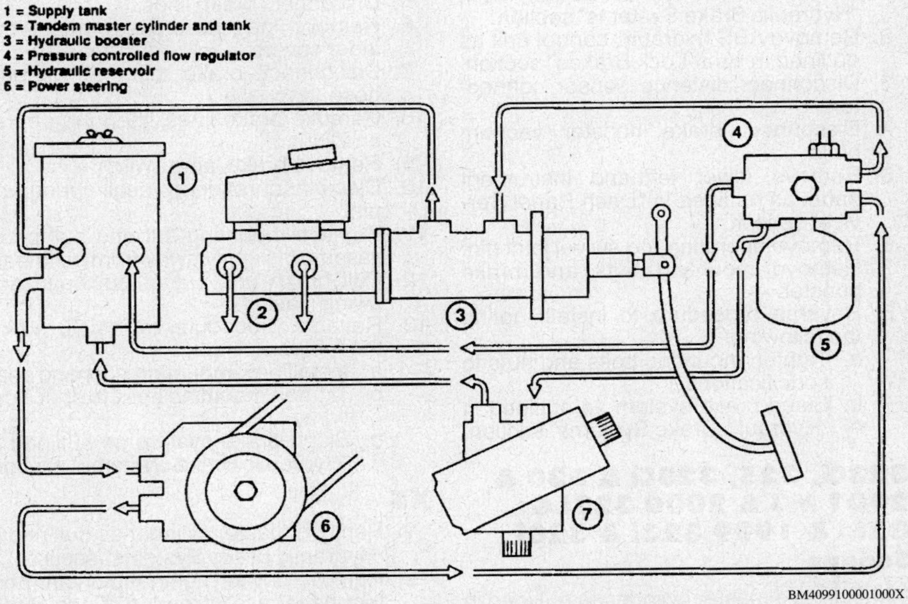

Fig. 1 Hydraulic system components

Brake will continue to operate even if the power unit fails. This mean the conventional brake system and the power assist system are completely separate.

DIAGNOSIS & TESTING

BRAKE BOOSTER LOW-PRESSURE TEST

1. Disconnect brake booster vacuum hose.
2. Install vacuum test tool No. 34 3 100, or equivalent, between booster and check valve.
3. Start engine and build up partial vacuum.
4. Switch engine off.
5. Press brake pedal to set partial vacuum of no more than 12 psi.
6. When brake pedal is not pressed, partial vacuum is allowed to drop no more than 0.87 psi during one minute.
7. If partial vacuum is not within specifications, proceed as follows:
   a. Inspect line connections for vacuum seal.
   b. Replace vacuum non-return valve.
   c. Inspect seal between brake booster and master cylinder.
   d. If partial vacuum is not within specifications during repeat test, replace brake booster.

POWER BRAKE UNIT SERVICE

HYDRAULIC POWER FLOW REGULATOR, REPLACE

1. With engine off, discharge hydraulic reservoir by operating brake pedal approximately 20 times with same force required for full stop braking action.
2. Disconnect circulating pressure warning and hydraulic pressure switches electrical connectors.
3. Disconnect power flow regulator hydraulic lines.

4. Remove mounting bolts and power flow regulator.
5. Reverse procedure to install, noting the following:
   a. Ensure all connections and pipes are free from dirt.
   b. Tighten mounting nuts and bolts to specifications.

POWER BRAKE BOOSTER, REPLACE

M3, Z3, 318, 325, 328 & 330

Z3, 318, 323is & 328is & 1998-99 M3, 328i & 1998 323i & 1999 323i & 328i Convertibles

1. Remove master cylinder as outlined in "Hydraulic Brake Systems" section.
2. Remove ABS hydraulic control unit as outlined in "Anti-Lock Brakes" section.
3. Disconnect distance sensor connector.
4. Disconnect brake booster vacuum hose.
5. Remove lower lefthand instrument panel as outlined in "Dash Panel Service" section.
6. Remove operating rod swivel joint pin.
7. Remove mounting buts and brake booster.
8. Reverse procedure to install, noting the following:
   a. Tighten mounting bolts and nuts to specifications.
   b. Bleed brake system as outlined in "Hydraulic Brake Systems" section.

323Ci, 325, 328Ci & 330 & 2001 M3 & 2000 323i & 328i & 1999 323i & 328i Sedans

1. Remove master cylinder as outlined in "Hydraulic Brake Systems" section.
2. Remove ABS hydraulic control unit as outlined in "Anti-Lock Brakes" section.
3. **On models equipped with Dynamic Stability Control (DSC),** remove pre-booster pump.
4. **On all models,** remove pedal assembly panel.
5. Remove locking clamp.
6. Remove mounting nuts.
7. Disconnect brake pedal actuating pin from brake booster pressure rod.
8. Remove brake booster by tilting toward engine, then lift upward.
9. Reverse procedure to install, noting the following:
   a. Tighten mounting bolts and nuts to specifications.
   b. Bleed brake system as outlined in "Hydraulic Brake Systems" section.

M5, 525, 528, 530 & 540

1. Remove mircofilter and air duct.
2. Remove brake fluid from master cylinder using suitable syringe.
3. Remove clutch master cylinder supply hose.
4. Disconnect reservoir from master cylinder by tilting to side.
5. Disconnect brake lines.
6. Remove line aperture and master cylinder covers.
7. Disconnect brake booster vacuum hose.
8. Remove brake lines, then plug bores and lines.
9. Remove brake lamp switch.
10. Disconnect retainer, recoil spring and pin.
11. Remove mounting nut and pull pedal assembly slightly away from bulkhead.
12. Pull brake unit out of bulkhead and swing it aside.
13. Reverse procedure to install, noting the following:
    a. Install new mounting nuts and seal.
    b. Tighten mounting bolts to specifications.
    c. Bleed brake system as outlined in "Hydraulic Brake Systems" section.

X5

1. Remove master cylinder as outlined in "Hydraulic Brake Systems" section.
2. Remove lower righthand instrument trim panel as outlined in "Dash Panel Service" section.
3. **On models equipped with manual transmission,** proceed as follows:
   a. Remove reinforcement plate and switch unit.
   b. Remove clutch switch
   c. Remove retainer and disconnect rod pin.
   d. Remove mounting bolts and set clutch master cylinder in footwell with lines connected.
4. **On all models,** disconnect lug and retainer, then remove rod pin.
5. Disconnect brake lamp switch connector.
6. Remove mounting bolts and bearing pedestal
7. Remove emergency siren with holder.
8. Disconnect arms from wiper motor.
9. Swivel linkage aside, then disconnect cover/cowl and foul up.
10. Remove brake booster by swivelling toward engine, then upward.
11. Reverse procedure to install, noting the following:
    a. Install new mounting nuts and seal.
    b. Tighten mounting bolts to specifications.
    c. Bleed brake system as outlined in "Hydraulic Brake Systems" section.

740 & 750

1. Remove master cylinder as outlined in "Hydraulic Brake Systems" section.
2. Remove lefthand windshield wiper arm.
3. Move and lock hood into assembly position.
4. Disconnect rubber seal and cover from left to middle of windshield by disconnecting clamps then pulling it up.
5. Remove mounting screws and cover.
6. Remove cover behind brake booster and line feed through.
7. Disconnect brake booster vacuum line.
8. Remove brake lamp switch.
9. Disconnect retainer and recoil spring.
10. Withdraw rod pin.
11. Loose mounting nuts and bolts, then pull pedal assembly slightly away from bulkhead.
12. Pull brake unit out of bulkhead and swing it aside.
13. Reverse procedure to install, noting the following:
    a. Install new mounting nuts and seal.
    b. Tighten mounting bolts to specifications.
    c. Bleed brake system as outlined in "Hydraulic Brake Systems" section.

TIGHTENING SPECIFICATIONS

Year	Component	Torque, Ft. Lbs.
1998–2001	Adapter To Power Flow Regulator	12
	Brake Booster To Pedal Assembly	16
	Hydraulic Line Coupling To Brake Booster	23
	Hydraulic Line To Brake Booster On Power Flow Regulator	23
	Hydraulic Line To Pressure Reservoir	29
	Hydraulic Line To Pressure Reservoir On Power Flow Regulator	35
	Hydraulic Line To Steering Gear On Power Flow Regulator	37
	Hydraulic Line To Power Steering Pump On Power Flow Regulator	29
	Hydraulic Warning Switch To Power Flow Regulator	13
	Orifice Valve To Brake Booster	26
	Reservoir To Power Flow Regulator	37
	Return Line To Oil Tank On Power Flow Regulator	12

Anti-Lock Brakes

NOTE: On Air Bag Equipped Models, Refer To "Air Bag System Precautions" Located In The Front Of This Manual For System Disarming & Arming Procedures.

NOTE: Prior To Performing Any Service Operations Listed In This Section, Consult The "Technical Service Bulletins" Section For Related Information.

INDEX

	Page No.
Description	2-184
ABS Less Stability & Traction Control	2-184
ABS w/Stability & Traction Control	2-184
Diagnosis & Testing	2-184
Accessing Diagnostic Trouble Codes	2-184
Clearing Diagnostic Trouble Codes	2-185
Connector Terminal Identification	2-185
Diagnostic Trouble Code Interpretation	2-185
Wiring Diagrams	2-185
Precautions	2-184
Air Bag Systems	2-184
Battery Ground Cable	2-184
System Service	2-185
Brake System Bleed	2-185
Component Replacement	2-185
Control Unit	2-185
Front Speed Sensor	2-186
Hydraulic Unit	2-185
Rear Speed Sensor	2-186
Technical Service Bulletins	2-186
ABS/ASC Warning Lamp On	2-186
ASC Lamp On	2-186
Troubleshooting	2-184

PRECAUTIONS

AIR BAG SYSTEMS

Refer to "Air Bag System Precautions" in the front of this manual for system disarming and arming procedures.

BATTERY GROUND CABLE

Prior to service, disconnect battery ground cable and isolate as required.

DESCRIPTION

ABS LESS STABILITY & TRACTION CONTROL

The Anti-Lock Brake System (ABS) consists of a control unit, hydraulic unit, speed sensors and wiring harness, **Fig. 1.** Each speed sensor has a gear wheel which runs past the permanently magnetized edge of the speed sensor installed in the wheel hub. The rotary motion of the wheels is recorded by inductive sensors and an electric signal is sent to the electronic control unit.

The electronic control unit is located in a compartment on the right side of the engine compartment. This control unit inputs acceleration, deceleration and slip factors from the electronic speed sensors, which are proportional to wheel velocity. The unit then issues control commands to the electronically operated valves in the hydraulic unit. If the control unit detects a defect in the wiring harness or system electronics, the monitoring circuit will switch off the ABS, which ensures normal use of the brake system during an ABS malfunction. The ABS indicator lamp will then go On to notify the driver of a system malfunction.

The hydraulic unit, located in the engine compartment, is integrated with the rest of the conventional brake system. The unit has three-way valves which control hydraulic pressure to the wheel cylinders. Three pressure phases, pressure holding, pressure build-up and pressure drop adapt themselves to road conditions based on information from the control unit.

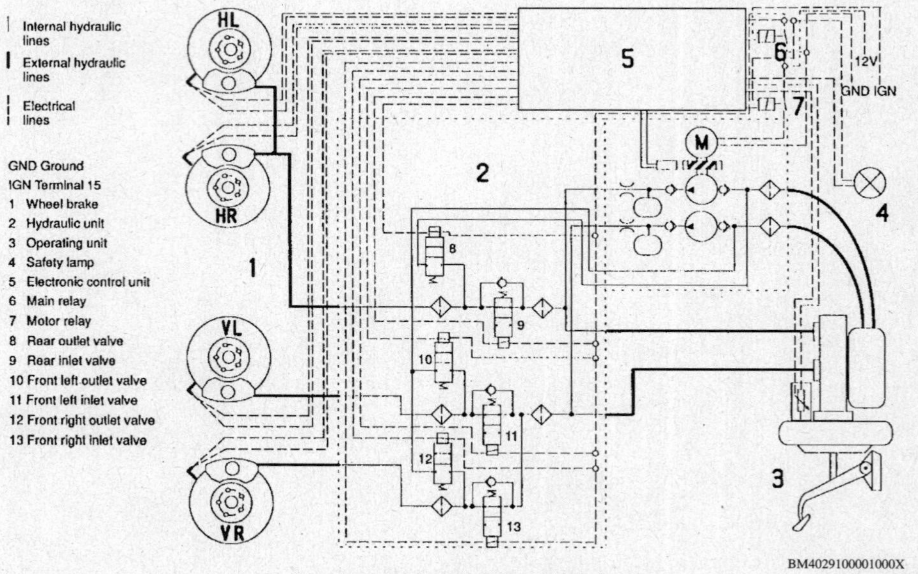

Fig. 1 Anti-lock brake system

The electronically driven return delivery pump returns brake fluid from the wheel cylinders while dropping pressure to the appropriate brake circuit. The pump is designed as a two-piston pump so the circuits of the dual brake circuit remain separated.

ABS w/STABILITY & TRACTION CONTROL

ABS and ABS 5 systems combined with Automatic Stability Control (ASC), (ASC/T) and Dynamic Stability Control (DSC) use ABS components combined with additional systems to offer stability and traction control.

TROUBLESHOOTING

Refer to "Diagnosis & Testing."

DIAGNOSIS & TESTING

Accessing Diagnostic Trouble Codes

Diagnosis is only available using the BMW Diagnostic System. Refer to BMW testing system manufacturer's instructions to diagnosis ABS malfunctions.

Diagnostic Trouble Code Interpretation

Refer to **Fig. 2** for Diagnostic Trouble Code (DTC) interpretation.

Wiring Diagrams

Refer to **Figs. 3 through 13** for wiring diagrams

Connector Terminal Identification

Refer to **Figs. 14 through 18** for connector terminal identification.

Clearing Diagnostic Trouble Codes

Refer to BMW service tester owners manual for instructions on clearing codes.

SYSTEM SERVICE

Brake System Bleed

Refer to "Hydraulic Brake Systems," for procedures.

Component Replacement

HYDRAULIC UNIT

M3, Z3, 318, 323, 325, 328 & 330

Z3, 318, 323is & 328is & 1998-99 M3, 328i & 1998 323i & 1999 323i & 328i Convertibles

1. Ensure ignition switch is in Off position.
2. Remove Mass Air Flow (MAF) sensor from air filter housing.
3. Disconnect cruise control drive motor as required.
4. Remove brake fluid from master cylinder using suitable syringe.
5. Disconnect central connector.
6. Mark brake lines for installation alignment.
7. Disconnect brake lines at master cylinder and hydraulic control unit.
8. Disconnect suction hose from pump body elbow. **Catch escaping brake fluid in suitable container.**
9. Remove mounting nut and hydraulic unit
10. Reverse procedure to install. Bleed brake system as outlined in "Hydraulic Brake Systems" section.

Number	Defect description
17	Front left inlet valve faulty
18	Front left outlet valve faulty
20	Front right inlet valve faulty
24	Front right outlet valve faulty
33	Rear axle inlet valve faulty
34	Rear axle outlet valve faulty
68	Microprocessor in control unit faulty or defective
72	Internal defect in control unit
81	Front left speed sensor not connected or faulty
82	Front right speed sensor not connected or faulty
84	Rear left speed sensor not connected or faulty
88	Rear right speed sensor not connected or faulty
97	Front left speed signal not plausible
98	Front right speed signal not plausible
100	Rear left speed signal not plausible
104	Rear right speed signal not plausible
113	Front left speed information not detected
114	Front right speed information not detected
116	Rear left speed information not detected
120	Rear right speed information not detected
132	Speed position sensor signal faulty or not connected
136	Serious defect in brake hydraulic system
145	Pump not operating
152	Warning brake hydraulic/pedal position sensor defective
161	Front left outlet valve malfunction
162	Front right outlet valve malfunction
164	Rear axle outlet valve malfunction
255	Access to memory in control unit defective

BM4029100004000X

Fig. 2 DTC interpretation

323Ci, 325, 328Ci & 330 & 2001 M3 & 2000 323i & 328i & 1999 323i & 328i Sedans

1. Remove end firewall and seal.
2. Disconnect vacuum lines and electrical connector.
3. Remove master cylinder as outlined in "Hydraulic Brake Systems" section.
4. Mark brake lines for installation alignment.
5. Disconnect brake lines.
6. Disconnect connector.
7. remove brake lines with rubber grommet from body and press toward engine. **Do not bend brake lines.**
8. Remove mounting bolts and hydraulic unit.
9. Reverse procedure to install. Bleed brake system as outlined in "Hydraulic Brake Systems" section.

M5, 525, 528, 530, 540, 740 & 750

1. Remove brake fluid from master cylinder using suitable syringe.
2. Disconnect connector.
3. Mark brake lines for installation reference.
4. **On 1999–2001 models,** disconnect pressure sensor connector.
5. **On all models,** remove mounting screws and hydraulic unit.
6. Reverse procedure to install. Bleed brake system as outlined in "Hydraulic Brake Systems" section.

X5

1. Load and lock brake pedal with suitable support.
2. **On 4.4i models,** remove equipment carrier.
3. **On 3.0i models,** remove intake air filter housing.
4. **On all models,** disconnect auxiliary water pump and connector, then position pump aside, as required.
5. Mark brake lines for installation reference.
6. Disconnect brake lines.
7. Disconnect pressure sensor connector.
8. Remove mounting bolts and hydraulic unit.
9. Reverse procedure to install. Bleed brake system as outlined in "Hydraulic Brake Systems" section.

CONTROL UNIT

M3, Z3, 318, 323, 325, 328 & 330

Z3, 318, 323is & 328is & 1998-99 M3, 328i & 1998 323i & 1999 323i & 328i Convertibles

1. Disconnect connector.
2. Remove mounting bolts and control unit with bracket.
3. Remove mounting bolts and control unit.
4. Remove cap covering control unit.
5. Reverse procedure to install.

323Ci, 325, 328Ci & 330 & 2001 M3 & 2000 323i & 328i & 1999 323i & 328i Sedans

1. Disconnect lock and connector.
2. Remove mounting screws and control unit.
3. Reverse procedure to install.

M5, 525, 528, 530, 540, 740 & 750

1998

1. Ensure ignition switch is in off position.
2. Remove lower glove compartment trim.
3. Remove mounting bolts and control unit.
4. Reverse procedure to install.

1999-2001

1. Disconnect connector.
2. Remove mounting bolts and control module.
3. Reverse procedure to install.

X5

1. **On 4.4i models,** remove lefthand headlamp and equipment carrier.
2. **On all models,** disconnect auxiliary water pump and connector, then position pump aside, as required.
3. Disconnect connector.
4. Remove mounting bolts and hydraulic unit.
5. Reverse procedure to install.

FRONT SPEED SENSOR

1. Raise and support vehicle, then remove tire and wheel assembly.
2. Open ABS sensor protective box.
3. Disconnect connector.
4. Remove mounting bolt and sensor.
5. Reverse procedure to install. Lubricate replacement sensor with Staborax NBU 12/k, or equivalent.

REAR SPEED SENSOR

1. Raise and support vehicle, then remove tire and wheel assembly.
2. Remove wheelhousing panels as required.
3. Open ABS sensor protective box as required.
4. Disconnect connector.
5. Remove mounting bolt and sensor.
6. Reverse procedure to install. Lubricate replacement sensor with Staborax NBU 12/k, or equivalent.

TECHNICAL SERVICE BULLETINS

ASC LAMP ON

Z3, 323is & 328is & 1998-99 328i & 1998 323i & 1999 323i & 328i Convertibles

On some of these models the ASC lamp may be illuminated with Diagnostic Trouble Code (DTC) 50 stored.

This condition may be caused by intermittent high resistance at plug connectors.

To correct this condition, proceed as follows:

1. Disconnect Throttle Position Sensor (TPS) and ASC control module connectors.
2. Clean connectors with suitable zero residue electrical contact cleaner.

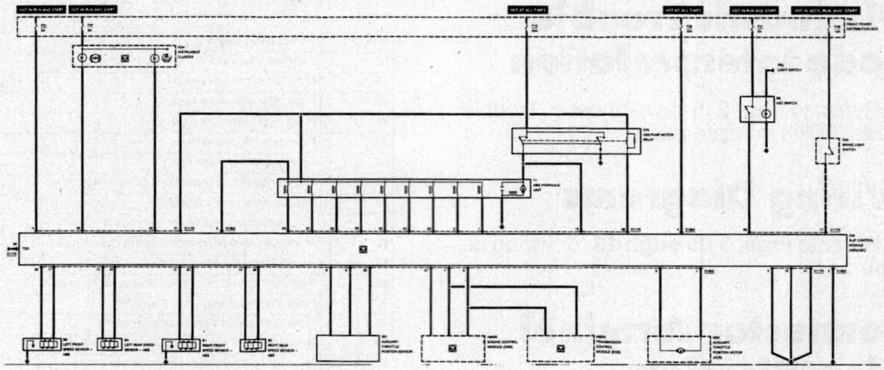

BM4020100037010X

Fig. 3 Wiring diagram (Part 1 of 5). Z3 1.9

3. Apply Stabilant 22A Electrical Contact Enhancer, or equivalent, to connectors.
4. Connect connectors.

528, 540, 740 & 750

On some of these models the ASC lamp may be on with no Diagnostic Trouble Code (DTC) set. The lamp goes off when the underhood diagnostic connector cap is removed.

This condition may be caused by incorrect diagnostic connector cap.

To correct this condition install proper diagnostic connector cap (part No. 12 52 1 703 202).

ABS/ASC WARNING LAMP ON

528, 540, 740 & 750

On some of these models built between September 1998 and March 1999 may have the ABS/ASC warning lamp on with Diagnostic Trouble Codes (DTCs) 67 or 112.

This condition may be caused by microscopic cracks in the ABS sensors.

To correct this condition install revised ABS sensors as follows:

1. **On 740 and 750 models,** as follows:
   a. Front (part No. 34 52 1 165 532.
   b. Rear (part No. 34 52 1 165 533.
2. **On 528 and 540 sedan models,** as follows:
   a. Front (part No. 34 52 1 165 534.
   b. Rear (part No. 34 52 1 165 535.
3. **On 528 and 540 sports wagon models,** as follows:
   a. Front (part No. 34 52 1 165 534.
   b. Rear (part No. 34 52 1 165 536.

323i & 328i

On some of these models built before September 1998 the ABS and/or ASC warning lamp may be on with Diagnostic Trouble Codes (DTCs) 31 or 41 set.

This condition may be caused by faulty rear wheel speed sensor.

To correct this condition install revised rear wheel speed sensors (part No. 34 52 1 164 652) with production date No. 2208 or later.

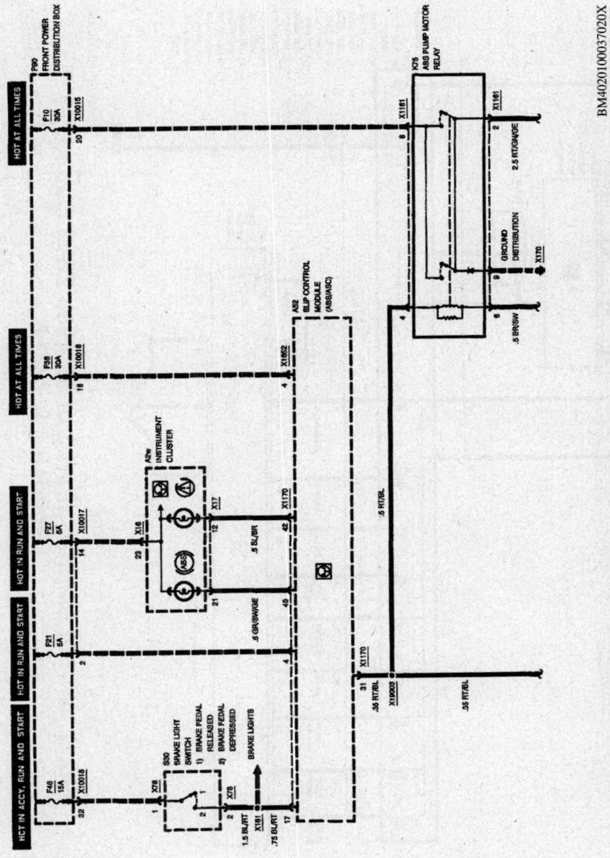

BM40201000370 20X

Fig. 3 Wiring diagram (Part 2 of 5). Z3 1.9

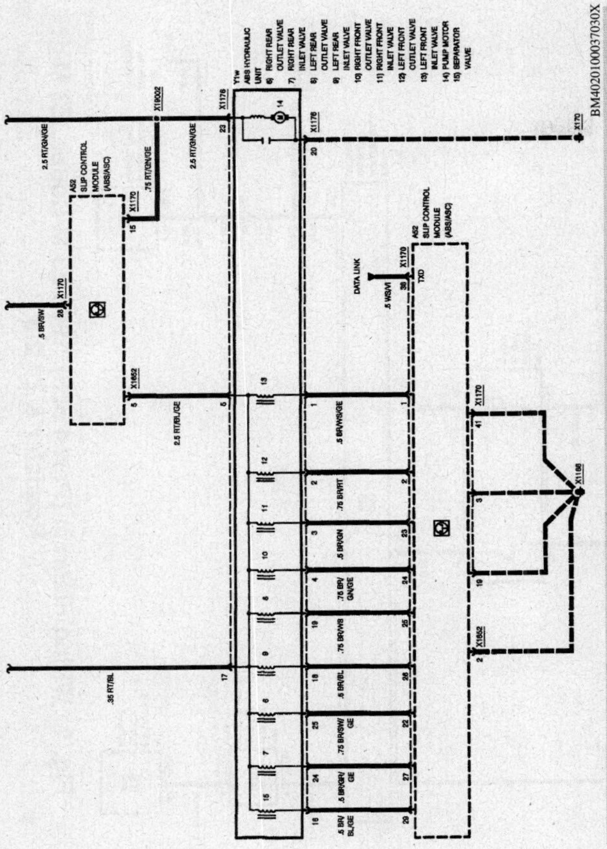

BM40201000370 30X

Fig. 3 Wiring diagram (Part 3 of 5). Z3 1.9

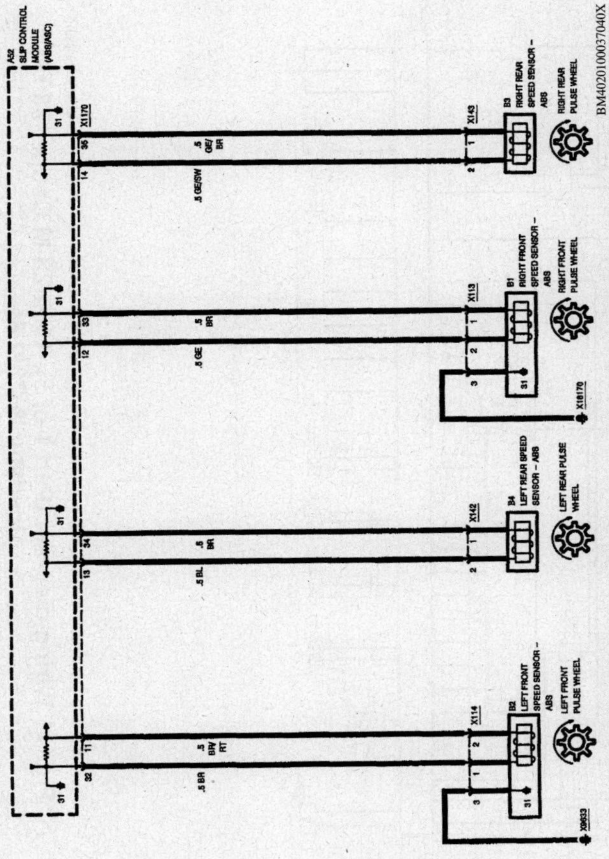

BM40201000370 40X

Fig. 3 Wiring diagram (Part 4 of 5). Z3 1.9

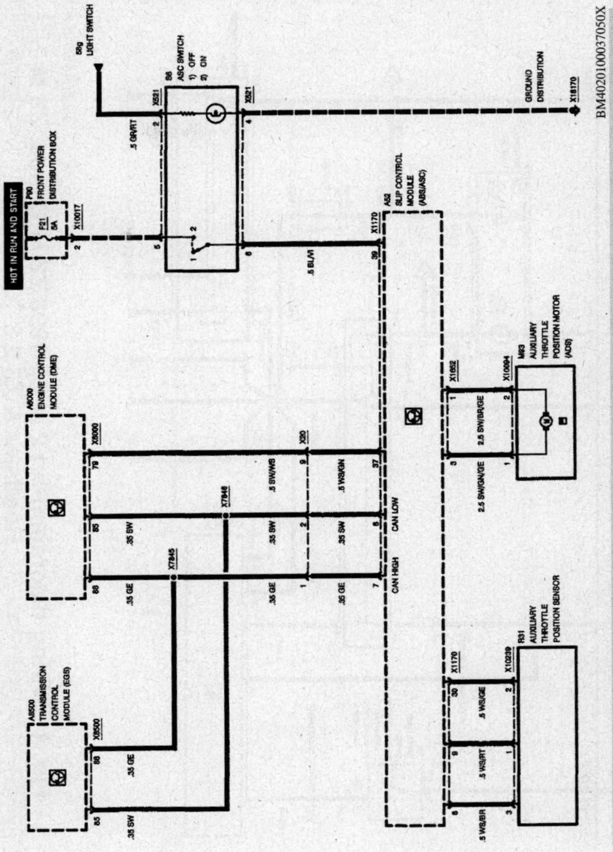

BM40201000370 50X

Fig. 3 Wiring diagram (Part 5 of 5). Z3 1.9

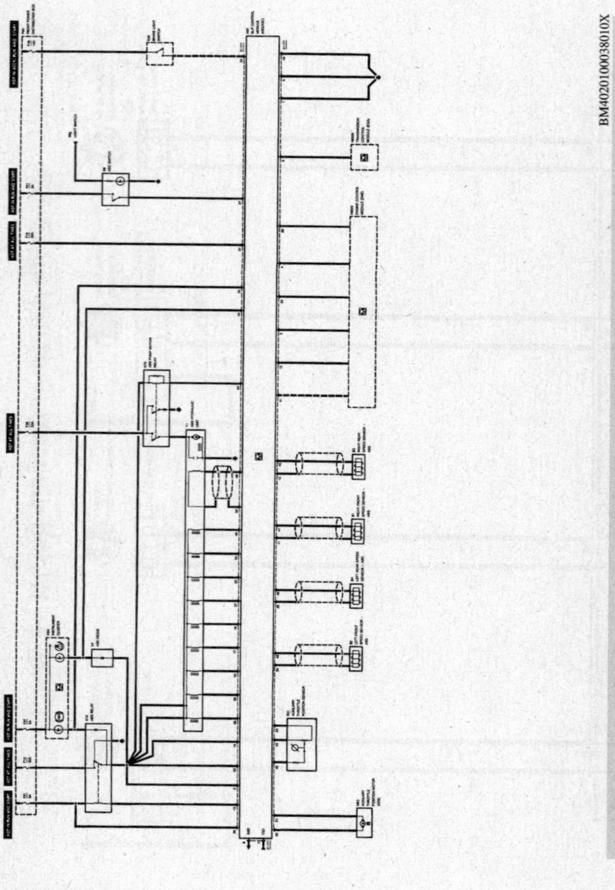

BM4020100038010X

Fig. 4 Wiring diagram (Part 1 of 5). 1998 Z3 M Coupe, Z3 M Roadster & Z3 2.8

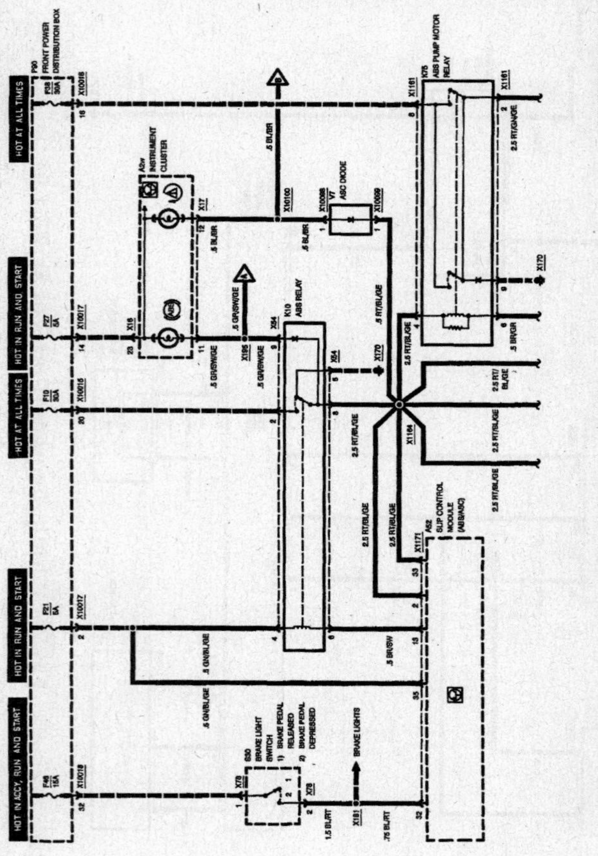

BM4020100038020X

Fig. 4 Wiring diagram (Part 2 of 5). 1998 Z3 M Coupe, Z3 M Roadster & Z3 2.8

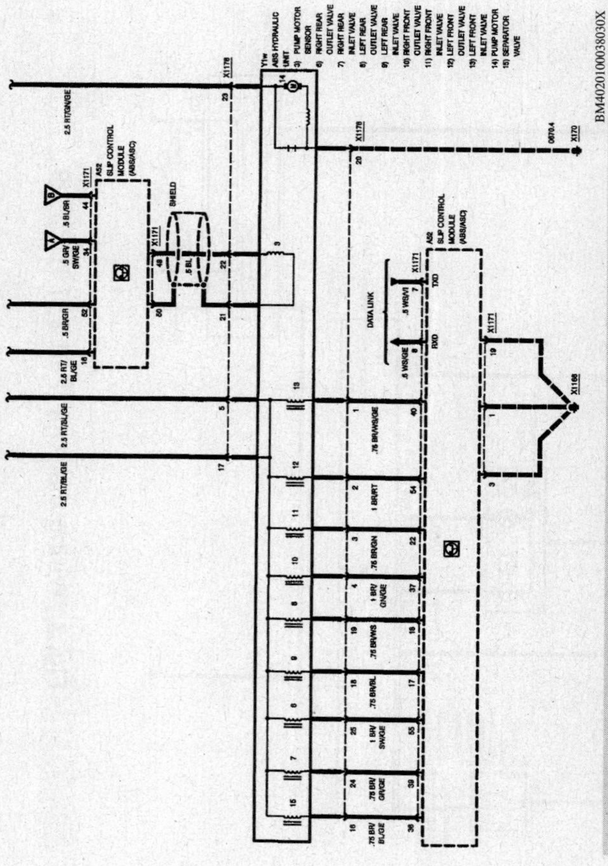

BM4020100038030X

Fig. 4 Wiring diagram (Part 3 of 5). 1998 Z3 M Coupe, Z3 M Roadster & Z3 2.8

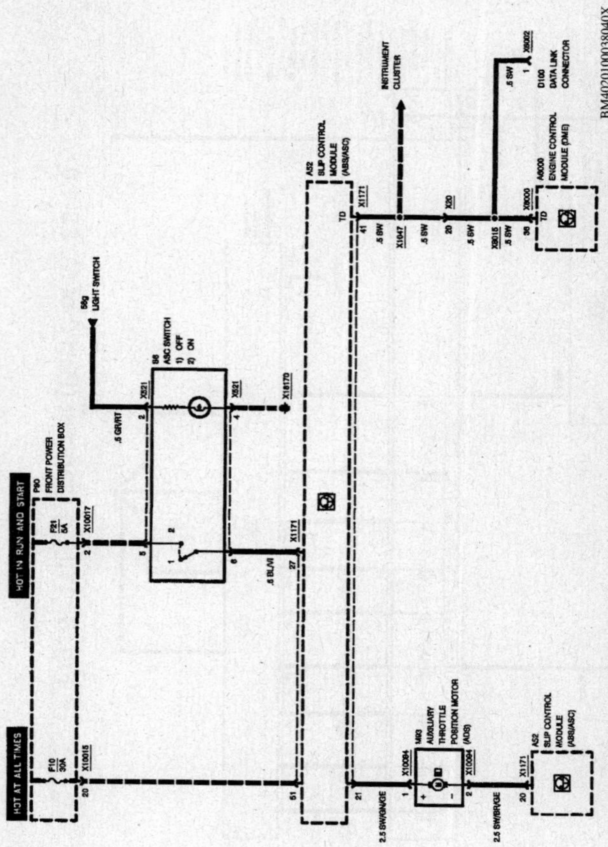

BM4020100038040X

Fig. 4 Wiring diagram (Part 4 of 5). 1998 Z3 M Coupe, Z3 M Roadster & Z3 2.8

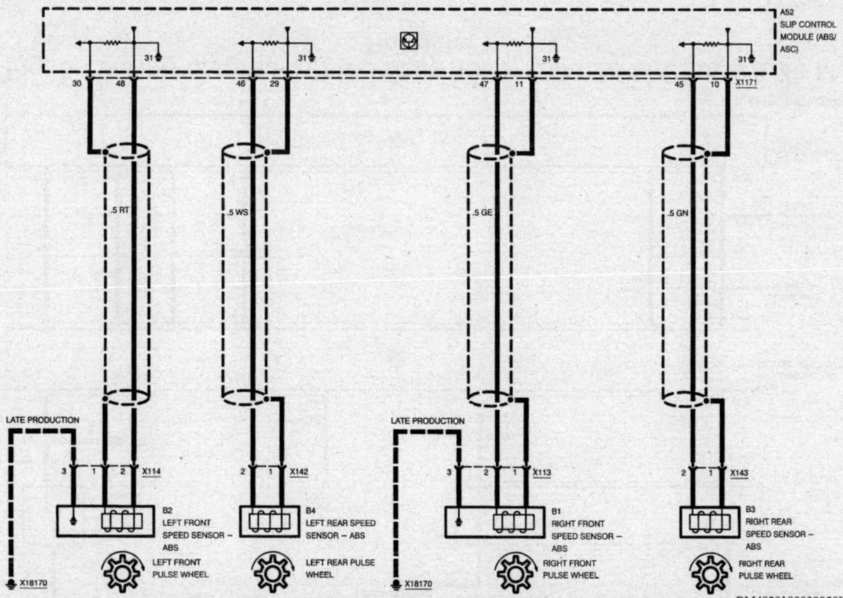

BM4020100038050X

Fig. 4 Wiring diagram (Part 5 of 5). 1998 Z3 M Coupe, Z3 M Roadster & Z3 2.8

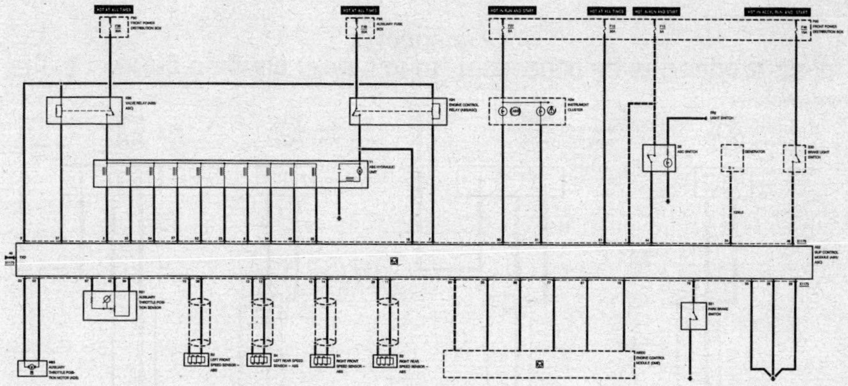

BM4020100040010X

Fig. 5 Wiring diagram (Part 1 of 6). 1999–2000 Z3 M Coupe & Z3 M Roadster

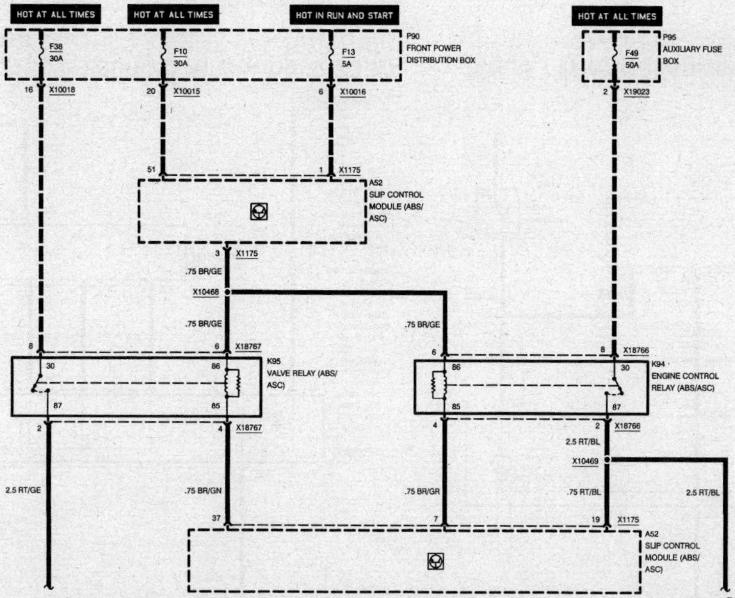

BM4020100040020X

Fig. 5 Wiring diagram (Part 2 of 6). 1999–2000 Z3 M Coupe & Z3 M Roadster

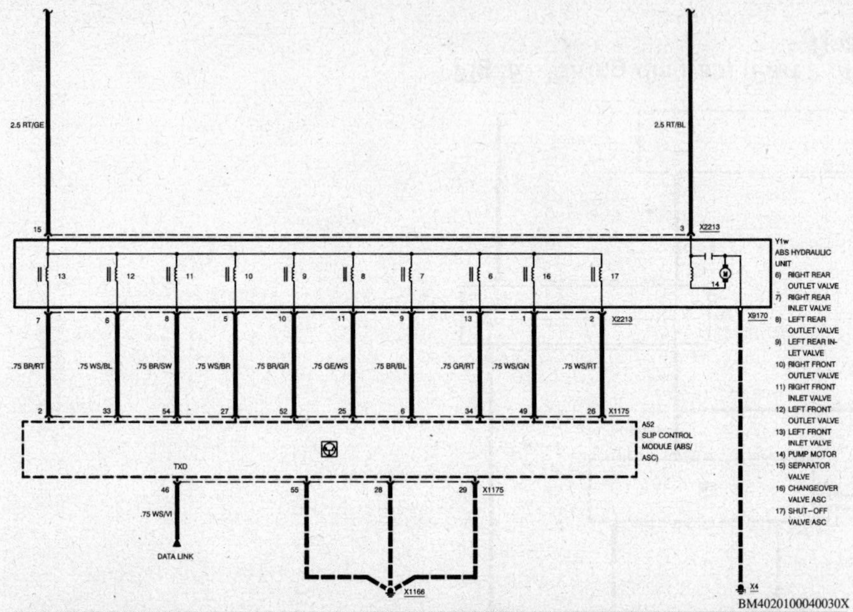

Fig. 5 Wiring diagram (Part 3 of 6). 1999–2000 Z3 M Coupe & Z3 M Roadster

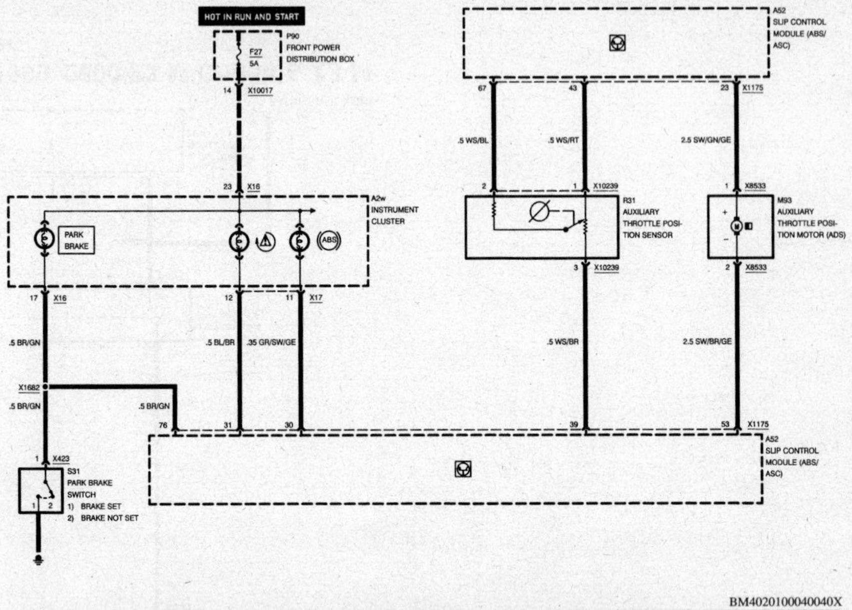

Fig. 5 Wiring diagram (Part 4 of 6). 1999–2000 Z3 M Coupe & Z3 M Roadster

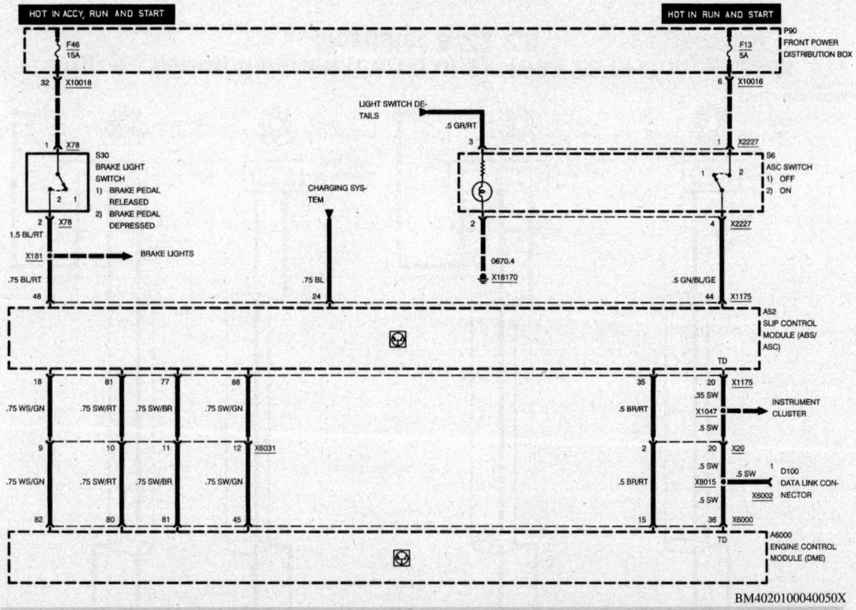

Fig. 5 Wiring diagram (Part 5 of 6). 1999–2000 Z3 M Coupe & Z3 M Roadster

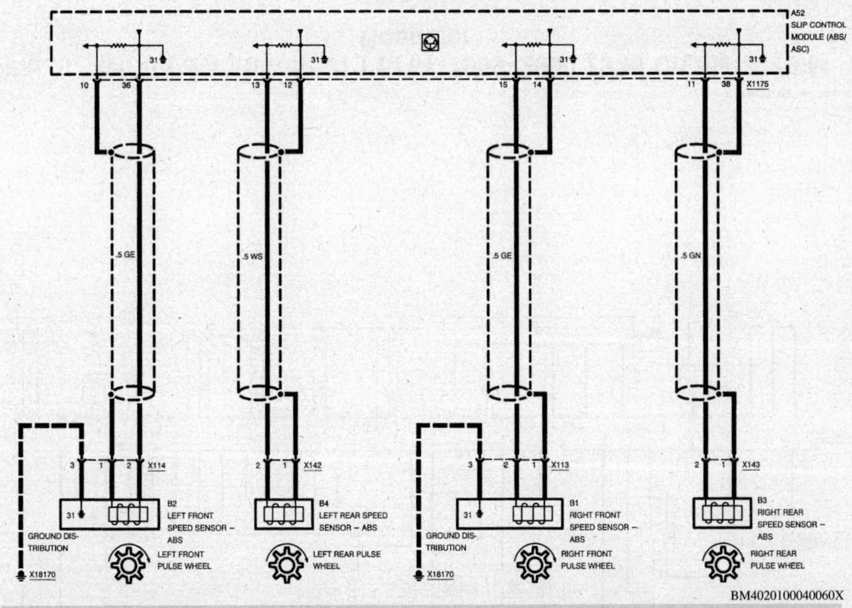

Fig. 5 Wiring diagram (Part 6 of 6). 1999–2000 Z3 M Coupe & Z3 M Roadster

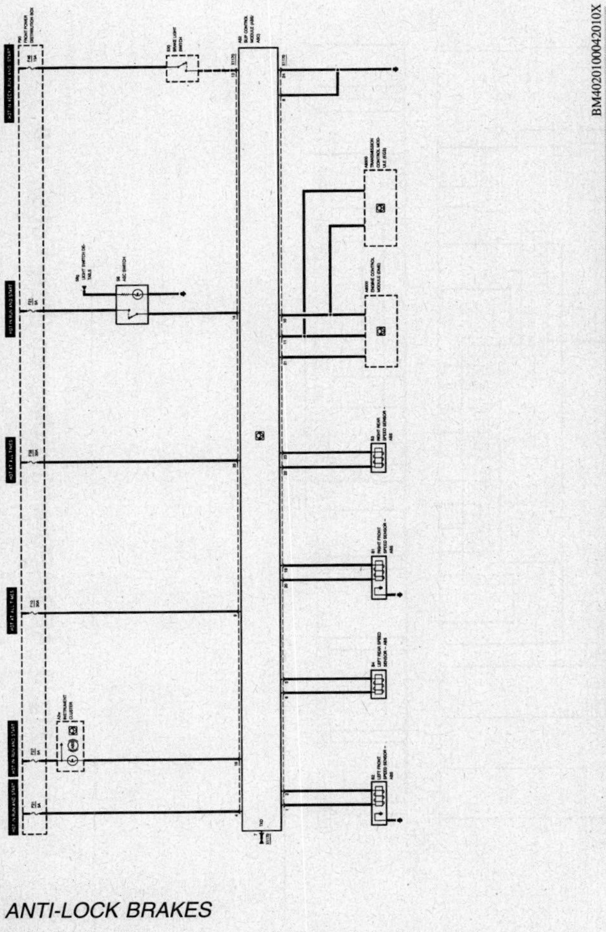

BM4020100042010X

Fig. 6 Wiring diagram (Part 1 of 4). Z3 2.3 & 1999–2000 Z3 2.8

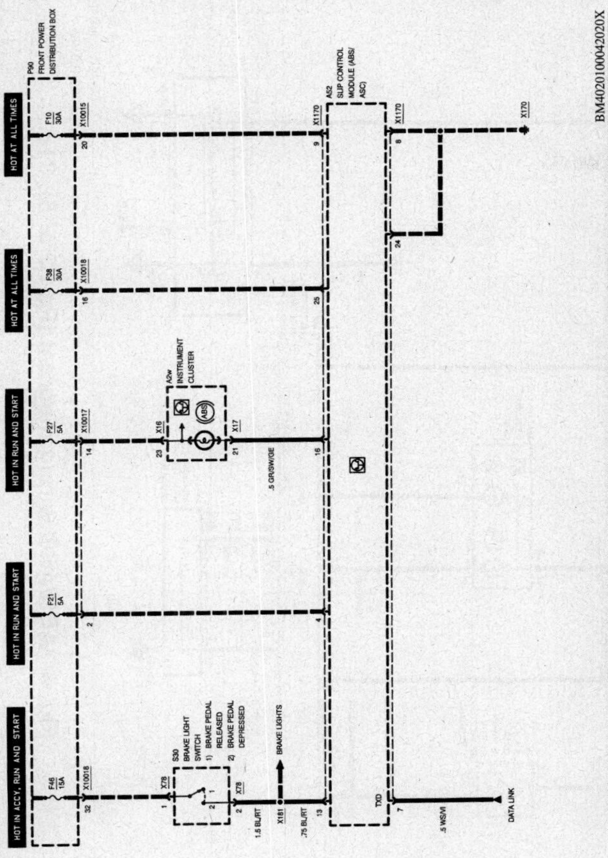

BM4020100042020X

Fig. 6 Wiring diagram (Part 2 of 4). Z3 2.3 & 1999–2000 Z3 2.8

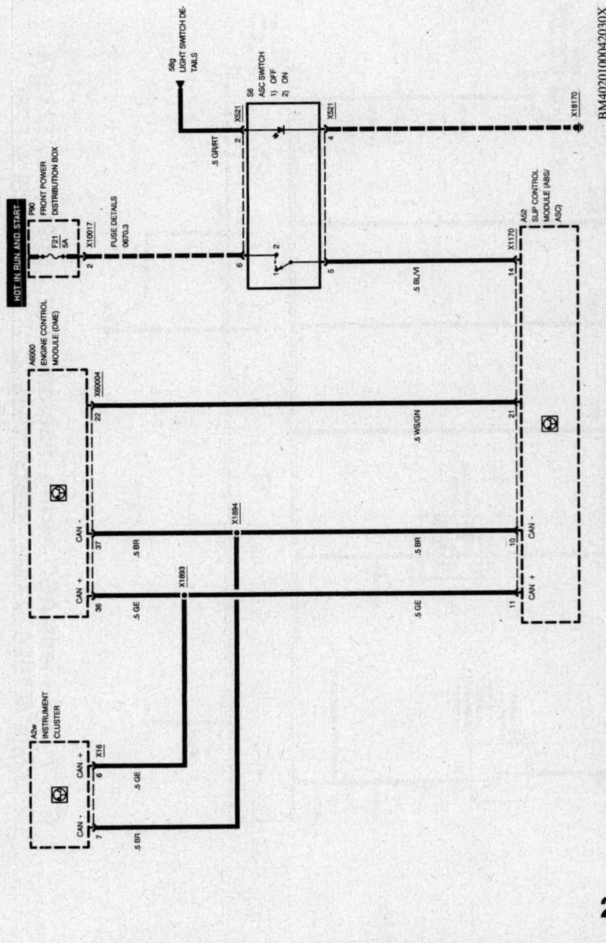

BM4020100042030X

Fig. 6 Wiring diagram (Part 3 of 4). Z3 2.3 & 1999–2000 Z3 2.8

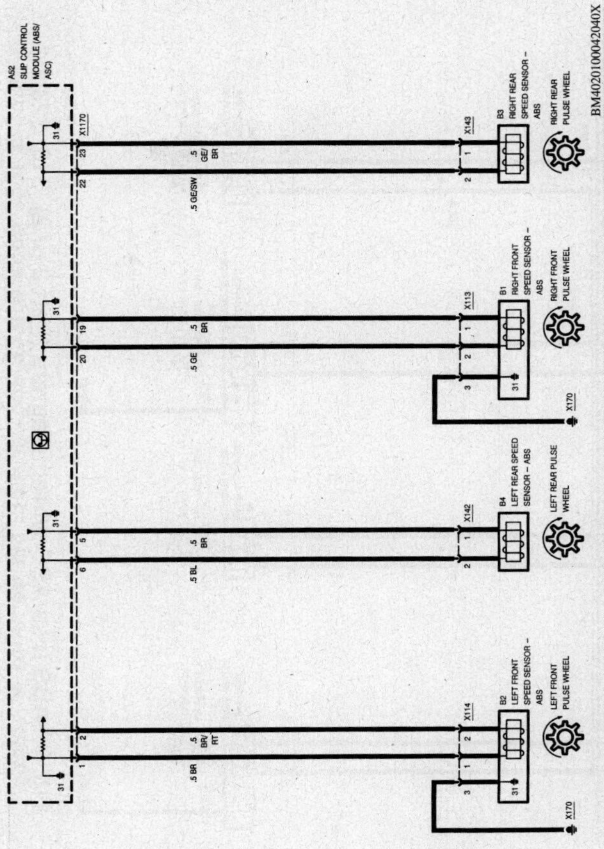

BM4020100042040X

Fig. 6 Wiring diagram (Part 4 of 4). Z3 2.3 & 1999–2000 Z3 2.8

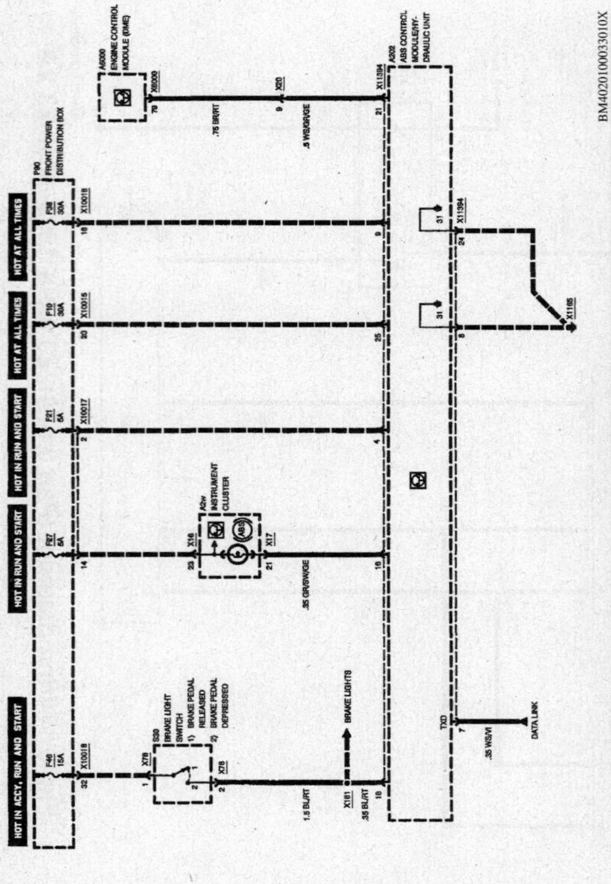

BM4020100033010X

Fig. 7 ABS less ASC wiring diagram (Part 1 of 2). 318, 323is & 328is & 1998–99 M3, 328i & 1998 323i & 1999 323i & 328i Convertibles

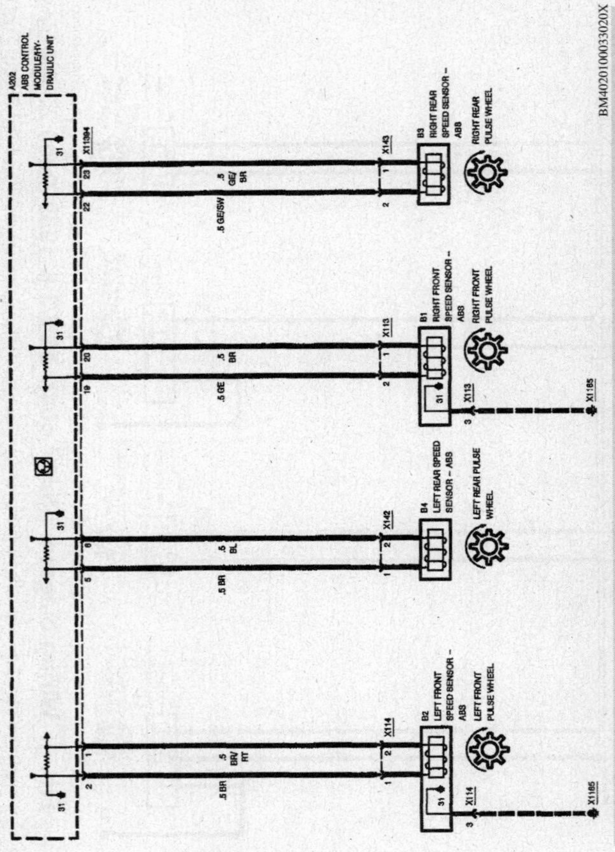

BM4020100033020X

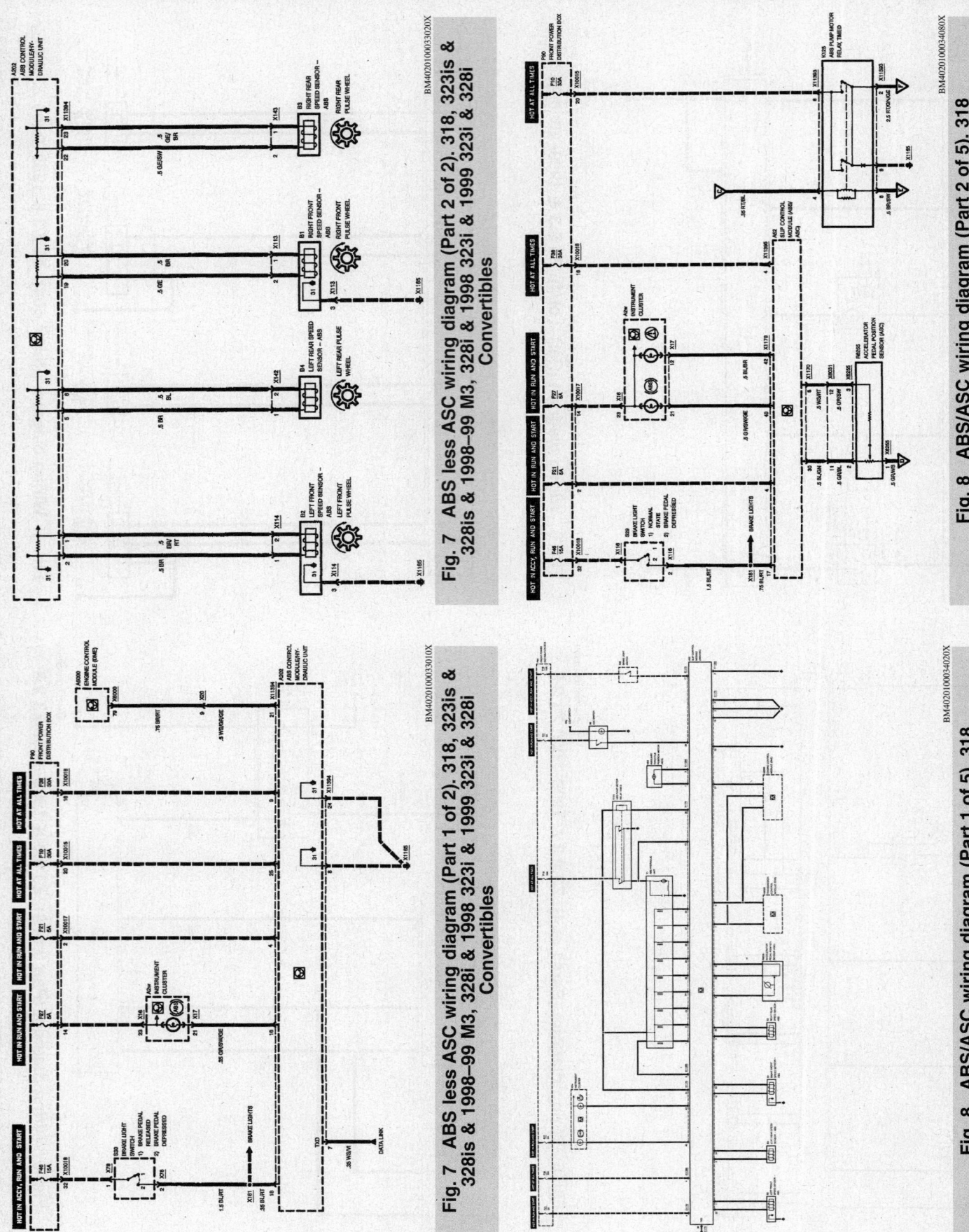

Fig. 7 ABS less ASC wiring diagram (Part 2 of 2). 318, 323is & 328is & 1998–99 M3, 328i & 1998 323i & 1999 323i & 328i Convertibles

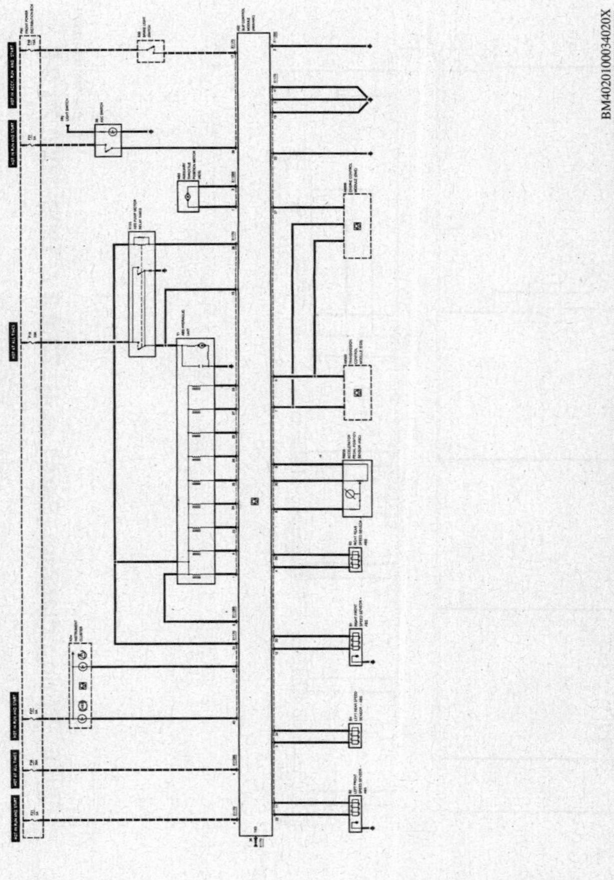

BM4020100034020X

Fig. 8 ABS/ASC wiring diagram (Part 1 of 5). 318

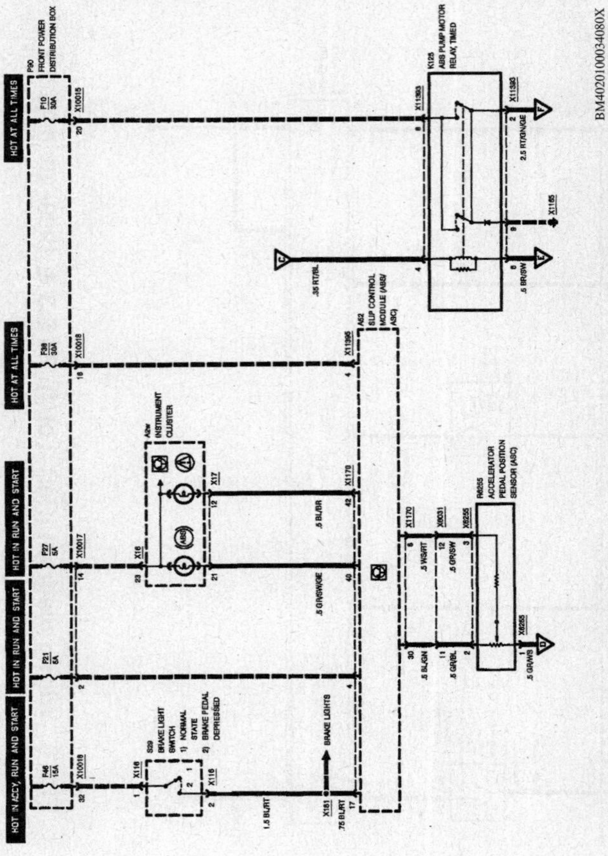

BM4020100034080X

Fig. 8 ABS/ASC wiring diagram (Part 2 of 5). 318

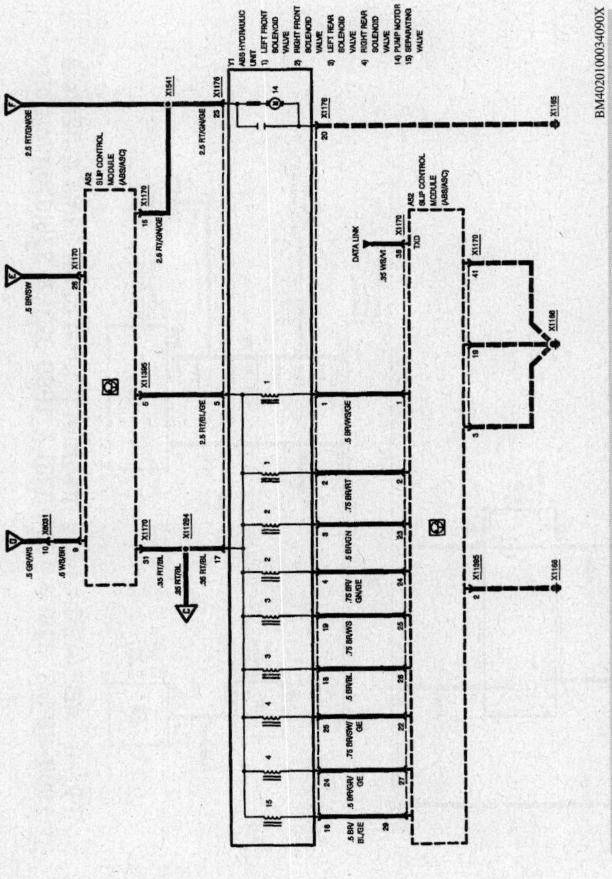

Fig. 8 ABS/ASC wiring diagram (Part 3 of 5). 318

BM402010003409 0X

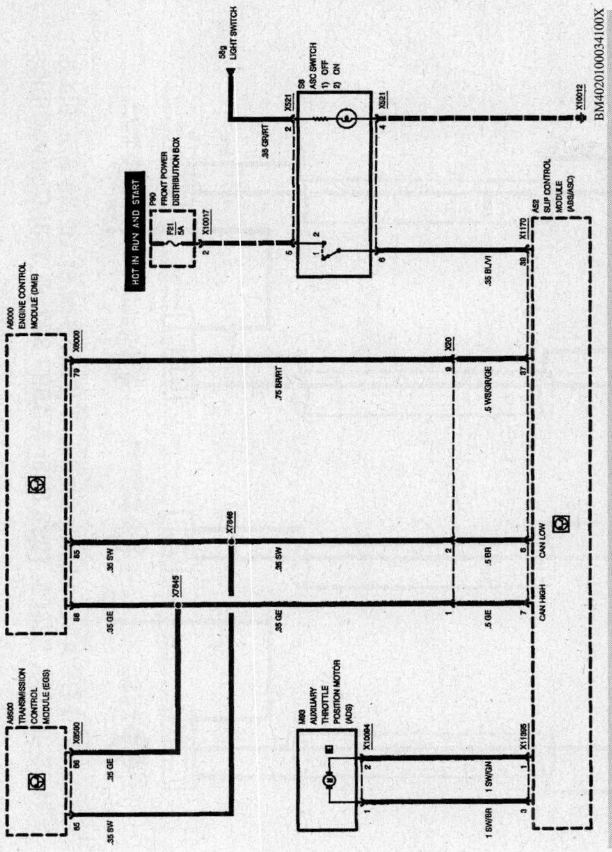

Fig. 8 ABS/ASC wiring diagram (Part 4 of 5). 318

BM402010003410 0X

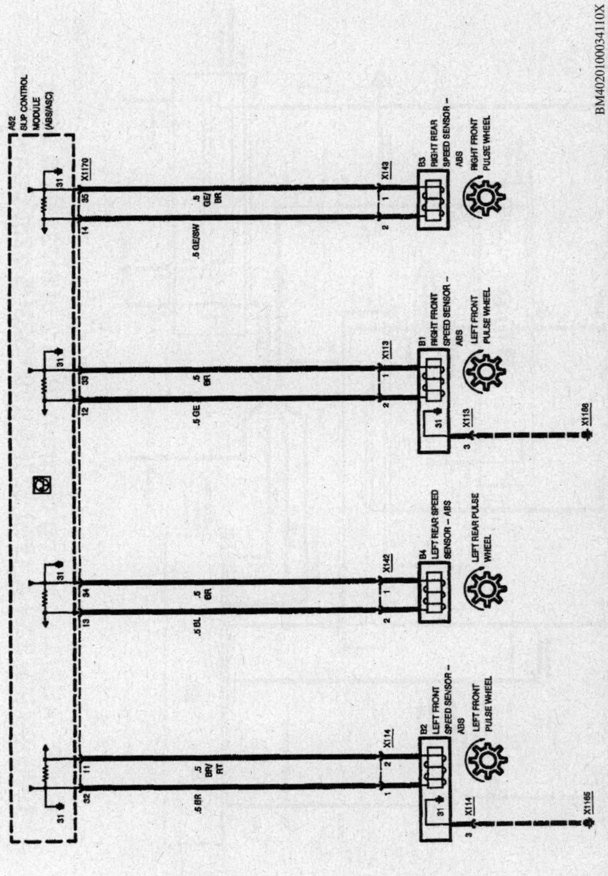

Fig. 8 ABS/ASC wiring diagram (Part 5 of 5). 318

BM402010003411 0X

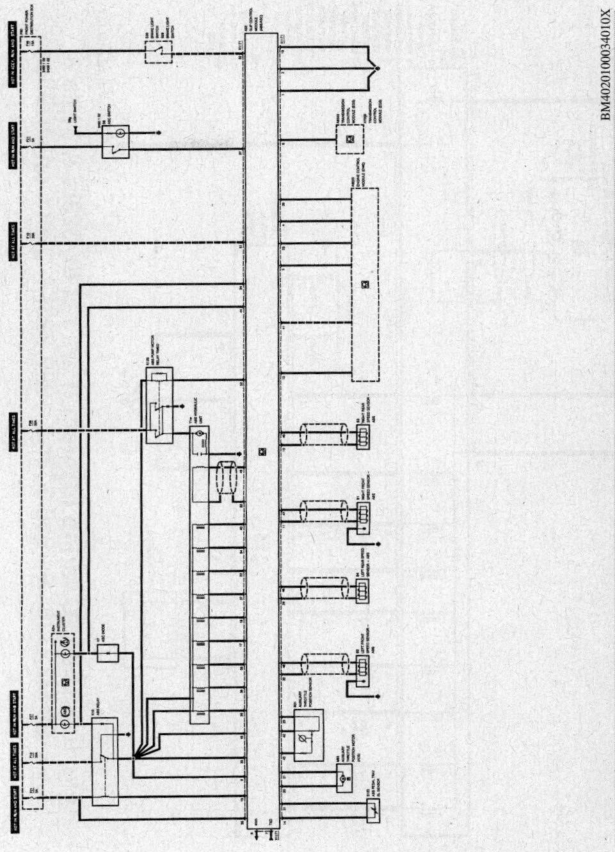

Fig. 9 ABS/ASC wiring diagram (Part 1 of 6). 323is & 328is & 1998–99 M3, 328i & 1998 323i & 1999 323i & 328i Convertibles

BM402010003401 0X

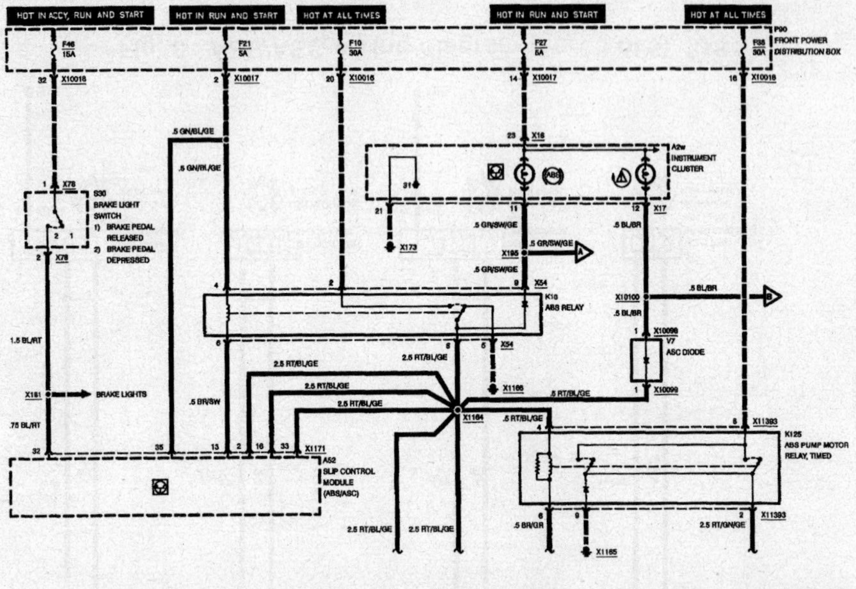

BM4020100034030X

Fig. 9 ABS/ASC wiring diagram (Part 2 of 6). 323is & 328is & 1998–99 M3, 328i & 1998 323i & 1999 323i & 328i Convertibles

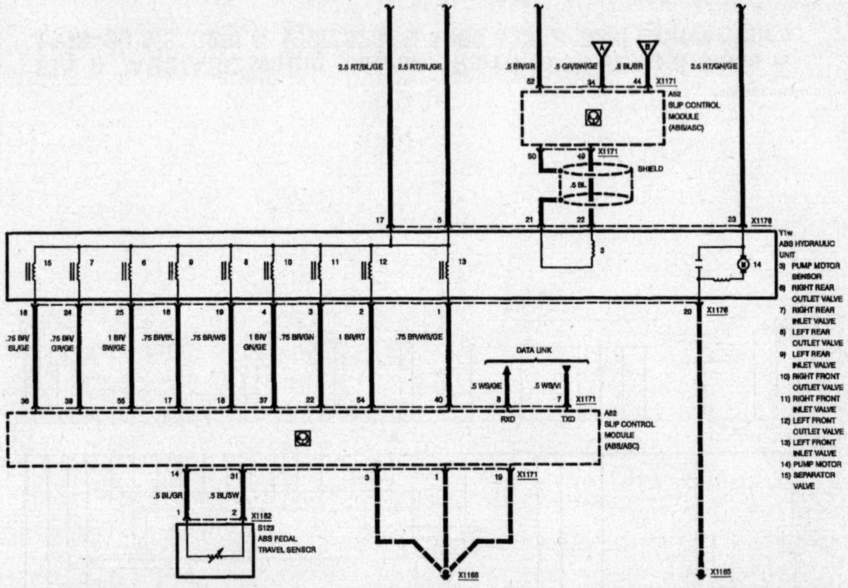

BM4020100034040X

Fig. 9 ABS/ASC wiring diagram (Part 3 of 6). 323is & 328is & 1998–99 M3, 328i & 1998 323i & 1999 323i & 328i Convertibles

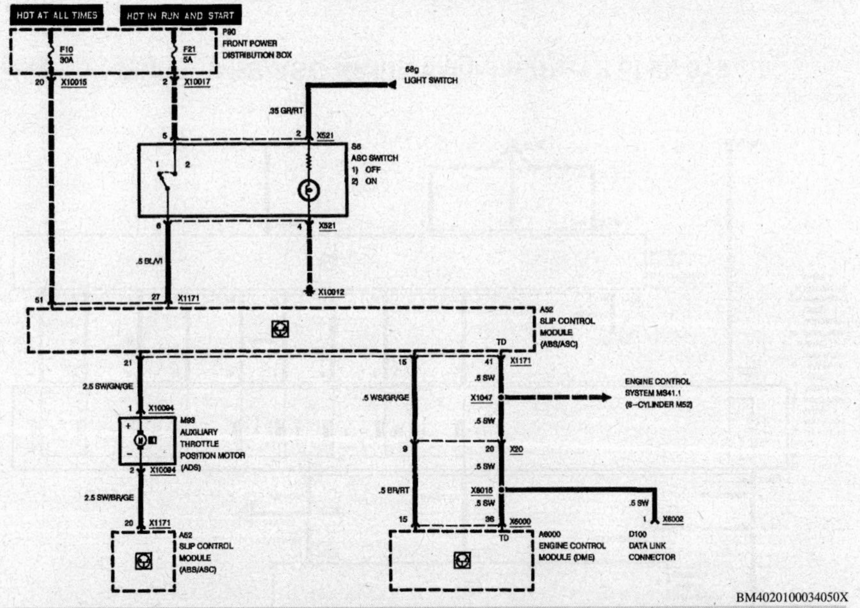

BM4020100034050X

Fig. 9 ABS/ASC wiring diagram (Part 4 of 6). 323is & 328is & 1998–99 M3, 328i & 1998 323i & 1999 323i & 328i Convertibles

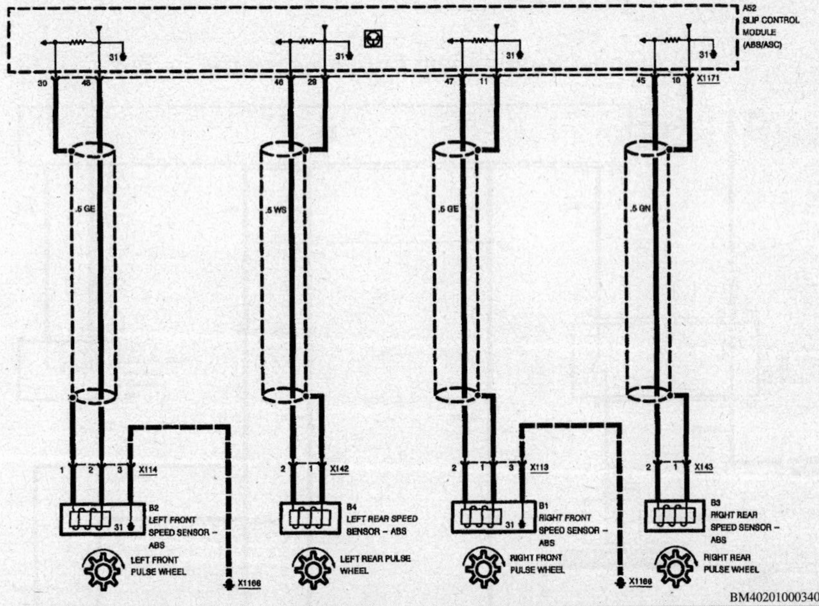

BM4020100034060X

Fig. 9 ABS/ASC wiring diagram (Part 5 of 6). 323is & 328is & 1998–99 M3, 328i & 1998 323i & 1999 323i & 328i Convertibles

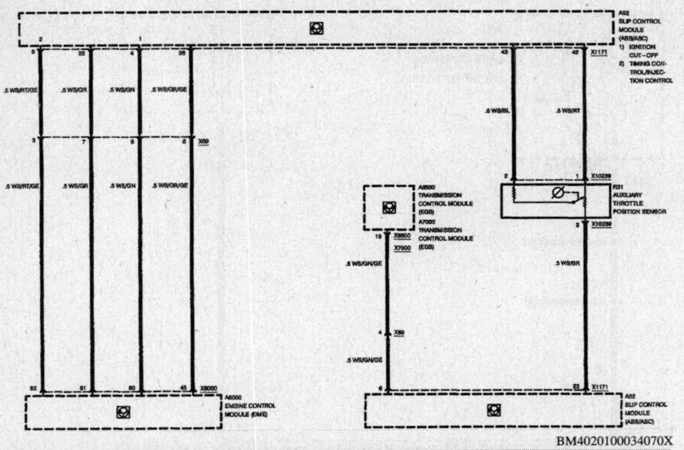

Fig. 9 ABS/ASC wiring diagram (Part 6 of 6). 323is & 328is & 1998–99 M3, 328i & 1998 323i & 1999 323i & 328i Convertibles

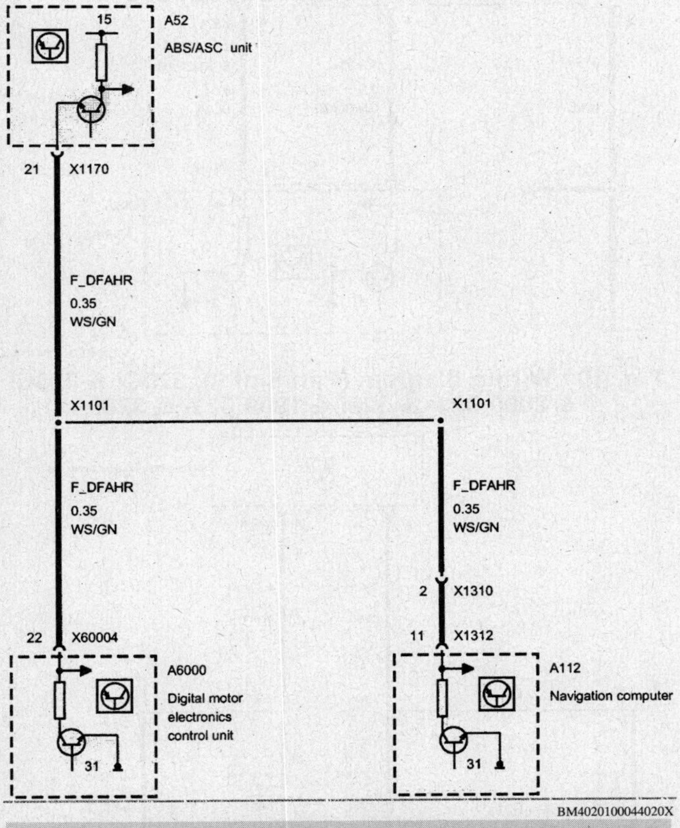

Fig. 10 Wiring diagram (Part 2 of 9). 323Ci & 328Ci & 2000 323i & 328i & 1999 323i & 328i

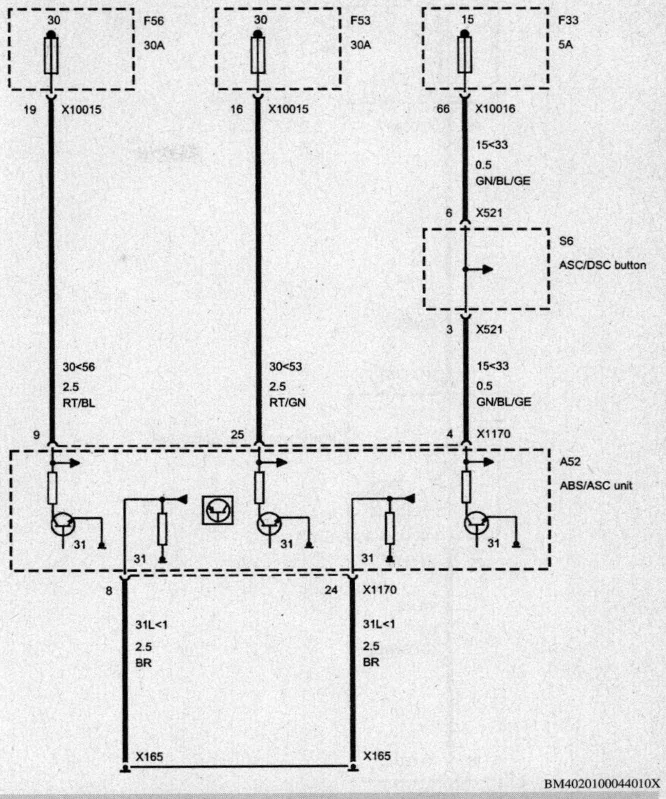

Fig. 10 Wiring diagram (Part 1 of 9). 323Ci & 328Ci & 2000 323i & 328i & 1999 323i & 328i Sedans

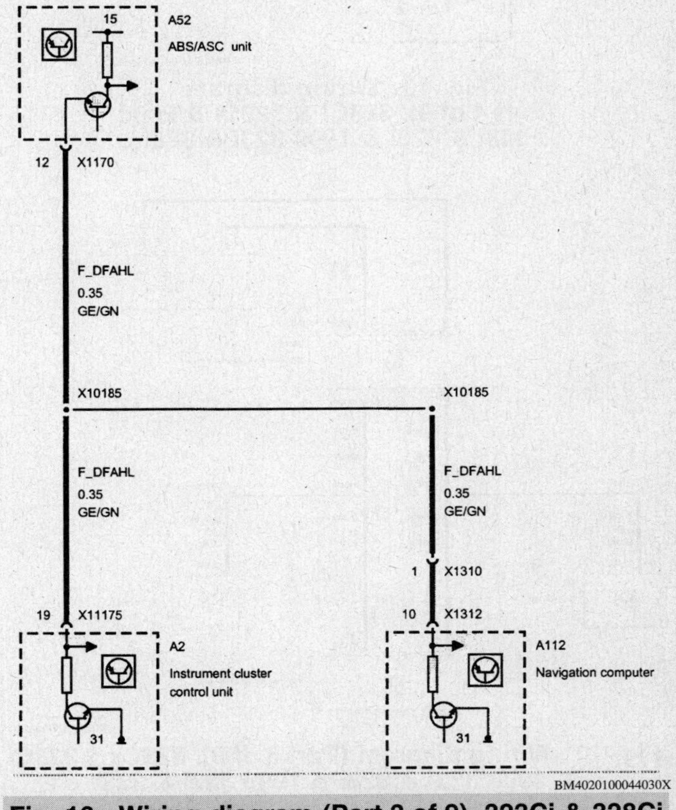

Fig. 10 Wiring diagram (Part 3 of 9). 323Ci & 328Ci & 2000 323i & 328i & 1999 323i & 328i

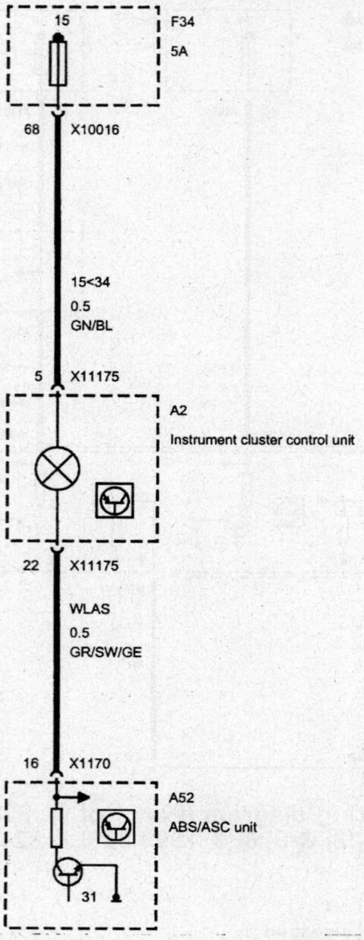

BM4020100044040X

Fig. 10 Wiring diagram (Part 4 of 9). 323Ci & 328Ci & 2000 323i & 328i & 1999 323i & 328i

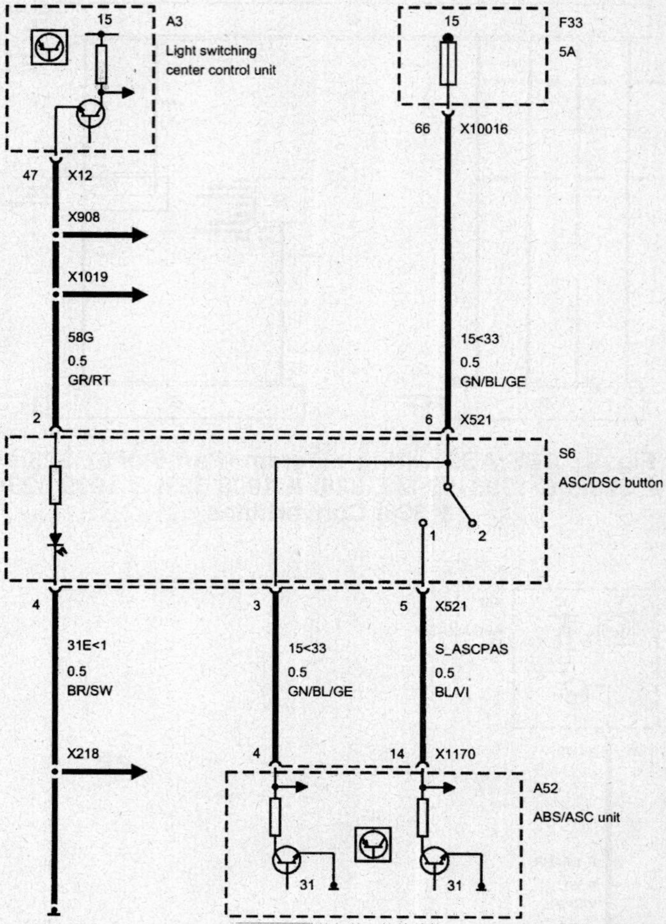

BM4020100044090X

Fig. 10 Wiring diagram (Part 5 of 9). 323Ci & 328Ci & 2000 323i & 328i & 1999 323i & 328i

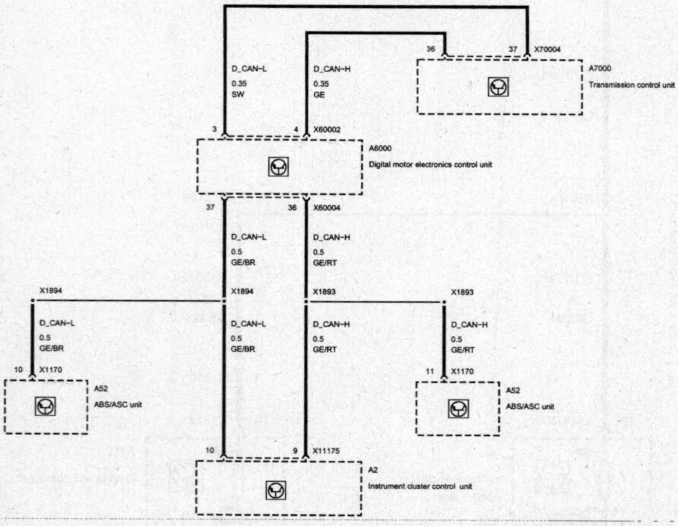

BM4020100044050X

Fig. 10 Wiring diagram (Part 6 of 9). 323Ci & 328Ci & 2000 323i & 328i & 1999 323i & 328i

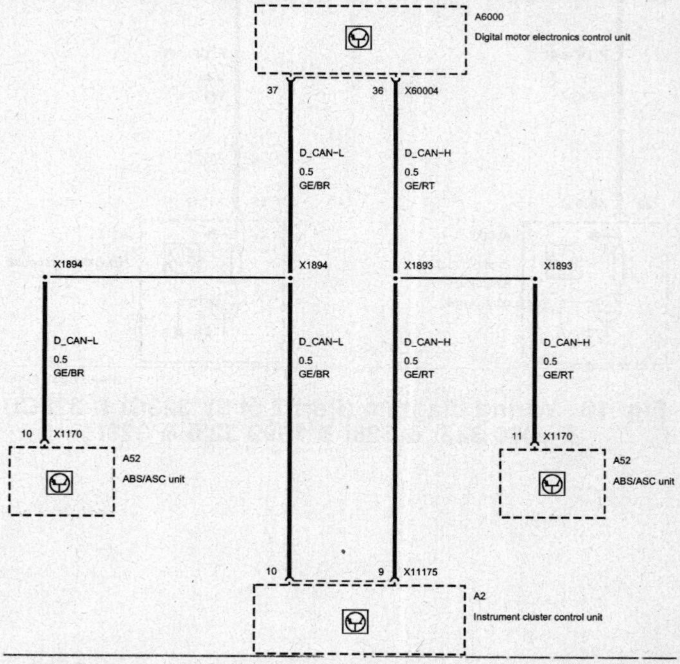

BM4020100044060X

Fig. 10 Wiring diagram (Part 7 of 9). 323Ci & 328Ci & 2000 323i & 328i & 1999 323i & 328i

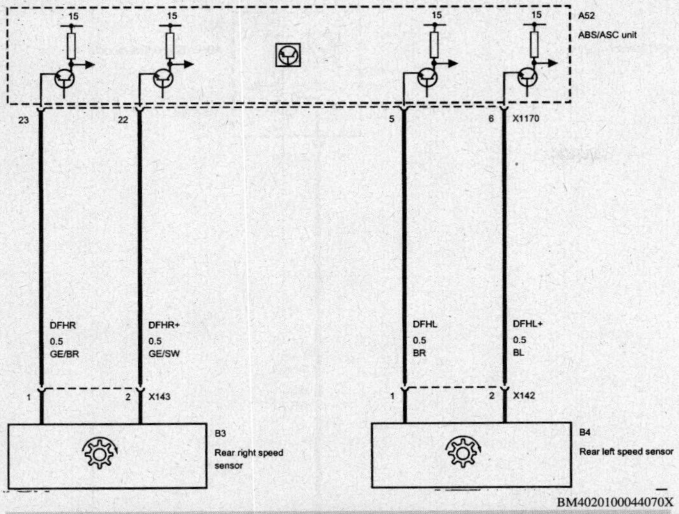

Fig. 10 Wiring diagram (Part 8 of 9). 323Ci & 328Ci & 2000 323i & 328i & 1999 323i & 328i

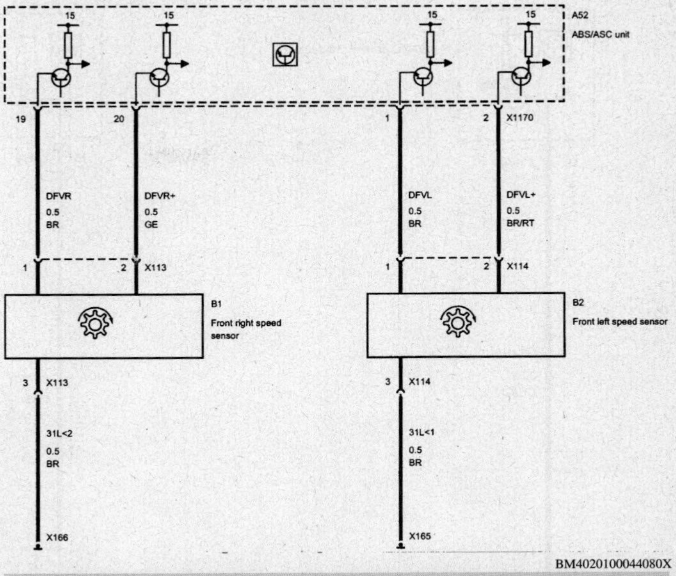

Fig. 10 Wiring diagram (Part 9 of 9). 323Ci & 328Ci & 2000 323i & 328i & 1999 323i & 328i

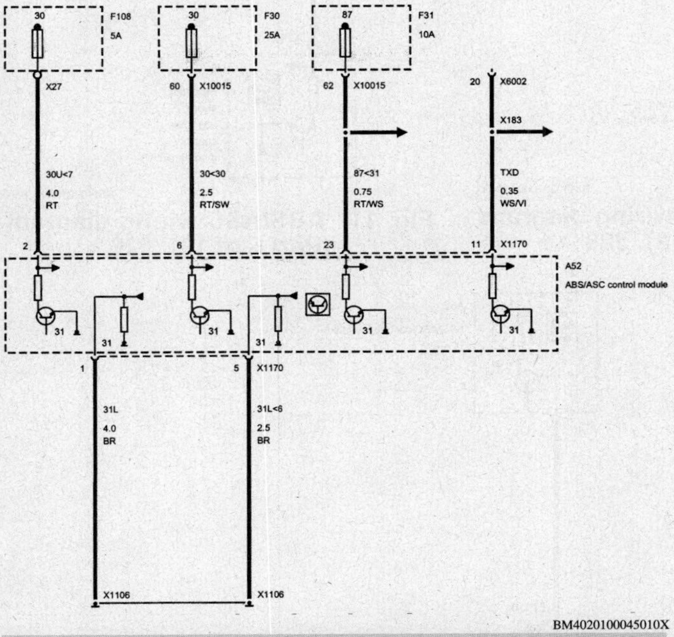

Fig. 11 ABS/ASC wiring diagram (Part 1 of 12). 528

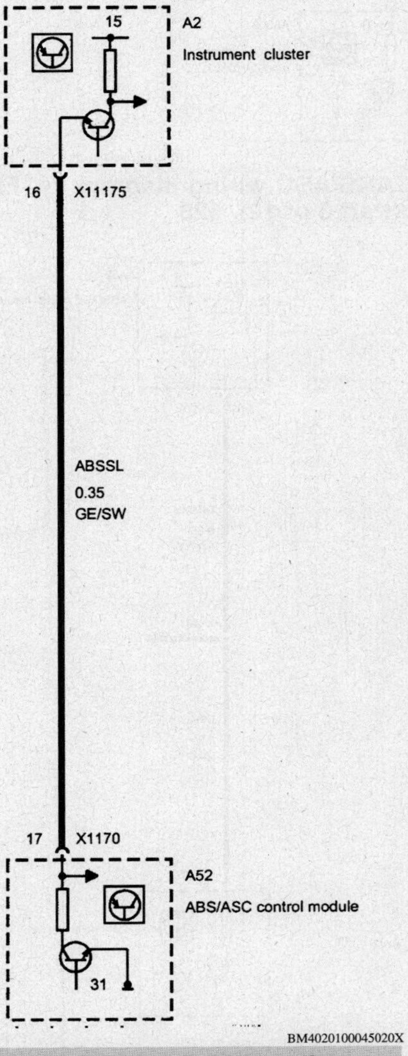

Fig. 11 ABS/ASC wiring diagram (Part 2 of 12). 528

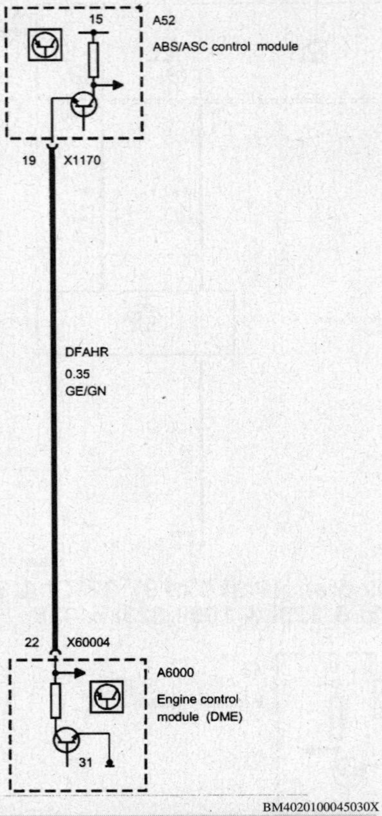

Fig. 11 ABS/ASC wiring diagram (Part 3 of 12). 528

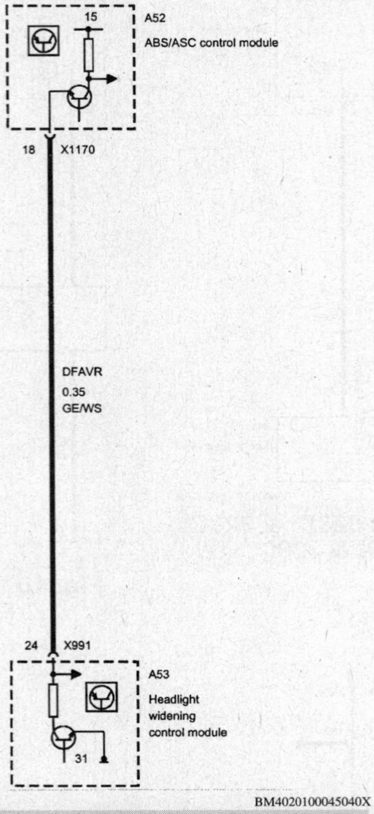

Fig. 11 ABS/ASC wiring diagram (Part 4 of 12). 528

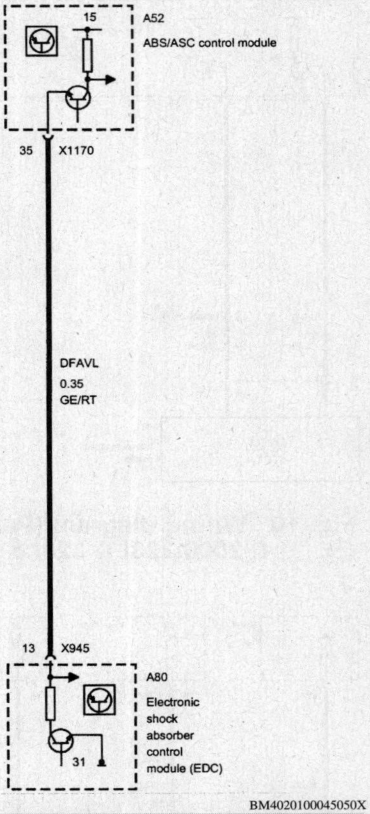

Fig. 11 ABS/ASC wiring diagram (Part 5 of 12). 528

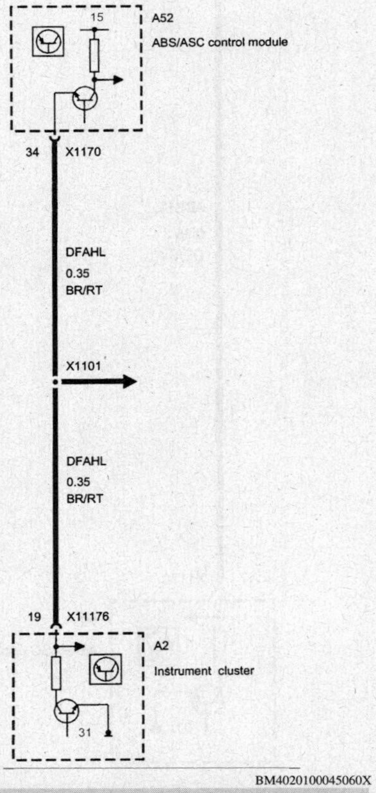

Fig. 11 ABS/ASC wiring diagram (Part 6 of 12). 528

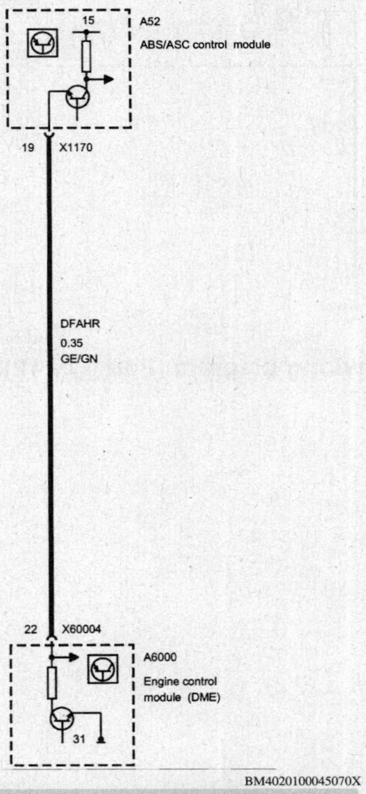

Fig. 11 ABS/ASC wiring diagram (Part 7 of 12). 528

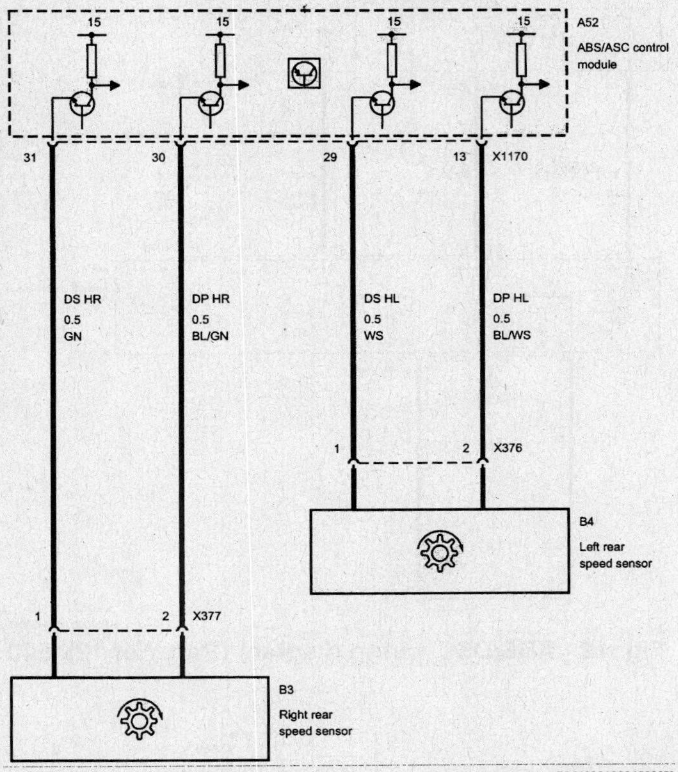

BM4020100045080X

Fig. 11 ABS/ASC wiring diagram (Part 8 of 12). 528

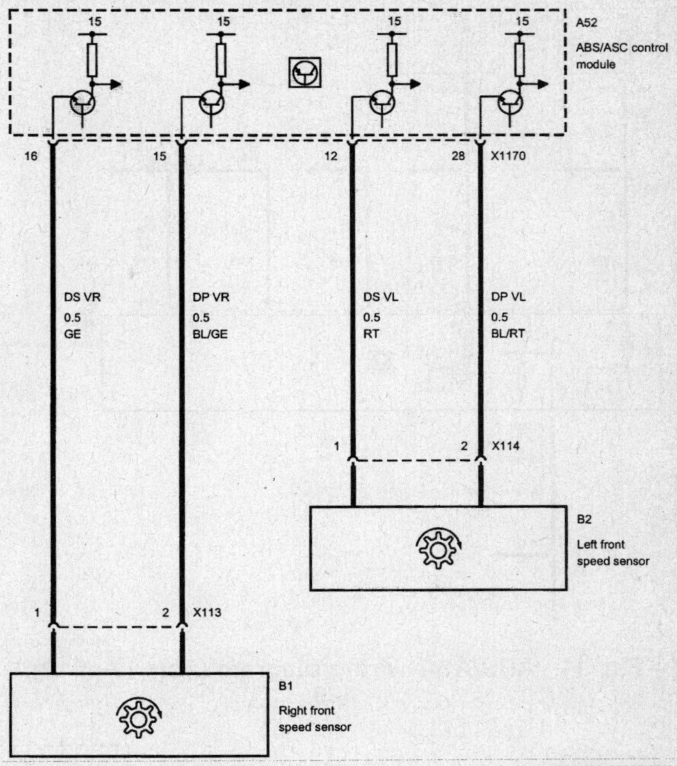

BM4020100045090X

Fig. 11 ABS/ASC wiring diagram (Part 9 of 12). 528

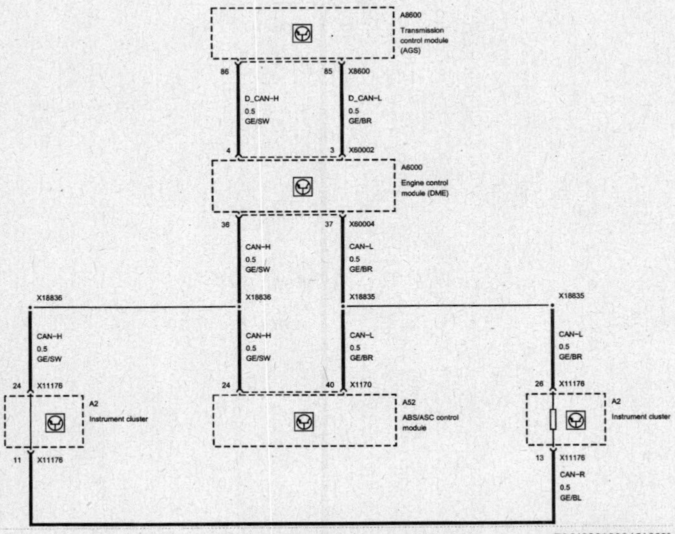

BM4020100045100X

Fig. 11 ABS/ASC wiring diagram (Part 10 of 12). 528

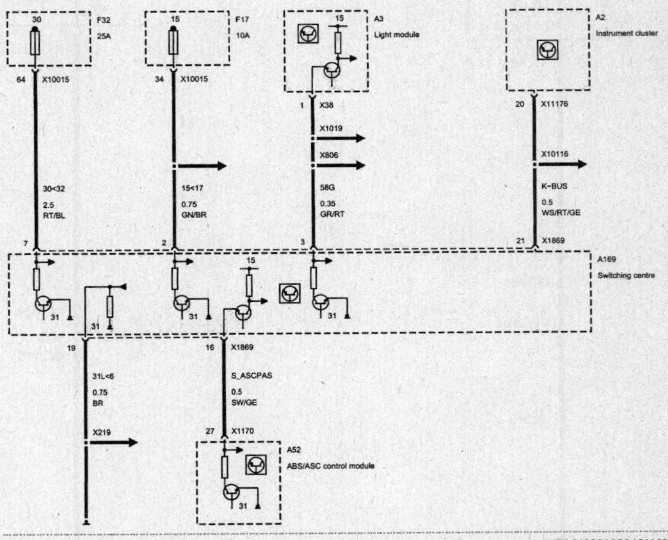

BM4020100045110X

Fig. 11 ABS/ASC wiring diagram (Part 11 of 12). 528

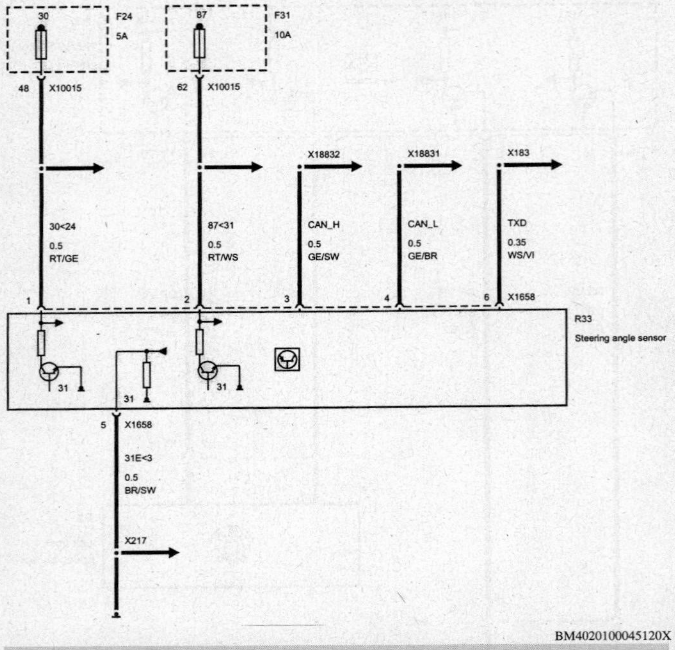

Fig. 11 ABS/ASC wiring diagram (Part 12 of 12). 528

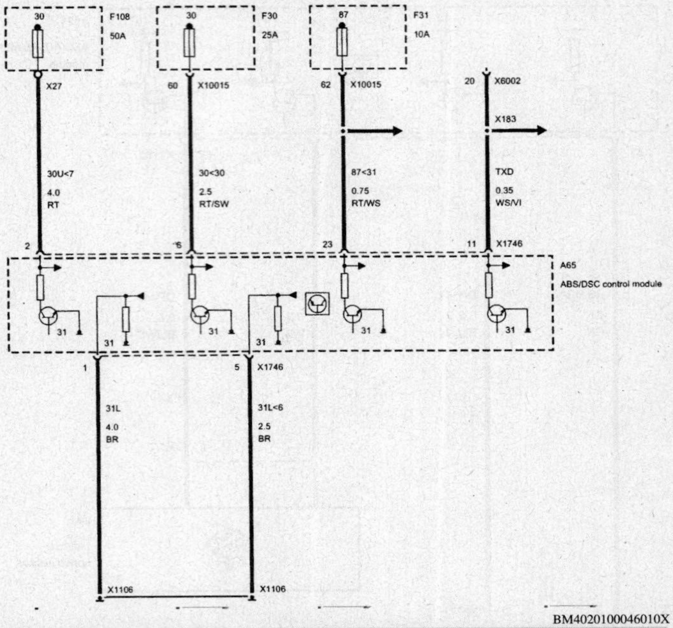

Fig. 12 ABS/DSC wiring diagram (Part 1 of 12). 540

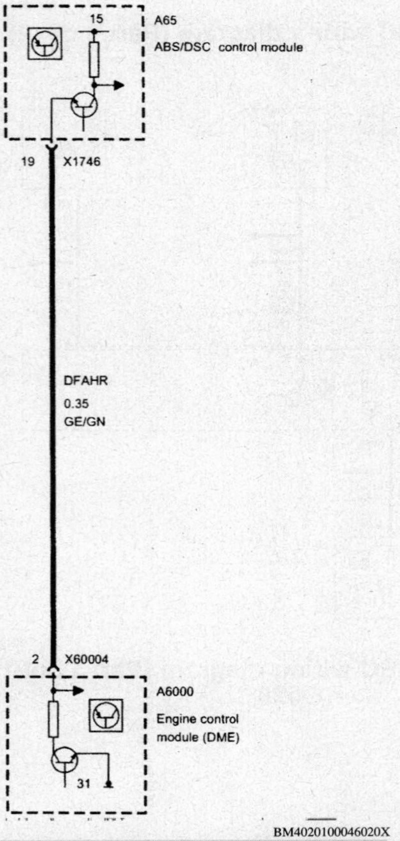

Fig. 12 ABS/DSC wiring diagram (Part 2 of 12). 540

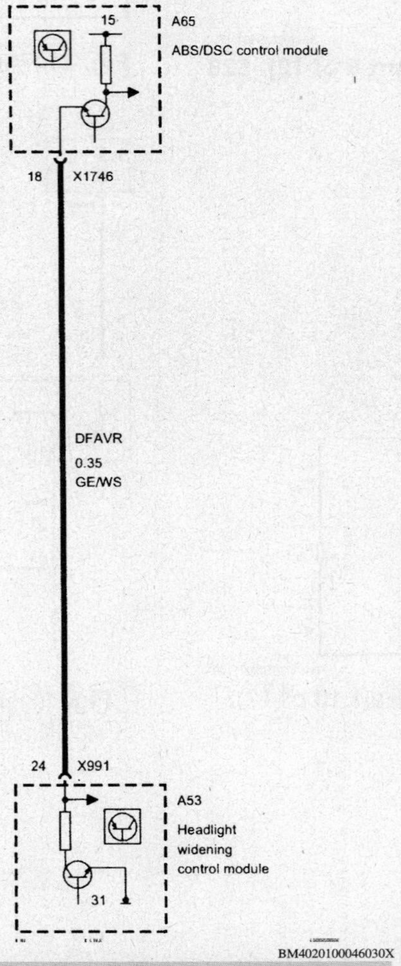

Fig. 12 ABS/DSC wiring diagram (Part 3 of 12). 540

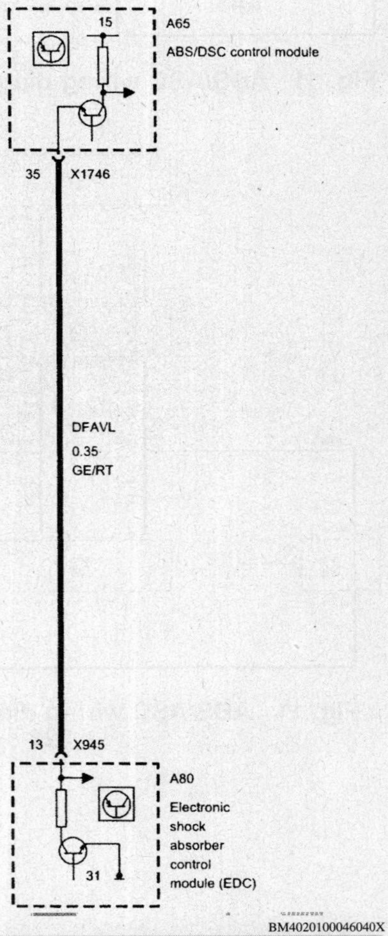

Fig. 12 ABS/DSC wiring diagram (Part 4 of 12). 540

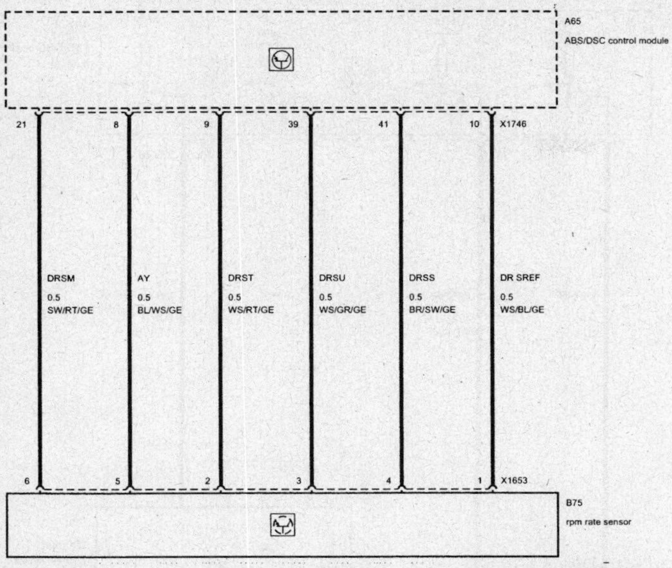

BM4020100046050X

Fig. 12 ABS/DSC wiring diagram (Part 5 of 12). 540

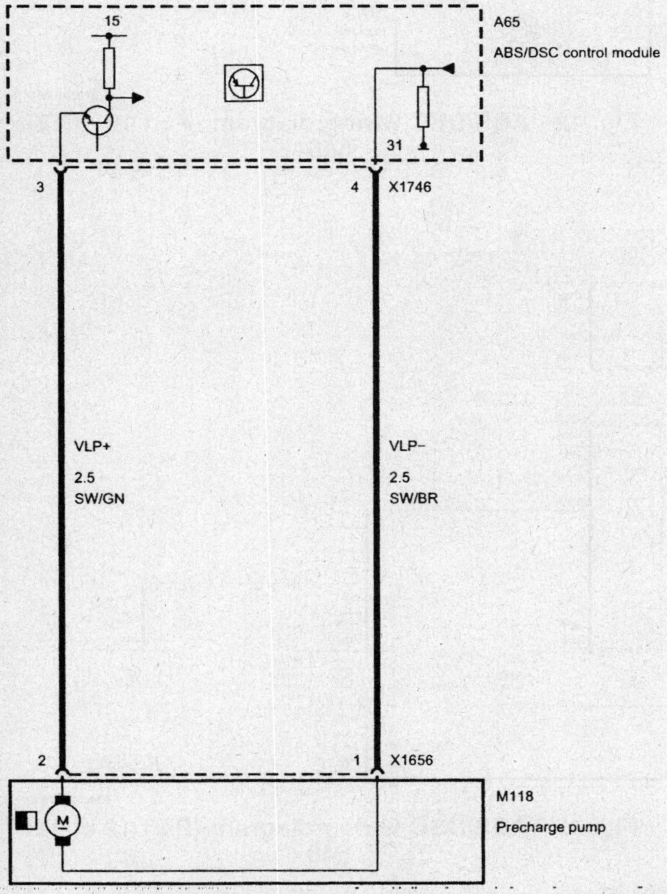

BM4020100046070X

Fig. 12 ABS/DSC wiring diagram (Part 7 of 12). 540

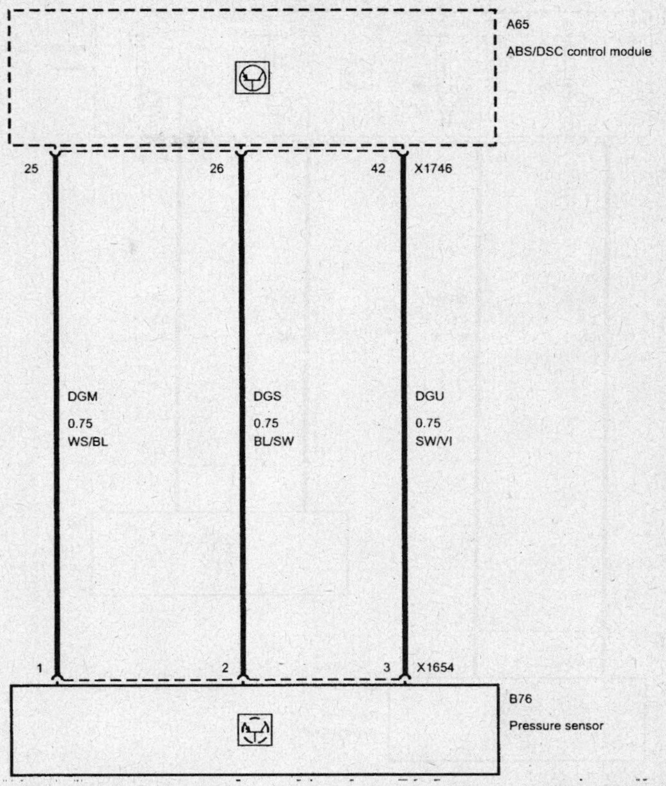

BM4020100046060X

Fig. 12 ABS/DSC wiring diagram (Part 6 of 12). 540

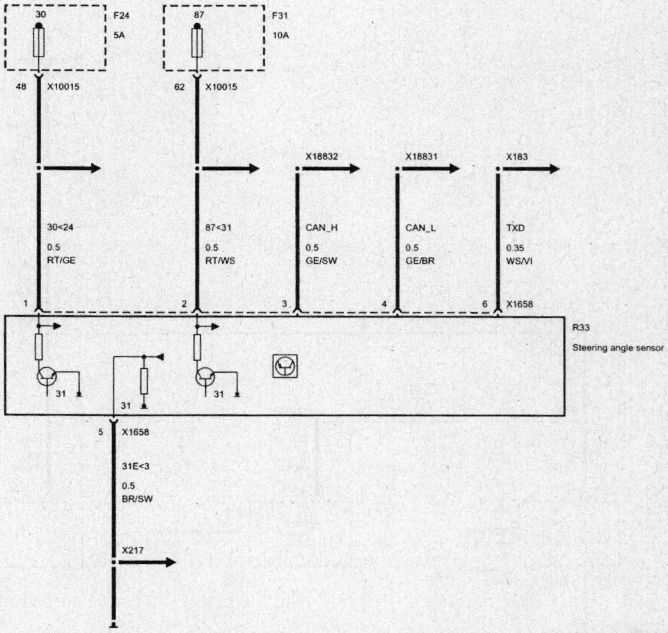

BM4020100046080X

Fig. 12 ABS/DSC wiring diagram (Part 8 of 12). 540

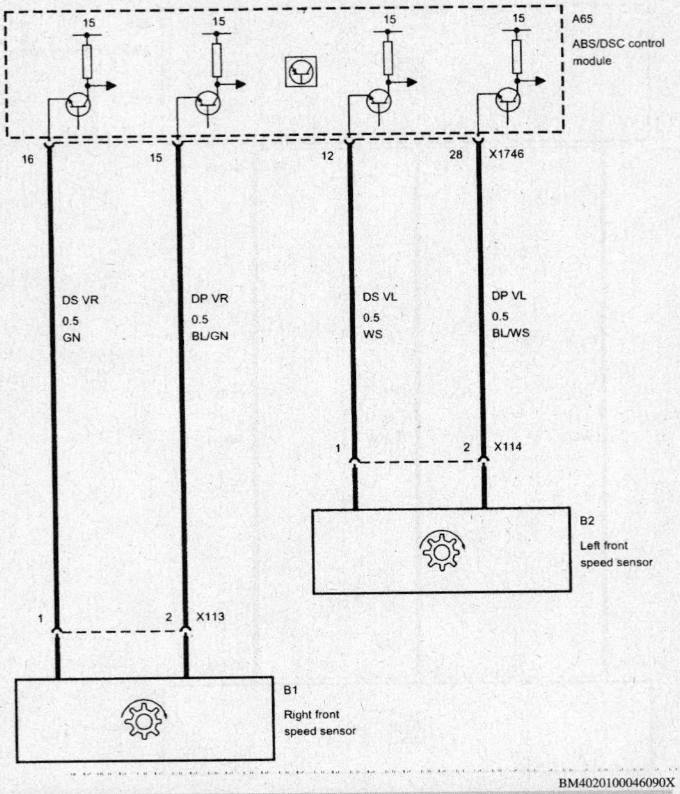

Fig. 12 ABS/DSC wiring diagram (Part 9 of 12). 540

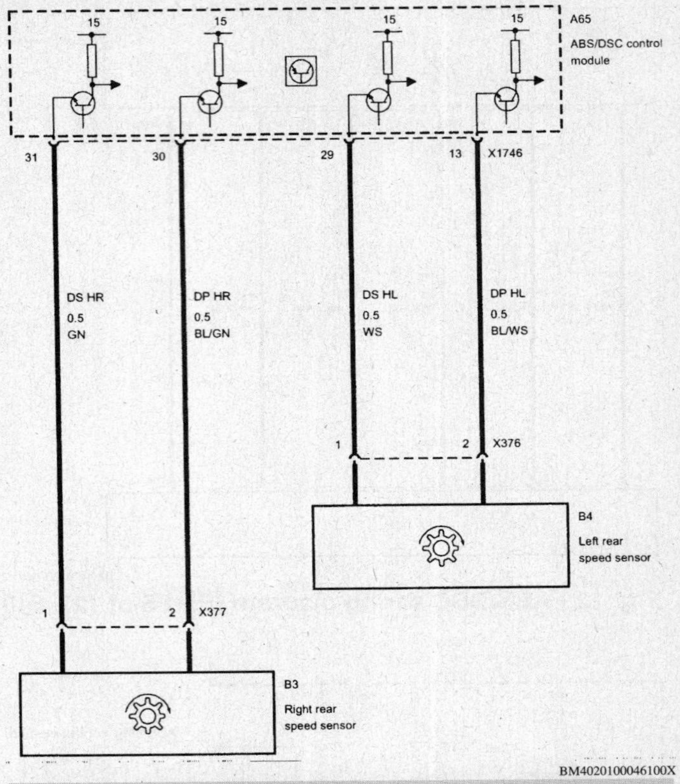

Fig. 12 ABS/DSC wiring diagram (Part 10 of 12). 540

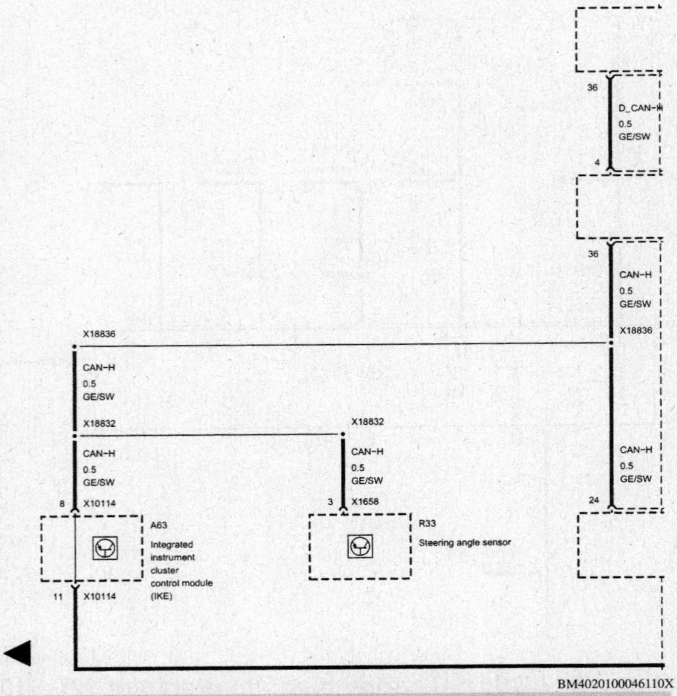

Fig. 12 ABS/DSC wiring diagram (Part 11 of 12). 540

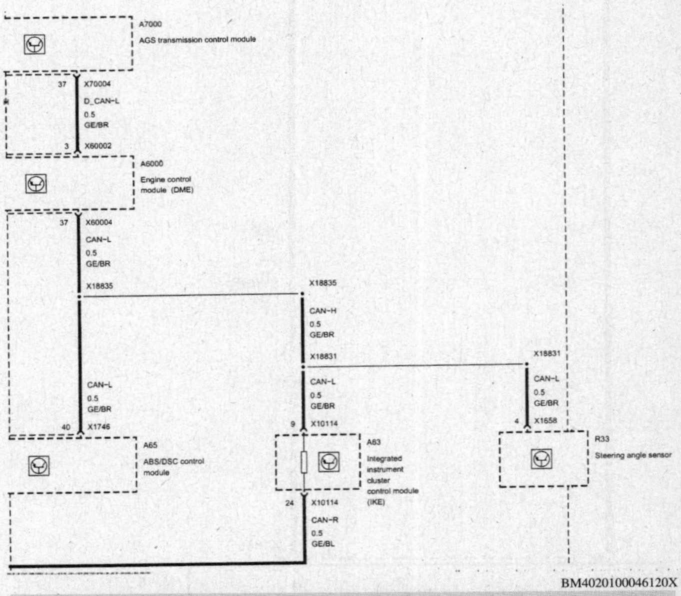

Fig. 12 ABS/DSC wiring diagram (Part 12 of 12). 540

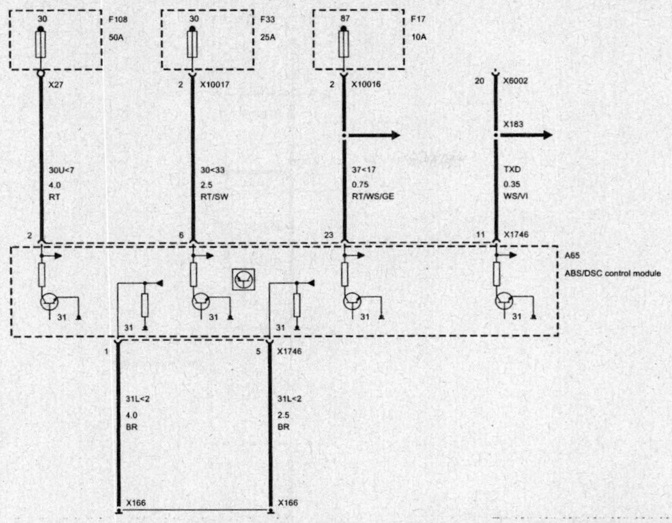

BM4020100047010X

Fig. 13 ABS/DSC wiring diagram (Part 1 of 13). 740 & 750

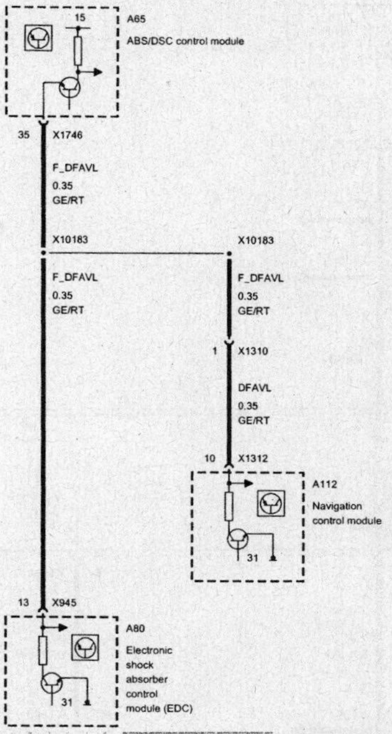

BM4020100047020X

Fig. 13 ABS/DSC wiring diagram (Part 2 of 13). 740 & 750

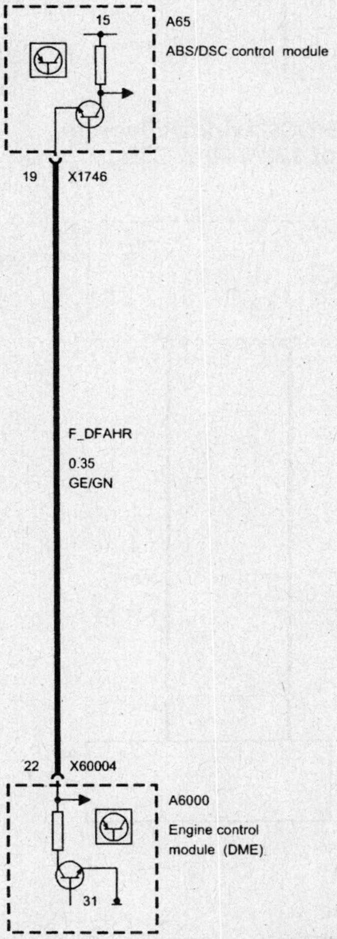

BM4020100047030X

Fig. 13 ABS/DSC wiring diagram (Part 3 of 13). 740 & 750

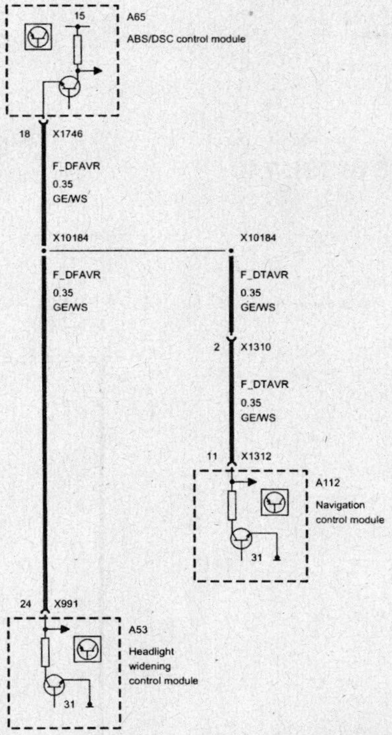

BM4020100047040X

Fig. 13 ABS/DSC wiring diagram (Part 4 of 13). 740 & 750

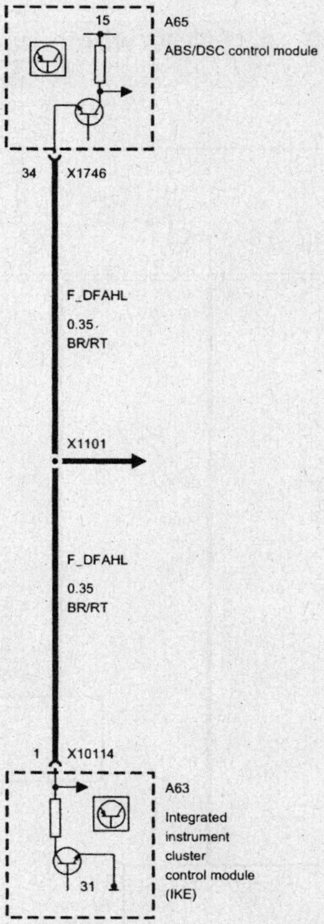

BM4020100047050X

Fig. 13 ABS/DSC wiring diagram (Part 5 of 13). 740 & 750

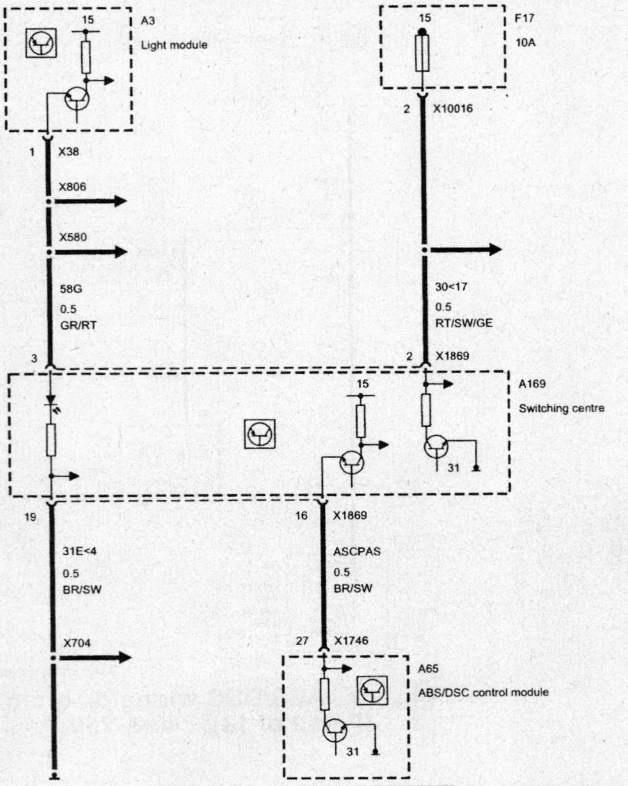

Fig. 13 ABS/DSC wiring diagram (Part 6 of 13). 740 & 750

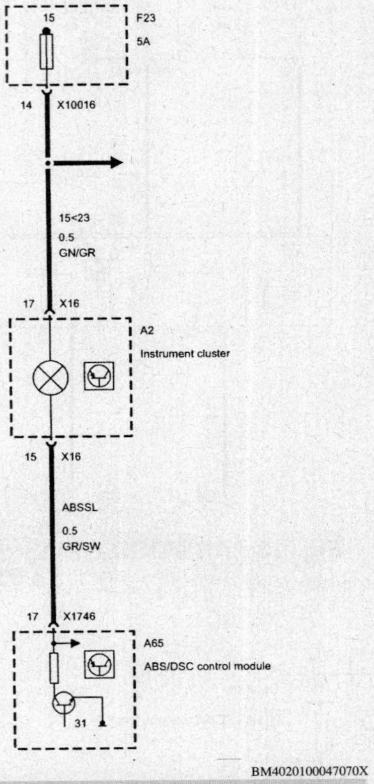

Fig. 13 ABS/DSC wiring diagram (Part 7 of 13). 740 & 750

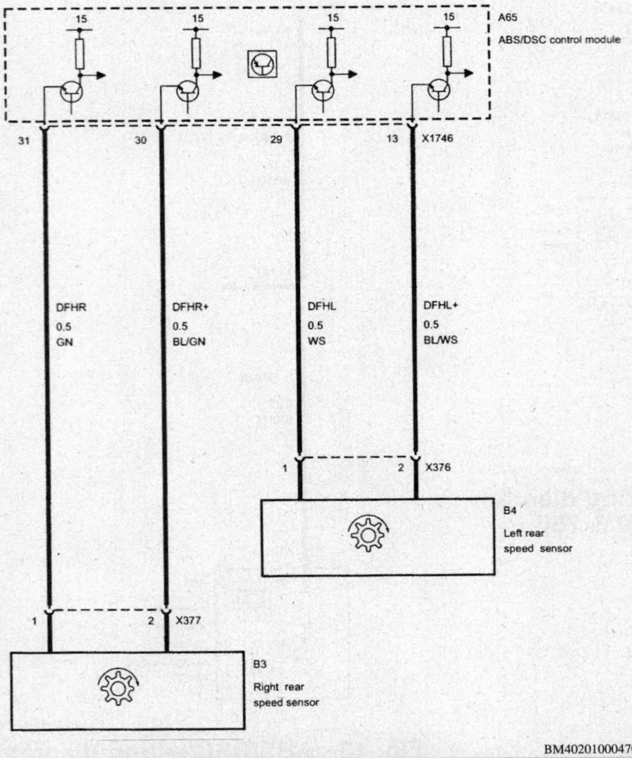

Fig. 13 ABS/DSC wiring diagram (Part 8 of 13). 740 & 750

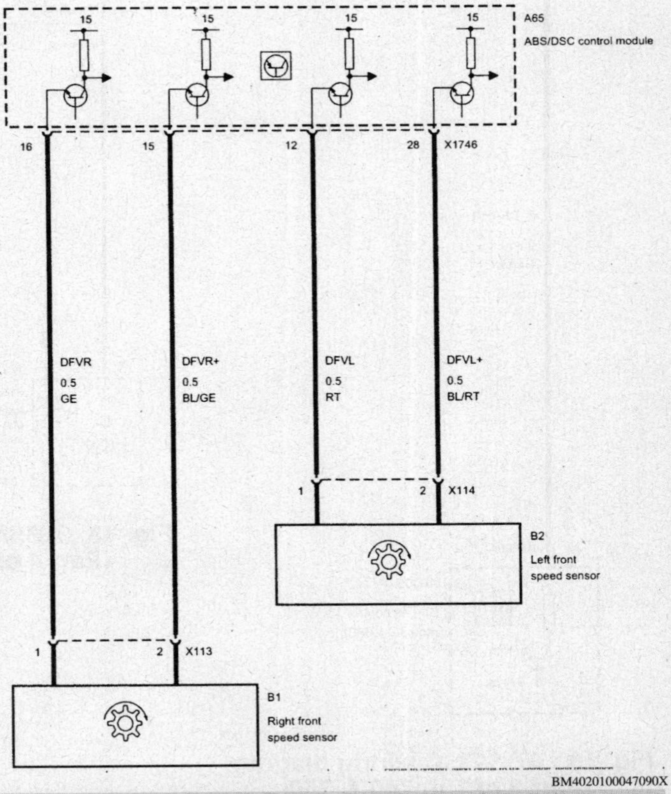

Fig. 13 ABS/DSC wiring diagram (Part 9 of 13). 740 & 750

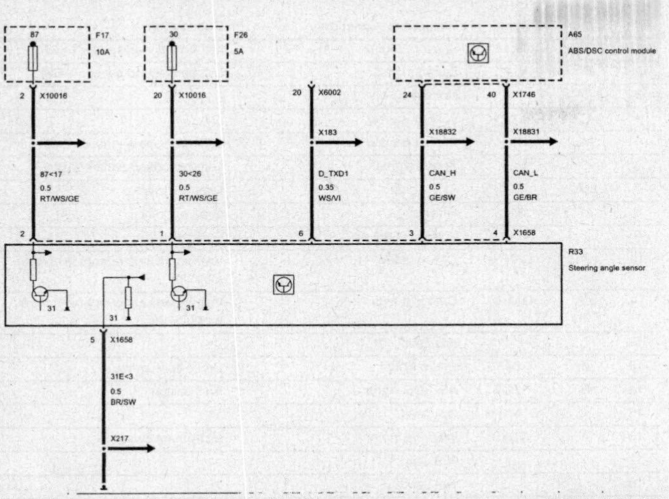

BM4020100047100X

Fig. 13 ABS/DSC wiring diagram (Part 10 of 13). 740 & 750

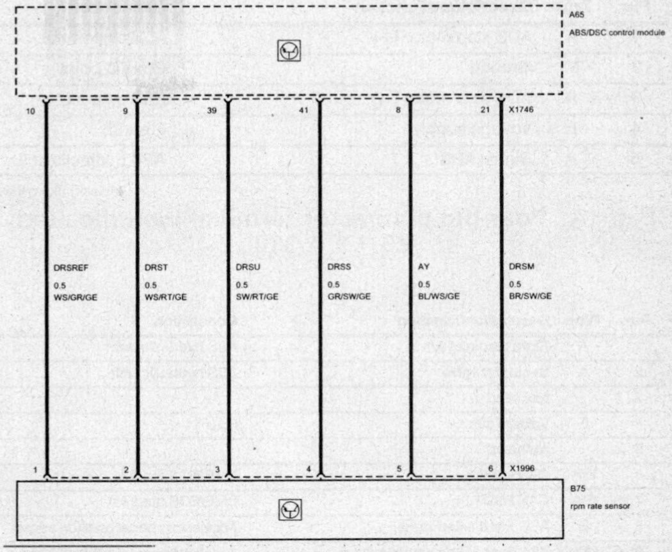

BM4020100047110X

Fig. 13 ABS/DSC wiring diagram (Part 11 of 13). 740 & 750

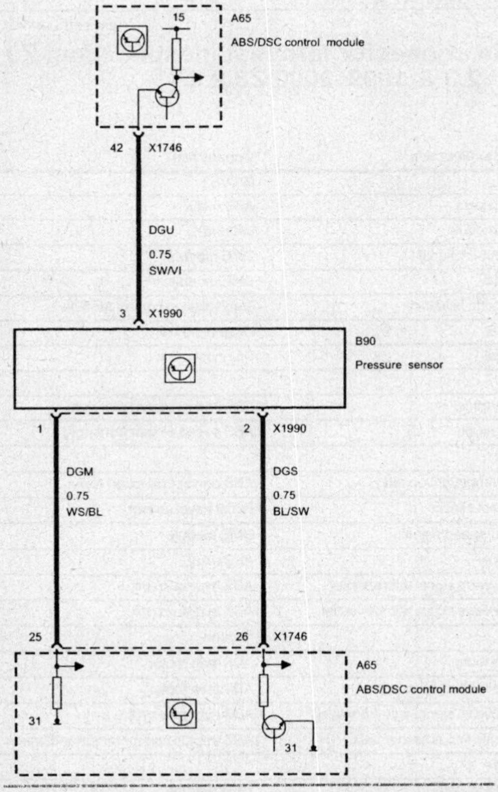

BM4020100047120X

Fig. 13 ABS/DSC wiring diagram (Part 12 of 13). 740 & 750

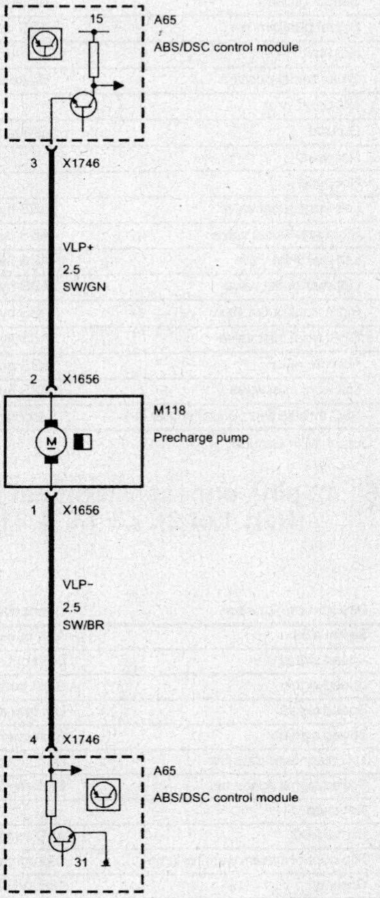

BM4020100047130X

Fig. 13 ABS/DSC wiring diagram (Part 13 of 13). 740 & 750

Pin	Type	Description/Function	Connection
1	A	ADS step motor (+)	ADS step motor
2	M	Ground	Ground point
3	A	ADS step motor (−)	ADS step motor
4	E	Voltage supply	Fuse 38
5	A	Signal ABS	ABS hydraulic unit

BM4020100039000X

Fig. 14 Four-pin connector terminal identification. Z3 1.9 & 318

Pin	Type	Description/Function	Connection
1	A	Right rear inlet valve	ABS hydraulic unit
2	A	Separator valve	ABS hydraulic unit
3		Not used	
4	E	Voltage supply	Fuse 21
5		Not used	
6	E/A	CAN LOW	DME/EGS module
7	E/A	CAN HIGH	DME/EGS module
8	E	ASC throttle flap signal	Accelerator pedal position sensor
9	E	ASC throttle flap potentiometer (−)	Accelerator pedal position sensor
10		Not used	
11	A	Sensor ground	Left front speed sensor ABS
12	A	Sensor ground	Right front speed sensor ABS
13	A	Sensor ground	Left rear speed sensor ABS
14	A	Sensor ground	Right rear speed sensor ABS
15	E	Signal pump motor	ABS pump motor relay
16		Not used	
17	E	Brake pedal position	Brake light switch
18		Not used	
19	M	Ground	Ground point
20		Not used	
21		Not used	
22	A	Left front outlet valve	ABS hydraulic unit
23	A	Right rear outlet valve	ABS hydraulic unit
24	A	Left rear inlet valve	ABS hydraulic unit
25	A	Left rear outlet valve	ABS hydraulic unit
26	A	Right front outlet valve	ABS hydraulic unit
27	A	Right front inlet valve	ABS hydraulic unit
28	A	Activate relay	ABS pump motor relay
29	A	Left front inlet valve	ABS hydraulic unit
30	E	ASC throttle flap potentiometer (+)	Accelerator pedal position sensor

E = Input, A = Output, M = Ground

BM4020100036010X

Fig. 16 42-pin connector terminal identification (Part 1 of 2). Z3 1.9 & 318

Pin	Type	Description/Function	Connection
31	A	Signal ABS	ABS pump motor relay/Hydraulic unit
32	E	Speed signal	Left front speed sensor ABS
33	E	Speed signal	Right front speed sensor ABS
34	E	Speed signal	Left rear speed sensor ABS
35	E	Speed signal	Right rear speed sensor ABS
36	E/A	TxD diagnostic data link	Data link connector
37	A	Speed signal right rear	DME module
38		Not used	
39	E	Signal ASC	ASC switch
40	E	Slip control system warning lamp	Slip control module (ASC)
41	M	Ground	Ground point
42	A	Signal ASC	Instrument cluster

BM4020100036020X

Fig. 16 42-pin connector terminal identification (Part 2 of 2). Z3 1.9 & 318

Pin	Type	Signal	Description/Function	Connection
1	M	VL−	Sensor ground	Left front speed sensor (ABS)
2	E	VL+	Speed signal	Left front speed sensor (ABS)
3			Not used	
4	E	15A21	Voltage supply	Fuse 21
5	M	HL−	Sensor ground	Left rear speed sensor (ABS)
6	E	HL+	Speed signal	Left rear speed sensor (ABS)
7	E/A	TXD	TXD signal	Diagnostic link
8	M	31L	Ground	Ground point
9	E	30<10	Voltage supply	Fuse 10
10	E/A	CAN−	CAN bus low	Instrument cluster/engine control module
11	E/A	CAN+	CAN bus high	Instrument cluster/engine control module
12			Not used	
13	E	54	Brake signal	Brake light switch
14	E	ASCS	ASC-ON-signal	ASC switch
15			Not used	
16	A	WLAS	Warning lamp	Instrument cluster
17			Not used	
18			Not used	
19	M	VR−	Sensor ground	Right front speed sensor (ABS)
20	E	VR+	Speed signal	Right front speed sensor (ABS)
21	A	DFAHR	Right rear speed signal	Engine control module (DME)
22	E	HR+	Speed signal	Right rear speed sensor (ABS)
23	M	HR−	Sensor ground	Right rear speed sensor (ABS)
24	M	31L	Ground	Ground point
25	E	30<38	Voltage supply	Fuse 38

BM4020100043000X

Fig. 15 25-pin connector terminal identification. Z3 2.3 & 1999–2000 Z3 2.8

Pin	Type	Description/Function	Connection
1	M	Ground	Ground
2	E	Battery voltage	ABS relay
3	M	Ground, module	Ground
4	E	Ignition cut-off signal	DME module
5	A	EML signal	DME module
6	A	Transmission influence	Transmission control module
7	E/A	TxD signal	Diagnostic link
8	A	RxD signal	Diagnostic link
9		Not used	
10	A	Sensor ground	ABS speed sensor rear right
11	A	Sensor ground	ABS speed sensor front right
12		Not used	
13	A	ABS-power protection relay	ABS power protection relay
14	E	Pedal travel sensor	Pedal travel sensor
15	A	Right rear speed signal	DME module
16	E	Plus supply	ABS relay
17	A	Solenoid valve signal left rear inlet	ABS hydraulic unit
18	A	Solenoid valve signal left rear outlet	ABS hydraulic unit
19	M	Ground	Ground
20	A	ADS step motor (−)	ADS step motor
21	A	ADS step motor (+)	ADS step motor
22	A	Solenoid valve signal right front inlet	ABS hydraulic unit
23	E	ASC throttle flap potentiometer (−)	ASC throttle flap motor potentiometer
24	·	Not used	
25	E	Signal idle speed	DME module
26	A	Throttle flap position	DME module
27	E	ASC switch signal	ASC witch
28		Not used	
29	A	Sensor ground	ABS speed sensor rear left
30	A	Sensor ground	ABS speed sensor front left

E = Input, A = Output, M = Ground

BM4020100035010X

Fig. 17 55-pin connector terminal identification (Part 1 of 2). 323is & 328is & 1998–99 M3, 328i & 1998 323i & 1999 323i & 328i Convertibles & 1998 Z3 M Coupe, Z3 M Roadster & Z3 2.8).

Pin	Type	Description/Function	Connection
31	E	Pedal travel sensor	Pedal travel sensor
32	E	Brake signal	Brake light switch
33	E	Plus supply	ABS relay
34	A	ABS lamp control	Instrument cluster
35	E	Ignition signal	Fuse 21
36	A	Separator valve	ABS hydraulic unit
37	A	Solenoid valve signal right front outlet	ABS hydraulic unit
38		Not used	
39	A	Right rear inlet valve	ABS hydraulic unit
40	A	Solenoid valve signal left front inlet	ABS hydraulic unit
41	E	Speed signal	DME module
42	E	ASC throttle flap potentiometer (+)	ASC throttle flap potentiometer
43	E	ASC throttle flap signal	ASC throttle flap potentiometer
44	A	ASC lamp control	Instrument cluster
45	E	Speed sensor signal rear right	Speed sensor rear right
46	E	Speed sensor signal rear left	Speed sensor rear left
47	E	Speed sensor signal front right	Speed sensor front right
48	E	Speed sensor signal front left	Speed sensor front left
49	E	Pump motor sensor signal	ABS hydraulic unit
50	E	Shield pump motor sensor	ABS hydraulic unit
51	E	Plus supply	Front power distribution box
52	A	ABS pump motor relay	ABS pump motor relay
53		Not used	
54	A	Solenoid valve signal left front outlet	ABS hydraulic unit
55	A	Right rear outlet valve	ABS hydraulic unit

BM4020100035020X

Fig. 17 55-pin connector terminal identification (Part 2 of 2). 323is & 328is & 1998–99 M3, 328i & 1998 323i & 1999 323i & 328i Convertibles & 1998 Z3 M Coupe, Z3 M Roadster & Z3 2.8).

Pin	Type	Description/Function	Connection
98	E	Voltage supply	Fuse 13
99	A	Left front inlet valve	ABS hydraulic unit
100	A	Voltage supply	Valve – Engine control relay
101		Not used	
102		Not used	
103	A	Right rear inlet valve	ABS hydraulic unit
104	A	Activare relay	Engine control relay
105		Not used	
106		Not used	
107	M	Sensor ground	ABS speed sensor front left
108	E	Speed signal	ABS speed sensor rear right
109	M	Sensor ground	ABS speed sensor rear left
110	E	Speed signal	ABS speed sensor rear left
111	M	Sensor ground	ABS speed sensor front right
112	E	Speed signal	ABS speed sensor front right
113		Not used	
114		Not used	
115	E	Engine signal 1	Engine control module (DME)
116	E	Relay activation feedback	Engine control relay
117	E	Speed signal	Engine control module (DME)
118		Not used	
119		Not used	
120	A	ADS step motor (+)	ADS step mototr
121	E	Charge indicator	Generator
122	A	Left rear outlet valve	ABS hydraulic unit
123	A	Shut-off valve (ASC)	ABS hydraulic unit
124	A	Right front outlet valve	ABS hydraulic unit
125	M	Ground	Ground point
126	M	Ground	Ground point
127	A	ABS lamp control	Instrument cluster

E = Input, A = Output, M = Ground

BM4020100041010X

Fig. 18 185-pin connector terminal identification (Part 1 of 3). 1999–2000 Z3 M Coupe & Z3 M Roadster

Pin	Type	Description/Function	Connection
128	A	ASC lamp control	Instrument cluster
129		Not used	
130	A	Left front outlet valve	ABS hydraulic unit
131	A	Right rear outlet valve	ABS hydraulic unit
132	A	Right rear speed signal	Engine control module (DME)
133	E	Speed signal	ABS speed sensor front left
134	A	Activare relay	Valve relay
135	M	Sensor ground	ABS speed sensor rear right
136	A	Throttle position sensor (–)	Auxiliary throttle position sensor
137		Not used	
138		Not used	
139		Not used	
140	A	Throttle position sensor (+)	Auxiliary throttle position sensor
141	E	ASC-ON-signal	ASC switch
142		Not used	
143	E/A	TXD signal	Diagnostic link
144		Not used	
145	E	Brake signal	Brake light switch
146	A	Changeover valve (ASC)	ABS hydraulic unit
147		Not used	
148	E	Voltage supply	Fuse 10
149	A	Left rear inlet valve	ABS hydraulic unit
150	A	ADS step motor (–)	ADS step motor
151	A	Right front inlet valve	ABS hydraulic unit
152	M	Ground	Ground point
153		Not used	
154		Not used	
155		Not used	
156		Not used	
157		Not used	
158		Not used	
159		Not used	

E = Input, A = Output, M = Ground

BM4020100041020X

Fig. 18 185-pin connector terminal identification (Part 2 of 3). 1999–2000 Z3 M Coupe & Z3 M Roadster

Pin	Type	Description/Function	Connection
160		Not used	
161		Not used	
162		Not used	
163		Not used	
164	E	ASC throttle flap signal	Auxiliary throttle position sensor
165		Not used	
166		Not used	
167		Not used	
168		Not used	
169		Not used	
170		Not used	
171		Not used	
172		Not used	
173	E	Signal park brake set	Park brake switch
174	E	Engine signal 3	Engine control module (DME)
175		Not used	
176		Not used	
177		Not used	
178	E	Engine signal 2	Engine control module (DME)
179		Not used	
180		Not used	
181		Not used	
182		Not used	
183		Not used	
184		Not used	
185	E	Throttle flap position	Engine control module (DME)

BM4020100041030X

Fig. 18 185-pin connector terminal identification (Part 3 of 3). 1999–2000 Z3 M Coupe & Z3 M Roadster

Automatic Transmissions

TABLE OF CONTENTS

	Page No.
APPLICATION CHART	2-208
4L30-E AUTOMATIC TRANSMISSION	2-210
5L40-E AUTOMATIC TRANSMISSION	2-227
ZF 5HP AUTOMATIC TRANSMISSIONS	2-216

Application Chart

Model	Chassis Series	Engine		Transmission	
		Series	Liter	Model	Type
1998					
M3	E36	S52	3.2L	5HP-18	A5S 310Z
Z3 1.9	E36/7	M44	1.9L	4L30-E	A4S 270R
Z3 2.8	E36/7	M52	2.8L	4L30-E	A4S 270R
318i	E36	M44	1.9L	4L30-E	A4S 270R
318ti	E36/5	M44	1.9L	4L30-E	A4S 270R
323i, is	E36	M52	2.5L	4L30-E	A4S 270R
328i, is	E36	M52	2.8L	4L30-E	A4S 270R
528i	E39	M52	2.8L	4L30-E	A4S 270R
540i	E39	M62	4.4L	5HP-24	A5S 440Z
740i, iL	E38	M62	4.4L	5HP-24	A5S 440Z
750iL	E38	M73	5.4L	5HP-30	A5S 560Z
1999					
M3	E36	S52	3.2L	5HP-18	A5S 310Z
Z3 Coupe	E36/7	M52 TU	2.8L	4L30-E	A4S 270R
Z3 2.3	E36/7	M52 TU	2.5L	4L30-E	A4S 270R
Z3 2.8	E36/7	M52 TU	2.8L	4L30-E	A4S 270R
318ti	E36/5	M44	1.9L	4L30-E	A4S 270R
323i, is Coupe & Convertible	E36	M52	2.5L	4L30-E	A4S 270R
323i Sedan	E46	M52 TU	2.5L	5L40-E	A5S 360R
328i, is Coupe & Convertible	E36	M52	2.8L	4L30-E	A4S 270R
328i Sedan	E46	M52 TU	2.8L	5L40-E	A5S 360R
528i	E39	M52 TU	2.8L	4L30-E	A4S 270R
540i	E39	M62	4.4L	5HP-24	A5S 440Z
740i, iL	E38	M62	4.4L	5HP-24	A5S 440Z
750iL	E38	M73	5.4L	5HP-30	A5S 560Z
2000					
X5	E53	M62	4.4L	5L40-E	A5S 360R
Z3 Coupe	E36/7	M52 TU	2.8L	4L30-E	A4S 270R
Z3 2.3	E36/7	M52 TU	2.5L	4L30-E	A4S 270R
Z3 2.8	E36/7	M52 TU	2.8L	4L30-E	A4S 270R
323Ci, i①	E46	M52 TU	2.5L	5L40-E	A5S 360R
323Ci, i②	E46	M52 TU	2.5L	5HP-19	A5S 325Z
328Ci, i	E46	M52 TU	2.8L	5L40-E	A5S 360R
528i	E39	M52 TU	2.8L	5L40-E	A5S 360R
540i	E39	M62	4.4L	5HP-24	A5S 440Z
740i, iL	E38	M62	4.4L	5HP-24	A5S 440Z
750iL	E38	M73	5.4L	5HP-30	A5S 560Z

Continued

Model	Chassis Series	Engine		Transmission	
		Series	Liter	Model	Type
2001					
X5 3.0i	E53	M54	3.0L	5L40-E	A5S 360R
X5 4.4i	E53	M62	4.4L	5HP-24	A5S 360R
Z3 2.5i	E36/7	M54	2.5L	5L40-E	—
Z3 3.0i	E36/7	M54	3.0L	5L40-E	—
325Ci, i	E46	M54	2.5L	5HP-19	A5S 325Z
325xi	E46	M54	2.5L	5L40-E	A5S 390R
330Ci, i	E46	M54	3.0L	5HP-19	A5S 325Z
330xi	E46	M54	3.0L	5L40-E	A5S 390R
525i Sedan	E39	M54	2.5L	5L40-E	—
525i Sport Wagon	E39	M54	2.5L	5L40-E	—
530i	E39	M54	3.0L	5L40-E	—
540i	E39	M62	4.4L	5HP-24	A5S 440Z
740i, iL	E38	M62	4.4L	5HP-24	A5S 440Z
750iL	E38	M73	5.4L	5HP-30	A5S 560Z

① — Built before March 2000.
② — Built after March 2000.

4L30-E Automatic Transmission

NOTE: On Air Bag Equipped Models, Refer To "Air Bag System Precautions" Located In The Front Of This Manual For System Disarming & Arming Procedures.

INDEX

	Page No.
Adjustments	2-212
Brake Band	2-212
Shift Interlock	2-212
Shift Selector	2-212
Description	2-210
In-Vehicle Repairs	2-212
Output Flange Oil Seal, Replace	2-213
Pressure Regulator, Replace	2-213
Pulse Sender, Replace	2-213
Solenoid Valves, Replace	2-212
Transmission Control Unit (TCU), Replace	2-213
Valve Body, Replace	2-212
Maintenance	2-211
Fluid Change	2-212
Fluid Check	2-211
Precautions	2-210
Air Bag Systems	2-210
Battery Ground Cable	2-210
Tightening Specifications	2-215
Transmission, Replace	2-213
Installation	2-214
Removal	2-213
Troubleshooting	2-210
Converter Lock-Up Clutch Does Not Apply	2-211
Converter Lock-Up Clutch Not Releasing	2-211
Converter Lock-Up Clutch Rattling	2-211
Delayed Shift From N to D	2-210
Engine Can Be Started In All Positions	2-210
Engine Cannot Be Started in N Or P	2-210
Filler Pipe Oil Loss	2-211
Hard Engaging Jolt From N to D Position	2-210
Leak Between Transmission Case & Extension	2-211
Leak Between Transmission Case & Oil Sump	2-211
Leaks	2-211
No Downshift	2-211
No Engine Brake Effect In D Position	2-211
No Kickdown Shifts, Only Partial Load/Full Load Shifts	2-211
No Kickdown	2-211
No Reverse Gear	2-210
No S (Standard) Program	2-211
No Shifts, Car Remains In Shifted Gear	2-211
No W (Winter) Program	2-211
No 1-2 Upshift	2-210
No 2-3 Upshift	2-211
No 3-4 Upshift	2-211
Oil Cooler Pipe Oil Loss	2-211
Oil Loss Through Vent	2-211
Output Oil Loss	2-211
Park Position Does Not Engage	2-210
Park Position Does Not Hold (Slips)	2-210
Poor Acceleration	2-210
Transmission Oil Temperature Too High	2-211
Transmission Plug Oil Loss	2-211
Vehicle Moves Or Creep In N Position	2-210
Wrong Shift Points, Oscillating Shifts	2-211
1-2 Shift Problems	2-211
1st Gear Slip Or Shake	2-210
2-3 Shift Problems	2-211
3-4 Shift Problems	2-211

PRECAUTIONS

AIR BAG SYSTEMS

Refer to "Air Bag System Precautions" in the front of this manual for system disarming and arming procedures.

BATTERY GROUND CABLE

Prior to service, disconnect battery ground cable and isolate as required.

DESCRIPTION

The 4L30-E is an electronically controlled four-speed automatic transmission with a lock-up clutch type converter, **Fig. 1.** Two planetary gears sets, five multiple disc clutches, one sprag and one roller clutch, and a brake band are used to provide four forward speeds and reverse. Shift control is hydraulic, where as shift pattern, shift quality and lock-up clutch are controlled electronically through five solenoid valves.

TROUBLESHOOTING

ENGINE CANNOT BE STARTED IN N OR P

1. Selector lever not in N or P.
2. Shift linkage between selector lever and transmission not correctly adjusted.
3. Transmission switch faulty.

ENGINE CAN BE STARTED IN ALL POSITIONS

1. Selector lever not in N or P.
2. Shift linkage between selector lever and transmission not correctly adjusted.
3. Transmission switch faulty.

PARK POSITION DOES NOT ENGAGE

1. Shift linkage between selector lever and transmission not correctly adjusted.
2. Excessive friction in parking lock mechanism.

PARK POSITION DOES NOT HOLD (SLIPS)

1. Shift linkage between selector lever and transmission not correctly adjusted.

DELAYED SHIFT FROM N TO D

1. Transmission oil level too low.
2. Insufficient oil pressure.

1ST GEAR SLIP OR SHAKE

1. Insufficient oil pressure.
2. Torque converter faulty.
3. Brake band not correctly adjusted.
4. Brake band oil circuit oil loss.
5. 4th gear freewheel faulty.
6. Planetary gear set freewheel faulty.

NO REVERSE GEAR

1. Shift linkage between selector lever and transmission not correctly adjusted.
2. Oil filter dirty.
3. Reverse gear clutch faulty.

VEHICLE MOVES OR CREEP IN N POSITION

1. Shift linkage between selector lever and transmission not correctly adjusted.
2. Brake band adjusted too tight.

HARD ENGAGING JOLT FROM N TO D POSITION

1. Brake band locked or faulty.

POOR ACCELERATION

1. Emergency shift program activated.
2. Torque converter faulty.

NO 1-2 UPSHIFT

1. Shift linkage between selector lever and transmission not correctly adjusted.
2. Solenoid valve/supply wire faulty.
3. 2nd gear clutch oil loss.

1-2 SHIFT PROBLEMS

1. 2nd gear clutch oil pressure incorrect.
2. 2nd gear clutch oil loss.
3. 1/2 gear clutch pressure reservoir valve seized or leaks.

NO 2-3 UPSHIFT

1. Shift linkage between selector lever and transmission not correctly adjusted.
2. Solenoid valve/supply wire faulty.
3. Valve body shift valve faulty.

2-3 SHIFT PROBLEMS

1. Brake band not adjusted correctly.
2. Solenoid valve brake band faulty/blocked.
3. 3rd gear clutch oil loss.
4. Brake band reservoir return pipe oil loss.
5. Oil pressure incorrect.

NO 3-4 UPSHIFT

1. Shift linkage between selector lever and transmission not correctly adjusted.
2. Solenoid valve/supply wire faulty.
3. 3rd gear clutch oil loss.

3-4 SHIFT PROBLEMS

1. 4th gear clutch oil loss.
2. Oil pressure incorrect.
3. 4th gear overdrive clutch does not release.

CONVERTER LOCK-UP CLUTCH DOES NOT APPLY

1. Solenoid valve/supply wire faulty.
2. Oil circuit oil loss.

CONVERTER LOCK-UP CLUTCH RATTLING

1. Torque converter faulty.
2. Insufficient oil pressure.

CONVERTER LOCK-UP CLUTCH NOT RELEASING

1. Solenoid valve/supply wire faulty.
2. Return pipe plugged.

NO S (STANDARD) PROGRAM

1. Program switch faulty.
2. Supply wire break.

NO W (WINTER) PROGRAM

1. Program switch faulty.
2. Supply wire break.

NO KICKDOWN

1. Kickdown switch faulty.
2. Supply wire break.

NO DOWNSHIFT

1. Solenoid valves 1/2 and 3/4 faulty, supply wire faulty.
2. Valve body shift valves faulty.

NO ENGINE BRAKE EFFECT IN D POSITION

1. 4th gear overdrive clutch defective.

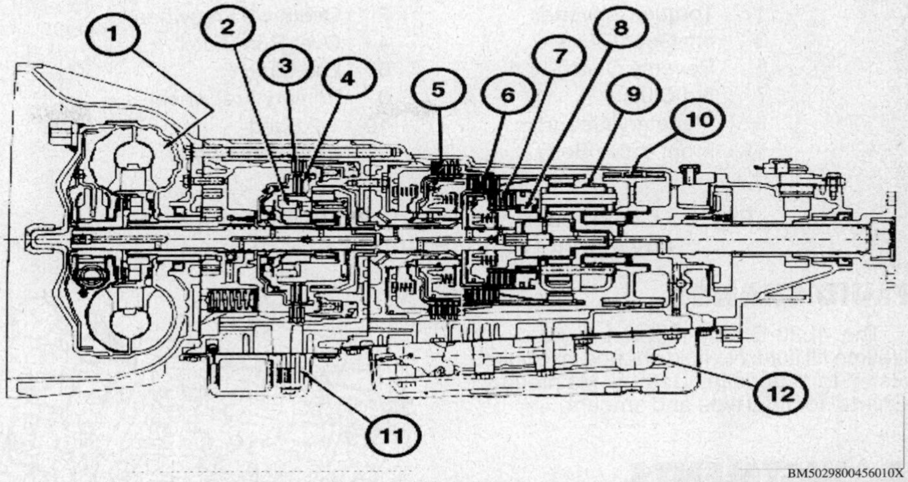

Fig. 1 Cross-section view of 4L30-E four-speed automatic transmission (Part 1 of 2)

2. Oil circuit oil loss.

TRANSMISSION OIL TEMPERATURE TOO HIGH

1. Oil level too high.
2. Converter lock-up clutch not functioning.
3. Extreme load in emergency running program or M program.

OIL LOSS THROUGH VENT

1. Oil level too high.
2. Converter lock-up clutch not functioning.
3. Extreme load in emergency running program or M program.

LEAKS

1. Input shaft O-ring faulty.
2. Converter leaks at welded seam.
3. Converter radial oil seal leaks.

LEAK BETWEEN TRANSMISSION CASE & OIL SUMP

1. Oil sump gasket damaged.

TRANSMISSION PLUG OIL LOSS

1. O-ring faulty.
2. Transmission plug not tight.

OUTPUT OIL LOSS

1. Output radial oil seal damaged.

FILLER PIPE OIL LOSS

1. Filler pipe sealing plug faulty.

LEAK BETWEEN TRANSMISSION CASE & EXTENSION

1. Mounting bolts loose.
2. Gasket damaged.

OIL COOLER PIPE OIL LOSS

1. Coupling loose.
2. Oil cooler pipe damaged.
3. Transmission oil cooler leak.

WRONG SHIFT POINTS, OSCILLATING SHIFTS

1. Engine idling speed too high or low.
2. Idling speed control valve faulty.

NO KICKDOWN SHIFTS, ONLY PARTIAL LOAD/FULL LOAD SHIFTS

1. Wire harness faulty.
2. Kickdown switch faulty.
3. Kickdown switch not adjusted correctly.

NO SHIFTS, CAR REMAINS IN SHIFTED GEAR

1. No positive supply/fuse faulty.
2. Signal wire faulty.
3. Switch faulty.

MAINTENANCE

FLUID CHECK

1. Warm vehicle and transmission.
2. Park vehicle of level area without load.
3. Use suitable programmed scan tool to ensure transmission fluid temperature is 68–86°F. **Do not check fluid level if temperature is more than 122°F, as level will be too low.**
4. With engine running, switch air conditioning on.
5. Fully apply parking brake and firmly press brake pedal.
6. Move gear selector lever through each gear position, pausing briefly in each gear.
7. With engine running, place selector lever in Park position.
8. Remove filler plug.
9. If small stream of oil runs out, fluid level is correct.
10. If no oil runs out, fluid level is too low. Add oil until it starts to overflow.
11. Install oil filler plug with engine running and tighten to specifications.

1	Torque Converter	2	Overdrive Freewheel
3	4th Gear Clutch	4	Over Run Clutch
5	Reverse Clutch	6	2nd Clutch
7	3rd Clutch	8	Primary Freewheel
9	Planetary Geartrain	10	1-2 Band
11	Front Valve Body	12	Rear Valve Body

BM5029800456020X

Fig. 1 Cross-section view of 4L30-E four-speed automatic transmission (Part 2 of 2)

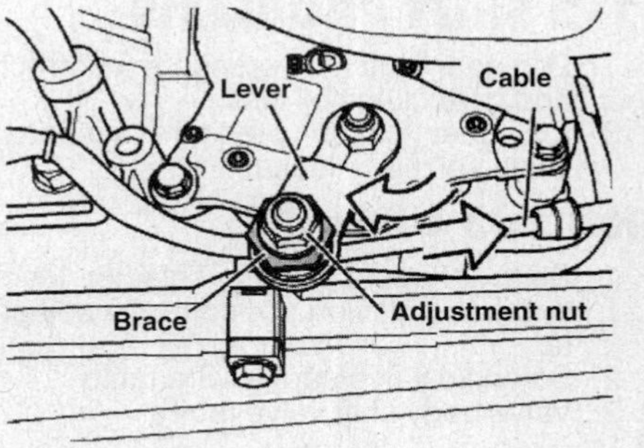

BM5029800457000X

Fig. 2 Selector adjustment

FLUID CHANGE

The 4L30-E transmission is filled with lifetime fill fluid. No fluid change is required. Refer to "Lubricant Data & Maintenance Charts" for fluid type and amount.

ADJUSTMENTS

SHIFT SELECTOR

1. Place selector lever in P position.
2. Brace bolt using holder tool No. 24 5 220, or equivalent, and loosen adjusting nut, **Fig. 2.**
3. Press lever forward to park position.
4. Press cable rod in direction opposite travel and release.
5. Secure cable rod with nut. Torque adjusting nut to specifications.
6. Ensure console and shifter assembly are properly secured.
7. Disconnect shift selector rod (1) from lower end of shift selector lever (2),
8. Rotate transmission lever (3) toward rear of vehicle, then forward two detents into Neutral position.
9. Place manual shift lever (4) in Neutral position and hold lever against forward stop in neutral gate (5).
10. Adjust selector rod length until pin (6) will freely enter hole in lower shift lever, with manual lever held forward against stop.
11. Shorten selector rod by rotating pin and adjuster 1–2 turns, reconnect rod to lower selector lever, then check transmission for proper operation.

SHIFT INTERLOCK

1. Move selector lever into P position (front detent).
2. Loosen adjusting screw enough to move cable slightly in axial direction to bracket.
3. Remove key from ignition switch.
4. Press interlock lever down into limit position.
5. Tighten adjusting screw to specifications.

BRAKE BAND

1. Raise and support vehicle.
2. Remove plug and drain transmission fluid into suitable container.
3. Remove oil pan.
4. Remove mounting bolts using socket tool No. 24 5 180, or equivalent, and oil filter.
5. Remove mounting bolts using socket tool, then the servo piston cover and gasket.

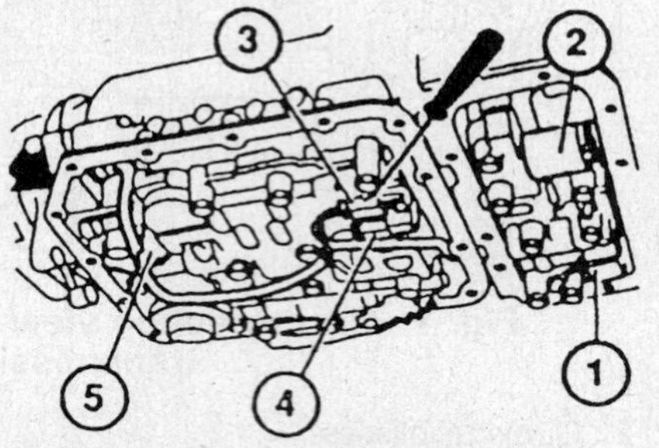

Copyrighted Material Reprinted with Permission from Hydra-Matic Div., GM Corp.

TH5029100038000X

Fig. 3 Solenoid valve electrical connectors

6. Grip servo piston fitting using suitable open end wrench and loosen locknut.
7. While holding fitting using open end wrench, tighten adjusting bolt to specifications.
8. Loosen adjusting bolt five turns and tighten locking nut.
9. Clean cover sealing surface.
10. Install cover with new gasket and tighten mounting bolts to specifications.
11. Install new oil filter and tighten mounting bolts to specifications.
12. Clean oil pan sealing surface.
13. Install oil pan with new gasket and new microencapsulated bolts.
14. Tighten oil pan mounting bolts evenly and only once to specifications. **Do not tighten diagonally or any further.**

IN-VEHICLE REPAIRS

VALVE BODY, REPLACE

Removal

1. Remove both oil pans and the transmission fluid filter.
2. Disconnect solenoid valve electrical connectors 1–5, **Fig. 3.**
3. Remove transfer case valve body mounting bolts using socket tool No. 24 5 180, or equivalent.
4. Remove transfer case valve body, then remove servo piston cover.
5. Remove main body valve body mounting bolts using socket tool No. 24 5 180, or equivalent.
6. Carefully lift off main valve body with gasket, pulling overrun valve connecting lever off of pawl. Overrun valve should remain in main valve body.
7. Separate transfer plate from valve body and remove gasket.

Installation

1. Mount gasket and transfer plate on main valve body. Center gasket using alignment tool No. 24 5 140, or equivalent.
2. Place two check balls in main case, **Fig. 4.** Secure check balls with petroleum jelly.
3. Secure gasket with petroleum jelly and place main valve body on main case. Attach connecting lever on overrun valve and operating lever.
4. Install main valve body mounting bolts and tighten crosswise.
5. Secure lockplate, then install servo piston cover.
6. Place check ball in transfer case. Secure with petroleum jelly.
7. Ensure check ball is installed at position (1), **Fig. 5.** Mount gasket (2) with oval opening (3) at check ball. Mount transfer plate (4) and second gasket (5).
8. Place transfer case valve body on transfer case and install mounting bolts. Tighten bolts in a crossing pattern.
9. Connect solenoid valve plugs and install transmission fluid pans.

SOLENOID VALVES, REPLACE

1. Drain fluid and remove transmission fluid pan.
2. Remove 2nd/3rd gear solenoid, 1st/2nd and 3rd/4th gear and converter lockup clutch solenoid valves as follows:
   a. Carefully pry off solenoid valve electrical connector using suitable screwdriver. **Do not pull on wires.**
   b. Pull out solenoid valve securing pin.
   c. Pull solenoid valve out of valve body.
3. Remove brake band solenoid valve as follows:
   a. Remove transmission fluid filter.
   b. Carefully pry off electrical connector using suitable screwdriver. **Do not pull on wires.**
   c. Press in solenoid valve, and pull out securing pin using pliers, then remove brake band solenoid valve.
4. Reverse procedure to install. Coat seals with petroleum jelly.

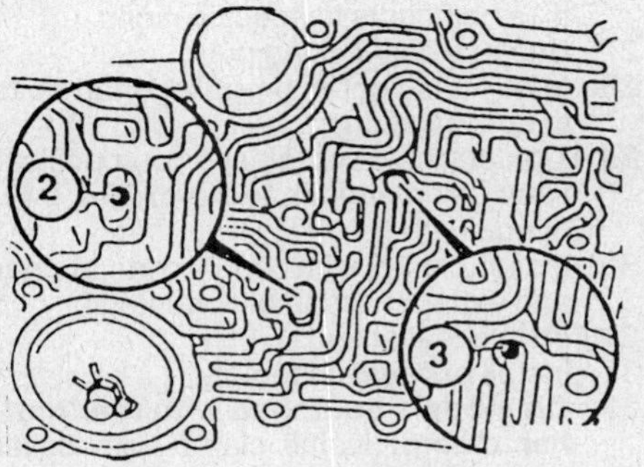

Copyrighted Material Reprinted with Permission from Hydra-Matic Div., GM Corp.

TH5029100039000X

Fig. 4 Main valve body check ball location

PRESSURE REGULATOR, REPLACE

1. Drain fluid and remove pan.
2. Carefully remove pressure regulator electrical wires and remove mounting bolt.
3. Remove mounting clip, then remove pressure regulator.
4. Reverse procedure to install. Install mounting clip with curved surface facing out.

PULSE SENDER, REPLACE

1. Drain fluid and remove pan.
2. Disconnect pulse sender electrical connector and remove mounting bolt.
3. Pull or press out pulse sender.
4. Reverse procedure to install. Lubricate O-ring with petroleum jelly.

OUTPUT FLANGE OIL SEAL, REPLACE

1. Disconnect propeller shaft.
2. Remove output flange by securing using holder tool No. 23 0 020, or equivalent, and loosening collar nut using suitable socket.
3. Lift out radial oil seal.
4. Reverse procedure to install, noting the following:
   a. Lubricate sealing lip with transmission fluid.
   b. Drive radial oil seal using installation tool No. 23 1 370, or equivalent.

TRANSMISSION CONTROL UNIT (TCU), REPLACE

The transmission control is located on the right side of the engine compartment.

1. Remove battery from vehicle, then remove control unit cover.
2. **On 318 models,** remove DME control unit from holder to allow access to TCU.
3. **On all models,** press TCU downward off of spring retainers.
4. Pull TCU forward through opening.
5. Reverse procedure to install.

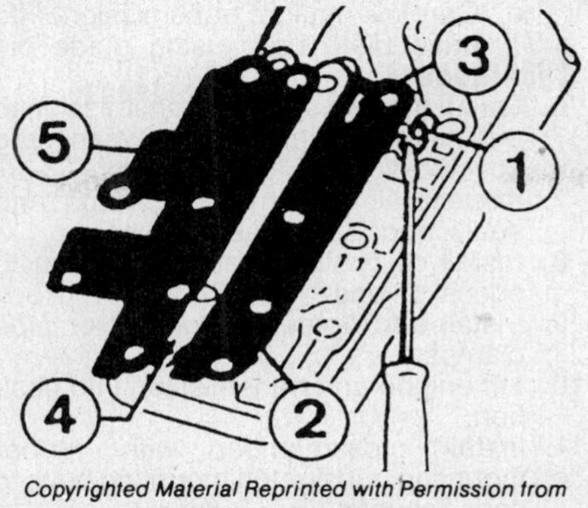

Copyrighted Material Reprinted with Permission from Hydra-Matic Div.,,GM Corp.

TH5029100040000X

Fig. 5 Transfer case valve body check ball location

TRANSMISSION

REPLACE

REMOVAL

1. **On models equipped with Automatic Speed Control and Traction Control (ASC+T),** remove throttle body to prevent damage when removing transmission.
2. **On all models,** raise and support vehicle.
3. Drain transmission fluid into suitable container.
4. Disconnect oxygen sensor and unclip cable from retainer.
5. Loosen exhaust manifold flange bolts.
6. Loosen exhaust bracket clamp.
7. Disconnect rubber ring on rear axle carrier.
8. If rear muffler is bracket mount, disconnect left and righthand rear retaining brackets.
9. If rear muffler is clamp mount, Loosen collar nut with clamp on final muffler.
10. Remove exhaust system downward.
11. Remove heat shield.
12. Remove exhaust assembly mounting brackets and clamp.
13. Loosen threaded sleeve a few turns using wrench tool No. 26 1 040, or equivalent.
14. Remove propeller shaft transmission mounting bolts.
15. Remove joint disc transmission mounting bolts.
16. Remove center mount mounting bolts or nuts. **Do not let propeller shaft fall into joints.**
17. Bend propeller shaft down at center mount and remove from transmission centering pin. Tie up to one side.
18. Remove shifting cable.
19. Turn bayonet lock counterclockwise, remove plug and lift wiring harness out of holder.
20. Disconnect speed sender connector.
21. Remove crankcase side opening cover.
22. Remove torque converter to drive flange mounting bolts using socket tool No. 24 1 110, or equivalent.

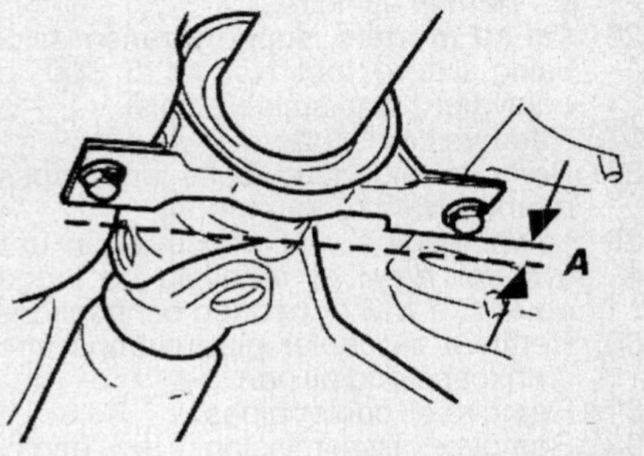

BM5029800459000X

Fig. 6 Center bearing mount preload

23. **On Z3 with 1.9L engine and 318 models, if supporting engine from above,** proceed as follows:
    a. Ensure wipers are in park position and remove wiper arms.
    b. Remove air collector grille cover.
    c. Loosen end wall wiring harness and bend insulation sheet to one side.
    d. Remove cable channel screws.
    e. Press wiper wiring harness to one side.
    f. Remove mounting screws and wiring harness holder.
    g. Remove air collector by pulling up and towards driver's side.
    h. Remove cable duct from engine rear.
    i. Mount fixture tool No. 00 0 200, or equivalent, and hook to crankcase eye.
    j. Tighten spindle.
24. **On Z3 with 1.9L engine and 318 models, if supporting engine from below,** proceed as follows:
    a. Attach engine rear loading fixture tool No. 11 8 022, or equivalent, to left and righthand control arms.
    b. Ensure engine oil pan rest securely on tool.
    c. Tighten knurled screws until tool contacts engine oil pan.
25. **On Z3 with 2.5L and 2.8L engines, and 323 models,** proceed as follows:
    a. Ensure wipers are in park position and remove wiper arms.
    b. Remove air collector grille cover.
    c. Loosen end wall wiring harness and bend insulation sheet to one side.
    d. Remove cable channel screws.
    e. Press wiper wiring harness to one side.
    f. Remove mounting screws and wiring harness holder.
    g. Remove air collector by pulling up and toward driver's side.
    h. Remove injection pipe cover.
    i. Install engine mounting fixture tool No. 11 0 030, or equivalent, through intake manifold and into crankcase bracket.
    j. Mount fixture tool No. 00 0 200, or equivalent, and attach to engine mounting fixture.

k. Tighten spindle.
26. **On all models,** support transmission using fixture tool No. 24 5 300, or equivalent, and suitable hoist.
27. Remove cross tube.
28. Remove mounting bolts and crossmember with rubber mount.
29. Lower engine and transmission until cylinder head or manifold no longer abuts fire wall or heating connections.
30. Remove oil cooler pipe clamps from crankcase and oil pan.
31. Remove oil cooler pipes.
32. Remove transmission to engine mounting bolts.
33. Secure torque converter to transmission housing using fixture tool No. 24 4 080, or equivalent. Flat side of fixture must face converter.
34. Remove transmission from engine.

INSTALLATION

1. Inspect dowel sleeves and replace as necessary.
2. Ensure cover plate is correctly positioned.
3. Secure torque converter to transmission housing using fixture tool No. 24 4 080, or equivalent. Flat side of fixture must face converter.
4. Support and lift transmission into position using suitable hoist.
5. **On models equipped with sheet metal flywheel,** proceed as follows:
   a. Drive plate bore must point perpendicularly to guard opening center.
   b. Turn transmission torque converter until tab bores point to flywheel bores center.
   c. Install guide pin tool No. 24 2 300, or equivalent, into tab.
   d. Lift transmission until drive plate bore is reached.
   e. Carefully guide transmission into drive plate bore using guide pin tool.
6. **On all models,** tighten transmission to engine mounting bolts with washers to specifications.
7. Inspect oil cooler pipe O-rings and seals, and replace as necessary.
8. Install oil cooler pipes and tighten to specifications.
9. Install and tighten all oil cooler pipe clamps.
10. Lift engine and transmission into position.
11. Install crossmember with rubber mounting and tighten mounting bolts to specifications.
12. Remove engine support.
13. Install air collector, wiring harness holder and mounting screws.
14. Install cable channel mounting screws.
15. Bend insulation sheet back and tighten wiper wiring harness.
16. Install air collector grille, then the wiper arms.
17. Install cross tube.
18. Install torque converter to drive flange bolts and tighten to specifications using socket tool No. 24 1 110, or equivalent.
19. Connect speed sender connector.
20. Install wire harness, plug and bayonet lock.
21. Install shifting cable.
22. Inspect center propeller shaft bearing and replace as necessary.
23. Coat center bearing with Molykote Longterm 2 grease, or equivalent.
24. Install joint onto transmission and bend shaft up into position.
25. Preload center mount forward 0.0787–0.1575 inch, **Fig. 6.**
26. Replace stop nuts and tighten final drive joint nuts to specifications.
27. Replace self-locking nuts.
28. Install and tighten propeller shaft bolts to specifications.
29. Tighten threaded sleeve to specifications using wrench tool No. 26 1 040, or equivalent.
30. Install clamp with long collar at rear and exhaust assembly brackets.
31. Install heat shield.
32. Install exhaust assembly.
33. **On models equipped with rear muffler clamp,** install clamp with collar nut.
34. **On models equipped with rear muffler bracket,** proceed as follows:
   a. Inspect rubber mount for damage and replace as necessary.
   b. Preload rubber mount forward 0.59 inch.
   c. Connect left and righthand side rear retaining brackets.
35. **On all models,** inspect rubber gaskets and replace as necessary.
36. Install rubber ring on rear axle carrier.
37. Install exhaust bracket clamp.
38. Inspect exhaust manifold seal and replace as necessary.
39. Lightly coat exhaust manifold threads with suitable copper paste and install new self-locking nuts.
40. Align exhaust bracket without tension.
41. Ensure tailpipe is properly positioned relative to body cutout. If necessary, loosen flange joint and rubber suspensions, align and fasten.
42. Clip cable to retainer and connect oxygen sensor connector.
43. **On models equipped with Automatic Speed Control and Traction Control (ASC+T),** install throttle body.

TIGHTENING SPECIFICATIONS

Year	Component	Torque, Ft. Lbs.
1998–2000	Brake Band Adjusting Bolt	44①
	Brake Band Adjusting Bolt Locknut	15
	Converter Bell Housing	31
	Extension	24
	Intermediate Plate	18
	Manual Shift Shaft Lever	84①
	Oil Cooler Pipe, Front	15
	Oil Cooler Pipe, Rear	27
	Oil Filler Plug	26
	Oil Filter	15
	Oil Pan	108①
	Output Flange Collar Nut	74
	Parking Lock Holder	84①
	Parking Lock Spring Plug	12
	Pressure Regulator	84①
	Propeller Shaft Center Support	15
	Propeller Shaft Coupling	44
	Propeller Shaft Slinging Ring	84①
	Propeller Shaft Universal Joint (M10 8.8)	35
	Propeller Shaft Universal Joint	②
	Reinforcement Plate	17
	Servo Piston Cover	18
	Shift Cable	11
	Shift Cable Adjusting Screw	84①
	Shift Console To Tunnel	60①
	Shift Interlock	60①
	Shift Switch	40①
	Solenoid Valve	84①
	Torque Converter Bell Housing Radial Seal	27①
	Torque Converter Radial Seal	27①
	Torque Converter To Flywheel	③
	Torque Converter Oil Pan	108①
	Transmission To Engine	④
	Valve Body	15

① — Inch lbs.
② — M10 10.9, 44 ft. lbs.; M12 8.8, 60 ft. lbs.; M12 10.9, 74 ft. lbs.
③ — M8, 19 ft. lbs.; M10, 33 ft. lbs.
④ — M8 Hex, 18 ft. lbs.; M8 Torx, 15 ft. lbs.; M10 Hex, 33 ft. lbs.; M10 Torx, 31 ft. lbs.; M12 Hex, 60 ft. lbs.; M12 Torx, 53 ft. lbs.

ZF 5HP Automatic Transmissions

NOTE: On Air Bag Equipped Models, Refer To "Air Bag System Precautions" Located In The Front Of This Manual For System Disarming & Arming Procedures.

INDEX

	Page No.
Adjustments	2-219
Gearshift Linkage	2-219
Shift Interlock	2-219
Shift Selector	2-219
Description	2-216
In-Vehicle Repairs	2-219
Bearing, Replace	2-223
Transmission Extension	2-223
EPROM, Replace	2-219
Oil Filter, Replace	2-221
Oil Pan, Replace	2-220
ZF 5HP-18EH Transmission	2-220
ZF 5HP-24EH Transmission	2-220
ZF 5HP-30EH Transmission	2-220
Oil Seal, Replace	2-221
Manual Shift Valve Shaft	2-222
Output Flange	2-221
Position Switch	2-222
Output Flange, Replace	2-222
ZF 5HP-18EH Transmission	2-222
ZF 5HP-30EH Transmission	2-223
Parking Lock, Replace	2-221
Pressure Regulator, Replace	2-221
Pulse Generators, Replace	2-221
ZF 5HP-18EH Transmission	2-221
ZF 5HP-24EH & ZF 5HP-30EH Transmissions	2-221
Shift Cable, Replace	2-220
Shift Selector, Replace	2-219
Solenoid Valves, Replace	2-221
ZF 5HP-18EH Transmission	2-221
ZF 5HP-24EH Transmission	2-221
ZF 5HP-30EH Transmission	2-221
Transmission Control Unit (TCU), Replace	2-223
528, 540, 740 & 750	2-223
M3 & 328	2-223
Valve Body, Replace	2-220
ZF 5HP-18EH Transmission	2-220
ZF 5HP-24EH Transmission	2-220
ZF 5HP-30EH Transmission	2-221
Wiring Harness, Replace	2-221
ZF 5HP-24EH & ZF 5HP-30EH Transmissions	2-221
Maintenance	2-219
Fluid Change	2-219
Fluid Check	2-219
Precautions	2-216
Air Bag Systems	2-216
Battery Ground Cable	2-216
Tightening Specifications	2-226
Transmission, Replace	2-223
540, 740 & 750	2-224
M3 & 328	2-223
X5	2-225
Troubleshooting	2-216
Back-up Lights Do Not Light	2-217
Converter Bell Housing Oil Leak	2-218
Converter Lock-Up Clutch Always Engaged (Engine Dies When Moving Off In D)	2-218
Engine Can Be Started In All Positions	2-217
Engine Cannot Be Started in N Or P	2-216
Engine Dies From 2-3/3-2 Shift (Overlapped Control)	2-218
Engine Dies From 4-5/5-4 Shift (Overlapped Control)	2-218
Engine Dies When Stopping Car In Position D	2-218
Engine Spins In 2-1 Shift	2-218
Engine Spins In 2-3/3-2 Shift	2-218
Engine Spins In 4-3 Shift	2-218
Engine Spins In 4-5/5-4 Shift	2-218
Hard Engaging Jolt From N to R or P to R Position	2-217
Hard Engaging Jolt In Position R	2-217
Hard Shift Impact N to D	2-217
Hard Shift Jolts	2-217
Leak Between Transmission Case & Oil Sump	2-218
Manual Shift Valve Shaft Leaks	2-218
No Converter Lock-Up Clutch	2-218
No Engine Braking	2-218
No Kickdown Shifts, Only Partial Load/Full Load Shifts	2-219
No Manual 4-3/3-2 Downshifts	2-218
No Manual 5-4 Downshift	2-218
No Position Forward Or Reverse Engagement	2-218
No Reverse Gear	2-217
No S (Standard) Program Or S Program Only	2-219
No Shift (Warm Or Cold)	2-217
No Shifts, Car Remains In Shifted Gear	2-219
No Transmission Power In Position D	2-217
No W (Winter) Program Or W Program Only	2-219
No 1-2 Shift	2-217
No 1st Gear, No Braking Action	2-218
No 2-1 Shift	2-217
No 2-3 Shift	2-217
No 3-2 Shift	2-217
No 3-4 Shift	2-217
No 4-3 Shift	2-217
No 4-5 Shift	2-217
No 5-4 Shift	2-217
Noise In All Positions	2-218
Oil Cooler Pipes Leak	2-219
Output Shaft Leaks	2-218
Park Position Does Not Engage	2-216
Park Position Does Not Hold (Slips)	2-216
Shift From Full Load To Kickdown Too Long	2-218
Shift Speed & Quality Generally Not Good	2-219
Shift Transition Too Hard	2-218
Shift Transitions In Zero Load Positions, Full Load Shifts Too Hard	2-218
Shift Transitions Of Full Load Shifts & Kickdown Shifts Too Long	2-218
Transmission Case Plugs Leak	2-219
Transmission Plug Leaks	2-218
Vehicle Moves In 2nd Gear	2-217
Vehicle Moves In 3rd Gear	2-217
Vehicle Moves In 4th Gear	2-218
Vehicle Moves Or Creep	2-217
Wrong Shift Points, Oscillating Shifts	2-219

PRECAUTIONS

AIR BAG SYSTEMS

Refer to "Air Bag System Precautions" in the front of this manual for system disarming and arming procedures.

BATTERY GROUND CABLE

Prior to service, disconnect battery ground cable and isolate as required.

DESCRIPTION

These transmissions are electronically controlled, five-speed units with a lock-up clutch type torque converters, **Fig. 1.** Three planetary gear sets (Wilson gearing), three rotating multiple disc clutches, four multiple disc brake-clutches and two sprag clutches (freewheelers) are used to provide the five forward speeds and reverse operation.

TROUBLESHOOTING

PARK POSITION DOES NOT ENGAGE

1. Shift linkage between selector lever and transmission not correctly adjusted.
2. Excessive friction in parking lock mechanism.

PARK POSITION DOES NOT HOLD (SLIPS)

1. Shift linkage between selector lever and transmission not correctly adjusted.

ENGINE CANNOT BE STARTED IN N OR P

1. Shift linkage between selector lever

and transmission not correctly adjusted.
2. Transmission switch faulty.
3. Starter motor inhibit relay or power line defective.

ENGINE CAN BE STARTED IN ALL POSITIONS

1. Shift linkage between selector lever and transmission not correctly adjusted.
2. Transmission switch faulty.
3. Starter motor inhibit relay or power line defective.

NO REVERSE GEAR

1. Shift linkage between selector lever and transmission not correctly adjusted.
2. Clutch B destroyed.
3. Brakes D destroyed. (There will also be no engine braking effect in position 2, 1st gear, in this case.)
4. Brake G destroyed.
5. Valve body faulty.
6. Signal wire to solenoid No. 3 grounded.
7. Reverse gear valve piston lock not in parked position.

HARD ENGAGING JOLT FROM N TO R OR P TO R POSITION

1. Idling speed too high.
2. Valve body faulty.

HARD SHIFT JOLTS

1. Modulation valve malfunctions.
2. Pressure regulator wire faulty.
3. Pressure regulator faulty.

HARD ENGAGING JOLT IN POSITION R

1. Brakes D damper malfunctions.
2. Modulation pressure too high.
3. Pressure regulator wire faulty.
4. Pressure regulator faulty.

BACK-UP LIGHTS DO NOT LIGHT

1. Transmission switch faulty.
2. Shift actuation between selector lever and transmission set incorrectly.

VEHICLE MOVES OR CREEP

1. Shift linkage between selector lever and transmission not correctly adjusted.
2. Clutch A faulty (welded solid).

NO TRANSMISSION POWER IN POSITION D

1. Clutch A destroyed.
2. 1st gear one-way gear faulty.
3. Shift linkage between selector lever and transmission not correctly adjusted.
4. Clutch A damper malfunctions.
5. Pressure regulator wire faulty.
6. Pressure regulator faulty.
7. Modulation valve malfunctions.

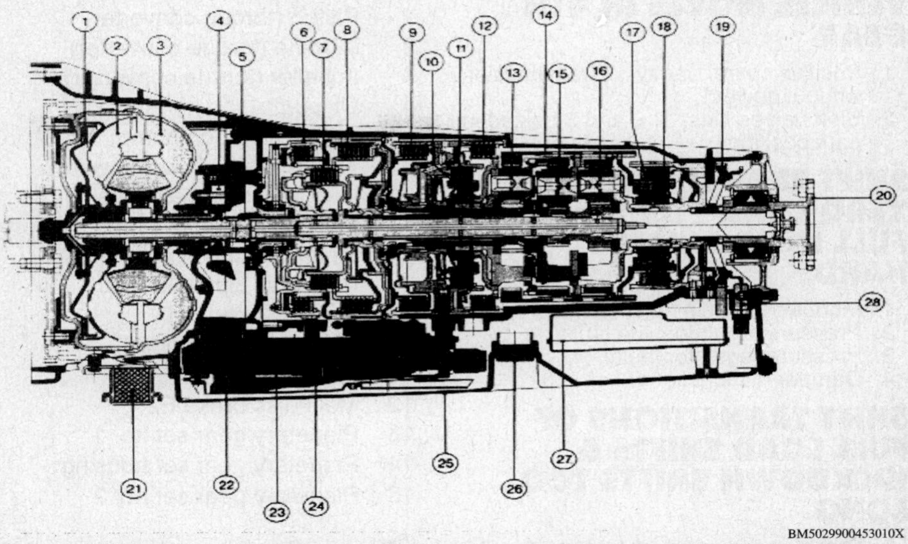

Fig. 1 Cross-section view of ZF five-speed automatic transmission (Part 1 of 2)

HARD SHIFT IMPACT N TO D

1. Idling speed too high.
2. Valve body faulty.

NO SHIFT (WARM OR COLD)

1. Valve body faulty.

NO 1-2 SHIFT

1. Output speed sensor wire faulty.
2. Output speed sensor faulty.
3. Solenoid No. 1 signal wire grounded.
4. Shift valve No. 1 seized in park position.
5. Damper C2 or clutch valve C1 seized.
6. Shift valve No. 3 seized in park position.
7. Brakes C1 and C2 faulty.
8. Insufficient brakes C1 and C2 oil supply.

NO 2-1 SHIFT

1. Solenoid No. 1 signal or positive wire faulty.
2. Solenoid No. 1 faulty.
3. Shift valve seized in pushed position.
4. Valve body faulty.

NO 2-3 SHIFT

1. Solenoid No. 2 signal wire faulty.
2. Solenoid No. 2 faulty.
3. Shift valve No. 2 seized in pushed position.
4. Pulling valve No. 2-3 seized in parked position.
5. Clutch F faulty.
6. Clutch F oil supply insufficient.

NO 3-2 SHIFT

1. Solenoid No. 2 signal or positive wire faulty.
2. Shift valve seized in parked position.
3. Pulling valve No. 2-3 seized in pushed position.

NO 3-4 SHIFT

1. Solenoid No. 3 signal wire ground.
2. Solenoid No. 3 faulty.
3. Shift valve seized in pushed position.
4. Damper E seized.
5. Clutch E faulty.
6. Clutch E oil supply insufficient.

NO 4-3 SHIFT

1. Solenoid No. 3 signal or positive wire faulty.
2. Shift valve No. 3 seized in park position.
3. Brake band C2 faulty. Shift 1-2 is not working properly.
4. Insufficient brake C2 oil supply.

NO 4-5 SHIFT

1. Shift valve No. 1 signal or positive lead defective.
2. Shift valve No. 4 seized in parked position.
3. Damper C2 blocked.

Valve body faulty.

NO 5-4 SHIFT

1. Solenoid No. 1 signal wire grounded.
2. Solenoid No. 1 faulty.
3. Shift valve No. 4 seized in pushed position.
4. Clutch A faulty. No 1st to 4th gear.

VEHICLE MOVES IN 2ND GEAR

1. Solenoid No. 1 signal or positive wire faulty. No 5th gear.
2. Shift valve No. 1 seized in park position.

VEHICLE MOVES IN 3RD GEAR

1. Solenoids Nos. 1 and 2 signal or positive wire faulty. No 5th gear.)
2. Shift valves Nos. 1 and 2 seized in park position.

1	Piston (torque converter)
2	Turbine (torque converter)
3	Impeller (torque converter)
4	Oil pump (crescent moon pump)
5	Transmission housing with integral clutch bell housing
6	Multi-disc clutch C
7	Multi-disc clutch A
8	Multi-disc clutch B
9	Multi-disc clutch D
10	Freewheel, 2nd gear
11	Multi-disc brake E1
12	Multi-disc brake E2
13	Planetary gear set no. 1
14	Planetary gear set housing
15	Planetary gear set no. 2
16	Planetary gear set no. 3
17	Freewheel, 1 st gear
18	Multi-disc brake F
19	Park gear wheel
20	Output flange
21	Oil cooler
22	Oil filter
23	Hydraulic shift unit
24	Speed sensor (turbine)
25	Oil sump
26	Oil filter plug (level checks/ adjustments)
27	Reservoir
28	Speed sensor (output)

BM5029900453020X

Fig. 1 Cross-section view of ZF five-speed automatic transmission (Part 2 of 2)

VEHICLE MOVES IN 4TH GEAR

1. Positive wire faulty. (Transmission without power.)
2. Shift valves Nos. 1, 2 and 3 seized in park position.

SHIFT TRANSITIONS IN ZERO LOAD POSITIONS, FULL LOAD SHIFTS TOO HARD

1. Modulation valve function not proper.
2. Pressure regulator wire faulty.
3. Pressure regulator faulty.
4. Damper malfunctions.

SHIFT TRANSITIONS OF FULL LOAD SHIFTS & KICKDOWN SHIFTS TOO LONG

1. Pressure reducing valves Nos. 1 and 2 not working properly.
2. Modulation valve function not proper.
3. Pressure regulator faulty.

ENGINE DIES FROM 2-3/ 3-2 SHIFT (OVERLAPPED CONTROL)

1. Shift Valve No. 4 signal or positive lead faulty.
2. Solenoid No. 4 faulty.
3. Damper G aperture clogged.
4. Damper F moves too hard.
5. Pull valve 2-3/3-2 moves too hard.

ENGINE DIES FROM 4-5/ 5-4 SHIFT (OVERLAPPED CONTROL)

1. Shift Valve No. 5 signal or positive lead faulty.
2. Solenoid No. 5 faulty.
3. Pull/push valve No. 2 moves too hard.
4. Damper C2 malfunctions.
5. Pull valve 4-5/5-4 moves too hard.
6. Damper A moves too hard.

ENGINE DIES WHEN STOPPING CAR IN POSITION D

1. Solenoid No. 6 signal wire grounded.
2. Converter lock-up clutch valve seized in pushed position.
3. Solenoid No. 6 faulty.

SHIFT FROM FULL LOAD TO KICKDOWN TOO LONG

1. Plates broken.
2. Valve body faulty.

ENGINE SPINS IN 2-1 SHIFT

1. Poor friction torque at plates.
2. 1st gear one-way gear not working properly.

ENGINE SPINS IN 2-3/3-2 SHIFT

1. Poor friction torque at plates.
2. Valve body faulty.

ENGINE SPINS IN 4-3 SHIFT

1. Poor friction torque at plates.
2. 3rd gear one-way gear not working properly.

ENGINE SPINS IN 4-5/5-4 SHIFT

1. Poor friction torque at plates.
2. Valve body faulty.

NO ENGINE BRAKING

1. Clutch A damaged.
2. Valve body faulty.

NO MANUAL 5-4 DOWNSHIFT

1. Clutch A damaged.
2. Valve body faulty.

NO MANUAL 4-3/3-2 DOWNSHIFTS

Valve body faulty.

NO 1ST GEAR, NO BRAKING ACTION

1. Clutch D faulty.
2. Valve body faulty.

SHIFT TRANSITION TOO HARD

1. Torque converter faulty.
2. Valve body faulty.

NO CONVERTER LOCK-UP CLUTCH

1. Solenoid No. 6 signal or positive wire faulty.
2. Solenoid No. 6 faulty.
3. Torque converter faulty.
4. Valve body faulty.

CONVERTER LOCK-UP CLUTCH ALWAYS ENGAGED (ENGINE DIES WHEN MOVING OFF IN D)

1. Torque converter faulty.
2. Valve body faulty.

NO POSITION FORWARD OR REVERSE ENGAGEMENT

1. Driver pressed off impeller.

NOISE IN ALL POSITIONS

1. Fluid level too low.
2. Valve body leaks.
3. Oil filter dirty.
4. Oil filter round seal missing/faulty.

CONVERTER BELL HOUSING OIL LEAK

1. Oil pump body round seal leaks.
2. Pump body round seal leaks.
3. Converter radial oil seal leaks.

LEAK BETWEEN TRANSMISSION CASE & OIL SUMP

1. Mounting bolts loose.
2. Gasket faulty.

OUTPUT SHAFT LEAKS

1. Output flange radial oil seal leaks.
2. Transmission extension O-ring leaks.

MANUAL SHIFT VALVE SHAFT LEAKS

1. Radial oil seal faulty.

TRANSMISSION PLUG LEAKS

1. Nut loose.
2. O-ring faulty.

Fig. 2 Oil filler plug

TRANSMISSION CASE PLUGS LEAK

1. Plugs loose.
2. Seals faulty.

OIL COOLER PIPES LEAK

1. Oil cooler pipes loose.
2. O-rings faulty.

WRONG SHIFT POINTS, OSCILLATING SHIFTS

1. Engine idling speed too high or low.
2. Idling speed control valve faulty.

NO KICKDOWN SHIFTS, ONLY PARTIAL LOAD/FULL LOAD SHIFTS

1. Wire harness faulty.
2. Kickdown switch faulty.
3. Kickdown switch not adjusted correctly.

NO S (STANDARD) PROGRAM OR S PROGRAM ONLY

1. Signal wire to program switch faulty.
2. Program switch faulty.

NO W (WINTER) PROGRAM OR W PROGRAM ONLY

1. Signal wire to program switch faulty.
2. Program switch faulty.

NO SHIFTS, CAR REMAINS IN SHIFTED GEAR

1. No positive supply/fuse faulty.
2. Signal wire faulty.
3. Switch faulty.

SHIFT SPEED & QUALITY GENERALLY NOT GOOD

1. Temperature sensor not working properly.

MAINTENANCE

FLUID CHECK

1. Warm vehicle and transmission to operating temperature.
2. Park vehicle of level area without load.
3. Use suitable programmed scan tool to ensure transmission fluid temperature is 86–122°F. **Do not check fluid level if temperature is more than 122°F, as level will be too low.**
4. With engine running, switch air conditioning on.
5. Fully apply parking brake and firm press brake pedal.
6. Move gear selector lever through each gear position, pausing briefly in each gear.
7. With engine running, place selector lever in Park position.
8. Remove filler plug, **Fig. 2.**
9. If small stream of oil runs out, fluid level is correct.
10. If no oil runs out, fluid level is too low. Add oil until it starts to overflow.
11. Install oil filler plug with engine running and tighten to specifications.

FLUID CHANGE

Transmission is filled with lifetime fill fluid. No fluid change is required.

ADJUSTMENTS

SHIFT SELECTOR

1. Place selector lever in P position.
2. Brace bolt using holder tool No. 24 5 210, or equivalent, and loosen adjusting nut, **Fig. 3.**
3. Press lever forward to park position.
4. Press cable rod in direction opposite travel and release.
5. Secure cable rod with nut. Torque adjusting nut to specifications.
6. Ensure console and shifter assembly are properly secured.
7. Disconnect shift selector rod (1) from lower end of shift selector lever (2).
8. Rotate transmission lever (3) toward rear of vehicle, then forward two detents into Neutral position.
9. Place manual shift lever (4) in Neutral position and hold lever against forward stop in neutral gate (5).
10. Adjust selector rod length until pin (6) will freely enter hole in lower shift lever, with manual lever held forward against stop.
11. Shorten selector rod by rotating pin and adjuster 1–2 turns, reconnect rod to lower selector lever, then check transmission for proper operation.

SHIFT INTERLOCK

Refer to "4L30-E Automatic Transmission" for shift interlock adjustment procedure.

GEARSHIFT LINKAGE

1. Move selector lever to PARK position.
2. Raise and support vehicle.
3. Use holder tool No. 24 5 220, or equivalent, to counterhold gearshift cable rod to transmission shift arm attaching bolt, **Fig. 4.**
4. Loosen gearshift cable rod to transmission shift arm attaching bolt.
5. Push transmission shift arm towards front of transmission.
6. Push gearshift cable rod towards rear of transmission.

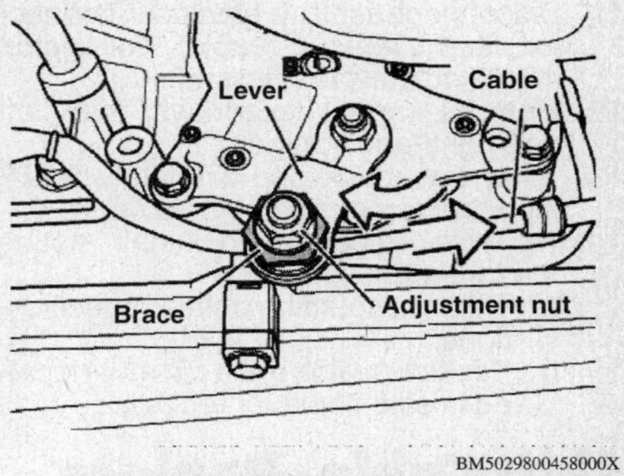

Fig. 3 Selector adjustment

7. **Torque** gearshift cable rod to transmission shift arm attaching bolt to 7–9 ft. lbs.

IN-VEHICLE REPAIRS

EPROM, Replace

This procedure has been revised by a Technical Service Bulletin.

1. Lay control module on suitable Three M static protection mat, or equivalent.
2. Carefully bend up taps.
3. Remove retaining pin using suitable small screwdriver and needle nose pliers.
4. Remove cover mounting Torx screws.
5. Remove EPROM protective cap by inserting suitable small screwdriver into cap side slot.
6. Remove EPROM using suitable IC extractor tool and carefully pulling it out of socket. **Do not touch EPROM pins.**
7. Reverse procedure to install, noting to following:
   a. Ensure all pins are straight.
   b. Align EPROM and socket notches.
   c. Ensure all pins insert into socket correctly and completely.
   d. Ensure cover taps do not contact PC board pins.

Shift Selector, Replace

1. Place selector lever in P position.
2. Brace bolt using holder tool No. 24 5 210, or equivalent, and loosen adjusting nut.
3. Brace head, loosen nut and remove cable from bracket.
4. Pull off hand and remove lift out rubber gaiter.
5. Lift out finisher and pull cable connector off.
6. Remove mounting bolts and position switch.
7. Press ventilation grill up and remove cup holder/tray.
8. Slide down, pull out and remove ventilation grill.
9. Remove mounting bolts and nuts, then the tray cover.
10. Remove switches by pressing out of finisher and Disconnecting cable connector.

11. Disconnect ashtray electrical connector, then remove cable, connector, mounting bolts and finisher.
12. Remove mounting screws, then left and righthand trim panels.
13. Slide tray back approximately 0.787 inch and remove selector lever.
14. Reverse procedure to install, noting the following:
    a. Tighten mounting bolts to specifications.
    b. Position switch drive pin must locate in selector lever recess.

Shift Cable, Replace

1. Remove selector lever.
2. Pull cable retaining plate off and lift retaining disc out.
3. Pull cable out of selector lever ball shell.
4. Remove cable with rubber sleeve.
5. Reverse procedure to install.

Oil Pan, Replace

ZF 5HP-18EH TRANSMISSION

REMOVAL

1. Raise and support vehicle.
2. Drain transmission fluid into suitable container.
3. Remove mounting bolts and oil pan.
4. Clean oil pan and magnetic washers.

INSTALLATION

1. Clean gasket and replace as necessary.
2. Install magnetic washers into oil pan.
3. Fit rounded bracket on oil pan edges.
4. Evenly tighten mounting bolts in several passes to specifications.

ZF 5HP-24EH TRANSMISSION

REMOVAL

1. Raise and support vehicle.
2. Drain transmission fluid into suitable container.
3. Remove mounting bolts, then the oil pan and gasket.
4. Remove exhaust carrier.
5. Clean oil pan and magnetic washers.

INSTALLATION

1. Clean seal and replace as necessary.
2. Install magnetic washers into oil pan.
3. Install exhaust carrier free from tension.
4. Fit straight shoulder brackets on side or concave brackets on front and rear of oil pan edges.
5. Evenly tighten mounting bolts in several passes to specifications.

ZF 5HP-30EH TRANSMISSION

1. Raise and support vehicle.
2. Drain transmission fluid into suitable container.
3. Remove mounting bolts and oil pan.
4. Remove expansion tank from oil pan.
5. Remove clips and magnets.

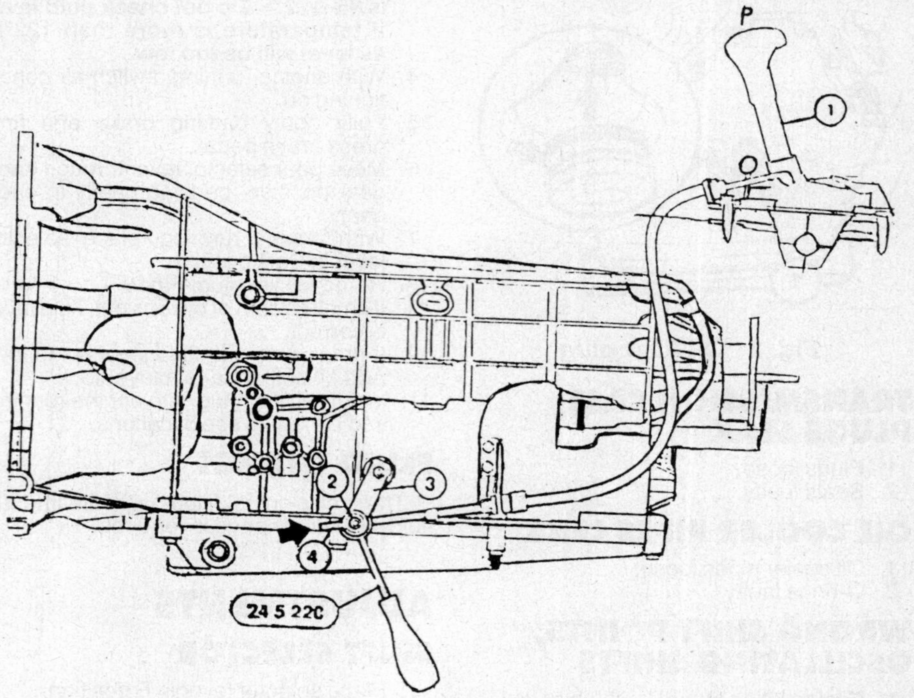

Fig. 4 Gearshift linkage adjustment

6. Clean magnets.
7. Reverse procedure to install, noting the following:
    a. Install new gasket and hold in place with petroleum jelly.
    b. Tighten mounting bolts to specifications.

Valve Body, Replace

ZF 5HP-18EH TRANSMISSION

1. Raise and support vehicle.
2. Remove oil pan as outlined under "Oil Pan, Replace."
3. Remove mounting bolts and oil filter.
4. Remove mounting bolts and valve body cover.
5. Remove mounting bolts. **Only remove bolts with 0.4725 inch heads, Fig. 5.**
6. Turn connector to left and remove.
7. Remove retaining clip and press cable connector into transmission case.
8. Remove valve body with wiring harness.
9. Reverse procedure to install, noting the following:
    a. Install dowel pin in transmission case.
    b. Selector lever spigot must engage slide valve groove.
    c. Coat new O-rings with petroleum jelly.
    d. Tighten mounting bolts to specifications.

ZF 5HP-24EH TRANSMISSION

REMOVAL

1. Raise and support vehicle.
2. Remove transmission oil pan as outlined under "Oil Pan, Replace."
3. Remove shifting cable.
4. Unlock and remove cable connector.
5. Press retaining clip to right and disconnect housing plug.
6. Press housing into transmission.
7. Remove mounting bolt, retainer and pulse generator.
8. Remove mounting screws and filter.
9. Remove five outer edge valve body mounting bolts.
10. Remove 17 large head valve body mounting bolts, except for one in valve center.
11. Grip valve body and remove last large head mounting bolt.
12. Remove valve body from transmission housing.

INSTALLATION

1. Ensure dowel pin is located in valve body.
2. Install valve body and ensure dowel pin engages housing bore.
3. Ensure locating disc journal inserts into slide valve groove.
4. Install large head (M6x60) mounting bolts and tighten to specifications.
5. Install outside edge mounting bolts and tighten to specifications.
6. Install new filter O-ring and coat with petroleum jelly.
7. Install oil filter and tighten mounting bolts to specifications.
8. Install pulse generator, retainer and tighten mounting bolt to specifications.
9. Install new O-rings with petroleum jelly on cable connector.
10. Install connector with turn lock engaging guide groove into transmission housing.

11. Lock retaining clip, then the cable connector.
12. Install shifting cable.
13. Install oil pan.

ZF 5HP-30EH TRANSMISSION

REMOVAL

1. Raise and support vehicle.
2. Remove transmission oil pan as outlined under "Oil Pan, Replace."
3. Remove oil container with magnetic disc.
4. Remove mounting bolt, impulse sensor and retaining clip. Note cable routing for assembly.
5. Remove mounting bolts and oil filter.
6. Remove retaining clip and press cable connector into transmission case. Note position for assembly.
7. Remove large head valve body mounting bolts.
8. Remove valve body.

INSTALLATION

1. Install valve body. Ensure unit lies flat.
2. Ensure detent disc spigot engages slide valve groove.
3. Tighten valve body mounting bolts to specifications in several passes.
4. Install new O-rings coated with petroleum jelly.
5. Install connector through transmission case housing.
6. Install connector retaining clip.
7. Install new oil filter O-ring coated with petroleum jelly.
8. Install oil filter and tighten mounting bolts to specifications.
9. Install impulse sensor, retaining clip and mounting bolt. Tighten mounting bolt to specifications.
10. Clean and install magnetic disc.
11. Install oil container.
12. Install new pan gasket and oil pan.
13. Tighten oil pan mounting bolts to specifications.

Oil Filter, Replace

Replace as described in "Valve Body, Replace."

Parking Lock, Replace

Refer to "4L30-E Automatic Transmission" for parking lock replacement procedure.

Solenoid Valves, Replace

ZF 5HP-18EH TRANSMISSION

1. Remove oil pan as outlined under "Oil Pan, Replace."
2. Disconnect valve body plug connector.
3. Fold retaining tabs down and remove cable.
4. Disconnect solenoid connectors.

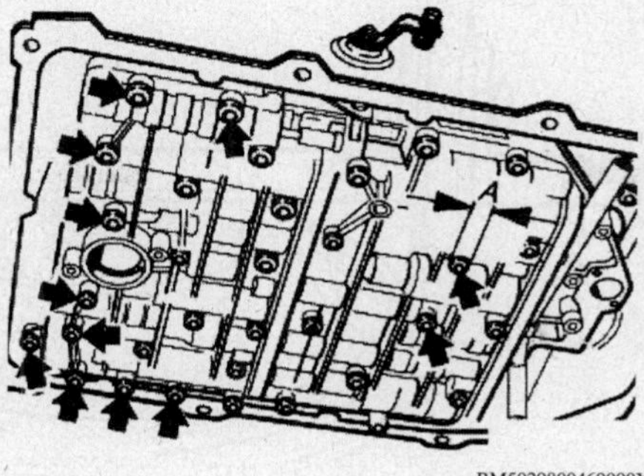

Fig. 5 Valve body mounting bolts. ZF 5HP-18EH transmission

5. Remove mounting bolts and solenoid valves.
6. Reverse procedure to install, noting the following:
   a. Coat new O-rings with ATF oil or petroleum jelly.
   b. Tighten mounting bolts to specifications.

ZF 5HP-24EH TRANSMISSION

1. Raise and support vehicle.
2. Remove oil pan as outlined under "Oil Pan, Replace."
3. Disconnect solenoid valves and pressure regulators connectors.
4. Remove wiring harness.
5. Remove mounting screws and retaining plate.
6. Note pressure regulators and solenoid valves location for assembly.
7. Remove pressure regulators.
8. Remove mounting screws and solenoid valves.
9. Reverse procedure to install, noting the following:
   a. Coat new O-rings with ATF oil.
   b. Tighten solenoid mounting screws to specifications.
   c. Install retaining plate with inside curved surface facing valve body.
   d. Tighten mounting screws to specifications.

ZF 5HP-30EH TRANSMISSION

1. Remove valve body as outlined under "Valve Body, Replace."
2. Disconnect solenoid valve connectors. **Do not pull off wires.**
3. Remove mounting screws and holder.
4. Remove solenoids by pulling out.
5. Reverse procedure to install, noting the following:
   a. Install holder with lightly curved side facing valve housing.
   b. Tighten holder mounting screws to specifications.

Pressure Regulator, Replace

Pressure regulator cannot be replaced separately as modulation pressure has to be adjusted. **Only transmission manufacturer can adjust modulation pressure.**

Pulse Generators, Replace

ZF 5HP-18EH TRANSMISSION

1. Remove valve body as outlined under "Valve Body, Replace."
2. Remove generator connector.
3. Remove mounting screws and pulse sender.
4. Reverse procedure to install. Tighten mounting screws to specifications.

ZF 5HP-24EH & ZF 5HP-30EH TRANSMISSIONS

1. Raise and support vehicle.
2. Remove oil pan as outlined under "Oil Pan, Replace."
3. Remove mounting screw, retainers and pulse generator.
4. Disconnect connector from generator.
5. Reverse procedure to install. Tighten mounting screws to specifications.

Wiring Harness, Replace

ZF 5HP-24EH & ZF 5HP-30EH TRANSMISSIONS

1. Raise and support vehicle.
2. Remove wiring harness from solenoid valves as outlined in "Solenoid Valves, Replace."
3. Remove wiring harness from pulse generators as outlined in "Pulse Generators, Replace."
4. Release cable retainers and remove wiring harness.
5. Reverse procedure to install. Tighten mounting screws to specifications.

Oil Seal, Replace

OUTPUT FLANGE

ZF 5HP-18EH TRANSMISSION

Removal

1. Raise and support vehicle.
2. Remove exhaust system as outlined in "Transmission, Replace."
3. Remove heat shield.
4. Remove heat shield, then left and righthand splash guard brackets.
5. Support transmission using fixture tool No. 24 5 300, or equivalent, and suitable hoist.
6. Remove oxygen sensor cable from transmission crossmember.
7. Remove mounting bolts and transmission crossmember.
8. Disconnect propeller shaft from transmission and suspend to one side and outlined in "Transmission, Replace."

9. Remove mounting bolts and transmission extension.
10. Clamp take-up support tool No. 24 1 220, or equivalent, into suitable vise.
11. Fit transmission extension to support tool.
12. Knock cotter pin out of grooved nut.
13. Remove grooved nut using pin wrench tool No. 24 1 170, or equivalent.
14. Remove transmission extension from support tool.
15. Remove output flange from extension.
16. Lift radial seal out using suitable screwdriver.

Installation

1. Install new seal flush using impact drift tool No. 24 1 190 and handle tool No. 0 5 500, or equivalents.
2. Coat radial seal sealing lip and output flange sealing surface with transmission oil.
3. Install output flange into transmission extension.
4. Fix transmission extension to fixture tool and vise.
5. Install grooved nut and tighten to specifications with pin wrench.
6. Peen grooved not to secure.
7. Remove transmission extension from fixture.
8. Install spacer disc and new O-ring.
9. If new output flange or bearing is installed, adjust end float as described in "Output Flange, Replace."
10. Install mounting bolts and tighten to specifications.
11. Connect propeller shaft to transmission as described in "Transmission, Replace."
12. Install transmission crossmember and tighten mounting bolts to specifications.
13. Install oxygen sensor cable on transmission crossmember.
14. Remove transmission support.
15. Install heat shields, and left and right-hand splash guard brackets.
16. Install exhaust system as described in "Transmission, Replace."

ZF 5HP-30EH TRANSMISSION

Removal

1. Remove exhaust system as outlined in "Transmission, Replace."
2. Remove heat shields, then the left and righthand splash guard brackets.
3. Support transmission using fixture tool No. 24 0 170, or equivalent, and suitable hoist.
4. Unclip oxygen sensors cable from transmission crossmember.
5. Remove mounting bolts and crossmember.
6. Disconnect propeller shaft from transmission flange and tie to one side as described in "Transmission, Replace."
7. Remove mounting bolts and transmission extension.
8. Clamp fixture tool No. 24 0 190, or equivalent, in suitable vise.
9. Attach transmission extension to fixture.
10. Knock grooved nut cotter pin back.
11. Remove grooved nut using wrench tool

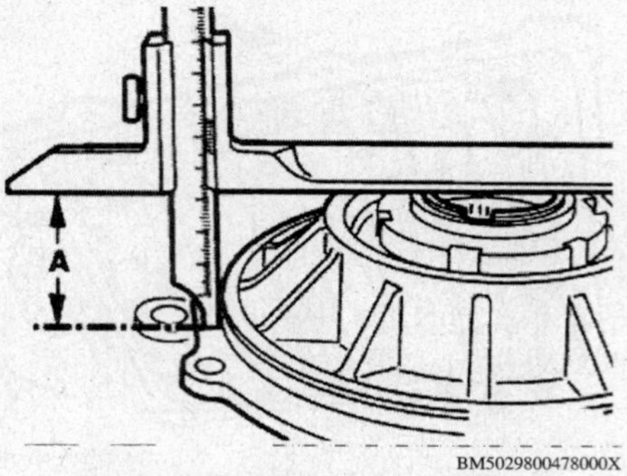

Fig. 6 Extension housing A measurement. ZF 5HP-30EH transmission

No. 24 4 110, or equivalent.
12. Remove transmission extension from fixture.
13. Remove output flange from mounting.
14. Lift out radial seal.

Installation

1. Drive new radial seal in place using impact drift tool No. 24 4 090, and handle tool No. 00 5 500, or equivalents.
2. Coat radial seal sealing lips and output flange sealing surface with transmission oil.
3. Install output flange.
4. Mount transmission extension in fixture.
5. Install groove nut and tighten to specifications.
6. Peen grooved nut to secure.
7. If install new output flange or bearing, adjust end float as described under "Output Flange, Replace."
8. Remove transmission extension from fixture.
9. Install transmission extension with new O-ring.
10. Tighten extension mounting bolts to specifications.
11. Connect propeller shaft to transmission flange as outlined in "Transmission, Replace."
12. Install crossmember and tighten mounting bolts to specifications.
13. Clip oxygen sensors cable to crossmember.
14. Remove transmission support.
15. Install splash guard left and righthand brackets, then the heat shields.
16. Install exhaust system as outlined in "Transmission, Replace."

MANUAL SHIFT VALVE SHAFT

ZF 5HP-18EH TRANSMISSION

Removal

1. Remove shifting cable.
2. Remove mounting nut and shifting lever.
3. Remove radial seal using seal removal tool No. 24 5 260, or equivalent.

Installation

1. Install sleeve tool No. 24 1 200, or equivalent, over shift valve shaft.
2. Lubricate radial oil seal sealing lip with transmission oil.
3. Drive radial oil seal as far as case.
4. Remove sleeve tool.
5. Install selector lever and tighten mounting nut to specifications.
6. Install shifting cable.

ZF 5HP-30EH TRANSMISSION

Removal

1. Remove shifting cable.
2. Remove mounting nut and shifting lever.
3. Remove radial seal using seal removal tool No. 24 5 260, or equivalent.

Installation

1. Install sleeve tool No. 24 5 490, or equivalent, over shift valve shaft.
2. Lubricate radial oil seal sealing lip with transmission oil.
3. Slide radial oil seal onto manual shift valve shaft.
4. Press radial seal into transmission case using bushing tool No. 24 5 250, or equivalent.
5. Remove special tools.
6. Install selector lever and tighten mounting nut to specifications.
7. Install shifting cable.

POSITION SWITCH

ZF 5HP-30EH TRANSMISSION

Removal

1. Remove mounting bolts and heat shield.
2. Remove mounting bolts and position switch from manual shift valve shaft.
3. Remove radial seal using seal removal tool No. 24 5 260, or equivalent.

Installation

1. Install sleeve tool No. 24 5 490, or equivalent, over shift valve shaft.
2. Lubricate radial oil seal sealing lip with transmission oil.
3. Slide radial oil seal onto manual shift valve shaft.
4. Press radial seal into transmission using bushing tool No. 24 5 250, or equivalent.
5. Remove special tools.
6. Install position switch and mounting bolts.
7. Install heat shield and mounting bolts.

Output Flange, Replace

ZF 5HP-18EH TRANSMISSION

1. Remove output flange as described under "Seal, Replace."
2. Clamp transmission extension into suitable vise.
3. Press output flange against vise. Flange must be free.
4. Measure distance from collar mount to sealing face (Example, 0.3937 inch).
5. Measure distance from collar mount to

output flange face (Example, 0.2953 inch).
6. Remove sprag wheel shim.
7. Press sprag wheel inwards.
8. Measure distance from transmission case sealing face to sprag wheel recess (Example, 0.1575 inch).
9. Subtract second measure from first (Example, 0.3937 minus 0.2953 = 0.0984 inch).
10. Subtract previous measure from sprag wheel recess measurement (Example, .1575 minus 0.0984 = 0.0591 inch).
11. Correct shim thickness is difference between previous measurement and end float of 0.0059–0.0138 inch. (Example, 0.0591 minus 0.0059 = 0.0532 inch or 0.0591 minus 0.0138 = 0.0453 inch).
12. Install suitable shim to obtain correct end float.

ZF 5HP-30EH TRANSMISSION

1. Remove output flange as described under "Oil Seal, Replace."
2. Clamp transmission extension in suitable vise.
3. Press output flange into extension. **Output flange must be free.**
4. Measure A on transmission extension, **Fig. 6.**
5. Remove sprag wheel shim.
6. Press sprag wheel in.
7. Measure B on sprag wheel, **Fig. 7.**
8. Subtract measurement A for B.
9. Determine shim thickness using previous result and chart, **Fig. 8.**

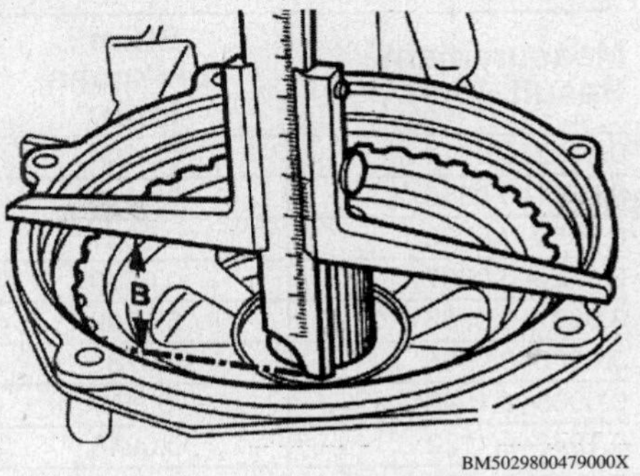

Fig. 7 Extension housing B measurement. ZF 5HP-30EH transmission

Bearing, Replace

TRANSMISSION EXTENSION

ZF 5HP-18EH TRANSMISSION

1. Remove output flange as outlined under "Output Flange, Replace."
2. Remove circlip and ball cage.
3. Heat transmission extension around inner bearing race to approximately 176°F with hot air blower.
4. Press outer bearing race and remove ball cage.
5. Reverse procedure to install, noting following.
   a. Heat transmission extension around inner bearing race to approximately 176°F with hot air blower.
   b. Press in outer bearing race.

ZF 5HP-30EH TRANSMISSION

1. Remove output flange as under "Output Flange, Replace."
2. Remove both inner bearing races.
3. Remove retaining ring, then the ball cage.
4. Heat transmission extension around inner bearing race to approximately 176°F with hot air blower.
5. Press out outer bearing race.
6. Reverse procedure to install, noting the following.
   a. Heat transmission extension around inner bearing race to approximately 176°F with hot air blower.
   b. Install ball cage.
   c. Press in outer bearing race.
   d. Ensure proper installation direction.

Transmission Control Unit (TCU), Replace

M3 & 328

Refer to "4L30-E Automatic Transmission" for transmission control unit replacement.

528, 540, 740 & 750

1. Turn ignition switch to Off position.
2. Remove mounting bolts and electronics box cover.
3. Disconnect connector and remove control unit.
4. Reverse procedure to install. Tighten mounting bolts to specifications.

TRANSMISSION

REPLACE

M3 & 328

Removal

1. **On models equipped with Automatic Speed Control and Traction Control (ASC+T),** remove throttle body to prevent damage when removing transmission.
2. **On all models,** raise and support vehicle.
3. Disconnect oxygen sensor and unclip cable from retainer.
4. Loosen exhaust manifold flange bolts.
5. Loosen exhaust bracket clamp.
6. Disconnect rubber ring on rear axle carrier.
7. If rear muffler is bracket mount, disconnect left and righthand rear retaining brackets.
8. If rear muffler is clamp mount, Loosen collar nut with clamp on final muffler.
9. Remove exhaust system downward.
10. Remove heat shield.
11. Remove exhaust assembly mounting brackets and clamp.
12. Remove transmission joint mounting bolts.
13. Loosen threaded sleeve a few turns using wrench tool No. 26 1 040, or equivalent.
14. Remove center mount mounting bolts or nuts. **Do not let propeller shaft fall into joints.**
15. Bend propeller shaft down at center mount and remove from transmission centering pin. Tie up to one side.
16. Drain transmission fluid into suitable container. as required, remove filler pipe.
17. Remove shifting cable.
18. Turn bayonet lock counterclockwise, pull plug off and lift wire harness from holder.
19. Lift transmission wire harness from holder and remove oxygen sensor plug from holder.
20. Remove crankcase and oil sump oil cooler pipe clamps.
21. Remove holder and pull transmission oil cooler pipe out.
22. Remove cover guard, then the torque converter to drive flange mounting bolts using socket tool No. 24 1 110, or equivalent. Rotate engine using front central bolt in 120° stages.
23. Support transmission using fixture tool No. 24 5 300, or equivalent, and suitable hoist.
24. Ensure wipers are in park position and remove wiper arms.
25. Remove air collector grille cover.
26. Loosen end wall wiring harness and bend insulation sheet to one side.
27. Remove cable channel screws.
28. Press wiper wiring harness to one side.
29. Remove mounting screws and wiring harness holder.
30. Remove air collector by pulling up and toward driver's side.
31. Remove injection pipe cover.
32. Install engine mounting fixture tool No. 11 2 370, or equivalent, through intake manifold and into crankcase bracket.
33. Mount fixture tool No. 00 0 200, or equivalent, and attach to engine mounting fixture.
34. Tighten spindle.
35. Remove cross tube.
36. Remove suspension gravity center holder.
37. Remove crossmember mounting bolts.
38. Lower transmission enough that there is no fire wall or heater connection contact.
39. Remove transmission to engine mounting bolts.
40. Secure torque converter to transmission housing using fixture tool No. 24 4 080, or equivalent. Flat side of fixture must face converter.
41. Remove transmission from engine.

Installation

1. Inspect dowel sleeves and replace as necessary.
2. Ensure cover plate is correctly positioned.
3. Secure torque converter to transmission housing using fixture tool No. 24 4 080, or equivalent. Flat side of fixture must face converter.

4. Support and lift transmission into position using suitable hoist.
5. **On models equipped using sheet metal flywheel,** proceed as follows:
   a. Drive plate bore must point perpendicularly to guard opening center.
   b. Turn transmission torque converter until tab bores point to flywheel bores center.
   c. Install guide pin tool No. 24 2 300, or equivalent, into tab.
   d. Lift transmission until drive plate bore is reached.
   e. Carefully guide transmission into drive plate bore using guide pin tool.
6. **On all models,** tighten transmission to engine mounting bolts with washers to specifications.
7. Center transmission and tighten crossmember mounting bolts to specifications.
8. Install suspension gravity center holder and cross tube.
9. Install cross tube.
10. Remove engine support.
11. Install air collector, wiring harness holder and mounting screws.
12. Install cable channel mounting screws.
13. Bend insulation sheet back and tighten wiper wiring harness.
14. Install air collector grille, then the wiper arms.
15. Remove transmission support.
16. Install torque converter to drive flange bolts and tighten to specifications using socket tool No. 24 1 110, or equivalent.
17. Inspect oil cooler pipe O-rings and replace as necessary.
18. Install oil cooler pipes and holder.
19. Connect oxygen sensor plug and wire harness.
20. Connect shifting cable.
21. Install joint onto transmission and bend shaft up into position.
22. Preload center mount forward 0.0787–0.1575 inch.
23. Ensure final drive flange and universal joint are aligned as marked during removal.
24. Tighten threaded sleeve to specifications using wrench tool No. 26 1 040, or equivalent.
25. Replace stop nuts and tighten flexible coupling mounting nuts to specifications from flange side only.
26. Install clamp with long collar at rear and exhaust assembly brackets.
27. Install heat shield.
28. Install exhaust assembly.
29. **On models with rear muffler clamp,** install clamp with collar nut.
30. **On models with rear muffler bracket,** proceed as follows:
   a. Inspect rubber mount for damage and replace as necessary.
   b. Preload rubber mount forward 0.59 inch.
   c. Connect left and righthand side rear retaining brackets.
31. **On all models,** inspect rubber gaskets and replace as necessary.
32. Install rubber ring on rear axle carrier.
33. Install exhaust bracket clamp.
34. Inspect exhaust manifold seal and replace as necessary.
35. Lightly coat exhaust manifold threads with suitable copper paste and install new self-locking nuts.
36. Align exhaust bracket without tension.
37. Ensure tailpipe is properly positioned relative to body cutout. If necessary, loosen flange joint and rubber suspensions, align and fasten.
38. Clip cable to retainer and connect oxygen sensor connector.
39. **On models equipped with Automatic Speed Control and Traction Control (ASC+T),** install throttle body.

Measurement Result, Inch.	Shim Thickness, Inch.
0.0492–0.0571	0.0394
0.0571–0.0650	0.0472
0.0650–0.0728	0.0551
0.0728–0.0807	0.0630
0.0807–0.0886	0.0709
0.0886–0.0965	0.0787
0.0965–0.1043	0.866
0.1043–0.1122	0.0945
0.1122–0.1201	0.1024
0.1201–0.1280	0.1102
0.1280–0.1358	0.1181
0.1358–0.1437	0.1260

Fig. 8 Output shaft shim thickness. ZF 5HP-30EH transmission

540, 740 & 750

Removal

1. Raise and support vehicle.
2. **On 750 models,** remove noise insulation cover by pressing interlocks down.
3. **On all models,** remove rear underbody protection and front axle support heat baffle plate.
4. Support exhaust system using fixture tool No. 31 2 220, or equivalent, and suitable hoist.
5. Disconnect left and righthand oxygen sensors connections.
6. Disconnect exhaust system from exhaust manifold.
7. Disconnect rear muffler rubber mount on rear axle.
8. Disconnect left and righthand rear mufflers clamping brackets.
9. Remove exhaust system.
10. Remove heat shields and left and righthand splash guard brackets.
11. Remove shifting cable.
12. Remove lefthand front axle support heat shield.
13. Remove engine oil pan oil line brackets.
14. **On 750 models,** remove power steering pump oil line bracket.
15. **On all models,** position suitable oil container, then remove banjo bolt and oil line.
16. Remove return cap and oil line.
17. **On 540 and 740 models,** support transmission using take-up support tool No. 24 0 250, or equivalent, base plate tool No. 24 5 301, or equivalent, and suitable hoist.
18. **On 750 models,** support transmission using mount tool No. 24 0 170, or equivalent, and suitable hoist.
19. **On all models,** disconnect oxygen sensor cable on transmission crossmember.
20. Remove mounting bolts and transmission crossmember.
21. **On 750 models,** remove heat shield.
22. **On all models,** remove flexible coupling transmission mounting bolts.
23. Brace propeller shaft at center mount and remove mounting bolts. **Do not allow propeller shaft to drop into joints.**
24. Bend propeller shaft down at center bearing, then remove from transmission output flange and tie up to one side.
25. Disconnect plug and connectors.
26. Remove cover guard, then the torque converter to drive flange mounting bolts using socket tool No. 24 1 110, or equivalent.
27. Remove impulse sensor cable connector.
28. Fit engine support spacer tool No. 11 7 310, or equivalent, between engine oil pan and front axle support.
29. Ensure center track rod is not excessively loaded when transmission is removed by turning front wheel to righthand lock.
30. Lower transmission until engine oil pan is supported on spacer tool.
31. Secure torque converter in position using clamping tool No. 24 4 131, or equivalent.
32. Remove transmission to engine mounting bolts.
33. Move transmission back and remove by lowering.

Installation

1. Inspect dowel sleeves and replace as necessary.
2. Secure torque converter to transmission housing using clamping tool No. 24 4 131, or equivalent.
3. Install guide pin tool No. 24 2 300, or equivalent, into thread bore.
4. Lift transmission until drive plate bore is reached.
5. Turn torque converter until guide pin aligns with drive plate bore.
6. Attach transmission input flange to engine output flange.
7. Drive plate bore must be accessible from oil pan aperture.
8. Install transmission to engine mounting bolts and washer, then tighten to specifications.
9. Remove torque converter clamping tool.
10. Lift transmission and remove spacer tool.
11. Install torque converter to drive flange mounting bolts using socket tool No. 24 1 110, or equivalent, and tighten to specifications.
12. Connect impulse sensor and plug.
13. Install joint onto transmission and bend shaft up into position.

14. Preload center mount forward 0.0787–0.1575 inch.
15. Ensure final drive flange and universal joint are aligned as marked during removal.
16. Tighten threaded sleeve to specifications using wrench tool No. 26 1 040, or equivalent.
17. Replace stop nuts and tighten flexible coupling mounting nuts to specifications from flange side only.
18. Install heat shield.
19. Install transmission crossmember and tighten mounting bolts to specifications.
20. Connect oxygen sensor cable on crossmember.
21. Remove transmission support.
22. Replace O-rings and install oil lines and brackets.
23. Install power steering pump oil line bracket.
24. Install front lefthand axle support heat shield.
25. Install shifting cable.
26. Install left and righthand splash guard brackets, then the heat shields.
27. Install exhaust system.
28. Install left and righthand rear mufflers clamping brackets. Preload clamps 0.59 inch
29. Install rear muffler rubber mount on rear axle.
30. Install new inner sealing rings, then connect exhaust system to exhaust manifold.
31. Connect left and righthand oxygen sensors connections.
32. Remove exhaust system support fixture.
33. Install rear underbody protection and front axle support heat baffle plate.
34. Install noise insulation by pressure down on interlocks until engagement is heard.

X5

1. Remove exhaust system.
2. Remove mounting bolts and reinforcement plate.
3. Remove front splash guard.
4. Remove left and righthand heat shields.
5. Disconnect oxygen sensor cable.
6. Release stabilizer bar.
7. Remove rear heat shield.
8. Remove front propeller shaft to differential carrier joint mounting bolts.
9. Remove front propeller shaft from transfer case.
10. Disconnect vent line.
11. Remove selector lever mounting nut.
12. Disconnect shifter cable.
13. Remove transmission oil cooler lines from engine oil pan.
14. Remove power steering pump oil lines' bracket.
15. Place suitable oil pan under engine, then disconnect banjo bolt and remove oil line.
16. Disconnect oil return line.
17. Move oil lines to lefthand side.
18. Support transmission and transfer case with suitable jack and fixture tools Nos. 24 5 301 and 24 0 250, or equivalents.
19. Disconnect oxygen sensor cable from transmission crossmember and transmission.
20. Remove mounting bolts and transmission crossmember.
21. Remove propeller shaft as outlined in "Rear Axle & Suspension" section.
22. Disconnect connect and cable from transmission.
23. Disconnect impulse sensor connector.
24. Remove cover, then the torque converter mounting bolts using socket tool No. 24 1 110, or equivalent. Turn engine in normal rotational direction to access all mounting bolts.
25. Support front of engine with suitable jack.
26. Turn front wheels to righthand lock.
27. Hold torque converter in place using clamp tool No. 24 4 131/132, or equivalent.
28. Remove transmission mounting bolts, then pull transmission and transfer case toward vehicle rear and lower.
29. Remove transfer case from transmission.
30. Reverse procedure to install. Tighten mounting bolts and nuts to specifications.

TIGHTENING SPECIFICATIONS

Year	Component	Torque, Ft. Lbs.
1998–2001	Adapter Housing	31
	Center Support Hub	18
	Crossmember	15
	Electronics Box Cover	39①
	Extension Bearing	89
	Extension Housing	18
	Oil Cooler Pipe, Front	15
	Oil Cooler Pipe, Rear	27
	Oil Filler Plug	26
	Oil Filter (ZF 5HP-18 & ZF5HP-19)	53①
	Oil Filter (ZF 5HP-24 & ZF 5HP-30)	44①
	Oil Pan	108①
	Oil Pump	②
	Output Flange Grooved Nut	89
	Pressure Regulator Retaining Plate	44①
	Propeller Shaft Coupling	44
	Propeller Shaft Center Support	15
	Propeller Shaft Slinging Ring	84①
	Propeller Shaft Universal Joint	③
	Pulse Generator (ZF 5HP-18, ZF 5HP-19 & ZF 5HP-24EH)	44①
	Pulse Generator (ZF 5HP-30)	④
	Reinforcement Plate	17
	Selector Lever	84①
	Shift Cable	11
	Shift Cable Adjusting Screw	84①
	Shift Console To Tunnel	60①
	Shift Interlock	60①
	Shift Switch	40①
	Solenoid (ZF 5HP-18EH)	44①
	Solenoid (ZF 5HP-30EH)	53①
	Solenoid Holder	44①
	Solenoid Retaining Plate	44①
	Torque Converter	33
	Torque Converter Housing Radial Seal	26①
	Transmission To Engine	⑤
	Valve Body (ZF 5HP-18, ZF 5HP19 & ZF 5HP-24)	72①
	Valve Body (ZF 5HP-30EH,	⑥

① — Inch lbs.
② — M5, 44 inch lbs.; M6, 84 inch lbs.
③ — M10 8.8, 35 ft. lbs.; M10 10.9, 44 ft. lbs.; M12 8.8, 60 ft. lbs.; M12 10.9, 74 ft. lbs.
④ — M5, 53 inch lbs.; M8, 17 ft. lbs.
⑤ — M8 Hex, 18 ft. lbs.; M8 Torx, 15 ft. lbs.; M10 Hex, 33 ft. lbs; M10 Torx, 31 ft. lbs.; M12 Hex, 60 ft. lbs.; M12 Torx, 53 ft. lbs.
⑥ — M6x12, 53 inch lbs.; M6x55, 72 inch lbs.

5L40-E Automatic Transmission

NOTE: On Air Bag Equipped Models, Refer To "Air Bag System Precautions" Located In The Front Of This Manual For System Disarming & Arming Procedures.

INDEX

	Page No.
Adjustments	2-227
Shift Interlock	2-227
Shift Selector	2-227
Description	2-227
In-Vehicle Repairs	2-227
Converter Clutch Lock-Up Pressure Regulator	2-228
Oil Filter, Replace	2-228
Oil Pan, Replace	2-227
Oil Seal, Replace	2-228
Output Flange, Replace	2-228
Pressure Regulator, Replace	2-228
Pulse Generators, Replace	2-228
Shift Selector, Replace	2-227
Solenoid Valves, Replace	2-228
Switch	2-228
Transmission Control Unit (TCU), Replace	2-228
Valve Body, Replace	2-227
Wiring Harness, Replace	2-228
Maintenance	2-227
Fluid Change	2-227
Fluid Check	2-227
Precautions	2-227
Air Bag Systems	2-227
Battery Ground Cable	2-227
Tightening Specifications	2-229
Transmission, Replace	2-228
325xi & 330xi	2-229
525, 528 & 530	2-229
X5	2-228
Z3 & 323	2-228

PRECAUTIONS

AIR BAG SYSTEMS

Refer to "Air Bag System Precautions" in the front of this manual for system disarming and arming procedures.

BATTERY GROUND CABLE

Prior to service, disconnect battery ground cable and isolate as required.

DESCRIPTION

The 5L40-E is a five-speed General Motors Strasbourg turbo-hydromatic automatic transmission.

MAINTENANCE

FLUID CHECK

1. Warm vehicle and transmission to operating temperature.
2. Park vehicle of level area without load.
3. Use suitable programmed scan tool to ensure transmission fluid temperature is 86–122°F. **Do not check fluid level if temperature is more than 122°F, as level will be too low.**
4. With engine running, switch air conditioning on.
5. Fully apply parking brake and firm press brake pedal.
6. Move gear selector lever through each gear position, pausing briefly in each gear.
7. With engine running, place selector lever in Park position.
8. Remove filler plug, **Fig. 1.**
9. If small stream of oil runs out, fluid level is correct.
10. If no oil runs out, fluid level is too low. Add oil until it starts to overflow.
11. Install oil filler plug with engine running and tighten to specifications.

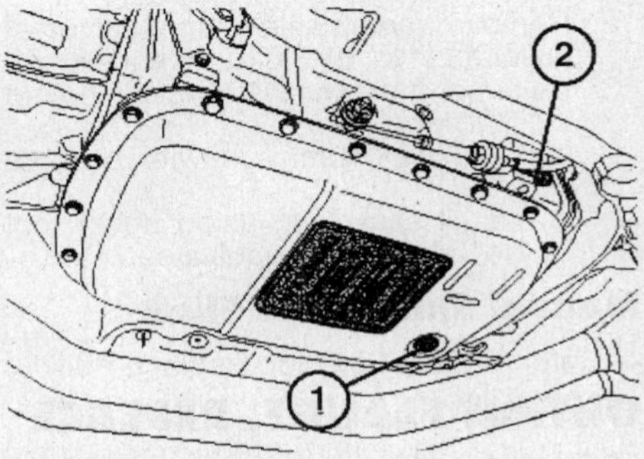

1- Drain plug
2- Filler plug

BM5020100569000X

Fig. 1 Oil filler plug

FLUID CHANGE

Transmission is filled with lifetime fill fluid. No fluid change is required.

ADJUSTMENTS

SHIFT SELECTOR

1. Place selector lever in P position.
2. Grip clamping piece and loosen mounting nut,
3. Press lever forward to park position.
4. Press cable rod in direction opposite travel and release.
5. Secure cable rod with nut. Torque adjusting nut to specifications.

SHIFT INTERLOCK

Refer to "4L30-E Automatic Transmission" for shift interlock adjustment procedure.

IN-VEHICLE REPAIRS

SHIFT SELECTOR, REPLACE

Removal

1. Hold clamping piece and remove cable nut.
2. Remove mounting nut and shift lever.
3. Screw fixture tool No. 24 5 361, or equivalent, into radial seal.
4. Remove radial seal by install fixture tool No. 24 5 362, or equivalent, into previous installed tool.

Installation

1. Install seat set adapter sleeve onto manual shift valve shaft.
2. Coat sealing lips with suitable ATF.
3. Push radial seal onto manual shaft as far as possible.
4. Remove adapter sleeve.
5. Draw seal into housing using installation tools Nos. 24 5 363/364, or equivalent.
6. Adjust selector as outlined under "Adjustments."

OIL PAN, REPLACE

1. Drain transmission fluid into suitable container.
2. Remove mounting bolts, oil pan and gasket.
3. Reverse procedure to install, noting the following:
   a. Install gasket and drain plug oil sealing ring.
   b. Install all mounting bolts until head contact is made.
   c. Tighten mounting bolts to specifications.

VALVE BODY, REPLACE

1. Remove oil pan and screen.
2. Disconnect connectors and temperature sensor.

3. Mark mounting bolts for installation alignment.
4. Remove mounting bolts and valve body.
5. Remove seals.
6. Reverse procedure to install, noting the following:
   a. Install new seals.
   b. Adjust gap between detent spring and disk to .031 inch.
   c. Tighten mounting bolts and nuts to specifications.

OIL FILTER, REPLACE

1. Remove oil pan as outlined under "Oil Pan, Replace."
2. Remove screen.
3. If sealing ring remained in pump housing, remove it.
4. Reverse procedure to install, noting the following:
   a. If sealing ring remained in pump housing, replace it and screen.
   b. Replace gaskets as required.

CONVERTER CLUTCH LOCK-UP PRESSURE REGULATOR

1. Remove oil pan and screen.
2. Lift out retaining spring and remove pressure regulator.
3. Reverse procedure to install. Coat regulator with suitable ATF.

SOLENOID VALVES, REPLACE

1. Remove oil pan.
2. Disconnect connectors.
3. Lift out retaining spring and remove pressure regulator.
4. Reverse procedure to install. Coat regulator with suitable ATF.

PRESSURE REGULATOR, REPLACE

1. Remove oil pan and screen.
2. Disconnect connector.
3. Lift out retaining spring and remove pressure regulator.
4. Reverse procedure to install. Coat regulator with suitable ATF.

PULSE GENERATORS, REPLACE

1. Remove oil pan.
2. Disconnect connectors.
3. Remove mounting bolt and pulse generator.
4. Reverse procedure to install.

SWITCH

1. Remove oil pan.
2. Move selector level to D position.
3. Remove selector unit as outlined under "Shift Selector, Replace."
4. Remove spring pin and manual shift valve shaft only as far as required to remove switch.
5. Secure parking gear rack with suitable pliers. **Do not remove parking gear rack.**
6. Disconnect parking gear rack detent disk. **Do not move rack more than .39 inch.**
7. Remove transmission switch with detent disk. Remove disk.
8. Reverse procedure to install.

WIRING HARNESS, REPLACE

1. Remove oil pan.
2. Remove righthand rear plug.
3. Remove fluid screen.
4. Disconnect valve body connectors.
5. Disconnect temperature sensor.
6. Remove retaining clip with suitable screwdriver and push plug into transmission.
7. Remove wiring harness.
8. Reverse procedure to install, noting the following:
   a. Coast sealing rings with suitable petroleum jelly.
   b. Install new pump housing sealing ring.

OIL SEAL, REPLACE

Output Flange

1. Remove output flange as outlined under "Output Flange, Replace."
2. Remove radial seal using universal puller tool No. 00 5 010, or equivalent.
3. Reverse procedure to install, noting the following:
   a. Coat new seal lips with suitable ATF.
   b. Install seal flush using driver tool No, 24 1 090, or equivalent.

Manual Shift Valve Shaft

Refer to "Shift Selector, Replace."

OUTPUT FLANGE, REPLACE

1. Remove exhaust system.
2. Remove heat shields.
3. Support transmission with suitable jack and fixture tools Nos. 24 5 301/305, or equivalent.
4. Remove mounting bolts and crossmember.
5. Remove propeller shaft as outlined in "Rear Axle & Suspension" section.
6. **On models equipped less spring washer,** hold output flange with holder tool No. 23 0 020, or equivalent, then remove mounting nut and flange.
7. **On models equipped with spring washer,** remove mounting nut, spring washer and output flange.
8. **On all models,** reverse procedure to install, noting the following:
   a. Install output flange nut with suitable retaining compound.
   b. Tighten mounting bolts and nuts to specifications.

TRANSMISSION CONTROL UNIT (TCU), REPLACE

Z3

The transmission control is located on the right side of the engine compartment.

1. Remove battery then the control unit cover.
2. Press TCU downward off of spring retainers.
3. Pull TCU forward through opening.
4. Reverse procedure to install.

TRANSMISSION

REPLACE

X5

1. Remove exhaust system.
2. Remove righthand heat shield.
3. Disconnect oxygen sensor cable.
4. Remove mounting bolts and reinforcement plate.
5. Remove engine front underguard.
6. Release stabilizer bar.
7. Remove front propeller shaft to differential carrier joint mounting bolts.
8. Remove front propeller shaft from transfer case.
9. Disconnect vent line.
10. Remove mounting bolts and exhaust bracket.
11. Remove selector lever mounting nut.
12. Disconnect shifter cable.
13. Disconnect connector and disconnect transmission housing cable.
14. Remove transmission oil cooler lines from engine oil pan.
15. Place suitable oil pan under engine, then disconnect banjo bolt and remove oil line.
16. Support transmission and transfer case with suitable jack and fixture tools Nos. 24 5 301 and 24 5 305, or equivalents.
17. Disconnect oxygen sensor cable from transmission crossmember and transmission.
18. Remove mounting bolts and transmission crossmember.
19. Remove propeller shaft as outlined in "Rear Axle & Suspension" section.
20. Remove cover, then the torque converter mounting bolts using socket tool No. 24 1 110, or equivalent. Turn engine in normal rotational direction to access all mounting bolts.
21. Remove transmission mounting bolts, then pull transmission and transfer case toward vehicle rear and lower.
22. Remove transfer case from transmission.
23. Reverse procedure to install. Tighten mounting bolts and nuts to specifications.

Z3 & 323

1. Remove air intake hood.
2. Disconnect fan cowl and position upward.
3. Remove microfilter housing and heater bulkhead.
4. Remove mounting bolts and reinforcement plate, as required.
5. Remove engine underguard.
6. Remove mounting bolts and front end reinforcement.
7. Remove exhaust system.
8. Remove heat shields.
9. Remove shift selector nut and disconnect cable.
10. Support transmission with suitable jack and fixture tools Nos. 24 5 301 and 34 5 305, or equivalents.
11. Remove mounting bolts and crossmember.
12. Remove propeller shaft as outlined in "Rear Axle & Suspension" section.
13. Lower transmission until cylinder head

touches bulkhead.
14. Support engine with engine bar tool No. 11 8 022, or equivalent.
15. Disconnect connector and cable.
16. Remove mounting bolt and disconnect oil cooler lines.
17. Remove cover, then the torque converter mounting bolts using socket tool No. 24 1 110, or equivalent. Turn engine in normal rotational direction to access all mounting bolts.
18. Hold torque converter in place using clamping tools Nos. 24 4 131 and 24 4 135, or equivalent.
19. Remove transmission mounting bolts, then pull transmission and transfer case toward vehicle rear and lower.
20. Remove transfer case from transmission.
21. Reverse procedure to install. Tighten mounting bolts and nuts to specifications.

325XI & 330XI

1. Remove air intake hood.
2. Disconnect fan cowl and position upward.
3. Remove microfilter housing and heater bulkhead.
4. Support engine with fixture tool No. 00 0 200, or equivalent.
5. Remove righthand engine mount top nut and lefthand engine mount bottom nut.
6. Remove front, middle and rear engine underguards.
7. Remove exhaust system.
8. Remove heat shields.
9. Remove shift selector nut and disconnect cable.
10. Remove propeller shaft as outlined in "Rear Axle & Suspension" section.
11. Remove front propeller shaft to differential carrier joint mounting bolts.
12. Remove front propeller shaft from transfer case.
13. Remove righthand heat shield.
14. Remove engine underguard righthand bracket.
15. Support transmission with suitable jack and fixture tools Nos. 24 5 301 and 34 5 305, or equivalents.
16. Remove mounting bolts and crossmember.
17. Disconnect connector and cable.
18. Remove transfer case as outlined in "Transfer Case" section.
19. Lower transmission.
20. Remove mounting bolt and disconnect oil cooler hydraulic lines.
21. Disconnect steering column from steering gear as outlined in "Front Suspension & Steering" section.
22. Raise engine.
23. Remove lefthand engine mount.
24. Remove mounting bolt then press vacuum tank off exhaust flap control.
25. Remove cover, then the torque converter mounting bolts using socket tool No. 24 1 110, or equivalent. Turn engine in normal rotational direction to access all mounting bolts.
26. Hold torque converter in place using clamping tools Nos. 24 4 131 and 24 4 135, or equivalent.
27. Remove transmission mounting bolts, then pull transmission toward vehicle rear and lower.
28. Reverse procedure to install. Tighten mounting bolts and nuts to specifications.

525, 528 & 530

1. Remove exhaust system.
2. Remove underbody protection.
3. Remove heat shields.
4. Release stabilizer bar.
5. Remove mounting screws and exhaust suspension.
6. Remove lefthand body protector holder.
7. Support transmission and transfer case with suitable jack and fixture tools Nos. 24 5 301 and 24 5 305, or equivalents.
8. Remove mounting bolts and transmission crossmember.
9. Remove propeller shaft as outlined in "Rear Axle & Suspension" section.
10. Remove mounting nut and disconnect shift cable.
11. Disconnect connector and disconnect transmission housing cable.
12. Disconnect cooler lines and collect fluid in suitable container.
13. Insert fixture tool No. 11 7 370, or equivalent between engine oil sump and front axle support.
14. Support engine at front using suitable jack.
15. Remove cover, then the torque converter mounting bolts using socket tool No. 24 1 110, or equivalent. Turn engine in normal rotational direction to access all mounting bolts.
16. Hold torque converter in place using clamping tools Nos. 24 4 131 and 24 4 135, or equivalent.
17. Remove transmission mounting bolts, then pull transmission toward vehicle rear and lower.
18. Reverse procedure to install. Tighten mounting bolts and nuts to specifications.

TIGHTENING SPECIFICATIONS

Year	Component	Torque, Ft. Lbs.
1999–2001	Converter Housing Radial Seal	27①
	Crossmember	16
	Drain/Fill Plugs	13
	Extension Housing	17
	Oil Pan	88①④
	Output Flange	③
	Position Switch	88①
	Pulse Sender	97①
	Rubber Mount	16
	Support Tube	31
	Torque Converter	33
	Transmission To Engine	②
	Valve Body	97①

① — Inch lbs.
② — M8 Hex, 18 ft. lbs.; M8 Torx, 15 ft. lbs.; M10 Hex, 33 ft. lbs; M10 Torx, 31 ft. lbs.; M12 Hex, 60 ft. lbs.; M12 Torx, 53 ft. lbs.
③ — Less spring washer, 22 ft. lbs.; w/spring washer, 44 ft. lbs.
④ — Tighten in order. Do not tighten in diagonal sequence.

Front Wheel Drive Axles

NOTE: On Air Bag Equipped Models, Refer To "Air Bag System Precautions" Located In The Front Of This Manual For System Disarming & Arming Procedures.

INDEX

	Page No.
Driveshaft Service	2-230
Joint, Replace	2-230
Precautions	2-230
Air Bag Systems	2-230
Battery Ground Cable	2-230

PRECAUTIONS

AIR BAG SYSTEMS

Refer to "Air Bag System Precautions" in the front of this manual for system disarming and arming procedures.

BATTERY GROUND CABLE

Prior to service, disconnect battery ground cable and isolate as required.

DRIVESHAFT SERVICE

JOINT, REPLACE

WHEEL SIDE

Removal

1. Place driveshaft in vice with suitable protective jaws.
2. Disconnect retainers and pull gaiter back.
3. Press joint off with pressure on retaining ring.
4. Lever out retaining ring.
5. Pull gaiter over splined shaft.

Installation

1. Clean all parts with suit clean shop rag.
2. Grease constant velocity joint with suitable fresh grease.
3. Install new retaining ring.
4. Press joint on until retaining ring snaps into place.

TRANSMISSION SIDE

Removal

1. Place driveshaft in vice with suitable protective jaws.
2. Disconnect retainers and pull gaiter back.
3. Disconnect tulip element.
4. Remove retaining ring.
5. Disconnect tripod star from splined shaft.
6. Pull gaiter over splined shaft.

Installation

1. Clean all parts with suit clean shop rag.
2. Install new retaining ring.
3. Install tripod star flat side to retaining ring.
4. Assemble gaiter and adapter before pushing gaiter over splined shaft.
5. Grease constant velocity joint with suitable fresh grease.

Drive Axles

NOTE: On Air Bag Equipped Models, Refer To "Air Bag System Precautions" Located In The Front Of This Manual For System Disarming & Arming Procedures.

INDEX

	Page No.
Adjustments	2-235
Differential Case	2-236
Pinion	2-235
Ring Gear & Pinion Tooth Contact Check	2-236
Assemble	2-235
Disassemble	2-231
Drive Axle Specifications	2-237
Backlash	2-237
Differential Friction Torque	2-237
Precautions	2-231
Air Bag Systems	2-231
Battery Ground Cable	2-231
Subassembly Service	2-231
Differential	2-231
Limited Slip Differential	2-233
One-Piece Differential	2-231
Two-Piece Differential	2-233
Output Shaft	2-231
Tightening Specifications	2-238

PRECAUTIONS

AIR BAG SYSTEMS

Refer to "Air Bag System Precautions" in the front of this manual for system disarming and arming procedures.

BATTERY GROUND CABLE

Prior to service, disconnect battery ground cable and isolate as required.

DISASSEMBLE

1. Remove axle housing assembly and mount in suitable holding fixture.
2. Bend down lock tab on pinion nut, then measure and record total assembly rotating torque, turning pinion shaft nut using suitable torque wrench.
3. Remove axle housing rear cover and drain lubricant.
4. Pry out drive axle flanges using suitable lever.
5. Mount suitable dial indicator on housing with pointer bearing against ring gear tooth, **Fig. 1.**
6. Measure and record ring gear and pinion backlash.
7. Punch matching marks between side bearing caps and case.
8. Remove caps along with shims, then the drive flange seals.
9. **Side bearing cap and shim assemblies are used to determine ring gear and pinion backlash and side bearing preload. Retain shim packs with respective side bearing caps and keep assemblies separate to aid assembly.**
10. Remove differential assembly from housing.
11. Measure and record pinion rotating torque using suitable torque wrench, **Fig. 2.**
12. Hold pinion flange using suitable tool, then remove pinion nut and lock plate.
13. Remove pinion flange and flange seals using suitable puller.
14. Press drive pinion and rear bearing assembly from housing, then remove front pinion bearing and spacer from housing. **Do not damage bearing or bearing surfaces.**
15. Remove front bearing outer race from housing using suitable puller and place bearing race with bearing, **Fig. 3.**
16. Inspect rear pinion bearing, then remove from pinion, using suitable puller.
17. Remove rear pinion bearing race from housing using suitable puller and place race with bearing.
18. Remove pinion depth adjusting shim and retain for assembly, **Fig. 4.**
19. Remove speed sensor from housing.
20. Clean housing, covers and flanges with solvent and blow dry with compressed air, ensuring all foreign material is removed. **Keep all components in order, noting installation position of bearings, races, covers and shims to ensure proper assembly. Any component that is reused should be installed in original position.**

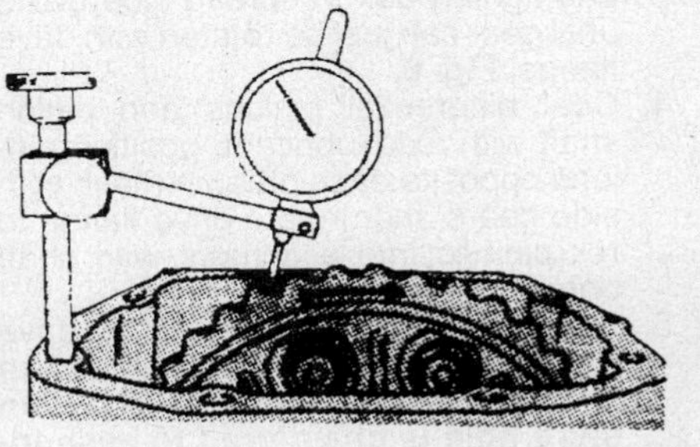

BM3019100001000X

Fig. 1 Ring gear & pinion backlash measurement

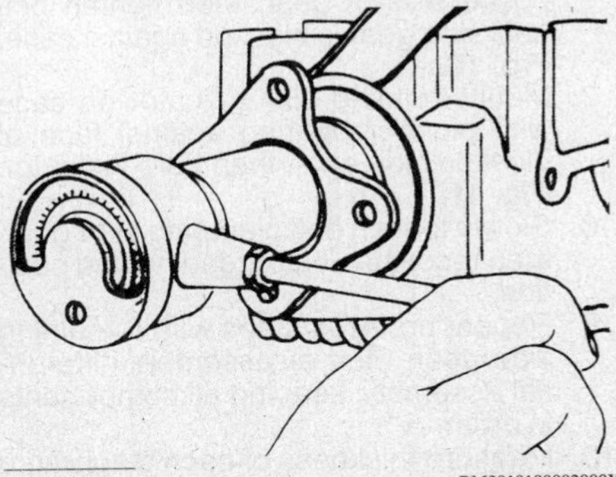

BM3019100002000X

Fig. 2 Rotating torque measurement

SUBASSEMBLY SERVICE

Output Shaft

1. Remove output shaft from final drive and rear axle shaft.
2. Remove sealing cover and circlip.
3. Remove clamp and dust cover.
4. Press output shaft from Constant Velocity (CV) joint, ensuring bearing inner race is resting on counter pressure plate. **Do not disassemble CV joint.**
5. Place dust cover and inside cover on output shaft. Ensure joint is installed with collar on inner race facing output shaft.
6. Clean threads of joint to remove grease, then apply suitable sealant. Ensure sealant does not enter ball passages.
7. Press on joint with cap and install circlip. **If only one side was disassembled, sealing cover of other side has to be removed to press on joint.**
8. Pack joint and dust cover with suitable joint grease, then clean dust cover sealing surface.
9. Apply adhesive to large diameter end of dust cover and secure with new clamps.
10. Apply sealant to sealing cover and install.
11. Reinstall output shaft.

Differential

ONE-PIECE DIFFERENTIAL

DISASSEMBLE

1. **On models with rear axle speed sensor,** remove pulse spider using suitable puller.
2. **On all models,** inspect differential

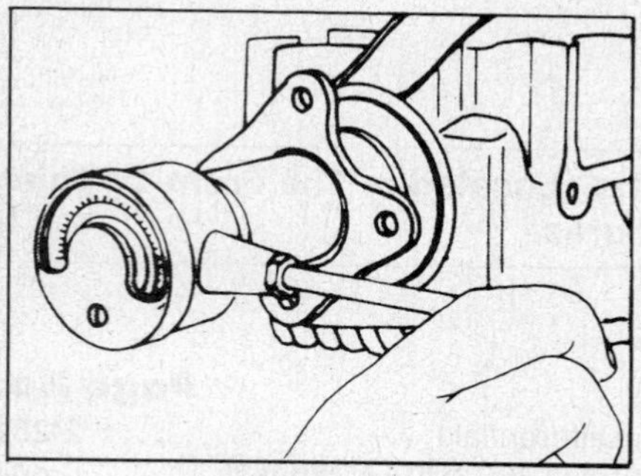

Fig. 3 Pinion bearing race replacement

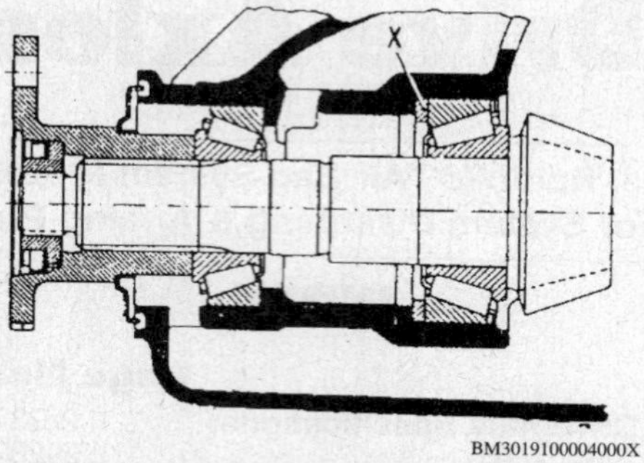

Fig. 4 Pinion, bearing & depth shim (X) installation

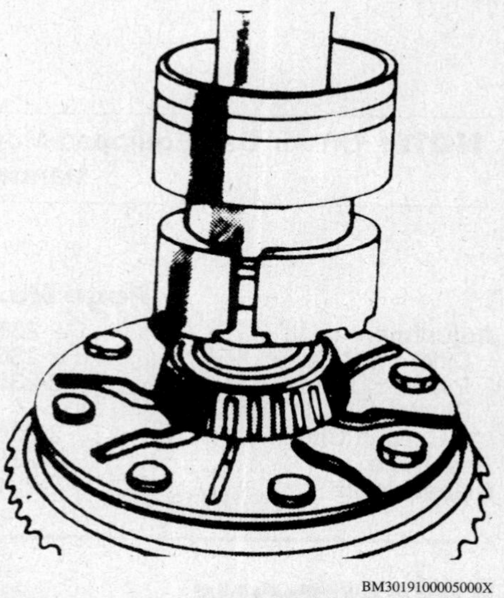

Fig. 5 Standard differential case bearing removal

case side bearings and remove, as required, using suitable puller, **Fig. 5.**

3. If differential case bearings are replaced, press bearing races from side bearing caps and housing (as equipped), using spacers. Take care not to distort caps and note installation position of bearing race shims, as required.
4. Remove and discard ring gear mounting bolts, then tap gear from case.
5. Drive out pin securing pinion shaft, then remove shaft from case.
6. **On 740 and 750 models,** drive pinion shaft out of retaining ring in direction A and remove shaft, **Fig. 6.**
7. **On all models,** mount differential case in vise with one side gear opening facing up, taking care not to damage machined surfaces.
8. Insert drive flange into side gear and rotate flange to position differential pinions at openings in case, **Fig. 7.**
9. Remove pinions and side gears along with shims and diaphragm springs. **Keep all components in order to ensure proper assembly. Components which are reused should be installed in original position.**

CLEANING & INSPECTION

1. Clean components with solvent, blow dry with compressed air, then coat components with axle lubricant to retard corrosion.
2. Mate side bearings with races and check operation. Replace damaged, scored or improperly operating bearings.
3. Inspect pinions and side gears and replace as an assembly if teeth are broken, excessively worn or deeply scored.
4. Inspect case for damaged or distorted ring gear flange, and worn side gear bores and bearing surfaces.
5. Inspect ring gear for damage, distortion, and uneven or excessive wear. **Ring gear and pinion must be replaced as an assembly.**

ASSEMBLE & ADJUSTMENT

328

1. Coat side gears with axle lubricant and install diaphragm springs with concave side toward gear, **Fig. 8.**
2. Mount side gear assemblies in case, then center gears by inserting drive flanges. **Side gear shims are not installed until side gear clearance has been measured.**
3. Install side gear spreader assembly and tighten bolt to spread side gears until gear can just be rotated with drive flange, **Fig. 9.**
4. Coat differential pinions and pinion shaft with axle lubricant, position pinions opposite each other in mesh with side gears, then rotate drive flange to roll pinions into alignment with shaft bores in case.
5. Remove spreader tool and drive flange, insert pinion shaft and secure shaft with lockpin. **One end of pinion shaft hole is chamfered to ease installation of lockpin.**
6. Position washer against face of side gear, thread bolt into washer from opposite side of gear, then tighten bolt until side gear is blocked against case, **Fig. 10.**
7. Mount suitable dial indicator on case with plunger bearing against face of blocked side gear, then zero indicator, **Fig. 11.**
8. Slowly loosen bolt clamping side gear, then record indicator reading and position.
9. Repeat previous steps with remaining side gear, then disassemble differential assembly, keeping all components in order.
10. Measure thickness of each diaphragm spring noting position and record measurement.
11. Add measured spring thickness to appropriate clearance measured during gauging procedure and record sum.
12. Obtain thickness of shim necessary to provide proper side gear clearance by subtracting desired clearance from sum obtained in previous step. Clearance should be 0.0008–0.0028 inch. **Select shim to provide clearance as close to 0.0008 inch as possible.**
13. Reassemble differential as outlined, installing selected shims in proper positions, then inspect clearance as previously outlined.
14. Install two guide pins in bolt holes on opposite sides of ring gear, heat ring gear to 212° F, and mount on differential case.
15. Apply suitable thread locking compound to new ring gear bolts, then remove guide pins and install ring gear bolts hand tight.
16. Evenly tighten ring gear bolts in crossing pattern to specifications.
17. Press side bearings onto case and bearing races into bearing caps, ensuring bearings and races remain matched during assembly.
18. Ensure drive flange lock rings are properly positioned, with both ends of ring seated in groove, then press speed sensor spider onto differential case using spacer tool No. 33 1 304, or equivalent.

528

1. Ensure lock ring for pinion shaft is properly seated in groove.
2. Coat side gears with axle lubricant, then install diaphragm spring and shim on each gear with inside curved surface of spring facing gear, **Fig. 8.**
3. Mount side gear assemblies in case, then insert drive flanges to center gears.
4. Install spreader tool, then tighten bolt on tool until side gear can just be turned with drive flange, **Fig. 9.**
5. Coat differential pinions and shaft with axle lubricant, position pinions opposite each other in mesh with side gears, then rotate drive flange to roll pinions into alignment with shaft bores in case.
6. When pinions are properly aligned, remove spreader tool, insert tapered mandrel through pinion and case bores, from direction E, **Fig. 6.**
7. Fit chamfered end of pinion shaft into mandrel, then press pinion shaft into position. Install puller tool No. 00 8 500, or equivalent, on case while forcing screw bearing on pinion shaft.
8. If hydraulic press is used, monitor applied force carefully, and stop pressing when pressure reading increases, indicating that clip has engaged groove in shaft. **Applying excessive force after clip engages groove in shaft**

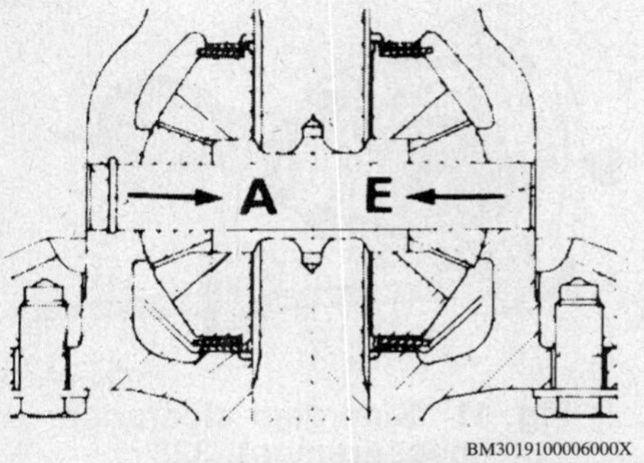

Fig. 6 Standard differential pinion shaft removal. 740 & 750

will damage retaining clip. Do not push back on pinion shaft after engaging clip.

9. If press is not available, press shaft in by hand until 3/8 to 3/4 inch of shaft remains protruding from case.
10. Tighten forcing screw to specifications. **Lubricate forcing screw prior to tightening, and ensure force is applied to pinion shaft in an even, progressive manner.**
11. Position washer against face of side gear and thread bolt into washer from opposite side of gear, then tighten bolt hand tight, **Fig. 10.**
12. Mount suitable dial indicator on case with plunger bearing against face of side gear, then zero indicator, **Fig. 11.**
13. Tighten bolt to compress diaphragm spring, then record indicator reading.
14. Loosen bolt and rotate side gear, checking play as previously outlined at evenly spaced positions.
15. Repeat previous for remaining side gear, taking average of three readings for each gear.
16. If average reading for each gear is not 0.0012–0.0040 inch, disassemble differential and replace side gear shims as required, to obtain specified clearance. **Select shims to provide clearance as close to .0012 inch as possible.**
17. After replacing shims, repeat clearance check to ensure proper adjustment.
18. Install guide pins in two opposite ring gear bolt holes, heat gear to 212° F, then mount gear on case.
19. Apply locking compound to threads of new ring gear bolts, remove guide pins and install bolts hand tight.
20. Tighten ring gear bolts evenly in crossing pattern to specifications.
21. Press side bearings onto differential case and bearing races into bearing caps, ensuring bearings and races remain matched.
22. Ensure drive flange retaining rings are properly installed with both ends of ring fully seated in case groove.

TWO-PIECE DIFFERENTIAL

DISASSEMBLE

Keep all components in order during service.

1. Remove mounting bolts, differential case cover and side gear assembly.

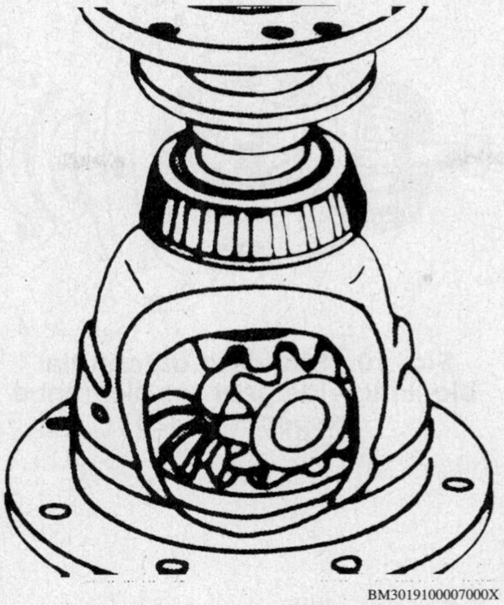

Fig. 7 Standard differential pinion removal

2. Remove differential pinion and pinion shaft assemblies, noting position for installation.
3. Remove side gears, along with shim and diaphragm spring from each case half, keeping components in order for assembly.
4. Remove ring gear and side bearings as outlined for "One-Piece Differentials."

CLEANING & INSPECTION

1. Clean components with solvent, dry with compressed air and coat components with axle lubricant to prevent corrosion.
2. Inspect components and replace any that are damaged, distorted or excessively worn.

ASSEMBLE & ADJUST

Components that are to be reused should be installed in original position to ensure proper operation.

1. Install ring gear side gear and one pinion shaft/pinion gear assembly, then the case cover. Tighten mounting bolts to specifications.
2. Mount suitable dial indicator on case with plunger inserted through drive flange opening and bearing against face of side gear.
3. Press side gear into contact with pinions using screwdriver, then zero dial indicator.
4. Pull side gear back against case and record dial indicator reading.
5. Subtract 0.002 inch from measurement obtained , then select side gear shim and spring as close as possible to remainder to obtain 0.002–0.004 inch side gear clearance.
6. Repeat previous steps with case cover side gear.
7. Disassemble unit, install selected shims and springs on respective side gears with concave side of spring facing gear, **Fig. 8.**

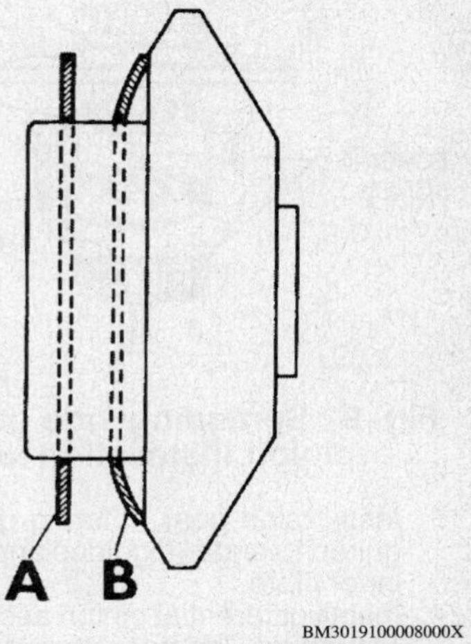

Fig. 8 Side gear thrust washer & diaphragm spring installation. Except limited slip differential

8. Coat all components with axle lubricant, reverse disassembly procedure to complete assembly. Evenly tighten case cover bolts to specifications crossing pattern.

LIMITED SLIP DIFFERENTIAL

DISASSEMBLE

1. Remove ring gear and case side bearings, as outlined under "One-Piece Differential."
2. Evenly loosen mounting bolts and remove cover.
3. Invert case over work surface and allow component stack to slide from case, tapping case using mallet to aid removal, **Fig. 12. Keep all components in order to ensure proper assembly. Components that are to be reused should be installed in original position to ensure proper operation.**

INSPECTION

1. Clean components with solvent and blow dry with compressed air.
2. Replace inner and outer plates if coating, splines or tabs are worn, or if they fail to operate properly.
3. Check fit of thrust rings in case and replace as needed if rings bind or stick, or if excessive play is evident.
4. Replace side gears and pinion assemblies if teeth are damaged or excessively worn, or if side gear splines are worn.

ASSEMBLE

Coat all components w/specified axle lubricant during assembly.

328

1. Install side gear diaphragm spring (2) and thrust washer (3) in case with concave side of spring and thrust washer oil grooves facing up.
2. Install clutch pack diaphragm spring (4) with concave side facing differential shaft, then install outer plate, inner plate and thrust ring.

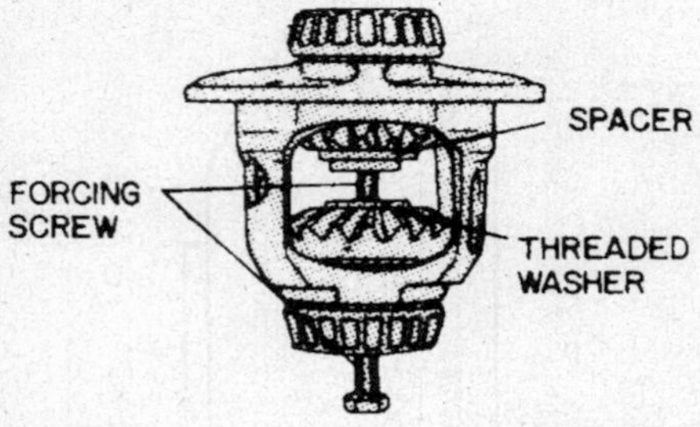

BM3019100009000X

Fig. 9 Spreading side gears for pinion installation. 328

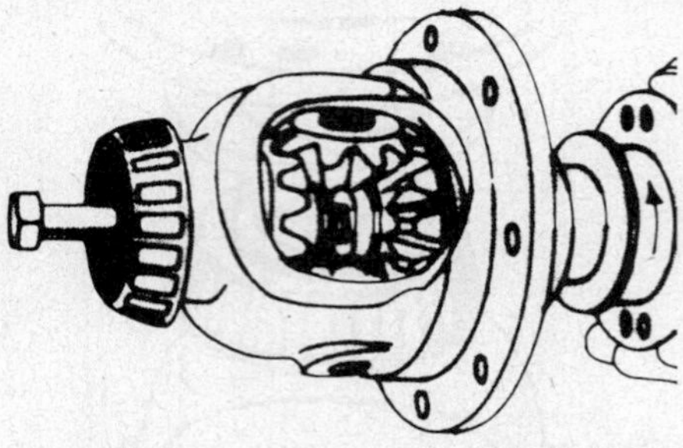

BM3019100010000X

Fig. 10 Standard differential blocking side gear for clearance inspection. 328

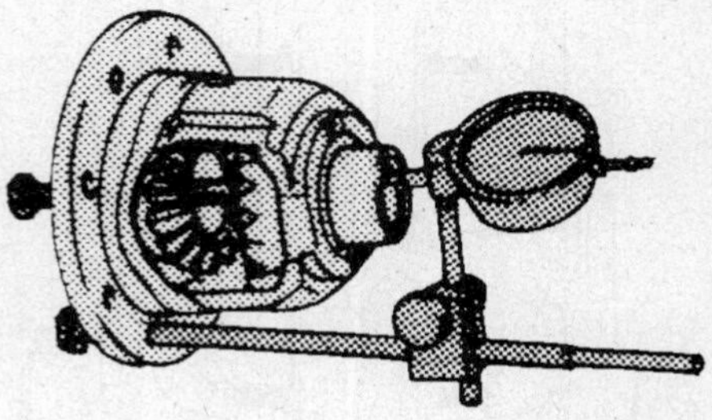

BM3019100011000X

Fig. 11 Side gear clearance measurement. 328

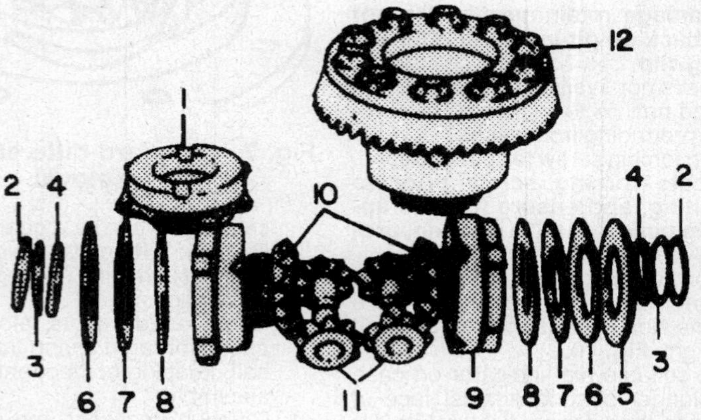

BM3019100013000X

Fig. 12 Exploded view of limited slip differential

3. Install side gear, rotating gear as required to engage guides and splines in inner plate.
4. Install differential pinion assembly and remaining side gear, ensuring components are properly seated.
5. Install thrust ring, inner plate, and outer plate ensuring tabs and splines of plates are properly engaged.
6. Install clutch pack diaphragm spring with concave side facing down.
7. Install side gear diaphragm spring (2) and thrust washer (3) into cover with concave side of spring and thrust washer oil grooves facing toward inside of case. **Use grease to hold spring and thrust washer in position during case installation.**
8. Apply thread locking compound to case cover bolts, install case cover and mounting bolts ensuring thrust washer and spring remain in position. Tighten evenly to specifications crossing pattern.

740 & 750

1. Install side gear trust washer (2) with oil grooves facing down and diaphragm spring (3) with concave side facing up, **Fig. 12.**
2. Install stepped washer with smooth side toward diaphragm spring and tab engaged in case notch.
3. Install spacer and clutch pack diaphragm spring (5), with concave side of spring facing up.
4. Install outer plate, inner plate and thrust ring, ensuring guide tabs are properly engaged.
5. Install side gear, turning gear to engage inner plate splines or guides.
6. Install differential pinion and shaft assembly.
7. Install remaining side gear and pressure ring, ensuring components are properly seated.
8. Install inner plate, outer plate and clutch pack diaphragm spring (5) with concave side of spring facing down, **Fig. 12.**
9. Install side gear thrust washer (2) and diaphragm spring (3) in case cover, with thrust washer oil grooves facing cover and concave side of spring facing inside of case.
10. Install stepped washer in cover with smooth side toward diaphragm spring and tab engaged in cover notch. **Use grease to retain thrust washers and spring in cover during assembly.**
11. Temporarily install cover assembly, ensuring thrust washers and springs remain in place, then evenly tighten mounting bolts to specifications.
12. Install drive flanges, then mount assembly in fixture with one drive flange blocked to prevent rotation.
13. Fabricate suitable tool to allow remaining drive flange to be rotated using torque wrench, then check assembly slip torque by rotating one flange while the other flange is blocked.
14. Slip torque is controlled by the thickness of the outer clutch plates. If slip torque is less than specified, install thicker outer plates; if torque exceeds specifications, install thinner outer plates. When replacing clutch plates to adjust slip torque, ensure clutch assembly clearance is maintained within the specified 0.004–0.016 inch.
15. After slip torque is properly established, install case cover as previously outlined using thread locking compound on mounting bolts, then tighten mounting bolts to specifications crossing pattern.

ADJUSTMENT

Side Gear Clearance

1. Install pressure rings, side gears and differential pinion gear and shaft assembly in case, ensuring components are properly seated, **Fig. 12.**
2. Measure dimension A from case cover mounting flange to outer face of side gear and record measurement, **Fig. 13.**
3. Measure dimension B from raised portion of case to center depression and dimension C from raised portion of case to mounting flange, **Fig. 14.**
4. Subtract dimension C from B and record remainder.
5. Add remainder obtained earlier to dimension A obtained obtain total side gear clearance.
6. Select a combination of thrust washers, diaphragm springs and stepped washers, for each side having total thickness of one half of the total side gear clearance minus 0.004 inch.

Clutch Assembly Clearance

1. Install spacer , outer plate, inner plate, thrust ring and side gear in differential case, ensuring side gear is properly seated. **Thrust washers, stepped washers, and diaphragm springs, as equipped, are not installed until assembly clearances have been measured.**
2. Install differential pinion assembly, ensuring pinion shafts are located in thrust ring notches.
3. Install remaining side gear with hub facing up, then the thrust ring, inner plate and outer plate.
4. Ensure components are properly seated, then measure and record distance A from case cover mounting surface to top of outer plate, **Fig. 15.**
5. Measure and record dimension B from

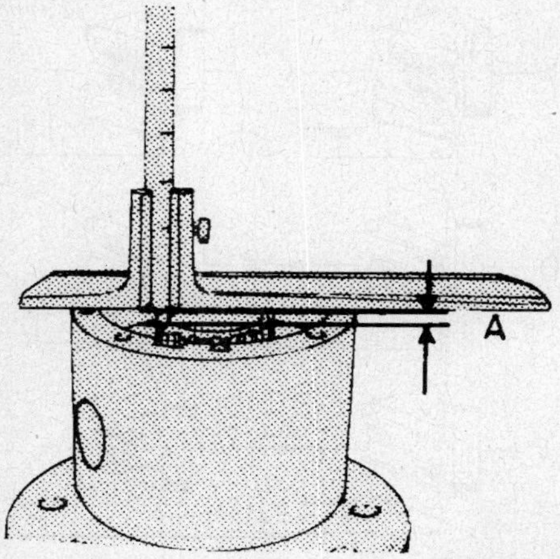

Fig. 13 Limited slip case assembly depth for side gear clearance measurement

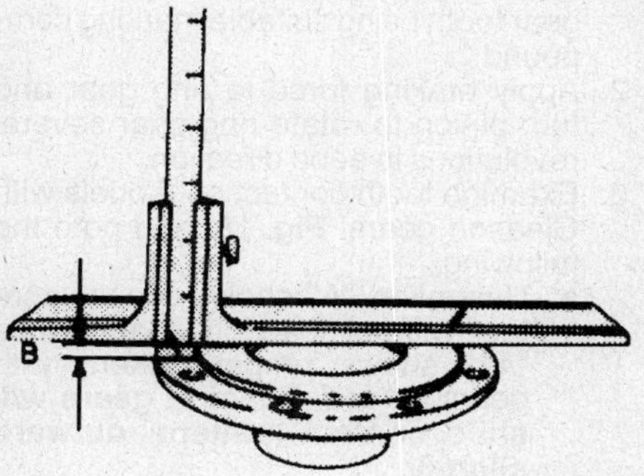

Fig. 16 Measuring case cover flange depth for clutch pack clearance. Limited slip differential

raised portion of case cover to cover mounting surface, **Fig. 16.**

6. Measure and record combined thickness C of diaphragm springs.
7. An assembly clearance of 0.004–0.016 inch is necessary to prevent total compression of clutch pack diaphragm springs. Obtain total assembly clearance as follows:
8. Add recorded case cover height B to total diaphragm thickness C.
9. Subtract sum obtained in previous step from assembly height A to obtain clutch assembly clearance.
10. If remainder obtained in previous step is not 0.004–0.016 inch, replace outer plates as required to obtain specified clearance.
11. If assembly clearance is less than specified, select and install thinner outer plates. If assembly clearance is greater than specified, install thicker outer plates. **Select plates to obtain clearance as close to 0.004 inch as possible.**
12. Install selected outer plates as previously outlined and ensure assembly clearance is within specifications.
13. Remove selected components from case, keeping components in order for final assembly.

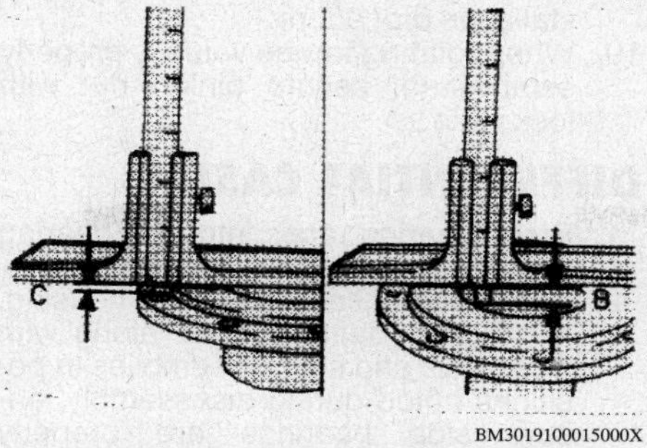

Fig. 14 Limited slip case center & flange depth for side gear clearance measurement

ASSEMBLE

After rear axle disassembly and component replacement, pinion depth, pinion bearing preload, side bearing preload, and ring gear and pinion backlash must be adjusted to specifications, and proper ring gear and pinion tooth contact must be established to ensure proper operation. If existing ring gear and pinion, pinion bearings and housing are reused, pinion depth can be properly established using the shim removed during disassembly. However, if any of these components are replaced, pinion depth must be measured and adjusted prior to axle housing assembly.

When reusing ring gear and pinion assemblies, backlash should be adjusted to value measured during disassembly to maintain the established tooth contact pattern. If ring gear and pinion are replaced, examine markings on gears to ensure a matched set is being installed, and note the type of gears supplied for replacement in order to ensure proper tooth contact pattern adjustment. Klingelnberg gears are generally stamped with the letter K and the tooth height and tooth back remain constant. Gleason type gears are generally stamped with the letter H or F and the gear teeth are higher and wider on the outside than the inside. Do not install gear sets unless matching marks are the same, and also note modification numbers stamped or etched on the pinion which indicate, in one hundredths of a millimeter, necessary modifications to the nominal pinion depth setting.

ADJUSTMENTS

PINION

1. Record thickness of pinion depth adjusting shim removed during disassembly and record pinion depth modification code etched or stamped on pinion.
2. Install pinion depth shim in rear bearing race bore, then press front and rear pinion bearing races into housing using forcing screw and adapters.
3. Press rear bearing onto pinion shaft.
4. Lubricate pinion bearings, insert pinion bearing into housing and install front bearing, then seat front bearing on pinion using forcing screw and spacer, **Fig. 17. Collapsible spacer and**

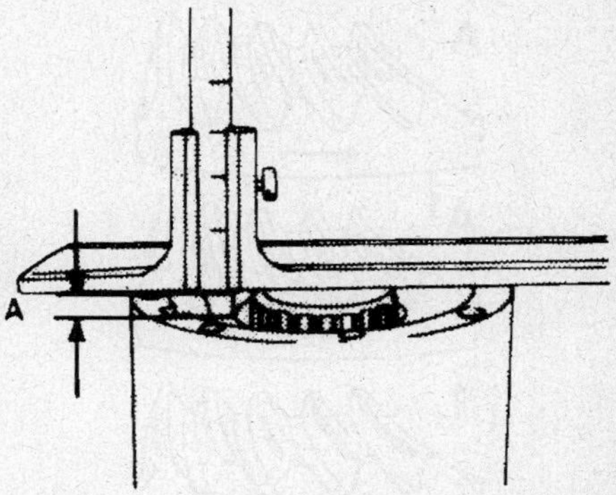

Fig. 15 Measuring case assembly depth for clutch pack clearance. Limited slip differential

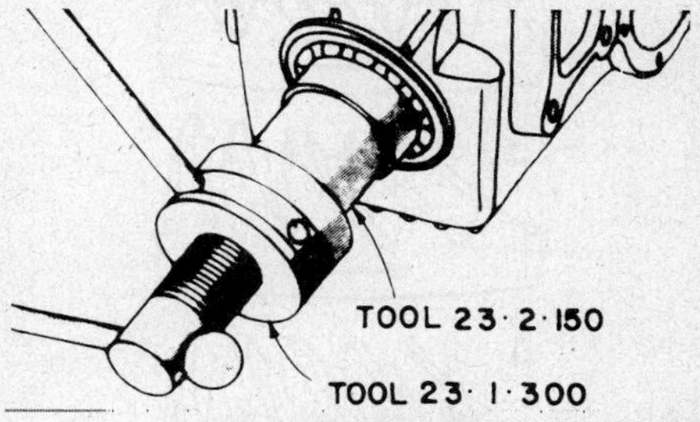

Fig. 17 Front pinion bearing installation

flange seal are not installed until pinion depth has been established.

5. Install pinion flange and nut, then tighten nut to obtain specified bearing preload, rotating pinion and checking preload after each adjustment, **Fig. 2.**
6. Position depth gauge arbor over gauge block, install suitable dial indicator in gauge arbor with approximately 0.20 inch preload, then secure and zero dial indicator.
7. Use the following tools, or equivalents, to measure pinion depth:
   a. **On 328 models,** arbor, 33 1 481; block (.276 inch), 33 1 482.
   b. **Except 328 models,** arbor, 33 1 461; block (.374 inch), 33 1 462.
8. **On all models,** position gauge block on face of pinion and mount arbor, then the dial indicator assembly in side bearing cover bores in case with dial indicator plunger bearing against gauge block.
9. Obtain measured pinion depth by adding dial indicator reading to gauge block height and record sum.
10. Factor recorded pinion depth modification number with nominal pinion depth to obtain desired pinion depth. **Modification number is expressed as 1⁄100 of a millimeter. If modification number is stamped with plus (+) sign add that value to nominal depth; if number is stamped with minus (–) sign subtract that value. Nominal pinion depths are as follows:**
    a. **On 328 models,** 0.355 inch.
    b. **Except 328 models,** 0.453 inch.
11. **On all models,** select shim to obtain desired pinion depth as follows:

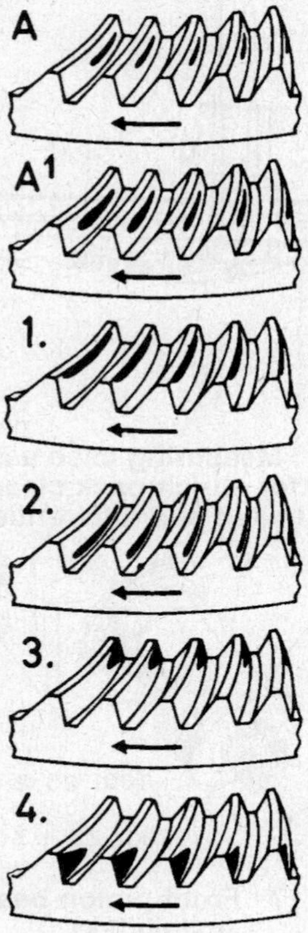

Fig. 18 Ring gear & pinion tooth contact inspection. Gleason gears

a. If desired pinion depth is greater than measured pinion depth, subtract the difference between the values from the installed shim thickness, and select shim accordingly.
b. If desired pinion depth is less than measured pinion depth, add the difference between the two values to the installed shim thickness and select shim accordingly.

12. Remove pinion assembly, rear bearing race and shim.
13. Install selected pinion depth shim, then press rear bearing race into housing as previously described.
14. Lubricate pinion bearings, insert pinion assembly into housing, then install collapsible spacer and front bearing on pinion shaft.
15. Seat front bearing on pinion shaft using forcing screw and spacer, then install pinion flange seal, **Fig. 17.**
16. Install pinion flange and nut along with pinion nut lock plate.
17. Hold pinion flange and **torque** pinion nut to 108 ft. lbs., rotating pinion to ensure bearings are properly seated, then check preload with suitable torque wrench, **Fig. 2.**
18. If pinion bearing preload is more than approximately 2 inch lbs. greater than value recorded during disassembly, or if specified pinion nut torque cannot be obtained without bottoming nut, replace collapsible spacer and repeat installation procedure.
19. When rotating torque value is properly established, secure pinion nut with lock plate.

DIFFERENTIAL CASE

1. Press bearing races into side bearing caps.
2. Install differential assembly in housing.
3. Install side bearing caps, along with new seals and shim assemblies in positions noted during disassembly, ensure side bearings are properly aligned in races, then tighten cap bolts to specifications.
4. Measure total assembly rotating torque, turning pinion using suitable torque wrench, **Fig. 2.**
5. If rotating torque is not 4–6 inch lbs. greater than pinion bearing preload, increase or decrease side bearing cap shim thickness, as needed, to obtain specified value.
6. After proper side bearing preload has been established, mount suitable dial indicator on case with plunger bearing against ring gear tooth at right angle to tooth, **Fig. 1.**
7. Secure pinion, rock ring gear back and forth and read backlash dial indicator.
8. If backlash is not within specifications, adjust as follows:
   a. If backlash is greater than specified, decrease thickness of bearing cap shims on ring gear tooth side and increase thickness of shims on opposite side by an equal amount. **Do not alter total shim pack thickness when adjusting backlash as side bearing preload will be affected. If shim thickness is decreased on one side, increase thickness of shims on opposite side.**
   b. If backlash is less than specified, increase thickness of side bearing cap shims on ring gear tooth side and decrease thickness of shims on opposite side by an equal amount.
9. Perform tooth contact pattern check as outlined and correct assembly adjustments to obtain proper tooth contact.
10. After proper ring gear and pinion tooth contact has been established, ensure drive flange retaining clips are properly installed in case grooves, then install new drive flange seals.
11. Lubricate drive flange seal lips, then install drive flanges.
12. Install rear cover using new gasket or seal, and the electronic speed sensor.

RING GEAR & PINION TOOTH CONTACT CHECK

Proper ring gear and pinion tooth contact is essential for proper rear axle operation. After performing basic adjustments outlined previously, slight modifications may be required to ensure proper contact. Tooth contact is adjusted by making modifications to the pinion depth and ring gear backlash settings.

1. Coat drive and coast face of each ring gear tooth using suitable marking compound.

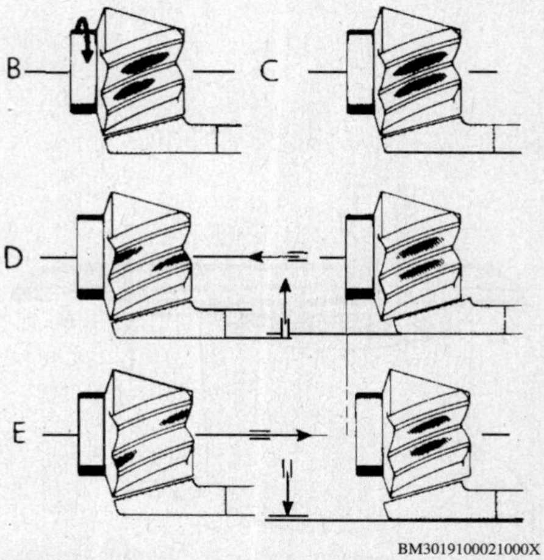

Fig. 19 Ring gear & pinion tooth contact inspection. Klingelnberg gears

2. Apply braking force to ring gear and turn pinion to rotate ring gear several revolutions in each direction.
3. Examine tooth contact on models with Gleason gears, **Fig. 18,** and note the following:
   a. Illustration "A" shows proper contact without load on gears, while "A1" shows proper pattern with gears loaded. **Loading gears will shift contact pattern outward slightly.**
   b. Illustration "1," high narrow contact pattern, indicates excessive pinion depth. Increase pinion depth shim and increase backlash setting slightly to compensate.
   c. Illustration "2," deep narrow contact, indicates insufficient pinion depth. Decrease thickness of pinion depth shim and reduce backlash slightly to compensate.
   d. Illustration "3," short contact pattern on toe end of ring gear, indicates insufficient backlash. Increase backlash, and if further correction is required increase thickness of pinion depth shim slightly.
   e. Illustration "4," short contact pattern on heel of ring gear, indicates excessive backlash. Decrease backlash, and if further correction is required, decrease thickness of pinion depth shim slightly.
4. Examine tooth contact pattern on models with Klingelnberg gear referring to **Fig. 19,** and note the following:
   a. Proper tooth contact pattern without load is shown in "B," and proper contact with load on gears is shown in "C."
   b. Pattern shown in "D" can be corrected by decreasing pinion depth shim thickness (moving pinion away from ring gear) and slightly decreasing backlash to compensate.
   c. Pattern shown in "E" can be corrected by increasing pinion shim

thickness (moving pinion toward ring gear) and slightly increasing backlash to compensate.

5. Other possible incorrect contact patterns and the necessary corrections are shown in **Fig. 20.**
6. Perform indicated corrections in assembly adjustments, ensure pinion preload and total assembly preload are properly adjusted, then recheck contact pattern. **If pinion depth shim must be replaced, use new collapsible spacer when installing pinion.**

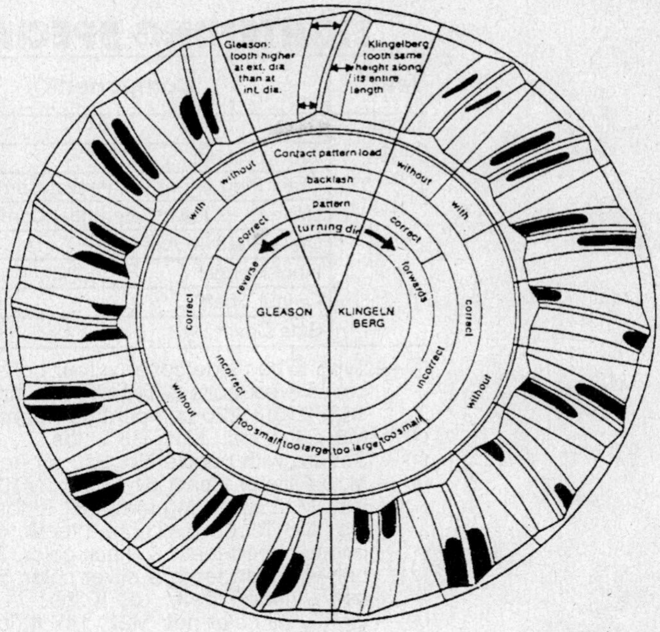

BM3019100022000X

Fig. 20 Ring gear & pinion tooth contact correction chart

DRIVE AXLE SPECIFICATIONS

BACKLASH

Models	Backlash, Inch	Minimum Input Flange Radial Runout, Inch	Shaft Seal Friction Torque, Inch Lbs.
All	0.0024–0.0055	0.0028	1.77

DIFFERENTIAL FRICTION TORQUE

Type	Manufacturer	Torque, Inch lbs.
Type G (Eight-Bolt)	FAG	19.469–45.929
	Koyo	21.062–42.124
	Timken	20.354–45.664
	SKF	17.699–38.053
Type K (Four-Bolt)	FAG	14.199–24.735
	Koyo	11.239–23.451
	SKF	12.389–23.008
	Timken	12.832–23.451
Type M (Six-Bolt)	FAG	13.982–28.850
	Koyo	10.885–24.159
	SKF	11.504–22.124
	Timken	11.062–30.008

TIGHTENING SPECIFICATIONS

Year	Component①	Torque, Ft. Lbs.
1998–2001	Cover	②③
	Crown Wheel	③⑦
	Drain Plug, Front Differential Carrier	48
	Drain Plug, Rear Differential Carrier	52
	Drive Shaft To Axle Shaft	⑤
	Input Flange	⑧
	Output Shaft	④
	Side Cover	③⑥

① — Type K has side cover w/four bolts; Type M has side cover w/six bolts & Type G has side cover w/eight bolts. 168, 215 & 220 compact do not have side covers.
② — M8, 24 ft. lbs.; M10, 35 ft. lbs.
③ — Secure with Loctite No. 270, or equivalent.
④ — M10 Fillister Head, 61 ft. lbs.; M10 w/locking teeth, 71 ft. lbs.; M12 w/locking teeth, 81 ft. lbs.; M10 Torx bolt, 61 ft. lbs.; M8 Torx bolt w/ribbed teeth, 47 ft. lbs.; M10 Torx bolt w/ribbed teeth & black color, 74 ft. lbs.; M10 Torx bolt w/ribbed teeth & silver color, 59 ft. lbs.; M12 Torx bolt w/ribbed teeth, 100 ft. lbs.
⑤ — Lightly oil color nut: M22, 147 ft. lbs.; M24, 184 ft. lbs.; M27 except X5, 221 ft. lbs.; M27 X5, 310 ft. lbs.
⑥ — Type M & G, 16 ft. lbs.; Type K, 88 inch lbs., plus 18 inch lbs., then an additional 40° plus 5°.
⑦ — M10, 37 ft. lbs. plus 27 inch lbs., then tighten 40° plus 3°; M12 & M14, 74 ft. lbs. plus 88 inch lbs., then tighten 50° plus 5°.
⑧ — M20, 129 ft. lbs.; M20, 136 ft. lbs.; M22, 155 ft. lbs.

Traction Control Systems

INDEX

Page No.		Page No.		Page No.	
Description	2-239	**System Service**	2-239	Rotating Speed Sensor	2-239
Diagnosis & Testing	2-239	Component Replacement	2-239		

DESCRIPTION

Dynamic Stability Control (DSC) optimizes traction by electronic means, with the system sensing wheel-speed differences and reducing engine torque and/or applying individual rear-wheel brakes.

DIAGNOSIS & TESTING

Refer "Anti-Lock Brakes" section

SYSTEM SERVICE

Refer "Anti-Lock Brakes" section

Component Replacement

ROTATING SPEED SENSOR

M5, 525, 528, 530 & 540

1998

1. Remove driver's seat.
2. Remove lower lefthand door pillar trim panel.
3. Raise floor trim panel and fold aside.
4. Disconnect connector.
5. Remove mounting bolts and sensor.
6. Reverse procedure to install.

1999–2001

1. Remove driver's seat.
2. Remove front entrance cover strip.
3. Raise floor trim panel and fold aside.
4. Disconnect connector.
5. Remove mounting bolts and sensor.
6. Reverse procedure to install.

X5

1. Remove rear cup holder.
2. Remove mounting bolts and sensor.
3. Disconnect connector.
4. Reverse procedure to install.

323Ci, 325, 328Ci & 330 & 2001 M3 & 2000 323i & 328i & 1999 323i & 328i SEDAN

1. Remove driver's seat.
2. Remove A-pillar footwell trim panel.
3. Raise floor trim panel and move insulating wedge approximately 0.315–0.394 inch forward.
4. Remove mounting bolts.
5. Turn sensor counterclockwise and remove to left.
6. Disconnect connector.
7. Remove mounting bolts and sensor from bracket.
8. Reverse procedure to install.

740 & 750

1998

1. Remove driver's seat.
2. Remove front inner rocker panel cover strip.
3. Raise floor trim panel and fold aside.
4. Pull soundproofing sheet out.
5. Remove sensor cover.
6. Disconnect connector.
7. Remove mounting bolts and sensor.
8. Reverse procedure to install.

1999–2001

1. Remove driver's seat.
2. Remove lower lefthand door pillar trim.
3. Raise floor trim panel and fold aside.
4. Disconnect connector.
5. Remove mounting bolts and sensor.
6. Reverse procedure to install.

Active Suspension Systems

NOTE: On Air Bag Equipped Models, Refer To "Air Bag System Precautions" Located In The Front Of This Manual For System Disarming & Arming Procedures.

INDEX

	Page No.
Component Replacement	2-240
Ride Height Sensor	2-240
Description	2-240
Description	2-240
Diagnosis & Testing	2-240
Precautions	2-240
Air Bag Systems	2-240
Battery Ground Cable	2-240

PRECAUTIONS

AIR BAG SYSTEMS

Refer to "Air Bag System Precautions" in the front of this manual for system disarming and arming procedures.

BATTERY GROUND CABLE

Prior to service, disconnect battery ground cable and isolate as required.

DESCRIPTION

Suspension is adjusted automatically depending on driving conditions and mode selected by driver. The system is capable of self-diagnosis after switching on ignition. If no faults are observed, a control lamp corresponding with the selected mode of suspension will light up in the program button.

Solenoid valves on the shock absorbers are activated by the control unit and adapt the absorbing force to driving conditions. For this purpose, the control unit processes electronic speed signals and signals from the following components: Front and rear body acceleration sensors, axial acceleration sensor, steering angle sensor and road speed sensor.

DIAGNOSIS & TESTING

COMPONENT REPLACEMENT

RIDE HEIGHT SENSOR

1. Disconnect connectors.
2. Remove mounting nut and disconnect control rod.
3. Remove mounting bolts and sensor.
4. Reverse procedure to install. **On 525, 528, 530, 540, 740 & 750 models,** ensure front sensor bracket is located between cast lugs and tab correctly seated.

Engine Rebuilding Specifications

INDEX

	Page No.
Camshaft	2-242
Crankshaft, Bearings & Rods	2-242
Cylinder Block	2-244
Cylinder Head, Valve Guide & Valve Seats	2-241
Pistons, Pins & Rings	2-243
Valves	2-241

CYLINDER HEAD, VALVE GUIDE & VALVE SEATS

All measurements given in inches, unless otherwise specified.

Engine		Cylinder Head Height		Valve Guides			Valve Seats		
Liter	Series	Standard	Machining Limit	Inside Diameter	Stem To Guide Clearance Intake	Stem To Guide Clearance Exhaust	Seat Angle, Degrees	Seat Width Intake	Seat Width Exhaust
1.9L	M44	5.5124	5.4946	0.2362–0.2441	0.0197	0.0197	45	1.2757	1.1852
2.5L	M52	5.5124	5.5005	0.2362–0.2441	0.0197	0.0197	45	1.2757	1.1576
2.8L	M52	5.5124	5.5005	0.2362–0.2441	0.0197	0.0197	45	1.2757	1.1576
3.0L	M54	5.5124	5.5005	0.2362–0.2441	0.0197	0.0197	45	1.2757	1.1576
3.2L	S52	5.5124	①	0.2362–0.2441	0.0197	0.0197	45	1.1497–1.1655	1.0316–1.0473
	S54	5.7466–5.7506	①	—	—	—	45	1.3584	1.1812
4.4L	M62	5.5124	5.5005	0.2362–0.2441	0.0197	0.0197	45	1.3584	1.1812
5.4L	S73	5.5124	5.5045	0.2756–0.2835	0.0197	0.0197	45	1.6340	1.4017

① — Do not machine head.

VALVES

All measurements given in inches, unless otherwise specified.

Engine		Intake		Exhaust		Face Angle, Degrees	Valve Tip Clearance (Between Valve & Guide)
Liter	Series	Head Diameter	Stem Diameter	Head Diameter	Stem Diameter		
1.9L	M44	1.2993	0.2362	1.2009	0.2362	45	0.0197
2.5L	M52 & M54	1.2993	0.2362	1.2009	0.2362	45	0.0197
2.8L	M52	1.2993	0.2362	1.2009	0.2362	45	0.0197
3.0L	M54	1.2993	0.2362	1.2009	0.2362	45	0.0197
3.2L	S52	1.1812	0.2362	1.0631	0.2362	45	0.0197
	S54	—	—	—	—	—	—
4.4L	M62	1.3781	0.2362	1.2009	0.2362	45	0.0197
5.4L	S73	1.6537	0.2362	1.4175	0.2362	45	0.0197

CAMSHAFT

All measurements given in inches, unless otherwise specified.

Engine		Bearing Width	Runout	
Liter	Series		Radial	Axial
1.9L	M44	0.7875	0.0016–0.0032	0.0026–0.0059
2.5L	M52 & M54	0.7875	0.0008–0.0021	0.0059–0.0130
2.8L	M52	0.7875	0.0008–0.0021	0.0059–0.0130
3.0L	M54	0.7875	0.0008–0.0021	0.0059–0.0130
3.2L	S52	0.7875	0.0008–0.0021	①
	S54	0.8072	0.0011–0.0021②③	0.0039–0.0072
4.4L	M62	.8702–0.8741	0.0016–0.0029	0.0079–0.0142
5.4L	M73	0.8662–0.8702	0.0016–0.0032	0.0059–0.0130

① — Intake, 0.0031–0.0058 inch; Exhaust, 0.0031–0.0066 inch.
② — Bearing points 2–7.
③ — Bearing point 1, 0.0013–0.0026 inch.

CRANKSHAFT, BEARINGS & RODS

All measurements given in inches, unless otherwise specified.

Engine		Crankshaft						Connecting Rod	
		Main Journal Diameter, Std.			Endplay		Center Main Bearing Runout, Max.	Journal Diameter, Std.	Endplay, Radial
Liter	Series	Yellow	Green	White	Radial	Axial			
1.9L	M44	2.3618–2.3620	2.3615–2.3618	2.3613–2.3615	0.0008–0.0018	0.0032–0.0064	0.0059	1.7718–1.7728	0.0004–0.0020
2.5L	M52 & M54	2.3618–2.3620	2.3615–2.3618	2.3613–2.3615	0.0008–0.0023	.0032–0.0064	0.0079	1.7718–1.7728	0.0007–0.0022
2.8L	M52	2.3618–2.3620	2.3615–2.3618	2.3613–2.3615	0.0008–0.0023	.0032–0.0064	0.0079	1.7718–1.7728	0.0007–0.0022
3.0L	M54	2.3618–2.3620	2.3615–2.3618	2.3613–2.3615	0.0008–0.0023	.0032–0.0064	0.0079	1.7718–1.7728	0.0007–0.0022
3.2L	S52	2.3618–2.3620	2.3615–2.3618	2.3613–2.3615	0.0008–0.0023	.0032–0.0064	0.0079	1.7718–1.7728	0.0007–0.0022
	S54	2.3618–2.36201①②	2.3615–2.3618①③	2.3613–2.3615①④	0.0007–0.0020	0.0056–0.0099	—	2.0868–1.0873	0.0012–0.0028
4.4L	M62	2.7556–2.7558	2.7553–2.7555	2.7550–2.7552	0.0008–0.0018	.0033–0.0101	0.0059	1.8900–1.8904	0.0008–0.0022
5.4L	M73	2.9524–2.9527	2.9521–2.9524	2.9519–2.5921	0.0010–0.0020	0.0033–0.0101	0.0059	1.7718–1.7722	.0006–0.0023

① — Bearing points 2–7.
② — Bearing point 1, 2.3610–2.3623 inches.
③ — Bearing point 1, 2.3607–2.3610 inches.
④ — Bearing Point 2, 2.3605–2.3607 inches.

PISTONS, PINS & RINGS

All measurements given in inches, unless otherwise specified.

Engine Liter	Engine Series	Piston Diameter, Std.	Piston To Bore Clearance	Piston & Cylinder Wear Clearance, Max.	Ring End Gap First Comp.	Ring End Gap Second Comp.	Ring End Gap Oil	Ring Side Clearance First Comp.	Ring Side Clearance Second Comp.	Ring Side Clearance Oil
1.9L	M44	3.3462	0.0004–0.0016	0.0059	0.0079–0.0393	0.0079–0.0393	0.0157–0.0551	0.0008–0.0079	0.0008–0.0039	①
2.5L	M52	3.3066	0.0004–0.0016	0.0059	0.0039–0.0118	0.0079–0.0157	0.0098–0.0197	0.0008–0.0024	0.0012–0.0026	0.0008–0.0024
	M54	3.3072	0.0004–0.0016	0.0059	0.0079–0.0157	0.0079–0.0157	0.0079–0.0177	0.0008–0.0024	0.0008–0.0024	0.0006–0.0024
2.8L	M52	3.3066	0.0004–0.0016	0.0059	0.0039–0.0118	0.0079–0.0157	0.0098–0.0197	0.0008–0.0024	0.0012–0.0026	0.0008–0.0024
3.0L	M54	3.3072	0.0004–0.0016	0.0059	0.0079–0.0157	0.0079–0.0157	0.0079–0.0177	0.0008–0.0024	0.0008–0.0024	0.0006–0.0024
3.2L	S52	3.4002–3.4009	0.0010–0.0023	0.0044	0.0098–0.0157	0.0079–0.0157	0.0098–0.0197	0.0012–0.0026	0.0008–0.0022	0.0008–0.0022
	S54	3.4238–3.4245	0.0010–0.0023	0.0059	0.0079–0.0139	0.0138–0.0236	0.0098–0.0197	0.0012–0.0028	0.0006–0.0024	0.0008–0.0024
4.4L	M62	3.6215–3.6222	.0002–0.0015	0.0039	0.0039–0.0118	0.0079–0.0157	0.0079–0.0354	0.0008–0.0024	0.0008–0.0024	①
5.4L	M73	②	0.0004–0.0013	0.0039	0.0059–0.0138	0.0079–0.0157	0.0157–0.0551	0.0008–0.0022	0.0008–0.0022	①

① — Not measurable.

② — Size A, 3.3458–3.3464 inches;
Size B, 3.3464–3.3469 inches.

CYLINDER BLOCK

All measurements given in inches, unless otherwise specified.

Engine		Bore				Total Wear Clearance Between Piston & Cylinder
Liter	Series	Standard	Limit	Taper, Max	Out Of Round, Max.	
1.9L	M44	3.3468–3.3473	3.3783–3.3670	0.0004	0.0004	0.0059
2.5L	M52 & M54	3.3074–3.3078	3.3173–3.3177	0.0004	0.0002	0.0059
2.8L	M52	3.3074–3.3078	3.3271–3.3275	0.0004	0.0002	0.0059
3.0L	M54	3.3074–3.3078	3.3271–3.3275	0.0004	0.0002	0.0059
3.2L	S52	3.4019–3.4025	3.4098–3.4103	0.0004	0.0002	0.0044
	S54	3.4255–3.4261	3.4334–3.4340	0.0004	0.0002	0.0059
4.4L	M62	3.6224–3.6230	—	0.0003	—	0.0039
5.4L	M73	3.3468–3.3472	3.3669–3.3673	0.0004	0.0004	0.0039

JAGUAR

INDEX OF SERVICE OPERATIONS

Page No.

AIR BAG SYSTEM PRECAUTIONS 0-12
ACTIVE SUSPENSION SYSTEM 3-102
AIR QUALITY STANDARDS 0-23
AUTOMATIC TRANSMISSIONS 3-78
BRAKES
Anti-Lock Brakes 3-55
Disc Brakes 3-51
Hydraulic Brake Systems 3-53
Power Brake Units 3-54
COMPUTER RELEARN PROCEDURES 0-10
DRIVE AXLES 3-99
ELECTRICAL
Air Bags 3-38
Air Conditioning 3-28
Alternators 3-34
Alternator, Replace 3-4
Blower Motor, Replace 3-6
Coil Pack, Replace 3-5
Combination Switch, Replace 3-6
Cooling Fans 3-30
Cruise Controls 3-35
Dash Panels 3-46
Evaporator Core, Replace 3-7
Fuel Pump Relay Location 3-4
Fuse Boxes & Relays 3-4
Fuse Panel & Flasher Location 3-4
Headlamp Switch, Replace 3-5
Heater Core, Replace 3-6
Ignition Lock, Replace 3-5
Ignition Switch, Replace 3-5
Instrument Cluster, Replace 3-6
Passive Restraints 3-38
Precautions 3-4
Relay Center Location 3-4
Speed Controls 3-35
Starter Motors 3-31
Starter, Replace 3-4
Steering Columns 3-48
Steering Wheel, Replace 3-6
Stop Light Switch, Replace 3-6
Technical Service Bulletins 3-7
Wiper Motor, Replace 3-6
Wiper Systems 3-36
ELECTRICAL SYMBOL IDENTIFICATION 0-33

Page No.

FRONT SUSPENSION & STEERING
Ball Joint, Replace 3-22
Ball Joint Inspection 3-22
Coil Spring, Replace 3-23
Control Arm, Replace 3-23
Crossmember, Replace 3-24
Description 3-22
Power Steering 3-49
Power Steering Gear, Replace 3-24
Power Steering Pump, Replace 3-25
Shock Absorber, Replace 3-23
Stabilizer Bar, Replace 3-23
Tightening Specifications 3-25
Wheel Bearing, Adjust 3-22
Wheel Bearing, Replace 3-22
Wheel Hub, Replace 3-22
REAR AXLE & SUSPENSION
Coil Spring, Replace 3-20
Description 3-19
Differential Carrier, Replace 3-20
Hub & Bearing, Replace 3-20
Hub & Bearing Service 3-20
Rear Axle, Replace 3-19
Rear Axle Shaft, Replace 3-20
Shock Absorber, Replace 3-20
Stabilizer Bar, Replace 3-21
Tightening Specifications 3-21
SERVICE REMINDER & WARNING LAMP RESET PROCEDURES 0-14
SPECIFICATIONS
Fluid Capacities & Cooling System Data 3-3
Front Wheel Alignment Specifications 3-2
General Engine Specifications 3-2
Lubricant Data 3-3
Rear Wheel Alignment Specifications 3-2
Tune Up Specifications 3-2
TRACTION CONTROL SYSTEM 3-101
VEHICLE IDENTIFICATION 0-3
VEHICLE MAINTENANCE SCHEDULES 0-45
WHEEL ALIGNMENT
Front Wheel Alignment 3-26
Preliminary Inspection 3-26

Page No.

Rear Wheel Alignment 3-27
Technical Service Bulletins 3-27
Vehicle Ride Height 3-27
Wheel Alignment Specifications 3-2
WIRE COLOR CODE IDENTIFICATION 0-33
3.0L ENGINE
Camshaft, Replace 3-10
Crankshaft Rear Oil Seal, Replace 3-10
Crankshaft Seal, Replace 3-10
Cylinder Head, Replace 3-9
Engine Mount, Replace 3-8
Engine Rebuilding Specifications 3-104
Engine, Replace 3-8
Exhaust Manifold, Replace 3-9
Front Cover, Replace 3-9
Intake Manifold, Replace 3-8
Oil Pan, Replace 3-10
Oil Pump, Replace 3-10
Pistons, Pins & Rings 3-10
Precautions 3-8
Radiator, Replace 3-11
Serpentine Drive Belt 3-10
Thermostat, Replace 3-10
Tightening Specifications 3-11
Timing Chain, Replace 3-9
Valve Cover, Replace 3-9
Water Pump, Replace 3-10
4.0L ENGINE
Camshaft, Replace 3-16
Crankshaft Rear Oil Seal, Replace 3-16
Crankshaft Seal, Replace 3-16
Cylinder Head, Replace 3-13
Engine Mount, Replace 3-12
Engine Rebuilding Specifications 3-104
Exhaust Manifold, Replace 3-13
Front Cover, Replace 3-14
Intake Manifold, Replace 3-12
Oil Pan, Replace 3-16
Oil Pump, Replace 3-16
Pistons, Pins & Rings 3-16
Precautions 3-12
Radiator, Replace 3-17
Serpentine Drive Belt 3-16
Supercharger, Replace 3-17
Technical Service Bulletins 3-17
Thermostat, Replace 3-16
Tightening Specifications 3-18
Timing Chain, Replace 3-14
Valve Cover, Replace 3-13
Water Pump, Replace 3-17

Specifications

GENERAL ENGINE SPECIFICATIONS

Engine, Liters	Year	Fuel System	Bore & Stroke, Inches	Compres-sion Ratio	Horsepower @ RPM	Torque Ft. Lbs @ RPM	Normal Oil Pressure, psi
3.0L①	2000–01	SFI	3.50 x 3.13	10.5	240 @ 6800	281 @ 6100	—
4.0L	1998–99	SFI	3.39 x 3.39	10.8	290 @ 6100	284 @ 4200	55.1
	1998–99②	SFI	3.39 x 3.39	9.00	370 @ 6150	387 @ 3600	65.25
	2000–01①	SFI	3.39 x 3.39	10.75	281 @ 6100	287 @ 4300	—

MPFI — Multi-Point Fuel Injection

① — S-Type.

② — Supercharged.

TUNE UP SPECIFICATIONS

Year & Engine	Spark Plug Gap Inch	Ignition Timing			Curb Idle Speed②		Fast Idle Speed②		Fuel Pres-sure, psi	Valve Lash, Inch	
		Firing Order	Timing BTDC	Timing Mark	Man. Trans.	Auto. Trans.	Man. Trans.	Auto. Trans.		Intake	Exhaust
1998–99											
4.0L	.052	④	①	③	—	①	—	①	—	—	—
2000–01											
3.0L	—	—	—	—	—	—	—	—	—	.007–.009C	.009–.011C
4.0L	.052	④	①	③	—	①	—	①	—	.007–.009C	.009–.011C

BTDC — Before Top Dead Center
C — Cold
N — Neutral
① — Controlled by engine management system.

② — When adjusting idle speed, set parking brake & block drive wheels.
③ — Equipped w/crankshaft position sensor.

④ — Firing order 1-5-4-2-6-3-7-8.

FRONT WHEEL ALIGNMENT SPECIFICATIONS

Model	Year	Caster Angle Deg.		Camber Angle Deg.		Toe-In Deg.
		Limits	Desired	Limits	Desired	
S-Type	2000–01	+7.79 to +8.79	+8.29	–.65 to +.35	–.15	0 to +.3°
XJ8	1998–2001	+4 to +8②	+6②	–1.2 to +0①	–.6①	+.1° to +.4°
XK8	1998–2001	+5 to +8②	+6.5②	–.9 to +.3①	–.6①	0° to +.4°

① — LH & RH balanced within 1°.

② — LH & RH balanced within 1.2°.

REAR WHEEL ALIGNMENT SPECIFICATIONS

Model	Year	Camber Angle Deg.		Toe-Out
		Limits	Desired	
S-Type	2000–01	–1.45 to —.55	–1.0	–.17 to +.33°
XJ8	1998–2001	–1.2 to 0	–.6	–.1 to +.76°
XK8	1998–2001	–.9 to –1	–.5	+.1 to +.5°

FLUID CAPACITIES & COOLING SYSTEM DATA

Year	Model	Cooling Capacity Qts.	Coolant Type	Radiator Cap Relief Pressure, lbs.	Thermo. Opening Temp. °F	Fuel Tank Gals.	Engine Oil Qts.①	Transmission Oil		Rear Axle Oil Pts.
								Man. Trans. Pts.	Auto. Trans. Qts.②	
1998	XJR	12.7	⑤	—	—	21.4		—	—	4.0
	XJ8	10.6	⑤	—	183	21.4	6.9	—	—	4.0
	XK8	10.6	⑤	—	183	21.4	6.9	—	③	3.8
1999–2001	XJR	12.7	⑥	—	—	21.4	7.7	—	—	4.0
	XJ8	10.6	⑥	—	—	23.1	6.9	—	10.6	4.0
	XK8	10.6	⑥	—	—	19.9	6.9	—	—	3.8
2000–01	S-Type	⑦	⑧	—	—	18.4	④	—	9.5	3.2

① — With filter change.
② — Approximate. Make final inspection w/dipstick.
③ — "Filled For Life" design. No routine inspection is required, nor is a dipstick provided. Fill to bottom of filler plug hole w/transmission at operating temperature.
④ — 3.0L, 6.8 qts.; 4.0L, 7.2 qts.
⑤ — Ethylene glycol meeting specification ESD-M97B49-A.
⑥ — Jaguar orange Extended Life Coolant (XLC) part No. JLM 20972/2 (1 liter) or part No. JLM 20972/3 (5 liter), or an equivalent meeting specification WSS-M97B44-D.
⑦ — 3.0L, 10.5 qts.; 4.0L, 11 qts.
⑧ — Jaguar premium cooling system fluid, part No. E2FZ-19549–AA or B.

LUBRICANT DATA

Model	Year	Lubricant Type						
		Transmission		Hydraulic Clutch Fluid	Transfer Case	Rear Axle	Power Steering	Brake System
		Manual	Automatic					
XJR	1998–2001	—	①	—	—	③	Dexron III	Super DOT 4
XJ8	1998–2001	—	②	—	—	③	Dexron III	Super DOT 4
XK8	1998–2001	—	②	—	—	③	Dexron III	Super DOT 4
S-Type	2000–01	—	④	Super DOT 4	—	⑤	Dexron III	Super DOT 4

① — Shell ATF 3403-M115, or equivalent.
② — Esso ATF LT 71141, or equivalent.
③ — Shell Spirax Super TS 90, or equivalent.
④ — Mercon, XT-5–QM, or equivalent.
⑤ — M2C192A Synthetic or equivalent

Electrical

NOTE: On Air Bag Equipped Models, Refer To "Air Bag System Precautions" Located In The Front Of This Manual For System Disarming & Arming Procedures.

INDEX

	Page No.
Air Bags	3-38
Air Conditioning	3-28
Alternators	3-34
Alternator, Replace	3-4
3.0L Engine	3-4
4.0L Engine	3-5
Blower Motor, Replace	3-6
S-Type	3-6
XJ8, XK8 & XJR	3-6
Coil Pack, Replace	3-5
3.0L Engine	3-5
4.0L Engine	3-5
Combination Switch, Replace	3-6
Cooling Fans	3-30
Cruise Controls	3-35
Dash Panels	3-46
Evaporator Core, Replace	3-7
S-Type	3-7
XJ8 & XJR	3-7
XK8	3-7
Fuel Pump Relay Location	3-4
Fuse Boxes & Relays	3-4
XJ8 & XJR	3-4
Fuse Panel & Flasher Location	3-4
Headlamp Switch, Replace	3-5
Heater Core, Replace	3-6
S-Type	3-6
XJ8 & XJR	3-6
XK8	3-6
Ignition Lock, Replace	3-5
XJ8, XK8 & XJR	3-5
Ignition Switch, Replace	3-5
S-Type	3-5
XJ8, XK8 & XJR	3-5
Instrument Cluster, Replace	3-6
Passive Restraints	3-38
Precautions	3-4
Air Bag Systems	3-4
Battery Connection	3-4
Battery Ground Cable	3-4
Relay Center Location	3-4
Speed Controls	3-35
Starter Motors	3-31
Steering Columns	3-48
Starter, Replace	3-4
S-Type	3-4
XJ8, XK8 & XJR	3-4
Steering Wheel, Replace	3-6
Stop Light Switch, Replace	3-6
Technical Service Bulletins	3-7
High Ignition Off Drain, Intermittent Permanent Power Feed Loss	3-7
Wiper Motor, Replace	3-6
Wiper Systems	3-36

PRECAUTIONS

AIR BAG SYSTEMS

Refer to "Air Bag System Precautions" in the front of this manual for system disarming and arming procedures.

BATTERY GROUND CABLE

Prior to service, disconnect battery ground cable and isolate as required.

BATTERY CONNECTION

Whether one or both cables are disconnected, a minimum of 30 seconds must elapse between disconnection of the first cable and connection of the last cable. **A clean final connection must be made. Do not allow temporary contact.**

1. Connect battery terminal.
2. Reset clock.
3. Enter radio security code. Refer to Sound System Manual if required.
4. Cycle both windows up and down to establish upper and lower datum points as follows:
   a. Turn ignition On.
   b. Lower glass to stop and hold switch in Down position for at least five seconds.
   c. Raise glass fully and hold switch in Up position for at least five seconds.
   d. Turn ignition Off.

FUSE PANEL & FLASHER LOCATION

The fuse panel is located under the lefthand side of the instrument panel. The flasher module is located behind the instrument panel, near the wiper switch.

FUSE BOXES & RELAYS

XJ8 & XJR

There are six fuse box assemblies, five of which have conventional, replaceable fuses. The High Power Protection Module does not have conventional fuses. It comprises three 250-Amp fusible links to protect the starting circuit (two connected in parallel) and the battery positive supply to the other fuse boxes. Refer to **Fig. 1** for fuse boxes and relay locations.

FUEL PUMP RELAY LOCATION

The fuel pump relay is located in the engine compartment relay center.

RELAY CENTER LOCATION

The relay centers are located on the lefthand and righthand of the engine compartment, on inner fenders and righthand and lefthand of rear inner fenders.

STARTER

REPLACE

XJ8, XK8 & XJR

1. **On XK8 models,** open driver's door to allow side windows to drop. Ensure doors remain open until battery is disconnected.
2. **On all models,** raise and support vehicle.
3. Remove power steering rack as outlined in "Front Suspension & Steering" section.
4. Disconnect starter motor main terminal wire, then the solenoid terminal wire.
5. Remove mounting bolts and starter motor.
6. Reverse procedure to install. **Torque** starter mounting bolts to 28–35 ft. lbs.

S-TYPE

1. Raise and support vehicle, then remove electrical connector protective cover.
2. Disconnect starter motor electrical connector, then the oxygen sensor and remove oxygen sensor.
3. Detach oxygen sensor harness connector, disconnect ground cable.
4. Remove harness retaining bracket, then the starter motor bolts and starter.
5. Reverse procedure to install. **Torque** starter motor to 18 ft. lbs.

ALTERNATOR

REPLACE

3.0L ENGINE

1. Release tensioner and remove accessory drive belt, then the alternator splash shield.
2. Detach alternator battery cable protective cover, then the positive cable nut.
3. Remove alternator retaining nut, then the alternator.
4. Reverse procedure to install. **Torque**

alternator nut to 35 ft. lbs. and cable nut to 108 inch lbs.

4.0L ENGINE

1. Remove air cleaner assembly.
2. Remove twin fan and motor assembly from behind radiator.
3. **On models equipped with supercharger,** remove supercharger drive belt and belt tensioner.
4. **On all models,** remove serpentine drive belt.
5. Raise and support vehicle.
6. Remove air intake duct from alternator.
7. Disconnect alternator harness from alternator.
8. Remove lower mounting bolt and position harness mounting bracket aside.
9. **On models equipped with supercharger,** proceed as follows:
   a. Lower vehicle.
   b. Position supercharger water pump harness multiplug from retaining bracket.
   c. Remove nuts mounting U-bracket and pump.
   d. Position pump to allow access to alternator.
10. **On all models,** remove upper mounting bolt and withdraw alternator from mounting bracket.
11. Reverse procedure to install. **Torque** lower mounting bolt to 28–35 ft. lbs. and upper mounting bolt to 13–18 ft. lbs.

COIL PACK

REPLACE

3.0L ENGINE

1. **On righthand bank,** remove intake manifold as outlined under "Intake Manifold Replace."
2. **On lefthand bank,** remove engine cover.
3. **On all banks,** disconnect electrical connector from ignition coil.
4. Remove retaining bolt, then the ignition coil.
5. Reverse procedure to install. **Torque** coil bolts to 48 inch lbs.

4.0L ENGINE

1. Remove air intake tube and air cleaner assembly cover.
2. Remove mounting screws and pull coil cover clear.
3. Pull harness from retaining clips and disconnect relevant coil connector.
4. Remove mounting bolts and ignition coil.
5. Reverse procedure to install. **Torque** coil bolts and coil cover screws to 36–60 inch lbs.

IGNITION LOCK

REPLACE

XJ8, XK8 & XJR

Removal

1. Remove steering column lower cover.

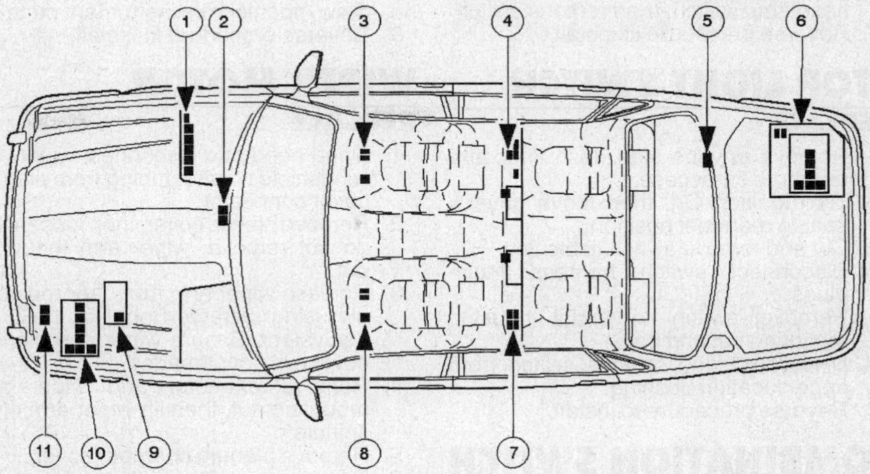

Item	Description
1	Engine and Transmission Control Module Compartment Relays (RH Steering opposite)
2	Front Firewall Relays
3	Front Seat Relays - Right Hand Side
4	Heelboard - Right Hand Side
5	High Power Protection Module
6	Trunk Fuse Box
7	Heelboard - Left Hand Side
8	Front Seat Relays - Left Hand Side
9	Engine Management Fuse Box
10	Engine Compartment Fuse Box
11	Engine Compartment Front Relays

JC1049800003000X

Fig. 1 Fuse boxes and relay locations. XJ8 & XJR

2. Insert ignition key into steering column lock.
3. Turn key to auxiliary position No. I.
4. Remove lock barrel by pressing retaining peg, then withdraw lock barrel from steering lock.

Installation

1. Insert ignition key into lock barrel.
2. Align lock barrel to steering column lock.
3. Install lock barrel to steering column lock by fully seating lock barrel to steering column lock and ensuring peg has engaged.
4. Remove ignition key from lock.
5. Install steering column lower cover.

IGNITION SWITCH

REPLACE

XJ8, XK8 & XJR

1. Remove dash panel under cover, then upper and lower column covers.
2. Remove and disconnect ignition switch electrical connector from mounting bracket.
3. Remove ignition switch from lock assembly by remove mounting screws.
4. Reverse procedure to install.

S-TYPE

1. Remove retaining screws, then the lower instrument panel.
2. Disconnect headlamp adjustment switch, then remove driver side air duct.
3. Remove hood latch release handle support plate, then the ignition switch upper and lower bolts.
4. Disconnect transmission lock actuator cable.
5. Disconnect ignition switch, then remove it.
6. Reverse procedure to install.

HEADLAMP SWITCH

REPLACE

1. Remove retaining screws, then the lower instrument panel.

2. Disconnect electrical connector from headlamp switch, then remove switch.
3. Reverse procedure to install.

STOP LIGHT SWITCH

REPLACE

1. Remove driver's side dash liner and armature for access.
2. Turn ignition On, then move driver's seat to rearmost position.
3. Cut and remove switch cable tie.
4. Disconnect switch harness multi-plugs.
5. Remove switch to pedal housing mounting nut and bolt.
6. Disconnect and remove switch from upper location bushing.
7. Reverse procedure to install.

COMBINATION SWITCH

REPLACE

1. Remove lower dash panel.
2. Remove steering column lower and upper covers.
3. Remove driver air bag module and outlined in "Air Bag System."
4. Ensure steering wheel is centered.
5. Remove steering wheel.
6. Disconnect cancellation module, wiper/washer switch and flasher/ headlamp electrical connectors.
7. Remove switch assemblies/ cancellation module by unscrewing switch gear mounting screws.
8. Remove switch assemblies from cancellation module and mounting bracket.
9. Remove cancellation module from mounting bracket.
10. Reverse procedure to install.

STEERING WHEEL

REPLACE

1. Remove air bag module as outlined in "Air Bag System."
2. Center front wheels and lock steering wheel by removing ignition key.
3. Slightly loosen nut securing steering wheel to shaft.
4. Pull steering wheel to release from shaft. Remove mounting nut and steering wheel.
5. Reverse procedure to install. **Torque** steering wheel mounting bolt to 26–33 ft. lbs.

INSTRUMENT CLUSTER

REPLACE

1. Turn ignition key to II position, then adjust steering column to lowest and fully extended position.
2. Turn ignition key to 0 position.
3. Remove steering wheel as outlined in this section.
4. Remove lower dash panel from driver's side.
5. Remove instrument panel veneer panel.
6. Disconnect major gauge harness electrical connectors under dash.
7. Loosen and remove four major gauge module mounting screws and withdraw module from instrument panel.
8. Reverse procedure to install.

WIPER MOTOR

REPLACE

1. Open hood and disconnect wiper arm windshield washer tubing from plenum cover connector.
2. Remove plastic cover, then loosen, but do not remove, wiper arm mounting nut.
3. Release wiper arm from tapered spindle using extractor tool No. 18G2, or equivalent. Ensure wiper and plenum cover are not damaged.
4. Remove extractor and wiper arm mounting nut, then lift wiper arm off of spindle.
5. Remove plenum chamber cover.
6. Remove mounting bolt and driver side water deflector.
7. **On convertible models,** remove driver's side firewall brace mounting bolts and brace.
8. **On all models,** cut strap attaching wiper motor electrical connector to mounting bracket and disconnect electrical connector.
9. Remove wiper motor mounting bolts and motor with linkage.
10. Reverse procedure to install.

BLOWER MOTOR

REPLACE

XJ8, XK8 & XJR

Driver's Side

1. Remove lower and upper steering column covers, then the driver's knee bolster.
2. Remove steering wheel as outlined in this section.
3. Remove upper steering column and center console.
4. Remove mounting bolts and footwell blower duct.
5. Cut console wiring harness tie strap.
6. Remove blower duct mounting screws and disconnect blower electrical connector.
7. Loosen firewall mounting nut, then remove mounting bolts and blower assembly.
8. Reverse procedure to install.

Passenger's Side

1. Remove shift selector panel, then the console and fascia veneers.
2. Remove radio and center console switch module, then the console.
3. Remove steering wheel as outlined in this section.
4. Remove lower and upper steering column covers, then the driver's knee bolster.
5. Remove combination switch as outlined in this section, then the glove compartment.
6. Remove dash panel.
7. Remove mounting bolts and footwell blower duct.
8. Cut console wiring harness tie strap.
9. Remove blower duct mounting screws and disconnect blower electrical connector.
10. Loosen firewall mounting nut, then remove mounting bolts and blower assembly.
11. Reverse procedure to install.

S-TYPE

1. Remove blower motor cover, then the blower motor.
2. Disconnect electrical connector from blower motor. **Prior to removing a wheel that is to be reused, clean any corrosion from blower motor shaft to prevent damage to wheel mounting diameter.**
3. Remove push clip, then the wheel from motor.
4. Reverse procedure to install.

HEATER CORE

REPLACE

XJ8 & XJR

1. Remove dash panel as outlined in "Dash Panel, Service."
2. Remove mounting screw and footwell duct.
3. Disconnect cool air bypass servo motor connector, then remove bracket mounting screws.
4. Position suitable cloth to absorb coolant leaking from hoses, then remove mounting brackets.
5. Remove mounting clamps and heater hoses. Plug openings.
6. Remove mounting screws, retaining plate and heater core.
7. Reverse procedure to install, using new O-rings.

XK8

1. Remove upper steering column, then drain radiator coolant into suitable container.
2. Remove mounting screw and footwell duct.
3. Remove center gauge module, then the dash panel as outlined in "Dash Panel, Service."
4. Disconnect cool air bypass servo motor connector, then remove bracket mounting screws.
5. Position suitable cloth to absorb coolant leaking from hoses, then remove mounting brackets.
6. Remove mounting clamps and heater hoses. Plug openings.
7. Remove mounting screws, retaining plate and heater core.
8. Reverse procedure to install, using new O-rings.

S-TYPE

1. Remove evaporator core housing from vehicle.
2. Remove blower motor, then the heater core pipe retaining bracket.
3. Disconnect blower control relay electrical connector, then remove retaining bolts and blower motor housing.
4. Remove blower motor control relay, then the foam insulation.

5. Remove evaporator core housing bolts, then unclip fastener and separate evaporator core housing.
6. Remove A/C radiator and heater core.
7. Reverse procedure to install.

EVAPORATOR CORE

REPLACE

XJ8 & XJR

1. Remove heater core as outlined in this section.
2. Disconnect connectors, then remove lower mounting and air conditioning control module.
3. Remove mounting screw and position evaporator pipe firewall seal plate aside.
4. Position heater temperature sensor wiring harness aside and disconnect connector.
5. Disconnect connector, then remove mounting screws and footwell servo motor.
6. Disconnect heater and evaporator sensor connectors.
7. Remove mounting bolts, clips and upper case from lower.
8. Remove evaporator core and disconnect sensor.
9. Reverse procedure to install.

XK8

1. Recover air conditioning refrigerant as outlined in "Air Conditioning."
2. Drain coolant into suitable container.
3. Remove dash panel as outlined under "Dash Panel, Replace."
4. Remove mounting bolts and disconnect evaporator air conditioning lines under hood. Plug openings.
5. Disconnect spring band clips and heater hoses. Plug openings.
6. Remove steering column upper mounting bracket/brace to fire wall mounting bolt.
7. Remove mounting bolts to firewall and transmission tunnel, then the brace
8. Remove mounting screws and fan motor ducts.
9. Disconnect heater electrical connector.
10. Disconnect air conditioning control module electrical connectors.
11. Disconnect condensate drain tubes.
12. Remove evaporator line support bracket.
13. Remove mounting nuts and evaporator core by clearing lines through firewall grommet.
14. Reverse procedure to install using new O-rings. **Torque** evaporator core mounting nuts to 44–62 inch lbs. and line mounting bolts to 44–88 inch lbs.

S-TYPE

1. Recover air conditioning refrigerant as outlined in "Air Conditioning."
2. Drain engine coolant into a suitable container, then disconnect heater hose assemble from heater core.
3. Disconnect manifold and tube assembly from thermostatic expansion valve.
4. Remove evaporator core housing nuts and washers.
5. Remove instrument panel as outlined under "Dash Panel Service."
6. Remove pin-type retainers, then the heater duct assembly.
7. Unclip driver side wiring harness, then the passenger side.
8. Remove evaporator core housing bolts, then disconnect heater wiring harness electrical connector.
9. Remove evaporator core housing.
10. Reverse procedure to install.

TECHNICAL SERVICE BULLETINS

HIGH IGNITION OFF DRAIN, INTERMITTENT PERMANENT POWER FEED LOSS

2000–01 S-Type

On these models, VINs L000001–L70801, these conditions may be accompanied by phantom headlamp flashes once at 30 minutes or one hour after the ignition has been turned Off and energizing of the four luggage compartment ignition power relays.

To correct this condition, proceed as follows:

1. Turn ignition Off.
2. Probe back of General Electronic Control Module (GECM) electrical connector FH59 pin 6 (orange and green wire) using a suitable voltmeter. Reading should remain at battery voltage.
3. Watch for any voltage change for approximately 10 minutes.
4. If reading is a steady battery voltage, proceed as follows:
   a. Disconnect GECM connector FH59.
   b. Disconnect primary junction box electrical connector FH7. This is a gray 6-way connector located uppermost of junction box in central position.
   c. Connect one ohmmeter lead to FH59 pin 6 and other to pin 2 (orange and yellow wire).
   d. Note resistance, which should be less than 1 ohm.
5. If voltage is considerably lower or resistance is higher than specified, obtain a forward harness bypass lead part No. XR8 22981, then proceed as follows:
   a. Record all owner's preferred settings, such as clock 12/24 selection, CD compress mode, navigation volume and voice volume defaults, transmission mode, radio presets and compass calibrations and zone.
   b. Disconnect and isolate battery ground cable.
   c. Remove lefthand and righthand A-pillar trim panels.
   d. Disconnect GECM connector FH59.
   e. Disconnect primary junction box electrical connector FH7.
   f. Connect proper ends of bypass lead to junction box and disconnected connector.
   g. Pull carpeting away from firewall and both footwells.
   h. Route bypass lead from junction box around footwell to console. Tape to firewall at regular intervals.
   i. Route bypass lead through opening at front edge of HVAC assembly across to opposite side.
   j. Position bypass lead inline connector within HVAC housing. **Ensure connector will not rattle when vehicle is in motion.**
   k. Route bypass lead across footwell toward lefthand A-pillar. Tape to firewall at regular intervals.
   l. Remove connector FH59 pin 6 (orange and green wire) using a suitable terminal removal tool.
   m. Cut off terminal and insulate with a termination splice and heatshrink tubing, then tape lead to harness.
   n. Insert bypass lead terminal into redundant aperture.
   o. Secure any excess bypass lead so it will not rattle when vehicle is in motion.
   p. Connect connector FH59 to GECM.
   q. Install carpeting and A-pillar trim panels.
   r. Connect battery and reset owner's preferred settings.

3.0L Engine

NOTE: On Air Bag Equipped Models, Refer To "Air Bag System Precautions" Located In The Front Of This Manual For System Disarming & Arming Procedures.

NOTE: Prior To Performing Any Service Operations Listed In This Section, Consult The "Technical Service Bulletins" Section For Related Information.

INDEX

	Page No.
Camshaft, Replace	3-10
Crankshaft Rear Oil Seal, Replace	3-10
Crankshaft Seal, Replace	3-10
Cylinder Head, Replace	3-9
Engine Mount, Replace	3-8
Engine Rebuilding Specifications	3-104
Engine, Replace	3-8
Exhaust Manifold, Replace	3-9
Front Cover, Replace	3-9
Intake Manifold, Replace	3-8
Oil Pan, Replace	3-10
Oil Pump, Replace	3-10
Pistons, Pins & Rings	3-10
Precautions	3-8
Air Bag Systems	3-8
Battery Connection	3-8
Battery Ground Cable	3-8
Radiator, Replace	3-11
Serpentine Drive Belt	3-10
Replacement	3-10
Routing	3-10
Thermostat, Replace	3-10
Tightening Specifications	3-11
Timing Chain, Replace	3-9
Valve Cover, Replace	3-9
Water Pump, Replace	3-10

PRECAUTIONS

AIR BAG SYSTEMS

Refer to "Air Bag System Precautions" in the front of this manual for system disarming and arming procedures.

BATTERY GROUND CABLE

Prior to service, disconnect battery ground cable and isolate as required.

BATTERY CONNECTION

Whether one or both cables are disconnected, a minimum of 30 seconds must elapse between disconnection of the first cable and connection of the last cable. **A clean final connection must be made. Do not allow temporary contact.**

1. Connect terminal to battery.
2. Reset clock.
3. Enter radio security code.
4. Turn ignition On.
5. Lower glass to stop and hold switch in down position for at least five seconds.
6. Raise glass fully and hold switch in up position for at least five seconds.
7. Turn ignition Off.

ENGINE MOUNT

REPLACE

1. Raise and support vehicle, then remove lefthand and righthand lower engine mount retaining nuts.
2. Lower vehicle, then remove lefthand and righthand upper engine retaining nuts.
3. Raise engine, then support it with three-bar engine support and remove engine mount.
4. Reverse procedure to install.

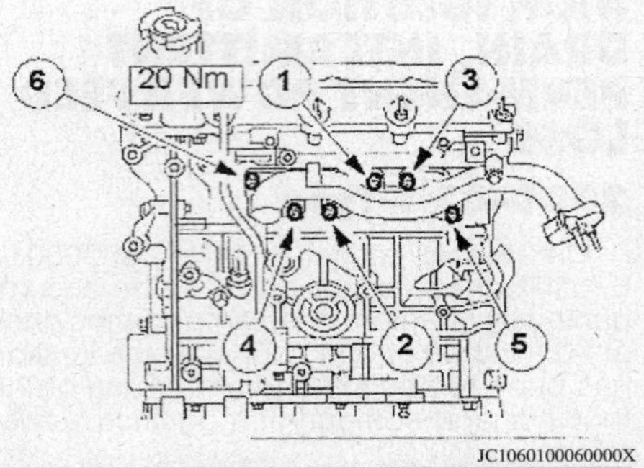

Fig. 1 Exhaust manifold tightening sequence

ENGINE

REPLACE

1. Remove intake manifold as outlined under "Intake Manifold Replace."
2. Remove air cleaner outlet tube, then the air cleaner.
3. Remove engine cover, then the radiator as outlined under "Radiator Replace."
4. Remove starter motor as outlined under "Starter Replace," then drain engine oil into a suitable container.
5. **On models equipped with manual transmission,** disconnect oxygen sensors, then remove support brackets.
6. Detach both rear muffler exhaust hangers, then support exhaust system.
7. Remove catalytic converters, then the exhaust system.
8. Remove transmission as outlined under "Transmission Replace."
9. **On models equipped with automatic transmission,** remove automatic transmission oil cooler tubes bracket, then the transmission wiring harness.
10. **On all models,** remove alternator splash shield, then the alternator positive cable protective cover.
11. Remove alternator positive cable nut, then power steering tube bracket.
12. Lower vehicle, then disconnect fuel supply spring lock coupling.
13. Remove oil level indicator, then the PCV valve tube.
14. Remove engine breather tube assembly, then the coolant by-pass tube assembly and purge inlet tube.
15. Remove EGR valve vacuum hose, then the coolant hoses.
16. Remove coolant hose assembly, then the power steering hose.
17. Remove engine wiring harness electrical connector, then the powertrain control module.
18. Raise vehicle, then remove A/C compressor supply and return tubes.
19. Remove power steering tube bracket retaining bolts, then the tube.
20. Remove lower engine mount retaining nuts, then lower vehicle and remove upper engine mount retaining nuts.
21. Remove engine assembly, using a suitable engine lift tool.
22. Reverse procedure to install. Tighten bolts and nuts to specifications.

INTAKE MANIFOLD

REPLACE

1. Drain engine coolant into a suitable container.
2. Remove throttle body as outlined under "Engine Performance & Driveability."
3. Disconnect EGR vacuum regulator valve (EVR) electrical connector, then

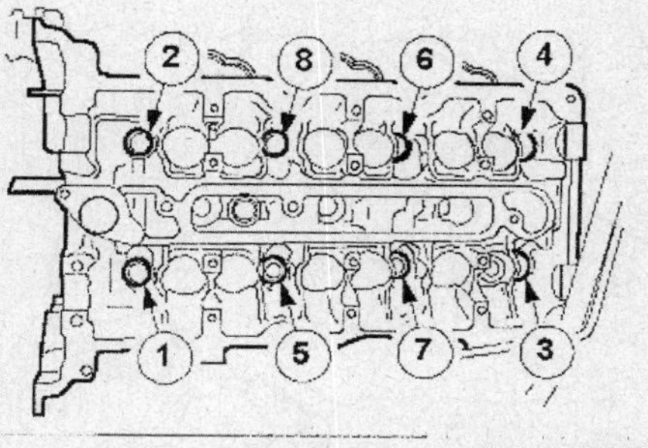

Fig. 2 Cylinder head bolts removal sequence

the vacuum hose connector from EGR vacuum regulator valve.
4. Disconnect electrical connector, then remove intake manifold tuning valve cover.
5. Disconnect differential pressure feedback EGR sensor electrical connector, then the hoses from differential pressure EGR sensor.
6. Disconnect inlet and outlet intake manifold coolant hoses, then the EGR valve vacuum hose and purge control valve (PCV) hose.
7. Disconnect purge line tube, then detach EGR valve.
8. Remove intake manifold bracket bolts, then the intake manifold securing bolt and fuel pulse damper protective bracket.
9. Displace intake manifold, then disconnect engine breather hose and intake manifold tuning valve electrical connector.
10. Remove intake manifold and discard gasket.
11. Reverse procedure to install. **Note: Intake manifold retaining bolts in positions 1, 2, 3 and 4 are longer than the retaining bolts in positions 5, 6, 7 and 8.**

EXHAUST MANIFOLD

REPLACE

1. Raise and support vehicle, then disconnect pre-catalytic converter oxygen sensor electrical connector and remove sensor.
2. Disconnect post-catalytic converter oxygen sensor electrical connector, then remove sensor.
3. Loosen three way catalytic converter downpipe exhaust clamp, then detach converter from exhaust manifold and remove.
4. Lower vehicle, then remove exhaust manifold heat shield.
5. Remove exhaust manifold and discard gasket.
6. Reverse procedure to install, noting the following:
   a. Install a new gasket.
   b. Tighten nuts and bolts in sequence as shown, **Fig. 1.**

CYLINDER HEAD

REPLACE

1. Remove camshafts as outlined under "Camshaft Replace."
2. Remove PCV valve tube, then disconnect fuel injection harness electrical connector.
3. Disconnect fuel pulse damper electrical connector and vacuum hose.
4. Detach fuel supply manifold and lower intake manifold. Discard lower intake manifold gaskets.
5. Remove coolant crossover tube, discard O-ring seals.
6. Disconnect catalytic converter electrical connectors, then remove catalytic converters.
7. Disconnect following electrical connectors over cylinder head for clarity:
   a. Knock sensor electrical connector.
   b. Audio suppressor electrical connector.
   c. Camshaft position electrical connector.
   d. Cylinder head earth strap.
8. Remove crankcase tube bracket retaining nut, then the oil level indicator tube.
9. Remove righthand and lefthand cylinder heads retaining bolts in sequence, **Fig. 2.** Remove exhaust manifold. Clean and inspect cylinder head and cylinder block.
10. Reverse procedure to install, noting the following:
    a. Tighten cylinder head bolts in indicated sequence in six stages, **Fig. 3.**
    b. Stage 1, tighten to 30 ft. lbs.
    c. Stage 2, additional 90°.
    d. stage 3, loosen 360° (one full turn) in reverse order.
    e. Stage 4, tighten to 30 ft. lbs.
    f. Stage 5, tighten 90°.
    g. Stage 6, additional 90°

VALVE COVER

REPLACE

1. Remove engine cover, then detach engine breather tube.
2. Detach throttle body wiring harness, then the wiring harness from valve cover.
3. Remove ignition coils, then the cylinder head temperature sensor and valve cover. Discard valve cover gasket.
4. Reverse procedure to install.

FRONT COVER

REPLACE

1. Remove valve covers as outlined under "Valve Cover Replace."
2. Remove water pump as outlined under "Water Pump Replace."
3. Remove crankshaft vibration damper.
4. Remove oil pan as outlined under "Oil Pan Replace."

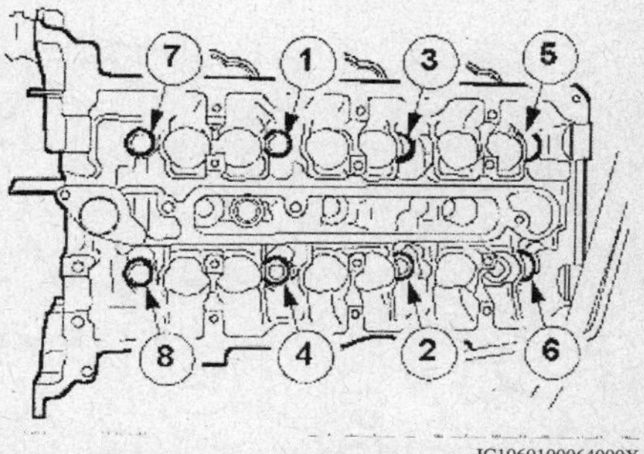

Fig. 3 Cylinder head bolts tightening sequence

5. Remove fuel supply manifold retaining bolt, then the accessory drive belt tensioner.
6. Remove idler pulley assembly, then the upper power steering pump bolts.
7. Disconnect crankshaft position sensor electrical connector, then raise and support vehicle.
8. Remove power steering pipe bracket retaining bolt, then detach power steering pipe and drain fluid into a suitable container.
9. Detach power steering pipe, then remove upper alternator bolt.
10. Remove engine cover retaining bolts in sequence, **Fig. 4.**
11. Detach engine wiring harness, then the front cover. Discard engine front cover gasket.
12. Reverse procedure to install, noting the following:
    a. Apply silicone sealant WSE-M4G323-A6 or equivalent to front cover.
    b. Tighten engine front cover bolts in sequence as shown, **Fig. 5.**

TIMING CHAIN

REPLACE

1. Remove engine front cover as outlined under "Front Cover Replace."
2. Install crankshaft pulley bolt and washer. **Rotate crankshaft clockwise until the colored timing chains align with marks on camshaft sprocket and crankshaft sprocket, to position engine to top dead center (TDC) No. 1 cylinder prior to removal and installation of camshaft.**
3. Remove crankshaft position sensor pulse wheel, then the crankshaft pulley bolt and washer.
4. Ensure crankshaft sprocket marks align with timing chain colored link.
5. Remove righthand chain tensioner, then the chain tensioner arm.
6. Remove righthand timing chain, then the chain guide.
7. Remove lefthand chain tensioner, then the chain tensioner arm.
8. Remove lefthand timing chain, then the chain guide.
9. Remove crankshaft sprocket.

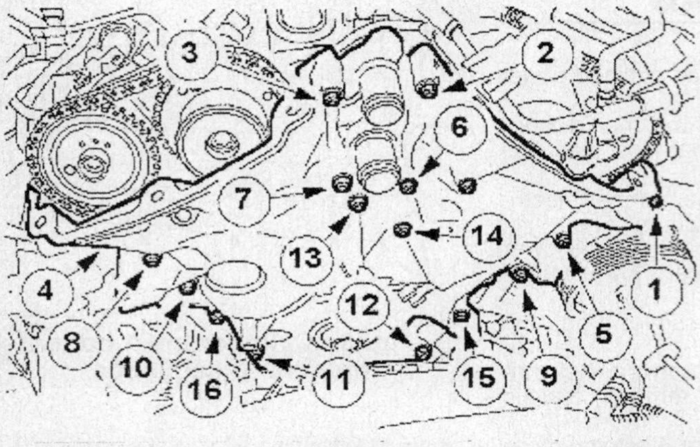

JC1060100061000X

Fig. 4 Engine front cover bolts removal sequence

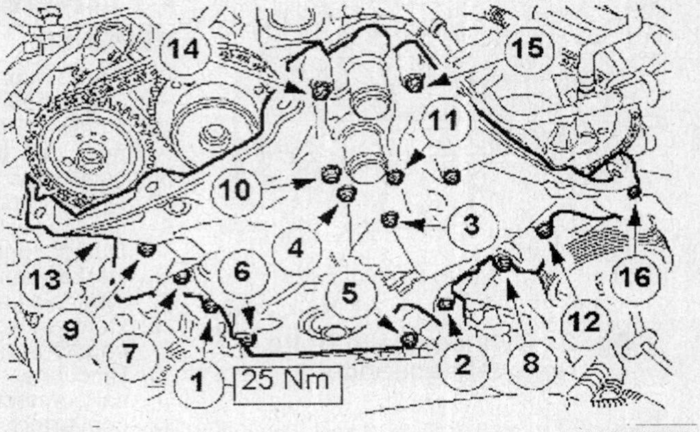

JC1060100062000X

Fig. 5 Engine front cover bolts tightening sequence

10. Reverse procedure to install.

CAMSHAFT

REPLACE

1. Remove timing chains, as outlined under "Timing Chain Replace."
2. Remove camshaft bearing cap bolts evenly, then the camshaft bearing caps.
3. Remove camshafts.
4. Reverse procedure to install.

PISTONS, PINS & RINGS

The pistons are open ended skirt design with flat upper surfaces to reduce heat absorption. Three piston rings, two compression and one oil control, are installed on each piston. Each piston is installed on a wrist pin which operates in a lead/bronze bushing installed in the connecting rod.

CRANKSHAFT SEAL

REPLACE

1. Drain engine coolant into a suitable container.
2. Release tensioner and remove accessory drivebelt.
3. Lower vehicle, then remove upper shield.
4. Remove throttle body as outlined under "Engine Performance & Driveability."
5. Detach coolant hose from housing assembly, then remove upper radiator mounting bracket.
6. Detach hose assembly from water pump and lower hose.
7. Remove hose assembly.
8. Using tool Nos. 303-D055 and 303-D121 or equivalents remove crankshaft vibration damper.
9. Using tool No. 303-409 or equivalent, remove crankshaft front oil seal.
10. Reverse procedure to install noting the following:
    a. Install oil seal using tool No. 303–335 or equivalent.
    b. Install crankshaft damper using tool 303-102 or equivalent.

CRANKSHAFT REAR OIL SEAL

REPLACE

1. Remove transmission and drive plate.
2. Remove seal using seal removal tool No. 303-519, or equivalent.
3. Reverse procedure to install seal with tool No. 303–178

OIL PAN

REPLACE

1. Remove alternator as outlined under "Alternator Replace."
2. Drain engine oil into suitable container.
3. Disconnect A/C compressor electrical connector, then remove A/C compressor retaining bolts and support A/C compressor using tie straps.
4. Detach power steering tube bracket.
5. **On models equipped with automatic transmission,** detach bracket for automatic transmission oil cooler tubes.
6. **On all models,** support engine with a suitable engine support beam.
7. Detach lower arm, then disconnect rotational sensor electrical connector.
8. Remove steering gear retaining bolts, then the crossmember.
9. Remove oil pan to transmission housing bolts.
10. Remove oil pan retaining bolts, then discard gasket. Clean and inspect oil pan and cylinder block sealing surfaces.
11. Reverse procedure to install.

OIL PUMP

REPLACE

1. Remove timing chains, as outlined under "Timing Chain Replace."
2. Remove and discard engine oil filter. **Do not drop two oil pump tube retaining bolts into oil pan during removal. Replace oil tube, remove and discard O-ring seal.**
3. Remove mounting bolts and oil pump.
4. Reverse procedure to install with new gasket. Tighten mounting bolts to specifications.

SERPENTINE DRIVE BELT

ROUTING

Refer to **Fig. 6** for serpentine drive belt routing.

REPLACEMENT

1. Raise and support vehicle, then remove and discard drivebelt tensioner clip.
2. Rotate belt tensioner counterclockwise using a 3/8 inch square drive bar, then remove drive belt.
3. Reverse procedure to install.

THERMOSTAT

REPLACE

1. Drain cooling system into suitable container.
2. Lower vehicle, then disconnect intake air temperature sensor electrical connector and engine breather hoses.
3. Remove air cleaner outlet tube, then the thermostat housing.
4. Remove thermostat from housing.
5. Reverse procedure to install with new seal.

WATER PUMP

REPLACE

1. Drain cooling system into suitable container.
2. Remove accessory drive belt.
3. Remove upper shield, then the throttle body as oulined under, "Engine Performance & Driveability."
4. Remove coolant hose from housing assembly, then upper radiator mounting bracket.
5. Detach hose assembly from water

pump and lower hose, then remove hose assembly.
6. Remove intake manifold support bracket, then coolant hoses from water pump.
7. Remove water pump from engine.
8. Reverse procedure to install.

RADIATOR

REPLACE

1. Drain cooling system into suitable container.
2. Recover A/C refrigerant as outlined in "Air Conditioning."
3. Remove air cleaner outlet tube, then the air cleaner and upper shield.
4. Remove radiator mounting brackets, then disconnect electric fan motor and conditioning pressure switch electrical connector.

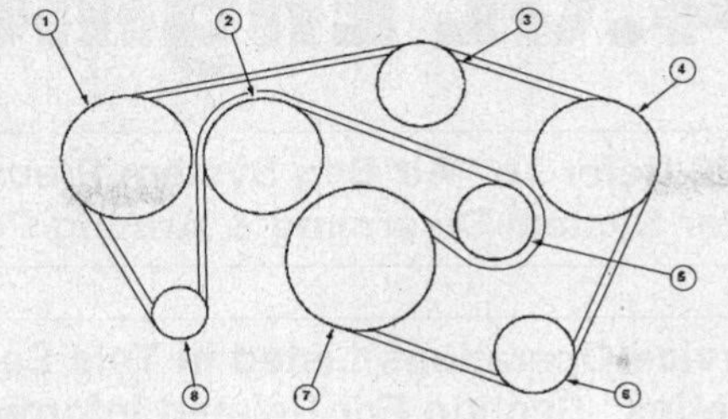

Item	Description
1	Belt idler pulley
2	Water pump pulley
3	Belt idler pulley
4	Power steering pump pulley
5	Belt tensioner
6	Air conditioning pump pulley
7	Crankshaft pulley
8	Generator pulley

JC1060100065000X

Fig. 6 Drive belt routing

5. Detach air conditioning receiver dryer, then disconnect heater valve electrical connector.
6. Remove lower radiator splash shield, then the cooling duct from fan shroud assembly.
7. Remove fan shroud retaining clips, then lower vehicle. Remove screws and fan shroud assembly.
8. Seal line and evaporator with plugs, then detach air conditioning line.
9. Raise vehicle, then remove lower radiator splash shield
10. Remove lower coolant hose, then A./C condenser.
11. Remove retaining screws, then the automatic transmission/power steering cooler.
12. Lower vehicle, then remove radiator foam trim and radiator.
13. Reverse procedure to install.

TIGHTENING SPECIFICATIONS

Year	Component	Torque, Ft. Lbs.
2000–01	Accessory Drive Belt	18
	Accessory Belt Idler Pulley	18
	A/C Compressor	18
	A/C Compressor Bracket	18
	Alternator	35
	Auto. Trans. To Oil Pan	84①
	Camshaft Bearing Caps	84①
	Coolant By-Pass tube	84①
	Crankshaft Pulley	②
	Cylinder Head	③
	EGR Tube	30
	EGR Valve	18
	Engine Front Cover	18
	Engine Mount Bracket	32
	Engine Mount To Crossmember	49
	Exhaust Manifold	15
	Flywheel	59
	Intake Manifold	84①
	Oil Pan	18
	Oil Pump	84①
	Power Steering Bracket	84①
	Power Steering Pump	18
	Spark Plugs	11
	Timing Chain Guide	18
	Timing Chain Tensioner	18
	Valve Cover	84①
	Water Pump	18

① — Inch lbs.

② — Torque bolt to 88 ft. lbs, then loosen (minimum 1 turn), torque to 37 ft. lbs. Angle torque to 90°.

③ — Tighten in sequence and in six stages: Stage 1, tighten to 30 ft. lbs.; stage 2, tighten additional 90°; stage 3, loosen 360° (one full turn); stage 4, tighten to 30 ft. lbs.; stage 5 tighten 90°; stage 6, tighten additional 90°.

4.0L Engine

NOTE: On Air Bag Equipped Models, Refer To "Air Bag System Precautions" Located In The Front Of This Manual For System Disarming & Arming Procedures.

NOTE: Prior To Performing Any Service Operations Listed In This Section, Consult The "Technical Service Bulletins" Section For Related Information.

INDEX

	Page No.
Camshaft, Replace	3-16
Crankshaft Rear Oil Seal, Replace	3-16
Crankshaft Seal, Replace	3-16
Front	3-16
Cylinder Head, Replace	3-13
Engine Mount, Replace	3-12
Rear Mount	3-12
Engine Rebuilding Specifications	3-104
Exhaust Manifold, Replace	3-13
Front Cover, Replace	3-14
Intake Manifold, Replace	3-12
Oil Pan, Replace	3-16
Oil Pump, Replace	3-16
Pistons, Pins & Rings	3-16
Precautions	3-12
Air Bag Systems	3-12
Battery Connection	3-12
Battery Ground Cable	3-12
Fuel System Pressure Relief	3-12
Radiator, Replace	3-17
Serpentine Drive Belt	3-16
Replacement	3-16
Routing	3-16
Supercharger, Replace	3-17
Technical Service Bulletins	3-17
Cylinder Head Rear Oil Leak	3-17
Low Coolant Level Warning Lamp Lighting	3-17
Start-Up Noise	3-17
Thermostat, Replace	3-16
Tightening Specifications	3-18
Timing Chain, Replace	3-14
Primary	3-14
Secondary	3-15
Valve Cover, Replace	3-13
Water Pump, Replace	3-17

PRECAUTIONS

AIR BAG SYSTEMS

Refer to "Air Bag System Precautions" in the front of this manual for system disarming and arming procedures.

FUEL SYSTEM PRESSURE RELIEF

Always relieve fuel system pressure before disconnecting any fuel system component.

1. Ensure ignition is switched off and remove valve cap from fuel crossover pipe.
2. Place suitable cloth under valve to collect any spillage.
3. Place suitable container for collecting fuel, adjacent to vehicle.
4. Connect fuel injector pressure test equipment tool No. JD 209, or equivalent, to valve on fuel crossover pipe.
5. Follow manufacture's instructions supplied with fuel injector pressure test equipment to depressurize fuel system.

BATTERY GROUND CABLE

Prior to service, disconnect battery ground cable and isolate as required.

BATTERY CONNECTION

Whether one or both cables are disconnected, a minimum of 30 seconds must elapse between disconnection of the first cable and connection of the last cable. **A clean final connection must be made. Do not allow temporary contact.**

1. Connect terminal to battery.
2. Reset clock.
3. Enter radio security code.
4. Turn ignition On.
5. Lower glass to stop and hold switch in down position for at least five seconds.
6. Raise glass fully and hold switch in up position for at least five seconds.
7. Turn ignition Off.

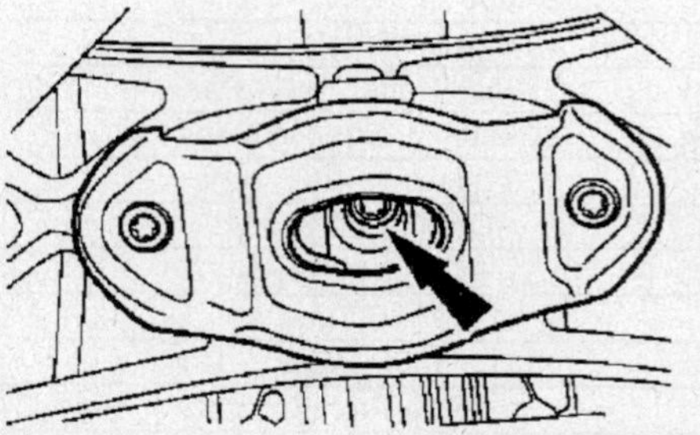

Fig. 1 Rear engine mount replacement

ENGINE MOUNT

REPLACE

REAR MOUNT

1. Raise and support vehicle.
2. Remove engine to rear mounting rubber to transmission mounting bolt, **Fig. 1.**
3. Support transmission with suitable transmission jack.
4. Loosen rear crossmember to vehicle floor mounting bolts (1), **Fig. 2.**
5. Remove mounting rubber to crossmember mounting bolts (2).
6. Remove mounting rubber (3).
7. Reverse procedure to install. Tighten mounting bolts to specifications.

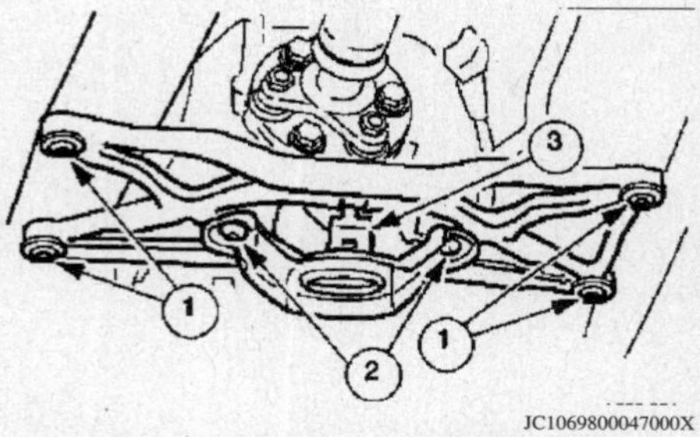

Fig. 2 Rear crossmember replacement

INTAKE MANIFOLD

REPLACE

1. Disconnect from righthand valve cover breather pipe.
2. Disconnect MAF connector.
3. Remove vacuum pipe to induction elbow strap.
4. Disconnect throttle body intake tube.
5. Remove air cleaner assembly.
6. Disconnect all electrical connectors, then the throttle body vacuum lines.
7. Disconnect throttle body throttle cables.
8. Disconnect throttle body coolant hoses and plug.
9. Remove mounting bolts and throttle body.
10. Disconnect intake manifold vacuum lines.
11. Remove intake manifold elbow support.
12. Disconnect fuel injectors' electrical connectors.
13. Disconnect fuel feed hose at Quick Fit connector using Quick Fit tool No. JD

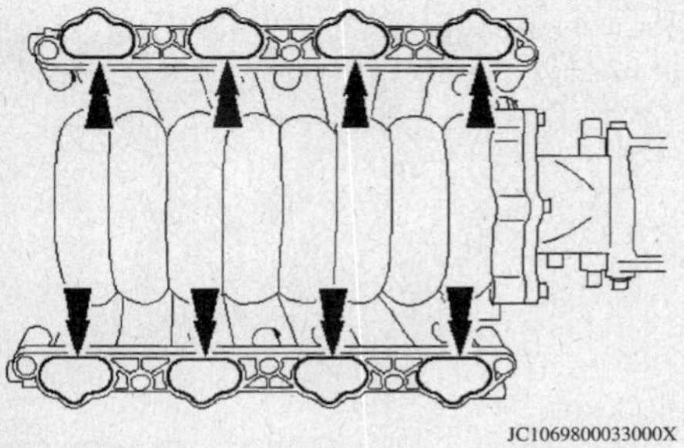

Fig. 3 Intake port seal replacement

182, or equivalent.

14. Disconnect fuel return hose at Quick Fit connector using Quick Fit tool No. JD 203, or equivalent.
15. Remove mounting bolts and intake manifold.
16. Remove and intake manifold ports seals, **Fig. 3.**
17. Reverse procedure to install. Tighten mounting bolts and nuts to specifications.

EXHAUST MANIFOLD

REPLACE

1. Raise and support vehicle.
2. Remove lefthand and righthand upstream catalytic converters.
3. Remove front muffler.
4. Remove air cleaner assembly.
5. Lower vehicle and remove front section of lefthand exhaust manifold to cylinder head mounting bolts.
6. Raise and support vehicle.
7. Remove steering rack mounting bolts on driver's side.
8. Loosen but do not remove steering rack mounting bolts on passenger side.
9. Remove rear section of lefthand exhaust manifold to cylinder head mounting bolts.
10. Remove manifold and gasket.
11. Lower vehicle and disconnect righthand exhaust manifold EGR pipe.
12. Remove front section of righthand exhaust manifold to cylinder head mounting bolts.
13. Raise and support vehicle.
14. Remove rear section of exhaust manifold to cylinder head mounting bolts.
15. Remove manifold and gasket. Discard manifold and EGR gaskets.
16. Reverse procedure to install noting the following:
    a. Clean manifold faces, EGR pipe flange and mating faces on cylinder head.
    b. Use suitable M8 x 1.25 thread tap to clean out threads of each manifold mounting bolt hole, in cylinder heads.
    c. Replace all manifold mounting bolts.

CYLINDER HEAD

REPLACE

This procedure has been revised by a Technical Service Bulletin.

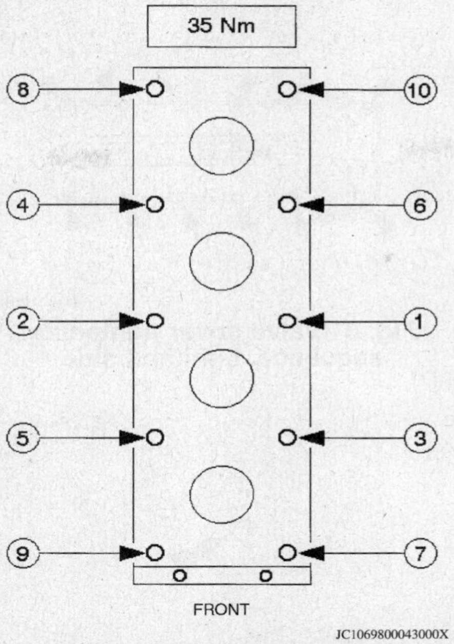

Fig. 4 Cylinder head tightening sequence. Righthand bank

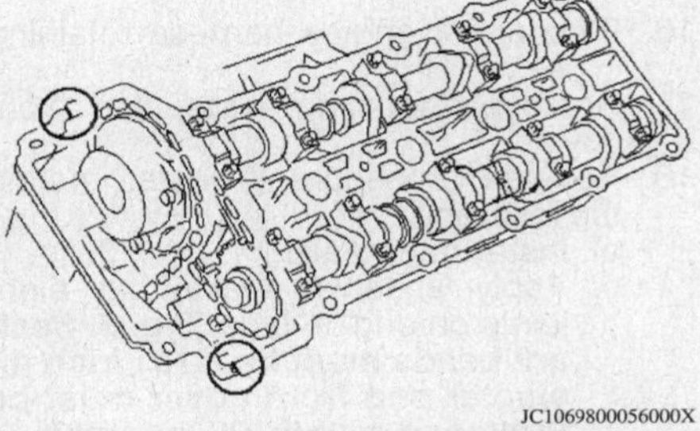

Fig. 6 Valve cover sealant location

1. Remove front cover as outlined under "Front Cover, Replace."
2. Remove intake manifold as outlined in this section.
3. Disconnect hoses and electrical connector from coolant outlet pipe.
4. Remove coolant outlet pipe discarding sealing rings from outlet pipe grooves.
5. Remove catalytic converter to exhaust manifold mounting nuts.
6. Remove cylinder block VVT bushing carrier.
7. Remove timing chains as outlined under "Timing Chain, Replace."
8. Remove cylinder head secondary chain tensioner.
9. Remove timing chain guide marking guide orientation.
10. Remove camshaft caps mounting bolts by loosening evenly, in stages.
11. Remove camshaft caps marking orientation.
12. Each cap is marked with its position (number) and orientation (an arrow).
13. Remove tappets and shims. Mark tapped position for installation. Retain shim with original tappet.
14. Mark inside face of each tappet with cylinder head original position.

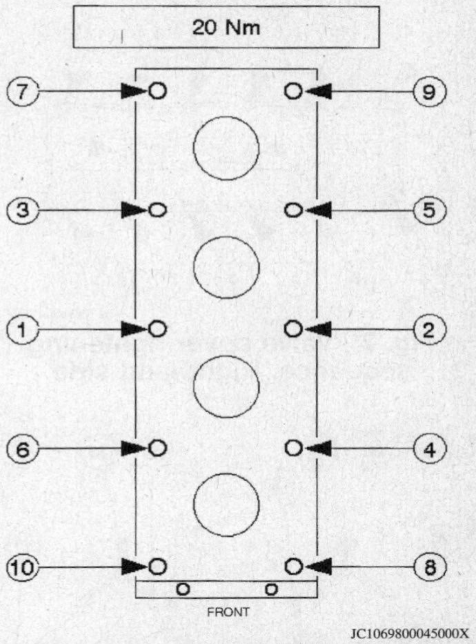

Fig. 5 Cylinder head tightening sequence. Lefthand bank

15. Remove residual coolant from cylinder head using suitable syringe.
16. Remove cylinder head and gasket marking position for installation.
17. Reverse procedure to install noting the following:
    a. Install new downpipe catalyst flange gasket.
    b. Install cylinder head bolts, hand tighten only.
    c. **Torque** M10 cylinder head bolts to 15 ft. lbs. in sequence, **Figs. 4 and 5.**
    d. **Torque** M10 bolts to 26 ft. lbs. in sequence.
    e. Tighten M10 bolts an additional 90° in sequence.
    f. Final tighten M10 bolts an additional 90° in sequence.
    g. **Torque** two M8 bolts at front of cylinder head to 17–20 ft. lbs.
    h. Apply suitable EP-90 oil to camshaft bearing surfaces and lobes.
    i. Install camshafts with timing flats uppermost. Tighten mounting bolts to specifications.

VALVE COVER

REPLACE

1. Remove coil packs from spark plugs as outlined in "Electrical" section.
2. Release engine harness to valve cover clips.
3. Remove valve cover mounting bolts.
4. Separate and discard valve cover seals bolt seals.
5. Reverse procedure to install noting the following:
    a. Apply sealant to joint between front cam cover and cylinder head, **Fig. 6.**
    b. Install valve cover immediately after applying sealant.
    c. Tighten valve cover bolts to specifications in sequence, **Figs. 7 and 8.**

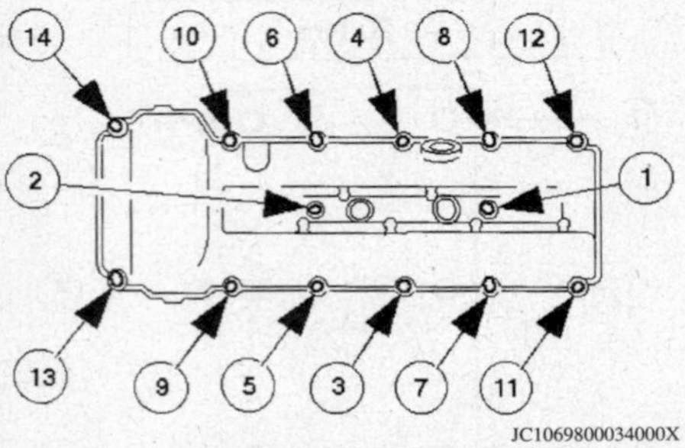

Fig. 7 Valve cover tightening sequence. Righthand side

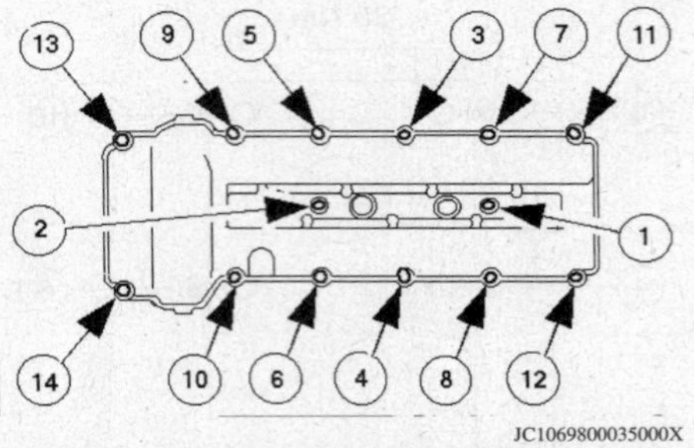

Fig. 8 Valve cover tightening sequence. Lefthand side

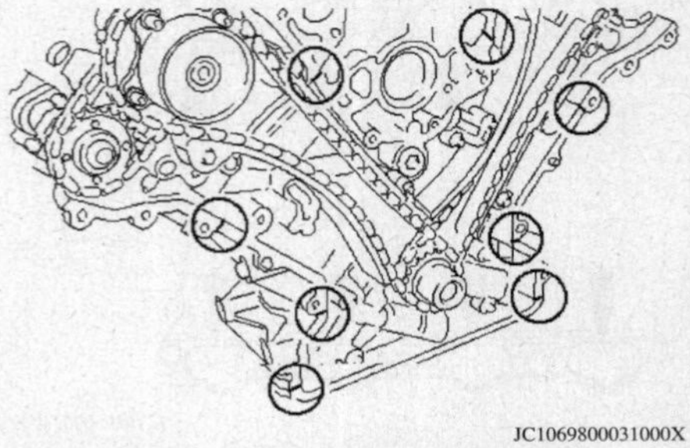

Fig. 9 Sealant application locations

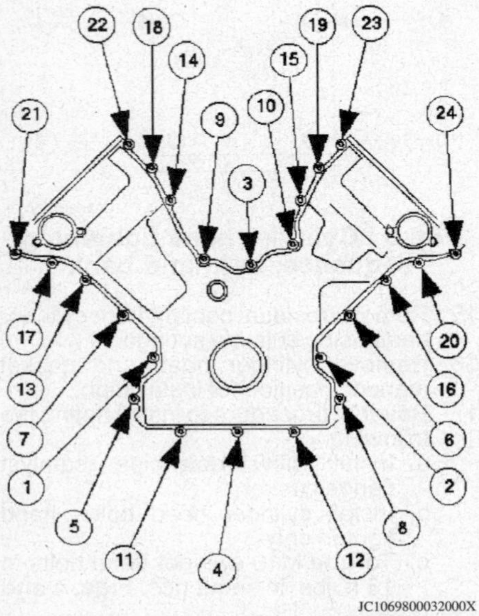

Fig. 10 Front cover tightening sequence

FRONT COVER

REPLACE

1. Drain coolant into suitable container.
2. Remove radiator top hose.
3. Loosen water pump pulley mounting bolts.
4. Remove accessory drive belt.
5. Remove water pump pulley.
6. Remove belt tensioner assembly.
7. Remove front accessory drive idler pulley.
8. Remove crankshaft damper. Refer to "Crankshaft Oil Seal, Replace."
9. Remove engine covers. **Do not damage plastic fixings or rubber inserts.**
10. Disconnect intake tube from throttle body and air cleaner cover, then the Mass Air Flow (MAF) sensor electrical connector.
11. Remove intake tube/MAF/air cleaner assembly.
12. Remove EVAP canister purge valve.
13. Remove plug coil packs. Refer to "Electrical."
14. Remove valve covers as outlined in this section.
15. Remove cylinder heads' variable valve timing solenoids.

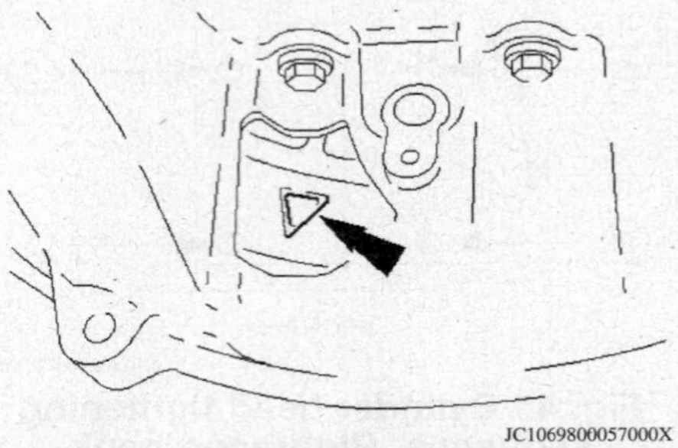

Fig. 11 Triangular arrow indent

16. Disconnect engine harness retaining clips.
17. Remove mounting bolts and front cover.
18. Reverse procedure to install, noting the following:
    a. Install new seals.
    b. Apply suitable sealant to eight joints on engine face, **Fig. 9. Sealant beads must be .1181 inch diameter and front cover must be tightened within 20 minutes of sealant application.**
    c. Tighten front cover bolts to specifications in sequence, **Fig. 10.**

TIMING CHAIN

REPLACE

PRIMARY

RIGHTHAND BANK

Removal

1. Remove front cover as outlined in this section.
2. Remove Variable Valve Timing (VVT) bushing carrier.
3. Raise and support vehicle.
4. Remove crankshaft position sensor.
5. Install damper mounting bolt to crankshaft and hand tighten.
6. Rotate crankshaft until triangular arrow indent on drive plate is visible through access hole, **Fig. 11. Ensure timing flat on each camshaft is uppermost.**
7. Fit crankshaft setting peg tool No. JD 216, or equivalent, to crankshaft position sensor location, **Fig. 12.**
8. Remove damper mounting bolt from crankshaft and lower vehicle.
9. Install camshaft locking tool No. JD

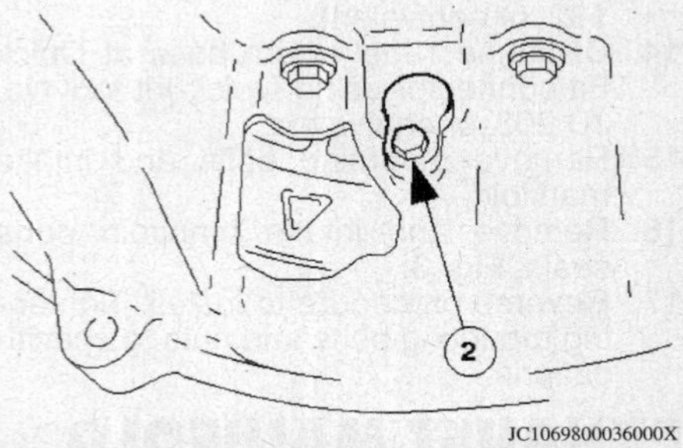

Fig. 12 Crankshaft setting peg location

215, or equivalent, to righthand bank camshafts, **Fig. 13.**

10. Loosen camshaft sprocket mounting bolt.
11. Loosen camshaft VVT unit mounting bolt.
12. Remove primary chain tensioner, **Fig. 14.**
13. Remove chain tensioner blade, then the chain from VVT unit and crankshaft sprocket.
14. If required, remove crankshaft sprocket.
15. Clean and inspect all relevant components.

Installation

This procedure has been revised by a Technical Service Bulletin.

1. Install crankshaft sprocket. **Teeth on righthand and lefthand bank crankshaft sprockets must be out of phase with each other, Fig. 15. If they are in phase after installation, remove sprocket, turn it on its vertical axis and install.**
2. Install chain tensioning tool No. JD 217, or equivalent, to exhaust camshaft sprocket.
3. Install primary chain over crankshaft sprocket and VVT unit sprocket. Ensure there is no slack of drive side of chain. **VVT unit must not be rotated on camshaft.**
4. Install chain tensioner blade and tighten to specifications.
5. Insert suitable thin rigid wire through hole in end of tensioner piston to displace ball from non-return valve seat.
6. Press piston fully into tensioner body with wire in position. Remove wire.
7. Install tensioner to cylinder block and

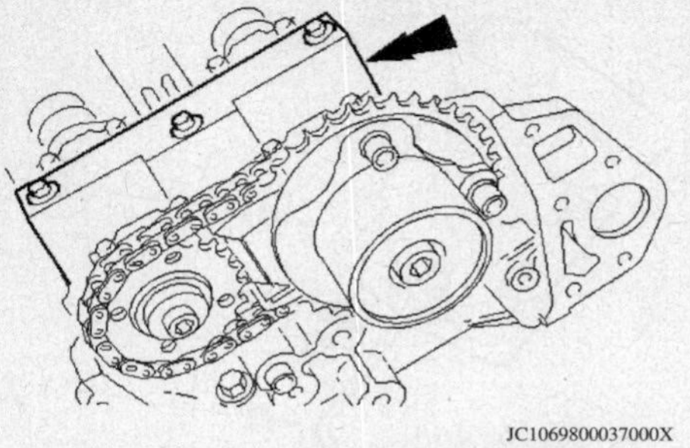

Fig. 13 Camshaft locking tool location

mating slot on tensioner blade rear face.

8. Take up slack by installing wedge tool No. JD 218, or equivalent, between primary chain tensioner and tensioner blade.
9. Tension chain on its drive side by applying counterclockwise force to secondary chain tensioner tool.
10. Tighten exhaust sprocket mounting bolt to specifications while applying force to sprocket and chain
11. Tighten VVT unit mounting bolt to specifications while applying force to exhaust sprocket and chain. **Ensure wedge is still in place.**
12. Remove camshaft locking and wedge tools.
13. Raise and support vehicle.
14. Remove crankshaft setting tool.
15. Install crankshaft position sensor and lower vehicle.
16. Install new VVT bushing carrier sealing ring and carrier oil way O-ring.
17. Install VVT bushing carrier and tighten to specifications.
18. Install front cover as outlined in this section.

LEFTHAND BANK

Removal

1. Remove front cover as outlined in this section.
2. Remove lefthand and righthand bank Variable Valve Timing (VVT) bushing carriers.
3. Raise and support vehicle.
4. Remove crankshaft position sensor.
5. Install damper mounting bolt to crankshaft and hand tighten.
6. Rotate crankshaft until triangular arrow indent on drive plate is visible through access hole, **Fig. 11. Ensure timing flat on each camshaft is uppermost.**
7. Fit crankshaft setting peg tool No. JD 216, or equivalent, to crankshaft position sensor location, **Fig. 12.**
8. Remove damper mounting bolt from crankshaft and lower vehicle.
9. Install camshaft locking tool No. JD 215, or equivalent, to righthand bank camshafts, **Fig. 13.**
10. Loosen camshaft sprocket mounting bolt.
11. Loosen camshaft VVT unit mounting bolt.
12. Remove primary chain tensioner, **Fig. 14.**

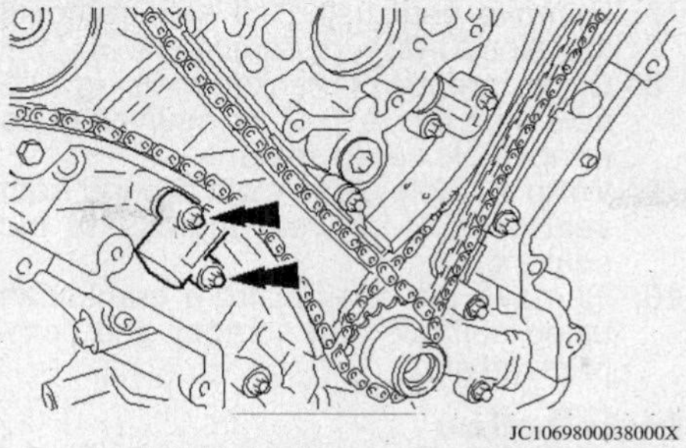

Fig. 14 Primary tensioner removal. Righthand bank

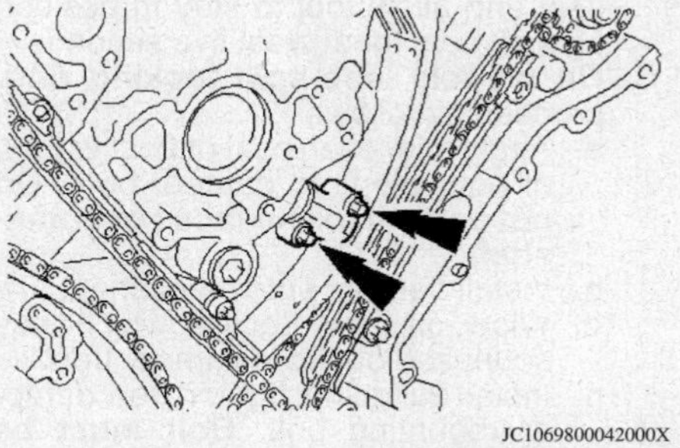

Fig. 16 Primary chain tensioner. Lefthand bank

13. Remove chain tensioner blade, then the chain from VVT unit and crankshaft sprocket.
14. Remove camshaft locking tool and transfer it to lefthand bank camshafts.
15. Loosen camshaft exhaust sprocket mounting bolt.
16. Loosen camshaft VVT unit mounting bolt.
17. Remove primary chain tensioner, **Fig. 16.**
18. Remove chain tensioner blade, then the chain from VVT unit and crankshaft sprocket.
19. If required, remove sprocket from crankshaft.
20. Clean and inspect all relevant components.

Installation

This procedure has been revised by a Technical Service Bulletin.

1. Install crankshaft sprocket. **Teeth on righthand and lefthand bank crankshaft sprockets must be out of phase with each other, Fig. 15. If they are in phase after installation, remove sprocket, turn it on its vertical axis and install.**
2. Remove camshaft locking tool and transfer to righthand bank.
3. Install chain tensioning tool No. JD 217, or equivalent, to exhaust camshaft sprocket.
4. Install primary chain to position over crankshaft sprocket and VVT unit sprocket. Ensure there is no slack of drive side of chain. **VVT unit must not be rotated on camshaft.**
5. Install chain tensioner blade and tighten to specifications.
6. Insert suitable thin rigid wire through hole in end of tensioner piston to displace ball from non-return valve seat.

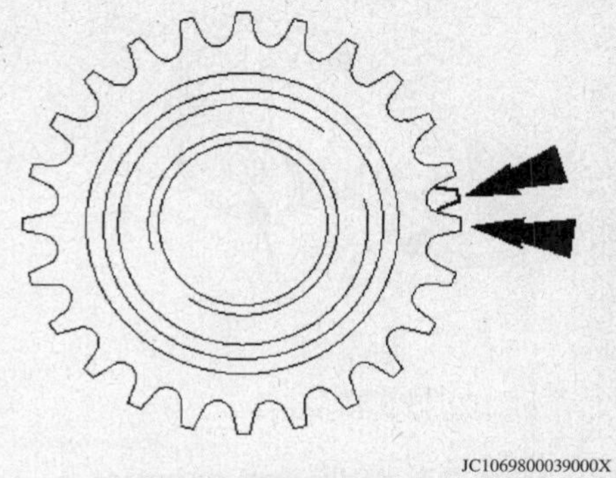

Fig. 15 Crankshaft sprockets

7. Press piston fully into tensioner body. Remove wire.
8. Install tensioner to cylinder block and mating slot on tensioner blade rear face.
9. Take up slack by installing wedge tool No. JD 218, or equivalent, between primary chain tensioner and tensioner blade.
10. Tension chain on its drive side by applying counterclockwise force to secondary chain tensioner tool.
11. Tighten exhaust sprocket mounting bolt to specifications while applying force to sprocket and chain.
12. Tighten VVT unit mounting bolt to specifications while applying force to exhaust sprocket and chain. **Ensure wedge is still in place.**
13. Remove camshaft locking, chain tensioning and wedge tools.
14. Raise and support vehicle.
15. Remove crankshaft setting tool.
16. Install crankshaft position sensor and lower vehicle.
17. Install new VVT bushing carriers sealing ring and carrier oil way O-rings.
18. Install VVT bushing carriers and tighten to specifications.
19. Install front cover as outlined in this section.

SECONDARY

REMOVAL

1. Remove primary chain as outlined in this section.
2. Remove VVT unit and exhaust cam sprocket mounting bolts, **Fig. 17. Do not tamper with VVT mechanism to sprockets mounting bolts. VVT is sealed at factory to proper valve timing specifications for engine and is supplied only as complete unit.**
3. Remove VVT unit, exhaust sprocket and secondary chain as an assembly by releasing chain from tensional which is still secured to cylinder head.
4. Clean and inspect all relevant components.

INSTALLATION

This procedure has been revised by a Technical Service Bulletin.

1. Insert suitable thin rigid wire through

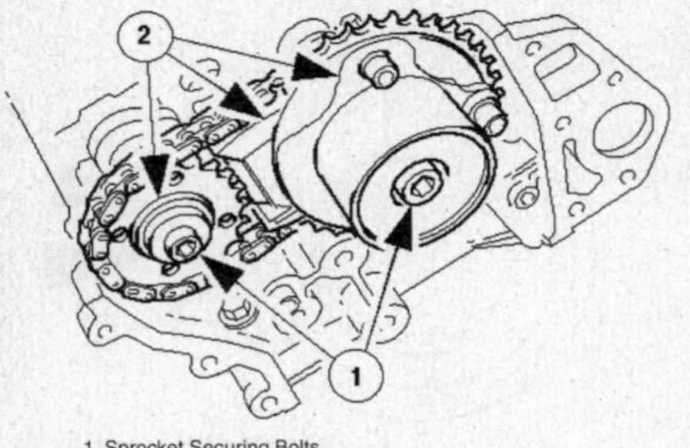

1. Sprocket Securing Bolts
2. Sprockets and Securing Tensioner

JC1069800040000X

Fig. 17 VVT and exhaust sprocket assemblies

hole in end of tensioner piston to displace ball from non-return valve seat, **Fig. 18.**
2. Press piston fully into tensioner body then remove wire.
3. Assemble VVT unit, exhaust camshaft sprocket and chain.
4. Install assembly to camshafts with chain properly positioned over tensioner, VVT unit to inlet and sprocket to exhaust.
5. Install but do not tighten VVT unit and exhaust sprocket mounting bolts.
6. Tension chain at exhaust camshaft sprocket with chain tensioning tool No. JD 217, or equivalent. Remove tool.
7. Install primary chain as outlined in this section.

CAMSHAFT

REPLACE

Refer to "Cylinder Head, Replace" for camshaft replacement.

PISTONS, PINS & RINGS

The pistons are open ended skirt design with flat upper surfaces (dished on supercharged engines) to reduce heat absorption. Three piston rings, two compression and one oil control, are installed on each piston. Each piston is installed on a wrist pin which operates in a lead/bronze bushing installed in the connecting rod.

CRANKSHAFT SEAL

REPLACE

FRONT

Removal

1. Remove front accessory drive belt.
2. Remove twin fan and motor assembly for access.
3. Remove damper mounting bolt using crankshaft locking tool No. 18G 1437, or equivalent. Remove locking tool from damper.
4. Remove damper using damper extractor tool 303–588, or equivalents.
5. Remove thrust button from end of crankshaft.
6. Remove split locking ring and O-ring from damper.
7. Remove seal using oil seal removal tool No. JD-234, or equivalent.
8. Clean threads of crankshaft using suitable plug tap M16x2, or equivalent, to remove old cured sealant.
9. Wrap suitable clean cloth around front seal area to prevent ingress of old sealant.
10. Remove old sealant from crankshaft using suitable soft scraper and compressed air.

Installation

1. Install new oil seal using oil seal replacer tool No. JD-235, or equivalent.
2. Only tighten tool sufficiently to seat seal and allow tool to stay in position against seal for at least five seconds.
3. **On models less split locking ring,** proceed as follows:
   a. Apply thin, even coat of Loctite 648, or equivalent, to damper bore. **Do not apply it to end faces or crankshaft.**
   b. Install damper onto crankshaft.
   c. Wipe off any Loctite which has squeezed out from damper front.
   d. Install but do not tighten new damper mounting bolt. **Bolt must be tightened within seven minutes of Loctite being applied.**
   e. Install crankshaft locking tool No. 18G 1437, or equivalent, and tighten damper mounting bolt to specifications.
4. **On models equipped with split locking ring,** proceed as follows:
   a. Install new O-ring to damper, then apply suitable petroleum jelly to damper bore and O-ring seal.
   b. Install damper, then the split locking ring inside damper center bore.
   c. Install but do not tighten new damper mounting bolt. **Bolt must be tightened within seven minutes of Loctite being applied.**
   d. Install crankshaft locking tool No. 18G 1437, or equivalent, and tighten damper mounting bolt to specifications.
5. **On all models,** remove locking tool.
6. Install accessory drive serpentine belt.
7. Install twin fan and motor assembly.

CRANKSHAFT REAR OIL SEAL

REPLACE

1. Remove transmission and drive plate.
2. Remove seal using seal removal tool No. 303-538, or equivalent.
3. Reverse procedure to install seal with tool, noting the following:
   a. **Torque** drive plate mounting bolts in crisscross pattern to 10–12 ft. lbs.
   b. Final **torque** drive plate mounting bolts in crisscross pattern to 70–92 ft. lbs.

OIL PAN

REPLACE

1. Raise and support vehicle.
2. Drain engine oil into suitable container.

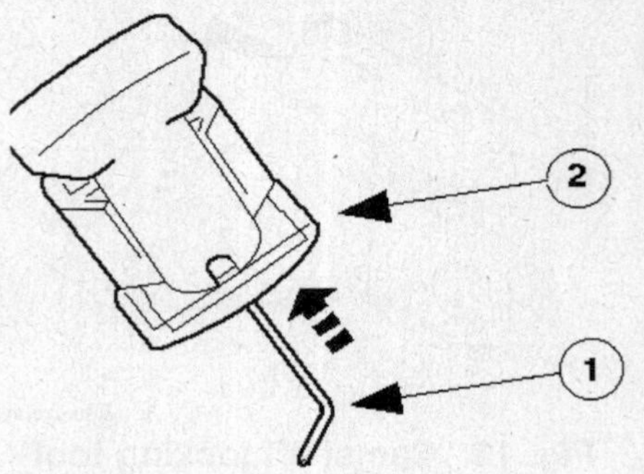

1. Secondary Chain Tensioner.
2. Thin Rigid Wire.

JC1069800041000X

Fig. 18 Secondary chain tensioner

3. Remove oil pan mounting bolts.
4. Remove pan and gasket.
5. Reverse procedure to install pan, noting the following:
   a. Clean and inspect sealing faces.
   b. Install new seal into locating positions in groove, working around from one corner.
   c. Tighten bolts to specifications in sequence, **Fig. 19.**

OIL PUMP

REPLACE

1. Remove engine compartment cover.
2. Remove crankshaft sprocket as outlined in "Timing Chain, Replace."
3. Remove mounting bolts and oil pump.
4. Reverse procedure to install with new gasket. Tighten mounting bolts to specifications.

SERPENTINE DRIVE BELT

ROUTING

Refer to **Fig. 20** for serpentine drive belt routing.

REPLACEMENT

1. Install spanner wrench tool No. JD-230, or equivalent, on belt tensioner pulley center bolt.
2. Turn tool counterclockwise against spring tension.
3. While holding tensioner against spring tension, remove drive belt.
4. Reverse procedure to install.

THERMOSTAT

REPLACE

1. Drain cooling system into suitable container.
2. Remove radiator bottom hose from thermostat housing.
3. Remove thermostat housing.
4. Remove thermostat from housing.
5. Reverse procedure to install with new seal.

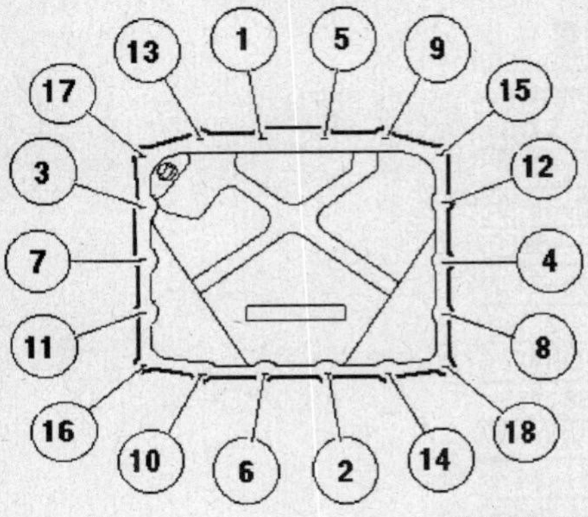

Fig. 19 Oil pan bolt tightening sequence

WATER PUMP

REPLACE

1. Drain cooling system into suitable container.
2. **On models equipped with supercharger,** remove supercharger drive belt.
3. **On all models,** loosen water pump pulley mounting bolts.
4. Remove accessory drive belt.
5. Remove water pump pulley.
6. Remove mounting bolts and water pump
7. Remove and discard water pump gasket and water pump O-ring seal.
8. Reverse procedure to install with new gasket and O-ring seal. Tighten mounting bolts to specifications.

RADIATOR

REPLACE

1. Drain cooling system into suitable container.
2. Recover A/C refrigerant as outlined in "Air Conditioning."
3. Disconnect both gas struts.
4. Set engine cover fully forward to service access position and support with suitable block. **Do not damage engine cover or radiator grille.**
5. Remove twin fan and motor assembly.
6. Disconnect radiator to expansion tank hose from radiator.
7. Raise and support vehicle.
8. Disconnect transmission oil cooler lower line. Plug line and opening.
9. Lower vehicle.
10. Disconnect transmission oil cooler upper line. Plug line and opening.
11. Disconnect fan switch harness connector.
12. Disconnect radiator upper and lower hoses.
13. Remove radiator top retaining panel mounting bolts.
14. Disconnect condenser discharge hose, then plug hose and opening.
15. Remove retaining panel and radiator.
16. Remove condenser and fan switch from radiator.
17. Reverse procedure to install. Tighten mounting bolts to specifications.

SUPERCHARGER

REPLACE

1. Drain cooling system into suitable container.
2. Remove air cleaner cover and intake assembly.
3. Remove throttle assembly.
4. Remove EGR valve.
5. Remove induction elbow to elbow support plate mounting bolt at induction elbow righthand side.
6. Disconnect brake servo vacuum line.
7. Loosen but do not remove induction elbow support plate to engine bracket lower mounting bolts.
8. Remove induction elbow to supercharger mounting bolts.
9. Disconnect intercooler pipes' induction elbow hoses and remove assembly.
10. Disconnect coolant hoses and vacuum line from supercharger outlet duct.
11. Remove outlet clamp plate mounting bolts.
12. Remove supercharger duct mounting bolts. **Ensure coolant does not drip into supercharger.**
13. Blank supercharger outlet body with suitable tape to prevent ingress of foreign matter.
14. Disconnect remaining intercoolers coolant hoses and position to facilitate supercharger removal.
15. Remove engine coolant outlet pipe, then the supercharger drive belt.
16. Position intercooler inlet and outlet hoses clear of supercharger.
17. Remove mounting bolts and supercharger.
18. Reverse procedure to install. Tighten mounting bolts to specifications.

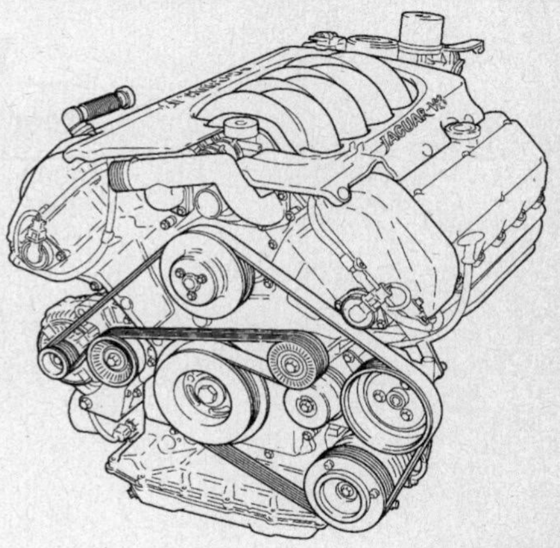

Fig. 20 Serpentine drive belt routing

TECHNICAL SERVICE BULLETINS

START-UP NOISE

Models Before Engine No. 98102106XX

On these models there may be a rattling noise when the engine is started.

This condition may be caused by secondary timing chain tensioners' resonance. To correct this condition, install revised secondary timing chain tensioners part No. NCA 2017AF for A-bank and part No. NCA 2017BE for B-bank.

CYLINDER HEAD REAR OIL LEAK

On these models there may be oil leaks at rear of cylinder head face.

This condition may be caused by oil leaking past manufacturing plugs. To correct this condition, install "Dowty" oil sealing washers part No. JWV 114003 and bolts part No. JZS 100098 in cylinder head rear face inner holes.

LOW COOLANT LEVEL WARNING LAMP LIGHTING

On these models, the low coolant level warning lamp may remain lit even with a proper coolant level.

This condition may be caused by sensor's captive float sticking in down position. To correct this condition, replace reservoir.

TIGHTENING SPECIFICATIONS

Year	Component	Torque, Ft. Lbs.
1998–2001	Camshaft Cap	80–97①
	Continuously Variable Valve Timing Unit	22–30⑥
	Crankshaft Position Sensor	71–106①
	Crossmember, Rear	16–21
	Cylinder Head	②
	Damper, Less Locking Ring	59③
	Damper, w/Locking Ring	268–285
	Drive Plate	⑤
	Engine Coolant Sensor	11–14
	Engine Mount, Rear	22–29
	Exhaust Cam Sprocket	85–92
	Exhaust Manifold	13
	Exhaust Manifold To Downpipe Catalyst	44–59
	Fuel Injector	35–53①
	Front Cover	97–115①
	Induction Elbow	13–18
	Induction Elbow, By-Pass Valve	71–106①
	Induction Elbow, Support	12–15
	Intake Manifold	15–16
	Intercooler Inlet Assembly	13–18
	Oil Pan	97–115④
	Oil Pump	97–115①
	Radiator Top Panel	71–88①
	Supercharger	13–18
	Thermostat Cove	71–88①
	Throttle Body	13–18
	Timing Chain Guide	88–124①
	Timing Chain Tensioner	88–124①
	Timing Chain Tensioner Blade	9–12
	Variable Valve Timing Bushing Carrier	14–17
	Variable Valve Timing Solenoid	88–124①
	Variable Valve Timing Unit	85–92①
	Water Pump	97–124①
	Water Pump Pulley	88–124①
	Valve Cover	88–97①

① — Inch lbs.

② — Refer to “Cylinder Head, Replace” for tightening specifications & sequence.

③ — Final tighten an additional 80°.

④ — Refer to “Oil Pan, Replace” for tightening sequence.

⑤ — Refer to “Crankshaft Rear Oil Seal, Replace” for tightening specifications & sequence.

⑥ — Final **torque** to 63–66 ft. lbs.

Rear Axle & Suspension

NOTE: On Air Bag Equipped Models, Refer To "Air Bag System Precautions" Located In The Front Of This Manual For System Disarming & Arming Procedures.

NOTE: Prior To Performing Any Service Operations Listed In This Section, Consult The "Technical Service Bulletins" Section For Related Information.

INDEX

	Page No.
Coil Spring, Replace	3-20
Description	3-19
Differential Carrier, Replace	3-20
XJ8, XK8 & XJR	3-20
Hub & Bearing, Replace	3-20
Hub & Bearing Service	3-20
Hub Bearing End Float	3-20
Rear Axle, Replace	3-19
S-Type	3-19
XJ8, XK8 & XJR	3-19
Rear Axle Shaft, Replace	3-20
Shock Absorber, Replace	3-20
Stabilizer Bar, Replace	3-21
Tightening Specifications	3-21

DESCRIPTION

These cars utilize an independent rear suspension, **Figs. 1 and 2.**

REAR AXLE

REPLACE

XJ8, XK8 & XJR

A-Frame

1. Raise and support vehicle.
2. **On XK8 convertible models,** remove rear support strut mounting bolts.
3. **On all models,** remove A-frame to final drive mounting bolts.
4. Remove A-frame to final drive unit front bracket inner mounting nuts and bolts.
5. Support final drive with suitable jack and wooden block under drive flange.
6. Remove both A-frame outer bushing to body and bracket mounting bolts.
7. Remove both bracket to body mounting bolts and A-frame outer bushings.
8. Lower final drive approximately .9844 inch.
9. Remove A-frame to final drive unit front bracket intermediate mounting bolts.
10. Remove A-frame to final drive unit mounting bracket and tie rod outer mounting bolts.
11. Support A-frame by hand and remove final drive unit casing mounting bolts.
12. Remove A-frame.
13. Reverse procedure to install. Tighten mounting bolts and nuts to specifications.

Monostrut

This procedure has been revised by a Technical Service Bulletin.

1. Raise and support vehicle, then remove rear tire and wheel assemblies.
2. **On XK8 convertible models,** remove mounting bolts and rear support struts.
3. **On all models,** mark driveshaft to coupling for install alignment.
4. Remove mounting nuts and bolts, then position drive shaft aside.
5. Disconnect both exhaust tail pipes from rear mountings.
6. Support suspension subframe with suitable jack.
7. Remove monostrut to control arm-tie assembly mounting bolts.
8. Remove monostrut to body bracket mounting bolts.
9. Remove bushing center and bracket mounting bolts, then the bracket.
10. Lower final drive approximately .9844 inch.
11. Remove monostrut through righthand wheelhousing.
12. Reverse procedure to install. Tighten mounting nuts and bolts to specifications.

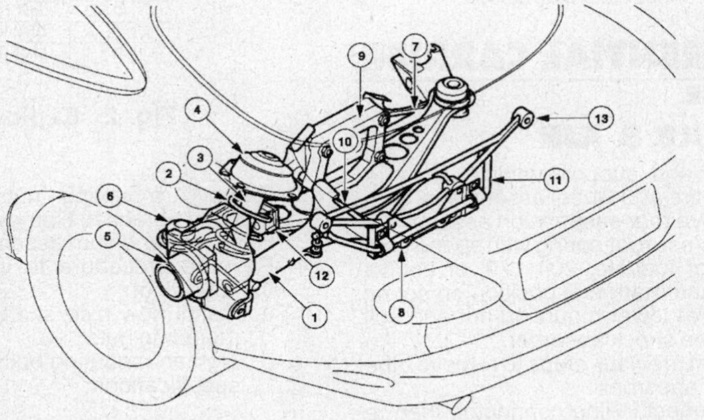

Item	Description
1	Lower Wishbone
2	Suspension Spring
3	Damper
4	Upper Spring Seat
5	Hub Carrier
6	'A' Frame
7	Wide Mounting Frame

Item	Description
8	Wishbone Tie Assembly
9	Pendulum
10	Wishbone Fulcrum Pin
11	Stabilizer Bar
12	Bump Stop
13	Monostrut

JC2039700002000X

Fig. 1 Exploded view of rear suspension. XJ8, XK8 & XJR

S-TYPE

1. Loosen wheel nut, then raise and support vehicle.
2. Remove wheel, then the axle shaft hub nut.
3. Detach brake caliper, unclip ABS sensor harness and remove.
4. Detach outer tie rod, then the lower arm from hub assembly.
5. Remove brake disc, then detach hub assembly from driveshaft.
6. Using a suitable pry tool, detach axle shaft from differential housing. **Do not damage differential seal.**

7. **Under no circumstances must flexible coupling be loosened or removed from driveshaft.**
8. Mark position of driveshaft in relation to differential flange, mark position of balance nut in relation to differential flange and mark position of each nut and bolt in relation to transmission flexible joint.
9. Disconnect axle assembly breather tube from crossmember, then support axle assembly. **When supporting axle assembly, use a suitable packing material to prevent damage to underside of casing.**
10. Ensure not to lose washer when removing forward axle retaining bolt.
11. Remove axle assembly.
12. Reverse procedure to install. Tighten bolts and nuts to specifications.

REAR AXLE SHAFT

REPLACE

Refer to "Rear Axle Replace."

DIFFERENTIAL CARRIER

REPLACE

XJ8, XK8 & XJR

1. Raise and support vehicle, then remove tire and wheel assemblies.
2. Remove rear suspension assembly.
3. Compress rear spring with spring compressor tool No. 204 179, or equivalent, and mark tool position on spring.
4. Remove lower mounting nut and bolt, then the shock absorber.
5. Repeat previous steps to remove other shock absorber.
6. Disconnect in-line connector, then remove out frame clips and clear parking brake cable through frame.
7. Remove mounting nut and lower fulcrum shaft.
8. Remove axle shaft drive flange nuts.
9. Support axle shaft assembly, then remove hub fulcrum. Mark and remove camber adjustment spacer.
10. Repeat previous steps to remove other axle shaft.
11. Remove mounting bolts and final drive nose plate.
12. Position axle assembly on supported by suitable wooden blocks.
13. Remove stabilizer bar link to control arm mounting nuts.
14. Remove mounting nut and pivot bolt.
15. Mark and remove front spacer and rear washers, then remove control arm.
16. Repeat previous steps to remove other control arm.
17. Remove mounting nuts, washers and control arm tie assembly.
18. Remove mounting nuts and bolts, then the tie rods. Mark and remove spacers.
19. Position assembly to access A frame. **Rear axle oil may flow from breather.**
20. Remove rear mounting bracket, final drive and wide mounting bracket mounting bolts, then the A frame.
21. Remove A frame rear mounting bracket from final drive.
22. Remove mounting nuts and wide mounting bracket. Remove washers.
23. Remove pendulum assembly.
24. Reverse procedure to install, noting the following:
    a. Install new axle shaft drive flange mounting nuts.
    b. Tighten mounting bolts and nuts to specifications.

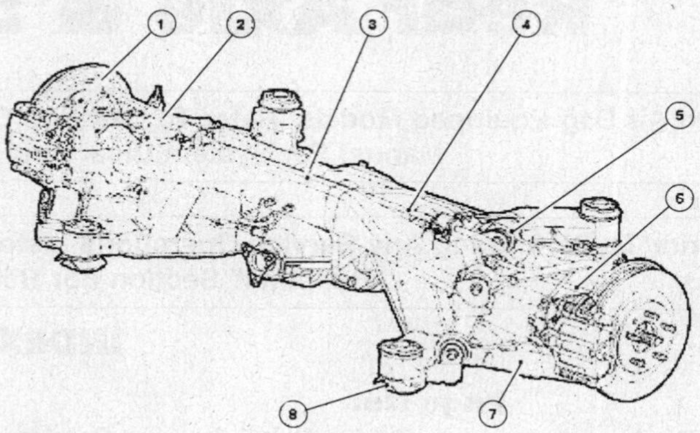

Item	Description
1	Hub carrier
2	Anti-roll bar link
3	Crossmember
4	Stabilizer bar
5	Upper arm
6	Tie rod
7	Lower arm
8	Bushings

JC2030100009000X

Fig. 2 Exploded view of rear suspension. S-Type

HUB & BEARING

REPLACE

1. Remove wheel, then the axle shaft nut.
2. Remove caliper, then ABS sensor and outer tie rod.
3. Detach lower arm from hub assembly, then the disc brake.
4. Detach hub assembly from driveshaft and remove.
5. Remove hub from bearing using a suitable hand press.
6. Remove inner bearing race from hub, then the circlip.
7. Using a suitable tool, remove bearing from hub carrier.
8. Reverse procedure to install.

HUB & BEARING SERVICE

HUB BEARING END FLOAT

The hub bearing end float is controlled by a spacer located next to the universal joint on the halfshaft. Spacers are available in .109–.151 inch thicknesses in .003 inch increments.

End float specification is .001–.003 inch. Adjust if more than .0004 inch beyond specification.

Inspection

1. Raise and support rear of vehicle.
2. Remove wheel and gently tap hub.
3. Clamp backlash gauge tool No. JD-13A, or equivalent, to hub carrier so dial gauge stylus contacts hub flange. Record reading.
4. Move hub to fullest extent using two levers and record reading.
5. If reading difference exceeds .004 inch, adjust as outlined under "Adjustment."

Adjustment

1. Remove hub and carrier assembly.
2. Remove halfshaft spacer and measure thickness.
3. Determine thickness of spacer required to obtain proper end float and install onto halfshaft.

SHOCK ABSORBER

REPLACE

1. Remove luggage compartment side trim panel, then disconnect active suspension damper electrical connector.
2. Remove wheel, then support strut and spring assembly. **Failure to follow these instructions may result in personal injury.**
3. Remove shock absorber assembly.
4. Reverse procedure to install.

COIL SPRING

REPLACE

Refer to "Shock Absorber Replace."

STABILIZER BAR

REPLACE

1. Raise and support vehicle.
2. **On S-type models,** remove bolts, then the crossmember.
3. **On all models,** remove stabilizer bar to links mounting nuts and bolts.
4. Remove mounting bolts and stabilizer bar brackets.
5. Remove stabilizer bar and bushings.
6. Reverse procedure to install, noting the following:
   a. Do not tighten link mounting bolts and nuts until last.
   b. Tighten mounting bolts and nuts to specifications.

TIGHTENING SPECIFICATIONS

Year	Component	Torque, Ft. Lbs.
XJ8, XK8 & XJR		
1998–2001	A-Frame Outer Bushing	59–74
	A-Frame To Final Drive	63–85
	A-Frame To Rear Mounting Bracket	66–81
	A-Frame To Wide Mounting Bracket	63–77
	Axle Shaft Drive Flange	60–73
	Control Arm To Final Drive	63–77
	Drive Shaft To Coupling	44
	Final Drive Nose Plate	29–38
	Fulcrum Shaft	66–81
	Monostrut To Body Bracket	65–87
	Monostrut To Control Arm Tie	57–76
	Pendulum	118–148
	Pivot Bolt	60–74
	Rear Strut	50–68
	Shock Absorber Lower Mount	59–74
	Shock Absorber Mount To Body	13–17
	Shock Absorber Upper	23–29
	Spring Seat To Body Securing Nuts	48–60①
	Stabilizer Bar Bracket	30–40
	Stabilizer Bar Link	22–30
	Tie Rod To Final Drive	63–77
	Tie Rod To Wide Mounting Bracket	63–85
	Upper Link Assembly, A Frame End	19–26
	Upper Link Assembly, Differential End	16–22
	Wide Mounting Bracket To Body	18–22
	Wide Mounting Bracket To Final Drive	118–148
S-TYPE		
2000–01	ABS Sensor	84①
	Axle Front Mounting	55
	Axle Rear Mounting	89
	Brake Caliper Carrier	41
	Crossmember	76
	Final Drive Flexible Joint	63
	Hub Nut	302
	Lower Arm	111
	Shock Absorber Top	41
	Shock Absorber Lower	98
	Stabilizer Bar	41
	Tie Bar Outer	74
	Upper Arm Outer	66
	Wheel Lug Nuts	86–102

① — Inch lbs.

Front Suspension & Steering

NOTE: On Air Bag Equipped Models, Refer To "Air Bag System Precautions" Located In The Front Of This Manual For System Disarming & Arming Procedures.

NOTE: Prior To Performing Any Service Operations Listed In This Section, Consult The "Technical Service Bulletins" Section For Related Information.

INDEX

	Page No.
Ball Joint, Replace	3-22
Ball Joint Inspection	3-22
Coil Spring, Replace	3-23
S-Type	3-23
XJ8, XK8 & XJR	3-23
Control Arm, Replace	3-23
Lower	3-23
Upper	3-23
Crossmember, Replace	3-24
XJ8, XK8 & XJR	3-24
Description	3-22
Power Steering	3-49
Power Steering Gear, Replace	3-24
Power Steering Pump, Replace	3-25
S-Type	3-25
XJ8, XK8 & XJR	3-25
Shock Absorber, Replace	3-23
S-Type	3-23
XJ8, XK8 & XJR	3-23
Stabilizer Bar, Replace	3-23
S-Type	3-24
XJ8, XK8 & XJR	3-23
Tightening Specifications	3-25
Wheel Bearing, Adjust	3-22
Wheel Bearing, Replace	3-22
S-Type	3-22
XJ8, XK8 XJR	3-22
Wheel Hub, Replace	3-22

DESCRIPTION

The cars utilizes an independent double control arm front suspension, **Figs. 1 and 2.**

WHEEL BEARING

ADJUST

Wheel bearings are adjusted by tightening the adjusting nut to eliminate all play and then backing the nut off slightly to provide .003–.001 inch play.

WHEEL BEARING

REPLACE

XJ8, XK8 XJR

Removal

1. Raise and support vehicle, then remove front tire and wheel assembly.
2. Remove front brake disc. Do not allow brake caliper to hand by brake hose.
3. Remove wheel speed sensor from vertical link.
4. Remove steering arm tie rod mounting nut, then the tie rod end using ball joint end taper separator tool No. JD 100, or equivalent.
5. Remove upper control arm ball joint mounting nut, then the ball joint using ball joint taper separator tool No. JD 219, or equivalent.
6. Remove lower control arm ball joint mounting nut, then the ball joint using ball joint taper separator tool.
7. Remove vertical link and hub assembly.
8. Remove mounting bolts and brake disc shield.
9. Secure vertical link and hub assembly in suitable vise using hub holding tool No. JD 227, or equivalent.
10. Remove rotor nut spring clip.
11. Remove rotor nut using ABS rotor nut socket tool No. 206 066A, or equivalent.
12. Install vertical link and hub assembly into hub removal collets tool No. JC 225, or equivalent, on suitable press bed.
13. Press hub out of vertical link with suitable press and hub remover tool No. JC 224, or equivalent.
14. Remove vertical link circlips.
15. Remove wheel bearing from vertical link using wheel bearing remover tool No. JD 237, or equivalent, and suitable press.

Installation

1. Install new vertical link outboard circlip with ears at lowest bore point.
2. Press wheel bearing into vertical link using wheel bearing replacer tool No. JD 238, or equivalent, and suitable press.
3. Install new vertical link inboard circlip with ears at lowest bore point.
4. Install hub into vertical link using hub replacer tool No. JD 236, or equivalent, and suitable press.
5. Position hub and vertical link in suitable vise using hub holding tool.
6. Ensure grease deflector ring is installed with .0197 gap between ring and rotor end.
7. Install rotor hub and tighten nut to specifications using ABS rotor nut socket.
8. Install rotor nut spring clip into hub retaining holes and rotor nut castellated slots. If slots are not aligned, tighten rotor nut until spring slip engages slots. **Do not loosen rotor nut to engage clip.**
9. Install disc shield and tighten mounting bolts to specifications.
10. Install upper control arm ball joint into vertical link and tighten mounting nut to specifications.
11. Install lower control arm ball joint into vertical link and tighten mounting nut to specifications.
12. Install steering arm tie rod end into steering arm and tighten mounting nut to specifications.
13. Install wheel speed sensor to vertical link and tighten to specifications.
14. Install brake disc.

S-TYPE

1. Remove front brake disc, then disconnect ABS sensor.
2. Remove wheel hub retaining bolts, then the hub.
3. Using a suitable tool, press out bearing.
4. Reverse procedure to install.

WHEEL HUB

REPLACE

Refer to "Wheel Bearing, Replace."

BALL JOINT INSPECTION

1. Raise and support vehicle.
2. Grasp top and bottom of front tire.
3. While shaking tire and wheel and assembly, inspect for any ball joint movement.
4. If ball joint shows any movement, replace ball joint.

BALL JOINT

REPLACE

1. Remove tie rod lock nut, then separate ball joint from lower arm.

2. Detach upper arm from wheel knuckle, then remove wheel knuckle.
3. Remove wheel hub, then using tool No. 204–271 or equivalent, remove ball joint.
4. Reverse procedure to install, noting the following:
   a. Install ball join using installation tool No. 204–272 or equivalent.

COIL SPRING

REPLACE

XJ8, XK8 & XJR

1. Remove shock absorber as outlined under "Shock Absorber, Replace."
2. Mount spring in suitable coil spring compressor tool, place tool in suitable vise and compress spring.
3. Remove mounting nut, upper mounting and shock absorber.
4. Mark tool position on spring, then slowly release spring pressure, counting number of turns.
5. Remove lower retaining arms, tool, spring pan and spring packers.
6. Reverse procedure to install.

S-TYPE

1. Remove front wheel, then disconnect Dynamic Stability Control electrical connector.
2. Remove suspension turret nuts, then the shock absorber nut and bolt.
3. Remove strut and spring assembly.
4. Reverse procedure to install.

SHOCK ABSORBER

REPLACE

XJ8, XK8 & XJR

1. Raise and support vehicle, then remove tire and wheel assembly.
2. Support suspension weight with suitable jack placed under lower control arm.
3. Remove covers, disconnect adaptive suspension connector and remove upper mounting nuts.
4. Remove lower mounting nut. **Do not remove lower mounting bolt just yet.**
5. Carefully lower supporting jack while guiding shock absorber and upper mounting studs through body. Stop lowering jack when studs have passed through body.
6. Mark washers and shims, then remove mounting nut, fulcrum shaft and disconnect upper control arm from crossmember.
7. Remove lower mounting bolt, then the shock absorber and spring. **Do not stretch brake lines.**
8. Align upper control arm in crossmember and temporarily install fulcrum shaft.
9. Remove spring as outlined in this section.
10. Reverse procedure to install. Tighten mounting bolts and nuts to specifications.

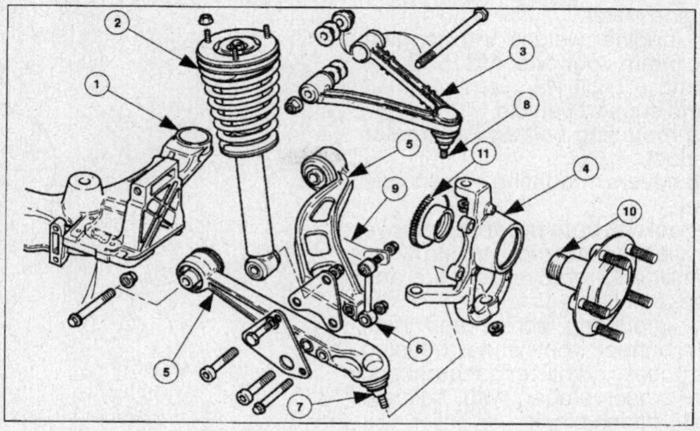

Item	Description
1	Aluminum Crossbeam
2	Co–axial Spring and Damper
3	Upper Wishbone
4	Vertical Link and Bearings Assembly
5	Lower Wishbone
6	Stabilizer Bar Link
7	Lower Wishbone Ball Joint
8	Upper Wishbone Ball Joint
9	Stabilizer Bar
10	Front Hub
11	Hub Nut/ABS Rotor

JC2029700005000X

Fig. 1 Exploded view of front suspension. XJ8, XJ8 & XJR

S-TYPE

Refer to "Coil Spring Replace," for replacement procedure.

CONTROL ARM

REPLACE

UPPER

XJ8, XK8 & XJR

1. Raise and support vehicle, then remove front tire and wheel assembly.
2. Remove tie strap and position ABS speed sensor harness away from upper control arm.
3. Remove mounting nut, then disconnect upper control arm ball joint from vertical link using ball joint taper separator tool No. JD 219, or equivalent. **Do not allow vertical link to hang on brake hose.**
4. Mark washer and shim position for install alignment.
5. Remove mounting nut, fulcrum bolt and upper control arm.
6. Reverse procedure to install. Tighten mounting bolts and nuts to specifications.

S-Type

1. Remove front wheel, then detach upper arm from wheel knuckle.
2. Remove upper arm bolts, then the upper arm from vehicle.
3. Reverse procedure to install.

LOWER

XJ8, XK8 & XJR

1. Raise and support vehicle, then remove front tire and wheel assembly.
2. Remove mounting nut and bolt, then disconnect stabilizer bar from lower control arm.
3. **Support vertical link. Do not allow vertical link to hang on upper ball joint.**
4. Remove mounting nut, then disconnect lower ball joint from vertical link using ball joint taper separator tool No. JD 219, or equivalent.
5. Remove mounting nut and bolt, then disconnect shock absorber from lower mounting.
6. Remove clamp bolt, then disconnect steering column from pinion shaft.
7. Disconnect steering rack transducer connector.
8. Remove tie straps and insulation rubbers, then disconnect hose from steering rack.
9. Remove bracket mounting bolts and carefully lower steering rack. **Do not allow steering rack to hang on power steering lines.**
10. Mark fulcrum or eccentric bolt position.
11. Remove mounting nuts and bolts, then the lower control arm.

S-Type

1. Remove strut and spring assembly as outlined under "Coil Spring Replace."
2. Detach stabilizer bar from lower arm, then the lower ball joint.
3. Separate lower arm, then remove it.
4. Reverse procedure to install.

STABILIZER BAR

REPLACE

XJ8, XK8 & XJR

1. Disconnect retaining pegs and remove

both engine cover.
2. Support engine weight with engine support beam tool No. MS 53D, or equivalent.
3. Raise and support vehicle.
4. Remove mounting bolt and alternator cooling duct.
5. Remove covers, mounting screws and undertray.
6. **On XK8 convertible models,** remove mounting bolts and cruciform strut.
7. **On all models,** remove front tire and wheel assemblies.
8. Remove mounting screw and bolt, then disconnect front wheel housing liners to access stabilizer bar brackets.
9. Support crossmember with suitable jack and wooden block.
10. Remove mounting bolts and crossmember mounting brackets.
11. Remove mounting bolts and disconnect front engine mounts from crossmember.
12. Remove mounting nut and bolt, then disconnect shock absorbers from lower mountings.
13. Remove mounting nut and disconnect link from stabilizer bar. **Counterhold ball-pin flats to prevent dust cover from twisting.**
14. Remove center mounting bolt and disconnect crossmember rear mountings from body.
15. Lower crossmember for stabilizer bar bracket access.
16. Remove mounting bolts, brackets and bushings, then the stabilizer bar.
17. Reverse procedure to install, noting the following:
    a. Apply suitable lubricant to bushings and install with split facing rear.
    b. Tighten mounting bolts and nuts to specifications.

S-TYPE

1. Remove radiator shield, then the A/C pipe retaining bracket screws and pipe.
2. Detach stabilizer bar from stabilizer link arms.
3. Remove stabilizer bar bolts, then the stabilizer.
4. Reverse procedure to install.

CROSSMEMBER

REPLACE

XJ8, XK8 & XJR

1. Disconnect retaining pegs and remove both engine cover.
2. Support engine weight with engine support beam tool No. MS 53D, or equivalent.
3. Raise and support vehicle.
4. Remove mounting bolt and alternator cooling duct.
5. Remove covers, mounting screws and undertray.
6. **On XK8 convertible models,** remove mounting bolts and cruciform strut.
7. **On all models,** remove front tire and wheel assemblies.
8. Remove dust cap, connect hose to bleed nipple and suitable container, then release bleed nipple and drain brake fluid.
9. Pump brake pedal until fluid stops draining, then tighten bleed nipple, remove hose and install dust cover.
10. Repeat previous procedure on other side.
11. Disconnect union nuts, then remove locknuts and brake hoses. Plug brake hoses and lines.
12. Remove tie straps and disconnect ABS sensor connectors.
13. Disconnect steering rack transducer electrical connector.
14. Remove tie straps and insulation rubbers, then disconnect steering rack hose.
15. Remove mounting bolt and disconnect hose retaining plate from pinion housing.
16. Position suitable container under pinion housing, disconnect hoses and drain fluid. Remove O-ring seals, then plug hoses and pinion housing ports.
17. Ensure steering is center, then remove clamp bolt and disconnect steering column from pinion shaft.
18. Support crossmember with suitable jack and wood block.
19. Remove mounting bolts and crossmember front mounting brackets.
20. Remove mounting bolts and disconnect both front engine mounts.
21. Support hub. **Do not allow hub weight to hang on ball joints.**
22. Remove lower mounting nuts and bolts, then disconnect front shock absorbers.
23. Remove center mounting bolts and disconnect crossmember rear mountings.
24. Remove crossmember.
25. Reverse procedure to install. Tighten mounting bolts and nuts to specifications.

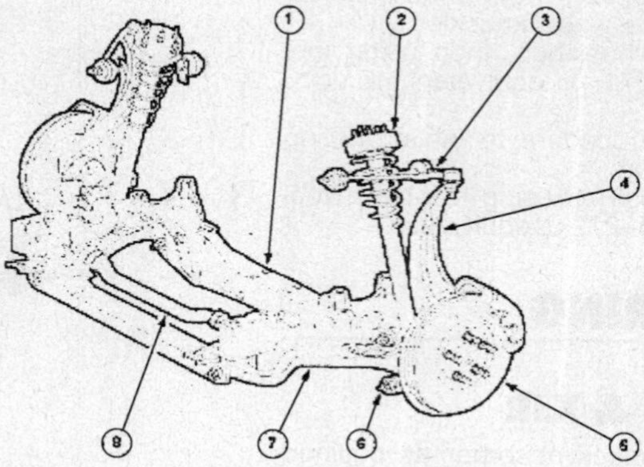

1
Front cross member
2
Spring and strut assembly
3
Upper arm
4
Wheel knuckle
5
Hub assembly
6
Stabilizer bar connecting arm
7
Lower arm
8
Stabilizer bar

JC2020100006000X

Fig. 2 Exploded view of front suspension. S-Type

POWER STEERING GEAR

REPLACE

1. Center steering wheel, then lock in position and remove key.
2. Install steering wheel locking tool No. 211–263 or equivalent, failure to do so may cause damage to steering wheel clock- spring.
3. Raise and support vehicle, then disconnect actuator electrical connector.
4. Remove power steering tube bracket retaining bolt, the steering gear shaft pinch bolt.
5. Disconnect power steering supply and return tubes, then drain fluid into a suitable container and discard washer seals.
6. Disconnect both tie rod ends,
7. Remove retaining bolts, then the steering gear.
8. Reverse procedure to install, noting the following:
    a. Install a new power steering reservoir.

b. Tighten all bolts and nuts to specifications.

POWER STEERING PUMP

REPLACE

XJ8, XK8 & XJR

1. Disconnect and plug steering pump hoses and lines.
2. Remove mounting bolts and pump assembly.
3. Plug pump openings and remove drive coupling.
4. Reverse procedure to install. Tighten mounting bolts to specifications.

S-TYPE

1. Remove air cleaner outlet tube, then the air cleaner.
2. Release tensioner and remove accessory drive belt, then raise and support vehicle.
3. Disconnect power steering feed tube and drain power steering fluid into a suitable container.
4. Remove power steering pump lower attaching bolt, then lower vehicle.
5. Disconnect power steering pump feed hose.
6. Remove retaining bolts, then the power steering pump.
7. Reverse procedure to install, noting the following:
   a. Install a new power steering reservoir.
   b. Install new union O-ring.
   c. Use steering gear oil No.WSA-M2C195–A or equivalent.

TIGHTENING SPECIFICATIONS

Year	Component	Torque, Ft. Lbs.
XJ8, XK8 & XJR		
1998–2001	ABS Rotor	199–243
	Control Arm Ball Joint	44–59
	Crossmember, Front Mount	57–76
	Crossmember, Rear Mount	57–76
	Cruciform Strut	50–68
	Disc Shield	80–97①
	Engine Mount To Crossbeam	25–34
	Lower Ball Joint	44–59
	Lower Control Arm Fulcrum Bolt	83–113
	Lower Control Arm Shock Absorber Bracket	94–127
	Pinion Housing Hose Retaining Plate	80–97①
	Shock Absorber Lower Mount	44–60
	Shock Absorber Lower Mount Bracket	29–41
	Shock Absorber Upper Mount	19–25
	Steering Column Clamp	16–21
	Steering Rack	30–37
	Stabilizer Bar Bracket	16–21
	Stabilizer Bar Link	44–59
	Steering Arm Tie Rod	52–63
	Upper Ball Joint	44–59
	Upper Control Arm Fulcrum	72–97
	Wheel Speed Sensor	62–80①
S-TYPE		
2000–01	Brake caliper	76
	Lower Arm To Knuckle	111
	Lower Arm To Subframe	129
	Power Steering Pump Bracket	84①
	Power Steering Pump	18
	Power Steering Pump Supply Tube	35
	Power Steering Gear	95
	Stabilizer Bar	41
	Stabilizer Bar Clamp	41
	Shock Absorber Top With/DSC	20
	Shock Absorber Top Without/DSC	37
	Steering Gear Supply Tubes	24
	Strut Tower	21
	Strut To Lower Arm	129
	Tie Rod End Lock Nut	30
	Tie Rod End To Wheel Knuckle	74
	Wheel Hub Nuts	66

① — Inch lbs.

Wheel Alignment

NOTE: On Air Bag Equipped Models, Refer To "Air Bag System Precautions" Located In The Front Of This Manual For System Disarming & Arming Procedures.

NOTE: Prior To Performing Any Service Operations Listed In This Section, Consult The "Technical Service Bulletins" Section For Related Information.

INDEX

	Page No.
Front Wheel Alignment	3-26
S-Type	3-26
XJ8 & XJR	3-26
XK8	3-26
Preliminary Inspection	3-26
Rear Wheel Alignment	3-27
S-Type	3-27
XJ8 & XJR	3-27
Technical Service Bulletins	3-27
Vehicle Pulls To One Side	3-27
Vehicle Ride Height	3-27
Wheel Alignment Specifications	3-2

PRELIMINARY INSPECTION

1. Ensure tires are inflated to proper pressure.
2. Ensure tire and wheel assemblies are properly balanced.
3. Center steering wheel at straight ahead position.
4. Vehicle must be unladen with full fuel tank.
5. Bounce front and rear of vehicle to settle suspension.

FRONT WHEEL ALIGNMENT

XJ8 & XJR

1. Lower control arm eccentric fulcrum bolts are rotated to adjust camber and caster.
2. Adjusting front bolt alters caster angle with small effect on camber angle.
3. Adjusting rear bolt alters camber angle with small effect on caster angle.

XK8

Caster

1. Raise and support vehicle, then remove front tire and wheel assemblies.
2. Make shim positions.
3. Remove mounting nut and fulcrum bolt, then secure control arm.
4. **Total number of shims on each fulcrum bolt must remain the same.**
5. To increase positive caster, decrease front shim thickness and increase rear.
6. To decrease positive caster, increase front shim thickness and decrease rear.
7. Two thick and two thin shims are allocated to each control arm fulcrum bolt.
8. Blue paint coded .0630 inch shims effect caster by .4.°
9. Red paint coded .0354 inch shims effect caster by .2.°
10. Align control arm to crossbeam, then install fulcrum bolt, shims, washers and nut. **Torque** nut to 72–97 ft. lbs.
11. Install tire and wheel assemblies, then lower vehicle.
12. Inspect caster. Adjust camber and toe as required.

Camber

Lower control arm fulcrum bolt may have to be replaced with eccentric fulcrum bolt to adjust camber.

1. Factory set position will have eccentric bolt indicator strip at 6 o'clock position.
2. Rotating bolt 90° so that indicator strip is outboard of bolt center will move lower control arm rear fulcrum out.
3. Depending on original camber angle, this with decrease positive camber or increase negative camber.
4. Rotating bolt 90° so that indicator strip is inboard of bolt center will move lower control arm rear fulcrum in.
5. Depending on original camber angle, this with increase positive camber or decrease negative camber.
6. **Torque** bolt to 83–113 ft. lbs.

S-TYPE

Less Adjustment Cam Bolts

Check wheel alignment, follow equipment manufacturers instructions.

1. Remove alternator splash shield, then detach lower steering column from steering gear. Discard pinch bolt.
2. Remove steering gear from crossmember, discard lock nuts.
3. Raise and support front of vehicle on No. 2 crossmember, then position two 4 inch X 4 inch pieces of wood between No. 2 crossmember and lifting device.
4. Remove and discard lower arm front lock nut and bolt.
5. Install caster adjustment cam bolt and a new lock nut, bolt should be installed from rear with cam lobe down. **Cam must be seated between cam guides on No. 1 crossmember.**
6. Reposition steering gear, then remove and discard lower arm rear lock nut and bolt.
7. Install camber adjustment cam bolt from rear with lobe down. **Cam must be seated in groove in No. 2 crossmember.**
8. Lower front of vehicle, then install new lock nut, steering gear, new pinch bolt and connect steering column lower shaft to steering gear.

With Adjustment Cam Bolts

Check wheel alignment, follow equipment manufacturers instructions.

1. For vehicles requiring caster adjustment, slacken lock nut, then rotate lower arm caster adjustment cam bolt to adjust caster.
2. Recheck alignment setting, follow manufacturers instructions. Readjust as required.
3. Adjustments to camber impact toe settings, therefore camber and toe may need to be adjusted at same time to achieve correct values.
4. Slacken tie rod end lock nut and remove steering gear boot clamp. Clean and lubricate lock nut and tie rod threads.
5. Do not allow steering gear boot to twist when tie rod is rotated. Rotate tie rod to adjust toe.
6. To aid accurate camber and toe measurements, support front suspension lower arm by hand while rotating camber adjustment cam bolt.
7. Rotate lower arm camber adjustment cam bolt to adjust camber.
8. Repeat above camber adjustment steps until correct camber and toe measurements are achieved.
9. Tighten caster adjustment cam bolt lock nut, then the camber adjustment cam bolt lock nut.
10. Tighten tie rod end lock nut, then install steering gear boot clamp.
11. Recheck alignment setting, follow equipment manufacturer's instructions and readjust as required.
12. Install alternator splash shield.

REAR WHEEL ALIGNMENT

XJ8 & XJR

Rear wheel toe-in is adjusted by rotating lower control arm outer end eccentric mounting bolt.

S-TYPE

Loosen lock nuts, then clean and lubricate lock nut and toe link threads. Rotate toe link to adjust toe settings, tighten lock nut and recheck toe settings.

VEHICLE RIDE HEIGHT

On the S-Type models the front ride height measurements should be, front 15.1 inches and rear 15.05 inches. On the XJ models settings are to be checked with the vehicle at curb height (unladen, with full tank of gas. On the XK models ride height is measured from the ground to the apex of the wheel arch, through the wheel center line. Measurements should be, front 28.4 inches and rear 28.7 inches.

TECHNICAL SERVICE BULLETINS

VEHICLE PULLS TO ONE SIDE

1998 XJR

On these models, the vehicle may pull to one side although alignment values are within specifications.

This condition may be caused by differences between lefthand and righthand camber balance combined with lefthand and righthand caster balance. To correct this condition, proceed as follows:

1. Calculate camber balance by subtracting lefthand camber from righthand camber.
2. Calculate caster balance by subtracting lefthand caster from righthand caster.
3. Calculate pull index by subtracting caster balance from camber balance.
4. If vehicle pulls to right, adjust caster settings to make pull index more negative.
5. If vehicle pulls to left, adjust caster settings to make pull index more positive. **Do not exceed -6 pull index.**

Air Conditioning

NOTE: On Air Bag Equipped Models, Refer To "Air Bag System Precautions" Located In The Front Of This Manual For System Disarming & Arming Procedures.

NOTE: Prior To Performing Any Service Operations Listed In This Section, Consult The "Technical Service Bulletins" Section For Related Information.

INDEX

	Page No.
A/C Specifications	3-29
Belt Tension	3-29
Charging System	3-29
Description	3-28
Climate Control System	3-28
Leak Test	3-28
Oil Charge	3-29
S Type	3-29
XJR, XJ8, XKR & XK8	3-29
Precautions	3-28
Air Bag Systems	3-28
Battery Ground Cable	3-28
R-134a Systems	3-28
System Evacuation	3-28

PRECAUTIONS

R-134A SYSTEMS

R-134a is a non-toxic, non-flammable, clear, odorless, liquefied gas.

R-134a refrigerant is not compatible with R-12 refrigerant. Even small amounts of R-12 in an R-134a system can cause lubricant contamination, improper A/C performance or compressor failure. Never add R-12 to an R-134a system.

New service ports have been added to compressor to prevent charging system with R-12 refrigerant. **R-134a systems require a special compressor lubricant.**

Avoid breathing R-134a refrigerant and lubricant vapor or mist. Exposure may irritate eyes, nose and throat. Use only approved service equipment to recover R-134a systems.

Before replenishing refrigerant or refrigerant oil, ensure product compatibility with the system being serviced. Refer to "A/C Specifications."

AIR BAG SYSTEMS

Refer to "Air Bag System Precautions" in the front of this manual for system disarming and arming procedures.

BATTERY GROUND CABLE

Prior to service, disconnect battery ground cable and isolate as required.

DESCRIPTION

CLIMATE CONTROL SYSTEM

AIR CONDITIONING ELECTRIC CONTROL MODULE

The control module is located on the righthand side of A/C unit, controls the function of the system. These functions include: in-vehicle temperature control, in-vehicle humidity control and air flow volume and distribution.

Solar Sensor

The solar sensor is mounted on top of the instrument panel, between the instrument panel defrost grilles. This sensor is constructed around a photo diode to measure direct sunlight.

Ambient Temperature Sensor

The ambient temperature sensor is located within the lefthand brake cooling duct. This sensor detects exterior air temperature.

Evaporator Temperature Sensor

Located next to the evaporator fins, this sensor detects the air temperature leaving the evaporator.

Vehicle Speed Sensor

This sensor detects road speed from the instrument cluster. This signal is required to control the blower fan speed changes to minimize the effect of ram air. This signal also determines the frequency at which the ambient air temperature sensor updates.

Compressor On Signal

This signal line monitors the compressor relay to inform the A/CCM of the compressor status and to facilitate lock detecting and error sensing.

Motorized In-Vehicle Aspirator (MIA)

The MIA detects the air temperature within the passenger compartment when air conditioning is selecting. A small motor driven fan draws air across a thermistor, which changes its electrical resistance in response to changes in air temperature, converting air temperature into a electrical signal.

Compressor Lock Signal

This signal provides the A/CCM with compressor rotation speed. This is then compared with engine rotation speed. If the ratio of the compressor speed against engine speed drops below the A/CCM limits, indicating compressor/belt slippage, the compressor clutch is disengaged.

Servo Motor Control

The system incorporates several servo motors which direct the flow of air through the air conditioning system. The motors are driven by the A/CCM signals. Servo motor position is monitored via a feedback potentiometer situated within the motor housing.

Blower Motor Control

The A/CCM controls two blower motors, delivering air flow through the evaporator at variable fan speeds. The blower motors are regulated by power transistor modules which provide linear variation of blower speed. The blower motors are inhibited when engine coolant temperature is below 86°F.

LEAK TEST

Fault conditions associated with low refrigerant charge weight and low pressure may be caused by leakage. Leaks traced to mechanical connections may be caused by torque relaxation or joint face contamination. Evidence of oil around these areas is an indication of leaks. When inspecting for non-visible leaks, only use a dedicated R-134a type electronic analyzer and apply probe all around the joint or connection.

If a leaks is traced to a joint, ensure the fixing is tightened properly before any other action is taken. **Never use an R-12 or flame type analyzer.**

SYSTEM EVACUATION

Moisture can be highly destructive and may cause internal blockages due to freezing or compressor oil contamination. Once the system has been opened for repairs or the refrigerant charge recovered, all traces of moisture must be removed before charging the system. **Follow charging station manufacturer's instructions for evacuating system.**

CHARGING SYSTEM

R-134a recovery will depend on the basic characteristics of the individual recovery station. Follow manufacturer's instructions completely. Compressor oil may be drawn out of system during this process. Note quantity of oil recovered so it may be replaced.

Do not vent refrigerant directly to atmosphere. Do not mix R-134a and R-12 refrigerants.

OIL CHARGE

S TYPE

1. Drain and discard new compressor transit lubricating oil.
2. Drain, measure and discard old compressor lubricating oil.
3. Measure oil recovered from system evacuation separator.
4. If less than 3 ounces of oil was drained, add 3 ounces of new oil.
5. If 3–5 ounces was drained, add equal amount of oil plus 1 ounce.
6. If more than 5 ounces was drain, add only 5 ounces to system.
7. If installing new condenser or evaporator, add 1 ounce of new oil.

XJR, XJ8, XKR & XK8

1. Drain and discard new compressor transit lubricating oil.
2. Drain, measure and discard old compressor lubricating oil.
3. Measure oil recovered from system evacuation separator.
4. Add amount of new oil to system equal to sum of old compressor and separator oil measurements.
5. If installing new condenser or evaporator, add 1.36 fl. oz. new oil.

A/C SPECIFICATIONS

Year	Refrigerant		Compressor Oil Viscosity	Total System Oil Capacity, Oz.	Compressor Clutch Air Gap, Inch
	Capacity, Lbs.	Type			
S TYPE					
2000–01	①	R-134a	②	3.00–5.00	0.010–0.030
XJR & XJ8					
1998–2001	1.42–1.53	R-134a	②	5.44–6.80	0.010–0.030
XKR & XK8					
1998–2001	1.31–1.53	R-134a	②	5.44–6.80	0.010–0.030

① — Refer to underhood label.

② — Special polyalkyleneglycol (PAG) lubricant required.

BELT TENSION

These engine incorporates a serpentine drive belt and there are no adjustments.

Cooling Fans

NOTE: On Air Bag Equipped Models, Refer To "Air Bag System Precautions" Located In The Front Of This Manual For System Disarming & Arming Procedures.

NOTE: Electrical Symbol & Wire Color Code Identification Located In The Front Of This Manual May Be Used As An Aid When Using Wiring Circuits Found In This Section.

INDEX

	Page No.
Component Diagnosis & Testing	3-30
Wiring Diagrams	3-30
Component Replacement	3-30
Fan	3-30
Motor	3-31
Description	3-30
Precautions	3-30
Battery Ground Cable	3-30

PRECAUTIONS

BATTERY GROUND CABLE

Prior to service, disconnect battery ground cable and isolate as required.

DESCRIPTION

On models equipped less a supercharger, a single, variable speed cooling fan motor is attached to a fan shroud located behind the radiator. The speed is determined by the Cylinder Head Temperature (CHT) on the 3.0L engine or the Engine Coolant Temperature (ECT) sensor, on the 4.0L engine. The air conditioning pressure and transmission oil temperature contributes to the cooling fan speed on both engines. Under hot operating conditions, the fan may continue to operate for four minutes after the engine has been switched off. An electric water pump runs for 1–10 minutes on the 4.0L engine only.

On models equipped with a supercharger, the two radiator cooling fans are mounted in a cowl assembly within the cooling module. The fans are controlled by the ECM dependent on the demand from the cooling system (temperature) or the air conditioning system (pressure). Outputs from the ECM control the radiator fans control module, located behind the lefthand side of the bumper, to operate the fans in the series mode (slow), parallel mode (fast) or Off modes. Hysteresis in the temperature and pressure switching values prevents hunting between modes. Under hot operating conditions, the fans may continue to operate for some time after the engine has been switched off, but will stop automatically when the coolant temperature has been sufficiently reduced. The Engine Coolant Temperature (ECT) sensor is located in the coolant outlet pipe and reacts to engine coolant temperature changes, providing an input to the Engine Control Module (ECM). The sensor has a negative temperature coefficient so that the sensor resistance decreases as temperature rises.

COMPONENT DIAGNOSIS & TESTING

The complexity of electronics involved with the body processor and the two multiplexed communication networks which are associated with it, preclude the use of workshop general electrical test equipment. Therefore, reference should be made to the Portable Diagnostic Unit (PDU) user guide for detailed instruction on testing the cooling fan system. The PDU systematically tests and analyzes all electrical functions of the cooling fans. Where a fault is indicated, some basic diagnostic methods may be required to confirm that connections are good and that wiring is not damaged, before replacing component.

Wiring Diagrams

For cooling fan wiring diagrams refer to "Jaguar" chapter in "Engine Performance & Driveability" portion of this manual.

COMPONENT REPLACEMENT

FAN

S Type

1. Drain cooling system into suitable container.
2. **On models equipped with 3.0L engine,** remove outlet tube and air cleaner, then the upper shield.
3. **On models equipped with 4.0L engine,** remove the air cleaner.
4. **On all models,** remove radiator mounting brackets.
5. Disconnect upper coolant hose.
6. Disconnect electric fan motor and air conditioning pressure switch electrical connectors.
7. **On models equipped with 4.0L engine,** proceed as follows:
   a. Disconnect auxiliary water pump electrical connector.
   b. Disconnect air conditioning receiver dryer.
   c. Disconnect auxiliary water pump.
8. **On all models,** disconnect air conditioning receiver dryer.
9. Disconnect heater valve electrical connector.
10. Raise and support vehicle.
11. Remove lower radiator splash shield.
12. Disconnect cooling duct from fan shroud assembly.
13. Remove fan shroud retaining clips.
14. Lower vehicle.
15. Remove mounting bolt, fan and shroud assembly **Do not damage radiator.**
16. Reverse procedure to install.

XJR, XJ8, XKR & XK8

1. Remove battery cover.
2. Disconnect cooling fans' harness connectors.
3. Cut and remove each fan harness strap on lower support leg.
4. Disconnect fans' connectors.
5. Disconnect fan mounting frame harness from clip. Place harness aside.
6. Remove two fan to radiator mounting bolts.
7. Remove fan and motor assembly.
8. Remove mounting grommets and spacer tubes from the assembly.
9. Reverse procedure to install. Ensure fan and motor assembly locates into lower mountings.

MOTOR

S Type

1. Remove fan as outlined under "Fan."
2. Remove fan motor assembly.
3. Disconnect electrical connector.
4. Remove mounting nuts and fan motor.
5. Reverse procedure to install.

XJR, XJ8, XKR & XK8

1. Remove twin cooling fans as outlined in this section.
2. Remove mounting nuts, then the fan and motor unit.
3. Remove spacers and rubber mountings.
4. Reverse procedure to install.
5. Remove fans and outlined under "Fan."
6. Remove three mounting nuts, then the fan and motor.
7. Remove spacers and three fan rubber mountings.
8. Reverse procedure to install.

Starter Motors

INDEX

Page No.		Page No.		Page No.	
Diagnosis & Testing	3-31	Engine Cranks Slowly	3-31	Wiring Diagrams	3-31
Symptom Related Diagnosis	3-31	Engine Does Not Crank	3-31	**Starter Specifications**	3-33

DIAGNOSIS & TESTING

Wiring Diagrams

Refer to **Figs. 1 through 3** for wiring diagrams.

Symptom Related Diagnosis

ENGINE DOES NOT CRANK

1. Inspect battery.
2. If battery is in satisfactory condition, proceed to "Starter Relay Test."
3. If battery us not in satisfactory condition, replace it as required.

Starter Relay Test

1. Turn ignition switch to RUN position.
2. If starter relay make audible click, proceed to "Starter Battery Voltage Test."
3. If there is no click, proceed to "Starter Relay Ignition Voltage Test."

Starter Battery Voltage Test

1. Measure voltage between starter connector AS006 and ground.
2. If voltage is more than 10 volts, proceed to "Starter Ground Test."
3. If voltage is not as specified, repair starter motor permanent live supply circuit.

Starter Ground Test

1. Measure resistance between starter outer casing and ground.
2. If resistance is less than 2 Ohm, proceed to "Starter Switch Live Test."
3. If resistance is not as specified, repair starter ground strap or connections.

Starter Switch Live Test

1. Turn ignition switch is to RUN position.
2. Measure voltage between starter connector SS2-1 and ground.
3. If measurement is more than 10 volts, install new starter motor.
4. If measurement is not as specified, proceed to "Permanent Live Voltage To Starter Relay Test."

Permanent Live Voltage To Starter Relay Test

1. Remove starter relay.
2. Measure voltage between connector 30 and ground.
3. If measurement is more than 10 volts, repair starter switch live circuit from starter relay to starter.
4. If measurement is not as specified, inspect fuse 14 (30A) in front PDB. If fuse satisfactory, repair starter relay permanent live supply circuit.

Ignition Voltage To Starter Relay, Test

1. Remove starter relay.
2. Measure voltage between connector 86 and ground.
3. If measurement is more than 10 volts, proceed to "Ground Supply To Starter Relay Test."
4. If voltage is not as specified, proceed to "Primary Junction Box Fuse Test."

Ground Supply To Starter Relay Test

1. Measure resistance between starter relay connector 85 and ground.
2. If resistance is less than 5 ohms, install new starter.
3. If resistance is not as specified, proceed to "Ground Supply Circuit Test."

Ground Supply Circuit Test

1. Measure resistance between starter relay connector 85 and instrument pack FC15-18.
2. If resistance is less than 5 ohms, diagnose anti-theft system.
3. If resistance is not as specified, repair ground circuit between starter relay and instrument pack.

Primary Junction Box Fuse Test

1. Inspect fuse No. 1
2. If fuse is in satisfactory condition, proceed to "Transmission Range Switch Test."
3. If fuse is not in satisfactory condition, proceed to "Short To Ground Test."

Short To Ground Test

1. Measure resistance between starter relay connector 86 and ground.
2. If resistance is more than 10,000 ohms, install new fuse.
3. If resistance is not as specified, repair short to ground between primary junction box and starter relay.

Transmission Range Switch Test

1. Disconnect transmission range switch electrical connector.
2. Inspect resistance between connector GB6-10 and GB6-12 on transmission range switch with gearshift selector in PARK or NEUTRAL position.
3. If resistance is less than 5 ohms, inspect circuitry between primary junction box and starter relay.
4. If resistance is not as specified, install new transmission range switch.

ENGINE CRANKS SLOWLY

Voltage Drop Test

1. Measure voltage between starter motor permanent voltage supply terminal and positive battery terminal with ignition key in START position.
2. If voltage drops, proceed to "Ground Connection Test."
3. If voltage does not drop, clean and tighten all positive battery cable connections.
4. If condition persists, install new positive battery cable.

Ground Connection Test

1. Measure voltage between starter motor case and battery negative terminal with ignition key in START position.
2. If measurement is less than 0.5 volts, diagnose battery and charging system.
3. If measurement is not as specified, clean and tighten all negative battery cable connections, starter motor mounting and body to engine ground strap.
4. If condition persists, install new negative battery cable.

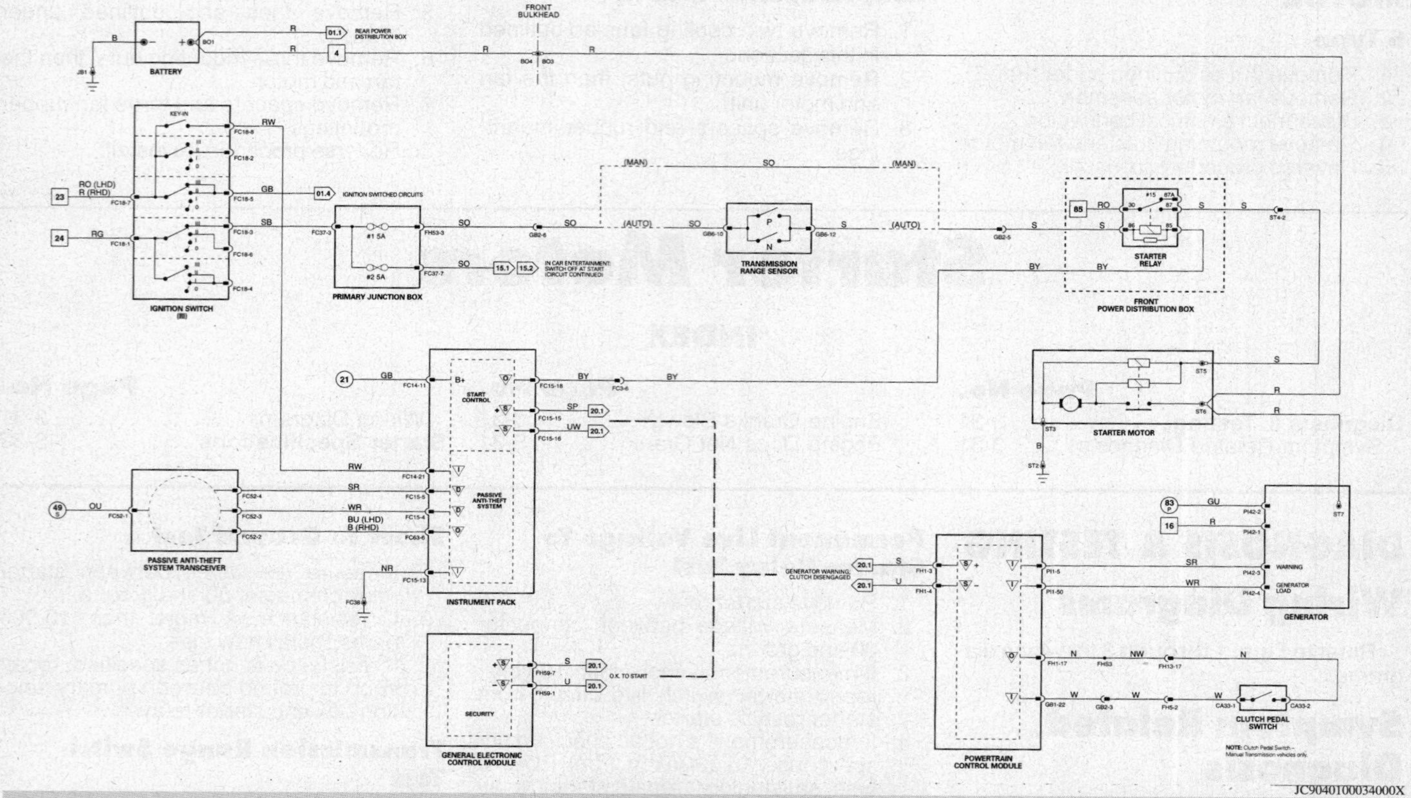

JC9040100034000X

Fig. 1 Wiring diagram. S Type

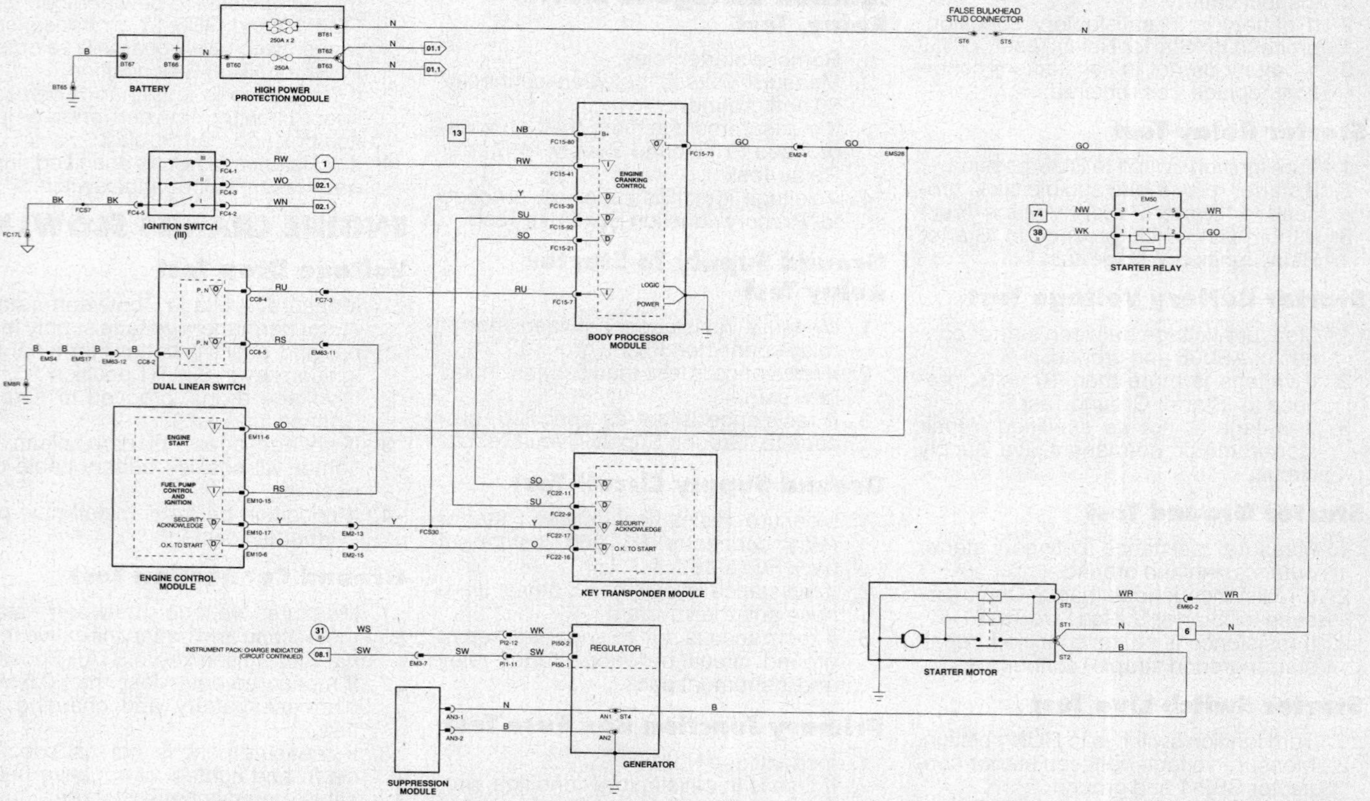

JC9040000011020X

Fig. 2 Wiring diagram. XJR & XKR

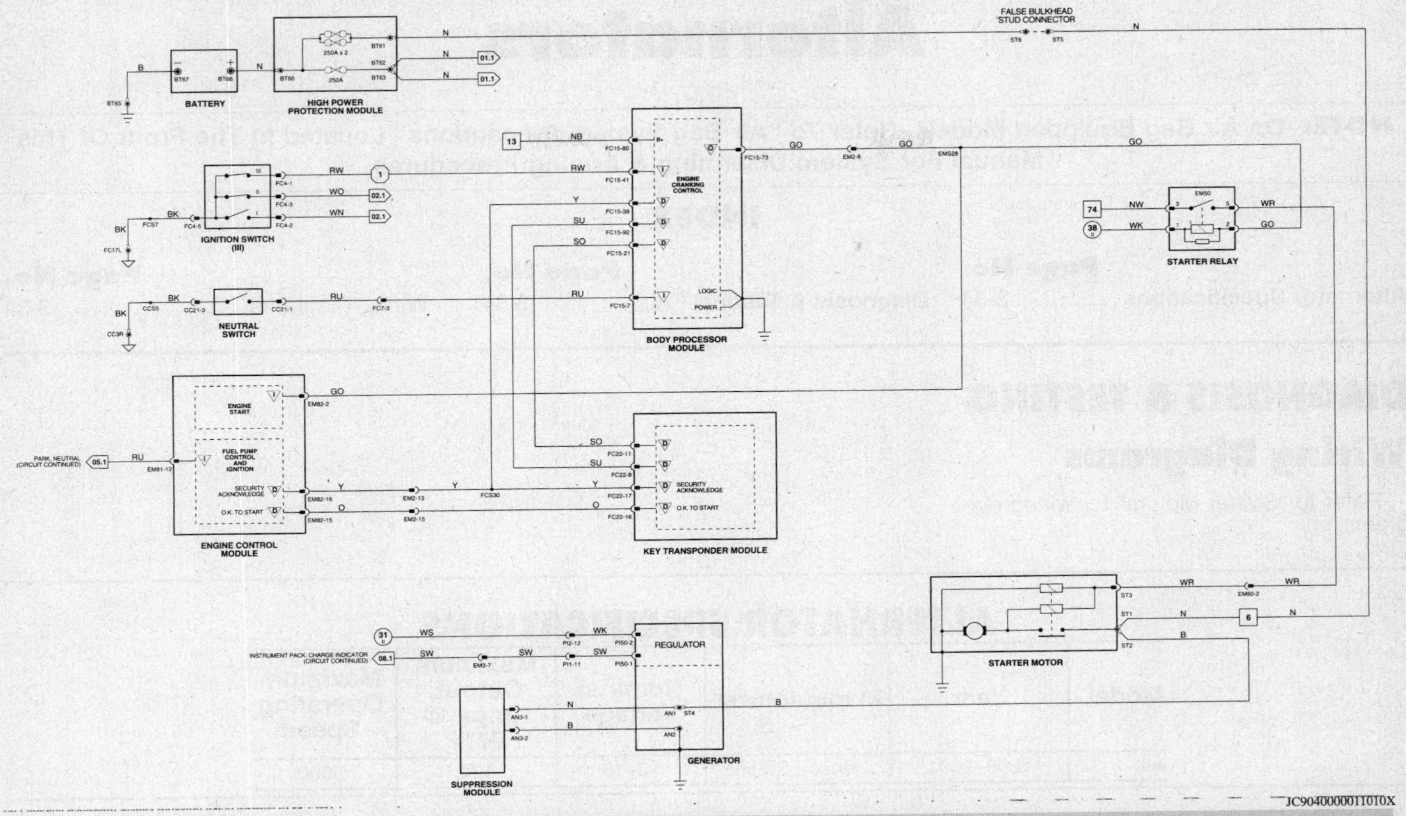

Fig. 3 Wiring diagram. XJ8 & XK8

STARTER SPECIFICATIONS

Starter Model	Rating	No Load			Load			Contact Closing		
	Output, kW	Time, Seconds	Voltage	Current, Amps	Speed, Max. RPM	Voltage	Current Amps	Speed, Max. RPM	Voltage	Gap, Nominal, Inch
Nippon Denso Type RA1.4	1.4	30	11.5	90	3000	8.5	350	1000	8	0.118

Alternators

NOTE: On Air Bag Equipped Models, Refer To "Air Bag System Precautions" Located In The Front Of This Manual For System Disarming & Arming Procedures.

INDEX

	Page No.
Alternator Specifications	3-34
Diagnosis & Testing	3-34
Wiring Diagrams	3-34

DIAGNOSIS & TESTING

Wiring Diagrams

Refer to "Starter Motors" for wiring diagrams.

ALTERNATOR SPECIFICATIONS

Model	Year	Manufacturer	Nominal Voltage	Maximum Output, Amps @ 77°F	Maximum Operating Speed
All	1998–2001	Denso L3B-HE	13–15	120	5000

Speed Control Systems

NOTE: On Air Bag Equipped Models, Refer To "Air Bag System Precautions" Located In The Front Of This Manual For System Disarming & Arming Procedures.

NOTE: Electrical Symbol & Wire Color Code Identification Located In The Front Of This Manual May Be Used As An Aid When Using Wiring Circuits Found In This Section.

INDEX

	Page No.
Adjustments	3-35
Switch	3-35
Component Replacement	3-35
Speed Control Deactivator Switch (Brake Pedal Switch)	3-35
Speed Control Switch	3-35
Precautions	3-35
Battery Ground Cable	3-35
System Diagnosis & Testing	3-35

PRECAUTIONS

BATTERY GROUND CABLE

Prior to service, disconnect battery ground cable and isolate as required.

ADJUSTMENTS

SWITCH

1. Rotate lock plug 65° counterclockwise.
2. Pull switch plunger out to its full extent.
3. Fully depress brake pedal.
4. Install switch.
5. Slowly release brake pedal until one click is heard.
6. Release brake pedal.

SYSTEM DIAGNOSIS & TESTING

For cruise control systems diagnosis and testing refer to "Jaguar" chapter in "Engine Performance & Driveability" portion of this manual.

COMPONENT REPLACEMENT

SPEED CONTROL DEACTIVATOR SWITCH (BRAKE PEDAL SWITCH)

1. Remove mounting screws and disconnect driver's side instrument panel lower panel.
2. Disconnect headlamp adjustment switch.
3. Remove mounting screws and driver's air duct.
4. Remove speed control deactivator switch.
5. Disconnect speed control deactivator switch electrical connector.
6. Reverse procedure to install.

SPEED CONTROL SWITCH

Remove driver's air bag module as outlined in "Air Bag System" section.

Disconnect cruise control switch electrical connector.

Remove two mounting screws and cruise control switch.

Reverse procedure to install.

Wiper Systems

NOTE: On Air Bag Equipped Models, Refer To "Air Bag System Precautions" Located In The Front Of This Manual For System Disarming & Arming Procedures.

INDEX

	Page No.
Component Diagnosis & Testing	3-36
Accessing Diagnostic Trouble Codes	3-36
Clearing Diagnostic Trouble Codes	3-36
Diagnostic Trouble Code Interpretation	3-36
Wiring Diagrams	3-36
Precautions	3-36
Air Bag Systems	3-36
Battery Ground Cable	3-36

PRECAUTIONS

AIR BAG SYSTEMS

Refer to "Air Bag System Precautions" in the front of this manual for system disarming and arming procedures.

BATTERY GROUND CABLE

Prior to service, disconnect battery ground cable and isolate as required.

COMPONENT DIAGNOSIS & TESTING

The complexity of electronics involved with the body processor and the two multiplexed communication networks which are associated with it, preclude the use of workshop general electrical test equipment. Therefore, reference should be made to the Portable Diagnostic Unit (PDU) user guide for detailed instruction on testing the wipers and washers. The PDU systematically tests and analyses all electrical functions of wipers and washers. Where a fault is indicated, some basic diagnostic methods may be required to confirm that connections are good and that wiring is not damaged, before replacing component.

Accessing Diagnostic Trouble Codes

Diagnostic Trouble Codes (DTCs) are accessed by connecting a suitable programmed scan tool to the Data Link Connector (DLC) and following the tool manufacturer's instructions. The DLC is located on the instrument panel adjacent to the driver's side A-pillar.

Diagnostic Trouble Code Interpretation

Refer to **Fig. 1** for Diagnostic Trouble Code (DTC) interpretation.

Code	Description	MIL	Possible Causes
B1479	Washer Fluid Lever Switch Circuit Fault	Yes	GECM To Fluid Lever Switch Circuit: Open Circuit, Short Circuit To Ground, Short Circuit To B+ Voltage
			Washer Fluid Level Switch Ground Fault
			Washer Fluid Level Switch Failure

Fig. 1 Body Control Module DTC Interpretation

Wiring Diagrams

Refer to **Figs. 2 and 3** for wiring diagrams.

Clearing Diagnostic Trouble Codes

Follow scan tool manufacturer's instructions.

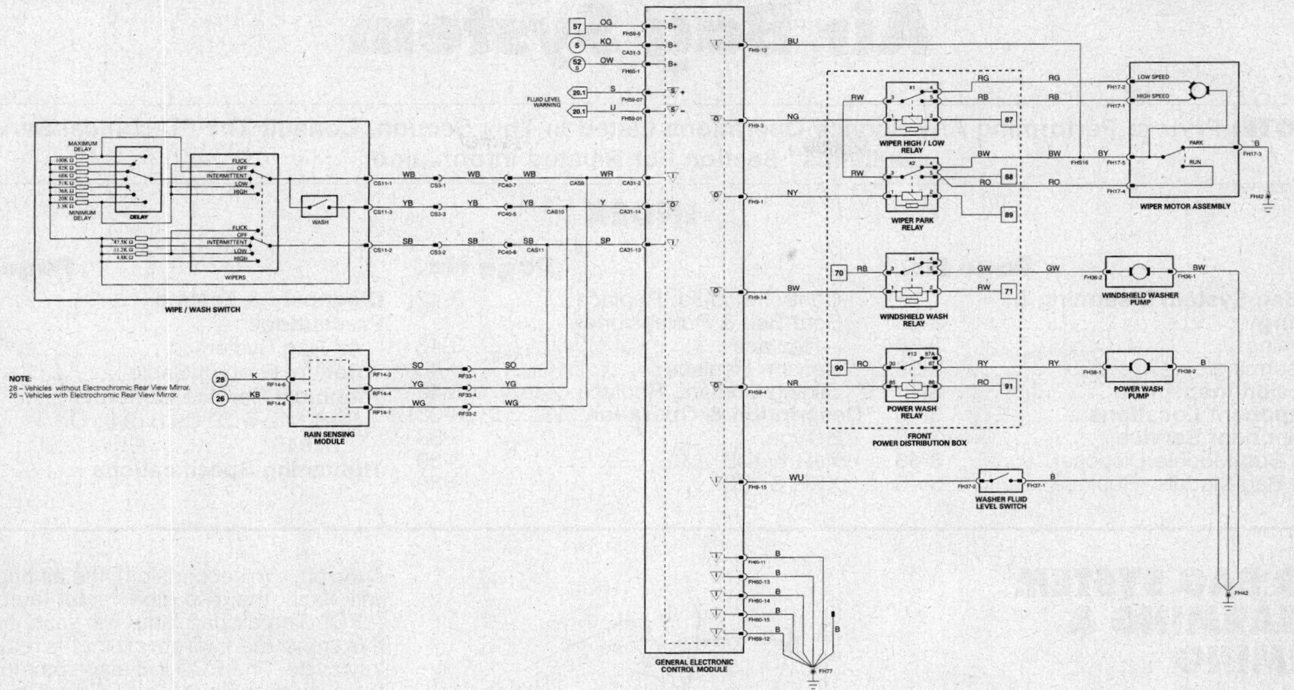

JC9040100033000X

Fig. 2 Wiring diagram. S Type

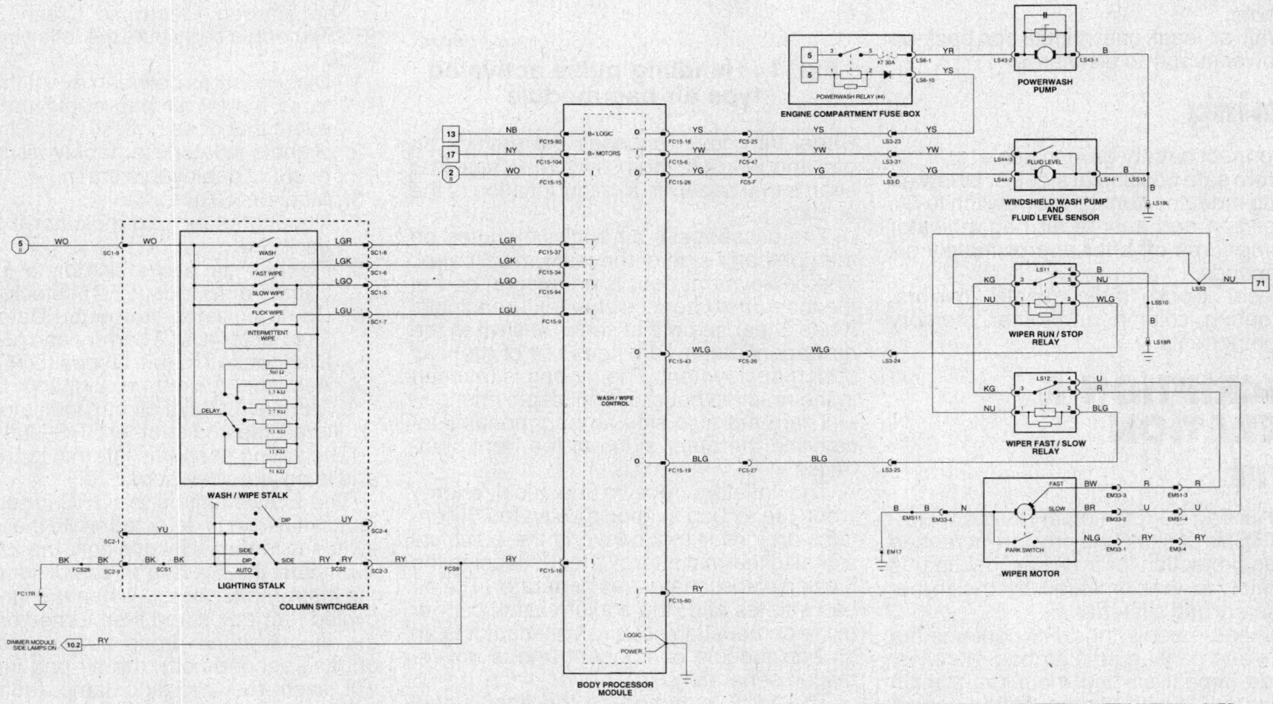

JC9040000023000X

Fig. 3 Wiring diagram. XJR, XJ8, XKR & XK8

Air Bag System

NOTE: Prior to Performing Any Service Operations Listed In This Section, Consult The "Technical Service Bulletins" Section For Related Information.

INDEX

	Page No.
Air Bag System Disarming & Arming	3-38
Arming	3-38
Disarming	3-38
Collision Inspection	3-40
Component Locations	3-40
Component Service	3-40
Air Bag Module Disposal	3-43
Air Bag Module, Replace	3-40
Control Module, Replace	3-42
Seat Belt & Pretensioner, Replace	3-43
Sensor, Replace	3-43
Sliding Contact, Replace	3-42
Description & Operation	3-38
S Type	3-38
XJR & XJ8	3-39
XKR & XK8	3-39
Diagnosis & Testing	3-40
Precautions	3-40
Air Bag System	3-40
Battery Ground Cable	3-40
Technical Service Bulletins	3-44
SRS MIL w/DTCs B1944 Or B1945	3-44
Tightening Specifications	3-45

AIR BAG SYSTEM DISARMING & ARMING

Disarming

1. Record clock, radio, seats, mirrors, steering column and other memory component settings.
2. Turn ignition switch to Lock position and remove key.
3. Disconnect and isolate battery ground cable.
4. Wait at least one minute for back-up power supply to discharge.

Arming

1. Connect battery ground cable.
2. From safe position at sides or below air bag modules, turn ignition switch to On position and ensure air bag indicator lamp turns off after approximately six seconds.
3. Reset clock, radio, seats, mirrors, steering column and other memory components.

DESCRIPTION & OPERATION

S TYPE

The air bag Supplemental Restraint System (SRS) is designed to provide increased collision protection for front seat occupants in addition to that provided by the three-point safety belt system.

On these models the SRS contains the driver's and passenger's air bag modules, two side impact air bag modules, a main control module with integral safing sensor and back-up power supply, two side impact sensors, a dedicated wiring harness and the instrument panel mounted air bag warning lamp.

The driver's air bag is located in the center of the steering wheel. The steering wheel trim cover encases the driver's air bag module and horn switch. It has tear seams that separate to allow inflation of the air bag.

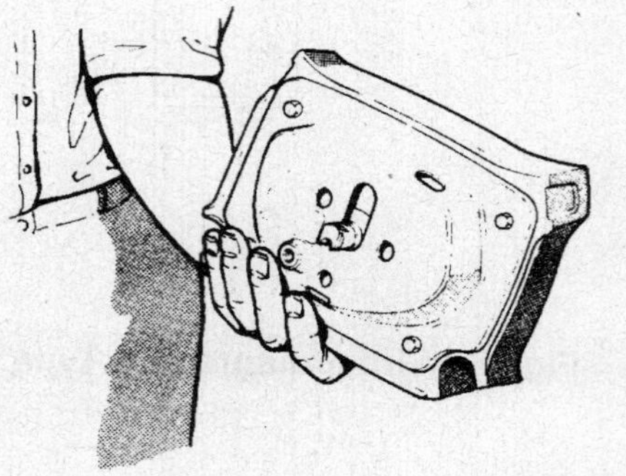

JC8019400022000X

Fig. 1 Handling pulse activated type air bag module

The passenger's air bag is mounted on the righthand side of the instrument panel. The deployment door is an integral part of the instrument panel with a textured finish. It has a tear seam that separates when the air bag inflates and hinges out of the way during deployment. The air bag is retained in the reaction housing until deployment.

There are also side air bag modules located in the outer sides of the front seatbacks.

The inflators receive electrical energy when the air bag sensor is activated. It contains an igniter that converts the electrical signal to thermal energy (heat), causing the ignition of the inflator gas generator. The air bag inflates after the sodium azide/copper oxide combustion occurs. The inflator is an air bag module component and is not replaced separately.

The ECS, mounted on the floor tunnel under the instrument panel, monitors the SRS for fault conditions. If a condition is detected while the ignition is On, the ECS will light the instrument cluster air bag lamp. When the ignition is cycled Off and On, after the eight-second prove out (six seconds on, two seconds off), the air bag lamp will flash the two-digit lamp fault code (LFC). The air bag lamp will flash the LFC five times, then will stay lit for the rest of the key cycle. The ECS will also communicate the current and historical DTCs through the data link connector (DLC), using the Portable Diagnostic Unit (PDU). If the air bag lamp does not operate and the system detects a fault condition, the ECS will activate an audible chime. This will be a series of five sets of five tone bursts. If the chime or buzzer should sound, the SRS and air bag lamp require service.

The air bag Electronic Crash Sensor (ECS) module carry outs the following functions:

1. Discriminates between event that warrants frontal air bag deployment and event that does not.
2. Signals inflators to deploy air bags in event of deployable crash.
3. Monitors SRS for faults.
4. Illuminates air bag indicator if fault is detected.
5. Flashes air bag indicator to indicate Lamp Fault Code (LFC) detected.
6. Communicates through Data Link Connector (DLC) current and historical Diagnostic Trouble Codes (DTCs).
7. Activates chime in Lighting Control Module (LCM) if air bag indicator is not available and another SRS fault exists.

The safing sensor is internal to the ECS and is not serviced separately.

The ECS monitors the SRS for possible faults. If a fault is detected while the ignition switch is in the RUN position, the ECS will illuminate the air bag indicator located in the instrument cluster. When the ignition is cycled (turned off and then turned on) after the eight-second prove out (six seconds on, two seconds off), the air bag indicator will flash the two-digit lamp fault code (LFC). The air bag indicator will flash the LFC five times, then it will remain illuminated for the rest of the key cycle. The ECS will also communicate the current and historical DTCs through the data link connector (DLC), using the Portable Diagnostic Unit

JC8019400023000X

Fig. 2 Storing pulse activated type air bag module

(PDU). If the air bag indicator does not function and the system detects a fault condition, the ECS will activate an audible chime. The chime is a series of five sets of five-tone bursts. If the chime or buzzer is heard, the SRS and the air bag indicator requires service.

Lamp fault codes are prioritized. If two or more faults occur at the same time, the fault having the highest priority will be displayed first. After that fault has been corrected, the next highest priority fault will be displayed

The ECS includes an internal backup power supply. This feature provides sufficient backup power to deploy the air bags in the event the battery or battery cables are damaged in a collision before the safing function in the ECS (RCM) closes. The Back Up Power Supply (BPS) gives sufficient power for 150 milli-seconds to close safing functions to fire or deploy air bags. The backup power supply will deplete its stored energy approximately one minute after the battery ground cable is disconnected.

The electrical system that supports the air bag supplemental restraint system (SRS):

1. Is powered from battery and ignition
2. Provides electrical path from ECS to air bag modules.
3. Provides electrical path from ECS to air bag indicator and On Board Diagnostics Two (OBD II) connector.
4. Provides electrical path from ECS to Vehicle Emergency System (VEMS).

XJR & XJ8

The Supplemental Restraint System (SRS) is designed to provide driver and front seat passenger protection. The air bag system can only be activated when the ignition switch is in II or III position.

The driver's air bag is located in the center of the steering wheel.

The passenger's air bag mounts in the instrument panel.

The side impact air bags are located in a cavity formed by the foam padding on the outside of the front seat backrests.

A Single-Point Sensing unit (SPS) is mounting on the transmission tunnel, below the radio. It provides fully electronic impact sensing, control and diagnostics for the front air bags.

Deployment of each side impact air bag is initiated by a Side Impact Sensing Module (SISM) installed in the adjacent B-pillar.

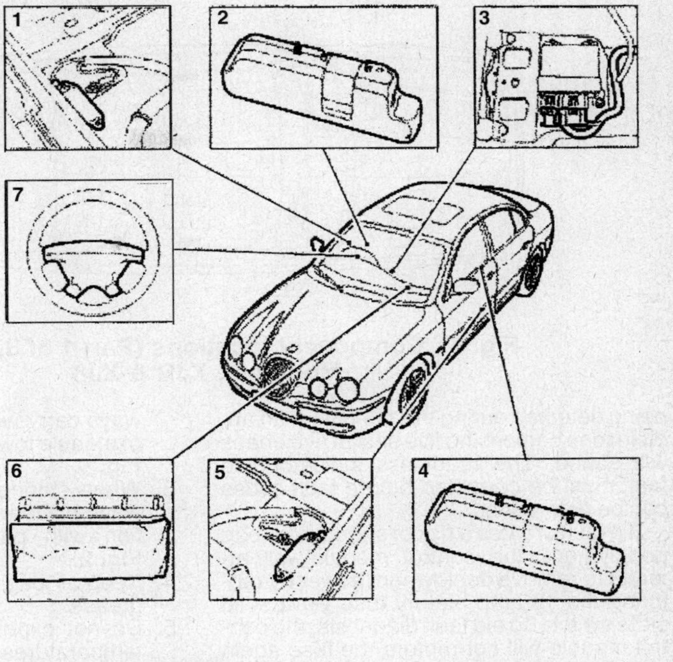

Item	Description
1	Electronic Crash Sensor (Restraints control module RCM)
2	Driver Side Air bag Module
3	Air Bag Electronic Crash Sensor (ECS) Module
4	Driver Side Air bag Module
5	Electronic Crash Sensor
6	Passenger Air Bag Module
7	Driver Air Bag Module

JC8010100054000X

Fig. 3 Component location. S Type

Each SISM senses and electronically processes a crash pulse and if this exceeds the must fire threshold, transmits a fire signal to the SPS unit. Neither the non-struck side air bag nor the frontal restraint system will be deployed under these conditions.

A pyrotechnic front seat belt pretensioning device with independent electronic sensing and retractor unit is install at the base of each B-pillar. Seat belt pretensioning activated when a front impact of sufficient force occurs within 30° of the vehicle center line. Under such an impact, electronic sensor in the retractor unit fire, igniting the pretensioner gas generator. The gas generator initiates a chemical reaction, producing gases under pressure. Gas pressure drives the piston/cable up a tube, rotating the retractor spindlier and removing excess slack from the seat belt. When the pretensioner unit has been activated, the seat belt will lock and cannot be retracted or pulled from the reel. If a seat belt pretensioner activates, a small quantity (less than one quart) of gas is produced containing nitrogen, oxygen and water vapor.

XKR & XK8

The Supplemental Restraint System (SRS) consists of the driver's and passenger's air bag modules, a control module with integral safing sensor and back-up power supply, two crash sensors, a dedicated wiring harness, front seat belt pretensioners, and the instrument panel mounted air bag warning lamp.

The driver's air bag is located in the center of the steering wheel. The passenger's air bag is in the instrument panel.

The control module with integral safing sensor and diagnostic capability is installed on the righthand A-pillar. The control module also incorporates independent back-up battery power supplies to ensure air bag deployment in the event of loss of main battery power in a crash.

The two primary crash sensors are hard wired to the air bags and installed forward of the radiator, inboard of the headlamps. An electronic extension of the primary sensor (dwell enhancement) is incorporated in the control module and maintains deployment circuity in the event of a loss of primary sensor signals. A disarm feature is also incorporated that isolates deployment power from the air bag system until a primary sensor closes. The air bag system will only be activated when the ignition switch is in II or III position and the air bags will only deploy if at least one primary sensor and safing sensor are made.

The SRS system control module continuously monitors all systems components and wiring connections for faults. If a fault occurs in the readiness indication line, a code written into the non-volatile memory of the control module is transmitted to the system cluster to displace a continuous LED warning. In the event of a further fault

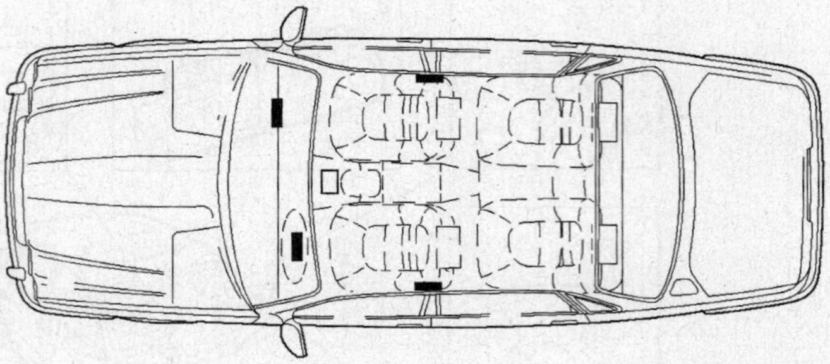

JC8010100055010X

Fig. 4 Component locations (Part 1 of 3, Air Bag Modules). XJR & XJ8

being detected during this condition, an audible tone comprising five sets of five beeps will sound. The readiness indicator line fault must be corrected before fault codes can be determined.

If a fault creates a risk of spurious air bag deployment, the control module will attempt to remove deployment power by rapturing the 10-amp battery fuse via a solid state switch. To aid fault diagnosis, the control module will not rupture the fuse again until the fault is rectified and cleared. The 10-amp battery fuse must not be renewed until the system has been disarmed. The fuse (F4) is located in the fuse-box at the driver's end of the instrument panel.

Each front seat belt has an electrically fired pyrotechnic operated pretensioning retractor until installed at the base of the B-pillar. In the event of severe frontal impact, these provide additional occupant protection by removing any excess slack from the seat belts.

Seat belt pretensioning activated when a front impact of sufficient force occurs within 30° of the vehicle centerline. Under such an impact, an impact sensing/control module installed on the transmission tunnel generates a 12-volt firing signal to each pretensioner. Receipt of this signal directly triggers a pyrotechnic igniter unit. The resulting detonation propels a train of steel balls through a tube to a ball trap where they are directed onto an impeller mounted on the reel spindlier. Rapid rotation of the impeller simultaneously rotates the seat belt reel, preventing forward movement of the occupant. When a pretensioner has been activated, the seat belt will lock and cannot be retracted or pulled from the reel.

The pretensioner reel assemblies provide standard Emergency Locking Retraction (ELR) under rapid vehicle deceleration and incorporate Automatic Locking Retraction (ALR), enabling child seats to be fully restrained by the seat belt.

PRECAUTIONS

AIR BAG SYSTEM

1. To avoid unwanted deployment and possible personal injury, always disarm SRS prior to performing service procedures. Refer to "Air Bag System Disarming & Arming."
2. When handling an air bag module, always carry with pad side and pin side of module toward either side of person, **Fig. 1.**
3. When storing an air bag module, always place in secure, clean dry location with pad side facing upward, **Fig. 2.**
4. Keep air bag assembly free of oil and grease.
5. Do not expose air bag assembly to temperatures above 200° F.
6. Do not use SRS components from another vehicle. Always install new components.
7. Inspect all components prior to installation. Do not install any that appear to have been improperly handled or stored or show any signs of damage.
8. When performing service procedures, do not expose SRS components to heat guns, welding or spray guns.
9. Do not paint air bag to correct cosmetic flaws. It must be replaced.
10. When handling deployed air bag assembly, suitable face shield and rubber gloves should be worn. Vehicle interior and HVAC ducts should be vacuumed. If sinus or throat irritation is encountered during air bag removal, exit vehicle and breathe fresh air. If skin irritation is encountered, flush affected area with cool water. If any type of irritation continues, consult physician. Wash hands and rinse thoroughly with water after handling deployed air bag assembly.
11. A deployed air bag should be removed as outlined under "Component Service." After unit has been removed, it should be placed in heavy duty plastic bag, sealed securely, then placed with automotive scrap.
12. If an undeployed air bag is to be discarded, contact Jaguar for disposal procedures.

BATTERY GROUND CABLE

Prior to service, disconnect battery ground cable and isolate as required.

COMPONENT LOCATIONS

Refer to **Figs. 3 through 5** for component locations.

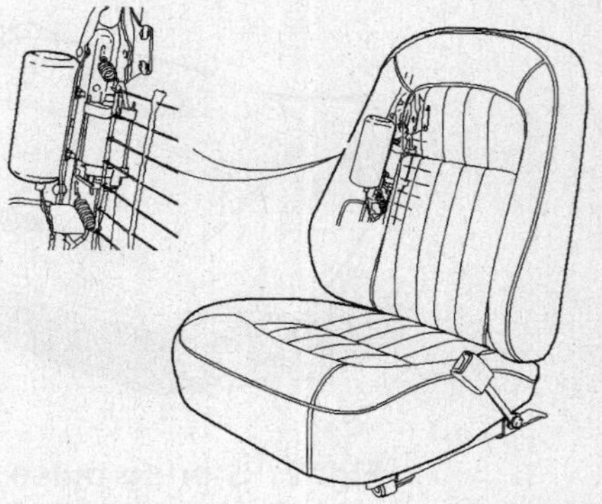

JC8010100055020X

Fig. 4 Component locations (Part 2 of 3, Side Impact Air Bag Module). XJR & XJ8

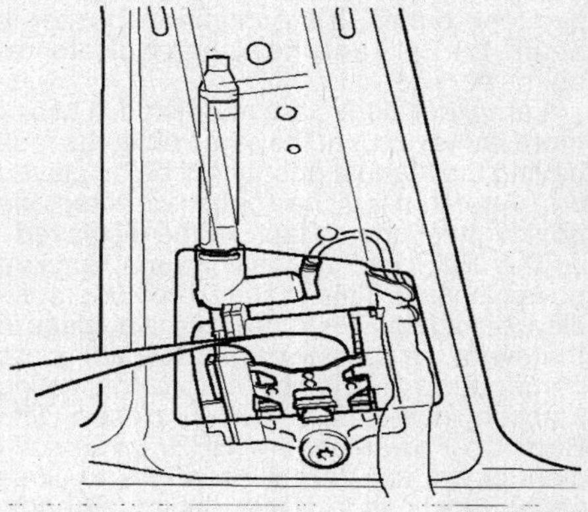

JC8010100055030X

Fig. 4 Component locations (Part 3 of 3, Pyrotechnic Seat Belt Pretensioner). XJR & XJ8

DIAGNOSIS & TESTING

Refer to MOTOR's "Air Bag Manual" for diagnosis and testing.

COLLISION INSPECTION

On vehicles which have experienced an SRS deployment, certain components must be replaced. To determine which components require replacement, refer to the "General Information" section located at the front of this manual.

All system components including the steering wheel, steering column, instrument panel and knee bolsters should be inspected for dents, cracks, exposure to excessive heat and other damage and replaced as required. When repairing the vehicle, the SRS must be disarmed as outlined under "Air Bag System Disarming & Arming."

COMPONENT SERVICE

AIR BAG MODULE, REPLACE

DRIVER'S

1. Ensure steering wheel is aligned

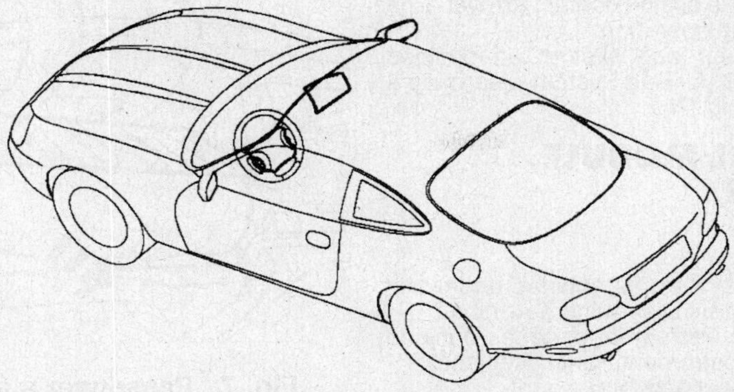

JC8010100056010X

Fig. 5 Component locations (Part 1 of 3, Air Bag Modules). XKR & XK8

straight-ahead and at lowest tilt position.
2. Disarm system as outlined under "Air Bag System Disarming & Arming."
3. Turn steering wheel 90° to left and remove air bag module mounting bolt.
4. Turn steering wheel 180° to right and remove air bag module mounting bolt.
5. Remove module and disconnect electrical connector, **Fig. 6.**
6. Reverse procedure to install, noting the following:
   a. Tighten mounting bolts to specifications in two stages.
   b. Arm system as outlined under "Air Bag System Disarming & Arming."

PASSENGER'S

S Type

1. Disarm air bag system as outlined under "Air Bag System Disarming & Arming."
2. Remove instrument panel as outlined under "Instrument Panel, Replace."
3. Remove passenger side floor air duct.
4. Disconnect passenger's air bag module electrical connector.
5. Remove mounting bolts and passenger's air bag module. **Do not disassemble module or any of its components.**
6. Reverse procedure to install, noting the following:
   a. Ensure wiring and electrical connectors are properly routed to avoid pinching.
   b. Tighten mounting bolts, nuts and screws to specifications.
   c. Arm system as outlined under "Air Bag System Disarming & Arming."

XJR & XJ8

1. Disarm system as outlined under "Air Bag System Disarming & Arming."
2. Open glove compartment, then loosen and remove four top mounting screws.
3. Loosen and remove two glove compartment lower outer mounting screws.
4. Remove glove compartment and disconnect two lamp electrical connectors.
5. Remove mounting clips and position air bag module deployment door aside. Discard clips.
6. Remove air bag module and tether bracket mounting nuts and washers. Discard nuts and washers.
7. Disconnect electrical connector and remove air bag module, **Fig. 7.**
8. Remove mounting bolts and air bag tether bracket. Discard mounting bolts.
9. Reverse procedure to install, noting the following:
   a. Install new mounting nuts and washers. Tighten to specifications.
   b. Arm air bag system as outlined under "Air Bag System Disarming & Arming."

XKR & XK8

1. Disarm system as outlined under "Air Bag System Disarming & Arming."
2. Open glove compartment and remove mounting screws. **Do not disturb two inner screws. These are for compartment alignment, not for retention.**
3. Disconnect footwell and glove compartment lamp connectors.
4. Remove glove compartment.
5. Remove two air bag module mounting bolts. Discard bolts.
6. Remove deployment door bracket mounting bolts and partially withdraw bracket.
7. Disconnect air bag module electrical connector.
8. Remove two lower tether bracket mounting bolts.
9. Remove air bag module, **Fig. 7.**
10. Remove mounting bolts and air bag tether bracket. Discard mounting bolts.
11. Reverse procedure to install, noting the following:
    a. Install new mounting bolts. Tighten to specifications.
    b. Align glove compartment and door to instrument panel before final tightening begins.
    c. Arm air bag system as outlined under "Air Bag System Disarming & Arming."

SIDE IMPACT

S Type

1. Disarm air bag system as outlined under "Air Bag System Disarming & Arming."
2. Remove front seat backing panel.

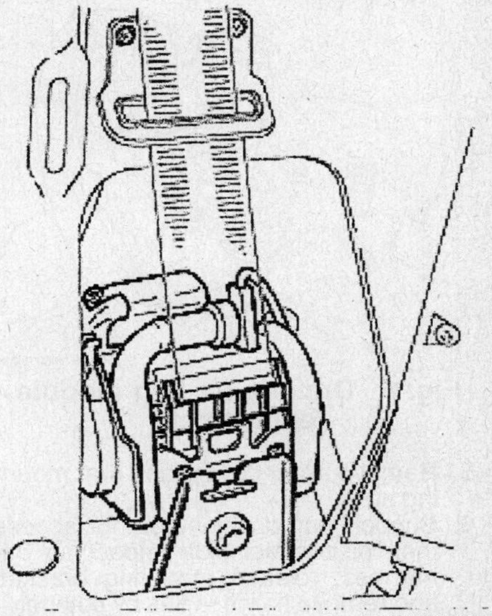

JC8010100056020X

Fig. 5 Component locations (Part 2 of 3, Pyrotechnic Seat Belt Pretensioner). XKR & XK8

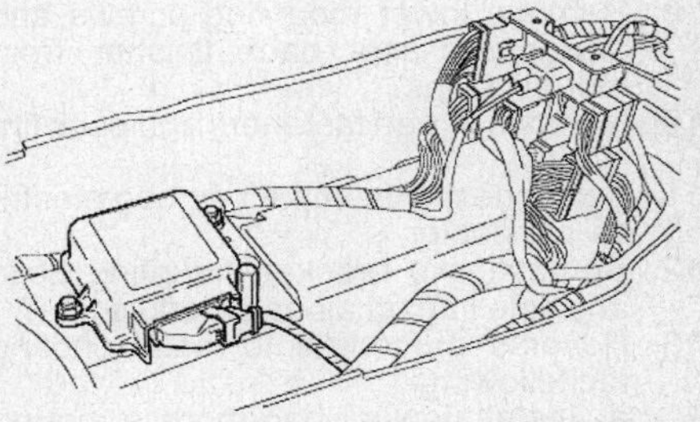

JC8010100056030X

Fig. 5 Component locations (Part 3 of 3, Impact Sensing/ Control Module). XKR & XK8

3. Remove clips and seat covering.
4. Disconnect side impact air bag module electrical connector.
5. Remove mounting screws and side impact air bag module from material pocket.
6. Reverse procedure to install, noting the following:
   a. Ensure wiring and electrical connectors are properly routed to avoid pinching.
   b. Tighten mounting bolts, nuts and screws to specifications.
   c. Arm system as outlined under "Air Bag System Disarming & Arming."

XJR & XJ8

Replace the complete seat assembly if the side impact air bag has deployed because of a collision. However, the side impact air bag can be replaced by itself if only a DTC or fault has occurred.

1. Disarm system as outlined under "Air Bag System Disarming & Arming."
2. Move seat to full rearward position and remove front mounting bolts.
3. Move steering wheel to full forward position.
4. Ensure squab is fully upright and move seat to full forward position.

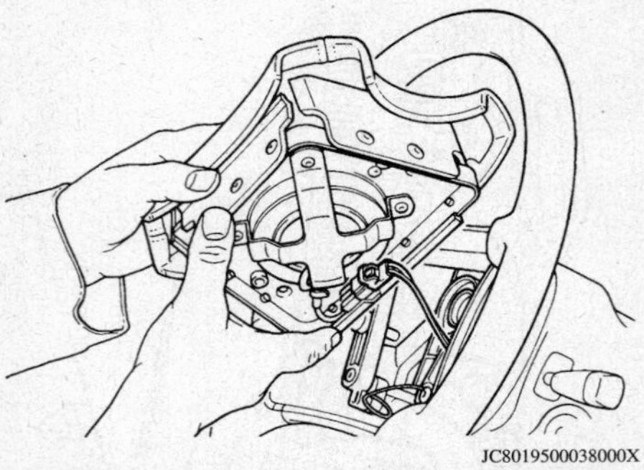

Fig. 6 Driver's air bag module replacement

5. Remove slider covers and rear mounting bolts.
6. Support and position seat for access, then disconnect side impact air bag harness, release mounting brackets and remove harness ties by cutting.
7. Loosen mounting bolt and remove seat belt anchor. Bolt remains with anchor.
8. Remove seat. **Do not damage side impact air bag.**
9. Remove lower mounting screws and disconnect seat back finisher from mounting lips.
10. Remove fir tree fasteners and back finisher.
11. Disconnect side impact air bag electrical connector.
12. Remove two bracket mounting bolts and side impact air bag module.
13. Reverse procedure to install, noting the following:
    a. Install new air bag module mounting bolts, nuts and washers. Tighten to specifications.
    b. Install new hog rings using suitable hog ring pliers.
    c. Arm air bag system as outlined under "Air Bag System Disarming & Arming."

SLIDING CONTACT, REPLACE

S TYPE

1. Disarm air bag system as outlined under "Air Bag System Disarming & Arming."
2. Remove mounting screws, disconnect clip and remove driver side lower instrument panel.
3. Remove driver's air bag module as outlined under "Air Bag Module, Replace."
4. Remove steering wheel as described under "Instrument Panel, Replace."
5. Remove steering column lower shroud.
6. Disconnect steering column adjustment switch electrical connector.
7. Record markings and orientation for installation, then remove mounting screws and sliding contact.
8. Reverse procedure to install, noting the following:
    a. Ensure markings and orientation are properly aligned.
    b. Ensure sliding contact arrows align during operation.
    c. Arm air bag system as outlined under "Air Bag System Disarming & Arming."

CONTROL MODULE, REPLACE

S TYPE

1. Disarm system as outlined under "Air Bag System Disarming & Arming."
2. Remove instrument panel as outlined under "Instrument Panel, Replace."
3. Disconnect park brake boot.
4. Disconnect center console upper section.
5. Disconnect cigarette lighter electrical connector.
6. Remove center console upper section.
7. Disconnect transmission mode, traction control and cellular phone electrical connectors, as required.
8. Disconnect center console.
9. Remove center console lower front mounting screws and rear compartment.
10. Disconnect and remove lower center console.
11. Disconnect control module electrical connectors.
12. Remove mounting bolts and control module.
13. Reverse procedure to install, noting the following:
    a. Ensure electrical connectors and wiring are properly routed to avoid pinching.
    b. Tighten mounting bolts, nuts and screws to specifications.
    c. Arm system as outlined under "Air Bag System Disarming & Arming."

XJR & XJ8

1. Disarm air bag system as outlined under "Air Bag System Disarming & Arming."
2. Apply suitable masking tape to sides of J-gate surround trim.
3. Remove surround trim by prying with suitable screwdriver in slot in front of trim.
4. Apply parking brake and turn ignition to II position
5. Depress brake pedal, move transmission gear selector lever to N position and turn ignition key to O position.
6. Disconnect battery ground connection.
7. Remove two center console veneer panel mounting nuts and screws.
8. Position panel aside, then disconnect Sport mode and cruise control On/Off switch connectors.
9. Remove panel with switches. Remove and discard plate bushes.
10. Remove veneer panel and disconnect locating tongue from upper console slot.
11. Disconnect electrical connectors and antenna lead-in, then remove radio.
12. Disconnect control module electrical connector.

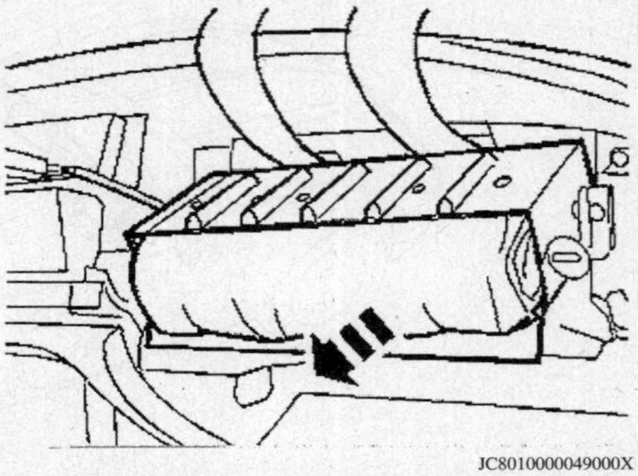

Fig. 7 Passenger's air bag module replacement. XJR, XJ8, XKR & XK8

13. Remove mounting bolts and control module.
14. Reverse procedure to install, noting the following:
    a. Ensure electrical connectors and wiring are properly routed to avoid pinching.
    b. Ensure markings and orientation are properly aligned.
    c. Tighten control module mounting bolts to specifications.
    d. Arm air bag system as outlined under "Air Bag System Disarming & Arming."

XKR & XK8

1. Disarm air bag system as outlined under "Air Bag System Disarming & Arming."
2. Move power passenger's seat fully rearward and turn ignition switch to Off position.
3. Disconnect body processor module harness.
4. Remove mounting nuts and body processor module.
5. Remove footwell air ducts.
6. Remove footwell to air conditioning duct mounting screw and disconnect electrical connector.
7. Remove footwell lamp and bracket.
8. Disconnect instrument panel harness fasteners from righthand instrument panel end panel and position aside.
9. Disconnect air bag control module harness connectors, then the instrument panel harness to passenger compartment harness connectors and position for access, **Fig. 8.**
10. Remove bracket, instrument panel and control module upper mounting bolts.
11. Remove control module.
12. Reverse procedure to install, noting the following:
    a. Install module mounting bracket outer bolts. Do not tighten yet.
    b. Install module and instrument panel mounting bolt. Do not tighten yet.
    c. Tighten control module upper mounting bolt first, then remaining mounting bolts.
    d. Arm system as outlined under "Air Bag System Disarming & Arming."

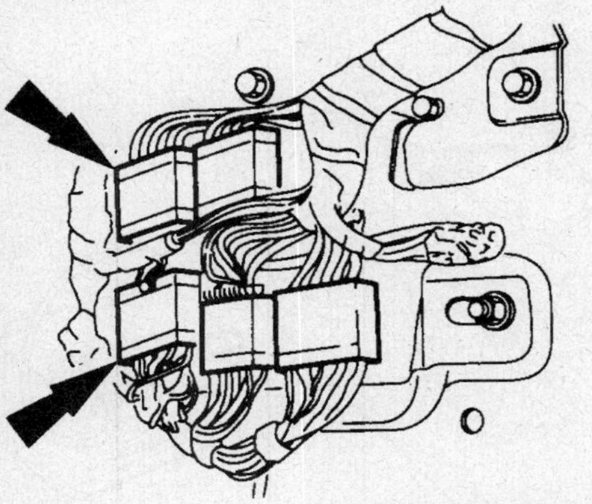

JC8019700044000X

Fig. 8 Control module replacement. XKR & XK8

SENSOR, REPLACE

PRIMARY

XKR & XK8

1. Disarm system as outlined under "Air Bag System Disarming & Arming."
2. Open hood.
3. Remove sensor harness from mounting bracket and disconnect connector.
4. Remove mounting bolts and sensor, **Fig. 9.**
5. Reverse procedure to install.

SIDE IMPACT

S Type

1. Disarm system as outlined under "Air Bag System Disarming & Arming."
2. Disconnect door opening weather-strip.
3. Remove seat belt anchoring bolt trim cover and seat belt height adjuster.
4. Remove front and rear passenger compartment scuff plates, then the lower and upper B-pillar trim panels.
5. Move seat to full rearward position, then remove front bolts and washers.
6. Move seat to full forward position, then remove rear mounting bolts and washers.
7. Remove seat mounting feet trim covers.
8. Remove rear mounting nuts, tilt seat forward and disconnect electrical connectors.
9. Remove seat outer trim panel.
10. Disconnect seat belt lower anchor and remove seat. **Do not snag seat or damage track.**
11. Disconnect electrical connector, then remove mounting bolts and side impact sensor.
12. Remove mounting bolts and side impact sensor.
13. Reverse procedure to install, noting the following:
    a. Tighten mounting bolts, nuts and screws to specifications.
    b. Arm air bag system as outlined under "Air Bag System Disarming & Arming."

XJR & XJ8

1. Disarm system as outlined under "Air Bag System Disarming & Arming."
2. Remove seat belt upper anchor and belt guide.
3. Remove B-pillar interior trim panel.
4. Remove side impact sensor mounting nuts.
5. Lower sensor and disconnect electrical connector.
6. Remove side impact sensor.
7. Reverse procedure to install, noting the following:
    a. Tighten mounting nuts to specifications.
    b. Arm air bag system as outlined under "Air Bag System Disarming & Arming."

SINGLE POINT

XJR & XJ8

1. Disarm air bag system as outlined under "Air Bag System Disarming & Arming."
2. Remove J-gate surround, center console veneer panel and radio as described in under "Electrical" section.
3. Disconnect electrical connector, then remove mounting bolts and Single Point Sensor (SPS).
4. Reverse procedure to install, noting the following:
    a. Tighten mounting bolts to specifications.
    b. Arm air bag system as outlined under "Air Bag System Disarming & Arming."

SEAT BELT & PRETENSIONER, REPLACE

XJR & XJ8

1. Position seat in full forward position and turn ignition Off.
2. Disarm system as outlined under "Air Bag System Disarming & Arming."
3. Remove front seat belt upper anchor and trim. Discard felt washer from slider stud.
4. Remove front seat belt escutcheon.
5. Loosen seat belt lower anchor bolt, washers and spacer.
6. Remove B-pillar casing.
7. Route seat belt anchor plate through B-pillar casing, then remove casing.
8. Loosen and remove two seat belt guide to B-pillar mounting bolts and position guide along seat belt.
9. Remove mounting bolt, seat belt and pretensioner.
10. Reverse procedure to install, noting the following:
    a. Install felt washer onto height adjuster stud with paper backing facing outward.
    b. Tighten mounting bolts, nuts and screws to specifications.
    c. Arm air bag system as outlined under "Air Bag System Disarming & Arming."

XKR & XK8

1. Disarm air bag system as outlined under "Air Bag System Disarming & Arming."
2. Remove rear seat cushion and backrest.

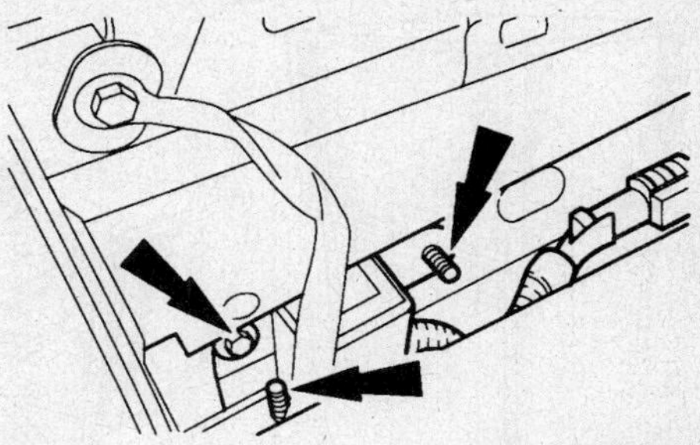

JC8019700043000X

Fig. 9 Primary impact sensor replacement. XKR & XK8

3. Remove front seat belt upper anchor plate and trim.
4. Remove front seat belt escutcheon.
5. **On coupe models,** remove escutcheon from rear quarter casing.
6. **On all models,** disconnect front seat belt lower anchor bar.
7. **On coupe models,** release rear quarter casing fasteners and position casing for access.
8. **On all models,** route seat belt anchor plates through rear quarter casing apertures and remove casing.
9. Remove seat belt guide to B-pillar mounting bolts and position belt guide along belt.
10. Remove pretensioner arming bolt located directly below upper mounting bolt.
11. Remove two pretensioner to B-pillar mounting bolts.
12. Remove seat belt and pretensioner.
13. Reverse procedure to install, noting the following:
    a. Ensure pretensioner is properly aligned with its locating holes.
    b. Tighten mounting bolts, nuts and screws to specifications.
    c. Arm air bag system as outlined under "Air Bag System Disarming & Arming."

AIR BAG MODULE DISPOSAL

When handling deployed air bags, always wear rubber gloves, chemical resistance goggles and an approved mask. After handling, immediately wash hands and exposed skin with mild soap and water.

When scrapping a vehicle, SRS components must be deployed beforehand.

AIR BAG DEPLOYMENT

Outside Vehicle

1. Disarm system as outlined under "Air Bag System Air Bag System Disarming & Arming."
2. Assemble deployment cage outdoors away from people, animals and objects, **Fig. 10.**
3. Secure SRS component in cage.
4. Clamp mesh guard in place.
5. Connect 33 foot link harness to SRS component.
6. If cage is not available, SRS component can be wedged under stack of four used tires. Secure tires together with suitable rope or wire.

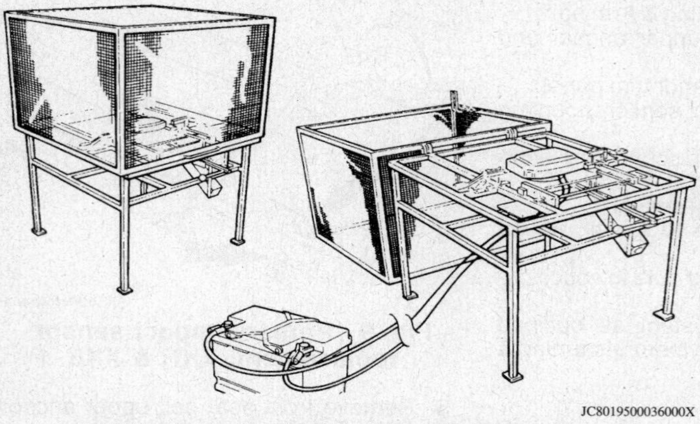

Fig. 10 In-cage air bag deployment

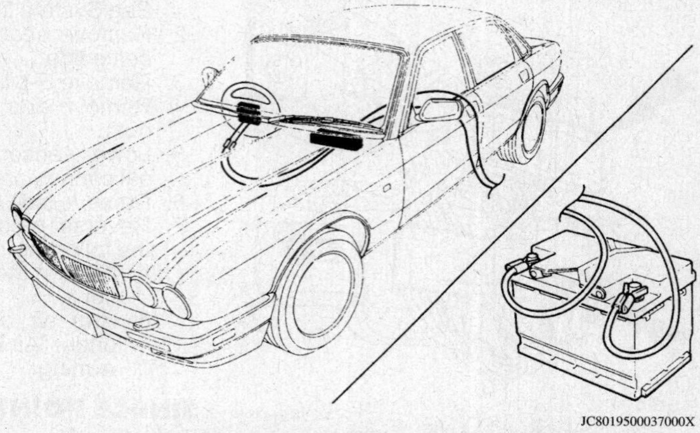

Fig. 11 In-vehicle air bag module deployment

7. Ensure no people, animals or objects are within 33 feet of cage or tire stack.
8. Move back 33 feet and connect link harness crocodile clips to Jaguar deployment tool No. 418-S135, or equivalent.
9. Connect deployment tool to fully charged 12-volt battery.
10. Depress both deployment tool switches. SRS component should deploy immediately.
11. Allow SRS component 30 minutes to cool before handling.
12. Open guard and remove SRS component.
13. Seal SRS component in plastic bag.
14. If there are any problems or if SRS component fails to deploy, contact Jaguar for further information.

In-Vehicle

1. Disarm system as outlined under "Air Bag System Disarming & Arming."
2. Remove driver's and passenger's lower instrument panels and knee bolster.
3. Disconnect air bag connectors from spiral cassette.
4. Cut wires leading from SRS component as required.
5. Pass 33 foot link harness through window opening, **Fig. 11.**
6. Connect harness using insulation displacement connector and two crocodile clips.
7. Close vehicle doors, leaving window open.
8. Ensure no people, animals or objects are within 33 feet of vehicle.
9. Move back 33 feet and connect link harness crocodile clips to Jaguar deployment tool No. 418-S135, or equivalent.
10. Connect deployment tool to fully charged 12-volt battery.
11. Depress both deployment tool switches. SRS component should deploy immediately.
12. Allow SRS component 30 minutes to cool before handling.
13. If there are any problems or if SRS component fails to deploy, contact Jaguar for further information.

TECHNICAL SERVICE BULLETINS

SRS MIL w/DTCS B1944 OR B1945

1998 XK8

On some of these models built between VINs 018108–018384, the air bag Malfunction Indicator Lamp (MIL) may remain lit with Diagnostic Trouble Code (DTC) B1944 or P1945 stored in SRS control module.

This condition may be caused by poor grounding of the impact sensors. The vehicle may have been assembled using plain bolts instead of the correct paint-cutting bolts.

To correct this condition, proceed as follows:

1. Remove sensor.
2. Clean two threads on sensor and one thread on body using 6 x 1 mm tap. Clean away any pain chips.
3. Install sensor and repeat procedure on other sensor.
4. Clear stored DTCs.

TIGHTENING SPECIFICATIONS

Year	Component	Torque/ Ft. Lbs.
S TYPE		
2000–01	Air Bag Control Module	106①
	Air Bag Module, Driver's	106①
	Air Bag Module, Passenger's	80①
	Air Bag Module, Side Impact	62①
	Height Adjuster	30
	Horn Contact	44①
	Instrument Panel	15
	Retractor	30
	Seat Belt Buckle, Front	30
	Seat Belt Buckle, Rear	35
	Seat Belt, Rear Outboard	30
	Seat, Bolts	29
	Seat, Nuts	35
	Seat Belt To Track, Front	30
	Side Impact Sensor	106①
	Steering Column	13
	Steering Column Pinch Bolt	22
	Steering Wheel Bolt	26
XJR & XJ8		
1998–2001	Air Bag Module, Driver's	35–44①
	Air Bag Module, Passenger's	44–62①
	Air Bag Module, Passenger's Door	35①
	Air Bag Module, Side	80–97①
	Front Seat Belt	22–29
	Front Seat Belt Guide To B/C-Pillar	71–88①
	Front Seat Belt Height Adjuster To B/C-Pillar	18–19
	Rear Seat Belt	22–29
	Seat Belt Upper Anchor To Height Adjuster	22–29
	Single Point Impact Sensor	44–62①
	Single Point Sensor	44–62①
	Steering Wheel	24–33
XKR & XK8		
1998–2001	Air Bag Module, Passenger	62–88①
	Air Bag Module, Passenger's Door	44–62①
	Pillar Loop (Coupe)	22–29
	Pretensioner, Lower	25–34
	Pretensioner, Upper	62–88①
	Pretensioner Arming Pin	62–88①
	Pretensioner Mounting, Top	62–88①
	Seat Belt Guide	62–88①
	Seat Belt Height Adjuster, Front	13–17
	Seat Belt Inertia Reel, Front	27–34
	Seat Belt Inertia Reel, Rear	25–34
	Seat Belt Slider Bar, Front	25–34
	Seat Buckle, Front	25–34
	Seat Buckle, Rear	44–59
	Steering Wheel	24–33
	Webbing Guide Bracket	62–88①

① — Inch lbs.

Dash Panel Service

NOTE: On Air Bag Equipped Models, Refer To "Air Bag System Precautions" Located In The Front Of This Manual For System Disarming & Arming Procedures.

INDEX

	Page No.
Dash Panel, Replace	3-46
S Type	3-46
XJR, XJ8, XKR & XK8	3-46
Floor Console, Replace	3-46
S Type	3-46
XJR, XJ8, XKR & XK8	3-46
Precautions	3-46
Air Bag Systems	3-46
Battery Ground Cable	3-46

PRECAUTIONS

AIR BAG SYSTEMS

Refer to "Air Bag System Precautions" in the front of this manual for system disarming and arming procedures.

BATTERY GROUND CABLE

Prior to service, disconnect battery ground cable and isolate as required.

FLOOR CONSOLE

REPLACE

S TYPE

1. Disconnect parking brake boot and console upper section.
2. Disconnect cigarette lighter electrical connector.
3. Remove console upper section and disconnect electrical connectors.
4. Disconnect console and remove lower console front screws.
5. Remove console rear compartment and disconnect lower console.
6. Remove lower console by pulling rearward, **Fig. 1.**
7. Reverse procedure to install.

XJR, XJ8, XKR & XK8

1. Position gear selector and passenger seat for access.
2. Turn ignition switch to II position.
3. Apply brake and move gear selector to D position.
4. Adjust passenger seat to fully forward position and tilt squab forward.
5. Turn ignition to 0 position.
6. Remove J-gate surround from selector.
7. Remove center console veneer panel mounting screws and mounting plates.
8. Position veneer panel for access and disconnect panel switch electrical connectors.
9. Remove console end trim cover and remove two rear securing bolts.
10. Remove forward mounting bolts and disconnect all electrical connections.
11. Remove console.
12. Reverse procedure to install.

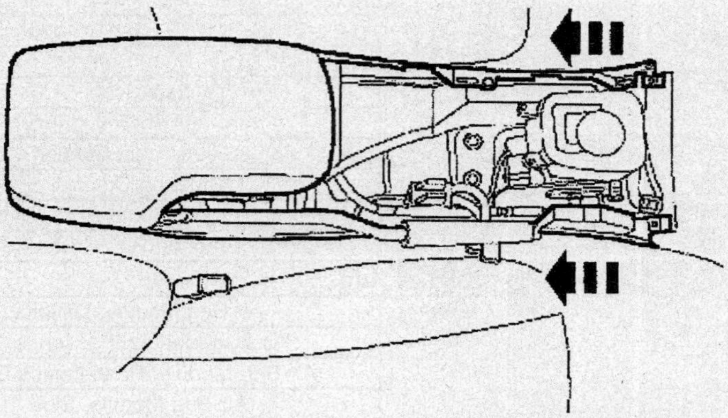

Fig. 1 Lower console removal. S Type

DASH PANEL

REPLACE

S TYPE

1. Remove steering wheel as outlined in "Electrical" section.
2. Remove driver's side lower panel and disconnect headlamp adjustment switch.
3. Remove driver's side air duct and hood latch release handle supporting plate.
4. Disconnect steering column electrical connectors.
5. Remove steering column pinch bolt and upper nuts.
6. Remove steering column.
7. Remove mounting screws and disconnect center control panel, **Fig. 2.**
8. Disconnect heated seat switch, climate control unit, satellite navigation screen and audio system electrical connectors.
9. Remove center control panel.
10. Remove instrument panel end panel and plug.
11. Remove driver's side mounting bolts and disconnect instrument panel.
12. Disconnect instrument panel electrical connectors and antenna cable.
13. Disconnect floor covering from transmission tunnel.
14. Remove instrument panel to transmission tunnel mounting bolts.
15. Disconnect air conditioning electrical connector.
16. Remove glove compartment trim panel and disconnect electrical connectors, **Fig. 3.**
17. Remove passenger's side end panel and disconnect lower windscreen trim panel electrical connector.
18. Remove lower windscreen trim panel.
19. Remove remaining mounting bolts and instrument panel.
20. Reverse procedure to install.

XJR, XJ8, XKR & XK8

1. Open glove compartment lid and remove instrument panel mounting screws.
2. Remove glove compartment and crossmember to lower instrument panel outer mounting screws.
3. Position glove compartment for access, then disconnect footwell and glove compartment lamp electrical connectors.
4. Remove glove compartment assembly complete with crossmember.
5. Remove glove compartment to crossmember outer mounting screws and glove compartment.
6. Remove lower dash panel to instrument panel crossmember mounting screws.

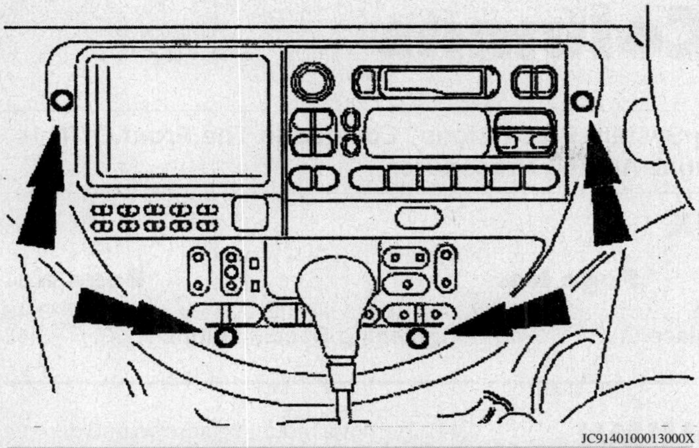

Fig. 2 Center control panel. S Type

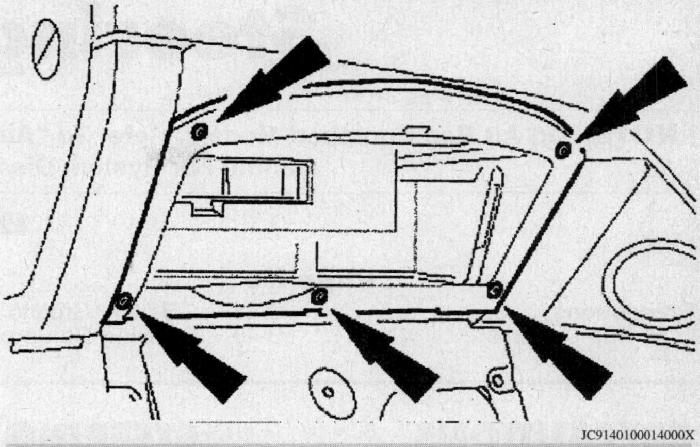

Fig. 3 Glove compartment trim panel. S Type

7. Remove lower dash panel upper mounting screws and position lower dash panel rearward for access.
8. Disconnect air conditioning aspirator and valet switch harnesses electrical connectors.
9. Remove mounting screws and stowage compartment lid.
10. Release tangs and remove valet switch.
11. Remove mounting nuts and air conditioning aspirator mounting bracket.
12. Release tangs and remove aspirator vent.
13. Remove lower dash panel.
14. Remove floor console as outlined under "Floor Console."
15. Remove steering wheel as outlined in "Electrical" section.
16. Remove steering column upper and lower covers.
17. Remove front seats.
18. Disconnect J-gate and gearshift interlock solenoid harness electrical connectors.
19. Remove mounting nuts and position J-gate to transmission tunnel assembly for access.
20. Remove mounting bolts and instrument panel to transmission tunnel side brackets.
21. Remove instrument panel central bracket to transmission tunnel mounting bolts.
22. Remove lefthand A pillar lower trim pad.
23. Disconnect instrument panel harness electrical connectors at lefthand A-pillar.
24. Remove A pillar post ground cable mounting nut and cable eyelets from stud.
25. Remove mounting nuts and position hood release lever aside.
26. Remove instrument panel to lefthand A pillar mounting bolts.
27. Disconnect harness rear electrical connector.
28. Disconnect front electrical connector and position aside.
29. Disconnect steering column righthand electrical connectors.
30. Remove mounting screws and footwell lamp mounting bracket.
31. Remove steering column upper mounting bracket mounting nuts.
32. Move steering column down from mounting bracket and position for access.
33. Remove righthand A pillar inner trim pad.
34. Remove righthand A pillar mounting nut and disconnect ground cable.
35. Disconnect righthand A pillar electrical connectors.
36. Disconnect fuse box power cable and remove instrument panel righthand mounting bolts.
37. Remove instrument panel to righthand A pillar mounting bolts.
38. Remove instrument panel speakers and central trim cover, then disconnect electrical connectors.
39. Remove solar sensor from instrument panel by prying upward, then disconnecting electrical connector.
40. Remove upper instrument panel to firewall mounting bolts.
41. Disconnect left and righthand harnesses at center console rear mounting bracket.
42. Disconnect gear selector cable stud and strap, then position J-gate for instrument panel removal.
43. Fold tunnel lefthand side carpet back for access and cut through strap ICE cable attaching harness.
44. Disconnect lefthand tunnel side harness fasteners.
45. Fold tunnel righthand side carpet back for access, then disconnect tunnel side harness fasteners.
46. Remove instrument panel to firewall mounting bracket mounting bolts.
47. Carefully lift inscribed tread plate finishers using suitable thin one inch wide scraper.
48. Remove mounting screws and tread plate.
49. Remove carpet to tunnel, seat location and toe board fasteners.
50. Lift weather stripping from each door frame and remove carpet clips from door frame.
51. Disconnect hand brake switch harness electrical connector.
52. Release seat harness fasteners.
53. Remove mounting nut and ground cable eyelet from floor stud.
54. Remove instrument panel harness ground cable mounting nuts at each side of tunnel, ground eyelets from studs.
55. Remove harness from each side of tunnel and coil. Strap coils them to ICE console mounting bracket.
56. Remove instrument panel rearward off support dowels, guiding power cable through righthand fuse box.
57. Reverse procedure to install.

Steering Columns

NOTE: On Air Bag Equipped Models, Refer To "Air Bag System Precautions" Located In The Front Of This Manual For System Disarming & Arming Procedures.

INDEX

	Page No.
Precautions	3-48
Air Bag Systems	3-48
Battery Ground Cable	3-48
Steering Column, Replace	3-48
S Type	3-48
Tightening Specifications	3-48

PRECAUTIONS

AIR BAG SYSTEMS

Refer to "Air Bag System Precautions" in the front of this manual for system disarming and arming procedures.

BATTERY GROUND CABLE

Prior to service, disconnect battery ground cable and isolate as required.

STEERING COLUMN

REPLACE

S TYPE

1. Remove steering wheel as outlined in "Electrical" section.
2. Remove mounting screws and disconnect clips, then remove driver's side instrument panel lower panel.
3. Disconnect headlamp adjustment switch.
4. Remove mounting screws and driver's side air duct.
5. Remove hood latch release handle supporting plate mounting screws.
6. Disconnect steering column electrical connectors.
7. Remove steering column pinch bolt.
8. Disconnect steering column mounting nuts and support steering column weight.
9. Remove steering column and disconnect steering lock electrical connector.
10. Reverse removal procedure to install. Tighten mounting bolts and nuts to specifications.

TIGHTENING SPECIFICATIONS

Year	Component	Torque, Ft. Lbs.
S TYPE		
2000–01	Column	13
	Horn Contact Switch	44①
	Pinch Bolt	26
	Steering Wheel	26
XJR & XJ8		
1998–2001	Column Cover	35–44①
	Column To Lower Bracket	12–17
	Column To Universal Joint	16–21
	Column To Upper Bracket	16–21
	Driver's Air Bag	35–44①
	Pinch Bolt	16–21
	Steering Wheel	25–34
	Switchgear	35–44①
	Upper Bracket To Body	16–21
XKR & XK8		
1998–2001	Column Cover	13①
	Column To Lower Bracket	16–21
	Column To Universal Joint	16–21
	Column To Upper Bracket	16–21
	Driver's Air Bag	35–44①
	Pinch Bolt	16–21
	Steering Wheel	25–34
	Switchgear	35–44①
	Universal Joint	16–21
	Upper Bracket To Body	16–21

① — Inch lbs.

Power Steering

NOTE: On Air Bag Equipped Models, Refer To "Air Bag System Precautions" Located In The Front Of This Manual For System Disarming & Arming Procedures.

NOTE: Prior To Performing Any Service Operations Listed In This Section, Consult The "Technical Service Bulletins" Section For Related Information.

INDEX

	Page No.
Description	3-49
Diagnosis & Testing	3-49
Pressure Test	3-49
Power Steering Pressure Specifications	3-49
Power Steering System Service	3-49
Adjustments	3-50
Steering Gear	3-50
Component Service	3-50
Pinion Valve Housing & Seal	3-50
Power Steering System Bleed	3-49
Precautions	3-49
Air Bag Systems	3-49
Battery Ground Cable	3-49
Technical Service Bulletins	3-50
Power Steering Noise	3-50
Tightening Specifications	3-50

POWER STEERING PRESSURE SPECIFICATIONS

Model	Year	Minimum Flow, Gal. per Min.	Minimum Relief Valve Pressure, psi	Maximum Relief Valve Pressure, psi
All	1998–2001	—	1470	1600

PRECAUTIONS

AIR BAG SYSTEMS

Refer to "Air Bag System Precautions" in the front of this manual for system disarming and arming procedures.

BATTERY GROUND CABLE

Prior to service, disconnect battery ground cable and isolate as required.

DESCRIPTION

Oil flow through the control valve is continuous. When the wheels are in the straight-ahead position, low oil pressure is applied to each side of the piston. As the steering wheel is turned, a small torsion bar within the assembly allows a few degrees of rotation before actually turning the pinion. This rotation is used to open and close ports in the control valve. To ensure the torsion bar is twisted, the hydraulic pressure directed to one side of the piston is also increased to a maximum, returning to minimum when the load on the torsion bar from the setting wheel is zero. The increase in pressure being proportional to the twist in the torsion bar.

Hydraulic pressure is provided by a vane-type, non-submerged pump, driven directly from engine auxiliary shaft.

To prevent the hydraulic pressure from exceeding maximum, a flow control valve is connected to the outlet port of the pump.

DIAGNOSIS & TESTING

The complexity of electronics involved with the body processor and the two multiplexed communication networks which are associated with it, preclude the use of workshop general electrical test equipment. Therefore, reference should be made to the Portable Diagnostic Unit (PDU) user guide for detailed instruction on testing the power steering system. The PDU systematically tests and analyses all electrical functions of power steering system. Where a fault is indicated, some basic diagnostic methods may be required to confirm that connections are good and that wiring is not damaged, before replacing component.

Pressure Test

This procedure has been revised by a Technical Service Bulletin.

1. Raise and support vehicle, then inspect entire power assisted steering system for damage, leaks and alignment.
2. Start engine and turn steering lock to lock inspecting connections and joints for leaks.
3. Connect pressure tester tool No. J25323-D using adapter tool No. J28579, or equivalents, in series with PAS fluid circuit. **Fluid must enter gauge end of tester through thicker high pressure hose.**
4. Thread dog leg adapter pipe tool No. J28579, or equivalent, into PAS pump high pressure fitting.
5. Connect other tester hose to PAS high pressure hose previously disconnected from pump.
6. Run engine at idle.
7. Pressure should be 100–150 psi.
8. Hold steering wheel at full lock and read maximum pressure. Pressure should be 1100–1200 psi.
9. If pressure is less than 1470–1600 psi, center steering wheel, close pressure test valve for not more than five seconds and record maximum pump pressure.
10. If maximum pressure is 1470–1600 psi, rack may have excessive internal leak.
11. If maximum pressure is less than 1470 psi, pump may have valve seized in open position, or be worn and inefficient.

POWER STEERING SYSTEM SERVICE

Power Steering System Bleed

1. Ensure reservoir is filled to bottom of filler neck.
2. Wait for any air to escape and top up again.
3. Turn steering lock to lock 2–3 times without engine running.
4. Top up reservoir fluid level.
5. Start engine and immediately top of reservoir as air escapes.
6. With engine idling, turn steering lock to lock 2–3 times.
7. Top up reservoir fluid level.
8. When no further fluid level changes occur, idle engine for an additional 20 minutes to vent any remaining air.
9. Adjust fluid level.
10. Stop engine and allow fluid to settle for at least 30 minutes.
11. Start engine to vent any further air. Adjust fluid level as required.

Component Service

PINION VALVE HOUSING & SEAL

Removal

1. Remove steering rack as outlined in "Front Suspension & Steering" section.
2. Ensure plugs stay in place.
3. Position rack with pinion housing up in vise fitted with suitable jaw protectors.
4. Remove plugs and drain fluid into suitable container.
5. Rotate pinion shaft lock to lock three times to dispel as much fluid as possible, then install plugs.
6. Align centralizing cap as outlined under "Adjustments."
7. Remove protective dirt shield, **Fig. 1.**
8. Disconnect union nuts, then remove oil transfer lines. **Do not distort lines.** Place lines in clean plastic bag.
9. Remove O-rings and plug transfer ports.
10. Mark transducer alignment for installation alignment.
11. Remove mounting screws and transducer. Place transducer in clean plastic bag.
12. Remove O-rings and filter.
13. Mark pinion valve housing for installation alignment.
14. Remove mounting screws and pinion valve housing using a steady upward twisting motion. **Excessive force and rocking may damage rotary valve O-ring seals.**
15. Remove pinion housing to steering rack main body O-ring seal.
16. Cover rotary valve assembly with clean plastic bag.

Installation

1. Install new O-ring seal in steering rack body.
2. Install oil seal protector tool (provided with seal kit) on pinion shaft splines.
3. Grease pinion seal lip with Texando F020, or equivalent.
4. Install pinion valve housing using steady downward twisting motion. **Excessive force and rocking may damage rotary valve O-ring seals.**
5. Remove seal protector tool and tighten mounting screws to specifications.
6. Install new O-ring seals on transfer lines. Lightly grease seals with Texando F020, or equivalent.
7. Remove plugs, install transfer lines and tighten union nuts to specifications.
8. Install new filter in pinion housing transducer port and O-ring seals to transducer. Lightly grease seals with Texando F020, or equivalent.
9. Install transducer to install marks, then tighten new mounting screws to specifications.
10. Smear small amount of Texando F020, or equivalent grease, into pinion valve housing cavity.
11. Install new dirt protection shield. Ensure centralizing index peg is properly located. **Centralizing peg will shear.**
12. Operate steering rack lock to lock, ensuring free movement without tight spots.
13. Centralize steering rack as outlined under "Adjustments."
14. Remove rack from vise and install.

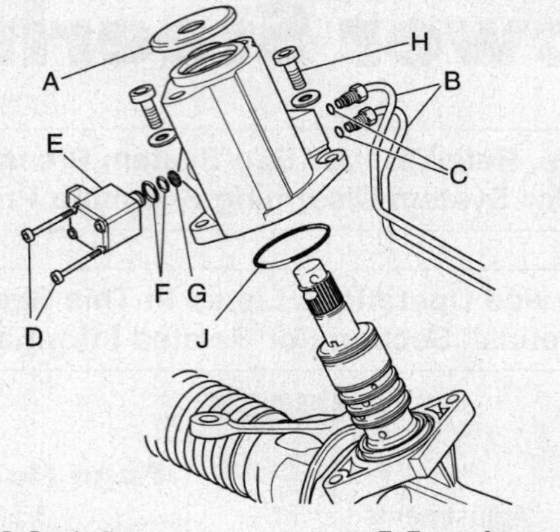

Fig. 1 Pinion valve housing & seal replacement

Adjustments

STEERING GEAR

XJR, XJ8, XKR & XK8

Align marker on centralizing cap with pinion housing locator.

TECHNICAL SERVICE BULLETINS

POWER STEERING NOISE

2000 S Type

On some of these models built between VINs L00600–L06869 there may be hissing or whining noises with the engine running and the steering off-center.

This condition may be caused by the pinion housing check valve.

To correct this condition install valve repair kit (part No. JLM 21299) as follows:

1. Open hood.
2. Raise and support vehicle.
3. Clean pinion housing and fluid lines.
4. Disconnect upper fluid line and allow fluid to drain into suitable container.
5. Remove stepped adapter nut where line union nut was threaded.
6. Remove check valve from pinion housing.
7. Install new check valve that does not have hole through center. **Copper colored spring should not be visible.**
8. Remove and discard stepped adapter nut Teflon seal.
9. Lubricate new seal with suitable clean power steering fluid.
10. Connect O-ring and line to union nut. **Torque** to 18 ft. lbs.
11. Fill power steering reservoir with fresh power steering fluid.
12. Bleed power steering fluid system using suitable vacuum pump and adapter tool No. 416-001-01, or equivalent.

TIGHTENING SPECIFICATIONS

Year	Component	Torque, Ft. Lbs.
1998–2001	Pinion Valve	13
	Rack To Crossmember	30–37
	Transducer	27①
	Transfer Lines	62①
	Tube	13–17
	Upper Fluid Line To Pinion Housing	18

① — Inch Lbs.

Disc Brakes

NOTE: On Air Bag Equipped Models, Refer To "Air Bag System Precautions" Located In The Front Of This Manual For System Disarming & Arming Procedures.

INDEX

	Page No.
Brake Pad Service	3-51
Front, Replace	3-51
Rear, Replace	3-51
Brake System Bleed	3-51
Caliper Service	3-51
Front, Replace	3-51
Rear, Replace	3-51
Disc Brake Specifications	3-52
Precautions	3-51
Air Bag Systems	3-51
Battery Ground Cable	3-51
Relieving Line Pressure	3-51
Rotor, Replace	3-51
Tightening Specifications	3-52

PRECAUTIONS

AIR BAG SYSTEMS

Refer to "Air Bag System Precautions" in the front of this manual for system disarming and arming procedures.

RELIEVING LINE PRESSURE

Discharge hydraulic accumulator by depressing brake pedal until pedal becomes difficult to operate (approximately 20 times).

BATTERY GROUND CABLE

Prior to service, disconnect battery ground cable and isolate as required.

BRAKE SYSTEM BLEED

Refer to "Hydraulic Brake Systems."

BRAKE PAD SERVICE

FRONT, REPLACE

S Type

1. Raise and support vehicle, then remove tire and wheel assembly.
2. Detach ABS sensor from clips.
3. Remove and discard mounting bolt.
4. Pivot caliper upwards.
5. Remove pads.
6. Compress piston and reverse procedure to install.

XJR, XJ8, XKR & XK8

1. Raise and support vehicle, then remove tire and wheel assembly.
2. Remove covers and guide pins, then the caliper.
3. **Do not allow caliper to hang by brakes hoses.**
4. Remove brake pads from carrier.
5. Compress piston and reverse procedure to install.

REAR, REPLACE

S Type

1. Raise and support vehicle, then remove rear tire and wheel assemblies.
2. Disconnect parking brake cable.
3. Remove caliper guide pin retaining bolts and disconnect caliper from anchor plate.
4. Secure caliper and anchor plate assembly aside using suitable wire.
5. Remove pads.
6. Reverse procedure to install. Tighten guide pins to specifications.

XJR, XJ8, XKR & XK8

1. Raise and support vehicle, then remove rear tire and wheel assemblies.
2. Remove retaining spring, covers, guide pins and caliper. **Do not allow caliper to hang by brakes hoses.**
3. Remove brake pads from carrier.
4. Reverse procedure to install. Tighten guide pins to specifications.

CALIPER SERVICE

FRONT, REPLACE

S Type

1. Raise and support vehicle, then remove tire and wheel assembly.
2. Apply suitable brake pedal hold down tool and adjust pedal down approximately 1.6 inches.
3. Install suitable bleeder bottle on nipple and loose. Remove brake pipe.
4. Remove guide pin mounting bolt and caliper.
5. Reverse procedure to install. Tighten mounting bolts to specifications.

XJR, XJ8, XKR & XK8

1. Raise and support vehicle, then remove tire and wheel assembly.
2. Remove caliper retaining spring and feed hose.
3. Plug feed hose and caliper.
4. Remove caps, guide pins and caliper.
5. Remove brake pads.
6. Remove mounting bolts and caliper carrier from vertical link.
7. Remove brake dust from caliper, carrier, wheel, wheel hub and rotor.
8. Reverse procedure to install. Tighten mounting bolts to specifications.

REAR, REPLACE

S Type

1. Raise and support vehicle, then remove tire and wheel assembly.
2. Disconnect tangs and parking brake cable.
3. Apply suitable brake pedal hold down tool and adjust pedal down approximately 1.6 inches.
4. Install suitable bleeder bottle on nipple and loose. Remove brake pipe.
5. Remove guide pin mounting bolt and caliper.
6. Reverse procedure to install. Tighten mounting bolts to specifications.

XJR, XJ8, XKR & XK8

Refer to "Front, Replace" for rear caliper replacement procedure.

ROTOR

REPLACE

1. Remove brake caliper as outlined under "Caliper Service."
2. Remove mounting bolt and brake disc.
3. Reverse procedure to install. Pump brake pedal several times to position brake pads.

DISC BRAKE SPECIFICATIONS

Model	Year	Front Disc Brake						Rear Disc Brake					
		Brake Lining Wear Limit, Inch②	Rotor					Brake Lining Wear Limit, Inch②	Rotor				
			Thickness, Inch			Thickness Variation Parallelism Inch	Lateral Run Out (T.I.R.) Inch		Thickness, Inch			Thickness Variation Parallelism Inch	Lateral Run-Out (T.I.R.) Inch
			Nominal	Min. Refinish	Discard Limit①				Nominal	Min. Refinish	Discard Limit①		
S Type	2000–01	—	1.200	—	1.120	0.0004	0.003	—	0.800	—	0.740	0.0004	0.002
XJR & XJ8	1998–99	0.079	1.102	—	1.024	—	0.004	0.079	1.102	—	1.023	—	0.006
	2000–01	0.295	1.260	—	1.181	—	0.002	0.295	1.102	—	1.023	—	0.001
XKR & XK8	1997–99	0.079	1.102	—	1.024	—	0.004	0.079	1.102	—	1.023	—	0.006
	2000–01	0.295	1.260	—	1.181	—	0.002	0.295	1.102	—	1.023	—	0.001

① — Discard thickness is stamped on rotor.

② — Original equipment type brake lining.

TIGHTENING SPECIFICATIONS

Year	Component	Torque, Ft. Lbs.
S TYPE		
2000–01	Caliper Anchor	76
	Guide Pin	24
	Hose Union	35
XJR, XJ8, XKR & XK8		
1998–2001	Caliper to Vertical Link	88–118
	Guide Pin	18–22

① — Inch lbs.

Hydraulic Brake Systems

NOTE: On Air Bag Equipped Models, Refer To "Air Bag System Precautions" Located In The Front Of This Manual For System Disarming & Arming Procedures.

INDEX

	Page No.
Brake System Bleed	3-53
Component Replacement	3-53
Master Cylinder	3-53
Component Service	3-53
Master Cylinder	3-53

COMPONENT REPLACEMENT

MASTER CYLINDER

1. Remove brake fluid reservoir cap cover and disconnect brake fluid level indicator wires.
2. Remove reservoir cap and filter.
3. Drain fluid from master cylinder using suitable syringe.
4. Disconnect and plug master cylinder brake lines.
5. Operate brake pedal approximately 10 times to ensure there is no vacuum remaining in servo.
6. Remove master cylinder from power booster.
7. Reverse procedure to install, noting the following:
   a. **Torque** master cylinder to servo bolts to 16–20 ft. lbs.
   b. Bleed hydraulic brake system.

COMPONENT SERVICE

MASTER CYLINDER

1. Remove master cylinder as outlined in this section.
2. Carefully pry out master cylinder hydraulic line adapters from sealing grommets.
3. Remove sealing grommets from master cylinder by levering out using suitable screwdriver.
4. Press primary piston stop pin in to relieve secondary piston stop pin pressure.
5. Remove front grommet sealing housing stop pin. Maintain pressure on primary piston and remove circlip.
6. Remove primary/secondary pistons and spring assemblies by tapping master cylinder open flanged end on suitable wooden block. Compressed air may have to be applied to master cylinder front delivery port.
7. Piston and spring assemblies must be kept together. If springs are being mixed, secondary piston spring is slightly thicker and longer than primary piston spring.
8. Remove spring, spring seat and seal from front end of secondary piston (1), **Fig. 1.**
9. Carefully pry seal (2) from rear of secondary piston.

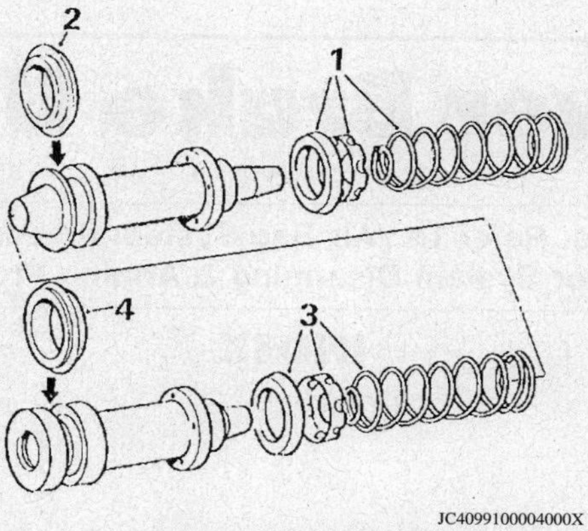

Fig. 1 Spring, spring seat & seal removal

10. Remove spring, spring seat and seal (3) from front end of primary piston.
11. Carefully pry seal (4) from rear of primary piston.
12. Discard all seals, clean components with cleaning fluid and suitable dry lint free cloth.
13. Examine piston and bore of master cylinder for visible signs of scoring, ridges and corrosion.
14. Apply clean brake fluid to all seals.
15. Carefully insert rear seal in secondary piston groove. Ensure seal lip faces toward primary piston.
16. Insert front seal, spring seat and spring to secondary piston front end. Ensure seal lip faces away from primary piston.
17. Carefully insert rear seal in primary piston groove. Ensure seal lip faces forward, away from circlip groove.
18. Insert seal, spring seat and spring to primary piston front end, with seal lip facing forward, away from circlip grooves.
19. Carefully secure master cylinder in suitable vise and lubricate piston seals with new brake fluid.
20. Insert secondary piston assembly to master cylinder until front seal rests centrally in cylinder opening. **Ensure seal is not trapped.**
21. Gently install piston into cylinder bore by slowly rotate and rock assembly, **Fig. 2.**
22. Once front seal has entered cylinder bore, slowly insert piston in one continuous movement.

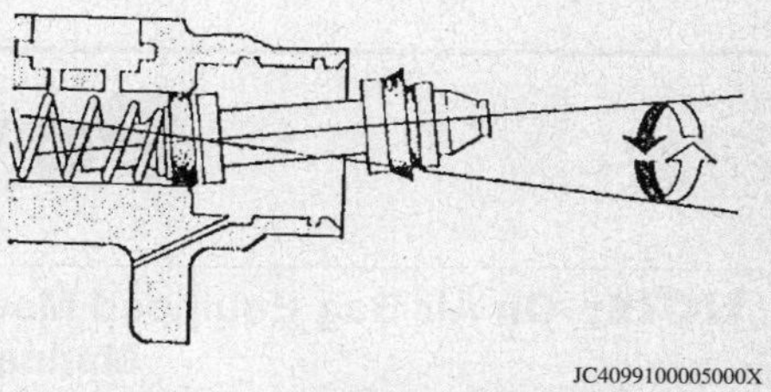

Fig. 2 Piston assembly

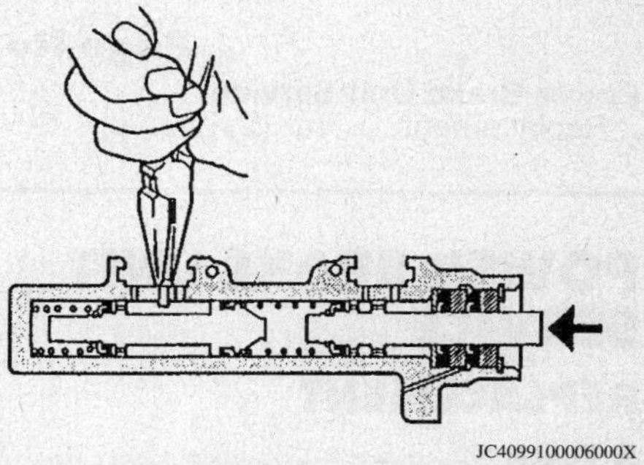

Fig. 3 Secondary piston stop pin assembly

23. Repeat procedure with primary piston assembly.
24. Press primary piston into bore and connect circlip.
25. Fully insert primary piston and install secondary piston stop pin, **Fig. 3.**
26. Insert sealing grommets to master cylinder, **Fig. 4.**
27. Lubricate and press hose adapters into sealing grommets.
28. Remove cylinder plugs, apply grease to operating rod socket and install master cylinder to booster.
29. Install master cylinder mounting nuts.
30. Remove brake lines' plugs and connect to master cylinder.
31. Fill reservoir with new brake fluid and bleed brake system.

BRAKE SYSTEM BLEED

1. Raise and support vehicle.
2. Start bleeding procedure at righthand rear wheel.
3. Remove bleeder screw dust cap, then attach suitable one-way bleed valve and hose to bleed screw.

4. Place hose end in suitable container, then loosen bleed screw ½ turn.
5. Pump brake pedal until clear, air-free fluid flows from bleed screw.
6. Adjust reservoir fluid level as required. Tighten bleed screw.
7. Repeat procedure for lefthand rear wheel.
8. Adjust reservoir fluid level as required.
9. Repeat procedure on front wheels.

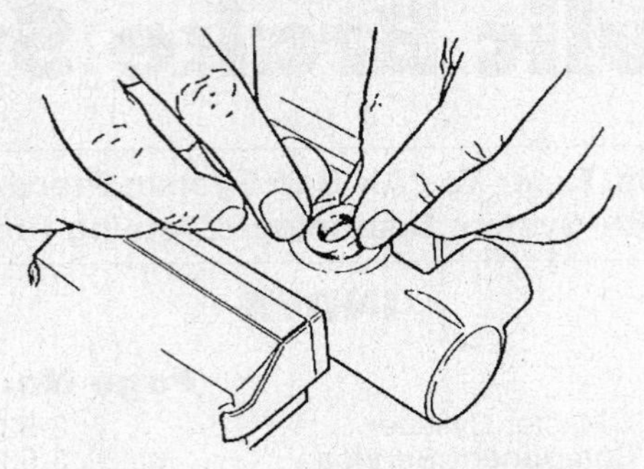

Fig. 4 Sealing grommet installation

10. Apply pressure to brake pedal, then inspect all bleed screws and lines for leakage.

Power Brake Units

NOTE: On Air Bag Equipped Models, Refer To "Air Bag System Precautions" Located In The Front Of This Manual For System Disarming & Arming Procedures.

INDEX

	Page No.
Power Brake Unit Service	3-54
Replacement	3-54

POWER BRAKE UNIT SERVICE

REPLACEMENT

S Type

1. Remove wiper arms.
2. Remove cowl grille.
3. Remove engine compartment brace.
4. Remove master cylinder as outlined in "Hydraulic Brake Systems" section.
5. Disconnect expansion tank.
6. Remove mounting screws and disconnect clips, then remove driver's side instrument panel lower panel.
7. Disconnect fuel flap and luggage compartment release switch electrical connector.
8. Remove mounting screws and driver's side air duct.
9. Disconnect hood latch release handle supporting plate.
10. Remove clip and brake booster retaining pin.
11. Remove mounting nuts and brake booster with non-return valve/vacuum pipe assembly.
12. Reverse procedure to install, noting the following:

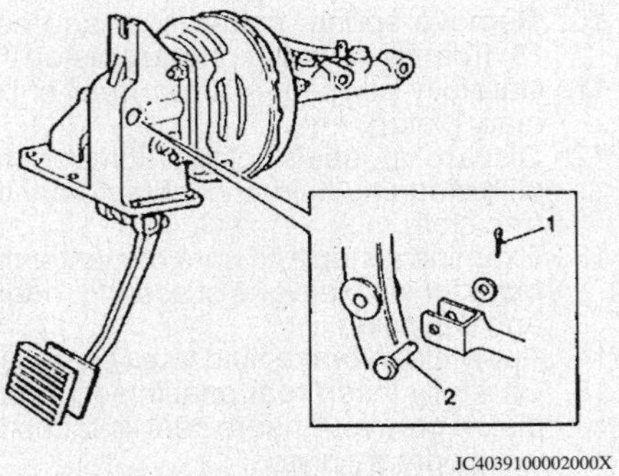

Fig. 1 Booster removal

   a. Install new brake booster/pedal box gasket.
   b. **Torque** mounting nuts to 22 ft. lbs.
   c. **Torque** expansion tank to 62 inch lbs.

XJR, XJ8, XKR & XK8

1. Remove engine compartment stabilizer bar located above brake booster.
2. Pry vacuum elbow from booster, then remove master cylinder/booster mounting nuts.
3. Loosen throttle cable/bracket locknut and disconnect kickdown switch feed wires.
4. Disconnect throttle cable from turntable, then remove fluid reservoir mounting bolts.
5. Remove reservoir from mounting bracket and position away from area.
6. Remove pedal housing nuts/bolts.
7. Ease master cylinder away from booster mounting studs. Lift pedal box/booster assembly clear of vehicle.
8. Remove retaining pin (1) from pushrod clevis pin, then remove clevis pin, **Fig. 1**.
9. Remove booster unit mounting nuts and reservoir mounting bracket.
10. Remove booster from pedal box.
11. Reverse procedure to install, noting the following:
   a. **Torque** master cylinder to booster nuts to 16–20 ft. lbs.
   b. **Torque** pedal box to body 11–13 ft. lbs.
   c. **Torque** reservoir to bracket to 24–36 inch lbs.
   d. **Torque** booster to pedal box to 8–10 ft. lbs.

Anti-Lock Brakes

NOTE: On Air Bag Equipped Models, Refer To "Air Bag System Precautions" Located In The Front Of This Manual For System Disarming & Arming Procedures.

NOTE: Electrical Symbol & Wire Color Code Identification Located In The Front Of This Manual May Be Used As An Aid When Using Wiring Circuits Found In This Section.

NOTE: Prior To Performing Any Service Operations Listed In This Section, Consult The "Technical Service Bulletins" Section For Related Information.

INDEX

	Page No.
Description	3-55
Diagnosis & Testing	3-55
Accessing Diagnostic Trouble Codes	3-55
Clearing Diagnostic Trouble Codes	3-74
Component Locations	3-56
Diagnostic Tests	3-56
1285: Booster Solenoid Output Circuit Failure	3-71
B1342: ABS Control Module Fault	3-56
B1342: CAN Circuit Failure	3-56
B1342: DSC (Dynamic Stability Control) Control Module Fault	3-57
B1485: Stop Lamp Switch Input Circuit Short To Positive Voltage	3-57
B1676: Battery Voltage Out Of Range	3-58
C1095: Hydraulic Pump Motor Circuit Failure	3-60
C1137: Control Module Internal Circuit Failure	3-60
C1145: Wheel Speed Sensor Circuit Righthand Front Electrical Failure	3-60
C1155: Wheel Speed Sensor Circuit Lefthand Front Electrical Failure	3-62
C1165: Wheel Speed Sensor Circuit Righthand Rear Electrical Failure	3-63
C1175: Wheel Speed Sensor Circuit Lefthand Rear Electrical Failure	3-65
C1233: Wheel Speed Sensor Circuit Lefthand Front Signal Failure	3-66
C1234: Wheel Speed Sensor Circuit Righthand Front Signal Failure	3-67
C1235: Wheel Speed Sensor Circuit Righthand Rear Signal Failure	3-67
C1236: Wheel Speed Sensor Circuit Lefthand Rear Signal Failure	3-67
C1267: Modulator Valve Failure	3-68
C1277: Steering Wheel Angle 1 & 2 Circuit Failure	3-68
C1278: Steering Wheel Angle 1 & 2 Signal Fault	3-69
C1279: Yaw Rate Sensor Circuit Failure	3-69
C1280: Yaw Rate Sensor Signal Fault	3-70
C1281: Lateral Accelerometer Circuit Failure	3-70
C1282: Lateral Accelerometer Signal Failure	3-71
C1286: Booster Mechanical Fault	3-71
C1287: Booster Pedal Force Switch Circuit Failure	3-71
C1288: Pressure Transducer Main/Primary Input Circuit Failure	3-72
C1289: Pressure Transducer Redundant/Secondary Input Circuit Failure	3-73
C1730: Reference Voltage Out Of Range	3-73
Diagnostic Trouble Code Interpretation	3-56
Wiring Diagrams	3-56
Precautions	3-55
Air Bag Systems	3-55
Battery Ground Cable	3-55
System Service	3-74
Brake System Bleed	3-74
Fluid Intake Hose	3-74
Component Replacement	3-74
ABS/Traction Control Control Module (ABS/TCCM)	3-75
Hydraulic Control Unit (HCU)	3-74
Lateral Acceleration & Rotation Sensors	3-75
Steering Wheel Rotation Sensor	3-75
Wheel Speed Sensor	3-75
Technical Service Bulletins	3-75
DTC 1145, 1155, 1233 or 1234	3-75
Troubleshooting	3-55

PRECAUTIONS

AIR BAG SYSTEMS

Refer to "Air Bag System Precautions" in the front of this manual for system disarming and arming procedures.

BATTERY GROUND CABLE

Prior to service, disconnect battery ground cable and isolate as required.

DESCRIPTION

The anti-lock braking system eliminates wheel lock by controlling hydraulic pressure applied to the brake calipers. This system, which is assisted by the power hydraulic system, also reduces tire wear and improves vehicle stability during severe braking conditions. Modulation of hydraulic pressure is achieved by a modulator containing three solenoid actuated valves; one valve in each hydraulic line to front calipers and one in a common hydraulic line to rear calipers. Each valve is controlled by an Electronic Control Unit (ECU) which also activates a hydraulic pump to return used fluid back to the modulator. The ECU contains electronic circuits which actuate the valve solenoids from inputs generated by speed sensors comprising variable reluctance coils located close to an exciter disc attached to each wheel hub. Each wheel deceleration rate is then calculated and pressure is applied to the calipers.

TROUBLESHOOTING

Refer to **Fig. 1** for troubleshooting.

DIAGNOSIS & TESTING

Accessing Diagnostic Trouble Codes

Diagnostic Trouble Codes (DTCs) are accessed by connecting a suitable programmed scan tool to the Data Link Connector (DLC) and following the tool manufacturer's instructions. The DLC is located on the instrument panel adjacent to the driver's side A-pillar.

Diagnostic Trouble Code Interpretation

Refer to **Figs. 2 and 3** for Diagnostic Trouble Code (DTC) interpretation.

Component Locations

Refer to **Figs. 4 and 5** for component locations.

Wiring Diagrams

Refer to **Figs. 6 through 8** for wiring diagrams.

Diagnostic Tests

B1342: ABS CONTROL MODULE FAULT

S TYPE

Check Voltage Supply To ABS Control Module

1. Switch ignition switch to OFF position.
2. Disconnect ABS control module electrical connector FH33.
3. Measure voltage between ABS control module electrical connector FH33 pin 25, (R) and ground FH33 pin 8, (B).
4. If measurement is less than 12 volts, proceed to "Check Voltage Supply Between Fuse 14 At Front Power Distribution Box."
5. If measurement is not as specified, proceed to "Check Voltage Supply To ABS Control Module."

Check Voltage Supply Between Fuse 14 At Front Power Distribution Box

1. Measure voltage supply between fuse 14 at front power distribution box and ground.
2. If measurement is less than 12 volts, proceed as follows:
   a. Install new fuse.
   b. If fuse fails check front distribution box.
3. If measurement is not as specified, repair circuit between ABS electrical connector FH33 pin 25, (R) and output side of fuse 14 at front power distribution box.

Check Voltage Supply To ABS Control Module

1. Measure voltage between ABS control module electrical connector pin FH33 pin 9, (R) and ground FH33, pin 8 (B).
2. If measurement Is less than 12 volts, proceed to "Check Voltage Supply From Fuse 22 At Front Power Distribution Box."
3. If measurement is not as specified, proceed to "Check Voltage Supply To ABS Control Module."

Trouble	Cause	Remedy
Long brake pedal	Brake caliper piston or caliper guide pins sticking	Service or renew caliper or caliper guide pins
	Worn / damaged brake pads	Renew brake pads
Vibration during braking	Worn / damaged brake pads	Renew brake pads
	Loose caliper mounting bolts	Tighten caliper mounting bolts
	Insufficient grease on sliding parts	Apply grease where necessary
	Foreign material or scratches on brake rotor contact surface	Clean brake rotor contact surface
	Damaged brake rotor contact surface	Renew brake rotor
Poor braking performance	Leak in hydraulic system	Repair leak. Check all pipework connections. Refill and bleed the system
	Air in system	Check the system for leaks and bleed brakes
	Worn / damaged brake pads	Renew brake pads
	Foreign material on brake pads	Examine brake pads and clean or renew as necessary
	Brake caliper piston malfunction	Renew faulty brake caliper piston
	Tandem master cylinder malfunction	Service or renew tandem master cylinder
	Vacuum booster fault	Renew vacuum booster
	Disconnected or damaged vacuum hose	Renew vacuum hose
	Low brake fluid level	Check for leaks, refill and bleed the system
Brakes pull to one side	Worn / damaged brake pads	Renew brake pads
	Foreign material on brake pad	Examine brake pads and clean or renew as necessary
	Failing valves in ABS valve block	Renew valve block
	Abnormal wear or distortion on front brake rotor	Examine front brake rotor and service or renew as necessary
	Incorrect wheel alignment	Carry out wheel alignment.
	Incorrect tire pressure	Inflate tire to correct pressure
Brakes do not release	No brake pedal free play	Adjust brake pedal free play
	Vacuum booster binding	Renew vacuum booster
	Tandem master cylinder return port faulty	Clean return port on tandem master cylinder
	Faulty valve in ABS valve block	Renew valve block
Excessive pedal travel	Leak in hydraulic system	Repair leak. Check all pipework connections. Refill and bleed the system
	Air in system	Check the system for leaks and bleed brakes

JC4029900019010X

Fig. 1 Troubleshooting (Part 1 of 2)

Check Voltage Supply From Fuse 22 At Front Power Distribution Box

1. Measure voltage supply from fuse 22 at front power distribution box.
2. If measurement is less than 12 volts, proceed as follows:
   a. Install new fuse.
   b. If fuse fails, check front distribution box.
3. If measurement is not as specified, repair circuit between ABS electrical connector FH33 pin 9, (R) and output side of fuse 22 at front power distribution box.

Check Voltage Supply To ABS Control Module

1. Measure voltage between ABS control module electrical connector FH33 pin 20, (KY) and ground FH33, pin 8 (B).
2. If measurement Is less than 12 volts, proceed to "Check Voltage Supply From Fuse 3 At Primary Junction Box."
3. If measurement is not as specified, proceed to "Check Ground Supply To ABS Control Module."

Check Voltage Supply From Fuse 3 At Primary Junction Box

1. Measure voltage supply from fuse 3 at primary junction box.
2. If measurement is less than 12 volts, proceed as follows:
   a. Install new fuse.
   b. If fuse fails, check front distribution box.
3. If measurement is not as specified, repair circuit between ABS control module electrical connector FH33 pin 9, (R) and output side of fuse 3 at primary junction box.

Check Ground Supply To ABS Control Module

1. Measure resistance between ABS control module electrical connector FH33 pin 8, (B) and ground.
2. If resistance is less than 0.5 ohms, proceed to "Check Ground Supply To ABS Control Module."
3. If resistance is not as specified, repair circuit between ABS control module electrical connector FH33 pin 8, (B) and ground.

Check Ground Supply To ABS Control Module

1. Measure resistance between ABS control connector FH33 pin 24, (B) and ground.
2. If resistance is less than 0.5 ohms, install new ABS control module.
3. Repair circuit between ABS control module electrical connector FH33 pin 24, (B) and ground point FH42.

B1342: CAN CIRCUIT FAILURE

XJR, XJ8, XKR & XK8

Measure Connector Resistance (Ignition Off)

1. Measure resistance on connector LF037 between pin 5 and pin 015.
2. If resistance is 120 ohms, vehicle is satisfactory.

3. If resistance is not as specified, proceed to "Check Electrical Continuity (1) (Ignition Off)."

Check Electrical Continuity (1) (Ignition Off)

1. Check for continuity between LS027/005 and connector EM007/082, then LS027/015 and EM007/083.
2. If there is continuity, proceed to "Check Electrical Continuity (2) (Ignition Off),"
3. If there is no continuity, inspect harness from ABS to TCM for damage. Repair required.

Check Electrical Continuity (2) (Ignition Off)

1. Check for continuity between J1692 connector CC006/011 and LS027/005, then CC006/010 and LS027/015.
2. If there is continuity, proceed to "Check For Short Circuit (1) (Ignition Off)."
3. If there is no continuity, check for continuity between vehicle ECU's.

Check For Short Circuit (1) (Ignition Off)

1. Check for short circuit between CAN wires.
2. If there Is short circuit, check harness. Repair as required.
3. If there is no short circuit, proceed to "Check For Short Circuit (2) (Ignition On)."

Check For Short Circuit (2) (Ignition On)

1. Check if either line is shorted to ground or +12V.
2. If either line is shorted to ground or +12V, Check harness. Repair as required.
3. If there is no short to ground or +12V, replace ABS/TCS module.

B1342: DSC (DYNAMIC STABILITY CONTROL) CONTROL MODULE FAULT

S TYPE

Check Voltage Supply To DSC Control Module

1. Switch ignition to OFF position.
2. Disconnect DSC control module electrical connector FH51.
3. Measure voltage between DSC control module electrical connector FH51 pin 16, (R) and ground.
4. If measurement is less than 12 volts, proceed to "Check Voltage Supply From Fuse 14 At Front Power Distribution Box."
5. If measurement is not as specified, proceed to "Check Voltage Supply To DSC Control Module."

Check Voltage Supply From Fuse 14 At Front Power Distribution Box

1. Measure voltage supply from fuse 14 at front power distribution box.
2. If measurement is less than 12 volts, proceed as follows:

Trouble	Cause	Remedy
Excessive pedal travel (Cont'd)	Worn tandem master cylinder piston seals or scored cylinder bore	Renew tandem master cylinder
	'knock back'. Excessive brake rotor run–out or loose wheel bearings	Check brake rotor run–out and renew as necessary. Adjust wheel bearing
Brakes grab	Brake pads contaminated by grease or brake fluid	Renew brake pads. Check pipework for leaks
	Brake pads distorted, cracked or loose	Renew brake pads
	Loose caliper mounting bolts or guide pins	Check caliper and repair / renew as necessary
Brakes drag	Seized or incorrectly adjusted parking brake or cable	Examine parking brake and repair / renew as necessary
	Broken or weak parking brake return springs	Renew parking brake return springs
	Caliper pistons seized	Examine calipers and repair / renew as necessary
	Brake pedal binding at pivot points	Examine brake pedal bushings and repair / renew as necessary
	Vacuum booster binding	Renew vacuum booster
	Tandem master cylinder faulty	Examine tandem master cylinder and repair / renew as necessary
Hard brake pedal when pressed	Lack of vacuum at the vacuum booster	Check vacuum hose. Repair or renew as necessary
	Tandem master cylinder pushrod binding	Renew tandem master cylinder
	Frozen tandem master cylinder piston	Renew tandem master cylinder
	Brake caliper piston or caliper guide pins seized	Examine caliper and renew / repair as necessary
Excessive brake noise	Worn brake pads	Renew brake pads
	Bent or cracked parking brake shoes	Renew parking brake shoes
	Foreign objects in brake pads or parking brake shoes	Examine brake pads and and parking brake shoes. Clean or renew as necessary
	Broken / loose parking brake hold down springs or return springs	Examine parking brake assembly. Repair or renew as necessary
	Loose caliper mounting bolts	Re–torque caliper mounting bolts

JC4029900019020X

Fig. 1 Troubleshooting (Part 2 of 2)

   a. Install new fuse.
   b. If fuse fails check front distribution box.
3. If measurement is not as specified, repair circuit between DSC electrical connector FH51 pin 16, (R) and output side of fuse 14 at front power distribution box.

Check Voltage Supply To DSC Control Module

1. Measure voltage between FH51 pin 33, (R) and ground FH51 pin 32, (B).
2. If measurement is less than 12 volts, proceed to "Check Voltage Supply From Fuse 22 At Front Power Distribution Box."
3. If measurement is not as specified, proceed to "Check Voltage Supply To DSC Control Module."

Check Voltage Supply From Fuse 22 At Front Power Distribution Box

1. Measure voltage supply from fuse 22 at front power distribution box.
2. If measurement is less than 12 volts, proceed as follows:
   a. Install new fuse.
   b. If fuse fails check front distribution box.
3. If measurement is not as specified, repair circuit between DSC control module electrical connector FH51 pin 33, (R) and output side of fuse 22 at front power distribution box.

Check Voltage Supply To DSC Control Module

1. Measure voltage between FH51 pin 22, (KY) and ground FH51 pin 32, (B).
2. If measurement is less than 12 volts, proceed to "Check Voltage Supply From Fuse 3 At Primary Junction Box."
3. If measurement is not as specified, proceed to "Check Ground Supply To DSC Control Module."

Check Ground Supply To DSC Control Module

1. Measure resistance between DSC control module electrical connector FH51 pin 32, (B) and ground.
2. If resistance is less than 0.5 ohms, proceed to "Check Ground Supply To DSC Control Module."
3. If resistance is not as specified, repair circuit between DSC control module electrical connector FH51 pin 32, (B) and ground point FH42.

Check Ground Supply To DSC Control Module

1. Measure resistance between DSC control module electrical connector FH51 pin 15, (B) and ground.
2. If resistance is less than 0.5 ohms, install new DSC control module.
3. If resistance is not as specified, repair circuit between DSC control module electrical connector FH51 pin 15, (B) and ground point FH42.

B1485: STOP LAMP SWITCH INPUT CIRCUIT SHORT TO POSITIVE VOLTAGE

S TYPE LESS DSC

Check Stop Lamp Switch Circuit For Short To Positive Voltage

1. Turn ignition switch to OFF position.
2. Disconnect ABS control module electrical connector FH33.
3. Switch ignition to RUN position.
4. Measure for voltage between ABS control module electrical connector FH33 pin 2, (OG) and ground FH33 pin 8, (B).

DTC	CM	SYSTEM	FAULT DESCRIPTION	MIL	POSSIBLE CAUSES
C1095	ABS/ TCCM	Anti-lock braking / traction control	Pressure pump circuit fault CUSTOMER SYMPTOM: ABS/TC MIL warnings; ABS/TC inoperative	Y	ABS/TCCM failure
C1095	DSCCM	Dynamic stability control	Pressure pump circuit fault CUSTOMER SYMPTOM: DSC MIL warnings; DSC inoperative	Y	DSCCM failure
C1145	ABS/ TCCM	Anti-lock braking / traction control	RH front wheel speed sensor circuit fault CUSTOMER SYMPTOM: ABS/TC MIL warnings; below 3 mph system inhibited; above 3 mph the system is disabled	Y	ABS/TCCM to wheel speed sensor signal circuit (FH33-3): open circuit, short circuit to ground, short circuit to B+ voltage, high resistance RH front wheel speed sensor failure
C1145	DSCCM	Dynamic stability control	RH front wheel speed sensor circuit fault CUSTOMER SYMPTOM: DSC MIL warnings; below 3 mph system inhibited; above 3 mph the system is disabled	Y	DSCCM to wheel speed sensor signal circuit (FH51-34): open circuit, short circuit to ground, short circuit to B+ voltage, high resistance RH front wheel speed sensor failure
C1155	ABS/ TCCM	Anti-lock braking / traction control	LH front wheel speed sensor circuit fault CUSTOMER SYMPTOM: ABS/TC MIL warnings; below 3 mph system inhibited; above 3 mph the system is disabled	Y	ABS/TCCM to wheel speed sensor signal circuit (FH33-17): open circuit, short circuit to ground, short circuit to B+ voltage, high resistance LH front wheel speed sensor failure
C1155	DSCCM	Dynamic stability control	LH front wheel speed sensor circuit fault CUSTOMER SYMPTOM: DSC MIL warnings; below 3 mph system inhibited; above 3 mph the system is disabled	Y	DSCCM to wheel speed sensor signal circuit (FH51-02): open circuit, short circuit to ground, short circuit to B+ voltage, high resistance LH front wheel speed sensor failure

JC4020100034010X

Fig. 2 DTC interpretation (Part 1 of 14). S Type

5. If there is a voltage value, proceed to "Check Continuity Of Brake Lamp Switch."
6. If there is no voltage, install new ABS control module.

Check Continuity Of Brake Lamp Switch

1. Disconnect brake lamp switch electrical connector.
2. Measure resistance across brake lamp switch.
3. If resistance is less than 0.5 ohms, install new brake lamp switch.
4. If resistance is not as specified, repair wire between brake lamp switch electrical connector CA37 pin 2, (OU) and ABS control module electrical connector FH33 pin 2, (OG).

S TYPE w/DSC

Check Stop Lamp Switch Circuit For Short To Positive Voltage

1. Turn ignition switch to OFF position.
2. Disconnect DSC control module electrical connector FH51.
3. Switch ignition to RUN position.
4. Measure for voltage between DSC control module electrical connector FH51 pin 21, and ground FH51 pin 32, (B).
5. If there is a voltage value, proceed to "Check Continuity Of Brake Lamp Switch."
6. If there is no voltage, install new DSC control module.

Check Continuity Of Brake Lamp Switch

1. Disconnect brake lamp switch electrical connector.
2. Measure resistance across brake lamp switch.
3. If resistance is less than 0.5 ohms, install new brake lamp switch.
4. If resistance is not as specified, repair wire between brake lamp switch electrical connector CA37 pin 2, (OU) and DSC control module electrical connector FH51 pin 21, (OG).

B1676: BATTERY VOLTAGE OUT OF RANGE

S TYPE LESS DSC

Check Voltage Supply To ABS Control Module

1. Switch ignition to OFF position.
2. Disconnect ABS control module electrical connector FH33.
3. Measure voltage between ABS control module electrical connector FH33 pin 25, (R) and ground.
4. If voltage is less than 12 volts, proceed to "Check Voltage Supply From Fuse 14 At Front Power Distribution Box."
5. If voltage is not as specified, proceed to "Check Voltage Supply To ABS Control Module."

Check Voltage Supply From Fuse 14 At Front Power Distribution Box

1. Measure voltage supply from fuse 14 at front power distribution box.
2. If measurement is less than 12 volts, install new fuse.
3. If measurement is not as specified, repair circuit between ABS electrical connector FH33 pin 25, (R) and output side of fuse 14 at front power distribution box.

Check Voltage Supply To ABS Control Module

1. Measure voltage between ABS electrical connector FH33 pin 9, (R) and ground FH33 pin 8, (B).
2. If voltage is less than 12 volts, proceed to "Check Voltage Supply From Fuse 22 At Front Power Distribution Box."
3. If voltage is not as specified, proceed to "Check Voltage Supply To ABS Control Module."

Check Voltage Supply From Fuse 22 At Front Power Distribution Box

1. Measure voltage supply from fuse 22 at front power distribution box.
2. If measurement is less than 12 volts, proceed as follows:
   a. Install new fuse.
   b. If fuse fails, check front power distribution box.
3. If measurement is not as specified, repair circuit between ABS electrical connector FH33 pin 9, (R) and output side of fuse 22 at front power distribution box.

Check Voltage Supply To ABS Control Module

1. Measure voltage between ABS electrical connector FH33 pin 20, (KY) and ground.

DTC	CM	SYSTEM	FAULT DESCRIPTION	MIL	POSSIBLE CAUSES
C1165	ABS/ TCCM	Anti-lock braking / traction control	RH rear wheel speed sensor circuit fault CUSTOMER SYMPTOM: ABS/TC MIL warnings; below 3 mph (5 km/h) system inhibited; above 3 mph the system is disabled	Y	ABS/TCCM to wheel speed sensor signal circuit (FH33-7): open circuit, short circuit to ground, short circuit to B+ voltage, high resistance RH rear wheel speed sensor failure
C1165	DSCCM	Dynamic stability control	RH rear wheel speed sensor circuit fault CUSTOMER SYMPTOM: DSC MIL warnings; below 3 mph (5 km/h) system inhibited; above 3 mph the system is disabled	Y	DSCCM to wheel speed sensor signal circuit (FH51-37): open circuit, short circuit to ground, short circuit to B+ voltage, high resistance RH rear wheel speed sensor failure
C1175	ABS/ TCCM	Anti-lock braking / traction control	LH rear wheel speed sensor circuit fault CUSTOMER SYMPTOM: ABS/TC MIL warnings; below 3 mph (5 km/h) system inhibited; above 3 mph the system is disabled	Y	ABS/TCCM to wheel speed sensor signal circuit (FH33-21): open circuit, short circuit to ground, short circuit to B+ voltage, high resistance LH rear wheel speed sensor failure
C1175	DSCCM	Dynamic stability control	LH rear wheel speed sensor circuit fault CUSTOMER SYMPTOM: DSC MIL warnings; below 3 mph (5 km/h) system inhibited; above 3 mph the system is disabled	Y	DSCCM to wheel speed sensor signal circuit (FH51-04): open circuit, short circuit to ground, short circuit to B+ voltage, high resistance LH rear wheel speed sensor failure
C1233	ABS/ TCCM	Anti-lock braking / traction control	LH front wheel speed signal fault – detectable at vehicle speed > 12.5 mph CUSTOMER SYMPTOM: ABS/TC MIL warnings	Y	LH front wheel speed sensor failure
C1233	DSCCM	Dynamic stability control	LH front wheel speed signal fault – detectable at vehicle speed > 12.5 mph CUSTOMER SYMPTOM: DSC MIL warnings	Y	LH front wheel speed sensor failure

JC4020100034020X

Fig. 2 DTC interpretation (Part 2 of 14). S Type

2. If measurement is less than 12 volts, proceed to "Check Voltage Supply From Fuse 3 At Primary Junction Box."
3. If measurement is not as specified, install new ABS control module.

Check Voltage Supply From Fuse 3 At Primary Junction Box

1. Measure voltage supply from fuse 3 at primary junction box.
2. If measurement is less than 12 volts, proceed as follows:
   a. Install new fuse.
   b. If fuse fails, check primary junction box.
3. If measurement is not as specified, repair circuit between ABS electrical connector FH33 pin 9, (R) and output side of fuse 3 at primary junction box.

S TYPE w/DSC

Check Voltage Supply To DSC Control Module

1. Switch ignition to OFF position.
2. Disconnect DSC control module electrical connector FH51.
3. Measure voltage between DSC control module electrical connector FH51 pin 16, (R) and ground FH51 pin 32, (B).
4. If voltage is less than 12 volts, proceed to "Check Voltage Supply From Fuse 14 At Front Power Distribution Box."
5. If voltage is not as specified, proceed to "Check Voltage Supply To DSC Control Module."

Check Voltage Supply From Fuse 14 At Front Power Distribution Box

1. Measure voltage supply from fuse 14 at front power distribution box.
2. If measurement is less than 12 volts, install new fuse.
3. If measurement is not as specified, repair circuit between DSC electrical connector FH51 pin 16, (R) and output side of fuse 14 at front power distribution box.

Check Voltage Supply To DSC Control Module

1. Measure voltage between ABS electrical connector FH51 pin 33, (R) and ground FH51 pin 32, (B).
2. If voltage is less than 12 volts, proceed to "Check Voltage Supply From Fuse 22 At Front Power Distribution Box."
3. If voltage is not as specified, proceed to "Check Voltage Supply To DSC Control Module."

Check Voltage Supply From Fuse 22 At Front Power Distribution Box

1. Measure voltage supply from fuse 22 at front power distribution box.
2. If measurement is less than 12 volts, proceed as follows:
   a. Install new fuse.
   b. If fuse fails, check front power distribution box.
3. If measurement is not as specified, repair circuit between DSC electrical connector FH51 pin 33, (R) and output side of fuse 22 at front power distribution box.

Check Voltage Supply To DSC Control Module

1. Measure voltage between ABS electrical connector FH51 pin 22, (KY) and ground FH51 pin 32, (B).
2. If measurement is less than 12 volts, proceed to "Check Voltage Supply From Fuse 3 At Primary Junction Box."
3. If measurement is not as specified, install new DSC control module.

Check Voltage Supply From Fuse 3 At Primary Junction Box

1. Measure voltage supply from fuse 3 at primary junction box.
2. If measurement is less than 12 volts, proceed as follows:
   a. Install new fuse.
   b. If fuse fails, check primary junction box.
3. If measurement is not as specified, repair circuit between DSC electrical connector FH51 pin 33, (R) and output side of fuse 3 at primary junction box.

DTC	CM	SYSTEM	FAULT DESCRIPTION	MIL	POSSIBLE CAUSES
C1234	ABS/ TCCM	Anti-lock braking / traction control	RH front wheel speed signal fault – detectable at vehicle speed > 12.5 mph CUSTOMER SYMPTOM: ABS/TC MIL warnings	Y	RH front wheel speed sensor failure
C1234	DSCCM	Dynamic stability control	RH front wheel speed signal fault – detectable at vehicle speed > 12.5 mph CUSTOMER SYMPTOM: DSC MIL warnings	Y	RH front wheel speed sensor failure
C1235	ABS/ TCCM	Anti-lock braking / traction control	RH rear wheel speed signal fault – detectable at vehicle speed > 12.5 mph CUSTOMER SYMPTOM: ABS/TC MIL warnings	Y	RH rear wheel speed sensor failure
C1235	DSCCM	Dynamic stability control	RH rear wheel speed signal fault – detectable at vehicle speed > 12.5 mph CUSTOMER SYMPTOM: DSC MIL warnings	Y	RH rear wheel speed sensor failure
C1236	ABS/ TCCM	Anti-lock braking / traction control	LH rear wheel speed signal fault – detectable at vehicle speed > 12.5 mph CUSTOMER SYMPTOM: ABS/TC MIL warnings	Y	LH rear wheel speed sensor failure
C1236	DSCCM	Dynamic stability control	LH rear wheel speed signal fault – detectable at vehicle speed > 12.5 mph CUSTOMER SYMPTOM: DSC MIL warnings	Y	LH rear wheel speed sensor failure

JC4020100034030X

Fig. 2 DTC interpretation (Part 3 of 14). S Type

C1095: HYDRAULIC PUMP MOTOR CIRCUIT FAILURE

S TYPE

Check Resistance Of ABS Or DSC Hydraulic Pump

1. Turn ignition switch to OFF position.
2. Disconnect ABS or DSC hydraulic pump electrical connector.
3. Measure resistance across hydraulic pump electrical connector.
4. If resistance is 0.4 ohms, install new ABS or DSC control module.
5. If resistance is not as specified, install new ABS or DSC hydraulic pump.

XJR, XJ8, XKR & XK8

Check Condition Of Fuse

1. Inspect fuse 18 (30A fuse) located in underhood fusebox.
2. If fuse is satisfactory, proceed to "Measure Connector Resistance."
3. If fuse is not satisfactory, replace as required.

Measure Connector Resistance

1. Measure resistance between pins 1 and 2 of flylead going to ABS pump.
2. If resistance is less than 20 ohms, proceed to "Measure Connector Voltage."
3. If resistance is not as specified, replace HCU.

Measure Connector Voltage

1. Disconnect connector LF037, then measure voltage between pins 9 and 24.
2. If measurement is approximately 12 volts, replace HCU.
3. If measurement is not as specified, proceed to "Inspect Harness/Connectors."

Inspect Harness/Connectors

1. Inspect harness/connectors from ABS module to fusebox for damage, corrosion, bent and/or pushed back pins.
2. If there is damage, repair as required.
3. If there is no damage, replace HCU.

C1137: CONTROL MODULE INTERNAL CIRCUIT FAILURE

XJR, XJ8, XKR & XK8

CHECK CONDITION OF FUSE

1. Inspect fuse 4 (5A fuse) located in underhood fusebox.
2. If fuse is satisfactory, proceed to "Measure Connector Resistance."
3. If fuse is not satisfactory, replace as required.

Measure Connector Resistance

1. Disconnect connector LF037, then measure voltage between pins 20 and 24.
2. If measurement is approximately 12 volts, replace ABS/TCS module.
3. If measurement is not as specified, proceed to "Inspect Harness/Connectors."

Inspect Harness/Connectors

1. Inspect harness/connectors from ABS module to fusebox for damage, corrosion, bent and or pushed back pins.
2. If there is damage, repair as required.
3. If these is no damage, replace HCU.

C1145: WHEEL SPEED SENSOR CIRCUIT RIGHTHAND FRONT ELECTRICAL FAILURE

S TYPE LESS DSC

Check Wheel Speed Sensor Resistance

1. Turn ignition switch to OFF position.
2. Disconnect ABS control module electrical connector FH33.
3. Measure resistance between the ABS control module electrical connector FH33 pin 3, (WR) and FH33 pin 4, (YR).
4. If resistance is 6–7 ohms, install new ABS control module.
5. If resistance is not as specified, install new wheel speed sensor.

S TYPE w/DSC

Check Wheel Speed Sensor Resistance

1. Turn ignition switch to OFF position.
2. Disconnect DSC control module electrical connector FH51.
3. Measure resistance between the DSC control module electrical connector FH51 pin 34, (WR) and FH51 pin 35, (YR).
4. If resistance is 6–7 ohms, install new DSC control module.
5. If resistance is not as specified, install

DTC	CM	SYSTEM	FAULT DESCRIPTION	MIL	POSSIBLE CAUSES
C1277	DSCCM	Dynamic stability control	Steering angle rate sensor circuit fault CUSTOMER SYMPTOM: DSC MIL warnings	Y	DSCCM to steering angle rate sensor signal circuit(s) (FH51-14, FH51-47): open circuit, short circuit to ground, short circuit to B+ voltage, high resistance Steering angle rate sensor failure NOTE: Control module calibration using PDU is required when the fault is repaired and the DTC is cleared. MIL will flash to indicate that configuration is required.
C1278	DSCCM	Dynamic stability control	Steering angle rate signal fault CUSTOMER SYMPTOM: DSC MIL warnings	Y	Steering angle rate sensor failure NOTE: Control module calibration using PDU is required when the fault is repaired and the DTC is cleared. MIL will flash to indicate that configuration is required.
C1279	DSCCM	Dynamic stability control	Yaw velocity sensor circuit fault CUSTOMER SYMPTOM: DSC MIL warnings	Y	DSCCM to yaw velocity sensor signal circuit (FH51-27): open circuit, short circuit to ground, short circuit to B+ voltage, high resistance Yaw velocity sensor failure NOTE: Control module calibration using PDU is required when the fault is repaired and the DTC is cleared. MIL will flash to indicate that configuration is required.
C1280	DSCCM	Dynamic stability control	Yaw velocity signal fault CUSTOMER SYMPTOM: DSC MIL warnings	Y	Yaw velocity sensor failure NOTE: Control module calibration using PDU is required when the fault is repaired and the DTC is cleared. MIL will flash to indicate that configuration is required.

JC4020100034040X

Fig. 2 DTC interpretation (Part 4 of 14). S Type

new wheel speed sensor.

XJR, XJ8, XKR & XK8

Mechanical Check

1. Check sensor fitted condition (air gap).
2. Ensure sensor gap 0.0055–0.0658 inch.
3. Ensure sensor face is free of foreign matter.
4. Inspect sensor wheel for damaged.
5. Ensure sensor wheel is free of foreign matter.
6. If mechanic check is satisfactory, proceed to "Check Sensor Continuity."
7. If mechanic check is not satisfactory, repair as required.

Check Sensor Continuity

1. Turn ignition switch to 0 position.
2. Disconnect FR001 on top of hub assembly.
3. Measure resistance between sensor pins 1 and 2.
4. If resistance is 1040–1160 ohms, do not reconnect, then proceed to "Check Sensor Output."
5. If resistance is not as specified, replace wheel speed sensor.

Check Sensor Output

The observed voltage will fluctuate and be proportional to the wheel speed.

1. With righthand front wheel raised, spin wheel and note output voltage from sensor at FR001/001 and FR001/002.
2. If measurement is more than 0 volts and less than 5 volts, proceed to "Check Harness Signal Continuity."
3. If measurement is not as specified, replace wheel speed sensor

Check Harness Signal Continuity

LS027 may be released by pulling the top mounted plunger upwards, this will release and simultaneously withdraw the connector from the ABS/TCS.

1. Disconnect LS027 behind headlamp assembly.
2. Measure resistance between LS027/003 and FR001/002, then LS027/004 and FR001/001.
3. If resistance is less than 0.5 ohms, Do not reconnect, then proceed to "Check Harness Short To Ground."
4. If resistance is not as specified, proceed as follows:
   a. Inspect harness and connectors LS027/003 and 004, then LS002/002 and 001, FR001/002 and 001 for damage, corrosion, bent and/or pushed back pins.
   b. Check for continuity between all pins.
   c. Repair as required.

Check Harness Short To Ground

1. Measure insulation resistance between ground LS29L (adjacent to the ABS pump) and LS027/003, ground LS29L and LS027/004.
2. If resistance is more than 10,000 ohms, do not reconnect, then proceed to "Check Harness Short Core To Core."
3. If resistance is not as specified, proceed as follows:
   a. Inspect harness and connectors LS027/003 and 004, LS002/002 and 001, FR001/002 and 001 for damage, corrosion, bent and/or pushed back pins.
   b. Check for resistance against ground between all connectors and ground LS29L.
   c. Repair as required.

Check Harness Short Core To Core

1. Measure insulation resistance between LS027/003 and LS027/004.
2. If resistance is more than 10,000 ohms, proceed to "Check For Short To B+."
3. If resistance is not as specified, inspect harness and connectors LS027/003 and 004, LS002/002 and 001, FR001/002 and 001 for damage, corrosion, bent and/or pushed back pins. Repair as required.

Check For Short To B+

1. Turn ignition switch to II position.
2. Measure voltage between ground LS29L and LS027/003, ground LS29L and LS027/004.
3. If measurement is 0 volts, proceed to "Check For Short To Ignition."
4. If measurement is not as specified, inspect harness and connectors LS027/

DTC	CM	SYSTEM	FAULT DESCRIPTION	MIL	POSSIBLE CAUSES
C1281	DSCCM	Dynamic stability control	Lateral accelerometer circuit fault CUSTOMER SYMPTOM: DSC MIL warnings	Y	DSCCM to lateral accelerometer signal circuit (FH51-29): open circuit, short circuit to ground, short circuit to B+ voltage, high resistance Lateral accelerometer failure NOTE: Control module calibration using PDU is required when the fault is repaired and the DTC is cleared. MIL will flash to indicate that configuration is required.
C1282	DSCCM	Dynamic stability control	Lateral accelerometer signal fault CUSTOMER SYMPTOM: DSC MIL warnings	Y	Lateral accelerometer failure NOTE: Control module calibration using PDU is required when the fault is repaired and the DTC is cleared. MIL will flash to indicate that configuration is required.
C1283	DSCCM	Dynamic stability control	DSCCM active brake booster release switch test signal fault CUSTOMER SYMPTOM: DSC MIL warnings	Y	DSCCM failure NOTE: Control module calibration using PDU is required when the fault is repaired and the DTC is cleared. MIL will flash to indicate that configuration is required.
C1284	GECM	Instrument pack	Oil pressure switch circuit fault CUSTOMER SYMPTOM: Oil pressure MIL always on (if short circuit to ground)	N	GECM to oil pressure switch circuit (FH59-9): open circuit, short circuit to ground, short circuit to B+ voltage Oil pressure switch ground fault (high resistance) Oil pressure switch failure
C1285	DSCCM	Dynamic stability control	Active brake booster solenoid drive circuit fault CUSTOMER SYMPTOM: DSC MIL warnings	Y	DSCCM to active brake booster solenoid drive circuit (FH51-08): open circuit, short circuit to ground, short circuit to B+ voltage, high resistance Active brake booster solenoid failure NOTE: Control module calibration using PDU is required when the fault is repaired and the DTC is cleared. MIL will flash to indicate that configuration is required.

JC4020100034050X

Fig. 2 DTC interpretation (Part 5 of 14). S Type

003 and 004, LS002/002 and 001, FR001/002 and 001 for damage, corrosion, bent and/or pushed back pins. Repair as required.

Check For Short To Ignition

1. Turn ignition switch to 0 position.
2. Measure resistance between ground LS027/020 and LS027/003, ground LS027/020 and LS027/004.
3. If resistance is more than 10,000 ohms, ensure DTC as been eliminated.
4. If resistance is not as specified, inspect harness and connectors LS027 for damage, corrosion, bent and or pushed back pins. Repair as required.

C1155: WHEEL SPEED SENSOR CIRCUIT LEFTHAND FRONT ELECTRICAL FAILURE

S TYPE LESS DSC

Check Wheel Speed Sensor Resistance

1. Turn ignition switch to OFF position.
2. Disconnect ABS control module electrical connector FH33.
3. Measure resistance between the ABS control module electrical connector FH33 pin 17, (W) and FH33 pin 18, (Y).
4. If resistance is 6–7 ohms, install new ABS control module.
5. If resistance is not as specified, install new wheel speed sensor where required.

S TYPE w/DSC

Check Wheel Speed Sensor Resistance

1. Turn ignition switch to OFF position.
2. Disconnect DSC control module electrical connector FH51.
3. Measure resistance between the DSC control module electrical connector FH51 pin 02, (W) and FH51 pin 01, (Y).
4. If resistance is 6–7 ohms, install new DSC control module.
5. If resistance is not as specified, install new wheel speed sensor where required.

XJR, XJ8, XKR & XK8

Mechanical Check

1. Check sensor fitted condition (air gap).
2. Ensure sensor gap 0.0055–0.0658 inch.
3. Ensure sensor face free of foreign matter.
4. Inspect sensor wheel for damaged.
5. Ensure sensor wheel is free of foreign matter.
6. If mechanic check is satisfactory, proceed to "Check Sensor Continuity."
7. If mechanic check is not satisfactory, repair as required.

Check Sensor Continuity

1. Turn ignition switch to 0 position.
2. Disconnect FL001 on top of hub assembly.
3. Measure resistance between sensor pins 1 and 2.
4. If resistance is 1040–1160 ohms, do not reconnect, then proceed to "Check Sensor Output."
5. If resistance is not as specified, replace wheel speed sensor.

Check Sensor Output

The observed voltage will fluctuate and be proportional to the wheel speed.

1. With lefthand front wheel raised, spin wheel and note output voltage from sensor at FR001/001 and FR001/002.
2. If measurement is more than 0 volts and less than 5 volts, proceed to "Check Harness Signal Continuity."
3. If measurement is not as specified, replace wheel speed sensor

Check Harness Signal Continuity

LS027 may be released by pulling the top mounted plunger upwards, this will release and simultaneously withdraw the connector from the ABS/TCS.

1. Disconnect LS027 behind headlamp assembly.
2. Measure resistance between LS027/017 and FL001/002, LS027/018 and FL001/001.
3. If resistance is less than 0.5 ohms, Do not reconnect, then proceed to "Check Harness Short To Ground."
4. If resistance is not as specified, proceed as follows:
   a. Inspect harness and connectors LS027/017 and 018, LS001/002 and 001, FL001/002 and 001 for damage, corrosion, bent and/or pushed back pins.
   b. Check for continuity between all pins.
   c. Repair as required.

DTC	CM	SYSTEM	FAULT DESCRIPTION	MIL	POSSIBLE CAUSES
C1286	DSCCM	Dynamic stability control	Active brake booster mechanical fault CUSTOMER SYMPTOM: DSC MIL warnings	Y	Active brake booster brake pedal fault Active brake booster vacuum fault Active brake booster failure NOTE: Control module calibration using PDU is required when the fault is repaired and the DTC is cleared. MIL will flash to indicate that configuration is required.
C1287	DSCCM	Dynamic stability control	Active brake booster release switch circuit fault CUSTOMER SYMPTOM: DSC MIL warnings	Y	DSCCM to release switch reference voltage circuit (FH51-40): open circuit, short circuit to ground, short circuit to B+ voltage, high resistance Active brake booster release switch failure NOTE: Control module calibration using PDU is required when the fault is repaired and the DTC is cleared. MIL will flash to indicate that configuration is required.
C1288	DSCCM	Dynamic stability control	Primary brake pressure sensor circuit fault CUSTOMER SYMPTOM: DSC MIL warnings	Y	DSCCM to primary brake pressure sensor sensing circuit (FH51-26): open circuit, short circuit to ground, short circuit to B+ voltage, high resistance DSCCM to primary brake pressure sensor reference voltage / ground circuit(s) (FH51-10, FH51-43): open circuit, short circuit to ground, short circuit to B+ voltage, high resistance Primary brake pressure sensor failure NOTE: Control module calibration using PDU is required when the fault is repaired and the DTC is cleared. MIL will flash to indicate that configuration is required.

JC4020100034060X

Fig. 2 DTC interpretation (Part 6 of 14). S Type

Check Harness Short To Ground

1. Measure insulation resistance between ground LS29L (adjacent to the ABS pump) and and LS027/017, ground LS29L and LS027/018.
2. If resistance is more than 10,000 ohms, do not reconnect, then proceed to "Check Harness Short Core To Core."
3. If resistance is not as specified, proceed as follows:
   a. Inspect harness and connectors LS027/017 and 018, LS001/002 and 001, FL001/002 and 001 for damage, corrosion, bent and/or pushed back pins.
   b. Check for resistance against ground between all connectors and ground LS29L.
   c. Repair as required.

Check Harness Short Core To Core

1. Measure insulation resistance between LS027/017 and LS027/018.
2. If resistance is more than 10,000 ohms, proceed to "Check For Short To B+."?
3. If resistance is not as specified, inspect harness and connectors LS027/017 and 018, LS001/002 and 001, FL001/002 and 001 for damage, corrosion, bent and/or pushed back pins. Repair as required.

Check For Short To B+

1. Turn ignition switch to II position.
2. Measure voltage between ground LS29L and LS027/017, ground LS29L and LS027/018.
3. If measurement is 0 volts, proceed to "Check For Short To Ignition."
4. If measurement is not as specified, inspect harness and connectors LS027/017 and 018, LS001/002 and 001, FL001/002 and 001 for damage, corrosion, bent and/or pushed back pins. Repair as required.

Check For Short To Ignition

1. Turn ignition switch to 0 position.
2. Measure resistance between ground LS027/020 and LS027/017, ground LS027/020 and LS027/018.
3. If resistance is more than 10,000 ohms, ensure DTC as been eliminated.
4. If resistance is not as specified, inspect harness and connectors LS027 for damage, corrosion, bent and or pushed back pins. Repair as required.

C1165: WHEEL SPEED SENSOR CIRCUIT RIGHTHAND REAR ELECTRICAL FAILURE

S TYPE LESS DSC

Check Wheel Speed Sensor Resistance

1. Turn ignition switch to OFF position.
2. Disconnect ABS control module electrical connector FH33.
3. Measure resistance between the ABS control module electrical connector FH33 pin 6, (YG) and FH33 pin 7, (WG).
4. If resistance is 6–7 ohms, install new ABS control module.
5. If resistance is not as specified, install new wheel speed sensor where required.

S TYPE w/DSC

Check Wheel Speed Sensor Resistance

1. Turn ignition switch to OFF position.
2. Disconnect DSC control module electrical connector FH51.
3. Measure resistance between the DSC control module electrical connector

DTC	CM	SYSTEM	FAULT DESCRIPTION	MIL	POSSIBLE CAUSES
C1289	DSCCM	Dynamic stability control	Secondary brake pressure sensor circuit fault CUSTOMER SYMPTOM: DSC MIL warnings	Y	DSCCM to secondary brake pressure sensor sensing circuit (FH51-28): open circuit, short circuit to ground, short circuit to B+ voltage, high resistance DSCCM to secondary brake pressure sensor reference voltage / ground circuit(s) (FH51-12, FH51-45): open circuit, short circuit to ground, short circuit to B+ voltage, high resistance Secondary brake pressure sensor failure NOTE: Control module calibration using PDU is required when the fault is repaired and the DTC is cleared. MIL will flash to indicate that configuration is required.
C1414	RCM	SRS airbag system	Incorrect control module fitted	Y	Replace RCM (correct part number)
C1416	ADCM	Suspension adaptive damping (CATS)	RH front damper solenoid circuit short circuit to B+ voltage CUSTOMER SYMPTOM: Dampers default to firm; fault message	M	ADCM to RH front damper solenoid circuit(s) (CA11- 7, CA11-8): short circuit to B+ voltage RH front damper solenoid failure
C1417	ADCM	Suspension adaptive damping (CATS)	RH front damper solenoid circuit short circuit ground CUSTOMER SYMPTOM: Dampers default to firm; fault message	M	ADCM to RH front damper solenoid circuit(s) (CA11- 7, CA11-8): short circuit to ground RH front damper solenoid failure
C1419	ADCM	Suspension adaptive damping (CATS)	RH front damper solenoid circuit open circuit CUSTOMER SYMPTOM: Dampers default to firm; fault message	M	RH front damper solenoid disconnected ADCM to RH front damper solenoid circuit(s) (CA11- 7, CA11-8): open circuit RH front damper solenoid failure

JC4020100034070X

Fig. 2 DTC interpretation (Part 7 of 14). S Type

FH51 pin 37, (YG) and FH51 pin 38, (WG).

4. If resistance is 6–7 ohms, install new DSC control module.
5. If resistance is not as specified, install new wheel speed sensor.

XJR, XJ8, XKR & XK8

Mechanical Check

1. Check sensor fitted condition (air gap).
2. Ensure sensor gap 0.0055–0.0658 inch.
3. Ensure sensor face is free of foreign matter.
4. Inspect sensor wheel for damaged.
5. Ensure sensor wheel is free of foreign matter.
6. If mechanic check is satisfactory, proceed to "Check Sensor Continuity."
7. If mechanic check is not satisfactory, repair as required.

Check Sensor Continuity

1. Turn ignition switch to 0 position.
2. Disconnect RA002 on rear of hub assembly.
3. Measure resistance between sensor pins 1 and 2.
4. If resistance is 1040–1160 ohms, do not reconnect, then proceed to "Check Sensor Output."
5. If resistance is not as specified, replace wheel speed sensor.

Check Sensor Output

The observed voltage will fluctuate and be proportional to the wheel speed.

1. With righthand rear wheel raised, spin wheel and note output voltage from sensor at RA002/001 and RA002/002.
2. If measurement is more than 0 volts and less than 5 volts, proceed to "Check Harness Signal Continuity."
3. If measurement is not as specified, replace wheel speed sensor

Check Harness Signal Continuity

LS027 may be released by pulling the top mounted plunger upwards, this will release and simultaneously withdraw the connector from the ABS/TCS.

1. Disconnect LS027 behind headlamp assembly.
2. Measure resistance between LS027/007 and RA002/002, LS027/006 and RA002/001.
3. If resistance is less than 0.5 ohms, Do not reconnect, then proceed to "Check Harness Short To Ground."
4. If resistance is not as specified, proceed as follows:
   a. Inspect harness and connectors LS027/006 and 007, LS003/007 and 008, CA009/001 and 002, RA002/001 and 002 for damage, corrosion, bent and/or pushed back pins.
   b. Check for continuity between all pins.
   c. Repair as required.

Check Harness Short To Ground

1. Measure insulation resistance between ground LS29L (adjacent to the ABS pump) and and LS027/006, ground LS29L and LS027/007.
2. If resistance is more than 10,000 ohms, do not reconnect, then proceed to "Check Harness Short Core To Core."
3. If resistance is not as specified, proceed as follows:
   a. Inspect harness and connectors LS027/006 and 007, LS003/007 and 008, CA009/001 and 002, RA002/001 and 002 for damage, corrosion, bent and/or pushed back pins.
   b. Check for resistance against ground between all connectors and ground LS29L.
   c. Repair as required.

Check Harness Short Core To Core

1. Measure insulation resistance between LS027/006 and LS027/007.
2. If resistance is more than 10,000 ohms, proceed to "Check For Short To B+."
3. If resistance is not as specified, inspect harness and connectors LS027/006

DTC	CM	SYSTEM	FAULT DESCRIPTION	MIL	POSSIBLE CAUSES
C1421	ADCM	Suspension adaptive damping (CATS)	LH front damper solenoid circuit short circuit to B+ voltage CUSTOMER SYMPTOM: Dampers default to firm; fault message	M	ADCM to LH front damper solenoid circuit(s) (CA11- 5, CA11-6): short circuit to B+ voltage LH front damper solenoid failure
C1422	ADCM	Suspension adaptive damping (CATS)	LH front damper solenoid circuit short circuit ground CUSTOMER SYMPTOM: Dampers default to firm; fault message	M	ADCM to LH front damper solenoid circuit(s) (CA11- 5, CA11-6): short circuit to ground LH front damper solenoid failure
C1424	ADCM	Suspension adaptive damping (CATS)	LH front damper solenoid circuit open circuit CUSTOMER SYMPTOM: Dampers default to firm; fault message	M	LH front damper solenoid disconnected ADCM to LH front damper solenoid circuit(s) (CA11- 5, CA11-6): open circuit LH front damper solenoid failure
C1425	ADCM	Suspension adaptive damping (CATS)	RH rear damper solenoid circuit short circuit ground CUSTOMER SYMPTOM: Dampers default to firm; fault message	M	ADCM to RH rear damper solenoid circuit(s) (CA11- 1, CA11-2): short circuit to ground RH rear damper solenoid failure
C1426	ADCM	Suspension adaptive damping (CATS)	RH rear damper solenoid circuit short circuit to B+ voltage CUSTOMER SYMPTOM: Dampers default to firm; fault message	M	ADCM to RH rear damper solenoid circuit(s) (CA11- 1, CA11-2): short circuit to B+ voltage RH rear damper solenoid failure
C1427	ADCM	Suspension adaptive damping (CATS)	RH rear damper solenoid circuit open circuit CUSTOMER SYMPTOM: Dampers default to firm; fault message	M	RH rear damper solenoid disconnected ADCM to RH rear damper solenoid circuit(s) (CA11- 1, CA11-2): open circuit RH rear damper solenoid failure

JC4020100034080X

Fig. 2 DTC interpretation (Part 8 of 14). S Type

and 007, LS003/007 and 008, CA009/001 and 002, RA002/001 and 002 for damage, corrosion, bent and/or pushed back pins. Repair as required.

Check For Short To B+

1. Turn ignition switch to II position.
2. Measure voltage between ground LS29L and LS027/006, ground LS29L and LS027/007.
3. If measurement is 0 volts, proceed to "Check For Short To Ignition."
4. If measurement is not as specified, inspect harness and connectors LS027/006 and 007, LS003/007 and 008, CA009/001 and 002, RA002/001 and 002 for damage, corrosion, bent and/or pushed back pins. Repair as required.

Check For Short To Ignition

1. Turn ignition switch to 0 position.
2. Measure resistance between ground LS027/020 and LS027/006, ground LS027/020 and LS027/007.
3. If resistance is more than 10,000 ohms, ensure DTC as been eliminated.
4. If resistance is not as specified, inspect harness and connectors LS027 for damage, corrosion, bent and or pushed back pins. Repair as required.

C1175: WHEEL SPEED SENSOR CIRCUIT LEFTHAND REAR ELECTRICAL FAILURE

S TYPE LESS DSC

Check Wheel Speed Sensor Resistance

1. Turn ignition switch to OFF position.
2. Disconnect ABS control module electrical connector FH33.
3. Measure resistance between the ABS control module electrical connector FH33 pin 21, (WU) and FH33 pin 22, (YU).
4. If resistance is 6–7 ohms, install new ABS control module.
5. If resistance is not as specified, install new wheel speed sensor where required.

S TYPE w/DSC

Check Wheel Speed Sensor Resistance

1. Turn ignition switch to OFF position.
2. Disconnect DSC control module electrical connector FH51.
3. Measure resistance between the DSC control module electrical connector FH51 pin 04, (WU) and FH51 pin 05, (YU).
4. If resistance is 6–7 ohms, install new DSC control module.
5. If resistance is not as specified, install new wheel speed sensor where required.

XJR, XJ8, XKR & XK8

Mechanical Check

1. Check sensor fitted condition (air gap).
2. Ensure sensor gap 0.0055–0.0658 inch.
3. Ensure sensor face is free of foreign matter.
4. Inspect sensor wheel for damaged.
5. Ensure sensor wheel is free of foreign matter.
6. If mechanic check is satisfactory, proceed to "Check Sensor Continuity."
7. If mechanic check is not satisfactory, repair as required.

Check Sensor Continuity

1. Turn ignition switch to 0 position.
2. Disconnect LA002 on rear of hub assembly.
3. Measure resistance between sensor pins 1 and 2.
4. If resistance is 1040–1160 ohms, do not reconnect, then proceed to "Check Sensor Output."
5. If resistance is not as specified, replace wheel speed sensor.

DTC	CM	SYSTEM	FAULT DESCRIPTION	MIL	POSSIBLE CAUSES
C1430	ADCM	Suspension adaptive damping (CATS)	LH rear damper solenoid circuit open circuit CUSTOMER SYMPTOM: Dampers default to firm; fault message	M	LH rear damper solenoid disconnected ADCM to LH rear damper solenoid circuit(s) (CA11-3, CA11-4): open circuit LH rear damper solenoid failure
C1431	ADCM	Suspension adaptive damping (CATS)	LH rear damper solenoid circuit short circuit to B+ voltage CUSTOMER SYMPTOM: Dampers default to firm; fault message	M	ADCM to LH rear damper solenoid circuit(s) (CA11-3, CA11-4): short circuit to B+ voltage LH rear damper solenoid failure
C1432	ADCM	Suspension adaptive damping (CATS)	LH rear damper solenoid circuit short circuit ground CUSTOMER SYMPTOM: Dampers default to firm; fault message	M	ADCM to LH rear damper solenoid circuit(s) (CA11-3, CA11-4): short circuit to ground LH rear damper solenoid failure
C1435	ADCM	Suspension adaptive damping (CATS)	Rear vertical accelerometer sensing circuit fault CUSTOMER SYMPTOM: Dampers default to firm; fault message	M	Rear vertical accelerometer incorrectly oriented ADCM to rear vertical accelerometer sensing circuit (CA12-10): open circuit, short circuit to ground, short circuit to B+ voltage Rear vertical accelerometer failure
C1446	GECM	Instrument pack	Parking brake switch circuit fault CUSTOMER SYMPTOM: Drive away door locking inoperative (manual transmission vehicles)	N	GECM to parking brake switch circuit (CA31-19): open circuit, short circuit to ground, short circuit to B+ voltage Parking brake switch ground fault (high resistance) Parking brake switch failure
C1455	ADCM	Suspension adaptive damping (CATS)	Front vertical accelerometer sensing circuit fault CUSTOMER SYMPTOM: Dampers default to firm; fault message	M	Front vertical accelerometer incorrectly oriented ADCM to front vertical accelerometer sensing circuit (CA12-12): open circuit, short circuit to ground, short circuit to B+ voltage Front vertical accelerometer failure

JC4020100034090X

Fig. 2 DTC interpretation (Part 9 of 14). S Type

Check Sensor Output

The observed voltage will fluctuate and be proportional to the wheel speed.

1. With lefthand rear wheel raised, spin wheel and note output voltage from sensor at LA002/001 and LA002/002.
2. If measurement is more than 0 volts and less than 5 volts, proceed to "Check Harness Signal Continuity."
3. If measurement is not as specified, replace wheel speed sensor

Check Harness Signal Continuity

LS027 may be released by pulling the top mounted plunger upwards, this will release and simultaneously withdraw the connector from the ABS/TCS.

1. Disconnect LS027 behind headlamp assembly.
2. Measure resistance between LS027/021 and LA002/002, LS027/022 and LA002/001.
3. If resistance is less than 0.5 ohms, Do not reconnect, then proceed to "Check Harness Short To Ground."
4. If resistance is not as specified, proceed as follows:
   a. Inspect harness and connectors LS027/022 and 021, LS003/009 and 010, CA029/001 and 002, LA002/001 and 002 for damage, corrosion, bent and/or pushed back pins.
   b. Check for continuity between all pins.
   c. Repair as required.

Check Harness Short To Ground

1. Measure insulation resistance between ground LS29L (adjacent to the ABS pump) and and LS027/022, ground LS29L and LS027/021.
2. If resistance is more than 10,000 ohms, do not reconnect, then proceed to "Check Harness Short Core To Core."
3. If resistance is not as specified, proceed as follows:
   a. Inspect harness and connectors LS027/022 and 021, LS003/009 and 010, CA029/001 and 002, LA002/001 and 002 for damage, corrosion, bent and/or pushed back pins.
   b. Check for resistance against ground between all connectors and ground LS29L.
   c. Repair as required.

Check Harness Short Core To Core

1. Measure insulation resistance between LS027/022 and LS027/021.
2. If resistance is more than 10,000 ohms, proceed to "Check For Short To B+."
3. If resistance is not as specified, inspect harness and connectors LS027/022 and 021, LS003/009 and 010, CA029/001 and 002, LA002/001 and 002 for damage, corrosion, bent and/or pushed back pins. Repair as required.

Check For Short To B+

1. Turn ignition switch to II position.
2. Measure voltage between ground LS29L and LS027/022, ground LS29L and LS027/021.
3. If measurement is 0 volts, proceed to "Check For Short To Ignition."
4. If measurement is not as specified, inspect harness and connectors LS027/022 and 021, LS003/009 and 010, CA029/001 and 002, LA002/001 and 002 for damage, corrosion, bent and/or pushed back pins. Repair as required.

Check For Short To Ignition

1. Turn ignition switch to 0 position.
2. Measure resistance between ground LS027/020 and LS027/021, ground LS027/020 and LS027/022.
3. If resistance is more than 10,000 ohms, ensure DTC as been eliminated.
4. If resistance is not as specified, inspect harness and connectors LS027 for damage, corrosion, bent and or pushed back pins. Repair as required.

C1233: WHEEL SPEED SENSOR CIRCUIT LEFTHAND FRONT SIGNAL FAILURE

S TYPE LESS DSC

Check Wheel Speed Sensor Resistance

1. Turn ignition switch to OFF position.
2. Disconnect ABS control module electrical connector FH33.
3. Measure resistance between ABS control module electrical connector FH33 pin 3, (WR) and FH33 pin 4, (YR).
4. If resistance is 6–7 ohms, install new ABS control module.
5. If resistance is not as specified, install new wheel speed sensor where required.

DTC	CM	SYSTEM	FAULT DESCRIPTION	MIL	POSSIBLE CAUSES
C1515	ADCM	Suspension adaptive damping (CATS)	Lateral accelerometer sensing circuit fault CUSTOMER SYMPTOM: Dampers default to firm; fault message	M	Lateral accelerometer incorrectly oriented ADCM to lateral accelerometer sensing circuit (CA12-11): open circuit, short circuit to ground, short circuit to B+ voltage Lateral accelerometer failure
C1699	RPACM	Reverse parking aid	LH sensor circuit short circuit to B+ voltage CUSTOMER SYMPTOM: Reverse parking aid inoperative	Y	RPACM to LH sensor sense circuit (CA112-11): short circuit to B+ voltage RPACM to LH sensor power supply circuit (CA112-15): short circuit to B+ voltage
C1700	RPACM	Reverse parking aid	LH sensor circuit short circuit fault CUSTOMER SYMPTOM: Reverse parking aid inoperative	Y	RPACM to LH sensor sense circuit (CA112-11): open circuit, short circuit ground RPACM to LH sensor ground circuit (CA112-16): open circuit, short circuit ground
C1701	RPACM	Reverse parking aid	LH sensor fault CUSTOMER SYMPTOM: Reverse parking aid inoperative	Y	LH sensor failure
C1702	RPACM	Reverse parking aid	RH sensor circuit short circuit to B+ voltage CUSTOMER SYMPTOM: Reverse parking aid inoperative	Y	RPACM to RH sensor sense circuit (CA112-24): short circuit to B+ voltage RPACM to RH sensor power supply circuit (CA112-15): short circuit to B+ voltage
C1703	RPACM	Reverse parking aid	RH sensor circuit short circuit fault CUSTOMER SYMPTOM: Reverse parking aid inoperative	Y	RPACM to RH sensor sense circuit (CA112-24): open circuit, short circuit ground RPACM to RH sensor ground circuit (CA112-16): open circuit, short circuit ground

JC4020100034100X

Fig. 2 DTC interpretation (Part 10 of 14). S Type

S TYPE w/DSC

Check Wheel Speed Sensor Resistance

1. Turn ignition switch to OFF position.
2. Disconnect DSC control module electrical connector FH51.
3. Measure resistance between DSC control module electrical connector FH51 pin 34, (WR) and FH51 pin 35, (YR).
4. If resistance is 6–7 ohms, install new DSC control module.
5. If resistance is not as specified, install new wheel speed sensor where required.

XJR, XJ8, XKR & XK8

Refer to "C1155: Wheel Speed Sensor Circuit Lefthand Front Electrical Failure."

C1234: WHEEL SPEED SENSOR CIRCUIT RIGHTHAND FRONT SIGNAL FAILURE

S TYPE LESS DSC

Check Wheel Speed Sensor Resistance

1. Turn ignition switch to OFF position.
2. Disconnect ABS control module electrical connector FH33.
3. Measure resistance between ABS control module electrical connector FH33 pin 17, (W) and FH33 pin 18, (Y).
4. If resistance is 6–7 ohms, install new ABS control module.
5. If resistance is not as specified, install new wheel speed sensor where required.

S TYPE w/DSC

Check Wheel Speed Sensor Resistance

1. Turn ignition switch to OFF position.
2. Disconnect DSC control module electrical connector FH51.
3. Measure resistance between DSC control module electrical connector FH51 pin 02, (W) and FH51 pin 01, (Y).
4. If resistance is 6–7 ohms, install new DSC control module.
5. If resistance is not as specified, install new wheel speed sensor where required.

XJR, XJ8, XKR & XK8

Refer to "C1145: Wheel Speed Sensor Circuit Righthand Front Electrical Failure."

C1235: WHEEL SPEED SENSOR CIRCUIT RIGHTHAND REAR SIGNAL FAILURE

S TYPE LESS DSC

Check Wheel Speed Sensor Resistance

1. Turn ignition switch to OFF position.
2. Disconnect ABS control module electrical connector FH33.
3. Measure resistance between ABS control module electrical connector FH33 pin 6, (YG) and FH33 pin 7, (WG).
4. If resistance is 6–7 ohms, install new ABS control module.
5. If resistance is not as specified, install new wheel speed sensor where required.

S TYPE w/DSC

Check Wheel Speed Sensor Resistance

1. Turn ignition switch to OFF position.
2. Disconnect DSC control module electrical connector FH51.
3. Measure resistance between DSC control module electrical connector FH51 pin 38, (YG) and FH51 pin 37, (WG).
4. If resistance is 6–7 ohms, install new DSC control module.
5. If resistance is not as specified, install new wheel speed sensor where required.

XJR, XJ8, XKR & XK8

Refer to "C1165: Wheel Speed Sensor Circuit Righthand Rear Electrical Failure."

C1236: WHEEL SPEED SENSOR CIRCUIT LEFTHAND REAR SIGNAL FAILURE

S TYPE LESS DSC

Check Wheel Speed Sensor Resistance

1. Turn ignition switch to OFF position.
2. Disconnect ABS control module electrical connector FH33.
3. Measure resistance between ABS control module electrical connector FH33 pin 21, (WU) and FH33 pin 22, (YU).
4. If resistance is 6–7 ohms, install new ABS control module.
5. If resistance is not as specified, install new wheel speed sensor where required.

DTC	CM	SYSTEM	FAULT DESCRIPTION	MIL	POSSIBLE CAUSES
C1704	RPACM	Reverse parking aid	RH sensor fault CUSTOMER SYMPTOM: Reverse parking aid inoperative	Y	RH sensor failure
C1705	RPACM	Reverse parking aid	Center LH sensor circuit short circuit to B+ voltage CUSTOMER SYMPTOM: Reverse parking aid inoperative	Y	RPACM to center LH sensor sense circuit (CA112-10): short circuit to B+ voltage RPACM to center LH sensor power supply circuit (CA112-15): short circuit to B+ voltage
C1706	RPACM	Reverse parking aid	Center LH sensor circuit short circuit fault CUSTOMER SYMPTOM: Reverse parking aid inoperative	Y	RPACM to center LH sensor sense circuit (CA112-10): open circuit, short circuit ground RPACM to center LH sensor ground circuit (CA112-16): open circuit, short circuit ground
C1707	RPACM	Reverse parking aid	Center LH sensor fault CUSTOMER SYMPTOM: Reverse parking aid inoperative	Y	Center LH sensor failure
C1708	RPACM	Reverse parking aid	Center RH sensor circuit short circuit to B+ voltage CUSTOMER SYMPTOM: Reverse parking aid inoperative	Y	RPACM to center RH sensor sense circuit (CA112-23): short circuit to B+ voltage RPACM to center RH sensor power supply circuit (CA112-15): short circuit to B+ voltage
C1709	RPACM	Reverse parking aid	Center RH sensor circuit short circuit fault CUSTOMER SYMPTOM: Reverse parking aid inoperative	Y	RPACM to center RH sensor sense circuit (CA112-23): open circuit, short circuit ground RPACM to center RH sensor ground circuit (CA112-16): open circuit, short circuit ground

JC4020100034110X

Fig. 2 DTC interpretation (Part 11 of 14). S Type

S TYPE w/DSC

Check Wheel Speed Sensor Resistance

1. Turn ignition switch to OFF position.
2. Disconnect DSC control module electrical connector FH51.
3. Measure resistance between DSC control module electrical connector FH51 pin 04, (WU) and FH51 pin 05, (YU).
4. If resistance is 6–7 ohms, install new DSC control module.
5. If resistance is not as specified, install new wheel speed sensor where required.

XJR, XJ8, XKR & XK8

Refer to "C1175: Wheel Speed Sensor Circuit Lefthand Rear Electrical Failure."

C1267: MODULATOR VALVE FAILURE

XJR, XJ8, XKR & XK8

Check Condition Of Fuse

1. Check fuse located in underhood fusebox, fuse 16.
2. If fuse is satisfactory, proceed to "Measure Connector Voltage."
3. If fuse is not satisfactory, replace as required.

Measure Connector Voltage

1. Disconnect connector LF037, then measure voltage between pins 25 and 24.
2. If measurement is approximately 12 volts, replace HCU.
3. If measurement is not as specified, proceed to "Inspect Harness/Connectors."

Inspect Harness/Connectors

1. Inspect harness/connectors from ABS module to fusebox for damage, corrosion, bent and/or pushed back pins.
2. If damage is found, repair as required.
3. If no damage is found, replace HCU.

C1277: STEERING WHEEL ANGLE 1 & 2 CIRCUIT FAILURE

S TYPE

Check Voltage Supply To Steering Wheel Angle Sensor Circuit

1. Remove driver side instrument panel lower panel.
2. Disconnect steering wheel angle sensor electrical connector FC16.
3. Disconnect steering wheel angle sensor electrical connector FC16.
4. Switch ignition to RUN position.
5. Measure voltage between steering wheel angle sensor electrical connector FC16 pin 1, (GO) and ground.
6. If measurement is less than 12 volts, proceed to "Check Voltage Supply From Primary Junction Box To Steering Wheel Angle Sensor Circuit+."
7. If measurement is not as specified, proceed to "Check Steering Wheel Angle Sensor Ground Supply Circuit."

Check Voltage Supply From Primary Junction Box To Steering Wheel Angle Sensor Circuit+

1. Remove righthand lower A pillar trim pillar
2. Measure voltage between steering wheel angle sensor circuit electrical connector FC13 pin 11, (GO) and ground.
3. If measurement is less than 12 volts, proceed to "Check Voltage Supply From Primary Junction Box To Steering Wheel Angle Sensor Circuit+."
4. If measurement is not as specified, repair steering wheel angle sensor circuit between electrical connector FC13 pin 11, (GO) and electrical connector FC16 pin 1, (GO).

Check Voltage Supply From Primary Junction Box To Steering Wheel Angle Sensor Circuit+

1. Measure voltage between steering wheel angle sensor circuit electrical connector FC13 pin 10, (GU) and ground.
2. If measurement is less than 12 volts, proceed to "Check Voltage Supply From Primary Junction Box To Steering Wheel Angle Sensor Circuit+."
3. If measurement is not as specified, install new steering wheel angle sensor circuit electrical connector FC13.

Check Voltage Supply From Primary Junction Box To Steering Wheel Angle Sensor Circuit+

1. Measure voltage supply from fuse 5 at primary junction box.
2. If measurement is less than 12 volts, proceed as follows:
   a. Install new fuse.
   b. If fuse fails check primary junction box.
3. If measurement is not as specified, repair circuit between steering wheel

DTC	CM	SYSTEM	FAULT DESCRIPTION	MIL	POSSIBLE CAUSES
C1710	RPACM	Reverse parking aid	Center RH sensor fault CUSTOMER SYMPTOM: Reverse parking aid inoperative	Y	Center RH sensor failure
C1730	DSCCM	Dynamic stability control	DSCCM sensor reference voltage supply not within specification	Y	DSCCM failure NOTE: Control module calibration using PDU is required when the fault is repaired and the DTC is cleared. MIL will flash to indicate that configuration is required.
C1742	RPACM	Reverse parking aid	Parking aid sounder circuit fault CUSTOMER SYMPTOM: Reverse parking aid inoperative	Y	RPACM to sounder circuit(s) (CA112-14, CA114-17): open circuit, short circuit to ground Parking aid sounder failure
C1743	RPACM	Reverse parking aid	Parking aid sounder circuit short circuit to B+ voltage CUSTOMER SYMPTOM: Reverse parking aid inoperative	Y	RPACM to sounder circuit(s) (CA112-14, CA114-17): short circuit to B+ voltage
C1748	RPACM	Reverse parking aid	Reverse parking aid switch circuit fault CUSTOMER SYMPTOM: Reverse parking aid switch inoperative	N	RPACM to switch circuit (CA112-7): open circuit, short circuit to ground, short circuit to B+ voltage Reverse parking aid switch ground fault Reverse parking aid switch failure
C1805	ABS/ TCCM	Anti-lock braking / traction control	ABS/TCCM mismatched with PCM (powertrain control module) CUSTOMER SYMPTOM: ABS/TC MIL warnings	Y	Replace ABS/TCCM

JC4020100034120X

Fig. 2 DTC interpretation (Part 12 of 14). S Type

angle sensor circuit electrical connector FC13 pin 10, (GU) and output side of fuse 3 at primary junction box.

Check Steering Wheel Angle Sensor Ground Supply Circuit

1. Measure resistance between steering wheel angle sensor electrical connector FC16 pin 4, (NY) and ground.
2. If resistance is less than 0.5 ohms, install new steering wheel angle sensor.
3. If resistance is not as specified, proceed to "Check Continuity Of Steering Wheel Angle Sensor Ground Supply Circuit."

Check Continuity Of Steering Wheel Angle Sensor Ground Supply Circuit

1. Switch ignition to OFF position.
2. Disconnect DSC control module electrical connector FH51.
3. Measure resistance between steering wheel angle sensor electrical connector FC16 pin 4, (NY) and DSC control module electrical connector FH51 pin 30, (NY).
4. If resistance is less than 0.5 ohms, proceed to "Check Steering Wheel Angle Sensor Ground Supply Circuit For Short To Ground."
5. If resistance is not as specified, repair circuit between steering wheel angle sensor electrical connector FC16 pin 4, (NY) and DSC control module electrical connector FH51 pin 30, (NY).

Check Steering Wheel Angle Sensor Ground Supply Circuit For Short To Ground

1. Measure resistance between DSC control module electrical connector FH51 pin 30, (NY) and ground.
2. If resistance is less than 0.5 ohms, repair circuit between steering wheel angle sensor electrical connector FC16 pin 4, (NY) and DSC control module electrical connector FH51 pin 30, (NY).
3. If resistance is not as specified, install new DSC control module.

C1278: STEERING WHEEL ANGLE 1 & 2 SIGNAL FAULT

S TYPE

Check Steering Wheel Angle 1 & 2 Sensor Signal

1. Remove driver side instrument panel lower panel.
2. Disconnect steering wheel angle sensor electrical connector FC16.
3. Disconnect steering wheel angle sensor electrical connector FC16.
4. Measure steering wheel angle sensor resistances between FC16 pin 3, and FC16 pin 4, FC16 pin 2, and FC16 pin 4.
5. If resistance is 6–8 ohms, proceed to "Check Continuity Of Wheel Angle 1 & 2 Signal Circuit."
6. If resistance is not as specified, install new steering wheel angle sensor.

Check Continuity Of Wheel Angle 1 & 2 Signal Circuit

1. Disconnect DSC control module electrical connector FH51.
2. Measure wheel angle 1 and 2 signal circuit resistance between FC16 pin 3, (WR) and FH51 pin 14, (WR) FC16 pin 2, (S) and FH51 pin 47, (S).
3. If resistance is less than 0.5 ohms, proceed to "Check Wheel Angle 1 & 2 Signal Circuit For Short To Ground."
4. If resistance is not as specified, repair necessary wheel angle signal circuit.

Check Wheel Angle 1 & 2 Signal Circuit For Short To Ground

1. Measure wheel angle 1 and 2 signal circuit resistance between FC16 pin 3, (WR) and ground FC16 pin 2, (S) and ground.
2. If resistance is less than 0.5 ohms, repair necessary wheel angle signal circuit.
3. If resistance is not as specified, install new DSC control module.

C1279: YAW RATE SENSOR CIRCUIT FAILURE

S TYPE

Check Continuity Of Yaw Rate Sensor Supply Circuit

1. Disconnect yaw rate sensor electrical connector CA40.

DTC	CM	SYSTEM	FAULT DESCRIPTION	MIL	POSSIBLE CAUSES
C1805	DSCCM	Dynamic stability control	DSCCM mismatched with PCM (powertrain control module) CUSTOMER SYMPTOM: DSC MIL warnings	Y	Replace DSCCM (correct part number)
C1920	RPACM	Reverse parking aid	Reverse parking aid state illumination circuit fault CUSTOMER SYMPTOM: Reverse parking aid inoperative	N / Y	RPACM to switch STATE LED circuit (CA112-19): open circuit, short circuit to ground Reverse parking aid switch ground fault Reverse parking aid switch failure
C1924	ADCM	Variable assist steering	Variable assist steering actuator circuit fault CUSTOMER SYMPTOM: "Steering feel" incorrect	N	GECM to variable assist steering actuator circuit FH60-9: open circuit, short circuit to ground, short circuit to B+ voltage, high resistance Variable assist steering actuator failure
C1925	ADCM	Variable assist steering	Variable assist steering actuator circuit fault CUSTOMER SYMPTOM: "Steering feel" incorrect	N	GECM to variable assist steering actuator circuit FH60-2: open circuit, short circuit to ground, short circuit to B+ voltage, high resistance Variable assist steering actuator failure
C1960	DSCCM	Dynamic stability control	Brake switch circuit fault (RECM brake switch message does not agree with DSCCM brake switch message) CUSTOMER SYMPTOM: DSC MIL warnings	Y	DSCCM to brake switch circuit: open circuit, short circuit to ground, short circuit to B+ voltage, high resistance RECM to brake switch circuit: open circuit, short circuit to ground, short circuit to B+ voltage, high resistance

JC4020100034130X

Fig. 2 DTC interpretation (Part 13 of 14). S Type

2. Disconnect DSC control module electrical connector FH51.
3. Measure resistance between yaw rate sensor electrical connector CA40 pin 3, (YR) and DSC control module electrical connector FH51 pin 44, (YR).
4. If resistance is less than 0.5 ohms, proceed to "Check Yaw Rate Sensor Supply Circuit For Short To Ground."
5. If resistance is not as specified, repair circuit between yaw rate sensor electrical connector CA40 pin 3, (YR) and DSC control module electrical connector FH51 pin 44, (YR).

Check Yaw Rate Sensor Supply Circuit For Short To Ground

1. Measure resistance between yaw rate sensor electrical connector CA40 pin 3, (YR) and ground FH51 pin 32, (B).
2. If resistance is less than 0.5 ohms, repair circuit between yaw rate sensor electrical connector CA40 pin 3, (YR) and DSC control module electrical connector FH51 pin 44, (YR).
3. If resistance is not as specified, proceed to "Check Continuity Of Yaw Rate Sensor Signal Ground Circuit."

Check Continuity Of Yaw Rate Sensor Signal Ground Circuit

1. Measure resistance between yaw rate sensor electrical connector CA40 pin 2, (NR) and DSC control module electrical connector FH51 pin 11, (NR).
2. If resistance is less than 0.5 ohms, proceed to "Check Yaw Rate Sensor Signal Ground Circuit For Short To Ground."
3. If resistance is not as specified, repair circuit between yaw rate sensor electrical connector CA40 pin 2, (NR) and DSC control module electrical connector FH51 pin 11, (NR).

Check Yaw Rate Sensor Signal Ground Circuit For Short To Ground

1. Measure resistance between yaw rate sensor electrical connector CA40 pin 2, (NR) and ground FH51 pin 32, (B).
2. If resistance is less than 0.5 ohms, repair circuit between yaw rate sensor electrical connector CA40 pin 2, (NR) and DSC control module electrical connector FH51 pin 11, (NR).
3. If resistance is not as specified, install new DSC control module.

C1280: YAW RATE SENSOR SIGNAL FAULT

S TYPE

Check Continuity Of Yaw Rate Sensor Signal Input Circuit

1. Measure resistance between yaw rate sensor electrical connector CA40 pin 1, (WR) and DSC control module electrical connector FH51 pin 27, (WR).
2. If resistance is less than 0.5 ohms, proceed to "Check Yaw Rate Sensor Signal Input Circuit For Short To Ground."
3. If resistance is not as specified, repair circuit between yaw rate sensor electrical connector CA40 pin 1, (WR) and DSC control module electrical connector FH51 pin 27, (WR).

Check Yaw Rate Sensor Signal Input Circuit For Short To Ground

1. Measure resistance between yaw rate sensor electrical connector CA40 pin 1, (WR) and ground FH51 pin 32, (B).
2. If resistance is less than 0.5 ohms, repair circuit between yaw rate sensor electrical connector CA40 pin 1, (WR) and DSC control module electrical connector FH51 pin 27, (WR).
3. If resistance is not as specified, install new DSC control module.

C1281: LATERAL ACCELEROMETER CIRCUIT FAILURE

S TYPE

Check Continuity Of Lateral Accelerometer Supply Circuit

1. Disconnect lateral accelerometer electrical connector CA39.
2. Disconnect DSC control module electrical connector FH51.
3. Measure resistance between lateral accelerometer electrical connector CA39 pin 3, (YU) and DSC control module electrical connector FH51 pin 46, (YU).
4. If resistance is less than 0.5 ohms, proceed to "Check Lateral Accelerometer Supply Circuit For Short To Ground."
5. If resistance is not as specified, repair circuit between lateral accelerometer electrical connector CA39 pin 3, (YU) and DSC control module electrical connector FH51 pin 46, (YU).

Check Lateral Accelerometer Supply Circuit For Short To Ground

1. Measure resistance between lateral accelerometer electrical connector CA39 pin 3, (YU) and ground FH51 pin 32, (B).
2. If resistance is less than 0.5 ohms, repair circuit between lateral accelerometer electrical connector CA39 pin 3, (YU) and DSC control module electrical connector FH51 pin 46, (YU).
3. If resistance is not as specified, proceed to "Check Continuity Of Lateral

Accelerometer Signal Ground Circuit."

Check Continuity Of Lateral Accelerometer Signal Ground Circuit

1. Measure resistance between lateral accelerometer electrical connector CA39 pin 1, (NU) and DSC control module electrical connector FH51 pin 13, (NU).
2. If resistance is less than 0.5 ohms, proceed to "Check Lateral Accelerometer Signal Ground Circuit For Short To Ground."
3. If resistance is not as specified, repair circuit between lateral accelerometer electrical connector CA39 pin 1, (NU) and DSC control module electrical connector FH51 pin 13, (NU).

Check Lateral Accelerometer Signal Ground Circuit For Short To Ground

1. Measure resistance between lateral accelerometer electrical connector CA39 pin 1, (NU) and ground FH51 pin 32, (B).
2. If resistance is less than 0.5 ohms, repair circuit between lateral accelerometer electrical connector CA39 pin 1, (NU) and DSC control module electrical connector FH51 pin 13, (NU).
3. If resistance is not as specified, install new DSC control module.

C1282: LATERAL ACCELEROMETER SIGNAL FAILURE

S TYPE

Check Continuity Of Lateral Accelerometer Signal Input Circuit

1. Measure resistance between lateral accelerometer electrical connector CA39 pin 2, (NU) and DSC control module electrical connector FH51 pin 29, (NU).
2. If resistance is less than 0.5 ohms, repair circuit between lateral accelerometer electrical connector CA39 pin 2, (NU) and DSC control module electrical connector FH51 pin 29, (NU).
3. If resistance is not as specified, proceed to "Check Lateral Accelerometer Signal Input Circuit For Short To Ground."

Check Lateral Accelerometer Signal Input Circuit For Short To Ground

1. Measure resistance between lateral accelerometer electrical connector CA39 pin 2, (NU) and ground.
2. If resistance is less than 0.5 ohms, repair circuit between lateral accelerometer electrical connector CA39 pin 2, (NU) and DSC control module electrical connector FH51 pin 29, (NU).

DTC	Diagnostic Trouble Code.	
CM	The control module(s) the DTC is associated with:	
	ABS/TC	Anti-lock braking / traction control
	ADCM	Adaptive damping
	DSCCM	Dynamic stability control
	GECM	General electronic control module
	RCM	Restraints control module
	RECM	Rear electronic control module
	RPACM	Reverse parking aid control module
MIL	Y = System MIL (if fitted) is activated.	
	N = System MIL (if fitted) is not activated.	
	M = Message displayed.	

JC4020100034140X

Fig. 2 DTC interpretation (Part 14 of 14). S Type

3. If resistance is not as specified, install new DSC control module.

1285: BOOSTER SOLENOID OUTPUT CIRCUIT FAILURE

S TYPE

Check Continuity Of Booster Solenoid Output Circuits

1. Disconnect brake booster solenoid electrical connector FH56.
2. Measure resistance between brake booster solenoid electrical connector and DSC control module electrical connector:
   a. FH56 pin 1, (WG) and FH51 pin 06, (WG).
   b. FH56 pin 2, (SO) and FH51 pin 07, (SO).
3. If resistance is less than 0.5 ohms, proceed to "Check Booster Solenoid Output Circuits For Shorts To Ground."
4. If resistance is not as specified, repair necessary circuit between brake booster solenoid electrical connector pin and DSC control module electrical connector pin.

Check Booster Solenoid Output Circuits For Shorts To Ground

1. Measure resistance between brake booster solenoid electrical connector FH56 pin 1, (WG) and ground FH56 pin 2, (SO) and ground.
2. If resistance is less than 0.5 ohms, repair necessary circuit between brake booster solenoid electrical connector pin and DSC control module electrical connector pin.
3. If resistance is not as specified, install new DSC module.

C1286: BOOSTER MECHANICAL FAULT

S TYPE

Check Brake Booster Vacuum Pipe

1. Switch ignition to RUN position.
2. Check vacuum pipe to brake booster.
3. If vacuum pipe broken or disconnected, install new vacuum pipe.
4. If vacuum pipe is satisfactory, proceed to "Check Brake Booster Solenoid."

Check Brake Booster Solenoid

1. Switch ignition to OFF position.
2. Disconnect brake booster electrical connector, FH56.
3. Measure resistance between pins 3 (NR) and 4 (WR) of brake booster solenoid.
4. If resistance is 1–2 ohms, proceed to "Check Continuity Of Brake Booster Solenoid Circuit."
5. If resistance is not as specified, install new brake booster.

Check Continuity Of Brake Booster Solenoid Circuit

1. Disconnect DSC control module electrical connector, FH51.
2. Measure resistance between brake booster solenoid electrical connector and DSC control module electrical connector:
   a. FH56 pin 4, (WR) and FH51 pin 08, (WR).
   b. FH56 pin 3, (NR) and FH51 pin 24, (NR).
3. If resistance is less than 0.5 ohms, proceed to "Check Brake Booster Solenoid Circuit For Short To Ground."
4. If resistance is not as specified, repair necessary circuit between brake booster solenoid electrical connector pin and DSC control module electrical connector pin.

Check Brake Booster Solenoid Circuit For Short To Ground

1. Measure resistance between brake booster solenoid electrical connector and DSC control module electrical connector:
   a. FH56 pin 4, (WR) and ground.
   b. FH56 pin 3, (NR) and ground.
2. If resistance is less than 0.5 ohms, repair necessary circuit between brake booster solenoid electrical connector pin and DSC control module electrical connector pin.
3. If resistance is not as specified, install new DSC control module.

C1287: BOOSTER PEDAL FORCE SWITCH CIRCUIT FAILURE

S TYPE

Check Voltage Supply To Brake Booster

1. Disconnect brake booster electrical connector, FH56.
2. Switch ignition to RUN position.
3. Measure voltage between brake booster electrical connector FH56 pin 5, (NG) and ground.
4. If measurement is less than 12 volts, proceed to "Check Continuity Of Brake Booster Voltage Supply Circuit."

DTC	FAULT DESCRIPTION	MONITORING CONDITIONS	ABS MIL	DEFAULT ACTION	POSSIBLE CAUSES
C1095	Pump motor failure	Drive vehicle to activate ABS / ASC or TC. Stop vehicle. Drive vehicle > 25 mph	YES	System switches off	Pump motor to CM circuit: high resistance, open circuit or short circuit to ground or B+ voltage Pump motor failure
C1137	Control module internal circuit failure	Ignition ON > 8 minutes	YES*	System switches off	CM ground circuits: high resistance, open circuit or short circuit to B+ voltage CM power circuits: high resistance, open circuit or short circuit to ground CM failure
C1145	Wheel speed sensor circuit right front electrical failure	Drive vehicle > 12.5 mph > 2 minutes	YES	System: – Switches off >3 mph – Inhibited < 3 mph	Wheel speed sensor open or short circuit Wheel speed sensor to CM circuit: high resistance, open circuit or short circuit to ground Wheel speed sensor failure CM failure
C1155	Wheel speed sensor circuit left front electrical failure	Drive vehicle > 12.5 mph > 2 minutes	YES	System: – Switches off > 3 mph – Inhibited < 3 mph	Wheel speed sensor open or short circuit Wheel speed sensor to CM circuit: high resistance, open circuit or short circuit to ground Wheel speed sensor failure CM failure
C1165	Wheel speed sensor circuit right rear trigger electrical failure	Drive vehicle > 12.5 mph > 2 minutes	YES*	System: – Switches off > 3 mph – Inhibited < 3 mph	Wheel speed sensor open or short circuit Wheel speed sensor to CM circuit: high resistance, open circuit or short circuit to ground Wheel speed sensor failure CM failure
C1175	Wheel speed sensor circuit left rear electrical failure	Drive vehicle > 12.5 mph > 2 minutes	YES*	System: – Switches off > 3 mph – Inhibited < 3 mph	Wheel speed sensor open or short circuit Wheel speed sensor to CM circuit: high resistance, open circuit or short circuit to ground Wheel speed sensor failure CM failure

* OBD II fault – If the fault occurs on two consecutive trips, the ECM will flag this DTC and the CHECK ENGINE MIL will be activated.

JC4020100033010X

Fig. 3 DTC interpretation (Part 1 of 3). XJR, XJ8, XKR & XK8

5. If measurement is not as specified, install new brake booster.

Check Continuity Of Brake Booster Voltage Supply Circuit

1. Switch ignition to OFF position.
2. Disconnect DSC control module electrical connector, FH51.
3. Measure resistance between brake booster electrical connector FH56 pin 5, (NG) and DSC control module electrical connector FH51 pin 40, (NG).
4. If resistance is 1–2 ohms, proceed to "Check Brake Booster Voltage Supply Circuit For Short To Ground."
5. If resistance is not as specified, repair circuit between brake booster electrical connector FH56 pin 5, (NG) and DSC control module electrical connector FH51 pin 40, (NG).

Check Brake Booster Voltage Supply Circuit For Short To Ground

1. Measure resistance between brake booster electrical connector FH56 pin 5, (NG) and ground.
2. If resistance is less than 0.5 ohms, repair circuit between brake booster electrical connector FH56 pin 5, (NG) and DSC control module electrical connector FH51 pin 40, (NG).

3. If resistance is not as specified, install new DSC control module.

C1288: PRESSURE TRANSDUCER MAIN/ PRIMARY INPUT CIRCUIT FAILURE

S TYPE

Measure VREF Voltage At Pressure Transducer Main Input Circuit Electrical Connector

1. Switch ignition to OFF position.
2. Disconnect primary pressure transducer electrical connector FH54.
3. Switch ignition to RUN position.
4. Measure VREF voltage at primary pressure transducer electrical connector between FH54 pin 1, (NY) and FH54 pin 3, (YB).
5. If measurement is 4–6 volts, proceed to "Check Pressure Transducer Primary Input Circuit For Shorts To Ground."
6. If measurement is not as specified, install new DSC control module

Check Pressure Transducer Primary Input Circuit For Shorts To Ground

1. Switch ignition to OFF position.
2. Disconnect DSC module electrical connector FH51.
3. Measure resistance between primary pressure transducer input circuit electrical connector FH54 pin 2, (WB) and ground.
4. If resistance is less than 0.5 ohms, repair circuit between primary pressure transducer input electrical connector FH54 pin 2, (WB) and DSC module electrical connector pin FH51 pin 26, (WB).
5. If resistance is not as specified, proceed to "Check Continuity Of Pressure Transducer Primary Input Circuit."

Check Continuity Of Pressure Transducer Primary Input Circuit

1. Measure resistance between pressure transducer primary input circuit electrical connector FH54 pin 2, (WB) and DSC module electrical connector FH51 pin 26, (WB).

DTC	FAULT DESCRIPTION	MONITORING CONDITIONS	ABS MIL	DEFAULT ACTION	POSSIBLE CAUSES
C1233	Wheel speed sensor circuit left front signal failure	Drive vehicle > 25 mph > 2 minutes	YES	System switches off > 12.5 mph or > 2 min.	Wheel speed sensor circuit to CM: open circuit or short circuit to ground Wheel speed sensor open circuit or short circuit Incorrect wheel speed sensor to reluctor air gap CM failure Solenoid valve failure
C1234	Wheel speed sensor circuit right front signal failure	Drive vehicle > 25 mph > 2 minutes	YES	System switches off > 12.5 mph or > 2 min.	Wheel speed sensor circuit to CM: open circuit or short circuit to ground Wheel speed sensor open circuit or short circuit Incorrect wheel speed sensor to reluctor air gap CM failure Solenoid valve failure
C1235	Wheel speed sensor circuit right rear signal failure	Drive vehicle > 25 mph > 2 minutes	YES	System switches off > 12.5 mph or > 2 min.	Wheel speed sensor circuit to CM: open circuit or short circuit to ground Wheel speed sensor open circuit or short circuit Incorrect wheel speed sensor to reluctor air gap CM failure Solenoid valve failure
C1236	Wheel speed sensor circuit left rear signal failure	Drive vehicle > 25 mph > 2 minutes	YES	System switches off > 12.5 mph or > 2 min.	Wheel speed sensor circuit to CM: open circuit or short circuit to ground Wheel speed sensor open circuit or short circuit Incorrect wheel speed sensor to reluctor air gap CM failure Solenoid valve failure
C1267	Modulator valve failure	Drive vehicle > 25 mph	YES	System switches off	ABS system sensors, wiring or connectors: intermittent open circuit, short circuit or short circuit to ground or B+ voltage Electronic (RFI) interference Modulator valve failure CM failure

JC4020100033020X

Fig. 3 DTC interpretation (Part 2 of 3). XJR, XJ8, XKR & XK8

2. If resistance is less than 0.5 ohms, install new pressure transducer.
3. If resistance is not as specified, repair circuit between primary pressure transducer input electrical connector FH54 pin 2, (WB) and DSC module electrical connector pin FH51 pin 26, (WB).

C1289: PRESSURE TRANSDUCER REDUNDANT/SECONDARY INPUT CIRCUIT FAILURE

S TYPE

Measure VREF Voltage At Pressure Transducer Redundant Input Circuit Electrical Connector

1. Switch ignition to OFF position.
2. Disconnect secondary pressure transducer electrical connector FH55.
3. Switch ignition to RUN position.
4. Measure VREF voltage at primary pressure transducer electrical connector between FH55 pin 1, (NY) and FH55 pin 3, (YB).
5. If measurement is 4–6 volts, refer "Check Pressure Transducer Secondary Input Circuit For Shorts To Ground."
6. If measurement is not as specified, install new DSC control module.

Check Pressure Transducer Secondary Input Circuit For Shorts To Ground

1. Switch ignition to OFF position.
2. Disconnect DSC module electrical connector FH51.
3. Measure resistance between primary pressure transducer input circuit electrical connector FH55 pin 2, (WB) and ground.
4. If resistance is less than 0.5 ohms, repair circuit between primary pressure transducer input electrical connector FH55 pin 2, (WB) and DSC module electrical connector pin FH51 pin 26, (WB).
5. If resistance is not as specified, proceed to "Check Continuity Of Pressure Transducer Primary Input Circuit."

Check Continuity Of Pressure Transducer Primary Input Circuit

1. Measure resistance between pressure transducer primary input circuit electrical connector FH55 pin 2, (WB) and DSC module electrical connector FH51 pin 26, (WB).
2. If resistance is less than 0.5 ohms, install new pressure transducer.
3. If resistance is not as specified, repair circuit between primary pressure transducer input electrical connector FH55 pin 2, (WB) and DSC module electrical connector pin FH51 pin 26, (WB).

C1730: REFERENCE VOLTAGE OUT OF RANGE

S TYPE

Check DSC Sensor Reference Voltage

1. Disconnect necessary DSC sensor.
2. Switch ignition to RUN position.
3. Measure DSC sensor voltage supply between:
   a. FH19 pin 2, and ground.
   b. CV3 pin 2, and ground.
   c. FH44 pin 2, and ground.
   d. CV6 pin 2, and ground.
4. If measurement in 4–6 volts, proceed to "C1145, C1155, C1165 or C1175."
5. If measurement is not as specified, proceed to "Check Continuity Of DSC Sensor Reference Voltage Supply Circuit."

Check Continuity Of DSC Sensor Reference Voltage Supply Circuit

1. Switch ignition to OFF position.
2. Disconnect DSC control module electrical connector FH51.
3. Measure DSC sensor voltage supply circuit resistance between:
   a. FH19 pin 2, (W) and FH51 pin 2, (W).
   b. CV3 pin 2, (WU) and FH51 pin 4, (WU).
   c. FH44 pin 2, (WR) and FH51 pin 34, (WR).
   d. CV6 pin 2, (WG) and FH51 pin 37, (WG)
4. If resistance is less than 0.5 ohms, proceed to "Check DSC Sensor Reference Voltage Supply Circuit For Short To Ground."
5. If resistance is not as specified, repair necessary DSC sensor voltage supply circuit.

Check DSC Sensor Reference Voltage Supply Circuit For Short To Ground

1. Measure DSC sensor voltage supply circuit resistance between:
   a. FH19 pin 2, and ground.
   b. CV3 pin 2, and ground.

DTC	FAULT DESCRIPTION	MONITORING CONDITIONS	ABS MIL	DEFAULT ACTION	POSSIBLE CAUSES
B1342	CAN circuit malfunction	Drive vehicle > 12.5 mph	YES	TC/ASC switches off	CAN open circuit fault CAN short circuit fault CM failure
B1676	Supply voltage out of range	Drive vehicle > 12.5 mph > 1500 rpm	YES	System: - Switches off > 19 volts - Inhibited < 9 volts	Battery to CM B+ supply circuit: open circuit or high resistance Battery failure, loose terminals Charging system failure CM failure

JC4020100033030X

Fig. 3 DTC interpretation (Part 3 of 3). XJR, XJ8, XKR & XK8

c. FH44 pin 2, and ground.
d. CV6 pin 2, and ground.
2. If resistance less than 0.5 ohms, repair necessary DSC sensor voltage supply circuit.
3. If resistance is not as specified, install new DSC control module.

Clearing Diagnostic Trouble Codes

Follow scan tool manufacturer's instructions.

SYSTEM SERVICE

Brake System Bleed

Bleeding the ABS system is not a routine maintenance operation and is only required when part of the system has been disconnected or the fluid is contaminated.

During the bleeding procedure, it is important that the level of fluid in the reservoir is maintained at approximately. 0787 inch below the bottom of the filler neck. Motor/pump unit cannot charge accumulator if air and not fluid, is standing on low pressure side of pump.

If motor/pump unit, fluid intake hose or hydraulic unit of ABS system has been removed or disconnected, bleed as outlined under "Fluid Intake Hose."

Do not allow pump motor to run continuously for more than two minutes. If for any reason the motor does overrun two minutes, turn ignition Off immediately and allow motor to cool for at least ten minutes.

The following bleeding procedure is for all maintenance work except motor/pump unit, fluid intake hose or actuation unit.

1. Ensure vehicle is on level surface and standing still.
2. Turn ignition Off and discharge accumulator by operating brake pedal until it is difficult to engage (approximately 20 times).
3. Ensure reservoir is approximately. 0787 inch below bottom of filler neck.
4. Open one bleed nipple, fully depress brake pedal and hold.
5. Turn ignition On and wait minimum of 15 seconds, until fluid flows air free.
6. Close bleed nipple and release pedal slowly.
7. Turn ignition Off and bleed remaining rear caliper using same procedure.

FLUID INTAKE HOSE

The following bleeding procedure is to be used for all procedures involving the motor/pump unit, fluid intake hose or actuation unit.

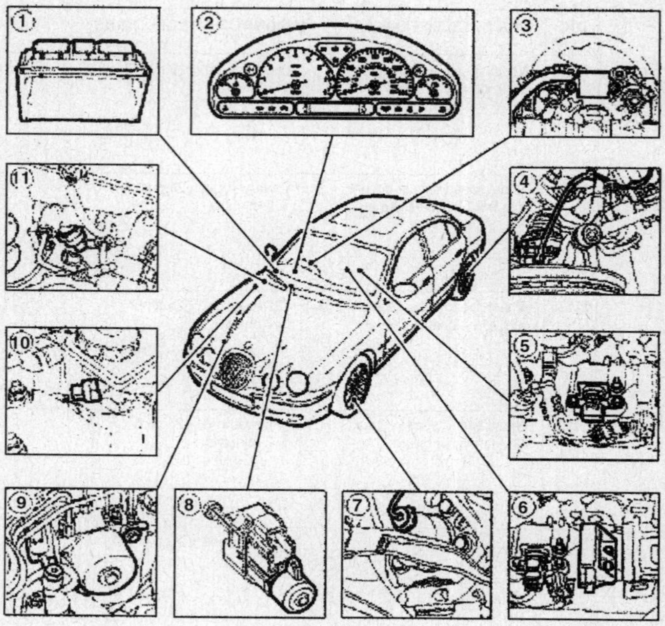

1
Powertrain control module
2
Instrument cluster
3
Steering wheel rotation sensor
4
Wheel speed sensor - rear
5
Lateral accelerometer sensor
6
Yaw rate sensor
7
Wheel speed sensor - front
8
Brake pedal switch
9
Interactive vehicle dynamics module
10
Master cylinder pressure sensor
11
Master cylinder pressure sensor

JC4020100035000X

Fig. 4 Component locations. S Type

1. Ensure vehicle is standing still and ignition is Off.
2. Fill fluid reservoir to approximately. 0787 inch below bottom of filler neck.
3. Disconnect fluid intake hose at pump and allow fluid to flow into a container until it is air free.
4. Ensure plastic elbow O-ring is not damaged and reconnect hose while fluid is flowing.
5. Switch ignition On and operate brake pedal several times.
6. If motor/pump unit is charging, fluid level in reservoir will decrease. Upper cutout point should be reached in less than 60 seconds.

Component Replacement

HYDRAULIC CONTROL UNIT (HCU)

1. Raise and support vehicle.
2. Connect suitable bleed tube and container to lefthand front and rear caliper bleed nipples.
3. Open bleed nipples.
4. Press and hold brake pedal down approximately 2.4 inches using suitable hold down tool.
5. **Torque** front caliper bleed nipple to

35–53 inch lbs.
6. **Torque** rear caliper bleed nipple to 71–97 inch lbs.
7. Remove bleed tube and container.
8. Disconnect ABS/TCCM electrical connectors.
9. Disconnect union nuts and inlet brake tubes. Plug and cap tubes and ports.
10. Disconnect union nuts and outlet brake tubes. Plug and cap tubes and ports.
11. Remove mounting bolts and HCU. **Do not distort brake tubes.**
12. Reverse procedure to install, noting the following:
    a. **On S type models, torque** HCU mounting bolts to 18 ft. lbs.
    b. **On XJR, XJ8, XKR and XK8 models, torque** HCU mounting bolts to 71–88 inch lbs.
    c. **On XJR, XJ8, XKR and XK8 models, torque** HCU bracket bolts to 88–124 inch lbs.

ABS/TRACTION CONTROL CONTROL MODULE (ABS/TCCM)

1. Remove HCU as outlined under "Hydraulic Control Unit (HCU)."
2. Disconnect ABS/TCCM electrical connector.
3. Remove mounting bolts and ABS/TCCM
4. Reverse procedure to install.

WHEEL SPEED SENSOR

XJR, XJ8, XKR & XK8

1. Raise and support vehicle.
2. Disconnect ABS sensor electrical connector.
3. Remove mounting bolt and sensor
4. Reverse procedure to install. **Torque** sensor mounting bolt to 71–88 inch lbs.

S TYPE

This procedure has been revised by a Technical Service Bulletin.

1. Raise and support vehicle.
2. Disconnect ABS sensor electrical connector.
3. Press retaining clip flat toward wheel speed sensor until sensor is released.
4. Remove sensor from bearing housing. Replace as required.

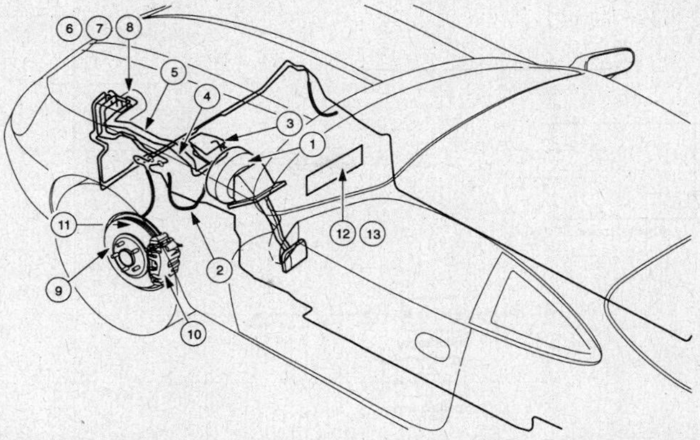

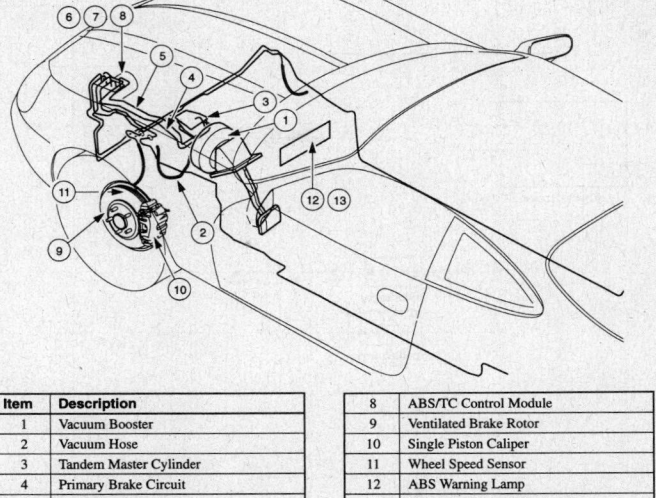

Item	Description
1	Vacuum Booster
2	Vacuum Hose
3	Tandem Master Cylinder
4	Primary Brake Circuit
5	Secondary Brake Circuit
6	Hydraulic Pump/Motor Unit
7	Valve Block
8	ABS/TC Control Module
9	Ventilated Brake Rotor
10	Single Piston Caliper
11	Wheel Speed Sensor
12	ABS Warning Lamp
13	Brake Fluid Level Warning Lamp

JC4029900023000X

Fig. 5 Component locations. XJR, XJ8, XKR & XK8

5. Remove and discard retaining clip and O-ring.
6. Reverse procedure to install, noting the following:
    a. Install new sensor housing O-ring and retaining clip.
    b. Apply continuous approximately 0.098 inch thick bead of Loctite Permatex Ultra Blue sealant, or equivalent, 0.195 inch from flange to sensor, **Fig. 9.** Bead must completely encircle sensor.

LATERAL ACCELERATION & ROTATION SENSORS

1. Remove center console as outlined in "Dash Panel Service" section.
2. Remove air duct.
3. Disconnect yaw rate sensor electrical connector.
4. Remove mounting bolts and yaw rate sensor.
5. Reverse procedure to install.

STEERING WHEEL ROTATION SENSOR

1. Remove upper steering column as outlined in "Steering Column" section.
2. Remove mounting screws and steering angle sensor.
3. Reverse procedure to install.

TECHNICAL SERVICE BULLETINS

DTC 1145, 1155, 1233 OR 1234

S Type

On some of these models there may be Diagnostic Trouble Codes (DTCs) 1145, 1155, 1233 or 1234 set.

This condition may be caused water in the wheel speed sensors.

To correct this condition, inspect for water damage or poor sealing between the sensor and wheel bearing housing. Replace the wheel bearing and speed sensor if water is visible on the tip of the sensor. **Do not separate the sensor from the new wheel bearing assembly since it is fully sealed into the bearing housing.** The sensor can be replaced separately only if there is no evidence of water entry.

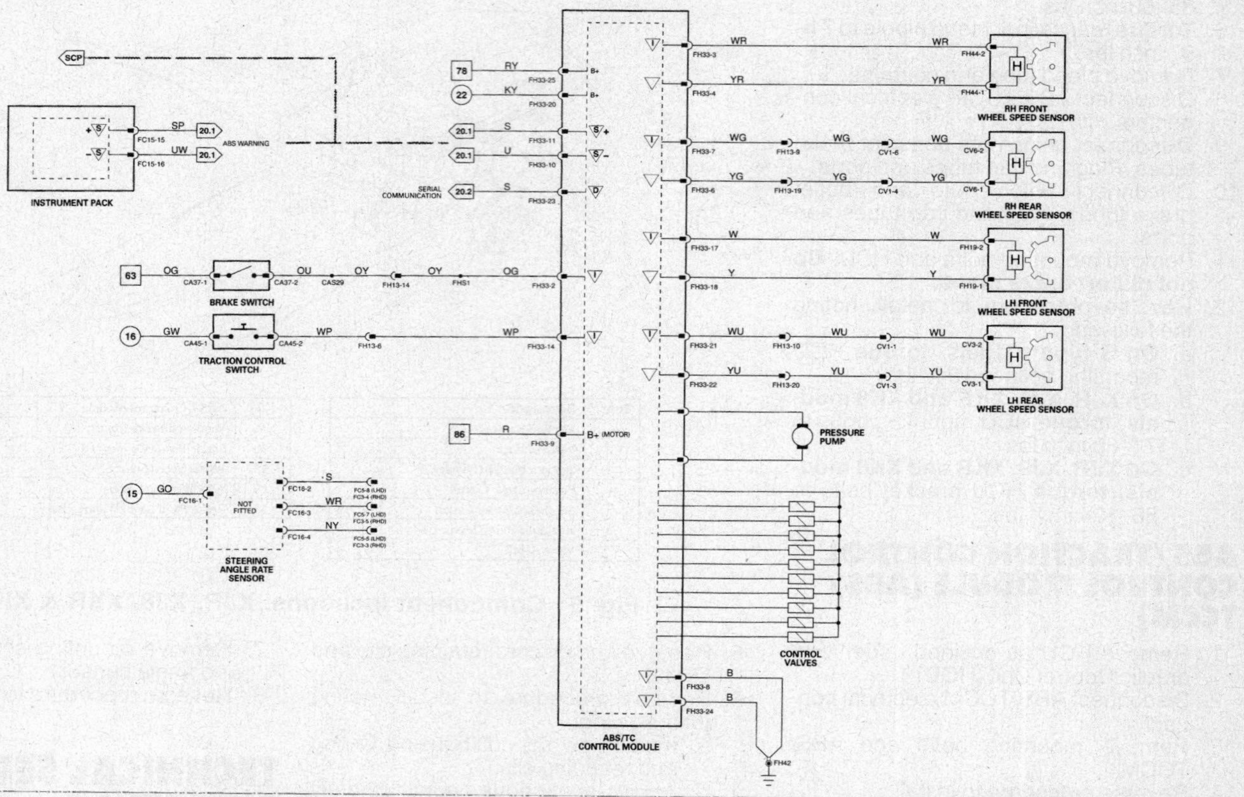

Fig. 6 ABS/traction control wiring diagram. S Type

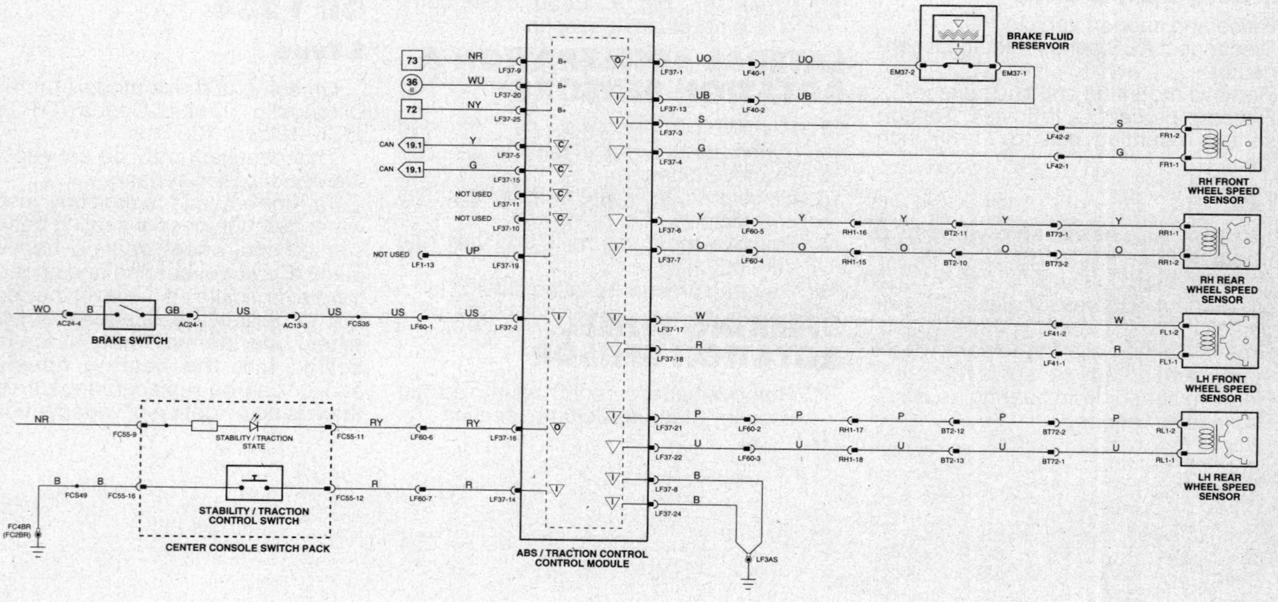

Fig. 7 ABS/traction control wiring diagram. XJR, XJ8, XKR & XK8

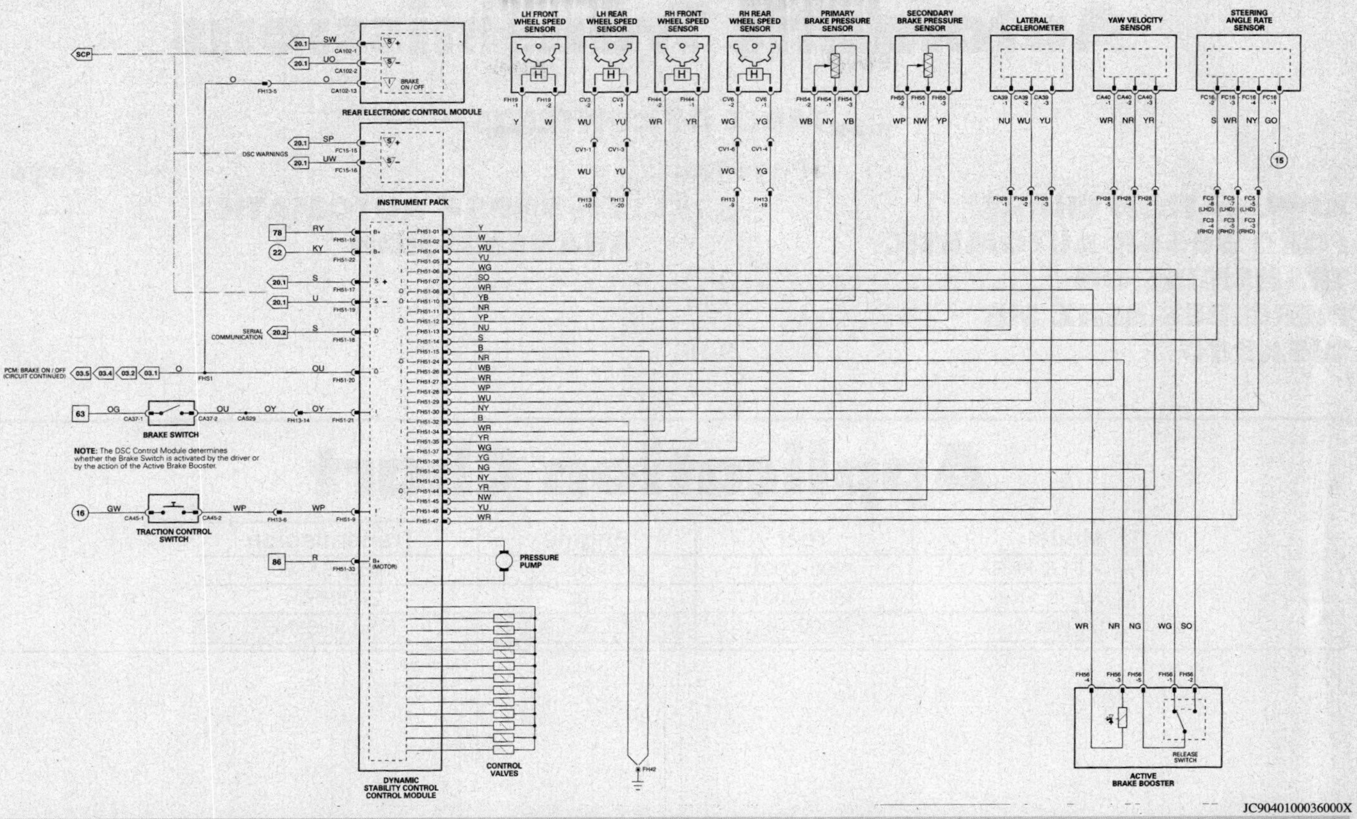

JC9040100036000X

Fig. 8 DSC wiring diagram. S Type

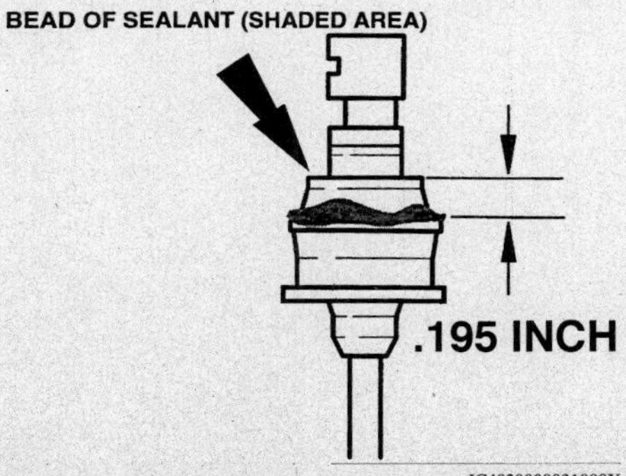

JC4020000031000X

Fig. 9 Sensor sealant application

Automatic Transmissions

TABLE OF CONTENTS

Page No.

APPLICATION CHART 3-78
FORD 5R55N AUTOMATIC TRANSMISSION 3-79
MERCEDES-BENZ MB W5A580 3-96
ZF-5HP24 AUTOMATIC TRANSMISSION 3-91

Application Chart

Model	Year	Engine	Transmission
XJR & XKR	1998–2001	4.0L	MB W5A580
XJ8 & XK8	1998–2001	4.0L	ZF-5HP24
S Type	2000–01	3.0L & 4.0L	Ford 5R55NF

Ford 5R55N Automatic Transmission

NOTE: On Air Bag Equipped Models, Refer To "Air Bag System Precautions" Located In The Front Of This Manual For System Disarming & Arming Procedures.

INDEX

	Page No.
Adjustments	3-88
Selector Cable	3-88
Description	3-79
Identification	3-79
Maintenance	3-88
Fluid Change	3-88
Fluid Filter	3-88
Fluid Inspection	3-88
Precautions	3-79
Air Bag Systems	3-79
Battery Ground Cable	3-79
Technical Service Bulletins	3-89
Shift Lever Will Not Release From Park	3-89
Tightening Specifications	3-90
Transmission, Replace	3-88
Installation	3-88
Removal	3-88
Troubleshooting	3-80
Delayed Forward & Reverse Engagement	3-80
Delayed Or Soft Forward Engagement	3-80
Delayed Or Soft Reverse Engagement	3-80
Engine Braking In All Gears	3-80
Engine Will Not Crank	3-80
Erratic Shift Or All Shifts Missing	3-80
External Leaks	3-80
Fluid Venting Or Foaming	3-80
Harsh Forward & Reverse Engagement	3-81
Harsh Forward Engagement	3-80
Harsh Reverse Engagement	3-81
Harsh Shift	3-81
Harsh 1-2 Shift	3-81
Harsh 1st Gear Engagement—Manual Range Only	3-81
Harsh 2-1 Shift	3-81
Harsh 2-3 Shift	3-81
Harsh 3-2 Shift	3-81
Harsh 3-4 Shift	3-82
Harsh 4-3 Shift	3-82
Harsh 4-5 Shift	3-82
Harsh 5-4 Shift	3-82
Improper Shift Timing—Early Or Late Shift	3-82
Improper Shift Timing—Erratic Or Hunting	3-82
No Engagement In Any Gear	3-82
No Engine Braking In Manual 1st Gear Range	3-83
No Engine Braking In Manual 2nd Gear Range	3-83
No Engine Braking In Manual 3rd Gear Range	3-83
No Engine Braking In Manual 4th Gear Range	3-83
No Forward Movement In Any Gear Position	3-83
No Forward Movement In D5 Or D4	3-83
No Park Range	3-83
No Reverse	3-84
No 1-2 Shift	3-84
No 1st Gear—Manual 1st Gear Range	3-84
No 1st or 2nd Gear In Drive—Engages in Higher Gear	3-84
No 2-1 Shift	3-84
No 2–3 Shift	3-84
No 2nd & 5th Gears	3-84
No 2nd Gear—Manual 2nd Gear Range	3-84
No 3-2 Shift	3-85
No 3-4 Shift	3-85
No 3rd, 4th & 5th Gears	3-84
No 4-3 Shift	3-85
No 4-5 Shift	3-85
No 5-4 Shift	3-85
Noise/Vibration In Forward Or Reverse	3-82
Poor Transmission Performance	3-85
Shift Lever Effort High	3-85
Slip/Chatter In Manual 1st Gear	3-85
Slip/Chatter In Manual 2nd Gear	3-86
Slip/Chatter In Manual 3rd Gear	3-86
Soft Or Slipping 1-2 Shift	3-86
Soft Or Slipping 2-1 Shift	3-86
Soft Or Slipping 2-3 Shift	3-86
Soft Or Slipping 3-2 Shift	3-87
Soft Or Slipping 3-4 Shift	3-87
Soft Or Slipping 4-3 Shift	3-87
Soft Or Slipping 4-5 Shift	3-87
Soft Or Slipping 5-4 Shift	3-87
Soft Shift Or Slipping	3-86
Torque Converter Clutch Always Applied—Vehicle Stalls	3-87
Torque Converter Clutch Cycling, Shudder Or Chatter	3-87
Torque Converter Clutch Does Not Apply	3-87
Transmission Overheats	3-87
Vehicle Movement With Gear Selector In N Range	3-88

PRECAUTIONS

AIR BAG SYSTEMS

Refer to "Air Bag System Precautions" in the front of this manual for system disarming and arming procedures.

BATTERY GROUND CABLE

Prior to service, disconnect battery ground cable and isolate as required.

IDENTIFICATION

The 5R55N transmission can be identified by the transmission service ID tag located on the transmission, **Fig. 1.**

DESCRIPTION

The 5R55N incorporates the following features; five forward speeds, electronic shift, pressure and torque converter controls, electronic gearshift indicator, three compound planetary gearsets, three bands, four multi-plate clutches and three one way clutches.

Electronic shift control allows for torque converter clutch modulation, closed loop shift control, adaptive shift control for consistent shift quality throughout lifespan of transmission, reactive shift scheduling to react to throttle position and rate of throttle change, OD lockout in manual in D4 shifter position and manual shift capability with optional select shift transmission.

Transmission shift points are controlled by the PCM. The PCM calculates shift point based on input from various sensors and driver inputs. When a shift error DTC is set, the fault must occur four times consecutively. When a torque converter clutch DTC is set, the fault must occur five times consecutively.

The electronic gearshift indicator appears with the key in Run position and displays the same gear selection as shown on the range selector floor console next to range selector lever. If an E flashes or remains on, a transmission fault is present.

With the 5R55N, diagnosis using an output state control (OSC) method in conjunction with pinpoint tests is possible. There are two OSC modes of operation. They are the bench mode and the drive mode. Each may be used as required when performing diagnostics.

TROUBLESHOOTING

DELAYED OR SOFT FORWARD ENGAGEMENT

1. Vehicle wiring harness and PCM.
2. Pressure control solenoid B.
3. Low line pressures.
4. Valve body:
   a. Not tightened to specifications.
   b. Separator plate damaged.
   c. Contamination.
   d. Valves or springs damaged, improperly assembled, missing, stuck or bore damage.
5. OD servo:
   a. Servo retaining ring damaged.
   b. Piston and cover seals damaged.
   c. Damage to anchor pins in transmission case.
6. OD band:
   a. Band damaged.
   b. Servo damaged or worn.
   c. Improper adjustment.
   d. Anchor pin damage or wear.
7. Center support:
   a. Not tightened to specifications.
   b. Seal rings or bearing damaged.
   c. Outside diameter of case bore damaged.
   d. Support damaged or leaking.
8. Forward clutch:
   a. Piston or seal damage.
   b. Check ball damaged, missing, not sealing or off location.
   c. Friction elements damaged or worn.
   d. Return springs damaged.

DELAYED FORWARD & REVERSE ENGAGEMENT

1. Vehicle wiring harness and PCM.
2. Transmission range sensor.
3. Transmission fluid temperature sensor.
4. Improper fluid level or poor fluid quality.
5. High line pressures.
6. Valve body:
   a. Not tightened to specifications.
   b. Separator plate damage.
   c. Contamination.
   d. Valves or springs damaged, misassembled, missing, stuck or bore damaged.
7. Fluid pump:
   a. Not tightened to specifications.
   b. Damaged pump gasket.
   c. Porosity, cross leaks, ball missing or plugged hole.

DELAYED OR SOFT REVERSE ENGAGEMENT

1. Vehicle wiring harness and PCM.
2. Pressure control solenoid C.
3. Low line pressure.
4. Valve body:

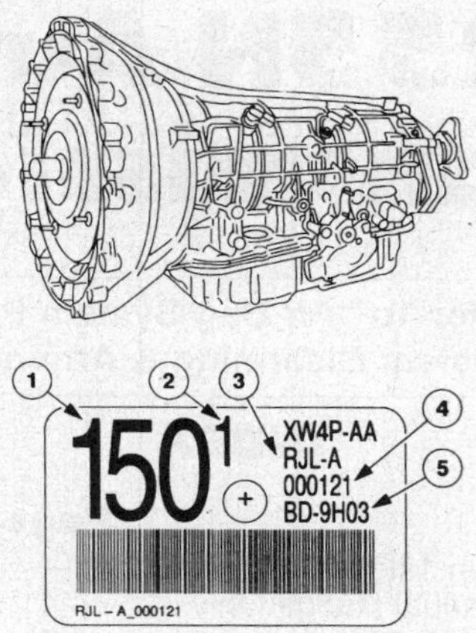

Item	Description
1	Model number
2	Assemble level
3	Build code
4	Serial number
5	Build date (YMDD)

FM5020001664000X

Fig. 1 Transmission identification

   a. Not tightened to specifications.
   b. Separator plate damaged.
   c. Contamination.
   d. Valves or springs damaged, improperly assembled, missing, stuck or bore damage.
5. Direct clutch assembly:
   a. Piston or seals damaged.
   b. Check ball damaged, missing, not seating or off location.
   c. Friction components worn or damaged.
   d. Damaged return springs.
6. Reverse servo:
   a. Servo retaining ring damaged.
   b. Piston and cover seal damage.
   c. Anchor pins in transmission case damaged.
7. Reverse band:
   a. Damaged band.
   b. Servo worn or damaged.
   c. Improper adjustment.
   d. Anchor pin damage or wear.

ENGINE BRAKING IN ALL GEARS

1. Vehicle wiring harness and PCM.
2. Shift solenoid D.

ENGINE WILL NOT CRANK

1. Vehicle wiring harness and PCM.
2. Transmission range sensor.
3. Shift cable or transmission range sensor damaged or misaligned.
4. Transmission fluid pump seized.
5. Flexplate or adapter plate damage.

ERRATIC SHIFT OR ALL SHIFTS MISSING

1. Vehicle wiring harness and PCM.
2. Torque converter clutch solenoid.
3. Pressure control solenoids A, B and C.
4. Output shaft speed sensor.
5. Transmission range sensor.
6. Intake air temperature sensor.
7. Vehicle speed sensor input.
8. Improper fluid level.
9. Poor fluid quality.
10. Shift cable or transmission range sensor damaged or misaligned.
11. Improper fluid pressures.
12. Valve body:
    a. Not tightened to specifications.
    b. Separator plate damaged.
    c. Contamination.
    d. Valves or springs damaged, improperly assembled, missing, stuck or bore damage.
13. Fluid pump:
    a. Not tightened to specifications.
    b. Damaged pump gasket.
    c. Porosity, cross leaks, ball missing or plugged hole.
14. OD planetary damaged.
15. Center support:
    a. Not tightened to specifications.
    b. Seal rings or bearing damaged.
    c. Outside diameter of case bore damaged.
    d. Support damaged or leaking.
16. Direct clutch and intermediate clutch:
    a. Piston or seals damaged.
    b. Check ball damaged, missing, not seating or off location.
    c. Friction elements damaged or worn.
    d. Return springs damaged.
17. Intermediate one-way clutch worn, damaged or improperly assembled.

EXTERNAL LEAKS

1. Output shaft speed sensor.
2. Intermediate shaft speed sensor.
3. Turbine shaft speed sensor.
4. Transmission range sensor.
5. Improper fluid level.
6. Case vent damaged.
7. Failed gaskets or seals.

FLUID VENTING OR FOAMING

1. Improper fluid level.
2. Contaminated transmission fluid.
3. Fluid pump:
   a. Not tightened to specifications.
   b. Damaged pump gasket.
   c. Porosity, cross leaks, ball missing or plugged hole.
4. Intermediate servo:
   a. Servo retaining ring damaged.
   b. Piston and cover seals damaged.
   c. Damage to anchor pins in transmission case.
5. Intermediate band:
   a. Band damaged.
   b. Servo damaged or worn.
   c. Improper adjustment.
   d. Anchor pin damage or wear.
6. Case vent damaged.
7. Transmission overheating.

HARSH FORWARD ENGAGEMENT

1. Vehicle wiring harness or PCM.
2. Pressure control solenoid A.
3. Pressure control solenoid C.
4. High line pressures.
5. Valve body:
   a. Not tightened to specifications.
   b. Separator plate damaged.

c. Contamination.
d. Valves or springs damaged, improperly assembled, missing, stuck or bore damage.

6. OD servo:
   a. Servo retaining ring damaged.
   b. Piston and cover seals damaged.
   c. Damage to anchor pins in transmission case.
7. OD band:
   a. Band damaged.
   b. Servo damaged or worn.
   c. Improper adjustment.
   d. Anchor pin damage or wear.
8. Center support:
   a. Not tightened to specifications.
   b. Seal rings or bearing damaged.
   c. Outside diameter of case bore damaged.
   d. Support damaged or leaking.
9. Forward clutch and intermediate clutch:
   a. Piston or seal damage.
   b. Check ball damaged, missing, not sealing or off location.
   c. Friction elements damaged or worn.
   d. Return springs damaged.

HARSH FORWARD & REVERSE ENGAGEMENT

1. Vehicle wiring harness and PCM.
2. Transmission range sensor.
3. Transmission fluid temperature sensor.
4. Improper fluid level or poor fluid quality.
5. High line pressures.
6. Valve body:
   a. Not tightened to specifications.
   b. Separator plate damage.
   c. Contamination.
   d. Valves or springs damaged, misassembled, missing, stuck or bore damaged.
7. Forward clutch and intermediate clutch:
   a. Piston or seal damage.
   b. Check ball damaged, missing, not sealing or off location.
   c. Friction elements damaged or worn.
   d. Return springs damaged.

HARSH REVERSE ENGAGEMENT

1. Vehicle wiring harness and PCM.
2. Pressure control solenoid C.
3. High line pressures.
4. Valve body:
   a. Not tightened to specifications.
   b. Separator plate damaged.
   c. Contamination.
   d. Valves or springs damaged, improperly assembled, missing, stuck or bore damage.
5. Direct clutch, forward clutch, intermediate clutch and reverse clutch:
   a. Piston or seals damaged.
   b. Check ball damaged, missing, not seating or off location.
   c. Friction components worn or damaged.
   d. Damaged return springs.
6. Reverse servo:
   a. Servo retaining ring damaged.
   b. Piston and cover seal damage.
   c. Anchor pins in transmission case damaged.
7. Reverse band:
   a. Damaged band.
   b. Servo worn or damaged.
   c. Improper adjustment.
   d. Anchor pin damage or wear.

HARSH SHIFT

1. Vehicle wiring harness and PCM.
2. Shift solenoids A, B and C.
3. Pressure control solenoids A, B and C.
4. Intermediate shaft speed sensor.
5. Transmission range sensor.
6. Transmission fluid temperature sensor.
7. Intake air temperature sensor.
8. Vehicle speed sensor input.
9. Improper fluid pressures.
10. Valve body:
    a. Not tightened to specifications.
    b. Separator plate damaged.
    c. Contamination.
    d. Valves or springs damaged, improperly assembled, missing, stuck or bore damage.
11. Damaged input shaft.
12. OD, intermediate or reverse servo:
    a. Servo retaining ring damaged.
    b. Piston and cover seals damaged.
    c. Damage to anchor pins in transmission case.
13. OD, intermediate or reverse band:
    a. Band damaged.
    b. Servo damaged or worn.
    c. Improper adjustment.
    d. Anchor pin damage or wear.
14. Center shaft assembly damage.
15. Center shaft one-way clutch damage.
16. Forward or intermediate clutch:
    a. Piston or seals damaged.
    b. Check ball damaged, missing, not seating or off location.
    c. Friction elements damaged or worn.
    d. Return springs damaged.
17. Output shaft damage.
18. Damaged transmission case.

HARSH 1ST GEAR ENGAGEMENT—MANUAL RANGE ONLY

1. Vehicle wiring harness and PCM.
2. Pressure control solenoid B.
3. Turbine shaft speed sensor.

HARSH 1-2 SHIFT

1. Vehicle wiring harness and PCM.
2. Shift solenoid C.
3. Pressure control solenoid B.
4. Turbine shaft speed sensor.
5. Transmission range sensor.
6. Transmission fluid temperature sensor.
7. Improper fluid pressures.
8. Valve body:
   a. Not tightened to specifications.
   b. Separator plate damaged.
   c. Contamination.
   d. Valves or springs damaged, improperly assembled, missing, stuck or bore damage.
9. OD servo:
   a. Servo retaining ring damaged.
   b. Piston and cover seals damaged.
   c. Damage to anchor pins in transmission case.
10. OD band:
    a. Band damaged.
    b. Servo damaged or worn.
    c. Improper adjustment.
    d. Anchor pin damage or wear.
11. Direct clutch or intermediate clutch:
    a. Piston or seals damaged.
    b. Check ball damaged, missing, not seating or off location.
    c. Friction components damaged or worn.
    d. Return springs damaged.

HARSH 2-1 SHIFT

1. Vehicle wiring harness and PCM.
2. Shift solenoid C.
3. Pressure control solenoid B.
4. Turbine shaft speed sensor.
5. Transmission range sensor.
6. Transmission fluid temperature sensor.
7. Improper fluid pressures.
8. Valve body:
   a. Not tightened to specifications.
   b. Separator plate damaged.
   c. Contamination.
   d. Valves or springs damaged, improperly assembled, missing, stuck or bore damage.
9. Direct clutch or intermediate clutch:
   a. Piston or seals damaged.
   b. Check ball damaged, missing, not seating or off location.
   c. Friction components damaged or worn.
   d. Return springs damaged.
10. Direct one-way clutch worn, damaged or improperly assembled.

HARSH 2-3 SHIFT

1. Vehicle wiring harness and PCM.
2. Shift solenoid B.
3. Pressure control solenoid A.
4. Turbine shaft speed sensor.
5. Intermediate shaft speed sensor.
6. Transmission range sensor.
7. Transmission fluid temperature sensor.
8. Improper fluid pressures.
9. Valve body:
   a. Not tightened to specifications.
   b. Separator plate damaged.
   c. Contamination.
   d. Valves or springs damaged, improperly assembled, missing, stuck or bore damage.
10. Direct clutch or intermediate clutch:
    a. Piston or seals damaged.
    b. Check ball damaged, missing, not seating or off location.
    c. Friction components damaged or worn.
    d. Return springs damaged.
11. Direct one-way clutch worn, damaged or improperly assembled.

HARSH 3-2 SHIFT

1. Vehicle wiring harness and PCM.
2. Shift solenoid C.
3. Pressure control solenoid B.
4. Turbine shaft speed sensor.
5. Intermediate shaft speed sensor.
6. Transmission range sensor.

7. Transmission fluid temperature sensor.
8. Improper fluid pressures.
9. Valve body:
   a. Not tightened to specifications.
   b. Separator plate damaged.
   c. Contamination.
   d. Valves or springs damaged, improperly assembled, missing, stuck or bore damage.
10. OD servo:
    a. Servo retaining ring damaged.
    b. Piston and cover seals damaged.
    c. Damage to anchor pins in transmission case.
11. OD band:
    a. Band damaged.
    b. Servo damaged or worn.
    c. Improper adjustment.
    d. Anchor pin damage or wear.
12. Direct clutch or intermediate clutch:
    a. Piston or seals damaged.
    b. Check ball damaged, missing, not seating or off location.
    c. Friction components damaged or worn.
    d. Return springs damaged.

HARSH 3-4 SHIFT

1. Vehicle wiring harness and PCM.
2. Shift solenoid A.
3. Pressure control solenoid C.
4. Transmission range sensor.
5. Transmission fluid temperature sensor.
6. Improper fluid pressures.
7. Valve body:
   a. Not tightened to specifications.
   b. Separator plate damaged.
   c. Contamination.
   d. Valves or springs damaged, improperly assembled, missing, stuck or bore damage.
8. Center support:
   a. Not tightened to specifications.
   b. Seal rings or bearing damaged.
   c. Outside diameter of case bore damaged.
   d. Support damaged or leaking.
9. Direct clutch or intermediate clutch:
   a. Piston or seals damaged.
   b. Check ball damaged, missing, not seating or off location.
   c. Friction components damaged or worn.
   d. Return springs damaged.

HARSH 4-3 SHIFT

1. Vehicle wiring harness and PCM.
2. Shift solenoid A.
3. Pressure control solenoid A.
4. Transmission range sensor.
5. Transmission fluid temperature.
6. Improper fluid pressures.
7. Valve body:
   a. Not tightened to specifications.
   b. Separator plate damaged.
   c. Contamination.
   d. Valves or springs damaged, improperly assembled, missing, stuck or bore damage.
8. Direct clutch or intermediate clutch:
   a. Piston or seals damaged.
   b. Check ball damaged, missing, not seating or off location.

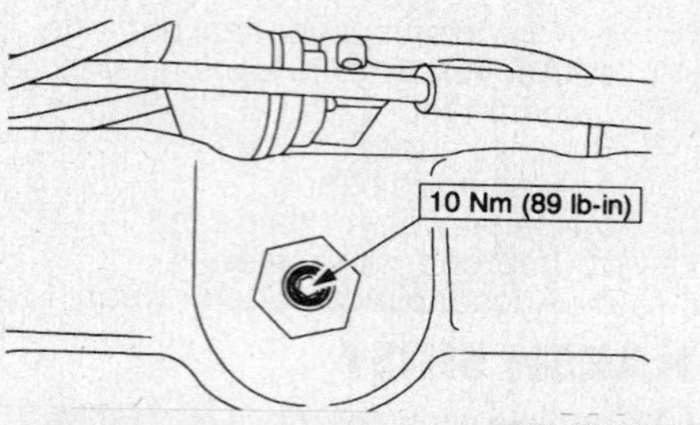

Fig. 2 Fluid level indicator plug

   c. Friction components damaged or worn.
   d. Return springs damaged.

HARSH 4-5 SHIFT

1. Vehicle wiring harness and PCM.
2. Shift solenoid C.
3. Pressure control solenoid B.
4. Turbine shaft speed sensor.
5. Transmission range sensor.
6. Transmission fluid temperature sensor.
7. Improper fluid pressures.
8. Valve body:
   a. Not tightened to specifications.
   b. Separator plate damaged.
   c. Contamination.
   d. Valves or springs damaged, improperly assembled, missing, stuck or bore damage.
9. OD servo:
   a. Servo retaining ring damaged.
   b. Piston and cover seals damaged.
   c. Damage to anchor pins in transmission case.
10. OD band:
    a. Band damaged.
    b. Servo damaged or worn.
    c. Improper adjustment.
    d. Anchor pin damage or wear.

HARSH 5-4 SHIFT

1. Vehicle wiring harness and PCM.
2. Shift solenoid C.
3. Pressure control solenoid C.
4. Turbine shaft speed sensor.
5. Transmission range sensor.
6. Transmission fluid temperature sensor.
7. Improper fluid pressures.
8. Valve body:
   a. Not tightened to specifications.
   b. Separator plate damaged.
   c. Contamination.
   d. Valves or springs damaged, improperly assembled, missing, stuck or bore damage.
9. Direct clutch:
   a. Piston or seals damaged.
   b. Check ball damaged, missing, not seating or off location.
   c. Friction components damaged or worn.
   d. Return springs damaged.
10. Direct one-way clutch worn, damaged or improperly assembled.

IMPROPER SHIFT TIMING—EARLY OR LATE SHIFT

1. Vehicle wiring harness and PCM.
2. Output shaft speed sensor.
3. Intake air temperature sensor.
4. Improper fluid level or poor fluid quality.
5. Valve body:
   a. Not tightened to specifications.
   b. Separator plate damaged.
   c. Contamination.
   d. Valves or springs damaged, improperly assembled, missing, stuck or bore damage.
6. OD servo:
   a. Servo retaining ring damaged.
   b. Piston and cover seals damaged.
   c. Damage to anchor pins in transmission case.
7. OD band:
   a. Band damaged.
   b. Servo damaged or worn.
   c. Improper adjustment.
   d. Anchor pin damage or wear.

IMPROPER SHIFT TIMING—ERRATIC OR HUNTING

1. Vehicle wiring harness and PCM.
2. Output shaft speed sensor.
3. Intake air temperature sensor.
4. Improper fluid level or poor fluid quality.
5. Valve body:
   a. Not tightened to specifications.
   b. Separator plate damaged.
   c. Contamination.
   d. Valves or springs damaged, improperly assembled, missing, stuck or bore damage.

NOISE/VIBRATION IN FORWARD OR REVERSE

1. Vehicle wiring harness and PCM.
2. Torque converter clutch solenoid.
3. Pressure control solenoids A, B and C.
4. Fluid pump:
   a. Not tightened to specifications.
   b. Damaged pump gasket.
   c. Porosity, cross leaks, ball missing or plugged hole.
5. Intermediate clutch:
   a. Piston or seals damaged.
   b. Check ball damaged, missing, not seating or off location.
   c. Friction elements damaged or worn.
   d. Return springs damaged.
6. Low one-way clutch worn, damaged or improperly assembled.
7. Flexplate or adapter plate damage or improperly aligned.

NO ENGAGEMENT IN ANY GEAR

1. Vehicle wiring harness and PCM.
2. Pressure control solenoid B.
3. Improper fluid level.
4. Poor fluid quality.
5. Shift cable or transmission range sensor damaged or misaligned.
6. Valve body:
   a. Not tightened to specifications.
   b. Separator plate damage.
   c. Contamination.
   d. Valves or springs damaged, misassembled, missing, stuck or bore damaged.
7. Damaged input shaft.
8. Fluid pump:
   a. Not tightened to specifications.
   b. Damaged pump gasket.

c. Porosity, cross leaks, ball missing or plugged hole.
9. OD planetary damage.
10. Damaged center shaft.
11. One way clutch damage.
12. Forward clutch and intermediate clutch:
   a. Piston or seal damage.
   b. Check ball damaged, missing, not sealing or off location.
   c. Friction elements damaged or worn.
   d. Return springs damaged.
13. Forward or reverse planetary damage.
14. Output shaft damage.
15. Torque converter:
   a. Damaged flexplate or adapter plate.
   b. Damaged impeller hub.
   c. Damaged turbine hub.
16. Worn, damaged or improperly assembled direct one-way clutch.

NO ENGINE BRAKING IN MANUAL 1ST GEAR RANGE

1. Vehicle wiring harness and PCM.
2. Shift solenoid A, C and D.
3. Pressure control solenoid A and B.
4. Improper fluid level.
5. Improper fluid pressures.
6. Fluid pump:
   a. Not tightened to specifications.
   b. Damaged pump gasket.
   c. Porosity, cross leaks, ball missing or plugged hole.
7. Coast clutch:
   a. Piston or seals damaged.
   b. Check ball damaged, missing, not seating or off location.
   c. Friction elements damaged or worn.
   d. Return springs damaged.
8. Reverse servo:
   a. Servo retaining ring damaged.
   b. Piston and cover seals damaged.
   c. Damage to anchor pins in transmission case.
9. Reverse band:
   a. Band damaged.
   b. Servo damaged or worn.
   c. Improper adjustment.
   d. Anchor pin damage or wear.

NO ENGINE BRAKING IN MANUAL 2ND GEAR RANGE

1. Vehicle wiring harness and PCM.
2. Shift solenoid A, C and D.
3. Pressure control solenoid A.
4. Improper fluid level.
5. Improper fluid pressures.
6. Reverse servo:
   a. Servo retaining ring damaged.
   b. Piston and cover seals damaged.
   c. Damage to anchor pins in transmission case.
7. Reverse band:
   a. Band damaged.
   b. Servo damaged or worn.
   c. Improper adjustment.
   d. Anchor pin damage or wear.

NO ENGINE BRAKING IN MANUAL 3RD GEAR RANGE

1. Vehicle wiring harness and PCM.
2. Shift solenoid A, B and C.
3. Pressure control solenoid A and B.
4. Reverse pressure switch.
5. Improper fluid level.
6. Improper fluid pressures.
7. Valve body:
   a. Not tightened to specifications.
   b. Separator plate damaged.
   c. Contamination.
   d. Valves or springs damaged, improperly assembled, missing, stuck or bore damage.
8. Fluid pump:
   a. Not tightened to specifications.
   b. Damaged pump gasket.
   c. Porosity, cross leaks, ball missing or plugged hole.
9. Coast clutch or intermediate clutch:
   a. Piston or seals damaged.
   b. Check ball damaged, missing, not seating or off location.
   c. Friction elements damaged or worn.
   d. Return springs damaged.
10. Center support:
   a. Not tightened to specifications.
   b. Seal rings or bearing damaged.
   c. Outside diameter of case bore damaged.
   d. Support damaged or leaking.
11. Intermediate servo:
   a. Servo retaining ring damaged.
   b. Piston and cover seals damaged.
   c. Damage to anchor pins in transmission case.
12. Intermediate band:
   a. Band damaged.
   b. Servo damaged or worn.
   c. Improper adjustment.
   d. Anchor pin damage or wear.
13. Low one-way clutch worn, damaged or improperly assembled.

NO ENGINE BRAKING IN MANUAL 4TH GEAR RANGE

1. Vehicle wiring harness and PCM.
2. Shift solenoid D.
3. Pressure control solenoid B.
4. Improper fluid level.
5. Valve body:
   a. Not tightened to specifications.
   b. Separator plate damaged.
   c. Contamination.
   d. Valves or springs damaged, improperly assembled, missing, stuck or bore damage.
6. Fluid pump:
   a. Not tightened to specifications.
   b. Damaged pump gasket.
   c. Porosity, cross leaks, ball missing or plugged hole.
7. Coast clutch or forward clutch:
   a. Piston or seals damaged.
   b. Check ball damaged, missing, not seating or off location.
   c. Friction elements damaged or worn.
   d. Return springs damaged.

NO FORWARD MOVEMENT IN ANY GEAR POSITION

1. Vehicle wiring harness and PCM.
2. Pressure control solenoid B.
3. Valve body:
   a. Not tightened to specifications.
   b. Separator plate damage.
   c. Contamination.
   d. Valves or springs damaged, misassembled, missing, stuck or bore damaged.
4. Center support:
   a. Not tightened to specifications.
   b. Seal rings or bearing damaged.
   c. Outside diameter of case bore damaged.
   d. Support damaged or leaking.
5. Forward clutch and intermediate clutch:
   a. Piston or seal damage.
   b. Check ball damaged, missing, not sealing or off location.
   c. Friction elements damaged or worn.
   d. Return springs damaged.
6. Forward planet damage.
7. Low one-way clutch worn, damaged or improperly assembled.

NO FORWARD MOVEMENT IN D5 OR D4

1. Vehicle wiring harness and PCM.
2. Pressure control solenoid B.
3. Improper fluid level or poor fluid quality.
4. Forward clutch assembly:
   a. Seals or piston damaged.
   b. Check ball damaged, missing, not seating or off location.
   c. Friction components worn or damaged.
   d. Damaged return springs.
5. OD servo:
   a. Servo retaining ring damaged.
   b. Piston and cover seals damaged.
   c. Damage to anchor pins in transmission case.
6. OD band:
   a. Band damaged.
   b. Servo damaged or worn.
   c. Improper adjustment.
   d. Anchor pin damage or wear.
7. Damaged transmission case.

NO PARK RANGE

1. Shift cable or transmission range sensor damaged or misaligned.
2. Manual control lever assembly damage.
3. Manual valve inner lever pin damage.
4. Spring rod damage.
5. Manual valve inner lever damage.
6. Manual valve lever shaft retaining pin damage.
7. Park gear, parking pawl or pawl return spring.
8. Park or guide plate.
9. Parking actuating rod.
10. Parking pawl shaft.

11. Manual lever or detent spring damaged or improperly assembled.
12. External linkage damaged.

NO REVERSE

1. Vehicle wiring harness and PCM.
2. Pressure control solenoid C.
3. Shift solenoid B.
4. Valve body:
   a. Not tightened to specifications.
   b. Separator plate damaged.
   c. Contamination.
   d. Valves or springs damaged, improperly assembled, missing, stuck or bore damage.
5. Direct clutch, forward clutch, intermediate clutch and reverse clutch assembly:
   a. Piston or seals damaged.
   b. Check ball damaged, missing, not seating or off location.
   c. Friction elements damaged or worn.
   d. Return springs damaged.
6. Reverse servo:
   a. Servo retaining ring damage.
   b. Piston and cover seal damage.
   c. Anchor pins in transmission case damaged.
7. Reverse band:
   a. Damaged band.
   b. Servo worn or damaged.
   c. Improper adjustment.
   d. Anchor pin wear or damage.

NO 1ST GEAR—MANUAL 1ST GEAR RANGE

1. Vehicle wiring harness and PCM.
2. Shift solenoid A and B.
3. Pressure control solenoid B and C.
4. Improper fluid pressures.
5. Valve body:
   a. Not tightened to specifications.
   b. Separator plate damaged.
   c. Contamination.
   d. Valves or springs damaged, improperly assembled, missing, stuck or bore damage.
6. Damaged OD planetary.
7. Worn, damaged or improperly assembled direct one-way or low one-way clutch.

NO 1ST OR 2ND GEAR IN DRIVE—ENGAGES IN HIGHER GEAR

1. Vehicle wiring harness and PCM.
2. Shift solenoid A, B and C.
3. Transmission range sensor.
4. Improper fluid pressures.
5. Valve body:
   a. Not tightened to specifications.
   b. Separator plate damaged.
   c. Contamination.
   d. Valves or springs damaged, improperly assembled, missing, stuck or bore damage.
6. Intermediate clutch assembly:
   a. Piston or seals damaged.
   b. Check ball damaged, missing, not seating or off location.
   c. Friction elements damaged or worn.

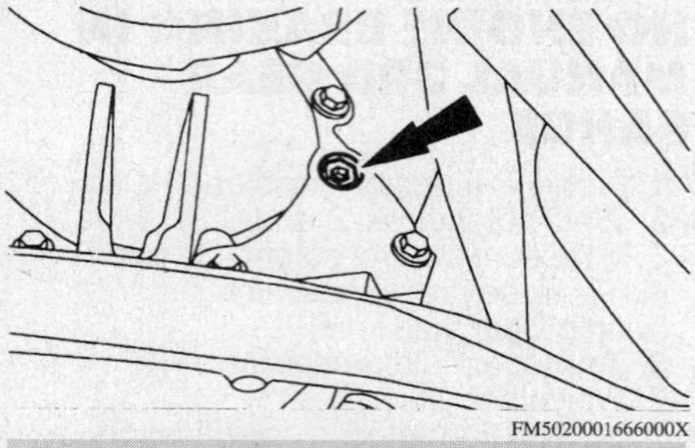

Fig. 3 Fluid fill plug location

   d. Return springs damaged.
7. Worn, damaged or improperly assembled direct one-way or low one-way clutch.

NO 2ND GEAR—MANUAL 2ND GEAR RANGE

1. Vehicle wiring harness and PCM.
2. Shift solenoid A, B and C.
3. Pressure control solenoid B.
4. Improper fluid pressures.
5. Valve body:
   a. Not tightened to specifications.
   b. Separator plate damaged.
   c. Contamination.
   d. Valves or springs damaged, improperly assembled, missing, stuck or bore damage.
6. OD servo:
   a. Servo retaining ring damaged.
   b. Piston and cover seals damaged.
   c. Damage to anchor pins in transmission case.
7. OD band:
   a. Band damaged.
   b. Servo damaged or worn.
   c. Improper adjustment.
   d. Anchor pin damage or wear.
8. Intermediate one-way clutch or low one-way clutch worn, damaged or improperly assembled.

NO 2ND & 5TH GEARS

1. Vehicle wiring harness and PCM.
2. Pressure control solenoid A and B.
3. Intermediate clutch:
   a. Piston or seals damaged.
   b. Check ball damaged, missing, not seating or off location.
   c. Friction elements damaged or worn.
   d. Return springs damaged.

NO 3RD, 4TH & 5TH GEARS

1. Vehicle wiring harness and PCM.
2. Pressure control solenoid A and B.
3. Fluid pump:
   a. Not tightened to specifications.
   b. Damaged pump gasket.
   c. Porosity, cross leaks, ball missing or plugged hole.
4. OD band:
   a. Band damaged.
   b. Servo damaged or worn.
   c. Improper adjustment.
   d. Anchor pin damage or wear.
5. OD planetary assembly damaged.

NO 1-2 SHIFT

1. Vehicle wiring harness and PCM.
2. Shift solenoid C.
3. Pressure control solenoid B.
4. Output shaft speed sensor.
5. Transmission range sensor.
6. Intake air temperature sensor.
7. Vehicle speed sensor input.
8. Improper fluid level or poor fluid quality.
9. Improper fluid pressures.
10. Valve body:
    a. Not tightened to specifications.
    b. Separator plate damaged.
    c. Contamination.
    d. Valves or springs damaged, improperly assembled, missing, stuck or bore damage.
11. OD servo:
    a. Servo retaining ring damaged.
    b. Piston and cover seals damaged.
    c. Damage to anchor pins in transmission case.
12. OD band:
    a. Band damaged.
    b. Servo damaged or worn.
    c. Improper adjustment.
    d. Anchor pin damage or wear.
13. OD planetary damaged.
14. Forward clutch or intermediate clutch:
    a. Piston or seals damaged.
    b. Check ball damaged, missing, not seating or off location.
    c. Friction elements damaged or worn.
    d. Return springs damaged.

NO 2-1 SHIFT

1. Vehicle wiring harness and PCM.
2. Shift solenoid A.
3. Pressure control solenoid A.
4. Output shaft speed sensor.
5. Transmission range sensor.
6. Improper fluid pressures.
7. Valve body:
   a. Not tightened to specifications.
   b. Separator plate damaged.
   c. Contamination.
   d. Valves or springs damaged, improperly assembled, missing, stuck or bore damage.
8. Forward clutch or intermediate clutch and reverse clutch assembly:
   a. Piston or seals damaged.
   b. Check ball damaged, missing, not seating or off location.
   c. Friction elements damaged or worn.
   d. Return springs damaged.

NO 2-3 SHIFT

1. Vehicle wiring harness and PCM.
2. Shift solenoid B.
3. Pressure control solenoid A.
4. Output shaft speed sensor.
5. Transmission range sensor.
6. Improper fluid pressures.
7. Valve body:
   a. Not tightened to specifications.
   b. Separator plate damaged.

c. Contamination.
d. Valves or springs damaged, improperly assembled, missing, stuck or bore damage.
8. Forward clutch or intermediate clutch:
a. Piston or seals damaged.
b. Check ball damaged, missing, not seating or off location.
c. Friction elements damaged or worn.
d. Return springs damaged.
9. Intermediate one-way clutch worn, damaged or improperly assembled.

NO 3-2 SHIFT

1. Vehicle wiring harness and PCM.
2. Shift solenoid A.
3. Pressure control solenoid A.
4. Output shaft speed sensor.
5. Transmission range sensor.
6. Improper fluid pressures.
7. Valve body:
a. Not tightened to specifications.
b. Separator plate damaged.
c. Contamination.
d. Valves or springs damaged, improperly assembled, missing, stuck or bore damage.
8. OD servo:
a. Servo retaining ring damaged.
b. Piston and cover seals damaged.
c. Damage to anchor pins in transmission case.
9. OD band:
a. Band damaged.
b. Servo damaged or worn.
c. Improper adjustment.
d. Anchor pin damage or wear.
10. Forward clutch or intermediate clutch and reverse clutch assembly:
a. Piston or seals damaged.
b. Check ball damaged, missing, not seating or off location.
c. Friction elements damaged or worn.
d. Return springs damaged.

NO 3-4 SHIFT

1. Vehicle wiring harness and PCM.
2. Shift solenoid A.
3. Pressure control solenoid C.
4. Output shaft speed sensor.
5. Transmission range sensor.
6. Transmission control switch.
7. Improper fluid pressures.
8. Valve body:
a. Not tightened to specifications.
b. Separator plate damaged.
c. Contamination.
d. Valves or springs damaged, improperly assembled, missing, stuck or bore damage.
9. Center support:
a. Not tightened to specifications.
b. Seal rings or bearing damaged.
c. Outside diameter of case bore damaged.
d. Support damaged or leaking.
10. Direct clutch, forward clutch or intermediate clutch:
a. Piston or seals damaged.
b. Check ball damaged, missing, not seating or off location.
c. Friction elements damaged or worn.
d. Return springs damaged.

NO 4-3 SHIFT

1. Vehicle wiring harness and PCM.
2. Shift solenoid A.
3. Pressure control solenoid A.
4. Output shaft speed sensor.
5. Transmission range sensor.
6. Transmission control switch.
7. Improper fluid pressures.
8. Valve body:
a. Not tightened to specifications.
b. Separator plate damaged.
c. Contamination.
d. Valves or springs damaged, improperly assembled, missing, stuck or bore damage.
9. Forward or direct clutch:
a. Piston or seals damaged.
b. Check ball damaged, missing, not seating or off location.
c. Friction elements damaged or worn.
d. Return springs damaged.

NO 4-5 SHIFT

1. Vehicle wiring harness and PCM.
2. Shift solenoid C.
3. Pressure control solenoid B.
4. Output shaft speed sensor.
5. Transmission range sensor.
6. Transmission control switch.
7. Improper fluid pressures.
8. Valve body:
a. Not tightened to specifications.
b. Separator plate damaged.
c. Contamination.
d. Valves or springs damaged, improperly assembled, missing, stuck or bore damage.
9. OD servo:
a. Servo retaining ring damaged.
b. Piston and cover seals damaged.
c. Damage to anchor pins in transmission case.
10. OD band:
a. Band damaged.
b. Servo damaged or worn.
c. Improper adjustment.
d. Anchor pin damage or wear.

NO 5-4 SHIFT

1. Vehicle wiring harness and PCM.
2. Shift solenoid C.
3. Pressure control solenoid C.
4. Output shaft speed sensor.
5. Transmission range sensor.
6. Transmission control switch.
7. Improper fluid pressures.
8. Valve body:
a. Not tightened to specifications.
b. Separator plate damaged.
c. Contamination.
d. Valves or springs damaged, improperly assembled, missing, stuck or bore damage.
9. Direct clutch:
a. Piston or seals damaged.
b. Check ball damaged, missing, not seating or off location.
c. Friction elements damaged or worn.
d. Return springs damaged.

POOR TRANSMISSION PERFORMANCE

1. Vehicle wiring harness and PCM.
2. Shift solenoid A, B and C.
3. Pressure control solenoid A, B and C.
4. Output shaft speed sensor.
5. Turbine shaft speed sensor.
6. Transmission fluid temperature sensor.
7. Transmission range sensor.
8. Improper fluid level.
9. Input shaft damage.
10. Center shaft damage.
11. One-way clutch damage.
12. Forward clutch or intermediate clutch:
a. Piston or seals damaged.
b. Check ball damaged, missing, not seating or off location.
c. Friction elements damaged or worn.
d. Return springs damaged.
13. Torque converter one-way clutch slipping.
14. Improper torque converter used in rebuild.

SHIFT LEVER EFFORT HIGH

1. Vehicle wiring harness and PCM.
2. Shift cable or transmission range sensor damaged or misaligned.
3. Valve body:
a. Not tightened to specifications.
b. Separator plate damaged.
c. Contamination.
d. Valves or springs damaged, improperly assembled, missing, stuck or bore damage.
4. Manual control lever assembly damage.
5. Manual valve inner lever pin damage.
6. Spring rod damage.
7. Manual valve inner lever damage.
8. Manual valve lever shaft retaining pin damage.

SLIP/CHATTER IN MANUAL 1ST GEAR

1. Vehicle wiring harness and PCM.
2. Pressure control solenoid A and B.
3. Improper fluid level or poor fluid quality.
4. Improper fluid pressures.
5. Valve body:
a. Not tightened to specifications.
b. Separator plate damaged.
c. Contamination.
d. Valves or springs damaged, improperly assembled, missing, stuck or bore damage.
6. Fluid pump:
a. Not tightened to specifications.
b. Damaged pump gasket.
c. Porosity, cross leaks, ball missing or plugged hole.
7. Forward clutch:
a. Piston or seals damaged.
b. Check ball damaged, missing, not seating or off location.
c. Friction elements damaged or worn.
d. Return springs damaged.
8. Reverse servo:
a. Servo retaining ring damaged.
b. Piston and cover seals damaged.

c. Damage to anchor pins in transmission case.
9. Reverse band:
   a. Band damaged.
   b. Servo damaged or worn.
   c. Improper adjustment.
   d. Anchor pin damage or wear.
10. Direct one-way or low one-way clutch worn, damaged or improperly assembled.

SLIP/CHATTER IN MANUAL 2ND GEAR

1. Vehicle wiring harness and PCM.
2. Pressure control solenoid A and B.
3. Improper fluid level or poor fluid quality.
4. Improper fluid pressures.
5. Fluid pump:
   a. Not tightened to specifications.
   b. Damaged pump gasket.
   c. Porosity, cross leaks, ball missing or plugged hole.
6. OD or reverse servo:
   a. Servo retaining ring damaged.
   b. Piston and cover seals damaged.
   c. Damage to anchor pins in transmission case.
7. OD or reverse band:
   a. Band damaged.
   b. Servo damaged or worn.
   c. Improper adjustment.
   d. Anchor pin damage or wear.
8. OD planetary damage.
9. Forward clutch:
   a. Piston or seals damaged.
   b. Check ball damaged, missing, not seating or off location.
   c. Friction components damaged or worn.
   d. Return springs damaged.
10. Low one-way clutch worn, damaged or improperly assembled.

SLIP/CHATTER IN MANUAL 3RD GEAR

1. Vehicle wiring harness and PCM.
2. Pressure control solenoid A and B.
3. Improper fluid level or poor fluid quality.
4. Improper fluid pressures.
5. Fluid pump:
   a. Not tightened to specifications.
   b. Damaged pump gasket.
   c. Porosity, cross leaks, ball missing or plugged hole.
6. OD or intermediate servo:
   a. Servo retaining ring damaged.
   b. Piston and cover seals damaged.
   c. Damage to anchor pins in transmission case.
7. OD or intermediate band:
   a. Band damaged.
   b. Servo damaged or worn.
   c. Improper adjustment.
   d. Anchor pin damage or wear.
8. Forward clutch or intermediate clutch:
   a. Piston or seals damaged.
   b. Check ball damaged, missing, not seating or off location.
   c. Friction elements damaged or worn.
   d. Return springs damaged.

PID: Temperature (°F)	Add Fluid (ml)	Add Fluid (oz.)
122	232	8
130	334	11
140	407	14
150	501	17
160	590	20
170	703	24
175	762	26
180	850	29
190	938	32
200	1026	35

FM5020001667000X

Fig. 4 Fluid temperature/fluid amount chart

9. Direct one-way or low one-way clutch worn, damaged or improperly assembled.

SOFT SHIFT OR SLIPPING

1. Vehicle wiring harness and PCM.
2. Shift solenoids A, B and C.
3. Pressure control solenoids A, B and C.
4. Intermediate shaft speed sensor.
5. Transmission fluid temperature sensor.
6. Intake air temperature sensor.
7. Vehicle speed sensor input.
8. Improper fluid level or poor fluid quality.
9. Improper fluid pressures.
10. Valve body:
    a. Not tightened to specifications.
    b. Separator plate damaged.
    c. Contamination.
    d. Valves or springs damaged, improperly assembled, missing, stuck or bore damage.
11. Fluid pump:
    a. Not tightened to specifications.
    b. Damaged pump gasket.
    c. Porosity, cross leaks, ball missing or plugged hole.
12. Coast clutch, direct clutch, forward clutch or intermediate clutch:
    a. Piston or seals damaged.
    b. Check ball damaged, missing, not seating or off location.
    c. Friction elements damaged or worn.
    d. Return springs damaged.
13. Center support:
    a. Not tightened to specifications.
    b. Seal rings or bearing damaged.
    c. Outside diameter of case bore damaged.
    d. Support damaged or leaking.
14. Intermediate or reverse servo:
    a. Servo retaining ring damage.
    b. Piston and cover seals damaged.
    c. Anchor pin damage in transmission case.
15. Intermediate or reverse band:
    a. Band damaged.
    b. Servo damaged or worn.
    c. Improper adjustment.
    d. Anchor pin damage or wear.
16. Damaged transmission case.

SOFT OR SLIPPING 1-2 SHIFT

1. Vehicle wiring harness and PCM.
2. Shift solenoid C.
3. Pressure control solenoid B.
4. Transmission fluid temperature sensor.
5. Intake air temperature sensor.
6. Vehicle speed sensor input.
7. Improper fluid level or poor fluid quality.
8. Improper fluid pressures.
9. Valve body:
   a. Not tightened to specifications.
   b. Separator plate damaged.
   c. Contamination.
   d. Valves or springs damaged, improperly assembled, missing, stuck or bore damage.
10. OD servo:
    a. Servo retaining ring damaged.
    b. Piston and cover seals damaged.
    c. Damage to anchor pins in transmission case.
11. OD band:
    a. Band damaged.
    b. Servo damaged or worn.
    c. Improper adjustment.
    d. Anchor pin damage or wear.

SOFT OR SLIPPING 2-1 SHIFT

1. Vehicle wiring harness and PCM.
2. Shift solenoid C.
3. Pressure control solenoid B.
4. Transmission fluid temperature sensor.
5. Improper fluid pressures.
6. Valve body:
   a. Not tightened to specifications.
   b. Separator plate damaged.
   c. Contamination.
   d. Valves or springs damaged, improperly assembled, missing, stuck or bore damage.

SOFT OR SLIPPING 2-3 SHIFT

1. Vehicle wiring harness and PCM.
2. Shift solenoid A.
3. Pressure control solenoid A.
4. Intermediate shaft speed sensor.
5. Transmission fluid temperature sensor.
6. Improper fluid pressures.
7. Valve body:
   a. Not tightened to specifications.
   b. Separator plate damaged.
   c. Contamination.
   d. Valves or springs damaged, improperly assembled, missing, stuck or bore damage.
8. Intermediate servo:
   a. Servo retaining ring damaged.
   b. Piston and cover seals damaged.
   c. Damage to anchor pins in transmission case.
9. Intermediate band:
   a. Band damaged.
   b. Servo damaged or worn.
   c. Improper adjustment.

d. Anchor pin damage or wear.
10. Intermediate clutch:
    a. Piston or seals damaged.
    b. Check ball damaged, missing, not seating or off location.
    c. Friction components damaged or worn.
    d. Return springs damaged.
11. Direct one-way clutch worn, damaged or improperly assembled.

SOFT OR SLIPPING 3-2 SHIFT

1. Vehicle wiring harness and PCM.
2. Shift solenoid C.
3. Pressure control solenoid B.
4. Intermediate shaft speed sensor.
5. Transmission fluid temperature sensor.
6. Improper fluid pressures.
7. Valve body:
    a. Not tightened to specifications.
    b. Separator plate damaged.
    c. Contamination.
    d. Valves or springs damaged, improperly assembled, missing, stuck or bore damage.
8. OD servo:
    a. Servo retaining ring damaged.
    b. Piston and cover seals damaged.
    c. Damage to anchor pins in transmission case.
9. OD band:
    a. Band damaged.
    b. Servo damaged or worn.
    c. Improper adjustment.
    d. Anchor pin damage or wear.
10. Direct one-way clutch worn, damaged or improperly assembled.

SOFT OR SLIPPING 3-4 SHIFT

1. Vehicle wiring harness and PCM.
2. Shift solenoid A.
3. Pressure control solenoid C.
4. Transmission fluid temperature sensor.
5. Improper fluid pressures.
6. Valve body:
    a. Not tightened to specifications.
    b. Separator plate damaged.
    c. Contamination.
    d. Valves or springs damaged, improperly assembled, missing, stuck or bore damage.
7. Center support:
    a. Not tightened to specifications.
    b. Seal rings or bearing damaged.
    c. Outside diameter of case bore damaged.
    d. Support damaged or leaking.
8. Direct clutch:
    a. Piston or seals damaged.
    b. Check ball damaged, missing, not seating or off location.
    c. Friction components damaged or worn.
    d. Return springs damaged.

SOFT OR SLIPPING 4-3 SHIFT

1. Vehicle wiring harness and PCM.
2. Shift solenoid A.
3. Pressure control solenoid A.
4. Transmission fluid temperature sensor.
5. Improper line pressures.
6. Valve body:
    a. Not tightened to specifications.
    b. Separator plate damaged.
    c. Contamination.
    d. Valves or springs damaged, improperly assembled, missing, stuck or bore damage.
7. Intermediate clutch:
    a. Piston or seals damaged.
    b. Check ball damaged, missing, not seating or off location.
    c. Friction components damaged or worn.
    d. Return springs damaged.

SOFT OR SLIPPING 4-5 SHIFT

1. Vehicle wiring harness and PCM.
2. Shift solenoid C.
3. Pressure control solenoid B.
4. Transmission fluid temperature sensor.
5. Improper fluid pressures.
6. Valve body:
    a. Not tightened to specifications.
    b. Separator plate damaged.
    c. Contamination.
    d. Valves or springs damaged, improperly assembled, missing, stuck or bore damage.
7. OD servo:
    a. Servo retaining ring damaged.
    b. Piston and cover seals damaged.
    c. Damage to anchor pins in transmission case.
8. OD band:
    a. Band damaged.
    b. Servo damaged or worn.
    c. Improper adjustment.
    d. Anchor pin damage or wear.

SOFT OR SLIPPING 5-4 SHIFT

1. Vehicle wiring harness and PCM.
2. Shift solenoid C.
3. Pressure control solenoid C.
4. Transmission fluid temperature sensor.
5. Improper fluid pressures.
6. Valve body:
    a. Not tightened to specifications.
    b. Separator plate damaged.
    c. Contamination.
    d. Valves or springs damaged, improperly assembled, missing, stuck or bore damage.
7. Direct clutch:
    a. Piston or seals damaged.
    b. Check ball damaged, missing, not seating or off location.
    c. Friction components damaged or worn.
    d. Return springs damaged.
8. Direct one-way clutch worn, damaged or improperly assembled.

TORQUE CONVERTER CLUTCH ALWAYS APPLIED—VEHICLE STALLS

1. Vehicle wiring harness and PCM.
2. Torque converter clutch solenoid.
3. Valve body:
    a. Not tightened to specifications.
    b. Separator plate damaged.
    c. Contamination.
    d. Valves or springs damaged, improperly assembled, missing, stuck or bore damage.
4. Torque converter internal failure preventing engagement or piston application.
5. Low one-way clutch worn, damaged or improperly assembled.

TORQUE CONVERTER CLUTCH CYCLING, SHUDDER OR CHATTER

1. Vehicle wiring harness and PCM.
2. Torque converter clutch solenoid.
3. Transmission fluid contamination.
4. Valve body:
    a. Not tightened to specifications.
    b. Separator plate damaged.
    c. Contamination.
    d. Valves or springs damaged, improperly assembled, missing, stuck or bore damage.
5. Torque converter internal leakage or clutch material damaged.

TORQUE CONVERTER CLUTCH DOES NOT APPLY

1. Vehicle wiring harness and PCM.
2. Torque converter clutch solenoid.
3. Transmission fluid temperature sensor.
4. Improper fluid pressures.
5. Valve body:
    a. Not tightened to specifications.
    b. Separator plate damaged.
    c. Contamination.
    d. Valves or springs damaged, improperly assembled, missing, stuck or bore damage.
6. Fluid pump:
    a. Not tightened to specifications.
    b. Damaged pump gasket.
    c. Porosity, cross leaks, ball missing or plugged hole.
7. Torque converter internal failure preventing engagement or piston application.

TRANSMISSION OVERHEATS

1. Vehicle wiring harness and PCM.
2. Shift solenoid A, B and C.
3. Pressure control solenoid A, B and C.
4. Transmission fluid temperature sensor.
5. Improper fluid level.
6. Improper fluid pressures.
7. Valve body:
    a. Not tightened to specifications.
    b. Separator plate damaged.
    c. Contamination.
    d. Valves or springs damaged, improperly assembled, missing, stuck or bore damage.
8. Fluid pump:
    a. Not tightened to specifications.
    b. Damaged pump gasket.
    c. Porosity, cross leaks, ball missing or plugged hole.
9. Case vent damaged.

10. Torque converter one-way clutch.
11. Excessive slip from torque converter.
12. Restriction in transmission cooling system.
13. Excessive trailer tow load.
14. Poor engine performance.

VEHICLE MOVEMENT WITH GEAR SELECTOR IN N RANGE

1. Improper fluid level.
2. Improper fluid pressure.

MAINTENANCE

FLUID INSPECTION

1. Install a suitable scan tool to vehicle Data Link Connector (DLC) and monitor transmission fluid temperature.
2. Start engine and allow vehicle to idle until transmission fluid temperature reaches at least 120°F.
3. Move gearshift selector lever through all gear ranges allowing transmission to engage in each gear.
4. Place selector lever in Park position and apply parking brake.
5. Raise and support vehicle. Ensure vehicle is level within 2–3°.
6. Place a suitable drain pan under transmission.
7. With engine running and transmission in Park position, remove fluid level indicator plug (small inner plug) using a suitable 3⁄16 inch hex key, **Fig. 2. Do not remove drain plug (large nut).**
8. Allow fluid to drain. When fluid is a thin stream or drip, it is at correct level. If no fluid drains, fluid must be added.
9. If fluid must be added, remove fill plug from extension housing using a suitable 5⁄16 inch hex key, **Fig. 3.**
10. Determine temperature of transmission fluid.
11. If fluid is above 122°F, refer to **Fig. 4** to determine proper amount of fluid to add.
12. If fluid is below 122°F, fill transmission until fluid drains from fluid level hole as a thin stream or drip.
13. Install fluid level plug and tighten to specifications.
14. Install fluid fill plug and tighten to specifications.

FLUID CHANGE

1. Raise and support vehicle.
2. Ensure vehicle is level within 2–3°.
3. Place a suitable drain pan under transmission.
4. Remove drain plug and allow fluid to drain, **Fig. 5.**
5. Remove torque converter housing plug.
6. Remove and discard torque converter drain plug allowing fluid to drain completely.
7. Install transmission oil pan drain plug and tighten to specifications.
8. Install a new torque converter drain plug and tighten to specifications.

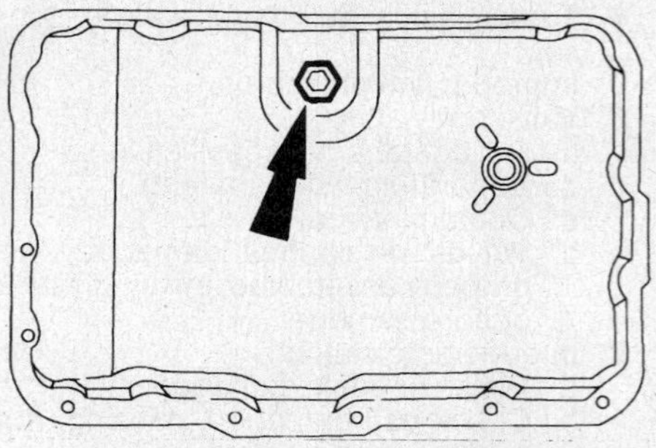

Fig. 5 Fluid drain plug

9. Install converter housing access plug.
10. Fill transmission to proper level. Refer to "Fluid Capacities & Cooling System Data" and "Lubricant Data" and charts for fluid quantity and type.
11. Inspect fluid level as outlined under "Fluid Inspection."

FLUID FILTER

1. Raise and support vehicle.
2. Remove drain plug draining fluid into a suitable container, **Fig. 5.**
3. Remove shift cable bracket.
4. Remove fluid pan attaching bolts, then the pan and gasket.
5. Remove two filter attaching bolts, then the filter.
6. Clean and inspect transmission pan and magnet.
7. Lubricate new filter O-ring seals with clean automatic transmission fluid.
8. Install filter and tighten to specifications.
9. Inspect pan gasket for damage. If gasket is not damaged, it may be reused.
10. Install transmission pan and tighten to specifications in a crisscross pattern.
11. Tighten shift cable bracket to specifications.
12. Add fluid to transmission as outlined under "Fluid Inspection."

ADJUSTMENTS

SELECTOR CABLE

1. Disconnect parking brake boot and center console upper section.
2. Disconnect cigar lighter electrical connector.
3. Remove center console upper section.
4. Disconnect transmission mode and traction control electrical connectors.
5. Move selector lever to R position.
6. Loosen selector cable lock nut.
7. Disconnect selector cable.
8. Raise and support vehicle.
9. Transmission selector lever has its own detent mechanism. There is no need to hold it after engaging gear.
10. Move rotary position switch to R position.
11. Lower vehicle.
12. Move selector lever to R position.
13. Connect selector cable. **Do not tighten selector lever lock nut.**
14. Move selector lever to D position.
15. Hold selector lever applying light pressure and hand tighten rear lock nut, then the front lock nut.
16. Move selector lever to different gear lever positions.
17. When D is selected ensure it sits as close as possible to D and 4 position in each corner.
18. Tighten selector lever lock nut.
19. Install center console upper section.
20. Connect transmission mode and traction control electrical connectors.
21. Connect cigarette lighter electrical connector.
22. Install center console upper section.
23. Clip together parking brake boot.

TRANSMISSION

REPLACE

REMOVAL

1. Place selector lever in N position.
2. Remove driveshaft.
3. **On models equipped with 3.0L engine,** remove starter motor.
4. **On models equipped with 4.0L engine,** disconnect Crankshaft Position (CKP) sensor electrical connector.
5. **On all models,** remove heat shields and disconnect oxygen sensor connector block.
6. Remove the rubber access cover and four torque converter nuts. Rotate torque converter to gain access to remaining nuts.
7. Disconnect oil cooler tubes from oil pan.
8. Disconnect oil cooler tubes from automatic transmission. Allow fluid to drain into suitable container.
9. Disconnect gear selector cable.
10. Support transmission with suitable jack.
11. Remove mounting bolts and lower transmission.
12. Remove transmission mount mounting bolts.
13. Disconnect Output Shaft Speed (OSS) sensor electrical connector.
14. Disconnect transmission range (TR) sensor electrical connector.
15. Disconnect protective cover.
16. Disconnect transmission body electrical connector.
17. Loosen mounting nut and disconnect Intermediate Shaft Speed (ISS) sensor and Turbine Shaft Speed (TSS) sensor electrical connectors.
18. Disconnect wiring harness from transmission housing.
19. Remove upper and lower transmission housing mounting bolts.
20. Remove transmission. **Do not let torque converter drop out of transmission.**

INSTALLATION

1. Ttorque converter must remain at correct installation depth throughout whole installation procedure.

2. Torque converter hub must engage fully in the oil pump drive gear.
3. Ensure installation depth between transmission flange and torque converter centering spigot for correct clearance.
4. Apply thin layer of suitable high-temperature grease to torque converter centering spigot bore.
5. Secure transmission to suitable jack with chain.
6. Raise transmission into place.
7. Install lower and upper transmission housing mounting bolts.
8. Install four torque converter nuts.
9. Rotate torque converter to gain access for remaining nuts.
10. Attach wiring harness to transmission housing.
11. Connect ISS and TSS sensor electrical connectors.
12. Connect transmission body electrical connector.
13. Tighten mounting nut.
14. Connect TR sensor electrical connector.
15. Attach protective cover.
16. Connect OSS electrical connector.
17. Raise rear of transmission.
18. Install transmission mount mounting bolts.
19. Attach gear selector cable and install mounting bolts.
20. Connect gear selector cable.
21. Attach oil cooler tubes to automatic transmission.
22. Attach oil cooler tubes to oil pan.
23. Install rubber access cover.
24. Attach oxygen sensor connector block.
25. Install heat shields.
26. **On models equipped with 4.0L engine,** connect CKP sensor electrical connector.

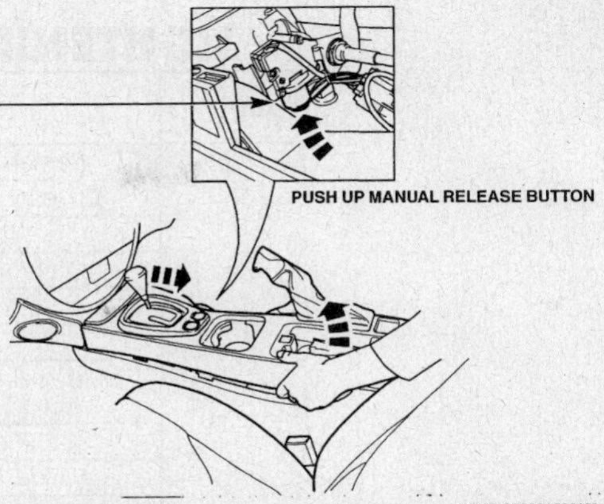

Fig. 6 Console trim plate removal for accessing interlock solenoid. 2000 S-Type

27. **On models equipped with 3.0L engine,** install starter motor.
28. **On all models,** install driveshaft.

TECHNICAL SERVICE BULLETINS

SHIFT LEVER WILL NOT RELEASE FROM PARK

2000 S Type

On some of these models the shift lever might not release from the Park position.

This condition may be caused by a discharged battery or other electrical fault conditions.

To correct this condition, the interlock mechanism can be manually released so the shift lever can be shifted into Neutral, as follows:

1. Fully apply parking brake.
2. Remove parking brake lever trim panel.
3. Lift up console lid.
4. Carefully lift console trim plate from rear, **Fig. 6. Catch seven trim clips so they can be used again.**
5. Raise manual plunger.
6. Hold plunger in raised position and move shift lever to Neutral.
7. Install console trim plate with seven clips after repairs.

TIGHTENING SPECIFICATIONS

Year	Component	Torque/Ft. Lbs.
2000–01	Center Support To Case Screw	96①
	Driveshaft Length Adjustment Nut	58
	Extension Housing	29
	Fill Plug To Extension Housing	15
	Filter To Case	89①
	Fluid Cooler	89①
	Fluid Level Indicator Plug To Drain Pipe Assembly	89①
	Fluid Pan Drain Plug	19
	Fluid Pump Assembly To Case	18
	Fluid Pump Housing Screws	18
	Intermediate & OD Band Adjustment Locknut	40
	Intermediate Shaft Speed Sensor	89①
	Manual Control Valve Detent Spring	89①
	Manual Valve Inner Lever Nut	35
	Output Shaft Flange Nut	97
	Output Shaft Speed Sensor	89①
	Pressure Tap Plug To Case	10
	Reverse Servo	89①
	Separator Plate To Valve Body	89①
	Solenoid Body	71①
	Torque Converter Drain Plug	89①
	Transmission Cooler Line Nut To Transmission Case Fitting	30
	Transmission Cooler Line To Transmission Case	35
	Transmission Mount To Extension Housing Center Screw	30
	Transmission Mount To Extension Housing Screws	37
	Transmission Pan To Case	96①
	Transmission Range Sensor	89①
	Turbine Shaft Speed Sensor	89①
	Valve Body	89①
	Valve Body Cover Plate	89①
	Wiring Harness To Solenoid Body	44①

① — Inch lbs.

ZF-5HP24 Automatic Transmission

NOTE: On Air Bag Equipped Models, Refer To "Air Bag System Precautions" Located In The Front Of This Manual For System Disarming & Arming Procedures.

INDEX

	Page No.
Adjustments	3-92
Gearshift Interlock Solenoid	3-92
Selector Cable	3-92
Description	3-91
In-Vehicle Repairs	3-92
Input/Output Speed Sensor	3-93
Internal Harness	3-93
Pressure Regulator Valve/Shift Solenoid	3-92
Rear Extension Housing & O-Ring Seal	3-93
Rear Extension Housing Oil Seal	3-93
Transmission Control Module	3-93
Valve Body	3-93
Maintenance	3-91
Fluid Change	3-91
Fluid Inspection	3-91
Precautions	3-91
Air Bag Systems	3-91
Battery Ground Cable	3-91
Tightening Specifications	3-95
Transmission, Replace	3-93
Installation	3-94
Removal	3-93
Troubleshooting	3-91
Default To Fifth Gear	3-91
Default To Fourth Gear	3-91
Harsh Shifts, Engine Stalling	3-91
Mode Switch State Lamp Not Working	3-91
No Torque Converter Lock-Up	3-91
Normal Transmission Operation But Fault Codes Stored	3-91
Out Of Sequence Shift	3-91
Poor Or Reduced Shift Quality	3-91
Sport Mode Will Not Select	3-91

PRECAUTIONS

AIR BAG SYSTEMS

Refer to "Air Bag System Precautions" in the front of this manual for system disarming and arming procedures.

BATTERY GROUND CABLE

Prior to service, disconnect battery ground cable and isolate as required.

DESCRIPTION

The ZF-5HP24 is a five-speed automatic transmission and uses advanced microprocessor control, **Fig. 1.** A 32-bit electronic Transmission Control Module (TCM) determines optimal gearshift points depending on vehicle speed, engine load, and selector position. Shift-energy management is controlled via a message from the TCM to the engine, requesting a reduction in engine torque during gearshifts. The TCM synchronizes the transmission clutches with engine torque and can adjust engine torque up to 30 times per second. This allows for smooth shifts between gears.

TROUBLESHOOTING

NORMAL TRANSMISSION OPERATION BUT FAULT CODES STORED

1. Output speed sensor circuit fault.
2. TCM faulty.
3. ABS system fault.
4. Position switch and D to 4 switch circuit fault.
5. P, R, 4 circuit fault.

SPORT MODE WILL NOT SELECT

Mode switch circuit fault.

MODE SWITCH STATE LAMP NOT WORKING

1. Mode switch supply.
2. Mode switch circuit fault.

POOR OR REDUCED SHIFT QUALITY

Transmission temperature sensor circuit.

OUT OF SEQUENCE SHIFT

1. Output/input speed sensor circuit fault.
2. Mechanical fault.

NO TORQUE CONVERTER LOCK-UP

1. P, R, 4 circuit fault.
2. Mechanical fault.

HARSH SHIFTS, ENGINE STALLING

1. P, R, 4 circuit fault.
2. Mechanical fault.

DEFAULT TO FOURTH GEAR

1. Solenoid/pressure regulator supply from TCM.
2. J-gate or selector cable out of adjustment.
3. D to 4th switch.
4. Rotary position switch circuit.
5. Input speed sensor circuit fault.
6. Input speed sensor faulty.
7. Solenoids 1, 2, or 3 circuit failure.
8. TCM faulty.
9. ABS fault.
10. CAN circuit fault between ABS/TCCM and TCM.
11. Output speed sensor circuit fault.
12. Pressure regulator, solenoid or speed sensor circuit fault.
13. Mechanical fault.
14. Pressure regulators 1, 2, 3, 4 or 5 circuit fault.
15. Power supply to TCM.
16. Vehicle battery charging system fault.
17. Incompatible ECM, ABS/TCCM, TCM or INST.
18. CAN circuit failure.
19. Faulty ECM.
20. CAN circuit fault between ECM and TCM.

DEFAULT TO FIFTH GEAR

1. Output speed sensor circuit fault.
2. Mechanical fault.
3. Output/input speed sensor.

MAINTENANCE

FLUID INSPECTION

1. Start engine with vehicle in Park position.
2. Idle engine at 600–750 RPM.
3. Remove fluid level/filler plug, **Fig. 2.**
4. Shift selector lever from Park to Drive, Drive to Reverse, and Reverse to Park pausing for at least three seconds in each position.
5. Add fluid until it starts to overflow from level/filler plug.
6. Install fluid level/filler plug.
7. Ensure fluid temperature has not exceeded 122° F.

FLUID CHANGE

The transmission fluid is filled for life and does not require changing except for prolonged driving under severe conditions. Routine level inspection is not required and a dipstick is not provided. A level/filler plug is fitted for service level inspection and filling if required.

1. Raise and support vehicle, then drain fluid into suitable container.
2. Install drain plug using new O-ring and tighten to specification.
3. Lower vehicle.
4. Ensure TCM is connected and functioning properly.

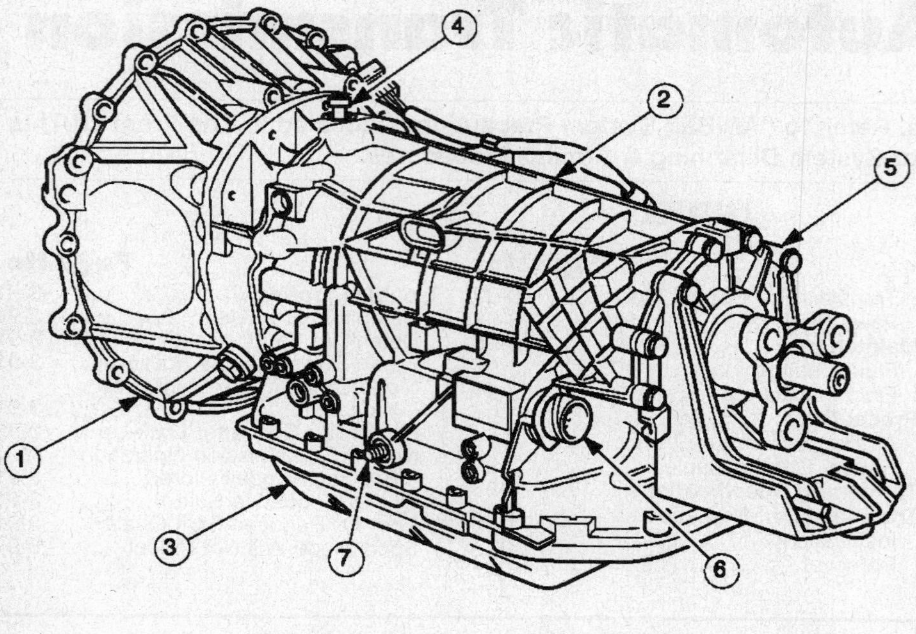

Item	Description
1	Torque converter housing
2	Transmission casing
3	Fluid pan
4	Transmission breather
5	Rear extension housing
6	16-way connector
7	Gear selector shaft

JC5029800040000X

Fig. 1 ZF-5HP24 automatic transmission

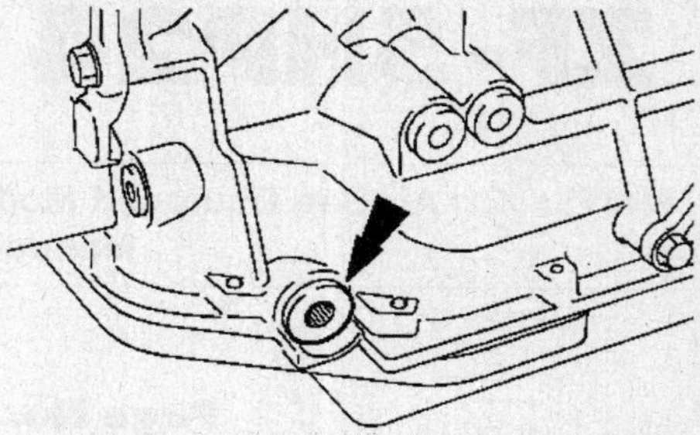

JC5029800041000X

Fig. 2 Fluid level/filler plug location

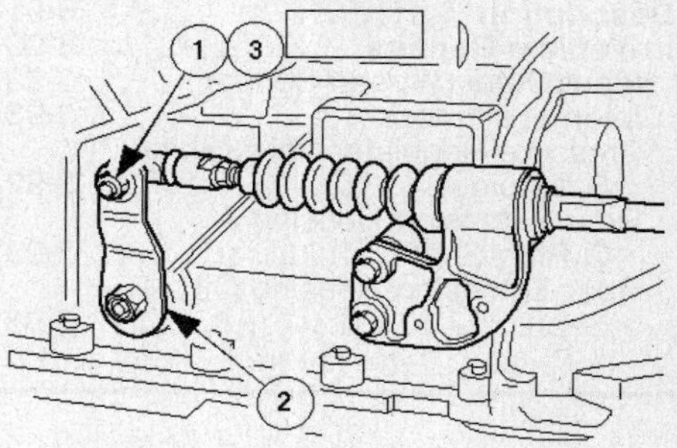

1. Inner cable
2. Selector lever
3. Inner cable

JC5029800049000X

Fig. 3 Selector cable neutral position

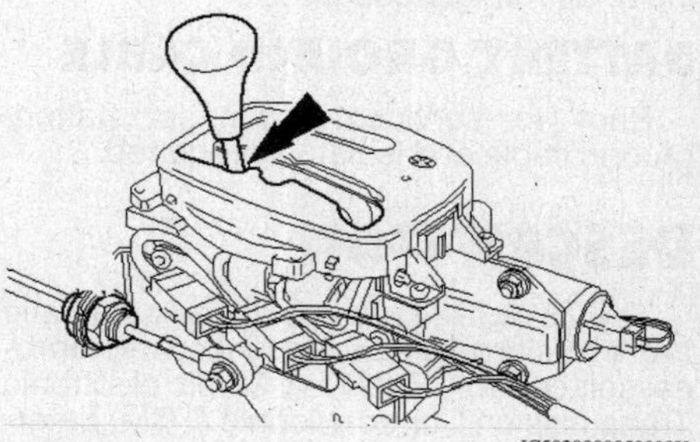

JC5029800050000X

Fig. 4 Selector cable adjustment

5. Position vehicle on level surface and let stand for at least two minutes.
6. Ensure transmission fluid temperature is below 86° F.
7. Start engine with vehicle in Park position.
8. Idle engine 600–750 RPM.
9. Remove fluid level/filler plug, **Fig. 2.**
10. Shift selector lever from Park to Drive, Drive to Reverse, and Reverse to Park pausing for at least three seconds in each position.
11. Fill fluid until it starts to overflow from level/filler plug.
12. Install fluid level/filler plug.
13. Ensure fluid temperature has not exceeded 122° F.

ADJUSTMENTS

SELECTOR CABLE

1. Place gear selector lever in Neutral position.
2. Remove J-gate finish panel, then the veneer panel assembly.
3. Remove center console assembly.
4. Loosen selector cable locking nuts away from abutment.
5. Ensure selector is in Neutral position as follows:
   a. Disconnect inner cable from selector lever at transmission, **Fig. 3.**
   b. With lever moved fully rearward, push lever forward two detents to achieve Neutral position.
   c. Reconnect inner cable.
6. Ensure transmission selector does not move from Neutral position during adjustment.
7. Position shifter in Neutral detent.
8. Adjust nuts to lock against bracket without moving set position of either shift lever or selector lever, **Fig. 4. Torque** locknuts 16–21 ft. lbs.
9. Install center console, veneer panel and J-gate finish panel.

GEARSHIFT INTERLOCK SOLENOID

1. Remove J-gate finish panel, then the veneer panel.
2. Remove interlock solenoid actuating lever cover.
3. Place gear selector in Neutral position.
4. Loosen solenoid mounting bolts, **Fig. 5.**
5. Hold selector lever midway between Park and Reverse positions.
6. Move solenoid rearward, against spring pressure to take up free play.
7. Tighten solenoid locking bolts to specifications.
8. Ensure interlock actuating lever has no freeplay with selector lever midway between Park and Reverse.
9. Install interlock actuating lever cover, veneer panel and J-gate finish panel.

IN-VEHICLE REPAIRS

PRESSURE REGULATOR VALVE/SHIFT SOLENOID

1. Raise and support vehicle, then drain transmission fluid into suitable container.
2. Remove mounting bolts and oil pan.
3. Disconnect regulator/solenoid electrical connectors.
4. Remove righthand rear valve body mounting screws.

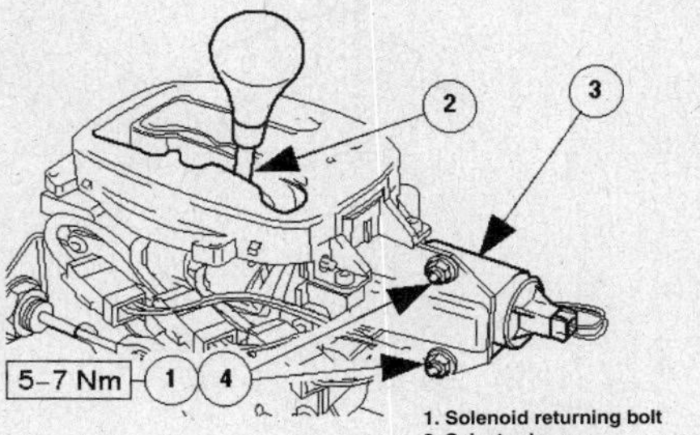

1. Solenoid returning bolt
2. Selector lever
3. Solenoid
4. Solenoid retaining nuts

JC5029800051000X

Fig. 5 Gearshift interlock solenoid adjustment

5. Remove mounting screws and pressure regulator/solenoid retaining plate, **Fig. 6.**
6. Reverse procedure to install with new regulator O-ring. Tighten mounting bolts to specifications.

INPUT/OUTPUT SPEED SENSOR

1. Raise and support vehicle, then drain transmission fluid into suitable container.
2. Remove mounting bolts and oil pan.
3. Remove bracket mounting screw and speed sensor.
4. Disconnect speed sensor electrical connector.
5. Reverse procedure to install. Tighten fasteners to specification.

TRANSMISSION CONTROL MODULE

1. Remove engine compartment passenger's side trim panel.
2. Remove mounting screws and ECM/TCM housing cover.
3. Disconnect TCM harness connector.
4. Remove TCM from housing.
5. Reverse procedure to install.

INTERNAL HARNESS

1. Remove input/output speed sensor as outlined in this section.
2. Remove selector cable abutment bracket mounting bolts, then position bracket for access to multi-plug.
3. Release locking lever and disconnect harness multi-plug.
4. Push harness multi-plug into transmission case, then remove multi-plug retaining clip.
5. Disconnect eight solenoid/regulator connectors.
6. Release retaining clips and remove harness, **Fig. 7.**
7. Reverse procedure to install. Tighten fasteners to specification.

REAR EXTENSION HOUSING & O-RING SEAL

1. Place selector lever in Neutral position.
2. Raise and support vehicle.
3. Remove front muffler.
4. Place suitable transmission jack under transmission.

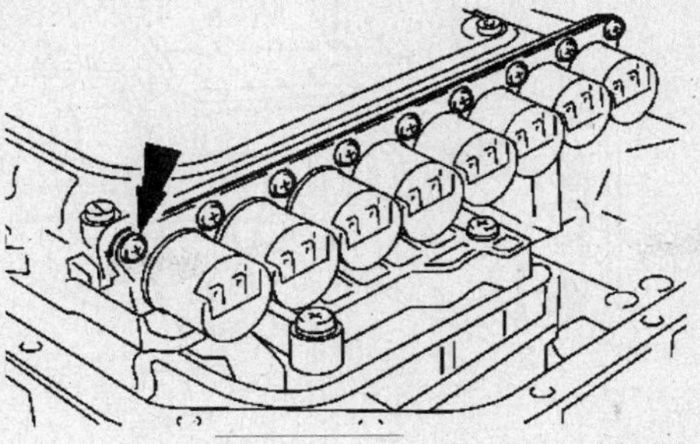

JC5029800042000X

Fig. 6 Pressure regulator/ solenoid retaining plate

5. Remove mounting bolts and engine rear mounting bracket.
6. Lower transmission.
7. Mark position of coupling to drive flange for installation.
8. Remove three transmission drive flange to flexible coupling mounting bolts. **Do not remove driveshaft to flexible coupling mounting bolts.**
9. Remove mounting bolts and rear extension housing assembly. Mark bolts for installation.
10. Remove O-ring.
11. Reverse procedure to install using new O-ring. Tighten mounting bolts to specifications.

REAR EXTENSION HOUSING OIL SEAL

Removal

1. Remove rear extension housing as outlined in this section.
2. Install driveshaft flange wrench tool No. 205-053, or equivalent, to transmission drive coupling.
3. Position tool and housing assembly in suitable vise.
4. Knock back coupling nut staked areas using suitable punch,.
5. Remove coupling nut using coupling nut socket tool No. 307-356, or equivalent.
6. Remove driveshaft flange wrench tool from coupling and drive coupling from housing.
7. Remove extension housing oil seal using suitable seal puller.

Installation

1. Clean oil seal mating faces.
2. Lubricate oil seal.
3. Install oil seal using oil seal replacement tool No. 307-358, or equivalent.
4. Install driveshaft flange wrench tool No. 205-053, or equivalent, to transmission drive coupling.
5. Install drive coupling to housing while holding housing in suitable soft jawed vise.
6. **Torque** coupling nut to 80–98 ft. lbs. using coupling nut socket tool No. 307-356, or equivalent.
7. Stake coupling nut at two positions.
8. Install rear extension housing. Tighten mounting bolts to specifications.

VALVE BODY

1. Remove input/output speed sensor as

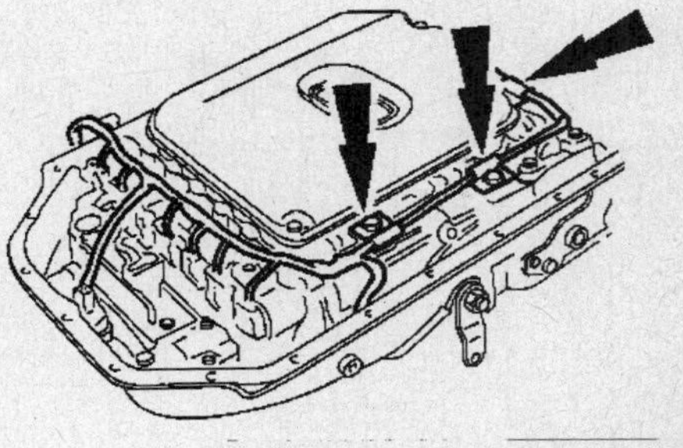

JC5029800043000X

Fig. 7 Internal harness replacement

outlined in this section, then the speed sensor.
2. Disconnect five pressure regulator and three solenoid connectors.
3. Release internal harness from retaining clips and position aside.
4. Loosen valve body to transmission case mounting screws and allow valve body to drain into a suitable container.
5. Remove mounting screws and valve body.
6. Reverse procedure to install. Tighten mounting bolts to specification.

TRANSMISSION

REPLACE

REMOVAL

1. Place gear selector in Neutral position.
2. Remove engine covers.
3. Remove air intake tube and air cleaner assembly.
4. Install engine lifting bracket tool No. 303-536, or equivalent, at righthand rear of engine.
5. Remove coolant header tank mounting bolt, then position tank aside.
6. Install engine lifting bracket tool No. 303-536, or equivalent, at lefthand rear of engine.
7. Support engine using engine support fixture tool No. 303-021, or equivalent.
8. Adjust and locate stands in lefthand and righthand fender channels, then tighten beams, **Fig. 8.**
9. Raise and support vehicle.
10. Remove lefthand and righthand upstream catalytic converters.
11. Remove front muffler.
12. Drain transmission fluid into suitable container.
13. Support transmission with suitable transmission jack.
14. Remove bracket mounting bolts and engine rear mounting.
15. Disconnect driveshaft from transmission drive flange. **Mark position of coupling to drive flange for installation alignment.**
16. Remove transmission drive flange to flexible coupling mounting bolts. **Do not remove driveshaft to flexible coupling mounting bolts.**
17. Lower transmission.
18. Remove gear selector cable ball pin to selector lever nut, **Fig. 9.**

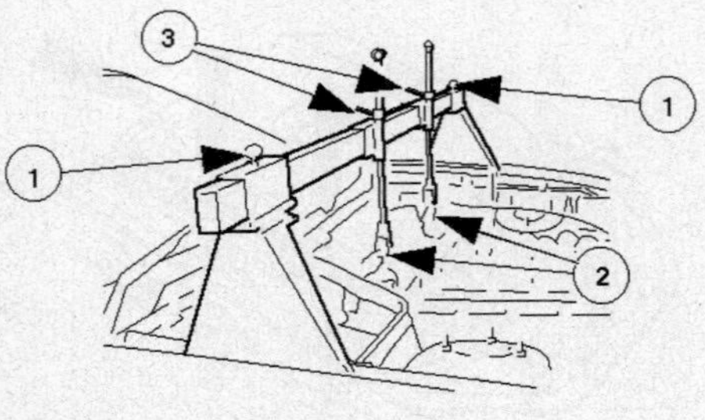

1.Beam adjustment.
2. Lifting brackets.
3. Support hook adjusters.

JC5029800044000X

Fig. 8 Engine support fixture installation

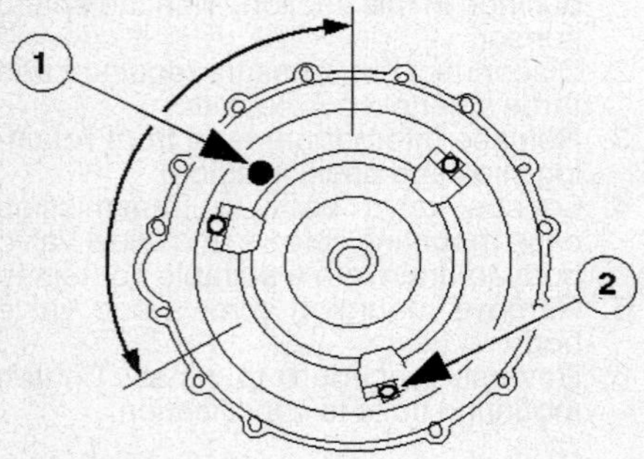

1. Blue dot alignment
2. Bolt access hole

JC5029800047000X

Fig. 11 Torque converter blue dot alignment

19. Remove selector cable to transmission casing bolts, then disconnect cable from transmission.
20. Disconnect transmission harness multi-plug.
21. Remove mounting bolts and rotary switch.
22. Disconnect fluid cooler pipes.
23. Remove flexplate access cover.
24. Remove three torque converter to drive plate mounting bolts.
25. Remove lefthand and righthand catalyst mounting brackets.
26. Remove engine harness connector mounting bracket mounting bolts and position aside.
27. Position righthand side cooler pipe aside.
28. Remove four upper transmission to engine mounting bolts, then the ground lead bolt.
29. Remove upper cooler pipe clip to

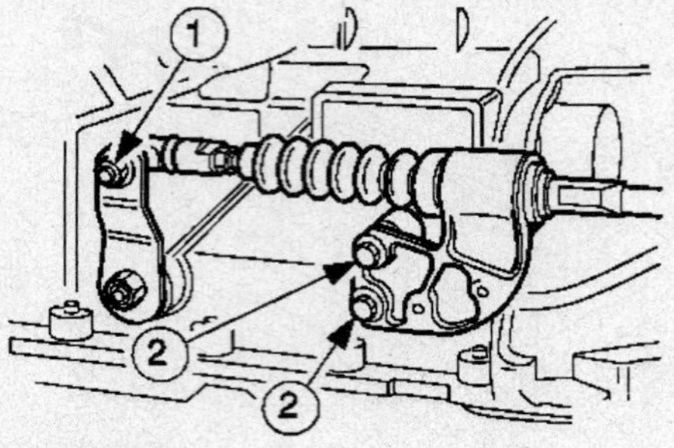

1.Lever nut.
2. Selector cable bolts.

JC5029800045000X

Fig. 9 Gear selector cable removal

transmission case bolt from lefthand side of transmission.

30. Remove remaining six transmission case to cylinder block mounting bolts.
31. Remove transmission assembly.

INSTALLATION

1. Clean all mating surfaces.
2. Apply Molykote lubricant, or equivalent, to torque converter spigot.
3. Rotate crankshaft to position orange dot within indicated sector, **Fig. 10.**
4. Keeping dot within sector, align nearest converter bolt hole.
5. Rotate torque converter to position blue dot within indicated sector, **Fig. 11.**
6. Keeping dot within sector, align nearest bolt hole.
7. Loosely assemble cooler pipe clip, ground lead and catalyst brackets.
8. Tighten transmission mounting bolts to specifications in sequence, **Fig. 12.**
9. Tighten remaining bolts in any order to specifications.
10. Install engine harness connector mounting bracket and tighten mounting bolts to specification.
11. Align driveshaft marks, then connect drive shaft. Tighten mounting bolts to specification.
12. Install rear mount. Tighten mounting bolts to specification. **Ensure hooks of engine support beam are not trapped before tightening bolts.**
13. Remove transmission jack.
14. Install torque converter to flexplate bolts and tighten to specification.

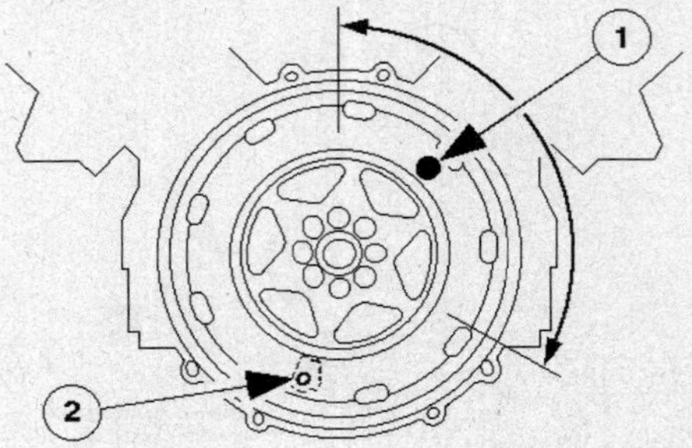

1. Orange dot alignment
2. Bolt access hole

JC5029800046000X

Fig. 10 Drive plate orange dot alignment

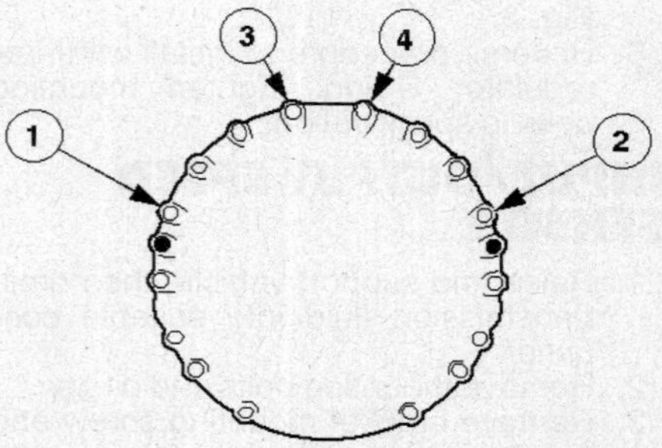

JC5029800048000X

Fig. 12 Transmission bolt tightening sequence

15. Connect transmission harness multi-plug.
16. Connect selector cable to lever and abutment bracket to transmission casing. Tighten mounting bolts to specification.
17. Install rotary switch and tighten to specification.
18. Connect fluid cooler pipes to transmission using new O-ring seals. Tighten mounting bolts to specification.
19. Remove engine support beam.
20. Install lefthand and righthand upstream catalytic converters, then the front muffler.
21. Lower vehicle.
22. Position cooler header tank and tighten mounting bolts to specifications.
23. Install air intake tube and air cleaner assembly.
24. Install engine covers.

TIGHTENING SPECIFICATIONS

Year	Component	Torque, Ft. Lbs.
1998–2001	Cooler Header Tank	35–44
	Drain Plug	19–24
	Driveshaft	55–65
	Fluid Cooler Pipe	13–17
	Gearshift Interlock Solenoid	44–62①
	Harness Connector Mounting Bracket	10–13
	Input Speed Sensor	44①
	Oil Pan	78–96①
	Output Speed Sensor	12①
	Pressure Regulator/Solenoid Plate	44①
	Rear Extension Housing	16–18
	Rear Mount, Center	22–30
	Rear Mount, Outer	16–21
	Rotary Switch	60–84①
	Selector Cable Abutment	60–84①
	Selector Cable To Lever	60–84①
	Torque Converter To Flexplate	32–42
	Valve Body	72①

① — Inch lbs.

Mercedes-Benz MB W5A580

NOTE: Refer To The "Mercedes-Benz" Section In This Manual For Procedures Not Found In This Section.

NOTE: On Air Bag Equipped Models, Refer To "Air Bag System Precautions" Located In The Front Of This Manual For System Disarming & Arming Procedures.

NOTE: Prior To Performing Any Service Operations Listed In This Section, Consult The "Technical Service Bulletins" Section For Related Information.

INDEX

	Page No.
Adjustments	3-97
Selector Cable	3-97
In-Vehicle Repairs	3-97
Rear Seal, Replace	3-97
Valve Body, Replace	3-97
Maintenance	3-96
Fluid Change	3-96
Precautions	3-96
Air Bag Systems	3-96
Battery Ground Cable	3-96
Technical Service Bulletins	3-97
Electrical Connector Oil Leak	3-97
Tightening Specifications	3-98
Transmission, Replace	3-97
Troubleshooting	3-96
Drive Does Not Engage	3-96
Engine May Be Started In Positions Other Than Park Or Neutral	3-96
Lower Ratios Will Not Hold	3-96
No Neutral Position	3-96
Noise/Rattle From J-Gate	3-96
Reverse Does Not Engage	3-96
Shift Lever Detent Indistinct in 3 Causing Poor Location	3-96
Shift Lever Has No Effect Upon Transmission & Resistance Cannot Be Felt	3-96
Shift Lever Position Not Aligned Properly	3-96
Shift Lever Vibration	3-96
Shift May Be Moved From Park Without Brake Pedal Operation	3-96
Shift Stuck In Park	3-96
Vehicle Rolls in Park	3-96

PRECAUTIONS

AIR BAG SYSTEMS

Refer to "Air Bag System Precautions" located in the front of this manual for system disarming & arming procedures.

BATTERY GROUND CABLE

Prior to service, disconnect battery ground cable and isolate as required.

TROUBLESHOOTING

SHIFT STUCK IN PARK

1. Selector cable seized.
2. Interlock solenoid not operating.
3. Operator sequence error.

VEHICLE ROLLS IN PARK

1. Improper cable adjustment.
2. Faulty parking pawl.

REVERSE DOES NOT ENGAGE

1. Improper cable adjustment.
2. Transmission fluid level improper.

NO NEUTRAL POSITION

1. Improper cable adjustment.
2. Transmission faulty.

DRIVE DOES NOT ENGAGE

1. Improper cable adjustment.
2. Transmission fluid level improper.
3. Transmission faulty.

LOWER RATIOS WILL NOT HOLD

1. Excessive engine temperature.
2. DLS fault.

SHIFT LEVER HAS NO EFFECT UPON TRANSMISSION & RESISTANCE CANNOT BE FELT

1. Cable disconnected or broken.
2. Transmission selector problem.
3. Shift lever drive pin adrift.

SHIFT LEVER POSITION NOT ALIGNED PROPERLY

Sliding block drive pin displaced.

SHIFT LEVER DETENT INDISTINCT IN 3 CAUSING POOR LOCATION

DLS detent fault.

SHIFT MAY BE MOVED FROM PARK WITHOUT BRAKE PEDAL OPERATION

1. Interlock latch fault.
2. Solenoid permanently activated.

ENGINE MAY BE STARTED IN POSITIONS OTHER THAN PARK OR NEUTRAL

1. Improper cable adjustment.
2. DLS fault.

SHIFT LEVER VIBRATION

1. Loose selector assembly.
2. Cable isolation fault.

NOISE/RATTLE FROM J-GATE

1. Debris in mechanism.
2. Worn J-gate track gasket.
3. Loose selector disc seal.

MAINTENANCE

FLUID CHANGE

It is not required to change the transmission fluid in normal service and routine level inspection is not required. The sealed dipstick tube is installed for service requirements only. The dipstick is available as a special tool only and is not permanently installed on the vehicle.

1. Raise and support vehicle.
2. Remove drain plug from transmission pan.
3. Break off dipstick tube plug locking plate.
4. Push locking pin downward into plug, then remove dipstick tube plug.
5. Push locking pin through tube plug and discard pin.
6. Pour approximately four quarts of fluid into transmission.
7. Place gear selector in Park position and start engine.
8. Pour approximately three quarts of fluid into transmission.

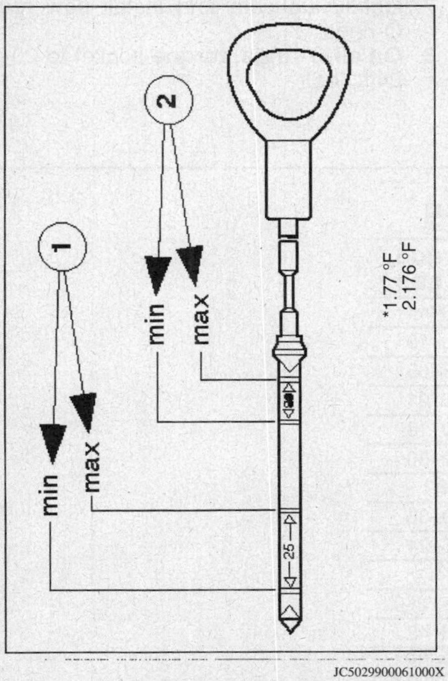

Fig. 1 Fluid level inspection

9. Cycle gear selector from Park to Drive, Drive to Reverse and Reverse to Park.
10. Inspect transmission fluid temperature to select appropriate dipstick calibration, **Fig. 1.**
11. Insert dipstick tool No. 307-379, or equivalent, until it stops.
12. Remove dipstick and inspect level.
13. Correct fluid level as required.
14. Seat tube plug, then engage and fully seat new locking pin.
15. Inspect for leaks.

ADJUSTMENTS

SELECTOR CABLE

Refer to "Adjustments" in the "ZF-5HP24 Automatic Transmission" section for selector cable adjustment procedure.

IN-VEHICLE REPAIRS

REAR SEAL, REPLACE

1. Place gear selector in Neutral position.
2. Raise and support vehicle.
3. Remove front muffler.
4. Remove rear crossmember.
5. Mark position of coupling to drive flange, then disconnect driveshaft from transmission drive flange.
6. Remove three transmission drive flange to flexible coupling retaining bolts. **Do not remove driveshaft to flexible coupling retaining bolts.**
7. Secure driveshaft wrench tool No. 205-053, or equivalent, to output shaft flange.
8. Remove staked portion from output shaft keyway.
9. Remove and discard flange nut, then the output shaft flange.
10. Remove and discard oil seal.
11. Reverse procedure to install. Tighten mounting bolts to specification.

VALVE BODY, REPLACE

1. Raise and support vehicle.
2. Remove righthand catalytic converter.
3. Remove harness lower mounting bolt and heat shield.
4. Release locking lever, then disconnect transmission link harness connector.
5. Remove center mounting bolt, then the female connector.
6. Drain transmission fluid into suitable container.
7. Remove mounting bolts and oil pan.
8. Pull disengage pick-up O-ring and location tang, then remove filter.
9. Remove mounting screw and selector detent lead spring.
10. Remove leaf spring to valve body dowel.
11. Remove mounting bolts and valve body.
12. Reverse procedure to install. Tighten mounting bolts to specifications.

TRANSMISSION

REPLACE

1. Place selector lever in Neutral position.
2. Remove engine covers.
3. Remove air intake tube and air cleaner cover assembly.
4. Disconnect transmission link lead connector.
5. Remove EMS harness mounting bracket.
6. Install engine lifting bracket tool No. 307-536, or equivalent, at righthand rear of engine.
7. Remove lefthand side enclosure panel, then the center trim panel.
8. Disconnect bleed pipe, then remove header tank mounting bolts.
9. Move coolant header tank for access.
10. Install engine lifting bracket tool No. 307-536, or equivalent, at lefthand rear of engine.
11. Support engine using engine support tool No. 307-021, or equivalent.
12. Raise and support vehicle.
13. Remove lefthand and righthand upstream catalytic converter, then the front muffler.
14. Drain transmission fluid into suitable container.
15. Support transmission with suitable transmission jack.
16. Remove rear crossmember center bolt.
17. Remove body mounting bolts and rear crossmember.
18. Mark position of driveshaft coupling to drive flange, then disconnect driveshaft from transmission drive flange.
19. Remove transmission drive flange to flexible coupling mounting bolts. **Do not remove driveshaft to flexible coupling mounting bolts.**
20. Lower transmission.
21. Remove selector cable ball pin to selector lever nut, then lower transmission for access.

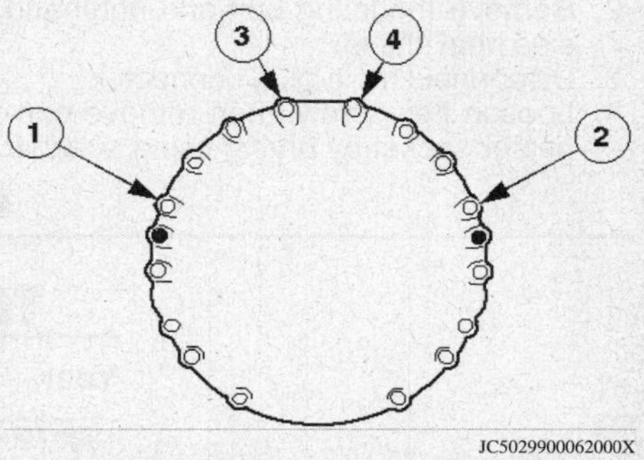

Fig. 2 Transmission case bolts tightening sequence

22. Remove selector cable to transmission case mounting bolts.
23. Remove bracket to transmission case mounting bolts and transmission harness multi-plugs.
24. Disconnect fluid cooler pipes.
25. Remove flexplate access cover.
26. Remove three torque converter to flexplate mounting bolts.
27. Remove lefthand and righthand catalyst mounting bracket mounting bolts, then the brackets.
28. Position cooler pipe to gain access on righthand side.
29. Remove transmission to engine mounting bolts as follows:
    a. Two top transmission to engine mounting bolts.
    b. Two starter motor power cable clip mounting bolts.
    c. Ground lead bolt.
    d. Cooler upper pipe clip to transmission case mounting bolt.
    e. Remaining six transmission case to cylinder block bolts.
30. Remove transmission.
31. Reverse procedure to install, noting the following:
    a. Apply lubricant Molykote, or equivalent, to torque converter spigot.
    b. Tighten transmission case to cylinder block mounting bolts to specifications in sequence, **Fig. 2.**
    c. Tighten remaining bolts in any order.
    d. Tighten mounting bolts and nuts to specifications.

TECHNICAL SERVICE BULLETINS

ELECTRICAL CONNECTOR OIL LEAK

1998 XJR

On some of these models there may be an oil leak near the electrical connector on the righthand side of the transmission.

This condition may be caused by the connector O-ring seals.

To correct this condition, proceed as follows:

1. Raise and support vehicle, then drain transmission fluid into suitable container.

2. Remove mounting bolt and righthand side heat shield.
3. Disconnect multi-plug connector.
4. Loosen hex screw, then remove connector socket by prying using suitable lever. Mounting screw remains with connector.
5. **If O-rings are black,** install new sleeve part No. JLM 21109.
6. **If O-rings are red,** proceed to next step.
7. Lightly lubricate and install new red O-rings.
8. **On all O-rings, torque** socket to 20–24 ft. lbs.

TIGHTENING SPECIFICATIONS

Year	Component	Torque, Ft. Lbs.
1998–2001	Coolant Header	35–44
	Dipstick Tube	10–13
	Driveshaft	55–65
	Front Muffler Bracket	16–21
	Harness Connector Support Bracket	10–13
	Oil Cooler Pipes	22–30
	Output Flange	89
	Rear Crossmember, Center	29–38
	Rear Crossmember, Outer	16–21
	Selector Cable	84①
	Selector Detent Leaf Spring	60–72①
	Torque Converter To Flexplate	33–42
	Transmission Link Harness	32–39
	Transmission To Cylinder Block	33–42
	Valve Body	60–72①

① — Inch lbs.

Drive Axles

INDEX

Page No.		Page No.		Page No.	
Drive Axle, Replace	3-99	S Type	3-99	**Tightening Specifications**	3-100
		XJR, XJ8, XKR & XK8	3-99		

DRIVE AXLE

REPLACE

S TYPE

1. Raise and support vehicle, then remove rear tire and wheel assemblies.
2. Remove axle shaft hub nut.
3. Disconnect brake caliper as outlined in "Disc Brake" section.
4. Disconnect harness and ABS sensor.
5. Disconnect outer tie rod.
6. Disconnect lower arm from hub assembly.
7. Remove brake disc as outlined in "Disc Brake" section.
8. Disconnect hub assembly from driveshaft.
9. Disconnect axle shaft from differential housing using suitable pry tool. **Do not damage differential seal.**
10. Remove axle shaft from differential housing.
11. **Do not loosen or remove flexible coupling.**
12. Mark driveshaft to flange for installation alignment.
13. Mark balance nut to flange for installation alignment.
14. Mark position of each nut and bolt to transmission flexible joint for installation alignment.
15. Disconnect driveshaft from differential flange.
16. Disconnect breather tube from crossmember.
17. Support axle assembly using suitable jack. **Use packing material to prevent damage to the underside of the casing.**
18. Remove mounting bolts and axle assembly. **Do not lose washer or mix positions.**
19. Reverse procedure to install, noting the following:
    a. Ensure driveshaft nuts and bolts are installed in correct locations.
    b. Install installation tool No. 205-461, or equivalent.
    c. Install new axle shaft circlip.
    d. **Do not fully engage axle shaft into the differential housing.**
    e. Install axle shaft, then remove special tool.
    f. Fully engage axle shaft into differential housing.

XJR, XJ8, XKR & XK8

1. Raise and support vehicle, then remove tire and wheel assemblies.
2. Remove rear suspension assembly.
3. Compress rear spring with spring compressor tool No. 204 179, or equivalent, and mark tool position on spring.
4. Remove lower mounting nut and bolt, then the shock absorber.
5. Repeat previous steps to remove other shock absorber.
6. Disconnect in-line connector, then remove out frame clips and clear parking brake cable through frame.
7. Remove mounting nut and lower fulcrum shaft.
8. Remove axle shaft drive flange nuts.
9. Support axle shaft assembly, then remove hub fulcrum. Mark and remove camber adjustment spacer.
10. Repeat previous steps to remove other axle shaft.
11. Remove mounting bolts and final drive nose plate.
12. Position axle assembly on supported by suitable wooden blocks.
13. Remove stabilizer bar link to control arm mounting nuts.
14. Remove mounting nut and pivot bolt.
15. Mark and remove front spacer and rear washers, then remove control arm.
16. Repeat previous steps to remove other control arm.
17. Remove mounting nuts, washers and control arm tie assembly.
18. Remove mounting nuts and bolts, then the tie rods. Mark and remove spacers.
19. Position assembly to access A frame. **Rear axle oil may flow from breather.**
20. Remove rear mounting bracket, final drive and wide mounting bracket mounting bolts, then the A frame.
21. Remove A frame rear mounting bracket from final drive.
22. Remove mounting nuts and wide mounting bracket. Remove washers.
23. Remove pendulum assembly.
24. Reverse procedure to install, noting the following:
    a. Install new axle shaft drive flange mounting nuts.
    b. Tighten mounting bolts and nuts to specifications.

TIGHTENING SPECIFICATIONS

Year	Component	Torque, Ft. Lbs.
S TYPE		
2000–01	ABS Sensor	88①
	Differential, Front Mount	55
	Differential, Rear Mount	89
	Flexible Joint	63
	Hub Nut	302
	Lower Arm, Outer	111
	Tie Bar, Outer	74
XJR, XJ8, XKR & XK8		
1998–2001	A Frame To Nose Plate	66–81
	A Frame To Rear Mounting Bracket	62–84
	A Frame To Wide Mounting Bracket	62–77
	Axle Shaft To Final Drive Flange	60–73
	Axle Shaft To Hub	223–347
	Damper, Lower	59–74
	Drive Shaft Flexible Coupling	55–65
	Final Drive Nose Plate	27–37
	Lower Fulcrum	66–81
	Pendulum To Final Drive	118–147
	Tie Rod To Final Drive	62–57
	Tie Rod To Wide Mounting Bracket	62–84
	Wishbone Pivot	62–74
	Wishbone Tie To Final Drive	62–77

① — Inch Lbs.

Traction Control Systems

NOTE: On Air Bag Equipped Models, Refer To "Air Bag System Precautions" Located In The Front Of This Manual For System Disarming & Arming Procedures.

INDEX

	Page No.
Description	3-101
Automatic Stability Control (ASC)	3-101
Dynamic Stability Control (DSC)	3-101
Diagnosis & Testing	3-101
Precautions	3-101
Air Bag Systems	3-101
Battery Ground Cable	3-101
Depressurizing System	3-101
System Service	3-101

PRECAUTIONS

AIR BAG SYSTEMS

Refer to "Air Bag System Precautions" in the front of this manual for system disarming and arming procedures.

DEPRESSURIZING SYSTEM

The rear struts, control valve and connecting lines contain gas and oil maintained at a high pressure. The system must be depressurized prior to service.

This system is filled with Jaguar/ Castrol Hydraulic System Mineral Oil (HMSO). If any other fluid is used, the system will become contaminated and must be flushed.

1. Operate brake pedal repeatedly until pedal becomes difficult to operate.
2. Raise and support rear of vehicle.
3. Attach suitable piece of hose to line bleed screw (1), located on three way line connector at lefthand rear side of ride height pressure line, **Fig. 1.**
4. Place free end of hose in drain container.
5. Loosen line bleed screw ½ turn and allow fluid to drain into container.
6. Tighten bleed screw and lower vehicle.
7. Add new fluid as required to reservoir. **Never use old fluid.**

BATTERY GROUND CABLE

Prior to service, disconnect battery ground cable and isolate as required.

DESCRIPTION

AUTOMATIC STABILITY CONTROL (ASC)

The ASC utilizes the ABS sensing arrangement to provide the maximum traction force to propel the vehicle. The ASC is switched on when the engine is started. The system can be switched off by pressing the ASC OFF (the switched is marked TRAC OFF on vehicles fitted with traction control). The switch, which is situated in the center console switchpack, lights up to warn that the system is switched off. An ASC amber warning light flashes on the instrument panel when the system detects a spinning wheel. The ASC system uses engine intervention to reduce the torque delivered to the drive wheels to prevent them spinning. Engine torque is reduced in three ways: The throttle is moved towards the closed position. The ignition is retarded. Fuel is cut-off at the cylinder injectors. Wheel spin is detected by the wheel speed sensors and communicated to the ABS/ TCCM. The ABS/TCCM uses information from the controller area network (CAN) to calculate the torque that the engine should produce to stop the wheel spinning. Torque reductions are then requested from the engine control module (ECM) through the CAN. The throttle is then positioned to provide the target torque, which has been calculated to prevent wheel spin. During the transient phase of torque reduction the fuel is cut-off and the ignition retarded. Both the fuel cut-off and ignition retard will be restored to normal when the throttle is set to its new position. The ASC uses a brake control modulator with six solenoid valves: three normally open inlet valves and three normally closed outlet valves.

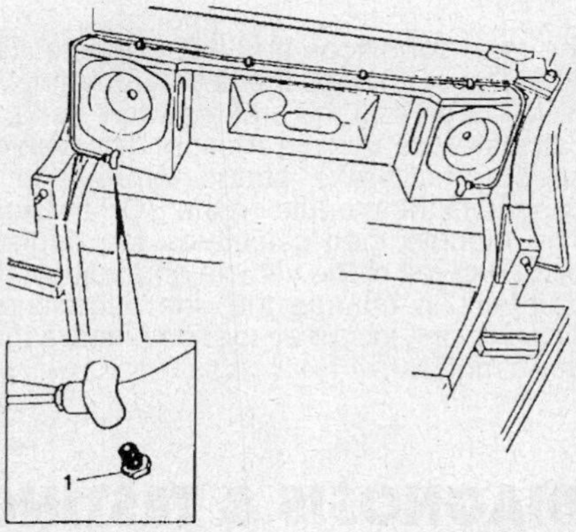

Fig. 1 Hydraulic system depressurization

DYNAMIC STABILITY CONTROL (DSC)

The DSC system manages the braking systems to enhance the driver control of the vehicle. The DSC system continually monitors the steering wheel angle, master cylinder brake pressures, front and rear wheel speeds, vehicle yaw rate and lateral acceleration. The yaw rate sensor supplies an analog signal to the DSC module which monitors the vehicles angular rotation around it's central axis. The lateral accelerometer also sends an analog signal to the DSC module which monitors the vehicles rate of acceleration from its central axis in a sideways direction. The driver effected parameters are continually monitored via the brake master cylinder pressure sensors and the steering wheel sensor. DSC is enabled/disabled via the traction control ON/OFF switch.

DIAGNOSIS & TESTING

Refer "Anti-Lock Brakes" section

SYSTEM SERVICE

Refer "Anti-Lock Brakes" section

Active Suspension Systems

NOTE: On Air Bag Equipped Models, Refer To "Air Bag System Precautions" Located In The Front Of This Manual For System Disarming & Arming Procedures.

INDEX

	Page No.
Description	3-102
Diagnosis & Testing	3-102
Accessing Diagnostic Trouble Codes	3-102
Clearing Diagnostic Trouble Codes	3-102
Diagnostic Trouble Code Interpretation	3-102
Wiring Diagrams	3-102
Precautions	3-102
Air Bag Systems	3-102
Battery Ground Cable	3-102
Depressurizing System	3-102
System Service	3-102
Control Module, Replace	3-102
Sensor, Replace	3-102

PRECAUTIONS

AIR BAG SYSTEMS

Refer to "Air Bag System Precautions" in the front of this manual for system disarming and arming procedures.

DEPRESSURIZING SYSTEM

The rear struts, control valve and connecting lines contain gas and oil maintained at a high pressure. The system must be depressurized prior to service.

This system is filled with Jaguar/Castrol Hydraulic System Mineral Oil (HMSO). If any other fluid is used, the system will become contaminated and must be flushed.

1. Operate brake pedal repeatedly until pedal becomes difficult to operate.
2. Raise and support rear of vehicle.
3. Attach suitable piece of hose to line bleed screw (1), located on three way line connector at lefthand rear side of ride height pressure line.
4. Place free end of hose in drain container.
5. Loosen line bleed screw ½ turn and allow fluid to drain into container.
6. Tighten bleed screw and lower vehicle.
7. Add new fluid as required to reservoir. **Never use old fluid.**

BATTERY GROUND CABLE

Prior to service, disconnect battery ground cable and isolate as required.

DESCRIPTION

The active damping ride control (ADRC) system is designed to control excessive body motions in bounce pitch and roll while maintaining/improving ride and feel. ADRC controls the settings of the four vehicle dampers between firm and soft based on the road conditions and driver inputs. The ADRC system uses the accelerometer, vehicle speed and the brake switch status to calculate the vehicle motion. The vehicle speed and brake status information is passed to the module on the SCP network. The module then calculates the bounce, pitch and roll of the vehicle and adjusts the dampers to change the ride accordingly. This will only occur at speeds of more than three mph.

DIAGNOSIS & TESTING

The complexity of electronics involved with the body processor and the two multiplexed communication networks which are associated with it, preclude the use of workshop general electrical test equipment. Therefore, reference should be made to the Portable Diagnostic Unit (PDU) user guide for detailed instruction on testing the ADRC system. The PDU systematically tests and analyses all electrical functions of ADRC. Where a fault is indicated, some basic diagnostic methods may be required to confirm that connections are good and that wiring is not damaged, before replacing component.

Accessing Diagnostic Trouble Codes

Diagnostic Trouble Codes (DTCs) are accessed by connecting a suitable programmed scan tool to the Data Link Connector (DLC) and following the tool manufacturer's instructions. The DLC is located on the instrument panel adjacent to the driver's side A-pillar.

Diagnostic Trouble Code Interpretation

Refer to **Fig. 1** for Diagnostic Trouble Code (DTC) interpretation.

Wiring Diagrams

Refer to **Fig. 2** for wiring diagrams.

Clearing Diagnostic Trouble Codes

Follow scan tool manufacturer's instructions.

SYSTEM SERVICE

CONTROL MODULE, REPLACE

1. Remove spare tire and wheel assembly.
2. Disconnect ADRC module electrical connectors.
3. Remove ADRC module.
4. Reverse procedure to install.

SENSOR, REPLACE

LATERAL

Front

1. Disconnect ADRC lateral sensor electrical connector.
2. Remove lateral sensor.
3. Reverse procedure to install.

Rear

1. Remove luggage compartment trim panel.
2. Disconnect rear electronics module (REM) bracket.
3. Disconnect ADRC rear vertical sensor electrical connector.
4. Remove vertical sensor.
5. Reverse procedure to install.

VERTICAL

1. Disconnect ADRC vertical sensor electrical connector.
2. Disconnect sensor bracket.
3. Remove vertical sensor.
4. Reverse procedure to install.

Code	Description	MIL	Possible Causes
B1342	Control Module Failure	Yes	DSCCM Failure
B1485	Brake Lamp Switch Circuit Fault	No	Brake Switch Battery Power Supply Open Circuit
			DSCCM To Brake Switch Circuit Open Circuit, Short Circuit To Ground, Short Circuit To B+ Voltage
			Brake Switch Failure
B1676	Battery Voltage Out Of Range (9–16 Volts)	Yes	Charging System Low/High Voltage Fault
B2477	Control Module Incorrectly Configured	Message	Replace ABS/TCCM

Fig. 1 Body Control Module DTC Interpretation

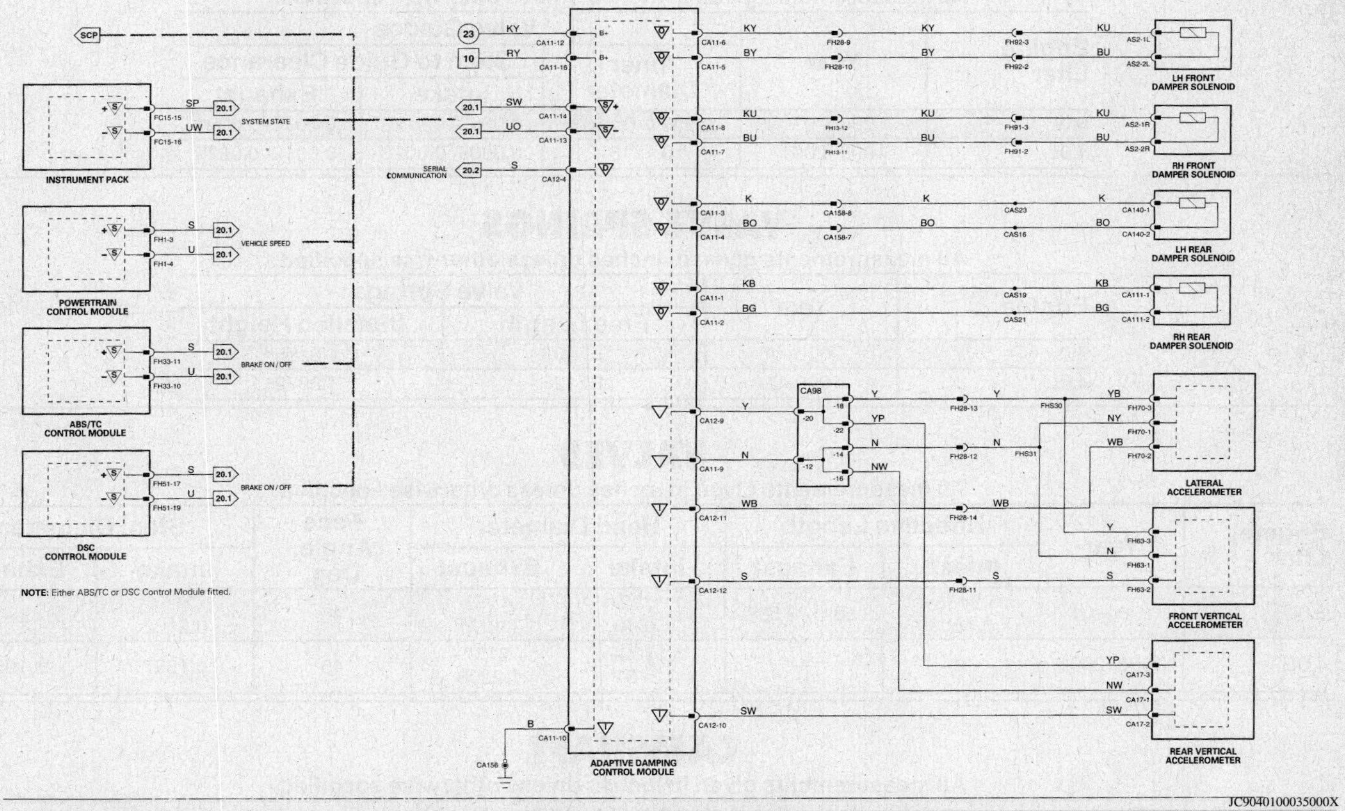

Fig. 2 Wiring diagram. S Type

Engine Rebuilding Specifications

INDEX

	Page No.		Page No.		Page No.
Camshaft	3-104	Valve Seats	3-104	Valves	3-104
Cylinder Head, Valve Guide &		Valve Springs	3-104		

CYLINDER HEAD, VALVE GUIDE & VALVE SEATS

All measurements given in inches unless otherwise specified.

Engine, Liter	Year	Valve Guides		
		Inner Diameter	Stem to Guide Clearance	
			Intake	Exhaust
3.0L	2000–01	0.2171–0.2183	0.0009–0.0126	0.0014–0.0031
4.0L	1998–2001	0.1713	0.0009–0.0023	0.0012–0.0026

VALVE SPRINGS

All measurements given in inches unless otherwise specified.

Engine	Year	Valve Springs	
		Free Length	Installed Height
3.0L	2000–01	1.7403	1.3155
4.0L	1998–99	1.7128	1.3072

VALVES

All measurements given in inches unless otherwise specified.

Engine, Liter	Year	Effective Length		Head Diameter		Face Angle, Deg.	Stem Diameter	
		Intake	Exhaust	Intake	Exhaust		Intake	Exhaust
3.0L	2000–01	3.5488–3.5803	3.5311–3.5389	1.3722–1.3840	1.1753–1.1871	45	0.2154–0.2162	0.2142–0.2157
4.0L	1998–2001	—	—	1.3702–1.3781	1.2137–1.2206	45	0.1957	0.1954

CAMSHAFT

All measurements given in inches unless otherwise specified.

Engine, Liter	Year	Endplay	Camshaft Bearing Clearance	Runout	Out Of Round
3.0L	2000–01	0.0028–0.0059	0.0010–0.0030	0.0016	0.0005
4.0L	1998–99	0.0069	0.0014–0.0030	0.0028	0.0002

LAND ROVER

INDEX OF SERVICE OPERATIONS

Page No.

AIR BAG SYSTEM PRECAUTIONS 0-12
AIR QUALITY STANDARDS 0-23
AUTOMATIC TRANSMISSIONS 4-42
BRAKES
Anti-Lock Brakes 4-40
Disc Brakes 4-38
CLUTCH & MANUAL TRANSMISSION
Adjustments 4-14
Clutch, Replace 4-14
Hydraulic System Service 4-14
Precautions 4-14
Tightening Specifications 4-14
Transmission, Replace 4-14
COMPUTER RELEARN PROCEDURE 0-10
ELECTRICAL
Air Bags 4-30
Air Conditioning 4-23
Alternator, Replace 4-4
Blower Motor, Replace 4-6
Coil Pack, Replace 4-4
Combination Switch, Replace . 4-5
Cooling Fans 4-27
Distributor, Replace 4-4
Dash Panels 4-36
Evaporator Core, Replace 4-8
Fuel Pump Relay Location 4-4
Fuse Panel & Flasher Location 4-4
Heater Core, Replace 4-6
Ignition Lock, Replace 4-4
Ignition Switch, Replace 4-5
Instrument Cluster, Replace ... 4-5
Neutral Safety Switch, Replace 4-5
Passive Restraints 4-30
Precautions 4-4
Radio, Replace 4-5
Starter, Replace 4-4
Steering Columns 4-37
Steering Wheel, Replace 4-5
Stop Light Switch, Replace ... 4-5
Wiper Motor, Replace 4-5
ELECTRICAL SYMBOL IDENTIFICATION 0-33
FRONT SUSPENSION & STEERING
Coil Spring, Replace 4-19
Front Drive Axles 4-65
Power Steering Gear, Replace 4-19
Power Steering Pump, Replace 4-20
Power Steering System Bleed 4-20
Precautions 4-19
Radius Arm, Replace 4-19
Shock Absorber, Replace 4-19
Tightening Specifications 4-20
Torsion Bar, Replace 4-19
REAR AXLE & SUSPENSION
Coil Spring, Replace 4-15
Rear Axle, Replace 4-15
Shock Absorber, Replace 4-15
Tightening Specifications 4-16
Torsion Bar, Replace 4-15
SERVICE REMINDER & WARNING LAMP RESET PROCEDURES 0-14
SPECIFICATIONS
Fluid Capacities & Cooling System Data 4-3
Front Wheel Alignment Specifications 4-2
General Engine Specifications 4-2
Lubricant Data 4-3
Tune Up Specifications 4-2
TRANSFER CASE
Fluid Change 4-17
Tightening Specifications 4-18
Transfer Cases 4-50
Transfer Case, Replace 4-17
VEHICLE IDENTIFICATION . 0-3
VEHICLE LIFT POINTS 0-24
VEHICLE MAINTENANCE SCHEDULES 0-45
WHEEL ALIGNMENT
Front Wheel Alignment 4-22
Preliminary Inspection 4-22
Wheel Alignment Specifications 4-2
WIRE COLOR CODE IDENTIFICATION 0-33
4.0L & 4.6L ENGINES
Camshaft, Replace 4-12
Compression Pressures 4-9
Cylinder Head, Replace 4-11
Engine Rebuilding Specifications 4-65
Engine, Replace 4-9
Exhaust Manifold, Replace 4-11
Front Cover, Replace 4-12
Fuel Filter, Replace 4-13
Fuel Pump, Replace 4-13
Intake Manifold, Replace 4-10
Oil Pan, Replace 4-12
Precautions 4-9
Serpentine Drive Belt 4-12
Thermostat, Replace 4-12
Tightening Specifications 4-13
Timing Chain, Replace 4-12
Valve Adjustment 4-12
Valve Cover, Replace 4-11
Water Pump, Replace 4-12

Specifications

GENERAL ENGINE SPECIFICATIONS

Year	Engine	Fuel System	Bore & Stroke	Compression Ratio	Maximum Brake H.P. @ RPM	Maximum Torque Ft. Lbs. @ RPM	Normal Oil Pressure, psi @ 2500 RPM
1998	4.0L	Fuel Inj.	3.70 x 2.80	9.35	190 @ 4750	236 @ 3000	30–40
	4.6L	Fuel Inj.	3.70 x 3.22	9.35	225 @ 4750	280 @ 3000	34–37
1999–2001	4.0L	Fuel Inj.	3.70 x 2.80	9.40	188 @ 4750	251 @ 2600	30–40
	4.6L	Fuel Inj.	3.70 x 3.22	9.60	240 @ 5000	285 @ 3500	34–37

TUNE UP SPECIFICATIONS

Year & Engine	Spark Plug Gap, Inch	Ignition Timing			Curb Idle Speed, RPM②		Valve Lash
		Firing Order	Timing, °BTDC①	Timing Mark Location	Man. Trans.	Auto. Trans.	
4.0L	.035	③	—	—	680-720	680-720	④
4.6L	.035	③	—	—	680-720	680-720	④

BTDC — Before Top Dead Center

N — Neutral

① — At specified curb idle speed.

② — When adjusting idle speed, set parking brake & chock drive wheels.

③ — Cylinder, numbering front to rear, left bank, 1, 3, 5, 7; right bank, 2, 4, 6, 8. Firing order, 1–8–4–3–6–5–7–2.

④ — Equipped w/hydraulic tappets.

FRONT WHEEL ALIGNMENT SPECIFICATIONS

Model	Year	Caster Angle, Deg.	Camber Angle, Deg.	Toe-Out, Inch	Swivel Pin Inclination, Deg.
Discovery	1998–2001	+3	0	0 to -.08	7
Range Rover HSE & SE	1998–2001	+4	0	-.02 to -.07	8

FLUID CAPACITIES & COOLING SYSTEM DATA

Year	Model	Coolant Capacity, Qts.	Radiator Cap Relief Pressure, Lbs.	Thermo. Opening Temp., °F	Fuel Tank, Gals.	Engine Oil, Qts.①	Transmission Oil		Transfer Case, Pts.	Front & Rear Drive Axles, Pts.
							Man. Trans., Pts.	Auto. Trans., Qts.②		
1998–2001	Discovery	10.50	15	190	23.0	5.2	5.7	9.60	4.9	3.6
	Range Rover 4.0 SE	12.00	15	190	26.4	7.0	5.7	10.25	5.0	3.6
	Range Rover 4.6 HSE	12.00	15	190	26.4	7.0	5.7	11.60	5.0	3.6

① — With filter change.

② — Approximate, make final check w/dipstick.

LUBRICANT DATA

Model	Year	Lubricant Type					
		Transmission		Transfer Case	Rear Axle	Power Steering	Brake System
		Manual	Automatic				
Discovery	1998–2001	Dexron IID	Dexron IID/IIE/III	90 GL-4/5	90 GL-4/5	Dexron IID/IIE/III	DOT 4
Range Rover 4.0 SE	1998–2001	Dexron IID/IIE/III	Dexron IID/IIE/III	Dexron IID/IIE/III	80W/90W GL-4/5	Dexron IID/IIE/III	DOT 4
Range Rover 4.6 HSE	1998–2001	Dexron IID	Dexron IID/IIE/III	Dexron IID/IIE/III	90 GL-4/5	Dexron IID/IIE/III	DOT 4

Electrical

NOTE: On Air Bag Equipped Models, Refer To "Air Bag System Precautions" Located In The Front Of This Manual For System Disarming & Arming Procedures.

INDEX

	Page No.
Air Bags	4-30
Air Conditioning	4-23
Alternator, Replace	4-4
Discovery & Range Rover	4-4
Blower Motor, Replace	4-6
Discovery	4-6
New Range Rover	4-6
Coil Pack, Replace	4-4
Combination Switch, Replace	4-5
Cooling Fans	4-27
Dash Panels	4-36
Distributor, Replace	4-4
Evaporator Core, Replace	4-8
Discovery	4-8
New Range Rover	4-8
Fuel Pump Relay Location	4-4
Discovery & New Range Rover	4-4
Fuse Panel & Flasher Location	4-4
Discovery	4-4
Range Rover	4-4
Heater Core, Replace	4-6
Discovery	4-6
New Range Rover	4-6
Ignition Lock, Replace	4-4
Ignition Switch, Replace	4-5
Instrument Cluster, Replace	4-5
Neutral Safety Switch, Replace	4-5
Passive Restraints	4-30
Precautions	4-4
Air Bag Systems	4-4
Battery Ground Cable	4-4
Radio, Replace	4-5
Starter, Replace	4-4
Steering Columns	4-37
Steering Wheel, Replace	4-5
Stop Light Switch, Replace	4-5
Less Anti-Lock Brakes	4-5
With Anti-Lock Brakes	4-5
Wiper Motor, Replace	4-5
Front	4-5
Headlamp	4-6
Rear	4-6

PRECAUTIONS

AIR BAG SYSTEMS

Refer to "Air Bag System Precautions" in the front of this manual for system disarming and arming procedures.

BATTERY GROUND CABLE

Prior to service, disconnect battery ground cable and isolate as required.

FUSE PANEL & FLASHER LOCATION

DISCOVERY

The interior fuse box is located behind the lefthand side of the instrument panel, below the steering column.

The underhood fuse box is located on the front righthand side of the engine compartment.

The hazard/flasher unit is located in the underhood fuse box.

RANGE ROVER

The interior fuse box is located behind the lefthand side of the instrument panel, left of the steering column.

The underhood fuse box is located on the front righthand side of the engine compartment.

The hazard/flasher unit is located on the interior fuse box.

FUEL PUMP RELAY LOCATION

DISCOVERY & NEW RANGE ROVER

The fuel pump relay is located on the righthand side of the engine compartment, in the relay module.

STARTER

REPLACE

1. Raise and support vehicle.
2. Disconnect leads from solenoid and starter.
3. Remove heat shield, if required.
4. Remove starter mounting bolts, then the starter.
5. Reverse procedure to install. **Torque** mounting bolts to 33 ft. lbs.

ALTERNATOR

REPLACE

DISCOVERY & RANGE ROVER

1. Remove radiator fan cowl.
2. Rotate drive belt tensioner to release tension from drive belt, then remove drive belt.
3. Remove two alternator to bracket attaching bolts.
4. Disconnect electrical connectors, then remove alternator.
5. Reverse procedure to install.

DISTRIBUTOR

REPLACE

1. Disconnect vacuum hose and remove distributor cap.
2. Mark position of rotor on distributor housing, then remove rotor.
3. Make alignment marks on distributor housing and front cover.
4. Release distributor retaining clamp.
5. Disconnect amplifier unit electrical connector, then remove distributor.
6. Reverse procedure to install, noting the following:
   a. Install new O-ring to distributor housing.
   b. Prior to installing distributor, turn distributor drive until center line of rotor is 30° counterclockwise from mark made during removal.
   c. When installing distributor it may be necessary to align oil pump drive shaft to engage distributor drive shaft into slot.

COIL PACK

REPLACE

1. Disconnect high tension leads from coil pack and position aside. **Note position of leads for installation reference.**
2. Disconnect ignition coil electrical connector, then remove four coil bracket retaining nuts.
3. Remove ignition coil bracket from intake manifold.
4. Remove terminal cover and remove two electrical lead retaining nuts.
5. Remove electrical leads from terminals. **Note position of leads for installation reference.**
6. Remove three ignition coil to bracket Torx screws, then separate coil from bracket.
7. Reverse procedure to install.

IGNITION LOCK

REPLACE

1. Remove steering column shroud.
2. Remove access panel from under steering column.
3. Remove knee pad attaching screws, then the knee pad.
4. Disconnect ignition switch electrical connector from fuse box.
5. Disconnect ignition switch main feed electrical connector.
6. Remove bulb holder from steering column lock shroud.
7. Tap head of ignition lock shear bolts in a counterclockwise direction.

8. Remove and discard shear bolts.
9. Remove ignition lock from steering column.
10. Reverse procedure to install.

IGNITION SWITCH

REPLACE

1. Remove steering column shroud.
2. Remove access panel from under steering column.
3. Remove knee pad attaching screws, then the knee pad.
4. Disconnect ignition switch electrical connector from fuse box.
5. Disconnect ignition switch main feed electrical connector.
6. Remove ignition switch from column.
7. Reverse procedure to install.

NEUTRAL SAFETY SWITCH

REPLACE

1. Raise and support vehicle.
2. Disconnect switch electrical connector.
3. Remove switch clamp retaining bolt, then the clamp.
4. Remove switch from transmission.
5. Reverse procedure to install.

STOP LIGHT SWITCH

REPLACE

LESS ANTI-LOCK BRAKES

1. Remove lower trim panel from under lefthand side of instrument panel.
2. Depress brake pedal, then remove rubber protector from switch.
3. Remove switch to bracket retaining nut.
4. Disconnect switch electrical connector, then remove switch from bracket.
5. Reverse procedure to install. Adjust stop lamp switch as follows:
   a. With switch in installed position, connect an ohmmeter across switch terminals.
   b. Screw switch in until an open circuit exists across terminals when pedal is released and continuity exists as soon as pedal is depressed.
   c. Tighten locknut.

WITH ANTI-LOCK BRAKES

1. Remove lower trim panel from under lefthand side of instrument panel.
2. Disconnect electrical connector from switch.
3. Depress brake pedal to gain access to the front of the switch.
4. Pull sleeve and plunger of switch fully forward.
5. Remove switch from top of brake pedal.
6. Reverse procedure to install.

COMBINATION SWITCH

REPLACE

1. Remove steering column shroud.
2. Remove steering wheel as outlined under "Steering Wheel, Replace."

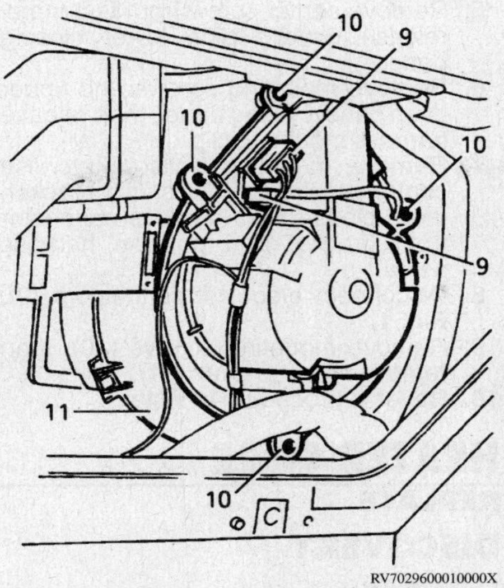

Fig. 1 Blower motor replacement. New Range Rover

3. Remove switch retaining screws.
4. Using a small screwdriver, release retaining catch between switch and casing.
5. Disconnect electrical connector, then remove switch.
6. Reverse procedure to install.

STEERING WHEEL

REPLACE

1. Disconnect both battery cables.
2. Position front wheels in straight-ahead direction.
3. Disarm air bag as outlined under "Air Bag System Precautions."
4. Remove air bag module as follows:
   a. Turn steering wheel 90° to access air bag module retaining screws on rear of steering wheel.
   b. Remove air module retaining screws, then disconnect module electrical connector.
   c. Remove module from vehicle.
   d. Return steering wheel to straight-ahead position.
5. Remove steering wheel trim pad and disconnect horn connector.
6. Disconnect cruise control electrical connector.
7. Remove steering wheel retaining nut and steering wheel.
8. Position cruise control cassette with tape to prevent damage.
9. Reverse procedure to install, noting the following:
   a. Ensure road wheels are in straight-ahead direction.
   b. Ensure cruise control cassette is properly positioned.
   c. **Torque** steering wheel nut to 32 ft. lbs.

INSTRUMENT CLUSTER

REPLACE

1. Position steering wheel for access.
2. Remove screws securing trim panel, then the panel.
3. Disconnect instrument cluster lighting rheostat connector.
4. Remove instrument cluster attaching screws, then the cluster by pulling lower panel brackets downward and outward.
5. Disconnect instrument connectors on rear of cluster, noting their positions.
6. Carefully remove cluster to prevent damage.
7. Reverse procedure to install.

RADIO

REPLACE

1. Remove radio trim panel.
2. Insert radio removal tools No. SMD 4091, or equivalent, into slots on left and right sides of radio. Press removal tools to release radio.
3. Pull radio rearward, then disconnect antenna and electrical connectors from rear of radio.
4. Reverse procedure to install.

WIPER MOTOR

REPLACE

FRONT

Discovery

1. Remove wiper arms.
2. Remove securing nuts, then the steel and rubber washer from wiper spindles.
3. Open hood and remove rubber seal from cowl flange
4. Disconnect tubing from washer jets.
5. Remove center bolt and retaining clips from cowl, then the center section of the cowl.
6. Remove wiper motor ground strap.
7. Remove motor/linkage support plate.
8. Lift out motor/linkage assembly and disconnect motor connector.
9. Remove motor spindle nut and release rotary connecting link from spindle.
10. Separate motor from support plate and detach linkage retaining clips. Note locations of flat and wavy washers for installation reference.
11. Reverse procedure to install.

Range Rover

1. Remove wiper arms.
2. Remove locknuts and grommets from wiper arm spindles.
3. Remove hood and deck panel.
4. Remove clips securing wiper arm linkage to spindles and motor crank, then disconnect linkage.
5. Remove lower grommets from spindles.
6. Remove screw securing hood torsion bar bracket and disconnect bracket from torsion bar.
7. Remove remaining screws securing motor and linkage assembly to bulkhead.
8. Remove motor from mounting location and disconnect electrical connector.
9. Remove mounting plate from motor.
10. Reverse procedure to install.

REAR

Discovery

1. Remove rear door trim panel.
2. Remove spare tire.
3. Remove wiper arm and grommet.
4. Remove nut, plain washer and seal from drive spindle.
5. From inside door, disconnect wiper motor leads from door harness at connector.
6. Remove bolts securing motor mounting bracket and ground lead to inner door panel.
7. Remove motor and bracket assembly from door.
8. Remove bracket from motor.
9. Reverse procedure to install.

Range Rover

1. Lower rear headliner to gain access to wiper motor assembly.
2. Remove wiper arm.
3. Loosen, but do not remove nut securing wiper motor spindle to body.
4. Disconnect wiper motor connector.
5. Remove bolts securing wiper motor to inner body.
6. Support wiper motor and remove loosened spindle nut, then remove motor from body.
7. Reverse procedure to install.

HEADLAMP

1. Remove wiper blade.
2. Remove headlamp assembly.
3. Disconnect wiper motor electrical connector.
4. Remove spindle seal.
5. Remove motor to headlamp assembly attaching nuts.
6. Remove wiper motor.
7. Reverse procedure to install.

BLOWER MOTOR

REPLACE

DISCOVERY

1. Remove four toe board attaching studs, then the toe board.
2. Remove four glove box attaching screws.
3. Release glove box catch and remove glove box.
4. Disconnect blower motor electrical harness.
5. Remove three blower motor attaching screws, then the blower motor.
6. Reverse procedure to install.

NEW RANGE ROVER

1. Remove center screw from fasteners and release closing panel to access glove compartment hinge, then remove mounting bolts and hinges.
2. Open glove compartment lid, then remove mounting screws and release glove compartment.
3. Disconnect lamp connect and cable latch, then remove glove compartment.
4. Release clips securing harness to dash panel.
5. Remove center screw from fasteners, release driver's side lower closing panel.
6. Remove mounting screws and upper dash panel closing panel, then release harness mounting clip.
7. Remove mounting bolts and cruise control electronic control unit bracket, then release SRS harness connector from bracket and position harness aside.
8. Disconnect electrical connectors (9), **Fig. 1.**
9. Remove mounting screws (10), then remove motor and fan (11).
10. Reverse procedure to install.

HEATER CORE

REPLACE

DISCOVERY

Less A/C

1. Drain cooling system.
2. Release clips and disconnect coolant hoses from heater pipes.
3. Remove facia assembly.
4. Disconnect harness electrical connector from heater blower motor.
5. Remove heater blower housing assembly to body attaching bolt and nuts, then blower.
6. Disconnect two drain tubes from base of heater.
7. Remove two console bracket to tunnel attaching crews, then bracket.
8. Disconnect radio antenna cable from behind heater pipes.
9. Remove four nuts and one bolt securing heater to body.
10. Remove heater assembly from vehicle.
11. Remove two screws securing heater righthand and lefthand footwell outlet duct to heater casing and remove ducts.
12. Remove two matrix pipe bracket to heater casing attaching screws.
13. Remove pipe clamp to heater casing attaching screw, then clamp.
14. Remove matrix from heater.
15. Remove heater core from heater assembly.
16. Reverse procedure to install.

With A/C

1. Drain cooling system.
2. Evacuate A/C system.
3. Release heater hose clips and disconnect heater hoses from heater.
4. Remove two A/C pipes to evaporator bolts, then disconnect pipes and discard O-rings.
5. Remove facia.
6. Disconnect blower motor electrical connector.
7. Remove two blower housing to body attaching nuts, then blower motor.
8. Disconnect two drain tubes from base of heater.
9. Remove two console bracket to tunnel attaching screws, then bracket.
10. Release radio coaxial cable from behind heater pipes.
11. Protect carpet from coolant spillage.
12. Remove four nuts and 1 bolt securing heater to body.
13. Remove heater from vehicle.
14. Remove two heater righthand and lefthand footwell outlet duct to heater casing attaching screws, then ducts.
15. Remove two matrix pipe bracket to heater casing attaching screws.
16. Remove pipe clamp to heater casing attaching screw, then clamp.
17. Remove matrix from heater.
18. Remove heater core from heater assembly.
19. Reverse procedure to assembly.

NEW RANGE ROVER

1. Drain cooling system into suitable container, then loosen hose clips and remove hoses from heater pipes.
2. Remove mounting screws and release electric window switch pack from center console, then disconnect electrical connector and remove switch over handbrake.
3. Disconnect rear footwell lamp electrical connector.
4. Remove mounting screws and base, then remove nuts at console rear.
5. Move both front seats fully rearward.
6. Remove mounting screws and release sprag clips, then remove side panels from dash panel.
7. Remove mounting screw and left rear of gear lever applique, then disengage forward clips.
8. Disconnect cigar lighter connector and release lighter bulb, then remove applique.
9. Remove screws and automatic shift lever.
10. Remove screws and lift selector graphics plate, then disconnect electrical connector and remove graphics plate.
11. Remove mounting clip and clevis pin, then raise park brake lever to vertical position.
12. Lift console rear, disconnect rear vent ducts and remove center console.
13. Remove mounting bolt securing steering column to universal joint.
14. Remove mounting bolts securing universal joint to intermediate shaft and steering box.
15. Ensure front wheels are set straight ahead and remove key from ignition switch. **To center steering, align input shaft rib with two marks on steering box casing. Moving steering wheel with intermediate shaft removed could damage rotary coupler leading to air bag and steering wheel mounted switches malfunctions.**
16. Push universal joint up splines to disengage from steering box, then remove intermediate shaft from steering column.
17. Remove fasteners below steering column and release closing panel from dash panel, then disconnect footwell lamp connector and remove closing panel.
18. Remove screw covers and screws, then release dash panel closing panel, disconnect driver's lap vent duct and

remove panel.
19. Remove mounting screws and release instrument cluster from dash panel, then disconnect fuel filler door release switch connector and remove cluster.
20. Release steering column tilt lever, then fully extend and lower column.
21. Remove screws, release upper steering column cover from side fillet clips and remove.
22. Remove screws, release from side fillet clips and remove lower steering column cover.
23. Remove screws and release turn indicator switch stalk from column, then disconnect electrical connector.
24. Remove screws and release wiper switch stalk from column, then disconnect electrical connector.
25. Disconnect ignition switch, "key in" sensor, rotary coupler and air bag system electrical connectors.
26. Remove clips securing air bag wiring harness to steering column harness, then remove clip securing steering column wiring harness.
27. Remove bulb from lock barrel and bulb harness from clip.
28. Disconnect shift interlock electrical connector.
29. Remove driver's blower motor housing duct from heater.
30. Remove bulkhead mounting bolts and pedal box mounting bolts and nuts, then remove steering column.
31. Lift side finisher seal and remove mounting screws, then remove windshield side finisher.
32. Remove cover, nut and wiper arms.
33. Release clips and remove lower windshield finisher.
34. Remove screws and righthand plenum panel, then lift lefthand plenum panel and disconnect hood wiring harness connector.
35. Release harness sleeve and remove lefthand plenum panel, then remove mounting screws and center plenum panel.
36. Remove wiper spindle housing covers, nuts and washer, then disconnect windshield heater electrical connector and disconnect connector to driver's side clip.
37. Remove bolts and scuttle side panel, then disconnect wiper motor electrical connector.
38. Remove mounting bolts, then wiper motor and linkage assembly.
39. Disconnect passenger side heated screen connector and release from clip.
40. Remove bolts and scuttle side panel, then heater intake pollen filters.
41. Remove bolts and both pollen filter housings.
42. Remove radio applique, then use suitable extractor(s) and release radio from dash panel.
43. Disconnect antenna leads, electrical connectors and compact disc autochanger connector, then remove radio.
44. Remove door opening seal next to A pillar lower trim panel, then remove bolts and foot rest.

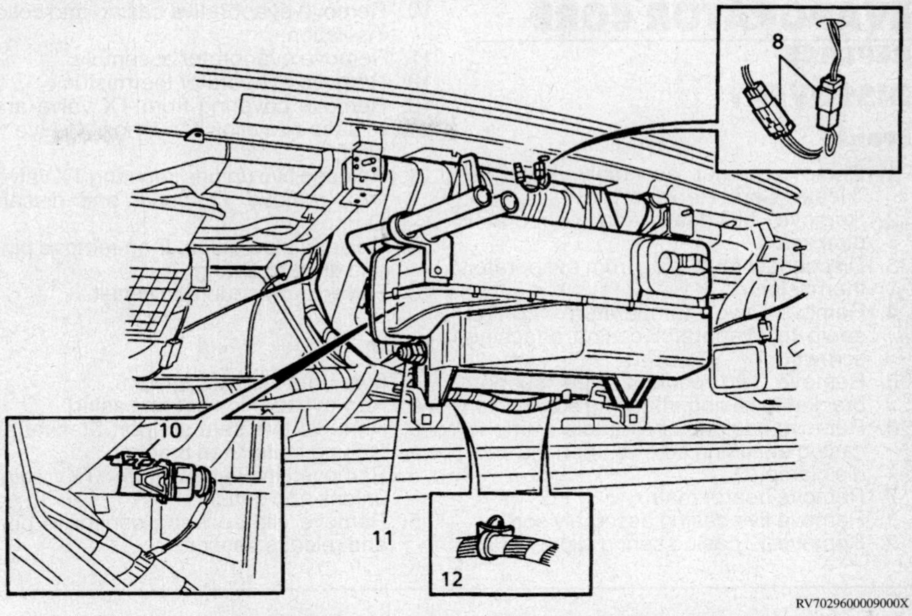

Fig. 2 Heater unit replacement. New Range Rover

45. Remove screw, release sprag clip and remove A pillar lower trim panels.
46. Remove screw, trim studs and seat base trim, then release sprag clips and remove driver's side carpet retainer.
47. Remove fasteners, release closing panel from passenger side of dash panel, then disconnect footwell lamp and diagnostic connectors, and remove closing panel.
48. Remove bolts and center dash panel bracket, then disconnect body electrical control module connector.
49. Remove nut and ground wires from stud at base of driver's side A pillar, then disconnect electrical connectors and base of each A pillar.
50. Release body electrical control module harness from sill and route to avoid fouling during dash panel removal.
51. Disconnect electrical connectors and release vacuum hose from brake and clutch switches, then disconnect air bag connector from main harness.
52. Disconnect electrical connector from air bag and route harness to avoid fouling during dash panel removal.
53. Raise and support vehicle, then remove front wheels.
54. Remove screws and mud flaps, then remove studs and wheelwell liners.
55. Remove fasteners and air cleaner baffles, then disconnect crash sensor connectors.
56. Remove battery tray and air cleaner bolts, then raise air cleaner and battery tray to access crash sensor harness.
57. Release crash sensor harness clips from valance, release grommets and feed harnesses through valance into wheelwells.
58. Release crash sensor harness clips in wheelwells, release grommets and feed harnesses through bulkhead into dash panel, then route harnesses to avoid fouling during dash panel removal.
59. Recover refrigerant, then remove thermostatic expansion valve clamp bolt.
60. Remove pipes and O-rings from valve. Seal pipes and valve ports.
61. Remove dash panel mounting bolts from scuttle panel, nuts and washers from A pillar bases, and bolt from pedal box.
62. Carefully remove dash panel through driver's door.
63. Remove screws from face level vent ducts and slide inserts away from heater unit, then remove passenger side blower duct.
64. Remove screws, release heater control panel and disconnect electrical connectors, then remove heater control panel.
65. Remove screws and release dash panel switch pack to access front heater mounting bolts.
66. Disconnect solar sensor and alarm LED connectors (8), then push flyleads into ducting, **Fig. 2.**
67. Release clip securing harness to ducting and position solar sensor/LED harness aside.
68. Release clip hold water temperature sensor (10) to heater core inlet and position sensor aside, then disconnect evaporator sensor connector (11).
69. Release clips (12) hold harness to heater unit base, then remove heater unit mounting bolts.
70. With assistant holding harness away from heater unit, remove unit.
71. Remove screws and righthand duct from heater, then remove pipe bracket mounting screw.
72. Remove screws and righthand servo, then release clips and remove core and pipe assembly.
73. Remove mounting screws and pipe assembly, then discard O-rings.
74. Reverse procedure to install, using new O-rings lubricated with antifreeze.

EVAPORATOR CORE

REPLACE

DISCOVERY

Front

1. Remove heater assembly. Refer to "Heater Core, Replace."
2. Remove bulkhead and evaporator pipe seals.
3. Disconnect multi-plug from evaporator thermistor.
4. Remove two temperature control servo to evaporator casing attaching screws.
5. Remove two coolant pipe support bracket to casing attaching screws.
6. Remove coolant pipe saddle clamp to casing attaching screws, then the saddle clamp.
7. Remove heater matrix.
8. Remove five casing assembly screws.
9. Remove 12 casing spring clips.
10. Remove evaporative casing and collet insulation.
11. Remove evaporator assembly.
12. Remove evaporator thermistor.
13. Remove covering from TX valve and release two clips securing TX valve to pipe.
14. Release two unions securing TX valve, then remove TX valve and discard O-rings.
15. Release pipe union, then remove pipe and discard O-ring.
16. Reverse procedure to install.

Rear

1. Evacuate rear A/C system.
2. Remove rear lower trim casing.
3. Remove five seat support bracket attaching bolts, then bracket.
4. Remove insulation from TXV pipe unions and sensor.
5. Remove clip securing sensor to pipe and release sensor.
6. Loosen TXV pipe unions, then disconnect pipes and remove TXV.
7. Remove and discard O-rings.
8. Remove relay from support bracket.
9. Remove ducting seal.
10. Remove four lower casing attaching screws, then lower casing.
11. Remove six screws and four clips attaching main casing.
12. Remove top half of casing.
13. Loosen and disconnect evaporator pipes, then remove evaporator.
14. Remove and discard evaporator pipe O-rings.
15. Reverse procedure to install.

NEW RANGE ROVER

1. Remove heater unit as described under "Heater Core, Replace."
2. Remove center vent duct screw.
3. Remove mounting bolts and evaporator core.
4. Reverse procedure to install.

4.0L & 4.6L Engines

NOTE: On Air Bag Equipped Models, Refer To "Air Bag System Precautions" Located In The Front Of This Manual For System Disarming & Arming Procedures.

INDEX

	Page No.
Camshaft, Replace	4-12
Compression Pressures	4-9
Cylinder Head, Replace	4-11
Engine Rebuilding Specifications	4-65
Engine, Replace	4-9
Exhaust Manifold, Replace	4-11
1998	4-11
1999-2001	4-11
Front Cover, Replace	4-12
Fuel Filter, Replace	4-13
Fuel Pump, Replace	4-13
Intake Manifold, Replace	4-10
Lower	4-10
Upper	4-10
Oil Pan, Replace	4-12
Precautions	4-9
Air Bag Systems	4-9
Battery Ground Cable	4-9
Fuel System Pressure Relief	4-9
Serpentine Drive Belt	4-12
Belt Tension Check	4-12
Replacement	4-12
Routing	4-12
Thermostat, Replace	4-12
Tightening Specifications	4-13
Timing Chain, Replace	4-12
Valve Adjustment	4-12
Valve Cover, Replace	4-11
Left	4-11
Right	4-11
Water Pump, Replace	4-12

PRECAUTIONS

AIR BAG SYSTEMS

Refer to "Air Bag System Precautions"in the front of this manual for system disarming and arming procedures.

BATTERY GROUND CABLE

Prior to service, disconnect battery ground cable and isolate as required.

FUEL SYSTEM PRESSURE RELIEF

The fuel injection system retains residual pressure when the vehicle is not operating. The fuel system pressure must be released before performing any engine repair procedure.

1. Remove fuel pump relay.
2. Start engine.
3. Run engine until it stalls.
4. After engine stalls, crank engine two or three times to ensure fuel pressure is released.
5. Turn ignition switch off and install fuel pump relay.

COMPRESSION PRESSURES

1. Start and run vehicle until normal operating temperatures are reached.
2. Remove all spark plugs.
3. Disconnect coil leads.
4. Insert compression gauge into spark plug hole and turn engine over until compression stabilizes.
5. Pressure should read 150–177 psi.
6. If pressure is less than 150 psi, inspect valves and/or rings for damage, wear or not properly adjusted.
7. Low pressure in adjoining cylinders may indicate a faulty head gasket.

ENGINE

REPLACE

1. Release fuel pressure as outlined under "Precautions."
2. Remove hood and battery.
3. Remove Electronic Control Module (ECM).
4. Remove fuel supply line at fuel rail and fuel return line at pressure regulator.
5. Remove purge valve from shock tower.
6. Remove RAM housing and air flow sensor.
7. Remove air cleaner assembly.
8. Disconnect throttle cable and position aside.
9. Remove battery tray.
10. Remove bolts from fuse box and position aside. Disconnect engine harness connectors from fuse box.
11. Remove engine harness and ground cables from engine.
12. Without disconnecting pressure lines, remove A/C compressor from mounting and position aside.
13. Remove cooling fan and viscous coupling.
14. Remove front grille, hood platform support, and air deflectors.
15. Remove washer bottle filler neck.
16. Disconnect engine and transmission oil cooler lines. Plug lines and position aside.
17. Disconnect coolant hoses from thermostat housing.
18. Remove power steering fluid reservoir from radiator, then the hoses from power steering pump.
19. Remove electrical connectors from transmission oil temperature sensor.
20. Remove radiator and cooling fans.
21. **On models with manual transmission,** perform the following:
    a. Using a suitable brake hose clamp, clamp flexible clutch hose.
    b. Disconnect flexible clutch hose at transmission pipe, and position aside.
22. **On all models,** remove window switch pack from center console, then the console.

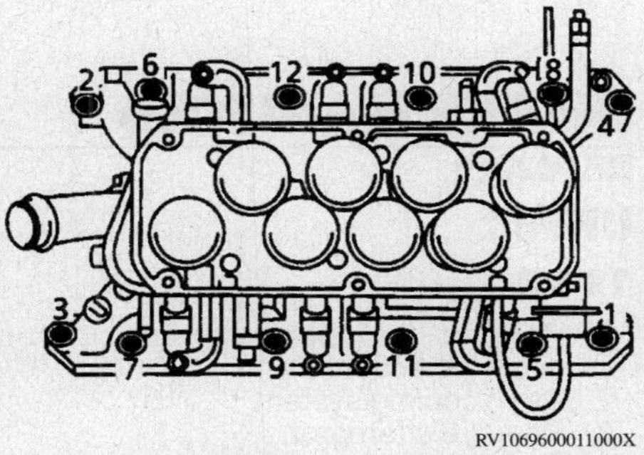

Fig. 1 Intake manifold bolt removal sequence

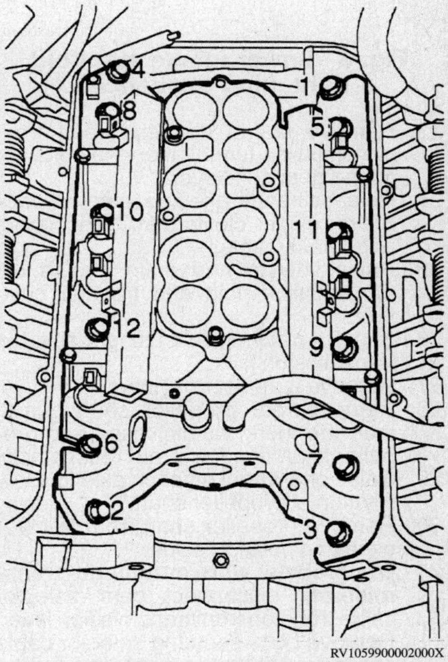

Fig. 2 Lower intake manifold loosening sequence

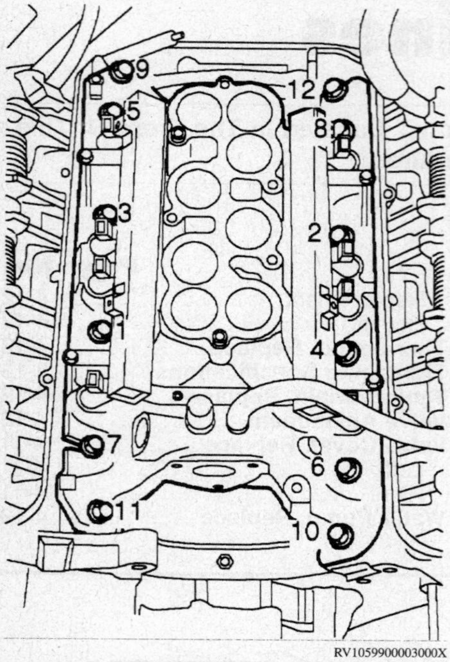

Fig. 3 Lower intake manifold tightening sequence

23. Remove sound deadener pad from transmission tunnel, then the bolts securing gear shift lever.
24. Release handbrake and remove handbrake cable clevis pin. Disconnect handbrake cable.
25. Raise vehicle and drain engine oil, transmission fluid and transfer case fluid.
26. Support transmission using a suitable transmission jack.
27. Remove exhaust front pipe.
28. Remove rear propeller shaft guard, then the mark transfer case and propeller shaft flanges to aid reassembly.
29. Raise one wheel on each axle to allow rotation of propeller shaft.
30. Remove propeller shaft from transfer case and position aside.
31. **On models with automatic transmission,** disconnect gear selector cable trunnion from transmission lever. Remove bolts securing selector cable abutment bracket to transmission and position aside.
32. **On all models,** lower transmission and disconnect electrical connectors.
33. Remove engine mount nuts and discard.
34. Remove oil filler cap to avoid damage during engine lifting.
35. Place protective cloth over plenum chamber to avoid damage.
36. Attach suitable lifting bracket and hoist.
37. Lift engine slightly upward and forward, then remove engine and transmission. **Engine and transmission assembly must be tilted at a 45° angle before it can be removed from engine compartment.**
38. Reverse procedure to install noting:
    a. Bleed clutch hydraulic system.
    b. Adjust gear selector lever cable.

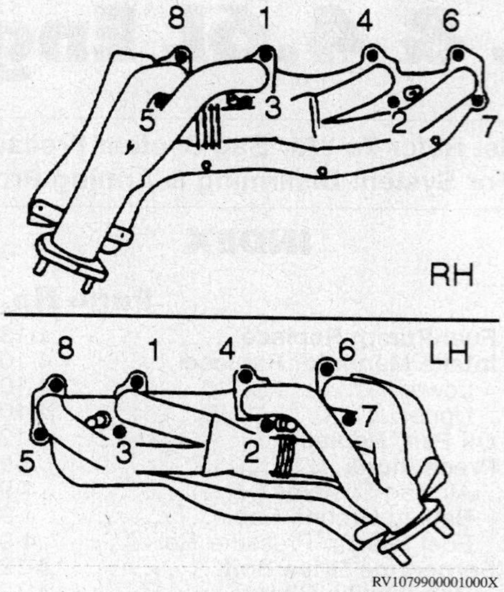

Fig. 4 Exhaust manifold tightening sequence. 1999–2001

c. Tighten to specification.

INTAKE MANIFOLD

REPLACE

UPPER

1998

1. Release fuel pressure as outlined under "Precautions."
2. Drain cooling system
3. Remove alternator.
4. Remove plenum chamber.
5. Disconnect purge and crankcase breather hoses from ram pipe housing.
6. Disconnect coolant temperature and temperature gauge sensor connectors.
7. Disconnect fuel temperature sensor and injector connectors.
8. Disconnect fuel feed and return lines from fuel rail.
9. Remove fuel rail and ignition coil from intake manifold and position aside.
10. Disconnect coolant hoses from intake manifold and plenum.
11. Remove harness from both sides of intake manifold.
12. Remove upper intake manifold bolts in sequence, **Fig. 1.**
13. Remove upper intake manifold, then the gasket and seals. Discard gasket and seals.
14. Reverse procedure to install noting the following:
    a. Ensure to install new gasket and seals.
    b. Reversing bolt removal sequence shown in **Fig. 1, torque** bolts in two steps: first to 7 ft. lbs., then to 38 ft. lbs.

1999–2001

1. Remove gas struts from hood. Then support hood on hinge extension arms.
2. Loosen two clips securing air intake

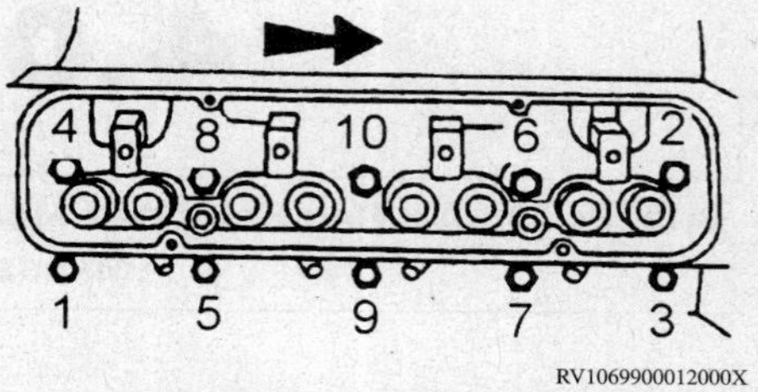

Fig. 5 Cylinder head bolt loosening sequence

hose then remove air intake hose and disconnect harness from clip on hose.
3. Remove clip attaching IAC hose to air intake hose and remove air intake hose.
4. Remove two abutment bracket to plenum chamber attaching bolts, then position aside.
5. Disconnect throttle and cruise control cables from clips and throttle cams and position aside.
6. Disconnect EVAP pipe from plenum chamber and clip on upper manifold.
7. Disconnect TP sensor electrical connector.
8. Remove clip attaching breather hose to throttle body and release breather hose.
9. Remove clip and disconnect IAC hose from plenum chamber.
10. Position a suitable container below throttle body to collect coolant.
11. Remove coolant hose to throttle body retaining clamps and disconnect hoses.
12. Remove clip and disconnect engine breather hose from plenum chamber.
13. Remove bolt securing coolant rails.
14. Remove two cables ties attaching engine harness to clip on upper manifold.
15. Release HT leads from clips on upper inlet manifold.
16. Disconnect IAC valve electrical connector.
17. Remove two ignition coil assembly retaining bolts.
18. Loosen two bolts attaching bottom of coils to block but do not remove bolts.
19. Remove six upper manifold attaching bolts, then the upper manifold.
20. Remove upper manifold gasket.
21. Reverse procedure to install, noting to install and tighten manifold bolts in diagonal sequence to specifications.

LOWER

1. Remove right and left rocker cover gaskets.
2. Disconnect ignition coil electrical connectors.
3. Remove coil assembly attaching bolts, then the coil assemblies.
4. Disconnect fuel rail and fuel injector electrical connectors.
5. Position suitable cloth to catch any fuel spillage, then disconnect fuel pipe.
6. Remove auxiliary drive belt.
7. Remove alternator electrical connector securing nuts, then disconnect electrical connectors.
8. Release clip securing top hose to outlet pipe and release hose.

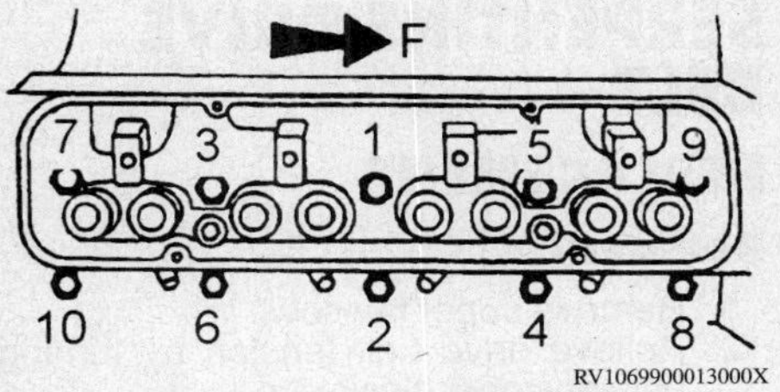

Fig. 6 Cylinder head bolt tightening sequence

9. Remove two alternator attaching bolts, then the alternator.
10. **On models equipped with A/C,** disconnect electrical connector from A/C compressor, then remove four compressor attaching bolts and the compressor.
11. **On all models,** remove two PAS pump to mounting bracket bolts, then position PAS pump aside.
12. Remove idler pulley to mounting bracket bolt, then the pulley.
13. Remove four mounting bracket bolts and one nut, then the mounting bracket.
14. Remove four top hose outlet pipe attaching bolts, then the outlet pipe.
15. Remove and discard O-ring.
16. Disconnect ECT sensor electrical connector.
17. Remove 12 lower intake manifold attaching bolts in sequence, **Fig. 2.**
18. Remove intake manifold and gasket.
19. Reverse procedure to install, noting the following:
    a. Using sequence shown in **Fig. 3, torque** lower intake manifold bolts to 8 ft. lbs., then to 38 ft. lbs.

EXHAUST MANIFOLD

REPLACE

1998

1. Raise and support vehicle.
2. Disconnect front exhaust pipe from manifold.
3. On left manifold, remove or disconnect the following:
    a. Air intake hose from plenum chamber.
    b. Harness from intake hose clip.
    c. Air flow meter from air cleaner and harness connector.
    d. Purge hose from RAM pipe housing.
    e. Purging valve from shock tower.
4. On right manifold, remove or disconnect the following:
    a. Spark plug leads and position aside. **Mark leads for installation reference**
    b. Spark plug lead clip from rocker cover.
    c. Loosen, but do not remove, righthand shock absorber top mounting bolt to provide additional clearance for heat shield removal
5. Remove heat shield.
6. Remove exhaust manifolds and gaskets.
7. Reverse procedure to install, noting the following:
    a. Ensure mating surfaces are clean.
    b. Coat threads of bolts with anti-seize compound.
    c. Install new gaskets.
    d. Install new locking tabs.
    e. Tighten to specification.

1999-2001

1. Raise and support vehicle.
2. Remove front pipe flange to exhaust manifold attaching nuts.
3. Disconnect front pipe from exhaust manifold, then remove gaskets.
4. Lower vehicle, then disconnect MAF sensor electrical connector and remove harness from clip on air intake hose.
5. Remove clip and disconnect hose from IAC valve.
6. Loosen clip and disconnect air intake hose from throttle body.
7. Remove two clips attaching MAF sensor to air cleaner.
8. Remove MAF sensor, hose assembly and O-ring.
9. Disconnect spark plug caps, then high tension leads from clips on rocker cover and place aside.
10. Loosen righthand shack absorber top mounting bolt.
11. Remove steering column intermediate shaft.
12. Remove exhaust manifold heat shield attaching bolts, then the heat shield.
13. Remove exhaust manifold to cylinder head attaching bolts, then the exhaust manifold and gaskets.
14. Reverse procedure to install, noting to tighten exhaust manifold bolt in sequence **Fig. 4** to specifications.

CYLINDER HEAD

REPLACE

1. Remove rocker shaft assembly.
2. Mark heads "LH" and "RH" for installation reference.
3. Remove and discard ten cylinder head to cylinder block attaching bolts in sequence, **Fig. 5.**
4. Remove cylinder head from dowels and remove cylinder head.
5. Remove and discard cylinder head gasket.
6. Reverse procedure to install, noting the following:
    a. Clean mating surfaces of cylinder head and cylinder block.
    b. Ensure all bolt holes are clean.
    c. Lightly oil and install cylinder head bolts.
    d. **Torque** cylinder head bolts in three steps in sequence, **Fig. 6.** First to 15 ft. lbs., next turn bolts another 90° and finally an additional 90.°

VALVE COVER

REPLACE

LEFT

1. Drain engine coolant and relieve fuel system pressure.

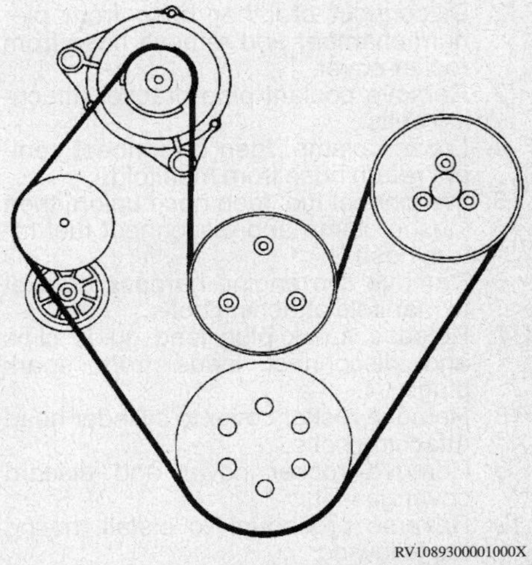

Fig. 7 Drive belt routing. Less A/C

2. Loosen air intake hose to plenum chamber clamp, then disconnect hose from plenum.
3. Remove cotter pin from throttle cable clevis pin, then the clevis pin.
4. Release and remove kick down cable clevis pin.
5. Disconnect throttle cable from bracket.
6. Remove kick down cable front lock nut, then disconnect cable from bracket.
7. Disconnect purge and breather hoses from plenum chamber.
8. Disconnect TPC and IACV electrical connectors.
9. Disconnect coolant hoses from plenum chamber.
10. Remove plenum chamber to intake manifold attaching bolts, then the manifold from plenum. **Place cloth over ram housing.**
11. Remove clamp securing dipstick tube to valve cover.
12. Release spark plug leads from guide clips and disconnect leads from spark plugs.
13. Remove valve cover to cylinder attaching bolts, then the cover.
14. Reverse procedure to install, noting the following:
    a. Using a suitable brush, apply a thin coat of impact adhesive Bostick part No. 1775, or equivalent, to mating surfaces of cylinder head and rocker cover. **Allow surfaces to stand for 30 minutes before installing valve cover.**
    b. Place one end of gasket into cover recess with edge firmly against recess wall, holding remainder of gasket clear. Working around cover pressing gasket into place, ensure edge firmly contacts recess wall.
    c. Apply a thin coat of sealant Loctite No. 577, or equivalent, to sealing face of plenum chamber.

RIGHT

1. Drain engine coolant and relieve fuel system pressure.

2. Disconnect breather hose from plenum chamber and remove hose from rocker cover.
3. Remove coolant pipe bracket attaching bolts.
4. Loosen clamp, then disconnect coolant return hose from manifold.
5. Disconnect fuel feed hose union, then loosen clamp and disconnect fuel return hose.
6. Remove two engine harness bracket to manifold attaching bolts.
7. Release spark plug lead guide clips and disconnect leads from spark plugs.
8. Remove rocker cover to cylinder head attaching bolts.
9. Remove rocker cover and discard cover gasket.
10. Reverse procedure to install, noting the following:
    a. Using a suitable brush, apply a thin coat of impact adhesive Bostick part No. 1775, or equivalent, to mating surfaces of cylinder head and rocker cover. **Allow surfaces to stand for 30 minutes before installing valve cover.**
    b. Place one end of gasket into cover recess with edge firmly against recess wall, holding remainder of gasket clear. Working around cover pressing gasket into place, ensure edge firmly contacts recess wall.

VALVE ADJUSTMENT

These engines utilize hydraulic tappets and are not adjustable.

FRONT COVER

REPLACE

1. Drain cooling system, then remove radiator as outlined under "Radiator, Replace."
2. Remove water pump pulley.
3. Remove coolant hose from water pump.
4. Raise and support vehicle, then disconnect oil cooler hoses from front cover and position aside. Plug hoses and connections.
5. Disconnect oil pressure switch electrical connector.
6. Disconnect camshaft sensor electrical connector.
7. Remove front cover attaching bolts.
8. Loosen four oil pump attaching bolts.
9. Remove front cover and oil seal.
10. Remove and discard gasket.
11. Reverse procedure to install, noting the following:
    a. Apply Hylosil jointing compound to position gasket on cover.
    b. Lubricate new front seal with engine oil.
    c. Apply a small amount of Loctite 242, or equivalent, to threads of attaching bolts.

TIMING CHAIN

REPLACE

1. Secure flywheel and remove crankshaft pulley bolt.

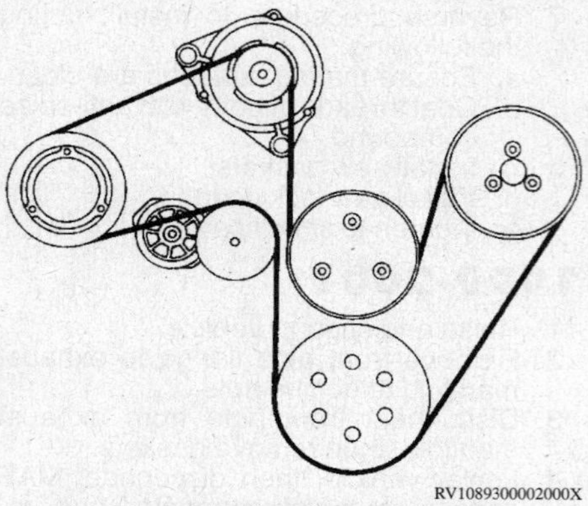

Fig. 8 Drive belt routing. With A/C

2. Remove crankshaft pulley.
3. Remove sump.
4. Remove nut and washers attaching oil pick-up pipe to stud.
5. Remove two bolts securing oil pick-up to oil pump cover, withdraw pipe from cover and discard O-ring.
6. Remove oil pick-up pipe and spacer from stud.
7. Remove bolt securing camshaft sensor to timing cover.
8. Remove sensor and discard O-ring.
9. Release harness connector from mounting bracket.
10. Noting fitted position, remove nine bolts securing timing cover to cylinder block, then cover.
11. Remove camshaft gear attaching bolt.
12. Remove timing chain and gears as an assembly, then woodruff key.
13. Remove and discard gasket.
14. Remove and discard oil seal from timing cover.
15. Reverse procedure to install.

CAMSHAFT

REPLACE

1. Remove tappets and keep in order with their respective pushrods.
2. Remove two bolts attaching camshaft thrust plate to cylinder block, then plate.
3. Slide camshaft out of cylinder block, ensuring not to damage bearings in cylinder block.
4. Reverse procedure to install.

OIL PAN

REPLACE

1. Drain engine oil.
2. Remove oil pan bolts and nuts.
3. Clean and degrease mating surfaces of pan, front cover and engine block.
4. Apply suitable silicone sealant to mating surface of oil pan.
5. Reverse procedure to install. Tighten to specification.

SERPENTINE DRIVE BELT

REPLACEMENT

Removal

1. Remove upper fan cowl.
2. Relieve drive belt tension by turning belt tensioner clockwise.
3. Remove belt from alternator pulley, then release tensioner pulley.
4. Remove drive belt. **If reusing belt, mark direction of rotation on belt.**

Installation

1. Clean drive belt pulley grooves and check grooves for any damage.
2. Position belt around all pulleys except alternator pulley, refer to "Belt Routing" for correct belt position.
3. Turn belt tensioner clockwise, then install belt onto alternator pulley
4. Ensure belt is squarely located on pulleys, with all grooves engaged
5. Release tensioner, then install upper fan cowl.

ROUTING

Refer to **Figs. 7 and 8** for drive belt routings.

BELT TENSION CHECK

1. With engine running, watch drive belt tensioner movement.
2. If tensioner has more than 12 mm of movement (play), replace tensioner.
3. Check tensioner. If tensioner arm and spring case contact each other, replace tensioner.
4. Using a suitable belt tension gauge, check belt tension several times at same point on belt away from tensioner, run engine between checks.
5. **On models with A/C,** if belt tension is less than 66 psi, replace drive belt.
6. **On models less A/C,** if belt tension is less than 60 psi, replace drive belt.

THERMOSTAT

REPLACE

1. Partially drain coolant from cooling system.
2. Loosen hose clamp and disconnect radiator top hose from thermostat housing.
3. Remove thermostat.
4. Reverse procedure to install.

WATER PUMP

REPLACE

1. Drain engine coolant.
2. Remove cooling fan and viscous coupling assembly.
3. Loosen water pump pulley bolts.
4. Remove water pump drive belt.
5. Remove water pump pulley.
6. Disconnect inlet hose from water pump.
7. Remove water pump and gasket.
8. Reverse procedure to install. Tighten to specification.

FUEL PUMP

REPLACE

1. Relieve fuel system pressure as outlined under "Precautions."
2. Siphon at least two gallons of fuel from fuel tank into a suitable container.
3. Remove carpet from cargo space floor and tailgate, then fold back cargo space sound insulation to expose fuel pump access panel.
4. Remove access panel, then disconnect multi-plug from fuel sender unit.
5. Disconnect fuel lines from fuel pump.
6. Using retaining ring removal tool No. LRS-19-001, or equivalent, remove fuel pump retaining ring, then the fuel pump from fuel tank.
7. Reverse procedure to install.

FUEL FILTER

REPLACE

1. Relieve fuel system pressure as outlined under "Precautions."
2. Raise and support vehicle.
3. Filter is mounted on the frame rail, near the righthand rear wheelwell opening
4. Clean area around fuel line connections to prevent dirt from entering system.
5. Remove fuel lines from filter. Plug fuel lines to prevent dirt from entering the system.
6. Remove filter bracket attaching bolts, then separate filter from bracket.
7. Reverse procedure to install.

TIGHTENING SPECIFICATIONS

Year	Component	Torque, Ft. Lbs.
1998–2001	A/C Compressor Bolts	17
	A/C Compressor Lines	11
	Camshaft Gear Bolt	37
	Cylinder Head Bolts	②
	Engine Mount Nuts	33
	Exhaust Front Pipe To Intermediate Pipe	18
	Exhaust Front Pipe To Manifold Nuts	37
	Exhaust Manifold	40
	Front Cover	16
	Fuel Line To Fuel Rail	12
	Gasket Clamp Bolts	13
	Gear Lever	18
	Ignition Coil Bracket	72③
	Intake Manifold	①
	Linkage Bracket To Plenum	72③
	Oil Cooler Lines	22
	Oil Pan	18
	Oil Pan Drain Plug	32
	Plenum Chamber	18
	Power Steering Lines	12
	Propeller Shaft Flange	35
	Shock Absorber Top Mount Bolt	63
	Transmission Crossmember to Chassis	33
	Valve Cover	84③
	Water Jacket To Plenum	10
	Water Pump	16
	Water Pump Pulley	18

① — Refer to "Intake Manifold, Replace" for tightening procedure.
② — Refer to "Cylinder Head, Replace" for tightening procedure.
③ — Inch lbs.

Clutch & Manual Transmission

INDEX

	Page No.
Adjustments	4-14
Clutch, Replace	4-14
Hydraulic System Service	4-14
Master Cylinder, Replace	4-14
Slave Cylinder, Replace	4-14
System Bleed	4-14
Precautions	4-14
Air Bag Systems	4-14
Battery Ground Cable	4-14
Tightening Specifications	4-14
Transmission, Replace	4-14

PRECAUTIONS

AIR BAG SYSTEMS

Refer to "Air Bag System Precautions" in the front of this manual for system disarming and arming procedures.

BATTERY GROUND CABLE

Prior to service, disconnect battery ground cable and isolate as required.

ADJUSTMENTS

These clutches are not adjustable.

HYDRAULIC SYSTEM SERVICE

MASTER CYLINDER, REPLACE

1. Drain hydraulic fluid from system.
2. Disconnect fluid pipe from master cylinder. Plug master cylinder fluid port and seal end of hydraulic pipe to prevent contamination.
3. Remove instrument panel trim panel from under steering column.
4. Remove retaining washer and clevis pin attaching master cylinder push rod to clutch pedal.
5. Remove master cylinder from firewall.
6. Reverse procedure to install. Bleed hydraulic system.

SLAVE CYLINDER, REPLACE

1. Drain hydraulic fluid from slave cylinder bleed valve.
2. Disconnect fluid pipe from slave cylinder.
3. Remove two slave cylinder to backing plate attaching bolts.
4. Remove slave cylinder and dust cover from backing plate.
5. Reverse procedure to install, noting the following:
   a. Coat both sides of backing plate with waterproof jointing compound Hylomar P232M, or equivalent.
   b. Bleed hydraulic system.

SYSTEM BLEED

1. Fill master cylinder with fluid. Maintain fluid level during bleeding procedure.
2. Attach a clear plastic tube to slave cylinder bleed screw.
3. Place other end of tube in a jar containing hydraulic fluid.
4. Loosen bleed screw.
5. Pump clutch pedal, pausing at end of each stroke, until fluid from tubing is free of air.
6. Hold clutch pedal down and tighten bleed screw.
7. Check fluid level.

CLUTCH

REPLACE

1. Remove Transmission following the procedures under "Transmission, Replace."
2. Disconnect push rod gaiter from clutch.
3. Remove slave cylinder and position aside.
4. Remove flywheel access cover.
5. Remove clutch housing bolts, then disengage release lever from release bearing.
6. Mark position of clutch housing, then remove.
7. Loosen, then remove clutch cover bolts in a diagonal pattern.
8. Remove clutch friction plate.
9. Reverse procedure to install noting the following:
   a. Ensure all matting surfaces are clean.
   b. Apply Molycote FB 180, or equivalent grease to splines.
   c. Position friction plate on flywheel using alignment tool No. LRT-12-001, or equivalent.
   d. Tighten to specification.

TRANSMISSION

REPLACE

1. Remove cooling fan assembly.
2. Remove shift lever knobs from console.
3. Remove console assembly.
4. Remove sound deadener pad from transmission tunnel.
5. Remove gear shift lever.
6. Release handbrake and remove handbrake cable clevis pin. Disconnect handbrake cable.
7. Raise and support vehicle.
8. Drain oil from transfer case, transmission and extension housing.
9. Remove exhaust front pipe.
10. Remove rear propeller shaft guard, then mark transfer case and propeller shaft flanges for installation reference.
11. Raise one wheel on each axle to allow rotation of propeller shaft.
12. Remove propeller shaft from transfer case and position aside.
13. Disconnect electrical connectors from transfer case and transmission.
14. Remove cooler pipe adaptor from transmission.
15. Remove banjo bolts securing breather pipes to transmission and transfer case. Position breather pipes aside.
16. Position a suitable jack under transmission/transfer case assembly.
17. Remove harness bracket from transmission.
18. Remove transmission to engine attaching bolts, then the transmission/transfer case assembly.
19. Reverse procedure to install noting the following:
   a. Align friction plate on flywheel using alignment tool No. LRT-12-001, or equivalent.
   b. Tighten to specification.

TIGHTENING SPECIFICATIONS

Year	Component	Torque, Ft. Lbs.
1998–2001	Clutch Cover	30
	Clutch Housing	30
	Clutch Slave Cylinder	33
	Gear Shift Lever Mounting	33
	Propeller Shafts	35
	Transmission To Bellhousing	33

Rear Axle & Suspension

INDEX

	Page No.
Coil Spring, Replace	4-15
Rear Axle, Replace	4-15
Discovery	4-15
New Range Rover	4-15
Shock Absorber, Replace	4-15
Tightening Specifications	4-16
Torsion Bar, Replace	4-15

REAR AXLE

REPLACE

DISCOVERY

1. Drain brake hydraulic system, then raise and support vehicle.
2. Support rear axle weight with suitable hydraulic jack.
3. **On models with ABS,** disconnect ABS wiring harness multi-plug at jump hose bracket.
4. **On all models,** remove shock absorbers from lower brackets.
5. Disconnect flexible brake hose at connection under floor.
6. Disconnect lower links at axle, then mark differential and propeller shaft flanges for installation reference.
7. Remove propeller shaft nuts and bolts, then lower propeller shaft and tie to one side.
8. Disconnect pivot bracket ball joint at axle bracket.
9. Remove coil spring plate bolts, then the plates.
10. Lower axle and remove springs.
11. Disconnect torsion bar links from axle as follows:
    a. Remove nuts, bolts, washers and rubber bushings from ball joint links, then the lower torsion bar to clear links.
    b. Remove cotter pin and loosen castellated nut a few turns.
    c. Remove ball joint using ball joint puller tool No. 18G 1063A, or equivalent.
    d. Remove castellated nut and ball joint link.
12. Remove rear axle.
13. Reverse procedure to install. Bleed brake system.

NEW RANGE ROVER

1. Raise and support vehicle.
2. Remove rear wheels.
3. Support axle using suitable jack.
4. Disconnect rear propeller shafts from differential and position propeller shaft aside.
5. Disconnect shock absorbers from axle.
6. Depressurize air suspension system using suitable electronic diagnostic tool.
7. Remove "R" clips retaining air springs to axle.
8. Remove panhard rod and position aside.
9. Disconnect ABS electrical connector from body bracket.
10. Disconnect and plug brake lines.
11. Remove banjo bolt and strap securing breather hose to axle, then the plug hose.
12. Remove height sensors from trailing arms, then the bolts securing trailing arms to axle.
13. Remove axle from vehicle.
14. Reverse procedure to install, noting the following:
    a. Tighten to specification.
    b. Bleed brake system.
    c. Run engine to repressurize air suspension system.

SHOCK ABSORBER

REPLACE

1. Raise and support vehicle, then remove wheels.
2. Support rear axle weight with suitable jack.
3. Remove shock absorber to axle bracket nut, then the shock absorber from bracket.
4. Remove upper shock absorber nut, then the shock absorber.
5. Remove mounting bracket and mounting bushings as necessary.
6. Reverse procedure to install.

COIL SPRING

REPLACE

1. Raise and support vehicle, then remove wheels.
2. Support rear axle weight with suitable jack, then disconnect shock absorbers at one end.
3. Position suitable coil spring compressor on spring and compress spring evenly.
4. Lower axle to free spring from upper seat. **Do not lower axle further than rear brake flexible hose will allow.**
5. Remove spring retainer plate, then the road spring and spring isolator.
6. Remove spring seat.
7. Reverse procedure to install.

TORSION BAR

REPLACE

1. Mark position of rubber bushings on torsion bar.
2. Remove bushing strap nuts, bolts and washers.
3. Remove ball joint link nuts, bolts, washers and rubber bushings, then the torsion bar.
4. Position rubber bushings on torsion bar, then install joint toward axle.
5. Install torsion bar with bushing straps. Ensure ball joint link arms point down.
6. Loosely install ball joint link bolts, washers and new Nyloc nuts. Tighten to specifications.
7. Install bolt, washers and rubber bushings, then the torsion bar to ball joint links.

TIGHTENING SPECIFICATIONS

Year	Component	Torque, Ft. Lbs.
DISCOVERY		
1998–2001	Ball Joint Link Arm Nuts	29
	Ball Joint Link Bolts	49
	Bushing Strap Nuts	22
	Pivot Bracket Ball Joint	126
	Propeller Shaft To Drive Pump	34
	Torsion Bar To Ball Joint Links	49
	Wheel Lug Nuts	80
NEW RANGE ROVER		
1998–2001	Axle To Trailing Arm	①
	Panhard Rod To Axle	148
	Propeller Shaft To Flange	35
	Shock Absorber to Axle	33
	Shock Absorber Top Mount	92
	Trailing Arm To Chassis	118
	Wheel Lug Nuts	80

① — M16 bolts, 118 ft. lbs.; M12 bolts, 92 ft. lbs.

Transfer Case

INDEX

	Page No.
Fluid Change	4-17
Tightening Specifications	4-18
Transfer Case, Replace	4-17
Discovery	4-17
Range Rover	4-17

FLUID CHANGE

1. Raise and support vehicle.
2. Clean immediate area around filler level and drain plug.
3. Place a suitable container under transfer case drain plug, then remove drain plug.
4. Thoroughly clean drain plug threads and apply suitable thread sealant.
5. Install drain plug and tighten to specifications.
6. Fill transfer case with fluid specified in "Lubricant Data," until fluid seeps from filler hole.
7. Wipe away any surplus oil, then thoroughly clean filler plug threads and apply suitable thread sealant.
8. Install filler plug and tighten to specifications.

TRANSFER CASE

REPLACE

DISCOVERY

1. Site vehicle on hoist.
2. Remove fan cowl from radiator.
3. Remove transfer gear lever knob and gaiter.
4. Raise and support vehicle, drain transfer case oil.
5. Detach heat shield at front exhaust pipe to manifold.
6. Disconnect O2 sensor connectors.
7. Remove catalytic converter assembly.
8. Remove chassis crossmember from under transfer case.
9. Remove heat shield from speedometer cable at transfer case.
10. Remove clamp and disconnect speedometer from transfer case. Tie cable to one side.
11. Disconnect propeller shafts from transfer case and tie aside.
12. Remove bolts retaining silencer front and rear securing brackets and tie silencer to one side.
13. Manufacture a suitable adaptor plate to transfer case hoist, **Fig. 1.**
14. Place four 1.250 inches long spacers between top of hoist and adaptor plate at securing points and secure adaptor plate to hoist.
15. Remove four center bolts from transfer case bottom cover, and install adaptor plate.
16. Adjust hoist to take weight off transfer case.
17. Remove tie bar, transfer case to transmission.
18. Remove nuts and bolts securing right hand transmission mounting bracket to chassis, then the nut from rubber mounting and withdraw bracket.
19. Repeat for left mounting bracket. Removal of these fixings will also free speedometer transducer bracket.
20. Lower hoist until rear brake drum clears passenger footwell. **Ensure engine does not crush any components while lowering.**
21. Loosen park brake adjustment nut.
22. Remove park brake drum.
23. Remove park brake assembly complete from rear output flange.
24. Disconnect leads from transfer case temperature sensor and differential lock warning light switch.
25. Remove banjo bolt from breather pipe, retrieve sealing washers and lay pipe aside.
26. Remove cotter pin and washers securing differential lock to connecting rod and disconnect rod from lever.
27. Select low range transfer case position.
28. Remove high/low rod lower lock nut and remove rod from yoke.
29. Position hoist jack channel under bellhousing.
30. Using a suitable wooden block support transmission and bellhousing.
31. Remove upper and lower bolts securing transfer case to transmission.
32. Install guide studs tool No. 18G 1425, or equivalent, to transmission and move transfer case rearwards to detach.
33. Reverse procedure to install noting the following:
    a. Select P in transmission, with low range and differential lock selected in transfer case.
    b. Clean threads of four bottom cover bolts and coat with Loctite 290, or equivalent, and install with spring washers. **Torque** to 18 ft. lbs.
    c. Add correct grade of oil to transfer case to oil level plug hole, see "Lubricant Data Charts" for fluid type and capacity.
    d. Ensure parking brake operation is correct and adjust if necessary.

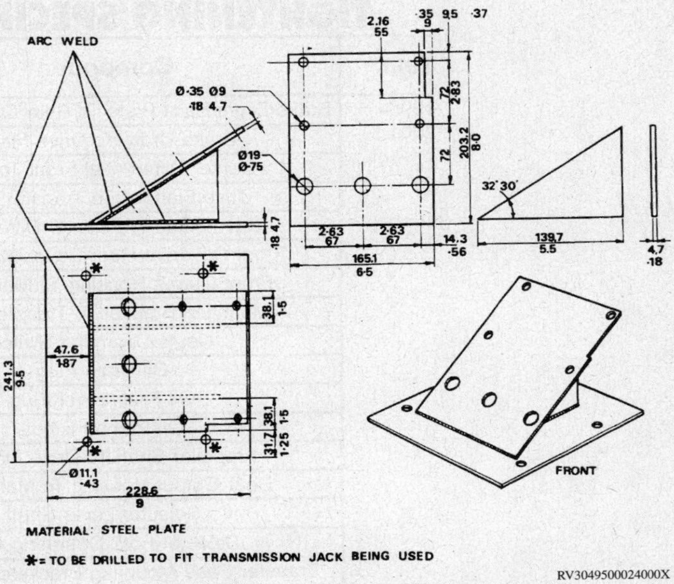

Fig. 1 Adaptor plate. Discovery

RANGE ROVER

1. Site vehicle on hoist and chock wheels.
2. Remove fan blade assembly. **Nut securing viscous unit has lefthand threads.**
3. Disconnect airflow meter to plenum chamber hose.
4. **On models with manual transmission,** remove two gear lever knobs.
5. **On models with automatic transmission,** remove gear selector.
6. **On all models,** remove floor mounted console assembly.
7. Remove padding from top of transmission tunnel.

8. Loosen pinch bolt and remove upper gear lever.
9. Remove screws and detach high low lever and main gear lever retaining plates.
10. Raise and support vehicle.
11. Drain oil from transfer case and reinstall plug, tightening to specifications.
12. **On V8 models,** disconnect O2 sensor and front exhaust sections.
13. **On V8 models,** remove chassis cross member secured by eight nuts and bolts.
14. **On all models,** mark each drive flange for reassembly and disconnect front and rear propeller shafts from transfer case. Tie shafts to one side.
15. Disconnect speed transducer electrical connector.
16. Remove transmission brake drum, then the four bolts securing back plate to transfer case and tie assembly aside complete with handbrake cable.
17. Raise transmission jack and support to transfer case.
18. Remove six bolts securing transfer case to transmission.
19. Release transfer case from transmission and lower transfer case.
20. Reverse procedure to install.

TIGHTENING SPECIFICATIONS

Year	Component	Torque, Ft. Lbs.
1998–2001	Brake Drum Back Plate To Rear Output Housing	54
	Brake Drum To Drive Flange	18
	Center Differential Front To Rear	44
	Drive Flanges To Transfer Case	165
	Driven Gear To Center Differential	37
	Front Cover To Rear Cover-Main Case	30
	Front Output Housing To Main Case	24
	Mounting Bracket To Transfer Case	75
	Neutral Warning Switch	35
	Oil Drain Plug	18
	Oil Filler/Level Plug	18
	Oil Pump Fixings	5
	Propeller Shaft To Drive Flanges	34
	Rear Output Housing To Main Case	30
	Selector Lever Shaft	6
	Selector Fork Operating Arm	6
	Transfer Case Mounting Brackets To Chassis	33

Front Suspension & Steering

INDEX

	Page No.
Coil Spring, Replace	4-19
Power Steering Gear, Replace	4-19
Discovery	4-19
New Range Rover	4-19
Power Steering Pump, Replace	4-20
Discovery	4-20
New Range Rover	4-20
Power Steering System Bleed	4-20
Precautions	4-19
Air Bag Systems	4-19
Battery Ground Cable	4-19
Radius Arm, Replace	4-19
Discovery	4-19
New Range Rover	4-19
Shock Absorber, Replace	4-19
Tightening Specifications	4-20
Torsion Bar, Replace	4-19

PRECAUTIONS

AIR BAG SYSTEMS

Refer to "Air Bag System Precautions" in the front of this manual for system disarming and arming procedures.

BATTERY GROUND CABLE

Prior to service, disconnect battery ground cable and isolate as required.

COIL SPRING

REPLACE

1. Remove front shock absorber as outlined under "Shock Absorber, Replace."
2. Lower axle enough to free spring. **Avoid over stretching brake hoses. If necessary, loosen hose connector locknuts to allow hoses to follow axle.**
3. Remove spring.
4. Remove shock absorber bracket securing ring nut, then the ring.
5. Reverse procedure to install.

SHOCK ABSORBER

REPLACE

1. Raise and support vehicle, then remove wheels.
2. Support front axle weight with suitable jack.
3. Remove shock absorber lower fixing, then the cup washer, rubber bushing and seating washer.
4. Remove shock absorber bracket nuts and washers, then the shock absorber and bracket as an assembly.
5. Remove lower seating washer, rubber bushing and cup washer.
6. Remove shock absorber to mounting bracket nut, then the mounting bracket.
7. Remove top seating washer, rubber bushing and cup washer.
8. Reverse procedure to install.

TORSION BAR

REPLACE

1. Mark position of rubber bushings on torsion bar.
2. Remove bushing strap nuts, bolts and washers, then the straps
3. Remove ball joint link nuts, bolts, washers and rubber bushings from ball joint links.
4. Remove torsion bar from vehicle.
5. Position bushings on torsion bar. **Ensure split points toward axle on righthand bushing and away from axle on lefthand bushing.**
6. Install torsion bar with straps. **To ensure correct fit, angled sides of bar should point down.**
7. Loosely install strap bolts, washers and Nyloc nuts.
8. Install ball joint link bolts, washers and rubber bushings with new nuts to ball joint links. Tighten to specifications.
9. Tighten strap nuts to specifications.

RADIUS ARM

REPLACE

DISCOVERY

1. Raise and support vehicle, then remove wheels.
2. Support front axle weight with suitable jack.
3. Remove radius arm to chassis side member nut, washer and bushing, then disconnect track rod at ball joint.
4. Remove radius arm to axle bolt, then lower radius arm front end to clear axle and remove from vehicle.
5. Press out bushings.
6. Reverse procedure to install, noting the following:
   a. Press in new bushings. Press on outer edge of bushing and not inner rubber.
   b. Tighten radius arm to chassis nut and radius arm to axle bolt to specifications.

NEW RANGE ROVER

1. Raise and support vehicle, then remove wheels.
2. Depressurize air suspension system using suitable electronic diagnostic and service tool.
3. Remove front wheel.
4. Remove anti-roll bar.
5. Disconnect track rod from swivel hub and position aside.
6. Disconnect height sensor link from radius arm.
7. Support front axle weight with suitable jack.
8. Remove radius arm to axle bolt, then radius arm from chassis bracket.
9. Press out bushings using bushing tool No. LRT-60-003, or equivalent.
10. Reverse procedure to install, noting the following:
    a. Press in new bushings. Press on outer edge of bushing and not inner rubber.
    b. Tighten radius arm to chassis nut and radius arm to axle bolt to specifications.

POWER STEERING GEAR

REPLACE

DISCOVERY

1. Raise and support vehicle and remove wheel.
2. Ensure steering wheel is centered, then install centralizing bolt to steering box.
3. Remove three bolts attaching intermediate shaft and universal joint.
4. Push intermediate shaft upwards then release and remove universal joint.
5. Position container to catch oil spillage.
6. Remove bolt attaching PAS pipe bracket to steering box, release pipes and discard O-rings.
7. Remove panhard rod attaching nut and bolt, then rod.
8. Remove drag link to drop arm attaching nut.
9. Using ball joint tool No. LRT-57–036 or equivalent, disconnect taper joint and release drag link.
10. Remove four steering box attaching bolts, then box.
11. Remove centralizing bolt from steering box.
12. Reverse procedure to install.

NEW RANGE ROVER

1. Raise and support vehicle.
2. Drain and remove windshield washer reservoir.
3. Remove nut connecting drag link to drop arm, then separate using removal tool No. LRT-57-018, or equivalent.
4. Remove bolts securing steering column lower universal joint to steering gear.
5. Slide universal joint upward on column to clear gear pinion.
6. Disconnect feed and return lines from steering gear. Plug openings to prevent contamination.

7. Remove power steering gear to chassis side member bolts, then the gear.
8. Reverse procedure to install, noting the following:
   a. Tighten to specification.
   b. Fill with suitable steering fluid according to specifications, then bleed system as outlined under "Power Steering System Bleed." **Do not start engine until reservoir is full as pump will be damaged.**
   c. Test drive vehicle for proper operation.

POWER STEERING PUMP

REPLACE

DISCOVERY

1. Remove drive belt. Refer to "Serpentine Drive Belt."
2. Remove air intake hose cable ties.
3. Loosen three clips attaching air intake hose then remove hose.
4. **On models equipped with ACE,** remove three bolts securing ACE pump, then position pump aside.
5. **On models equipped with A/C,** disconnect A/C compressor electrical connector, then remove four A/C compressor bolts and compressor, then position aside.
6. **On all models,** remove three power steering pump pulley attaching bolts, then pulley.
7. Position suitable tray to catch spillage and disconnect power steering pump pressure pipe.
8. Remove clip and disconnect power steering pump inlet hose.
9. Remove idler pulley.
10. Remove oil cooling pipe bracket bolt and bracket.
11. Remove two power steering pump bolts and power steering pump.
12. Remove four auxiliary housing bolts and one nut, then pull housing forward to release power steering pump.
13. Reverse procedure to install.

NEW RANGE ROVER

1. Remove power steering pump drive belt as outlined under "Engine, Replace."
2. Hold steering pump pulley while removing pulley bolts, then remove pulley.
3. Position container to catch power steering fluid.
4. Remove power steering pump reservoir hose clamp, then disconnect high pressure line from steering pump. **Plug openings to prevent contamination.**
5. Remove bolts securing pump and compressor mounting bracket to engine.
6. Remove bolts securing steering pump to mounting plate.
7. Remove pump assembly.
8. Reverse procedure to install noting following:
   a. Tighten to specifications.
   b. Bleed power steering system as outlined under "Power Steering System Bleed."

POWER STEERING SYSTEM BLEED

1. Ensure power steering pump fluid reservoir reaches dipstick maximum, then run engine to normal operating temperature.
2. Turn steering wheel 45° in both directions to open valve in steering gear.
3. Check reservoir fluid level and adjust as necessary.
4. With engine at idle speed, loosen bleed screw, then, when fluid seeps past bleed screw retighten screw, noting the following:
   a. **Do not maintain pressure for more than 30 seconds in one minute to avoid overheating fluid and damaging seals.**
   b. **Maintain maximum fluid level in reservoir.**
   c. **Do not increase engine speed or move steering wheel.**
5. Check fluid level, then check for fluid leaks.
6. Road test vehicle.

TIGHTENING SPECIFICATIONS

Year	Component	Torque, Ft. Lbs.
DISCOVERY		
1998–2001	A/C Compressor Bolts	16
	ACE Pump Bolts	16
	Ball Joint Link	49
	Drag Link To Drop Arm Nut	29
	High Pressure Pipe To Power Steering Pump	14
	Power Steering Gear Bolts	58
	Power Steering Gear Pipes (14mm)	11
	Power Steering Gear Pipes (16mm)	14
	Power Steering Gear To UV Joint Pinch Bolt	18
	Power Steering Pump Bolts	16
	Power Steering Pump Pulley Bolt	84①
	Power Steering Pump Reservoir Hose Clamp	27①
	Radius Arm To Axle Bolt	142
	Radius Arm To Chassis Nut	126
	Rubber Bushing Strap Nuts	22
	Tie Bar Bolts	②
	Tie Bar Nut	79
	Wheel Lug Nuts	80

Continued

TIGHTENING SPECIFICATIONS—Continued

Year	Component	Torque, Ft. Lbs.
NEW RANGE ROVER		
1998–2001	Banjo Bolt (M14)	22
	Banjo Bolt (M16)	37
	Drag Link To Drop Arm Nut	59
	High Pressure Line To Power Steering Pump	12
	Lifting Bracket To Power Steering Pump	13
	Power Steering Gear Bleed Screw	36①
	Power Steering Gear To Chassis Bolts	92
	Power Steering Pump & Compressor Bracket Bolts	30
	Power Steering Pump Bolts	13
	Power Steering Pump Pulley Bolt	18
	Radius Arm To Axle Bolt	63
	Radius Arm To Chassis Nut	118
	Shock Absorber Lower Mount	33
	Shock Absorber Upper Mount	92
	Steering Column Universal Joint To Pinion	18
	Wheel Lug Nuts	80

① — Inch lbs.
② — 58 ft. lbs., then loosen one complete turn.

Wheel Alignment

INDEX

	Page No.		Page No.		Page No.
Front Wheel Alignment	4-22	Toe	4-22	**Wheel Alignment Specifications**	4-2
Caster & Camber	4-22	**Preliminary Inspection**	4-22		

PRELIMINARY INSPECTION

1. Ensure tires are inflated to correct pressure, then check for uneven wear.
2. Inspect front wheel bearings, suspension arm and ball joints for damage and replace as necessary.
3. Inspect steering gear for damage and adjust as necessary.
4. Inspect shocks for damage and replace as necessary.
5. Rock vehicle backward and forward and bounce it upward and downward to settle vehicle prior to alignment.
6. Ensure vehicle is unloaded and on a suitable alignment rack according to manufacturers instructions. **When measuring equipment is attached and front wheels are on turntables, apply brake to prevent improper vehicle movement.**

FRONT WHEEL ALIGNMENT

CASTER & CAMBER

Front wheel caster and camber are preset by the manufacturer and are not adjustable. If caster and camber are not as indicated under "Front Wheel Alignment Specifications," inspect suspension components for damage, modification or excessive wear.

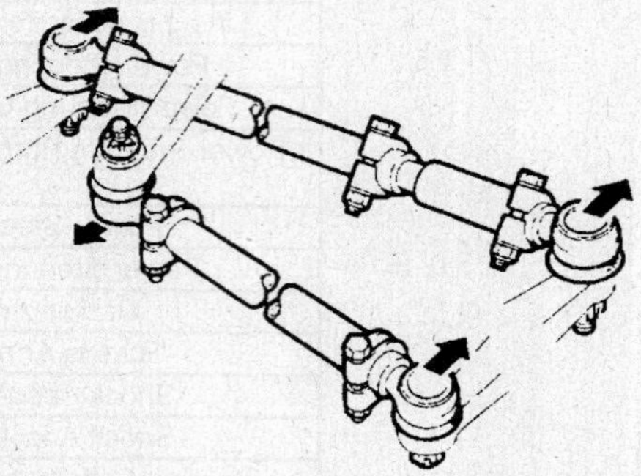

Fig. 1 Toe adjustment

TOE

1. Check toe-out setting as follows:
   a. Ensure vehicle is on level ground with wheels in straight-ahead position.
   b. Push vehicle forward and back to settle linkage, then measure toe-out at horizontal center line of wheels.
   c. **On Defender, Discovery and Range Rover, torque** clamp bolts to 10 ft. lbs.
   d. **On New Range Rover, torque** 8 mm bolts to 16 ft. lbs. and 10 mm bolts to 35 ft. lbs.
2. **On all models,** loosen adjuster sleeve clamp, then rotate adjuster to lengthen or shorten track rod.
3. When toe-out is correct, tap steering linkage ball joint in direction specified, **Fig. 1,** to maximum of travel. This ensures full unrestricted working travel.
4. Tighten clamp bolts as specified.

Air Conditioning

NOTE: On Air Bag Equipped Models, Refer To "Air Bag System Precautions" Located In The Front Of This Manual For System Disarming & Arming Procedures.

INDEX

	Page No.
A/C Specifications	4-27
Charging System	4-26
Evacuating System	4-25
Using Charging Station	4-26
Using Vacuum Pump	4-25
Oil Charge	4-26
Precautions	4-23
Air Bag Systems	4-23
Battery Ground Cable	4-23
Product Compatibility	4-23
Refrigerant Recovery	4-25
System Inspection	4-23
Compressor	4-24
Condenser	4-24
Evaporator	4-25
Receiver/Drier	4-25
Refrigerant Line Restrictions	4-25
Thermostatic Expansion Valve	4-25
Troubleshooting	4-23
Blower Controls	4-23
Compressor Controls	4-23
Refrigerant System	4-23
System	4-23

PRECAUTIONS

AIR BAG SYSTEMS

Refer to "Air Bag System Precautions" in the front of this manual for system disarming and arming procedures.

PRODUCT COMPATIBILITY

Before replenishing refrigerant or refrigerant oil, ensure product is compatible with the system being serviced. Refer to "Specifications" in the front of this manual.

BATTERY GROUND CABLE

Prior to service, disconnect battery ground cable and isolate as required.

TROUBLESHOOTING

BLOWER CONTROLS

1. Check maxi-fuse, engine compartment fuse and dash panel fuse box.
2. If front blower motor does not stop running with fan speed switch in on position, replace fan speed switch.
3. If fresh air does not enter engine passenger compartment with air supply selector switch in Outside Air position, check air recirculation solenoid and linkage.
4. If blower motor(s) run with ignition key removed, replace ignition load relay.
5. If blower motor(s) run, but not at fan speed switch indicated speed, replace fan speed switch.

COMPRESSOR CONTROLS

1. If front blower motor does not run normally, refer to "Blower Controls."
2. Check engine compartment and dash panel fuses.
3. Verify refrigerant pressures are within specifications.

SYSTEM

For A/C system troubleshooting, refer to **Figs. 1 and 2.**

REFRIGERANT SYSTEM

For refrigerant system troubleshooting, refer to **Figs. 3 and 4.**

FAULT	CAUSE	REMEDY
A. BLOWER MOTOR INOPERATIVE OR SLOW RUNNING	1. Incorrect voltage. 2. Open or defective fuse or relay. 3. Loose wire connection including ground. 4. Switch open or defective. 5. Tight, worn, or burnt motor bearings. 6. Open rotor windings. 7. Worn motor brushes. 8. Shaft binding-blade misaligned. 9. Defective resistors	1. Check voltage. 2. Check and replace as necessary. 3. Check system wires; tighten all connections. 4. Replace switch. 5. Replace motor. 6. Replace motor. 7. Replace motor. 8. Check alignment. Repair or replace as necessary. 9. Rectify or replace.
B. COMPRESSOR CLUTCH INOPERATIVE	1. Incorrect voltage. 2. Open or defective fuse or relay. 3. Defective thermostat control or pressure switch. 4. Shorted or open field coil. 5. Bearing seized (clutch will not (disengage). 6. Refrigeration circuit problem causing heavy load and excessive drive torque.	1. Check voltage. 2. Check and replace as necessary. 3. Replace thermostat or pressure switch. 4. Replace coil. 5. Replace clutch pulley assembly. 6. Check and rectify.
C. COMPRESSOR CLUTCH NOISY	1. Incorrect alignment. 2. Loose belt. 3. Compressor not mounted securely. 4. Bearing in clutch-pulley assembly not pressed in. 5. Low voltage to clutch. 6. Clutch will not spin freely. 7. Oil on clutch face. 8. Slipping clutch. 9. Overloaded or locked compressor. 10. Icing.	1. Check alignment; repair as necessary. 2. Adjust to proper tension. 3. Repair as necessary. 4. Remove clutch and replace clutch pulley assembly. 5. Check connections and voltage. 6. Refer to B5 above. 7. Check compressor seals for leaks. 8. Refer to C5 above. Then check air gap. 9. Repair or replace compressor. 10. Check for suction line frosting. Replace expansion valve if necessary. Replace receiver/drier if necessary.
D. CONDENSER VIBRATION	1. Motor and/or blades improperly mounted. 2. Foreign matter build-up on blades. 3. Excessive wear of motor bearings.	1. Check mountings, adjust as necessary. 2. Clean blades with a suitable non-inflammable cleaner. 3. Replace motor.

RV7019600022000X

Fig. 1 A/C system troubleshooting. Discovery

SYSTEM INSPECTION

While a detailed diagnostic procedure for all air conditioning systems would be impractical due to the many variations in construction and operation, there are three fundamental components of a total diagnosis:

1. Refrigerant systems must have an adequate, but not excessive charge.
2. Determination must be made whether the refrigerant system is governed by a cycling clutch compressor or by valves which control evaporator pressure.
3. The air distribution system (blower motor, switches, vacuum lines and air ducts) must be operational before checking the refrigerant system.

Check the blower; if inoperative, examine switches, fuses, connections, wiring and the blower motor. If blower is operating but the air output is low, check for loose wire connections or shorts, undercharged battery, dirty or loose switch contacts, or a faulty blower motor. Inspect the air distribution system for obstructions and ensure proper door operation.

If the blower is circulating the air but there is no cooling, check the compressor drive belt; ensure it is not broken or slipping. If the pulley is turning but the compressor shaft is not, check the magnetic clutch. On models equipped with a cycling clutch, the following hand check method

Symptom - Condenser Fan Motor Inoperative or Slow Running.

POSSIBLE CAUSE	REMEDY
1. Blown fuse.	1. Check and renew fuse 34.
2. Loose electrical connections.	2. Check and tighten all relevant connections.
3. Worn internal motor components.	3. Renew fan motor.

Symptom - Condenser Fan Motor and/or Condenser Vibration.

POSSIBLE CAUSE	REMEDY
1. Fan motor and/or blades out of alignment.	1. Check for visual damage.
2. Fan motor/s out of balance.	2. Balance fan motors.
3. Build up of debris on fan blades.	3. Clean blades with a suitable non-inflamable cleaner.
4. Excessive wear of fan motor bearings.	4. Renew condenser fan and motor assembly.
5. Condenser unit not mounted securely.	5. Secure as necessary.

RV7019600024010X

Fig. 2 A/C system troubleshooting (Part 1 of 3). New Range Rover

POSSIBLE CAUSE	REMEDY
1. Blown air conditioning system fuse.	1. Check and renew fuse 8 or 17.
2. Loose electrical connections.	2. Check and tighten all electrical connections.
3. Defective electrical or mechanical components.	3. Renew compressor.
4. Refrigerant circuit problem.	4. Check and rectify.

Symptom - Compressor Clutch Noisy

POSSIBLE CAUSE	REMEDY
1. Loose drive belt.	1. Check drive belt tensioner or renew drive belt.
2. Compressor not mounted securely.	2. Secure as necessary.
3. Bearing in clutch pulley not pressed in.	3. Renew compressor.
4. Clutch will not spin freely.	4. Renew compressor.
5. Oil on clutch face.	5. Check compressor seals for leaks; if apparent, renew compressor.
6. Slipping clutch.	6. Renew compressor.
7. Compressor pump seizing.	7. Renew compressor.
8. Icing.	8. Check for suction line frosting. Renew expansion valve or receiver/drier, if necessary.

Symptom - Blower Motors Inoperative or Slow Running.

POSSIBLE CAUSE	REMEDY
1. Blown fuse.	1. Check and renew fuse 42 or 43.
2. Loose electrical connections.	2. Check and tighten all relevant connections.
3. Worn internal motor components.	3. Renew blower motor/s.

RV7019600024020X

Fig. 2 A/C system troubleshooting (Part 2 of 3). New Range Rover

Symptom - Blower Motor vibration

POSSIBLE CAUSE	REMEDY
1. Blower motor/fan out of alignment.	1. Check for visual damage.
2. Blower motor/s out of balance.	2. Balance or renew motor/fan assembly.
3. Excessive wear of motor bearings.	3. Renew motor/fan assembly.
4. Blower motor not mounted securely.	4. Secure as necessary.

Symptom - Air conditioning system inoperative

POSSIBLE CAUSE	REMEDY
1. Blown air conditioning system fuse.	1. Check and renew fuses 8 or 17.
2. Switch control panel/ ECU faulty.	2. Check and renew fuse 8 or fit new switch control panel.

RV7019600024030X

Fig. 2 A/C system troubleshooting (Part 3 of 3). New Range Rover

will determine whether the problem lies in the refrigerant system or further testing of the distribution system is required.

1. With engine warmed up and at normal idle, set selector lever to Norm, temperature lever to Cold and blower on Hi.
2. Place one hand on the evaporator inlet pipe and the other on the receiver/drier surface with the compressor engaged.
3. If both surfaces are the same temperature and colder than ambient temperature, refrigerant system is normal.
4. If the inlet pipe is cooler than the receiver/drier surface, refrigerant system is low on charge. Add small amounts of refrigerant until both feel the same temperature. Then add 14 ozs. (one can) of additional refrigerant.
5. If inlet pipe is frosted over and receiver/drier surface is warmer, proceed as in step 4.

The individual components of the refrigerant system will often give clear signs of their malfunctioning. Use the following general descriptions to pinpoint faulty components.

COMPRESSOR

A faulty compressor will display one or more of the following symptoms: noise, seizure, leakage or low inlet and discharge pressure. A steady, resonant noise from the compressor is not necessarily an indication of a problem, but irregular metallic rattling may indicate broken parts and should be investigated. A thumping noise from the compressor and a cool, sweating suction line into it may indicate an overcharged system. Check seizure by disengaging the magnetic clutch and rotating the driven plate. If the compressor is seized, the driven plate will not rotate.

False compressor seizure may occur after an extended period of disuse or storage. Lubricating oil drains away from the polished surfaces of ball seats and axial plate and the compressor appears to be seized. Use a clutch hub holding tool to turn the compressor in the opposite direction of rotation at least three revolutions. Check for false compressor seizure if compressor has not been used in a month or longer.

If compressor is not seized but will not rotate, check for current at magnetic coil. Low discharge pressure may be caused by faulty seals within the compressor, a restriction in the compressor or elsewhere, or by a low refrigerant charge. The compressor must have the correct amount of the proper viscosity oil. Excess oil will restrict refrigerant circulation and reduce compressor outlet pressure.

CONDENSER

The condenser may malfunction either due to leakage or restriction. If restricted, compressor discharge pressure will be excessive. Icy or frosty spots on the condenser will indicate a partial restriction within the condenser. Ensure all foreign matter is removed from the front of the condenser. Similarly, bent cooling fins will block air flow

FAULT	CAUSE	REMEDY
A. HIGH HEAD PRESSURE	1. Overcharge of refrigerant. 2. Air in system. 3. Condenser air passage clogged with dirt or other foreign matter. 4. Condenser fan motor defective. 5. Incorrect voltage to fan motor.	1. Discharge, evacuate and charge system. 2. Discharge system, fit new drier, evacuate and charge system. 3. Clean condenser of debris. 4. Replace motor. 5. Check voltage.
B. LOW HEAD PRESSURE	1. Undercharge of refrigerant; evident by bubbles in sight glass while system is operating 2. Split compressor gasket or leaking valves. 3. Defective compressor.	1. Evacuate and charge system. Check for leakage. 2. Replace gasket and/or reed valve. Fit new drier, evacuate and charge system. 3. Repair or replace compressor.
C. HIGH SUCTION PRESSURE	1. Loose drive belt 2. Refrigerant flooding through evaporator into suction line; evident by ice on suction line and suction service valve. 3. Expansion valve stuck open. 4. Leaking compressor valves, valve gaskets and/or service valves. 5. Receiver/drier blocked; evident by temperature difference between input and output lines.	1. Check belt tension. 2. Check thermobulb. Bulb should be securely clamped to clean horizontal section of copper suction pipe. 3. Replace expansion valve. 4. Replace valves and/or gaskets. Fit new drier evacuate and charge system. 5. Fit new drier, evacuate and charge system.
D. LOW SUCTION	1. Expansion valve thermobulb not operating. 2. Expansion valve sticking closed. 3. Moisture freezing in expansion valve orifice. Valve outlet tube will frost while inlet hose tube will have little or no frost. System operates periodically. 4. Dust, paper scraps, or other debris restricting evaporator blower grille 5. Defective evaporator blower motor, wiring, or blower switch.	1. Warm thermobulb with hand. Suction should rise rapidly to 1.4 bar 20 lb/in² or more. If not replace expansion valve. 2. Check inlet side screen. Clean if clogged. Refer to C-2 and C-3. 3. Fit new drier, evacuate and charge system. 4. Clean grilles as required. 5. Refer to blower motor.

RV7019600023010X

Fig. 3 Refrigerant system troubleshooting (Part 1 of 2). Discovery

FAULT	CAUSE	REMEDY
E. NOISY EXPANSION VALVE (steady hissing)	1. Low refrigerant charge; evident by bubbles in sight glass.	1. Leak test. Repair or replace components as required.
F. INSUFFICIENT COOLING	1. Expansion valve not operating properly. 2. Low refrigerant charge-evident by bubbles in sight glass. 3. Compressor not pumping.	1. Refer to C-2, C-3, D-1 and E. 2. Refer to B-1 and E. 3. Refer to B-2 and B-3
G. COMPRESSOR BELT SLIPPING	1. Belt tension. 2. Excessive head pressure. 3. Incorrect alignment of pulleys or worn belt not riding properly. 4. Nicked or broken pulley. 5. Seized compressor.	1. Adjust belt tension. 2. Refer to A-1 through A-4 and C-6. 3. Repair as needed. 4. Replace as needed. 5. Replace compressor.
H. ENGINE NOISE AND/OR VIBRATION	1. Loose or missing mounting bolts. 2. Broken mounting bracket. 3. Loose flywheel or clutch retaining bolt. 4. Rough idler pulley bearing. 5. Bent, loose, or improperly mounted engine drive pulley. 6. Defective compressor bearing. 7. Insecure mountings of accessories; generator, power steering, air filter, etc. 8. Excessive head pressure. 9. Incorrect compressor oil level.	1. Repair as necessary. 2. Replace bracket. 3. Repair as necessary. 4. Replace bearing. 5. Repair as necessary. 6. Replace bearing. 7. Repair as necessary. 8. Refer to A-1, A-2, A-3 A-4 and C-6. 9. Refer to compressor Oil Level Check.

RV7019600023020X

Fig. 3 Refrigerant system troubleshooting (Part 2 of 2). Discovery

through the condenser and result in high discharge pressures.

EVAPORATOR

A faulty evaporator will provide insufficient cooling to the vehicle. The core may be restricted with dirt, the case may be cracked, or a seal may be leaking sufficiently to prevent cooling. If evaporator restriction is due to icing, the expansion valve, capillary tube or suction throttling valve, if equipped, may be at fault and should be investigated.

Since there is a constant condensation of atmospheric moisture on the outside of the evaporator coils, ensure that the draining system is unobstructed and clean. **Some vehicles have an auxiliary evaporator in the trunk or between the headliner and the roof.**

RECEIVER/DRIER

A restriction inside the receiver/drier will result in high head pressures if the restriction is on the inlet side of the unit. A restriction at the outlet side will cause low head pressures and little or no cooling. An exceedingly cold receiver/drier may be restricted.

If the system has been in service for a considerable amount of time, the desiccant element may have lost its moisture absorbing ability. This condition is indicated by the constant presence of small bubbles in the sight glass if equipped and a wide difference in temperature between the inlet and outlet receiver/drier lines.

THERMOSTATIC EXPANSION VALVE

Faulty expansion valves will be indicated by low suction and discharge pressures on the manifold gauge set. In most cases the power element fails and the valve closes. Occasionally the inlet screen becomes clogged with contamination or desiccant beads loose in the system.

REFRIGERANT LINE RESTRICTIONS

1. A restricted suction line is indicated by low suction pressure at the compressor, low discharge pressure and little or no cooling.
2. A restricted discharge line will usually cause the pressure relief valve to open.
3. A restricted liquid line will cause low suction and discharge pressures and little or no cooling.

REFRIGERANT RECOVERY

R-134a systems require the use of special service equipment designed specifically for R-134a systems. R-12 servicing equipment cannot be used on R-134a systems.

R-12 recovery stations cannot be used on R-134a systems. A separate recovery station must be used on R-134a systems. The refrigerants are not compatible and will contaminate the R-12 recovery station.

The use of refrigerant recovery and recycling stations allows the recovery and reuse of refrigerant after contaminants and moisture have been removed.

When using a recovery or recycling station, follow the manufacturer's operating instructions, noting the following:

1. **Use extreme caution and observe all safety and service precautions related to use of refrigerants.**
2. Connect refrigerant recycling station hose(s) to vehicle A/C service port(s) and recovery station inlet fitting. Hoses used should have shutoff devices or check valve within 12 inches of hose ends to minimize introduction of air into recycling station and to minimize amount of refrigerant release when hose(s) is disconnected.
3. Turn recycling station On to start recovery process. Allow recycling station to pump refrigerant from A/C system until station pressure gauge indicates vacuum.
4. After vehicle A/C system has been evacuated, close station inlet valve, if equipped.
5. Turn station Off. On some stations the pump will automatically be turned Off by a low pressure switch.
6. Allow vehicle A/C system to remain closed for approximately two minutes. Observe vacuum level indicated on gauge. If pressure does not rise, disconnect recycling station hose(s).
7. If system pressure rises, repeat steps 3 through 6 until vacuum level remains stable for two minutes.
8. Service A/C system as necessary. then evacuate and recharge A/C system.

EVACUATING SYSTEM

USING VACUUM PUMP

Vacuum pumps suitable for removing air

Symptom - High Head Pressure

POSSIBLE CAUSE	REMEDY
1. Overcharge of refrigerant.	1. Discharge, evacuate and recharge system.
2. Air in system.	2. Discharge system, fit new receiver/drier, evacuate and recharge system.
3. Condensor air passage blocked with dirt etc.	3. Clean condenser of debris.
4. Condenser fan motor/s defective.	4. Renew motor/s.
5. Loose compressor drive belt.	5. Check drive belt tensioner or renew drive belt.
6. Siezed compressor.	6. Renew compressor.

Symptom - Low Head Pressure

POSSIBLE CAUSE	REMEDY
1. Undercharge of refrigerant; evident by bubbles in sight glass while system is operating	1. Evacuate and recharge system.
2. Leaking compressor valves.	2. Renew compressor.
3. Defective compressor.	3. Renew compressor.

Symptoms - High Suction Pressure

POSSIBLE CAUSE	REMEDY
1. Loose drive belt.	1. Check drive belt tensioner or renew drive belt.
2. Refrigerant flooding through evaporator into suction line; evident by ice on suction line.	2. Renew expansion valve.
3. Expansion valve stuck open.	3. Renew expansion valve.
4. Leaking compressor valves.	4. Renew compressor.
5. Receiver/drier blocked; evident by temperature difference between input and output lines.	5. Fit new receiver/drier, evacuate and recharge system.

RV7019600025010X

Fig. 4 Refrigerant system troubleshooting (Part 1 of 2). New Range Rover

Symptoms - Low Suction Pressure

POSSIBLE CAUSE	REMEDY
1. Expansion valve sticking or closed.	1. Clean or if renew if necessary.
2. Moisture freezing in expansion valve orifice. Valve outlet tube will frost while inlet tube will have little or no frost.	2. Fit new receiver/drier, evacuate and recharge system.
3. Debris restricting external air intake grille.	3. Clean air intake grille.
4. Blocked air inlet housing filters.	4. Renew air filters.
5. Defective blower motor/s, blown fuse/s or loose electrical connections.	5. Check and renew fuses 42 or 43, tighten all relevant wiring connections or renew blower motor/s.

Symptom - Noisy Expansion Valve (Steady hissing)

POSSIBLE CAUSE	REMEDY
1. Low refrigerant charge; evident by bubbles in sight glass.	1. Test system for leaks; renew components as required.

Symptom - Insufficient Cooling

POSSIBLE CAUSE	REMEDY
1. Expansion valve not operating efficiently.	1. Renew expansion valve.
2. Low refrigerant charge; evident by bubbles in sight glass.	2. Test system for leaks. Evacuate system and renew components as required. Recharge system.
3. Compressor not pumping.	3. Renew compressor.

RV7019600025020X

Fig. 4 Refrigerant system troubleshooting (Part 2 of 2). New Range Rover

and moisture from A/C systems are commercially available. A specification for system pump down used here is 28-29½ inches vacuum. This reading can be attained at or near sea level only. For each 1000 feet of altitude this operation is performed, the reading will be 1 inch vacuum higher. For example, at 5000 feet elevation, only 23-24½ inches of vacuum can be obtained. **The system refrigerant must be completely recovered before it can be evacuated. Damage to the vacuum pump will result if pressurized refrigerant is allowed to enter.**

1. Connect vacuum pump to gauge manifold. With gauges connected into system, remove cap from vacuum hose connector. Install center hose from gauge manifold to vacuum pump connector mid-position high and low side compressor service valve (if used). Open high and low side gauge manifold hand valves.
2. Operate vacuum pump a minimum of 30 minutes for air and moisture removal. Watch compound gauge to see that system pumps down into a vacuum. System will reach 28-29½ inches Hg vacuum in a maximum of five minutes. If system does not pump down, check all connections and leak test if necessary.
3. Close gauge manifold hand valves and shutoff vacuum pump.
4. Check ability of system to hold vacuum. Watch compound gauge to see that gauge does not rise at a faster rate than one inch vacuum every four or five minutes. If compound gauge rises at too rapid a rate, install partial charge and leak test. Then recover refrigerant as outlined above.
5. If system holds vacuum, charge system with refrigerant

USING CHARGING STATION

A vacuum pump is built into the charging station and is constructed to withstand repeated and prolonged use without damage. Complete moisture removal from the system is possible only with a vacuum pump constructed for the purpose.

The system refrigerant must be completely recovered before it can be evacuated. Damage to the vacuum pump may result if pressurized refrigerant is allowed to enter.

1. Connect hose to vacuum pump, if system refrigerant was recovered through charging station.
2. Open low side gauge hand valve of charging station.
3. Connect station into 110 volt current.
4. Turn vacuum pump on according to instructions for specific station being used.
5. Evacuate system with the vacuum pump until the low pressure gauge reads at least 28 inches of vacuum. Continue evacuating system for an additional 15 minutes for routine system servicing or 20 to 30 minutes, if any parts have been replaced.
6. Close low side gauge hand valve, then turn vacuum pump off.
7. Check ability of system to hold vacuum. Watch low side gauge to see that gauge does not rise at a faster rate than one inch of vacuum every four to five minutes. If low side gauge rises at too rapid a rate, install partial charge and leak test. Then evacuate system again.
8. If system hold vacuum, charge system with refrigerant.

CHARGING SYSTEM

Use instructions provided with charging station. Follow these procedures to prevent charging station from being accidentally exposed to high-side vehicle system pressure:

1. Do not connect high pressure line to A/C system.
2. Always keep high pressure valve closed on charging station.
3. Perform all evacuation and charging through receiver/drier low-side pressure service fitting.

OIL CHARGE

Remove defective components. Add the proper amount of oil to each replacement component. Most recovery/recycling equipment will measure the amount of oil being removed. This is the amount of oil to be added back to the system, follow manufactures instructions provided with the recovery/recycling station.

A/C SPECIFICATIONS

Model	Year	Refrigerant		System Oil		Compressor Clutch Air Gap, Inch.
		Capacity, Lbs.	Type	Polyalkaline Glycol (PAG) Type	Total System Capacity, Oz.	
Discovery Less Rear A/C	1998-2001	1.98	R134a	ND Oil 8	—	—
Discovery w/Rear A/C	1998-2001	2.5	R134a	ND Oil 8	—	—
New Range Rover	1998–2001	2.76	R134a	Sanden SP10	—	—

Cooling Fans

NOTE: On Air Bag Equipped Models, Refer To "Air Bag System Precautions" Located In The Front Of This Manual For System Disarming & Arming Procedures.

INDEX

	Page No.
Component Replacement	4-27
Condenser Fan, Replace	4-27
Precautions	4-27
Air Bag Systems	4-27
Battery Ground Cable	4-27
System Diagnosis & Testing	4-27
A/C Mode	4-27
Condenser Fan Motor	4-27
Condenser Fan Relay	4-27
Fan Timer	4-27
Temperature Switch	4-27

PRECAUTIONS

AIR BAG SYSTEMS

Refer to "Air Bag System Precautions" in the front of this manual for system disarming and arming procedures.

BATTERY GROUND CABLE

Prior to service, disconnect battery ground cable and isolate as required.

SYSTEM DIAGNOSIS & TESTING

CONDENSER FAN RELAY

For condenser fan relay testing refer to Test A, **Fig. 1.**

A/C MODE

For A/C mode testing refer to Test C, **Fig. 2.**

CONDENSER FAN MOTOR

For condenser fan motor testing refer to Test E, **Fig. 3.**

TEMPERATURE SWITCH

For temperature switch testing refer to Test F, **Fig. 4.**

FAN TIMER

For fan timer testing refer to Test G, **Fig. 5.**

COMPONENT REPLACEMENT

CONDENSER FAN, REPLACE

Discovery

1. Remove condenser as described in "Component Replacement & Adjustment" section.
2. Remove bolts mounting fan cowl to condenser, then remove bolts mounting fan motor to cowl.
3. Remove fan motor assembly, then remove fan blade mounting screws and blades.
4. Reverse procedure to install.

New Range Rover

1. Remove screws and grille, then raise and support vehicle.
2. Disconnect fog lamp connectors and breather hoses, then release clips mounting bumper ends to mounting brackets.
3. Remove bolt access plugs from valance and bolts, then remove bumper assembly.
4. Lower vehicle, then recover refrigerant as outlined in "Air Conditioning" section.
5. Remove mounting bolts, release hood release cable and remove hood.
6. Disconnect electrical connectors, remove mounting bolts and condenser cooling fans.
7. Reverse procedure to install.

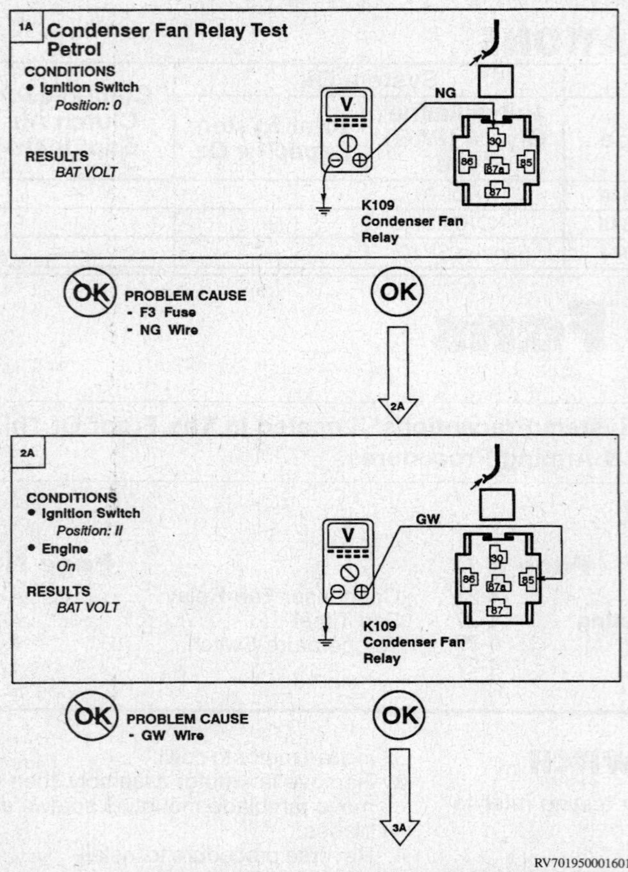

Fig. 1 Test A: Condenser Fan Relay (Part 1 of 2)

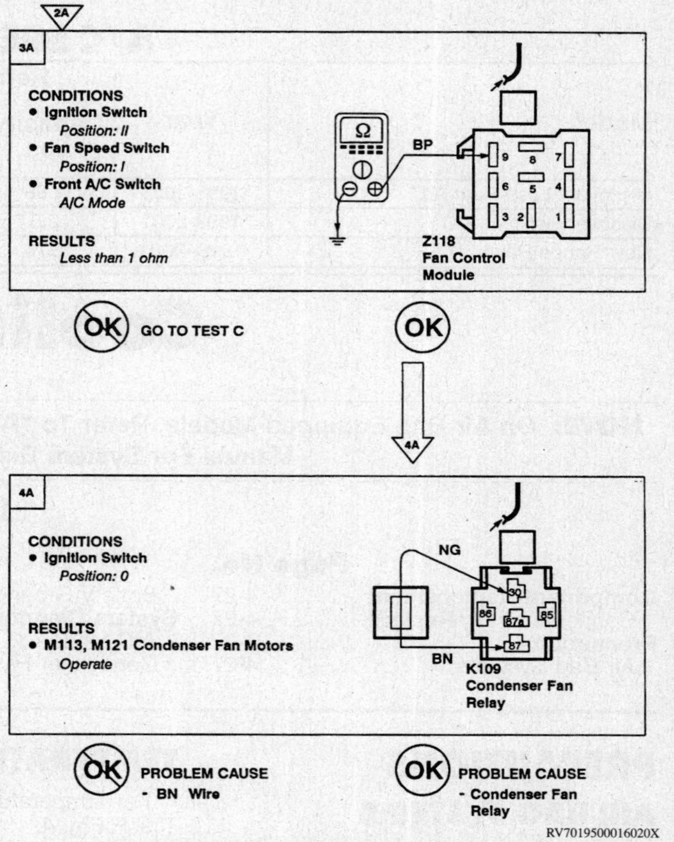

Fig. 1 Test A: Condenser Fan Relay (Part 2 of 2)

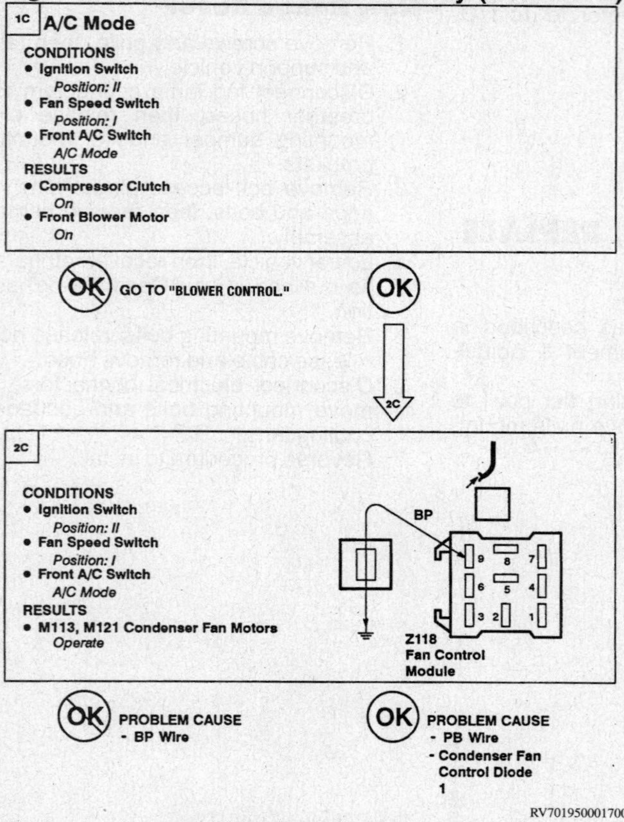

Fig. 2 Test C: A/C Mode

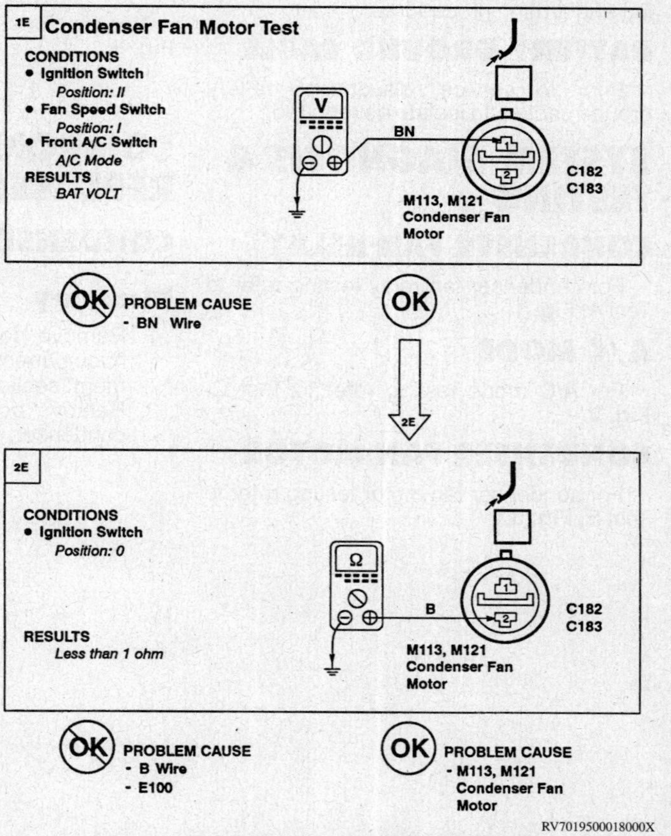

Fig. 3 Test E: Condenser Fan Motor

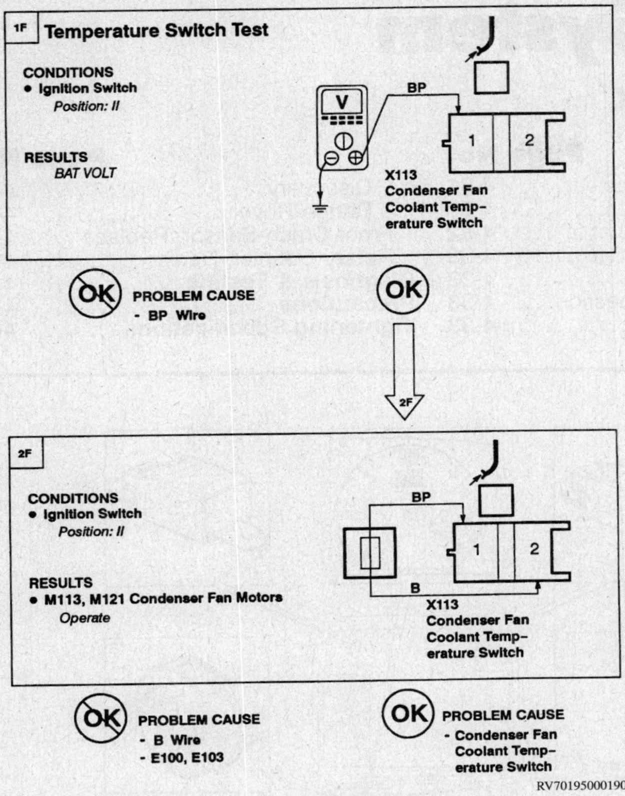

Fig. 4 Test F: Temperature Switch

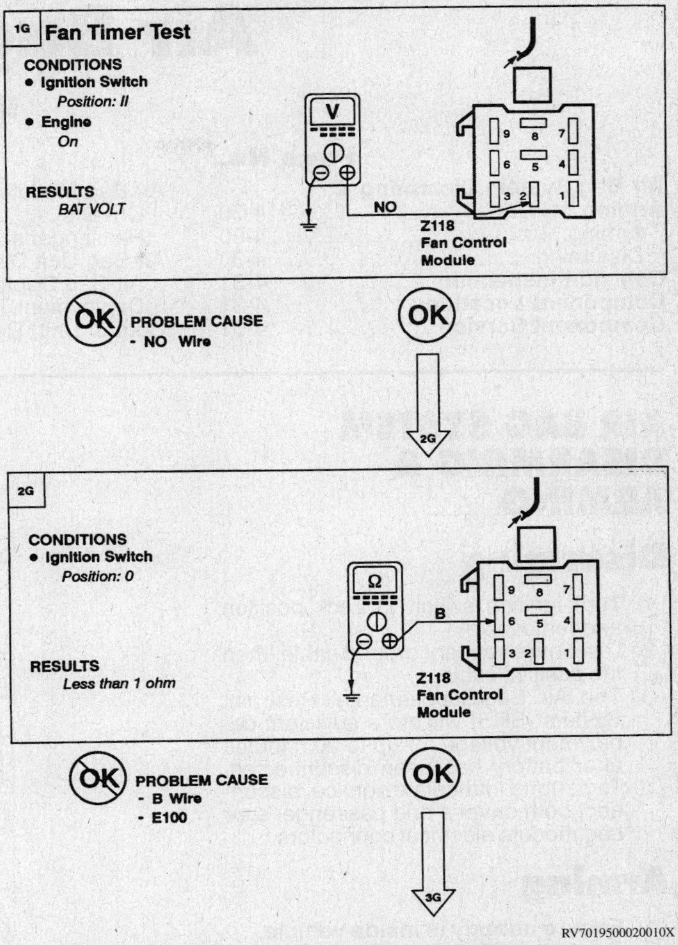

Fig. 5 Test G: Fan Timer (Part 1 of 3)

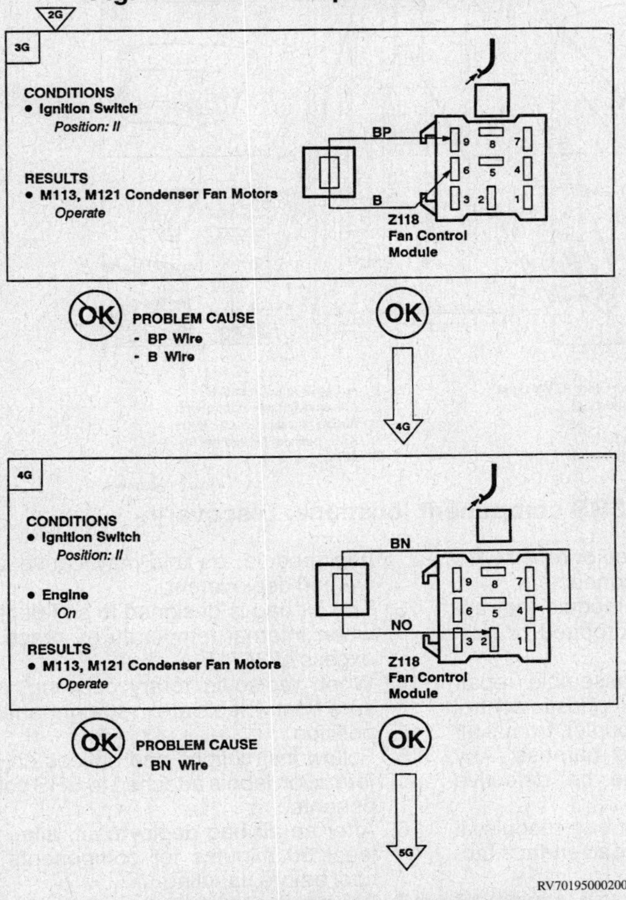

Fig. 5 Test G: Fan Timer (Part 2 of 3)

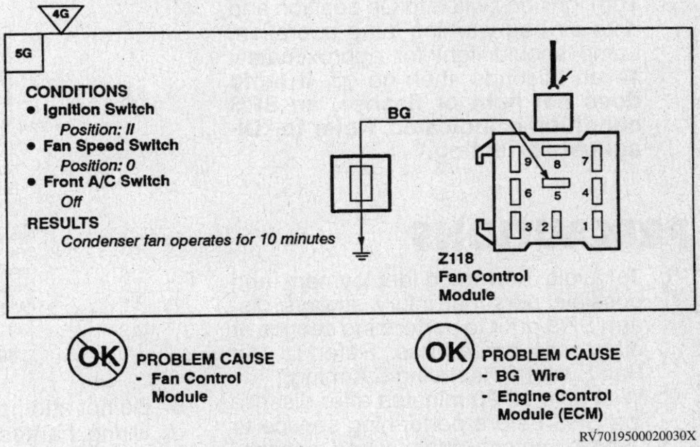

Fig. 5 Test G: Fan Timer (Part 3 of 3)

Air Bag System

INDEX

	Page No.
Air Bag System Disarming & Arming	4-30
Arming	4-30
Disarming	4-30
Collision Inspection	4-31
Component Locations	4-31
Component Service	4-31
Air Bag Module, Replace	4-31
Driver's	4-31
Passenger's	4-32
Air Bag Unit Disposal	4-33
Air Bag Deployment	4-33
Deployment Tool Inspection	4-33
Control Unit, Replace	4-33
Discovery	4-33
Range Rover	4-33
Front Crash Sensor, Replace	4-32
Rotary Coupler, Replace	4-32
Diagnosis & Testing	4-31
Precautions	4-30
Tightening Specifications	4-35

AIR BAG SYSTEM DISARMING & ARMING

Disarming

1. Turn ignition switch to Lock position and remove key.
2. Disconnect battery ground cable, then the positive cable.
3. The Air Bag/Supplemental Restraint System (SRS) will store sufficient deployment voltage for up to 20 minutes after battery has been disconnected. To perform immediate service, disconnect both driver's and passenger's air bag module electrical connectors.

Arming

1. **Ensure nobody is inside vehicle.**
2. Connect battery positive cable, then the ground cable.
3. Turn ignition switch to On position and note air bag warning lamp operation. Lamp should light for approximately seven seconds, then go off. **If lamp does not light or flashes, an SRS condition is indicated. Refer to "Diagnosis & Testing."**

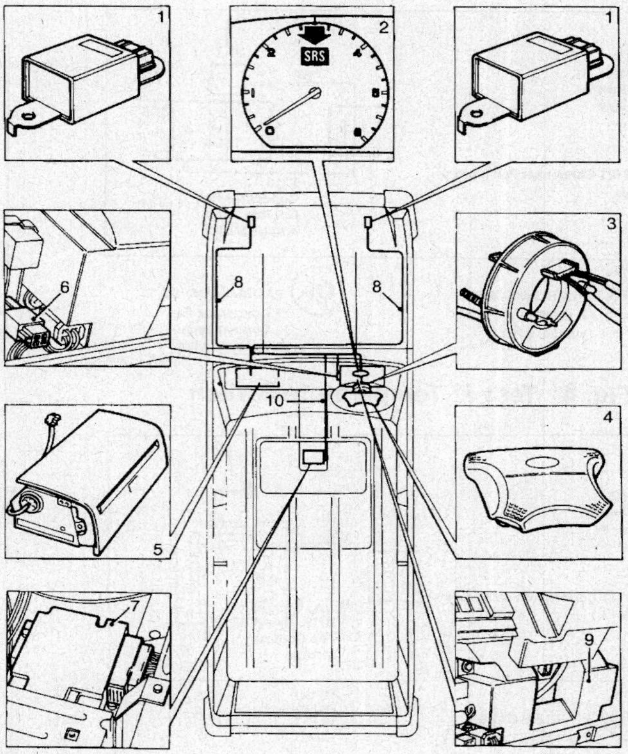

1. Airbag crash sensors (pre 97MY only)
2. SRS warning light (airbag)
3. Rotary coupler
4. Driver's airbag module
5. Passenger's airbag module
6. Airbag diagnostic socket
7. Airbag diagnostic control unit
8. Airbag harness (Pre 97 MY)
9. Knee bolsters (where fitted)
10. Airbag harness

RV8019800027000X

Fig. 1 SRS component locations. Discovery

PRECAUTIONS

1. To avoid unwanted deployment and possible personal injury, always disarm SRS prior to performing service or diagnostic procedures. Refer to "Air Bag System Disarming & Arming."
2. Wait at least 20 minutes after disarming SRS before performing service to vehicle, unless driver's and passenger's air bags have been disconnected from system.
3. Always remove key from ignition prior to servicing vehicle.
4. When troubleshooting SRS, always inspect Diagnostic Trouble Codes (DTCs) prior to disconnecting battery.
5. Never use SRS components from another vehicle. Always install new components.
6. Do not paint air bag to correct cosmetic flaws. It must be replaced.
7. SRS wiring can be identified by a special yellow outer protective covering.
8. Do not attempt to splice or repair SRS wiring, harnesses or connectors.
9. Replace any air bag module that appears to have been dropped or mishandled.
10. Do not attempt to disassemble, repair or tamper with SRS diagnostic control unit, module, rotary coupler, frontal air bag sensor or wiring harness. Any components found to be defective must be replaced.
11. When handling an air bag module, it should be placed with pad surface facing upward.
12. Never use electrical test equipment such as analog ohmmeters on an air bag module, as this may cause unwanted deployment.
13. The air bag is designed to self-deploy when internal temperatures reach in excess of 347° F.
14. When replacing rotary coupling, ensure front wheels are in straight-ahead position.
15. Follow instructions and notices on information labels attached to SRS components.
16. After an air bag deployment, allow at least 30 minutes for components to cool before handling.
17. Always store air bags in a secure area, such as an approved steel cabinet.

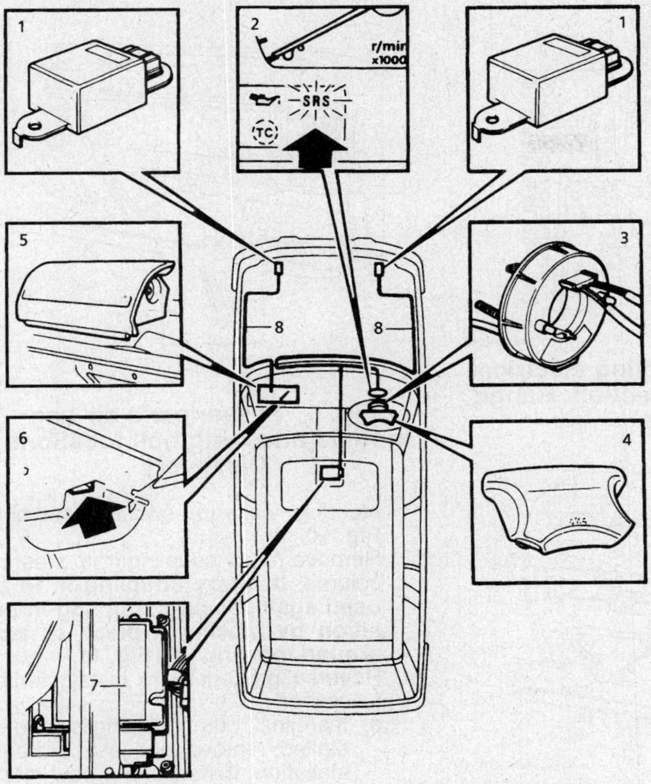

1. Airbag crash sensors
2. SRS warning light (airbag)
3. Rotary coupler
4. Driver's airbag module
5. Passenger's airbag module
6. Airbag diagnostic socket
7. Airbag diagnostic control unit
8. Airbag harness

RV8019700025000X

Fig. 2 SRS component locations w/front sensors. Range Rover

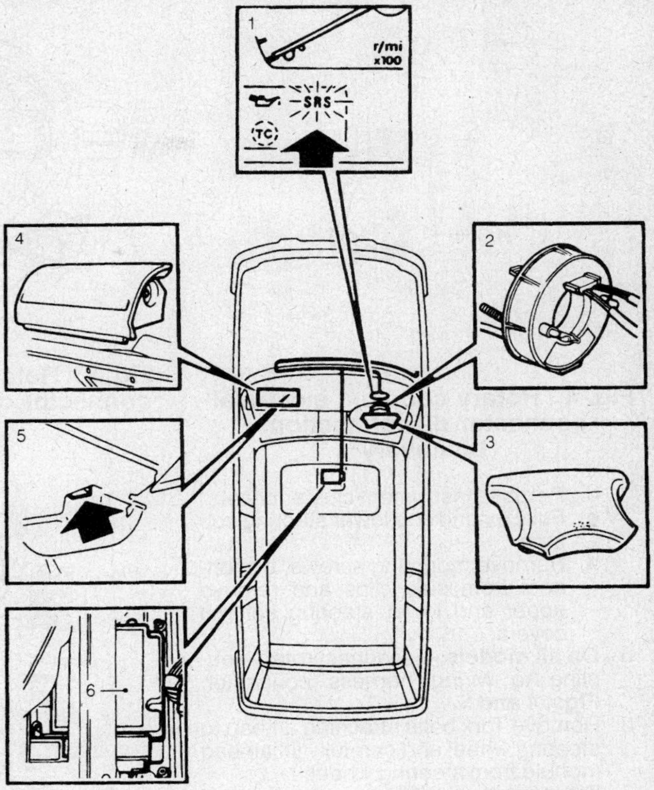

1. SRS warning light (airbag)
2. Rotary coupler
3. Driver's airbag module
4. Passenger's airbag module
5. Airbag diagnostic socket
6. Airbag diagnostic control unit (DCU)

RV8019700026000X

Fig. 3 SRS component locations less front sensors. Range Rover

18. Do not allow heat, grease, oil, detergents or water to contact air bag.
19. Avoid direct exposure of sensors and wiring harness to heat guns, welding equipment or spraying equipment.
20. Ensure all SRS wiring harnesses are properly routed and that all connectors are properly seated.
21. When installing a replacement front sensor, use only mounting screws supplied with sensor. Tighten front, then the rear mounting bolt to specifications.
22. Wear gloves, safety glasses and protective clothing with long sleeves when handling deployed air bag module components, as materials emitted during deployment may irritate eyes, nose, throat and skin. If materials contact skin, run cool water over affected area. If nasal or throat irritation is experienced, exit vehicle for fresh air until irritation ceases. If irritation continues, seek medical attention.
23. Ensure no people, animals or objects are inside vehicle before arming SRS.

COMPONENT LOCATIONS

Refer to **Figs. 1 through 3** for SRS component locations. (Illustrations are for right-hand drive models.)

DIAGNOSIS & TESTING

The SRS diagnosis unit fault code memory can only be accessed by using Land Rover Test Book, or equivalent. For system diagnosis, follow tester tool manufacturer's instructions.

COLLISION INSPECTION

On vehicles that have experienced an SRS deployment, certain system components must be replaced. To determine which components require replacement, refer to the "General Information" section located at the front of this manual.

To ensure proper SRS operation on a vehicle involved in a collision, perform procedures as outlined under "Diagnosis & Testing."

COMPONENT SERVICE

Air Bag Module, Replace

DRIVER'S

1. **On Discovery models,** position steering wheel 90° from straight-ahead position.
2. **On all models,** disarm SRS as outlined under "Air Bag System Disarming & Arming."
3. **On Discovery models,** remove lower lefthand instrument panel cover.
4. **On Range Rover models,** proceed as follows:
   a. Remove fascia closing panel covers and mounting screws.
   b. Disconnect driver's lap vent duct and fascia closing panel.
   c. Remove instrument cluster bezel mounting screws and disconnect fuel filter door release switch connector.

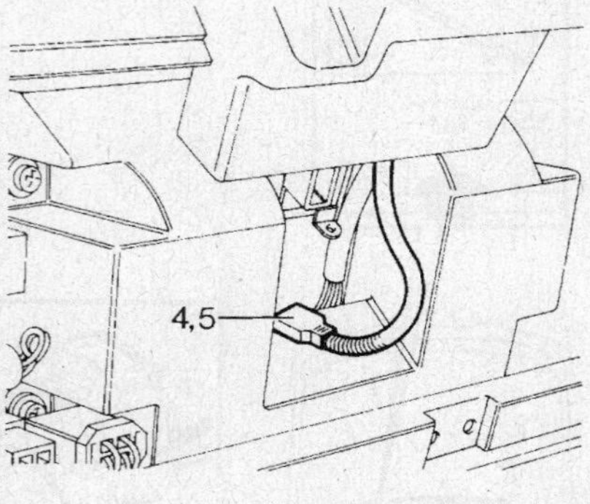

RV8019400003000X

Fig. 4 Rotary coupling electrical connector disconnection. Discovery

d. Remove instrument cluster bezel.
e. Fully extend and lower steering column.
f. Remove mounting screws, disconnect from side clips and remove upper and lower steering column covers.

5. **On all models,** disconnect rotary coupling to wiring harness connector, **Figs. 4 and 5.**
6. Remove Torx bolts attaching air bag to steering wheel and carefully lift air bag module from steering wheel.
7. Disconnect electrical connector, remove air bag module and position in a secure, clean, dry location with pad side facing upward.
8. Reverse procedure to install. Tighten attaching bolts to specifications.

PASSENGER'S

DISCOVERY

1. Disarm SRS as outlined under "Air Bag System Disarming & Arming."
2. Open glove compartment and disconnect connector.
3. Remove front and rear Torx bolts attaching air bag to instrument panel, **Fig. 6.**
4. Carefully lift air bag from instrument panel, **Fig. 7,** and position in a secure, clean, dry location with pad side facing upward.
5. Remove air bag module.
6. Reverse procedure to install. Tighten attaching bolts to specifications.

RANGE ROVER

1. Disarm SRS as outlined under "Air Bag System Disarming & Arming."
2. Remove fasteners and access panel, then the glove compartment hinge bolts.
3. Open glove compartment, remove mounting screws and release compartment from fascia.
4. Disconnect lamp connector and cable latch.
5. Remove glove compartment, then disconnect passenger's air bag module electrical connector, **Fig. 8.**
6. Remove Torx bolts attaching air bag to instrument panel.
7. Carefully lift air bag module from instrument panel, then disconnect connector.
8. Remove air bag module, **Fig. 9,** and position in a secure, clean, dry location with pad side facing upward.
9. Reverse procedure to install. Tighten mounting bolts to specifications.

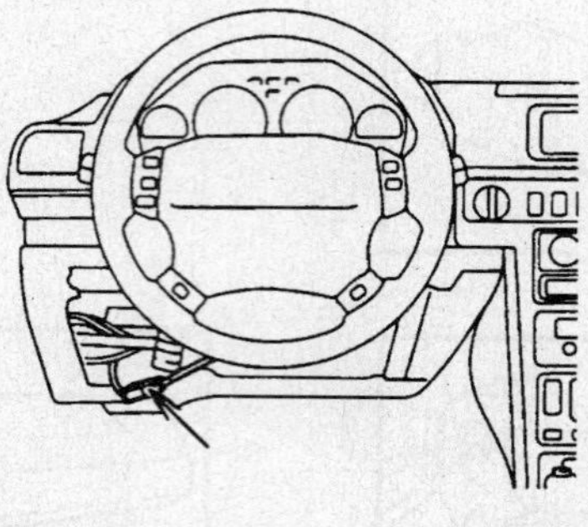

RV8019400004000X

Fig. 5 Rotary coupling electrical connector disconnection. Range Rover

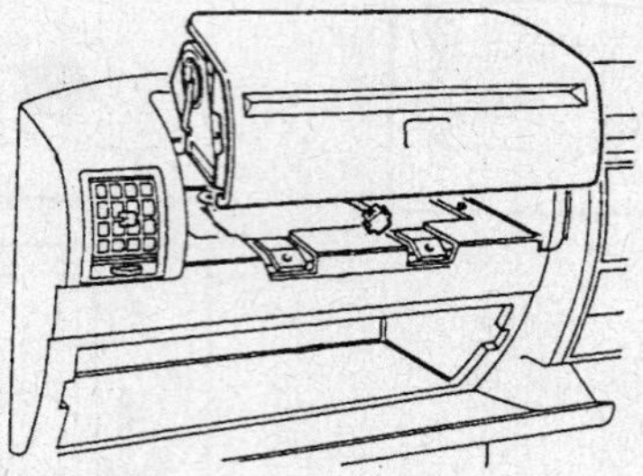

RV8019400007000X

Fig. 7 Passenger's air bag module removal. Discovery

Rotary Coupler, Replace

1. Place front wheels in straight-ahead position.
2. Disarm SRS as outlined under "Air Bag System Disarming & Arming."
3. Remove driver's air bag module as outlined under "Air Bag Module, Replace."
4. Disconnect speed control electrical connector from rotary coupling, if equipped, and release wiring harness clip on steering wheel.
5. Loosen but do not remove steering wheel retaining nut.
6. Release steering wheel from taper, remove steering wheel retaining nut and washer.
7. Remove wheel from column.
8. Feed wiring harness through hole in steering wheel, then remove wheel.
9. Remove turnbuckles and lower instrument panel.
10. Remove lower and upper steering column covers.
11. Disconnect rotary coupling connectors.
12. Release two rotary coupling clips from steering column switch assembly, **Fig. 10.**
13. Remove rotary coupling from steering column. **If rotary coupling is to be used again, secure coupling in position by placing a piece of tape around molding (A), Fig. 11.**
14. Reverse procedure to install, noting following:
    a. If original rotary coupling is to be installed, remove tape just before installation. If installing a new rotary coupling, ensure sealing tape is not broken, **Fig. 12.**
    b. If necessary, center rotary coupling. Rotate rotary coupling counterclockwise until resistance is encountered. Turn rotary coupling 2½ turns in the clockwise direction to center.
    c. Ensure rotary coupling electrical connectors are securely installed.
    d. After completing rotary coupling and steering wheel installation, cycle steering wheel from lock to lock approximately five times and note operation. If steering feels heavy or if noise is present, replace rotary coupler.

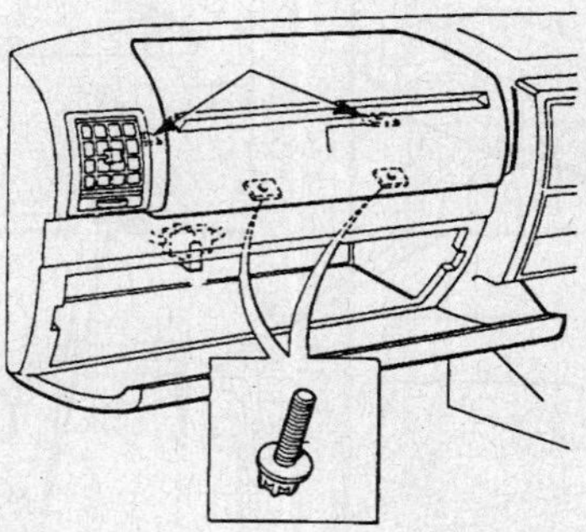

RV8019400006000X

Fig. 6 Passenger's air bag module attaching bolt locations. Discovery

Front Crash Sensor, Replace

1. Disarm SRS as outlined under "Air Bag System Disarming & Arming."
2. Disconnect sensor electrical connector.
3. Remove mounting bolts and front crash sensor.
4. Remove front crash sensor.
5. Reverse procedure to install, noting the following:
    a. Ensure sensor electrical connectors are securely installed.
    b. If equipped with markings, ensure sensor is installed with arrow marking facing toward front.
    c. Ensure front crash sensor is properly mounted to body with no gaps between sensor and body, **Fig. 13.**
    d. Tighten front then rear mounting bolt to specifications. Use only

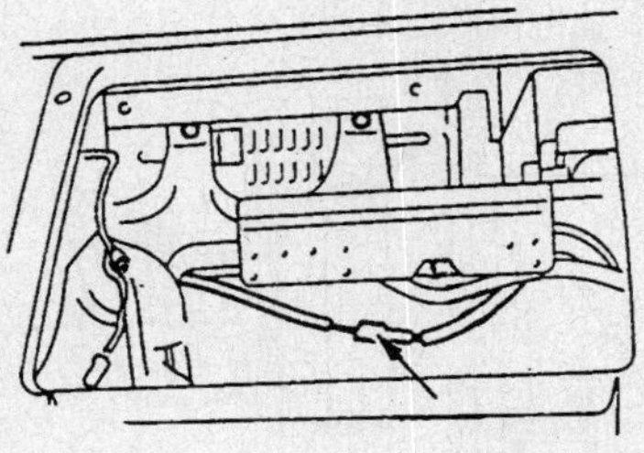

RV8019400008000X

Fig. 8 Passenger's air bag module electrical connector location. Range Rover

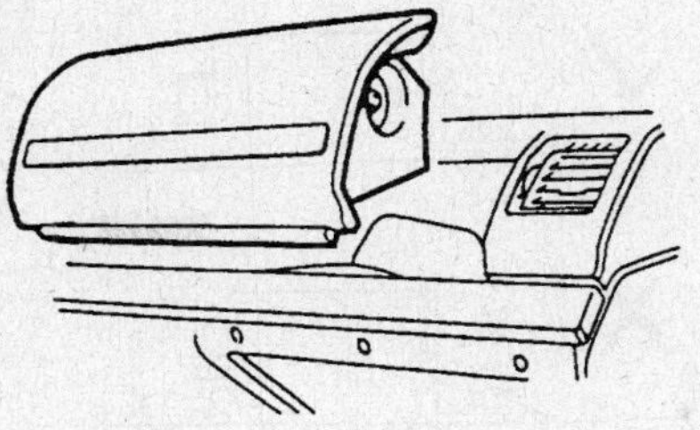

RV8019400009000X

Fig. 9 Passenger's air bag module removal. Range Rover

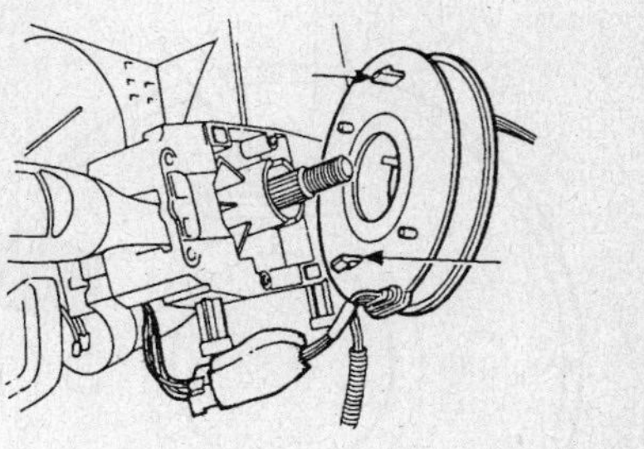

RV8019400010000X

Fig. 10 Rotary coupling clip locations

mounting bolts supplied with sensor.

Control Unit, Replace

DISCOVERY

1. Disarm SRS as outlined under "Air Bag System Disarming & Arming."
2. Remove transfer and transmission selector lever and knob assembly.
3. Remove center console rubber mat and switch panel mounting screws.
4. Disconnect electrical connector and remove switch panel.
5. Release electric front seat switches, disconnect connectors and remove.
6. Release hand brake, and remove parking cable clip and clevis pin.
7. Remove center console mounting screws, raise hand brake lever and pull center console to rear for access.
8. Disconnect cigarette and bulb connector, and remove center console assembly.
9. Disconnect electrical connector from control unit.
10. Remove two mounting screws and control unit.
11. Reverse procedure to install. Tighten mounting screws to specifications.

RANGE ROVER

1. Disarm SRS as outlined under "Air Bag System Disarming & Arming."
2. Remove mounting screws, release electric window switch pack and disconnect connectors.
3. Remove electric window switch pack over hand brake.
4. Disconnect rear footwell lamp connect and remove console bin base.
5. Remove center console mounting screws and move front seats fully rearward.
6. Remove mounting screws, release clips and remove side panels.
7. Remove rear mounting screws and raise transmission selector lever finish panel rear to disengage front clips.
8. Disconnect cigarette lighter and lamp connectors, and remove transmission selector lever finish panel.
9. **On models equipped with manual transmission,** remove selector lever knob, then the center console mounting bolts.
10. **On models equipped with automatic transmission,** remove mounting bolts and selector lever, then the mounting screws, electric connector and selector graphic plate.

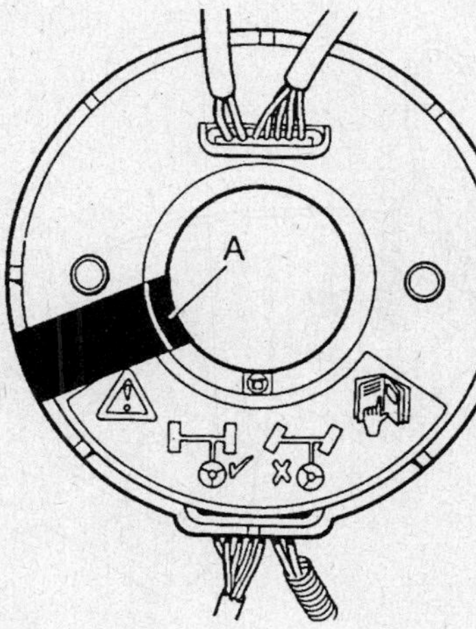

RV8019400011000X

Fig. 11 Rotary coupling clip in position

11. **On all models,** remove parking brake lever clip and clevis pin, and raise lever to vertical position.
12. Raise center console rear to disengage rear vent ducts and remove console.
13. Lift sound deadener pad rear from transmission tunnel and disconnect control module connector.
14. Disconnect connectors from bracket, **Fig. 14.**
15. Remove mounting bolts and control unit.
16. Reverse procedure to install. Tighten mounting bolts to specifications.

Air Bag Unit Disposal

When handling a deployed air bag assembly, a face shield and rubber gloves should be worn. If sinus or throat irritation is encountered during air bag removal, exit vehicle and breathe fresh air. If skin irritation is encountered, flush affected area with cool water. If any type of irritation continues, consult a physician. Wash hands and rinse thoroughly with water after handling a deployed air bag assembly.

A deployed air bag unit should be removed as outlined under "Air Bag Unit, Replace." Wait at least 30 minutes before handling a deployed air bag

Any undeployed air bag unit must be deployed prior to disposal.

1. Place tape over air bag exhaust vents so no additional powder will escape into vehicle.
2. Remove air bag from vehicle as outlined under "Component Service."
3. Place deployed air bag in a sturdy, sealed vinyl bag for disposal with other automotive scrap.
4. Use a vacuum cleaner to remove residual powder from vehicle interior. Work from outside to center of vehicle.
5. Vacuum HVAC ducts.
6. Run blower motor at low speed and vacuum any powder expelled from the plenum.
7. It may be necessary to vacuum vehicle a second time to ensure all powder is recovered.

DEPLOYMENT TOOL INSPECTION

1. Insert deployment tool No. SMD 4082/1, or equivalent, blue and yellow connectors into corresponding tool sockets, **Fig. 15.**
2. Connect red deployment tool lead to battery positive post and black lead to battery negative post.
3. Deployment tool red READY lamp should light.
4. Depress and hold both tool buttons.
5. Tool's green DEFECTIVE lamp should light.
6. Release buttons and red lamp should light.
7. Disconnect leads from battery and tool.

AIR BAG DEPLOYMENT

INSIDE VEHICLE

Driver's

1. Disarm SRS as outlined under "Air Bag System Disarming & Arming."
2. Open vehicle windows and doors, then remove battery from vehicle.
3. Remove lefthand lower instrument panel trim cover and knee bolster.
4. Disconnect driver's air bag module electrical connector.
5. Connect deployment harness tool No. SMD 4082/5, or equivalent, to air bag

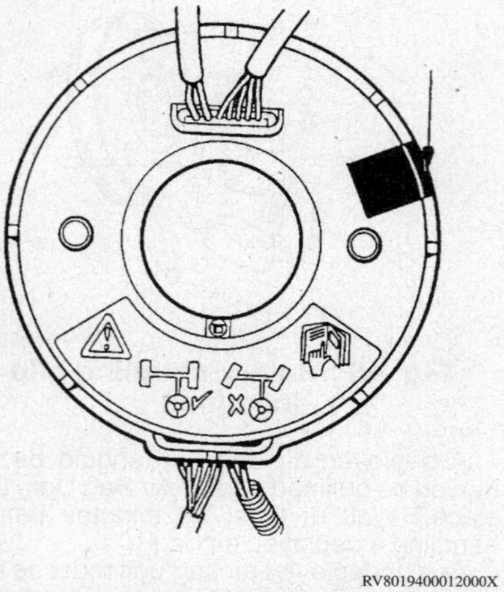

Fig. 12 Rotary coupling tape inspection

steering column harness connector, then uncoil harness and route as far away from vehicle as possible.
6. Position a fully charged 12 volt battery and deployment tool away from vehicle.
7. Ensure battery is not connected to deployment tool, then connect deployment harness to tool.
8. At a location as far away from vehicle as possible, connect deployment tool to battery positive, then negative posts, **Fig. 16.**
9. Ensure no people, animals or objects are within 45 ft. of vehicle.
10. Depress both tool buttons to deploy air bag. **Allow deployed components 30 minutes to cool.**
11. **If air bag fails to deploy, do not go near module. Contact Land Rover dealer for disposal procedures.**

Passenger's

1. Disarm SRS as outlined under "Air Bag System Disarming & Arming."
2. Open vehicle windows and doors, then remove battery from vehicle.
3. Remove glove compartment, release and disconnect air bag connector.
4. Connect deployment harness tool No. SMD 4082/5, or equivalent, to air bag connector, then uncoil harness and route as far away from vehicle as possible.
5. Position a fully charged 12 volt battery and deployment tool away from vehicle.
6. Ensure battery is not connected to deployment tool, then connect deployment harness to tool.
7. At a location as far away from vehicle as possible, connect deployment tool to battery positive, then negative posts.
8. Ensure no people, animals or objects are within 45 ft. of vehicle.
9. Depress both tool buttons to deploy air bag. **Allow deployed components 30 minutes to cool.**

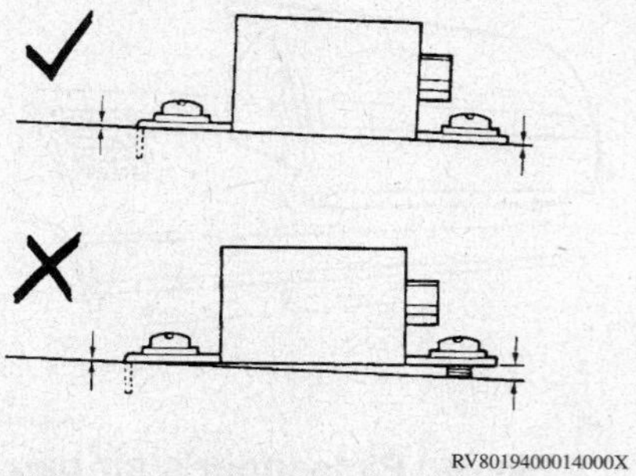

Fig. 13 Front crash sensor installation

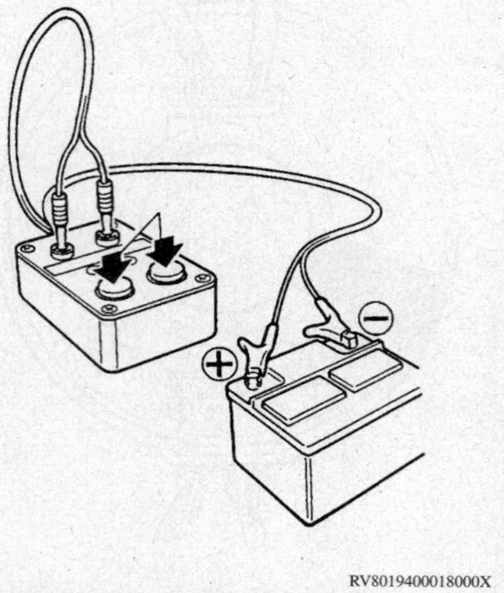

Fig. 15 Air bag module deployment tool inspection

10. **If air bag fails to deploy, do not go near module. Contact Land Rover dealer for disposal procedures.**

OUTSIDE VEHICLE

Driver's

1. Disarm SRS as outlined under "Air Bag System Disarming & Arming."
2. Remove module as outlined under "Air Bag Module, Replace."
3. Position air bag deployment bracket tool No. SMD 4082/6, or equivalent, in a suitable vise. **Ensure vise jaws grip tool above bottom flange, then tighten vise.**
4. Position air bag bracket tools No. SMD 4082/7, or equivalent, to tool and lightly tighten bolts.
5. Position air bag module to tool and secure with attachments.
6. Ensure air bag module and tool are secure.
7. Connect deployment harness tool No. SMD 4082/4, or equivalent, to air bag electrical connector.
8. Ensure battery is not connected to deployment tool, then connect deployment harness to tool.
9. At a location as far away from air bag module as possible, connect deployment tool to a fully charged 12 volt bat-

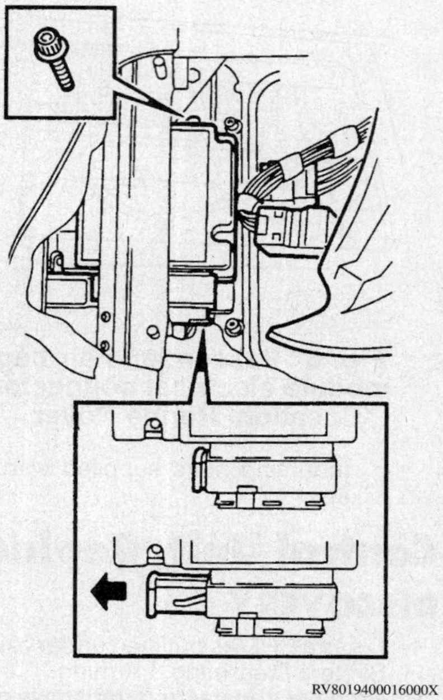

Fig. 14 Control unit replacement. Range Rover

tery positive, then negative posts.
10. Ensure no people, animals or objects are within 45 ft. of air bag unit.
11. Depress both tool buttons to deploy air bag. **Allow 30 minutes for deployed components to cool.**
12. **If air bag fails to deploy, do not go near module. Contact Land Rover dealer for disposal procedures.**

Passenger's

1. Disarm SRS as outlined under "Air Bag System Disarming & Arming."
2. Remove module as outlined under "Driver's Air Bag Module, Replace."
3. Position air bag deployment bracket tool No. SMD 4082/7, or equivalent, in a suitable vise. **Ensure vise jaws grip tool above bottom flange, then tighten vise.**
4. Position air bag to tool and secure with attachments.
5. Ensure air bag module and tool are secure.
6. Connect deployment harness tool No. SMD 4082/4, or equivalent, to air bag electrical connector.
7. Ensure battery is not connected to deployment tool, then connect deployment harness to tool.
8. At a location as far away from air bag module as possible, connect deployment tool to a fully charged 12 volt battery positive, then negative posts.
9. Ensure no people, animals or objects are within 45 ft. of air bag unit.
10. Depress both tool buttons to deploy air bag. **Allow 30 minutes for deployed components to cool.**
11. **If air bag fails to deploy, do not go near module. Contact Land Rover dealer for disposal procedures.**

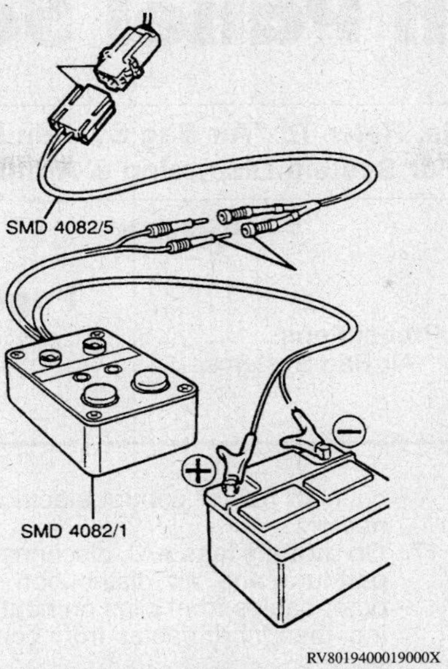

Fig. 16 Air bag deployment tool connections

TIGHTENING SPECIFICATIONS

Year	Component	Torque/ Ft. Lbs.
DISCOVERY		
1998–2001	Air Bag Diagnosis Control Unit	7
	Air Bag Module, Driver's	5.9
	Air Bag Module, Passenger's	5.9
	Steering Wheel Nut	37
RANGE ROVER		
1998–2001	Air Bag Module, Driver's	7
	Air Bag Module, Passenger's	7
	Steering Wheel Bolt	24

Dash Panel Service

NOTE: On Air Bag Equipped Models, Refer To "Air Bag System Precautions" Located In The Front Of This Manual For System Disarming & Arming Procedures.

INDEX

	Page No.
Dash Panel, Replace	4-36
Discovery	4-36
Range Rover	4-36
Precautions	4-36
Air Bag Systems	4-36
Battery Ground Cable	4-36
Microprocessor Radios	4-36

PRECAUTIONS

AIR BAG SYSTEMS

Refer to "Air Bag System Precautions" in the front of this manual for system disarming and arming procedures.

MICROPROCESSOR RADIOS

On models equipped with microprocessor radios, always switch radio off before disconnecting or connecting battery ground cable to prevent damage to the radio.

BATTERY GROUND CABLE

Prior to service, disconnect battery ground cable and isolate as required.

DASH PANEL

REPLACE

DISCOVERY

1. Remove radio cassette player.
2. Remove steering wheel.
3. Remove steering column cover.
4. Remove center console.
5. Remove "A" pillar trim panels.
6. Remove six lower panel to dash panel attaching clips.
7. Remove two instrument cowl screws from clips on dash panel.
8. Disconnect electrical connectors from switches in instrument cowl, then remove cowl.
9. Remove four gauge assembly to instrument panel attaching screws.
10. Disconnect two electrical connectors from gauge assembly and remove assembly.
11. Remove instrument panel access panel.
12. Remove four steering column bracket to instrument panel retaining nuts.
13. Disconnect three main body harness to instrument panel harness electrical connectors.
14. Disconnect instrument panel electrical connector from fuse panel.
15. Remove four glove box retaining bolts, then box.
16. **On models equipped with A/C,** disconnect heater control electrical connector.
17. **On models less A/C,** disconnect temperature and air distribution control outer cables from clips on heater casing, then inner cables from control levers.
18. **On all models,** Separate blue section from In Car Entertainment (ICE) electrical connector.
19. Disconnect coaxial cables from instrument panel.
20. Disconnect electrical connector from passenger side air bag module.
21. Disconnect electrical connector from blower motor.
22. Working through glove box opening, remove air bag module attaching bolts.
23. Remove four lower instrument panel to transmission tunnel mounting bracket bolts.
24. Remove four lower instrument panel to "A" pillar bracket attaching bolts.
25. Remove instrument panel from vehicle.
26. Reverse procedure to install. Note that if renewing instrument panel, transfer old components to new panel as necessary.

RANGE ROVER

1. Drain cooling system.
2. Loosen heater pipe attaching clips, then disconnect hoses.
3. Remove center console.
4. Remove steering column.
5. Remove wiper motor and linkage.
6. Disconnect passenger side heated front screen electrical connector, then release connector from clip.
7. Remove six side panel attaching bolts, then panel.
8. Remove heater intake pollen filters.
9. Remove eight pollen filter housing attaching screws, then housing.
10. Remove radio.
11. Remove door opening seal adjacent to "A" pillar lower trim panels.
12. Remove three foot rest attaching bolts through "A" pillar lower trim, then foot rest.
13. Remove both "A" pillar lower trim panel attaching screws, then pull panel to disconnect clip.
14. Remove fuse cover from driver's site seat base trim.
15. Remove screw and two trim studs, then seat base trim.
16. Remove four clips, then driver's side carpet retainer.
17. Remove two fasteners attaching lower closing panel to passenger side of instrument panel.
18. Disconnect footwell lamp and diagnostic electrical connector, then remove closing panel.
19. Remove four instrument panel center bracket attaching bolts, then bracket.
20. Disconnect four Body Electrical Control Module (BECM) electrical connectors.
21. Remove ground wire attaching nut at base of driver's side "A" pillar, then disconnect ground wire from stud.
22. Disconnect electrical connectors at base of "A" pillars.
23. Disconnect BECM harness from sill, then route into instrument panel to prevent fouling as panel is removed.
24. Disconnect electrical connectors and vacuum hose from brake and clutch switches.
25. Disconnect air bag module electrical connector from main harness.
26. Disconnect electrical connector from SRS control module
27. Remove both front wheel arch liners.
28. Remove two air cleaner baffle fasteners from beneath lefthand side wheel arch, then baffle.
29. Disconnect both air bag crash sensor electrical connectors.
30. Remove four battery tray attaching bolts and two air cleaner to valance attaching bolts.
31. Raise air cleaner and battery tray for access to crash sensor harness clips.
32. Disconnect clips attaching each crash sensor harness to valance.
33. Remove harness grommets and feed both harnesses through valance into wheel arches.
34. **On models equipped with A/C:** proceed as follows:
    a. Evacuate and recover refrigerant from A/C system.
    b. Remove bolt securing pipe clamp

to Thermostatic Expansion Valve (TXV).

c. Disconnect pipes from TXV and remove O-rings, then seal pipes and ports of TXV.

35. **On all models,** remove four instrument panel to firewall attaching bolts.
36. Remove instrument panel to base of "A" pillar retaining nuts and washers.
37. Remove instrument panel to pedal box attaching bolt.
38. Remove instrument panel out through driver's side doorway.
39. Remove rubber seals from air intake ducts.
40. Remove rear heater duct connecting tubes.
41. Reverse procedure to install. Note that if renewing instrument panel, transfer old components to new panel as necessary.

Steering Columns

NOTE: On Air Bag Equipped Models, Refer To "Air Bag System Precautions" Located In The Front Of This Manual For System Disarming & Arming Procedures.

INDEX

	Page No.
Precautions	4-37
Air Bag Systems	4-37
Battery Ground Cable	4-37
Microprocessor Radios	4-37
Steering Column, Replace	4-37
Discovery	4-37
Range Rover	4-37

PRECAUTIONS

AIR BAG SYSTEMS

Refer to "Air Bag System Precautions" in the front of this manual for system disarming and arming procedures.

MICROPROCESSOR RADIOS

On models equipped with microprocessor radios, always switch radio off before disconnecting or connecting battery ground cable to prevent damage to the radio.

BATTERY GROUND CABLE

Prior to service, disconnect battery ground cable and isolate as required.

STEERING COLUMN

REPLACE

DISCOVERY

1. Remove steering column intermediate shaft.
2. Remove rotary coupler.
3. Open instrument panel lower access panel.
4. Remove steering column covers.
5. Disconnect electrical connectors illumination bulb from passive coil and remove passive coil.
6. Disconnect two electrical connectors from wiper switch assembly.
7. Disconnect two electrical connectors from light switch assembly.
8. Loosen screw and remove switch assembly.
9. Disconnect ignition switch electrical connector.
10. Disconnect electrical from ignition switch housing.
11. Disconnect harness from column clip.
12. Remove four steering column assembly to instrument panel rail attaching nuts, then steering column.
13. Reverse procedure to install.

RANGE ROVER

1. Remove intermediate steering shaft.
2. Remove four knee bolster panel attaching screws from under steering column.
3. Disconnect footwell lamp electrical connector, then remove knee bolster from instrument panel.
4. Remove steering column covers.
5. Remove indicator switch stalk to column attaching screws.
6. Remove wiper switch stalk to column attaching screws.
7. Remove ignition switch, "key in" sensor, rotary coupler and air bag system electrical connectors.
8. Remove two clips securing air bag harness to steering column harness.
9. Remove clip securing harness to column.
10. Remove illumination bulb then harness from retaining clip.
11. Disconnect electrical connector from ignition shift interlock solenoid.
12. Remove duct from driver's side blower motor housing.
13. Remove duct from heater unit.
14. Remove two steering column to firewall attaching bolts.
15. Remove two nuts and two bolts attaching steering column to pedal box.
16. Remove steering column assembly.
17. Reverse procedure to install.

Disc Brakes

INDEX

	Page No.
Brake Pad Service	4-38
Replacement	4-38
Brake System Bleed	4-38
Discovery	4-38
Range Rover	4-38
Caliper Service	4-38
Replacement	4-38
Disc Brake Specifications	4-39
Parking Brake Service	4-38
Hand-Brake Adjustment	4-38
Rotor, Replace	4-38
Tightening Specifications	4-39

BRAKE SYSTEM BLEED

DISCOVERY

Do not allow fluid level in master cylinder to fall below "MIN" mark during bleeding. Do not fill reservoir above "MAX" level.

1. Raise and support vehicle.
2. Ensue all pipe and hose connections are secure with no signs of leakage.
3. Ensure fluid level in brake reservoir is at "MAX" level.
4. Attach bleed tube to front passenger side brake caliper bleed screw, then submerge tube end into suitable container containing brake fluid.
5. Apply pressure to brake pedal several times, then apply steady pressure.
6. Loosen bleed screw to release brake fluid and air. Allow pedal to return unassisted.
7. Depress brake pedal steadily through its full stroke and allow to return unassisted. Repeat procedure until a flow of clean air-free fluid is purged into container, then tighten brake caliper bleed screw with brake pedal fully depressed.
8. Fill brake fluid reservoir to "MAX" level.
9. Repeat procedure at each wheel in sequence, continuing with front driver's side, then rear driver's side and finally rear passenger's side.
10. Apply brakes and check for leakage.
11. Lower vehicle then road test. Pedal should have short firm travel when applied.

RANGE ROVER

1. Switch ignition off.
2. Operate brake pedal approximately 30 times. Pedal travel will increase slightly and reduced resistance will be felt as pressure decreases.
3. Wait for 60 seconds, press brake pedal four more times to ensure that all pressure is evacuated from system.
4. Fill fluid reservoir with specified fluid to "MAX" level.
5. Bleed master cylinder by opening bleed screw on booster. When fluid appears, close bleed screw.
6. Fit tube to bleed screw.
7. Open bleed screw, depress pedal slowly and progressively.
8. Close bleed screw and release brake pedal.
9. Repeat steps 7 and 8 until fluid is clear of air bubbles.
10. Open bleed screw, fully depress pedal then close bleed screw.
11. Bleed front calipers, driver's side caliper first as follows:
    a. Open bleed screw.
    b. Depress brake pedal slowly and progressively.
    c. Close bleed screw at bottom of each stroke, then release pedal.
12. Repeat step 11 until fluid is clear of air bubbles.
13. Open bleed screw again. Fully depress brake pedal and close bleed screw.
14. Repeat steps 11 and 13 for passenger side caliper.
15. Bleed two booster bleed screws, starting at front bleed screw, open bleed screw and depress brake pedal, then switch ignition on.
16. Allow fluid to flow until clear of air bubbles.
17. Switch ignition to off, then close bleed screw and release pedal.
18. Repeat steps 15 through 17 for rear booster bleed screw.
19. Bleed each rear caliper, driver's side caliper first. Open bleed screw, depress brake pedal slowly and progressively.
20. Switch ignition to on for four seconds. Switch off ignition for four seconds. Repeat until fluid is clear of air bubbles.
21. Switch ignition to off, then close bleed screw and release pedal.
22. Switch ignition to on, then wait for ABS pump to stop running. Press brake pedal down firmly and fully release it five times.
23. With ignition in on position, repeat front caliper bleed procedure, using only lower to thirds of pedal travel when bleeding.
24. Repeat step 22.
25. Check and fill reservoir fluid level as required.

BRAKE PAD SERVICE

REPLACEMENT

1. Raise and support vehicle.
2. Remove front or rear wheels as necessary.
3. Remove bolt from lower guide pin of each caliper.
4. Swivel caliper upwards and remove brake pads.
5. Using piston clamp tool No. LRT-70-500, press caliper pistons fully into bores.
6. Clean faces of pistons and pad locations in caliper.
7. Check condition of guide pin boots, replace if damaged.
8. Reverse procedure to install.

CALIPER SERVICE

REPLACEMENT

1. Raise and support vehicle and remove wheels.
2. Clamp brake hose to prevent fluid loss.
3. Remove brake hose banjo bolt and discard sealing washers.
4. Remove two guide pin bolts and remove caliper housing from carrier.
5. Reverse procedure to install.

ROTOR

REPLACE

1. Raise and support vehicle, then remove wheels.
2. Remove two bolts attaching brake caliper to swivel hub.
3. Release caliper and tie aside clear of brake disc.
4. Remove screw securing disc to drive flange.
5. Remove brake disc from drive flange.
6. Reverse procedure to install.

PARKING BRAKE SERVICE

HAND-BRAKE ADJUSTMENT

Discovery

1. Ensure hand-brake lever is fully released.
2. Raise and support rear of vehicle.
3. Tighten brake shoe adjusting bolt until brake drum is locked, then back off adjusting bolt 1½ turns.
4. Ensure brake drum is free to rotate.
5. Lower vehicle.
6. Recheck hand-brake operation. Hand brake should be fully engaged in three clicks. If not, then cable requires adjustment.
7. Remove switch panel from center console.
8. Remove hand-brake lever boot from center console.
9. Rotate adjuster counterclockwise to increase cable tension or clockwise to decrease cable tension.
10. Recheck hand-brake operation and repeat as necessary.

11. Install hand-brake lever boot and switch panel to center console.

Range Rover

1. Raise and support rear of vehicle.
2. Tighten brake shoe adjusting bolt until brake drum is locked, then back off adjusting bolt 1½ turns.
3. Ensure brake drum is free to rotate.
4. Recheck hand-brake operation. Hand brake should be fully engaged in three clicks. If not, then cable requires adjustment.
5. Ensure hand-brake lever is fully released.
6. Raise and support rear of vehicle.
7. From underside of vehicle, adjust length of outer parking brake cable, then tighten lock nut.
8. Lower vehicle.
9. Recheck hand-brake operation and repeat as necessary.

DISC BRAKE SPECIFICATIONS

Disc Rotors						Disc Pads	
Model	Type	Nominal Thickness	Minimum Refinish Thickness	Thickness variation (Parallelism)	Lateral Runout (T.I.R.)	Thickness New/Inches	Minimum Thickness/Inches
Discovery	Front	.980-.988	.866	—	.006	—	.079
	Rear	.492-.500	.461	—	.006	—	.079
Range Rover	Front	1.00	.870	—	.006	—	.800
	Rear	.500	.460	—	.006	—	.800

TIGHTENING SPECIFICATIONS

Year	Component	Torque/ Ft. Lbs.
DISCOVERY		
1998–2001	Banjo Bolt	24
	Caliper Pivot Bolt	22
	Disc To Drive Flange	10
	Front Caliper Bolts	129
	Lug Nuts	103
	Rear Caliper Bolts	70
RANGE ROVER		
1998–2001	Caliper Pivot Bolt	22
	Disc Shield	72①
	Disc To Drive Flange	18
	Front Caliper Bolts	122
	Lug Nuts	80
	Rear Caliper Bolts	74

① — Inch lbs.

Anti-Lock Brakes

NOTE: On Air Bag Equipped Models, Refer To "Air Bag System Precautions" Located In The Front Of This Manual For System Disarming & Arming Procedures.

INDEX

	Page No.
Description	4-40
Diagnosis & Testing	4-40
Accessing Diagnostic Trouble Codes	4-40
Clearing Diagnostic Trouble Codes	4-40
Precautions	4-40
Air Bag Systems	4-40
Battery Ground Cable	4-40
Microprocessor Radios	4-40
System Service	4-40
Brake System Bleed	4-40
Component Replacement	4-40
ABS Pump & Motor	4-41
Accumulator	4-40
Hydraulic Booster Unit	4-40
Modulator Unit	4-41
SLABS ECU	4-41
Troubleshooting	4-40

PRECAUTIONS

AIR BAG SYSTEMS

Refer to "Air Bag System Precautions" in the front of this manual for system disarming and arming procedures.

MICROPROCESSOR RADIOS

On models equipped with microprocessor radios, always switch radio off before disconnecting or connecting battery ground cable to prevent damage to the radio.

BATTERY GROUND CABLE

Prior to service, disconnect battery ground cable and isolate as required.

DESCRIPTION

The ABS modulator is a 4 channel unit that controls the supply of hydraulic pressure to the brakes in response to inputs from the SLABS ECU. The modulator is attached by three mounting bushes to a bracket on the LH inner front wing and connected to the primary and secondary hydraulic circuits downstream of master cylinder assembly. Three electrical connectors link the ABS modulator to the vehicle wiring.

TROUBLESHOOTING

When the ignition is switched to on, the SLABS ECU performs a check of the brake related warning lamps as part of the power up procedure. The warning lamps are illuminated for approximately 3 seconds and then turn off. If a fault warning lamp remains illuminated after the lamp check, a fault has been detected and repair action is required. The warning lamp will turn off when vehicle speed exceeds 5 mph.

If the lamp remains on or subsequently illuminates with ignition in on position, a fault in the ABS system is indicated. This self monitoring procedure is repeated frequently while the ignition is on. If a fault is detected during self monitoring, the lamp will illuminate indicating that one or more wheels are not under ABS control.

DIAGNOSIS & TESTING

Accessing Diagnostic Trouble Codes

Fault codes and diagnostic routines can be accessed by connecting Testbook or equivalent scan tool to the vehicles diagnostic connector located in the driver's footwell and follow the instructions given by the tool manufacturer.

Clearing Diagnostic Trouble Codes

Clear fault codes using a Testbook or equivalent scan tool, following the instructions given by the tool manufacturer.

SYSTEM SERVICE

Brake System Bleed

Refer to "Disc Brakes" section for brake system bleed procedures.

Component Replacement

ACCUMULATOR

Range Rover

1. Switch ignition off.
2. Operate brake pedal approximately 30 times. Pedal travel will increase slightly and reduced resistance will be felt as pressure decreases.
3. Wait for 60 seconds, press brake pedal four more times to ensure that all pressure is evacuated from system.
4. Position cloth under accumulator to catch any fluid spillage.
5. Remove accumulator and discard O-ring.
6. Reverse procedure to install.

HYDRAULIC BOOSTER UNIT

Range Rover

1. Switch ignition off.
2. Operate brake pedal approximately 30 times. Pedal travel will increase slightly and reduced resistance will be felt as pressure decreases.
3. Wait for 60 seconds, press brake pedal four more times to ensure that all pressure is evacuated from system.
4. Remove two bolts attaching fuel filter assembly to chassis turret, then position filter aside.
5. Position cloth under booster to collect fluid spillage.
6. Release clip from fluid reservoir hose at pump and disconnect hose.
7. Allow fluid to drain into suitable container, then plug hose and pump.
8. Disconnect hose from reservoir, then plug hose and reservoir.
9. **On models equipped with manual transmission,** reposition container beneath clutch master cylinder feed hose. Disconnect clutch hose from reservoir and allow fluid to drain, then plug hose and reservoir.
10. **On all models,** disconnect two electrical connectors from hydraulic booster unit.
11. Disconnect fluid level switch electrical connector.
12. Remove banjo bolt securing high pressure hose to pump. Discard sealing washers, then plug hose and pump.
13. Unscrew pipe unions from booster. Plug pipes and booster.
14. Remove closing panel and stop lamp switch.

15. Release booster push rod from brake pedal.
16. Remove two bolts attaching booster assembly to pedal box, then booster.
17. Remove banjo bolt securing high pressure hose to booster. Then discard sealing washers and plug hose and booster.
18. Reverse procedure to install noting the following:
    a. **Torque** banjo bolt to 18 ft. lbs.
    b. **Torque** booster attaching bolts to 33 ft. lbs.
    c. **Torque** union nuts to 10 ft. lbs.

MODULATOR UNIT

Discovery

1. Position cloth under modulator to absorb fluid spillage.
2. Disconnect three electrical connectors from ABS modulator.
3. Disconnect two inlet brake pipe unions from pump side of modulator.
4. Disconnect four outlet brake pipe unions from top of modulator.
5. Loosen three nuts securing modulator to mounting bracket.
6. Remove modulator from mounting bracket.
7. Remove three rubber mounts from modulator.
8. Reverse procedure to install noting the following:
    a. **Torque** modulator mounting bracket nuts to 7 ft. lbs.
    b. **Torque** 13mm unions to 16 ft. lbs.
    c. **Torque** 11mm unions to 10 ft. lbs.

SLABS ECU

Discovery

1. Remove five electrical connectors from SLABS ECU from under right-hand side lower corner of instrument panel.
2. Remove electrical connector from ACE ECU.
3. Remove lower nut and loosen upper nut securing SLABS and ACE ECU bracket to body.
4. Remove ECU's and bracket assembly.
5. Remove four nuts attaching SLABS ECU and then ECU.
6. Reverse procedure to install.

ABS PUMP & MOTOR

Range Rover

1. Remove accumulator.
2. Position cloth to catch fluid spillage.
3. Release clip securing reservoir hose to pump.
4. Disconnect reservoir hose, then plug hose and connection.
5. Remove banjo bolt attaching high pressure hose to pump. Collect sealing washers and discard, then plug hose and connection.
6. Disconnect electrical connectors from motor and pressure switch.
7. Remove three nuts securing pump/motor assembly to valance, then assembly.
8. Collect rubber mounts and inserts from pump brackets.
9. Remove and discard ABS pump relay.
10. Reverse procedure to install noting the following:
    a. **Torque** pump assembly to valance to 72 inch lbs.
    b. Position high pressure hose to pump, ensuring correct location of banjo timing peg into slot. **Torque** banjo bolt to 18 ft. lbs.

Automatic Transmissions

NOTE: On Air Bag Equipped Models, Refer To "Air Bag System Precautions" Located In The Front Of This Manual For System Disarming & Arming Procedures.

INDEX

	Page No.
Adjustments	4-42
Kickdown Cable	4-42
Application Chart	4-42
Description	4-42
Identification	4-42
In-Vehicle Repairs	4-43
ECU, Replace	4-44
Extension Housing, Replace	4-44
Fluid Cooler, Replace	4-43
Governor & Hub Assembly, Replace	4-44
Inhibitor Switch, Replace	4-45
Kickdown Cable, Replace	4-46
Oil Screen, Replace	4-43
Oil Sump, Replace	4-43
Parking Pawl, Replace	4-45
Selector Position Switch, Replace	4-45
Selector Shaft Oil Seal, Replace	4-45
Shift Cable, Replace	4-43
Valve Body, Replace	4-43
Maintenance	4-42
Fluid Change	4-42
Fluid Check	4-42
Precautions	4-42
Air Bag Systems	4-42
Battery Ground Cable	4-42
Tightening Specifications	4-49
Transmission, Replace	4-47
Discovery	4-47
Range Rover	4-47
Troubleshooting	4-42

APPLICATION CHART

Model/Year	Automatic Transmission
1998–2001	
Discovery	ZF 4HP22
Range Rover 4.0L	ZF 4HP22
Range Rover 4.6L	ZF 4HP24

PRECAUTIONS

AIR BAG SYSTEMS

Refer to "Air Bag System Precautions" in the front of this manual for system disarming and arming procedures.

BATTERY GROUND CABLE

Prior to service, disconnect battery ground cable and isolate as required.

IDENTIFICATION

Refer to **Fig. 1** for transmission identification.

DESCRIPTION

These transmissions consist of a three element torque converter that delivers power to a four speed epicyclic transmission. To accommodate the extra engine power of 4.6L models the ZF4HP24 unit has a larger torque converter and oil cooler. First and second gears are reduction ratios, third is direct and forth is an overdrive gear for high speed cruising. A lock-up clutch, integral with the torque converter, operates to engage in third and fourth gear, **Fig. 2.**

TROUBLESHOOTING

Refer to **Fig. 3** when troubleshooting transmission.

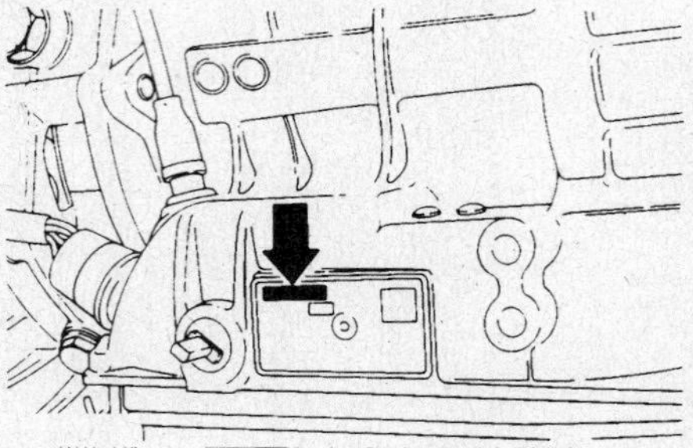

Fig. 1 Transmission identification location

MAINTENANCE

FLUID CHECK

1. Ensure vehicle is on level ground.
2. Start and run engine in park or neutral.
3. Check fluid level on dipstick.
4. If not between two markings on dipstick, fill to specifications. Refer to "Lubricant Data & Maintenance Charts" for fluid amount and type.

FLUID CHANGE

1. Raise and support vehicle.
2. Remove drain plug and drain transmission fluid.
3. Disconnect fluid filler tube from pan.
4. Remove six pan attaching bolts and drop pan.
5. Remove oil pick-up tube attaching bolt, then the tube. Collect spacer.
6. Remove filter from valve block, then the O-ring and discard.
7. Reverse procedure to install noting the following:
   a. Tighten to specifications.
   b. Refer to "Lubricant Data & Maintenance Charts" for fluid amount and type.

ADJUSTMENTS

KICKDOWN CABLE

Discovery

1. Remove split pin and clevis pin, then disconnect kickdown cable from lever.
2. Remove split pin and clevis pin, then disconnect throttle cable from lever.
3. Adjust position of kickdown cable locknuts so that dimension "A" is 1.1 inches, **Fig. 4.** With cable held in this position, there should be six threads exposed to the rear of the bracket, dimension "B".
4. Tighten both locknuts.
5. Connect kickdown cable to lever and secure with clevis pin and split pin.
6. Connect throttle cable to lever and secure with clevis pin and split pin.
7. Pull back rubber boot on kickdown cable until crimped nipple is visible.
8. Rotate knurled plug on throttle cable until crimped nipple is. 039 inch from end of threads, dimension "C".
9. Install rubber boot.

Range Rover

1. Adjust cable sheath to achieve a crimp gap of. 009–.049 inch.

2. Hold cable sheath while tightening locknuts.
3. Ensure vehicle is on level ground with parking brake applied.
4. Check oil level with engine at idle with neutral selected, after selecting each gear.

IN-VEHICLE REPAIRS

OIL SUMP, REPLACE

DISCOVERY

1. Raise and support vehicle.
2. Drain oil and install plug with new seal.
3. Detach heat shield at front exhaust pipe to manifold.
4. Disconnect electrical connectors from Lambda sensors.
5. Remove catalytic converter assembly.
6. Remove chassis cross-member from under transmission.
7. Disconnect dipstick tube at oil sump.
8. Loosen dipstick attaching bolt at bell housing and move dipstick aside.
9. Remove clamps attaching oil sump. Note their locations for installation reference.
10. Remove gasket and clean gasket mating faces.
11. Install oil sump using a new gasket.
12. Connect dipstick tube to oil sump and tighten bolt at bell housing.
13. Install chassis cross member.
14. Install catalytic converter assembly
15. Connect electrical connectors to Lambda sensors.
16. Connect heat shield front pipe to manifold.
17. Refill transmission using correct grade of oil. Refer to "Lubricant Data & Maintenance Charts" for fluid amount and type.

OIL SCREEN, REPLACE

DISCOVERY

1. Raise and support vehicle.
2. Drain oil and install plug with new seal.
3. Remove heat shield from front exhaust pipe.
4. Disconnect electrical connectors from Lambda sensors.
5. Remove catalytic converter assembly.
6. Remove chassis cross-member from under transmission.
7. Disconnect dipstick tube at oil sump.
8. Loosen dipstick attaching bolt at bell housing and move dipstick aside.
9. Remove clamps attaching oil sump. Note their locations for installation reference.
10. Remove gasket and clean gasket mating faces.
11. Remove attaching screws, then the oil screen and suction pipe.
12. Detach suction pipe from oil screen, discard O-ring seal.
13. Reverse procedure to install, noting the following:
    a. Clean oil screen and suction pipe.
    b. Use a light grease to hold O-rings in place.
    c. Install oil screen and suction pipe with spacer.
    d. Install new oil sump gasket.

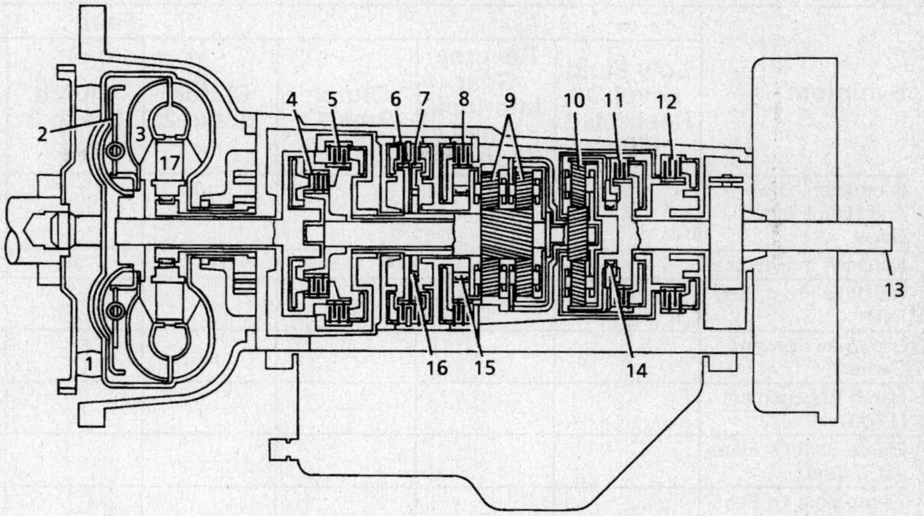

1. Input/impeller
2. Converter lock-up clutch
3. Turbine
4. Clutch, forward drive
5. Clutch, reverse drive
6. Clutch, brake
7. Clutch, brake
8. Clutch, brake
9. Epicyclic gear set
10. Epicyclic gear set
11. Clutch
12. Clutch, brake
13. Input to transfer box
14. Freewheel (one way clutch)
15. Freewheel (one way clutch)
16. Freewheel (one way clutch)
17. Stator and one way clutch

RV5029500002000X

Fig. 2 Cross sectional view of transmission

    e. Refer to "Lubricant Data & Maintenance Charts" for fluid amount and type.

RANGE ROVER

1. Raise and support vehicle.
2. Drain transmission fluid.
3. Remove fluid filler tube from pan.
4. Remove six bolts attaching fluid pan to transmission, then the fluid pan.
5. Remove gasket and discard.
6. Remove oil pick-up tube attaching bolt, then the pick-up tube.
7. Remove remaining two bolts attaching filter to valve block.
8. Remove filter, then the O-rings. Discard O-rings.
9. Reverse procedure to install.

FLUID COOLER, REPLACE

RANGE ROVER

1. Remove engine oil cooler.
2. Remove four air deflector trim studs, then the deflectors.
3. Position a suitable container under fluid cooler to collect any spilled fluid.
4. Unscrew fluid cooler pipe union nuts and discard O-rings.
5. Plug cooler and pipes.
6. Remove four bolts attaching fluid cooler to radiator attaching bracket.
7. Remove fluid cooler.
8. Reverse procedure to install, noting the following.
    a. Tighten to specifications.
    b. Lubricate new O-rings with clean fluid.
    c. Refer to "Lubricant Data & Maintenance Charts" for fluid amount and type.

VALVE BODY, REPLACE

DISCOVERY

1. Raise and support vehicle.
2. Drain oil and install plug with new seal.
3. Remove exhaust heat shield from front exhaust pipe.
4. Disconnect electrical connectors from Lambda sensors.
5. Remove catalytic converter assembly.
6. Remove chassis crossmember from under transmission.
7. Remove dipstick tube at oil sump.
8. Loosen dipstick attaching bolt at bell housing and move dipstick aside.
9. Remove clamps attaching oil sump. Note their locations for installation reference.
10. Remove gasket and clean gasket mating faces.
11. Remove attaching screws and remove oil screen and suction pipe. Discard O-ring seal.
12. Remove attaching screws, then the valve body from casing, **Fig. 5.**
13. Reverse procedure to install. Refer to "Lubricant Data & Maintenance Charts" for fluid amount and type.

SHIFT CABLE, REPLACE

RANGE ROVER

1. Raise and support vehicle.
2. Slacken selector cable trunnion locknut, then remove split pin and release trunnion from transmission lever.
3. Select P position. Position lever on transmission fully forward.
4. Adjust trunnion until a sliding fit in transmission lever is achieved.
5. Connect trunnion to lever and install split pin, then tighten locknut.

Symptom	Fault								
	Low Fluid Level Or Restricted Filter	Reverse Gear Interlock Valve Seized	Clutch Brake 1	Clutch Brake 2	Clutch Brake 3	Clutch Brake 4	Clutch A	Clutch B	Clutch C
Intermittent Drive And High Pitched Noise	X	—	—	—	—	—	—	—	—
No Drive In Reverse	X	X	—	—	X	—	—	—	—
No Drive From Stop In D	X	—	—	—	—	—	X	—	—
Slip In All Forward Gears	X	—	—	—	—	—	X	—	—
Harsh Engagement N To D	—	—	—	—	—	—	X	—	—
Fierce Shift Or Flare 1st To 2nd	—	—	—	—	—	—	—	—	—
Fierce Shift Or Flare 2nd To 3rd	—	—	—	—	—	—	—	X	—
No 3rd Gear	—	—	—	—	—	—	—	X	—
No 4th Gear D Selected	—	—	—	—	—	X	—	—	—
No Engine Braking Selected 3rd	—	—	—	—	—	—	—	—	X
1st Selected No Engine Braking	—	—	—	—	X	—	—	—	—
2nd Selected No Engine Braking	—	—	X	—	—	—	—	—	—
Vehicle Drives Forward In N	—	—	—	—	—	—	X	—	—

Fig. 3 Troubleshooting chart (Part 1 of 3)

ECU, REPLACE

RANGE ROVER

1. Move left hand front seat fully rearwards and raise cushion for access.
2. Disconnect battery negative lead.
3. Remove three trim attaching screws from seat base and trim.
4. Remove two screws attaching cover to ECU, then the cover.
5. Release electrical connector from ECU.
6. Remove screw attaching ECU, then the ECU.
7. Reverse procedure to install.

EXTENSION HOUSING, REPLACE

DISCOVERY

Removal

1. Remove transfer case. Refer to "Transfer Case" in this section for removal procedures.
2. Drain fluid from automatic transmission.
3. Remove bolts attaching left hand attaching bracket to extension housing and withdraw bracket.
4. Remove transfer gear lever housing attaching bolts and move housing aside.
5. Remove attaching bolts and withdraw extension housing from over coupling shaft. Remove and discard gasket.
6. Place extension housing on bench and remove oil seal.
7. Ensure that all surfaces are clean and housing is free from damage. If damage is found and housing has to be renewed remove dowels from face of existing housing and install in new housing.
8. Using oil seal replacer tool No. LST108 or equivalent, install a new oil seal in housing.

Installation

1. Install extension housing to transmission, with a new gasket, ensuring oil seal is not damaged by extension shaft.
2. Secure housing with nine bolts.
3. Install transfer gear lever housing to top of extension housing.
4. Install attaching bracket to extension housing.
5. Install transfer gear box.
6. Refill transmission using correct grade of oil. Refer to "Lubricant Data & Maintenance Charts" for fluid amount and type.

GOVERNOR & HUB ASSEMBLY, REPLACE

DISCOVERY

Removal

1. Remove extension housing as previously outlined in this section.
2. Remove extension shaft retaining bolt, withdraw shaft and discard O-ring seal. If TDI vehicle remove spacer.
3. Remove governor assembly.
4. Remove park gear from governor assembly.
5. Detach governor housing.
6. Remove security clip and counter weight.
7. Remove and discard O-ring seal from output shaft and three seal rings from F-clutch housing.
8. Clean all components.
9. If necessary detach parking pawl by removing guide plates and withdrawing mechanism.

Installation

1. Install parking pawl mechanism if removed.
2. Remove, lubricate and install new seal rings to F-clutch housing shaft, ensure they are correctly seated.
3. Apply petroleum jelly to a new O-ring seal. Install to output shaft
4. Install park gear to governor assembly tightening screws to correct torque.
5. Install governor assembly to output shaft.
6. Install extension shaft with spacer if TDI. Install new O-ring under bolt head.
7. Install extension housing, avoid damaging seal.
8. Install transfer gear lever housing to extension housing.
9. Install attaching bracket to extension housing.
10. Install transfer transmission.
11. Refill transmission using correct grade

Symptom	Fault								
	1st-2nd Shift Valve	2nd-3rd Shift Valve	3rd-4th Upshift Valve	4th-3rd Down-shift Valve	Direct Drive Clutch Control Valve	Hystere-sis Valve	Governor Valve	Modula-tor Valve	Torque Converter Control Valve
Fierce Shift Or Flare 1st To 2nd	—	—	—	—	—	—	—	X	—
Fierce Shift Or Flare 2nd To 3rd	—	—	—	—	—	—	—	X	—
No 3rd Gear	—	X	—	—	—	—	—	—	—
No 4th Gear D Selected	—	—	X	X	—	—	—	—	—
None Or Harsh Engagement Of Direct Drive Clutch	—	—	—	—	X	X	—	—	—
Direct Drive Clutch Shift Point Incorrect	—	—	—	—	X	X	X	—	X
Drives In D But Immediately Upshifts To 3rd	—	X	—	—	—	—	—	—	—
D Position Starts in 2nd	X	X	—	—	—	—	—	—	—
D Position Starts In 3rd	X	X	—	—	—	—	—	—	—
No Kickdown 4th To 3rd	—	—	—	X	—	—	—	—	—
No Upshift At Light Throttle	X	X	X	—	—	—	X	—	—
No Downshift Manually From 3rd To 2nd	—	X	—	—	—	—	X	—	—
No Downshift Manually From 2nd To 1st Below 28 mph	X	—	—	—	—	—	X	—	—

Fig. 3 Troubleshooting chart (Part 2 of 3)

of oil. Refer to "Lubricant Data & Maintenance Charts" for fluid amount and type.

SELECTOR POSITION SWITCH, REPLACE

NEW RANGE ROVER

Removal

1. Ensure vehicle is in P position, raise and support vehicle.
2. Remove nut attaching selector lever to selector shaft. Release lever.
3. Release switch electrical connector from bracket. Disconnect from vehicle harness.
4. Remove position switch attaching nut and bolt.
5. Disconnect switch from selector shaft and remove breather hose.
6. Remove switch.

Installation

1. Ensure P is selected by rotating selector shaft fully clockwise.
2. Engage N by rotating selector shaft counterclockwise by two detents.
3. Connect breather hose to switch, then the electrical connector to vehicle harness attaching to bracket.
4. Engage switch on selector shaft install nut and bolt to stud.
5. Install setting tool No. LRT-44–011 or equivalent, to shaft.
6. Insert setting pin into tool and rotate switch until setting pin engages with hole in switch.
7. Tighten nut and bolt and remove setting tool.
8. Install selector lever to shaft and secure with nut.

PARKING PAWL, REPLACE

1. Remove transfer case. Refer to "Transfer Case" in this section for removal procedures.
2. Remove transfer case selector housing.
3. Loosen extension housing attaching bolts.
4. Remove extension housing. Do not damage extension housing seal.
5. Remove extension shaft, retaining bolt and O-ring.
6. Remove governor assembly with parking wheel.
7. Remove guide plate bolt, then the guide plate from transmission case.
8. Remove pin, parking pawl and spring.
9. Reverse procedure to install.

INHIBITOR SWITCH, REPLACE

1. Raise and support vehicle.
2. Disconnect inhibitor switch electrical connector.
3. Remove inhibitor switch retaining plate.
4. Remove inhibitor switch and O-ring seal.
5. Clean inhibitor switch and mating face on casing.
6. Install and lubricate new O-ring seal to switch.
7. Secure with retaining plate and bolt.
8. Connect electrical connector to harness.

SELECTOR SHAFT OIL SEAL, REPLACE

DISCOVERY

1. Raise and support vehicle.
2. Detach heat shield at front exhaust pipe to manifold and electric from O2 sensors.
3. Remove catalytic converter assembly and crossmember from under transmission.
4. Engage low range gear in transfer case and support transmission with transmission jack.
5. Remove transfer case chassis attaching bracket nuts and bolts noting location of speedometer cable bracket for installation.
6. Remove selector lever from shaft, then

Symptom	Fault								
	Pump Failure	Primary Regulator	No 2 Freewheel	Governor Sleeve	Throttle Valve Adj.	2 Position Interlock Valve	1 Position Interlock Valve	Clutch Brake CB1	Clutch Brake CB2
No Drive From Stop In D	X	X	X	—	—	—	—	—	—
Slip In All Forward Gears	X	X	—	—	—	—	—	—	—
Harsh Engagement N to D	—	X	—	—	—	—	—	—	—
Fierce Shift Or Flare 1st To 2nd	—	—	—	—	—	—	—	X	X
D Position Starts In 2nd	—	—	—	X	—	—	—	—	—
D Position Starts In 3rd	—	—	—	X	—	—	—	—	—
Upshift/DownShift/ Kickdown Incorrect Speeds	—	X	—	—	X	—	—	—	—
No Downshift Manually From 3rd to 2nd	—	—	—	—	—	X	—	—	—
No Downshift Manually From 2nd To 1st Below 28 mph	—	—	—	—	—	—	X	—	—

Fig. 3 Troubleshooting chart (Part 3 of 3)

the selector shaft seal from casing.
7. Clean selector shaft seal and seal mating faces.
8. Install selector shaft oil seal installer tool No. LST 114 or equivalent, over selector shaft.
9. Lubricate new oil seal and position seal on tool.
10. Install tool outer sleeve and screw on nut to drive seal on housing.
11. Remove tool from shaft.
12. Reverse procedure to install.

RANGE ROVER

1. Raise and support vehicle.
2. Remove gear changer lever.
3. Remove oil seal from casing.
4. Clean selector shaft seal and seal mating faces.
5. Install selector shaft oil seal installer tool No. LST 114 or equivalent, over selector shaft.
6. Lubricate new oil seal and position seal on tool.
7. Install tool outer sleeve and screw on nut to drive seal on housing
8. Remove tool from shaft.
9. Install gear selector lever and tighten to specifications.

KICKDOWN CABLE, REPLACE

DISCOVERY

1. Raise and support vehicle.
2. Place gear selector in Neutral.
3. Disconnect kickdown cable at throttle linkage.
4. Remove outer cable locknut.
5. Disconnect cable from attaching bracket.
6. Disconnect cable from cylinder head bracket.
7. Feed cable through to underside of vehicle.
8. Drain oil and install plug with new seal.
9. Remove exhaust heat shield from front exhaust pipe.
10. Disconnect electrical connectors from Lambda sensors.
11. Remove catalytic converter assembly.
12. Remove chassis crossmember from under transmission.
13. Disconnect dipstick tube from oil sump, then loosen attaching bolt at bell housing and move dipstick aside.
14. Remove clamps attaching oil sump. Note their locations for installation reference.
15. Pull kickdown inner cable to fully open valve cam, then wedge cam into this position.
16. Disconnect cable from cam by pushing inner cable into outer casing, then separate cable nipple from cam.
17. Compress cable tangs and remove cable from transmission, using removal tool No. LST112, or equivalent.
18. If cable is to be reinstalled remove O-ring seal and clean cable assembly.
19. Reverse procedure to install, noting the following:
    a. Lubricate new O-ring seal with transmission fluid.
    b. Install oil pan using a new gasket.
    c. Install catalytic converter assembly.
    d. Refer to "Adjustments" in this section for kickdown cable adjustment.
    e. Tighten locknuts and recheck gap.
    f. Refill transmission using correct grade of oil. Refer to "Lubricant Data & Maintenance Charts" for fluid amount and type.

RANGE ROVER

Removal

1. Disconnect kickdown cable from engine.
2. Raise and support vehicle.
3. Drain transmission oil.
4. Remove front exhaust assembly and chassis crossmember.
5. Remove oil level tube, six retaining plates and bolts and sump.
6. Loosen three bolts, remove oil screen.
7. Loosen 13 remaining bolts, remove control unit.
8. Locate selector cam, remove nipple, holding kickdown cable from seat.
9. Using kickdown cable remover tool No. LST 112 or equivalent, remove cable and its housing from casing and discard.

Installation

1. Install new cable and new O-ring into casing,
2. Spring load cam by turning once before installing. Install nipple into cam seat.
3. Install control unit after cleaning face with a lint free rag. Ensure selector shaft locates into gear shift fork. Install 13 bolts loosely.
4. Place selector linkage setting gauge tool No. LST 109 or equivalent, in position. Gently press control unit in direction shown in **Fig. 6** and tighten to specifications.
5. Remove setting gauge, install oil screen.
6. Install sump with a new gasket.
7. Install six retaining plates.
8. Install oil filler tube.

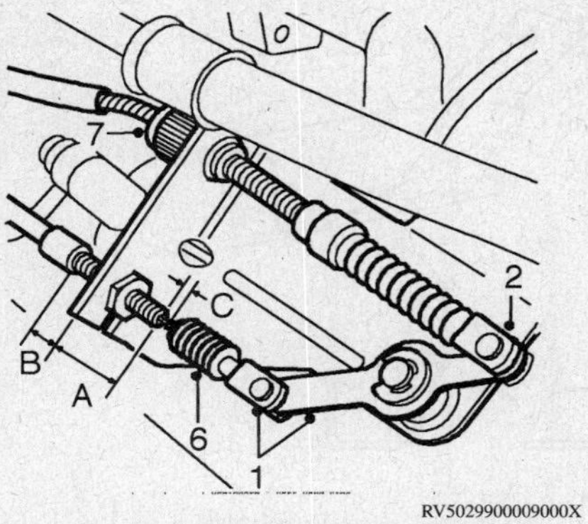

Fig. 4 Kickdown cable adjustment. Discovery

9. Install sump plug with new seal.
10. Install chassis crossmember and exhaust assembly.
11. Fill transmission to specifications, refer to "Lubricant Data & Maintenance Charts" for fluid amount and type.
12. Connect kickdown cable to engine.

TRANSMISSION

REPLACE

RANGE ROVER

1. Remove fan blade assembly. **Fan blade has lefthand threads.**
2. **On V8 models,** remove air intake hose from plenum chamber.
3. **On all models,** disconnect kickdown cable from throttle linkage, then the transmission breather pipes from rear of engine.
4. Remove transmission dipstick.
5. Select low range, unscrew and remove transfer case knob and cigar lighter.
6. Remove surround from gear selector panel.
7. Pry out wood veneer panel from center console, and disconnect electrical connectors from switches.
8. Remove screws securing center console to floor, and two clips at front.
9. Disconnect electrical connectors from window switch and to selector graphics panel and remove inset panel.
10. Disconnect electrical leads to cigar lighter.
11. Remove sound deadening trim from top of transmission tunnel, then the retaining plate from transfer case.
12. Raise and support vehicle.
13. Drain transmission fluid and reinstall plug.
14. **On V8 models,** disconnect electrical connectors to oxygen sensors and remove front exhaust sections and chassis crossmember.
15. **On all models,** disconnect transmission oil cooler pipes and plug hoses and connections.
16. Remove dipstick tube from transmission.
17. Disconnect propeller shafts at output flanges and tie aside.
18. Disconnect electrical connector from speed transducer, then the main selector cable and rod from transmission, tie aside.
19. Disconnect inhibitor switch.
20. Remove transmission brake drum and four bolts securing back plate of transfer case and tie assembly aside complete with hand-brake.
21. Remove two bolts and cover plate from bottom of transmission bell housing.
22. Rotate engine to remove bolts securing drive plate to torque converter.
23. Position transmission jack on rear output housing to support weight of transmission assembly.
24. Remove fixings and withdraw transfer case mountings.
25. Install a suitable adaptor plate to transmission hoist, **Fig. 7.** Raise hoist and position under transfer case securing fixture to transfer case mounting points, **Fig. 8.**
26. Remove mounts to transmission and transfer case, then the crossmember.
27. Raise and position jack under transmission.
28. Support engine and remove bellhousing bolts and lower transmission.
29. Inspect flex plate for damage, replace if necessary.
30. Reverse procedure to install noting the following:
    a. Coat drive plate to torque converter bolts with Loctite 270, or equivalent.
    b. Install new exhaust gaskets.
    c. **Torque** cooler pipe adaptor bolts to 31 ft. lbs. Bell housing mounting bolts to 34 ft. lbs., extension housing bolts to 34 ft. lbs., Bottom cover to converter housing to 72 inch lbs. and converter housing cover bolts to 72 inch lbs.

DISCOVERY

1. Select low range with transfer gear lever, then remove knob and gaiter.
2. Remove insulated pad from rocker cover and inlet manifold.
3. Disconnect electrical connectors from top of brake fluid reservoir.
4. Release electrical harness from clips along top of bulkhead and pull over to one side.
5. Disconnect breather pipe from rear of cylinder head then kickdown cable at fuel injection pump.
6. Drain coolant from cooling system and remove upper radiator hose.
7. Disconnect turbo charger hose from inter-cooler.
8. Remove starter heat shield, then the starter.
9. Remove converter to flex drive plate bolts through starter aperture.
10. Raise and support vehicle.
11. Drain transmission and transfer case fluids.
12. Disconnect speedometer cable from transfer case, then the associated clipping.
13. Remove rear propeller shaft, disconnect front propeller shaft at transfer case and tie aside.
14. Remove front exhaust front pipe, bolts attaching front and center silencer attaching brackets and tie silencer to side.
15. Disconnect oil cooler pipes from transmission plugging pipes and connections.

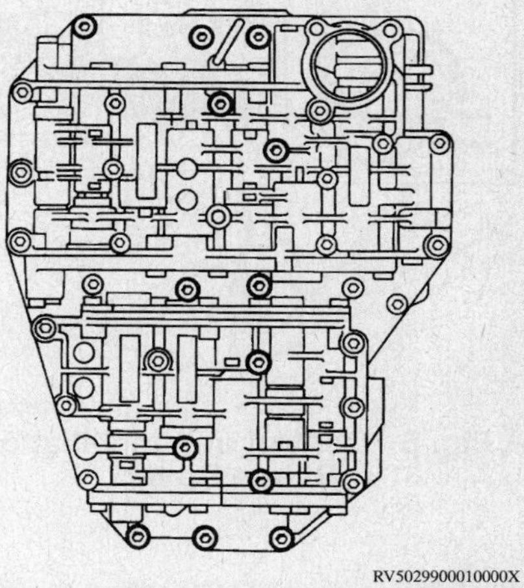

Fig. 5 Valve body attaching bolt locations. Discovery

16. Remove bolt attaching retaining bracket to sump and move cooler pipes aside.
17. Disconnect selector cable from lever.
18. Disconnect inhibitor switch electrical connectors, then the park brake cable from linkage to park brake lever.
19. Disconnect electrical connections from differential lock switch on transfer case.
20. Remove two lower bolts from transfer case input bearing support plate.
21. Assemble suitable support cradle to transmission hoist, **Fig. 9.**
22. Raise hoist and secure cradle to transfer case input bearing support plate using bolts removed.
23. Disconnect transmission attaching brackets from crossmember and remove crossmember.
24. Lower transmission to access items attached to top of transmission.
25. Remove left hand transmission attaching bracket assembly.
26. Remove ties from breather pipes and harnesses.
27. Remove nut attaching transmission oil filler tube to bell housing.
28. Disconnect union nut at transmission sump and remove oil filler tube, then install plug.
29. Support engine using a wooden block with a suitable jack.
30. Remove nut attaching kickdown cable bracket to bell housing.
31. Remove two bolts attaching top of bell housing to flywheel housing, then the nuts attaching bell housing to flywheel housing and withdraw transmission assembly from engine.
32. Inspect flex plate for damage, replace if necessary.
33. Reverse procedure to install noting the following:
    a. Coat drive plate to torque converter bolts with Loctite 270 or equivalent.
    b. Install new exhaust gaskets.
    c. Tighten to specifications.

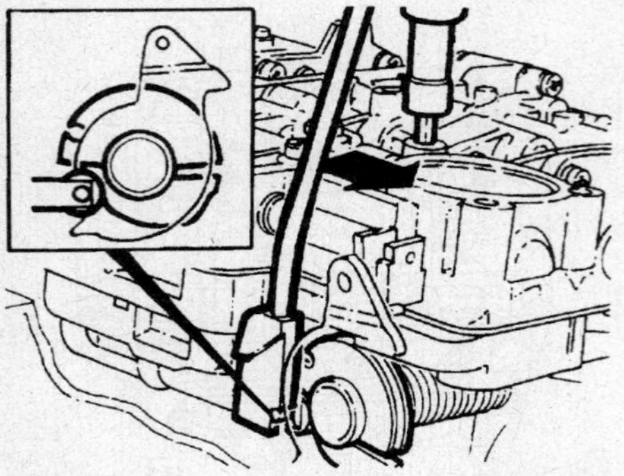

RV5029500003000X

Fig. 6 Control unit installation. Range Rover

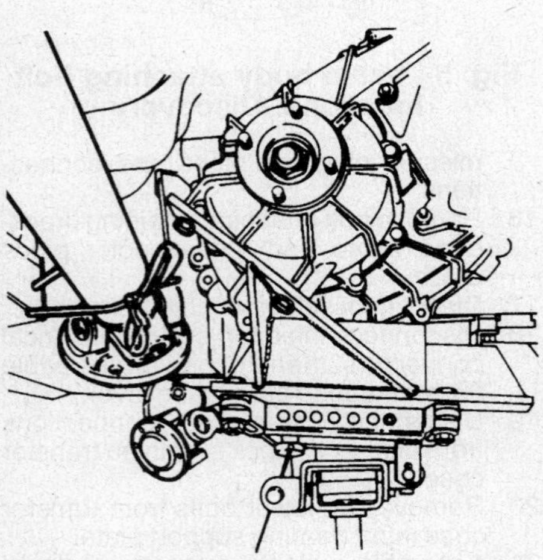

RV5029500005000X

Fig. 8 Adaptor plate location. Range Rover

Adaptor plate for removing Borg Warner transfer gearbox. This can be manufactured locally to drawing shown.

Material: Steel BS 1449 Grade 4 or 14.
Drill holes marked * to fit hoist used.

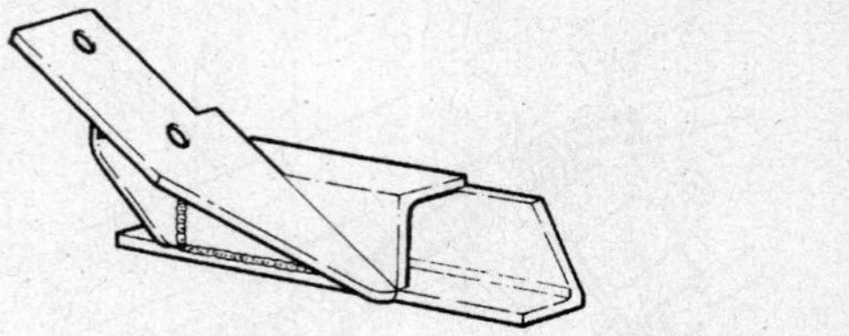

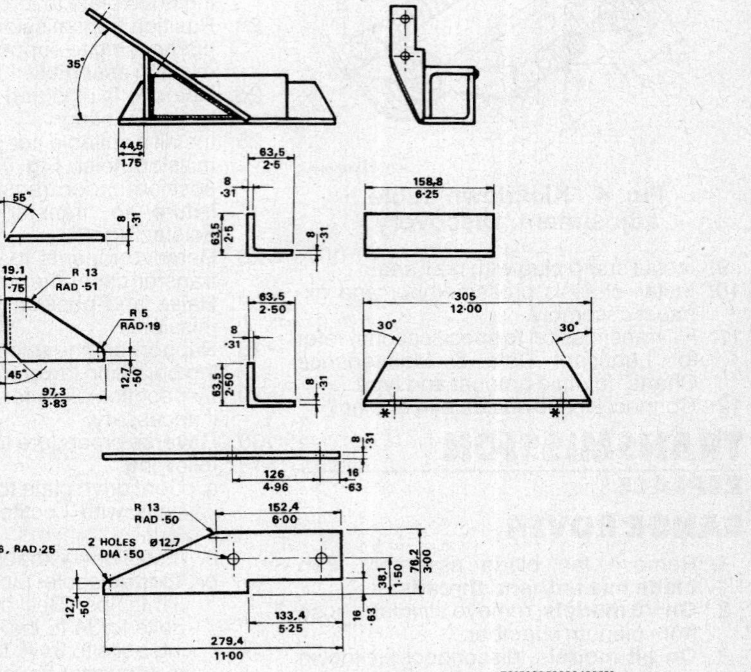

RV5029500004000X

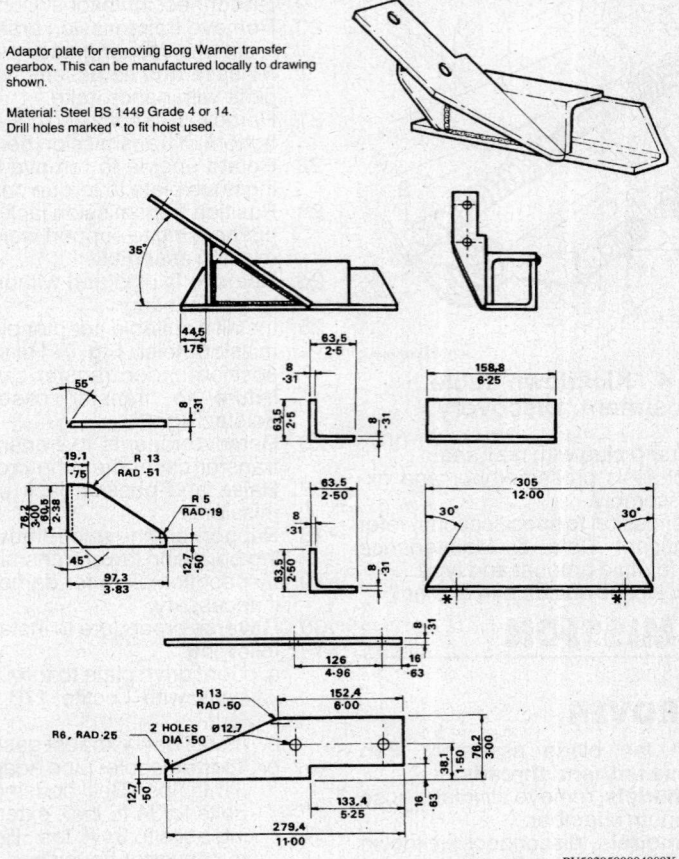

Fig. 7 Transfer case adapter plate. Range Rover

The assembled transfer gearbox, automatic gearbox and torque converter is removed from underneath the vehicle. Using a transmission hoist with an adaptor plate for securing the assembly to the hoist. The adaptor can be manufactured locally to the drawing below or purchased from:- Straight Set Engineering, England. Tel.0909 480055

WARNING: When using a transmission hoist it is essential to follow the hoist manufacturers instructions.

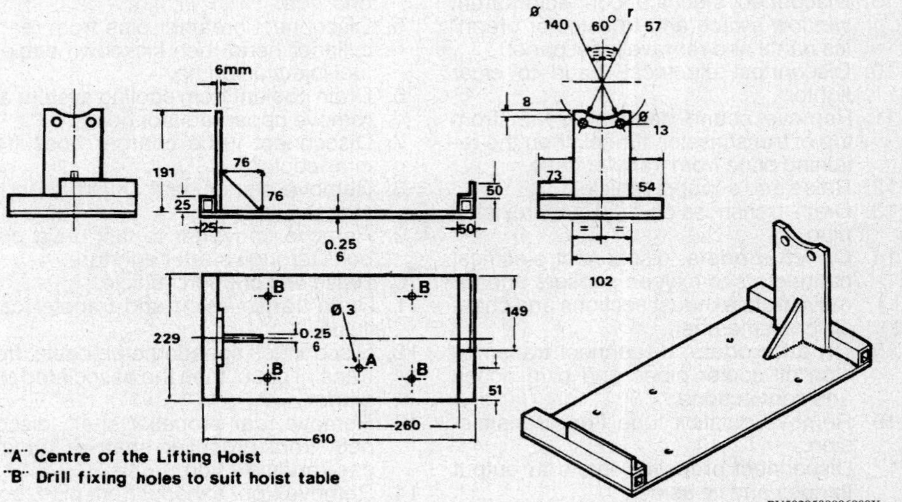

"A" Centre of the Lifting Hoist
"B" Drill fixing holes to suit hoist table

RV5029500006000X

Fig. 9 Adaptor plate. Discovery

TIGHTENING SPECIFICATIONS

Year	Component	Torque/ Ft. Lbs.
DISCOVERY		
1998–2001	Adapter To Crankshaft	60
	Bell Housing Mounting Bolts	34
	Bottom Cover To Converter Housing	84①
	Clutch F Attaching Screws	84①
	Converter Housing Cover Bolts	84①
	Cooler Adapter Bolts	30
	Coupling Shaft To Mainshaft	30
	Drive Plate To Converter	28
	Drive Plates To Crankshaft Adapter	29
	Extension Housing Bolts	16
	Fluid Filler Tube	50
	Fluid Filter	72①
	Gearbox To Engine	30
	Governor Mounting Screws	84①
	Intermediate Plate Plugs (M14)	29
	Intermediate Plate Plugs (M20)	36
	Pan Bolts	72①
	Parking Pawl Attaching Screw	84①
	Pick Up Tube	72①
	Pump Attaching Screws	84①
	Selector Lever To Gearbox	18
	Selector Shaft Mounting Bracket To Chassis Bolts	22
	Strut (Threaded End)	30
	Sump Mounting Screws	72①
	Sump Plug	84①
	Valve Body Mounting Bolts	72①
RANGE ROVER		
1998–2001	Cooler Pipes	22
	Drive Plate To Converter	33
	Fluid Filler Tube	52
	Fluid Filter Screen	72①
	Gear Selector Nut	18
	Propeller Shaft Nuts & Bolts	35
	Retaining Plates	72①
	Selector Linkage Bolts	72①
	Sump Plug	72①
	Transmission Mounting Assembly	33
	Transmission To Engine Housing Bolts	31

① — Inch lbs.

Transfer Cases

NOTE: On Air Bag Equipped Models, Refer To "Air Bag System Precautions" Located In The Front Of This Manual For System Disarming & Arming Procedures.

INDEX

	Page No.
Application Chart	4-50
Assemble	4-51
Borg Warner 44–62	4-54
LT230Q, LT230SE & LT230T	4-51
Disassemble	4-50
Borg Warner 44–62	4-50
LT230Q, LT230SE & LT230T	4-50
Tightening Specifications	4-64

APPLICATION CHART

Model	Borg Warner Transfer Case	LT230Q, LT230SE & LT230T Transfer Case
Range Rover	X	—
Discovery	—	X

DISASSEMBLE

LT230Q, LT230SE & LT230T

Before disassembling transfer case, thoroughly clean the exterior of the transfer case. If the transfer case oil has not been drained, drain the oil into a suitable container.

Refer to **Figs. 1 through 8** when disassembling or assembling these transfer cases.

1. Loosen bolt to release transmission brake adjustment.
2. Remove countersunk screw(s) securing transmission brake drum, then the drum.
3. Scribe suitable alignment marks between transmission brake backplate and rear output housing.
4. Remove four transmission brake back plate attaching bolts.
5. Remove Allen screw securing vehicle speed sensor.
6. Remove vehicle speed sensor and discard O-ring.
7. Remove six bottom cover attaching bolts, then the cover.
8. **On models up to serial No. 288709E,** remove and discard gasket.
9. **On all models,** release staking from intermediate shaft nut, remove and discard nut.
10. Remove bolt securing anti-rotation plate, remove plate.
11. Using a soft metal drift on threaded end of intermediate shaft, drive shaft out of main casing.
12. Remove and discard O-ring from intermediate shaft.
13. Remove and discard O-ring from main casing.
14. Wrap a suitable length of wire around intermediate gears and using assistance, lift gears out of main casing.
15. Remove and discard two taper roller bearings from intermediate gears.
16. Remove and discard collapsible spacer from intermediate gears. **Do not remove bearing tracks at this stage.**
17. Remove five bolts and stud nut securing cover plate/power take-off cover, recover clip. **Note position of stud nut and harness/speedometer cable clip.**
18. Remove cover plate/power take-off cover.
19. **On models up to serial No. 288709E,** remove and discard gasket.
20. **On all models,** remove two countersunk screws securing mainshaft input gear bearing housing.
21. **On models up to serial No. 288709E,** remove bearing housing and the gasket.
22. **On models from serial No. 288709E,** remove mainshaft input gear bearing housing. **Do not remove mainshaft input gear bearing track at this stage.**
23. **On all models,** remove mainshaft input gear together with taper roller bearings.
24. Remove and discard mainshaft oil seal from main casing.
25. Remove six bolts securing high/low cross shaft housing, then the cross shaft housing.
26. **On models up to serial No. 288709E,** remove and discard gasket.
27. **On all models,** loosen locknut and remove differential lock warning lamp switch from front output housing.
28. Remove eight bolts securing front output housing to main casing, note position of longest bolt.
29. Remove front output housing.
30. **On models up to serial No. 288709E,** remove and discard gasket.
31. **On all models,** remove bolts and washers securing rear output housing to main casing, note their position for installation reference.
32. Remove rear output housing.
33. **On models up to serial No. 288709E,** remove and discard gasket.
34. **On all models,** remove plug securing high/low selector shaft detent spring and ball.
35. Remove detent spring.
36. Remove ball using a stick magnet. **Suitably identify plug, detent spring and ball to their installed positions, do not interchange with differential lock selector shaft detent components.**
37. Remove differential assembly together with high/low selector shaft and fork.

BORG WARNER 44-62

1. Thoroughly clean exterior of transfer case.
2. Drain transfer case oil into a suitable container.
3. Remove the brake drum assembly.
4. Remove six bolts and withdraw rear output housing complete with output shaft, **Fig. 9.**
5. Remove eight bolts and withdraw front output housing complete with viscous unit, **Fig. 10.**
6. Remove 11 bolts attaching front and rear cover together.
7. Clean any previous sealant from threads of bolts.
8. Using two suitable levers between cast lugs on outer edges of casing, carefully separate front cover from rear cover. **Do not lever between mating faces.**
9. Mark one chain link and corresponding tooth on transfer sprocket with an identification line. **This is to ensure balance of unit when reassembled with original components and to ensure chain is installed correct way up.**
10. Remove circlip retaining transfer sprocket to transfer shaft.
11. Place two thin pieces of wood on joint face to prevent damage and using two suitable levers behind differential assembly carefully lever differential bearing from its bore while simultaneously easing transfer sprocket off transfer shaft to maintain alignment during removal, **Fig. 11.**

12. Remove transfer sprocket and differential assembly from chain.
13. Install a screw driver between anti-rotation dowel and snap ring gently pry snap ring out of groove.
14. Withdraw carrier complete with transfer shaft, then the anti-rotation dowel.
15. Using Torx bit 25 remove screw attaching selector arm to selector lever shaft, **Fig. 12.**
16. Remove retaining clip attaching selector fork arm to selector lever shaft.
17. Using Torx bit 25 remove screw retaining selector lever.
18. Remove selector lever shaft from case and fork assembly.
19. Withdraw selector fork assembly and selector sleeve.
20. Retrieve selector plunger and spring from rear cover.
21. Turn case over and pry end cap off planetary set housing.
22. Remove circlip retaining sun gear shaft.
23. Turn casing over and remove large snap ring retaining planetary set, **Fig. 13.**
24. Withdraw annulus and planetary set housing, complete with oil pump, feed pipe and filter.

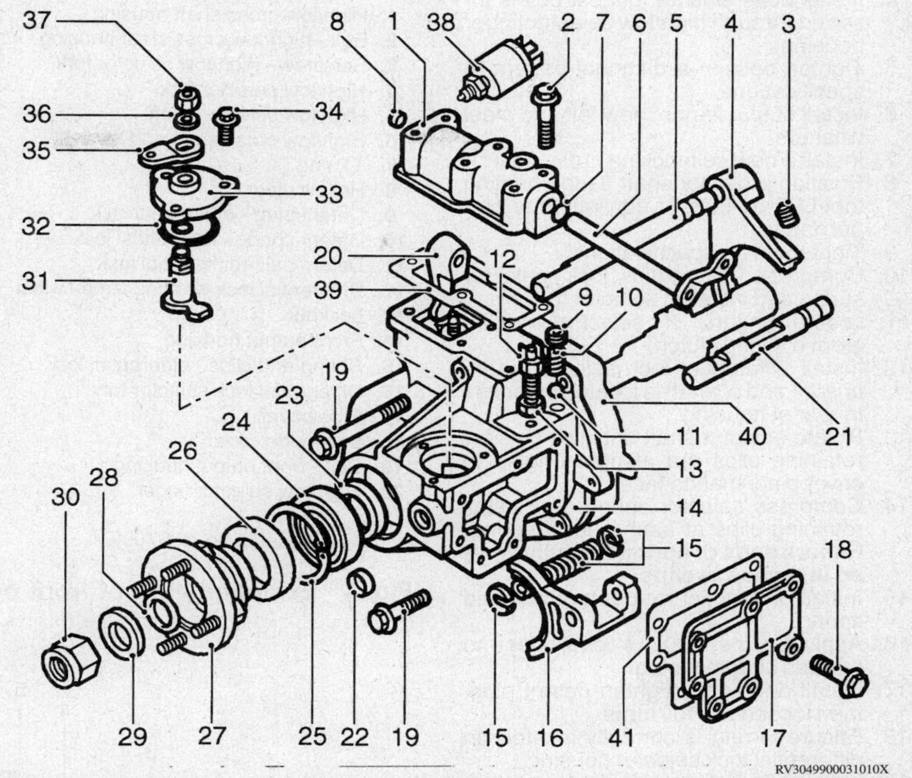

Fig. 1 Exploded view of front output housing (Part 1 of 2). LT230Q & LT230T

ASSEMBLE

LT230Q, LT230SE & LT230T

Mainshaft Input Gear Bearing Preload

1. Position mainshaft input gear assembly in main casing.
2. **On models up to serial No. 288709E,** install a new mainshaft input gear bearing housing gasket, dry on main casing.
3. **On all models,** install mainshaft input gear bearing housing and finger tighten bolts and stud nut.
4. Install mainshaft and engage spline.
5. Install spring balance tool No. LRT-41-005, or equivalent, then secure a length of cord to split pin of the tool, attach other end of cord to a spring balance.
6. Tension cord and note load to turn figure recorded on spring balance when mainshaft rotates.
7. Ensure measurement obtained is within specified load to turn limits: Load to turn - bearing preload = 16-63 ft. lbs.
8. If load to turn measurement is not as specified, remove mainshaft input gear bearing housing.
9. Using a soft metal drift, carefully drive input gear bearing track out of bearing housing and remove shim. **If bearing track is damaged during this operation, a new track must be installed.**
10. Measure thickness of shim removed and select a thicker or thinner shim from the range available. **Shims are available rising in thickness by increments of. 0009 inch. A thicker shim will increase load to turn, a thinner shim will decrease load to turn.**
11. Install selected shim and using a suitable mandrel, install input gear bearing track and repeat load to turn check as necessary until load to turn is as specified.
12. Record final load to turn figure. Differential load to turn/bearing preload

Differential Load To Turn/ Bearing Preload

1. Position high/low selector shaft and fork to differential ensuring that fingers of selector fork are located in high/low selector sleeve.
2. Position high/low selector shaft and differential in main casing.
3. **On models up to serial No. 288709E,** install a new front output housing gasket on main casing.
4. **On all models,** install front output housing, ensure splines of output shaft are engaged in differential and internal splines of dog clutch are engaged with teeth of output shaft.
5. Install and finger tighten eight bolts, ensure longest bolt is inserted through high/low selector finger housing.
6. Select high or low gear.
7. Wrap a length of cord around exposed splines of high/low selector hub, attach other end of cord to a spring balance.
8. Tension cord and note load to turn measurement recorded on spring balance when differential rotates.
9. Ensure measurement obtained is within specified load to turn limits: Load to turn - bearing preload = 9.5-32 ft. lbs.
10. If load to turn measurement is not as specified, remove front output housing.
11. Remove output shaft, dog clutch and bearing spacer.
12. Using a soft metal drift, carefully drive differential bearing track out of front output housing and remove shim.
13. Measure thickness of shim removed and select a thicker or thinner shim from the range available. **A thicker shim will increase load to turn, a thinner shim will decrease load to turn.**
14. Install selected shim and differential bearing track.
15. Install output shaft, dog clutch and bearing spacer. Ensuring chamfer on spacer is positioned towards threaded end of shaft and flange on dog clutch is towards splined end of shaft.
16. Repeat load to turn check as necessary until load to turn is as specified.
17. Remove front output housing.
18. **On models up to serial No. 288709E,** retain gasket on main casing.

Front Output Housing

1. **On models from serial No. 288709E,** apply Hylomar RTV 102 sealant, or equivalent to mating flange of front output housing.
2. **On all models,** install front output housing, ensure splines of output shaft are engaged in differential and internal splines of dog clutch are engaged with teeth of output shaft.
3. Apply Loctite 290, or equivalent to threads of bolts.

4. Install bolts, ensure longest bolt is inserted through high/low selector finger housing.
5. Tighten bolts in a diagonal pattern to specifications.
6. Install output flange, new felt and steel washers.
7. Install a new self-locking nut.
8. Position propeller shaft flange holding tool LRT-51-003, or equivalent to output flange.
9. Tighten nut to specifications.
10. Compress differential lock selector spring and install in selector fork.
11. Locate fingers of selector fork in groove in dog clutch.
12. Install differential lock selector shaft, ensure end of shaft is located in recess in rear of housing.
13. Rotate selector shaft until two flats for retaining clips are at right angles to cover plate mating face.
14. Compress selector spring and install retaining clips at each end of spring. **Ensure ends of spring are fully seated in recess in clips.**
15. Install differential lock detent ball and spring.
16. Apply Loctite 290, or equivalent to threads of detent plug.
17. Install and lightly tighten detent plug, then loosen two full turns.
18. Ensure O-ring is correctly located on differential lock selector housing.
19. Install differential lock selector assembly, ensure selector finger is located in recess of differential lock selector shaft.
20. Apply Loctite 290, or equivalent to threads of bolts, then install and tighten to specifications.
21. Operate differential lock selector lever and ensure differential lock detent ball engages and disengages with grooves in selector shaft. Screw detent plug in or out until setting is correct.
22. Install differential lock warning lamp switch.
23. **On models up to serial No. 288709E,** apply grease to new high/low selector housing gasket, position gasket on front output housing.
24. **On models from serial No. 288709E,** apply Hylosil RTV 102 sealant, or equivalent, to mating flange of high/low selector housing.
25. **On all models,** install housing, ensure high/low selector finger is located in recess of high/low selector shaft.
26. Install bolts and tighten to specifications.

Rear Output Housing

1. **On models up to serial No. 288709E,** position a new gasket on main casing.
2. **On models from serial No. 288709E,** apply Hylosil RTV 102 sealant, or equivalent, to mating flange of rear output housing.
3. **On all models,** install rear output housing, ensure splines of output shaft are engaged in differential.
4. Apply Loctite 290, or equivalent, to threads of bolts and shoulder bolt.
5. Install washers to bolts.

1. High/low cross shaft housing
2. Bolt - high/low cross shaft housing
3. Setscrew - high/low selector fork
4. High/low selector fork
5. High/low selector shaft
6. High/low cross shaft and lever
7. 'O' ring
8. Hollow plug
9. Detent plug - differential lock
10. Detent spring - differential lock
11. Detent ball - differential lock
12. Differential lock warning lamp switch
13. Locknut
14. Front output housing
15. Spring and clips - differential lock
16. Differential lock selector fork
17. Side cover
18. Bolt - side cover
19. Bolt - front output housing
20. High/low selector finger
21. Differential lock selector shaft
22. Plug
23. Bearing spacer
24. Output shaft bearing
25. Circlip
26. Oil seal
27. Output shaft flange and mud shield
28. Felt washer
29. Steel washer
30. Self-locking nut
31. Differential lock selector finger and shaft
32. 'O' rings
33. Differential lock selector housing
34. Bolt - housing
35. Selector lever
36. Washer
37. Self-locking nut
38. Neutral warning switch - if fitted
39. Gasket - high/low cross shaft housing *
40. Gasket - front output housing *
41. Gasket - side cover plate *

* Up to serial no. 288709E

RV3049900031020X

Fig. 1 Exploded view of front output housing (Part 2 of 2). LT230Q & LT230T

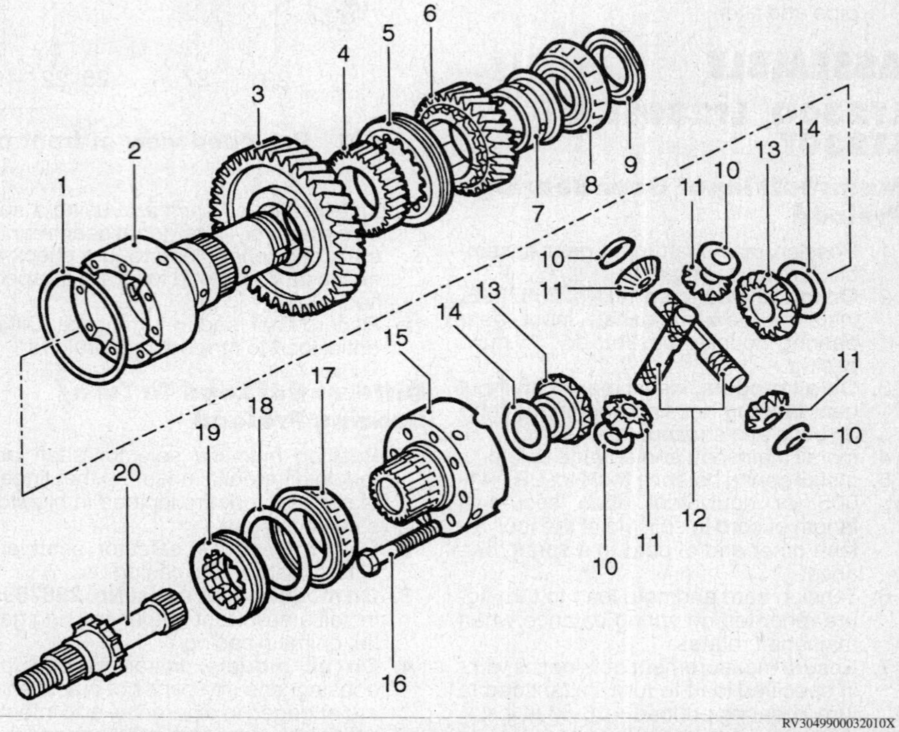

RV3049900032010X

Fig. 2 Exploded view of differential (Part 1 of 2). LT230Q & LT230T

6. Install bolts and tighten in a diagonal pattern to specification.
7. Install output flange, new felt and steel washers to output shaft.
8. Install a new self-locking nut.
9. Position propeller shaft flange holding tool No. LRT-51-003, or equivalent, to output flange and tighten nut.
10. Lubricate new O-ring with recommended oil and install onto vehicle speed sensor.
11. Install vehicle speed sensor and tighten Allen screw.

Intermediate Gears

1. Install a new collapsible spacer into intermediate gears, then the bearings into bearing tracks.
2. Wrap a suitable length of wire around intermediate gears and with assistance, lower gears into main casing. Ensure gears mesh with input and differential gears. **Do not remove wire at this stage.**

3. Lubricate new O-rings with recommended oil and install onto intermediate shaft and main casing.
4. Raise intermediate gears until dummy shaft part No. LRT-41-004, or equivalent, can be inserted from front output housing side of main casing.
5. Install intermediate shaft into position while at the same time removing dummy shaft.
6. Remove wire from around intermediate gears.
7. Rotate intermediate shaft until retaining plate can be inserted into slot in shaft.
8. Apply Loctite 290, or equivalent, to threads of retaining plate bolt, then install and tighten.
9. Install and lightly tighten new intermediate shaft nut

Intermediate Gear Load To Turn/Bearing Preload

1. Ensure spring balance tool No. LRT-41-005, or equivalent, is engaged into mainshaft and cord is attached to split pin of tool.
2. Tension cord and note load to turn measurement recorded on spring balance.
3. Compare this measurement with final load to turn measurement recorded in "Bearing Preload Recorded For Mainshaft Input Gear." Intermediate gear load to turn bearing preload is correct when mainshaft input gear load to turn measurement has increased by 15–37 ft. lbs.
4. To increase the load to turn, tighten intermediate shaft nut in small stages, check load to turn measurement at end of each stage. **Take great care not to overtighten nut as this will cause excessive bearing preload. If load to turn figure is inadvertently exceeded, a new collapsible spacer must be installed.**
5. Stake flange of intermediate shaft nut into recess of intermediate shaft.
6. Remove tool No. LRT-41-005, or equivalent.
7. **On models up to serial No. 288709E,** install and tighten countersunk screws to secure mainshaft input gear bearing housing.
8. **On all models,** remove bolts securing housing.
9. **On models from serial No. 288709E,** remove bearing housing, then apply Hylosil RTV 102, or equivalent, sealant to main casing mating face of bearing housing. Position housing on main casing and install countersunk screws.
10. **On all models,** apply Hylosil RTV 102 sealant, or equivalent, or position a new dry gasket to mating face of cover plate/power take-off cover.
11. Position plate/cover on bearing housing, ensure bolt holes are aligned.
12. Position clip to stud nut.
13. Apply Loctite 290, or equivalent, to threads of bolts and stud nut.
14. Install bolts and stud nut, then tighten in a diagonal pattern to specifications.

1. Retaining ring
2. Differential carrier - rear half
3. Low range gear
4. High/low hub
5. High/low selector sleeve
6. High range gear
7. High range gear bush
8. Differential rear bearing
9. Bearing retaining nut
10. Dished thrust washers
11. Planet gears
12. Cross shafts
13. Sun gears
14. Selective thrust washers
15. Differential carrier - front half
16. Bolt - differential carriers
17. Differential front bearing
18. Selective shim
19. Dog clutch
20. Front output shaft

RV3049900032020X

Fig. 2 Exploded view of differential (Part 2 of 2). LT230Q & LT230T

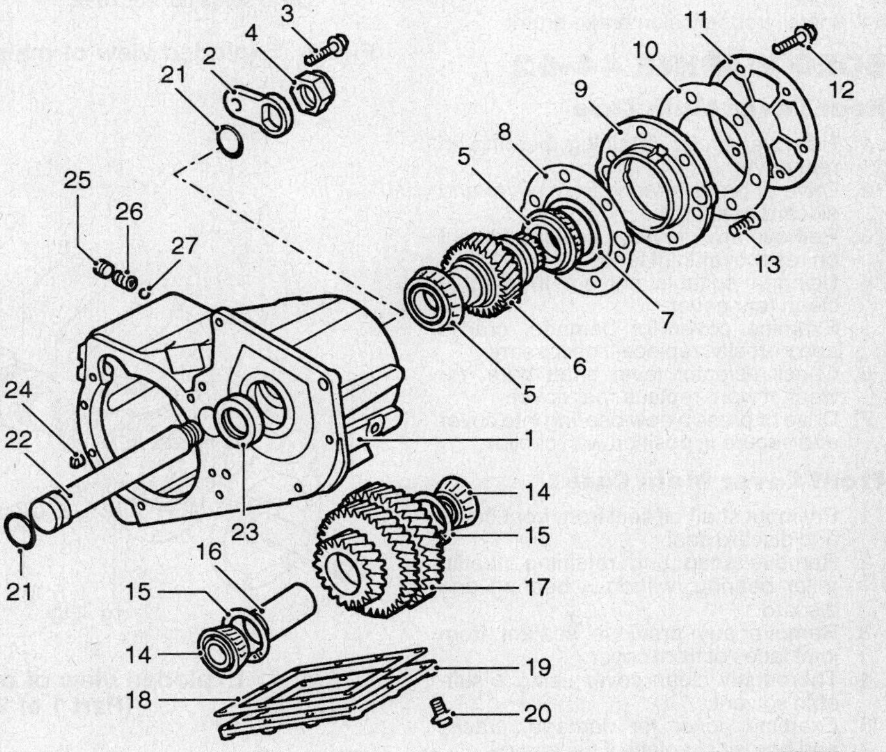

RV3049900033010X

Fig. 3 Exploded view of main casing (Part 1 of 2). LT230Q & LT230T

Bottom Cover

1. **On models up to serial No. 288709E,** position new bottom cover gasket on main casing.
2. **On models from serial No. 288709E,** apply Hylosil RTV 102, or equivalent, sealant to mating face of bottom cover.
3. **On all models,** install bottom cover.
4. Apply Loctite 290 to threads of bottom cover attaching bolts.
5. Install bolts in positions shown and tighten in a diagonal pattern to specifications.

High/Low Selector Shaft Detent

1. Install detent ball and spring.
2. Apply Loctite 290, or equivalent, to threads of detent plug.
3. Install and lightly tighten plug, then loosen two full turns.
4. Operate high/low selector lever and ensure detent ball engages and disengages with grooves in selector shaft. Screw plug in or out until setting is correct.

Differential Lock Warning Lamp Switch Adjustment

1. Move differential lock selector fork to differential locked position.
2. Connect a 12V test lamp and battery to differential lock switch.
3. Screw switch in until test lamp is illuminated, then screw switch in a half turn further, tighten locknut.
4. Disengage differential lock, ensure test lamp goes out.
5. Remove test lamp.
6. **On models up to serial No. 288709E,**

apply grease to a new gasket and install in differential lock side cover.
7. **On models from serial No. 288709E,** apply Hylosil RTV 102, or equivalent, sealant to mating face of differential lock side cover.
8. **On all models,** install side cover and cover attaching bolts, tighten to specifications.

Transmission Brake

1. Apply Hylosil RTV 102, or equivalent, sealant to mating face of rear output housing.
2. Position brake backplate on rear output housing, ensure marks are aligned.
3. Install bolts and tighten to specifications.
4. Install transmission brake drum.

BORG WARNER 44-62

Rear Cover Main Case

1. Remove circlip retaining bearing in rear cover.
2. Drive or press bearing from cover and discard bearing.
3. Remove any previous sealant evident on rear cover joint faces.
4. Using a suitable solvent thoroughly clean rear cover.
5. Examine cover for damage, cracks and porosity, replace if necessary.
6. Check selector lever shaft bore, for wear. If worn replace rear cover.
7. Drive or press a new bearing into cover and secure in position with circlip.

Front Cover Main Case

1. Pry input shaft oil seal from front cover and discard seal.
2. Remove snap ring retaining needle roller bearing, withdraw bearing and discard.
3. Remove any previous sealant from joint faces of front cover.
4. Thoroughly clean cover using a suitable solvent.
5. Examine cover for damage, cracks and porosity, replace if necessary.
6. Check inside edges of case for witness marks which may indicate a chain that has stretched.
7. Lubricate a new oil seal. Using seal installer tool No. LST550–6 or equivalent, in conjunction with bearing and oil seal replacer tool No. 18G134 or equivalent, install seal open side leading, until face of seal is. 039 inch. below surface of boss, **Fig. 14.**
8. Lubricate a new needle roller bearing and drive or press bearing into its recess until contact is made with shoulder at bottom of bore.
9. Install snap ring to retain bearing.

Planetary Set (Epicyclic Unit) & Oil Pump

The Epicylic unit and oil pump are serviced as a complete assembly, if after inspection either of the units is found to be worn or damaged a complete new assembly must be installed.

1. Remove annulus from planetary set.

1. Main casing
2. Retaining plate
3. Bolt - retaining plate
4. Stake nut - intermediate shaft
5. Bearings - mainshaft input gear
6. Mainshaft input gear *
7. Selective shim
8. Gasket **
9. Mainshaft input gear bearing housing
10. Gasket **
11. Cover plate/power take-off cover *
12. Bolt - cover plate
13. Countersunk screw - bearing housing
14. Bearings - intermediate gears
15. Circlips
16. Collapsible spacer
17. Intermediate gears
18. Gasket **
19. Bottom cover plate
20. Bolt - bottom cover plate
21. 'O' rings - intermediate shaft
22. Intermediate shaft
23. Mainshaft oil seal
24. Locating dowel
25. Detent plug - high/low selector
26. Detent spring - high/low selector
27. Detent ball - high/low selector

* Defender mainshaft input gear and Discovery power take-off cover plate illustrated
** Up to serial no. 288709E

RV3049900033020X

Fig. 3 Exploded view of main casing (Part 2 of 2). LT230Q & LT230T

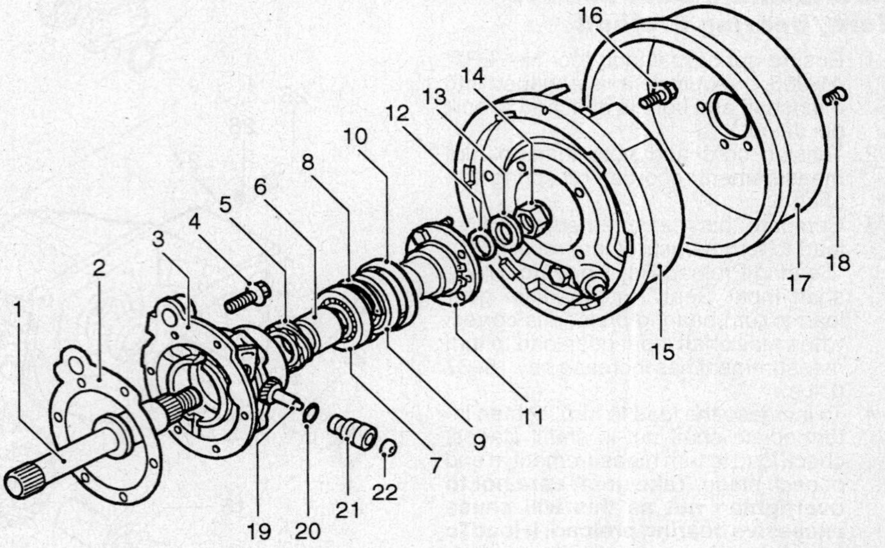

Fig. 4 Exploded view of output housing & transmission brake (Part 1 of 2). LT230Q & LT230T

2. Thoroughly clean all components using a suitable solvent.
3. Examine helical teeth of annulus for wear or damage.
4. Examine planetary gears and high/low gear teeth for wear or damage.
5. Check end float of four planet gears, between end of gear and planetary set carrier. End float of each planet gear should not exceed. 033 inch, **Fig. 15.**
6. Check end float of sun gear to planetary set carrier by using a dial indicator, position base on top of assembly and zero indicator on end of sun gear shaft, lift shaft and check end float. End float should not exceed. 033 inch, **Fig. 16.**
7. To aid in reassembly, mark an identification line on edges of oil pump plates. **The front plate of oil pump is stamped "Top," center bearing plate is stamped "Rear," and rear plate is stamped "Top Rear."**
8. Remove four bolts attaching pump front and rear plates, separating pump by removing plungers, spring and bearing plate.
9. Depress retaining clips, remove oil pick up pipe and rubber connection tubes. Examine tubes and pipes for damage or fractures.
10. Clean pump components and check for damage and wear such as blueing of pump, plungers, scoring of center bearing center plate. If any wear is evident a new planetary set must be Installed, as pump is a part of complete assembly.
11. Thoroughly clean oil pick up filter. examine filter screen for damage and blockage, replace or clean filter as necessary.
12. Clean sealant from oil pump attaching screws.
13. Prior to assembly lubricate pump components with clean oil.
14. Install plate stamped "Top" to sun gear shaft with word "Top" facing planetary assembly, **Fig. 17.**
15. Install plungers and spring noting that flats on plungers must be uppermost to

enable "Top Rear" plate to be installed.
16. Compress plungers and install middle bearing plate with word "Rear" uppermost.
17. Align offset fixings holes and also noting previously marked identification mark.
18. Install top rear plate with words "Top Rear" uppermost.
19. Apply Loctite 242 or equivalent, to threads of four screws and install screws, tightening to specifications.
20. Install rubber connection tube and oil pick up pipe to oil pump and retaining clip.
21. Install rubber connection tube to filler end of pipe and install clip.
22. Push filter into tube.
23. Lubricate planetary set and annulus with clean oil.
24. Position annulus around planetary set, install assembly to rear cover, locating oil pump inlet port in groove at bottom of planetary set housing, sun gear shaft in bearing and lugs on outer edge of annulus in anti rotation lugs, **Fig. 18. It may be necessary to tap sun gear shaft into bearing to enable large ring gear snap ring to be installed.**
25. Install snap ring with stepped ends adjacent to selector shaft bore.
26. Turn rear cover over and install circlip to retain sun gear shaft.
27. Remove any previous sealant from end cap. Apply Dow Corning 732 silicon sealant or equivalent, to outside diameter of rear cover, evenly tap cap into position.
28. If necessary reposition filter on oil pick up pipe until lug on filter can be pushed into slot in rear cover.

Selector Fork

1. Remove retaining clip and separate fork from arm, **Fig. 19.**
2. Detach two nylon slippers from selector fork feet and discard.
3. Thoroughly clean all components.
4. Examine fork, arm and pivot pin for wear. Replace as necessary.
5. Remove O-ring and discard. Examine shaft and lever for wear and damage, replace as necessary.
6. Examine selector sleeve teeth and internal splines for damage and wear. Replace as necessary.
7. Install new nylon slippers to fork.
8. Assemble fork to selector arm and secure in position using a new retaining clip.
9. Lightly lubricate and install spring and selector plunger.
10. While compressing plunger and spring, install selector fork, operating arm assembly and selector sleeve simultaneously, **Fig. 20.**
11. Select neutral gear position at operating arm.
12. Install a new O-ring to selector lever shaft.
13. Lubricate O-ring and install lever assembly to rear cover, noting that when fully assembled lever should lie parallel with joint face of rear cover.
14. Install a new retaining clip to secure selector fork operating arm to selector lever shaft.
15. Remove any previous sealant from Torx screw. Align selector lever shaft groove to retaining screw hole, apply a small amount of Loctite 242 or equivalent, to threads of screw and tighten to specifications.
16. Install Torx screw to selector fork operating arm and tighten to specifications.

1. Rear output shaft
2. Gasket *
3. Rear output housing
4. Bolt - rear output housing
5. Speedometer drive gear
6. Spacer
7. Output shaft bearing
8. Circlip
9. Oil seal
10. Mud shield
11. Output shaft flange
12. Felt washer
13. Steel washer
14. Self-locking nut
15. Transmission brake backplate
16. Bolt - transmission brake backplate
17. Transmission brake drum
18. Countersunk screw
19. Speedometer driven gear
20. 'O' ring
21. Speedometer driven gear housing
22. Seal

* Up to serial no. 288709E

RV3049900034020X

Fig. 4 Exploded view of output housing & transmission brake (Part 2 of 2). LT230Q & LT230T

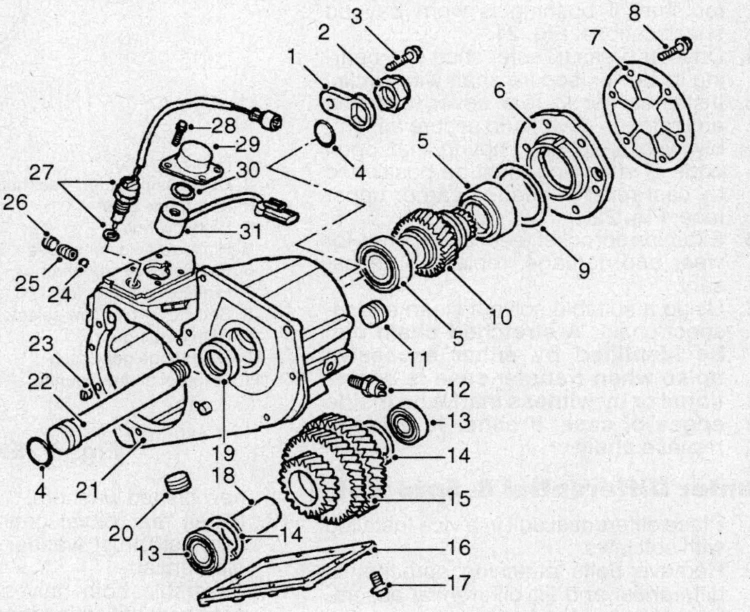

1 Retaining plate
2 Stake nut - intermediate shaft
3 Bolt - retaining plate
4 'O' rings - intermediate shaft
5 Bearings and outer tracks - mainshaft input gear
6 Mainshaft input gear bearing housing
7 Cover plate
8 Bolt - cover plate
9 Selective shim
10 Mainshaft input gear
11 Oil filler/level plug
12 Oil temperature switch - if fitted
13 Bearings and outer tracks - intermediate gears
14 Circlips
15 Intermediate gears
16 Bottom cover plate
17 Bolt - bottom cover plate
18 Selective spacer
19 Mainshaft oil seal
20 Oil drain plug
21 Main casing
22 Intermediate shaft
23 Locating dowel
24 Detent ball - high/low selector
25 Detent spring - high/low selector
26 Detent plug - high/low selector
27 Neutral warning switch
28 Bolt - interlock solenoid cover
29 Cover - interlock solenoid
30 Belleville washer - interlock solenoid
31 Interlock solenoid

RV3049900027000X

Fig. 5 Exploded view of main casing. LT230SE

Bearing Carrier

1. Remove circlip and drive or press transfer shaft from bearing.
2. Remove circlip retaining bearing in carrier.
3. Drive or press bearing from carrier and discard bearing.
4. Clean and examine carrier for cracks and general condition. Replace if necessary.
5. Press or drive a new bearing into carrier and secure with circlip.

Transfer Shaft

1. Clean transfer shaft.
2. Visually examine external splines for damage and wear, if worn replace with new component.
3. Check phosphor bronze bushing for wear by measuring internal diameter of bushing. Bushing diameter must not exceed 1.516 inch. Install a new transfer shaft if bushing is worn beyond specifications, **Fig. 21.**
4. Drive or press transfer shaft into bearing in carrier, secure shaft with circlip.
5. Install carrier to rear cover, then the anti rotation dowel and secure assembly with snap ring, noting that open ends of snap ring must be positioned by cast relief in bearing carrier upper face, **Fig. 22.**
6. Examine sprocket teeth and splines for wear and damage, replace if necessary.
7. Using a suitable solvent clean and inspect chain. **A stretched chain can be identified by either excessive noise when transfer case is operational or by witness marks on inside edges of case. If either is evident, replace chain.**

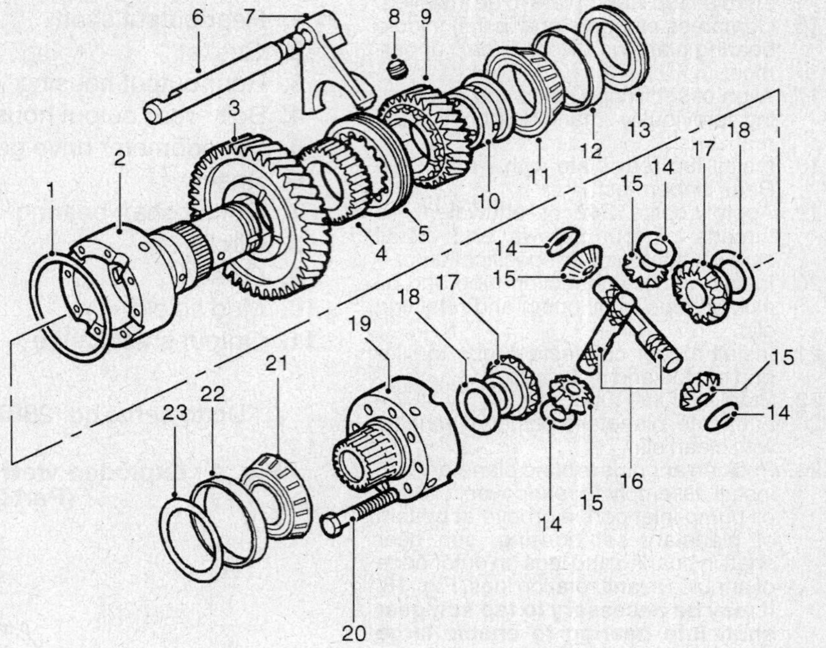

1 Retaining ring
2 Differential carrier - rear half
3 Low range gear
4 High/low hub
5 High/low selector sleeve
6 High/low selector shaft
7 High/low selector fork
8 Setscrew - high/low selector fork
9 High range gear
10 High range gear bush
11 Differential rear bearing
12 Bearing outer track
13 Bearing retaining nut
14 Dished thrust washers
15 Planet gears
16 Cross shafts
17 Sun gears
18 Selective thrust washers
19 Differential carrier - front half
20 Bolt - differential carriers
21 Differential front bearings
22 Bearing outer track
23 Selective shim

RV3049900028000X

Fig. 6 Exploded view of differential. LT230SE

Center Differential & Sprocket

1. Place differential unit in a vice Installed with soft jaws.
2. Remove bolts attaching sprocket to differential and lift differential assembly from sprocket.
3. Examine sprocket teeth for wear and damage, replace if necessary.
4. Using a suitable two legged puller, ease bearings from differential assembly and discard bearings.
5. Secure front half of differential unit in a vice with soft jaws, remove eight retaining bolts attaching front and rear halves of assembly together, lift off rear part of differential unit, **Fig. 23.**
6. Remove rear upper bevel gear and thrust washer.
7. Remove pinion gears and dished washers along with cross shaft.
8. Remove front lower bevel gear and thrust washer from front half of differential unit.
9. Remove front half of differential unit from vice and clean all components. Examine for wear or damage, replace if necessary.
10. Secure front half of differential unit in soft jaw vice, **Fig. 24.**
11. Install front bevel gear without thrust washer and lightly lubricate.
12. Install cross shaft, pinion gears and new dished washers.
13. Install rear bevel gear together with thinnest thrust washer to rear half of differential.
14. Assemble both halves of differential noting identification marks.
15. Install bolts and tighten to specifications.
16. Invert differential unit in vice, install front output housing to differential, locating viscous splines on front bevel gear.
17. Install drive flange to viscous unit and place brake drum on top of drive flange, secure with nut. Ensure gears are free to operate.
18. Tie a length of string around brake drum, attach a spring balance to free end and carefully tension string until a load to turn is achieved, Alternatively use a torque wrench applied to drive flange nut. Rotate brake drum slowly by hand to overcome initial load, **Fig. 25.**
19. Gears that have been run will rotate smoothly and will require a **torque** of five inch. lbs., equivalent force using a spring balance 1 ft. lb. New gears will rotate with a rough feel and will require a **torque** of not more than 20 inch. lbs., equivalent force using a spring balance 3.8 lbs. **Keep all components lubricated when carrying out these adjustments.**
20. Change thrust washer for a thicker one if torque reading is too low an recheck torque. Five thrust washers are available in. 003 inch steps ranging from. 041 to. 057 inch.
21. Dismantle unit when rear bevel gear thrust washer has been selected.
22. Remove and retain rear bevel gear and thrust washer combination.
23. Repeat procedure to obtain correct thrust washer for front bevel gear, it is not necessary to install rear bevel gear when checking front bevel gear rolling resistance.
24. When thrust washer has been selected for bevel gear, again dismantle differential unit and retain thrust washer and front bevel gear combination.
25. Install thrust washer and front bevel gear into front half of differential unit.
26. Install pinion gears with dished washers to cross shaft, then the assembly to differential unit.
27. Install thrust washer and rear bevel gear to rear half of differential unit.
28. Align both haves of differential noting identification marks. Secure both haves together with eight bolts tighten bolts to specifications, **Fig. 23.**
29. Check overall torque required to turn

differential, this should be approximately equal to both bevel gears added together.
30. Drive or press new bearings onto differential, noting smaller of two bearings is installed in rear half of differential.
31. Install center differential sprocket to differential. **Face of sprocket with relieved threads must contact flange of differential housing.**
32. Install new bolts and tighten evenly to specifications.
33. Place differential assembly and transfer sprocket inside chain. **If original components are being used observe identification marks previously applied to chain and transfer sprocket.**
34. Carefully tap differential bearing into its bore while easing transfer sprocket onto transfer shaft.
35. Ensure transfer sprocket is fully down and secure sprocket to transfer shaft with circlip.
36. Ensure joint faces of front and rear covers are clean and apply a bead of Dow Corning 732 silicone sealant or equivalent, on joint face of rear cover and evenly spread sealant over face. **Do not over apply sealant.**
37. Install front cover, secure with 11 bolts and tighten evenly to specifications. **Do not wipe away surplus sealant which is forced out of joint.**

Rear Output Housing

1. Support rear output housing by output shaft in a soft jaw vice.
2. Using Adjustable flange holding wrench tool No. 18G1205 or equivalent, restrain drive flange, release and remove nylon lock nut and plain washer attaching drive flange to output shaft, withdraw rubber seal. Discard nut and seal.
3. Remove drive flange from output shaft and examine for damage or wear particularly seal running surface.
4. If surface is corroded or a groove has been worn by previous seal, replace flange.
5. Pry speedometer sleeve and driven gear from housing, **Fig. 26.**
6. Examine gear teeth for wear, replace if necessary.
7. Pry oil seal from sleeve and remove O-ring, discard both seal and O-ring.
8. Clean sleeve and drive or press output shaft from housing.
9. Clean and inspect splines and speedometer drive gear for wear or damage, replace if necessary.
10. **While output shaft is removed from rear output housing, check rolling resistance of viscous unit as follows:**
    a. Testing should be carried out in an ambient temperature of 68°F.
    b. Secure output shaft in soft jaw vice, gripping flange splines, **Fig. 27.**
    c. With viscous unit still installed in front output housing place assembly on rear output shaft spline.
    d. Apply a clockwise **torque** of 20 ft. lbs. to output flange nut.

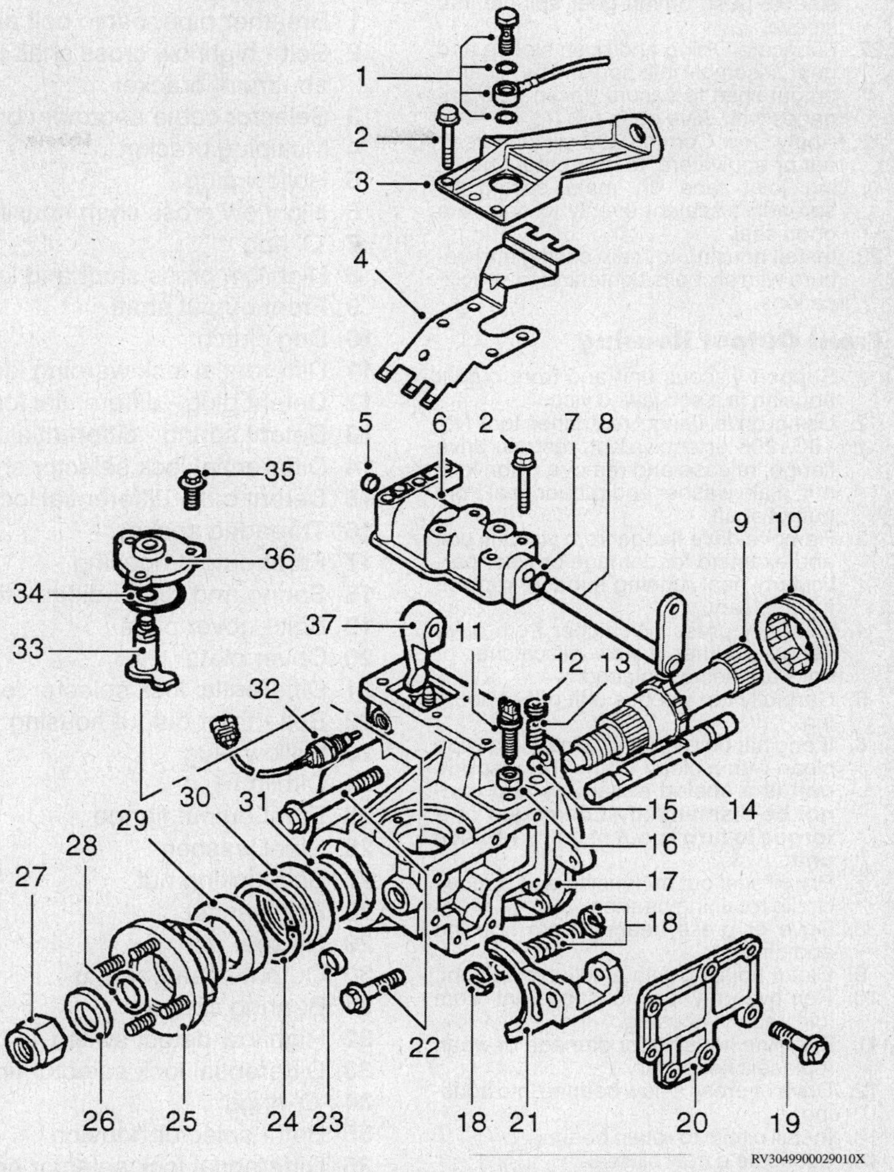

Fig. 7 Exploded view of front output housing (Part 1 of 2). LT230SE

    e. If no resistance to turn is felt, unit requires replacement.
    f. If resistance to turn is felt, apply a clockwise **torque** of 15 ft. lbs., to output flange nut for one minute, this should result in a rotation of approximately 25°–30°.
    g. If no rotation or a greater force is required, unit requires replacement.
11. Pry dust shield, then oil seal off rear output housing, **Fig. 28.**
12. Remove circlip retaining bearing.
13. Drive or press bearing from housing and discard.
14. Remove any previous sealant from housing joint face.
15. Thoroughly clean all components with a suitable solvent.
16. Examine housing for damage or wear, replace if necessary.
17. Drive or press new bearing into housing until bearing contacts shoulder.
18. Install circlip.
19. Lubricate a new oil seal. Using oil seal replacer tool No. 18G1422 or equivalent, install seal lip side leading until it contacts circlip.
20. Install dust shield.
21. Place ball bearing in indent on output shaft, install speedometer drive gear to shaft and secure together with circlip.
22. Press or drive output shaft into housing until shoulder of shaft contacts bearing.
23. Lubricate oil seal bearing surface of drive flange and install flange followed by a new rubber seal.
24. Install steel washer and secure flange to shaft using a new nut. Tighten to specifications.
25. Lubricate new speedometer sleeve oil seal and press seal into top of sleeve.
26. Install a new O-ring to outside of

sleeve, push driven gear spindle into sleeve.

27. Lubricate O-ring and push sleeve and gear assembly into housing by rotating output shaft to ensure driven gear engages with drive gear.
28. Apply Dow Corning 732 silicone sealant or equivalent, to rear output housing joint face on main casing by spreading sealant evenly to ensure a good seal.
29. Install housing to main casing and secure with six bolts tightening to specifications.

Front Output Housing

1. Support viscous unit and front output housing in a soft jawed vice.
2. Using drive flange restrainer tool No. 18G1205 or equivalent, restrain drive flange, release and remove nylon lock nut, plain washer and rubber seal from output shaft.
3. Remove drive flange from viscous unit and examine for damage or wear particularly seal running surface, replace if necessary.
4. Carefully press oil catcher from drive flange if either a new oil catcher or bolts are being replaced.
5. Carefully tap viscous unit out of housing.
6. If original unit is being reinstalled wipe clean with a clean cloth. **The viscous unit is a sealed assembly and cannot be dismantled, if damaged or if torque to turn is out of limits replace unit.**
7. Pry oil seal out of housing and remove circlip retaining bearing.
8. Drive or press bearing from housing and discard.
9. Clean housing with a suitable solvent.
10. Remove any previous sealant from joint face of housing.
11. Examine housing for damage or wear, replace if necessary.
12. Drive or press a new bearing into housing.
13. Install circlip to retain bearing.
14. Lubricate a new oil seal.
15. Using oil seal replacing tool No. 18G1422 or equivalent, install seal lip side of seal leading until it contacts circlip.
16. Carefully tap viscous unit into housing until it contacts circlip.
17. Lubricate lips of seal and install flange followed by a new rubber seal.
18. Install steel washer and secure flange with a new nut tightening to specifications.

1 Breather pipe, banjo bolt and sealing washers
2 Bolt - high/low cross shaft housing and abutment bracket
3 Selector cable abutment bracket
4 Multiplug bracket
5 Hollow plug
6 High/low cross shaft housing
7 'O' ring
8 High/low cross shaft and lever
9 Front output shaft
10 Dog clutch
11 Differential lock warning lamp switch
12 Detent plug - differential lock
13 Detent spring - differential lock
14 Differential lock selector shaft
15 Detent ball - differential lock
16 Threaded spacer
17 Front output housing
18 Spring and clips - differential lock
19 Bolt - cover plate
20 Cover plate
21 Differential lock selector fork
22 Bolt - front output housing
23 Hollow plug
24 Circlip
25 Front output flange
26 Steel washer
27 Self-locking nut
28 Felt washer
29 Oil seal
30 Output shaft bearing
31 Bearing spacer
32 High/low detect switch
33 Differential lock selector finger and shaft
34 'O' rings
35 Bolt - selector housing
36 Differential lock selector housing
37 High/low selector finger

RV3049900029020X

Fig. 7 Exploded view of front output housing (Part 2 of 2). LT230SE

19. Apply Dow Corning 732 silicone sealant or equivalent, to output housing joint face of main casing spreading sealant evenly to ensure a good seal.
20. Install housing to main case a secure in position with eight bolts tightened evenly to specifications.

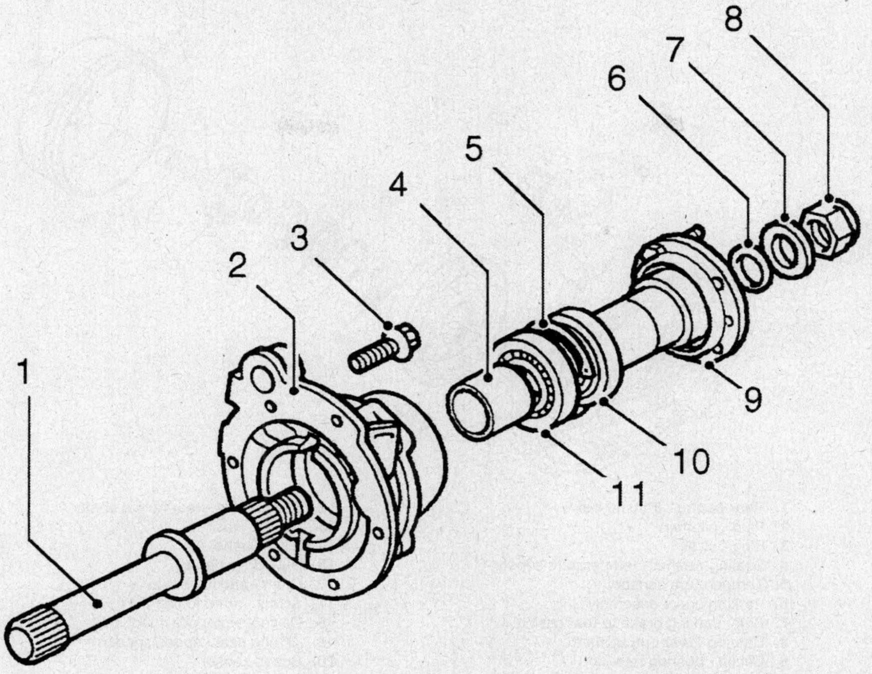

1 Rear output shaft
2 Rear output housing
3 Bolt - rear output housing
4 Spacer
5 Circlip
6 Felt washer
7 Steel washer
8 Self-locking nut
9 Rear output flange
10 Oil seal
11 Output shaft bearing

RV3049900030000X

Fig. 8 Exploded view of rear output housing. LT230SE

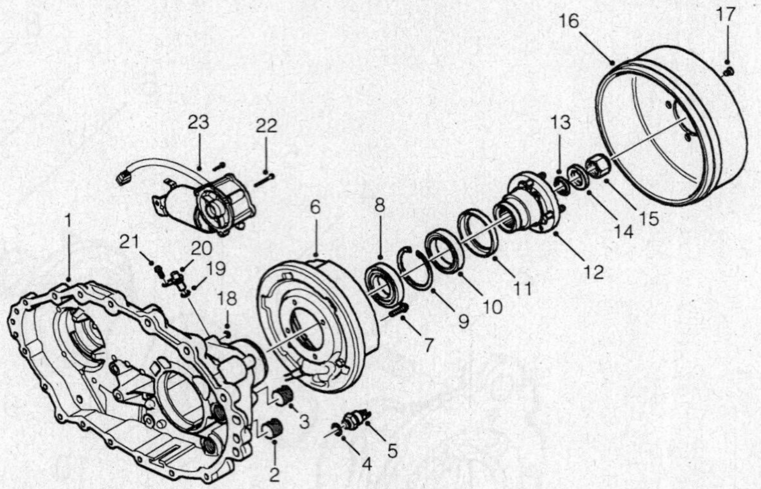

1. Rear casing - transfer box
2. Plug - oil drain
3. Plug - oil fill
4. Sealing washer - temperature sensor
5. Temperature sensor
6. Parking brake assembly
7. Bolt - parking brake to rear casing
8. Bearing - rear output shaft
9. Circlip - bearing retention
10. Oil seal - rear output shaft
11. Dust shroud
12. Drive flange - rear output shaft
13. Sealing washer
14. Plain washer
15. Nut - drive flange
16. Drum - parking brake
17. Screw - drum to flange
18. Oil seal - interlock spool shaft
19. 'O' ring seal - speed sensor
20. Speed sensor
21. Bolt - speed sensor
22. Bolt - ratio control motor to rear casing
23. Ratio control motor

RV3049500002000X

Fig. 9 Exploded view of rear output housing. Borg Warner 44–62

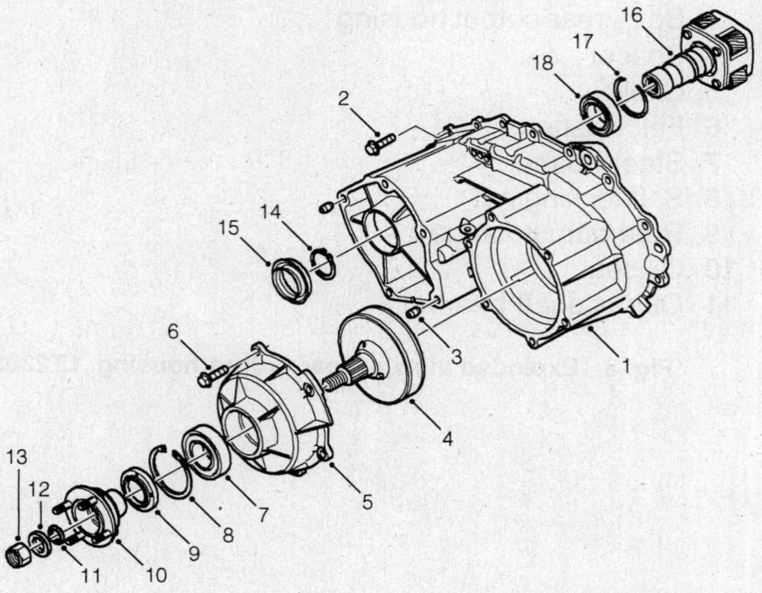

1. Front casing - transfer box
2. Bolt - front casing to rear casing
3. Dowel - transfer box to gearbox
4. Viscous coupling
5. Housing - viscous coupling
6. Bolt - viscous coupling housing to front casing
7. Bearing - front output shaft
8. Circlip - bearing retention
9. Oil seal - front output shaft
10. Drive flange - front output shaft
11. Sealing washer
12. Plain washer
13. Nut - drive flange
14. Circlip - epicyclic gear to bearing
15. Oil seal - input shaft
16. Epicyclic gear set
17. Circlip - bearing retention
18. Bearing - input shaft

RV3049500003000X

Fig. 10 Exploded view of front output housing. Borg Warner 44–62

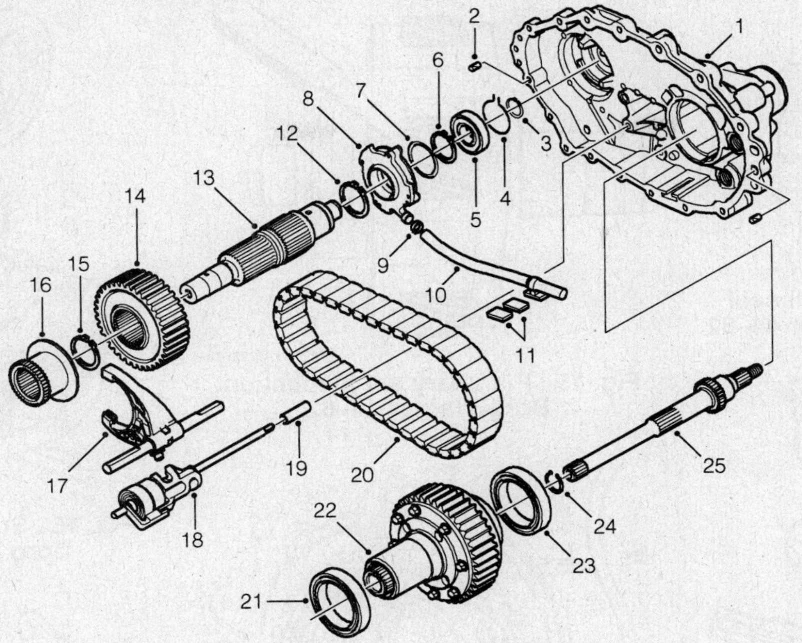

1. Rear casing - transfer box
2. Dowel - front casing to rear casing
3. Circlip - bearing retention
4. Snap ring - bearing to rear casing
5. Bearing - intermediate shaft
6. Circlip - oil pump retention
7. Shim
8. Oil pump
9. Clip - hose to pump
10. Hose and strainer
11. Magnet
12. Circlip - gear retention
13. Intermediate shaft
14. Gear
15. Circlip - gear retention
16. Reduction hub
17. Selector fork assembly
18. Interlock spool
19. Tube spacer
20. Morse chain
21. Bearing - differential
22. Differential assembly
23. Bearing - differential
24. Circlip - gear retention
25. Rear output shaft

RV3049500004000X

Fig. 11 Transfer sprocket & chain. Borg Warner 44–62

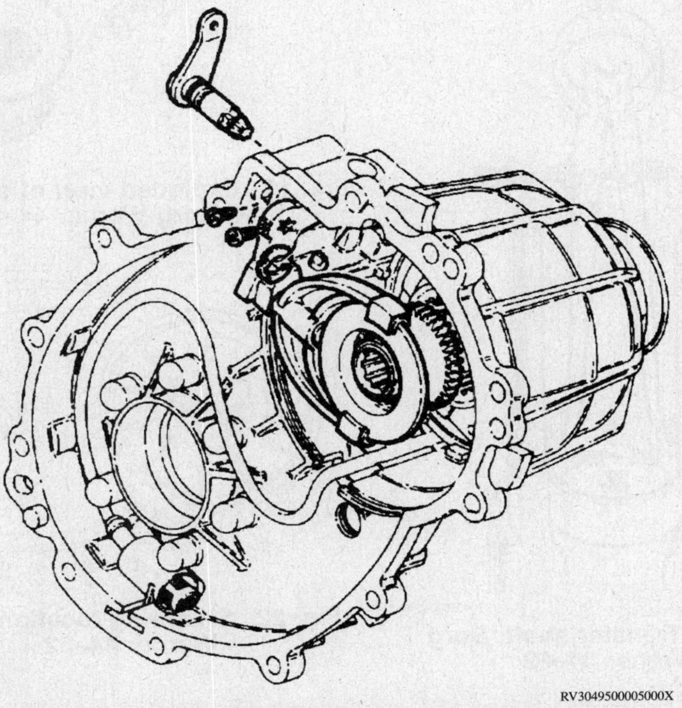

RV3049500005000X

Fig. 12 Selector fork assembly. Borg Warner 44–62

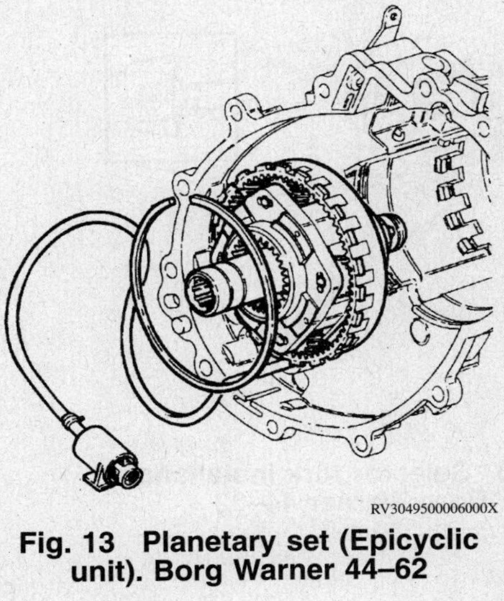

RV3049500006000X

Fig. 13 Planetary set (Epicyclic unit). Borg Warner 44–62

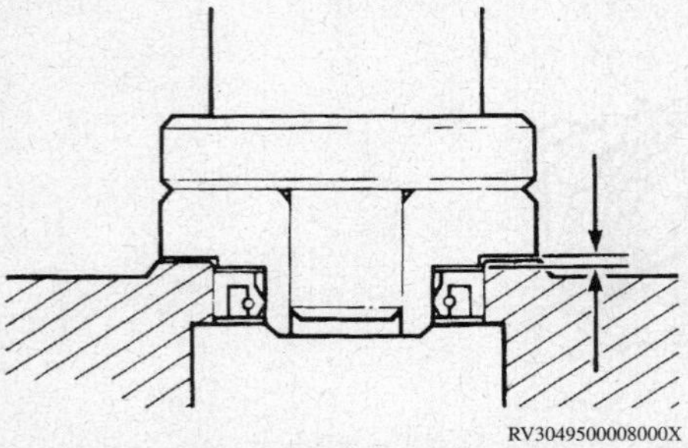

Fig. 14 Front cover oil seal installation. Borg Warner 44–62

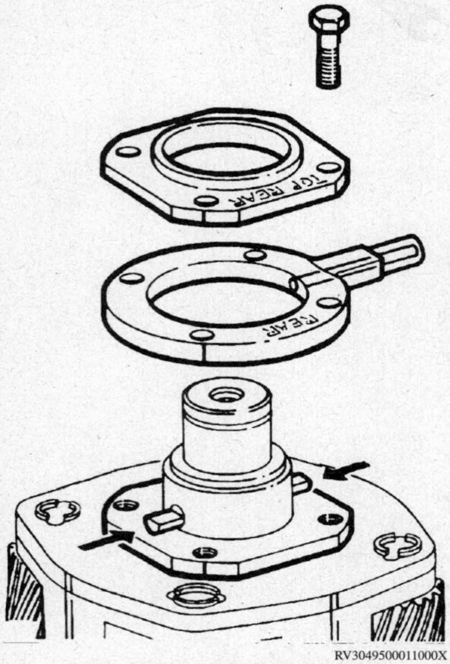

Fig. 17 Oil pump & filter installation. Borg Warner 44–62

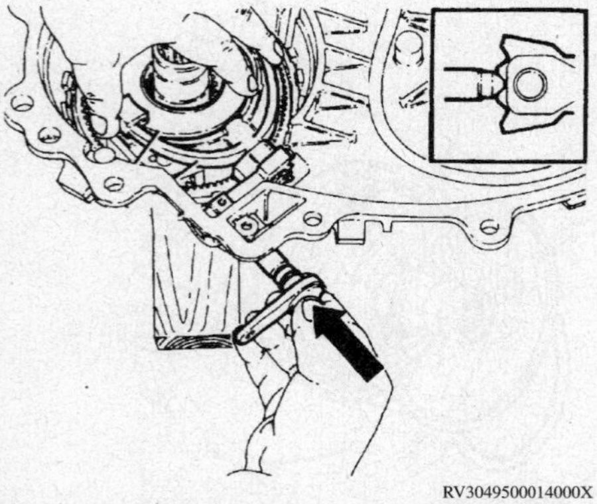

Fig. 20 Selector fork installation. Borg Warner 44–62

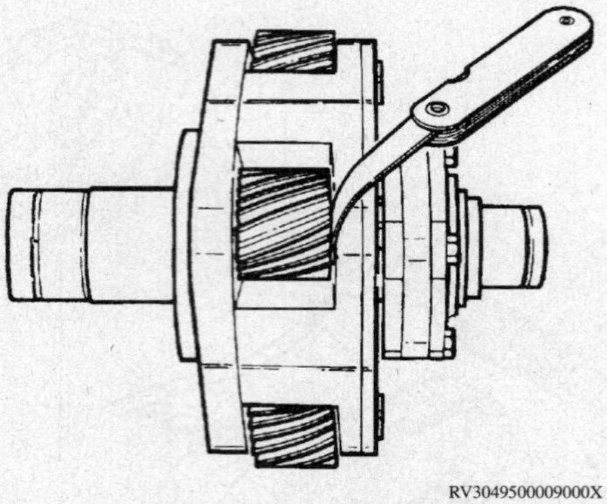

Fig. 15 Planetary set inspection. Borg Warner 44–62

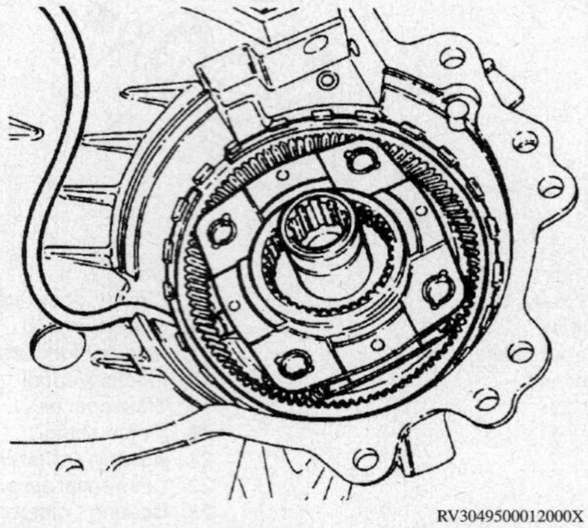

Fig. 18 Planetary set & annulus. Borg Warner 44–62

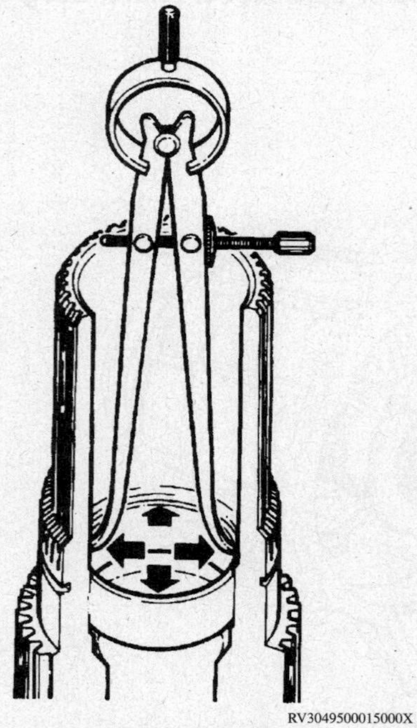

Fig. 21 Transfer shaft. Borg Warner 44–62

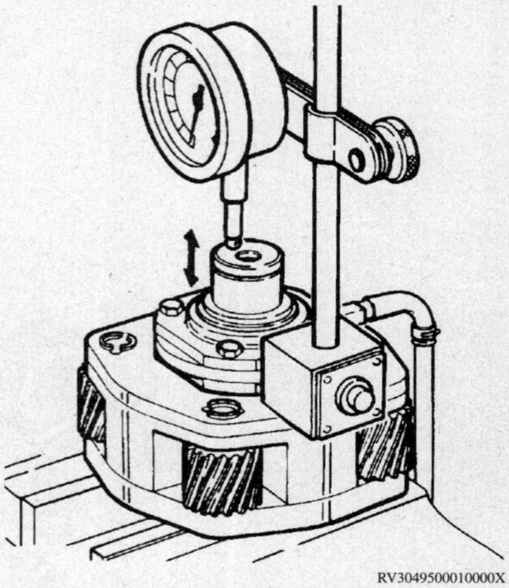

Fig. 16 Sun gear inspection. Borg Warner 44–62

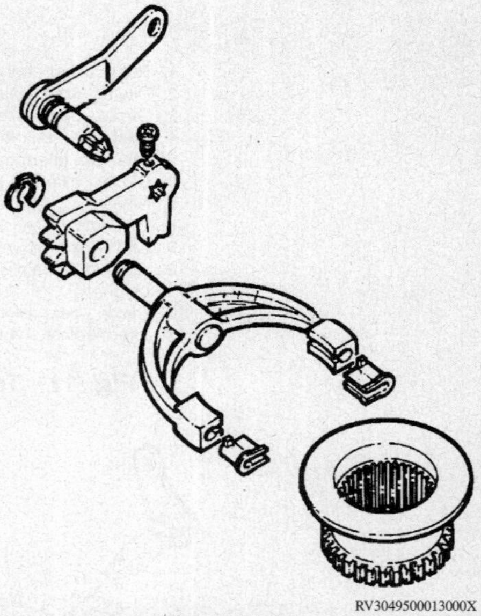

Fig. 19 Exploded view of selector fork. Borg Warner 44–62

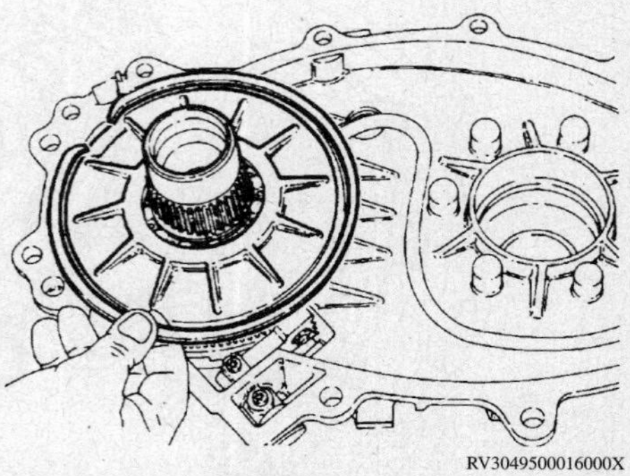

Fig. 22 Snap ring location. Borg Warner 44–62

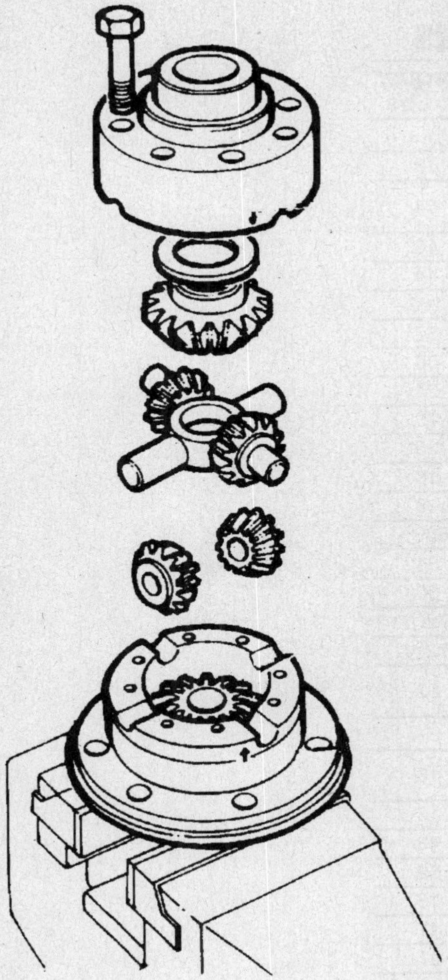

RV3049500017000X

Fig. 23 Exploded view of center differential. Borg Warner 44–62

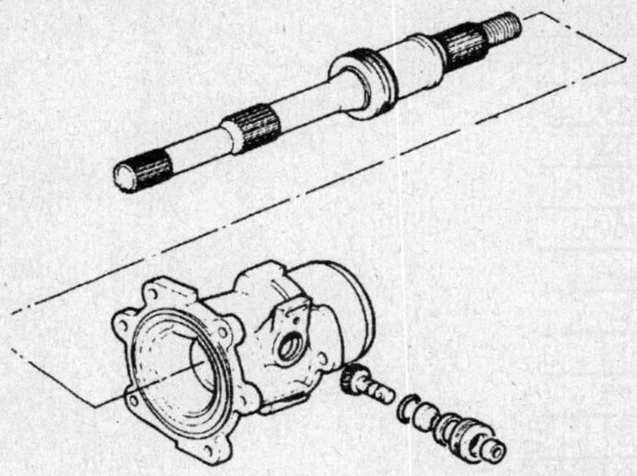

RV3049500020000X

Fig. 26 Exploded view of rear output housing. Borg Warner 44–62

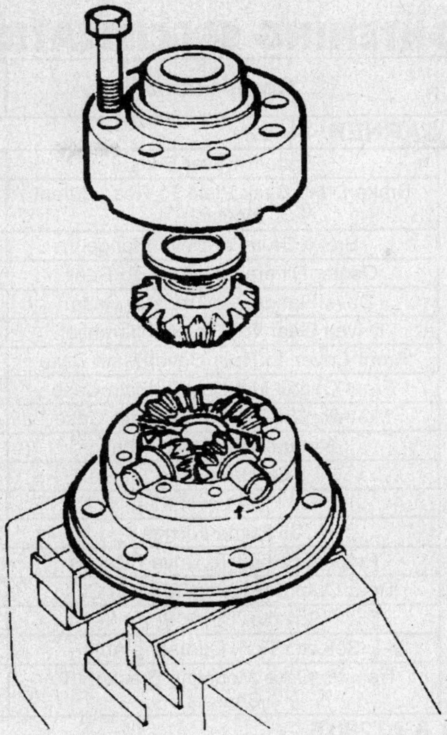

RV3049500018000X

Fig. 24 Differential pinions. Borg Warner 44–62

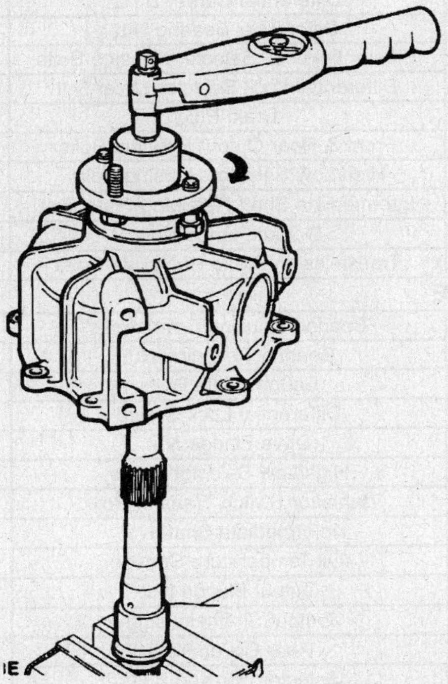

RV3049500021000X

Fig. 27 Viscous unit rolling resistance. Borg Warner 44–62

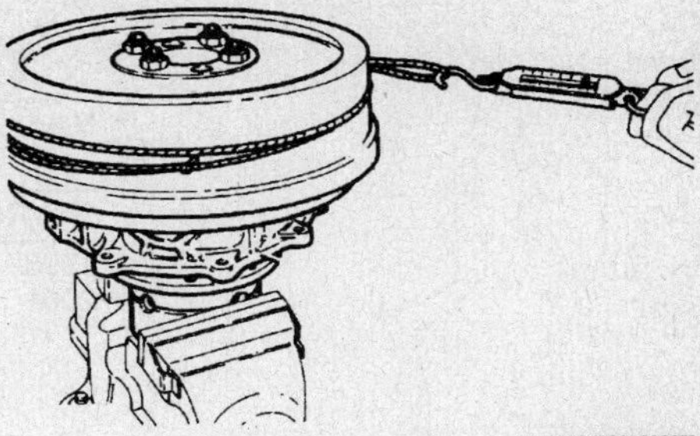

RV3049500019000X

Fig. 25 Differential pinions rolling resistance. Borg Warner 44–62

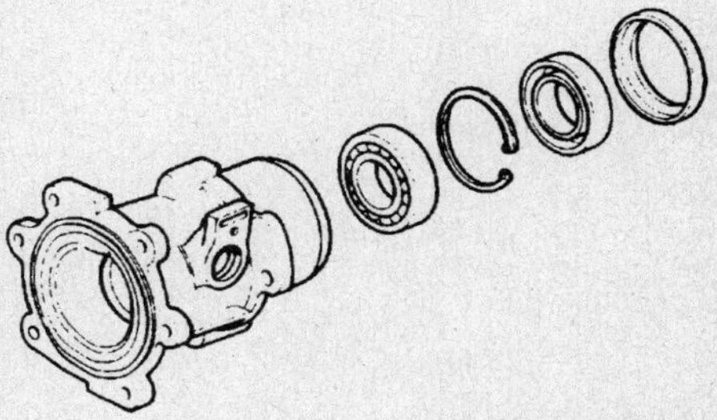

RV3049500022000X

Fig. 28 Rear output housing bearing replacement. Borg Warner 44–62

TIGHTENING SPECIFICATIONS

Year	Component	Torque/ Ft. Lbs.
BORG WARNER 44–62		
1998–2001	Bottom Cover Bolts	18
	Brake Drum Back Plate To Rear Output Housing	54
	Brake Drum To Drive Flange	18
	Center Differential Front To Rear	44
	Drive Flanges To Transfer Case	165
	Driven Gear To Center Differential	37
	Front Cover To Rear Cover-Main Case	30
	Front Output Housing To Main Case	24
	Mounting Bracket To Transfer Case	75
	Neutral Warning Switch	35
	Oil Drain Plug	18
	Oil Filler/Level Plug	18
	Oil Pump Fixings	60①
	Propeller Shaft To Drive Flanges	34
	Rear Output Housing To Main Case	30
	Selector Lever Shaft	72①
	Selector Fork Operating Arm	72①
	Transfer Case Mounting Brackets To Chassis	33
LT230Q & LT230T		
1998–2001	Bearing Housing Cover Plate Bolts & Stud Nut	18
	Bottom Cover Bolts	18
	Differential Carrier Bolts	43
	Differential Bearing Nut	52
	Differential Lock Selector Housing Bolts	18
	Differential Lock Selector Lever Nut	11
	Drain Plug	22
	Front & Rear Output Housing Bolts	18
	High/Low Selector Housing Bolts	18
	Intermediate Shaft Retaining Plate Bolt	18
	Output Flange Nuts	34
	Transmission Brake Backplate Bolts	50
LT230SE		
1998–2001	Bearing Housing/Cover Bolts	18
	Bearing Retaining Nut	53
	Bottom Plate Bolts	18
	Differential Lock Switch	96①
	Drive Flange Nut	109
	High/Low Selector Cable	22
	Inhibitor Switch Transfer Box	19
	Intermediate Shaft Nut	65
	Oil Temperature Sensor	31
	Output Flange Nut	119
	Output Shaft Housing	18
	Rear Cover Plate	18
	Selector Housing Bolts	18
	Side Cover Bolts	18
	Transfer Box To Gearbox Bolts	33

① — Inch lbs.

Front Wheel Drive Axles

DRIVESHAFT

REPLACE

1. Remove center cap from front wheel, release stake from drive shaft nut, then loosen nut.
2. Raise and support vehicle.
3. Remove caliper, disc and disc shield.
4. Disconnect ABS sensor electrical connector then remove ABS sensor and bushing from hub.
5. Remove four bolts securing hub to carrier.
6. Remove hub from carrier, then hub and drive shaft.
7. Remove drive shaft nut, then shaft assembly from hub.
8. Remove drive shaft seal from axle casing.
9. Reverse procedure to install, noting the following:
   a. **Torque** hub and driveshaft bolts to 100 ft. lbs.
   b. **Torque** drive shaft nut to 192 ft. lbs.

Engine Rebuilding Specifications

INDEX

	Page No.		Page No.		Page No.
Camshaft	4-65	Cylinder Head, Valve Guide & Valve Seats	4-65	Pistons, Pins & Rings	4-66
Crankshaft, Bearings & Rods	4-66	Oil Pump	4-66	Valve Springs	4-65
Cylinder Block	4-66			Valves	4-65

CYLINDER HEAD, VALVE GUIDE & VALVE SEATS

All Measurements Given In Inches Unless Otherwise Specified.

Engine Liter	Cylinder Head		Valve Guides			Valve Seats			Valve Clearance	
	Warpage Limit	Minimum Height	Standard Inside Diameter	Stem To Guide Clearance		Seat Angle	Seat Width		Intake	Exhaust
				Intake	Exhaust		Intake	Exhaust		
4.0L	—	—	—	.0010–.0026	.0015–.0031	45	—	—	①	①
4.6L	—	—	—	.0010–.0026	.0015–.0031	45–46	—	—	①	①

① — Hydraulic self-adjusting.

VALVE SPRINGS

All Measurements Given In Inches Unless Otherwise Specified.

Engine Liter	Valve Springs	
	Free Length	Fitted Length
4.0L	1.92	1.61
4.6L	—	1.59–1.61

VALVES

All Measurements Given In Inches Unless Otherwise Specified.

Engine Liter	Valves		
	Stem Diameter		Face Angle, Degrees
	Intake	Exhaust	
4.0L	.3411–.3417	.3406–.3412	45
4.6L	.3411–.3417	.3406–.3412	45–46

CAMSHAFT

All Measurements Given In Inches Unless Otherwise Specified.

Engine Liter	Camshaft Journal Diameter	Camshaft Bearing Clearance	Camshaft Endplay	Lifter Diameter	Lifter To Bore Clearance
4.0L	①	①	.002–.014	—	—
4.6L	①	①	.002–.014	—	—

① — Non-serviceable.

CRANKSHAFT, BEARINGS & RODS

All Measurements Given In Inches Unless Otherwise Specified.

Engine Liter	Crankshaft			Bearing Clearance		Connecting Rod Side Clearance
	Standard Journal Diameter		Endplay	Main Bearing	Connecting Rod Bearing	
	Main Bearing	Connecting Rod				
4.0L	2.4995–2.5000	2.185–2.1855	.004–.008	.00059–.00063	—	—
4.6L	2.4995–2.5000	2.20–2.21	.004–.008	.0004–.002	—	—

PISTONS, PINS & RINGS

All Measurements Given In Inches Unless Otherwise Specified.

Engine Liter	Piston Std. Diameter	Piston Pin Diameter	Piston Pin To Piston Clearance	Piston Ring End Gap			Piston Ring Side Clearance		
				Top	Second	Oil	Top	Second	Oil
4.0L	—	—	.0009–.0026	.012–.020	.0151–.0256	.0150–.0551	.0476–.0484	.0582–.0587	.1181
4.6L	—	—	.0008–.0026	.0118–.0197	.0157–.0256	.0150–.0551	—	—	—

CYLINDER BLOCK

All Measurements Given In Inches Unless Otherwise Specified.

Engine, Liter	Cylinder Bore Std. Diameter
4.0L	3.7008-3.7024
4.6L	3.7008-3.7024

MERCEDES-BENZ

INDEX OF SERVICE OPERATIONS

	Page No.
ACTIVE SUSPENSION SYSTEM	5-321
AIR BAG SYSTEM PRECAUTIONS	0-12
AIR QUALITY STANDARDS	0-23
AUTOMATIC TRANSMISSIONS	5-295
BRAKES	
Anti-Lock Brakes	5-247
Disc Brakes	5-235
Hydraulic Brake Systems	5-242
Power Brake Units	5-244
CLUTCH & MANUAL TRANSMISSION	5-122
Adjustments	5-122
Clutch, Replace	5-122
Technical Service Bulletins	5-122
Transmission, Replace	5-122
COMPUTER RELEARN PROCEDURES	0-10
DRIVE AXLES	5-305
ELECTRICAL	
Air Bags	5-214
Air Conditioning	5-191
Alternators	5-210
Alternator, Replace	5-16
Automatic Seat Belts	5-220
Blower Motor, Replace	5-22
Combination Switch, Replace	5-18
Cooling Fans	5-195
Cruise Controls	5-212
Dash Gauges	5-197
Dash Panels	5-221
Evaporator Core, Replace	5-28
Fuel Pump Relay Location	5-15
Fuse Panel & Flasher Location	5-15
Headlamp Switch, Replace	5-18
Heater Core, Replace	5-23
Ignition Coil, Replace	5-17
Ignition Lock, Replace	5-17
Instrument Cluster, Replace	5-20
Passive Restraints	5-214
Precautions	5-15
Radio, Replace	5-20
Relay Center Location	5-15
Speed Controls	5-212
Starter Motors	5-209
Starter, Replace	5-15
Steering Columns	5-222
Steering Wheel, Replace	5-19
Stop Light Switch, Replace	5-18
Technical Service Bulletins	5-29
Wiper Motor, Replace	5-21
Wiper Systems	5-213
ELECTRICAL SYMBOL IDENTIFICATION	0-33
FRONT SUSPENSION & STEERING	
Ball Joint, Replace	5-154
Ball Joint Boot, Replace	5-154
Ball Joint Inspection	5-153
Coil Spring, Replace	5-155
Control Arm, Replace	5-156
Control Arm Bushing, Replace	5-159
Driveshaft, Replace	5-153
Hub & Bearing Service	5-152
Hub, Bearing & Seal, Replace	5-151
Power Steering	5-230
Power Steering Gear, Replace	5-164
Power Steering Pump, Replace	5-165
Power Steering System Bleed	5-166
Precautions	5-151
Shock Absorber, Replace	5-155
Spring Link, Replace	5-163
Stabilizer Bar, Replace	5-162
Steering Knuckle, Replace	5-160
Strut, Replace	5-155
Technical Service Bulletins	5-166
Tension Strut, Replace	5-163
Tie Rod, Replace	5-164
Tightening Specifications	5-168
Wheel Bearing, Adjust	5-151
FRONT WHEEL DRIVE	
Axle Bearing Seal, Replace	5-175
Axle Shaft, Replace	5-174
Differential Carrier, Replace	5-175
Intermediate Shaft, Replace	5-175
Pinion Flange Seal, Replace	5-175
Precautions	5-174
Stabilizer Bar, Replace	5-176
Steering Knuckle & Ball Joint, Replace	5-176
Tightening Specifications	5-177
REAR AXLE & SUSPENSION	
Camber Strut, Replace	5-135
Coil Spring, Replace	5-134
Differential Carrier, Replace	5-127
Hub & Bearing, Replace	5-131
Hub & Bearing Service	5-132
Precautions	5-124
Propeller Shaft, Replace	5-129
Propeller Shaft Centering Sleeve, Replace	5-131
Propeller Shaft Intermediate Bearing, Replace	5-131
Rear Axle, Replace	5-124
Rear Axle Shaft, Replace	5-126
Rear Wheel Spindle, Replace	5-133
Shock Absorber, Replace	5-134
Spindle Knuckle, Replace	5-133
Spring Linkage, Replace	5-137
Spring Linkage Bushing, Replace	5-137
Technical Service Bulletins	5-140
Tension Arm, Replace	5-136
Thrust Arm, Replace	5-136
Tightening Specifications	5-142
Torque Strut, Replace	5-134
Torsion Rod, Replace	5-138
Track Rod, Replace	5-139
SPECIFICATIONS	
Engine Identification	5-4
Fluid Capacities & Cooling System Data	5-13
Front Wheel Alignment Specifications	5-9
General Engine Specifications	5-6
Lubricant Data	5-13
Rear Wheel Alignment Specifications	5-11
Tune Up Specifications	5-8
TRANSFER CASE	
Description	5-147
Technical Service Bulletins	5-147
Tightening Specifications	5-149
Transfer Case, Replace	5-147
TRACTION CONTROL SYSTEMS	5-318
VACUUM PUMPS	5-246
VEHICLE IDENTIFICATION	0-3
VEHICLE LIFT POINTS	0-24
VEHICLE MAINTENANCE SCHEDULES	0-45
WHEEL ALIGNMENT	5-178
Front Wheel Alignment	5-178
Inspection	5-178
Preliminary Inspection	5-178
Rear Wheel Alignment	5-180
Technical Service Bulletins	5-182
Vehicle Ride Height	5-180
Wheel Alignment Specifications	5-9
104 SIX-CYLINDER GASOLINE ENGINE	
Belt Tension Data	5-52
Camshaft, Replace	5-50
Camshaft Adjuster, Replace	5-50
Compression Pressure	5-45
Cooling System Bleed	5-52
Crankshaft Damper, Replace	5-48
Crankshaft Rear Oil Seal, Replace	5-51
Crankshaft Seal, Replace	5-50
Cylinder Head, Replace	5-47
Engine Rebuilding Specifications	5-344
Engine, Replace	5-46
Engine Mount, Replace	5-46
Exhaust Manifold, Replace	5-47
Front Cover, Replace	5-48
Front Cover Seal, Replace	5-49
Fuel Filter, Replace	5-53
Fuel Pump, Replace	5-53
Hydraulic Lifters, Replace	5-48
Intake Manifold, Replace	5-47
Main & Rod Bearings	5-50
Oil Cooler, Replace	5-52
Oil Pump, Replace	5-52
Oil Sump, Replace	5-51
Piston & Rod Assembly	5-50
Precautions	5-45
Radiator, Replace	5-53
Serpentine Drive Belt	5-52
Technical Service Bulletins	5-53
Thermostat, Replace	5-52
Tightening Specifications	5-54
Timing Chain, Replace	5-49
Timing Chain Tensioner, Replace	5-49
Valve Adjustment	5-48

Page No.

Valve Cover, Replace 5-48
Water Pump, Replace 5-52

111 FOUR-CYLINDER GASOLINE ENGINE

Belt Tension Data 5-39
Camshaft, Replace 5-37
Camshaft Adjuster, Replace... 5-37
Compression Pressure......... 5-32
Cooling System Bleed 5-39
Crankshaft Damper, Replace.. 5-36
Crankshaft Rear Oil Seal, Replace 5-38
Crankshaft Seal, Replace..... 5-38
Cylinder Head, Replace....... 5-35
Engine Rebuilding Specifications................. 5-344
Engine, Replace 5-33
Engine Mount, Replace 5-33
Exhaust Manifold, Replace.... 5-34
Front Cover, Replace 5-36
Front Cover Seal, Replace.... 5-37
Fuel Filter, Replace 5-40
Fuel Pump, Replace 5-40
Hydraulic Lifters, Replace..... 5-36
Intake Manifold, Replace...... 5-34
Main & Rod Bearings 5-37
Oil Pan, Replace.............. 5-38
Oil Pump, Replace............ 5-39
Oil Sump, Replace............ 5-38
Piston & Rod Assembly 5-37
Precautions.................. 5-32
Radiator, Replace............. 5-40
Serpentine Drive Belt 5-39
Supercharger, Replace 5-40
Technical Service Bulletins.... 5-41
Thermostat, Replace.......... 5-39
Tightening Specifications...... 5-43
Timing Chain, Replace........ 5-37
Timing Chain Tensioner, Replace 5-37
Valve Adjustment 5-35
Valve Cover, Replace 5-35
Water Pump, Replace 5-39

112 V6 & 113 V8 GASOLINE ENGINES

Balance Shaft, Replace....... 5-71
Belt Tension Data............ 5-78
Camshaft, Replace 5-71
Compression Pressure........ 5-57
Cooling System Bleed 5-78
Crankshaft Damper, Replace.. 5-69
Crankshaft Rear Oil Seal, Replace 5-72
Crankshaft Seal, Replace..... 5-72
Cylinder Head, Replace....... 5-67
Engine Rebuilding Specifications................. 5-344
Engine, Replace 5-62
Engine Mount, Replace 5-57
Exhaust Manifold, Replace.... 5-67
Front Cover, Replace 5-69
Fuel Filter, Replace 5-81
Fuel Pump, Replace 5-81
Hydraulic Lifters, Replace..... 5-69
Intake Manifold, Replace...... 5-66
Main & Rod Bearings 5-71
Oil Cooler, Replace 5-78

Page No.

Oil Pan, Replace............. 5-73
Oil Pump, Replace........... 5-77
Piston & Rod Assembly 5-71
Precautions.................. 5-56
Radiator, Replace............ 5-79
Rocker Arms, Replace 5-69
Serpentine Drive Belt 5-78
Technical Service Bulletins.... 5-81
Thermostat, Replace.......... 5-79
Tightening Specifications...... 5-83
Timing Chain, Replace........ 5-70
Timing Chain Tensioner, Replace 5-71
Valve Adjustment 5-69
Valve Cover, Replace 5-68
Water Pump, Replace 5-79

119 V8 GASOLINE ENGINE

Belt Tension Data............ 5-94
Camshaft, Replace 5-90
Camshaft Adjuster, Replace... 5-91
Compression Pressure........ 5-85
Cooling System Bleed 5-94
Crankshaft Damper, Replace.. 5-89
Crankshaft Rear Oil Seal, Replace 5-92
Crankshaft Seal, Replace..... 5-92
Cylinder Head, Replace....... 5-88
Engine Rebuilding Specifications................. 5-344
Engine, Replace 5-86
Engine Mount, Replace 5-85
Exhaust Manifold, Replace.... 5-87
Front Cover, Replace 5-89
Front Cover Seal, Replace.... 5-90
Fuel Filter, Replace 5-95
Fuel Pump, Replace 5-95
Hydraulic Lifters, Replace..... 5-89
Intake Manifold, Replace...... 5-87
Main & Rod Bearings 5-92
Oil Cooler, Replace 5-94
Oil Pump, Replace............ 5-93
Oil Sump, Replace............ 5-93
Piston & Rod Assembly 5-92
Precautions.................. 5-85
Radiator, Replace............. 5-94
Serpentine Drive Belt 5-94
Technical Service Bulletins.... 5-96
Thermostat, Replace.......... 5-94
Tightening Specifications...... 5-96
Timing Chain, Replace........ 5-90
Timing Chain Tensioner, Replace 5-90
Valve Adjustment 5-88
Valve Cover, Replace 5-88
Water Pump, Replace 5-94

120 V12 GASOLINE ENGINE

Belt Tension Data............ 5-108
Camshaft, Replace 5-104
Camshaft Adjuster, Replace... 5-105
Compression Pressure........ 5-98
Cooling System Bleed 5-108
Crankshaft Damper, Replace.. 5-102
Crankshaft Rear Oil Seal, Replace 5-106
Crankshaft Seal, Replace..... 5-106

Page No.

Cylinder Head, Replace....... 5-101
Engine Rebuilding Specifications................. 5-344
Engine, Replace 5-99
Engine Mount, Replace 5-98
Exhaust Manifold, Replace.... 5-101
Front Cover, Replace 5-102
Front Cover Seal, Replace.... 5-103
Fuel Filter, Replace 5-109
Fuel Pump, Replace 5-108
Intake Manifold, Replace...... 5-101
Main & Rod Bearings 5-106
Oil Cooler, Replace 5-107
Oil Pan, Replace.............. 5-106
Oil Pump, Replace............ 5-107
Piston & Rod Assembly 5-105
Precautions.................. 5-98
Radiator, Replace............. 5-108
Serpentine Drive Belt 5-108
Technical Service Bulletins.... 5-109
Thermostat, Replace.......... 5-108
Tightening Specifications...... 5-111
Timing Chain, Replace........ 5-104
Timing Chain Tensioner, Replace 5-104
Valve Adjustment 5-102
Valve Cover, Replace 5-102
Water Pump, Replace 5-108

606 DIESEL ENGINE

Belt Tension Data............ 5-117
Camshaft, Replace 5-115
Camshaft Timing Inspection... 5-116
Compression Pressure........ 5-112
Cooling System Bleed 5-118
Crankshaft Damper, Replace.. 5-114
Crankshaft Rear Oil Seal, Replace 5-116
Crankshaft Seal, Replace..... 5-116
Cylinder Head, Replace....... 5-114
Engine Rebuilding Specifications................. 5-344
Engine, Replace 5-113
Engine Mount, Replace 5-113
Exhaust Manifold, Replace.... 5-114
Front Cover, Replace 5-115
Fuel Filter, Replace 5-118
Fuel Pump, Replace 5-118
Intake Manifold, Replace...... 5-113
Main & Rod Bearings 5-116
Oil Pan, Replace.............. 5-117
Oil Pump, Replace............ 5-117
Oil-To-Water Cooler, Replace . 5-117
Piston & Rod Assembly 5-116
Pre-combustion Chamber, Replace 5-114
Precautions.................. 5-112
Radiator, Replace............. 5-118
Serpentine Drive Belt 5-117
Technical Service Bulletins.... 5-119
Thermostat, Replace.......... 5-118
Tightening Specifications...... 5-120
Timing Chain, Replace........ 5-115
Timing Chain Tensioner, Replace 5-115
Turbocharger, Replace........ 5-118
Valve Adjustment 5-114
Valve Cover, Replace 5-114
Water Pump, Replace 5-118

Specifications

ENGINE IDENTIFICATION

Model	Chassis Series	Engine Series	Engine Displacement, Liters
1998			
C230	202.023	111.974	2.3L
C280	202.029	112.920	2.8L
CL500	140.070	119.980	5.0L
CL600	140.076	120.982	6.0L
CLK320	208.365	112.940	3.2L
E300	210.025	606.962③	3.0L
E320	210.065	112.941	3.2L
E320 4MATIC	210.082	112.941	3.2L
E320 (Wagon)	210.265	112.941	3.2L
E320 (Wagon) 4MATIC	210.282	112.941	3.2L
ML320	163.154	112.942	3.2L
S320 (SWB)	140.032	104.994	3.2L
S320 (LWB)	140.033	104.994	3.2L
S420	140.043	119.981	4.2L
S500	140.051	119.980	5.0L
S600	140.057	120.982	6.0L
SL500	129.067	119.982	5.0L
SL600	129.076	120.983	6.0L
SLK230	170.447	111.973①	2.3L
1999			
C43②	202.033	113.944	4.3L
C230	202.024	111.975①	2.3L
C280	202.029	112.920	2.8L
CL500	140.070	119.980	5.0L
CL600	140.076	120.982	6.0L
CLK320	208.365	112.940	3.2L
CLK320 Cabriolet	208.465	112.940	3.2L
CLK430	208.370	113.943	4.3L
E300	210.025	606.962③	3.0L
E320	210.065	112.941	3.2L
E320 4MATIC	210.082	112.941	3.2L
E320 (Wagon)	210.265	112.941	3.2L
E320 (Wagon) 4MATIC	210.282	112.941	3.2L
E430	210.070	113.940	4.3L
ML320	163.154	112.942	3.2L
ML430	163.172	112.942	4.3L
S320 (SWB)	140.032	104.994	3.2L
S320 (LWB)	140.033	104.994	3.2L
S420	140.043	119.981	4.2L
S500	140.051	119.980	5.0L
S600	140.057	120.982	6.0L
SL500	129.068	113.961	5.0L
SL600	129.076	120.983	6.0L
SLK230	170.447	111.973①	2.3L
2000			
C43②	202.033	113.944	4.3L
C230	202.024	111.975①	2.3L
C280	202.029	112.920	2.8L
CL500	215.375	113.960	5.0L
CLK320	208.365	112.940	3.2L
CLK320 Cabriolet	208.465	112.940	3.2L

Continued

ENGINE IDENTIFICATION—Continued

Model	Chassis Series	Engine Series	Engine Displacement, Liters
2000			
CLK430	208.370	113.943	4.3L
CLK430 Cabriolet	208.470	113.943	4.3L
E55②	210.074	113.980	5.5L
E320	210.065	112.941	3.2L
E320 4MATIC	210.082	112.941	3.2L
E320 (Wagon)	210.265	112.941	3.2L
E320 (Wagon) 4MATIC	210.282	112.941	3.2L
E430	210.070	113.940	4.3L
E430 4MATIC	210.083	113.940	4.3L
ML55②	163.174	113.981	5.5L
ML320	163.154	112.942	3.2L
ML430	163.172	113.942	4.3L
S430	220.170	113.941	4.3L
S500	220.175	113.960	5.0L
SL500	129.068	113.961	5.0L
SL600	129.076	120.983	6.0L
SLK230	170.447	111.973①	2.3L
2001			
C240	203.061	112.912	2.4L
C320	203.064	112.946	3.2L
CL55②	215.373	113.982	5.5L
CL500	215.375	113.960	5.0L
CL600	215.378	137.970	6.0L
CLK55②	208.374	113.984	5.5L
CLK320	208.365	112.940	3.2L
CLK320 Cabriolet	208.465	112.940	3.2L
CLK430	208.370	113.943	4.3L
CLK430 Cabriolet	208.470	113.943	4.3L
E55②	210.074	113.980	5.5L
E320	210.065	112.941	3.2L
E320 4MATIC	210.082	112.941	3.2L
E320 (Wagon)	210.265	112.941	3.2L
E320 (Wagon) 4MATIC	210.282	112.941	3.2L
E430	210.070	113.940	4.3L
E430 4MATIC	210.083	113.940	4.3L
ML55②	163.174	113.981	5.5L
ML320	163.154	112.942	3.2L
ML430	163.172	113.942	4.3L
S55②	220.173	113.982	5.5L
S430	220.170	113.941	4.3L
S500	220.175	113.960	5.0L
S600	220.178	137.970	6.0L
SL500	129.068	113.961	5.0L
SL600	129.076	120.983	6.0L
SLK230	170.449	111.983①	2.3L
SLK320	170.465	112.947	3.2L

LWB — Long Wheelbase.
SWB — Short Wheelbase.
① — Supercharged.
② — Modified by AMG.
③ — Diesel Engine.

GENERAL ENGINE SPECIFICATIONS

Engine, Liter	Model	Engine Series	Fuel Injection	Bore & Stroke, Inches	Com-pression Ratio	Maximum Brake, HP @ RPM	Maximum Torque, Ft. Lbs. @ RPM	Oil Pressure @ 3000 RPM (psi)①
1998								
2.3L	C230	111.974	ME-SFI 2.0	3.58 x 3.48	10.4	148 @ 5500	162 @ 4000	43.5
	SLK230	111.973②	ME-SFI 2.1	3.58 x 3.48	8.8	185 @ 5300	200 @ 2500–4800	43.5
2.8L	C280	112.920	ME-SFI 2.0	3.54 x 2.89	10.0	194 @ 5800	195 @ 3000–4600	43.5
3.0L③	E300	606.962	IFI	3.43 x 3.31	22.0	174 @ 5000	244 @ 1600–3000	43.5
3.2L	CLK320	112.940	ME-SFI 2.0	3.54 x 3.30	10.0	215 @ 5500	229 @ 3000–4600	43.5
	E320	112.941	ME-SFI 2.0	3.54 x 3.30	10.0	221 @ 5500	232 @ 3000–4800	43.5
	ML320	112.942	ME-SFI 2.0	3.54 x 3.30	10.0	215 @ 5500	233 @ 3000	43.5
	S320	104.994	ME-SFI 2.0	3.54 x 3.30	10.0	228 @ 5600	232 @ 3750	43.5
4.2L	S420	119.981	ME-SFI 1.0	3.62 x 3.11	11.0	275 @ 5700	295 @ 3900	43.5
5.0L	CL500 & S500	119.980	ME-SFI 1.0	3.80 x 3.35	11.0	315 @ 5600	347 @ 3900	43.5
	SL500	119.982	ME-SFI 1.0	3.80 x 3.35	11.0	315 @ 5600	345 @ 3900	39–80
6.0L	CL600 & S600	120.982	ME-SFI 1.0	3.50 x 3.16	10.0	389 @ 5200	420 @ 3800	43.5
	SL600	120.983	ME-SFI 1.0	3.50 x 3.16	10.0	389 @ 5200	420 @ 3800	43.5
1999								
2.3L	C230	111.975②	ME-SFI 2.1	3.58 x 3.48	8.8	185 @ 5300	200 @ 2500–4800	43.5
	SLK230	111.973②	ME-SFI 2.1	3.58 x 3.48	8.8	185 @ 5300	200 @ 2500–4800	43.5
2.8L	C280	112.920	ME-SFI 2.0	3.54 x 2.89	10.0	194 @ 5800	195 @ 3000–4600	43.5
3.0L③	E300	606.962	IFI	3.43 x 3.31	22.0	174 @ 5000	244 @ 1600–3000	43.5
3.2L	CLK320	112.940	ME-SFI 2.0	3.54 x 3.30	10.0	215 @ 5500	229 @ 3000–4600	43.5
	E320	112.941	ME-SFI 2.0	3.54 x 3.30	10.0	221 @ 5500	232 @ 3000–4800	43.5
	ML320	112.942	ME-SFI 2.0	3.54 x 3.30	10.0	215 @ 5500	233 @ 3000	43.5
	S320	104.994	ME-SFI 2.0	3.54 x 3.30	10.0	228 @ 5600	232 @ 3750	43.5
4.2L	S420	119.981	ME-SFI 1.0	3.62 x 3.11	11.0	275 @ 5700	295 @ 3900	43.5
4.3L	C43	113.944	ME-SFI 2.0	3.54 x 3.30	10.0	302 @ 5850	302 @ 3250–5000	43.5
	CLK430	113.943	ME-SFI 2.0	3.54 x 3.30	10.0	275 @ 5750	295 @ 3000–4000	43.5
	E430	113.940	ME-SFI 2.0	3.54 x 3.30	10.0	275 @ 5750	295 @ 3000–4000	43.5
	ML430	113.942	ME-SFI 2.0	3.54 x 3.30	10.0	268 @ 5500	288 @ 3000–4500	43.5
5.0L	CL500 & S500	119.980	ME-SFI 1.0	3.80 x 3.35	11.0	315 @ 5600	347 @ 3900	43.5
	SL500	119.983	ME-SFI 1.0	3.80 x 3.35	10.0	302@ 5600	339 @ 2700–4250	43.5
6.0L	CL600 & S600	120.982	ME-SFI 1.0	3.50 x 3.16	10.0	389 @ 5200	420 @ 3800	43.5
	SL600	120.983	ME-SFI 1.0	3.50 x 3.16	10.0	389 @ 5200	420 @ 3800	43.5
2000								
2.3L	C230	111.975②	ME-SFI 2.0	3.58 x 3.48	8.8	185 @ 5300	200 @ 2500–4800	43.5
	SLK230	111.973②	ME-SFI 2.1	3.58 x 3.48	8.8	185 @ 5300	200 @ 2500–4800	43.5
2.8L	C280	112.920	ME-SFI 2.0	3.54 x 2.89	10.0	194 @ 5800	195 @ 3000–4600	43.5

Continued

GENERAL ENGINE SPECIFICATIONS—Continued

Engine, Liter	Model	Engine Series	Fuel Injection	Bore & Stroke, Inches	Com-pression Ratio	Maximum Brake, HP @ RPM	Maximum Torque, Ft. Lbs. @ RPM	Oil Pressure @ 3000 RPM (psi)①
3.2L	CLK320	112.940	ME-SFI 2.0	3.54 x 3.30	10.0	215 @ 5700	229 @ 3000–4600	43.5
	E320	112.941	ME-SFI 2.0	3.54 x 3.30	10.0	221 @ 5500	232 @ 3000–4800	43.5
	ML320	112.942	ME-SFI 2.0	3.54 x 3.30	10.0	215 @ 5500	233 @ 3000	43.5
4.3L	CLK430	113.943	ME-SFI 2.0	3.54 x 3.30	10.0	275 @ 5750	295 @ 3000–4000	43.5
	E430	113.940	ME-SFI 2.0	3.54 x 3.30	10.0	275 @ 5750	295 @ 3000–4000	43.5
	ML430	113.942	ME-SFI 2.0	3.54 x 3.30	10.0	268 @ 5500	288 @ 3000–4500	43.5
	S430	113.941	ME-SFI 2.0	3.54 x 3.31	10.0	275 @ 5750	295 @ 3000–4000	43.5
5.0L	CL500	113.960	ME-SFI 2.0	3.82 x 3.31	10.0	302 @ 5600	339 @ 2700–4250	43.5
	S500 & SL500	113.961	ME-SFI 2.0	3.82 x 3.31	10.0	302 @ 5600	339 @ 2750–5250	43.5
5.5L	E55	113.980	ME-SFI 2.0	3.82 x 3.62	10.5	349 @ 5500	391 @ 3000	43.5
	ML55	113.981	ME-SFI 2.0	3.82 x 3.62	10.5	342 @ 5500	376 X 3000	43.5
6.0L	SL600	120.983	ME-SFI 2.0	3.20 x 3.16	10.0	389 @ 5200	420 @ 3800	—
2001								
2.3L	SLK230	111.983②	ME-SFI 2.1	3.58 x 3.48	9.0	190 @ 5300	200 @ 2500–4800	43.5
2.4L	C240	112.912	ME-SFI 2.8	3.54 x 2.69	10.5	168 @ 5500	177 @ 4500	43.5
3.2L	C320	112.946	ME-SFI 2.8	3.54 x 3.31	10.0	215 @ 5700	221 @ 3000–4600	43.5
	CLK320	112.940	ME-SFI 2.8	3.54 x 3.31	10.0	215 @ 5700	229 @ 3000–4600	43.5
	E320	112.941	ME-SFI 2.8	3.54 x 3.30	10.0	221 @ 5500	232 @ 3000–4000	43.5
	ML320	112.942	ME-SFI 2.8	3.54 x 3.31	10.0	215 @ 5500	233 @ 3000	43.5
	SLK320	112.947	ME-SFI 2.8	3.54 x 3.31	10.0	215 @ 5700	229 @ 3000–4600	43.5
4.3L	CLK430	113.943	ME-SFI 2.8	3.54 x 3.31	10.0	275 @ 5750	295 @ 3000–4400	43.5
	ML430	113.942	ME-SFI 2.8	3.54 x 3.31	10.0	268 @ 5500	288 @ 3000–4500	43.5
	E430	113.940	ME-SFI 2.8	3.54 x 3.30	10.0	275 @ 5750	295 @ 3000–4000	43.5
	S430	113.941	ME-SFI 2.8	3.54 x 3.31	10.0	275 @ 5750	295 @ 3000–4400	43.5
5.0L	CL500 & S500	113.960	ME-SFI 2.8	3.82 x 3.31	10.0	302 @ 5600	339 @ 2700–4250	43.5
	SL500	113.96	ME-SFI 2.8	3.82 x 3.31	10.0	302 @ 5600	339 @ 2700–4250	43.5
5.5L	CL55 & S55	113.982	ME-SFI 2.8	3.82 x 3.62	10.5	354 @ 5500	391 @ 3000	43.5
	CLK55	113.984	ME-SFI 2.8	3.82 x 3.62	10.5	342 @ 500	376 @ 3000	43.5
	E55	113.980	ME-SFI 2.8	3.82 x 3.62	10.5	349 @ 5500	391 @ 3000	43.5
	ML55	113.981	ME-SFI 2.8	3.82 x 3.62	10.5	342 @ 5500	376 @ 3000	43.5
6.0L	CL600 & S600	137.970	ME-SFI 2.7	3.31 x 3.43	10.0	362 @ 5500	391 @ 4100	—
	SL600	120.983	ME-SFI 1.0	3.50 x 3.16	10.0	389 @ 5200	420 @ 3800	—

① — Minimum. ② — Supercharged. ③ — Turbo-diesel engine.

TUNE UP SPECIFICATIONS

Model	Spark Plug Gap, Inch	Ignition			Curb Idle Speed, RPM①	Fuel Pressure, psi③	Valve Lash, Inch	
		Firing Order	Timing Deg. BTDC.	Timing Mark			Intake	Exhaust
1998								
C43	.032	⑮	⑩	⑦	—	54–61	⑨	⑨
C230	.032	⑬	5–20⑤	⑦	680–850N	54–61	⑨	⑨
C280	.032	⑭	5–25⑩	⑦	650–800N	54–61	⑨	⑨
CL500	.032	⑧	5–20④	⑦	600–750N	54–61	⑨	⑨
CL600	.032	②	5–20④	⑦	600–750N	54–61	⑨	⑨
CLK320	.032	⑭	5–25⑩	⑦	650–800N	54–61	⑨	⑨
E320	.032	⑭	5–25⑩	⑦	650–800N	54–61	⑨	⑨
E430	.032	⑮	⑩	⑦	—	54–61	⑨	⑨
ML320	.032	⑭	5–25⑩	⑦	650–800N	54–61	⑨	⑨
S320	.032	⑥	5–20⑤	⑦	600–800N	54–61	⑨	⑨
S420	.032	⑧	5–20④	⑦	600–750N	54–61	⑨	⑨
S500	.032	⑧	5–20④	⑦	600–750N	54–61	⑨	⑨
S600	.032	②	5–20④	⑦	600–750N	54–61	⑨	⑨
SL500	.032	⑧	5–20④	⑦	600–750N	54–61	⑨	⑨
SL600	.032	②	5–20④	⑦	600–750N	54–61	⑨	⑨
SLK230	.032	⑬	5–20⑤	⑦	680–850N	54–61	⑨	⑨
1999								
C43	.032	⑮	⑩	⑦	—	54–61	⑨	⑨
C230	.032	⑬	5–20⑤	⑦	680–850N	54–61	⑨	⑨
C280	.032	⑭	5–25⑩	⑦	650–800N	54–61	⑨	⑨
CL500	.032	⑧	5–20④	⑦	600–750N	54–61	⑨	⑨
CL600	.032	②	5–20④	⑦	600–750N	54–61	⑨	⑨
CLK320	.032	⑭	5–25⑩	⑦	650–800N	54–61	⑨	⑨
CLK430	.032	⑮	⑩	⑦	—	54–61	⑨	⑨
E320	.032	⑭	5–25⑩	⑦	650–800N	54–61	⑨	⑨
E430	.032	⑮	⑩	⑦	—	54–61	⑨	⑨
ML320	.032	⑭	5–25⑩	⑦	650–800N	54–61	⑨	⑨
ML430	.032	⑮	⑩	⑦	—	54–61	⑨	⑨
S320	.032	⑥	5–20⑤	⑦	650–800N	54–61	⑨	⑨
S420	.032	⑧	5–20④	⑦	600–750N	54–61	⑨	⑨
S500	.032	⑧	5–20④	⑦	600–750N	54–61	⑨	⑨
S600	.032	②	5–20④	⑦	600–750N	54–61	⑨	⑨
SL500	.032	⑮	⑩	⑦	—	54–61	⑨	⑨
SL600	.032	②	5–20④	⑦	600–750N	54–61	⑨	⑨
SLK230	.032	⑬	5–20⑤	⑦	680–850N	54–61	⑨	⑨
2000								
C43	.032	⑮	⑩	⑦	—	54–61	⑨	⑨
C230	.032	⑬	5–20⑤	⑦	680–850N	54–61	⑨	⑨
C280	.032	⑭	5–25⑩	⑦	650–800N	54–61	⑨	⑨
CL500	.032	⑮	⑩	⑦	—	54–61	⑨	⑨
CLK320	.032	⑭	5–25⑩	⑦	650–800N	54–61	⑨	⑨
CLK430	.032	⑮	⑩	⑦	—	54–61	⑨	⑨
E55	.032	⑮	⑩	⑦	—	54–61	⑨	⑨
E320	.032	⑭	5–25⑩	⑦	650–800N	54–61	⑨	⑨
E430	.032	⑮	⑩	⑦	—	54–61	⑨	⑨
ML55	.032	⑮	⑩	⑦	—	54–61	⑨	⑨
ML320	.032	⑭	5–25⑩	⑦	650–800N	54–61	⑨	⑨
ML430	.032	⑮	⑩	⑦	—	54–61	⑨	⑨
S430	.032	⑮	⑩	⑦	—	54–61	⑨	⑨
S500	.032	⑮	⑩	⑦	—	54–61	⑨	⑨
SL500	.032	⑮	⑩	⑦	—	54–61	⑨	⑨
SL600	.032	②	5–20⑩	⑦	600–750N	54–61	⑨	⑨

Continued

TUNE UP SPECIFICATIONS—Continued

Model	Spark Plug Gap, Inch	Ignition			Curb Idle Speed, RPM①	Fuel Pressure, psi③	Valve Lash, Inch	
		Firing Order	Timing Deg. BTDC.	Timing Mark			Intake	Exhaust
2001								
C240	.032	⑭	5–25⑪	⑦	650–800N	54–61	⑨	⑨
C320	.032	⑭	5–25⑪	⑦	650–800N	54–61	⑨	⑨
CL55	.032	⑮	⑪	⑦	—	54–61	⑨	⑨
CL500	.032	⑮	⑪	⑦	—	54–61	⑨	⑨
CL600	—	②	⑫	—	—	—	⑨	⑨
CLK55	.032	⑮	⑪	⑦	—	54–61	⑨	⑨
CLK320	.032	⑭	5–25⑪	⑦	650–800N	54–61	⑨	⑨
CLK430	.032	⑮	⑪	⑦	—	54–61	⑨	⑨
E55	.032	⑮	⑪	⑦	—	54–61	⑨	⑨
E320	.032	⑭	5–25⑪	⑦	650–800N	54–61	⑨	⑨
E430	.032	⑮	⑪	⑦	—	54–61	⑨	⑨
ML55	.032	⑮	⑪	⑦	—	54–61	⑨	⑨
ML320	.032	⑭	5–25⑪	⑦	650–800N	54–61	⑨	⑨
ML430	.032	⑮	⑪	⑦	—	54–61	⑨	⑨
S55	.032	⑮	⑪	⑦	—	54–61	⑨	⑨
S430	.032	⑮	⑪	⑦	—	54–61	⑨	⑨
S500	.032	⑮	⑪	⑦	—	54–61	⑨	⑨
S600	—	②	⑫	—	—	—	⑨	⑨
SL500	.032	⑮	⑩	⑦	—	54–61	⑨	⑨
SL600	—	②	5–20⑩	⑦	600–750N	54–61	⑨	⑨
SLK230	.032	⑬	5–20⑤	⑦	680–850N	54–61	⑨	⑨
SLK320	.032	⑭	5–25⑪	⑦	650–800N	54–61	⑨	⑨

BTDC — Before Top Dead Center
N — Neutral
① — When adjusting idle speed, set parking brake & chock driver wheels.
② — Cylinder numbering front to rear, righthand bank, 1, 2, 3, 4, 5, 6; lefthand hand bank, 7, 8, 9, 10, 11, 12. Firing order 1-12-5-8-3-10-6-7-2-11-4-9.
③ — Less vacuum.
④ — Equipped w/ME-1.0 engine management system, non-adjustable.
⑤ — Equipped w/ME-2.1 engine management system, non-adjustable.
⑥ — Firing order 1-5-3-6-2-4.
⑦ — Equipped w/crankshaft position sensor.
⑧ — Cylinder numbering front to rear, righthand bank, 1, 2, 3, 4; lefthand hand bank, 5, 6, 7, 8. Firing order 1-5-4-8-6-3-7-2.
⑨ — Equipped w/hydraulic valve lash adjusters.
⑩ — Equipped w/ME-2.0 engine management system, non-adjustable.
⑪ — Equipped w/ME-2.8 engine management system, non-adjustable.
⑫ — Equipped w/ME-2.7 engine management system, non-adjustable.
⑬ — Cylinder numbering front to rear, 1, 2, 3, 4. Firing order 1–3–4–2.
⑭ — Cylinder numbering front to rear, righthand bank, 1, 2, 3; lefthand bank, 4, 5, 6. Firing order, 1–4–3–6–2–5.
⑮ — Cylinder numbering front to rear, righthand bank, 1, 2, 3, 4; lefthand bank, 5, 6, 7, 8. Firing order, 1–5–4–2–6–3–7–8.

FRONT WHEEL ALIGNMENT SPECIFICATIONS

Models	Caster Angle, Degrees①		Camber Angle, Degrees①		Toe, Degrees②		Ball Joint Inspection
	Limits	Desired	Limits	Desired	Limits	Desired	
C43	+4 47/60 to 4 9/10	+4 57/60	-1 1/20 to -1 11/30	-1/6	+1/4 to 7/12	+5/12	③
C230 & C280 Less Level Control	+4 1/12 to + 4 11/20	+4 5/12	-7/10 to -6/15	-1/2	+1/4 to +7/12	+5/12	③
C230 & C280 w/Level Control	+4 3/10 to +4 23/30	+4 1/2	-7/10 to -6/15	-1/2	+1/4 to +7/12	+5/12	③
C240 & C320	+10 11/30 to +10 9/10	+10 43/60	-11/15 to -1/15	-6/15	+1/20 to +37/60	+1/3	③
2000–01 CL500 & 2001 CL600	+9 1/6 to +9 8/15	+9 3/10	-1 13/30 to -23/30	-1 1/10	+11/30 to +7/10	+8/15	③
CLK55	+4 47/60 to +5 7/20	+5 1/60	-1 1/20 to -1 11/30	-1/6	+1/4 to +7/12	+5/12	③
CLK320 & CLK430 Cabriolet	+4 7/15 to +4 11/12	+4 7/10	-1 3/10 to -53/60	-1 14/15	+1/4 to +7/12	+5/12	③
CLK320 & CLK430 Less Level Control	+4 2/3 to +5 1/30	+4 9/10	-1 3/10 to -53/60	-1 14/15	+1/4 to +7/12	+5/12	③
CLK320 & CLK430 w/Level Control	+4 9/10 to +5 1/3	+5	-1 3/10 to -53/60	-1 14/15	+1/4 to +7/12	+5/12	③
E55	+5 37/60 to +5 13/15	+5 2/3	-11/12 to -1 4/15	-1 1/30	0 to +1/3	+1/6	③
E300, E320 & E430 Sedan Less 4MATIC Less Level Control	+5 1/60 to +5 1/2	+5 1/5	-11/30 to -2/3	-31/60	0 to +1/3	+1/6	③
E300, E320 & E430 Sedan less 4MATIC w/Level Control	+5 7/10 to +5 3/10	+5 6/15	-11/30 to -2/3	-31/60	0 to +1/3	+1/6	③
E320 Wagon Less 4MATIC	+4 47/60 to +5 1/4	+5	-13/60 to 1/2	-19/60	0 to +1/3	+1/6	③
E320 & E430 w/4MATIC Less Level Control	+4 4/5 to +5 4/15	+5 1/10	-29/30 to -1 3/5	-1 7/60	0 to +1/3	+1/6	③
E320 & E430 w/4-MATC w/Level Control	+5 to +5 11/30	+5 11/60	-29/30 to -1 3/5	-1 7/60	0 to +1/3	+1/6	③
1998–99 CL500, CL600, S320, S420, S500 & S600④	+9 5/6 to +10 5/6	+10° 1/3	-2/3 to 0	-1/3	+5/12 to +3/4	+7/12	③
S430 & 2000–01 S500 & 2001 S600	+8 4/5 to 10 1/15	+8 14/15	-1 7/60 to -9/20	-47/60	+11/30 to +7/10	+8/15	③
SL500 & SL600 less ADS④	+9 3/4 to +10 3/4	+10 1/4	-5/6 to -1/4	-7/12	+1/6 to +1/2	+1/3	③
SL500 & SL600 w/ADS④	+9 11/12 to +10 11/12	+10 5/12	-1 to -1/2	-5/6	+1/6 to +1/2	+1/3	③
SLK230 & SLK320	+4 57/60 to +5 9/20	+5 1/5	-1 31/60 to -1 1/15	-1 13/60	+1/6 to +1/2	+1/3	③

① — Measurements are vehicle level dependent. Refer to "Wheel Alignment" section.

② — Toe-in (+); toe-out (-).

③ — Refer to "Ball Joint Inspection" as outlined in "Front Suspension & Steering."

④ — With 0° toe-in.

REAR WHEEL ALIGNMENT SPECIFICATIONS

Model	Toe, Degrees① Total		Ride Height②		Camber Angle, Degrees	
	Limits	Desired	Inches	Angle, Degrees	Limits	Desired
C43, C230 & C280	+13/30 to +2/3	+11/20	+1.5750	+3.9	-1 to 0	-1/2
			+1.1812	+2.9	-1 1/4 to -1/4	-3/4
			+.7875	+1.8	-1 1/2 to -1/2	-1
			+.3937	+.7	-1 3/4 to -3/4	-1 1/4
			0	-.4	-2 to -1	-1 1/2
			-.3937	-1.5	-2 1/4 to -1 3/4	-1 3/4
			-.7875	-2.5	-2 1/2 to -1 1/2	-2
			-1.1812	-3.6	-2 3/4 to -1 3/4	-2 3/4
			-1.5750	-4.7	-3 1/15 to -2 1/5	-2 17/30
			-1.9687	-5.8	-3 11/30 to -2 11/20	-2 13/15
C240 & C320	+13/30 to +2/3	+11/20	—	-.9	-2 19/60 to -1 19/60	-1 49/60
			—	-.6	-2 7/30 to -1 7/30	-1 11/15
			—	-.3	-2 1/10 to -1 1/10	-1 3/5
			—	0	-2 1/60 to -1 1/60	-1 31/60
			—	+.3	-1 9/10 to -9/10	-1 7/15
			—	+.6	-1 5/6 to -5/6	-1 6/15
			—	+.9	-1 5/6 to -5/6	-1 1/3
			—	+1.2	-1 23/30 to -23/30	-1 1/3
			—	+1.5	-1 7/10 to -7/10	-1 1/5
2000–01 CL500 & 2001 CL600	+7/15 to +7/10	+7/12	—	-1.3	-29/60 to -1 29/60	-59/60
	+29/60 to +43/60	+3/5	—	-1.8	-7/12 to -1 7/12	-1 1/12
	+31/60 to +3/4	+19/30	—	-2.3	-41/60 to -1 41/60	-1 11/60
	+8/15 to +23/30	+39/60	—	-2.8	-47/60 to -1 47/60	-1 17/60
	+17/30 to +4/5	+41/60	—	-3.3	-9/10 to -1 9/10	-1 6/150
CLK55, CLK320 & CLK430	+13/30 to +2/3	+11/20	+1.5750	+3.9	-1 to 0	-1/2
			+1.1812	+2.9	-1 1/4 to -1/4	-3/4
			+.7875	+1.8	-1 1/2 to -1/2	-1
			+.3937	+.7	-1 3/4 to -3/4	-1 1/4
			0	-.4	-2 to -1	-1 1/2
			-.3937	-1.5	-2 1/4 to -1 3/4	-1 3/4
			-.7875	-2.5	-2 1/2 to -1 1/2	-2
			-1.1812	-3.6	-2 3/4 to -1 3/4	-2 3/4
			-1.5750	-4.7	-3 1/15 to -2 1/5	-2 17/30
			-1.9687	-5.8	-3 11/30 to -2 11/20	-2 13/15
1998–99 CL500, CL600, S320, S420, S500 & S600	+1/2 to +3/4	+7/12	+1.5750	—	-13/15 to +2/15	-11/30
			+1.1812	—	-1 to 0	-1/2
			+.7875	—	-1 1/6 to -1/6	-2/3
			+.3937	—	-1 4/15 to -4/15	-23/30
			0	—	-1 1/2 to -1/2	-1
			-.3937	—	-1 3/4 to -3/4	-1 1/4
			-.7875	—	-1 59/60 to -59/60	-1 29/60
			-1.1812	—	-2 7/30 to -1 7/30	-1 11/15
			-1.5750	—	-2 1/2 to -1 1/2	-2
			-1.9687	—	-2 47/60 to -1 47/60	-2 17/60
E55, E300, E320 & E430	+13/30 to +2/3	+11/20	+1.5750	+3	-1 1/5 to -1/5	-7/10
			+1.1812	+2	-1 11/30 to -11/30	-13/15
			+.7875	+2	-1 17/30 to -17/30	-1 1/15
			+.3937	0	-1 47/60 to -47/60	-1 17/60
			0	-1.1	-2 to -1	-1 1/2
			-.3937	-2.1	-2 4/15 to -4/15	-1 11/15
			-.7875	-3.1	-2 29/60 to -29/60	-1 59/60
			-1.1812	-4.1	-2 14/15 to -1 14/15	-2 4/15
			-1.5750	-5.1	-3 1/15 to -2 1/15	-2 17/30
			-1.9687	-6.1	-3 11/30 to -2 11/30	-2 13/15

Continued

REAR WHEEL ALIGNMENT SPECIFICATIONS—Continued

Model	Toe, Degrees①		Ride Height②		Camber Angle, Degrees	
	Total					
	Limits	Desired	Inches	Angle, Degrees	Limits	Desired
S430, 2000–01 S500 & 2001 S600	+7/15 to +7/10	+7/12	—	+.1	-7/30 to -1 7/30	-11/15
	+29/60 to +43/60	+3/5	—	-.4	-19/60 to -1 19/60	-49/60
	+31/60 to +3/4	+19/30	—	-.9	-5/12 to -1 5/12	-11/12
	+33/60 to +47/60	+2/3	—	-1.4	-1/2 to -1 1/2	-1
	+17/30 to +4/5	+42/60	—	1.9	-3/5 to -1 3/5	-1 1/10
SL500 & SL600	+1/3 to 7/12	+5/16	+1.5750	—	-1 to 0	-1/2
			+1.1812	—	-1 1/4 to -1/4	-3/4
			+.7875	—	-1 1/2 to -1/2	-1
			+.3937	—	-1 3/.4 to -3/4	-1 1/4
			0	—	-2 to -1	-1 1/2
			-.3937	—	-2 1/4 to -1 1/4	-1 3/4
			-.7875	—	-2 1/2 to -1 1/2	-2
			-1.1812	—	-2 3/4 to -1 3/4	-2 1/4
			-1.5750	—	-3 1/15 to -1 47/60	-2 17/30
			-1.9687	—	-3 11/30 to -2 11/30	-2 13/15
SLK230 & SLK320	+13/30 to +2/3	+11/20	+1.5750	+3.9	-1 to 0	-1/2
			+1.1812	+2.9	-1 1/4 to -1/4	-3/4
			+.7875	+1.8	-1 1/2 to -1/2	-1
			+.3937	+.7	-1 3/4 to -3/4	-1 1/4
			0	-.4	-2 to -1	-1 1/2
			-.3937	-1.5	-2 1/4 to -1 3/4	-1 3/4
			-.7875	-2.5	-2 1/2 to -1 1/2	-2
			-1.1812	-3.6	-2 3/4 to -1 3/4	-2 3/4
			-1.5750	-4.7	-3 1/15 to -2 1/5	-2 17/30
			-1.9687	-5.8	-3 11/30 to -2 11/20	-2 13/15

①— Toe-in (+); toe-out (-).

②— Measure w/model specific tools as outlined under "Wheel Alignment."

FLUID CAPACITIES & COOLING SYSTEM DATA

These capacities has been revised by a Technical Service Bulletin.

Model	Year	Cooling System Capacity, Qts.	Coolant Type	Thermo. Opening Temp., °F	Fuel Tank, Gals.	Engine Oil Refill, Qts.①	Auto. Trans., Qts.②④	Rear Axle Oil, Pts.	Front Axle Oil, Pts.	Transfer Case, Pts.
C43	1999–2000	11.6	Ethylene Glycol	185–192	16.4	7.9	9.9	2.5	—	—
C230	1998–2000	9.0	Ethylene Glyco	189	16.4	6.5	7.9	2.4	—	—
C240	2001	11.1	Ethylene Glyco	185–192	16.2	8.5	—	2.3	—	—
C280	1998–2000	10.0	Ethylene Glyco	185–192	16.4	8.5	9.9	3.0	—	—
C320	2001	11.1	Ethylene Glyco	185–192	16.2	8.5	—	2.5	—	—
CL55	2001	—	Ethylene Glyco	185–192	23.3	7.9	—	—	—	—
CL500	1998–99	17.4	Ethylene Glyco	180	26.4	8.5	9.9	3.0	—	—
	2000–01	13.5	Ethylene Glyco	185–192	23.3	8.5	—	3.4	—	—
CL600	1998–99	19.6	Ethylene Glyco	189	26.4	10.7	9.9	3.0	—	—
	2001	12.7	Ethylene Glyco	—	23.3	9.5	—	3.4	—	—
CLK55	2001	11.6	Ethylene Glyco	185–192	16.4	7.9	—	2.5	—	—
CLK320	1998–2001	10.0	Ethylene Glyco	185–192	16.4	8.5	7.7	2.5	—	—
CLK430	1999–2001	11.6	Ethylene Glyco	185–192	16.4	7.9	9.9	2.5	—	—
E55	2000–01	11.6	Ethylene Glyco	185–192	21.1	7.9	—	3.4	—	—
E300③	1998–99	10.6	Ethylene Glyco	185	21.2	8.5	7.5	2.5	—	—
E320	1998–2001	10.6	Ethylene Glyco	185–192	⑤	8.5	7.9	2.5	.95	1.8
E430	1998–201	11.6	Ethylene Glyco	185–192	21.1	8.5	9.9	⑧	—	—
ML55		—	Ethylene Glyco	185–192	19.0⑥	7.9	—	—	—	—
ML320	1998–2001	11.6	Ethylene Glyco	185–192	19.0⑥	8.5	7.9	3.2	2.4	3.0
ML430	1999–2001	12.2	Ethylene Glyco	185–192	19.0⑥	8.5	9.9	—	—	—
S55	2001	—	Ethylene Glyco	185–192	23.2	7.9	—	—	—	—
S320	1998–99	15.3	Ethylene Glyco	189	26.4	7.4	7.5	2.8	.9	
S420	1998–99	17.4	Ethylene Glyco	185	26.4	8.5	9.9	3.0	—	—
S430	2000–01	12.2	Ethylene Glyco	185–192	23.2	8.5	—	3.4	—	—
S500	1998–99	17.4	Ethylene Glyco	185	26.4	8.5	9.9	3.0	—	—
	2000–01	12.2	Ethylene Glyco	185–192	23.2	8.5	—	3.4	—	—
S600	1998–99	19.6	Ethylene Glyco	189	26.4	10.7	9.9	3.0	—	—
	2001	12.7	Ethylene Glyco	—	23.2	9.5	—	3.4	—	—

Continued

FLUID CAPACITIES & COOLING SYSTEM DATA—Continued

These capacities has been revised by a Technical Service Bulletin.

Model	Year	Cooling System Capacity, Qts.	Coolant Type	Thermo. Opening Temp., °F	Fuel Tank, Gals.	Engine Oil Refill, Qts.①	Auto. Trans., Qts.②④	Rear Axle Oil, Pts.	Front Axle Oil, Pts.	Transfer Case, Pts.
SL500	1998	16.4	Ethylene Glyco	185	21.1	8.5	9.9	3.0	—	—
	1999–2001	13.5	Ethylene Glyco	185–192	21.1	8.5	9.9	2.8	—	—
SL600	1998–2001	21.1	Ethylene Glyco	189	21.1	10.7	9.9	3.0	—	—
SLK230	1998–2000	9.5	Ethylene Glyco	189	14.0	5.9	7.5	2.3	—	—
	2001	9.5	Ethylene Glyco	189	15.9	5.9	—	—	—	—
SLK320	2001	9.5	Ethylene Glyco	185–192	15.9	8.5⑦	—	—	—	—

① — Includes filter.
② — Approximate drain & refill, make final check w/dipstick.
③ — Diesel.
④ — Life-fill.
⑤ — Sedan 21.1 gals; Wagon 18.5 gals.
⑥ — Plug 2.6 gals reserve.
⑦ — Manual transmission, 3.2 pts.
⑧ — Up to Jan. 31, 1998, 2.7 pts.; as of Feb. 1, 1998, 3.4 pts.

LUBRICANT DATA

Model	Lubricant Type							
	Transmission		Hydraulic Clutch Fluid	Transfer Case	Drive Axle		Power Steering	Brake System
	Automatic	Manual			Front	Rear		
All	③	ATF Type A⑥	DOT 4+	ATF④⑦	SAE 85W-90②	SAE 85W-90②	ATF Type A①⑤⑧	DOT 4+

① — Mercedes-Benz No. 000 989 88 03, or equivalent.
② — Mercedes-Benz No. 001 989 17 03, or equivalent.
③ — Mercedes-Benz Life-Fill ATF No. 000 989 21 03 10, or equivalent.
④ — Mercedes-Benz No. 000 989 92 03, or equivalent.
⑤ — On E55, E300, E320 and E430 models w/common reservoir for steering and level control, Mercedes-Benz No. 001 989 2003 10, or equivalent, hydraulic fluid.
⑥ — Mercedes-Benz No. 000 989 26 03, or equivalent.
⑦ — ML55, ML320 & ML430 models, Mercedes-Benz Life-Fill ATF No. 000 989 21 03 10, or equivalent.
⑧ — On S430 & 2000–01 S500 & 2000 S600 models, Pentosin CHF 11S or Mercedes-Benz No. A 001 989 24 03, or equivalent, hydraulic fluid.

Electrical

NOTE: On Air Bag Equipped Models, Refer To "Air Bag System Precautions" Located In The Front Of This Manual For System Disarming & Arming Procedures.

NOTE: Prior To Performing Any Service Operations Listed In This Section, Consult The "Technical Service Bulletins" Section For Related Information.

INDEX

Page No.

Air Bags 5-214
Air Conditioning 5-191
Alternators 5-210
Alternator, Replace 5-16
C230, E300 & SLK230 5-16
C240 & C320 5-16
C280, CLK320 & E320 5-16
S320 5-16
S420 & 1998–99 CL500 & S500 5-16
S430 & 2000–01 CL500 & S500 5-16
SL600 5-17
1998 SL500 5-17
1998–99 CL600 & S600 5-17
Automatic Seat Belts 5-220
Blower Motor, Replace 5-22
C240 & C320 5-22
C43, C230 & C280 5-22
CLK55, CLK320, CLK430, SLK230 & SLK320 5-22
E55, E300, E320 & E430 5-23
S320, S420 & 1998–99 CL500, CL600, S500 & S600 5-22
S430 & 2000–01 CL500 & S500 & 2001 CL600 & S600 5-23
SL500 & SL600 5-23
Combination Switch, Replace 5-18
C240 & C320 5-18
C43, C230, C280, CLK55, CLK320, CLK430, E55, E300, E320, E430, SLK230 & SLK320 5-18
S320 & S420 & 1998–99 CL500, CL600, S500 & S600 5-19
S430 & 2000–01 CL500 & S500 & 2001 CL600 & S600 5-19
SL500 & SL600 5-19
Cooling Fans 5-195
Cruise Controls 5-212
Dash Gauges 5-197
Dash Panel Service 5-221
Evaporator Core, Replace 5-28
C240 & C320 5-28
C43, C230, C280, CLK55, CLK320, CLK430, E55, E300, E320, E430, SLK230 & SLK320 5-28
S320 & S420 & 1998–99 CL500, CL600, S500 & S600 5-28
S430 & 2000–01 CL500 & S500 & 2001 CL600 & S600 5-29
SL500 & SL600 5-29
Fuel Pump Relay Location 5-15
C43, C230, C240, C280, C320, CLK55, CLK320, CLK430, SLK230 & SLK320 5-15
CL500, CL600, S320, S420, S500, S600, SL500 & SL600 5-15
E320 & E430 5-15
ML320 & ML430 5-15
Fuse Panel & Flasher Location 5-15
Headlamp Switch, Replace 5-18
C240 & C320 5-18
C43, C230 & C280 5-18
S320 & S420 & 1998–99 CL500, CL600, S500 & S600 5-18
S430 & 2000–01 CL500 & S500 & 2000 CL600 & S600 5-18
Heater Core, Replace 5-23
C240 & C320 5-24
C43, C230 & C280 5-23
CLK55, CLK320 & CLK430 5-24
E55, E300, E320 & E430 5-26
S320 & S420 & 1998–99 CL500, CL600, S500 & S600 5-24
S430 & 2000–01 CL500 & S500 & 2001 CL600 & S600 5-26
SL500 & SL600 5-27
SLK230 & SLK320 5-28
Ignition Coil, Replace 5-17
104 & 111 Engines 5-17
112 & 113 Engines 5-17
119 Engine 5-17
Ignition Lock, Replace 5-17
C43, C230, C280, SLK230 & SLK320 5-17
CLK55, CLK320 & CLK430 5-17
E55, E300, E320 & E430 5-17
S320, S420, SL500 & SL600 & 1998–99 CL500, CL600, S500 & S600 5-18
Instrument Cluster, Replace 5-20
C240 & C320 5-20
C43, C230, C280, CLK55, CLK320, CLK430, E55, E300, E320 & E430 5-20
S320 & S420 & 1998–99 CL500, CL600, S500 & S600 5-20
S430 & 2000–01 CL500 & S500 & CL600 & S600 5-20
SLK230 & SLK320 5-20
Passive Restraints 5-214
Precautions 5-15
Air Bag Systems 5-15
Battery Ground Cable 5-15
Radio Coded Anti-Theft System 5-15
Radio, Replace 5-20
C240 & C320 & S430 & 2000–01 CL500 & S500 & 2001 CL600 & S600 5-20
C43, C230, C280, CLK55, CLK320, CLK430, E55, E320, E430, ML55, ML320, ML430, S320, S420, SLK230 & SLK320 & 1998–99 CL500, CL600, S500 & S600 5-20
SL500 & SL600 5-20
Relay Center Location 5-15
Speed Controls 5-212
Starter Motors 5-209
Starter, Replace 5-15
C230 & SLK230 5-15
C240 & C320 5-15
C280 & CLK320 5-15
E300 5-15
E320 5-16
S320 5-16
S420 & 1998–99 CL500 & S500 5-16
SL600 & 1998 SL500 5-16
1998–99 CL600 & 6500 5-16
Steering Columns 5-222
Steering Wheel, Replace 5-19
C43, C230, C280, E55, E300, E320, E430, S320, S420, SL500 & SL600 & 1998–99 CL500, CL600, S500 & S600 5-19
CLK55, CLK320, CLK430, SLK230 & SLK320 5-19
S430 & 2000–01 CL500 & S500 & 2000 CL600 & S600 5-19
Stop Light Switch, Replace 5-18
Technical Service Bulletins 5-29
Battery Discharges & Vehicle Cannot Be Started 5-30
Blower Motor Noisy 5-31
Engine Cannot Be Started 5-31
Engine Dies When Transmission Shift Into Gear Or When Parking 5-30
Fog Lamps Not Operating 5-30
Ignition Key Difficult To Remove 5-31
Instrument Cluster Liquid Crystal Display Not Readable 5-31
Instrument Cluster Loose 5-31
MIL & Indicator Lamps Illuminate Briefly 5-31
Oil Level Below Min. Or Oil Sensor Faulty Indicated On Instrument Cluster 5-30
Parktronic All Segments On & Warning Tone Sounds 5-29
Parktronic System Displays Implausible Warning Tone While Standing 5-30
Parktronic Warning Display Active For No Reason 5-29
Radio Continues To Operate After Ignition Key Is Remove 5-31
Starter Defective Or Corroded 5-31

Page No.
Starter Occasionally Does Not Operate 5-31
Steering Wheel Clacking
Noises 5-31
Turn Signal Occasionally Fails .. 5-29
Wiper Motor, Replace 5-21
Front 5-21
Rear 5-22
Wiper Systems 5-213

PRECAUTIONS

AIR BAG SYSTEMS

Refer to "Air Bag System Precautions" in front of this manual for system disarming and arming procedures.

BATTERY GROUND CABLE

Prior to service, disconnect battery ground cable and isolate as required.

RADIO CODED ANTI-THEFT SYSTEM

Anti-theft radios have a coded theft protection circuit. The CODE card must be obtained before disconnecting battery, removing radio fuse or removing the radio. **The serial number from the radio must match the CODE card.**

After service has been performed proceed as follows:

1. Connect radio power and turn key to position No. 2.
2. Turn radio to On position. Word "CODE" will appear on display.
3. Enter first digit of anti-theft code from CODE card. "CODE" will disappear and entered digit will appear followed by four dashes.
4. Enter next four digits, when all five are entered first digit flashes again.
5. Press SC, Seek or Tune button to confirm code.
6. If "WAIT" appears on radio panel, proceed as follows:
   a. Radio will allow three coding attempts only before entering lock-up mode and won't respond to controls.
   b. Leave radio on for 15–60 minutes, then radio will unlock and allow three addition coding attempts.
   c. Third lockout period (after nine failed coding attempts) will last 24 hours.
   d. Radio must be left on during enter 24-hour period until "CODE" appears.
7. When "CODE" appears, repeat coding attempt.

FUSE PANEL & FLASHER LOCATION

The main fuse panel is located in the lefthand rear corner of the engine compartment.

On C43, C230, C240, C280, C320, CLK55, CLK320, CLK430, SLK230 and SLK320 models, the auxiliary fuse panel is located in the righthand front corner of the luggage compartment. There is an auxiliary fuse in the righthand rear corner of the engine compartment and righthand front corner of the luggage compartment.

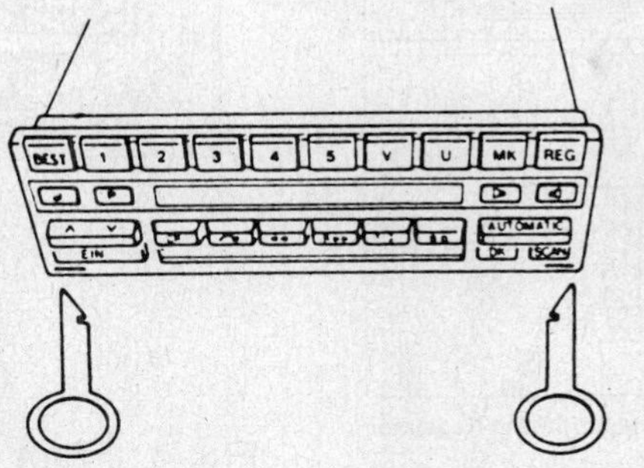

MB9039100001000X

Fig. 1 Radio replacement. S320, S420, SLK230 & SLK320 & 1998–99 CL500, CL600, S500 & S600

On E300, E320, E430 & E55 models there are auxiliary fuse panels under the rear seat and on the lefthand side of the instrument panel.

On S320 and S420 and 1998–99 CL500, CL600, S500 and S600 models there is an auxiliary fuse panel on the righthand side of the luggage compartment.

On S430, CL55 and 2000–01 CL500 and S500 and 2000 CL600 and S600 models there is an auxiliary fuse panel on the righthand side of the engine compartment.

On SL500 and SL600 models there are auxiliary fuse panels located in the lefthand rear corner of the engine compartment and in the front of the luggage compartment.

FUEL PUMP RELAY LOCATION

C43, C230, C240, C280, C320, CLK55, CLK320, CLK430, SLK230 & SLK320

The fuel pump relay is located in the righthand front corner of the luggage compartment.

CL500, CL600, S320, S420, S500, S600, SL500 & SL600

The fuel pump relay is located in the righthand side of the luggage compartment.

E320 & E430

The fuel relay pump is located next to the battery below the rear seat cushion, in the rear fuse box.

ML320 & ML430

The fuel pump relay is located in the electrical box on the lefthand side of the engine compartment.

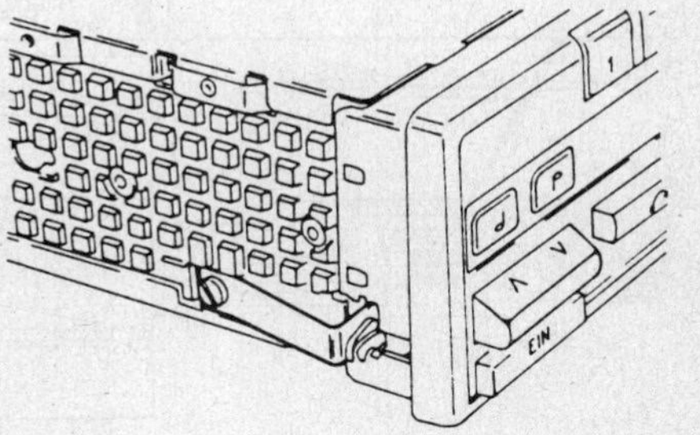

MB9039100002000X

Fig. 2 Radio spring location. S320 & S420 & 1998–99 CL500, CL600, S500 & S600

RELAY CENTER LOCATION

Relay center is located on lefthand front side of engine compartment.

STARTER

REPLACE

C230 & SLK230

1. **On C230 models,** remove engine compartment bottom cover.
2. **On all models,** disconnect electrical connectors.
3. Remove mounting bolts, then the cable and hose brackets.
4. Remove mounting bolts starter.
5. Reverse procedure to install. **Torque** starter mounting bolts to 31 ft. lbs.

C240 & C320

1. Remove engine compartment bottom cover.
2. Remove catalytic converter or front exhaust system
3. Disconnect electrical connectors.
4. Remove mounting bolts and bracket.
5. Remove starter.
6. Reverse procedure to install. **Torque** starter mounting bolts to 31 ft. lbs.

C280 & CLK320

1. Remove engine compartment bottom cover.
2. Remove engine mount and/or front engine carrier.
3. Disconnect electrical connectors.
4. Remove mounting bolts and bracket.
5. Remove starter.
6. Reverse procedure to install. **Torque** starter mounting bolts to 43 ft. lbs.

E300

1. Remove engine compartment bottom cover.
2. Disconnect electrical connectors.
3. Remove mounting bolts and bracket.

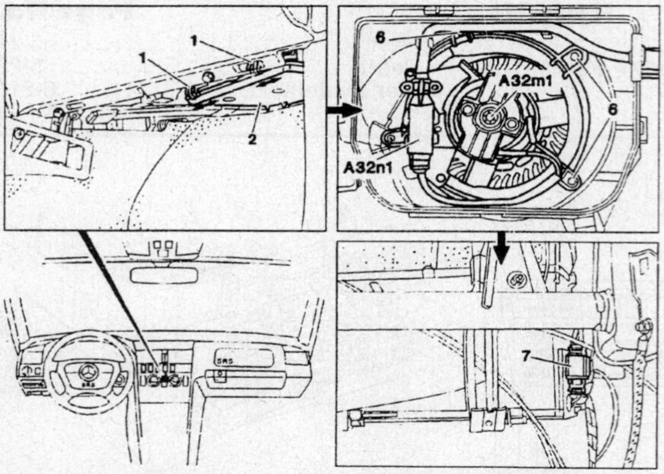

1 Locking Mount 2 Cover 6 Bolt 7 Connector A32m1 Blower Motor A32n1 Regulator

MB7020000124000X

Fig. 3 Blower motor replacement. C43, C230 & C280

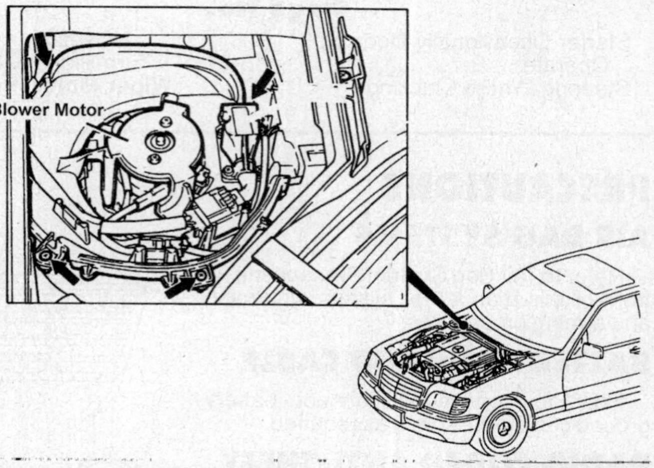

MB7020000094000X

Fig. 4 Front blower motor replacement. S320, S420 & 1998–99 CL500, CL600, S500 & S600

4. Remove starter from below.
5. Reverse procedure to install. **Torque** starter mounting bolts to 31 ft. lbs.

E320

1. Remove engine compartment bottom cover.
2. **On models equipped with 4MATIC,** remove propeller shaft guard.
3. **On all models,** remove righthand side catalytic converter or exhaust system front section.
4. Disconnect electrical connectors.
5. Remove mounting bolts and starter motor.
6. Reverse procedure to install. **Torque** starter mounting bolts to 31 ft. lbs.

S320

1. Remove engine compartment rear panel.
2. Remove Automatic Locking Differential/Acceleration Slip Regulation (ASD/ASR) hose holder, as required.
3. Remove starter motor mounting bolts.
4. Disconnect electrical cable.
5. Remove starter motor.
6. Reverse procedure to install. **Torque** starter mounting bolts to 41 ft. lbs.

S420 & 1998–99 CL500 & S500

1. Remove engine compartment rear panel.
2. Remove mounting bolts, nut and shield.
3. Disconnect electrical wiring from starter.
4. Remove starter mounting bolts and starter motor.
5. Reverse procedure to install. **Torque** starter mounting bolts to 41 ft. lbs.

1998–99 CL600 & 6500

1. Remove engine compartment rear panel.
2. Turn steering to full lefthand lock.
3. Disconnect electrical wiring from starter.
4. Remove starter mounting bolts and starter motor.
5. Reverse procedure to install. **Torque** starter mounting bolts to 41 ft. lbs.

SL600 & 1998 SL500

1. **On SL600 models,** turn steering to full lefthand lock.
2. **On all models,** remove engine compartment bottom panel.
3. Disconnect righthand pitman arm and loosen righthand strut stiffener.
4. **On 1998 SL500 models,** remove starter shield mounting bolts and nut.
5. **On all models,** remove starter shield.
6. Remove holder and disconnect cables.
7. Remove mounting bolts and starter.
8. Reverse procedure to install. **Torque** starter mounting bolts to 31 ft. lbs.

ALTERNATOR

REPLACE

C230, E300 & SLK230

1. Remove drive belt.
2. **On C230 and SLK230 models,** remove engine compartment bottom panel.
3. **On E300 models,** remove bottom soundproofing covers.
4. **On all models,** remove protective cover, as required, and disconnect electrical connectors.
5. Remove mounting bolts and alternator from bottom.
6. Reverse procedure to install. **Torque** alternator mounting bolts to 31 ft. lbs.

C240 & C320

1. Remove air cleaner housing and intake air scoop.
2. Remove drive belt.
3. Disconnect electrical connectors.
4. Remove mounting bolts, spacer sleeve and alternator from bottom.
5. Reverse procedure to install. **Torque** alternator mounting bolts to 31 ft. lbs.

C280, CLK320 & E320

1. Remove engine compartment bottom cover.
2. Remove viscous fan clutch and drive belt.
3. Disconnect electrical connectors.
4. Remove mounting bolts and alternator from bottom.
5. Reverse procedure to install. **Torque** alternator mounting bolts to 44 ft. lbs.

S320

1. Remove drive belt.
2. Remove engine compartment panels.
3. Disconnect electrical connector
4. Remove mounting bolts and alternator.
5. Reverse procedure to install.

S420 & 1998–99 CL500 & S500

1. Remove drive belt.
2. Remove engine compartment panels.
3. Remove crossmember below radiator.
4. Remove fan cowl.
5. Disconnect electrical connector
6. Remove automatic transmission oil line mounting screw.
7. Remove mounting bolts and alternator.
8. Reverse procedure to install.

S430 & 2000–01 CL500 & S500

1. Remove drive belt.
2. Remove mounting nut and pivot coolant expansion tank aside. **Do not remove tank.**
3. Remove righthand side air intake duct.
4. Remove engine cover.
5. Remove radiator.
6. Remove alternator mounting bolts.
7. Disconnect electrical connectors.
8. Remove alternator.
9. Reverse procedure to install. **Torque**

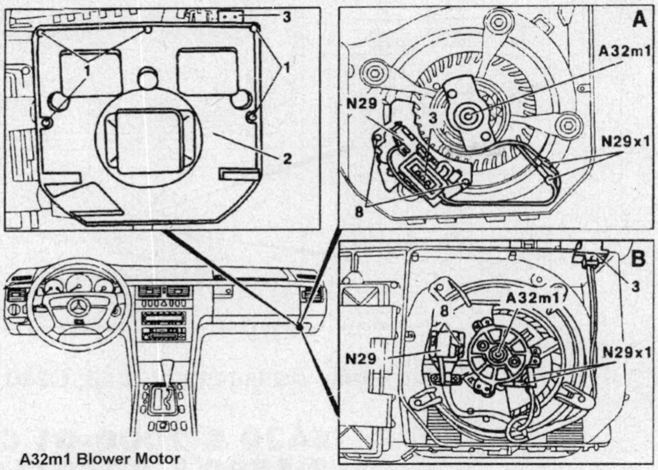

A32m1 Blower Motor
1 Bolt 2 Cover 3 Connecto r8 Bolt N29 Regulator N29x1 Connector

MB7020000123000X

Fig. 5 Blower motor replacement. E55 E300, E320 & E430

mounting bolts to 31 ft. lbs.

1998–99 CL600 & S600

1. Remove drive belt.
2. Remove engine compartment panels.
3. Remove side member torsion bar.
4. Disconnect electrical connector
5. Remove automatic transmission oil line mounting screw.
6. Remove mounting bolts and alternator.
7. Reverse procedure to install.

1998 SL500

1. Remove engine compartment bottom panel.
2. **On models equipped with bowl-type alternator,** remove viscous fan clutch.
3. **On all models,** remove electrical cables.
4. Remove drive belt.
5. **On models equipped with compact alternator,** remove left and righthand torsion bar spring leaf rockers.
6. **On all models,** remove mounting bolts and alternator.
7. Reverse procedure to install, noting the following:
   a. Replace self-locking bolts on left and righthand torsion bar spring leaf rockers, and controller connecting lever rod.
   b. **Torque** circuit 30 cable mounting nut to 11 ft. lbs.
   c. **Torque** circuit 61 cable mounting nut to 35 inch lbs.
   d. **Torque** alternator mounting bolt to 31 ft. lbs.

SL600

1. Release cooling system pressure.
2. Remove engine compartment bottom panel.
3. Remove electrical cables.
4. Remove drive belt.
5. Disconnect controller connecting lever rod.
6. Remove ATF line mounting bolt.
7. **On models equipped with compact alternator,** remove left and righthand torsion bar spring leaf rockers.
8. **On all models,** remove mounting bolts and alternator.
9. Reverse procedure to install, noting the following:
   a. Replace self-locking bolts on left and righthand torsion bar spring leaf rockers, and controller connecting lever rod.
   b. **Torque** circuit 30 cable mounting nut to 11 ft. lbs.
   c. **Torque** circuit 61 cable mounting nut to 35 inch lbs.
   d. **Torque** alternator mounting bolt to 31 ft. lbs.

IGNITION COIL

REPLACE

104 & 111 ENGINES

1. Remove mounting bolt and cable duct cover.
2. Disconnect cables and remove ignition coils.
3. Reverse procedure to install.

112 & 113 ENGINES

1. **On S430 and 2000–01 CL500 and S500 models,** unclip engine face engine cover.
2. **On all models,** remove engine trim panel or air cleaner from cylinder head covers.
3. Remove mounting bolts.
4. Disconnect spark plug connectors.
5. Remove ignition coils.
6. Reverse procedure to install. **Torque** mounting bolt to 71 inch lbs.

119 ENGINE

1. Remove mounting bolts and cover.
2. Remove coil. Mark cable routing for installation.
3. Reverse procedure to install.

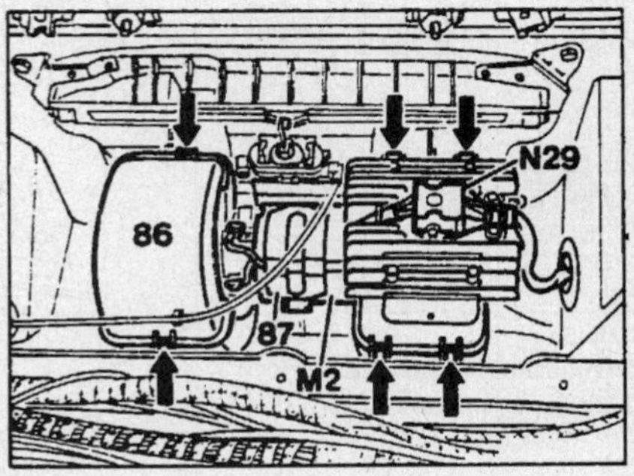

M2 Connector N29 Blower Controller
86 Cover 87 Retaining Strap

MB7020000083000X

Fig. 6 Blower motor replacement. SL500 & SL600

IGNITION LOCK

REPLACE

C43, C230, C280, SLK230 & SLK320

Removal

1. Press out instrument panel escutcheon using suitable small screwdriver.
2. Remove transponder coil from steering lock cylinder.
3. Push sleeve tool No. 202 589 00 14 00, or equivalent, onto cap and turn lock cylinder to position 1.
4. Unlock lock cylinder by turning cap counterclockwise 90°, then remove.

Installation

1. Spray lock cylinder outside with cylinder grease No. 001 989 26 51 00, or equivalent.
2. Install cylinder in cap.
3. Push key through cap and up to lock cylinder stop.
4. Align lock cylinder indentations with steering lock recesses, then push lock cylinder into steering lock.
5. Turn cap with sleeve approximately 90° clockwise until it locks in position.
6. Turn key to 0 position and remove with sleeve.
7. Press on escutcheon.
8. Install transponder coil.

CLK55, CLK320 & CLK430

1. Remove cover below instrument panel.
2. Remove mounting screws and bottom righthand side of instrument panel.
3. Remove instrument panel escutcheon using claw-type wrench tool No. 210 589 00 07 00, or equivalent.
4. Remove electronic ignition/starter switch.
5. Remove shift lock by pressing retaining clips together and drawing shaft lock forward out of retaining lugs.
6. Reverse procedure to install.

E55, E300, E320 & E430

1. Remove cover below instrument panel.

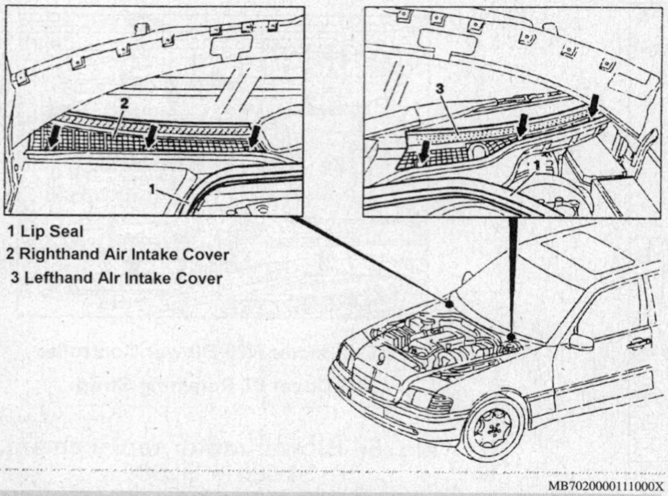

Fig. 7 Left & righthand air intake cover replacement. C43, C230, C280, CLK55, CLK320 & CLK430

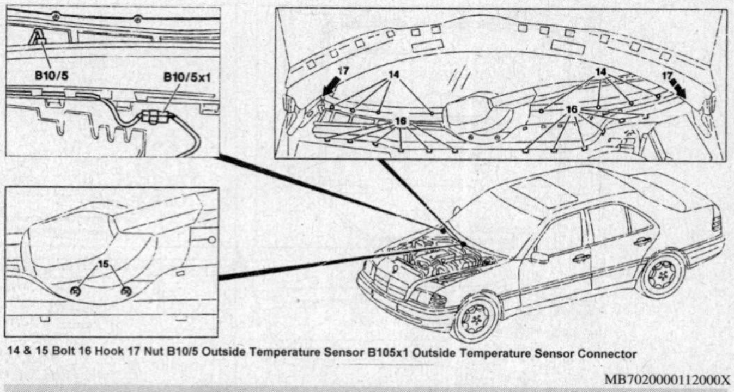

Fig. 8 Air intake replacement. C43, C230 & C280

2. Remove instrument panel escutcheon using claw-type wrench tool No. 210 589 00 07 00, or equivalent.
3. Remove electronic ignition/starter switch.
4. Remove shift lock by pressing retaining clips together and drawing shaft lock forward out of retaining lugs.
5. Reverse procedure to install.

S320, S420, SL500 & SL600 & 1998-99 CL500, CL600, S500 & S600

Removal

1. Remove transponder coil from lock cylinder.
2. Push sleeve tool No. 202 589 00 14 00, or equivalent onto cap and turn lock cylinder to position 1 with key.
3. Unlock and remove cylinder by turning cap counterclockwise through 90°.

Installation

1. Spray lock cylinder outside with cylinder grease No. 001 989 26 51 00, or equivalent.
2. Install in covering cap.
3. Push key through cap as far as lock cylinder stop.
4. Push lock cylinder into steering lock until cylinder and steering lock recesses align.
5. Turn cap with sleeve approximately 90° clockwise until it locks into position.
6. Turn key to position 0 and remove with sleeve.
7. Push cap onto protective sleeve until snap ring locks.
8. Install transponder coil from lock cylinder.

HEADLAMP SWITCH

REPLACE

C43, C230 & C280

1. Remove cover below instrument panel.
2. Remove switch control knob by pulling it off.
3. Remove bulb, then remove nut and cover.
4. Remove switch by turning to it to left.
5. Disconnect electrical connector.
6. Reverse procedure to install.

C240 & C320

1. Remove cover below instrument panel.
2. Pull out parking brake release and remove mounting bolt.
3. Remove switch. Disconnect electrical connector.
4. Reverse procedure to install.

S320 & S420 & 1998-99 CL500, CL600, S500 & S600

1. Remove lower instrument panel cover.
2. Remove steering column adjustment control button.
3. Remove switch locking element by pressing with suitable screwdriver.
4. Remove bulb, then the mounting screws and panel cover.
5. Remove mounting screw, nut and cover.
6. Remove pneumatic line, as required.
7. Disconnect lighting electrical connector.
8. Remove switch by turning it to left.
9. Disconnect electrical connector.
10. Reverse procedure to install.

S430 & 2000-01 CL500 & S500 & 2000 CL600 & S600

1. Pull out and release parking brake.
2. Remove mounting screw, cover and switch.
3. Disconnect electrical connector.
4. Unhook parking brake cable.
5. Reverse procedure to install.

STOP LIGHT SWITCH

REPLACE

1. Remove cover below instrument panel.
2. Disconnect electrical connector.
3. Press locking device, turn and remove stop lamp switch.
4. Withdraw actuating pin completely.
5. Press brake pedal, insert and turn switch until locking devices engages.
6. Switch is self-adjusting.

COMBINATION SWITCH

REPLACE

C43, C230, C280, CLK55, CLK320, CLK430, E55, E300, E320, E430, SLK230 & SLK320

1. Remove steering wheel as described under "Steering Wheel, Replace."
2. Remove air bag contact spiral.
3. Remove cover below instrument panel.
4. Remove mounting bolts and bracket.
5. Disconnect electrical connectors.
6. Remove casing tube with combination and cruise control switches.
7. Remove cruise control switch from casing.
8. Remove combination switch from casing.
9. Reverse procedure to install.

C240 & C320

1. Remove steering wheel as described under "Steering Wheel, Replace."
2. Remove air bag contact spiral.

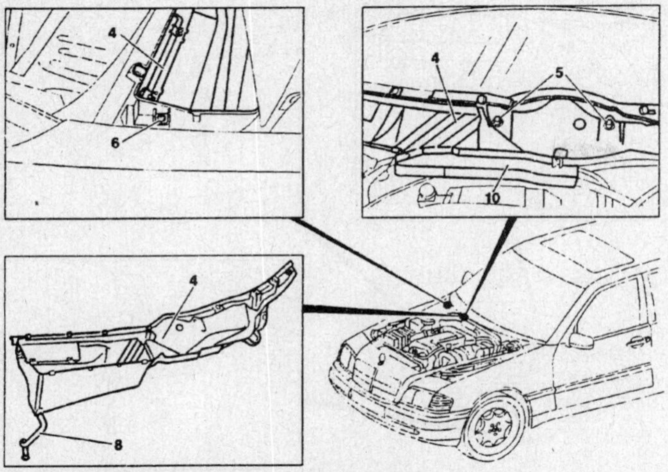

4 Water Collector 5 Rubber Wiper Mount 8 Water Drain 10 Wiring Duct

MB7020000110000X

Fig. 9 Water collector replacement. C43, C230, C280, CLK55, CLK320 & CLK430

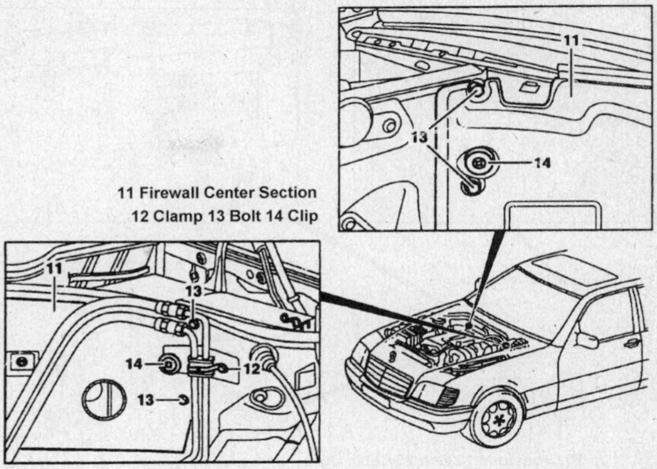

MB7020000113000X

Fig. 10 Firewall center section replacement. C43, C230 & C280

3. Remove mounting bolts and cruise control switch. Disconnect electrical connectors.
4. Remove combination switch from casing. Disconnect electrical connectors.
5. Reverse procedure to install.

S320 & S420 & 1998-99 CL500, CL600, S500 & S600

1. Remove steering wheel as described under "Steering Wheel, Replace."
2. Remove mounting screws, cover plate and contact spiral.
3. Remove steering angle sensor.
4. Remove instrument panel lower cover.
5. Disconnect combination and cruise control switches electrical connectors.
6. Remove casing tube cover.
7. Remove cruise control switch from casing tube.
8. Remove combination switch from casing tube.
9. Reverse procedure to install.

S430 & 2000-01 CL500 & S500 & 2001 CL600 & S600

1. Remove steering wheel as described under "Steering Wheel, Replace."
2. Remove mounting screws and horn/air bag clock spring contact.
3. Remove steering angle sensor.
4. Loosen mounting bolt and remove steering column switch module.
5. Remove cover and cruise control switch.
6. Remove steering column adjustment and entry/exit switch module.
7. Remove combination switch.
8. Reverse procedure to install

SL500 & SL600

1. Remove steering wheel as described under "Steering Wheel, Replace."
2. Remove instrument panel lower cover.
3. Remove mounting screws, cover plate and contract spiral.
4. Disconnect combination switch electrical connector by moving bracket.
5. Disconnect cruise control switch connector.
6. Disconnect cable duct clips on reinforcement bracket under steering column.
7. Remove steering column cover.
8. Remove cruise control switch from steering column cover.
9. Remove combination switch from steering column cover.
10. Reverse procedure to install.

STEERING WHEEL

REPLACE

C43, C230, C280, E55, E300, E320, E430, S320, S420, SL500 & SL600 & 1998-99 CL500, CL600, S500 & S600

1. Remove driver's air bag module as described in "Passive Restraints" section.
2. Remove countersunk bolt and disconnect electrical connectors.
3. Remove steering wheel.
4. Reverse procedure to install, noting the following:
   a. Align steering wheel splines recesses with steering shaft marking.
   b. **Torque** new countersunk bolt to 61 ft. lbs.
   c. **On models equipped with Adaptive Damping System (ADS) and Electronic Stability Program (ESP),** start and idle engine, then turn steering wheel lock to lock to activate steering angle sensor. ADS or ESP malfunction indicator lamp should go out.

CLK55, CLK320, CLK430, SLK230 & SLK320

1. **On CLK55, CLK320 and CLK430 models,** remove electronic ignition key.
2. **On all models,** remove driver's air bag module as described in "Passive Restraints" section.
3. Remove countersunk bolt and disconnect electrical connectors.
4. Remove steering wheel guiding through air bag cable.
5. Reverse procedure to install, noting the following:
   a. Align steering wheel splines recesses with steering shaft marking.
   b. **Torque** new countersunk bolt to 61 ft. lbs.
   c. **On models equipped with Electronic Stability Program (ESP),** start and idle engine, then turn steering wheel lock to lock to activate steering angle sensor. ESP malfunction indicator lamp should go out.

S430 & 2000-01 CL500 & S500 & 2000 CL600 & S600

1. Adjust steering column to full extension.
2. Remove driver's air bag module as described in "Passive Restraints" section.
3. Remove countersunk bolt and disconnect electrical connectors.
4. Remove steering wheel.
5. Reverse procedure to install, noting the following:
   a. **Torque** new countersunk bolt to 61 ft. lbs.
   b. Start and idle engine, then turn steering wheel lock to lock to activate steering angle sensor.

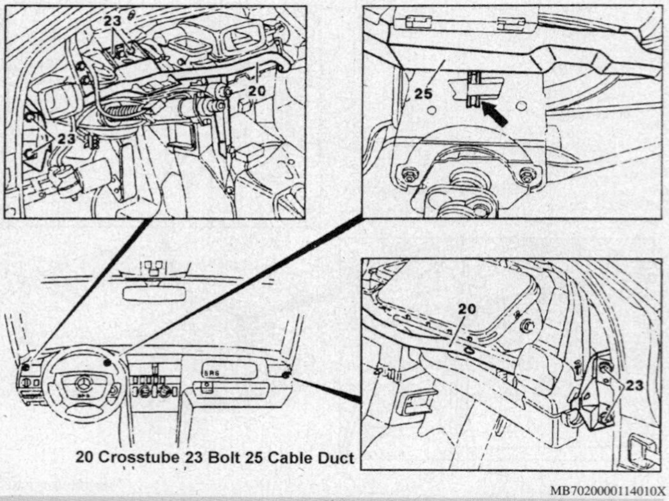

Fig. 11 Evaporator core replacement (Part 1 of 3). C43, C230 & C280

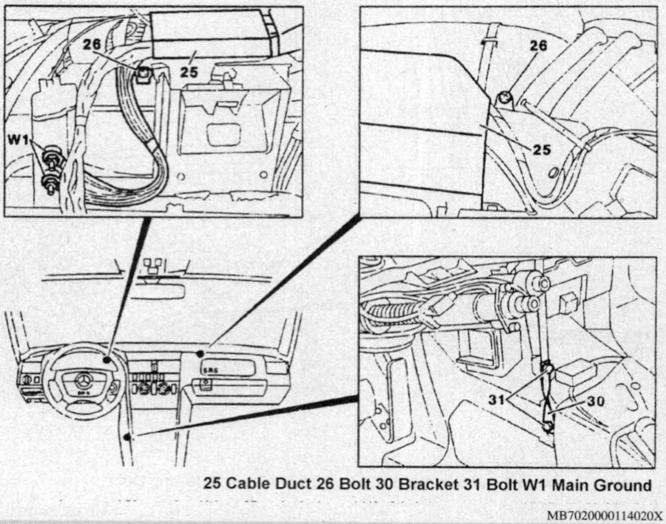

Fig. 11 Evaporator core replacement (Part 2 of 3). C43, C230 & C280

INSTRUMENT CLUSTER

REPLACE

C43, C230, C280, CLK55, CLK320, CLK430, E55, E300, E320 & E430

1. Pull adjustable steering wheel out.
2. Insert pull hook tool No. 140 589 02 33 00, or equivalent, between instrument panel padding and instrument cluster approximately .3 inch deep with curved end pointing down and turn tool 90° toward instrument cluster.
3. Pull hook tool until it engages instrument cluster recess.
4. Alternately pull left and righthand sides of cluster out approximately .2 inch with hook tool.
5. Pull instrument cluster out.
6. Disconnect electrical connectors and remove cluster.
7. Reverse procedure to install.

C240 & C320

1. Insert pull hook tool No. 140 589 02 33 00, or equivalent, between instrument panel padding and instrument cluster approximately .3 inch deep with curved end pointing down and turn tool 90° toward instrument cluster.
2. Pull hook tool until it engages instrument cluster recess.
3. Alternately pull left and righthand sides of cluster out approximately .2 inch with hook tool.
4. Pull instrument cluster out.
5. Disconnect electrical connectors.
6. Remove instrument cluster.
7. Reverse procedure to install.

S320 & S420 & 1998-99 CL500, CL600, S500 & S600

1. **On models equipped with manual steering column adjustment,** remove steering wheel as described under "Steering Wheel, Replace."
2. **On all models,** disconnect contract spiral.
3. Remove steering angle sensor.
4. Insert pull hook tool No. 140 589 02 33 00, or equivalent, between instrument panel padding and instrument cluster approximately .3 inch deep with curved end pointing down and turn tool 90° toward instrument cluster.
5. Pull hook tool until it engages instrument cluster recess.
6. Alternately pull left and righthand sides of cluster out approximately .2 inch with hook tool.
7. Remove instrument cluster.
8. Reverse procedure to install.

S430 & 2000-01 CL500 & S500 & CL600 & S600

1. Pull steering wheel and column out and down.
2. Push on side and pull instrument cluster out.
3. Disconnect electrical connectors and remove instrument cluster.
4. Reverse procedure to install.

SLK230 & SLK320

1. Pull adjustable steering wheel out.
2. Remove steering wheel as described under "Steering Wheel, Replace."
3. Remove mounting screws and instrument cluster cover.
4. Remove mounting screws and pull instrument cluster forward.
5. Disconnect electrical connectors and remove instrument cluster.
6. Reverse procedure to install.

RADIO

REPLACE

C43, C230, C280, CLK55, CLK320, CLK430, E55, E320, E430, ML55, ML320, ML430, S320, S420, SLK230 & SLK320 & 1998-99 CL500, CL600, S500 & S600

1. Push retaining springs back and pull radio out using radio removal key tools No. 000 833 03 61, or equivalent, **Figs. 1 and 2.**
2. Disconnect electrical connectors.
3. Reverse procedure to install.

C240 & C320 & S430 & 2000-01 CL500 & S500 & 2001 CL600 & S600

1. Remove center console cover.
2. Remove mounting bolts and pull radio out.
3. Disconnect fiber optic cable and electrical connectors.
4. Remove radio.
5. Reverse procedure to install.

SL500 & SL600

1. Press radio into console at cover outer left and righthand corners.
2. Insert removal plate tools No. 129 589 00 05 00, or equivalent, approximately .02 inch from faceplate outer edges at 45° angle from bottom between cover and wooden molding against stop.

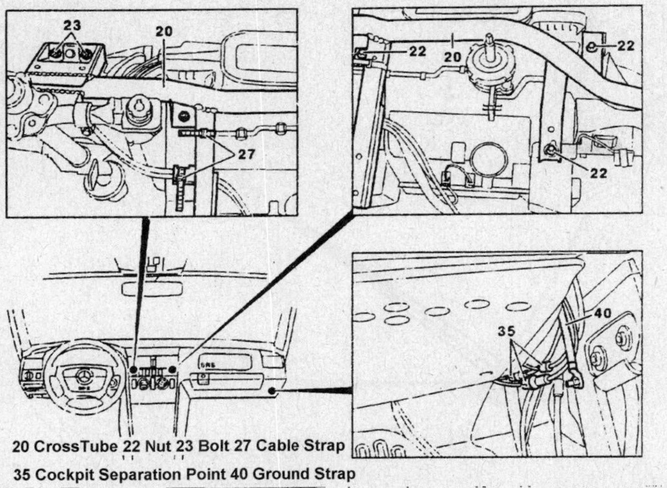

20 CrossTube 22 Nut 23 Bolt 27 Cable Strap
35 Cockpit Separation Point 40 Ground Strap

MB7020000114030X

Fig. 11 Evaporator core replacement (Part 3 of 3). C43, C230 & C280

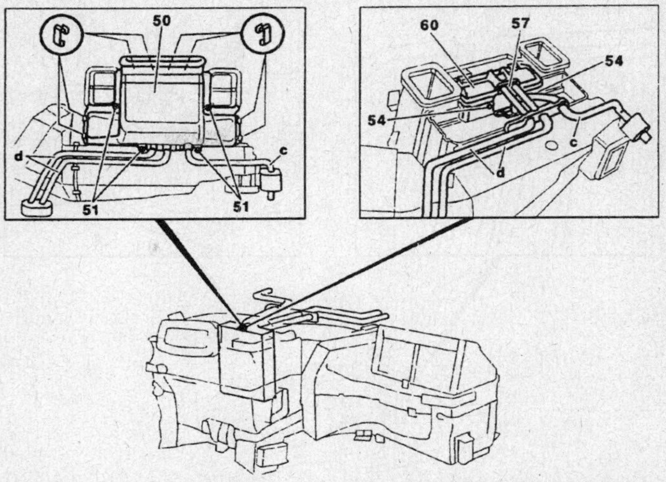

50 Cover 51, 54& 57 Bolts 60 Heater Core c Supply Hose d Return Hose

MB7020000105010X

Fig. 12 Heat core replacement (Part 1 of 2). C43, C230, C280, CLK320, CLK430, E55, E300, E320, E430 & SLK230

3. Lift slightly and pull tools out.
4. Disconnect electrical connectors.
5. Remove radio.
6. Reverse procedure to install.

WIPER MOTOR

REPLACE

FRONT

C43, C230, C280, CLK55, CLK320, CLK430, E55, E300, E320 & E430

1. Remove key from ignition switch.
2. Remove cover, mounting screw and wiper arm.
3. Open hood, raise to vertical position and remove air inlet.
4. Remove cover below wiper system.
5. Remove system mounting nuts.
6. **On C43, C230 and C280 models,** remove screw from rubber mount behind engine partition. **Access is difficult.**
7. **On CLK320 and CLK430 models,** open rubber mount clamp.
8. **On all models,** disconnect wiper motor electrical connector.
9. Remove wiper system with rubber bushing. **Do not damage windshield.**
10. Mark basic gear head seating for installation alignment.
11. Remove motor shaft nut and press crank arm off shaft.
12. Remove mounting bolts and wiper motor.
13. Reverse procedure to install, noting the following:
    a. Ensure motor is in park position.
    b. Ensure wiper gear head marking align.
    c. Install crank arm and wiper linkage in extended position.
    d. Ensure distance between wiper gear head and windshield is .1969 inch.
    e. **Torque** shaft nut to 14 ft. lbs.
    f. **Torque** wiper motor mounting bolts to 44 inch lbs.

C240 & C320

1. Remove key from ignition switch.
2. Remove water collector and SAM control module cover.
3. Disconnect control module electrical connector.
4. Remove wiring harness.
5. Remove mounting screw, bolts and wiper system.
6. Cut cable straps.
7. Press lefthand articulated rod from ball joint and remove. **Do not loosen or remove mounting nut.**
8. Remove mounting screws and wiper motor from linkage.
9. Reverse procedure to install, noting the following:
    a. **Torque** wiper motor mounting bolts to 115 inch lbs.
    b. **Torque** system mounting screw to firewall to 71 inch lbs.
    c. **Torque** system mounting screw to body to 15 ft. lbs.

S320 & S420 & 1998–99 CL500, CL600, S500 & S600

1. Remove key from ignition switch.
2. Open hood, then remove mounting nut and wiper arm.
3. Raise wiper head to vertical position.
4. Disconnect main air flap elements' vacuum lines.
5. Remove air collection box mounting screws.
6. Disconnect temperature sensor from lefthand side of air collection box.
7. Remove air collection box.
8. Remove air filter with cover.
9. Remove lefthand cover.
10. Remove righthand cover mounting screws.
11. Press off righthand wiper arm mount rubber ring.
12. Remove righthand cover.
13. Remove wiper system.
14. Disconnect wiper system relay electrical connector.
15. Remove righthand wiper arm mount mounting bolts.
16. Remove system mounting nut, bolt and screws.
17. Push wiring harness with rubber grommet into water box.
18. Remove wiper system to left.
19. Open cover plate, then remove mounting screw and wiper arm. Mark arm for installation alignment.
20. Press off linkage snow guard.
21. Remove wiper motor shaft mounting nut.
22. Press off snow guard.
23. Remove mounting bolts and wiper motor.
24. Disconnect wiper motor electrical connector.
25. Reverse procedure to install, noting the following:
    a. Ensure wiper motor is in park position.
    b. **Torque** motor mounting bolts to 10–13 ft. lbs.
    c. Crank arm and push rod must be parallel.
    d. **Torque** motor shaft nut to 41–44 ft. lbs.
    e. **Torque** stop screws to 88 inch lbs.
    f. **Torque** wiper arm mounting bolts to 88 inch lbs.
    g. Ensure distance between wiper gear head and windshield is .4331 inch.

S430 & 2000–01 CL500 & S500 & 2001 CL600 & S600

1. Move wiper system to park position.
2. Remove key from ignition switch.
3. Open hood and move to upright position.
4. Remove mounting nuts and wiper arms.
5. Remove four spreading rivets, then pull water deflector out of channel.
6. Remove four wiper system mounting nuts and disconnect wiper motor electrical connector.

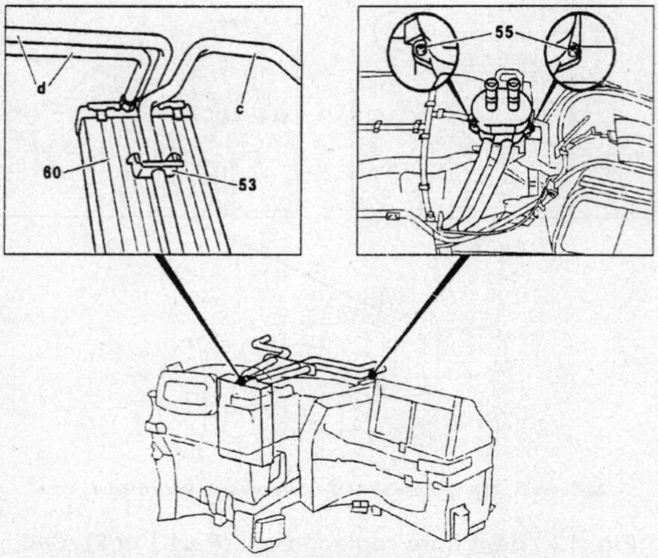

53 Bracket 55 Bolts 60 Heater Core c Supply Hose d Return Hose

MB7020000105020X

Fig. 12 Heat core replacement (Part 2 of 2). C43, C230, C280, CLK320, CLK430, E55, E300, E320, E430 & SLK230

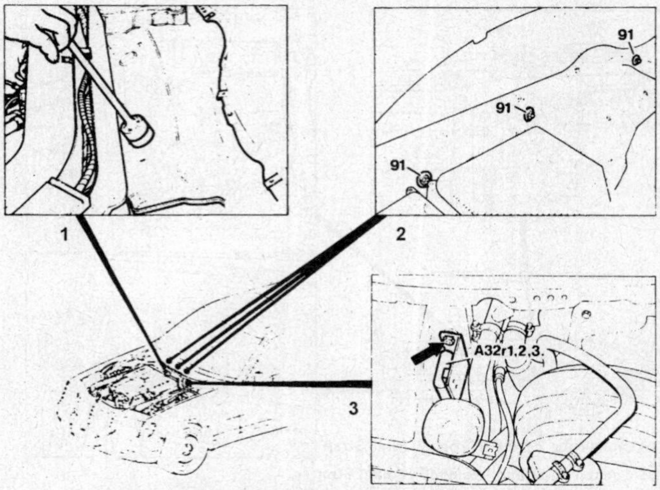

91 Firewall Mounting Nuts A32r1,2,3 Preresistor Group

MB7020000092000X

Fig. 13 Front heater core housing replacement. S320 & S420 & 1998–99 CL500, CL600, S500 & S600

7. Remove wiper system.
8. Remove shaft nut and crank with linkage.
9. Disconnect mount connector.
10. Remove mounting screws and motor.
11. Reverse procedure to install, noting the following:
    a. **Torque** wiper motor mounting screws to 83 inch lbs.
    b. **Torque** shaft nut to 15 ft. lbs.
    c. **Torque** wiper system mounting nuts to 15 ft. lbs.
    d. **Torque** wiper arm mounting nut to 25 ft. lbs.

SL500 & SL600

1. Remove key from ignition switch.
2. Remove air intake cover.
3. Remove righthand cover above electrical components.
4. Remove side cover hose.
5. Move wiper system to maximum extension.
6. Remove plastic cover, mounting screw and wiper arm.
7. Remove mounting nuts, screws and cable strap.
8. Disconnect relay electrical connector.
9. Remove wiper motor with gearbox by pushing wiring harness through firewall with rubber grommet.
10. Remove mounting nut and press off crank arm.
11. Remove mounting screws and wiper motor.
12. Reverse procedure to install, noting the following:
    a. Move wiper motor to park position.
    b. Ensure linkage is perpendicular above shaft center.
    c. Ensure distance between wiper gear head and windshield is .1969 inch.
    d. **Torque** wiper motor mounting screws to 44 inch lbs.
    e. **Torque** wiper motor shaft nut to 14 ft. lbs.

SLK230 & SLK320

1. Remove key from ignition switch.
2. Open hood to upright position.
3. Remove cap, mounting nut and wiper arm.
4. Remove air inlet.
5. Remove control module box cover.
6. Disconnect wiper motor connector from multi-function control module.
7. Remove control module box and heat exchanger rubber grommets.
8. Remove drain.
9. Remove mounting screw, nuts and wiper system.
10. Remove wiper motor shaft nut and press crank arm off.
11. Remove mounting screws and wiper motor.
12. Reverse procedure to install, noting the following:
    a. Ensure motor is in park position.
    b. Ensure distance between wiper gear head and windshield is .1969 inch.
    c. **Torque** wiper motor mounting screws to 97 inch lbs.
    d. **Torque** shaft mounting nut to 19 ft. lbs.

REAR

E320

1. Remove key from ignition switch.
2. Remove tailgate trim panel.
3. Open cover plate, then remove mounting screw and wiper arm.
4. Disconnect electrical connector.
5. Remove mounting bolts and wiper motor.
6. Reverse procedure to install.

BLOWER MOTOR

REPLACE

C43, C230 & C280

1. Remove passenger side blower motor cover below instrument panel.
2. Push locking mounts to one side and fold cover down, **Fig. 3.**
3. Disconnect electrical connector.
4. Remove mounting bolts and blower regulator.
5. Remove mounting bolts and blower motor.
6. Reverse procedure to install.

C240 & C320

1. Remove passenger side blower motor cover below instrument panel.
2. Disconnect electrical connector.
3. Remove mounting screws and blower motor with controller.
4. Reverse procedure to install.

CLK55, CLK320, CLK430, SLK230 & SLK320

1. Remove passenger side blower motor cover below instrument panel.
2. Disconnect electrical connector.
3. Slide catch mounts to side and swing cover down.
4. Disconnect electrical connectors.
5. Remove mounting bolts and blower regulator.
6. Remove mounting bolts and blower motor.
7. Reverse procedure to install.

S320, S420 & 1998–99 CL500, CL600, S500 & S600

Front

1. Remove air collector as outlined under "Heater Core, Replace."
2. Remove dust filter.
3. Disconnect electrical connector.

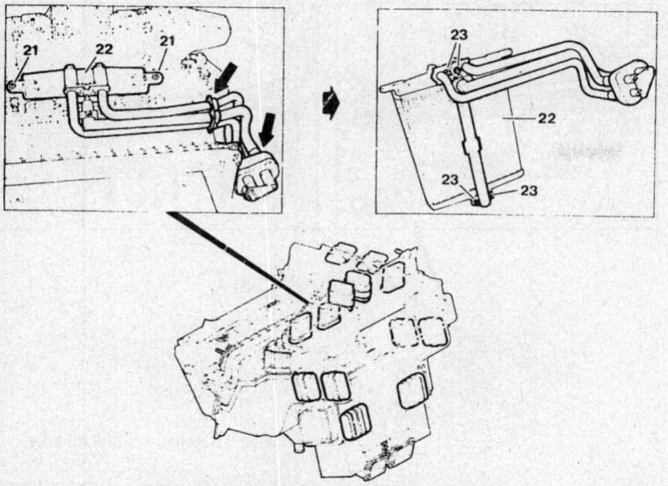

21 Mounting Bolts 22 Heater Core 23 Pipes

MB7020000093000X

Fig. 14 Front heater core replacement. S320 & S420 & 1998–99 CL500, CL600, S500 & S600

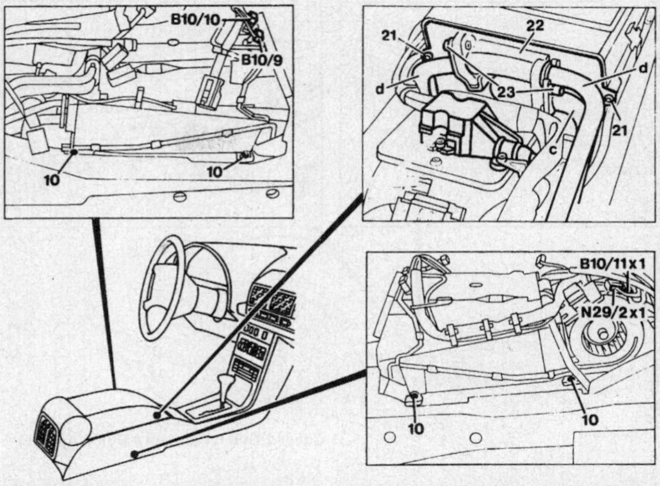

N10/9 & 10 Temperature Sensor N10/11x1 Connections N29/2x1 Connector c & d Hose 10, 21 & 23 Bolt 22 Heater Corer

MB7020000102000X

Fig. 15 Rear air condition unit replacement. S320 & S420 & 1998–99 CL500, CL600, S500 & S600

4. Remove mounting bolts and blower motor, **Fig. 4.**
5. Reverse procedure to install.

Rear

1. Drain coolant into suitable container.
2. Remove rear control module as previously outlined.
3. Remove center console as outlined under "Heater Core, Replace."
4. Remove heater core supply and return lines.
5. Disconnect heat exchanger temperature sensor connectors.
6. Remove clips and blower housing.
7. Remove mounting bolt and blower controller.
8. Remove blower motor.
9. Reverse procedure to install.

S430 & 2000–01 CL500 & S500 & 2001 CL600 & S600

Front

1. Remove cover below instrument panel.
2. Disconnect blower connector.
3. Remove mounting bolts and cover.
4. Disconnect blower regulator.
5. Remove mounting bolts and blower motor.
6. Reverse procedure to install.

Rear

1. Recover refrigerant as outlined under "Air Conditioning."
2. Remove air conditioning housing as outlined under "Evaporator Core, Replace."
3. Remove rear blower regulator.
4. Remove clips and motor housing.
5. Remove clips and disconnect housing.
6. Remove mounting bolts and rear blower motor.
7. Reverse procedure to install.

E55, E300, E320 & E430

1. Remove blower motor cover below passenger side instrument panel.
2. Disconnect blower connector, **Fig. 5.**
3. Remove mounting bolt and cover.
4. Remove regulator connector.
5. Remove mounting bolts and regulator.
6. Remove mounting bolts and blower motor.
7. Reverse procedure to install.

SL500 & SL600

1. Remove key from ignition switch.
2. Remove air inlet cover.
3. Remove electrical components right-hand cover and hose from side cover.
4. Move wiper system to maximum extension.
5. Pull plastic cover down and off, then remove mounting screw and wiper arm.
6. Remove mounting nuts, bolts and wiper motor mounting clip.
7. Disconnect wiper motor electrical connector.
8. Remove wiper motor with gearbox. Push wiring harness through firewall with rubber grommet.
9. Remove mounting bolts, then the left and righthand cowl water drains.
10. Remove mounting rivets and bolts, then the center partition wall.
11. Remove mounting bolts, housing and rubber stopper.
12. Remove mounting clips, cover and blower controller, **Fig. 6.**
13. Remove strap, disconnect connector and remove blower motor.
14. Reverse procedure to install, noting the following:
    a. Ensure blower motor is properly inserted into mounting bracket.
    b. Ensure wiper motor is in park position.
    c. **Torque** wiper motor linkage mounting bolts to 44 inch lbs.
    d. Ensure wiper linkage is perpendicular above wiper motor shaft center.
    e. **Torque** wiper motor shaft nut to 14 ft. lbs.
    f. Ensure gaps between wiper gear head and windshield, and wiper arm and blade are .197 inch.

HEATER CORE

REPLACE

C43, C230 & C280

1. Recover refrigerant as outlined under "Air Conditioning."
2. Drain coolant into suitable container.
3. Remove lip seal and mounting clips, then the left and righthand air intake covers, **Fig. 7.**
4. Remove mounting nuts, bolts and clips, then the air intake cover, **Fig. 8.**
5. Remove wiper arm.
6. Remove cover under wiper system.
7. Remove wiper system mounting nuts.
8. Remove rubber mount bolt and clamp.
9. Disconnect wiper system electrical connector.
10. Remove wiper system with rubber bushing.
11. Remove water collector rubber mounts and mounting clips, **Fig. 9.**
12. Disconnect wiring duct.
13. Remove clamp and disconnect fuel lines.
14. Remove mounting bolts and clips, then the firewall center section, **Fig. 10.**
15. Remove cover, then the engine and ABS control modules.
16. Remove mounting screws and loosen control module box.
17. Remove water collector.
18. Remove expansion valve.
19. Disconnect water hoses and plug openings.
20. Remove instrument panel and center console.

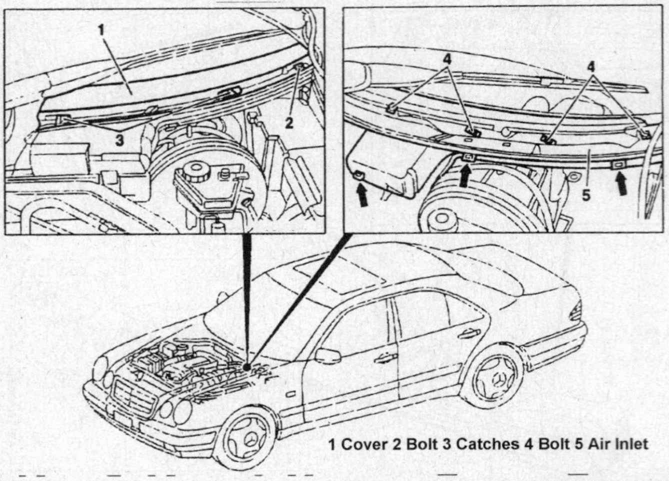

Fig. 16 Lefthand air inlet replacement. E55, E300, E320 & E430

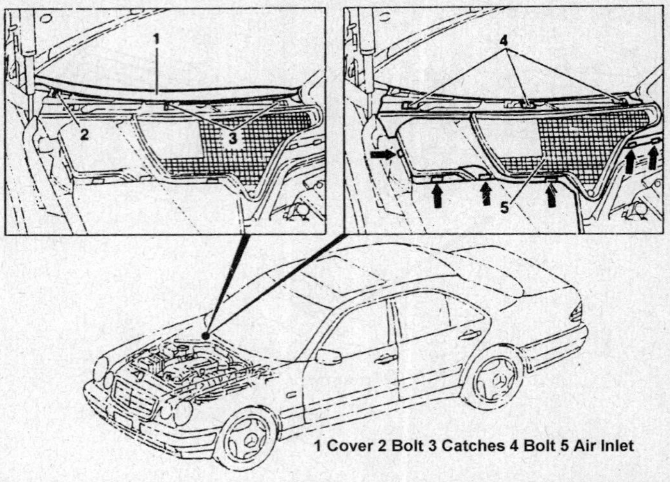

Fig. 17 Righthand air inlet replacement. E55, E300, E320 & E430

21. Remove left and righthand floor covering.
22. Remove steering column as described in "Steering Column" section.
23. Remove mounting bolts and cable duct, **Fig. 11.**
24. Remove mounting bolts and nuts, then the cross tube.
25. Disconnect electrical cables at ground point.
26. Open cable strap.
27. Remove left and righthand side rear air ducts.
28. Disconnect vacuum lines at cockpit separation point.
29. Remove righthand ground strap.
30. Disconnect blower motor electrical connector.
31. Remove left and righthand side air duct nozzles.
32. Remove mounting bolts and clips, then the cover, **Fig. 12.**
33. Loosen water pipe mounting bolts.
34. Remove heater core with water pipes.
35. Remove water pipes from heater core.
36. Reverse procedure to install, noting the following:
    a. Install new O-rings.
    b. Ensure gap between wiper gear head and windshield, and wiper arm and blade is .197 inch.

C240 & C320

1. Move adjustable steering column out and down.
2. Open hood and relieve cooling system pressure.
3. Remove engine compartment bottom cover.
4. Drain cooling systems into suitable container.
5. Remove steering wheel as described under "Steering Wheel, Replace."
6. Remove cover under driver's side of instrument panel.
7. Remove bottom section of driver's side instrument panel.
8. Remove instrument cluster as described under "Instrument Cluster, Replace."
9. Remove accelerator pedal, then fold back front floor covering.
10. Remove lefthand rear air duct.
11. Remove steering column from instrument panel carrier as described in "Steering Column" section and swing down into footwell. **Do not remove bottom steering shaft from coupling.**
12. Remove three tensioning springs and fitting.
13. Pull out socket yokes and discard.
14. Remove hot water lines from core. Plug lines and openings.
15. Remove mounting screws, bracket and heater core.
16. Reverse procedure to install, noting the following:
    a. Install new seals.
    b. Install new socket yokes.
    c. Install new self-locking nuts and bolts.

CLK55, CLK320 & CLK430

1. Drain coolant into suitable container.
2. Recover refrigerant as outlined under "Air Conditioning."
3. Remove expansion valve and plug openings.
4. Remove lip seal and mounting clips, then the left and righthand air intake covers, **Fig. 7.**
5. Remove mounting nuts, bolts and clips, then the air intake cover.
6. Remove wiper arm.
7. Remove cover under wiper system.
8. Remove wiper system mounting nuts.
9. Remove rubber mount bolt and clamp.
10. Disconnect wiper system electrical connector.
11. Remove wiper system with rubber bushing.
12. Remove water collector rubber mounts and mounting clips, **Fig. 9.**
13. Disconnect wiring duct.
14. Remove clamp and disconnect fuel lines.
15. Remove mounting bolts and clips, then the firewall center section.
16. Remove cover, then the engine and ABS control modules.
17. Remove mounting screws and loosen control module box.
18. Remove water collector.
19. Disconnect water hoses and plug openings.
20. Remove instrument panel and center console.
21. Disconnect squid, then remove mounting nuts and passenger air bag.
22. Remove insulating mat.
23. Remove mounting bolt and main ground.
24. Remove wiring duct mounting screw.
25. Remove mounting nut and disconnect steering column.
26. Remove mounting nut and disconnect heater core temperature sensor.
27. Remove mounting bolt and bracket.
28. Remove side nozzles, and left and righthand air ducts.
29. Expose electrical cables.
30. Disconnect righthand A-pillar ground.
31. Remove mounting nut, and left and righthand A-pillar mounting bolts, then the crosstube.
32. Disconnect cockpit vacuum lines at separation point.
33. Disconnect connector and remove heater housing.
34. Disconnect evaporator temperature sensor.
35. Remove mounting bolts and clips, then the cover, **Fig. 12.**
36. Loosen water pipe mounting bolts.
37. Remove heater core with water pipes.
38. Remove water pipes from heater core.
39. Reverse procedure to install. Install new O-rings.

S320 & S420 & 1998–99 CL500, CL600, S500 & S600

Front

1. Recover refrigerant as outlined under "Air Conditioning."
2. Remove key from ignition switch
3. Raise wiper arms to vertical position.
4. Remove air collector rubber seal.

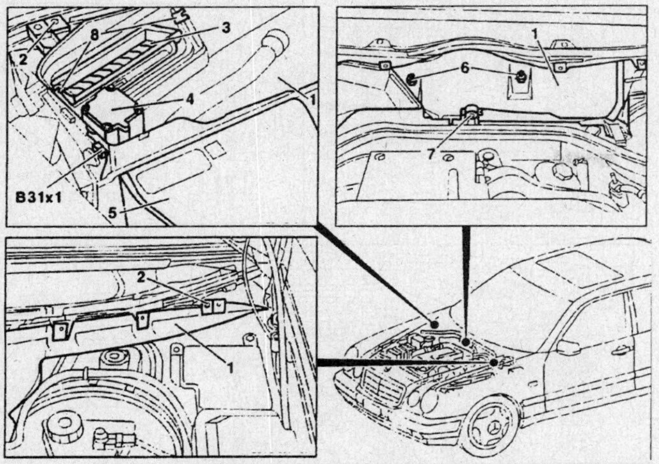

1 Water Collector 2 Plastic Rivet 3 Main Air Flap 4 Smog Sensor 5 Control Module Box
6 Wiper Ruber Pads 7 WIper Unit Mount 8 Air Intake Clips
B31x1 Smog Sensor Connector

MB7020000118010X

Fig. 18 Water collector replacement (Part 1 of 2). E55, E300, E320 & E430

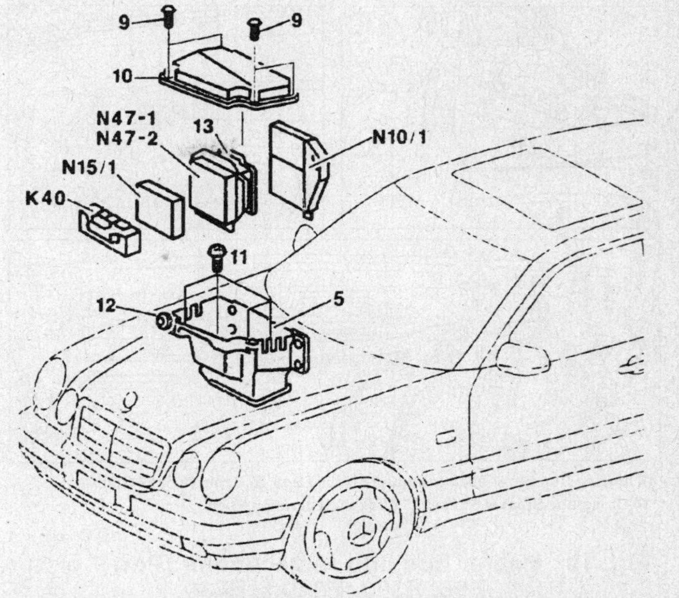

5 Conrol Module Box 9 Cover Bolt 10 Cover 11 Bolt
12 Clamping Screw 13 Engine Control Module K40 Relay Unit
N10-1 Multi-Function Control Module
N15-1 Automatic Transmission Control Module
N47-1 ASR/SPS Control Module N47-2 ETS/SPS Control Module

MB7020000118020X

Fig. 18 Water collector replacement (Part 2 of 2). E55, E300, E320 & E430

5. Disconnect main air flap vacuum lines.
6. Turn wiper system surface heating thermal valve to left, unclip and remove temperature sensor.
7. Disconnect temperature sensor and remove lefthand air collecting box.
8. Remove air intake cover using remover tool No. 140 589 00 98 00, or equivalent.
9. Remove mounting bolts and lefthand wiper system cover.
10. Remove mounting bolts rubber ring and righthand wiper system cover.
11. Ensure wiper system is in end position.
12. Disconnect wiper relay connector.
13. Remove righthand wiper arm mounting bolts.
14. Remove wiper motor mounting bolts and nuts.
15. Push wiper electrical cable with rubber grommet into water box.
16. Remove wiper system.
17. Remove water collector rubber seal using remover tool No. 140 589 00 07 00, or equivalent.
18. Remove mounting bolts and water collector, **Fig. 13.**
19. Remove heater core hoses and plug openings.
20. Remove mounting nut and preresistor group.
21. Remove firewall mounting nuts, then disconnect blower motor electrical connectors.
22. Remove both front floor mats.
23. Remove switches or cover plates from both sides of center console cover to provide access to cover mounting bolts.
24. Remove center console cover mounting bolts and cover.
25. Remove gearshift lever cover, then the radio assembly.
26. Pull heater and blower, and vent lever control knobs off.
27. Remove control shafts mounting nuts.
28. Remove center console cover plate.
29. Remove mounting bolts and center console.
30. Remove left and righthand instrument panel lower covers.
31. Push drivers seat to rearmost position.
32. Remove heater upper insulation cover.
33. Remove rear footwell and rear outlet air ducts.
34. Disconnect rear air outlet cable.
35. Disarm air bag system as outlined in the front of this manual.
36. Disconnect connector, remove mounting bolts and air bag system control module.
37. Remove ignition switch.
38. Remove mounting bolts and nuts, then the crossbrace.
39. Remove mounting bolts and nuts, then the left and righthand stiffening tubes.
40. Remove mounting nuts and heater housing brackets.
41. Remove mounting bolts and nuts, then Disconnect switch over valve block and remove righthand bearing tube.
42. Remove defroster outlet mounting nuts.
43. Remove left and righthand air outlet ducts.
44. Remove connector and blower harness.
45. Disconnect main air flap vacuum line.
46. Disconnect valve block vacuum line.
47. Remove heater housing.
48. Remove clamps and mounting bolts, then the heater core, **Fig. 14.**
49. Disconnect heater core pipes.
50. Reverse procedure to install, noting the following:
    a. Install new O-rings.
    b. **Torque** wiper system mounting bolts to 88 inch lbs.
    c. **Torque** wiper motor mounting nut to 15 ft. lbs. and bolt to 16 ft. lbs.
    d. Ensure wiper arm to windshield gap is .433 inch.

Rear

1. Raise and support vehicle.
2. Remove mounting bolts and panelling behind righthand side front member, **Fig. 15.**
3. Remove supply and return hoses and drain coolant into suitable container. Plug openings.
4. Remove front control module as previously outlined.
5. Remove center console as previously outlined under "Heater Core, Replace."
6. Disconnect connectors.
7. Expose electrical lines around rear air conditioning unit.
8. Remove evaporator temperature sensor.
9. Remove blower housing as outlined under "Blower Motor, Replace."
10. Remove heater core pipes and plug openings.

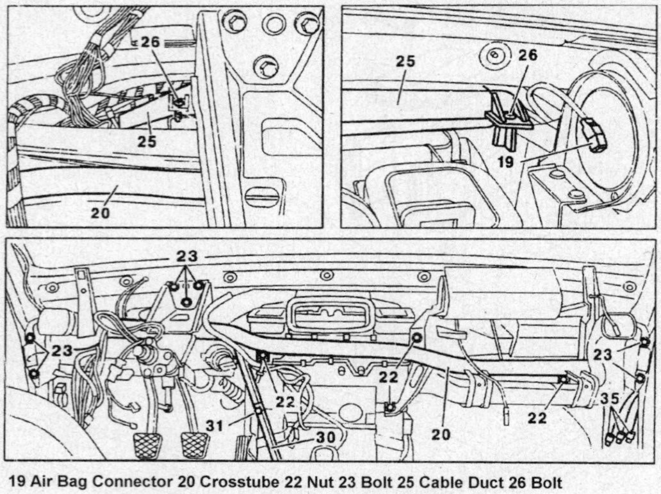

19 Air Bag Connector 20 Crosstube 22 Nut 23 Bolt 25 Cable Duct 26 Bolt
30 Crosstube Bracket 31 Bolt 35 Cockpit Separation Point

MB7020000115010X

Fig. 19 Heater housing replacement (Part 1 of 2). E55, E300, E320 & E430

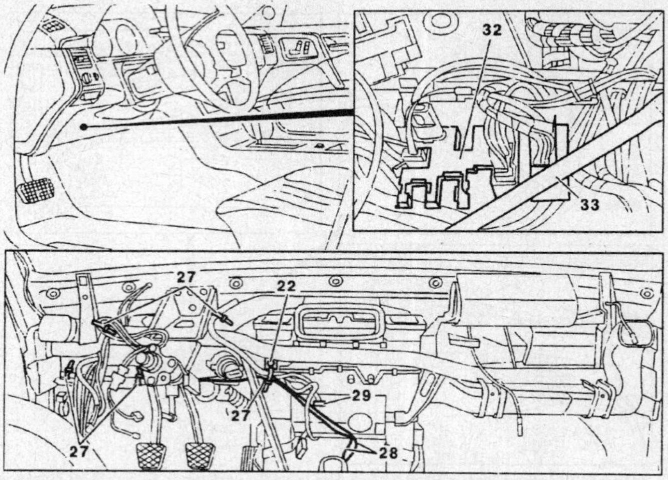

20 Crosstube, 22 Nut, 27 Cable Strap 28 Shift Lock Control Cables
29 Heater Core Temperature Sensor Connector 32 Jacket Tube Separation Point
33 Brace

MB7020000115020X

Fig. 19 Heater housing replacement (Part 2 of 2). E55, E300, E320 & E430

11. Remove mounting bolts and heater core.
12. Reverse procedure to install. Install new O-rings.

S430 & 2000-01 CL500 & S500 & 2001 CL600 & S600

Front

1. Recover refrigerant as outlined under "Air Conditioning."
2. Drain coolant into suitable container.
3. Remove wiper system.
4. Remove spreading rivets and water deflector.
5. Disconnect multifunction sensor connector.
6. Remove air and water collector boxes.
7. Disconnect expansion valve pressure lines and plug openings.
8. Remove clamps and coolant hoses from heater housing.
9. Remove instrument panel and center console.
10. Remove rear compartment air ducts.
11. Remove left and righthand front floor covering.
12. Remove left and righthand rear air ducts.
13. Remove left and righthand side vent and footwell air ducts.
14. Disconnect front passenger air bag.
15. Disconnect blower motor connector.
16. Disconnect ignition switch connector.
17. Disconnect stepper motor electronic control module.
18. Disconnect left and righthand heater core temperature sensors.
19. Disconnect evaporator core temperature sensor.
20. Remove steering column mounting bolts.
21. Remove lefthand A-pillar and fire wall mounting bolts.
22. Remove A/C housing mounting nut.
23. Remove lefthand transmission tunnel mounting bolt.
24. Remove righthand A-pillar mounting bolts.
25. Remove mounting bolts and wiring harness line duct.
26. Separate crosstube cable straps.
27. Remove crosstube.
28. Remove heater housing.
29. Remove receiver as outlined under "Receiver, Replace."
30. Remove mounting clips and bolts, then the cover.
31. Remove hot water feed clamp, then the hot water return pipe.
32. Remove heater core with water pipes.
33. Remove clips and water pipes.
34. Reverse procedure to install, noting the following:
    a. Install new cable straps.
    b. Install new O-rings.

Rear

1. Drain coolant into suitable container.
2. Remove control module as previously outlined.
3. Remove center console.
4. Disconnect rear evaporator temperature sensor connector.
5. Disconnect wiring harness from upper housing section.
6. Remove clips and upper housing section.
7. Remove mounting screw and disconnect hoses.
8. Remove heater core.
9. Replace receiver as outlined under "Receiver, Replace."
10. Reverse procedure to install. **Torque** coolant line separation point to 71 inch lbs.

E55, E300, E320 & E430

1. Drain coolant into suitable container.
2. Recover refrigerant as outlined under "Air Conditioning."
3. Remove expansion valve and plug openings.
4. Remove mounting bolt, catches and lefthand air inlet, **Fig. 16.**
5. Remove mounting bolts, catches and righthand air inlet cover to left, **Fig. 17.**
6. Remove mounting bolt, catches and righthand air inlet.
7. Remove cover, mounting bolt and windshield wiper arm.
8. Remove rubber pads, mounting bolt and windshield wiper mount.
9. Remove water collector clips and plastic rivet, **Fig. 18.**
10. Disconnect smog sensor connector.
11. Remove mounting bolts and control module cover.
12. Remove multifunction control module.
13. Remove clamping screw and mounting screws, then move control module box upper section forward.
14. Remove water collector.
15. Remove heater core hoses and plug openings.
16. Remove switches or cover plates from both sides of center console cover to provide access to cover mounting bolts.
17. Remove center console cover mounting bolts and cover.
18. Remove gearshift lever cover, then the radio.
19. Pull heater and blower controls, and vent lever control knobs off.
20. Remove control shafts' retaining nuts.
21. Remove center console cover plate.
22. Remove mounting bolts and center console.
23. Remove left and righthand instrument panel lower covers.
24. Push drivers seat to rearmost position.
25. Remove glove box and disconnect glove box light electrical connectors.
26. Remove trunk air ducts.
27. Remove left and righthand floor covering.
28. Remove left and righthand rear compartment air ducts.
29. Disconnect ignition switch.
30. Remove steering column as described

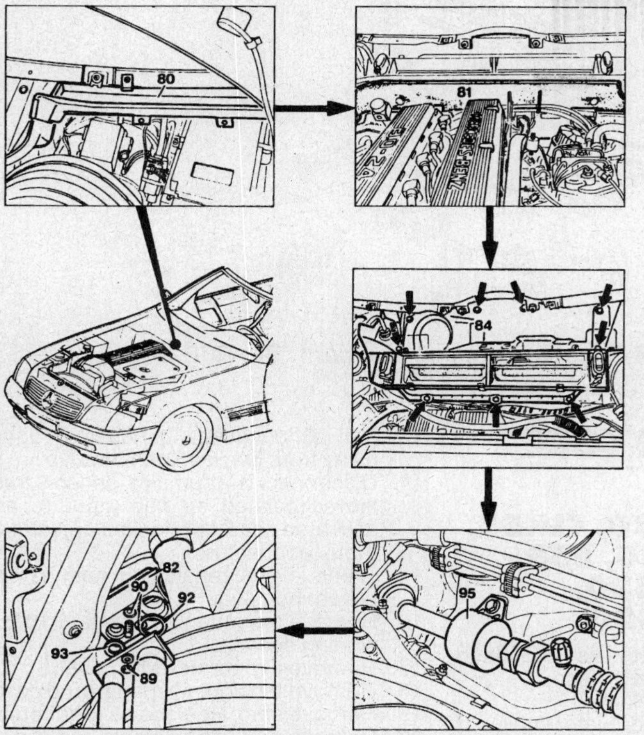

80 Water Drain 81 Center Partition Wall 82 Expansion Valve 84 Housing 89 Expansion Pipe Nut 90 Mounting Bolts 92 O-ring 95 Clip

MB7020000080000X

Fig. 20 Heater core housing replacement. SL500 & SL600

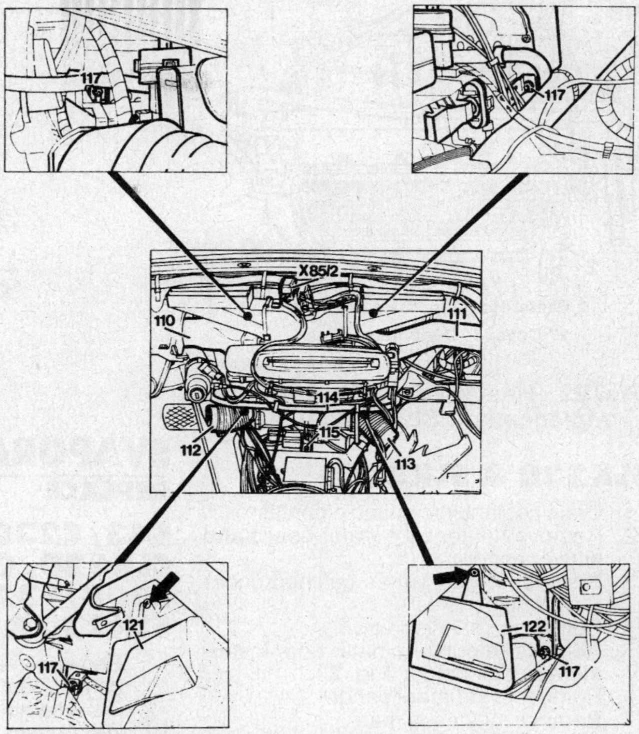

X85/2 12-Pin Connector 110 & 111 Defrost Air Duct 112 & 113 Heater Duct Hose 114 Cross Strut 115 Bracket 117 Mounting Nuts 121 & 122 Air Scoop

MB7020000081000X

Fig. 21 Heater core replacement. SL500 & SL600

in "Steering Column" section.
31. Disconnect passenger air bag.
32. Disconnect vacuum lines at cockpit separation point, **Fig. 19.**
33. Disconnect blower motor connector.
34. Disconnect fresh/recirculating air flap vacuum valve.
35. Disconnect heater core temperature sensor connector.
36. Loosen steering column separation point brace holder.
37. Open cable straps.
38. Disconnect shift lock control cables, steering wheel lock and pedal assembly.
39. Remove mounting bolt and bracket.
40. Remove mounting bolts and nuts, then the crosstube.
41. Remove left and righthand nozzle air ducts.
42. Remove mounting bolts, disconnect and lay cable duct aside.
43. Remove heater housing.
44. Disconnect evaporator temperature sensor connector.
45. Remove mounting bolts and clips, then the cover, **Fig. 12.**
46. Loosen water pipe mounting bolts.
47. Remove heater core with water pipes.
48. Remove water pipes from heater core.
49. Reverse procedure to install. Install new O-rings.

SL500 & SL600

1. Recover refrigerant as outlined under "Air Conditioning."
2. Drain coolant into suitable container.
3. Remove wiper systems as previously outlined under "Blower Motor, Replace."
4. Remove mounting bolts, then the left and righthand cowl water drains, **Fig. 20.**
5. Remove mounting rivets and bolts, then the center partition wall.
6. Loosen clamps and remove heater hoses.
7. Remove mounting nut and expansion valve piping.
8. Remove mounting bolts and expansion valve.
9. Remove both front floor mats.
10. Remove switches or cover plates from both sides of center console cover to access cover mounting bolts.
11. Remove mounting bolts and center console cover.
12. Remove gearshift lever cover, then the radio assembly.
13. Pull control knobs off heater and blower controls, and vent lever.
14. Remove retaining nuts from control shafts mounting nuts.
15. Remove center console cover plate.
16. Remove mounting bolts and center console.
17. Remove right and lefthand instrument panel lower covers.
18. Push drivers seat to rearmost position.
19. Remove instrument panel.
20. Disconnect electrical plug, then the defroster ducts, **Fig. 21.**
21. Remove cross strut and disconnect heater duct hoses.
22. Remove bracket and air scoops.
23. Disconnect switchover valve block connecting plate, then the vacuum lines.
24. Remove mounting nuts and heater box, **Fig. 22.**
25. Remove mounting clip and bolts, then the heater core.
26. Disconnect pipes.
27. Reverse procedure to install, noting the following:
    a. Install new O-rings.
    b. **Torque** expansion valve mounting bolts to 62–115 inch lbs.
    c. **Torque** expansion valve piping nut to 85–88 inch lbs.
    d. Install medium-green/yellow vacuum line to connecting plate switchover valve block 0, medium-green/light blue to 1, dark red to 2 and medium-green/white to 3.

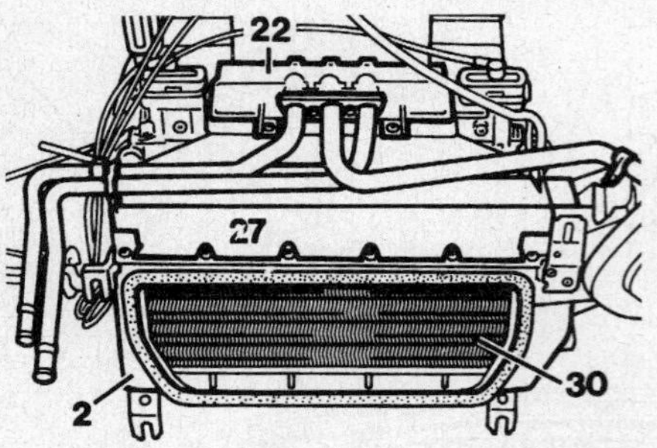

2 Heater Housing 22 Heater Core
27 Cover 30 Evaporator Core

MB7020000082000X

Fig. 22 Heater & evaporator core replacement. SL500 & SL600

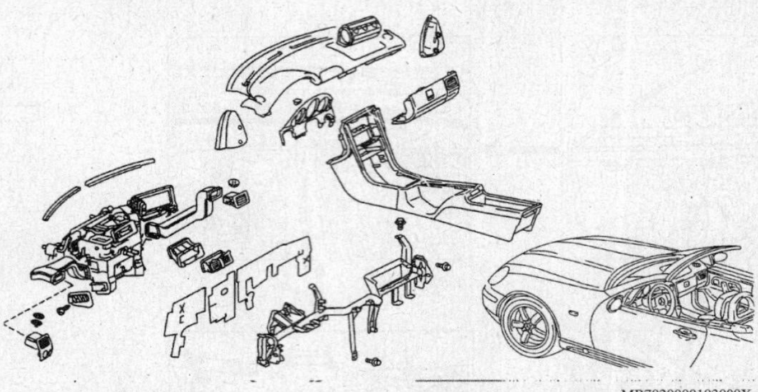

MB7020000103000X

Fig. 23 Heater core replacement. SLK230 & SLK320

SLK230 & SLK320

1. Drain coolant into suitable container.
2. Remove heater core water hoses and plug openings.
3. Recover refrigerant as outlined under "Air Conditioning."
4. Remove expansion valve.
5. Remove mounting nuts and instrument cluster holder, **Fig. 23.**
6. Remove instrument panel.
7. Remove insulating mats.
8. Remove mounting bolts and pivot steering column out of working area.
9. Remove Infra Red (IR) Drive Authorization System (DAS) control module.
10. Separate crosstube cable straps.
11. Disconnect body tunnel electrical wires.
12. Remove mounting bolts and nuts, then the steering column.
13. Disconnect front passenger air bag squib electrical connector.
14. Remove left and righthand heating ducts.
15. Remove heater housing and body tunnel mounting nuts.
16. Remove A-pillar mounting bolts, **Fig. 24.**
17. Disconnect vacuum reservoir connector.
18. Remove crosstube.
19. Disconnect heater core temperature sensor.
20. Disconnect fresh/recirculating air flap switchover valve.
21. Disconnect evaporator temperature sensor connector.
22. Disconnect heater housing cable straps.
23. Remove heater housing.
24. Remove evaporator core housing.
25. Remove mounting bolts and clips, then the cover, **Fig. 12.**
26. Loosen water pipe mounting bolts.
27. Remove heater core with water pipes.
28. Remove water pipes from heater core.
29. Reverse procedure to install. Install new O-rings.

EVAPORATOR CORE

REPLACE

C43, C230, C280, CLK55, CLK320, CLK430, E55, E300, E320, E430, SLK230 & SLK320

1. Remove heater core as described under "Heater Core, Replace."
2. Disassemble valve block.
3. Disconnect vacuum actuator lines.
4. Remove clips and disconnect blower box from air distributor box.
5. Remove mounting screw and gasket, **Fig. 25.**
6. Remove distributor box upper section.
7. Remove evaporator.
8. Remove mounting bolts and expansion valve.
9. Reverse procedure to install. **Torque** expansion valve mounting bolts to 71 inch lbs.

C240 & C320

1. Open hood and release cooling system pressure.
2. Remove engine compartment bottom paneling and drain cooling system into suitable container.
3. Recover refrigerant as outlined under "Air Conditioning."
4. Move front seats to rear.
5. Remove accelerator pedal, then fold lefthand floor covering back.
6. Remove lefthand rear compartment air duct.
7. Fold righthand floor covering back and remove righthand rear compartment air duct.
8. Remove and discard drier cartridge.
9. Remove nut and pressure lines with retaining plate. Plug openings.
10. Remove clamps and hot water hoses. Plug openings.
11. Remove condensation water hoses.
12. Disconnect evaporator temperature sensor electrical connector.
13. Pull air conditioning housing slightly away from firewall, then remove.
14. Disconnect air humidity sensor, fresh air/recirculated air flap actuator and activated charcoal filer flap adjustment motor connectors.
15. Remove five tensioning springs and blower housing.
16. Remove mounting screws and 10 tensioning springs.
17. Remove evaporator with cover.
18. Remove tensioning springs and cover.
19. Remove seal. Replace as required.
20. Remove mounting screws and expansion valve. Plug openings.
21. Remove evaporator.
22. Reverse procedure to install, noting the following:
    a. Moisten housing seal with soap solution. **Do not use oil seal**
    b. Grease housing guides with long-life grease No. 000 989 63 51, or equivalent.
    c. Install new O-rings.
    d. Install new drier cartridge.

S320 & S420 & 1998-99 CL500, CL600, S500 & S600

Front

1. Remove heater core as described under "Heater Core, Replace."
2. **On models equipped with charcoal canister,** remove cover, evacuate pneumatic gasket with tester tool No. 201 589 13 21 00 00 42 80, or equivalent, and remove charcoal canister.
3. **On models less charcoal canister,** remove damping mat.
4. **On all models,** remove clips and mounting bolts, then the defroster outlet nozzles, **Fig. 26.**
5. Remove mounting bolts and recirculating air flap vacuum valve.
6. Remove mounting bolts and blower housing.
7. Remove clips and mounting screws, then the bypass flap.

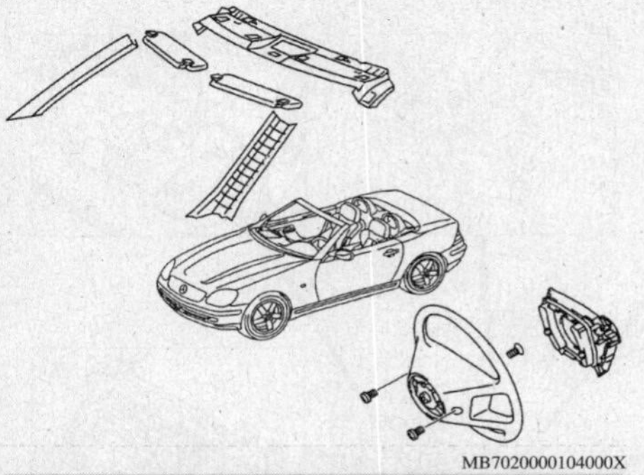

Fig. 24 A-pillar replacement. SLK230 & SLK320

8. Remove threaded plate and mounting bolt.
9. Disconnect recirculating air element actuating linkage.
10. Remove mounting nuts and bolts, then the retaining frame with studs. **Carefully pull sealing strips off around joints.**
11. Separate air conditioner unit housing sections.
12. Remove evaporator core.
13. Reverse procedure to install.

Rear

1. Recover refrigerant as outlined under "Air Conditioning."
2. Raise support vehicle.
3. Remove mounting bolts and panelling behind righthand side front member, **Fig. 15.**
4. Remove supply and return hoses and drain coolant into suitable container. Plug openings.
5. Remove front seats.
6. Remove front control module as previously outlined.
7. Remove center console as previously outlined under "Heater Core, Replace."
8. Remove mounting bolt, then the expansion valve suction and pressure lines. Plug openings.
9. Disconnect connectors.
10. Expose electrical lines around rear air conditioning unit.
11. Remove mounting bolt and heater core hot water line. Plug openings.
12. Remove rear air conditioning unit.
13. Remove mounting clips and blower housing.
14. Remove evaporator temperature sensor.
15. Remove mounting bolts and heater core.
16. Remove clips and evaporator, **Fig. 27.**
17. Reverse procedure to install. Install new O-rings.

S430 & 2000–01 CL500 & S500 & 2001 CL600 & S600

Front

1. Remove heater core as described under "Heater Core, Replace."
2. Disconnect stepper motor connectors.
3. Remove clips and disconnect stepper motor connectors.
4. Remove clips and air distribution housing upper section.
5. Remove evaporator core.
6. Remove mounting bolts and expansion valve.
7. Remove receiver as outlined under "Receiver, Replace."
8. Reverse procedure to install, noting the following:
   a. Install new O-rings lubricated with suitable compressor oil.
   b. **Torque** expansion valve mounting bolt to 88 inch lbs.

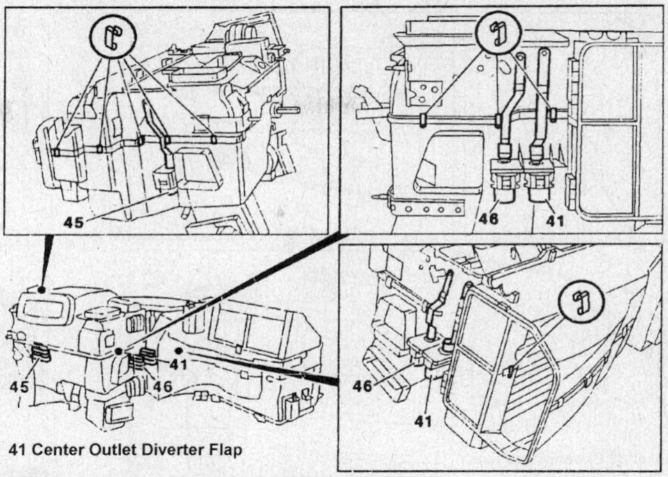

41 Center Outlet Diverter Flap

45 Lefthand Center Outlet Blend Flap 46 Righthand Center Outlet Blend Flap

MB70200001250100X

Fig. 25 Evaporator core replacement (Part 1 of 2). C43, C230, C280, CLK55, CLK320, CLK430, E55, E300, E320 & E430

Rear

1. Recover refrigerant as outlined under "Air Conditioning."
2. Drain coolant into suitable container.
3. Remove front seats.
4. Remove rear control module as previously outlined.
5. Remove center console.
6. Fold left and righthand rear floor covering back.
7. Remove heater core mounting bolt.
8. Disconnect connector.
9. Remove mounting bolt and refrigerant lines. Plug openings.
10. Remove clips and air ducts.
11. Remove mounting bolts and rear housing.
12. Remove clips and upper housing section.
13. Remove evaporator core.
14. Replace receiver as outlined under "Receiver, Replace."
15. Reverse procedure to install, noting the following:
    a. Install new O-rings lubricated with suitable compressor oil.
    b. **Torque** lines to 71 inch lbs.

SL500 & SL600

1. Remove heater core as described under "Heater Core, Replace."
2. Loosen cover mounting bolts and clips.
3. Press clips down and remove evaporator core, **Fig. 22.**
4. Reverse procedure to install.

TECHNICAL SERVICE BULLETINS

TURN SIGNAL OCCASIONALLY FAILS

E300, E320 & E430

On some of these models built between VIN 085154–100856, the turn signal may occasionally fail.

This condition may be caused by multifunction control module multi-point connector not being properly soldered.

To correct this condition, install control module with production date of FD 96W06.

PARKTRONIC WARNING DISPLAY ACTIVE FOR NO REASON

1998–99 E300, E320 & E430

On some of these models built before July 1999, the Parktronic System (PTS) may come on without apparent reason

This condition may be caused by the front or rear bumper wiring harness.

To correct this condition, install revised wiring harness (front part No. A 210 540 58 09 or rear part No. A 210 540 57 09).

PARKTRONIC ALL SEGMENTS ON & WARNING TONE SOUNDS

CL500, CL600, S320, S420, S430, S500 & S600

On some of these models, **Fig. 28,** the Parktronic System (PTS) may display all 7 or 8 bars and sound an acoustic warning.

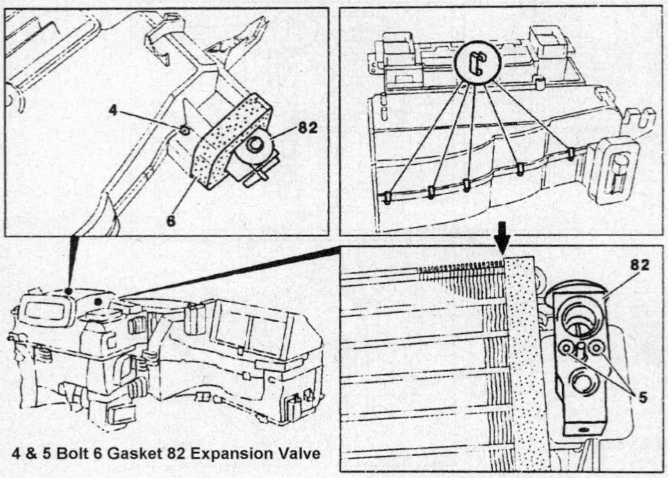

4 & 5 Bolt 6 Gasket 82 Expansion Valve

MB7020000125020X

Fig. 25 Evaporator core replacement (Part 2 of 2). C43, C230, C280, CLK55, CLK320, CLK430, E55, E300, E320 & E430

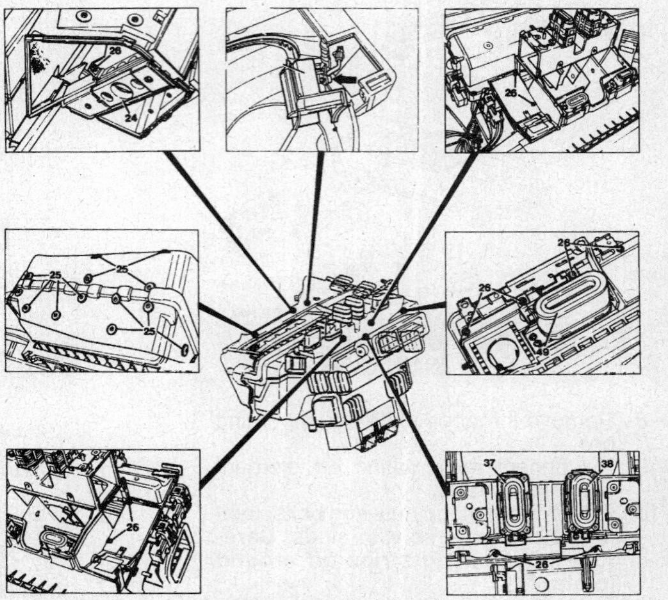

24 Threaded Plate 25 Clips 26 Mounting Bolts 37 & 38 Defroster Outlets
49 Recirculating Flap

MB7020000097000X

Fig. 26 Front evaporator core replace. S320 & S420 & 1998–99 CL500, CL600, S500 & S600

This condition may be caused by prolonged oscillations of the PTS sensors in the bumpers from structure-borne sound transmitted from the sensor to the metallic spring washer resulting in a "tuning fork" effect.

To correct this condition, proceed as follows:

1. **On sedan models,** proceed as follows:
   a. Remove bumper.
   b. Remove spacer ring, spring washer and nut.
   c. Install revised, grooved spacer ring (part No. 000 542 02 51), damper ring (par No. 140 546 00 79) and toothed nut (part No. 140 542 00 72).
2. **On couple models,** proceed as follows:
   a. Remove bumper.
   b. Unclip spring clip.
   c. Remove decoupling and PTS sensor housing.
   d. Install using decoupling ring from kit (part No. 001 540 40 17).

PARKTRONIC SYSTEM DISPLAYS IMPLAUSIBLE WARNING TONE WHILE STANDING

S320, S420, S500 & S600

On some of these models built before VIN A336001, the parktronic system may display implausible warning tone and bar graph while standing.

This condition may be caused by faulty ultrasonic sensor mounts.

To correct this condition, install improved dampening ring, spacer with location tab and locknut.

FOG LAMPS NOT OPERATING

E300, E320 & E430

On some of these models the fog lamps may not operate.

This condition may be caused by water condensation on connectors.

To correct this condition, install revised, 11.8-inch long fog lamp wiring harness and connector (kit No. 000 540 21 05)

BATTERY DISCHARGES & VEHICLE CANNOT BE STARTED

2000–01 CL500

On some of these models built before VIN 004585, the battery may discharge and the vehicle cannot be started.

This condition may be caused by the Active Body Control (ABC) control module remaining active when the vehicle is locked. This usually happens when the vehicle is locked more than one minute after shutting off vehicle and closing doors.

To correct this condition, proceed as follows:

1. Shut vehicle off, close doors and lock immediate using remove control.
2. Measure quiescent current consumption. Consumption should be less than 50 mAmps.
3. Shut vehicle off, close doors and wait two minutes before locking using remove control.
4. If quiescent current is approximately 350 mAmps, replace ABC control module (part No. 022 545 08 32 27).

ENGINE DIES WHEN TRANSMISSION SHIFT INTO GEAR OR WHEN PARKING

1998–99 CL500, CL600, S320, S420, S500 & S600

On some of these models the engine may die when the transmission is shifted into gear or when parking.

This condition may be caused by moisture in the starter lockout switch.

To correct this condition, proceed as follows:

1. Inspect starter lockout switch for corrosion.
2. Replace switch.
3. Replace transmission wiring harness.

OIL LEVEL BELOW MIN. OR OIL SENSOR FAULTY INDICATED ON INSTRUMENT CLUSTER

1998–99 CL500, CL600, S320, S420, S500 & S600

On some of these models the instrument cluster may indicate "Oil Level Below Min." Or "Oil Sensor Faulty" for approximately eight seconds after engine start. No Diagnostic Trouble Codes (DTCs) are stored.

Model	Before VIN	
	Front	Rear
Coupe	385366	385366
Sedan	324327	336001

Fig. 28 PTS application chart. CL500, CL600, S320, S420, S430, S500 & S600

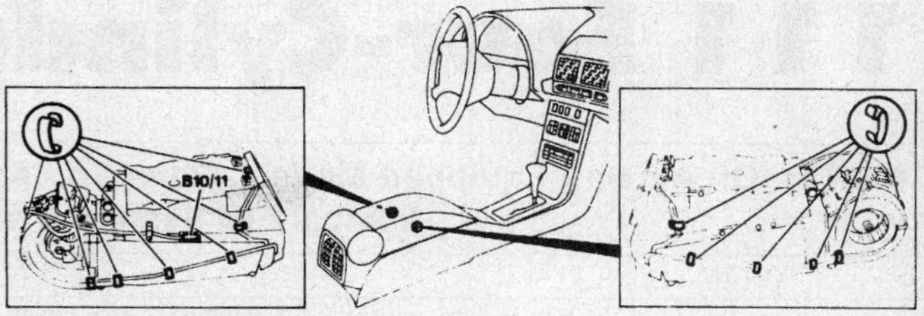

B10/11 Evaporator Temperature Sensor

MB7020000106000X

Fig. 27 Rear evaporator replacement. S320 & S420 & 1998–99 CL500, CL600, S500 & S600

This condition may be caused by discharged or defective battery.

To correct this condition, inspect battery. Charge or replace battery, as required.

ENGINE CANNOT BE STARTED

1998-99 CL500, CL600, S320, S420, S500 & S600

On some of these models the engine cannot be started or occasionally stalls.

This condition may be caused by low voltage.

To correct this condition, tighten battery pole clamp bolts.

BLOWER MOTOR NOISY

C43, C230, C280, E55, E300, E320 & E430

On some of these models the heater blower motor may be noisy.

This condition may be caused by the air intake below the windshield be obstructed with leaves or other debris.

To correct this condition, proceed as follows:

1. Remove air intake covers.
2. Clean passages.
3. Remove heater blower motor.
4. Clean blower motor.

STARTER DEFECTIVE OR CORRODED

C230, E300, S320 & SLK230

On some of these models the starter may be defective or corroded.

This condition may be caused by water running over starter.

To correct this condition, proceed as follows:

1. Replace starter.
2. Remove water collector.
3. Install revised water drain (part No. 210 832 01 25).

STARTER OCCASIONALLY DOES NOT OPERATE

E43, C280, CLK320, CLK430, E55, E320, E430, ML55, ML320, ML430, S430 & SLK320 & 1999-2001 SL500 & 2000-01 S500

On some of these models that starter may occasionally no operate. The starting operation being interrupted before engine can start. The tachometer may jump toward 2000 RPM momentarily while starting.

To correct this condition, proceed as follows:

1. Remove starter.
2. Lightly coat starter ring gear teeth with paste No. 000 989 76 41.
3. Ensure excess grease is not applied as this can interfere with sensor signal pickup.

STEERING WHEEL CLACKING NOISES

C43, C230, C280, E55, E300, E320, E430, SL500 & SL600 & 1998-99 S320, S420, S500 & S600

On some of these models the steering wheel may make a clacking noise.

This condition may be caused by loose contact bridge mounting screws.

To correct this condition, remove air bag module and tighten Torx mounting screws to 44 inch lbs.

MIL & INDICATOR LAMPS ILLUMINATE BRIEFLY

C43, C230, C280, E55, E300, E320 & E430

On some of these models the Malfunction Indicator Lamp (MIL) and instrument cluster indicator lamps may briefly illuminate when the ignition switch is to turned to ON position.

This condition may be caused by an open circuit in the wiring harness between the alternator and instrument cluster.

To correct this condition, inspect the wiring and repair as required.

INSTRUMENT CLUSTER LOOSE

CL500, CL600, S320, S420, S500 & S600

On some of these models the instrument cluster may be loose

To correct this condition, remove instrument cluster and glue felt pieces to rubber retention tabs.

IGNITION KEY DIFFICULT TO REMOVE

C43, C230 & C280

On some of these models the ignition key may be difficult to remove from the ignition switch.

To correct this condition, adjust shift interlock cable.

RADIO CONTINUES TO OPERATE AFTER IGNITION KEY IS REMOVE

SL500 & SL600

On some of these models the radio may continue to operate after the ignition key is remove from the switch.

To correct this condition, replace the ignition switch.

INSTRUMENT CLUSTER LIQUID CRYSTAL DISPLAY NOT READABLE

C43, C230 & C280

On some of these models the instrument cluster Liquid Crystal Display (LSD) may not be readable.

To correct this condition, inspect individual illumination bulbs before replacing cluster

111 Four-Cylinder Gasoline Engine

NOTE: On Air Bag Equipped Models, Refer To "Air Bag System Precautions" Located In The Front Of This Manual For System Disarming & Arming Procedures.

NOTE: Prior To Performing Any Service Operations Listed In This Section, Consult The "Technical Service Bulletins" Section For Related Information.

INDEX

	Page No.
Belt Tension Data	5-39
Camshaft, Replace	5-37
Camshaft Adjuster, Replace	5-37
Installation	5-37
Removal	5-37
Compression Pressure	5-32
Cooling System Bleed	5-39
Crankshaft Damper, Replace	5-36
Crankshaft Rear Oil Seal, Replace	5-38
Installation	5-38
Removal	5-38
Crankshaft Seal, Replace	5-38
Installation	5-38
Removal	5-38
Cylinder Head, Replace	5-35
Engine Rebuilding Specifications	5-344
Engine, Replace	5-33
Less Supercharger	5-33
With Supercharger	5-33
Engine Mount, Replace	5-33
Front	5-33
Rear	5-33
Exhaust Manifold, Replace	5-34
1998–2000	5-34
2001	5-35
Front Cover, Replace	5-36
Cylinder Head	5-36
Timing Case	5-36
Front Cover Seal, Replace	5-37
Fuel Filter, Replace	5-40
Fuel Pump, Replace	5-40
C230	5-40
SLK230	5-40
Hydraulic Lifters, Replace	5-36
Intake Manifold, Replace	5-34
Less Supercharger	5-34
With Supercharger	5-34
Main & Rod Bearings	5-37
Oil Pan, Replace	5-38
Oil Pump, Replace	5-39
Oil Sump, Replace	5-38
Less Supercharger	5-38
With Supercharger	5-38
Piston & Rod Assembly	5-37
Precautions	5-32
Air Bag Systems	5-32
Battery Ground Cable	5-32
Fuel Pressure Relief Procedure	5-32
Radio Coded Anti-Theft System	5-32
Radiator, Replace	5-40
Serpentine Drive Belt	5-39
Belt, Replace	5-39
Routing	5-39
Tensioner, Replace	5-39
Supercharger, Replace	5-40
1998–2000	5-40
2001	5-41
Technical Service Bulletins	5-41
Arrhythmia Noise at Idle	5-41
Chain Tensioner Oil Leak	5-41
Engine Cannot Be Started	5-41
Engine Does Not Start	5-41
Engine Oil Above Max. Level	5-41
Exhaust Manifold Chatter	5-42
Oil Leak Between Cylinder Head & Timing Case Cover	5-41
Rear Oil Leak	5-41
Rear Oil Leak	5-42
Righthand Oil Leak	5-42
Valve Cover Leak	5-42
Thermostat, Replace	5-39
Tightening Specifications	5-43
Timing Chain, Replace	5-37
Timing Chain Tensioner, Replace	5-37
Valve Adjustment	5-35
Valve Cover, Replace	5-35
1998–2000	5-35
2001	5-35
Water Pump, Replace	5-39
1998–2000	5-39
2001	5-40

PRECAUTIONS

AIR BAG SYSTEMS

Refer to "Air Bag System Precautions" in front of this manual for system disarming and arming procedures.

BATTERY GROUND CABLE

Prior to service, disconnect battery ground cable and isolate as required.

RADIO CODED ANTI-THEFT SYSTEM

Anti-theft radios have a coded theft protection circuit. The CODE card must be obtained before disconnecting battery, removing radio fuse or removing the radio. **The serial number from the radio must match the CODE card.**

After service has been performed proceed as follows:

1. Connect radio power and turn key to position No. 2.
2. Turn radio to On position. Word "CODE" will appear on display.
3. Enter first digit of anti-theft code from CODE card. "CODE" will disappear and entered digit will appear followed by four dashes.
4. Enter next four digits, when all five are entered first digit flashes again.
5. Press SC, Seek or Tune button to confirm code.
6. If "WAIT" appears on radio panel, proceed as follows:
   a. Radio will allow three coding attempts only before entering lock-up mode and won't respond to controls.
   b. Leave radio on for 15–60 minutes, then radio will unlock and allow three addition coding attempts.
   c. Third lockout period (after nine failed coding attempts) will last 24 hours.
   d. Radio must be left on during enter 24-hour period until "CODE" appears.
7. When "CODE" appears, repeat coding attempt.

FUEL PRESSURE RELIEF PROCEDURE

1. Ensure ignition switch is in Off position.
2. Remove fuel pump protective box.
3. Disconnect fuel pump negative terminal.
4. Start engine and allow to run until it stalls from fuel starvation.
5. Crank engine to ensure pressure is released.

COMPRESSION PRESSURE

1. Warm engine to normal operating temperature of 176°F.
2. Remove spark plug.
3. Crank engine with starter several times to eliminate cylinder combustion residues. **Do not crank engine with ignition switch or with compression tester contact switch.**

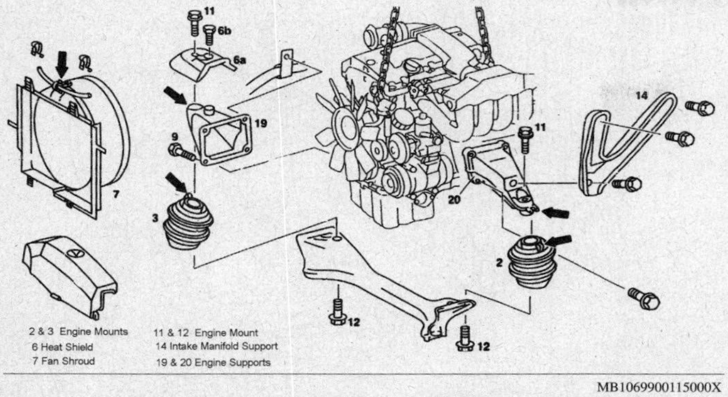

Fig. 1 Front engine mount replacement

4. Install suitable compression tester into spark plug bore.
5. Open throttle valves wide open.
6. Crank engine with starter eight revolutions. **Do not crank engine with ignition switch or with compression tester contact switch.**
7. Record compression readings.
8. **On 1998 models equipped less supercharger,** normal compression pressure should measure 160–218 psi.
9. **On 1998–2000 models equipped with supercharger,** normal compression pressure should measure 109–152 psi.
10. **On all models,** maximum permissible difference between individual cylinders is 22 psi.

ENGINE MOUNT

REPLACE

FRONT

1. Remove intake manifold support mounting bolts, **Fig. 1.**
2. Remove steering idler arm heat shield from righthand engine mount.
3. Remove engine mount bolt from engine support.
4. Remove engine mount bolt from frame crossmember.
5. Raise engine at front suspension lug, noting the following:
   a. **Do not damage injection line to front suspension lug.**
   b. Loosen power steering hose, as required.
   c. **On SLK230 models,** do not overstretch coolant hose.
6. **On all models,** remove engine support mounting bolts with engine mount from crankcase. Righthand engine mount bolt is not accessible because of supercharger.
7. **On SLK230 models,** loosen steering shock absorber if removing lefthand engine mount.
8. **On all models,** remove engine mounts.
9. Remove engine supports.
10. Remove heat shield from engine mount.
11. Reverse procedure to install, noting following:
    a. Engine mount anti-twist lug must engage engine support retaining grooves.
    b. **On models equipped with automatic transmission,** ensure transmission wiring harness routing.
    c. **On all models,** tighten mounting bolts to specifications.

REAR

1. Support transmission with suitable jack.
2. Remove rear engine support crossmember mounting bolts, **Fig. 2.**
3. Remove mounting bolts and rear engine mount.
4. Reverse procedure to install. Tighten mounting bolts to specifications.

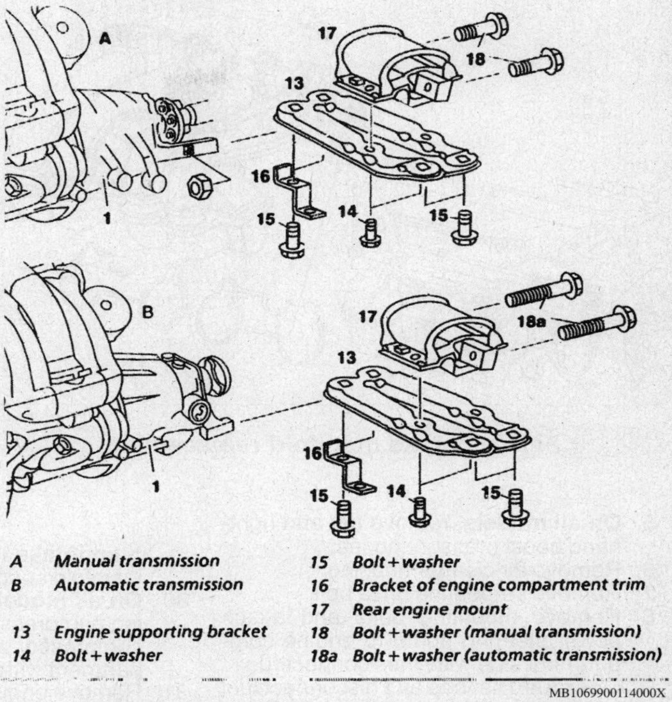

Fig. 2 Rear engine mount replacement

ENGINE

REPLACE

LESS SUPERCHARGER

1. Remove viscous fan clutch. **Clutch has lefthand threads.**
2. Remove radiator as described under "Radiator, Replace."
3. Remove Hot Film Mass (HFM) air flow sensor, as required.
4. Remove air cleaner crosspipe and cover.
5. Remove serpentine drive belt.
6. Attach 15.75 x 26.77 x .039-inch sheet metal or plastic guard plate to condenser.
7. Remove lefthand wheelhousing liner, component partition covers and windshield washer reservoir.
8. Disconnect engine wiring harness.
9. Disconnect purge switchover valve.
10. Disconnect accelerator control cable.
11. Open fuel filler cap and disconnect fuel lines at connection fitting.
12. Disconnect intake manifold vacuum line at brake booster.
13. Disconnect automatic transmission switchover valve vacuum lines.
14. Remove hydraulic fluid from power steering pump reservoir.
15. Disconnect power steering pump fluid lines.
16. **On models equipped with level control,** drain pressurized fluid system.
17. **On all models,** remove coolant hoses from cylinder head and water pump.
18. Remove air conditioning compressor mounting bolts. Place compressor at bottom of engine compartment with hose connected.
19. Drain cooling system into suitable container.
20. Disconnect transmission shifting rods.
21. Remove driveshaft and transmission mounting bolts.
22. Remove rear engine mount as outlined under "Engine Mount, Replace."
23. Remove front engine mount body and front suspension support mounting bolts.
24. Attach suitable engine hoist to both lifting eyes and remove engine.
25. Reverse procedure to install. Tighten mounting bolts to specifications.

WITH SUPERCHARGER

1. Remove engine compartment trim panel.
2. Remove radiator as described under "Radiator, Replace."
3. Attach 15.75 x 26.77 x .039-inch sheet metal or plastic guard plate to condenser.
4. **On SLK230 models,** remove coolant expansion reservoir.

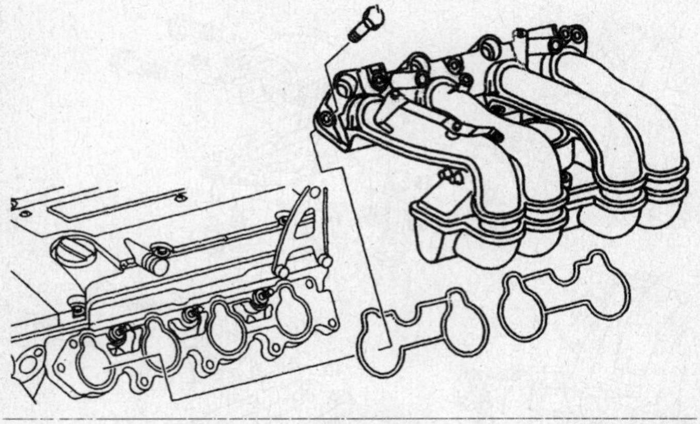

Fig. 3 Intake manifold replacement

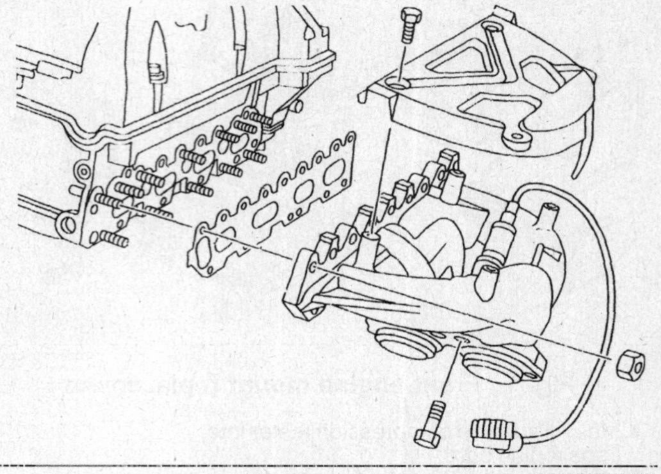

Fig. 4 Exhaust manifold replacement

5. **On all models,** remove left and right-hand boost pressure hoses.
6. Remove air cleaner housing.
7. Remove serpentine drive belt.
8. Remove mounting bolts and attach power steering pump to engine compartment side with lines connected.
9. Open fuel filler cap and disconnect fuel lines.
10. **On 1999–2000 C230 models,** remove lefthand wheelhousing liner, component partition covers and windshield washer reservoir.
11. **On SLK230 models,** remove module box cover.
12. **On all models,** disconnect engine wiring harness.
13. Disconnect purge switchover valve.
14. Disconnect throttle control cable.
15. Remove intake manifold vacuum line to brake booster vacuum lines.
16. **On 1999–2000 C230 models,** disconnect automatic transmission switchover valve vacuum lines.
17. **On all models,** remove coolant hoses from cylinder head and water pump.
18. Remove exhaust system to exhaust manifold and transmission intermediate bearing mounting bolts.
19. **On SLK230 models,** remove steering shock absorber.
20. **On all models,** remove rear engine mount as outlined under "Engine Mount, Replace.".
21. Remove propeller shaft to transmission mounting bolts.
22. Disconnect park lock interlock cable. Ensure transmission selector lever is in P position.
23. Disconnect transmission electric control unit plug connections.
24. Disconnect transmission shifting rods.
25. Remove slave cylinder and attach to vehicle with line connected, as required.
26. Remove front engine mount body mounting bolts.
27. Attach suitable engine hoist to both lifting eyes.
28. Lift engine enough to remove air condition compressor mounting bolts from above.
29. **On models equipped with aluminum intake manifold,** remove intake manifold support mounting bolts.
30. **On all models,** remove air conditioning compressor mounting bolts. Place compressor at bottom of engine compartment with hose connected.
31. Remove engine.
32. Reverse procedure to install, noting the following:
    a. Adjust park lock interlock.
    b. Adjust throttle control cable.

INTAKE MANIFOLD

REPLACE

LESS SUPERCHARGER

1. Remove air cleaner cross pipe.
2. Remove fuel rail with injectors.
3. Disconnect vacuum hoses and electrical connectors.
4. Disconnect engine wiring harness bracket.
5. Disconnect crankshaft position and knock sensors.
6. Disconnect starter connector.
7. Remove Idle Speed Control (ISC) actuator.
8. Disconnect throttle control from intake manifold.
9. Remove mounting bolts, nuts and intake manifold, **Fig. 3.**
10. Reverse procedure to install noting following:
    a. Install new gasket.
    b. Tighten mounting bolts to specifications.
    c. Inspect idle speed.

WITH SUPERCHARGER

1998–2000

1. Remove fuel rail with injectors.
2. Remove Idle Speed Control (ISC) actuator.
3. Disconnect vacuum lines and electrical connectors.
4. Disconnect throttle control from intake manifold.
5. Disconnect engine wiring harness bracket.
6. Disconnect crankshaft position and knock sensors.
7. Disconnect starter motor electrical connector.
8. Remove mounting bolts and intake manifold, **Fig. 3.**
9. Reverse procedure to install noting following:
    a. Install new gasket.
    b. Tighten mounting bolts to specifications.
    c. Inspect idle speed.

2001

1. Remove intake manifold trim panel with rubber mounts.
2. Remove fuel rail and injectors.
3. Remove electronic accelerator actuator.
4. Remove secondary air injection switchover valve bracket mounting bolts.
5. Disconnect pressure and altitude correction sensors.
6. Disconnect oxygen sensor upstream from catalytic converter, then the oil level indicator sensor and air conditioning compressor.
7. Disconnect engine wiring harness from intake manifold bracket and set aside.
8. Disconnect intake manifold vacuum lines.
9. Disconnect crankshaft position and knock sensors.
10. Disconnect starter motor electrical connectors.
11. Remove mounting bolts and intake manifold.
12. Reverse procedure to install noting following:
    a. Install new gasket.
    b. Tighten mounting bolts to specifications.
    c. Inspect idle speed.

EXHAUST MANIFOLD

REPLACE

1998–2000

1. Remove oxygen sensor, **Fig. 4.**

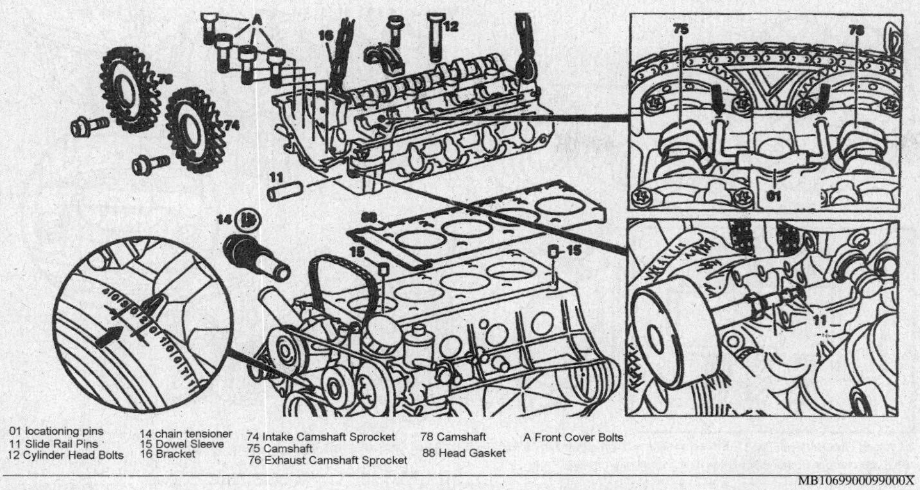

Fig. 5 Cylinder head replacement

2. **On models equipped with supercharger,** remove supercharger compressor suction connection.
3. **On all models,** remove exhaust manifold rivet nuts as required.
4. Remove gasket.
5. Remove exhaust manifold
6. Reverse procedure to install, noting the following:
   a. Clean manifold mounting surface and apply dots exhaust sealing compound No. A 001 989 25 20, or equivalent, to new gasket.
   b. Coat oxygen sensor threads with hot lubricating paste No. 000 989 76 51, or equivalent.
   c. Tighten rivet nuts to specifications.

2001

1. Remove inlet and pressure connections.
2. Remove supercharger heat shield.
3. Separate exhaust manifold to front exhaust pipe flange.
4. Remove mounting nuts and exhaust manifold.
5. Reverse procedure to install, noting the following:
   a. Install new gasket.
   b. Tighten mounting nuts to specifications.

CYLINDER HEAD

REPLACE

This procedure has been revised by a Technical Service Bulletin.

1. Drain cooling system into suitable container.
2. Remove exhaust system to exhaust manifold mounting bolts.
3. Remove exhaust manifold bracket mounting bolts at transmission.
4. Remove thermostat housing.
5. Disconnect cylinder head electrical connector.
6. Remove mounting bolts and swivel intake manifold to side with lines connected.
7. Disconnect crankcase ventilation line below intake manifold/cylinder head at T connection flange.
8. Disconnect partial intake manifold preheater connectors.
9. Disconnect coolant hose at cylinder head rear.
10. Remove front cover at cylinder head described under "Front Cover, Replace."
11. Remove dipstick guide tubes mounting bolts.
12. Rotate crankshaft to 20–30° after cylinder No. 1 ignition TDC, **Fig. 5.**
13. Lock camshafts with locating pin tools No. 111 589 03 15 00, or equivalent.
14. Mark camshaft sprockets and timing chain for installation alignment.
15. Remove chain tensioner.
16. Remove cylinder head guide rail using impact extractor tool No. 116 589 20 33 00, or equivalent.
17. Remove exhaust and intake camshaft sprocket with adjuster tool No. 000 589 01 10 00, or equivalent.
18. Remove intake camshaft adjuster.
19. Remove first camshaft bearing cap and bolt, then install cylinder head removal bracket with bearing cap bolts.
20. Remove side rail pins.
21. Remove cylinder head to timing case cover mounting bolts.
22. Loosen cylinder head mounting bolts in reverse tightening sequence, **Fig. 6. Ensure engine is cool.**
23. Attach suitable engine hoist to cylinder head bracket and rear engine suspension eye.
24. Remove cylinder head using suitable hoist.
25. Reverse procedure to install, noting the following:
   a. Clean contact surfaces and threaded holes, then inspect for cracks and flatness.
   b. Install new head gasket.
   c. Ensure slide rails stay together.
   d. Locate cylinder head using dowel sleeves.
   e. Replace bolts that are not 4.0161–4.1243 inches long, **Fig. 7.**
   f. Oil cylinder head mounting bolts thread and head contact surfaces.
   g. **Torque** cylinder bolts to 41 ft. lbs. in sequence **Fig. 6.**

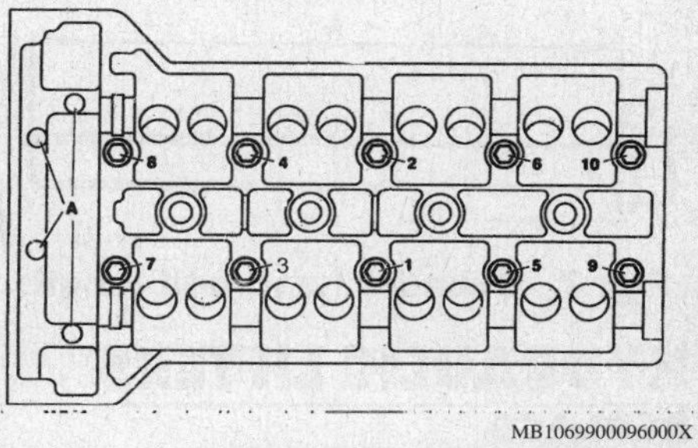

Fig. 6 Cylinder head tightening sequence

   h. Tighten cylinder bolts an additional 90° in sequence.
   i. Finally tighten cylinder bolts an additional 90° in sequence.
   j. Pressure test cooling system after engine has reached operating temperature and gasket has swollen.
   k. Install new cylinder head to timing case cover mounting bolts.
   l. Oil new bolts head contact surface,
   m. Coat guide rail pins with suitable sealant.
   n. Install new camshaft sprocket mounting bolts.

VALVE COVER

REPLACE

1998–2000

1. Remove cover at top front of engine.
2. Remove cover at engine compartment partition.
3. Remove recess cover on top of head cover.
4. Remove crankcase ventilation line and spark plug connectors from head cover.
5. Remove electric cable of oxygen sensor and electric cable of hot film air mass sensor.
6. Remove transmission dipstick.
7. Remove mounting bolts, head cover and gasket.
8. Reverse procedure to install noting following:
   a. Replace gasket, as required.
   b. Install new rivet nuts.
   c. Inspect for leaks around edge of head cover and in spark plug recesses, with engine running.

2001

1. Remove mounting bolts and spark plug cover.
2. Remove ignition coils.
3. Disconnect automatic transmission dipstick guide tube from cylinder head.
4. Remove mounting screws and valve cover.
5. Reverse procedure to install, noting the following:
   a. Replace gasket, as required.
   b. Tighten mounting bolts to specifications.

VALVE ADJUSTMENT

This engine is equipped with hydraulic lifters and requires no valve adjustment,

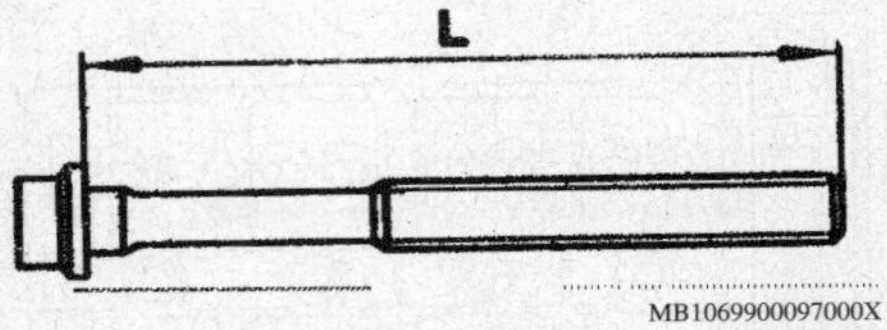

Fig. 7 Cylinder head bolt length

HYDRAULIC LIFTERS

REPLACE

1. Remove camshafts as outlined under "Camshaft, Replace."
2. Remove hydraulic lifters using suitable rubber suction cup. **Do not use magnet.**
3. Reverse procedure to install.

CRANKSHAFT DAMPER

REPLACE

1. Remove viscous fan coupling and fan shroud, **Fig. 8.**
2. **On models equipped with supercharger,** remove supercharger drive belt.
3. **On all models,** remove serpentine drive belt.
4. Rotate engine until cylinder No. 1 piston is to TDC. **Ensure Woodruff key faces vertically.**
5. Install crankshaft/starter ring gear locking plate tool No. 601 589 02 40 00, or equivalent.
6. Remove central bolt and dished washers.
7. Remove pulley/vibration damper using two-arm puller tool No. 000 589 88 33 00, or equivalent.
8. Reverse procedure to install, noting the following:
   a. Inspect hub for scoring. If wear groove is visible, replace radial seal.
   b. Ensure groove is aligned crankshaft Woodruff key.
   c. Oil dished washers and central bolt thread.
   d. Fit dished washers with curved side facing bolt head.
   e. Tighten central bolt to specifications.

FRONT COVER

REPLACE

CYLINDER HEAD

1. Remove valve cover as described under "Valve Cover, Replace.".
2. Remove thermostat housing, **Fig. 9.**
3. **On 1998–2000 models equipped with supercharger,** disconnect supercharger and bypass flap connectors, then remove compressor line bracket at front cover.
4. **On 2001 models,** disconnect supercharger, bypass flap, camshaft adjuster, coolant temperature sensor and alternator connectors.
5. **On all models,** remove mounting bolts and cylinder head front cover.

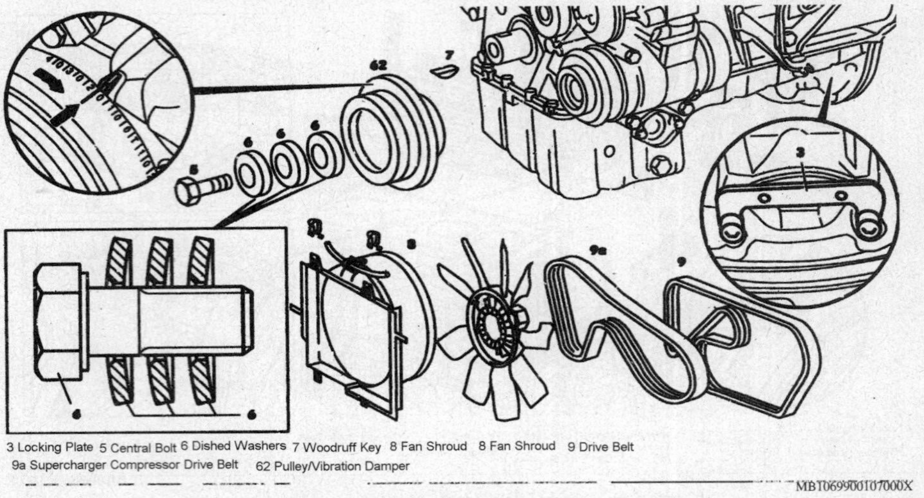

Fig. 8 Vibration damper replacement

6. Reverse procedure to install, noting the following:
   a. Replace O-ring and coat cover to cylinder head sealing surfaces with Omnifit sealant No. FD 3041, or equivalent.
   b. Tighten mounting bolts to specifications.

TIMING CASE

This procedure has been revised by a Technical Service Bulletin.

1. Remove air cleaner.
2. **On models equipped with supercharger,** remove lefthand charge air hose complete with Hot Film Mass (HFM) air flow sensor.
3. **On all models,** remove oil filter. Ensure oil filter oil flows into oil sump.
4. Remove oil sump as described under "Oil Sump, Replace."
5. **On 1998–2000 models,** remove viscous fan coupling.
6. **On all models,** remove fan shroud.
7. **On models equipped with supercharger,** remove supercharger drive belt.
8. **On all models,** drain cooling system into suitable container.
9. **On models equipped with supercharger,** remove supercharger compressor.
10. **On all models,** remove alternator bracket and belt tensioner.
11. Remove cylinder head front cover as outlined under "Front Cover, Replace."
12. Remove water pump.
13. Remove power steering pump belt pulley.
14. **On models equipped with aluminum intake manifold,** remove mounting bolts and brackets.
15. **On all models,** remove mounting bolts and power steering pump with oil lines connected.
16. **On 2001 models,** remove dipstick guide tube mounting bolt.
17. **On 1998–2000 models,** rotate crankshaft to 20–30° after cylinder No. 1 ignition TDC.
18. **On 2001 models,** rotate crankshaft to 25° after cylinder No. 1 ignition TDC.
19. **On all models,** lock camshafts with locating pin tools No. 111 589 03 15 00, or equivalent.
20. Mark camshaft sprockets and timing chain for installation alignment.
21. Remove chain tensioner.
22. Remove exhaust and inlet camshaft sprockets with adjuster tool No. 000 589 01 10 00, or equivalent.
23. Remove inlet camshaft with adjuster.
24. Remove slide rail pins.
25. Remove cylinder head to timing case cover mounting bolts.
26. Remove crankshaft damper as described under "Crankshaft Damper, Replace.".
27. Mark timing case cover mounting bolts to crankcase for installation alignment.
28. Remove remaining timing case cover mounting bolts.
29. Remove timing case cover. **Do not damage cylinder head gasket.**
30. Reverse procedure to install, noting following:
    a. Clean timing case and crankcase sealing surfaces.
    b. Coat sealing surfaces with Omnifit sealant No. FD 3401, or equivalent. **Ensure no sealant gets into chain tensioner oil supply chamber, Fig. 10.**
    c. Replace front crankshaft radial seal and install new O-ring.
    d. When install cover, pull timing chain tight so no chain loop forms between crankshaft sprocket and chain locking stud.
    e. Install new timing case cover bolts. Oil bolt head contact surfaces.
    f. Tighten case cover mounting bolts to specifications.
    g. Coat slide rail pins with Omnifit sealant No. FD 3401, or equivalent.
    h. Install new camshaft sprocket mounting bolts.
    i. Tighten camshaft adjuster mounting bolts to specifications.

j. If chain tensioner is slackened: remove, disassemble and assemble.

FRONT COVER SEAL

REPLACE

Refer to "Front Cover, Replace" for front cover seal replacement.

TIMING CHAIN

REPLACE

1. Remove valve cover, **Fig. 11.**
2. Remove spark plugs.
3. Position cylinder No. 1 piston to 20° after TDC.
4. Lock intake and exhaust camshaft in position with pins tool No. 111 589 03 15 00, or equivalent.
5. Remove chain tensioner.
6. Wedge timing chain in position against camshaft sprockets with wedges tool No. 111 589 19 61 00, or equivalent.
7. Separate timing chain.
8. Reverse procedure to install. Inspect valve cover for leaks.

TIMING CHAIN TENSIONER

REPLACE

1. Remove top part of air cleaner.
2. **On models equipped with supercharger,** remove supercharger.
3. **On all models,** position cylinder No. 1 piston at 20° after TDC.
4. Cover alternator with clean cloth.
5. Loosen tensioner end piece one turn, **Fig. 12.**
6. Remove chain tensioner.
7. Reverse procedure to install. Tighten tensioner and end piece to specifications.

CAMSHAFT

REPLACE

1. Remove cylinder head front cover.
2. Position cylinder No. 1 piston at 30° after TDC.
3. Mark camshaft sprockets and timing chain for installation alignment.
4. Remove chain tensioner as outlined under "Timing Chain Tensioner, Replace."
5. Remove exhaust camshaft sprocket and timing chain from intake camshaft sprocket.
6. Rotate camshafts unit they are free of tension using wrench tool No. 104 589 01 01 00, or equivalent.
7. Remove camshaft bearing cap. **Mark bearing caps for installation in original position.**
8. Remove camshafts.
9. Reverse procedure to install, noting the following:
   a. Ensure base circles rest against hydraulic lifters.
   b. Install bearing caps in original positions.
   c. Install new sprocket mounting bolts.

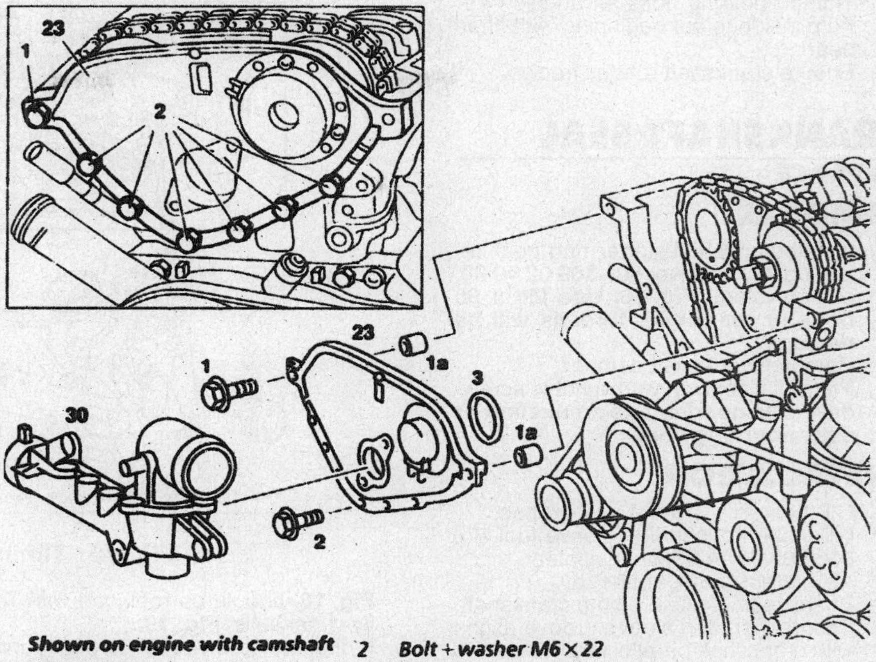

Shown on engine with camshaft adjustment
1 Bolt + washer M8×35
1a Dowel sleeve
2 Bolt + washer M6×22
3 O-ring
23 Cover at front of cylinder head
30 Coolant thermostat housing

Fig. 9 Cylinder head front cover replacement

CAMSHAFT ADJUSTER

REPLACE

REMOVAL

1. Remove cylinder head front cover.
2. **On 1998–2000 models,** position cylinder No. 1 piston at 20° after TDC.
3. **On 2001 models,** position cylinder No. 1 piston at 25° after TDC.
4. **On all models,** lock camshafts in position with pins tool No. 111 589 03 15 00, or equivalent, through camshaft bearing caps rear into camshaft flanges.
5. Mark timing chain and camshaft sprockets for installation alignment.
6. Remove chain tensioner as outlined under "Timing Chain Tensioner, Replace."
7. Remove exhaust camshaft sprocket with adjuster tool No. 000 589 01 10 00, or equivalent.
8. Remove intake camshaft adjuster.

INSTALLATION

1. Install adjuster onto intake camshaft.
2. Install sprocket onto exhaust camshaft with timing chain using new collar bolts.
3. Tighten camshaft sprocket mounting bolts to specifications.
4. Install timing chain tensioner.
5. Remove locking pins and rotate engine crankshaft twice.
6. Inspect basic camshaft positioning.
7. Install cylinder head front cover.
8. Install valve cover.
9. Tighten mounting bolts to specifications.

PISTON & ROD ASSEMBLY

Assemble piston and rod so the piston crown arrow or colored dot is facing travel direction, **Fig. 13** for piston and rod assembly. The marking and retaining grooves in the rod are positioned to the lefthand (inlet) side. The shoulder on one of the piston pin hubs must face away from travel direction.

The pistons are identified relative to the crankcase with code letters A, X and B, **Fig. 14.** Match pistons to cylinder bore, **Fig. 15.**

Tighten connecting rod bolts to specifications.

MAIN & ROD BEARINGS

Crankshaft bearing caps are consecutively number beginning with first crankshaft bearing cap at front.

1. Crankshaft bearing caps are interference-fitted. When correctly installed, crankshaft bearing cap lugs face toward lefthand (intake) side when view in travel direction.
2. Replace bolts with shank length of more than 2.512 inches.
3. Thrust washer oil grooves must face toward crankcase thrust collars.
4. Bearing cap thrust washes have two anti-twist locating lugs
5. Oil thread and head contact surface of bolts.
6. **Torque** crankshaft bearing bolts to 41 ft. lbs.

7. Tighten bearing bolts an addition 95° from inside to out beginning with fitted bearing.
8. Ensure crankshaft rotates freely.

CRANKSHAFT SEAL

REPLACE

REMOVAL

1. Install crankshaft/starter ring gear retaining lock tool No. 601 589 02 40 00, or equivalent, **Fig. 16. Use M6 x 90 bolts or rear cover threads will be damage.**
2. Remove crankshaft damper.
3. Pry radial seal out with suitable screwdriver. **Do not damage crankshaft or seal mounting bore.**

INSTALLATION

1. Oil sealing lip. **Do not use grease.**
2. Fit seal onto insertion sleeve tool No. 606 589 00 14 00, or equivalent.
3. Align crankshaft parallel key.
4. Push insertion sleeve onto crankshaft.
5. Ensure insertion sleeve groove aligns with crankshaft parallel key.
6. Draw insertion sleeve with central bolt and washer.
7. Ensure radial seal is at right angles to crank journal.

CRANKSHAFT REAR OIL SEAL

REPLACE

Production engines are equipped with the radial seal vulcanized to the end cover. This end cover is not a replacement part. Install end cover with interference-fit radial seal.

REMOVAL

1. Remove transmission and clutch, as required.
2. Install crankshaft/starter ring gear retaining lock tool No. 601 589 02 40 00, or equivalent. **Use M6 x 90 bolts or rear cover threads will be damage.**
3. Remove mounting bolts and driven plate or flywheel.
4. Remove mounting bolts, **Fig. 17.**
5. Pry end cover off with radial seal. **Do not damage oil sump gasket.**
6. Remove seal.

INSTALLATION

1. Clean contact surfaces of end cover and coat with Loctite 574 sealant, or equivalent.
2. Oil radial seal sealing lip and mating contact surface. **Do not use grease.**
3. Place inner part of insertion tool No. 111 589 08 43 00, or equivalent, onto crankshaft.
4. Press new radial seal into new end cover at rear.
5. Install mounting bolts, cover first and tighten to specifications.
6. Inspect engine rear for oil leaks before installing transmission.
7. Standard stretch shank flywheel bolts, **Fig. 18,** should be replaced with Torx flywheel bolts, **Fig. 19.**
8. If diameter d is not .3150–.3347 inch, or length L is not .8662 inch, **Fig. 18,** bolt must be replaced.
9. Torx L length should be 1.1222 inches, **Fig. 19.**
10. Tighten mounting bolts to specifications.

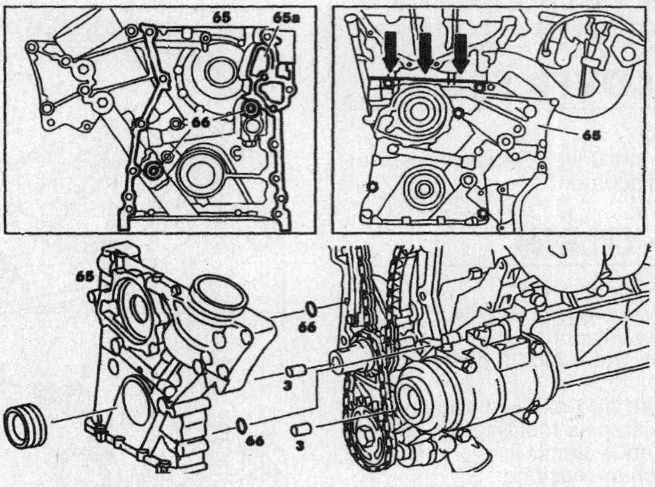

3 Dowel Sleeve 65 Timing Case Cover 65a Oil Supply Chamber 66 O-Ring

MB1069900100000X

Fig. 10 Timing case replacement

OIL PAN

REPLACE

For 1998–2000 models, refer to "Oil Sump, Replace."

1. Drain coolant and engine oil into suitable containers.
2. Disconnect lefthand charge air line at Hot Film Mass (HFM) air flow sensor.
3. Disconnect righthand charge air line at supercharger.
4. Remove intake air scoop and air cleaner.
5. Remove exhaust system to manifold mounting bolts.
6. Disconnect oil level sensor connector.
7. Clamp and disconnect power steering pump oil return hose.
8. Remove front engine mount bottom bolts.
9. Attach suitable engine hoist to front and rear engine lifting eyes, then evenly raise engine front and rear.
10. Remove mounting bolts, oil pan and gasket. Record bolt lengths and diameters for installation in original postilions.
11. Reverse procedure to install noting following:
    a. Clean sealing surfaces.
    b. Install new gasket.
    c. Install pan and align to rear contact surface on transmission. If not aligned to transmission properly noise and vibration problems may result.
    d. Inspect for leaks with engine running.
    e. Tighten mounting bolts to specifications.

OIL SUMP

REPLACE

For 2001 models, refer to "Oil Pan, Replace."

LESS SUPERCHARGER

1. Remove front axle torsion bar.
2. Drain cooling system and oil into suitable containers.
3. Remove fan shroud and place over fan.
4. Remove exhaust system mounting bolts at exhaust manifold.
5. Disconnect oil level sensor electrical connector.
6. Remove front engine mounts' bottom mounting bolt.
7. Loosen coolant hoses at thermostat housing.
8. Remove rear engine mount bottom mounting bolts.
9. Attach suitable engine hoist to front and rear engine suspension lugs, then lift engine evenly at front and rear.
10. Remove mounting bolts, oil pan and gasket. **Mark mounting bolts lengths and diameters for installation.**
11. Reverse procedure to install noting following:
    a. Clean sealing surfaces.
    b. Install new gasket.
    c. Install pan and align to rear contact surface on transmission. If not aligned to transmission properly noise and vibration problems may result.
    d. Inspect for leaks with engine running.
    e. Tighten mounting bolts to specifications.

WITH SUPERCHARGER

1. Drain cooling system and oil into suitable containers.
2. Remove fan shroud and place over fan.
3. Disconnect supercharger lefthand

charge air pipe at Hot Film Mass (HFM) air flow sensor and righthand charge air pipe at compressor.
4. Remove intake air cowl and pull air cleaner housing out of body fixture.
5. **On C230 models,** remove electrical cable mounting bolt at terminal block circuit 30 in lefthand footwell.
6. **On all models,** remove exhaust system mounting bolts at exhaust manifold.
7. Disconnect oil level sensor electrical connector.
8. **On SLK230 models,** loosen coolant hoses at thermostat housing.
9. **On all models,** pinch off and disconnect power steering pump oil return hose.
10. Remove front engine mounts' bottom mounting bolt.
11. Remove rear engine mount bottom mounting bolts.
12. Attach suitable engine hoist to front and rear engine suspension lugs, then lift engine evenly at front and rear.
13. Remove mounting bolts, oil sump and gasket. **Mark mounting bolts lengths and diameters for installation, Fig. 20.**
14. Reverse procedure to install noting following:
    a. Clean sealing surfaces.
    b. Install new gasket.
    c. Install pan and align to rear contact surface on transmission. If not aligned to transmission properly noise and vibration problems may result.
    d. Inspect for leaks with engine running.
    e. Tighten mounting bolts to specifications.

OIL PUMP

REPLACE

1. Remove oil sump as outlined under "Oil Sump, Replace."
2. Remove oil pump drive gear and chain as follows:
    a. **On all models equipped less supercharger,** gear is press fit.
    b. **On SLK230 models with engines as of No. 018931,** gear is press fit.
    c. **On C230 models with engines as of No. 008240,** gear is press fit.
    d. **On all engines except as previously listed,** remove mounting bolts, drive gear and chain.
3. Remove mounting bolts and oil pump.
4. Reverse procedure to install, noting the following:
    a. Fill pump with engine oil before installing.
    b. Clean oil pump filter.
    c. **On models equipped with press fit gear,** install new O-ring seal.
    d. **On all models,** align dowel sleeves in front holes.
    e. Install drive gear with curve side facing oil pump.

BELT TENSION DATA

Belt tension is maintained by an automatic belt tensioner.

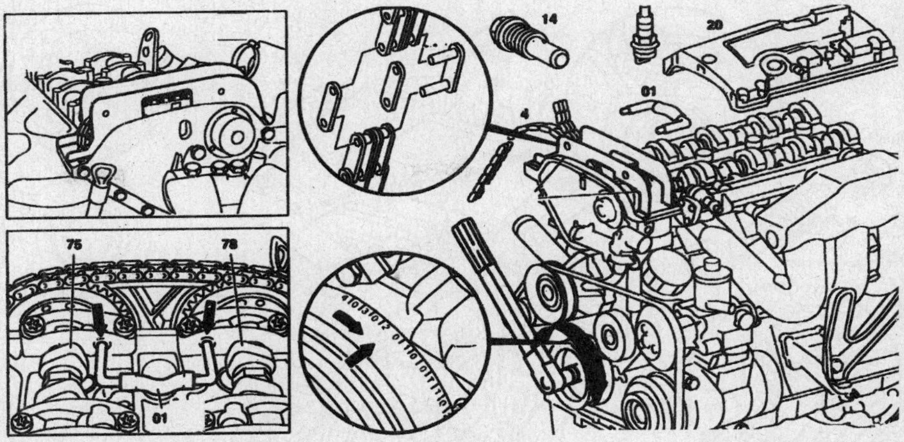

01 Positioning Pins 02 Holding Device 4 Timing Chain 14 Chain Tensioner 20 Cylinder Head Cover 75 Intake Camshaft 78 Exhaust Camshaft

MB1069900110000X

Fig. 11 Timing chain replacement

SERPENTINE DRIVE BELT

BELT, REPLACE

1. Remove viscous fan coupling and fan shroud.
2. Loosen tensioning arm and pulley counterclockwise at stud bolt. **Do not swivel arm at pulley nut.**
3. Remove belt.
4. Reverse procedure to install.

ROUTING

Refer to **Figs. 21 and 22** for drive belt routing.

TENSIONER, REPLACE

Less Supercharger

1. Remove belt as outlined under "Belt, Replace."
2. Remove tensioning pulley mounting bolt.
3. Remove tensioning device shock absorber.
4. Remove bracket mounting bolt.
5. Swivel tensioning arm and fix in position.
6. Remove mounting bolt and tensioning device.
7. Reverse procedure to install. Tighten mounting bolts to specifications.

With Supercharger

1. Remove belt as outlined under "Belt, Replace."
2. Remove tensioning pulley mounting bolt.
3. Remove mounting bolt and tensioning device.
4. Reveres procedure to install.
5. Tighten mounting bolts to specifications.

COOLING SYSTEM BLEED

1. Push float down using suitable screwdriver.
2. Adjust coolant level to marking slowly.
3. Switch heater to Max and warm engine by running at moderate RPM.
4. Adjust coolant level constantly to expansion chamber mark.
5. When coolant temperature reaches 140–150°F, close coolant expansion reservoir using cooling system cap.

THERMOSTAT

REPLACE

1. Drain radiator coolant into suitable container.
2. Remove front cover.
3. **On models equipped with supercharger,** remove charge air pipe bracket from cover.
4. **On all models,** disconnect coolant hoses.
5. Remove mounting bolts, housing and thermostat. **Do not remove thermostat from housing.**
6. Reverse procedure to install using new O-rings.

WATER PUMP

REPLACE

1998–2000

1. Remove viscous fan clutch. **Bolts have lefthand threads.**
2. Drain cooling system into suitable container.
3. Disconnect coolant hoses.
4. Loosen belt pulley bolts and washers, then remove drive belt.
5. Remove mounting bolts and water pump pulley.
6. Remove mounting bolts and water pump.
7. Reverse procedure to install, noting following:
    a. Clean coolant pump sealing surfaces.
    b. Install new gasket and seal with Ominfit FD 3042 sealing agent, or equivalent.
    c. Tighten mounting bolts to specifications.

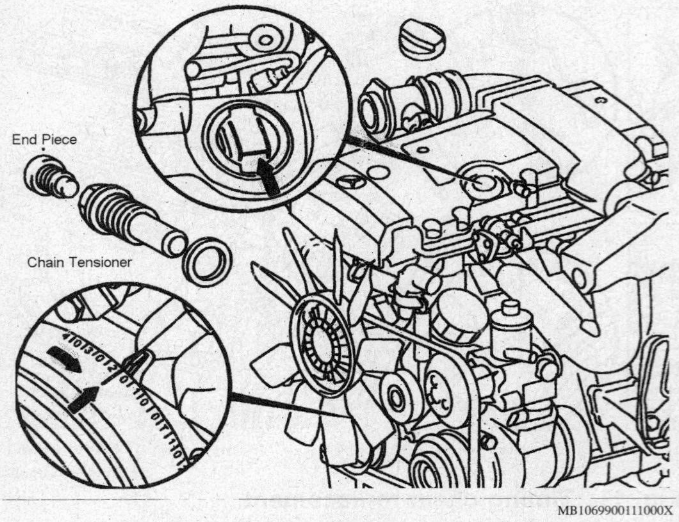

Fig. 12 Chain tensioner replacement

2001

1. Drain cooling system into suitable container.
2. Remove coolant expansion reservoir mount bolts at front crossmember.
3. Disconnect fan connector.
4. Disconnect coolant lines from top and bottom of fan shroud.
5. Remove clamps and fan shroud.
6. Disconnect coolant hoses.
7. Loosen belt pulley bolts and washers, then remove drive belt.
8. Remove mounting bolts and water pump pulley.
9. Remove mounting bolts and water pump.
10. Reverse procedure to install, noting following:
    a. Clean coolant pump sealing surfaces.
    b. Install new gasket and seal with Ominfit FD 3042 sealing agent, or equivalent.
    c. Tighten mounting bolts to specifications.

RADIATOR

REPLACE

1. Drain cooling system into suitable container.
2. **On 1998–2000 models,** remove viscous fan clutch and fan shroud.
3. **On 2001 models,** remove fan shroud as described under "Water Pump, Replace."
4. **On models equipped with automatic transmission,** remove ATF cooler lines.
5. **On all models,** remove upper frame crossmember, protective blower grille and air deflecting elements.
6. Remove condenser from radiator and leave on vehicle with lines connected.
7. Remove radiator hoses.
8. Remove radiator.
9. Reverse procedure to install. Insert attachment lugs in rubber grommets of lower cross member.

FUEL PUMP

REPLACE

C230

1. Relieve fuel pressure as described under "Precautions."
2. Pinch suction, delivery and degassing hoses using clamps tool Nos. 000 589 40 37 00, or equivalent, **Fig. 23.**
3. Remove cap nuts.
4. Mark spacer/adapter for installation alignment.
5. Disconnect electrical connectors.
6. Remove fuel pump.
7. Reverse procedure to install. Tighten banjo bolt and cap nuts to specifications.

SLK230

1998–2000

1. Relieve fuel pressure as described under "Precautions."
2. Pinch suction and delivery hoses using clamps tool Nos. 000 589 40 37 00, or equivalent.
3. Remove cap nuts.
4. Remove fuel pump.
5. Reverse procedure to install. Tighten banjo bolt and cap nuts to specifications.

2001

1. Relieve fuel pressure as described under "Precautions."
2. Remove fuel pump cover.
3. Pinch suction and delivery hoses using clamps tool Nos. 000 589 40 37 00, or equivalent.
4. Remove clamps and disconnect electrical connectors.

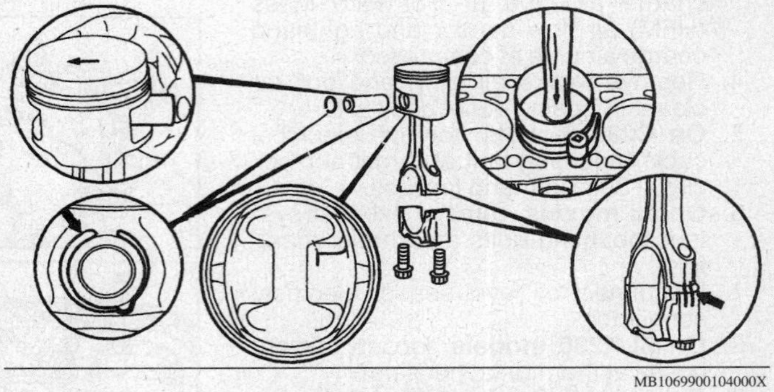

Fig. 13 Piston & rod assembly

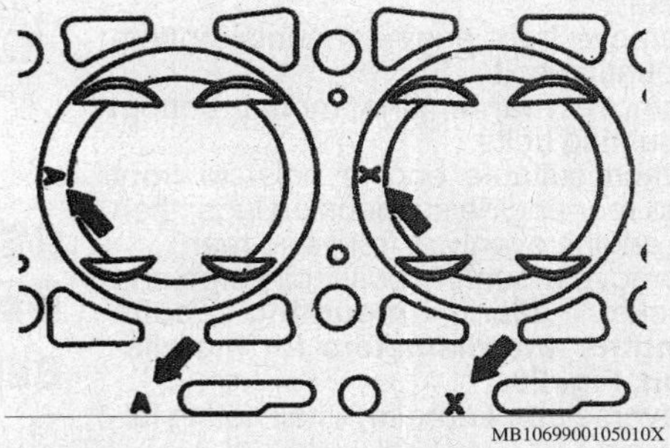

Fig. 14 Piston to crankcase codes

5. Remove fuel pump.
6. Reverse procedure to install.

FUEL FILTER

REPLACE

Refer to "Fuel Pump, Replace" for fuel filter replacement.

SUPERCHARGER

REPLACE

1998–2000

1. Drain cooling system into suitable container.
2. Remove air cleaner.
3. Disconnect suction and pressure lines at supercharger. Seal supercharger openings.
4. **On C230 models,** pinch off secondary air injection valve suction connection and disconnect vacuum hose.
5. **On all models,** remove sensor block cover at front of cylinder head.
6. Disconnect electromagnetic clutch connector, **Fig. 24.**
7. Remove water pump to radiator hose.
8. Remove shroud and fan.
9. Remove supercharger drive belt.
10. **On SLK230 models,** remove pressure connection at compressor.
11. **On all models,** remove mounting bolts and supercharger compressor.
12. Reverse procedure to install, noting the following:
    a. Install bottom mounting bolt before install supercharger.
    b. Tighten mounting bolts to specifications.

Cylinder Bore Identification	Approved Pistons	Additional Code For Ordering Pistons
A	A or X	52 For A Pistons
X	A or X or B	54 For X Pistons
B	B or X	56 For B Pistons

Fig. 15 Piston to bore application chart

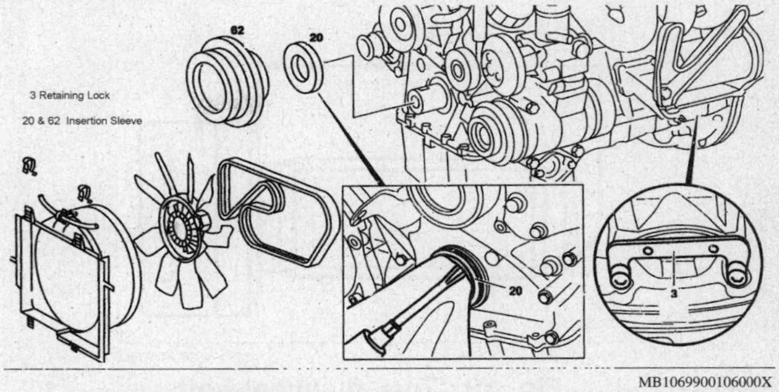

Fig. 16 Front crankshaft radial seal replacement

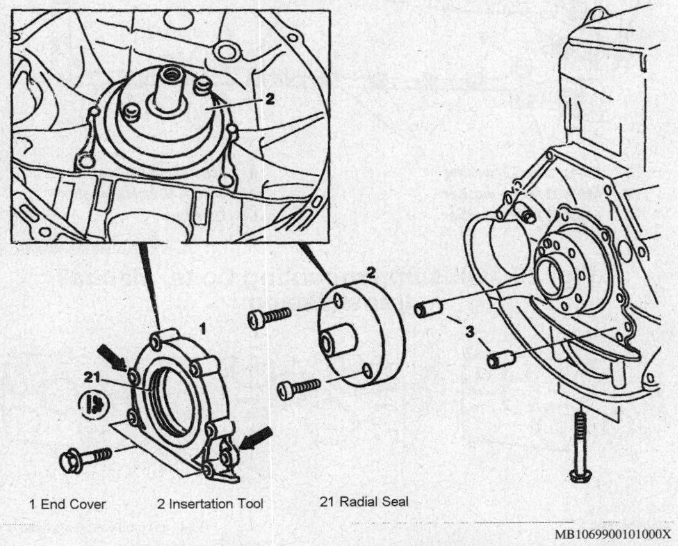

Fig. 17 End cover replacement

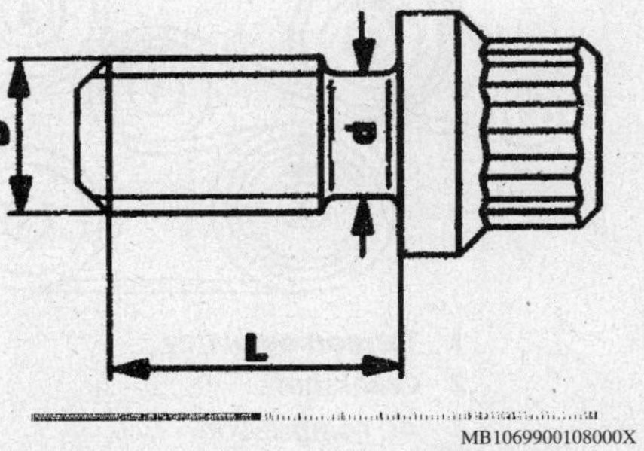

Fig. 18 Stretch shank flywheel bolt. Standard

2001

1. Remove inlet and pressure connections.
2. Remove drive belt.
3. Remove mounting bolts and supercharger.
4. Reverse procedure to install.

TECHNICAL SERVICE BULLETINS

ENGINE DOES NOT START

On some of these models equipped with Brake Assist (BAS) control module, occasionally the engine may not start, the touch/start feature may not work or the engine may go into limp home mode.

This condition may be caused by moisture/corrosion in the connector or the BAS control module.

To correct this condition, proceed as follows:

1. Inspect CAN/power supply connector No. 3 for moisture and corrosion. Repair as required.
2. If condition is still present, replace BAS control module.

ARRHYTHMIA NOISE AT IDLE

On some of these models there may be a arrhythmia noise at idle with engine coolant temperature more than 104°F.

This condition may be caused by a chain tensioner spill valve.

To correct this condition, replace the chain tensioner.

ENGINE CANNOT BE STARTED

1999 C230 & SLK230

On some of these models with engine control modules built between Sept. 2, 1998 and Feb. 19, 1999, the started will not crank the engine and the ME-SFI cannot be diagnosed.

This condition may be caused by the engine control module.

To correct this condition replace engine control modules built between Sept. 2, 1998 and February 19, 1999. Production date is stamped on part number label at upper righthand corner of bar code. Code No. 980902 equals Sept. 2, 1998.

OIL LEAK BETWEEN CYLINDER HEAD & TIMING CASE COVER

On some of these models there may be a high oil leak between the cylinder head and timing case cover.

This condition may be caused by mounting bolts being too loose.

To correct this condition, proceed as follows:

1. Remove top front cover.
2. Remove camshaft gears.
3. Remove and discard four front cover mounting bolts.
4. Install new mounting bolts.
5. **Torque** bolts to 13 ft. lbs.
6. Tighten bolts an additional 90°.

ENGINE OIL ABOVE MAX. LEVEL

On some of these models the engine oil level may be above the Max. mark dip stick or by the oil sensor.

This condition may be caused by diesel or fuel oil or other subsequent additives in the fuel that did not burn and collected in the engine oil pan.

To correct this condition, proceed as follows:

1. Replace engine oil.
2. Drain fuel tank of foreign substances.
3. Do not replace sensor.

CHAIN TENSIONER OIL LEAK

On some of these models built before Dec. 15, 1997, there may be an oil leak at the chain tensioner.

To correct this condition, replace chain tensioner end element and sealing ring.

REAR OIL LEAK

C230

On some of these models there may be an oil leak from rear of engine.

This condition may be caused by torn or creased oil pan gasket.

To correct this condition, install new oil pan gasket (Use only Reinz Co. gasket code No. AFM 32/2).

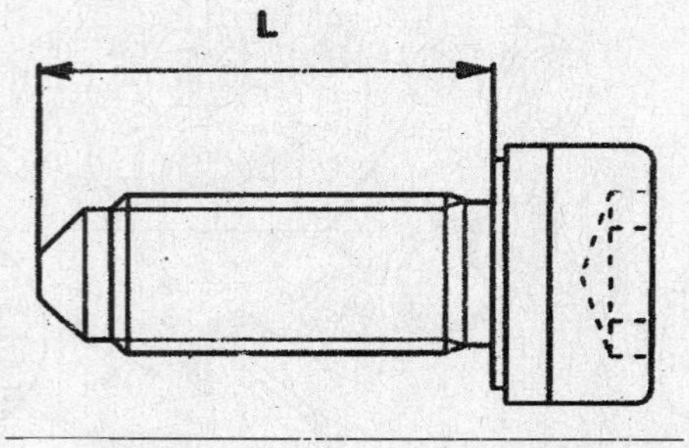

MB1069900109000X

Fig. 19 Torx flywheel bolt

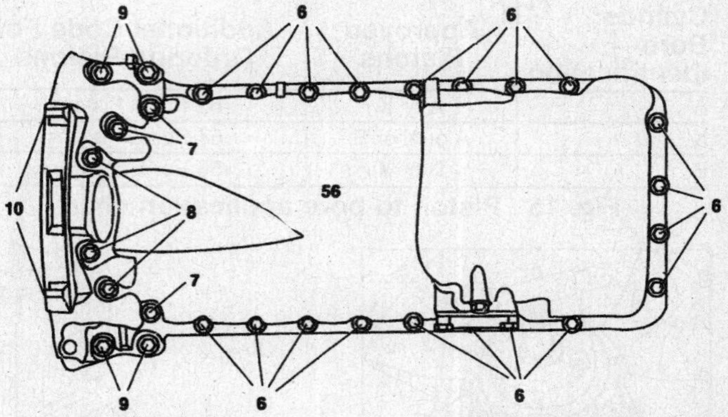

6 M6×20 bolt+washer
7 M6×35 bolt+washer
8 M6×85 bolt+washer
9 M8×40 bolt+washer
10 M10×40 bolt+washer
56 Oil sump

MB1069900103000X

Fig. 20 Oil sump mounting bolts. Manual transmission

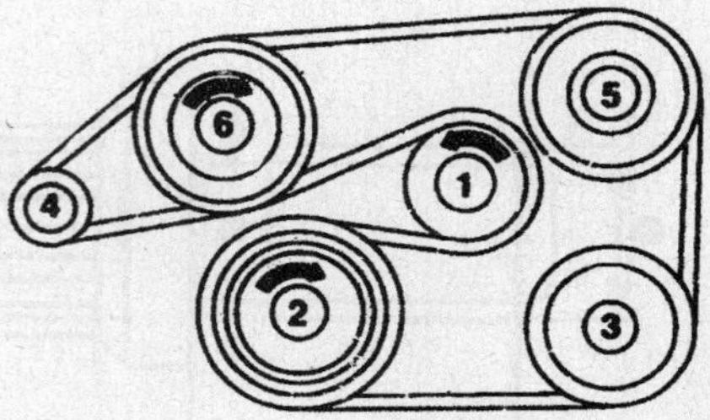

1 Tensioning pulley
2 Crankshaft
3 AC compressor
4 Alternator
5 Power steering pump
6 Coolant pump

MB1069900113000X

Fig. 21 Serpentine drive belt routing. Less supercharger

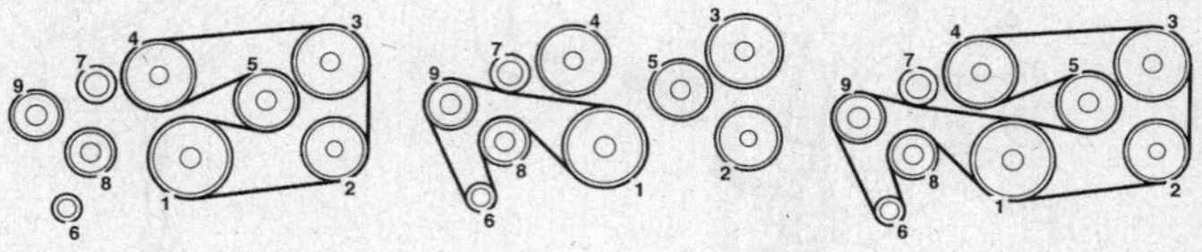

Routing, Belt I

Routing, Belt II

Routings combined, Belts I and II

1 Crankshaft
2 Air conditioner compressor
3 Power steering pump
4 Coolant pump
5 Idler pulley
6 Generator (alternator)
7 Idler pulley
8 Idler pulley
9 Supercharger

MB1139800048000X

Fig. 22 Serpentine drive belt routing. With supercharger

RIGHTHAND OIL LEAK

On some of these models there may be an engine oil leak on the righthand hand side.

To correct this condition, proceed as follows:

1. Install new cylinder head gasket.
2. Install cover gasket on oil-free front cover using Loctite No. 5900 sealant, or equivalent.

REAR OIL LEAK

On some of these models there may be an oil leak from rear of engine.

This condition may be caused by insufficient surface pressure between oil pan and rear end cap.

To correct this condition, proceed as follows:

1. Install new oil pan gasket
2. Thoroughly clean sealing surfaces using suitable stainless steel toothbrush. **Seal surfaces must be absolutely oil free.**
3. Apply Loctite 5900 sealant, or equivalent, to seal surfaces, **Fig. 25.**
4. Assembly must occur within 10 minutes of sealant application.
5. Cure at least two hours before running engine.

VALVE COVER LEAK

C230

On some of these models there may be valve cover leaks.

This condition may be caused by valve cover mounting bolts tightening torque loss because of paint residue on bolts' underside.

To correct this condition, **torque** valve cover mounting bolts to 88 inch lbs.

EXHAUST MANIFOLD CHATTER

On some of these models there may be an exhaust manifold chatter.

This condition may be caused by the exhaust manifold head shield.

To correct this condition, install heat shield with two-layer sandwiched construction (part No. 111 140 04 34).

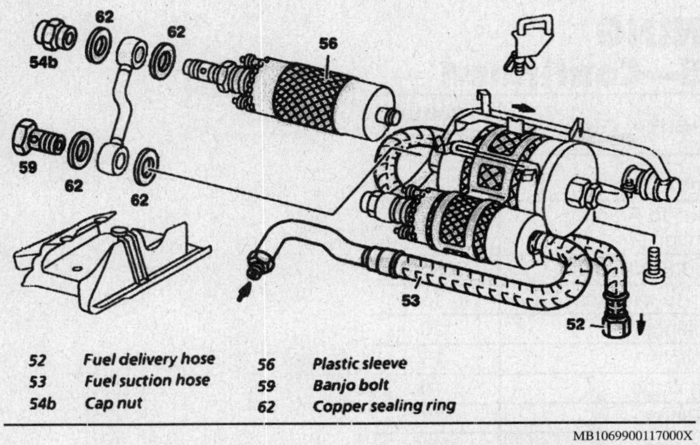

Fig. 23 Fuel pump replacement. C230

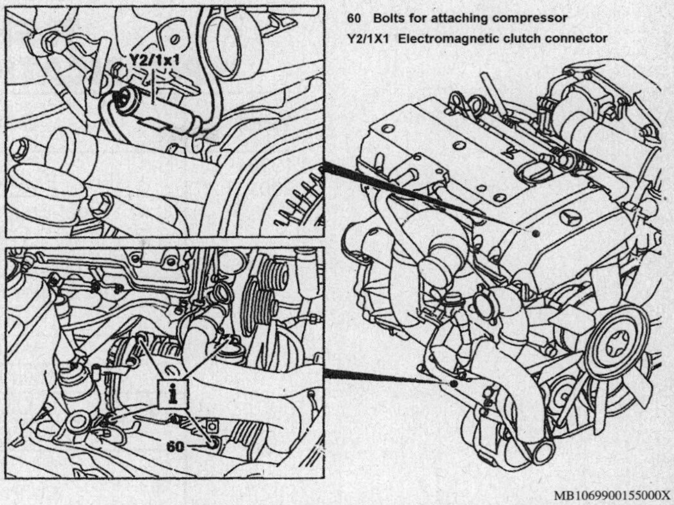

Fig. 24 Supercharger replacement

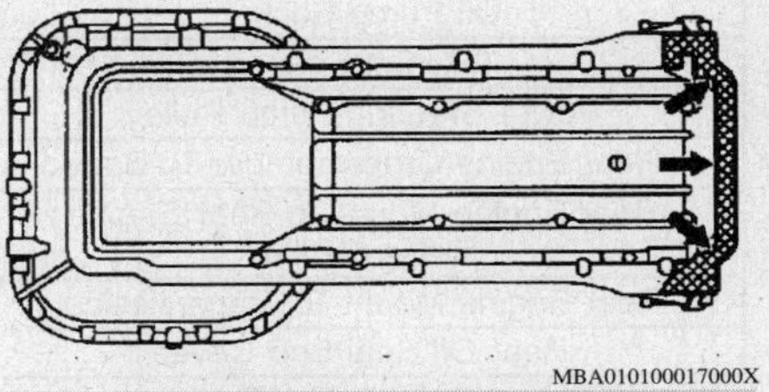

Fig. 25 Rear end cap sealant area. 111 engine

TIGHTENING SPECIFICATIONS

Year	Component	Torque, Ft. Lbs.
1998–2001	ATF Lines	15
	Camshaft	31
	Camshaft Adjuster	15⑤
	Camshaft Bearing Caps	15
	Camshaft Control Plunger Armature	44①⑥
	Camshaft Sprocket	15⑥
	Camshaft Gear To Flange Shaft	48
	Connecting Rod	33⑥
	Crankshaft Damper	221
	Cylinder Head	③
	Cylinder Head Cover	88①
	Cylinder Head Front Cover (M6)	88①
	Cylinder Head Front Cover (M8)	18
	Cylinder Head To Timing Case	13⑥
	Drive Plate	④
	End Cover	88①
	Exhaust Manifold (1998–2000)	22
	Exhaust Manifold (2001)	25
	Exhaust Manifold Front Exhaust Pipe Flange	15
	Flywheel	④

Continued

TIGHTENING SPECIFICATIONS—Continued

Year	Component	Torque, Ft. Lbs.
1998–2001	Front Engine Mount To Bracket	41
	Front Engine Mount To Frame Crossmember	18
	Front Engine Support Heat Shield	88①
	Front Engine Bracket To Crankcase	15
	Fuel Line Fittings	20
	Intake Manifold	15
	Main Bearing Caps	②
	Oil Drain Plug	18
	Oil Level Sensor	88①
	Oil Pan/Sump (M6)	88①
	Oil Pan/Sump (M8)	18
	Oil Pump (Hex Head)	18
	Oil Pump (Torx)	13
	Oil Pump Socket	24
	Oxygen Sensor	41
	Power Steering Pump Pulley	22
	Rear Engine Crossmember To Body	29
	Rear Engine Mount To Rear Engine Crossmember	18
	Rear Engine Mount To Transmission	29
	Rear Oil Seal End Cover	88①
	Serpentine Drive Belt Tensioner	18
	Spark Plugs	18–22
	Supercharger	15
	Thermostat Housing Cover (M6)	80①
	Thermostat Housing Cover (M8)	18
	Timing Case	18
	Timing Case To Cylinder Head	13⑥
	Timing Chain Tensioner End Piece	29
	Timing Chain Tensioner Housing	59
	Transmission Bell Housing To Oil Pan	29
	Valve Cover (1998–2000)	72①
	Valve Cover (2001)	88①
	Vibration Damper	221
	Viscous Clutch Bearing Body	30
	Viscous Clutch Fan	88①
	Water Pump (M6)	88①
	Water Pump (M8)	18
	Water Pump Pulley	88①

① — Inch lbs.
② — Refer to "Main & Rod Bearings" for tightening specifications and sequence.
③ — Refer to "Cylinder Head, Replace" for tightening specifications and sequence.
④ — **Torque** stretch shank bolts to 29 ft. lbs., then tighten an additional 90°; Torque Torx bolts to 33 ft. lbs., then tighten an additional 90.°
⑤ — Tighten an additional 60.°
⑥ — Tighten an additional 90.°

104 Six-Cylinder Gasoline Engine

NOTE: On Air Bag Equipped Models, Refer To "Air Bag System Precautions" Located In The Front Of This Manual For System Disarming & Arming Procedures.

NOTE: Prior To Performing Any Service Operations Listed In This Section, Consult The "Technical Service Bulletins" Section For Related Information.

INDEX

	Page No.
Belt Tension Data	5-52
Camshaft, Replace	5-50
Installation	5-50
Removal	5-50
Camshaft Adjuster, Replace	5-50
Installation	5-50
Removal	5-50
Compression Pressure	5-45
Cooling System Bleed	5-52
Crankshaft Damper, Replace	5-48
Less Integrated Hub	5-48
With Integrated Hub	5-48
Crankshaft Rear Oil Seal, Replace	5-51
Integrated Radial Shaft Seal	5-51
Press-Fitted Radial Shaft Seal	5-51
Crankshaft Seal, Replace	5-50
Installation	5-51
Removal	5-50
Cylinder Head, Replace	5-47
Engine Rebuilding Specifications	5-344
Engine, Replace	5-46
Engine Mount, Replace	5-46
Front	5-46
Rear	5-46
Exhaust Manifold, Replace	5-47
Front Cover, Replace	5-48
Cylinder Head	5-48
Timing Case	5-49
Front Cover Seal, Replace	5-49
Cylinder Head	5-49
Fuel Filter, Replace	5-53
Fuel Pump, Replace	5-53
Hydraulic Lifters, Replace	5-48
Intake Manifold, Replace	5-47
Main & Rod Bearings	5-50
Oil Cooler, Replace	5-52
Air-To-Oil	5-52
Oil-To-Coolant Heat Exchanger	5-52
Oil Pump, Replace	5-52
Oil Sump, Replace	5-51
Piston & Rod Assembly	5-50
Precautions	5-45
Air Bag Systems	5-45
Battery Ground Cable	5-45
Fuel Pressure Relief Procedure	5-45
Radio Coded Anti-Theft System	5-45
Radiator, Replace	5-53
Serpentine Drive Belt	5-52
Belt Tensioner, Replace	5-52
Belt, Replace	5-52
Routing	5-52
Technical Service Bulletins	5-53
Chain Tensioner Oil Leak	5-53
Engine Does Not Start	5-53
Irregular Belt Drive Or Coolant Pump Knocking Noises At Idle	5-53
Oil Pump Howling Or Humming After Cold Start	5-53
Thermostat, Replace	5-52
Tightening Specifications	5-54
Timing Chain, Replace	5-49
Timing Chain Tensioner, Replace	5-49
Installation	5-49
Removal	5-49
Valve Adjustment	5-48
Valve Cover, Replace	5-48
Water Pump, Replace	5-52

PRECAUTIONS

AIR BAG SYSTEMS

Refer to "Air Bag System Precautions" in front of this manual for system disarming and arming procedures.

BATTERY GROUND CABLE

Prior to service, disconnect battery ground cable and isolate as required.

RADIO CODED ANTI-THEFT SYSTEM

Anti-theft radios have a coded theft protection circuit. The CODE card must be obtained before disconnecting battery, removing radio fuse or removing the radio. **The serial number from the radio must match the CODE card.**

After service has been performed proceed as follows:

1. Connect radio power and turn key to position No. 2.
2. Turn radio to On position. Word "CODE" will appear on display.
3. Enter first digit of anti-theft code from CODE card. "CODE" will disappear and entered digit will appear followed by four dashes.
4. Enter next four digits, when all five are entered first digit flashes again.
5. Press SC, Seek or Tune button to confirm code.
6. If "WAIT" appears on radio panel, proceed as follows:
   a. Radio will allow three coding attempts only before entering lock-up mode and won't respond to controls.
   b. Leave radio on for 15–60 minutes, then radio will unlock and allow three addition coding attempts.
   c. Third lockout period (after nine failed coding attempts) will last 24 hours.
   d. Radio must be left on during enter 24-hour period until "CODE" appears.
7. When "CODE" appears, repeat coding attempt.

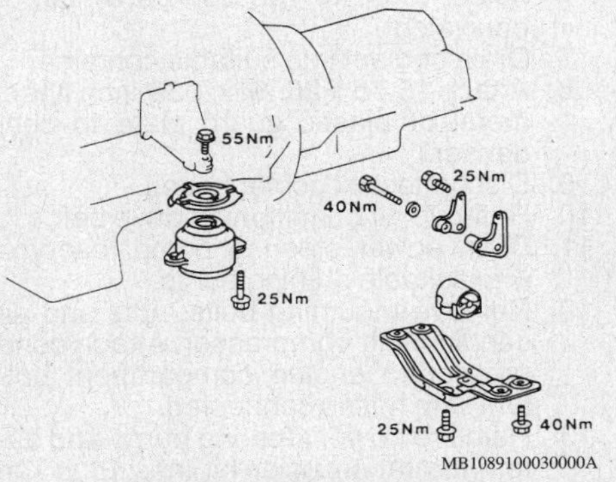

Fig. 1 Engine mounts

FUEL PRESSURE RELIEF PROCEDURE

1. Ensure ignition switch is in Off position.
2. Remove fuel pump protective box.
3. Disconnect fuel pump negative terminal.
4. Start engine and allow to run until it stalls from fuel starvation.
5. Crank engine to ensure pressure is released.

COMPRESSION PRESSURE

1. Warm engine to normal operating temperature.
2. Remove spark plug.
3. Crank engine several times to eliminate cylinder combustion residues. **Do not crank engine with ignition switch.**

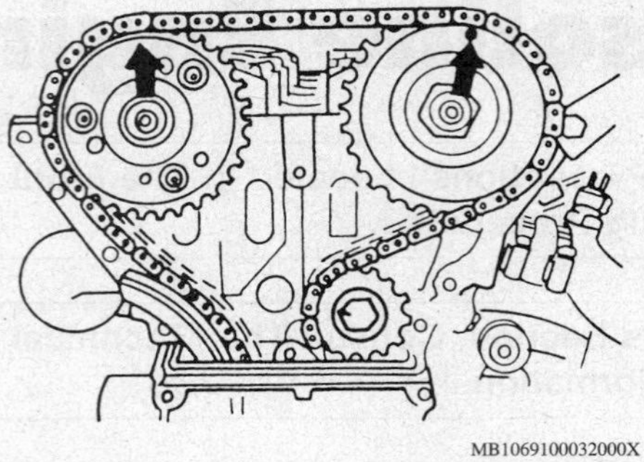

Fig. 2 Timing chain alignment mark

4. Install suitable compression tester into spark plug bore.
5. Open throttle valves wide open.
6. Crank engine with starter eight revolutions. **Do not crank engine with ignition switch or with compression tester contact switch.**
7. Record compression readings.
8. Normal compression pressure should measure 145–203 psi.
9. Maximum permissible difference between individual cylinders is 22 psi.

ENGINE MOUNT

REPLACE

FRONT

1. Remove air cleaner air intake scoop.
2. Remove engine compartment bottom panel.
3. Remove bottom mounting bolt and raise engine slightly, **Fig. 1.**
4. Remove upper mounting bolt, mounts and shield.
5. Remove engine mount with engine carrier.
6. Reverse procedure to install, noting the following:
   a. Engine mount torsion pin must be located in shield hole and engine carrier retaining slot.
   b. Tighten mounting bolts to specifications.

REAR

1. Support transmission using suitable jack stands.
2. Loosen kick-down switch and oxygen sensor cable ties on engine support.
3. Remove mounting bolts and engine carrier, **Fig. 1.**
4. Loosen engine mount mounting bolt.
5. Reverse procedure to install, noting the following:
   a. Engine mount position is fixed by mount slot and bracket recess.
   b. Tighten mounting bolts and nuts to specifications.

ENGINE

REPLACE

The engine and transmission are removed as an assembly.

1. Remove lower engine compartment cover.
2. Remove air cleaner.

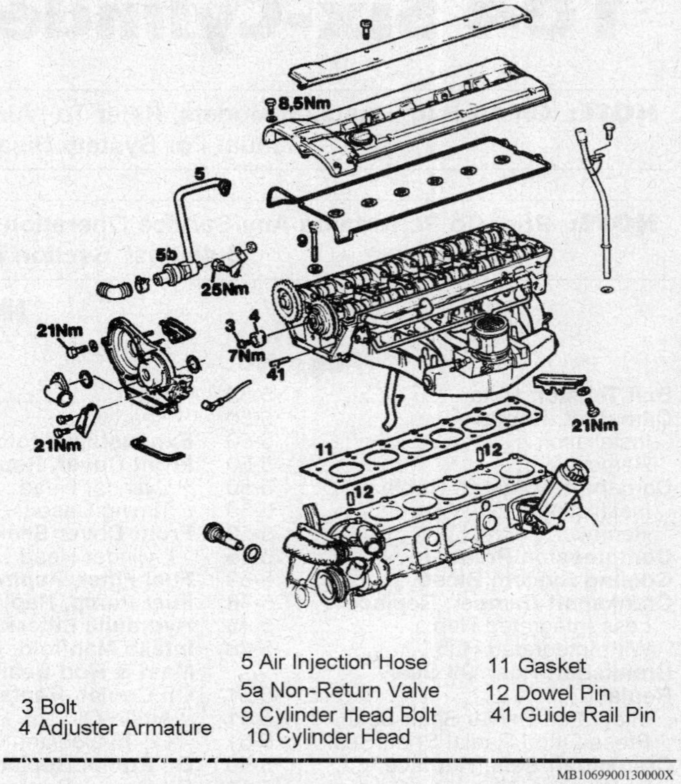

Fig. 3 Cylinder head replacement

3. Remove radiator as outlined under "Radiator, Replace."
4. Remove upper frame crossmember.
5. Remove locking pin, then turn fan shroud ring to left and place it over fan.
6. Remove viscous fan clutch mounting bolts while holding fan with counterholder tool No. 120 589 02 01 00, or equivalent.
7. Drain coolant into suitable container.
8. Attach 15.75 x 26.77 x .039-inch sheet metal or plastic guard plate to condenser.
9. Disconnect oil cooler hoses.
10. Remove air conditioning drive belt.
11. Drain power steering pump reservoir with suitable priming pump.
12. Remove mounting bolts, nuts and air conditioning compressor. Attach compressor to engine compartment bottom with hoses connected.
13. Remove power steering pump and automatic transmission oil lines. Plug and seal hoses and openings.
14. Relieve fuel pressure as described under "Precautions."
15. Open fuel tank filler cap.
16. Remove and seal fuel pump hoses and vacuum lines.
17. Disconnect Bowden cable from accelerator control lever.
18. Disconnect heater return hose.
19. Remove engine compartment cover and righthand cable duct.
20. Disconnect engine wiring connectors.
21. Release clip and place engine wiring harness on engine.
22. Disconnect ignition control module crankshaft position sensor, engine control module and knock sensor connectors.
23. Disconnect brake pressure regulator vacuum hoses.
24. Disconnect evaporative emission control system suction hose on lefthand wheelwell.
25. Disconnect diagnostic socket electrical connector.
26. Remove exhaust system and front heat shields.
27. Remove starter motor electrical connectors.
28. Mark propeller shaft and transmission flex joint for installation alignment, then remove mounting bolts.
29. Loosen propeller shaft intermediate bearing mounting bolts. **Do not remove.**
30. Loosen clamping nut and push propeller shaft as far back as possible.
31. Loosen strap and remove cable from kickdown solenoid valve.
32. Remove mounting bolt and pulse generator from automatic transmission.
33. Remove transmission ground cable.
34. Disconnect starter lockout switch connector.
35. Disconnect transmission overload protection connector using two suitable screwdrivers.
36. Attach suitable engine hoist to lifting lugs and adjust so engine can be lifted horizontally.
37. Support transmission with suitable transmission jack.
38. Remove rear engine support bolts. Do not remove rear engine mount.

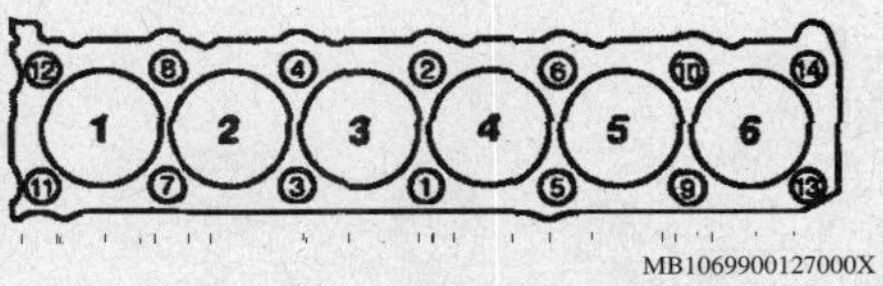

Fig. 4 Cylinder head tightening sequence

39. Remove exhaust bracket from transmission.
40. Remove left and righthand engine mount bolts.
41. Attach 12.60 x 14.96 x .039-inch sheet metal or plastic guard plate to engine compartment wall.
42. Tilt engine and transmission, then remove. **Do not damage rear lifting lug or oil filter.**
43. Remove engine by lifting.
44. Reverse procedure to install, noting the following:
    a. Install righthand engine mount on front suspension before installing engine. Lefthand engine mount can be installed with engine.
    b. Adjust throttle cable.
    c. Inspect engine mounts and replace as required.
    d. Inspect hoses and replace as required.
    e. Adjust transmission pressure control cable.
    f. Fan cast part number must face radiator.
    g. Ensure fan shroud studs engage fan shroud.
    h. Tighten all mounting nuts and bolt to specifications.

INTAKE MANIFOLD

REPLACE

1. Remove air cleaner crosspipe.
2. Relieve fuel pressure as described under "Precautions."
3. **On models equipped with integrated oil and water cooler,** remove oil filter.
4. **On all models,** remove fuel rail.
5. Disconnect fuel lines.
6. Remove fuel injectors.
7. Disconnect vacuum lines and electrical connectors.
8. Disconnect throttle control level cable.
9. Remove ram manifold.
10. Reverse procedure to install, noting the following:
    a. Do not trap vacuum lines or electrical wires.
    b. Inspect rubber boots and replace as required.
    c. Install new resonance intake manifold gasket.
    d. Install new fuel injector and rail O-rings.
    e. Tighten mounting bolts to specifications.
    f. Inspect idle speed.

EXHAUST MANIFOLD

REPLACE

1. Remove exhaust manifold rivet nuts as required.

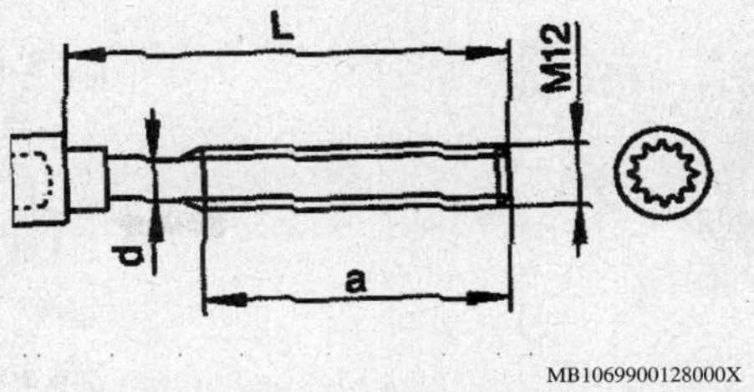

Fig. 5 Cylinder head bolt measurement

2. Remove gasket.
3. Remove exhaust manifold.
4. Reverse procedure to install, noting the following:
    a. Install gaskets with metal side toward cylinder head.
    b. Clean manifold mounting surface and apply dots exhaust sealing compound No. A 001 989 25 20, or equivalent, to new gasket.
    c. Coat oxygen sensor threads with hot lubricating paste No. 000 989 76 51, or equivalent.
    d. Tighten rivet nuts to specifications.

CYLINDER HEAD

REPLACE

Engine must be cold when performing this procedure. Remove cylinder head complete with intake and exhaust manifolds.

1. Drain coolant into suitable container, then disconnect cylinder head coolant hoses.
2. Set cylinder No. 1 piston at ignition TDC.
3. Remove cylinder head front cover as outlined under "Front Cover, Replace."
4. Mark timing chain and camshaft sprockets for installation alignment, **Fig. 2.**
5. Remove guide rail or friction rail pin using impact extractor tool No. 116 589 20 33 00 and threaded bolt tool No. 116 589 02 34 00, or equivalents, **Fig. 3.**
6. Remove guide sprocket and bearing body.
7. Remove camshaft adjuster armature.
8. Remove timing chain from camshaft.
9. Disconnect position sensor at righthand wheelhouse.
10. Loosen cable ties, disconnect electrical connectors and remove engine wiring harness.
11. Disconnect speed control linkage.
12. Disconnect intake manifold vacuum lines.
13. Remove exhaust system mounting bolts at exhaust manifold flange.
14. Disconnect secondary air injection hose at cylinder head.
15. Disconnect secondary air injection non-return valve and remove bracket mounting bolts.
16. Remove dipstick guide tube and intake manifold support mounting bolts
17. Remove dipstick guide tube.
18. Disconnect crankcase air admission combination support hose.
19. Release fuel tank pressure by briefly opening fuel filler cap.

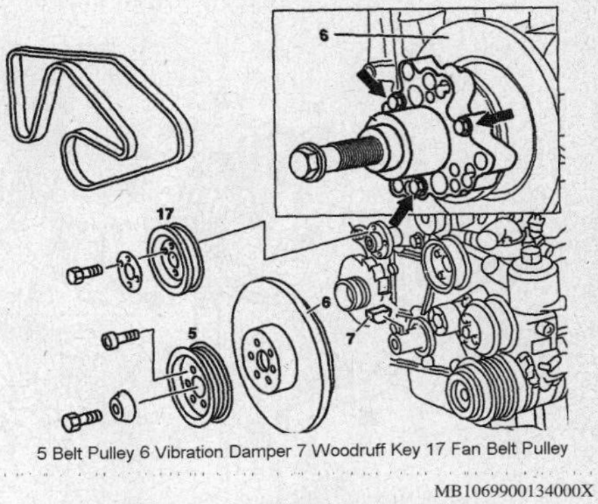

Fig. 6 Crankshaft damper replacement. With integrated hub

20. Open fuel tank filler cap to relieve tank pressure.
21. Disconnect fuel lines.
22. Remove automatic transmission oil dipstick guide tube.
23. Disconnect Bowden control cable from accelerator lever.
24. Loosen water pump hose clamps and remove return line.
25. Loosen in stages and remove cylinder head mounting bolts in reverse tightening sequence, **Fig. 4.**
26. Remove camshaft bearing caps Nos. 9 and 13.
27. Install lifting lugs tool No. 104 589 00 40 00, or equivalent.
28. Remove cylinder head using suitable engine hoist and lifting tackle.
29. Reverse procedure to install, noting following:
    a. Clean cylinder head bolts and threaded holes.
    b. Install new cylinder head gasket.
    c. Ensure dowel pins are correctly located.
    d. Turn camshaft so camshaft flange holes lower edge are level with cylinder head top. Inspect with .1575 inch pin.
    e. Ensure cylinder No. 1 piston is at TDC.
    f. Measure length L of cylinder head bolts prior to installation, **Fig. 5.** If length is more than 6.4376 inches, replace bolt.
    g. Lubricate cylinder head bolts and washer contact surfaces with engine oil.
    h. Adjust throttle cable.
    i. Install new secondary air injection hose seal.
    j. Guide rail pin thread must be located at front in direction of travel when installed.
    k. **Torque** cylinder head bolts to 41 ft. lbs. in sequence, **Fig. 4.**
    l. Tighten head bolts an additional 90° in sequence.
    m. Final bolts tighten an additional 90° in sequence.
    n. **Do not pressure test cooling system until engine has reached normal operating temperature and cylinder head gasket has swollen.**

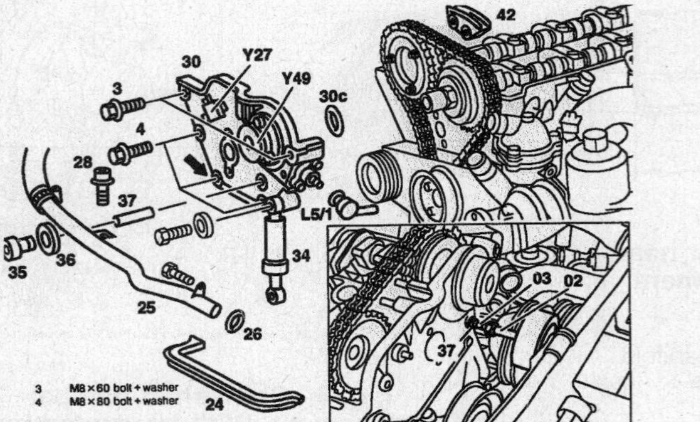

02 Impact Extractor
03 Threaded Insert
24 Shaped Rubber Gasket
25 Heater Water Return Hose
26 Seal
30 Front Cover
30c Seal
35 Screw Plug
36 Seal
37 Top Guide Rail Pin
42 Guide Rail
L5/1 Camshaft Position Sensor Connection
Y49 Camsahft Adjustment Actuator Connector

MB1069900121000X

Fig. 7 Cylinder head front cover replacement

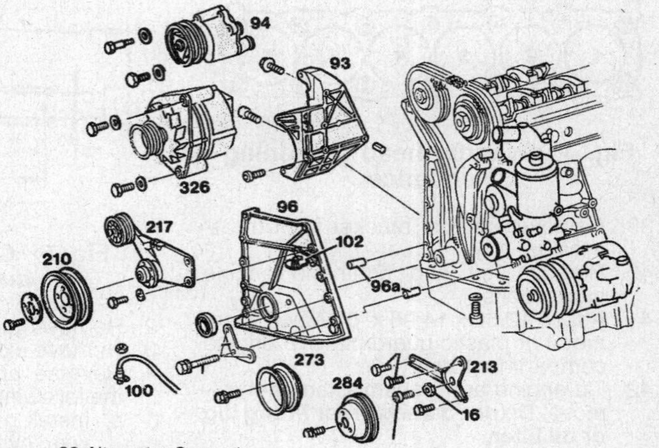

93 Alternator Support
94 Air Pump
96 Timing Case Cover
100 TDC Sensor
102 TDC Sensor Bracket
210 Can Clutch Pulley
213 Tension Device
217 Fan Bearing Bracket
273 Water Pump Pulley
284 Power Steering Pump Pulley
326 Alterator

MB1069900119000X

Fig. 8 Timing case cover replacement

VALVE COVER

REPLACE

1. Remove ignition coils.
2. Remove cylinder head front cover.
3. Remove mounting bolts with spacer sleeves from valve cover.
4. Remove valve cover, gaskets and shaft seals.
5. Reverse procedure to install, noting the following:
   a. Remove grease from gasket sealing groove.
   b. **Do not grease new gasket.**
   c. Inspect for leaks especially at rear gaskets and spark plug recesses.

VALVE ADJUSTMENT

This engine is equipped with hydraulic lifters and requires no valve adjustment,

HYDRAULIC LIFTERS

REPLACE

1. Remove camshafts as outlined under "Camshaft, Replace."
2. Remove hydraulic lifters using suitable rubber suction cup. **Do not use magnet.**
3. Reverse procedure to install.

CRANKSHAFT DAMPER

REPLACE

LESS INTEGRATED HUB

1. Remove viscous fan clutch.
2. Attach 15.75 x 26.77 x .039-inch sheet metal or plastic guard plate to condenser.
3. Turn engine until cylinder No. 1 piston is at TDC. Crankshaft Woodruff key should be facing up.
4. Loosen fan belt pulley mounting bolts and remove serpentine drive belt.
5. Remove belt from fan and plate.
6. Remove crankshaft/ring gear retaining lock.
7. Remove mounting bolts, belt pulley and vibration damper.
8. Remove mounting bolts and dished or conical washers.
9. Remove hub using puller tool No. 103 589 00 33 00, or equivalent.
10. Reverse procedure to install, noting the following:
    a. Align Woodruff key, push hub on and turn to determine if crankshaft slot is aligned with key.
    b. Fit dished washer with curved side facing vibration damper.
    c. Oil bolt thread and washers.
    d. Tighten mounting bolts to specifications.

WITH INTEGRATED HUB

1. Remove viscous fan clutch.
2. Remove radiator.
3. Turn engine until cylinder No. 1 piston is at TDC. Crankshaft Woodruff key should be facing up.
4. Loosen fan belt pulley mounting bolts and remove serpentine drive belt, **Fig. 6.**
5. Remove fan pulley and plate.
6. Remove crankshaft/ring gear retaining lock.
7. Remove mounting bolts and belt pulley.
8. Remove center bolt and conical washers.
9. Remove vibration damper using puller tool No. 129 589 01 33 00, or equivalent.
10. Reverse procedure to install, noting the following:
    a. Align Woodruff key, push hub on and turn to determine if crankshaft slot is aligned with key.
    b. Tighten mounting bolts to specifications.

FRONT COVER

REPLACE

CYLINDER HEAD

1. Remove coolant connection fitting.
2. Remove guide rail at top, **Fig. 7.**
3. Remove heater coolant hose at fan bearing bracket and water pump.
4. Disconnect camshaft position sensor and camshaft adjustment actuator connectors.
5. Disconnect secondary air injection vacuum lines and switchover valve connectors.
6. Remove mounting bolt and push tensioning device shock absorber down, if equipped.
7. Remove screw plug and seal.
8. Remove top guide rail pin using impact extractor tool No. 116 589 20 33 00 and threaded insert tool No. 116 589 01 34 00, or equivalents.
9. Remove mounting bolts and front valve cover. **Do not apply pressure to cover when removing.**
10. Reverse procedure to install, noting the following:
    a. Replace cover seal.
    b. Apply sealant No. 002 989 45 30, or equivalent, on left and righthand joints to form dot.
    c. Install new shaped rubber gasket without sealant into oil-free groove.
    d. Coat top side of gasket with engine oil.
    e. Coat cover contact surfaces with sealant No. 002 989 45 30, or equivalent.
    f. Ensure shaped rubber gasket does not shift when front cover is installed.
    g. Tighten mounting bolts to specifications.
    h. Replace coolant hose seal.

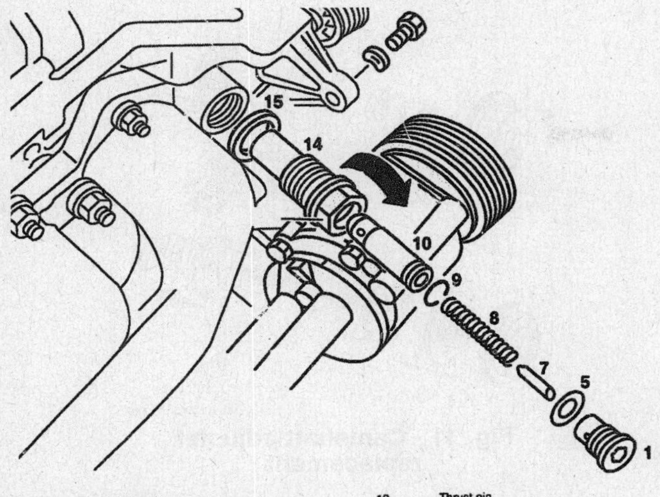

1 Screw plug
2 Ball (return flow shutoff valve)
3 Compression spring
4 Ball guide
5 Aluminium seal
7 Filler pin
8 Compression spring
9 Detent spring
10 Thrust pin
11 Ball
12 Compression spring
13 Thrust piece (press-fitted)
14 Chain tensioner housing
15 Aluminium seal
16 Timing case cover

MB1069900137000X

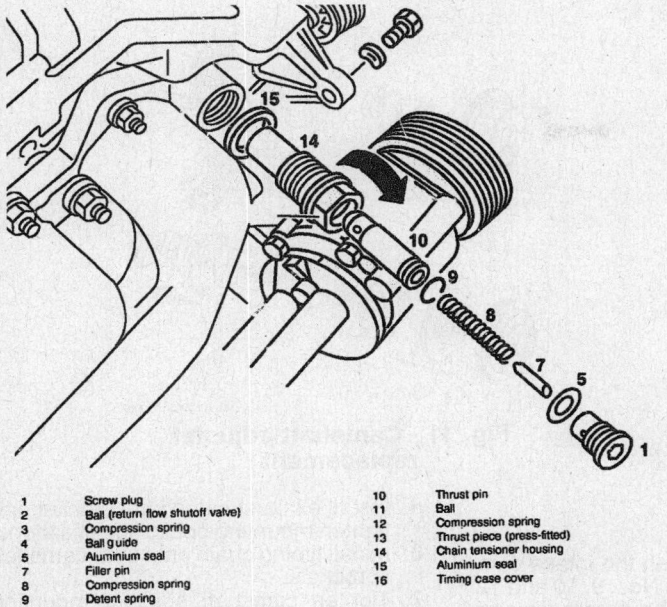

Fig. 9 Timing chain tensioner replacement

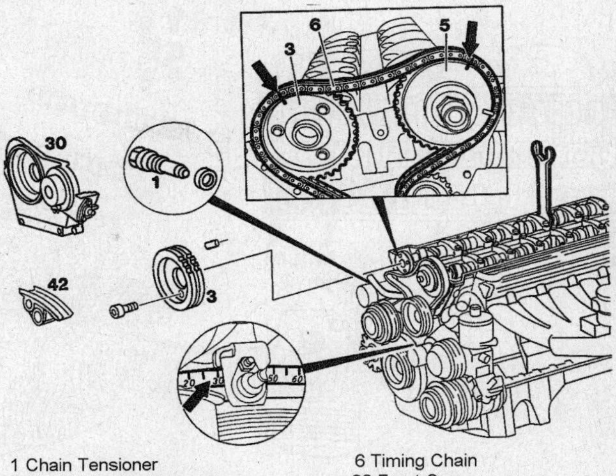

1 Chain Tensioner
3 Exhaust Camshaft Sprocket
5 Intake Camshaft Sprocket
6 Timing Chain
30 Front Cover
42 Top Guide Rail

MB1069900136010X

Fig. 10 Camshaft replacement (Part 1 of 2)

i. If chain tensioner is move one detent in pressure direction, it must be removed to avoid over tensioning chain.

TIMING CASE

1. Remove air cleaner and intake air scoop.
2. Remove engine compartment bottom cover.
3. Remove viscous fan clutch.
4. Loosen fan clutch, water pump and power steering pump pulleys' mounting bolts, **Fig. 8.**
5. Remove serpentine drive belt.
6. Remove mounting bolts, fan clutch, water pump and power steering pump pulleys.
7. Remove pulley belt vibration damper.
8. Remove cap and release cooling system pressure.
9. Remove cylinder head front cover as outlined under "Front Cover, Replace."
10. Mark timing chain and sprockets for installation alignment, then remove timing chain.
11. Remove mounting bolts and swing tensioning device bracket aside.
12. Remove air pump and set aside with lines attached.
13. Remove fan bearing bracket.
14. Remove TDC sensor with cable and place aside. Sensor remains on case cover.
15. Disconnect alternator electrical connector.
16. Remove mounting bolt and alternator with support.
17. Remove timing case cover front and bottom mounting bolts.
18. Remove timing case cover with TDC sensor. **Do not damage oil sump gasket.**
19. Reverse procedure to install, noting the following:
    a. Inspect oil sump gasket and replace as required.
    b. Clean timing case cover and crankcase sealing surfaces.
    c. Apply even coating of sealant No. 002 989 47 20, or equivalent, to timing case cover sealing surface.
    d. Ensure dowel pins are installed in correct positions.
    e. Install alternator support front and side mounting bolts until they contact. Tighten front mounting bolt first.
    f. Tighten mounting bolts to specifications.
    g. Install new water pump heater hose seal.

FRONT COVER SEAL

REPLACE

CYLINDER HEAD

Removal

Pry radial shaft seal out using suitable screwdriver and clean cloth. **Do not damage camshaft or seal mounting hole.**

Installation

1. Install insertion sleeve tool No. 103 489 01 14 00, or equivalent.
2. Coat radial seal sealing lip with engine oil. **Do not use grease.**
3. Fit seal flush with sleeve. **Seal must be vertical to camshaft.**

TIMING CHAIN

REPLACE

This procedure has been revised by a Technical Service Bulletin.

1. Remove spark plugs.
2. Remove timing chain tensioner as described under "Timing Chain Tensioner, Replace."
3. Remove front cover and top guide rail.
4. Cover timing case with clean cloth.
5. Separate chain pin at exhaust camshaft sprocket using separating tool No. 602 589 02 33 00 and thrust spindle tool No. 602 589 04 63 00, or equivalents.
6. Pry plate off timing chain with suitable screwdriver.
7. Press out double link.
8. Connect old timing chain with riveted link and center plate to new timing chain.
9. Rotate engine with suitable wrench socket in engine rotational direction pulling new chain in. Hold timing chain meshed at exhaust camshaft sprocket.
10. Pull timing chain bottom free end out of case.
11. Rotate crankshaft until new timing chain can be connected with riveted link.

TIMING CHAIN TENSIONER

REPLACE

REMOVAL

1. Remove mounting bolts, then swivel air pump to side with lines and wires connected, **Fig. 9.**
2. Cover alternator with clean cloth.
3. Loosen screw plug approximately one turn. **Once plug as been loosened, tensioner must be removed.**
4. Remove chain tensioner.
5. Remove screw plug with seal, filler pin and compression spring.
6. Press thrust pin with detent spring out in pressure direction.

INSTALLATION

1. Install chain tensioner housing and tighten to specifications.

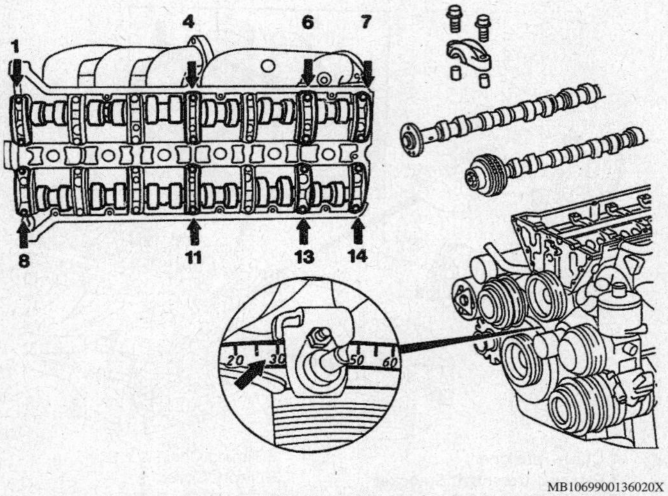

Fig. 10 Camshaft replacement (Part 2 of 2)

2. Install thrust pin with detent spring, compression spring and filler pin.
3. Stick new seal to screwplug with suitable grease.
4. Install screwplug with new seal and tighten to specifications.

CAMSHAFT

REPLACE

REMOVAL

1. Remove valve cover.
2. Rotate crankshaft until cylinder No. 1 piston is at 30° before ignition TDC. At this position, camshafts can rotate without valves touching piston crowns, **Fig. 10.**
3. Remove chain tensioner.
4. Remove cylinder head front cover.
5. Mark timing chain and camshaft sprockets for installation alignment.
6. Remove exhaust camshaft sprocket.
7. Remove timing chain from intake camshaft sprocket
8. Turn camshafts so cylinder No. 2 cam lobes press on lifter centers using wrench tool No. 104 589 00 01 00, or equivalent.
9. Remove exhaust camshaft bearing caps Nos. 1, 4, 6 and 7; and intake camshaft bearing caps Nos. 8, 11, 13 and 14.
10. Loosen remaining camshaft bearing caps one turn at a time until pressure is eliminated. **Do not twist camshafts when loosen or tightening bearing caps.**
11. Remove intake and exhaust camshafts.

INSTALLATION

1. Inspect lifters for ease of movement. Replace as required.
2. Oil bearing points and lifters.
3. Ensure cylinder No. 1 pistons is at 30° BTDC.
4. Install intake and exhaust camshafts. Cam lobes must face down and center at cylinder No. 2.
5. Install exhaust camshaft bearing caps Nos. 2, 3 and 5, then the intake camshaft bearings caps Nos. 9, 10 and 12. Bearing caps must be installed in original positions.
6. Tighten camshaft bearing caps alternately one turn at a time to specifications.
7. Hold camshafts using wrench tool No. 104 589 00 01 00, or equivalent.
8. Tighten remaining camshaft bearing caps alternately one turn at a time to specifications.
9. Install exhaust camshaft sprocket and tighten to specifications.
10. Install timing chain. Ensure timing marks align.
11. Install front cover and top guide rail.
12. Install chain tensioner.

CAMSHAFT ADJUSTER

REPLACE

REMOVAL

1. Position cylinder No. 1 piston at ignition TDC.
2. Remove cylinder head front cover, **Fig. 11.**
3. Mark timing chain and camshaft sprockets for installation alignment.
4. Remove mounting bolt and armature while counterholding armature.
5. Remove mounting nut and cover with ring.
6. Remove exhaust camshaft sprocket mounting bolts, sprocket and positioning piston.

INSTALLATION

1. Install flanged shaft onto camshaft with locating pin. Tighten new mounting bolt to specifications.
2. Install positioning piston onto flanged shaft, turning to left while holding timing chain up.
3. Install camshaft sprocket onto positioning piston, turning to right while holding timing chain up.
4. Install cover with ring and mount nut. Do not tighten nut now.

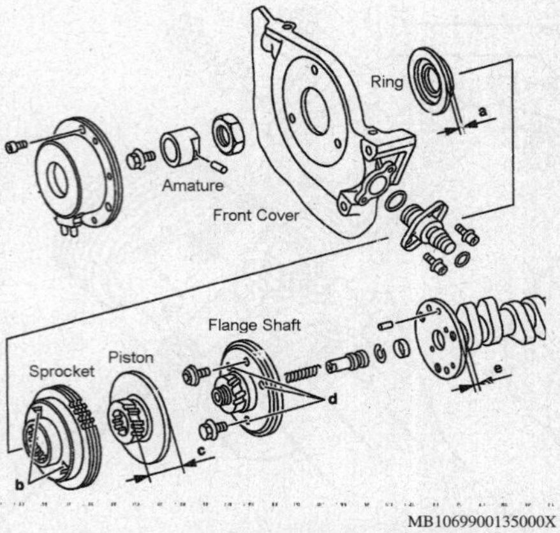

Fig. 11 Camshaft adjuster replacement

5. Install exhaust camshaft sprocket and tighten mounting bolt to specifications.
6. Install timing chain onto both camshaft sprockets.
7. Tighten camshaft adjuster mounting nut to specifications.
8. Install armature onto control plunger and tighten to specifications. **Armature roll pin must align with control plunger flat face.**
9. Install cylinder head front cover.

PISTON & ROD ASSEMBLY

Assemble piston and rod so the piston crown arrow is facing travel direction for piston and rod assembly, **Fig. 12.**

The pistons are identified relative to the crankcase with code letters A, X and B. Match pistons to cylinder bore, **Fig. 13.**

Connecting rod bolt maximum shank length is 2.083 inches.

Tighten connecting rod bolts to specifications.

MAIN & ROD BEARINGS

Replace mounting bolt if shank is more than 2.512 inches.

1. Oil bearing shells in crankcase.
2. Oil crankshaft bearing points.
3. Oil bearing caps with bearing shells.
4. Oil bolt threads and contact surfaces.
5. Thrust washer of original thickness must always be inserted on one side in crankcase and bearing cap.
6. Oil grooves must face toward contact surface of crankshaft and be oiled.
7. Anti-twist lock is on bearing cap thrust washer.
8. Tighten crankshaft bearing bolts to specifications. Rotate crankshaft while tightening bolts to detect any jamming.

CRANKSHAFT SEAL

REPLACE

REMOVAL

1. Remove belt pulley/vibration damper.

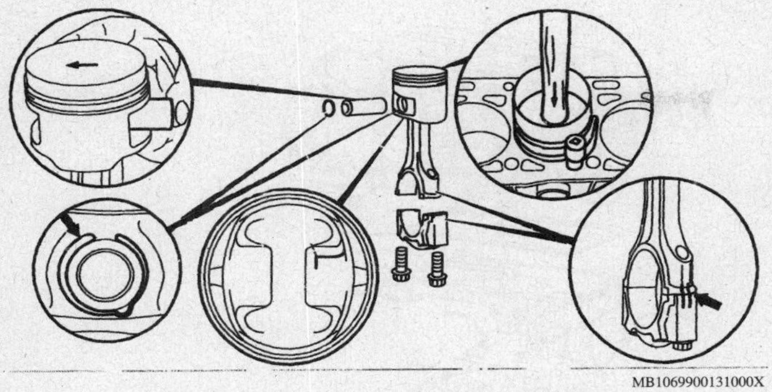

Fig. 12 Piston & rod assembly

Cylinder Bore Identification	Approved Pistons	Additional Code For Ordering Pistons
A	A or X	52 For A Pistons
X	A or X or B	54 For X Pistons
B	B or X	56 For B Pistons

Fig. 13 Piston to bore application chart

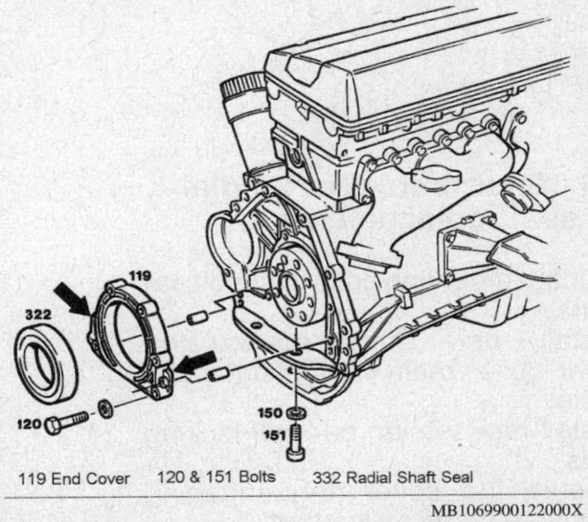

Fig. 14 End cover replacement

2. Pry out radial shaft seal using clean cloth suitable screwdriver. **Do not damage crankshaft and seal mounting hole.**

INSTALLATION

1. If bearing surface has grooves, install repair radial shaft seal with sealing lip offset .079 inch inside or press standard radial seal approximately .079 inch deeper.
2. Oil radial shaft seal sealing lip with engine oil. **Do not use grease.**
3. Install seal in insertion sleeve tool No. 601 589 03 14 00, or equivalent.
4. Install insertion sleeve so groove aligns with Woodruff key.
5. Pull seal in as far as stop using bolt and four dished washers.
6. Install belt pulley/vibration damper.

CRANKSHAFT REAR OIL SEAL

REPLACE

These procedures have been revised by a Technical Service Bulletin.

End cover with integrated radial shaft seal should be replaced with end cover with press-fitted radial shaft seal.

INTEGRATED RADIAL SHAFT SEAL

Removal

1. Remove automatic transmission.
2. Remove crankshaft/ring gear retaining lock.
3. Remove mounting bolts.
4. Remove drive plate and ring gear.
5. Remove mounting bolts and end cover, **Fig. 14.**
6. Remove plates and seal.
7. Clean sealing surface.

Installation

1. Install radial seal with sealing lip offset to inside.
2. Coat end cover sealing surface with sealant No. 001 989 45 20 10, or equivalent.
3. Coat radial shaft seal sealing lip with engine oil. **Do not use grease.**
4. Install insertion tool No 601 589 03 43 02, or equivalent, to crankshaft flange.
5. Press end cover with radial seal over insertion tool.
6. **Torque** mounting bolts (120) to 80 inch lbs., then bolts (151) to 88 inch lbs.
7. Replace drive plate mounting stretch bolts if shank diameter is less than .315 inch.
8. Replace drive plate mounting stretch bolts if shank length is more than .8859 inch.
9. Replace drive plate mounting Torx bolts.
10. Install drive plate and tighten mounting bolts to specifications.

PRESS-FITTED RADIAL SHAFT SEAL

Removal

1. Remove automatic transmission.
2. Remove crankshaft/ring gear retaining lock.
3. Remove mounting bolts.
4. Remove drive plate.
5. Pry out seal using clean cloth and suitable screwdriver, **Fig. 15.**

Installation

1. Inspect bearing surface.
2. If bearing surface has grooves, install repair version radial shaft seal with sealing lip offset .1181 inch inside.
3. Deburr mounting hole.
4. Bolt inner part of insertion tool No. 601 589 03 43 00, or equivalent, to crankshaft.
5. Coat radial shaft seal sealing lip with engine oil. **Do not use grease.**
6. Install seal and press as far as stop with outer part of insertion tool.
7. Replace drive plate mounting stretch bolts if shank diameter is less than .315 inch.
8. Replace drive plate mounting stretch bolts if shank length is more than .8859 inch.
9. Replace drive plate mounting Torx bolts.
10. Install drive plate and tighten mounting bolts to specifications.

OIL SUMP

REPLACE

1. Remove air intake scoop.
2. Remove fan cowl and bottom engine compartment cover.
3. Drain engine oil into suitable container.
4. Remove left and righthand front engine mount bolts from below.
5. Remove mounting nuts and lower torsion bar, **Fig. 16.**
6. Disconnect oil level switch and oil pressure electrical connector.
7. Remove automatic transmission and oil cooler oil lines from oil sump.
8. Remove torsion bar.
9. Raise engine far enough for cylinder head to rest against compartment wall using engine support bar tool No. 140 589 01 6100, or equivalent.
10. Remove front axle springs.
11. Remove steering coupling mounting bolt and push steering spindle up.
12. Support front axle with suitable vehicle jack.
13. Remove front axle rear mounting point plastic covers.
14. Remove front axle main mounting point bolts.
15. Lower front axle until it is hanging clear at shock absorbers and top control arms. **Do not damage hoses and lines.**
16. Remove mounting bolts, then the oil sump by pulling front axle forward and down. **Do not damage oil dipstick guide tube and oil pump stainer.**
17. Reverse procedure to install, noting the following:
    a. Align contact surface to transmission before tightening sump mounting bolts.

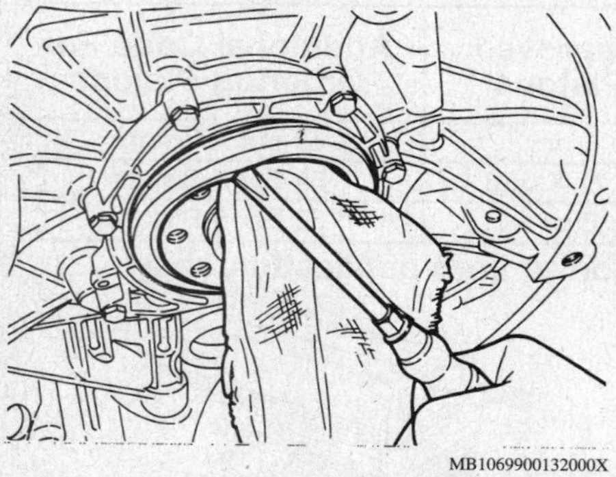

Fig. 15 Rear crankshaft radial seal replacement

b. Tighten mounting bolts to specifications.
c. Install new microencapsulated front axle main mounting point bolts.
d. Install new torsion bar self-locking nuts.
e. Ensure fan cover ring engaging point are correctly located.

OIL PUMP

REPLACE

1. Remove oil sump as outlined under "Oil Sump, Replace."
2. Remove mounting bolt and oil pump drive sprocket, **Fig. 17.**
3. Remove mounting bolts and oil pump.
4. Reverse procedure to install, noting the following:
   a. Ensure oil pump drive gear with convex face toward oil pump.
   b. Tighten mounting bolts to specifications.

OIL COOLER

REPLACE

OIL-TO-COOLANT HEAT EXCHANGER

1. Remove resonance intake manifold.
2. Remove oil filter screw cover and drain engine oil into suitable container.
3. Drain cooling system into suitable container.
4. Disconnect cooler coolant hose.
5. Disconnect line to resonance intake manifold bottom.
6. Disconnect hose from crankcase to heat exchanger.
7. Remove mounting bolts and heat exchanger.
8. Reverse procedure to install, noting the following:
   a. Clean sealing surfaces and install new gaskets.
   b. Maintain clearance between hose clips and starter solenoid switch.
   c. Ensure accelerator control linkage does not get jammed by top and bottom hose clips.
   d. Install new O-ring.

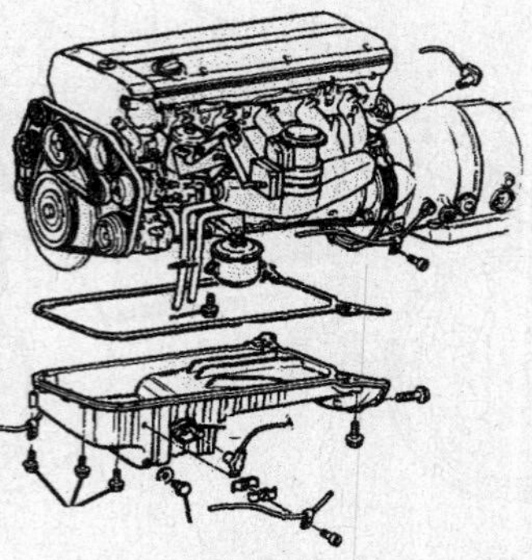

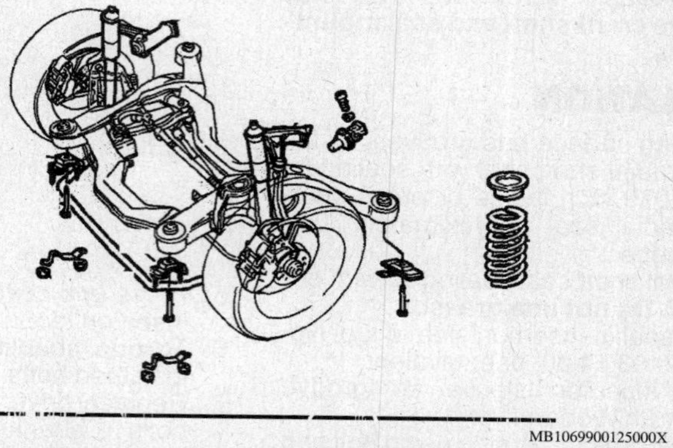

Fig. 16 Oil sump replacement

AIR-TO-OIL

1. Remove engine compartment bottom cover.
2. Remove oil lines.
3. Remove metal hold and lift cooler out from mounting points.
4. Reverse procedure to install.

BELT TENSION DATA

Belt tension is maintained by an automatic belt tensioner.

SERPENTINE DRIVE BELT

BELT, REPLACE

1. Remove viscous fan clutch.
2. Swivel tensioning pulley clockwise.
3. Remove belt.
4. Install new belt.
5. Swivel tensioning pulley clockwise at nut.

ROUTING

Refer to **Fig. 18** for serpentine belt routing. Install in numerical order.

BELT TENSIONER, REPLACE

1. Remove fan shroud and viscous fan clutch.
2. Loosen water pump pulley bolts.
3. Remove serpentine drive belt.
4. Remove water pump and tensioner pulleys.
5. Remove mounting bolt and tensioner.
6. Reverse procedure to install. Tighten mounting bolts to specifications.

COOLING SYSTEM BLEED

1. Fill cooling system to markings.
2. Turn heater to On position.
3. Warm engine at moderate RPM until thermostat opens.
4. Adjust coolant level as required.

THERMOSTAT

REPLACE

1. Drain cooling system into suitable container.
2. Remove thermostat housing mounting bolts.
3. Remove thermostat.
4. Reverse procedure to install, noting the following:
   a. Thermostat ball valve must be at highest point.
   b. Install new seal.

WATER PUMP

REPLACE

1. Drain cooling systems into suitable container.
2. Remove air cleaner.
3. Remove drive belt.
4. Remove mounting bolts and place power steering pump aside with lines attached.

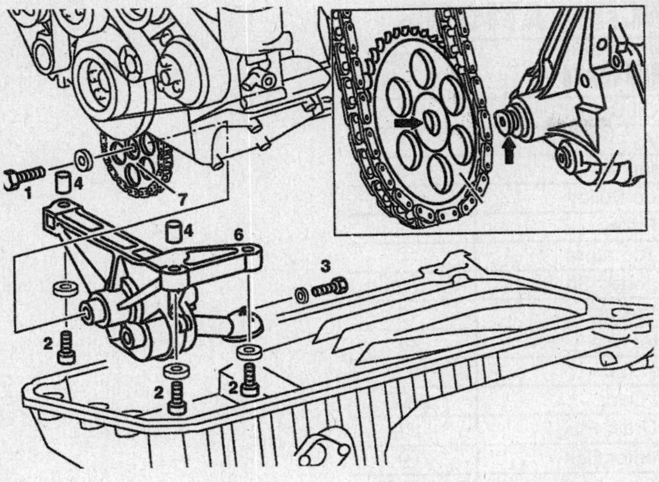

Fig. 17 Oil pump replacement

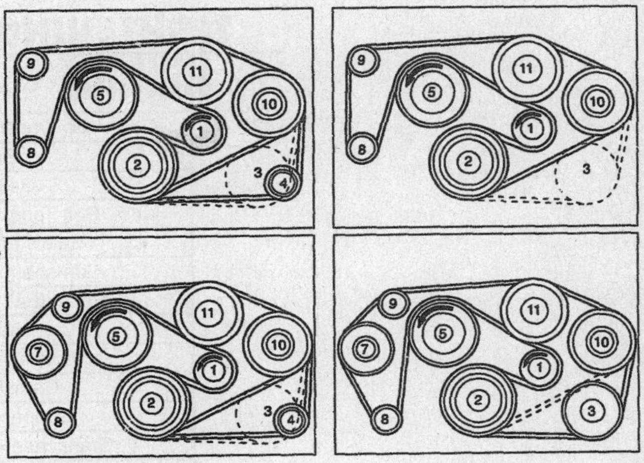

Fig. 18 Serpentine belt routing

5. Remove mounting screws and hot water return line.
6. Remove coolant line.
7. Remove mounting bolts and water pump.
8. Reverse procedure to install, noting the following:
   a. Install new seal.
   b. Tighten mounting bolts to specifications.

RADIATOR

REPLACE

1. Remove fan shroud.
2. Drain cooling system into suitable container.
3. Disconnect coolant hoses.
4. Disconnect automatic transmission oil cooler lines.
5. Remove air scoop.
6. Remove radiator plastic strips.
7. Remove radiator to condenser mounting bolt.
8. Remove radiator.
9. Reverse procedure to install, noting the following:
   a. Radiator studs must be inserted into rubber pads on bottom crossmember.
   b. Tighten mounting bolts to specifications.
   c. Adjust positioning bar by turning adjusting screw with suitable screwdriver until adjusted bar rests slightly pretensioner against upper frame crossmember.

FUEL PUMP

REPLACE

1. Relieve fuel pressure as described under "Precautions."
2. Pinch suction, delivery and degassing hoses using clamps tool Nos. 000 589 40 37 00, or equivalent.
3. Remove cap nuts.
4. Mark spacer/adapter for installation alignment.
5. Disconnect electrical connectors.
6. Remove fuel pump.
7. Reverse procedure to install. Tighten banjo bolt and cap nuts to specifications.

FUEL FILTER

REPLACE

Refer to "Fuel Pump, Replace" for fuel filter replacement.

TECHNICAL SERVICE BULLETINS

ENGINE DOES NOT START

On some of these models equipped with Brake Assist (BAS) control module, occasionally the engine may not start, the touch/start feature may not work or the engine may do into limp home mode.

This condition may be caused by moisture/corrosion in the connector or the BAS control module.

To correct this condition, proceed as follows:

1. Inspect CAN/power supply connector No. 3 for moisture and corrosion. Repair as required.
2. If condition is still present, replace BAS control module.

CHAIN TENSIONER OIL LEAK

On some of these models built before Dec. 15, 1997, there may be an oil leak at the chain tensioner.

To correct this condition, replace chain tensioner end element and sealing ring.

IRREGULAR BELT DRIVE OR COOLANT PUMP KNOCKING NOISES AT IDLE

On some of these models there may be an irregular knocking noise from the belt drive or coolant pump at idle with engine warm.

This condition may be caused by irregular belt tensioning with self-damping feature.

To correct this condition, proceed as follows:

1. Remove drive belt and idler pulley.
2. Install smaller diameter idler pulley.
3. Through clean all pulleys.
4. Ensure there is no residues on V-belt.
5. Install shorter drive belt.

OIL PUMP HOWLING OR HUMMING AFTER COLD START

1998 S320

On some of these models the oil pump may howl or hum after a cold start from idle to 2000 RPM.

This condition may be caused by the oil pump.

To correct this condition, replace the oil pump.

TIGHTENING SPECIFICATIONS

Year	Component	Torque, Ft. Lbs.
1998–99	Automatic Transmission Oil Cooler Lines	15
	Belt Pulley	⑦
	Belt Tensioner	18
	Belt Tensioner Guide Pulley	21
	Belt Tensioner Pulley	33
	Camshaft Adjuster Armature	②
	Camshaft Adjuster Flanged Shaft	15⑥
	Camshaft Bearing Cap	15
	Camshaft Adjuster Nut	48
	Camshaft Sprocket	15⑥
	Connecting Rod Caps	22③
	Crankcase Coolant Drain Plug	22
	Crankshaft Front Center Bolt	④
	Crankshaft/Ring Gear Retaining Lock	88①
	Cylinder Head	⑤
	Cylinder Head Cover	80①
	Cylinder Head Front Cover	15
	Drive Plate	33⑧
	Engine Compartment Lower Cover	18
	Engine Removal Bracket	15
	Fan	88①
	Fan Bearing Bracket	15
	Fan Belt Pulley	106①
	Fan Clutch To Bearing Housing	33
	Front Engine Mount, Lower	18
	Front Engine Mount, Upper	41
	Fuel Rail	18
	Fuel Lines	18–22
	Guide Sprocket	26
	Heat Exchanger	15
	Hose Clamps	13①
	Main Rod Bearing	41⑧
	Oil Cooler Line	22
	Oil Drain Plug	18
	Oil Pump (M6)	80①
	Oil Pump (M8)	15
	Oil Pump Sprocket	24
	Oil Sump (M6)	80①
	Oil Sump (M8)	15
	Oil Sump (M10)	30
	Power Steering Pump Pulley	24
	Propeller Shaft Clamping Nuts	22–30
	Radiator Drain Plug	13①
	Rear Engine Carrier (M8)	18
	Rear Engine Carrier (M10)	30
	Rear Engine Mount	30
	Spark Plugs	18–22
	Tensioning Device	55
	Thermostat Housing	80①
	Timing Chain Tensioner Housing	59
	Timing Chain Tensioner Screwplug	30
	Timing Case Cover (M6)	80①
	Timing Case Cover (M8)	15
	Timing Case To Oil Pan	88①
	Upper Fame Crossmember	80①
	Valve Cover	80①

Continued

TIGHTENING SPECIFICATIONS—Continued

Year	Component	Torque, Ft. Lbs.
1998–99	Vibration Damper	④
	Viscous Fan Clutch	33
	Water Hose Clips	22①
	Water Pump	18
	Water Pump Pulley	24

① — Inch lbs.
② — Bolt w/washer, 62 inch lbs.; new collar bolt, 44 inch lbs., then tighten an additional 90.°
③ — Tighten an additional 90–100.°
④ — With four dished washers, 295 ft. lbs.; w/conical washers, 273 ft. lbs.
⑤ — Refer to "Cylinder Head, Replace" for tightening specifications.
⑥ — Tighten an additional 60.°
⑦ — Less integrated hub, 24 ft. lbs.; w/integrated hub, 11 ft. lbs.
⑧ — Tighten an additional 90.°

112 V6 & 113 V8 Gasoline Engines

NOTE: On Air Bag Equipped Models, Refer To "Air Bag System Precautions" Located In The Front Of This Manual For System Disarming & Arming Procedures.

NOTE: Prior To Performing Any Service Operations Listed In This Section, Consult The "Technical Service Bulletins" Section For Related Information.

INDEX

	Page No.
Balance Shaft, Replace	5-71
Belt Tension Data	5-78
Camshaft, Replace	5-71
Installation	5-71
Removal	5-71
Compression Pressure	5-57
Cooling System Bleed	5-78
Crankshaft Damper, Replace	5-69
Crankshaft Rear Oil Seal, Replace	5-72
Installation	5-72
Removal	5-72
Crankshaft Seal, Replace	5-72
Installation	5-72
Removal	5-72
Cylinder Head, Replace	5-67
Engine Mount, Replace	5-57
Front	5-57
Lefthand	5-61
Rear	5-60
Righthand	5-61
Engine Rebuilding Specifications	5-344
Engine, Replace	5-62
C43, C280, CLK55, CLK320, CLK430, E55 & E430 & 1999–2001 SL500	5-62
E320	5-64
ML55, ML320 & ML430	5-64
S430 & 2000–01 S500	5-65
Exhaust Manifold, Replace	5-67
C43, C280, CLK55, CLK320 & CLK430	5-67
E55, E320 & E430	5-67
ML55, ML320 & ML430	5-67
S430 & 1999–2001 SL500 & 2000–01 CL500 & S500	5-67
Front Cover, Replace	5-69
Fuel Filter, Replace	5-81
ML55, ML320 & ML430	5-81
Fuel Pump, Replace	5-81
E55, E320 & E430	5-81
ML55, ML320 & ML430	5-81
S430 & 1999–2001 SL500 & 2000–01 S500	5-81
Hydraulic Lifters, Replace	5-69
Intake Manifold, Replace	5-66
Main & Rod Bearings	5-71
Main Bearings	5-71
Rod Bearings	5-72
Oil Cooler, Replace	5-78
Oil Pan, Replace	5-73
C43, C280, CLK55, CLK320 & CLK430	5-73
E320	5-75
E55 & E430	5-73
ML55, ML320 & ML430	5-75
S430 & 2000–01 S500	5-76
1999–2001 SL500	5-77
Oil Pump, Replace	5-77
Piston & Rod Assembly	5-71
Precautions	5-56
Air Bag Systems	5-56
Battery Ground Cable	5-56
Fuel Pressure Relief Procedure	5-56
Radio Coded Anti-Theft System	5-56
Radiator, Replace	5-79
C43 & C280	5-79
CLK55, CLK320 & CLK430	5-79
E55, E320 & E430	5-80
ML55, ML320 & ML430	5-80
S430 & 2000–01 S500 & 2001 CL600 & S600	5-80
1999–2001 SL500	5-80
Rocker Arms, Replace	5-69
Serpentine Drive Belt	5-78
Belt, Replace	5-78
Routing	5-78
Tensioner, Replace	5-78
Technical Service Bulletins	5-81
Drive Belt Flutters Or Bangs At Idle	5-82
Engine Cannot Be Started	5-82
Engine Does Not Start	5-81
Engine Oil Above Max. Level	5-82
Oil Leak From Lefthand Drain Opening	5-81
Oil Level Warning Lamp On	5-82
Thermostat, Replace	5-79
Tightening Specifications	5-83
Timing Chain, Replace	5-70
Timing Chain Tensioner, Replace	5-71
Valve Adjustment	5-69
Valve Cover, Replace	5-68
Water Pump, Replace	5-79

PRECAUTIONS

AIR BAG SYSTEMS

Refer to "Air Bag System Precautions" in front of this manual for system disarming and arming procedures.

BATTERY GROUND CABLE

Prior to service, disconnect battery ground cable and isolate as required.

RADIO CODED ANTI-THEFT SYSTEM

Anti-theft radios have a coded theft protection circuit. The CODE card must be obtained before disconnecting battery, removing radio fuse or removing the radio. **The serial number from the radio must match the CODE card.**

After service has been performed proceed as follows:

1. Connect radio power and turn key to position No. 2.
2. Turn radio to On position. Word "CODE" will appear on display.
3. Enter first digit of anti-theft code from CODE card. "CODE" will disappear and entered digit will appear followed by four dashes.
4. Enter next four digits, when all five are entered first digit flashes again.
5. Press SC, Seek or Tune button to confirm code.
6. If "WAIT" appears on radio panel, proceed as follows:
   a. Radio will allow three coding attempts only before entering lock-up mode and won't respond to controls.
   b. Leave radio on for 15–60 minutes, then radio will unlock and allow three addition coding attempts.
   c. Third lockout period (after nine failed coding attempts) will last 24 hours.
   d. Radio must be left on during enter 24-hour period until "CODE" appears.
7. When "CODE" appears, repeat coding attempt.

FUEL PRESSURE RELIEF PROCEDURE

1. Ensure ignition switch is in Off position.
2. Remove fuel pump protective box.
3. Disconnect fuel pump negative terminal.
4. Start engine and allow to run until it stalls from fuel starvation.

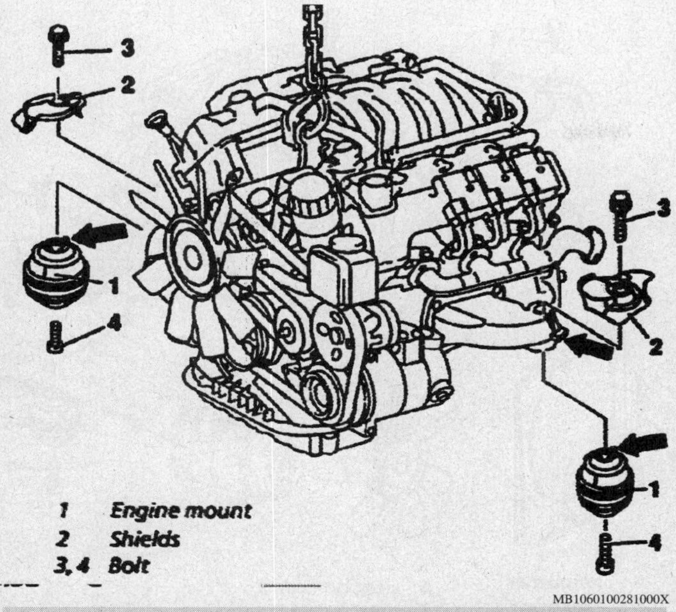

Fig. 1 Front engine mount replacement. C43, C280 & CLK320

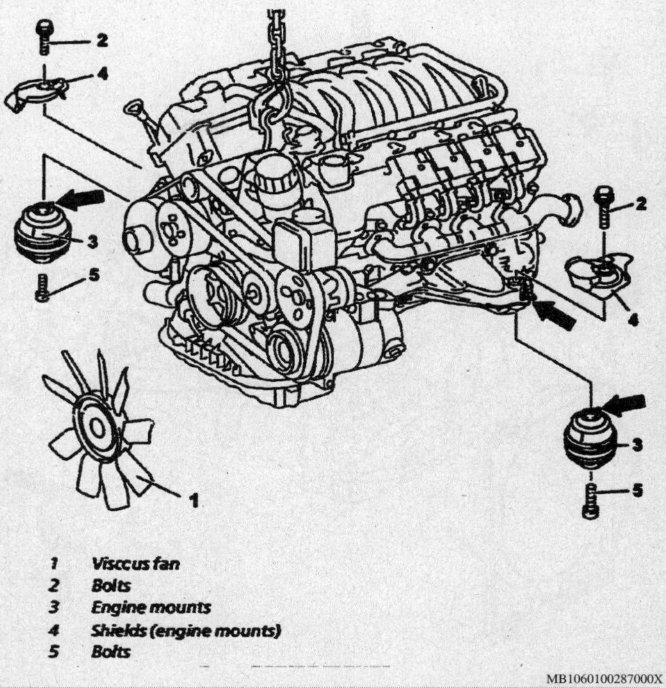

Fig. 2 Front engine mount replacement. CLK55 & CLK430

5. Crank engine to ensure pressure is released.

COMPRESSION PRESSURE

1. Warm engine to normal operating temperature (176°F).
2. Remove engine trim panel, air cleaner and resonance pipe.
3. **On ML320 and ML430 models,** remove fuse and relay module heat shield.
4. **On all models,** remove one spark plug from each cylinder.
5. Remove ignition coils.
6. Crank engine several times to eliminate cylinder combustion residues using starter motor. **Do not crank engine with ignition switch; use compression tester contact switch.**
7. Install suitable compression tester into spark plug bore.
8. Open throttle valves wide open.
9. Crank engine with starter at least eight revolutions. **Do not crank engine with ignition switch; use compression tester contact switch.**
10. Record compression readings.
11. **On C43, C280, C320, CLK320, CLK430, E320, E430, ML320, ML430, S430 and SLK320 and 1999–2001 SL500 and 2000–01 CL500 and S500 models,** compression readings should be as follows:
    a. Normal compression pressure should measure 174–203 psi.
    b. Compression wear limit is 131 psi.
12. **On C240, CL55, CLK55, E55, ML55 and S55 models,** compression readings should be as follows:
    a. Normal compression pressure should measure 159–189 psi.
    b. Compression wear limit is 145 psi.
13. **On all models,** maximum permissible difference between individual cylinders is 22 psi.

ENGINE MOUNT

REPLACE

FRONT

C43, C280 & CLK320

1. Remove engine trim panel or air cleaner off cylinder head covers.
2. If removing righthand engine mount, remove battery ground cable.
3. Support engine with suitable frame lifting device, noting the following:
    a. Two rear engine support frame supports must be seated on shock absorber supports.
    b. Two front support with rubber buffers must be seated on front panel.
4. Remove front axle carrier engine mount bolt, **Fig. 1.**
5. Remove steering shock absorber at drag link.
6. Remove drag link mounting nuts at pitman arm and relay lever. Counterhold ball stud, as required.
7. Remove drag link by pressing it off pitman arm and relay lever using suitable puller.
8. Remove relay lever shield.
9. Remove engine support bracket engine mount bolts.
10. Raise engine at front lifting eye, noting the following:
    a. Ensure engine rear does not touch body.
    b. Do not overextend coolant hoses.
    c. Do not overextend lefthand engine mount ground cable at front axle carrier.
11. Remove shields and engine mounts.
12. Reverse procedure to install, noting the following:
    a. **On C43 models,** harder engine mounts are fitted than on standard vehicles.
    b. **On all models,** anti-twist lock should be located in engine support slots.
    c. Shields' recesses should located in supports' anti-twist locks.
    d. Clean drag link tapers free of grease and press ball joints firmly into pitman arm.
    e. Install thrust piece at appropriate joint.
    f. Install new dray link self-locking nuts.
    g. Tighten mounting bolts and nuts to specifications.

CLK55 & CLK430

1. Remove engine compartment paneling.
2. Remove front axle carrier engine mount bolts, **Fig. 2.**
3. Remove engine trim panel from cylinder head covers.
4. If removing righthand engine mount, disconnect battery ground cable.
5. Remove viscous fan mounting nut while counterholding pulley socket bolts with suitable wrench. Mounting nut has righthand threads.
6. Remove fan clutch.
7. Remove Mass Air Flow (MAF) sensor with air intake pipe.

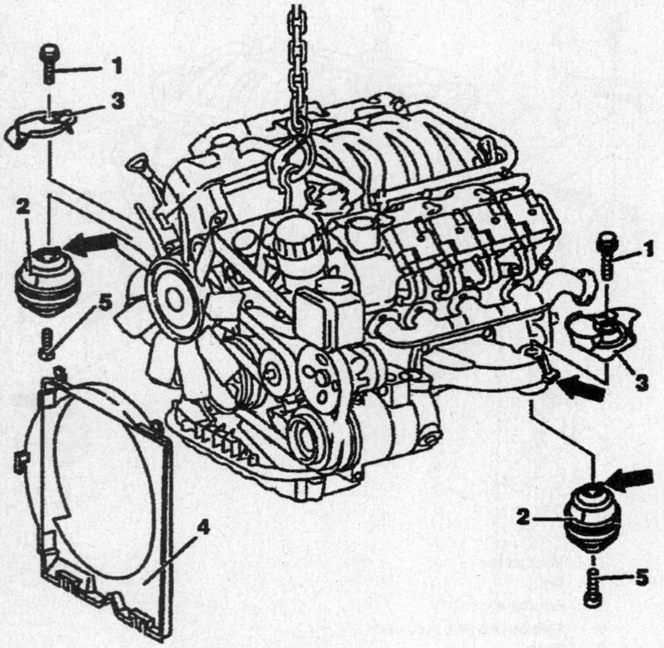

1 Bolts
2 Engine mount
3 Shields (engine mounts)
4 Fan shroud
5 Bolts

MB1060100285000X

Fig. 3 Front engine mounting replacement. E55 & E430 Less 4MATIC

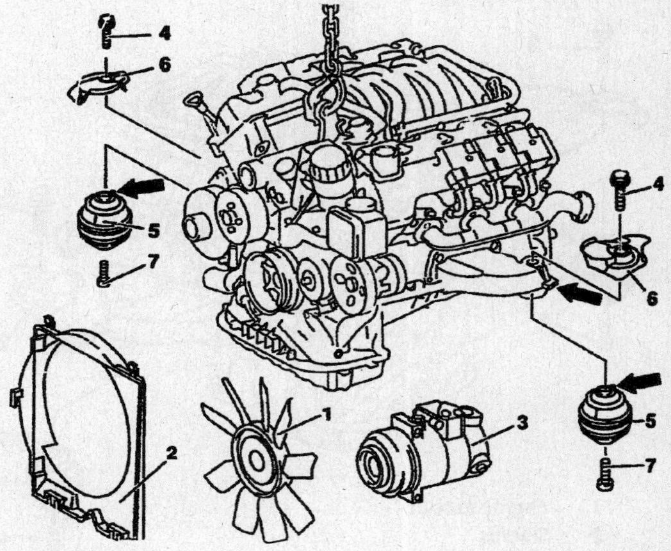

1 Viscous fan
2 Fan shroud
3 AC compressor
4 Bolts
5 Engine mounts
6 Shields (engine support)
7 Bolts

MB1060100286000X

Fig. 4 Front engine mount replacement. E320 Less 4MATIC

8. Support engine with suitable frame lifting device, noting the following:
   a. Remove specified valve position sensor.
   b. Two rear engine support frame supports must be seated on shock absorber supports.
   c. Two front support with rubber buffers must be seated on front panel.
9. Raise engine at front lifting eye, noting the following:
   a. Ensure engine rear does not touch body.
   b. Do not overextend coolant hoses.
10. Remove engine support bracket engine mount bolts.
11. Remove shields and engine mounts.
12. Reverse procedure to install, noting the following:
    a. Engine mount anti-twist locks must engage engine supports' retaining slots.
    b. Shields' recesses should located in supports' anti-twist locks.
    c. Tighten mounting bolts and nuts to specifications.

E55

1. Remove middle engine panel.
2. Remove engine support engine mount bolts, **Fig. 3.**
3. Remove engine mount shields.
4. Remove engine trim panel or air cleaner from off cylinder head covers.
5. Remove fan shroud. **Do not remove viscous fan.**
6. Install suitable bolts into shock absorber mounts from below on left and righthand sides.
7. Slide top shock absorber rubber mount with plate and screw on nut.
8. Install rear supports on engine lifting frame toll No. 140 589 01 61 00, or equivalent.
9. Install engine lifting frame. Ensure no cables or hoses are pinched.
10. Raise engine, noting the following:
    a. Ensure engine rear does not touch body.
    b. Do not overextend coolant hoses.
11. Remove front axle carrier engine mount bolts.
12. Remove engine mounts.
13. Reverse procedure to install, noting the following:
    a. Engine mount anti-twist locks must engage engine supports' retaining slots.
    b. Shields' recesses should located in supports' anti-twist locks.
    c. Tighten mounting bolts and nuts to specifications.

E320

Less 4MATIC

1. Remove engine trim panel.
2. If removing righthand engine mount, remove battery ground cable.
3. If removing lefthand engine mount, proceed as follows:
   a. Remove viscous fan mounting nut while counterholding pulley socket bolts with suitable wrench. Mounting nut has righthand threads.
   b. Remove fan clutch.
   c. Remove fan shroud.
   d. Remove serpentine drive belt.
4. Install suitable bolts into shock absorber mounts from below on left and righthand sides.
5. Slide top shock absorber rubber mount with plate and screw on nut.
6. Install rear supports on engine lifting frame toll No. 140 589 01 61 00, or equivalent.
7. Install engine lifting frame. Ensure no cables or hoses are pinched.
8. Fasten shackle with chain to two support beam tools No. 210 589 00 61 00, or equivalent, holes from front.
9. Fasten engine at rear with suitable chain in engine suspension eyes and shackle on support beam.
10. Remove engine compartment paneling.
11. If removing lefthand engine mount, remove air conditioning compressor mounting bolts. **Do not disconnect compressor refrigerant lines.**
12. Remove engine support engine mount bolts, **Fig. 4.**
13. Remove engine mount shields.
14. Raise engine. Ensure engine rear does not touch body.
15. Remove front axle engine mount bolts.
16. Remove engine mounts.
17. Reverse procedure to install, noting the following:
    a. Engine mount anti-twist locks must engage engine supports' retaining slots.
    b. Shields' recesses should located in supports' anti-twist locks.

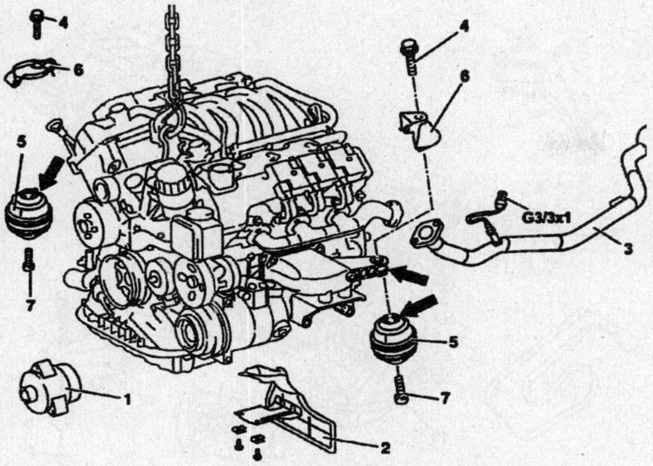

Fig. 5 Front engine mount replacement. E320 & E430 w/4MATIC

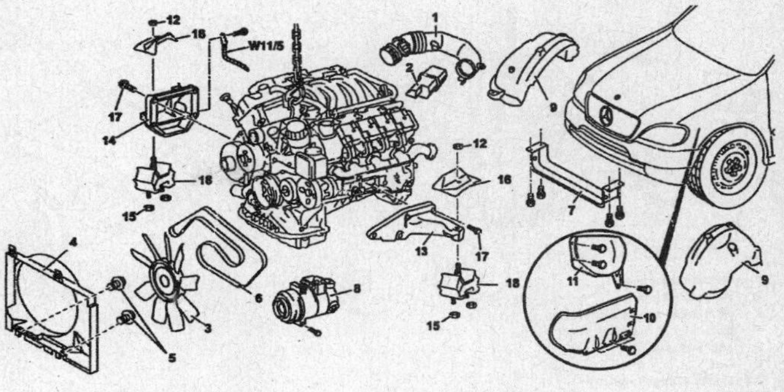

Fig. 6 Front engine mount replacement. ML55 & ML430

c. Install new engine support to crankcase mounting bolts.
d. Tighten mounting bolts and nuts to specifications.

With 4MATIC

1. If removing righthand engine mount, remove battery ground cable.
2. Remove serpentine drive belt.
3. If removing righthand engine mount, remove alternator.
4. Remove engine trim panel.
5. If removing lefthand engine mount, disconnect O2 sensor connector.
6. Remove middle engine trim panel.
7. Install suitable bolts into shock absorber mounts from below on left and righthand sides.
8. Slide top shock absorber rubber mount with plate and screw on nut.
9. Install rear supports on engine lifting frame toll No. 140 589 01 61 00, or equivalent.
10. Install engine lifting frame. Ensure no cables or hoses are pinched.
11. Fasten shackle with chain to two support beam tools No. 210 589 00 61 00, or equivalent, holes from front.
12. Fasten engine at rear with suitable chain in engine suspension eyes and shackle on support beam.
13. Remove steering shield, **Fig. 5.**
14. If removing lefthand engine mount, remove exhaust pipe.
15. Remove engine support engine mount bolts.
16. Remove engine mount shield.
17. Raise engine, noting the following:
    a. Ensure engine rear does not touch body.
    b. Do not overextend coolant hoses.
    c. Do not damage drive shaft and cup seals.
18. Remove front axle carrier engine mount bolts.
19. Remove engine mounts.
20. Reverse procedure to install, noting the following:
    a. Anti-twist lock should be located in engine support slots.
    b. Shields' recesses should located in supports' anti-twist locks.
    c. Tighten mounting bolts and nuts to specifications.

E430

Less 4MATIC

Refer to "E55".

With 4MATIC

Refer to "E320".

ML55 & ML430

1. If removing righthand engine mount, disconnect battery ground cable.
2. Remove engine trim panel.
3. Disconnect Hot Film Mass (HFM) air flow sensor and resonance pipe, **Fig. 6.**
4. **On ML430 models,** proceed as follows:
    a. Remove viscous fan mounting nut while counterholding pulley socket bolts with suitable wrench. Mounting nut has righthand threads.
    b. Remove fan clutch.
    c. If removing lefthand engine mount, remove fan shroud.
5. **On all models,** if removing lefthand engine mount, remove serpentine drive belt.
6. If removing lefthand engine mount, remove air baffle.
7. If removing lefthand engine mount, remove air conditioning compressor mounting bolt. Attach compressor to bottom of engine compartment with lines connected.
8. Remove wheelwell lines.
9. If removing lefthand engine mount, remove engine mount shields.
10. Remove engine bracket top mounting nuts.
11. If removing lefthand engine mount, press power steering hydraulic fluid line out of holder.
12. Remove engine mount nut at frame.
13. Install Kent-Moore CH6340 Baar engine support frame, or equivalent, with its supports on inner fold of left and righthand fenders.
14. Raise engine at front lifting eye, noting the following:
    a. Ensure engine does not touch body.
    b. Do not overextend coolant lines and electrical cables.
15. Remove engine mount shields.
16. If removing righthand engine mount, disconnect ground cable at righthand engine bracket.
17. Remove engine bracket at crankcase mounting bolts.
18. Remove engine brackets with mounts. Record marking and position for installation.
19. Reverse procedure to install, noting the following:
    a. Install new engine bracket to crankcase mounting bolts.
    b. Tighten mounting bolts and nuts to specifications.

ML320

1. If removing righthand engine mount, remove battery ground cable.
2. Remove wheelwell liners.
3. Remove air cleaner housing.
4. Remove viscous fan mounting nut while counterholding pulley socket bolts with suitable wrench. Mounting nut has righthand threads.
5. Remove fan clutch.
6. If removing lefthand engine mount, remove heat shield, **Fig. 7.**
7. If removing lefthand engine mount, press power steering oil line out of fixture.

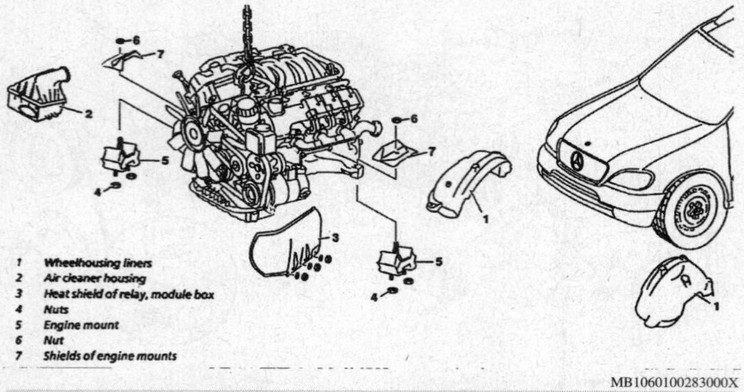

Fig. 7 Front engine mount replacement. ML320

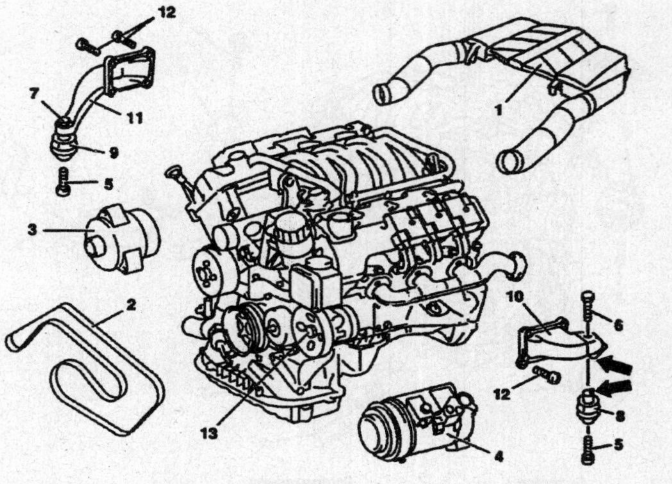

Fig. 8 Front engine mount replacement. S430 & 2000–01 S500

8. Remove engine mount nuts.
9. Support engine with Kent-Moore frame tool No. CH-6340, or equivalent. Engine support frame mounts on inner fold of left and righthand fenders.
10. Remove engine support engine mount nuts.
11. Remove engine mount shields.
12. Raise engine at front lifting eye, noting the following:
    a. Ensure engine rear does not touch body.
    b. Do not overextend coolant hoses.
    c. Do not overextend ground cable.
13. Remove engine mounts.
14. Reverse procedure to install, noting the following:
    a. Anti-twist lock should be located in engine support slots.
    b. Shields' recesses should located in supports' anti-twist locks.
    c. Tighten mounting bolts and nuts to specifications.

S430 & 2000–01 S500

Righthand

1. Disconnect battery ground cable.
2. Remove engine compartment bottom cover.
3. Remove air cleaner housing, **Fig. 8.**
4. Remove alternator.
5. Remove front axle carrier engine mount bolts. Remove both sides regardless if removing only one engine mount.
6. Disconnect engine front cover.
7. Mount Blitz M. Schneider engine bearer frame tool No. 3745-001, or equivalent, between fender fixing bolts.
8. Connect front shackle into engine lifting eye at air pump.
9. Raise engine at front lifting eye, noting the following:
    a. Ensure engine rear does not strike body.
    b. Ensure cables and hoses are not trapped.
10. Remove righthand engine supporting bracket bolt at crankcase.
11. Remove righthand engine supporting bracket engine mount bolt.
12. Remove engine mount and bracket.
13. Reverse procedure to install, noting the following:
    a. Engine mount anti-twist lock should engage engine supporting bracket slot.
    b. Install new engine bracket to crankcase mounting bolts.
    c. Tighten mounting bolts to specifications.

Lefthand

1. Remove power steering pump, **Fig. 8.**
2. Remove air conditioning compressor.
3. Disconnect battery ground cable.
4. Disconnect engine front cover.
5. Mount Blitz M. Schneider engine bearer frame tool No. 3745-001, or equivalent, between fender fixing bolts.
6. Connect front shackle into engine lifting eye at air pump.
7. Raise engine at front lifting eye, noting the following:
    a. Ensure engine rear does not strike body.
    b. Ensure cables and hoses are not trapped.
8. Remove lefthand engine supporting bracket bolt at crankcase.
9. Remove lefthand engine supporting bracket engine mount bolt.
10. Remove engine mount and bracket.
11. Reverse procedure to install, noting the following:
    a. Engine mount anti-twist lock should engage engine supporting bracket slot.
    b. Install new engine bracket to crankcase mounting bolts.
    c. Tighten mounting bolts to specifications.

SL500

1. If removing righthand engine mount, remove battery ground cable.
2. Remove engine compartment trim paneling.
3. Remove front axle carrier engine mount bolt, **Fig. 9.**
4. Remove air cleaner off cylinder head covers.
5. Remove viscous fan mounting nut while counterholding pulley socket bolts with suitable wrench. Mounting nut has righthand threads.
6. Remove fan clutch.
7. Remove Hot Film Mass (HFM) air flow sensor with air intake pipe.
8. Remove engine support engine mount bolts.
9. Support engine with suitable frame lifting device.
10. Raise engine at front lifting eye, noting the following:
    a. Ensure engine rear does not touch body.
    b. Do not overextend coolant hoses.
11. Remove shields and engine mount.
12. Reverse procedure to install, noting the following:
    a. Anti-twist lock should be located in engine support slots.
    b. Shields' recesses should located in supports' anti-twist locks.
    c. Tighten mounting bolts and nuts to specifications.

REAR

C43, C280, CLK320, CLK430, E320 & E430 & 1999–2001 SL500

1. Support transmission with suitable jack.
2. Remove mounting bolts and rear engine supporting bracket, **Fig. 10.**
3. Remove mounting bolts and rear engine mount.

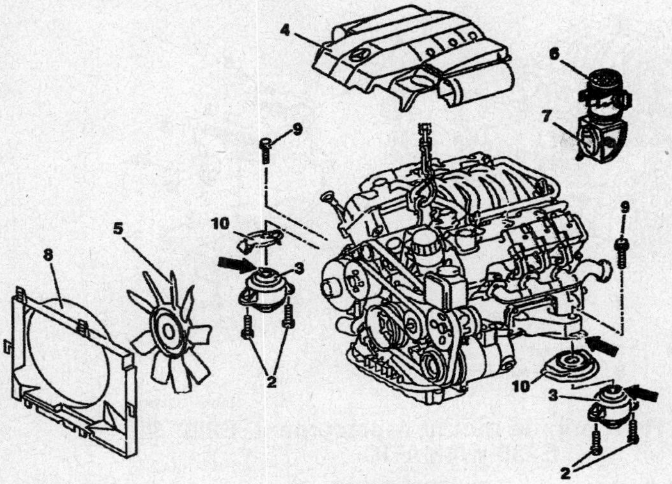

Fig. 9 Front engine mount replacement. 1999–2001 SL500

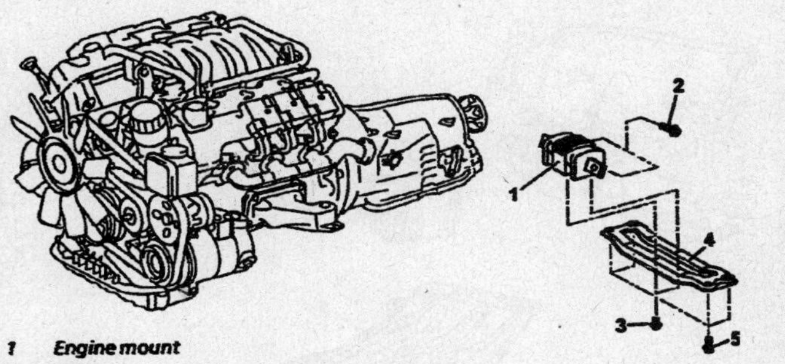

Fig. 10 Rear engine mount replacement. C43, C280, CLK320, CLK430, E320 & E430 & 1999–2001 SL500

4. Reverse procedure to install. Tighten mounting bolts and nuts to specifications.

CL600, S430, S500 & S600

1. Support transmission with suitable jack.
2. Remove mounting bolt and rear engine supporting bracket, **Fig. 11.**
3. Remove mounting bolt and rear engine mount.
4. Reverse procedure to install. Tighten mounting bolts and nuts to specifications.

E320 & E430 w/4MATIC

1. Remove rear engine support to mount bolts, **Fig. 12.**
2. Remove rear engine support to body mounting bolts.
3. Remove rear engine support.
4. Remove rear engine mount bolts.
5. Remove rear engine mount with brackets.
6. Reverse procedure to install, noting the following:
   a. Anti-twist locks must be located in engine mount recesses.
   b. Tighten mounting bolts and nuts to specifications.

RIGHTHAND

C43, C280, CLK55, CLK320, CLK430, E55 & E430

1. **On C43, C280, CLK55, CLK320 and CLK430 models,** remove engine compartment bottom cover.
2. **On all models,** remove front engine mounts.
3. Remove engine support to crankcase mounting bolt, **Figs. 13 and 14.**
4. Remove righthand engine support.
5. Reverse procedure to install, noting the following:
   a. Install new mounting bolt.
   b. Do not jam electrical cables between engine support and crankcase.
   c. Tighten mounting bolt to specifications.

E320

Less 4MATIC

Refer to "C43, C280, CLK55, CLK320, CLK430, E55 & E430."

With 4MATIC

1. Remove front engine mounts.
2. Remove shield, **Fig. 15.**
3. Remove front drive gear.
4. Remove engine support to crankcase mounting bolt.
5. Remove engine support.
6. Reverse procedure to install, noting the following:
   a. Install new support to crankcase mounting bolt.
   b. Tighten mounting bolts to specifications.

ML320

1. Remove front engine mounts.
2. Remove engine support to crankcase mounting bolt, **Fig. 16.**
3. Remove engine support. **Do not damage alternator housing.**
4. Reverse procedure to install, noting the following:
   a. Install new mounting bolt.
   b. Do not jam electrical cables between engine support and crankcase.
   c. Tighten mounting bolt to specifications.

SL500

1. Remove front engine mounts.
2. Remove serpentine drive belt.
3. Remove alternator mounting bolt.
4. Remove engine support to crankcase mounting bolt, **Fig. 17.**
5. Remove engine support.
6. Reverse procedure to install.
   a. Install new support to crankcase mounting bolt.
   b. Tighten mounting bolts to specifications.

LEFTHAND

C43, C280, CLK55, CLK320 & CLK430

1. Disconnect fan motor and remove fan shroud.
2. Remove serpentine drive belt.
3. Remove engine compartment bottom cover.
4. Remove front engine mounts.
5. **On CLK320 models,** disconnect ATF line fixture at oil pan.
6. **On all models,** remove air conditioning compressor mounting bolt, **Fig. 18.** Attach compressor to engine compartment bottom with lines connected.
7. Remove ground cable mounting bolt at engine support.
8. Remove engine support to crankcase mounting bolt.
9. Remove lefthand engine support.
10. Reverse procedure to install, noting the following:
    a. Install new mounting bolt.
    b. Do not jam electrical cables between engine support and crankcase.
    c. Tighten mounting bolt to specifications.

E55 & E430

1. Remove front engine mounts.
2. Remove serpentine drive belt.
3. Remove air conditioning compressor mounting bolt, **Fig. 19.** Attach compressor to engine compartment bottom with lines and cables connected.
4. Remove engine support to crankcase mounting bolt.
5. Remove engine support with bracket.
6. Remove mounting bolt and bracket.
7. Reverse procedure to install, noting the following:
   a. Install new support to crankcase mounting bolt.

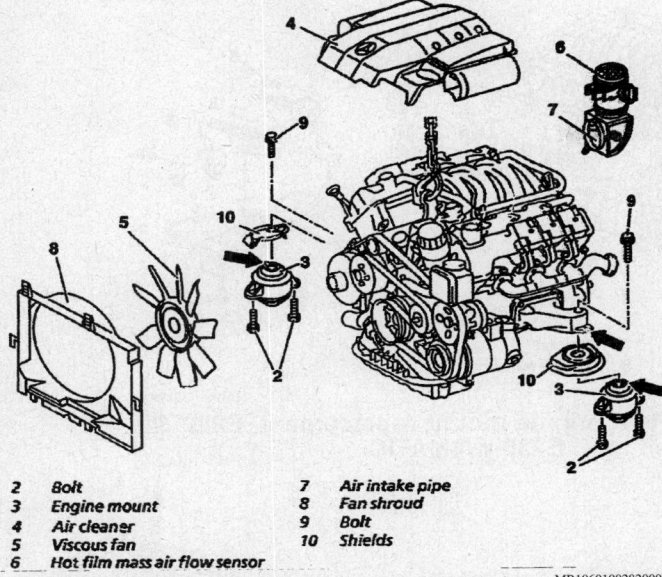

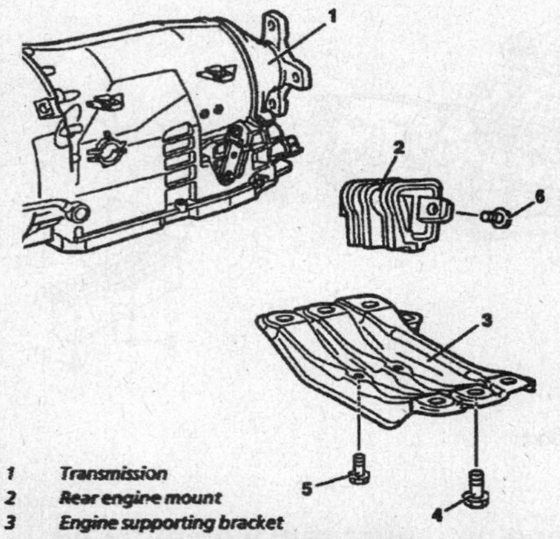

Fig. 11 Rear engine mount replacement. CL600, S430, S500 & S600

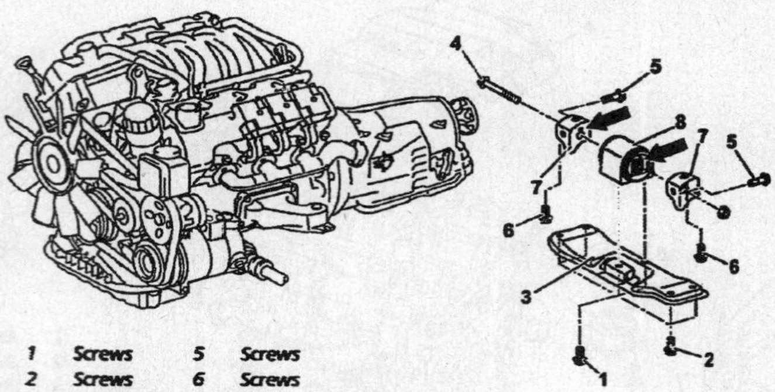

Fig. 12 Rear engine mount replacement. E320 & E430 w/4MATIC

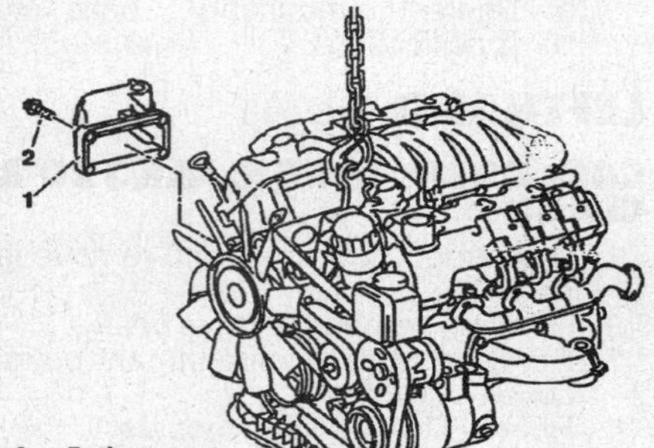

Fig. 13 Righthand engine support replacement. C43, C280, CLK55, CLK320 & CLK430 & E320 Less 4MATIC

   b. Tighten mounting bolts to specifications.

E320

Less 4MATIC

1. Remove front engine mounts.
2. Remove engine support to crankcase mounting bolt, **Fig. 18.**
3. Remove lefthand engine support.
4. Reverse procedure to install, noting the following:
   a. Install new mounting bolt.
   b. Tighten mounting bolt to specifications.

With 4MATIC

1. Remove front engine mounts.
2. Remove serpentine drive belt.
3. Remove air conditioning compressor mounting bolt, **Fig. 20.** Attach compressor to engine compartment bottom with lines and cables connected.
4. Remove retaining bracket to engine oil pan mounting bolt.
5. Remove engine support to crankcase

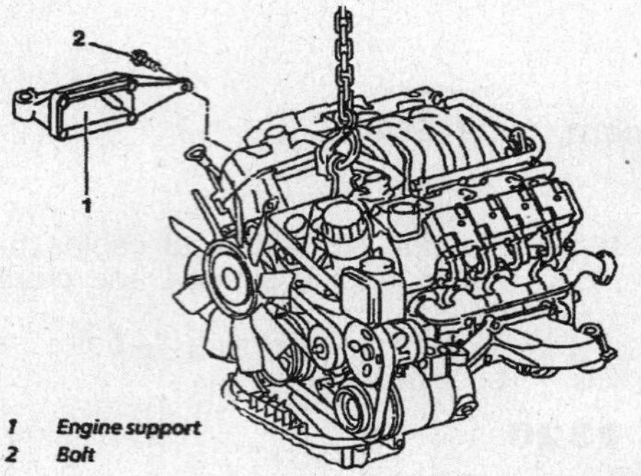

Fig. 14 Righthand engine support replacement. E55 & E430

mounting bolt.
6. Remove engine support with bracket.
7. Remove mounting bolt and bracket.
8. Reverse procedure to install, noting the following:
   a. Install new support to crankcase mounting bolt.
   b. Tighten mounting bolts to specifications.

ML320

1. Remove front engine mounts.
2. Remove serpentine drive belt.
3. Remove air conditioning compressor mounting bolt, **Fig. 21.** Attach compressor to engine compartment bottom with lines connected.
4. Remove engine support to crankcase mounting bolt.
5. Remove lefthand engine support.
6. Reverse procedure to install, noting the following:
   a. Install new mounting bolt.
   b. Tighten mounting bolt to specifications.

SL500

1. Remove front engine mounts.
2. Remove serpentine drive belt.
3. Remove air conditioning compressor mounting bolt, **Fig. 22.** Attach compressor to engine compartment bottom with lines and cables connected.
4. Remove engine support to crankcase

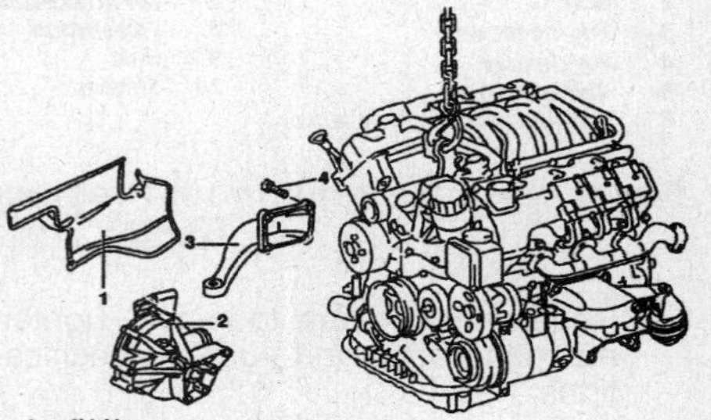

Fig. 15 Righthand engine support replacement. E320 w/4MATIC

mounting bolt.
5. Remove engine support.
6. Reverse procedure to install.
   a. Install new support to crankcase mounting bolt.
   b. Tighten mounting bolts to specifications.

ENGINE

REPLACE

C43, C280, CLK55, CLK320, CLK430, E55 & E430 & 1999–2001 SL500

This procedure has been revised by a Technical Service Bulletin.

1. Remove engine trim panel or air cleaner from cylinder head covers.
2. Inspect engine rear lifting eyes. Replace eyes that are stamped with Mercedes emblem and two digit number.
3. Remove engine compartment paneling.
4. Drain radiator coolant into suitable container.
5. Drain engine oil into suitable container.
6. Disconnect automatic transmission oil lines. Seal and plug connections and openings.
7. **On C43, C280, CLK55, CLK430, E55 and E430 and 1999–2001 SL500 models,** remove viscous fan mounting

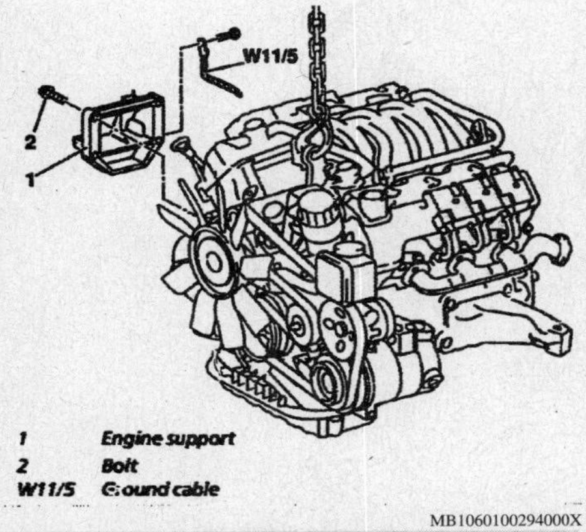

Fig. 16 Righthand engine support replacement. ML320

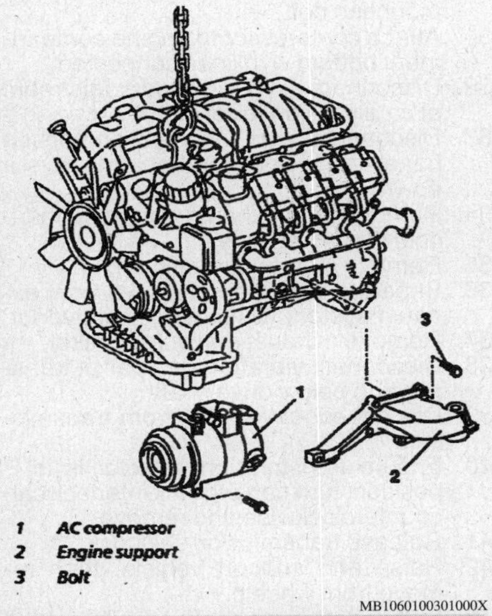

Fig. 19 Lefthand engine support replacement. E55 & E430

nut while counterholding pulley socket bolts with suitable wrench. Mounting nut has righthand threads.

8. **On all models,** disconnect fan connector and remove shroud.
9. **On C280, CLK320 and E430 models,** proceed as follows:
   a. Remove air cleaner housing
   b. Disconnect Hot Film Mass (HFM) air flow sensor.
   c. Remove resonance pipe to cylinder head mounting bolt.
   d. Remove resonance piper with body. **Do not damage plastic plate.**
10. **On C43, CLK55, CLK430 and E55 and 1999–2001 SL500 models,** remove Hot Film Mass (HFM) air flow sensor with air intake pipe.
11. **On all models,** disconnect water pump and thermostat housing coolant hoses.
12. **On C43, C280, CLK55, CLK320 and CLK430 models,** disconnect expansion reservoir top hose.

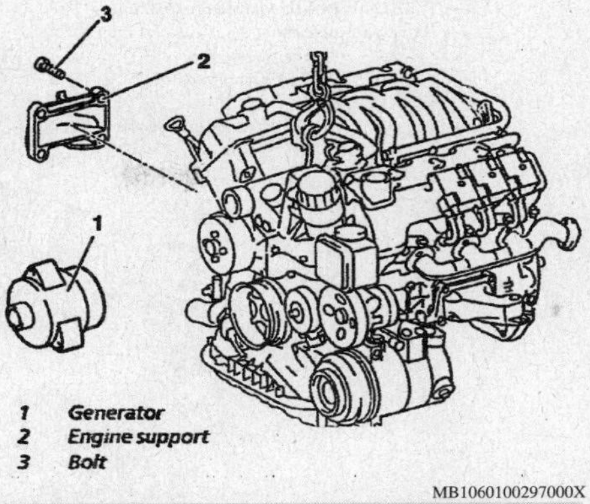

Fig. 17 Righthand engine support replacement. 1999–2001 SL500

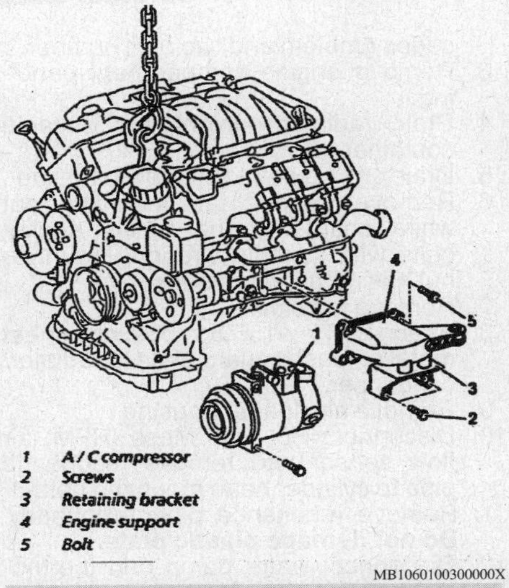

Fig. 20 Lefthand engine support replacement. E320 w/4MATIC

13. **On all models,** remove radiator.
14. Attach 15.75 x 26.77 x .039-inch sheet metal or plastic guard plate to condenser.
15. Disconnect brake servo vacuum line at rear of intake manifold.
16. Remove power steering pump fluid with suitable handpump.
17. Disconnect power steering pump oil lines. Seal and plug connections and openings.
18. Disconnect automatic transmission and power steering pump lines from oil pan.
19. Disconnect purge control valve vacuum hose.
20. Relieve fuel pressure as outlined under “Precautions.”
21. Disconnect fuel rail fuel line.
22. Disconnect heater hose at firewall.
23. Remove control module box cover.
24. Disconnect vacuum distributor gray hose next to control module box.
25. Remove engine management control module by pulling locking bar up and disconnecting connectors.
26. **On E55, E320 and E430 models,** disconnect control module box connectors.

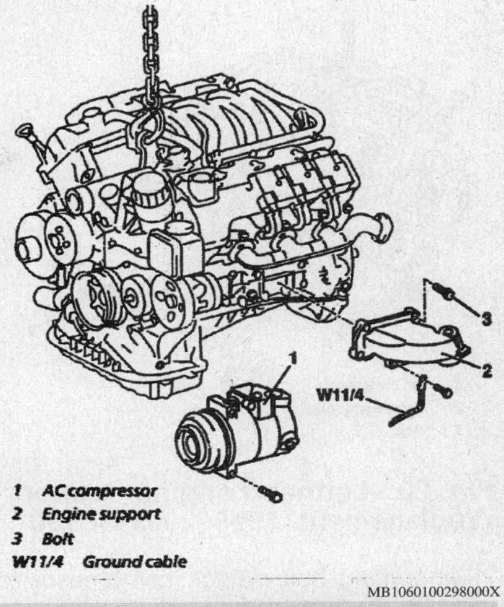

Fig. 18 Lefthand engine support replacement. C43, C280, CLK55, CLK320 & CLK430 & E320 less 4MATIC

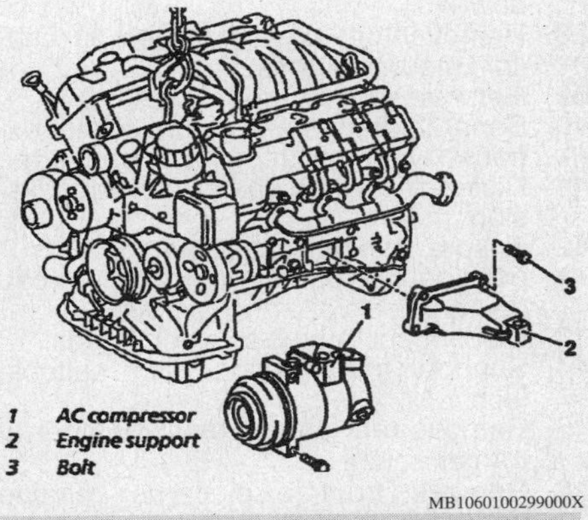

Fig. 21 Lefthand engine support replacement. ML320

27. **On all models,** disconnect alternator wiring harness.
28. **On E55, E320 and E430 models,** remove block mounting bolt in righthand footwell by removing cable cover and pulling protective cap off.
29. **On C43, C280, CLK55, CLK320 and CLK430 and 1999–2001 SL500 models,** remove terminal block mounting bolt in lefthand footwell by remove cable cover and pulling protective cap off.
30. **On all models,** remove heat shield and disconnect automatic transmission central connector.
31. Remove floor mounting bolt and engine ground strap.
32. Remove engine wiring harness.
33. Remove serpentine drive belt.
34. Disconnect air conditioning compressor connector.
35. Remove air conditioning compressor

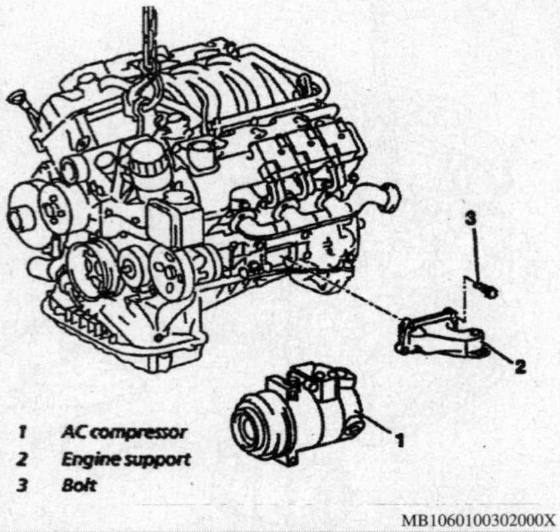

Fig. 22 Lefthand engine support replacement. 1999–2001 SL500

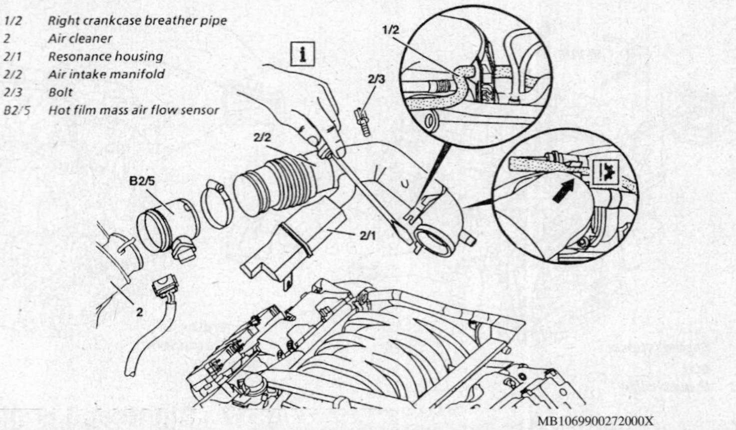

Fig. 23 HFM air flow sensor replacement. C280, CLK320, E320, E430 & ML320

mounting bolt. Attach compressor to engine compartment bottom with lines connected.

36. Disconnect oxygen sensors upstream of catalytic converter.
37. Disconnect front suspension torsion bar at frame side member and swivel it down.
38. Remove front exhaust system to manifold mounting bolts.
39. Remove support mounting nuts.
40. Separate flange and remove front exhaust system with catalytic converter.
41. Disconnect drive shaft from transmission.
42. Ensure transmission selector is in P position, turn parking lock interlock cab counterclockwise and remove.
43. Disconnect transmission shift rods.
44. Support transmission with suitable jack.
45. Remove rear engine crossmember at transmission.
46. Remove front axle carrier engine mount bolts.
47. **On 1999–2001 SL500 models,** press level control pressure line out of oil pan fixture.
48. **On CLK55, CLK320, CLK430, E55 and E430 models,** install suitable engine removal fixture.
49. **On all models,** attach suitable engine hoist to lifting eyes.
50. Lower engine rear and remove.
51. Reverse procedure to install, noting the following:
    a. Install new exhaust system bracket and support mounting nuts.
    b. Tighten mounting bolts and nuts to specifications.

E320

Less 4MATIC

Refer to "C43, C280, CLK55, CLK320, CLK430, E55 & E430 & 1999–2001 SL500."

With 4MATIC

This procedure has been revised by a Technical Service Bulletin.

1. Remove engine trim panel.
2. Inspect engine rear lifting eyes. Replace eyes that are stamped with Mercedes emblem and two digit number.
3. Remove engine compartment paneling.
4. Drain radiator coolant into suitable container.
5. Drain engine oil into suitable container.
6. Remove viscous fan mounting nut while counterholding pulley socket bolts with suitable wrench. Mounting nut has righthand threads.
7. Remove fan clutch.
8. Attach 26.77 x 15.75 x .039 inch sheet metal or plastic guard plate to radiator/condenser.
9. Remove air cleaner housing.
10. Disconnect Hot Film Mass (HFM) air flow sensor and remove resonance pipe to cylinder head mounting bolt.
11. Remove resonance piper with body. **Do not damage plastic plate.**
12. Disconnect water pump and thermostat housing coolant hoses.
13. Remove power steering pump fluid with suitable handpump.
14. Disconnect power steering pump lines. Plug openings.
15. Disconnect brake servo vacuum line at rear or intake manifold rear.
16. Relieve fuel pressure as described under "Precautions."
17. Remove fuel rail fuel line.
18. Disconnect heater hose at firewall.
19. Disconnect ground cable.
20. Remove control module box trim panel.
21. Disconnect vacuum line at rear of intake manifold.
22. Release locking bar and disconnect control module connector.
23. Disconnect relay module connector.
24. Remove ground cable mounting bolt next to control module box.
25. Disconnect cable cover, pull off protective cap and remove terminal block mounting bolt in righthand footwell.
26. Remove heat shield and disconnect automatic transmission central connector.
27. Remove engine ground and remove wiring harness.
28. Remove serpentine drive belt.
29. Disconnect automatic transmission oil lines. Plug and seal connections and openings.
30. Remove air conditioning compressor mounting bolt.
31. Attach compressor to engine compartment bottom with lines connected.
32. Disconnect oxygen sensors upstream of catalytic converter.
33. Disconnect front suspension torsion bar at frame side member and swivel it down.
34. Remove front exhaust system to manifold mounting bolts.
35. Remove support mounting nuts.
36. Separate flange and remove front exhaust system with catalytic converter.
37. Remove exhaust manifold bracket.
38. Disconnect vibration damper at transmission below drive shaft.
39. Disconnect drive shaft from transmission.
40. Ensure transmission selector is in P position, turn parking lock interlock cab counterclockwise and remove.
41. Release transmission shift lock.
42. Raise and support vehicle, then remove front wheels.
43. Disconnect input shafts from front axle gear and remove. **Do not damage seals.**
44. Support transmission and remove engine crossmember as described under "Engine Mount, Replace."
45. Remove front axle carrier front engine mount bolts.
46. Disconnect air conditioning compressor electrical connector.
47. Disconnect power steering pump ground cable.
48. Attach suitable engine hoist to engine lifting eyes.
49. Lower engine to rear and lift out.
50. Reverse procedure to install, noting the following:
    a. Tighten mounting bolts and nuts to specifications.
    b. Install new exhaust manifold bracket nuts.
    c. Install new torsion bar bolts.

ML55, ML320 & ML430

This procedure has been revised by a Technical Service Bulletin.

1. Remove engine trim panel.
2. Inspect engine rear lifting eyes. Replace eyes that are stamped with Mercedes emblem and two digit number.

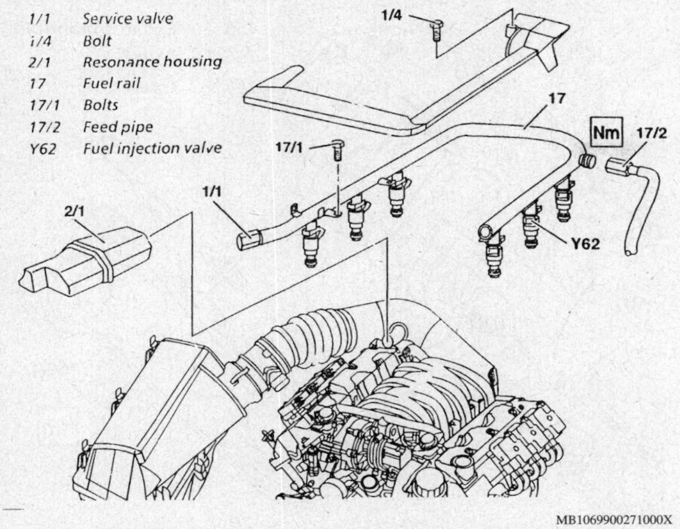

Fig. 24 Fuel injection rail replacement.

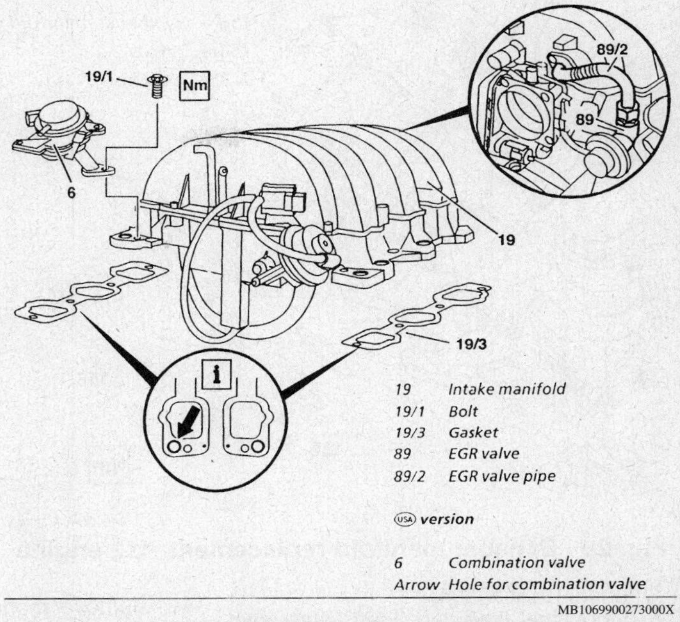

Fig. 25 Intake manifold replacement

3. **On ML430 models,** remove air baffle.
4. **On all models,** drain cooling system into suitable container.
5. Drain engine oil into suitable container.
6. **On ML320 and ML430 models,** remove viscous fan mounting nut while counterholding pulley socket bolts with suitable wrench. Mounting nut has righthand threads.
7. **On all models,** disconnect fan connector and remove shroud .
8. Attach 15.75 x 26.77 x .039-inch sheet metal or plastic guard plate to condenser.
9. Remove coolant expansion reservoir.
10. Remove air cleaner housing
11. Disconnect Hot Film Mass (HFM) air flow sensor and remove resonance pipe to cylinder head mounting bolt.
12. Remove resonance piper with body. **Do not damage plastic plate.**
13. Disconnect water pump and thermostat housing coolant hoses.
14. **On ML55 and ML430 models,** remove radiator.
15. **On all models,** disconnect brake servo vacuum line at intake manifold rear.
16. Remove power steering pump fluid with suitable handpump.
17. Disconnect power steering pump lines. Seal and plug connections and openings.
18. Disconnect purge control valve vacuum hose.
19. Relieve fuel pressure as described under "Precautions."
20. Disconnect fuel line.
21. Disconnect heater hose at cylinder head rear.
22. Disconnect ground cable.
23. Disconnect alternator and battery positive cables.
24. Disconnect positive cable fixture next to water pump.
25. Disconnect relay module fuse connector.
26. Release locking arm and disconnect control module connector.
27. Remove engine to frame ground cable mounting bolt.
28. Remove serpentine drive belt.
29. Disconnect air conditioning compressor connector.
30. Remove air conditioning compressor mounting bolt. Attach compressor to engine compartment bottom with lines and cables connected.
31. **On ML55 and ML430 models,** remove wheelwell liner and heat shield.
32. **On all models,** raise and support front suspension.
33. Remove front spring.
34. Disconnect oxygen sensor connectors.
35. Loosen clips and disconnect front from rear exhaust system.
36. Remove exhaust system support mounting nuts.
37. Remove exhaust system to manifold mounting bolts.
38. Remove front exhaust system with catalytic converters.
39. Support exhaust system and remove bracket.
40. Remove torque converter mounting bolts from starter ring gear.
41. Disconnect oxygen sensor connectors as transmission.
42. Remove starter mounting bolts. **Do not disconnect electrical cables.**
43. Remove transmission bell housing mounting bolts, noting the following:
    a. **On ML320 models,**do not loosen top two bolts now.
    b. **On ML55 and ML430 models,** do not loosen two bottom bolts now.
44. **On all models,** remove engine mount nuts. Before remove lefthand mount, press power steering oil line out of fixture.
45. Remove automatic transmission oil filler pipe mounting bolt from righthand cylinder head.
46. Attach suitable engine hoist to lifting eyes with suitable fixture.
47. Raise engine. Ensure engine and parts do not touch body.
48. Install suitable transmission support on crossmember and into transmission recess.
49. Remove remaining two transmission bell housing mounting bolts.
50. Ensure engine does not strike radiator or condenser.
51. Remove engine.
52. Reverse procedure to install, noting the following:
    a. Ensure torque converter aligns with three starter ring gear recesses.
    b. Install new exhaust system bracket and support mounting nuts.
    c. Tighten mounting bolts and nuts to specifications.

S430 & 2000-01 S500

This procedure has been revised by a Technical Service Bulletin.

1. Inspect engine rear lifting eyes. Replace eyes that are stamped with Mercedes emblem and two digit number.
2. Remove engine compartment bottom panel.
3. Drain radiator coolant into suitable container.
4. Drain engine oil into suitable container.
5. Disconnect engine front cover.
6. Remove air cleaner housing with intake pipes.
7. Remove shroud and fan.
8. Attach 26.77 x 15.75 x .039 inch sheet metal or plastic guard plate to radiator/ condenser.
9. Disconnect water pump hoses.
10. Disconnect thermostat and expansion reservoir hoses.
11. Disconnect brake booster vacuum line at rear of intake manifold.
12. Remove power steering pump oil into suitable container.
13. Disconnect purge control valve vacuum line.
14. Relieve fuel pressure as described

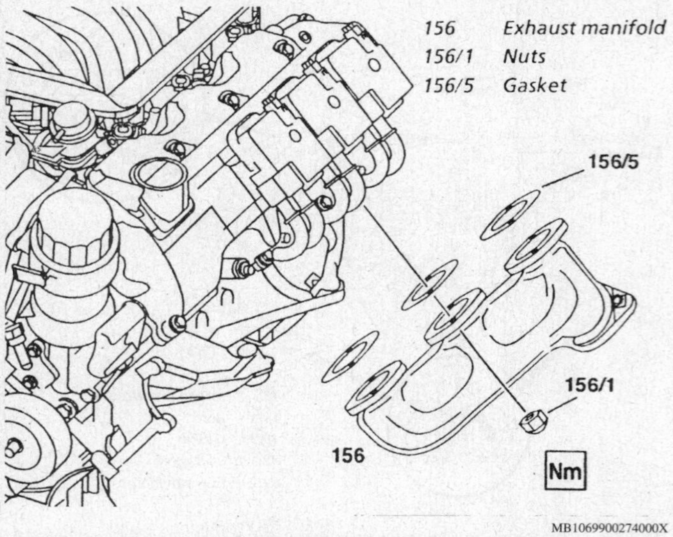

Fig. 26 Exhaust manifold replacement. 112 engine

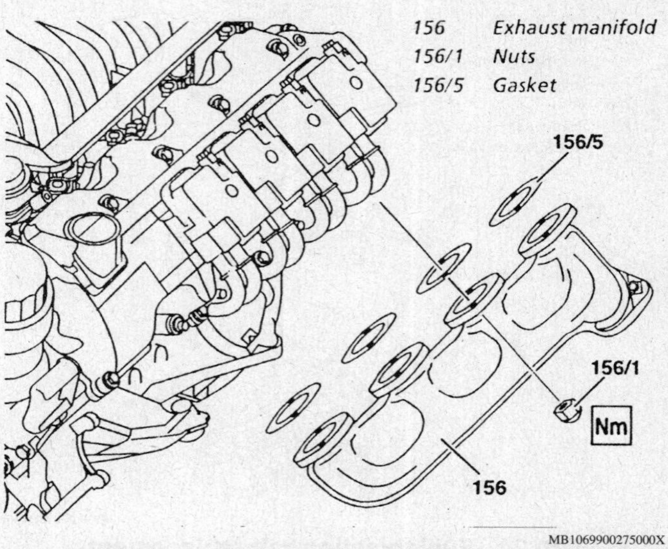

Fig. 27 Exhaust manifold replacement. 113 engine

under "Precautions."
15. Open fuel filler cap, then disconnect fuel line.
16. Disconnect firewall heater hose.
17. Remove righthand front relay module cover.
18. Release locking arm and disconnect control module connectors.
19. Disconnect relay module connectors.
20. Disconnect fuse carrier from relay module.
21. Disconnect ground cable from suspension tower.
22. Disconnect ground cable at power steering pump.
23. Remove heat shield and open protective cap, then remove terminal block wiring harness mounting bolt on outside of righthand footwell.
24. Remove heat shield and disconnect automatic transmission electrical connector.
25. Disconnect transmission ground attached to rear engine mount.
26. Remove wiring harness.
27. Remove serpentine drive belt.
28. Disconnect ATF lines. Plug openings.
29. Disconnect air conditioning compressor connection.
30. Remove compressor mounting bolt.
31. Attach compressor to engine compartment bottom with lines connected.
32. Support rear exhaust system.
33. Disconnect oxygen sensors connectors.
34. Remove front/rear exhaust system flanged connection mounting bolts and nuts.
35. Remove front exhaust system to exhaust manifold mounting bolts.
36. Remove front exhaust system to bracket mounting nuts.
37. Remove catalytic converters/front exhaust system.
38. Remove transmission exhaust bracket.
39. Disconnect transmission shift rod.
40. Remove rear engine crossmember as described under "Engine Mount, Replace."
41. Remove mounting bolts and disconnect driveshaft from transmission.
42. Remove front axle carrier engine mount bolts as described under "Engine Mount, Replace."
43. Attach suitable engine lifting hoist to lifting eyes.
44. Lower engine at rear and remove. **Ensure engine rear does not touch firewall.**
45. Reverse procedure to install, noting the following.
    a. Install new front exhaust system to bracket mounting nuts.
    b. Tighten mounting bolts and nuts to specifications.

INTAKE MANIFOLD

REPLACE

This procedure has been revised by a Technical Service Bulletin.

1. **On S430 and 1999–2001 SL500 and 2000–01 CL500 and S500 models,** remove engine front end trim panel.
2. **On all models,** remove engine trim panel or air cleaner from cylinder head covers.
3. **On C280, CLK320, E320, E430 and ML320 models,** proceed as follows:
    a. Remove air intake pipe accelerator actuator lock using suitable screwdriver to press catch down, **Fig. 23.**
    b. Remove righthand crankcase ventilation line.
    c. Remove air cleaner.
    d. Remove resonance housing.
    e. Remove air intake pipe.
    f. Disconnect electrical connector and remove Hot Film Mass (HFM) air flow sensor.
4. **On S430 and 1999–2001 SL500 and 2000–01 CL500 and S500 models,** proceed as follows:
    a. Remove air filter with intake pipes.
    b. Disconnect Hot Film Mass (HFM) air flow sensor electrical connector.
    c. Disconnect crankcase vent hose from air intake pipe.
    d. Disconnect electronic accelerator actuator cable.
    e. Remove HFM air flow sensor by pressing lug down with suitable screwdriver.
5. **On ML55 and ML430 models,** proceed as follows:
    a. Open expansion reservoir cap and relieve pressure.
    b. Remove expansion reservoir overflow hose.
    c. Remove expansion reservoir coolant lines. Collect coolant in suitable container.
    d. Disconnect expansion reservoir.
    e. Disconnect expansion reservoir electrical connector.
    f. Remove expansion reservoir.
    g. Remove crankcase ventilation vacuum hose.
    h. Remove air intake pipe to cylinder head cover mounting bolt.
    i. Remove Mass Air Flow (MAF) sensor mounting bolt.
    j. Disconnect air intake pipe by pressing lock down with suitable screwdriver.
    k. Remove resonance housing.
    l. Disconnect electrical connector and remove air intake pipe from hot film MAF sensor.
6. **On all models,** remove valve covers as outlined under "Valve Cover, Replace."
7. Remove plastic cover and relieve fuel pressure through service valve as outlined under "Precautions,", **Fig. 24.**
8. Disconnect fuel line and injection valve electrical connector.
9. Remove mounting bolts and fuel rail with injectors.
10. Disconnect vacuum lines and electrical connectors.
11. Remove EGR valve line union nut, **Fig. 25.** Counterhold connection when loosening.
12. Remove mounting bolts and combination valves.

13. Remove mounting bolts and intake manifold
14. Reverse order to install, noting the following:
    a. Align gaskets with stud bolts.
    b. Replace injector O-rings as required.
    c. Oil O-rings before installing fuel rail.
    d. Tighten mounting bolts to specifications.

EXHAUST MANIFOLD

REPLACE

C43, C280, CLK55, CLK320 & CLK430

1. Disconnect oxygen sensors.
2. Remove exhaust system.
3. If removing righthand exhaust manifold, remove air cleaner.
4. Remove ignition coils.
5. If removing lefthand exhaust manifold, remove washer fluid reservoir and loosen front axle carrier lefthand engine mount bolt.
6. Remove mounting nuts, **Figs. 26 and 27.**
7. lefthand front engine mount mounting bolts when removing lefthand exhaust manifold, **Figs. 26.**
8. If removing lefthand exhaust manifold, push engine to right, then pull manifold up and out.
9. If removing righthand exhaust manifold, remove downward.
10. Reverse procedure to install, noting the following:
    a. Install new gaskets.
    b. Tighten new mounting nuts to specifications.

E55, E320 & E430

1. Disconnect oxygen sensor connector.
2. Remove exhaust system.
3. Remove air cleaner.
4. If removing righthand exhaust manifold, remove water circulation pump and place aside.
5. Remove ignition coils.
6. Remove mounting nuts and exhaust manifold, **Figs. 26 and 27.**
7. Reverse procedure to install, noting the following:
    a. Install new gaskets.
    b. Tighten new mounting nuts to specifications.

ML55, ML320 & ML430

1. Remove front tire and wheel assemblies.
2. Remove wheelwell liners.
3. If removing lefthand exhaust manifold, remove shield.
4. Remove exhaust system flanged connection mounting bolts.
5. Remove front exhaust pipe transmission bracket.
6. Remove mounting nuts and exhaust manifold.
7. Reverse procedure to install, noting the following:
    a. Install new gaskets.
    b. Install new front exhaust pipe transmission bracket nuts.

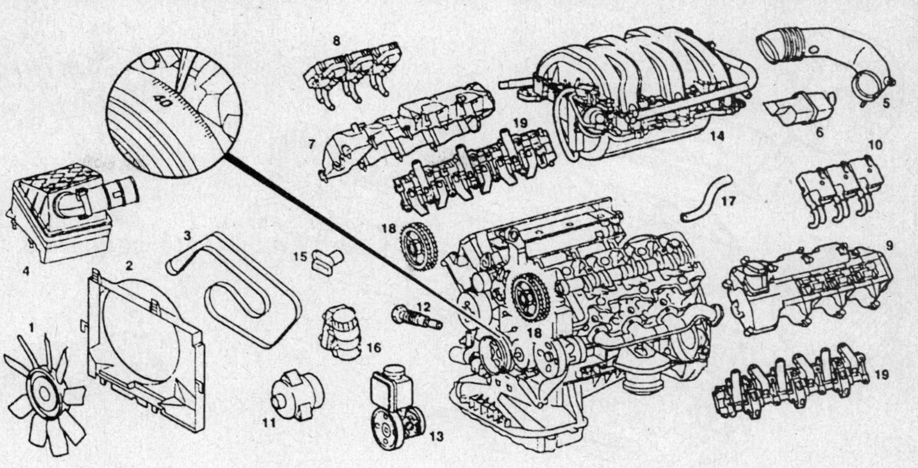

1 Viscous fan
2 Fan shroud
3 Poly V-belt
4 Air cleaner housing with HFM-SFI
5 Resonance pipe
6 Resonance body
7 Right cylinder head cover
8 Right ignition coils
9 Left cylinder head cover
10 Left ignition coils
11 Generator
12 Chain tensioner
13 Power steering pump with reservoir
14 Intake manifold
15 Camshaft position sensor
16 Oil filter housing
17 Heating hose
18 Camshaft gears
19 Camshaft bearing bridges

MB1069900239000X

Fig. 28 Cylinder head replacement (Part 1 of 2)

    c. Tighten new mounting nuts to specifications.

S430 & 1999–2001 SL500 & 2000–01 CL500 & S500

1. Remove catalytic converter or front exhaust system.
2. Remove air cleaner housing.
3. Remove ignition coils.
4. Remove mounting nuts and exhaust manifold.
5. Reverse procedure to install, noting the following:
    a. Install new gasket.
    b. Tighten new mounting nuts to specifications.

CYLINDER HEAD

REPLACE

Remove cylinder heads only when engine is cold.

1. Remove engine compartment paneling.
2. **On ML320 models,** remove air baffle.
3. **On all models,** drain radiator coolant into suitable container.
4. Remove engine trim panel or air cleaner from cylinder head covers.
5. **On C280, CLK55, CLK430, E55, E320, E430, ML320 and ML430 and 1999–2001 SL500 models,** remove viscous fan mounting nut while counterholding pulley socket bolts with suitable wrench, **Fig. 28.** Mounting nut has righthand threads.
6. **On all models,** disconnect fan connection and remove shroud.
7. Attach 15.75 x 26.77 x .039-inch sheet metal or plastic guard plate to condenser.
8. **On C280, CLK320, E320, E430, ML55, ML320 and ML430 models,** remove air cleaner housing.
9. **On all models,** disconnect Hot Film Mass (HFM) air flow sensor and remove resonance pipe with body. **Do not damage plastic plate at intake manifold rear.**
10. Remove HFM air flow sensor.
11. Relieve fuel pressure as outlined under "Precautions."
12. Remove fuel rail fuel line.
13. Remove ignition coils and valve covers.
14. Remove intake manifold as outlined under "Intake Manifold, Replace."
15. If removing righthand cylinder head, remove Camshaft Position (CMP) sensor.
16. Remove serpentine drive belt.
17. Disconnect coolant line at lefthand cylinder head.
18. **On C43 models,** remove coolant line at righthand cylinder head.
19. **On ML55 and ML430 models,** proceed as follows:
    a. Remove wheelwell liner.
    b. Remove heat shield.
    c. Support exhaust system.
    d. Remove exhaust bracket.
20. **On all models,** disconnect exhaust system from manifold as described under "Engine, Replace."
21. Rotate crankshaft in engine rotation direction to set cylinder No. 1 piston at 40° after ignition TDC, noting the following:
    a. Crankshaft damper and timing case cover marks must align.
    b. Camshaft groove should point toward inner V.
    c. **Engine must not be rotate backward.**
22. Lock camshafts with fixing plate tools No. 112 589 00 32 00, 112 589 01 32

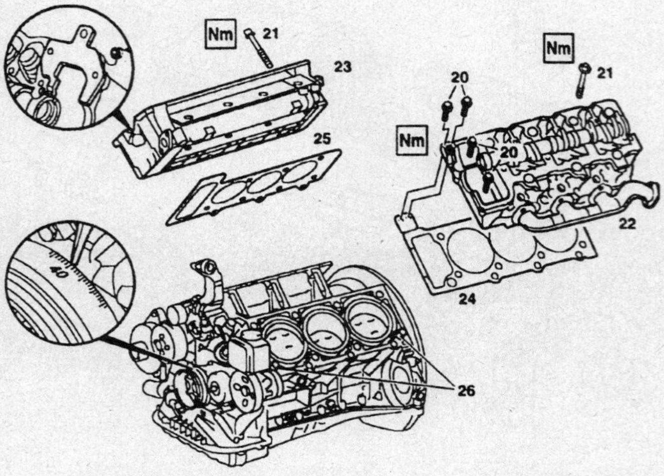

20 M8x30 cylinder head bolts
21 M11x141.5 cylinder head bolts
22 Left cylinder head
23 Right cylinder head
24 Left cylinder head gasket
25 Right cylinder head gasket
26 Dowel sleeves

MB1069900240000X

Fig. 28 Cylinder head replacement (Part 2 of 2)

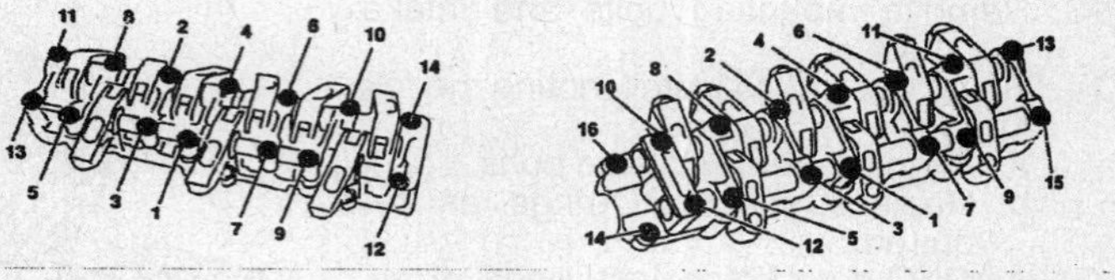

MB1069900253000A

Fig. 29 Camshaft bearing bridge tightening sequence. C240, C280, C320, CLK320, ML320 & SLK320

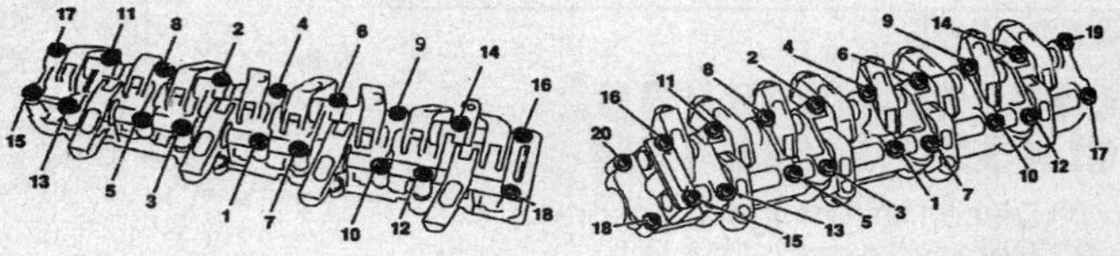

MB1069900254000A

Fig. 30 Camshaft bearing bridge tightening sequence. C43, E55, E430, CLK55, CLK430, ML55, ML430, S55 S430 & 1999–2001 SL500

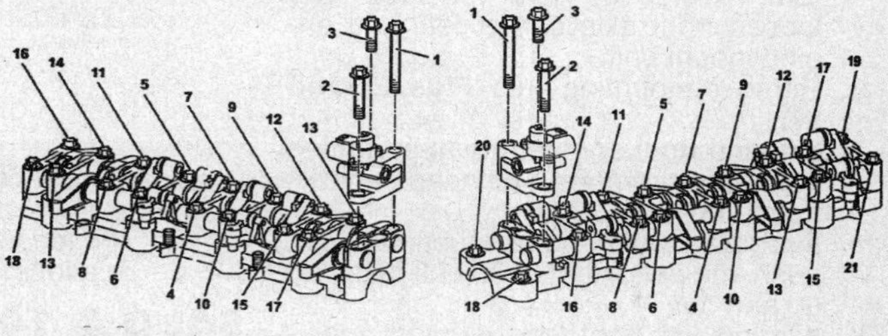

MB1060100319000X

Fig. 31 Camshaft bearing bridge tightening sequence. 2000–01 CL500 & S600

00, or equivalents.

23. **On CLK55, CLK430, ML55 and ML430 and 1999–2001 SL500 models,** proceed as follows:
    a. Remove oil filter housing.
    b. Remove oil filter element an allow oil to drain into pan.
    c. Remove oil-water heat exchanger mounting bolts.
    d. **Do not pinch coolant lines.**
    e. Remove mounting bolt and oil filter housing.
24. **On all models,** remove chain tensioner.
25. **On CLK55, CLK430, ML55 and ML430 and 1999–2001 SL500 models,** tie timing chain tight on both camshaft sprockets with suitable cable straps.
26. **On C280, CLK320, E55, E320, E430, ML320 and S430 and 2000–01 S500 models,** proceed as follows:
    a. Tie timing chain tight on righthand camshaft sprocket with suitable cable strap.
    b. Mark lefthand camshaft sprocket to timing chain relationship for installation.
27. Remove mounting bolts and camshaft sprockets using open-end wrench tool No. 112 589 00 01 00 and insertion tool No. 112 589 01 03 00, or equivalents.
28. **On 2000–01 CL500 and S500 models,** remove cylinder shutoff valve by pushing into oil paper. Ensure O-ring is not damaged and pressed out of oil pipe groove.
29. **On all models,** loosen camshaft bearing bridge bolts in stages in reverse of tightening sequence, **Figs. 29 through 31.**
30. Remove cylinder head to timing case cover mounting bolts.
31. Loosen cylinder head bolts in sequence, **Figs. 32 and 33.**
32. Reverse procedure to install, noting the following:
    a. **Do not disassemble camshaft bearing bridge.** If damaged, replace complete cylinder head with camshaft bearing bridge.
    b. Oil cylinder head bolts' threads and head contact surface.
    c. Replace cylinder head bolts with shank length more than 5.5714 inches.
    d. If blowholes are present in cylinder sealing surface, apply .0315 inch thick Loctite No. 5900 silicone sealant, or equivalent.
    e. Cylinder head must be installed within 10 minutes of silicone application.
    f. Align cylinder head using dowel sleeves.
    g. **Torque** cylinder head bolts to 15 ft. lbs. in sequence, **Figs. 34 and 35.**
    h. **Torque** bolts to 37 ft. lbs. in sequence.
    i. Tighten cylinder head bolts an additional 60–70° in sequence.
    j. Final tighten bolts an additional 60–70° in sequence.
    k. **Torque** camshaft bearing bridge M7x45 bolts to 11 ft. lbs. in sequence, **Figs. 29 through 31.**
    l. **Torque** new camshaft bearing bridge M7x84, M7x90 and M7x120 bolts to 88 inch lbs. in sequence.
    m. Final tighten M7x84M7x90 and M7x120 bolts an additional 90° in sequence.
    n. Inspect basic camshaft timing position.
    o. **On CLK55, CLK430, ML55 and ML430 and 1999–2001 SL500 models,** install new oil filter housing seal.

VALVE COVER

REPLACE

1. Remove air cleaner housing and engine cover.
2. Remove resonance body, **Fig. 36.**
3. Disconnect connector and remove resonance pipe mounting bolt with Hot Film Mass (HFM) air flow sensor at valve cover.
4. Remove automatic transmission dipstick guide tube mounting bolt.
5. Remove ignition coils mounting bolts.
6. Mark connectors, cover and ignition coils for installation.
7. Disconnect spark plug connectors.
8. Disconnect vacuum hose.
9. If removing lefthand valve cover, disconnect crankcase ventilation hoses.
10. Relieve fuel pressure as described under "Precautions."
11. Disconnect fuel rail fuel line.
12. Remove mounting bolts and valve covers.
13. Reverse procedure to install, noting the following:
    a. Ensure gasket is correctly located.
    b. Tighten mounting bolts to specifications.

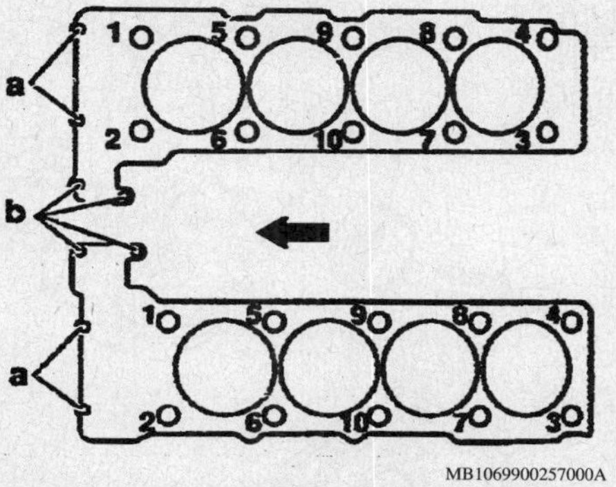

Fig. 33 Cylinder head bolt slackening sequence. 113 engine

VALVE ADJUSTMENT

This engine is equipped with hydraulic lifters and requires no valve adjustment,

ROCKER ARMS

REPLACE

1. Remove camshaft bearing bridge as outlined under "Cylinder Head, Replace."
2. Heat camshaft bearing bridge evenly to not more than 302°F.
3. Place bridge on board and knock rocker arm shaft out by striking .591 inch diameter extraction drift tool No. 112 589 00 15 00, or equivalent, with suitable hammer.
4. Remove extraction tool.
5. Reverse procedure to install, noting the following:
   a. Assembly rocker arms on .627 inch diameter guide shaft tool No. 112 589 02 31 00, or equivalent, .709 inch diameter guide shaft tool No. 112 589 03 31 00, or equivalent.

HYDRAULIC LIFTERS

REPLACE

This procedure has been revised by a Technical Service Bulletin.

1. Remove camshaft bearing bridge as outlined under "Cylinder Head, Replace."
2. Mark lifters for installation in original position.
3. Press lifter out of rocker arm using suitable .0787 inch drift. **Do not use magnet.**
4. Reverse procedure to install. Disc slots at rocker arm top must face down toward lifter.

CRANKSHAFT DAMPER

REPLACE

This procedure has been revised by a Technical Service Bulletin.

1. Remove viscous fan mounting nut while counterholding pulley socket bolts with suitable wrench, **Fig. 37.** Mounting nut has righthand threads.
2. **On C43, C280, E55, E320, E430, CLK320, ML55, ML320, ML430, S430, S500 and SLK320 and 1999–**

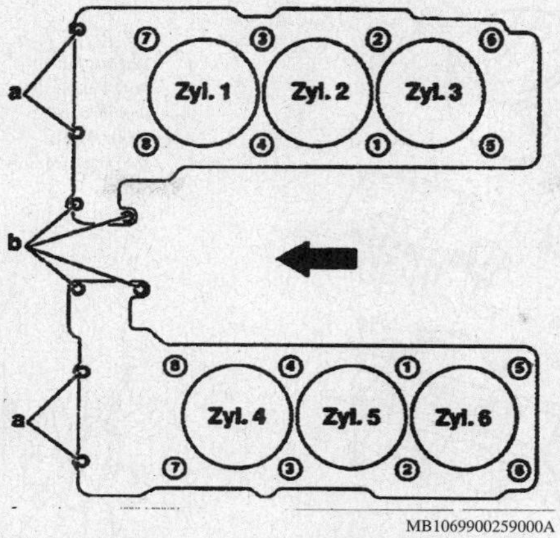

Fig. 34 Cylinder head bolt tightening sequence. 112 engine

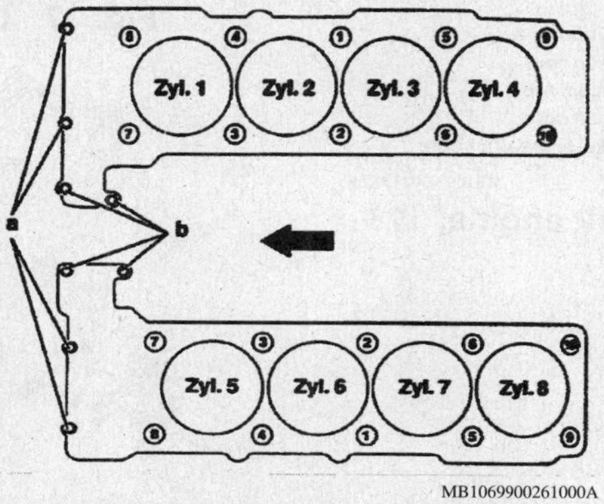

Fig. 35 Cylinder head bolt tightening sequence. 113 engine

2001 SL500 models disconnect fan and remove shroud.

3. **On all models,** remove serpentine drive belt.
4. **On ML55 and ML430 models,** proceed as follows:
   a. Remove protective grille.
   b. Remove radiator front clips.
   c. Remove front end crossmember
5. **On models equipped with manual transmission,** install retaining lock tool No. 112 589 03 40 00, or equivalent, into starter opening and engage ring gear.
6. **On all models,** remove central bolt using counterholder extension tool No. 112 589 00 40 00, or equivalent.
7. Remove pulley/vibration damper.
8. Reverse procedure to install, noting the following:
   a. Oil central bolt threads.
   b. Installation positions is set by parallel key or spring wedge.
   c. Tighten mounting bolts to specifications.

FRONT COVER

REPLACE

1. Remove engine compartment paneling.
2. Drain radiator coolant into suitable container.
3. Remove engine trim panel or air cleaner from cylinder head covers.

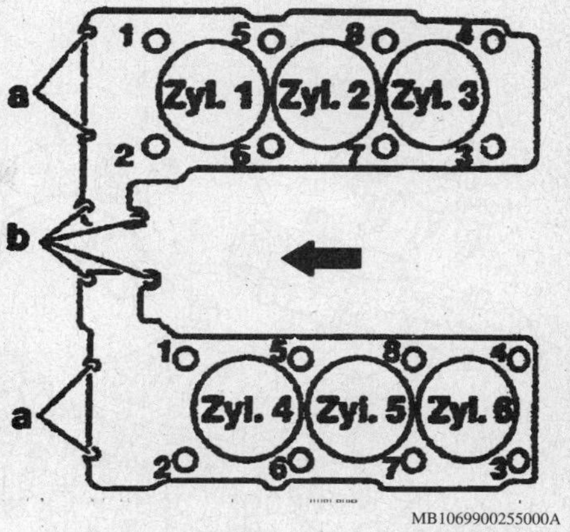

Fig. 32 Cylinder head bolt slackening sequence. 112 engine

4. **On C43, C280, CLK55, CLK430, E55, E320, E430, ML320 and ML430 and 2000–01 S500 models,** remove viscous fan mounting nut while counterholding pulley socket bolts with suitable wrench, **Fig. 38.** Mounting nut has righthand threads.
5. Disconnect fan connector and remove shroud.
6. Attach 15.75 x 26.77 x .039-inch sheet metal or plastic guard plate to condenser.
7. Remove serpentine drive belt.
8. Remove valve covers as outlined under "Valve Cover, Replace."
9. **On E320 models equipped with 4MATIC,** remove cylinder heads as described under "Cylinder Head, Replace."
10. **On all models,** disconnect water pump and thermostat coolant hoses.
11. Remove air conditioning compressor mounting bolt. Attach compressor to engine compartment bottom with lines connected.
12. Remove oil pan as outline under "Oil Pan, Replace."
13. Remove serpentine drive belt tensioner.
14. Remove crankshaft damper as outlined under "Crankshaft Damper, Replace."
15. Remove timing chain tensioner as described under "Timing Chain Tensioner, Replace."
16. Remove oil filter housing with oil-water heat exchanger.
17. Remove mounting bolts and set power steering pump with reservoir aside with lines connected.
18. Remove plastic cover and disconnect water pump pulley.
19. Remove air pump.
20. Disconnect Engine Coolant Temperature (ECT) sensor connector.
21. Remove mounting bolts and timing case cover. Mark bolt size, length and location for installation, **Fig. 39.**
22. Reverse procedure to install, noting the following:
    a. Clean front case sealing surfaces.
    b. Apply Loctite No. 5203 sealant, or equivalent, to bolts marked with arrows, **Fig. 39.**

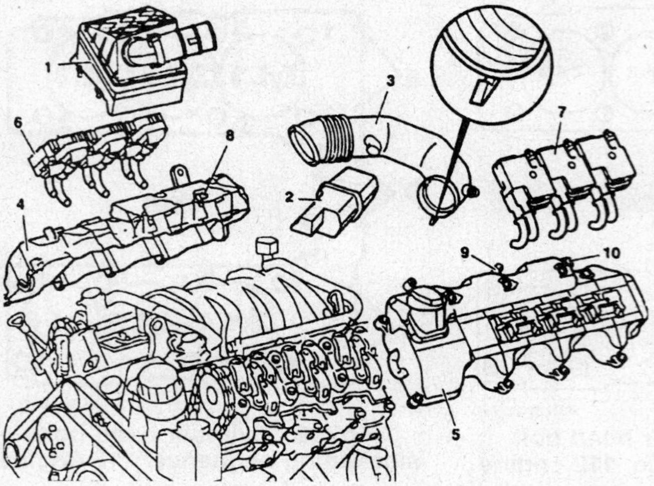

1 Air cleaner housing with HFM-SFI
2 Resonance body
3 Resonance pipe
4 Right cylinder head cover
5 Left cylinder head
6 Right ignition coils
7 Left ignition coils
8 Right vacuum hose
9 Left vacuum hose
10 Left crankcase breather hose

MB1069900238000X

Fig. 36 Valve cover replacement. 112 engine, 113 engine similar

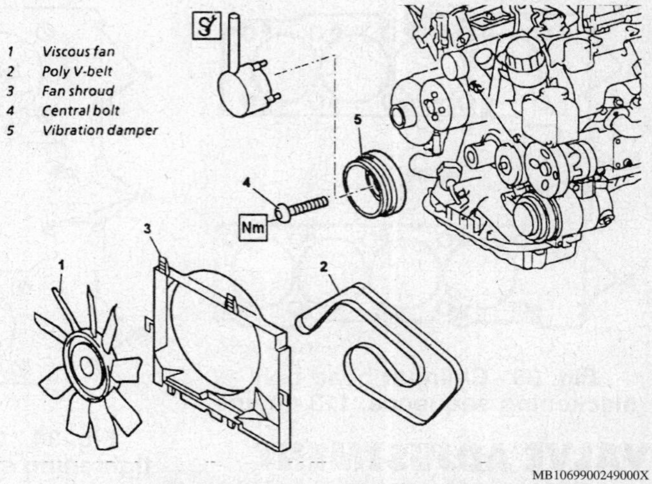

MB1069900249000X

Fig. 37 Crankshaft damper replacement

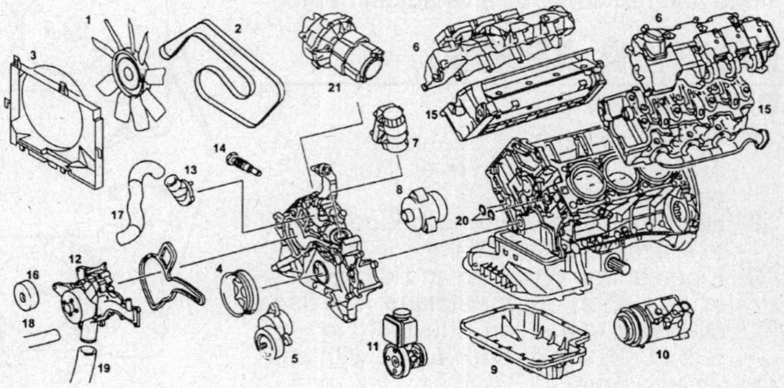

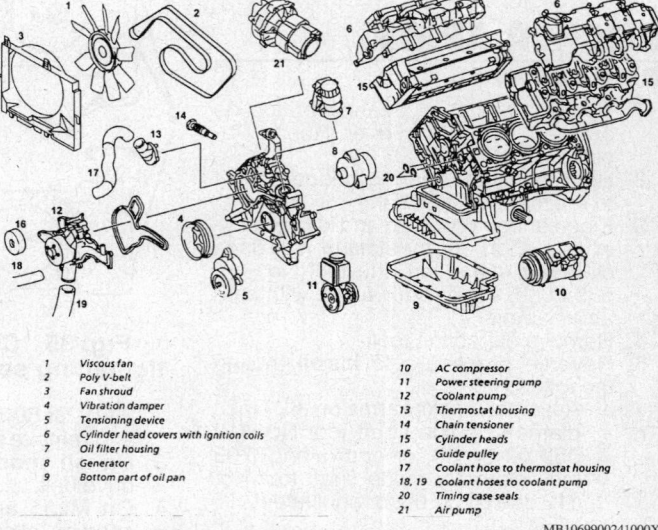

1 Viscous fan
2 Poly V-belt
3 Fan shroud
4 Vibration damper
5 Tensioning device
6 Cylinder head covers with ignition coils
7 Oil filter housing
8 Generator
9 Bottom part of oil pan
10 AC compressor
11 Power steering pump
12 Coolant pump
13 Thermostat housing
14 Chain tensioner
15 Cylinder heads
16 Guide pulley
17 Coolant hose to thermostat housing
18, 19 Coolant hoses to coolant pump
20 Timing case seals
21 Air pump

MB1069900241000X

Fig. 38 Timing case cover replacement

c. Apply .059–.098 inch bead of Loctite 5900 sealant, or equivalent, to sealing surfaces A, C, D and around bolt hole G, **Fig. 40.**
d. **Do not spread bead. Ensure sealant does not get into oil galleries.**
e. Install cover within 10 minutes of sealant application.
f. Install new timing case seals.
g. Install new crankshaft seal as described under "Crankshaft Seal, Replacement."
h. Tighten mounting bolts to specifications.

TIMING CHAIN

REPLACE

This procedure has been revised by a Technical Service Bulletin.

The 113 engine does not use a balance shaft.

1. Remove one spark plug from each cylinder.
2. Remove valve covers as outlined under "Valve Cover, Replace."
3. **On C43, C280, E55, E320, E430, CLK55, CLK430, ML320 and ML430 and 1999–2001 SL500 models,** remove viscous fan mounting nut while counterholding pulley socket bolts with suitable wrench. Mounting nut has righthand threads.
4. **C43, C280, E55, E320, E430, CLK55, CLK320, CLK430, ML55, ML320, ML430 and S430 and 1999–2001 SL500 and 2000–01 S500 models,** disconnect fan connector and remove shroud.
5. **On all models,** position engine with cylinder No. 1 at 40° after TDC, **Fig. 41,** noting the following:
   a. **Do not crank engine backward.**
   b. Because of unevenly long timing chain travel path, it may be necessary to crank engine up to 14 times before chain cooper platers align with camshaft sprocket marks.
   c. Left and righthand camshafts' grooves point in direction of inner V and are centered on cylinder head cover mating surface.
   d. **On models equipped with air pump,** remove combination valve mounting bolts before inserting righthand locating plate.
   e. **On all models,** fit two locating plate tools No. 112 589 00 32 00, or equivalent, flush onto left and righthand cylinder heads and into camshaft slots.
   f. **On 112 engines,** balance shaft crankcase front and balancing weight marks must align. Marks can be seen through lefthand timing case shaft approximately .867 inch below cylinder head and valve cover parting surface when cylinder head is removed.
   g. **On all models,** remove locking plates.
6. Remove chain tensioner as described under "Timing Chain Tensioner, Replace."
7. Remove Camshaft Position (CMP) sensor.
8. Crank engine in rotational direction until separating link can easily be accessed. Link is on righthand side of copper plate.
9. Remove righthand camshaft bearing bridge as described under "Cylinder Head, Replace."
10. Install holding bush tool No. 112 589 05 04 00, or equivalent, onto righthand camshaft. Tighten bolts until they contact.
11. Install holding tools No. 112 589 04 40 00, or equivalent, onto left and righthand cylinder heads.
12. Separate and remove timing chain.
13. Cover timing case recess with suitable clean cloth. **Parts dropped into timing case must be removed.**
14. Reverse procedure to install, noting the following:
    a. Draw in new timing chain by joining new chain to old, **Fig. 42.**

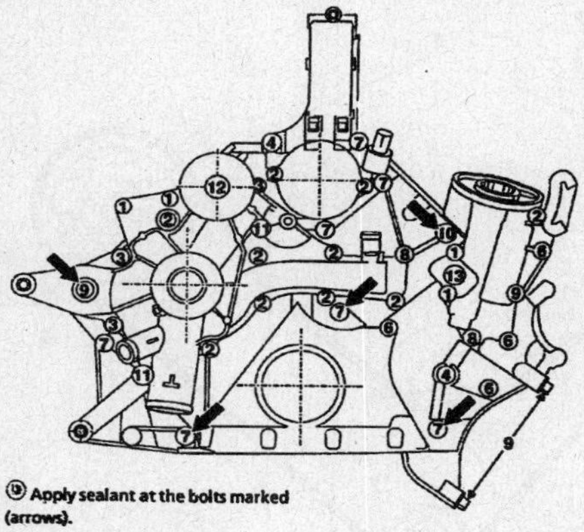

1	M6 X 19	6	M8 X 34	10	M8 X 100
2	M6 X 23	7	M8 X 70	11	M8 X 110
3	M6 X 43	8	M8 X 80	12	M8 X 140
4	M8 X 30	9	M8 X 90	13	M12 x 1.5

MB1069900262000A

Fig. 39 Timing case cover bolt sizes, lengths, sealant & locations

b. **On models equipped with air pump,** install new combination valve seal.
c. **On all models,** tighten mounting bolts to specifications.

TIMING CHAIN TENSIONER

REPLACE

This procedure has been revised by a Technical Service Bulletin.

1. **On C43, C280, E55, E320, E430, CLK55, CLK430, ML320 and ML430 and 1999–2001 SL500 models,** remove viscous fan mounting nut while counterholding pulley socket bolts with suitable wrench, **Fig. 43.** Mounting nut has righthand threads.
2. **On all models,** disconnect fan connector and remove shroud.
3. Remove serpentine drive belt.
4. Remove alternator.
5. Remove timing chain tensioner.
6. Reverse procedure to install with new seal. Tighten tensioner to specifications.

CAMSHAFT

REPLACE

This procedure has been revised by a Technical Service Bulletin.

REMOVAL

1. Remove valve cover as outlined under "Valve Cover, Replace," **Fig. 44.**
2. Rotate crankshaft to set cylinder No. 1 piston at 40° after TDC.
3. Remove timing chain tensioner as outlined under "Timing Chain Tensioner, Replace."
4. Remove Camshaft Position (CMP) sensor.
5. Tie camshaft sprocket and timing chain together with cable strap.
6. Remove mounting bolt and camshaft sprocket.
7. Remove camshaft bearing bridge as described under "Cylinder Head, Replace."
8. Remove camshaft.

INSTALLATION

1. Oil contact surfaces.
2. Ensure end cover is correctly located on camshaft end face.
3. Install camshaft bearing bridge as outlined under "Cylinder Head, Replace."
4. Rotate camshaft so groove centers to cylinder head contact surface in direction of inner V, **Fig. 41.**
5. Install camshaft sprocket and tighten mounting bolt to specifications.
6. Remove cable straps.
7. Install CMP sensor.
8. Install chain tensioner.
9. Ensure engine timing is correct.
10. Install valve cover.

BALANCE SHAFT

REPLACE

1. Remove engine as described under "Engine, Replace."
2. Remove automatic transmission and drive plate.
3. Remove end cover as outlined under "Crankshaft Rear Oil Seal, Replace."
4. Remove valve covers as outlined under "Valve Cover, Replace," **Fig. 45.**
5. Rotate crankshaft to set cylinder No. 1 piston at 40° after ignition TDC. **Do not rotate engine backward.**
6. Remove oil pan as outlined under "Oil Pan, Replace."
7. Remove timing case front cover as outlined under "Front Cover, Replace." **Do not damage cylinder head gaskets.**
8. **Do not remove cylinder heads.**
9. Remove Camshaft Position (CMP) sensor.
10. Remove righthand camshaft sprocket.
11. Remove rear balancing weight.
12. Remove mounting bolt, front locking plate and balance shaft.
13. Reverse procedure to install, noting the following:
    a. Fix rear weight to balance using suitable pin or drift.
    b. Replace weight mounting bolt if shank length is more than 1.996 inches.
    c. Tighten mounting bolts to specifications.

PISTON & ROD ASSEMBLY

1. Match piston to bore and install with arrow in drive direction, **Fig. 46.**
2. Piston ring gaps must be offset 120°.
3. Turn crankshaft until connecting rod does not butt against connecting rod journal when inserting piston into cylinder.
4. Connecting rod and bearing caps are "cracked" and must not be fitted in wrong way around, **Fig. 47.**

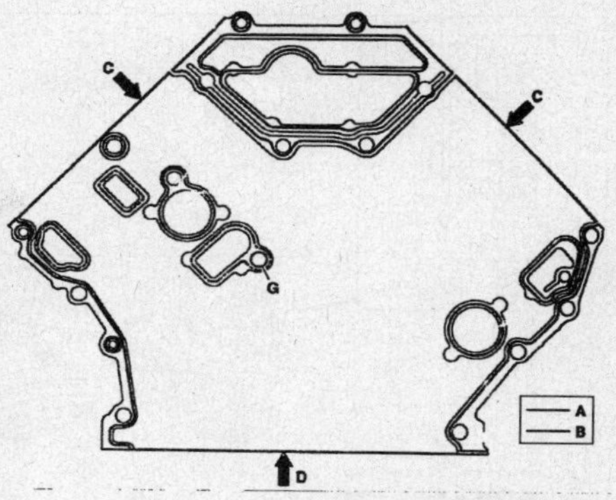

MB1060100304000X

Fig. 40 Timing case cover sealing surfaces

MAIN & ROD BEARINGS

MAIN BEARINGS

This procedure has been revised by a Technical Service Bulletin.

1. Top main bearings halves are assigned to journal by colored coding on rear of main bearing shells and number or chisel punches stamped on crankcase, **Fig. 48.**
2. Any assigned color and numerical combinations may be fitted together.
3. Bottom main bearing halves are assigned to journal by initial letter of particular color, **Fig. 49.**
4. Bottom main bearing halves color coding is on rear of bearing halves.
5. Initial letters are engraved on crankshaft journal. **Keep order colors are engraved on crankshaft.**
6. Ensure shell anti-twist locks are located in crankcase and bearing cap recesses.
7. Thrust washers are assigned to fit bearing cap by numbers engraved on crankshaft journal, **Fig. 50.**
8. Thrust washer oil grooves must face crankshaft web.
9. Thrust washer anti-twist locks must be located in bearing cap slots.
10. Moisten bolts' threads and head contact surfaces with engine oil.
11. **Torque** crankshaft bearing cap M8 bolts to 15 ft. lbs. in sequence, **Figs. 51 and 52.**
12. Final tighten crankshaft bearing cap M8 bolts an additional 90° in sequence.
13. **Torque** crankshaft side bolt bearing cap M8 bolts to 22 ft. lbs in sequence.
14. **Torque** crankshaft bearing cap M10 bolts to 22 ft. lbs in sequence.
15. Final tighten crankshaft bearing cap M10 bolts an additional 90° in sequence.
16. If angle tightener is not available, continue turning bolt through specified angle with socket wrench and bar in one movement. **Do not use torque wrench.**

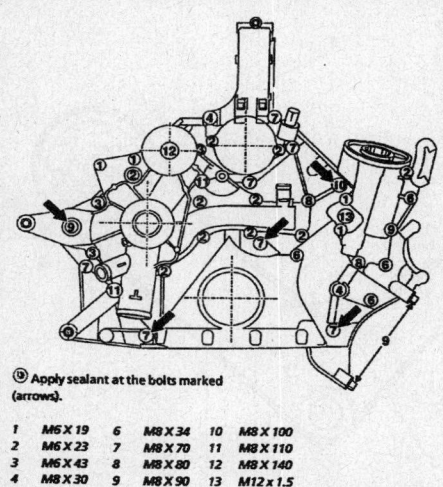

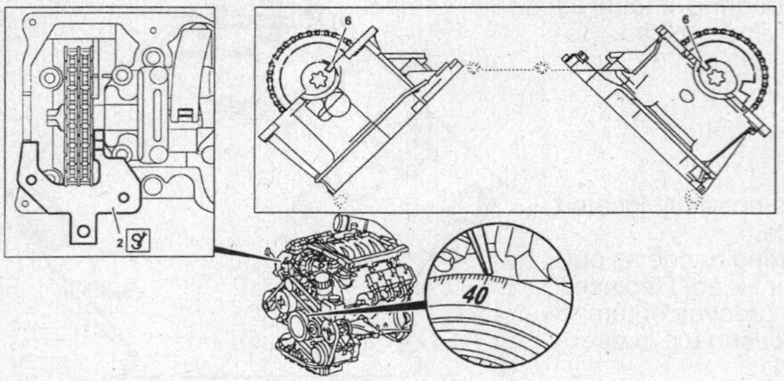

2 Locating Plate Tool No. 112 589 00 32 000
6 Camshaft Slot Inner V

MB1069900250000X

Fig. 41 Camshaft timing

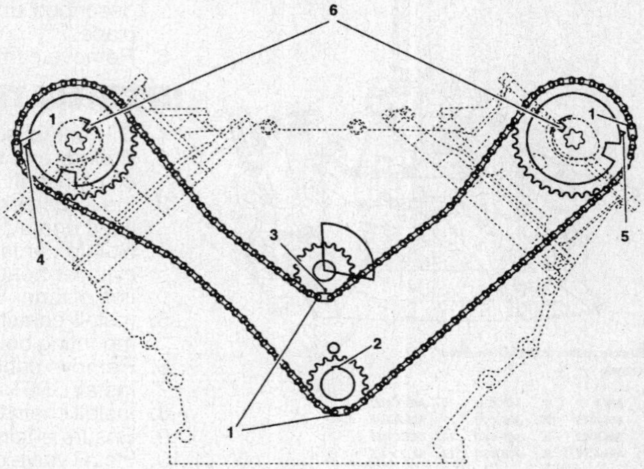

1	Copper-plated link
2	Groove in crankshaft
3	Mark on balance shaft sprocket
4	Mark on right camshaft gear
5	Mark on left camshaft gear
6	Groove in camshaft

MB1069900237000X

Fig. 42 Timing chain replacement. 112 engine

ROD BEARINGS

1. Assign connecting rod bearings to bearing caps by color spot on reverse side of bearing shells, **Fig. 53.**
2. Sequence of individual color combinations on connecting rod bearing journals is not fixed.
3. Bearing shells with oil bores must be used.
4. Anti-twist locks must sit in rod and cap grooves, **Fig. 47.**
5. Replace connecting rod bolts with shank length of more than 1.874 inches.
6. Lightly coat bolt threads and head contact surfaces with engine oil.
7. **Torque** connecting rod bolts to 44 inch lbs.
8. **Torque** rod bolts to 18 ft. lbs.
9. Final tighten bolts an additional 90°. If angle tightener is not available, continue turning bolt through specified angle with socket wrench and bar in one movement. **Do not use torque wrench.**

CRANKSHAFT SEAL

REPLACE

REMOVAL

1. Remove engine compartment paneling.
2. **On ML430 models,** remove air guide.
3. **On C43, C280, CLK55, CLK430, E55, E320, E430, ML320 and ML430 and 1999–2001 SL500 models,** remove viscous fan mounting nut while counterholding pulley socket bolts with suitable wrench, **Fig. 54.** Mounting nut has righthand threads.
4. **On C43, C280, CLK55, CLK320, CLK430, E55, E320, E430, ML55, ML320, ML430, S430 and SLK320 and 1999–2001 SL500 and 2000–01 S500 models,** disconnect fan connector and remove shroud.
5. **On all models,** remove serpentine drive belt.
6. **On C43, C280, CLK55, CLK320, CLK430, E55, E320, E430, ML55, ML320, ML430, and S430 and 1999–2001 SL500 and 2000–01 S500 models,** remove crankshaft damper as outlined under "Crankshaft Damper, Replace."
7. **On all models,** remove radial seal using suitable screwdriver and clean cloth. **Do not damage crankshaft or mounting hole.**

INSTALLATION

1. Ensure circumference and radial seal sealing lip and matching contact surface are free of oil and grease.
2. Fit new seal onto front crankshaft radial seal insertion tool No. 611 589 00 14 00, or equivalent.
3. Align crankshaft parallel key and push tool on.
4. Drive tool on with central bolt as far as stop.
5. Remove insertion tool.
6. Draw insertion sleeve tool No. 119 589 01 14 00, or equivalent, on with central bolt as far as stop.
7. Remove sleeve.
8. Continue to reverse removal procedure to install.
9. Tighten mounting bolts to specifications.

CRANKSHAFT REAR OIL SEAL

REPLACE

This procedure has been revised by a Technical Service Bulletin.

Factory-fitted crankshaft radial seal cannot be replaced. Install new end cover.

REMOVAL

1. Remove transmission.
2. Remove crankshaft/ring gear retaining lock and driven plate, **Fig. 55.**
3. Remove mounting bolts and end cover, **Fig. 56. Use suitable angled screwdriver to carefully lever off end cover at arrow points.**
4. Remove seal. **Do not use screwdriver to press out seal if end cover is installed.**

INSTALLATION

1. Install end cover, then seal.
2. Apply .059–.098 inch bead of Loctite 5900 sealant, or equivalent, to sealing surfaces E, arrow D and G, **Fig. 57.**
3. **Do not spread bead. Ensure sealant does not get into oil galleries.**
4. Install cover within 10 minutes of sealant application.
5. Ensure dowel sleeves are correctly positioned.
6. Install inner part of rear crankshaft radial seal insertion tool No. 111 589 08 43 00, or equivalent, onto crankshaft.
7. Ensure circumference and radial seal sealing lip and matching contact surface are free of oil and grease.
8. Push new seal over tool and onto crankshaft journal.
9. Ensure seal is at right angles to crankshaft stub.
10. Fit insertion tool with offset chamfer and tighten screw until resistance is felt.
11. Remove tool.
12. Ensure clearance between end cover and seal is approximately .039 inch around entire circumference.
13. Tighten mounting bolts to specifications.

This procedure has been revised by a Technical Service Bulletin.

Factory-fitted crankshaft radial seal cannot be replaced. Install new end cover.

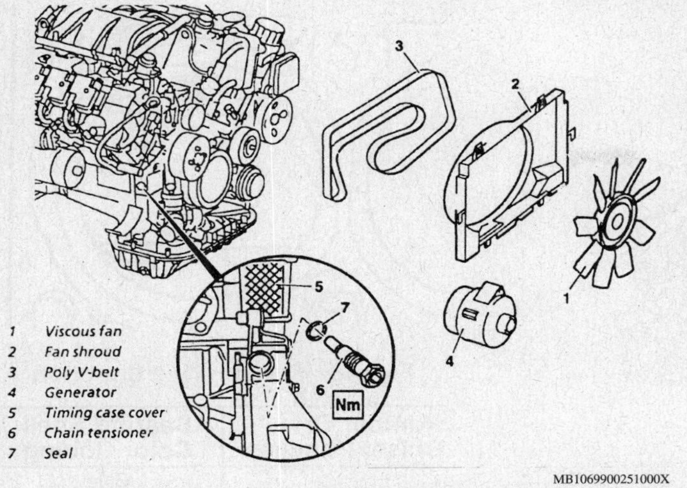

Fig. 43 Timing chain tensioner replacement

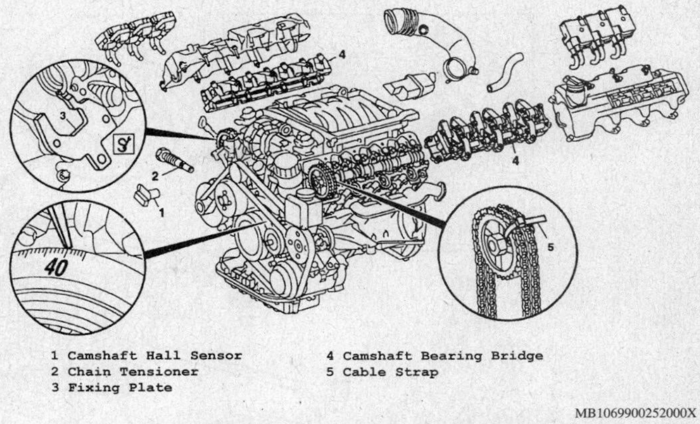

Fig. 44 Camshaft replacement. 112 engine

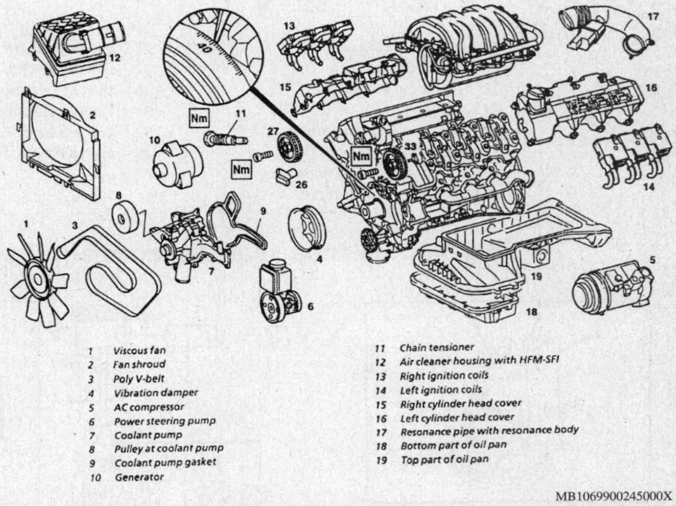

Fig. 45 Balance shaft replacement (Part 1 of 2)

OIL PAN

REPLACE

C43, C280, CLK55, CLK320 & CLK430

This procedure has been revised by a Technical Service Bulletin.

1. Remove engine compartment paneling.
2. Drain engine oil into suitable container.
3. Remove engine trim panel or air cleaner off cylinder head covers.
4. **On C43, C280, CLK55 and CLK430 models,** remove viscous fan mounting nut while counterholding pulley socket bolts with suitable wrench, **Fig. 58.** Mounting nut has righthand threads.
5. **On C43, C280 and CLK320 models,** disconnect fan connector and remove shroud.
6. **On C280 and CLK320 models,** disconnect Hot Film Mass (HFM) air flow sensor and remove resonance pipe with body, **Do not damage plastic plate.**
7. **On C43, CLK55 and CLK430 models,** remove Hot Film Mass (HFM) air flow sensor with air intake pipe.
8. **On all models,** remove anti-roll bar.
9. Disconnect ATF lines fixtures at bottom and top of oil pan.
10. Disconnect positive cable at top oil pan.
11. **On CLK55 and CLK430 models,** proceed as follows:
    a. Disconnect oxygen sensors' electrical connectors.
    b. Remove lefthand catalytic converter as described under "Engine, Replace."
12. **On all models,** disconnect oil level sensor electrical connector.
13. Disconnect AFT lines on left and righthand sides at transmission bell housing, noting the following:
    a. Catch fluid in suitable container.
    b. Seal and plug connections and openings.
14. Remove ground cable mounting bolt from front axle carrier lefthand engine support.
15. Remove mounting bolt and oil pipe from dipstick.
16. Remove mounting bolts and bottom part of oil pan.
17. Remove front axle carrier front engine mount bolts as outlined under "Engine Mount, Replace."
18. Install suitable engine support frame and hook to engine suspension eyes.
19. Raise engine, noting the following:
    a. Ensure engine and attachments do not touch body.
    b. Do not overextend coolant hoses.
20. Remove oil pan mounting bolts. Record lengths, diameters and locations for installation, **Figs. 59 and 60.**
21. Remove oil pan to the front. Rotate crankshaft slightly, as required.
22. Reverse procedure to install, noting the following:
    a. Apply .0591–.0984 inch bead of Loctite 5900 sealant, or equivalent, to sealing surfaces, **Figs. 61 through 63. Do not spread bead. Ensure sealant does not get into oil galleries.**
    b. Install pan within 10 minutes of sealant application.
    c. Ensure cables or hoses are not pinched.
    d. Install new oil pipe seal.
    e. Tighten mounting bolts to specifications.

E55 & E430

This procedure has been revised by a Technical Service Bulletin.

1. Remove engine compartment paneling.
2. Drain engine oil into suitable container.
3. Remove engine trim panel or air cleaner off cylinder head covers.
4. Remove viscous fan mounting nut while counterholding pulley socket bolts with suitable wrench, **Fig. 64.** Mounting nut has righthand threads.
5. Disconnect fan connector and remove shroud.
6. **On E320 and E430 models,** disconnect Hot Film Mass (HFM) air flow sensor and remove resonance pipe with body, **Do not damage plastic plate.**
7. **On E55 models,** remove Hot Film Mass (HFM) air flow sensor with air intake pipe.
8. **On all models,** disconnect ATF lines fixtures at bottom and top of oil pan.
9. Remove mounting bolts and bottom part of oil pan.
10. Disconnect oil level sensor electrical connector.

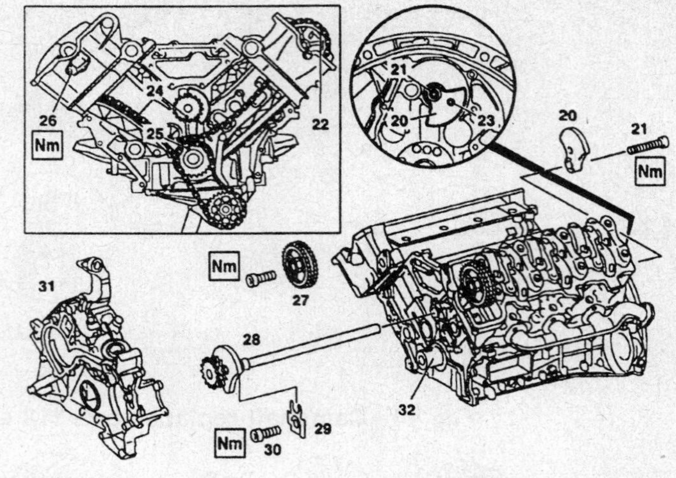

20	Rear balancing weight
21	M8 X 50 collar bolt
22	Left camshaft marking
23	Locating hole
24	Balancing shaft markings
25	Crankshaft markings
26	Camshaft position sensor
27	Right camshaft sprocket
28	Balancing shaft
29	Locking plate for balancing shaft
30	Screw of locking plate M7 X 16.5
31	Timing case cover
32	Crankshaft
33	Left camshaft sprocket

MB1069900246000X

Fig. 45 Balance shaft replacement (Part 2 of 2)

MB1060100317000X

Fig. 46 Piston drive direction

Number Or Chisel Punches	Bearing Shell Color Coding
1	Blue
2	Yellow
3	Red

Fig. 48 Top main bearing assignment

Laser Inscription	Color Coding
v	Purple
w	White
r	Red
g	Yellow
b	Blue

Fig. 49 Bottom main bearing assignment

Journal Inscription	Thrust Wash Designation
0	N
1	N1

Fig. 50 Thrust washer assignment

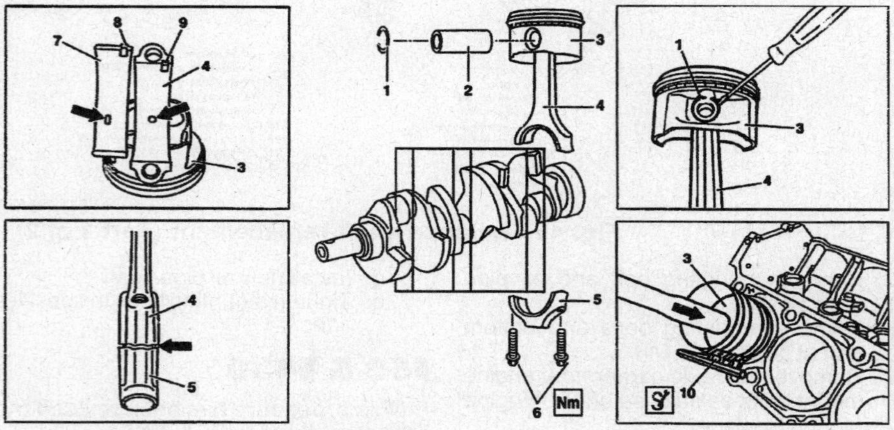

1	Circlip
2	Piston pin
3	Piston
4	Connecting rod
5	Connecting rod bearing cap
6	Connecting rod bolts
7	Connecting rod bearing shell
8	Anti-twist lock
9	Groove
10	Piston ring clamp

MB1060100318000X

Fig. 47 Pistons, connecting rods and bearings

11. Remove mounting bolt and oil pipe from dipstick.
12. Disconnect AFT lines on left and right-hand sides at transmission bell housing, noting the following:
    a. Catch fluid in suitable container.
    b. Seal and plug connections and openings.
13. Remove front axle carrier front engine mount bolts as outlined under "Engine Mount, Replace."
14. Install engine support frame tool No. 140 589 01 61 00, or equivalent, and hook to engine suspension eyes.
15. Raise engine, noting the following:
    a. Ensure engine and attachments do not touch body.
    b. Do not overextend coolant hoses.
16. Support front axle carrier with suitable jack using adapter tool No. 210 589 01 62 00, or equivalent.
17. Remove steering coupling bolt.
18. Unclamp front spring.
19. Remove front axle carrier ATF line fixture mounting bolt.
20. Remove front axle carrier mounting bolts.
21. Lower front axle carrier.
22. Remove oil pan mounting bolts. Record lengths, diameters and locations for installation, **Figs. 59 and 60.**
23. Remove oil pan to the front. Rotate crankshaft slightly, as required.
24. Reverse procedure to install, noting the following:
    a. Apply .0591–.0984 inch bead of Loctite 5900 sealant, or equivalent, to sealing surfaces, **Figs. 61 through 63. Do not spread bead. Ensure sealant does not get into oil galleries.**
    b. Install pan within 10 minutes of sealant application.
    c. Insert front axle carrier locating pins in longitudinal member holes.
    d. Install new front axle carrier mounting bolts. **Do not install at an angle.**
    e. **Do not use impact wrench to install front axle carrier mounting bolts.**
    f. **Do not retap front axle carrier longitudinal member.**
    g. Install new steering joint bolt and nut.
    h. Ensure cables or hoses are not pinched.
    i. Install new oil pipe seal.
    j. Tighten mounting bolts to specifications.

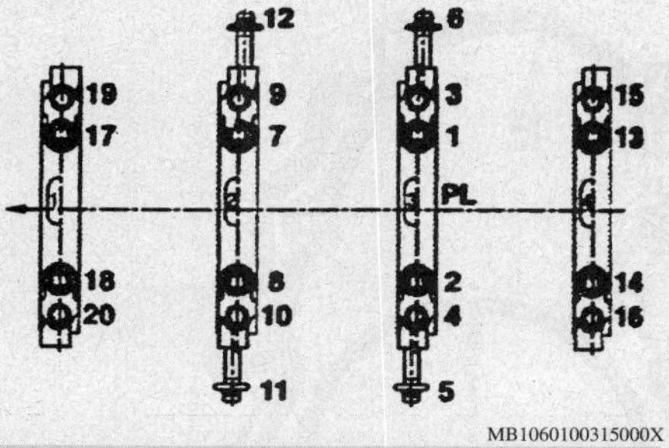

Fig. 51 Main bearing tightening sequence. 112 engine

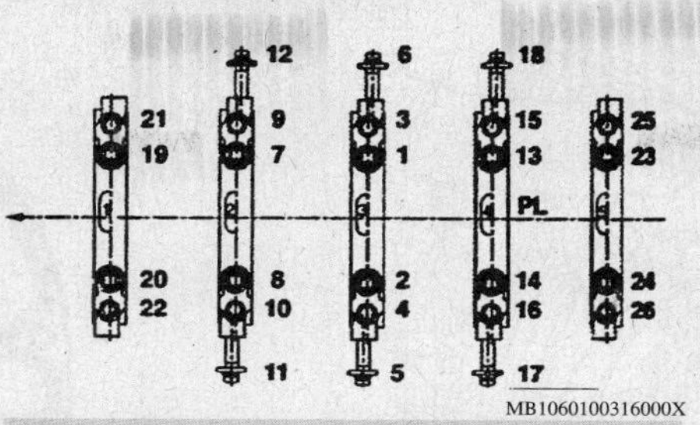

Fig. 52 Main bearing tightening sequence. 113 engine

Top Half Conrod	Bottom Half Conrod Bearing Cap
Yellow	Yellow
Blue	Red
Red	Blue

Fig. 53 Connecting rod bearing assignments

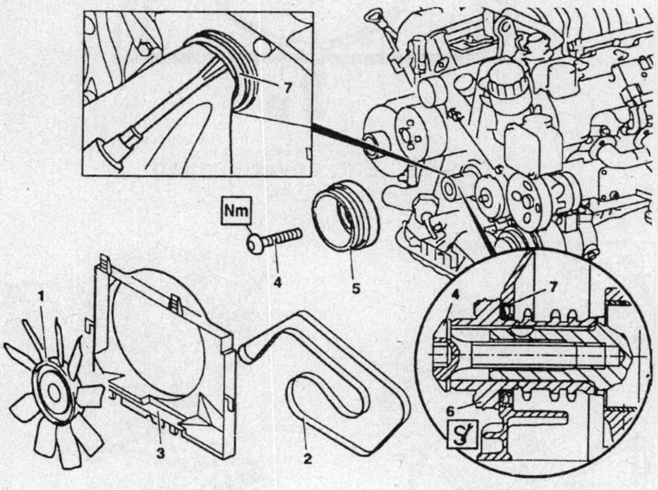

Fig. 54 Front crankshaft seal replacement

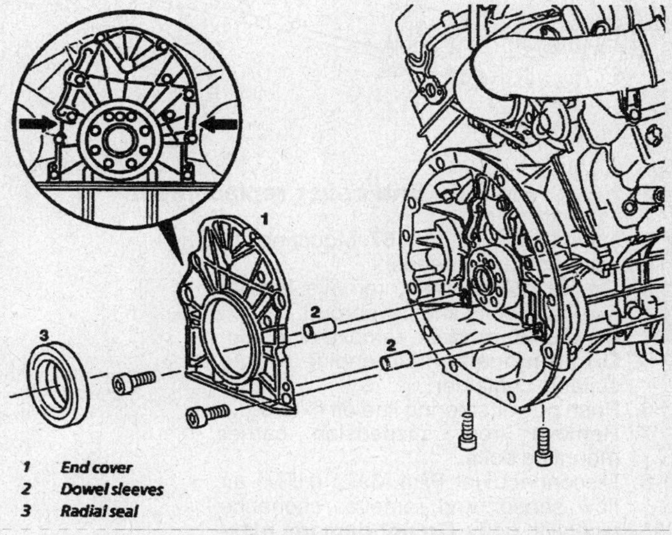

Fig. 55 Flywheel replacement

E320

Less 4MATIC

Refer to "E55 & E430."

With 4MATIC

This procedure has been revised by a Technical Service Bulletin.

1. Remove engine compartment paneling.
2. Drain engine oil into suitable container.
3. Remove engine trim panel or air cleaner off cylinder head covers.
4. Remove viscous fan mounting nut while counterholding pulley socket bolts with suitable wrench, **Fig. 65.** Mounting nut has righthand threads.
5. Disconnect fan connector and remove shroud.
6. Disconnect Hot Film Mass (HFM) air flow sensor and remove resonance pipe with body, **Do not damage plastic plate.**
7. Remove mounting bolts and bottom part of oil pan.
8. Disconnect oil level sensor electrical connector.
9. Remove mounting bolt and oil pipe from dipstick.
10. Raise and support vehicle, the remove front wheels.
11. Remove exhaust system as described under "Engine, Replace."
12. Disconnect front drive shafts from drive gear. **Do not damage drive shaft seals.**
13. Remove front drive gear.
14. Remove front axle carrier front engine mount bolts as outlined under "Engine Mount, Replace."
15. Install engine support frame tool No. 140 589 01 61 00, or equivalent, and hook to engine suspension eyes.
16. Raise engine, noting the following:
    a. Ensure engine and attachments do not touch body.
    b. Do not overextend coolant hoses.
17. Support front axle carrier with suitable jack using adapter tool No. 210 589 01 62 00, or equivalent.
18. Remove steering coupling bolt.
19. Remove front axle carrier ATF line fixture mounting bolt.
20. Remove front axle carrier mounting bolts.
21. Lower front axle carrier.
22. Remove oil pan mounting bolts. Record lengths, diameters and locations for installation, **Fig. 66.**
23. Remove oil pan to the front. Rotate crankshaft slightly, as required.
24. Reverse procedure to install, noting the following:
    a. Apply .0591–.0984 inch bead of Loctite 5900 sealant, or equivalent, to sealing surfaces, **Figs. 61 and 63. Do not spread bead. Ensure sealant does not get into oil galleries.**
    b. Install pan within 10 minutes of sealant application.
    c. Insert front axle carrier locating pins in longitudinal member holes.
    d. Install new front axle carrier mounting bolts. **Do not install at an angle.**
    e. **Do not use impact wrench to install front axle carrier mounting bolts.**
    f. **Do not retap front axle carrier longitudinal member.**
    g. Install new steering joint bolt and nut.
    h. Ensure cables or hoses are not pinched.
    i. Install new oil pipe seal.
    j. Tighten mounting bolts to specifications.

ML55, ML320 & ML430

1. Remove engine trim panel.
2. **On ML320 and ML320 models,** remove viscous fan mounting nut while counterholding pulley socket bolts with

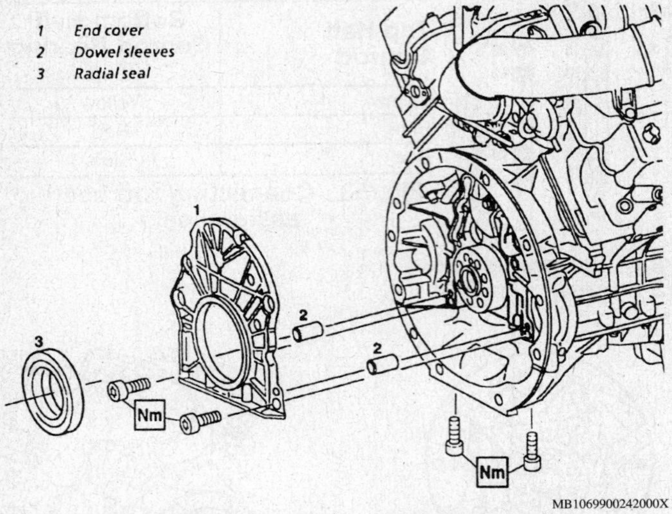

Fig. 56 End cover replacement

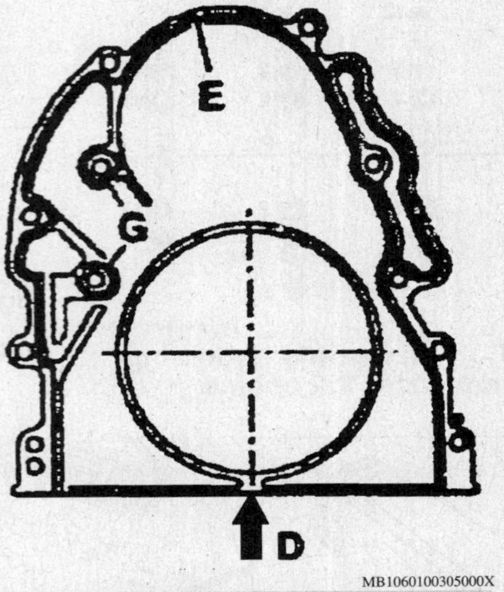

Fig. 57 End cover sealing surfaces

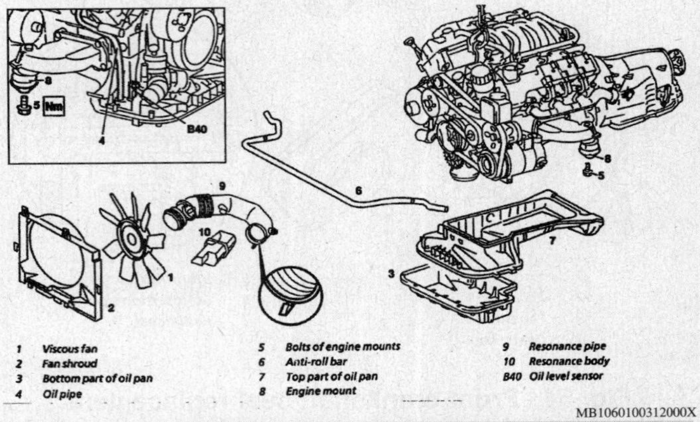

Fig. 58 Top oil pan replacement. C43, C280, ML55, ML320 & ML430

suitable wrench, **Fig. 67.** Mounting nut has righthand threads.

3. **On ML320 models,** remove bottom mounting bolts and fan shroud.
4. **On ML430 models,** remove air guide.
5. **On all models,** drain engine oil into suitable container.
6. Push power steering line off fixture.
7. Remove front suspension carrier mounting bolts.
8. Disconnect Hot Film Mass (HFM) air flow sensor and remove resonance pipe with body, **Do not damage plastic plate.**
9. Install suitable engine support frame attached to engine lifting eyes.
10. Raise engine, noting the following:
    a. Ensure engine does not touch body.
    b. Do not overextend coolant hoses.
    c. Do not overextend ground. Disconnect as required.
11. Remove mounting bolts and bottom oil pan.
12. Disconnect oil level sensor connector and remove cable strap at oil pipe, **Fig. 68.**
13. Remove mounting bolt and oil pipe.
14. Remove oil pan mounting bolts. Record lengths, diameters and locations for installation, **Figs. 59 and 60.**
15. Remove oil pan to the front. Rotate crankshaft slightly, as required.
16. Reverse procedure to install, noting the following:
    a. Apply .0591–.0984 inch bead of Loctite 5900 sealant, or equivalent, to sealing surfaces, **Figs. 61, 63 and 69 . Do not spread bead. Ensure sealant does not get into oil galleries.**
    b. Install pan within 10 minutes of sealant application.
    c. Ensure cables or hoses are not pinched.
    d. Install new oil pipe seal.
    e. Tighten mounting bolts to specifications.

S430 & 2000-01 S500

This procedure has been revised by a Technical Service Bulletin.

1. Remove lower engine compartment paneling.
2. Drain engine oil into suitable container.
3. Remove front axle carrier front engine mount bolts as outlined under "Engine Mount, Replace."
4. Install suitable engine support frame and hook to engine suspension eyes.
5. Raise engine, noting the following:
    a. Ensure engine and attachments do not touch body.
    b. Do not overextend coolant hoses.
6. Remove steering coupling bolt.
7. Support front axle carrier with suitable jack using suitable transmission plate.
8. Lower front axle carrier. **Do not disconnect power steering pump lines.**
9. Disconnect oil level sensor electrical connector.
10. Remove mounting bolts and bottom part of oil pan.
11. Remove mounting bolt and oil pipe from dipstick.
12. Remove oil pan mounting bolts. Record lengths, diameters and locations for installation, **Fig. 60.**
13. Remove oil pan to the front. Rotate crankshaft slightly, as required.
14. Reverse procedure to install, noting the following:
    a. Apply .0591–.0984 inch bead of Loctite 5900 sealant, or equivalent, to sealing surfaces, **Figs. 63 and 69. Do not spread bead. Ensure sealant does not get into oil galleries.**
    b. Install pan within 10 minutes of sealant application.
    c. Insert front axle carrier locating pins in longitudinal member holes.
    d. Install new front axle carrier mounting bolts.
    e. Install new steering joint bolt and nut.
    f. Ensure cables or hoses are not pinched.
    g. Install new oil pipe seal.
    h. Tighten mounting bolts to specifications.

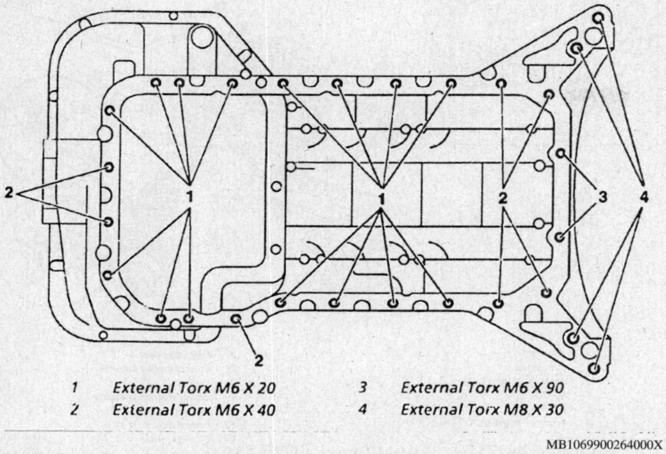

Fig. 59 Oil pan bolt sizes, lengths & locations. 112 engine less 4MATIC

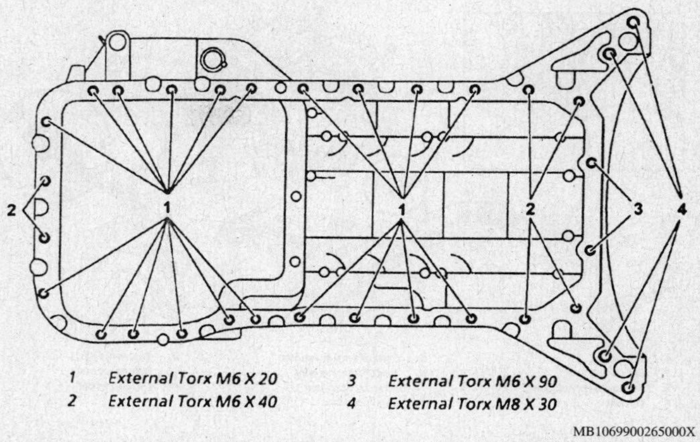

Fig. 60 Oil pan bolt sizes, lengths & locations. 113 engine

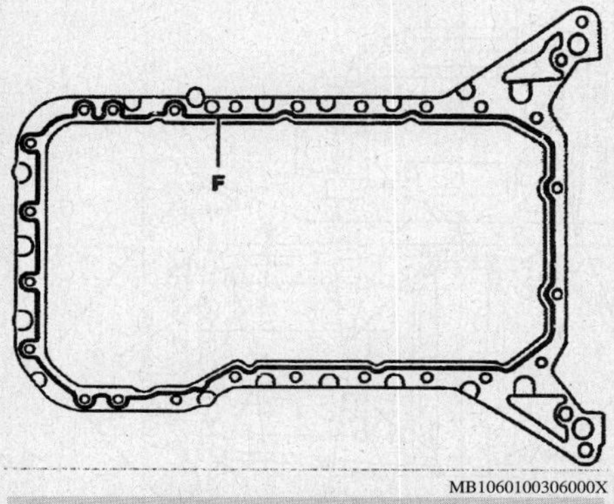

Fig. 61 Top oil pan sealing surfaces. 112 engine

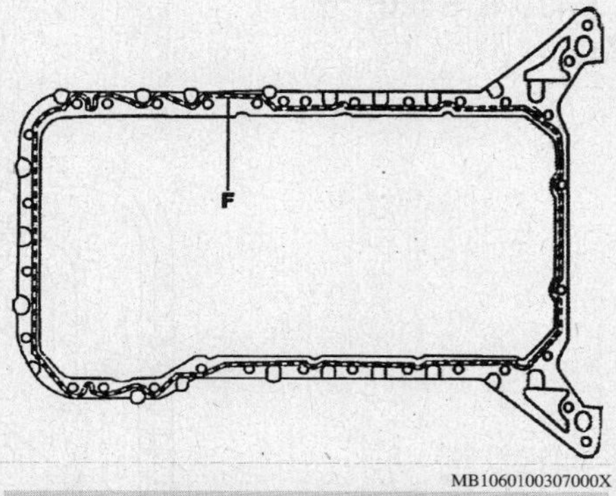

Fig. 62 Top oil pan sealing surfaces. C43, CLK55, CLK430, E55 & E430 & 1999–2001 SL500

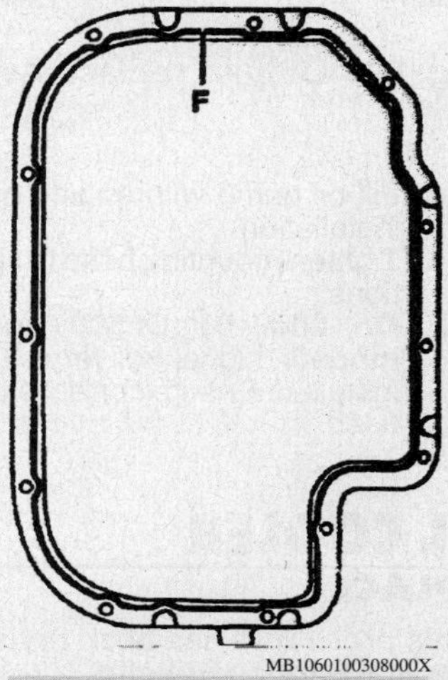

Fig. 63 Bottom oil pan sealing surfaces

1999–2001 SL500

This procedure has been revised by a Technical Service Bulletin.

1. Remove engine compartment paneling, **Fig. 70.**
2. Drain engine oil into suitable container.
3. Remove air cleaner off cylinder head covers.
4. Remove viscous fan mounting nut while counterholding pulley socket bolts with suitable wrench. Mounting nut has righthand threads.
5. Remove Hot Film Mass (HFM) air flow sensor with air intake pipe.
6. Disconnect AFT lines on left and right-hand sides at transmission bell housing, noting the following:
   a. Catch fluid in suitable container.
   b. Seal and plug connections and openings.
7. Remove mounting bolts and bottom part of oil pan.
8. Disconnect oil level sensor connector.
9. Remove front axle carrier front engine mount bolts as outlined under "Engine Mount, Replace."
10. Remove mounting bolt and oil pipe from dipstick.
11. Install suitable engine support frame and hook to engine suspension eyes.
12. Raise engine, noting the following:
    a. Ensure engine and attachments do not touch body.
    b. Do not overextend coolant hoses.
13. Remove engine support engine mount bolts.
14. Remove engine mount as described under "Engine Mount, Replace."
15. Remove oil pan mounting bolts. Record lengths, diameters and locations for installation, **Fig 60.**
16. Remove oil pan to the front. Rotate crankshaft slightly, as required.
17. Reverse procedure to install, noting the following:
    a. Apply .0591–.0984 inch bead of Loctite 5900 sealant, or equivalent, to sealing surfaces, **Figs. 62 and 63. Do not spread bead. Ensure sealant does not get into oil galleries.**
    b. Install pan within 10 minutes of sealant application.
    c. Ensure cables or hoses are not pinched.
    d. Install new oil pipe seal.
    e. Tighten mounting bolts to specifications.

OIL PUMP

REPLACE

This procedure has been revised by a Technical Service Bulletin.

1. Remove oil pan bottom as outlined under "Oil Pan, Replace."
2. Remove oil pump mounting bolts, push back chain tensioner and remove chain, **Fig. 71.**
3. Remove oil pump.
4. Reverse procedure to install, noting the following:
   a. Ensure oil return flow check valve is correctly located.
   b. Clean oil pump strainer.

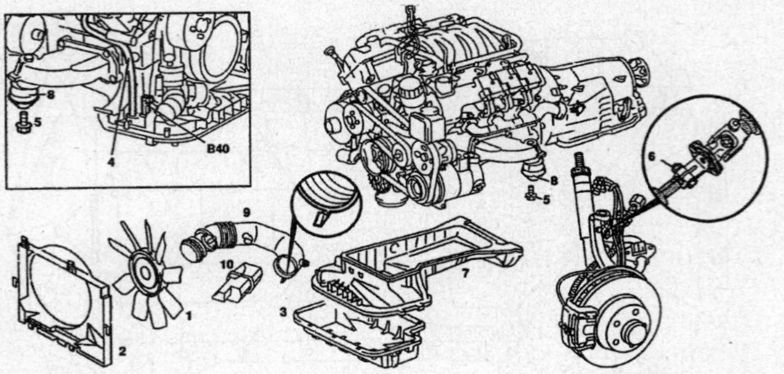

1 Viscous fan
2 Fan shroud
3 Bottom part of oil pan
4 Oil pipe
5 Bolts of engine mounts
6 Bolt of steering joint
7 Top part of oil pan
8 Engine mount
9 Resonance pipe
10 Resc.nance body
B40 Oil level sensor
15 Bolts of front axle carrier
16 Front axle carrier
17 Fixture
18 Oil line

MB1060100303000X

Fig. 64 Oil pan replacement. E55 & E430 & E320 less 4MATIC

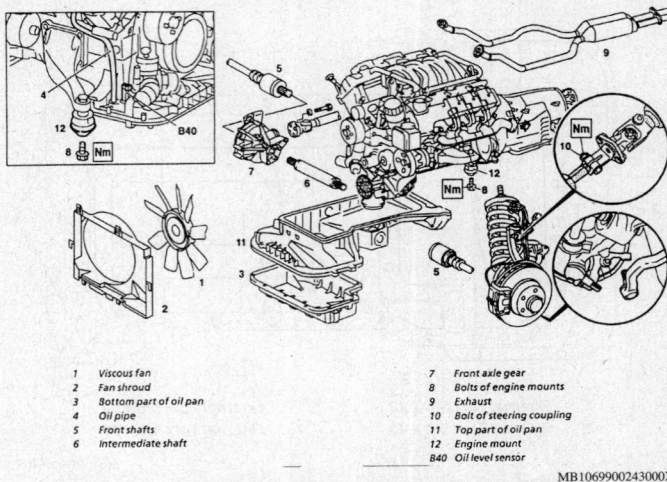

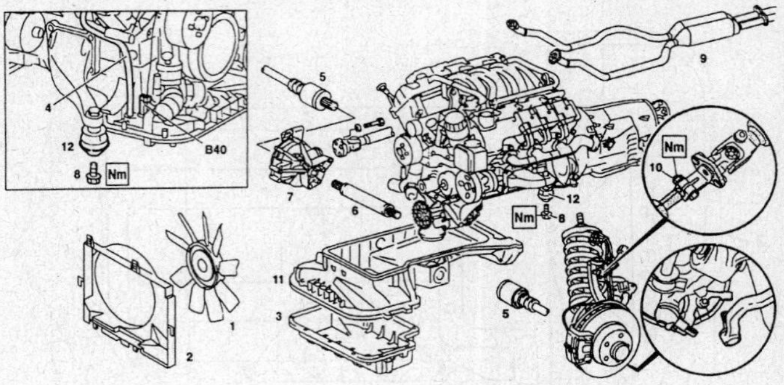

1 Viscous fan
2 Fan shroud
3 Bottom part of oil pan
4 Oil pipe
5 Front shafts
6 Intermediate shaft
7 Front axle gear
8 Bolts of engine mounts
9 Exhaust
10 Bolt of steering coupling
11 Top part of oil pan
12 Engine mount
B40 Oil level sensor

MB1069900243000X

Fig. 65 Oil pan replacement. E320 w/4MATIC

c. Fill oil pump with engine oil before installation.
d. Tighten mounting bolts to specifications.
e. **On 2000–01 CL500 and S500 models,** higher delivery oil pump is installed. Ensure correct oil pump is used.

OIL COOLER

REPLACE

This procedure has been revised by a Technical Service Bulletin.

1. **On S430 and 2000–01 S500 models,** disconnect engine face end cover.
2. **On all models,** remove engine trim panel of air cleaner from cylinder head covers.
3. **On C43, C280, CLK55, CLK430, E55, E320, E430, ML320, ML430 and SLK320 and 1999–2001 SL500 models,** remove viscous fan mounting nut while counterholding pulley socket bolts with suitable wrench. Mounting nut has righthand threads.
4. **On all models,** disconnect fan connector and remove shroud.
5. Remove oil filter housing and filter element allowing oil to flow back oil pan.
6. Drain radiator coolant into suitable container.
7. Disconnect oil-to-water heat exchanger coolant hoses.
8. Remove air pump as required.
9. Remove mounting bolts and heat exchanger at oil filter housing.
10. Reverse procedure to install, noting the following:
    a. Install new seals.
    b. Tighten mounting bolts to specifications.

BELT TENSION DATA

Belt tension is maintained by an automatic belt tensioner.

SERPENTINE DRIVE BELT

BELT, REPLACE

1. **On C43, C280, CLK55, CLK430, E55, E320, E430, ML320, ML430 and SLK320 and 1999–2001 SL500 models,** remove viscous fan mounting nut while counterholding pulley socket bolts with suitable wrench. Mounting nut has righthand threads.
2. **On all models,** disconnect fan connector and remove shroud.
3. Remove fan shroud.
4. Loosen belt by swiveling tensioning pulley stud bolt counterclockwise.
5. Lock tensioning pulley using suitable .1969 inch pin or drift.
6. **On SLK320 models equipped with manual transmission,** remove shock absorber mounting bolts.

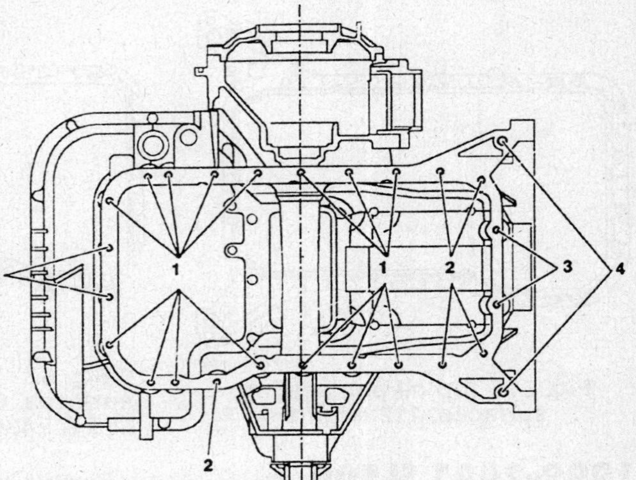

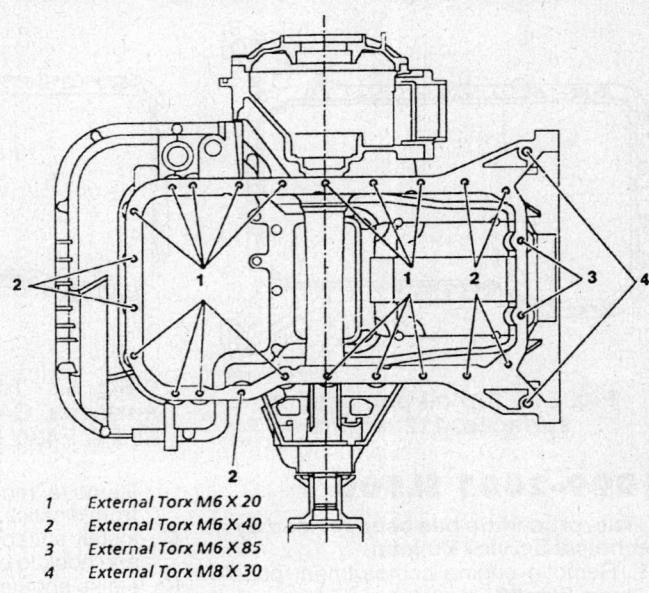

1 External Torx M6 X 20
2 External Torx M6 X 40
3 External Torx M6 X 85
4 External Torx M8 X 30

MB1069900263000X

Fig. 66 Oil pan bolt sizes, lengths & locations. E320 w/4MATIC

7. **On all models,** remove tensioning device
8. Remove belt.
9. Reverse procedure to install. Tighten mounting bolts to specifications.

ROUTING

Refer to **Fig. 72** for serpentine belt routing.

TENSIONER, REPLACE

1. Remove belt as outlined under "Belt, Replace."
2. Remove mounting bolt and tensioner.
3. Reverse procedure to install. Tighten mounting bolts to specifications.

COOLING SYSTEM BLEED

1. Fill cooling system.

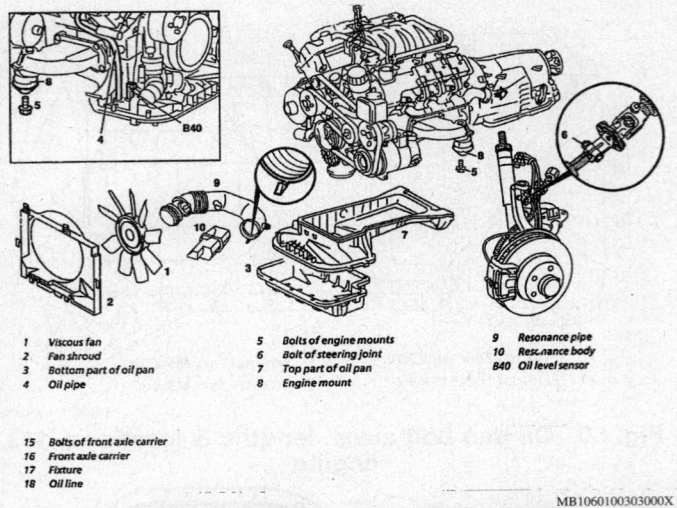

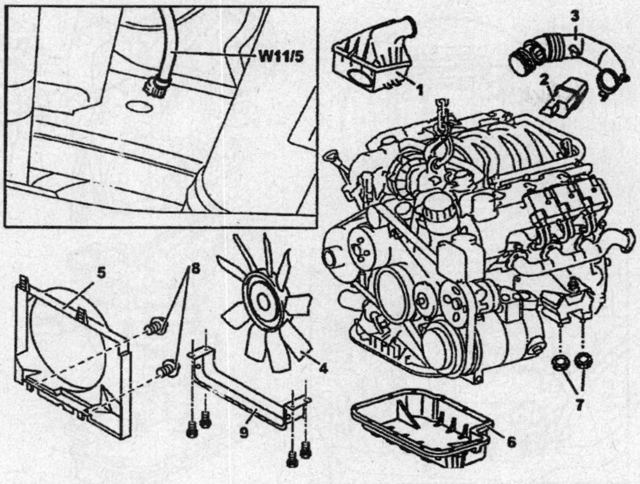

1	Air cleaner housing	6	Bottom part of oil pan
2	Resonance body	7	Nuts
3	Resonance pipe	8	Bolts of fan shroud
4	Viscous fan	9	Air guide
5	Fan shroud	W11/5	Ground cable from engine to vehicle frame

MB1060100309000X

Fig. 67 Bottom oil pan replacement. ML55, ML320 & ML430

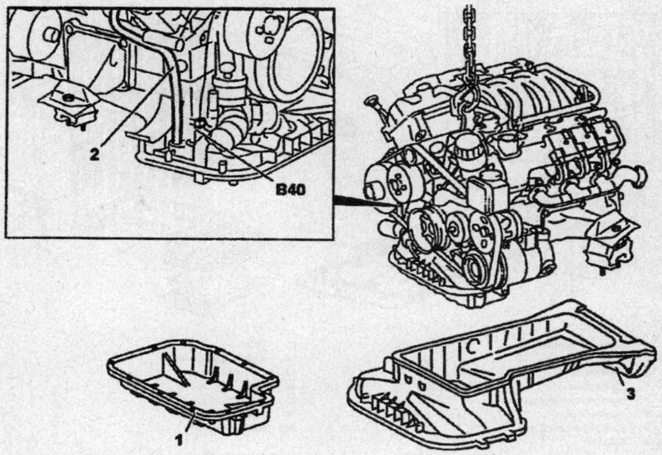

1	Bottom part of oil pan
2	Oil pipe
3	Top part of oil pan
B40	Oil level sensor

MB1060100310000X

Fig. 68 Top oil pan replacement. ML55, ML320 & ML430

2. Turn heater to On.
3. Warm engine by running at moderate RPM.
4. Adjust coolant level as required.
5. When coolant has reached operating temperature (140–158°F), seal system by installing cap at radiator or expansion tank.

THERMOSTAT

REPLACE

1. Drain radiator coolant into suitable container.
2. **On S430 and 2000–01 S500 models,** disconnect engine front end clip.
3. **On all models,** remove engine trim panel or air cleaner from cylinder head covers.
4. Disconnect coolant hose.
5. Remove mounting bolts, housing and thermostat. Thermostat cannot be remove from housing.
6. Reverse procedure to install, noting the following:
   a. Install new seal.
   b. Tighten mounting bolts to specifications.

WATER PUMP

REPLACE

1. **On S430 and 2000–01 S500 models,** disconnect engine front end clip.
2. **On all models,** remove engine trim panel or air cleaner from cylinder head covers.
3. **On C43, C280, CLK55, CLK430, E55, E320, E430, ML320, ML430 and 1999–2001 SL500 models,** remove viscous fan mounting nut while counterholding pulley socket bolts with suitable wrench, **Fig. 73.** Mounting nut has righthand threads.

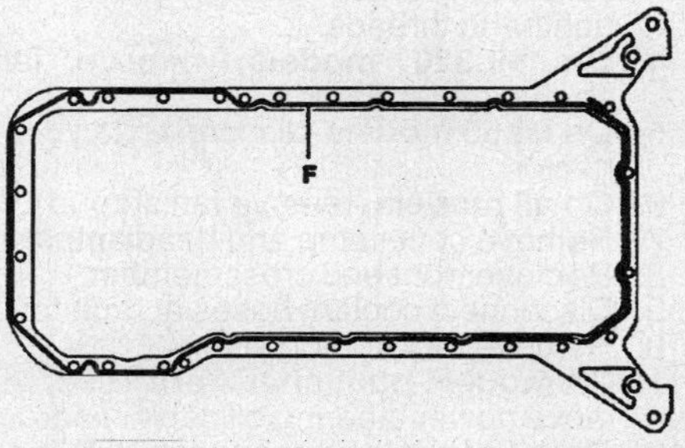

MB1060100311000X

Fig. 69 Top oil pan sealing surfaces. ML55, ML430 & S430 & 2000–01 CL500

4. **On all models,** disconnect fan connector and remove shroud.
5. Drain radiator coolant into suitable container.
6. Remove serpentine drive belt as described under "Serpentine Drive Belt."
7. Disconnect coolant hoses.
8. Disconnect coolant hose to oil cooler.
9. Remove mounting bolts and pulley.
10. Remove mounting bolts and water pump.
11. Reverse procedure to install, noting the following:
    a. Install new gasket.
    b. Tighten mounting bolts to specifications.

RADIATOR

REPLACE

C43 & C280

1. Remove engine compartment panel.
2. Drain radiator coolant into suitable container.
3. Remove viscous fan mounting nut while counterholding pulley socket bolts with suitable wrench. Mounting nut has righthand threads.
4. Disconnect fan connector and remove shroud.
5. Remove protective grille.
6. Remove radiator bottom ATF line fixture mounting bolt.
7. Disconnect ATF lines from radiator. Plug and seal lines and openings.
8. **On C43 models,** remove air cleaner air inlet pipe.
9. **On all models,** remove clips and front end crossmember.
10. Disconnect coolant hoses at radiator.
11. Remove condenser mounting bolts.
12. Remove radiator.
13. Reverse procedure to install, noting the following:
    a. Ensure mounting studs engage rubber grommets at bottom crossmember.
    b. Tighten mounting bolts to specifications.

CLK55, CLK320 & CLK430

1. Remove engine compartment panel.
2. Drain radiator coolant into suitable container.
3. **On CLK430 models,** remove front engine compartment bottom cover.
4. **On CLK55 and CLK430 models,** remove viscous fan mounting nut while counterholding pulley socket bolts with suitable wrench. Mounting nut has righthand threads.
5. **On all models,** disconnect fan connector and remove shroud.
6. **On CLK55 and CLK430 models,** remove protective grille.
7. **On all models,** remove radiator bottom ATF line fixture mounting bolt.
8. Disconnect ATF lines from radiator. Plug and seal lines and openings.
9. **On CLK55 and CLK430 models,** remove both air liner pipes.
10. **On all models,** remove clips and front end crossmember.

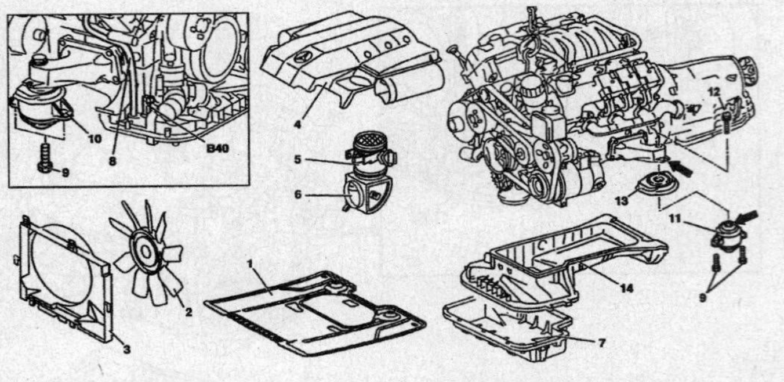

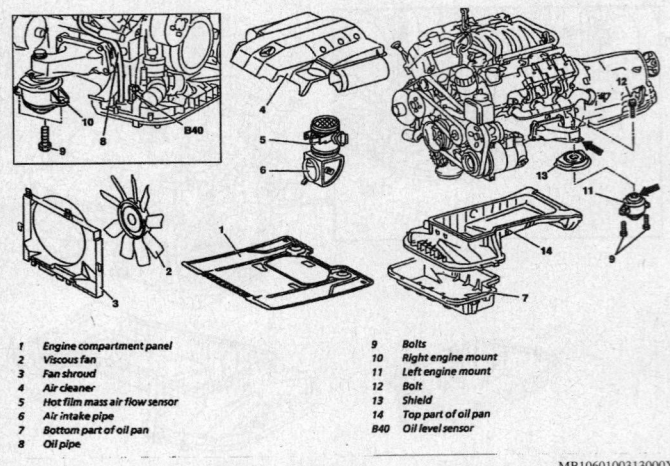

1 Engine compartment panel
2 Viscous fan
3 Fan shroud
4 Air cleaner
5 Hot film mass air flow sensor
6 Air intake pipe
7 Bottom part of oil pan
8 Oil pipe
9 Bolts
10 Right engine mount
11 Left engine mount
12 Bolt
13 Shield
14 Top part of oil pan
B40 Oil level sensor

MB1060100313000X

Fig. 70 Top oil pan replacement. 1999–2001 SL500

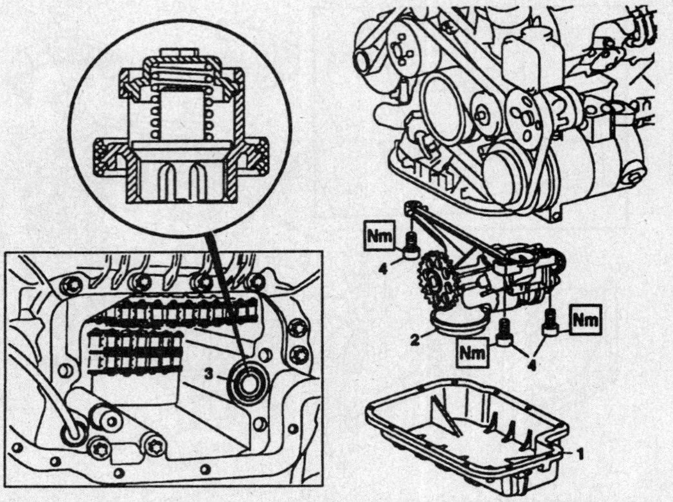

1 Bottom part of oil pan
2 Oil pump
3 Oil return flow check valve
4 Bolts of oil pump

MB1069900266000X

Fig. 71 Oil pump replacement

11. Disconnect coolant hoses at radiator.
12. Remove condenser mounting bolts.
13. Remove radiator.
14. Reverse procedure to install, noting the following:
    a. Ensure mounting studs engage rubber grommets at bottom crossmember.
    b. Tighten mounting bolts to specifications.

E55, E320 & E430

1. Remove engine compartment panel.
2. Drain radiator coolant into suitable container.
3. **On E430 models,** remove front engine compartment bottom cover.
4. **On all models,** remove viscous fan mounting nut while counterholding pulley socket bolts with suitable wrench. Mounting nut has righthand threads.
5. Disconnect fan connector and remove shroud.
6. Remove protective grille.
7. **On E320 models,** remove radiator bottom ATF line fixture mounting bolt.
8. **On all models,** disconnect ATF lines from radiator. Plug and seal lines and openings.
9. Remove air cleaner air inlet pipe.
10. **On models equipped less 4MATIC,** remove clips and front end crossmember.
11. **On all models,** disconnect coolant hoses at radiator.
12. Remove condenser mounting bolts.
13. Remove radiator.
14. Reverse procedure to install, noting the following:
    a. Ensure mounting studs engage rubber grommets at bottom crossmember.
    b. Tighten mounting bolts to specifications.

ML55, ML320 & ML430

If replacing radiator on models built before May 1998, power steering oil cooler is integrated into new radiators.

1. **On ML430 models,** remove air baffle.
2. **On all models,** drain cooling system into suitable container.
3. **On ML320 and ML430 models,** remove viscous fan mounting nut while counterholding pulley socket bolts with suitable wrench. Mounting nut has righthand threads.
4. **On ML320 models,** remove fan shroud metal clamps.
5. **On ML55 models,** disconnect fan connector.
6. **On all models,** remove fan shroud.
7. Remove cover strip and headlamps.
8. Remove front end crossmember.
9. Disconnect coolant hoses at radiator.
10. Remove radiator top seal.
11. **On models built after April 1998,** remove power steering oil cooler lines.
12. **On all models,** disconnect AFT lines at radiator. Plug and seal lines and openings.
13. Remove fan grille.
14. Remove condenser mounting bolts. **Do not disconnect lines.**
15. Remove condenser to radiator insulators.
16. Remove mounting bolts and place air condition receiver to side with lines connector.
17. Disconnect condenser from radiator.
18. Remove radiator.
19. Remove mounting clamps and air guides.
20. Reverse procedure to install, noting the following:
    a. Install new air guides' clamps.
    b. Ensure radiator studs engage crossmember bottom rubber pads.
    c. Tighten mounting bolts and nuts to specifications.

S430 & 2000-01 S500 & 2001 CL600 & S600

1. Remove engine compartment bottom panel.
2. Drain radiator coolant into suitable container.
3. Remove air cleaner air intake pipes.
4. Remove fan shroud retaining lugs' mounting screws.
5. Disconnect fan electrical connector.
6. **On 2001 CL600 and S600 models,** remove fan shroud coolant hose mounting clips.
7. **On all models,** disconnect coolant hoses from radiator.
8. Remove ATF line mounting plate bolts.
9. Remove fan shroud with retaining lugs.
10. Disconnect ATF lines from radiator. Plug and seal lines and openings.
11. Remove air conditioning condenser mounting nuts.
12. Remove bracket mounting bolts and radiator.
13. Reverse procedure to install, noting the following:
    a. Ensure radiator stubs locate in crossmember bottom rubber pads.
    b. Tighten mounting bolts and nuts to specifications.

1999-2001 SL500

1. Remove engine compartment panels.
2. Drain radiator coolant into suitable container.
3. Remove viscous fan mounting nut while counterholding pulley socket bolts with suitable wrench. Mounting nut has righthand threads.
4. Disconnect fan connector and remove fan shroud.
5. Remove cover.
6. Disconnect coolant hoses.
7. Disconnect ATF lines at radiator. Plug and seal lines and openings.
8. Disconnect ATF line radiator fixture.
9. Remove mounting clips and front end crossmember.
10. Disconnect air conditioning compressor line fixture.
11. Remove three mounting bolts and condenser.
12. Remove radiator.
13. Reverse procedure to install, noting the following:
    a. Ensure radiator studs engage crossmember bottom rubber pads.

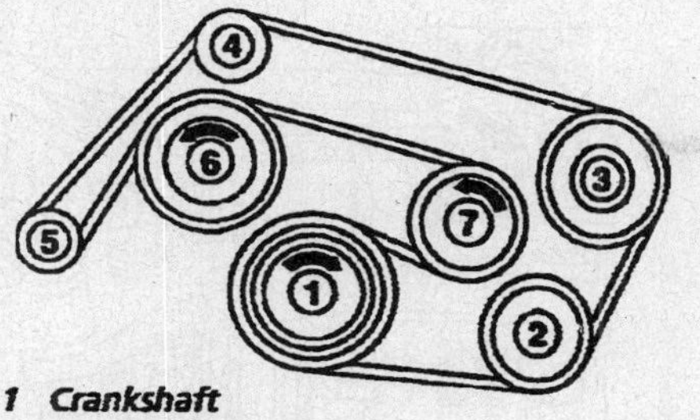

Fig. 72 Serpentine belt routing

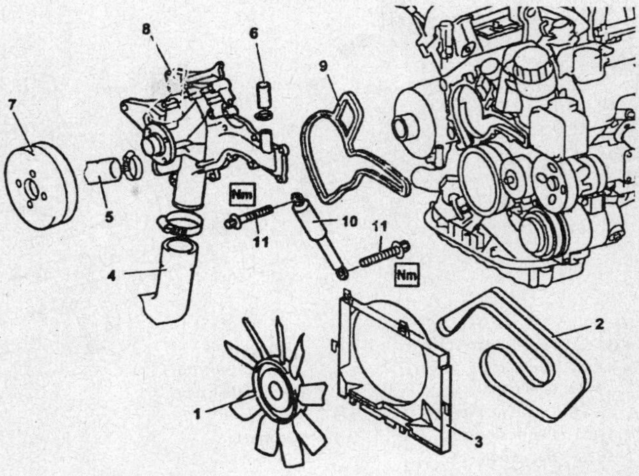

Fig. 73 Water pump replacement

  b. Ensure condenser is located on two radiator mounts.
  c. Tighten mounting bolts and nuts to specifications.

FUEL PUMP

REPLACE

E55, E320 & E430

1. Relieve fuel pressure as described under "Precautions."
2. Remove banjo bolt, **Figs. 74 and 75.**
3. **On E320 station wagon models,** do not pinch fuel hose at elbow.
4. **On all models,** pinch off and disconnect fuel lines.
5. Remove fuel pump.
6. Reverse procedure to install, noting the following:
   a. Plastic sleeve must project at both sides of bracket. Replace as required.
   b. Install new copper seals.

ML55, ML320 & ML430

1. Relieve fuel pressure as described under "Precautions."
2. Remove lefthand rear seat mounting bracket, raise seat and support with suitable 20-inch long wooden block, **Fig. 76.**
3. Turn carpeting up to expose fuel pump body. **Do not bend carpeting.**
4. Remove body cover by heating cover with hot air fan to loosen sealant.
5. Disconnect electrical connector.
6. Disconnect fuel lines using pliers No. 163 589 00 37 00, or equivalent. **Do not kink fuel lines.**
7. **If fuel pump is working,** proceed as follows:
   a. Disconnect fuel feed line from fuel rail. **Collect spilled fuel.**
   b. Connect suitable 10 mm fuel hose to fuel feed line and insert other end into suitable container.
   c. Remove fuel pump relay.
   d. Bridge relay, turn ignition switch to On position and drain fuel tank into suitable container. If tank is full, this procedure may take approximately 15 minutes.
8. **If fuel pump is not working,** proceed as follows:
   a. Connect adapter hose No. 168 589 00 91 00 and extractor hose No. 168 589 00 90 00, or equivalents, to fuel feed line and drain fuel tank into suitable container using suitable suction pump.
9. **On all models,** remove union nut using pronged wrench tool No. 163 589 01 07 00, or equivalent.
10. Remove fuel pump.
11. Reverse procedure to install, noting the following:
    a. Install new seal
    b. Tighten new union nut to specifications.
    c. Tighten seat mounting bolts to specifications.

S430 & 1999-2001 SL500 & 2000-01 S500

1. Relieve fuel pressure as described under "Precautions."
2. Remove fuel pump cover.
3. Pinch of fuel suction and pressure hoses.
4. Disconnect electrical connections.
5. Remove fuel pump.
6. Reverse procedure to install. Install new fuel hose clamps.

FUEL FILTER

REPLACE

ML55, ML320 & ML430

1. Relieve fuel pressure as outlined under "Precautions."
2. Remove fuel tank filler cap to release fuel tank pressure.
3. Remove lefthand rear tire and wheel assembly.
4. Remove plastic wheelwell liner.
5. Remove fuel feed and return flow lines using pliers tool No. 163 589 00 37 00, or equivalent, **Fig. 77. Do not kink fuel lines.**
6. Disconnect spring chamber breather line.
7. Loosen mounting clamp and pull filter with pressure regulator to front.
8. Reverse procedure to install. Tighten clamp to specifications.

TECHNICAL SERVICE BULLETINS

ENGINE DOES NOT START

On some of these models equipped with Brake Assist (BAS) control module, occasionally the engine may not start, the touch/start feature may not work or the engine may do into limp home mode.

This condition may be caused by moisture/corrosion in the connector or the BAS control module.

To correct this condition, proceed as follows:

1. Inspect CAN/power supply connector No. 3 for moisture and corrosion. Repair as required.
2. If condition is still present, replace BAS control module.

OIL LEAK FROM LEFTHAND DRAIN OPENING

C280, CLK320, E320 & ML320

On some of these models through No. 074999, there may be an oil leak from the lefthand side drain opening.

This condition may be caused by missing of damaged oil duct screw connection sealing ring at front in crankcase V.

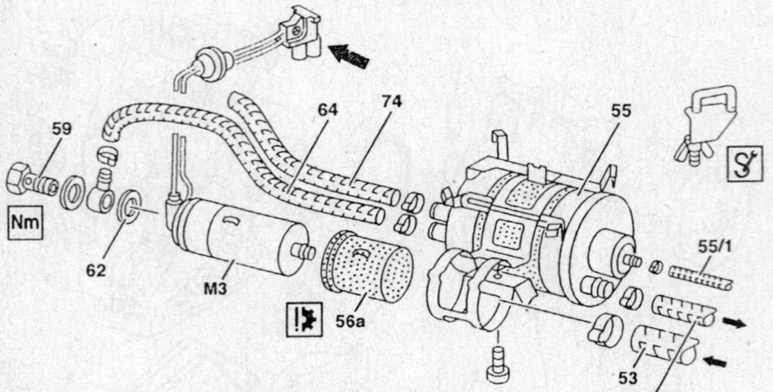

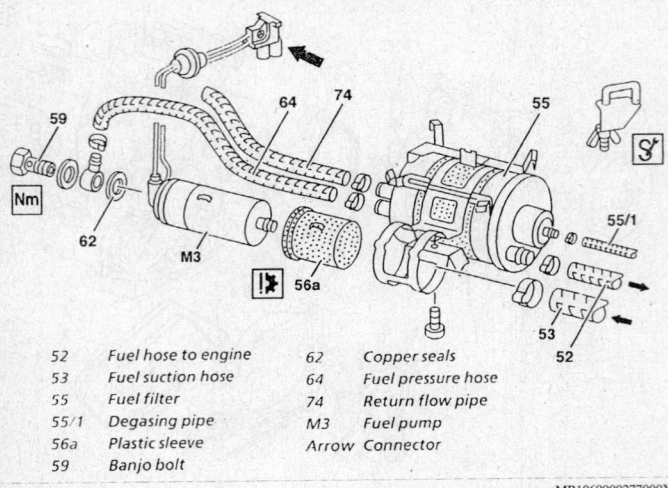

52	Fuel hose to engine	62	Copper seals
53	Fuel suction hose	64	Fuel pressure hose
55	Fuel filter	74	Return flow pipe
55/1	Degasing pipe	M3	Fuel pump
56a	Plastic sleeve	Arrow	Connector
59	Banjo bolt		

MB1069900277000X

Fig. 74 Fuel pump replacement. E55, E320 & E430

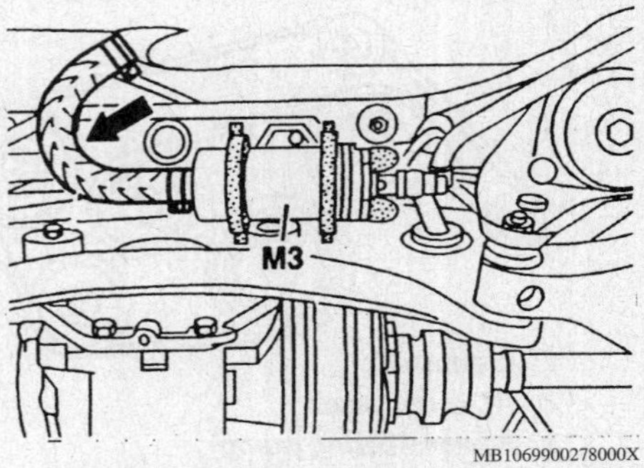

Fig. 75 Fuel pump replacement. E320 station wagon

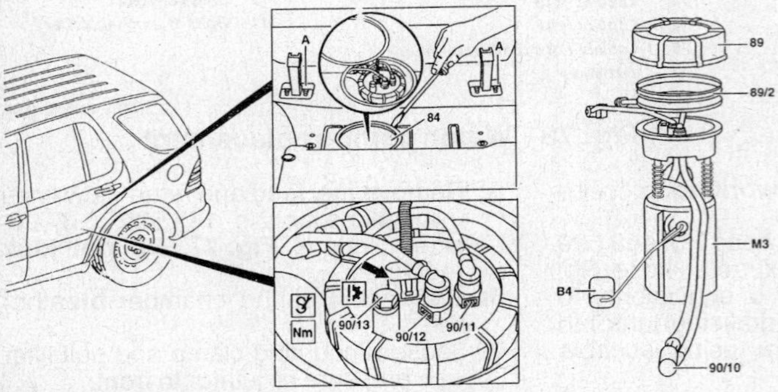

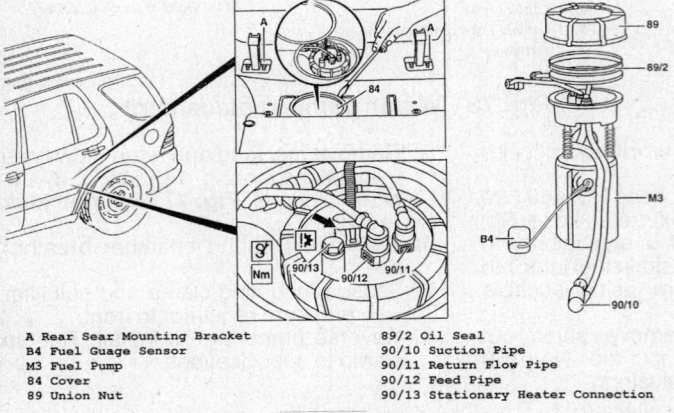

A Rear Sear Mounting Bracket	89/2 Oil Seal
B4 Fuel Guage Sensor	90/10 Suction Pipe
M3 Fuel Pump	90/11 Return Flow Pipe
84 Cover	90/12 Feed Pipe
89 Union Nut	90/13 Stationary Heater Connection

MB1069900276000X

Fig. 76 Fuel pump replacement. ML55, ML320 & ML430

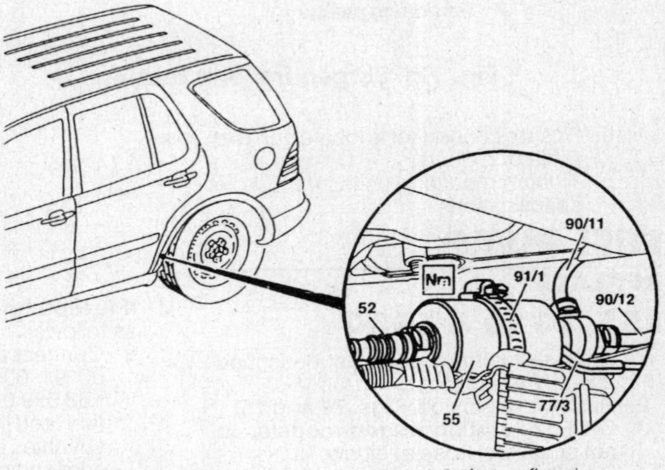

52	Fuel pipe to engine	90/11	Fuel return flow pipe
55	Fuel filter with pressure regulator	90/12	Fuel feed pipe
77/3	Connection of spring chamber breather	91/1	Clip

MB1069900279000X

Fig. 77 Fuel filter replacement. ML320 & ML430

To correct this condition, proceed as follows:

1. Remove intake manifold.
2. Replace sealing ring.

ENGINE CANNOT BE STARTED

1999 C280, CLK320, ML320 & E320

On some of these models with engine control modules built between Sept. 2, 1998 and February 19, 1999, the started will not crank the engine and the ME-SFI cannot be diagnosed.

This condition may be caused by the engine control module.

To correct this condition replace engine control modules built between Sept. 2, 1998 and February 19, 1999. Production date is stamped on part number label at upper righthand corner of bar code. Code No. 980902 equals Sept. 2, 1998.

ENGINE OIL ABOVE MAX. LEVEL

On some of these models the engine oil level may be above the Max. mark dip stick or by the oil sensor.

This condition may be caused by diesel or fuel oil or other subsequent additives in the fuel that did not burn and collected in the engine oil pan.

To correct this condition, proceed as follows:

1. Replace engine oil.
2. Drain fuel tank of foreign substances.
3. Do not replace sensor.

OIL LEVEL WARNING LAMP ON

On some of these models the oil level warning lamp may come on or the Flexible Service System (FSS) instrument cluster may display message "Oil Level Below Minimum" or "Oil Sensor Defective." Diagnostic Trouble Code (DTC) P1178 or P1179 may be also be stored.

To correct this condition replace oil sensor with model with white label sticker running number of more than 10700000. Ensure different length bolts are installed in original positions.

DRIVE BELT FLUTTERS OR BANGS AT IDLE

On some of these models built before June 1, 1998, the drive belt may flutter or bang at low or idle engine speeds.

This condition may be caused by contaminated belt tensioner friction damping strip.

To correct this condition, proceed as follows:

1. Replace belt tensioner.
2. If condition still exists, tighten air conditioning compressor mounting bolts.

TIGHTENING SPECIFICATIONS

Year	Component	Torque, Ft. Lbs.
1998–2001	Air Conditioning Compressor	15
	Alternator	31
	Automatic Transmission Oil Line	15
	Balance Shaft Balancing Weight	15④
	Balance Shaft Locking Plate	11
	Camshaft Bearing Bridge	②
	Camshaft Hall Sensor	71①
	Camshaft Sprocket	37④
	Central Bolt	147③
	Crankcase Coolant Drain Plug	22
	Crankshaft Damper	147③
	Crankshaft Front Center Bolt	147③
	Cylinder Head	⑤
	Cylinder Head To Timing Case Front Cover	15
	Drag Link	37⑧
	Driven Plate	33④
	Drive Shaft To Transmission (M10)	29
	Drive Shaft To Transmission (M12)	44
	End Cover	88①
	Exhaust Manifold	12
	Exhaust Pipe Flange	15
	Engine Support To Crankcase	15④
	Fan To Viscous Clutch	88①
	Flywheel	33④
	Front Axle Carrier	96
	Front Cover To Crankcase (Timing Case)	15
	Front Engine Mount To Bracket	48⑨
	Front Engine Mount To Engine Carrier	41⑩
	Front Engine Mount To Engine Support	41⑪
	Front Engine Mount To Engine Support	48⑫
	Front Engine Mounts To Front Axle Carrier	26⑬
	Front Engine Mounts To Front Axle Carrier	18⑭
	Fuel Filter Clamp	27①
	Fuel Filter Or Pump Banjo	18
	Fuel Pump Union Nut	48
	Fuel Rail Line	28
	Heat Exchanger	97①
	Ignition Coil	71①
	Intake Manifold	15
	Oil Cooler	97①
	Oil Filter Cover	18
	Oil Filter Housing	52
	Oil Pan (M6)	88①
	Oil Pan	⑦
	Oil Pan Drain Plug	22
	Power Steering Pump	⑥
	Oil Pan To Oil Pan	88①
	Power Steering Pump Return Line	18①
	Power Steering Pump High Pressure Line	33
	Oil Pump	15
	Oil-Water Heat Exchanger	97①
	Propeller Shaft Clamping Nuts	22–30
	Radiator Drain Plug	13–18①
	Rear Engine Mount Tensioning	29⑩
	Rear Engine Crossmember To Body	29⑮
	Rear Engine Mount To Crossmember	22⑯

Continued

TIGHTENING SPECIFICATIONS—Continued

Year	Component	Torque, Ft. Lbs.
1998–2001	Rear Engine Mount To Crossmember	26⑩
	Rear Engine Mount To Transmission (M8)	18⑩
	Rear Engine Mount To Transmission (M10)	29⑰
	Rear Seat	37⑱
	Serpentine Drive Belt Tensioner	⑦
	Serpentine Drive Belt Tensioner Shock Absorber	18
	Shock Absorber To Drag Link	29⑲
	Spark Plugs	21
	Starter Motor	43
	Steering Coupling	15
	Thermostat Housing	88①
	Timing Case Front Cover To Crankcase	15
	Timing Chain Tensioner	59
	Timing Case Cover	15
	Timing Case To Oil Pan	88①
	Torque Converter	31
	Valve Cover	88①
	Vibration Damper	147③
	Viscous Clutch	33
	Water Pump	⑥
	Water Pump Pulley	88①
	Wheel Bolts	111

①— Inch lbs.
②— Refer to "Cylinder Head, Replace" for tightening sequence.
③— Tighten an additional 95.°
④— Tighten an additional 90.°
⑤— Refer to "Cylinder Head, Replace" for tightening specifications and sequence.
⑥— Not pretapped, 26 ft. lbs.; pretapped, 15 ft. lbs.
⑦— M6, 88 inch lbs., M8, 15 ft. lbs; Not pretapped, 10 ft. lbs.; pretapped, 88 inch lbs.
⑧— C43, C280 & CLK320.
⑨— ML55 & ML430.
⑩— E320 & E430 w/4MATIC.
⑪— C43, C280, CLK55, CLK320, CLK430, E55, E320, E430 & S430 & 1999–2001 S500 & SL500.
⑫— ML320.
⑬— C43, C280, CLK55, CLK320, CLK430, E55, E320, E430, ML55, ML320, ML430, S430 & 1999–2001 S500.
⑭— 1999–2001 SL500.
⑮— C43, C280, CL600, SLK320, CLK430, E320, E430, S430, S500 & S600 & 1999–2001 SL500.
⑯— C43, C280, CL600, CLK320, CLK430, S430, S500 & S600 & E320 & E430 less 4MATIC & 1999–2001 SL500.
⑰— C43, C280, CL600, CLK320, CLK430, E320, E430, S430, S500 & S600 & 1999–2001 SL500.
⑱— ML55, ML320 & ML430.
⑲— C43, C280 & CLK320.

119 V8 Gasoline Engine

NOTE: On Air Bag Equipped Models, Refer To "Air Bag System Precautions" Located In The Front Of This Manual For System Disarming & Arming Procedures.

NOTE: Prior To Performing Any Service Operations Listed In This Section, Consult The "Technical Service Bulletins" Section For Related Information.

INDEX

	Page No.
Belt Tension Data	5-94
Camshaft, Replace	5-90
Installation	5-91
Removal	5-90
Camshaft Adjuster, Replace	5-91
Installation	5-91
Removal	5-91
Compression Pressure	5-85
Cooling System Bleed	5-94
Crankshaft Damper, Replace	5-89
Crankshaft Rear Oil Seal, Replace	5-92
Installation	5-92
Removal	5-92
Crankshaft Seal, Replace	5-92
Installation	5-92
Removal	5-92
Cylinder Head, Replace	5-88
Engine Mount, Replace	5-85
Front	5-85
Rear	5-86
Engine Rebuiding Specifications	5-344
Engine, Replace	5-86
Exhaust Manifold, Replace	5-87
Lefthand	5-87
Righthand	5-88
Front Cover, Replace	5-89
Cylinder Head	5-89
Timing Case	5-89
Front Cover Seal, Replace	5-90
Cylinder Head	5-90
Fuel Filter, Replace	5-95
Fuel Pump, Replace	5-95
Hydraulic Lifters, Replace	5-89
Intake Manifold, Replace	5-87
Main & Rod Bearings	5-92
Connecting Rod	5-92
Main Bearings	5-92
Oil Cooler, Replace	5-94
1998 SL500	5-94
Oil Pump, Replace	5-93
1998 SL500	5-93
Oil Sump, Replace	5-93
Piston & Rod Assembly	5-92
Precautions	5-85
Air Bag Systems	5-85
Battery Ground Cable	5-85
Radio Coded Anti-Theft System	5-85
Radiator, Replace	5-94
1998 SL500	5-94
S420 & 1998–99 CL500 & S500	5-94
Serpentine Drive Belt	5-94
Belt, Replace	5-94
Routing	5-94
Tensioner, Replace	5-94
Technical Service Bulletins	5-95
Coolant Loss	5-95
Engine Oil Above Max. Level	5-95
Excessive Smoke After Starting	5-95
Loud Rattling Noise During Cold Start	5-95
Tappet Noise	5-95
Valve Area Ticking Or Low Oil Pressure	5-95
Thermostat, Replace	5-94
Tightening Specifications	5-96
Timing Chain, Replace	5-90
Timing Chain Tensioner, Replace	5-90
Valve Adjustment	5-88
Valve Cover, Replace	5-88
Water Pump, Replace	5-94

PRECAUTIONS

AIR BAG SYSTEMS

Refer to "Air Bag System Precautions" in front of this manual for system disarming and arming procedures.

BATTERY GROUND CABLE

Prior to service, disconnect battery ground cable and isolate as required.

RADIO CODED ANTI-THEFT SYSTEM

Anti-theft radios have a coded theft protection circuit. The CODE card must be obtained before disconnecting battery, removing radio fuse or removing the radio. **The serial number from the radio must match the CODE card.**

After service has been performed proceed as follows:

1. Connect radio power and turn key to position No. 2.
2. Turn radio to On position. Word "CODE" will appear on display.
3. Enter first digit of anti-theft code from CODE card. "CODE" will disappear and entered digit will appear followed by four dashes.
4. Enter next four digits, when all five are entered first digit flashes again.
5. Press SC, Seek or Tune button to confirm code.
6. If "WAIT" appears on radio panel, proceed as follows:
   a. Radio will allow three coding attempts only before entering lock-up mode and won't respond to controls.
   b. Leave radio on for 15–60 minutes, then radio will unlock and allow three addition coding attempts.
   c. Third lockout period (after nine failed coding attempts) will last 24 hours.
   d. Radio must be left on during enter 24-hour period until "CODE" appears.
7. When "CODE" appears, repeat coding attempt.

COMPRESSION PRESSURE

1. Warm engine to normal operating temperature.
2. Remove spark plug.
3. Crank engine with starter several times to eliminate cylinder combustion residues.
4. Install suitable compression tester into spark plug bore.
5. Open throttle valves wide open.
6. Crank engine with starter eight revolutions.
7. Record compression readings.
8. Normal compression pressure should measure 145–203 psi.
9. Maximum permissible difference between individual cylinders is 22 psi.

ENGINE MOUNT

REPLACE

FRONT

S420 & 1998–99 CL500 & S500

1. Remove intake air scoops.
2. Remove engine compartment bottom cover.
3. Remove fan shroud and place over fan.
4. Remove mounting bolts from bottom, **Fig. 1.**
5. Raise engine at front lifting eye approximately .196 inch.

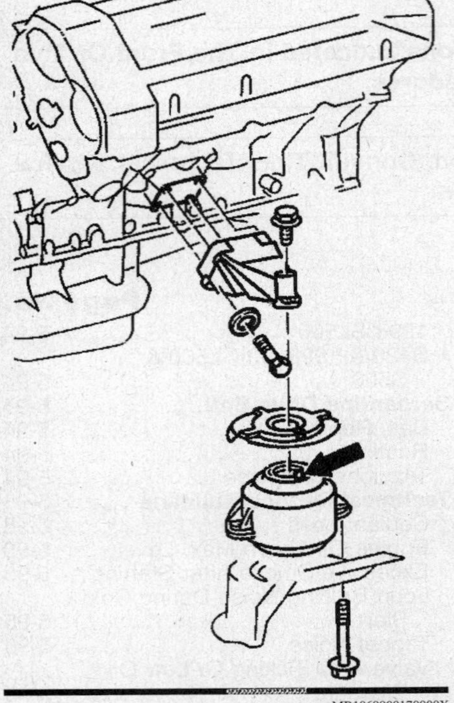

Fig. 1 Front engine mount replacement. S420 & 1998–99 CL500 & S500

6. Remove engine carrier mounting bolts.
7. Raise engine approximately 1.575 inches. **Ensure accelerator control at rear and coolant hoses are not damaged.**
8. Remove engine mount with shield and carrier.
9. Remove mounting bolts and engine mount from carrier. Remove shield.
10. Reverse procedure to install, noting the following:
    a. Engine mount anti-twist locks must engage shield openings and carriers' retaining slots.
    b. Tighten mounting bolts to specifications.
    c. Ensure fan shroud four engaging points are correctly located.

1998 SL500

1. Remove intake air scoops.
2. Remove fan shroud and place over fan.
3. Remove engine compartment bottom cover.
4. Remove mounting bolts from bottom, **Fig. 2.**
5. Remove air conditioning drag link.
6. Raise engine at front lifting eye. **Ensure accelerator control at rear and coolant hoses are not damaged.**
7. Remove upper mounting bolts and engine mount with shield.
8. Reverse procedure to install, noting the following:
    a. Engine mount anti-twist locks must

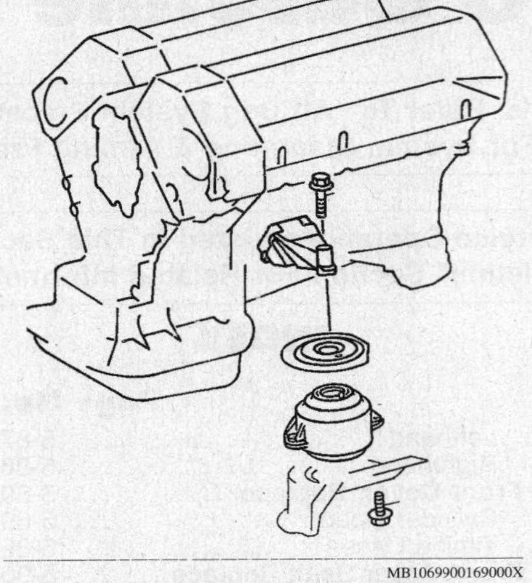

Fig. 2 Front engine mount replacement. 1998 SL500

engage shield openings and carriers' retaining slots.
    b. Tighten mounting bolts to specifications.
    c. Ensure fan shroud four engaging points are correctly located.

REAR

1. Support transmission suitable jack.
2. Disconnect kickdown electrical cable straps.
3. Remove mounting bolts and engine carrier, **Figs. 3 and 4.**
4. Remove mounting bolt and rear engine mount.
5. Reverse procedure to install, noting the following:
    a. Ensure backing plate is installed.
    b. Tighten mounting bolts to specifications.

ENGINE

REPLACE

1. Remove air cleaner.
2. Remove engine compartment bottom cover.
3. Remove radiator as outlined under "Radiator, Replace."
4. Drain cooling system into suitable container.
5. Attach 15.75 x 26.77 x .039-inch sheet metal or plastic guard plate to condenser.
6. **On S420 and 1998–99 CL500 and S500 models,** disconnect hood release cable.
7. **On all models,** disconnect coolant hose at intake manifold rear and connection line at crankcase rear.
8. Remove fan shroud and place over fan.
9. Counterhold viscous fan with hub holding wrench tool No. 603 589 00 40 00, or equivalent.
10. Remove mounting bolts and viscous fan.
11. Remove serpentine drive belt.

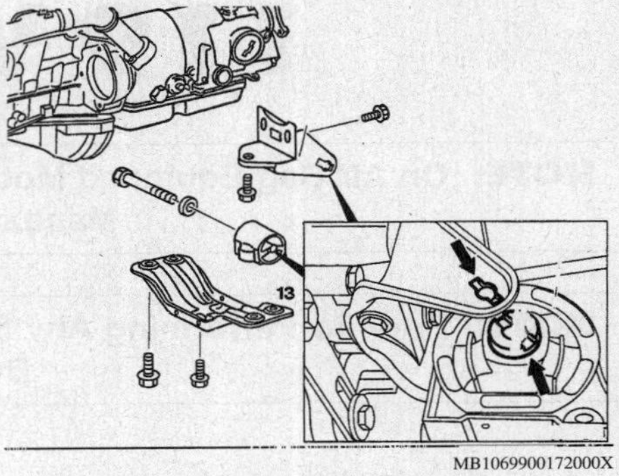

Fig. 3 Rear engine mount replacement. S420 & 1998–99 CL500 & S500

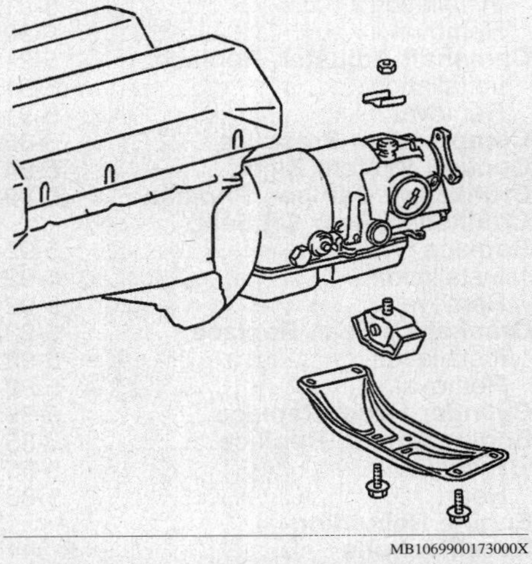

Fig. 4 Rear engine mount replacement. 1998 SL500

12. Relieve fuel pressure as described under "Precautions."
13. Open fuel filler cap to release tank pressure.
14. Disconnect and seal fuel lines using clamp tools No. 000 589 40 37 00, or equivalent.
15. Disconnect electrical connectors and vacuum lines.
16. Disconnect brake servo vacuum line.
17. Remove power steering pump reservoir oil with hand pump tool No. 112 589 00 72 00, or equivalent.
18. Disconnect power steering pump lines. Plug and seal lines and openings.
19. Disconnect air pump and plug connection, as required.
20. **On S420 and 1998–99 CL500 and S500 models,** remove mounting bolts and oil cooler line bracket.
21. **On all models,** disconnect oil cooler lines at air-to-oil cooler and seal.
22. **On models equipped with level control,** disconnect high pressure hose.
23. **On all models,** remove line bolt behind air conditioning compressor.
24. Remove air conditioning compressor and place aside with lines connected.
25. Disconnect oxygen sensor connection.

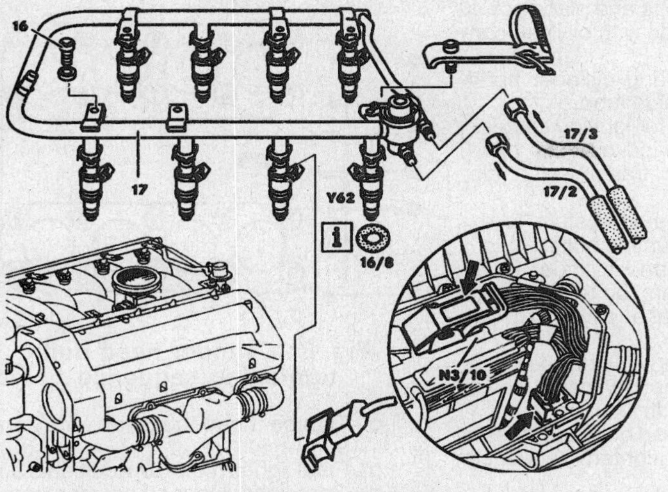

16	Screws	17/2	Fuel return pipe	N3/10	ME control module
16/8	O-rings	17/3	Fuel feed pipe	Arrow	Coupling
17	Fuel rail	Y62	Fuel injection valve	Arrow	Connector

MB1069900178000X

Fig. 5 Fuel rail replacement

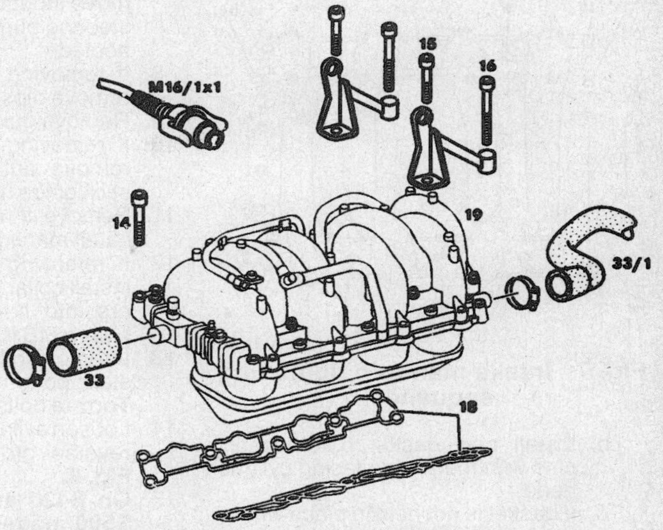

14, 15 & 16 Mounting Bolts 18 Gasket 19 Intake Manifold
33 & 33/1 Water Hoses M16/1x1 Actuator

MB1069900177000X

Fig. 6 Intake manifold replacement

26. Remove engine compartment bottom panel.
27. Separate exhaust manifold catalytic converter or front exhaust system from exhaust manifold flange.
28. Disconnect and remove crosspipe.
29. **On 1998–99 CL500 and S500 models,** remove engine carrier.
30. **On S420 and 1998 SL500 models,** remove lefthand mount carrier mounting nuts.
31. **On 1998 SL500 models,** remove lefthand crossmember and rubber mount.
32. **On all models,** remove complete exhaust system.
33. Remove mounting bolts and starter shield.
34. **On 1998 SL500 models,** disconnect starter electrical connector.
35. **On all models,** remove starter and alternator wiring harness from engine and transmission.
36. Disconnect propeller shaft from flexible coupling. Coupling remains on transmission.
37. Loosen propeller shaft clamping nut and intermediate bearing attachment.
38. Disconnect transmission ground cable.
39. Remove rear engine carrier without engine mount as outlined under "Engine Mount, Replace."
40. Remove transmission exhaust bracket.
41. Disconnect transmission shift rod.
42. Disconnect transmission electrical connectors.
43. Remove left and righthand front engine mounts as outlined under "Engine Mount, Replace."
44. Attach suitable engine hoist to lifting eyes.
45. Remove engine.
46. Reverse procedure to install, noting the following.
    a. Inspect engine mounts and replace as required.
    b. Inspect coolant, oil and fuel hoses. Replace as required.
    c. Install new propeller shaft to flexible coupling self-locking nuts.
    d. Tighten mounting bolts and nuts to specifications.
    e. Adjust automatic transmission control pressure cable.
    f. Inspect idle speed.

INTAKE MANIFOLD

REPLACE

1. Relieve fuel pressure as described under "Precautions."
2. Disconnect brake servo vacuum line and crankcase ventilation hoses.
3. Disconnect diaphragm pressure regulator vacuum line.
4. Place suitable shop rag under fuel lines, then disconnect fuel feed and return lines, **Fig. 5.**
5. Disconnect fuel injector couplings.
6. Disconnect ME control module and connector couplings.
7. Remove lefthand ignition coils' cover.
8. Disconnect intake manifold electrical connectors and cables.
9. Remove mounting bolts and fuel rail with injectors. Cover fuel injector openings.
10. Disconnect connector and remove Hot Film Mass (HFM) air flow sensor.
11. Partially drain cooling system into suitable container.
12. Disconnect actuator connector and check valve vacuum line, **Fig. 6**
13. Disconnect intake manifold front and rear coolant hoses.
14. Remove intake manifold mounting bolts. Mark bolt locations and lengths for installation.
15. Remove intake manifold.
16. Reverse procedure to install, noting the following:
    a. Install new gasket.
    b. Ensure no vacuum lines, or electrical cables are jammed by intake manifold.
    c. Oil mounting bolts' threads with suitable assembly oil.
    d.
    e. **Torque** bolts from top to bottom of intake manifold to 18 ft. lbs. Bolts from intake manifold to cylinder head to 18–22 ft. lbs. in sequence, **Fig. 7.**
    f. Ensure electronic accelerator actuator electrical cable is routed correctly.
    g. Install new fuel injector O-rings.
    h. Adjust throttle cable.
    i. Inspect idle speed.

EXHAUST MANIFOLD

REPLACE

LEFTHAND

This procedure has been revised by a Technical Service Bulletin.

1. Remove engine compartment bottom cover.
2. Remove exhaust manifold and system crosspipe.
3. Remove fan shroud.
4. Remove front lefthand side engine mount bolts as outlined under "Engine Mount, Replace."
5. Remove exhaust manifold self-locking mounting bolts. Mark bolt locations and lengths for installation.
6. Relieve fuel pressure as outlined under "Precautions.".
7. Place suitable shop rag under and disconnect fuel lines.
8. Raise engine at oil sump using suitable telescoping lift.
9. Remove exhaust manifold.
10. Reverse procedure to install, noting the following:
    a. Clean sealing surfaces.

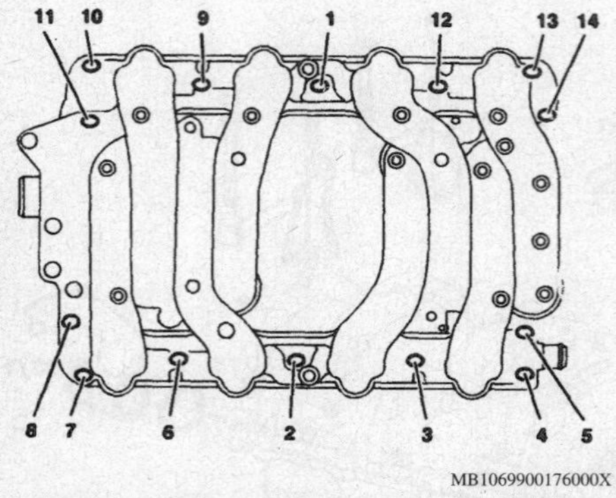

Fig. 7 Intake manifold tightening sequence

b. Install new gasket onto locating pins with metal side facing cylinder head.
c. If gasket is not held in place with locating pins, apply exhaust sealing compound No. A 001 989 25 20, or equivalents, in dots.
d. Install new self-locking mounting bolts.
e. Tighten mounting bolts to specifications.

RIGHTHAND

This procedure has been revised by a Technical Service Bulletin.

1. Remove engine compartment bottom cover.
2. Remove complete exhaust system.
3. Remove exhaust manifold self-locking mounting bolts. Mark bolt locations and lengths for installation.
4. Raise engine at oil sump using suitable telescoping lift.
5. Remove exhaust manifold.
6. Reverse procedure to install, noting the following:
   a. Clean sealing surfaces.
   b. Install new gasket onto locating pins with metal side facing cylinder head.
   c. If gasket is not held in place with locating pins, apply exhaust sealing compound No. A 001 989 25 20, or equivalents, in dots.
   d. Install new self-locking mounting bolts.
   e. Tighten mounting bolts to specifications.

CYLINDER HEAD

REPLACE

Perform this procedure only when engine is cold.

1. Drain coolant into suitable container.
2. Remove valve covers as outlined under "Valve Cover, Replace."
3. Remove intake manifold as outlined under "Intake Manifold, Replace."
4. Remove cylinder head front cover as outlined during "Front Cover, Replace."
5. Remove cylinder head guide rail.
6. Remove camshaft adjuster as outlined under "Camshaft Adjuster, Replace."
7. If removing lefthand cylinder head, remove mounting bolts and place power steering pump aside with oil lines connected.
8. If removing righthand cylinder head, remove dipstick guide tube.
9. Remove guide rail for ignition cables.
10. If removing righthand cylinder head, remove automatic transmission dipstick guide tube.
11. Remove front exhaust system to exhaust manifold mounting bolts.
12. If removing righthand cylinder head, install collar bolts and bolts with washers into timing case cover. **Torque** bolts to 18 ft. lbs.
13. If removing lefthand cylinder head, install bolts into timing case cover. **Torque** bolts to 18 ft. lbs.
14. Loosen cylinder head bolts in stages in reverse order of tighten sequence, **Fig. 8.**
15. **On S420 and 1998–99 CL500 and S500 models,** bolt No. 10 cannot be removed with cylinder head installed.
16. **On all models,** remove remaining head bolts. Mark cylinder head bolt locations and lengths for installation.
17. Remove intake camshaft first and fourth bearing caps.
18. Replace bearing caps with bracket tools No. 119 589 01 40 00, or equivalent.
19. Attach suitable engine hoist to bracket tools.
20. Raise and support cylinder heads, then remove remaining head bolts and cylinder head.
21. Reverse procedure to install, noting the following:
   a. Clean cylinder head bolt tapped holes.
   b. Install new cylinder head gaskets.
   c. Ensure dowel sleeves or roll pins are correctly positioned.
   d. Oil cylinder head bolt threads and bolt head contact surfaces.
   e. Closed-deck cylinder heads' combustion chambers are oval on one side.
   f. Open-deck cylinder heads' combustion chambers are straight on both sides.
   g. Closed-deck cylinder head bolts are phosphatized with chrome-plated washers.
   h. Open-deck cylinder head bolts are chrome-plated with phosphatized washers.
   i. Heli-Coil inserts may be used on closed-deck cylinder head engine crankcases.
   j. Heli-Coil inserts cannot be used on open-deck cylinder head engine crankcases.
   k. Replace closed-deck head bolts with shank length of more than 6.4061 inches.
   l. Replace open-deck short head bolts with shank length of more than 6.4061 inches.
   m. Replace open-deck long head bolts with shank length of more than 8.7253 inches.
   n. **Torque** cylinder head bolts to 41 ft. lbs.

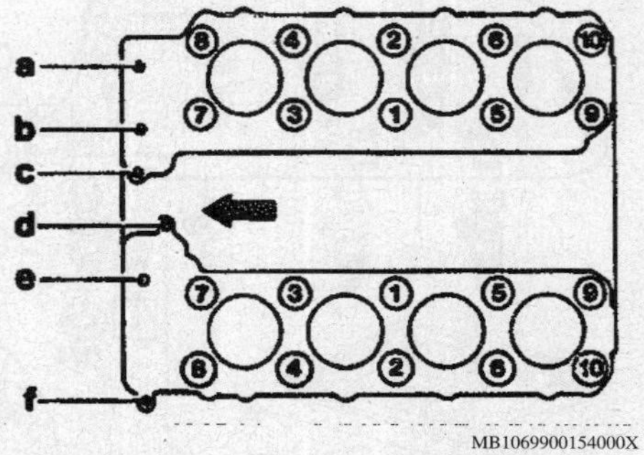

Fig. 8 Cylinder head bolt tightening sequence

   o. Tighten head bolts an additional 90°.
   p. Final tighten bolts an additional 90°.
   q. Coat upper lefthand power steering pump mounting bolt with sealant No. 002 989 47 20 10, or equivalent.
   r. Do not pressure test cooling system until after engine has reached operating temperature and cylinder head gaskets have swelled.

VALVE COVER

REPLACE

1. Remove air cleaner.
2. Disconnect crankcase ventilation lines, **Fig. 9.**
3. Remove engine wiring harness mounting bolt from righthand cylinder head cover.
4. Disconnect brake servo vacuum line at intake manifold.
5. Remove high voltage distributor covers.
6. Relieve fuel pressure as outlined under "Precautions."
7. Open fuel filler cap to relieve fuel tank pressure.
8. Disconnect fuel lines using box wrench bit tool No. 000 589 68 03 00, or equivalent.
9. Remove spark plug cables and ignition coil covers.
10. Remove ignition coils.
11. Remove valve cover mounting bolts with seals. Mark different length mounting bolts for installation.
12. Remove valve covers with gaskets and shaft seals.
13. Reverse procedure to install, noting the following:
   a. Install seals.
   b. Ensure valve cover gaskets overlap correctly at rear. Replace gaskets as required.
   c. Ensure crankcase ventilation siphon at lefthand cover is correctly located in drain hole.
   d. Tighten mounting bolts to specifications.
   e. Fuel lines must not touch valve or engine covers.

VALVE ADJUSTMENT

This engine is equipped with hydraulic lifters and requires no valve adjustment,

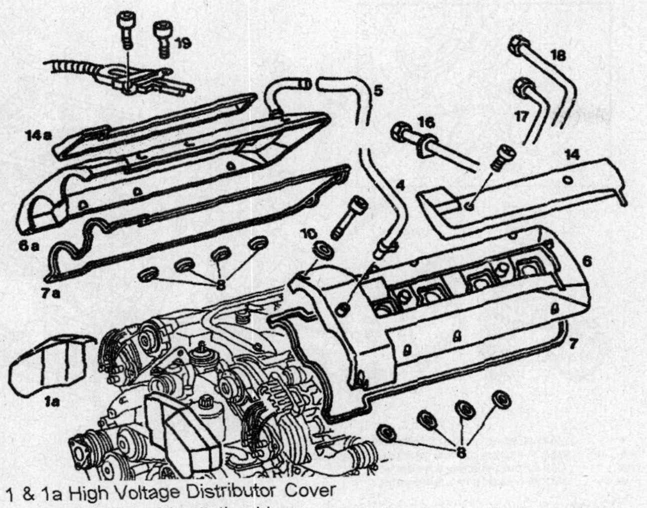

1 & 1a High Voltage Distributor Cover
4 & 5 Crankcase Ventilation Lines
6 & 6a Valve Cover
7 & 7a Gaskets
8 Shaft Seals
10 Seals
14 & 14a Shaft, Spark Plug Cable & Ignition Coil Cover
16 Brake Servo Vacuum Line
17 & 18 Fuel Lines
19 Engine Wiring Harness

MB1069900147000X

Fig. 9 Valve cover replacement

HYDRAULIC LIFTERS

REPLACE

1. Remove camshaft as outlined under "Camshaft, Replace."
2. Mark lifters for installation in original position.
3. Remove lifter using suitable rubber suction cup. **Do not use magnet.**
4. Reverse procedure to install.

CRANKSHAFT DAMPER

REPLACE

1. Remove fan shroud and place over fan.
2. Counterhold viscous fan with hub holding wrench tool No. 603 589 00 40 00, or equivalent.
3. Remove mounting bolts and viscous fan.
4. Remove serpentine drive belt tensioning device.
5. Remove alternator.
6. Attach 15.75 x 26.77 x .039-inch sheet metal or plastic guard plate to radiator.
7. Remove viscous fan coupling bearing bracket, **Fig. 10.**
8. Remove mounting bolts air conditioning compressor carrier.
9. Turn engine until cylinder No. 1 piston is at TDC. Crankshaft Woodruff key should be facing up.
10. Install retaining lock tool No. 116 589 01 40 00, or equivalent, on crankshaft/ring gear.
11. Remove central bolt with tapered washer. Replace tapered washer with conical washer.
12. Remove vibration damper.
13. Reverse procedure to install, noting the following:
    a. Align Woodruff key, push hub on and turn to determine if crankshaft slot is aligned with key.
    b. Tighten mounting bolts to specifications.

FRONT COVER

REPLACE

CYLINDER HEAD

1. Remove valve covers as described under "Valve Cover, Replace."
2. Remove serpentine drive belt.
3. **If removing lefthand cylinder head cover,** proceed as follows:
    a. Remove mounting bolt and wiring harness retaining bracket.
    b. Remove power steering pump plate mounting bolts.
    c. Set mounting plate with power steering pump and lines connected aside.
4. **If removing righthand cylinder head cover,** remove support mounting and set secondary air injection pump aside.
5. Remove camshaft adjuster solenoid.
6. Remove mounting bolts and front cover.
7. Reverse procedure to install, noting the following:
    a. Coat front cover contact surfaces and mounting bolts with sealant No. 002 989 47 20 00, or equivalent.
    b. Ensure front covers mount on dowel pins.

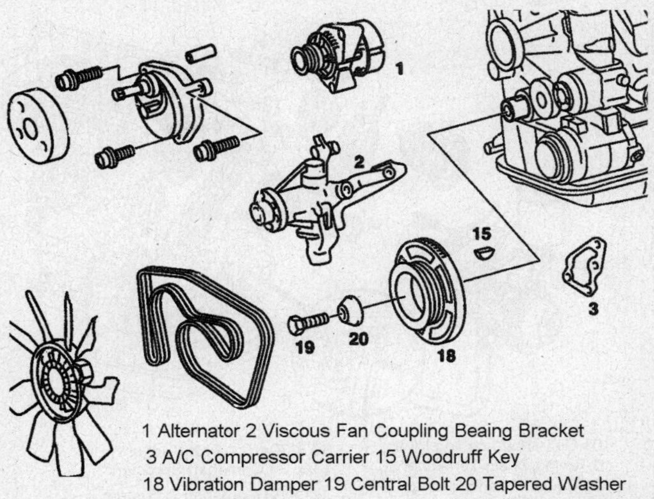

1 Alternator 2 Viscous Fan Coupling Beaing Bracket
3 A/C Compressor Carrier 15 Woodruff Key
18 Vibration Damper 19 Central Bolt 20 Tapered Washer

MB1069900158000X

Fig. 10 Crankshaft damper replacement

    c. Tighten mounting bolts to specifications.

TIMING CASE

1. Remove timing chain tensioner as described under "Timing Chain Tensioner, Replace," **Fig. 11.**
2. Remove valve covers as outlined under "Valve Cover, Replace."
3. Turn crankshaft until cylinder No. 1 piston is at 45° before TDC.
4. Lock camshafts in positions with locking pins No. 111 589 03 15 00, or equivalent.
5. **If removing lefthand cylinder head cover,** proceed as follows:
    a. Remove mounting bolt and wiring harness retaining bracket.
    b. Remove power steering pump plate mounting bolts.
    c. Set mounting plate with power steering pump and lines connected aside.
6. **On all models,** remove mounting bolts and cylinder head front covers as outlined under "Cylinder Head, Replace."
7. Mark camshaft sprockets and timing chain for installation alignment.
8. Remove timing chain tensioners as outlined under "Timing Chain Tensioner, Replace."
9. Remove camshaft adjusters and exhaust camshaft sprockets as outlined under "Camshaft, Replace."
10. Remove vibration damper as outlined under "Crankshaft Damper, Replace."
11. Remove oil sump as outlined under "Oil Sump, Replace." **Do not damage gasket.**
12. Remove water pump as outlined under "Water Pump, Replace."
13. Remove screwplug with seal.
14. Remove tensioning rail pin using impact puller tool No. 1116 589 20 33 00 and threaded insert tool No. 116 589 01 34 00, or equivalents.
15. Remove tensioning rail.
16. Install timing case cover collar bolts with washers. **Torque** bolts to 15 ft. lbs.
17. Remove front crankshaft radial seal as

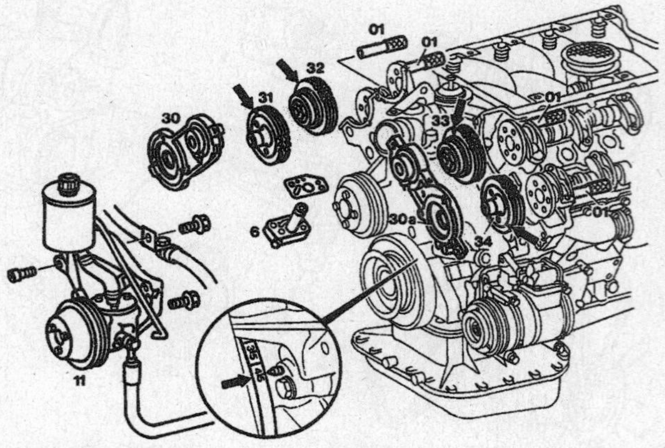

01 Camshaft Locking Pins
6 Timing Chain Tensioner
11 Power Steering Pump
30 & 30a Top Front Covers
31 & 34 Camshaft Sprockets
32 & 33 Camshaft Adjusters

MB1069900148010X

Fig. 11 Timing case replacement (Part 1 of 3)

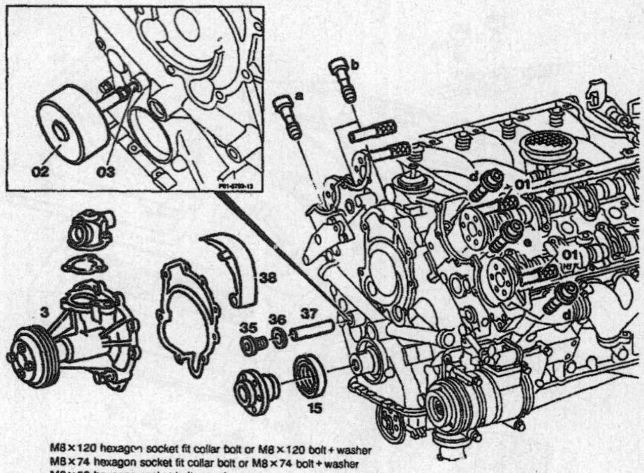

a M8×120 hexagon socket fit collar bolt or M8×120 bolt + washer
b M8×74 hexagon socket fit collar bolt or M8×74 bolt + washer
d M8×50 hexagon socket bolt + washer
e M8×75 hexagon socket bolt + washer

02 Impact Puller 03 Threaded Insert 3 Water Pump
15 Front Crankshaft Radial Seal
35 Screwplug 36 Seal 37 Tensioning Rail Pin 38 Tensioning Rail

MB1069900148020X

Fig. 11 Timing case replacement (Part 2 of 3)

outlined under "Crankshaft Seal, Replace,"

18. Remove oil pump as outlined under "Oil Pump, Replace." **Disconnect oil pump chain at crankshaft sprocket using bent piece of metal.**
19. Remove mounting bolts and timing case cover. **Do not damage cylinder head gaskets.**
20. Reverse procedure to install, noting the following:
    a. Install new O-rings.
    b. Clean sealing surfaces and coat with sealant No. 002 989 47 20 10, or equivalent.
    c. Coat cylinder head gaskets with engine oil.
    d. Ensure dowel sleeves and pins are correctly positioned.
    e. Install new front crankshaft radial seal.
    f. Install new tensioning rail pin screwplug seal.
    g. Replace oil sump gasket as required.
    h. Coat power steering mounting bolt with sealant No. 002 989 47 20 10, or equivalent.

FRONT COVER SEAL

REPLACE

CYLINDER HEAD

Cover Installed

1. Pry seal out with suitable screwdriver. **Do not damage camshaft or seal mounting hole.**
2. Install insertion sleeve tool No. 119 589 00 14 00, or equivalent.
3. Coat new seal sealing lip with engine oil. **Do not use grease.**
4. Fit seal onto sleeve tool.
5. Press seal in. **Seal must be vertical to camshaft.**

Cover Removed

1. Pry seal out with suitable screwdriver. **Do not damage mounting hole.**
2. Fit seal to drift tool No. 119 589 01 15 00, or equivalent.
3. Press seal in with drift tool.

TIMING CHAIN

REPLACE

1. Remove valve covers as outlined under "Valve Cover, Replace."
2. Remove viscous fan clutch.
3. Remove spark plugs.
4. Rotate crankshaft to set cylinder No. 1 piston at 45° before ignition TDC.
5. Install pin tool No. 111 589 03 15 00, or equivalent, into righthand cylinder head intake and exhaust camshaft sprocket.
6. Remove chain tensioner as outlined under "Timing Chain Tensioner, Replace."
7. Install release device tool No. 119 589 01 63 03, or equivalent, into top detents, **Fig. 12.**
8. Fit pusher tool No. 119 589 01 63 00, or equivalent, onto top guide rail.
9. Remove front part of guide rail by pushing pusher tool down.
10. Remove mounting bolt, guide rail and rubber gasket.
11. Lock timing chain to righthand cylinder head camshaft sprockets with wedge tools No. 110 589 03 59 00, or equivalent, **Fig. 13.**
12. Remove cylinder head front cover as outlined under "Front Cover, Replace."
13. Grind open chain pin between intake and exhaust camshaft sprockets, then push out double link.
14. Connect new timing chain to old with riveted link, middle plate and outer plate.
15. Remove locking pins from camshaft sprockets.
16. Remove intake camshaft wedge from chain.
17. Loosen exhaust camshaft wedge slightly.
18. Rotate crankshaft in engine rotational direction with suitable wrench socket, while holding chain meshed at intake and exhaust camshaft sprockets. **Do not allow timing chain to jump when turned.**
19. Pull new timing chain in while pulling old chain out.
20. Rotate crankshaft until ends of new chain can be connected with riveted link.
21. Lock timing chain to righthand cylinder head camshaft sprockets with wedge tools.
22. Connect chain with link and center plate.

TIMING CHAIN TENSIONER

REPLACE

1. Remove righthand valve cover as outlined under "Valve Cover, Replace."
2. Rotate crankshaft to set cylinder No. 1 piston at 45° before ignition TDC.
3. Install pin tool No. 111 589 03 15 00, or equivalent, into exhaust camshaft sprocket.
4. Remove secondary air pump and/or alternator as required to gain access.
5. Remove timing chain tensioner mounting bolt and nut. **Do not allow engine oil to flow into alternator.**
6. Remove chain tensioner with gasket. **Do not tilt chain tensioner.**
7. Reverse procedure to install. Tighten mounting bolts and nuts to specifications.

CAMSHAFT

REPLACE

REMOVAL

The bearing caps are numbered consecutively being at the front of the righthand exhaust camshaft. The numbers are cast into

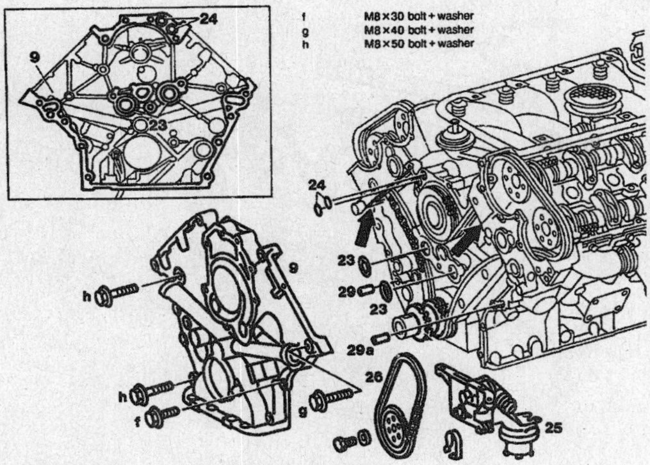

9 Front Cover 25 Oil Pump
23 & 24 O-Rings 29 Dowel Sleeve 29a Dowel Pin

MB1069900148030X

Fig. 11 Timing case replacement (Part 3 of 3)

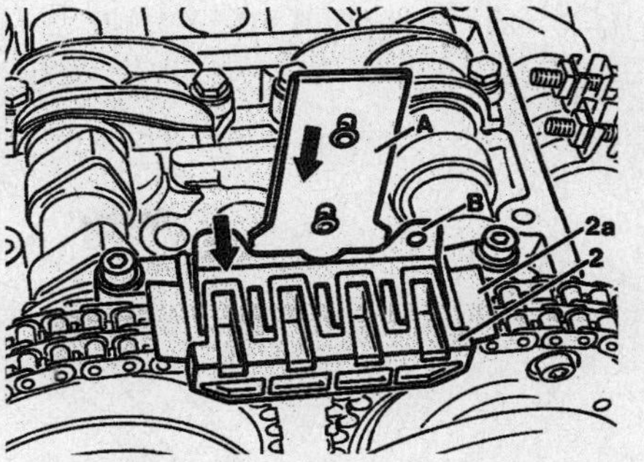

2 Guide Rail Front Part 2a Guide Rail w/Rubber Gasket
A Push B Release Device

MB1069900161000X

Fig. 12 Top guide rail replacement

the cylinder head. The bearing caps must be installed in original positions.

The camshaft are sensitive to fracturing and must not be twisted when removing and installing camshaft bearing caps.

If a camshaft is removed, other camshafts must be secured with fixing pins to prevent turning.

1. Turn crankshaft to set cylinder No. 1 piston at 45° before TDC, **Fig. 14.**
2. Remove cylinder head front covers as outlined under "Front Cover, Replace."
3. Mark camshaft sprockets and timing chain for installation alignment.
4. Remove timing chain tensioner as outlined under "Timing Chain Tensioner, Replace."
5. Remove top slide rails.
6. Lift timing chain off camshaft sprockets.
7. Rotate camshaft with wrench tool No. 119 589 00 01 00, or equivalent, until only cams' base circle is touch hydraulic lifter, noting the following:
   a. Righthand exhaust and intake camshafts rotate approximately six teeth in engine's rotational direction.
   b. Lefthand intake camshaft rotates approximately 10 teeth in opposition of engine's rotational direction.
   c. Lefthand exhaust camshaft rotates approximately 14 teeth in engine's rotational direction.
8. Loosen camshaft bearing caps alternately.
9. Remove bearing caps and camshafts with sprockets and adjusters.

INSTALLATION

Bearing caps are centered by camshaft bearing points when bolts are tighten to specifications.

1. Install lefthand intake and exhaust camshafts with timing chain fitter free of tension.
2. Ensure guide bearing point No. 3 is correctly positioned.
3. Oil bearing caps, install and tighten uniformly to specifications.
4. Inspect camshaft ease of movement by rotating with wrench tool No. 119 589 00 01 00, or equivalent.
5. Rotate lefthand exhaust camshaft and fit timing chain at marked position. Secure camshaft sprocket with pin tool No. 111 589 03 15 00, or equivalent.
6. Rotate lefthand intake camshaft and fit timing chain at marked position. Secure camshaft sprocket with pin tool No. 111 589 03 15 00, or equivalent.
7. Ensure camshafts are in retarded position, **Fig. 15.**
8. Install righthand intake and exhaust camshafts with timing chain fitter free of tension.
9. Ensure guide bearing point No. 3 is correctly positioned.
10. Oil bearing caps, install and tighten uniformly to specifications.
11. Inspect camshaft ease of movement by rotating with wrench tool No. 119 589 00 01 00, or equivalent.
12. Rotate righthand intake camshaft and fit timing chain at marked position. Secure camshaft sprocket with pin tool No. 111 589 03 15 00, or equivalent.
13. Ensure camshafts are in retarded position.
14. Rotate righthand exhaust camshaft and fit timing chain at marked position. Secure camshaft sprocket with pin tool No. 111 589 03 15 00, or equivalent.
15. Install top slide rails.
16. Install timing chain tensioner.
17. Install cylinder head front covers.

CAMSHAFT ADJUSTER

REPLACE

REMOVAL

1. Remove cylinder head front cover(s) as outlined under "Front Cover, Replace."
2. Turn engine to cylinder No. 1 piston is at 45 before ignition TDC.
3. Lock camshafts with pin tools No. 111 589 03 15 00, or equivalent.
4. Mark timing chain and camshaft sprockets for installation alignment.
5. Remove chain tensioner as outlined under "Timing Chain Tensioner, Replace."
6. Remove top guide rails. If removing righthand camshaft adjust, remove only righthand guide.
7. Remove righthand camshaft sprocket.
8. Remove mounting bolt and armature, **Fig. 16.**
9. Remove nut, cover, lefthand camshaft sprocket with adjusting piston and conical spring.
10. Remove mounting bolts and flanged shaft.

INSTALLATION

1. Ensure dowel pin is correctly located.
2. Install flange shaft onto intake camshaft and tighten new collar bolts to specifications.
3. Install spherical spring and push adjusting piston onto flange shaft fixed by blocked tooth.
4. Install thrust nut with socket tool No. 111 589 01 40 00, or equivalent.
5. Install intake camshaft sprocket into adjusting piston splines fixed by block tooth. Hold timing chain up.
6. Loosen thrust nut while holding camshaft adjuster together.
7. Install cover.
8. Install mounting nut with flat face pointing toward camshaft adjuster.
9. Tighten mounting nut to specifications while counterholding camshaft with wrench tool No. 119 589 00 01 00, or equivalent.
10. Install armature to fixed control plunger position. Armature and control plunger must move freely from stop to stop.
11. Install new armature mounting bolt and tighten to specifications.
12. Start chain installation on lefthand exhaust camshaft sprocket and it in opposite direction of engine rotation.
13. Install cover.
14. Coat solenoid sealing surface with sealant No. 002 989 47 20 10, or equivalent.
15. Install solenoid and tighten mounting

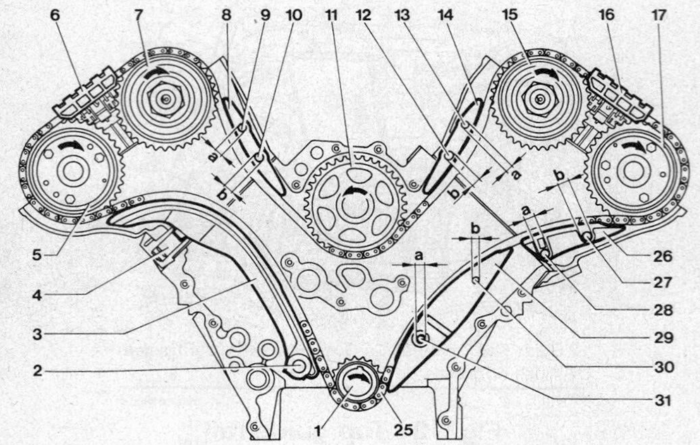

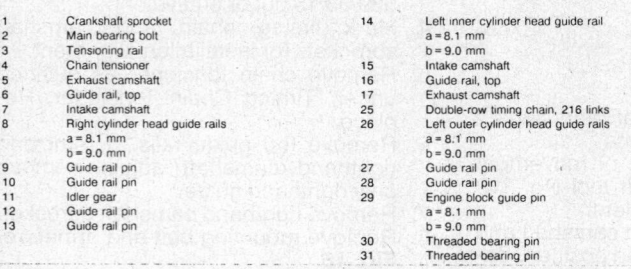

1	Crankshaft sprocket	14	Left inner cylinder head guide rail a = 8.1 mm b = 9.0 mm
2	Main bearing bolt	15	Intake camshaft
3	Tensioning rail	16	Guide rail, top
4	Chain tensioner	17	Exhaust camshaft
5	Exhaust camshaft	25	Double-row timing chain, 216 links
6	Guide rail, top	26	Left outer cylinder head guide rails a = 8.1 mm b = 9.0 mm
7	Intake camshaft	27	Guide rail pin
8	Right cylinder head guide rails a = 8.1 mm b = 9.0 mm	28	Guide rail pin
9	Guide rail pin	29	Engine block guide pin a = 8.1 mm b = 9.0 mm
10	Guide rail pin	30	Threaded bearing pin
11	Idler gear	31	Threaded bearing pin
12	Guide rail pin		
13	Guide rail pin		

MB1069200085000X

Fig. 13 Timing chain

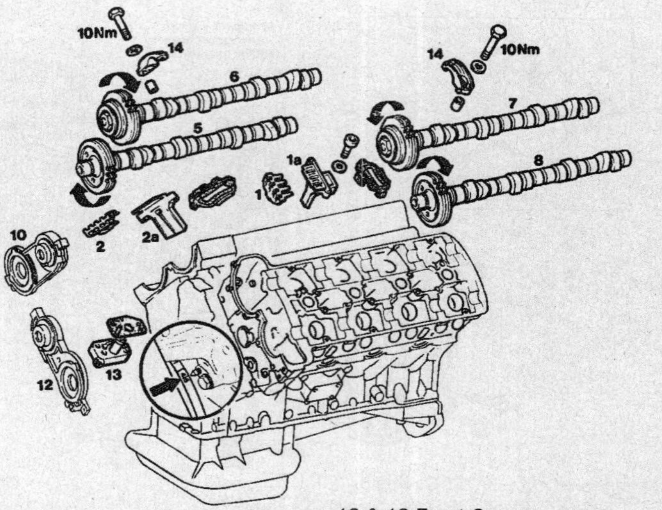

1,1a, 2 & 2a Tip Slide Rails
5, 6, 7 & 8 Camshafts
10 & 12 Front Covers
13 Chain Tensioner
14 Camshaft Bearing Caps

MB1069900160000X

Fig. 14 Camshaft replacement

bolts to specifications.

PISTON & ROD ASSEMBLY

Cylinder and piston identifications must match. Pistons with numerals may be installed in crankcase with letter grouping, but not vice versa, **Fig. 17.**

MAIN & ROD BEARINGS

MAIN BEARINGS

Standard bearing shells and thrust washers are installed at third crankshaft (fit) bearing.

1. Match top bearing shell color codes to chisel points on crankcase, **Fig. 18.**
2. Match bottom bearing shell color codes to crankshaft color code, **Fig. 19.**
3. Mark stud bolts depth and collar diameter for replacement installation.
4. Stud bolts may only be used once.
5. Heli-coil inserts may not be used for crankshaft bearing caps.
6. Oil threads and contact surfaces of nuts and side bolts.
7. Identical thrust washers are inserted on both sides of crankcase and bearing cap.
8. Bearing cap thrust washers face two anti-twist retaining lugs.
9. Thrust washer oil grooves must face toward crank webs.
10. Tighten stud bolts, nuts and side bolts to specifications in sequence, **Fig. 20.**

CONNECTING ROD

1. Install conrod bearing cap with identification facing each other.
2. Moisten contact surface with engine oil.
3. Replace bolts if shank length is more than 2.0829 inches.
4. Moisten bolt threads and contact surface with engine oil.
5. **Torque** bolts to 29 ft. lbs.
6. Loosen bolts, then **torque** to 22 ft. lbs.
7. Final tighten bolts an additional 90°. If angle tightener is not available, continue turning bolt through specified angle with socket wrench and bar in one movement. **Do not use torque wrench.**

CRANKSHAFT SEAL

REPLACE

REMOVAL

1. Remove belt pulley, vibration damper and hub, **Fig. 21.**
2. Pry out radial seal using suitable screwdriver and clean cloth. **Do not damage crankshaft or seal mounting bore.**

INSTALLATION

1. Deburr mounting hole.
2. Oil radial seal sealing lip. **Do not use grease.**
3. Install seal onto insertion sleeve tool No. 119 589 01 14 00, or equivalent.
4. Draw as far as stop with bolt and four Belleville spring washers. Seal must be perpendicular to hub.
5. If hub has running marks, install radial seal offset .1181 inch inside.

CRANKSHAFT REAR OIL SEAL

REPLACE

REMOVAL

1. Remove transmission.
2. Remove lefthand front exhaust crosspipe.
3. Remove lefthand starter motor recess cover.
4. Install crankshaft/ring gear lock tool No. 119 589 00 40 00, or equivalent.
5. Remove mounting bolt and ignition control module with bracket.
6. Remove mounting bolts and driven plate, **Fig. 22.**
7. Remove end plate mounting bolts. Mark bolt locations and lengths for installation.
8. Press off end plate with radial seal using M8 bolts at tapped holes. **Do not damage oil sump gasket.**

INSTALLATION

1. Clean crankcase and end cover sealing surfaces carefully.
2. Coat end cover sealing surface with sealant No. 002 989 45 20, or equivalent. **Do not get sealant into oil gallery.**
3. Coat radial seal between dust and sealing lip with engine oil. **Do not use grease.**
4. Coat end cover underside with sealant No. 002 989 00 20 10, or equivalent.
5. Push end cover with radial seal over

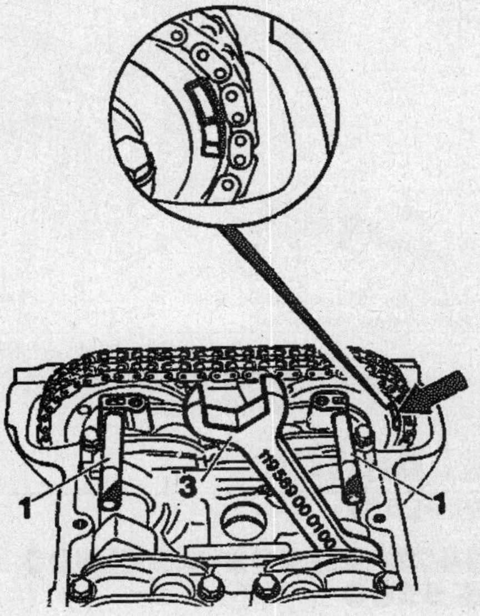

1 Locating Pins

3 Wrench

MB1069900146000X

Fig. 15 Camshaft retarded position

inner part of insertion tool No. 117 589 00 43 00, or equivalent.

6. Bolt insertion tool onto crankcase. **Do not damage oil sump gasket.**
7. Tighten rear bolts, then bottom bolts to specifications.
8. Ensure driven plate and plate base engage dowel pin.
9. Tighten driven plate mounting bolts to specifications.

OIL SUMP

REPLACE

1. Raise hood to vertical position.
2. Remove air scoops.
3. Remove fan shroud and place over fan.
4. Counterhold viscous fan with hub holding wrench tool No. 603 589 00 40 00, or equivalent.
5. Remove mounting bolts and viscous fan.
6. Remove drive belt tensioning device.
7. Remove TDC sensor.
8. Remove dipstick guide tube at air pump bracket.
9. Remove engine compartment bottom panel.
10. Drain engine oil into suitable container.
11. Remove front oil sump bracket.
12. Remove belt pulley/crankshaft vibration damper as outlined under "Crankshaft Damper, Replace."
13. Remove mounting bolts, washers and guide pulley carrier.
14. Remove mounting bolts, washers and nuts and air conditioning compressor. Attach compressor to engine compartment side with lines and wires connected.
15. Remove mounting bolts and air conditioning compressor carrier.

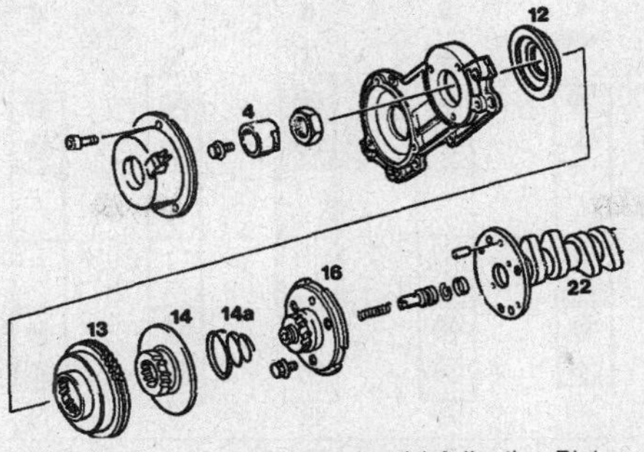

4 Armature 12 Cover 13 Sproket 14 Adjusting Piston 14a Conical Spring 16 Flanged Shaft 22 Camshaft

MB1069900159000X

Fig. 16 Camshaft adjuster replacement

Chisel Point	Crankshaft Bearing Cap Color	Top Bearing Shell Color
1	Blue	Blue
2	Yellow	Yellow
3	Red	Red

Fig. 18 Top bearing shell chart

16. Remove mounting bolts and alternator.
17. Remove mounting bolts and alternator bracket.
18. Remove mounting bolts and dipstick guide tube.
19. Remove left and righthand front engine mounts as described under "Engine Mount, Replace."
20. Remove front axle springs and shock absorber.
21. Install engine support bar tool No. 140 589 01 61 00, or equivalent.
22. Remove shield and disconnect steering coupling.
23. Support front axle with support tool No. 140 589 00 62 00, or equivalent, and suitable vehicle jack.
24. Remove front axle rear covers and mounting bolts.
25. Lower front axle enough to remove sump. Do not overextend brake and steering gear hoses.
26. Remove automatic transmission and cooler oil lines from sump.
27. Disconnect knock sensors electric cable at rear of power steering pump bracket.
28. Remove oil sump mounting bolts. Mark mounting bolts for installation alignment.
29. Remove oil sump.
30. Reverse procedure to install, noting the following:
    a. Clean sealing surfaces.
    b. Install new gasket.
    c. Apply Ominvisc sealant No. 002 989 45 20, or equivalent, to rear area of oil sump and crankcase.
    d. Align oil sump real contact face with transmission.
    e. Install new oil drain plug seal.
    f. Before install near microencapsulated front axle rear mounting bolts, clean body thread taps.
    g. Tighten mounting bolts to specifications.

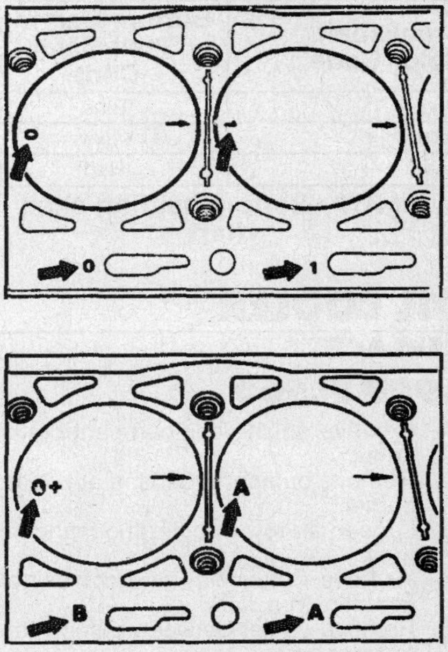

MB1069900156000X

Fig. 17 Piston & cylinder identification

OIL PUMP

REPLACE

1998 SL500

1. Remove engine compartment bottom cover.
2. Drain engine oil into suitable container.
3. Disconnect oil sump bottom part cable strap.
4. Disconnect automatic transmission oil line from oil sump, **Fig. 23.**
5. **On models equipped with level control,** disconnect high pressure flexible hose from oil sump.
6. **On all models,** remove mounting bolts and oil sump bottom.
7. Place crankshaft first journal balance weight horizontally.
8. Remove mounting bolt and oil level sensor.
9. Loosen oil pump drive sprocket mounting bolt.
10. Remove oil pump mounting bolts.
11. Tilt oil pump to rear, then remove mounting bolt and drive sprocket.
12. Remove oil pump.
13. Reverse procedure to install, noting the following:
    a. Prime oil pump before installing.
    b. Prevent tensioning bar spring from turning by inserting suitable screwdriver when tightening mounting bolt.
    c. Install drive sprocket with curved side toward pump.
    d. Install new gasket.
    e. Tighten mounting bolts to specifications.

Crankshaft Color Code	Bottom Bearing Shell Color Code
Blue	Blue
Yellow	Yellow
Red	Red

Fig. 19 Bottom bearing shell chart

OIL COOLER

REPLACE

1998 SL500

1. Remove engine compartment bottom panel.
2. Remove bumper mounting at radiator carrier.
3. Loosen air-to-oil cooler mounting line nuts.
4. Remove Cotter pins and cooler from mounting brackets.
5. Remove cooler between bumper and radiator carrier.
6. Reverse procedure to install. Tighten mounting nuts to specifications.

BELT TENSION DATA

Belt tension is maintained by an automatic belt tensioner.

SERPENTINE DRIVE BELT

BELT, REPLACE

1. Remove fan shroud ring and place over fan.
2. Swivel mounting counterclockwise with suitable wrench, **Fig. 24.**
3. Remove belt.
4. Inspect pulley surfaces and replace as required.
5. Install belt.

ROUTING

Refer to **Fig. 25** for serpentine drive belt routing.

TENSIONER, REPLACE

1. Remove drive belt as outlined under "Belt, Replace."
2. Remove mounting bolt with tensioning nut from bracket.
3. Reverse procedure to install. Tighten mounting bolts and nuts to specifications.

COOLING SYSTEM BLEED

1. Fill cooling system to markings.
2. Turn heater to On position.
3. Warm engine at moderate RPM until thermostat opens.
4. Adjust coolant level as required.

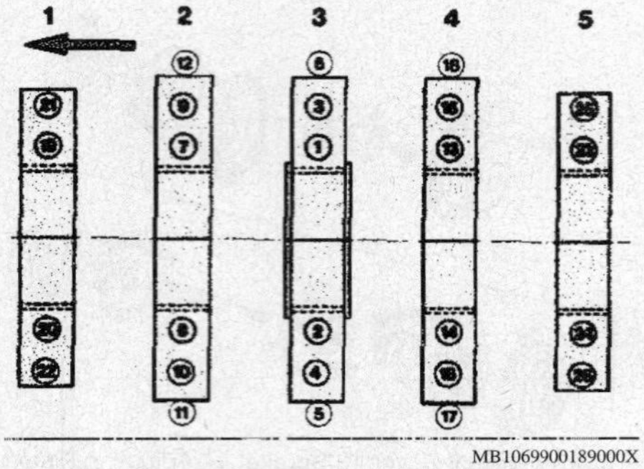

Fig. 20 Crankshaft bearing cap tightening sequence

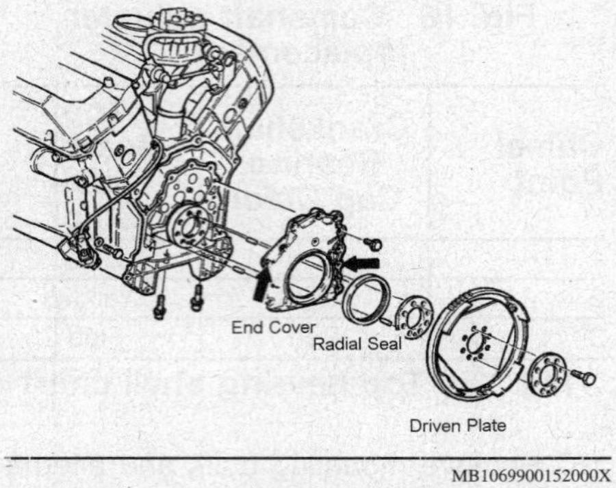

Fig. 22 End cover replacement

THERMOSTAT

REPLACE

1. Drain radiator coolant into suitable container.
2. **On 1998 SL500 models,** remove dipstick guide tube from cylinder head.
3. **On all models,** disconnect thermostat housing coolant hose.
4. Remove thermostat.
5. Remove procedure to install. Ball valve must be at highest point.

WATER PUMP

REPLACE

1. Remove fan shroud and place over fan.
2. Counterhold viscous fan with hub holding wrench tool No. 603 589 00 40 00, or equivalent.
3. Remove mounting bolts and viscous fan.
4. Remove crankshaft vibration damper as outlined under "Crankshaft Damper, Replace."
5. Remove coolant hoses, **Fig. 26.**
6. Remove mounting bolts and connection cover with lifting eye.
7. Remove mounting bolts and water pump.
8. Reverse procedure to install, noting the following:
   a. Install new gaskets.
   b. Water pump mounting bolts are different lengths, **Fig. 27.**
   c. Tighten mounting bolts to specifications.

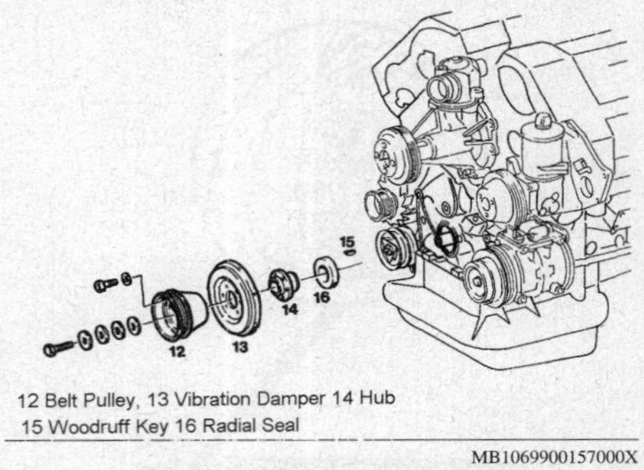

Fig. 21 Crankshaft seal replacement

RADIATOR

REPLACE

S420 & 1998-99 CL500 & S500

1. Remove engine compartment bottom cover.
2. Drain radiator coolant into suitable container.
3. Disconnect automatic transmission oil lines.
4. Disconnect coolant hoses.
5. Remove air scoops.
6. Remove mounting bolts and cross panel.
7. Remove locking pin, then turn shroud ring to left and place over fan.
8. Remove flat spring and fan shroud.
9. Remove plastic strips.
10. Disconnect hood release cable.
11. Remove air conditioning condenser mounting bolts.
12. Remove radiator.
13. Reverse procedure to install, noting the following:
    a. Radiator mounting studs must engage crossmember rubber pads.
    b. Insert fan shroud retaining catches into radiator mounting points.
    c. Ensure fan shroud ring four engaging points are correctly located.
    d. Adjust positioning strip by turning adjusting bolt using suitable adjusting tool until adjusting stop is resting with slight tension against radiator crosspanel.
    e. Tighten mounting bolts to specifications.

1998 SL500

1. Remove fan shroud.
2. Drain radiator coolant into suitable container.
3. Disconnect coolant hoses at radiator.
4. Disconnect automatic transmission oil lines at radiator.
5. Remove air scoop.
6. Remove mounting bolts, strut and crossmember.
7. Loosen air conditioning line bracket.
8. Remove mounting bolts and air conditioning condenser.
9. Remove radiator.
10. Reverse procedure to install, noting the following:
    a. Ensure radiator studs are inserted

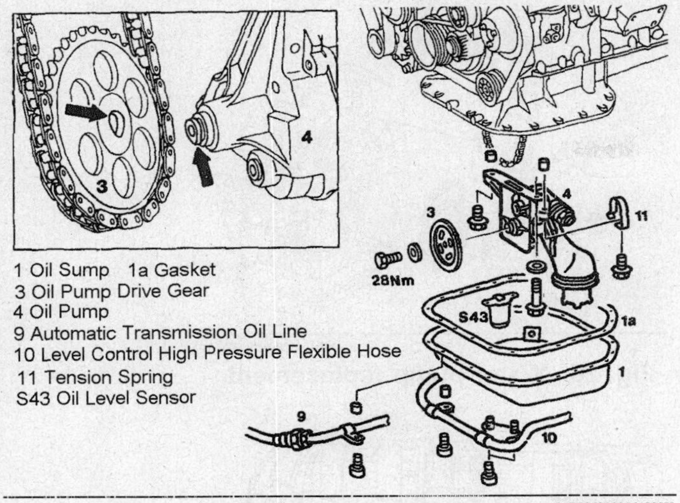

Fig. 23 Oil pump replacement. 1998 SL500

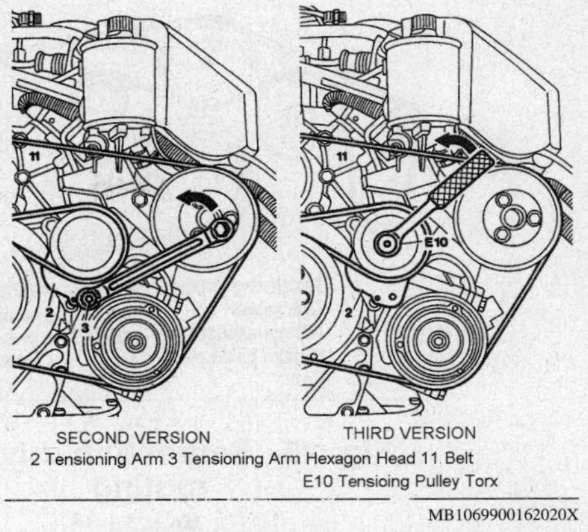

Fig. 24 Serpentine belt replacement

into crossmember bottom rubber pads.

b. Ensure condenser mounts on both rubber pads.
c. Raise condenser while installing radiator, then inset into radiator catches.
d. Tighten mounting bolts to specifications.

FUEL PUMP

REPLACE

1. Pinch off fuel delivery hose.
2. Remove cap nut or banjo bolt.
3. Remove mounting bracket.
4. Reverse procedure to install, noting the following:
   a. Plastic sleeve must project at both sides of bracket. Replace sleeve as required.
   b. Install new cooper sealing rings.
   c. Tighten connections to specifications.

FUEL FILTER

REPLACE

Refer to "Fuel Pump, Replace" for fuel filter replacement.

TECHNICAL SERVICE BULLETINS

ENGINE OIL ABOVE MAX. LEVEL

On some of these models the engine oil level may be above the Max. mark dip stick or by the oil sensor.

This condition may be caused by diesel or fuel oil or other subsequent additives in the fuel that did not burn and collected in the engine oil pan.

To correct this condition, proceed as follows:

1. Replace engine oil.
2. Drain fuel tank of foreign substances.
3. Do not replace sensor.

LOUD RATTLING NOISE DURING COLD START

On some of these models there may be a loud rattling noise during cold start.

This condition may be caused by a leaky oil filter return allowing oil to run out of the camshaft adjuster and oil filter housing.

To correct this condition, install a return valve repair kit (part No. 119 184 01 30).

TAPPET NOISE

On some of these models there may be tappet noise.

This condition may be caused by a missing exhaust camshaft side oil bridge, **Fig. 28.**

To correct this condition, install oil bridge cover

EXCESSIVE SMOKE AFTER STARTING

On some of these models there may be excessive smoke after starting.

This condition may be caused by missing or loose .4331 inch diameter closing plug in lefthand cylinder head.

To correct this condition, proceed as follows:

1. Remove lefthand valve cover.
2. Inspect timing chain housing for closing plug in lefthand cylinder head air injection gallery behind timing chain rail between chain rail pins. If plug is missing proceed to next step.
3. Remove spark plug and inspect for oil foiling. Clean or replace as required.
4. Remove catalyst and inspect for oil contamination. Empty excess oil.
5. Rotate crankshaft to set cylinder No. 1 piston at 45° BTDC.
6. Install holding pin tools No. 119 589 00 15 00, or equivalent, in left and righthand camshaft sprockets.
7. Mark timing chain to lefthand hand exhaust camshaft sprocket for installation alignment.
8. Remove lefthand cylinder head cover.
9. Remove timing chain tensioner.
10. Remove lefthand exhaust camshaft sprocket.
11. Inspect for loose closing plug.
12. Remove timing chain rail.
13. Remove .8662 inch diameter freeze plug from front of lefthand cylinder head.
14. Close timing chain housing opening with clean rags.
15. Cut .5906 inch deep M12x1.5 thread into air injection gallery closing plug hole. Lubricate thread tap during tapping.
16. Thorough clean thread hole and air injection gallery of aluminum shavings.
17. Install Allen screw closing plug flush with cylinder head surface using heat-proof Loctite 642 sealant, or equivalent.
18. Install .8662 inch diameter freeze plug in front of lefthand cylinder head using heat-proof Loctite 642 sealant, or equivalent.
19. **Ensure missing plug is recovered.**

VALVE AREA TICKING OR LOW OIL PRESSURE

On some of these models there may be a valve area ticking or low oil pressure.

This condition may be caused by missing closing plug in oil feed tube between camshafts.

To correct this condition, proceed as follows:

1. Inspect oil feed tubes for loose or missing closing plugs.
2. Replace plugs as required.
3. **Ensure missing plugs are removed from valve area or oil pan.**

COOLANT LOSS

On some of these models there may be coolant loss with evidence of coolant on alternator.

This condition may be caused by hose clamps being improperly installed onto elbow-shaped coolant hose between water pump and viscous fan clutch carrier.

To correct this condition, install new coolant hose and clamps with a least .0787 inch of hose extending beyond clamps.

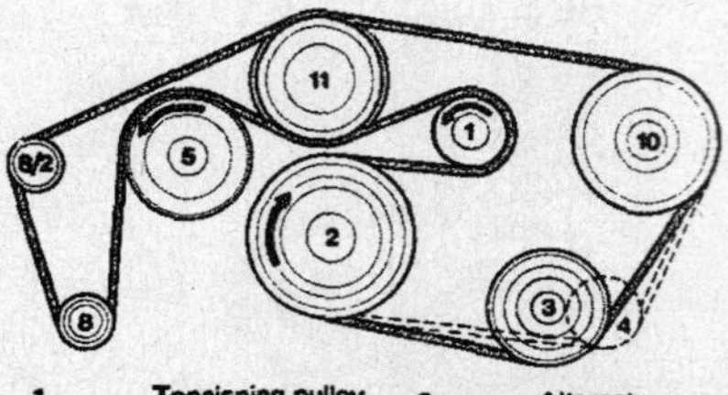

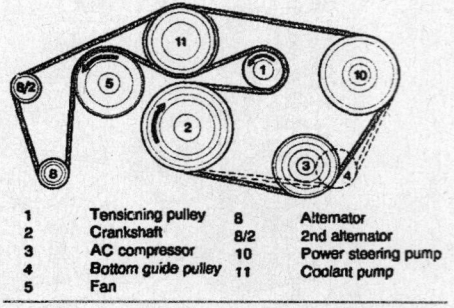

1	Tensioning pulley	8	Alternator
2	Crankshaft	8/2	2nd alternator
3	AC compressor	10	Power steering pump
4	*Bottom guide pulley*	11	Coolant pump
5	Fan		

MB1069900163020X

Fig. 25 Serpentine drive belt routing

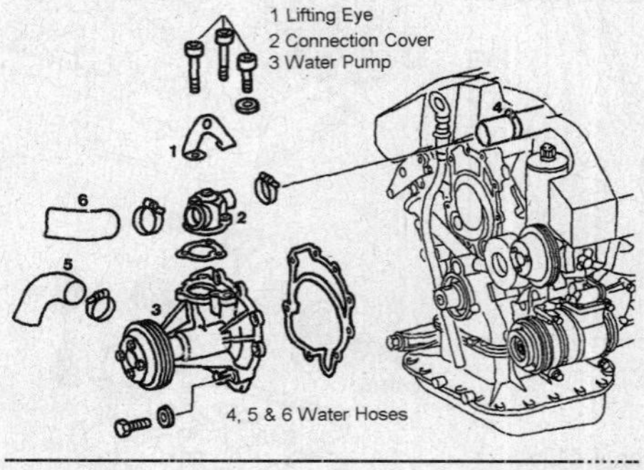

Fig. 26 Water pump replacement

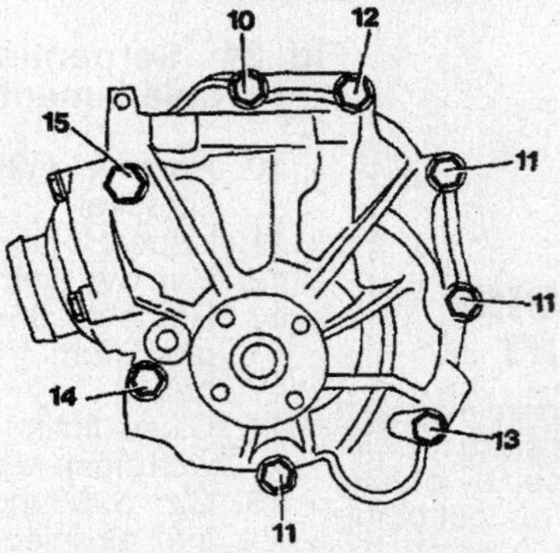

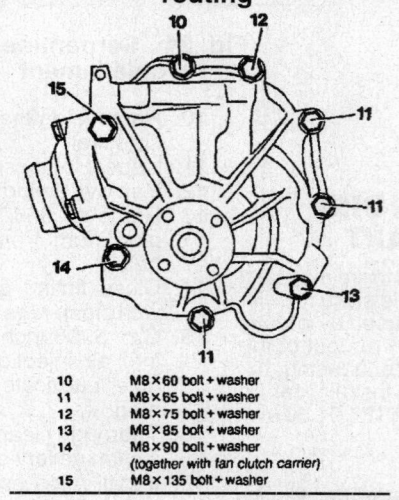

10	M8×60 bolt + washer
11	M8×65 bolt + washer
12	M8×75 bolt + washer
13	M8×85 bolt + washer
14	M8×90 bolt + washer *(together with fan clutch carrier)*
15	M8×135 bolt + washer

MB1069900166000X

Fig. 27 Water pump mounting bolts

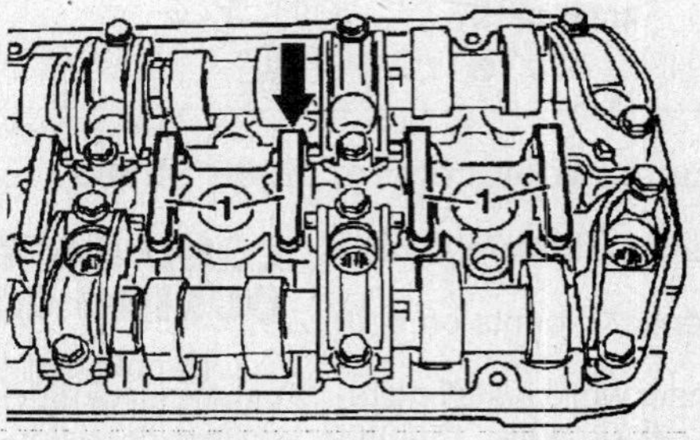

Fig. 28 Oil bridge cover replacement. 119 engine

TIGHTENING SPECIFICATIONS

Year	Component	Torque, Ft. Lbs.
1998–2001	Air Conditioning Compressor	15
	Air Conditioning Compressor Carrier (M6)	80①
	Air Conditioning Compressor Carrier (M8)	15
	Alternator Carrier	15
	Automatic Transmission Oil Lines	15
	Belt Tensioner	734
	Belt Tensioner Idler Pulley	22
	Camshaft Bearing Cap	97①
	Camshaft Sprocket	13
	Camshaft Timing Adjuster Armature	44①②
	Camshaft Timing Adjuster Flange Shaft	15⑧
	Camshaft Timing Adjuster Nut	48
	Camshaft Timing Adjuster Solenoid	88①
	Connecting Rod Bolts	⑥
	Crankshaft Bearing Stud	22④
	Crankshaft Bearing Stud (M10x1 Nut)	37④
	Crankshaft Bearing Stud (M10x40 Side Bolt)	37④.
	Crankcase Coolant Drain Plug	22
	Crankshaft Front Center Bolt	147②
	Crankshaft Vibration Damper	147②
	Cylinder Head Bolts	③

Continued

TIGHTENING SPECIFICATIONS—Continued

Year	Component	Torque, Ft. Lbs.
1998–2001	Cylinder Head Front Cover	18
	Distributor Driver	80①
	Distributor Rotor	22①
	Driven Plate	22–30⑦
	End Cover	80①
	Exhaust Crosspipe	18
	Exhaust Manifold	22
	Exhaust Pipe to Exhaust Manifold	15
	Exhaust Rear Crossmember (SL500)	88
	Fan Bearing Bracket	15
	Fan Pulley	88①
	Fan To Clutch	88①
	Front Engine Carrier (M8)	18
	Front Engine Carrier (M10)	30
	Front Engine Mount	18
	Front Engine Mount To Carrier	41
	Front Engine Mount To Front Suspension Carrier	22
	Front Suspension Carrier	18
	Fuel Pump Banjo Bolt or Cap Nut	18–22
	Guide Pulley	15
	Intake Manifold	⑤
	Oil Drain Plug	29
	Oil Lines	22
	Oil Pump	15
	Oil Pump Socket	21
	Oil Sump (M6)	97①
	Oil Sump (M8)	18
	Oil Sump (M10)	29
	Power Steering Pump	15
	Power Steering Pump Reservoir	80①
	Rear Engine Carrier (M8)	18
	Rear Engine Carrier (M10)	30
	Rear Engine Mount	⑨
	Secondary Air Injection Pump	18
	Serpentine Drive Belt Adjusting Bolt	74
	Spark Plugs	18–22
	Thermostat Housing Cover	88①
	Timing Case Cover	15
	Timing Chain Tensioner	18
	Timing Chain Top Guide Rail	80①
	Valve Cover	80①
	Viscous Fan	88①
	Viscous Fan Clutch	33
	Water Hose	88①
	Water Pump	15
	Water Pump Pulley	88①

① — Inch lbs.
② — Tighten an addition 90.°
③ — Refer to "Cylinder Head, Replace" for tightening procedure.
④ — Refer to "Main & Rod Bearings" for tightening sequence.
⑤ — Refer to "Intake Manifold, Replace" for tightening specifications and sequence.
⑥ — Refer to "Main & Rod Bearings" for tighten specifications and sequence.
⑦ — Tighten an additional 90–100.°
⑧ — Tighten an addition 60.°
⑨ — CL500, S420 & S500, 30 ft. lbs.; 1998 SL500, 52 ft. lbs.

120 V12 Gasoline Engine

NOTE: On Air Bag Equipped Models, Refer To "Air Bag System Precautions" Located In The Front Of This Manual For System Disarming & Arming Procedures.

NOTE: Prior To Performing Any Service Operations Listed In This Section, Consult The "Technical Service Bulletins" Section For Related Information.

INDEX

	Page No.
Belt Tension Data	5-108
Camshaft, Replace	5-104
Installation	5-105
Removal	5-104
Camshaft Adjuster, Replace	5-105
Installation	5-105
Removal	5-105
Compression Pressure	5-98
Cooling System Bleed	5-108
Crankshaft Damper, Replace	5-102
Crankshaft Rear Oil Seal, Replace	5-106
End Cover	5-106
Seal	5-106
Crankshaft Seal, Replace	5-106
Removal	5-106
Cylinder Head, Replace	5-101
Engine, Replace	5-99
CL600 & S600	5-99
SL600	5-100
Engine Mount, Replace	5-98
Front	5-98
Rear	5-99
Engine Rebuilding Specifications	5-344
Exhaust Manifold, Replace	5-101
Lefthand	5-101
Righthand	5-101
Front Cover, Replace	5-102
Cylinder Head	5-102
Timing Case	5-103
Front Cover Seal, Replace	5-103
Cylinder Head	5-103
Fuel Filter, Replace	5-109
Fuel Pump, Replace	5-108
Intake Manifold, Replace	5-101
Main & Rod Bearings	5-106
Oil Cooler, Replace	5-107
CL600 & S600	5-107
SL600	5-107
Oil Pan, Replace	5-106
CL600 & S600	5-106
SL600	5-106
Oil Pump, Replace	5-107
CL600 & S600	5-107
SL600	5-107
Piston & Rod Assembly	5-105
Precautions	5-98
Air Bag Systems	5-98
Battery Ground Cable	5-98
Radio Coded Anti-Theft System	5-98
Radiator, Replace	5-108
CL600 & S600	5-108
SL600	5-108
Serpentine Drive Belt	5-108
Belt, Replace	5-108
Routing	5-108
Tensioner, Replace	5-108
Technical Service Bulletins	5-109
Chain Tensioner Oil Leak	5-109
Engine Dies After Cold Start	5-109
Engine Oil Above Max. Level	5-109
Exhaust System Rattle	5-109
Thermostat, Replace	5-108
Tightening Specifications	5-111
Timing Chain, Replace	5-104
Timing Chain Tensioner, Replace	5-104
Installation	5-104
Removal	5-104
Valve Adjustment	5-102
Valve Cover, Replace	5-102
Water Pump, Replace	5-108

PRECAUTIONS

AIR BAG SYSTEMS

Refer to "Air Bag System Precautions" in front of this manual for system disarming and arming procedures.

BATTERY GROUND CABLE

Prior to service, disconnect battery ground cable and isolate as required.

RADIO CODED ANTI-THEFT SYSTEM

Anti-theft radios have a coded theft protection circuit. The CODE card must be obtained before disconnecting battery, removing radio fuse or removing the radio. **The serial number from the radio must match the CODE card.**

After service has been performed proceed as follows:

1. Connect radio power and turn key to position No. 2.
2. Turn radio to On position. Word "CODE" will appear on display.
3. Enter first digit of anti-theft code from CODE card. "CODE" will disappear and entered digit will appear followed by four dashes.
4. Enter next four digits, when all five are entered first digit flashes again.
5. Press SC, Seek or Tune button to confirm code.
6. If "WAIT" appears on radio panel, proceed as follows:
   a. Radio will allow three coding attempts only before entering lock-up mode and won't respond to controls.
   b. Leave radio on for 15–60 minutes, then radio will unlock and allow three addition coding attempts.
   c. Third lockout period (after nine failed coding attempts) will last 24 hours.
   d. Radio must be left on during enter 24-hour period until "CODE" appears.
7. When "CODE" appears, repeat coding attempt.

COMPRESSION PRESSURE

1. Warm engine to normal operating temperature of 176°F.
2. Remove spark plug.
3. Crank engine with compression tester contact switch several times with throttle closed and parking brake applied to eliminate cylinder combustion residues.
4. Install suitable compression tester into spark plug bore.
5. Open throttle valves wide open.
6. Crank engine with starter eight revolutions.
7. Record compression readings.
8. Normal compression pressure should measure 145–203 psi.
9. Maximum permissible difference between individual cylinders is 22 psi.

ENGINE MOUNT

REPLACE

FRONT

CL600 & S600

1. Remove air cleaner with Mass Air Flow (MAF) sensor, **Fig. 1.**
2. Remove fan cowl ring and place over fan.
3. Remove engine compartment bottom cover.
4. Remove front engine mount bottom mounting bolts.
5. Remove drag link.

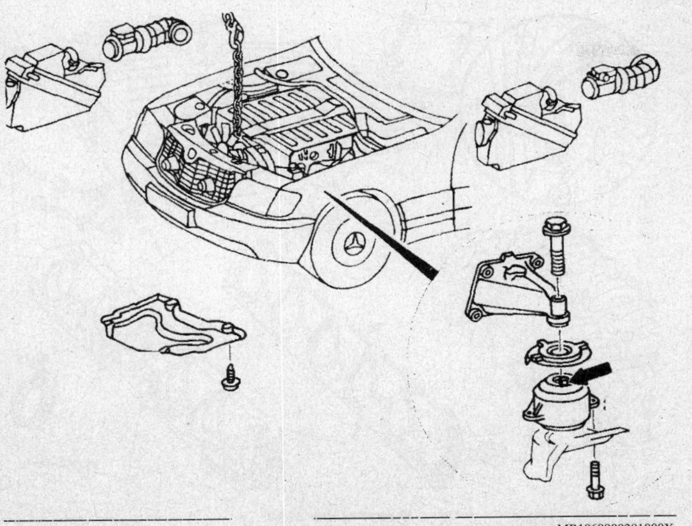

MB1069900201000X

Fig. 1 Front engine mount replacement. CL600 & S600

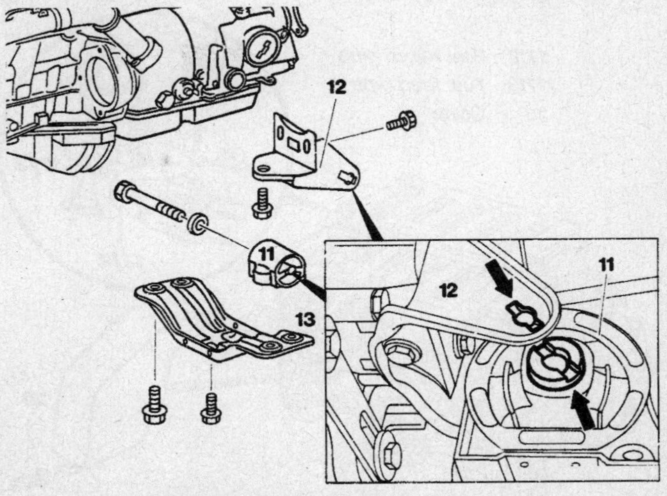

11 Engine Mount 12 Bracket 13 Engine Carrier

MB1069900202000X

Fig. 2 Rear engine mount replacement

6. Disconnect righthand engine oil cooler line at cooler crossmember.
7. Raise engine slightly. **Do not damage coolant hoses.**
8. If removing lefthand engine mount, disconnect secondary air injection line at cylinder head and crankcase.
9. If removing righthand engine mount, disconnect secondary air injection line at cylinder head and engine carrier, then the dipstick guide tube.
10. Remove top mounting bolts.
11. Remove front engine mounts.
12. Reverse procedure to install, noting the following.
    a. Ensure engine mount retention locks mount into shield openings and engine carrier retaining slots.
    b. Install new O-rings.
    c. Ensure fan cowl ring four catch points are correctly located.
    d. Tighten mounting bolts to specifications.

SL600

1. Remove air cleaner with Mass Air Flow (MAF) sensor.
2. Remove fan cowl.
3. Remove mounting bolts and exhaust system from exhaust manifold and transmission intermediate bearing.
4. If removing front lefthand engine mount, remove front exhaust pipe.
5. If removing righthand engine mount, remove shield above steering arm.
6. Remove top and bottom mounting bolts.
7. Raise engine slightly and remove shields.
8. Remove front engine mounts.
9. Reverse procedure to install, noting the following:
    a. Ensure engine mount retention locks mount into shield openings and engine carrier retaining slots.
    b. Tighten mounting bolts to specifications.

REAR

1. Support transmission with suitable jack.
2. **On SL600 models,** disconnect kickdown switch electrical cable from engine carrier.
3. **On CL600 and S600 models,** disconnect kickdown switch and oxygen sensor electrical cables from engine carrier.
4. **On all models,** remove mounting bolts and engine carrier, **Fig. 2.**
5. Remove mounting bolts and engine mount.
6. Reverse procedure to install, noting the following:
    a. Ensure engine mount retention locks mount into shield openings and engine carrier retaining slots.
    b. Tighten mounting bolts to specifications.

ENGINE

REPLACE

CL600 & S600

1. Remove air cleaner with Mass Air Flow (MAF) sensor.
2. Remove engine compartment bottom cover.
3. Remove radiator as outlined under "Radiator, Replace."
4. Disconnect lefthand automatic transmission oil line.
5. Attach 15.75 x 26.77 x .039-inch sheet metal or plastic guard plate to condenser.
6. Disconnect hood release cable.
7. Disconnect heater coolant hose at engine rear.
8. Remove viscous fan clutch, fan and serpentine drive belt.
9. Open fuel filler cap to relieve tank pressure, then disconnect and seal fuel lines.
10. Remove ignition control modules covers, then disconnect Crankshaft Position (CKP) and knock sensors connectors, and vacuum lines.
11. Remove diagnostic sockets' mounting bolts, then disconnect TDC sensor and rear diagnostic socket.
12. Remove high voltage distributors' covers and disconnect ignition cable No. 4.
13. Remove cable cover.
14. Disconnect two-way valve, automatic transmission and ignition control modules' vacuum lines.
15. Disconnect camshaft position (CMP) sensors intermediate, engine separation point connectors, CMP and knock sensors connectors from.
16. Remove air admission cover, then the cable mount by pulling cable up and removing mounting bolt.
17. Disconnect secondary air injection pump connector at righthand wheelhouse.
18. Disconnect air conditioning compressor, power steering pump and ground cable connectors at lefthand wheelhouse.
19. Disconnect accelerator control cable.
20. Disconnect brake servo vacuum line at intake manifold and evaporative emission control system lines at throttle valve actuators.
21. Remove power steering pump reservoir oil with handpump tool No. 112 589 00 72 00, or equivalent.
22. Disconnect return line, high pressure flexible hose, high pressure hose and oil lines at power steering pump.
23. Remove oil cooler and air conditioning lines' bracket.
24. Disconnect oil cooler lines at air-to-oil cooler.
25. Disconnect righthand oil cooler line from radiator crossmember.
26. Remove air conditioning compressor mounting bolt and oil pressure switch.
27. Remove compete exhaust system.
28. Drain cooling system into suitable container.
29. Remove starter motor harness shield and disconnect connectors.

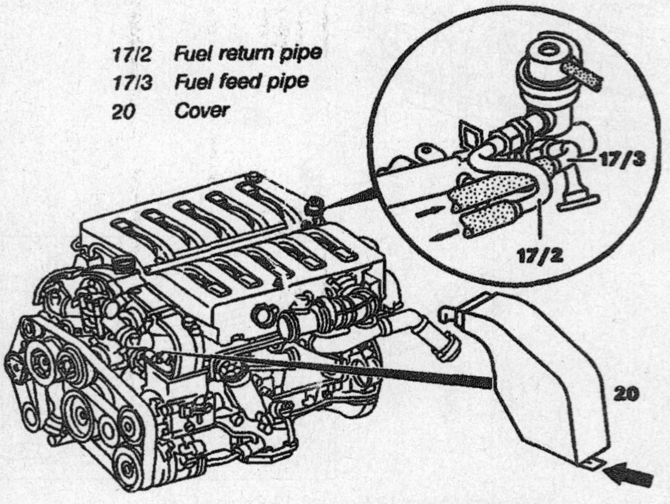

Fig. 3 Intake manifold replacement (Part 1 of 2)

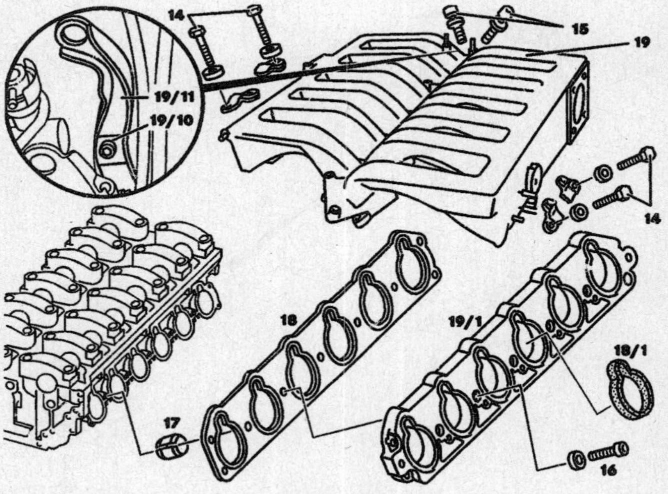

Fig. 3 Intake manifold replacement (Part 2 of 2)

30. Disconnect propeller shaft from transmission flexible coupling and push shaft back.
31. Remove transmission exhaust bracket carrier and disconnect ground cable.
32. Support transmission with suitable jack and remove rear engine carrier without engine mount as outlined under "Engine Mount, Replace."
33. Lower transmission.
34. Disconnect automatic transmission shift rod and starter lockout switch connector.
35. Disconnect transmission overload protection, kickdown, electronic speedometer and E-S model selector connectors.
36. Remove left and righthand front engine mount mounting bolts as outlined under "Engine Mount, Replace."
37. Attach suitable engine hoist to three lifting eyes.
38. Raise engine and transmission enough to disconnect air conditioning compressor bracket and place aside with lines attached.
39. Tilt engine and transmission, then remove. **Do not rest engine on oil pan.**
40. Reverse procedure to install, noting the following:
    a. Install new air-to-oil cooler line seals.
    b. Install new propeller shaft to flexible shaft self-locking nuts.
    c. Adjust throttle cable.
    d. Adjust automatic transmission control pressure cable.
    e. Inspect idle speed.

SL600

1. Remove engine compartment bottom cover and complete exhaust system.
2. Remove transmission exhaust bracket carrier.
3. Remove left and righthand air cleaners.
4. Remove radiator as outlined under "Radiator, Replace."
5. Remove serpentine drive belt.
6. Attach 15.75 x 26.77 x .039-inch sheet metal or plastic guard plate to condenser.
7. Drain cooling system into suitable container.
8. Disconnect propeller shaft from transmission flexible coupling and push shaft back.
9. Disconnect transmission ground cable and support transmission with suitable jack.
10. Remove rear engine carrier as outlined under "Engine Mount, Replace." and lower transmission.
11. Disconnect automatic transmission shift rod and starter lockout switch connector. Protect starter lockout switch with suitable locking element.
12. Disconnect transmission overload protection kickdown valve, second driving mode switchover valve and electronic speedometer connectors.
13. Remove left and righthand front engine mount mounting bolts as outlined under "Engine Mount, Replace."
14. Remove righthand, front exhaust shield.
15. Disconnect starter motor electrical connector and holder.
16. Disconnect oil pressure sensor connector.
17. Remove mounting bolts and place air conditioning compressor aside with lines attached.
18. Disconnect air-to-oil cooler lines.
19. Disconnect high pressure flexible hose at oil sump bottom.
20. Disconnect and seal fuel lines.
21. Remove power steering pump reservoir oil using handpump tool No. 112 589 00 72 00, or equivalent.
22. Disconnect return hose, high pressure flexible hose, high pressure hose and oil line at power steering pump.
23. Disconnect brake servo vacuum line and accelerator control cable.
24. Remove engine compartment upper covers.
25. Disconnect wiring harness connectors.
26. Remove component partition.
27. Disconnect diagnostic sockets and TDC sensor connectors
28. Disconnect Distributor Ignition (DI) control modules' crankshaft position and knock sensors' connectors.
29. Disconnect DI vacuum lines.
30. Disconnect Camshaft Position (CMP) sensors' connectors.
31. Disconnect electronic accelerator pedal actuator connectors at left and righthand wheelhouse.
32. Disconnect secondary air pump connector.
33. Disconnect purge line at both throttle valve actuators, upshift delay switchover valve, automatic transmission at right of component partition and intake manifold vacuum lines.
34. Disconnect alternator wiring harness.
35. Disconnect Exhaust Gas Recirculation (EGR) switchover valves connectors on left and righthand intake manifolds.
36. Disconnect ignition cable No. 4 at high voltage distributor and ignition coil.
37. Disconnect lefthand cylinder head cover ground cable.
38. Disconnect air conditioning compressor connector.
39. Attach suitable engine hoist to three lifting eyes.
40. Move engine and transmission into tilted position and raise sightly.
41. Disconnect heater hose at rear, then remove engine and transmission. **Do not rest engine on oil pan.**
42. Reverse procedure to install, noting the following:
    a. Install new air-to-oil cooler line seals.
    b. Tighten mounting bolts and nuts to specifications.

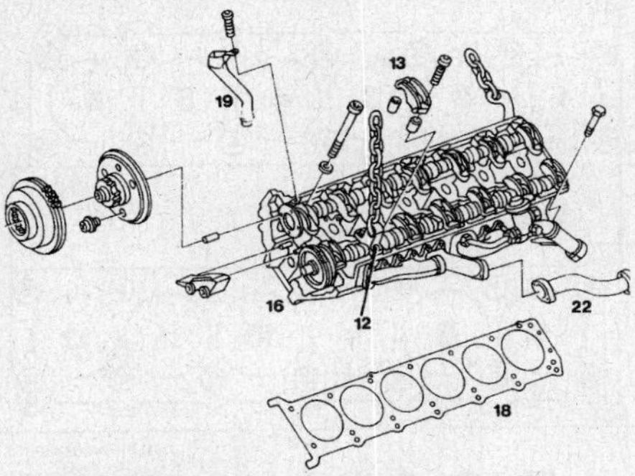

12 Lifting Bracket 13 Camshaft Bearing Caps
16 Cylinder Head 18 Gasket 19 Ventilation Line
22 Exhaust Pipe

MB1069900186010X

Fig. 4 Cylinder head replacement (Part 1 of 2). Lefthand

c. Adjust throttle cable.
d. Adjust automatic transmission control pressure cable.
e. Inspect idle speed.

INTAKE MANIFOLD

REPLACE

1. Remove air cleaner.
2. Remove electronic accelerator actuator with throttle valve body.
3. Remove cable duct cover above intake manifold.
4. Remove intake manifold covers.
5. Remove electric wiring straps on fuel rail.
6. Remove ignition coils.
7. Disconnect vacuum lines at intake manifold. Mark for installation.
8. Relieve fuel pressure through fuel rail service valve.
9. Place suitable shop rags to collect spilled fuel, then disconnect fuel feed and return lines, **Fig. 3.**
10. Disconnect brake unit vacuum lines at intake manifold left and righthand sides.
11. Remove mounting bolts and air inlet plenum chamber.
12. Remove intake manifold mounting bolts. Mark bolt size, length and positions for installation.
13. Remove bracket mounting screws and servopump expansion tank with lines connected.
14. Remove intake manifold.
15. Remove intermediate flange.
16. Reverse procedure to install, noting the following:
    a. Install new gasket
    b. Replace shaped rubber seals.
    c. Ensure no vacuum lines or electrical wiring is jammed between intake manifold and block.
    d. Tighten mounting bolts to specifications starting in middle and working to outside.
    e. Adjust accelerator control and inspect idle speed.

10 Water Hose 18 Gasket

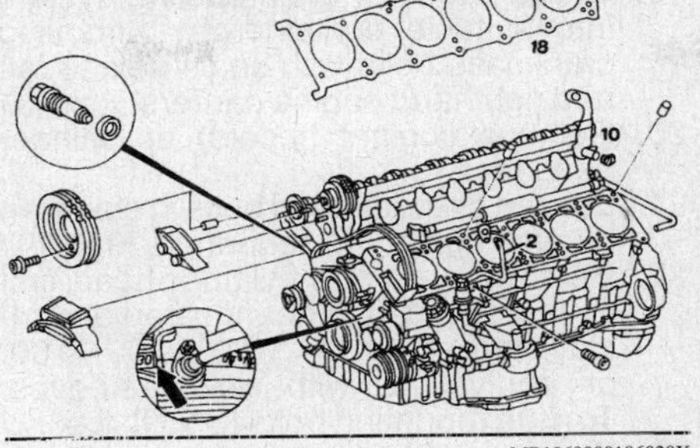

MB1069900186020X

Fig. 4 Cylinder head replacement (Part 2 of 2). Lefthand

EXHAUST MANIFOLD

REPLACE

LEFTHAND

Front

1. Remove complete exhaust system.
2. Disconnect secondary air injection line at cylinder head and engine block, then press to outside.
3. Remove self-locking nuts.
4. Remove lefthand front exhaust manifold.
5. Reverse procedure to install, noting the following:
    a. Gasket metal side faces toward cylinder head.
    b. Apply dots of sealant No. A 001 989 25 20, or equivalent, to gaskets facilitate installation.
    c. Install new self-locking nuts.
    d. Tighten mounting nuts to specifications.

Rear

1. Remove lefthand front exhaust manifold as outlined under "Exhaust Manifold, Replace."
2. Remove electronic accelerator actuator with throttle valve body.
3. Remove Exhaust Gas Recirculation (EGR) valve.
4. **On CL600 and S600 models,** remove lefthand front engine mount as outlined under "Engine Mount, Replace."
5. **On all models,** remove self-locking nuts.
6. Pull engine to right and remove lefthand rear exhaust manifold.
7. Reverse procedure to install, noting the following:
    a. Gasket metal side faces toward cylinder head.
    b. Apply dots of sealant No. A 001 989 25 20, or equivalent, to gaskets facilitate installation.
    c. Install new self-locking nuts.
    d. Tighten mounting nuts to specifications.

RIGHTHAND

Front

1. Remove complete exhaust system.
2. Remove alternator, air pump and dipstick guide tube.

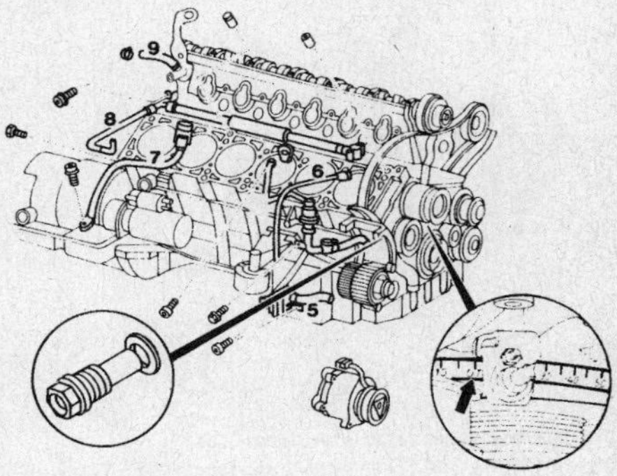

5 Secondary Air Pump Air Cleaner
6 Oil Pan Dipstick Guide Tube
7 Automatic Transmission Dipstick Guide Tube
8 Crankcase Ventilation Line
9 Water Hose

MB1069900187010X

Fig. 5 Cylinder head replacement (Part 1 of 2). Righthand

3. Disconnect secondary air injection line at cylinder head and engine supporting bracket, then press to outside.
4. Remove self-locking nuts.
5. Remove righthand front exhaust manifold.
6. Reverse procedure to install, noting the following:
    a. Gasket metal side faces toward cylinder head.
    b. Apply dots of sealant No. A 001 989 25 20, or equivalent, to gaskets facilitate installation.
    c. Install new self-locking nuts.
    d. Tighten mounting nuts to specifications.

Rear

1. Remove righthand front exhaust manifold as outlined under "Exhaust Manifold, Replace."
2. Remove Exhaust Gas Recirculation (EGR) valve.
3. Remove electronic accelerator actuator with throttle valve body.
4. **On SL600 models,** remove steering idler arm and starter cover, then the automatic transmission dipstick guide tube.
5. **On all models,** remove self-locking nuts.
6. Remove righthand rear exhaust manifold.
7. Reverse procedure to install, noting the following:
    a. Gasket metal sides faces toward cylinder head.
    b. Apply dots of sealant No. A 001 989 25 20, or equivalent, to gaskets facilitate installation.
    c. Install new self-locking nuts.
    d. Tighten mounting nuts to specifications.

CYLINDER HEAD

REPLACE

Remove cylinder heads with camshafts only when engine is cold.

1. **On CL600 and S600 models,** remove engine as outlined under "Engine, Replace."

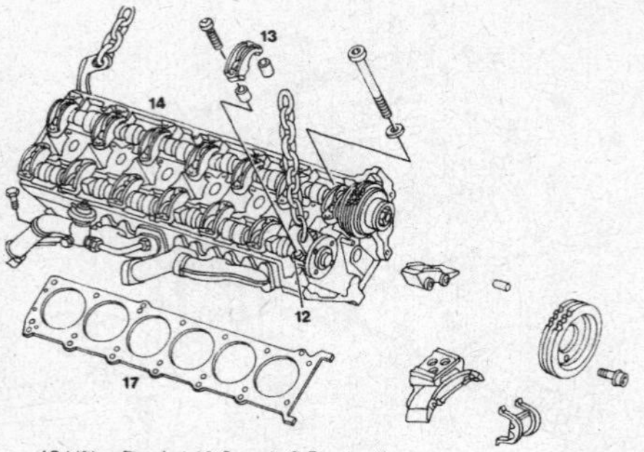

12 Lifting Bracket 13 Camshaft Bearing Caps
14 Cylinder Head 17 Gasket

MB1069900187020X

Fig. 5 Cylinder head replacement (Part 2 of 2). Righthand

2. **On all models,** remove cylinder head front covers as outlined under "Front Cover, Replace."
3. Remove chain tensioner as outlined under "Timing Chain Tensioner, Replace."
4. Remove chain rail housing.
5. Rotate crankshaft to set cylinder No. 1 piston at 30° after ignition TDC. Camshafts can be rotated without valves contacting piston crowns.
6. Mark camshaft sprockets and timing chain for installation alignment.
7. Remove ventilation line from lefthand cylinder head, **Fig. 4.**
8. Remove lefthand cylinder head guide rail pin using impact extractor tool No. 116 589 20 33 00 and threaded insert tool No. 116 589 02 34 00, or equivalents.
9. **On CL600 and S600 models,** remove mounting bolts and secondary air injection air cleaner.
10. **On all models,** remove secondary air injection line mounting bolts on righthand cylinder head and engine carry, **Fig. 5.**
11. **On CL600 and S600 models,** remove secondary air injection line mounting bolts on oil pan.
12. **On all models,** remove secondary air injection line mounting bolts on lefthand cylinder head and crankcase below front exhaust manifold.
13. **On CL600 and S600 models,** remove secondary air injection line mounting bolt on lefthand engine carrier.
14. **On SL600 model,** proceed as follows:
    a. Remove exhaust system to exhaust manifold mounting bolts.
    b. Remove exhaust system at transmission exhaust bracket carrier.
    c. Remove front manifold mounting exhaust pipe mounting bolt to gain access to crankcase drain plug.
15. **On all models,** remove mounting bolt and turn oil pan dipstick to side.
16. Remove automatic transmission dipstick guide tube at righthand cylinder head from crankcase and transmission. Seal automatic transmission hole.
17. Remove crankcase ventilation line from righthand cylinder head.
18. **On CL600 and S600 models,** remove exhaust manifold mounting bolts at crankcase rear.
19. **On all models,** drain cooling system into suitable container by removing crankcase bolts with seals next to left and righthand engine carriers.
20. Remove coolant hose(s) at cylinder head rear.
21. Loosen cylinder head bolts in stages in reverse tightening sequence, **Fig. 6.**
22. Remove righthand cylinder head first exhaust camshaft bearing cap and install bracket tool No. 104 589 00 40 00, or equivalent, with dowel sleeves. **Torque** mounting bolts to 15 ft. lbs.
23. Remove lefthand cylinder head second exhaust camshaft bearing cap and install bracket tool No. 104 589 00 40 00, or equivalent, with dowel sleeves. **Torque** mounting bolts to 15 ft. lbs.
24. Attach suitable engine hoist to bracket tool and rear engine suspension point, lift and remove cylinder head. **Do not damage tensioning or guide rails.**
25. Reverse procedure to install, noting the following:
    a. Install new cylinder head gasket.
    b. Replace cylinder head bolts with shanks longer than 6.393 inches.
    c. Clean threaded holes.
    d. Oil cylinder head bolt threads and head contact surface.
    e. **Torque** cylinder head bolts to 55 ft. lbs. in sequence, **Fig. 6.**
    f. Tighten head bolts an additional 90° in sequence
    g. Final tighten bolts an additional 90° in sequence.
    h. Install new oil pan dipstick O-ring as required.
    i. Install new secondary air injection gaskets.
    j. Guide rail pin thread must be positioned to front in direction of travel.
    k. Do not pressure test cooling system until engine has reached operating temperature and cylinder head gaskets have swelled.

VALVE COVER

REPLACE

1. Remove intake manifold as previous described.
2. Remove viscous fan clutch.
3. Install guard plate tool No. 120 589 06 31 00, or equivalents, into intake ports.
4. Remove high voltage distributor shields, **Fig. 7.**
5. Remove spark plug cable ducts mounting bolts from covers.
6. Remove lefthand high voltage distributor and holder.
7. Remove Camshaft Position (CMP) sensor.
8. Remove spark plug cables ducts with high voltage distributor and spark plug connectors.
9. Disconnect crankcase ventilation lines bracket.
10. Remove mounting bolt and dipstick guide tube from righthand cover.
11. Remove bolts, seals and washers. Record bolt locations and lengths for installation reference.
12. **On SL600 models,** remove lefthand valve cover ground strap.

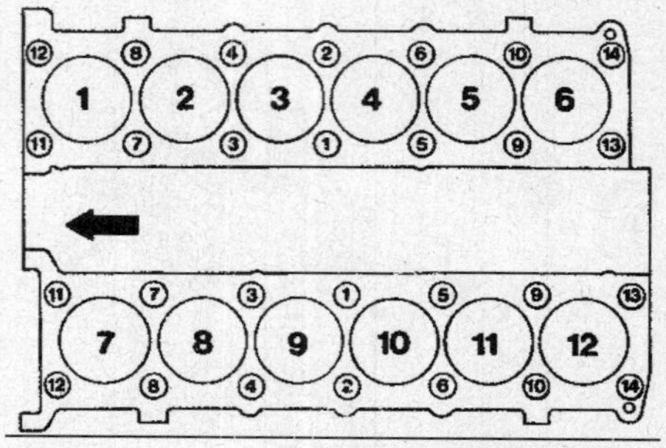

MB1069900188000X

Fig. 6 Cylinder head bolt tightening sequence

13. **On all models,** remove valve covers with gaskets and duct seals.
14. Reverse procedure to install, noting the following:
    a. Ensure valve cover gaskets are correctly install, especially at rear.
    b. Tighten mounting bolts to specifications.

VALVE ADJUSTMENT

This engine is equipped with hydraulic lifters and requires no valve adjustment,

CRANKSHAFT DAMPER

REPLACE

1. Remove engine compartment bottom cover.
2. Remove viscous fan.
3. Attach 15.75 x 26.77 x .039-inch sheet metal or plastic guard plate to radiator front.
4. Rotate crankshaft to set cylinder No. 1 piston at TDC so crankshaft Woodruff key is vertical.
5. Loosen fan and water pump pulley mounting bolts, **Fig. 8.**
6. Remove serpentine drive belt.
7. Remove tensioning pulley mounting bolt.
8. Remove mounting bolts, fan and water pump pulleys.
9. Install crankshaft/ring gear retaining lock tool No. 602 589 00 40 00, or equivalent.
10. Remove hub bolt and pulley with vibration damper.
11. Reverse procedure to install, noting the following:
    a. Ensure crankshaft Woodruff key engages hub slot.
    b. Tighten mounting bolts to specifications.

FRONT COVER

REPLACE

CYLINDER HEAD

1. Remove valve covers as outlined under "Valve Cover, Replace."
2. **On CL600 and S600 models,** remove radiator as outlined under "Radiator, Replace,"
3. **On all models,** remove serpentine drive belt and thermostat housing.
4. Remove guide pulley.

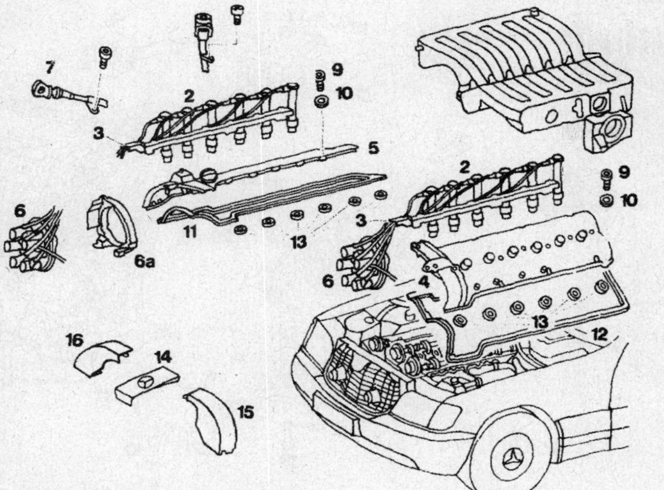

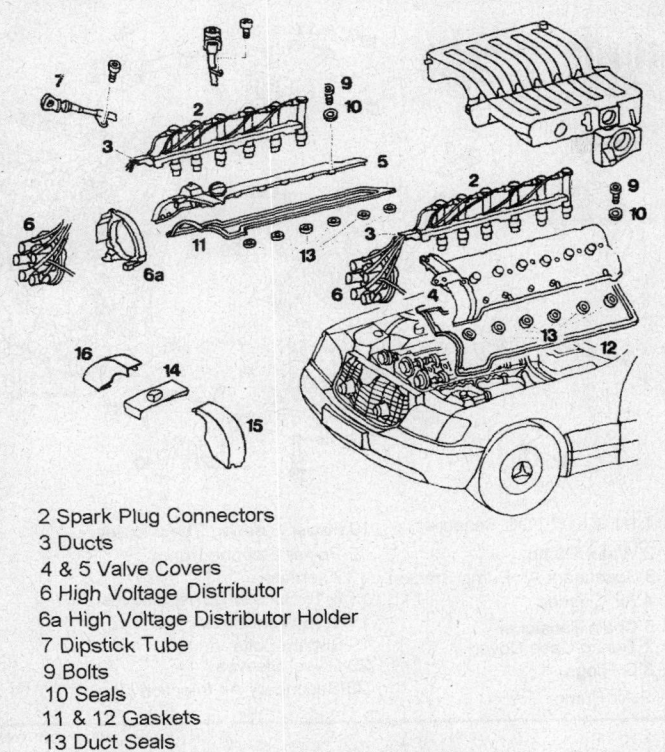

2 Spark Plug Connectors
3 Ducts
4 & 5 Valve Covers
6 High Voltage Distributor
6a High Voltage Distributor Holder
7 Dipstick Tube
9 Bolts
10 Seals
11 & 12 Gaskets
13 Duct Seals
14, 15 & 16 High Voltage Distributor Covers

MB1069900179000X

Fig. 7 Valve cover replacement

5. Fit guard plate No. 120 589 06 31 00 onto intake ports.
6. **On SL600 models,** disconnect upper coolant hose at radiator.
7. **On all models,** remove distributor rotor and follower, **Fig. 9.**
8. Remove protective cover and seal.
9. Remove mounting bolts and move power steering pump reservoir upward with hoses.
10. Remove mounting bolts and bracket. Mark mounting bolt locations and lengths for installation.
11. Remove mounting bolts and disconnect power steering pump connection fitting.
12. Remove mounting bolts and cylinder head front covers.
13. Reverse procedure to install, noting the following:
    a. Clean cylinder head front cover sealing surfaces and timing case shaped groove.
    b. Install new coolant passage shaped rubber gasket and O-ring.
    c. Inspect guide rail bridge shaped gaskets and replace as required.
    d. Apply dots of sealant No. 001 989 61 20, or equivalent, into timing case cover oil-free groove at cylinder head joint.
    e. Install new shaped gasket without sealant into oil-free groove and coat top with little engine oil.
    f. Coat front cover to cylinder head contact surfaces with sealant No. 002 989 00 20 10, or equivalent.
    g. Install insertion sleeve tool No. 103 589 01 14 00, or equivalent, onto exhaust camshaft.
    h. Coat radial seal sealing lip for engine oil.
    i. Ensure bottom shaped rubber gasket does not move out of position.
    j. Tighten mounting bolts to specifications, starting with bottom bolts.
    k. Install new power steering pump connection seal.
    l. Distributor follower slot must engage camshaft locating pin.

TIMING CASE

1. Remove cylinder head front covers as outlined under "Front Cover, Replace."
2. Remove water pump, **Fig. 10.**
3. Remove air cleaner and Mass Air Flow (MAF) sensor.
4. Remove air pump and alternator.
5. Rotate crankshaft to set cylinder No. 1 piston at 30° after TDC. Camshafts can be rotated without valves contact pistons' crowns.
6. Mark camshaft sprockets and timing chain for installation alignment.
7. Remove crankshaft vibration damper as outlined under "Crankshaft Damper, Replace."
8. Remove power steering pump belt pulley by placing drive belt over pulley, installing holder tool No. 603 589 00 40 00, or equivalent, removing mounting bolts and pulley.
9. Remove mounting bolts and push power steering pump aside with oil lines connected.
10. Disconnect TDC sensors at cover.

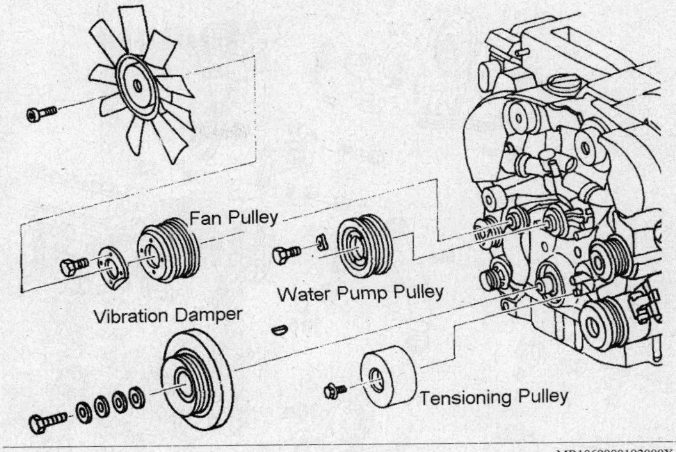

MB1069900192000X

Fig. 8 Crankshaft damper replacement

11. Remove mounting bolts and secondary air pump air cleaner.
12. Remove mounting bolts and secondary air pump bracket.
13. **On SL600 models,** remove mounting bolt, alternator harness bracket, shutoff valve vacuum line bracket and secondary air injection line.
14. **On all models,** remove timing chain tensioner as outlined under "Timing Chain Tensioner, Replace."
15. Remove mounting bolts and timing case cover. Mark mounting bolt locations and lengths for installation.
16. Reverse procedure to install, noting the following:
    a. Coat sealing surfaces with sealant No. 002 989 00 20 10, or equivalent.
    b. Ensure no sealant gets into oil gallery or separator.
    c. Install new O-rings.
    d. Ensure dowel sleeves are correctly positioned.
    e. Tighten front mounting bolts to specifications first.
    f. Ensure secondary air pump bracket mounting bolts' dowel sleeves are correctly installed.

FRONT COVER SEAL

REPLACE

CYLINDER HEAD

1. **On CL600 and S600 models,** remove radiator as outline under "Radiator, Replace."
2. **On all models,** if removing righthand seal, remove viscous fan, **Fig. 11.**
3. Remove shield caps and high voltage distributor with holder.
4. Remove distributor rotor, screw and follower.
5. Remove guard seal with seal.
6. Pry radial seal out with suitable screwdriver and clean cloth. **Do not damage camshaft and seal mounting hole.**
7. Reverse procedure to install, noting the following:
    a. Install insertion sleeve tool No. 103 589 01 14 00, or equivalent.

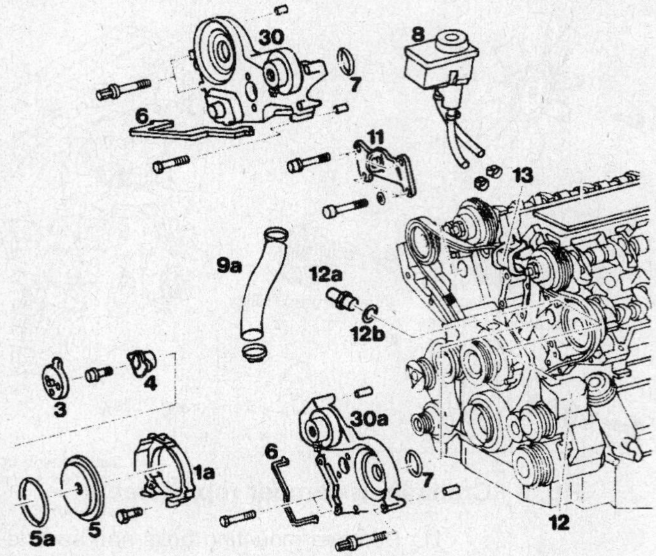

3 Distributor Rotor 4 Distributor Follower 5 Protective Cover
5a Seal 6 Shaped Rubber Gaskets 7 O-Rings
8 Power Steering Pump Reservoir 9a Water Hose
11 Bracket 12 Power Steering Pump
12a Power Steering Pump Oil Line Connection Fitting
12b Seal 13 Guide Rail Bridge
30 & 30a Cylinder Head Front Covers

MB1069900181000X

Fig. 9 Cylinder head front cover replacement

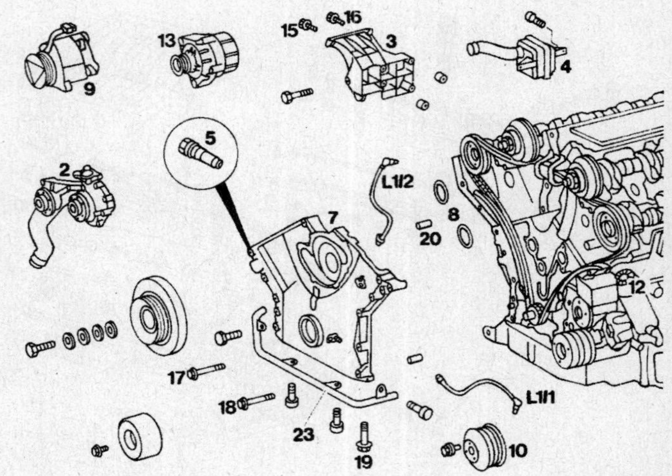

L1/1 & L1/2 TDC Sensors
2 Water Pump
3 Secondary Air Pump Bracket
4 Air Cleaner
5 Chain Tensioner
7 Timing Case Cover
8 O-Rings
9 Air Pump
10 Power Steering Pump Pulley
12 Power Steering Pump
13 Alternator
15 & 16 Bolts w/Dowel Sleeves
17 & 18 Front Bolts
19 Bottom Bolts
20 Dowel Sleeves
23 Secondary Air Injection Line

MB1069900180000X

Fig. 10 Timing case cover replacement

b. Coat radial seal sealing lip with engine oil. **Do not use grease.**
c. Fit seal onto insertion sleeve and press flush using shop-made sleeve. **Seal must be vertical to camshaft.**
d. Distributor follower slot must engage camshaft locating pin.
e. **On CL600 and S600 models,** clip TDC sensors cables into left and righthand holders.
f. **On CL600 and S600 models,** clip oil lines into lefthand holder.
g. **On SL600 models,** clip ignition cable No. 4 into righthand holder.
h. **On all models,** clip TDC sensor cables into lefthand holder.
i. Tighten mounting bolts to specifications.

TIMING CHAIN

REPLACE

1. Remove cylinder head front covers as outlined under "Front Cover, Replace," **Fig. 12.**
2. Remove timing chain tensioner as outlined under "Timing Chain Tensioner, Replace."
3. Remove spark plug.
4. Cover chain box with clean cloth.
5. Grind open both chain pins at double link at righthand exhaust camshaft sprocket.
6. Press of plate with suitable screwdriver and push out ground open double link.
7. Connect new timing chain to old chain with rivet link and middle plate.
8. Rotate crankshaft in engine rotation direction using wrench tool No. 001 589 65 09 00, or equivalent. Hold chain by hand and ensure it meshes into lefthand exhaust sprocket teeth.
9. Pull bottom freed timing chain end out of chain box.
10. Continue rotating crankshaft under end of new timing chain can be connected with rivet link.

TIMING CHAIN TENSIONER

REPLACE

REMOVAL

1. Remove drive belt, **Fig. 13.**
2. Remove righthand air cleaner with Mass Air Flow (MAF) sensor.
3. Remove righthand intake air scoop and secondary air pump.
4. Turn crankshaft to set cylinder No. 1 piston at 30° after ignition TDC.
5. Loosen tensioner plug approximately one turn.
6. Remove chain tensioner.
7. Remove plug with sealing ring and thrust spring with filler pin.
8. Press thrust bolt out with catch spring in thrust direction.

INSTALLATION

1. Stick new seal to housing with suitable grease.
2. Install chain tensioner housing with new seal and tighten to specifications.
3. Install thrust bolt into housing with catch spring and pressure spring with filler pin.
4. Install plug and tighten to specifications.

CAMSHAFT

REPLACE

The camshaft code numbers are at righthand cylinder head bearing points No. 3 and 10, and lefthand cylinder head bearing points No. 17 and 24 behind the bearing caps. The camshaft bearing caps numbers are cast into the cylinder heads. The camshaft bearings must be installed in original positions.

The camshafts are very sensitive to fracturing and must be removed and installed free of tension.

REMOVAL

1. Remove cylinder head front covers as outlined under "Front Cover, Replace," **Fig. 14.**
2. Turn crankshaft to set cylinder No. 1 piston to 30 after ignition TDC. Camshafts can be rotated without valves contacting piston crowns.
3. Mark camshaft sprockets and timing chain for installation alignment.
4. Remove timing chain tensioner as underlined under "Timing Chain Tensioner, Replace."
5. Remove righthand guide rail mounting bolts.
6. Remove mounting bolts and righthand exhaust camshaft sprocket.

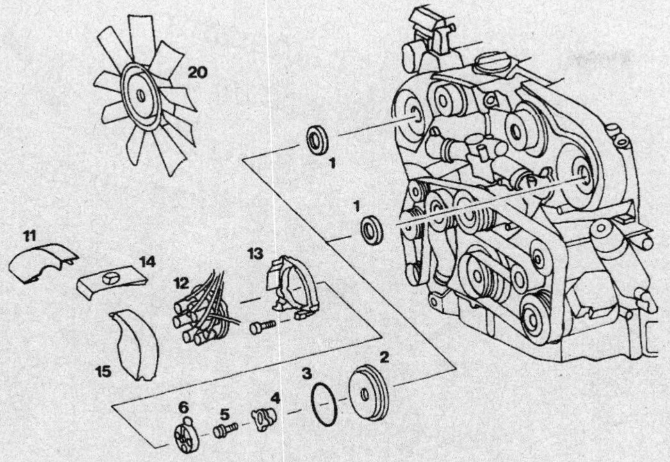

1 Radial Seal
2 Guard Cover
3 Seals
4 Distributor Follower
5 Distributor Screw
6 Distributor Rotor
11 Shield Cap
12 High Voltage Distributor
13 High Voltage Distributor Holder
14 & 15 Shield Caps
20 Viscous Fan

MB1069900182000X

Fig. 11 Cylinder head front cover seal replacement

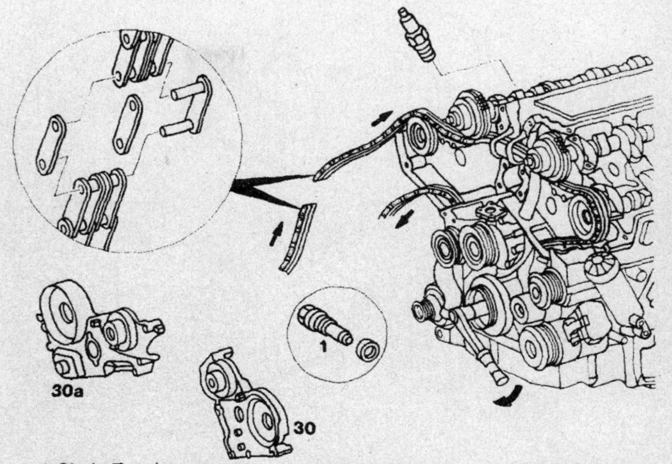

1 Chain Tensioner
30 & 30a Cylinder Head Front Covers

MB1069900196000X

Fig. 12 Timing chain replacement

7. Loosen timing chain by rotating righthand intake camshaft in rotational direction using wrench tool No. 104 589 01 01 00, or equivalent.
8. Remove righthand guide rail from bearing pin.
9. Rotate lefthand intake camshaft in rotational direction using wrench tool No. 104 589 01 01 00, or equivalent.
10. Remove lefthand guide rail from bearing pin.
11. Remove mounting bolts and lefthand cylinder head exhaust camshaft sprocket.
12. Turn camshaft using wrench tool No. 104 589 01 01 00, or equivalent, until cylinders Nos. 3 and 9 cam tips are pressing hydraulic lifter centers.
13. Remove camshaft bearing caps mounting bolts except for cylinders Nos. 3 and 9. Bearing cap No. 15 is removed with intake camshaft.
14. Loosen cylinders Nos. 3 and 9 camshaft bearing caps one turn at a time. **Camshafts must not be tilted when loosening camshaft bearing caps.**
15. Remove bearings caps and intake and exhaust camshafts.
16. Inspect hydraulic lifters for movement ease.

INSTALLATION

1. Oil bearing points and hydraulic lifters.
2. Install intake and exhaust camshafts into bearing points with cylinders Nos. 3 and 9 tips pointing down and centered.
3. Align intake and exhaust camshafts axially at axial bearing.
4. Install cylinders Nos. 3 and 9 bearing caps.
5. Tighten mounting bolts to specifications one turn at a time while holding camshafts with wrench tool No. 104 589 01 01 00, or equivalent. **Camshafts must not be tilted when tightening camshaft bearing caps.**
6. Install remaining camshaft bearing caps and tighten mounting bolts to specifications.
7. Rotate exhaust and intake camshafts in opposite of rotational direction when installing timing chain.
8. Install chain tensioner.

CAMSHAFT ADJUSTER

REPLACE

REMOVAL

1. Remove cylinder head front covers as outlined under "Front Cover, Replace" **Fig. 15.**
2. Turn crankshaft to set cylinder No. 1 piston to 30 after ignition TDC. Camshafts can be rotated without valves contacting piston crowns.
3. Mark camshaft sprockets and timing chain for installation alignment.
4. Remove timing chain tensioner as outlined under "Timing Chain Tensioner, Replace."
5. Remove righthand guide rail mounting bolts.
6. Remove mounting bolts and righthand exhaust camshaft sprocket.
7. Loosen timing chain by rotating righthand intake camshaft in rotational direction using wrench tool No. 104 589 01 01 00, or equivalent.
8. Remove righthand guide rail from bearing pin.
9. Rotate lefthand intake camshaft in rotational direction using wrench tool No. 104 589 01 01 00, or equivalent.
10. Remove lefthand guide rail from bearing pin.
11. Remove mounting bolt and armature.
12. Remove mounting nut while holding camshaft with wrench tool No. 104 589 01 01 00, or equivalent.
13. Remove disc, camshaft sprocket and adjusting piston.
14. Remove flange shaft from intake camshaft.

INSTALLATION

1. Ensure flange shaft locking pin is correctly located and install flange shaft.
2. Tighten flange shaft new mounting bolts to specifications while holding camshaft with wrench tool No. 104 589 01 01 00, or equivalent.
3. Install adjusting piston onto flange shaft to proper position by rotating clockwise.
4. Install sprocket onto adjusting piston to proper position by rotating counterclockwise.
5. Install disc and mounting nut.
6. Ensure mounting nut locking slot is at front.
7. Tighten mounting nut to specifications while holding camshaft with wrench tool No. 104 589 01 01 00, or equivalent.
8. Install armature. Armature roll pin must coincide with control piston flat face.
9. Tighten mounting bolt to specifications.
10. Install guide rails and cylinder head front covers.

PISTON & ROD ASSEMBLY

Piston identification number, group number and driving direction arrow are ink stamped on piston crown. Also, piston identification number and group number are stamped into side near wrist pin, **Fig. 16.**

1. Install piston so piston code number next to piston pin and group number are pointing to travel direction.
2. Connecting rod identification must face outside of engine.
3. Replace connecting rod bolt if shank length is more than 2.0828 inches.
4. Oil bolt and nut threads and contact surfaces.

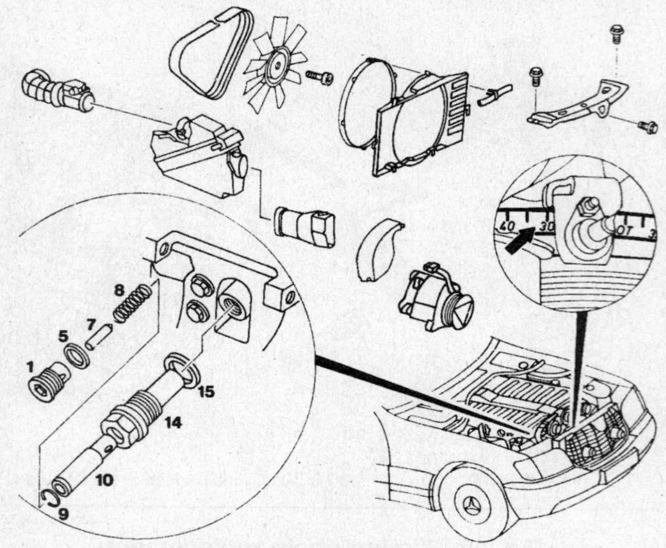

Fig. 13 Timing chain tensioner replacement

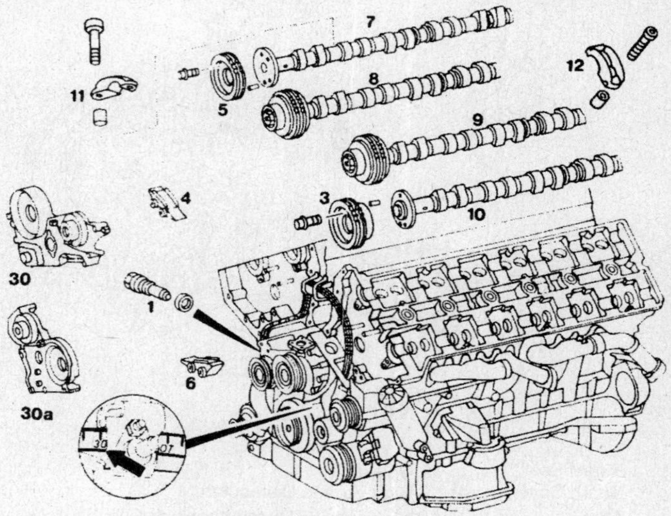

Fig. 14 Camshaft replacement

5. Tighten connecting rod bolts to specifications.

MAIN & ROD BEARINGS

1. Oil bolt and nuts threads, head and contact surfaces
2. Tighten bearing caps to specifications in sequence, **Fig. 17.**

CRANKSHAFT SEAL

REPLACE

REMOVAL

1. Remove crankshaft damper as outlined under "Crankshaft Damper, Replace."
2. Pry shaft seal out with suitable screwdriver and clean cloth. **Do not damage crankshaft or seal mounting bore.**
3. Remove mounting bore burrs.
4. If there are wear grooves in vibration damper, install shaft seal offset .1181 inch.
5. Oil shaft seal sealing lip. **Do not use grease.**
6. Attach shaft seal to side on installation sleeve tool No. 119 589 01 14 00, or equivalent.
7. Align Woodruff key and slide installation sleeve on.
8. Ensure crankshaft Woodruff key engages sleeve groove.
9. Tighten installation sleeve against stop with bolt and four plate springs. **Shaft seal must be at right angles to hub.**
10. Install crankshaft vibration damper, **Fig. 18.**
11. Tighten mounting bolt to specifications.

CRANKSHAFT REAR OIL SEAL

REPLACE

END COVER

1. Remove transmission and driven plates with ring gear.
2. Remove end cover mounting bolts, **Fig. 19.** Mark bolt locations and lengths for installation.
3. Remove end cover with radial seal and gasket by pressing off. **Do not damage oil pan gasket.**
4. Reverse procedure to install, noting the following:
   a. Clean sealing surface.
   b. Install new gasket without sealant.
   c. Coat radial seal between dust and sealing lips with engine oil. **Do not use grease.**
   d. Install with insertion tool No. 117 589 00 43 00, or equivalent.
   e. Tilt end cover back slight when fitting.
   f. Replace driven plate mounting bolts with shank diameter of less than .3662 inch or shank length of more than .9253 inch.

SEAL

1. Remove transmission and driven plates.
2. Pry seal out with suitable screwdriver and clean cloth. **Do not damage crankshaft and seal mounting hole.**
3. Both inner part of insertion tool No. 117 589 00 43 00, or equivalent, to crankshaft.
4. Coat radial seal between dust and sealing lips with engine oil. **Do not use grease.**
5. Fit seal to inner part of insertion tool and install as far as stop.
6. Ensure dust lip is resting on crankshaft.

OIL PAN

REPLACE

SL600

1. Remove engine as outlined under "Engine, Replace."
2. Remove alternator.
3. Drain engine oil into suitable container.
4. Disconnect automatic transmission oil lines at pan.
5. Disconnect oil press sensor connector, **Fig. 20.**
6. Remove mounting bolts, bottom oil pan and gasket.
7. Remove mounting bolts and intake manifold support.
8. Disconnect oil level sensor connector.
9. Remove inside oil pan mounting bolts.
10. Remove dipstick guide tube, **Fig. 21.**
11. Remove crankshaft vibration damper.
12. Remove secondary air injection line.
13. Remove mounting bolts, pan and gasket. Mark mounting bolt position and length for installation.
14. Reverse procedure to install, noting the following:
    a. Align rear contact surface to transmission.
    b. Install new engine pan drain plug seal.
    c. Install new dipstick guide tube seal.
    d. Tighten mounting bolts to specifications.

CL600 & S600

1. Remove drive belt and air cleaner with Mass Air Flow (MAF) sensor.
2. Remove engine compartment bottom cover.
3. Drain engine oil into suitable container, **Fig. 22**

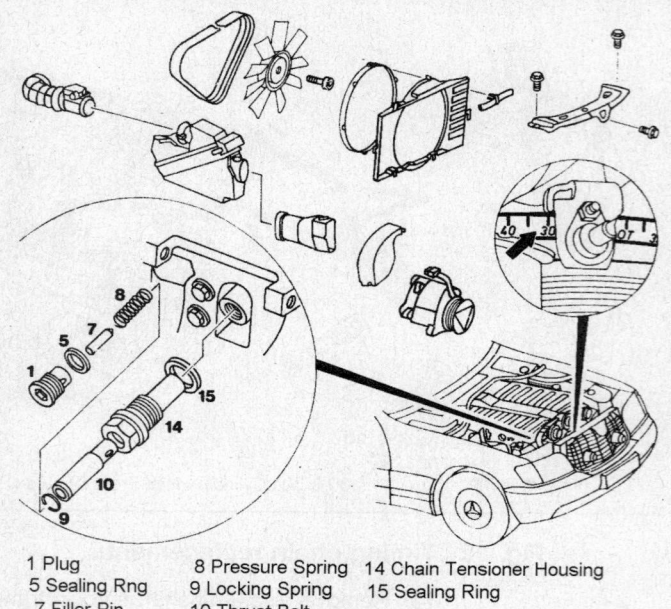

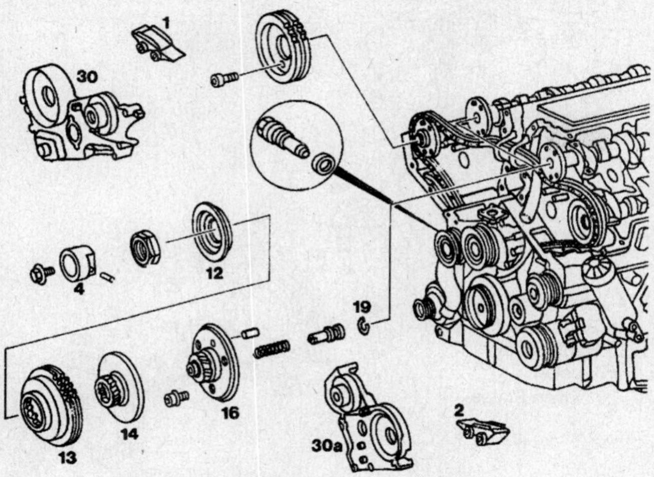

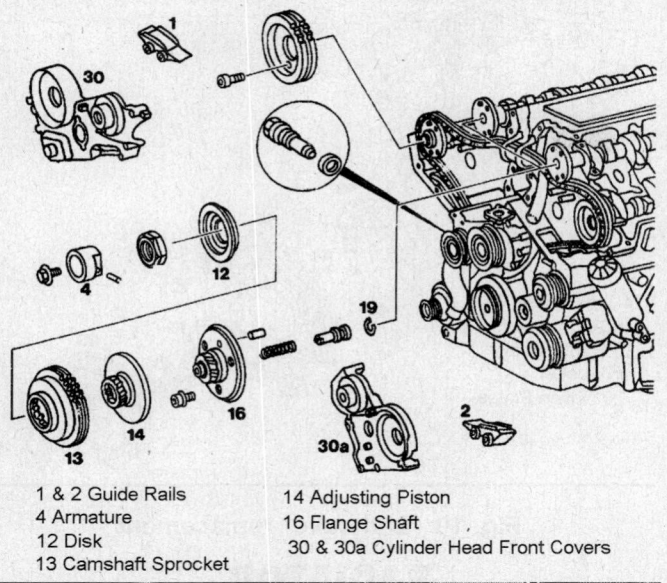

1 & 2 Guide Rails
4 Armature
12 Disk
13 Camshaft Sprocket
14 Adjusting Piston
16 Flange Shaft
30 & 30a Cylinder Head Front Covers

MB1069900193000X

Fig. 15 Camshaft adjuster replacement

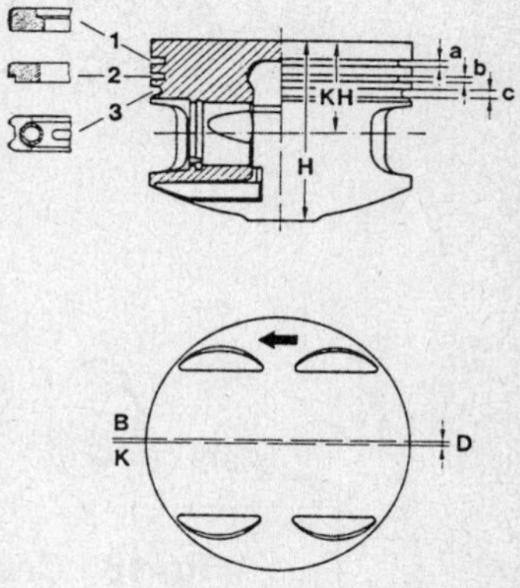

1	Rectangular compression ring with inside chamfer
2	Tapered oil scraper ring
3	Chamfered oil control ring with expander spring
a	1.54-1.55 mm
b	2.00-2.01 mm
c	3.00-3.01 mm
B	Wrist pin center
D	Wrist pin offset = 1.1 mm
H	Piston height
K	Piston center

MB1069100049000X

Fig. 16 Piston dimensions

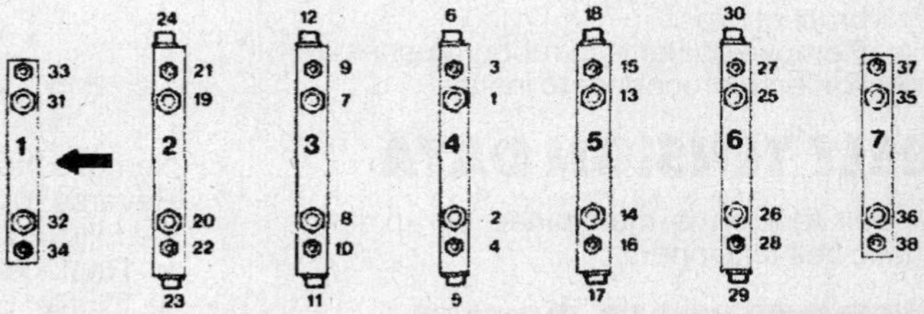

MB1069900190000X

Fig. 17 Crankshaft bearing cap tightening sequence

4. Disconnect oil pressure sensor wire from oil pan bottom and connector from oil filter.
5. Disconnect automatic transmission oil line from lefthand side of oil pan.
6. Disconnect secondary air injection line from oil pan bottom, then remove from left and righthand sides of engine support.
7. Remove mounting bolts and oil pan bottom part.
8. Remove mounting bolts inside oil pan.
9. Remove front axle torsion bar and springs.
10. Remove shock absorber bottom mounting bolts.
11. Remove front engine mounts' bottom bolts.
12. Remove both ignition control modules' covers.
13. Install engine support bracket tool No. 140 589 01 61 00, or equivalent.
14. Connect front and rear engine support eyes to support tool and lift engine slightly.
15. Remove dipstick guide tube from righthand cylinder head.
16. Remove mounting bolts and push steering gear shielding plate aside.
17. Loosen mounting bolt and unhook joint from steering column.
18. Support front axle with jack attachment tool No. 140 589 00 62 00, or equivalent.
19. Remove covers and microencapsulated bolts from front axle rear.
20. Lower front axle until oil pan can be removed. **Ensure brake and steering gear hydraulic lines are not damaged.**
21. Remove alternator.
22. Disconnect automatic transmission oil lines from oil pan.
23. Disconnect air oil cooler and air conditioning compressor lines from lefthand front of oil pan.
24. Remove oil dipstick guide tube from oil pan.
25. Remove rear oil pan and remain mounting bolts. Mark mounting bolt locations and lengths for installation.
26. Remove oil pan down toward front.
27. Reverse procedure to install, noting the following:
    a. Replace oil pan gasket.
    b. Replace oil dipstick guide tube sealing ring as required.
    c. Clean front axle body mounting threads and install new microencapsulated mounting bolts.
    d. Install new oil pan bottom part gasket as required.
    e. Install new oil level sensor sealing ring.
    f. Install new oil pan drain plug seal.
    g. Before tightening mounting bolts, ensure rear surface contacts transmission.
    h. Tighten mounting bolts to specifications.

OIL PUMP

REPLACE

CL600 & S600

1. Remove oil pan as outlined under "Oil Pan, Replace."
2. Remove oil level sensor, **Fig. 23.**
3. Remove mounting bolt and drive gear.
4. Remove mounting bolts, washer and pump.
5. Reverse procedure to install, noting the following:
    a. Fill pump with oil before installing.
    b. Clean compensating strainer.
    c. Install gear with curved side toward pump.
    d. Tighten mounting bolts to specifications.

SL600

1. Remove engine compartment bottom cover.
2. Drain engine oil into suitable container.
3. Remove mounting bolts, **Fig. 24.**
4. Disconnect oil pump from front dowel sleeves and push to rear.
5. Remove drive gear from pump.
6. Remove pump.
7. Reverse procedure to install, noting the following:
    a. Fill pump with oil before installing.
    b. Clean compensating strainer.
    c. Install gear with curved side toward pump.
    d. Tighten mounting bolts to specifications.

OIL COOLER

REPLACE

CL600 & S600

1. Remove engine compartment bottom cover.
2. Remove mounting bolts and disconnect oil lines from air-to-oil cooler.
3. Remove mounting bolts and brackets with rubber bushes.
4. Remove cooler at mounting brackets.
5. Reverse procedure to install. Bracket retaining lug must engage mounting bracket recess.

SL600

1. Remove front air scoop.
2. Remove mounting bolts and disconnect oil lines from air-to-oil cooler.

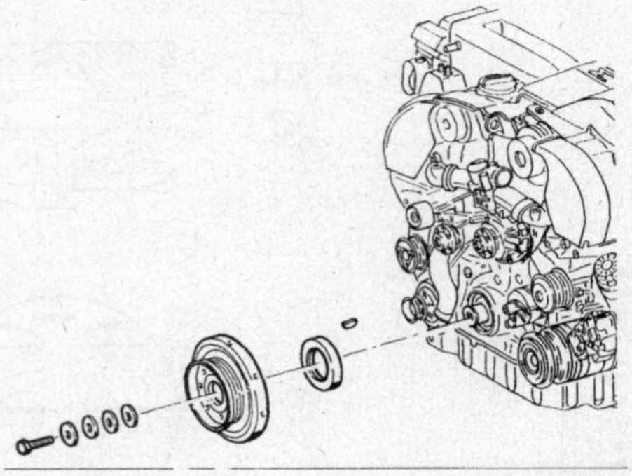

Fig. 18 Crankshaft seal replacement

3. Remove left and righthand mounting bracket clips.
4. Remove cooler with rubber bushes.
5. Reverse procedure to install.

BELT TENSION DATA

Belt tension is maintained by an automatic belt tensioner.

SERPENTINE DRIVE BELT

BELT, REPLACE

1. Loosen tensioning puller with suitable wrench as far as stop.
2. Remove belt.
3. Install belt beginning at tensioning pulley and vibration damper.
4. Allow tensioning arm to return to tensioning position.

ROUTING

Refer to **Fig. 25** for serpentine drive belt routing.

TENSIONER, REPLACE

1. Remove viscous fan and drive belt.
2. Remove mounting bolt and tensioner.
3. Reverse procedure to install. Tighten mounting bolts to specifications.

COOLING SYSTEM BLEED

1. Fill cooling system to prescribed level.
2. Turn heater on.
3. Warm engine at moderate speed until thermostat opens.
4. Adjust coolant level as required.

THERMOSTAT

REPLACE

1. Drain cooling system into suitable container.
2. Remove fan shroud ring and place over fan.
3. Disconnect coolant hoses.
4. Remove thermostat housing cover mounting bolts and swivel housing forward 90.°
5. Remove mounting bolts, holder and housing.
6. Remove thermostat.
7. Reverse procedure to install, noting the following:
   a. Replace sealing ring.
   b. Profile plate must catch housing cover recesses.
   c. Thermostat ball valve must be at highest point.
   d. Install new seals as required.
   e. Tighten mounting bolts to specifications.
   f. Ensure fan shroud ring four catch studs are properly located in shroud.

WATER PUMP

REPLACE

1. Remove radiator as outlined under "Radiator, Replace."
2. Remove thermostat as outlined under "Thermostat, Replace." **Fig. 26.**
3. Loosen viscous fan and water pump pulleys' mounting bolts.
4. Remove drive belt.
5. Remove fan and water pump pulleys.
6. Remove mounting bolt and guide pulley.
7. Disconnect lower coolant hose at pump.
8. Remove mounting bolts and water pump. Mark bolts' locations, size and length for installation.
9. Reverse procedure to install, noting the following:
   a. **On SL600 models,** lead ignition cable No. 4 passes behind water pump.
   b. **On CL600 and S600 models,** TDC sensor cable passes behind water pump.
   c. **On all models,** clean sealing surfaces.
   d. Install new gasket.
   e. Tighten mounting bolts to specifications.

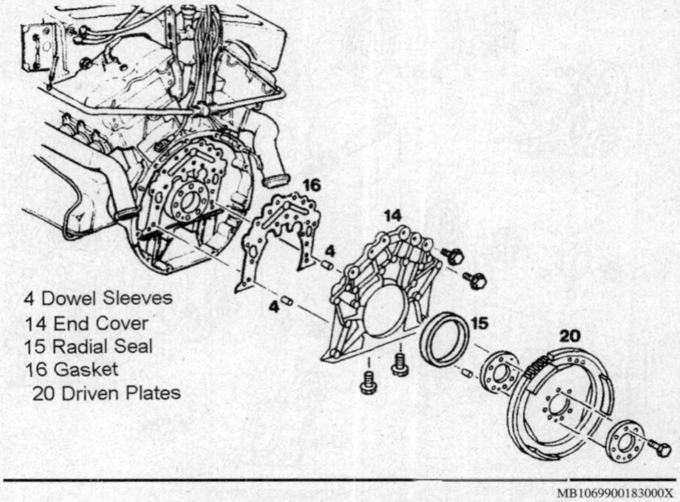

Fig. 19 End cover replacement

RADIATOR

REPLACE

CL600 & S600

1. Remove fan cowl.
2. Release pressure in expansion tank by opening cap.
3. Drain cooling system into suitable container.
4. Disconnect automatic transmission cooling lines.
5. Disconnect coolant hoses.
6. Remove radiator plastic strips.
7. Remove front air scoops.
8. Disconnect hood release cable.
9. Remove condenser.
10. Remove radiator.
11. Reverse procedure to install, noting the following:
    a. Radiator mounting studs must be installed into rubber pads at bottom crossmember.
    b. Adjusting bar must rest slightly pretensioner against front crossmember.

SL600

1. Remove fan cowl.
2. Release pressure in expansion tank by opening cap.
3. Drain cooling system into suitable container.
4. Disconnect automatic transmission cooling lines.
5. Disconnect coolant hoses.
6. Remove flat spring by unclipping.
7. Remove condenser.
8. Remove radiator.
9. Reverse procedure to install. Radiator mounting studs must be installed into rubber pads at bottom crossmember.

FUEL PUMP

REPLACE

1. Pinch off fuel suction and delivery hoses using clamp tool No. 000 589 40 37 00, or equivalent, **Fig. 27.**

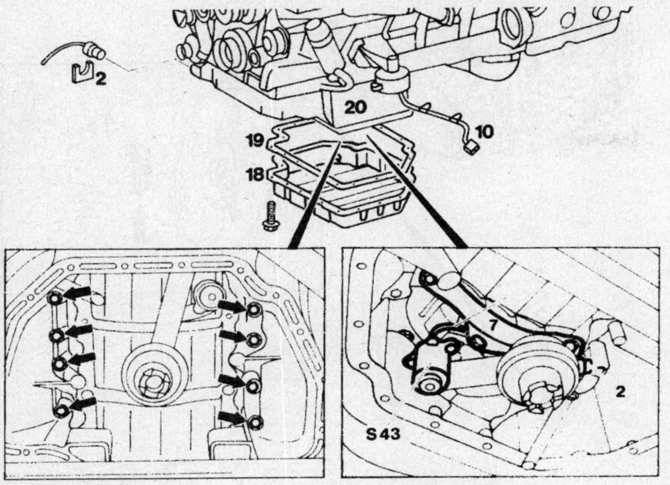

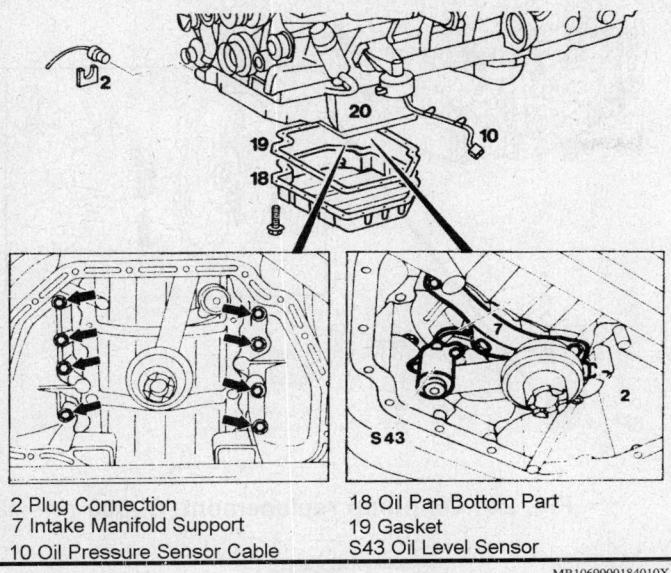

2 Plug Connection
7 Intake Manifold Support
10 Oil Pressure Sensor Cable
18 Oil Pan Bottom Part
19 Gasket
S43 Oil Level Sensor

MB1069900184010X

Fig. 20 Oil pan bottom replacement. SL600

2. Remove cap nut or banjo bolt.
3. Remove fuel pump.
4. Reverse procedure to install, noting the following:
   a. Replace copper sealing rings.
   b. Tighten banjo bolt or cap nut to specifications.
   c. Plastic sleeve must project at both sides of bracket.

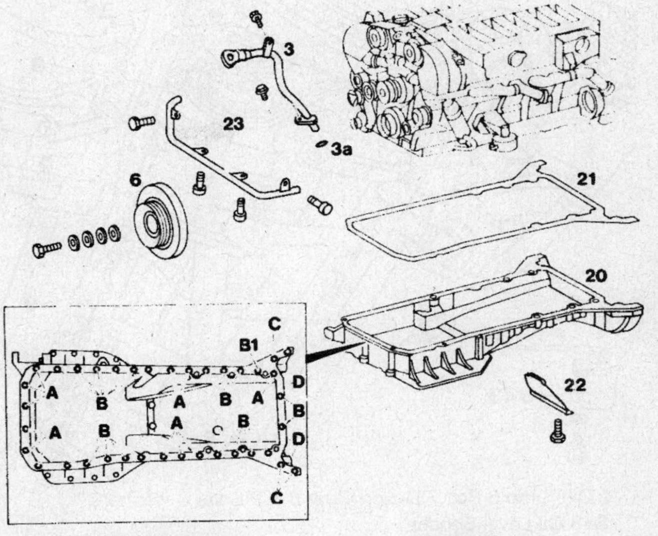

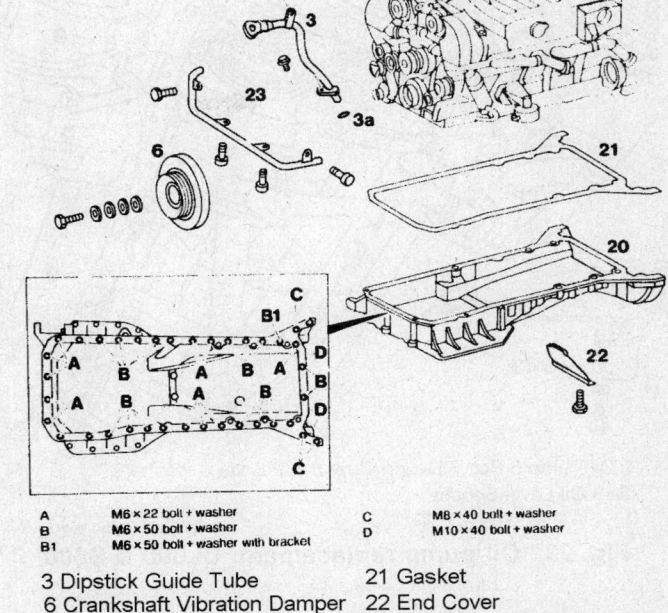

A M6 × 22 bolt + washer
B M6 × 50 bolt + washer
B1 M6 × 50 bolt + washer with bracket
C M8 × 40 bolt + washer
D M10 × 40 bolt + washer

3 Dipstick Guide Tube
6 Crankshaft Vibration Damper
20 Oil Pan
21 Gasket
22 End Cover
23 Secondary Air Injection Line

MB1069900184020X

Fig. 21 Oil pan replacement. SL600

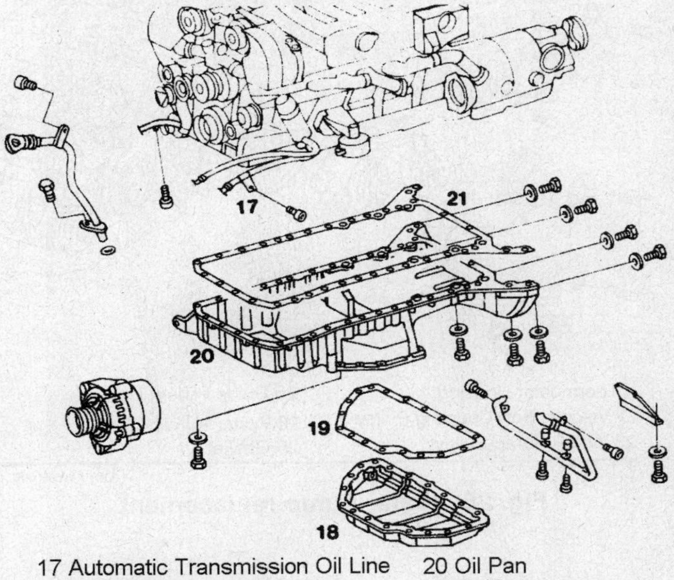

17 Automatic Transmission Oil Line
18 Oil Pan Bottom Part
19 Gasket
20 Oil Pan
21 Gasket

MB1069900185000X

Fig. 22 Oil pan replacement. CL600 & S600

FUEL FILTER

REPLACE

Refer to "Fuel Pump, Replace" for fuel filter replacement.

TECHNICAL SERVICE BULLETINS

ENGINE OIL ABOVE MAX. LEVEL

On some of these models the engine oil level may be above the Max. mark dip stick or by the oil sensor.

This condition may be caused by diesel or fuel oil or other subsequent additives in the fuel that did not burn and collected in the engine oil pan.

To correct this condition, proceed as follows:

1. Replace engine oil.
2. Drain fuel tank of foreign substances.
3. Do not replace sensor.

ENGINE DIES AFTER COLD START

On some of these models the engine may die after cold start during deceleration or after sudden acceleration.

This condition may be caused by the camshaft moving back to retarded position to slowly.

To correct this condition install revised camshafts (lefthand part No. 120 050 46 01 and righthand part No. 120 050 45 01) and adjusters (part No . 120 050 03 47).

EXHAUST SYSTEM RATTLE

On some of these models there may be an exhaust system rattling noise that decreases with engine speed between 3000–1000 RPM.

This condition may be caused by a loose exhaust manifold inner shell.

To correct this condition, proceed as follows:

1. Remove catalytic converter or exhaust system front section.
2. Remove exhaust manifold.
3. Inspect inner shell for tight seat. Replace damaged and opposing exhaust manifolds, as required.

CHAIN TENSIONER OIL LEAK

On some of these models built before Dec. 15, 1997, there may be an oil leak at the chain tensioner.

To correct this condition, replace chain tensioner end element and sealing ring.

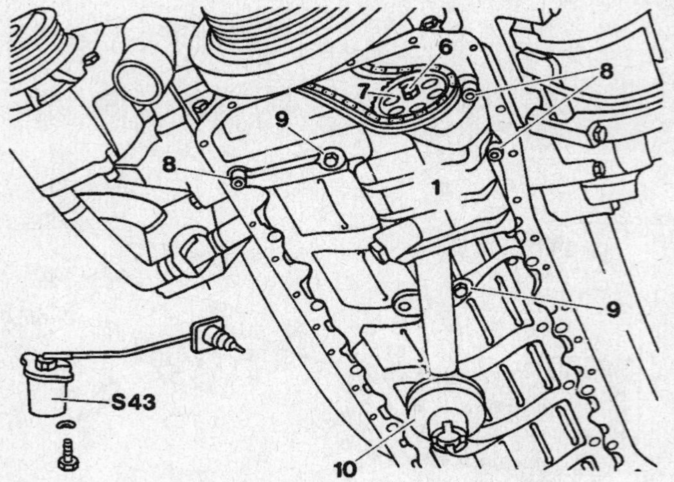

1 Oil Pump 6 Bolt 7 Driven Gear 8 & 9 Bolts & washers
S43 Oil Level Sensor

MB1069900199000X

Fig. 23 Oil pump replacement. CL600 & S600

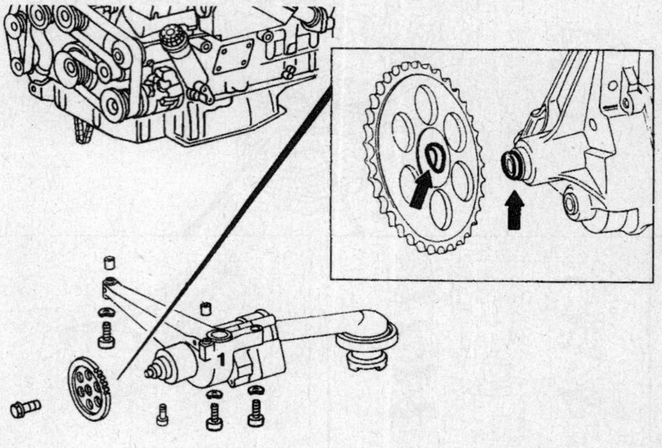

MB1069900198000X

Fig. 24 Oil pump replacement. SL600

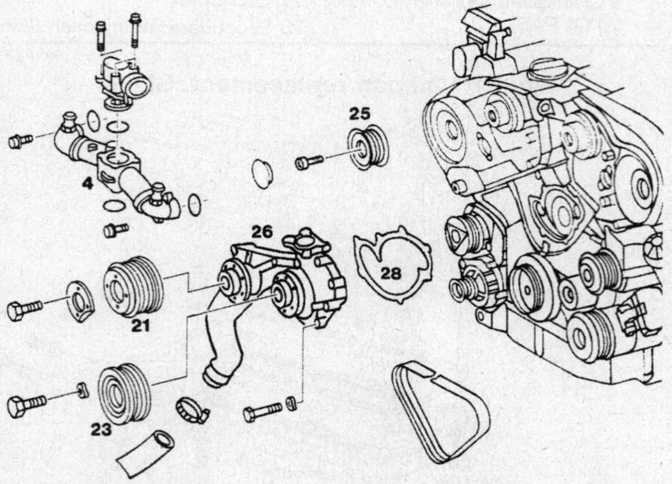

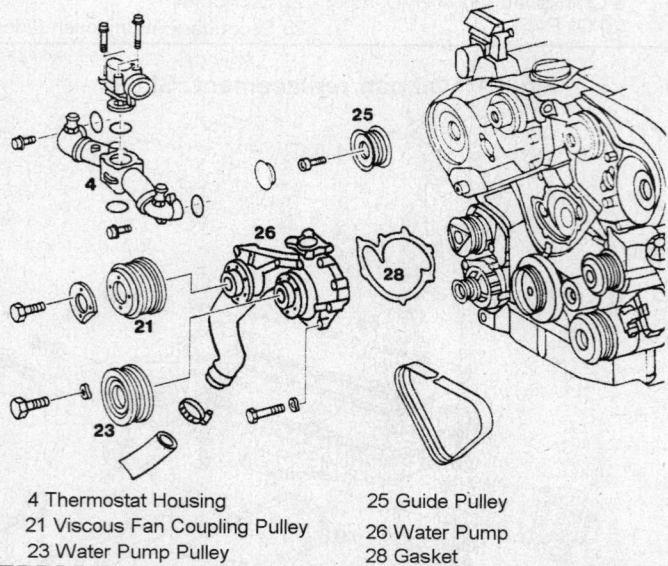

4 Thermostat Housing
21 Viscous Fan Coupling Pulley
23 Water Pump Pulley
25 Guide Pulley
26 Water Pump
28 Gasket

MB1069900200000X

Fig. 26 Water pump replacement

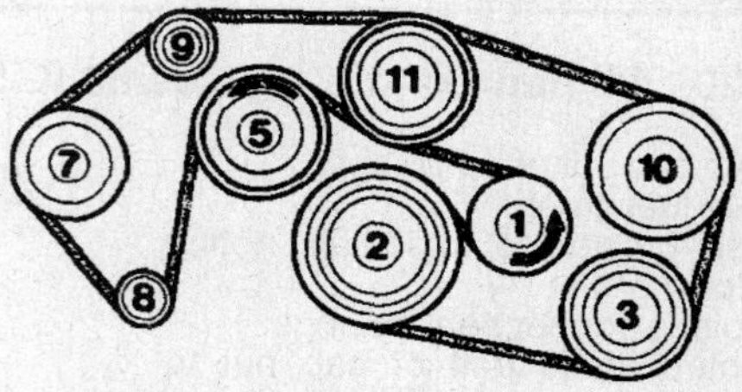

1 Tensioning pulley (without grooves)
2 Crankshaft
3 AC compressor
5 Fan
7 Secondary air pump
8 Generator
9 Top guide pulley
10 Power steering pump
11 Coolant pump

MB1069900197000X

Fig. 25 Serpentine drive belt routing

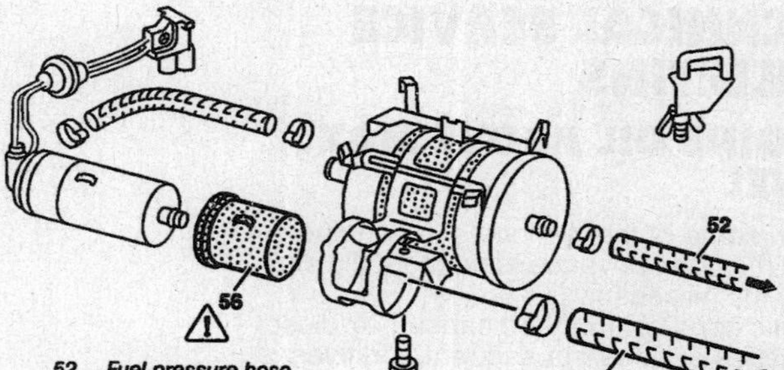

52 Fuel pressure hose
53 Fuel suction hose
56a Plastic sleeve

MB1069900205000X

Fig. 27 Fuel pump replacement

TIGHTENING SPECIFICATIONS

Year	Component	Torque, Ft. Lbs.
1998–2001	Automatic Transmission Oil Lines	15
	Belt Idler Pulley	25.8
	Camshaft Bearing Cap	15
	Camshaft Timing Adjuster Nut	48
	Camshaft Timing Flange Shaft	15(2)
	Connecting Rod Bolts	30(2)
	Crankcase Coolant Drain Plug	22
	Crankshaft Front Center Bolt	295
	Crankcase Rear Cover	6.6
	Cylinder Head Bolts	(3)
	Cylinder Head Front Cover	15
	Distributor Follower	12
	Distributor Rotor	30(1)
	Driven Plates	22–30(5)
	End Cover	80(1)
	Exhaust Manifold	22
	Front Engine Mount, Bottom	18
	Front Engine Mount, Top	41
	Fuel Pump Cap Or Banjo	18–22
	Intake Manifold	18–22
	Main Bearing Cap Nuts (M8)	22(4)
	Main Bearing Cap Nuts (M10)	37(4)
	Main Bearing Cap Side Bolts	22(4)
	Oil Cooler Lines	22
	Oil Pan Bottom	18
	Oil Pan Drain Plug	30
	Oil Pan (M6)	80(1)
	Oil Pan (M8)	18
	Oil Pan (M10)	30
	Oil Pressure Sensor	11
	Oil Pressure Switch	11
	Oil Pump Gear	21
	Oil Pump (M6)	80(1)
	Oil Pump (M8)	15
	Propeller Shaft	33
	Radiator Drain Plug	13(1)
	Rear Engine Carrier (M8)	18
	Rear Engine Carrier (M10)	30
	Rear Engine Mount	30
	Secondary Air Pump Bracket	18
	Serpentine Drive Belt Tensioner	28
	Tensioning Pulley	28
	Thermostat Housing Cover	80(1)
	Thermostat Housing Holder	15
	Timing Case Cover (M6)	80(1)
	Timing Case Cover (M8)	15
	Timing Chain Tensioner Housing	59
	Valve Cover	80(1)
	Vibration Damper	295
	Viscous Fan Clutch	33
	Viscous Fan Pulley	88(1)
	Water Hose Clamps	22(1)
	Water Pump	15
	Water Pump Pulley	88(1)

(1) — Inch lbs.
(2) — Tighten an additional 90.°
(3) — Refer to "Cylinder Head, Replace" for tightening procedure.
(4) — Refer to "Main & Rod Bearings" for tightening sequence.
(5) — Tighten an additional 90–100.°

606 Diesel Engine

NOTE: On Air Bag Equipped Models, Refer To "Air Bag System Precautions" Located In The Front Of This Manual For System Disarming & Arming Procedures.

NOTE: Prior To Performing Any Service Operations Listed In This Section, Consult The "Technical Service Bulletins" Section For Related Information.

INDEX

	Page No.
Belt Tension Data	5-117
Camshaft, Replace	5-115
Installation	5-116
Removal	5-115
Camshaft Timing Inspection	5-116
Compression Pressure	5-112
Cooling System Bleed	5-118
Crankshaft Damper, Replace	5-114
Crankshaft Rear Oil Seal, Replace	5-116
Interference-Fit Seal	5-116
Vulcanized Seal	5-116
Crankshaft Seal, Replace	5-116
Cylinder Head, Replace	5-114
Engine Rebuilding Specifications	5-344
Engine, Replace	5-113
Engine Mount, Replace	5-113
Front	5-113
Rear	5-113
Exhaust Manifold, Replace	5-114
Front Cover, Replace	5-115
Fuel Filter, Replace	5-118
Fuel Pump, Replace	5-118
Intake Manifold, Replace	5-113
Main & Rod Bearings	5-116
Oil Pan, Replace	5-117
Oil Pump, Replace	5-117
Oil-To-Water Cooler, Replace	5-117
Piston & Rod Assembly	5-116
Precautions	5-112
Air Bag Systems	5-112
Battery Ground Cable	5-112
Radio Coded Anti-Theft System	5-112
Pre-Combustion Chamber, Replace	5-114
Radiator, Replace	5-118
Serpentine Drive Belt	5-117
Belt, Replace	5-117
Routing	5-117
Tensioner, Replace	5-117
Technical Service Bulletins	5-119
Engine Does Not Start	5-119
High Oil Consumption	5-119
Increase Engine RPM, Blue Engine Smoke Or High Oil Consumption	5-119
Low Oil Level Warning Lamp Illuminates Briefly Or Excessive Valve Train Noise At Operating Temperature	5-119
Oil Loss, Shaft/Cylinder Head Cover Fills w/Oil	5-119
Oil Pan Leak	5-119
Thermostat, Replace	5-118
Tightening Specifications	5-120
Timing Chain, Replace	5-115
Timing Chain Tensioner, Replace	5-115
Turbocharger, Replace	5-118
Valve Adjustment	5-114
Valve Cover, Replace	5-114
Water Pump, Replace	5-118

PRECAUTIONS

AIR BAG SYSTEMS

Refer to "Air Bag System Precautions" in front of this manual for system disarming and arming procedures.

BATTERY GROUND CABLE

Prior to service, disconnect battery ground cable and isolate as required.

RADIO CODED ANTI-THEFT SYSTEM

Anti-theft radios have a coded theft protection circuit. The CODE card must be obtained before disconnecting battery, removing radio fuse or removing the radio. **The serial number from the radio must match the CODE card.**

After service has been performed proceed as follows:

1. Connect radio power and turn key to position No. 2.
2. Turn radio to On position. Word "CODE" will appear on display.
3. Enter first digit of anti-theft code from CODE card. "CODE" will disappear and entered digit will appear followed by four dashes.
4. Enter next four digits, when all five are entered first digit flashes again.
5. Press SC, Seek or Tune button to confirm code.
6. If "WAIT" appears on radio panel, proceed as follows:
   a. Radio will allow three coding attempts only before entering lock-up mode and won't respond to controls.
   b. Leave radio on for 15–60 minutes, then radio will unlock and allow three addition coding attempts.
   c. Third lockout period (after nine failed coding attempts) will last 24 hours.
   d. Radio must be left on during enter 24-hour period until "CODE" appears.
7. When "CODE" appears, repeat coding attempt.

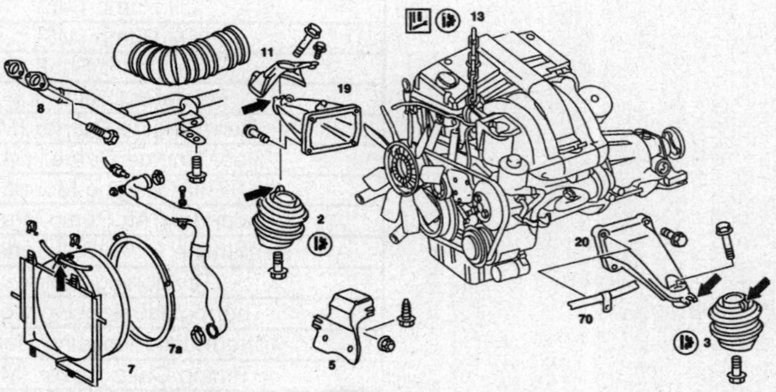

2 & 3 Engine Mount 5 Steering idler Arm 7 Fan Shroud 7a Fan Shroud Ring 8 Exhaust System 11 Engine Mount 19 & 20 Engine Support Arm 21 & 70 Transmission Wiring Harness

MB1069900228000X

Fig. 1 Front engine mount replacement

COMPRESSION PRESSURE

1. Warm engine to operating temperature (approximately 176°F)
2. Remove nozzle holder.
3. Disconnect starter harness connector.
4. Ensure transmission is in neutral.

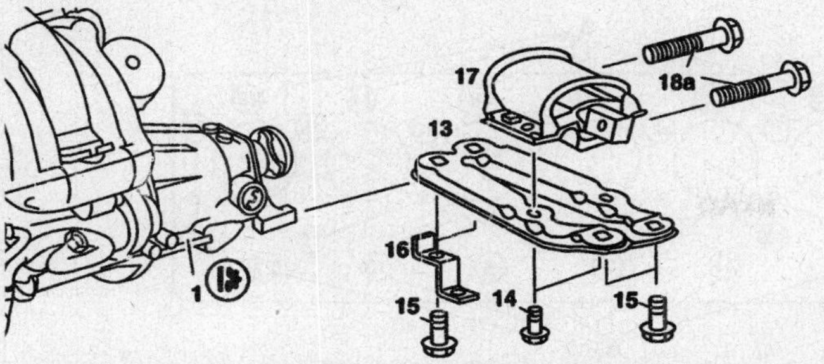

Fig. 2 Rear engine mount replacement

5. Crank engine over several times to clean out residue using compression tester contact switch. **Do not use starter to crank engine.**
6. Install suitable compression checker into precombustion chamber.
7. Crank engine at least nine revolutions using compression tester contact switch. **Do not use starter to crank engine.**
8. Record compression readings.
9. Normal compression pressure should be 421–508 psi.
10. Maximum permissible difference between individual cylinders should not be more than 44 psi.

ENGINE MOUNT

REPLACE

FRONT

1. Remove fan shroud and place over viscous fan.
2. Remove exhaust system mounting bolts at exhaust manifold and side support, **Fig. 1.**
3. Remove mounting bolts at engine supporting arm.
4. Remove mounting bolts at frame side rail or front axle carrier.
5. Attach suitable engine hoist to front lifting eye. **Ensure injection pipe is not damaged.**
6. Ensure engine rear is not touching body. **Do not overtension coolant hoses.**
7. Remove mounting bolts at engine support arm.
8. Remove lefthand engine mount mounting bolts at engine supporting arm.
9. Disconnect automatic transmission oil lines from engine mounts.
10. Remove engine mounts and remove shields.
11. Reverse procedure to install. Engine mount anti-twist locks must engage supporting arms retaining slots.

REAR

1. Support transmission with suitable jack.
2. Remove rear engine crossmember mounting bolts, **Fig. 2.**
3. Remove mounting bolts and rear engine mount.
4. Reverse procedure to install. Tighten mounting bolts to specifications.

ENGINE

REPLACE

1. Remove air intake hose and air cleaner housing.
2. Remove engine compartment bottom cover.
3. Drain cooling system into suitable container.
4. Disconnect and seal automatic transmission oil lines.
5. Remove radiator as outlined under "Radiator, Replace."
6. Disconnect coolant hoses at cylinder head and oil filter housing.
7. Attach 15.75 x 26.77 x .039-inch sheet metal or plastic guard plate to condenser.
8. Remove engine component compartment cover.
9. Disconnect engine compartment/transmission connect on righthand side of engine compartment.
10. Disconnect fuse and relay module electrical connectors.
11. Disconnect IRI inline injection pump connector at component partition panel.
12. Remove splash panel rubber seal and cables behind trim panel.
13. Disconnect glow output stage connector.
14. Disconnect starter wiring harness.
15. Disconnect terminal block circuit in lefthand footwell.
16. Disconnect engine ground and remove engine wiring harness.
17. Remove exhaust system mounting bolts at turbocharger intermediate flange and transmission.
18. Remove boost pressure hoses.
19. Remove serpentine drive belt.
20. Disconnect vacuum lines. Mark lines for installation.
21. Remove oil from power steering pump reservoir and disconnect lines.

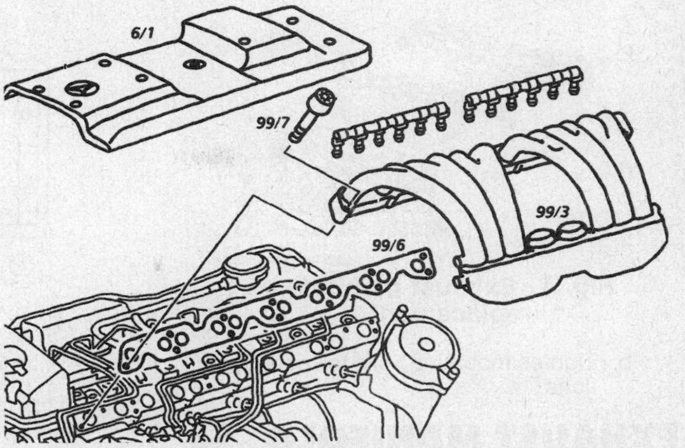

Fig. 3 Intake manifold replacement

22. **On models equipped with self-leveling suspension,** drain pressurized oil system into suitable container.
23. **On all models,** disconnect engine oil cooler lines.
24. Disconnect air conditioning compressor electrical connector.
25. Remove mounting bolts and attach air conditioning compressor to engine compartment bottom with lines connected.
26. Disconnect fuel lines.
27. Disconnect transmission shift rods.
28. Remove mounting bolts and push propeller shaft back.
29. Disconnect automatic transmission interlock electrical connectors.
30. Remove transmission righthand side guard plate.
31. Disconnect automatic transmission electrical connectors.
32. Remove front engine mount lower mounting bolts.
33. Support transmission with suitable jack.
34. Remove rear engine mount.
35. Attach suitable engine hoist to engine lifting eyes. **Do not damage injection pipe when attaching to front lifting eye.**
36. Attach chain to exhaust manifold and third lifting hook.
37. Remove engine.
38. Reverse procedure to install. Tighten mounting bolts and nuts to specifications.

INTAKE MANIFOLD

REPLACE

1. Remove crankcase ventilation, **Fig. 3.**
2. Remove cylinder head cover shaft trim.
3. Remove mounting bolts and intake manifold.
4. Cover intake ports.
5. Remove vacuum pipe.
6. Reverse procedure to install, noting the following:
   a. Install new O-rings.

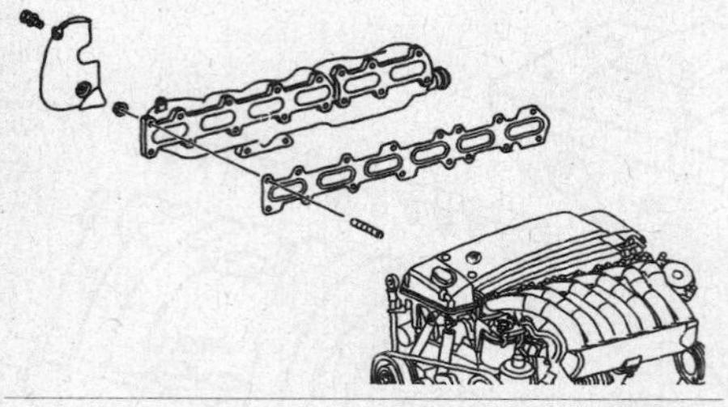

Fig. 4 Exhaust manifold replacement

b. Tighten mounting bolts to specifications.

EXHAUST MANIFOLD

REPLACE

1. **On 1998 models,** remove turbocharger as outlined under "Turbocharger, Replace."
2. **On all models,** remove mounting nuts, **Fig. 4.**
3. Remove exhaust pipe mounting bolts.
4. Remove exhaust manifold.
5. Reverse procedure to install. Tighten mounting bolts and nuts to specifications.

CYLINDER HEAD

REPLACE

This procedure has been revised by a Technical Service Bulletin.

Cylinder head must be removed with engine cold.

1. Remove engine compartment bottom cover.
2. Drain cooling system into suitable container.
3. Remove radiator as outlined under "Radiator, Replace."
4. Remove serpentine drive belt.
5. Remove valve cover as outlined under "Valve Cover, Replace."
6. Remove intake manifold as outlined under "Intake Manifold, Replace."
7. Disconnect coolant hoses at cylinder head.
8. Disconnect cylinder head vacuum lines. Mark for installation.
9. Remove camshaft housing.
10. Remove injection nozzles.
11. Open fuel cap to relieve fuel tank pressure and disconnect fuel lines.
12. Disconnect cylinder head engine wiring harness.
13. Remove oil filter.
14. Remove mounting bolt and place fuel filter aside with lines connected.
15. Remove guide rail pin using impact extractor tool No. 116 589 20 33 00, threaded insert tool No. 116 589 01 34 00 and puller tool No. 605 589 00 33 00, or equivalents, then the guide rail.
16. Remove cylinder head to front cover mounting bolts.
17. Disconnect oil delivery and return flow pipes, then the charge air pipe at turbocharger.
18. Loosen cylinder head bolts in reverse tighten sequence, **Fig. 5.**

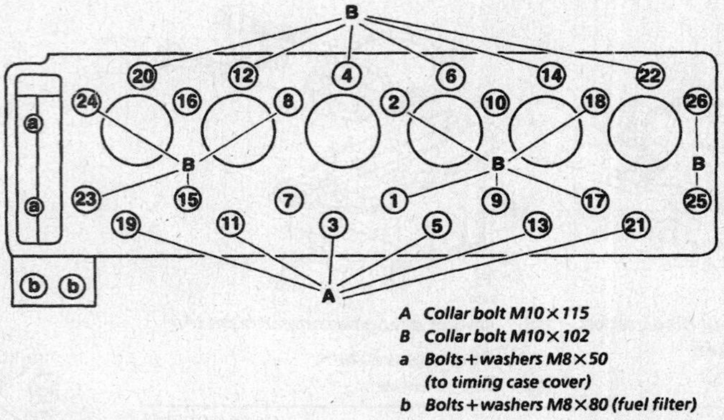

Fig. 5 Cylinder head tightening sequence

19. Install bracket tools No. 119 589 01 40 00, or equivalent, to first and last exhaust end camshaft bearings.
20. Remove cylinder head.
21. Reverse procedure to install, noting following:
    a. Clean sealing surfaces.
    b. Replace M10x115 cylinder head bolts with shank lengths more than 4.6068 inches and M10x102 bolts with shank lengths more than 4.0949 inches.
    c. Oil cylinder head bolts' threads and contact surfaces.
    d. Install new gasket using dowel sleeves to correctly locate.
    e. Coat bottom guide rail pin with sealant No. Loctite 574 sealant, or equivalent.
    f. **Torque** cylinder head bolts to 11 ft. lbs.
    g. **Torque** head bolts to 26 ft. lbs.
    h. Tighten bolts an additional 90°.
    i. Allow head to settle for at least 10 minutes and final tighten an additional 90°.
    j. Ensure guide rail is correctly located at chain housing and installed to stop.
    k. Install guide rail with mounting holes facing up and open side facing opposite travel direction.
    l. Install new timing chain tensioner seal.
    m. Do not pressure test cooling system until engine has reached operating temperature and head gasket as swollen and sealed.

PRE-COMBUSTION CHAMBER

REPLACE

1. Remove valve cover as outlined under "Valve Cover, Replace."
2. Remove shaft cover bushes.
3. Remove injection nozzles.
4. Remove glow plugs.
5. Remove prechamber threaded ring using serrated wrench tool No. 604 589 01 09 00, or equivalent.
6. Knock out prechamber using impact extractor tool No. 602 589 00 33 00, or equivalent.
7. Reverse procedure to install, noting the following:
    a. Prechamber collar lug rests against cylinder head recess.
    b. Oil threaded rings before installing.
    c. Tighten threaded ring and mounting bolts to specifications.

VALVE COVER

REPLACE

1. Remove charge air distribution pipe.
2. Remove injection lines.
3. Remove cylinder head trim panel.
4. Remove cover with gasket.
5. Reverse procedure to install, noting the following:
    a. Install new gasket as required.
    b. Ensure trim panel bushes are correctly located.
    c. Install new seal.
    d. Install trim panel using new self-tapping screws.
    e. **Do not jam leak oil pipe between trim panel and cylinder head.**

VALVE ADJUSTMENT

This engine is equipped with hydraulic lifters and requires no valve adjustment,

CRANKSHAFT DAMPER

REPLACE

1. Remove radiator as outlined under "Radiator, Replace."
2. Remove water pump pulley.
3. Install crankshaft/ring gear locking plate.
4. Remove mounting bolts and damper pulley, **Fig. 6.**
5. Remove mounting bolt and crankshaft damper.
6. Reverse procedure to install, noting the following:
    a. Fix align parallel key in place with grease.
    b. Ensure groove is aligned with crankshaft key.
    c. Tighten mounting bolts to specifications.

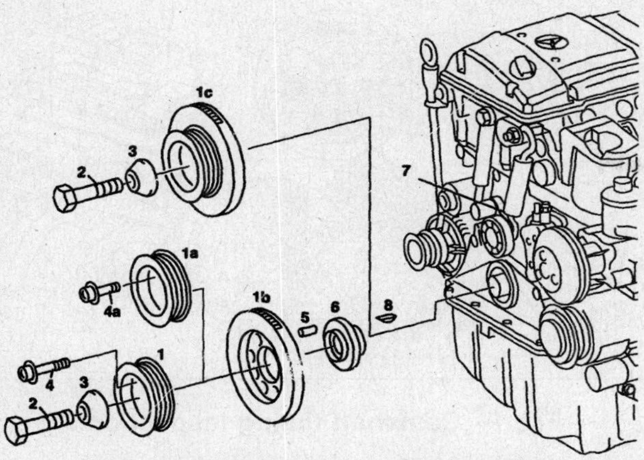

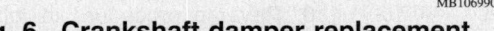

1 Belt pulley (engine 605/606 1st version)
1a Belt pulley (engine 604 1st version)
1b Vibration damper (engine 605/606 1st version)
1c Belt pulley/vibration damper with hub engine 604, 605, 606 (2nd version)
2 Central bolt M18×1.5×50
3 Washer
4 Hexagon socket bolt+washer M8×25 (6 in total) engine 605/606
4a hexagon socket bolt+washer M8×12 (6 in total) engine 604
5 Dowel pin
6 Hub
7 Tensioning pulley
8 Woodruff key

MB1069900220000X

Fig. 6 Crankshaft damper replacement

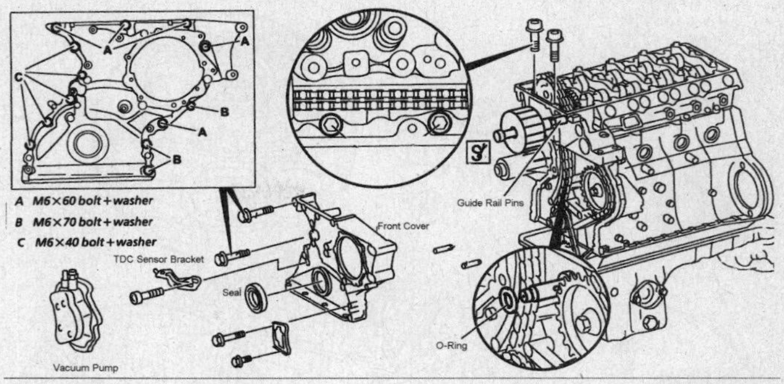

MB1069900215000X

Fig. 7 Front cover replacement

FRONT COVER

REPLACE

1. Remove viscous fan coupling.
2. Remove serpentine drive belt.
3. Remove radiator as outlined under "Radiator, Replace."
4. Remove water pump and power steering pump pulleys.
5. Remove valve cover as outlined under "Valve Cover, Replace."
6. Remove vacuum pump, **Fig. 7.**
7. Turn engine crankshaft to set cylinder No. 1 piston at TDC.
8. Install crankshaft/ring gear locking plate.
9. Remove oil-water heat exchanger at oil pan.
10. Remove crankshaft damper as outlined under "Crankshaft Damper, Replace."
11. Remove alternator bracket.
12. Remove front cover to oil pan mounting bolts. Loosen remaining oil pan mounting bolts.
13. Disconnect cylinder head front coolant hose.
14. Remove mounting bolts and set power steering pump aside with lines connected.
15. Remove mounting bolt and set fuel filter aside with lines connected.
16. Remove guide rail pin using impact extractor tool No. 116 589 20 33 00, threaded insert tool No. 116 589 01 34 00 and puller tool No. 605 589 00 33 00, or equivalents, then the guide rail.
17. If replacing front cover, remove belt tensioner.
18. Remove injection pump mounting bolts from front cover.
19. Remove TDC sensor bracket mounting bolt.
20. Remove cylinder head to front cover mounting bolts.
21. Remove front cover mounting bolts. Mark bolt size, length and location for installation.
22. Remove front cover. **Do not damage cylinder head or oil pan gaskets.**
23. Reverse procedure to install, noting the following:
    a. Clean sealing surfaces and coat with Omnifit FD 3041 sealant, or equivalent.
    b. Tighten mounting bolts to specification.
    c. Install TDC mounting bracket bolt with pointer aligned with damper TDC mark.
    d. Coat bottom guide rail pin with sealant No. Loctite 574 sealant, or equivalent.
    e. Ensure guide rail is correctly located at chain housing and installed to stop.
    f. Install guide rail with mounting holes facing up and open side facing opposite travel direction.

TIMING CHAIN

REPLACE

1. Remove viscous fan coupling.
2. Remove chain tensioner as outlined under "Timing Chain Tensioner, Replace."
3. Remove valve cover as outlined under "Valve Cover, Replace."
4. Cover chain case with suitable cloth and grind off timing chain link pins.
5. Attach new timing chain to old with connecting link.
6. Slowly turn crankshaft in engine rotational direction while simultaneously raising old timing chain until connecting link is against camshaft timing sprocket upper most point. **Timing chain must remain meshed while rotating camshaft and crankshaft sprockets.**
7. Remove old timing chain and connect ends of new timing chain with connecting link.
8. Install chain tensioner.

TIMING CHAIN TENSIONER

REPLACE

1. Rotate crankshaft and set cylinder No. 1 piston at ignition TDC.
2. Remove chain tensioner.
3. Reverse procedure to install. When installing tensioner, proceed as follows:
    a. Place chain tensioner with thrust pin facing downward into container of engine oil. Ensure flange is submerged in oil.
    b. Press thrust bolt 7–10 times slowly downward against stop.
    c. Install new sealing ring.
    d. Tighten tensioner to specifications.

CAMSHAFT

REPLACE

The camshaft bearing on 606 engine are constructed as bearing bridge with intake and exhaust camshaft bearing having a common bearing cap.

REMOVAL

1. Remove valve cover as outlined under "Valve Cover, Replace."
2. Turn crankshaft to set cylinder No. 1 piston at ignition TDC.
3. Install crankshaft/starter ring locking tool.
4. Mark camshaft sprocket to timing chain for installation. Strap timing chain to sprockets.
5. Remove timing chain tensioner as outlined under "Timing Chain Tensioner, Replace."
6. Remove mounting bolts and camshaft sprockets with chain attached, **Fig. 8.**
7. Remove bearing caps Nos. 2 and 5 mounting bolts.
8. Install M7x41 bolts and **torque** to 11 ft. lbs.
9. Remove bearing caps except for Nos. 3 and 6.
10. Loosen bearing caps Nos. 3 and 6, one

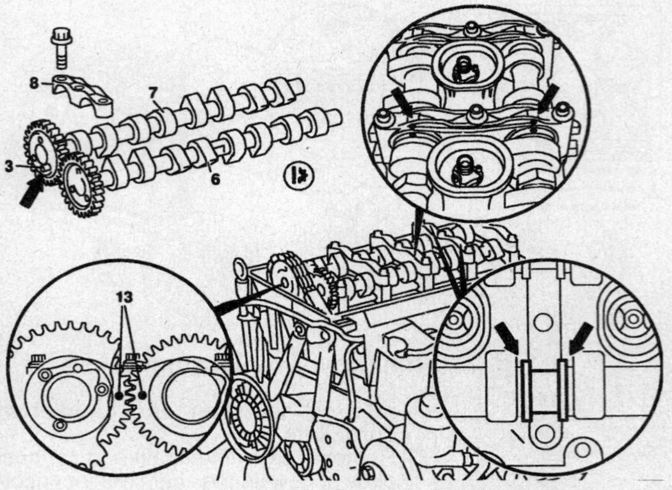

3 Dowel Pin 6 Intake Camshaft 7 Exhaust Camshaft 8 Bearing Cap
13 Alignment Holes

MB1069900222000X

Fig. 8 Camshaft replacement

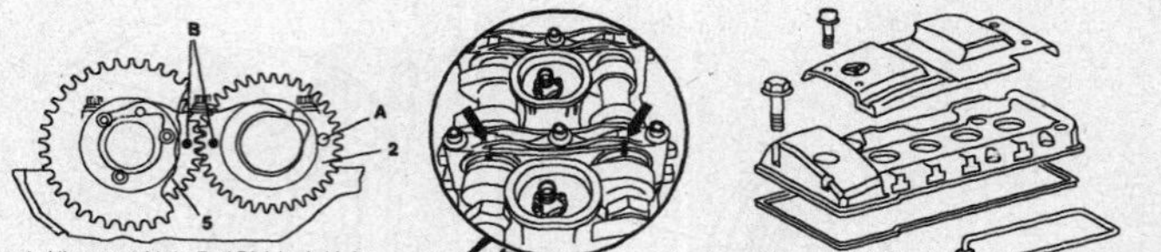

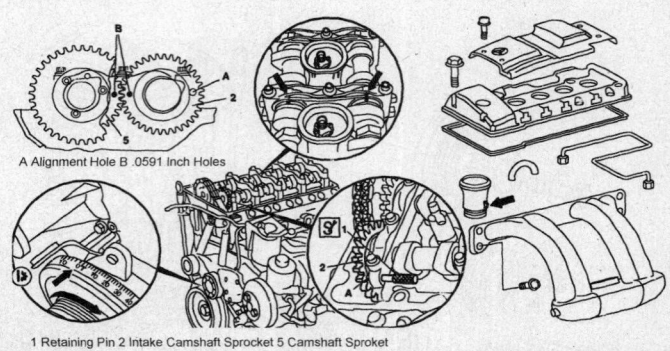

A Alignment Hole B .0591 Inch Holes

1 Retaining Pin 2 Intake Camshaft Sprocket 5 Camshaft Sproket

MB1069900221000X

Fig. 9 Camshaft timing inspection

turn at a time and pressure is eliminated. **Camshafts, must not be twisted when loosening bearing caps.**

11. Remove bearing caps.
12. Remove intake and exhaust camshafts, then the shaft trim panel bushes.
13. Remove camshaft.
14. Reverse procedure to install, noting following:

INSTALLATION

The camshafts are very sensitive to fracturing. **Ensure they are installed free of stresses.**

1. Install shaft trim panels bushes with new seals. Lug should align with camshaft housing notch.
2. Inspect hydraulic lifters for movement ease.
3. Align intake and exhaust camshafts at axial bearing.
4. Install camshafts so sprocket markings are opposite each other and camshaft and bearing caps are aligned.
5. Install bearing caps in original positions.
6. Tighten mounting bolts evenly, one turn at a time to specifications.
7. Ensure cylinder No. 1 piston is at ignition TDC.
8. Install locking pin through first camshaft bearing cap into intake camshaft sprocket hole.
9. Install sprockets with new mounting bolts.
10. Ensure sprocket dowel pins are correctly installed.
11. Ensure sprocket and timing chain marks are aligned.
12. Instal timing chain tensioner with new seal.

CAMSHAFT TIMING INSPECTION

1. Rotate crankshaft to set cylinder No. 1 piston at ignition TDC.
2. Install locking pin tools No. 111 589 03 15 00, or equivalent, through camshaft bearing cap No. 1 into intake camshaft sprocket, **Fig. 9.**
3. Ensure .0591 inch camshaft sprocket holes are opposite each other.

PISTON & ROD ASSEMBLY

1. Connecting rod and bearing caps are marked together.
2. Install piston with arrow in direction of travel.
3. Connecting rod marking and retaining slots are on lefthand (intake) side.
4. **Do not mix top and bottom connecting rod bearing shells.**
5. Connecting rod and bearing cap markings face each other.
6. Tighten connecting rod bolts to specifications.

MAIN & ROD BEARINGS

1. Crankshaft bearing caps are numbered consecutively, beginning with first crankshaft bearing at front.
2. Replace crankshaft bearing cap bolts with shank length more than 2.5121 inches.
3. Thrust washer oil grooves should face toward crankshaft collars.
4. Oil bolts thread and head contact surfaces.
5. Tighten bolts from inside to outside beginning at fit bearing.
6. Ensure crankshaft rotates freely.

CRANKSHAFT SEAL

REPLACE

This procedure has been revised by a Technical Service Bulletin.

1. Remove radiator as outlined under “Radiator, Replace.”
2. Remove water pump pulley.
3. Install crankshaft/ring gear locking plate.
4. Remove crankshaft damper as outlined under “Crankshaft Damper, Replace.”
5. Pray out radial seal with suitable screwdriver and clean cloth, **Fig. 10. Do not damage crankshaft or mounting hole.**
6. Reverse procedure to install, noting the following:
   a. Install seal using insertion tools Nos. 606 589 00 14 00 and 601 589 03 14 00, or equivalents.
   b. Tighten mounting bolts to specifications.

CRANKSHAFT REAR OIL SEAL

REPLACE

INTERFERENCE-FIT SEAL

Removal

1. Remove transmission.
2. Remove driven plates.
3. Remove radial seal with suitable screwdriver and clean cloth, **Fig. 11. Do not damage crankshaft or seal mounting bore.**

Installation

1. Deburr and clean mounting bore.
2. If there are wear grooves in crankshaft flange, use insertion tool No. 111 589 08 43 00, or equivalent, with shoulder to install new seal .1181 inch further.
3. Bolt inner part of insertion tool to crankshaft.
4. Coast radial seal sealing lip and mating surfaces with engine oil. **Do not use grease.**
5. Fit radial seal to insertion tool inner part.
6. Press seal into end cover as far as stop using insertion tool.

VULCANIZED SEAL

1. Remove transmission and driven plates.
2. Remove end cover mounting bolts, **Fig. 12.**
3. Pry end cover with radial seal off lugs. **Do not damage oil pan gasket.**

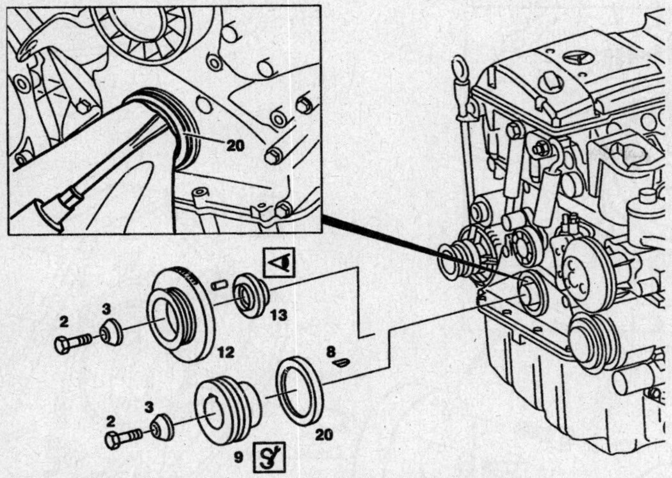

2 Central bolt M18×1.5×50
3 Washer
8 Woodruff key
9 Insertion sleeve for standard or repair position
12 Belt pulley/vibration damper
13 Hub (engine 604, 605, 606, 1st version)
20 Radial seal

MB1069900218000X

Fig. 10 Crankshaft seal replacement

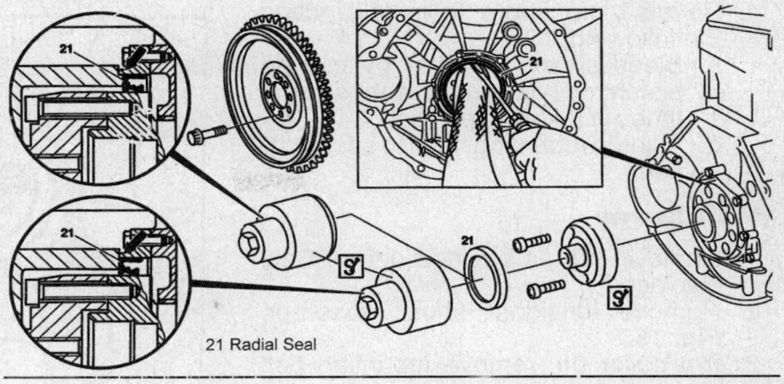

MB1069900219000X

Fig. 11 Crankshaft rear seal replacement

4. Reverse procedure to install, noting the following:
   a. Press new vulcanized radial seal into new end cover using insertion tool No. 111 589 08 43 00, or equivalent.
   b. Coat radial seal sealing lip and mating surface with oil. **Do not use grease.**
   c. Clean sealing surfaces and coat with Loctite 574 sealant, or equivalent.
   d. Ensure dowel sleeves are correctly located. **Do not damage oil pan gasket.**
   e. Coat mounting bolt threads with sealant.
   f. Tighten horizontal end cover mounting bolts to specifications, then the vertical bolts.

OIL PAN

REPLACE

1. Drain engine oil into suitable container.
2. Disconnect fan shroud and place over fan.
3. Remove power steering pump oil with suitable handpump.
4. Disconnect power steering pump oil lines.
5. Disconnect lefthand front intake manifold electric cable and at front lefthand frame floor.
6. Remove front springs.
7. Remove front engine mounts' mounting bolts at front axle carrier.
8. Disconnect exhaust system from exhaust manifold.
9. Attach suitable support bar and raise engine.
10. Support front axle carrier with suitable jack.
11. Remove steering coupling clamping bolt.
12. Remove mounting bolts and lower front axle carrier.
13. Disconnect oil level sensor.
14. Remove oil pan mounting bolts. Mark size, length and location for installation.
15. Push automatic transmission oil lines aside slightly and remove oil pan downward.
16. Reverse procedure to install, noting the following:
    a. Install new gasket with a little grease.
    b. Ensure dowel sleeves are correctly located.
    c. Ensure oil level sensor bracket is correctly located.
    d. Tighten mounting bolts to specifications.
    e. Ensure ground strap is correctly positioned on transmission bell housing.
    f. Ensure automatic transmission oil lines and wiring harness are correctly located.
    g. Align oil pan with transmission joint face.

OIL PUMP

REPLACE

1. Remove oil pan as outlined under "Oil Pan, Replace."
2. Remove mounting bolt and sprocket with chain.
3. Remove mounting bolts and oil pump.
4. Reverse procedure to install, noting the following:
   a. Install oil sprocket with curve side facing pump.
   b. Tighten mounting bolts to specifications.

OIL-TO-WATER COOLER

REPLACE

1. Drain cooling system into suitable container.
2. Remove starter.
3. Drain engine oil into suitable container.
4. Remove intake manifold support bracket mounting bolt at oil filter.
5. Disconnect oil filter electrical connector.
6. Remove mounting bolts and oil filter housing, **Fig. 13.**
7. Remove oil-to-water heat exchanger oil filter mounting bolt.
8. Disconnect crankcase connection fittings.
9. Reverse procedure to install, noting the following:
   a. Coat connection fittings with coolant before installing. **Do not use engine oil.**
   b. Install new O-rings.
   c. Install new oil filter housing gasket.

BELT TENSION DATA

Belt tension is maintained by an automatic belt tensioner.

SERPENTINE DRIVE BELT

BELT, REPLACE

1. Remove viscous fan coupling.
2. Relieve belt tension by pushing spring tensioning lever.
3. Remove belt.
4. Reverse procedure to install.

ROUTING

Refer to "603 Diesel Engine" for serpentine drive belt routing.

TENSIONER, REPLACE

Less Lever

1. Remove belt as outlined under "Belt, Replace."
2. Remove water pump pulley, **Fig. 14.**
3. Remove shock absorber.

4. Reverse procedure to install, noting the following:
   a. Bleed shock absorber by moving piston rod back and forward several times in installed position.
   b. Tighten mounting bolts to specifications.

With Lever

1. Remove belt as outlined under "Belt, Replace."
2. Remove tensioner shock absorber, **Fig. 15.**
3. Pry cover off, remove mounting bolt and tensioning pulley.
4. Pry cover off and remove bearing pin.
5. Remove tensioning lever.
6. Reverse procedure to install, noting the following:
   a. Clean bearing pin threads and coat with Omnifit 100 M orange sealant, or equivalent.
   b. Bleed shock absorber by moving piston rod back and forward several times in installed position.
   c. Tighten mounting bolts to specifications.

COOLING SYSTEM BLEED

1. Remove cylinder head lefthand front plug.
2. Fill system with coolant.
3. Close plug as soon as coolant flows out.
4. Set heater to maximum and warm engine by running at moderate speeds.
5. Adjust fluid level as required.
6. When coolant has reached 140–158°F, cap radiator and expansion tank.

THERMOSTAT
REPLACE

1. Drain cooling system into suitable container.
2. Remove mounting bolts and thermostat housing.
3. Remove thermostat.
4. Reverse procedure to install, noting the following:
   a. Install new O-ring.
   b. Thermostat recess must align with housing rib.

WATER PUMP
REPLACE

1. Drain cooling system into suitable container.
2. Remove viscous fan coupling.
3. Loosen water pump pulley mounting bolts and remove drive belt, **Fig. 16.**
4. Rotate crankshaft to set cylinder No. 1 piston at TDC.
5. Remove TDC sensor.
6. Remove mounting bolts and water pump.
7. Reverse procedure to install, noting the following:
   a. Clean sealing surfaces and install new gasket.

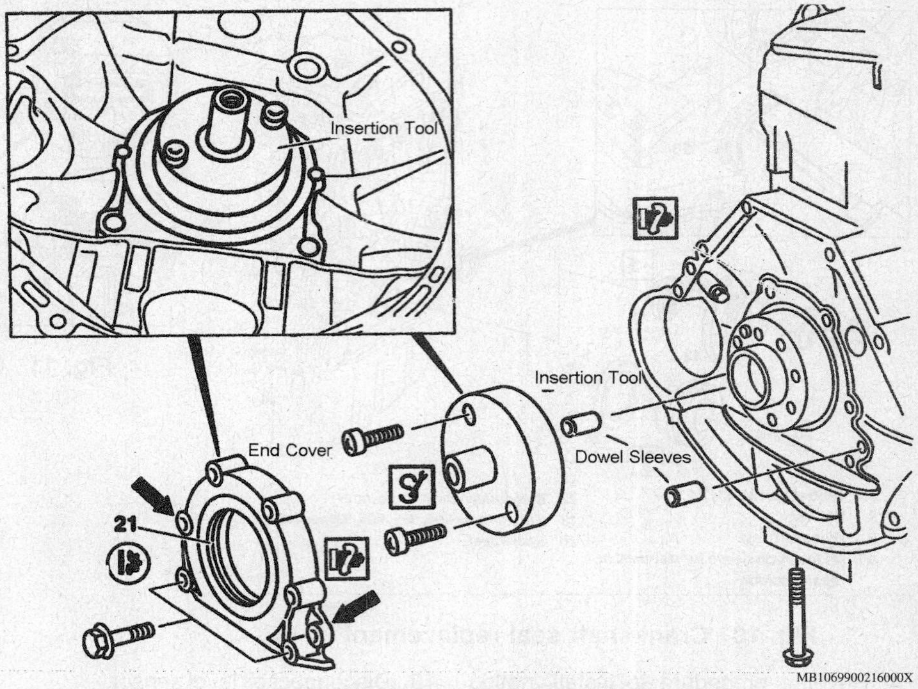

Fig. 12 End cover replacement

b. Ensure dowel sleeves are correctly located.
c. Tighten mounting bolts to specifications.

RADIATOR
REPLACE

1. Remove engine compartment bottom cover.
2. Drain cooling system into suitable container.
3. Remove charge air cooler mounting bolts.
4. Remove automatic transmission oil line bracket at radiator.
5. Remove condenser line bracket mounting bolt at lefthand side member.
6. Disconnect automatic transmission oil lines.
7. Disconnect coolant hoses.
8. Remove flat springs and fan shroud.
9. Remove additional fan and radiator panel.
10. Remove righthand hood lock and disconnect hood release cable.
11. Remove condenser mounting bolts.
12. Tilt radiator toward engine and disconnect condenser from radiator mounting plates beginning on righthand side.
13. Remove radiator by lifting up and out.
14. Attach 15.75 x 26.77 x .039-inch sheet metal or plastic guard plate to condenser.
15. Reverse procedure to install, noting the following:
    a. Coat condenser rubber block with silicone paste No. 000 989 84 51, or equivalent.
    b. Tighten mounting bolts to specifications.

TURBOCHARGER
REPLACE

1. Disconnect air intake and charged air hoses, **Fig. 17.**
2. Remove exhaust pipe clamp.
3. Disconnect oil line from turbocharger and loosen at engine block, then turn pipe away.
4. Remove oil drain line.
5. Remove mounting nuts and turbocharger.
6. Reverse procedure install, noting the following:
   a. Install new oil drain line O-ring as required.
   b. Tighten mounting nuts to specifications.

FUEL PUMP
REPLACE

1. Remove air cleaner.
2. Disconnect fuel suction and pressure lines.
3. Remove mounting nuts and fuel pump from fuel injection pump.
4. Reverse procedure to install with new gasket.

FUEL FILTER
REPLACE

1. Remove mounting bolt and O-rings.
2. Remove filter.
3. Reverse procedure to install. Install new O-rings

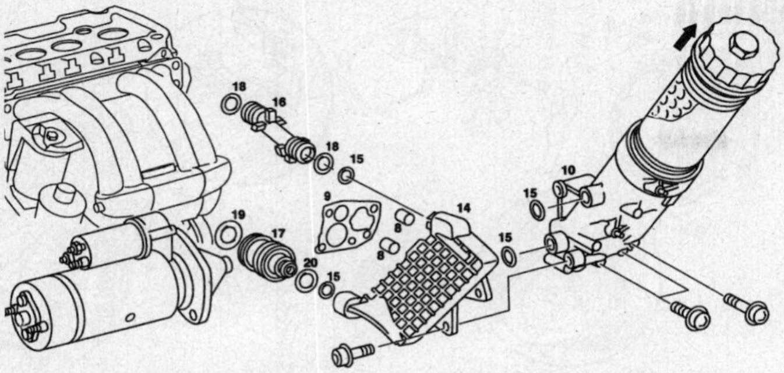

8 Dowel Sleeves 9 Gasket 10 Oil Filter Housing 14 Oil-To-Water Heat Exchanger 15, 18, 19 & 20 O-Rings
16 & 17 Fittings

MB1069900226000X

Fig. 13 Oil-to-water heat exchanger replacement

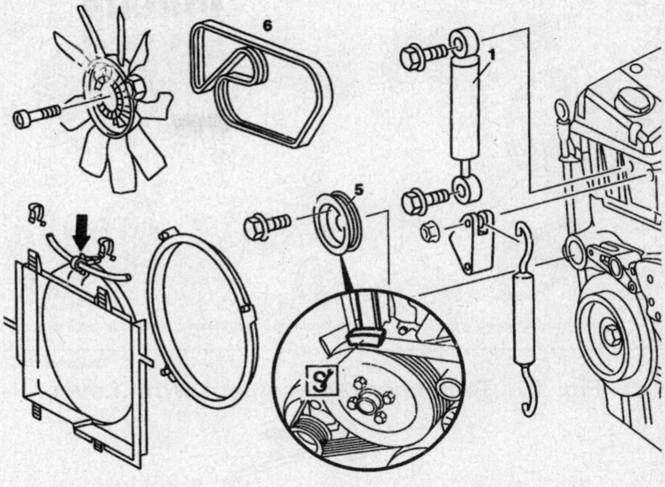

1 Shock Absorber 5 Water Pump Pulley 6 Serpentine Belt

MB1069900224000X

Fig. 14 Tensioner replacement. Less lever

TECHNICAL SERVICE BULLETINS

OIL LOSS, SHAFT/ CYLINDER HEAD COVER FILLS w/OIL

On some of these models there may be engine oil loss or the shaft/cylinder head cover may fill with oil.

This condition may be caused by leaking shaft/cylinder head cover O-ring, porous shaft seal, camshaft housing/cylinder head leaky O-ring and camshaft housing porous.

To correct this condition, proceed as follows:

1. Remove cylinder head cover and replace O-ring.
2. Inspect shaft cover O-rings for damage and brittleness. Replace as required.
3. If shaft cover O-rings are satisfactory, inspect camshaft housing/cylinder head O-ring. Replace as required.
4. If camshaft housing/cylinder head O-ring is not leaking or damaged, replace camshaft housing with all bearing caps.

HIGH OIL CONSUMPTION

On some of these models oil consumption may be high (more than one quart per 625 miles).

This condition may be caused by the pistons and rings.

To correct this condition, proceed as follows:

1. Inspect engine for external oil leaks. Repair as required.
2. Replace pistons or rings only when cylinder bores does not indicate abnormal wear and is within cylinder shape and concentricity tolerances, and honing marks are visible and undamaged.
3. Revised piston rings (part No. 003 030 98 24) have been installed on standard production engines beginning on Jan. 15, 1999, (No. 2 056 671) and replacement engine beginning March 3, 1999, (No. 67 419, except 67 464–67 473).

ENGINE DOES NOT START

On some of these models equipped with Brake Assist (BAS) control module, occasionally the engine may not start, the touch/start feature may not work or the engine may do into limp home mode.

This condition may be caused by moisture/corrosion in the connector or the BAS control module.

To correct this condition, proceed as follows:

1. Inspect CAN/power supply connector No. 3 for moisture and corrosion. Repair as required.
2. If condition is still present, replace BAS control module.

OIL PAN LEAK

On some of these models there may be a gasket oil leak at joint between timing case cover and engine block.

To correct this condition install new oil gasket and apply OmniVisc sealant 1050, or equivalent, to sealing surfaces, **Fig. 18.**

LOW OIL LEVEL WARNING LAMP ILLUMINATES BRIEFLY OR EXCESSIVE VALVE TRAIN NOISE AT OPERATING TEMPERATURE

On some of these models the low oil level warning lamp may illuminate briefly or there may be excessive valve train noise at operating temperatures.

This condition may be caused by loose camshaft end cap.

To correct this condition, proceed as follows:

1. Remove valve cover.
2. Inspect front and rear camshafts for loose and missing end covers.
3. If covers have dropped out, remove camshaft.
4. Remove camshaft end caps (Part No. 000443 018003).
5. **Ensure missing covers are removed from cylinder head oil return channels.**

INCREASE ENGINE RPM, BLUE ENGINE SMOKE OR HIGH OIL CONSUMPTION

On some of these models there may be increase engine RPM, blue engine smoke or high oil consumption.

This condition may be caused by excessive oil leakage at first camshaft bearing caps allowing engine oil to be sucked into combustion chambers through the crankcase ventilation system.

To correct this condition, proceed as follows:

1. Remove cover and cylinder head cover.
2. Disconnect preshaped hose between crankcase ventilation system pressure valve and cylinder head cover oil separation chamber.
3. Increase engine speed to 3000 RPM.
4. If oil separator fills with oil, remove cylinder head cover.
5. Turn engine using starter motor.
6. If oil runs out between first camshaft bearing and camshaft gears for intake and exhaust camshafts, replace camshaft bearing housing will bearing caps.
7. Remove prechambers and inspect.
8. If prechamber material is worn off or there are cracks in burner holes or ball pins are damages, replace as required.
9. Inspect precombustion chambers. Replace as required.

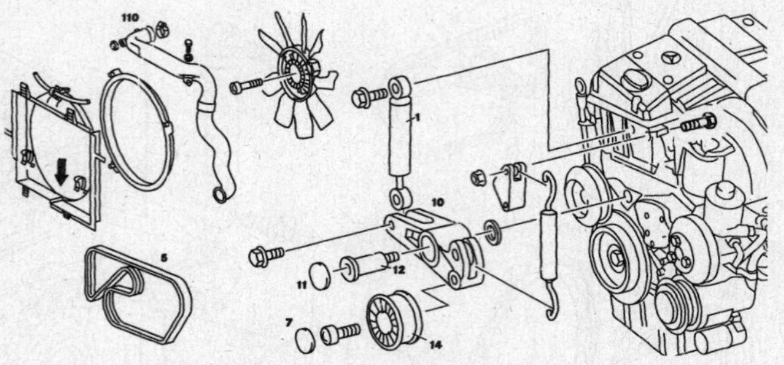

1 Shock Absorber 5 Serpentine Belt 7 & 11 Covers 10 Tensioning Lever 12 Bearing Pin 14 Tensioning Pulley

MB1069900223000X

Fig. 15 Tensioner replacement. With Lever

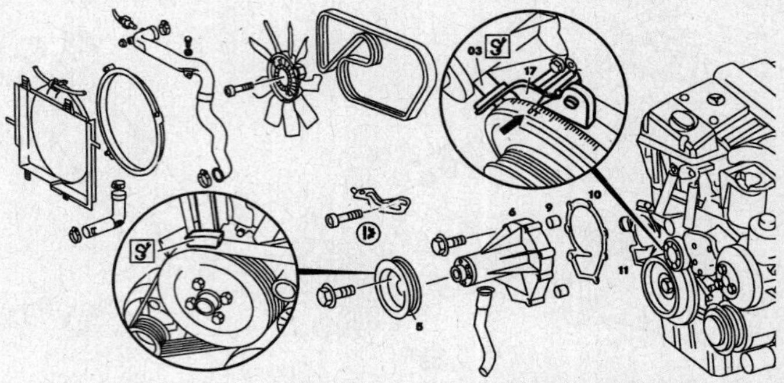

5 Water Pump Pulley 6 Water Pump 9 Dowel Sleeves 10 Gasket 11 Pump Housing 17 TDC Sensor Backet

MB1069900227000X

Fig. 16 Water pump replacement

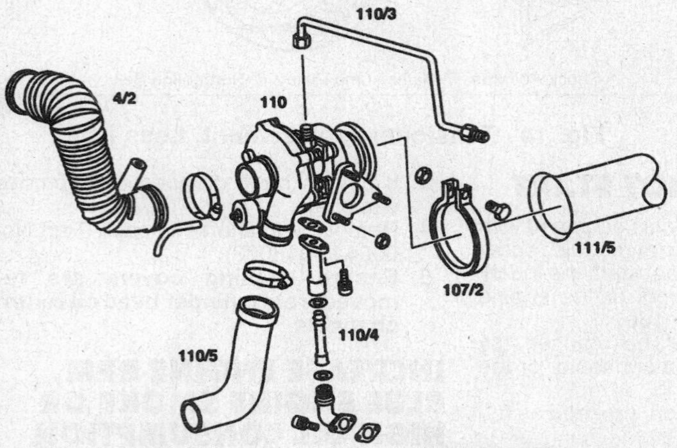

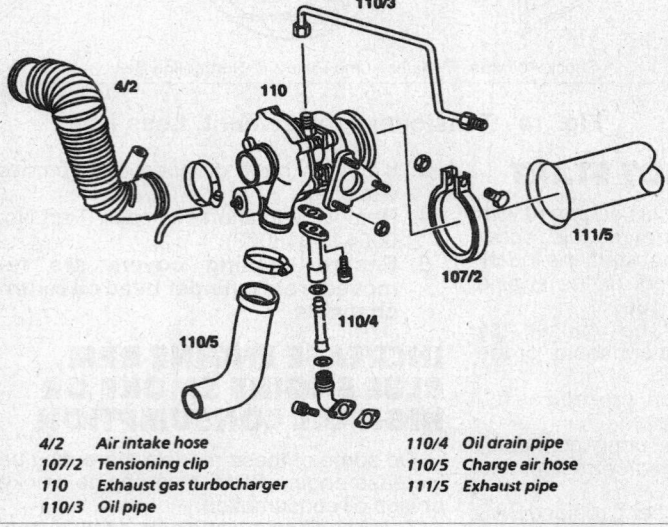

4/2 Air intake hose
107/2 Tensioning clip
110 Exhaust gas turbocharger
110/3 Oil pipe
110/4 Oil drain pipe
110/5 Charge air hose
111/5 Exhaust pipe

MB1069900234000X

Fig. 17 Tubrocharger replacement

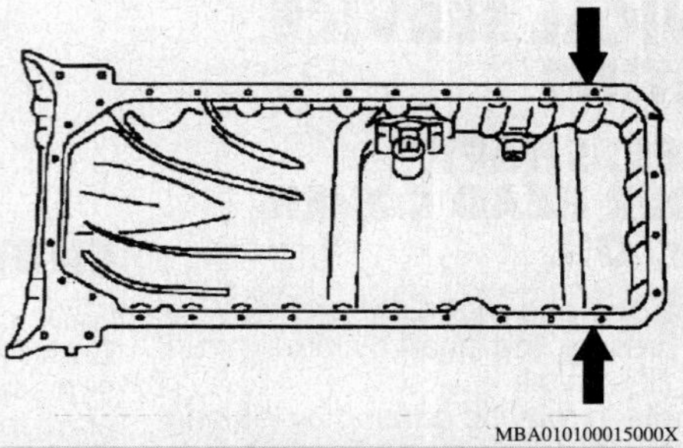

MBA010100015000X

Fig. 18 Oil pan gasket sealant application. 606 engine

TIGHTENING SPECIFICATIONS

Year	Component	Torque, Ft. Lbs.
1998–99	Air Conditioning Compressor	17
	Automatic Transmission Oil Lines	15
	Belt Tensioner Lever Bearing Pin	73.8
	Camshaft Bearing Caps	11
	Camshaft Housing Bolts	11
	Camshaft Sprocket	13
	Connecting Rod Caps	30②
	Crankcase Coolant Drain Plug	22
	Crankshaft Damper	148⑤
	Crankshaft Pulley	18
	Crossmember	30
	Cylinder Head Bolts	③
	Cylinder Head To Front Cover	18
	Drive Shaft Clamp	22–30
	Drive Shaft Intermediate Flange	18
	Drive Shaft To Transmission	33
	Driven Plate	26⑤
	End Cover	88①
	Engine Supporting Arm To Crankcase	15

Continued

TIGHTENING SPECIFICATIONS—Continued

Year	Component	Torque, Ft. Lbs.
1998–99	Exhaust Manifold	22
	Front Cover	88①
	Front Cover To Cylinder Head	18
	Front Engine Mount Shield	88①
	Front Engine Mount To Frame Crossmember (M8)	18
	Front Engine Mount To Frame Crossmember (M10)	30
	Front Engine Mount To Front Axle Carrier	30
	Front Engine Mount To Supporting Arm	41
	Injection Pump Flange	15
	Intake Manifold (M5)	88①
	Intake Manifold (M7)	15
	Main Bearing Caps	41④
	Oil Cooler Lines	22
	Oil Pan Drain Plug (M12)	22
	Oil Pan Drain Plug (M14)	18
	Oil Pan (M6)	88①
	Oil Pan (M8)	18
	Oil Pressure Sensor	11
	Oil Pump	18
	Oil Pump Socket	24
	Oil Sump To Transmission Bell Housing	30
	Power Steering Pump High Pressure Hose (M14)	18–22
	Power Steering Pump High Pressure Hose (M16)	26–37
	Power Steering Pump Line	26–33
	Power Steering Pump Oil Lines	22
	Precombustion Chamber Threaded Ring	96
	Rear Engine Crossmember To Body	29
	Rear Engine Mount to Rear Engine Crossmember	18
	Rear Engine Mount To Transmission	29
	Serpentine Belt Tensioning Lever Bearing Pin	74
	Serpentine Belt Tensioning Lever Shock Absorber To Cylinder Head	25
	Serpentine Belt Tensioning Lever Shock Absorber To Tensioning Level	15
	Serpentine Belt Tensioning Lever Bearing Pin	18
	Serpentine Belt Tensioning Pulley	22
	Thermostat Housing Cover	88①
	Timing Chain Housing Cover (M6)	88①
	Timing Chain Housing Cover (M8)	18
	Timing Chain Tensioner	59
	Turbocharger Exhaust Manifold Flange	15
	Turbocharger Exhaust Pipe Clamp	18
	Valve Cover	88①
	Viscous Fan Clutch	18
	Water Pump Pulley	88①

①— Inch lbs.
②— Tighten an additional 90–100.°
③— Refer to "Cylinder Head, Replace" for tightening procedure.
④— Refer to "Main & Rod Bearings" for tightening sequence.
⑤— Tighten an additional 90.°

Clutch & Manual Transmission

INDEX

Page No.		Page No.		Page No.	
Adjustments	5-122	Clutch Pedal Occasionally Sticks	5-122	And/Or Transmission Rattling	5-122
Clutch, Replace	5-122	Gear Shift Lever Vibrations		Rattling Noises At Idle	5-122
Technical Service Bulletins	5-122			**Transmission, Replace**	5-122

ADJUSTMENTS

Clutch is hydraulic operated and required no adjustment.

CLUTCH

REPLACE

1. Remove transmission as outlined under "Transmission, Replace."
2. Loosen mounting bolts 1–1.5 turns.
3. Remove pressure plate and clutch disk.
4. Reverse procedure to install. **Torque** mounting bolts to 18 ft. lbs.

TRANSMISSION

REPLACE

1. Support transmission with suitable jack.
2. Remove rear support with engine mount as outlined in appropriate engine section.
3. Remove exhaust bracket and U-mount.
4. Remove heat shield bracket.
5. Remove mounting bolts and disconnect front drive shaft.
6. Disconnect exhaust system at rear mount and suspend with suitable belt.
7. Remove speedometer shaft and speed sensor.
8. Disconnect clutch cable.
9. Disconnect shift rods.
10. Remove transmission ground strap.
11. Remove mounting bolts and transmission.
12. Reverse procedure to install.

TECHNICAL SERVICE BULLETINS

RATTLING NOISES AT IDLE

SLK230

On some of these models there may be a rattling noise at idle with transmission in neutral and air conditioning compressor on.

This condition may be caused by engine vibrations being transmitted to the transmission.

To correct this condition, install revised clutch disc (part No. 006 250 67 03).

CLUTCH PEDAL OCCASIONALLY STICKS

SLK230

On some of these models the clutch pedal may occasionally stick.

This condition may be caused by thermal overload on slave cylinder forming vapor bubbles.

To correct this condition, proceed as follows:

1. Remove clutch slave cylinder and clutch line.
2. Remove shield, as required.
3. Install insulated slave cylinder (part No. 210 290 00 11).
4. Install insulated clutch line (part No. 210 290 28 13).

GEAR SHIFT LEVER VIBRATIONS AND/OR TRANSMISSION RATTLING

SLK230

On some of these models there may be gear shift lever vibrations and/or transmission rattling noises. Vibration or rattling may occur in 1st and/or 2nd gear.

This condition may be caused by shift arm blocks vibrating in shift collar groove.

To correct this condition, remove old shift arm/slider and install new 1st/2nd gear fork.

Rear Axle & Suspension

NOTE: Prior To Performing Any Service Operations Listed In This Section, Consult The "Technical Service Bulletins" Section For Related Information.

INDEX

	Page No.
Camber Strut, Replace	5-135
C240 & C320	5-135
C43, C230, C280, CLK55, CLK320, CLK430, E55, E300, E320, E430, SL500, SL600, SLK230 & SLK320	5-135
S320 & S420 & 1998–99 CL500, CL600, S500 & S600	5-135
S430 & 2000–01 CL500, CL600, S500 & S600	5-136
Coil Spring, Replace	5-134
Differential Carrier, Replace	5-127
C240 & C320	5-127
C43, C230, C280, CLK55, CLK320, CLK430, SLK230 & SLK320	5-127
E55, E300, E320 & E430	5-127
S320 & S420 & 1998–99 CL500, CL600, S500 & S600	5-127
S430 & 2000–01 CL500, CL600, S500 & S600	5-128
SL500 & SL600	5-128
Hub & Bearing, Replace	5-131
C43, C230, C240, C280, C320, CLK55, CLK320, CLK430, E55, E300, E320, E430, SL500, SL600, SLK230 & SLK320	5-131
S320 & S420 & 1998–99 CL500, CL600, S500 & S600	5-132
S430 & 2000–01 CL500, CL600, S500 & S600	5-132
Hub & Bearing Service	5-132
Precautions	5-124
Battery Ground Cable	5-124
Propeller Shaft, Replace	5-129
C43, C230, C280, CLK55, CLK320, CLK430, SLK230 & SLK320	5-129
E55, E300, E320 & E430	5-129
ML55, ML320 & ML430	5-129
S320 & S420 & 1998–99 CL500, CL600, S500 & S600	5-129
S430 & 2000–01 CL500 & S500 & 2001 CL600 & S600	5-130
SL500 & SL600	5-130
Propeller Shaft Centering Sleeve, Replace	5-131
Propeller Shaft Intermediate Bearing, Replace	5-131
C43, C230, C280, CLK55, CLK320, CLK430, E55, E300, E320, E430, S320, S430, SL500, SL600, SLK230 & SLK320 & 1998–99 CL500, CL600, S500 & S600	5-131
S430 & 2000–01 CL500, CL600, S500 & S600	5-131
Rear Axle, Replace	5-124
C240 & C320	5-124
C43, C230, C280, CLK55, CLK320, CLK430, SLK230 & SLK320	5-124
E55, E300, E320 & E430	5-125
S320 & S420 & 1998–99 CL500, CL600, S500 & S600	5-125
S430 & 2000–01 CL500, CL600, S500 & S600	5-125
SL500 & SL600	5-126
Rear Axle Shaft, Replace	5-126
Rear Wheel Spindle, Replace	5-133
C240 & C320	5-133
C43, C230, C280, CLK55, CLK320, CLK430, E55, E300, E320, E430, SL500, SL600, SLK230 & SLK320	5-133
S320 & S420 & 1998–99 CL500, CL600, S500 & S600	5-134
S430 & 2000–01 CL500, CL600, S500 & S600	5-134
Shock Absorber, Replace	5-134
C43, C230, C280, CLK55, CLK320, CLK430, E55, E300, E320, E430, SL500, SL600, SLK230 & SLK320	5-134
S320 & S420 & 1998–99 CL500, CL600, S500 & S600	5-134
Spindle Knuckle, Replace	5-133
C43, C230, C280, CLK55, CLK320, CLK430, E55, E300, E320, E430, SL500, SL600, SLK230 & SLK320	5-133
S320 & S420 & 1998–99 CL500, CL600, S500 & S600	5-133
Spring Linkage, Replace	5-137
C43, C230, C240, C280, C320, CLK55, CLK320, CLK430, E55, E300, E320, E430, SL500, SL600, SLK230 & SLK320	5-137
S320 & S420 & 1998–99 CL500, CL600, S500 & S600	5-137
S430 & 2000–01 CL500, CL600, S500 & S600	5-137
Spring Linkage Bushing, Replace	5-137
C43, C230, C280, CLK55, CLK320, CLK430, E55, E300, E320, E430, SL500, SL600, SLK230 & SLK320	5-137
S320 & S420 & 1998–99 CL500, CL600, S500 & S600	5-138
Technical Service Bulletins	5-140
Air Suspension MIL On	5-140
Drive Line Vibration At 50–62 mph	5-140
Driveline Or Rear Axle Humming Drone	5-141
Howling/Whistling From Rear	5-141
Howling/Whistling Sound From Propeller Shaft	5-141
Knocking Noise	5-141
Rear Axle Low Speed Rumble On Uneven Roads	5-140
Rear Axle Strain In Sharp Curves	5-141
Tension Arm, Replace	5-136
C240 & C320	5-136
Thrust Arm, Replace	5-136
C43, C230, C280, CLK55, CLK320, CLK430, E55, E300, E320, E430, SL500, SL600, SLK230 & SLK320	5-136
S320 & S420 & 1998–99 CL500, CL600, S500 & S600	5-136
S430 & 2000–01 CL500, CL600, S500 & S600	5-137
Tightening Specifications	5-142
Torque Strut, Replace	5-134
C240 & C320	5-134
C43, C230, C280, CLK55, CLK320, CLK430, E55, E300, E320, E430, SL500, SL600, SLK230 & SLK320	5-134
S320 & S420 & 1998–99 CL500, CL600, S500 & S600	5-134
Torsion Rod, Replace	5-138
C43, C230, C280, CLK55, CLK320, CLK430, E55, E300, E320, E430, SLK230 & SLK320	5-138
S320 & S420 & 1998–99 CL500, CL600, S500 & S600	5-138
SL500 & SL600	5-138
Track Rod, Replace	5-139
C240 & C320	5-139
C43, C230, C280, CLK55, CLK320, CLK430, E55, E300, E320, E430, SL500, SL600, SLK230 & SLK320	5-139
S320 & S420 & 1998–99 CL500, CL600, S500 & S600	5-139
S430 & 2000–01 CL500, CL600, S500 & S600	5-140

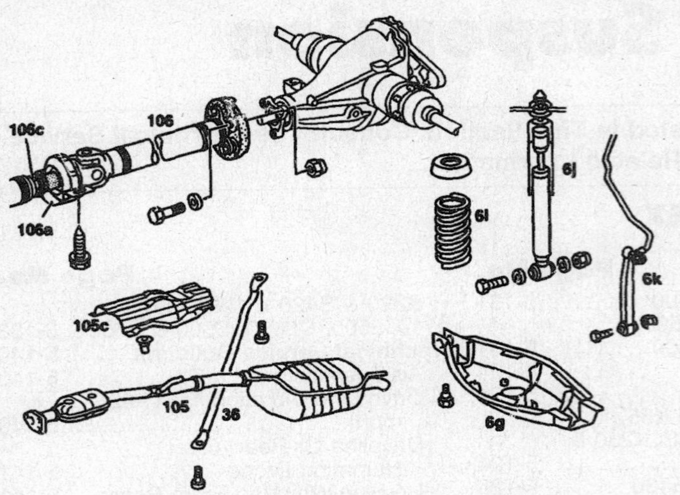

1c & 1d Front & Rear Axle Suspension
6g Spring Link Cover 6i Rear Spring
6j Shock Absorber
6k Torsion Bar/Connecting Rod
36 Frame Crossbraces
105 Exhaust System 105c Exhaust Shield
106 Propellor Shaft
106a Propellopr Shaft Intermediate Bearing
106c Clamping Nut

MB2039900004000X

Fig. 1 Rear axle replacement (Part 1 of 2). C43, C230, C280, CLK55, CLK320, CLK430, SLK230 & SLK320

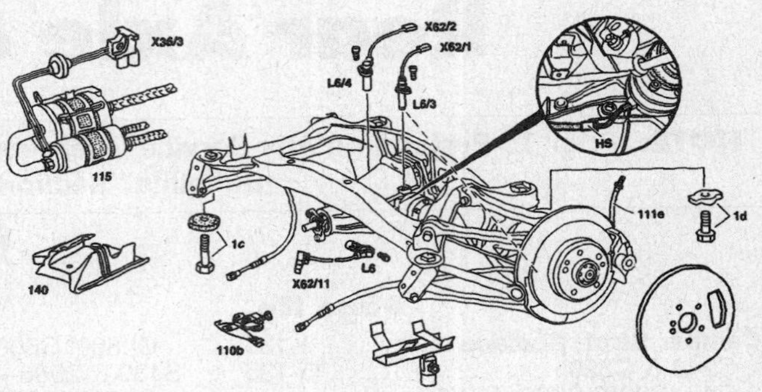

1c & 1d Front & Rear Mounts
115 Fuel Pump Assembly
140 Fuel Pump Assembly Cover
HS Hydraulic Line
L6 rear Axle Speed Sensor
L6/3 & L6/4 Left & Righthand Rear Axle Speed Sensors
X36/3 Fuel Pump Wiring Connector
X62/1 & X62/2 Rear Speed Sensor/Brake Lining Wear Indicator

MB2039900005000X

Fig. 1 Rear axle replacement (Part 2 of 2). C43, C230, C280, CLK55, CLK320, CLK430, SLK230 & SLK320

PRECAUTIONS

BATTERY GROUND CABLE

Prior to service, disconnect battery ground cable and isolate as required.

REAR AXLE

REPLACE

C43, C230, C280, CLK55, CLK320, CLK430, SLK230 & SLK320

1. Drain rear axle oil into suitable container.
2. Remove mounting bolts, front and rear rubber mounts, **Fig. 1.**
3. Remove mounting bolts, spring link cover and rear springs.
4. Remove mounting bolts and shock absorbers or spring strut.
5. Remove mounting bolts and torsion rod connecting rod.
6. **On SLK230 and SLK320 models,** remove mounting bolts and frame cross braces.
7. **On all models,** remove exhaust system and shield.
8. Disconnect propeller shaft at joint flange. Attach shaft to reinforcement bracket.
9. Disconnect propeller shaft intermediate bearing.
10. **On C43, C230 and C280 models,** disconnect propeller shaft compression joint.
11. **On all models,** disconnect automatic cable length compensator or intermediate lever control cables.
12. Disconnect and seal frame floor brake hoses.
13. Disconnect fuel pump and secure with suitable wire. Remove cover.
14. Disconnect rear axle speed sensors.
15. Disconnect fuel pump electrical connector.
16. Disconnect left and righthand speed sensor/brake lining wear indicator connectors.
17. Disconnect ABS speed sensors.
18. Remove rear axle.
19. Reverse procedure to install, noting the following:
    a. Inspect ABS rear axle speed sensors magnetic tip and install new O-ring.
    b. Recut frame floor threads with tap.
    c. Install new self-locking bolts and nuts.
    d. Ensure brake hoses are not twisted.
    e. Maintain .5906 inch clearance between brake hose and axle parts.
    f. Tighten mounting bolts and nuts to specifications.
    g. Bleed brake system.
    h. Inspect vehicle rear axle ride height.
    i. Inspect headlamp adjustment.

C240 & C320

1. Remove strap mounting bolts and raise rear seat bench and remove cover.
2. Raise and support vehicle.
3. Disconnect rear brake control cable at intermediate lever and housing, **Fig. 2.**
4. Remove tire and wheel assemblies.
5. Remove exhaust system as outlined under "Engine, Replace" in appropriate engine section.
6. Raise front part and remove rear of exhaust shielding plate.
7. Remove propeller shaft intermediate bearing mounting bolts.
8. Disconnect propeller shaft as outlined under "Propeller Shaft, Replace."
9. Remove torsion bar. Connecting rods remain on wheel carriers.
10. Remove brake hoses. Plug and seal hoses and openings.
11. Disconnect left and righthand rear axle vehicle speed sensor connections.
12. Remove rear spring.
13. Disconnect shock absorber at spring link.
14. Remove four rear underbody paneling mounting nuts.
15. Support rear axle with suitable transmission jack.
16. Remove rear axle suspension front and rear mounting bolts.
17. Drain rear axle fluid into suitable container.
18. Remove rear axle rearward. **Do not bend paneling too much.**
19. Reverse procedure to install, noting the following:
    a. Install new self-locking nuts.
    b. Tighten mounting bolts to

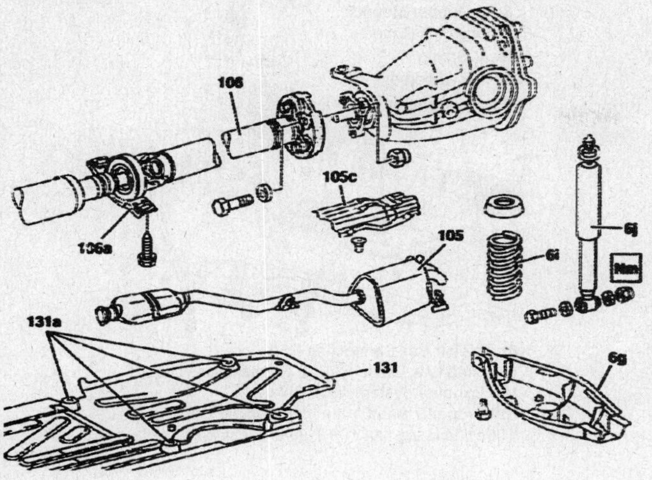

1c Bolt
1d Bolt
6i Rear Spring
6j Shock Absorber
6r Torsion Bar
105 Exhaust System
105c Exhaust Shielding Plate
106 Propeller Shaft
106a Propeller Shaft Intermediate Bearing
110c Rear Brake Control Cables Internedate Lever Housing
110d Rear Brake Control Cables Internedate Lever
111e Brake Hoses
131 Underbody Paneling
131a Nut
16/2X1 Rear Axle Vehicle Speed Sensor

MB2030100050000X

Fig. 2 Rear axle replacement. C240 & C320

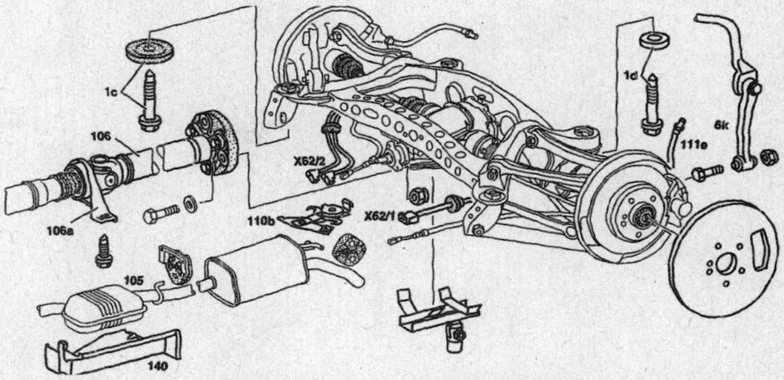

1c & 1d Rubber Mounts 6k Torsion Bar Connecting Rod 105 Exhaust System
106 Propeller Shaft 106a Intermediate Bering 110b Parking Brake Cable
111e Brake Hose 140 Fuel Pump Assembly X62/1 Speed Sensor Connector
X62/1 Speed Sensor/Brake Pad Wear Connector

MB2039900028000X

Fig. 3 Rear axle replacement. E55, E300, E320 & E430

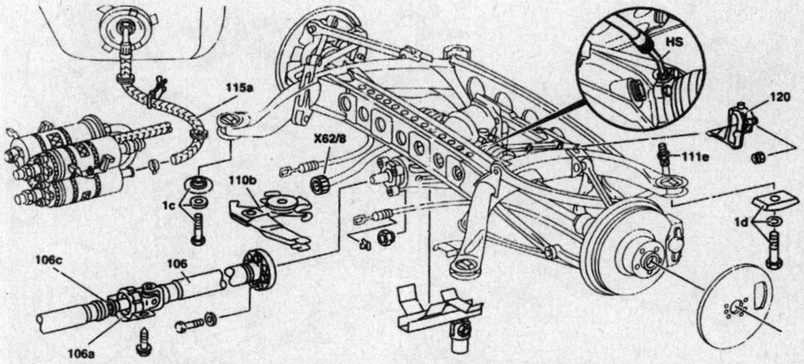

1c Front Mounting Rubber 1d Rear Mounting Rubber106 Propellor Shaft 106a Intermediate Bearing
106c Clamping Nut 110b Parking Brake Automative Slack Adjuster 111e Brake Hose 115a Fuel Hose
120 Level Controller Bracket HS Hydraulic Line X62/8 Rear Axle Distibutor Connector

MB2039900016000X

Fig. 4 Rear axle replacement. S320 & S420 & 1998–99 CL500, CL600, S500 & S600

specifications.

E55, E300, E320 & E430

1. Remove rear springs, **Fig. 3.**
2. Remove mounting bolts and shock absorbers or spring strut.
3. Remove mounting bolts, then the front and rear rubber mounts,
4. Remove mounting bolts and torsion rod connecting rod.
5. Remove exhaust system.
6. Disconnect propeller shaft and intermediate bearing.
7. Disconnect automatic cable length compensator.
8. Disconnect and seal frame floor brake hoses.
9. Remove fuel pump cover.
10. Disconnect rear axle speed sensors.
11. Drain rear axle oil into suitable container.
12. Remove mounting bolts and frame cross braces.
13. Disconnect propeller shaft compression joint.
14. Disconnect fuel pump and secure with suitable wire. Remove cover.
15. Disconnect and seal hydraulic line (HS).
16. Disconnect fuel pump electrical connector.
17. Disconnect left and righthand speed sensor/brake lining wear indicator connectors.
18. Disconnect ABS speed sensors.
19. Remove rear axle.
20. Reverse procedure to install, noting the following:
    a. Install new self-locking bolts and nuts.
    b. Tighten mounting bolts and nuts to specifications.
    c. Bleed brake system.
    d. Inspect vehicle rear axle ride height.
    e. Inspect headlamp adjustment.

S320 & S420 & 1998-99 CL500, CL600, S500 & S600

1. Remove complete exhaust system.
2. Remove rear springs.
3. Remove rear shock absorbers.
4. **On models equipped with ADS or level control,** remove rear spring struts.
5. **On all models,** remove front and rear mounting bolts, **Fig. 4.**
6. Disconnect propeller shaft intermediate bearing.
7. Disconnect parking brake automatic slack adjuster and remove rear brake cable.
8. Disconnect and seal frame floor brake hose
9. Pinch fuel tank to pump hose with clamp tool No. 000 589 40 37 00, or equivalent, and disconnect.
10. **On models equipped with ADS or level control,** remove level control bracket, then disconnect and seal ADS hydraulic lines.
11. **On all models,** disconnect rear axle distributor connector and remove rear axle.
12. Reverse procedure to install, noting the following:
    a. Recut frame floor mounting bolt threads.
    b. Install new self-locking bolts and nuts.
    c. Tighten mounting bolts and nuts to specifications.
    d. Inspect and adjust rear axle ride height as required.
    e. Adjust headlamp aim as required.

S430 & 2000-01 CL500, CL600, S500 & S600

1. Raise and support vehicle.
2. Remove rear tire and wheel assemblies.
3. Remove exhaust system as outlined under “Engine, Replace” in appropriate engine section.
4. Disconnect brake cables from parking brake automatic slack adjuster, **Fig. 5.**
5. Remove propeller shaft intermediate bearing mounting bolts.
6. Disconnect propeller shaft from differential carrier as outlined under “Propeller Shaft, Replace.”
7. Disconnect righthand rear brake pad contact sensor, then the left and righthand wheel speed sensors.

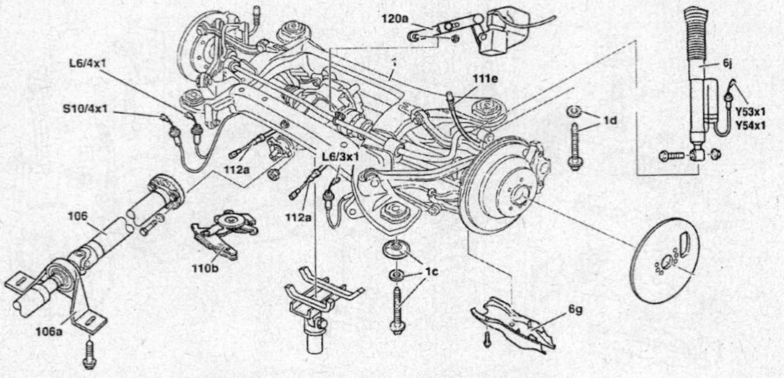

1 Rear Axle 1c, d Bolts 6g Spring Link Cover 6j Spring Stut 106 Propeller Shaft
106a Propeller Shaft Intermediate Bearing 110b Automatic Slack Adjuster
111e Brake Hose 112 Brake Cables 120a Level Sensor Control Rod
L6/4x1 Righthand Rear Wheel Speed Sensor S10/4x1 Righthand Rear Brake Pad Contact Sensor
Y53x1 Damping Valve Unit Connector Y54x1 Damping Valve Unit Connector

MB2030100054000X

Fig. 5 Rear axle replacement. S430 & 2000–01 CL500, CL600, S500 & S600

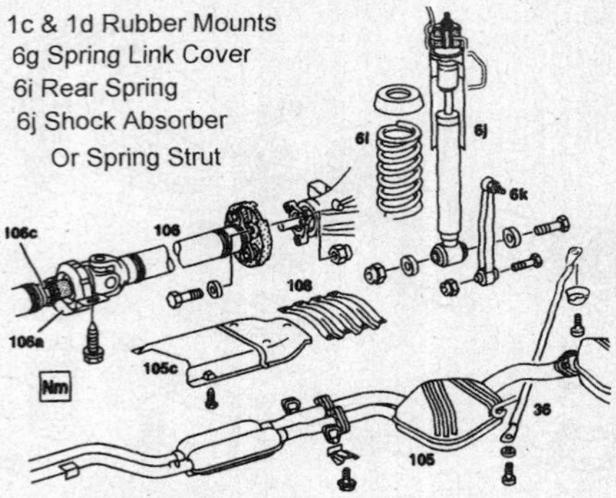

6k Torsion Bar Connecting Rod
6l Spring Link Guide Rail 36 Frame Cross Braces
105 Exhaust System 105c Shield
106 Propellor Shaft 106a Intermediate Bearing
106c Clamping Nut 108 Tunnel Closing Plate

MB2039900025000X

Fig. 6 Rear axle replacement (Part 1 of 2). SL500 & SL600

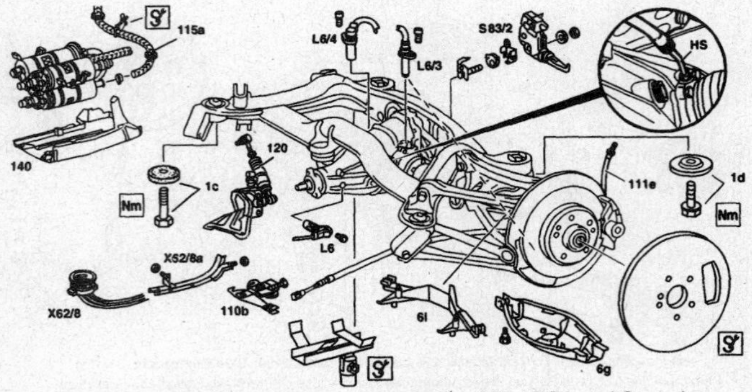

110b Idler Lever 111e Brake Hose 115a Fuel Hose 120 ADS Level Control
140 Fuel Pump HS Hydraulic Line L6 Rear Axle Speed Sensor
L6/3 & L6/4 Rear Axle Speed Sensors S83/2 & S83/s Roll-Over Bar Switches
X62/8 Rear Axle Distributor X62/8a Guide Rail

MB2039900026000X

Fig. 6 Rear axle replacement (Part 2 of 2). SL500 & SL600

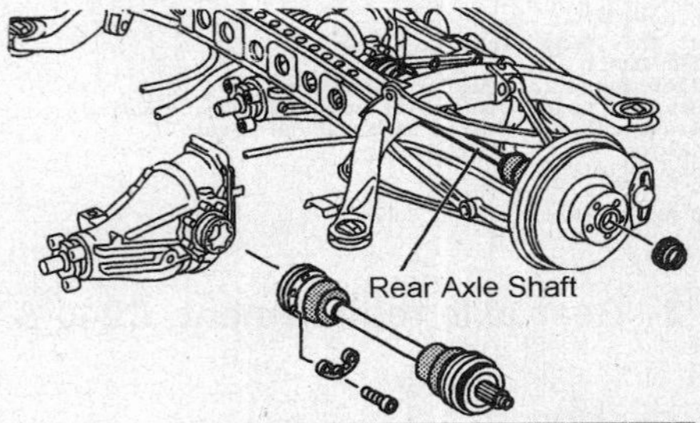

MB2039900014000X

Fig. 7 Rear axle shaft replacement. C240, C320, S320 & S420 & 1998–99 CL500, CL600, S500 & S600

8. Disconnect left and righthand damping valve unit connectors.
9. Remove pin, expanding rivet and spring link cover.
10. Disconnect strut from spring link.
11. Disconnect torsion bar level sensor control rod.
12. Disconnect brake hoses. Seal and plug lines and openings.
13. Support rear axle assembly with suitable jack.
14. Remove front and rear axle mounting bolts.
15. Remove axle.
16. Reverse procedure to install. Tighten mounting bolts and nuts to specifications.

SL500 & SL600

1. Drain rear axle oil into suitable container.
2. Remove front and rear mounting bolts, then the rubber mounts, **Fig. 6.**
3. Remove rear springs.
4. Remove rear shock absorbers or spring strut.
5. Remove torsion bar connecting rod.
6. Remove spring link guide rail.
7. Remove frame cross braces.
8. Remove complete exhaust system and shield.
9. Disconnect propeller shaft at joint flange.
10. Disconnect propeller shaft intermediate bearing.
11. Disconnect propeller shaft clamping nut.
12. Remove tunnel closing plate.
13. Remove parking brake idler lever.
14. Disconnect and seal frame floor brake hose.
15. Disconnect fuel hose.
16. **On models equipped with ADS,** remove level sensor connecting rod.
17. **On all models,** remove fuel pump cover.
18. **On models equipped with ADS,** disconnect and seal ADS hydraulic lines.
19. **On all models,** disconnect rear axle speed sensor and remove roll-over bar rear axle switch.
20. Disconnect rear axle distributor connector and cable guide rail.
21. Remove rear axle.
22. Reverse procedure to install, noting the following:
    a. Recut frame floor mounting bolt threads.
    b. Install new self-locking bolts and nuts.
    c. Adjust roll-over bar switch.
    d. Tighten mounting bolts and nuts to specifications.
    e. Inspect and adjust rear axle ride height as required.
    f. Adjust headlamp aim as required.

REAR AXLE SHAFT

REPLACE

Do not move vehicle with rear axle shafts removed.

1. Remove exhaust system from flanged connection.
2. **On SL600 and SL600 models equipped with ADS,** disconnect level controller or sensor control rod.
3. **On all models,** remove rear axle shaft collared nut, **Figs. 7 and 8.**
4. Remove shaft flange with puller and installation tool No. 210 589 03 43 00 and holder tool No. 210 589 01 40 00, or equivalents.
5. Loosen locking bolts.
6. Move rear axle shafts into approximately horizontal position, push together and remove obliquely down at an angle from connecting flange.
7. Reverse procedure to install, noting the following:
    a. If shafts seized, shaft and flange

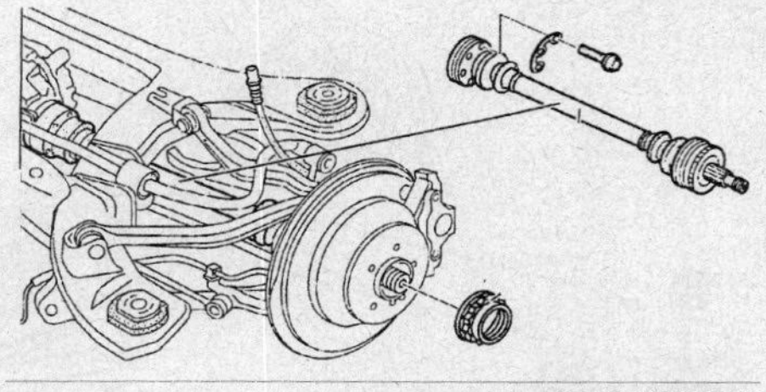

MB2030100060000X

Fig. 8 Rear axle shaft replacement. C430 & 2000–01 CL500, CL600, S500 & S600

splined shaft profile must be cleaned mechanically before installation.

b. Inspect constant velocity joints, rubber boots and covers for leaks and damage.
c. If outer constant velocity joint is damaged, replace complete rear axle shaft.
d. If inner constant velocity joint, boots and covers are damaged or leaking, replace as required.
e. Install new collared nut.
f. Install new self-locking bolts and washers.
g. Lightly lubricate bolt threads and head supports.
h. Tighten mounting bolts and nuts to specifications.

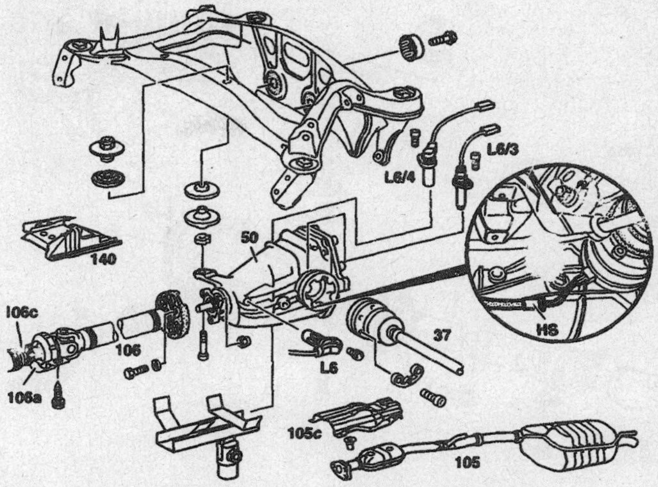

HS Hydraulic Line L6 Rear Axle Speed Sensor
L6/3 & L6/4 Rear Axle Speed Sensor
37 Rear Axle Shafts 50 Rear Axle Center Support
105 Exhaust System 105c Exhaust Shield
106 Propellor Shaft
106a Propellor Shaft Intermediate Bearing
106c Propellor Shaft Clamping Nut
140 Fuel Pump Assembly

MB2039900015000X

Fig. 9 Differential carrier replacement. C43, C230, C280, CLK55, CLK320, CLK430, SLK230 & SLK320

DIFFERENTIAL CARRIER

REPLACE

C43, C230, C280, CLK55, CLK320, CLK430, SLK230 & SLK320

1. Drain rear axle oil into suitable container.
2. **On C43, C230 and C280 models equipped with ASD,** removal and seal hydraulic line (HS), **Fig. 9.**
3. **On all models,** disconnect rear axle speed sensor.
4. Remove exhaust system from flange connection and exhaust shield.
5. **On C43, C230 and C280 models,** disconnect propeller shaft compression joint.
6. **On all models,** disconnect propeller shaft intermediate bearing.
7. Disconnect propeller shaft at differential carrier and mount on reinforcement bracket.
8. Remove fuel pump cover and disconnect pump at rubber rings.
9. Remove rear axle shafts as outlined under "Rear Axle Shaft, Replace."
10. Support differential carrier with suitable jack.
11. Remove mounting bolts and stop plate.
12. Remove mounting bolts and differential carrier.
13. Remove rear axle breather.
14. Reverse procedure to install, noting the following:
    a. Install new self-locking bolts and nuts.
    b. Lightly lubricate bolt threads and head supports.
    c. Ensure differential carrier is centered in rear axle carrier using removal and installation tool No. 210 589 02 43 00, or equivalent.
    d. Tighten mounting bolts to specifications.

C240 & C320

1. Raise and support vehicle.
2. Remove exhaust shielding plate, **Fig. 10.**
3. Remove propeller shaft intermediate bearing mounting bolts.
4. Disconnect propeller shaft from differential carrier as outlined under "Propeller Shaft, Replace."
5. Remove righthand rear axle shaft as outlined under "Rear Axle Shaft, Replace"
6. Support differential carrier with suitable jack.
7. Remove rear center assembly mounting bolts.
8. Remove front center assembly mounting bolts.
9. Drain rear axle fluid into suitable container.
10. Pull differential carrier to right off lefthand rear axle shaft.
11. Pull rear axle shaft out of differential carrier.
12. Remove differential.
13. Reverse procedure to install. Tighten mounting bolts and nuts to specifications.

E55, E300, E320 & E430

1. Drain rear axle oil into suitable container.
2. Remove propeller shaft intermediate bearing, **Fig. 11.**
3. Disconnect propeller shaft at differential carrier.
4. Remove rear axle shafts as outlined under "Rear Axle Shaft, Replace."
5. Support differential carrier with suitable jack.
6. Remove mounting bolts and differential carrier.
7. Remove rear axle vent.
8. Reverse procedure to install, noting the following:
    a. Install new self-locking bolts and nuts.
    b. Tighten mounting bolts to specifications.

S320 & S420 & 1998–99 CL500, CL600, S500 & S600

1. Removal and seal unit, **Fig. 12.**
2. Drain rear axle oil into suitable container.
3. Remove complete exhaust system and exhaust shield.
4. Loosen propeller shaft clamping nut.
5. Disconnect propeller shaft intermediate bearing.
6. Disconnect propeller shaft at differential carrier.
7. Remove rear axle shafts as outlined under "Rear Axle Shaft, Replace."

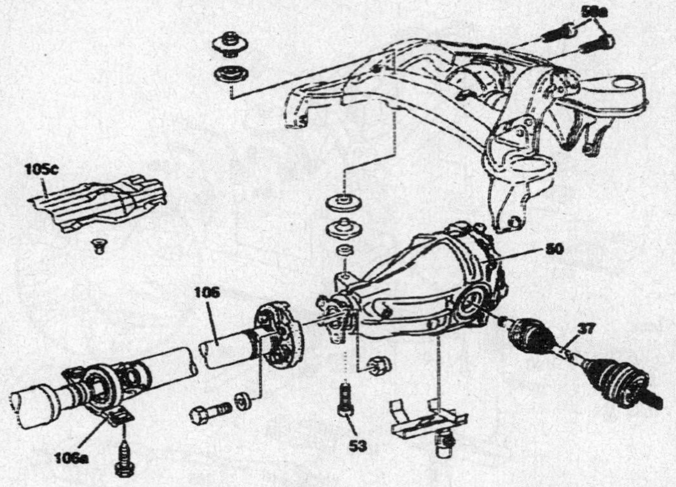

37 Rear Axle Shaft
50 Differential Carrier
50a Differential Carrier Suspension
53 Front Center Assembly Suspension
105c Exhaust Shielding Plate
106 Propeller Shaft
106a Propeller Shaft Intermediate Bearing

MB2030100053000X

Fig. 10 Differential carrier replacement. C240 & C320

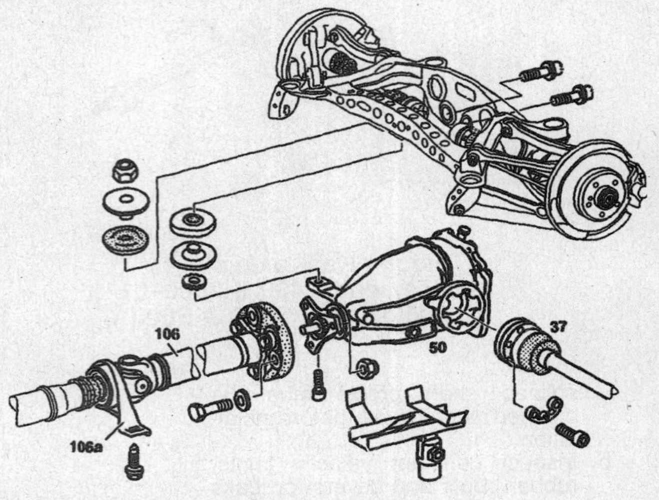

37 Rear Axle Shafts 50 Differential Carrier
106 Propeller Shaft 106a Intermediate Bearing

MB2039900029000X

Fig. 11 Differential carrier replacement. E55, E300, E320 & E430

8. Disconnect fuel pump and electrical connector.
9. Support differential carrier with suitable jack.
10. Remove extension carrier mounting bolts.
11. Disconnect front center suspension.
12. Disconnect hydraulic line (HS).
13. Remove mounting bolts and differential carrier.
14. Disconnect VSS sensor(s) and bracket.
15. Remove rear axle breather.
16. Reverse procedure to install, noting the following:
    a. Install new breather.
    b. Install new self-locking bolts and nuts.
    c. Install new propeller shaft to differential carrier mounting nuts.
    d. Lightly lubricate bolt threads and head supports.
    e. Tighten mounting bolts to specifications.

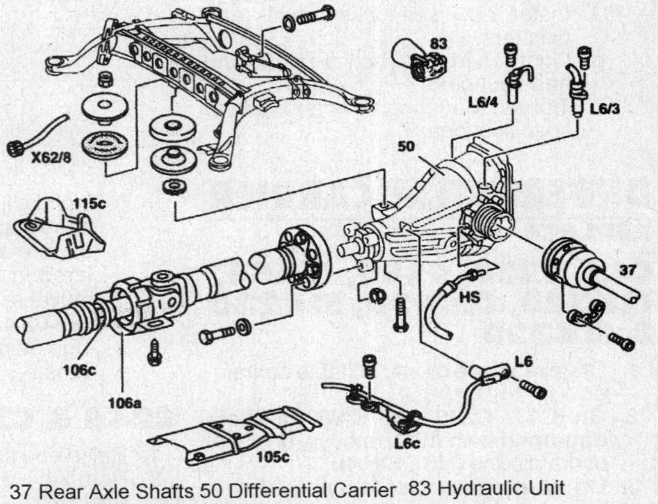

37 Rear Axle Shafts 50 Differential Carrier 83 Hydraulic Unit
105c Exhaust Head Shield 106 Propellor Shaft
106a Intermediate Bearing 106c Clamping Nut
L6, L6/3 & L6/4 VSS Sensor L6c Bracket

MB2039900024000X

Fig. 12 Differential carrier replacement. S320 & S420 & 1998–99 CL500, CL600, S500 & S600

S430 & 2000–01 CL500, CL600, S500 & S600

1. Raise and support vehicle.
2. Remove exhaust system as outlined under "Engine, Replace" in appropriate engine section.
3. Remove axle shaft from connecting flange as outlined under "Rear Axle Shaft, Replace," **Fig. 13.**
4. Remove propeller shaft intermediate bearing mounting bolts.
5. Disconnect propeller shaft from differential carrier as outlined under "Propeller Shaft, Replace."
6. Support differential carrier with suitable jack.
7. Remove extension carrier mounting nuts.
8. Remove front center assembly mounting bolts.
9. Remove differential.
10. Reverse procedure to install. Tighten mounting bolts and nuts to specifications.

SL500 & SL600

1. Drain rear axle oil into suitable container.
2. Removal and seal hydraulic line (HS), **Fig. 14.**
3. Disconnect rear axle speed sensor.
4. Remove lefthand frame cross braces,
5. Remove complete exhaust system and exhaust shield.
6. Remove tunnel closing plate.
7. Disconnect propeller shaft clamping nut or compression joint.
8. Remove propeller shaft intermediate bearing.
9. Remove cable guide rail. **Do not tension cables.**
10. Remove rear axle shafts as outlined under "Rear Axle Shaft, Replace."
11. Support differential carrier with suitable jack.
12. Remove mounting bolts and differential carrier.
13. Remove rear axle breather.

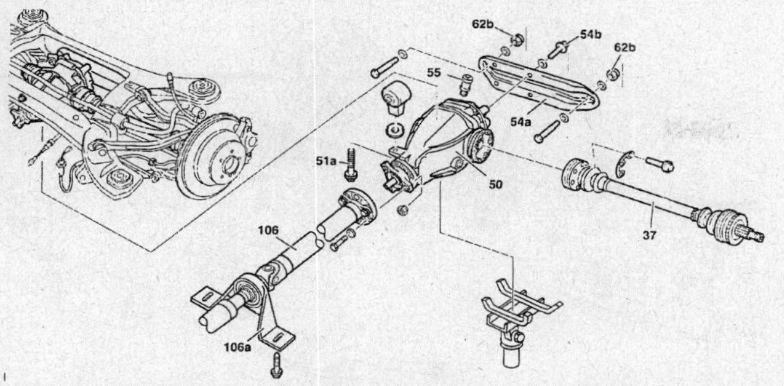

MB2030100061000X

Fig. 13 Differential carrier replacement. S430 & 2000–01 CL500, CL600, S500 & S600

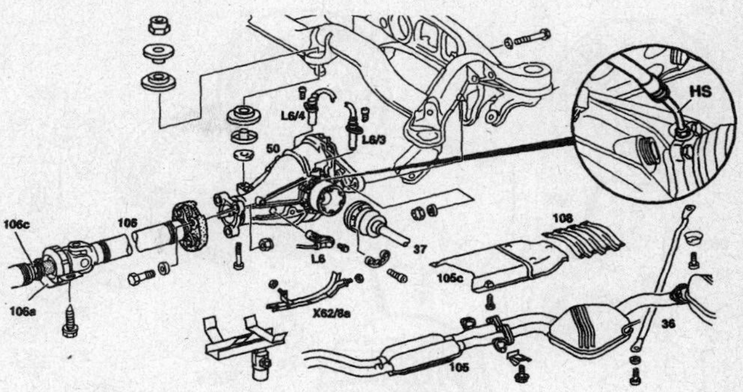

HS Hydraulic Line L6, L6/3 & L6/4 Rear Axle Speed Sensors
36 Frame Cross Braces 37 Rear Axle Shafts 50 Differential Carrier
105 Exhaust System 105c Head Shield 106 Propellor Shaft
106a Intermediate Bearing 106c Clamping Nut 108 Tunnel Closing Plate
X62/8a Cable Guide Rail

MB2039900027000X

Fig. 14 Differential carrier replacement. SL500 & SL600

14. Reverse procedure to install, noting the following:
    a. Install new self-locking bolts and nuts.
    b. Tighten mounting bolts to specifications.

PROPELLER SHAFT

REPLACE

C43, C230, C280, CLK55, CLK320, CLK430, SLK230 & SLK320

1. **On SLK230 and SLK320 models,** remove lefthand frame cross brace, **Fig. 15.**
2. **On C43, C230 and C280 models,** remove exhaust system downstream of connector.
3. **On CLK55, CLK320, CLK430, SLK230 and SLK320 models,** disconnect exhaust system suspension rubbers and support at rear muffler.
4. **On all models,** disconnect exhaust shield from tunnel.
5. Remove rear transverse bridge and reinforcement brace.
6. Loosen clamping nut.
7. Loosen intermediate bearing mounting bolts.
8. **On CLK55, CLK320, CLK430, SLK230 and SLK320 models,** remove rear engine mount.
9. **On all models,** remove mounting bolts and nuts, then disconnect front propeller shaft from transmission. Flexible disc remains on propeller shaft.
10. Remove mounting bolts and nuts, then disconnect rear propeller shaft from differential carrier. Flexible disc remains on propeller shaft.
11. Loosen flexible discs fitted sleeves using suitable six-inch long, .3974–.4725 inch diameter steel drift.
12. Support propeller shaft.
13. Remove intermediate bearing mounting bolts.
14. Disconnect propeller shaft from transmission and differential carrier centering pins, then remove to rear.
15. Reverse procedure to install, noting the following:
    a. Coat splined shaft section with suitable Molykote grease.
    b. Pack centering bushes with suitable multipurpose grease.
    c. Install new self-locking bolts and nuts.
    d. Tighten mounting bolts and nuts to specifications.
    e. Do not tighten intermediate bearing mounting bolts until flexible disks have been fastened to transmission and differential carrier.

E55, E300, E320 & E430

1. Disconnect middle or rear muffler suspension and lower exhaust system at muffler and support, **Fig. 16.**
2. Remove exhaust heat shield and reinforcement brace.
3. Remove seat belt bracket.
4. Remove mounting bolts and nuts, then disconnect front propeller shaft from transmission. Flexible disc remains on propeller shaft.
5. Remove mounting bolts and nuts, then disconnect rear propeller shaft from differential carrier. Flexible disc remains on propeller shaft.
6. Loosen flexible discs fitted sleeves using suitable six-inch long, .3974–.4725 inch diameter steel drift.
7. Support propeller shaft.
8. Remove intermediate bearing mounting bolts.
9. Disconnect propeller shaft from transmission and differential carrier centering pins, then remove to rear.
10. Reverse procedure to install, noting the following:
    a. Coat splined shaft section with suitable Molykote grease.
    b. Pack centering bushes with suitable multipurpose grease.
    c. Install new self-locking bolts and nuts.
    d. Tighten mounting bolts and nuts to specifications.
    e. Do not tighten intermediate bearing mounting bolts until flexible discs have been fastened to transmission and differential carrier.

ML55, ML320 & ML430

1. Remove front propeller shaft to transfer case mounting bolts and washers, **Figs. 17 and 18.**
2. Remove rear propeller shaft to rear differential carrier section mounting bolts.
3. **On ML320 models,** remove intermediate bearing mounting bolts.
4. **On all models,** remove propeller shaft to rear.
5. Reverse procedure to install.
    a. Center front propeller shaft and transfer case flange.
    b. Install new mounting bolts and washers.
    c. Do not twist intermediate bearing when tightening mounting bolts.
    d. Tighten mounting bolts to specifications.

S320 & S420 & 1998–99 CL500, CL600, S500 & S600

1. Disconnect exhaust system and shields, **Fig. 19.**
2. Remove fuel pump cover.
3. Remove seat belt bracket mounting bolts.
4. Remove mounting bolts and propeller shaft reinforcement bridge.
5. Remove clamping nut,
6. Loosen intermediate bearing mounting bolts.
7. Remove mounting bolts and nuts, then disconnect front propeller shaft from transmission. Flexible disc remains on propeller shaft.
8. Remove mounting bolts and nuts, then disconnect rear propeller shaft from differential carrier. Flexible disc remains on propeller shaft.
9. Loosen flexible discs fitted sleeves using suitable six-inch long, .3974–.4725 inch diameter steel drift.
10. Support propeller shaft.
11. Remove intermediate bearing mounting bolts.

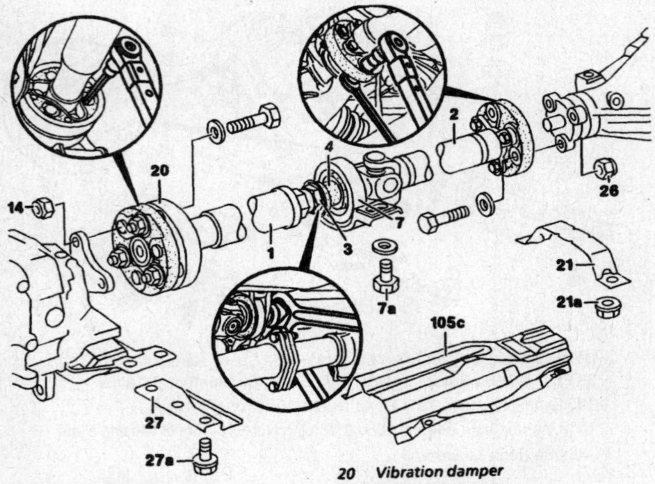

1 Front propellor shaft
2 Rear propellor shaft
3 Propellor shaft clamping nut
4 Rubber boot
7 Propellor shaft intermediate bearing
7a Bolt
20 Vibration damper
21 Transverse bridge
21a Bolts
26 Nut
27 Reinforcement brace
27a Bolt
105c Exhaust shield on tunnel
105d Plate nut

MB2039900039000X

Fig. 15 Propeller shaft replacement. C43, C230, C280, CLK55, CLK320, CLK430, SLK230 & SLK320

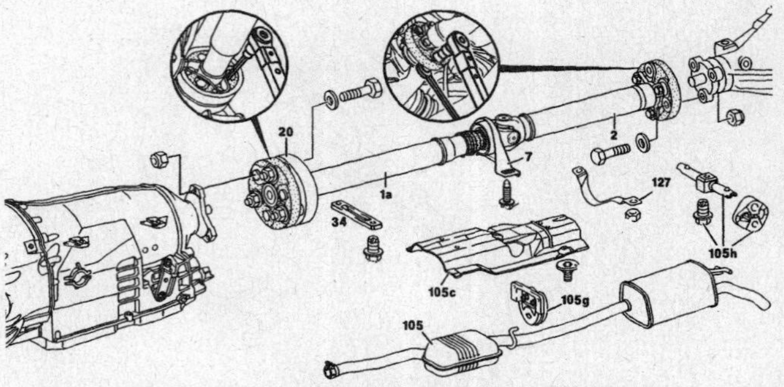

1a Front Propeller Shaft 2 Rear Propeller Shaft 7 Intermediate Bearing 20 Flexible Disks 34 Reinforcement Brace 105 Exhaust System 105c Heat Shield 105g & 105h Suspension 127 Seat Belt Bracket

MB2039900037000X

Fig. 16 Propeller shaft replacement. E55, E300, E320 & E430

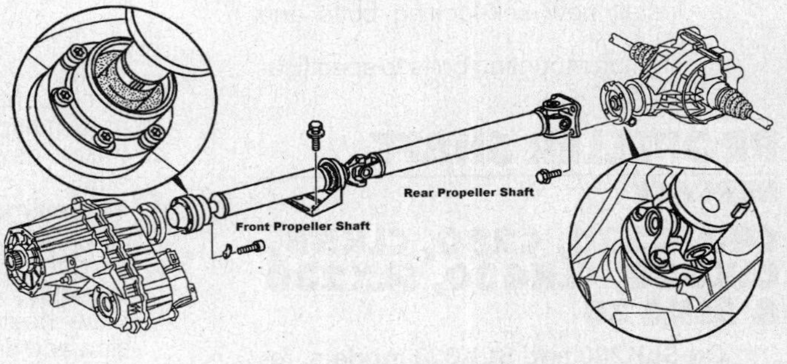

MB2030100045000X

Fig. 17 Propeller shaft replacement. ML320

12. Disconnect propeller shaft from transmission and differential carrier centering pins, then remove to rear.
13. Reverse procedure to install, noting the following:
    a. Coat splined shaft section with suitable Molykote grease.
    b. Pack centering bushes with suitable multipurpose grease.
    c. Install new self-locking bolts and nuts.
    d. Tighten mounting bolts and nuts to specifications.
    e. Do not tighten intermediate bearing mounting bolts until flexible discs have been fastened to transmission and differential carrier.

S430 & 2000–01 CL500 & S500 & 2001 CL600 & S600

1. Remove exhaust system from flange back as described under "Engine, Replace" in appropriate engine section.
2. Remove mounting bolts and rear reinforcement bridge, **Fig. 20.**
3. Disconnect front exhaust shield from exhaust shield.
4. Disconnect exhaust shield from tunnel.
5. Remove mounting bolts and front reinforcement bridge.
6. Loosen intermediate bearing mounting bolts.
7. Remove mounting bolts and disconnect propeller shaft from transmission. Flexible disk remains with propeller shaft.
8. Remove mounting bolts and disconnect propeller shaft from differential carrier. Flexible disk remains with propeller shaft.
9. Loosen flexible discs fitted sleeves using suitable six-inch long, .3974–.4725 inch diameter steel drift.
10. Remove intermediate shaft mounting bearings.
11. Pull propeller shaft off transmission and differential carrier spigots, then remove rear.
12. Reverse procedure to install, noting the following:
    a. Smear shaft splines with Molykote long-life grease, or equivalent.
    b. Pack two centering sleeves' cavities with suitable multipurpose grease.
    c. Install new heat shield sheet metal nuts and screws.
    d. Install new self-locking nuts.
    e. Tighten mounting bolts and nuts to specifications.

SL500 & SL600

1. Remove lefthand crossbrace with reinforcing plate, **Fig. 21.**
2. Remove complete exhaust system, exhaust shield and tunnel closing panel.
3. Disconnect reinforcement bridge.
4. Loosen slide connection clamp.
5. Remove mounting bolt and nuts, then disconnect front propeller shaft from transmission. Flexible disc remains with propeller shaft.
6. Remove mounting bolts and nuts, then disconnect rear propeller shaft from differential carrier. Flexible disc remains with propeller shaft.
7. Loosen flexible discs fitted sleeves using suitable six-inch long, .3974–.4725 inch diameter steel drift.
8. Remove intermediate bearing mounting bolts.
9. Disconnect propeller shaft from transmission and differential carrier centering pins, then remove to rear.
10. Separate front and rear propeller shafts, as required.
11. Reverse procedure to install, noting the following:
    a. Coat splined shaft section with suitable Molykote grease.
    b. Pack centering bushes with suitable multipurpose grease.
    c. Install new self-locking bolts and nuts.
    d. Tighten mounting bolts and nuts to specifications.
    e. Do not tighten intermediate bearing mounting bolts until flexible discs have been fastened to transmission and differential carrier.

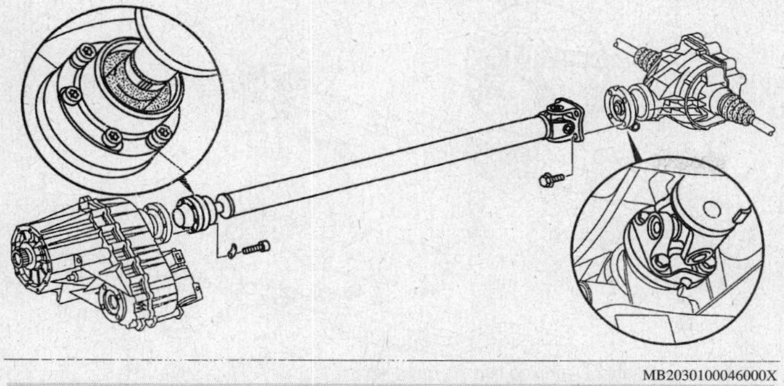

Fig. 18 Propeller shaft replacement. ML430

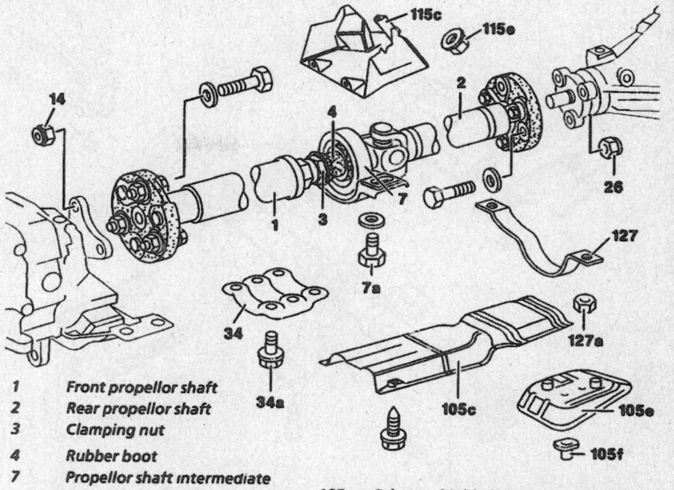

Fig. 19 Propeller shaft replacement. S320 & S420 & 1998–99 CL500, CL600, S500 & S600

PROPELLER SHAFT INTERMEDIATE BEARING

REPLACE

C43, C230, C280, CLK55, CLK320, CLK430, E55, E300, E320, E430, S320, S430, SL500, SL600, SLK230 & SLK320 & 1998-99 CL500, CL600, S500 & S600

1. Remove propeller shaft as outlined under "Propeller Shaft, Replace."
2. Separate front and rear propeller shafts at clamp or slide connection, **Fig. 22.**
3. Remove joint fork rubber boot.
4. Remove rubber mount with grooved ball bearing and front protective cap using two-arm puller tool No. 000 589 88 33 00 and pulling arms tools No. 129 509 00 34 00, or equivalent.
5. **On C280, CLK55, CLK320, CLK430, E55, E300, E320, E430, S320, S420, SL500, SL600, SLK230 and SLK320 and 1998–99 CL500, CL600, S500 & S600 models,** there is no protective cap.
6. **On C43, C280, CLK55, CLK320, CLK430, E55, E300, E320, E430, SL500, SL600, SLK230 and SLK320 models,** press groove ball bearing out of rubber mount using removal and installation tool No. 116 589 09 43 00, or equivalent.
7. **On C230 models,** press groove ball bearing out of rubber mount using removal and installation tool No. 201 589 09 43 00, or equivalent.
8. **On all models,** reverse procedure to install, noting the following:
   a. Install new protective cap on deep-groove ball bearing as required.
   b. Press rubber mount with grooved ball bearing on to joint fork using alignment tool No. 126 589 03 15 00 and drift punch No. 201 589 07 15 00, or equivalents.
   c. Replace joint fork rubber boot, as required.
   d. Tighten mounting bolts and nuts to specifications.

S430 & 2000-01 CL500, CL600, S500 & S600

1. Remove propeller shaft as outlined under "Propeller Shaft, Replace."
2. Disconnect front and rear shafts at side connect, **Fig. 23.**
3. Remove front shaft rubber boot.
4. Remove rubber mount with deep-grooved ball bearing using two-arm puller tool No. 000 589 88 33 00 and arms No. 129 589 00 34 00, or equivalents.
5. Remove deep-grooved ball bearing by pressing out using removal/installation tool No. 116 589 09 43 00, or equivalent.
6. Reverse procedure to install, noting the following:
   a. Smear shaft splines with Molykote long-life grease, or equivalent.
   b. Press ball bearing into joint fork using drift tool No. 126 589 03 15 00, or equivalent.
   c. Tighten mounting bolts to specifications.

PROPELLER SHAFT CENTERING SLEEVE

REPLACE

1. Remove propeller shaft as outlined under "Propeller Shaft, Replace."
2. Mark flexible disks to three- or four-arm flange alignment for installation, **Fig. 24.**
3. Remove flexible disks.
4. Loosen flexible disks fitted sleeves using suitable six-inch long, .3974–.4725 inch diameter steel drift.
5. Separate front and rear propeller shafts at slide connection.
6. Drive centering sleeve out of propeller shaft with suitable cold chisel. If sleeve cannot be driven out, proceed as follows:
   a. Drill .3934 hole approximately .5906 inch from end face at right angle through sleeve.
   b. Insert suitable drift through hole and remove centering sleeve out using two suitable assembly levers.
7. Inspect centering sleeves and replace as required.
8. Reverse procedure to install, noting the following:
   a. Coat splined shaft section with suitable Molykote grease.
   b. Pack centering bushes with suitable multipurpose grease.
   c. Install new self-locking bolts and nuts.
   d. Tighten mounting bolts and nuts to specifications.
   e. Do not tighten intermediate bearing mounting bolts until flexible disks have been fastened to transmission and differential carrier.

HUB & BEARING

REPLACE

C43, C230, C240, C280, C320, CLK55, CLK320, CLK430, E55, E300, E320, E430, SL500, SL600, SLK230 & SLK320

1. Remove rear axle shaft as outlined under "Rear Axle Shaft, Replace."
2. Remove brake disc and parking brake shoes, **Fig. 25.**
3. **On models equipped less 4MATIC,**

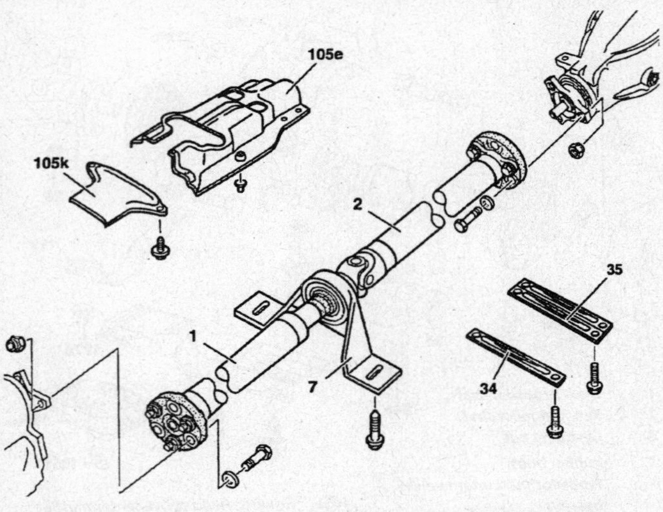

1	*Front propellor shaft with slide connection*	34	*Front reinforcement bridge*
2	*Rear propellor shaft*	35	*Rear reinforcement bridge*
7	*Propellor shaft intermediate bearing*	105e	*Exhaust heat shield above center muffler*
		105k	*Front exhaust heat shield*

MB2030100047000X

Fig. 20 Propeller shaft replacement. S430 & 2000–01 CL500 & S500 & 2001 CL600 & S600

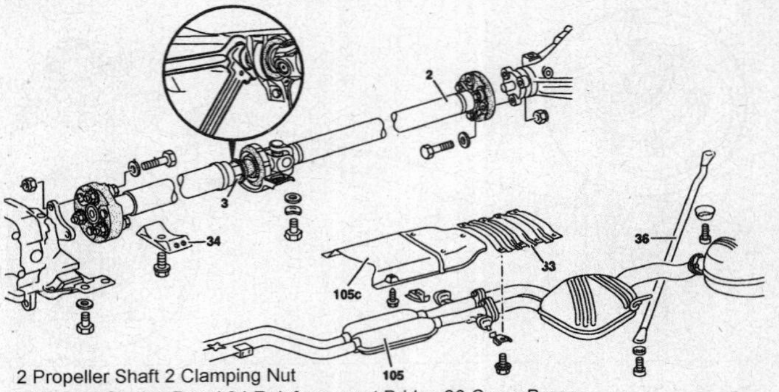

2 Propeller Shaft 2 Clamping Nut
33 Tunnel Closing Panel 34 Reinforcement Bridge 36 Cross Brace
105 Exhaust System 105a Shield

MB2039900036000X

Fig. 21 Propeller shaft replacement. SL500 & SL600

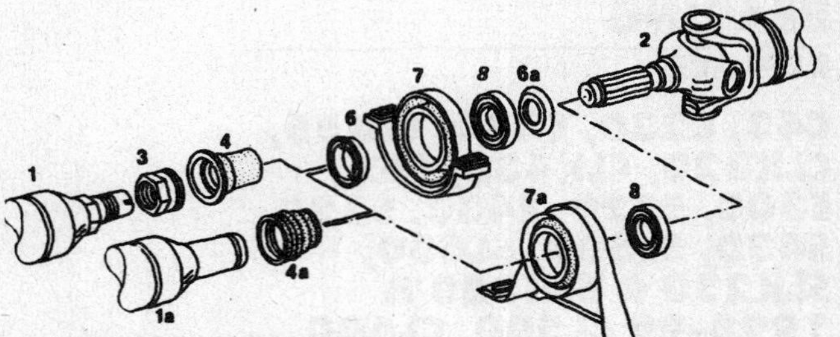

1	***Front propeller shaft with clamp connection***	6a	***Rear protective cap (fork side)***
1a	***Front propeller shaft with slide connection***	7	***Rubber mount, models 129, 140, 202 and 208***
2	***Rear propeller shaft***	7a	***Rubber mount, model 210***
3	***Propeller shaft clamping nut***	8	***Grooved ball bearing***
4/4a	***Rubber boot (optional)***		
6	***Front protective cap (shaft side)***		

MB2039900040000X

Fig. 22 Propeller shaft intermediate bearing replacement. C43, C230, C280, CLK55, CLK320, CLK430, E55, E300, E320, E430, S320, S430, SL500, SL600, SLK230 & SLK320 & 1998–99 CL500, CL600, S500 & S600

remove rear axle shaft flange by pulling out using removal installation tool No. 140 589 03 61 00, or equivalent.

4. **On models equipped with 4MATIC,** remove rear axle shaft flange by pulling out using removal installation tool No. 140 589 08 43 00, or equivalent.
5. **On all models,** remove locking ring.
6. Remove pull two-row angular ball bearing using extractor/puller tool No. 124 589 05 43 00, or equivalent.
7. Pull inner bearing race off rear axle shaft flange.
8. Reverse procedure to install, noting the following:
   a. Install new self-locking nuts.
   b. Ensure thrust plate rest snugly against inner bearing race when installing.
   c. Rear axle shaft must be horizontal when tightening camber, strut, torque strut, thrust arm, track rod and spring link mounting nuts.
   d. Tighten mounting bolts and nuts to specifications.

S320 & S420 & 1998–99 CL500, CL600, S500 & S600

1. Remove rear axle shaft as outlined under "Rear Axle Shaft, Replace," **Fig. 26.**
2. Remove brake disk and parking brake shoes.
3. Remove rear axle shaft flange by pulling out using removal installation tool No. 210 589 03 43 00, or equivalent.
4. Remove locking ring.
5. Remove pull two-row angular ball bearing using extractor/puller tool No. 124 589 05 43 00, or equivalent.
6. Pull inner bearing race off rear axle shaft flange.
7. Reverse procedure to install, noting the following:
   a. Install new self-locking nuts.
   b. Ensure thrust plate rest snugly against inner bearing race when installing.
   c. Rear axle shaft must be horizontal when tightening camber, strut, torque strut, thrust arm, track rod and spring link mounting nuts.
   d. Tighten mounting bolts and nuts to specifications.

S430 & 2000–01 CL500, CL600, S500 & S600

1. Remove axle shaft as outlined under "Rear Axle Shaft, Replace."
2. Remove brake caliper and disc. Support caliper with suitable wire.
3. Remove parking brake shoes.
4. Remove spindle as outlined under "Rear Wheel Spindle, Replace."
5. Remove locking ring, **Fig. 27.**
6. Remove bearings using removal/installation tool No. 140 689 08 43 00, or equivalent, from spindle.
7. Remove inner bearing from axle shaft flange.
8. Reverse procedure to install, noting the following:
   a. Install new self-locking nuts.
   b. Ensure thrust plate rest snugly against inner bearing race when installing.
   c. Rear axle shaft must be horizontal when tightening camber, strut, torque strut, thrust arm, track rod and spring link mounting nuts.
   d. Tighten mounting bolts and nuts to specifications.

HUB & BEARING SERVICE

If lateral or radial runout is more than .0118 inch, replace rear axle shaft flange.

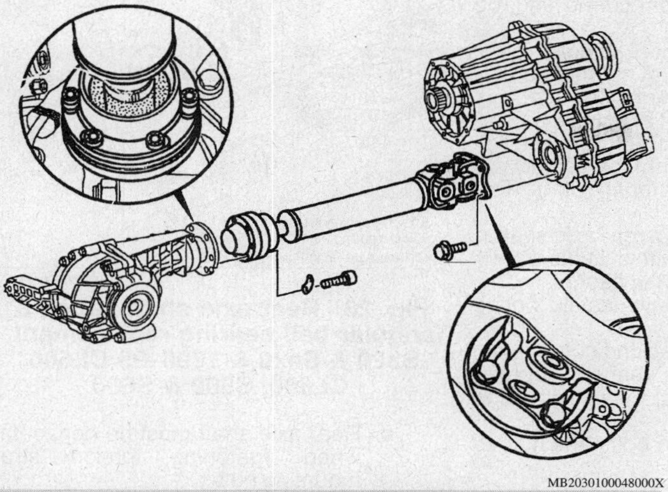

Fig. 23 Propeller shaft intermediate bearing replacement. S430 & 2000–01 CL500, CL600, S500 & S600

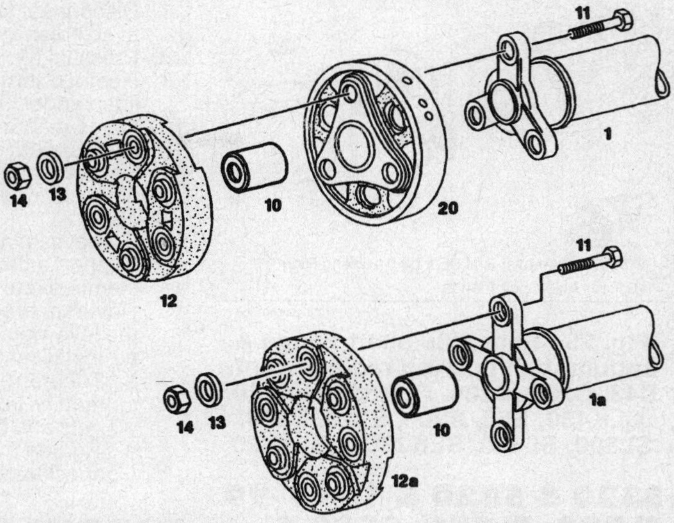

1	*Front propellor shaft with three-arm flange*	*12*	*Flexible disk for three-arm flange*
1a	*Front propellor shaft with four-arm flange*	*12a*	*Flexible disk for four-arm flange*
10	*Centering sleeve*	*13*	*Washer*
11	*Bolt*	*14*	*Nut*
		20	*Vibration damper*

MB2039900042000X

Fig. 24 Propeller shaft centering sleeve replacement

SPINDLE KNUCKLE

REPLACE

C43, C230, C280, CLK55, CLK320, CLK430, E55, E300, E320, E430, SL500, SL600, SLK230 & SLK320

1. Disconnect brake pad wear indicator cable clip on spring link.
2. Remove mounting bolt and nut, then disconnect spring line from spindle.
3. Press spindle up and out of spring link.
4. Remove knuckle.
5. Reverse procedure to install, noting the following:
   a. Install new self-locking nuts.
   b. Do not damage rubber boots when installing spring link.
   c. Rear axle shaft must be horizontal when tightening camber, strut, torque strut, thrust arm, track rod and spring link mounting nuts.
   d. Tighten mounting bolts and nuts to specifications.

S320 & S420 & 1998–99 CL500, CL600, S500 & S600

1. Remove mounting bolt and nut, then disconnect spring line from spindle.
2. Press spindle out of spring link.
3. Install spindle knuckle mounting bolt into spring link bore.
4. Remove knuckle.
5. Reverse procedure to install, noting the following:
   a. Install new self-locking nuts.
   b. Do not damage rubber boots when installing spring link.
   c. Rear axle shaft must be horizontal when tightening camber, strut, torque strut, thrust arm, track rod and spring link mounting nuts.
   d. Tighten mounting bolts and nuts to specifications.

REAR WHEEL SPINDLE

REPLACE

C43, C230, C280, CLK55, CLK320, CLK430, E55, E300, E320, E430, SL500, SL600, SLK230 & SLK320

1. Remove parking brake shoes.
2. Remove camber strut as outlined under "Camber Strut, Replace," **Fig. 28.**
3. Remove torque strut as outline under "Torque Strut, Replace."
4. Remove track rod as outline under "Track Rod, Replace."
5. Remove thrust arm as outline under "Thrust Arm, Replace."
6. Remove spring link as outline under "Spring Linkage, Replace."
7. Remove spindle from rear axle shaft.
8. Remove rear axle shaft collared nut.
9. Pull rear axle shaft flange out as outlined under "Hub & Bearing, Replace."
10. Remove rear brake control cable and splash shield.
11. Remove rear axle speed sensors.
12. Reverse procedure to install, noting the following:
    a. Install new collared nut.
    b. Tighten collared nut to specifications.
    c. Lock collared nut with suitable caulker so there is no gap between groove and locking tab.
    d. Install new self-locking bolts and nuts.
    e. Rear axle shaft must be horizontal when tightening camber, strut, torque strut, thrust arm, track rod and spring link mounting nuts.
    f. Tighten mounting bolts and nuts to specifications.
    g. Inspect and adjust rear toe-in as required.

C240 & C320

1. Remove rear axle shaft nut.
2. Raise and support vehicle.
3. Remove tire and wheel assembly.
4. Remove brake disc as outlined in "Disc Brakes" section, **Fig. 29.**
5. Remove parking brake shoes.
6. Remove torsion bar connecting rod.
7. Disconnect brake control cable at spindle.
8. Remove spindle wheel speed sensor.
9. Remove camber strut at spindle as outlined under "Camber Strut, Replace."
10. Remove tension arm at spindle as outlined under "Tension Arm, Replace."
11. Remove torque strut at spindle as outlined under "Torque Strut, Replace."
12. Remove track rod at spindle as outlined under "Track Rod, Replace."
13. Press rear axle shaft out of rear axle shaft flange. **Do not damage speed sensor exciter ring or sleeve.**
14. Remove spring link at spindle as outlined under "Spring Linkage, Replace."
15. Remove spindle
16. Reverse procedure to install, noting the following:
    a. Install new self-locking nuts.
    b. Ensure rear axle shafts is approximately horizontal when tightening nuts and bolts.
    c. Tighten mounting bolts and nuts to specifications.

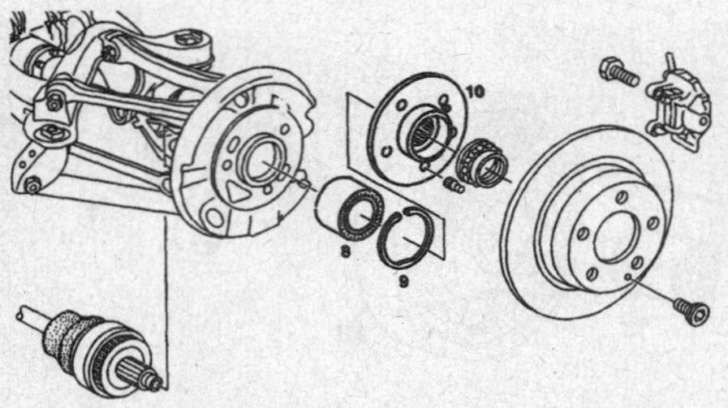

8 Two-row Angular Ball Bearing 9 Locking Ring
10 Rear Axle Shaft Flange

MB2039900013000X

Fig. 25 Rear axle shaft flange & angular ball bearing replacement. C43, C230, C280, CLK55, CLK320, CLK430, E55, E300, E320, E430, SL500, SL600, SLK230 & SLK320

S320 & S420 & 1998–99 CL500, CL600, S500 & S600

1. Remove parking brake shoes, **Fig. 30.**
2. Remove spindle speed sensor.
3. Remove camber strut as outline under "Camber Strut, Replace,"
4. Remove torque strut as outline under "Torque Strut, Replace."
5. Remove track rod as outline under "Track Rod, Replace."
6. Remove thrust arm as outline under "Thrust Arm, Replace."
7. Remove spring link as outline under "Spring Linkage, Replace."
8. Remove torsion rod connecting rod.
9. Remove spindle from rear axle shaft.
10. Remove rear axle shaft collared nut.
11. Pull rear axle shaft flange out as outlined under "Hub & Bearing, Replace."
12. Remove rear brake control cable.
13. Reverse procedure to install, noting the following:
    a. Install new collared nut.
    b. Tighten collared nut to specifications.
    c. Lock collared nut with suitable caulker so there is no gap between groove and locking tab.
    d. Install new self-locking bolts and nuts.
    e. Rear axle shaft must be horizontal when tightening camber, strut, torque strut, thrust arm, track rod and spring link mounting nuts.
    f. Tighten mounting bolts and nuts to specifications.
    g. Inspect and adjust rear toe-in as required.

S430 & 2000–01 CL500, CL600, S500 & S600

1. Raise and support vehicle.
2. Remove rear axle shaft nut, **Fig. 31.**
3. Remove rear wheel, brake caliper and disc.
4. Remove parking brake shoes and brake cable.
5. Remove left and righthand rear wheel speed sensors.
6. Remove spring link at spindle as outlined under "Spring Linkage, Replace."
7. Disconnect torsion bar connecting rod at spindle.
8. Press tie rod joint out of spindle.
9. Remove thrust arm at spindle as outlined under "Thrust Arm, Replace."
10. Remove torque strut at spindle as outlined under "Torque Strut, Replace."
11. Remove camber strut at spindle as outlined under "Camber Strut, Replace."
12. Remove spindle from rear axle shaft.
13. Support axle shaft with suitable wire.
14. Remove rear axle shaft flange.
15. Reverse procedure to install, noting the following:
    a. Install new self-locking nuts.
    b. Ensure rear axle shafts is approximately horizontal when tightening nuts and bolts.
    c. Tighten mounting bolts and nuts to specifications.

TORQUE STRUT

REPLACE

C43, C230, C280, CLK55, CLK320, CLK430, E55, E300, E320, E430, SL500, SL600, SLK230 & SLK320

1. **On C43, C230, C280, CLK55, CLK320, CLK430, SL500, SL600, SLK230 and SLK320 models,** press spindle forward to release tension.
2. **On all models,** remove mounting bolts and torque strut, **Fig. 32.**
3. Reverse procedure to install, noting the following:
    a. Install new self-locking nuts.
    b. Rear axle shaft must be horizontal when tightening torsion strut mounting nuts.
    c. Tighten mounting bolts and nuts to specifications.

C240 & C320

1. Raise and support vehicle.
2. Remove mounting bolts and nuts.
3. Remove cover and torque strut.
4. Reverse procedure to install, noting the following:
    a. Install new self-locking nuts.
    b. Ensure rear axle shafts is approximately horizontal when tightening nuts and bolts.
    c. Tighten mounting bolts and nuts to specifications.

S320 & S420 & 1998–99 CL500, CL600, S500 & S600

1. Remove fixed caliper and brake disk.
2. Remove mounting bolts, **Fig. 33.**
3. Mark eccentric discs relation to rear axle carrier for installation and remove.
4. Reverse procedure to install, noting the following:
    a. Install new self-locking nuts and fitted bolt.
    b. Install eccentric disks with notes toward back (number and letters in travel direction).

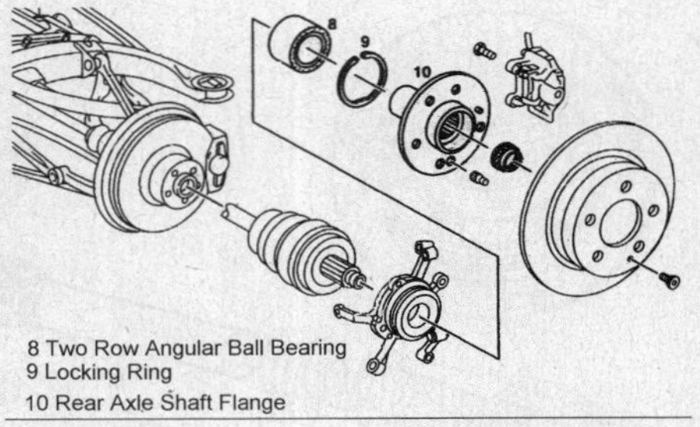

MB2039900023000X

Fig. 26 Rear axle shaft flange & angular ball bearing replacement. S320 & S420 & 1998–99 CL500, CL600, S500 & S600

    c. Rear axle shaft must be horizontal when tightening torsion strut mounting nuts.
    d. Tighten mounting bolts and nuts to specifications.

SHOCK ABSORBER

REPLACE

C43, C230, C280, CLK55, CLK320, CLK430, E55, E300, E320, E430, SL500, SL600, SLK230 & SLK320

1. Vehicle must be on tires and wheels.
2. Remove upper shock absorber fixings, **Fig. 34.**
3. Remove plate and rubber mount
4. Raise and support vehicle.
5. Remove spring link as outlined under "Spring Linkage, Replace."
6. Remove mounting nut and shock absorber.
7. Remove mounting parts.
8. Reverse procedure to install, noting the following:
    a. Inspect mounting parts and replace as required.
    b. Install new self-locking nuts.
    c. Tighten mounting bolts and nuts to specifications.

S320 & S420 & 1998–99 CL500, CL600, S500 & S600

1. Vehicle must be on tires and wheels.
2. Steady piston rod with suitable Allen wrench, **Fig. 35.**
3. Remove upper shock absorber fixings.
4. Raise and support vehicle.
5. Remove spring link as outlined under "Spring Linkage, Replace."
6. Remove mounting nut and shock absorber.
7. Remove mounting parts.
8. Reverse procedure to install, noting the following:
    a. Install new self-locking nuts.
    b. Tighten mounting bolts and nuts to specifications.

COIL SPRING

REPLACE

1. Raise and support vehicle.

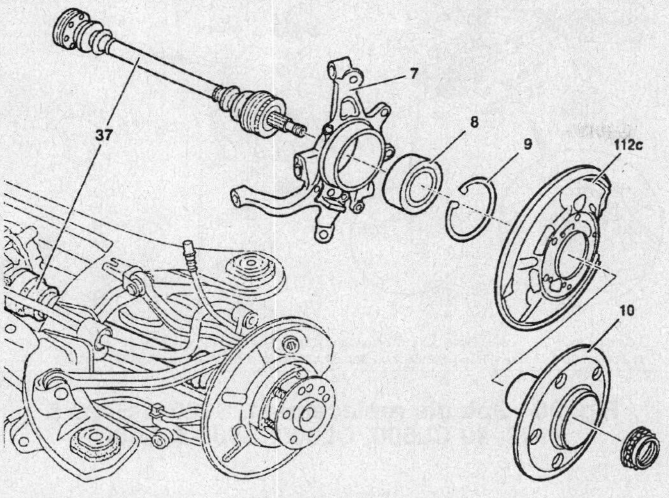

7 Wheel Carrier 8 Bearing9 Locking Ring10 Rear Axle Shaft Flange 12 Collar Nut 37 Rear Axle Shaft
112 Brake Splash Shield

MB2030100059000X

Fig. 27 Hub & bearing replacement. S430 & 2000–01 CL500, CL600, S500 & S600

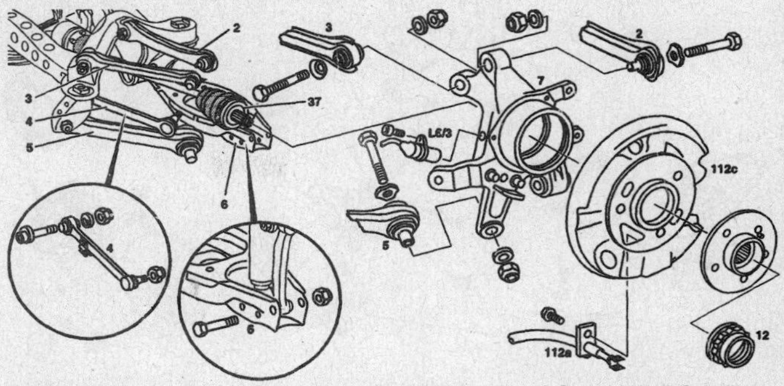

2 Camber Strut 3 Torque Sturt 4 Track Rod 5 Thrust Arm 6 Sprink Link 7 Spindle
12 Collared Nut 37 Rear Axle Shaft 112a Rear Brake Control Cable
112c Brake Splash Shield L6/3 & L6/4 Rear Axle Speed Sensors

MB2039900012000X

Fig. 28 Rear wheel spindle replacement. C43, C230, C280, CLK55, CLK320, CLK430, E55, E300, E320, E430, SL500, SL600, SLK230 & SLK320

2. Remove spring link cover, **Fig. 36.**
3. **On SL500 and SL600 models,** when removing lefthand rear spring, remove cross brace.
4. **On SLK230 and SLK320 models,** remove cross brace.
5. **On models equipped with ASR,** disconnect brake pad wear indicator cable from spring link. Mark cable routing.
6. **On all models,** install suitable clamping plates so 4–5 spring coils will be preloaded with clamping plate recesses towards vehicle inside.
7. Raise spring link until rear axle shaft is approximately horizontal.
8. Install clamping tool No. 202 589 02 31 00, or equivalent, into clamping plates and lock upper clamping plate.
9. Tension spring. **Do not use impact wrench.** Mark clamping plates relative to spring coil for installation.
10. Loosen spring link and remove spring with rubber mount.
11. Reverse procedure to install, noting the following:
    a. Spring link impression bore must be exposed after spring is released. Probe spring end with .1181 inch wire.
    b. Install new self-locking nuts.
    c. Rear axle shaft must be horizontal when tightening mounting nuts.
    d. Tighten mounting bolts and nuts to specifications.
    e. Inspect and adjust headlamp aim.

CAMBER STRUT

REPLACE

C43, C230, C280, CLK55, CLK320, CLK430, E55, E300, E320, E430, SL500, SL600, SLK230 & SLK320

1. **On E55, E300, E320 and E430 models,** if camber strut to rear axle carrier mounting bolt is installed from front, front and rear axle rubber mountings cannot be removed.
2. **On all models,** remove mounting bolts, front and rear axle rubber mounting.
3. Remove camber strut, **Fig. 37.**
4. Reverse procedure to install, noting the following:
    a. Recut frame floor mounting threads with tap.
    b. Install new self-locking bolts and nuts.
    c. Rear axle shaft must be horizontal when tightening camber strut mounting bolts.
    d. Tighten mounting bolts and nuts to specifications.

C240 & C320

1. Raise and support vehicle.
2. Remove tension arm at wheel carrier mounting bolt, **Fig. 38.**
3. Press down on camber strut and remove mounting bolts.
4. Remove camber strut.
5. Reverse procedure to install, noting the following.
    a. Install new self-locking nuts.
    b. Ensure rear axle shafts is approximately horizontal when tightening nuts and bolts.
    c. Tighten mounting bolts and nuts to specifications.

S320 & S420 & 1998-99 CL500, CL600, S500 & S600

1. Remove spring link lining.
2. Remove mounting bolts and front and rear rubber mounts, **Fig. 39.**
3. Remove camber strut mounting bolts and nuts.
4. Remove camber strut fixing bolt.
5. Disconnect shock absorber or spring strut from spring link.
6. Clamp springs with suitable clamp. Mark clamping plates position for installation.
7. Remove camber strut.
8. Reverse procedure to install, noting the following:
    a. Recut frame floor mounting threads with tap.
    b. Ensure spring link impression bore is exposed after spring clamp is released. Inspect with .1181 inch diameter wire.
    c. Install new self-locking bolts and nuts.
    d. Ensure there is sufficient clearance between new strut fixing bolt and frame floor.
    e. Mount camber strut on spindle side with large radius.
    f. Rear axle shaft must be horizontal when tightening camber strut mounting bolts.

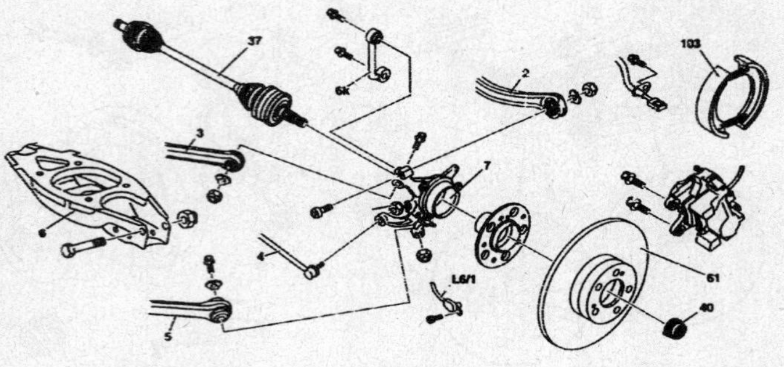

2 Camber Strut
3 Tension Arm
4 Track Rod
5 Spring Link
7 Wheel Carrier
37 Rear Axle Shaft
40 Twelve-Point Collared Nut
61 Brake Disc
103 Brake Shoes Of Parking Brake
111 Fixed Caliper
6k Torsion Bar Connecting Rod
L6/1 Speed Sensor

MB2030100052000X

Fig. 29 Rear wheel spindle replacement. C240 & C320

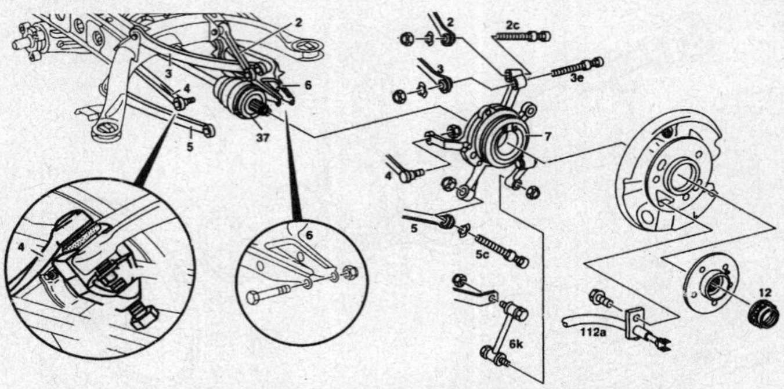

2 Camber Strut, 2C, 3e & 5c Fitted Bolts 3 Torque Strut 4 Track Rod 5 Thrust Arm 6 Spring Link 6k Torsion Bar Connecting Rod 7 Spindle 12 Collared Nut 37 Rear Axle Shaft 112a Rear Brake Cable

MB2039900022000X

Fig. 30 Spindle replacement. S320 & S420 & 1998–99 CL500, CL600, S500 & S600

g. Tighten mounting bolts and nuts to specifications.

S430 & 2000–01 CL500, CL600, S500 & S600

1. Raise and support vehicle.
2. Remove rear tire and wheel assembly.
3. Remove brake caliper and disc.
4. Disconnect torque strut from wheel carrier.
5. Remove mounting bolts and camber strut. Push down on torque strut when removing camber strut mounting bolts.
6. Reverse procedure to install, noting the following.
   a. Install new self-locking nuts.
   b. Ensure rear axle shafts is approximately horizontal when tightening nuts and bolts.
   c. Tighten mounting bolts and nuts to specifications.

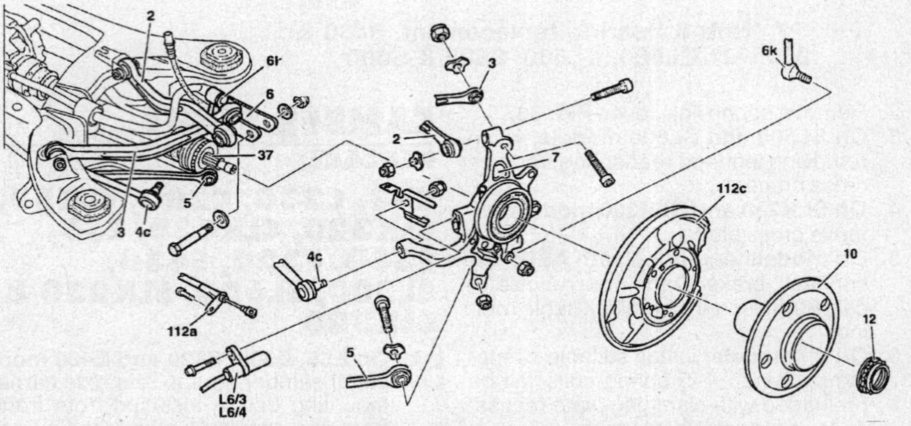

2 Camber Strut 3 Torque Strut 4c Tie Rod Joint 5 Thrust Arm 6 Spring Link 6k Torison Bar Connecting Rod 7 Wheel Carrier 10 Rear Axle Shaft Flange 12 Collar Nut 37 Rear Axle Shaft 112a Rear Brake Cable L6/3 Lefthand Rear Wheel Speed Sensor L6/4 Righthand Rear Wheel Speed Sensor

MB2030100058000X

Fig. 31 Rear wheel spindle replacement. S430 & 2000–01 CL500, CL600, S500 & S600

TENSION ARM

REPLACE

C240 & C320

1. Raise and support vehicle.
2. Remove rear tire and wheel assemblies.
3. Remove torsion bar. Connecting rods remain on wheel carriers.
4. Remove underbody paneling four rear mounting nuts. **Do not bend panel too much.**
5. Disconnect fuel lines and hold fuel filter to side.
6. Remove exhaust shielding.
7. Remove propeller shaft intermediate bearing mounting bolts.
8. Disconnect propeller shaft from different carrier flange as outlined under "Propeller Shaft, Replace."
9. Support differential carrier with suitable jack.
10. Remove rear axle front and rear suspension bolts on one side.
11. Drain rear axle fluid into suitable container. Push rear axle away from fuel tank using suitable lever.
12. Remove mounting bolts and tension arm.
13. Reverse procedure to install, noting the following:
    a. Install new self-locking nuts.
    b. Tighten mounting bolts and nuts to specifications.

THRUST ARM

REPLACE

C43, C230, C280, CLK55, CLK320, CLK430, E55, E300, E320, E430, SL500, SL600, SLK230 & SLK320

1. Remove mounting bolts, **Fig. 40.**
2. Remove thrust arm cover.
3. Remove bracket.
4. Remove thrust arm.
5. Reverse procedure to install, noting the following:
   a. Install new self-locking nuts.
   b. Rear axle shaft must be horizontal when tightening thrust arm mounting nuts.
   c. Tighten mounting bolts and nuts to specifications.

S320 & S420 & 1998–99 CL500, CL600, S500 & S600

1. Remove mounting bolts, **Fig. 41.**
2. Remove fitted bolt.
3. Remove thrust arm cover.
4. Remove thrust arm.
5. Reverse procedure to install, noting the following:
   a. Install new self-locking nuts and fitted bolt.
   b. Rear axle shaft must be horizontal when tightening thrust arm mounting nuts.
   c. Tighten mounting bolts and nuts to specifications.

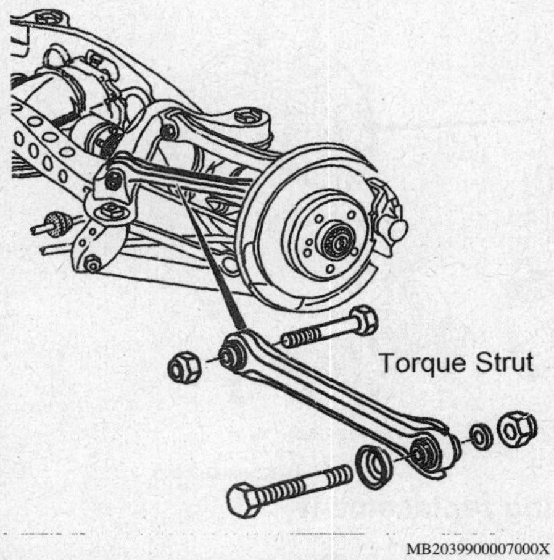

Fig. 32 Torque strut replacement. E55, E300, E320 & E430

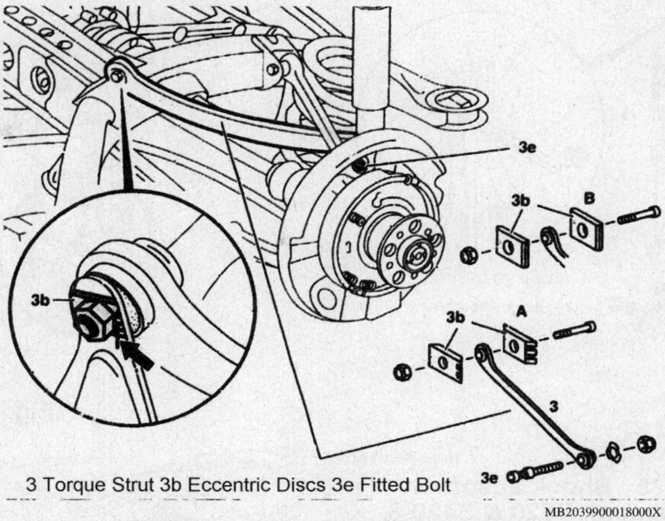

Fig. 33 Torque strut replacement. S320 & S420 & 1998–99 CL500, CL600, S500 & S600

S430 & 2000–01 CL500, CL600, S500 & S600

1. Raise and support vehicle.
2. Remove thrust arm cover, **Fig. 42.**
3. Remove mounting bolts and thrust arm.
4. Reverse procedure to install, noting the following:
   a. Install new self-locking nuts and fitted bolt.
   b. Rear axle shaft must be horizontal when tightening thrust arm mounting nuts.
   c. Tighten mounting bolts and nuts to specifications.

SPRING LINKAGE

REPLACE

C43, C230, C240, C280, C320, CLK55, CLK320, CLK430, E55, E300, E320, E430, SL500, SL600, SLK230 & SLK320

1. Remove rear spring.
2. Remove mounting bolts, **Figs. 43 and 44.**
3. Remove bushing as outlined under "Spring Linkage Bushing, Replace."
4. Remove cover.
5. Disconnect shock absorber or spring strut at spring link.
6. Disconnect torsion rod connecting rod.
7. **On SL600 and SL500 models equipped with ASR, ETS and ESP,** remove spring link guide rail.
8. **On SL500, SL600, SLK230 and SLK320 models,** remove frame cross brace.
9. **On all models,** remove spring linkage.
10. Reverse procedure to install, noting the following:
    a. Install new self-locking nuts.
    b. Rear axle shaft must be horizontal when tightening spring link mounting bolts and nuts.
    c. Tighten mounting bolts and nuts to specifications.

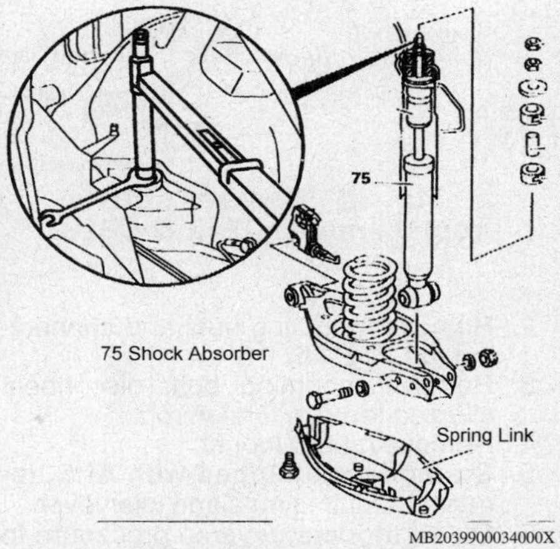

Fig. 34 Shock absorber replacement. C43, C230, C280, CLK55, CLK320, CLK430, E55, E300, E320, E430, SL500, SL600, SLK230 & SLK320

S320 & S420 & 1998–99 CL500, CL600, S500 & S600

1. Remove rear spring.
2. Disconnect shock absorber or spring strut at spring link.
3. Remove mounting bolts, **Fig. 45.**
4. Remove bushing as outlined under "Spring Linkage Bushing, Replace."
5. Remove spring linkage.
6. Reverse procedure to install, noting the following:
   a. Install new self-locking nuts.
   b. Rear axle shaft must be horizontal when tightening spring link mounting bolts and nuts.
   c. Tighten mounting bolts and nuts to specifications.

S430 & 2000–01 CL500, CL600, S500 & S600

1. Remove exhaust system as outlined under "Engine, Replace" in appropriate engine section.
2. Remove pin, expanding rivet and spring linkage cover.
3. Raise and support vehicle.
4. Remove mounting bolts and spring linkage.
5. Disconnect spring strut from spring linkage.
6. Reverse procedure to install, noting the following:
   a. Install new self-locking nuts.
   b. Rear axle shaft must be horizontal when tightening spring link mounting bolts and nuts.
   c. Tighten mounting bolts and nuts to specifications.

SPRING LINKAGE BUSHING

REPLACE

C43, C230, C280, CLK55, CLK320, CLK430, E55, E300, E320, E430, SL500, SL600, SLK230 & SLK320

1. Press bushing out of spring using removal/installation tool No. 129 589 01 43 00, or equivalent.
2. If bushing is jammed, first press small overlap as far as spring link using suitable flat thrust plate.
3. Press bushing into spring link until each steel sleeve end is original distance from housing using removal/installation tool.

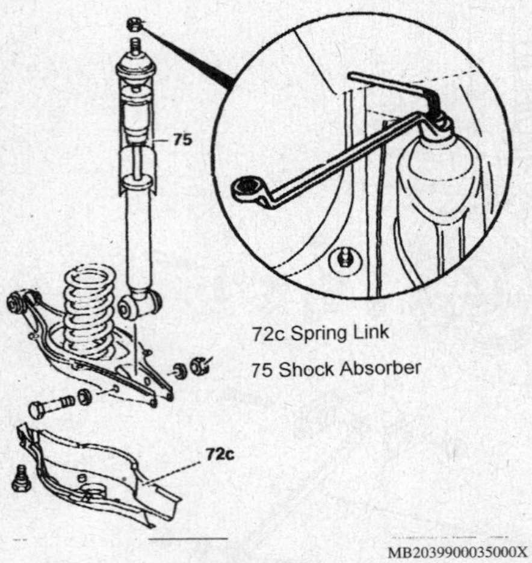

Fig. 35 Shock absorber replacement. S320 & S420 & 1998–99 CL500, CL600, S500 & S600

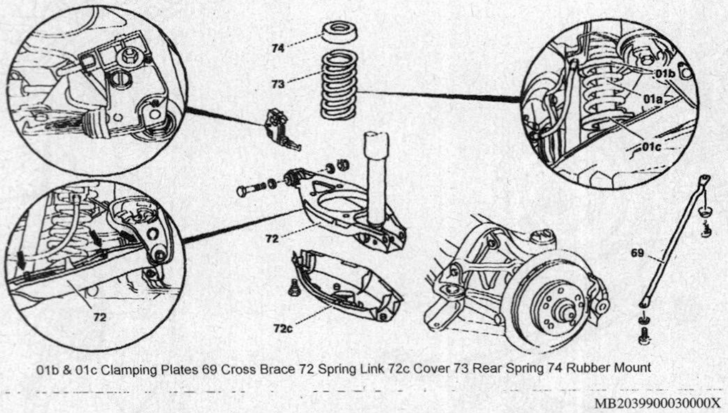

Fig. 36 Rear spring replacement

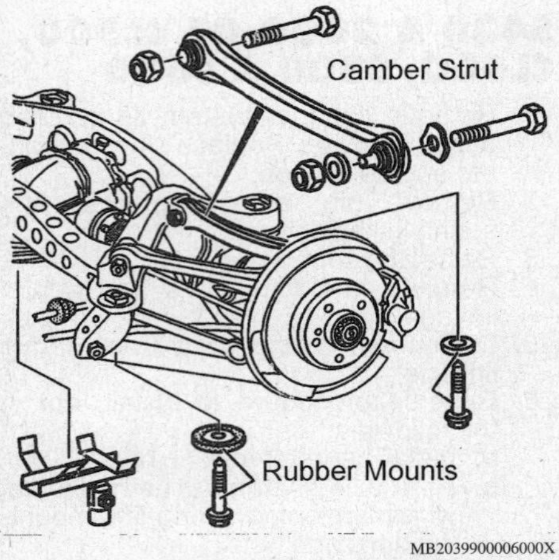

Fig. 37 Camber strut replacement. E55, E300, E320 & E430

S320 & S420 & 1998-99 CL500, CL600, S500 & S600

1. Press bushing out of spring using removal/installation tool No. 140 589 05 43 00, or equivalent.
2. If bushing is jammed, first press small overlap as far as spring link using suitable flat thrust plate.
3. Press bushing into spring link until it abuts spring link bush using removal/ installation tool.

TORSION ROD

REPLACE

C43, C230, C280, CLK55, CLK320, CLK430, E55, E300, E320, E430, SLK230 & SLK320

1. Remove rear axle as outlined under "Rear Axle Shaft, Replace."

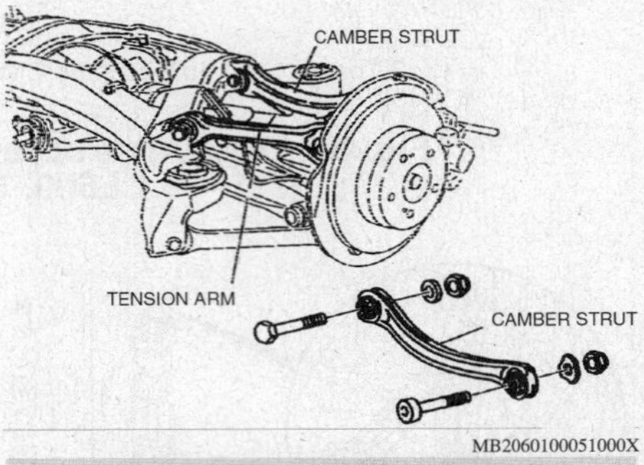

Fig. 38 Camber strut replacement. C240 & C320

2. Remove mounting nuts and connecting rod, **Fig. 46.**
3. Remove mounting bolt, disconnect clip and remove torsion rod.
4. Remove rubber mount.
5. **On models equipped with ADS,** remove mounting nuts and idler lever.
6. **On all models,** reverse procedure to install, noting the following:
   a. Install new self-locking bolts and nuts.
   b. Lubricate rubber mounts with Naphthalene H No. 000 989 01 60, or equivalent.
   c. Tighten mounting bolts and nuts to specifications.

S320 & S420 & 1998-99 CL500, CL600, S500 & S600

1. Remove differential carrier as outlined under "Differential Carrier, Replace."
2. Remove mounting nuts and connecting rods, **Fig. 47.**
3. Remove mounting nuts and clamps.
4. Disconnect fuel hose between tank and pump.
5. **On models equipped with ADS,** remove mounting bolts and intermediate lever.
6. **On all models,** remove torsion rod.
7. Remove rubber mounts.
8. Reverse procedure to install, noting the following:
   a. Install new self-locking bolts.
   b. Lubricate rubber mounts with Naphthalene H No. 000 989 01 60,

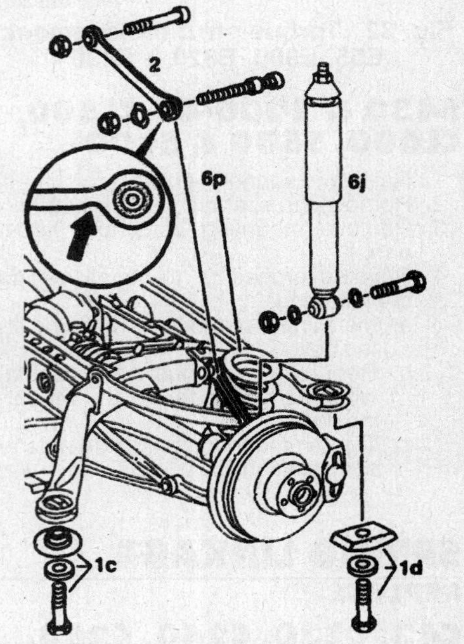

1c & 1d Rubber Mounts
2 Camber Strut
6j Shock Absorber Or Spring Strut

MB2039900017000X

Fig. 39 Camber strut replacement. S320 & S420 & 1998–99 CL500, CL600, S500 & S600

or equivalent.
   c. Align torsion bar.
   d. **On models equipped with ADS,** intermediate lever face must align with torsion rod face.
   e. **On all models,** tighten mounting bolts and nuts to specifications.

SL500 & SL600

1. Remove rear axle as outlined under "Rear Axle Shaft, Replace."
2. Remove mounting nuts and connecting rod, **Fig. 48.**
3. Remove clamps and torsion rod.
4. Remove rubber mounts.
5. **On models equipped with ADS,** remove mounting nuts and intermediate linkage.

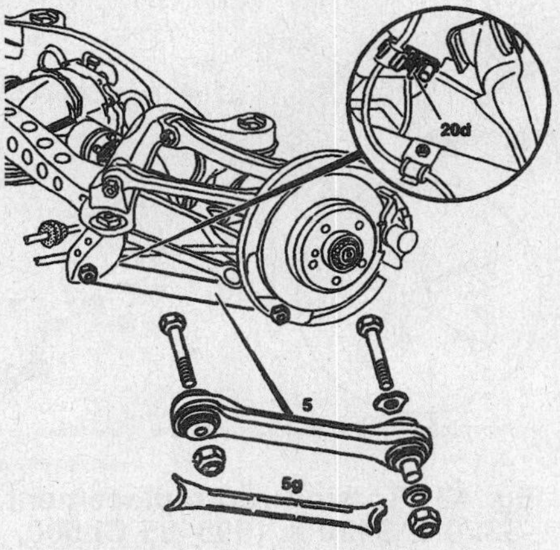

5 Thrust Arm 5g Cover 20d Bracket

MB2039900009000X

Fig. 40 Thrust arm replacement. E55, E300, E320 & E430

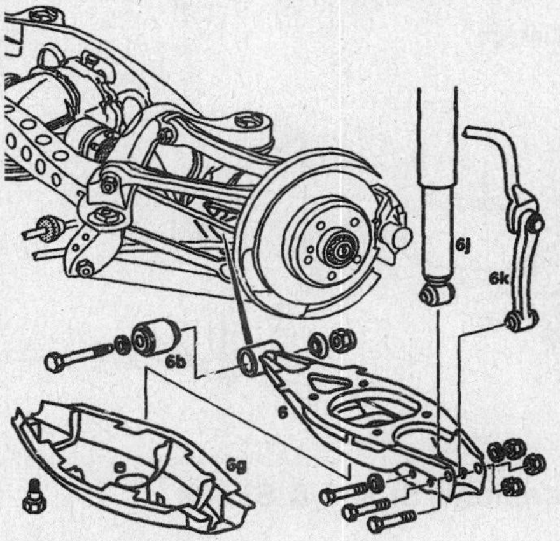

6 Spring Link 6b Bushing
6j Shock Absorber
6k Torison Bar Connecting Rod

MB2039900010000X

Fig. 43 Spring linkage replacement. C240, C320, E55, E300, E320 & E430

6. **On all models,** reverse procedure to install, noting the following:
   a. Install new self-locking bolts and nuts.
   b. Lubricate rubber mounts with Naphthalene H No. 000 989 01 60, or equivalent.
   c. **On models equipped with ADS,** intermediate linkage must align with torsion rod flat.
   d. **On all models,** ensure torsion rod is centered.
   e. Tighten mounting bolts and nuts to specifications.

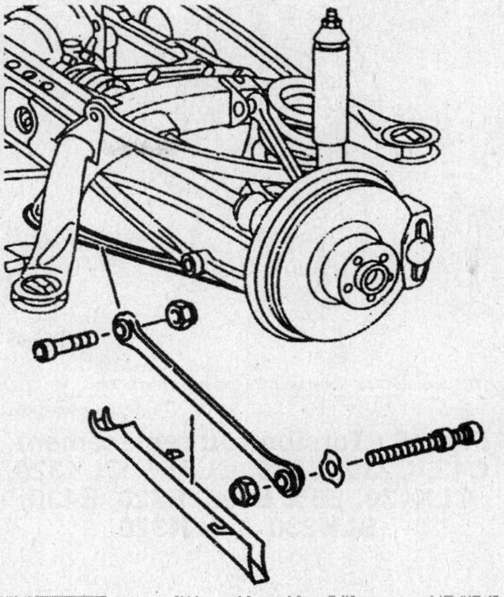

MB2039900020000X

Fig. 41 Thrust arm replacement. S320 & S420 & 1998–99 CL500, CL600, S500 & S600

TRACK ROD

REPLACE

C43, C230, C280, CLK55, CLK320, CLK430, E55, E300, E320, E430, SL500, SL600, SLK230 & SLK320

1. Mark eccentric bolt to rear axle carrier position for installation.
2. Remove mounting bolts, **Fig. 49.**
3. Remove rubber mounts.
4. Remove bracket.
5. Disconnect rear axle speed sensor cable.
6. Remove track rod.
7. Reverse procedure to install, noting the following:
   a. Clean grease off spindle ball pin and conical seat.
   b. Press ball pin firmly into conical seat and secure with Allen wrench as required.
   c. Install new self-locking nuts.
   d. Rear axle shaft must be horizontal when tightening track rod mounting nuts.
   e. Tighten mounting bolts and nuts to specifications.
   f. Inspect and adjust rear toe-in as required.

C240 & C320

1. Raise and support vehicle.
2. Mark cam bolt and eccentric disc for installation alignment.
3. Remove torsion bar connecting rod.
4. Remove mounting bolts, nuts and track rod using thrust piece tool No.

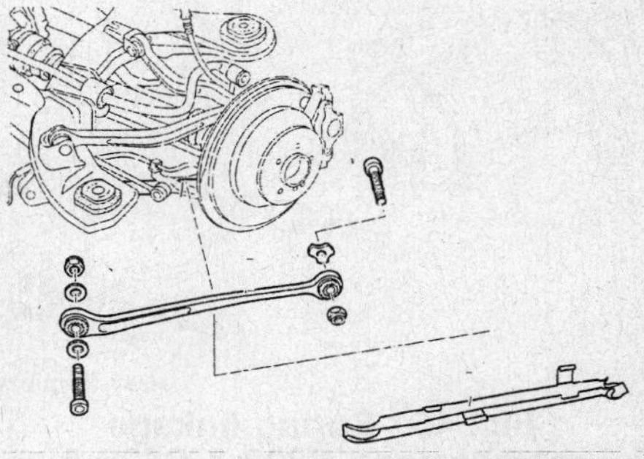

MB2030100057000X

Fig. 42 Thrust arm replacement. S430 & 2000–01 CL500, CL600, S500 & S600

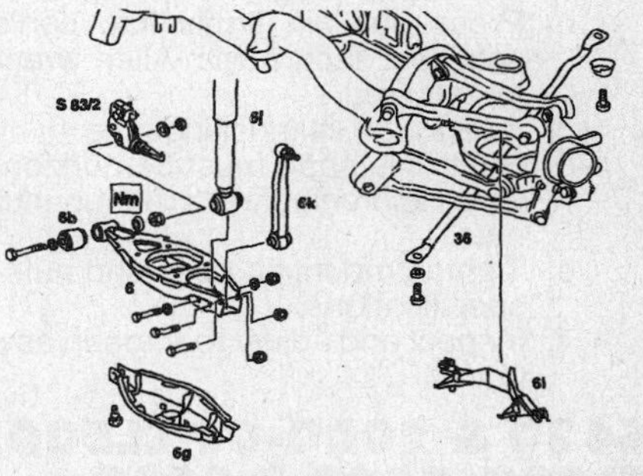

6 Spring Link 6b Bushing 6g Spring Link Cover
6j Shock Absorber
6k Torison Bar Connecting Rod
61 Spring Link Guide Rail 36 Frame Cross Brace
S83/2 & S83/3 Roll-Over Bar Rear Axle Switch

MB2039900011000X

Fig. 44 Spring linkage replacement. SL500 & SL600

210 589 04 63 00 and puller tool No. 210 589 01 33 00, or equivalents.

5. Reverse procedure to install, noting the following:
   a. Install new self-locking nuts.
   b. Press ball head bolt into cone and hold with suitable Allen wrench, as required.
   c. Ensure rear axle shaft is approximately horizontal when tightening mounting nuts.
   d. Inspect and adjust rear axle toe, as required.

S320 & S420 & 1998–99 CL500, CL600, S500 & S600

This procedure has been revised by a Technical Service Bulletin.

1. Mark cam bolt to rear axle carrier position for installation.
2. Remove mounting bolts and rubber mounts, **Fig. 50.**
3. Remove track rod.
4. Reverse procedure to install, noting the following:

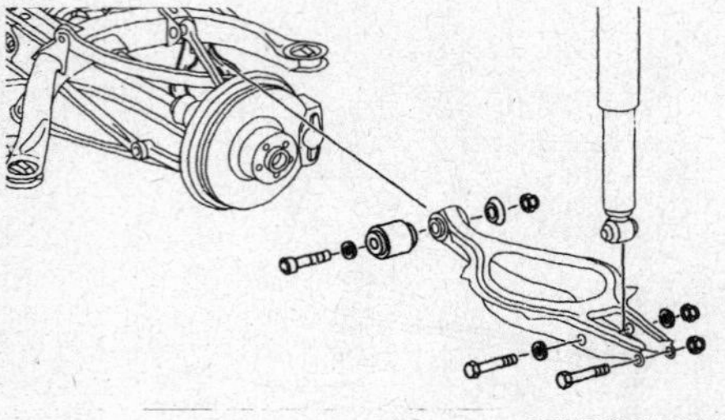

Fig. 45 Spring linkage replacement. S320 & S420 & 1998–99 CL500, CL600, S500 & S600

a. Clean grease off spindle ball pin and conical seat.
b. Press ball pin firmly into conical seat and secure with Allen wrench as required.
c. Install new self-locking nuts.
d. Rear axle shaft must be horizontal when tightening track rod mounting nuts.
e. Tighten mounting bolts and nuts to specifications.
f. Inspect and adjust rear toe-in as required.

S430 & 2000–01 CL500, CL600, S500 & S600

1. Raise and support vehicle.
2. Remove mounting nut, **Fig. 51.**
3. Press track rod joint out of wheel carrier using thrust piece tool No. 201 589 05 63 00 and puller tool No. 140 589 00 33 00, or equivalents.
4. Mark cam bolt to rear axle carrier position for installation alignment.
5. Reverse procedure to install, noting the following:
   a. Install new self-locking nuts.
   b. Press ball head bolt into cone and hold with suitable Allen wrench, as required.
   c. Ensure rear axle shaft is approximately horizontal when tightening mounting nuts.
   d. Inspect and adjust rear axle toe, as required.

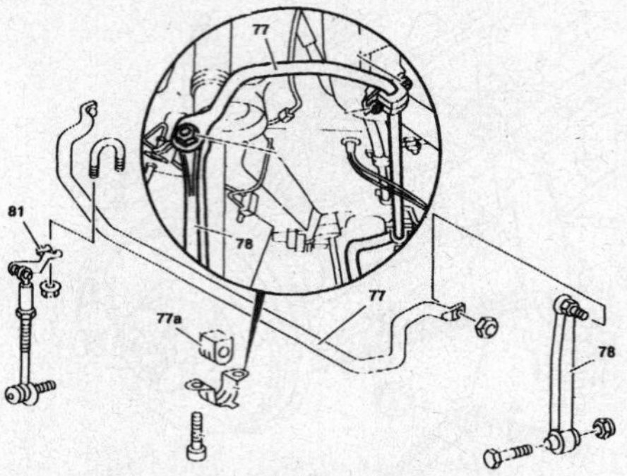

Fig. 46 Torsion rod replacement. C43, C230, C280, CLK55, CLK320, CLK430, E55, E300, E320, E430, SLK230 & SLK320

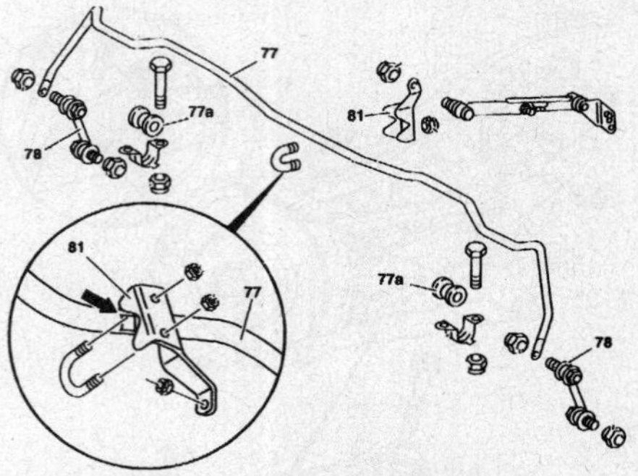

Fig. 47 Torsion rod replacement. S320 & S420 & 1998–99 CL500, CL600, S500 & S600

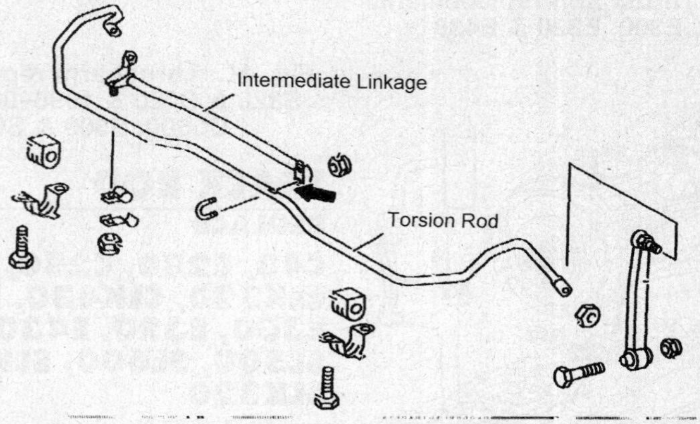

Fig. 48 Torsion rod replacement. SL500 & SL600

TECHNICAL SERVICE BULLETINS

AIR SUSPENSION MIL ON

S430, 2000–01 S500 & 2001 S600

On some of these models the air suspension MIL may be on (instrument cluster reads "Air suspension ... visit workshop."

This condition may be caused by water in level sensor connectors.

To correct this condition, proceed as follows:

1. Disconnect level sensor connector. Pneumatic suspension Diagnostic Trouble Codes (DTCs) may help determine which sensor to inspect, **Fig. 52.**
2. Inspect for water. Clean as required.
3. Close off connector chamber to which wires are not attached.

DRIVE LINE VIBRATION AT 50–62 MPH

1998–99 CL500, CL600, S420 & S500

On some of these, **Fig. 53,** there may be a drive line vibration at 50–62 mph.

This condition may be caused by drive train imbalance being transferred to the body via the propeller shaft intermediate bearing.

To correct this condition, proceed as follows:

1. Visually inspect propeller shaft and intermediate bearing, nothing the following:
   a. Models with yellow dot intermediate bearing mounting bracket or white color ring on rear propeller shaft tube are satisfactory.
   b. On models less markings, proceed to next step.
2. Remove, balance and install drive wheels.
3. If condition is still present, replace propeller shaft intermediate bearing, **Fig. 53,** and grooved ball bearing (part No. 003 981 23 25).

REAR AXLE LOW SPEED RUMBLE ON UNEVEN ROADS

S320 & S420 & 1998–99 CL500, CL600, S500 & S600

On some of the these models equipped with level control system or self-leveling suspension with ADS there may be a rear axle rumbling noise at low speed on uneven roads.

This condition may be caused by vibrations being transmitted to the body.

To correct this condition, proceed as follows:

1. Remove left and righthand rear spring struts.
2. Clamp spring strut into suitable vise in pressure line connection area.
3. Warm spring strut mount at rubberized screw connection with suitable air drier
4. Unscrew with suitable pipe wrench. Turn several times to left and right, then heat stud again to prevent breaking off.
5. Cut spring strut thread (M10 x 1), remove grease and coat with Loctite No. 270, or equivalent,
6. Install new spring strut mount (part No. 140 320 09 44).
7. Install spring strut, noting the following:

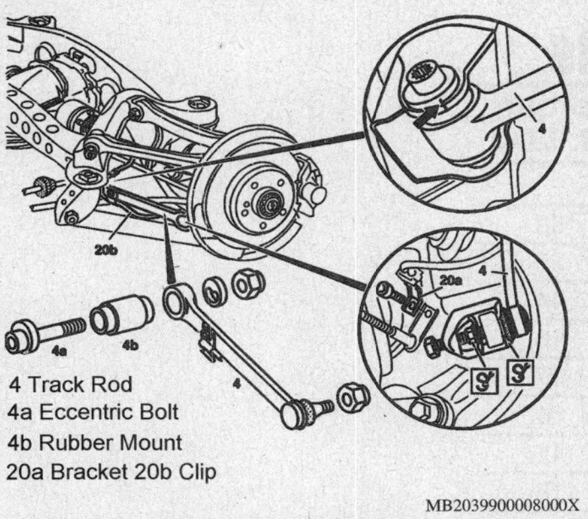

Fig. 49 Track rod replacement. E55, E300, E320 & E430

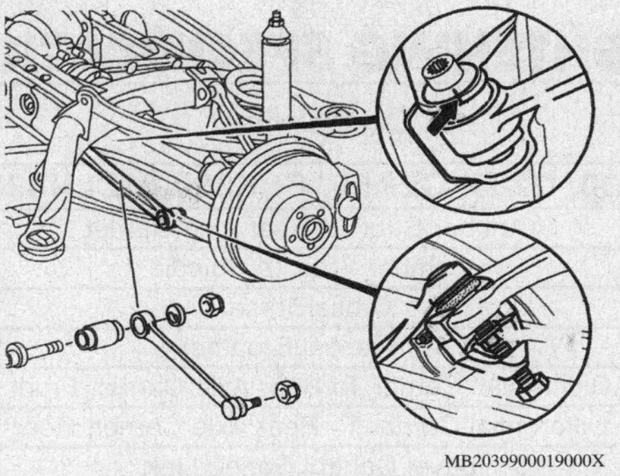

Fig. 50 Track rod replacement. S320 & S420 & 1998–99 CL500, CL600, S500 & S600

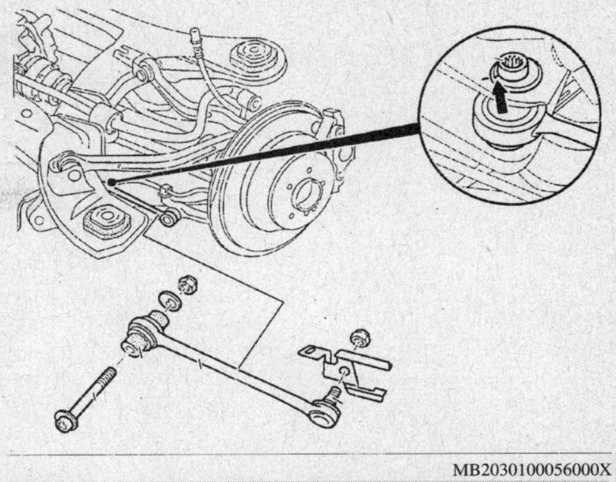

Fig. 51 Track rod replacement. S430 & 2000–01 CL500, CL600, S500 & S600

Code	Interpretation
C1121	Front Lefthand Body Acceleration Sensor
C1122	Front Righthand Body Acceleration Sensor
C1123	Rear Righthand Body Acceleration Sensor
C1132	Front Lefthand Level Sensor
C1133	Front Righthand Level Sensor
C1135	Rear Axle Level Sensor
C1144	Pneumatic Suspension Pressure Sensor

Fig. 52 Air suspension DTC interpretation. S430, 2000–01 S500 & 2001 S600

Model	Up To VIN	Propeller Shaft Intermediate Bearing Part No.
CL500	126831	140 410 08 81
CL600	136831	140 410 10 81
S420	136628	140 410 07 81
S500	136835	140 410 07 81

Fig. 53 Propeller shaft intermediate bearing application chart. 1998–99 CL500, CL600, S420 & S500

a. New mounts do not installation aid.
b. Attempt to install in original position.
c. Ensure sufficient clearance at hose.
d. **Torque** spring strut to frame floor mounting nut to 29 ft. lbs.
e. **Torque** spring strut to spring link mounting nut to 74 ft. lbs.
f. **Torque** control pressure line connection to 22 ft. lbs.

REAR AXLE STRAIN IN SHARP CURVES

S320

On some of these models equipped with Automatic Locking Differential (ASD), there may be strain at the rear axle in sharp curves or when parking.

This condition may be caused by slight locking effect of limited slip differential.

To correct this condition, proceed as follows:

1. Remove rear axle.
2. Disassembly center section.
3. Remove one friction plate with lining on both sides per side and replace with steel plates (part No. 140 350 64 23).

HOWLING/WHISTLING FROM REAR

C43, C230, C280, SL500 & SL600

On some of these models there may be a howling or whistling from the rear.

This condition may be caused by the rear wheel bearing seal not turning with bearing inner race.

To correct this condition, replace wheel bearing, noting the following:

1. If replacement bearing is from vendor FAG (bearing seal is red), proceed as follows:
   a. Apply Loctite Prism No. 401 to bearing seal and inner race at 12, 3, 6 and 9 o'clock positions.
   b. Turn inner race until sealing material is evenly distributed in seal groove.
   c. Repeat procedure on opposite side of bearing.
2. If replacement bearing is from vender SNR (bearing seal is blue), Loctite application is not required.

HOWLING/WHISTLING SOUND FROM PROPELLER SHAFT

2000 C43, C230, C280, CLK55, CLK320, CLK430, E55, E320, E430, SL500, SL600, SLK230 & SLK320

On some of these models there may be a howling or whistling sound from the propeller shaft area when the temperature is cold at approximately 37 mph.

This condition may be caused by the propeller shaft intermediate bearing sealing plate hitting against the bearing inner race.

To correct this condition, replace the propeller shaft intermediate bearing.

DRIVELINE OR REAR AXLE HUMMING DRONE

S320 & S420 & 1998–99 CL500, CL600, S500 & S600

On some of these models there may be a driveline or rear axle humming drone.

This condition may be caused by propeller shaft/rear axle balance tolerances.

To correct this condition, exactly match weight of all propeller shaft flex mounting bolts, nuts and washers to within .001 oz.

KNOCKING NOISE

S320 & S420 & 1998–99 CL500, CL600, S500 & S600

On some of these models there may be a knocking noise in the rear axle stabilized bar or spindle area.

This condition may be caused by loose stabilized bar connecting rod mounting nuts.

To correct this condition, install new self-locking nuts and **torque** to 30 ft. lbs.

TIGHTENING SPECIFICATIONS

Year	Component	Torque, Ft. Lbs.
C43, C230, C280, CLK55, CLK320 & CLK430		
1998–2001	Camber Strut To Rear Axle Carrier	52
	Camber Strut To Spindle	29
	Cross Brace	44
	Differential Breather	18
	Differential Carrier To Rear Axle Carrier, Front	37
	Differential Carrier To Rear Axle Carrier, Rear	81
	Level Control Spring Link	41
	Propeller Shaft Front Reinforcement Brace	15
	Propeller Shaft Intermediate Bearing w/Collar & Centering Tip	22
	Propeller Shaft Intermediate Bearing w/ Washer	18
	Propeller Shaft Rear Crossbrace	44
	Propeller Shaft Reinforcement Brace	18
	Propeller Shaft To Transmission Or Differential Carrier (M10)	29
	Propeller Shaft To Transmission Or Differential Carrier (M12)	44
	Propeller Shaft Transverse Bridge (C43, C320, C280, CLK55, CLK320 & CLK430)	29
	Propeller Shaft Transverse Bridge (SLK230 & SLK320)	18
	Rear Axle Carrier	66
	Rear Axle Shaft To Connecting Flange	52
	Rear Axle Shaft To Flange Collared Nut	162
	Reinforcement Brace, Front	18
	Shock Absorber To Frame Floor	13
	Shock Absorber To Frame Floor Lock Nut	22
	Shock Absorber To Spring Link	41
	Spring Linkage Connecting Rod	15
	Spring Link To Rear Axle Carrier	52
	Spring Link To Spindle	89
	Spring Strut	41
	Stop Plate	81
	Thrust Arm To Rear Axle Carrier	52
	Thrust Arm To Spindle	29
	Torsion Rod Connecting Rod	22
	Torsion Rod Connecting Rod To Spring Link	15
	Torsion Rod Idler Lever	88①
	Torsion Rod Rubber Mount	15
	Torque Strut	52
	Track Rod To Rear Axle Carrier	52
	Track Rod To Wheel Carrier (Silver Or Blue, M10x1)	18
	Track Rod To Wheel Carrier (Silver Or Blue, M10x1.5 & Yellow M10x1)	22
	Track Rod To Spindle	26
C240 & C320		
2001	Brake Control Cable	15
	Brake Line	10
	Camber Strut	52
	Differential Carrier To Front Of Rear Axle Carrier	37
	Differential Carrier To Rear Of Rear Axle Carrier	81

Continued

TIGHTENING SPECIFICATIONS—Continued

Year	Component	Torque, Ft. Lbs.
C240 & C320		
2001	Drive Pinion To Joint Flange	133
	Propeller Shaft Intermediate Bearing	22
	Propeller Shaft To Rear Axle (M10)	29
	Propeller Shaft To Rear Axle (M12)	44
	Rear Axle Breather	18
	Rear Axle Carrier	52
	Rear Axle Oil Filler Screw	37
	Rear Axle Shaft Nut	162
	Rear Axle Shaft To Connecting Flange	52
	Rear Axle Speed Sensor	71①
	Shock Absorber To Spring Link	41
	Spring Link To Rear Axle Carrier	52
	Spring Link To Wheel Carrier	88
	Tension Arm To Wheel Carrier	52
	Torque Strut	52
	Torsion Bar Bracket	22
	Torsion Bar Connecting Rod	29
	Track Rod	52
	Wheel Lug Bolt	81
CL500, CL600, S320, S420, S500 & S600		
1998–99	Camber Strut	52
	Collared Nut	236
	Differential Carrier To Rear Axle Carrier, Front	33
	Fixed Caliper To Semi-Trailing Arm Or Spindle	85
	Level Control Spring Strut To Spring Link	74
	Propeller Shaft Clamping Nut	29
	Propeller Shaft Intermediate Bearing w/Collar & Centering Tip	22
	Propeller Shaft Intermediate Bearing w/ Washer	18
	Propeller Shaft Reinforcement Bridge	18
	Propeller Shaft To Transmission Or Differential Carrier	44
	Rear Axle Carrier Front Center Piece	33
	Rear Axle Carrier Rear Center Piece	74
	Rear Axle Carrier To Frame Floor	52
	Rear Axle Shaft To Connecting Flange (M10)	52
	Rear Axle Shaft To Connecting Flange (M12)	74
	Reinforcement Bridge	18
	Seat Belt Bracket	199
	Shock Absorber To Frame Floor	29
	Shock Absorber To Spring Link	74
	Spring Link To Rear Axle Carrier	52
	Spring Link To Spindle	89
	Thrust Arm	52
	Torque Strut	52
	Torsion Rod Connecting Rod	29
	Torsion Rod Intermediate Lever	88①
	Torsion Rod Rubber Mount	15
	Track Rod To Rear Axle Carrier	52
	Track Rod To Spindle (Silver Or Blue)	18
	Track Rod To Spindle (Yellow)	22
	Transmission Exhaust Bracket	18

Continued

TIGHTENING SPECIFICATIONS—Continued

Year	Component	Torque, Ft. Lbs.
CL500, CL600, S430, S500 & S600		
2000–01	Brake Line	10
	Breather	22
	Camber Strut	52
	Differential Carrier To Extension (Blue or Silver)	52
	Differential Carrier To Extension (Yellow)	59
	Differential Carrier To Front Center (Blue or Silver)	41
	Differential Carrier To Front Center (Yellow)	33
	Level Sensor Control Rod	88①
	Propeller Shaft Intermediate Bearing	22
	Propeller Shaft Reinforcement Bridge	17
	Propeller Shaft To Transmission Or Differential Carrier	44
	Rear Axle Carrier	70
	Rear Axle Oil Filler	37
	Rear Axle Shaft Collared Nut	236
	Rear Axle Shaft To Flange (M10)	52
	Rear Axle Shaft To Flange (M12)	73
	Rear Extension Carrier To Rear Axle	73
	Spring Linkage To Rear Axle Carrier	88
	Spring Linkage To Wheel Carrier	52
	Spring Strut	81
	Thrust Arm	52
	Tie Rod To Wheel Carrier	22
	Torque Strut	52
	Torsion Bar Connecting Rod	29
	Track Rod To Rear Axle Carrier	52
	Track Rod To Wheel Carrier	22
E55, E300, E320 & E430		
1998–2001	Camber Strut To Rear Axle Carrier	52
	Camber Strut To Spindle	29
	Differential Carrier To Rear Axle Carrier, Front	33
	Propeller Shaft Front Reinforcement Brace	18
	Propeller Shaft Intermediate Bearing (E300)	②
	Propeller Shaft To Transmission Or Differential Carrier (M10)	29
	Propeller Shaft To Transmission Or Differential Carrier (M12)	44
	Level Control Spring Strut	41
	Rear Axle Carrier Rubber Mount	66
	Rear Axle Shaft To Flange Collared Nut (Less 4MATIC)	162
	Rear Axle Shaft To Flange Collared Nut (w/4MATIC)	236
	Rear Axle Shaft To Connecting Flange	52
	Reinforcement Brace	18
	Seat Belt Bracket	206
	Shock Absorber To Frame Floor	12
	Shock Absorber To Frame Floor Lock Nut	22
	Shock Absorber To Spring Link	41

Continued

TIGHTENING SPECIFICATIONS—Continued

Year	Component	Torque, Ft. Lbs.
E55, E300, E320 & E430		
1998–2001	Spring Linkage Connecting Rod	15
	Spring Link To Rear Axle Carrier	52
	Spring Link To Spindle	89
	Spring Strut	41
	Thrust Arm To Rear Axle Carrier	52
	Thrust Arm To Spindle	29
	Torque Strut	52
	Torsion Rod Connecting Rod	22
	Torsion Rod Connecting Rod To Spring Link	18
	Torsion Rod Idler Lever	88①
	Torsion Rod Rubber Mount	15
	Track Rod To Rear Axle Carrier	52
	Track Rod To Wheel Carrier (Silver Or Blue, M10x1)	18
	Track Rod To Wheel Carrier (Silver Or Blue, M10x1.5 & Yellow M10x1)	22
	Track Rod To Spindle	26
ML55, ML320 & ML430		
1998–2001	Propeller Shaft, Front To Transfer Case	29
	Propeller Shaft, Rear To Differential Carrier	37
	Propeller Shaft Intermediate Bearing	29
SL500 & SL600		
1998–2001	Camber Strut To Rear Axle Carrier	52
	Camber Strut To Spindle	29
	Cross Brace	89
	Differential Breather	22
	Differential Carrier To Rear Axle Carrier, Front	33
	Differential Carrier To Rear Axle Carrier, Rear	70
	Level Control Spring Strut	41
	Propeller Shaft Clamping Nut	29
	Propeller Shaft Intermediate Bearing (w/Collar & Centering Tip)	22
	Propeller Shaft Intermediate Bearing (w/ Washer)	18
	Propeller Shaft To Transmission Or Differential Carrier (M10)	29
	Propeller Shaft To Transmission Or Differential Carrier (M12)	44
	Propeller Shaft Front Reinforcement Bridge	18
	Propeller Shaft Rear Crossbrace	88
	Propeller Shaft Tunnel Closing Panel	18
	Rear Axle Carrier Rubber Mount	66
	Rear Axle Carrier To Frame Floor	52
	Rear Axle Shaft To Connecting Flange (M10)	52
	Rear Axle Shaft To Connecting Flange (M12)	74
	Rear Axle Shaft To Flange Collared Nut	162
	Rear Cross Brace	89
	Shock Absorber To Frame Floor	13
	Shock Absorber To Frame Floor Lock Nut	22
	Shock Absorber To Spring Link	41
	Spring Linkage Connecting Rod	15
	Spring Link To Rear Axle Carrier	52
	Spring Link To Spindle	89
	Spring Strut	41

Continued

TIGHTENING SPECIFICATIONS—Continued

Year	Component	Torque, Ft. Lbs.
SL500 & SL600		
1998–2001	Thrust Arm To Rear Axle Carrier	52
	Thrust Arm To Spindle	29
	Torque Strut	52
	Torsion Rod Connecting Rod	22
	Torsion Rod Connecting Rod To Spring Link	18
	Torsion Rod Intermediate Linkage	88①
	Torsion Rod Rubber Mount	21
	Track Rod To Rear Axle Carrier	52
	Track Rod To Spindle	26
	Tunnel Closing Plate	18
SLK230 & SLK320		
1998–99	Camber Strut To Rear Axle Carrier	52
	Camber Strut To Spindle	29
	Cross Brace	44
	Differential Breather	18
	Differential Carrier To Rear Axle Carrier, Front	37
	Differential Carrier To Rear Axle Carrier, Rear	81
	Level Control Spring Link	41
	Propeller Shaft Intermediate Bearing w/Collar & Centering Tip	22
	Propeller Shaft Intermediate Bearing w/ Washer	18
	Propeller Shaft To Transmission Or Differential Carrier (M10)	29
	Propeller Shaft To Transmission Or Differential Carrier (M12)	44
	Propeller Shaft Transverse Bridge	29
	Rear Axle Carrier	66
	Rear Axle Shaft To Connecting Flange	52
	Rear Axle Shaft To Flange Collared Nut	162
	Reinforcement Brace	15
	Shock Absorber To Frame Floor	13
	Shock Absorber To Frame Floor' Lock Nut	22
	Shock Absorber To Spring Link	41
	Spring Linkage Connecting Rod	15
	Spring Link To Rear Axle Carrier	52
	Spring Link To Spindle	89
	Spring Strut	41
	Stop Plate	81
	Thrust Arm To Rear Axle Carrier	52
	Thrust Arm To Spindle	29
	Torsion Rod Connecting Rod	22
	Torsion Rod Connecting Rod To Spring Link	15
	Torsion Rod Idler Lever	88①
	Torsion Rod Rubber Mount	15
	Torque Strut	52
	Track Rod To Rear Axle Carrier	52
	Track Rod To Spindle	26

① — Inch lbs.

② — E300 models, 18 ft. lbs.; E55, E320 & E430 models, 22 ft. lbs.

Transfer Case

INDEX

	Page No.
Description	5-147
ML320 & ML430	5-147
Technical Service Bulletins	5-147
Knocking Noise When Accelerator Released Or Depressed Suddenly	5-147
Low Range Indicator Lamp On w/Low Range Switch Not Activated	5-147
Tightening Specifications	5-149
Transfer Case, Replace	5-147
E320 w/4MATIC	5-147

DESCRIPTION

ML320 & ML430

The ML320 and ML430 transfer case is a full-time four-wheel drive design with an open center differential utilizing a double planetary gear set, **Fig. 1.** It incorporates another planetary gear set that is electrically shifted for either high or low range. A chain connects the front and rear output shafts.

The control unit is located on the tunnel below the console, behind the shifter.

The transfer case is contained in an aluminum housing that is flange-connected directly to the five-speed automatic transmission.

The double planetary gear differential is on the output shaft driving the rear driveshaft. A gear meshed into the rear of the double planetary gear set drives the front driveshaft through a multi-link chain. A drum style ring gear connects the intermediate shaft to the output shaft through the planetary pinion gears.

The two-speed front planetary gear set located on the input shaft as part of the carrier has a 1:1 ratio high range. The low range, off-road reduction is 2.64:1. The low range gearing uses helical cut gears for quiet operation.

ML vehicles built through early 1998 have a Series 1 transfer case with a 50–50% torque split. Vehicle built later have a Series 2 transfer case with a 48–52% torque split.

TRANSFER CASE

REPLACE

E320 w/4MATIC

1. Remove mounting bolts, shield and exhaust bracket, **Fig. 2.**
2. Suspend rear exhaust on V-belt.
3. Remove shield above propeller shaft.
4. Remove tunnel strut mounting bolts.
5. Remove transfer case vibration damper mounting bolts.
6. Disconnect rear propeller shaft from transfer case.
7. Support automatic transmission with suitable jack.
8. Remove rear engine mount engine support.
9. Disconnect front propeller shaft from transfer case.
10. Lower engine and transmission slightly.
11. Position suitable container under transfer case.
12. Remove mounting bolts and transfer case.
13. Remove plug and drain residual oil by tilting transfer case.
14. Reverse procedure to install, noting the following:
    a. Clean sealing surfaces and coat with Omnifit FD 3041 sealing compound, or equivalent.
    b. Tighten mounting bolts and nuts to specifications.
    c. Inspect and correct fluid level as required.

TECHNICAL SERVICE BULLETINS

LOW RANGE INDICATOR LAMP ON w/LOW RANGE SWITCH NOT ACTIVATED

ML320

On some of these models the low range indicator lamp may come on and remain on after starting engine in low ambient temperature even thought he low range switch is not activated.

This condition may be caused by no CAN signal from the transfer case control module.

To correct this condition, replace the transfer case control module.

KNOCKING NOISE WHEN ACCELERATOR RELEASED OR DEPRESSED SUDDENLY

E320

On some of these models there may be a knocking noise when the accelerator is released or depressed suddenly.

This condition is caused by additional play in the 4X4 drive.

To correct this condition, proceed as follows:

1. Remove transfer case.
2. Disassemble transfer case.
3. Remove transmission cover from housing.
4. Mount transfer case on assembly support.
5. Replace planetary gear set (part No. 210 270 11 43).
6. Notify owner and place following message in owner's manual: **CAUTION!!! Do not tow vehicle on one axle! If vehicle cannot be loaded, remove propeller shaft to towed axle!**

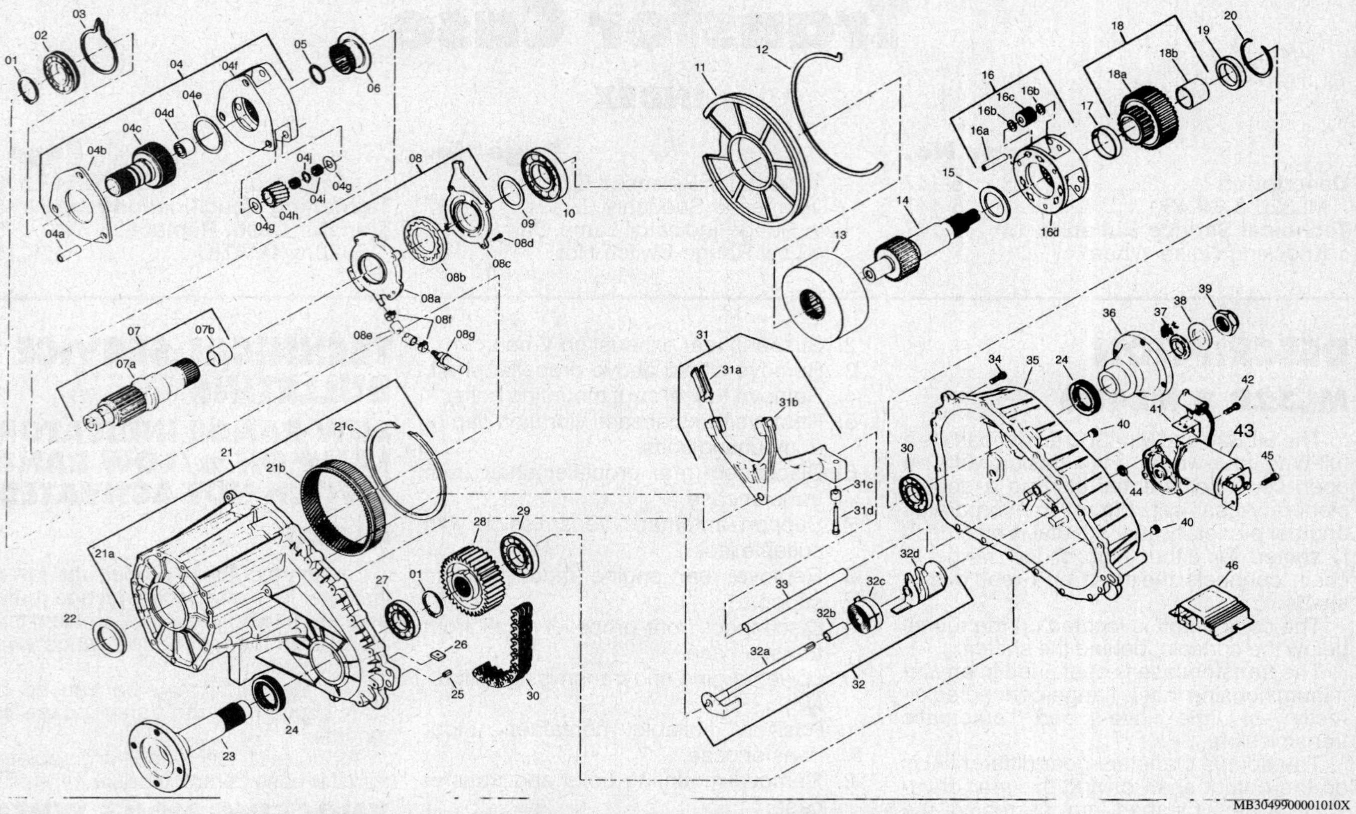

Fig. 1 Exploded view of transfer case (Part 1 of 2)

Item No.	Description	Qty
01	Ring, Snap	1
02	Bearing, Ball	1
03	Ring, Snap	1
04*	Asm. - Carrier Complete	1
04a	Shaft, Pinion	3
04b	Plate, Planet Carrier	1
04c	Shaft, Input	1
04d	Bearing, Needle	1
04e	Washer, Thrust	1
04f	Carrier, Planet	1
04g	Washer, Thrust	6
04h	Gear, Pinion	3
04i	Bearing, Needle	90
04j	Spacer, Pinion	3
05	Washer, Thrust	1
06	Hub, Reduction	1
07*	Asm. - Intermediate Shaft	1
07a	Shaft, Intermediate	1
07b	Bushing	1
08*	Asm. - Gerotor Pump	1
08a	Cover, Gerotor Pump	1
08b	Gear Sot. Gerotor	1
08c	Gerotor Pump Body	1
08d	Bolt	4
08e	Hose	1
08f	Clamp, Hose	2
08g	Lube Pickup & Filter	1
09	Washer, Thrust	1
10	Bearing, Ball	1
11	Support, Ball Bearing	1
12	Ring, Retaining	1
13	Gear, Differential Ring	1
14	Shaft, Rear Output	1
15	Washer, Thrust	1
16*	Asm. - Carrier Complete	1
16a	Shaft, Pinion	6
16b	Washer, Thrust	12
16c	Gear, Pinion	6
16d	Carrier, Planet	1
17	Spacer	1
18*	Asm. - Upper Sprocket	1
18a	Sprocket, Upper Drive	1
18b	Bushing	1

Item No.	Description	Qty
19	Spacer	1
20	Ring, Retaining	1
21*	Asm. - Case	1
21a	Case, Transfer	1
21b	Gear Ring-Reduction	1
21c	Ring, Retaining	1
22	Seal, Oil	1
23	Shaft, Lower Output	1
24	Seal, Oil	2
25	Dowel, Spring Pin	2
26	Magnet	1
27	Bearing, Ball	1
28	Sprocket, Lower Drive	1
29	Bearing, Ball	2
30*	Asm. - Chain, Drive	1
31*	Asm. - Reduction Shift Fork	1
31a	Facing, Shift Fork	2
31b	Fork, Shift Reduction	1
31c	Cam Follower	1
31d	Pin, Shift Fork	1
32*	Asm. - Shift Shaft	1
32a	Shaft, Shift	1
32b	Spacer	1
32c	Spring, Torsion	1
32d	Cam, Electric Shift	1
33	Rail, Shift	1
34	Bolt, Hex Flange Head	18
35	Cover, Transfer Case	1
36	Flange, Companion	1
37	Seal, Oil	1
38	Washer	1
39	Nut, Stake	1
40	Plug, Drain	2
41	Bracket, Motor	1
42	Bolt, Metric Hex Head	3
43	Shift Motor	1
44	Seal, Oil	1
45	Cap Screw, Hex Head	1
46	Electronic Control Unit	1
47	RTV (Neutral Cure)	AR

▭ Indicates Sub-Assembly
* Serviced Only as Sub-Assembly

MB3049900001020X

Fig. 1 Exploded view of transfer case (Part 2 of 2)

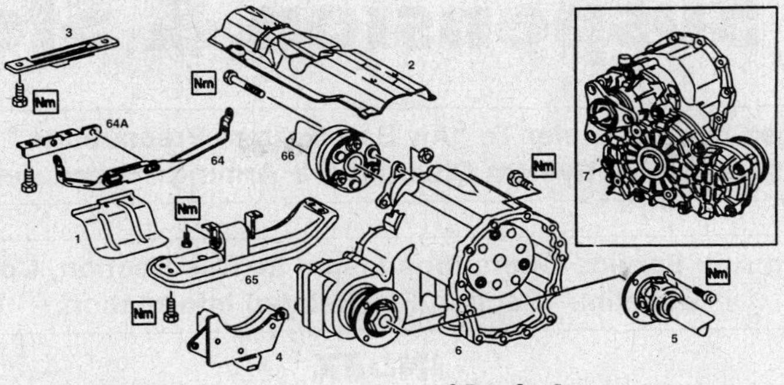

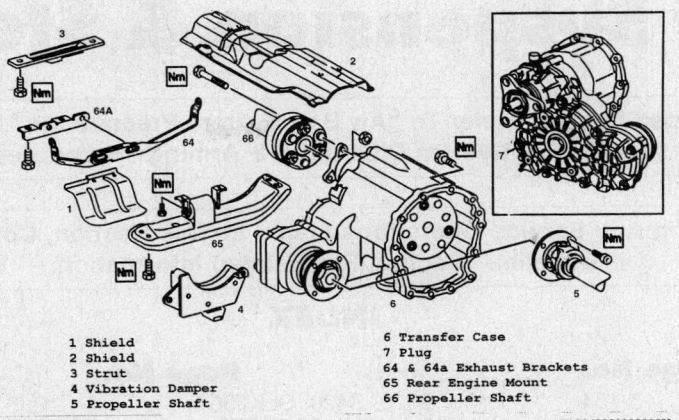

Fig. 2 Transfer case replacement. E320 w/4MATIC

TIGHTENING SPECIFICATIONS

Year	Component	Torque, Ft. Lbs.
E320 w/4MATIC		
1998–2001	Oil Plug	22
	Propeller Shaft	18
	Rear Engine Crossmember	30
	Transfer Case To Transmission	18
	Transmission Engine Mount	30

Front Suspension & Steering

NOTE: On Air Bag Equipped Models, Refer To "Air Bag System Precautions" Located In The Front Of This Manual For System Disarming & Arming Procedures.

NOTE: Prior To Performing Any Service Operations Listed In This Section, Consult The "Technical Service Bulletins" Section For Related Information.

INDEX

Page No.

Ball Joint, Replace 5-154
- C43, C230, C280, CLK55, CLK320, CLK430, E55, E300, E430, SLK230 & SLK320 5-154
- E320 5-154
- S320 & S420 & 1998–99 CL500, CL600, S500 & S600 . 5-154
- S430 & 2000–01 CL500, CL600, S500 & S600 5-154
- SL500 & SL600................. 5-154

Ball Joint Boot, Replace......... 5-154
Ball Joint Inspection 5-153
- Installed 5-153
- Removed 5-154

Coil Spring, Replace............. 5-155
- C43, C230, C280, CLK55, CLK320, CLK430, E55, E300, E430, S320, S420, SLK230 & SLK320 & 1998–99 CL500, CL600, S500 & S600 & E320 Less 4MATIC 5-155
- E320 w/4MATIC 5-155

Control Arm, Replace 5-156
- Lower........................... 5-157
- Upper........................... 5-156

Control Arm Bushing, Replace.. 5-159
- C43, C230, C280, SLK230 & SLK320....................... 5-159
- CLK55, CLK320 & CLK430 5-159
- E320 5-160
- E55, E300 & E430.............. 5-159
- S320 & S420 & 1998–99 CL500, CL600, S500 & S600 . 5-159
- SL500 & SL600................. 5-160

Driveshaft, Replace.............. 5-153
- E320 w/4MATIC 5-153
- ML55, ML320 & ML430......... 5-153

Hub & Bearing Service 5-152
- C43, C230, C280, CLK55, CLK320, CLK430, E55, E300, E320, E430, SLK230 & SLK320....................... 5-152
- S320 & S420 & 1998–99 CL500, CL600, S500 & S600 . 5-153
- SL500 & SL600................. 5-153

Hub, Bearing & Seal, Replace... 5-151
- C43, C230, C280, CLK55, CLK320, CLK430, E55, E300, E430, S320, S420, SLK230 & SLK320 & 1998–99 CL500, CL600, S500 & S600 5-151
- E320 5-152
- S430 & 2000–01 CL500, CL600, S500 & S600 5-152
- SL500 & SL600................. 5-152

Power Steering Gear, Replace .. 5-164
- C43, C230, C280, CLK55, CLK320, CLK430, SL500, SL600, SLK230 & SLK320.... 5-164
- E55, E300, E320 & E430 5-164
- S320 & S420 & 1998–99 CL500, CL600, S500 & S600 . 5-164
- S430 & 2000–01 CL500, CL600, S500 & S600 5-165

Power Steering Pump, Replace . 5-165
- C230, E300, S320, S420, SL600, SLK230 & 1998–99 CL500, CL600, S500 & S600 & 1998 SL500 5-165
- C43, C240, C280, C320, CLK55, CLK320, CLK430, E55, E320, E430 & S430 & 2000–01 CL500, CL600, S500 & S600 5-166

Power Steering System Bleed... 5-166
Precautions...................... 5-151
- Air Bag Systems............... 5-151
- Battery Ground Cable........... 5-151
- Radio Coded Anti-Theft System. 5-151

Shock Absorber, Replace 5-155
- C43, C230, C280, CLK55, CLK320, CLK430, E55, E300, E430, SLK230 & SLK320 5-155
- CLK55, CLK320, CLK430, S320 & S420 & 1998–99 CL500, CL600, S500 & S600 5-156
- E320 5-155

Spring Link, Replace 5-163
- S430 & 2000–01 CL500, CL600, S500 & S600 5-163

Stabilizer Bar, Replace 5-162
- C43, C230, C280, CLK55, CLK320, CLK430, SLK230 & SLK320....................... 5-162
- E320 5-163
- E55, E300 & E430.............. 5-163
- S320 & S420 & 1998–99 CL500, CL600, S500 & S600 . 5-162
- SL500 & SL600................. 5-163

Steering Knuckle, Replace 5-160
- C43, C230, C280, CLK55, CLK320, CLK430, SLK230 & SLK320....................... 5-160
- E320 5-161
- E55, E300 & E430.............. 5-160
- S320 & S420 & 1998–99 CL500, CL600, S500 & S600 . 5-161
- S430 & 2000–01 CL500, CL600, S500 & S600 5-162
- SL500 & SL600................. 5-162

Strut, Replace 5-155
- SL500 & SL600................. 5-155

Technical Service Bulletins 5-166
- Air Suspension MIL On 5-166
- Front Axle Rumbling On Undulating Or Poor Roads.... 5-167
- High-Pitched Metallic Knocking When Starting To Drive & At Slow Speeds 5-167
- Insufficient Power Steering Assistance.................. 5-167
- Knocking Noise From Front Axle When Steering............... 5-166
- Leaking Front Wheel Bearing Grease Cap 5-167
- Power Steering Oil Cooler Leak. 5-167
- Single Knocking Noise When Stopping w/Light Brake Pressure...................... 5-167
- Squeaking Noises When Steering 5-166
- Steering Stiff & Possible Noises. 5-166
- Steering Wheel Vibration Or Shimmy....................... 5-167

Tension Strut, Replace 5-163
- S430 & 2000–01 CL500, CL600, S500 & S600 5-163

Tie Rod, Replace 5-164
- Inner 5-164
- Outer 5-164

Tightening Specifications 5-168
Wheel Bearing, Adjust........... 5-151

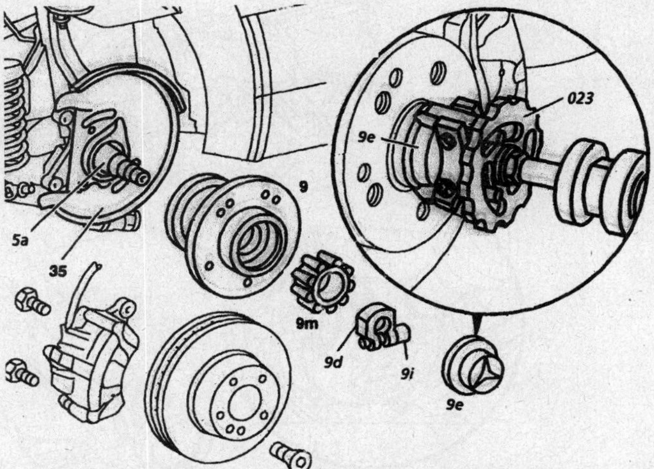

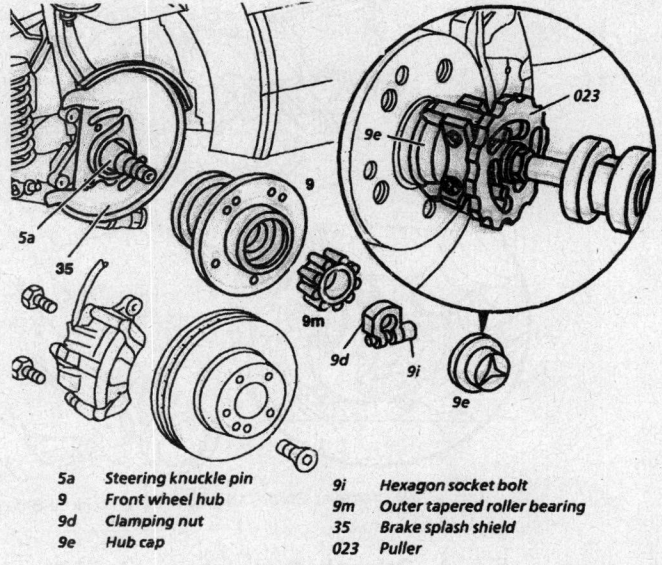

5a	*Steering knuckle pin*	9i	*Hexagon socket bolt*
9	*Front wheel hub*	9m	*Outer tapered roller bearing*
9d	*Clamping nut*	35	*Brake splash shield*
9e	*Hub cap*	023	*Puller*

MB2029900061000X

Fig. 1 Hub & bearing replacement. C43, C230, C280, CLK55, CLK320, CLK430, E55, E300, E430, S320, S420, SLK230 & SLK320 & 1998–99 CL500, CL600, S500 & S600

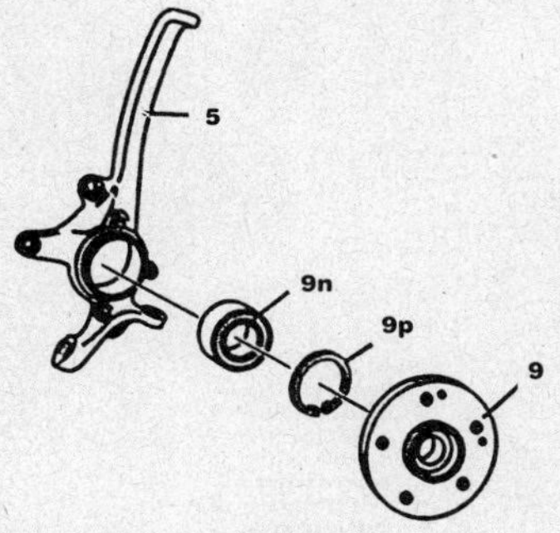

5 Steering Knuckle
9 Front Axle Shaft Flange
9n Two-row Angular-contact Ball Bearing
9p Circlip

MB2029900070000X

Fig. 2 Hub replacement. E320 w/4MATIC

PRECAUTIONS

AIR BAG SYSTEMS

Refer to "Air Bag System Precautions" in front of this manual for system disarming and arming procedures.

BATTERY GROUND CABLE

Prior to service, disconnect battery ground cable and isolate as required.

RADIO CODED ANTI-THEFT SYSTEM

Anti-theft radios have a coded theft protection circuit. The CODE card must be obtained before disconnecting battery, removing radio fuse or removing the radio. **The serial number from the radio must match the CODE card.**

After service has been performed proceed as follows:

1. Connect radio power and turn key to position No. 2.
2. Turn radio to On position. Word "CODE" will appear on display.
3. Enter first digit of anti-theft code from CODE card. "CODE" will disappear and entered digit will appear followed by four dashes.
4. Enter next four digits, when all five are entered first digit flashes again.
5. Press SC, Seek or Tune button to confirm code.
6. If "WAIT" appears on radio panel, proceed as follows:
   a. Radio will allow three coding attempts only before entering lock-up mode and won't respond to controls.
   b. Leave radio on for 15–60 minutes, then radio will unlock and allow three addition coding attempts.
   c. Third lockout period (after nine failed coding attempts) will last 24 hours.
   d. Radio must be left on during enter 24-hour period until "CODE" appears.
7. When "CODE" appears, repeat coding attempt.

WHEEL BEARING

ADJUST

1. Raise and support vehicle.
2. Remove front tire and wheel assembly.
3. Secure brake disc to wheel hub assembly by installing wheel bolt opposite locking bolt.
4. Press brake pads away from brake disc.
5. Remove hub cap using puller tool No. 116 589 22 33 00, or equivalent.
6. Attach dial gauge stand tool No. 363 589 02 21 00, or equivalent, on front wheel hub and set suitable dial gauge to approximately .0787 inch preload.
7. Inspect wheel bearing play by vigorously pulling and pushing on flange.
8. Turn wheel hub several turns before each measurement. Hub must not turn during measurement.
9. If bearing play is more than .002 inch, proceed as follows:
   a. Loosen clamping nut bolt.
   b. While rotating wheel hub, turn clamping nut until hub can only be turned with effort.
   c. Loosen clamping nut until there is play. Release tension by tapping steering knuckle pin with suitable plastic mallet.
   d. Adjust wheel bearing play to .0004–.0007 by alternately turning clamping nut, then pulling and pushing vigorously on wheel hub.
   e. **Torque** bolt to 71 inch lbs. and inspect wheel bearing play, again.
   f. Fill hub cap with .529 oz. suitable high-temperature roller bearing grease.
   g. Drive hub cap on using drift tool No. 124 589 00 15 00, or equivalent.
   h. Pump brake several times to build up pressure and apply brake pads.

HUB, BEARING & SEAL

REPLACE

C43, C230, C280, CLK55, CLK320, CLK430, E55, E300, E430, S320, S420, SLK230 & SLK320 & 1998–99 CL500, CL600, S500 & S600

1. Raise and support vehicle, then remove front tire and wheel assembly.
2. Remove brake disc, **Fig. 1.**
3. Remove hub cap.
4. Loosen bolt, then remove clamping nut and tapered roller bearing.
5. Remove front wheel hub. If hub is seized use impact extractor tool No. 201 589 10 33 00, or equivalent.
6. Reverse procedure to install, noting the following:
   a. Coat seal ring and pack space between sealing lip and tapered roller bearings with suitable high-temperature roller bearing grease.
   b. Push front wheel hub with inner tapered roller bearing and radial seal ring onto steering knuckle pin.
   c. Adjust wheel bearing play as outlined under "Wheel Bearing, Adjust."

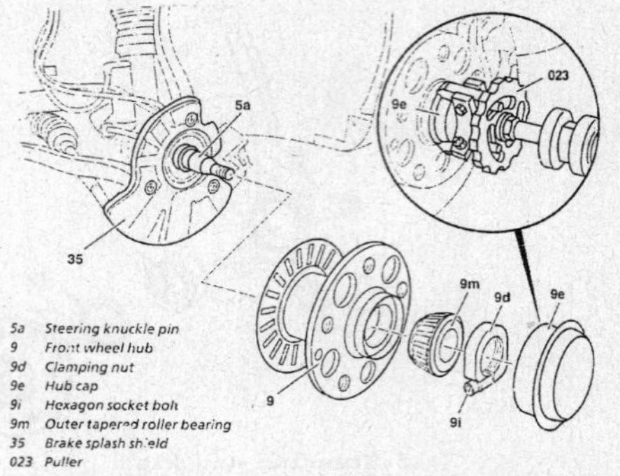

Fig. 3 Hub & bearing replacement. S430 & 2000–01 CL500, CL600, S500 & S600

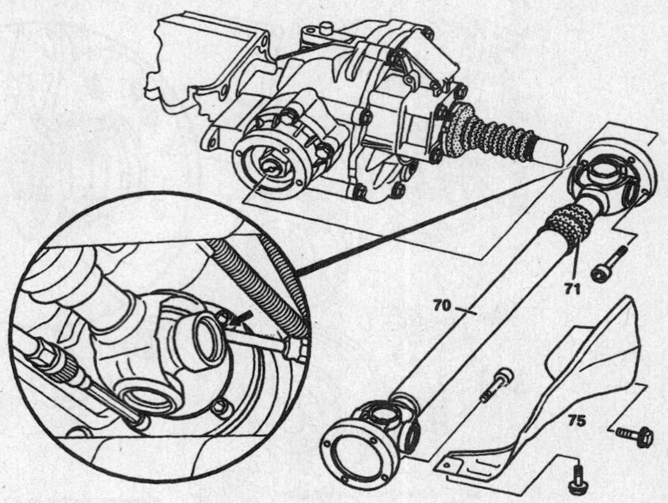

70 Propeller Shaft 71 Rubber Boot 75 Heat Shield

MB2029900058000X

Fig. 4 Driveshaft replacement. E320 w/4MATIC

E320

Less 4MATIC

Refer to "C43, C230, C280, CLK55, CLK320, CLK430, E55, E300, E320, E430, S320, S420, SLK230 & SLK320 & 1998–99 CL500, CL600, S500 & S600."

With 4MATIC

1. Remove steering knuckle as outlined under "Steering Knuckle, Replace."
2. Place steering knuckle in suitable press.
3. Press front axle shaft flange out using thrust piece from extractor tool No. 202 589 04 43 00, or equivalent, **Fig. 2.**
4. Remove circlip using suitable pliers.
5. Pull two-row angular-contact ball bearing out using removal tool No. 124 589 05 34 00, or equivalent.
6. Clamp front axle shaft flange in suitable vise with aluminum jaws.
7. Place thrust piece tool No. 000 589 03 34 00, or equivalent, on front axle shaft flange.
8. Screw clamping pliers onto puller tool No. 001 589 50 33 00, or equivalent, and tighten.
9. Guide pliers complete over bearing inner race and tighten at upper grooves.
10. Remove bearing inner race from front axle shaft flange.
11. Reverse procedure to install, noting the following:
    a. Install two-row angular-contact ball bearing out using installation tool No. 124 589 05 34 00, or equivalent.
    b. Ensure gasket points inward.
    c. Ensure circlip is correctly seated in groove.
    d. Install front axle shaft flange in two-row angular contact ball bearing using installation tool No. 124 589 05 43 00, or equivalent.
    e. Ensure thrust washer abuts tapered roller bearing correctly.

S430 & 2000–01 CL500, CL600, S500 & S600

1. Raise and support vehicle, then remove tire and wheel assembly.
2. Remove brake disc.
3. Remove hub cap using dust cover removal/installation tool No. 116 589 22 33 00, or equivalent, **Fig. 3.**
4. Loosen mounting bolt, then remove clamping nut and tapered roller bearing.
5. Remove hub.
6. Reverse procedure to install, noting the following:
    a. Coat seal ring and pack space between sealing lip and tapered roller bearings with suitable high-temperature roller bearing grease.
    b. Push front wheel hub with inner tapered roller bearing and radial seal ring onto steering knuckle pin.
    c. Adjust wheel bearing play as outlined under "Wheel Bearing, Adjust."

SL500 & SL600

1. Raise and support vehicle, then remove tire and wheel assembly.
2. Remove brake disc.
3. Remove hub cap using puller tool No. 116 589 22 93 00, or equivalent.
4. Loosen mounting bolt and remove clamping nut from steering knuckle.
5. Remove hub. If seated tightly, use puller tool No. 201 589 10 33 00, or equivalent.
6. Remove tapered roller bearing inner race using puller tool No. 001 589 50 33 00 and collet chuck tool No. 210 589 03 34 00, or equivalents.
7. Remove radial sealing ring from steering knuckle.
8. Inspect brake guard for distortion and cracks. Replace as required.
9. Inspect hub as outlined under "Hub & Bearing Service."
10. Inspect steering knuckle pin for wear and discoloration. Replace as required.
11. Reverse procedure to install, noting the following:
    a. Coat steering knuckle radial seal contact surface and pack space between sealing and dust lips with suitable high-temperature roller bearing grease.
    b. Adjust wheel bearing play as outlined under "Wheel Bearing, Adjust."
    c. Tighten bolt to specifications.
    d. Fill hub cap with .529 oz. suitable high-temperature roller bearing grease.
    e. Drive hub cap on using drift tool No. 124 589 00 15 00, or equivalent.

HUB & BEARING SERVICE

C43, C230, C280, CLK55, CLK320, CLK430, E55, E300, E320, E430, SLK230 & SLK320

1. Remove front wheel hub as outlined under "Hub, Bearing & Seal, Replace."
2. Knock out inner tapered roller bearing and radial seal using punch tool No. 202 589 00 15 00, or equivalent.
3. Knock out outer tapered roller bearing race using punch tool.
4. Pull inner tapered roller bearing race out of front wheel hub using pulling-out tool No. 202 589 00 33 00, or equivalent.
5. Clean tapered roller bearings and front wheel hub.
6. Inspect tapered roller bearings and races.
7. Inspect front wheel hub tapped holes and rotor teeth for damage.
8. Pull bearing races into front wheel hub

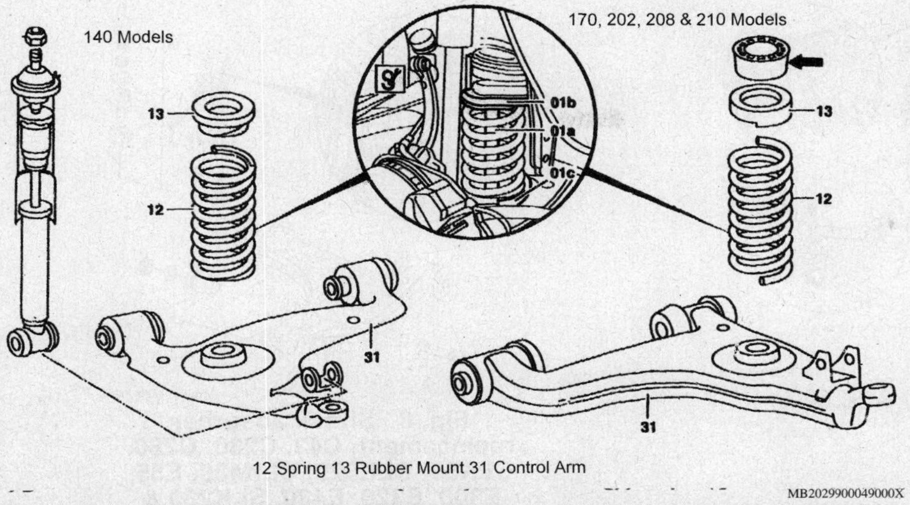

Fig. 5 Front spring replacement. C43, C230, C280, CLK55, CLK320, CLK430, E55, E300, E320, E430, S320, S420, SLK230 & SLK320 & 1998–99 CL500, CL600, S500 & S600

using pulling tool No. 201 589 01 43 00, or equivalent.

9. Coat radial seal ring contact surface, then pack space between sealing and dust lips with suitable high-temperature wheel bearing grease.
10. Pull radial seal ring to front wheel stop using puller tool.
11. Pack wheel hub with suitable grease.
12. Install outer tapered roller bearing in front hub.
13. Install front wheel hub.

S320 & S420 & 1998–99 CL500, CL600, S500 & S600

1. Remove front wheel hub as outlined under "Hub, Bearing & Seal, Replace."
2. Knock out inner tapered roller bearing and radial seal using punch tool No. 140 589 00 15 00, or equivalent.
3. Knock out outer tapered roller bearing race using punch tool.
4. Pull inner tapered roller bearing race out of front wheel hub using pulling-out tool No. 140 589 11 33 00, or equivalent.
5. Clean tapered roller bearings and front wheel hub.
6. Inspect tapered roller bearings and races.
7. Inspect front wheel hub tapped holes and rotor teeth for damage.
8. Pull bearing races into front wheel hub using pulling tool No. 140 589 00 43 00, or equivalent.
9. Coat radial seal ring contact surface, then pack space between sealing and dust lips with suitable high-temperature wheel bearing grease.
10. Pull radial seal ring to front wheel stop using puller tool.
11. Pack wheel hub with suitable grease.
12. Install outer tapered roller bearing in front hub.
13. Install front wheel hub.

SL500 & SL600

1. Remove outer tapered roller bearing.
2. Drive inner tapered roller bearing and radial sealing ring out of hub using drift tool No. 202 589 00 15 00, or equivalent.
3. Remove inner tapered roller bearing outer race using puller tool No. 201 589 00 33 00, or equivalent.
4. Driver outer tapered roller bearing outer race out using drift tool No. 202 589 00 15 00, or equivalent.
5. Thoroughly wash tapered roller bearing with outer race and front wheel hub with benzine or suitable cold cleaner.
6. Inspect condition of inner and outer races' tracks as well as tapered rollers' end surfaces.
7. Tapered roller bearings with smooth gray marks on rollers may be reused.
8. Inspect inner tapered roller bearing for damage to roller cage or roller faces where sealing ring was removed.
9. Inspect threaded wheel bolt bores.
10. When replacing tapered roller bearings, replace bearing races.
11. Install outer races in hub using puller tool No. 201 589 01 43 00, or equivalent.
12. Ensure thrust washers are correctly seated.
13. **On SL500 and SL600 models,** use 1.5872 ounces of suitable high-temperature roller bearing grease.
14. **On all models,** thoroughly pack inner tapered roller bearing roller cage with suitable roller bearing grease.
15. **On all models,** install inner race with roller cage in hub and apply grease to rollers' faces.
16. Pack space between radial sealing ring sealing and dust lips with suitable high-temperature roller bearing grease.
17. Install radial sealing ring with puller tool No. 201 589 01 43 00, or equivalent.
18. Fill hub cap with .529 oz. suitable high-

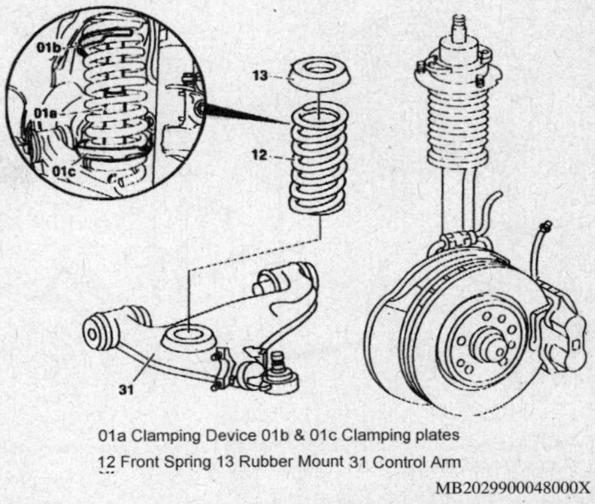

Fig. 6 Front spring replacement. SL500 & SL600

temperature roller bearing grease.

19. Thoroughly pack outer tapered roller bearing with suitable roller bearing grease and install in wheel hub.

DRIVESHAFT

REPLACE

E320 w/4MATIC

1. Remove righthand side exhaust heat shield, **Fig. 4.**
2. Remove propeller shaft mounting bolts.
3. Remove propeller shaft.
4. If rubber boot must be replaced, proceed as follows:
   a. Pull universal joint off propeller shaft.
   b. Remove rubber boot.
5. Reverse procedure to install, noting the following:
   a. Coat splined shaft profile with Molykote grease, or equivalent.
   b. Push rubber boot with universal joint onto propeller shaft, ensuring markings align.
   c. Steady propeller shaft with suitable screwdriver when tightening mounting bolts to specifications.

ML55, ML320 & ML430

1. Remove propeller shaft to transfer case mounting bolts and washers.
2. Remove propeller shaft to front differential carrier mounting bolts.
3. Remove propeller shaft to front.
4. Reverse procedure to install, noting the following:
   a. Ensure front differential carrier flange and propeller shaft are perfectly centered.
   b. Tighten mounting bolts to specifications.

BALL JOINT INSPECTION

INSTALLED

1. Attach compression tool No. 129 589 06 21 00, or equivalent, as close as possible to ball joint.
2. Raise and lower compression tool.
3. Replace ball joint if any play is felt.

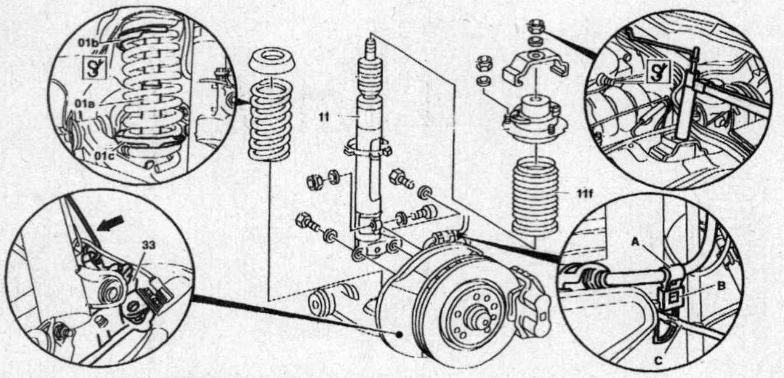

01a Clamping Tool 01b & 01c Clamping Plates 11 Strut 11c Rubber Mount 11f Boot 33 Steering Knuckle
A Clips B Cable Bracket C ABS Speed Sensor Cable

MB2029900054000X

Fig. 7 Strut replacement. SL500 & SL600

REMOVED

1. Place six-inch long pipe over ball joint.
2. If pipe cannot be moved side to side without play, jamming or cracking noises, replace ball joint.
3. Inspect boot for cracks and damage. Replace boot and ball joint as required.
4. Ensure wire clamping rings are correctly installed.

BALL JOINT

REPLACE

C43, C230, C280, CLK55, CLK320, CLK430, E55, E300, E430, SLK230 & SLK320

Shock absorber must be install to replace ball joint.

1. Raise and support vehicle, then remove tire and wheel assembly.
2. Remove ball joint mounting nuts.
3. Install thrust plate tool No. 140 589 00 63 00, or equivalent, onto ball pivot.
4. Press ball joint out using puller tool No, 202 589 02 33 00, or equivalent.
5. Remove ball joint nut.
6. Reverse procedure to install, noting the following:
   a. Install new self-locking bolts and nuts.
   b. Tighten mounting bolts and nuts to specifications.

E320

Less 4MATIC

Refer to "C43, C230, C280, CLK55, CLK320, CLK430, E55, E300, E430, SLK230 & SLK320."

With 4MATIC

The shock absorber does not have to be removed.

1. Raise and support vehicle, then remove front tire and wheel assembly.
2. Remove front axle shaft nut.
3. Remove nut, then press tie rod joint out of steering knuckle using thrust piece tool No. 140 589 00 63 00 and puller tool No. 202 589 02 33 00, or equivalents.
4. Pull steering knuckle outward and move front axle shaft out of flange.
5. Tie steering knuckle to one side using suitable wire.
6. Support steering knuckle by clamp suitable piece of wood at top between steering knuckle and front spring.
7. Tie front axle shaft to one side. **Do not damage rubber boots and speed sensor rotor.**
8. Remove nut, and press lower ball joint out of steering knuckle using thrust piece tool No. 140 589 00 63 00 and puller tool No. 202 589 09 33 00, or equivalents.
9. Reverse procedure to install, noting the following:
   a. Replace self-locking nuts.
   b. Install new front axle shaft nut, tighten to specifications and secure with caulker so there is no gap between groove and locking tab.
   c. Tighten mounting bolts and nuts to specifications.

S320 & S420 & 1998-99 CL500, CL600, S500 & S600

Shock absorber must be install or spring removed to replace ball joint.

1. Raise and support vehicle, then remove tire and wheel assembly.
2. Remove brake disc and splash shield locking bolt.
3. Remove steering knuckle ball joint mounting nut.
4. Install thrust plate tool No. 140 589 24 63 00, or equivalent, onto ball pivot.
5. Press brake disc and splash shield out, then press ball joint out of steering knuckle using puller tool No, 140 589 09 33 00, or equivalent.
6. Remove control arm ball joint nut.
7. Install thrust plate tool onto ball pivot.
8. Press ball joint out of control arm using puller tool.
9. Reverse procedure to install, noting the following:

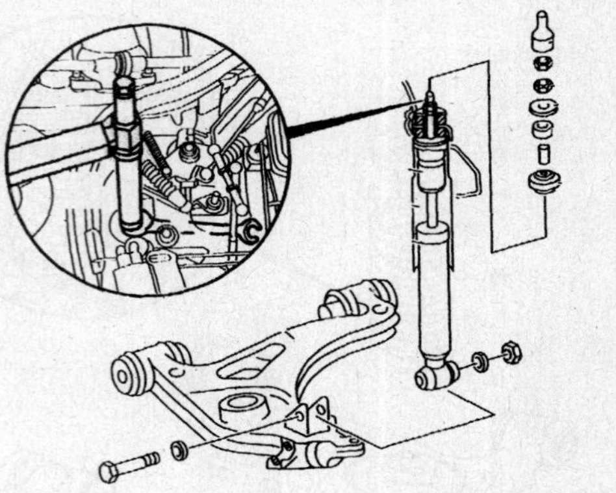

MB2029900056000X

Fig. 8 Shock absorber replacement. C43, C230, C280, CLK55, CLK320, CLK430, E55, E300, E320, E430, SLK230 & SLK320

   a. Install new self-locking bolts and nuts.
   b. Tighten mounting bolts and nuts to specifications.

S430 & 2000-01 CL500, CL600, S500 & S600

1. Remove steering knuckle as outlined under "Steering Knuckle, Replace."
2. Remove ball joint using removal/installation tool No. 220 589 03 43 00, or equivalent.
3. Reverse procedure to install.

SL500 & SL600

On SL500 models, control arm ball joint area is welded and joint cannot be replaced.

1. Remove control arm as outlined under "Control Arm, Replace."
2. Clamp control arm in suitable vise and install press-out sleeve tool No. 107 589 01 43 00, or equivalent.
3. Press ball joint out.
4. Install ball joint into control arm with ball joint mark aligned with control arm center.
5. Place press-out sleeve tool thrust piece on ball joint and press in.
6. Ensure ball joint and rubber boot are correctly seated.

BALL JOINT BOOT

REPLACE

1. Remove control arm as outlined under "Control Arm, Replace."
2. Remove clamping wire.
3. Remove boot.
4. Push new boot into housing.
5. Push wire clamping wing onto assembly sleeve tool No. 201 589 03 14 00, or equivalent, until it reached cylindrical part.
6. Place sleeve on joint and push wire clamping ring onto boot.

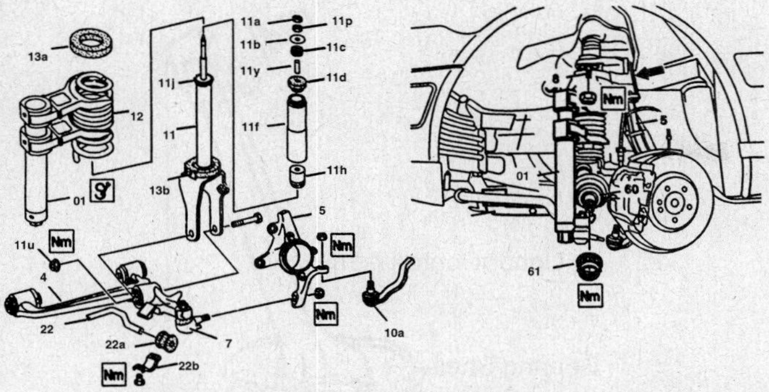

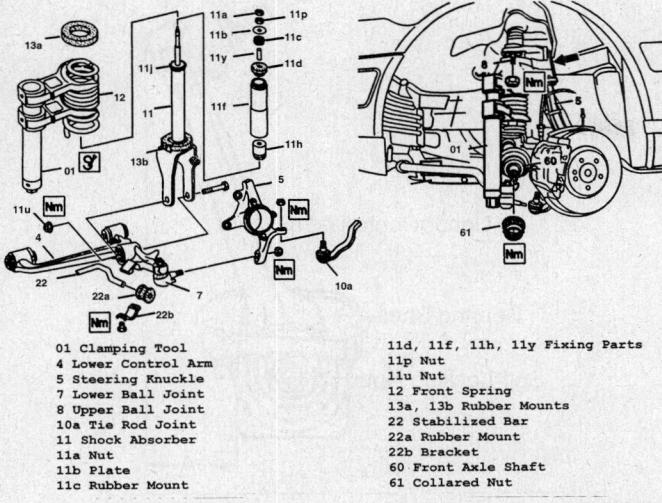

01 Clamping Tool
4 Lower Control Arm
5 Steering Knuckle
7 Lower Ball Joint
8 Upper Ball Joint
10a Tie Rod Joint
11 Shock Absorber
11a Nut
11b Plate
11c Rubber Mount
11d, 11f, 11h, 11y Fixing Parts
11p Nut
11u Nut
12 Front Spring
13a, 13b Rubber Mounts
22 Stabilized Bar
22a Rubber Mount
22b Bracket
60 Front Axle Shaft
61 Collared Nut

MB2029900068000X

Fig. 9 Shock absorber replacement. E320 w/4MATIC

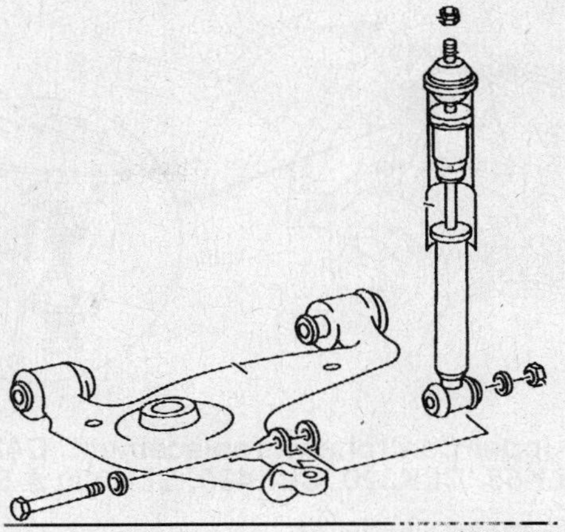

MB2029900055000X

Fig. 10 Shock absorber replacement. CLK55, CLK320, CLK430, S320 & S420 & 1998–99 CL500, CL600, S500 & S600

COIL SPRING

REPLACE

C43, C230, C280, CLK55, CLK320, CLK430, E55, E300, E430, S320, S420, SLK230 & SLK320 & 1998–99 CL500, CL600, S500 & S600 & E320 LESS 4MATIC

1. **On C43, C230, C280, CLK55, CLK320, CLK430, E55, E300, E320, E430, S320, S420, SLK230 and SLK320 and 1998–99 CL500, CL600, S500 and S600 models,** disconnect upper shock absorber mounting.
2. **On all models,** raise and support vehicle.
3. **On S320 & S420 and 1998–99 CL500, CL600, S500 and S600 models,** vehicle weight must rest on tires and wheels.
4. **On all models,** install suitable clamping plates at top and bottom of spring to preload 7–8 coils, **Figs. 5 and 6.**
5. Turn clamping plate recesses toward vehicle inside.
6. Install suitable clamping device in plates and lock upper clamping plate. Retaining lugs must engage upper clamping plate recesses.
7. Tension spring. **Do not use impact wrench.**
8. Remove spring with rubber mount.
9. Mark clamping plate alignment with spring coil for installation.
10. Reverse procedure to install, noting the following:
    a. Ensure rubber mount fits correctly in front end.
    b. Ensure spring coil fits correctly in control arm impression.
    c. Inspect and adjust headlamp aim as required.

E320 w/4MATIC

1. Remove shock absorber as outlined under "Shock Absorber, Replace"
2. Remove spring from shock absorber.
3. Reverse procedure to install, noting the following:
    a. Ensure rubber mounts are correctly positioned.
    b. Attach rubber mounts to spring with adhesive tape
    c. Righthand coil spring rubber mount arrow must point in direction of travel.
    d. Lefthand coil spring rubber mount arrow must point in direction opposite travel.

STRUT

REPLACE

SL500 & SL600

1. Raise and support vehicle, then remove front tire and wheel assembly.
2. Install suitable clamping plates at top and bottom of spring to preload 7–8 coils, **Fig. 7.**
3. Turn clamping plate recesses toward vehicle inside.
4. Install suitable clamping device in plates and lock upper clamping plate. Retaining lugs must engage upper clamping plate recesses.
5. Tension spring. **Do not use impact wrench.**
6. Remove upper strut mounting.
7. Remove ABS speed sensor cable by disconnect clips and bracket.
8. Disconnect strut from steering knuckle. Secure steering knuckle with suitable hook.
9. Remove strut and rubber mount.
10. Reverse procedure to install, noting the following:
    a. Install new self-locking bolts and nuts.
    b. Slightly tighten upper mounting bolt until steering knuckle abuts strut on inside, then tighten lower bolts to specification.
    c. Tighten mounting bolts and nuts to specifications.
    d. Inspect and adjust front wheel alignment as required.

SHOCK ABSORBER

REPLACE

C43, C230, C280, CLK55, CLK320, CLK430, E55, E300, E430, SLK230 & SLK320

Vehicle weight must be on tire and wheel assembly with disconnect upper shock absorber mount.

1. Disconnect upper shock absorber mounting nut, **Fig. 8.**
2. Remove plate and rubber mount.
3. Raise and support vehicle.
4. Remove control arm mounting bolt and shock absorber, then the mounting parts.
5. Reverse procedure to install, noting the following:
    a. Install new self-locking nuts.
    b. Tighten mounting bolts and nuts to specifications.

E320

Less 4MATIC

Refer to "C43, C230, C280, CLK55, CLK320, CLK430, E55, E300, E430, SLK230 & SLK320."

With 4MATIC

1. Raise and support vehicle, then remove front tire and wheel assembly.
2. Remove front axle shaft nut, **Fig. 9.**
3. Disconnect shock absorber brake hose bracket.
4. Move speed sensor cables and brake lining contact sensor out of guides.
5. Remove nut, then press tie rod joint out of steering knuckle using thrust piece

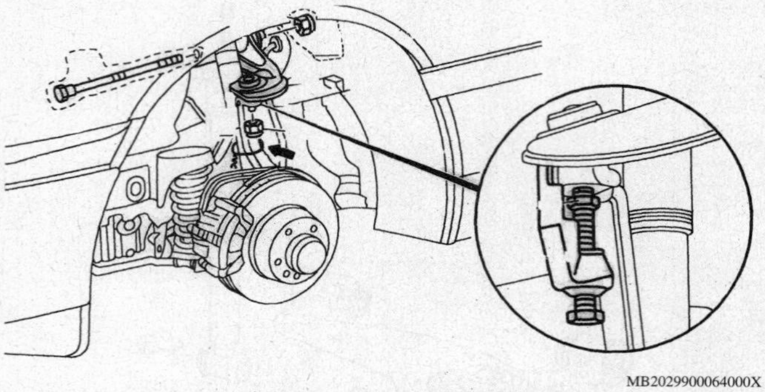

Fig. 11 Upper control arm replacement. C43, C230, C280, CLK55, CLK320, CLK430, SLK230 & SLK320

tool No. 140 589 00 63 00 and puller tool No. 202 589 02 33 00, or equivalents.
6. Remove nut, and press lower ball joint out of steering knuckle using thrust piece tool No. 140 589 00 63 00 and puller tool No. 202 589 09 33 00, or equivalents.
7. Pull steering knuckle out and move front axle shaft out of flange.
8. Remove nut, then press upper ball joint out of steering knuckle using thrust piece tool No. 210 589 04 63 00 and puller tool No. 124 589 03 33 00, or equivalents.
9. Attach steering knuckle to upper control arm with shop-made hook.
10. Remove engine compartment lower cover.
11. Cover steering knuckle and front axle carrier with suitable cloths.
12. Pry front axle shaft out using suitable screwdriver. **Do not damage rubber boot and speed sensor rotor.**
13. Disconnect stabilized bar bracket on lower control arms and remove rubber mount.
14. Install tension tool No. 210 589 00 31 00, or equivalent, and plates, on at least six spring coils. Spring must be located behind clamping plate lug.
15. Mark clamping plates relative to spring coils.
16. Remove shock absorber upper mounting nut, plate and rubber mount .
17. Remove shock absorber lower control arm mounting nut.
18. Remove shock absorber with shackle and spring.
19. Remove front axle shaft.
20. Remove upper fixing parts, inspect and replace as required.
21. Reverse procedure to install, noting the following:
    a. Install new self-locking bolts and nuts.
    b. Attach rubber mounts to spring with adhesive tape
    c. Righthand coil spring rubber mount arrow must point in direction of travel.
    d. Lefthand coil spring rubber mount arrow must point in direction opposite travel.
    e. Inspect front axle shaft rubber boots and replace as required.
    f. Inspect front axle shaft groove circlip and replace as required.
    g. Align joint to almost horizontal when press front axle shaft in.
    h. Install new front axle shaft nut, tighten to specifications and secure with caulker so there is no gap between groove and locking tab.
    i. Tighten mounting bolts and nuts to specifications.

CLK55, CLK320, CLK430, S320 & S420 & 1998–99 CL500, CL600, S500 & S600

Vehicle weight must be on tire and wheel assembly with disconnect upper shock absorber mount.

1. Steady piston rod using suitable Allen wrench, **Fig. 10.**
2. Disconnect upper shock absorber mounting nut.
3. Raise and support vehicle.
4. Remove control arm mounting bolt and shock absorber.
5. Reverse procedure to install, noting the following:
    a. Install new self-locking nuts.
    b. Tighten mounting bolts and nuts to specifications.

CONTROL ARM

REPLACE

Tighten control arm bearings only with vehicle weight on tires.

UPPER

C43, C230, C280, CLK55, CLK320, CLK430, SLK230 & SLK320

Shock absorber must be installed to replace upper control arm.

1. Remove upper ball joint mounting bolt, **Fig. 11.**

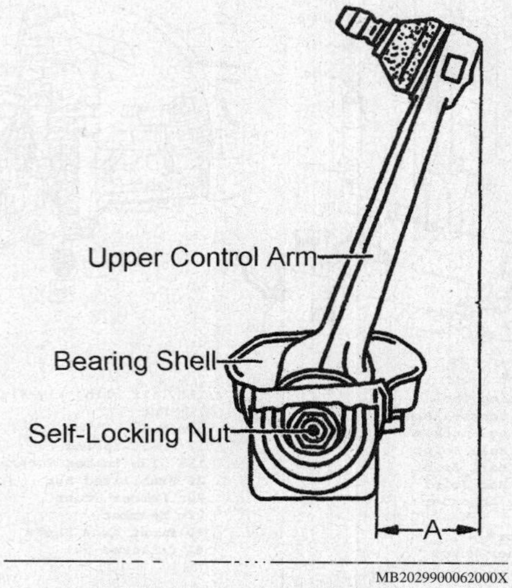

Fig. 12 Upper control arm inclination angle. S320 & S420 & 1998–99 CL500, CL600, S500 & S600

2. Install thrust piece tool No. 210 589 04 63 00, or equivalent, onto ball pivot.
3. Press ball joint out of upper control arm using puller tool No. 124 589 03 33 00, or equivalent.
4. Secure steering knuckle to shock absorber spring dome. **Do not tension brake line or electric cables.**
5. **On SLK230 and SLK320 models,** remove air cleaner housing if removing righthand upper control arm.
6. **On all models,** remove mounting bolts and upper control arm.
7. If dimension A, **Fig. 12,** is not 2.4806 inches, proceed as follows:
    a. Loosen self-locking nut.
    b. Adjust inclination to specifications.
    c. Tighten self-locking nut.
8. Reverse procedure to install, noting the following:
    a. Install new self-locking bolts and nuts.
    b. Fill upper clamp joint separator slot with suitable wax preservative.
    c. Tighten mounting bolts and nuts to specifications.

E55, E300 & E430

Shock absorber must be installed to replace upper control arm.

1. Remove upper ball joint mounting bolt, **Fig. 13.**
2. Install thrust piece tool No. 210 589 04 63 00, or equivalent, onto ball pivot.
3. Press ball joint out of upper control arm using puller tool No. 124 589 03 33 00, or equivalent.
4. Secure steering knuckle to shock absorber spring dome. **Do not tension brake line or electric cables.**
5. Remove windshield washer reservoir if removing lefthand upper control arm.
6. Remove air cleaner is removing righthand upper control arm.
7. Remove wheel housing plastic cover and steady nut by using suitable box wrench.

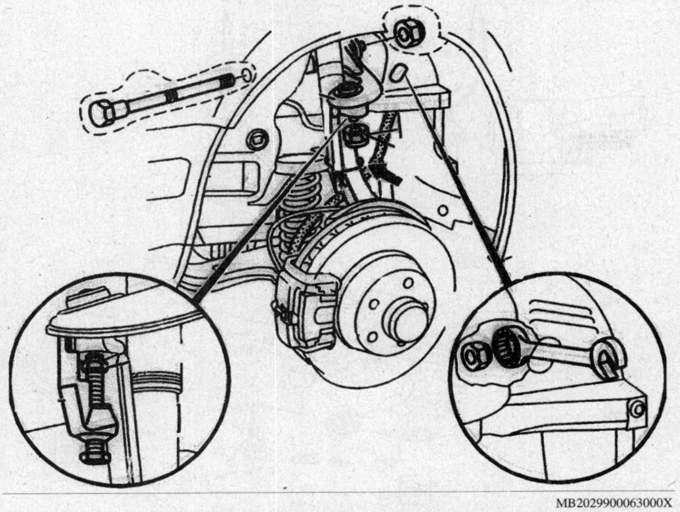

Fig. 13 Upper control arm replacement. E55, E300, E320 & E430

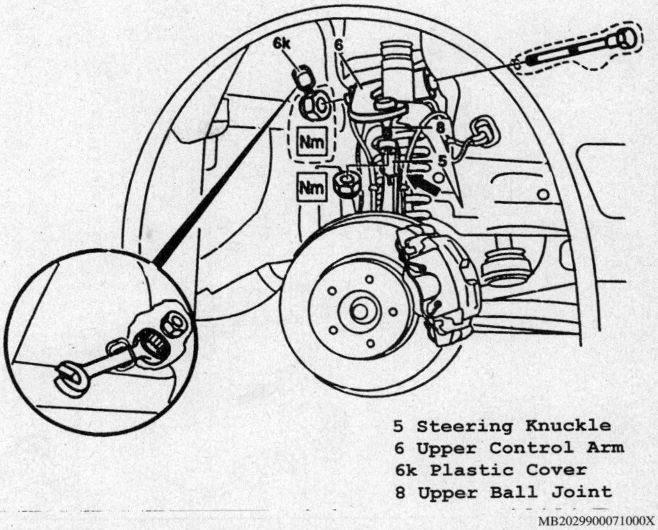

Fig. 14 Upper control arm replacement. E320 w/4MATIC

8. Remove mounting bolts and upper control arm.
9. Inspect arm inclination angle as described under "C43, C230, C280, CLK55, CLK320, CLK430, SLK230 & SLK320" and adjust as required.
10. Reverse procedure to install, noting the following:
   a. Install new self-locking bolts and nuts.
   b. Fill upper clamp joint separator slot with suitable wax preservative.
   c. Tighten mounting bolts and nuts to specifications.

E320

Less 4MATIC

Refer to "E55, E300 & E430."

With 4MATIC

The shock absorber does not have to be removed.

1. Raise and support vehicle, then remove front tire and wheel assembly.
2. Remove nut, then press tie rod joint out of steering knuckle using thrust piece tool No. 140 589 00 63 00 and puller tool No. 202 589 02 33 00, or equivalents, **Fig. 14.**
3. Secure steering knuckle to spring using suitable wire. **Do not tension brake lines or electrical cables.**
4. If removing lefthand upper control arm, proceed as follows:
   a. Disconnect windshield washer reservoir and swivel out of way.
   b. Remove BAS control module.
   c. Remove BAS diaphragm travel sensor.
5. If removing righthand upper control arm, proceed as follows:
   a. Remove air cleaner.
   b. Remove wheel housing plastic cover.
   c. Steady nut using suitable box wrench.
6. Remove control arm.
7. Reverse procedure to install, noting the following:
   a. Replace self-locking bolts and nuts.
   b. Guide lefthand mounting bolt through ABS hydraulic unit under bracket.
   c. Tighten mounting bolts and nuts to specifications.

S320 & S420 & 1998-99 CL500, CL600, S500 & S600

Shock absorber must be installed or spring remove to replace upper control arm.

1. Remove steering knuckle to upper control arm mounting nut
2. Press bolt out of clamped joint. Expand seized clamped joint with suitable spreader tool No. 140 589 02 31 00, or equivalent.
3. Attach steering knuckle to spring dome. **Do not tension brake lines and electrical cables.**
4. Remove mounting bolts and upper control arm with bearing shell.
5. Inspect arm inclination angle as described under "C43, C230, C280, CLK55, CLK320, CLK430, SLK230 & SLK320" and adjust as required.
6. Reverse procedure to install, noting the following:
   a. Install new self-locking bolts and nuts.
   b. Fill upper clamp joint separator slot with suitable wax preservative.
   c. Tighten mounting bolts and nuts to specifications.

S430 & 2000-01 CL500, CL600, S500 & S500

1. Raise and support vehicle, then remove tire and wheel assembly.
2. Disconnect level sensor connector and connecting rod, **Fig. 15.**
3. Press ball joint out of control arm using thrust piece tool No. 210 589 04 63 00 and puller tool No. 202 589 02 33 00, or equivalents.
4. Secure steering knuckle aside with suitable wire. **Do not tension lines or wires.**
5. Remove mounting bolts and upper control arm.
6. Reverse procedure to install. Tighten mounting bolts and nuts to specifications.

LOWER

C43, C230, C280, CLK55, CLK320, CLK430, SLK230 & SLK320

1. Raise and support vehicle, then remove front tire and wheel assembly
2. Remove front spring as outlined under "Coil Spring, Replace."
3. Screw thrust plate tool No. 140 589 24 63 00, or equivalent, onto ball pivot.
4. Press ball joint out of steering knuckle using puller tool No. 202 589 02 33 00, or equivalent.
5. Remove shock absorber from lower control arm.
6. **On SLK230 and SLK320 models,** remove engine compartment lower cover.
7. **On all models,** mark eccentric bolts position relative to frame for installation alignment, then loosen nuts and press out bolts.
8. Remove lower control arm ball joint mounting nut.
9. Screw thrust plate tool No. 140 589 24 63 00, or equivalent, onto ball pivot.
10. Press ball joint out of lower control arm using puller tool No. 202 589 02 33 00, or equivalent.
11. Remove control arm.
12. Reverse procedure to install, noting the following:
   a. Install new self-locking nut and tighten to specifications.
   b. Inspect and adjust front wheel alignment as required.
   c. Tighten eccentric bolts when vehicle weight is resting on tires and front wheels are properly aligned.

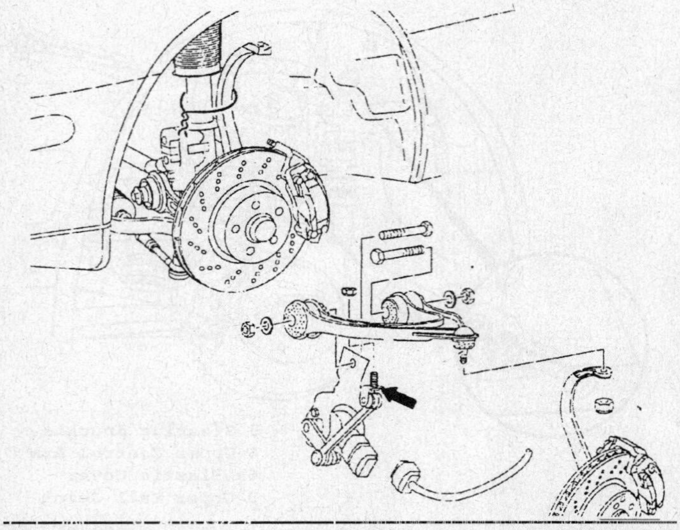

MB2020100080000X

Fig. 15 Upper control arm replacement. S430 & 2000–01 CL500, CL600, S500 & S500

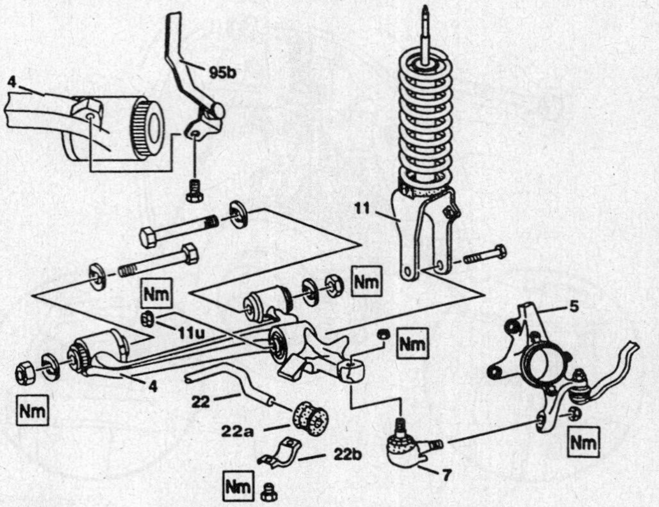

4 Lower Control Arm
5 Steering Knuckle
7 Lower Ball Joint
11 Shock Absorber
22 Stabilizer Bar
22a Rubber Mount
22b Bracket
95b Headlamp Levelling Device

MB2029900072000X

Fig. 16 Lower control arm replacement. E320 w/4MATIC

S320 & S420 & 1998–99 CL500, CL600, S500 & S600

1. Remove spring as outlined under "Coil Spring, Replace."
2. Remove brake disc and splash shield locking bolt.
3. Remove ball joint nut.
4. Screw thrust plate tool No. 140 589 24 63 00, or equivalent, onto ball pivot.
5. Press brake disc and splash shield outward, then press ball joint out of steering knuckle using puller tool No. 140 589 09 33 00, or equivalent.
6. Remove shock absorber from control arm.
7. Remove lower control arm.
8. Remove ball joint nut.
9. Screw thrust plate tool onto ball pivot.
10. Press ball joint out of steering knuckle using puller tool.
11. Reverse procedure to install, noting the following:
    a. Install new self-locking nut and tighten to specifications.
    b. Inspect and adjust front wheel alignment as required.
    c. Tighten eccentric bolts when vehicle weight is resting on tires and front wheels are properly aligned.

E55, E300 & E430

1. Raise and support vehicle, then remove front tire and wheel assembly
2. Remove front spring as outlined under "Coil Spring, Replace."
3. Remove stabilizer bar from lower control arm.
4. Remove ball joint mounting nut.
5. Screw thrust plate tool No. 140 589 24 63 00, or equivalent, onto ball pivot.
6. Press ball joint out of steering knuckle using puller tool No. 202 589 02 33 00, or equivalent.
7. Remove mounting bolts and lower control arm from frame.
8. Remove lower control arm ball joint mounting nut.
9. Screw thrust plate tool No. 140 589 24 63 00, or equivalent, onto ball pivot.
10. Press ball joint out of lower control arm using puller tool No. 202 589 02 33 00, or equivalent.
11. Remove control arm.
12. Reverse procedure to install, noting the following:
    a. Install new self-locking nut and tighten to specifications.
    b. Inspect and adjust front wheel alignment as required.
    c. Tighten eccentric bolts when vehicle weight is resting on tires and front wheels are properly aligned.

E320

Less 4MATIC

Refer to "E55, E300 & E430."

With 4MATIC

1. Raise and support vehicle, then remove front tire and wheel assembly.
2. Remove engine compartment lower cover.
3. Disconnect stabilized bar brackets on lower control arms and remove rubber mounts, **Fig. 16.**
4. If remove righthand side lower control arm, disconnect headlamp leveling linkage.
5. Remove nut, then press upper ball joint out of steering knuckle using thrust piece tool No. 210 589 04 63 00 and puller tool No. 124 589 03 33 00, or equivalents.
6. Disconnect shock absorber from lower control arm.
7. Remove nut, and press lower ball joint out of steering knuckle using thrust piece tool No. 140 589 00 63 00 and puller tool No. 202 589 09 33 00, or equivalents.
8. Remove control arm.
9. Reverse procedure to install, noting the following:
    a. Replace self-locking bolts and nuts.
    b. Tighten mounting bolts and nuts to specifications.
    c. Inspect and adjust front wheel alignment as required.

SL500 & SL600

1. Raise and support vehicle, then remove tire and wheel assembly.
2. Remove lower engine compartment cover.
3. Remove front spring as outlined under "Coil Spring, Replace."
4. Remove mounting nuts and stabilizer bar bracket.
5. Press eccentric bolts out and remove lower control arm.
6. Remove bolt and nut clamping steering knuckle to ball joint.
7. Remove steering knuckle from ball joint. If knuckle is corroded, loosen clamping joint by expanding slot using spread tool No. 140 589 02 31 00, or equivalent.
8. Reverse procedure to install, noting the following:
    a. Install new ball joint self-locking nut and tighten to specifications.
    b. Pack clamped joint slot with preservation wax No. 000 986 33 70 10, or equivalent.
    c. Install new stabilized bracket mounting nuts and tighten to specifications.
    d. Inspect and adjust front wheel alignment as required.
    e. Tighten eccentric bolts when vehicle weight is resting on tires and front wheels are properly aligned.

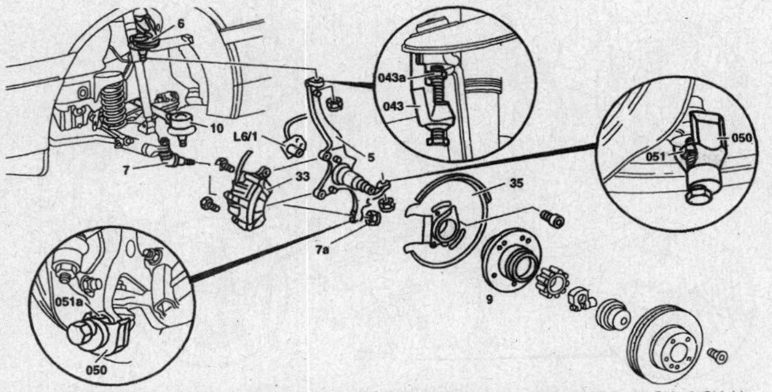

5 Steering Knuckle 6 Upper Control Arm 7 Ball Joint 9 Front Wheel Hub 10 Tie Rod 35 Brake Splash Shield 043 Puller 043a Thrust Piece 050 Puller 051 Thrust Piece L6/1 VSS Sensor

MB2029900067000X

Fig. 17 Steering knuckle replacement. C43, C230, C280, CLK55, CLK320, CLK430, SLK230 & SLK320

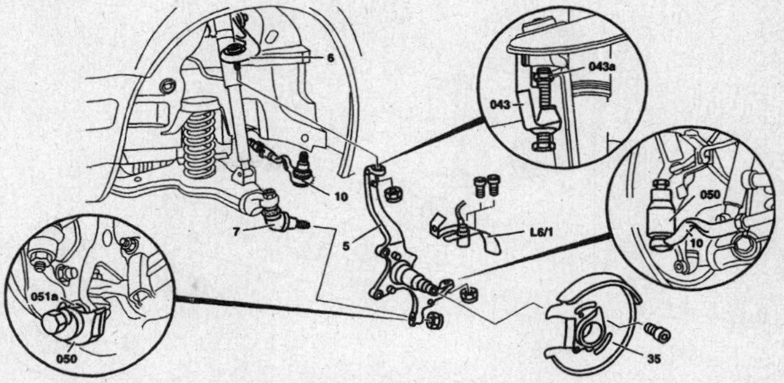

5 Steering Knuckle 6 Upper Control Arm 7 Ball Joint 10 Tie Rod 35 Brake Splash Shield 043 Puller 043a Thrust Piece 050 Puller 051a Thrust Piece L6/1 VSS Sensor

MB2029900066000X

Fig. 18 Steering knuckle replacement. E55, E300, E320 & E430

CONTROL ARM BUSHING

REPLACE

C43, C230, C280, SLK230 & SLK320

FRONT

1. Remove lower control arm as outlined under “Control Arm, Replace.”
2. Clamp control arm in suitable vise with aluminum jaws.
3. Loosen bushing sleeve with suitable drift punch.
4. Disconnect outer steel casing with suitable flat chisel. **Do not damage mounting eye.**
5. Remove bushing.
6. Cleaning mounting bore.
7. Smear bushing with thin film of lubricant No. 000 989 03 67, or equivalent. **Do not use oil or grease.**
8. Insert bushing and spacer sleeve with flats perpendicular to control arm installed position.
9. Pull bushing and spacer sleeve to stop using installation tool No. 202 589 01 43 00, or equivalent.
10. Install lower control arm.

REAR

1. Remove lower control arm as outlined under “Control Arm, Replace.”
2. Clamp control arm in suitable vise with aluminum jaws.
3. Pull bushing out using thrust piece and sleeve tool No. 202 589 01 43 00, or equivalent.
4. Cleaning mounting bore.
5. Smear bushing with thin film of lubricant No. 000 989 03 67, or equivalent. **Do not use oil or grease.**
6. Insert bushing with flats at 90° angle to control arm center weld seam from back (view in travel direction).
7. Pull bushing and spacer sleeve to stop using installation tool No. 202 589 01 43 00, or equivalent.
8. Install lower control arm.

CLK55, CLK320 & CLK430

FRONT

Refer to “C43, C230, C280, SLK230 & SLK320” for front bushing replacement.

REAR

1. Remove lower control arm as outlined under “Control Arm, Replace.”
2. Clamp control arm in suitable vise with aluminum jaws.
3. Mount removal tool No. 208 589 00 43 00, or equivalent, clamping washer between control arm eye and rubberized stop ring collar.
4. Insert tool sleeve in clamping washer, thrust washer and thrust piece. Thrust washer straight pins point outward.
5. Remove hydraulic mount.
6. Cleaning mounting bore. **Do not use any oil, lubricant or grease containing acid.**
7. Insert hydraulic mount into control arm from behind viewed from direction of travel. Parallel surfaces of bearing core must be at 90° angle to control arm center weld seam.
8. Pull hydraulic mount to stop using tool thrust washers. Thrust washer straight pins point inwards.
9. Press washer flush with bearing core with tool thrust washer and thrust piece.
10. Install lower control arm.

S320 & S420 & 1998–99 CL500, CL600, S500 & S600

FRONT

1. Remove lower control arm as outlined under “Control Arm, Replace.”
2. Clamp control arm in suitable vise with aluminum jaws.
3. Loosen bushing with suitable drift punch.
4. Hammer bushing outer steel casing down with suitable flat chisel. **Do not damage mounting eye.**
5. Remove bushing.
6. Cleaning mounting bore.
7. Smear bushing with lubricant No. 000 989 03 67, or equivalent. **Do not use oil or grease.**
8. Insert bushing and spacer sleeve with flats perpendicular to control arm installed position.
9. Pull bushing and spacer sleeve to stop using installation tool No. 140 589 11 43 00, or equivalent.
10. Install lower control arm.

REAR

1. Remove lower control arm as outlined under “Control Arm, Replace.”
2. Clamp control arm in suitable vise with aluminum jaws.
3. Mount bowls of removal tool No. 140 589 11 43 00, or equivalent, between control arm eyes and rubberized stop ring collar.
4. Install tool sleeve bowls and remove hydraulic mount.
5. Cleaning mounting bore.
6. Smear bushing with thin film of lubricant No. 000 989 03 67, or equivalent. **Do not use oil or grease.**
7. Insert hydraulic mount with offset recess toward control arm weld seam horizontal.
8. Pull hydraulic mount until it abuts lower control arm collar using installation tool No. 140 589 11 43 00, or equivalent.
9. Install lower control arm.

E55, E300 & E430

FRONT

1. Remove lower control arm as outlined under “Control Arm, Replace.”
2. Clamp control arm in suitable vise with aluminum jaws.
3. Loosen outer steel washer with suitable flat chisel.
4. Remove hydraulic mount using thrust piece and three-arm tool No. 210 589 00 43 00, or equivalent.
5. Cleaning mounting bore.
6. Insert hydraulic mount with at 90° angle to lower control arm welding seam.
7. Draw hydraulic mount in until it abuts control arm collar using sleeve and thrust piece tool No. No. 210 589 00 43 00, or equivalent. **Do not use impact wrench.**
8. Install lower control arm.

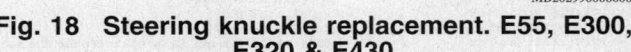

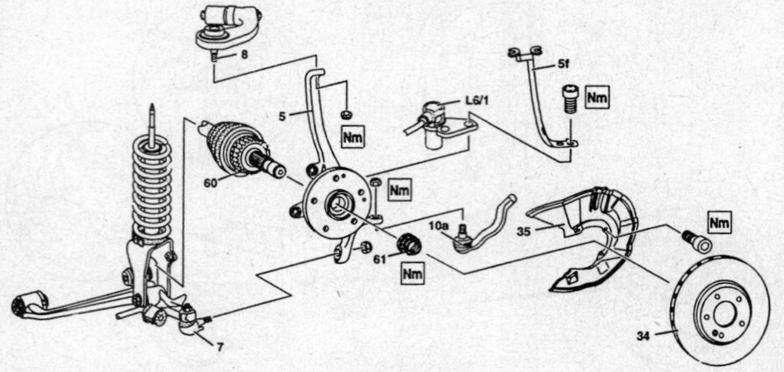

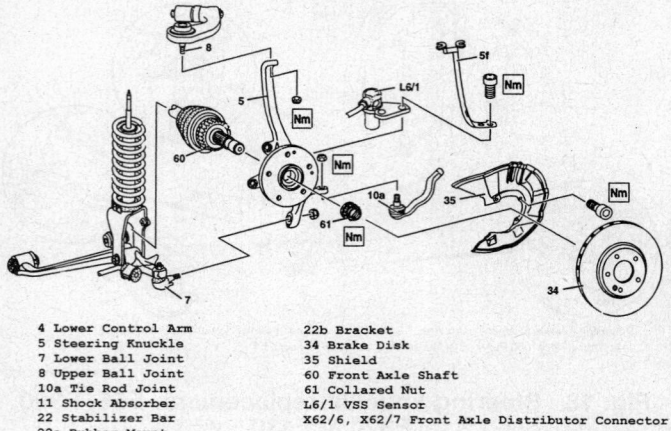

4 Lower Control Arm
5 Steering Knuckle
7 Lower Ball Joint
8 Upper Ball Joint
10a Tie Rod Joint
11 Shock Absorber
22 Stabilizer Bar
22a Rubber Mount
22b Bracket
34 Brake Disk
35 Shield
60 Front Axle Shaft
61 Collared Nut
L6/1 VSS Sensor
X62/6, X62/7 Front Axle Distributor Connector

MB2029900073000X

Fig. 19 Steering knuckle replacement. E320 w/4MATIC

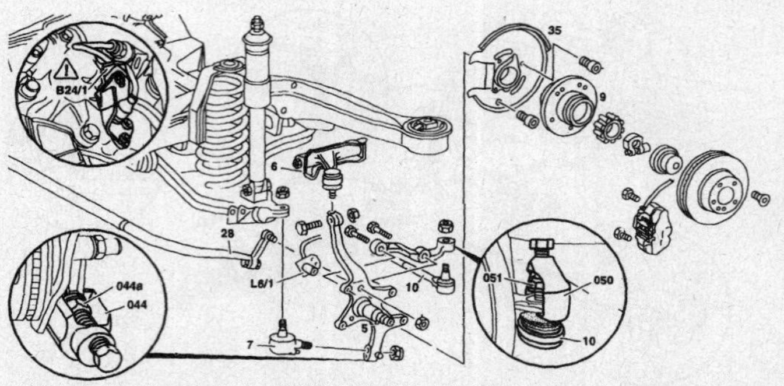

5 Steering Knuckle 6 Upper Control Arm 7 Ball Joint 9 Wheel Hub10 Tie Rod 28 Stablizer Bar Connecting Rod 35 Brake Splash Shield 044 Puller 0441 Thrust Piece 050 Puller 051 Thrust Piece B24/1 Wheel Acceleration Sensor L6/1 VSS Sensor

MB2029900065000X

Fig. 20 Steering knuckle replacement. S320 & S420 & 1998–99 CL500, CL600, S500 & S600

REAR

1. Remove lower control arm as outlined under "Control Arm, Replace."
2. Clamp control arm in suitable vise with aluminum jaws.
3. Remove front bushing as outlined under "Front."
4. Press out outer bushing using thrust piece, supporting washer and shaft of puller tool No. 202 589 00 43 00, or equivalent.
5. Pull out inner bushing using thrust piece, supporting washer and shaft of puller tool.
6. Cleaning mounting bore.
7. Insert bushing with lugs at 90° angle to control arm weld seam.
8. Pull bushing into control arm up to stop using thrust piece and clamp bolt of puller tool.
9. Install lower control arm.

E320

LESS 4MATIC

Refer to "E55, E300 & E430."

WITH 4MATIC

Front

1. Remove lower control arm as outlined under "Control Arm, Replace."
2. Clamp control arm in suitable vise with aluminum jaws.
3. Loose steel disk using suitable flat chisel and remove.
4. Pull bushing out using thrust piece, tensioning screw, thrust piece and nut of removal tool No. 210 589 00 43 00, or equivalent.
5. Install bushing with parallel surfaces at 90° to control arm.
6. Install bushing until it abuts control arm collar using thrust piece, tensioning screws, thrust piece and nut of installation tool No. 210 589 00 43 00, or equivalent.
7. Press on outer steel disk.

Rear

1. Remove front bushing as outlined under "Front."
2. Press outer bushing out using tensioning screw, supporting ring, thrust piece, nut and spindle of removal tool No. 210 589 00 43 00, or equivalent.
3. Press inner bushing out using thrust piece of removal tool.
4. Install bushing with rubber mount lugs correctly positioned.
5. Install bushing with spacer sleeve using two thrust pieces, nut and tensioning screw of installation tool No. 210 589 01 43 00, or equivalent, as far as stop.

SL500 & SL600

Replace bushings in complete pairs.

1. Remove control arm as outlined under "Control Arm, Replace."
2. Clamp control arm is suitable vise.
3. Countersink clamping sleeve flared rim with .9844 inch, 90° countersink.
4. Drive clamping sleeve out. If tightly seated, drill sleeve halfway.
5. Drive bushing out using suitable drift.
6. Thorough clean mounting bore and rub down with emery cloth, as required.
7. Coat bushing circumference and control arm mounting bore with Naphtolen or suitable soft soap. **Do not use grease.**
8. **On rear mounts,** install bushing so flats are vertical.
9. **On front mounts,** install bushing so flats are horizontal.
10. **On all mounts,** press bushing into control arm in vise.
11. Ensure bushing lugs engage thrust piece recess.
12. Install clamping sleeve.
13. Install puller tool No. 201 589 06 33 00, or equivalent, so thrust pieces is on closed side and unflared side of clamping sleeve points toward housing.
14. Clamp in vise and press together as far as possible.
15. Ensure bushing and clamping sleeve are perfectly seated against contact surfaces.

STEERING KNUCKLE

REPLACE

C43, C230, C280, CLK55, CLK320, CLK430, SLK230 & SLK320

Shock absorber must be installed to replace steering knuckle.

1. Raise and support vehicle, then remove front tire and wheel assembly.
2. Remove brake disc.
3. Remove front wheel hub as outlined under "Hub, Bearing & Seal, Replace," **Fig. 17.**
4. Remove brake splash shield.
5. Remove front axle VSS sensor and brake pad wear indicator.
6. Remove tie rod from steering knuckle using puller tool No. 202 589 02 33 00 and thrust piece tool No. 140 589 00 63 00, or equivalents.
7. Remove steering knuckle ball joint using puller tool No. 202 589 02 33 00 and thrust piece tool No. 140 589 00 63 00, or equivalents.
8. Remove steering knuckle from upper control arm using puller tool No. 124 589 03 33 00 and thrust piece tool No. 210 589 04 63 00, or equivalents.
9. Reverse procedure to install, noting the following:
   a. Install new self-locking bolts and nuts.
   b. Tighten mounting bolts and nuts to specifications.
   c. Inspect and adjust front wheel alignment as required.

E55, E300 & E430

Shock absorber must be installed to replace steering knuckle.

1. Raise and support vehicle, then remove front tire and wheel assembly.
2. Remove brake disc.
3. Remove front wheel hub as outlined under "Hub, Bearing & Seal, Replace," **Fig. 18.**
4. Remove front axle VSS sensor and brake pad wear indicator.
5. Remove tie rod from steering knuckle using puller tool No. 202 589 02 33 00 and thrust piece tool No. 140 589 00 63

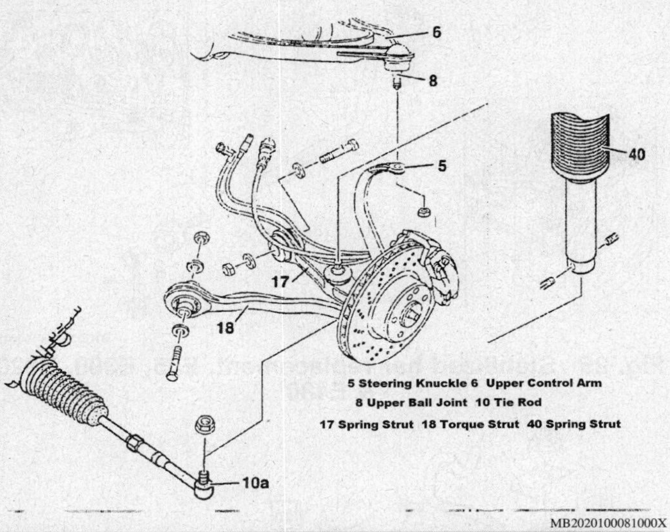

MB2020100081000X

Fig. 21 Front suspension replacement. S430 & 2000–01 CL500, CL600, S500 & S600

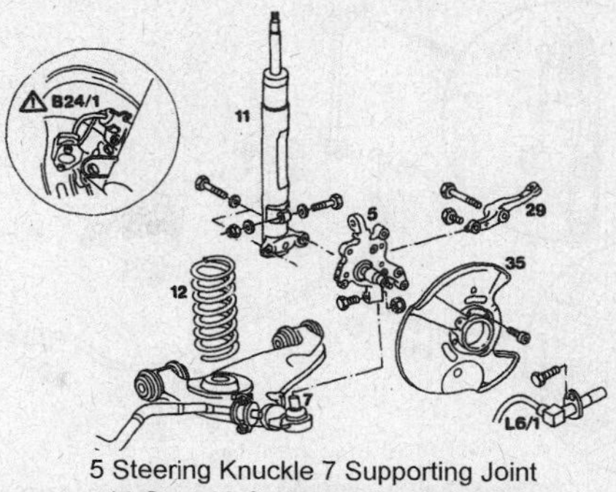

5 Steering Knuckle 7 Supporting Joint
11 Strut 12 Spring 35 Brake Guard
B24/1 Wheel Sensor :6/1 ABS Speed Sensor

MB2029900057000X

Fig. 22 Steering knuckle replacement. SL500 & SL600

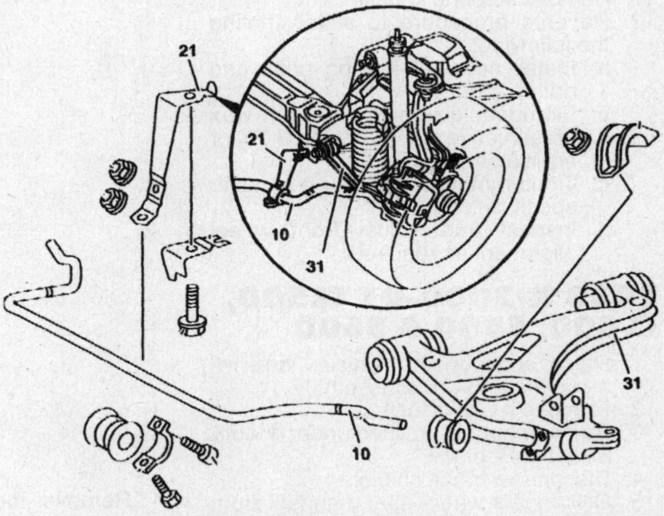

10 Stablized Bar 21Spring Leaf Swivelling Lever 31 Control Arm

MB2029900052000X

Fig. 23 Stabilized bar replacement. C43, C230, C280, CLK55, CLK320, CLK430, SLK230 & SLK320

00, or equivalents.

6. Remove steering knuckle ball joint using puller tool No. 202 589 02 33 00 and thrust piece tool No. 140 589 00 63 00, or equivalents.
7. Remove steering knuckle from upper control arm using puller tool No. 124 589 03 33 00 and thrust piece tool No. 210 589 04 63 00, or equivalents.
8. Reverse procedure to install, noting the following:
   a. Install new self-locking bolts and nuts.
   b. Tighten mounting bolts and nuts to specifications.
   c. Inspect and adjust front wheel alignment as required.

E320

Less 4MATIC

Refer to "E55, E300 & E430."

With 4MATIC

The shock absorber does not have to be removed.

1. Raise and support vehicle, then remove front tire and wheel assembly.
2. Remove front axle shaft nut, **Fig. 19.**
3. Disconnect front axle distributor connector.
4. Remove speed sensor cables and brake lining wear indicator fro guides. Mark positions for installation.
5. Remove brake disc and disconnect brake splash shield from steering knuckle.
6. Disconnect lefthand VSS and remove bracket.
7. Remove nut, then press tie rod joint out of steering knuckle using thrust piece tool No. 140 589 00 63 00 and puller tool No. 202 589 02 33 00, or equivalents.
8. Remove nut, and press lower ball joint out of steering knuckle using thrust piece tool No. 140 589 00 63 00 and puller tool No. 202 589 09 33 00, or equivalents.
9. Remove nut, then press upper ball joint out of steering knuckle using thrust piece tool No. 210 589 04 63 00 and puller tool No. 124 589 03 33 00, or equivalents.
10. Remove steering knuckle forward, moving front axle shaft out of flange.
11. Reverse procedure to install, noting the following:
    a. Install new self-locking bolts and nuts.
    b. Install new front axle shaft nut, tighten to specifications and secure with caulker so there is no gap between groove and locking tab.
    c. Tighten mounting bolts and nuts to specifications.
    d. Inspect and adjust front wheel alignment as required.

S320 & S420 & 1998–99 CL500, CL600, S500 & S600

Shock absorber must be installed to replace steering knuckle.

1. Remove front wheel hub as outlined under "Hub, Bearing & Seal, Replace," **Fig. 20.**
2. Remove brake splash shield.
3. Remove stabilized bar connecting rod from steering knuckle.
4. Remove front axle VSS sensor and brake pad wear indicator.
5. **On models equipped with ADS,** remove wheel acceleration sensor.
6. **On all models,** remove tie rod from steering knuckle using puller tool No. 140 589 00 33 00 and thrust piece tool No. 140 589 00 63 00, or equivalents.
7. Remove steering knuckle ball joint using puller tool No. 140 589 09 33 00 and thrust piece tool No. 140 589 24 63 00, or equivalents.
8. Remove upper wishbone mounting nut and press steering knuckle out of clamped joint. If clamped joint seized, expand with suitable spreader.
9. Remove tie rod from steering knuckle arm using puller tool No. 140 589 00 33 00 and thrust piece tool No. 140 589 00 63 00, or equivalents.
10. Remove steering knuckle arm for

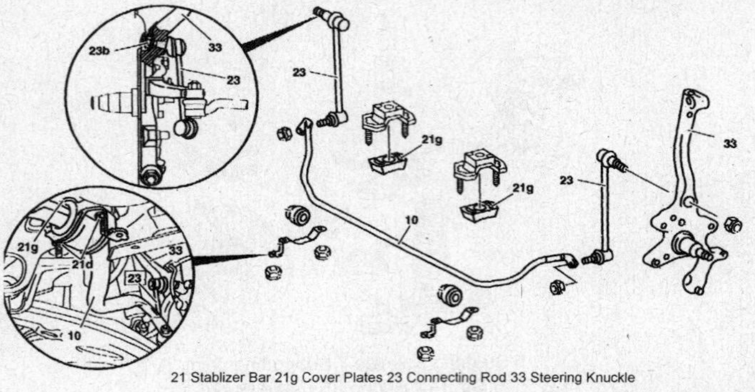

Fig. 24 Stabilizer bar replacement. S320 & S420 & 1998–99 CL500, CL600, S500 & S600

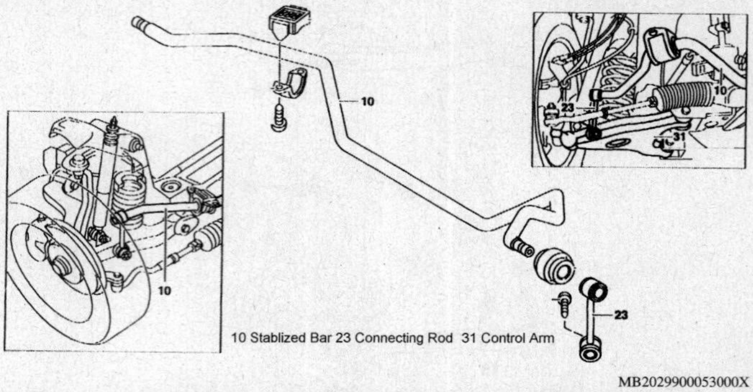

Fig. 25 Stabilized bar replacement. E55, E300, E320 & E430

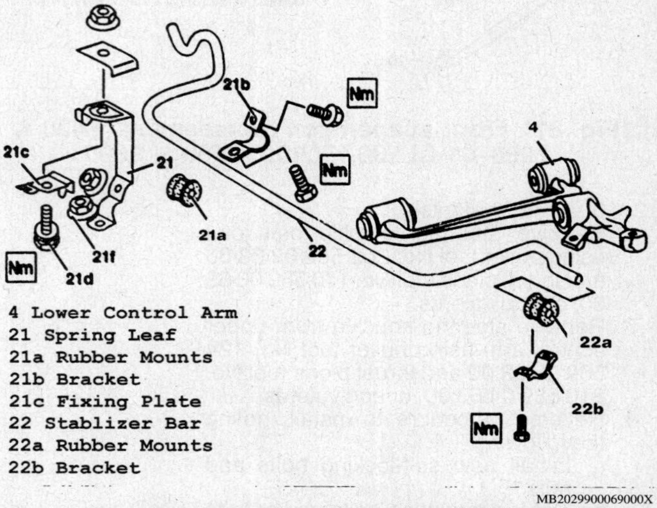

Fig. 26 Stabilizer bar replacement. E320 w/4MATIC

steering knuckle.

11. Remove steering knuckle.
12. Reverse procedure to install, noting the following:
    a. Install new self-locking bolts and nuts.
    b. Fill upper clamped joint with wax preservative No. 000 986 33 70, or equivalent.
    c. Tighten mounting bolts and nuts to specifications.
    d. Inspect and adjust front wheel alignment as required.

S430 & 2000–01 CL500, CL600, S500 & S600

1. Raise and support vehicle, then remove tire and wheel assembly.
2. Remove brake disc.
3. Remove hub as outlined under "Hub & Bearing, Replace."
4. Disconnect brake shield.
5. Disconnect wheel speed sensor from steering knuckle.
6. Press tie rod ball joint out of steering knuckle using thrust piece tool No. 140 589 00 63 00 and puller tool No. 124 589 03 33 00, or equivalents, **Fig. 21.**
7. Press upper ball joint out of steering knuckle using thrust piece tool No. 210 589 04 63 00 and puller tool No. 202 589 02 33 00, or equivalents.
8. Press torque strut out of steering knuckle using thrust piece tool No. 140 589 00 63 00, puller tool No. 220 589 00 33 00 and press tool No. 163 589 03 43 00, or equivalents. **Do not disconnect torque strut from front axle carrier.**
9. Press spring link out of steering knuckle using thrust piece tool No. 140 589 00 63 00, puller tool No. 220 589 00 33 00 and press tool No. 163 589 03 43 00, or equivalents. **Do not disconnect spring link from front axle carrier.**
10. Remove steering knuckle.
11. Reverse procedure to install.

SL500 & SL600

1. Raise and support vehicle, then remove tire and wheel assembly.
2. Remove wheel hub as outlined under "Hub, Bearing & Seal, Replace."
3. Disconnect ABS speed sensor, **Fig. 22.**
4. Remove mounting bolts and brake guard.
5. Remove spring as outlined under "Coil Spring, Replace."
6. Remove steering knuckle arm to steering knuckle mounting bolts.
7. **On models equipped with ADS,** remove wheel acceleration sensor from righthand steering knuckle.
8. **On all models,** remove strut mounting bolts and nuts.
9. Remove bolt and nut clamping steering knuckle to ball joint.
10. Remove steering knuckle from ball joint. If knuckle is corroded, loosen clamping joint by expanding slot using spread tool No. 140 589 02 31 00, or equivalent.
11. Reverse procedure to install, noting the following:
    a. Install new ball joint self-locking nut and tighten to specifications.
    b. Pack clamped joint slot with preservation wax No. 000 986 33 70 10, or equivalent.
    c. Install new microencapsulated mounting bolts and tighten to specifications.
    d. Tighten mounting bolts to specifications.
    e. Inspect and adjust wheel alignment as required.

STABILIZER BAR

REPLACE

C43, C230, C280, CLK55, CLK320, CLK430, SLK230 & SLK320

1. Remove mounting nuts and control arm bracket, **Fig. 23.**
2. Remove mounting nuts and stabilizer bar bracket.
3. Remove mounting bolt, spring leaf swiveling lever and mounting plate. Mark levers for installation. Left and righthand side are mounted differently.
4. Remove stabilized bar and rubber mounts.
5. Reverse procedure to install, noting the following:
    a. Install new self-locking bolts and nuts.
    b. Align stabilizer bar.
    c. Install bracket mounting bolt first because of preload.
    d. Tighten mounting bolts and nuts to specifications.

S320 & S420 & 1998–99 CL500, CL600, S500 & S600

1. Remove connecting rod mounting nuts, **Fig. 24.**

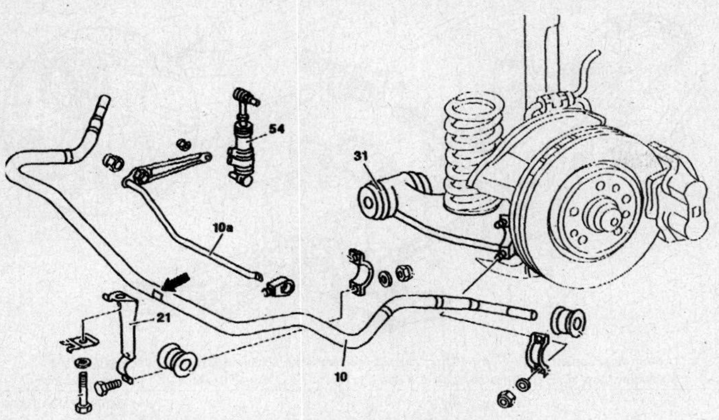

10 Stablized Bar 10a Intermediate Linkage 21 Spring Leaf Swivelling Lever
31 Control Arm 54 Control Rod

MB2029900050000X

Fig. 27 Stabilizer bar replacement. SL500 & SL600

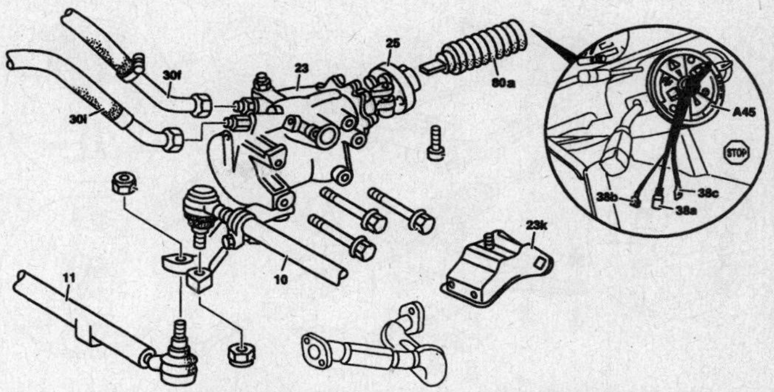

10 Tie Rod 11 Pitman Arm 23 Steering Gear 23k Heat Shield 25 Steering Coupling 30f Return Line
30i High Pressure Hose 80a Steering Shaft

MB6029900006000X

Fig. 28 Steering gear replacement. C43, C230, C280, CLK55, CLK320, CLK430, SL500, SL600, SLK230 & SLK320

2. Remove mounting nuts and brackets.
3. Remove stabilized bar and rubber mounts.
4. Remove front axle carrier cover plates.
5. If required, remove connecting rod as follows:
   a. Remove brake caliper and disk.
   b. Loosen steering knuckle to connecting rod nut half its thread length.
   c. Loosen steering knuckle connecting rod taper by hammering gently on mounting nut.
   d. Remove connecting rod.
6. Reverse procedure to install, noting the following:
   a. Smear rubber mounts' inside with naphthalene H lubricant No. 000 989 01 60, or equivalent.
   b. Install new self-locking bolts and nuts.
   c. Align stabilizer bar.
   d. Tighten mounting bolts and nuts to specifications.

E55, E300 & E430

1. Remove connecting rod mounting bolt, **Fig. 25.**
2. Remove mounting bolts and bracket from cover plates.
3. Remove stabilized bar.
4. Remove connecting rod.
5. Remove rubber mount.
6. Reverse procedure to install, noting the following:
   a. Smear rubber mounts' inside with naphthalene H lubricant No. 000 989 01 60, or equivalent.
   b. Install new self-locking bolts and nuts.
   c. Align stabilizer bar.
   d. Tighten mounting bolts and nuts to specifications.

E320

Less 4MATIC

Refer to "E55, E300 & E430."

With 4MATIC

1. Remove engine compartment lower cover.
2. Disconnect control arm bracket, **Fig. 26.**
3. Disconnect spring leaf swinging bracket.
4. Remove stabilized bar.
5. Mark spring leaf swinging bracket for installation and disconnect. Left and righthand brackets differ.
6. Remove rubber mounts.
7. Reverse procedure to install, noting the following:
   a. Install new self-locking bolts and nuts.
   b. Center stabilizer bar.
   c. Tighten mounting bolts and nuts to specifications.

SL500 & SL600

1. **On models equipped with ADS,** remove mounting nuts and intermediate linkage control rod, **Fig. 27.**
2. **On all models,** remove wishbone bracket mounting nuts.
3. Remove spring leaf swiveling lever bracket mounting nuts.
4. Remove mounting bolt, spring leaf swiveling lever and mounting plate.
5. Remove stabilizer bar through engine compartment cover side.
6. Remove rubber mounts.
7. **On models equipped with ADS,** remove intermediate linkage from stabilizer bar.
8. **On all models,** reverse procedure to install, noting the following:
   a. **On models equipped with ADS,** slide bush with hexagon side forward onto stabilizer bar. Ensure intermediate linkage and stabilizer bar faces align.
   b. **On all models,** install new self-locking bolts and nuts.
   c. Align stabilizer bar.
   d. Tighten mounting bolts and nuts to specifications.

TENSION STRUT

REPLACE

S430 & 2000-01 CL500, CL600, S500 & S600

1. Raise and support vehicle, then remove tire and wheel assembly.
2. Remove brake caliper. **Do not disconnect brake lines. Hang caliper with suitable wire.**
3. Press upper ball joint out of steering knuckle using thrust piece tool No. 210 589 04 63 00 and puller tool No. 202 589 02 33 00, or equivalents, **Fig. 21.**
4. Swivel steering knuckle outward.
5. Press torque strut out of steering knuckle using thrust piece tool No. 140 589 00 63 00, puller tool No. 220 589 00 33 00 and press tool No. 163 589 03 43 00, or equivalents.
6. Disconnect engine compartment from fender inner liner and swivel fender liner back.
7. Remove mounting bolt, nut and tension strut. **If repair kit has been installed, do not turn bolt.**
8. Reverse procedure to install, noting the following:
   a. **Do not torque** strut mounting bolt until vehicle weight is on wheels.
   b. Tighten mounting bolts and nuts to specifications.

SPRING LINK

REPLACE

S430 & 2000-01 CL500, CL600, S500 & S600

1. Raise and support vehicle, then remove tire and wheel assembly.
2. Press torque strut out of steering knuckle using thrust piece tool No. 140 589 00 63 00, puller tool No. 220 589 00 33 00 and press tool No. 163 589 03 43 00, or equivalents, **Fig. 21. Do not disconnect torque strut from front axle carrier.**
3. Press tie rod ball joint out of steering knuckle using thrust piece tool No. 140 589 00 63 00 and puller tool No. 124 589 03 33 00, or equivalents.
4. **On models equipped with AIRmatic,** remove mounting nut and disconnect connecting rod.
5. **On all models,** remove mounting bolts and disconnect spring strut from spring link with suitable lever.
6. Press spring link out of steering knuckle using thrust piece tool No. 140 589

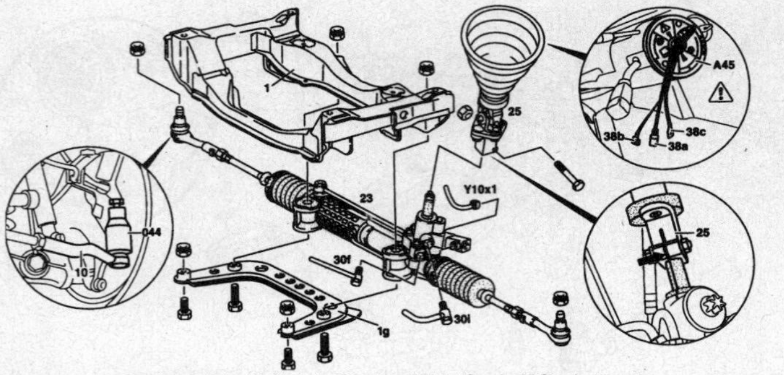

1 Front Axle Carrier 1g Retainer 10 Tie Rods 23 Rack-And-Pinion Steering25 Steering Coupling 30f Return line 30i High-Pressure Hose Y10x1 Connector

MB6029900007000X

Fig. 29 Steering gear replacement. E55, E300, E320 & E430

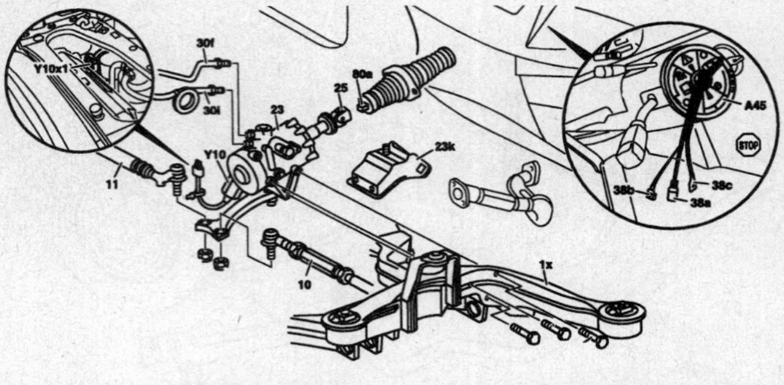

1x Front Axle Carrier 10 Tie Rod 11 Drag Link 23 Steering Gear 23k Heat Shield 25 Steering Coupling 30f Return Line 30i High Pressure Hose 80a Steering Shaft A45 Contact Spiral Y10x1 P-Valve Connector

MB6029900005000X

Fig. 30 Steering gear replacement. S320 & S420 & 1998–99 CL500, CL600, S500 & S600

00 63 00, puller tool No. 220 589 00 33 00 and press tool No. 163 589 03 43 00, or equivalents.
7. **On models equipped with Active Body Control (ABC),** remove right-hand spring link, disconnect pressure control unit on righthand side of front axle frame and tie up with suitable wire.
8. **On all models,** remove mounting bolt, nut and spring link. **Do not turn bolt.**
9. Reverse procedure to install.

TIE ROD

REPLACE

INNER

1. Remove outer tie rod joint nut.
2. Remove tire rod using thrust piece tool No. 140 589 00 63 00 and puller tool No. 202 589 02 33 00, or equivalent.
3. Inspect bellows and replace as required.
4. Ensure steering is centered and remove inner tie rod joint from steering rack.
5. Reverse procedure to install, noting the following:
   a. Install new self-locking nuts.
   b. Tighten nuts to specifications.

OUTER

1. Steady ball pivot with suitable Allen wrench and remove tie rod nut.
2. Press tie rod off using thrust piece tool No. 140 589 00 63 00 and puller tool No. 140 589 00 33 00, or equivalents.
3. Clean grease off taper.
4. Press tie rod ball joints securely into steering arm.
5. Install new mounting nuts and tighten to specifications.

POWER STEERING GEAR

REPLACE

C43, C230, C280, CLK55, CLK320, CLK430, SL500, SL600, SLK230 & SLK320

1. Move adjustment steering column out full extend.
2. Remove power steering pump oil with hand pump tool No. 210 589 00 71 00, or equivalent.
3. **On SLK230 and SLK320 models,** remove aerodynamic molding.
4. **On SL500 and SL600 models,** disconnect tie rod from pitman arm, **Fig. 28.**
5. **On all models,** disconnect drag link from pitman arm.
6. **On SL500 models,** remove exhaust connecting pipe.
7. **On SL500 and SL600 models,** remove heat shield.
8. **On all models,** disconnect and seal return line and high pressure stretch hose.
9. Remove ignition key and allow steering lock to engage. **Do not allow steering wheel to turn or contact spiral will be damaged beyond repair.**
10. Disconnect steering shaft from steering coupling.
11. **On SLK230 and SLK320 models,** proceed as follows:
    a. Disconnect frame longitudinal member ground strap.
    b. Disconnect left and righthand engine mount lower mounting bolts.
    c. Raise engine approximately 1.575 inches and push to right.
12. **On all models,** remove mounting bolts and move steering gear out of shaft. Remove steering gear. **Do not force.**
13. Reverse procedure to install, noting the following:
    a. Install new mounting bolts and nuts.
    b. Tighten mounting bolts and nuts to specifications.
    c. Align steering shaft marking line with housing cover.
    d. Fill and bleed power steering pump as outlined under "Power Steering System Bleed,"
    e. Inspect front wheel alignment and adjust as required.

E55, E300, E320 & E430

1. Remove power steering pump oil using hand pump tool 210 589 00 71 00, or equivalent.
2. **On models equipped with level control,** disconnect and seal feed line clamp tool No. 000 589 40 37 00, or equivalent.
3. **On all models,** remove ignition key and allow steering lock to engage. **Do not allow steering wheel to turn or contact spiral will be damaged beyond repair.**
4. Remove tie rod joint self-locking nut, then press out steering knuckle joint using thrust piece tool No. 140 589 00 63 00 and puller tool No. 202 589 02 33 00, or equivalents, **Fig. 29.**
5. **On models equipped with 4MATIC,** remove steering cap seals' heat shield.
6. **On all models,** disconnect and seal return line and high pressure stretch hose.
7. Disconnect steering coupling from rack-and-pinion control valve. **Do not force.**
8. Disconnect P-valve connector on left-hand front end and expose steering gear cable harness.
9. Disconnect retaining front mounting bolts.
10. Remove mounting bolts and power steering rack-and-pinion.
11. Reverse procedure to install, noting the following.
    a. Install new mounting bolts and nuts.
    b. Tighten mounting bolts and nuts to specifications.
    c. Align steering shaft marking line with housing cover.
    d. Fill and bleed power steering pump as outlined under "Power Steering System Bleed,"
    e. Inspect front wheel alignment and adjust as required.

S320 & S420 & 1998–99 CL500, CL600, S500 & S600

1. Move steering column out its full extent.
2. Remove power steering pump oil using hand pump tool 210 589 00 71 00, or equivalent.
3. Disconnect P-valve connector on left-hand front end and expose steering gear cable harness, **Fig. 30.**
4. Disconnect tie rod and drag link at pitman arm.
5. **On 1998–99 CL500, CL600, S500**

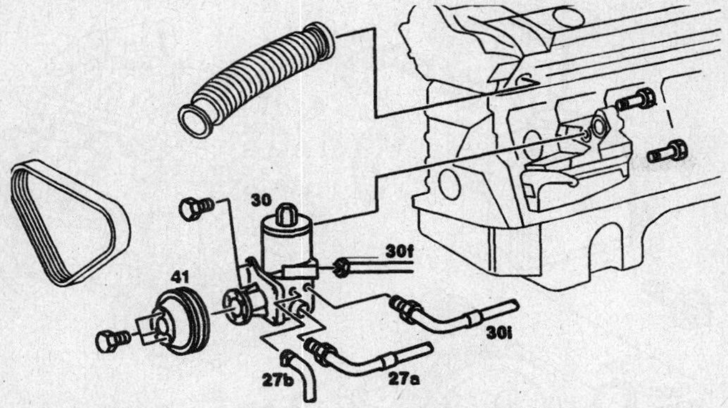

27a High Pressure Hose 27b Suction Line 27c & 27d Oil Line
30 Power Steering Pump 30f Return Line 30i High Pressure Hose
41 Belt Pulley

MB6029900008000X

Fig. 31 Power steering pump replacement. C230, E300, S320, SLK230 & SLK320

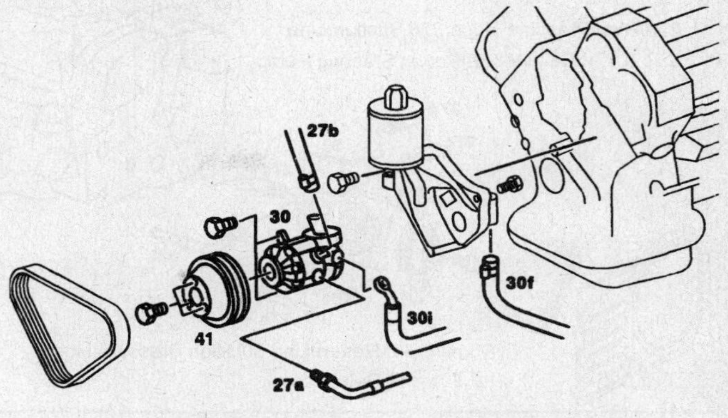

27a High Pressure Hose 27b Suction Line 27c & 27d Oil Line
30 Power Steering Pump 30f Return Line 30i High Pressure Hose
41 Belt Pulley

MB6029900009000X

Fig. 32 Power steering pump replacement. S420 & 1998–99 CL500, CL600, S500 & S600 & 1998 SL500

and S600 models, remove exhaust connecting pipe and heat shield.

6. **On all models,** disconnect and seal return line and high pressure stretch hose.
7. Remove ignition key and allow steering lock to engage. **Do not allow steering wheel to turn or contact spiral will be damaged beyond repair.**
8. Disconnect steering shaft from steering coupling.
9. Remove mounting bolls and steering gear.
10. Reverse procedure to install, noting the following:
    a. Install new mounting bolts and nuts.
    b. Tighten mounting bolts and nuts to specifications.
    c. Align steering shaft marking line with housing cover.
    d. Fill and bleed power steering pump as outlined under "Power Steering System Bleed,"
    e. Inspect front wheel alignment and adjust as required.

S430 & 2000–01 CL500, CL600, S500 & S600

1. Raise and support vehicle, then remove front tire and wheel assemblies.
2. Remove power steering pump oil using hand pump tool 210 589 00 71 00, or equivalent.
3. Center steering wheel and lock using holding tool No. 129 589 01 21 00, or equivalent.
4. Remove center and rear lower engine compartment paneling.
5. Press tie rod ball joint out of steering knuckle using thrust piece tool No. 140 589 00 63 00 and puller tool No. 124 589 03 33 00, or equivalents.
6. Remove lower steering shaft coupling bolt.
7. Pull lower steering shaft out of coupling using suitable tool. **Do not use hammering or sever force.**
8. Disconnect SPS solenoid valve connector.
9. Remove retaining plate to front axle carrier mounting bolts.
10. Loosen rack and pinion plate to front axle carrier mounting bolts.
11. Remove high pressure and return flow lines. Seal and plug lines and openings.
12. Remove mounting bolts and rack and pinion with retaining plate.
13. Reverse procedure to install, noting the following:
    a. Install new self-locking bolts and nuts.
    b. Push lower steering column into coupling as far as stop.
    c. Install new sealing rings.
    d. Tighten mounting bolts and nuts to specifications.
    e. Bleed system.

POWER STEERING PUMP

REPLACE

C230, E300, S320, S420, SL600, SLK230 & 1998–99 CL500, CL600, S500 & S600 & 1998 SL500

Less Level Control

1. Remove reservoir oil using hand pump tool No. 210 589 00 71 00, or equivalent.
2. Remove air intake hose, fan shroud, ignition, distributor, etc., as required to expose power steering pump.
3. Remove drive belt.
4. **On models equipped with ZF power steering pump,** remove belt pulley.
5. **On all models,** disconnect and seal high pressure stretch hose and return line using suitable blind plugs, **Figs. 31 through 33.**
6. **On SLK230 and SLK320 models,** disconnect oil cooler lines.
7. **On CL600 and SL600 models,** disconnect oil lines.
8. **On all models,** disconnect and remove power steering pump.
9. Reverse procedure to install, noting the following:
    a. Tighten mounting bolts and nuts to specifications.
    b. Bleed system as outlined under "Power Steering System Bleed."

With Level Control

1. **On C230, S320, S420, SL600, SLK230 and SLK320 and 1998–99 CL500, CL600, S500 and S600 and 1998 SL500 models,** remove reservoir oil using hand pump tool No. 210 589 00 71 00, or equivalent.
2. **On E300 models,** disconnect and seal reservoir oil feed line using clamp tool No. 000 589 40 37 00, or equivalent.
3. **On all models,** remove air intake hose, fan shroud, ignition, distributor, etc., as required to expose power steering pump.
4. Remove drive belt.
5. **On models equipped with ZF power steering pump,** remove belt pulley.
6. **On all models,** disconnect and seal high pressure stretch hose and return line using suitable blind plugs, **Figs. 31 through 33.**
7. Remove and seal high pressure stretch hose and suction line using suitable blind plugs.
8. **On SLK230 and SLK320 models,** disconnect oil cooler lines.
9. **On CL600 and SL600 models,** disconnect oil cooler lines.
10. **On all models,** disconnect and remove power steering pump.
11. Reverse procedure to install, noting the following:
    a. Tighten mounting bolts and nuts to specifications.
    b. Bleed system as outlined under

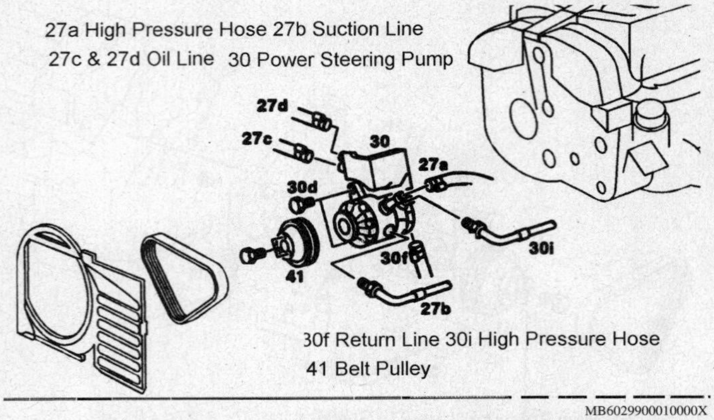

Fig. 33 Power steering pump replacement. CL600, S600 & SL600

"Power Steering System Bleed."

C43, C240, C280, C320, CLK55, CLK320, CLK430, E55, E320, E430 & S430 & 2000–01 CL500, CL600, S500 & S600

Less Level Control

1. Remove fan, shroud and drive belt.
2. Remove reservoir oil using hand pump tool No. 210 589 00 71 00, or equivalent.
3. Disconnect return line and high-pressure hose, **Fig. 34.**
4. Remove mounting bolts, power steering pump and reservoir.
5. Remove reservoir by pressing locking ring out using suitable screwdriver.
6. Reverse procedure to install, noting the following:
   a. Tighten mounting bolts and nuts to specifications.
   b. Bleed system as outlined under "Power Steering System Bleed."

With Level Control

1. Remove fan, shroud and drive belt.
2. **On C280 and CLK55, CLK320 and CLK430 and 1999–2001 SL500 and 2000–01 SL600 models,** remove reservoir oil using hand pump tool No. 210 589 00 71 00, or equivalent.
3. **On E55, E320 and E430 models,** disconnect and seal reservoir oil feed line using clamp tool No. 000 589 40 37 00, or equivalent.
4. **On all models,** disconnect return line and high-pressure hose, **Fig. 34.**
5. Disconnect tandem pump pressure and intake lines. Seal intake line with clamp and plug high-pressure line.
6. Remove mounting bolts and power steering pump.
7. **On C280, CLK55, CLK320 and CLK430 and 1999–2001 SL500 and 2000–01 SL600 models,** remove reservoir by pressing locking ring out using suitable screwdriver.
8. **On all models,** reverse procedure to install, noting the following:

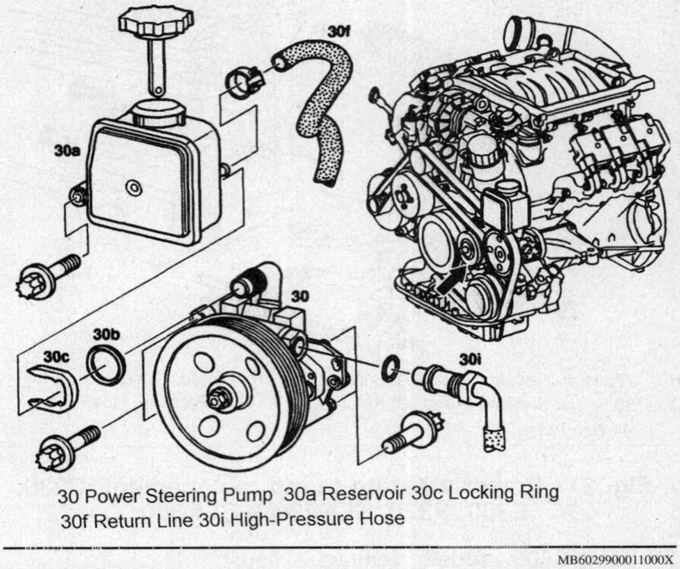

Fig. 34 Power steering pump replacement. C43, C240, C280, C320, CLK55, CLK320, CLK430, E55, E320, E430 & S430 & 1999–2001 SL500 & 2000–01 CL500, CL600, S500, S600 & SL600

   a. Tighten mounting bolts and nuts to specifications.
   b. Bleed system as outlined under "Power Steering System Bleed."

POWER STEERING SYSTEM BLEED

1. Start engine 2–3 times to automatic bleed system.
2. Turn steering from lock-to-lock several times with engine running.
3. Adjust fluid level.

TECHNICAL SERVICE BULLETINS

STEERING STIFF & POSSIBLE NOISES

E300, E320 & E430

On some of these models the steering may be stiff and/or have noises.

This condition may be caused by contact between the bottom and sealing ring or mismatched boot and sealing ring.

To correct this condition, proceed as follows:

1. Apply grease No. 001 989 46 51, or equivalent, to firewall side boot on steering column on contact surface between boot and sealing ring.
2. If condition still exists, remove boot.
3. Ensure boot number and sealing ring diameter match, **Fig. 35.**

KNOCKING NOISE FROM FRONT AXLE WHEN STEERING

S430 & 2000–01 S500 & 2001 S600

On some of these models there may be a front axle knocking noise when steering.

This condition may be caused by a broken control arm mount.

To correct this condition, replace control arm.

SQUEAKING NOISES WHEN STEERING

C43, C230 & C280

On some of these models there may be a squeaking noise when steering.

This condition may be caused by torn sealing bellows.

To correct this condition, proceed as follows:

1. Inspect sealing bellows.
2. If bellows is damaged, replace support joint.
3. Ensure sealing bellows rotates on ball joint when wheels are turned.

AIR SUSPENSION MIL ON

S430, 2000–01 S500 & 2001 S600

On some of these models the air suspension MIL may be on (instrument cluster reads "Air suspension ... visit workshop."

This condition may be caused by water in level sensor connectors.

To correct this condition, proceed as follows:

1. Disconnect level sensor connector.

Boot Part No.	Sealing Ring Outer Diameter, Inch
210 462 08 96	1.4765
210 462 01 96	1.6537
210 462 05 96	1.6537
210 462 09 96	1.6537

Fig. 35 Steering boot sealing ring application chart. E300, E320 & E430

Code	Interpretation
C1121	Front Lefthand Body Acceleration Sensor
C1122	Front Righthand Body Acceleration Sensor
C1123	Rear Righthand Body Acceleration Sensor
C1132	Front Lefthand Level Sensor
C1133	Front Righthand Level Sensor
C1135	Rear Axle Level Sensor
C1144	Pneumatic Suspension Pressure Sensor

Fig. 36 Air suspension DTC interpretation. S430, 2000–01 S500 & 2001 S600

Pneumatic suspension Diagnostic Trouble Codes (DTCs) may help determine which sensor to inspect, **Fig. 36.**

2. Inspect for water. Clean as required.
3. Close off connector chamber to which wires are not attached.

FRONT AXLE RUMBLING ON UNDULATING OR POOR ROADS

1998–99 CL500, CL600, S320, S420, S500 & S600

On some of these models there may be front axle rumbling on undulating or poor roads.

This condition may be caused by worn out front axle torsion bar connecting rod.

To correct this condition, inspect the torsion bar connecting rod play. Replace as required.

STEERING WHEEL VIBRATION OR SHIMMY

1998–99 CL500, CL 600, S320, S420, S500 & S600

On some of these models there may be a steering wheel vibration or shimmy.

This condition may be caused by tire flat spots.

To correct this condition, proceed as follows:

1. Install hydraulic bearings on bottom control arm mounts. Hydraulic bearings are standard after VIN A 096 694.
2. Adjust wheel bearing play to .0004 inch.
3. If condition still exists, inspect tires for flat spots. Replace as required.

E55, E300, E320 & E430

On some of these models there may be a vibration or shimmy in the steering wheel.

This condition may be caused by bottom wishbone hydraulic rubber mount wear or liquid loss.

To correct this condition, proceed as follows:

1. Inspect hydraulic rubber mount.
2. If there is visible leakage at arrows or crackling in shaded area, replace mount.

HIGH-PITCHED METALLIC KNOCKING WHEN STARTING TO DRIVE & AT SLOW SPEEDS

CL500, CL600, S320, S420, S500 & S600 w/ADS

On some of these models there may be a high-pitch metallic knocking noise when starting and at slow speeds.

This condition may be caused by jammed shock absorber piston suddenly releasing.

To correct this condition, replace shock absorber.

LEAKING FRONT WHEEL BEARING GREASE CAP

C43, C230 & C280

On some of these models the front wheel bearing grease cap may leak.

This condition may be caused by rough sealing surfaces.

To correct this condition, replace leaking cap as follows:

1. Fill cap with .4332 oz. of suitable high-temperature bearing grease.
2. Thoroughly clean contact surfaces of cap and front wheel hub.
3. Seal contact surfaces with Hylomar sealant No. 001 989 25 20, Omnifit 1050 sealant No. 002 989 45 20, or equivalent.

SINGLE KNOCKING NOISE WHEN STOPPING w/LIGHT BRAKE PRESSURE

C43, C230 & C280

On some of these models there may be a single knocking noise when stopping with light brake pressure.

This condition may be caused by excessive lower control arm bushing movement.

To correct this condition, replace lower control arm front bushing.

INSUFFICIENT POWER STEERING ASSISTANCE

S420, S500 & S600

On some of these models there may be insufficient power steering assistance.

This condition may be caused by narrowing of hoses between reservoir and power steering pump.

To correct this condition, inspect, then correct installation and hose routing

POWER STEERING OIL COOLER LEAK

S320

On some of these models there may be an oil leak at the power steering oil cooler.

This condition may be caused by vibration crack.

To correct this condition, install new power steering cooler tube with formed return hose and curved steel return line. Assemble tension free.

TIGHTENING SPECIFICATIONS

Year	Component	Torque, Ft. Lbs.
C43, C230, C280, CLK55, CLK320 & CLK430		
1998–2001	Ball Joint	77
	Ball Joint To Control Arm	77
	Brake Line	10
	Brake Splash Shield	18
	Control Arm, Lower To Bracket	18
	Control Arm, Lower To Frame	88
	Control Arm, Lower To Shock Absorber	41
	Control Arm, Upper To Frame	48
	Control Arm, Upper To Steering Knuckle	33
	Disc Brake Locking	88①
	Engine Mount To Crossmember (C230)	18
	Power Steering Pump	18
	Power Steering Pump High Pressure Line (M14)	22
	Power Steering Pump High Pressure Line (M16)	37
	Power Steering Pump Pulley	22
	Power Steering Pump Return Line	30
	Shock Absorber To Control Arm	41
	Shock Absorber Upper	13
	Shock Absorber Upper, Lock Nut	22
	Stabilizer Bar Spring Leaf Swiveling Lever Bottom Bracket	15
	Stabilizer Bar Spring Leaf Swiveling Lever (M8)	15
	Stabilizer Bar Spring Leaf Swiveling Lever Side Member	44
	Stabilizer Bar Spring Leaf Swiveling Lever Top Bracket	30
	Stabilizer Bar To Control Arm	15
	Steering Coupling	22
	Steering Gear	52
	Steering Gear Line, High-Pressure	22
	Steering Gear Line, Return	30
	Steering Knuckle To Ball Joint	33
	Steering Knuckle To Upper Control Arm	77
	Tandem Pump High-Pressure Hose	18
	Tie Rod To Steering Knuckle	37
	VSS Sensor	18
CL500, CL600, S320, S420, S430, S500 & S600		
1998–99	Ball Joint, Control Arm	74
	Ball Joint, Steering Knuckle	103
	Brake Disc Locking Bolt	88①
	Brake Lines	10
	Brake Splash Shield	18
	Control Arm, Lower To Ball Joint	74
	Control Arm, Lower To Front Axle Carrier	133
	Control Arm, Lower To Steering Knuckle	104
	Control Arm, Upper To Steering Knuckle	92
	Engine Mount To Front Axle Carrier	18
	Front Axle Carrier To Front End	96
	Power Steering Pump	18
	Power Steering Pump High Pressure Line (M14)	22

Continued

TIGHTENING SPECIFICATIONS—Continued

Year	Component	Torque, Ft. Lbs.
CL500, CL600, S320, S420, S430, S500 & S600		
1998–99	Power Steering Pump High Pressure Line (M16)	37
	Power Steering Pump Pulley	22
	Power Steering Pump Return Line	30
	Shock Absorber To Control Arm	74
	Shock Absorber Upper	30
	Stabilizer Bar	15
	Stabilizer Connecting Rod	59
	Stabilizer Connecting Rod To Steering Knuckle	30
	Steering Coupling (M8)	18
	Steering Coupling (M10)	22
	Steering Coupling (Torx)	15
	Steering Gear	37(2)(3)
	Steering Gear High Pressure Switch	30
	Steering Gear Lines	30
	Steering Shaft	15
	Steering Shaft, Lower To Upper	81
	Tandem Pump High-Pressure Hose	18
	Tie Rod To Steering Arm	37
2000–01	Control Arm, Upper To Frame	37
	Control Arm, Upper To Steering Knuckle	33
	Power Steering Hose, Return Flow To Rack And Pinion	33
	Power Steering Hose, Pressure To Rack and Pinion	29
	Power Steering Pump	(5)
	Power Steering Pump High-Pressure Hose	29
	Power Steering Pump Return Hose	18(1)
	Rack And Pinion	81
	Spring Link To Front Axle Carrier	111
	Spring Link To Steering Knuckle	59
	Spring Strut To Spring Link	15
	Steering Shaft Coupling	18
	Tie Rod To Steering Knuckle	37(4)
	Torque Strut To Front Axle Carrier	111
	Torque Strut To Steering Knuckle	59
	Vehicle Speed Sensor To Steering Knuckle	18
E55, E300 & E430		
1998–2001	Ball Joint	77
	Brake Lines (E300)	13
	Brake Lines (E430)	10
	Brake Splash Shield	18
	Control Arm, Lower	88
	Control Arm, Upper To Frame	48
	Control Arm, Upper To Steering Knuckle (Bolt)	33
	Control Arm, Upper To Steering Knuckle (Nut)	88
	Front Axle Support	96
	Front Engine Mount To Front Axle Support (E300)	(6)

Continued

TIGHTENING SPECIFICATIONS—Continued

Year	Component	Torque, Ft. Lbs.
E55, E300 & E430		
1998–2001	Power Steering Pump	18
	Power Steering Pump High Pressure Line (M14)	22
	Power Steering Pump High Pressure Line (M16)	37
	Power Steering Pump Pulley	22
	Power Steering Pump Return Line	30
	Shock Absorber To Control Arm	41
	Shock Absorber Upper	13
	Shock Absorber Upper, Lock Nut	22
	Stabilizer Bar	15
	Stabilizer Bar Connecting Rod	59
	Stabilize Bar To Steering Knuckle	30
	Steering Coupling	15
	Steering Gear Front Axle Retaining Plate	37
	Steering Gear Lines	30
	Steering Knuckle To Ball Joint	77
	Steering Knuckle Upper Control Arm	33
	Steering Rack-And-Pinion	37②
	Tandem Pump High-Pressure Hose	18
	Tie Rod To Steering Knuckle	52
	Tie Rod To Steering Rack	81
	VSS Sensor	18
E320 LESS 4MATIC		
1998–2001	Ball Joint	77
	Brake Lines	13
	Brake Splash Shield	18
	Control Arm, Lower	88
	Control Arm, Upper To Frame	48
	Control Arm, Upper To Steering Knuckle (Bolt)	33
	Control Arm, Upper To Steering Knuckle (Nut)	88
	Front Axle Support	96
	Front Engine Mount To Front Axle Support	30
	Power Steering Pump	18
	Power Steering Pump High Pressure Line (M14)	22
	Power Steering Pump High Pressure Line (M16)	37
	Power Steering Pump High Pressure Line (E320)	33
	Power Steering Pump Pulley	22
	Power Steering Pump Return Line	30
	Shock Absorber To Control Arm	41
	Shock Absorber Upper	13
	Shock Absorber Upper, Lock Nut	22
	Stabilizer Bar	15
	Stabilizer Bar Connecting Rod	59
	Stabilize Bar To Steering Knuckle	30
	Steering Coupling	15

Continued

TIGHTENING SPECIFICATIONS—Continued

Year	Component	Torque, Ft. Lbs.
E320 LESS 4MATIC		
1998–2001	Steering Gear Front Axle Retaining Plate	37
	Steering Gear Lines	30
	Steering Knuckle To Ball Joint	77
	Steering Knuckle Upper Control Arm	33
	Steering Rack-And-Pinion	37②
	Tandem Pump High-Pressure Hose	18
	Tie Rod To Steering Knuckle	52
	Tie Rod To Steering Rack	81
	VSS Sensor	18
E320 w/4MATIC		
1998–2001	Ball Joint, Lower	77
	Ball Joint, Upper	33
	Brake Line	13
	Brake Splash Shield	18
	Control Arm, Lower	81
	Control Arm, Upper	37
	Drive Shaft	26
	Front Axle Carrier	96
	Front Axle Shaft Nut	206
	Front Axle Speed Sensor	44
	Front Engine Mount To Front Axle Carrier	26
	Propeller Shaft	26
	Shock Absorber	13
	Shock Absorber Lock Nut	22
	Shock Absorber To Control Arm	136
	Stabilizer Bar Bracket To Control Arm	15
	Stabilizer Bar Spring Leaf Swinging Bracket	30
	Stabilizer Bar Spring Leaf Swinging Bracket To Front Axle Carrier	44
	Steering Coupling	15
	Steering Gear Line	30
	Steering Knuckle Lower Ball Joint	77
	Steering Knuckle Upper Ball Joint	33
	Tandem Pump High-Pressure Hose	18
	Tie Rod To Steering Knuckle	44
ML55, ML320 & ML430		
1998–2001	Power Steering Pump	⑤
	Power Steering Pump High-Pressure Hose	29
	Power Steering Pump Return Hose	18①
	Propeller Shaft To Front Differential Carrier	37
	Propeller Shaft To Transfer Case	29
SL500 & SL600		
1998–2001	Ball Joint, Lower	77
	Ball Joint, Upper	33
	Brake Disc Locking Bolt	88①
	Brake Guard	88①
	Power Steering Pump	18
	Power Steering Pump High Pressure Line (M14)	22
	Power Steering Pump High Pressure Line (M16)	37
	Power Steering Pump Pulley	22
	Power Steering Pump Return Line	30

Continued

TIGHTENING SPECIFICATIONS—Continued

Year	Component	Torque, Ft. Lbs.
SL500 & SL600		
1998–2001	Shock Absorber Lock Nut	22
	Shock Absorber Nut	13
	Shock Absorber To Control Arm	136
	Stabilized Bar Bracket	15
	Stabilizer Bar Intermediate Linkage	88①
	Stabilizer Bar To Control Arm	15
	Stabilizer Bar To Spring Leaf Swiveling Lever	15
	Stabilizer Spring Leaf Swiveling Lever To Side Member	44
	Steering Coupling	22
	Steering Gear	52
	Steering Gear Line, High-Pressure	22
	Steering Gear Line, Return	30
	Steering Knuckle	59
	Strut	59
	Strut Rubber Mount	15
	Strut/Steering Knuckle Clamping Joint (M12)	81
	Strut/Steering Knuckle Clamping Joint (M14)	148
	Strut To Steering Knuckle (M12)	81
	Strut To Steering Knuckle (M14)	148
	Tandem Pump High-Pressure Hose	18
	Wheel Bearing Adjusting Bolt	106①
SLK230 & SLK320		
1998–2001	Ball Joint	77
	Brake Line	10
	Brake Splash Shield	18
	Control Arm, Lower To Bracket	18
	Control Arm, Lower To Frame	88
	Control Arm, Lower To Shock Absorber	41
	Control Arm, Upper To Frame	48
	Control Arm, Upper To Steering Knuckle	33
	Disc Brake Locking	88①
	Engine Mount To Crossmember	18
	Power Steering Pump	18
	Power Steering Pump High Pressure Line	33
	Power Steering Pump Pulley	22
	Power Steering Pump Return Line	30
	Shock Absorber Upper	13
	Shock Absorber Upper, Lock Nut	22
	Shock Absorber To Control Arm	41
	Stabilizer Bar Spring Leaf Swiveling Lever Bottom Bracket	15
	Stabilizer Bar Spring Leaf Swiveling Lever (M8)	15
	Stabilizer Bar Spring Leaf Swiveling Lever Side Member	44
	Stabilizer Bar Spring Leaf Swiveling Lever Top Bracket	30
	Stabilizer Bar To Control Arm	15
	Steering Coupling	22
	Steering Gear	52
	Steering Gear Line, High-Pressure	22
	Steering Gear Line, Return	30

Continued

TIGHTENING SPECIFICATIONS—Continued

Year	Component	Torque, Ft. Lbs.
SLK230 & SLK320		
1998–2001	Steering Knuckle To Ball Joint	33
	Steering Knuckle To Upper Control Arm	33
	Tandem Pump High-Pressure Hose	18
	Tie Rod To Steering Knuckle	37
	VSS Sensor	18

① — Inch lbs.
② — Tighten an addition 90.°
③ — Do not exceed 103 ft. lbs.
④ — Tighten an addition 60°.
⑤ — Balcony mount or engine block, 18 ft. lbs.; Self-tapping, uncut, 26 ft. lbs.; precut 15 ft. lbs.
⑥ — E300 models, 22 ft. lbs.; E430 models, 30 ft. lbs.

Front Wheel Drive

NOTE: On Air Bag Equipped Models, Refer To "Air Bag System Precautions" Located In The Front Of This Manual For System Disarming & Arming Procedures.

INDEX

	Page No.
Axle Bearing Seal, Replace	5-175
E320 w/4MATIC	5-175
Axle Shaft, Replace	5-174
E320 w/4MATIC	5-174
Differential Carrier, Replace	5-175
E320 w/4MATIC	5-175
Intermediate Shaft, Replace	5-175
E320 w/4MATIC	5-175
Pinion Flange Seal, Replace	5-175
E320 w/4MATIC	5-175
Precautions	5-174
Air Bag Systems	5-174
Battery Ground Cable	5-174
Radio Coded Anti-Theft System	5-174
Stabilizer Bar, Replace	5-176
Steering Knuckle & Ball Joint, Replace	5-176
Tightening Specifications	5-177

PRECAUTIONS

AIR BAG SYSTEMS

Refer to "Air Bag System Precautions" in front of this manual for system disarming and arming procedures.

BATTERY GROUND CABLE

Prior to service, disconnect battery ground cable and isolate as required.

RADIO CODED ANTI-THEFT SYSTEM

Anti-theft radios have a coded theft protection circuit. The CODE card must be obtained before disconnecting battery, removing radio fuse or removing the radio. **The serial number from the radio must match the CODE card.**

After service has been performed proceed as follows:

1. Connect radio power and turn key to position No. 2.
2. Turn radio to On position. Word "CODE" will appear on display.
3. Enter first digit of anti-theft code from CODE card. "CODE" will disappear and entered digit will appear followed by four dashes.
4. Enter next four digits, when all five are entered first digit flashes again.
5. Press SC, Seek or Tune button to confirm code.
6. If "WAIT" appears on radio panel, proceed as follows:
   a. Radio will allow three coding attempts only before entering lock-up mode and won't respond to controls.
   b. Leave radio on for 15–60 minutes, then radio will unlock and allow three addition coding attempts.
   c. Third lockout period (after nine failed coding attempts) will last 24 hours.
   d. Radio must be left on during enter 24-hour period until "CODE" appears.
7. When "CODE" appears, repeat coding attempt.

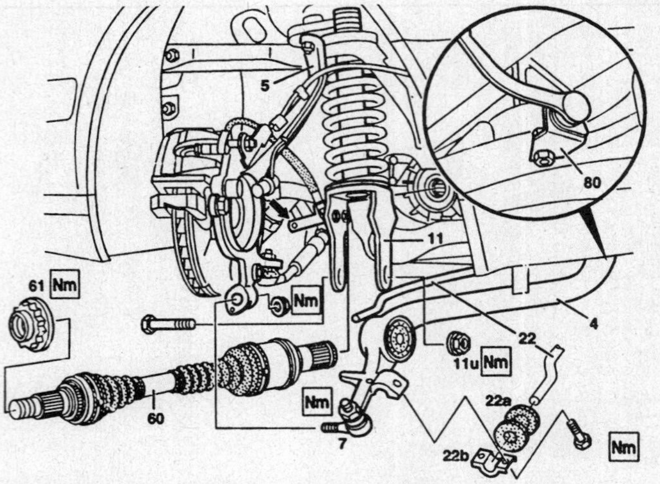

4 Lower Control Arm
5 Steering Knuckle
7 Lower Ball Joint
11 Shock Absorber
22 Stablizer Bar
22a Rubber Mount
22b Bracket
60 Front Axle Shaft
61 Collared Nut
80 Headlamp Levelling Device

MB3039900015000X

Fig. 1 Front axle shafts replacement. E320 w/4MATIC

AXLE SHAFT

REPLACE

E320 w/4MATIC

1. Remove front axle shaft nut, **Fig. 1.**
2. Remove engine compartment lower cover.
3. Disconnect brake line bracket on shock absorber shackle.
4. Disconnect stabilized bar bracket from lower control arm and remove rubber mount.
5. If removing righthand axle, disconnect headlamp leveling linkage.
6. Remove nut, and press lower ball joint out of steering knuckle using thrust piece tool No. 140 589 00 63 00 and puller tool No. 140 589 09 33 00, or equivalents.
7. Disconnect shock absorber from lower control arm.
8. Disconnect lower control arm mounting nuts on axle carrier.
9. Press stabilized bar over lower control arm mounting bracket.
10. Pull steering knuckle out and move front axle shaft out of flange.
11. Cover steering knuckle and front axle carrier with cloths.
12. Press shaft out using suitable screwdriver. **Do not damage rubber boots and speed sensor rotor.**
13. If boot cover replacement is required, proceed as follows:
    a. Disconnect rubber boots from joint, **Fig. 2.**
    b. Drive outer joint ring off using suitable open end wrench.
    c. Inner joint cannot be removed.
    d. Pull rubber boots off front axle shaft.
14. Reverse procedure to install, noting the following:
    a. Install new self-locking bolts and nuts.

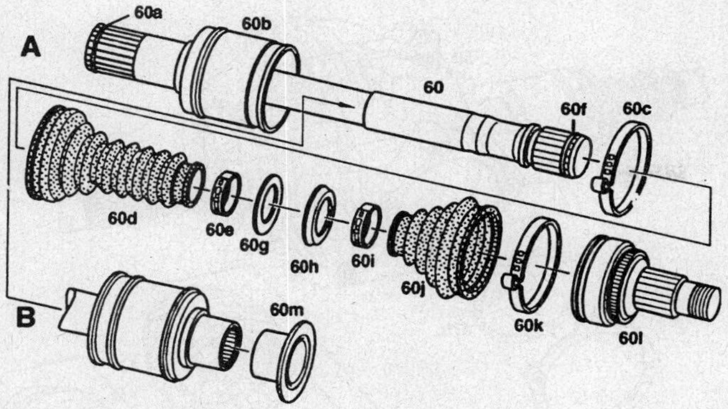

Fig. 2 Front axle shaft rubber boot replacement. E320 w/4MATIC

b. Place suitable assembly sleeve on front axle splined shaft and push rubber boots on.
c. Push disk spring and intermediate ring onto front axle shaft.
d. Press outer joint ring on. Circlip must lock into joint hub.
e. Align front axle shaft joint to almost horizontal before pressing in.
f. Install front axle shaft flange in two-row angular contact ball bearing using installation tool No. 124 589 05 43 00, or equivalent.
g. Tighten mounting bolts and nuts to specifications.
h. Tighten control arm mounting nuts when vehicle weight is on tires.

INTERMEDIATE SHAFT

REPLACE

E320 w/4MATIC

1. Remove lefthand front axle shaft as outlined under "Axle Shaft, Replace," **Fig. 3.**
2. Remove circlip.
3. Remove intermediate shaft from oil pan.
4. Remove deep-groove ball bearing circlip.
5. Remove deep-groove ball bearing using two-arm puller tool No. 000 589 88 33 00, or equivalent.
6. Reverse procedure to install, noting the following:
   a. Press new deep-groove ball bearing with bearing inner race underneath.
   b. Ensure intermediate shaft circlip is correctly seated.

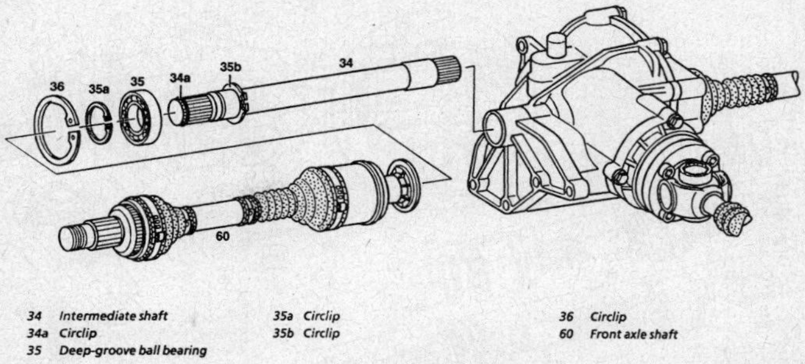

Fig. 3 Intermediate shaft replacement. E320 w/4MATIC

DIFFERENTIAL CARRIER

REPLACE

E320 w/4MATIC

1. Remove front axle shaft nut, **Fig. 4.**
2. Remove engine compartment lower cover.
3. Disconnect oxygen sensors.
4. Remove complete exhaust system.
5. Remove front axle drive propeller shaft as outlined under "Front Suspension & Steering" "Driveshaft, Replace."
6. Remove nut, and press lower ball joint out of steering knuckle using thrust piece tool No. 140 589 00 63 00 and puller tool No. 202 589 09 33 00, or equivalents.
7. Pull steering knuckle out and mover front axle shafts out of flange.
8. Tie steering knuckle to one side with suitable wire.
9. Cover steering knuckle and front axle carrier with cloths.
10. Press front axle shafts out using suitable screwdriver. **Do not damage rubber boots and speed sensor rotors.**
11. Remove intermediate shaft circlip.
12. Pull intermediate shaft out of front axle drive.
13. Remove mounting bolts and disconnect front axle drive to engine mount bracket.
14. Remove front axle drive collared bolts.
15. Remove mounting bolts on left and righthand integral carrier engine mount.
16. Raise engine approximately 1.9687 inches. **Do not trap or damage parts.**
17. Install drift punch tool No. 210 589 01 15 00, or equivalent, in righthand outer radial seal ring.
18. Remove differential carrier.
19. Reverse procedure to install, noting the following:
   a. Ensure intermediate shaft circlip is correcting seated.
   b. Inspect front axle shaft groove circlip and replace as required.
   c. Align front axle shaft joint to almost horizontal before pressing in.
   d. Install front axle shaft flange in two-row angular contact ball bearing using installation tool No. 124 589 05 43 00, or equivalent.
   e. Tighten mounting bolts and nuts to specifications.

PINION FLANGE SEAL

REPLACE

E320 w/4MATIC

1. Remove front axle drive propeller shaft as outlined under "Front Suspension & Steering" "Driveshaft, Replace."
2. Position suitable container under axle drive housing.
3. Mark bearing cover to housing for installation alignment.
4. Remove drive pinion bearing cover, **Fig. 5.**
5. Remove spacer washer and O-ring.
6. Attach pin wrench tool No. 210 589 02 40 00, or equivalent, to drive pinion with bearing cover and clamp into suitable vise.
7. Remove mounting nut.
8. Pull flange off using two-arm puller tool No. 000 589 88 33 00, or equivalent.
9. Press radial seal ring out with suitable screwdriver.
10. Reverse procedure to install, noting the following:
   a. Install new self-locking nuts.
   b. Coat radial seal ring sealing lip with suitable hypoid transmission oil.
   c. Press radial seal ring flush with bearing cover using suitable drift punch.
   d. Tighten mounting bolts and nuts to specifications.

AXLE BEARING SEAL

REPLACE

E320 w/4MATIC

Righthand Outer

1. Remove axle shaft as outlined under "Axle Shaft, Replace," **Fig. 6.**

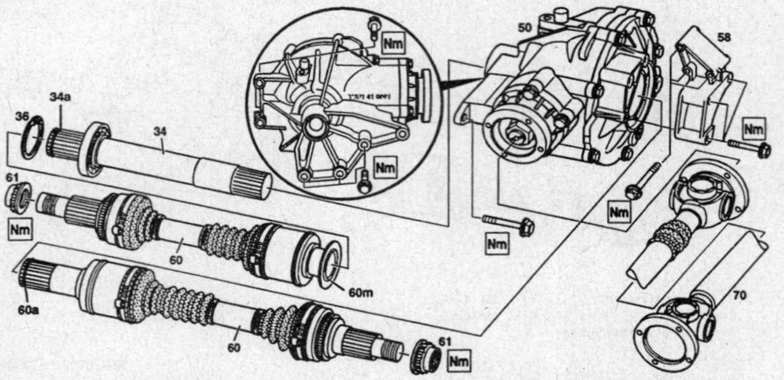

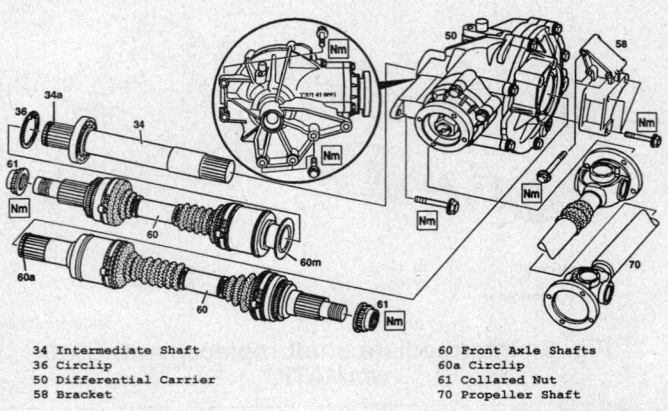

Fig. 4 Front axle replacement. E320 w/4MATIC

2. Pull radial seal ring out using countering support tool No. 000 589 34 33 00 and 1.3781–1.8112 inches internal extractor tool No. 000 589 34 33 00, or equivalents.
3. Coast radial seal ring sealing lips with suitable hypoid transmission oil.
4. Press seal into housing using drift punch tool No. 210 589 01 15 00, or equivalent, and suitable extension.

Lefthand Inner

1. Clamp differential carrier on assembly trestle tool No. 129 589 00 31 00, or equivalent.
2. Disconnect bearing cover.
3. Remove differential from carrier.
4. Pull radial seal ring out using countering support tool No. 000 589 333 33 00 and .9844–1.5750 inches internal extractor tool No. 000 589 33 33 00, or equivalents.
5. Coat radial seal ring sealing lip with suitable hypoid transmission oil.
6. Press seal ring in housing using drift punch tool No. 210 589 00 15 00, or equivalent. Ring inside must point toward punch.
7. Clean bearing cover sealing surface and coat with Hylomar sealing agent No. 001 989 25 20, or equivalent.

STEERING KNUCKLE & BALL JOINT

REPLACE

Refer to "Front Suspension & Steering."

STABILIZER BAR

REPLACE

Refer to "Front Suspension & Steering."

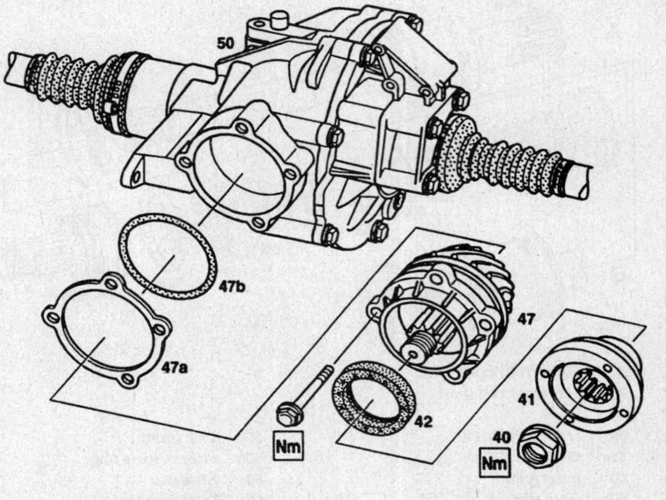

Fig. 5 Drive pinion seal ring replacement. E320 w/4MATIC

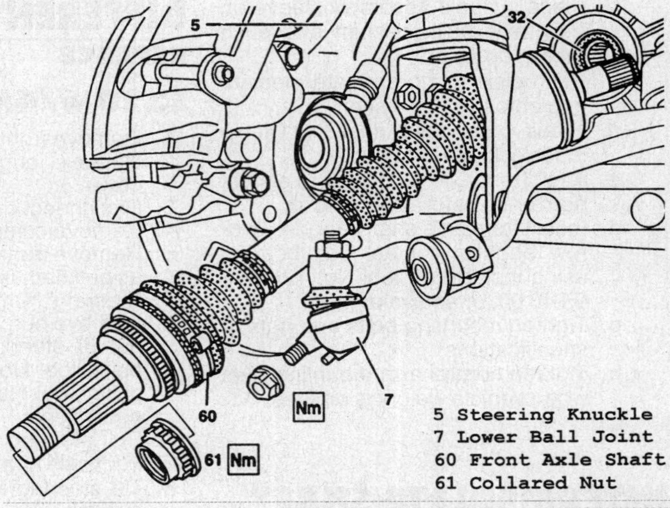

Fig. 6 Outer righthand front axle drive seal ring replacement. E320 w/4MATIC

TIGHTENING SPECIFICATIONS

Year	Component	Torque, Ft. Lbs.
E320 w/4MATIC		
1998–2001	Ball Joint, Lower	77
	Bearing Cover (M8)	26
	Bearing Cover (M10)	48
	Drive Pinion Cover	26
	Drive Pinion Flange	350
	Engine Mount Mounting Bracket	18
	Front Axle Drive To Engine Oil Pan	48
	Front Axle Shaft Nut	206
	Front Engine Mount To Front Axle Carrier	26
	Lower Control Arm To Axle Carrier	81
	Oil Filler	22
	Shock Absorber To Lower Control Arm	136

Wheel Alignment

INDEX

	Page No.
Front Wheel Alignment	5-178
Ball-Point, Adjust	5-179
Camber & Caster, Adjust	5-178
Toe-In, Adjust	5-179
Inspection	5-178
Preliminary Inspection	5-178
Rear Wheel Alignment	5-180
Camber, Adjust	5-180
Toe-In, Adjust	5-180
Technical Service Bulletins	5-182
Increase Tire Wear	5-182
Vehicle Veers To Right On Level Road	5-182
Vehicle Ride Height	5-180
Adjust	5-180
Measurement	5-180
Wheel Alignment Specifications	5-9

PRELIMINARY INSPECTION

1. Ensure vehicle oil and coolant levels are correct.
2. **On C43, C230, C240, C280, C320, CLK55, CLK320, CLK430, E55, E300, E320, E430, ML55, ML 320, ML 430, SL500, SL600, SLK230 and SLK320 and 1998–99 CL 500, CL600, S320, S420, S500 and S600 models,** if fuel tank is not full, compensate for lack of fuel by adding weight in trunk.
3. **On all models,** ensure spare tire and tool kit are properly located.
4. Ensure vehicle is unladen. Remove any luggage or equipment.
5. Ensure tire pressures are correct.
6. Inspect tires' wear pattern, tread depth and for damage.
7. Inspect wheels for damage.
8. Inspect vehicle for damage.
9. Inspect chassis and supporting body for corrosion.
10. Inspect components and pipes for leaks.

Front Axle Level Degrees	Camber, Degrees①	Inches
+2.1	0	-1 1/30
+1.4	-.1969	-1 3/20
+.6	-.3974	-1 4/15
-.1	-.5906	-1 11/30

① — Tolerance, plus or minus 1/3°; Maximum difference between left and righthand sides, 1/3°.

Fig. 1 Camber specification. C43 & CLK55

INSPECTION

Perform alignment inspections in order.

On 2000–01 S430 and S500 and 2001 S600 models, do not check chassis alignment when engine is hot. As spring struts may be heated which may influence vehicle level.

1. Drive vehicle onto suitable electronic measuring system.
2. Inspect wheel bearing play.
3. Inspect steering mechanism.
4. Inspect bellows.
5. Unlock rotary and sliding plates.
6. Install brake pedal winch tool No. 000 589 18 31 00, or equivalent.
7. Ensure transmission selector is in P position.
8. Open driver's window and turn ignition switch to OFF position.
9. Get out of vehicle and close doors.
10. Attach quick-action clamp tools No. 124 589 01 31 00, or equivalent, to front and rear wheels.
11. Attach and adjust measuring heads.
12. Perform initial measurements.
13. Inspect vehicle ride height at front and rear axles. Adjust as required.
14. Inspect ball point position.
15. Inspect rear axle toe-in. Adjust as required.
16. Inspect front axle camber and caster. Adjust as required.
17. **On ML55, ML320 and ML430 models,** inspect rear axle camber and caster. Adjust as required.
18. **On all models,** inspect front axle toe-in. Adjust as required.
19. Perform initial measurements.
20. Remove measuring heads and brake pedal winch.
21. Drive vehicle off measuring system and lock rotary plates.

FRONT WHEEL ALIGNMENT

CAMBER & CASTER, ADJUST

C43, C230, C280, CLK55, CLK320, CLK430, E55, E300, E320, E430, SLK230 & SLK320

1. Inspect and adjust vehicle level as outlined under "Vehicle Ride Height."
2. Inspect camber, **Figs. 1 through 8.**
3. Inspect caster, **Figs. 9 through 17.**
4. Raise and support vehicle.
5. Clamp spring. **Handle preloaded springs and parts with suitable clamping tools, only.**
6. Install repair set (19b) tool No. BA40.20-P-1005-01A, or equivalent, and screw nut until it abuts, **Figs. 18 though 23.** Do not tighten now.
7. Unclamp spring and lower vehicle.
8. Push and pull suspension several times to deflect.
9. Inspect and adjust vehicle level as outlined under "Vehicle Ride Height."
10. **On models equipped less 4MATIC, torque** repair set nut to 88 ft. lbs.
11. **On models equipped with 4MATIC, torque** repair set nut to 81 ft. lbs.
12. **On all models,** adjust camber and caster.
13. Adjust rear, then front axle toe-ins.

C240 & C320

1. Inspect and adjust vehicle level as outlined under "Vehicle Ride Height."
2. Inspect camber, **Fig. 24.**
3. Inspect caster, **Fig. 25.**
4. Raise and support vehicle.
5. Install repair bolt and tighten nut as far as is will go. **Do not tighten so transverse strut or radius rod can turn when suspension is compressed or rebounded.**
6. Inspect vehicle front axle level.
7. **Torque** repair kit nut to 111 ft. lbs.. **Adjusting screw must not be turned and must be countered when tightening nut.**
8. Adjust camber and caster, **Figs. 26 and 27.**

1998-99 CL500, CL600, S320, S420, S500 & S600

1. Inspect and adjust vehicle level as outlined under "Vehicle Ride Height."
2. Inspect camber and caster. Refer to "Specifications."
3. Install caster measuring tool No. 140 589 03 21 00, or equivalent, (04) on steering knuckle mounting points, **Fig. 28.**
4. Adjust camber with front cam bolt (19) and caster with rear cam bolt (20) at control arm mount (4), **Fig. 29.**

Front Axle Level Degrees	Camber, Degrees①	Inches
+7.8	+1.5750	-6/15
+7.1	+1.3781	-27/60
+6.4	+1.1812	-1/2
+5.6	+.9844	-17/30
+4.9	+.7875	-13/20
+4.2	+.5906	-43/60

① — Tolerance, plus or minus 1/3°; Maximum difference between left and righthand sides, 1/3°.

Fig. 2 Camber specification. C230 & C280

Front Axle Level Degrees	Camber, Degrees①	Inches
+3.5	+.3975	-49/60
+2.8	+.1969	-9/10
+2.1	0	-1 1/30
+1.4	-.1969	-1 3/20
+.6	-.3974	-1 4/15
-.1	-.5906	-1 11/30

① — Tolerance, plus or minus 1/3°; Maximum difference between left & righthand sides, 1/3°.

Fig. 3 Camber specification. CLK320 & CLK430

Front Axle Level Degrees	Camber, Degrees①	Inches
+2.9	-.1969	-11/12
+2.2	-.3974	-1 1/30
+1.4	-.5906	-1 3/20
+.7	-.7875	-1 4/15

① — Tolerance, plus or minus 1/3°; Maximum difference between left and righthand sides, 1/3°.

Fig. 4 Camber specification. E55

Front Axle Level Degrees	Camber, Degrees①	Inches
+7.9	+1.1812	-1/3
+7.2	+.9844	-23/60
+6.5	+.7875	-7/15
+5.8	+.5906	-8/15
+5.0	+.3974	-37/60
+4.3	+.1969	-43/60
+3.6	0	-49/60

① — Tolerance, plus or minus 1/3°; Maximum difference between left and righthand sides, 1/3°.

Fig. 5 Camber specification. E300 & E320 & E430 sedan less 4MATIC

5. **Torque** cam bolt nut to 133 ft. lbs.

S430 & 2000–01 CL500 & S500 & 2001 CL600 & S600

1. Inspect and adjust vehicle level as outlined under "Vehicle Ride Height."
2. Inspect camber, **Figs. 30 and 31.**
3. Inspect caster, **Figs. 32 and 33.**
4. Raise and support vehicle.
5. Install repair bolt and tighten nut as far as is will go. **Do not tighten so transverse strut or radius rod can turn when suspension is compressed or rebounded.**
6. Inspect vehicle front axle level.
7. **Torque** repair kit nut to 88 ft. lbs.
8. Adjust camber and caster, **Figs. 34 and 35.**

SL500 & SL600

1. Inspect and adjust vehicle level as outlined under "Vehicle Ride Height."
2. Inspect camber and caster. Refer to "Specifications."
3. Install caster measuring tool No. 201 589 02 21 00, or equivalent, (04a) on steering knuckle mounting points, **Fig. 36.**
4. Loosen and tighten bracket (22b) on control arms, **Fig. 37.**
5. Adjust camber with front cam bolt (19) and caster with rear cam bolt (20) at control arm mount (4), **Fig. 38.**
6. **Torque** cam bolt nut to 88 ft. lbs. and bracket nut to 15 ft. lbs.

TOE-IN, ADJUST

1. Fix steering wheel in centered position with holder tool No. 129 589 01 21 00, or equivalent.
2. **On C43, C230, C280, CLK55, CLK320, CLK430, SLK230 and SLK320 models,** steering gear is centered when steering coupling separating joint and steering gear marking notch are aligned.
3. **On C240, C280, E55, E300, E320 and E430 models,** steering gear is centered when cap marking line aligns with rotary slide valve marking notch.
4. **On 1998–99 CL500, CL600, S320, S420, S500 and S600 models,** steering gear is centered when steering coupling clamping slot aligns with steering gear line.
5. **On S430 and 2000–01 CL500 and S500 and 2001 CL600 and S600 models,** steering gear is centered when cap marks align with rotary-spool valve notch.
6. **On SL500 and SL600 models,** steering gear is centered when gear marks align above each other.
7. **On all models,** offset steering wheel by no more than one tooth, as required.
8. Install Beissbarth wheel spreader tool No. 860 000 883, or equivalent, and adjust toe-in by rotating tie rods.
9. **On C43, C230, C280, CLK55, CLK320, CLK430, CL500, CL600, S320, S420, S500, S600, SLK230 and SLK320 models, torque** lock nuts to 37 ft. lbs.
10. **On C240, C320, E300, E320, E430 and S430 and 2000–01 CL500 and S500 and 2001 CL600 and S600 models, torque** lock nuts to 44 ft. lbs.
11. **On SL500 and SL600 models, torque** holder to 15 ft. lbs. and clamp to 37 ft. lbs.

BALL-POINT, ADJUST

C43, C230, C280, CLK55, CLK320, CLK430, S420, SL500, SL600, SLK230 & SLK320

1. Install control arm measuring tool No. 201 589 00 21 00, or equivalent, on wishbone bolted connection and position to zero on scale using suitable plum bob.
2. Position ball point position in straight-ahead position, **Fig. 39.**
3. Adjust by sliding drag link cylindrical section.
4. If ball point cannot be adjusted at steering idler arm, correct at pitman arm of offsetting the splined section of the shaft.
5. If ball point position is more than .1969 inch out of tolerance, inspect steering idler arm bearing.
6. **Torque** steering idler arm to bearing bush to 22 ft. lbs.

1998–99 CL500, CL600, S320, S500 & S600

1. Install control arm measuring tool No. 140 589 00 21 00, or equivalent, on wishbone bolted connection and position to zero on scale using suitable plum bob.
2. Position ball point position in straight-ahead position, **Fig. 39.**

Front Axle Level	Camber, Degrees①	
Degrees		Inches
+10.1	+1.7781	-1/5
+9.3	+1.5750	-7/30
+8.6	+1.3781	-17/60
+7.9	+1.1812	-1/3
+7.2	+.9844	-23/60
+6.5	+.7875	-7/15
+5.8	+.5906	-8/15

① — Tolerance, plus or minus 1/3°; Maximum difference between left and righthand sides, 1/3°.

Fig. 6 Camber specification. E320 wagon less 4MATIC

Front Axle Level	Camber, Degrees①	
Degrees		Inches
+2.9	-.1969	-11/12
+2.2	-.3974	-1 1/30
+1.4	-.5906	-1 3/20
+.7	-.7875	-1 4/15
0	-.9844	-1 6/15
-.7	-1.1812	-1 11/20
-1.4	-1.3781	-1 7/10

① — Tolerance, plus or minus 1/3°; Maximum difference between left and righthand sides, 1/3°.

Fig. 7 Camber specification. E320 & E430 w/4MATIC

3. Adjust by sliding tie rod.
4. If ball point cannot be adjusted at steering idler arm, correct at pitman arm of offsetting the splined section of the shaft.
5. If ball point position is more than .1969 inch out of tolerance, inspect steering idler arm bearing.
6. **Torque** steering idler arm to bearing bush to 26 ft. lbs.

Front Axle Level	Camber, Degrees①	
Degrees		Inches
+4.2	+.5906	-43/60
+3.5	+.3937	-49/60
+2.8	+.1969	-9/10
+2.1	0	-1 1/30
+1.4	-.1969	-1 3/20
+.6	-.3937	-1 4/15
-.1	-.5906	-1 11/30

① — Tolerance, plus or minus 1/3°; Maximum difference between left and righthand sides, 1/3°.

Fig. 8 Camber specification. SLK230 & SLK320

REAR WHEEL ALIGNMENT

CAMBER, ADJUST

The rear wheel camber cannot be adjusted. Inspect and adjust vehicle lever as outlined under "Front Wheel Alignment." Too great a different in rear wheel camber may be the result of too much vehicle level different left to right, bent camber strut or floor frame damage.

TOE-IN, ADJUST

1. Inspect and adjust vehicle lever as outlined under "Front Wheel Alignment."
2. Adjust toe-in with left and righthand tie rod (60) cam bolts (60a) at rear axle carrier (50), **Fig. 40.**
3. **Torque** cam bolt to 52 ft. lbs.

VEHICLE RIDE HEIGHT

MEASUREMENT

USING PLUMB TOOL

C43, C230, C280, CLK320, CLK430, E55, E300, E320, E430, SL500, SL600, SLK230 & SLK320

1. Install front axle measuring tool No. 201 589 00 21 00, or equivalent, between control arm mount fixing bolts with contact arm on control arm.
2. From center of vehicle record tool plumb value.
3. **On SLK230 models,** loosen righthand rear frame brace and swivel to one side.
4. **On all models,** place rear axle measuring tool No. 201 589 01 21 00, or equivalent, swivel arm on inside of spring link with contact arm on rear axle shaft.
5. From center of vehicle record tool plumb value.
6. **On models equipped with Acceleration Slip Regulation (ASR),** remove spring link bracket.
7. **On all models,** if vehicle is not within specifications, **Fig. 41,** adjust by changing springs or spring rubber mounts.
8. **On models equipped with level control,** do not modify level controller connecting rod to adjust vehicle that is too low.
9. **Torque** rear cross brace to frame floor mounting bolt to 44 ft. lbs.

1998–99 CL500, CL600, S320, S420, S500 & S600

1. Install front axle measuring tool No. 140 589 01 21 00, or equivalent, between control arm mount eccentric bolts with contact arm on control arm.
2. From center of vehicle record tool plumb value.
3. Install rear axle measuring tool No. 140 589 02 21 00, or equivalent, on rear axle shaft.
4. From center of vehicle record tool plumb value.
5. If vehicle is not within specifications, **Fig. 41,** adjust by changing springs or spring rubber mounts.
6. **On models equipped with level control,** do not modify level controller connecting rod to adjust vehicle that is too low.

USING ELECTRONIC TOOL

1. Install measuring plate in front suspension lower wishbone recess with plate groove at 90° angle to travel direction.
2. Install sensor on measuring plate with connecting cable toward vehicle center and record left and righthand front inclination angle using Romess Rogg electronic inclination measuring instrument tool No. 09606, or equivalent.
3. Install measuring sensor on rear drive shaft with connecting cable toward vehicle center and record left and righthand rear inclination angle using electronic inclination measuring instrument tool.
4. If vehicle is not within specifications, **Fig. 42,** adjust by changing springs or spring rubber mounts.
5. **On models equipped with level control,** do not modify level controller connecting rod to adjust vehicle that is too low.

ADJUST

C43, C230, C280, CLK320, CLK430, E55, E300, E320, E430, SLK230 & SLK320

1. Measure vehicle ride height as outlined under "Measurement"
2. Ensure level control oil level is correct.
3. Install angled retainer tool No. 202 589 00 63 00, or equivalent, to rear axle carrier rear mount and secure with pin.

Front Axle Level		Rear Axle Level		Caster,
Degrees	Inches	Degrees	Inches	Degrees①
+2.1	0	-.9	-.1969	$5\frac{13}{60}$
		-.4	0	$5\frac{7}{60}$
		-.2	+.1969	5
		+.7	+.3974	$4\frac{9}{10}$
		+1.2	+.5906	$4\frac{47}{60}$
		+1.8	.7875	$4\frac{41}{60}$
+1.4	-.1969	-.9	-.1969	$5\frac{13}{60}$
		-.4	0	$5\frac{7}{60}$
		-.2	+.1969	$5\frac{1}{60}$
		+.7	+.3974	$4\frac{9}{10}$
		+1.2	+.5906	$4\frac{4}{5}$
		+1.8	.7875	$4\frac{41}{60}$
+.6	-.3974	-.9	-.1969	$5\frac{7}{30}$
		-.4	0	$5\frac{2}{15}$
		-.2	+.1969	$5\frac{1}{60}$
		+.7	+.3974	$4\frac{11}{12}$
		+1.2	+.5906	$4\frac{4}{5}$
		+1.8	.7875	$4\frac{7}{10}$
-.1	-.5906	-.9	-.1969	$5\frac{7}{30}$
		-.4	0	$5\frac{2}{15}$
		-.2	+.1969	$5\frac{1}{30}$
		+.7	+.3974	$5\frac{11}{12}$
		+1.2	+.5906	$4\frac{49}{60}$
		+1.8	.7875	$4\frac{43}{60}$

① — Tolerance, plus or minus ⅓°; Maximum difference between left & righthand sides, ⅓°.

Fig. 9 Caster specification. C43

4. Pull vehicle rear down to specified control point, **Fig. 43,** with puller tool No. 201 589 11 31 00, or equivalent, and suitable chains to simulate loaded condition.
5. Install measuring tool No. 201 589 01 21 00, or equivalent, on inside of spring link and scan rear axle shaft with tool's contact arm.
6. Loosen lock nuts, and shorten or extend level controller connecting rod with adjusting screw until suitable .1575 inch alignment tool can be pushed through adjusting lever hole and into level controller positioning hole.

1998-99 CL500, CL600, S320, S420, S500 & S600

1. Measure vehicle ride height as outlined under "Measurement"
2. Ensure level control oil level is correct.
3. Install angled retainer tool No. 140 589 37 63 00, or equivalent, to rear axle carrier rear mount and secure with pin.
4. Pull vehicle rear down to specified control point, **Fig. 43,** with puller tool No. 201 589 11 31 00, or equivalent, and suitable chains to simulate loaded condition.
5. Install measuring tool No. 140 589 02 21 00, or equivalent, on inside of spring link and scan rear axle shaft with tool's contact arm.
6. Loosen lock nuts, and shorten or extend level controller connecting rod with adjusting screw until suitable .1575 inch alignment tool can be pushed through adjusting lever hole and into level controller positioning hole.

Front Axle Level		Rear Axle Level		Caster,
Degrees	Inches	Degrees	Inches	Degrees①
+7.8	+1.5750	+1.2	+.5906	$4\frac{43}{60}$
		+1.8	+.7875	$4\frac{37}{60}$
		+2.3	+.9844	$4\frac{1}{2}$
		+2.9	+1.1812	$4\frac{6}{15}$
		+3.4	+1.3781	$4\frac{3}{10}$
		+3.9	+1.5750	$4\frac{11}{60}$
		+4.5	+1.7718	$4\frac{1}{12}$
+7.1	+1.3781	+1.2	+.5906	$4\frac{11}{15}$
		+1.8	+.7875	$4\frac{37}{60}$
		+2.3	+.9844	$4\frac{31}{60}$
		+2.9	+1.1812	$4\frac{5}{12}$
		+3.4	+1.3781	$4\frac{3}{10}$
		+3.9	+1.5750	$4\frac{1}{5}$
		+4.5	+1.7718	$4\frac{1}{12}$
+6.4	+1.1812	+1.2	+.5906	$4\frac{11}{15}$
		+1.8	+.7875	$4\frac{19}{30}$
		+2.3	+.9844	$4\frac{8}{15}$
		+2.9	+1.1812	$4\frac{5}{12}$
		+3.4	+1.3781	$4\frac{19}{60}$
		+3.9	+1.5750	$4\frac{1}{5}$
		+4.5	+1.7718	$4\frac{1}{12}$
+5.6	+.9844	+1.2	+.5906	$4\frac{3}{4}$
		+1.8	+.7875	$4\frac{19}{30}$
		+2.3	+.9844	$4\frac{8}{15}$
		+2.9	+1.1812	$4\frac{13}{30}$
		+3.4	+1.3781	$4\frac{19}{60}$
		+3.9	+1.5750	$4\frac{13}{60}$
		+4.5	+1.7718	$4\frac{1}{10}$
+4.9	+.7875	+1.2	+.5906	$4\frac{3}{4}$
		+1.8	+.7875	$4\frac{39}{60}$
		+2.3	+.9844	$4\frac{11}{20}$
		+2.9	+1.1812	$4\frac{13}{30}$
		+3.4	+1.3781	$4\frac{1}{3}$
		+3.9	+1.5750	$4\frac{13}{60}$
		+4.5	+1.7718	$4\frac{1}{10}$
+4.2	+.5906	+1.2	+.5906	$4\frac{23}{30}$
		+1.8	+.7875	$4\frac{13}{20}$
		+2.3	+.9844	$4\frac{11}{20}$
		+2.9	+1.1812	$4\frac{13}{30}$
		+3.4	+1.3781	$4\frac{1}{3}$
		+3.9	+1.5750	$4\frac{13}{60}$
		+4.5	+1.7718	$4\frac{7}{60}$

① — Tolerance, plus or minus ⅓°; Maximum difference between left and righthand sides, ⅓°.

Fig. 10 Caster specification. C230 & C280

SL500 & SL600

With Adaptive Damping System (ADS) w/Level Control

1. Ensure level control oil level is correct and level adjustment switch is in Off position.
2. Measure front and read ride height.
3. If height is not within specifications, **Fig. 41,** disconnect front and rear axle level controllers' connecting rods.
4. With engine idling, adjust axles' heights using level controller lever.
5. Adjust level from bottom up until specified values are obtained.
6. Fix lever with .1574 inch alignment tool in center position.
7. Turn engine Off.
8. Adjust connecting rod(s) to length and

Front Axle Level		Rear Axle Level		Caster, Degrees①
Degrees	Inches	Degrees	Inches	
+2.1	0	-1.5	-.3974	$5\frac{19}{60}$
		-.9	-.1969	$5\frac{13}{60}$
		-.4	0	$5\frac{7}{60}$
		+.2	+.1969	5
		+.7	+.3974	$4\frac{9}{10}$
+1.4	-.1969	-1.5	-.3974	$5\frac{1}{3}$
		-.9	-.1969	$5\frac{13}{60}$
		-.4	0	$5\frac{7}{60}$
		+.2	+.1969	$5\frac{1}{60}$
		+.7	+.3974	$4\frac{9}{10}$
+.6	-.3974	-1.5	-.3974	$5\frac{1}{3}$
		-.9	-.1969	$5\frac{7}{30}$
		-.4	0	$5\frac{2}{15}$
		+.2	+.1969	$5\frac{1}{60}$
		+.7	+.3974	$4\frac{11}{12}$
-.1	-.5906	-1.5	-.3974	$5\frac{7}{20}$
		-.9	-.1969	$5\frac{7}{30}$
		-.4	0	$5\frac{2}{15}$
		+.2	+.1969	$5\frac{1}{30}$
		+.7	+.3974	$4\frac{11}{12}$

① — Tolerance, plus or minus ⅓°; Maximum difference between left and righthand sides, ⅓°.

Fig. 11 Caster specification. CLK55

install on level controller lever without tension.

9. Adjust vehicle headlamps.

With Adaptive Damping System (ADS II) w/Electronic Level Control

1. Ensure level control oil level is correct and level adjustment switch is in Off position.
2. Measure front and rear ride height.
3. If height is not within specifications, disconnect front and rear axle level controllers' connecting rods.
4. If vehicle is not within specifications, **Fig. 41,** connect Hand-Held Tester (HHT) tool No. 965 589 00 01 00, or equivalent, to Data Link Connector (DLC).
5. With engine idling, select menu "FA/RA level adjustment."
6. Lower vehicle with HHT. If level is not obtained, terminate program with "STOP."
7. Adjust vehicle with HHT Raising and "STOP" when level is obtained.
8. Store adjust level in HHT as specified value 0.
9. Turn engine Off and clear Diagnostic Trouble Code (DTC) memory. If vehicle was more than 1.7718 inches low, DTC was stored.

TECHNICAL SERVICE BULLETINS

INCREASE TIRE WEAR

E55

On some of these AMG models there may be increased tire inner shoulder wear.

This condition may be caused by the vehicle being to low and/or the front toe-in/camber may be out of tolerance.

To correct this condition, proceed as follows:

1. Adjust vehicle front and rear axle height to upper tolerance range.
2. Reduce front axle camber in positive direction.
3. Adjust overall toe-in with deviation of $\frac{3}{10}$°.

Front Axle Level		Rear Axle Level		Caster, Degrees①
Degrees	Inches	Degrees	Inches	
+3.5	+.3975	-.4	0	$5\frac{1}{10}$
		-.2	+.1969	$4\frac{59}{60}$
		+.7	+.3974	$4\frac{53}{60}$
		+1.2	+.5906	$4\frac{23}{30}$
		+1.8	+.7875	$4\frac{2}{3}$
		+2.3	+.9844	$4\frac{17}{30}$
		+2.9	+1.1812	$4\frac{9}{20}$
+2.8	+.1969	-.4	0	$5\frac{1}{10}$
		-.2	+.1969	5
		+.7	+.3974	$4\frac{53}{60}$
		+1.2	+.5906	$4\frac{47}{60}$
		+1.8	+.7875	$4\frac{2}{3}$
		+2.3	+.9844	$4\frac{17}{30}$
		+2.9	+1.1812	$4\frac{7}{15}$
+2.1	0	-.4	0	$5\frac{1}{10}$
		-.2	+.1969	5
		+.7	+.3974	$4\frac{9}{10}$
		+1.2	+.5906	$4\frac{47}{60}$
		+1.8	+.7875	$4\frac{41}{60}$
		+2.3	+.9844	$4\frac{7}{12}$
		+2.9	+1.1812	$4\frac{7}{15}$
+1.4	-.1969	-.4	0	$5\frac{7}{60}$
		-.2	+.1969	$5\frac{1}{60}$
		+.7	+.3974	$4\frac{9}{10}$
		+1.2	+.5906	$4\frac{4}{5}$
		+1.8	+.7875	$4\frac{41}{60}$
		+2.3	+.9844	$4\frac{7}{12}$
		+2.9	+1.1812	$4\frac{29}{60}$
+.6	-.3974	-.4	0	$5\frac{2}{15}$
		-.2	+.1969	$5\frac{1}{60}$
		+.7	+.3974	$4\frac{11}{12}$
		+1.2	+.5906	$4\frac{4}{5}$
		+1.8	+.7875	$4\frac{7}{10}$
		+2.3	+.9844	$4\frac{3}{5}$
		+2.9	+1.1812	$4\frac{29}{60}$
-.1	-.5906	-.4	0	$5\frac{2}{15}$
		-.2	+.1969	$5\frac{1}{30}$
		+.7	+.3974	$4\frac{11}{12}$
		+1.2	+.5906	$4\frac{49}{60}$
		+1.8	+.7875	$4\frac{43}{60}$
		+2.3	+.9844	$4\frac{3}{5}$
		+2.9	+1.1812	$4\frac{1}{2}$

① — Tolerance, plus or minus ⅓°; Maximum difference between left and righthand sides, ⅓°.

Fig. 12 Caster specification. CLK320 & CLK430

VEHICLE VEERS TO RIGHT ON LEVEL ROAD

E55, E300, E320 & E430

On some of the models, the vehicle may veer to the right on level road.

To correct this condition, procedure as follows:

1. Measure chassis alignment.
2. Release tension on front axle rubber

Front Axle Level		Rear Axle Level		Caster, Degrees①
Degrees	Inches	Degrees	Inches	
+2.9	-.1969	-2.1	-.3973	$5\frac{11}{12}$
		-1.6	-.1969	$5\frac{49}{60}$
		-1.1.	0	$5\frac{43}{60}$
		-.6	+.1969	$5\frac{37}{60}$
		0	+.3974	$5\frac{31}{60}$
+2.2	-.3974	-2.1	-.3973	$5\frac{14}{15}$
		-1.6	-.1969	$5\frac{5}{6}$
		-1.1.	0	$5\frac{11}{15}$
		-.6	+.1969	$5\frac{19}{30}$
		0	+.3974	$5\frac{8}{15}$
+1.4	-.5906	-2.1	-.3973	$5\frac{57}{60}$
		-1.6	-.1969	$5\frac{51}{60}$
		-1.1.	0	$5\frac{3}{4}$
		-.6	+.1969	$5\frac{13}{20}$
		0	+.3974	$5\frac{8}{15}$
+.7	-.7875	-2.1	-.3973	$5\frac{29}{60}$
		-1.6	-.1969	$5\frac{13}{15}$
		-1.1.	0	$5\frac{3}{4}$
		-.6	+.1969	$5\frac{13}{20}$
		0	+.3974	$5\frac{11}{20}$

① — Tolerance, plus or minus ⅓°; Maximum difference between left and righthand sides, ⅓°.

Fig. 13 Caster specification. E55

mounts at bottom/top wishbone and torsion bar mount on longitudinal member. Loosen mounting bolts.

3. Load vehicle with three 150 lbs. bags or pull vehicle down on alignment rack by compressing suspension .315 inch.
4. Tighten loosened bolts and inspection alignment. Correct alignment as required.
5. If vehicle stills veers to right, rotate tires.
6. If vehicle stills veers to right, check condition with another set of tires.
7. If vehicle stills veers to right, proceed as follows:
   a. Increase lefthand camber in positive direction (e.g. -⅔° to -⅓°
   b. Decrease righthand camber in negative direction (e.g. -⅔° to 1°).

Front Axle Level	Rear Axle Level	Caster, Degrees①		
Degrees	Inches		Degrees	Inches
+7.9	+1.1812	-1.1	0	$5\frac{37}{60}$
		-.6	+.1969	$5\frac{31}{60}$
		0	+.3974	$5\frac{5}{12}$
		+.5	+.5906	$5\frac{19}{60}$
		+1.0	+.7875	$5\frac{13}{60}$
		+1.5	+.9844	$5\frac{7}{60}$
		+2.0	+1.1812	$5\frac{1}{60}$
		+2.5	+1.3781	$4\frac{11}{12}$
+7.2	+.9844	-1.1	0	$5\frac{19}{30}$
		-.6	+.1969	$5\frac{8}{15}$
		0	+.3974	$5\frac{13}{30}$
		+.5	+.5906	$5\frac{1}{3}$
		+1.0	+.7875	$5\frac{7}{30}$
		+1.5	+.9844	$5\frac{2}{15}$
		+2.0	+1.1812	$5\frac{1}{30}$
		+2.5	+1.3781	$4\frac{11}{12}$
+6.5	+.7875	-1.1	0	$5\frac{13}{20}$
		-.6	+.1969	$5\frac{11}{20}$
		0	+.3974	$5\frac{19}{30}$
		+.5	+.5906	$5\frac{7}{20}$
		+1.0	+.7875	$5\frac{7}{20}$
		+1.5	+.9844	$5\frac{3}{20}$
		+2.0	+1.1812	$5\frac{1}{30}$
		+2.5	+1.3781	$4\frac{14}{15}$
+5.8	+.5906	-1.1	0	$5\frac{2}{3}$
		-.6	+.1969	$5\frac{17}{30}$
		0	+.3974	$5\frac{9}{20}$
		+.5	+.5906	$5\frac{7}{20}$
		+1.0	+.7875	$5\frac{1}{4}$
		+1.5	+.9844	$5\frac{3}{20}$
		+2.0	+1.1812	$5\frac{3}{60}$
		+2.5	+1.3781	$4\frac{57}{60}$
+5.0	+.3974	-1.1	0	$5\frac{2}{3}$
		-.6	+.1969	$5\frac{17}{30}$
		0	+.3974	$5\frac{7}{15}$
		+.5	+.5906	$5\frac{11}{30}$
		+1.0	+.7875	$5\frac{4}{15}$
		+1.5	+.9844	$5\frac{1}{6}$
		+2.0	+1.1812	$5\frac{1}{15}$
		+2.5	+1.3781	$4\frac{29}{30}$

Fig. 14 Caster specification (Part 1 of 2). E300 & E320 & E430 sedan less 4MATIC

Front Axle Level	Rear Axle Level	Caster, Degrees①		
Degrees	Inches		Degrees	Inches between left & righthand sides, 1/3°.
+4.3	+.1969	-1.1	0	5 41/60
		-.6	+.1969	5 7/12
		0	+.3974	5 29/60
		+.5	+.5906	5 23/60
		+1.0	+.7875	5 17/60
		+1.5	+.9844	5 11/60
		+2.0	+1.1812	5 1/12
		+2.5	+1.3781	4 59/60
+3.6	0	-1.1	0	5 7/10
		-.6	+.1969	5 3/5
		0	+.3974	5 1/2
		+.5	+.5906	5 6/15
		+1.0	+.7875	5 3/10
		+1.5	+.9844	5 1/5
		+2.0	+1.1812	5 1/10
		+2.5	+1.3781	5

① — Tolerance, plus or minus 1/3°; Maximum difference between left & righthand sides, 1/3°.

Fig. 14 Caster specification (Part 2 of 2). E300 & E320 & E430 sedan less 4MATIC

Front Axle Level		Rear Axle Level		Caster, Degrees①
Degrees	Inches	Degrees	Inches	
10.1	+1.7781	+.5	+.5906	5 4/15
		+1.0	+.7875	5 1/6
		+1.5	+.9844	5 1/15
		+2.0	+1.1812	4 29/30
		+2.5	+1.3781	4 13/15
		+3.0	+1.5750	4 23/30
9.3	+1.5750	+.5	+.5906	5 17/60
		+1.0	+.7875	5 11/60
		+1.5	+.9844	5 1/12
		+2.0	+1.1812	4 59/60
		+2.5	+1.3781	4 53/60
		+3.0	+1.5750	4 47/60
8.6	+1.3781	+.5	+.5906	5 3/10
		+1.0	+.7875	5 1/5
		+1.5	+.9844	5 1/10
		+2.0	+1.1812	5
		+2.5	+1.3781	4 9/10
		+3.0	+1.5750	4 4/5
+7.9	+1.1812	+.5	+.5906	5 19/60
		+1.0	+.7875	5 13/60
		+1.5	+.9844	5 7/60
		+2.0	+1.1812	5 1/60
		+2.5	+1.3781	4 11/12
		+3.0	+1.5750	4 49/60
+7.2	+.9844	+.5	+.5906	5 1/3
		+1.0	+.7875	5 7/30
		+1.5	+.9844	5 2/15
		+2.0	+1.1812	5 1/30
		+2.5	+1.3781	4 11/12
		+3.0	+1.5750	4 49/60
+6.5	+.7875	+.5	+.5906	5 7/20
		+1.0	+.7875	5 7/20
		+1.5	+.9844	5 3/20
		+2.0	+1.1812	5 1/30
		+2.5	+1.3781	4 14/15
		+3.0	+1.5750	4 5/6
+5.8	+.5906	+.5	+.5906	5 7/20
		+1.0	+.7875	5 1/4
		+1.5	+.9844	5 3/20
		+2.0	+1.1812	5 3/60
		+2.5	+1.3781	4 57/60
		+3.0	+1.5750	4 51/60

① — Tolerance, plus or minus 1/3°; Maximum difference between left and righthand sides, 1/3°.

Fig. 15 Caster specification. E320 wagon less 4MATIC

Front Axle Level		Rear Axle Level		Caster,
Degrees	Inches	Degrees	Inches	Degrees①
+2.9	-.1969	+.5	+.5906	$5\frac{5}{12}$
		+1.0	+.7875	$5\frac{19}{60}$
		+1.5	+.9844	$5\frac{13}{60}$
		+2.0	+1.1812	$5\frac{7}{60}$
		+2.5	+1.3781	5
		+3.0	+1.5750	$4\frac{9}{10}$
		+3.5	+1.7718	$4\frac{4}{5}$
+2.2	-.3974	+.5	+.5906	$5\frac{113}{30}$
		+1.0	+.7875	$5\frac{1}{3}$
		+1.5	+.9844	$5\frac{13}{60}$
		+2.0	+1.1812	$5\frac{7}{60}$
		+2.5	+1.3781	$5\frac{1}{60}$
		+3.0	+1.5750	$4\frac{11}{12}$
		+3.5	+1.7718	$4\frac{49}{60}$
+1.4	-.5906	+.5	+.5906	$5\frac{13}{30}$
		+1.0	+.7875	$5\frac{1}{3}$
		+1.5	+.9844	$5\frac{7}{30}$
		+2.0	+1.1812	$5\frac{2}{15}$
		+2.5	+1.3781	$5\frac{1}{30}$
		+3.0	+1.5750	$4\frac{14}{15}$
		+3.5	+1.7718	$4\frac{5}{6}$
+.7	-.7875	+.5	+.5906	$5\frac{9}{20}$
		+1.0	+.7875	$5\frac{7}{20}$
		+1.5	+.9844	$5\frac{1}{4}$
		+2.0	+1.1812	$5\frac{3}{20}$
		+2.5	+1.3781	$5\frac{1}{20}$
		+3.0	+1.5750	$4\frac{57}{60}$
		+3.5	+1.7718	$4\frac{51}{60}$
0	-.9844	+.5	+.5906	$5\frac{7}{15}$
		+1.0	+.7875	$5\frac{11}{30}$
		+1.5	+.9844	$5\frac{4}{15}$
		+2.0	+1.1812	$5\frac{1}{6}$
		+2.5	+1.3781	$5\frac{1}{12}$
		+3.0	+1.5750	$4\frac{29}{30}$
		+3.5	+1.7718	$4\frac{13}{15}$
-.7	-1.1812	+.5	+.5906	$5\frac{29}{60}$
		+1.0	+.7875	$5\frac{23}{60}$
		+1.5	+.9844	$5\frac{17}{60}$
		+2.0	+1.1812	$5\frac{11}{60}$
		+2.5	+1.3781	$5\frac{1}{12}$
		+3.0	+1.5750	$4\frac{59}{60}$
		+3.5	+1.7718	$4\frac{53}{60}$
-1.4	-1.3781	+.5	+.5906	$5\frac{1}{2}$
		+1.0	+.7875	$5\frac{26}{15}$
		+1.5	+.9844	$5\frac{23}{10}$
		+2.0	+1.1812	$5\frac{1}{5}$
		+2.5	+1.3781	$5\frac{1}{12}$
		+3.0	+1.5750	$4\frac{59}{60}$
		+3.5	+1.7718	$4\frac{53}{60}$

① — Tolerance, plus or minus ⅓°; Maximum difference between left and righthand sides, ⅓°.

Fig. 16 Caster specification. E320 & E430 w/4MATIC

Front Axle Level		Rear Axle Level		Caster,
Degrees	Inches	Degrees	Inches	Degrees①
+4.2	+.5906	-.2	+.1969	$5\frac{9}{20}$
		+.7	+.3937	$5\frac{1}{3}$
		+1.2	+.5906	$5\frac{1}{5}$
		+1.8	+.7879	$5\frac{1}{12}$
		+.2.3	+.9844	$4\frac{29}{30}$
+3.5	+.3937	-.2	+.1969	$5\frac{13}{30}$
		+.7	+.3937	$5\frac{19}{60}$
		+1.2	+.5906	$5\frac{1}{5}$
		+1.8	+.7879	$5\frac{1}{12}$
		+.2.3	+.9844	$4\frac{29}{30}$
+2.8	+.1969	-.2	+.1969	$5\frac{13}{30}$
		+.7	+.3937	$5\frac{19}{60}$
		+1.2	+.5906	$5\frac{1}{5}$
		+1.8	+.7879	$5\frac{1}{12}$
		+.2.3	+.9844	$4\frac{29}{30}$
+2.1	0	-.2	+.1969	$5\frac{13}{30}$
		+.7	+.3937	$5\frac{19}{60}$
		+1.2	+.5906	$5\frac{1}{5}$
		+1.8	+.7879	$5\frac{1}{15}$
		+.2.3	+.9844	$4\frac{57}{60}$
+1.4	-.1969	-.2	+.1969	$5\frac{13}{30}$
		+.7	+.3937	$5\frac{19}{60}$
		+1.2	+.5906	$5\frac{11}{60}$
		+1.8	+.7879	$5\frac{1}{15}$
		+.2.3	+.9844	$4\frac{57}{60}$
+.6	-.3937	-.2	+.1969	$5\frac{5}{12}$
		+.7	+.3937	$5\frac{3}{10}$
		+1.2	+.5906	$5\frac{11}{60}$
		+1.8	+.7879	$5\frac{1}{15}$
		+.2.3	+.9844	$4\frac{57}{60}$
-.1	-.5906	-.2	+.1969	$5\frac{5}{12}$
		+.7	+.3937	$5\frac{3}{10}$
		+1.2	+.5906	$5\frac{11}{60}$
		+1.8	+.7879	$5\frac{1}{15}$
		+.2.3	+.9844	$4\frac{57}{60}$

① — Tolerance, plus or minus ⅓°; Maximum difference between left and righthand sides, ⅓°.

Fig. 17 Caster specification. SLK230 & SLK320

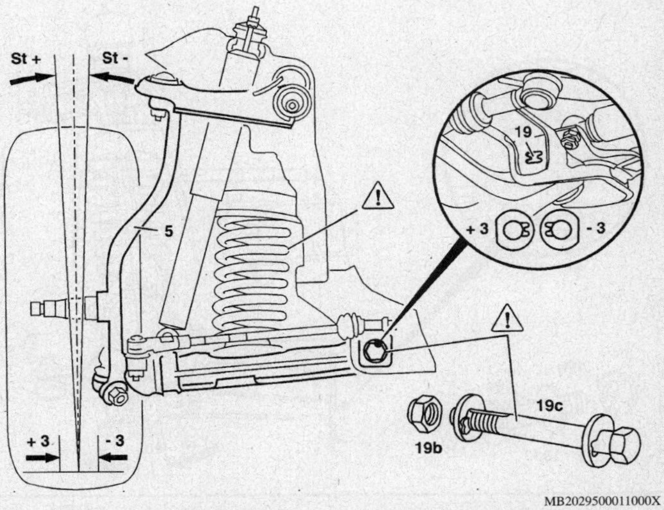

Fig. 18 Camber adjustment. C43, C230, C280, CLK55, CLK320, CLK430, SLK230 & SLK320

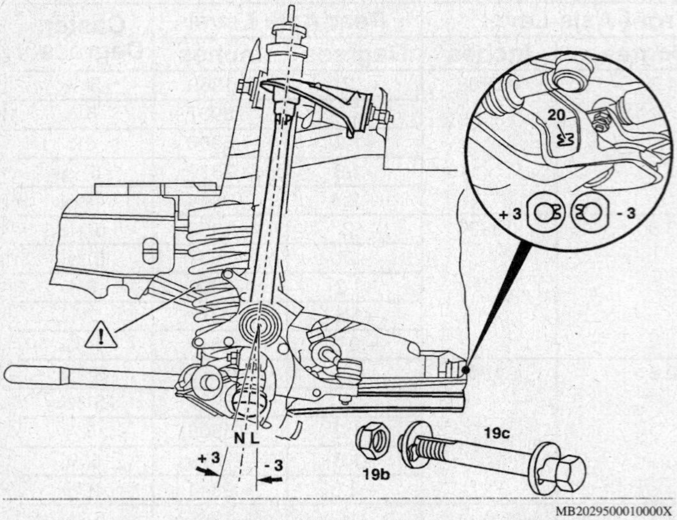

Fig. 19 Caster adjustment. C43, C230, C280, CLK55, CLK320, CLK430, SLK230 & SLK320

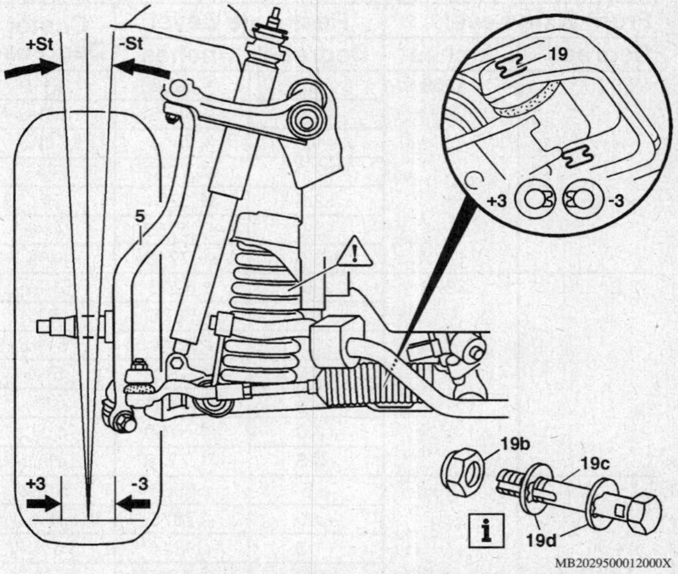

Fig. 20 Camber adjustment. E55, E300, E320 & E430 less 4MATIC

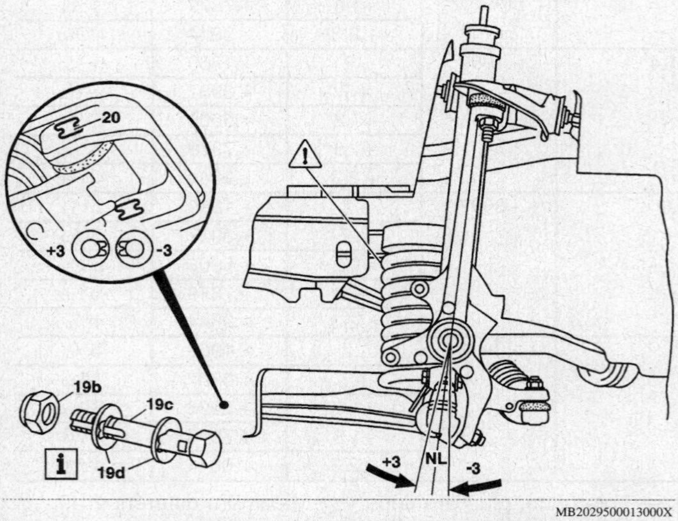

Fig. 21 Caster adjustment. E55, E300, E320 & E430 less 4MATIC

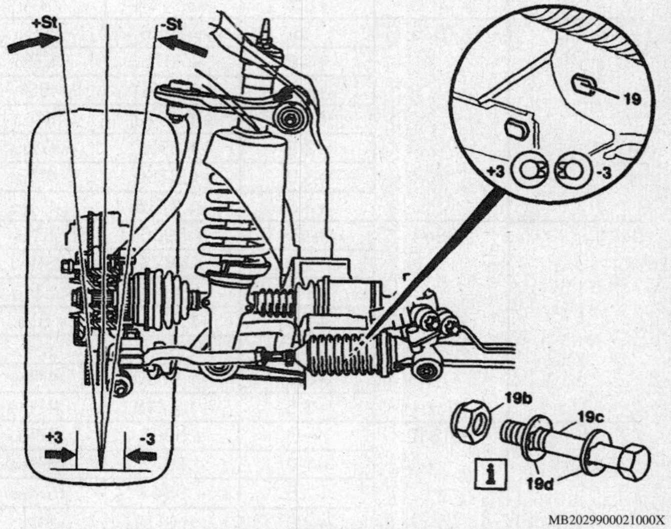

Fig. 22 Camber adjustment. E320 & E430 w/4MATIC

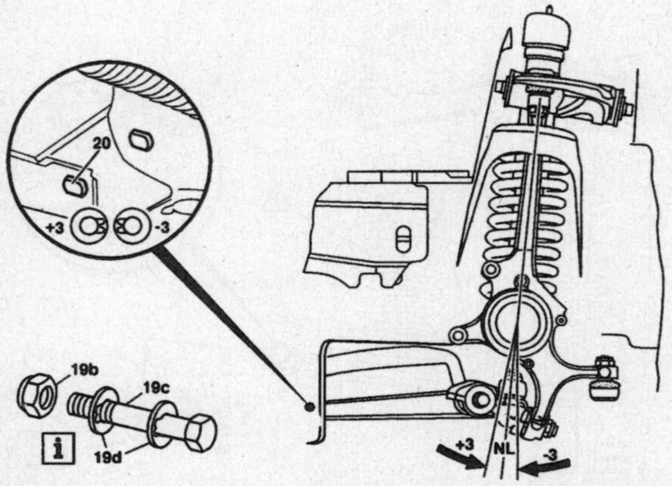

Fig. 23 Caster adjustment. E320 & E430 w/4MATIC

Front Axle Level, Degrees	Camber, Degrees①
6.9	-6/15
5.9	-9/20
5.0	-31/60
4.1	-17/30
3.2	-7/12

① — Tolerance, plus or minus 1/3°; Maximum difference between left & righthand sides, 6/15°.

Fig. 24 Camber specifications. C240 & C280

Front Axle Level, Degrees	Rear Axle Level, Degrees	Caster, Degrees①
8.3	-1.2	+10 5/6
	-.6	+10 3/4
	0	+10 2/3
	+.6	+10 11/20
	+1.2	+10 9/20
	+1.8	+10 1/3
7.4	-1.2	+10 53/60
	-.6	+10 4/5
	0	+10 41/60
	+.6	+10 7/12
	+1.2	+10 7/15
	+1.8	+10 7/20
6.5	-1.2	+10 14/15
	-.6	+10 5/6
	0	+10 43/60
	+.6	+10 3/5
	+1.2	+10 29/60
	+1.8	+10 11/30
5.6	-1.2	+10 59/60
	-.6	+10 53/60
	0	+10 23/30
	+.6	+10 19/30
	+1.2	+10 31/60
	+1.8	+10 6/15
4.7	-1.2	+11 1/30
	-.6	+10 11/12
	0	+10 4/5
	+.6	+10 41/60
	+1.2	+10 17/30
	+1.8	+10 7/15

① — Tolerance, plus or minus 1/2°.

Fig. 25 Caster specifications. C240 & C320

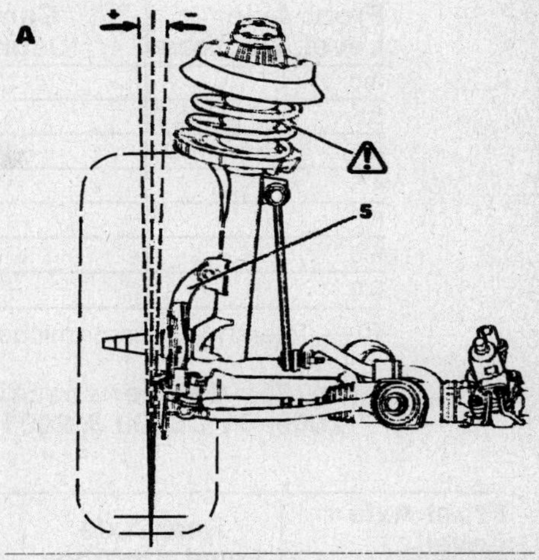

MB2020100075000X

Fig. 26 Camber adjustment. C240 & C320

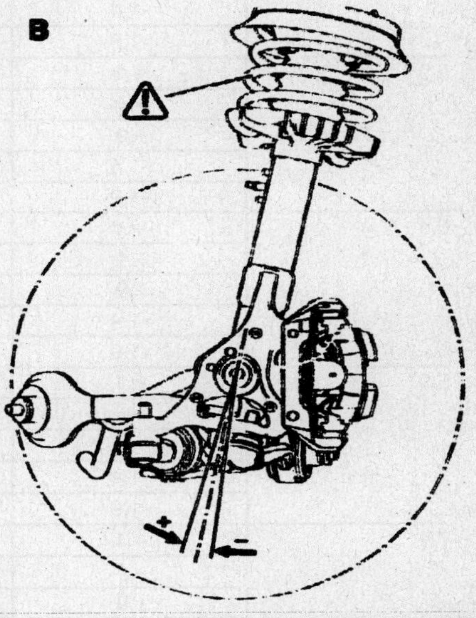

MB2020100076000X

Fig. 27 Caster adjustment. C240 & C320

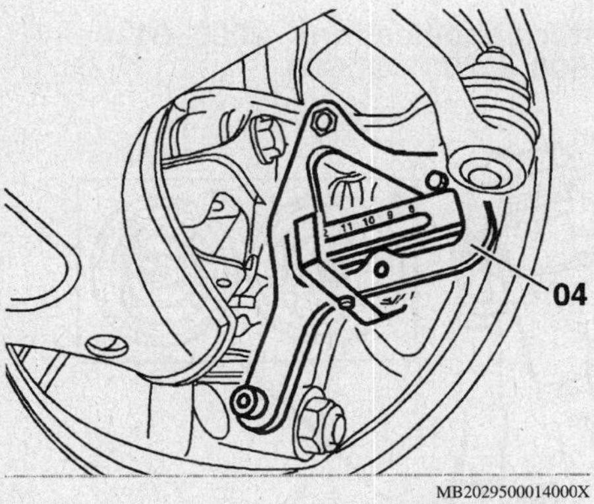

MB2029500014000X

Fig. 28 Caster measurement. CL500, CL600, S320, S420, S500 & S600

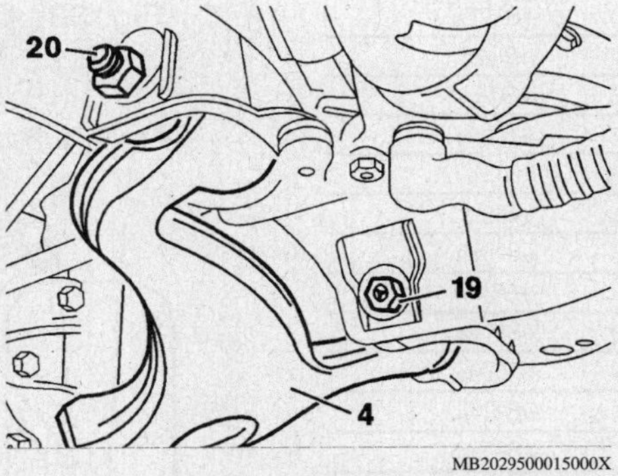

MB2029500015000X

Fig. 29 Camber & caster adjustment. CL500, CL600, S320, S420, S500 & S600

Front Axle Level, Degrees	Camber, Degrees①
5.4	-11/12
5.9	-9/10
6.4	-5/6
6.9	-47/60
7.4	-43/60
7.9	-19/30
8.4	-17/30

① — Tolerance, plus or minus 1/3°

Fig. 30 Camber specifications. S430 & 2000–01 S500 & 2001 S600

Front Axle Level, Degrees	Camber, Degrees①
3.0	-1 17/60
3.5	-1 7/30
4.0	-1 3/20
4.5	-1 1/10
5.0	-1 1/30
5.5	-29/30
6.0	-53/60

① — Tolerance, plus or minus 1/3°

Fig. 31 Camber specifications. 2000–01 CL500 & 2001 CL600

Front Axle Level, Degrees	Rear Axle Level, Degrees	Caster, Degrees①
5.4	+.1	+8 5/6
	-.4	+8 53/600
	-.9	+8 59/60
	-1.4	+9 1/12
	-1.9	+9 1/6
5.9	+.1	+8 29/30
	-.4	+8 13/15
	-.9	+8 29/30
	-1.4	+9 1/15
	-1.9	+9 1/6
6.4	+.1	+8 3/4
	-.4	+8 51/60
	-.9	+8 14/15
	-1.4	+9 1/30
	-1.9	+9 2/15
6.9	+.1	+4 11/15
	-.4	+8 5/6
	-.9	+8 14/15
	-1.4	+9 1/30
	-1.9	+9 7/60
7.4	+.1	+8 43/60
	-.4	+8 49/60
	-.9	+8 11/12
	-1.4	+9 1/60
	-1.9	+9 1/10
7.9	+.1	+8 7/10
	-.4	+8 4/5
	-.9	+8 9/10
	-1.4	+8 59/60
	-1.9	+9 1/12
8.4	+.1	+8 41/60
	-.4	+8 47/60
	-.9	+8 53/60
	-1.4	+8 29/30
	-1.9	+9 1/15

① — Tolerance, plus or minus 1/2°.

Fig. 32 Caster specifications. S430 & 2000–01 S500 & 2001 S600

Front Axle Level, Degrees	Rear Axle Level, Degrees	Caster, Degrees①
3.0	-1.3	+9 3/20
	-1.8	+9 7/30
	-2.3	+9 7/20
	-2.8	+9 13/30
	-3.3	+9 8/15
3.5	-1.3	+9 2/15
	-1.8	+9 13/60
	-2.3	+9 1/3
	-2.8	+9 5/12
	-3.3	+9 31/60
4.0	-1.3	+9 7/60
	-1.8	+9 1/5
	-2.3	+9 19/60
	-2.8	+9 6/15
	-3.3	+9 29/60
4.5	-1.3	+9 1/12
	-1.8	+9 11/60
	-2.3	+9 3/10
	-2.8	+9 23/60
	-3.3	+9 7/15
5.0	-1.3	+9 1/15
	-1.8	+9 1/6
	-2.3	+9 17/60
	-2.8	+9 11/30
	-3.3	+9 7/15
5.5	-1.3	+9 1/20
	-1.8	+9 3/20
	-2.3	+9 4/15
	-2.8	+9 1/3
	-3.3	+9 13/30
6.0	-1.3	+9 1/30
	-1.8	+9 2/15
	-2.3	+9 1/4
	-2.8	+9 19/60
	-3.3	+9 5/12

① — Tolerance, plus or minus 1/2°.

Fig. 33 Caster specifications. 2000–01 CL500 & 2001 CL600

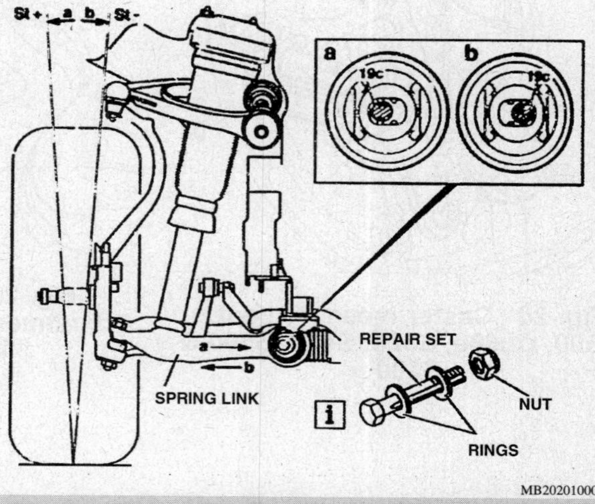

Fig. 34 Camber adjustment. S430 & 2000–01 CL500 & S500 & 2001 CL600 & S600

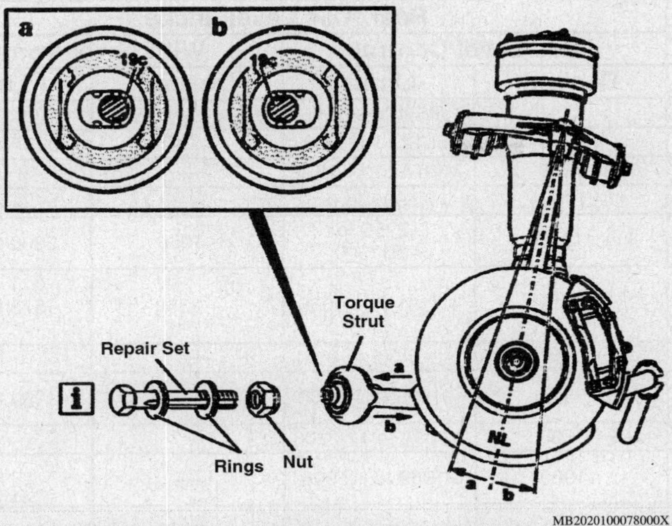

Fig. 35 Caster adjustment. S430 & 2000–01 CL500 & S500 & 2001 CL600 & S600

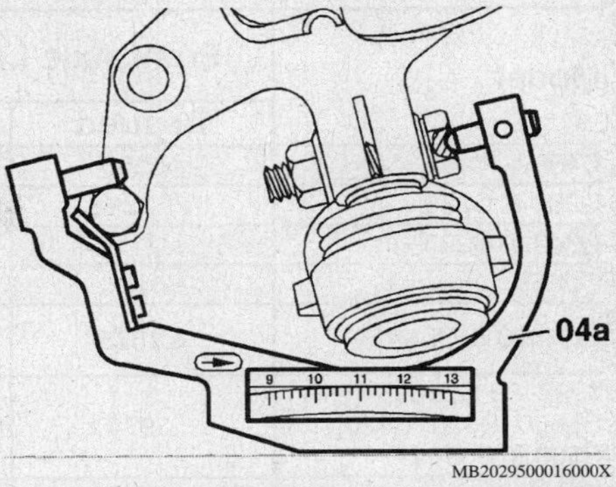

Fig. 36 Caster measurement. SL500 & SL600

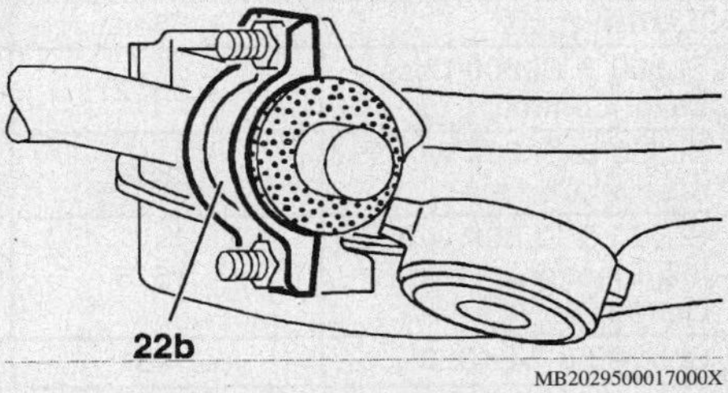

Fig. 37 Bracket adjustment. SL500 & SL600

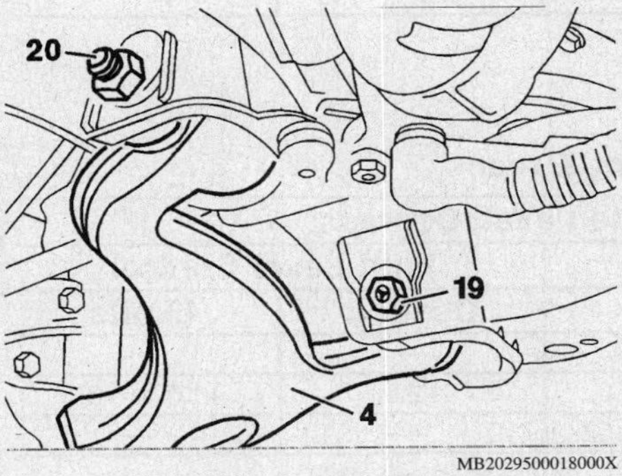

Fig. 38 Camber & caster adjustment. SL500 & SL600

Model	Ball Point Position, Inch	
	Desired	Limits
C230 & C280	1.2206	1.1418–1.2953
CLK320 & CLK430	1.2206	1.1418–1.2953
1998–99 CL500, CL600, S320, S420, S500 & S600	.3974	.3450–.4725
SL500 & SL600	.9056	.8269–.9844
SLK230 & SLK320	1.2009	1.1222–1/2797

Fig. 39 Ball point position specifications

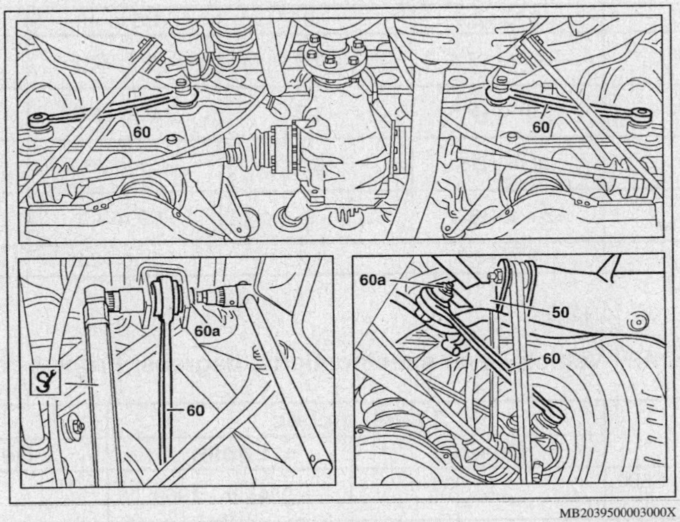

Fig. 40 Rear wheel toe-in adjustment. C43, C230, C280, CLK55, CLK320, CLK430, E55, E300, E320, E430, SL500, SL600, SLK230 & SLK320 & 1998–99 CL500, CL600, S320, S420, S500 & S600

Model	Front Axle Level, Inches		Rear Axle Level, Inches			
			Less Level Control		With Level Control	
	Desired	Limits	Desired	Limits	Desired	Limits
C43	-.5906	-.9844 to -.3931	0	-.3974 to +.1969	—	—
C230 & C280	+1.1812	+.5906 to +1.5750	+.9450	+.5512 to +1.3387	+.7875	+.3937 to +1.1812
C240 & C280	+.3150	-.2756 to +.7087	+.7875	+.3974 to +1.1812	—	—
CLK55	-.5906	-.9844 to -.3931	-.1969	-.5906 to 0	—	—
CLK320 & CLK430	+.1575	-.4331 to +.5512	+.1181①	-.2756 to +.5119①	-.1969	-.5906 to +.5906
1998–99 CL500, CL600, S320, S420, S500 & S600	.3974	-.1969 to +.7879	+.5119	+.1181 to +.9056	+.2362	-.1575 to +.6300
E55	-.7087	-1.1025 to -.5119	-.1969	-.3974 to 0	—	—
E300, E320 & E430 Sedan	+.3544	-.2362 to +.7481	+.5512	+.1525 to +.9450	+.1969	-.1969 to +.5906
E320 Wagon	+.3544	-.2362 to +.7481	+.8269	+.4331 to +1.2206	—	—
SL500 & SL600 Less Level Control	+.5512	-.0394 to +.950	+.1969	-.1969 to +.5906	—	—
SL500 & SL600 w/ADS & Level Control②	-.2362	-.6300 to +.1575	—	—	-.2362	-.6300 to +.1575
SL500 & SL600 w/ADS II & Electronic Level Control②	+.1575	-.2362 to +.6300	—	—	-.2756	-.6694 to +.1182
SLK230 & SLK320	+.1181	-.4725 to +.5119	+.3150	-.0787 to + .7087	—	—

① — Cabriolet, Desired: +.4331 inch; Limits: +.0394 to +.8269 inch.
② — With level switch off.

Fig. 41 Vehicle level specifications, inches. Front & rear

Model	Front Axle Level, Degrees		Rear Axle Level, Degrees			
			Less Level Control		With Level Control	
	Desired	Limits	Desired	Limits	Desired	Limits
C43	+1.3	-.1 to +2.0	+.4	-.7 to +.9	—	—
C230 & C280	+6.4	+4.3 to +7.8	+3.0	+2.0 to +4.0	+2.5	+1.5 to +3.5
C240 & C320	+6.9	+4.8 to + 8.3	+2.57	+1.57 to +3.57	—	—
2000–01 CL500 & 2001 CL600	+4.5	+3.0 to +6.0	-2.3	-1.3 to -2.3	—	—
CLK55	+1.3	-.1 to +2.0	-.2	-1.3 to +.4	—	—
CLK320 & CLK430	+2.6	+.5 to +3.0	+.7①	-.3 to +1.7①	-.2	-1.3 to +.8
E55	+2.2	+.7 to +2.9	-.8	-1.8 to -.2	—	—
E300, E320 & E430 Sedan less 4MATIC	+6.0	+3.9 to +7.4	+1.2	+.2 to +2.2	+.3	-.7 to +1.3
E320 Wagon less 4MATIC	+8.2	+6.1 to +9.6	+1.9	+.9 to +2.9	—	—
E320 & E430 w/ 4MATIC	+1.2	-.9 to +2.6	+2.3	+1.3 to +3.3	+1.9	+.9 to +2.9
S430 & 2000–02 S500 & 2001 S600	+6.9	+5.4 to +8.3	-.9	-1.9 to +.1	—	—
SLK230 & SLK320	+2.5	+.4 to +3.9	+1.2	+.2 to +2.2	—	—

Cabriolet, Desired: + 1.6°; Limits: +.6° to +2.6°.

Fig. 42 Vehicle level specifications, degrees. Front & rear

Model	Level, Inches		Level, Degrees	
	Desired	Limits	Desired	Limits
1998–99 CL500, CL600, S320, S420, S500 & S600	-.5906	-.9844 to -.1969	—	—
C230 & C280	0	-.3937 to +.3937	+.4	-.6 to +1.4
CLK320 & CLK430	-.9844	-1.3781 to -.5906	-2.3	-3.3 to -1.3
E300, E320 & E430 less 4MATIC	-.3150	-.7057 to +.0788	-1.1	-2.1 to -.1
E320 & E430 w/4MATIC	0	-.3937 to +.3937	-.3	-1.3 to +.7

Fig. 43 Vehicle level specifications at rear axle control point

Air Conditioning

NOTE: Prior To Performing Any Service Operations Listed In This Section, Consult The "Technical Service Bulletins" Section For Related Information.

INDEX

	Page No.
A/C Specifications	5-194
Oil Charge	5-192
Performance Test	5-191
Refrigerant Capacity & Pressure	5-191
Refrigerant Capacity	5-191
Precautions	5-191
Air Bag Systems	5-191
Battery Ground Cable	5-191
Product Compatibility	5-191
R-134a Systems	5-191
System Evacuation	5-192
Technical Service Bulletins	5-192
Automatic Climate Control Switches To Emergency Mode	5-192
Auxiliary Fan Runs Constantly	5-192
Auxiliary Fan Runs Continuously At High Speed	5-193
Blower Inoperative Or Produces Low Air Flow	5-193
Droning, Growling At 2500–4500 RPM	5-192
Magnetic Clutch Overheats, Compressor Does Not Operate	5-192
Whistling During or After Operating Air Recirculation	5-192
Window Condensation	5-193

PRECAUTIONS

R-134A SYSTEMS

R-134a is a non-toxic, non-flammable, clear, odorless, liquefied gas.

R-134a refrigerant is not compatible with R-12 refrigerant. Even small amounts of R-12 in an R-134a system can cause lubricant contamination, improper A/C performance or compressor failure. Never add R-12 to an R-134a system.

New service ports have been added to compressor to prevent charging system with R-12 refrigerant. **R-134a systems require a special compressor lubricant.**

Avoid breathing R-134a refrigerant and lubricant vapor or mist. Exposure may irritate eyes, nose and throat. Use only approved service equipment to recover R-134a systems.

AIR BAG SYSTEMS

On air bag equipped models, refer to "Air Bag System Precautions" located in the front of this manual for system disarming and arming procedures.

BATTERY GROUND CABLE

Prior to service, disconnect battery ground cable and isolate as required.

PRODUCT COMPATIBILITY

Before replenishing refrigerant or refrigerant oil, ensure product compatibility with the system being serviced. Refer to "A/C Specifications."

PERFORMANCE TEST

The vehicle must not be exposed to the sun before and during the tests.

REFRIGERANT CAPACITY

1. Inspect compressor drive belt.
2. Inspect auxiliary fan operation by turning ignition switch to On position and short pressure switch flat terminals. Auxiliary fan should start running at first speed.
3. Bridge temperature switch two-pole coupling and auxiliary fan should start running at second speed.
4. Ensure fan rotates clockwise.
5. Pull pressure switch cable, turn A/C system on and operate engine at idle speed of at least 750 RPM.
6. Clear fluid reservoir sight glass.
7. Connect pressure switch cable and observe sight glass.
8. Shortly before electromagnetic coupling is switched on, refrigerant should rise and subsequently flow through without bubbles.
9. If compressor does not switch on, proceed as follows:
   a. Bridge pressure switch cables.
   b. If compressor still does not switch on, inspect compressor cutout.
   c. If compressor still does not switch on, inspect compressor activation circuits.
10. Set temperature control to Min. position.
11. Set function to A/C and turn blower on High.
12. Open center and lateral nozzles, then turn fresh air switch off.
13. Insert suitable thermometer in left or righthand center nozzle.
14. Set suitable thermometer approximately 79 inches from driver's side outside vehicle.
15. Open windows and close vehicle doors.
16. Run engine at approximately 2000 RPM.
17. After approximately five minutes record center nozzle outlet and outside temperatures.
18. Compare temperatures with **Fig. 1.**
19. Air outlet temperature on center nozzle must not be less than 77°F.
20. If valve is not obtained, inspect temperature sensor evaporator resistance and supply cables. Replace as required.
21. If no fault can be found, replace control unit.

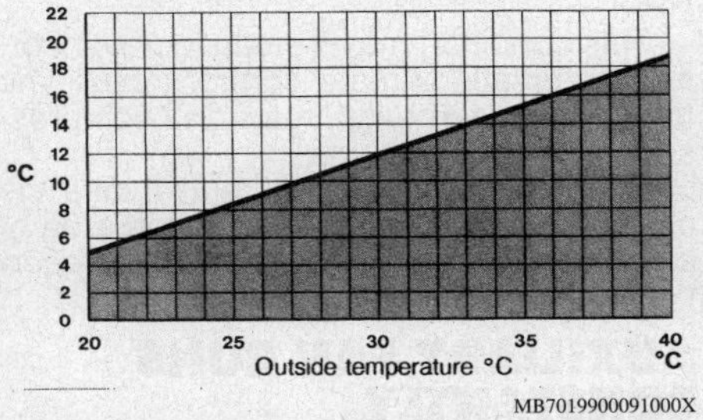

Fig. 1 Inside/outside temperature graph

REFRIGERANT CAPACITY & PRESSURE

1. Set up "Refrigerant Capacity" test.
2. Place hygrometer into center console tray.
3. Remove caps and connect hose to suitable suction pressure or high pressure gauges.
4. **On models equipped with four-cylinder engines,** remove temperature switch coupling and bridge terminals so that engine fan electromagnetic coupling runs during test.
5. **On all models,** run engine at approximately 2000 RPM.
6. After approximately 10 minutes, record temperatures and pressures as well as hygrometer.
7. Compare readings with **Figs. 2 and 3.** Specified valves are maximum and may not be exceeded.
8. If suction pressure is too low and high pressure too high, inspect the following:
   a. Expansion valve.
   b. Fluid Reservoir.
   c. Condenser.
   d. Evaporator.
9. If suction pressure is too high and high pressure too low, inspect expansion valve.
10. If suction pressure and high pressure

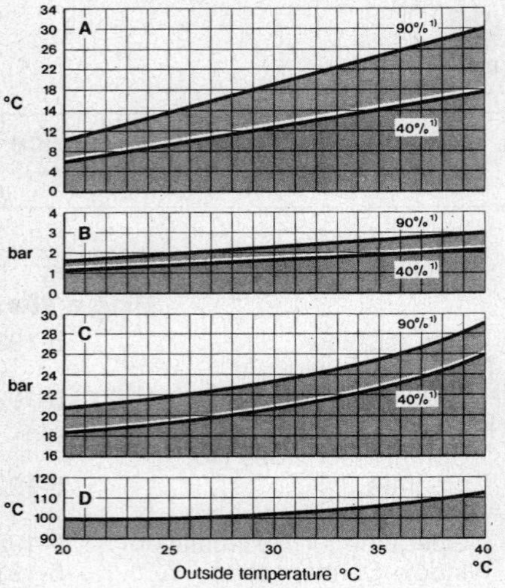

Fig. 2 Humidity/pressure/ temperature charts. Gasoline engines

are identical, inspect compressor.

11. If outlet temperature is too low or high, inspect the following:
    a. Temperature sensor evaporator.
    b. Power supply cables.
    c. Control unit.

SYSTEM EVACUATION

1. Remove high and low service valve protective caps.
2. Connect manifold gauge set, open gauge set valves, and close filling cylinder or refrigerant container valve, **Fig. 4.**
3. Operate vacuum pump and evacuate system for at least 15 minutes.
4. Once 0.918–1.02 psi vacuum is reached, close gauge valves.
5. Close filling cylinder valve and stop vacuum pump.
6. After at least 10 minutes, open gauge valves.
7. If vacuum pressure is below specifications more than 0.153 psi, system has not been evacuated long enough or a system leak is indicated.

OIL CHARGE

1. Drain and measure oil from compressor being replaced.
2. Drain and measure oil from new compressor.
3. Fill new compressor with same amount oil drained from old compressor plus 0.68 ounce.
4. If replacing other components, proceed as follows:
    a. Add 1.35 ounces of oil if system suddenly lost refrigerant, such as line break.
    b. Add 0.68 ounce of oil if replacing condenser.
    c. Add 1.35 ounces of oil if replacing evaporator.
    d. Add 0.34 ounce of oil if replacing dehydrator.
    e. Add 0.68 ounce of oil if replacing intake line.
    f. Add 0.68 ounce of oil if replacing delivery line.

TECHNICAL SERVICE BULLETINS

DRONING, GROWLING AT 2500–4500 RPM

S320

On some of these models there may be droning or growling between 2500–4500 RPM.

This condition may be caused by incorrect automatic climate control intake line routing between evaporator and compressor.

To correct this condition, route intake line correctly. Ensure correct routing in area of electrical switchover valves and fluid reservoir.

AUXILIARY FAN RUNS CONSTANTLY

C230, C280, CLK55, CLK320, CLK430, E55, E320 & E430

On some of these models the electronic cooling or auxiliary fan(s) may run constantly, even with the ignition switched off.

This condition may be caused by water entering in the fuse and relay box.

To correct this condition, proceed as follows:

1. Inspect righthand front fuse and relay box for water leakage.
2. Remove fuse module relay box and Signal Acquisition and Control Module (SAM).
3. Inspect contacts between fuse module/relay box and SAM for corrosion.
4. If there is corrosion or copper oxide present, replace fuse module/relay box and SAM.
5. Fuse and relay box over is only splash proof, not water proof. **Do not spray water directly on fuse and relay box.**

MAGNETIC CLUTCH OVERHEATS, COMPRESSOR DOES NOT OPERATE.

1998 E300 & E320

On some of these models built between Feb. 1 and May, 31, 1998, the air conditioning compressor magnetic clutch may overheat and the compressor not operate.

This condition may be caused by an interference voltage spike from the engine control module via the direct lead.

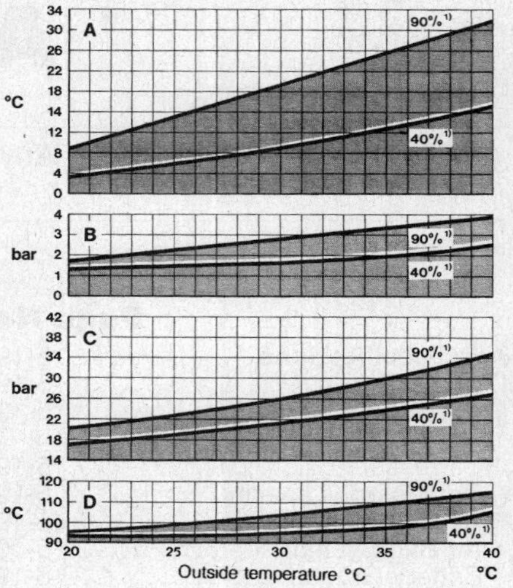

Fig. 3 Humidity/pressure/ temperature charts. Diesel engines

To correct this condition, proceed as follows:

1. Replace push button control module with new unit having increased input capacitor.
2. Replace compressor. Parts numbers remain same.

AUTOMATIC CLIMATE CONTROL SWITCHES TO EMERGENCY MODE

CLK55, CLK320 & CLK430

On some of these models the automatic air conditioning may switch to emergency operation and jump to 72°F.

This condition may be caused by incorrect version coding.

To correct this condition, perform onboard version coding.

WHISTLING DURING OR AFTER OPERATING AIR RECIRCULATION

S320 & S420 & 1998-99 CL500, CL600, S500 & S600

On some of these models there may be a whistling noise after operating air recirculation switch or during automatic air recirculation.

This condition may be caused by air recirculation flap chaffing against rubber seal.

To correct this condition, proceed as follows:

1. Remove righthand side under dash panel dust filter.
2. Position air recirculation flap to open position.
3. Lubricate area on lefthand side where

recirculation flap chafes rubber seal using suitable grease.

AUXILIARY FAN RUNS CONTINUOUSLY AT HIGH SPEED

S320 & S420 & 1998-99 CL500, CL600, S500 & S600

On some of these models the auxiliary fan may run continuously at high speed (third stage).

This condition may be caused air conditioning pressure sensor not functioning as the result of water entering wiring harness or connector.

To correct this condition, proceed as follows:

1. Diagnosis sensor values.
2. If refrigerant pressure is more than 406 psi, install new refrigerant pressure sensor.
3. Inspect wiring harness for water. Dry as required.
4. Seal wiring harness at junction before sensor with insulating tape.

WINDOW CONDENSATION

C43, C230 & C280

On some of these models there may be condensation on windows.

This condition may be caused by a broken fresh air/recirculation air flap actuator return spring.

To correct this condition, proceed as follows:

1. Remove air conditioning/heater case.
2. Remove fresh air/recirculated air flap housing.
3. Install fresh air/recirculated air flap new actuator.

BLOWER INOPERATIVE OR PRODUCES LOW AIR FLOW

All Models Equipped w/ Automatic Air Conditioning

On some of these models the air conditioning system may operate with little or no A/C vent air flow.

This condition may be caused by the electronic blower regulator.

To correct this condition, proceed as follows:

1. Remove blower housing cover and air filter.

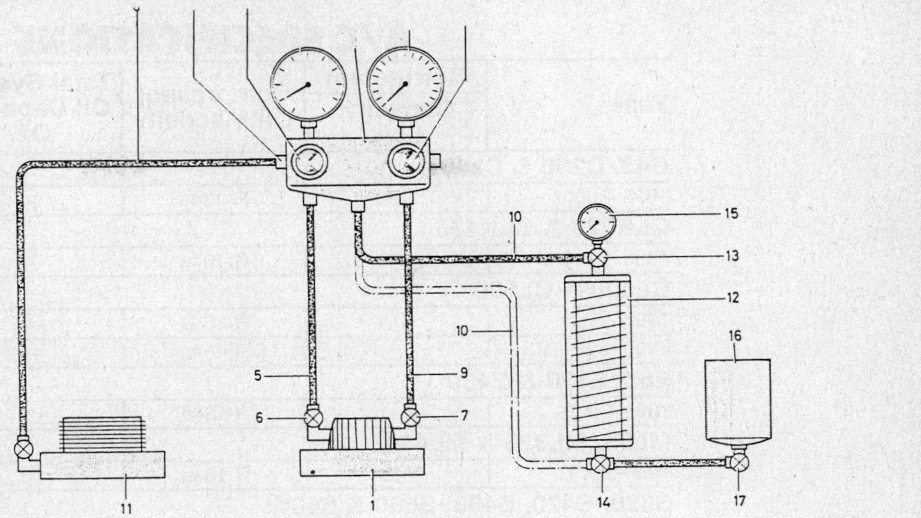

A Valve on suction pressure gauge
B Valve on high-pressure gauge
C Schrader valve on assembly tester
1 Refrigerant compressor
2 Assembly tester
3 Suction pressure gauge
4 High-pressure gauge
5 Hose line
6 Service valve (suction end)
7 Service valve (pressure end)
8 Hose line
9 Hose line
10 Hose line
11 Vacuum pump
12 Filling cylinder
13 Upper valve
14 Lower valve
15 Pressure gauge
16 Refrigerant bottle with R 12
17 Valve on refrigerant bottle

MB7029100012000X

Fig. 4 Refrigerant system service connections

2. Connect suitable ammeter to blower motor red wire.
3. Start engine and set A/C to EC and Max blower speed mode.
4. Ensure highest speed has been selected, then enter diagnostic mode by pressing REST button and select step 10, blower control voltage.
5. Reading should be at least five volts.
6. Current draw should be approximately 28 amps or more for at least 10 minutes.
7. If blower shuts down prematurely, proceed as follows:
   a. Remove blower regulator.
   b. Clean blower housing contact surfaces using line free cloth.
   c. Apply thin, even layer of suitable thermal compound to contact surface.
   d. Position regulator onto blower housing contact surface.
   e. Carefully move regulator around slightly to obtain good adhesion.
   f. Install and tighten mounting screws slightly. Tighten screw in round hole, then screw in slotted hole.
   g. Route wiring harness, connect connector and secure with clips.
8. If current draw is obtained or blower is not running, proceed as follows:
   a. Bypass regulator by connecting blower motor blue wire using suitable bridge and short to ground (blower housing).
   b. If current draw value is obtained, remove regulator.
   c. If value is not obtained, replace blower motor.
9. If blower motor still does not run, proceed as follows:
   a. Measure blower side motor control and terminal No. 15 voltages at blower motor plug without separating connection.
   b. Measure regulator side motor control and terminal No. 15 voltages at blower motor plug without separating connection.
   c. Large difference in voltage or no voltage on regulator side, clean contacts.

A/C SPECIFICATIONS

Year	Refrigerant Capacity, Lbs.	Compressor Oil Viscosity	Total System Oil Capacity, Oz.	Type
C43, C230 & C280				
1998–2000	1.80	R-134a	②	5.20
CLK320 & CLK430				
1998–2001	—	R-134a	②	—
CL500 & CL600				
1998–99	①	R-134a	②	—
2000–01	—	R-134a	—	—
E55, E320 & E430				
1998–2001	2.11	R-134a	②	4.73
ML55, ML320 & ML430				
1998–2001	1.70	R-134a	②	—
S320, S420, S430, S500 & S600				
1998–1999	①	R-134a	②	5.41
2000–01	—	R-134a	—	—
SL500 & SL600				
1998–2001	2.01	R-134a	②	4.73
SLK230 & SLK320				
1998–2001	1.80	R-134a	②	—

① — Front A/C, 2.43 lbs., w/rear A/C, 2.6 lbs.
② — Special Poly Alkaline Glycol (PAG) lubricant, Mercedes-Benz No. 001 989 08 03 or equivalent.

Cooling Fans

NOTE: On Air Bag Equipped Models, Refer To "Air Bag System Precautions" Located In Front Of This Manual For System Disarming And Arming Procedures.

NOTE: Prior To Performing Any Service Operations Listed In This Section, Consult The "Technical Service Bulletins" Section For Related Information.

INDEX

	Page No.
Component Replacement	5-195
Electric Cooling Fan, Replace	5-195
Description	5-195
C43, C230 & C280	5-195
S320 & S420 & 1998–99 CL500, CL600, S500 & S600	5-195
Precautions	5-195
Air Bag Systems	5-195
Battery Ground Cable	5-195
Technical Service Bulletins	5-196
Auxiliary Fan Runs Constantly	5-196

PRECAUTIONS

AIR BAG SYSTEMS

Refer to "Air Bag System Precautions" in front of this manual for system disarming and arming procedures.

BATTERY GROUND CABLE

Prior to service, disconnect battery ground cable and isolate as required.

DESCRIPTION

C43, C230 & C280

The two auxiliary fans are controlled by the A/C push-button control module via the auxiliary fan relays (two stages), **Fig. 1**, and auxiliary fan pre-resistor, **Fig. 2**.

First stage switch on refrigerant pressure point is 232 psi; off is 188 psi. Second stage switch on refrigerant pressure point is 290 psi; off is 247 psi. First stage switch on temperature (from engine coolant temperature sensor) is 212°F; off is 184°F. Second stage switch on refrigerant temperature is 239°F; off is 225°F. Fans will not engage in first stage if ambient temperature is below 41°F.

S320 & S420 & 1998–99 CL500, CL600, S500 & S600

The two auxiliary fans are controlled by the automatic A/C push-button control unit via auxiliary fan relays, **Fig. 3**, and pre-resistor, **Fig. 4**.

The automatic A/C push-button control unit receives inputs from sensor on low press/high pressure A/C compressor cut-out and engine coolant temperature sensor. First stage engagement will not take place when ambient temperature is less than 41°F, but does take place above 50°F.

Refrigerant pressure switch on points for first, second and third stages are 203, 247 and 290 psi, respectively. Switch off points are: 174, 203 and 247 psi. Coolant temperature switch on points are: 212, 225 and 239°F. Switch off point are: 203, 212 and 225°F.

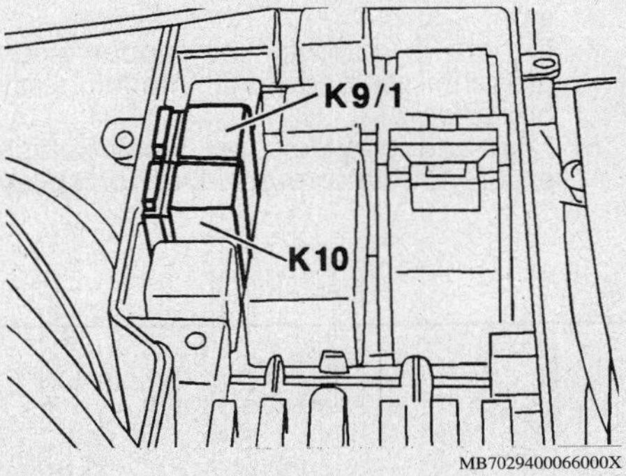

Fig. 1 Auxiliary fan relay locations. C43, C230 & C280

COMPONENT REPLACEMENT

ELECTRIC COOLING FAN, REPLACE

Refer to **Figs. 5 and 6,** for cooling fan replacement.

E300, E320 & E430

1. Remove protective grate by turning plastic clips 90°.
2. Remove cover by remove clips.
3. Disconnect electrical connector.
4. Remove upper clips, mounting screws and upper frame crossmember.
5. Move hood release control cable to rear.
6. Remove mounting screw, disconnect horn electrical lead on crossmember and move hang brace with horn to side.
7. Remove mounting bolts and auxiliary fan.
8. Remove fan shroud by disconnecting clips.
9. Remove drive belt.
10. Remove mounting bolts and fan motor from carrier.
11. Reverse procedure to install. **Torque** frame crossmember and brace mounting bolts to 62–115 inch lbs.

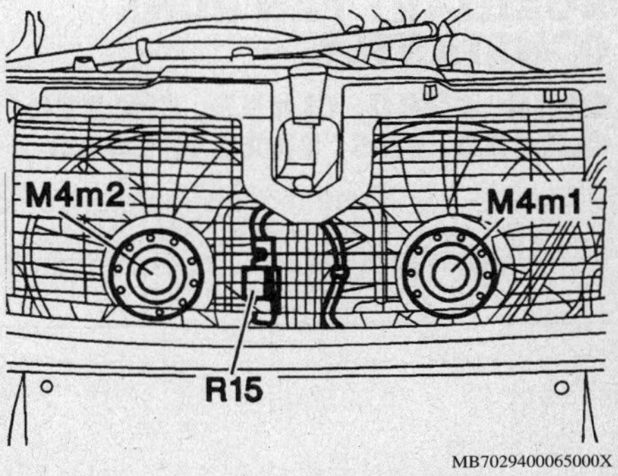

Fig. 2 Auxiliary fan and pre-resistor locations. C43, C230 & C280

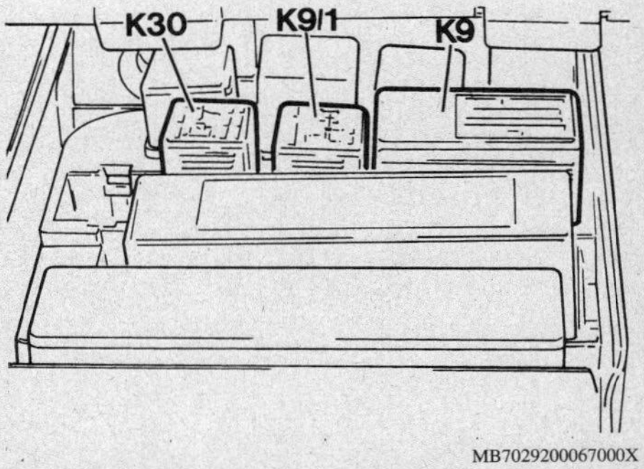

Fig. 3 Auxiliary fan relay locations. S320 & S420 & 1998–99 CL500, CL600, S500 & S600

SL500 & SL600

1. Remove radiator with condenser as described in appropriate engine section.
2. Press out six clips and remove box frame.
3. Disconnect electric connector.
4. Loosen clamps.
5. Remove three mounting bolts and separate auxiliary fan from condenser.
6. Remove two mounting bolts and holder.
7. Reverse procedure to install.

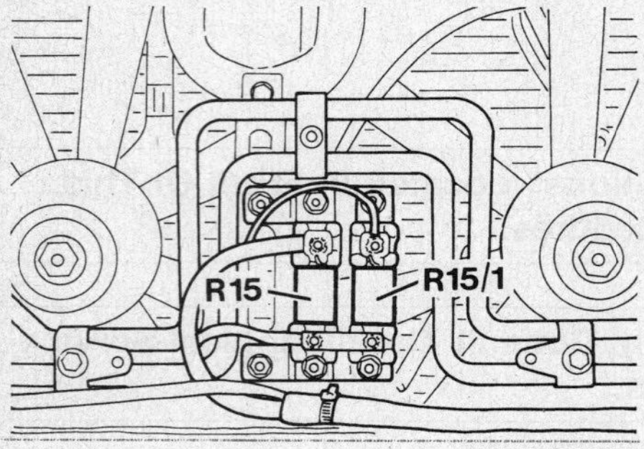

Fig. 4 Pre-resistor locations between auxiliary fans. S320 & S420 & 1998–99 CL500, CL600, S500 & S600

TECHNICAL SERVICE BULLETINS

AUXILIARY FAN RUNS CONSTANTLY

C230, C280, CLK55, CLK320, CLK430, E55, E320 & E430

On some of these models the electronic cooling or auxiliary fan(s) may run constantly, even with the ignition switched off.

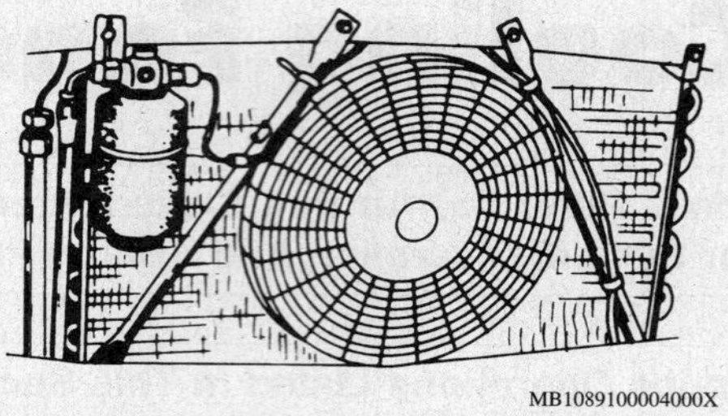

Fig. 5 Single electric cooling fan

This condition may be caused by water entering in the fuse and relay box.

To correct this condition, proceed as follows:

1. Inspect righthand front fuse and relay box for water leakage.
2. Remove fuse module relay box and Signal Acquisition and Control Module (SAM).
3. Inspect contacts between fuse module/relay box and SAM for corrosion.
4. If there is corrosion or copper oxide present, replace fuse module/relay box and SAM.
5. Fuse and relay box over is only splash proof, not water proof. **Do not spray water directly on fuse and relay box.**

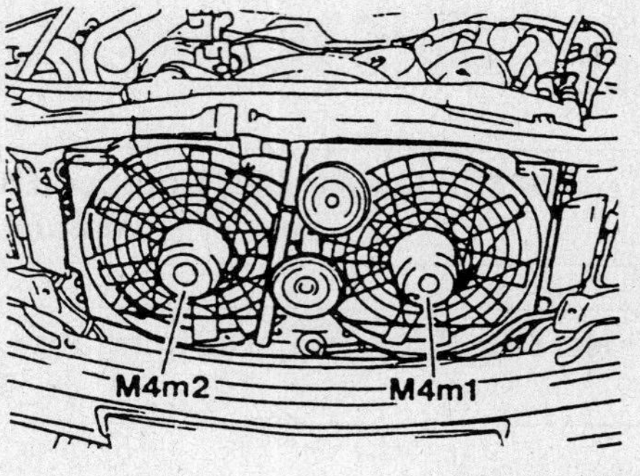

Fig. 6 Dual electric cooling fans

Dash Gauges

NOTE: Prior To Performing Any Service Operations Listed In This Section, Consult The "Technical Service Bulletins" Section For Related Information.

INDEX

	Page No.
Diagnostic Chart Index	5-205
Gauges	5-197
Component Locations	5-197
Function Tests	5-197
Symbol Explanation	5-197
Symptom Related Diagnosis	5-197
Tests	5-197
Meters	5-197
Precautions	5-197
Air Bag Systems	5-197
Battery Ground Cable	5-197
Speedometer	5-197
Technical Service Bulletins	5-208
Fuel Gauge Inoperative Or Reads Incorrectly	5-208
Fuel Gauge Occasionally Drops To Zero After Coasting	5-208
Lamp Failure Indicator Does Not Go Out	5-208
MIL Lamps Illuminate Only Briefly During Bulb Check	5-208
Oil Pressure Gauge Intermittently Drops To Zero Without Warning Lamp Illumination	5-208
Outside Air Temperature Gauge Reads Too Low	5-208
Warning Lamps	5-197
Warning System	5-197
Fuel Gauge Reads ¼ Tank High After Instrument Cluster Replacement	5-208

PRECAUTIONS

AIR BAG SYSTEMS

Refer to "Air Bag System Precautions" in front of this manual for system disarming and arming procedures.

BATTERY GROUND CABLE

Prior to service, disconnect battery ground cable and isolate as required.

GAUGES

SYMBOL EXPLANATION

Refer to **Figs. 1 through 3** for explanations of symbols, connections and Steps included in the charts.

COMPONENT LOCATIONS

Refer to **Figs. 4 through 9** for component locations.

SYMPTOM RELATED DIAGNOSIS

Refer to **Figs. 10 and 11** for symptom related diagnosis.

FUNCTION TESTS

1. Turn ignition key to 2 position.
2. All malfunction indicator/warning lamps must illuminate.
3. Start engine.
4. At more than 480 RPM, all indicator/warning lamps are to extinguish.
5. Independent of engine operation, the following lamps must go out:
   a. SRS MIL after four seconds.
   b. Safety belt warning lamp after six seconds.

TESTS

C43, C230, C280, CLK320, CLK430, E300, E320 & E430

Less Flexible Service System (FSS)

Perform test as directed, **Figs. 12 through 15.**

With Flexible Service System (FSS)

Perform test as directed, **Figs. 16 and 17.**

S320, S420 & SL600 & 1998-99 CL500, CL600, S500 & S600 & 1998 SL500

Less Flexible Service System (FSS)

Perform test as directed, **Figs. 18 through 21.**

With Flexible Service System (FSS)

Perform test as directed, **Figs. 22 through 25.**

SLK230

Less Flexible Service System (FSS)

Perform test as directed, **Figs. 26 and 27.**

With Flexible Service System (FSS)

Perform test as directed, **Figs. 28 and 29.**

METERS

Refer to "Gauges."

WARNING LAMPS

Refer to "Gauges."

WARNING SYSTEM

Refer to "Gauges."

SPEEDOMETER

Refer to "Gauges."

Description	Symbol
ABS adaptor	
Socket box tester 35-pole	
Socket box tester 126-pole	
Signal generator	
Hand–held tester (HHT)	
Impulse counter scan tool	
On-off ratio tester	
Pressure gauge	
Digital multimeter	
Resistance substitution unit	
Bridge	
DANGER! High Voltage	ϟ
Brake pad wear indicator	(◯)

Description	Symbol
Pin	
Socket	)—
Battery	
DC generator	Ⓖ
DC motor	Ⓜ
Capacitor	
Coil	
Resistance	
Ground	⊥
Systems check O.K.	√
Fault	F
Grater than	>
Smaller than	<
Short circuit	⌐¬
Short circuit to positive	⌐¬ +

Description	Symbol
Short circuit to ground	⌐¬ −
Open circuit	—//—
Direct current measured with multimeter	Ⓐ
Alternating current measured w/multimeter	Ⓐ
Direct voltage measured w/multimeter	Ⓥ
Alternating voltage measured w/multimeter	Ⓥ
Resistance measured with multimeter	Ω
Signal generator Square wave form	Ⓖ
Signal generator Sine form	Ⓖ
Oscilloscope	
Adaptor wire with LED	

MB9099900093010X

Fig. 1 Test equipment & component symbols explanation (Part 1 of 2)

Description	Symbol
Top air outlets	
Top, bottom and door air outlets	
Bottom air outlets	
Top and bottom air outlets	
Normal setting	
Economy setting	
Center and side air outlets	
Automatic function	AUTOMATIC
Automatic blower speed regulation	AUTO
Defrost	

Description	Symbol
Recirculating air	
Minimum blower speed	
Maximum blower speed	
Dehumidify	
Normal setting (cooling)	
A/C compressor Off	EC
A/C On/Off (USA only)	A/C
Off (no air intake)	O
° C	C
° F	F
Residual engine heat utilization	REST

MB9099900093020X

Fig. 1 Test equipment & component symbols explanation (Part 2 of 2)

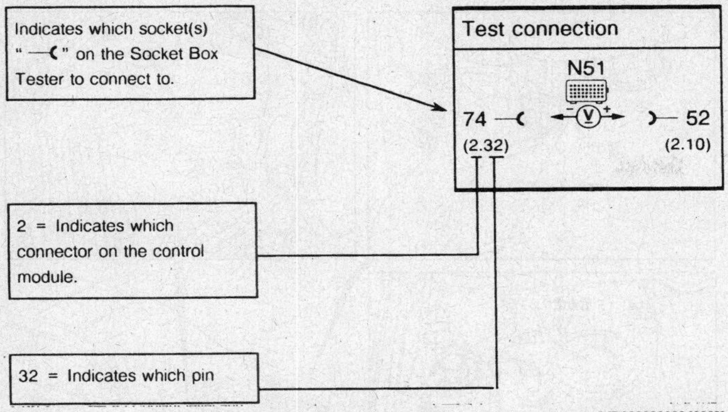

MB9099900026000X

Fig. 2 Test connections explanation

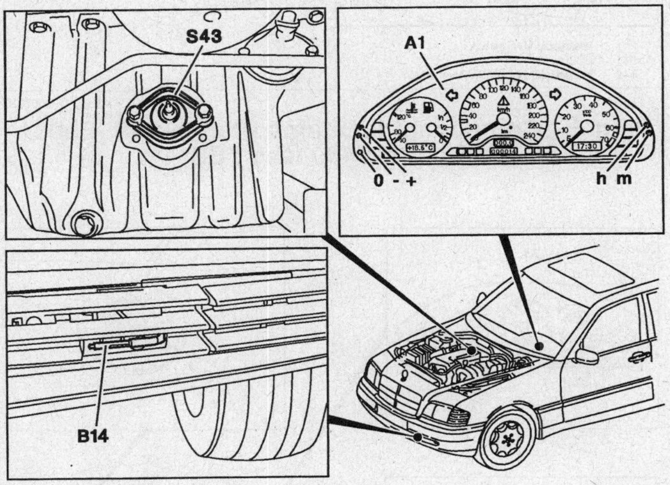

A1 Instrument cluster
B14 Outside temperature indicator temperature sensor
S43 Oil level switch

MB9099900063010X

Fig. 4 Component locations (Part 1 of 4). C43, C230 & C280 less FSS

N47 Instrument cluster
S12 Parking brake switch
S42 Windshield washer fluid level switch
W3 Ground (left front wheel housing at ignition coil)

MB9099900063030X

Fig. 4 Component locations (Part 3 of 4). C43, C230 & C280 less FSS

- to a test step within the same test

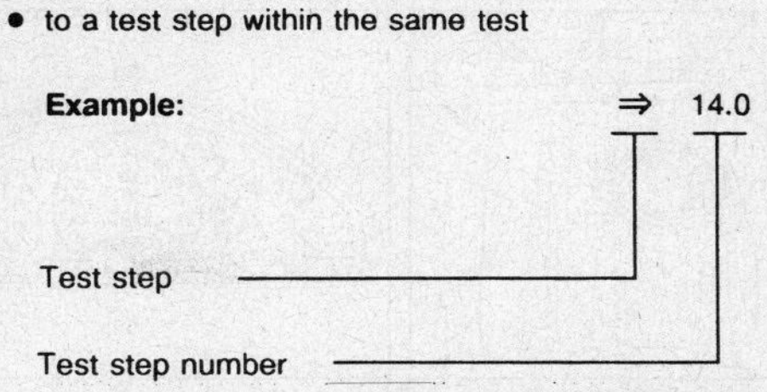

MB9099900027000X

Fig. 3 Test step explanation

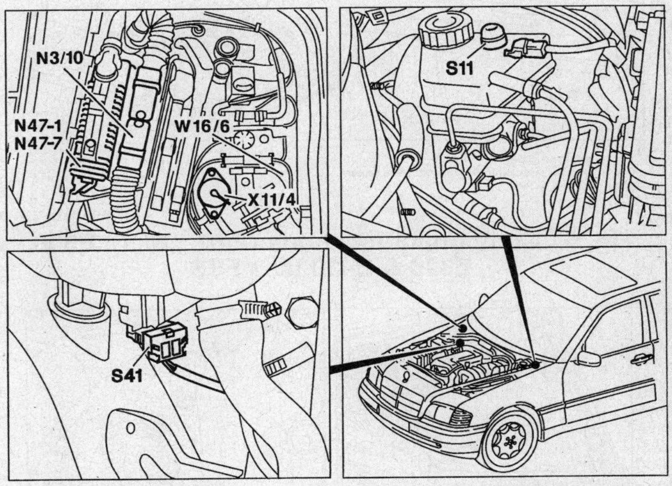

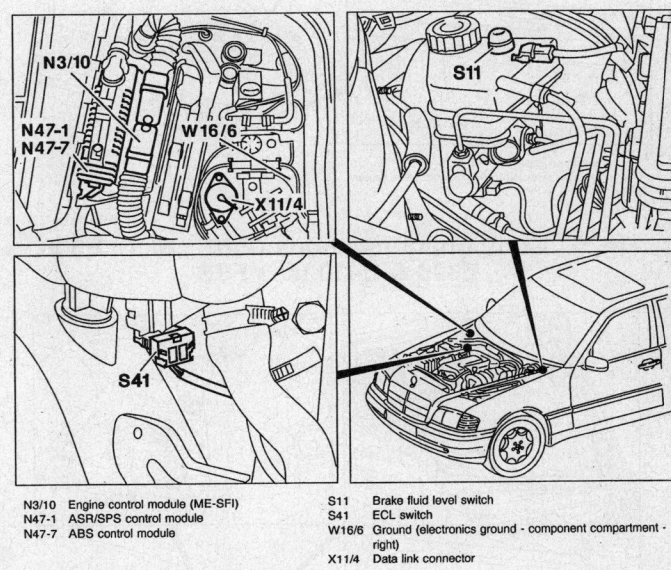

N3/10 Engine control module (ME-SFI)
N47-1 ASR/SPS control module
N47-7 ABS control module
S11 Brake fluid level switch
S41 ECL switch
W16/6 Ground (electronics ground - component compartment - right)
X11/4 Data link connector

MB9099900063020X

Fig. 4 Component locations (Part 2 of 4). C43, C230 & C280 less FSS

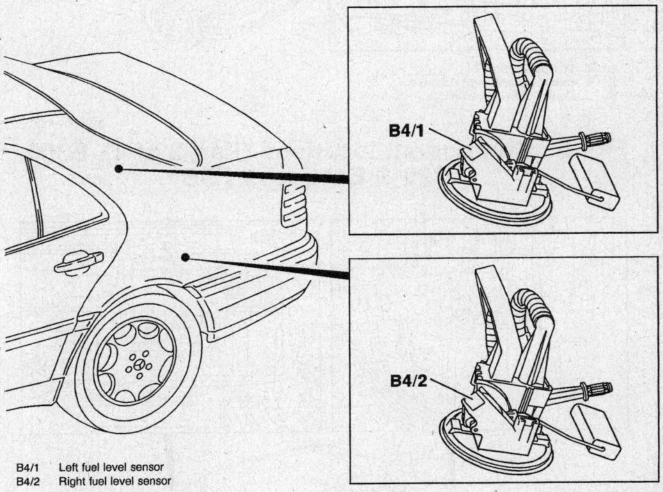

B4/1 Left fuel level sensor
B4/2 Right fuel level sensor

MB9099900063040X

Fig. 4 Component locations (Part 4 of 4). C43, C230 & C280 less FSS

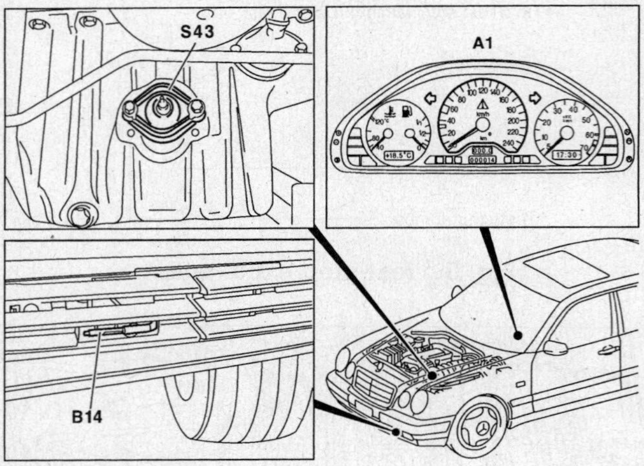

A1 Instrument cluster
B14 Outside temperature indicator temperature sensor
S43 Oil level switch

MB9099900062010X

Fig. 5 Component locations (Part 1 of 4). E300, E320 & E430 less FSS

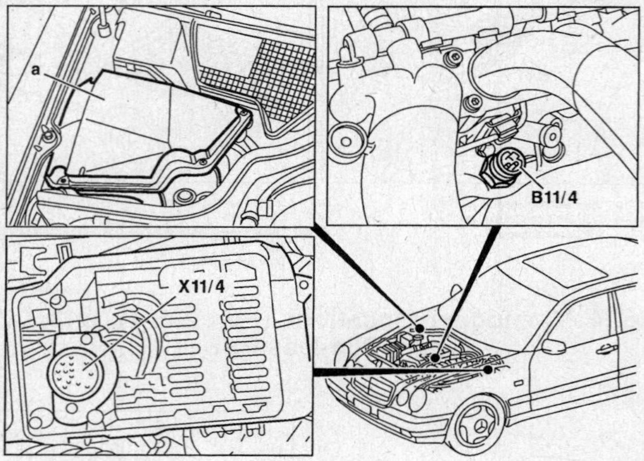

B11/4 ECT sensor (IFI)
X11/4 Data link connector (DTC readout)
a Control module box (plastic)

MB9099900062030X

Fig. 5 Component locations (Part 3 of 4). E300, E320 & E430 less FSS

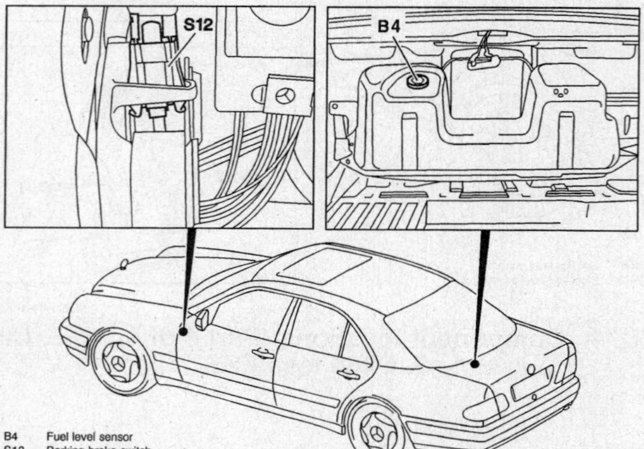

B4 Fuel level sensor
S12 Parking brake switch

MB9099900062040X

Fig. 5 Component locations (Part 4 of 4). E300, E320 & E430 less FSS

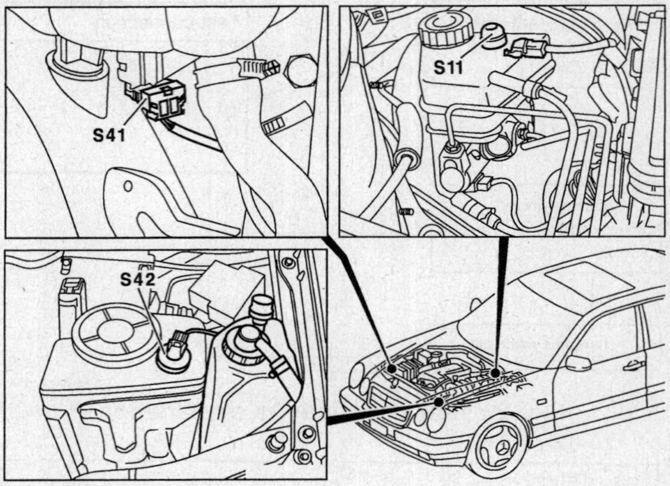

S11 Brake fluid level switch
S41 ECL switch
S42 Windshield washer fluid level switch

MB9099900062020X

Fig. 5 Component locations (Part 2 of 4). E300, E320 & E430 less FSS

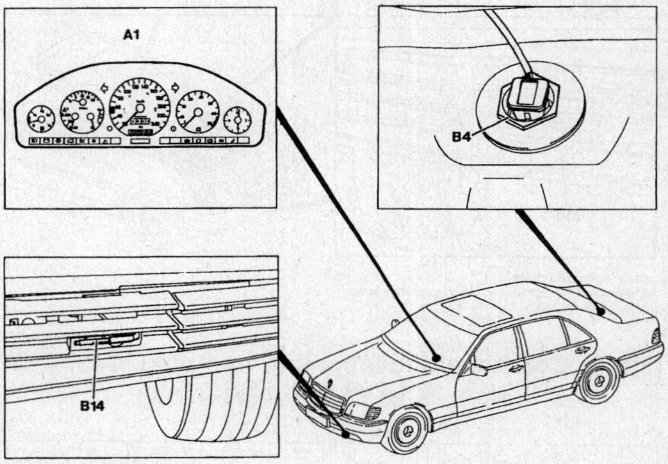

A1 Instrument cluster
B4 Fuel level sensor
B14 Outside temperature indicator temperature sensor

MB9099900064010X

Fig. 6 Component locations (Part 1 of 2). S320 & S420 & 1998–99 CL500, CL600, S500 & S600 less FSS

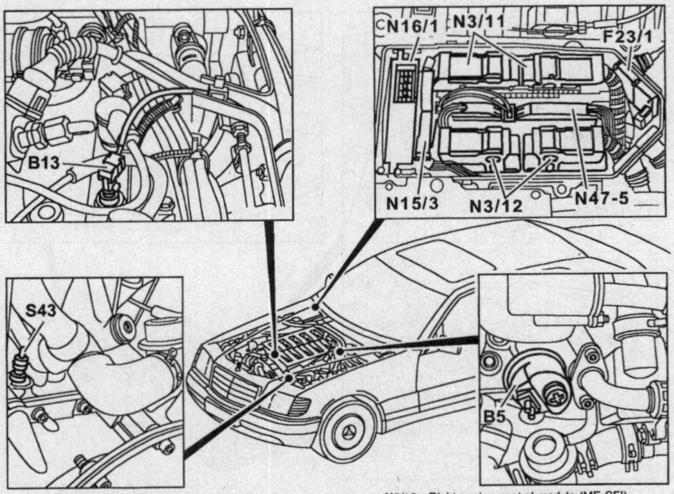

B5 Oil pressure sensor (Engine 119: right front; engine 104, 120: left rear
B13 ECT sensor
F23/1 Control module box
N3/11 Left engine control module (ME-SFI)
N3/12 Right engine control module (ME-SFI)
N15/3 Transmission control module
N16/1 Base module
N47-5 ESP - SPS control module
S43 Oil level switch (Engine 119: right side of oil pan; engine 104, 120: left side of oil pan)

MB9099900064020X

Fig. 6 Component locations (Part 2 of 2). S320 & S420 & 1998–99 CL500, CL600, S500 & S600 less FSS

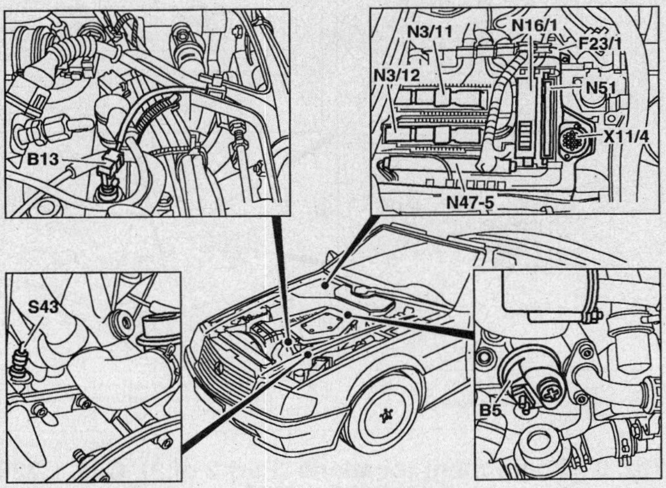

B5 Oil pressure sensor (Engine 119: right front; engine 104, 120: left rear)
B13 ECT sensor
F23/1 Control module box
N3/11 Left engine control module (ME-SFI)
N3/12 Right engine control module (ME-SFI)
N16/1 Base module
N47-5 ESP - SPS control module
N51 ADS control module
S43 Oil level switch (Engine 119: right side of oil pan; engine 104, 120: left side of oil pan)
X11/4 Data link connector

MB9099900066020X

Fig. 7 Component locations (Part 2 of 2). SL600 & 1998 SL500 less FSS

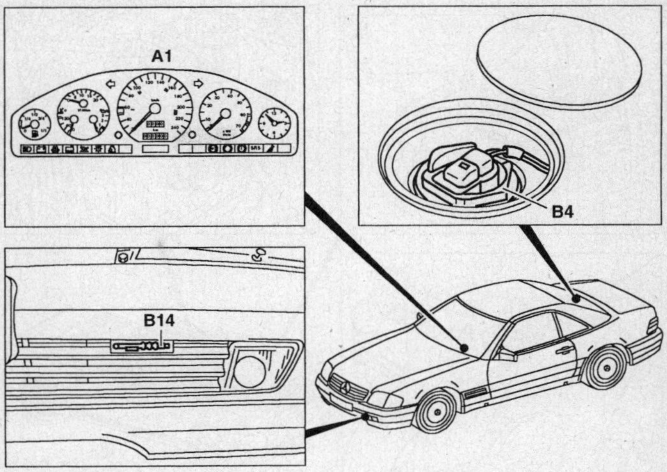

A1 Instrument cluster
B4 Fuel level sensor
B14 Outside temperature indicator temperature sensor

MB9099900066010X

Fig. 7 Component locations (Part 1 of 2). SL600 & 1998 SL500 less FSS

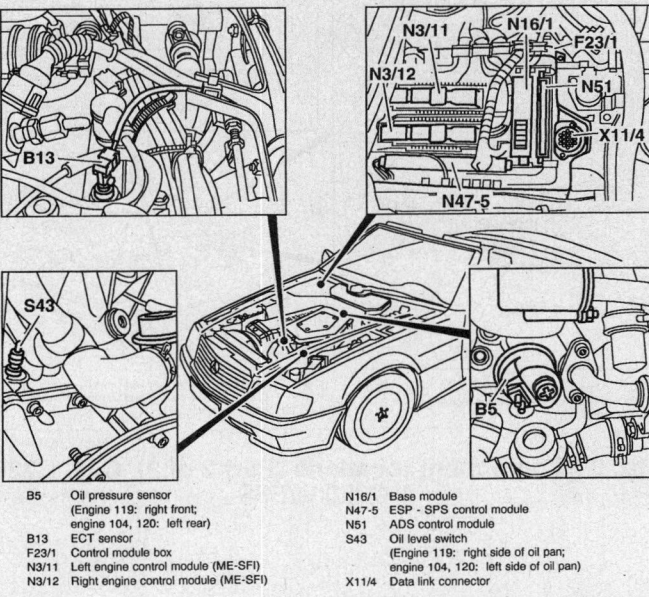

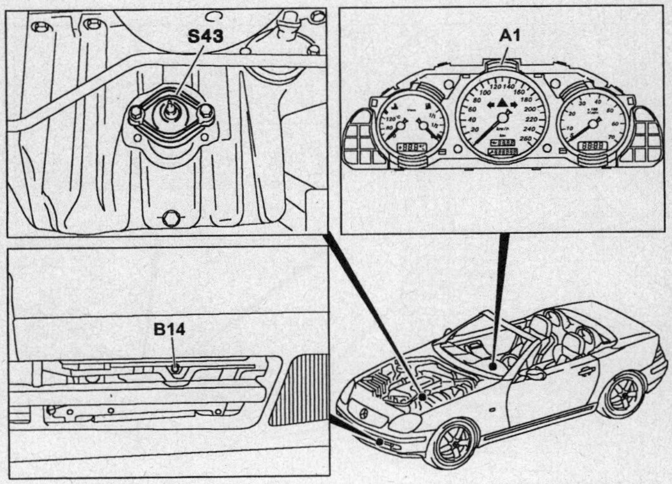

A1 Instrument cluster
B14 Outside temperature indicator temperature sensor
S43 Oil level switch

MB9099900061010X

Fig. 8 Component locations (Part 1 of 3). SLK230 less FSS

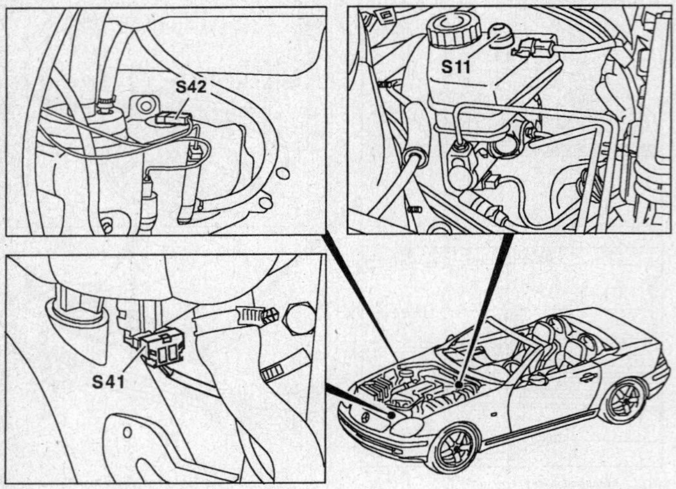

S11 Brake fluid switch
S41 ECL switch
S42 Windshield washer fluid level switch

MB9099900061020X

Fig. 8 Component locations (Part 2 of 3). SLK230 less FSS

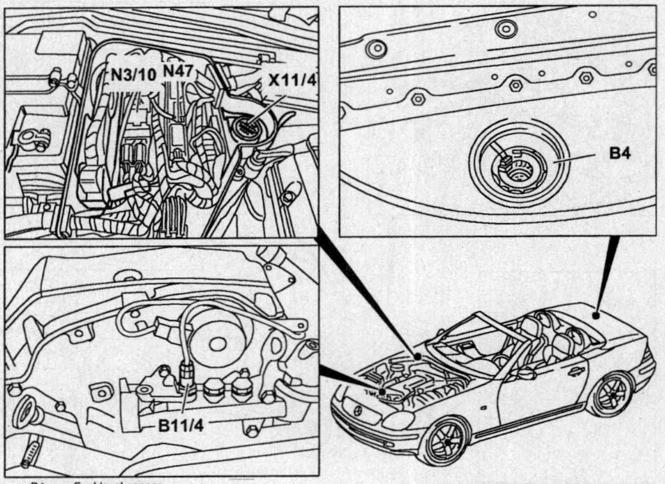

B4 Fuel level sensor
B11/4 ECT sensor (DFI,IFI)
N3/10 Engine control module (ME-SFI)
N47 Traction system control module
X11/4 Data link connector (DTC readout)

MB9099900061030X

Fig. 8 Component locations (Part 3 of 3). SLK230 less FSS

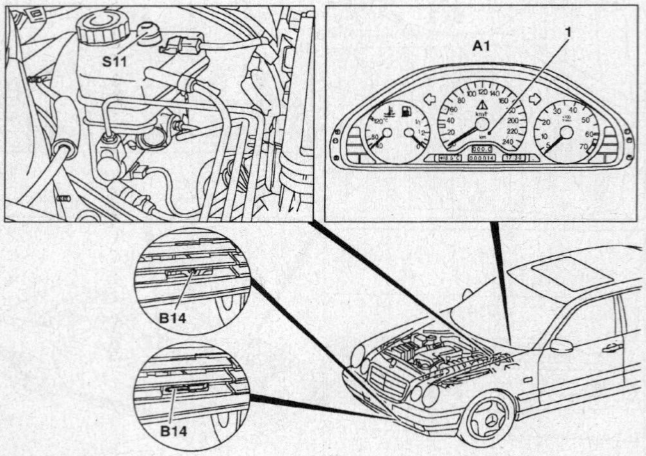

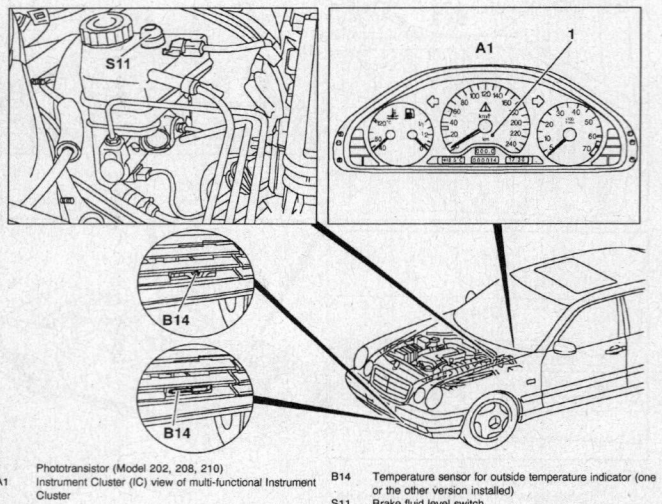

1 Phototransistor (Model 202, 208, 210)
A1 Instrument Cluster (IC) view of multi-functional Instrument Cluster
B14 Temperature sensor for outside temperature indicator (one or the other version installed)
S11 Brake fluid level switch

MB9099900054000X

Fig. 9 Component locations (Part 1 of 3). C43, C230, C280, CLK320, CLK430, E300, E320, E430, S320, S420, SL600 & SLK230 & 1998–99 CL500, CL600, S500 & S600 & 1998 SL500 w/FSS

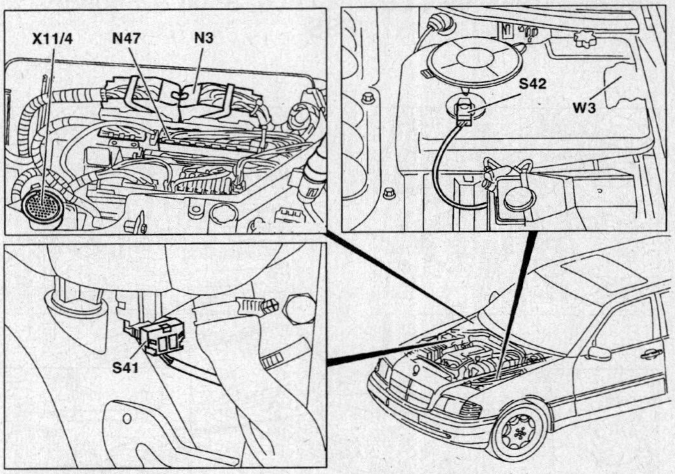

N3 Engine control module
N47 Traction systems control module
S41 ECL switch
S42 Windshield washer fluid level switch
W3 Ground (left front wheel well housing at ignition coil)
X11/4 Data link connector

MB9099900050010X

Fig. 9 Component locations (Part 2 of 3). C43, C230 & C280 w/FSS

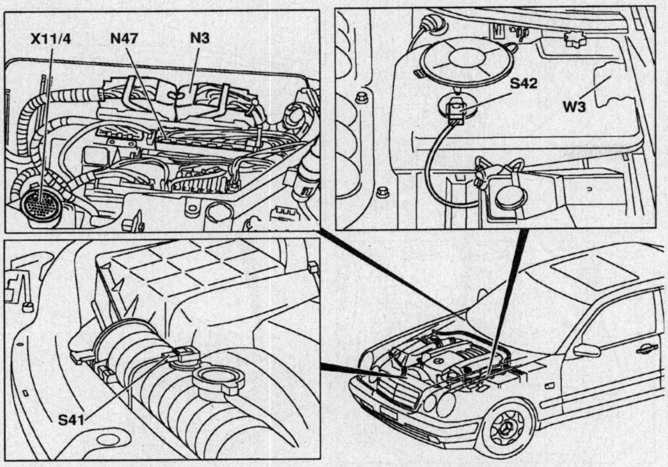

N3 Engine control module
N47 Traction systems control module
S41 ECL switch
S42 Windshield washer fluid level switch
W3 Ground (left front wheel well housing at ignition coil)
X11/4 Data link connector

MB9099900039000X

Fig. 9 Component locations (Part 2 of 3). CLK320 & CLK430 w/FSS

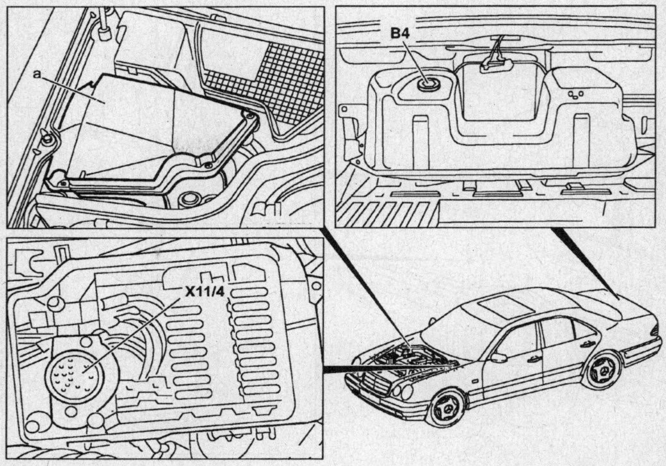

B4 Fuel level sensor
X11/4 Data link connector (DTC readout)
a Control module box

MB9099900038010X

Fig. 9 Component locations (Part 2 of 3). E300, E320 & E430 w/FSS

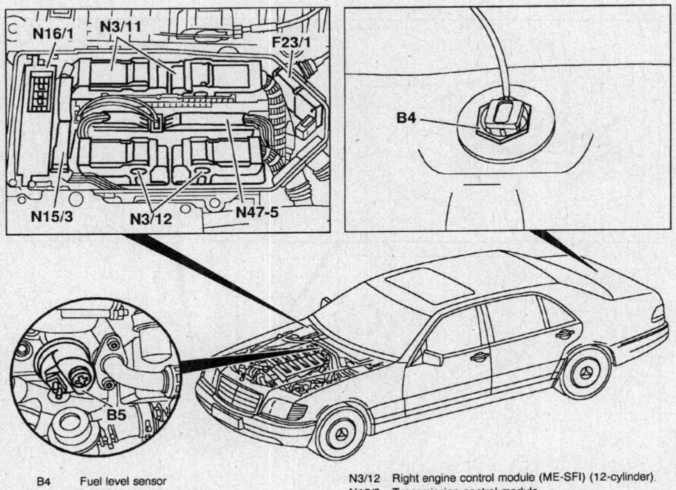

B4 Fuel level sensor
B5 Oil pressure sensor (Engine 119: right front; engine 104, 120: left rear)
F23/1 Control module box
N3/11 Left engine control module (ME-SFI) (12-cylinder)
N3/12 Right engine control module (ME-SFI) (12-cylinder)
N15/3 Transmission control module
N16/1 Base module
N47-5 ESP - SPS control module

MB9099900052000X

Fig. 9 Component locations (Part 2 of 3). S320, S420 & SL600 & 1998–99 CL500, CL600, S500 & S600 & 1998 SL500 w/FSS

B4 Fuel level sensor
N3/10 Engine control module (ME-SFI)
N47 Traction systems control module
X11/4 Data link connector

MB9099900051010X

Fig. 9 Component locations (Part 2 of 3). SLK230 w/FSS

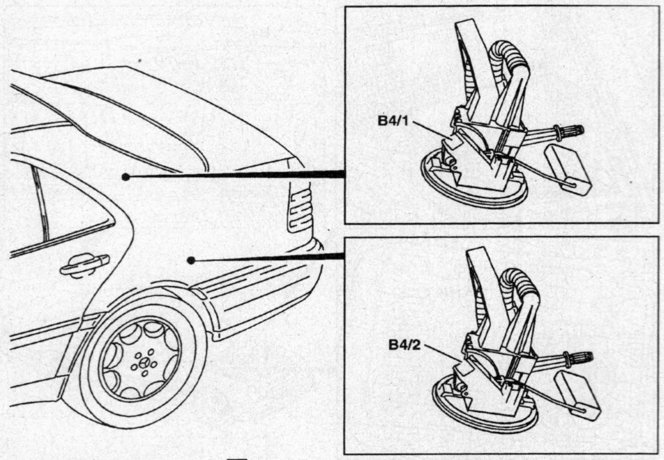

B4/1 Left fuel level sensor
B4/1 Right fuel level sensor

The fuel sensors are accessible from underneath of the vehicle.

MB9099900050020X

Fig. 9 Component locations (Part 3 of 3). C43, C230 & C280 w/FSS

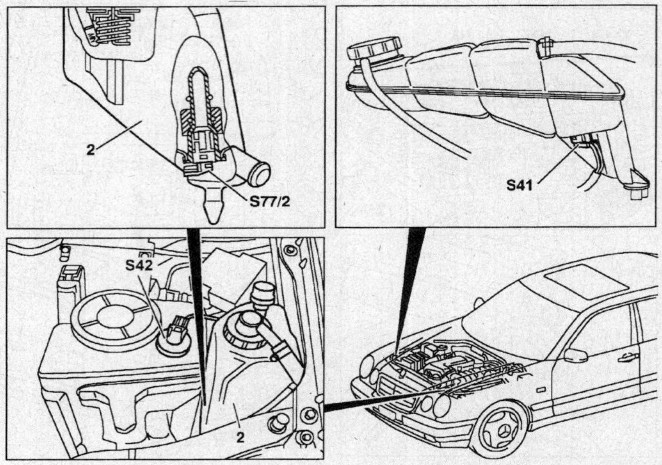

2 Power steering and leveling system hydraulic fluid container
S41 ECL switch
S42 Windshield washer fluid level switch
S77/2 Hydraulic fluid level switch

MB9099900038020X

Fig. 9 Component locations (Part 3 of 3). E300, E320 & E430 w/FSS

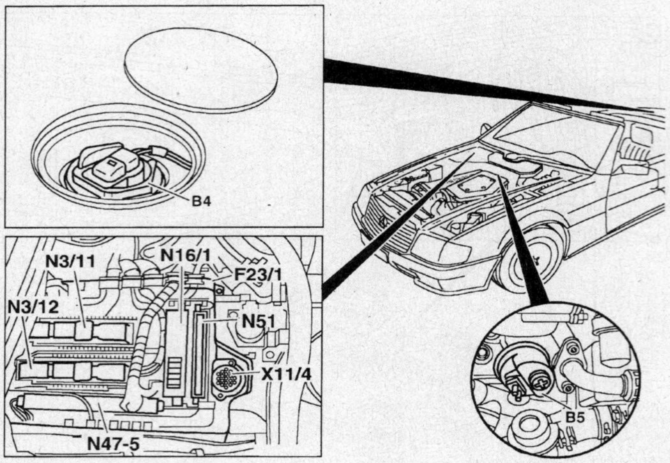

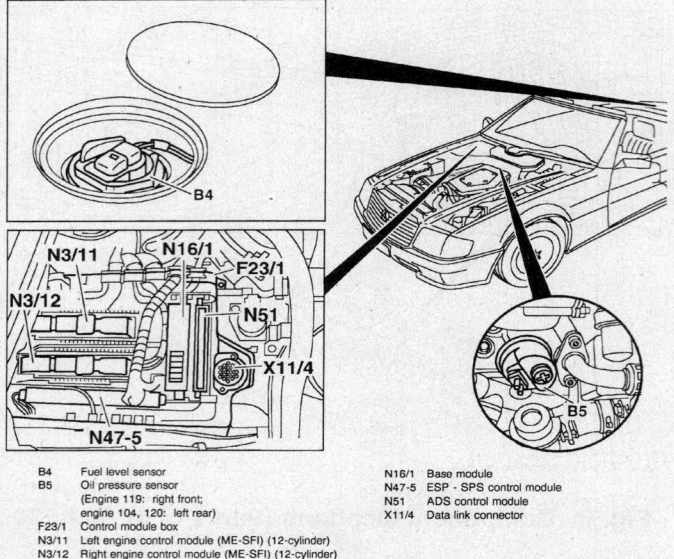

B4 Fuel level sensor
B5 Oil pressure sensor (Engine 119: right front; engine 104, 120: left rear)
F23/1 Control module box
N3/11 Left engine control module (ME-SFI) (12-cylinder)
N3/12 Right engine control module (ME-SFI) (12-cylinder)
N16/1 Base module
N47-5 ESP - SPS control module
N51 ADS control module
X11/4 Data link connector

MB9099900053000X

Fig. 9 Component locations. (Part 3 of 3) SL600 & 1998 SL500 w/FSS

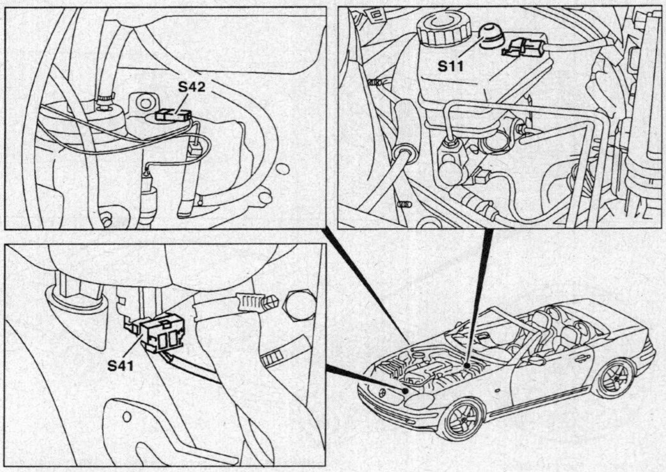

S11 Brake fluid level switch
S41 ECL switch
S42 Windshield washer fluid level switch

MB9099900051020X

Fig. 9 Component locations (Part 3 of 3). SLK230 w/FSS

Complaint/Problem	Possible cause	Test step/Remedy
Entire instrument cluster (A1) not functioning.	Power supply, Instrument cluster (A1)	Model 129: □ 23 ⇒ 1.0 Model 140: □ 24 ⇒ 1.0 Model 202: □ 25 ⇒ 1.0 Model 210: □ 26 ⇒ 1.0 Model 170: □ 27 ⇒ 1.0
Warning lamps/Indicator lamps are not functioning.	Power supply, Instrument cluster (A1)	Model 129: □ 23 ⇒ 1.0 Model 140: □ 24 ⇒ 1.0 Model 202: □ 25 ⇒ 1.0 Model 210: □ 26 ⇒ 1.0 Model 170: □ 27 ⇒ 1.0
Communication between HHT and instrumnet cluster not possible.	Wiring, Instrument cluster (A1)	Model 129: □ 23 ⇒ 2.0 Model 140: □ 24 ⇒ 2.0 Model 202: □ 25 ⇒ 2.0 Model 210: □ 26 ⇒ 2.0 Model 170: □ 27 ⇒ 2.0
Low engine coolant level (ECL) indicator lamp (A1e11), low windshield washer fluid level indicator lamp (A1e13) illuminated or does not function.	ECL switch (S41) Windshield washer fluid level switch (S42) Wiring Instrument cluster (A1)	Model 129: □ 23 ⇒ 3.0 Model 140: □ 24 ⇒ 3.0 Model 202: □ 25 ⇒ 3.0 Model 210: □ 26 ⇒ 3.0 Model 170: □ 27 ⇒ 3.0

MB9099900065000X

Fig. 10 Symptom Related Diagnosis. Less FSS

Complaint/Problem	Possible cause	Test step/Remedy
Entire instrument cluster (A1) not functioning.	Power supply, Instrument cluster (A1)	Model 129: □ 23 ⇒ 1.0 Model 140: □ 24 ⇒ 1.0 Model 170: □ 25 ⇒ 1.0 Model 202, 208, 210: □ 26 ⇒ 1.0
Warning lamps/Indicator lamps are not functioning.	Power supply, Instrument cluster (A1)	Model 129: □ 23 ⇒ 1.0 Model 140: □ 24 ⇒ 1.0 Model 170: □ 25 ⇒ 1.0 Model 202, 208, 210: □ 26 ⇒ 1.0
Communication between HHT and instrument cluster not possible.	Wiring, Instrument cluster (A1)	Model 129: □ 23 ⇒ 2.0 Model 140: □ 24 ⇒ 2.0 Model 170: □ 25 ⇒ 2.0 Model 202, 208, 210: □ 26 ⇒ 2.0
Low engine coolant level (ECL) indicator lamp (A1e11), low windshield washer fluid level indicator lamp (A1e13) illuminated - does not function.	ECL switch (S41) Windshield washer fluid level switch (S42) Wiring Instrument cluster (A1)	Model 129: □ 23 ⇒ 3.0 Model 140: □ 24 ⇒ 3.0 Model 170: □ 25 ⇒ 3.0 Model 202, 208, 210: □ 26 ⇒ 3.0
Warning lamps/Indicator lamps (brake fluid level, parking brake, brake pad wear, ABS, ETS, ASR, ESP) illuminate simultaneously and speedometer needle rests at the bottom stop.	Traction system control module (N47)	
Tachometer needle, ECT needle remain at rest on the bottom stop. Engine oil low level warning lamp illuminates.	Injection control module (N3)	

MB9099900055010X

Fig. 11 Symptom Related Diagnosis (Part 1 of 2). w/FSS

Complaint/Problem	Possible cause	Test step/Remedy
Warning lamps/Indicator lamps (brake fluid level, parking brake, brake pad wear, oil level, ABS, ETS, ASR, ESP) illuminate simultaneously and tachometer speedometer needle rests at the bottom stop.	CAN Bus disruption	Model 129: □ 23 ⇒ 4.0 Model 140: □ 24 ⇒ 4.0 Model 170: □ 25 ⇒ 4.0 Model 202, 208, 210: □ 26 ⇒ 4.0

MB9099900055020X

Fig. 11 Symptom Related Diagnosis (Part 2 of 2). w/FSS

DIAGNOSTIC CHART INDEX

Test	Description	Page No.	Fig. No.
C43, C230 & C280 LESS FLEXIBLE SERVICE SYSTEM (FSS)			
Test 25	Steps 1.0–2.0	5-206	12
	Steps 3.0–3.2	5-206	13
C43, C230, C280 w/FLEXIBLE SERVICE SYSTEM (FSS)			
Test 25	Steps 1.0–3.0	5-206	16
	Steps 3.1–4.2	5-206	17
CLK320 &m CLK430 w/FLEXIBLE SERVICE SYSTEM (FSS)			
Test 25	Steps 1.0–3.0	5-206	16
	Steps 3.1–4.2	5-206	17
E300, E320 & E430 LESS FLEXIBLE SERVICE SYSTEM (FSS)			
Test 26	Steps 1.0–2.0	5-206	14
	Steps 3.0–3.2	5-206	15
E300, E320 & E430 w/FLEXIBLE SERVICE SYSTEM (FSS)			
Test 25	Steps 1.0–3.0	5-206	16
	Steps 3.1–4.2	5-206	17
S320 & S420 & 1998–99 CL500, CL600, S500 & S600 LESS FLEXIBLE SERVICE SYSTEM (FSS)			
Test 24	Steps 1.0–2.0	5-206	18
	Steps 3.0–3.2	5-206	19
S320, S420 & 1998–99 CL500, CL600, S500 & S600 w/FLEXIBLE SERVICE SYSTEM (FSS)			
Test 24	Steps 1.0–3.0	5-207	22
	Steps 3.1–4.2	5-207	23
SL600 & 1998 SL500 LESS FLEXIBLE SERVICE SYSTEM (FSS)			
Test 23	Steps 1.0–2.0	5-207	20
	Steps 3.0–3.2	5-207	21
SL600 & 1998 SL500 w/FLEXIBLE SERVICE SYSTEM (FSS)			
Test 23	Steps 1.0–3.0	5-207	24
	Steps 3.1–4.2	5-207	25
Test 24	Steps 1.0–3.0	5-207	22
	Steps 3.1–4.2	5-207	23
SLK230 LESS FLEXIBLE SERVICE SYSTEM (FSS)			
Test 27	Steps 1.0–2.0	5-207	26
	Steps 3.0–3.2	5-207	27
SLK230 w/FLEXIBLE SERVICE SYSTEM (FSS)			
Test 25	Steps 1.0–3.0	5-208	28
	Steps 3.1–4.2	5-208	29

⇒	Test scope	Test connection	Test condition	Nominal value	Possible cause/Remedy
1.0	**Instrument cluster (A1)** Voltage supply Circuit 30	A1 3 —(-(V)+)— 11 (1A.3) (1A.11) 12 —(-(V)+)— 11 (1A.12) (1A.11)	Ignition: **OFF** Remove Instrument cluster (A1) Disconnect connector 1 (30-pole)	11 – 14 V	Fuse 10 in fuse and relay box (F1), Wiring, ⇒ 1.1
1.1	Voltage supply Circuit 15	A1 3 —(-(V)+)— 9 (1A.3) (1A.9)	Ignition: **ON**	11 – 14 V	Fuse 3 in fuse and relay box (F1), Wiring, A1
2.0	**HHT interface** Connection between A1 and data link connector (X11/4)	15—(-(Ω)+)— 11 X11/4 (1B.11)	Ignition: **OFF** Remove A1, Disconnect connector 1 (30-pole)	≤ 5 Ω	Wiring.

MB9099900058010X

Fig. 12 Test 25: Steps 1.0–2.0. C43, C230 & C280 less FSS

⇒	Test scope	Test connection	Test condition	Nominal value	Possible cause/Remedy
1.0	**Instrument cluster (A1)** Voltage supply Circuit 30	A1 3 —(-(V)+)— 11 (1A.3) (1A.11) 12 —(-(V)+)— 11 (1A.12) (1A.11)	Ignition: **OFF** Remove instrument cluster (A1) Disconnect connector 1 (30-pole)	11 – 14 V	Fuse 4 in fuse and relay box (F1), Wiring, ⇒ 1.1
1.1	Voltage supply Circuit 15	A1 3 —(-(V)+)— 9 (1A.3) (1A.9)	Ignition: **ON**	11 – 14 V	Fuse 7 in fuse and relay box (F1), Wiring, A1
2.0	**HHT interface** Connection between A1 and data link connector (X11/4)	15—(-(Ω)+)— 11 X11/4 (1B.11)	Ignition: **OFF** Remove A1, Disconnect connector 1 (30-pole)	≤ 5 Ω	Wiring.

MB9099900057010X

Fig. 14 Test 26: Steps 1.0–2.0. E300, E320 & E430 less FSS

⇒	Test scope	Test connection	Test condition	Nominal value	Possible cause/Remedy
1.0	**Instrument cluster (A1)** Voltage supply Circuit 30	A1 3 —(-(V)+)— 11 (1A.3) (1A.11) 12 —(-(V)+)— 11 (1A.12) (1A.11)	Ignition: **OFF** Remove instrument cluster (A1) Disconnect connector 1 (30-pole)	11 – 14 V	Model 202: fuse 30 Model 208: fuse 26 Model 210: fuse 4 in fuse and relay box (F1), Wiring, ⇒ 1.1
1.1	Voltage supply Circuit 15	A1 3 —(-(V)+)— 9 (1A.3) (1A.9)	Ignition: **ON**	11 – 14 V	Model 202: fuse 19 Model 208: fuse 19 Model 210: fuse 7 in fuse and relay box (F1), Wiring, A1
2.0	**HHT interface** Connection between A1 and data link connector (X11/4)	A1 15—(-(Ω)+)— 11 X11/4 (1B.11)	Ignition: **OFF** Remove A1, Disconnect connector 1 (30-pole)	≤ 5 Ω	Wiring.
3.0	**ECL and windshield washer level:** ECL level switch (S41), windshield washer level switch (S42) and wiring	A1 12 —(-(Ω)+)— 4 (1B.12) (1B.4)	Ignition: **OFF** Coolant level and windshield washer fluid level: OK Remove instrument cluster (A1) Disconnect connector 1 (30 pole).	233 - 297 Ω	Wiring ⇒ 3.1 Values O.K.: A1

MB9099900034010X

Fig. 16 Test 25: Steps 1.0–3.0. C43, C230, C280, CLK320, CLK430, E300, E320 & E430 w/FSS

⇒	Test scope	Test connection	Test condition	Nominal value	Possible cause/Remedy
1.0	**Instrument cluster (A1)** Voltage supply Circuit 30	A1 3 —(-(V)+)— 11 (1A.3) (1A.11) 12 —(-(V)+)— 11 (1A.12) (1A.11)	Ignition: **OFF** Remove instrument cluster (A1) Disconnect connector 1 (30-pole)	11 – 14 V	Fuse 17 in fuse and relay box (F3), Wiring, ⇒ 1.1
1.1	Voltage supply Circuit 15	A1 3 —(-(V)+)— 9 (1A.3) (1A.9)	Ignition: **ON**	11 – 14 V	Fuse 24 in fuse and relay box (F3), Wiring, A1
2.0	**HHT interface** Connection between A1 and data link connector (X11/4)	15—(-(Ω)+)— 11 X11/4 (1B.11)	Ignition: **OFF** Remove A1, Disconnect connector 1 (30-pole)	≤ 5 Ω	Wiring.

MB9099900059010X

Fig. 18 Test 24: Steps 1.0–2.0. S320 & S420 & 1998–99 CL500, CL600, S500 & S600 less FSS

⇒	Test scope	Test connection	Test condition	Nominal value	Possible cause/Remedy
3.0	**ECL and windshield washer level:** ECL level switch (S41), windshield washer level switch (S42) and wiring	A1 12 —(-(Ω)+)— 4 (1B.12) (1B.4)	Ignition: **OFF** Coolant level and windshield washer fluid level: OK Remove A1 Disconnect connector 1 (30 pole).	233 - 297 Ω	Wiring ⇒ 3.1 Values O.K.: A1
3.1	**ECL switch (S41)**	S41 1 — -(Ω)+ — 2	Ignition: **OFF** Remove expansion tank Disconnect connector at S41 Coolant level OK	102 - 120 Ω	S41 Values O.K.: ⇒ 3.2
3.2	**Windshield washer fluid level switch (S42)**	S42 1 — -(Ω)+ — 2	Ignition: **OFF** Disconnect connector at S42 Washer fluid level OK	145 - 185 Ω	S42

MB9099900058020X

Fig. 13 Test 25: Steps 3.0–3.2. C43, C230 & C280 less FSS

⇒	Test scope	Test connection	Test condition	Nominal value	Possible cause/Remedy
3.0	**ECL and windshield washer level:** ECL level switch (S41), windshield washer level switch (S42) and wiring	A1 12 —(-(Ω)+)— 4 (1B.12) (1B.4)	Ignition: **OFF** Coolant level and windshield washer fluid level: OK Remove instrument cluster (A1) Disconnect connector 1 (30 pole).	233 - 297 Ω	Wiring ⇒ 3.1 Values O.K.: A1
3.1	**ECL switch (S41)**	S41 1 — -(Ω)+ — 2	Ignition: **OFF** Remove expansion tank Disconnect connector at S41 Coolant level OK	102 - 120 Ω	S41 Values O.K.: ⇒ 3.2
3.2	**Windshield washer fluid level switch (S42)**	S42 1 — -(Ω)+ — 2	Ignition: **OFF** Disconnect connector at S42 Washer fluid level OK	145 - 185 Ω	S42

MB9099900057020X

Fig. 15 Test 26: Steps 3.0–3.2. E300, E320 & E430 less FSS

⇒	Test scope	Test connection	Test condition	Nominal value	Possible cause/Remedy
3.1	ECL switch (S41)	S41 1 — -(Ω)+ — 2	Ignition: **OFF** Remove expansion tank Disconnect connector at S41. Coolant level OK	102 - 120 Ω	S41 Values O.K.: ⇒ 3.2
3.2	Windshield washer fluid level switch (S42)	S42 1 — -(Ω)+ — 2	Ignition: **OFF** Disconnect connector at S42. Washer fluid level OK	145 - 185 Ω	S42
4.0	**CAN bus data lines resistance**	A1 1 —(-(Ω)+)— 2 (2B.1) (2B.20)	Ignition: **OFF** Disconnect connector 1 (All control modules are connected to CAN)	around 60 Ω	CAN: –//–, ⌐ ¬ – N47 N3 Values O.K.: ⇒ 4.1
4.1	CAN bus data lines Voltage Low-data line	⊥ -(V)+ A1)— 2 (2B.1)	Ignition: **ON**	around 2.3 V	N47 N3 Values O.K.: ⇒ 4.2
4.2	CAN bus data lines Voltage High-data line	⊥ -(V)+ A1)— 2 (2B.20)	Ignition: **ON**	around 2.6 V	N47 N3

MB9099900034020X

Fig. 17 Test 25: Steps 3.1–4.2. C43, C230, C280, CLK320, CLK430, E300, E320 & E430 w/FSS

⇒	Test scope	Test connection	Test condition	Nominal value	Possible cause/Remedy
3.0	**ECL and windshield washer level:** ECL level switch (S41), windshield washer level switch (S42) and wiring	A1 6 —(-(Ω)+)— 4 (1B.6) (1B.4)	Ignition: **OFF** Coolant level and windshield washer fluid level: OK Remove A1 Disconnect connector 1 (30 pole).	233 - 297 Ω	Wiring ⇒ 3.1 Values O.K.: A1
3.1	**ECL switch (S41)**	S41 1 — -(Ω)+ — 2	Ignition: **OFF** Remove expansion tank Disconnect connector at S41. Coolant level OK	102 - 120 Ω	S41 Values O.K.: ⇒ 3.2
3.2	**Windshield washer fluid level switch (S42)**	S42 1 — -(Ω)+ — 2	Ignition: **OFF** Disconnect connector at S42. Washer fluid level OK	145 - 185 Ω	S42

MB9099900059020X

Fig. 19 Test 24: Steps 3.0–3.2. S320 & S420 & 1998–99 CL500, CL600, S500 & S600 less FSS

⇒	Test scope	Test connection	Test condition	Nominal value	Possible cause/Remedy
1.0	**Instrument cluster (A1)** Voltage supply Circuit 30	A1 3 –< –(V)– >– 11 (1A.3) (1A.11) 12 –< –(V)– >– 11 (1A.12) (1A.11)	Ignition: **OFF** Remove A1 Disconnect connector 1 (30-pole)	11 – 14 V	Fuse 14 in fuse and relay box (F1), Wiring, ⇒ 1.1
1.1	Voltage supply Circuit 15, fused	A1 3 –< –(V)– >– 9 (1A.3) (1A.9)	Ignition: **ON**	11 – 14 V	Fuse 10 in fuse and relay box (F1), Wiring, A1
2.0	**HHT Interface** Connection between A1 and data link connector (X11/4)	15 –< –(Ω)– >– 11 X11/4 (1B.11)	Ignition: **OFF** Remove A1, Disconnect connector 1 (30-pole)	≤ 5 Ω	Wiring.

MB9099900060010X

Fig. 20 Test 23: Steps 1.0–2.0. SL600 & 1998 SL500 less FSS

⇒	Test scope	Test connection	Test condition	Nominal value	Possible cause/Remedy
3.0	**ECL and windshield washer level:** ECL level switch (S41), windshield washer level switch (S42) and wiring	A1 6 –< –(Ω)– >– 4 (1B.6) (1B.4)	Ignition: **OFF** Coolant level and windshield washer fluid level: OK Remove instrument cluster (A1) Disconnect connector 1 (30 pole).	233 - 297 Ω	Wiring ⇒ 3.1 Values O.K.: A1
3.1	**ECL switch (S41)**	S41 1 — –(Ω)– — 2	Ignition: **OFF** Remove expansion tank Disconnect connector at ECL switch (S41). Coolant level OK	102 - 120 Ω	S41 Values O.K.: ⇒ 3.2
3.2	**Windshield washer fluid level switch (S42)**	S42 1 — –(Ω)– — 2	Ignition: **OFF** Disconnect connector at S42. Washer fluid level OK	145 - 185 Ω	S42

MB9099900060020X

Fig. 21 Test 23: Steps 3.0–3.2. SL600 & 1998 SL500 less FSS

⇒	Test scope	Test connection	Test condition	Nominal value	Possible cause/Remedy
1.0	**Instrument cluster (A1)** Voltage supply Circuit 30	A1 3 –< –(V)– >– 11 (1A.3) (1A.11) 12 –< –(V)– >– 11 (1A.12) (1A.11)	Ignition: **OFF** Remove instrument cluster (A1) Disconnect connector 1 (30-pole)	11 – 14 V	Fuse 17 in fuse and relay box (F3), Wiring, ⇒ 1.1
1.1	Voltage supply Circuit 15	A1 3 –< –(V)– >– 9 (1A.3) (1A.9)	Ignition: **ON**	11 – 14 V	Fuse 24 in fuse and relay box (F3), Wiring, A1
2.0	**HHT Interface** Connection between A1 and data link connector (X11/4)	A1 15 –< –(Ω)– >– 11 X11/4 (1B.11)	Ignition: **OFF** Remove A1, Disconnect connector 1 (30-pole)	≤ 5 Ω	Wiring.
3.0	**ECL and windshield washer level:** ECL level switch (S41), windshield washer level switch (S42) and wiring	A1 6 –< –(Ω)– >– 4 (1B.6) (1B.4)	Ignition: **OFF** Coolant level and windshield washer fluid level: OK Remove A1 Disconnect connector 1 (30 pole)	233 - 297 Ω	Wiring ⇒ 3.1 Values O.K.: A1

MB9099900036010X

Fig. 22 Test 24: Steps 1.0–3.0. S320, S420 & SL600 & 1998–99 CL500, CL600, S500 & S600 & 1998 SL500 w/FSS

⇒	Test scope	Test connection	Test condition	Nominal value	Possible cause/Remedy
3.1	ECL switch (S41)	S41 1 — –(Ω)– — 2	Ignition: **OFF** Remove expansion tank Disconnect connector at S41. Coolant level OK	102 - 120 Ω	S41 Values O.K.: ⇒ 3.2
3.2	Windshield washer fluid level switch (S42)	S42 1 — –(Ω)– — 2	Ignition: **OFF** Disconnect connector at S42. Washer fluid level OK	145 - 185 Ω	S42
4.0	**CAN bus data lines resistance**	A1 9 –< –(Ω)– >– 10 (1B.9) (1B.10)	Ignition: **OFF** Disconnect connector 1 (All control modules are connected to CAN)	around 60 Ω	CAN: –//–, ⌐–¬– N47 N3 Values O.K.: ⇒ 4.1
4.1	CAN bus data lines Voltage Low-data line	A1 ⊥ –(V)– >– 9 (1B.9)	Ignition: **ON**	around 2.3 V	N47 N3 Values O.K.: ⇒ 4.2
4.2	CAN bus data lines Voltage High-data line	A1 ⊥ –(V)– >– 10 (1B.10)	Ignition: **ON**	around 2.6 V	N47 N3

MB9099900036020X

Fig. 23 Test 24: Steps 3.1–4.2. S320, S420 & SL600 & 1998–99 CL500, CL600, S500 & S600 & 1998 SL500 w/FSS

⇒	Test scope	Test connection	Test condition	Nominal value	Possible cause/Remedy
1.0	**Instrument cluster (A1)** Voltage supply Circuit 30	A1 3 –< –(V)– >– 11 (1A.3) (1A.11) 12 –< –(V)– >– 11 (1A.12) (1A.11)	Ignition: **OFF** Remove A1 Disconnect connector 1 (30-pole)	11 – 14 V	Fuse 14 in fuse and relay box (F1), Wiring, ⇒ 1.1
1.1	Voltage supply Circuit 15, fused	A1 3 –< –(V)– >– 9 (1A.3) (1A.9)	Ignition: **ON**	11 – 14 V	Fuse 10 in fuse and relay box (F1), Wiring, A1
2.0	**HHT Interface** Connection between A1 and data link connector (X11/4)	15 –< –(Ω)– >– 11 X11/4 (1B.11)	Ignition: **OFF** Remove A1, Disconnect connector 1 (30-pole)	≤ 5 Ω	Wiring.
3.0	**ECL and windshield washer level:** ECL level switch (S41), windshield washer level switch (S42) and wiring	A1 6 –< –(Ω)– >– 4 (1B.6) (1B.4)	Ignition: **OFF** Coolant level and windshield washer fluid level: OK Remove instrument cluster (A1) Disconnect connector 1 (30 pole).	233 - 297 Ω	Wiring ⇒ 3.1 Values O.K.: A1

MB9099900037010X

Fig. 24 Test 23: Steps 1.0–3.0. SL600 & 1998 SL500 w/FSS

⇒	Test scope	Test connection	Test condition	Nominal value	Possible cause/Remedy
3.1	ECL switch (S41)	S41 1 — –(Ω)– — 2	Ignition: **OFF** Remove expansion tank Disconnect connector at ECL switch (S41). Coolant level OK	102 - 120 Ω	S41 Values O.K.: ⇒ 3.2
3.2	Windshield washer fluid level switch (S42)	S42 1 — –(Ω)– — 2	Ignition: **OFF** Disconnect connector at S42. Washer fluid level OK	145 - 185 Ω	S42
4.0	**CAN bus data lines resistance**	A1 1 –< –(Ω)– >– 10 (1B.9) (1B.10)	Ignition: **OFF** Disconnect connector 1 (All control modules are connected to CAN)	around 60 Ω	CAN: –//–, ⌐–¬– N47 N3 Values O.K.: ⇒ 4.1
4.1	CAN bus data lines Voltage Low-data line	A1 ⊥ –(V)– >– 9 (1B.9)	Ignition: **ON**	around 2.3 V	N47 N3 Values O.K.: ⇒ 4.2
4.2	CAN bus data lines Voltage High-data line	A1 ⊥ –(V)– >– 10 (1B.10)	Ignition: **ON**	around 2.6 V	N47 N3

MB9099900037020X

Fig. 25 Test 23: Steps 3.1–4.2. SL600 & 1998 SL500 w/FSS

⇒	Test scope	Test connection	Test condition	Nominal value	Possible cause/Remedy
1.0	**Instrument cluster (A1)** Voltage supply Circuit 30	A1 3 –< –(V)– >– 11 (1A.3) (1A.11) 12 –< –(V)– >– 11 (1A.12) (1A.11)	Ignition: **OFF** Remove instrument cluster (A1) Disconnect connector 1 (30-pole)	11 – 14 V	Fuse 34 in fuse and relay box (F1), Wiring, ⇒ 1.1
1.1	Voltage supply Circuit 15	A1 3 –< –(V)– >– 9 (1A.3) (1A.9)	Ignition: **ON**	11 – 14 V	Fuse 37 in fuse and relay box (F1), Wiring, A1
2.0	**HHT Interface** Connection between A1 and data link connector (X11/4)	15 –< –(Ω)– >– 11 X11/4 (1B.11)	Ignition: **OFF** Remove A1, Disconnect connector 1 (30-pole)	≤ 5 Ω	Wiring.

MB9099900056010X

Fig. 26 Test 27: Steps 1.0–2.0. SLK230 less FSS

⇒	Test scope	Test connection	Test condition	Nominal value	Possible cause/Remedy
3.0	**ECL and windshield washer level:** ECL level switch (S41), windshield washer level switch (S42) and wiring	A1 12 –< –(Ω)– >– 4 (1B.12) (1B.4)	Ignition: **OFF** Coolant level and windshield washer fluid level: OK Remove instrument cluster (A1) Disconnect connector 1 (30 pole).	233 - 297 Ω	Wiring ⇒ 3.1 Values O.K.: A1
3.1	**ECL switch (S41)**	S41 1 — –(Ω)– — 2	Ignition: **OFF** Remove expansion tank Disconnect connector at S41 Coolant level OK	102 - 120 Ω	S41 Values O.K.: ⇒ 3.2
3.2	**Windshield washer fluid level switch (S42)**	S42 1 — –(Ω)– — 2	Ignition: **OFF** Disconnect connector at S42 Washer fluid level OK	145 - 185 Ω	S42

MB9099900056020X

Fig. 27 Test 27: Steps 3.0–3.2. SLK230 less FSS

⇒	Test scope	Test connection	Test condition	Nominal value	Possible cause/Remedy
1.0	**Instrument cluster (A1)** Voltage supply Circuit 30	A1 3 (1A.3) –V– 11 (1A.11) 12 (1A.12) –V– 11 (1A.11)	Ignition: **OFF** Remove Instrument cluster (A1) Disconnect connector 1 (30-pole)	11 – 14 V	Fuse 34 in fuse and relay box (F1), Wiring, ⇒ 1.1
1.1	Voltage supply Circuit 15	A1 3 (1A.3) –V– 9 (1A.9)	Ignition: **ON**	11 – 14 V	Fuse 37 in fuse and relay box (F1), Wiring, A1
2.0	**HHT interface** Connection between A1 and data link connector (X11/4)	15 X11/4 –Ω– A1 11 (1B.11)	Ignition: **OFF** Remove A1, Disconnect connector 1 (30-pole)	≤ 5 Ω	Wiring.
3.0	**ECL and windshield washer level:** ECL level switch (S41), windshield washer level switch (S42) and wiring	A1 12 (1B.12) –Ω– 4 (1B.4)	Ignition: **OFF** Coolant level and windshield washer fluid level: OK Remove A1 Disconnect connector 1 (30 pole).	233 - 297 Ω	Wiring ⇒ 3.1 Values O.K.: A1

MB9099900035010X

Fig. 28 Test 25: Steps 1.0–3.0. SLK230 w/FSS

⇒	Test scope	Test connection	Test condition	Nominal value	Possible cause/Remedy
3.1	ECL switch (S41)	S41 1 –Ω– 2	Ignition: **OFF** Remove expansion tank Disconnect connector at S41 Coolant level OK	102 - 120 Ω	S41 Values O.K.: ⇒ 3.2
3.2	Windshield washer fluid level switch (S42)	S42 1 –Ω– 2	Ignition: **OFF** Disconnect connector at S42 Washer fluid level OK	145 - 185 Ω	S42
4.0	**CAN bus data lines resistance**	A1 9 (1B.9) –Ω– 10 (1B.10)	Ignition: **OFF** Disconnect connector 1 (All control modules are connected to CAN)	around 60 Ω	CAN: –//–, ⌐ ¬ – N47 N3 Values O.K.: ⇒ 4.1
4.1	CAN bus data lines Voltage Low-data line	⊥ –V– A1 2 (2B.1)	Ignition: **ON**	around 2.3 V	N47 N3 Values O.K.: ⇒ 4.2
4.2	CAN bus data lines Voltage High-data line	⊥ –V– A1 2 (2B.20)	Ignition: **ON**	around 2.6 V	N47 N3

MB9099900035020X

Fig. 29 Test 25: Steps 3.1–4.2. SLK230 w/FSS

TECHNICAL SERVICE BULLETINS

LAMP FAILURE INDICATOR DOES NOT GO OUT

On some of these models the lamp failure indicator lamp may not go out with the engine running, the lights turned on and no defective lamps.

This condition may be caused by incorrect bulb wattage or poor electrical contacts.

To correct this condition, proceed as follows:

1. Ensure correct wattage bulbs are installed. Left and righthand lamps must have same wattage.
2. Inspect for poor electrical contacts at exterior lamp failure monitoring unit. Inspect for the following:
   a. Spread sockets.
   b. Cold soldering joints.
   c. Incorrect attachment.
3. Inspect for spread sockets at front directional signal connector.
4. Inspect taillamp units for insufficient tension on bulb contacts.
5. Tighten sockets with suitable pliers and replace parts as required.
6. Ensure all exterior lamps are working properly, include the often overlooked license plate lamps and center high-mounted stop lamp.

FUEL GAUGE READS 1/4 TANK HIGH AFTER INSTRUMENT CLUSTER REPLACEMENT

SL500 & SL600

On some of these models the fuel gauge may read 1/4 tank high after instrument cluster has been replaced.

This condition may be caused by instrument cluster coding.

To correct this condition, the old instrument cluster version coding has to be entered into the new cluster using the Hand-Held Tester (HHT) tool No. 965 589 00 01 00, or equivalent scan tool. If the old cluster version is not available, proceed as follows:

1. With HHT switch version coding to any other country.
2. Exit from HHT.
3. Enter from HHT.
4. Set country code to USA.
5. Set version coding options.

OUTSIDE AIR TEMPERATURE GAUGE READS TOO LOW

C43, C230 & C280

On some of these models the outside air temperature gauge may read approximately 18° too low after vehicle is driven short distance.

This condition may be caused by instrument cluster version code.

To correct this condition, install instrument cluster with K30 or higher version. **Do not install remanufactured part with suffix 80.**

MIL LAMPS ILLUMINATE ONLY BRIEFLY DURING BULB CHECK

C43, C230, C280, E300, E320 & E430

On some of these models the Malfunction Indicator Lamps (MIL) and warning lamps may illuminate only briefly after switching ignition switch to ON position. Alternator warning lamp does not illuminate.

This condition may be caused by open circuit between instrument cluster and alternator (circuit No. 61).

To correct this condition, repair circuit as required.

OIL PRESSURE GAUGE INTERMITTENTLY DROPS TO ZERO WITHOUT WARNING LAMP ILLUMINATION

S320 & S420 & 1998-99 CL500, CL600, S500 & S600

On some of these models the oil pressure gauge may intermittently drop to zero illuminating the warning lamp.

This condition may be caused by instrument cluster electronic circuit board.

To correct this condition, proceed as follows:

1. Ensure engine oil level is correct.
2. Ensure engine oil pressure is correct using separate suitable pressure gauge.
3. Replace instrument cluster electronic circuit board.
4. Replacing oil pressure sensor will not correct condition.

FUEL GAUGE OCCASIONALLY DROPS TO ZERO AFTER COASTING

S320 & S420 & 1998-99 CL500, CL600, S500 & S600

On some of these models the fuel gauge may occasionally drop to zero after coasting.

This condition may be caused by instrument cluster electronic circuit board.

To correct this condition, replace instrument cluster electronic circuit board.

FUEL GAUGE INOPERATIVE OR READS INCORRECTLY

C230 & C280

On some of the models built before VIN 007796, the fuel gauge may be inoperative or read incorrectly.

This condition may be caused by lefthand fuel tank chamber fuel level sensor wiring being pinched or cut.

To correct this condition, proceed as follows:

1. Remove lefthand fuel tank chamber fuel level sensor and inspect wiring.
2. If wiring is damaged, remove rear seat cushion.
3. Loosen wiring by removing tape.
4. Repair damage as required.

Starter Motors

NOTE: Prior To Performing Any Service Operations Listed In This Section, Consult The "Technical Service Bulletins" Section For Related Information.

INDEX

	Page No.
Application Chart	5-209
Technical Service Bulletins	5-209
Engine Will Not Crank	5-209
Metallic Starter Noise	5-209
Troubleshooting	5-209
Metallic Starter Noise When Engine Fires	5-209
Starter Cranks Slowly	5-209

APPLICATION CHART

Model	Year	Bosch Model
C43, CLK430, E430, ML430 & SL500	1999–2001	—
C280, CLK320, E320 & ML320	1998–2001	—
C230	1998–2000	DW 12 V 1.4 kW
E300	1998–99	EV 12 V 2.2 kW
E320	1998–2001	—
S320	1998–99	DW 12 V 1.7 kW
S420 & S500	1998–99	DW 12 V 1.7 kW
S600 & SL600	1998–99	DW 12 V 2.2 kW
SL500	1998	DW 12 V 1.7 kW
	1999–2001	—
SLK230	1998–2001	DW 12 V 1.4 kW

TROUBLESHOOTING

METALLIC STARTER NOISE WHEN ENGINE FIRES

1. Faulty tooth flank on ring gear.
2. Faulty starter.

STARTER CRANKS SLOWLY

1. Undercharged battery.
2. Incorrect engine oil viscosity.
3. Faulty electrical or ground connection.
4. Faulty starter.

TECHNICAL SERVICE BULLETINS

ENGINE WILL NOT CRANK

S320 & S420 & 1998-99 CL500, CL600, S500 & S600

On some of these models the engine may not crank.

This condition may be caused aftermarket electrical accessories being wired through front cigar lighter fuse.

To correct this condition, rewire voltage supply as follows:

1. Remove fuse box and locate wire coupling position 21.
2. Remove position 21 wiring connector and install at position 27.
3. Add "STARTER LOCK-OUT" fuse to position 19 fuse card.

METALLIC STARTER NOISE

On some of these gasoline engine models the starter may make metallic noises when engine starts.

This condition may be caused by bent ring gear tooth chamfers which cannot be seen with starter installed.

To correct this condition, activate starter without switching ignition switch to On position. If metallic noise is no longer heard, replace starter.

Alternators

NOTE: Prior To Performing Any Service Operations Listed In This Section, Consult The "Technical Service Bulletins" Section For Related Information.

INDEX

	Page No.
Alternator Specifications	5-211
Diagnosis & Testing	5-210
In-Vehicle Testing	5-210
Technical Service Bulletins	5-210
Alternator Pulley Loose	5-210
Alternator Whine	5-210
Battery Complete Discharges While Standing Very Short Time	5-211
Battery Discharges After Vehicle Is Inoperative For Extended Period	5-210
Battery Discharges	5-210
Battery Discharges	5-211
Battery Discharges	5-211
Troubleshooting	5-210
Lamp Does Not Light w/Ignition On	5-210
Lamp On At Idle & Gets Darker At Higher Speed	5-210
Lamp On w/Engine Running	5-210
Lamp On w/Ignition Switch & Engine Off	5-210

TROUBLESHOOTING

LAMP ON AT IDLE & GETS DARKER AT HIGHER SPEED

1. Faulty stator winding.
2. Faulty negative diode.
3. Faulty alternator.

LAMP DOES NOT LIGHT w/IGNITION ON

1. Faulty transition resistance.
2. Faulty pre-exiter circuit
3. Faulty alternator.

LAMP ON w/IGNITION SWITCH & ENGINE OFF

1. Faulty positive diode.
2. Faulty electrical or ground connection.
3. Faulty alternator.

LAMP ON w/ENGINE RUNNING

1. Faulty negative diodes.
2. Faulty exciter diodes.
3. Stator winding short to ground.
4. Faulty electrical or ground connection.
5. Faulty alternator.

DIAGNOSIS & TESTING

IN-VEHICLE TESTING

1. Ensure all battery and alternator connections, drive belt and battery are in good condition.
2. Connect suitable voltmeter across battery terminals.
3. Start engine and ensure charge indicator lamp turns off.
4. Run engine up at 3000 RPM with no additional loads on electrical system.
5. If measurement is 13–14.5 volts after two minutes, proceed to next step. If measurement is not within specifications, proceed as follows:
   a. If measurement is more than 14.5 volts, replace regulator.
   b. If regulator is in good condition, replace alternator.
   c. If measurement is less than 13 volts, eliminate transitional resistance at electrical connections in charging system.
   d. Check alternator diodes.
   e. **On SLK230 models,** inspect crash shut-off relay.
6. **On all models,** connect suitable multimeter across battery terminals and multi-meter with shunt resistor to circuit between alternator and circuit 30 connector in lefthand footwell.
7. Run engine at 2100–2500 RPM.
8. Load battery with multi-meter shunt resistor until maximum charging current is reached.
9. If regulate voltage drops below 12.7 volts, inspect alternator diodes.
10. **On SLK230 models,** inspect crash shut-off relay.

TECHNICAL SERVICE BULLETINS

ALTERNATOR WHINE

On some of these models the alternator may whine between 700–3000 RPM. At very low temperatures, alternator may whine from first minute of operation.

This condition may be caused by the alternator's magnetic field.

To correct condition, replace alternator.

ALTERNATOR PULLEY LOOSE

On some of these models the alternator pulley may be loose.

This condition may be caused by pulley mounting components setting condition.

To correct, proceed as follows:

1. Replace alternator. Tightening pulley will not insure permanent fix.
2. Remove alternator shaft nut and oil nut flange.
3. **Torque** shaft nut to 48–55 ft. lbs.

BATTERY DISCHARGES

S320 & S420 & 1998–99 CL500, CL600, S500 & S600

On some of these models the battery may discharge

This condition may be caused by a variety of conditions.

To correct this condition, proceed as follows:

1. If the doom lamp does not shut off approximately eight seconds after door is closed, proceed as follows:
   a. Disconnect battery negative cable for approximately 30 seconds.
   b. Connect battery cable.
   c. Code radio.
   d. Synchronize windows.
   e. **On models equipped with Adaptive Driving System (ADS),** activate steering angle sensor turning steering once from full left to full right with engine running.
   f. **On all models,** if condition continues, replace doom lamp assembly.
2. **On models equipped with activate charcoal filter,** proceed as follows:
   a. Measure rest current draw by automatic A/C push-button control module.
   b. If current draw is approximately 200 mA, inspect A/C push-button control module software status with suitable hand-held tester.
   c. If status is 06, replace A/C push-button control module.
3. **On all models,** if left or righthand turn signal lamps light up continuously with ignition switch in Off position, replace combination relay.
4. If alternator rest current draw is approximately 120 mA, replace alternator.

BATTERY DISCHARGES AFTER VEHICLE IS INOPERATIVE FOR EXTENDED PERIOD

On some of these models the battery

may discharge after the vehicle is inoperative for an extended period.

This condition may be caused by incorrectly connect electrical consumer.

To correct this condition, proceed as follows:

1. Measure current flow between battery and battery cables with suitable ampere meter set to milli-ampere. Do not use test lamp.
2. Remove ignition key, switch all consumers off and close doors.
3. Find fault by removing individual fuses and repair as required.
4. Some electronic systems with memory and time delay circuits operate with ignition off. Their current consumption should be considered normal as follows:
   a. Central locking system pump, maximum 15 mA.
   b. Dome lamp, maximum 10 mA.
   c. Becker electronic radio, maximum 20 mA.
   d. Safety belt extender systems, maximum 5 mA.
   e. Anti-theft system, maximum 10 mA.
   f. Antenna, maximum 2 mA.
   g. Electronic clock, maximum 3 mA.
   h. Electric seat adjustment memory (each seat), maximum 1 mA.
   i. When electronically controlled antenna is disconnect and connected, it will draw 2–3 amps for approximately 10 seconds.

BATTERY COMPLETE DISCHARGES WHILE STANDING VERY SHORT TIME

E300

On some of these models the battery may discharge after standing for a very short period for no apparent reason.

This condition may be caused by preglow time relay being stuck in glow mode.

To correct this condition, replace preglow time relay if contact spring appears blue in color.

BATTERY DISCHARGES

SL500 & SL600

On some of these models the battery may discharge.

This condition may be caused by roll bar control unit timed switch-off.

To correct this condition, proceed as follows:

1. Measure rest current draw between chassis ground and battery terminal with suitable digital multi-meter.
2. Ensure seat belts are not buckled, noting the following:
   a. One buckled seat belt draws 380 mA for approximately 60 minutes after ignition is switched to Off position.
   b. Two buckled seat belts draw 400 mA for approximately 60 minutes after ignition is switched to Off position.
3. If current draw is more than 360 mA, replace roll bar control unit.
4. If current draw is more than 220 mA, replace soft top control unit.

BATTERY DISCHARGES

On some of these models equipped with CD changer, battery may discharge.

This condition may be caused by CD changer current draw being too high.

To correct this condition, proceed as follows:

1. Remove ignition key.
2. Turn radio off.
3. Remove radio/CD changer fuse.
4. Connect suitable digital multi-meter set to mA in place of fuse.
5. Wait approximately six minutes for CD changer to complete loading sequence. **Do not operate radio or CD change during this six minute wait, or period will be extended an additional three minutes.**
6. Measure rest current.
7. If measurement is more than 20 mA, replace CD changer.

ALTERNATOR SPECIFICATIONS

Model	Year	Bosch No.	Amps
C230	1998–2000	NC 14 V 45/90A	90
C240	2001	—	—
C280	1998–2000	NC 14 V 70/115 A	90
C320	2001	—	—
CLK320	1998–2001	NC 14 V 70/115 A	90
CLK430	1999–2001	NC 14 V 90/150A	150
CL500	1998–99	NC 14 V 70/115A	115
	2000–01	NC 14 V 90/150A	150
CL600	1998–99	NC 14 V 70/115A	115
	2001	NF 14 V 90/150A	150
E300	1998–99	KC 14 V 45/90A	90
E320	1998–2001	NC 14 V 70/115 A	115
E430	1998–2001	NC 14 V 90/150A	150
ML320	1998–2001	NC 14 V 70/115 A	90
ML430	1999–2001	NC 14 V 90/150A	150
S320	1998–99	NC 14 V 70/115A	115
S420	1998–99	NC 14 V 70/115A	115
S430	2000–01	NC 14 V 90/150A	150
S500	1998–99	NC 14 V 70/115A	115
	2000–01	NC 14 V 90/150A	150
S600	1998–99	NC 14 V 70/115A	115
	2001	NF 14 V 90/150A	150
SL500	1998	NC 14 V 70/115A	115
	1999–2001	NC 14 V 90/150A	150
SL600	1998–2001	NC 14 V 70/115A	115
SLK230	1998–2001	NC 14 V 45/90A	90

Speed Control Systems

NOTE: On Air Bag Equipped Models, Refer To "Air Bag System Precautions" Located In Front Of This Manual For System Disarming And Arming Procedures.

NOTE: Refer To The "Traction Control Systems" Section For Acceleration Slip Regulation (ASR) And Electronic Traction System (ETS) Procedures.

NOTE: Prior To Performing Any Service Operations Listed In This Section, Consult The "Technical Service Bulletins" Section For Related Information.

INDEX

	Page No.
Adjustments	5-212
Connecting Rod	5-212
Component Replacement	5-212
Actuator	5-212
Coding Plug	5-213
Control Unit	5-213
Cruise Control Switch	5-212
Precautions	5-212
Air Bag Systems	5-212
Battery Ground Cable	5-212
System Diagnosis & Testing	5-212

PRECAUTIONS

AIR BAG SYSTEMS

Refer to "Air Bag System Precautions" in front of this manual for system disarming and arming procedures.

BATTERY GROUND CABLE

Prior to service, disconnect battery ground cable and isolate as required.

ADJUSTMENTS

CONNECTING ROD

E300 & E320

1. Remove air cleaner assembly.
2. Turn control cable adjustment bolt until spring has .12–0.20 inch of play.
3. Loosen connecting link lock bolts, ensuring throttle valve lever is against idle stop of throttle body.
4. Move connecting link lever to idle stop at acceleration pedal position sensor.
5. Swivel connecting link lever clockwise until link is apart.
6. Push loosened lock bolt toward accelerator pedal position sensor until stop pin is adjacent to hole, carefully push lever to stop and tighten lock bolt.
7. Turn ignition On, adjust control Bowden cable, depress accelerator cable to kickdown switch. **Do not activate kickdown switch.**
8. Push lever to wide open throttle, if not as indicated readjust screw.
9. Turn ignition Off, with accelerator pedal in idle position ensure no play in take up spring. If play indicated, adjust.

SL500 & SL600

1. Remove air cleaner assembly.
2. Turn control cable adjustment bolt until spring has 0.12–0.20 inch of play.
3. Remove spring loaded connecting link from accelerator pedal position sensor.
4. Disconnect connecting linkage from control shaft, remove accelerator pedal position sensor lever and move to idle stop.
5. Turn ignition On, ensure actuator lever moves to idle position, move connecting link lever in direction of actuator until transmission play is removed and adjust connecting linkage ensuring no tension.
6. Push accelerator pedal position sensor lever to wide open throttle, if throttle lever rests against wide open throttle with tension, electronic accelerator adjustment motor will shutdown (limp-home mode is operational).
7. Turn ignition Off, loosen actuator ball head nut and slide ball head in hole, tighten and retest.
8. Adjust pressure control cable knurled bolts enough to align opposite one another.
9. Turn ignition On, adjust control Bowden cable, depress accelerator cable to kickdown switch. **Do not activate kickdown switch.**
10. Push lever to wide open throttle, if not as indicated readjust screw.
11. Turn ignition Off, with accelerator pedal in idle position ensure no play in take up spring. If play indicated, adjust.

SYSTEM DIAGNOSIS & TESTING

Refer to "Electronic Accelerator" and "Idle Speed Control" in appropriate "Computerized Engine Controls" section.

COMPONENT REPLACEMENT

ACTUATOR

1. Disconnect actuator electrical connector and connecting rod.
2. Remove actuator cover, if equipped.
3. Remove actuator mounting bolts, remove actuator and mounting bracket as an assembly.
4. Reverse procedure to install.

CRUISE CONTROL SWITCH

Remove combination switch as described in "Electrical" section. After removing combination switch, remove screw attaching cruise control switch to combination switch and separate switches.

CONTROL UNIT

C280 w/ETS

If the Cruise Control/Idle Speed Control (CC/ISC) control module is replaced, or if a control module from another vehicle is temporarily installed, the Electronic Traction System (ETS) adaptation must be activated as follows:

1. Turn ignition switch to On position and wait three seconds.
2. Start engine and wait seven seconds.
3. Turn ignition switch to Off position.
4. Turn ignition switch to On position.
5. Remove lefthand side instrument panel undercover, if equipped.
6. Disconnect electrical connector from control unit.
7. Remove control unit to pedal bracket mounting screws, then the control unit.
8. Reverse procedure to install.

CODING PLUG

Coding plug is connected to control unit. Control unit is located under lefthand side of instrument panel. While compressing coding plug locking lugs, disconnect coding plug from control unit.

Wiper Systems

NOTE: On Air Bag Equipped Models, Refer To "Air Bag System Precautions" Located In Front Of This Manual For System Disarming And Arming Procedures.

NOTE: Prior To Performing Any Service Operations Listed In This Section, Consult The "Technical Service Bulletins" Section For Related Information.

INDEX

	Page No.
Component Replacement	5-213
Description	5-213
Headlamp Wiper System	5-213
Heated Windshield Washer	5-213
Precautions	5-213
Air Bag Systems	5-213
Battery Ground Cable	5-213
Wiper Systems	5-213

PRECAUTIONS

AIR BAG SYSTEMS

Refer to "Air Bag System Precautions" in front of this manual for system disarming and arming procedures.

WIPER SYSTEMS

Remove ignition key prior to servicing wiper system. With key in steering lock position 1 or 2, movement of wiper may cause automatic wiper park feature to engage.

BATTERY GROUND CABLE

Prior to service, disconnect battery ground cable and isolate as required.

DESCRIPTION

All models have a two-speed windshield wiper with an intermittent feature. The intermittent relay is attached to wiper motor assembly. In addition, a headlamp wiper system and a heated windshield washer features are available.

HEADLAMP WIPER SYSTEM

Headlamp cleaning system is operated by switching on headlamps and actuating combination switch. Wipers will operate as long as combination switch is actuated, they return to park position once switch is released. Two nozzles are located in respective wiper arm. headlamp cleaning system draws washer fluid from electrically heated washer fluid tank.

HEATED WINDSHIELD WASHER

Windshield washer fluid reservoir is heated by a heat exchanger connected to engine cooling circuit. Hoses from reservoir to washer nozzles and nozzles themselves are electrically heated. A thermoswitch switches on electrically heated components of windshield washer at an outside temperature below 41°F and off again at 59°F.

COMPONENT REPLACEMENT

Refer to "Electrical" section.

Passive Restraint Systems

TABLE OF CONTENTS

	Page No.		Page No.
AIR BAG SYSTEM	5-214	AUTOMATIC SEAT BELTS	5-220

Air Bag System

NOTE: Prior To Performing Any Service Operations Listed In This Section, Consult The "Technical Service Bulletins" Section For Related Information.

INDEX

	Page No.
Air Bag System Disarming & Arming	5-214
Arming	5-214
Disarming	5-214
Collision Inspection	5-216
Component Locations	5-215
Component Service	5-216
Air Bag Assemble Disposal	5-219
Air Bag Module, Replace	5-216
Clock Spring, Centering	5-218
Clock Spring, Replace	5-218
Control Module, Replace	5-217
Curtain Side Impact Sensor, Replace	5-218
Side Impact Sensor, Replace	5-218
Description & Operation	5-214
Diagnosis & Testing	5-215
Precautions	5-215
Scheduled Maintenance	5-215
Technical Service Bulletins	5-219
DTC 004 Or 007	5-219
DTC B1310 & B1311	5-219
Passenger's Air Bag Rattles	5-219
SRS MIL & ACSR Indicator Lamp On	5-219
Tightening Specifications	5-219
Wire Harness & Connector Repair	5-215

AIR BAG SYSTEM DISARMING & ARMING

Disarming

When the battery is disconnected, the vehicle electronic memory will be lost. Make note of radio stations and other codes. Never use a back-up power source to retain memory.

1. Obtain radio theft protection CODE card.
2. Place ignition switch in Off position and remove ignition key.
3. Disconnect all air bag squib Supplemental Restraint System (SRS) electrical connectors (red).
4. Wait 10 minutes before starting any repairs to allow back-up power supply to discharge.
5. If welding is to be performed on vehicle, disconnect and isolate battery ground cable.
6. Disconnect control module connector.

Arming

1. Ensure ignition is turned Off and nobody is inside vehicle.
2. Connect SRS red electrical connectors.
3. If disconnected, connect battery ground cable.
4. Turn ignition to On position. Air bag warning lamp should light for approximately four seconds and go off. If lamp fails to light or remains illuminated after 10 seconds, refer to "Diagnosis & Testing."

DESCRIPTION & OPERATION

The SRS includes the driver's and passenger's air bags, knee bolsters, three-point seat belts with automatic Emergency Tension Restraint (ETR) and door-mounted side impact air bags. The BabySmart system is also installed.

The C240, C320, CL55, CL500, CL600, ML55, ML320, ML430, S55, S430, S500 and S600 models have dual-stage driver's and passenger's air bags which can deploy at partial or full force depending on the severity of the impact.

On C240, C320, E55, CL55, CL500, CL600, E55, E320, E430, S55, S430, S500 and S600 models, current side impact air bags with nine air chambers span the entire length of the sides of the passenger compartment from A- to C-pillar.

On SL500 and SL600 models, a padded, leather-cover automatic roll bar pops up, locking in place if sensors detect an impending rollover. The driver can also raise and lower the bar intentionally by a switch on the console.

The driver's air bag is located below the steering wheel pad. The front passenger's air bag is located inside the upper righthand side of the instrument panel. The folded air bag and a tubular gas generator are located inside a plastic housing. The air bag is made of nylon material with gas permeable sides.

The door side impact air bags for each outboard passenger are located above the door armrest. When a side impact occurs, the side impact air bag will trigger, tearing open a seam in the door panel.

The side impact current air bags deploy out of the roof directly above the side windows in approximately 25 milliseconds.

The central triggering system for the front air bags and seat belt tensioners is connected to two additional sensors for the side impact air bags.

If voltage is interrupted during a collision, the driver's and front passenger's air bags will deploy within 100 milliseconds, but the ETR will not deploy. If the vehicle voltage drops below 9.5 volts for longer than 10 seconds, the air bag system warning lamp will light. Once voltage is more than 10 volts, the lamp will go off.

The control module is located on the transmission tunnel. This module processes vehicle deceleration information from a frontal impact. An arming switch is installed to interrupt the deployment circuit during normal driving mode. This allows system deployment only when the limits have been exceeded.

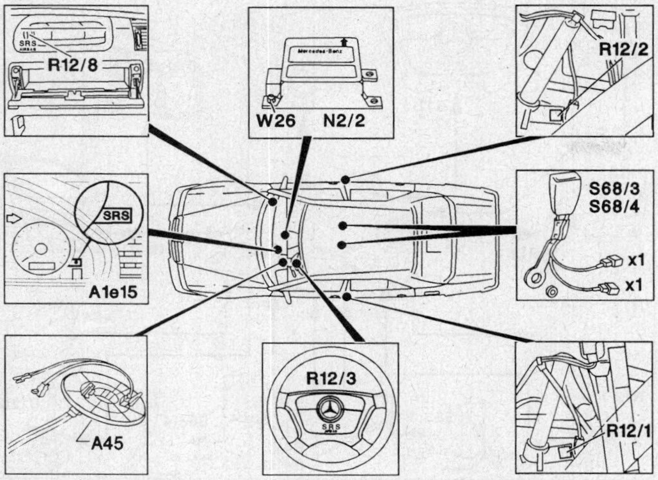

A1e15	SRS MIL	R12/3	Driver airbag squib
A45	Horn/airbag clock spring contact	R12/8	Front passenger airbag squib
N2/2	SRS control module	S68/3	Left front seat belt buckle switch (airbag/ETR) (USA)
R12/1	Left front ETR squib	S68/4	Right front seat belt buckle switch (airbag/ETR) (USA)
R12/2	Right front ETR squib	W26	Ground (SRS control module)

MB8019900096000X

Fig. 1 Component locations. C43, C230 & C280

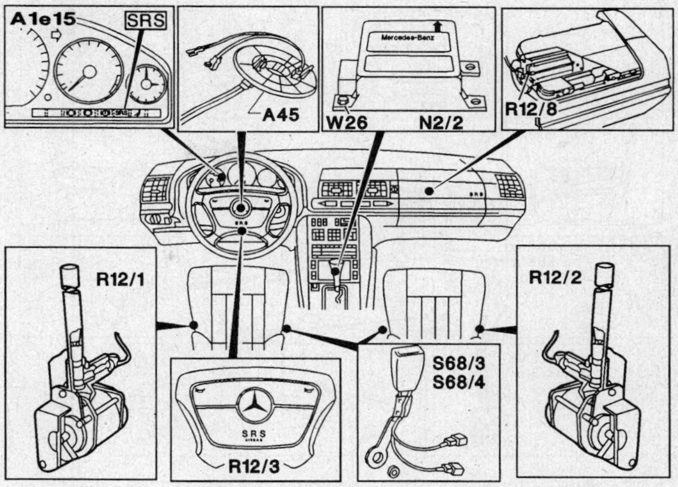

A1e15	SRS MIL	R12/3	Driver airbag squib
A45	Horn/airbag clock spring contact	R12/8	Front passenger airbag squib
N2/2	SRS control module	S68/3	Left front seat belt buckle switch (airbag/ETR) (USA)
R12/1	Left front ETR squib		
R12/2	Right front ETR squib	S68/4	Right front seat belt buckle switch (airbag/ETR) (USA)
		W26	Ground (SRS control module)

MB8019900094000X

Fig. 2 Component locations. S320 & S420 & 1998–99 CL500, CL600, S500 & S600

The control module detects longitudinal vehicle deceleration and generates a signal that is processed and sent to the threshold evaluation switch. When the limit is exceeded, information is given to the ETR and the SRS for proper deployment sequence.

If the sensor detects a minor front end impact, only one chamber of the gas generator is deployed so the driver's and passenger' air bags are not filled as fully or as quickly as in a severe front impact. In a more severe collision the second chamber is deployed 5–15 milliseconds later.

A sensor mat in the front passenger seat determines if someone is in the seat. If the seat is not occupied, the sensor will deactivate the passenger's air bag, as well as the righthand front passenger side impact air bag and seat belt pretensioner. The seat belt latch sensor determines how many passengers are in the vehicle and where they are sitting.

The BabySmart automatic child seat recognition systems uses a small resonator built into the special Mercedes-Benz BabySmart-compatible child safety seat to turn off the passenger's air bag. Side impact air bags and ETR remain active, only the passenger's air bag is inactive. When activated the "Air Bag Off" lamp on the center console confirms a BabySmart seat is installed.

The ETRs for all outboard seats belts remove seat belt slack just as the air bags begin to deploy. The driver and front passenger seats' belt force limiters relax the belts slightly as restraining forces build on the chest later in the collision sequence.

PRECAUTIONS

Prior to disconnecting any SRS electrical connectors, servicing any system components or other components located near an air bag system electrical connector, the system must be disarmed. Refer to "Air Bag System Disarming & Arming." Wait 10 minutes before starting any repairs. This in necessary to allow the system's back-up power supply to discharge.

Always observe the following safety precaution when working on the air bag system:

1. SRS components must not be opened or repaired. Always install new components.
2. If air bag module, crash sensor or control module have been dropped 18 inches or more, do not install that component into vehicle. It must be replaced.
3. Always replace damaged SRS components.
4. Do not paint air bag module to correct cosmetic flaws. It must be replaced.
5. Do not leave undeployed air bag module unattended if work is interrupted. Install into vehicle as soon as unit is removed from packaging.
6. Always store removed air bag module with pad facing upwards.
7. Air bag module must not be exposed to oil, grease, or cleaning solutions.
8. Do not expose air bag module to temperatures of more than 195°F for even brief periods during repair process. Keep unit clear of all heat sources.
9. Prior to service disconnect battery ground cable and isolate as required.
10. Remove any SRS component prior to performing repair or welding procedures in area of component.
11. Do not use electrical test equipment or analog ohmmeters on air bag module.
12. Do not expose sensors, wiring or other SRS components to heat guns, welding or spray guns.
13. SRS wiring should not be spliced, soldered or repaired. If wiring or connectors are found to be damaged or worn, wiring harness should be replaced. When replacing harness, ensure it is properly routed and all electrical connectors are securely installed.
14. Storage, transportation and disposal of air bag modules are subject to flammable solids laws.
15. Deployed air bag modules do not have to be disposed of as hazardous waste, but may be included with automotive metal scrap for recycling.
16. Thoroughly wash hands after handling deployed air bag module.

SCHEDULED MAINTENANCE

The driver's and passenger's air bag replacement date label is located on the left-hand B-pillar. The service life for the air bag modules is at least 15 years. New air bag replacement date labels are available from the vehicle manufacturer.

WIRE HARNESS & CONNECTOR REPAIR

The SRS wiring should not be spliced, soldered or repaired. If wiring or connectors are found to be damaged or worn, the harness should be replaced. When replacing the harness, ensure it is properly routed and all electrical connectors are securely installed.

COMPONENT LOCATIONS

Refer to **Figs. 1 through 6** for component locations.

DIAGNOSIS & TESTING

Refer to MOTOR's "Air Bag Manual" for diagnosis and testing.

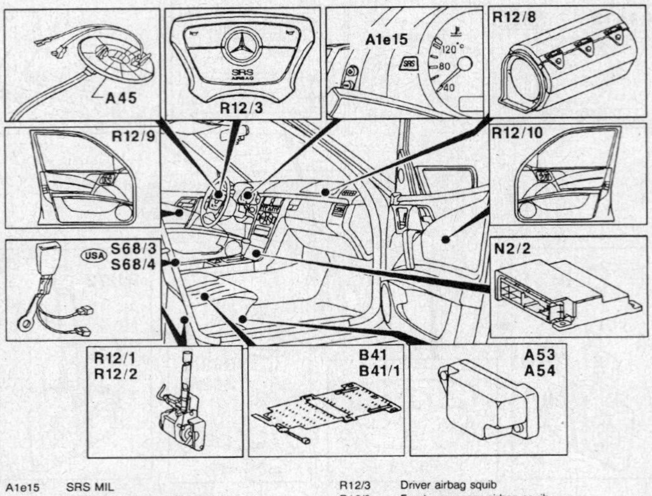

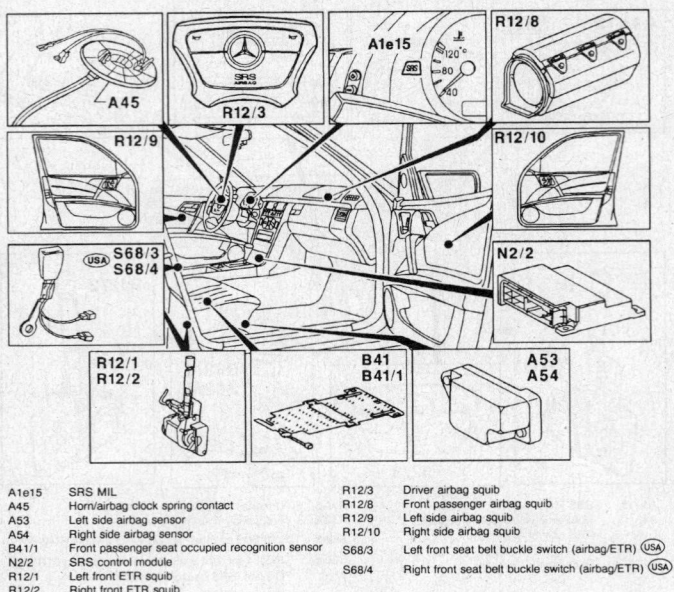

A1e15 SRS MIL
A45 Horn/airbag clock spring contact
A53 Left side airbag sensor
A54 Right side airbag sensor
B41/1 Front passenger seat occupied recognition sensor
N2/2 SRS control module
R12/1 Left front ETR squib
R12/2 Right front ETR squib
R12/3 Driver airbag squib
R12/8 Front passenger airbag squib
R12/9 Left side airbag squib
R12/10 Right side airbag squib
S68/3 Left front seat belt buckle switch (airbag/ETR) (USA)
S68/4 Right front seat belt buckle switch (airbag/ETR) (USA)

MB8019900097000X

Fig. 3 Component locations. E55, E300, E320 & E430

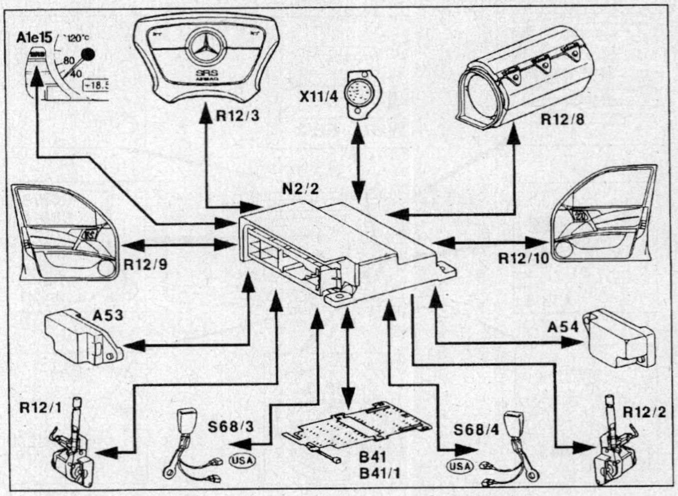

A1e15 SRS MIL
A53 Left side airbag sensor
A54 Right side airbag sensor
B41/1 Front passenger seat occupied recognition sensor
N2/2 SRS control module
R12/1 Left front ETR squib
R12/2 Right front ETR squib
R12/3 Driver airbag squib
R12/8 Front passenger airbag squib
R12/9 Left side airbag squib
R12/10 Right side airbag squib
S68/3 Left front seat belt buckle switch (airbag/ETR)
S68/4 Right front seat belt buckle switch (airbag/ETR)
X11/4 Data link connector (DTC readout)

MB8019600065000X

Fig. 4 Connection of components. E55, E300 & E320

COLLISION INSPECTION

To ensure proper SRS operation on any vehicle involved in a collision, perform procedures outlined under “Diagnosis & Testing.” All system components should be inspected for dents, cracks, exposure to excessive heat and other damage. All SRS wiring should be checked for chafing and interference with other vehicle components. On models with passenger's air bag, the instrument panel should also be inspected.

When repairing the vehicle, the SRS should be disarmed as outlined under “Air Bag System Disarming & Arming.” Also, when performing service procedures, do not expose components or wiring to heat guns, welding or spray guns.

COMPONENT SERVICE

AIR BAG MODULE, REPLACE

DRIVER'S

C43, C230, C240, C280, C320, CL55, CL500, CL600, E55, E300, E320, E430, S55, S430, S500 & S600

1. Disarm SRS as described under “Air Bag System Disarming & Arming.”
2. Remove mounting screws while holding air bag module.
3. Lift module and disconnect gas generator squib.
4. Remove air bag module.
5. Reverse procedure to install. Tighten mounting bolts to specifications.

CLK55, CLK320, CLK430, SLK230 & SLK320

1. Disarm SRS as described under “Air Bag System Disarming & Arming.”
2. Remove mounting screws while holding air bag module.
3. Lift module and disconnect gas generator squib.
4. Disconnect horn connector.
5. Remove air bag module.
6. Reverse procedure to install. Tighten mounting bolts to specifications.

PASSENGER'S

C43, C230, C240, C280, C320, CLK55, CLK320 & CLK430

1. Disarm SRS as described under “Air Bag System Disarming & Arming.”
2. Disconnect module connector.
3. Remove instrument panel.
4. Disconnect gas generator squib.
5. Remove mounting nuts and air bag module.
6. Reverse procedure to install.

CL55, CL500, CL600, S55, S320, S420, S430, S500 & S600

1. Disarm SRS as described under “Air Bag System Disarming & Arming.”
2. Remove glover compartment.
3. **On CL55, CL500 and CL600 models,** remove center and righthand side air nozzles.
4. **On all models,** disconnect passenger's air bag module squibs.
5. Remove mounting nuts and air bag module.
6. Reverse procedure to install.

E55, E300, E320 & E430

1. Disarm SRS as described under “Air Bag System Disarming & Arming.”
2. Disconnect module connector.
3. Remove instrument panel.
4. Disconnect gas generator squib.
5. Remove mounting nuts and air bag module.
6. Reverse procedure to install.

SL500 & SL600

1. Disarm SRS as described under “Air Bag System Disarming & Arming.”
2. Remove glove compartment.
3. Remove center air outlet.
4. Remove righthand speaker cover.
5. Remove righthand air outlet.
6. Remove cover below instrument panel.
7. Remove mounting bolts and air bag module.
8. Disconnect squibs.
9. Reverse procedure to install.

SLK230 & SLK320

1. Disarm SRS as described under “Air Bag System Disarming & Arming.”
2. Remove instrument panel top section.
3. Fold vapor barrier toward front.
4. Disconnect gas generator squib.
5. Remove mounting bolts and air bag module.
6. Reverse procedure to install.

SIDE

1. Disarm SRS as described under “Air Bag System Disarming & Arming.”
2. Remove door liners.
3. Drill retaining plate rivets out and remove side bag.
4. Disconnect squib connector.
5. Reverse procedure to install. If side bag has been deployed, replace door liner center section.

CURTAIN SIDE IMPACT

1. Disarm SRS as described under “Air

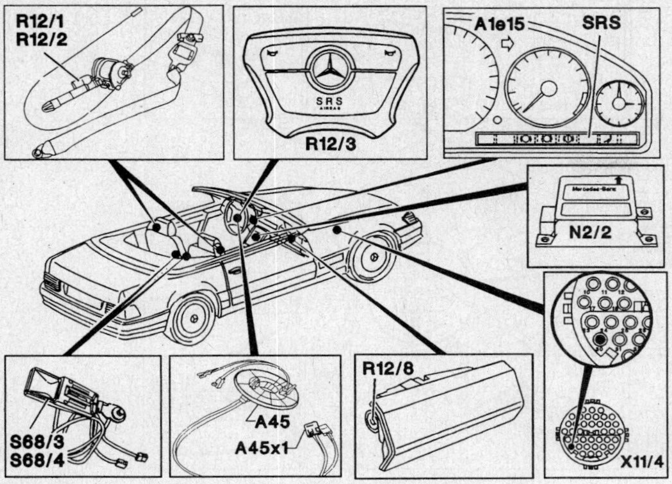

A1e15	SRS MIL	R12/3	Driver airbag squib
A45	Horn/airbag clock spring contact	R12/8	Front passenger airbag squib
A45x1	Horn/airbag clock spring contact connector	S68/3	Left front seat belt buckle switch (airbag/ETR) (USA)
N2/2	SRS control module	S68/4	Right front seat belt buckle switch (airbag/ETR) (USA)
R12/1	Left front ETR squib	X11/4	Data link connector, 38-pole (DTC readout)
R12/2	Right front ETR squib		

MB8019900093010X

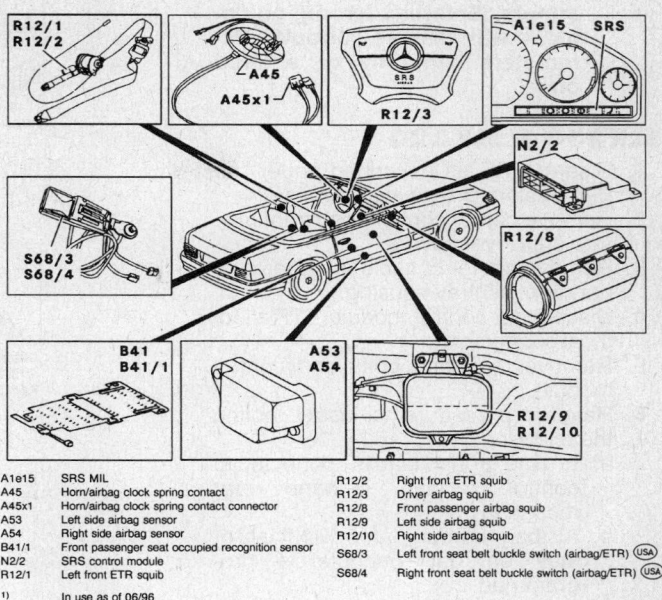

Fig. 5 Component locations (Part 1 of 2). SL500 & SL600

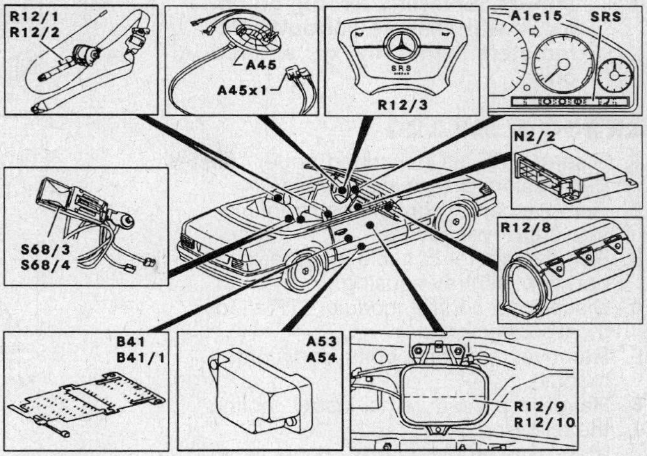

A1e15	SRS MIL	R12/2	Right front ETR squib
A45	Horn/airbag clock spring contact	R12/3	Driver airbag squib
A45x1	Horn/airbag clock spring contact connector	R12/8	Front passenger airbag squib
A53	Left side airbag sensor	R12/9	Left side airbag squib
A54	Right side airbag sensor	R12/10	Right side airbag squib
B41/1	Front passenger seat occupied recognition sensor	S68/3	Left front seat belt buckle switch (airbag/ETR) (USA)
N2/2	SRS control module	S68/4	Right front seat belt buckle switch (airbag/ETR) (USA)
R12/1	Left front ETR squib		
1)	In use as of 06/96		

MB8019900093020X

Fig. 5 Component locations (Part 2 of 2). SL500 & SL600

Bag System Disarming & Arming."
2. Remove headliner.
3. Disconnect connector.
4. Remove gas generator mounting nut.
5. Remove catch strap mounting screws and disconnect clips.
6. Remove plate mounting screws and curtain side impact air bag module from holder.
7. Reverse procedure to install.

CONTROL MODULE, REPLACE

The control module must be programmed using the Hand-Held Tester (HHT) tool No. 965 589 00 01 00, or equivalent scan tool.

C43, C230 & C280

1. Disarm SRS as described under "Air Bag System Disarming & Arming."
2. Remove transmission shift lever cover.
3. Open console storage compartment cover.
4. Remove lever cover by prying out, then disconnect electrical connector.
5. Remove mounting screws under ashtray, then the storage tray.
6. Remove mounting screws and ashtray, then disconnect electrical connector.
7. Disconnect control module ETR connector.
8. Remove mounting bolts and control module.
9. Reverse procedure to install, noting the following:
   a. Ensure ground lead is connected to control module ground.
   b. Air bag warning lamp will flash or stay on until module is programmed.
   c. Program vehicle equipment and parameters into control module using Hand-Held Tool (HHT) No 965 589 00 01 00, or equivalent scan tool. **Do not interrupt power supply. Entering wrong equipment will disable module. Parameters can only be entered once.**

C240, C320, CL55, CL500, CL600, S55, S320, S420, S430, S500 & S600

1. Disarm SRS as described under "Air Bag System Disarming & Arming."
2. Remove center console.
3. Disconnect control module ETR with air bag connector.
4. Remove mounting bolts and control module.
5. Reverse procedure to install, noting the following:
   a. Ensure ground lead is connected to control module lefthand rear mounting bolt.
   b. Air bag warning lamp will flash or stay on until module is programmed.
   c. Program vehicle equipment and parameters into control module using Hand-Held Tool (HHT) No 965 589 00 01 00, or equivalent scan tool. **Do not interrupt power supply. Entering wrong equipment will disable module. Parameters can only be entered once.**

CLK55, CLK320 & CLK430

1. Disarm SRS as described under "Air Bag System Disarming & Arming."
2. Remove transmission shift lever cover and ashtray housing.
3. Disconnect control module ETR electrical connector.
4. Remove mounting bolts and control module.
5. Reverse procedure to install, noting the following:
   a. Ensure ground lead is connected to control module lefthand rear mounting bolt.
   b. Air bag warning lamp will flash or stay on until module is programmed.
   c. Program vehicle equipment and parameters into control module using Hand-Held Tool (HHT) No 965 589 00 01 00, or equivalent scan tool. **Do not interrupt power supply. Entering wrong equipment will disable module. Parameters can only be entered once.**

E55, E300, E320 & E430

1. Disarm SRS as described under "Air Bag System Disarming & Arming."
2. Remove transmission shift lever cover.
3. Remove center console ashtray housing.
4. Disconnect control module ETR with air bag connector.
5. Remove mounting bolts and control module.
6. Reverse procedure to install, noting the following:
   a. Ensure ground lead is connected to control module lefthand rear mounting bolt.
   b. Air bag warning lamp will flash or stay on until module is programmed.
   c. Program vehicle equipment and parameters into control module using Hand-Held Tool (HHT) No 965 589 00 01 00, or equivalent scan tool. **Do not interrupt power**

supply. Entering wrong equipment will disable module. Parameters can only be entered once.

SLK230 & SLK320

1. Disarm SRS as described under "Air Bag System Disarming & Arming."
2. Remove center console and transmission shift lever covers.
3. Remove center console storage compartment ashtray housing.
4. Disconnect control module ETR electrical connector.
5. Remove mounting bolts and control module.
6. Reverse procedure to install, noting the following:
   a. Ensure ground lead is connected to control module lefthand rear mounting bolt.
   b. Air bag warning lamp will flash or stay on until module is programmed.
   c. Program vehicle equipment and parameters into control module using Hand-Held Tool (HHT) No 965 589 00 01 00, or equivalent scan tool. **Do not interrupt power supply. Entering wrong equipment will disable module. Parameters can only be entered once.**

SIDE IMPACT SENSOR, REPLACE

C43, C230, C240, C280, C320, CL55, CL500, CL600, S55, S320, S420, S430, S500 & S600

1. Disarm SRS as described under "Air Bag System Disarming & Arming."
2. Remove rear seat cushion.
3. Remove mounting screw.
4. Disconnect electrical connector.
5. Remove sensor.
6. Reverse procedure to install. Ensure arrow points toward outside.

CLK55, CLK320, CLK430, E55, E300, E320, E430, SL500, SL600, SLK230 & SLK320

1. Disarm SRS as described under "Air Bag System Disarming & Arming."
2. **On SLK230 and SLK320 models,** remove door sill molding.
3. **On all models,** remove front seat.
4. Expose sensor by folding floor covering to rear.
5. Disconnect electrical connector.
6. Remove mounting bolts and sensor.
7. Reverse procedure to install. Ensure arrow points toward outside.

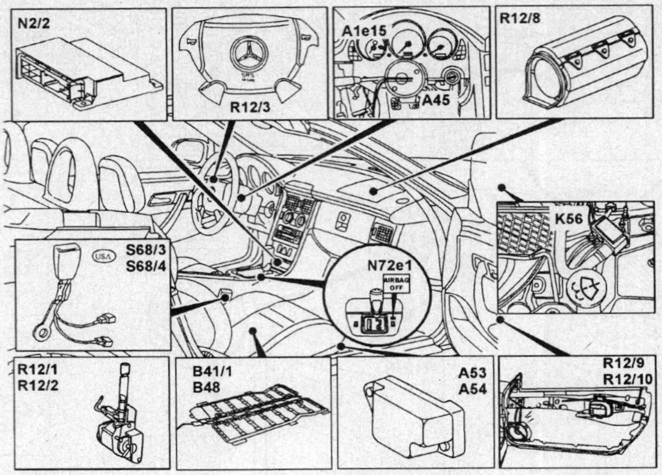

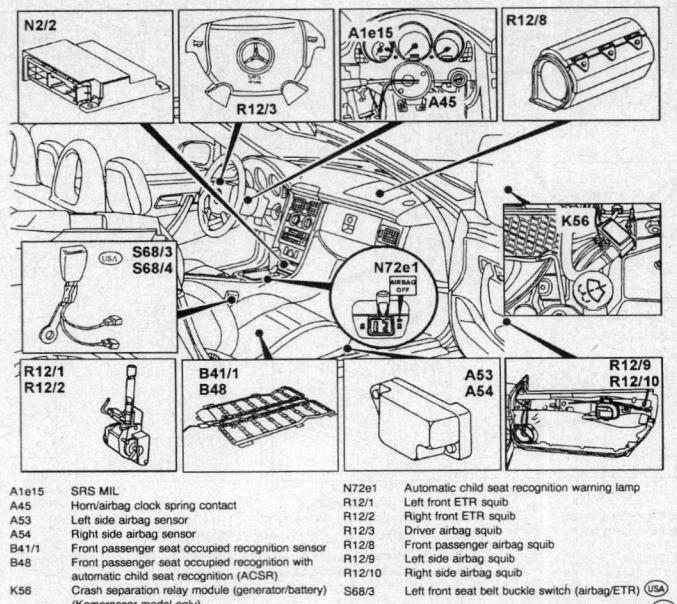

A1e15	SRS MIL	N72e1	Automatic child seat recognition warning lamp
A45	Horn/airbag clock spring contact	R12/1	Left front ETR squib
A53	Left side airbag sensor	R12/2	Right front ETR squib
A54	Right side airbag sensor	R12/3	Driver airbag squib
B41/1	Front passenger seat occupied recognition sensor	R12/8	Front passenger airbag squib
B48	Front passenger seat occupied recognition with automatic child seat recognition (ACSR)	R12/9	Left side airbag squib
		R12/10	Right side airbag squib
K56	Crash separation relay module (generator/battery) (Kompressor model only)	S68/3	Left front seat belt buckle switch (airbag/ETR) (USA)
N2/2	SRS control module	S68/4	Right front seat belt buckle switch (airbag/ETR) (USA)

MB8019900095000X

Fig. 6 Component locations. SLK230 & SLK320

CURTAIN SIDE IMPACT SENSOR, REPLACE

Refer to "Side Impact Sensor, Replace."

CLOCK SPRING, REPLACE

C43, C230, C280, CL500, CL600, E55, E300, E320, E430, S320, S420, S500, S600, SL500 & SL600

1. Place front wheels in the straight-ahead position.
2. Disarm system as described under "Air Bag System Disarming & Arming."
3. Remove steering wheel as outlined under "Electrical."
4. Remove cover below instrument panel.
5. Disconnect horn/air bag clock spring contact connector.
6. Disconnect FAN relay module clock spring contact connector.
7. Loosen mounting bolts until contact spring can be remove.
8. Carefully remove horn/air bag clock spring contact from jacket tube.
9. Remove clock spring.
10. Reverse procedure to install, noting the following:
    a. Ensure upper and lower contract spiral sections are clipped together, not pinched or kinked.
    b. **Do not apply grease.**
    c. Push horn/air bag clock spring contact as far as stop.
    d. Recess must align with fixing lug.
    e. Adjust distance between jacket tube upper bracket and locking ring to 1.1615–1.2001 inches.

CLK55, CLK320, CLK430, SLK230 & CLK320

1. Disarm system as described under "Air Bag System Disarming & Arming."
2. Remove steering wheel as outlined in "Electrical" section.
3. Loosen mounting bolts until contact spring can be remove.
4. Carefully contact spring from jacket tube.
5. Remove clock spring.
6. Reverse procedure to install, noting the following:
   a. Ensure upper and lower contract spiral sections are clipped together, not pinched or kinked.
   b. **Do not apply grease.**
   c. Push horn/air bag clock spring contact as far as stop.
   d. Recess must align with fixing lug.
   e. Adjust distance between jacket tube upper bracket and locking ring to 1.1615–1.2001 inches.

CLOCK SPRING, CENTERING

1. Turn mounting bolt into contact spiral.
2. Turn spiral counterclockwise until slightly resistance is felt.
3. Turn spiral approximately 2–2.5 half turns clockwise until mounting bolts can be backed out through openings.
4. Total rotation range is 5–6 turns.

AIR BAG ASSEMBLE DISPOSAL

When handling a deployed air bag assembly, a face shield and rubber gloves should be worn. Vehicle interior and HVAC ducts should be vacuumed. If sinus or throat irritation is encountered during air bag removal, exit vehicle and breathe fresh air. If skin irritation is encountered, flush affected area with cool water. If any type of irritation continues, consult a physician. Wash hands and rinse thoroughly with water after handling a deployed air bag assembly.

A deployed air bag should be removed as outlined under "Air Bag Module, Replace." Place tape over exhaust vents prior to air bag removal. After unit has been removed, it should be placed in a heavy duty plastic bag, sealed securely and placed with automotive scrap. To dispose of an undeployed air bag assembly, contact Mercedes-Benz.

TECHNICAL SERVICE BULLETINS

DTC B1310 & B1311

E55, E300, E320, E430 & S430 & 2000 S500

On some of these models Diagnostic Trouble Codes B1310 and B1311 may be set.

This condition may be caused by the air bag control module and the side impact air bag module not being of the same manufacture.

To correct this condition, replace the air bag control module or side impact air bag module to match.

DTC 004 OR 007

On some of these models there may be Diagnostic Trouble Codes (DTCs) 004 and/or 007.

This condition may be caused by poor contact at connect X28/23 (yellow connector behind radio).

To correct this condition, proceed as follows:

1. Replace connector X28/23.
2. Ensure pin assignments are correct, as follows:
   a. Brown/green wire should be pin 14 not 39.
   b. Blue/green wire should be pin 13 not 40.
   c. Violet wire should be pin 10 not 33.
   d. Green wire should be pin 11 not 34.

PASSENGER'S AIR BAG RATTLES

SL500 & SL600

On some of the models the passenger's front air bag may rattle.

This condition may be cause by the air bag module hitting the installation frame.

To correct this condition, remove the air bag models and install four 0.7874–0.9842 inch self-adhesive felt strips on inside of frame near corners.

SRS MIL & ACSR INDICATOR LAMP ON

SLK230

On some of these models built before VIN 004581, the SRS MIL and ACSR indicator lamp may be on.

This condition may be caused by insufficient insulation or improper crimping of electrical contacts at righthand front ESA connector under righthand front seat.

To correct this condition, crimp and solder all contacts as required.

TIGHTENING SPECIFICATIONS

Year	Component	Torque, Ft. Lbs.
1998–2001	Air Bag Module, Driver's	53①
	Air Bag Module, Passenger's	72①
	Control Module	88①
	Emergency Tensioning Retractor	26–30
	Seat Belt Guide, Front	22
	Seat Belt Guide, Rear (C240 & C320)	53①
	Seat Belt Guide, Rear (CL55, CL500 & CL600)	26
	Side Curtain Air Bag Module	44①
	Side Curtain Gas Generator	53①
	Steering Jacket Bracket	44①

① — Inch lbs.

Automatic Seat Belts

INDEX

	Page No.
Component Replacement	5-220
Control Module, Replace	5-220
Emergency Tensioning Retractor (ETR), Replace	5-220
Description	5-220
Precautions	5-220

PRECAUTIONS

Refer to "Air Bag System."

DESCRIPTION

The control module evaluates de-acceleration forces (acceleration in case of rear collisions) and when a certain value is exceeded, triggers the ETR retractors. If the front seat is not occupied, the ETR is not triggered. If the threshold value is medium, only the ETR is triggered and the air bag is not deployed. If the seat belt is not fastened, the ETR is not triggered, and even if the threshold value is medium, the air bag is deployed.

COMPONENT REPLACEMENT

EMERGENCY TENSIONING RETRACTOR (ETR), REPLACE

Left and righthand ETRs are not interchangeable. Ensure retractor is properly seated in arresting device. **Do not disassemble ETR.**

C240, C320, CLK55, CLK320, CLK430, E55, E300, E320 & E430

Front Seat

1. Disarm system as described under "Air Bag System Disarming & Arming."
2. Remove front and rear door sill molding, then the B-pillar panel.
3. Remove cover and seat belt end fitting mounting bolt.
4. Remove guide fitting mounting bolt and disconnect squibs connectors.
5. Remove mounting bolt and automatic belt retractor.
6. Reverse procedure to install.

Rear Seat

1. Disarm system as described under "Air Bag System Disarming & Arming."
2. Remove C-pillar paneling.
3. Remove seat belt mounting bolt and cover.
4. Remove guide fitting mounting bolt and disconnect squibs connectors.
5. Remove mounting bolt and automatic belt retractor.
6. Reverse procedure to install.

CL55, CL500 & CL600

Front

1. Disarm system as described under "Air Bag System Disarming & Arming."
2. Remove belt end fitting mounting bolt.
3. Press cover with suitable installation wedge.
4. Pull belt with end fitting through paneling.
5. Remove tensioning element from seat backrest.
6. Remove head restraint.
7. Remove ignition key.
8. Disconnect backrest upholstery from crossmember.
9. Disconnect ETR electrical connector.
10. Remove mounting bolts and disconnect crossmember from tensioning wire.
11. Remove mounting bolt and belt reel.
12. Remove mounting bolt and ETR.
13. Reverse procedure to install.

Rear

1. Disarm system as described under "Air Bag System Disarming & Arming."
2. Remove C-pillar paneling.
3. Remove inner side wall paneling.
4. Remove curtain side impact air bag mounting nuts.
5. Pull curtain side impact air bag out to access upper belt guide.
6. Remove upper belt guide mounting bolt.
7. Remove upper belt end fitting and guide belt out of cover.
8. Disconnect ETR ignition squibs.
9. Remove mounting bolt and belt reel.
10. Remove mounting bolts and ETR.
11. Reverse procedure to install.

SL500 & SL600

1. Disarm system as described under "Air Bag System Disarming & Arming."
2. Remove seat and backrest frame side trim.
3. If driver's seat is removed, remove backrest rear trim.
4. Slide seat cushion frame trim off.
5. Remove top belt reversing fitting trim.
6. Remove lower seat belt mounting bolts.
7. Disconnect belt lock cable.
8. Remove belt buckle from seat frame.
9. Raise heads rest adjusting device fully.
10. Remove mounting bolt and top belt reversing fitting.
11. Remove belt inertia reel mounting bolt.
12. Disconnect inertia reel connector.
13. Disconnect ETR squib.
14. Remove inertia reel from backrest.
15. Reverse procedure to install, noting the following:
    a. Ensure proper version (left or right-hand side) is installed.
    b. Tighten mounting bolts to specifications.

SLK230 & SLK320

1. Disarm system as described under "Air Bag System Disarming & Arming."
2. Remove upper mounting bolts and cover,
3. Remove lower mounting bolts and cover.
4. Pull edge guard off.
5. Remove seat belt end and upper belt guide mounting bolts.
6. Disconnect squib connector.
7. Remove mounting bolt and automatic belt retractor.
8. Reverse procedure to install, noting the following:
    a. Ensure proper version (left or right-hand side) is installed.
    b. Tighten mounting bolts to specifications.

CONTROL MODULE, REPLACE

Refer to "Air Bag System."

Dash Panel Service

NOTE: On Air Bag Equipped Models, Refer To "Air Bag System Precautions" Located In Front Of This Manual For System Disarming And Arming Procedures.

INDEX

	Page No.
Dash Panel, Replace	5-221
S320, S420, SL500 & SL600 & CL500, CL600, S500 & S600	5-221
Precautions	5-221
Air Bag Systems	5-221
Battery Ground Cable	5-221
Radio Coded Anti-Theft System	5-221

PRECAUTIONS

AIR BAG SYSTEMS

Refer to "Air Bag System Precautions" in front of this manual for system disarming and arming procedures.

BATTERY GROUND CABLE

Prior to service, disconnect battery ground cable and isolate as required.

RADIO CODED ANTI-THEFT SYSTEM

Anti-theft radios have a coded theft protection circuit. The CODE card must be obtained before disconnecting battery, removing radio fuse or removing the radio. **The serial number from the radio must match the CODE card.**

After service has been performed proceed as follows:

1. Reconnect radio power and turn key to position No. 2.
2. Turn radio to On position. The word "CODE" will appear on display.
3. Enter first digit of anti-theft code from CODE card. "CODE" will disappear and entered digit will appear followed by four dashes.
4. Enter the next four digits, when all five are entered the first digit flashes again.
5. Press SC, Seek or Tune button to confirm code.
6. If "WAIT" appears on radio panel, proceed as follows:
   a. Radio will allow three coding attempts only before entering lock-up mode and won't respond to controls.
   b. Leave radio on for 15–60 minutes, then radio will unlock and allow three addition coding attempts.
   c. The third lockout period (after nine failed coding attempts) will last 24 hours.
   d. Radio must be left on during enter 24-hour period until "CODE" appears.
7. When "CODE" appears, repeat coding attempt.

DASH PANEL

REPLACE

S320, S420, SL500 & SL600 & CL500, CL600, S500 & S600

1. Remove steering wheel assembly.
2. Remove instrument cluster.
3. Remove windshield reveal molding.
4. Turn glove box lock 45° with ignition key.
5. Install 1.77 inches minimum length, 0.059 inch diameter wire pin into hole at lock cylinder. Unhook lock cylinder catch and pull glove box lock from housing using key. **Do not remove key as lock tumblers may fall out.**
6. Remove instrument panel center air duct.
7. Remove light switch assembly.
8. Remove radio assembly.
9. Push heater control upward while pulling heater control rearward.
10. Disconnect heater control electrical connectors.
11. Remove box below radio assembly mounting screws and bend box gently inward to remove.
12. Lift shift rear cover to gain access and disconnect electrical connectors.
13. Remove shift cover plate.
14. Remove left and righthand side instrument panel air ducts.
15. Disconnect parking brake control cable, then remove handle and housing.
16. Remove hose from lefthand side air duct.
17. Disconnect glove box lock cylinder vacuum line.
18. Disconnect glove box plastic chain, remove mounting screws and pull upward to remove damping device.
19. Disconnect speaker electrical connectors.
20. Remove screws located behind gearshift.
21. Remove center console compartment carpet, using puller tool No. 126 589 03 33 00, or equivalent,
22. Remove center console compartment mounting screws.
23. Remove center console top front mounting screw.
24. Disconnect center console electrical connectors, lift slightly lift console and pull rearward approximately 1.18 inches.
25. Remove mounting screws and speaker and bracket.
26. Pull steering column upper cover upward.
27. Remove ignition cable from bracket on heater case.
28. Remove steering column upper mounting bolts.
29. Remove steering column lower jacket attaching nut and bolt.
30. Remove instrument panel left side brace tube mounting screw, and position tube downward and aside.
31. Lift instrument panel, disconnect any remaining electrical connectors.
32. Carefully pull right side of instrument panel rearward, moving ignition lock and steering column cover upward and outward.
33. Remove instrument panel.
34. Reverse procedure to install.

Steering Columns

NOTE: On Air Bag Equipped Models, Refer To "Air Bag System Precautions" Located In Front Of This Manual For System Disarming And Arming Procedures.

NOTE: Prior To Performing Any Service Operations Listed In This Section, Consult The "Technical Service Bulletins" Section For Related Information.

INDEX

	Page No.
Precautions	5-222
Air Bag Systems	5-222
Battery Ground Cable	5-222
Radio Coded Anti-Theft System	5-222
Steering Column, Replace	5-222
C43, C230, C280, CLK55, CLK320, CLK430, S320, S420, SL500, SL600 & SLK230 & 1998–99 CL500, CL600, S500 & S600	5-222
E55, E300, E320 & E430	5-222
S430 & 2000–01 CL500, CL600, S500 & S600	5-223
Steering Column Lock, Replace	5-223
C43, C230, C280, SLK230 & SLK320	5-223
CLK55, CLK320 & CLK430	5-224
E55, E300, E320 & E430	5-224
S320, S420, SL500 & SL600 & 1998–99 CL500, CL600, S500 & S600	5-223
Steering Column Service	5-224
Electrically Adjustable Jacket Tube	5-226
Fixed Jacket Tube	5-224
Manually Adjustable Jacket Tube	5-225
Technical Service Bulletins	5-228
Electric Steering Column Works Sporadically	5-228
Tightening Specifications	5-228

PRECAUTIONS

AIR BAG SYSTEMS

Refer to "Air Bag System Precautions" in front of this manual for system disarming and arming procedures.

BATTERY GROUND CABLE

Prior to service, disconnect battery ground cable and isolate as required.

RADIO CODED ANTI-THEFT SYSTEM

Anti-theft radios have a coded theft protection circuit. The CODE card must be obtained before disconnecting battery, removing radio fuse or removing the radio. **The serial number from the radio must match the CODE card.**

After service has been performed proceed as follows:

1. Reconnect radio power and turn key to position No. 2.
2. Turn radio to On position. The word "CODE" will appear on display.
3. Enter first digit of anti-theft code from CODE card. "CODE" will disappear and entered digit will appear followed by four dashes.
4. Enter the next four digits, when all five are entered the first digit flashes again.
5. Press SC, Seek or Tune button to confirm code.
6. If "WAIT" appears on radio panel, proceed as follows:
   a. Radio will allow three coding attempts only before entering lock-up mode and won't respond to controls.
   b. Leave radio on for 15–60 minutes, then radio will unlock and allow three addition coding attempts.
   c. The third lockout period (after nine failed coding attempts) will last 24 hours.
   d. Radio must be left on during enter 24-hour period until "CODE" appears.
7. When "CODE" appears, repeat coding attempt.

STEERING COLUMN

REPLACE

C43, C230, C280, CLK55, CLK320, CLK430, S320, S420, SL500, SL600 & SLK230 & 1998–99 CL500, CL600, S500 & S600

1. Remove cover below instrument panel.
2. Remove steering wheel as outlined in "Electrical" section.
3. Remove clock spring as outlined under "Passive Restraint Systems," **Figs. 1 and 2.**
4. **On models equipped with Adaptive Damping System (ADS),** remove steering angle sensor.
5. **On all models,** remove instrument cluster as outlined in "Electrical" section.
6. Remove steering lock as outlined under "Steering Column Lock, Replace."
7. Remove combination switch as outlined in "Electrical" section.
8. Remove jacket tube trim.
9. **On CLK320, CLK430 and SLK230 models,** disconnect clock spring/air bag module connector.
10. **On models equipped with adjustable steering column,** disconnect operating switch and reinforcement brace.
11. **On all models,** remove steering coupling upper mounting bolt.
12. Remove jacket tube lower mounting nuts and upper mounting bolts.
13. Remove jacket tube with lower steering shaft by pulling out of steering coupling. **Do not force. Lower steering shaft is sensitive to side force.**
14. Reverse procedure to install, noting the following:
    a. If lower steering shaft runout exceeds 0.0787 inch, replace lower steering shaft.
    b. Ensure jacket tube is in straight ahead position with triggering lugs pointed toward combination switch.
    c. Push lower steering shaft as far as steering coupling stop.
    d. **On models with manually adjustable jacket tube,** tighten lower mounting nuts first.
    e. **On models with electric jacket tube,** tighten upper mounting bolts first.
    f. **On all models,** ensure correct routing of adjustable steering column cable.
    g. Tighten mounting bolts and nuts to specifications.

E55, E300, E320 & E430

1. Remove cover below instrument panel.
2. Remove steering wheel as outlined in "Electrical" section
3. Remove instrument cluster as outlined in "Electrical" section.
4. Remove clock spring as outlined under "Passive Restraint Systems," **Fig. 3.**
5. **On models equipped with ADS or ESP,** remove steering angle sensor.
6. **On all models,** remove combination

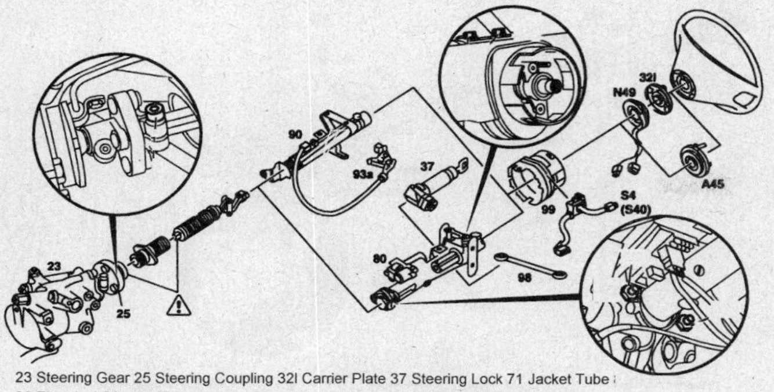

23 Steering Gear 25 Steering Coupling 32I Carrier Plate 37 Steering Lock 71 Jacket Tube
80 Electrical Steering Column Adjustment 90 Manual Steering Colum Adjustment
98 Reinforcement Brace 99 Jacket Tube Trim A45 Clock Spring N49 Steering Angle Sensor S4 Combination Switch

MB6049900012020X

Fig. 1 Adjustable steering column replacement. C43, C230, C280, CLK320, CLK430, S320, S420, S500, S600, SL500, SL600 & SLK230

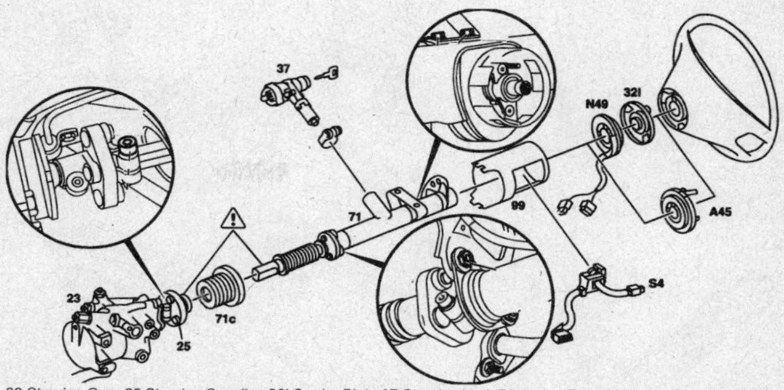

23 Steering Gear 25 Steering Coupling 32I Carrier Plate 37 Steering Lock 71 Jacket Tube 80 Lower Steering Shaft
98 Reinforcement Brace 99 Jacket Tube Trim A45 Clock Spring N49 Steering Angle Sensor S4 Combination Switch

MB6049900012010X

Fig. 2 Fixed steering column replacement. C43, C230, C280, CLK320, CLK430, S320, S420, S500, S600, SL500, SL600 & SLK230

switch as outlined in "Electrical" section.
7. Remove jacket tube trim.
8. Remove steering lock as outlined under "Steering Column Lock, Replace."
9. **On models equipped with electrically adjustable steering column,** disconnect connector.
10. **On E320 models,** remove steering coupling head shield.
11. **On all models,** remove steering coupling mounting bolt.
12. Press lower steering shaft out of steering couple. **Do not force. Expand clamp slot slightly, if required.**
13. Remove jacket tube lower mounting nuts and upper mounting bolts.
14. Remove jacket tube.
15. Reverse procedure to install, noting the following:
    a. Install new self-locking bolts and nuts.
    b. Tighten upper mounting bolts first.
    c. Install new tab washer on lower steering shaft and one thread of mounting nut to upper steering shaft.
    d. Attach lower steering shaft to mounting nut and but both parts to screw together until just before they lock in position in splines.
    e. Position upper steering shaft horizontal with combination switch reset cam on lefthand side. Lock in place with steering lock.
    f. Ensure jacket tube is in straight ahead position with triggering lugs pointed toward combination switch.
    g. Rotate lower steering shaft until joint fork points down or bolt-on flange flats are upright. Steering coupling double flat section should be horizontal and steering coupling fixing bolt groove on righthand side.
    h. Tighten mounting bolts and nuts to specifications.

S430 & 2000–01 CL500, CL600, S500 & S600

1. Ensure front wheels are pointed straight ahead and lower steering column to horizontal position.
2. Remove lower rear engine compartment lining.
3. Disconnect exhaust heat shields around steering shaft.
4. Remove lower steering shaft coupling bolt, **Fig. 4.**
5. Pull lower steering shaft out of coupling by inserting suitable tool into bore. **Do not hammer or force steering shaft. Do not use rubber boot or thermal protective washer to steady tool.**
6. Remove retaining plate mounting nuts.
7. Remove steering wheel as outlined in "Electrical" section.
8. Remove switch module.
9. Mark steering column to tube for installation alignment.
10. Remove instrument cluster as outlined in "Electrical" section.
11. Remove tube trim and disconnect connector.
12. Remove steering column covers.
13. Disconnect adjustment motors' and micro switch electrical connectors.
14. Remove transverse heating duct.
15. Remove electrical adjuster motor lower and upper mounting bolts.
16. Remove mounting bolts, reinforcement brace and steering column.
17. Reverse procedure to install, noting the following:
    a. Install new self-locking bolts and nuts.
    b. Tighten mounting bolts and nuts to specifications.

STEERING COLUMN LOCK

REPLACE

C43, C230, C280, SLK230 & SLK320

1. Remove cover below instrument panel.
2. Remove instrument cluster as outlined in "Electrical" section.
3. Remove transponder coil from steering lock cylinder.
4. Press out instrument panel escutcheon using suitable small screwdriver.
5. Push sleeve onto cap and turn lock cylinder to position 1.
6. Unlock lock cylinder by turning cap counterclockwise 90°, then remove.
7. Disconnect warning buzzer and ignition/starter switch connectors.
8. Disconnect parking lock interlock wire cable.
9. Loosen clamp, press locking pin in and remove steering lock.
10. Disconnect ignition/starter switch.
11. Remove washer and parking lock valve.
12. Reverse procedure to install, noting the following:
    a. Spray lock cylinder outside with cylinder grease No. 001 989 26 51 00, or equivalent.
    b. Install cylinder in cap.
    c. Steering lock must not be turned from position 1 or ignition/starter switch will be permanently jammed.
    d. Align lock cylinder indentations with steering lock recesses, then push lock cylinder into steering lock.
    e. Ensure locking pin locks into bearing tube bore.
    f. Turn lock cylinder clockwise 90° until it locks in position.

S320, S420, SL500 & SL600 & 1998–99 CL500, CL600, S500 & S600

1. Remove cover below instrument panel.
2. **On S320, S420, S500 and S600 models,** remove instrument cluster as outlined in "Electrical" section.
3. **On all models,** remove instrument panel escutcheon using claw-type wrench tool No. 210 589 00 07 00, or equivalent.
4. Remove transponder coil from steering lock cylinder.
5. Turn lock cylinder to position 1.
6. **On SL500 and SL600 models,** press connector locking catch and pull slide toward lock cylinder.
7. **On all models,** disconnect parking lock wire cable on protective sleeve.
8. Press locking pins on steering lock, then remove protective sleeve with

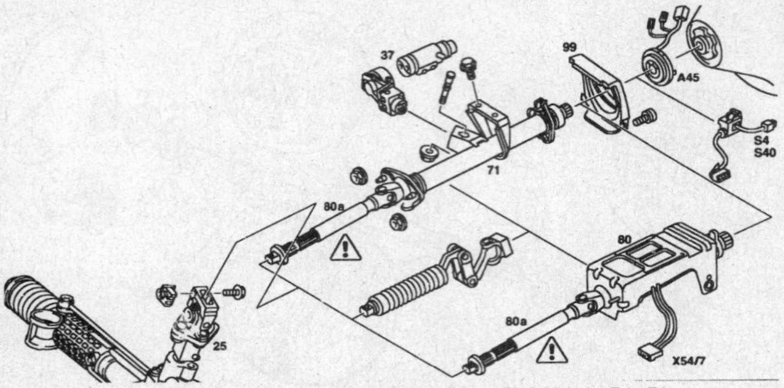

25 Steering Coupling 37 Steering Lock71 Jacket Tube 80a Lower Steering Shaft 99 Jacket Tube Trim
A45 Clock Spring N49 Steering Angle Sensor S4 Combination Switch
X54/7 Electrically Adjustable Steering Column Connector

MB6049900013000X

Fig. 3 Steering column replacement. E300, E320 & E430

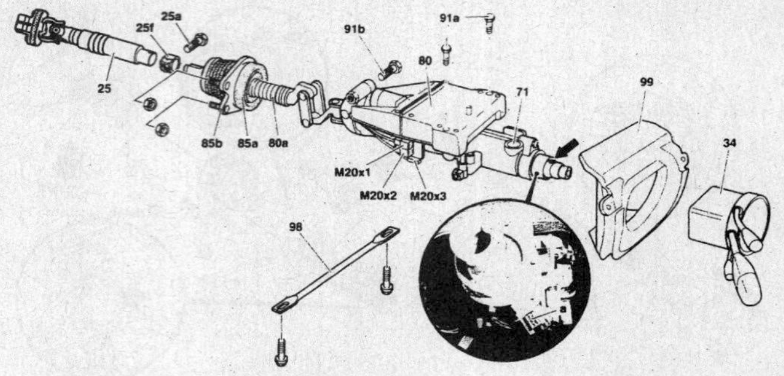

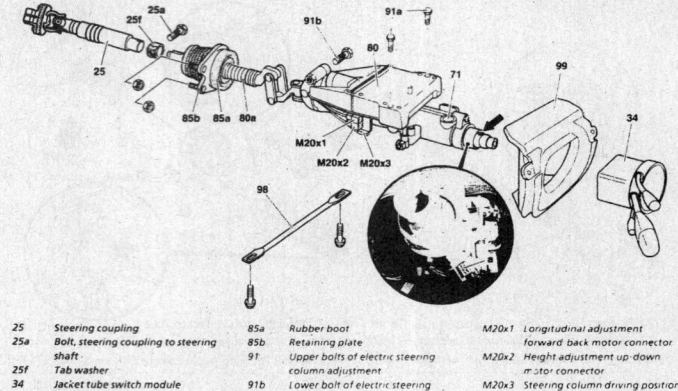

25	Steering coupling	85a	Rubber boot	M20x1	Longitudinal adjustment forward back motor connector
25a	Bolt, steering coupling to steering shaft	85b	Retaining plate	M20x2	Height adjustment up-down motor connector
25f	Tab washer	91	Upper bolts of electric steering column adjustment	M20x3	Steering column driving position microswitch connector
34	Jacket tube switch module	91b	Lower bolt of electric steering column adjustment		
71	Jacket tube	98	Reinforcement brace		
80	Electric steering column adjustment	99	Jacket tube trim	a	Connector on jacket tube
80a	Lower steering shaft				

MB6040100018000X

Fig. 4 Steering column replacement. S430 & 2000–01 CL500, CL600, S500 & S600

starter switch and lock cylinder.

9. Steering lock shift shaft must not be twisted out of position 1.
10. Remove mounting nut and remove pins upward. If required, loosen and carefully lower steering column at upper mounting bolts.
11. Remove steering lock from steering column.
12. Reverse procedure to install, noting the following:
    a. Spray lock cylinder outside with cylinder grease No. 001 989 26 51 00, or equivalent.
    b. Push cap onto protective sleeve until snap ring locks.
    c. Press ignition/starter switch and parking lock valve with lock shaft into protective cover until it locks.

CLK55, CLK320 & CLK430

1. Remove steering wheel as outlined in "Electrical" section.
2. Remove instrument cluster as outlined in "Electrical" section.
3. Remove cover below instrument panel.
4. Disconnect trim and jacket tube.
5. Remove mounting nut, then turn electronic ignition switch to position 1 and remove mounting bolt.
6. Disconnect electrical connector.
7. Remove electronic steering lock.
8. Reverse procedure to install. Install all jacket tube bolts and nuts, then tighten lower nuts first.

E55, E300, E320 & E430

Less Electronic Switch

Refer to "S320, S420, SL500, SL600 & 1998–99 CL500, CL600, S500 & S600."

With Electronic Switch

1. Remove cover below instrument panel.
2. Remove instrument panel escutcheon using claw-type wrench tool No. 210 589 00 07 00, or equivalent.
3. Press transponder coil out of lock cylinder.
4. Turn lock cylinder to position 1 and disconnect electrical connector.
5. Remove parking lock wire cable on protective sleeve.
6. Press locking pins on steering lock, then remove protective sleeve.
7. Steering lock shift shaft must not be twisted out of position 1.
8. **On models equipped with electrically adjustable steering column,** proceed as follows:
    a. Loosen contract spiral and turn signal switch contacts.
    b. Disconnect steering column jacket lining.
    c. Remove instrument cluster.
    d. Disconnect upper column mounting suspension.
    e. Lower steering column as far as possible.
9. **On all models,** loosen nuts through box-profile opening, then remove steering lock mounting bolts.
10. Remove steering lock from steering column.
11. Reverse procedure to install. Spray lock cylinder outside with cylinder grease No. 001 989 26 51 00, or equivalent.

STEERING COLUMN SERVICE

FIXED JACKET TUBE

C43, C230, C280, CLK55, CLK320, CLK430, SL500, SL600, SLK230 & SLK320

Disassemble

1. Remove mounting bolt and lower steering shaft, **Fig. 5.**
2. Visually inspect lower steering shaft runout.
3. Remove retaining ring, disk spring and thrust ring.
4. Remove locking and thrust rings by pushing steering shaft out slightly.
5. Press ball baring out of jacket tube using steering shaft.

Assemble

1. Press second ball bearing in using suitable tube.
2. Slide steering shaft in and press second ball bearing in.
3. Push thrust ring and locking rings together onto steering shaft. Ensure locking ring locks in upper steering shaft groove.
4. Slide thrust ring and disk spring on.
5. Mount retaining ring on steering shaft, then push on until disk spring is fully preloaded using suitable tube.
6. Attach lower steering shaft to upper steering shaft.

E55, E300, E320 & E430

Disassemble

1. Remove mounting bolt and lower steering shaft, **Fig. 6.**
2. Visually inspect lower steering shaft runout.
3. Remove disk spring and thrust ring.
4. Remove locking and thrust rings by sliding steering shaft out slightly.
5. Press ball baring out of jacket tube using steering shaft.

Assemble

1. Press new ball bearing in from above using suitable tube.
2. Slide steering shaft in and press second ball bearing in from below.
3. Push thrust ring and locking rings together onto steering shaft. Ensure locking ring locks in upper steering shaft groove.
4. Fit locking ring.
5. Slide thrust ring and disk spring on.
6. Install lower steering shaft on upper steering shaft. Disk spring must be fully preloaded.

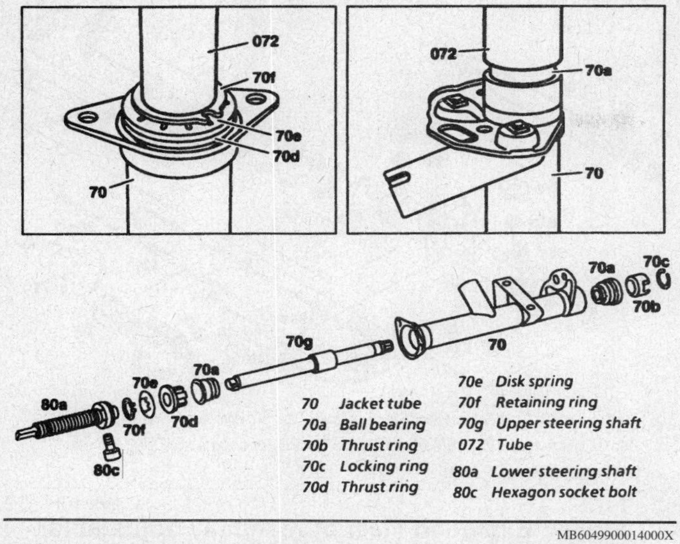

Fig. 5 Exploded view of steering fixed column. C43, C230, C280, CLK320, CLK430, SL500, SL600 & SLK230

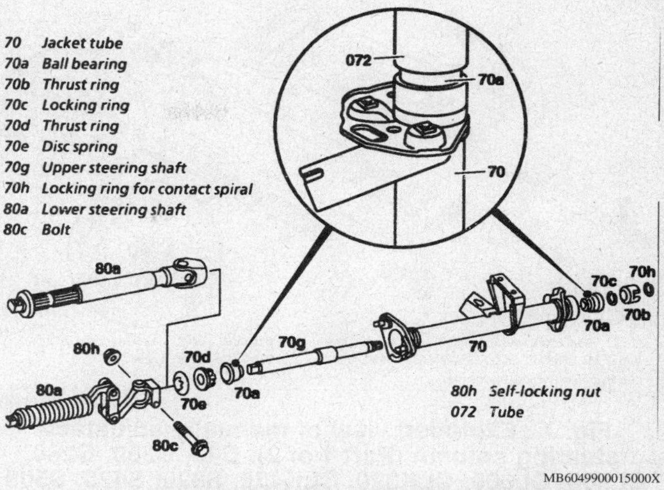

Fig. 6 Exploded view of fixed steering column. E300, E320 & E430

7. Tighten mounting bolt to specifications.

MANUALLY ADJUSTABLE JACKET TUBE

C43, C230, C280, CLK320, CLK430, S320, S420, SLK230 & SLK320 & 1998–99 CL500, CL600, S500 & S600

Disassemble

1. Remove seal cap from lower steering shaft, **Fig. 7.**
2. **On CL500, CL600, S320, S420, S500 and S600 models,** remove lower steering column from upper shaft by removing self-locking nut.
3. **On C43, C230, C280, CLK320, CLK430 and SLK230 models,** remove mounting bolt and disconnect lower steering shaft.
4. **On all models,** replace lower steering shaft if runout exceeds 0.0787 inch.
5. Disconnect hydraulic cylinder and control cable.
6. Remove guide screw.
7. Push or pull adjusting lever or handle and remove inner jacket tube from outer.
8. **On C43, C230, C280, CLK320, CLK430 and SLK230 models,** disconnect manual steering wheel adjustment handle and latching mechanism as follows:
   a. Remove plastic locking pin by pressing back in handle using suitable screwdriver.
   b. Press lever shaft out of handle.
   c. Remove latching mechanism plastic locking pin by pressing back using suitable screwdriver.
   d. Remove latching mechanism.
   e. Remove mounting bolt and handle.
9. **On all models,** disconnect control cables by turning and removing plastic clips.
10. Remove and visually inspect play adjusters.
11. Inspect plastic bearing.
12. **On CL500, CL600, S320, S420, S500 and S600 models,** disassemble inner jacket as follows:
    a. Remove locking nut and plate.
    b. Remove disk spring and thrust ring.
    c. Push steering shaft out slightly, then disconnect thrust and locking rings.
    d. Press ball bearing out of jacket tube using steering shaft.
13. **On CLK320, CLK430 and SLK230 models,** disassemble inner jacket as follows:
    a. Remove retaining ring or spacer washer using suitable pliers.
    b. Remove disk spring and thrust ring.
    c. Push steering shaft out slightly, then disconnect thrust and locking rings.
    d. Press ball bearing out of jacket tube using steering shaft.

Assemble

1. **On CL500, CL600, S320, S420, S500 and S600 models,** assemble inner jacket as follows:
   a. Press new ball bearing into of jacket tube up to stop, using suitable tube.
   b. Install steering shaft.
   c. Press in second ball bearing.
   d. Slide thrust and locking rings together onto steering shaft. Ensure locking ring locks in steering shaft groove.
   e. Push thrust ring, disk spring and new lock plate with retaining lugs toward locking nut.
   f. Install locking nut and **torque** slightly by hand to not more than 1.3 inch lbs.
   g. Ensure shaft has no axial play in tube and turns without binding.
2. **On C43, C230, C280, CLK320, CLK430 and SLK230 models,** assemble inner jacket as follows:
   a. Press new ball bearing as far as inner jacket tube stop using suitable pliers.
   b. Install steering shaft.
   c. Install second ball bearing as far as jacket tube stop.
   d. Push thrust and locking rings together onto steering shaft.
   e. Ensure locking ring locks into steering shaft groove.
   f. Install second locking ring.
   g. Slide thrust ring and disc spring or space washer on.
   h. Install retaining ring on steering shaft with round second (chamfer) toward disc spring or spacer washer.
   i. Press retaining ring until disc spring is fully preloaded using suitable tube.
3. **On all models,** install plastic bearing.
4. Lubricate inner jacket tube and push into outer tube.
5. Align inner jacket tube groove with guide screw, install and tighten guide screw.
6. Install play adjusters thrust pieces lightly into jacket tube until they abut.
7. **On CL500, CL600, S320, S420, S500 and S600 models,** connect and adjust control cables as follows:
   a. Connect control cables with spring.
   b. Release play adjusters against spring force.
   c. Turn play adjusters by hand and tighten by spring force.
   d. Adjust until dimension a at both spring cables at hook eyes is 3.5437 inches, **Fig. 8.**
   e. Press driver off adjusting bush.
8. **On CL500, CL600, S320, S420, S500 and S600 models,** connect and adjust control cable with adjusting switch or latching mechanism as follows:
   a. Install control cable with adjusting switch at bracket.
   b. Lock cable in position and install play adjusters.
   c. Adjust control cable to dimension b

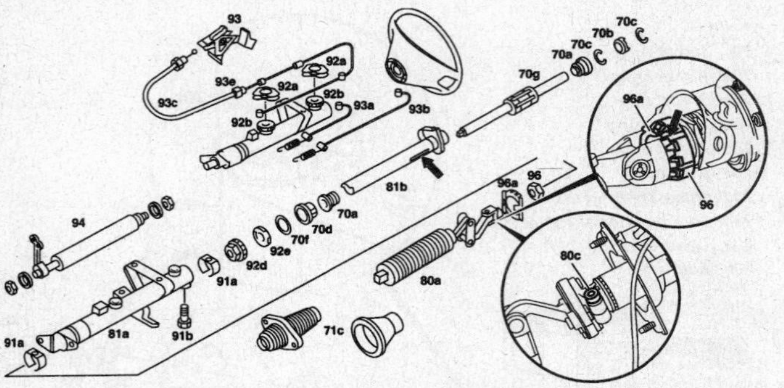

71c Cup Seal 80a Lower Steering Shaft 81a Outer Jacket Tube 81b Inner Jacket Tube 91a Plastic Bearing 91b Guide Screw 92a & 92b Play Adjusters 93 Lever 93a, 93b, 93c & 93e Control Cables 94 Hydraulic Cylinder 95 Handle

MB6049900018010X

Fig. 7 Exploded view of manually adjustable steering column (Part 1 of 2). C43, C230, C280, CL500, CL600, CLK320, CLK430, S320, S420, S500, S600 & SLK230

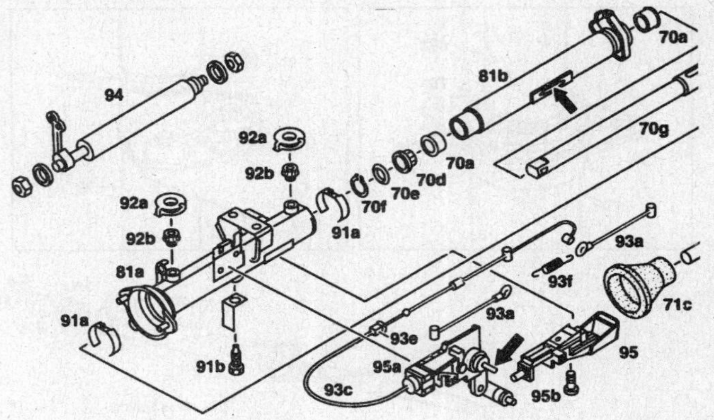

71c Cup Seal 80a Lower Steering Shaft 81a Outer Jacket Tube 81b Inner Jacket Tube 91a Plastic Bearing 91b Guide Screw 92a & 92b Play Adjusters 93 Lever 93a, 93b, 93c & 93e Control Cables 94 Hydraulic Cylinder 95 Handle

MB6049900018020X

Fig. 7 Exploded view of manually adjustable steering column (Part 2 of 2). CLK320, CLK430 & SLK230

by measuring between hydraulic cylinder bracket and lever, **Fig. 9.**

d. Operate release lever several times and adjust again.

9. **On C43, C230, C280, CLK320 and CLK430 models,** connect and adjust control cable with adjusting switch or latching mechanism as follows:
   a. Install control cable with adjusting switch at bracket.
   b. Lock cable in position and install play adjusters.
10. **On SLK230 models,** connect and adjust control cable with adjusting switch or latching mechanism as follows:
    a. Thread latching mechanism control cable through two brackets and lock in fixing device.
    b. Attach driver compression nipple on steering wheel side in lower clip row.
    c. Clip driver onto thrust piece.
    d. Attach control cable compression nipple in front driver low clip row onto thrust piece.
    e. Do not turn thrust pieces.
    f. There should be no slack in cable between ball and compression nipple or between compression nipples.
11. **On all models,** attach hydraulic cylinder control cable lever and install hydraulic cylinder onto jacket tube. Install flat nut and ball socket toward steering wheel.
12. **On CL500, CL600, S320, S420, S500 and S600 models,** install lower steering column as follows:
    a. Mount new lock plate on lower steering shaft and bend tap over.
    b. Install self-locking nut on upper steering shaft with one turn of thread.
    c. Position lower steering shaft onto nut and screw together by turning both pats until just before they lock in position in splines.
    d. Turn lower steering shaft until joint fork points down.
    e. Install suitable adjustable gauge into upper steering shaft groove.
    f. Install lower steering shaft joint fork

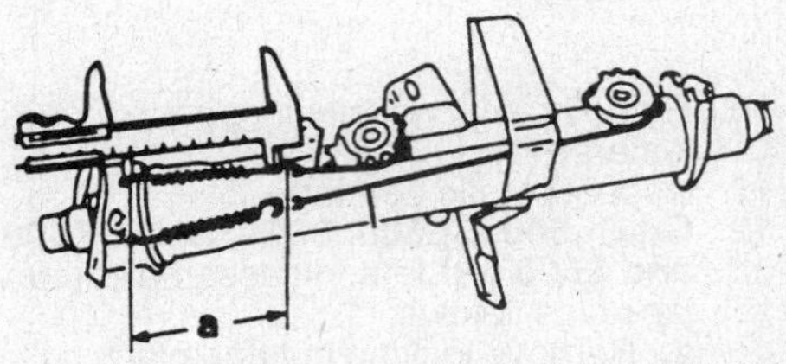

MB6049100007000X

Fig. 8 Control cable adjustment

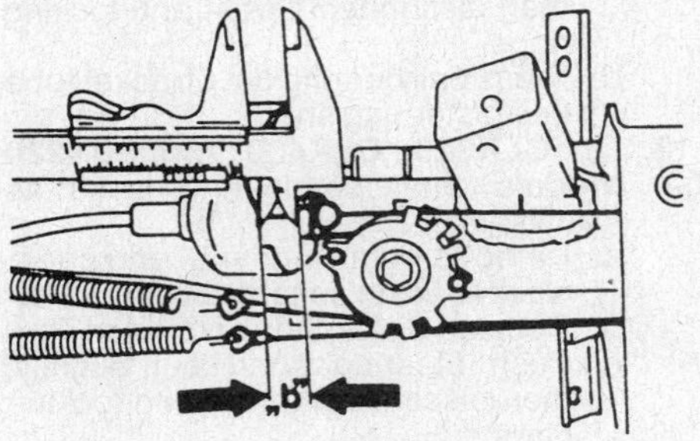

MB6049100008000X

Fig. 9 Control cable adjustment. With adjusting switch or latching mechanism

parallel to adjustment gauge. Continue to screw nut to position lower steering shaft.

g. Tighten nut to specifications. Steady shaft by mounting steering wheel.

13. **On C43, C230, C280, CLK320, CLK430 and SLK230 models,** install lower steering shaft as follows:
    a. Push lower steering shaft onto upper steering shaft retaining ring.
    b. Mounting bolt and thrust ring lug must be in same position.
    c. Fully preload disk spring by pressing against steering shaft.
    d. Install mounting bolt and tighten to specifications.
14. **On all models,** install lower steering shaft on upper.
15. Coat cup seal lightly with suitable lubricating grease and install.

ELECTRICALLY ADJUSTABLE JACKET TUBE

S320, S420, SL500 & SL600 & 1998-99 CL500, CL600, S500 & S600

Disassemble

1. Remove lower steering shaft cap seal, **Fig. 10.**
2. **On CL500, CL600, S320, S420, S500 and S600 models,** remove lower steering column from upper shaft by removing self-locking nut.
3. **On SL500 and SL600 models,** remove lower steering column as follows:
   a. Disconnect lower steering shaft from upper steering shaft splines as far as locking ring stop.
   b. Remove locking ring from upper steering shaft.
   c. Remove lower steering shaft.
4. **On all models,** remove lower bracket and position tilt adjustment in center position.
5. Remove tilt adjustment motor, then the telescopic adjustment motor.
6. Remove thrust pieces, spring packs and locking rings.
7. Remove bracket.
8. Remove cap screw, then pull inner jacket tube down and out of outer jacket tube.
9. **On CL500, CL600, S320, S420, S500 and S600 models,** disassemble inner jacket as follows:
   a. Remove locking nut and plate.
   b. Remove disk spring and thrust ring.
   c. Push steering shaft out slightly, then disconnect thrust and locking rings.
   d. Press ball bearing out of jacket tube using steering shaft.
10. **On SL500 and SL600 models,** disassemble inner jacket as follows:
    a. Remove locking ring, nut and plate.

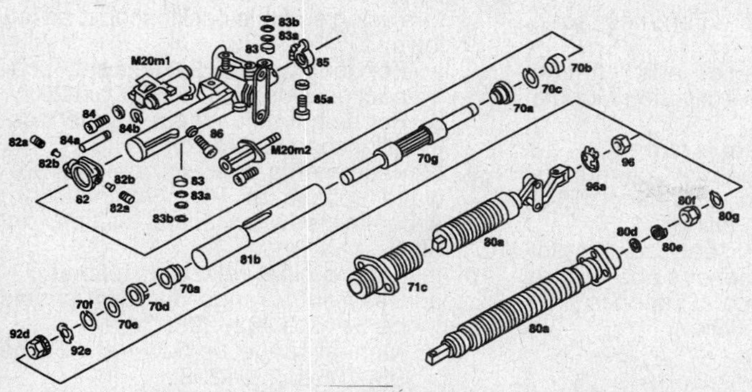

71c Cup Seal 80a Lower Steering Shaft 81b Innner Jacket Tube 82 Lower Bracket 83 Thrust Piece 83b Locking Ring 85 Bracket 86 Cap Screw M20m1 Telescopic Motor M20m2 Tolt Motor

MB6049900016000X

Fig. 10 Exploded view of electrically adjustable steering column. CL500, CL600, S320, S420, S500, S600, SL500 & SL600

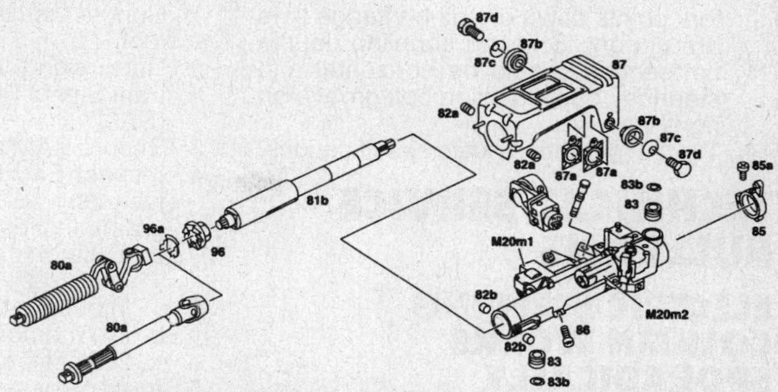

37 Steering Lock 80a Lower Steering Shaft 81b Inner Jacket Tube82a Fixing Bolt 83 Spring Packs 83b Locking Rings 85 Bracket 86 Guide Bolt 87 Console 87a Plastic Washers 87b Metal Ring 87d Fixing Bolt M20m1 Telescopic Adjustment Motor M20m2 Tilt Adjustment Motor

MB6049900017000X

Fig. 11 Exploded view of electrically adjustable steering column. E300, E320 & E430

b. Disconnect retaining ring using suitable pliers.
c. Remove disk spring and thrust ring.
d. Push steering shaft out slightly, then disconnect thrust and locking rings.
e. Press ball bearing out of jacket tube using steering shaft.

Assemble

1. If lateral runout is more than 0.0787 inch, replace lower steering shaft.
2. **On CL500, CL600, S320, S420, S500 and S600 models,** assemble inner jacket as follows:
   a. Press new ball bearing into of jacket tube up to stop, using suitable tube.
   b. Install steering shaft.
   c. Press in second ball bearing.
   d. Slide thrust and locking rings together onto steering shaft. Ensure locking ring locks in steering shaft groove.
   e. Push thrust ring, disk spring and new lock plate with retaining lugs toward locking nut.
   f. Install locking nut and **torque** slightly by hand to not more than 1.3 inch lbs.
   g. Ensure shaft has no axial play in tube and turns without binding.
3. **On SL500 and SL600 models,** assemble inner jacket as follows:
   a. Press new ball bearing into of jacket tube up to stop, using suitable tube.
   b. Install steering shaft.
   c. Press in second ball bearing.
   d. Slide thrust and locking rings together onto steering shaft. Ensure locking ring locks in steering shaft groove.
   e. Push thrust ring and disk spring on.
   f. Install retaining ring with chamfer towards disk spring on steering shaft and press on using suitable tube until disk spring is fully preloaded.
   g. Ensure shaft has no axial play in tube and turns without binding.
   h. Install new locking plate with retaining lugs pointing toward lock nut.
   i. Install locking nut and tighten slightly by hand.
   j. Install locking ring on upper steering shaft.
4. **On all models,** lubricate inner jack tube and push into outer jacket tube from below. Inner jacket must slide in without binding.
5. Install guide bolt, aligning inner jacket tube groove with cap screw.
6. Install telescopic adjustment motor.
7. Install thrust piece with disc springs and new locking ring.
8. Install upper, then lower brackets.
9. Install tilt adjustment motor.
10. **On CL500, CL600, S320, S420, S500 and S600 models,** install lower steering column as follows:
    a. Mount new lock plate on lower steering shaft and bend tap over.
    b. Install self-locking nut on upper steering shaft with one turn of thread.
    c. Position lower steering shaft onto nut and screw together by turning both pats until just before they lock in position in splines.
    d. Turn lower steering shaft until joint fork points down.
    e. Install suitable adjustable gauge into upper steering shaft groove.
    f. Install lower steering shaft joint fork parallel to adjustment gauge. Continue to screw nut to position lower steering shaft.
    g. Tighten nut to specifications. Steady shaft by mounting steering wheel.
11. **On SL500 and SL600 models,** install lower steering column as follows:
    a. Install torsion spring with winding offset end in flange.
    b. Screw tensioning nut onto flange until there is approximately 11.81–0.1575 inch between flange and tensioning nut.
    c. Connect lower steering shaft with upper.
    d. Turn clamping nut counterclockwise against torsion spring force until lower steering shaft can be pushed on.
    e. Upper thrust ring lug (combination switch reset cam) and lower shaft steering coupling fixing bolt milled recess must be in same position.
    f. Push lower steering shaft onto upper steering shaft splines until locking nut can be install between steering coupling flange and upper steering shaft flexible disk grove.
12. **On all models,** install cap seal.

E55, E300, E320 & E430

Disassemble

1. Remove steering lock.
2. Remove mounting nut, tab washer and lower steering shaft, **Fig. 11.**
3. Remove mounting bolts and slide console down off jacket tube.
4. Remove tilt, then the telescopic adjustment motors.
5. Remove locking rings, then the thrust piece with spring packs.
6. Remove bracket.
7. Remove guide bolt and pull inner jacket tube down and out.

Assemble

1. Lubricate inner jacket tube and push into outer tube from below.
2. Install guide bolt and align guide groove.
3. Install telescopic adjustment motor, then adjust jacket tube longitudinal to 0.0098–0.1181 inch.
4. Install thrust piece with spring packs, then the new locking ring.
5. Install tilt adjustment motor.
6. Press plastic washers and metal ring into console.
7. Install console over jacket tube, then the mounting bolts.
8. Install upper bracket.
9. Install new tab washer on lower steering shaft.
10. Install mounting nut on upper steering shaft with one thread.
11. Install lower steering shaft to nut and turn both parts together until just before they lock in position in splines.
12. Position upper steering shaft horizontal (combination switch reset cam is on lefthand side). Fix upper steering shaft in position using steering lock.
13. Rotate lower steering shaft until joint

fork points down or bolt-on flange flats are upright. Steering coupling double flat section should be horizontal and steering coupling fixing bolt groove on righthand side.

14. Tighten mounting nut to specifications.

TECHNICAL SERVICE BULLETINS

ELECTRIC STEERING COLUMN WORKS SPORADICALLY

S430 & 2000-01 S500

On some of these models the electric steering column easy entry and exit adjustment works sporadically or adjusts without apparent reason while driving. Diagnostic Trouble Code (DTC) B1410 may be set.

This condition may be caused by synchronization, hall sensors or connectors and wiring.

To correct this condition, proceed as follows:

1. Connect suitably programmed scan tool.
2. Read signal acquisition and lefthand front Signal Pick-Up Activation Module (SAM).
3. Ensure SAM software is current.
4. Inspect Electric Steering Column Adjustment (ESC) programming. Programming loss is as follows:
   a. During manual seat adjustment there is emergency operations: moves in two second intervals.
   b. No memory function.
   c. No entry function.
5. Inspect for synchronization.
6. If system is not synchronized, perform initialization via "control unit adaptation" and follow menu guide.
7. Manually synchronize, as follows:
   a. Manually move column to upper stop.
   b. Manually move column to front stop.
   c. Manually move column down until microswitch is actuated.
8. Inspect hall sensors in adjustment motors using suitable oscilloscope, as follows:
   a. For longitudinal adjustment, connect oscilloscope to SAM pin 20.
   b. For height adjustment, connect oscilloscope to SAM pin 21.
9. Measurements should be square-wave voltage at 10ms intervals. Inspect microswitch actual values, on/off.
10. Inspect nominal valves, as follows:
    a. Easy entry range up/down should be 5–15 to 292–298.
    b. Manual range up/down should be 95–105 to 292–298.
    c. Servomotor range forward/back should be 5–15 to 292–298.
11. Inspect connectors and wires.
12. It may be necessary to inspect the following linked control modules:
    a. Seat control module.
    b. Jacket tube module.
    c. Door control module.
    d. Electronic ignition lock.
13. If condition still exists, replace SAM.

TIGHTENING SPECIFICATIONS

Year	Component	Torque, Ft. Lbs.
C43, C230 & C280		
1998–2000	Clamping Screw	18
	Hydraulic Cylinder	106①
	Jacket Tube, Lower	71①
	Jacket Tube, Upper	15
	Steering Coupling	22
	Steering Shaft	81
S320, S420, CL500, CL600, S500 & S600		
1998–99	Bracket, Upper	44①
	Clamping Screw	18
	Guide Bolt	88①
	Hydraulic Cylinder	106①
	Jacket Tube, Lower	15
	Jacket Tube, Upper	15
	Steering Coupling (M8)	18
	Steering Coupling (M10)	22
	Steering Shaft	81
	Telescopic Adjustment Motor	15
	Tilt Adjustment Motor	88①
2000–01	Steering Column	15
	Steering Column Reinforcement Plate Boot	44①
	Steering Shaft Coupling	18
CLK320 & CLK430		
1998–2001	Clamping Screw	18
	Hydraulic Cylinder	106①
	Jacket Tube, Lower	71①
	Jacket Tube, Upper	15
	Steering Coupling	22
	Steering Shaft	81

Continued

TIGHTENING SPECIFICATIONS—Continued

Year	Component	Torque, Ft. Lbs.
E55, E300, E320 & E430		
1998–2001	Clamping Screw	18
	Console	15
	Guide Bolt	88①
	Jacket Tube, Lower	71①
	Jacket Tube, Upper	15
	Steering Coupling	15
	Steering Shaft	21
	Telescopic Motor	88①
	Tilt Adjustment Motor	44①
	Upper Bracket	44①
	Upper Steering Shaft, Electrically Adjustable Jacket Tube	81
SL500 & SL600		
1998–2001	Bracket, Upper	44①
	Clamping Screw	18
	Guide Bolt	88①
	Hydraulic Cylinder	106①
	Jacket Tube, Lower	15
	Jacket Tube, Upper	15
	Steering Coupling	22
	Telescopic Adjustment Motor	15
	Tilt Adjustment Motor	88①
SLK230 & SLK320		
1998–2001	Clamping Screw	18
	Jacket Tube, Lower	71①
	Jacket Tube, Upper	15
	Steering Coupling	22
	Steering Shaft	81

① — Inch lbs.

Power Steering

NOTE: Refer To The "Traction Control Systems" Section For Speed Sensitive Power Steering (SPS) Procedures.

INDEX

	Page No.
Diagnosis & Testing	5-230
Diagnostic Trouble Code Interpretation	5-230
Adaptive Damping Suspension (ADS)	5-230
Diagnostic Trouble Code Test	5-230
Code 003 or 004	5-230
Power Steering Pump Pressure Inspection	5-230
Power Steering System Bleed	5-230
Component Service	5-231
Power Steering Gear	5-231
Power Steering Pump	5-233
Power Steering System Service	5-230
Precautions	5-230
Air Bag Systems	5-230
Battery Ground Cable	5-230
Tightening Specifications	5-234

PRECAUTIONS

AIR BAG SYSTEMS

Refer to "Air Bag System Precautions" in front of this manual for system disarming and arming procedures.

BATTERY GROUND CABLE

Prior to service, disconnect battery ground cable and isolate as required.

DIAGNOSIS & TESTING

Power Steering Pump Pressure Inspection

1. Remove power steering/tandem pump cover.
2. **On C43, C230, C280, CL500, CL600, CLK320, CLK430, S320, S420, S500, S600, SL500 and SL600 models,** remove steering fluid from pump with hand pump tool No. 210 589 00 71 00, or equivalent.
3. **On E300, E320 and E430 models equipped less level control or ADS,** remove steering fluid from pump with hand pump.
4. **On E300, E320 and E430 models equipped with level control or ADS,** pinch reservoir supply line with clamp tool No. 000 589 40 37 000, or equivalent.
5. **On all models,** connect suitable pressure gauge between power steering pump and high pressure stretch hose.
6. **On E300, E320 and E430 models equipped with level control or ADS,** remove supply line clamp tool.
7. **On C43, C280, CL500, CL600, CLK320, CLK430, S320, S420, S500, S600, SL500 and SL600 models,** fill reservoir.
8. **On E300, E320 and E430 models equipped less level control or ADS,** fill reservoir.
9. **On all models,** start engine and run at approximately 1000 RPM.
10. Connect throttle valve and measure maximum operating pressure. **Do this briefly to avoid increasing fluid temperature.**

Model	Year	Maximum Operating Pressure, psi
C43	1998–99	1552–1668
C230	1998–2000	1334–1450
C280	1998–2000	1523–1668
CL500 & CL600	1998–99	1740–1885
	2000–01	1740–1842
CLK320 & CLK430	1998–2001	1523–1668
E300, E320 & E430	1998–2001	1552–1668
ML320 & ML430	1998–2001	1334–1450
S320	1998–99	1450–1595
SL500	1998	1595–1740
	1999–2001	1552–1668
SL600	1998–2000	1740–1885
S420, S500 & S600	1998–99	1740–1885
S430, S500 & S600	2000–01	1740–1842
SLK230	1998–99	1334–1450
SLK320	2001	1552–1668

Fig. 1 Power steering pump maximum operating pressures

Code	Interpretation
003	Lefthand Front Body Lateral Acceleration Sensor
004	Righthand Front Body Lateral Acceleration Sensor

Fig. 2 DTC interpretation. ADS

11. If pressure is not within specifications, **Fig. 1,** replace pump.
12. Turn engine off.
13. **On E300, E320 and E430 models equipped less level control or ADS,** remove steering fluid from pump with hand pump.
14. **On E300, E320 and E430 models equipped with level control or ADS,** pinch reservoir supply line with clamp tool No. 000 589 40 37 000, or equivalent.
15. **On all models,** connect suitable pressure gauge between power steering pump and high pressure stretch hose.
16. **On E300, E320 and E430 models equipped with level control or ADS,** remove supply line clamp tool.
17. **On C43, C230, C280, CL500, CL600, CLK320, CLK430, S320, S420, S500, S600, SL500 and SL600 models,** fill reservoir.
18. **On E300, E320 and E430 models equipped less level control or ADS,** fill reservoir.

Diagnostic Trouble Code Interpretation

ADAPTIVE DAMPING SUSPENSION (ADS)

This procedure has been revised by a Technical Service Bulletin

Refer to **Fig. 2.**

Diagnostic Trouble Code Test

CODE 003 OR 004

This procedure has been revised by a Technical Service Bulletin

1. Install new wiring harness.
2. Clean front body lateral acceleration sensor electrical connection pins.

POWER STEERING SYSTEM SERVICE

POWER STEERING SYSTEM BLEED

1. Start engine and allow it to run for one second.
2. Shut off engine and immediately top off reservoir to replace fluid sucked into

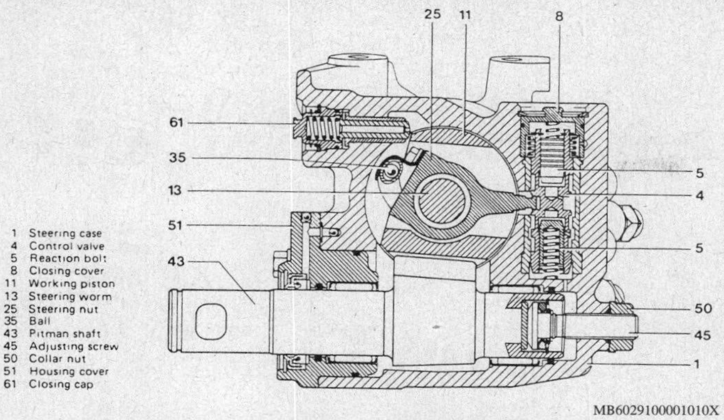

Fig. 3 Cross-sectional view of steering gear (Part 1 of 2)

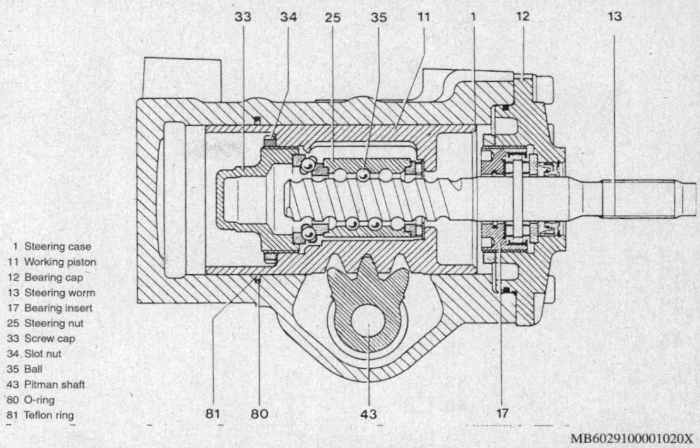

Fig. 3 Cross-sectional view of steering gear (Part 2 of 2)

system. Repeat this three times. **Never allow power steering pump to suck air.**

3. Turn wheel repeatedly to left and right to allow unit to bleed itself.
4. Start engine 2–3 times to automatic bleed system.
5. Turn steering from lock-to-lock several times with engine running.
6. Adjust fluid level.

Component Service

POWER STEERING GEAR

Refer to **Figs. 3 and 4** when servicing steering gear.

Disassemble

1. Position steering gear in suitable soft jawed vise.
2. Remove locking ring and mounting screw, and using puller tool No. 000 589 88 33 00, or equivalent, remove pitman arm from shaft.
3. **On first version steering gear,** remove hex nut and dowel sleeve.
4. **On all steering gears,** loosen closing screw and turn steering worm until nearly at right or lefthand lock.
5. Remove locking ring and thrust ring.
6. Remove locking ring.
7. Remove cover, spring, spring bolt and bushing.
8. Position steering to center position.
9. Remove steering case cover mounting screws.
10. Apply counter pressure to adjusting screws and remove self-locking hex nut.
11. Turn adjusting screw to right in steering center position.
12. Remove pitman shaft from steering case cover.
13. Remove bearing cap mounting screws.
14. Turn steering worm to left until bearing cap pulls slightly from case. **Do not turn to far as balls may fall from ball circuit.**
15. Remove bearing cap with steering worm.
16. Measure friction torque of ball circuit using measuring tool No. 116 589 03 21 00 or 201 589 59 00, or equivalents. If friction torque is not 0.44–4.43 inch lbs., replace steering nut.
17. Remove steering case cover from pitman shaft.
18. Remove locking ring from steering case cover.
19. Remove radial steering ring from case cover using suitable screwdriver.
20. Remove O-rings from case cover.
21. Remove adjusting screw locking ring and remove thrust ring.
22. Remove pitman shaft locking ring.
23. Remove adjusting screw with thrust washer.
24. Position bearing cap with steering worm in suitable work tray.
25. Unbend locking plate, remove screws, locking plate clamp and ball guide halves.
26. Remove steering worm from steering nut, ensure no balls are lost.
27. Remove bearing cap O-ring and position bearing cap in suitable soft jawed vise.
28. Remove bearing insert nut using socket tool Nos. 201 589 02 09 00 and 126 589 00 16 00, or equivalents.
29. Remove bearing insert from bearing cap.
30. Remove Teflon ring and O-ring from bearing cap.
31. Remove steering worm from bearing cap, remove axial bearing and washer from steering worm.
32. Remove bearing cap locking ring.
33. Remove bearing cap seal.
34. Install piston and secure with plug.
35. Remove slot nut and screw cover using slot wrench tool No. 201 589 01 07 00, or equivalent.
36. Remove outer race from screw cover.
37. Remove ball cage from steering cage.
38. Remove steering nut from piston.
39. Remove inner race and bearing ring from steering nut.
40. Remove axial needle cage and axial washer from working piston.
41. Remove locking nut from steering case.
42. Pull closing cap from steering case.
43. Remove O-ring from closing cap.
44. Remove control valve from steering case, ensuring reaction piston springs do not fall out.
45. Remove ring and O-ring from steering case.

Inspection

1. Inspect steering worm and steering nut, as follows:
   a. Check ball paths on steering worm and steering nut. If traces of wear are shown, replace steering.
2. Check bearing insert as follows:
   a. Check needle sleeve for wear.
   b. If wear is indicated, replace bearing insert.
3. Inspect pitman shaft, as follows:
   a. Check pitman shaft for wear at bearing points and for distortion or other damage. Replace pitman shaft, if required.
4. Inspect steering case, as follows:
   a. Check needle sleeve in steering case for wear. If required, replace.
5. Inspect housing cover, as follows:
   a. Check needle sleeve for wear. Completely replace housing cover, if needle bushing is damaged.
6. Check control valve, as follows:
   a. Check reaction piston in control valve for smooth operation. If required, remove reaction piston after removing locking ring and clean. **Do not interchange springs and compensating washers of both reaction pistons.**

Assemble

1. Press sealing ring in bearing cap to a depth of 0.193 inch using thrust plate tool No. 201 589 05 31 05, or equivalent.
2. Install locking ring to bearing cap.
3. Install positioning tool No. 201 589 05 31 00, or equivalent, to bearing cap and position in suitable soft jawed vise.
4. Install O-ring and Teflon ring to bearing insert.
5. Install bearing insert to bearing cap and tighten slightly, and install nut with chamfer toward bearing cap on bearing insert.
6. Measure friction torque of steering worm in bearing cap (sealing point only), by positioning measuring tool on steering worm splines. Friction torque

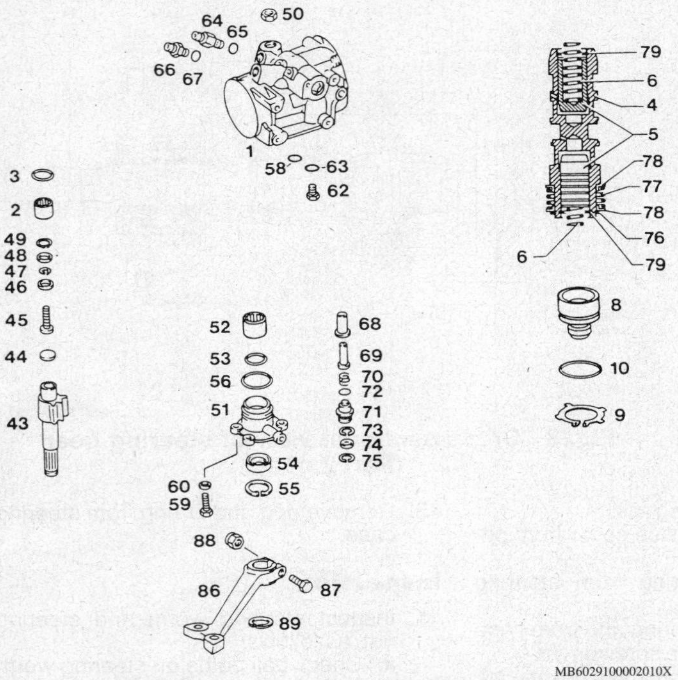

Fig. 4 Exploded view of steering gear (Part 1 of 3)

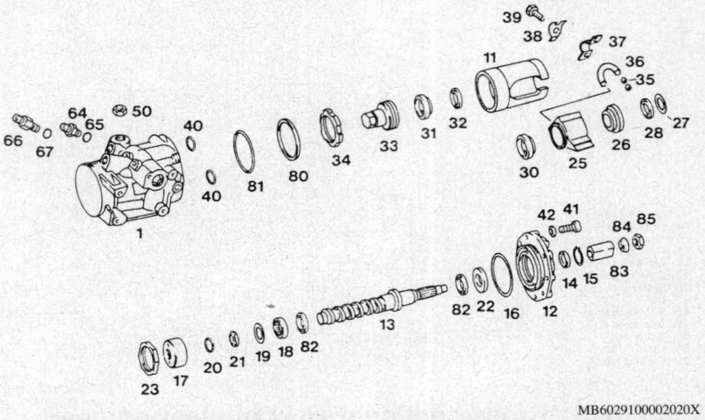

Fig. 4 Exploded view of steering gear (Part 2 of 3)

```
 1 Steering Case                     48 Thrust Ring
 2 Needle Sleeve (Pitman Shaft)      49 Locking Ring
 4 Control Valve                     50 Polystop Nut
 5 Reaction Piston                   51 Cover Screws
 8 Closing Cap                       52 Needle Sleeve
 9 Locking Nut                       53 O-Ring
10 O-Ring                            54 Radial Sealing Ring
12 Bearing Cap                       55 Locking Ring
13 Steering Worm                     56 O-Ring
15 Locking Ring                      62 Closing Screw
17 Bearing Insert                    68 Bushing
20 O-Ring                            69 Spring Bolt
21 Teflon Ring                       70 Compression Spring
22 Washer                            71 Closing Cover
25 Steering Nut                      73 Locking Ring
26 Bearing                           74 Thurst Ring
27 Axial Washer                      75 Locking Ring
28 Axial Need Cage                   77 Nut
30 Inner Race                        78 Head Screw
31 Outer Race                        79 Locking Ring
32 Ball Cage                         80 O-Ring
35 Steel Balls                       81 Nut
36 Ball Guide Halves                 82 Axial Bearing
37 Locking Plate Clamps              83 Dowel Sleeve
38 Locking Plate                     84 Adjusting Ring
39 Head Screw                        85 Hex Nut
40 Ball Guide Tube                   86 Pitman Arm
43 Pitmans Shaft                     87 Radial Sealing Ring
45 Adjusting Screw                   88 Outer Bearing Race
46 Thrust Washer                     89 Angular Ball Bearing
47 Locking Ring                      90 Inner Bearing Race
```

MB6029100002030X

Fig. 4 Exploded view of steering gear (Part 3 of 3)

should be less than or equal to 1 inch lbs.

7. Tighten bearing insert to with pin spanner until an additional 108 inch lbs. friction torque are measured.
8. Tighten slot nut to specifications and check friction torque, again.
9. Remove bearing cap from fixture, install O-rings.
10. Install working bearing into fixture and secure with plug.
11. Install axial washer and needle cage to working piston.
12. Install bearing ring and inner race to steering nut.
13. Install steering knuckle into working piston in such a manner that bearing ring rests on axial needle cage.
14. Install ball cage on steering nut.
15. Push outer race up to screw cover stop.
16. Install screw cover to working piston.
17. Install slot nut on screw cover and tighten slightly.
18. Clamp piston in fixture and adjust friction torque of steering nut in piston, while placing measuring device on straightedge of steering nut. Friction torque is 1 inch lbs.
19. Tighten screw cover until weight on measuring device will just turn steering nut. Secure screw cover with slot nut, tightening to specifications.
20. Remove working piston from device and place into assembly tray.
21. Install steering worm into steering nut until one ball circuit is completely shown through bore (for balls) in steering nut.
22. Install 16 balls into ball circuit while slowly turning steering worm to right.
23. Fill one ball guide half with grease and insert remaining six balls into this guide half. Attach other ball guide halves into steering nut. Mount fastening clip and install hex screws with serrated washers and tighten to specifications.
24. Position measuring fixture on splines of steering worm and measure friction torque of ball circuit. Friction torque of steering nut/steering worm should be 0.44–4.42 inch lbs. **If friction torque is not within this tolerance, replace complete ball circuit together with steering nut, steering worm and balls.**
25. Replace O-ring in steering case.
26. Install bearing cap O-ring to case.
27. Install O-ring on control valve.
28. Install reaction pin spring.
29. Install control valve to case, ensuring springs do not fall out.
30. Replace closing cover and knock closing cover into steering case by means of a plastic hammer.
31. Install locking ring into steering case in such a manner that lugs of ring are exerting pressure on closing cover. If required, knock-in locking ring slightly by means of a mandrel until correctly fitted in groove of steering case.
32. Carefully install working piston complete with steering worm, steering nut and bearing cap into steering case, while installing straightedge of steering nut into groove of control valve. **Do not use force.**
33. Turn bearing cap in such a manner, that oil duct on steering case is in alignment with oil bore on bearing cap. Watch out for correct seat of O-rings. Install hex bolts without snap rings and washers, and tighten to specifications.
34. Turn steering worm with center tooth gap resting against piston in center of steering case.
35. Insert O-rings into housing cover.
36. Insert adjusting screw, including thrust washer (46) and locking ring into pitman shaft, ensure of perfect seating of locking ring. **Install adjusting screw into pitman shaft with as little play as possible.**
37. Position thrust ring on adjusting screw and insert locking ring.
38. Place housing cover on pitman shaft and insert pitman shaft into steering housing. Ensure center tooth of pitman

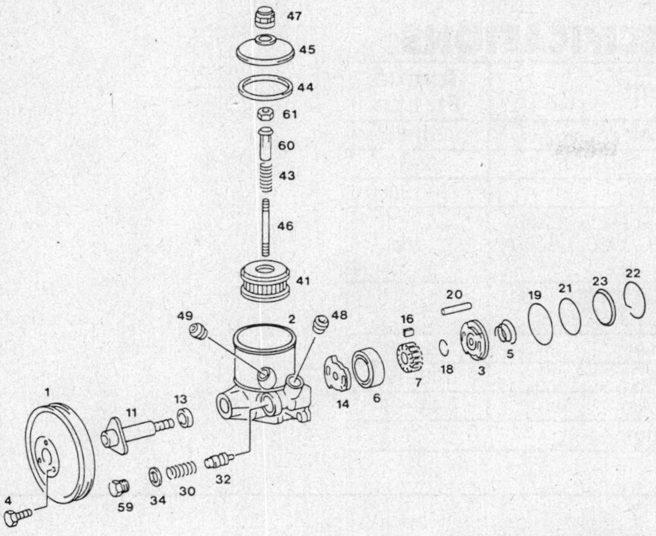

Fig. 5 Exploded view of power steering pump (Part 1 of 2)

1 Pulley
2 Pump Housing
3 Pressure Plate At Cover End
4 Head Screws
5 Compression Spring
6 Cam Ring
7 Rotor w/Blade
11 Drive Shaft
13 Radial Sealing Ring
14 Pressure Plate At Drive End
16 Blade
18 Locking Ring
19 O-Ring
20 Cylinder Pins
21 O-Ring
22 Circlip
23 Cover
30 Compression Spring
32 Valume Control Valve
34 Sealing Ring
41 Filter Pack
43 Compression Spring
44 Gasket
45 Closing Cap
46 Stud
47 Vent Cap
48 Sealing Cone
49 Sealing Cone
59 Closing Plug
60 Plastic Sleeve
61 Self-Locking Nut

MB6029100003010X

Fig. 5 Exploded view of power steering pump (Part 2 of 2)

shaft enters center tooth gap of working piston and that O-rings are correctly seated.

39. Install adjusting screw into steering case until it is hard to move.
40. Turn housing cover so that both oil ducts are one above other. Install hex bolts with new high-tension snap rings and tighten to specifications. **Housing cover is now attached to steering housing by means of four hex screws.**
41. Loosen adjusting screw until steering worm is easy to turn, measure friction torque of steering worm and measure friction value.
42. Adjust pressure mechanism of pitman shaft by turning adjusting screw to right until friction torque has increased by 3.5–5.3 inch lbs.
43. Install seal/lock collar nut on adjusting screw and tighten to specifications, while applying counterhold to adjusting screw.
44. Check total friction torque, again.
45. Slightly turn steering worm until working piston is no longer in steering center.
46. Install bushing and spring bolt to steering case.
47. Install compression spring to cap, install cap and spring to case.
48. Install cap locking ring.
49. Push thrust ring on cap and install locking ring.
50. Install dowel sleeve onto steering worm so that two surfaces are parallel with fastening points of steering and milled cut pointing toward pitman arm.
51. Install supporting ring and tighten to specifications.
52. Install pitman arm.

POWER STEERING PUMP

Refer to **Fig. 5** when servicing power steering pump.

Disassemble

1. Remove vent and closing caps.
2. Remove stud nut, sleeve, spring and filter pack.
3. Remove cover.
4. Remove circlip from housing and cove.
5. Remove spring and O-ring from housing.
6. Remove pressure plate.
7. Remove lock ring from driveshaft.
8. Loosen driveshaft from rotor and remove driveshaft using suitable hammer.
9. Remove rotor, cam ring and pressure plate.
10. Remove cylinder pins.
11. Remove radial sealing ring using suitable screwdriver.
12. Remove closing plug, compression spring and volume control valve.
13. Position volume control valve in suitable vise, remove valve ball, valve cone and compression spring.

Inspection

1. Check volume control valve and pump housing bore for scoring or damage, if indicated, replace pump.
2. Inspect rotor blades for grooves and blade on cam ring for wear, if indicated, replace.
3. Inspect pressure plates for scoring and wear, if indicated, replace.
4. Inspect driveshaft and bearing bushings for wear, if indicated, replace drive set.

Assemble

1. Install pressure relief valve to volume control valve and install compression ring, valve cone and valve ball.
2. Install volume control valve and compression spring.
3. Install closing plug with new sealing ring.
4. Press radial seal ring to housing.
5. Install driveshaft to housing.
6. Install pressure plate at drive end with recesses toward rotor.
7. Install cylinder pins.
8. Install rotor to driveshaft with chamfer on I.D. of rotor toward pressure plate at drive end.
9. Install locking ring to driveshaft groove.
10. Position cam ring on cylinder pins, ensuring proper cam location.
11. Install blade with rounded metallic side toward cam rings in rotor.
12. Install O-ring to housing.
13. Install pressure plate.
14. Install O-ring and position compression ring on pressure plate.
15. Install cover, then the circlip.
16. Install filter pack.
17. Install spring, sleeve, compress slightly and install new locking nut.

TIGHTENING SPECIFICATIONS

Year	Component	Torque, Ft. Lbs.
1998–2001	Bearing Cap	51–55
	Gear Slot	162–177
	Guide Ball	88–133①
	High Pressure Hose (C43, C230, C280, CLK55, CLK320, CLK430, S430, S500 & S600)	29
	High Pressure Hose (E300, E320, E430, ML320, ML430, SLK230 & SLK320)	33
	Housing Cover	22–26
	Pump Slot	148–176
	Seal/Lock Collar	44–48
	Support Ring	37

① — Inch lbs.

Disc Brakes

NOTE: On Air Bag Equipped Models, Refer To "Air Bag System Precautions" Located In Front Of This Manual For System Disarming And Arming Procedures.

NOTE: On Models Equipped With Anti-Lock Brake Systems, Refer To "Anti-Lock Brake Systems."

NOTE: Prior To Performing Any Service Operations Listed In This Section, Consult The "Technical Service Bulletins" Section For Related Information.

INDEX

	Page No.
Adjustments	5-239
Parking Brake	5-239
Brake Pad Service	5-235
Fixed Caliper Brake Pad, Replace	5-235
Floating Caliper Brake Pad, Replace	5-235
Brake System Bleed	5-235
Caliper, Replace	5-236
C230, C280, CLK320, CLK430, E300, E320, E430 & SLK230	5-236
C43, S320, S420, SL500 & SL600 & 1998–99 CL500, CL600, S500 & S600	5-236
S430 & 2000–01 CL500, CL600, S500 & S600	5-236
Caliper Service	5-236
Front	5-236
Rear	5-237
Disc Brake Specifications	5-240
Parking Brake Service	5-237
Foot Control Cable, Replace	5-238
Foot Control, Replace	5-237
Hand Lever, Replace	5-238
Parking Brake Rear Control Cable, Replace	5-238
Parking Brake Shoes, Replace	5-238
Precautions	5-235
Air Bag Systems	5-235
Battery Ground Cable	5-235
Rotor, Replace	5-237
Technical Service Bulletins	5-239
Brake Shudder During Cold Brake Application	5-239
Front Brake Shimmy & Vibration	5-239
Front Brake Squeal	5-239
Front Vibration After Severe Braking Although Brakes Not Operated	5-239
Parking Brake Does Not Make Ratcheting Noise During Application	5-239
Rear Brake Rattle	5-239
Rear Brake Squeal When Applied	5-239
Tightening Specifications	5-241

PRECAUTIONS

AIR BAG SYSTEMS

Refer to "Air Bag System Precautions"in front of this manual for system disarming and arming procedures.

BATTERY GROUND CABLE

Prior to service, disconnect battery ground cable and isolate as required.

BRAKE SYSTEM BLEED

Refer to procedure as outlined in "Hydraulic Brake Systems" section.

BRAKE PAD SERVICE

FLOATING CALIPER BRAKE PAD, REPLACE

C230

1. Disconnect wear sensor connector.
2. **On models equipped with cam on housing,** remove lower mounting bolt, steady sliding pin and remove floating caliper, securing with suitable hook.
3. **On all models,** inspect boots for damage and replace as required.
4. Remove brake pads.
5. Remove some brake fluid from reservoir.
6. Pull wear sensor out of lining back plate.
7. Push piston back using resetting tool No. 000 589 52 43 00, or equivalent.
8. Reverse procedure to install, noting the following:
   a. Clean brake pad contact surface in carrier and cylinder housing.
   b. **On models equipped with one wear sensor,** install sensor on outer brake pad.
   c. **On all models,** ensure U-bolt is parallel to brake pad lining upper edge.
   d. Install new mounting bolt and tighten to specifications.
   e. Coil excess wear sensor cable up in spiral shape.

C280, E300, E320, E430 & SLK230

1. Disconnect spring and removal wear sensor from connector.
2. Remove covers and guide pins.
3. Remove calipers with brake pads.
4. Remove wear sensor from lining back plate.
5. Remove some brake fluid from reservoir.
6. Pull wear sensor out of lining back plate.
7. Push piston back using resetting tool No. 000 589 52 43 00, or equivalent.
8. Reverse procedure to install, noting the following:
   a. Clean brake pad contact surface in carrier and cylinder housing.
   b. **On models equipped with one wear sensor,** install sensor on outer brake pad.
   c. **On all models,** ensure U-bolt is parallel to brake pad lining upper edge.

FIXED CALIPER BRAKE PAD, REPLACE

1. Disconnect wear sensor from connector.
2. Drive retaining pins out using suitable punch.
3. Remove brake pads using release lever tool No. 123 589 13 33 00, or equivalent.
4. Remove wear sensor from lining back plate or brake lining.
5. Remove some brake fluid from reservoir.
6. **On models equipped with four-piston caliper,** prevent pistons from sliding by securing opposing pairs with suitable plastic wedges.
7. **On all models,** push piston back using resetting tool No. 000 589 52 43 00, or equivalent. **Do not bend heat shield.**
8. Reverse procedure to install, noting the following:
   a. Drive retaining pins to stop using suitable drift punch.
   b. **Pads equipped less peripheral damping,** must be smeared lightly with brake pad paste on side surfaces.
   c. **Pads equipped with peripheral damping,** must be installed dry.

CALIPER

REPLACE

C43, S320, S420, SL500 & SL600 & 1998–99 CL500, CL600, S500 & S600

1. Disconnect and plug brake hoses, **Fig. 1.**
2. Disconnect wear sensor connector.
3. Remove connector, and if required, speed sensor.
4. Remove mounting bolts and caliper from steering knuckle or wheel carrier.
5. Reverse procedure to install, noting the following:
   a. Install new self-locking bolts and tighten to specifications.
   b. Only transparent (temperature resistance) wear sensors may be installed on rear axle.
   c. Front wear sensors' contacts must correspond to plug connectors.
   d. **On E430, S320 and S420 and 1998–99 CL500, CL600, S500 and S600 models equipped with Lucas fixed calipers,** wear sensors are installed on outer brake pad.
   e. **On all models,** install brake hose into locking plate so that it does not cafe on full lock turns with bump and rebound.
   f. Ensure brake hose is not twisted.
   g. Minimum 0.5906 inch clearance must be maintained between other axle parts under all driving conditions.
   h. Bleed braking systems as outlined in "Hydraulic Brake Systems" section.

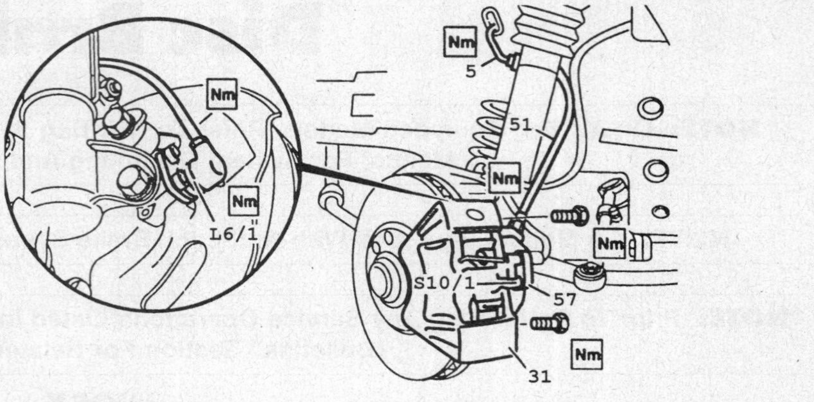

Fig. 1 Fixed or floating caliper replacement. C43, S320, S420, SL500 & SL600 & 1998–99 CL500, CL600, S500 & S600

C230, C280, CLK320, CLK430, E300, E320, E430 & SLK230

Front

1. Disconnect and plug brake hoses, **Fig. 2.**
2. Disconnect spring, then the wear sensor connector.
3. Disconnect wear sensor connector at floating caliper.
4. Remove covers and guide pins.
5. Remove mounting bolts and steady sliding pins.
6. Remove floating caliper with brake pads.
7. Reverse procedure to install, noting the following:
   a. Install inner brake pad in sliding caliper piston and outer pad in frame guide.
   b. Install new self-locking bolts and tighten to specifications.
   c. Install new microencapsulated wear sensor mounting bolts.
   d. Front wear sensors' contacts must correspond to plug connectors.
   e. **On models equipped with Lucas floating calipers,** wear sensors are installed on outer brake pad.
   f. **On models equipped with Teves floating calipers,** wear sensors are installed on inner brake pad.
   g. **On all models,** install brake hose into locking plate so that it does not cafe on full lock turns with bump and rebound.
   h. Ensure brake hose is not twisted.
   i. Minimum 0.5906 inch clearance must be maintained between other axle parts under all driving conditions.
   j. Bleed braking systems as outlined in "Hydraulic Brake Systems" section.

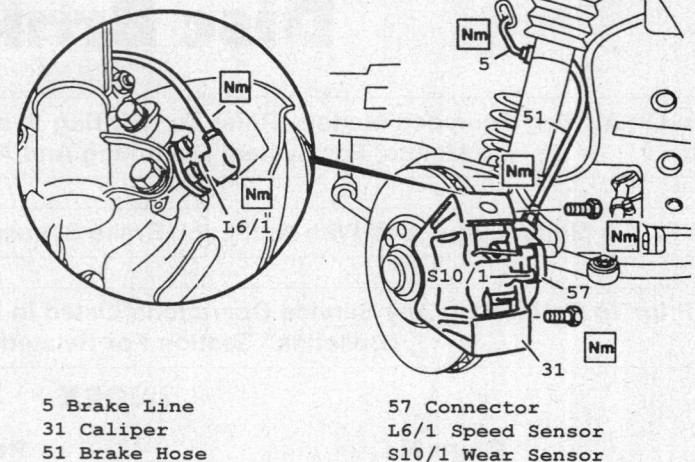

Rear

1. Disconnect and plug brake hoses, **Fig. 3.**
2. Disconnect righthand wear sensor connector.
3. **On C280 models equipped with ASR,** wear sensor not installed.
4. **On all models,** remove mounting bolts and caliper from wheel carrier.
5. Reverse procedure to install, noting the following:
   a. Install new self-locking bolts and tighten to specifications.
   b. Only transparent (temperature resistance) wear sensors may be installed on rear axle.
   c. Front wear sensors' contacts must correspond to plug connectors.
   d. Install brake hose into locking plate so that it does not cafe on full lock turns with bump and rebound.
   e. Ensure brake hose is not twisted.
   f. Minimum 0.5906 inch clearance must be maintained between other axle parts under all driving conditions.
   g. Bleed braking systems as outlined in "Hydraulic Brake Systems" section.

S430 & 2000–01 CL500, CL600, S500 & S600

Front

1. Raise and support vehicle, then remove tire and wheel assembly.
2. Disconnect brake hose from pipe and caliper. Plug lines and openings.
3. Disconnect brake pad wear sensor from connector.
4. Remove mounting bolt and connector.
5. Remove pads as outlined under "Brake Pad Service."
6. Remove mounting bolts and caliper.
7. Reverse procedure to install. Tighten mounting bolts to specifications.

Rear

1. Raise and support vehicle, then remove tire and wheel assembly.
2. Disconnect brake hose from pipe and caliper. Plug lines and openings.
3. Disconnect righthand rear brake pad wear sensor from connector.
4. Remove connector from caliper.
5. Remove mounting bolts and caliper.
6. Reverse procedure to install. Tighten mounting bolts to specifications.

CALIPER SERVICE

FRONT

FIXED

Disassemble

1. Press off dust cap
2. Insert 1.1025 inches thick metal segment (brake disc section) into fixed caliper and carefully force pistons out against stop with compressed air.
3. Remove piston using piston-turning pliers tool No. 000 589 50 37 00, or equivalent.

4. Remove piston seal from groove in cylinder bore.

Inspection

1. If piston is stuck or there are scores or rusted bores, replace complete caliper.
2. Remove deposits on piston with soft brass wire brush or rough cloth only. If there is noticeable damage to chrome plating, replace piston.
3. Inspect pistons and bores in fixed caliper for signs of wear. If bore is scored or rusty, replace complete floating caliper.
4. Remove piston coatings with soft brass wire brush or rough cleaning rag. **Do not use polishing or abrasive cloth.**
5. If chrome layer is damaged, replace piston.
6. Remove slight narrow rust points in bore with polishing cloth.
7. Remove severe rust point in groove front for piston seal with fine abrasive paper (180–500 grain).

Assemble

1. Lightly coat new piston seal with suitable brake fluid and install.
2. Install piston.
3. Press dust cap on using pliers tool No. 000 589 49 37 00, or equivalent.

FLOATING

Disassemble

1. Force piston out using compressed air and, if required, suitable piston turning pliers.
2. Remove dust cap.
3. Remove piston seal from groove in cylinder bore.

Inspection

1. If piston is stuck or there are scores or rusted bores, replace complete caliper.
2. Remove deposits on piston with soft brass wire brush or rough cloth only. If there is noticeable damage to chrome plating, replace piston.
3. Inspect pistons and bores in fixed caliper for signs of wear. If bore is scored or rusty, replace complete floating caliper.
4. Remove piston coatings with soft brass wire brush or rough cleaning rag. **Do not use polishing or abrasive cloth.**
5. If chrome layer is damaged, replace piston.
6. Remove slight narrow rust points in bore with polishing cloth.
7. Remove severe rust point in groove front for piston seal with fine abrasive paper (180–500 grain).

Assemble

1. Lightly coat new piston seal with suitable brake fluid and install.
2. Light coat cylinder bore with brake fluid.
3. Install inverted dust cap over piston and install into cylinder with piston. Push piston in with both hands.

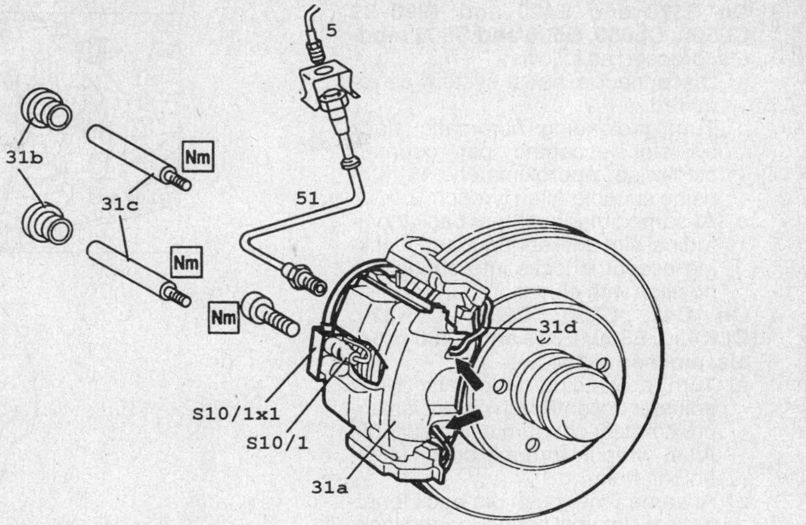

5 Brake Line
31a Caliper
31b Covers
31c Guide Pins
31d Spring
51 Brake Hose
57 Connector
L6/1 Speed Sensor
S10/1 Wear Sensor
S10/1x1 Brake Pad Wear Sensor

MB4079900013000X

Fig. 2 Front floating caliper replacement. E300 & E320

REAR

DISASSEMBLE

1. Remove heat shield.
2. Press off dust cap from housing with screwdriver.
3. Hold piston with resetting tool No. 000 589 52 43 00, or equivalent, and carefully press out opposing piston using compressed air. Remove piston with turning tongs if necessary.
4. Remove piston seal from groove in cylinder bore.

INSPECTION

1. If piston is stuck or there are scores or rusted bores, replace complete caliper.
2. Remove deposits on piston with soft brass wire brush or rough cloth only. If there is noticeable damage to chrome plating, replace piston.
3. Inspect pistons and bores in fixed caliper for signs of wear. If bore is scored or rusty, replace complete floating caliper.
4. Remove piston coatings with soft brass wire brush or rough cleaning rag. **Do not use polishing or abrasive cloth.**
5. If chrome layer is damaged, replace piston.
6. Remove slight narrow rust points in bore with polishing cloth.
7. Remove severe rust point in groove front for piston seal with fine abrasive paper (180–500 grain).

ASSEMBLE

1. Coat new seal with brake fluid and install.
2. Coat cylinder bore with brake fluid.
3. Install inverted dust cap over piston and install into cylinder with piston. Push piston in with both hands.
4. Inspect piston position using inspection gauge tool No. 000 589 35 23 00, or equivalent. If required, correct position using pliers tool No. 000 589 49 37 00, or equivalent, and suitable plates.

ROTOR

REPLACE

1. Remove caliper as outlined under "Caliper, Replace." **Do not disconnect brake hose.**
2. **On front rotors,** remove brake carrier from steering knuckle.
3. **On rear rotors,** disconnect parking brake.
4. **On all models,** remove mounting bolts and brake disc.
5. Reverse procedure to install, noting the following:
   a. Replace rotors in pairs only.
   b. Lightly lubricate new mounting bolts with suitable long-life grease.
   c. Ensure dowel or roll pins fit correctly into brake rotor.
   d. Adjust parking brake.

PARKING BRAKE SERVICE

FOOT CONTROL, REPLACE

1. **On S320, S420, SL500 and SL600 and 1998–99 CL500, CL600, S500, and S600 models,** remove exhaust system heat shield.
2. **On C43, C230, C280, E300, E320 and E430 models,** remove cover panel under rear squab.

3. **On S320 and S420 and 1998–99 CL500, CL600, S500 and S600 models,** proceed as follows:
   a. Disconnect exhaust system as required.
   b. Turn preloading automatic slack adjuster eccentric pin counterclockwise approximately ½ turn using suitable Allen wrench.
   c. At same time, push pin back longitudinal slot until spring-loaded locking eccentric locks into spring clip position with elevation.
4. **On C43, C230, C280, CLK320, CLK430, E300, E320 and E430 models,** proceed as follows:
   a. Turn preloading automatic slack adjuster eccentric pin clockwise approximately one turn using suitable Allen wrench through cover sheet oblong hole.
   b. At same time, push pin back longitudinal slot until spring-loaded locking eccentric locks into spring clip position with elevation.
5. **On S430 and 2000–01 CL500, CL600, S500 and S600 models,** preload automatic slack adjuster by lifting center spring clip and pushing with suitable screwdriver.
6. **On all models,** disconnect return spring.
7. **On SL500 and SL600 models,** loosen adjusting screw.
8. **On all models,** remove cover below instrument panel and floor covering at front.
9. Disconnect brake control cable from pedal bracket using clip remover tool No. 129 589 11 63 00, or equivalent.
10. Loosen lower mounting bolt(s) and unhook foot control with friction brake. **A-pillar press-in nut may fall out.**
11. Disconnect parking brake switch by lifting foot controls slightly.
12. Disconnect control cable and remove foot controls.
13. Reverse procedure to install. Release automatic slack adjuster by lifting spring clip using suitable screwdriver.

FOOT CONTROL CABLE, REPLACE

1. **On S320 and S420 and 1998–99 CL500, CL600, S500 and S600 models,** carefully lower transmission with suitable engine carrier. **Do not let engine touch component compartment wall.**
2. **On S320, S420, SL500 and SL600 and 1998–99 CL500, CL600, S500 and S600 models,** remove exhaust system heat shield.
3. **On C43, C230, C280, E300, E320 and E430 models,** remove cover panel under rear squab.
4. **On S320 and S420 and 1998–99 CL500, CL600, S500 and S600 models,** proceed as follows:
   a. Disconnect exhaust system as required.
   b. Turn preloading automatic slack adjuster eccentric pin counterclockwise approximately ½ turn using suitable Allen wrench.

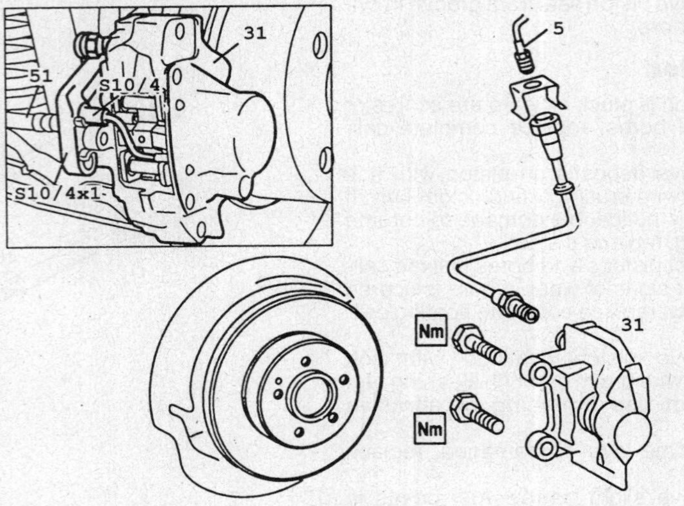

5 Brake Line
31 Caliper
51 Brake Hose
57 Connector
S10/4 Wear Sensor
S10/4x1 Brake Pad Wear Sensor

MB4079900014000X

Fig. 3 Rear fixed caliper replacement. C230, C280, CLK320, CLK430, E300, E320, E430 & SLK230

   c. At same time, push pin back longitudinal slot until spring-loaded locking eccentric locks into spring clip position with elevation.
5. **On C43, C230, C280, CLK320, CLK430, E300, E320 and E430 models,** proceed as follows:
   a. Turn preloading automatic slack adjuster eccentric pin clockwise approximately one turn using suitable Allen wrench through cover sheet oblong hole.
   b. At same time, push pin back longitudinal slot until spring-loaded locking eccentric locks into spring clip position with elevation.
6. **On S430 and 2000–01 CL500, CL600, S500 and S600 models,** proceed as follows:
   a. Remove rear cross bracket from frame floor.
   b. Disconnect rear bracket between center and rear muffler at rear axle, then the rear muffler bracket on the floor frame.
   c. Disconnect exhaust system until heat shield under propeller shaft an be removed.
   d. Preload automatic slack adjuster.
7. **On all models,** disconnect return spring.
8. **On SL500 and SL600 models,** loosen adjusting screw.
9. **On S430 and 2000–01 CL500, CL600, S500 and S600 models,** disconnect brake cable from idler lever by unscrews self-locking bolt.
10. **On all models,** remove cover below instrument panel and floor covering at front.
11. Disconnect brake control cable from pedal bracket using clip remover tool No. 129 589 11 63 00, or equivalent.
12. Remove cable.
13. Loosen transmission heat shield and guide cable through.
14. Disconnect driver's footwell and outside frame floor clips, then slide cable through rubber grommet.
15. Disconnect brake control cable from floor frame using clip remover tool No. 129 589 11 63 00, or equivalent.
16. Reverse procedure to install.

HAND LEVER, REPLACE

SLK230

1. Disconnect return spring and loosen adjusting bolt.
2. Loosen idler lever stud bolt.
3. Remove hand brake rubber handle.
4. Remove gate and rear center console.
5. Remove indicator lamp contact switch.
6. Remove mounting bolts and pull hand brake lever forward.
7. Reverse procedure to install, noting the following:
   a. Install new self-locking idler lever stud bolt.

PARKING BRAKE REAR CONTROL CABLE, REPLACE

1. Remove parking brake shoes.
2. Disconnect return spring.
3. **On SL500, SL600 and SLK230 models,** loosen adjustment screw.
4. **On all models,** disconnect front brake control cable from intermediate lever.
5. Disconnect brake control cables from compensating lever.
6. Disconnect brake control cables from frame floor using clip remover tool No. 129 589 11 63 00, or equivalent.
7. Remove wheel carrier mounting bolt and control cable.
8. Reverse procedure to install. Install new self-locking bolts.

PARKING BRAKE SHOES, REPLACE

1. Remove rear brake rotor as outlined

under "Rotor, Replace."
2. Disconnect control cable.
3. Remove brake shoes above rear axle shaft flange.
4. Disconnect return spring.
5. Remove expanding lock.
6. Reverse procedure to install, noting the following:
   a. If shoes are burnt, replace shoes and return springs.
   b. Smear all expanding lock bearing and sliding surfaces with suitable long-life grease.
   c. Smear thrust pad thread and adjusting wheel cylindrical section with suitable long-life grease.
   d. Return spring must be located below bolt.
   e. **On models equipped with internally ventilated rotors,** remove rotors.
   f. **On all models,** back adjuster off and insert into both brakes shoes so adjusting wheel points in direction of travel.
   g. Adjust parking brakes.

ADJUSTMENTS

PARKING BRAKE

1. Raise and support vehicle rear.
2. **On SL500, SL600 and SLK230 models,** loosen adjusting bolt.
3. **On all models,** remove one wheel bolt on both rear wheels. **Light alloy wheels must be removed.**
4. Turn adjuster until brake shoes contact and it is no longer possible to turn rear wheel, noting the following:
   a. Use suitable 0.1772 inch screw driver.
   b. Turn righthand side adjuster from bottom up.
   c. Turn lefthand side adjuster from top down.
5. Turn adjuster until it is possible to turn rear wheel freely. **Turn both sides back equal number of teeth.**
6. **On SL500, SL600 and SLK230 models,** turn adjusting bolt until there no cable sag.
7. **On all models,** operate parking brake several times.

TECHNICAL SERVICE BULLETINS

FRONT VIBRATION AFTER SEVERE BRAKING ALTHOUGH BRAKES NOT OPERATED

C43, C230 & C280

On some of these models built before VIN 002200, there may be a front vibration after severe braking even though the brakes are not being operated.

This condition may be caused by heat expanding the parking brake drum and contacting linings.

To correct this condition, proceed as follows:

1. Inspect parking brake linings. Replace as required.
2. Change parking brake adjustment from 0.020–0.236 to 0.315–0.354 inch.

FRONT BRAKE SQUEAL

S430 & 2000-01 S500

On some of these models the front brakes may squeal.

This condition may be caused by front brake pad friction vibration.

To correct this condition, install revised brake pads (part No. 003 420 18 20).

FRONT BRAKE SHIMMY & VIBRATION

S320 & S420 & 1998-99 CL500, CL600, S500 & S600

On some of these models there may be a front brake shimmy and vibration.

This condition may be caused by uneven wear or disc deformation because of heat.

To correct this condition, proceed as follows:

1. **On models equipped with four-piston fixed calipers,** proceed as follows:
   a. If equipped with Jurid 226 pads, clean or replace rotors.
   b. If not equipped with Jurid 226 pads, install Jurid 226 pads and new rotors.
2. **On models equipped with two-piston fixed calipers,** replace pads and rotors.
3. **On all models,** adjust front wheel bearing axial play to 0.0004 inch.

REAR BRAKE RATTLE

SL500 & SL600

On some of these models there may be a rear brake rattle while diving with the top down at slow speeds with the brakes released.

This condition may be caused by excessive brake pad clearance.

To correct this condition, install new rear brake calipers. Ensure maximum clearance between brake pad metal backing plate and caliper is 0.0197 inch.

BRAKE SHUDDER DURING COLD BRAKE APPLICATION

E300, E320 & E430

On some of these models there may be a brake shudder during cold brake application.

This condition may be caused by brake disc thickness variation.

To correct this condition, proceed as follows:

1. Measure rear brake disc lateral runout ½ inch from rotor outer edge.
2. If runout is more than 0.0031 inch, replace rear axle shaft flange, angular ball bearing and rotors.
3. If runout is less than 0.0031 inch, replace rotors.

PARKING BRAKE DOES NOT MAKE RATCHETING NOISE DURING APPLICATION

1998-99 Models

On some of these models the parking brake may not make ratcheting noise during application.

This condition may be caused by damaged ratcheting element teeth.

To correct this condition, install new ratcheting element and retaining pin.

REAR BRAKE SQUEAL WHEN APPLIED

S320, S420, SL500 & SL600 & 1998-99 CL500, CL600, S500 & S600

On some of these models the rear brakes may squeal when applied.

This condition may be caused by frictional vibration.

To correct this condition, proceed as follows:

1. Install brake pads with new anti-squeal back plate.
2. Remove 0.0397 inch of pad material using flat surface and 60 grit sandpaper.
3. Apply brake pad paste No. 001 989 47 51, or equivalent, to backing plate and hammer-shaped ends.

DISC BRAKE SPECIFICATIONS

Model	Year	Front Disc Brake						Rear Disc Brake					
		Brake Lining Wear Limit, Inch②	Rotor					Brake Lining Wear Limit, Inch②	Rotor				
			Thickness, Inch			Thickness Variation Parallelism Inch	Lateral Run Out (T.I.R.) Inch		Thickness, Inch			Thickness Variation Parallelism Inch	Lateral Run Out (T.I.R.) Inch
			Nominal	Min. Refinish	Discard Limit①				Nom-inal	Min. Refinish	Discard Limit①		
C43	1999–2000	0.079	1.102	1.023	1.000	—	0.005	0.079	0.394	0.347	0.315	—	0.006
C230	1998–2000	0.079	0.984	0.906	0.882	—	0.005	0.079	0.354	0.299	0.287	—	0.006
C240	2001	0.079	1.102	1.023	1.000	—	0.005	0.079	0.394	0.347	0.315	—	0.006
C280	1994–2000	0.079	0.984	0.906	0.882	—	0.005	0.079	0.354	0.299	0.287	—	0.006
C320	2001	0.079	1.102	1.023	1.000	—	0.005	0.079	0.394	0.347	0.315	—	0.006
CL55	2001	0.079	1.260	—	—	—	—	0.079	0.870	—	—	—	—
CL500	1998–99	0.079	1.181	1.122	10.079	—	0.003	0.079	0.866	0.787	0.764	—	0.004
	2000–01	0.079	1.300	—	—	—	—	0.079	0.866	0.787	0.764	—	0.004
CL600	1998–99	0.079	1.181	1.122	1.079	—	0.003	0.079	0.866	0.787	0.764	—	0.004
	2001	0.079	1.300	—	—	—	—	0.079	0.900	—	—	—	—
CLK55	2001	0.079	1.260	—	—	—	—	0.079	0.870	—	—	—	—
CLK320	1998–2001	0.079	1.102	1.023	1.000	—	0.005	0.079	0.394	0.347	0.315	—	0.006
CLK430	1998–2001	0.079	1.102	1.023	1.000	—	0.005	0.079	0.394	0.347	0.315	—	0.006
E55	2000–01	0.079	1.260	—	—	—	—	0.079	0.870	—	—	—	—
E300	1998–99	0.079	1.102	1.023	1.000	—	0.005	0.079	0.354	299	0.287	—	0.006
E320	1998–2001	0.079	1.102	1.023	1.000	—	0.005	0.079	0.394	0.347	0.315	—	0.006
E430	1998–2001	0.079	1.102	1.023	1.000	—	0.005	0.079	0.394	0.347	0.315	—	0.006
ML55	2000–01	0.079	1.260	—	—	—	—	0.079	0.550	—	—	—	—
ML320	2000–01	0.079	1.102	1.023	1.000	—	0.005	0.079	0.472	0.413	0.385	—	0.004
ML430	2000–01	0.079	1.260	—	—	—	—	0.079	0.550	—	—	—	—
S320	1998–2001	0.079	1.181	1.122	1.079	—	0.003	0.079	0.472	0.413	0.385	—	0.004
S420	1998–99	0.079	1.181	1.122	1.079	—	0.003	0.079	0.866	0.787	0.764	—	0.004
S430	2000–01	0.079	1.260	—	—	—	—	0.079	0.866	0.787	0.764	—	0.004
S500	1998–99	0.079	1.181	1.122	1.079	—	0.003	0.079	0.866	0.787	0.764	—	0.004
	2000–01	0.079	1.300	—	—	—	—	0.079	0.866	0.787	0.764	—	0.004
S600	1994–2000	0.079	1.181	1.122	1.079	—	0.003	0.079	0.866	0.787	0.764	—	0.004
S600	2001	0.079	1.300	—	—	—	—	0.079	0.900	—	—	—	—
SL500	1994–2001	0.079	1.024	1.00	1.079	—	0.003	0.079	⑤	④	③	—	0.006
SL600	1994–2001	0.079	1.181	1.122	1.079	—	0.003	0.079	0.866	0.787	0.764	—	0.004
SLK230	1998–2001	0.079	0.984	0.906	0.882	—	0.005		0.354	0.299	0.287	—	0.006
SLK320	2001	0.079	0.984	0.906	0.882	—	0.005		0.354	0.299	0.287	—	0.006

① — Discard thickness is stamped on rotor.

② — Minimum.

③ — Solid rotor, 0.315 inch; vented rotor, 0.764 inch.

④ — Solid rotor, 0.347 inch; vented rotor, 0.787 inch.

⑤ — Solid rotor, 0.394 inch; vented rotor, 0.866 inch.

TIGHTENING SPECIFICATIONS

Year	Component	Torque, Ft. Lbs.
1998–2001	Bleed Screw	53–71①
	Brake Hose To Caliper	13
	Brake Hose To Pipe (Except E300, E320 & E430)	10
	Brake Hose To Pipe (E300, E320 & E430)	13
	Caliper To Carrier, Floating	26
	Caliper To Steering Knuckle (C43, CL500, CL600, E300, E320 E430, S320, S420, S430, S500, S600, SL500 & SL600)	85
	Caliper To Wheel Carrier, Fixed (CL500, CL600, S320, S420, S430, S500 & S600)	85
	Caliper To Wheel Carrier, Fixed (C43 Less ASR & SL500)	37
	Caliper To Wheel Carrier, Fixed (C43 w/ASR & SL600)	52
	Caliper To Wheel Carrier (C230, C280 Less ASR, CLK320, CLK430 & SLK230)	37
	Caliper To Wheel Carrier (C280 w/ASR)	52
	Caliper To Wheel Carrier, Fixed (E300, E320 less 4MATIC & E430)	37
	Caliper To Wheel Carrier, Fixed (E320 w/4MATIC)	85
	Contact Sensor (S430 & 2000–01 CL500, CL600, S500 & S600)	88①
	Guide Pins	18
	Hand Brake Handle (SLK230)	15
	Parking Brake Control Cable	15
	Parking Brake Foot Controls	106①
	Rotor	89①
	Speed Sensor, Front (C43, CL500, CL600, E300, E320, E430, S320, S420, S500, S600, SL500 & SL600)	16
	Splash Shield	89①
	Wear Sensor	22

① — Inch lbs.

Hydraulic Brake Systems

NOTE: On Air Bag Equipped Models, Refer To "Air Bag System Precautions" Located In Front Of This Manual For System Disarming And Arming Procedures.

NOTE: On Models Equipped With Anti-Lock Brake Systems, Refer To "Anti-Lock Brake Systems."

NOTE: Prior To Performing Any Service Operations Listed In This Section, Consult The "Technical Service Bulletins" Section For Related Information.

INDEX

	Page No.
Brake System Bleed	5-242
Less ESP	5-242
With ESP	5-242
Component Replacement	5-242
Master Cylinder	5-242
Component Service	5-242
Master Cylinder	5-242
Precautions	5-242
Air Bag Systems	5-242
Battery Ground Cable	5-242
Technical Service Bulletins	5-243
Master Cylinder Bleeder Valve Fluid Leak	5-243
Tightening Specifications	5-243

PRECAUTIONS

AIR BAG SYSTEMS

Refer to "Air Bag System Precautions"in front of this manual for system disarming and arming procedures.

BATTERY GROUND CABLE

Prior to service, disconnect battery ground cable and isolate as required.

COMPONENT REPLACEMENT

MASTER CYLINDER

1. Remove brake fluid from reservoir.
2. Disconnect bolt and remove reservoir from tandem master brake cylinder.
3. Disconnect brake lines.
4. **On S430 and 2000–01 CL500, CL600, S500 and S600 models,** remove hinged support from master cylinder.
5. **On all models,** remove mounting bolts and master cylinder. **Do not tilt tandem brake master cylinder.**
6. Reverse procedure to install, using new sealing ring. Bleed brake system.

COMPONENT SERVICE

MASTER CYLINDER

Brake master cylinder must not be repaired. Replace only.

BRAKE SYSTEM BLEED

LESS ESP

1. Connect suitable brake fluid changing tool following tool manufacturer's instructions. Bleed pressure is 29 psi.
2. Open righthand rear brake caliper bleed screw and allow approximately 2.7 ounces of brake fluid to flow out without any bubbles.
3. Tighten bleed screw to specifications.
4. Repeat bleeding procedure at lefthand rear, righthand front and lefthand front calipers.
5. **On CL500, CL600, S320, S420, S430, S500 and S600 models,** open master cylinder bleed screw and allow brake fluid to flow without any bubbles. Tighten bleed screw to specifications.
6. **On all models,** operate brake pedal firmly several times to set brake disc and pad play.
7. With engine running, operate brake pedal with approximately 45–76 lbs.
8. Pressure must be held without brake pedal being depressed any further.
9. Inspect all connections for leaks.
10. Adjust brake fluid level as required.

WITH ESP

1. Disconnect master cylinder switchover valve.
2. **On SL600 models,** connect connector set tool No. 201 589 00 99 00, or equivalent, flat plug
   a. Remove fuse and relay box F1 fuse No. C.
   b. Connect shop-made wiring harness flat connector fuse No. C input.
   c. Remove hydraulic unit bracket ground round plug.
   d. Connect two-pin coupling to switchover valve.
   e. Actuate brake master cylinder switchover valve using wiring harness.
3. **On CL500, CL600, S420, S430, S500 and S600 models,** proceed as follows:
   a. Remove fuse and relay box F1 fuse No. 28.
   b. Connect shop-made wiring harness flat connector fuse No. 28 input.
   c. Remove hydraulic unit bracket ground round plug.
   d. Connect two-pin coupling to switchover valve.
   e. Actuate brake master cylinder switchover valve using wiring harness.
4. **On all models,** connect Hand-Held Tester (HHT) tool No. 965 589 00 01 00, or equivalent scan tool, to Data Link Connector (DLC).
5. Turn ignition switch to On position.
6. Follow HHT Bleeding Braking System menu.
7. Open righthand rear brake caliper bleed screw and allow approximately 2.7 ounces of brake fluid to flow out without any bubbles.
8. Tighten bleed screw to specifications.
9. Repeat bleeding procedure at lefthand rear, righthand front and lefthand front calipers.

10. **On CL500, CL600, S320, S420, S430, S500 and S600 models,** open master cylinder bleed screw and allow brake fluid to flow without any bubbles. Tighten bleed screw to specifications.
11. **On all models,** operate brake pedal firmly several times to set brake disc and pad play.
12. With engine running, operate brake pedal with approximately 45–76 lbs.
13. Pressure must be held without brake pedal being depressed any further.
14. Inspect all connections for leaks.
15. Adjust brake fluid level as required.

TECHNICAL SERVICE BULLETINS

MASTER CYLINDER BLEEDER VALVE FLUID LEAK

S320 & S420 & 1998-99 CL500, CL600, S500 & S600

On some of these models there may be a master cylinder bleeder valve fluid leak.

This condition may be caused by bleeder valve not being properly tightened.

To correct this condition, do not replace master cylinder. **Torque** bleeder valve to 106 inch lbs.

TIGHTENING SPECIFICATIONS

Year	Component	Torque, Ft. Lbs.
1998–2001	Bleed Screw	53–71①
	Hinged Support	80①
	Master Cylinder	15
	Wheel Bolt	85

① — Inch lbs.

Power Brake Units

NOTE: On Air Bag Equipped Models, Refer To "Air Bag System Precautions" Located In Front Of This Manual For System Disarming And Arming Procedures.

NOTE: On Models Equipped With Anti-Lock Brake Systems, Refer To "Anti-Lock Brake Systems."

NOTE: Prior To Performing Any Service Operations Listed In This Section, Consult The "Technical Service Bulletins" Section For Related Information.

INDEX

	Page No.
Diagnosis & Testing	5-244
Brake Booster	5-244
Non-Return Valve	5-244
Power Brake Unit Service	5-244
Brake Booster, Replace	5-244
Precautions	5-244
Air Bag Systems	5-244
Battery Ground Cable	5-244
Technical Service Bulletins	5-245
Bake Pedal Hard To Apply	5-245

PRECAUTIONS

AIR BAG SYSTEMS

Refer to "Air Bag System Precautions"in front of this manual for system disarming and arming procedures.

BATTERY GROUND CABLE

Prior to service, disconnect battery ground cable and isolate as required.

DIAGNOSIS & TESTING

NON-RETURN VALVE

1. Disconnect brake booster vacuum line.
2. Connect pressure tester tool No. 201 589 13 21 00, or equivalent, between brake booster and vacuum line.
3. Start engine and create 10.9–11.6 psi vacuum by opening and suddenly releasing throttle.
4. Turn engine off.
5. If vacuum drops more than 2.9 psi in 30 seconds, replace vacuum line.
6. **Torque** vacuum line to 22 ft. lbs.

BRAKE BOOSTER

1. Disconnect brake booster vacuum line.
2. Connect pressure tester tool No. 201 589 13 21 00, or equivalent, between brake booster and vacuum line.
3. Connect suitable pressure tester at brake caliper.
4. Connect Bosch pedal force meter tool No. 0 681 148 EFSV 57 B, or equivalent, to brake pedal.
5. Start engine and create 10.9–11.6 psi vacuum by opening and suddenly releasing throttle.
6. If slightly lower vacuum is achieves or vacuum is reduced immediately, proceed as follows:
   a. Inspect O-ring between brake booster and tandem master brake cylinder. Replace as required.
   b. Test non-return valve as outlined under "Non-Return Valve."
   c. **On models equipped with diesel engine,** inspect vacuum pump.
7. **On all models,** apply specified brake pedal force and measure line pressure.
8. Compare measurements to **Fig. 1.**
9. If line pressure is ±14.5 psi from specifications, replace brake booster.
10. Remove test equipment and bleed brake system at caliper were pressure tester was connected.
11. **Torque** vacuum line to 22 ft. lbs.
12. **Torque** bleed screws to 53–71 inch lbs.

POWER BRAKE UNIT SERVICE

BRAKE BOOSTER, REPLACE

C43, C230, C280, E300, E320, E430, S320, S420, SL500, SL600 & SLK230 & 1998–99 CL500, CL600, S500 & S600

1. Remove master cylinder as outlined in "Hydraulic Brake Systems" section.
2. Inspect master cylinder rear piston for leaks. If no leaks are visible, proceed as follows:
   a. Remove and measure brake fluid in booster.
   b. If there is more than 3.38 ounces of brake fluid, booster must be replaced.
3. Disconnect vacuum line at booster.
4. Remove cover below instrument panel.
5. Disconnect brake pedal return spring.
6. Disconnect pedal locking device and remove pin.
7. Remove carrier mounting nuts.
8. Remove brake booster. **Do not damage control housing.**
9. Inspect washer and replace as required.
10. Reverse procedure to install, noting the following:
    a. **Torque** vacuum line to 22 ft. lbs.
    b. **Torque** carrier mounting nuts to 15 ft. lbs.

CLK320 & CLK430

1. Remove cover below instrument panel.
2. Remove stop lamp switch.
3. Remove fuel lines bracket.
4. Remove component compartment rubber seal.
5. Remove clips and mounting nut, then push firewall sound insulation mat away from engine side.
6. Disconnect brake booster vacuum line.
7. Disconnect brake fluid level sensor.
8. Disconnect connector and remove BAS control module.
9. Remove mounting bolt and tile windshield washer fluid reservoir to one side.
10. Draw off reservoir brake fluid.
11. Remove brake lines.
12. Open fuse box, remove upper section and disconnect electric cables from duct.
13. Remove brake pedal locking device and pin.
14. Remove mounting nuts and brake booster. **Do not damage cup seal.**
15. Inspect washers between firewall and brake booster. Replace as required.
16. Remove master cylinder as outlined in "Hydraulic Brake Systems" section.
17. Inspect master cylinder rear piston for leaks. If no leaks are visible, proceed as follows:
    a. Remove and measure brake fluid in booster.
    b. If there is more than 3.38 ounces of

Model	Year	Brake Booster	Line Pressure, psi, @ Brake Pedal Pressure, psi, w/10.9–11.6 psi Vacuum				
			11.2	22.5	33.7	45.0	56.2
C43	1998–2000	Teves T52/4A/255 or Lucas/LSC 80	188–334	464–638	696–899	899–1131	1088–1320
C230	1998–2000	Teves T52/4A/255 or Lucas/LSC 80	188–334	464–638	696–899	899–1131	1088–1320
C280	1998–2000	Teves T52/4A/255 or Lucas/LSC 80	188–334	464–638	696–899	899–1131	1088–1320
CL500 & CL600	1998–99	Teves T52/4A/255-225	189–363	508–682	827–1001	1131–1334	1378–1523
	2000–01	—	319–435	609–754	870–1015	1160–1378	1450–1740
CLK320, & CLK430	1998–2001	Lucas	188–334	464–638	696–899	899–1131	1189–1378
E300	1998–99	Teves	218–363	551–725	827–1015	1044–1204	1189–1320
E320	1998–2001	Teves	116–261	479–580	754–885	986—1146	1189–1378
E430	1998–2001	Teves	116–261	479–580	754–885	986—1146	1189–1378
S320	1998–99	Teves T52/4A/225-210 or Lucas LSC 115	203–363	508–653	769–914	1030–1175	1262–1421
S420, S500 & S600	1998–99	Teves T52/4A/255-225	189–363	508–682	827–1001	1131–1334	1378–1523
S430, S500 & S600	2000–01	—	319–435	609–754	870–1015	1160–1378	1450–1740
SL500	1998–2001	Teves T52/4A/225-210 or Lucas LSC 115	203–363	508–653	769–914	1030–1175	1262–1421
SL600	1998–2001	Teves T52/4A/225-210	203–363	508–653	769–914	1030–1175	1262–1421
SLK230 & SLK320	1998–2001	Lucas	188–334	464–638	696–899	899–1131	1189–1378

Fig. 1 Power brake unit test specifications

brake fluid, booster must be replaced.

18. Reverse procedure to install, noting the following:
    a. **Torque** vacuum line to 22 ft. lbs.
    b. **On models equipped with BAS,** booster must be adapted to BAS control module using Hand-Held Tester (HHT) tool No. 965 589 00 01 00, or equivalent scan tool.

S430 & 2000-01 CL500, CL600, S500 & S600

1. Remove master cylinder as outlined in "Hydraulic Brake Systems" section.
2. Disconnect BAS diaphragm travel sensor.
3. Disconnect booster vacuum line.
4. Remove covers below foot controls.
5. Pull off booster to pedal locking element and remove pin.
6. Remove mounting nuts and brake booster.
7. Reverse procedure to install. **Torque** mounting nuts to 18 ft. lbs.

TECHNICAL SERVICE BULLETINS

BAKE PEDAL HARD TO APPLY

1999-2000 C230 & SLK230

On some of these models the brake pedal may be hard to apply when starting the engine cold.

This condition may be caused by the combination of cold start vacuum equalization, engine RPM required for catalyst warm up and vehicle position.

To correct this condition, proceed as follows:

1. Replace brake booster hose with revised unit (C230 part No. A 202 430 6029 or SLK230 part No. A 170 430 1729).
2. Replace crankcase vent hose between oil separator and air filter housing with revised unit (C230 part No. A 111 081 31 82 or SLK230 part No. A 111 081 3382) and connect it to brake booster hose venturi.

Vacuum Pumps

NOTE: On Air Bag Equipped Models, Refer To "Air Bag System Precautions" Located In Front Of This Manual For System Disarming And Arming Procedures.

NOTE: On Models Equipped With Anti-Lock Brake Systems, Refer To "Anti-Lock Brake Systems."

INDEX

	Page No.
Precautions	5-246
Air Bag Systems	5-246
Battery Ground Cable	5-246
Vacuum Pump, Replace	5-246

PRECAUTIONS

AIR BAG SYSTEMS

Refer to "Air Bag System Precautions"in front of this manual for system disarming and arming procedures.

BATTERY GROUND CABLE

Prior to service, disconnect battery ground cable and isolate as required.

VACUUM PUMP

REPLACE

1. Loosen fan shroud and remove viscous fan clutch.
2. Release drive belt and swing idler pulley to one side.
3. Disconnect vacuum line.
4. Remove mounting bolts and vacuum pump.
5. Reverse procedure to install, noting the following:
   a. Install new sealing washer.
   b. Turn crankshaft in engine rotation direction until drive cams contact injection timer and vacuum pump drive roller engages between cams.
   c. **Torque** mounting bolts to 89 inch lbs.

Anti-Lock Brakes

NOTE: On Air Bag Equipped Models, Refer To "Air Bag System Precautions" Located In Front Of This Manual For System Disarming And Arming Procedures.

NOTE: Prior To Performing Any Service Operations Listed In This Section, Consult The "Technical Service Bulletins" Section For Related Information.

INDEX

	Page No.
Description	5-247
Components	5-247
System	5-247
Diagnosis & Testing	5-247
Accessing Diagnostic Trouble Codes	5-248
Generic Scan Tool	5-248
Hand-Held Tester (HHT) Tool	5-248
Impulse Counter Scan Tool	5-248
Clearing Diagnostic Trouble Codes	5-249
Hand-Held Tester	5-249
Impulse Counter Scan Tool	5-249
Component Locations	5-249
Connector Terminal Identification	5-249
Diagnostic Tests	5-249
ABS, ASR, ETS & SPS	5-249
ABS, ESP & SPS	5-249
ABS	5-249
Diagnostic Trouble Code Interpretation	5-248
Function Tests	5-249
Symbol Explanation	5-247
Symptom Related Diagnosis	5-248
Wiring Diagrams	5-249
Diagnostic Chart Index	5-279
ABS, ASR, ETS & SPS	5-279
ABS, ESP & SPS	5-281
ABS	5-279
Precautions	5-247
Air Bag Systems	5-247
Battery Ground Cable	5-247
System Service	5-249
Brake System Bleed	5-249
Component Replacement	5-249
ABS Control Unit	5-249
ESP Charging Pump	5-250
ESP Pressurizing Piston Unit	5-250
Hydraulic Unit	5-249
Speed Sensor	5-249
Technical Service Bulletins	5-250
ABS Activates Or Warning Lamp Comes On When Braking At Speeds Less Than 10 MPH	5-252
ABS Control Lamp On, ABS Still Operating Normally	5-250
ABS Lamp Lights At Highway Speeds	5-251
ABS Lamp Lights Intermittently & Goes Out While Driving	5-251
ABS Lamp Lights Intermittently	5-251
ABS, ABS/ASR Warning Lamp Come On After Engine Is Started & Remains Lit Until Ignition Is Switched Off	5-251
ABS, ASR Or ETS MIL Illuminated	5-252
ASR MIL On After Engine Start, DTC C1022	5-251
ESP & ADS DTC C1140 & C1054 or 015, 016 & 017	5-250
ESP Activated Even In Slight Curves At Moderate Speed	5-251
ESP DTC C1120 or C1142	5-250
ESP DTC C1140 & C1504	5-250
ESP DTC C1140 & C1504	5-250
ESP DTC C1401 Or C1405	5-250
ESP React Too Sensitively At Slow Speeds In Tight Curves	5-251
Pedal Pulsates When Applying Brakes Lightly	5-251
Return Pump Runs Without Control, DTC C1401	5-251
Soft Brake Pedal Or Insufficient Braking At Front Or Rear Axle	5-251

PRECAUTIONS

AIR BAG SYSTEMS

Refer to "Air Bag System Precautions" in front of this manual for system disarming and arming procedures.

BATTERY GROUND CABLE

Prior to service, disconnect battery ground cable and isolate as required.

DESCRIPTION

SYSTEM

Four-wheel ABS uses a control unit, hydraulic actuator and wheel speed sensors to control brake fluid pressure and prevent wheel lock during severe braking conditions,

Basic ABS components are supplemented by an expanded hydraulic unit, a charging pump, a fourth wheel speed sensor and a more comprehensive electronic system for Acceleration Slip Regulation (ASR) and Electronic Traction System (ETS).

Integrated with ABS and traction control systems, Electronic Stability Program (ESP) detects slides and applies brake pressure to individual wheels to help maintain control.

COMPONENTS

Electronic Control Unit

There are several different control units available. To prevent interchanging control units there are two lugs cast in control unit connector and at front clasp there is a notch located in different positions for different model/engine combinations.

The control unit receives input from four wheel speed sensors, stop lamp switch, electronic accelerator control unit (for throttle valve actual position), snow chain switch and pressure reservoir switch. The control unit turns these input signals into output signals for the following components: hydraulic unit solenoid valves, relays (solenoid valves, return/pressure pump and ASR charging pump), electronic acceleration control unit, ASR indicator lamp, snow chain switch LED, ABS warning lamp and ASR warning lamp. From input signals control unit differentiates between three operational modes, normal operation, ABS operation and ASR operation.

Wheel Speed Sensors

On models equipped with only ABS, three wheel speed sensors are located in both front steering knuckle and in rear axle assembly.

Models equipped with ABS/ASR or ETS have speed sensors located at all four wheels. Single-edged tooth and long cable with a coaxial plug identifies front speed sensors. Lefthand rear speed sensor can be identified by E on plug and righthand by D on plug.

DIAGNOSIS & TESTING

Symbol Explanation

Refer to **Figs. 1 through 3** for explanations of symbols, connections and steps included in charts.

Description	Symbol
ABS adaptor	
Socket box tester 35-pole	
Socket box tester 126-pole	
Signal generator	
Hand–held tester (HHT)	
Impulse counter scan tool	
On-off ratio tester	
Pressure gauge	
Digital multimeter	
Resistance substitution unit	
Bridge	
DANGER! High Voltage	
Brake pad wear indicator	

Description	Symbol
Pin	
Socket	
Battery	
DC generator	
DC motor	
Capacitor	
Coil	
Resistance	
Ground	
Systems check O.K.	√
Fault	F
Resistance too high	> Ω
Resistance too low	< Ω
Short circuit to ground	┌┐ –

Description	Symbol
Short circuit to positive	┌┐ +
Open circuit	–//–
Short circuit	┌┐
Direct current measured with multimeter	
Alternating current measured w/multimeter	
Direct voltage measured w/multimeter	
Alternating voltage measured w/multimeter	
Resistance measured with multimeter	
Signal generator Square wave form	
Signal generator Sine form	
Oscilloscope	
Adaptor wire with LED	

MB7019600011000X

Fig. 1 Explanation of test equipment & component symbols

Accessing Diagnostic Trouble Codes

ABS systems with ASR or ETS may only be inspected using Hand-Held Tester (HHT) tool No. 965 589 00 01 00, or equivalent scan tool.

GENERIC SCAN TOOL

Follow tool manufacturers instructions and connect suitably programmed scan tool to generic scan tool connection X11/22, **Fig. 4.**

HAND-HELD TESTER (HHT) TOOL

1. Turn ignition switch to Off position.
2. **On models equipped with 16-pin Data Link Connector (DLC),** connect Hand-Held Tester tool No. 965 589 00 01 00, or equivalent scan tool, as follows:
   a. Attach test cable tool No. 965 589 00 50 00, or equivalent, to tester.
   b. Connect ground circuit 31 black wire to DLC socket No. 1, **Fig. 5.**
   c. Connect voltage circuit 15 white wire to socket No. 16.
   d. Connect circuit 30 red wire to battery positive terminal or X4/10 terminal block circuit 30.
   e. Connect yellow wire to diagnostic output socket of system being tested, refer to "Connector Terminal Identification."
3. **On models equipped with 38-pin DLC,** connect HHT tool No. 965 589 00 01 00, or equivalent scan tool, as follows:
   a. Connect tester to multiplexer cable tool No. 965 589 00 40 00, or equivalent.
   b. Turn multiplexer cable locking ring completely to left detent stop.
   c. Attach multiplexer cable to DLC via locking pins, **Fig. 6.**
   d. Turn multiplexer cable locking ring to right to lock to connector.
4. **On all models,** follow tool manufacturer's instructions.

IMPULSE COUNTER SCAN TOOL

1. **On models equipped with 16-pin data link connector,** connect impulse counter scan tool No. 124 589 19 21 00, or equivalent, as follows:
   a. Connect ground circuit 31 black wire to socket No. 1, **Fig. 5.**
   b. Connect ignition circuit 15 white wire to socket No. 16.
   c. Connect yellow wire to diagnostic output socket of system being tested, refer to "Connector Terminal Identification."
2. **On models equipped with 38-pin data link connector,** connect impulse counter scan tool No. 124 589 19 21 00, or equivalent, as follows:
   a. Connect adapter tool No. 140 589 14 63 00, or equivalent, to 38-pin DLC, **Fig. 6.**
   b. Connect voltage circuit 30 red wire to socket No. 3.
   c. Connect ground circuit 32 black wire to socket No. 1.
   d. Connect yellow wire to diagnostic output socket of system being tested, refer to "Connector Terminal Identification."
3. **On all models,** LED "U-Bat" lamp must light. If LED does not light, check voltage supply and tool fuse.
4. Turn ignition switch to On position, then press scan tool start button for 2–4 seconds.
5. Read and record Diagnostic Trouble Codes (DTCs) displayed.
6. Press scan tool start button again for 2–4 seconds to display next DTC.
7. Continue to press start button for 2–4 seconds until all DTCs have been displayed. If no other DTCs are stored, first DTC will be displayed, again.

Diagnostic Trouble Code Interpretation

Refer to **Figs. 7 through 10** for DTC interpretation.

Symptom Related Diagnosis

Refer to **Figs. 11 through 15** for symptom related diagnosis.

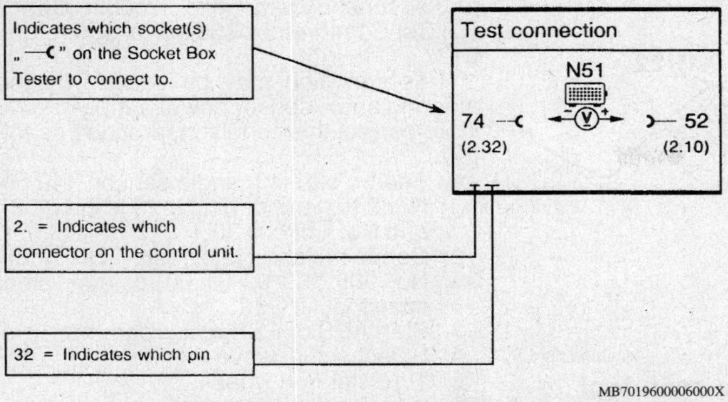

Fig. 2 Explanation of test connections

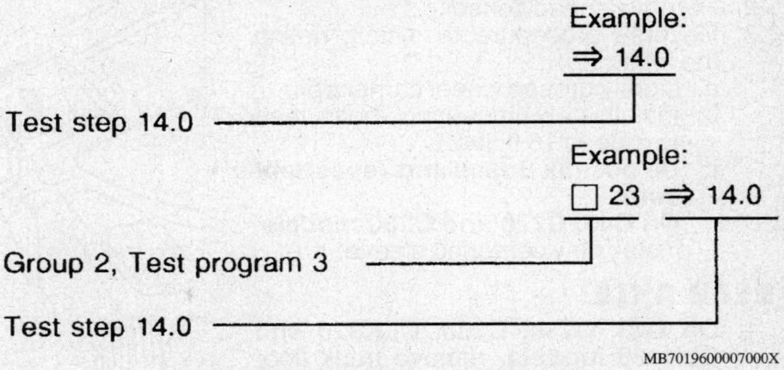

Fig. 3 Explanation of test step

Component Locations

Refer to **Figs. 16 through 24** for component locations.

Wiring Diagrams

Refer to **Figs. 25 through 38** for wiring diagrams.

Connector Terminal Identification

Refer to **Figs. 39 through 46** for connector terminal identification.

Function Tests

Refer to **Figs. 47 through 49** for function tests.

Diagnostic Tests

ABS

C230 & C280

1. Turn ignition switch to Off position.
2. Access ABS control module.
3. Connect 126-pin socket box tool No. 129 589 00 21 00 54, or equivalent, between ABS control module and connector using test cable tool No. 129 589 00 63 00, or equivalent.
4. Perform test as directed using suitable digital multi-meter, **Figs. 50 through 56.**

ABS, ASR, ETS & SPS

C43, C230, C280, E300, S320, S420, SL500, SL600 & SLK230 & 1998-99 CL500, CL600, S500 & S600

1. Turn ignition switch to Off position.
2. Disconnect traction control module.
3. Connect socket box tool No. 129 589 00 21 00, or equivalent, to control module using test cable tool No. 140 589 45 63 00, or equivalent.
4. Perform test as directed use suitable digital multi-meter, **Figs. 57 through 67.**

SL500 & SL600

1. Turn ignition switch to Off position.
2. Disconnect ASR/SPS or ETS/SPS control module.
3. Connect socket box tool No. 129 589 00 21 00, or equivalent, to module box and control module using test cable tool No. 140 589 39 63 00, or equivalent.
4. Perform test as directed use suitable digital multi-meter, **Figs. 68 through 83.**

ABS, ESP & SPS

E320, E430, S320, S420, SL500 & SL600 & 1998-99 CL500, CL600, S500 & S600

1. Turn ignition switch to Off position.
2. Disconnect ESP/SPS control module.
3. Connect socket box tool No. 129 589 00 21 00, or equivalent, to control module using test cable tool No. 140 589 45 63 00, or equivalent.
4. Perform test as directed use suitable digital multi-meter, **Figs. 84 through 99.**

Clearing Diagnostic Trouble Codes

The Diagnostic Trouble Codes will be cleared when the effected component has been repaired or replaced.

HAND-HELD TESTER

Follow tool manufacturer's instructions.

IMPULSE COUNTER SCAN TOOL

1. Press start button 2–4 seconds until Diagnostic Trouble Code (DTC) appears.
2. Wait three second, press start button and hold 6–8 seconds, erasing previously displayed DTC.
3. Erasing must begin within 20 seconds of DTC display. After 20 seconds, DTC can no longer be erased until displayed again.
4. Erase each stored DTC individually.

SYSTEM SERVICE

Brake System Bleed

Refer to procedure as outlined in "Hydraulic Brake Systems" section.

Component Replacement

HYDRAULIC UNIT

ABS

ASR/ETS/ESP

C43, C230, C280, CLK320, CLK430, E300, E320, E430, S320, S420, SL500, SL600 & SLK230 & 1998-99 CL500, CL600, S500 & S600

1. Turn ignition switch to Off position.
2. Disconnect hydraulic lines. Seal lines and connections.
3. Remove plastic caps and hydraulic unit.
4. Reverse procedure to install. **Torque** hydraulic lines to 11 ft. lbs.

ABS CONTROL UNIT

CLK320, CLK430, E300, E320, E430, S320, S420, SL500 & SL600 & 1998-99 CL500, CL600, S500 & S600

1. **On E300, E320 and E430 models,** disconnect vacuum line.
2. **On all models,** disconnect electrical connector.
3. Disconnect release switch/solenoid valve connector.
4. Disconnect diaphragm travel sensor connector.
5. Remove circlip and pull diaphragm travel sensor.
6. Remove control unit.
7. Reverse procedure to install, noting the following:
   a. Install new O-ring in brake booster groove and correctly seat.
   b. Rub diaphragm travel sensor front with spirit to ease installation through O-ring.

SPEED SENSOR

FRONT WHEEL

1. Remove mounting bolts.

2. Remove speed sensor.
3. Reverse procedure to install, noting the following:
   a. Lightly grease wheel carrier bore.
   b. Install new mounting bolts and **torque** to 16 ft. lbs.
   c. **Do not mix Bosch and Teves sensors.**
   d. **On C43, C230 and C280 models,** install new centering sleeve.

REAR AXLE

1. **On C43, C230, C280, CLK320 and CLK430 models,** remove trunk floor and cover.
2. **On SLK230 models,** remove vehicle floor vertical plate rubber grommet.
3. **On all models,** remove mounting bolt and speed sensor.
4. Reverse procedure to install. **Torque** new mounting bolt to 71 inch lbs.

ESP CHARGING PUMP

1. Turn ignition switch to Off position.
2. Disconnect hydraulic lines. Plug lines and control unit connections. **Do not mix lines.**
3. Remove mounting bolts and pump.
4. Reverse procedure to install. **Torque** mounting bolts to 11 ft. lbs.

ESP PRESSURIZING PISTON UNIT

1. Turn ignition switch to Off position.
2. Disconnect hydraulic lines. Plug lines and control unit connections. **Do not mix lines.**
3. Remove mounting bolts and pump.
4. Reverse procedure to install. **Torque** mounting bolts to 11 ft. lbs.

TECHNICAL SERVICE BULLETINS

ESP DTC C1140 & C1504

C43, C230, C280, CLK55, CLK320, CLK430, E55, E300, E320, E430 & SLK230

On some of these models there may be Electronic Stability Program (ESP) Diagnostic Trouble Codes (DTCs) C1140 and C1504.

This condition may be caused by steering angle sensor and contact spiral clearance.

To correct this condition, proceed as follows:

1. Read ESP DTC memory.
2. Check steering angle sensor supply voltage.
3. Measure steering angle sensor ground, pin No. 3. In relation to battery, it should be 12–14 volts. In relation to ground pole, less than one ohm.
4. Pin No. 4 (supply voltage circuit 30) to No. 3 should be 12–14 volts.
5. Pin No. 2 (supply voltage circuit 87) to No. 3 with ignition on, 12–14 volts. With ignition off, zero volts.
6. Measure clearance between steering angle sensor and contact spiral at five different points on circumference.

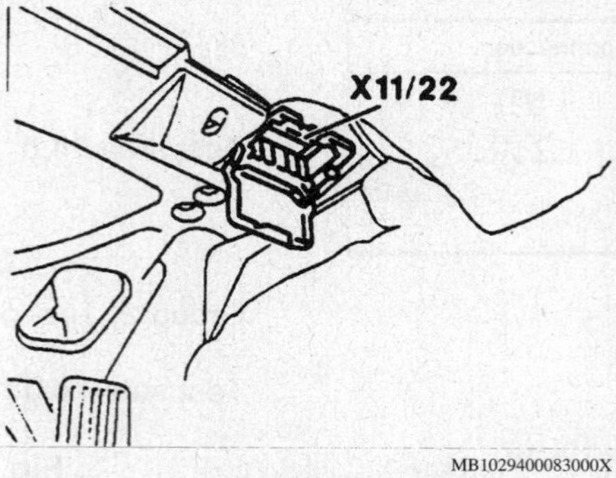

Fig. 4 Generic scan tool connection

7. If clearance is not 0.118–0.217 inch, adjust turn signal switch three-point mount.

ESP DTC C1401 OR C1405

C230, C240, CLK320, CLK430, E300, E320 & E430

On some of these models the Electronic Stability Program (ESP) may have Diagnostic Trouble Codes (DTCs) C1401 or C1405 stored. Code occurs only when putting vehicle in motion for first time after starting engine.

This condition may be caused by ESP control module software error.

To correct this condition, replace control module.

ESP DTC C1120 OR C1142

E43, C280, CLK55, CLK320, CLK430, E55, E320, E430 & S430 & 1999-2000 SL500 & 2000 CL500 & S500

On some of these models the Electronic Stability Program (ESP) may store Diagnostic Trouble Code (DTC) C1120 or C1142.

DTC C1120 usually occurs after the vehicle has been driven up a steep incline and through a 90° left or righthand curve immediately after starting the engine. The indicator lamp may come on after driving straight for approximately 100 yards.

DTC C1142 usually occurs when driving through curves with low lateral acceleration forces.

This condition may be caused by erroneous standstill calibration of yaw rate sensor or lateral acceleration sensor is monitored to precisely by ESP control module.

To correct this condition, install revised control module, **Fig. 100.**

ESP & ADS DTC C1140 & C1054 OR 015, 016 & 017

E55, E320, E430, S320, S420, SL500 & SL600 & 1998-99 S500 & S600

On some of these models there may be Electronic Stability Program (ESP) and Adaptive Damping System (ADS) steering angle sensor Diagnostic Trouble Codes (DTCs) C1140 and C1504 or 015, 016 and 017.

This condition may be caused by the steering angle sensor power supply.

To correct this condition, proceed as follows:

1. Ensure steering angle sensor N49 pin No. 2 is ground, pin No. 3 is circuit 87 and No. 4 circuit 30.
2. Connect Hand-Held Tester (HHT) tool No. 965 589 00 01 00, or equivalent scan tool, to DLC.
3. Start ADS or ESP test program.
4. Select actual valve menu.
5. Turn steering wheel.
6. If values change, replace steering angle sensor.
7. If values do not change, inspect distance between clock spring contact and jacket tube. Adjust as required.
8. If steering angle sensor cannot be initialized after starting engine, replace sensor.

ESP DTC C1140 & C1504

S430 & 2000-01 CL500 & S500

On CL500 models built before VIN 000532, and S430 and S500 models built before VIN 063525, there may be Electronic Stability Program (ESP) steering angle sensor Diagnostic Trouble Codes (DTCs) C1140 and C1504.

This condition may be caused by jacket tube control module voltage being too low.

To correct this condition, proceed as follows:

1. Disconnect battery.
2. Remove footwell paneling.
3. Cut cable on PIN No. 12 of cockpit connector X18 wiring harness.
4. Connect cut line with additional 23.6 inch length of suitable wire. Use solder end sleeve.
5. Route new lead to lefthand fuse and relay box fuse F25.
6. Release fuse carrier.
7. Disconnect fuse carrier from fuse and relay box.
8. Remove fuse F25.
9. Disconnect and cut off contact carrier connection.
10. Connect new connected lead to red/yellow lead removed from fuse carrier. Use solder end sleeve.
11. Reverse procedure to install. **Do not install fuse F25.**

ABS CONTROL LAMP ON, ABS STILL OPERATING NORMALLY

On some of these models the ABS control lamp may be illuminated, however the ABS is still operating normally.

This condition may be caused by low alternator output.

To correct this condition, proceed as follows:

1. Inspect alternator control lamp.
2. If alternator lamp is very dim, apply load to alternator.
3. If alternator makes humming noise under load, inspect alternator.

RETURN PUMP RUNS WITHOUT CONTROL, DTC C1401

C43, C230, C280, CLK55, CLK320 & CLK430

On some of these models the return pump may run without control and Diagnostic Trouble Code (DTC) C1401 may be set.

This condition may be caused by oxidation and creep currents in fuse box. Because of the uniform ABS wiring harness for both the Bosch and ITT systems, the plug for the return pump is not used on the ITT system. The plug lies loose in the fuse box lower area.

To correct this condition, clean and insulate the plug.

ASR MIL ON AFTER ENGINE START, DTC C1022

On some of these models the ASR MIL lamp may illuminate after engine start with Diagnostic Trouble Code C1022 stored. There are no engine operation complaints.

This condition may be caused by the ME-SFI 2.1 engine control module.

To correct this condition, replace the engine control module.

ESP ACTIVATED EVEN IN SLIGHT CURVES AT MODERATE SPEED

2000 C230

On some of these models built after February 2000, the Electronic Stability Program (ESP) starts regulating too early particularly in long curves for example freeway exists. There are control noises or a flashing indicator lamp without the vehicle oversteering noticeably.

This condition is caused by the ESP control module.

To correct this condition, proceed as follows:

1. Inspect the ESP control module part number status.
2. If control module part number is 202 545 47 32 with an imprinted status of "Q06," replace module with unit having "Q7" or higher status.
3. Control modules with "Q05" status or less are not affected.

ESP REACT TOO SENSITIVELY AT SLOW SPEEDS IN TIGHT CURVES

C230, C280, CLK320, E55, E320 & E430

On some of these models equipped with the Electronic Stability Program (ESP) may react too sensitively at walking speed in tight curves.

To correct this condition, replace the ESP control module, **Fig. 101.**

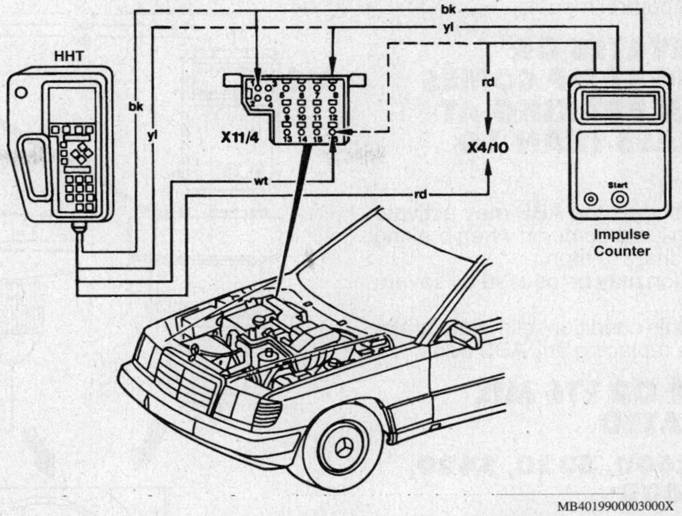

Fig. 5 Tool connection to 16-pin DLC

ABS LAMP LIGHTS INTERMITTENTLY & GOES OUT WHILE DRIVING

On some of these models the ABS lamp may intermittently be lit, then go out while driving.

This condition may be caused by low battery voltage.

To correct this condition, proceed as follows:

1. Test battery.
2. Test over voltage protection relay.
3. Inspect ABS power supply and ground wiring or loose connection.

ABS LAMP LIGHTS AT HIGHWAY SPEEDS

On some of these models the ABS lamp my light at highway speeds.

This condition may be caused by different size tires and rims on front and rear axles.

To correct this condition, install original equipment tire and rim sizes.

PEDAL PULSATES WHEN APPLYING BRAKES LIGHTLY

On some of these models the brake pedal may pulsate when lightly applying brakes not within ABS control range. The ABS lamp does not light.

This condition may be caused by defective speed sensor, the electronic control module or open circuit in ABS wiring harness at front axle speed sensor connector.

To correct this condition, proceed as follows:

1. Measure speed sensors resistance. Resistance should be 800–3700 ohms.
2. Remove speed sensor and inspect for damage or dirt accumulation.
3. Inspect rear axle speed sensor or metal chips on tip and clean as required.
4. Inspect speed sensor cable for interruptions in fastening clip areas. Stretch and flex cable in fastening area when inspecting continuity.

ABS LAMP LIGHTS INTERMITTENTLY

On some of these models the ABS lamp may light intermittently.

This condition may be caused by intermittent contact loss near either front axle speed sensor connector.

To correct this condition, repair harness within 20 inches of connector.

SOFT BRAKE PEDAL OR INSUFFICIENT BRAKING AT FRONT OR REAR AXLE

On some of these models there may be a soft brake pedal or insufficient braking at front or rear axle.

This condition may be caused by flow noises at vacuum line check valve.

To correct this condition, install new vacuum line with modified check valve (part No. 126 430 28 29 05).

ABS, ABS/ASR WARNING LAMP COME ON AFTER ENGINE IS STARTED & REMAINS LIT UNTIL IGNITION IS SWITCHED OFF

On some of these models the ABS and/or ABS/ASR warning lamp may come on after the engine is started and remain lit unit the ignition is switched Off. After numerous engine restarts, the condition may go away.

This condition may be caused by poor electrical connector or defective ABS control module.

To correct this condition, proceed as follows:

1. Tighten ground connect W10.
2. Remove hydraulic unit ground connection plug screw under motor relay/black.
3. Install toothed washer and screw.

4. Test ABS control module.

ABS ACTIVATES OR WARNING LAMP COMES ON WHEN BRAKING AT SPEEDS LESS THAN 10 MPH

On some models the ABS may activate or the warning lamp come on when braking at speed less than 10 mph.

This condition may be caused by severe brake squeal.

To correct this condition, eliminate brake sequel before replacing any ABS parts.

ABS, ASR OR ETS MIL ILLUMINATED

CL500, CL600, S320, S420, S500 & S600

On some of these models the ABS, ASR or ETS malfunction warning lamps may be illuminated without recording Diagnostic Trouble Codes (DTCs).

This condition may be caused by control module connector internal shorting contacts remaining closed in electrical contact adjacent to pins.

To correct this condition, carefully inspect plastic control module and harness connector spreading pins. If any damage is found, replace control module and electrical harness.

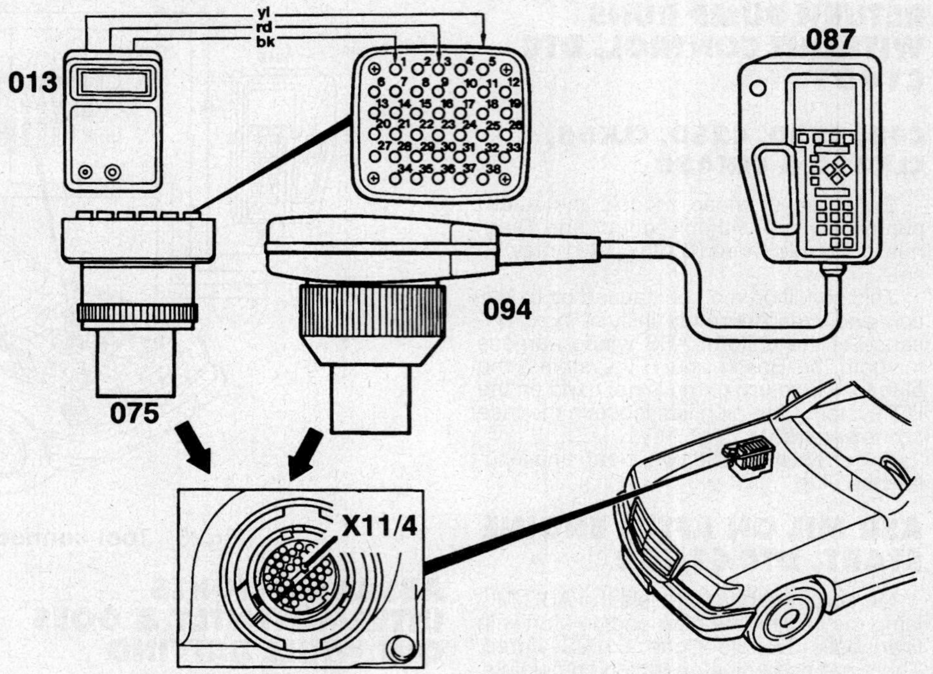

013	Impulse counter scan tool	094	Multiplexer, 965 589 00 40
075	Adaptor for impulse counter scan tool	X11/4	Data link connector
087	Hand–Held Tester (HHT)		

MB4019900004000X

Fig. 6 Tool connections to 38-pin DLC

Diagnostic trouble code (DTC)		Possible cause	Test step/Remedy
1	–	No faults recognized. In case of complaint:	☐ 23 (entire test)
2	002	Left front axle vehicle speed sensor (L6/1), open circuit	☐ 23 ⇒ 7.0
3	003	Right front axle vehicle speed sensor (L6/2), open circuit	☐ 23 ⇒ 9.0
4	004	Rear axle vehicle speed sensor (L6), open circuit	☐ 23 ⇒ 11.0
6	006	Left front axle solenoid valve (A7y1)	☐ 23 ⇒ 13.0
7	007	Right front axle solenoid valve (A7y2)	☐ 23 ⇒ 14.0
8	008	Rear axle solenoid valve (A7y3)	☐ 23 ⇒ 15.0
10	010	Return pump (A7m1) or return pump relay (A7k2)	☐ 23 ⇒ 6.0
11	011	Solenoid valve relay (A7k1)	☐ 23 ⇒ 5.0
15	015	ABS control module (N30)	Replace N30.
16	016	Implausible signal, vehicle speed sensors (L6/1, L6/2, L6) [2)]	☐ 23 ⇒ 7.0, 9.0, 11.0, Visual inspection.
17	017	Low battery voltage	☐ 23 ⇒ 1.0
25	025	Implausible signal, left front vehicle speed sensor (L6/1) [2)]	☐ 23 ⇒ 7.0
26	026	Implausible signal, right front vehicle speed sensor (L6/2) [2)]	☐ 23 ⇒ 9.0
27	027	Implausible signal, rear axle vehicle speed sensor (L6) [2)]	☐ 23 ⇒ 11.0

2) Rotor tooth count wrong or dirty/damaged, or wrong rear axle ratio, tires or wheels.

MB4029400039000X

Fig. 7 ABS DTC interpretation. C43, C230 & C280

DTC	Possible cause	Test step/Remedy
–	No fault in system	In case of complaint: □ 23 (entire test)
C 1000	Traction system control module (N47)	N47
C 1010	Battery voltage too low, circuit 87	□ 23 ⇒ 1.0
C 1011	Voltage supply for ASR/ETS/ESP hydraulic unit (A7/3) solenoid valve, short/open circuit	□ 23 ⇒ 5.0 □ 23 ⇒ 2.0
C 1012	Battery voltage too hi, circuit 87	□ 23 ⇒ 1.0
C 1020	CAN communication faulty	Wiring
C 1021	CAN communication with EA/CC/ISC control module (N4/1) interrupted	Read out DTC's from (N4/1)
C 1022	CAN communication with engine control module (ME-SFI) (N3/10) interrupted	Read out DTC's from (N3/10)
C 1024	CAN communication with transmission control module (N15/3) interrupted	Read out DTC's from (N15/3)
C 1100	Left front axle VSS sensor (L6/1), open circuit Left front axle VSS sensor (L6/1), loose connection Left front axle VSS sensor (L6/1), implausible [2]	□ 23 ⇒ 11.0
C 1101	Right front axle VSS sensor (L6/2), open circuit Right front axle VSS sensor (L6/2), loose connection Right front axle VSS sensor (L6/2), implausible [2]	□ 23 ⇒ 13.0

2) Rotor with incorrect tooth count, dirt accumulation on or damaged rotor, incorrect rear axle ratio, wrong wheel or tire size.
If DTC appears only after repair work, it was caused by applying the brakes or driving vehicle on a dynamometer, erase DTC.

MB0029900064010X

Fig. 8 ABS, ASR, ETS & SPS DTC interpretation (Part 1 of 4). C43, C230, S320, S420, SL500, SL600 & SLK230 & 1998–99 C280, CL500, CL600, E300, S500 & S600

DTC	Possible cause	Test step/Remedy
C 1102	**ETS/SRS:** Left rear axle VSS sensor (L6/3), open circuit Left rear axle VSS sensor (L6/3), loose connection Left rear axle VSS sensor (L6/3), implausible [2] **ABS:** Left axle VSS sensor (L6), open circuit Left axle VSS sensor (L6), loose connection Left axle VSS sensor (L6), implausible [2]	□ 23 ⇒ 15.0
C 1103	Right rear axle VSS sensor (L6/4), open circuit Right rear axle VSS sensor (L6/4), loose connection Right rear axle VSS sensor (L6/4), implausible [2]	□ 23 ⇒ 17.0
C 1104	Left front axle VSS sensor (L6/1), implausible [2]	□ 23 ⇒ 11.0
C 1105	Right front axle VSS sensor (L6/2), implausible [2]	□ 23 ⇒ 13.0
C 1106	**ETS/ASR:** Left rear axle VSS sensor (L6/3), implausible [2] **ABS:** Rear axle VSS sensor (L6), implausible [2]	□ 23 ⇒ 15.0
C 1107	Right rear axle VSS sensor (L6/4), implausible [2]	□ 23 ⇒ 17.0
C 1142	ABS lateral acceleration sensor (B24/2), short/open circuit	□ 23 ⇒ 8.0
C 1143	ABS lateral acceleration sensor (B24/2), implausible	□ 23 ⇒ 8.0
C 1200	Stop lamp switch (S9/1) short/open circuit S9/1 implausible	Wiring S/91

2) Rotor with incorrect tooth count, dirt accumulation on or damaged rotor, incorrect rear axle ratio, wrong wheel or tire size.
If DTC appears only after repair work, it was caused by applying the brakes or driving vehicle on a dynamometer, erase DTC.

MB0029900064020X

Fig. 8 ABS, ASR, ETS & SPS DTC interpretation (Part 2 of 4). C43, C230, S320, S420, SL500, SL600 & SLK230 & 1998–99 C280, CL500, CL600, E300, S500 & S600

DTC	Possible cause	Test step/Remedy
C 1300	ASR/ETS hydraulic unit, left front axle solenoid valve (hold) (A7/3y6), short/open circuit	□ 23 ⇒ 19.0
C 1301	ASR/ETS hydraulic unit, left front axle solenoid valve (hold) (A7/3y7), short/open circuit	□ 23 ⇒ 20.0
C 1302	ASR/ETS hydraulic unit, right front axle solenoid valve (hold) (A7/3y8), short/open circuit	□ 23 ⇒ 21.0
C 1303	ASR/ETS hydraulic unit, right front axle solenoid valve (release) (A7/3y9), short/open circuit	□ 23 ⇒ 22.0
C 1304	ASR/ETS hydraulic unit, left rear axle solenoid valve (hold) (A7/3y10), short/open circuit	□ 23 ⇒ 23.0
C 1305	ASR/ETS hydraulic unit, left rear axle solenoid valve (release) (A7/3y11), short/open circuit	□ 23 ⇒ 24.0
C 1306	ASR/ETS hydraulic unit, right rear axle solenoid valve (hold) (A7/3y12), short/open circuit	□ 23 ⇒ 25.0
C 1307	ASR/ETS hydraulic unit, right rear axle solenoid valve (release) (A7/3y13), short/open circuit	□ 23 ⇒ 26.0
C 1311	Switchover/solenoid valve (A7/3y5), short/open circuit	□ 23 ⇒ 27.0
C 1312	Master brake cylinder switchover valve (Y61)	□ 23 ⇒ 9.0
C 1313	ASR/ETS hydraulic unit, solenoid valve relay (A7/3k1)	N47

MB0029900064030X

Fig. 8 ABS, ASR, ETS & SPS DTC interpretation (Part 3 of 4). C43, C230, S320, S420, SL500, SL600 & SLK230 & 1998–99 C280, CL500, CL600, E300, S500 & S600

DTC	Possible cause	Test step/Remedy
C 1314	ASR/ETS hydraulic unit, solenoid valve relay (A7/3k1), voltage supply	□ 23 ⇒ 5.0 □ 23 ⇒ 2.0
C 1315	ASR/ETS hydraulic unit, inlet solenoid valve (A7/3y15)	□ 23 ⇒ 28.0
C 1401	High pressure return pump (A7/3m1) short/open circuit A7/3m1 will not turn off	□ 23 ⇒ 6.0
C 1500	VSS sensor implausible [2]	□ 23 ⇒ 11.0, 13.0, 15.0, 17.0
C 1501	SPS P-valve (Y10)	□ 23 ⇒ 7.0
C 1511	ETS/SPS control module (N47-2), not version coded	N47-2
C 1512	Brakes overheated	Brakes were momentarily overloaded, erase DTC.
C 1513	ASR/SPS (N47-1) OR ME-SFI (N3/10) engine control module, version coding incorrect	N47-1 N3/10
C 1514	SPS P-valve (Y10) adjustment data	□ 23 ⇒ 7.0 N47
C 1515	Version coding SPS	N47
C 1600	Temperature after engine is turned off	N47

2) Rotor with incorrect tooth count, dirt accumulation on or damaged rotor, incorrect rear axle ratio, wrong wheel or tire size.
If DTC appears only after repair work, it was caused by applying the brakes or driving vehicle on a dynamometer, erase DTC.

MB0029900064040X

Fig. 8 ABS, ASR, ETS & SPS DTC interpretation (Part 4 of 4). C43, C230, S320, S420, SL500, SL600 & SLK230 & 1998–99 C280, CL500, CL600, E300, S500 & S600

DTC		Possible cause	Test step/Remedy
1	–	No fault in system	In case of complaint: ☐ 23 (entire test), Check shorting pins
2	002	ASR/SPS (N47-1) or ETS/SPS (N47-2) control module	Replace control module.
3	003	Left front axle VSS sensor (L6/1), open circuit	☐ 23 ⇒ 13.0
4	004	Right front axle VSS sensor (L6/2), open circuit	☐ 23 ⇒ 15.0
5	005	Left rear axle VSS sensor (L6/3), open circuit	☐ 23 ⇒ 17.0
6	006	Right rear axle VSS sensor (L6/4), open circuit	☐ 23 ⇒ 19.0
7	007	Left front axle VSS sensor (L6/1), implausible [2]	☐ 23 ⇒ 13.0
8	008	Right front axle VSS sensor (L6/2), implausible [2]	☐ 23 ⇒ 15.0
9	009	Left rear axle VSS sensor (L6/3), implausible [2]	☐ 23 ⇒ 17.0
10	010	Right rear axle VSS sensor (L6/4), implausible [2]	☐ 23 ⇒ 19.0
11	011	VSS (L6/1, L6/2, L6/3, L6/4), implausible [2]	☐ 23 ⇒ 13.0, 15.0, 17.0, 19.0 Visually inspect.
12	012	ASR/ETS/ESP hydraulic unit, solenoid valve relay (A7/3k1)	☐ 23 ⇒ 8.0
13	013	ASR/ETS/ESP hydraulic unit, left front axle solenoid valve (hold) (A7/3y6)	☐ 23 ⇒ 21.0
14	014	ASR/ETS/ESP hydraulic unit, left front axle solenoid valve (release) (A7/3y7)	☐ 23 ⇒ 22.0

2) Rotor with incorrect tooth count, dirt accumulation on or damaged rotor, incorrect rear axle ratio, wrong wheel or tire size.
If DTC appears only after repair work, it was caused by applying the brakes or driving vehicle on a dynamometer, erase DTC.

MB0029600003010X

Fig. 9 ABS, ASR, ETS & SPS DTC interpretation (Part 1 of 4). SL500 & SL600

DTC		Possible cause	Test step/Remedy
15	015	ASR/ETS/ESP hydraulic unit, right front axle solenoid valve (hold) (A7/3y8)	☐ 23 ⇒ 23.0
16	016	ASR/ETS/ESP hydraulic unit, right front axle solenoid valve (release) (A7/3y9)	☐ 23 ⇒ 24.0
17	017	ASR/ETS/ESP hydraulic unit, left rear axle solenoid valve (hold) (A7/3y10)	☐ 23 ⇒ 25.0
18	018	ASR/ETS/ESP hydraulic unit, left rear axle solenoid valve (release) (A7/3y11)	☐ 23 ⇒ 26.0
19	019	ASR/ETS/ESP hydraulic unit, right rear axle solenoid valve (hold) (A7/3y12)	☐ 23 ⇒ 27.0
20	020	ASR/ETS/ESP hydraulic unit, right rear axle solenoid valve (release) (A7/3y13)	☐ 23 ⇒ 28.0
21	021	ASR/ETS/ESP hydraulic unit, switchover/solenoid valve (A7/3y5)	☐ 23 ⇒ 30.0
22	022	ASR/ETS/ESP hydraulic unit, inlet solenoid valve (A7/3y15)	☐ 23 ⇒ 29.0
23	023	**ASR only:** ASR system pressure too low	ASR hydraulic unit (A7/3)
24	024	ASR/ETS/ESP hydraulic unit, high-pressure/return pump relay (A7/3k2)	☐ 23 ⇒ 9.0 High-pressure/return pump (A7/3m1)
27	027	Stop lamp switch (S9/1)	☐ 23 ⇒ 11.0
28	028	Battery voltage too low, circuit 87	☐ 23 ⇒ 1.0
29	029	**ETS only:** Circuit 30, voltage supply	☐ 23 ⇒ 2.0
30	030	**ASR only:** CAN data bus to EA/CC/ISC control module (N4/1) interrupted	☐ 23 ⇒ 35.0

MB0029600003020X

Fig. 9 ABS, ASR, ETS & SPS DTC interpretation (Part 2 of 4). SL500 & SL600

DTC		Possible cause	Test step/Remedy
31	031	**ASR only:** CAN communication with LH-SFI or left and right LH-SFI control modules (N3/1 or N3/2 and N3/3) faulty CAN communication with engine control module (N3/4) faulty	☐ 23 ⇒ 35.0, Read out DTC
32	032	**ASR only:** CAN dcommunication with DI or left and right DI control module (N1/3 or N1/4 and N1/5) faulty	☐ 23 ⇒ 35.0
33	033	**ASR only:** CAN communication faulty in general	☐ 23 ⇒ 35.0,

MB0029600003030X

Fig. 9 ABS, ASR, ETS & SPS DTC interpretation (Part 3 of 4). SL500 & SL600

DTC		Possible cause	Test step/Remedy
34	034	**ETS only:** Brakes overheated	Brakes were momentarily overloaded, erase DTC.
35	035	**Model 129.076, 140.04/05/07:** Master brake cylinder switchover valve (Y61)	☐ 23 ⇒ 12.0
36	036	**Model 129.076, 140.04/05/07:** ABS lateral accelration sensor (B24/2), open circuit	☐ 23 ⇒ 32.0
37	037	**Model 129.076, 140.04/05/07:** ABS lateral accelration sensor (B24/2), implausible	☐ 23 ⇒ 32.0
38	038	**ETS only:** ETS/SPS control module (N47-2) not coded	Input code data into control module with HHT.
39	039	**Model 140:** ASR/SPS or ETS/SPS control module (N47-1 or N47-2)	Replace control module.
40	040	**Model 140:** SPS P-valve (Y10)	☐ 23 ⇒ 31.0
41	041	**Model 140:** ASR/SPS or ETS/SPS control module (N47-1 or N47-2)	Replace control module.

MB0029600003040X

Fig. 9 ABS, ASR, ETS & SPS DTC interpretation (Part 4 of 4). SL500 & SL600

DTC	Possible cause	Test step/Remedy
C 1000	ESP/SPS control module (N47-5)	Replace control module.
C 1010	Battery voltage too low, circuit 87	☐ 23 ⇒ 1.0 Battery charge low.
C 1011	ASR/ETS/ESP hydraulic unit solenoid valve voltage supply, open/short circuit	☐ 23 ⇒ 22.0
C 1020	CAN communication faulty in general	☐ 23 ⇒ 30.0
C 1022	CAN communication with right engine control module (ME-SFI, N3/12), interrupted	☐ 23 ⇒ 30.0 Read DTC (ME-SFI) memory
C 1023	CAN communication with left engine control module (ME-SFI, N3/11), interrupted	☐ 23 ⇒ 30.0 Read DTC (ME-SFI) memory
C 1024	CAN communication with transmission control module (N15/3), interrupted	Read DTC (ETC [722.6]) memory
C 1100	Left front axle VSS sensor (L6/1), open circuit Left front axle VSS sensor (L6/1), loose contact Left front axle VSS sensor (L6/1), implausible [2]	☐ 23 ⇒ 13.0
C 1101	Right front axle VSS sensor (L6/2), open circuit Right front axle VSS sensor (L6/2), loose contact Right front axle VSS sensor (L6/2), implausible [2]	☐ 23 ⇒ 15.0

[2]) Rotor with incorrect tooth count, dirt accumulation on or damage to rotor, incorrect rear axle ratio, wrong wheel or tire size.
If DTC appears only after repair work, it may be caused by applying the brakes or driving vehicle on a dynamometer, erase DTC.

MB0029900069010X

Fig. 10 ABS, ESP & SPS DTC interpretation (Part 1 of 4). E430, S320 & S420 & 1998–99 CL500, CL600, E320, S500, S600, SL500 & SL600

DTC	Possible cause	Test step/Remedy
C 1102	Left rear axle VSS sensor (L6/3), open circuit Left rear axle VSS sensor (L6/3), loose contact Left rear axle VSS sensor (L6/3), implausible [2]	☐ 23 ⇒ 17.0
C 1103	Right rear axle VSS sensor (L6/4), open circuit Right rear axle VSS sensor (L6/4), loose contact Right rear axle VSS sensor (L6/4), implausible [2]	☐ 23 ⇒ 19.0
C 1120	ESP yaw sensor (N64) signal wire, open/short circuit ESP yaw sensor (N64) reference wire, open/short circuit	☐ 23 ⇒ 28.0
C 1140	Steering angle sensor (N49), open/short circuit Steering angle sensor (N49), initialization	☐ 23 ⇒ 29.0
C 1141	ESP brake pressure sensor (B34)	☐ 23 ⇒ 9.0 ☐ 23 ⇒ 27.0
C 1142	ABS lateral acceleration sensor (B24/2), open/short circuit	☐ 23 ⇒ 26.0
C 1200	Stop lamp switch (S9/1), open/short circuit Stop lamp switch (S9/1), implausible	☐ 23 ⇒ 6.0
C 1300	ASR/ETS/ESP hydraulic unit, left front axle solenoid valve (hold) (A7/3y6)	☐ 23 ⇒ 23.0
C 1301	ASR/ETS/ESP hydraulic unit, left front axle solenoid valve (release) (A7/3y7)	☐ 23 ⇒ 23.0
C 1302	ASR/ETS/ESP hydraulic unit, right front axle solenoid valve (hold) (A7/3y8)	☐ 23 ⇒ 23.0
C 1303	ASR/ETS/ESP hydraulic unit, right front axle solenoid valve (release) (A7/3y9)	☐ 23 ⇒ 23.0

[2]) Rotor with incorrect tooth count, dirt accumulation on or damage to rotor, incorrect rear axle ratio, wrong wheel or tire size.
If DTC appears only after repair work, it may be caused by applying the brakes or driving vehicle on a dynamometer, erase DTC.

MB0029900069020X

Fig. 10 ABS, ESP & SPS DTC interpretation (Part 2 of 4). E430, S320 & S420 & 1998–99 CL500, CL600, E320, S500, S600, SL500 & SL600

DTC	Possible cause	Test step/Remedy
C 1304	ASR/ETS/ESP hydraulic unit, left rear axle solenoid valve (hold) (A7/3y10)	☐ 23 ⇒ 23.0
C 1305	ASR/ETS/ESP hydraulic unit, left rear axle solenoid valve (release) (A7/3y11)	☐ 23 ⇒ 23.0
C 1306	ASR/ETS/ESP hydraulic unit, right rear axle solenoid valve (hold) (A7/3y12)	☐ 23 ⇒ 23.0
C 1307	ASR/ETS/ESP hydraulic unit, right rear axle solenoid valve (release) (A7/3y13)	☐ 23 ⇒ 23.0
C 1308	ASR/ETS/ESP hydraulic unit, front axle precharge solenoid valve (A7/3y16)	☐ 23 ⇒ 24.0
C 1309	ASR/ETS/ESP hydraulic unit, rear axle precharge solenoid valve (A7/3y17)	☐ 23 ⇒ 24.0
C 1310	ASR/ETS/ESP hydraulic unit, front axle switchover valve (A7/3y18)	☐ 23 ⇒ 24.0
C 1311	ASR/ETS/ESP hydraulic unit, rear axle switchover valve (A7/3y19)	☐ 23 ⇒ 24.0
C 1312	Master brake cylinder switchover valve (Y61)	☐ 23 ⇒ 8.0
C 1313	ASR/ETS/ESP hydraulic unit, solenoid valve relay (A7/3k1)	Replace control module (N47-5)
C 1400	ASR/ESP charging pump (M15), open/short circuit	☐ 23 ⇒ 9.0
C 1401	ASR/ETS/ESP hydraulic unit, high-pressure/return pump (A7/3m1), open/short circuit ASR/ETS/ESP hydraulic unit, high-pressure/return pump (A7/3m1), does not turn off	☐ 23 ⇒ 10.0 ☐ 23 ⇒ 11.0

MB0029900069030X

Fig. 10 ABS, ESP & SPS DTC interpretation (Part 3 of 4). E430, S320 & S420 & 1998–99 CL500, CL600, E320, S500, S600, SL500 & SL600

DTC	Possible cause	Test step/Remedy
C 1500	VSS (L6/1, L6/2, L6/3, L6/4) implausible [2]	☐ 23 ⇒ 13.0, 15.0, 17.0, 19.0
C 1501	SPS P-valve (Y10)	☐ 23 ⇒ 12.0
C 1503	Pressure transfer piston unit	Check condition of rear brake pads Pressure transfer piston unit.
C 1504	System turned off	Steering angle sensor (N49) not initialized ☐ 23 ⇒ 29.0 Low voltage to ESP yaw rate sensor (N64) ☐ 23 ⇒ 28.0

[2]) Rotor with incorrect tooth count, dirt accumulation on or damage to rotor, incorrect rear axle ratio, wrong wheel or tire size.
If DTC appears only after repair work, it may be caused by applying the brakes or driving vehicle on a dynamometer, erase DTC.

MB0029900069040X

Fig. 10 ABS, ESP & SPS DTC interpretation (Part 4 of 4). E430, S320 & S420 & 1998–99 CL500, CL600, E320, S500, S600, SL500 & SL600

Complaint/Problem	Possible cause	Remedy/Test step
ABS malfunction indicator lamp (MIL) (A1e17) remains lit with engine running.		DTC memory DTC memory for base module
ABS malfunction indicator lamp (MIL) (A1e17) comes on and stays on while driving.		DTC memory
ABS malfunction indicator lamp (MIL) (A1e17) comes on and goes out while driving.	Voltage supply < 11 V, too many electrical consumers operating	Test generator (G2), DTC memory
ABS malfunction indicator lamp (MIL) (A1e17) does not come on with ignition **ON**.	Wiring ABS malfunction indicator lamp (MIL) (A1e17)	□ 23 ⇒ 2.0

MB4029400062000X

Fig. 11 ABS symptom related diagnosis. C43, C230 & C280

Complaint/Problem	Possible cause	Test step/Remedy
ASR MIL (A1e22) or ETS MIL (A1e35) and ABS MIL (A1e17) come when engine is running		Check voltage supply and ground, Read DTC memory
ETS MIL (A1e35) comes on while driving and after a while goes out	Rear axle brakes were momentarily overloaded.	Read DTC memory, Erase DTC 034
ASR MIL (A1e22) or ETS MIL (A1e35) and ABS MIL (A1e17) comes on while driving and does not go out		Read DTC memory
ASR MIL (A1e22) or ETS MIL (A1e35) and ABS MIL (A1e17) comes on while driving and then goes out	Vehicle system voltage < 11 V, too many electrical consumers in use.	Check voltage supply and ground alteration Check generator, Read DTC memory
ABS MIL (A1e17) does not come on with ignition turned on		□ 23 ⇒ 3.0
ASR MIL (A1e22) or ETS MIL (A1e35) does not come on with ignition turned on		□ 23 ⇒ 4.0
ABS MIL (A1e17) comes on with engine running after brake test or dynamometer use	Implausible rpm signal due to different rpm at front and rear axles.	Read, erase DTC memory

MB0029600004000X

Fig. 13 ABS, ASR, ETS & SPS symptom related diagnosis. SL500 & SL600

Complaint/Problem	Possible cause	Test step/Remedy
ASR MIL (A1e22) or ETS MIL (A1e35) or ABS MIL (A1e17) come when engine is running		Read out DTC using HHT.
ASR MIL (A1e22) or ETS MIL (A1e35) and ABS MIL (A1e17) comes on while driving and does not go out		Read out DTC using HHT.
ASR MIL (A1e22) or ETS MIL (A1e35) and ABS MIL (A1e17) comes on while driving and then goes out	Vehicle system voltage < 11 V, too many electrical consumers in use.	Check generator (G2), Read out DTC using HHT.
Brake pad wear indicator lamp (A1e6), low brake fluid/parking brake indicator lamp (A1e7), ASR warning lamp (A1e21), ETS warning lamp (A1e36), ABS MIL (A1e17), ASR MIL (A1e22) or ETS MIL (A1e35) will not come on when turning ignition on.	Data bus to instrument cluster	23 ⇒ 3.0 Read out DTC's instrument cluster
ABS MIL (A1e17) comes on with engine running after brake test or dynamometer use	Nonplausible rpm signal due to different rpm at front and rear axles.	Read out DTC, erase using HHT.
ETS only, ETS MIL (A1e35) comes on while driving and then after a while goes out (DTC code C 1512 is read out)	Rear brakes at one time were overloaded	Read out DTC, erase using HHT.

MB0029900065000X

Fig. 12 ABS, ASR, ETS & SPS symptom related diagnosis. C43, C230, S320, S420, SL500, SL600 & SLK230 & 1998–99 C280, CL500, CL600, E300, S500 & S600

Complaint/Problem	Possible cause	Test step/Remedy
ASR MIL (A1e22) or ETS MIL (A1e35) or ABS MIL (A1e17) come when engine is running		Read out DTC using HHT.
ASR MIL (A1e22) or ETS MIL (A1e35) and ABS MIL (A1e17) comes on while driving and does not go out		Read out DTC using HHT.
ASR MIL (A1e22) or ETS MIL (A1e35) and ABS MIL (A1e17) comes on while driving and then goes out	Vehicle system voltage < 11 V, too many electrical consumers in use.	Check generator (G2), Read out DTC using HHT.
Brake pad wear indicator lamp (A1e6), low brake fluid/parking brake indicator lamp (A1e7), ASR warning lamp (A1e21), ETS warning lamp (A1e36), ABS MIL (A1e17), ASR MIL (A1e22) or ETS MIL (A1e35) will not come on when turning ignition on.	Data bus to instrument cluster	23 ⇒ 3.0
ABS MIL (A1e17) comes on with engine running after brake test or dynamometer use	Nonplausible rpm signal due to different rpm at front and rear axles.	Read out DTC, erase using HHT.
ETS only, ETS MIL (A1e35) comes on while driving and then after a while goes out (DTC code C 1512 is read out)	Rear brakes at one time were overloaded	Read out DTC, erase using HHT.

MB4029500063000X

Fig. 14 ABS, ASR & ETS symptom related diagnosis. S320, S420, SL500 & SL600 & 1998–99 S500 & S600

Complaint/Problem	Possible cause	Test step/Remedy
ESP MIL (A1e42) or ABS MIL (A1e17) comes on with engine running		Check voltage supply and ground, Read DTC memory ☐ 12,
EPC MIL (A1e43) comes on with engine running	Fault in EA.	Read DTC memory ☐ 12, DM, Engines
ESP MIL (A1e42) or ABS MIL (A1e17) comes on while driving and does not go out		Read DTC memory ☐ 12
ESP MIL (A1e42) or ABS MIL (A1e17) comes on while driving and then goes out	Vehicle system voltage < 11 V, too many electrical consumers in use, loose power or ground connection.	Check voltage supply and ground, Check generator (G2), Read DTC memory ☐ 12 Wiring
ESP MIL (A1e42) or ABS MIL (A1e17) does not come on with ignition turned on	Lamp, Wiring.	☐ 23 ⇒ 3.0
ABS MIL (A1e17) comes on with engine running after brake test or dynamometer use	Implausible wheel speed signal due to different rpm at front and rear axles.	Read, erase DTC memory ☐ 12

MB0029900070000X

Fig. 15 ABS, ESP & SPS symptom related diagnosis. E430, S320 & S420 & 1998–99 CL500, CL600, E320, S500, S600, SL500 & SL600

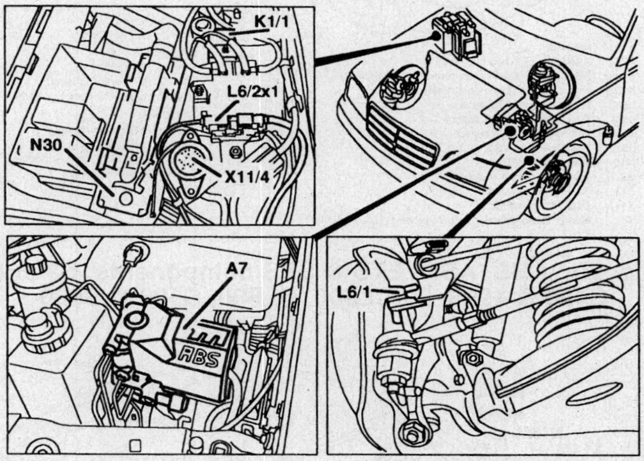

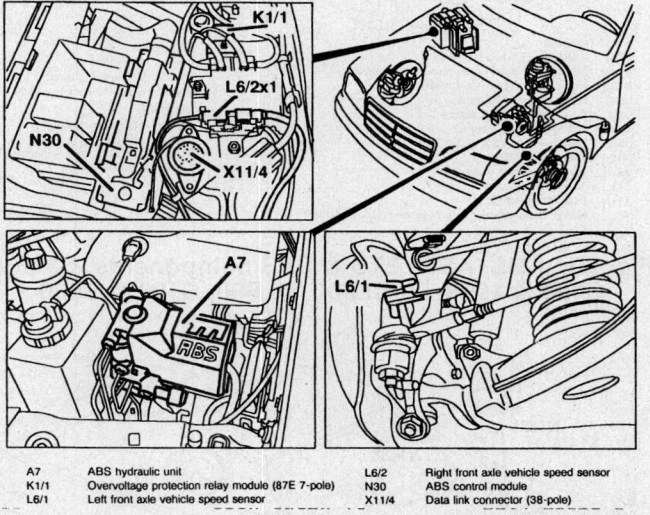

A7 ABS hydraulic unit
K1/1 Overvoltage protection relay module (87E 7-pole)
L6/1 Left front axle vehicle speed sensor
L6/2 Right front axle vehicle speed sensor
N30 ABS control module
X11/4 Data link connector (38-pole)

MB4029900007010X

Fig. 16 ABS components (Part 1 of 2). C43, C230 & C280 (CLK320, CLK430 & SLK230 similar)

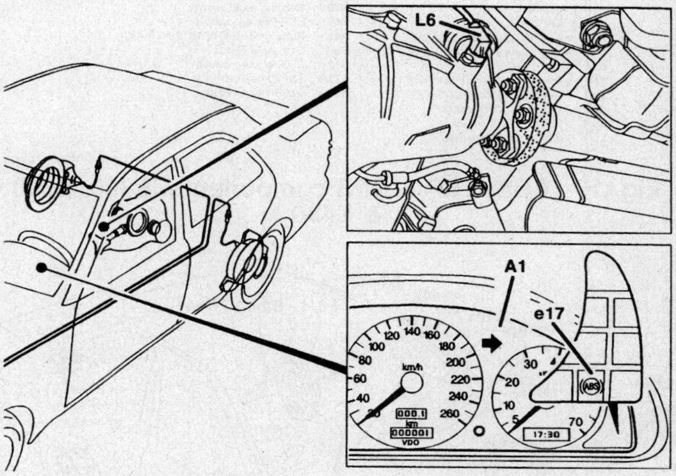

A1 Instrument cluster
A1e17 ABS malfunction indicator lamp
L6 Rear axle vehicle speed sensor

MB4029900007020X

Fig. 16 ABS components (Part 2 of 2). C43, C230 & C280 (CLK320, CLK430 & SLK230 similar)

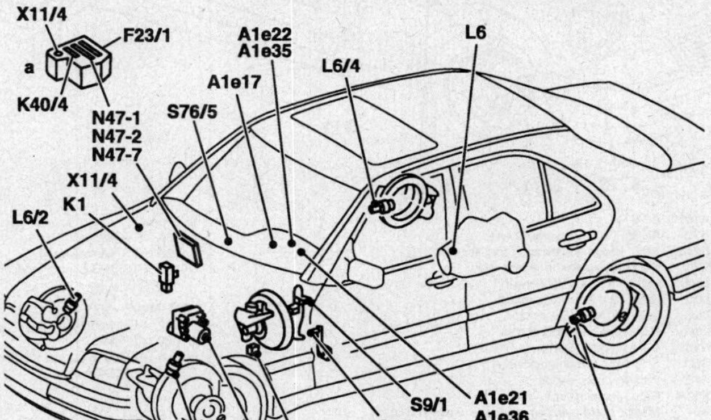

A1e17 ABS MIL
A7/3 ASR/ETS/ESP hydraulic unit
B23/1 Left front tire pressure indicator sensor
F23/1 Control module box
K1 Over voltage protection relay module
K20/1 High pressure/return pump relay
K40/4 Passsenger-side fuse and relay module box
L6/1 Left front axle VSS sensor
L6/2 Right front axle VSS sensor
L6/3 Left rear axle VSS sensor
L6/4 Right rear axle VSS sensor
S9/1 Stop lamp switch (4-pole)
S12 Parking brake switch
X11/4 Data link connector

ABS only
L6 Rear axle VSS sensor
N47-7 ABS control module

ETS only
A1e35 ETS MIL
A1e36 ETS warning lamp
N47-2 ETS/SPS control module

ASR only
A1e21 ASR warning lamp
A1e22 ASR MIL
N47-1 ASR/SPS control module
S76/5 ASR Off switch

MB4029900067000X

Fig. 17 ABS, AST, ETS & SPS components. C230 & C280

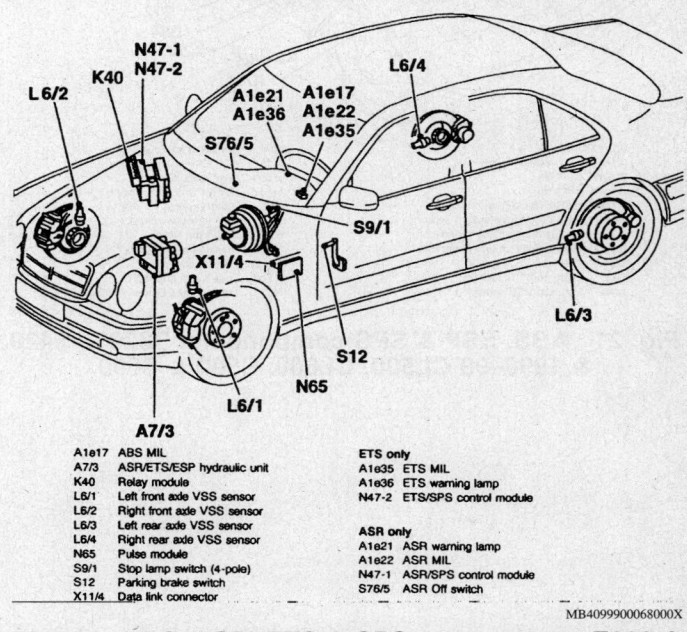

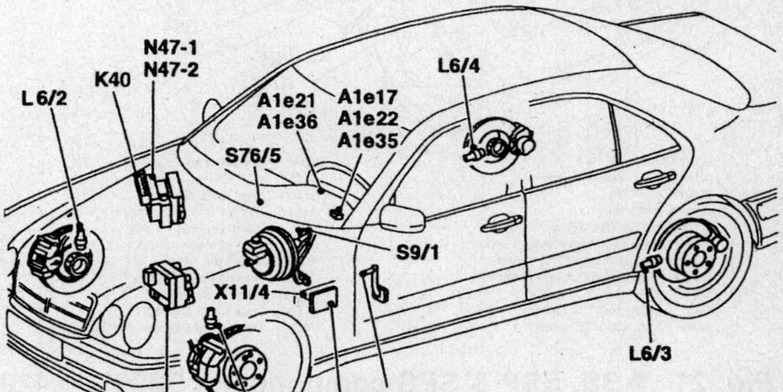

A1e17 ABS MIL
A7/3 ASR/ETS/ESP hydraulic unit
K40 Relay module
L6/1 Left front axle VSS sensor
L6/2 Right front axle VSS sensor
L6/3 Left rear axle VSS sensor
L6/4 Right rear axle VSS sensor
N65 Pulse module
S9/1 Stop lamp switch (4-pole)
S12 Parking brake switch
X11/4 Data link connector

ETS only
A1e35 ETS MIL
A1e36 ETS warning lamp
N47-2 ETS/SPS control module

ASR only
A1e21 ASR warning lamp
A1e22 ASR MIL
N47-1 ASR/SPS control module
S76/5 ASR Off switch

MB4099900068000X

Fig. 18 ABS, ASR, ETS & SPS components. E300 & E320

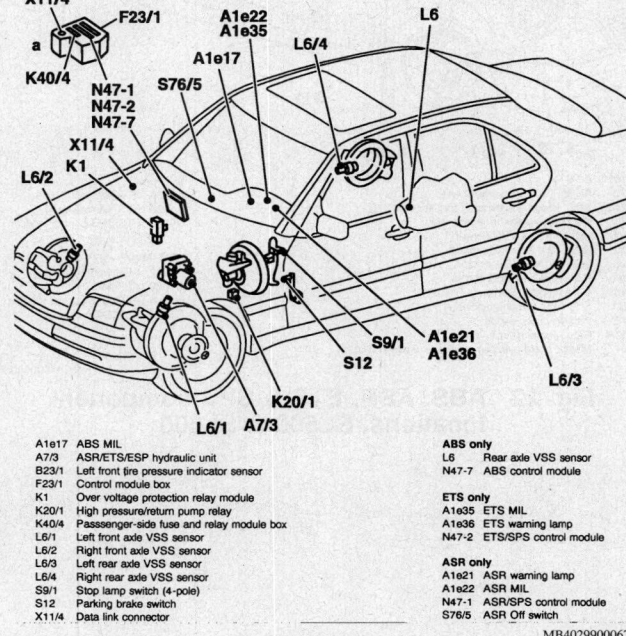

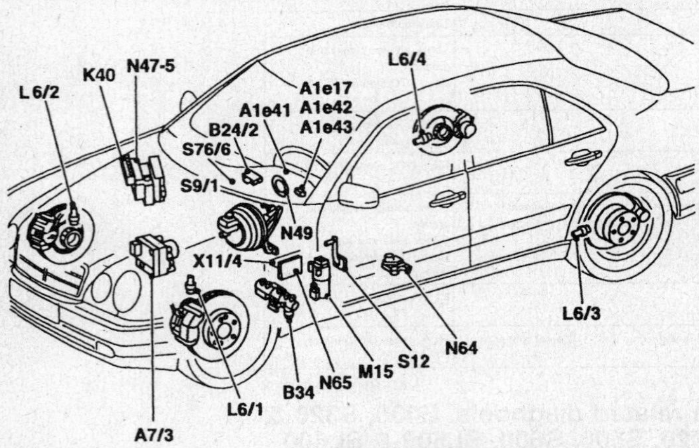

A1e17 ABS MIL
A1e41 ESP warning lamp
A1e42 ESP MIL
A1e43 EPC MIL
A7/3 ASR/ETS/ESP hydraulic unit
B24/2 ABS lateral acceleration sensor
B34 ESP brake pressure sensor
K40 Relay module (base function)
L6/1 Left front VSS sensor
L6/2 Right front VSS sensor
L6/3 Left rear VSS sensor
L6/4 Right rear VSS sensor
M15 ASR/ESP charging pump
N47-5 ESP/SPS control module
N49 Steering angle sensor
N64 ESP yaw rate sensor
N65 Pulse module (ETS/HCS/ATA,A/C)
S9/1 Stop lamp switch
S12 Parking brake switch
S76/6 ESP Off switch
X11/4 Data link connector

MB4099900072000X

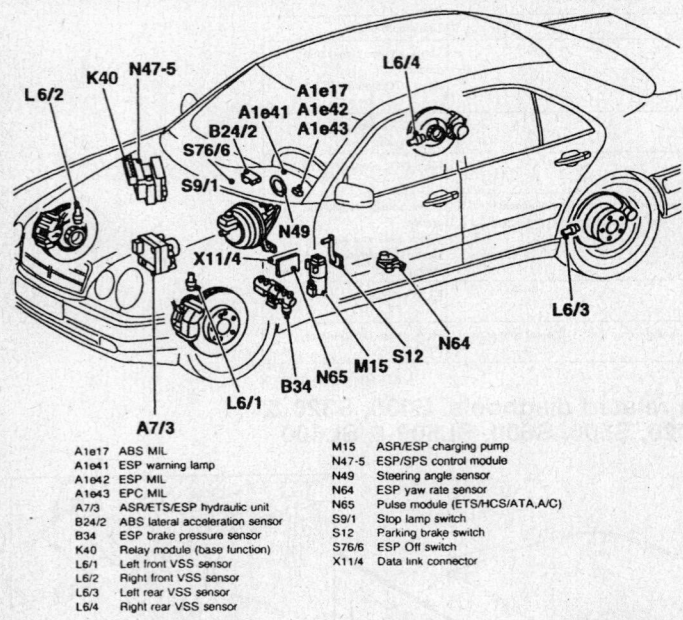

Fig. 19 ABS, ESP & SPS components. E300, E320 & E430

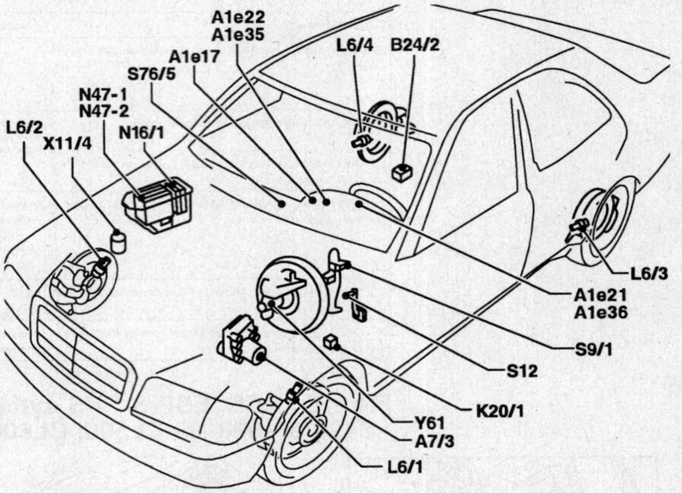

A1e17 ABS MIL
A7/3 ASR/ETS/ESP hydraulic unit
B24/2 ABS lateral acceleration sensor (140.04/05/07)
K20/1 High pressure/return pump relay
L6/1 Left front axle VSS sensor
L6/2 Right front axle VSS sensor
L6/3 Left rear axle VSS sensor
L6/4 Right rear axle VSS sensor
N16/1 Base module (BM)
S9/1 Stop lamp switch (4-pole)
S12 Parking brake switch
X11/4 Data link connector
Y61 Master brake cyllinder swichover valve (140.04/05/07)

ETS only
A1e35 ETS MIL
A1e36 ETS warning lamp
N47-2 ETS/SPS control module

ASR only
A1e21 ASR warning lamp
A1e22 ASR MIL
N47-1 ASR/SPS control module
S76/5 ASR Off switch

MB4029900065000X

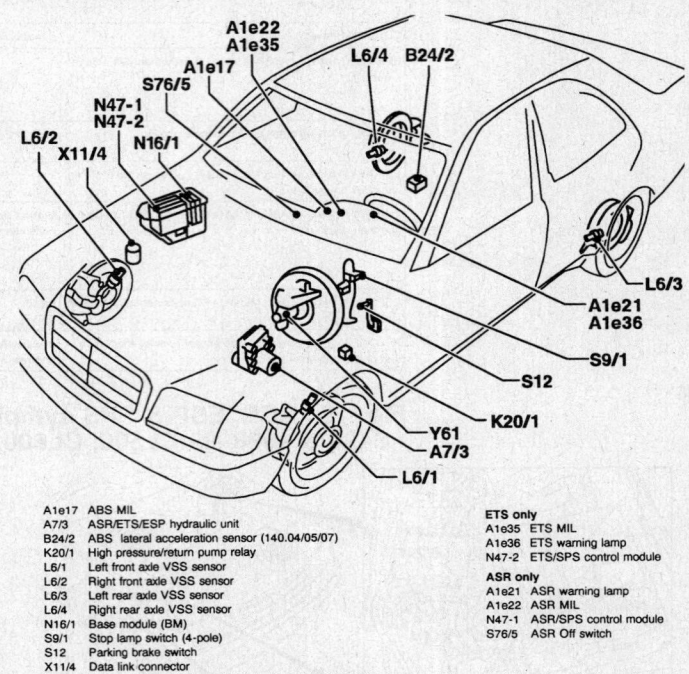

Fig. 20 ABS, ASR, ETS & SPS components. S320 & S420 & 1998–99 CL500, CL600, S500 & S600

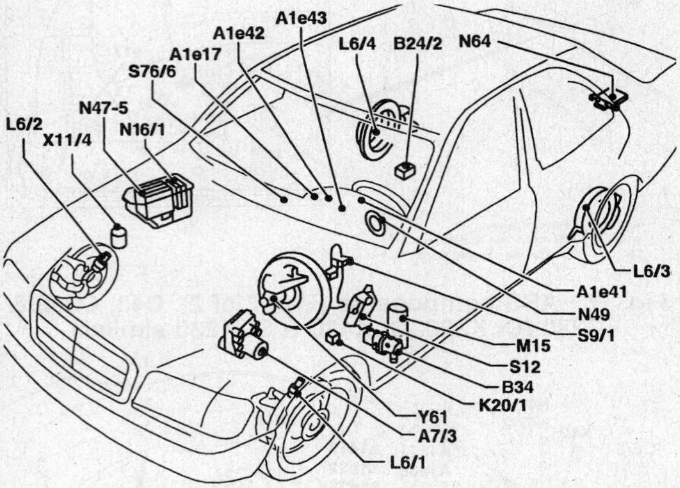

A1e17 ABS MIL
A1e41 ESP warning lamp
A1e42 ESP MIL
A1e43 EPC MIL
A7/3 ASR/ETS/ESP hydraulic unit
B24/2 ABS lateral acceleration sensor
B34 ESP brake pressure sensor
K20/1 High-pressure/return pump relay
L6/1 Left front VSS sensor
L6/2 Right front VSS sensor
L6/3 Left rear VSS sensor
L6/4 Right rear VSS sensor
M15 ASR/ESP charging pump
N16/1 Base module
N47-5 ESP/SPS control module
N49 Steering angle sensor
N64 ESP yaw rate sensor
S9/1 Stop lamp switch
S12 Parking brake switch
S76/6 ESP Off switch
X11/4 Data link connector
Y61 Master brake clinder switchover valve

MB4029900071000X

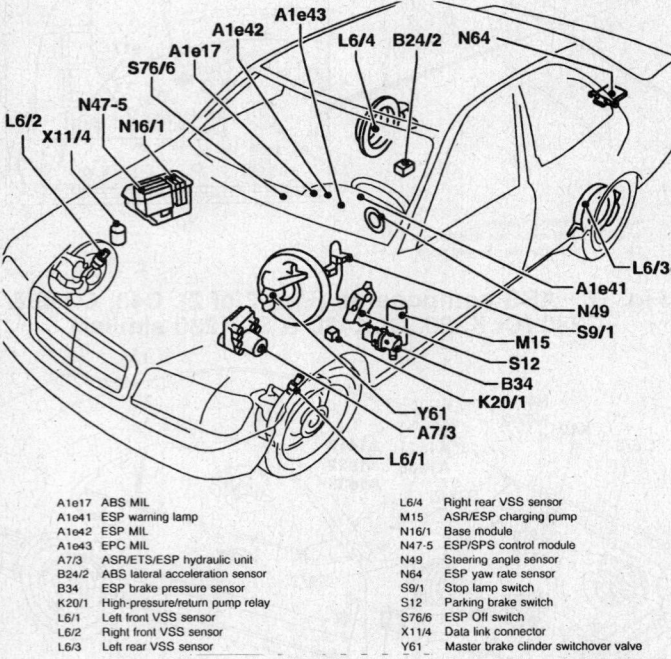

Fig. 21 ABS, ESP & SPS components. S320 & S420 & 1998–99 CL500, CL600, S500 & S600

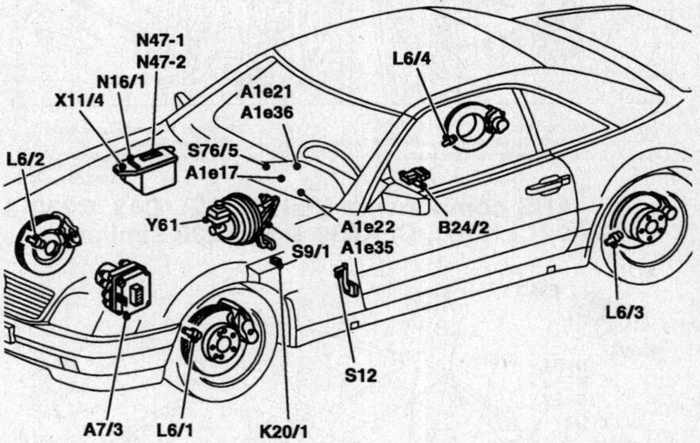

A1e17 ABS MIL
A7/3 ASR/ETS/ESP hydraulic unit
B24/2 ABS lateral acceleration sensor (129.076)
K20/1 High pressure/return pump relay
L6/1 Left front axle VSS sensor
L6/2 Right front axle VSS sensor
L6/3 Left rear axle VSS sensor
L6/4 Right rear axle VSS sensor
N16/1 Base module (BM)
S9/1 Stop lamp switch (4-pole)
S12 Parking brake switch
X11/4 Data link connector
Y61 Master brake cyllinder swichover valve (129.076)

ETS only
A1e35 ETS MIL
A1e36 ETS warning lamp
N47-2 ETS/SPS control module

ASR only
A1e21 ASR warning lamp
A1e22 ASR MIL
N47-1 ASR/SPS control module
S76/5 ASR Off switch

MB4029900064000X

Fig. 22 ABS, ASR, ETS & SPS component locations. SL500 & SL600

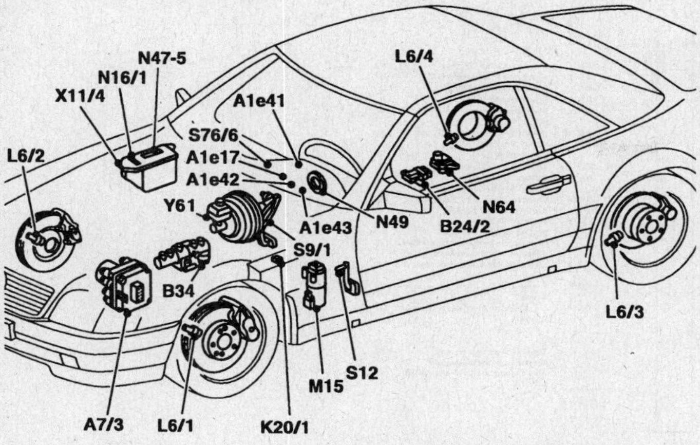

A1e17	ABS MIL	L6/4	Right rear VSS sensor
A1e41	ESP warning lamp	M15	ASR/ESP charging pump
A1e42	ESP MIL	N16/1	Base module
A1e43	EPC MIL	N47-5	ESP/SPS control module
A7/3	ASR/ETS/ESP hydraulic unit	N49	Steering angle sensor
B24/2	ABS lateral acceleration sensor	N64	ESP yaw rate sensor
B34	ESP brake pressure sensor	S9/1	Stop lamp switch
K20/1	High-pressure/return pump relay	S12	Parking brake switch
L6/1	Left front VSS sensor	S76/6	ESP Off switch
L6/2	Right front VSS sensor	X11/4	Data link connector
L6/3	Left rear VSS sensor	Y61	Master brake clinder switchover valve

MB4029900070000X

Fig. 23 ABS, ESP & SPS component locations. SL500 & SL600

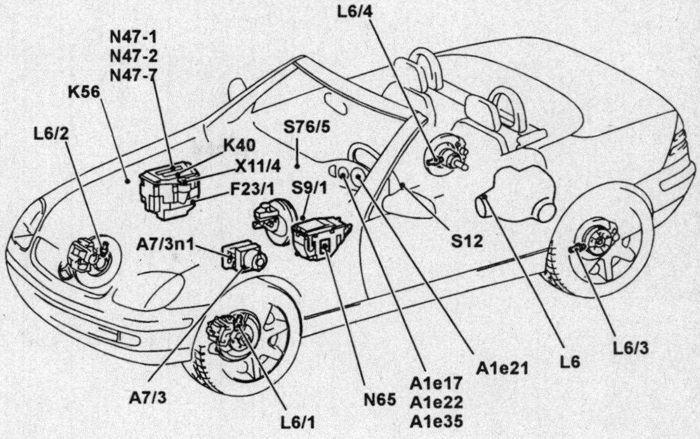

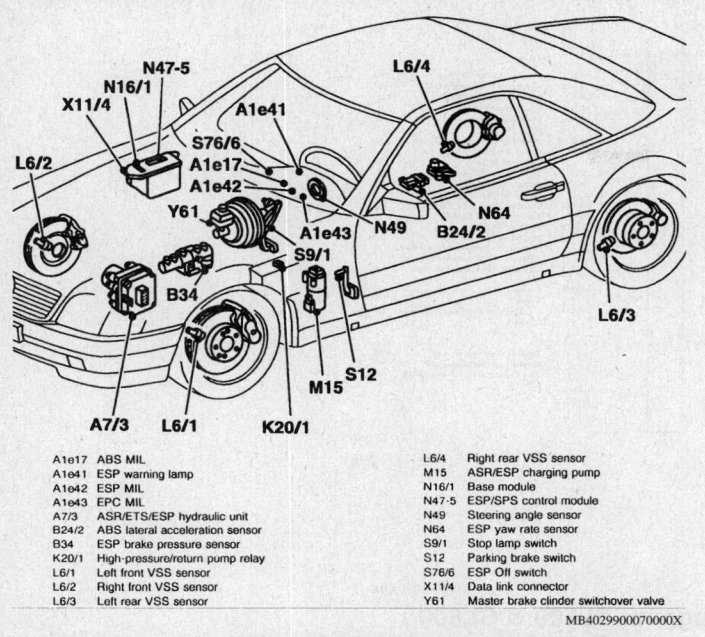

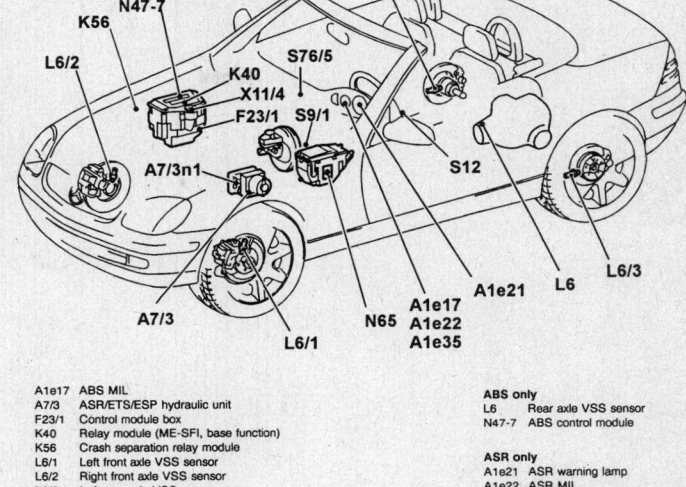

A1e17	ABS MIL
A7/3	ASR/ETS/ESP hydraulic unit
F23/1	Control module box
K40	Relay module (ME-SFI, base function)
K56	Crash separation relay module
L6/1	Left front axle VSS sensor
L6/2	Right front axle VSS sensor
L6/3	Left rear axle VSS sensor
L6/4	Right rear axle VSS sensor
N65	Pulse module (HCS, ATA, A/C)
S9/1	Stop lamp switch (4-pole)
S12	Parking brake switch
X11/4	Data link connector

ABS only

L6	Rear axle VSS sensor
N47-7	ABS control module

ASR only

A1e21	ASR warning lamp
A1e22	ASR MIL
N47-1	ASR/SPS control module
S76/5	ASR Off switch

MB4029900066000X

Fig. 24 ABS, ASR, ETS & SPS component locations. SLK230

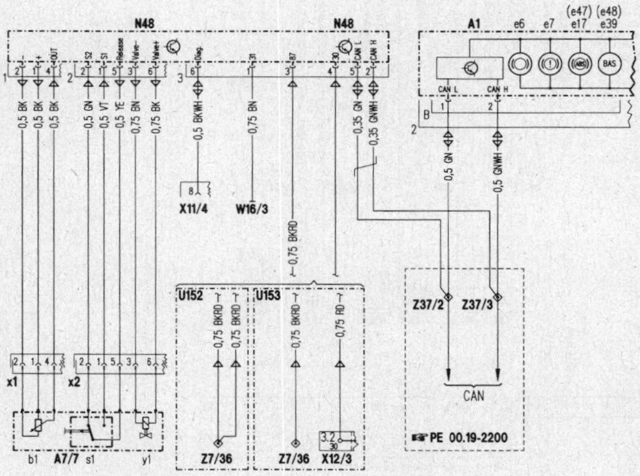

A1	Instrument cluster	11A
A1e6	Brake pad wear indicator lamp	12A
A1e7	Low brake fluid level/parking brake indicator lamp	13A
A1e17	ABS MIL	13A
A1e39	EA warning lamp	14A
A1e47	BAS/ESP MIL	13A
A1e48	BAS/ASR MIL	14A
A7/7	Brake booster (BAS)	2M
A7/7b1	Membrane travel sensor (BAS)	1M
A7/7s1	Release switch (BAS)	3M
A7/7x1	Membrane travel sensor connector (BAS)	1K
A7/7x2	Release switch/membrane travel sensor connector (BAS)	2K
A7/7y1	Solenoid valve (BAS)	4M
N48	BAS control module	4A 8A
U152	Valid for model 202	5H
U153	Valid for model 208	6H
W16/3	Ground (output ground - component compartment - left)	6F

X11/4	Data link connector (DTC readout)	5F
X12/3	Terminal block (circuit 30)	8M 13M
Z7/36	Circuit 87 M2e connector sleeve	5M 7M
Z37/2	Engine CAN-Bus (low) connector sleeve	10H
Z37/3	Engine CAN-Bus (high) connector sleeve	11H
	☞ PE 00.19-2200 CAN-Bus engine	

MB0029900079000X

Fig. 25 ABS wiring diagram. C43, C230, C280, CLK320 & CLK430

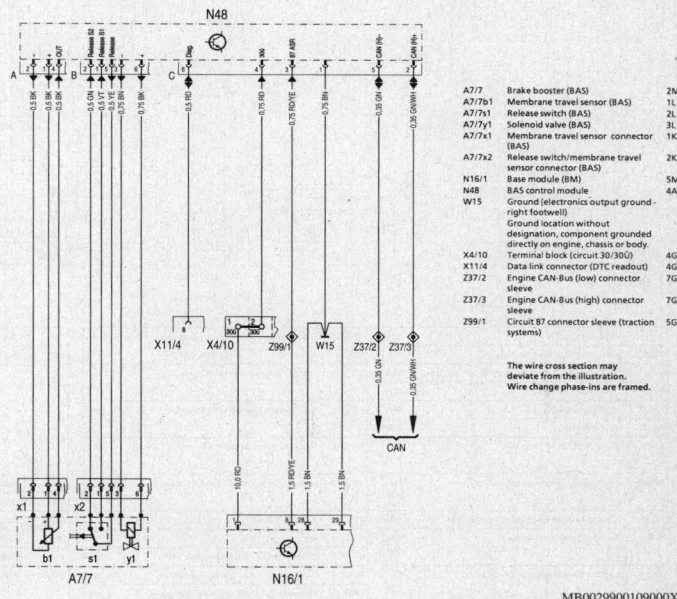

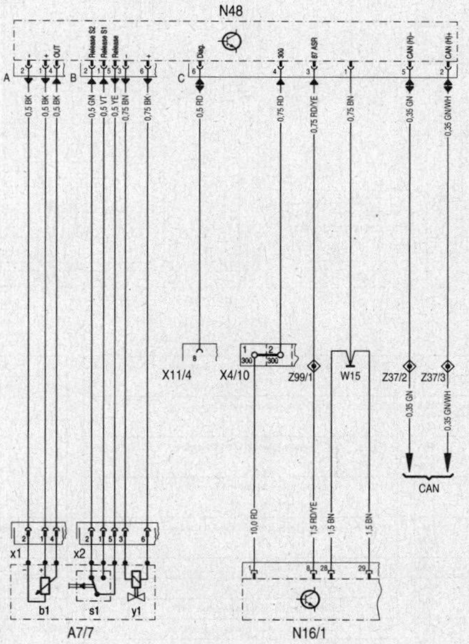

A7/7	Brake booster (BAS)	2M
A7/7b1	Membrane travel sensor (BAS)	1L
A7/7s1	Release switch (BAS)	2L
A7/7y1	Solenoid valve (BAS)	3L
A7/7x1	Membrane travel sensor connector (BAS)	1K
A7/7x2	Release switch/membrane travel sensor connector (BAS)	2K
N16/1	Base module (BM)	5M
N48	BAS control module	4A
W15	Ground (electronics output ground - right footwell) Ground location without designation, component grounded directly on engine, chassis or body.	
X4/10	Terminal block (circuit 30/30Ü)	4G
X11/4	Data link connector (DTC readout)	4G
Z37/2	Engine CAN-Bus (low) connector sleeve	7G
Z37/3	Engine CAN-Bus (high) connector sleeve	7G
Z99/1	Circuit 87 connector sleeve (traction systems)	5G

The wire cross section may deviate from the illustration. Wire change phase-ins are framed.

MB0029900109000X

Fig. 26 ABS wiring diagram. S320 & S420 & 1998–99 CL500, CL600, S500 & S600

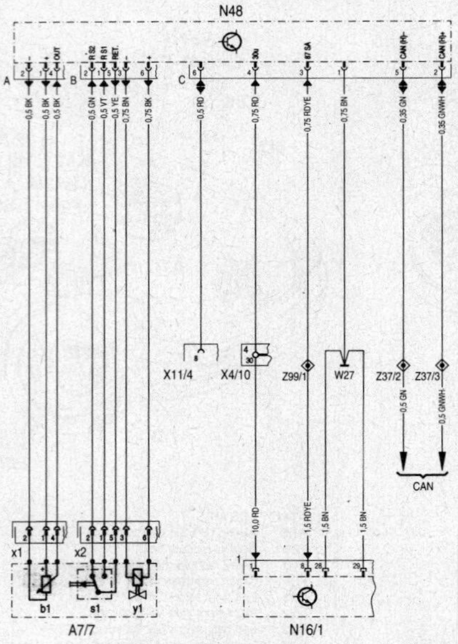

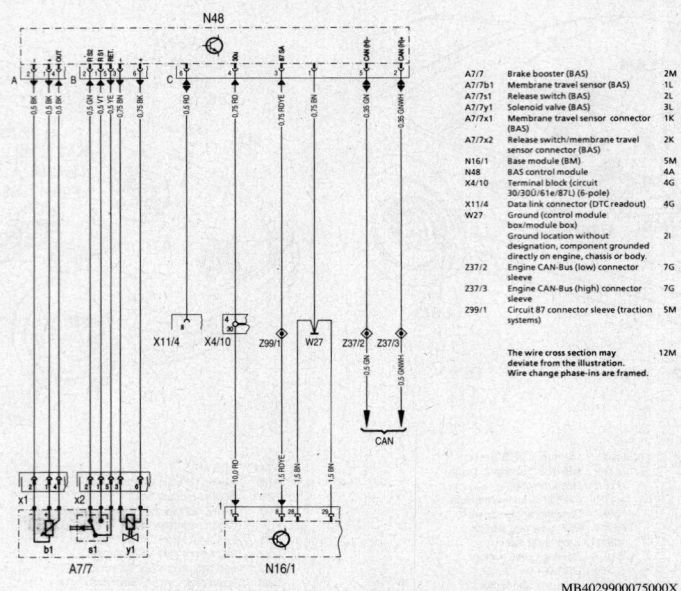

A7/7	Brake booster (BAS)	2M
A7/7b1	Membrane travel sensor (BAS)	1L
A7/7s1	Release switch (BAS)	2L
A7/7y1	Solenoid valve (BAS)	3L
A7/7x1	Membrane travel sensor connector (BAS)	1K
A7/7x2	Release switch/membrane travel sensor connector (BAS)	2K
N16/1	Base module (BM)	5M
N48	BAS control module	4A
X4/10	Terminal block (circuit 30/30Ü/61e/87L) (6-pole)	4G
X11/4	Data link connector (DTC readout)	4G
W27	Ground (control module box/module box)	
	Ground location without designation, component grounded directly on engine, chassis or body.	2I
Z37/2	Engine CAN-Bus (low) connector sleeve	7G
Z37/3	Engine CAN-Bus (high) connector sleeve	7G
Z99/1	Circuit 87 connector sleeve (traction systems)	5M
	The wire cross section may deviate from the illustration. Wire change phase-ins are framed.	12M

MB4029900075000X

Fig. 27 ABS wiring diagram. SL500 & SL600

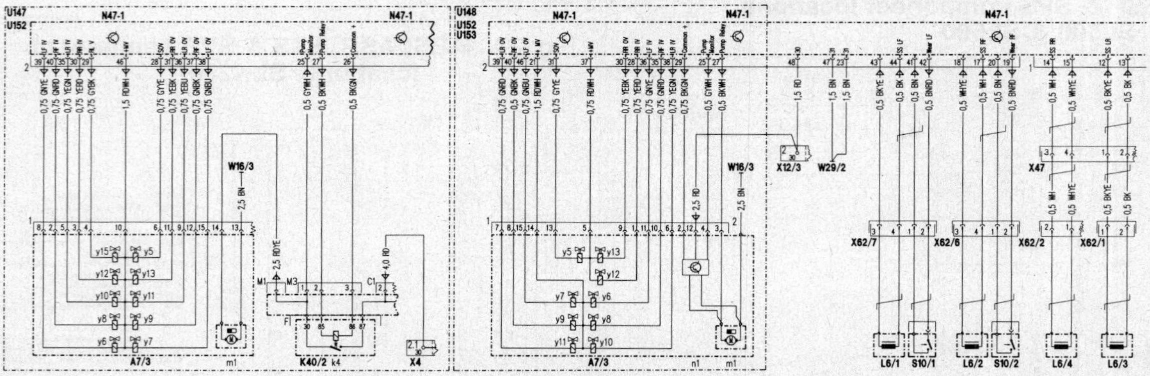

A1	Instrument cluster	62A
A1e6	Brake pad wear indicator lamp	64A
A1e7	Low brake fluid level/parking brake indicator lamp	65A
A1e17	ABS MIL	66A
A1e21	ASR warning lamp	64A
A1e48	BAS/ASR MIL	63A
A7/3	ASR/ETS/ESP hydraulic unit	5M 17M
A7/3m1	High-pressure/return pump	7M 20M
A7/3n1	Cycling module/high pressure return pump	19M
A7/3y5	Switchover/solenoid valve	5H 16H
A7/3y6	Left front axle solenoid valve (hold)	3L 17K
A7/3y7	Left front axle solenoid valve (release)	5L 16K
A7/3y8	Right front axle solenoid valve (hold)	3K 17K
A7/3y9	Right front axle solenoid valve (release)	5K 16K
A7/3y10	Left rear axle solenoid valve (hold)	3K 17L
A7/3y11	Left rear axle solenoid valve (release)	5K 16L
A7/3y12	Right rear axle solenoid valve (hold)	3I 17I
A7/3y13	Right rear axle solenoid valve (release)	5I 17H
A7/3y15	Inlet solenoid valve	3H
G1	Battery	35M
K40/2	Driver-side fuse and relay module box	9M
K40/2k4	High pressure/return pump relay module	10M
K40/4	Passenger-side fuse and relay module box	41M
K40/4f2	Fuse, traction system	43M
K40/4k1	Polarity protection relay	39M
L6/1	Left front axle VSS sensor	25M
L6/2	Right front axle VSS sensor	27M
L6/3	Left rear axle VSS sensor	31M
L6/4	Right rear axle VSS sensor	29M
N47-1	ASR/SPS control module	4A 11A 16A 21A 28A 36A 44A 53A 59A
N73	Electronic ignition lock control module	33M
S9/1	Stop lamp switch (4-pole)	46M
S10/1	Left front brake pad wear sensor	26M
S10/2	Right front brake pad wear sensor	28M
S12	Parking brake switch	58M
S76/5	ASR OFF switch	53M 55M
U147	Valid for Bosch system	1A
U148	Valid for Teves system	13A
U152	Valid for model 202	1B 13B 46F 52A
U153	Valid for model 208	13B 47F 54A
W1	Main ground (behind instrument cluster)	32H
W16/3	Ground (output ground - component compartment - left)	7F 21F
W16/4	Ground (output ground - component compartment - right)	38F
W19	Ground (right front seat crossmember)	55H
W29/2	Ground (right A-pillar)	23F 58H
X4	Terminal block (circuit 30, left footwell)	12M
X11/4	Data link connector (DTC readout)	41F
X12/3	Terminal block (circuit 30)	22F
X18	Interior/taillamp harness connector	46H
X20	Stop lamp switch intermediate connector (2-pole)	46K
X26/23	Engine compartment/cockpit connector	33F
X43/3	REST/CL connector, circuit 30Z	35F

MB0029900080010X

Fig. 28 ASR wiring diagram (Part 1 of 2). C43, C230, C280, CLK320 & CLK430

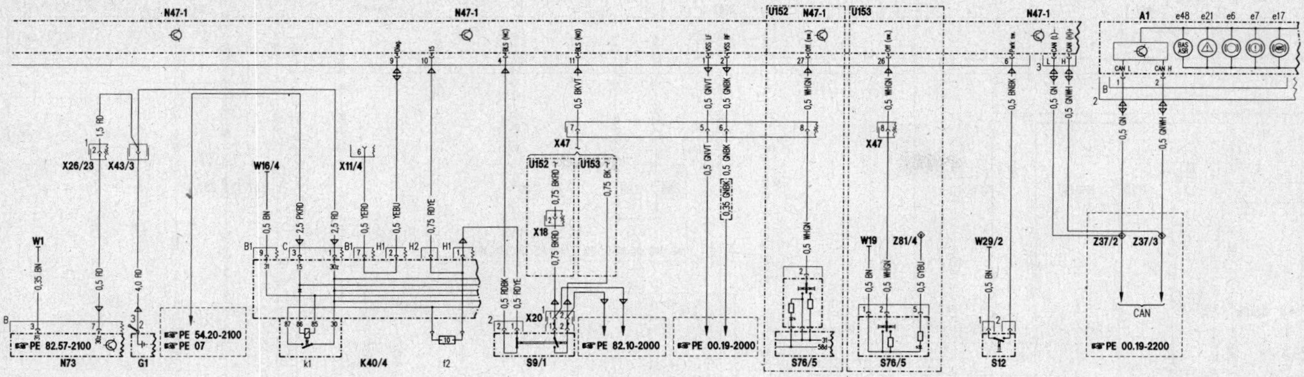

X47	Rear axle VSS sensor harness connector (2-pole) (right footwell)	29F 46E 55E
X62/1	Left rear axle VSS sensor/brake pad wear sensor connector	30H
X62/2	Right rear axle VSS sensor/brake pad wear sensor connector	29H
X62/6	Right front axle VSS sensor connector (component compartment)	26H
X62/7	Left front axle VSS sensor connector (component compartment)	24H
Z37/2	Engine CAN-Bus (low) connector sleeve	61H
Z37/3	Engine CAN-Bus (high) connector sleeve	62H
Z81/4	Circuit 58d connector sleeve (frame floor)	56H
	☞ PE 00.19-2000 Front axle VSS	
	☞ PE 00.19-2200 CAN-Bus engine	
	☞ PE 07 Mixture preparation	

☞ PE 54.20-2100 Driver-side fuse and relay module (K40/2)
☞ PE 82.10-2000 Exterior lighting
☞ PE 82.57-2100 Electronic ignition switch (N73)

MB0029900080020X

Fig. 28 ASR wiring diagram (Part 2 of 2). C43, C230, C280, CLK320 & CLK430

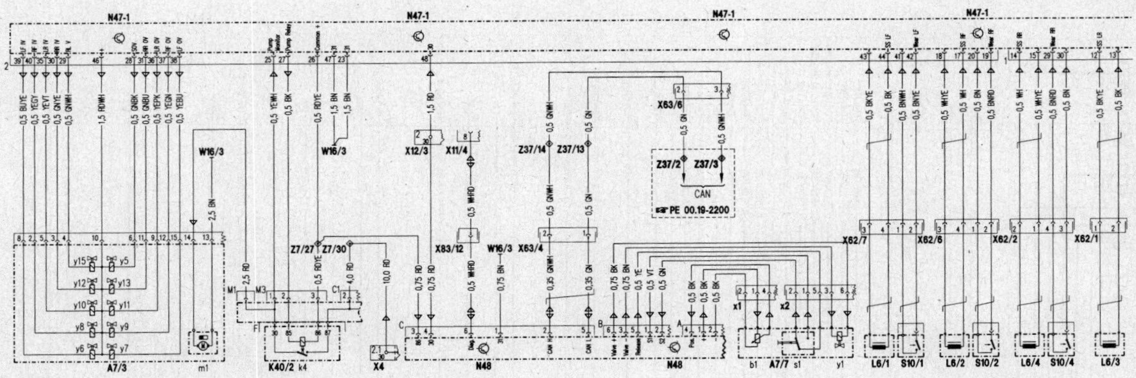

A1	Instrument cluster	55A
A1e6	Brake pad wear indicator lamp	57A
A1e7	Low brake fluid level/parking brake indicator lamp	58A
A1e17	ABS MIL	58A
A1e21	ASR warning lamp	57A
A1e49	BAS/ETS MIL	56A
A7/3	ASR/ETS/ESP hydraulic unit	4L
A7/3m1	High-pressure/return pump	6L
A7/3y5	Switchover/solenoid valve	4H
A7/3y6	Left front axle solenoid valve (hold)	3K
A7/3y7	Left front axle solenoid valve (release)	4K
A7/3y8	Right front axle solenoid valve (hold)	3K
A7/3y9	Right front axle solenoid valve (release)	4K
A7/3y10	Left rear axle solenoid valve (hold)	3J
A7/3y11	Left rear axle solenoid valve (release)	4J
A7/3y12	Right rear axle solenoid valve (hold)	3J
A7/3y13	Right rear axle solenoid valve (release)	4J
A7/3y15	Inlet solenoid valve	3H
A7/7	Brake booster (BAS)	21L
A7/7b1	Membrane travel sensor (BAS)	21L

A7/7s1	Release switch (BAS)	22L
A7/7x1	Membrane travel sensor connector (BAS)	20J
A7/7x2	Release switch/membrane travel sensor connector (BAS)	22J
A7/7y1	Solenoid valve (BAS)	23L
G1	Battery	32L
K40/2	Driver-side fuse and relay module box	8L
K40/2k4	High pressure/return pump relay module	9L
K40/4	Passenger-side fuse and relay module box	40L
K40/4f2	Fuse, traction system	42L
K40/4k1	Polarity protection relay	38L
L6/1	Left front axle VSS sensor	24L
L6/2	Right front axle VSS sensor	26L
L6/3	Left rear axle VSS sensor	30L
L6/4	Right rear axle VSS sensor	28L
N7-1	Illumination control module	46L

N47-1	ASR/SPS control module	4A 12A 20A 27A 36A 44A 51A
N48	BAS control module	14L 19L
N73	Electronic ignition lock control module	34L
S9/1	Stop lamp switch (4-pole)	44L
S10/1	Left front brake pad wear sensor	25L
S10/2	Right front brake pad wear sensor	27L
S10/4	Right rear brake pad wear sensor	29L
S12	Parking brake switch	52L
S76/5	ASR OFF switch	50L
W1	Main ground (behind instrument cluster)	33H
W15/1	Ground (right footwell)	50G
W16/3	Ground (output ground-left wheel housing)	6E 9E 14H
W16/4	Ground (output ground - right wheel housing)	37E

W18	Ground (left front seat crossmember)	52H
X4	Terminal block (circuit 30, left footwell)	11L 35E
X11/4	Data link connector (DTC readout)	13E 39E
X12/3	Terminal block (circuit 30)	12E
X62/1	Left rear axle VSS sensor/brake pad wear sensor connector	30H
X62/2	Right rear axle VSS sensor/brake pad wear sensor connector	28H
X62/6	Right front axle VSS sensor connector (component compartment)	26H
X62/7	Left front axle VSS sensor connector (component compartment)	24H
X63/4	CAN databus adaptor connector (2-pole)	15H
X63/6	CAN-Bus/15u connector	19D 32E 54H
X83/12	Brake assist diagnostic connector	13H
Z3/38	Circuit 15 (unfused) connector sleeve	34H

MB0029900096010X

Fig. 29 ASR wiring diagram (Part 1 of 2). E320 & E430

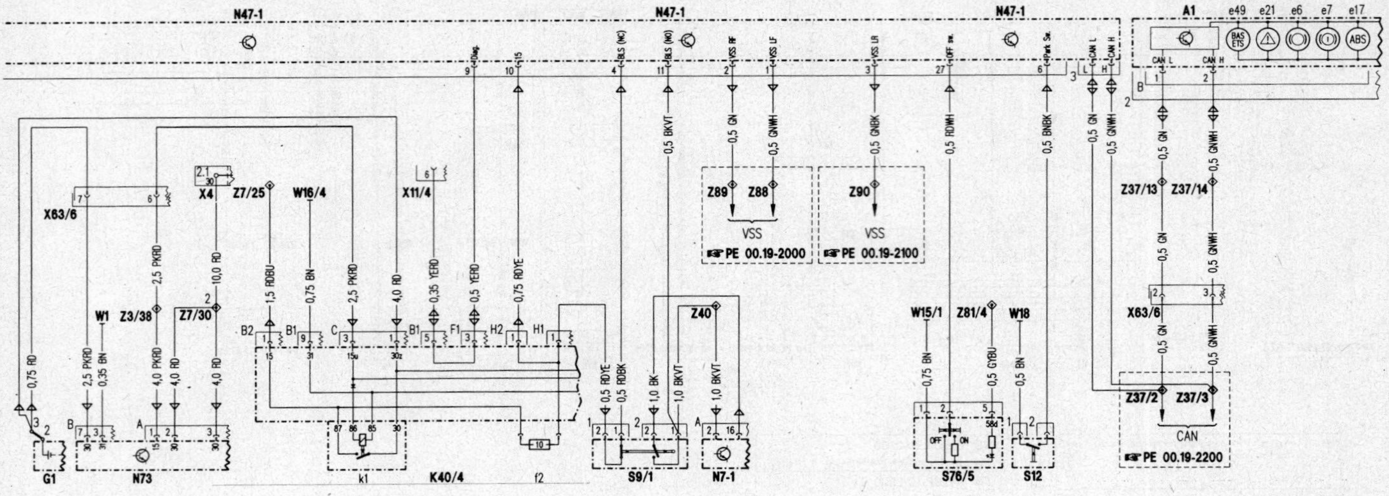

MB0029900096020X

Fig. 29 ASR wiring diagram (Part 2 of 2). E320 & E430

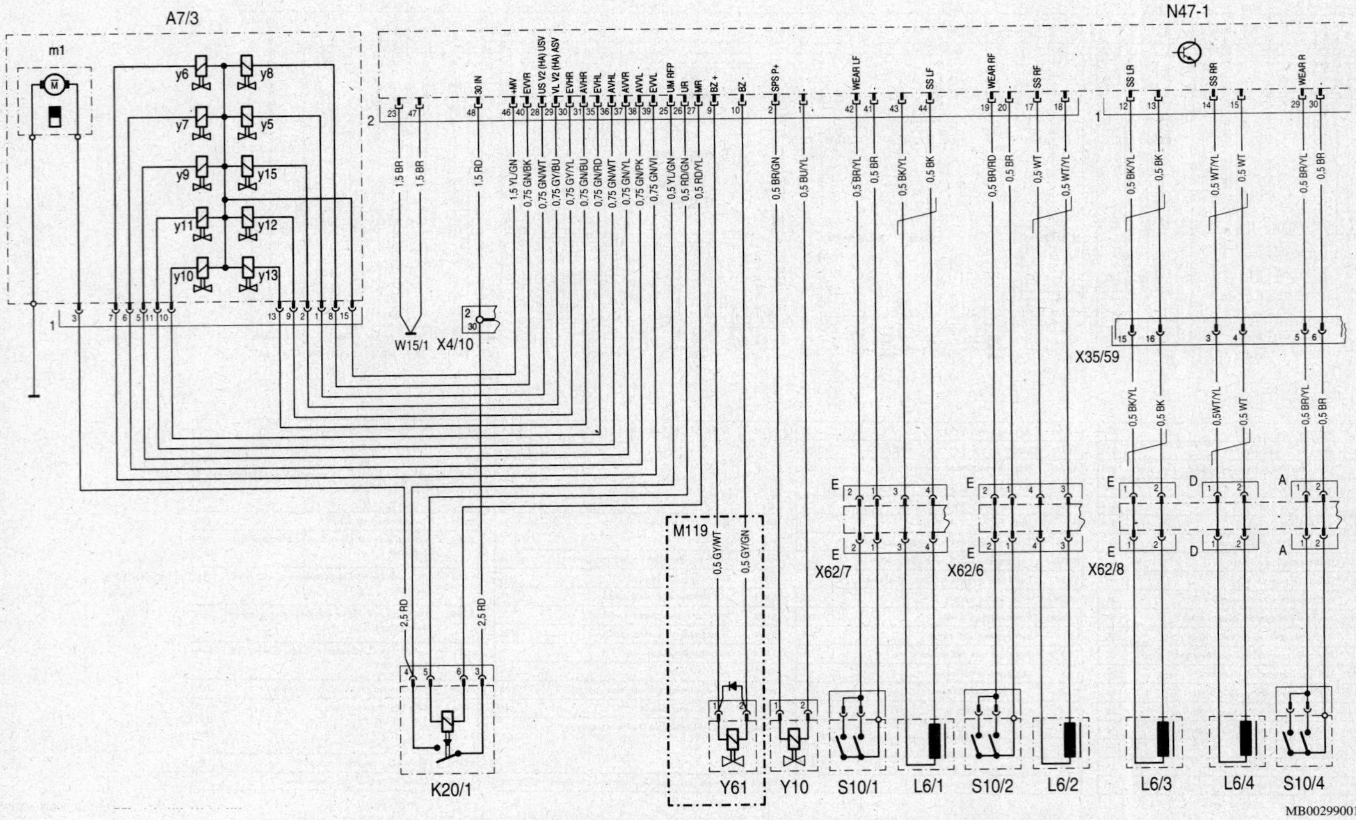

MB0029900108010X

Fig. 30 ASR wiring diagram (Part 1 of 5). S320 & 1998–99 S500

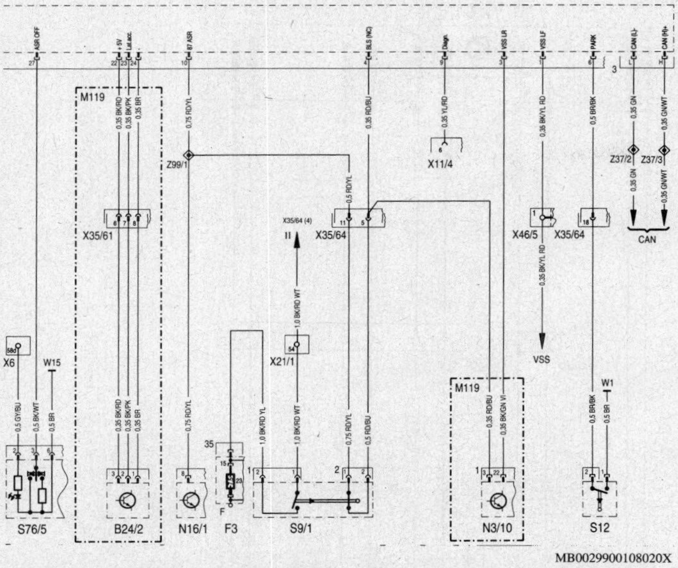

Fig. 30 ASR wiring diagram (Part 2 of 5). S320 & 1998–99 S500

A7/3	ASR/ETS/ESP hydraulic unit	3A
A7/3m1	High-pressure/return pump	1B
A7/3y5	Switchover/solenoid valve	4C
A7/3y6	Left front axle solenoid valve (hold)	3B
A7/3y7	Left front axle solenoid valve (release)	3C
A7/3y8	Right front axle solenoid valve (hold)	4B
A7/3y9	Right front axle solenoid valve (release)	3C
A7/3y10	Left rear axle solenoid valve (hold)	3E
A7/3y11	Left rear axle solenoid valve (release)	3D
A7/3y12	Right rear axle solenoid valve (hold)	4D
A7/3y13	Right rear axle solenoid valve (release)	4E
A7/3y15	Inlet solenoid valve	4C
B24/2	ABS lateral acceleration sensor	19M
F3	Fuse box (35-fuse, in fuse and relay box F1)	
F3-23	Fuse 23, circuit 15	21L
K20/1	High-pressure/return pump relay	6M
L6/1	Left front axle VSS sensor	12M
L6/2	Right front axle VSS sensor	13M
L6/3	Left rear axle VSS sensor	15M
L6/4	Right rear axle VSS sensor	16M
N3/10	Engine control module (ME-SFI)	26M
N16/1	Base module (BM)	20M
N47-1	ASR/SPS control module	15A
S9/1	Stop lamp switch (4-pole)	22M
S10/1	Left front brake pad wear sensor	11M
S10/2	Right front brake pad wear sensor	13M
S10/4	Right rear brake pad wear sensor	16M
S12	Parking brake switch	27M
S76/5	ASR OFF switch	17M
W1	Main ground (behind instrument cluster)	
W15	Ground (electronics output ground - right footwell)	
W15/1	Ground (electronics - right footwell)	
	Ground location without designation, component grounded directly on engine, chassis or body.	
X4/10	Terminal block (circuit 30/30Ü)	6F
X6	Terminal block (circuit 58d) (3- or 4-pole)	17H
X11/4	Data link connector (DTC readout)	25E
X21/1	Terminal block (stop lamp switch)	22H
X35/59	Compact harness/taillamp harness separation point	14F
X35/61	RPM rate sensor separation point	19F
X35/64	Compact harness/cockpit separation point (18-pole)	23F 27F
X46/5	Terminal block (right foot well)	26F
X62/6	Right front axle VSS sensor connector (component compartment)	12I
X62/7	Left front axle VSS sensor connector (component compartment)	11I
X62/8	Rear axle multiple circuit junction connector	14I
Y10	SPS P-valve	10M
Y61	Master brake cylinder switchover valve	9M
Z37/2	CAN-Engine-Bus (low) connector sleeve	28D
Z37/3	CAN-Engine-Bus (high) connector sleeve	28D
Z99/1	Circuit 87 connector sleeve (ASR/ETS)	20E

The wire cross section may deviate from the illustration. Wire change phase-ins are framed.

MB0029900108030X

Fig. 30 ASR wiring diagram (Part 3 of 5). S320 & 1998–99 S500

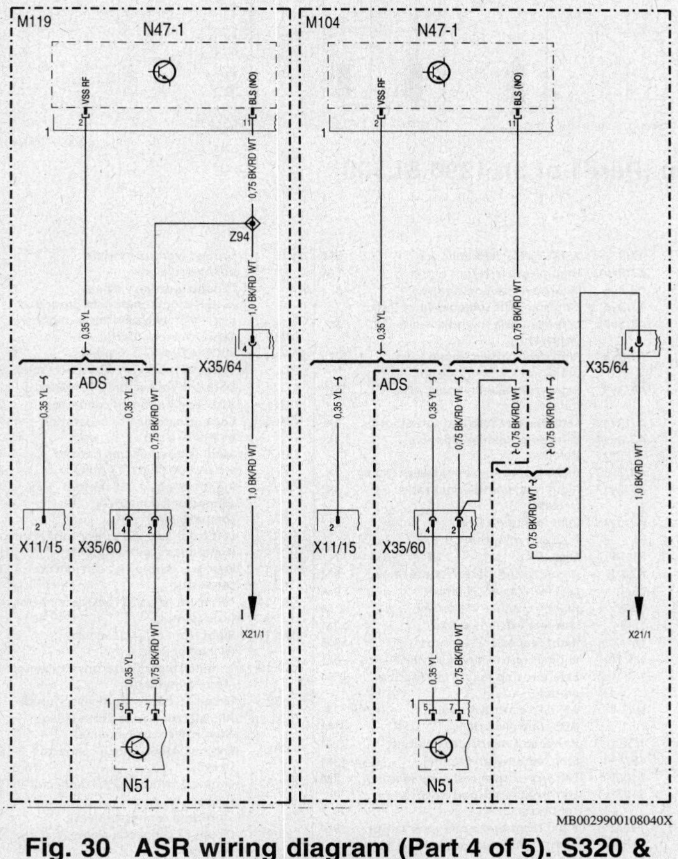

Fig. 30 ASR wiring diagram (Part 4 of 5). S320 & 1998–99 S500

N47-1	ASR/SPS control module
N51	ADS control module
	Ground location without designation, component grounded directly on engine, chassis or body.
X11/15	Diagnostic intermediate connector (taillamp harness) (16-pole)
X35/60	ADS separation point
X35/64	Compact harness/cockpit separation point (18-pole)
Z94	Stop lamp switch contact connector sleeve (feed from brake lamp switch - S9/1, n.o. contact)

The wire cross section may deviate from the illustration. Wire change phase-ins are framed.

MB0029900108050X

Fig. 30 ASR wiring diagram (Part 5 of 5). S320 & 1998–99 S500

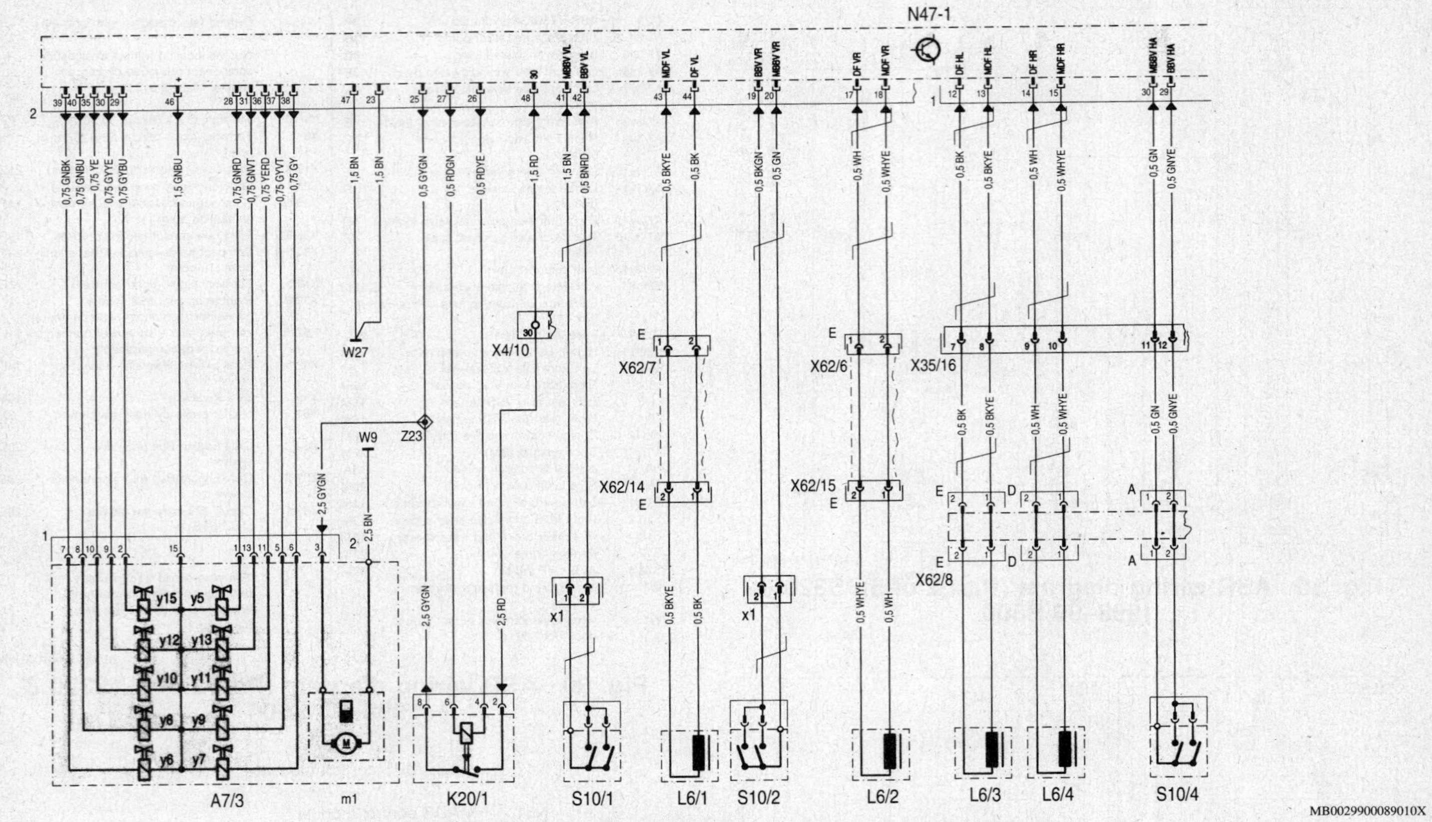

Fig. 31 ASR wiring diagram (Part 1 of 3). 1998 SL500

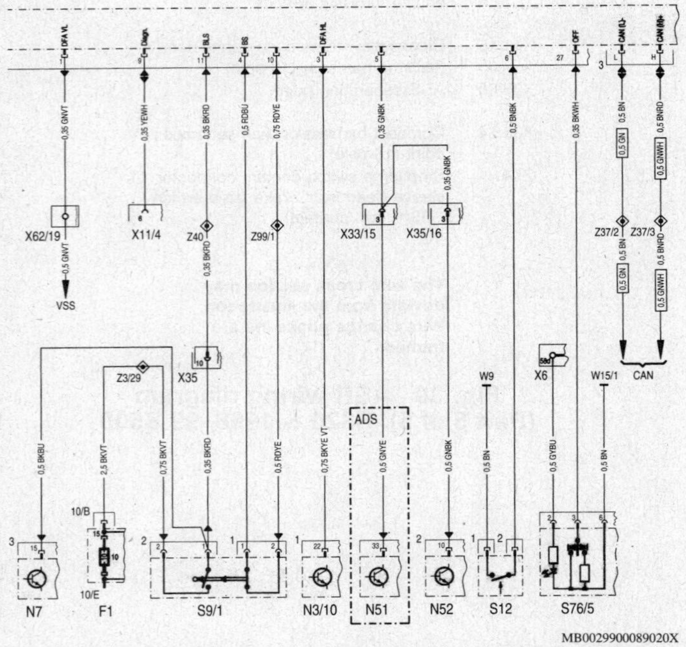

Fig. 31 ASR wiring diagram (Part 2 of 3). 1998 SL500

A7/3	ASR/ETS/ESP hydraulic unit	3M
A7/3m1	High-pressure/return pump	5M
A7/3y5	Switchover/solenoid valve	3I
A7/3y6	Left front axle solenoid valve (hold)	2L
A7/3y7	Left front axle solenoid valve (release)	3L
A7/3y8	Right front axle solenoid valve (hold)	2L
A7/3y9	Right front axle solenoid valve (release)	3L
A7/3y10	Left rear axle solenoid valve (hold)	2K
A7/3y11	Left rear axle solenoid valve (release)	3K
A7/3y12	Right rear axle solenoid valve (hold)	2K
A7/3y13	Right rear axle solenoid valve (release)	3K
A7/3y15	Inlet solenoid valve	2I
F1	Fuse and relay box	
F1f10	Fuse 10	17L
K20/1	High-pressure/return pump relay	6M
L6/1	Left front axle VSS sensor	9M
L6/2	Right front axle VSS sensor	11M
L6/3	Left rear axle VSS sensor	12M
L6/4	Right rear axle VSS sensor	13M
N3/10	Engine control module (ME-SFI)	20M
N7	Exterior lamp failure monitoring module	16M
N47-1	ASR/SPS control module	12A
N51	ADS control module	21M
N52	Power soft top control module.	22M
S9/1	Stop lamp switch (4-pole)	19M
S10/1	Left front brake pad wear sensor	7M
S10/1x1	Left front brake pad wear sensor connector	7I
S10/2	Right front brake pad wear sensor	9M
S10/2x1	Right front brake pad wear sensor connector	9I
S10/4	Right rear brake pad wear sensor	14M
S12	Parking brake switch	23M
S76/5	ASR OFF switch	24M
W9	Ground (at left headlamp unit)	
W15/1	Ground (electronics - right footwell)	
W27	Ground (control module box/module box) Ground location without designation, component grounded directly on engine, chassis or body.	
X4/10	Terminal block (circuit 30/30Ü/61e/87L) (6-pole)	7F
X6	Terminal block (circuit 58d) (2-pole)	24H
X11/4	Data link connector (DTC readout)	18E
X33/15	ADS/ engine-chassis connector	21E
X35	Cockpit/module box separation point (12-pole)	18H
X35/16	Module box/taillamp harness separation point (13-pole)	12F 22E
X62/6	Right front axle VSS sensor connector (component compartment)	10F
X62/7	Left front axle VSS sensor connector (component compartment)	8F
X62/8	Rear axle multiple circuit junction connector	12I
X62/14	Left front axle VSS sensor connector (axle spindle)	8H
X62/15	Right front axle VSS sensor connector (axle spindle)	10H
X62/19	Terminal block (left front VSS sensor - traction systems)	16E
Z3/29	Circuit 15 connector sleeve, (fused)	17H
Z23	ABS MIL connector sleeve (feed from ASR control module)	5G
Z37/2	Engine CAN-Bus (low) connector sleeve	25E
Z37/3	Engine CAN-Bus (high) connector sleeve	25E
Z40	Stop lamp connector sleeve	18E
Z99/1	Circuit 87 connector sleeve (traction systems)	19E

The wire cross section may deviate from the illustration. Wire change phase-ins are framed.

MB0029900089030X

Fig. 31 ASR wiring diagram (Part 3 of 3). 1998 SL500

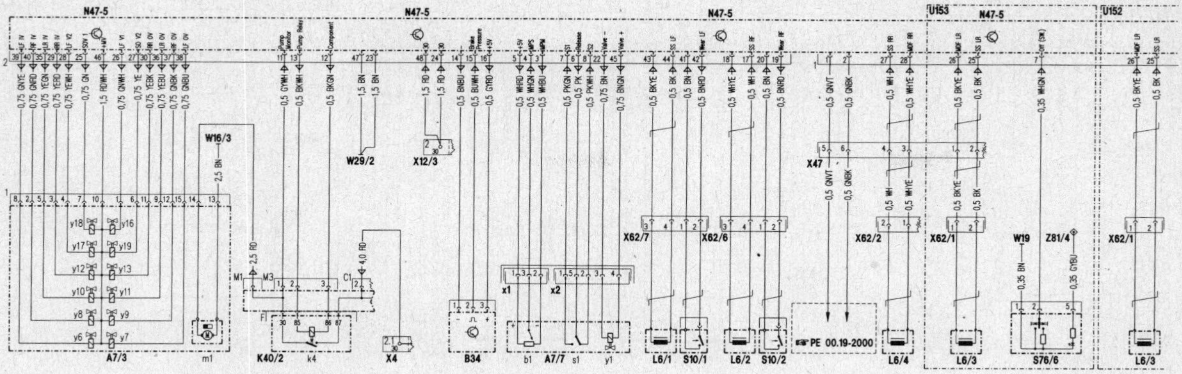

A1	Instrument cluster	68A
A1e6	Brake pad wear indicator lamp	70A
A1e7	Low brake fluid level/parking brake indicator lamp	71A
A1e17	ABS MIL	71A
A1e41	ESP warning lamp	69A
A1e47	BAS/ESP MIL	69A
A7/3	ASR/ETS/ESP hydraulic unit	4M
A7/3m1	High-pressure/return pump	6M
A7/3y6	Left front axle solenoid valve (hold)	3L
A7/3y7	Left front axle solenoid valve (release)	4L
A7/3y8	Right front axle solenoid valve (hold)	3K
A7/3y9	Right front axle solenoid valve (release)	4K
A7/3y10	Left rear axle solenoid valve (hold)	2K
A7/3y11	Left rear axle solenoid valve (release)	4K
A7/3y12	Right rear axle solenoid valve (hold)	2I
A7/3y13	Right rear axle solenoid valve (release)	4I
A7/3y16	Front axle precharge solenoid valve	4H
A7/3y17	Rear axle precharge solenoid valve	2H
A7/3y18	Front axle switchover solenoid valve	2H
A7/3y19	Rear axle switchover solenoid valve	4H

A7/7	Brake booster (BAS)	15M
A7/7b1	Membrane travel sensor (BAS)	15M
A7/7s1	Release switch (BAS)	16M
A7/7x1	Membrane travel sensor connector (BAS)	14K
A7/7x2	Release switch/membrane travel sensor connector (BAS)	15K
A7/7y1	Solenoid valve (BAS)	17M
B24/2	ABS lateral acceleration sensor	35M
B34	ESP brake pressure sensor	13M
F1	Fuse and relay box	58M 61M
F1f16	Fuse 16	61L
F1f19	Fuse 19	57L
G1	Battery	41M
K40/2	Driver-side fuse and relay module box	8M
K40/2k4	High pressure/return pump relay module	9M
K40/4	Passenger-side fuse and relay module box	48M
K40/4f2	Fuse, traction system	5OM
K40/4k1	Polarity protection relay	46M
K55	Stop lamp suppression relay module	59M

L6/1	Left front axle VSS sensor	18M
L6/2	Right front axle VSS sensor	20M
L6/3	Left rear axle VSS sensor	27M 31M
L6/4	Right rear axle VSS sensor	25M
N7	Exterior lamp failure monitoring module	54M
N7-1	Illumination control module	56M
N47-5	ESP/SPS/BAS control module	3A 12A 20A 27A 35A 44A 52A 60A
N49	Steering angle sensor	62M
N64	ESP yaw rate sensor	36M
N73	Electronic ignition lock control module	38M
S9/1	Stop lamp switch (4-pole)	52M
S10/1	Left front brake pad wear sensor	19M
S10/2	Right front brake pad wear sensor	21M
S12	Parking brake switch	64M

S76/6	ESP OFF switch	29M 33M
U152	Valid for model 202	30A 53H 57H
U153	Valid for model 208	26A 55H
W1	Main ground (behind instrument cluster)	38H
W16/3	Ground (output ground - component compartment - left)	6E 11F 44F
W16/4	Ground (output ground - component compartment - right)	45F
W19	Ground (right front seat crossmember)	28H 63E 64H
W29/2	Ground (right A-pillar)	10F
X4	Terminal block (circuit 30, left footwell)	11M
X4/28	Steering angle sensor connector	61H
X11/4	Data link connector (DTC readout)	47F

MB0029900081010X

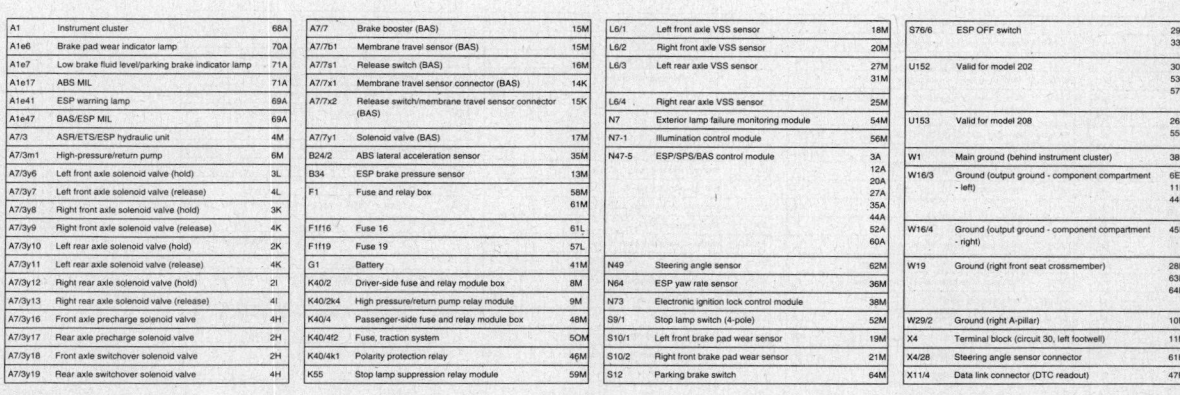

Fig. 32 ESP wiring diagram (Part 1 of 2). C43, C230, C280, CLK320 & CLK430

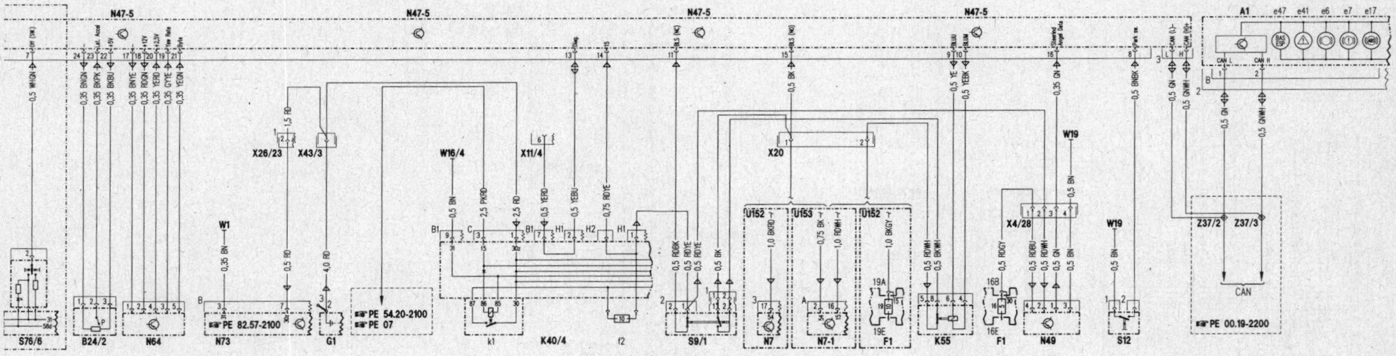

X12/3	Terminal block (circuit 30)	12F
X20	Stop lamp switch intermediate connector (2-pole)	54F
X26/23	Engine compartment/cockpit connector	40F
X43/3	REST/CL connector, circuit 30Z	41F
X47	Rear axle VSS sensor harness connector (2-pole) (right footwell)	23F
X62/1	Left rear axle VSS,sensor/brake pad wear sensor connector	26H 31H
X62/2	Right rear axle VSS sensor/brake pad wear sensor connector	24H
X62/6	Right front axle VSS sensor connector (component compartment)	20H
X62/7	Left front axle VSS sensor connector (component compartment)	18H
Z37/2	Engine CAN-Bus (low) connector sleeve	67H
Z37/3	Engine CAN-Bus (high) connector sleeve	68H
Z81/4	Circuit 58d connector sleeve (frame floor)	29H
	☞ PE 00.19-2000 Front axle VSS	

☞ PE 00.19-2200 CAN-Bus engine
☞ PE 07 Mixture preparation
☞ PE 54.20-2100 Driver-side fuse and relay module (K40/2)
☞ PE 82.57-2100 Electronic ignition switch (N73)

MB0029900081020X

Fig. 32 ESP wiring diagram (Part 2 of 2). C43, C230, C280, CLK320 & CLK430

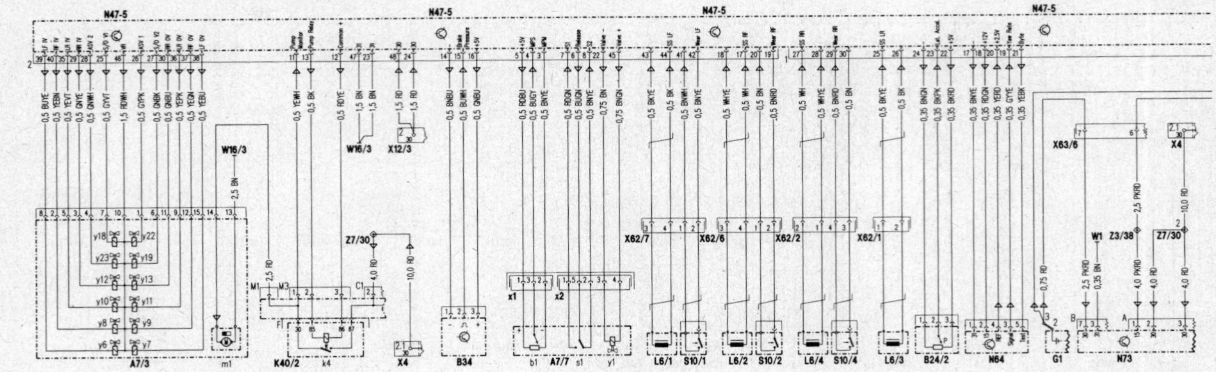

A1	Instrument cluster	54A
A1e6	Brake pad wear indicator lamp	57A
A1e7	Low brake fluid level/parking brake indicator lamp	57A
A1e17	ABS MIL	58A
A1e21	ASR warning lamp	56A
A1e49	BAS/ETS MIL	55A
A7/3	ASR/ETS/ESP hydraulic unit	4L
A7/3m1	High-pressure/return pump	6L
A7/3y6	Left front axle solenoid valve (hold)	3K
A7/3y7	Left front axle solenoid valve (release)	4K
A7/3y8	Right front axle solenoid valve (hold)	3K
A7/3y9	Right front axle solenoid valve (release)	4K
A7/3y10	Left rear axle solenoid valve (hold)	3J
A7/3y11	Left rear axle solenoid valve (release)	4J
A7/3y12	Right rear axle solenoid valve (hold)	3J
A7/3y13	Right rear axle solenoid valve (release)	4J
A7/3y18	Front axle switchover solenoid valve	2G
A7/3y19	Rear axle switchover solenoid valve	4H
A7/3y22	Front axle vacuum solenoid valve	4G
A7/3y23	Rear axle vacuum solenoid valve	3H

A7/7	Brake booster (BAS)	15L
A7/7b1	Membrane travel sensor (BAS)	14L
A7/7s1	Release switch (BAS)	15L
A7/7x1	Membrane travel sensor connector (BAS)	14J
A7/7x2	Release switch/membrane travel sensor connector (BAS)	15J
A7/7y1	Solenoid valve (BAS)	16L
B24/2	ABS lateral acceleration sensor	25L
B34	ESP brake pressure sensor	12L
F4	Rear fuse box	46L
F4f11	Fuse 11	46K
G1	Battery	28L
K40/2	Driver-side fuse and relay module box	7L
K40/2k4	High pressure/return pump relay module	9L
K40/4	Passenger-side fuse and relay module box	36L
K40/4f2	Fuse, traction system	38L
K40/4k1	Polarity protection relay	35L
K55	Stop lamp suppression relay module	43L
L6/1	Left front axle VSS sensor	18L
L6/1	Left front axle VSS sensor	20L

L6/3	Left rear axle VSS sensor	24L
L6/4	Right rear axle VSS sensor	22L
N7-1	Illumination control module	42L
N47-5	ESP/SPS/BAS control module	3A 12A 19A 28A 36A 45A 51A
N49	Steering angle sensor	48L
N64	ESP yaw rate sensor	27L
N73	Electronic ignition lock control module	30L
S9/1	Stop lamp switch (4-pole)	40L
S10/1	Left front brake pad wear sensor	18L
S10/2	Right front brake pad wear sensor	20L
S10/4	Right rear brake pad wear sensor	22L
S12	Parking brake switch	51L
S76/6	ESP OFF switch	50L
W1	Main ground (behind instrument cluster)	29H
W15/1	Ground (right footwell)	49G

W16/3	Ground (output ground-left wheel housing)	6E 9E
W16/4	Ground (output ground - right wheel housing)	34E
W18	Ground (left front seat crossmember)	51H
W19	Ground (right front seat crossmember)	48E
X4	Terminal block (circuit 30, left footwell)	11L 31E
X4/28	Steering angle sensor connector	47H
X11/4	Data link connector (DTC readout)	36E
X12/3	Terminal block (circuit 30)	11E
X62/1	Left rear axle VSS sensor/brake pad wear sensor connector	23H
X62/2	Right rear axle VSS sensor/brake pad wear sensor connector	21H
X62/6	Right front axle VSS sensor connector (component compartment)	19H
X62/7	Left front axle VSS sensor connector (component compartment)	17H
X63/6	CAN-Bus/15u connector	29E 54H

MB0029900098010X

Fig. 33 ESP wiring diagram (Part 1 of 2). E320 & E430

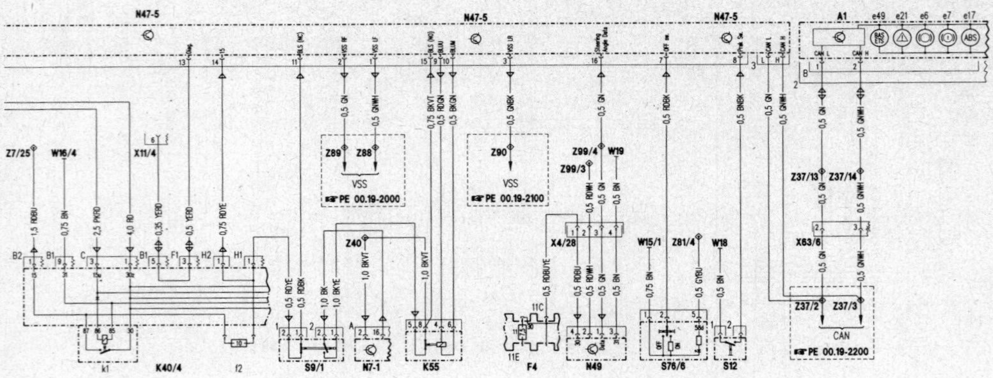

Z3/38	Circuit 15 (unfused) connector sleeve	30G
Z37/2	Engine CAN-Bus (low) connector sleeve	54j
Z7/25	Circuit 87 (unfused) connector sleeve (HFM-SFI/base module)	33E
Z7/30	Circuit 30 (unfused) connector sleeve	10G 31G
Z37/3	Engine CAN-Bus (high) connector sleeve	55J
Z40	Stop lamp connector sleeve	42G
Z81/4	Circuit 58d connector sleeve (frame floor)	50G
Z88	LF VSS sensor connector sleeve feed from traction system control modules	42E
Z89	Right front axle VSS sensor connector sleeve (feed from ABS - N30 or ASR - N30/1, N47-1, ETS-N47-2 control module)	41E
Z90	Left rear axle VSS sensor connector sleeve	45E
Z99/3	Circuit 87 connector sleeve (FFS)	47E
Z99/4	Steering angle sensor connector sleeve	48E
	☞ PE 00.19-2000 Front axle VSS	

☞ PE 00.19-2100 Rear axle VSS
☞ PE 00.19-2200 CAN-Bus engine

MB0029900098020X

Fig. 33 ESP wiring diagram (Part 2 of 2). E320 & E430

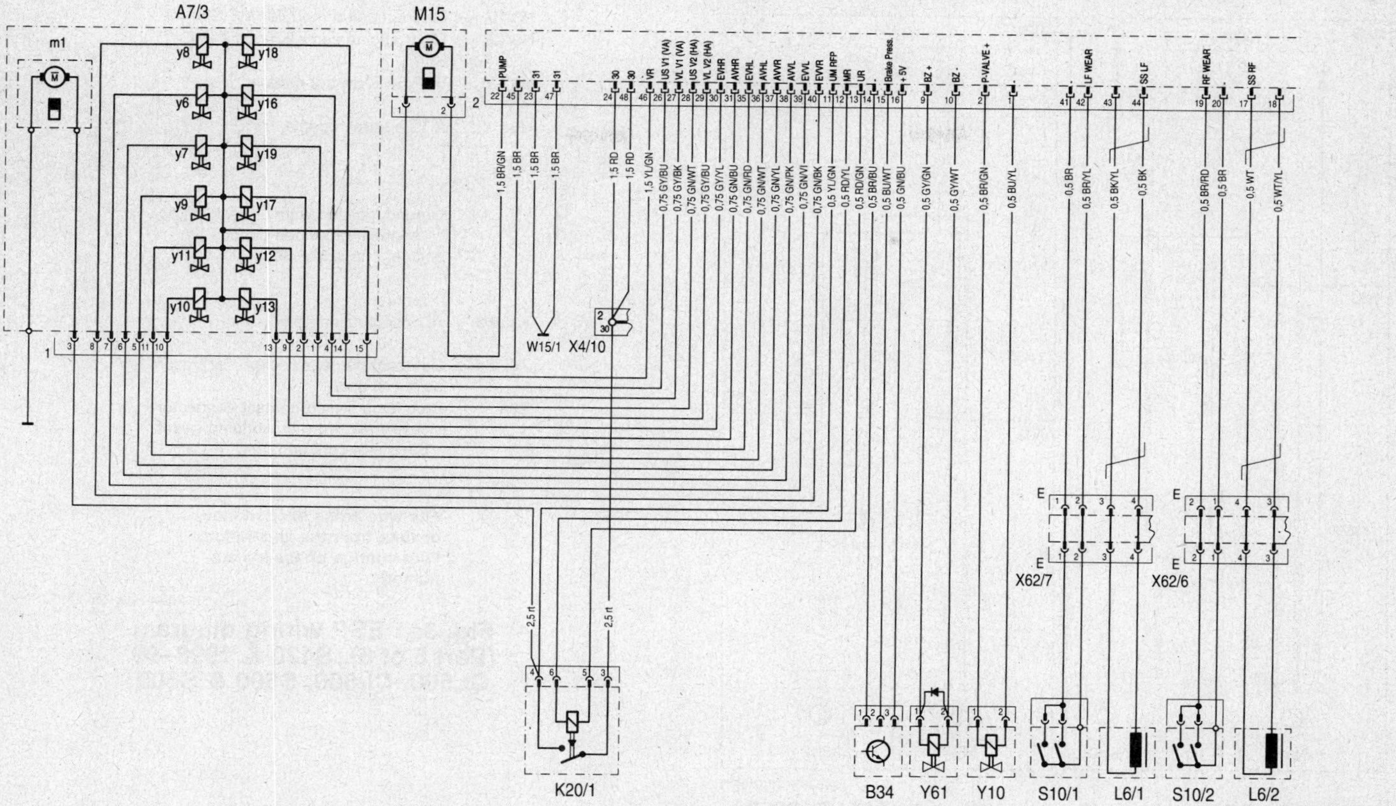

MB0029900105010X

Fig. 34 ESP wiring diagram (Part 1 of 5). S420 & 1998–99 CL500, CL600, S500 & S600

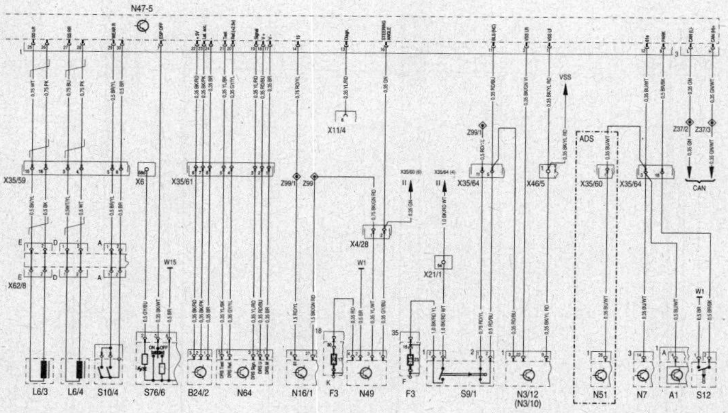

MB0029900105020X

Fig. 34 ESP wiring diagram (Part 2 of 5). S420 & 1998–99 CL500, CL600, S500 & S600

A1	Instrument cluster	33M
A7/3	ASR/ETS/ESP hydraulic unit	3A
A7/3m1	High-pressure/return pump	1B
A7/3y6	Left front axle solenoid valve (hold)	3B
A7/3y7	Left front axle solenoid valve (release)	3C
A7/3y8	Right front axle solenoid valve (hold)	3B
A7/3y9	Right front axle solenoid valve (release)	3D
A7/3y10	Left rear axle solenoid valve (hold)	3E
A7/3y11	Left rear axle solenoid valve (release)	3E
A7/3y12	Right rear axle solenoid valve (hold)	4E
A7/3y13	Right rear axle solenoid valve (release)	4E
A7/3y16	Front axle precharge solenoid valve	4B
A7/3y17	Rear axle precharge solenoid valve	4D
A7/3y18	Front axle switchover valve	4B
A7/3y19	Rear axle switchover valve	4C
B24/2	ABS lateral acceleration sensor	21M
B34	ESP brake pressure sensor	11M
F3	Fuse box (35-fuse, in fuse and relay box F1)	
F3-17	Fuse 17, circuit 30	24L
F3-23	Fuse 23, circuit 15	26L
K20/1	High-pressure/return pump relay	8M
L6/1	Left front axle VSS sensor	14M
L6/2	Right front axle VSS sensor	16M
L6/3	Left rear axle VSS sensor	17M
L6/4	Right rear axle VSS sensor	18M
M15	ASR/ESP charging pump	6A
N3/10	Engine control module (ME-SFI)	29M
N3/12	Right engine control module (ME-SFI)	29M
N7	Exterior lamp failure monitoring module	32M
N16/1	Base module (BM)	23M
N47-5	ESP/SPS control module	19A
N49	Steering angle sensor	25M
N51	ADS control module	31M
N64	ESP yaw rate sensor	22M
S9/1	Stop lamp switch (4-pole)	28M
S10/1	Left front brake pad wear sensor	13M
S10/2	Right front brake pad wear sensor	15M
S10/4	Right rear brake pad wear sensor	19M
S12	Parking brake switch	33M
S76/6	ESP OFF switch	20M
W1	Main ground (behind instrument cluster)	
W15	Ground (electronics output ground - right footwell)	
W15/1	Ground (electronics - right footwell)	
	Ground location without designation, component grounded directly on engine, chassis or body.	
X4/10	Terminal block (circuit 30/30Ū)	8F
X4/28	Steering angle sensor connector	25H
X6	Terminal block (circuit 58d) (3- or 4-pole)	20F
X11/4	Data link connector (DTC readout)	24E
X21/1	Terminal block (stop lamp switch)	27H
X35/59	Compact harness/taillamp harness separation point	16F
X35/60	ADS separation point	31F
X35/61	Yaw rate sensor separation point	21F
X35/64	Compact harness/cockpit separation point (18-pole)	28F 32F
X46/5	Terminal block (right foot well)	29F
X62/6	Right front axle VSS sensor connector (component compartment)	15I
X62/7	Left front axle VSS sensor connector (component compartment)	13I
X62/8	Rear axle multiple circuit junction connector	17I
Y10	SPS P-valve	13M
Y61	Master brake cylinder switchover valve	12M
Z37/2	CAN-Engine-Bus (low) connector sleeve	33D
Z37/3	CAN-Engine-Bus (high) connector sleeve	33D
Z99	Circuit 87 voltage supply from base module (N16/1) connector sleeve	24F
Z99/1	Circuit 87 connector sleeve (ASR/ETS)	23F 28E

The wire cross section may deviate from the illustration. Wire change phase-ins are framed.

MB0029900105030X

Fig. 34 ESP wiring diagram (Part 3 of 5). S420 & 1998–99 CL500, CL600, S500 & S600

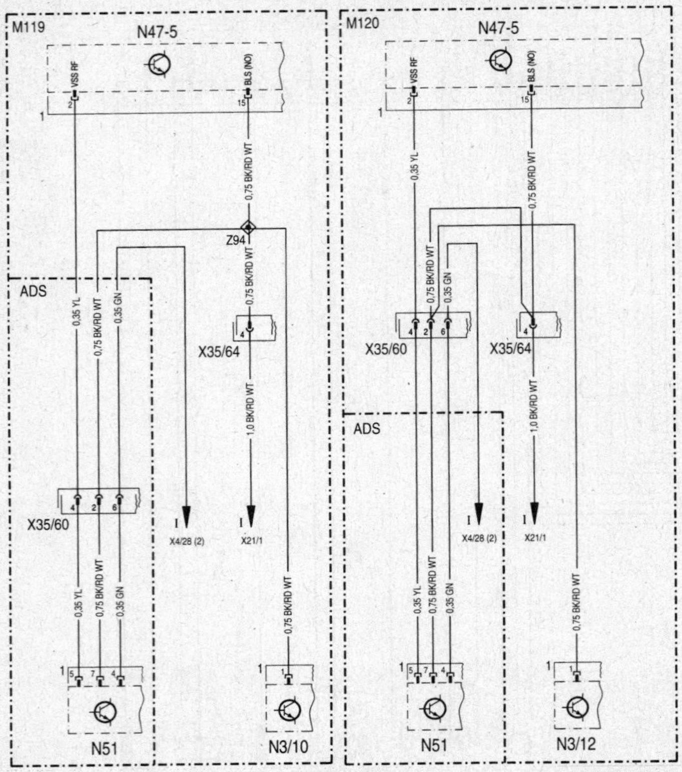

MB0029900105040X

Fig. 34 ESP wiring diagram (Part 4 of 5). S420 & 1998–99 CL500, CL600, S500 & S600

N3/10	Engine control module (ME-SFI)
N3/12	Right engine control module (ME-SFI)
N47-5	ESP/SPS control module
N51	ADS control module
	Ground location without designation, component grounded directly on engine, chassis or body.
X35/60	ADS separation point
X35/64	Compact harness/cockpit separation point (18-pole)
Z94	Stop lamp switch contact connector sleeve (feed from brake lamp switch - S9/1, n.o. contact)

The wire cross section may deviate from the illustration. Wire change phase-ins are framed.

MB0029900105050X

Fig. 34 ESP wiring diagram (Part 5 of 5). S420 & 1998–99 CL500, CL600, S500 & S600

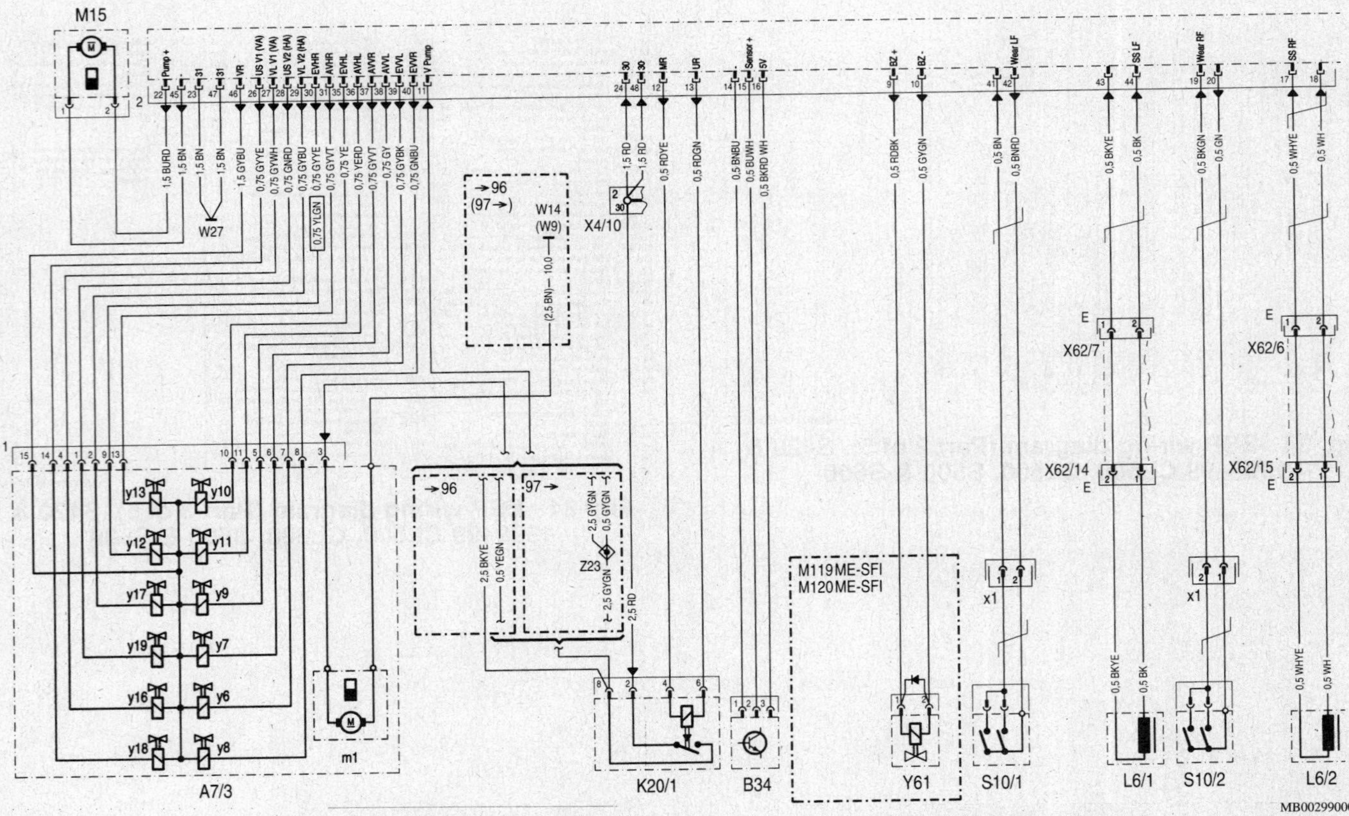

MB0029900087010X

Fig. 35 ESP wiring diagram (Part 1 of 4). SL600 & 1998 SL500

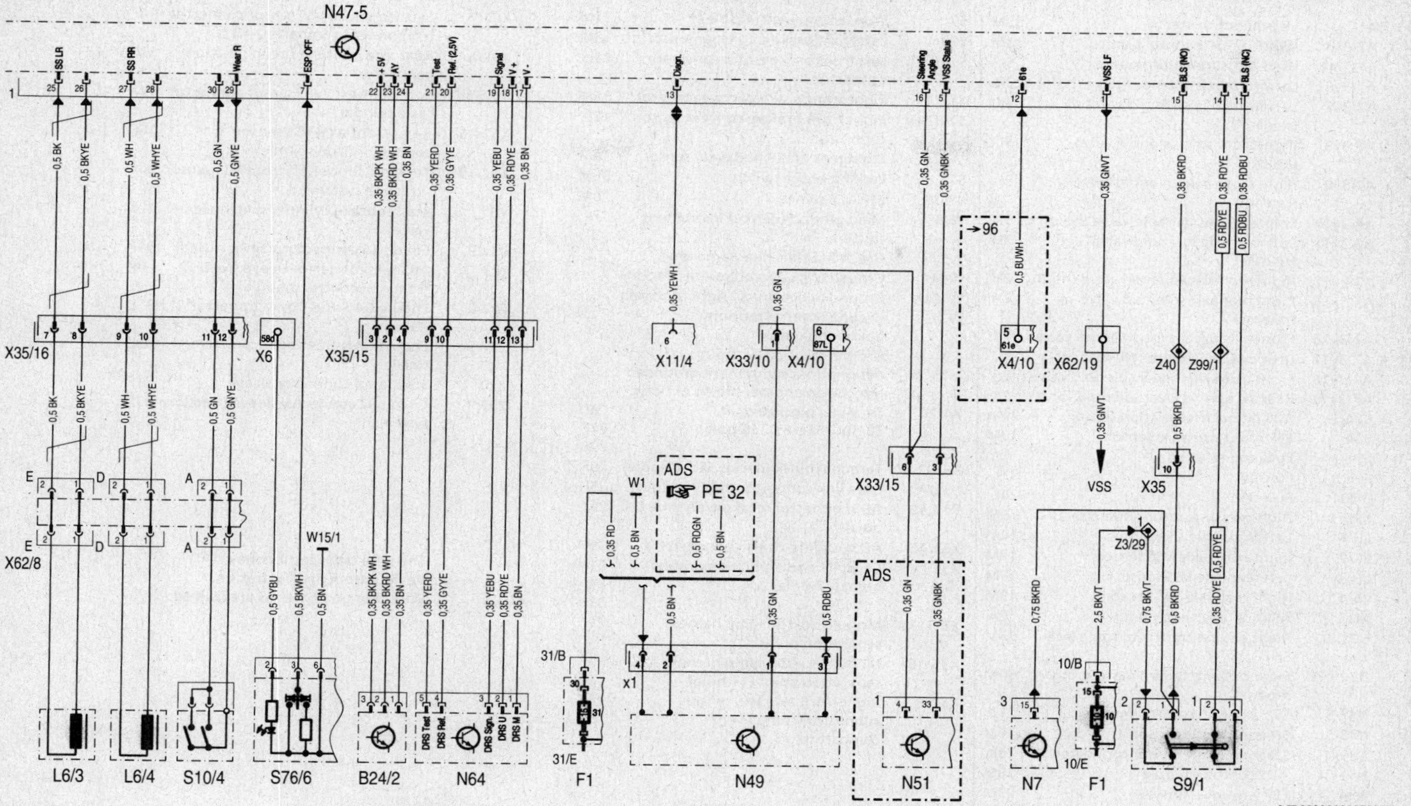

MB0029900087020X

Fig. 35 ESP wiring diagram (Part 2 of 4). SL600 & 1998 SL500

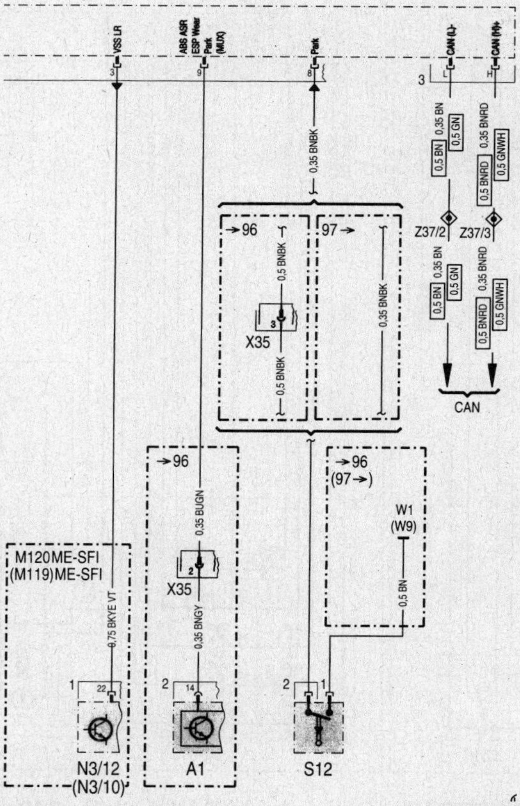

MB0029900087030X

Fig. 35 ESP wiring diagram (Part 3 of 4). SL600 & 1998 SL500

A1	Instrument cluster	35M
A7/3	ASR/ETS/ESP hydraulic unit	3M
A7/3m1	High-pressure/return pump	5L
A7/3y6	Left front axle solenoid valve (hold)	3K
A7/3y7	Left front axle solenoid valve (release)	3K
A7/3y8	Right front axle solenoid valve (hold)	3L
A7/3y9	Right front axle solenoid valve (release)	3I
A7/3y10	Left rear axle solenoid valve (hold)	3H
A7/3y11	Left rear axle solenoid valve (release)	3H
A7/3y12	Right rear axle solenoid valve (hold)	2H
A7/3y13	Right rear axle solenoid valve (release)	2H
A7/3y16	Front axle precharge solenoid valve	2K
A7/3y17	Rear axle precharge solenoid valve	2I
A7/3y18	Front axle switchover solenoid valve	2L
A7/3y19	Rear axle switchover solenoid valve	2K
B24/2	ABS lateral acceleration sensor	22M
B34	ESP brake pressure sensor	10M
F1	Fuse and relay box	
F1f10	Fuse 10	31L
F1f31	Fuse 31	24L
K20/1	High-pressure/return pump relay	8M
L6/1	Left front axle VSS sensor	14M
L6/2	Right front axle VSS sensor	17M
L6/3	Left rear axle VSS sensor	18M
L6/4	Right rear axle VSS sensor	19M
M15	ASR/ESP charging pump	2A
N3/12	Right engine control module (ME-SFI)	33M
N7	Exterior lamp failure monitoring module	30M
N47-5	ESP/SPS/BAS control module	21A
N49	Steering angle sensor	26M
N49x1	Steering angle sensor connector	25K
N51	ADS control module	28M
N64	ESP yaw rate sensor	23M
S9/1	Stop lamp switch (4-pole)	31M
S10/1	Left front brake pad wear sensor	13M
S10/1x1	Left front brake pad wear sensor connector	13I
S10/2	Right front brake pad wear sensor	15M
S10/2x1	Right front brake pad wear sensor connector	15I
S10/4	Right rear brake pad wear sensor	19M
S12	Parking brake switch	36M
S76/6	ESP OFF switch	20M
W1	Main ground (behind instrument cluster)	
W9	Ground (at left headlamp unit)	
W14	Ground (ABS hydraulic unit bracket)	
W15/1	Ground (electronics - right footwell)	
W27	Ground (control module box/module box)	
	Ground location without designation, component grounded directly on engine, chassis or body.	
X4/10	Terminal block (circuit 30/30Ü/61e/87L) (6-pole)	8D 27F 29F
X6	Terminal block (circuit 58d) (2-pole)	20F
X11/4	Data link connector (DTC readout)	25F
X33/10	ADS connector (cockpit/engine) (2-pole)	26F
X33/15	ADS/ engine-chassis connector	28H
X35	Cockpit/module box separation point (12-pole)	31H 34I 33F
X35/15	Module box/taillamp harness separation point	21F
X35/16	Module box/taillamp harness separation point (13-pole)	17F
X62/6	Right front axle VSS sensor connector (component compartment)	16F
X62/7	Left front axle VSS sensor connector (component compartment)	14F
X62/8	Rear axle multiple circuit junction connector	17I
X62/14	Left front axle VSS sensor connector (axle spindle)	14H
X62/15	Right front axle VSS sensor connector (axle spindle)	16H
X62/19	Terminal block (left front VSS sensor - traction systems)	30F
Y61	Master brake cylinder switchover valve	12M
Z3/29	Circuit 15 connector sleeve, (fused)	31H
Z23	ABS MIL connector sleeve (feed from ASR control module)	8I
Z37/2	Engine CAN-Bus (low) connector sleeve	37D
Z37/3	Engine CAN-Bus (high) connector sleeve	38D
Z40	Stop lamp connector sleeve	31F
Z99/1	Circuit 87 connector sleeve (traction systems)	32F

The wire cross section may deviate from the illustration. Wire change phase-ins are framed.

MB0029900087040X

Fig. 35 ESP wiring diagram (Part 4 of 4). SL600 & 1998 SL500

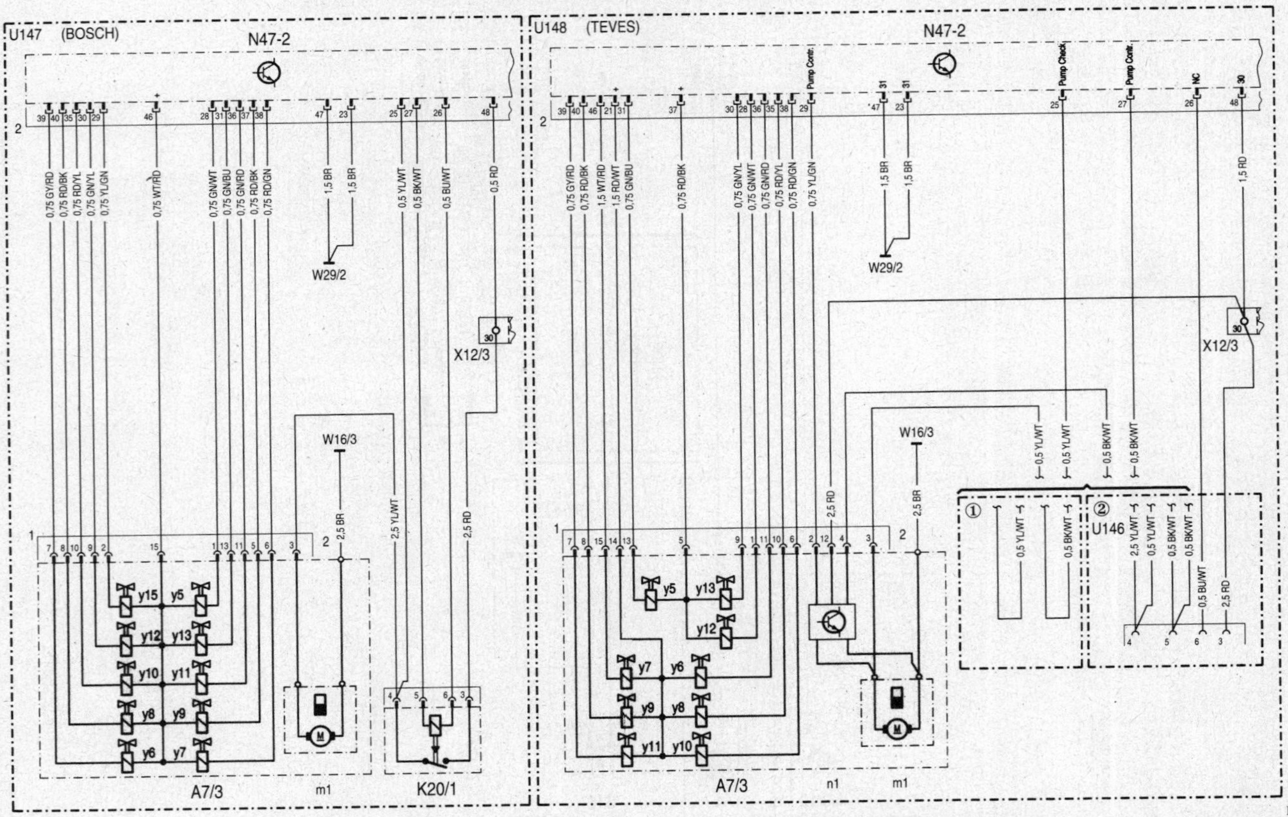

MB0029900078010X

Fig. 36 ETS wiring diagram (Part 1 of 3). C43, C230 & C280

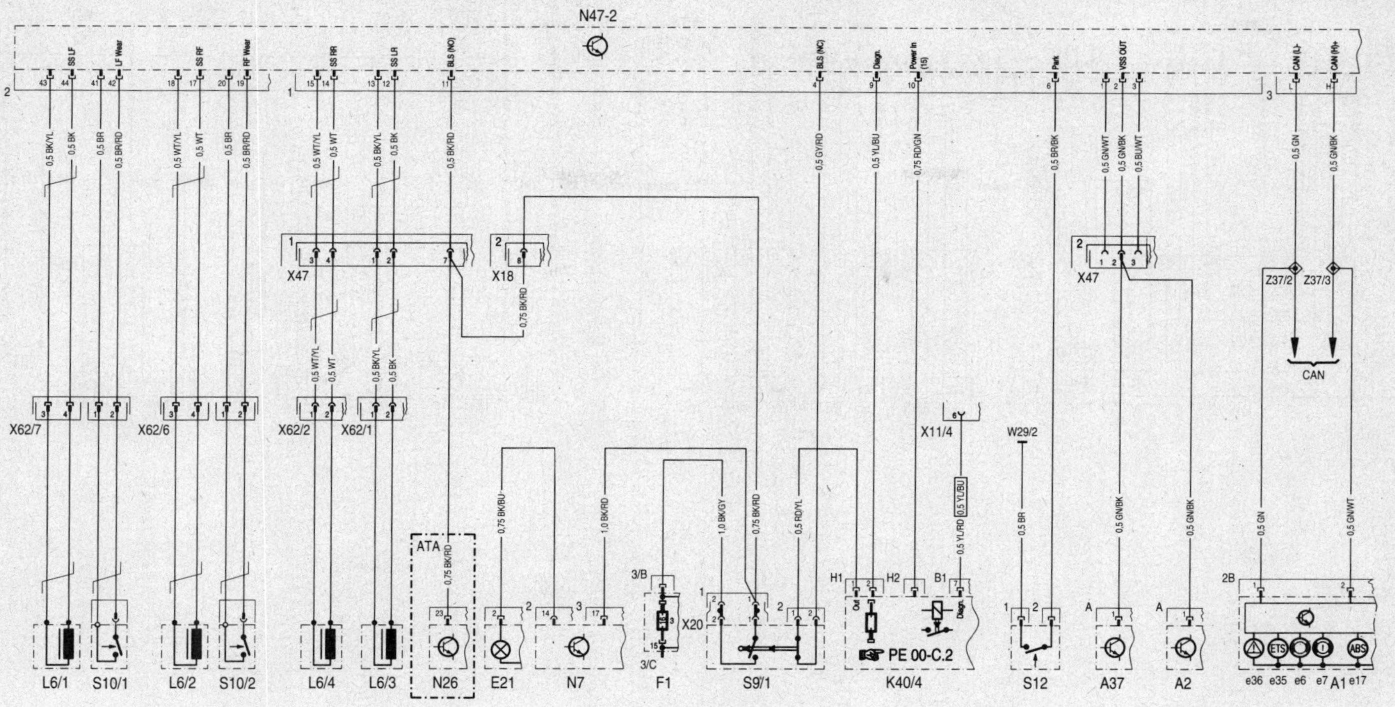

MB0029900078020X

Fig. 36 ETS wiring diagram (Part 2 of 3). C43, C230 & C280

A1	Instrument cluster	35M
A1e6	Brake pad wear indicator lamp	35M
A1e7	Low brake fluid level/parking brake indicator lamp	35M
A1e17	ABS MIL	36M
A1e35	ETS MIL	35M
A1e36	ETS warning lamp	34M
A2	Radio	33M
A7/3	ASR/ETS/ESP hydraulic unit	3M 10M
A7/3m1	High-pressure/return pump	5M 12M
A7/3n1	Cycling module/high pressure return pump	11M
A7/3y5	Switchover/solenoid valve	3I 9I
A7/3y6	Left front axle solenoid valve (hold)	2L 9K
A7/3y7	Left front axle solenoid valve (release)	3L 9K
A7/3y8	Right front axle solenoid valve (hold)	2L 9L
A7/3y9	Right front axle solenoid valve (release)	3L 9L
A7/3y10	Left rear axle solenoid valve (hold)	2K 9L
A7/3y11	Left rear axle solenoid valve (release)	3K 9L
A7/3y12	Right rear axle solenoid valve (hold)	2K 9K
A7/3y13	Right rear axle solenoid valve (release)	3K 9I
A7/3y15	Inlet solenoid valve	2I
A37	PSE control module	32M
E21	Center high mounted stop lamp (CHMSL)	24M
F1	Fuse and relay box	
F1-3	Fuse 3, circuit 15	26L
K20/1	High-pressure/return pump relay	6M
K40/4	Passenger-side fuse and relay module box	29M
L6/1	Left front axle VSS sensor	17M
L6/2	Right front axle VSS sensor	19M
L6/3	Left rear axle VSS sensor	22M
L6/4	Right rear axle VSS sensor	21M
N7	Exterior lamp failure monitoring module	25M
N26	ATA control module	23M
N47-2	ETS/SPS control module	4A 12A 25A
S9/1	Stop lamp switch (4-pole)	27M
S10/1	Left front brake pad wear sensor	18M
S10/2	Right front brake pad wear sensor	20M
S12	Parking brake switch	31M
U146	Component K20/1 not connected	
U147	Valid for Bosch system	
U148	Valid for Teves system	
W16/3	Ground (output ground - component compartment - left)	
W29/2	Ground (right A-pillar)	
	Ground location without designation, component grounded directly on engine, chassis or body.	
X11/4	Data link connector (DTC readout)	30H
X12/3	Terminal block (circuit 30/15 unfused) (3-pole)	7F 16F
X18	Interior/taillamp harness connector	24E
X20	Stop lamp switch intermediate connector (2-pole)	26L
X47	RPM sensor harness connector	21E 32E
X62/1	Left rear axle VSS sensor/brake pad wear sensor connector	22H
X62/2	Right rear axle VSS sensor/brake pad wear sensor connector	21H
X62/6	Right front axle VSS sensor connector (component compartment)	19H
X62/7	Left front axle VSS sensor connector (component compartment)	17H
Z37/2	CAN-Engine-Bus (low) connector sleeve	35E
Z37/3	CAN-Engine-Bus (high) connector sleeve	35E

The wire cross section may deviate from the illustration. Wire change phase-ins are framed.

MB0029900078030X

Fig. 36 ETS wiring diagram (Part 3 of 3). C43, C230 & C280

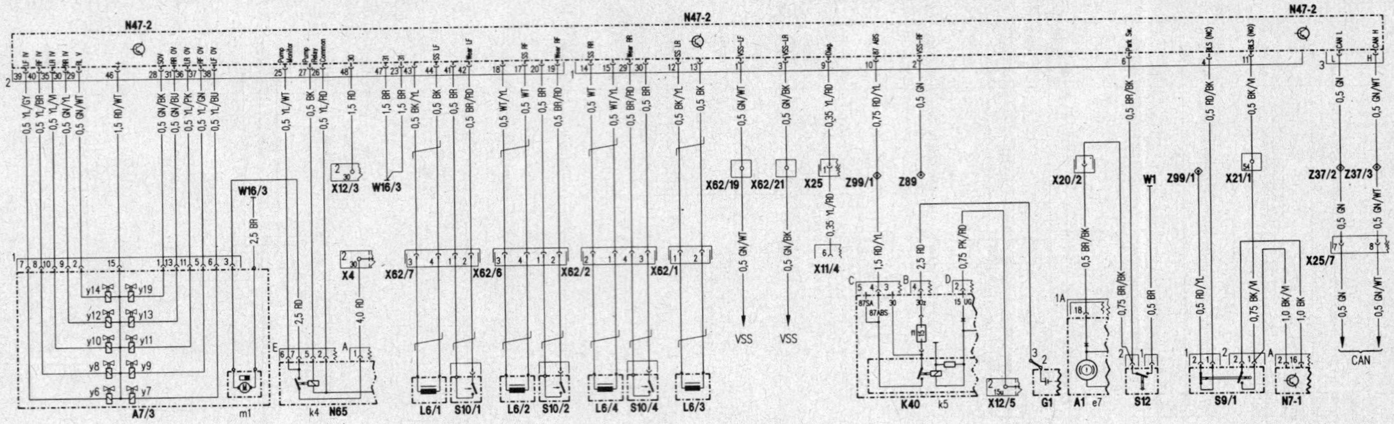

MB0029900092010X

Fig. 37 ETS wiring diagram (Part 1 of 2). E300

A1	Instrument cluster	26M
A1e7	Low brake fluid level/parking brake indicator lamp	27M
A7/3	ASR/ETS/ESP hydraulic unit	4M
A7/3m1	High-pressure/return pump	6M
A7/3y6	Left front axle solenoid valve (hold)	2L
A7/3y7	Left front axle solenoid valve (release)	4L
A7/3y8	Right front axle solenoid valve (hold)	2K
A7/3y9	Right front axle solenoid valve (release)	4K
A7/3y10	Left rear axle solenoid valve (hold)	2K
A7/3y11	Left rear axle solenoid valve (release)	4K
A7/3y12	Right rear axle solenoid valve (hold)	2I
A7/3y13	Right rear axle solenoid valve (release)	3I
A7/3y14	Return solenoid valve	2H
A7/3y19	Rear axle switchover valve	3H
G1	Battery	26M
K40	Relay module (HFM-SFI, HFM-LP, ME-SFI, EDC, base function)	22M
K40f1	ETS/ASR/ESP fuse	22K
K40k5	ETS/ASR relay	23M
L6/1	Left front axle VSS sensor	11M
L6/2	Right front axle VSS sensor	13M
L6/3	Left rear axle VSS sensor	17M
L6/4	Right rear axle VSS sensor	15M
N7-1	Illumination control module	31M
N47-2	ETS/SPS control module	4A 17A 32A
N65	Pulse module (ETS/HCS/ATA, A/C)	8M
N65k4	High-pressure/return pump relay module	8M
S9/1	Stop lamp switch (4-pole)	30M
S10/1	Left front brake pad wear sensor	11M
S10/2	Right front brake pad wear sensor	13M
S10/4	Right rear brake pad wear sensor	16M
S12	Parking brake switch	28M
W1	Main ground (behind instrument cluster)	28F
W16/3	Ground (output ground-left wheel housing)	6F 9F
X4	Terminal block (circuit 30, left footwell)	9H
X11/4	Data link connector (DTC readout)	20H
X12/3	Terminal block (circuit 30/15 unfused) (2-pole)	8F
X12/5	Terminal block, circuit 15/15R (FFS)	24M
X20/2	Foot parking brake intermediate connector	26F
X21/1	Terminal block (stop lamp switch)	30F
X25	Engine compartment/FFS connector, left and right	20F
X25/7	Engine compartment/FFS connector	32H
X62/1	Left rear axle VSS sensor/brake pad wear sensor connector	16H
X62/2	Right rear axle VSS sensor/brake pad wear sensor connector	14H
X62/6	Right front axle VSS sensor connector (component compartment)	12H
X62/7	Left front axle VSS sensor connector (component compartment)	10H
X62/19	Terminal block (left front VSS sensor - ASR/ETS)	18F
X62/21	Terminal block (left rear VSS sensor - ASR/ETS)	19F
Z37/2	CAN-Engine-Bus (low) connector sleeve	32F
Z37/3	CAN-Engine-Bus (high) connector sleeve	33F
Z89	Right front axle VSS sensor connector sleeve (feed from ABS - N30 or ASR - N30/1, N47-1, ETS-N47-2 control module)	22F
Z99/1	Circuit 87 connector sleeve (ASR/ETS)	21F 29F

MB0029900092020X

Fig. 37 ETS wiring diagram (Part 2 of 2). E300

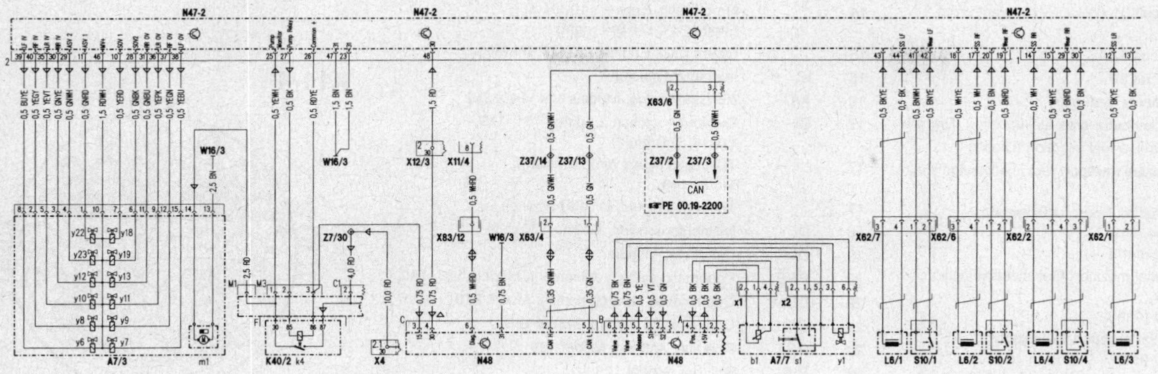

A1	Instrument cluster	52A	A7/7	Brake booster (BAS)	21L	N47-2	ETS/SPS control module	6A 12A 19A 28A 36A 45A 50A	X4	Terminal block (circuit 30, left footwell)	11L 35E
A1e6	Brake pad wear indicator lamp	54A	A7/7b1	Membrane travel sensor (BAS)	21L	N48	BAS control module	14L 19L	X11/4	Data link connector (DTC readout)	13E 39E
A1e7	Low brake fluid level/parking brake indicator lamp	55A	A7/7s1	Release switch (BAS)	22L	N73	Electronic ignition lock control module	34L	X12/3	Terminal block (circuit 30)	12E
A1e17	ABS MIL	55A	A7/7x1	Membrane travel sensor connector (BAS)	20J	S9/1	Stop lamp switch (4-pole)	44L	X62/1	Left rear axle VSS sensor/brake pad wear sensor connector	30H
A1e21	ASR warning lamp	54A	A7/7x2	Release switch/membrane travel sensor connector (BAS)	22J	S10/1	Left front brake pad wear sensor	25L	X62/2	Right rear axle VSS sensor/brake pad wear sensor connector	28H
A1e49	BAS/ETS MIL	53A	A7/7y1	Solenoid valve (BAS)	23L	S10/2	Right front brake pad wear sensor	27L	X62/6	Right front axle VSS sensor connector (component compartment)	26H
A7/3	ASR/ETS/ESP hydraulic unit	4L	G1	Battery	32L	S10/4	Right rear brake pad wear sensor	29L	X62/7	Left front axle VSS sensor connector (component compartment)	24H
A7/3m1	High-pressure/return pump	6L	K40/2	Driver-side fuse and relay module box	8L	S12	Parking brake switch	49L	X63/4	CAN databus adaptor connector (2-pole)	15H
A7/3y6	Left front axle solenoid valve (hold)	3K	K40/2k4	High pressure/return pump relay module	8L	W1	Main ground (behind instrument cluster)	33H	X63/6	CAN-Bus/15u connector	18D 32E 51H
A7/3y7	Left front axle solenoid valve (release)	4K	K40/4	Passenger-side fuse and relay module box	40L	W16/3	Ground (output ground-left wheel housing)	6E 9E 14H	X83/12	Brake assist diagnostic connector	13H
A7/3y8	Right front axle solenoid valve (hold)	3K	K40/4f2	Fuse, traction system	41L	W16/4	Ground (output ground - right wheel housing)	37E	Z3/38	Circuit 15 (unfused) connector sleeve	34G
A7/3y9	Right front axle solenoid valve (release)	4K	K40/4k1	Polarity protection relay	38L	W18	Ground (left front seat crossmember)	50H			
A7/3y10	Left rear axle solenoid valve (hold)	3J	L6/1	Left front axle VSS sensor	24L						
A7/3y11	Left rear axle solenoid valve (release)	4J	L6/2	Right front axle VSS sensor	26L						
A7/3y12	Right rear axle solenoid valve (hold)	3J	L6/3	Left rear axle VSS sensor	31L						
A7/3y13	Right rear axle solenoid valve (release)	4J	L6/4	Right rear axle VSS sensor	28L						
A7/3y18	Front axle switchover solenoid valve	4G	N7-1	Illumination control module	45L						
A7/3y19	Rear axle switchover solenoid valve	4H									
A7/3y22	Front axle vacuum solenoid valve	2G									
A7/3y23	Rear axle vacuum solenoid valve	3H									

MB0029900093010X

Fig. 38 ETS wiring diagram (Part 1 of 2). E320 w/4MATIC

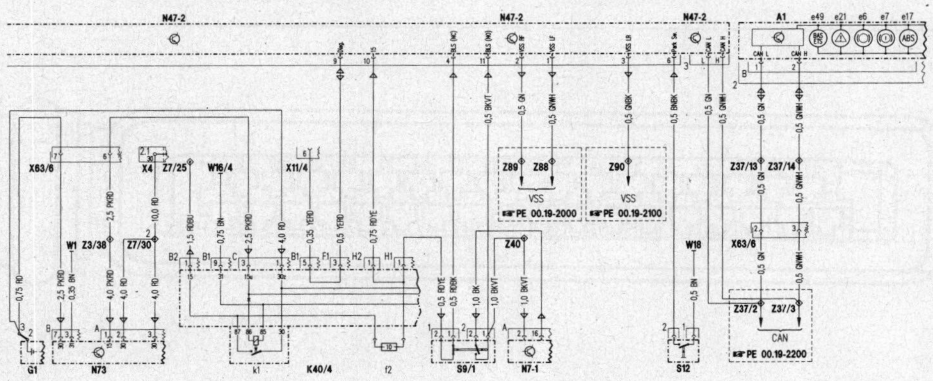

Z37/2	Engine CAN-Bus (low) connector sleeve	18E 51J
Z37/3	Engine CAN-Bus (high) connector sleeve	19E 52J
Z37/13	Engine CAN-Bus (low) connector sleeve	16E 51E
Z37/14	Engine CAN-Bus (high) connector sleeve	15E 52E
Z7/25	Circuit 87 (unfused) connector sleeve (HFM-SFI/base module)	36E
Z7/30	Circuit 30 (unfused) connector sleeve	10G 35G
Z40	Stop lamp connector sleeve	45G
Z88	LF VSS sensor connector sleeve feed from traction system control modules	46E
Z89	Right front axle VSS sensor connector sleeve (feed from ABS - N30 or ASR - N30/1, N47-1, ETS-N47-2 control module)	45E
Z90	Left rear axle VSS sensor connector sleeve	48E

PE 00.19-2000 Front axle VSS
PE 00.19-2100 Rear axle VSS
PE 00.19-2200 CAN-Bus engine

MB0029900093020X

Fig. 38 ETS wiring diagram (Part 2 of 2). E320 w/4MATIC

1		Ground, circuit 31 (W12, W15, electronics ground)
2		Voltage, circuit 87
3		Voltage, circuit 30
4	EDS	Electronic diesel system
4	DFI	Electronic distributor-type fuel injection (Diesel)
4	IFI	Electronic In-line fuel injection (Diesel)
4	HFM-SFI	HFM sequential multiport fuel injection/ignition, Engine 104
4	LH-SFI	LH sequential multiport fuel injection, Engines 104, 119 Engine 120 (right)
4	ME-SFI	ME sequential multiport fuel injection/ignition, Engine 119, Engine 120 (right)
5	LH-SFI	LH sequential multiport fuel injection, Engine 120 (left)
5	ME-SFI	ME sequential multiport fuel injection/ignition, Engine 120 (left)
6	ABS	Anti-lock brake system
6	ETS	Electronic traction system
6	ASR	Acceleration slip regulation
6	ESP	Electronic stability program
7	EA	Electronic accelerator
7	CC/ISC	Cruise control/idle speed control
8	BM	Base module
9	ASD	Automatic locking differential, Models 124, 129, 140
10	ETC	Electronic transmission control
10	ETC	Electronic transmission control (A/T 722.6)
11	ADS	Adaptive damping system
12	SPS	Speed-sensitive power steering
13		TNA-signal (gasoline), LH-SFI engines
13		TN-signal (gasoline), HFM-SFI engines
14		On-off ratio, Engine 119 LH-SFI, Engine 120 LH-SFI (right)
15		On-off ratio, Engine 120 LH-SFI (left)
15	IC	Instrument cluster
16	A/C	Air conditioning, Models 124, 140, 202
17	DI	Distributor ignition, Engines 104, 119, Engine 120 (right)
17		TD-speed signal (time division), Model 140
17		TN-speed signal, LH-SFI engines
18	DI	Distributor ignition, Engine 120 (left)
19	DM	Diagnostic module
20	PSE	Pneumatic system equipment, Models 129, 140
20	CCM	Combination control module, Model 210
21	CF	Convenience feature, Model 140
21	RST	Roadster soft top, Model 129
22	RB	Roll bar, Model 129
23	ATA	Anti-theft alarm
24-25		Not used
26	ASD	Automatic locking differential, Model 202
27		Not used
28	PTS	Parktronic system
29		Not used
30	AB	Airbag/ETR (SRS)
31	RCL	Remote central locking
32-33		Not used
34	CNS	Communication and navigation system
35		Not used
36		Not used
37-38		Not used

X11/4

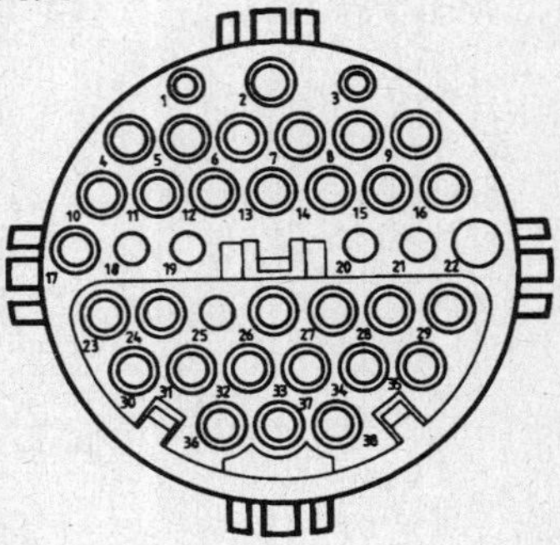

MB4019900001000X

Fig. 39 Data Link Connector 38-pin terminal identification. C43, C230, C280, E300, E320, E430, S320, S420, SL500 & SL600 & 1998–99 CL500, CL600, S500 & S600

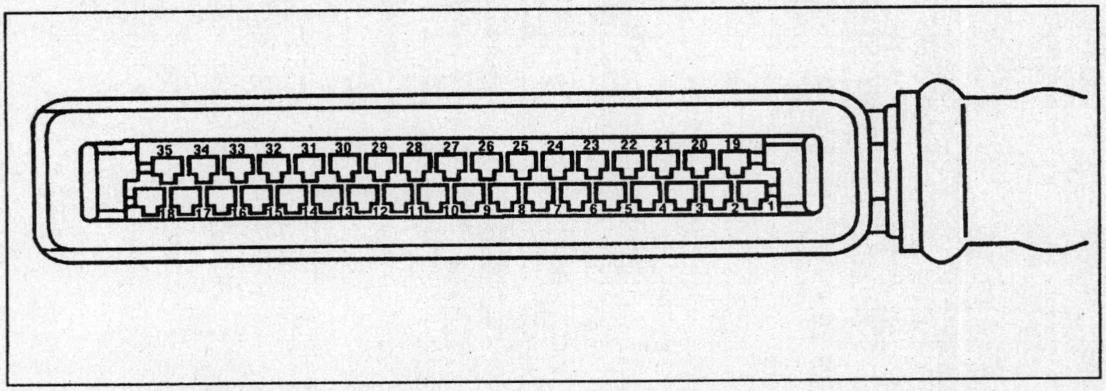

1	Circuit 87, voltage supply
2	Left front axle solenoid valve (A7y1) (–)
3	–
4	Left front axle vehicle speed sensor (L6/1) (–)
5	Left front vehicle speed sensor output
6	Left front axle vehicle speed sensor (L6/1) (+)
7	Rear axle vehicle speed sensor (L6) (+)
8	Rear axle vehicle speed sensor output
9	Rear axle vehicle speed sensor (L6) (–)
10	–
11	Right front axle vehicle speed sensor output
12-13	–
14	Return pump relay (A7k2) (monitor)
15	Circuit 61, voltage supply
16	–
17	Return pump relay (A7k2) and solenoid valve relay (A7k1), voltage supply
18	Rear axle solenoid valve (A7y3) (–)
19	–
20	Ground, (component compartment, right) (W16/4)
21	Right front axle vehicle speed sensor (L6/2) (–)
22	–
23	Right front axle vehicle speed sensor (L6/2) (+)
24-26	–
27	Solenoid valve relay (A7k1) (monitor)
28	–
29	ABS malfunction indicator lamp (A1e17)
30	Diagnosis output
31	–
32	Solenoid valve relay (A7k1) (+)
33	–
34	Ground, (component compartment, right) (W16/4)
35	Right front axle solenoid valve (A7y2) (–)

MB1049400059000X

Fig. 40 ABS control module connector terminal identification. C43, C230 & C280

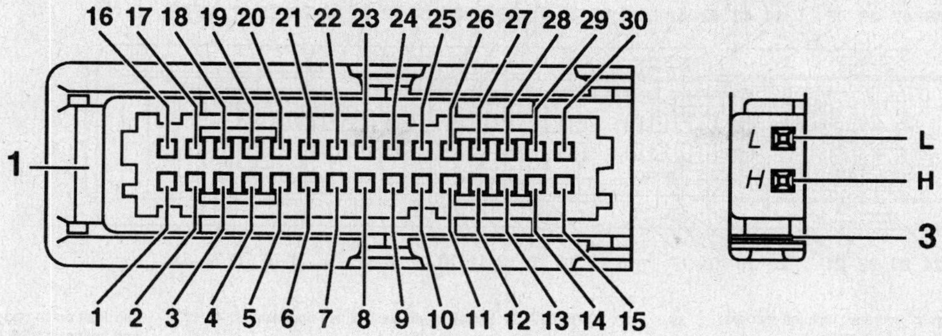

1	Left front axle VSS sensor (L6/1) output
2	Right front axle VSS sensor (L6/2) output
3	Left rear axle VSS sensor (L6/3) output
4	Stop lamp switch (4 pole) (S9/1) N.O. contact
5	VSS sensor output status
6	Parking brake switch (S12)
7	Data bus instrument cluster (instrument clusters without CAN connection)
8	Not used
9	Diagnostic output
10	Terminal 87 (voltage supply)
11	Stop lamp switch (S9/1) N.C. contact
12	Rear axle VSS sensor or left rear axle VSS sensor (L6) or (L6/3) (+)
13	Rear axle VSS sensor or left rear axle VSS sensor (L6) or (L6/3) (–)
14	**ETS, ASR:** Right rear axle VSS sensor (L6/4) (+)
15	**ETS, ASR:** Right rear axle VSS sensor (L6/4) (–)
16-25	not used
26	**ETS:** ETS signal
27	**ASR:** ASR OFF switch (S76/5)
28	Terminal 61
29-30	Right rear brake pad wear sensor (S10/4)
H	**ASR:** CAN data bus (+)
L	**ASR:** CAN data bus (–)

MB0029900067010X

Fig. 41 ABS, ETS, ASR control module interior harness connector 1 & CAN data bus connector 3. C43, C230, C280, E300, S320, S420, SL500, SL600 & SLK230 & 1998–99 CL500, CL600, S500 & S600

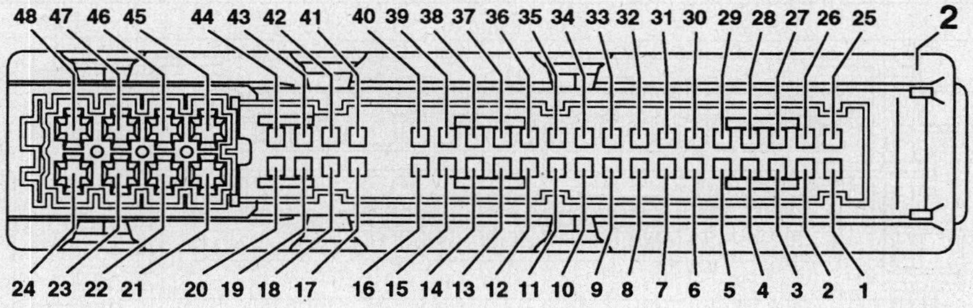

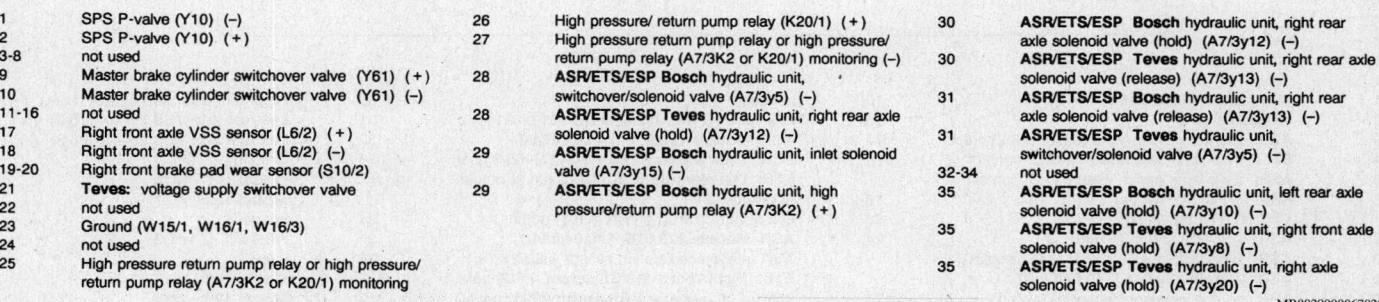

1	SPS P-valve (Y10) (–)
2	SPS P-valve (Y10) (+)
3-8	not used
9	Master brake cylinder switchover valve (Y61) (+)
10	Master brake cylinder switchover valve (Y61) (–)
11-16	not used
17	Right front axle VSS sensor (L6/2) (+)
18	Right front axle VSS sensor (L6/2) (–)
19-20	Right front brake pad wear sensor (S10/2)
21	**Teves:** voltage supply switchover valve
22	not used
23	Ground (W15/1, W16/1, W16/3)
24	not used
25	High pressure return pump relay or high pressure/ return pump relay (A7/3K2 or K20/1) monitoring
26	High pressure/ return pump relay (K20/1) (+)
27	High pressure return pump relay or high pressure/ return pump relay (A7/3K2 or K20/1) monitoring (–)
28	**ASR/ETS/ESP Bosch** hydraulic unit, switchover/solenoid valve (A7/3y5) (–)
28	**ASR/ETS/ESP Teves** hydraulic unit, right rear axle solenoid valve (hold) (A7/3y12) (–)
29	**ASR/ETS/ESP Bosch** hydraulic unit, inlet solenoid valve (A7/3y15) (–)
29	**ASR/ETS/ESP Bosch** hydraulic unit, high pressure/return pump relay (A7/3K2) (+)
30	**ASR/ETS/ESP Bosch** hydraulic unit, right rear axle solenoid valve (hold) (A7/3y12) (–)
30	**ASR/ETS/ESP Teves** hydraulic unit, right rear axle solenoid valve (release) (A7/3y13) (–)
31	**ASR/ETS/ESP Bosch** hydraulic unit, right rear axle solenoid valve (release) (A7/3y13) (–)
31	**ASR/ETS/ESP Teves** hydraulic unit, switchover/solenoid valve (A7/3y5) (–)
32-34	not used
35	**ASR/ETS/ESP Bosch** hydraulic unit, left rear axle solenoid valve (hold) (A7/3y10) (–)
35	**ASR/ETS/ESP Teves** hydraulic unit, right front axle solenoid valve (hold) (A7/3y8) (–)
35	**ASR/ETS/ESP Teves** hydraulic unit, right axle solenoid valve (hold) (A7/3y20) (–)

MB0029900067020X

Fig. 42 ABS, ETS, ASR control module engine harness connector 2 (Part 1 of 2). C43, C230, C280, E300, S320, S420, SL500, SL600 & SLK230 & CL500, CL600, S500 & S600

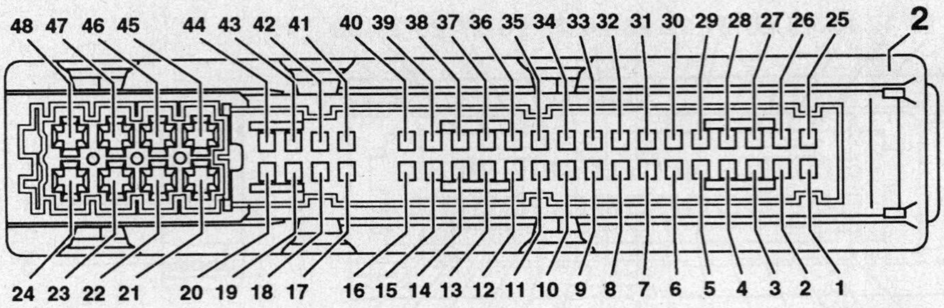

36 **ASR/ETS/ESP Boxch:** hydraulic unit, left rear axle solenoid valve (release) (A7/3y11) (–)
36 **ASR/ETS/ESP Boxch:** hydraulic unit, rear axle solenoid valve (release) (A7/3y21) (–)
36 **ASR/ETS/ESP Teves:** hydraulic unit, left front axle solenoid valve (hold) (A7/3y6) (–)
37 **ASR/ETS/ESP Bosch:** hydraulic unit, right front axle solenoid valve (release) (A73/y9) (–)
38 **ASR/ETS/ESP Bosch:** hydraulic unit, left front axle solenoid valve (release) (A73/y7) (–)
38 **ASR/ETS/ESP Teves:** hydraulic unit, left rear axle solenoid valve (hold) (A73/y10) (–)
38 **ASR/ETS/ESP Teves:** hydraulic unit, rear axle solenoid valve (hold) (A73/y20) (–)
39 **ASR/ETS/ESP Bosch:** hydraulic unit, left front axle solenoid valve (hold) (A7/3y6) (–)
39 **ASR/ETS/ESP Teves:** hydraulic unit, left rear axle solenoid valve (hold) (A7/3y11) (–)
39 **ASR/ETS/ESP Teves:** hydraulic unit, rear axle solenoid valve (release) (A7/3y21) (–)
40 **ASR/ETS/ESP Bosch:** hydraulic unit, right front axle solenoid valve (hold) (A7/3y8) (–)
40 **ASR/ETS/ESP Teves:** hydraulic unit, right front axle solenoid valve (release) (A7/3y9) (–)
41-42 Left front brake pad wear sensor (S10/1)
43 Left front axle VSS sensor (L6/1) (–)
44 Left front axle VSS sensor (L6/1) (+)
45 not used
46 **Bosch:** Solenoid valve voltage supply
46 **Bosch: ASR/ETS/ESP Bosch:** hydraulic unit, right front axle solenoid valve (release) (A7/3y7) (–)
47 Ground (W15/1, W16/1 W16/3)
48 Circuit 30 voltage

MB0029900067030X

Fig. 42 ABS, ETS, ASR control module engine harness connector 2 (Part 2 of 2). C43, C230, C280, E300, S320, S420, SL500, SL600 & SLK230 & CL500, CL600, S500 & S600

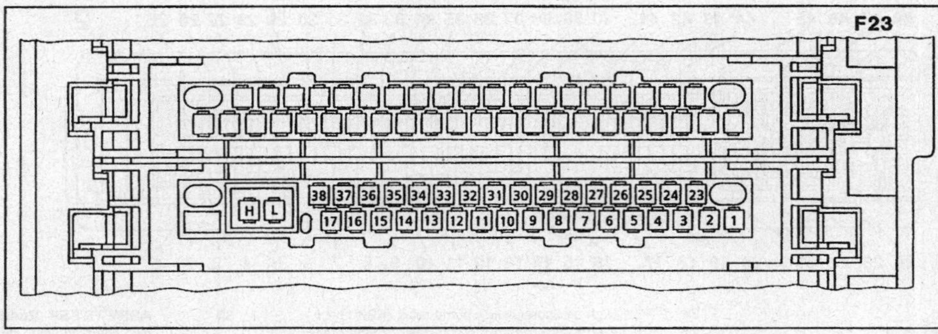

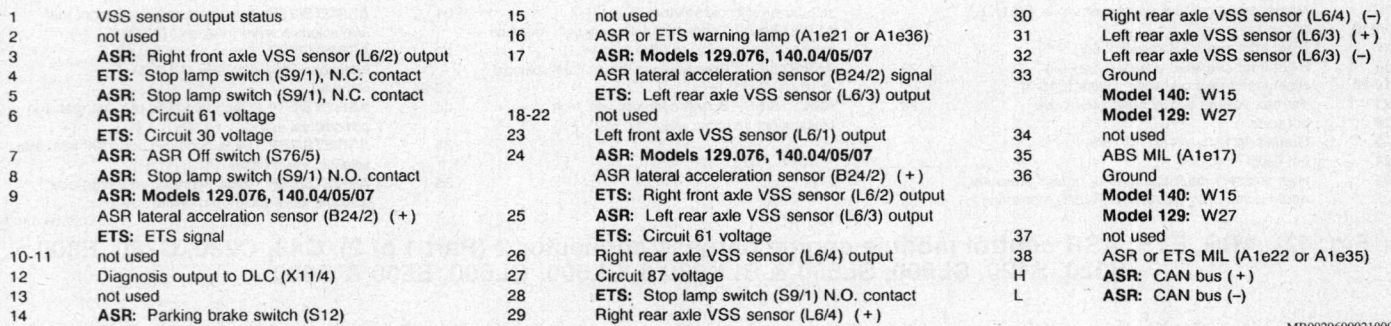

1 VSS sensor output status
2 not used
3 **ASR:** Right front axle VSS sensor (L6/2) output
4 **ETS:** Stop lamp switch (S9/1), N.C. contact
5 **ASR:** Stop lamp switch (S9/1), N.C. contact
6 **ASR:** Circuit 61 voltage
ETS: Circuit 30 voltage
7 **ASR:** ASR Off switch (S76/5)
8 **ASR:** Stop lamp switch (S9/1) N.O. contact
9 **ASR: Models 129.076, 140.04/05/07**
ASR lateral accelration sensor (B24/2) (+)
ETS: ETS signal
10-11 not used
12 Diagnosis output to DLC (X11/4)
13 not used
14 **ASR:** Parking brake switch (S12)
15 not used
16 ASR or ETS warning lamp (A1e21 or A1e36)
17 **ASR: Models 129.076, 140.04/05/07**
ASR lateral acceleration sensor (B24/2) signal
ETS: Left rear axle VSS sensor (L6/3) output
18-22 not used
23 Left front axle VSS sensor (L6/1) output
24 **ASR: Models 129.076, 140.04/05/07**
ASR lateral acceleration sensor (B24/2) (+)
ETS: Right front axle VSS sensor (L6/2) output
25 **ASR:** Left rear axle VSS sensor (L6/3) output
ETS: Circuit 61 voltage
26 Right rear axle VSS sensor (L6/4) output
27 Circuit 87 voltage
28 **ETS:** Stop lamp switch (S9/1) N.O. contact
29 Right rear axle VSS sensor (L6/4) (+)
30 Right rear axle VSS sensor (L6/4) (–)
31 Left rear axle VSS sensor (L6/3) (+)
32 Left rear axle VSS sensor (L6/3) (–)
33 Ground
Model 140: W15
Model 129: W27
34 not used
35 ABS MIL (A1e17)
36 Ground
Model 140: W15
Model 129: W27
37 not used
38 ASR or ETS MIL (A1e22 or A1e35)
H **ASR:** CAN bus (+)
L **ASR:** CAN bus (–)

MB0029600021000X

Fig. 43 ASR/SPS or ETS/SPS interior harness control module connector terminal identification. SL500 & SL600

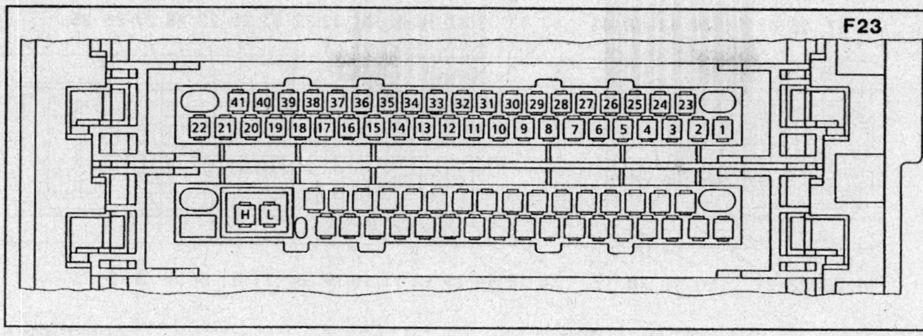

1	not used
2	ASR/ETS hydraulic unit, left rear axle solenoid valve (release) (A7/3y11) (–)
3	ASR/ETS hydraulic unit, right rear axle solenoid valve (hold) (A7/3y12) (–)
4	Master brake cylinder switchover valve (Y61)
5-6	not used
7	ASR/ETS hydraulic unit, high-pressure/return pump relay (A7/3k2) and solenoid valve relay (A7/3k1)
8-9	not used
10	Left front axle VSS sensor (L6/1) (–)
11-12	not used
13	Right front axle VSS sensor (L6/2) (–)
14-16	not used
17	ASR/ETS hydraulic unit, inlet solenoid valve (A7/3y15) (–)
18	ASR/ETS hydraulic unit, left front axle solenoid valve (hold) (A7/3y6) (–)
19	ASR/ETS hydraulic unit, switchover/solenoid valve (A7/3y5) (–)
20	ASR/ETS hydraulic unit, left front axle solenoid valve (release) (A7/3y7) (–)
21	**Model 140:** SPS P-valve (Y10) (–)
22	**Model 140:** SPS P-valve (Y10) (+)
23	ASR/ETS hydraulic unit, right rear axle solenoid valve (hold) (A7/3y12) (–)
24	ASR/ETS hydraulic unit, right rear axle solenoid valve (hold) (A7/3y13) (–)
25-26	not used
27	ASR/ETS hydraulic unit, solenoid valve relay (A7/3k1) (–)
28	ASR/ETS hydraulic unit, high-pressure/return pump relay (A7/3k2) (–)
29	not used
30	Left front axle VSS sensor (L6/1) (+)
31-33	not used
34	Right front axle VSS sensor (L6/2) (+)
35	not used
36	ASR/ETS hydraulic unit, high-pressure/return pump relay (A7/3k2) control
37	not used
38	ASR/ETS hydraulic unit, right front axle solenoid valve (hold) (A7/3y8) (–)
39	ASR/ETS hydraulic unit, right front axle solenoid valve (release) (A7/3y9) (–)
40-41	not used

MB0029600022000X

Fig. 44 ASR/SPS or ETS/SPS engine harness control module connector terminal identification. SL500 & SL600

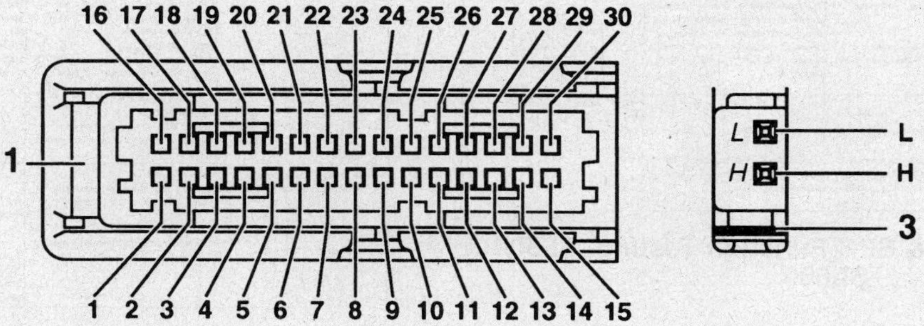

1	Left front axle VSS sensor (L6/1)
2	Right front axle VSS sensor (L6/2)
3	Left rear axle VSS sensor (L6/3)
4	Right rear axle VSS sensor (L6/4)
5	VSS sensor output status
6	not used
7	ESP OFF switch (S76/6)
8	Parking brake switch (S12)
9	Instrument cluster data bus (for vehicles without CAN connection to intrument cluster)
10	not used
11	Stop lamp switch (S9/1) N.C. contact
12	Circuit 61 voltage
13	Diagnosis output
14	Circuit 87 ABS voltage supply
15	Stop lamp switch (S9/1) N.O. contact
16	Steering angle sensor (N49)
17	ESP yaw rate sensor (N64) (–)
18	ESP yaw rate sensor (N64) (+)
19	ESP yaw rate sensor (N64) signal
20	ESP yaw rate sensor (N64) reference
21	ESP yaw rate sensor (N64) test
22	ABS lateral acceleration sensor (B24/2) (+)
23	ABS lateral acceleration sensor (B24/2) signal
24	ABS lateral acceleration sensor (B24/2) (–)
25	Left rear axle VSS sensor (L6/3) (+)
26	Left rear axle VSS sensor (L6/3) (–)
27	Right rear axle VSS sensor (L6/4) (+)
28	Right rear axle VSS sensor (L6/4) (–)
29-30	Right rear brake pad wear sensor (S10/4)
H	CAN data bus (+)
L	CAN data bus (–)

MB00299000720I0X

Fig. 45 ESP/SPS control module interior harness connector 1 & CAN data bus connector 3 terminal identification. E320, E430, S320, S420, SL500 & SL600 & 1998–99 CL500, CL600, S500 & S600

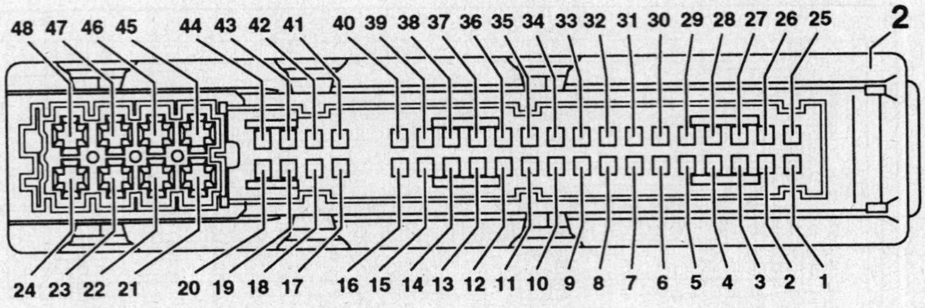

1	Model 140 with SPS P-valve (Y10) (–)
2	Model 140 with SPS P-valve (Y10) (+)
3-8	not used
9	Master brake cylinder switchover valve (Y61) (+) (models 129.067/076, 140)
10	Master brake cylinder switchover valve (Y61) (–) (models 129.067/076, 140)
11	Model 140, 129 (K20/1), model 210 (N65k4): high pressure/retun pump relay module
12	Model 140, 129 (K20/1), model 210 (N65k4): high pressure/retun pump relay module (–)
13	Model 140, 129 (K20/1), model 210 (N65k4): high pressure/retun pump relay module (+)
14	ESP brake pressure sensor (B34) (–)
15	ESP brake pressure sensor (B34) signal
16	ESP brake pressure sensor (B34) (+)
17	Right front axle VSS sensor (L6/2) (+)
18	Right front axle VSS sensor (L6/2) (–)
19-20	Right front brake pad wear sensor (S10/2)
21	not used
22	ASR/ESP charging pump (M15) (+)
23	Ground (model 129: W27, model 140: W16/1, model 210: W16/3)
24	Circuit 30 voltage
25	not used
26	ASR/ETS/ESP hydraulic unit, rear axle switchover valve (A7/3y18) (–)
27	ASR/ETS/ESP hydraulic unit, rear axle switchover valve (A7/3y18) precharge
28	ASR/ETS/ESP hydraulic unit, switchover/solenoid valve (A7/3y5) (–)
29	ASR/ETS/ESP hydraulic unit, switchover/solenoid valve (A7/3y5) precharge
30	ASR/ETS/ESP hydraulic unit, right rear axle solenoid valve (hold) (A7/3y12) (–)
31	ASR/ETS/ESP hydraulic unit, right rear axle solenoid valve (release) (A7/3y13) (–)
32-34	not used
35	ASR/ETS/ESP hydraulic unit, left rear axle solenoid valve (hold) (A7/3y10) (–)
36	ASR/ETS/ESP hydraulic unit, left rear axle solenoid valve (release) (A7/3y11) (–)
37	ASR/ETS/ESP hydraulic unit, right front axle solenoid valve (release) (A73/y9) (–)
38	ASR/ETS/ESP hydraulic unit, left front axle solenoid valve (release) (A73/y7) (–)
39	ASR/ETS/ESP hydraulic unit, left front axle solenoid valve (hold) (A7/3y6) (–)
40	ASR/ETS/ESP hydraulic unit, right front axle solenoid valve (hold) (A7/3y8) (–)
41-42	Right front brake pad wear sensor (S10/2)
43	Left front axle VSS sensor (L6/1) (–)
44	Left front axle VSS sensor (L6/1) (+)
45	ASR/ESP charging pump (M15) (–)
46	Solenoid valve voltage supply
47	Ground (model 129: W27, model 140: W16/1, model 210: W16/3)

MB0029900072020X

Fig. 46 ESP/SPS engine harness control module connector 2 terminal identification. E320, E430, S320, S420, SL500 & SL600 & 1998–99 CL500, CL600, S500 & S600

Test step/Test scope	Test condition	Nominal value	Possible cause/Remedy
⇒ 1.0 Brake torque control circuit	Lift rear of vehicle so that both rear wheels can be rotated freely. ⚠ **Secure vehicle !** Engine: **at Idle** Selector lever in transmission range "D". Apply WOT using accelerator pedal. ⚠ **CAUTION!** Should ASR not come into effect: Release accelerator pedal to idle speed.	The rear wheels are noticeably braked; simultaneously the high-pressure/return pump can audibly be heard operating. Engine speed is reduced to approx. 1000 rpm. The ASR warning lamp blinks.	☐ 23,
⇒ 2.0 ASR off function using ASR OFF switch (S76/5)	Engine: **at Idle** Selector lever in "N". Press ASR OFF switch (S76/5).	The ASR warning lamp illuminates.	☐ 23
	Selector lever in transmission range "D". Slowly depress accelerator pedal.	Engine speed is not reduced. The rear wheels are not braked. The ASR warning lamp blinks.	

MB0029600002000X

Fig. 47 ASR, ETS & SPS Function Testing. SL500 & SL600

Test step/Test scope	Test condition	Nominal value	Possible cause/Remedy
ASR only ⇒ 1.0 Brake torque control circuit	⚠ **Test cables are not to be hooked up to the HHT while performing function tests.**		Test, using HHT Engines HFM-SFI, EA, or ME-SFI
	Lift rear of vehicle so that both rear wheels can be rotated freely. ⚠ **Secure vehicle!** Engine: **at Idle** Selector lever in transmission range "D". Apply WOT using accelerator pedal.	The rear wheels are noticeably braked; simultaneously the return/pressure pump can audibly be heard operating. Engine speed is reduced to appprox. 1000 rpm. The ASR warning lamp (A1e21) will blink.	
	⚠ **CAUTION!** Should ASR not come into effect: Release accelerator pedal to idle speed.		
⇒ 2.0 Switching off ASR using ASR Off switch (S76/5).	Engine: **at Idle** Selector lever in transmission range "N". Press ASR OFF switch (S76/5).	The ASR warning lamp (A1e21) will remain on.	Test, using HHT
	Selector lever in transmission range "D". Slowly press on accelerator pedal.	The engine speed will not be reduced. The rear brakes will not be applied. The ASR warning lamp (A1e21) will blink.	

MB0029900063000X

Fig. 48 ASR Function Testing. C43, C230, C280, E300, S320, S420, SL500, SL600 & SLK230 & 1998–99 CL500, CL600, S500 & S600

Test step/Test scope	Test condition	Nominal value	Possible cause/Remedy
⇒ 1.0 Brake torque control circuit	⚠ **Test cables are not to be hooked up to the HHT while performing function tests.** Lift rear of vehicle so that both rear wheels can be rotated freely. ⚠ **Secure vehicle !** Engine: **at Idle** Selector lever in transmission range "D". Apply WOT using accelerator pedal. ⚠ **CAUTION!** Should ASR not come into effect: Release accelerator pedal to idle speed.	The rear wheels are noticeably braked; simultaneously the high-pressure/ return pump can audibly be heard operating. Engine speed is reduced to approx. 1000 rpm. The ESP warning lamp blinks.	□ 23,
⇒ 2.0 ESP off function using ESP OFF switch (S76/6)	Engine: **at Idle** Selector lever in "N". Press ESP OFF switch (S76/6). Selector lever in transmission range "D". Slowly depress accelerator pedal.	The ESP warning lamp illuminates. Engine speed is not reduced. The rear wheels are not braked. The ESP warning lamp blinks.	□ 23 ⇒ 25.0

MB0029900068000X

Fig. 49 ESP & SPS Function Testing. E320, E430, S320, S420, SL500 & SL600 & 1998–99 CL500, CL600, S500 & S600

DIAGNOSTIC CHART INDEX

ABS

Code	Description	Page No.	Fig. No.
C43, C230 & C280			
2	Test 23, Steps 7.0–8.1	5-282	53
3	Test 23, Steps 9.0–10.1	5-283	54
4	Test 23, Steps 11.0–12.1	5-283	55
6	Test 23, Steps 13.0–16.0	5-283	56
7	Test 23, Steps 13.0–16.0	5-283	56
8	Test 23, Steps 13.0–16.0	5-283	56
10	Test 23, Steps 5.1–6.1	5-282	52
11	Test 23, Steps 2.1–5.0	5-282	51
16	Test 23, Steps 7.0–8.1	5-282	53
	Test 23, Steps 9.0–10.1	5-283	54
	Test 23, Steps 11.0–12.1	5-283	55
17	Test 23, Steps 1.0–2.0	5-282	50
25	Test 23, Steps 7.0–8.1	5-282	53
26	Test 23, Steps 9.0–10.1	5-283	54
27	Test 23, Steps 11.0–12.1	5-283	55

ABS, ASR, ETS & SPS

Code	Description	Page No.	Fig. No.
C43, C230, C280, E300, S320, S420, SL500, SL600 & SLK230 & 1998–99 CL500, CL600, S500 & S600			
C1010	Test 23, Steps 1.0–1.1	5-283	57
	Test 23, Steps 1.2–3.0	5-284	58
C1011	Test 23, Steps 1.2–3.0	5-284	58
	Test 23, Steps 4.0–6.0	5-284	59
C1012	Test 23, Steps 1.0–1.1	5-283	57
	Test 23, Steps 1.2–3.0	5-284	58
C1100	Test 23, Steps 10.0–12.0	5-284	61
C1101	Test 23, Steps 12.1–14.1	5-285	62
C1102	Test 23, Steps 15.0–17.0	5-285	63
C1103	Test 23, Steps 15.0–17.0	5-285	63
C1104	Test 23, Steps 10.0–12.0	5-284	61

Continued

DIAGNOSTIC CHART INDEX —Continued

ABS, ASR, ETS & SPS—Continued

Code	Description	Page No.	Fig. No.
C43, C230, C280, E300, S320, S420, SL500, SL600 & SLK230 & 1998–99 CL500, CL600, S500 & S600			
C1105	Test 23, Steps 12.1–14.1	5-285	62
C1106	Test 23, Steps 15.0–17.0	5-285	63
C1107	Test 23, Steps 15.0–17.0	5-285	63
C1142	Test 23, Steps 6.1–9.0	5-284	60
C1143	Test 23, Steps 6.1–9.0	5-284	60
C1300	Test 23, Steps 17.1–20.0	5-285	64
C1301	Test 23, Steps 17.1–20.0	5-285	64
C1302	Test 23, Steps 21.0–23.0	5-285	65
C1303	Test 23, Steps 21.0–23.0	5-285	65
C1304	Test 23, Steps 21.0–23.0	5-285	65
C1305	Test 23, Steps 24.0–26.0	5-286	66
C1306	Test 23, Steps 24.0–26.0	5-286	66
C1307	Test 23, Steps 24.0–26.0	5-286	66
C1311	Test 23, Steps 27.0–28.0	5-286	67
C1312	Test 23, Steps 6.1–9.0	5-284	60
C1315	Test 23, Steps 27.0–28.0	5-286	67
C1401	Test 23, Steps 4.0–6.0	5-284	59
C1500	Test 23, Steps 10.0–12.0	5-284	61
	Test 23, Steps 12.1–14.1	5-285	62
	Test 23, Steps 15.0–17.0	5-285	63
C1501	Test 23, Steps 6.1–9.0	5-284	60
C1514	Test 23, Steps 6.1–9.0	5-284	60
C1515	Test 23, Steps 6.1–9.0	5-284	60
C3114	Test 23, Steps 4.0–6.0	5-284	59
SL500 & SL600			
—	Test 23, Steps 5.0–7.0	5-287	70
	Test 23, Steps 15.2–16.1	5-288	75
	Test 23, Steps 35.1–36.0	5-290	83
003	Test 23, Steps 11.0–13.1	5-287	73
004	Test 23, Steps 13.2–15.1	5-288	74
005	Test 23, Steps 17.0–18.0	5-288	76
006	Test 23, Steps 18.1–19.2	5-288	77
007	Test 23, Steps 11.0–13.1	5-287	73
008	Test 23, Steps 13.2–15.1	5-288	74
009	Test 23, Steps 17.0–18.0	5-288	76
010	Test 23, Steps 18.1–19.2	5-288	77
011	Test 23, Steps 11.0–13.1	5-287	73
	Test 23, Steps 13.2–15.1	5-288	74
	Test 23, Steps 17.0–18.0	5-288	76
	Test 23, Steps 18.1–19.2	5-288	77
012	Test 23, Steps 8.0–8.2	5-287	71
013	Test 23, Steps 10.0–22.0	5-289	78
014	Test 23, Steps 10.0–22.0	5-289	78
015	Test 23, Steps 23.0–26.0	5-289	79
016	Test 23, Steps 23.0–26.0	5-289	79
017	Test 23, Steps 23.0–26.0	5-289	79
018	Test 23, Steps 23.0–26.0	5-289	79
019	Test 23, Steps 27.0–30.0	5-289	80
020	Test 23, Steps 27.0–30.0	5-289	80
021	Test 23, Steps 27.0–30.0	5-289	80
022	Test 23, Steps 27.0–30.0	5-289	80
024	Test 23, Steps 9.0–10.0	5-287	72
027	Test 23, Steps 11.0–13.1	5-287	73
028	Test 23, Steps 1.0–1.2	5-286	68

Continued

DIAGNOSTIC CHART INDEX —Continued

ABS, ASR, ETS & SPS—Continued

Code	Description	Page No.	Fig. No.
C43, C230, C280, E300, S320, S420, SL500, SL600 & SLK230 & 1998–99 CL500, CL600, S500 & S600			
029	Test 23, Steps 2.0–4.0	5-286	69
030	Test 23, Steps 32.1–35.0	5-290	82
031	Test 23, Steps 32.1–35.0	5-290	82
032	Test 23, Steps 32.1–35.0	5-290	82
033	Test 23, Steps 32.1–35.0	5-290	82
035	Test 23, Steps 11.0–13.1	5-287	73
036	Test 23, Steps 31.0–32.0	5-289	81
037	Test 23, Steps 31.0–32.0	5-289	81
040	Test 23, Steps 31.0–32.0	5-289	81

ABS, ESP & SPS

Code	Description	Page No.	Fig. No.
E320, E430, S320, S420, SL500 & SL600 & 1998–99 CL500, CL600, S500 & S600			
—	Test 23, Steps 1.0–5.0	5-290	85
C1010	Test 23, Steps 1.0–1.2	5-290	84
C1011	Test 23, Steps 20.0–22.0	5-292	92
C1020	Test 23, Steps 30.0–30.2	5-294	99
C1022	Test 23, Steps 30.0–30.2	5-294	99
C1100	Test 23, Steps 12.0–13.2	5-291	88
C1101	Test 23, Steps 14.0–15.20	5-291	89
C1102	Test 23, Steps 16.0–17.2	5-292	90
C1103	Test 23, Steps 18.0–19.2	5-292	91
C1120	Test 23, Steps 26.1–28.0	5-293	97
C1140	Test 23, Steps 28.1–29.2	5-294	98
C1141	Test 23, Steps 26.1–28.0	5-293	97
C1142	Test 23, Steps 24.3–26.0	5-293	96
	Test 23, Steps 26.1–28.0	5-293	97
C1200	Test 23, Steps 6.0–8.0	5-291	86
C1300	Test, Steps 23.0–23.3	5-292	93
C1301	Test, Steps 23.0–23.3	5-292	93
C1302	Test, Steps 23.0–23.3	5-292	93
C1303	Test 23, Steps 23.4–23.7	5-293	94
C1304	Test 23, Steps 23.4–23.7	5-293	94
C1305	Test 23, Steps 23.4–23.7	5-293	94
C1306	Test 23, Steps 23.4–23.7	5-293	94
C1307	Test, Steps 23.0–23.3	5-292	93
	Test 23, Steps 23.8–24.2	5-293	95
C1308	Test 23, Steps 23.8–24.2	5-293	95
C1309	Test 23, Steps 23.8–24.2	5-293	95
C1310	Test 23, Steps 24.3–26.0	5-293	96
C1311	Test 23, Steps 23.8–24.2	5-293	95
	Test 23, Steps 24.3–26.0	5-293	96
C1312	Test 23, Steps 6.0–8.0	5-291	86
C1400	Test 23, Steps 8.1–11.1	5-291	87
C1402	Test 23, Steps 8.1–11.1	5-291	87
C1403	Test 23, Steps 8.1–11.1	5-291	87
C1500	Test 23, Steps 12.0–13.2	5-291	88
	Test 23, Steps 14.0–15.2	5-291	89
	Test 23, Steps 16.0–17.2	5-292	90
	Test 23, Steps 18.0–19.2	5-292	91
C1501	Test 23, Steps 12.0–13.2	5-291	88

Test step	DTC	Test scope	Test connection	Test condition	Nominal value	Possible cause/Remedy
⇒ 1.0	17	**ABS control module (N30)** Voltage supply Circuit 87 E	N30 20 – V – 1 34 – V – 1	Ignition: **ON**	11 – 14 V	⇒ 1.1, Wiring, Ground
⇒ 1.1		Voltage supply from overvoltage protection relay module (K1/1)	N30 W16/4 – V – 1 (Figure 5)	Ignition: **ON**	11 – 14 V	Fuse at K1/1, Wiring, K1/1.
⇒ 2.0		**ABS malfunction indicator lamp (MIL) (A1e17)**	N30 20 – V – 29	Ignition: **ON**	< 2 V A1e17: **ON**	Wiring, ABS MIL (A1e17), ⇒ 2.1
				Engine: **At idle**	10 – 14 V A1e17: **OFF**	Fault stored, Read DTC memory: ☐ 11, Wiring, ABS control module (N30).

MB4029400040000X

Fig. 50 Code 17: Test 23, Steps 1.0–2.0. C43, C230 & C280

Test step	DTC	Test scope	Test connection	Test condition	Nominal value	Possible cause/Remedy
⇒ 2.1		Diode in solenoid valve (A7k1)		Engine: **OFF** Disconnect ABS control module (N30).		Wiring, A7k1.
				Ignition: **ON** Engine: **At idle**	A1e17: **ON** A1e17: **ON**	
⇒ 3.0		**Diagnosis output**	N30 20 – V – 30	Ignition: **ON**	10 – 14 V	Wiring, ABS control module (N30).
⇒ 4.0		**Circuit 61 Voltage**	N30 20 – V – 15	Ignition: **ON**	< 1 V	Wiring, Generator (G2).
				Engine: **Start**	11 – 14 V	
⇒ 5.0	11	**Solenoid valve relay (A7k1)**		Ignition: **ON**		DTC stored, see ☐ 11(clear DTC), ⇒ 5.1 to 5.3
		Control	N30 27 – V – 17		10 – 14 V	
		Monitor	N30 20 – V – 32		11 – 14 V	Wiring.

MB4029400041000X

Fig. 51 Code 11: Test 23, Steps 2.1–5.0. C43, C230 & C280

Test step	DTC	Test scope	Test connection	Test condition	Nominal value	Possible cause/Remedy
⇒ 5.1		Voltage supply	N30 20 – V – 17	Ignition: **ON**	11 – 14 V	Wiring, ⇒ 1.0, ABS control module (N30).
⇒ 5.2		Coil resistance	N30 27 – Ω – 17	Ignition: **OFF** Disconnect ABS control module (N30).	40 – 80 Ω	Wiring, Solenoid valve relay (A7k1).
⇒ 5.3		Operational contact	N30 W14 – Ω – 32	Ignition: **OFF** Disconnect N30.	< 1 Ω	Wiring, Solenoid valve relay (A7k1),
⇒ 6.0	10	**Return pump relay (A7k2)** Voltage supply	N30 20 – V – 41	Ignition: **ON**	11 – 14 V	Wiring, ⇒ 6.1, Return pump (A7m1).
⇒ 6.1		Coil resistance	N30 17 – Ω – 28	Ignition: **OFF** Disconnect N30.	40 – 80 Ω	Wiring, Return pump (A7k2).

MB4029400042000X

Fig. 52 Code 10: Test 23, Steps 5.1–6.1. C43, C230 & C280

Test step	DTC	Test scope	Test connection	Test condition	Nominal value	Possible cause/Remedy
⇒ 7.0	2 16 25	**Left front axle vehicle speed sensor (L6/1)**	N30 4 – V – 6	Lift front of vehicle. Ignition: **ON** Rotate left front wheel.	> 0.1 V~	⇒ 7.1, ⇒ 7.2
⇒ 7.1		Insulation resistance	N30 20 – Ω – 6	Ignition: **OFF** Disconnect N30.	> 20 kΩ	Wiring.
⇒ 7.2		Internal resistance	N30 4 – Ω – 6	Ignition: **OFF** Disconnect (N30) from socket box.	0.8 – 3.7 kΩ	Wiring, L6/1.
⇒ 8.0		**Left front axle vehicle speed sensor output**	N30 20 – V – 5	Lift front of vehicle. Ignition: **ON** Rotate left front wheel.	> 3 V~	Wiring, ⇒ 7.0, ⇒ 8.1
⇒ 8.1		Circuit loading from connected control modules	N30 20 – Ω – 5	Ignition: **OFF** Disconnect N30.	> 5 kΩ	Wiring, Connected control modules (A1, A2, N4/1, N4/2, N22).

MB4029400043000X

Fig. 53 Codes 2, 16 & 25: Test 23, Steps 7.0–8.1. C43, C230 & C280

Test step DTC	Test scope	Test connection	Test condition	Nominal value	Possible cause/Remedy
⇒ 9.0 3 16 26	**Right front axle vehicle speed sensor (L6/2)**	N30 21 —< V >— 23	Lift front of vehicle. Ignition: **ON** Rotate right front wheel.	> 0.1 V~	⇒ 9.1, ⇒ 9.2
⇒ 9.1	Insulation resistance	N30 20 —< Ω >— 23	Ignition: **OFF** Disconnect N30.	> 20 kΩ	Wiring.
⇒ 9.2	Internal resistance	N30 21 —< Ω >— 23	Ignition: **OFF** Disconnect N30.	0.8 – 3.7 kΩ	Wiring, L6/2.
⇒ 10.0	**Right front axle vehicle speed sensor output**	N30 20 —< V >— 11	Lift front of vehicle. Ignition: **ON** Rotate right front wheel.	> 3 V~	Wiring, ⇒ 9.0, ⇒ 10.1
⇒ 10.1	Circuit loading from connected control modules	N30 20 —< Ω >— 11	Ignition: **OFF** Disconnect N30.	> 5 kΩ	Wiring, Connected control modules (N30/2).

MB4029400044000X

Fig. 54 Codes 3, 16 & 26: Test 23, Steps 9.0–10.1. C43, C230 & C280

Test step DTC	Test scope	Test connection	Test condition	Nominal value	Possible cause/Remedy
⇒ 13.0 6	**Left front axle solenoid valve (A7y1)** Internal resistance	N30 2 —< Ω >— 32	Ignition: **OFF** Disconnect N30.	0.7 – 2.2 kΩ	Wiring, ABS hydraulic unit (A7).
⇒ 14.0 7	**Right front axle solenoid valve (A7y2)** Internal resistance	N30 35 —< Ω >— 32	Ignition: **OFF** Disconnect N30.	0.7 – 2.2 kΩ	Wiring, ABS hydraulic unit (A7).
⇒ 15.0 8	**Rear axle vehicle solenoid valve (A7y3)** Internal resistance	N30 18 —< Ω >— 32	Ignition: **OFF** Disconnect N30.	0.7 – 2.2 kΩ	Wiring, ABS hydraulic unit (A7).
⇒ 16.0	**Stop lamp switch (2-pole) (S9)** N. O. contact	N30 20 —< V >— 25	Ignition: **ON** Brake not applied.	< 1 V	Wiring, S9.
			Brake applied.	11 – 14 V	

MB4029400046000X

Fig. 56 Codes 6, 7 & 8: Test 23, Steps 13.0–16.0. C43, C230 & C280

Test step DTC	Test scope	Test connection	Test condition	Nominal value	Possible cause/Remedy
⇒ 11.0 4 16 27	**Rear axle vehicle speed sensor (L6)**	N30 9 —< V >— 7	Lift rear of vehicle. Ignition: **ON** Rotate a rear wheel	> 0.1 V~	⇒ 11.1; ⇒ 11.2
⇒ 11.1	Insulation resistance	N30 20 —< Ω >— 7	Ignition: **OFF** Disconnect (N30).	>20 kΩ	Wiring.
⇒ 11.2	Internal resistance	N30 9 —< Ω >— 7	Ignition: **OFF** Disconnect N30.	0.6 – 3.2 kΩ	Wiring, L6.
⇒ 12.0	**Rear axle vehicle speed sensor output**	N30 20 —< V >— 8	Lift rear of vehicle. Ignition: **ON** Rotate a rear wheel.	> 3 V~	⇒ 11.0, ⇒ 12.1
⇒ 12.1	Circuit loading from connected control modules	N30 20 —< Ω >— 8	Disconnect N30. Ignition: **ON** Rotate a rear wheel.	>5 kΩ	Wiring, Connected control modules (N3/4, N4/2, N30/2).

MB4029400045000X

Fig. 55 Codes 4, 16 & 27: Test 23, Steps 11.0–12.1. C43, C230 & C280

⇒	DTC	Test scope	Test connection	Test condition	Nominal value	Possible cause/Remedy
1.0	C1010 C1012	**Control module (N47)** Circuit 87 Voltage supply	N47 57 —< V >—10 (2.23) (1.10) 81 —< V >— 10 (2.47) (1.10)	Ignition: **ON**	11 – 14 V	⇒ 1.1, ⇒ 1.2.
1.1		Voltage supply from: **model 202 without control module box** Overvoltage protection relay module (K1) **model 170, 210** Relay module (K40) **model 202 with control module box** Passenger side fuse and relay module box (K40/4) **models 129, 140** Base module (N16/1)	N47 ⊥ V >— 10 (1.10)	Ignition: **ON**	11 – 14 V	Fuse on K1, (model 202 without control module box) Fuse on K40 (170, 210) Fuse on K40/4 (model 202 with control module box) Fuse F3 on N16/1 (models 129, 140) Wiring K1 (model 202 without control module box) K40 (model170, 210) K40/4 (model 202 with control module box) N16/1 (models 129, 140)

MB0029900066010X

Fig. 57 Codes C1010 & C1012: Test 23, Steps 1.0–1.1. C43, C230, C280, E300, S320, S420, SL500, SL600 & SLK230 & 1998–99 CL500, CL600, S500 & S600

⇒		Test scope	Test connection	Test condition	Nominal value	Possible cause/Remedy
1.2		Ground wire **Model 202 without control module box** **Model 202 with control module box** **Model 140, 210** **Model 129** **Model 170** **Model 202 without control module box** **Model 202 with control module box** **Model 140, 210** **Model 129** **Model 170**	N47 W16/4 Ω — 57 (2.23) W29/2 W15/1 W27 W16 W16/4 Ω — 81 (2.47) W29/2 W15/1 W27 W16	Ignition: **OFF** **Disconnect** Traction control module (N47):	< 1 Ω	Wiring, Model 202 without control module box (W16/4) ground, component compartment - right Model 202 with control module box (W29/2) ground, left "A" pillar Model 140, 210; (W15/1) ground, right footwell. Model 129 (W27) contol module box/control module. Model 170 (W16) ground, component compartment
2.0	C 1010 C 1011 C 1012	**Traction control module (N47)** Circuit 30 Voltage supply	N47 57 (2.23) — V — 82 (2.48)	Ignition: **OFF**	11 – 14 V	Wiring. Model 210 only: Fuse on K40 Model 170.447 only: Crash separation relay module (K56)
3.0		**Data bus instrument cluster** (vehicles without CAN connection to instrument cluster)	N47 57 (2.23) — V — 17 (1.17)	Ignition: **ON**	3 - 4 V A1e6/7/17/21/22 /35/36: **ON**	Wiring, (N47).

MB0029900066020X

Fig. 58 Codes C1010, C1011 & C1012: Test 23, Steps 1.2–3.0. C43, C230, C280, E300, S320, S420, SL500, SL600 & SLK230 & 1998–99 CL500, CL600, S500 & S600

⇒		Test scope	Test connection	Test condition	Nominal value	Possible cause/Remedy
4.0		Diagnostic output	N47 57 (2.23) — V — 9 (1.9)	Ignition: **ON**	10 – 14 V	Wiring, (N47). K40/4 (model 202 with control module box).
5.0	C 1011 C 3114	**ASR/ETS/ESP hydraulic unit (A7/3)** Voltage supply for solenoid valve	N47 **Bosch** 57 (2.23) — V — 80 (2.46) **Teves** 57 (2.23) — V — 55 (2.21) 57 (2.23) — V — 71 (2.37)	Ignition: **On** **Bosch** **Teves**	11 – 14 V 5 - 10 V (voltage pulsed)	Wiring. Traction control module (N47)
6.0	C 1401	**High pressure/return pump relay (K20/1)** Voltage supply Model 129,140, 202 (Bosch ABS, ETS, ASR; Teves ABS): (K20/1) Model 210: (N65/k4) Model 202 (Teves ETS): (A7/3n1)	N47 57 (2.23) — V — 61 (2.27)	Ignition: **ON** **Bosch ABS, ETS ASR** **Teves ABS** **Teves ETS**	10 – 14 V 5 - 10 V (voltage pulsed)	Wiring. ⇒6.1

MB0029900066030X

Fig. 59 Codes C1011, C1401 & C3114: Test 23, Steps 4.0–6.0. C43, C230, C280, E300, S320, S420, SL500, SL600 & SLK230 & 1998–99 CL500, CL600, S500 & S600

⇒		Test scope	Test connection	Test condition	Nominal value	Possible cause/Remedy
6.1		**Bosch: ABS, ETS, ASR** **Teves: ABS** Coil resistance	N47 60 (2.26) — V — 61 (2.27)	Ignition: **OFF** Disconnect traction control module (N47)	40 - 80 Ω	Wiring Models 129, 140, 202: K20/1 Models 170, 210: N65k4
7.0	C 1501 C 1514 C 1515	**Model 140, 210 with SPS:** SPS P - valve (Y10) Coil resistance	N47 35 (2.1) — Ω — 36 (2.2)	Ignition: **OFF** Disconnect traction control module (N47)	3 - 8 Ω	Wiring, SPS P - valve (Y10)
8.0	C 1142 C 1143	**Models 129.076, 140.04/05/07** ABS lateral acceleration sensor (B24/2) Voltage supply	N47 57 (2.23) — V — 22 (1.22)	Ignition: **ON**	4.75 - 5.25 V	N47
9.0	C 1312	**Models 129.076, 140.04/05/07** Master brake cylinder switchover valve (Y61) Internal resistance	N47 44 (2.10) — Ω — 43 (2.9)	Ignition: **OFF** Disconnect traction control module (N47)	7 - 8 Ω	Wiring, Y61

MB0029900066040X

Fig. 60 Codes C1142, C1143, C1312, C1501, C1514 & C1515: Test 23, Steps 6.1–9.0. C43, C230, C280, E300, S320, S420, SL500, SL600 & SLK230 & 1998–99 CL500, CL600, S500 & S600

⇒		Test scope	Test connection	Test condition	Nominal value	Possible cause/Remedy
10.0		**ETS and cruise control only, vehicles without CAN connection to instrument cluster** ETS signal	N47-2 57 (2.23) — V — 26 (1.26)	Ignition: **ON** Engine: **at idle**	< 1V ETS MIL (A1e35) **ON** 11 - 14 V A1e35: **OFF**	Wiring N47-2
11.0	C 1100 C 1104 C 1500	Left front axle **VSS sensor (L6/1)** Internal resistance	N47 77 (2.43) — Ω — 78 (2.44)	Ignition: **OFF** Disconnect Traction control module (N47)	0.8 - 2.3 kΩ	Wiring, L6/1
11.1		Insulation resistance	N47 57 (2.23) — Ω — 77 (2.43)	Ignition: **OFF** Disconnect control module (N47).	>20 kΩ	Wiring, L6/1
12.0		Left front axle **VSS sensor (L6/1)** Output	N47 57 (2.23) — V — 1 (1.1)	Raise front of vehicle Ignition: **ON** Rotate left front tire by hand (> 1 rev./sec.)	>3 V~	Wiring, ⇒12.1, N47

MB0029900066050X

Fig. 61 Codes C1100, C1104 & C1500: Test 23, Steps 10.0–12.0. C43, C230, C280, E300, S320, S420, SL500, SL600 & SLK230 & 1998–99 CL500, CL600, S500 & S600

⇒	Code	Test scope	Test connection	Test condition	Nominal value	Possible cause/Remedy
12.1		Load with control modules connected	N47: 57 (2.23) – Ω – 1 (1.1)	Ignition: **OFF** Disconnect control module (N47).	> 5 kΩ	Wiring, Connected control modules ⇒ 11.0.
13.0	C 1101 C 1105 C 1500	**Right front axle VSS sensor (L6/2)** Internal resistance	N47: 52 (2.18) – Ω – 51 (2.17)	Ignition: **OFF** Disconnect control module (N47).	0.8 – 2.3 kΩ	Wiring, L6/2.
13.1		Insulation resistance	N47: 57 (2.23) – Ω – 52 (2.18)	Ignition: **OFF** Disconnect control module (N47).	> 20 kΩ	Wiring, L6/2.
14.0		**Right front axle VSS sensor (L6/2)** Output	N47: 57 (2.23) – V – 2 (1.2)	Raise front of vehicle Ignition: **ON** Rotate right front tire by hand (> 1 rev./sec.)	> 3 V ~	Wiring, ⇒ 14.1, N47.
14.1		Load with control modules connected	N47: 57 (2.23) – Ω – 2 (1.2)	Ignition: **OFF** Disconnect control module (N47).	> 5 kΩ	Wiring, Connected control modules ⇒ 13.0.

MB0029900066060X

Fig. 62 Codes C1101, C1105 & C1500: Test 23, Steps 12.1–14.1. C43, C230, C280, E300, S320, S420, SL500, SL600 & SLK230 & 1998–99 CL500, CL600, S500 & S600

⇒	Code	Test scope	Test connection	Test condition	Nominal value	Possible cause/Remedy
15.0	C 1102 C 1106 C 1500	**ABS: VSS sensor (L6) ASR or ETS: Left rear axle VSS sensor (L6/3)** Internal resistance	N47: 13 (1.13) – Ω – 12 (1.12)	Ignition: **OFF** Disconnect control module (N47).	0.6 – 1.8 kΩ	Wiring, L6/3. ⇒ 15.1
15.1		Insulation resistance	N47: 57 (2.23) – Ω – 13 (1.13)	Ignition: **OFF** Disconnect control module (N47).	> 20 kΩ	Wiring.
16.0		**ABS: VSS sensor (L6) ASR ETS: Left rear axle sensor (L6/3)** output	N47: 57 (2.23) – V – 3 (1.3)	Raise rear of vehicle Ignition: **ON** Rotate left rear tire by hand (> 1 rev./sec.)	> 3 V ~	Wiring, ⇒ 16.1, N47.
16.1		Load with control modules connected	N47: 57 (2.23) – Ω – 3 (1.3)	Ignition: **OFF** Disconnect control module (N47).	> 5 kΩ	Wiring, Connected control modules ⇒ 15.0.
17.0	C 1103 C 1107 C 1500	**ASR or ETS: Right rear axle VSS sensor (L6/4)** Internal resistance	N47: 15 (1.15) – Ω – 14 (1.14)	Ignition: **OFF** Disconnect control module (N47).	0.6 – 1.8 kΩ	Wiring, L6/4. ⇒ 17.1

MB0029900066070X

Fig. 63 Codes C1102, C1103, C1106, C1107 & C1500: Test 23, Steps 15.0–17.0. C43, C230, C280, E300, S320, S420, SL500, SL600 & SLK230 & 1998–99 CL500, CL600, S500 & S600

⇒	Code	Test scope	Test connection	Test condition	Nominal value	Possible cause/Remedy
17.1		Insulation resistance	N47: 57 (2.23) – Ω – 15 (1.15)	Ignition: **OFF** Disconnect control module (N47).	> 20 kΩ	Wiring
18.0		**VSS sensor status** Signal: vehicle standing	N47: 57 (2.23) – Ω – 5 (1.5)	Engine: **Idle**	> 3V ~	Wiring, N47
19.0	C 1300	**ASR/ETS hydraulic unit, left front axle solenoid valve (hold) (A7/3y6)** Internal resistance	N47: **Bosch** 73 (2.39) – Ω – 80 (2.46); **Teves** 70 (2.36) – Ω – 55 (2.21)	Ignition: **OFF** Disconnect control module (N47).	5.4 – 12.6 Ω	Wiring, A7/3.
20.0	C 1301	**ASR/ETS hydraulic unit, left front axle solenoid valve (release) (A7/3y7)** Internal resistance	N47: **Bosch** 72 (2.38) – Ω – 80 (2.46); **Teves** 80 (2.46) – Ω – 55 (2.21)	Ignition: **OFF** Disconnect control module (N47).	2.8 – 6.6 Ω	Wiring, A7/3.

MB0029900066080X

Fig. 64 Codes C1300 & C1301: Test 23, Steps 17.1–20.0. C43, C230, C280, E300, S320, S420, SL500, SL600 & SLK230 & 1998–99 CL500, CL600, S500 & S600

⇒	Code	Test scope	Test connection	Test condition	Nominal value	Possible cause/Remedy
21.0	C 1302	**ASR/ETS hydraulic unit, right front axle solenoid valve (hold) (A7/3y8)** Internal resistance	N47: **Bosch** 74 (2.40) – Ω – 80 (2.46); **Teves** 69 (2.35) – Ω – 55 (2.21)	Ignition: **OFF** Disconnect control module (N47).	5.4 – 12.6 Ω	Wiring, A7/3.
22.0	C 1303	**ASR/ETS hydraulic unit, right front axle solenoid valve (release) (A7/3y9)** Internal resistance	N47: **Bosch** 71 (2.37) – Ω – 80 (2.46); **Teves** 74 (2.40) – Ω – 55 (2.21)	Ignition: **OFF** Disconnect control module (N47).	2.8 – 6.6 Ω	Wiring, A7/3.
23.0	C 1304	**ABS hydraulic unit, rear axle solenoid valve (hold) (A7/3y20)** **ASR/ETS hydraulic unit, left rear axle solenoid valve (hold) (A7/3y10)** Internal resistance	N47: **Bosch** 69 (2.35) – Ω – 80 (2.46); **Teves** 72 (2.38) – Ω – 55 (2.21)	Ignition: **OFF** Disconnect control module (N47).	5.4 – 12.6 Ω	Wiring, A7/3.

MB0029900066090X

Fig. 65 Codes C1302, C1303 & C1304: Test 23, Steps 21.0–23.0. C43, C230, C280, E300, S320, S420, SL500, SL600 & SLK230 & 1998–99 CL500, CL600, S500 & S600

⇒	Code	Test scope	Test connection	Test condition	Nominal value	Possible cause/Remedy
24.0	C 1305	**ABS hydraulic unit, rear axle solenoid valve (relase) (A7/3y20)** **ASR/ETS hydraulic unit, left rear axle solenoid valve (release) (A7/3y11)** Internal resistance	**Bosch** 70 —< (2.36) N47 (module) –Ω– >— 80 (2.46) **Teves** 73—< (2.39) –Ω– >— 55 (2.21)	Ignition: **OFF** Disconnect control module (N47).	2.8 – 6.6 Ω	Wiring, A7/3.
25.0	C 1306	**ASR/ETS hydraulic unit, right rear axle solenoid valve (hold) (A7/3y12)** Internal resistance	**Bosch** 64 —< (2.30) N47 (module) –Ω– >— 80 (2.46) **Teves** 62—< (2.28) –Ω– >— 71 (2.37)	Ignition: **OFF** Disconnect control module (N47).	5.4 – 12.6 Ω	Wiring, A7/3.
26.0	C 1307	**ASR/ETS hydraulic unit, right rear axle solenoid valve (release) (A7/3y13)** Internal resistance	**Bosch** 65 —< (2.31) N47 (module) –Ω– >— 80 (2.46) **Teves** 64—< (2.30) –Ω– >— 71 (2.37)	Ignition: **OFF** Disconnect control module (N47).	2.8 – 6.6 Ω	Wiring, A7/3.

MB0029900066100X

Fig. 66 Codes C1305, C1306 & C1307: Test 23, Steps 24.0–26.0. C43, C230, C280, E300, S320, S420, SL500, SL600 & SLK230 & 1998–99 CL500, CL600, S500 & S600

⇒	Code	Test scope	Test connection	Test condition	Nominal value	Possible cause/Remedy
27.0	C 1311	**ASR/ETS hydraulic unit, switchover/solenoid valve (A7/3y5)** Internal resistance	**Bosch** 62 —< (2.28) N47 (module) –Ω– >— 80 (2.46) **Teves** 65—< (2.31) –Ω– >— 71 (2.37)	Ignition: **OFF** Disconnect control module (N47).	5.4 – 12.6 Ω	Wiring, A7/3.
28.0	C 1315	**ASR/ETS hydraulic unit, inlet solenoid valve (A7/3y15)** Internal resistance	**Bosch** 65 —< (2.29) N47 (module) –Ω– >— 80 (2.46)	Ignition: **OFF** Disconnect control module (N47).	5.4 – 12.6 Ω	Wiring, A7/3.

MB0029900066110X

Fig. 67 Codes C1311 & C1315: Test 23, Steps 27.0–28.0. C43, C230, C280, E300, S320, S420, SL500, SL600 & SLK230 & 1998–99 CL500, CL600, S500 & S600

⇒	Code	Test scope	Test connection	Test condition	Nominal value	Possible cause/Remedy
1.0	028	**ASR/SPS or ETS/SPS control module (N47-1 or N47-2)** Circuit 87 Voltage supply	N47-1 N47-2 (module) 74 —< (1.33) –V– >— 68 (1.27) 77 —< (1.36) –V– >— 68 (1.27)	Ignition: **ON**	11 – 14 V	⇒ 1.1, ⇒ 1.2
1.1		Voltage supply from base module (N16/1)	N47-1 N47-2 (module) ⊥ –V– >— 68 (1.27)	Ignition: **ON**	11 – 14 V	Fuse (F1) on N16/1,
1.2		Ground wire	**Model 129** W27 –Ω– N47-1 N47-2 (module) >— 74 (1.33) **Model 140** W15 **Model 129** W27 –Ω– >— 77 (1.36) **Model 140** W15	Ignition: **OFF** Control module (N47-1 or N47-2) disconnected. Disconnect ground wire.	< 1 Ω	**Model 129** Wiring, Ground (module box bracket) (W27). **Model 140** Wiring, Ground (electronics output ground - right footwell) (W15).

MB0029600005000A

Fig. 68 Code 028: Test 23, Steps 1.0–1.2. SL500 & SL600

⇒	Code	Test scope	Test connection	Test condition	Nominal value	Possible cause/Remedy
2.0 ETS only	029	**ETS/SPS control module (N47-2)** Circuit 30 Voltage supply	N47-2 (module) 74 —< (1.33) –V– >— 47 (1.6)	Ignition: **OFF**	11 – 14 V	Wiring.
3.0		**ABS MIL (A1e17)**	N47-1 N47-2 (module) 74 —< (1.33) –V– >— 76 (1.35)	Ignition: **ON** Engine: **at Idle**	< 2 V A1e17: **ON** 10 – 14 V A1e17: **OFF**	A1e17. Read DTC memory □ 12, Wiring, N47-1 or N47-2.
4.0		**ASR MIL or ETS MIL (A1e22 or A1e35)**	N47-1 N47-2 (module) 74 —< (1.36) –V– >— 79 (1.38)	Ignition: **ON** Engine: **at Idle**	< 2 V A1e22 or A1e35: **ON** 10 – 14 V A1e22 or A1e35: **OFF**	A1e22 or A1e35. Read DTC memory □ 12, Wiring, N47-1 or N47-2.

MB0029600006000A

Fig. 69 Code 029: Test 23, Steps 2.0–4.0. SL500 & SL600

⇒		Test scope	Test connection	Test condition	Nominal value	Possible cause/Remedy
5.0		**ASR or ETS warning lamp (A1e21 or A1e36)**	N47-1 N47-2 74 —< (1.33) V >— 57 (1.16)	Ignition: **ON**	< 2 V A1e21 or A1e36: **ON**	Wiring, A1e21 or A1e36.
				Engine: **at Idle**	10 – 14 V A1e21 or A1e36: **OFF**	Wiring.
6.0		**Diagnosis output**	N47-1 N47-2 74 —< (1.33) V >— 53 (1.12)	Ignition: **ON**	10 – 14 V	Wiring, N47-1 or N47-2.
7.0		**Circuit 61 Voltage supply**		Ignition: **ON**	OFF	Wiring, Generator (G2).
				Engine: **at Idle**	On	

MB0029600007000A

Fig. 70 Code —: Test 23, Steps 5.0–7.0. SL500 & SL600

⇒		Test scope	Test connection	Test condition	Nominal value	Possible cause/Remedy
8.0	012	**ASR/ETS/ESP hydraulic unit, solenoid valve relay (A7/3k1)** Voltage supply	N47-1 N47-2 74 —< (1.33) V >— 7 (2.7)	Ignition: **ON**	11 – 14 V	☐ 12, Wiring, ⇒ 8.1
		Control	N47-1 N47-2 27 —< (2.27) V >— 7 (2.7)			
8.1		Coil resistance	N47-1 N47-2 27 —< (1.27) Ω >— 7 (2.7)	Ignition: **OFF** Control module (N47-1 or N47-2) disconnected.	40 – 80 Ω	Wiring, A7/3k1, ⇒ 8.2
8.2		Working contact	N47-1 N47-2 74 —< (1.33) V >— 18 (2.18)	Ignition: **ON**	11 – 14 V	Wiring, A7/3k1.

MB0029600008000A

Fig. 71 Code 012: Test 23, Steps 8.0–8.2. SL500 & SL600

⇒		Test scope	Test connection	Test condition	Nominal value	Possible cause/Remedy
9.0	024	**ASR/ETS/ESP hydraulic unit, high-pressure/return pump relay (A7/3k2)** Voltage supply	N47-1 N47-2 74 —< (1.33) V >— 7 (2.7)	Ignition: **ON**	11 – 14 V	Wiring, ⇒ 9.1
9.1		Coil resistance	N47-1 N47-2 28 —< (2.28) Ω >— 7 (2.7)	Ignition: **OFF** Control module (N47-1 or N47-2) disconnected.	40 – 80 Ω	Wiring, A7/3k2.
9.2		Working contact	N47-1 N47-2 74 —< (1.33) V >— 36 (2.36); 77 —< (1.36) ⟵⟶ >— 36 (2.36)	Ignition: **ON** Control module (N47-1 or N47-2) disconnected.	11 – 14 V High-pressure/ return pump (A7/3m1) runs.	A7/3k2, A7/3m1, Wiring.
10.0		**Parking brake switch (S12)**		Engine: **at Idle** Apply parking brake.	On Parking brake indicator lamp (A1e7): **ON**	Wiring, S12, A1e7.
				Release parkng brake.	OFF A1e7: **OFF**	

MB0029600009000X

Fig. 72 Code 024: Test 23, Steps 9.0–10.0. SL500 & SL600

⇒		Test scope	Test connection	Test condition	Nominal value	Possible cause/Remedy
11.0	027	**Stop lamp switch (S9/1)** N.O. contact		Ignition: **ON** Brakes not applied. Brakes applied.	OFF On	Wiring, S9/1.
		N.C. contact		Brakes not applied. Brakes applied.	OFF On	
12.0	035	**Models 129.076, 140.04/05/07** **Master brake cylinder switchover valve (Y61)** Internal resistance	Y61 1 — Ω — 2	Ignition: **OFF** Pull connector off of Y61.	7 – 8 Ω	Y61.
13.0	003 007 011	**Left front axle VSS sensor (L6/1)**		Raise front of vehicle. Ignition: **ON** Rotate left front tire by hand (> 1 rev./sec.).	> 2 mph (3 km/h)	⇒ 13.1, ⇒ 13.2
13.1		Internal resistance	N47-1 N47-2 10 —< (2.10) Ω >— 30 (2.30)	Ignition: **OFF** Control module (N47-1 or N47-2) disconnected.	0.8 – 2.3 kΩ	Wiring, L6/1.

MB0029600010000X

Fig. 73 Codes 003, 007, 011, 027 & 035: Test 23, Steps 11.0–13.1. SL500 & SL600

⇒		Test scope	Test connection	Test condition	Nominal value	Possible cause/Remedy
13.2		Insulation resistance	N47-1 N47-2 74 —((1.33) Ω)— 10 (2.10)	Ignition: **OFF** Control module (N47-1 or N47-2) disconnected.	> 20 kΩ	Wiring, L6/1.
14.0		**Left front axle VSS sensor (L6/1) output**	N47-1 N47-2 74 —((1.33) V)— 64 (1.23)	Raise front of vehicle. Ignition: **ON** Rotate left front tire by hand (> 1 rev./sec.).	> 3 V ~	Wiring, ⇒ 14.1, N47-1 or N47-2.
14.1		Load with control modules connected	N47-1 N47-2 74 —((1.33) Ω)— 64 (1.23)	Ignition: **OFF** Control module (N47-1 or N47-2) disconnected.	> 5 kΩ	Wiring, Connected control modules (N4/1, N4/2, N22, etc.), ⇒ 13.0
15.0	004 008 011	**Right front axle VSS sensor (L6/2)**		Raise front of vehicle. Ignition: **ON** Rotate right front tire by hand (> 1 rev./sec.).	> 2 mph (3 km/h)	⇒ 15.1, ⇒ 15.2
15.1		Internal resistance	N47-1 N47-2 13 —((2.13) Ω)— 34 (2.34)	Ignition: **OFF** Control module (N47-1 or N47-2) disconnected.	0.8 – 2.3 kΩ	Wiring, L6/2.

MB0029600011000X

Fig. 74 Codes 004, 008 & 011: Test 23, Steps 13.2–15.1. SL500 & SL600

⇒		Test scope	Test connection	Test condition	Nominal value	Possible cause/Remedy
15.2		Insulation resistance	N47-1 N47-2 74 —((1.33) Ω)— 13 (2.13)	Ignition: **OFF** Control module (N47-1 or N47-2) disconnected.	> 20 kΩ	Wiring, L6/2.
16.0		**Right front axle VSS sensor (L6/2) output**	N47-1 N47-2 **ASR** 74 —((1.33) V)— 44 (1.3) **ETS** 74 —((1.33) V)— 65 (1.24)	Raise front of vehicle. Ignition: **ON** Rotate right front tire by hand (> 1 rev./sec.).	> 3 V ~	Wiring, ⇒ 16.1, N47-1 or N47-2.
16.1		Load with control modules connected	N47-1 N47-2 **ASR** 74 —((1.33) Ω)— 44 (1.3) **ETS** 74 —((1.33) Ω)— 65 (1.24)	Ignition: **OFF** control module (N47-1 or N47-2) disconnected.	> 5 kΩ	Wiring, Connected control modules (N16/1, N51, etc.), ⇒ 15.0

MB0029600012000X

Fig. 75 Code —: Test 23, Steps 15.2–16.1. SL500 & SL600

⇒		Test scope	Test connection	Test condition	Nominal value	Possible cause/Remedy
17.0	005 009 011	**Left rear axle VSS sensor (L6/3)**		Raise rear of vehicle. Ignition: **ON** Rotate left rear tire by hand (> 1 rev./sec.).	> 2 mph (3 km/h)	⇒ 17.1, ⇒ 17.2
17.1		Internal resistance	N47-1 N47-2 73 —((1.32) Ω)— 72 (1.31)	Ignition: **OFF** Control module (N47-1 or N47-2) disconnected.	0.6 – 1.8 kΩ	Wiring, L6/3.
17.2		Insulation resistance	N47-1 N47-2 74 —((1.33) Ω)— 73 (1.32)	Ignition: **OFF** Control module (N47-1 or N47-2) disconnected.	> 20 kΩ	Wiring, L6/3.
18.0		**Left rear axle VSS sensor (L6/3) output**	N47-1 N47-2 **ASR** 74 —((1.33) V)— 66 (1.25) **ETS** 74 —((1.33) V)— 58 (1.17)	Raise rear of vehicle. Ignition: **ON** Rotate left rear tire by hand (> 1 rev./sec.).	> 3 V ~	Wiring, ⇒ 18.1, N47-1 or N47-2.

MB0029600013000X

Fig. 76 Codes 005, 009 & 011: Test 23, Steps 17.0–18.0. SL500 & SL600

⇒		Test scope	Test connection	Test condition	Nominal value	Possible cause/Remedy
18.1		Load with control modules connected	N47-1 N47-2 **ASR** 74 —((1.33) Ω)— 66 (1.25) **ETS** 74 —((1.33) Ω)— 58 (1.17)	Ignition: **OFF** Control module (N47-1 or N47-2) disconnected.	> 5 kΩ	Wiring, Connected control modules (N3/4, N4/1, etc.), ⇒ 17.0
19.0	006 010 011	**Right rear axle VSS sensor (L6/4)**		Raise rear of vehicle. Ignition: **ON** Rotate right rear tire by hand (> 1 rev./sec.).	> 2 mph (3 km/h)	⇒ 19.1, ⇒ 19.2
19.1		Internal resistance	N47-1 N47-2 71 —((1.30) Ω)— 70 (1.29)	Ignition: **OFF** Control module (N47-1 or N47-2) disconnected.	0.6 – 1.8 kΩ	Wiring, L6/4.
19.2		Insulation resistance	N47-1 N47-2 74 —((1.33) Ω)— 71 (1.30)	Ignition: **OFF** Control module (N47-1 or N47-2) disconnected.	> 20 kΩ	Wiring, L6/4.

MB0029600014000X

Fig. 77 Codes 006, 010 & 011: Test 23, Steps 18.1–19.2. SL500 & SL600

⇒		Test scope	Test connection	Test condition	Nominal value	Possible cause/Remedy
20.0		**Right rear axle VSS sensor (L6/4) output**	N47-1 N47-2 74 (1.33) — V — 67 (1.26)	Raise rear of vehicle. Ignition: **ON** Rotate right rear tire by hand (> 1 rev./sec.).	> 3 V ~	⇒ 20.1, N47-1 or N47-2.
20.1		Load with control modules connected	N47-1 N47-2 74 (1.33) — Ω — 67 (1.26)	Ignition: **OFF** Control module (N47-1 or N47-2) disconnected.	> 5 kΩ	Wiring, Connected control modules (N3/4, N4/1, etc.), ⇒ 19.0
21.0	013	**ASR/ETS/ESP hydraulic unit, left front axle solenoid valve (hold) (A7/3y6)** Internal resistance	A7/3 1 — Ω — 12	Ignition: **OFF** Disconnect electrical connector on A7/3.	5.4 – 12.6 Ω	Wiring, A7/3.
22.0	014	**ASR/ETS/ESP hydraulic unit, left front axle solenoid valve (release) (A7/3y7)** Internal resistance	A7/3 1 — Ω — 13	Ignition: **OFF** Disconnect electrical connector on A7/3.	2.8 – 6.6 Ω	Wiring, A7/3.

MB0029600015000X

Fig. 78 Codes 013 & 014: Test 23, Steps 10.0–22.0. SL500 & SL600

⇒		Test scope	Test connection	Test condition	Nominal value	Possible cause/Remedy
23.0	015	**ASR/ETS/ESP hydraulic unit, right front axle solenoid valve (hold) (A7/3y8)** Internal resistance	A7/3 1 — Ω — 3	Ignition: **OFF** Disconnect electrical connector on A7/3.	5.4 – 12.6 Ω	Wiring, A7/3.
24.0	016	**ASR/ETS/ESP hydraulic unit, right front axle solenoid valve (release) (A7/3y9)** Internal resistance	A7/3 1 — Ω — 14	Ignition: **OFF** Disconnect electrical connector on A7/3.	2.8 – 6.6 Ω	Wiring, A7/3.
25.0	017	**ASR/ETS/ESP hydraulic unit, left rear axle solenoid valve (hold) (A7/3y10)** Internal resistance	A7/3 1 — Ω — 19	Ignition: **OFF** Disconnect electrical connector on A7/3.	5.4 – 12.6 Ω	Wiring, A7/3.
26.0	018	**ASR/ETS/ESP hydraulic unit, left rear axle solenoid valve (release) (A7/3y11)** Internal resistance	A7/3 1 — Ω — 18	Ignition: **OFF** Disconnect electrical connector on A7/3.	2.8 – 6.6 Ω	Wiring, A7/3.

MB0029600016000X

Fig. 79 Codes 015, 016, 017 & 018: Test 23, Steps 23.0–26.0. SL500 & SL600

⇒		Test scope	Test connection	Test condition	Nominal value	Possible cause/Remedy
27.0	019	**ASR/ETS/ESP hydraulic unit, right rear axle solenoid valve (hold) (A7/3y12)** Internal resistance	A7/3 1 — Ω — 20	Ignition: **OFF** Disconnect electrical connector on A7/3.	5.4 – 12.6 Ω	Wiring, A7/3.
28.0	020	**ASR/ETS/ESP hydraulic unit, right rear axle solenoid valve (release) (A7/3y13)** Internal resistance	A7/3 1 — Ω — 17	Ignition: **OFF** Disconnect electrical connector on A7/3.	2.8 – 6.6 Ω	Wiring, A7/3.
29.0	022	**ASR/ETS/ESP hydraulic unit, inlet solenoid valve (A7/3y15)** Internal resistance	A7/3 1 — Ω — 16	Ignition: **OFF** Disconnect electrical connector on A7/3.	5.4 – 12.6 Ω	Wiring, A7/3.
30.0	021	**ASR/ETS/ESP hydraulic unit, switchover/solenoid valve (A7/3y5)** Internal resistance	A7/3 1 — Ω — 21	Ignition: **OFF** Disconnect electrical connector on A7/3.	5.4 – 12.6 Ω	Wiring, A7/3.

MB0029600017000X

Fig. 80 Codes 019, 020, 021 & 022: Test 23, Steps 27.0–30.0. SL500 & SL600

⇒		Test scope	Test connection	Test condition	Nominal value	Possible cause/Remedy
31.0	040	**Model 140** **SPS P-valve (Y10)** Voltage supply	(scan tool)	Engine: **at Idle** Press MAX key Press MIN key	> 800 mA steering is light < 400 mA steering is heavy	⇒ 31.1, N47-1 or N47-2.
31.1		Coil resistance	N47-1 N47-2 21 (2.21) — Ω — 22 (2.22)	Ignition: **OFF** Control module (N47-1 or N47-2) disconnected.	3 – 8 Ω	Wiring, Y10.
32.0	036 037	**Models 129.076, 140.04/05/07** **ABS lateral accelration sensor (B24/2)** Static sensor signal (off) Dynamic sensor signal (on)	(scan tool)	Vigorously rock vehicle from side to side.	0 ± 1 m/s² > 1 m/s² Value changes with movement of vehicle	Wiring, B24/2, ⇒ 32.1

MB0029600018000X

Fig. 81 Codes 036, 037 & 040: Test 23, Steps 31.0–32.0. SL500 & SL600

⇒		Test scope	Test connection	Test condition	Nominal value	Possible cause/Remedy
32.1		Voltage suppply to sensor input	N47-1 65 (1.24) –(V)– 50 (1.9)	**Ignition: ON** Disconnect connector on B24/2.	4.75–5.25 V	Wiring, N47-1.
33.0 **ASR only**		**ASR OFF switch (S76/5)**		Press and hold switch S76/5: **ON** Release switch Press and hold switch S76/5: **OFF**	1 – 2 V 3.5 – 6 V < 1 V	Wiring, S76/5, N47-1.
34.0		**VSS sensor output status** Signal: Vehicle stationary	N47-1 74 (1.33) –(V)– 42 (1.1)	Engine: **at Idle**	> 3 V ~	⇒ 34.1
35.0 **ASR only**	030 031 032 033	**CAN bus**	N47-1 L –(Ω)– H	**Ignition: OFF** Disconnect contact module 2 or N47-1. Test directly at both wide connectors using an ohmmeter.	55 – 65 Ω	Data bus, ⇒ 35.1, ⇒ 35.2

MB0029600019000X

Fig. 82 Codes 030, 031, 032 & 033: Test 23, Steps 32.1–35.0. SL500 & SL600

⇒		Test scope	Test connection	Test condition	Nominal value	Possible cause/Remedy
35.1		**Engine 104, 119** **CAN element in LH-SFI or engine control module (N3/1 or N3/4)** Resistance	N3/1 N3/4 L –(Ω)– H	Disconnect control module (N3/1 or N3/4) and test directly on control module using an ohmmeter.	115 – 125 Ω	N3/1 or N3/4,
35.2		**CAN element in DI control module (N1/3, N1/4 or N1/5)** Resistance **Engine 104/119 LH-SFI** **Engine 120**	N1/3 3 –(Ω)– 4 N1/4 N1/5 3 –(Ω)– 4	Disconnect connector B on control module (N1/3, N1/4 or N1/5) and test directly on control module using an ohmmeter.	115 – 125 Ω	**Engine 104/119 LH-SFI** N1/3, **Engine 120** N1/4 or N1/5,
36.0 **ETS only**		**ETS signal**	N47-2 74 (1.33) –(V)– 50 (1.9)	Ignition: **ON** Engine: **at Idle**	< 1 V ETS MIL (A1e35): **ON** 10 – 14 V A1e35: **OFF**	Wiring, N47-2.

MB0029600020000X

Fig. 83 Code —: Test 23, Steps 35.1–36.0. SL500 & SL600

⇒		Test scope	Test connection	Test condition	Nominal value	Possible cause/Remedy
1.0	C 1010	**ESP/SPS control module (N47-5)** Circuit 87 Voltage supply	N47-5 57 (2.23) –(V)– 14 (1.14) 81 (2.47) –(V)– 14 (1.14)	Ignition: **ON**	11 – 14 V	⇒ 1.1, ⇒ 1.2
1.1		Voltage supply from: **Models 129, 140** Base module (N16/1) **Model 210** Relay module (K40)	N47-5 W15/1 –(V)– 14 (1.14)	Ignition: **ON**	11 – 14 V	Fuse (F3) on N16/1, DM, Wiring.
1.2		Ground wire **Model 129** W27 **Model 140** W15/1 **Model 210** W16/3 **Model 129** W27 **Model 140** W15/1 **Model 210** W16/3	N47-5 –(Ω)– 57 (2.23) –(Ω)– 81 (2.47)	Ignition: **OFF**	< 1 Ω	Wiring, **Model 129:** bracket ground (W27) (control module box/module box). **Model 140:** electronics- right footwell ground (W15/1). **Model 210:** output ground - left wheel housing ground (W16/3).

MB0029900071010X

Fig. 84 Code C1010: Test 23, Steps 1.0–1.2. E320, E430, S320, S420, SL500 & SL600 & 1998–99 CL500, CL600, S500 & S600

⇒		Test scope	Test connection	Test condition	Nominal value	Possible cause/Remedy
2.0		**ESP/SPS control module (N47-5)** Circuit 30 Voltage supply	N47-5 57 (2.23) –(V)– 58 (2.24) 57 (2.23) –(V)– 82 (2.48)	Ignition: **OFF**	11 – 14 V	Wiring.
3.0		**Instrument cluster data bus** (for vehicles without CAN connection to instrument cluster)	N47-5 57 (2.23) –(V)– 9 (1.9)	Ignition: **ON**	3 – 4 V A1e6, A1e7, A1e17, A1e41, A1e42: **ON.**	Wiring, N47-5.
4.0		**Diagnosis output**	N47-5 57 (2.23) –(V)– 13 (1.13)	Ignition: **ON**	10 – 14 V	Wiring, N47-5.
5.0		**Engine speed (rpm)**		Engine: **at Idle**	Engine speed	DM Engines

MB0029900071020X

Fig. 85 Code —: Test 23, Steps 1.0–5.0. E320, E430, S320, S420, SL500 & SL600 & 1998–99 CL500, CL600, S500 & S600

⇒		Test scope	Test connection	Test condition	Nominal value	Possible cause/Remedy
6.0	C 1200	**Stop lamp switch (S9/1)** N.O. contact N.C. contact		Brakes not applied. Brakes applied. Brakes not applied. Brakes applied.	OFF ON OFF ON	⇒ 6.1, Wiring, S9/1.
6.1		Circuit 15 Voltage supply		Brakes not applied. Brakes applied.	< 1 V 11 - 14 V	Wiring.
7.0		**Parking brake switch (S12)**		Engine: **at Idle** Apply parking brake. Release parking brake.	ON Parking brake indicator lamp (A1e7): **ON** OFF A1e7: **OFF**	Wiring, S12, A1e7.
8.0	C 1312	**Master brake cylinder switchover valve (Y61) (Models 129.067/076, 140 only)**		Press ON button. Press OFF button.	ON OFF Y61 audibly switches over.	⇒ 8.1, N47-5.

MB0029900071030X

Fig. 86 Codes C1200 & C1312: Test 23, Steps 6.0–8.0. E320, E430, S320, S420, SL500 & SL600 & 1998–99 CL500, CL600, S500 & S600

⇒		Test scope	Test connection	Test condition	Nominal value	Possible cause/Remedy
8.1		Internal resistance	N47-5 44 (2.10) —Ω— 43 (2.9)	Ignition: **OFF** Disconnect control module (N47-5).	7 – 8 Ω	Wiring, Y61.
9.0	C 1400	**ASR/ESP charging pump (M15)**		Activate M15. Brake pressure sensor.	M15 audibly runs. 3 - 15 bar	Wiring, M15.
10.0	C 1401	**ASR/ETS/ESP hydraulic unit, high-pressure/return pump (A7/3m1)**		Activate A7/3m1.	A7/3m1 audibly runs.	Wiring, ⇒ 11.0
11.0	C 1401	**High-pressure/return pump relay (K20/1)** **Model 129, 140: K20/1** **Model 210: N65k4** Voltage supply	N47-5 57 (2.23) —V— 47 (2.13)	Ignition: **ON**	11 – 14 V	Wiring, ⇒ 7.1
11.1		Coil resistance	N47-5 46 (2.12) —Ω— 47 (2.13)	Ignition: **OFF** Disconnect control module (N47-5).	40 – 80 Ω	Wiring, **Models 129, 140:** K20/1 (relay box). **Model 210:** Pulse module (N65).

MB0029900071040X

Fig. 87 Codes C1400, C1402 & C1403: Test 23, Steps 8.1–11.1. E320, E430, S320, S420, SL500 & SL600 & 1998–99 CL500, CL600, S500 & S600

⇒		Test scope	Test connection	Test condition	Nominal value	Possible cause/Remedy
12.0	C 1501	**SPS P-valve (Y10)** Voltage supply		Engine: **at Idle** Press MAX key Press MIN key	> 800mA steering is light < 400mA steering is heavy	⇒ 12.1, N47-5.
12.1		Coil resistance	N47-5 35 (2.1) —Ω— 36 (2.2)	Ignition: **OFF** Disconnect control module (N47-5).	3 – 8 Ω	Wiring, Y10.
13.0	C 1100 C 1500	**Left front axle VSS sensor (L6/1)**		Raise front of vehicle. Ignition: **ON** Rotate left front tire by hand (> 1 rev./sec.).	> 2 mph (3 km/h)	⇒ 13.1, ⇒ 13.2
13.1		Internal resistance	N47-5 77 (2.43) —Ω— 78 (2.44)	Ignition: **OFF** Disconnect control module (N47-5).	0.8 – 2.3 kΩ	Wiring, L6/1.
13.2		Insulation resistance	N47-5 57 (2.23) —Ω— 77 (2.43)	Ignition: **OFF** Disconnect control module (N47-5).	> 20 kΩ	Wiring, L6/1.

MB0029900071050X

Fig. 88 Codes C1100, C1500 & C1501: Test 23, Steps 12.0–13.2. E320, E430, S320, S420, SL500 & SL600 & 1998–99 CL500, CL600, S500 & S600

⇒		Test scope	Test connection	Test condition	Nominal value	Possible cause/Remedy
14.0		**Left front axle VSS sensor (L6/1) output**	N47-5 57 (2.23) —V— 1 (1.1)	Raise front of vehicle. Ignition: **ON** Rotate left front tire by hand (> 1 rev./sec.).	> 3 V ~	Wiring, ⇒ 14.1, N47-5.
14.1		Load with control modules connected	N47-5 57 (2.23) —Ω— 1 (1.1)	Ignition: **OFF** Disconnect control module (N47-5).	> 5 kΩ	Wiring, Connected control modules (N3/12, etc.), ⇒ 13.0
15.0	C 1101 C 1500	**Right front axle VSS sensor (L6/2)**		Raise front of vehicle. Ignition: **ON** Rotate right front tire by hand (> 1 rev./sec.).	> 2 mph (3 km/h)	⇒ 15.1, ⇒ 15.2
15.1		Internal resistance	N47-5 52 (2.18) —Ω— 51 (2.17)	Ignition: **OFF** Disconnect control module (N47-5).	0.8 – 2.3 kΩ	Wiring, L6/2.
15.2		Insulation resistance	N47-5 57 (2.23) —Ω— 52 (2.18)	Ignition: **OFF** Disconnect control module (N47-5).	> 20 kΩ	Wiring, L6/2.

MB0029900071060X

Fig. 89 Codes C1101 & C1500: Test 23, Steps 14.0–15.2. E320, E430, S320, S420, SL500 & SL600 & 1998–99 CL500, CL600, S500 & S600

⇒		Test scope	Test connection	Test condition	Nominal value	Possible cause/Remedy
16.0		**Right front axle VSS sensor (L6/2) output**	N47-5: 57 (2.23) — V — 2 (1.2)	Raise front of vehicle. Ignition: **ON** Rotate right front tire by hand (> 1 rev./sec.).	> 3 V ~	Wiring, ⇒ 16.1, N47-5.
16.1		Load with control modules connected	N47-5: 57 (2.23) — Ω — 2 (1.2)	Ignition: **OFF** Disconnect control module (N47-5).	> 5 kΩ	Wiring, Connected control modules, ⇒ 15.0
17.0	C 1102 C 1500	**Left rear axle VSS sensor (L6/3)**		Raise rear of vehicle. Ignition: **ON** Rotate left rear tire by hand (> 1 rev./sec.).	> 2 mph (3 km/h)	⇒ 17.1, ⇒ 17.2
17.1		Internal resistance	N47-5: 26 (1.26) — Ω — 25 (1.25)	Ignition: **OFF** Disconnect control module (N47-5).	0.6 – 1.6 kΩ	Wiring, L6/3.
17.2		Insulation resistance	N47-5: 57 (2.23) — Ω — 26 (1.26)	Ignition: **OFF** Disconnect control module (N47-5).	> 20 kΩ	Wiring.

MB0029900071070X

Fig. 90 Codes C1102 & C1500: Test 23, Steps 16.0–17.2. E320, E430, S320, S420, SL500 & SL600 & 1998–99 CL500, CL600, S500 & S600

⇒		Test scope	Test connection	Test condition	Nominal value	Possible cause/Remedy
18.0		**Left rear axle VSS sensor (L6/3) output**	N47-5: 57 (2.23) — V — 3 (1.3)	Raise rear of vehicle. Ignition: **ON** Rotate left rear tire by hand (> 1 rev./sec.).	> 3 V ~	Wiring, ⇒ 18.1, N47-5.
18.1		Load with control modules connected	N47-5: 57 (2.23) — Ω — 3 (1.3)	Ignition: **OFF** Disconnect control module (N47-5).	> 5 kΩ	Wiring, Connected control modules, ⇒ 17.0
19.0	C 1103 C 1500	**Right rear axle VSS sensor (L6/4)**		Raise rear of vehicle. Ignition: **ON** Rotate right rear tire by hand (> 1 rev./sec.).	> 2 mph (3 km/h)	⇒ 19.1, ⇒ 19.2
19.1		Internal resistance	N47-5: 28 (1.28) — Ω — 27 (1.27)	Ignition: **OFF** Disconnect control module (N47-5).	0.6 – 1.6 kΩ	Wiring, L6/4.
19.2		Insulation resistance	N47-5: 57 (2.23) — Ω — 28 (1.28)	Ignition: **OFF** Disconnect control module (N47-5).	> 20 kΩ	Wiring.

MB0029900071080X

Fig. 91 Codes C1103 & C1500: Test 23, Steps 18.0–19.2. E320, E430, S320, S420, SL500 & SL600 & 1998–99 CL500, CL600, S500 & S600

⇒		Test scope	Test connection	Test condition	Nominal value	Possible cause/Remedy
20.0		**Right rear axle VSS sensor (L6/4) output**	N47-5: 57 (2.23) — V — 4 (1.4)	Raise rear of vehicle. Ignition: **ON** Rotate right rear tire by hand (> 1 rev./sec.).	> 3 V ~	⇒ 20.1, N47-5.
20.1		Load with control modules connected	N47-5: 57 (2.23) — Ω — 4 (1.4)	Ignition: **OFF** Disconnect control module (N47-5).	> 5 kΩ	Wiring, Connected control modules, ⇒ 19.0
21.0		**VSS sensor output status** Signal: Vehicle stationary	N47-5: 57 (2.23) — V — 5 (1.5)	Ignition: **ON**	> 3 V ~	Wiring, N47-5.
22.0	C 1011	**ASR/ETS/ESP hydraulic unit (A7/3)** Solenoid valve voltage supply	N47-5: 57 (2.23) — V — 80 (2.46)	Ignition: **ON**	11 – 14 V	Wiring, N47-5.

MB0029900071090X

Fig. 92 Code C1011: Test 23, Steps 20.0–22.0. E320, E430, S320, S420, SL500 & SL600 & 1998–99 CL500, CL600, S500 & S600

⇒		Test scope	Test connection	Test condition	Nominal value	Possible cause/Remedy
23.0	C 1300 – C 1307	**ASR/ETS/ESP hydraulic unit (A7/3)** Solenoid valves (A7/3y6 – A7/3y13)		Raise vehicle. Activate all solenoid valves, one after the other. ON and apply brakes. OFF and apply brakes.	ON Wheels not braked. OFF Wheels braked.	Wiring, ⇒ 23.1 – 23.8
23.1	C 1300	**ASR/ETS/ESP hydraulic unit, left front axle solenoid valve (hold) (A7/3y6)** Internal resistance	N47-5: 80 (2.46) — Ω — 73 (2.39)	Ignition: **OFF** Disconnect control module (N47-5).	5.4 – 12.6 Ω	Wiring, A7/3.
23.2	C 1301	**ASR/ETS/ESP hydraulic unit, left front axle solenoid valve (release) (A7/3y7)** Internal resistance	N47-5: 80 (2.46) — Ω — 72 (2.38)	Ignition: **OFF** Disconnect control module (N47-5).	2.8 – 6.6 Ω	Wiring, A7/3.
23.3	C 1302	**ASR/ETS/ESP hydraulic unit, right front axle solenoid valve (hold) (A7/3y8)** Internal resistance	N47-5: 80 (2.46) — Ω — 74 (2.40)	Ignition: **OFF** Disconnect control module (N47-5).	5.4 – 12.6 Ω	Wiring, A7/3.

MB0029900071100X

Fig. 93 Codes C1300, C1301, C1302 & C1307: Test, Steps 23.0–23.3. E320, E430, S320, S420, SL500 & SL600 & 1998–99 CL500, CL600, S500 & S600

⇒	Code	Test scope	Test connection	Test condition	Nominal value	Possible cause/Remedy
23.4	C 1303	**ASR/ETS/ESP hydraulic unit, right front axle solenoid valve (release) (A7/3y9)** Internal resistance	N47-5: 80 (2.46) —Ω— 71 (2.37)	Ignition: **OFF** Disconnect control module (N47-5).	2.8 – 6.6 Ω	Wiring, A7/3.
23.5	C 1304	**ASR/ETS/ESP hydraulic unit, left rear axle solenoid valve (hold) (A7/3y10)** Internal resistance	N47-5: 80 (2.46) —Ω— 69 (2.35)	Ignition: **OFF** Disconnect control module (N47-5).	5.4 – 12.6 Ω	Wiring, A7/3.
23.6	C 1305	**ASR/ETS/ESP hydraulic unit, left rear axle solenoid valve (release) (A7/3y11)** Internal resistance	N47-5: 80 (2.46) —Ω— 70 (2.36)	Ignition: **OFF** Disconnect control module (N47-5).	2.8 – 6.6 Ω	Wiring, A7/3.
23.7	C 1306	**ASR/ETS/ESP hydraulic unit, right rear axle solenoid valve (hold) (A7/3y12)** Internal resistance	N47-5: 80 (2.46) —Ω— 64 (2.30)	Ignition: **OFF** Disconnect control module (N47-5).	5.4 – 12.6 Ω	Wiring, A7/3.

MB0029900071110X

Fig. 94 Codes C1303, C1304, C1305 & C1306: Test 23, Steps 23.4–23.7. E320, E430, S320, S420, SL500 & SL600 & 1998–99 CL500, CL600, S500 & S600

⇒	Code	Test scope	Test connection	Test condition	Nominal value	Possible cause/Remedy
23.8	C 1307	**ASR/ETS/ESP hydraulic unit, right rear axle solenoid valve (release) (A7/3y13)** Internal resistance	N47-5: 80 (2.46) —Ω— 65 (2.31)	Ignition: **OFF** Disconnect control module (N47-5).	2.8 – 6.6 Ω	Wiring, A7/3.
24.0	C 1308 C 1311	**ASR/ETS/ESP hydraulic unit(A7/3)** Solenoid valves (A7/3y16 – A7/3y19)		Raise vehicle. Activate all solenoid valves, one after the other. ON and apply service brake. OFF and apply service brake.	ON Wheel not braked. OFF Wheel braked.	Wiring, ⇒ 24.1 – 24.4
24.1	C 1308	**ASR/ETS/ESP hydraulic unit, front axle precharge solenoid valve (A7/3y16)** Internal resistance	N47-5: 80 (2.46) —Ω— 61 (2.27)	Ignition: **OFF** Disconnect control module (N47-5).	2.8 – 6.6 Ω	Wiring, A7/3.
24.2	C 1309	**ASR/ETS/ESP hydraulic unit, rear axle precharge solenoid valve (A7/3y17)** Internal resistance	N47-5: 80 (2.46) —Ω— 63 (2.29)	Ignition: **OFF** Disconnect control module (N47-5).	2.8 – 6.6 Ω	Wiring, A7/3.

MB0029900071120X

Fig. 95 Codes C1307, C1308, C1309 & C1311: Test 23, Steps 23.8–24.2. E320, E430, S320, S420, SL500 & SL600 & 1998–99 CL500, CL600, S500 & S600

⇒	Code	Test scope	Test connection	Test condition	Nominal value	Possible cause/Remedy
24.3	C 1310	**ASR/ETS/ESP hydraulic unit, front axle switchover valve (A7/3y18)** Internal resistance	N47-5: 80 (2.46) —Ω— 60 (2.26)	Ignition: **OFF** Disconnect control module (N47-5).	5.4 – 12.6 Ω	Wiring, A7/3.
24.4	C 1311	**ASR/ETS/ESP hydraulic unit, rear axle switchover valve (A7/3y19)** Internal resistance	N47-5: 80 (2.46) —Ω— 62 (2.28)	Ignition: **OFF** Disconnect control module (N47-5).	5.4 – 12.6 Ω	Wiring, A7/3.
25.0		**ESP Off switch (S76/6)**		Press and hold switch S76/6: **ON** Release switch Press and hold switch S76/6: **OFF**	1 – 2 V 3.5 – 6 V < 1 V	Wiring, S76/6, N47-5.
26.0	C 1142	**ABS lateral accelration sensor (B24/2)** Static sensor signal (off) Dynamic sensor signal (on)		 Vigorously rock vehicle from side to side.	0±1 m/s² > 1 m/s² Value changes with movement of vehicle.	Wiring, B24/2, ⇒ 26.1

MB0029900071130X

Fig. 96 Codes C1142, C1310 & C1311: Test 23, Steps 24.3–26.0. E320, E430, S320, S420, SL500 & SL600 & 1998–99 CL500, CL600, S500 & S600

⇒	Code	Test scope	Test connection	Test condition	Nominal value	Possible cause/Remedy
26.1	C 1142	Voltage suppply to sensor	N47-5: 24 (1.24) —V— 22 (1.22)	Ignition: **ON**	4.75–5.25 V	N47-5.
27.0	C 1141	**ESP brake pressure sensor (B34)** Dynamic sensor signal (on)		Apply service brake.	– 17.5 bar – +17.5 bar Value increase when service brake is applied.	⇒ 27.1, B34.
27.1		Voltage supply	N47-5: 48 (2.14) —V— 50 (2.16)	Ignition: **ON**	4.75–5.25 V	N47-5.
28.0	C 1120	**ESP yaw rate sensor (N64)** Static sensor signal (off) Dynamic sensor signal (on)		 Vigorously rock vehicle from side to side.	– 3.5 °/s – +3.5 °/s Value change > 0.5 °/s	⇒ 28.1, Wiring, N64.

MB0029900071140X

Fig. 97 Codes C1120, C1141 & C1142: Test 23, Steps 26.1–28.0. E320, E430, S320, S420, SL500 & SL600 & 1998–99 CL500, CL600, S500 & S600

⇒		Test scope	Test connection	Test condition	Nominal value	Possible cause/Remedy
28.1		Voltage suppply	N47-5 17 (1.17) — V — 18 (1.18)	Ignition: **ON**	11 – 14 V	N47-5.
29.0	C 1140	**Steering angle sensor (N49)**		Engine: **at Idle** Steering wheel in center position. Slowly turn steering wheel to left stop. Slowly turn steering wheel to right stop.	0° Value continuously changes.	Wiring, N49 not initialized, ⇒ 29.1, N47-5.
29.1		Circuit 30 Voltage supply	N49x1 2 — V — 4	Ignition: **OFF** Disconnect connector N49x1.	11 – 14 V	Wiring.
29.2		Circuit 87 Voltage supply	N49x1 2 — V — 3	Ignition: **ON**	11 – 14 V	Wiring.

MB0029900071150X

Fig. 98 Code C1140: Test 23, Steps 28.1—29.2. E320, E430, S320, S420, SL500 & SL600 & 1998–99 CL500, CL600, S500 & S600

⇒		Test scope	Test connection	Test condition	Nominal value	Possible cause/Remedy
30.0	C 1020 C 1022	**CAN data bus**		Engine: **at Idle**	Idle speed	Data bus, ⇒ 30.1, ⇒ 30.2
30.1		**Engine 119** **CAN element in engine control module (ME-SFI, N3/10)** Resistance	N3/10 60 — Ω — 61	Disconnect control module (N3/10) and test directly on control module using an ohmmeter.	235 – 245 Ω	N3/10,
		Engine 120 **CAN element in left or right engine control module (ME-SFI, N3/11 or N3/12)** Resistance	N3/11 or N3/12 60 — Ω — 61	Disconnect control module (N3/11 or N3/12) and test directly on control module using an ohmmeter.	235 – 245 Ω	N3/11 or N3/12,
30.2		**CAN element in RCL control module (N54)** Resistance	N54 L — Ω — H	Disconnect 2-pole connector on control module (N54) and test directly on control module using an ohmmeter.	115 – 125 Ω	N54.

MB0029900071160X

Fig. 99 Codes C1020 & C1022: Test 23, Steps 30.0–30.2. E320, E430, S320, S420, SL500 & SL600 & 1998–99 CL500, CL600, S500 & S600

Model	ESP Control Module Part No.	
	Old	New
C43, C280, CLK320 & CLK430	027 545 59 32	029 545 70 32
E55, E320 & E430	027 545 57 32	029 545 76 32

Fig. 100 ESP control module replacement

Model	Equipment	ESP Control Module Part No.
C230, C280 & CLK320	All	027 545 59 32
E55, E320 & E430	Less SPS	027 545 56 32
	w/SPS	027 545 57 32
	w/4MATIC	027 545 63 32

Fig. 101 ESP control module replacement

Automatic Transmissions

NOTE: On Air Bag Equipped Models, Refer To "Air Bag System Precautions" Located In Front Of This Manual For System Disarming And Arming Procedures.

NOTE: Prior To Performing Any Service Operations Listed In This Section, Consult The "Technical Service Bulletins" Section For Related Information.

INDEX

	Page No.
Adjustments	5-299
Parking Lock	5-299
Shift Linkage Rod	5-299
Application Chart	5-295
Description	5-296
Elecro-Hydraulic Control Unit	5-296
Mechanical	5-296
Identification	5-296
In-Vehicle Repairs	5-299
Electrohydraulic Control Module, Replace	5-299
Electronic Transmission Control (ETC) Control Module, Replace	5-299
Floor Selector, Replace	5-299
Maintenance	5-298
Fluid Change	5-298
Fluid Level Check	5-298
Precautions	5-296
Air Bag Systems	5-296
Battery Ground Cable	5-296
Radio Coded Anti-Theft System	5-296
Shift Lock System	5-301
Parking Lock Interlock, Replace	5-301
Technical Service Bulletins	5-302
Engine Dies When Transmission Shift Into Gear Or When Parking	5-302
Engine Reaches Cutout During 2-3 Upshift At Full Throttle Or Kickdown	5-302
Knocking Noise That Changes w/Engine Load	5-302
Select Lever Cannot Be Moved From P Position	5-302
Transmission In Emergency Running Mode, DTCs 012, 013, 108 & 109	5-302
Transmission In Emergency Running Mode, DTCs 051, 055, 147 or 151	5-302
Tightening Specifications	5-304
Transmission, Replace	5-300
C43, C230, C280, CLK55, CLK320, CLK430, E55, E300, E320, E430, S320, S420, SL500, SL600 & SLK230, SLK320 & 1998–99 CL500, CL600, S500 & S600	5-300
S430 & 2000–01 CL500, CL600, S500 & S600	5-301
Troubleshooting	5-296
Heavy Jerk When Engaging Drive Or Reverse	5-297
Heavy Shift Jerk During 4-3 Downshift	5-297
Heavy Shift Jerks When Changing Gears	5-297
No Brake Shifts, 4-3 & 3-2	5-298
No Kickdown Downshifts	5-298
No Reverse Gear Engagement	5-297
No Upshifts	5-297
Parking Lock Not Engaging	5-298
Selector Lever Positions R & P Will Not Engage	5-298
Shift Jerks In Partial Load Range	5-297
Temporarily No Transmission Engagement In Any Position, Immediately After Starting Engine	5-297
Transmission Slips During 2-3 Shift, Or Slips At First Then Grips Hard	5-297
Transmission Slips During 3-4 Shifts	5-297
Transmission Slips In All Selector Positions	5-296
Transmission Slips When Starting In 1st Or 2nd Or Will Not Move Forward; But Reverse Satisfactory	5-297
Upshifts In Lower Speed Range Only	5-298
Upshifts In Upper Speed Range Only	5-297
1st & Reverse Gear Too Loud	5-298
2nd Speed Slips Or Transmission Shifts From 1st To 2nd	5-297
3rd Gear Too Loud	5-298

APPLICATION CHART

Model	Year	Transmission
C43	1998–2000	722.631
C230	1998	722.600
	1999–2000	722.605
C240	2001	722.609
C280	1998–2000	722.606
C320	2001	—
CL55	2001	—
CL500	1998–99	722.620
	2000–01	722.633
CL600	1998–99	722.621
	2001	722.628
CLK55	2001	—
CLK320	1998–2001	722.607
CLK430	1999–2001	722.623
E55	1999–2001	722.624
E300	1998–99	722.608

Continued

APPLICATION CHART—Continued

Model	Year	Transmission
E320	1998–2001	722.607
		722.664 (4MATIC)
E430	1998–2001	722.623
	2001	— (4MATIC)
ML55	2000–01	—
ML320	1998–2001	722.662
ML430	1999–2001	722.663
S55	2001	—
S320	1998–99	722.605
S420	1998–99	722.622
S430	2000–01	722.632
S500	1998–99	722.620
	2000–01	722.633
S600	1998–99	722.621
	2001	722.628
SL500	1998	722.620
	1999–2001	722.624
SL600	1998–2001	722.621
SLK230	1998–2001	722.605
SLK320	2001	722.616

PRECAUTIONS

AIR BAG SYSTEMS

Refer to "Air Bag System Precautions" in front of this manual for system disarming and arming procedures.

BATTERY GROUND CABLE

Prior to service, disconnect battery ground cable and isolate as required.

RADIO CODED ANTI-THEFT SYSTEM

Anti-theft radios have a coded theft protection circuit. The CODE card must be obtained before disconnecting battery, removing radio fuse or removing the radio. **The serial number from the radio must match the CODE card.**

After service has been performed proceed as follows:

1. Reconnect radio power and turn key to position No. 2.
2. Turn radio to On position. The word "CODE" will appear on display.
3. Enter first digit of anti-theft code from CODE card. "CODE" will disappear and entered digit will appear followed by four dashes.
4. Enter the next four digits, when all five are entered the first digit flashes again.
5. Press SC, Seek or Tune button to confirm code.
6. If "WAIT" appears on radio panel, proceed as follows:
   a. Radio will allow three coding attempts only before entering lock-up mode and won't respond to controls.
   b. Leave radio on for 15–60 minutes, then radio will unlock and allow three addition coding attempts.
   c. The third lockout period (after nine failed coding attempts) will last 24 hours.
   d. Radio must be left on during enter 24-hour period until "CODE" appears.
7. When "CODE" appears, repeat coding attempt.

IDENTIFICATION

The identification code is stamped on the transmission housing or the identification plate.

DESCRIPTION

The 722.6 automatic transmission is an electronically controlled five-speed with a lock-up clutch in the torque converter, **Fig. 1.** The individual gear ratios are produced by three planetary gear sets. The fifth gear acts as an overdrive.

The gears are controlled electronically and hydraulically. The gears are shifted by a corresponding combination of three brakes, three clutches and two free-wheeling units.

The Electronic Transmission Control (ETC) or Transmission Control Module (TCM) allows a precise matching of the pressures to the respective operating conditions and to the engine performance during shifting.

The torque converter and transmission light allow metal housings are bolted together and centered via the outer brake carrier of brake B1. A coated intermediate metal shim serves as a gasket.

MECHANICAL

The mechanical part consists of the input and output shafts, a sun gear shaft and three planetary gear sets which are connected to each other.

On the transmission for high output engines, the planetary gear sets have four planetary gears. On the transmission for low output engines, the front and rear planetary gear set is equipped with three planetary gears.

Oil pressure for the torque converter lock-up clutch and clutch K2 is supplied through input shaft bores. Oil pressure for clutch K3 is routed through the output shaft. Lubrication oil is supplied and distributed through additional bores in both shafts.

The parking lock wheel and output flange are connected to the output shaft via a spline.

The front free-wheeling unit is supported on the stator shaft extension inside the transmission and connects in the lock position the front planetary gear set sun gear with the transmission housing. The rear free-wheeling unit connects in lock position the center planetary gear sung gear with the rear planetary gear set sun gear.

ELECRO-HYDRAULIC CONTROL UNIT

The electro-hydraulic control unit consists of the hydraulic control light allow valve body and an electrical control unit. The electrical control unit consists of a plastic carrier with electrical components positioned on the valve body.

TROUBLESHOOTING

TRANSMISSION SLIPS IN ALL SELECTOR POSITIONS

1. Check modulating pressure, adjust if possible. If not adjustable, check modulating pressure control guide for ease of operation.
2. Inspect vacuum line from intake pipe to vacuum control unit for any restrictions.

3. **On models equipped with diesel engines,** inspect vacuum control valve.
4. **On all models,** loosen oil cooler line on transmission oil cooler, start engine and inspect for hydraulic oil.
5. Disassemble shift valve housing, clean and ensure working pressure control valve is operational. Replace shift valve housing if necessary.
6. Remove and inspect primary pump. Replace as required.
7. Switch on control valve and inspect for ease of operation.
8. If working pressure is satisfactory, but there is still no engagement, inspect one-way clutch and wheel assembly.

2ND SPEED SLIPS OR TRANSMISSION SHIFTS FROM 1ST TO 2ND

1. Inspect control slide B1 for ease of operation. Replace shift valve housing if necessary.
2. Inspect lip sealing ring of brake band piston B1.
3. Inspect brake B1 and thrust body for B1.

TRANSMISSION SLIPS WHEN STARTING IN 1ST OR 2ND OR WILL NOT MOVE FORWARD; BUT REVERSE SATISFACTORY

1. Shift valve B2 inoperable, replace shift valve housing if necessary.
2. Inspect brake B2.
3. Inspect thrust pin of brake B2.
4. If vehicle moves forward in 2 position but will not move in 3 or D position, one-way clutch may be slipping.

TRANSMISSION SLIPS DURING 2-3 SHIFT, OR SLIPS AT FIRST THEN GRIPS HARD

1. Inspect and adjust modulating pressure.
2. Inspect shift valve housing.
3. Inspect front cover Teflon ring.
4. Inspect and replace clutch K1 inner plates.

TRANSMISSION SLIPS DURING 3-4 SHIFTS

1. Inspect and adjust modulating pressure.
2. Inspect shift valve housing.
3. Inspect Teflon rings of clutch K2 supporting flange.
4. Inspect and replace clutch K2 inner plates.

TEMPORARILY NO TRANSMISSION ENGAGEMENT IN ANY POSITION, IMMEDIATELY AFTER STARTING ENGINE

1. Inspect lubricating pressure ring on input shaft.
2. Inspect lubricating pressure valve in shift valve housing.

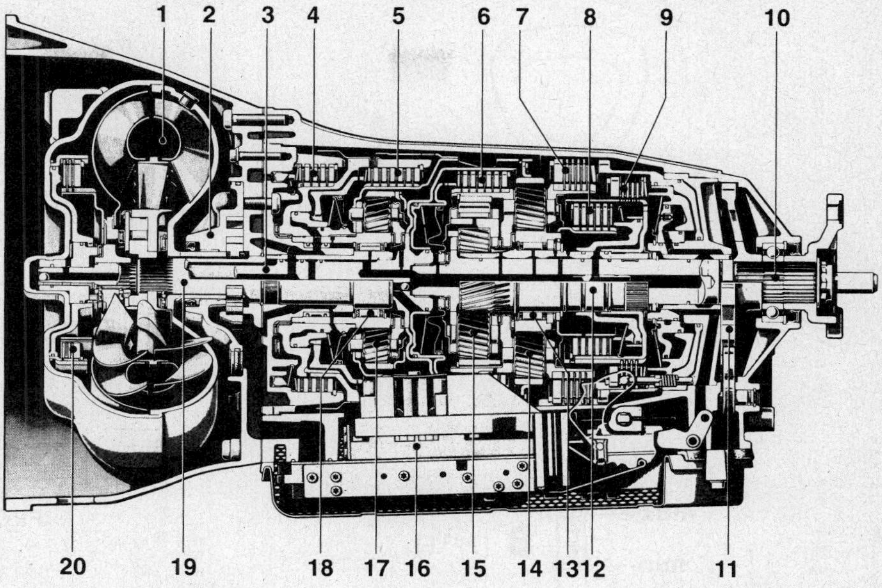

1	Torque converter	11	Parking lock wheel
2	ATF pump	12	Intermediate shaft
3	Input shaft	13	Free-wheeling unit F2
4	Brake B1	14	Rear planetary gear set
5	Clutch K1	15	Center planetary gear set
6	Clutch K2	16	Electro-hydraulic control unit
7	Brake B3	17	Front planetary gear set
8	Clutch K3	18	Free-wheeling unit F1
9	Brake B2	19	Stator shaft
10	Output shaft	20	Torque converter lock-up clutch

MB5029900058000X

Fig. 1 Cross-sectional views of automatic transmission. 722.6

NO REVERSE GEAR ENGAGEMENT

1. Inspect lining plates and lip sealing rings on piston LB3.
2. Inspect one-way clutch.

HEAVY JERK WHEN ENGAGING DRIVE OR REVERSE

1. Inspect and adjust idle speed as required.
2. Inspect and adjust modulating pressure.
3. Inspect vacuum lines and connections for leaks.
4. Inspect pressure pickup piston in shift valve housing for proper installation and ease of operation.

HEAVY SHIFT JERKS WHEN CHANGING GEARS

1. Inspect control pressure cable control adjustment.
2. Inspect and adjust modulating pressure.
3. Inspect vacuum line from intake pipe to vacuum control unit for any restrictions.
4. **On models equipped with diesel engines,** inspect vacuum control valve.
5. **On all models,** inspect for evidence of coolant in transmission fluid.

HEAVY SHIFT JERK DURING 4-3 DOWNSHIFT

1. Inspect lip sealing ring on release side B2.
2. Inspect and replace brake B2 as required.

SHIFT JERKS IN PARTIAL LOAD RANGE

1. Inspect control pressure cable control adjustment.
2. Inspect and adjust modulating pressure.
3. Inspect vacuum line from intake pipe to vacuum control unit for any restrictions.
4. **On models equipped with diesel engines,** inspect vacuum control valve.

NO UPSHIFTS

1. Inspect regulating pressure.
2. Inspect and clean centrifugal governor.
3. Inspect and clean shift valve housing.
4. Inspect if solenoid valve is binding in opened position or inspect kickdown switch.

UPSHIFTS IN UPPER SPEED RANGE ONLY

1. Inspect control pressure cable control adjustment.
2. Inspect regulating pressure, if regulated pressure is too low, replace centrifugal governor.
3. Ensure control pressure regulating

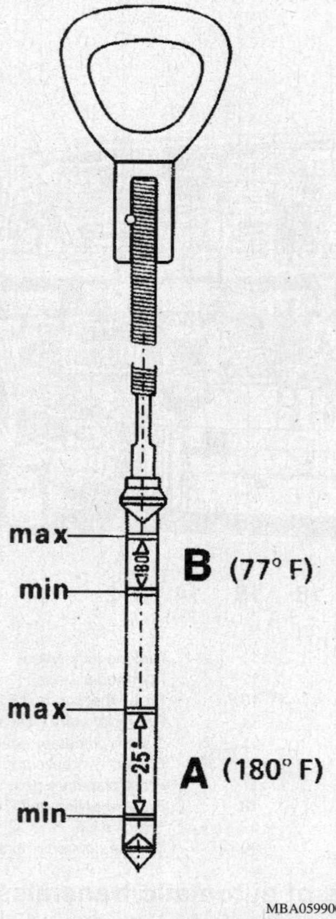

Fig. 2 Transmission dipstick

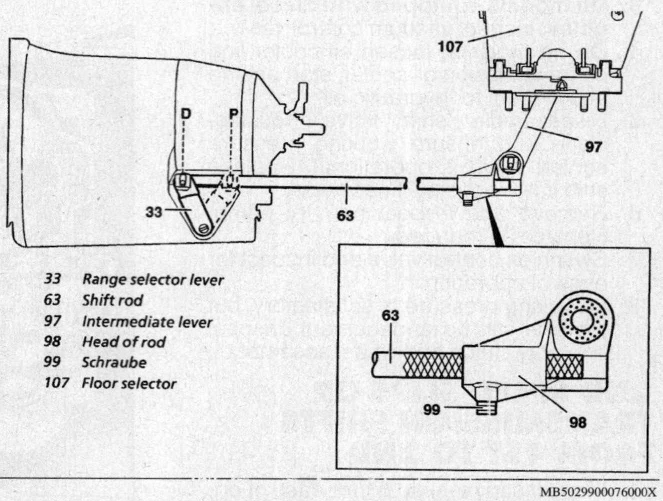

Fig. 3 Shift linkage rod adjustment

valve is operable.
4. Inspect if solenoid valve is binding in opened position or inspect kickdown switch.

UPSHIFTS IN LOWER SPEED RANGE ONLY

1. Inspect cable control for control pressure.
2. Inspect and adjust full throttle stop.
3. Inspect regulating pressure, if regulated pressure is too high, replace centrifugal governor.

NO KICKDOWN DOWNSHIFTS

1. Inspect engine throttle control cable and control pressure cable.
2. Inspect fuse for power supply to solenoid valves.
3. Inspect solenoid valves for proper operation.
4. Inspect operation of kickdown control valve in shift valve housing.

NO BRAKE SHIFTS, 4-3 & 3-2

1. Adjust cable control for control pressure.
2. Inspect vacuum lines and connections for leaks.
3. Ensure brake shift piston in shift valve housing is operable.

PARKING LOCK NOT ENGAGING

1. Inspect rear engine mount.
2. Inspect selector rod adjustment.

SELECTOR LEVER POSITIONS R & P WILL NOT ENGAGE

1. If lever will not engage with engine running, clean centrifugal governor and ensure proper operation.
2. If lever will not engage with engine stopped, repair detent piston in lower cover.

1ST & REVERSE GEAR TOO LOUD

Inspect and repair front gear assembly.

3RD GEAR TOO LOUD

Replace rear planetary gear assembly.

MAINTENANCE

The 722.6 transmission uses a "filled for life" fluid and does not require fluid level checking or changes.

FLUID LEVEL CHECK

This procedure has been revised by a Technical Service Bulletin.

If fluid checking is necessary because of repairs or diagnosis, a 722.6 transmission dipstick tool No. 140 589 15 21 00, or equivalent, is required. The tool is longer than necessary to permit use on several different applications.

The red locking clip will break-off and be destroyed during removal. A transmission dipstick tube cap red locking pin part No. 140 991 00 55, or equivalent, is required.

1. Place vehicle on level surface and engage parking brake.
2. Place selector lever in P position.
3. Remove locking pin with suitable tool, then press out pin remaining in cap downwards.
4. Start engine and allow to idle.
5. Shift through driving stages several times.
6. Insert dipstick as far as end stop permits.
7. Inspect level and correct as required, **Fig. 2.**
8. Drive vehicle until transmission is hot.
9. Wait at least two minutes.
10. With engine running, insert dipstick as far as end stop permits.
11. Inspect level and correct as required.
12. Mount cap on oil filler pipe and press in new lock pin until it locks into position.

FLUID CHANGE

1. Place selector lever in P position.
2. Raise and support vehicle, then remove engine compartment lining.
3. Remove transmission oil pan drain plug and drain fluid into suitable container.
4. After fluid has been drained, install drain plug tighten to specifications.
5. Fill transmission. Refer to "Lubricant Data" for fluid type and amount.

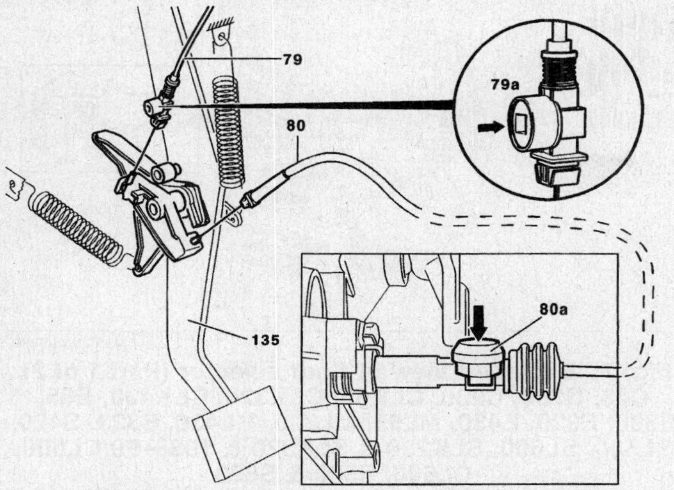

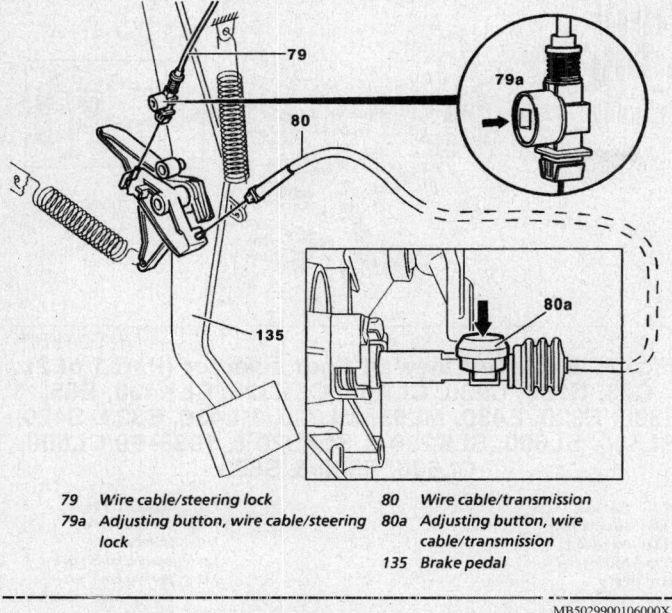

79 *Wire cable/steering lock*
79a *Adjusting button, wire cable/steering lock*
80 *Wire cable/transmission*
80a *Adjusting button, wire cable/transmission*
135 *Brake pedal*

MB5029900106000X

Fig. 4 Parking lock adjustment

ADJUSTMENTS

SHIFT LINKAGE ROD

C43, C230, C280, CLK320, CLK430, E300, E320, E430, S320, S420, SL500 & SL600 & 1998-99 CL500, CL600, S500 & S600

This procedure has been revised by a Technical Service Bulletin.

1. Place shift selector lever in D position.
2. Raise and support vehicle. Support all four wheels.
3. Mount rod heat on idler lever and lock with clips, **Fig. 3.**
4. Ensure both shift selector lever and transmission range selector lever are in D position. There are only four positions, from rear to front they are P, R, N and D.
5. Insert shift rod in rod head, attach range selector lever and lock with clips.
6. Tighten bolt securely, ensuring it presses against rod head. **Do not rotate rod and head. Do not move selector lever out of D position.**

S430 & 2000-01 CL500, CL600, S500 & S600

1. Place shift selector lever in D position.
2. Raise and support vehicle. Support all four wheels.
3. Remove heat shield.
4. Disconnect tab washers using suitable screwdriver, then the shift rod on idler lever.
5. Move range selector lever to R position and disconnect shift rod on range selector lever.
6. Remove rod end locking screw and make slot in locking screw using suitable tool.
7. Loosen threaded pin.
8. Connect shift rod into range selector lever.
9. Place range selector lever in D position.
10. Connect shift rod at idler lever.
11. Clip in new tab washers.
12. Tighten new threaded pin. **Do not move range selector lever out of D position.**
13. Ensure selector and transmission position align.
14. Install lock screw.

PARKING LOCK

1. Ensure selector lever is in position P.
2. Pretension spring on adjusting button, **Fig. 4.**
3. Turn ignition switch steering lock to O position.
4. Adjust wire cable/steering lock by pressing adjusting button (arrow).

IN-VEHICLE REPAIRS

ELECTROHYDRAULIC CONTROL MODULE, REPLACE

1. Place transmission selector in P position.
2. Remove mounting screws and heat shield, then disconnect 13-pin connector.
3. Turn guide bush bayonet lock counterclockwise and remove it.
4. Loosen guide bush and remove from transmission housing.
5. Remove oil pan drain plug and drain transmission fluid into suitable container.
6. Remove oil pan and filter.
7. Remove mounting bolts and electrohydraulic control module.
8. Reverse procedure to install, noting the following:

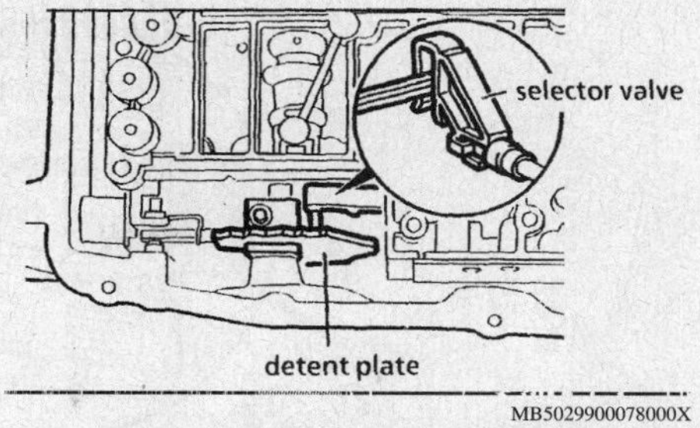

Fig. 5 Valve detent plate engagement

a. Ensure punched windows center in pulse rings.
b. Position punched window in pulse ring.
c. Install selector valve in detent plate driver, **Fig. 5.**

ELECTRONIC TRANSMISSION CONTROL (ETC) CONTROL MODULE, REPLACE

S430 & 2000-01 CL500, CL600, S500 & S600

1. Remove righthand fuse box cover.
2. Disconnect ETC connectors.
3. Remove ETC.
4. Reverse procedure to install.

FLOOR SELECTOR, REPLACE

C43, C230, C280, CLK55, CLK320, CLK430, E55, E300, E320, E430, ML55, ML320, ML430, S320, S420, SL500, SL600, SLK230 & SLK320 & 1998-99 CL500, CL600, S500 & S600

1. Unhook shift rod at intermediate lever by removing clip locking device, **Fig. 6.**
2. Remove center console.
3. **On ML320 and ML430 models,** remove insulation mat.
4. **On all models,** remove mounting bolts and disconnect switch plugs.
5. Remove floor selector, then the selector lever handle, **Fig. 7.**
6. Unclip cover and cap, then remove mounting screw.
7. Place selector lever in D position and unclip bearing bracket upper part.
8. Remove carrier from upper part of bearing bracket, then the gate guard.
9. Remove gear indicator and gear recognition switch.
10. Remove shift shaft and intermediate lever together, then the bracket with shift lock.
11. Remove shift shaft from bracket with shift lock.
12. Remove selector lever with fork end and at same time remove fuse and pull out pins.
13. Unscrew shift detent.
14. Remove left bearing bushing by removing pins from shift shaft and using a suitable press.
15. Remove pin and disconnect shift shaft

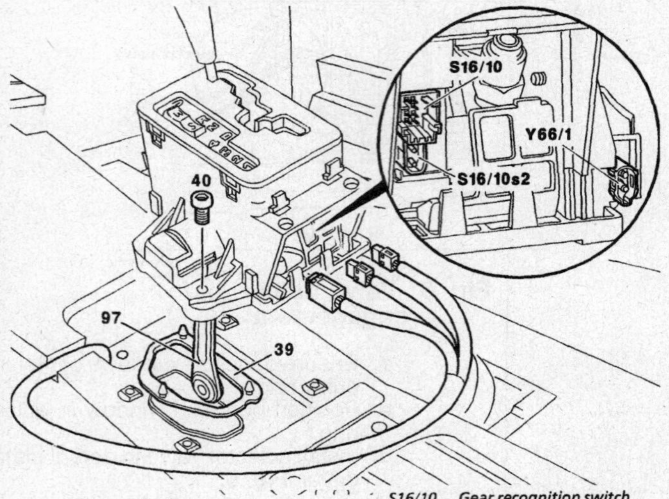

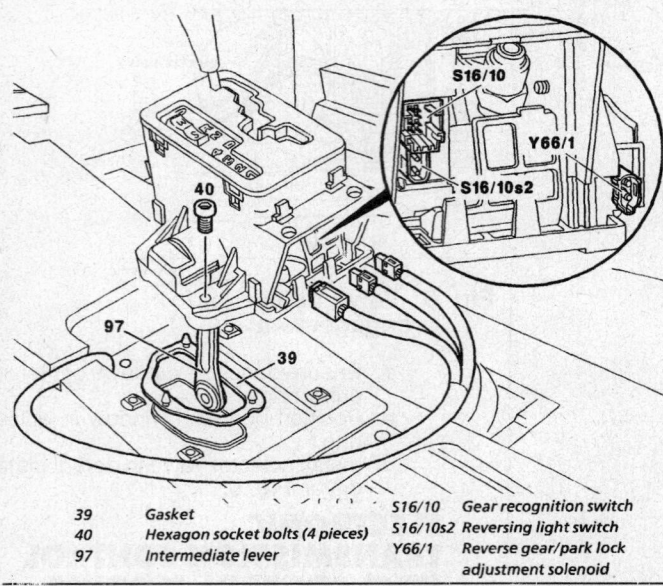

39	Gasket	S16/10	Gear recognition switch
40	Hexagon socket bolts (4 pieces)	S16/10s2	Reversing light switch
97	Intermediate lever	Y66/1	Reverse gear/park lock adjustment solenoid

MB5029900107000X

Fig. 6 Floor selector replacement. C43, C230, C280, CLK55, CLK320, CLK430, E55, E300, E320, E430, ML55, ML320, ML430, S320, S420, SL500, SL600, SLK230 & SLK320 & 1998–99 CL500, CL600, S500 & S600

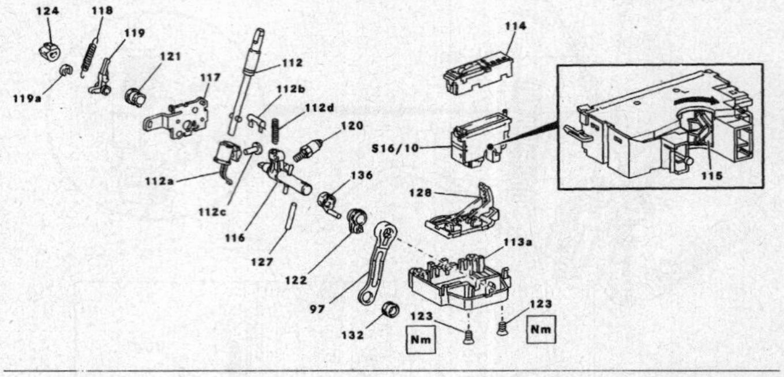

MB5029900108010X

Fig. 7 Exploded view of floor selector (Part 1 of 2). C43, C230, C280, CLK55, CLK320, CLK430, E55, E300, E320, E430, ML55, ML320, ML430, S320, S420, SL500, SL600, SLK230 & SLK320 & 1998–99 CL500, CL600, S500 & S600

97	Idler lever	119	Supporting lever
112	Selector lever	119a	Locking device
112a	Fork end	120	Shift detent
112b	Locking device	121	Bearing bush, right
112c	Pin	122	Bearing bush, left
112d	Spring	123	Hexagon socket screw
113a	Lower part of bearing bracket	124	Cam
114	Gear indicator	127	Pin
115	Driver	128	Shift pattern
116	Shift shaft	132	Bearing bush
117	Bracket with shift lock	136	Locking lever
118	Spring	S16/10	Gear recognition switch

MB5029900108020X

Fig. 7 Exploded view of floor selector (Part 2 of 2). C43, C230, C280, CLK55, CLK320, CLK430, E55, E300, E320, E430, ML55, ML320, ML430, S320, S420, SL500, SL600, SLK230 & SLK320 & 1998–99 CL500, CL600, S500 & S600

with intermediate lever from sleeve.

16. Remove right bearing bushing bracket.
17. Unhook spring and remove locking device, then the supporting lever.
18. Remove mounting screws, then the shift pattern from upper part of bearing bracket.
19. Reverse procedure to install, noting the following:
    a. Lever must be in position 1.
    b. Before installing shift shaft pin, lubricate lightly.
    c. Check bearing bushings for wear and Replace as required.
    d. Grease shift detent balls.
    e. Spring may jump out during installation.
    f. Install only preassembled components in lower part of the bearing bracket and grease bearing points.
    g. Gear recognition switch to shift shaft driver must be behind in direction of travel (arrow).
    h. Ensure gasket is positioned correctly.
    i. Place selector lever in N position.
    j. Apply battery voltage to adjustment solenoid.
    k. Loosen adjustment screw and adjust gap between locking lever and cam to 0.0079 inch, **Fig. 8.**
    l. Tighten adjustment screw.

S430 & 2000–01 CL500, CL600, S500 & S600

1. Disconnect shift rod at idler lever.
2. Remove center console.
3. Remove center rear nozzle air duct.
4. Remove three mounting bolts.
5. Disconnect connectors.
6. Disconnect shift lock cable on fitting by pulling lugs outward and pulling cable off.
7. Remove electronic shift lever module control module.
8. Reverse procedure to install.

TRANSMISSION

REPLACE

C43, C230, C280, CLK55, CLK320, CLK430, E55, E300, E320, E430, S320, S420, SL500, SL600 & SLK230, SLK320 & 1998–99 CL500, CL600, S500 & S600

1. **On C230, E300 and S420 and 1998–99 CL500 and S500 and 1998 SL500 models,** unscrew oil filler piper from engine.
2. **On SL600 and 1998–99 CL600 and S600 models,** remove mounting bolts and knock oil filler pipe out of transmission housing using suitable tool, **Fig. 9.**
3. **On all models,** remove oil pan drain plug and drain transmission fluid into suitable container, **Fig. 10.**
4. If transmission fluid is burnt or contains abrasives, flush oil cooler and lines.
5. Remove torque converter oil drain plug and drain transmission fluid into suitable container. If there are metal shavings in transmission fluid, replace torque converter.
6. Remove mounting screws and heat shield.
7. Turn guide bushing bayonet lock counterclockwise and disconnect Transmission Control Module (TCM) 13-pin connector.
8. Ensure transmission range selector lever is in P position.
9. **On C43, C230, C280, CLK55, CLK320, CLK430, E55, E300, E320, E430, ML55, ML320, ML430, S320, SLK230 and SLK320 models,** loosen parking interlock locking device with suitable tool and remove wire cable from transmission, **Fig. 11.**
10. **On S420, SL500 and SL600 and 1998–99 CL500, CL600, S500 and S600 models,** turn parking interlock cable counterclockwise and remove.
11. **On E320 models equipped with 4MATIC transmission,** remove rack-and-pinion steering retaining plate.
12. **On all models,** remove cover and torque converter to drive plate mounting bolts.
13. Remove left and righthand lines to oil cooler.
14. Remove clip lock and shift rod, then the exhaust bracket.
15. **On S420 and 1998–99 CL500 and S500 and SL500 models,** hang exhaust system at rear with V-belt.
16. **On SL600 and 1998–99 CL600 and**

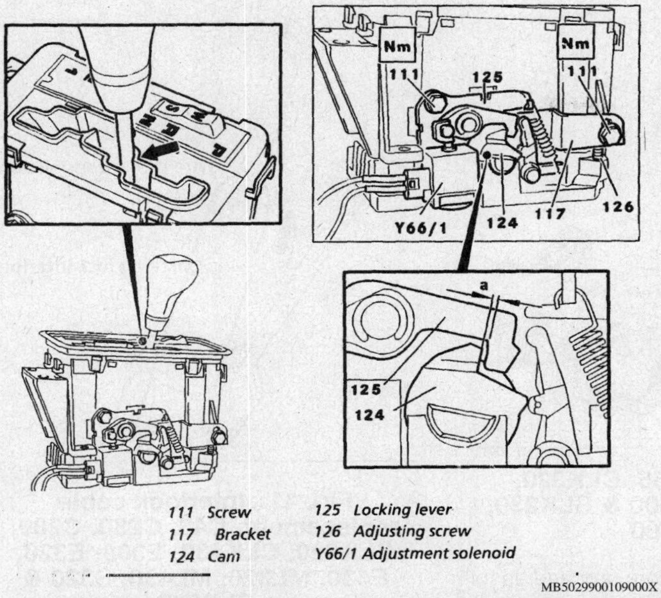

Fig. 8 Shift lock adjustment. C43, C230, C280, CLK55, CLK320, CLK430, E55, E300, E320, E430, ML55, ML320, ML430, S320, S420, SL500, SL600, SLK230 & SLK320 & 1998–99 CL500, CL600, S500 & S600

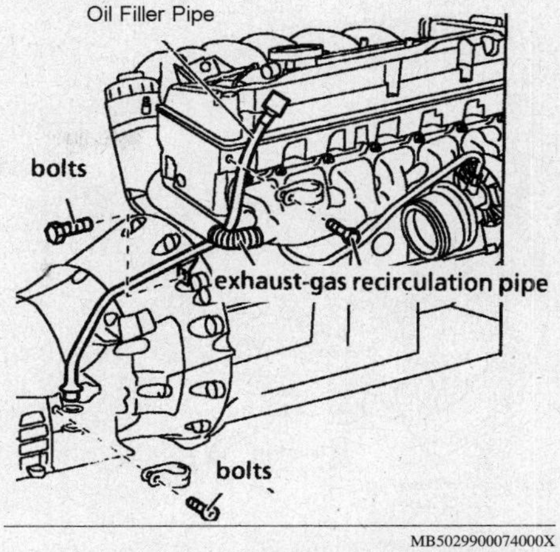

Fig. 9 Oil filler pipe replacement. SL600 & 1998–99 CL600 & S600

S600 models, remove exhaust system from connector.

17. **On C230, E300, S420 and SL600 and 1998–99 CL500, CL600, S500 and S600 and 1998 SL500 models,** remove engine support with rear engine mount.
18. **On all models,** remove front propeller shaft mounting bolts.
19. Remove transmission ground strap.
20. Secure torque converter.
21. Remove mounting bolts and transmission from crankcase downward at an angle.
22. Position transmission vertically.
23. Bolt handle tools No. 168 589 00 62 00, or equivalent, to torque converter and remove converter from transmission.
24. Reverse procedure to install, noting the following:
    a. Lightly lubricate torque converter input flange and crankshaft bearing journals with Molykote No. 000 989 63 51, or equivalent.
    b. Rotate torque converter back and forth to ensure splines mesh properly.
    c. Measure clearance A between transmission housing and torque converter attachment with suitable depth gauge, **Fig. 12.** If measurement is not as specified, **Fig. 13,** remove and install torque converter.
    d. Adjust shift rod as outlined under "Adjustments."
    e. Inspect and replace TCM connector O-ring as required.
    f. Install new oil filler pipe O-ring.

S430 & 2000–01 CL500, CL600, S500 & S600

1. Unscrew oil filter pipe from engine, **Fig. 14.**
2. Remove plug and drain transmission fluid into suitable container. If there are metal shavings in transmission fluid, replace torque converter.
3. Remove torque converter oil drain plug and drain transmission fluid into suitable container. If there are metal shavings in transmission fluid, replace torque converter.
4. Remove heat shield and disconnect 13-pin connector.
5. Remove cover and torque converter to drive plate mounting bolts.
6. Disconnect left and righthand lines to oil cooler.
7. Remove clip and disconnect shift rod from transmission.
8. Remove exhaust mount.
9. Support transmission with suitable jack and plate.
10. Remove engine support with rear mount.
11. Remove front propeller shaft to transmission flange mounting bolts.
12. Remove mounting bolts and transmission downward at an angle.
13. Position transmission vertically.
14. Bolt handle tools No. 168 589 00 62 00, or equivalent, to torque converter and remove converter from transmission.
15. Reverse procedure to install, noting the following:
    a. Lightly lubricate torque converter input flange and crankshaft bearing journals with Molykote No. 000 989 63 51, or equivalent.
    b. Rotate torque converter back and forth to ensure splines mesh properly.
    c. Adjust shift rod as outlined under "Adjustments."
    d. Inspect and replace TCM connector O-ring as required.
    e. Install new oil filler pipe O-ring.

SHIFT LOCK SYSTEM

PARKING LOCK INTERLOCK, REPLACE

S420, SL500 & SL600 & 1998–99 CL500, CL600, S500 & S600

1. Remove cover below lefthand side of instrument panel.
2. Ensure ignition switch is in steering lock position 1.
3. Unhook wire cable/steering lock by pressing in locking tongues, then at the same time press (arrows) against steering lock, **Fig. 15.**
4. Remove stop lamp switch.
5. Unhook wire cable/steering lock at release lever, **Fig. 16.**
6. Compress locking device, then at the same time push wire cable steering lock upwards and out of mount on pedal bearing bracket, **Fig. 17.**
7. Remove wire cable steering lock.
8. Remove entrance strip, then the A pillar footwell cover.
9. Unscrew accelerator pedal from floor panel.
10. Remove driver's side floor lining completely. **Do not fold floor carpet.**
11. Remove air duct for rear compartment heating.
12. Turn wire cable/transmission counterclockwise and pull it off, **Fig. 18.**
13. Remove tunnel rubber boot on tunnel.
14. Open cable straps behind cover on lefthand side of tunnel and remove wire cable from transmission.
15. Reverse procedure to install, noting the following:
    a. Attach wire cable/transmission in bracket on jacket tube.
    b. Place selector lever or range selector lever in P position and leave in position P when wire cable/transmission is removed.

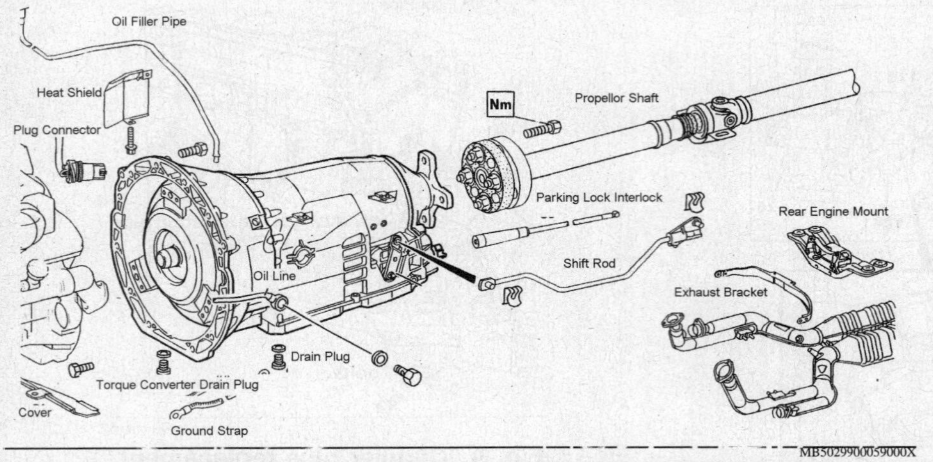

Fig. 10 Transmission replace. C43, C230, C280, CLK55, CLK320, CLK430, E55, E300, E320, E430, S320, S420, SL500, SL600 & SLK230, SLK320 & 1998–99 CL500, CL600, S500 & S600

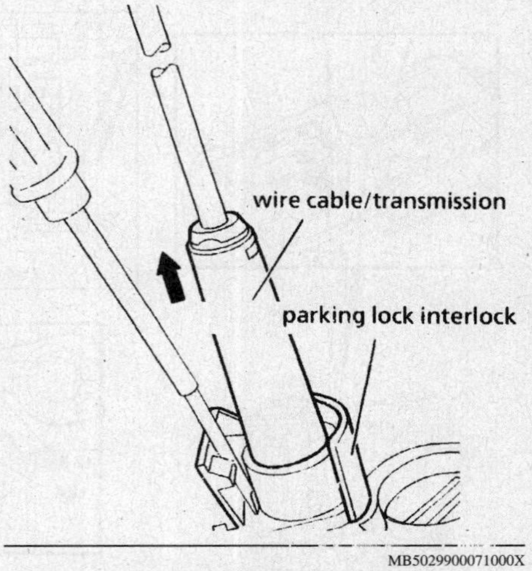

Fig. 11 Interlock cable replacement. C43, C230, C280, CLK320, CLK430, E300, E320, E430, ML320, ML430, S320 & SLK230

c. Attach wire cable transmission and turn clockwise.
d. Adjust wire cables for parking lock interlock.

TECHNICAL SERVICE BULLETINS

SELECT LEVER CANNOT BE MOVED FROM P POSITION

C230, C280, CLK320, CLK430, E300, E320, E430 & SLK230

On some of these models equipped with touch shift, the selector lever occasionally cannot be moved from P position with the brake applied.

This condition may be caused by the Electronic Selector Lever Module (ESM) not receiving a signal from the stop lamp switch.

To correct this condition replace the stop lamp switch.

ENGINE DIES WHEN TRANSMISSION SHIFT INTO GEAR OR WHEN PARKING

S320 & S420 & 1998–99 CL500, CL600, S500 & S600

On some of these models the engine may die when the transmission is shifted into gear or when parking.

This condition may be caused by moisture in the starter lockout switch.

To correct this condition, proceed as follows:

1. Inspect starter lockout switch for corrosion.
2. Replace switch.
3. Replace transmission wiring harness.

TRANSMISSION IN EMERGENCY RUNNING MODE, DTCS 012, 013, 108 & 109

On some of these models the transmission may be in emergency running mode with Diagnostic Trouble Codes (DTCs) 012, 013, 108 and/or 109.

This condition may be caused by worn lose connector on ETC control module or transmission connector, or defective output speed sensor.

To correct this condition, ensure connector has proper contact.

If condition still exists, replace conductor plate. **Do not replace complete valve body.**

TRANSMISSION IN EMERGENCY RUNNING MODE, DTCS 051, 055, 147 OR 151

On some of these models the transmission may be in emergency running mode with Diagnostic Trouble Codes (DTCs) 051, 055, 147 and/or 151.

This condition may be caused by worn input/output shaft Teflon rings.

To correct this condition, replace the transmission.

ENGINE REACHES CUTOUT DURING 2-3 UPSHIFT AT FULL THROTTLE OR KICKDOWN

On some of these models the engine may reach cutout during 2-3 upshift at full throttle or kickdown.

This condition may be caused by kickdown solenoid always being energized or not moving or the full throttle control pressure adjusted too high.

To correct this condition, proceed as follows:

1. Inspect kick down solenoid valve, kick down switch and fuel pump relay for binding or dirt. Replace as required.
2. Adjust control valve full throttle set screw approximately 1–2 turns clockwise, **Fig. 19.**

KNOCKING NOISE THAT CHANGES w/ENGINE LOAD

On some of these models there may be a knocking noise that changes with engine load.

To correct this condition, install new (gold colored) output shaft nut and **torque** to 147 ft. lbs.

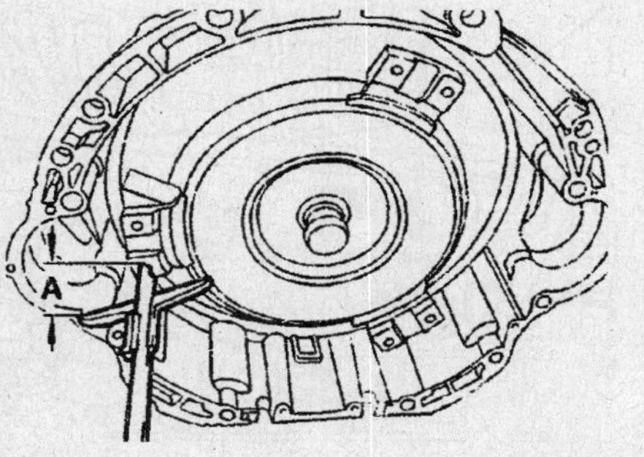

Fig. 12 Torque converter height measurement. C43, C230, C280, CLK55, CLK320, CLK430, E55, E300, E320, E430, S320, S420, SL500, SL600 & SLK230, SLK320 & 1998–99 CL500, CL600, S500 & S600

Model	Year	Torque Converter Installed Height, Inches
C43	1999–2000	0.7678
C230	1998–2000	0.2756
C280	1998–2000	0.7678
CL500	1998–99	1.0237
CL600	1998–99	0.7481
CLK320	1998–2001	0.7678
E300	1998–99	0.2756
E320	1998–2001	0.7678
E320 (4MATIC)	1998–2001	0.7678
ML320	1998–2001	0.7678
ML430	1999–2001	0.7678
S320	1998–99	0.2756
S420	1998–99	1.0237
S500	1998–99	1.0237
S600	1998–99	0.7481
SL500	1998–2001	1.0237
SL600	1998–2001	0.7481
SLK230	1998–2001	0.2756

Fig. 13 Torque converter installed height specifications. C43, C230, C280, CLK55, CLK320, CLK430, E55, E300, E320, E430, S320, S420, SL500, SL600 & SLK230, SLK320 & 1998–99 CL500, CL600, S500 & S600

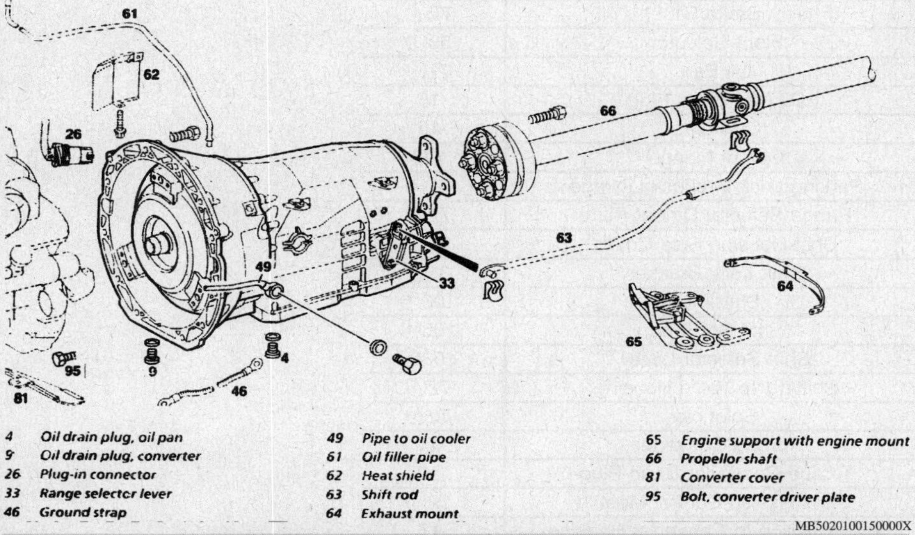

Fig. 14 Transmission replacement. S430 & 2000–01 CL500, CL600, S500 & S600

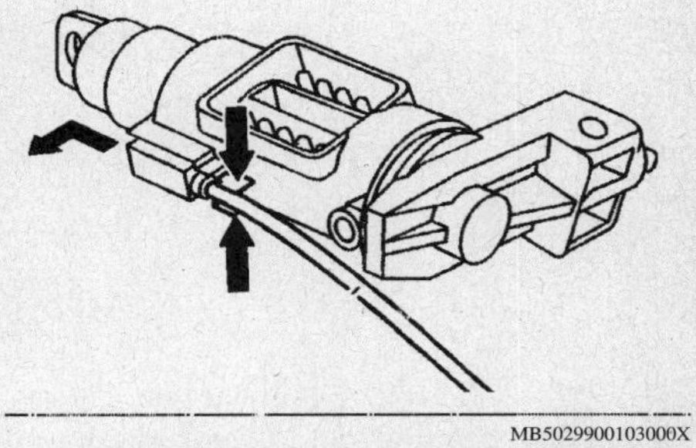

Fig. 15 Steering lock removal. S420, SL500 & SL600 & 1998–99 CL500, CL600, S500 & S600

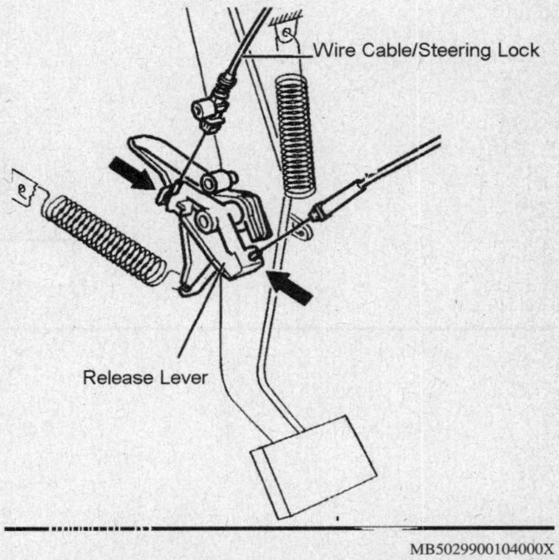

Fig. 16 Release lever. S420, SL500 & SL600 & 1998–99 CL500, CL600, S500 & S600

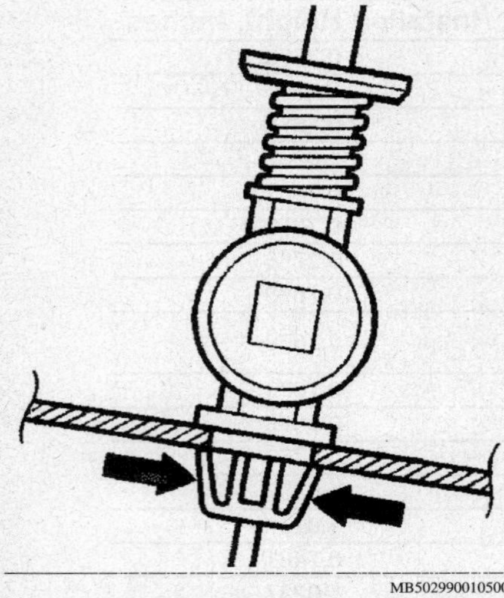

Fig. 17 Pedal bearing bracket. S420, SL500 & SL600 & 1998–99 CL500, CL600, S500 & S600

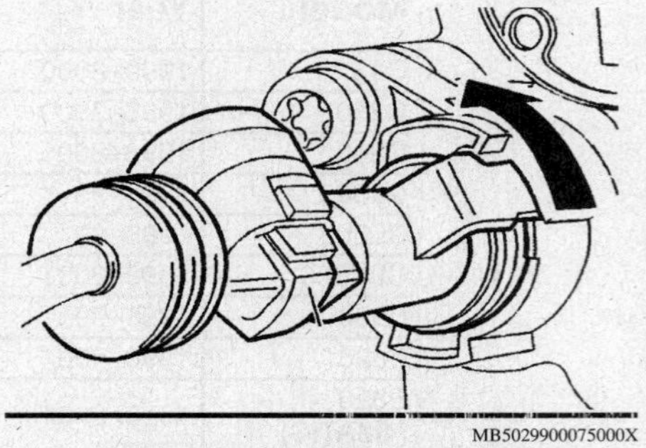

Fig. 18 Interlock cable replacement. S420, SL500 & SL600 & 1998–99 CL500, CL600, S500 & S600

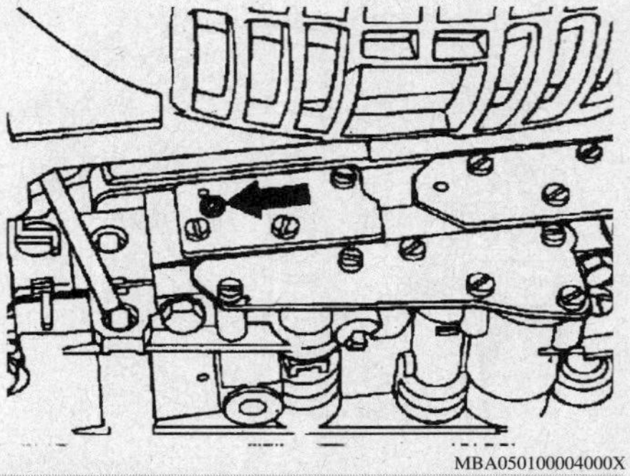

Fig. 19 Full throttle set screw adjustment

TIGHTENING SPECIFICATIONS

Year	Component	Torque, Ft. Lbs.
1998–2001	Brake B1	72①
	Floor Selector	53①
	Oil Pan	71①
	Oil Pan Drain Plug	15
	Oil Pump	15
	Output Flange	148
	Parking Lock Interlock Linkage	72①
	Range Selector Detent Plate	72①
	Shift Housing Side Cover	35①
	Shift Lock Bracket	31①
	Shift Rod	106①
	Shift Rod End	106①
	Shift Selector Lever	108①
	Shifting To Valve Housing	72①
	Solenoid	72①
	Torque Converter	31
	Torque Converter Drain Plug	12
	Transmission Control Module	72①
	Transmission to Converter Housing	15
	Valve Body	72①
	Valve Housing Side Cover	35①

① — Inch lbs.

Drive Axles

NOTE: On Air Bag Equipped Models, Refer To "Air Bag System Precautions" Located In Front Of This Manual For System Disarming And Arming Procedures.

NOTE: Prior To Performing Any Service Operations Listed In This Section, Consult The "Technical Service Bulletins" Section For Related Information.

INDEX

	Page No.
Adjustments	5-310
Bevel Gear & Crown Wheel Backlash	5-312
Drive Pinion	5-311
Rear Axle Housing Shim	5-310
Assemble	5-307
185 MM Rear Axle	5-307
198 MM Rear Axle	5-308
210 MM Rear Axle	5-309
Cleaning & Inspection	5-307
Diagnosis & Testing	5-312
Automatic Locking Differential (ASD)	5-312
Accessing Diagnostic Trouble Codes	5-312
Clearing Diagnostic Trouble Codes	5-313
Component Locations	5-312
Connector Terminal Identification	5-312
Diagnostic Tests	5-313
Diagnostic Trouble Code Interpretation	5-312
Hydraulic Tests	5-313
Mechanic Tests	5-313
Symbol Explanation	5-312
Diagnostic Chart Index	5-313
Disassemble	5-305
185 MM Rear Axle	5-305
198 MM Rear Axle	5-306
210 MM Rear Axle	5-306
Precautions	5-305
Air Bag Systems	5-305
Battery Ground Cable	5-305
Radio Coded Anti-Theft System	5-305
Subassembly Service	5-307
ASD Ring Cylinder	5-307
Differential	5-307
Technical Service Bulletins	5-316
ASD MIL Blinks When New Control Module Installed	5-316
Drivetrain Noise & Vibration	5-316
Tightening Specifications	5-317

PRECAUTIONS

AIR BAG SYSTEMS

Refer to "Air Bag System Precautions" in front of this manual for system disarming and arming procedures.

BATTERY GROUND CABLE

Prior to service, disconnect battery ground cable and isolate as required.

RADIO CODED ANTI-THEFT SYSTEM

Anti-theft radios have a coded theft protection circuit. The CODE card must be obtained before disconnecting battery, removing radio fuse or removing the radio. **The serial number from the radio must match the CODE card.**

After service has been performed proceed as follows:

1. Reconnect radio power and turn key to position No. 2.
2. Turn radio to On position. The word "CODE" will appear on display.
3. Enter first digit of anti-theft code from CODE card. "CODE" will disappear and entered digit will appear followed by four dashes.
4. Enter the next four digits, when all five are entered the first digit flashes again.
5. Press SC, Seek or Tune button to confirm code.
6. If "WAIT" appears on radio panel, proceed as follows:
   a. Radio will allow three coding attempts only before entering lock-up mode and won't respond to controls.
   b. Leave radio on for 15–60 minutes, then radio will unlock and allow three addition coding attempts.
   c. The third lockout period (after nine failed coding attempts) will last 24 hours.
   d. Radio must be left on during enter 24-hour period until "CODE" appears.
7. When "CODE" appears, repeat coding attempt.

DISASSEMBLE

185 MM REAR AXLE

1. Clamp rear axle center assembly in assembly support tool No. 129 589 03 31 00, or equivalent.
2. Remove end cover, **Fig. 1.**
3. Remove locking rings and both connecting flanges.
4. **On models equipped less ASD/ASR,** pry left and righthand radial seal rings out using suitable screwdriver.
5. **On models equipped with ASD,** remove left and righthand radial seal rings out using puller tool No. 129 589 02 33 00, or equivalent.
6. **On models equipped with ASR,** pry left and righthand radial seal rings out using suitable screwdriver.
7. **On models equipped with ASD,** remove hydraulic pipe, ring cylinder and oil deflector.
8. **On all models,** remove right then lefthand locking ring using spreader tool No. 126 589 00 31 00, or equivalent. Mark locking rings for assembly.
9. Install differential bevel gears assembly mandrel tool No. 116 589 18 61 00, or equivalent, on lefthand side and press differential to right until it abuts rear axle housing.
10. Remove both tapered roller bearing outer races and mark for assembly.
11. Remove differential.
12. Put differential on assembly mandrel and remove both tapered roller bearing inner races using puller tool No. 123 589 08 33 00, or equivalent. Mark races for assembly.
13. Loosen locking bolts and remove crown wheel. Mark crown wheel for assembly alignment.
14. Carefully press crown wheel out of differential.
15. Remove joint flange 12-point collared nut using Allen wrench tool No. 126 589 02 09 00, or equivalent.
16. Remove joint flange using puller tool No. 129 589 01 33 00, or equivalent. Mark flange for assembly alignment to drive pinion.
17. Press drive pinion out of rear axle housing using puller tool No. 000 589 65 33 00, or equivalent.
18. Pry radial seal ring out of rear axle using suitable screwdriver.
19. Remove tapered roller bearing inner race with thrust washer.
20. Mount removal and installation tool No. 201 589 02 43 00, or equivalent, on rear axle housing.
21. Pull large tapered roller bearing outer race out of housing with suitable thrust piece, then the shim.
22. Press small tapered roller bearing outer race out with suitable thrust piece. Remove tool.
23. Remove drive pinion spacer sleeve with thrust washer.

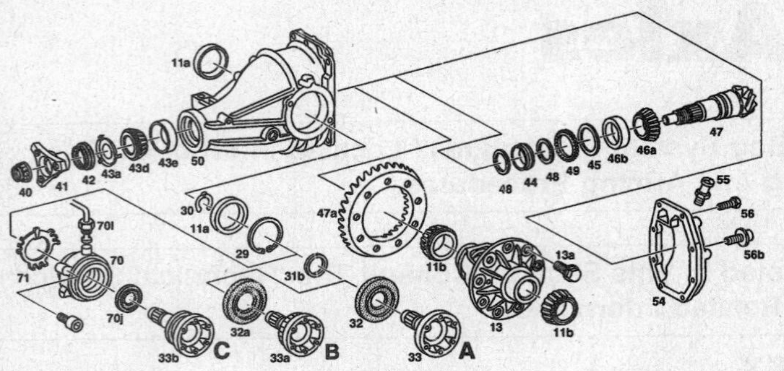

A Standard version
B ASR version
C ASD version

11a Tapered roller bearing outer race
11b Tapered roller bearing inner race
13 Differential
13a Locking bolts
29 Locking ring
30 Locking ring
31b Spacer ring
32 Radial seal ring (standard)
32a Radial seal ring (ASR)
33 Connecting flange (standard)
33a Connecting flange (ASR)
33b Connecting flange (ASD)
40 Twelve-point collared nut
41 Joint flange
42 Radial seal ring
43a Thrust washer
43d Tapered roller bearing inner race
43e Tapered roller bearing outer race
44 Spacer sleeve
45 Shim
46a Tapered roller bearing inner race
46b Tapered roller bearing outer race
47 Drive pinion
47a Crown wheel
48 Thrust washers
49 ABS gear
50 Rear axle housing
54 End cover
55 Rear axle breather
56 Bolt
56b Collared bolt
70 Ring cylinder
70j Radial seal ring (ASD)
70l Hydraulic pipe
71 Oil deflector

MB3019900004000X

Fig. 1 Exploded view of 185 mm rear axle

24. Remove ABS gear using two-arm puller tool No. 000 589 88 33 00, or equivalent.
25. Push puller tool No. 001 589 50 33 00, or equivalent, with suitable clamping pliers over tapered roll bearing inner race. Clamp securely behind rollers with roll pin.
26. Remove drive pinion tapered roller bearing inner race by pulling with tool.

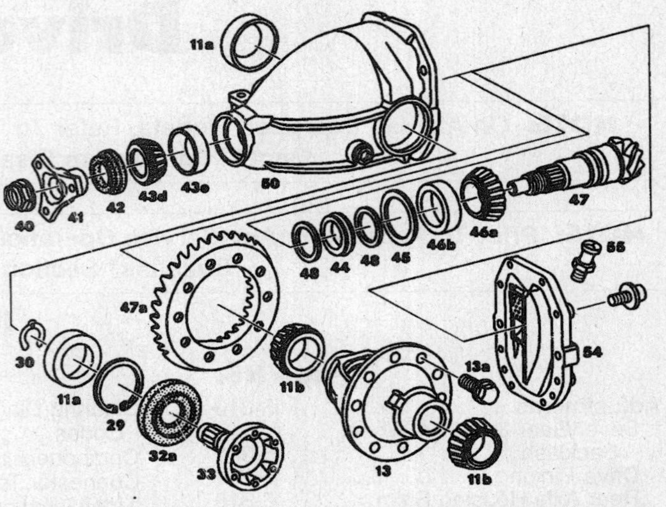

11a Tapered roller bearing outer race
11b Tapered roller bearing inner race
13 Differential housing
13a Locking bolts
29 Locking ring
30 Locking ring
32a Radial seal ring
33 Connecting flange
40 Hexagon collared nut
41 Joint flange
42 Radial seal ring
43d Tapered roller bearing inner race
43e Tapered roller bearing outer race
43e Tapered roller bearing outer race
44 Spacer sleeve
45 Shim
46a Tapered roller bearing inner race
46b Tapered roller bearing outer race
47 Drive pinion
47a Crown wheel
48 Bearing washers
50 Rear axle center piece
54 End cover
55 Rear axle breather

MB3019900008000X

Fig. 2 Exploded view of 198 mm rear axle

198 MM REAR AXLE

1. Clamp rear axle center assembly in assembly support tool No. 129 589 03 31 00, or equivalent.
2. Remove end cover, **Fig. 2.**
3. Remove locking rings and both connecting flanges.
4. Pry left and righthand radial seal rings out using suitable screwdriver.
5. Remove lefthand locking ring using expanding device using spreader tool No. 140 589 05 31 00, or equivalent. Mark locking ring for assembly.
6. Remove right locking ring. Mark locking ring for assembly.
7. Install differential bevel gears assembly mandrel tool No. 116 589 18 61 00, or equivalent, on righthand side and turn differential counterclockwise until it abuts rear axle housing.
8. Remove left and righthand tapered roller bearing outer races and mark for assembly.
9. Remove differential.
10. Remove both differential tapered roller bearing inner races using puller tool No. 123 589 08 33 00, or equivalent. Mark races for assembly.
11. Loosen locking bolts and remove crown wheel. Mark crown wheel for assembly alignment.
12. Carefully press crown wheel out of differential.
13. Remove joint flange 12-point collared nut using Allen wrench tool No. 126 589 01 07 00, or equivalent.
14. Disconnect joint flange using puller tool No. 129 589 01 33 00, or equivalent. Mark flange for assembly alignment to drive pinion.
15. Press drive pinion out of rear axle housing using puller tool No. 000 589 65 33 00, or equivalent.
16. Pry radial seal ring out of rear axle using suitable screwdriver.
17. Remove tapered roller bearing inner race with thrust washer.
18. Mount removal and installation tool No. 140 589 10 43 00, or equivalent, on rear axle housing.
19. Pull large tapered roller bearing outer race out of housing with suitable thrust piece.
20. Press small tapered roller bearing out of race with thrust piece, then the shim.
21. Remove drive pinion spacer sleeve with washer.
22. Push puller tool No. 001 589 50 33 00, or equivalent, with suitable clamping pliers over tapered roll bearing inner race. Clamp securely behind rollers with roll pin.
23. Remove drive pinion tapered roller bearing inner race by pulling with tool.

210 MM REAR AXLE

1. Clamp rear axle center assembly in assembly support tool No. 129 589 00 31 00, or equivalent.
2. Remove end cover, **Fig. 3.**
3. Remove circlips and both connecting flanges.
4. **On models equipped with ASD or ASR,** remove deep-groove ball bearing connecting flange using puller tool No. 001 589 50 33 00, or equivalent.
5. **On models equipped less ASD,** remove spacer rings.
6. **On models equipped with ASD,** disconnect hydraulic pipe.
7. **On all models,** remove mounting bolts, side bearing covers and shims. Mark together with shim for assembly. **Ensure differential gear does not fall out.**
8. Remove differential gear.
9. Mount bearing cover on removal and installation tool No. 129 589 02 43 00, or equivalent, then knock left and righthand radial seal rings out.
10. **On models equipped less ASD,** press both bearing cover tapered roller bearing outer races out using removal tool No. 116 589 00 35 00, or equivalent. Mark for assembly.
11. **On models equipped with ASD,** press both bearing cover tapered roller bearing outer races out using removal tool No. 129 589 02 43 00, or equivalent. Mark for assembly.
12. **On all models,** place differential on assembly mandrel tool No. 116 589 18 61 00, or equivalent.
13. Remove both differential gear tapered roller bearing inner races using puller tool No. 123 589 08 33 00, or equivalent. Mark for assembly.
14. Loosen locking bolts and disconnect ring gear.
15. Press ring gear from differential gear.
16. Remove joint flange 12-point collared nut using Allen wrench tool No. 129 589 01 07 00, or equivalent.
17. Remove joint flange using puller tool No. 129 589 01 33 00, or equivalent. Mark relative to drive pinion for assembly.

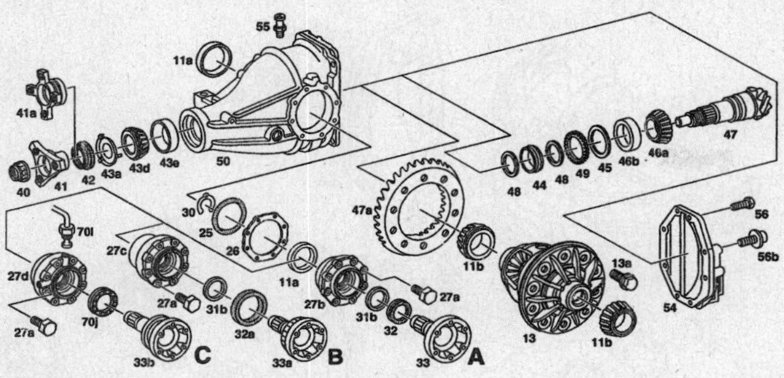

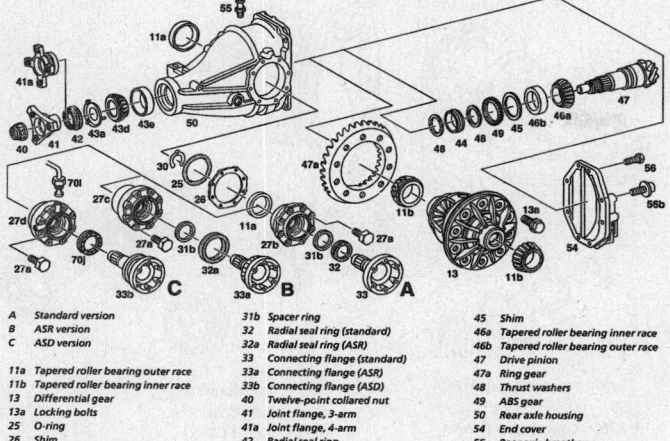

A Standard version
B ASR version
C ASD version

11a Tapered roller bearing outer race
11b Tapered roller bearing inner race
13 Differential gear
13a Locking bolts
25 O-ring
26 Shim
27a Hexagon bolt
27b Side bearing cover (standard)
27c Side bearing cover (ASR)
27d Side bearing cover (ASD)
30 Circlip
31b Spacer ring
32 Radial seal ring (standard)
32a Radial seal ring (ASR)
33 Connecting flange (standard)
33a Connecting flange (ASR)
33b Connecting flange (ASD)
40 Twelve-point collared nut
41 Joint flange, 3-arm
41a Joint flange, 4-arm
42 Radial seal ring
43a Thrust washer
43d Tapered roller bearing inner race
43e Tapered roller bearing outer race
44 Spacer sleeve
45 Shim
46a Tapered roller bearing inner race
46b Tapered roller bearing outer race
47 Drive pinion
47a Ring gear
48 Thrust washers
49 ABS gear
50 Rear axle housing
54 End cover
55 Rear axle breather
56 Bolt
56b Collared bolt
70j Radial seal ring (ASD)
70l Hydraulic pipe

MB3019900009000X

Fig. 3 Exploded view. 210 mm rear axle

18. Press drive pinion out of rear axle housing using puller tool No. 000 589 65 33 00, or equivalent.
19. Pry radial seal ring out using suitable screwdriver.
20. Remove tapered roller bearing inner race with thrust washer.
21. Install removal and installation tool No. 210 589 02 43 00, or equivalent, on rear axle housing.
22. Pull large tapered roller bearing outer race out with shim using suitable thrust piece.
23. Press small tapered roller bearing outer race out using suitable thrust piece.
24. Remove drive pinion spacer sleeve with thrust washers.
25. Remove BAS gear using two-arm puller tool No. 000 589 88 33 00, or equivalent.
26. Push puller tool No. 001 589 50 33 00, or equivalent, with suitable clamping pliers over tapered roll bearing inner race. Clamp securely behind rollers with roll pin.
27. Remove drive pinion tapered roller bearing inner race by pulling with tool.

SUBASSEMBLY SERVICE

DIFFERENTIAL

Disassemble

1. Install differential housing on plate disk tool No. 201 589 02 31 00, or equivalent, and mount tool in suitable vise.
2. Driver out roll and differential pins using suitable drift, **Figs. 4 and 5.**
3. Install assembly mandrels tool No. 116 589 18 61 00, or equivalent, and turn until differential bevel gears are upright in opening.
4. Remove bevel gears with spherical washers and side gears with thrust washers.

Assemble

1. Install assembly mandrel tool No. 116 589 18 61 00, or equivalent, into differential housing bores.
2. Mount both side gears with thrust washers on tool.
3. Install both bevel gears with spherical washers together, then precisely align in differential housing and screw in using assembly mandrel.
4. **On models equipped with 185 mm rear axles,** push assembly mandrel tool No. 123 589 06 15 00, or equivalent, into differential housing instead of differential pin.
5. **On models equipped with 198 and 210 mm rear axles,** push assembly mandrel tool No. 126 589 02 15 00, or equivalent, into differential housing instead of differential pin.
6. **On all models,** inspect friction torque of differential. Friction torque should be 4–22 ft. lbs.
7. **On models equipped with 185 mm rear axles,** drive differential pin into housing using drift punch tool No. 123 589 06 15 00, or equivalent.
8. **On models equipped with 198 mm rear axles,** drive differential pin into housing using drift punch tool No. 126 589 02 15 00, or equivalent.
9. **On all models,** drive new roll pin in until it seats centrally in differential pin.
10. Unclamp differential housing

ASD RING CYLINDER

Disassemble

1. Remove end cover, **Fig. 6.**
2. Pull off locking rings.
3. Remove connecting flange.
4. Pull off deep-grove ball bearing using puller tool No. 001 589 50 33 00, or equivalent.
5. Remove hydraulic pipe.
6. Remove ASD ring cylinder.
7. Remove mounting bolts and ring cylinder.
8. Remove oil deflector.

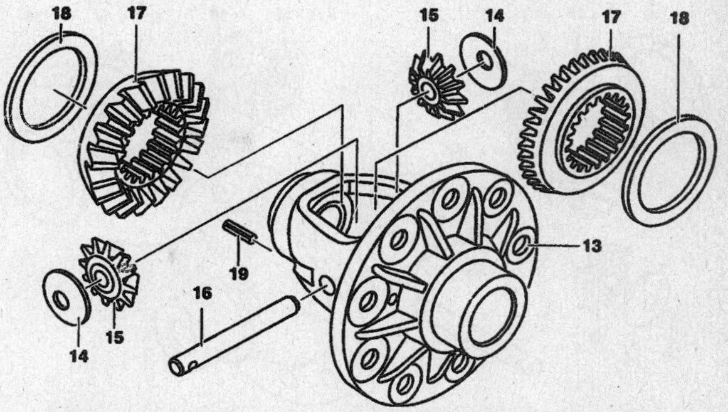

13 Differential Housing 14 Spherical Washers
15 Bevel Gears 16 Differential Pin 17 Side Gear
18 Thrust Washers19 Roll Pin

MB3019900005000X

Fig. 4 Exploded view of differential. 185 & 210 mm rear axle

Assemble

1. Coat new radial seal ring sealing lip with suitable universal hypoid transmission fluid.
2. Install oil deflector. Ensure correct seating in housing.
3. Coat ring cylinder O-ring periphery with suitable hydraulic fluid.
4. Install ring cylinder and tighten mounting bolts to specifications.
5. Install hydraulic pipe. Ensure good routing.
6. Install off deep-grove ball bearing with chamber or groove pointing toward shaft until it abuts flange using collet chuck tool No. 140 589 00 34 00, or equivalent,
7. Inspect connecting flange radial seal ring contact surface. If there are pronounced settling down scores, replace connecting flange.
8. Install connecting flange.
9. **Do not adjust axial play.**
10. Install new locking rings and ensure they are properly seated.
11. Clean sealing surfaces and coat with suitable sealing compound, then install end cover and tighten new mounting bolts to specifications.
12. Bleed ASD hydraulic system.

CLEANING & INSPECTION

1. Inspect connecting flange and joint flange.
2. If there are pronounced settling down scores because of radial seal ring, replace flanges.
3. Ensure drive pinion and crown wheel have matching numbers.

ASSEMBLE

185 MM REAR AXLE

1. Press tapered roller bearing inner race onto drive pinion using suitable sleeve.

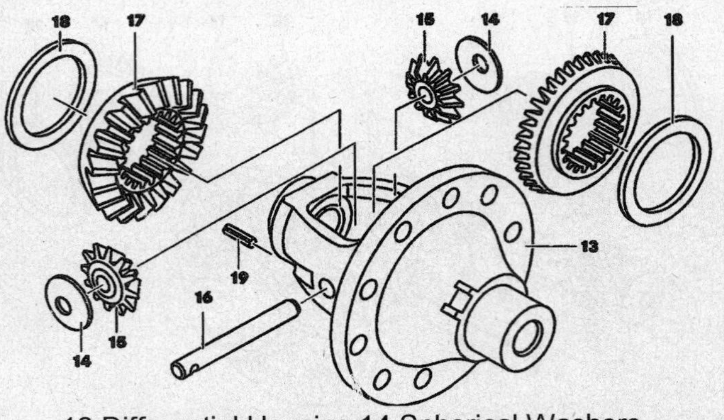

13 Differential Housing 14 Spherical Washers
15 Bevel Gears 16 Differential Pin 17 Side Gear
18 Thrust Washers19 Roll Pin

MB3019900006000X

Fig. 5 Exploded view of differential. 198 mm rear axle

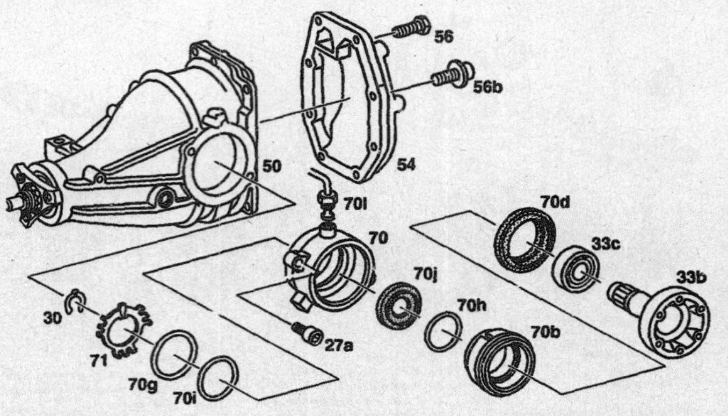

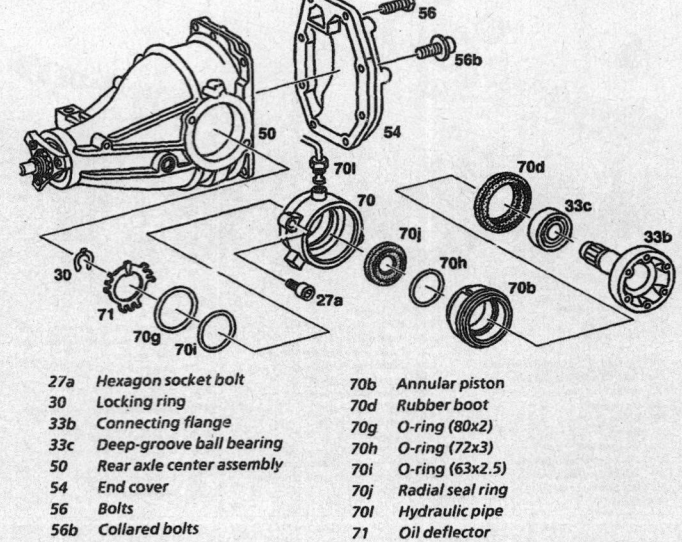

27a	*Hexagon socket bolt*	*70b*	*Annular piston*
30	*Locking ring*	*70d*	*Rubber boot*
33b	*Connecting flange*	*70g*	*O-ring (80x2)*
33c	*Deep-groove ball bearing*	*70h*	*O-ring (72x3)*
50	*Rear axle center assembly*	*70i*	*O-ring (63x2.5)*
54	*End cover*	*70j*	*Radial seal ring*
56	*Bolts*	*70l*	*Hydraulic pipe*
56b	*Collared bolts*	*71*	*Oil deflector*
70	*Ring cylinder*		

MB3019900007000X

Fig. 6 Exploded view of ASD ring cylinder. 185 mm rear axle

2. Press ABS gear onto drive pinion using suitable sleeve.
3. Install rear axle housing shim as outlined under "Adjustments."
4. Install tapered roller bearing outer races using pulling-in tool No. 116 589 11 61 00, or equivalent. **Do not tilt tapered roller bearing out races when pulling in.**
5. Place new spacer sleeve with thrust washers on both sides on drive pinions.
6. Support drive pinion with removal/installation tool No. 210 589 02 43 00, or equivalent, and install in rear axle housing.
7. Clip thrust washer on tapered roller bearing inner race.
8. Install tapered roller bearing inner race on drive pinion.
9. Coat new radial seal ring sealing lip with suitable universal hypoid transmission fluid and mount on drift punch tool No. 124 589 02 15 00, or equivalent.
10. Press tapered roller bearing inner race and drive pinion in with radial seal ring using puller tool No. 000 589 65 33 00, or equivalent. Remove tools.
11. Coat radial seal ring contact surface with suitable universal hypoid transmission fluid.
12. Push joint flange onto drive pinion.
13. Install new 12-point collared nut using Allen wrench tool No. 126 589 02 09 00, or equivalent.
14. Adjust friction torque of drive pinion bearing. Friction torque of drive pinion bearing should be 11–13 inch lbs.
15. Inspect adjustment dimension of drive pinion as outlined under "Adjustments."
16. Caulk slots on drive pinion nut to there is no gap between slot and locking tabs.
17. Warm to 167–185°F and install crown wheel on differential.
18. Press tapered roller bearing inner races onto differential using assembly mandrel tool No. 115 589 04 61 00 with assembly mandrel tool No. 116 589 18 61 00, or equivalents, as support in suitable vise.
19. Install differential and locate with alignment tool No. 126 589 00 15 00, or equivalent.
20. Remove lefthand alignment tool and together with lefthand tapered roller bearing outer race, press into until it abuts housing. Remove lefthand alignment tool.
21. Install lefthand locking ring using suitable locking pliers so locking ring points toward rib.
22. Remove righthand alignment tool.
23. Install righthand tapered roller bearing outer race.
24. Preload rear axle housing 0.1181 inch with expansion spreader tool No. 126 589 00 31 00, or equivalent. **Torque** mounting bolts to 30 ft. lbs. Ensure zero adjustment of dial gauge with contact arm is retained.
25. Install righthand locking ring using suitable pliers so locking ring groove points toward rib. Ensure rings is properly seated.
26. Unclamp rear axle housing and measure expanded dimension. Record measurement if not 0.0043–0.0067 inch.
27. Remove spreader.
28. Measure bevel gear and crown wheel backlash as outlined under "Adjustments."
29. Check locking ring for proper seating using alignment tool No. 126 589 00 15 00, or equivalent. Ring is correctly install when gap of less than 0.002 inch is visible between alignment tool and rear axle housing.
30. **On models equipped with ASD,** proceed as follows:
    a. Install oil deflector ensuring correct seating in housing.
    b. Coat O-ring periphery with suitable hydraulic fluid and install ring cylinder. Tighten mounting bolts to specifications.
    c. Install hydraulic pipe. Ensure good routing.
31. **On all models,** coat new radial seal ring outside diameter and sealing lip with suitable universal hypoid transmission fluid.
32. Press new radial seal ring into housing using drift punch tool No. 126 589 00 15 00, or equivalent.
33. **On models equipped less ASD,** push spacer rings onto connecting flanges.
34. **On all models,** install connecting flanges in differential.
35. Mount new locking rings on connecting flanges.
36. **On models equipped less ASD,** inspect axial play between connecting flange and differential housing. If axial play is not 0.0012–0.0118 inch, install greater or less thickness spacer ring to correct as required.
37. **On models equipped with ASD, do not adjust axial play.**
38. **On all models,** clean sealing surfaces and coat with suitable sealing compound, then install end cover and tighten new mounting bolts to specifications.
39. Remove rear axle center assembly from assembly support and fill with suitable rear axle oil.
40. Install new rear axle breather on end cover.
41. Bleed ASD hydraulic system.

198 MM REAR AXLE

1. Press tapered roller bearing inner race onto drive pinion using suitable sleeve.
2. Install rear axle housing shim as outlined under "Adjustments."
3. Install front and rear tapered roller bearing outer races up to housing stop using pulling-in tool No. 140 589 01 43 00, or equivalent. **Do not tilt tapered**

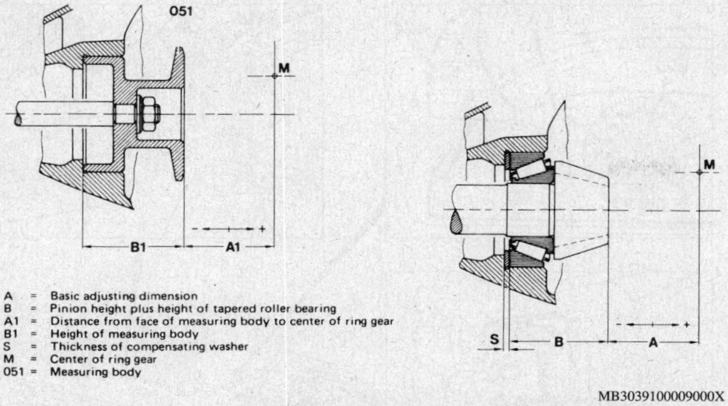

Fig. 7 Pinion & body height measurement

Diagnostic trouble code (DTC)		Possible cause	Test step/Remedy
1	–	No fault in system.	In case of complaint: ☐ 23 and ☐ 33 (entire test)
2	002	ASD control module (N30/2).	Replace N30/2.
3	003	Stop lamp switch (S9/1).	☐ 23⇒ 6.0 ☐ 23⇒ 7.0
4	004	Left front axle VSS sensor (L6/1) or from ABS control module (N30).	☐ 23⇒ 10.0
5	005	Right front axle VSS sensor (L6/2) or from ABS control module (N30).	☐ 23⇒ 9.0
6	006	Rear axle VSS sensor (L6) or from ABS control module (N30).	☐ 23⇒ 11.0
7	007	No VSS from any sensor (L6, L6/1, L6/2).	☐ 23⇒ 9.0 ☐ 23⇒ 10.0 ☐ 23⇒ 11.0
8	008	ASD valve (Y38) or stop lamp switch (S9/1).	☐ 23⇒ 6.0 ☐ 23⇒ 7.0 ☐ 23⇒ 8.0
9	009	**ASD without pressure reservoir (06/92 →)** VSS (L6, L6/1, L6/2) [2]	Visually inspect

[2] Rotor with incorrect tooth count, dirt accumulation on or damaged rotor, incorrect rear axle ratio, wrong wheel or tire size.

MB3029400001000A

Fig. 8 ASD DTC interpretation. C230 & C280

roller bearing out races when pulling in.

4. Place new spacer sleeve with thrust washers on both sides on drive pinions.
5. Support drive pinion with removal/installation tool No. 140 589 10 43 00, or equivalent, and install in rear axle housing.
6. Clip thrust washer on tapered roller bearing inner race.
7. Install tapered roller bearing inner race on drive pinion.
8. Coat new radial seal ring sealing lip with suitable universal hypoid transmission fluid and mount on drift punch tool No. 140 589 08 15 00, or equivalent.
9. Press tapered roller bearing inner race and drive pinion in with radial seal ring using puller tool No. 000 589 65 33 00, or equivalent. Remove tools.
10. Coat radial seal ring contact surface with suitable universal hypoid transmission fluid.
11. Push joint flange onto drive pinion.
12. Install new 12-point collared using Allen wrench tool No. 126 589 02 09 00, or equivalent.
13. Adjust friction torque of drive pinion bearing. Friction torque of drive pinion bearing should be 19–22 inch lbs.
14. Inspect adjustment dimension of drive pinion as outlined under "Adjustments."
15. Caulk slots on drive pinion nut to there is no gap between slot and locking tabs.
16. Warm to 167–185°F and install crown wheel on differential.
17. Press tapered roller bearing inner races onto differential housing using installation mandrel tool No. 116 589 08 61 00 with assembly mandrel tool No. 116 589 18 61 00, or equivalents, as support in suitable vise.
18. Install differential in rear axle housing.
19. Install assembly mandrel tool No. 116 589 18 61 00, or equivalent, into housing, then the righthand tapered roller bearing outer race in housing until it abuts tapered roller bearing inner race.
20. Install righthand locking ring in slot so oil bore is not covered using suitable circlip pliers. Ensure rings is properly seated.
21. Install lefthand tapered roller bearing outer race in rear axle housing.
22. Remove both assembly mandrels from differential.
23. Preload rear axle housing 0.1181 inch with expansion spreader tool No. 140 589 05 31 00, or equivalent. **Torque** mounting bolts to 30 ft. lbs. Ensure zero adjustment of dial gauge with contact arm is retained.
24. Install lefthand locking ring in slot so oil bore is not covered using suitable circlip pliers. Ensure rings is properly seated.
25. Release load on rear axle housing.
26. Unclamp rear axle housing and measure expanded dimension. Record measurement if not 0.0043–0.0067 inch.
27. Remove spreader.
28. Measure bevel gear and crown wheel backlash as outlined under "Adjustments."
29. Coat new radial seal ring outside diameter and sealing lip with suitable universal hypoid transmission fluid.
30. Press new radial seal ring into housing using drift punch tool No. 140 589 10 15 00, or equivalent.
31. Install connecting flanges in differential.
32. Mount new locking rings on connecting flanges using removal and installation tool No. 116 589 01 62 00, or equivalent.
33. Inspect axial play between connecting flange and differential housing. If axial play is not 0.0012–0.0118 inch, install greater or less thickness spacer ring to correct as required.
34. Clean sealing surfaces and coat with suitable sealing compound, then install end cover and tighten new mounting bolts to specifications.
35. Remove rear axle center assembly from assembly support and fill with suitable rear axle oil.
36. Install new rear axle breather on end cover.

210 MM REAR AXLE

1. Press tapered roller bearing inner race onto drive pinion using suitable sleeve.
2. Press ABS gear onto drive pinion using suitable sleeve.
3. Install rear axle housing shim as outlined under "Adjustments."
4. Install tapered roller bearing outer races using pulling-in tool No. 116 589 11 61 00, or equivalent. **Do not tilt tapered roller bearing out races when pulling in.**
5. Place new spacer sleeve with thrust washers on both sides on drive pinions.
6. Support drive pinion with removal/installation tool No. 210 589 02 43 00, or equivalent, and install in rear axle housing.
7. Clip thrust washer on tapered roller bearing inner race.
8. Install tapered roller bearing inner race on drive pinion.
9. Coat new radial seal ring sealing lip with suitable universal hypoid transmission fluid and mount on drift punch tool No. 124 589 02 15 00, or equivalent.
10. Press tapered roller bearing inner race and drive pinion in with radial seal ring using puller tool No. 000 589 65 33 00, or equivalent. Remove tools.
11. Coat radial seal ring contact surface with suitable universal hypoid transmission fluid.
12. Push joint flange onto drive pinion.
13. Install new 12-point collared nut using Allen wrench tool No. 126 589 02 09 00, or equivalent.
14. Adjust friction torque of drive pinion bearing. Friction torque of drive pinion bearing should be 11–13 inch lbs.
15. Inspect adjustment dimension of drive pinion as outlined under "Adjustments."
16. Caulk slots on drive pinion nut to there is no gap between slot and locking tabs.
17. Warm to 167–185°F and install ring gear on differential.
18. Press tapered roller bearing inner races onto differential using assembly mandrel tool No. 116 589 08 61 00 with assembly mandrel tool No. 116 589 18 61 00, or equivalents, as support in suitable vise.
19. **On models equipped less ASD,** press both new tapered roller bearing outer races into bearing cover using 3.4649 inches diameter washer and pulling-in tool No. 116 589 11 61 00, or equivalent.
20. **On models equipped with ASD,** press both new tapered roller bearing outer races into bearing cover using installation tool No. 129 589 02 43 00, or equivalent.

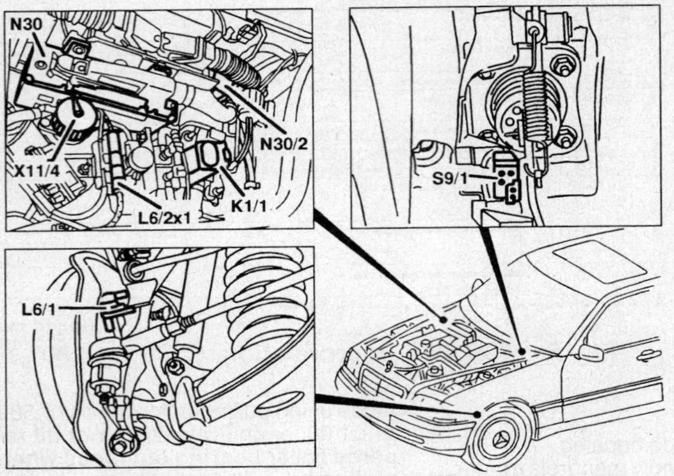

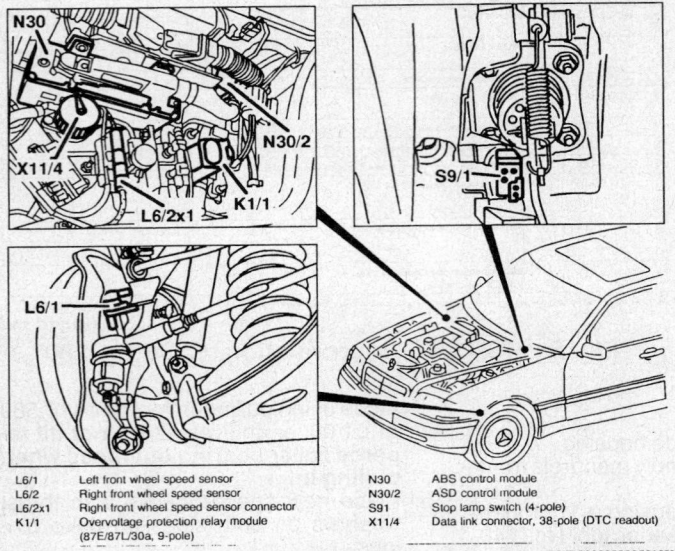

L6/1	Left front wheel speed sensor	N30	ABS control module
L6/2	Right front wheel speed sensor	N30/2	ASD control module
L6/2x1	Right front wheel speed sensor connector	S91	Stop lamp switch (4-pole)
K1/1	Overvoltage protection relay module (87E/87L/30a, 9-pole)	X11/4	Data link connector, 38-pole (DTC readout)

MB3029900005010X

Fig. 9 ASD engine compartment electrical component locations. C230 & C280

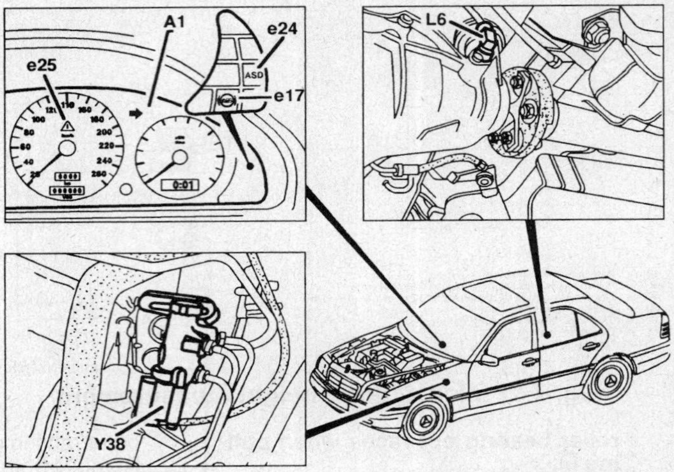

A1	Instrument cluster	A1e25	ASD function indicator lamp
A1e17	ABS malfunction indicator lamp	L6	Rear axle vehicle speed sensor
A1e24	ASD malfunction indicator lamp	Y38	ASD valve

MB3029900005020X

Fig. 10 ASD instrument cluster and chassis electrical component locations. C230 & C280

21. **On all models,** coat new radial seal ring sealing lip with suitable universal hypoid transmission fluid.
22. Mount bearing cover on removal and install tool No. 129 589 02 43 00, or equivalent, and press radial seal ring into cover as follows:
    a. **On models equipped less ASD/ ASR,** use drift punch tool No. 140 589 06 15 00, or equivalent.
    b. **On models equipped with ASR,** use drift punch tool No. 126 589 04 15 00, or equivalent.
    c. **On models equipped with ASD,** use drift punch tool No. 124 589 01 15 00, or equivalent.
23. **On all models,** coat bearing cover O-ring periphery with suitable universal hypoid transmission fluid.
24. Press side bearing covers into housing and install differential gear. Ensure bearing cover spring correctly seats.
25. Install stop tools No. 201 589 01 63 00, or equivalent, to support contact arm on left and righthand of rear axle housing.
26. Put contact arm for expanded dimension measure with dial gauge onto stops from below. Adjust dial to zero with 0.1181 inch preload.
27. **Torque** side bearing covers' mounting bolts to 18 ft. lbs.
28. Measure expanded dimension of housing with contact arm.
29. Record measurement if not 0.0059–0.0079 inch.
30. Remove tool.
31. Measure bevel gear and crown wheel backlash as outlined under "Adjustments."
32. Disconnect contact arm stops.
33. **On models equipped with ASD or ASR,** press deep-groove ball bearing connecting flange using suitable tube. On models with ASD, chamfer or groove must point toward shaft.
34. **On models equipped with ASD** install hydraulic pipe. Ensure good routing.
35. **On models equipped less ASD,** push spacer rings onto connecting flanges.
36. **On all models,** install connecting flanges in differential.
37. Install new circlips on connecting flanges.
38. **On models equipped less ASD,** inspect axial play between connecting flange and differential housing. If axial play is not 0.0012–0.0118 inch, install greater or less thickness spacer ring to correct as required.
39. **On models equipped with ASD, do not adjust axial play.**
40. **On all models,** clean sealing surfaces and coat with suitable sealing compound, then install end cover and tighten new mounting bolts to specifications.
41. Remove rear axle center assembly from assembly support and fill with suitable rear axle oil.
42. Install new rear axle breather on end cover.
43. Bleed ASD hydraulic system.

ADJUSTMENTS

REAR AXLE HOUSING SHIM

185 MM Rear Axle

1. Clamp suitable dial gauge in gauge stand tool No. 363 589 02 21 00, or equivalent, and mount on measuring plate tool No. 601 589 00 23 00, or equivalent.
2. Adjust dial gauge on gauge member tool No. 124 589 14 21 00, or equivalent, to zero under approximately 0.1181 inch preload.
3. Mount drive pinion tapered roller bearing outer race on inner race and attach magnetic plate tool No. 126 589 00 21 00, or equivalent.
4. Install drive pinion in measuring plate, then measure drive pinion height with tapered roller bearing and magnetic plate.
5. Record the difference between gauging member height and drive pinion with magnetic plate height.
6. Record the prefix (+ or -) number from the drive pinion end.
7. Add or subtract drive pinion value as required by the prefix from the first recorded measurement.
8. Install gauging member tool No. 124 589 14 21 00, or equivalent, in rear axle housing.
9. Install dial gauge tool No. 000 589 38 19 00, or equivalent, with measuring pin to measuring tool No. 126 589 00 22 00, or equivalent.
10. Press adjuster tool No. 126 589 00 22 00, or equivalent, against measuring device and adjust dial gauge to zero under 0.0787 inch preload.
11. Tighten clamp screw and correct zero position as required. Install measure device in rear axle housing from left-hand bore. Ensure measuring pin is not damage at bore.
12. Measure and record difference between adjusted gauge dimension and gauge member end face. Note correct negative or positive measurement.
13. Calculate shim thickness by adding or subtracting the three number as required.
14. Remove measuring device and gauging member.
15. Install calculate shim in rear axle housing.

198 MM Rear Axle

1. Clamp suitable dial gauge in gauge stand tool No. 363 589 02 21 00, or equivalent, and mount on measuring plate tool No. 140 589 16 23 00, or equivalent.
2. Adjust dial gauge on gauge member tool No. 140 589 14 21 00, or equivalent, to zero under approximately

0.1181 inch preload.

3. Mount drive pinion tapered roller bearing outer race on inner race and attach magnetic plate tool No. 140 589 41 63 00, or equivalent.
4. Install drive pinion in measuring plate, then measure drive pinion height with tapered roller bearing and magnetic plate.
5. Record the difference between gauging member height and drive pinion with magnetic plate height.
6. Record the prefix (+ or -) number from the drive pinion end.
7. Add or subtract drive pinion value as required by the prefix from the first recorded measurement.
8. Install gauging member tool No. 140 589 14 21 00, or equivalent, in rear axle housing using attachment piece tool No. 140 589 14 21 00, or equivalent.
9. Install lefthand measuring device race tool No. 140 589 41 63 00, or equivalent, outside inwards precisely up to rear axle housing stop.
10. Install righthand measuring device race tool No. 140 589 41 63 00, or equivalent, from inside outward precisely up to rear axle housing stop.
11. Install dial gauge tool No. 000 589 38 19 00, or equivalent, with measuring pin to measuring tool No. 126 589 00 21 00, or equivalent.
12. Press adjuster tool No. 126 589 00 21 00 against measuring device and adjust dial gauge to zero under 0.0787 inch preload.
13. Tighten clamp screw and correct zero position as required. Install measure device in rear axle housing from lefthand bore. Ensure measuring pin is not damage at bore.
14. Measure and record difference between adjusted gauge dimension and gauge member end face. Note correct negative or positive measurement.
15. Calculate shim thickness by adding or subtracting the three number as required.
16. Remove measuring device and gauging member.
17. Install calculate shim in rear axle housing.

210 MM Rear Axle

1. Clamp suitable dial gauge in gauge stand tool No. 363 589 02 21 00, or equivalent, and mount on measuring plate tool No. 601 589 00 23 00, or equivalent.
2. Adjust dial gauge on gauge member tool No. 116 589 07 21 00, or equivalent, to zero under approximately 0.1181 inch preload.
3. Mount drive pinion tapered roller bearing outer race on inner race and attach magnetic plate tool No. 116 589 01 21 00, or equivalent.
4. Install drive pinion in measuring plate, then measure drive pinion height with tapered roller bearing and magnetic plate.
5. Record the difference between gauging member height and drive pinion with magnetic plate height.

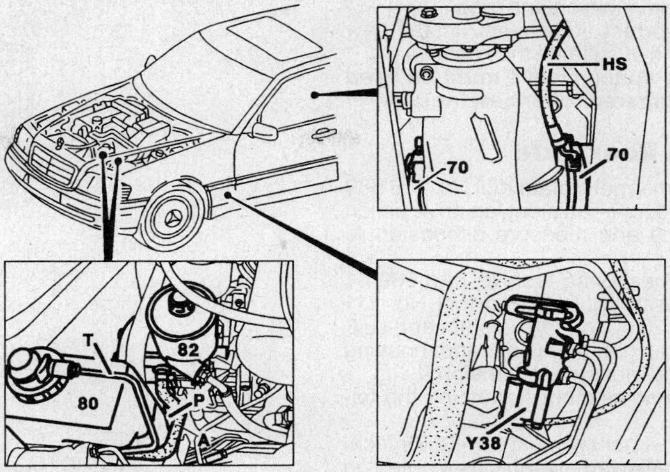

70 Ring cylinder
80 Oil reservoir
82 Tandem pump
83 Hydraulic unit without pressure reservoir
A Suction line - oil reservoir to pressure pump
HS Pressure line - hydraulic unit to ring cylinder
T Return line - hydraulic unit to oil reservoir
N Without leveling function:
Return line - hydraulic unit to oil reservoir
With leveing function:
Return line - leveling valve to oil reservoir
P Pressure line - pressure pump to hydraulic unit

MB3029900011000X

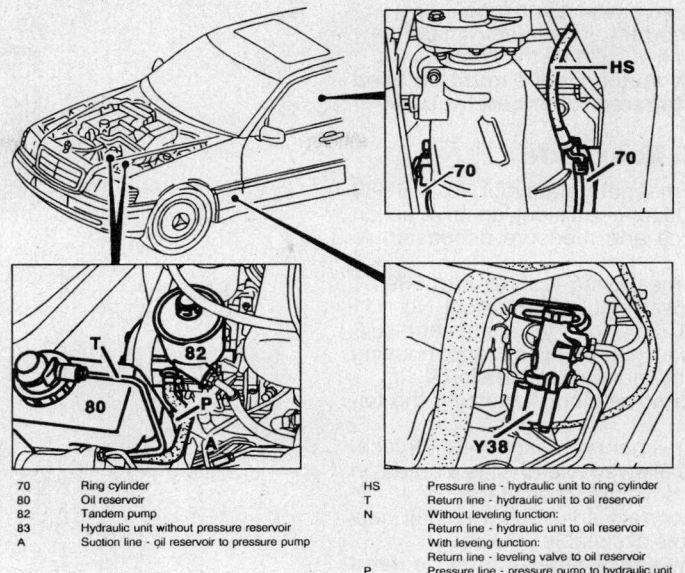

Fig. 11 ASD hydraulic component locations. C230 & C280

6. Record the prefix (+ or -) number from the drive pinion end.
7. Add or subtract drive pinion value as required by the prefix from the first recorded measurement.
8. Install gauging member tool No. 116 589 07 21 00, or equivalent, in rear axle housing.
9. Install suitable dial gauge tool with gauge stand tool No. 111 589 08 23 00 in adjustment gauge tool No. 115 589 05 21 00, or equivalents, and adjust dial gauge to zero under 0.1181 inch preload.
10. Install measuring tool No. 116 589 01 21 00, or equivalent, in lefthand housing bore.
11. Install gauge stand with dial gauge and record measurement.
12. Measure and record difference between adjusted gauge dimension and gauge member end face. Note correct negative or positive measurement.
13. Calculate shim thickness by adding or subtracting the three number as required.
14. Remove measuring device and gauging member.
15. Install calculate shim in rear axle housing.

DRIVE PINION

185 MM Rear Axle

1. Mount magnetic plate tool No. 126 589 00 21 00, or equivalent, on drive pinion end face and measure dimension A, **Fig. 7.**
2. Install dial gauge tool No. 000 589 38 19 00 with measuring pin in measuring device tool No. 126 589 00 21 00, or equivalents.
3. Press adjusting piece tool No. 126 589 00 21 00, or equivalent, against measuring device and adjust dial gauge to zero with 0.0787 inch preload.
4. Tighten clamping screw and ensure dial gauge maintains zero position.
5. Install measuring device from lefthand bore into housing. Ensure measuring pin does not damage housing bore.
6. Record adjustment A, nothing the following:
   a. Adjustment A must be -.0079 inch.
   b. The allowed tolerance is marked on the drive pinion end face.
   c. To correct adjustment, install new shims of suitable thickness.
   d. **New space sleeve must be used for tapered roller bearings.**

198 MM Rear Axle

1. Mount magnetic plate tool No. 140 589 41 63 00, or equivalent, on drive pinion end face and measure dimension A, **Fig. 7.**
2. Install lefthand measuring device race tool No. 140 589 41 63 00, or equivalent, from outside toward inside precisely up to housing stop.
3. Install righthand measuring device race tool No. 140 589 41 63 00, or equivalent, from inside outward precisely up to housing stop.
4. Install dial gauge tool No. 000 589 38 12 19 00 with measuring pin in measuring device tool No. 126 589 00 21 00, or equivalents.
5. Press adjusting piece tool No. 126 589 00 21 00, or equivalent, against measuring device and adjust dial gauge to zero with 0.0787 inch preload.
6. Tighten clamping screw and ensure dial gauge maintains zero position.
7. Install measuring device from lefthand bore into housing. Ensure measuring pin does not damage housing bore.
8. Record adjustment A, nothing the following:
   a. Adjustment A must be -.0079 inch.
   b. The allowed tolerance is marked on

the drive pinion end face.
c. To correct adjustment, install new shims of suitable thickness.
d. **New space sleeve must be used for tapered roller bearings.**

210 MM Rear Axle

1. Mount magnetic plate tool No. 116 589 01 21 00, or equivalent, on drive pinion end face and measure dimension A, **Fig. 7.**
2. Install measuring tool No. 116 589 01 21 00 with gauge stand tool No. 111 589 08 23 00, or equivalents, and suitable dial gauge in lefthand housing bore and measure dimension A.
3. Record adjustment A, nothing the following:
   a. Adjustment A must be -.0079 inch.
   b. The allowed tolerance is marked on the drive pinion end face.
   c. To correct adjustment, install new shims of suitable thickness.
   d. **New space sleeve must be used for tapered roller bearings.**

BEVEL GEAR & CROWN WHEEL BACKLASH

185 & 210 MM Rear Axle

1. Install backlash measuring instrument tool No. 210 589 03 21 00, or equivalent, with suitable dial gauge in differential housing lefthand bore, then clamp securely.
2. Zero dial gauge with 0.1181 inch preload.
3. Hold drive pinion securely at joint flange and alternately move dial gauge to left and right at handle, reading off gear backlash.
4. Repeat measure four times, always turning crown wheel approximately 90°.
5. Gear backlash should be 0.0031–0.0055 inch.
6. Remove measuring tools.
7. Tapered roller bearings and gear seat are correctly adjusted if rear axle housing expanded dimension and gear backlash are within specifications.
8. If expanded dimension and backlash are not within specifications, adjust with suitably thicker or thinner locking rings as follows:
   a. If gear backlash is correct, but expanded dimension is too small, install thicker (by missing amount) locking ring on both sides. Backlash will change slightly.
   b. If expanded dimension is correct, but gear backlash too large, install thinner (by missing amount) locking ring on lefthand assembly and thicker (by missing amount) locking ring by missing amount on righthand (crown wheel) side.
   c. If expanded dimension is correct, but gear backlash too small, install thicker (by missing amount) locking ring on lefthand assembly and thinner (by missing amount) locking ring by missing amount on righthand (crown wheel) side.

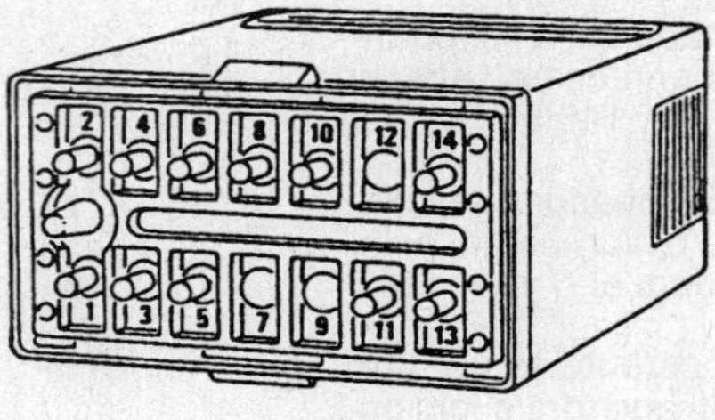

1	Rear axle VSS sensor (L6)
2	ASD MIL (A1e24)
3	Right front axle VSS sensor (L6/2)
4	ASD warning lamp (A1e25)
5	Left front axle VSS sensor (L6/1)
6	Data link connector (X11/4)
7	Not used
8	Ground **Model 124:** W10 **Model 129:** W16 **Model 201:** W10 **Model 202:** W16/4
9	Not used
10	ASD solenoid valve (Y38) (−)
11	Stop lamp switch (S9/1), N.O. contact
12	Not used
13	Circuit 61 voltage
14	Stop lamp switch (S9/1), N.C. contact and Circuit 87e voltage

MB3029900012000X

Fig. 12 ASD control module terminal identification. C230 & C280

198 MM Rear Axle

1. Install backlash measuring instrument tool No. 140 589 08 21 00, or equivalent, with suitable dial gauge in differential housing lefthand bore, then clamp securely.
2. Zero dial gauge with 0.1181 inch preload.
3. Hold drive pinion securely at joint flange and alternately move dial gauge to left and right at handle, reading off gear backlash.
4. Repeat measure four times, always turning crown wheel approximately 90°.
5. Gear backlash should be 0.0031–0.0055 inch.
6. Remove measuring tools.
7. Tapered roller bearings and gear seat are correctly adjusted if rear axle housing expanded dimension and gear backlash are within specifications.
8. If expanded dimension and backlash are not within specifications, adjust with suitably thicker or thinner locking rings as follows:
   a. If gear backlash is correct, but expanded dimension is too small, install thicker (by missing amount) locking ring on both sides. Backlash will change slightly.
   b. If expanded dimension is correct, but gear backlash too large, install thinner (by missing amount) locking ring on lefthand assembly and thicker (by missing amount) locking ring by missing amount on righthand (crown wheel) side.
   c. If expanded dimension is correct, but gear backlash too small, install thicker (by missing amount) locking ring on lefthand assembly and thinner (by missing amount) locking ring by missing amount on righthand (crown wheel) side.

DIAGNOSIS & TESTING

Automatic Locking Differential (ASD)

SYMBOL EXPLANATION

Refer "Anti-Lock Brakes" section.

ACCESSING DIAGNOSTIC TROUBLE CODES

Refer "Anti-Lock Brakes" section.

DIAGNOSTIC TROUBLE CODE INTERPRETATION

Refer to **Fig. 8** for DTC description and identification.

COMPONENT LOCATIONS

Refer to **Figs. 9 through 11** for component locations.

CONNECTOR TERMINAL IDENTIFICATION

Refer to **Fig. 12** for connector terminal identification.

Refer to "Anti-Lock Brakes" for data link connector terminal identification.

DIAGNOSTIC TESTS

C230 & C280

1. Turn ignition switch to Off position.
2. Remove plastic cover.
3. Remove ASD control module.
4. Connect socket box tool No. 129 589 00 21 00, or equivalent, to control module connector using test cable tool No. 124 589 28 63 00, or equivalent.
5. Perform test as directed using suitable digital multi-meter, **Figs. 13 through 17.**

HYDRAULIC TESTS

C230 & C280

1. Turn ignition switch to Off position.
2. Inspect oil reservoir level and correct as required.
3. Remove plastic cover.
4. Remove ASD control module.
5. Bridge ASD control module connector sockets No. 8 and 10.
6. Connect pressure gauge to ring cylinder.
7. Start engine and idle until pressure no longer increases. Test gauge pressure should be 3626 psi.
8. If pressure is not 725–914 psi, inspect hydraulic oil pump.

MECHANIC TESTS

C230 & C280

1. Turn ignition switch to Off position.
2. Ensure oil reservoir level is correct.
3. Raise and support vehicle on one side.
4. Attach frictional torque measurement adapter plate tool No. 140 589 00 46 00, or equivalent, using two opposing wheel bolts.
5. Install studs with shorter threads into rear axle shaft flange until they bottom.
6. Slide plate over studs and hand tighten knurled nuts.
7. Turn wheel 90° and record measurement using suitable torque wrench.
8. Disconnect ASD control module.
9. Install jumper wire between ASD control module connector sockets No. 8 and 10.
10. Return wheel to starting position.
11. Connect suitable pressure gauge to ring cylinder.
12. With engine at idle, measure hydraulic system pressure. Pressure should be 725–914 psi.
13. Turn wheel 90° and record measurement using suitable torque wrench.
14. Subtract first torque reading from second. **Torque** should be more than 74 ft. lbs.
15. If difference is less than 74 ft. lbs., replace center section.

CLEARING DIAGNOSTIC TROUBLE CODES

Refer "Anti-Lock Brakes" section.

DIAGNOSTIC CHART INDEX

Code	Description	Page No.	Fig. No.
C230 & C280			
—	Test 23, Steps 2.0–4.0	5-314	14
	Test 23, Steps 5.0–6.0	5-315	15
3	Test 23, Steps 7.0–8.1	5-315	16
8	Test 23, Steps 7.0–8.1	5-315	16
4	Test 23, Steps 9.0–11.0	5-316	17
5	Test 23, Steps 9.0–11.0	5-316	17
6	Test 23, Steps 9.0–11.0	5-316	17
7	Test 23, Steps 9.0–11.0	5-316	17
8	Test 23, Steps 1.0–1.2	5-314	13

Test step DTC	Test scope	Test connection	Test condition	Nominal value	Possible cause/Remedy
⇒ 1.0 8	**ASD control module (N30/2)** Voltage supply Circuit 87 E	N30/2 8 — V — 14	Ignition: **ON**	11 – 14 V	⇒ 1.1
⇒ 1.1	Voltage supply from overvoltage protection relay module (K1/1 or K1/2)	N30/2 ⊥ — V — 14	Ignition: **ON**	11 – 14 V	Fuse in K1/2, Wiring, K1/2, ⇒ 1.2
⇒ 1.2	Ground wire	**Models 124, 201** N30/2 W10 — Ω — 8 **Models 129, 202** N30/2 W16 — Ω — 8 W16/4	Ignition: **OFF**	< 1 Ω	Wiring, **Models 124** Ground (battery) (W10). **Model 202** Ground (component compartment, right) (W16/4).

MB3029900009010X

Fig. 13 Code 8: Test 23, Steps 1.0–1.2. C230 & C280

Test step DTC	Test scope	Test connection	Test condition	Nominal value	Possible cause/Remedy
⇒ 2.0	**Circuit 61 voltage**	N30/2 8 — V — 13	Ignition: **ON** Engine: **Start**	< 1.5 V 11 – 14 V	Wiring, Generator (G2).
⇒ 3.0	**Diagnosis output**	**X11/4 8-pole/16-pole** N30/2 5 — Ω — 6 **X11/4 38-pole** N30/2 26 — Ω — 6	Engine: **OFF**	< 1 Ω	Wiring, Data link connector (X11/4).
⇒ 4.0	**ASD warning lamp (A1e25)**	N30/2 8 — 4	Ignition: **ON**	A1e25: **ON**	Wiring, A1e25,

MB3029900009020X

Fig. 14 Code —: Test 23, Steps 2.0–4.0. C230 & C280

Test step	DTC	Test scope	Test connection	Test condition	Nominal value	Possible cause/Remedy
⇒ 5.0		**ASD MIL (A1e24)**	**Models 124, 129, 201**	Ignition: **ON**		Wiring, A1e24.
			N30/2 8 – 2	Bridge sockets 8 and 2.	A1e24: **ON**	Wiring.
			Model 202	Ignition: **ON**	A1e24: lamp goes **out** after 30 seconds.	Wiring, A1e24,
			N30/2 8 – 2	Bridge sockets 8 and 2.	A1e24: **ON**	
⇒ 6.0	3 8	**Stop lamp switch (S9/1)** N.O. contact	N30/2	Ignition: **OFF**		Fuse in overvoltage protection relay module (K1/2), Wiring, S9/1.
			8 – V – 11	Brake pedal not depressed.	< 1 V	
				Depress brake pedal.	11 – 14 V	

MB3029900009030X

Fig. 15 Code —: Test 23, Steps 5.0–6.0. C230 & C280

Test step	DTC	Test scope	Test connection	Test condition	Nominal value	Possible cause/Remedy
⇒ 7.0	3 8	**Stop lamp switch (S9/1)** N.C. contact	N30/2	Ignition: **ON**		Wiring, S9/1, ⇒ 8.0
			8 – V – 10	Brake pedal not depressed.	11 – 14 V	
				Depress brake pedal.	< 1 V	
⇒ 8.0	3 8	**ASD solenoid valve (Y38)** Function	N30/2 8 – 10	Ignition: **ON**	ASD valve switches on.	⇒ 8.1, Wiring.
				Depress brake pedal.	ASD valve switches off.	
⇒ 8.1	3 8	Coil resistance	Y38x1 1 – Ω – 2	Ignition: **OFF** Brake pedal not depressed.	5 – 7 Ω.	Wiring, Y38.

MB3029900009040X

Fig. 16 Codes 3 & 8: Test 23, Steps 7.0–8.1. C230 & C280

TECHNICAL SERVICE BULLETINS

ASD MIL BLINKS WHEN NEW CONTROL MODULE INSTALLED

C230 & C280

On some of these models the ASD MIL may blink when a new control module is installed.

This condition may be caused by front rotors to rear axle not being initialized.

To correct this condition, drive vehicle up to 19 mph without applying brakes. Once specified speed is obtained, front rotors to rear axle is initialized and brakes may be applied.

DRIVETRAIN NOISE & VIBRATION

On some of these model there may be noise and/or vibrations.

These conditions may be caused by engine, drive shaft imbalance, improper drive shaft angles, transmission and rear axle center piece.

To correct this conditions, follow the troubleshooting charts, **Fig. 18.**

Test step	DTC	Test scope	Test connection	Test condition	Nominal value	Possible cause/Remedy
⇒ 9.0	5 7	**Right front axle VSS sensor (L6/2)**	N30/2 8 —< -V+ >— 3	Raise front of vehicle. Ignition: **ON** Rotate right front wheel (approx. 1 rev./sec.).	> 3 V~	Wiring
⇒ 10.0	4 7	**Left front axle VSS sensor (L6/1)**	N30/2 8 —< -V+ >— 5	Raise front of vehicle. Ignition: **ON** Rotate left front wheel (approx. 1 rev./sec.).	> 3 V~	Wiring
⇒ 11.0	6 7	**Rear axle VSS sensor (L6)**	N30/2 8 —< -V+ >— 1	Raise rear of vehicle. Selector lever in: **N** Ignition: **ON** Rotate a rear wheel (approx. 1 rev./sec.).	> 3 V~	Wiring

MB3029900009050X

Fig. 17 Codes 4, 5, 6 & 7: Test 23, Steps 9.0–11.0. C230 & C280

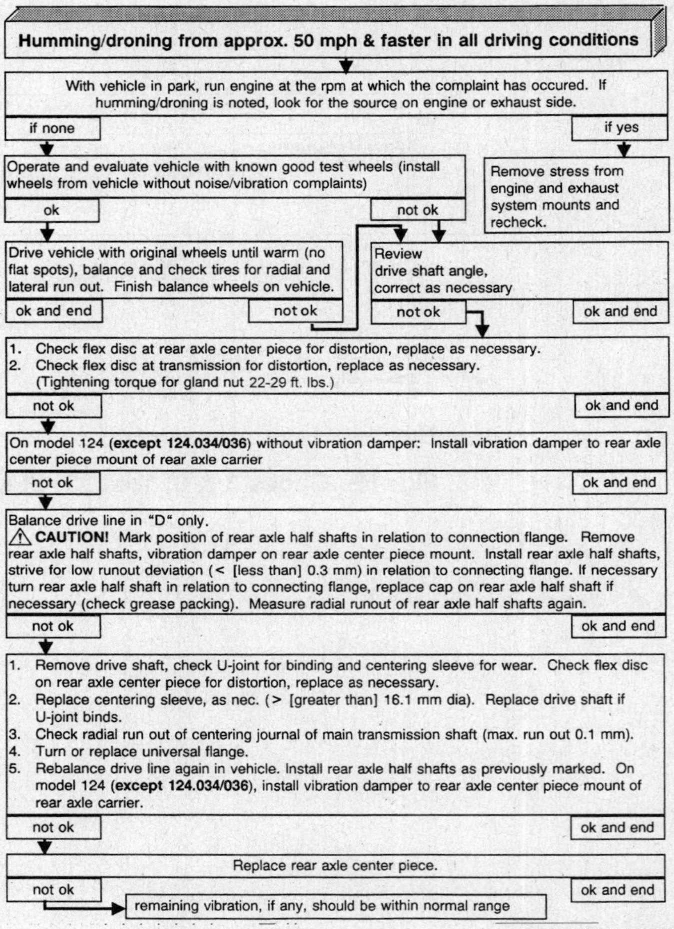

Humming/droning from approx. 50 mph & faster in all driving conditions
With vehicle in park, run engine at the rpm at which the complaint has occured. If humming/droning is noted, look for the source on engine or exhaust side.
if none
if yes
Operate and evaluate vehicle with known good test wheels (install wheels from vehicle without noise/vibration complaints)
Remove stress from engine and exhaust system mounts and recheck.
ok
not ok
Drive vehicle with original wheels until warm (no flat spots), balance and check tires for radial and lateral run out. Finish balance wheels on vehicle.
Review drive shaft angle, correct as necessary
ok and end
not ok
not ok
ok and end
1. Check flex disc at rear axle center piece for distortion, replace as necessary.
2. Check flex disc at transmission for distortion, replace as necessary. (Tightening torque for gland nut 22-29 ft. lbs.)
not ok
ok and end
On model 124 (except 124.034/036) without vibration damper: Install vibration damper to rear axle center piece mount of rear axle carrier
not ok
ok and end
Balance drive line in "D" only.
CAUTION! Mark position of rear axle half shafts in relation to connection flange. Remove rear axle half shafts, vibration damper on rear axle center piece mount. Install rear axle half shafts, strive for low runout deviation (< [less than] 0.3 mm) in relation to connecting flange. If necessary turn rear axle half shaft in relation to connecting flange, replace cap on rear axle half shaft if necessary (check grease packing). Measure radial runout of rear axle half shafts again.
not ok
ok and end
1. Remove drive shaft, check U-joint for binding and centering sleeve for wear. Check flex disc on rear axle center piece for distortion, replace as necessary.
2. Replace centering sleeve, as nec. (> [greater than] 16.1 mm dia). Replace drive shaft if U-joint binds.
3. Check radial run out of centering journal of main transmission shaft (max. run out 0.1 mm).
4. Turn or replace universal flange.
5. Rebalance drive line again in vehicle. Install rear axle half shafts as previously marked. On model 124 (except 124.034/036), install vibration damper to rear axle center piece mount of rear axle carrier.
not ok
ok and end
Replace rear axle center piece.
not ok
ok and end
remaining vibration, if any, should be within normal range

MBA039500001010X

Fig. 18 Drivetrain troubleshooting chart (Part 1 of 3)

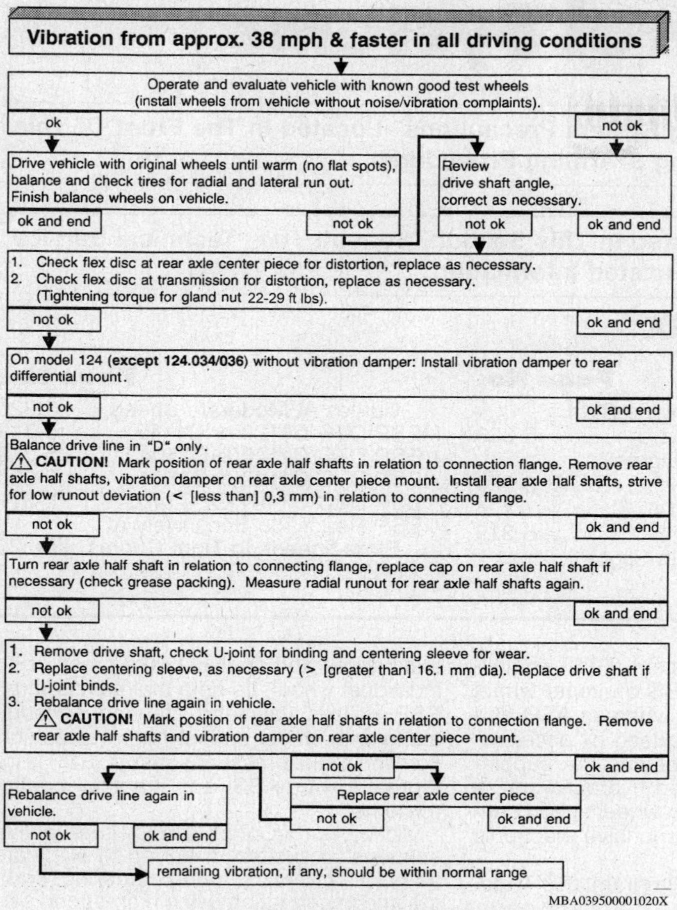

Fig. 18 Drivetrain troubleshooting chart (Part 2 of 3)

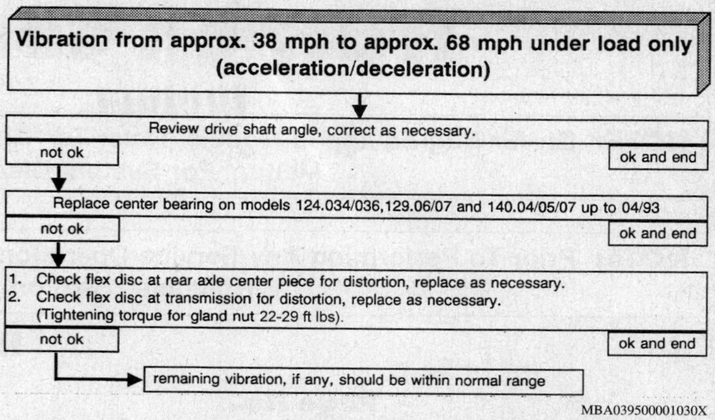

Fig. 18 Drivetrain troubleshooting chart (Part 3 of 3)

TIGHTENING SPECIFICATIONS

Year	Component	Torque, Ft. Lbs.
1998–2001	Breather (185 MM)	18
	Breather (198 & 210 MM)	22
	Crown Wheel	63
	End Cover	33
	Oil Filler & Drain	33
	Ring Cylinder	18

Traction Control Systems

NOTE: On Air Bag Equipped Models, Refer To "Air Bag System Precautions" Located In The Front Of This Manual For System Disarming & Arming Procedures.

NOTE: Prior To Performing Any Service Operations Listed In This Section, Consult The "Technical Service Bulletins" Section For Related Information.

INDEX

	Page No.
Application Chart	5-319
Description	5-318
Diagnosis & Testing	5-319
Precautions	5-318
Air Bag Systems	5-318
Battery Ground Cable	5-318
System Service	5-319
Technical Service Bulletins	5-319
ASR MIL On After Engine Start, DTC C1022	5-320
ASR Warning Lamp Lights Intermittently	5-320
ESP & ADS DTC C1140 & C1054 or 015, 016 & 017	5-319
ESP Activated Even In Slight Curves At Moderate Speed	5-320
ESP DTC C1120 or C1142	5-319
ESP DTC C1140 & C1504	5-319
ESP DTC C1140 & C1504	5-320
ESP DTC C1401 Or C1405	5-319
ESP React Too Sensitively At Slow Speeds In Tight Curves	5-320

PRECAUTIONS

AIR BAG SYSTEMS

Refer to "Air Bag System Precautions"in front of this manual for system disarming and arming procedures.

BATTERY GROUND CABLE

Prior to service, disconnect battery ground cable and isolate as required.

DESCRIPTION

Acceleration Slip Regulation (ASR) and Electronic Traction System (ETS) compliments ABS system. ABS prevents wheel lock-up during braking whereas ASR and ETS limit wheel spin caused by acceleration. Basic ABS components are supplemented by an expanded hydraulic unit, a charging pump, a fourth wheel speed sensor and a more comprehensive electronic system.

Electronic Stability Program (ESP) detects slides and applies brake pressure to individual wheels to help maintain control. ESP utilizes yaw and steering sensors, along with wheel speed, lateral acceleration and brake pressure sensors. ESP is integrated with ABS and traction control systems.

Active Body Control (ABC) is an active suspension system designed to eliminate body roll and pitch during cornering, braking and acceleration using high-speed servos and sensors.

APPLICATION CHART

Model	Year	ASR	ETS	ASD	ESP
C43	1999–2000	S	—	—	S
C230	1998	O	—	—	—
	1999	S	—	—	—
	2000	S	—	—	S
C240	2001	S	—	—	S
C280	1998–99	S	—	—	O
	2000	S	—	—	S
C320	2001	S	—	—	S
CL55	2000–01	S	—	—	S
CL500	1998–99	S	—	—	O
	2000–01	S	—	—	S
CL600	1998–99	S	—	—	S
	2001	S	—	—	S
CLK55	2001	S	—	—	S
CLK320	1998–99	S	—	—	O
	2000–01	S	—	—	S
CLK430	1999–2001	S	—	—	S
E55	2000–01	S	—	—	S
E300	1998–99	S	—	—	O
E320	1998–99	S	—	—	O
	2000–01	S	—	—	S

Continued

APPLICATION CHART—Continued

Model	Year	ASR	ETS	ASD	ESP
E430	1998	S	—	—	O
	1999–2001	S	—	—	S
ML55	2000–01	—	—	—	S
ML320	1998	—	S	—	—
	1999	—	S	—	S
	2000–01	—	—	—	S
ML430	1999	—	S	—	S
	2000–01	—	—	—	S
S55	2001	S	—	—	S
S320	1998–99	S	S	—	O
S420	1998–99	S	—	—	O
S430	2000–01	S	—	—	S
S500	1998–99	S	—	—	O
	2000–01	S	—	—	S
S600	1998–99	S	—	—	S
	2001	S	—	—	S
SL500	1998–98	S	—	—	O
	1999–2001	S	—	—	S
SL600	1998–2001	S	—	—	S
SLK230	1998–2001	S	—	—	—
SLK320	2001	S	—	—	—

O — Optional.
S — Standard.

DIAGNOSIS & TESTING

Refer "Anti-Lock Brakes" section

SYSTEM SERVICE

Refer "Anti-Lock Brakes" section

TECHNICAL SERVICE BULLETINS

ESP DTC C1140 & C1504

C43, C230, C280, CLK55, CLK320, CLK430, E55, E300, E320, E430 & SLK230

On some of these models there may be Electronic Stability Program (ESP) Diagnostic Trouble Codes (DTCs) C1140 and C1504.

This condition may be caused by steering angle sensor and contact spiral clearance.

To correct this condition, proceed as follows:

1. Read ESP DTC memory.
2. Check steering angle sensor supply voltage.
3. Measure steering angle sensor ground, pin No. 3. In relation to battery, it should be 12–14 volts. In relation to ground pole, less than one ohm.
4. Pin No. 4 (supply voltage circuit 30) to No. 3 should be 12–14 volts.
5. Pin No. 2 (supply voltage circuit 87) to No. 3 with ignition on, 12–14 volts. With ignition off, zero volts.
6. Measure clearance between steering angle sensor and contact spiral at five different points on circumference.
7. If clearance is not 0.118–0.217 inch, adjust turn signal switch three-point mount.

ESP DTC C1401 OR C1405

C230, C240, CLK320, CLK430, E300, E320 & E430

On some of these models the Electronic Stability Program (ESP) may have Diagnostic Trouble Codes (DTCs) C1401 or C1405 stored. Code occurs only when putting vehicle in motion for first time after starting engine.

This condition may be caused by ESP control module software error.

To correct this condition, replace control module.

ESP DTC C1120 OR C1142

E43, C280, CLK55, CLK320, CLK430, E55, E320, E430 & S430 & 1999-2000 SL500 & 2000 CL500 & S500

On some of these models the Electronic Stability Program (ESP) may store Diagnostic Trouble Code (DTC) C1120 or C1142.

DTC C1120 usually occurs after the vehicle has been driven up a steep incline and through a 90° left or righthand curve immediately after starting the engine. The indicator lamp may come on after driving straight for approximately 100 yards.

DTC C1142 usually occurs when driving through curves with low lateral acceleration forces.

This condition may be caused by erroneous standstill calibration of yaw rate sensor or lateral acceleration sensor is monitored to precisely by ESP control module.

To correct this condition, install revised control module, **Fig. 1.**

ESP & ADS DTC C1140 & C1054 OR 015, 016 & 017

E55, E320, E430, S320, S420, SL500 & SL600 & 1998-99 S500 & S600

On some of these models there may be Electronic Stability Program (ESP) and Adaptive Damping System (ADS) steering angle sensor Diagnostic Trouble Codes (DTCs) C1140 and C1504 or 015, 016 and 017.

This condition may be caused by the steering angle sensor power supply.

To correct this condition, proceed as follows:

1. Ensure steering angle sensor N49 pin No. 2 is ground, pin No. 3 is circuit 87 and No. 4 circuit 30.
2. Connect Hand-Held Tester (HHT) tool No. 965 589 00 01 00, or equivalent scan tool, to DLC.
3. Start ADS or ESP test program.
4. Select actual valve menu.
5. Turn steering wheel.
6. If values change, replace steering angle sensor.
7. If values do not change, inspect distance between clock spring contact and jacket tube. Adjust as required.
8. If steering angle sensor cannot be initialized after starting engine, replace

sensor.

ESP DTC C1140 & C1504

S430 & 2000-01 CL500 & S500

On CL500 models built before VIN 000532, and S430 and S500 models built before VIN 063525, there may be Electronic Stability Program (ESP) Diagnostic Trouble Codes (DTCs) C1140 and C1504.

This condition may be caused by jacket tube control module voltage being too low.

To correct this condition, proceed as follows:

1. Disconnect battery.
2. Remove footwell paneling.
3. Cut cable on PIN No. 12 of cockpit connector X18 wiring harness.
4. Connect cut line with additional 23.6 inch length of suitable wire. Use solder end sleeve.
5. Route new lead to lefthand fuse and relay box fuse F25.
6. Release fuse carrier.
7. Disconnect fuse carrier from fuse and relay box.
8. Remove fuse F25.
9. Disconnect and cut off contact carrier connection.
10. Connect new connected lead to red/yellow lead removed from fuse carrier. Use solder end sleeve.
11. Reverse procedure to install. **Do not install fuse F25.**

ASR MIL ON AFTER ENGINE START, DTC C1022

On some of these models the ASR MIL lamp may illuminate after engine start with Diagnostic Trouble Code C1022 stored. There are no engine operation complaints.

This condition may be caused by the ME-SFI 2.1 engine control module.

To correct this condition, replace the engine control module.

Model	ESP Control Module Part No.	
	Old	New
C43, C280, CLK320 & CLK430	027 545 59 32	029 545 70 32
E55, E320 & E430	027 545 57 32	029 545 76 32

Fig. 1 ESP control module replacement

Model	Equipment	ESP Control Module Part No.
C230, C280 & CLK320	All	027 545 59 32
E55, E320 & E430	Less SPS	027 545 56 32
	w/SPS	027 545 57 32
	w/4MATIC	027 545 63 32

Fig. 2 ESP control module replacement

ESP ACTIVATED EVEN IN SLIGHT CURVES AT MODERATE SPEED

2000 C230

On some of these models built after February 2000, the Electronic Stability Program (ESP) starts regulating too early particularly in long curves for example freeway exists. There are control noises or a flashing indicator lamp without the vehicle oversteering noticeably.

This condition is caused by the ESP control module.

To correct this condition, proceed as follows:

1. Inspect the ESP control module part number status.
2. If control module part number is 202 545 47 32 with an imprinted status of "Q06," replace module with unit having "Q7" or higher status.
3. Control modules with "Q05" status or less are not affected.

ESP REACT TOO SENSITIVELY AT SLOW SPEEDS IN TIGHT CURVES

C230, C280, CLK320, E55, E320 & E430

On some of these models equipped with the Electronic Stability Program (ESP) may react too sensitively at walking speed in tight curves.

To correct this condition, replace the ESP control module, **Fig. 2.**

ASR WARNING LAMP LIGHTS INTERMITTENTLY

On some of these models equipped with ASR, the warning lamp may intermittently light.

This condition may be caused by internal stop lamp switch contacts.

To correct this condition, install new stop lamp switch.

Active Suspension Systems

NOTE: On Air Bag Equipped Models, Refer To "Air Bag System Precautions" Located In The Front Of This Manual For System Disarming & Arming Procedures.

NOTE: Prior To Performing Any Service Operations Listed In This Section, Consult The "Technical Service Bulletins" Section For Related Information.

INDEX

Page No.

Component Replacement 5-342
Front Shock Absorber........... 5-342
Rear Damper Valve............ 5-342
Rear Level Controller 5-342
Rear Spring Actuator........... 5-342
Rear Strut 5-342
Description 5-321
Diagnosis & Testing 5-324
Accessing Diagnostic Trouble Codes 5-324
Clearing Diagnostic Trouble Codes 5-324
Component Locations........... 5-324
Connector Terminal Identification 5-324
Diagnostic Tests 5-324
S320 & S420 & 1998–99 CL500, CL600, S500 & S600 5-324
SL500 & SL600............... 5-324
Diagnostic Trouble Code Interpretation 5-324
Function Tests 5-324
Symbol Explanation............. 5-324
Symptom Related Diagnosis 5-324

Page No.

Wiring Diagrams................ 5-324
Diagnostic Chart Index 5-331
Inspection 5-322
Damping Inspection............ 5-323
Front Axle Strut Leak Inspection 5-323
Hydraulic Oil Pump Inspection .. 5-322
Hydraulic System Bleed......... 5-322
Internal Leakage Inspection..... 5-323
Leveling Valve Function Inspection 5-322
Leveling Valve Pressure Inspection 5-322
Valve Assemble Internal Leak Inspection 5-323
Vehicle Level Inspection 5-323
Precautions 5-321
Air Bag Systems................ 5-321
Battery Ground Cable........... 5-321
Technical Service Bulletins 5-343
ADS MIL Lit & DTC 14 Or 20 Set 5-343
ADS MIL Lit & DTC 3 Or 4 Set . 5-343
ADS MIL Lit & DTC 5 Set....... 5-343

Page No.

ADS MIL Lit & DTC 6, 7, 8 or 9 Set, But No Malfunction Found 5-343
ESP & ADS DTC C1140 & C1054 or 015, 016 & 017..... 5-343
ESP DTC C1120 or C1142....... 5-343
ESP DTC C1140 & C1504...... 5-343
ESP DTC C1401 Or C1405..... 5-343
Rear Suspension Knocking On Rough Roads At Low Speed .. 5-343
Troubleshooting 5-321
ADS MIL On w/Engine Running. 5-321
Damping Too Hard Or Soft...... 5-321
Hydraulic Oil Level Low......... 5-321
Vehicle Base Level Low 5-321
Vehicle Does Not Lift One Or Both Axles 5-321
Vehicle Front Axle Low 5-321
Vehicle Lowers At One Or Both Axles 5-321
Vehicle Lowers w/Engine Off.... 5-321
Vehicle Lowers w/Engine Running 5-321
Vehicle Rear Axle Low.......... 5-321

PRECAUTIONS

AIR BAG SYSTEMS

Refer to "Air Bag System Precautions"in front of this manual for system disarming and arming procedures.

BATTERY GROUND CABLE

Prior to service, disconnect battery ground cable and isolate as required.

DESCRIPTION

The Adaptive Damping System (ADS) automatically adjusts shock absorber firmness to suit driving conditions. ADS integrates axle level sensors, body acceleration sensors, steering angle sensor, control module, comfort/sport switch, level adjustment switch, rear axle height valve and shock absorber valves.

TROUBLESHOOTING

ADS MIL ON w/ENGINE RUNNING

1. Steering angle sensor may not have been initialized.
2. Turn steering wheel from full right to full left stop to initialize.
3. Inspect for Diagnostic Trouble Codes (DTC).

DAMPING TOO HARD OR SOFT

Inspect for Diagnostic Trouble Codes (DTC).

VEHICLE BASE LEVEL LOW

Inspect and repair leveling valve system.

VEHICLE LOWERS w/ENGINE OFF

1. Inspect for Diagnostic Trouble Codes (DTC).
2. Inspect for external leaks.
3. Inspect leveling valve pressure.

VEHICLE FRONT AXLE LOW

1. Inspect for Diagnostic Trouble Codes (DTC).
2. Inspect for external leaks.
3. Inspect front axle circuit for internal leaks.

VEHICLE REAR AXLE LOW

1. Inspect for Diagnostic Trouble Codes (DTC).
2. Inspect for external leaks.
3. Inspect rear axle circuit for internal leaks.

VEHICLE LOWERS AT ONE OR BOTH AXLES

1. Inspect for Diagnostic Trouble Codes (DTC).
2. Inspect for external leaks.
3. Inspect axle circuits for internal leaks.

HYDRAULIC OIL LEVEL LOW

Inspect for external leaks.

VEHICLE LOWERS w/ENGINE RUNNING

Inspect leveling functions.

VEHICLE DOES NOT LIFT ONE OR BOTH AXLES

Inspect leveling valve functions. Inspection valve assembly for internal leaks.

INSPECTION

HYDRAULIC SYSTEM BLEED

1. Disconnect high pressure flexible hose at steel line.
2. Hold suitable hose into suitable container.
3. Run engine unit oil exiting system is free of bubbles.

HYDRAULIC OIL PUMP INSPECTION

S320 & S420 & 1998–99 S500 & S600

1. Inspect and correct oil reservoir level. Increase oil fill quantity by one pint.
2. If oil reservoir is empty, bleed system as outlined under "Hydraulic System Bleed."
3. Set leveling valve levers to neutral position by disconnecting front and rear leveling valve levers' connecting rods.
4. Connect suitable drain hose to rear axle hydraulic system bleed screw and place other end into suitable container.
5. Depressurize rear axle hydraulic system by slowly opening bleeder screw.
6. Connect suitable test gauge to rear axle leveling valve bleed screw.
7. Set both leveling valve levers to F position.
8. Open pressure supply screw one turn, maximum.
9. Disconnect oil reservoir return line at oil reservoir and hold suitable hose into suitable measuring glass.
10. Start and idle engine.
11. Set HHT to hold position until pressure no longer increases. Rear axle leveling valve connection test gauge pressure should be 3626 psi.
12. Pressure should be more than 1740 psi with a delivery rate of more than 6.76 ounces per minute. If pressure is not as specified, proceed as follows:
    a. If pressure is less than 1740 psi and delivery rate is less than 6.76 ounces per minute, replace hydraulic oil pressure pump.
    b. If pressure is less than 1740 psi and delivery rate is more than 6.76 ounces per minute, replace rear axle leveling valve.
    c. If pressure more than 2219 psi, replace rear axle leveling valve.

SL500 & SL600

1. Inspect and correct oil reservoir level. Increase oil fill quantity by one pint.
2. If oil reservoir is empty, bleed system as outlined under "Hydraulic System Bleed."
3. Connect suitable drain hose to rear axle hydraulic system bleed screw and place other end into suitable container.
4. Depressurize rear axle hydraulic system by slowly opening bleeder screw.
5. Connect suitable test gauge to rear axle leveling valve bleed screw.
6. Hand-Held Tester (HHT) tool No. 865 589 00 01 00, or equivalent scan tool, to DLC.
7. Disconnect oil reservoir return line at oil reservoir and hold suitable hose into suitable measuring glass.
8. Start and idle engine.
9. Observe test gauge until pressure no longer increases. Rear axle leveling valve connection test gauge pressure should be 3626 psi.
10. Pressure should be more than 2611–2756 psi with a delivery rate of more than 6.76 ounces per minute. If pressure is not as specified, proceed as follows:
    a. If pressure is less than 2611 psi and delivery rate is less than 6.76 ounces per minute, replace hydraulic oil pressure pump.
    b. If pressure is less than 2611 psi and delivery rate is more than 6.76 ounces per minute, replace leveling valve.

🗎	Possible cause	Test step/Remedy
–	No fault in system.	In case of complaint: ☐ 23 (entire test) and ☐ 33
002	ADS control module (N51)	Replace N51.
003	Left front body acceleration sensor (B24/3)	☐ 23 ⇒ 7.0
004	Right front body acceleration sensor (B24/4)	☐ 23 ⇒ 8.0
005	Right rear body acceleration sensor (B24/6)	☐ 23 ⇒ 9.0
006	Left front axle damper valve assembly, front axle solenoid valve 1 (Y51y1)	☐ 23 ⇒ 13.0
007	Left front axle damper valve assembly, front axle solenoid valve 2 (Y51y2)	☐ 23 ⇒ 13.0
008	Right front axle damper valve assembly, front axle solenoid valve 1 (Y52y1)	☐ 23 ⇒ 14.0
009	Right front axle damper valve assembly, front axle solenoid valve 2 (Y52y2)	☐ 23 ⇒ 14.0
010	Left rear axle damper valve assembly, rear axle solenoid valve 1 (Y53y1)	☐ 23 ⇒ 15.0
011	Left rear axle damper valve assembly, rear axle solenoid valve 2 (Y53y2)	☐ 23 ⇒ 15.0
012	Right rear axle damper valve assembly, rear axle solenoid valve 1 (Y54y1)	☐ 23 ⇒ 16.0
013	Right rear axle damper valve assembly, rear axle solenoid valve 2 (Y54y2)	☐ 23 ⇒ 16.0
014	ADS MIL (A1e27)	☐ 23 ⇒ 5.0

MB2019500024010X

Fig. 1 DTC interpretation (Part 1 of 2). S320 & S420 & 1998–99 CL500, CL600, S500 & S600

LEVELING VALVE FUNCTION INSPECTION

S320 & S420 & 1998–99 CL500, CL600, S500 & S600

1. Inspect and correct oil reservoir level.
2. Set leveling valve levers to neutral position by disconnecting front and rear leveling valve levers' connecting rods.
3. Start and idle engine.
4. Set leveling valve lever to F position.
5. Vehicle should raise at respective axle.
6. If vehicle does not raise, proceed as outlined under "Leveling Valve Pressure Inspection."

LEVELING VALVE PRESSURE INSPECTION

S320 & S420 & 1998–99 CL500, CL600, S500 & S600

1. Inspect and correct oil reservoir level.
2. Set leveling valve levers to neutral position by disconnecting front and rear leveling valve levers' connecting rods.
3. Connect suitable drain hose and container to rear axle hydraulic system.
4. Depressurize rear axle hydraulic system by slowly opening bleeder screw.
5. Connect suitable test gauge to front axle leveling valve bleed screw.
6. Start and idle engine.
7. Inspect relief valve opening pressure by setting leveling valve lever to F position.
8. Observe test gauge until pressure no longer increases. Front axle leveling valve connection test gauge pressure should be 3626 psi.
9. If pressure is 1740–2219 psi, proceed to next step. If pressure is more than 2219 psi, replace leveling valve. If pressure is less than 1740 psi, proceed as outlined under "Hydraulic Oil Pump Inspection."
10. Inspect overflow valve function by setting leveling valve lever to F position.
11. Observe test gauge until pressure no longer increases. Front axle leveling valve connection test gauge pressure should be 3626 psi.
12. When pressure is approximately 1160 psi, set leveling valve lever to L position. Pressure should drop to approximately 435–522 psi.
13. If rear axle pressure is not as specified, replace leveling valve.

SL500 & SL600

1. Inspect and correct oil reservoir level.
2. Connect suitable drain hose and container to rear axle hydraulic system.
3. Depressurize rear axle hydraulic system by slowly opening bleeder screw.
4. Connect suitable test gauge to front axle leveling valve bleed screw.
5. Hand-Held Tester (HHT) tool No. 865 589 00 01 00, or equivalent scan tool, to DLC.
6. Start and idle engine.
7. Inspect relief valve opening pressure by setting HHT to hold position test gauge until pressure no longer increases. Rear axle leveling valve connection test gauge pressure should be 3626 psi.
8. If pressure is 2611–2756 psi, proceed to next step. If pressure is more than 2756 psi, replace leveling valve. If pressure is less than 2611 psi, proceed as outlined under "Hydraulic Oil Pump Inspection."
9. Inspect overflow valve function by selecting HHT release for five minutes.

Pressure should drop to approximately 479–522 psi.

10. If rear axle pressure is not as specified, replace leveling valve.

DAMPING INSPECTION

S320, S420, SL500 & SL600 & 1998-99 CL500, CL600, S500 & S600

1. Ensure oil reservoir level is correct.
2. Connect Hand-Held Tester (HHT) tool No. 965 589 00 01 00, or equivalent scan tool, to DLC.
3. Activate comfort/sport setting and set to hard damping.
4. Manually rock all four corners of vehicle.
5. Set to soft damping, and manually rock all four corners of vehicle.
6. If damping is not clearly difference between settings, replace damping valves.

VALVE ASSEMBLE INTERNAL LEAK INSPECTION

1. Inspect and correct oil reservoir level.
2. Set leveling valve levers to neutral position by disconnecting front and rear leveling valve levers' connecting rods.
3. Disconnect front axle and close steel line leak oil line.
4. Ensure oil reservoir level is correct, set leveling valve levers to neutral position and unscrew connecting rods at front and rear leveling valve levers.
5. Remove front axle struts leak oil line and close steel line.
6. Disconnect oil reservoir return line.
7. Start and idle engine.
8. Set front axle leveling valve lever to F position.
9. Move leveling valve to center position. If vehicle front axle does not raise, replace distributor valve or valve assembly. If front axle does raise, proceed to next step.
10. Set rear axle leveling valve lever to F position.
11. Move leveling valve to center position. If vehicle rear axle does not raise, replace distributor valve or valve assembly. If rear axle does raise, proceed to next step.
12. Turn engine Off and wait at least two minutes to allow valves to close.
13. Move both leveling valve levers to L position. If vehicle does not lower, replace distributor valve or valve assembly. If vehicle does lower, proceed to next step.
14. Disconnect reservoir return line, then attach suitable drain hose and place in measuring container. If more than 0.0676 ounce of oil leaks in four hours, replace distributor valve and valve assembly.

FRONT AXLE STRUT LEAK INSPECTION

1. Ensure vehicle is resting on wheels.
2. Disconnect left and righthand leak oil hoses leak oil line and place into suitable measuring container.

	Possible cause	Test step/Remedy
015	Steering angle sensor (N49)	☐ 23 ⇒ 10.0
016	Steering angle sensor (N49), incorrect signal	☐ 23 ⇒ 10.0
017	Steering angle sensor (N49) not initialized	☐ 23 ⇒ 11.0
018	Right front VSS signal from ASR/SPS control module (N47-1) or ETS/SPS control module (N47-2) or ESP/SPS control module (N47-5)	☐ 23 ⇒ 4.0
019	Comfort/sport switch (S45/1)	☐ 23 ⇒ 12.0
020	Voltage supply too low	☐ 23 ⇒ 1.0
021	Voltage supply too high	☐ 23 ⇒ 1.0
022	Stop lamp switch (S9/1)	☐ 23 ⇒ 6.0

MB2019500024020X

Fig. 1 DTC interpretation (Part 2 of 2). S320 & S420 & 1998–99 CL500, CL600, S500 & S600

3. If more than 0.0676 ounces of oil leaks in four hours, replace strut.

INTERNAL LEAKAGE INSPECTION

SL500 & SL600

Front Axle Circuit

Test only if front axle drops or does not hold position.

1. Ensure vehicle is resting on all four wheels.
2. Switch level control lock-out switch.
3. Inspect oil reservoir level and correct as required.
4. Disconnect suspension strut overflow oil return line.
5. Connect coupling and bleed screw to steel hydraulic lines.
6. If more than 0.0676 ounces of oil leaks in four hours, replace strut.
7. Disconnect oil reservoir return line, then connect suitable hose and measuring container.
8. If oil return flow does not stop after five minutes, replace leveling valve.

Rear Axle Circuit

Test only if rear axle drops or does not hold position.

1. Ensure vehicle is resting on all four wheels.
2. Switch level control lock-out switch.
3. Inspect oil reservoir level and correct as required.
4. Disconnect oil reservoir return line, then connect suitable hose and measuring container.
5. If oil return flow does not stop after five minutes, replace leveling valve.

VEHICLE LEVEL INSPECTION

1. Inspect oil reservoir level and correct as required.
2. Connect Hand-Held Tester (HHT) tool No. 965 589 00 01 00, or equivalent scan tool, to DLC.
3. Start and idle engine.
4. With level control switch in Off position, measure and record front and rear axle height between wheel and wheelhousing centers.
5. Raise vehicle to stage 1 (press switch once).
6. Measure and record front and rear axle height between wheel and wheelhousing centers. Ride height should increase more than 0.591 inch. If there is no front or rear height change, proceed as outlined under "Leveling Valve Pressure Inspection." If there is not height change at one end, proceed as outlined under "Internal Leakage Inspection" for appropriate axle.
7. Raise vehicle to stage 2 (press switch twice).
8. Measure and record front and rear axle height between wheel and wheelhousing centers. Ride height should increase more than 0.591 inch. If there is no front or rear height change, proceed as outlined under "Leveling Valve Pressure Inspection." If there is not height change at one end, proceed as outlined under "Internal Leakage Inspection" for appropriate axle.
9. Lower vehicle to normal height (press switch down twice).
10. Measure and record front and rear axle height between wheel and wheelhousing centers. Ride height should decrease more than 1.181 inches. If there is no front or rear height change, proceed as outlined under "Leveling Valve Pressure Inspection."

DIAGNOSIS & TESTING

Symbol Explanation

Refer "Anti-Lock Brakes" section.

Accessing Diagnostic Trouble Codes

Refer "Anti-Lock Brakes" section.

Diagnostic Trouble Code Interpretation

Refer to **Fig. 1** for DTC interpretation.

Symptom Related Diagnosis

Refer to **Figs. 2 through 3** for symptom related diagnosis.

Component Locations

Refer to **Figs. 4 through 8** for component locations.

Wiring Diagrams

Refer to **Figs. 9 and 10** for wiring diagrams.

Connector Terminal Identification

Refer to **Fig. 11** for connector terminal identification.

Refer to "Anti-Lock Brakes" for data link connector terminal identification.

Function Tests

Refer to **Figs. 12 through 13** for function testing.

Diagnostic Tests

S320 & S420 & 1998-99 CL500, CL600, S500 & S600

1. Turn ignition switch to Off position.
2. Disconnect ADS control module.
3. Connect socket box tool No. 129 589 00 21 00, or equivalent, to contact box and control module box using contact module 4 tool No. 140 589 04 63 00, or equivalent,
4. Perform test as directed using suitable digital multi-meter, **Figs. 14 through 25.**

SL500 & SL600

1. Turn ignition switch to Off position.
2. Disconnect ADS control module.
3. Remove mounting bolts and frame
4. Disconnect connector and remove from frame.
5. Connect socket box tool No. 129 589 00 21 00, or equivalent, to control module and connector using test cable tool No. 140 589 39 63 00, or equivalent.
6. Perform test as directed using suitable digital multi-meter, **Figs. 26 through 33.**

Clearing Diagnostic Trouble Codes

Refer "Anti-Lock Brakes" section.

Complaint/Problem	Possible cause	Test step/Remedy
ADS MIL (A1e27) comes on with engine running	Steering angle sensor (N49) not initialized DTC stored	Turn steering wheel from right to left stop. ☐ 12
Damping too hard/too soft		☐ 12 ☐ 35 ⇒ 1.0
Vehicle level too low (base level)		☐ 33 ⇒ 1.0
Vehicle lowers at rear axle		Visually check for external leaks.
Hydraulic oil level too low		Visually check for external leaks.

MB2019900052000X

Fig. 2 Symptom related diagnosis. S320 & S420 & 1998–99 CL500, CL600, S500 & S600

Complaint	Possible cause	Test step/Remedy
ADS MIL A1e27 on with engine running	Steering angle sensor (N49) not initialized. DTC's stored in DTC memory.	Steering angle sensor (N49) not initialized, turn steering wheel from right to left stop. DTC read out: read out DTC memory
Damping to hard/soft		DTC read out: read out DTC memory Damping Test Inspection
Vehicle height too low (normal height)		Test and repair vehicle height
Vehicle height dropped with engine OFF.		DTC read out: read out DTC memory. Visually inspect for leaks. Internal leakage, front axle circuit Inspection Internal leakage, rear axle circuit Inspection
Vehicle height dropped at front axle.		DTC read out: read out DTC memory. Visually inspect for leaks. Internal leakage, front axle circuit Inspection
Vehicle height dropped at rear axle.		DTC read out: read out DTC memory. Visually inspect for leaks. Internal leakage, rear axle circuit Inspection

MB2019900055010X

Fig. 3 Symptom related diagnosis (Part 1 of 2). SL500 & SL600

Complaint	Possible cause	Test step/Remedy
Vehicle height will not raise at one or both axles.		DTC read out: read out DTC memory. Visually inspect for leaks Leveling Valve Pressure Test Inspection Level Control Pressure Test Inspection Internal leakage, front axle circuit Inspection Internal leakage, rear axle circuit Inspection
Hydraulic oil level too low.		Visually inspect for leaks.

MB2019900055020X

Fig. 3 Symptom related diagnosis (Part 2 of 2). SL500 & SL600

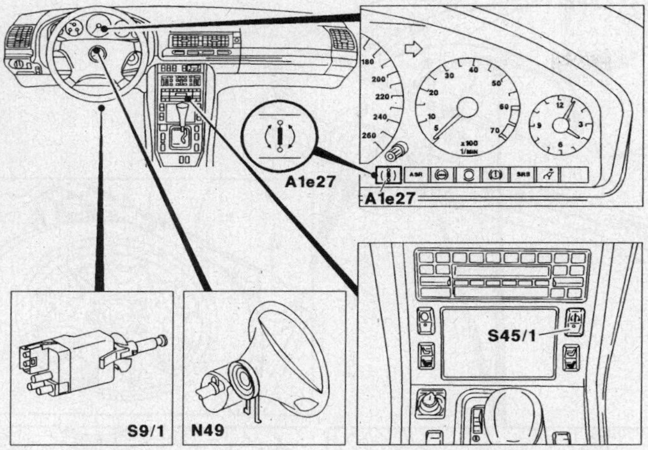

A1e27 ADS MIL
N49 Steering angle sensor
S9/1 Stop lamp switch
S45/1 Comfort/sport switch

MB2019900053000X

Fig. 4 ADS passenger compartment electric component locations. S320 & S420 & 1998–99 CL500, CL600, S500 & S600

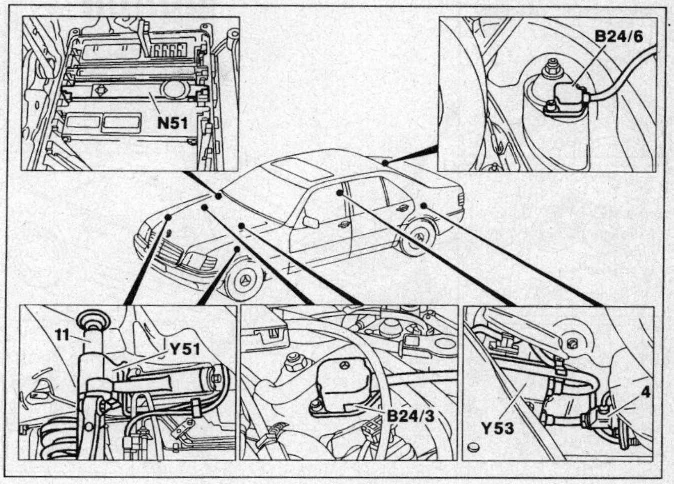

B24/3 Left front body acceleration sensor
B24/4 Right front body acceleration sensor (mirror image of B24/3)
B24/6 Right rear body acceleration sensor
N51 ADS control module
Y51 Left front axle damper valve assembly
Y52 Right front axle damper valve assembly (mirror image of Y51)
Y53 Left rear axle damper valve assembly
Y54 Right rear axle damper valve assembly (mirror image of Y53)

MB2019400025000X

Fig. 5 ADS engine & chassis electric component locations. S320 & S420 & 1998–99 CL500, CL600, S500 & S600

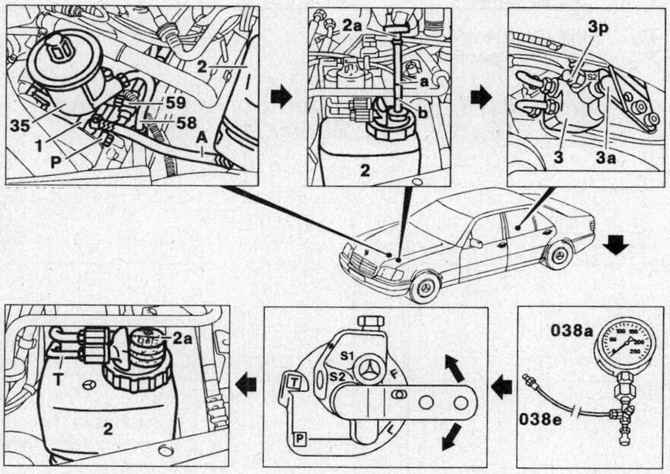

1 Hydraulic oil pump
2 Hydraulic oil reservoir
3 Leveling valve
3a Connecting lever
3p Bleeder screw
038a Test gauge
T Retrun line from leveling valve

MB2019900057000X

Fig. 6 ADS hydraulic component locations. S320 & S420 & 1998–99 CL500, CL600, S500 & S600

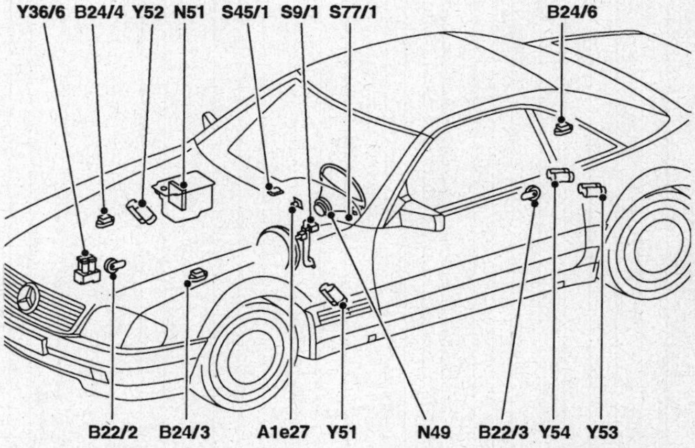

A1e27 ADS MIL
B22/2 Front axle level sensor
B22/3 Rear axle level sensor
B24/3 Left front body acceleration sensor
B24/4 Right front body acceleration sensor
B24/6 Right rear body acceleration sensor
N49 Steering angle sensor
N51 ADS control module
S9/1 Stop lamp switch (4-pole)
S45/1 Comfort/sport switch (ADS)
S77/1 Level adjustment switch
Y36/6 Rear axle height reduction valve
Y51 Left front axle damper valve assembly
Y52 Right front axle damper valve assembly (mirror image of Y51)
Y53 Left rear axle damper valve assembly
Y54 Right rear axle damper valve assembly (mirror image of Y53)

MB2019900058000X

Fig. 7 ADS electrical component locations. SL500 & SL600

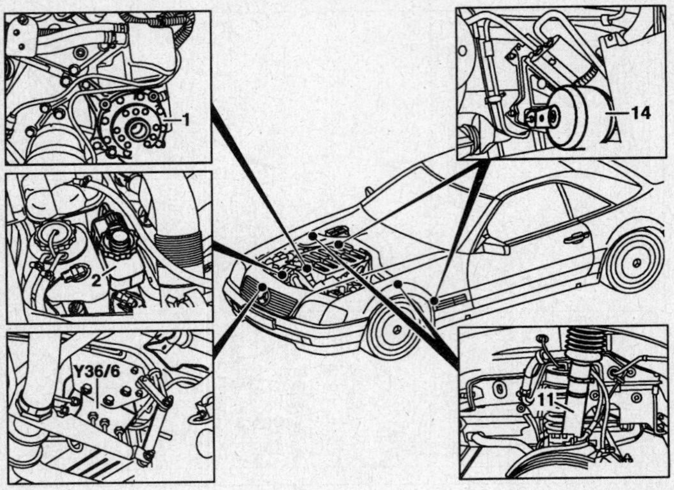

1 Hydraulic oil pump
2 Hydraulic oil reservoir
11 Front ADS suspension strut
14 Front pressure reservoir
Y36/6 Level adjustment valve

MB2019900059010X

Fig. 8 ADS hydraulic component locations (Part 1 of 2). SL500 & SL600

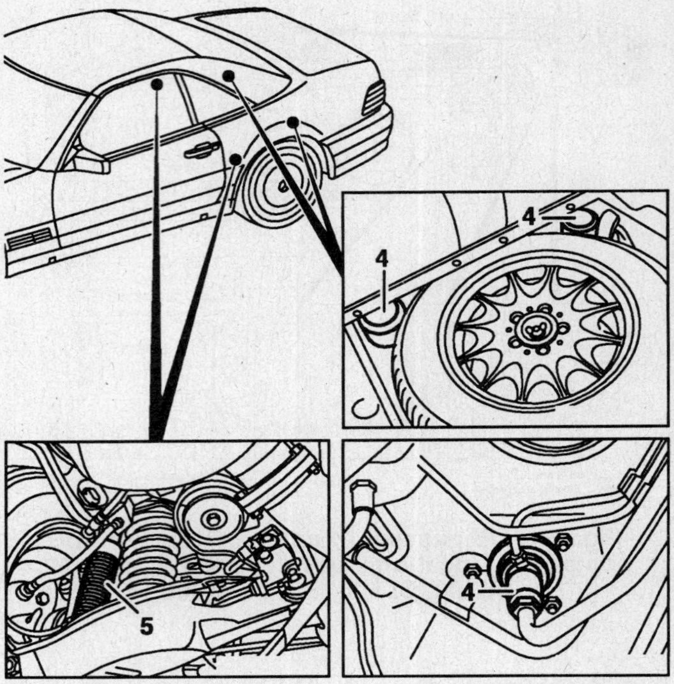

4 Hydraulic oil reservoir
5 Rear ADS suspension strut

MB2019900059020X

Fig. 8 ADS hydraulic component locations (Part 2 of 2). SL500 & SL600

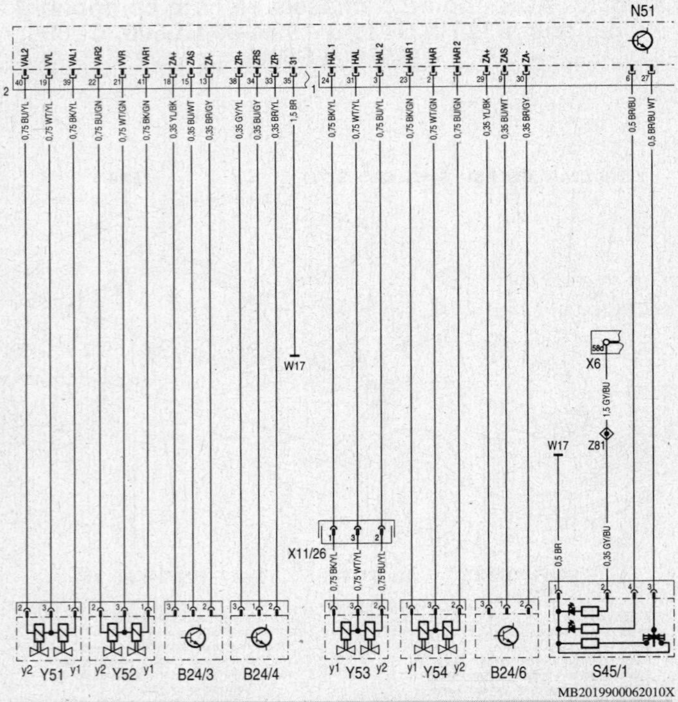

MB2019900062010X

Fig. 9 ADS wiring diagram (Part 1 of 3). S320 & S420 & 1998–99 CL500, CL600, S500 & S600

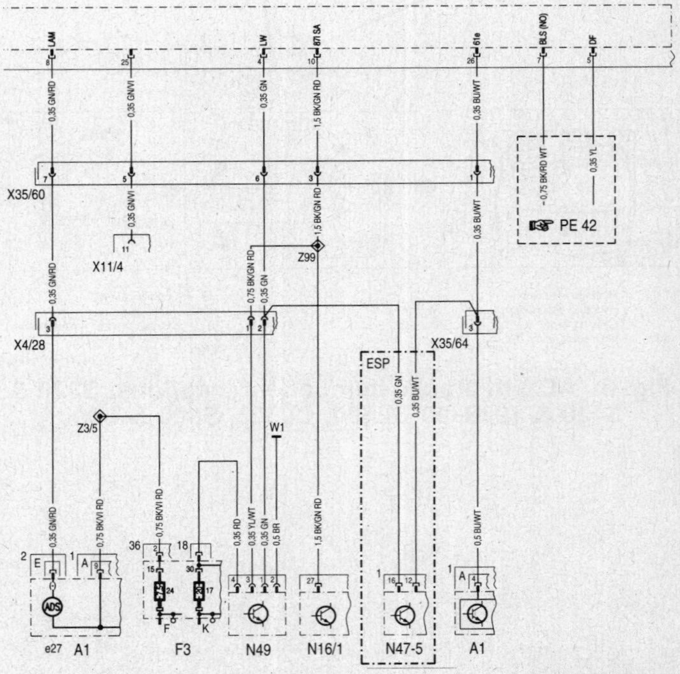

MB2019900062020X

Fig. 9 ADS wiring diagram (Part 2 of 3). S320 & S420 & 1998–99 CL500, CL600, S500 & S600

A1	Instrument cluster
A1e27	ADS MIL
B24/3	Left front body acceleration sensor
B24/4	Right front body acceleration sensor
B24/6	Right rear body acceleration sensor
F3	Fuse box (35-fuse, in fuse and relay box F1)
F3-17	Fuse 17, circuit 30
F3-24	Fuse 24, circuit 15
N16/1	Base module (BM)
N47-5	ESP/SPS control module
N49	Steering angle sensor
N51	ADS control module
S45/1	Comfort/sport switch (ADS)
W1	Main ground (behind instrument cluster)
W17	Ground (right rear seat)
	Ground location without designation, component grounded directly on engine, chassis or body.
X4/28	Steering angle sensor connector
X6	Terminal block (circuit 58d) (3- or 4-pole)
X11/4	Data link connector (DTC readout)
X11/26	ADS control module intermediate connector
X35/60	ADS separation point
X35/64	Compact harness/cockpit separation point (18-pole)
Y51	Left front axle damper valve assembly
Y51y1	Front axle solenoid valve 1
Y51y2	Front axle solenoid valve 2
Y52	Right front axle damper valve assembly
Y52y1	Front axle solenoid valve 1
Y52y2	Front axle solenoid valve 2
Y53	Left rear axle damper valve assembly
Y53y1	Rear axle solenoid valve 1
Y53y2	Rear axle solenoid valve 2
Y54	Right rear axle damper valve assembly
Y54y1	Rear axle solenoid valve 1
Y54y2	Rear axle solenoid valve 2
Z3/5	Circuit 15 connector sleeve (feed from F3-24 output 1)
Z81	Circuit 58d connector sleeve
Z99	Circuit 87 voltage supply from base module (N16/1) connector sleeve

The wire cross section may deviate from the illustration. Wire change phase-ins are framed.

MB2019900062030X

Fig. 9 ADS wiring diagram (Part 3 of 3). S320 & S420 & 1998–99 CL500, CL600, S500 & S600

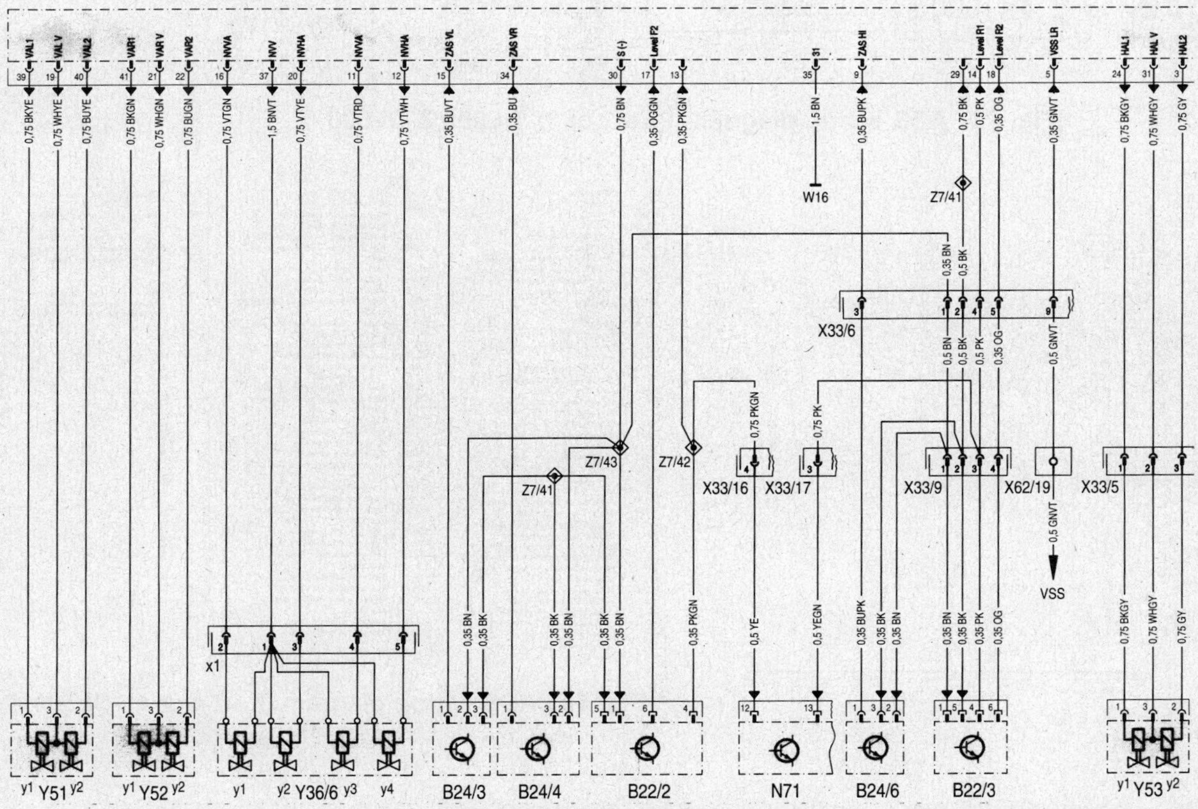

MB2019900064010X

Fig. 10 ADS wiring diagram (Part 1 of 4). SL500 & SL600

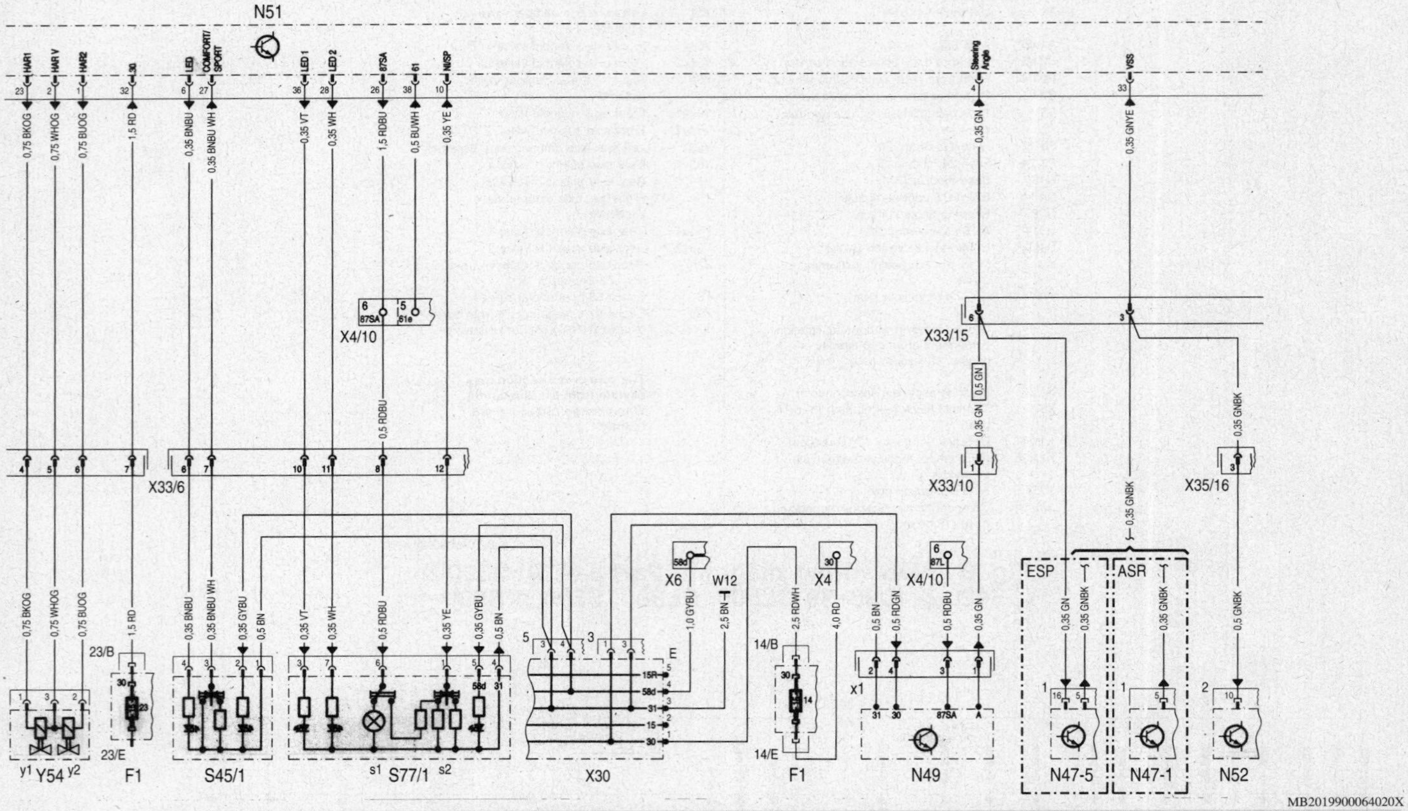

Fig. 10 ADS wiring diagram (Part 2 of 4). SL500 & SL600

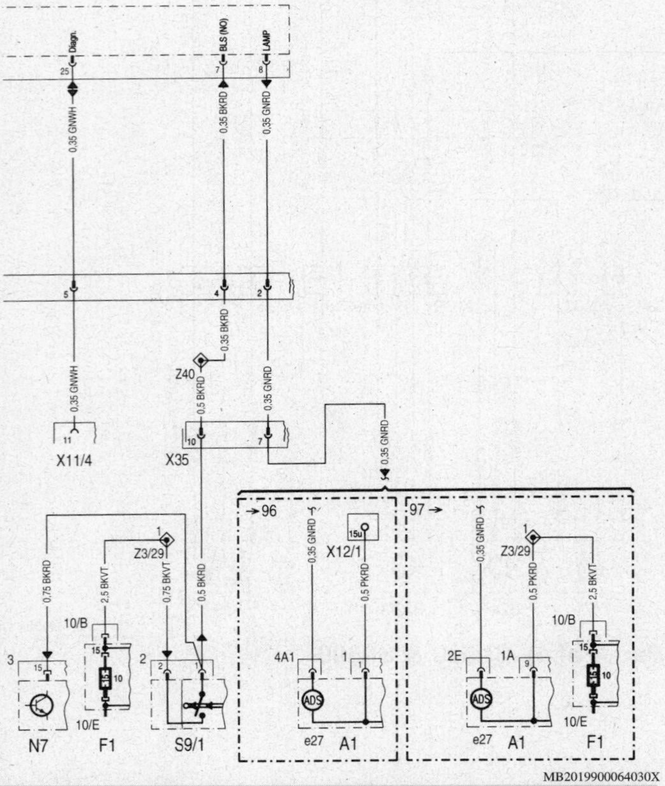

Fig. 10 ADS wiring diagram (Part 3 of 4). SL500 & SL600

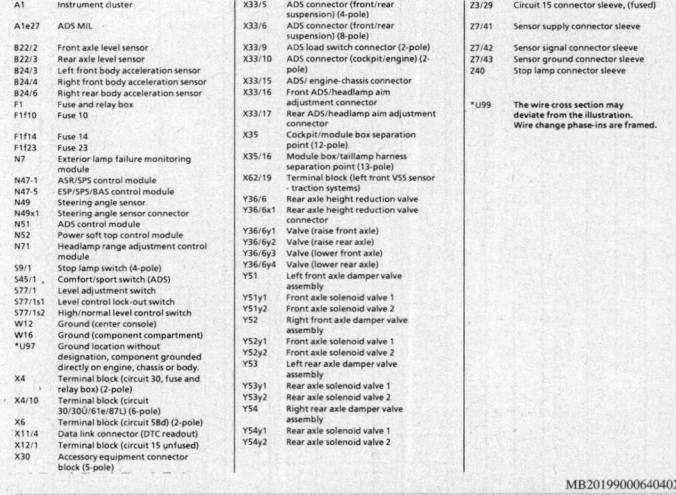

A1	Instrument cluster
A1e27	ADS MIL
B22/2	Front axle level sensor
B22/3	Rear axle level sensor
B24/3	Left front body acceleration sensor
B24/4	Right front body acceleration sensor
B24/6	Right rear body acceleration sensor
F1	Fuse and relay box
F1f10	Fuse 10
F1f14	Fuse 14
F1f23	Fuse 23
N7	Exterior lamp failure monitoring module
N47-1	ASR/SPS control module
N47-5	ESP/SPS/BAS control module
N49	Steering angle sensor
N49x1	Steering angle sensor connector
N51	ADS control module
N52	Power soft top control module
N71	Headlamp range adjustment control module
S9/1	Stop lamp switch (4-pole)
S45/1	Comfort/sport switch (ADS)
S77/1	Level adjustment switch
S77/1s1	Level control lock-out switch
S77/1s2	High/normal level control switch
W12	Ground (center console)
W16	Ground (component compartment)
*U97	Ground location without designation, component grounded directly on engine, chassis or body.
X4	Terminal block (circuit 30, fuse and relay box) (2-pole)
X4/10	Terminal block (circuit 30/30Ü/61e/87L) (6-pole)
X6	Terminal block (circuit 58d) (2-pole)
X11/4	Data link connector (DTC readout)
X12/1	Terminal block (circuit 15 unfused)
X30	Accessory equipment connector block (5-pole)
X33/5	ADS connector (front/rear suspension) (4-pole)
X33/6	ADS connector (front/rear suspension) (8-pole)
X33/9	ADS load switch connector (2-pole)
X33/10	ADS connector (cockpit/engine) (2-pole)
X33/15	ADS/ engine-chassis connector
X33/16	Front ADS/headlamp aim adjustment connector
X33/17	Rear ADS/headlamp aim adjustment connector
X35	Cockpit/module box separation point (12-pole)
X35/16	Module box/taillamp harness separation point (13-pole)
X62/19	Terminal block (left front VSS sensor - traction systems)
Y36/6	Rear axle height reduction valve
Y36/6x1	Rear axle height reduction valve connector
Y36/6y1	Valve (raise front axle)
Y36/6y2	Valve (raise rear axle)
Y36/6y3	Valve (lower front axle)
Y36/6y4	Valve (lower rear axle)
Y51	Left front axle damper valve assembly
Y51y1	Front axle solenoid valve 1
Y51y2	Front axle solenoid valve 2
Y52	Right front axle damper valve assembly
Y52y1	Front axle solenoid valve 1
Y52y2	Front axle solenoid valve 2
Y53	Left rear axle damper valve assembly
Y53y1	Rear axle solenoid valve 1
Y53y2	Rear axle solenoid valve 2
Y54	Right rear axle damper valve assembly
Y54y1	Rear axle solenoid valve 1
Y54y2	Rear axle solenoid valve 2
Z3/29	Circuit 15 connector sleeve, (fused)
Z7/41	Sensor supply connector sleeve
Z7/42	Sensor signal connector sleeve
Z7/43	Sensor ground connector sleeve
Z40	Stop lamp connector sleeve
*U99	The wire cross section may deviate from the illustration. Wire change phase-ins are framed.

MB2019900064040X

Fig. 10 ADS wiring diagram (Part 4 of 4). SL500 & SL600

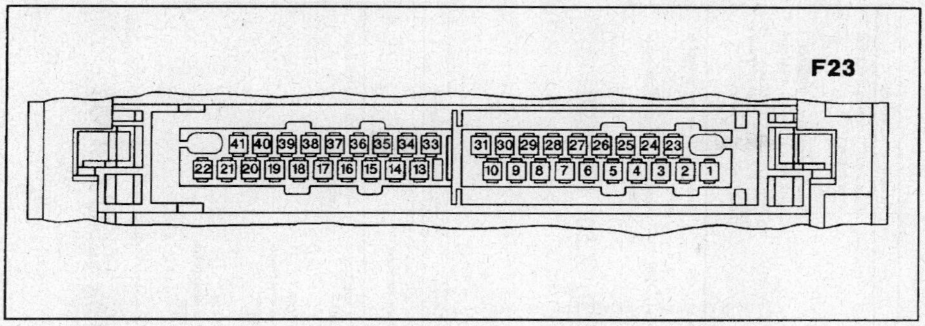

F23	Module box
1	Right rear axle damper valve assembly, valve 2 (Y54y2) (–)
2	Right rear axle damper valve assembly (Y54y1, Y54y2) (+)
3	Left rear axle damper valve assembly, valve 2 (Y53y2) (–)
4	Steering angle sensor (N49)
5	Processed right front VSS signal from ASR/SPS or ETS/SPS or ESP/SPScontrol module (N47-1 or N47-2 or N47-5)
6	Comfort/sport switch (S45/1), indicator lamp
7	Stop lamp switch (S9/1)
8	ADS MIL (A1e27)
9	Right rear body latertal acceleration sensor (B24/6) signal
10	Circuit 87 voltage supply (feed from N16/1)
11–12	not used
13	Left front body lateral acceleration sensor (B24/3) (–)
14	not used
15	Left front body lateral acceleration sensor (B24/3) signal
16–17	not used
18	Left front body lateral acceleration sensor (B24/3) (+)
19	Left front axle damper valve assembly (Y51y1, Y51y2) (+)
20	not used
21	Right front axle damper valve assembly (Y52y1, Y52y2) (+)
22	Right front axle damper valve assembly , valve 2 (Y52y2) (–)
23	Right rear axle damper valve assembly, valve 1 (Y54y1) (–)
24	Left rear axle damper valve assembly, valve 1 (Y53y1) (–)
25	Diagnosis output
26	Circuit 61
27	Comfort/sport switch (S45/1)
28	not used
29	Right rear body lateral acceleration sensor (B24/6) (+)
30	Right rear body lateral acceleration sensor (B24/6) (–)
31	Left rear axle damper valve assembly (Y53y1, Y53y2) (+)
32	not used
33	Right front body lateral acceleration sensor (B24/4) (–)
34	Right front body lateral acceleration sensor (B24/4) signal
35	Ground, component compartment (W16)
36–37	not used
38	Right front body lateral acceleration sensor (B24/4) (+)
39	Left front axle damper valve assembly, valve 1 (Y51y1) (–)
40	Left front axle damper valve assembly, valve 2 (Y51y2) (–)
41	Right front axle damper valve assembly valve 1 (Y52y1) (–)

MB2019500026000X

Fig. 11 ADS control module connector terminal identification. S320 & S420 & 1998–99 CL500, CL600, S500 & S600

Test step/Test scope	Test condition	Nominal value	Possible cause/Remedy
⇒ 1.0 ADS MIL (A1e27)	Ignition: **ON**	A1e27 comes on	Wiring, A1e27 □ 23 ⇒ 5.0, □ 23⇒ 1.0
	Engine: **at Idle**	A1e27 goes out	Steering angle sensor (N49) not initialized, turn steering wheel from right to left stop, □ 12, Wiring, Circuit 61 □ 23 ⇒ 2.0
⇒ 2.0 Comfort/sport switch (S45/1)	Switch (S45/1) set to: **Sport**	Indicator lamp in switch (S45/1): **ON**	Wiring, S45/1 □ 23 ⇒ 12.0.
	Switch (S45/1) set to: **Comfort**	Indicator lamp in switch (S45/1): **OFF**	

MB2019400009000A

Fig. 12 ADS function test. S320 & S420 & 1998–99 CL500, CL600, S500 & S600

Test step/Test scope	Test condition	Nominal value	Possible cause/Remedy
⇒ 1.0 ADS MIL (A1e27)	Ignition: **ON** Level adustment switch (S77/1) in normal position	A1e27: **ON**	Read out DTC memory and actual value display.
	Engine: **at Idle**	A1e27: **OFF**	Steering angle sensor (N49) not initialized, turn steering wheel from right to left stop. DTC read out: read out DTC memory and actual value display.
⇒ 2.0 Comfort/sport switch (S45/1)	Switch (S45/1) set to: **Sport**	LEDs' in switch (S45/1): **ON**	Read out DTC memory and actual value display.
	Switch (S45/1) set to: **Comfort**	LEDs' in switch (S45/1): **OFF**	Read out DTC memory and actual value display.

MB2019900054010X

Fig. 13 ADS function test (Part 1 of 3). SL500 & SL600

Test step/Test scope	Test condition	Nominal value	Possible cause/Remedy
⇒ 3.0 High/normal level control switch (S77/1s2)	Engine: **at Idle** High/normal level control switch (S77/1s2): **normal**	A1e27: **OFF** LEDs' in high/normal level control switch (S77/1s2): **OFF**	Read out DTC memory and actual value display.
Raise vehicle height	High/normal level control switch (S77/1s2): **stage 1** (press switch once)	One LED in S77/1s2 is **flashing.** Vehicle height is raised 15 mm. After reaching 15 mm LED remains lit. **Note:** Increase engine speed to 2000 rpm to speed up raising procedure.	Hydraulic oil pump Inspection. Test leveling valve pressure Inspection.
	High/normal level control switch (S77/1s2): **normal**	Vehicle height is lowering. LEDs' in S77/1s2: **OFF**	
Raise vehicle height	High/normal level control switch (S77/1s2): **stage 2** (press switch twice)	2 LEDs' in switch: **flashing.** Vehicle height raised 30 mm. After reaching 30 mm LEDs' remains lit. Note: Increase engine speed to 2000 rpm to speed up raising procedure.	Hydraulic oil pump Inspection. Test leveling valve pressure Inspection.

MB2019900054020X

Fig. 13 ADS function test (Part 2 of 3). SL500 & SL600

Test step/Test scope	Test condition	Nominal value	Possible cause/Remedy
Vehicle height (holding in stage 2)	Ignition: **OFF** ≥1 minute.	Vehicle height remains the same.	
⇒4.0 Level control lock-out switch (S77/1s1)	Ignition: **ON**	LEDs' in high/normal level control switch (S77/1s2): **ON.**	Read out DTC memory and actual value display.
	Press: level control lock-out switch (S77/1s1)	Lamps in S77/1s1: **ON** LEDs' in high/normal level control switch (S77/1s2): **OFF.**	
	Engine: **Idle**	Lamps in S77/1s1: **ON** LEDs' in high/normal level control switch (S77/1s2): **OFF.** A1e27: **ON**	

MB2019900054030X

Fig. 13 ADS function test (Part 3 of 3). SL500 & SL600

DIAGNOSTIC CHART INDEX

Code	Description	Page No.	Fig. No.
S320 & S420 & 1998–99 CL500, CL600, S500 & S600			
003	Test 23, Steps 7	5-333	17
004	Test 23, Step 8.0	5-334	18
005	Test 23, Step 9.0	5-334	19
006	Test 23, Step 13.0	5-336	22
007	Test 23, Step 13.0	5-336	22
008	Test 23, Step 14.0	5-336	23
009	Test 23, Step 14.0	5-336	23
010	Test 23, Step 15.0	5-337	24
011	Test 23, Step 15.0	5-337	24
012	Test 23, Step 16.0	5-337	25
013	Test 23, Step 16.0	5-337	25
014	Test 23, Steps 4.0–5.	5-332	15
015	Test 23, Steps 10.0–11.0	5-335	20
016	Test 23, Steps 10.0–11.0	5-335	20
017	Test 23, Steps 10.0–11.0	5-335	20
018	Test 23, Steps 4.0–5.1	5-332	15
019	Test 23, Steps 12.0–12.1	5-335	21
020	Test 23, Steps 1.0–3.0	5-332	14
021	Test 23, Steps 1.0–3.0	5-332	14
022	Test 23, Step 6.0	5-333	16
SL500 & SL600			
C1000	Test 23, Steps 1.0–3.0	5-338	26
C1010	Test 23, Steps 1.0–3.0	5-338	26
C1012	Test 23, Steps 1.0–3.0	5-338	26
C1121	Test 23, Steps 4.0–6.0	5-338	27
C1122	Test 23, Steps 4.0–6.0	5-338	27
C1123	Test 23, Steps 4.0–6.0	5-338	27
C1130	Test 23, Steps 4.0–6.0	5-338	27
C1131	Test 23, Steps 4.0–6.0	5-338	27
C1140	Test 23, Steps 4.0–6.0	5-338	27
C1320	Test 23, Steps 7.0–7.2	5-339	28
C1321	Test 23, Steps 7.0–7.2	5-339	28
C1322	Test 23, Steps 8.0–8.2	5-339	29
C1323	Test 23, Steps 8.0–8.2	5-339	29
C1324	Test 23, Steps 9.0–9.2	5-340	30
C1325	Test 23, Steps 9.0–9.2	5-340	30
C1326	Test 23, Steps 10.0–10.2	5-340	31
C1327	Test 23, Steps 10.0–10.2	5-340	31
C1328	Test 23, Steps 11.0–11.3	5-341	32
C1329	Test 23, Steps 11.0–11.3	5-341	32
C1330	Test 23, Steps 11.0–11.3	5-341	32
C1331	Test 23, Steps 11.0–11.3	5-341	32
C1331	Test 23, Steps 11.4–12.0	5-341	33
C1505	Test 23, Steps 1.0–3.0	5-338	26

⇒		Test scope	Test connection	Test condition	Nominal value	Possible cause/Remedy
1.0	020 021	**ADS control module (N51)** Circuit 87 SA Voltage supply	N51 35 —< V >— 10	Ignition: **ON**	11 – 14 V	⇒ 1.1, W15, Wiring.
1.1		Voltge supply from base module (N16/1)	N51 W16/1 V >— 10	Ignition: **ON**	11 – 14 V	Fuse (F3) on BM (N16/1), 1.1 or 1.2 □ 23, Wiring.
2.0		**Circuit 61 voltage**	N51 35 —< V >— 26	Ignition: **ON** Engine: **at Idle**	< 1 V 11 – 14 V	Wiring, Generator (G2).
3.0		**Diagnosis output**	N51 35 —< V >— 25	Ignition: **ON**	10 – 14 V	Wiring, ASD control module (N51).

MB2019400027000X

Fig. 14 Codes 020 & 021: Test 23, Steps 1.0–3.0. S320 & S420 & 1998–99 CL500, CL600, S500 & S600

⇒		Test scope	Test connection	Test condition	Nominal value	Possible cause/Remedy
4.0	018	**Right front VSS signal**	N51 35 —< V >— 5	Raise front of vehicle. Ignition: **ON** Turn right front wheel by hand (approx. 1 rev./s)	> 3 V ~	9.1 □ 23, Wiring, ADS control module (N51).
5.0	014	**ADS MIL (A1e27)**	N51 35 —< V >— 8	Ignition: **ON** Engine: **at Idle**	A1e27: **ON** < 1 V A1e27: **OFF** 11 – 14 V	Wiring, ⇒ 5.1, N51. Wiring, N51.
5.1		ADS MIL (A1e27)	N51 35 —< V >— 8	Ignition: **OFF** Disconnect N51. Ignition: **ON**	11 – 14 V	Wiring, A1e27.

MB2019400028000X

Fig. 15 Codes 014 & 018: Test 23, Steps 4.0–5.1. S320 & S420 & 1998–99 CL500, CL600, S500 & S600

⇒		Test scope	Test connection	Test condition	Nominal value	Possible cause/Remedy
6.0	022	**Stop lamp switch (S9/1)**	N51 35 —‹ V ›— 7	Ignition: **ON**		Wiring, S9/1.
				Brake pedal **not** applied	< 1 V	
				Brake pedal applied	11 – 14 V	

MB2019400029000X

Fig. 16 Code 022: Test 23, Step 6.0. S320 & S420 & 1998–99 CL500, CL600, S500 & S600

⇒		Test scope	Test connection	Test condition	Nominal value	Possible cause/Remedy
7.0	003	**Left front body lateral acceleration sensor (B24/3)** Voltage supply	N51 13 —‹ V ›— 18	Ignition: **ON**	4.75 – 5.25 V	Wiring, B24/3, ADS control module (N51).
		Static sensor signal (off)	N51 13 —‹ V ›— 15	Ignition: **ON**	2.35 – 2.65 V	Wiring, B24/3.
		Dynamic sensor signal (on)	N51 13 —‹ V ›— 15	Ignition: **ON** Vigorously move left front section of vehicle up and down by hand.	> 5 mV ~ **Note:** Value changes with movement of vehicle. Value can only be attained with digital multimeter set to mV ~.	B24/3.

MB2019400030000X

Fig. 17 Code 003: Test 23, Steps 7. S320 & S420 & 1998–99 CL500, CL600, S500 & S600

⇒		Test scope	Test connection	Test condition	Nominal value	Possible cause/Remedy
8.0	004	**Right front body lateral acceleration sensor (B24/4)** Voltage supply	N51 33 —(⊝V⊕)— 38	Ignition: **ON**	4.75 – 5.25 V	Wiring, B24/4, ADS control module (N51).
		Static sensor signal (off)	N51 33 —(⊝V⊕)— 34	Ignition: **ON**	2.35 – 2.65 V	Wiring, B24/4.
		Dynamic sensor signal (on)	N51 33 —(⊝V⊕)— 34	Ignition: **ON** Vigorously move right front section of vehicle up and down by hand.	> 5 mV ~ **Note:** Value changes with movement of vehicle. Value can only be attained with digital multimeter set to mV ~.	B24/4.

MB2019400031000X

Fig. 18 Code 004: Test 23, Step 8.0. S320 & S420 & 1998–99 CL500, CL600, S500 & S600

⇒		Test scope	Test connection	Test condition	Nominal value	Possible cause/Remedy
9.0	005	**Right rear body lateral acceleration sensor (B24/6)** Voltage supply	N51 30 —(⊝V⊕)— 29	Ignition: **ON**	4.75 – 5.25 V	Wiring, B24/6, ADS control module (N51).
		Static sensor signal (off)	N51 30 —(⊝V⊕)— 9	Ignition: **ON**	2.35 – 2.65 V	Wiring, B24/6.
		Dynamic sensor signal (on)	N51 30 —(⊝V⊕)— 9	Ignition: **ON** Vigorously move right rear section of vehicle up and down by hand.	> 5 mV ~ **Note:** Value changes with movement of vehicle. Value can only be attained with digital multimeter set to mV ~.	B24/6.

MB2019400032000X

Fig. 19 Code 005: Test 23, Step 9.0. S320 & S420 & 1998–99 CL500, CL600, S500 & S600

⇒	Code	Test scope	Test connection	Test condition	Nominal value	Possible cause/Remedy
10.0	015 016	**Steering angle sensor (N49)** Signal	N51 35 —< V >— 4	Ignition: **ON**	> 3 V ~	Wiring, ⇒ 10.1, ADS control module (N51).
10.1		Steering angle sensor (N49)	N51 35 —< V >— 4	Ignition: **OFF** Disconnect N51. Ignition: **ON**	> 3 V ~	Wiring, ⇒ 10.2, ⇒ 10.3, N49.
10.2		Circuit 30 voltage supply	N49x1 2 —< V >— 4	Ignition: **OFF** Disconnect N49x1.	11 – 14 V	Wiring.
10.3		Circuit 87 voltage supply	N49x1 2 —< V >— 3	Ignition: **ON**	11 – 14 V	Wiring.
11.0	017	**Steering angle sensor** Initialization		Engine: **at Idle** Turn steering wheel from right to left stop.	A1e27 goes out.	⇒ 5.0

MB2019400033000X

Fig. 20 Codes 015, 016 & 017: Test 23, Steps 10.0–11.0. S320 & S420 & 1998–99 CL500, CL600, S500 & S600

⇒	Code	Test scope	Test connection	Test condition	Nominal value	Possible cause/Remedy
12.0	019	**Comfort/sport switch (S45/1)**	N51 35 —< V >— 27	Ignition: **ON** Hold switch S45/1 in:		
				Comfort setting	< 1 V Indicator lamp in S45/1: **OFF**	Wiring, ADS control module (N51), S45/1.
				Release switch	11–14 V Indicator lamp in S45/1: **OFF**	Wiring, N51.
				Sport setting	4 – 6 V Indicator lamp in S45/1: **ON**	Wiring, ADS control module (N51), S45/1, ⇒ 12.1.
12.1		Indicator lamp in S45/1	N51 35 —< V >— 6	Release switch (S45/1)	11 – 14 V Indicator lamp in S45/1: **ON**	Wiring, N51.

MB2019400034000X

Fig. 21 Code 019: Test 23, Steps 12.0–12.1. S320 & S420 & 1998–99 CL500, CL600, S500 & S600

⇒		Test scope	Test connection	Test condition	Nominal value	Possible cause/Remedy
13.0	006 007	**Left front axle damper valve assembly (Y51)** Voltage supply	N51 35 — (V) — 19	Ignition: **ON**	11–14 V	Wiring, ADS control module (N51).
		Front axle solenoid valve 1 (Y51y1)	N51 39 — (Ω) — 19	Ignition: **OFF** Disconnect N51.	10 – 16 Ω	Wiring, Y51.
		Front axle solenoid valve 2 (Y51y2)	N51 40 — (Ω) — 19	Ignition: **OFF** Disconnect N51.	10 – 16 Ω	Wiring, Y51.

MB2019400035000X

Fig. 22 Codes 006 & 007: Test 23, Step 13.0. S320 & S420 & 1998–99 CL500, CL600, S500 & S600

⇒		Test scope	Test connection	Test condition	Nominal value	Possible cause/Remedy
14.0	008 009	**Right front axle damper valve assembly (Y52)** Voltage supply	N51 35 — (V) — 21	Ignition: **ON**	11–14 V	Wiring, ADS control module (N51).
		Front axle solenoid valve 1 (Y52y1)	N51 41 — (Ω) — 21	Ignition: **OFF** Disconnect N51.	10 – 16 Ω	Wiring, Y52.
		Front axle solenoid valve 2 (Y52y2)	N51 22 — (Ω) — 21	Ignition: **OFF** Disconnect N51.	10 – 16 Ω	Wiring, Y52.

MB2019400036000X

Fig. 23 Codes 008 & 009: Test 23, Step 14.0. S320 & S420 & 1998–99 CL500, CL600, S500 & S600

⇒		Test scope	Test connection	Test condition	Nominal value	Possible cause/Remedy
15.0	010 011	**Left rear axle damper valve assembly (Y53)** Voltage supply	N51 35 — V — 31	Ignition: **ON**	11–14 V	Wiring, ADS control module (N51).
		Rear axle solenoid valve 1 (Y53y1)	N51 24 — Ω — 31	Ignition: **OFF** Disconnect N51.	10 – 16 Ω	Wiring, Y53.
		Rear axle solenoid valve 2 (Y53y2)	N51 3 — Ω — 31	Ignition: **OFF** Disconnect N51.	10 – 16 Ω	Wiring, Y53.

MB2019400037000X

Fig. 24 Codes 010 & 011: Test 23, Step 15.0. S320 & S420 & 1998–99 CL500, CL600, S500 & S600

⇒		Test scope	Test connection	Test condition	Nominal value	Possible cause/Remedy
16.0	012 013	**Right rear axle damper valve assembly (Y54)** Voltage supply	N51 35 — V — 2	Ignition: **ON**	11–14 V	Wiring, ADS control module (N51).
		Rear axle solenoid valve 1 (Y54y1)	N51 23 — Ω — 2	Ignition: **OFF** Disconnect N51.	10 – 16 Ω	Wiring, Y54.
		Rear axle solenoid valve 2 (Y54y2)	N51 1 — Ω — 2	Ignition: **OFF** Disconnect N51.	10 – 16 Ω	Wiring, Y54.

MB2019400038000X

Fig. 25 Codes 012 & 013: Test 23, Step 16.0. S320 & S420 & 1998–99 CL500, CL600, S500 & S600

⇒		Test scope	Test connection	Test condition	Nominal value	Possible cause/Remedy
1.0	C 1000 C 1010 C 1012	**ADS control module (N51)** Circuit 87 SA Voltage supply	N51 35 —< —(V)— >—26	Ignition: **ON**	11 – 14 V	⇒ 1.1, W16, Wiring.
1.1		Voltge supply from base module (N16/1)	N51 ⊥ —(V)— >— 26	Ignition: **ON**	11 – 14 V	Fuse (F3) on BM (N16/1), 1.1 or □ 23, Wiring.
2.0		**Diagnosis output**	N51 35 —< —(V)— >— 25	Ignition: **ON**	10 – 14 V	Wiring, ADS control module (N51).
3.0	C 1505	ADS MIL (A1e27)	N51 35 —< —(V)— >— 8	Ignition: **OFF** Disconnect N51. Ignition: **ON**	11 – 14 V	Wiring, A1e27.

MB2019500042000A

Fig. 26 Codes C1000, C1010, C1012 & C1505: Test 23, Steps 1.0–3.0. SL500 & SL600

⇒		Test scope	Test connection	Test condition	Nominal value	Possible cause/Remedy
4.0	C 1121 C 1122 C 1123 C 1130 C 1131	**Voltage supply** Body acceleration sensors (B24/3/4/6) Front, rear axle level sensors (B22/2/3)	N51 30 —< —(V)— >— 29	Ignition: **ON**	4.75 - 5.25 V	ADS control module (N51)
5.0	C 1140	**Steering angle sensor (N49)** Voltage supply circuit 30	N51 N49x1 2 —< —(V)— >— 4	Ignition: **OFF** Disconnect steering angle sensor connecter (N49x1)	11 - 14 V	Wiring.
5.1		Voltage supply circuit 87	N51 N49x1 2 —< —(V)— >— 3	Ignition: **ON**	11 - 14 V	Wiring.
6.0	C 1140	**Steering angle sensor** Initialization		Engine: **at Idle** Turn steering wheel from right to left stop.	A1e27 goes out.	⇒ 5.0

MB2019500043000A

Fig. 27 Codes C1121, C1122, C1123, C1130, C1131 & C1140: Test 23, Steps 4.0–6.0. SL500 & SL600

⇒		Test scope	Test connection	Test condition	Nominal value	Possible cause/Remedy
7.0	C 1320 C 1321	**Left front axle damper valve assembly (Y51)** Voltage supply	N51 35 —(V)— 19	Ignition: **ON**	11–14 V	Wiring, ADS control module (N51).
7.1	C 1320	Front axle solenoid valve 1 (Y51y1)	N51 39 —(Ω)— 19	Ignition: **OFF** Disconnect N51.	10 – 16 Ω	Wiring, Y51
7.2	C 1321	Front axle solenoid valve 2 (Y51y2)	N51 40 —(Ω)— 19	Ignition: **OFF** Disconnect N51.	10 – 16 Ω	Wiring, Y51

MB2019500044000A

Fig. 28 Codes C1320 & C1321: Test 23, Steps 7.0–7.2. SL500 & SL600

⇒		Test scope	Test connection	Test condition	Nominal value	Possible cause/Remedy
8.0	C 1322 C 1323	**Right front axle damper valve assembly (Y52)** Voltage supply	N51 35 —(V)— 21	Ignition: **ON**	11–14 V	Wiring, ADS control module (N51).
8.1		Front axle solenoid valve 1 (Y52y1)	N51 41 —(Ω)— 21	Ignition: **OFF** Disconnect N51.	10 – 16 Ω	Wiring, Y52
8.2		Front axle solenoid valve 2 (Y52y2)	N51 22 —(Ω)— 21	Ignition: **OFF** Disconnect N51.	10 – 16 Ω	Wiring, Y52

MB2019500045000A

Fig. 29 Codes C1322 & C1323: Test 23, Steps 8.0–8.2. SL500 & SL600

⇒		Test scope	Test connection	Test condition	Nominal value	Possible cause/Remedy
9.0	C 1324 C 1325	**Left rear axle damper valve assembly (Y53)** Voltage supply	N51 35 —(V)— 31	Ignition: **ON**	11–14 V	Wiring, ADS control module (N51).
9.1	C 1324	Rear axle solenoid valve 1 (Y53y1)	N51 24 —(Ω)— 31	Ignition: **OFF** Disconnect N51.	10 – 16 Ω	Wiring, Y53
9.2	C 1325	Rear axle solenoid valve 2 (Y53y2)	N51 3 —(Ω)— 31	Ignition: **OFF** Disconnect N51.	10 – 16 Ω	Wiring, Y53

MB2019500046000A

Fig. 30 Codes C1324 & C1325: Test 23, Steps 9.0–9.2. SL500 & SL600

⇒		Test scope	Test connection	Test condition	Nominal value	Possible cause/Remedy
10.0	C 1326 C 1327	**Right rear axle damper valve assembly (Y54)** Voltage supply	N51 35 —(V)— 2	Ignition: **ON**	11–14 V	Wiring, ADS control module (N51).
10.1	C 1326	Rear axle solenoid valve 1 (Y54y1)	N51 23 —(Ω)— 2	Ignition: **OFF** Disconnect N51.	10 – 16 Ω	Wiring, Y54
10.2	C 1327	Rear axle solenoid valve 2 (Y54y2)	N51 1 —(Ω)— 2	Ignition: **OFF** Disconnect N51.	10 – 16 Ω	Wiring, Y54

MB2019500047000A

Fig. 31 Codes C1326 & C1327: Test 23, Steps 10.0–10.2. SL500 & SL600

⇒		Test scope	Test connection	Test condition	Nominal value	Possible cause/Remedy
11.0	C 1328 C 1329 C 1330 C 1331	**Rear axle height reduction valve (Y36/6)** Voltage supply	N51 35 —< —(V)— >— 37	Ignition: **ON**	11–14 V	Wiring, ADS control module (N51).
11.1	C 1328	**Valve (raise front axle) (Y36/6y1)**	N51 16 —< —(Ω)— >— 37	Ignition: **OFF** Disconnect N51.	7.5 – 12 Ω	Wiring, (Y36/6y1).
11.2	C 1329	**Valve (raise rear axle) (Y36/6y2)**	N51 20 —< —(Ω)— >— 37	Ignition: **OFF** Disconnect N51.	7.5 – 12 Ω	Wiring, (Y36/6y2).
11.3	C 1330	**Valve (lower front axle) (Y36/6y3)**	N51 11 —< —(Ω)— >— 37	Ignition: **OFF** Disconnect N51.	7.5 – 12 Ω	Wiring, (Y36/6y3).

MB2019500048000A

Fig. 32 Codes C1328, C1329, C1330 & C1331: Test 23, Steps 11.0–11.3. SL500 & SL600

⇒		Test scope	Test connection	Test condition	Nominal value	Possible cause/Remedy
11.4	C 1331	**Valve (lower rear axle) (Y36/6y4)**	N51 12 —< —(Ω)— >— 37	Ignition: **OFF** Disconnect N51.	7.5 – 12 Ω	Wiring, (Y36/6y4).
12.0		**Circuit 30 voltage supply**	N51 35 —< —(V)— >— 32	Engine: **OFF**	11 – 14 V	Fuse 23 in fuse and relaly box F1, Wiring.

MB2019500049000A

Fig. 33 Code C1331: Test 23, Steps 11.4–12.0. SL500 & SL600

COMPONENT REPLACEMENT

REAR STRUT

C43, C230, C280, E300, E320 & E430

The vehicle weight must be on the wheels to remove upper spring strut mounting.

1. Remove trunk trim.
2. Steady piston rod with suitable Allen wrench and remove upper mounting.
3. Remove washer and rubber mount.
4. Raise and support vehicle.
5. Disconnect level controller lever connecting rod or linkage.
6. **On C43, C230 and C280 models,** disconnect left and righthand stabilizer bar connecting rod.
7. **On all models,** connect suitable drain hose to level controller oil drain plug.
8. Slowly open drain plug and drain oil into suitable container.
9. Disconnect pressure line at connection between steel line and hose.
10. Disconnect pressure line on strut.
11. Disconnect spring link cover.
12. Remove strut.
13. Reverse procedure to install, noting the following:
    a. Ensure there is proper clearance between strut and wheelhousing, **Fig. 34.**
    b. **On all models,** Install new copper sealing rings on banjo bolt.
    c. **Torque** oil drain plug to 10 ft. lbs.
    d. **Torque** strut to frame floor nut to 11–13 ft. lbs.
    e. **Torque** strut to frame floor lock nut to 22 ft. lbs.
    f. **Torque** strut to spring link 41 ft. lbs.
    g. **Torque** pressure line banjo bolt to 18 ft. lbs.
    h. **Torque** stabilized bar connecting rod mounting nuts to 22 ft. lbs.

S320 & S420 & 1998–99 CL500, CL600, S500 & S600

The vehicle weight must be on the wheels to remove upper spring strut mounting.

1. Remove trunk trim.
2. Steady piston rod with suitable Allen wrench and remove upper mounting.
3. Raise and support vehicle.
4. Disconnect level controller lever connecting rod or linkage.
5. Connect suitable drain hose to level controller oil drain plug.
6. Slowly open drain plug and drain oil into suitable container.
7. Disconnect pressure line at connection between steel line and hose.
8. Disconnect spring link cover.
9. Remove strut.
10. Reverse procedure to install, noting the following:
    a. Install new copper sealing rings on banjo bolt.
    b. **Torque** oil drain plug to 10 ft. lbs.
    c. **Torque** strut to frame floor lock nut to 30 ft. lbs.
    d. **Torque** strut to spring link nut to 74 ft. lbs.
    e. **Torque** pressure line to 22 ft. lbs.

Side	Clearance At Rebound, Inch.	Clearance Ready To Drive, Inch.
C43, C230 & C280		
Lefthand	0.4331–0.5906	0.5512–0.7087
Righthand	0.0450–1.1025	1.0237–1.1812
E300, E320 & E430		
Lefthand	0.3347–0.4134	0.3347–0.4134
Righthand	0.4134–0.4922	0.4134–0.4922

Fig. 34 Strut to wheelhousing clearance. On C43, C230, C280, E300, E320 & E430

REAR SPRING ACTUATOR

C43, C230, C280, E300, E320, E430, S320 & S420 & 1998–99 CL500, CL600, S500 & S600

1. Connect suitable drain hose to level controller oil drain plug.
2. Slowly open drain plug and drain oil into suitable container.
3. Disconnect spring actuator pressure lines.
4. **On S320 and S420 and 1998–99 CL500, CL600, S500 and S600 models,** when removing lefthand actuator, disconnect exhaust system from floor mounts and secure with suitable hook.
5. **On C43, C230 and C280 models,** when removing lefthand actuator, remove trunk trim.
6. **On E300, E320 and E430 models,** remove spare wheel cover.
7. **On all models,** remove mounting nuts and spring actuator.
8. Reverse procedure to install, noting the following:
    a. **Torque** M10 pressure line to 11 ft. lbs., and M16 to 22 ft. lbs.
    b. **Torque** banjo bolt to 37 ft. lbs.

REAR LEVEL CONTROLLER

C43, C230, C280, E300, E320, E430, S320 & S420 & 1998–99 CL500, CL600, S500 & S600

1. Connect suitable drain hose to level controller oil drain plug.
2. Slowly open drain plug and drain oil into suitable container.
3. Disconnect level controller pressure and return lines.
4. Remove mounting bolts and level controller.
5. Reverse procedure to install, noting the following:
    a. Install new self-locking mounting bolts.
    b. **Torque** M10 pressure line to 11 ft. lbs., and M12 to 15 ft. lbs.

FRONT SHOCK ABSORBER

S320 & S420 & 1998–99 CL500, CL600, S500 & S600

The vehicle weight must be on the wheels to remove upper spring shock mounting.

1. Steady piston rod with suitable Allen wrench and remove upper mounting.
2. Mark shock absorber for installation alignment.
3. Turn shock absorber so damper valve points outward. **Do not allow valve to contact spring dome.**
4. Raise and support vehicle.
5. Disconnect damper valve electrical connector.
6. Disconnect shock absorber from control arm and remove downward.
7. Reverse procedure to install, noting the following:
    a. Ensure there is proper clearance between damper valve and upper control arm.
    b. **On E300, E320 and E430 models,** ensure damper valve points toward spring dome.
    c. **On all models,** ensure damper valve electrical cable is correctly routed.
    d. **On S320 and S420 and 1998–99 CL500, CL600, S500 and S600 models, torque** upper shock absorber mounting nut to 30 ft. lbs. and control arm to 74 ft. lbs.
    e. **On E300, E320 and E430 models, torque** upper shock absorber mounting nut to 26 ft. lbs. and control arm to 41 ft. lbs.

REAR DAMPER VALVE

1. Connect suitable drain hose to level controller oil drain plug.
2. Slowly open drain plug and drain oil into suitable container.
3. Disconnect pressure return lines.
4. Remove mount bolts, nuts and damper valve, then disconnect electrical connector.
5. Reverse procedure to install, noting the following:
    a. **Torque** M16 pressure line to 22 ft. lbs., and M18 to 32 ft. lbs.
    b. **Torque** lefthand damper valve mounting bolt to 18 ft. lbs., and righthand mounting nuts to 10 ft. lbs.

TECHNICAL SERVICE BULLETINS

ESP DTC C1140 & C1504

C43, C230, C280, CLK55, CLK320, CLK430, E55, E300, E320, E430 & SLK230

On some of these models there may be Electronic Stability Program (ESP) Diagnostic Trouble Codes (DTCs) C1140 and C1504.

This condition may be caused by steering angle sensor and contact spiral clearance.

To correct this condition, proceed as follows:

1. Read ESP DTC memory.
2. Check steering angle sensor supply voltage.
3. Measure steering angle sensor ground, pin No. 3. In relation to battery, it should be 12–14 volts. In relation to ground pole, less than one ohm.
4. Pin No. 4 (supply voltage circuit 30) to No. 3 should be 12–14 volts.
5. Pin No. 2 (supply voltage circuit 87) to No. 3 with ignition on, 12–14 volts. With ignition off, zero volts.
6. Measure clearance between steering angle sensor and contact spiral at five different points on circumference.
7. If clearance is not 0.118–0.217 inch, adjust turn signal switch three-point mount.

ESP DTC C1401 OR C1405

C230, C240, CLK320, CLK430, E300, E320 & E430

On some of these models the Electronic Stability Program (ESP) may have Diagnostic Trouble Codes (DTCs) C1401 or C1405 stored. Code occurs only when putting vehicle in motion for first time after starting engine.

This condition may be caused by ESP control module software error.

To correct this condition, replace control module.

ESP DTC C1120 OR C1142

E43, C280, CLK55, CLK320, CLK430, E55, E320, E430 & S430 & 1999-2000 SL500 & 2000 CL500 & S500

On some of these models the Electronic Stability Program (ESP) may store Diagnostic Trouble Code (DTC) C1120 or C1142.

DTC C1120 usually occurs after the vehicle has been driven up a steep incline and through a 90° left or righthand curve immediately after starting the engine. The indicator lamp may come on after driving straight for approximately 100 yards.

DTC C1142 usually occurs when driving through curves with low lateral acceleration forces.

Model	ESP Control Module Part No.	
	Old	New
C43, C280, CLK320 & CLK430	027 545 59 32	029 545 70 32
E55, E320 & E430	027 545 57 32	029 545 76 32

Fig. 35 ESP control module replacement

This condition may be caused by erroneous standstill calibration of yaw rate sensor or lateral acceleration sensor is monitored to precisely by ESP control module.

To correct this condition, install revised control module, **Fig. 35.**

ESP & ADS DTC C1140 & C1054 OR 015, 016 & 017

E55, E320, E430, S320, S420, SL500 & SL600 & 1998-99 S500 & S600

On some of these models there may be Electronic Stability Program (ESP) and Adaptive Damping System (ADS) steering angle sensor Diagnostic Trouble Codes (DTCs) C1140 and C1504 or 015, 016 and 017.

This condition may be caused by the steering angle sensor power supply.

To correct this condition, proceed as follows:

1. Ensure steering angle sensor N49 pin No. 2 is ground, pin No. 3 is circuit 87 and No. 4 circuit 30.
2. Connect Hand-Held Tester (HHT) tool No. 965 589 00 01 00, or equivalent scan tool, to DLC.
3. Start ADS or ESP test program.
4. Select actual valve menu.
5. Turn steering wheel.
6. If values change, replace steering angle sensor.
7. If values do not change, inspect distance between clock spring contact and jacket tube. Adjust as required.
8. If steering angle sensor cannot be initialized after starting engine, replace sensor.

ADS MIL LIT & DTC 6, 7, 8 OR 9 SET, BUT NO MALFUNCTION FOUND

S320 & S420 & 1998-99 CL500, CL600, S500 & S600

On some of these models the ADS Malfunction Indicator Lamp (MIL) may be lit and Diagnostic Trouble Codes 6, 7, 8 or 9 may be set, but no malfunction can be located.

This condition may be caused by solenoid valves' ground connections.

To correct this condition, proceed as follows:

1. Disconnect solenoid valves electrical harness.
2. Inspect all three solenoid valve electrical connections for continuity to valve housing using suitable ohmmeter.
3. If there is continuity, replace solenoid valve.

REAR SUSPENSION KNOCKING ON ROUGH ROADS AT LOW SPEED

S320 & S420 & 1998-99 CL500, CL600, S500 & S600

On some of these models there may be rear suspension knocking noise when driving on rough roads at low speeds.

This condition may be caused by vibrations being transferred to body.

To correct this condition replace strut upper mounts.

ADS MIL LIT & DTC 14 OR 20 SET

S320 & S420 & 1998-99 CL500, CL600, S500 & S600

On some of these modes the ADS Malfunction Indicator Lamp (MIL) may be lit with Diagnostic Trouble Codes (DTC) 14 or 20 set.

This condition may be caused by improperly mounted steering angle sensor.

To correct this condition, remove steering wheel and tighten steering angle sensor mounting screws.

ADS MIL LIT & DTC 3 OR 4 SET

S320 & S420 & 1998-99 CL500, CL600, S500 & S600

On some of these models the ADS Malfunction Indicator Lamp (MIL) may be lit with Diagnostic Trouble Codes (DTC) 3 or 4 set.

This condition may be caused by oxidized left or righthand front body lateral acceleration sensor connections.

To correct this condition, clean connections and replace wiring harness.

ADS MIL LIT & DTC 5 SET

S320 & S420 & 1998-99 CL500, CL600, S500 & S600

On some of these models the ADS Malfunction Indicator Lamp (MIL) may be lit with Diagnostic Trouble Code (DTC) 5 set.

This condition may be caused by steering angle sensor failure.

To correct this condition, remove steering wheel and replace steering angle sensor.

Engine Rebuilding Specifications

INDEX

	Page No.
Camshaft	5-346
Crankshaft, Bearings & Rods	5-346
Cylinder Block	5-348
Cylinder Head, Valve Guide & Valve Seats	5-344
Pistons, Pins & Rings	5-347
Valve Springs	5-345
Valves	5-345

CYLINDER HEAD, VALVE GUIDE & VALVE SEATS

All measurements given in inches, unless otherwise specified.

Engine		Cylinder Head			Valve Guides						Valve Seats		
Dis-place-ment, Liters	Series	Total Height	Mini-mum Height	War-page Limit	Standard Inside Diameter		Stem To Camshaft Bearing Distance (Stem To Guide Clearance)①				Seat Angle, Degrees	Seat Width	
							Standard		Repair				
					Intake	Exhaust	Intake	Exhaust	Intake	Exhaust		Intake	Exhaust
2.3L	111	5.3504–5.3543	5.3346	0.0031	0.2756–0.2762	0.2756–0.2762	0.9914–1.0119	0.9127–0.9332	0.9816–1.021	0.9028–0.9233	45	—	—
2.4L	112	—	—	—	—	—	—	—	—	—	—	—	—
2.8L	112	—	—	—	—	—	—	—	—	—	—	—	—
3.0L③	606	4.9946–5.0064②	4.9926②	0.0016	0.2362–0.2368	0.2756–0.2762	0.9332–0.9525	0.9332–0.9525	—	—	45	0.0394–0.0591	0.0315–0.0591
3.2L	104	5.3509–5.3549	5.3352	0.0031	0.2756–0.2762	0.2756–0.2762	0.9532–0.9745	0.8745–0.8958	0.9434–0.9651	0.8647–0.8863	45	0.0354–0.9433	0.0354–0.9433
	112	—	—	—	—	—	—	—	—	—	—	—	—
4.2L	119	④	⑤	0.0031	0.2756–0.2762	0.2756–0.2762	0.9083–0.9374	0.9083–0.9374	0.8984–0.9276	0.8984–0.9276	45	0.0315–0.0433	0.0394–0.0472
4.3L	113	—	—	—	—	—	—	—	—	—	—	—	—
5.0L	119	④	⑤	0.0031	0.2756–0.2762	0.2756–0.2762	0.9083–0.9374	0.9083–0.9374	0.8984–0.9276	0.8984–0.9276	45	0.0315–0.0433	0.0394–0.0472
	113	—	—	—	—	—	—	—	—	—	—	—	—
5.5L	113	—	—	—	—	—	—	—	—	—	—	—	—
6.0L	120	5.3509–5.3549	5.3352	0.0079	0.5313–0.5319	0.5313–0.5319	0.9532–0.9745	0.8745–0.8958	0.9434–0.9651	0.8647–0.8863	45	—	—
	137	—	—	—	—	—	—	—	—	—	—	—	—

① — Allowable distance between end of valve stem & base of camshaft bearing.
② — Less camshaft housing.
③ — Diesel.
④ — Height H1 in **Fig. A,** 5.1422–5.1462 inches; height He 5.7447–5.7486 inches.
⑤ — Height H1 in **Fig. A,** 5.1344 inches; height He 5.7368 inches.

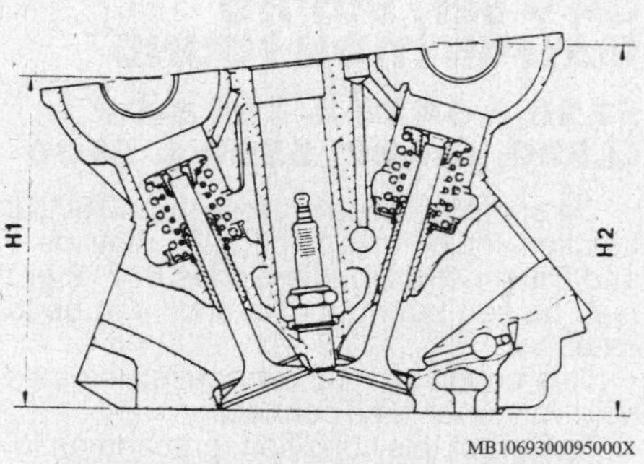

Fig. A Cylinder head height measurements. 119 engine

VALVE SPRINGS

All measurements given in inches, unless otherwise specified.

Engine Liters	Engine Series	Position	Free Length	Pretensioned Length, Inches @ lbs. L1	Pretensioned Length, Inches @ lbs. L2
2.3L	111	—	—	—	—
2.4L	112	—	—	—	—
2.8L	112	—	—	—	—
3.0L④	606	—	—	—	—
3.2L	104	Outer	1.8427	1.4529 @ 61–67	1.0828 @ 142–157
		Inner	1.8742	1.3347 @ 27–30	0.9647 @ 55–61
		Conical	1.8624	1.4450 @ 62–69	1.0749 @ 128–142
	112	—	—	—	—
4.2L	119	Outer	1.5750	1.2992 @ 51	0.9056 @ 129
		Inner	1.6380	1.1812 @ 22	0.7875 @ 46
		Conical	①	②	③
4.3L	113	—	—	—	—
5.0L	119	Outer	1.5750	1.2992 @ 51	0.9056 @ 129
		Inner	1.6380	1.1812 @ 22	0.7875 @ 46
		Conical	①	②	③
	113	—	—	—	—
5.5L	113	—	—	—	—
6.0L	120	—	—	—	—
	137	—	—	—	—

① — Purple or yellow/blue, 1.6065 inches; Purple/blue, 1.5789 inches; Purple or yellow/red, 1.6498 inches; Yellow/green, 1.6419 inches; purple/white, 1.6498 inches.

② — Purple or yellow/blue or purple/blue, 1.2993 inches @ 56 lbs.; Purple or yellow/red or purple/white, 1.2993 inches @ 47 lbs.; Yellow/green, 1.2993 inches @ 49 lbs.

③ — Purple or yellow/blue, 0.9253 inches @ 142 lbs.; Purple/blue, 0.9489 inches @ 135 lbs.; Purple or yellow/red or purple/white, 0.9647 inches @ 105 lbs.; Yellow/green, 0.9647 inches @ 107 lbs.

④ — Diesel

VALVES

All measurements given in inches, unless otherwise specified.

Engine Displacement, Liters	Series	Stem Diameter Intake	Stem Diameter Exhaust	Clearance① Installation Tolerance Intake	Clearance① Installation Tolerance Exhaust	Clearance① Wear Limit Intake	Clearance① Wear Limit Exhaust	Face Angle Degrees
2.3L	111	—	—	0.0394	0.0758	0.0591	0.0906	45
2.4L	112	—	—	—	—	—	—	—
2.8L	112	—	—	—	—	—	—	—
3.0L②	606	0.3132–0.3138	0.3522–0.3528	0.0512–0.0669	0.0512–0.0669	—	—	45
3.2L	104	0.2756	0.3150	0.0394	0.0748	0.0591	0.0906	45
	112	—	—	—	—	—	—	—
4.2L	119	0.2736–0.2744	0.2736–0.2744	—	—	—	—	45
4.3L	113	—	—	—	—	—	—	—
5.0L	119	0.2736–0.2744	0.2736–0.2744	—	—	—	—	45
	113	—	—	—	—	—	—	—
5.5L	113	—	—	—	—	—	—	—
6.0L	120	—	—	—	—	—	—	45
	137	—	—	—	—	—	—	—

① — Allowed depth of valve disk in relation to cylinder head mating face.

② — Diesel.

CAMSHAFT

All measurements given in inches, unless otherwise specified.

Engine Displacement, Liters	Series	Camshaft Journal Diameter: Standard	Camshaft Journal Diameter: Repair	Maximum Journal Runout	End Play: Radial	End Play: Axial
2.3L	111	1.0005–1.0090	1,1202–1.1206	—	—	0.0020–0.0059
2.4L	112	—	—	—	—	—
2.8L	112	—	—	—	—	—
3.0L①	606	—	—	—	—	—
3.2L	104	1.1790–1.1795	1.1983–1.1989	0.0016	0.0016–0.0029	0.0024–0.0083
	112	—	—	—	—	—
4.2L	119	1.1025–1.1039	1.1123–1.1230	0.0008	0.0021–0.0024	0.0020–0.0059
4.3L	113	—	—	—	—	—
5.0L	119	1.1025–1.1039	1.1123–1.1230	0.0008	0.0021–0.0024	0.0020–0.0059
	113	—	—	—	—	—
5.5L	113	—	—	—	—	—
6.0L	120	1.1791–1.1796	1.1589–1.1596	—	0.0016–0.0029	0.0024–0.0083
	137	—	—	—	—	—

① — Diesel.

CRANKSHAFT, BEARINGS & RODS

All measurements given in inches, unless otherwise specified.

Engine Displacement, Liters	Engine Series	Group	Crankshaft, Main Bearing Journal Diameter	Out Of Round	Bearing Play: Radial New	Bearing Play: Radial Limit	Bearing Play: Axial New	Bearing Play: Axial Limit	Connecting Rod, Journal Diameter
2.3L	111	—	2.2817–2.2823④	—	0.0012–0.0018	—	0.0039–0.0098	—	1.8881–1.8886②
2.4L	112	—	—	—	—	—	—	—	—
2.8L	112	—	—	—	—	—	—	—	—
3.0L①	606	—	2.4609–2.4617	0.0008	0.0012–0.0020	0.0031	0.0039–0.0098	0.0118	—
3.2L	104	B	2.2821–2.2823④	0.0001	0.0012–0.0018	—	0.0039–0.0098	—	1.8881–1.8886②
		G	2.2819–2.2821④	0.0001	0.0012–0.0018	—	0.0039–0.0098	—	1.8881–1.8886②
		R	2.2817–2.2819④	0.0001	0.0012–0.0018	—	0.0039–0.0098	—	1.8881–1.8886②
		W	2.2815—2.2817④	0.0001	0.0012–0.0018	—	0.0039–0.0098	—	1.8881–1.8886②
		V	2.2813–2.2815④	0.0001	0.0012–0.0018	—	0.0039–0.0098	—	1.8881–1.8886②
	112	—	—	—	—	—	—	—	—
4.2L	119	Blue	2.5184–2.5186③	0.0004	0.0008–0.0018	0.0035	0.0039–0.0087	0.0118	2.0317–2.0324
		Yellow	2.5182–2.5184③	0.0004	0.0008–0.0018	0.0035	0.0039–0.0087	0.0118	2.0317–2.0324
		Red	2.5180—2.5182③	0.0004	0.0008–0.0018	0.0035	0.0039–0.0087	0.0118	2.0317–2.0324
4.3L	113	—	—	—	—	—	—	—	—
5.0L	119	Blue	2.5184–2.5186③	0.0004	0.0008–0.0018	0.0035	0.0039–0.0087	0.0118	2.0317–2.0324
		Yellow	2.5182–2.5184③	0.0004	0.0008–0.0018	0.0035	0.0039–0.0087	0.0118	2.0317–2.0324
		Red	2.5180—2.5182③	0.0004	0.0008–0.0018	0.0035	0.0039–0.0087	0.0118	2.0317–2.0324
	113	—	—	—	—	—	—	—	—
5.5L	113	—	—	—	—	—	—	—	—

Continued

CRANKSHAFT, BEARINGS & RODS—Continued

All measurements given in inches, unless otherwise specified.

Engine Displacement, Liters	Engine Series	Group	Crankshaft, Main Bearing Journal Diameter	Out Of Round	Bearing Play Radial New	Bearing Play Radial Limit	Bearing Play Axial New	Bearing Play Axial Limit	Connecting Rod, Journal Diameter
6.0L	120	—	2.2813–2.2823④	0.0008	0.0010–0.0020	—	0.0039–0.0100	—	1.8882–1.8886②
	137	—	—	—	—	—	—	—	—

① — Diesel engine.
② — Fourth repair, 1.8488–1.8492 inches.
③ — Fourth repair, 2.4792–2.4766 inches.
④ — Fourth repair, 2.2425–2.2429 inches.

PISTONS, PINS & RINGS

All measurements given in inches, unless otherwise specified.

Engine Displacement, Liters	Engine Series	Group②	Piston Diameter (Std.)	Piston Pin Diameter	Piston Ring End Gap 1st	Piston Ring End Gap 2nd	Piston Ring End Gap 3rd	Piston Ring Side Clearance 1st	Piston Ring Side Clearance 2nd	Piston Ring Side Clearance 3rd
2.3L	111	—	—	—	—	—	—	0.0012–0.0024	0.0004–0.0020	0.0008–0.0024
2.4L	112	X	3.5386–3.5398	—	0.0079–0.0138	0.079–0.0157	—	—	—	—
2.8L	112	X	3.5386–3.5398	—	0.0079–0.0138	0.079–0.0157	—	—	—	—
3.0L①	606	—	—	—	—	—	—	—	—	—
3.2L	104	A	3.5387–3.5389	—	0.0079–0.0157	0.0079–0.0157	0.0079–0.0177	0.0006–0.0020	0.0008–0.0016	0.0004–0.0018
		X	3.5389–3.5392	—	0.0079–0.0157	0.0079–0.0157	0.0079–0.0177	0.0006–0.0020	0.0008–0.0016	0.0004–0.0018
		B	3.5391–3.53.94	—	0.0079–0.0157	0.0079–0.0157	0.0079–0.0177	0.0006–0.0020	0.0008–0.0016	0.0004–0.0018
	112	X	3.5386–3.5398	—	0.0079–0.0138	0.079–0.0157	—	—	—	—
4.2L	119	A	3.6217–3.6222	0.9450	—	—	—	0.0020–0.0031	0.0004–0.0012	0.0004–0.0016
		B	3.6221–3.6423	0.9450	—	—	—	0.0020–0.0031	0.0004–0.0012	0.0004–0.0016
		C	3.6224–3.6229	0.9450	—	—	—	0.0020–0.0031	0.0004–0.0012	0.0004–0.0016
4.3L	113	X	3.5386–3.5398	—	0.0079–0.0138	0.079–0.0157	—	—	—	—
5.0L	119	A	3.7988–3.7994	0.9450	—	—	—	0.0020–0.0031	0.0004–0.0012	0.0004–0.0016
		B	3.7992–3.7997	0.9450	—	—	—	0.0020–0.0031	0.0004–0.0012	0.0004–0.0016
		C	3.7996–3.8000	0.9450	—	—	—	0.0020–0.0031	0.0004–0.0012	0.0004–0.0016
	113	X	3.8182–3.8193	—	0.0079–0.0138	0.079–0.0157	—	—	—	—
5.5L	113	X	3.8182–3.8193	—	0.0079–0.0138	0.079–0.0157	—	—	—	—
6.0L	120	0	3.5034–3.5038	0.8660–0.8862	—	—	—	—	—	—
		1	3.5038–3.5042	0.8660–0.8862	—	—	—	—	—	—
		2	3.5042–3.5046	0.8660–0.8862	—	—	—	—	—	—
	137	—	—	—	—	—	—	—	—	—

① — Diesel.
② — Tolerance group letters or numbers are punched into piston crown & stamped into cylinder crankcase parting surface.

CYLINDER BLOCK

All measurements given in inches, unless otherwise specified.

Engine		Cylinder Bore Diameter				
Displace-ment, Liters	Series	①Tolerance Group	Standard	Limit	Cylinder Bore Taper Max.	Cylinder Bore Out Of Round Max.
2.3L	111	A	–3.57913.793	–3.59893.5993	0.0020	0.0020
		X	–3.57943.796	–3.59913.5993	0.0020	0.0020
		B	–3.57963.798	–3.59933.5995	0.0020	0.0020
2.4L	112	X	–3.53973.5403	–3.54963.5502	0.0012	—
2.8L	112	X	–3.53973.5403	–3.54963.5502	0.0012	—
②3.0L	606	A	–3.42553.4258	—	0.0020	0.0028
		X	–3.42583.4260	—	0.0020	0.0028
		B	–3.42603.4262	—	0.0020	0.0028
3.2L	104	A	–3.53973.5400	–3.55943.5596	0.0020	0.0020
		X	–3.54003.5402	–3.55963.5599	0.0020	0.0020
		B	–3.54023.5404	–3.55993.5601	0.0020	0.0020
	112	X	–3.53973.5403	–3.54963.5502	0.0012	—
4.2L	119 4.2L	A	–3.62243.6227	–3.66183.6621	0.0020	0.0020
		B	–3.62273.6230	–3.66213.6624	0.0020	0.0020
		C	–3.62303.6234	–3.66243.6627	0.0020	0.0020
4.3L	113	X	–3.53973.5403	–3.54963.5502	0.0012	—
5.0L	119 5.0L	A	–3.79963.7999	–3.83983.8392	0.0020	0.0020
		B	–3.79993.8002	–3.83923.8396	0.0020	0.0020
		C	–3.80023.8005	–3.83963.8399	0.0020	0.0020
	113	X	–3.81933.8299	–3.82913.8297	0.0012	—
5.5L	113	X	–3.81933.8299	–3.82913.8297	0.0012	—
6.0L	120	0	–3.50433.5046	–3.53183.5322	0.0020	0.0020
		1	–3.50463.5049	–3.53223.5325	0.0020	0.0020
		2	–3.50493.5052	–3.53253.5328	0.0020	0.0020
	137	—	—	—	—	—

① — Tolerance group letters or numbers are punched into piston& crown stamped into cylinder crankcase parting surface.

② — Diesel.

PORSCHE

INDEX OF SERVICE OPERATIONS

	Page No.
AIR BAG SYSTEM PRECAUTIONS	0-12
AUTOMATIC TRANSMISSIONS/ TRANSAXLES	6-92
BRAKES	
Anti-Lock Brakes	6-77
Disc Brakes	6-73
Hydraulic Brake Systems	6-76
Power Brake Units	6-77
CLUTCH & MANUAL TRANSMISSION	
Adjustments	6-36
Clutch, Replace	6-37
Differential, Replace	6-38
Hydraulic System Service	6-36
Maintenance	6-36
Tightening Specifications	6-39
Transmission, Replace	6-37
COMPUTER RELEARN PROCEDURES	0-10
ELECTRICAL	
Air Bags	6-68
Air Conditioning	6-57
Alterntors	6-66
Alternator, Replace	6-5
Blower Motor, Replace	6-6
Cooling Fans	6-58
Cruise Controls	6-67
Dash Gauges	6-61
Dash Panels	6-71
Evaporator Core, Replace	6-6
Fuel Pump Relay Location	6-4
Fuse Panel & Flasher Location	6-4
Headlamp Switch, Replace	6-5
Heater Core, Replace	6-6
Ignition Switch, Replace	6-5
Instrument Cluster, Replace	6-6
Passive Restraints	6-68
Precautions	6-4
Relay Center Location	6-4
Speed Control Systems	6-67
Starter Motors	6-66
Starter, Replace	6-4
Steering Wheel, Replace	6-6
Stop Light Switch, Replace	6-6
Wiper Motor, Replace	6-6
Wiper Transmission, Replace	6-6
ELECTRICAL SYMBOL IDENTIFICATION	0-33
FRONT SUSPENSION & STEERING	
Ball Joint, Replace	6-48
Ball Joint Inspection	6-48
Coil Spring & Strut Service	6-48
Control Arm, Replace	6-49
Driveshaft, Replace	6-47
Power Steering Gear, Replace	6-49
Precautions	6-47
Stabilizer Bar, Replace	6-49
Strut, Replace	6-48
Technical Service Bulletins	6-50
Tie Rod End, Replace	6-49
Tightening Specifications	6-53
Wheel Bearing, Replace	6-47
Wheel Carrier, Replace	6-47
REAR AXLE & SUSPENSION	
Coil Spring, Replace	6-44
Hub & Bearing, Replace	6-40
Maintenance	6-40
Rear Axle Shaft, Replace	6-40
Rear Suspension, Replace	6-40
Strut, Replace	6-41
Strut Service	6-42
Tightening Specifications	6-44
Trailing Arm Service	6-44
SERVICE REMINDER LAMP RESET	0-14
SPECIFICATIONS	
Fluid Capacities & Cooling System Data	6-3
Front Wheel Alignment Specifications	6-2
General Engine Specifications	6-2
Lubricant Data	6-3
Rear Wheel Alignment Specifications	6-3
Tune Up Specifications	6-2
VEHICLE IDENTIFICATION	0-3
VEHICLE LIFT POINTS	0-24
VEHICLE MAINTENANCE SCHEDULES	0-45
WHEEL ALIGNMENT	
Front Wheel Alignment	6-54
Preliminary Inspection	6-54
Rear Wheel Alignment	6-54
Vehicle Ride Height	6-55
Wheel Alignment Specifications	6-2
WIRE COLOR CODE IDENTIFICATION	0-33
2.5L & 3.2L ENGINES	
Air/Oil Separator, Replace	6-11
Camshaft, Replace	6-10
Cylinder Head, Replace	6-9
Engine Rebuilding Specifications	6-109
Engine, Replace	6-8
Engine Assemble	6-9
Engine Disassemble	6-9
Fuel Filter, Replace	6-11
Fuel Pump, Replace	6-11
Intake Manifold, Replace	6-9
Oil Cooler, Replace	6-11
Oil Pan, Replace	6-11
Oil Pump, Replace	6-11
Piston & Rod Assembly	6-10
Precautions	6-8
Serpentine Drive Belt	6-11
Technical Service Bulletins	6-11
Tightening Specifications	6-13
Valve Clearance Specifications	6-10
Water Pump, Replace	6-11
3.4L ENGINE	
Cooling System Bleed	6-19
Crankshaft Rear Oil Seal, Replace	6-18
Crankshaft Seal, Replace	6-18
Engine Rebuilding Specifications	6-109
Engine, Replace	6-14
Engine Assemble	6-15
Engine Disassemble	6-14
Fuel Filter, Replace	6-20
Fuel Pump, Replace	6-20
Precautions	6-14
Serpentine Drive Belt	6-19
Tightening Specifications	6-24
Valve Clearance Specifications	6-18
Water Pump, Replace	6-19
3.6L ENGINE	
Belt Tension Data	6-33
Camshaft, Replace	6-31
Compression Pressure	6-26
Crankshaft Seal, Replace	6-32
Cylinder Head, Replace	6-27
Engine Rebuilding Specifications	6-109
Engine, Replace	6-26
Engine Assemble	6-28
Engine Disassemble	6-27
Fuel Filter, Replace	6-33
Hydraulic Lifters, Replace	6-29
Piston & Rod Assembly	6-32
Pistons, Pins & Rings	6-32
Precautions	6-26
Rocker Arms	6-29
Tightening Specifications	6-34
Timing Chain, Replace	6-30
Timing Chain Tensioner, Replace	6-31
Turbocharger, Replace	6-33
Valve Clearance Specifications	6-29
Valve Guides	6-29

Specifications

GENERAL ENGINE SPECIFICATIONS

Engine, Liter	Fuel System	Bore x Stroke, Inch	Compression Ratio	Maximum HP @ RPM	Maximum Torque @ RPM	Normal Oil Pressure, psi @ RPM①
1998						
2.5L	MFI	3.37 X 2.84	11.0	201 @ 6000	181 @ 4500	73 @ 5000
3.6L	MFI	3.94 X 3.01	11.3	282 @ 6300	250 @ 5250	94 @ 5000
1999						
2.5L	MFI	3.37 X 2.84	11.0	201 @ 6000	181 @ 4500	73 @ 5000
3.4L	MFI	3.78 X 3.07	11.3	296 @ 6800	258 @ 4600	73 @ 5000
2000–01						
2.5L	MFI	3.37 X 2.84	11.0	201 @ 6000	181 @ 4500	73 @ 5000
3.2L	MFI	3.66 X 3.07	11.0	248 @ 6250	226 @ 4500	73 @ 5000
3.4L	MFI	3.78 X 3.07	11.3	296 @ 6800	258 @ 4600	73 @ 5000
3.6L	MFI	3.94 X 3.01	9.4	415 @ 6000	415 @ 4600	73 @ 5000

MFI — Multi-Port Fuel Injection

① — At 194°F.

TUNE UP SPECIFICATIONS

Model	Spark Plug Gap Inch	Ignition Timing		Curb Idle Speed		Fuel System Pressure, psi	Valve Clearance, inch
		Firing Order	Timing BTDC	Man. Trans.	Auto. Trans.		
1998							
2.5L	.031	1-6-2-4-3-5	③	—	—	52–58	①
3.6L	.026	1-6-2-4-3-5	③	800④	750D④	52–58②	①
1999							
2.5L	.031	1-6-2-4-3-5	③	—	—	52–58	①
3.4L	.032	1-6-2-4-3-5	③	660–740	660–740	52–58	①
2000–01							
2.5L	.031	1-6-2-4-3-5	③	—	—	52–58	①
3.2L	.031	1-6-2-4-3-5	③	—	—	52–58	①
3.4L	.032	1-6-2-4-3-5	③	660–740	660–740	52–58	①
3.6L	.032	1-6-2-4-3-5	③	660–740	660–740	52–58	①

D — Drive
N — Neutral
BTDC — Before Top Dead Center

① — Equipped w/hydraulic lash adjusters.
② — Key On, Engine Off.

③ — Controlled by DME (Digital Motor Electronics) control unit.
④ — 880 RPM w/A/C.

FRONT WHEEL ALIGNMENT SPECIFICATIONS

Model	Caster Angle, Degrees		Camber Angle, Degrees		Toe Angle, Degrees	Toe Difference Angle @ 20°	Ball Joint Wear
	Limits	Desired	Limits	Desired			
1998							
Boxster	$+7\frac{1}{12}$ to $+8\frac{1}{2}$	8	$-\frac{5}{12}$ to $+\frac{7}{12}$	$+\frac{1}{12}$	0 to $+\frac{1}{6}$	$-\frac{5}{6}$ to $-1\frac{5}{6}$	①
911 Carrera	$+4\frac{5}{6}$ to $+5\frac{7}{12}$	$+5\frac{1}{3}$	$-\frac{2}{3}$ to $-\frac{1}{6}$	$-\frac{1}{3}$	0 to $+\frac{1}{6}$	$-1\frac{1}{2}$ to $-\frac{1}{2}$②	①
1999–2001							
Boxster	$+7\frac{1}{12}$ to $+8\frac{1}{2}$	8	$-\frac{5}{12}$ to $+\frac{7}{12}$	$+\frac{1}{12}$	0 to $+\frac{1}{6}$	$-\frac{5}{6}$ to $-1\frac{5}{6}$	①
911	$+7\frac{1}{12}$ to $+8\frac{1}{2}$	8	$-\frac{1}{4}$ to $+\frac{1}{4}$	0	0 to $+\frac{1}{20}$	—	①

① — Refer to "Ball Joint Inspection" in "Front Suspension & Steering."

② — Models equipped w/Sport-type running gear: $-2\frac{1}{4}$ to $-1\frac{1}{4}$.°

REAR WHEEL ALIGNMENT SPECIFICATIONS

Model	Camber Angle, Deg.		Toe Per Wheel, Deg.①
	Limits	Desired	
1998			
Boxster	−1⅚ to −⅚	−1⅓	0 to +⅙
911 Carrera	−11/12 to −1 5/12	−1⅙	+1/12 to +3/12
1999–2001			
Boxster	−1⅚ to −⅚	−1⅓	0 to +⅙
911	−1⅙ to −1⅔	−1 5/12	0 to +⅙

① — Toe-in (+); toe-out (-).

FLUID CAPACITIES & COOLING SYSTEM DATA

Model	Cooling Capacity, Qts.	Fuel Tank Gals.	Engine Oil Refill Qts.②		Transmission Oil Pts.			
					Manual①	Automatic		
						Trans.		Final Drive
			Service	Dry③		Service	Dry③	
1998								
Boxster	—	15.3	8.7	—	4.8	—	20	1.7
911	—	19.4	10.0	12.15	7.6	6.0	19	1.8
1999								
Boxster	—	15.3	8.7	—	4.8	—	20	1.7
911 Carrera	24	17.0④	8.72	11.00	7.4	—	20	1.7
2000–01								
Boxster	—	15.3	8.7	—	4.8	—	20	1.7
911 Carrera	24	17.0④	8.72	11.00	7.4	—	20	1.7
911 Turbo	29.6	17.0⑤	9.25	13.2	8.0	—	19	1.3

① — Includes final drive.
② — With filter.
③ — After complete disassembly of entire system including coolers & lines.
④ — Reserve 2.6 gallons.
⑤ — Reserve 3.1 gallons.

LUBRICANT DATA

Year	Model	Lubricant Type			
		Transmission		Power Steering②	Brake System
		Manual	Automatic		
1998	Boxster	75W-90	Esso LT 71141	Pentosin CHF 11S	DOT 4
	911	75W-90 GL-5	Dexron IID①	Pentosin CHF 11S	DOT 4
1999–2001	Boxster	75W-90	Esso LT 71141	Pentosin CHF 11S	DOT 4
	911	SAE 90 GL5	Esso LT71141	Pentosin CHF 11S	DOT 4

① — Final drive, 75W-90 GL-5.
② — Pentosin CHF 11S may be mixed on models using Dexron IID. However, Dexron IID may not be added to system using Pentosin CHF 11S which includes models manufactured after March 25, 1996, Coupe VIN 99 9 TS 32 3082, Cabriolet VIN 99 3 TS 34 1781 and Targa VIN 99 8 TS 38 5439.

Electrical

NOTE: On Air Bag Equipped Models, Refer To "Air Bag System Precautions" Located In The Front Of This Manual For System Disarming & Arming Procedures.

INDEX

	Page No.
Air Bags	6-68
Air Conditioning	6-57
Alternators	6-66
Alternator, Replace	6-5
Boxster	6-5
911	6-5
Blower Motor, Replace	6-6
Boxster & 1999–2001 911	6-6
1998 911	6-6
Cooling Fans	6-58
Cruise Controls	6-67
Dash Gauges	6-61
Dash Panels	6-71
Evaporator Core, Replace	6-6
Boxster & 1999–2001 911	6-6
1998 911	6-7
Fuel Pump Relay Location	6-4
Boxster	6-4
911	6-4
Fuse Panel & Flasher Location	6-4
Boxster	6-4
911	6-4
Headlamp Switch, Replace	6-5
Heater Core, Replace	6-6
Ignition Switch, Replace	6-5
Boxster & 1999–2001 911	6-5
1998 911	6-5
Instrument Cluster, Replace	6-6
Boxster & 1999–2001 911	6-6
1998 911	6-6
Passive Restraints	6-68
Precautions	6-4
Air Bag Systems	6-4
Battery Ground Cable	6-4
Relay Center Location	6-4
Speed Control Systems	6-67
Starter Motors	6-66
Starter, Replace	6-4
Boxster	6-4
911	6-4
Steering Wheel, Replace	6-6
Stop Light Switch, Replace	6-6
Wiper Motor, Replace	6-6
Boxster & 1999–2001 911	6-6
1998 911	6-6
Wiper Transmission, Replace	6-6
Boxster & 1999–2001 911	6-6
1998 911	6-6

PRECAUTIONS

AIR BAG SYSTEMS

Refer to "Air Bag System Precautions" in the front of this manual for system disarming and arming procedures.

BATTERY GROUND CABLE

Prior to service, disconnect battery ground cable and isolate as required.

FUSE PANEL & FLASHER LOCATION

BOXSTER

The fuse and main relay panels are located on the footwell portion of the lefthand A-pillar. The luggage compartment relay panel is on the lefthand side of the rear luggage compartment.

911

1998

One fuse panel is located on the lefthand side of the luggage compartment, below the hydraulic unit cover. The other fuse panel is in on the carrier plate on the lefthand side of the engine compartment. The flasher is located on the center console.

1999–2001

The electric fuses are installed at the lower lefthand side A-pillar.

FUEL PUMP RELAY LOCATION

BOXSTER

The fuel pump relay is located on the footwell portion of the lefthand A-pillar, on the main relay panel.

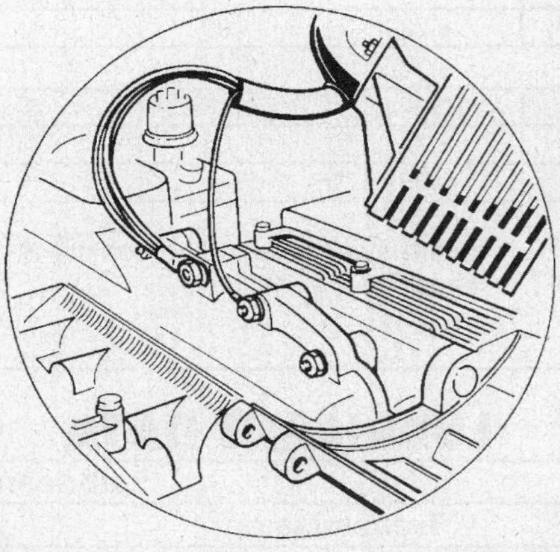

PR1129600002000X

Fig. 1 Alternator harness to engine ground wires. 911

911

1998

The fuel pump relay is located on the relay center, in the righthand rear of the luggage compartment.

1999–2001

The fuel pump relay is located on the footwell portion of the lefthand A-pillar, on the relay panel.

RELAY CENTER LOCATION

Refer to "Fuse Panel & Flasher Location" for relay locations.

STARTER

REPLACE

BOXSTER

1. Remove air guide between throttle body and air filter, then the vent line between intake manifold and oil separator.
2. Loosen intake manifold hose clamps and fuel pipe mounting bolts.
3. Loosen throttle body bracket, then swing intake manifold and throttle body upward approximately 45° and remove throttle body bracket.
4. Loosen cable and solenoid switch terminals, then remove starter mounting bolts and ground cable.
5. Remove starter with bracket.
6. Reverse procedure to install. **Torque** solenoid terminal nut to 60 inch lbs., terminal nut to 11 ft. lbs. and starter mounting bolts to 33 ft. lbs.

911

1998

Automatic Transmission

1. Remove engine guard and underside rear panel.
2. Remove air distributor pipe on left and right sides of transmission.
3. Loosen transmission mounting bolts and lower approximately .4 inch.
4. Disconnect solenoid electrical connectors.
5. Remove solenoid wire clamp and tie wrap from starter, then the oil pipe from body.
6. Remove starter bolts and ground strap.
7. Lift starter from support and rotate starter pinion toward engine oil filter.
8. Rotate starter ½ turn until solenoid

faces transmission, then carefully remove starter.
9. Reverse procedure to install. **Torque** starter mounting bolts to 30 ft. lbs. and transmission mounting bolts to 34 ft. lbs.

Manual Transmission

1. Remove engine guard.
2. Remove air distributor rail mounted on left and righthand sides of transmission.
3. Separate driveshaft from differential flange.
4. Disconnect solenoid electrical connectors.
5. Remove wire clamp holding solenoid wire to body, then the tie-wrap from starter.
6. Remove clutch slave cylinder attaching bolts and position slave cylinder aside. **Do not disconnect slave cylinder hydraulic line.**
7. Remove upper starter mounting nut using a 10 mm socket, two short extensions, transverse handle tool No. 425 and a shop made extension pipe.
8. Remove bolt from righthand side of starter assembly using transverse handle tool and extension pipe.
9. Use right hand to hold tool in place above transmission, remove remaining starter bolt with ground cable.
10. Remove starter from support.
11. Turn starter until solenoid points towards halfshaft and remove from below.
12. Reverse procedure to install, noting the following:
    a. Use two tie wraps to attach solenoid to alternator wire.
    b. **Torque** starter attaching bolts and nuts to 29 ft. lbs.
    c. When attaching halfshaft flange to transmission end, make sure mating surfaces are clean and free from grease. Apply a thin coat of copper paste to bolt threads and **torque** to 59 ft. lbs.

1999–2001

1. Remove air cleaner assembly.
2. Disconnect tank venting valve tube and electrical connector.
3. Disconnect idle speed positioner and throttle potentiometer electrical connectors.
4. Disconnect accelerator cable, then remove throttle body.
5. Disconnect vent line for oil separator at intake distributor.
6. Disconnect all hose clamps at intake distributor and push rubber sleeves to one side.
7. Pull out intake distributor towards the rear.
8. Disconnect starter motor electrical connectors.
9. Remove starter motor upper attaching bolt, using three long extensions, a universal joint and suitable socket.
10. Remove lower attaching bolt, then the starter.
11. Reverse procedure to install, noting the following:
    a. **Torque** starter motor attaching bolts to 33 ft. lbs.
    b. **Torque** M8 terminal nut to 11 ft. lbs.
    c. **Torque** M6 terminal nut to 60 inch lbs.
    d. Check air distributor and tubes for leaks.

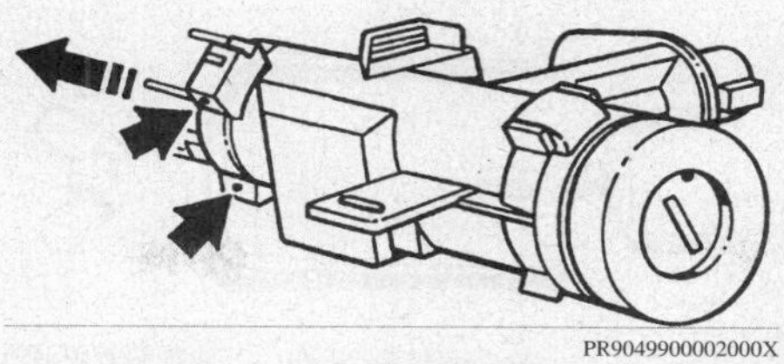

Fig. 2 Ignition switch removal. Boxster & 1999–2001 911

ALTERNATOR

REPLACE

BOXSTER

1. Remove righthand seat and open rear wall cover.
2. Disconnect alternator and starter battery power leads.
3. Remove serpentine drive belt as outlined in "2.5L & 3.2L Engines" section.
4. Remove righthand mount bolt and loosen lefthand mounting bolt three turns, then gently tab bolt to loosen threaded bushed in alternator arm, use a suitable aluminum mandrel to tap bolt.
5. Remove alternator from slotted bracket, then the deflection roller.
6. Turn alternator clockwise so swivel arm is near crankcase and the holding arm projects beyond the fastening eye.
7. Carefully pull alternator forward enough to disconnect electrical connections.
8. Remove alternator to front.
9. Reverse procedure to install. **Torque** M8 bolts to 11 ft. lbs., M10 bolts to 33 ft. lbs. and M16 bolts to 45–51 ft. lbs. **Alternator lead must be on top of starter lead when connecting battery power point.**

911

1998

Removal

1. Remove V-Belt cover and belt.
2. Remove fan wheel from alternator/cooling fan assembly using puller tool No. VW 202, or equivalent.
3. Disconnect alternator electrical connector, then the alternator harness to engine ground wires, **Fig. 1.**
4. Remove alternator mounting bolts and the alternator.

Installation

1. Install alternator into cooling fan housing. Ensure connections for B+ and terminal D+ are positioned opposite TDC line mark (located on edge of cooling fan housing).
2. Apply a thin coat of Loctite 270, or equivalent, to alternator shaft, and install alternator cooling fan wheel onto shaft. **Torque** fan wheel to 10 ft. lbs.
3. Install air guide shroud and connect alternator harness to engine ground wires.
4. Place alternator with cooling fan housing onto locating pin on crankcase and tighten retaining strap.
5. When installed properly, wiring harness will exit air guide shroud towards right.

1999–2001

1. Remove air cleaner assembly.
2. Remove accessory drive belt.
3. Disconnect vacuum switchover valve electrical connector, then remove switchover valve from bracket.
4. Remove bracket and the intake distributor.
5. Remove alternator attaching bolts and the idler pulley.
6. Turn alternator clockwise so swivel arm is near crankcase and holding arm projects beyond the fastening eye.
7. Carefully pull alternator back and disconnect electrical connector.
8. Reverse procedure to install, noting the following:
    a. **Torque** M16 bolts to 45–51 ft. lbs.
    b. **Torque** M10 bolts to 33 ft. lbs.
    c. **Torque** M8 nut to 11 ft. lbs.
    d. Replace vacuum brake booster sealing ring.

IGNITION SWITCH

REPLACE

BOXSTER & 1999–2001 911

1. Ensure ignition is in the "0" position.
2. Remove air duct from under lefthand side of instrument panel.
3. Disconnect ignition switch electrical connector.
4. Remove locking paint from threaded bores of ignition switch, **Fig. 2.**
5. Loosen ignition switch attaching screws with tool No. 9631, or equivalent.
6. Pull ignition switch from housing.
7. Reverse procedure to install.

1998 911

1. Remove ignition switch cover.
2. Drill out shear bolts and remove retaining screw.
3. Pull switch down far enough to allow removal of electrical connectors.
4. Remove ignition/starter switch retaining screws, then the switch.
5. Reverse procedure to install, tightening shear bolts until heads break off.

HEADLAMP SWITCH

REPLACE

1. Pull switch knob out as far as possible, press lower side locking element with suitable small screwdriver and remove knob.
2. Remove lefthand vent Torx screws and carefully pull side vent out of dash panel.

3. Remove electrical connectors and mounting nut.
4. Pull switch out approximately .2 inch, then turn clockwise and remove.
5. Reverse procedure to install. **Torque** mounting nut to 30 inch lbs.

STOP LIGHT SWITCH

REPLACE

1. Disconnect electrical connector.
2. Remove retaining screws, then the switch.
3. Reverse procedure to install.

STEERING WHEEL

REPLACE

1. Remove horn pad.
2. Remove air bag module as outlined in "Air Bag System" section.
3. Mark position of steering wheel to steering shaft.
4. Remove retaining nut, then the steering wheel with washer.
5. Reverse procedure to install. **Torque** retaining nut to 33 ft. lbs.

INSTRUMENT CLUSTER

REPLACE

BOXSTER & 1999-2001 911

1. Insert two small screwdrivers into small openings on each side of the hazard warning switch, then pull button off of switch.
2. Remove hazard warning switch from instrument cluster.
3. Remove instrument cluster attaching screw located inside warning switch opening.
4. Remove plug from lefthand side of instrument cluster, then the cluster attaching screw from opening.
5. Disconnect instrument cluster electrical connectors.
6. Remove instrument cluster from instrument panel.
7. Reverse procedure to install.

1998 911

1. Disconnect instrument cluster electrical connectors. Connectors are accessible through the luggage compartment.
2. **On models equipped with mechanical speedometer,** remove flex shaft knurled nut.
3. **On all models,** remove knurled instrument retaining nuts and retaining clamp.
4. Remove instrument cluster from instrument panel.
5. Reverse procedure to install.

WIPER MOTOR

REPLACE

BOXSTER & 1999-2001 911

1. Remove battery and windshield washer fluid tank covers.

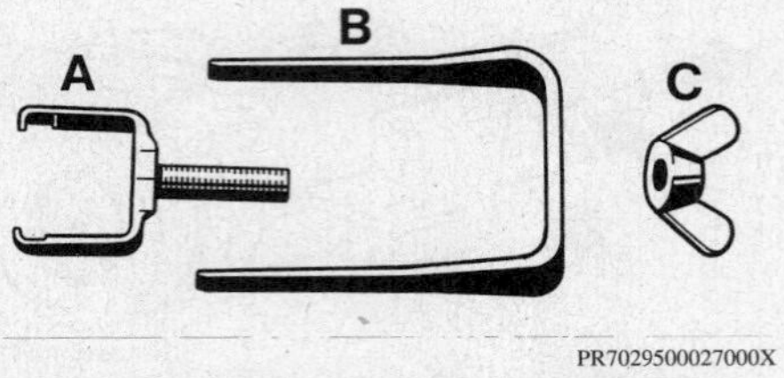

Fig. 3 Blower motor puller tool 9512. 1998 911

2. Remove attaching nut and wiper link.
3. Remove mounting bolts, raise link and pull motor downwards.
4. Disconnect electrical connector.
5. Reverse procedure to install, noting the following:
   a. Align link and motor in park position, marked with "0" on console.
   b. **Torque** mounting screw to 72 inch lbs. and mounting bolts to 7 ft. lbs.
   c. **Torque** link nut to 12 ft. lbs.

1998 911

1. Remove luggage compartment cover from rear of compartment.
2. Remove wiper arms and rubber discs below wiper arms, then the retaining hex nuts.
3. Remove wiper motor with linkage downward and disconnect electrical connector.
4. Remove wiper motor from linkage.
5. Reverse procedure to install.

WIPER TRANSMISSION

REPLACE

BOXSTER & 1999-2001 911

1. Remove heating and air conditioning system, battery and fluid tank covers.
2. Remove left and right wiper arms, then the cowl panel.
3. Remove lefthand dome strut and wiper link mounting bolts.
4. Disconnect wiper motor electrical connector.
5. Remove wiper link with motor.
6. Reverse procedure to install. **Torque** mounting bolts to 84 inch lbs. and wiper arm nut to 12 ft. lbs.

1998 911

Refer to "Wiper Motor, Replace."

BLOWER MOTOR

REPLACE

BOXSTER & 1999-2001 911

1. Remove footwell bulkhead and righthand air guide, then the blower motor electrical connector and wire.
2. Remove ballast resistor electrical connector.
3. Hold blower motor and remove housing lid mounting screws.
4. Carefully remove blower motor downward.
5. Reverse procedure to install.

1998 911

1. Remove heater and A/C unit cover attaching screws, then the cover.
2. Remove central electrical system fuse/relay box attaching bolts.
3. Remove wiring harness cover located on righthand side of fuse/relay box.
4. Disconnect electrical connector from blower housing cover and place fuse/relay box on fender.
5. On lefthand blower motor, remove reservoir and tank.
6. On left and righthand blower motors, disconnect blower electrical connector and remove firewall.
7. Separate connector and wiring harness from housing cover.
8. Remove knurled retaining nut, then remove clamp from housing cover using a screwdriver.
9. Remove blower housing cover, then the particle filter from housing duct.
10. Remove blower motor mounting bolts.
11. Place part (A) of blower motor puller tool No. 9512, or equivalent, onto shaft and turn to the right, **Fig. 3.**
12. Align cutouts in blower wheel with cutouts in blower housing.
13. Push part (B) of blower motor puller tool No. 9512, or equivalent, into cutouts of blower motor.
14. Tighten wing screw part (C) of blower motor puller tool No. 9512, or equivalent, until blower separates from housing.
15. Reverse procedure to install.

HEATER CORE

REPLACE

1. Remove heater and air conditioning system, battery and fluid reservoir covers.
2. Remove wiper motor and entire wiper link as outlined under "Wiper Transmission, Replace."
3. Remove righthand dome strut and bracket from cowl frame.
4. Clamp heater hoses shut and remove from core.
5. Remove heater core cover, release core and pull up to remove.
6. Reverse procedure to install, sealing cover with suitable butyl adhesive.

EVAPORATOR CORE

REPLACE

BOXSTER & 1999-2001 911

1. Recover A/C system refrigerant.
2. Remove instrument panel as outlined in "Dash Panel Service."
3. Disconnect heater and A/C unit electrical connectors.
4. Disconnect battery positive terminal from current distributor and current distributor front wall.
5. Disconnect both heater hoses from heater core and plug connections.
6. Remove heater and A/C unit to firewall attaching nuts.

7. Remove top righthand side heater and A/C unit bracket.
8. Carefully lower and remove heater and A/C unit from vehicle.
9. Remove evaporator core from heater and A/C unit.
10. Reverse procedure to install.

1998 911

1. Recover A/C system refrigerant.
2. Remove fuel tank as outlined under "Fuel Pump, Replace" in the "3.6L Engine" section.
3. Remove heater and A/C unit cover.
4. Remove central electrical system fuse/relay box attaching bolts.
5. Remove wiring harness cover located on righthand side of fuse/relay box.
6. Disconnect electrical connector from blower housing cover and place fuse/relay box on fender.
7. Disconnect blower electrical connector and remove firewall.
8. Remove fresh air cleaner grille.
9. Remove heater and A/C unit attaching bolts.
10. Disconnect refrigerant pipes from expansion valve. Plug pipes to prevent moisture or dirt from entering the system.
11. Disconnect pressure switch electrical connector.
12. Remove A/C piping bracket and position piping aside.
13. Disconnect condensation and water drain hoses, then push rubber grommets forward.
14. Remove radio, heater and A/C control panel and glove compartment.
15. Remove remaining heater and A/C unit attaching bolts and nuts.
16. Remove side panel and pull off right and left hot air induction flanges.
17. Disconnect servo motor and temperature mixing valves electrical connectors.
18. Separate wiring harness from heater and A/C regulator, then pull harness through to passenger compartment.
19. Beginning with righthand side, pull heater and A/C unit out of vehicle.
20. Remove evaporator core from heater and A/C unit.
21. Reverse procedure to install.

2.5L & 3.2L Engines

NOTE: On Air Bag Equipped Models, Refer To "Air Bag System Precautions" Located In The Front Of This Manual For System Disarming & Arming Procedures.

NOTE: Prior To Performing Any Service Operations Listed In This Section, Consult The "Technical Service Bulletins" Section For Related Information.

INDEX

	Page No.
Air/Oil Separator, Replace	6-11
Camshaft, Replace	6-10
Adjustment	6-10
Replacement	6-10
Cylinder Head, Replace	6-9
Installation	6-9
Removal	6-9
Engine Rebuilding Specifications	6-109
Engine, Replace	6-8
Engine Assemble	6-9
Engine Disassemble	6-9
Fuel Filter, Replace	6-11
Fuel Pump, Replace	6-11
Installation	6-11
Removal	6-11
Intake Manifold, Replace	6-9
Oil Cooler, Replace	6-11
Oil Pan, Replace	6-11
Oil Pump, Replace	6-11
Piston & Rod Assembly	6-10
Precautions	6-8
Air Bag Systems	6-8
Battery Ground Cable	6-8
Serpentine Drive Belt	6-11
Installation	6-11
Removal	6-11
Routing	6-11
Technical Service Bulletins	6-11
Coolant Hose Leaks	6-12
Oil Leak	6-12
Swollen Or Weak Coolant Hoses	6-11
Tightening Specifications	6-13
Valve Clearance Specifications	6-10
Water Pump, Replace	6-11

PRECAUTIONS

AIR BAG SYSTEMS

Refer to "Air Bag System Precautions" in the front of this manual for system disarming and arming procedures.

BATTERY GROUND CABLE

Prior to service, disconnect battery ground cable and isolate as required.

ENGINE

REPLACE

Engine and transmission are removed from under the vehicle. Transmission must be removed before the engine.

1. Remove engine covers and install body protective covers.
2. Raise and support vehicle.
3. Press out lining expanding rivets and disconnect rear luggage compartment engine wiring harness connectors.
4. Pull out control unit connector and push rubber boot through to engine compartment.
5. Remove spoiler and rear panel, then the right and lefthand wheel housing liners.
6. Remove transverse member panel.
7. Remove left and righthand transverse members, then the stabilizer at rear axle.
8. Disconnect oxygen sensor connector, then separate exhaust manifold and catalytic converter flange.
9. Place suitable transmission jack under muffler, remove mounting bolts and lower exhaust system.
10. Support engine on transport carrier with support bridge tool No. 10–22A and support tools No. 9591/A, or equivalents.
11. **On models equipped with manual transmission,** refer to "Clutch & Manual Transmission" section for removal procedure.
12. **On models equipped with automatic transmissions,** refer to "Automatic Transmissions" section for removal procedure.
13. **On all models,** remove underside panels.
14. Place a suitable container under water guide housing, then remove coolant expansion tank and disconnect vent line.
15. Remove water guide housing drain plug, clamp coolant hoses shut and drain coolant.
16. Disconnect accelerator cable, then remove deflection box cover and accelerator cable.
17. Remove power steering connecting line.
18. Remove return hose/servo pipe clips and brake booster vacuum hose.
19. Disconnect fuel return line.
20. **On models equipped with A/C,** proceed as follows:
    a. Remove lefthand seat and rear wall lining, then the engine compartment cover.
    b. Disconnect battery positive cable from engine and set aside.
    c. Remove power steering fluid from reservoir to below joint.
    d. Remove servo reservoir and seal joint from dirt.
    e. Remove compressor front mounting bolts and disconnect electrical connector.
    f. Remove mounting bolts between intake pipes and set compressor aside with hoses connected.
21. **On all models,** remove air flow sensor and throttle body suction hose.
22. Disconnect air flow sensor electrical connector.
23. Remove oil dipstick guide tube, then loosen spring band clamp and remove oil filler hose.
24. Place suitable container under fuel line and remove fuel feed hose.
25. Remove air pump ground strap.
26. Install retainer plate tool No. 9592, or equivalent, to crankcase and support engine with suitable jack.
27. Remove engine cross member, then release supporting bridge suspension hook and transporting shackle hook.
28. Carefully lower engine in stages watching engine for clearance.

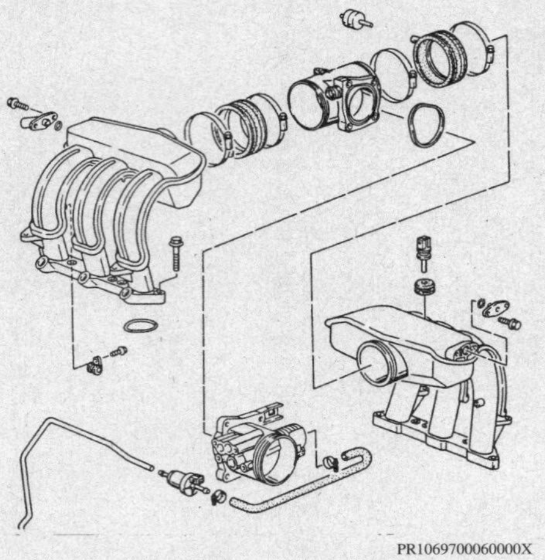

Fig. 1 Intake manifold (distributor) replacement

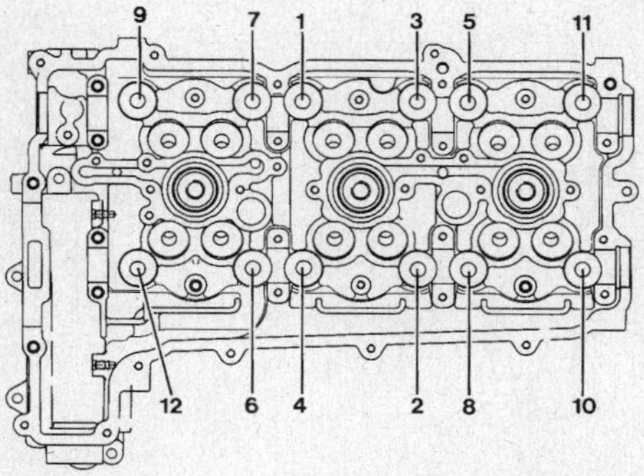

PR1069600047000X

Fig. 2 Cylinder head tightening sequence

29. Reverse procedure to install.

INTAKE MANIFOLD

REPLACE

Refer to **Fig. 1** for intake manifold (distributor) replacement.

CYLINDER HEAD

REPLACE

REMOVAL

1. Remove camshafts as outlined under "Camshaft, Replace."
2. Remove cylinder head attaching bolts.
3. Remove cylinder head and gasket.

INSTALLATION

Chain tensioner areas are different on individual cylinder heads. Front of cylinder heads are marked 1–3 and 4–6.

1. Apply a thin coat of engine oil to cylinder head bolts.
2. **Torque** cylinder head bolts to 22 ft. lbs. using tightening sequence shown in **Fig. 2.**
3. Completely loosen all cylinder head bolts.
4. **Torque** cylinder head bolts to 15 ft. lbs. in sequence.
5. Tighten bolts an additional 90° in sequence.
6. Tighten bolts another 90° in sequence.
7. Install camshafts as outlined under "Camshaft, Replace."

ENGINE DISASSEMBLE

1. Fasten cylinder bank 1–3 (18), **Fig. 3,** to engine holder tool No. 9589, or equivalent.
2. Remove intake manifold (distributor) as outlined under "Intake Manifold, Replace."
3. Remove serpentine drive belt as outlined under "Serpentine Drive Belt."
4. Remove deflection and tensioning rollers.
5. Remove oil pump as outlined under "Oil Pump, Replace."
6. Remove air/oil separator as outlined under "Air/Oil Separator, Replace"
7. Remove camshafts as outlined under "Camshaft, Replace."
8. Remove cylinder head.

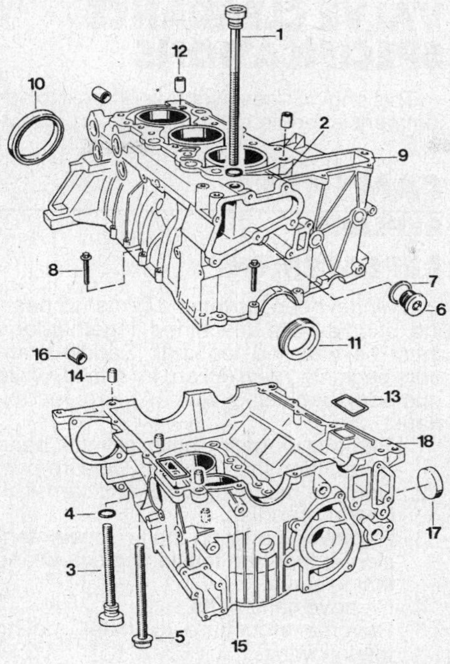

PR1069600044000X

Fig. 3 Engine service

9. Remove bearing housing bolts (1, 3 and 5) and O-rings (2 and 4), then the piston pin assembly bore plug (6) and sealing ring (7).
10. Remove crankcase bolts (8) and release intermediate shaft flange.
11. Remove oil pan and crankcase bolts.
12. Separate cylinder bank half 4–6 (9) from 1–3.
13. Remove crankcase sealing rings (10 and 11), dowel sleeves (12, 15 and 16), gaskets (13), cylindrical pins (14) and closure cap (17).
14. Remove pistons.
15. Remove mounting bolts and slide rail, then the circlip, washer and tensioning rail.
16. Remove intermediate shaft from oil separator, then the chains and O-ring from intermediate shaft.
17. Remove mounting bolts, gaskets and oil separator.
18. Remove bolts, bearing caps, connecting rods and bearing shell halves. Join rods and bearing caps and mark for installation. **Bearing caps must remain with appropriate rods and are not interchangeable.**
19. Remove thrust bearing bolts and separate bearing housing halves.
20. Remove crankcase bearing shelf halves and piston spray nozzles from cylinder bank (1–3).
21. Remove cylindrical and roll pin, and crankshaft.
22. Remove thrust plates, crankcase bearing shell halves, piston spray nozzles, dowel sleeves and tensioning rail pin from cylinder bank (4–6).

ENGINE ASSEMBLE

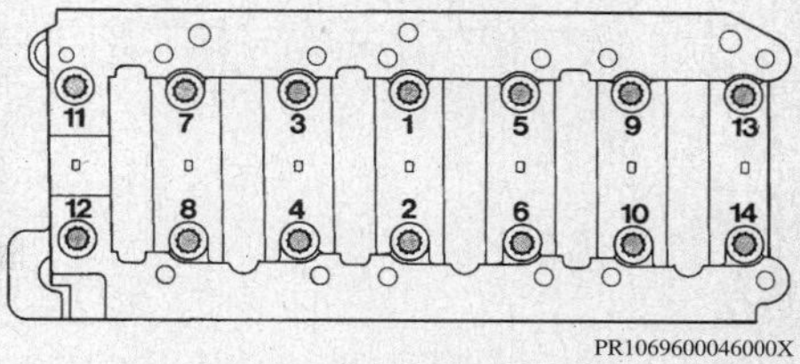

PR1069600046000X

Fig. 4 Thrust bearing bolt tightening sequence

1. Fasten cylinder bank 1–3 (18), **Fig. 3,** to engine holder tool No. 9589, or equivalent.
2. Clean bearing housing surface, especially in oil duct area, deburr edges and ensure dowel sleeves are correctly seated.
3. Ensure sealing balls are correctly caulked
4. Push dowel sleeves to stops of main thrust bearings seven, four and one of cylinder bank (4–6) bearing housing.
5. Press spray nozzles into take-up bores with .1575 inch plastic mandrel.
6. Lay crankshaft bearing shells in main thrust bearing with locating stud on dowel sleeve side and lightly oil running surfaces.
7. Install thrust plates in main thrust bearing four recess of cylinder bank (4–6) bearing housing with oil pockets facing pulley or flywheel side.
8. Install crankshaft and inspect thrust plates for correct seating.
9. Coat thrust bearing bolt threads and contact surfaces with oil. Install and **torque** bolts to 15 ft. lbs., then tighten an additional 90° in sequence shown in **Fig. 4.**
10. Insert gauge with gauge holder tool No. VW 387, or equivalent, into bearing housing and against crankshaft flange.
11. Press crankshaft against gauge by hand and set gauge to zero, then press crankshaft away from gauge and note reading. Crankshaft endplay should be .0031–.0098 inch.
12. Install connecting rod bearing shells into connecting rod. Lubricate sliding surface liberally with Optimol Olista Longtime 3 EP, or equivalent grease.
13. Join connecting rod and bearing cap. Rod bearing twist locks must face each other.
14. Coat bolt threads and contact surface with oil. Install and **torque** bolts to 15 ft. lbs., then tighten an additional 90.°
15. Inspect bearing housing sealing surfaces for damage and cleanliness. Grind off sharp edges.
16. Inspect intermediate shaft flange bearing for ease of movement and roughness.
17. Lightly oil and install intermediate shaft O-ring. **Do not twist O-ring.**
18. Install chain between crankshaft and intermediate drive sprockets.
19. Install slide and tensioning rails.
20. Turn intermediate shaft sprocket clockwise and inspect for upper chain area sag.
21. Before installing bearing housing to cylinder crankcase half (1–3), connect

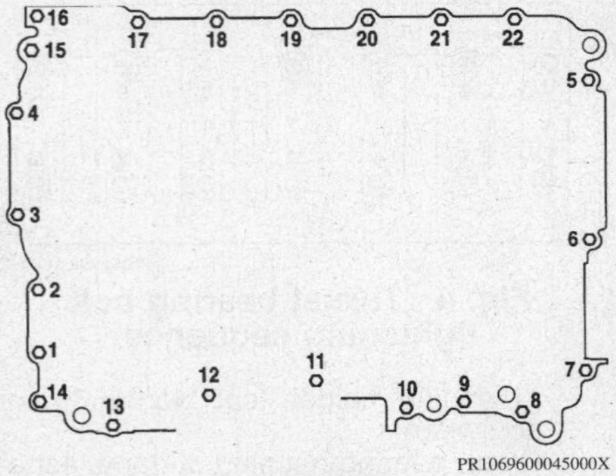

Fig. 5 Crankcase halves tightening sequence

crankshaft and intermediate shaft with O-ring.

22. Fit bearing housing mounting tool No. 9607, or equivalent, and workshop crane into dowel sleeves and carefully lower bearing housing.
23. Turn intermediate shaft flange so both flange lugs face upward with smaller gap towards each other just before final installation position.
24. Install slide rails and connect drive sprocket.
25. Install two plastic spacer sleeve tools No. 9613, or equivalent, with original cylinder head bolts to hold crankcase and bearing housing unit in place.
26. Turn engine until cylinders 1–3 face upward.
27. Assemble pistons as outlined under "Piston & Rod Assembly" and install.
28. Install cylinder head as outlined under "Cylinder Head, Replace."
29. Install camshafts as outlined under "Camshaft, Replace."
30. Install closure cap (17), cylindrical pins (14), new gaskets (13) and dowel sleeves (12, 15 and 16), **Fig. 3.**
31. Install flywheel crankcase sealing ring (11) with insertion device tool No. 9609, or equivalent, and pulley crankcase sealing rings (10) with insertion device tool No. 9610, or equivalent.
32. Apply a uniform .0591 inch bead of Drei Bond silicone type 1209, or equivalent, to cleaned sealing surface of cylinder crankcase half (4–6) and carefully set half in place so bead is not damaged. Halves must be bolted together within five minutes.
33. Tighten bolts to specifications in sequence shown in **Fig. 5.**
34. Install piston pin assembly bore plug (6) with new sealing ring and tighten to specifications.
35. Install bearing housing bolts (1, 3 and 5) with new O-rings (2 and 4) and tighten to specifications.
36. Install air/oil separator as outlined under "Air/Oil Separator."
37. Install oil pump as outlined under "Oil Pump, Replace."
38. Install deflection and tensioning rollers.
39. Install serpentine drive belt as outlined under "Serpentine Drive Belt."
40. Install intake manifold as outlined under "Intake Manifold, Replace."

VALVE CLEARANCE SPECIFICATIONS

This engine uses hydraulic lifters. No adjustment is required.

CAMSHAFT

REPLACE

REPLACEMENT

Cylinder head, cover and camshaft bearing saddles are machined together and must be installed together. Saddle numbers beginning with (E) are for intake, while numbers beginning with (A) are for exhaust.

1. Remove mounting bolts, cylinder head cover, then the camshaft closure cap.
2. Remove mounting bolts and camshaft bearing saddles.
3. Remove mounting bolts, chain tensioner, then the tensioning screw and timing chain.
4. Remove camshafts.
5. Reverse procedure to install, noting the following:
   a. Adjust camshaft timing as outlined under "Adjustment."
   b. Tighten bolts to specifications.
   c. Apply uniform .0591 inch bead of Drei Bond silicone type 1209, or equivalent, to clean sealing surface of cylinder head cover and carefully set in place so bead is not damaged. Head cover must be tightened in place within five minutes.
   d. Tighten cylinder head cover bolts to specification using sequence shown in **Fig. 6.**

ADJUSTMENT

Cylinder head, cover and camshaft bearing saddles are machined together and must be installed together. Saddle numbers beginning with (E) are for intake, while numbers beginning with (A) are for exhaust.

1. Turn crankshaft clockwise until belt pulley (OT) TDC mark aligns with fixing bore on crankcase, then lock pulley into position with dowel pin tool No. 9595, or equivalent.
2. Tension chain with auxiliary chain tensioner tool No. 9599, or equivalent.
3. Turn engine assembly until cylinder row (1–3) is facing upwards.
4. Install assembled camshafts into cylinder head in overlapping position.
5. Install camshaft hold-down tools No. 9611, or equivalent.
6. Install bearing saddles and tighten to specification, remove hold-down tools.
7. Install drive sprocket and driver, then hand tighten mounting bolts.
8. Turn engine assembly until cylinder row (4–6) is facing upwards.
9. Install camshaft hold-down tools No. 9611, or equivalent.
10. Install bearing saddles and tighten to specification, remove hold-down tools.
11. Apply uniform .0591 inch bead of Drei Bond silicone type 1209, or equivalent, to clean cylinder head cover sealing surface, then carefully set in place so bead is not damaged. Head cover must be tightened within five minutes.

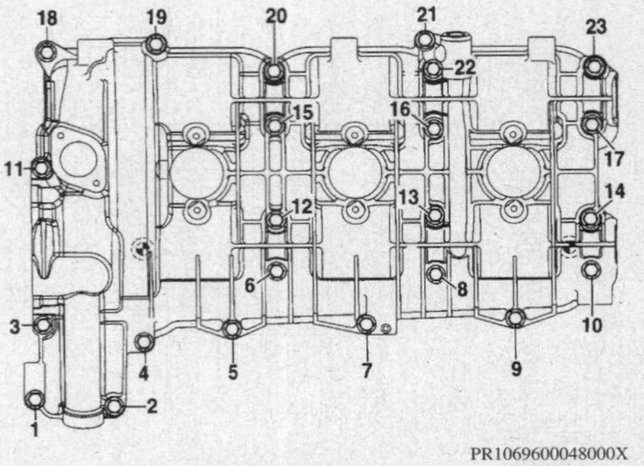

Fig. 6 Cylinder head cover tightening sequence

12. Seal cylinder head cover with suitable silicone, then install mounting bolts and tighten to specification in sequence, **Fig. 6.**
13. Turn engine assembly until cylinder row (1–3) is facing upwards.
14. Seal cylinder head cover with suitable silicone, then install mounting bolts and tighten to specification in sequence, **Fig. 6.**
15. Tension secondary chains with auxiliary chain tensioner tools.
16. Install camshaft timing locking tool No. 9612, or equivalent, and turn intake camshaft until device locking pin lies in camshaft bore.
17. Install chain sprocket bolts and tighten to specification, remove locking device.
18. Turn engine assembly until cylinder row (4–6) is facing upwards.
19. Remove pulley dowel pin and turn crankshaft one full revolution clockwise.

PISTON & ROD ASSEMBLY

1. Ensure circlip is seated securely and with opening opposite piston groove.
2. Put piston into retaining tool No. 9597, or equivalent, with circlip side facing down.
3. Install connecting rod with twist lock recesses diagonally opposite "TOP" marking, then the piston pin.
4. Install new circlip into conical assembly sleeve tool No. 9603, or equivalent.
5. Place assembly tool into assembly tube tool No. 9602, or equivalent.
6. Slide circlip from conical sleeve into assembly tube using assembly aid tool No. 9500/3, or equivalent. Ensure circlip is properly seated in tube.
7. Push assembly tube tool No. 9602, or equivalent, until circlip is in position.
8. Install assembly tube and thrust pin into piston pin eye, push thrust pin down until circlip is heard engaging ring groove.
9. Inspect for proper seating.

OIL PAN

REPLACE

1. Raise and support vehicle.
2. Drain engine oil into a suitable container.
3. Remove oil pan attaching bolts.
4. Separate oil pan from crankcase by lightly tapping at sides with a suitable plastic hammer.
5. Clean oil pan and crankcase sealing surfaces.
6. Seal oil pan sealing surface using Drei Bond Silikon part No. 1209, or equivalent.
7. After sealant has been applied, oil pan must be installed within 5 minutes.

OIL PUMP

REPLACE

1. Remove coolant drain plug and seal.
2. Remove mounting bolts, gaskets and oil pump coolant guide housing.
3. Remove driver and O-ring.
4. Remove plug along with guide pin, piston, spring and sealing ring.
5. Remove mounting bolts, oil pump cover, dowel sleeves and oil seal.
6. Remove mounting bolts, neck and gasket.
7. Remove temperature sensor with sealing ring.
8. Remove mounting bolts, closure cap and gasket.
9. Remove heat exchanger and O-rings.
10. Remove mounting bolts, oil return pumps and O-rings. **Do not lay pumps on drivers.**
11. Reverse procedure to install, noting the following:
    a. Install oil return pump for flywheel side of the (1–3) cylinder head with rotation direction arrow or "1–3" marking facing crankcase.
    b. Install oil return pump for pulley side of the (4–6) cylinder head with rotation direction arrow or "4–6" marking facing coolant temperature sensor.
    c. Install new gaskets, O-rings and sealing rings.
    d. Tighten bolts to specifications.

OIL COOLER

REPLACE

Refer to procedure as outlined under "Oil Pump, Replace."

AIR/OIL SEPARATOR

REPLACE

1. Remove oil pan as previously outlined.
2. Remove mounting bolts and bulkhead box.
3. Remove mounting bolts, O-rings and air/oil separators.
4. Remove O-ring, mounting bolts and oil suction pipe.
5. Remove O-ring, mounting bolt, oil probe holder and grommet.
6. Reverse procedure to install, noting the following:

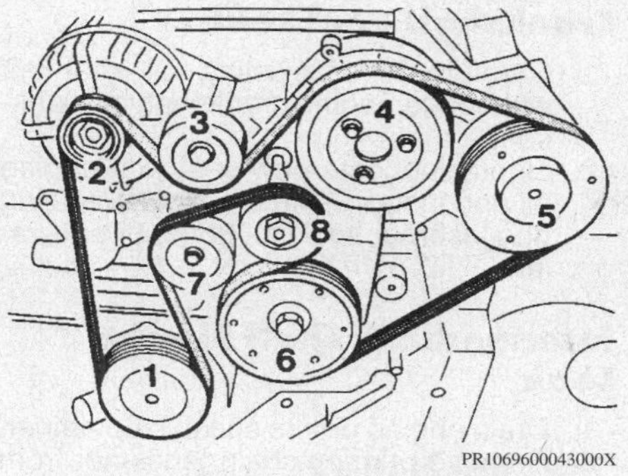

Fig. 7 Serpentine drive belt routing

a. Install new oil suction pipe mounting bolts and drain plug sealing ring.
b. Apply uniform .0591 inch bead of Drei Bond silicone type 1209, or equivalent, to clean oil pan sealing surface.
c. Carefully set oil pan in place so bead is not damaged. Oil pan must be installed within five minutes.
d. Tightening bolts to specifications.

SERPENTINE DRIVE BELT

ROUTING

Refer to **Fig. 7** for drive belt routing.

REMOVAL

1. Remove lefthand seat and disconnect electrical connector.
2. Remove mounting screws, rear wall lining and lid.
3. Mark belt rotational direction.
4. Turn tensioning roller clockwise and remove belt from pulleys.

INSTALLATION

1. Tension belt by hand and install in the following order:
    a. Water pump pulley.
    b. Alternator pulley.
    c. Deflection roller.
    d. Power steering pump pulley.
    e. Air conditioning compressor pulley.
    f. Crankshaft pulley.
    g. Tensioning roller.
2. Turn tensioning roller clockwise and simultaneously fit belt on deflection roller.
3. Slowly relieve tensioning roller.
4. Ensure belt is correctly positioned.
5. Install rear wall liner and lid, then the seat.

WATER PUMP

REPLACE

1. Remove underside panel and clamp coolant hoses shut.
2. Remove drain plug and drain coolant into suitable container.
3. Use suitable pliers to remove spring band clamps.
4. Remove righthand seat and disconnect electrical connector.
5. Remove mounting bolts and rear wall lining cover.
6. Remove serpentine drive belt as outlined under "Serpentine Drive Belt."
7. Remove mounting bolts and water pump. Use suitable flexible head socket wrench to reach lower righthand bolt.
8. Cut out metal seal between water pump and water guide housing.
9. Reverse procedure to install. Cut and install new metal combination seal. Tighten bolts to specification.

FUEL PUMP

REPLACE

REMOVAL

1. Remove holder, battery, mounting bolts and support cover.
2. Disconnect fuel line and electrical connectors.
3. Remove union nut with wrench No. VW 3117, or equivalent.
4. Remove residual fuel to suitable container.
5. Lift fuel gauge, disconnect electrical connector and remove fuel pipes.
6. Hold fuel pump with fuel proof glove, turn to left approximately 15° to disengage bayonet lock and remove pump.

INSTALLATION

1. Install fuel pump with housing edge facing fuel tank installation alignment markings.
2. Turn pump to right as far as stop, then check for proper seating by pulling up on pump.
3. Install sending unit, then turn until unit marks match tank markings.
4. Use wrench No. VW 3217, or equivalent, to tighten new union nut and sealing ring to specifications.
5. Install fuel lines and electrical connector.

FUEL FILTER

REPLACE

1. Remove underside cover.
2. Remove filter ground wire.
3. Place suitable container under filter and remove plug connection.
4. Remove mounting strap and filter.
5. Reverse procedure to install.

TECHNICAL SERVICE BULLETINS

SWOLLEN OR WEAK COOLANT HOSES

On these models, coolant hoses may be swollen and weak. This condition may be caused by Pentosin power steering fluid being spilled onto hoses.

To correct this condition, replace swollen hoses and use extreme caution when adding Pentosin to power steering system.

COOLANT HOSE LEAKS

On some of these models equipped with Tiptronic automatic transmission, the coolant hoses may leak near the transmission. This condition may be caused by insufficient clearance between cooling system hoses and metal pipes and not allowing spring loaded hose clamps enough closing pressure.

To correct this condition, replace spring loaded hose clamps with adjustable band hose clamps.

OIL LEAK

On some of these models, engine may leak oil from flywheel or torque converter drive plate area.

To correct this condition, remove transmission and flywheel or transmission drive plate. Determine from oil trail if leak is coming from crankshaft seal or intermediate shaft flange O-ring.

Crankshaft Seal Leak

1. Carefully lever existing oil seal out without damaging crankshaft or crankcase.
2. Lightly lubricate new seal with engine oil and install using crankcase sealing ring insertion tool No. 9609, or equivalent.

Intermediate Shaft Flange Leak

1. Drain engine oil into suitable container.
2. Remove primary chain tensioner from rear left side rear of crankcase, mounting horizontally next to oil filter.
3. Remove secondary chain tensioner from righthand cylinder head, mounted vertically in rear. **With tensioners removed, do not turn crankcase or chains will jump basic timing.**
4. Remove intermediate shaft flange mounting bolts.
5. Counter holding threaded stud with suitable screwdriver, remove counternut from flange center using special wrench tool No. 9110, or equivalent.
6. Remove flange and O-ring.
7. Lubricate new O-ring lightly with oil and install into flange groove. **Do not roll or cut O-ring on sharp flange edges. Remove sharp edges with emery cloth.**
8. Carefully install flange without applying pressure to threaded stud.
9. As soon as threaded stud emerges from flange center hole, install locking nut and pull flange into position. It may be necessary to pry flange into centered position.
10. After flange enters crankcase, counter hold threaded stud with suitable screwdriver and **torque** locknut to 108 inch lbs.
11. Install new mounting bolts and **torque** to 58 ft. lbs.
12. Install oil drain plug, **torque** to 37 ft. lbs., then fill engine with oil.

TIGHTENING SPECIFICATIONS

Year	Component	Torque, Ft. Lbs.
1998–2001	Air/Oil Separator	84④
	Alternator	33
	Bearing Housing	①
	Bearing Housing Oil Deflector	84④
	Camshaft Bearing Saddle	84④
	Camshaft Drive Pinion	11
	Camshaft Drive Plate	11
	Chain Tensioner	59
	Coolant Guide Housing	33
	Crankcase Bearing Housing	16
	Crankcase Screws	10
	Crankshaft Pulley	37②
	Connecting Rod Screws	①
	Cylinder Head	③
	Cylinder Head Cover	10
	Drive Plate	18②
	Flat-Base Tapped Housing	84④
	Flywheel	18②
	Hall Sender	84④
	Ignition Coil	84④
	Intake Pipe	84④
	Intermediate-Shaft Flange	84④
	Knock Sensor	13–17
	NTC Coolant Temperature	14–22
	Oil Filter	17–19
	Oil Level Sender	15
	Oil Pan	84④
	Oil Pan Plug	37
	Oil Pressure Duct Plug	84④
	Oil Pressure Switch	12–18
	Oil Suction Pipe	84④
	Oxygen Sensor	37–44
	Piston-Pin Plug	59
	Side Rail	84④
	Spark Plug	14–21
	Starter	33
	Thrust Plate	17
	Water Pump	84④

① — Refer to “Engine Assemble” for tightening specification and sequence.
② — Tighten an additional 90.°
③ — Refer to “Cylinder Head, Replace” for tightening specification and sequence.
④ — Inch lbs.

3.4L Engine

NOTE: On Air Bag Equipped Models, Refer To "Air Bag System Precautions" Located In The Front Of This Manual For System Disarming & Arming Procedures.

INDEX

	Page No.
Cooling System Bleed	6-19
Crankshaft Rear Oil Seal, Replace	6-18
Crankshaft Seal, Replace	6-18
Engine Rebuilding Specifications	6-109
Engine, Replace	6-14
Engine Assemble	6-15
Engine Disassemble	6-14
Fuel Filter, Replace	6-20
Fuel Pump, Replace	6-20
Precautions	6-14
Air Bag Systems	6-14
Battery Ground Cable	6-14
Serpentine Drive Belt	6-19
Replacement	6-19
Routing	6-19
Tightening Specifications	6-24
Valve Clearance Specifications	6-18
Water Pump, Replace	6-19

PRECAUTIONS

AIR BAG SYSTEMS

Refer to "Air Bag System Precautions" in the front of this manual for system disarming and arming procedures.

BATTERY GROUND CABLE

Prior to service, disconnect battery ground cable and isolate as required.

ENGINE

REPLACE

The entire engine/transmission assembly is removed in a downward direction.

1. Remove side covers from under side panel near rear jacking points, **Fig. 1.**
2. Raise and support vehicle.
3. Remove rear spoiler and side retaining brackets.
4. Remove coolant drain plug from coolant reservoir and drain coolant into a suitable container.
5. Install new sealing ring on drain plug and reinstall.
6. Lower vehicle.
7. Remove air cleaner assembly.
8. Disconnect oxygen sensor plug connectors.
9. Remove right and left coolant hoses.
10. Suck fluid out of power steering reservoir until level is just below joint.
11. Turn bayonet lock in direction indicated in **Fig. 2,** then pull hose off of reservoir. Immediately seal reservoir with a suitable plug.
12. Disconnect battery positive at B+ disconnection point, **Fig. 3.**
13. Remove disconnection point box retaining nuts and set box aside.
14. Mark accessory drive belt travel direction with a colored pen, then while turning tensioning pulley clockwise with a suitable 24 mm wrench, remove belt.
15. Remove A/C compressor bolts and disconnect electrical connector.
16. Remove compressor with hoses connected, then secure compressor aside with suitable wire.
17. Disconnect engine wiring harnesses

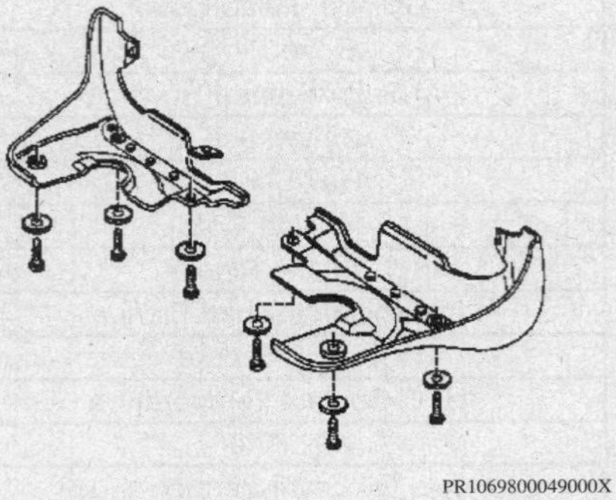

Fig. 1 Rear side covers

located on righthand side of engine compartment.

18. Disconnect vacuum line from brake booster.
19. Disconnect tank vent tube.
20. Disconnect fuel supply line and fuel return line.
21. Raise and support vehicle.
22. Remove rear axle drive shafts, diagonal braces, then the front and rear crossmembers, **Fig. 4.**
23. Disconnect ground strap between engine and body, then the accelerator cable.
24. Disconnect electrical connector and selector lever cable from transmission.
25. Remove transmission selector lever cable from cable mount.
26. Remove lower coolant hoses.
27. Ensure all hoses, electrical connectors and cables are no longer securing engine/transmission assembly to body.
28. Using suitable removal tools, place pre-fitted retainer plate tool No. 9592, or equivalent, on crankcase.
29. Place a suitable jack under pre-fitted retainer plate, then raise slightly.
30. Remove transmission mount retaining nuts.
31. Remove engine carrier to engine mount retaining nuts.
32. Lower engine/transmission assembly slowly and in steps.
33. Before removing engine/transmission assembly entirely from vehicle, disconnect power steering pressure and return lines from reservoir.

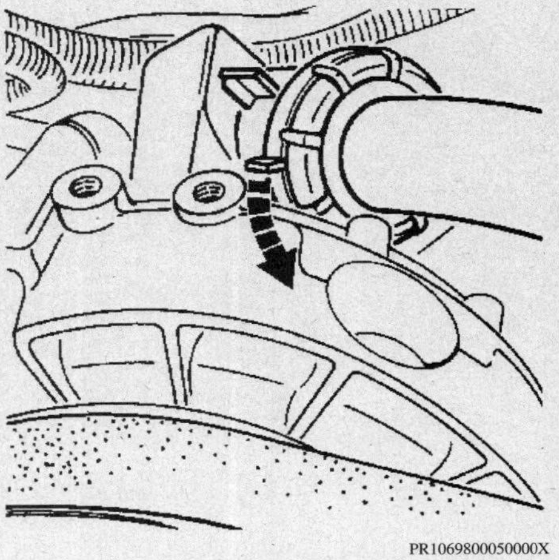

Fig. 2 Bayonet lock open

34. Remove engine/transmission assembly. **If vehicle is to be moved after engine/transmission assembly is removed, install rear crossmember to maintain structural strength.**
35. Reverse procedure to install.

ENGINE DISASSEMBLE

1. Remove intake distributor (manifold) assembly, **Fig. 5.**
2. Remove accessory belt deflection and tensioning rollers.
3. Disconnect accelerator cable and remove throttle body, pull off vacuum check valve.
4. Remove power steering supply tank from bracket, then pull supply tank up and off.
5. Remove power steering hydraulic pump attaching bolts, then the pump from engine.
6. Turn engine so engine oil pan is facing upward.
7. Remove oil drain plug and sealing ring, **Fig. 6.**
8. Remove oil pan attaching bolts, then the bulkhead box attaching bolts.
9. Remove air/oil separators attaching

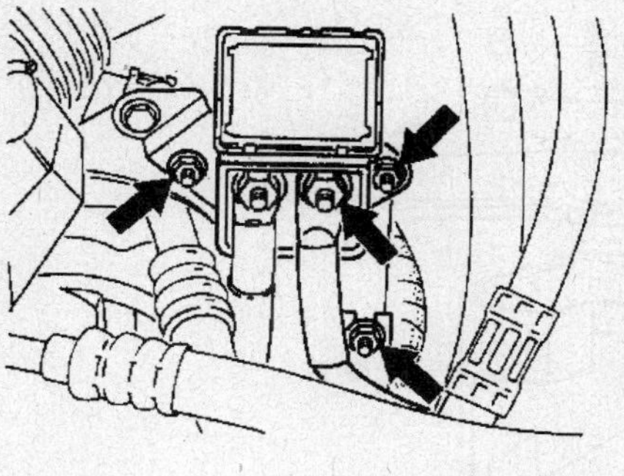

Fig. 3 B+ disconnection point

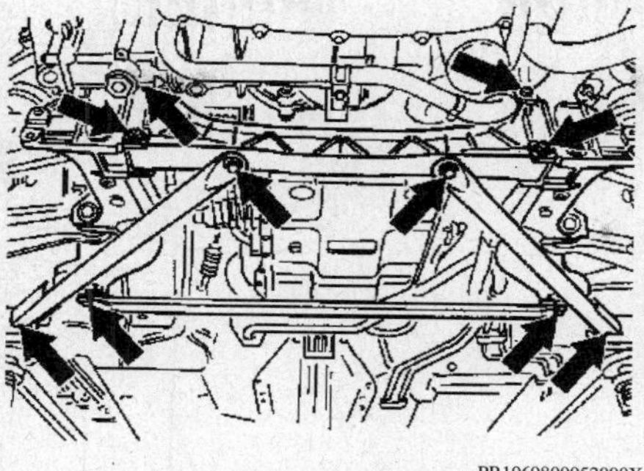

Fig. 4 Diagonal brace & crossmember removal

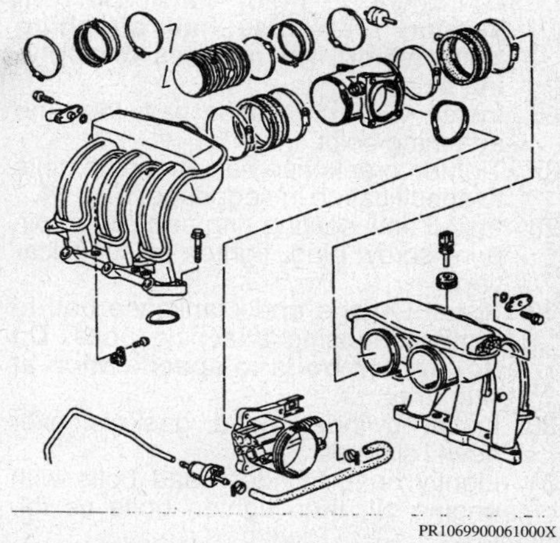

Fig. 5 Intake distributor assembly

bolts, then the air/oil separators and O-rings from crankcase.

10. Remove suction pipe attaching bolts, then the suction pipe and sealing ring.
11. Remove oil probe holder attaching bolt, then the holder and grommet.
12. Remove coolant drain plug and sealing ring, **Fig. 7.**
13. Remove oil pump and coolant guide housing attaching bolts, then the oil pump with coolant guide housing.
14. Remove oil pump and coolant guide housing gaskets.
15. Remove driver and O-ring.
16. Remove plug with guide pin, piston, spring and sealing ring.
17. Remove oil pump cover attaching bolts, then the cover and sealing ring.
18. Remove dowel sleeve, then the neck attaching bolts, neck and gasket.
19. Remove temperature sensor with the captive sealing ring.
20. Remove oil pump/coolant guide cap attaching bolt, then the cap and gasket.
21. Rotate engine so cylinder head cover is facing upward.
22. Remove cylinder head cover attaching bolts, **Fig. 8.**
23. Remove camshaft closure cap, then the tensioning bolt.
24. Remove exhaust camshaft bearing saddle attaching bolts, then the bearing saddle.
25. Remove intake camshaft bearing saddle attaching bolts, then the bearing saddle.
26. Remove camshaft tensioning element attaching bolts, then the tensioning element.
27. Remove timing chain.
28. Remove exhaust and intake camshafts.
29. Remove valve tappets, then the valve tappet guide attaching bolts. **Mark valve tappets for installation reference. Do not use magnetized tools or magnets to remove valve tappets.**
30. Remove shield attaching bolt and shield.
31. Remove outer cylinder attaching bolts.
32. Remove cylinder head attaching bolts, then the cylinder head and gasket.
33. Remove (4–6) crankcase half to intermediate housing attaching bolts and O-rings, **Fig. 9.**
34. Remove screw plug and sealing ring for bore of piston pin.
35. Remove (4–6) crankcase half to (1–3) crankcase half attaching bolts, then the (4–6) crankcase half.
36. Remove (1–3) crankcase half to intermediate housing attaching bolts and O-rings, then the (1–3) crankcase half.
37. Remove intermediate shaft sealing rings, dowel sleeves, gaskets, cylindrical pins and cap.
38. Remove slide rail attaching bolts, then the slide rail, **Fig. 10.**
39. Remove circlip, washer, tensioning rail and tensioning rail lining.
40. Remove intermediate shaft and intermediate shaft chain.
41. Remove camshaft drive chains.
42. Remove O-ring, then the oil separator to bearing housing attaching bolts.
43. Remove oil separator gaskets, then the oil separator from bearing housing.
44. Remove connecting rod bearing cap to connecting rod bolts.
45. Remove thrust bearing retaining bolts.
46. Remove thrust plates, then the crankshaft bearing shells.
47. Remove piston spray nozzles and dowel sleeves.

ENGINE ASSEMBLE

1. Ensure bearing housing sealing balls are in place, **Fig. 11.**
2. Install dowel sleeves into main thrust bearings as far as stop.
3. Press piston spray nozzles into take-up bore using a suitable plastic mandrel.
4. Apply a light coat of oil to crankshaft bearing shells, then lay shells in main thrust bearings and install locating stud on dowel sleeve side.
5. Install thrust plate in recess of main thrust bearing housing half. **Oil pockets must face pulley or flywheel side.**
6. Install crankshaft and check thrust plates for correct seating.
7. Lightly coat thrust bearing bolts with oil, then using tightening sequence **Fig. 12, torque** thrust bearing bolts to 15 ft. lbs., then an additional 90.°
8. Check crankshaft axial play as follows:
   a. Mount a suitable dial gauge onto bearing housing.
   b. Place gauge against crankshaft flange.
   c. Press crankshaft by hand against gauge and set gauge to zero.
   d. Press crankshaft away from gauge and observe gauge reading.
   e. Axial play should be .0032–.0098.
9. Apply a generous coat of Optimal Olista Longtime 3 P, or equivalent, grease to connecting rod bearing shells and connecting rod sliding surface.
10. Install connecting rod bearing shells into connecting rods.
11. Attach connecting rod and connecting rod bearing cap. Ensure connecting rod bearing twist lock recesses face each other.
12. Coat connecting rod bearing cap bolts with oil, then tighten to specification.
13. Check intermediate shaft and bearing housing sealing surfaces for damage or sharp edges, **Fig. 13.**
14. Check intermediate shaft flange bearing for ease of movement or roughness, replace shaft if necessary.
15. Apply a light coat of oil to O-ring, then install ring into groove of intermediate shaft.
16. Install chain between crankshaft drive sprocket and intermediate shaft drive sprocket.
17. Install slide and tensioning rails, then turn intermediate shaft sprocket slightly by hand in a clockwise direction and check for sag in upper chain area. If sag is apparent, check chain installation.
18. Before installing bearing housing into crankshaft half, place a suitable O-ring around crankshaft and intermediate shaft.
19. Install oil separator gaskets and attaching bolts, tighten to specification.
20. Install camshaft drive chains onto intermediate shaft, **Fig. 10.**
21. Install tensioning rail lining and tensioning rail.
22. Install washer, circlip, slide rail, then the tensioning and slide rail attaching bolts, tighten to specification.
23. Install (1–3) crankcase half, cap and dowel sleeves, **Fig. 9.**
24. Install cylindrical pins, gaskets, dowel sleeves and sealing rings.
25. Apply Drei Bond silicone type 1209, or

equivalent, to (4–6) crankcase half. **Tighten crankcase half attaching bolts within five minutes of applying sealer.**

26. Install (4–6) crankcase half, then the attaching bolts.
27. Tighten crankcase half attaching bolts to specification in sequence, **Fig. 14.**
28. Install new sealing ring and piston pin bore screw plug, tighten to specification.
29. Install O-rings and crankcase half to bearing housing attaching bolts. **Do not tighten bolts to specification at this time.**
30. Install cylinder head gaskets over dowel sleeves.
31. Lightly coat cylinder head bolts with engine oil, then tighten bolts as follows:
    a. **Torque** cylinder head bolts to 23 ft. lbs. in sequence, **Fig. 15.**
    b. Completely loosen all bolts.
    c. **Torque** bolts to 15 ft. lbs. in sequence.
    d. Tighten bolts an additional 60° in sequence.
    e. Tighten bolts an additional 60° in sequence.
32. Tighten crankcase half to bearing housing bolts to specification.
33. Install oil pump mounting studs into crankcase, **Fig. 7.**
34. Install oil pump cap gasket, cap, then the cap attaching bolts.
35. Install temperature sensor sealing ring, then the sensor.
36. Install coolant neck gasket, coolant neck, then the attaching bolts.
37. Install oil pump cover dowel sleeves, cover sealing ring, cover, then the cover attaching bolts.
38. Install sealing ring, spring, piston, then the plug with guide pin.
39. Install O-ring and oil pump driver.
40. Install oil pump and coolant guide housing gaskets, then the pump and guide housing. Tighten bolts to specification.
41. Install sealing ring, then the coolant drain plug.
42. Install oil probe holder, **Fig. 6.**
43. Install O-ring and oil suction pipe.
44. Install air/oil separators, then the bulkhead box.
45. Install oil pan, then the oil pan drain plug.
46. Install guide rail, then the guide rail attaching bolts. Tighten bolts to specification.
47. Turn crankshaft clockwise until bore "OT Zyl.1" in belt pulley is aligned with fixing bore on crankcase. Insert fixing pin tool No. 9595, or equivalent, to hold pulley in position.
48. Install auxiliary chain tensioner tool No. 9599, or equivalent, onto crankcase half of cylinder bank (4–6), hand tighten.
49. Install shield onto front of (1–3) cylinder head.
50. Prepare camshafts for installation as follows:
    a. Place intake and exhaust camshafts on a soft surface.

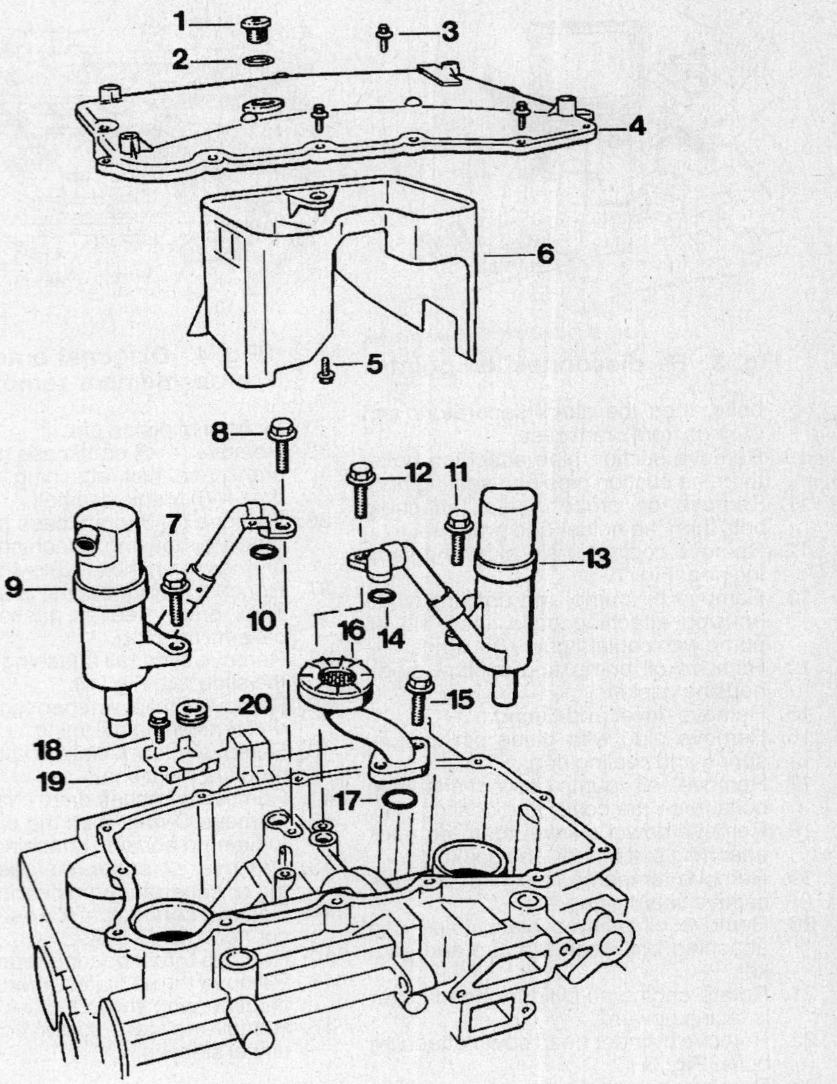

1. Oil Drain Plug
2. Sealing Ring
3. Oil Pan Bolts
4. Oil Pan
5. Bulkhead Box Bolts
6. Bulkhead Box
7. Air/Oil Separator Bolt
8. Air/Oil Separator Bolt
9. Air/Oil Separator
10. O-ring
11. Air/Oil Separator Bolt
12. Air/Oil Separator Bolt
13. Air/Oil Separator
14. O-ring
15. Oil Suction Pipe Bolt
16. Oil Suction Pipe
17. O-ring
18. Oil Probe Holder
19. Grommet

PR1069900063000X

Fig. 6 Air/oil separator assembly

    b. Place chain on camshaft drive sprockets, align chain links with marks on camshaft sprockets, **Fig. 16.**
    c. Install tensioning tool No. 9632, or equivalent, with groove in camshaft position sensor housing pointing upward, **Fig. 17.**

51. Install assembled camshafts on cylinder head (1–3) as follows:
    a. Turn engine on engine support until cylinder (1–3) faces upward.
    b. Install valve tappet guide, then tighten guide attaching bolts to specification.
    c. Install valve tappets.
    d. Install timing chain onto intake and exhaust camshafts.
    e. Align links in chain with camshaft sprockets, then install tensioning

element tool No. 9632, or equivalent.
- f. Place camshaft assembly into cylinder head. Ensure groove on camshaft position sensor cover is facing upward.
- g. Align camshafts with holding tool Nos. 9611 (inside cylinder head) and 9624 (outside cylinder head).
- h. Ensure bearing saddle dowel sleeves are properly seated in cylinder head.
- i. Grease bearing surface, then install bearing saddles.
- j. Tighten bearing saddle bolts evenly to specification. **Ensure bearing saddles are installed in the correct position by comparing pairing Nos. of cylinder head, cylinder head cover and bearing saddles.**
- k. Install Variocam and tighten to specification.
- l. Remove chain tensioning tool No. 9632, or equivalent.
- m. Install chain sprocket on exhaust camshaft and tighten to specification.
- n. Place driveplate on sprocket wheel and hand tighten bolts so sprocket can still be rotated.
- o. Install auxiliary chain tensioner tool No. 9599, or equivalent, without sealing ring on cylinder head and hand tighten, **Fig. 18.**
- p. Adjust **torque** bolt on sprocket wheel to 90 inch lbs.
- q. Remove camshaft holding device tool No. 9611 (inside cylinder head), or equivalent.
- r. Apply a bead of suitable silicone sealant to cylinder head to cylinder head cover sealing surface.
- s. Install cylinder head cover and tighten attaching bolts to specification.
- t. Remove camshaft holding tool No. 9624 (outside cylinder head), or equivalent.

52. Install assembled camshafts on cylinder head (4–6) as follows:
- a. Turn engine on engine support until cylinder (4–6) faces upward.
- b. Install valve tappet guide, then tighten guide attaching bolts to specification.
- c. Install valve tappets.
- d. Install timing chain onto intake and exhaust camshafts.
- e. Align links in chain with camshaft sprockets, then install tensioning element tool No. 9632, or equivalent.
- f. Place camshaft assembly into cylinder head. Ensure groove on camshaft position sensor cover is facing upward.
- g. Align camshafts with holding tool Nos. 9611 (inside cylinder head) and 9624 (outside cylinder head).
- h. Ensure bearing saddle dowel sleeves are properly seated in cylinder head.
- i. Grease bearing surface, then install bearing saddles.
- j. Tighten bearing saddle bolts evenly to specification. **Ensure bearing saddles are installed in the correct position by comparing pairing Nos. of cylinder head, cylinder head cover and bearing saddles.**
- k. Install Variocam and tighten to specification.
- l. Remove chain tensioning tool No. 9632, or equivalent.
- m. Install chain sprocket on exhaust camshaft and tighten to specification.
- n. Place driveplate on sprocket wheel and hand tighten bolts so sprocket can still be rotated.
- o. Install auxiliary chain tensioner tool No. 9599, or equivalent, without sealing ring on cylinder head and hand tighten, **Fig. 18.**
- p. Adjust **torque** bolt on sprocket wheel to 90 inch lbs.
- q. Remove camshaft holding device tool No. 9611 (inside cylinder head), or equivalent.
- r. Apply a bead of suitable silicone sealant to cylinder head to cylinder head cover sealing surface.
- s. Install cylinder head cover and tighten attaching bolts to specification.
- t. Remove camshaft holding tool No. 9624 (outside cylinder head), or equivalent.

53. Adjust camshaft timing for cylinder bank (1–3) as follows:
- a. Turn engine to installation position on support stand.
- b. Remove position pin from crankshaft pulley and turn crankshaft pulley 360° clockwise until pulley OT Zyl. 1 (TDC) mark is aligned with

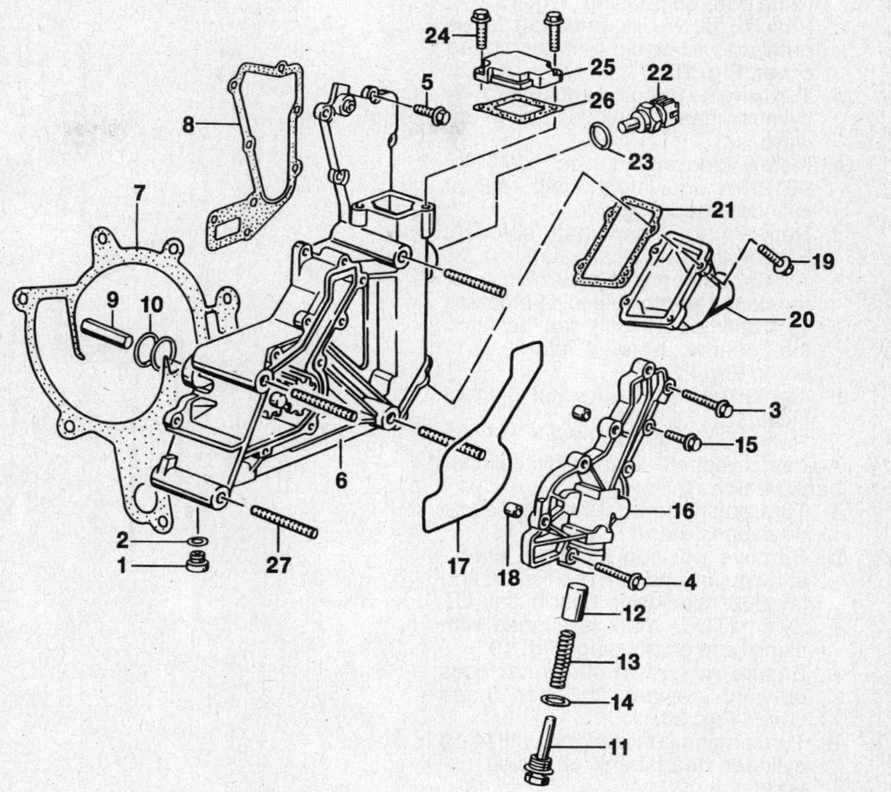

1. Coolant Drain Plug
2. Sealing Ring
3. Oil Pump & Coolant Guide Housing Bolt
4. Oil Pump & Coolant Guide Housing Bolt
5. Oil Pump & Coolant Guide Housing Bolt
6. Oil Pump & Coolant Guide
7. Gasket
8. Gasket
9. Driver
10. O-ring
11. Guide Pin Plug
12. Piston
13. Spring
14. Sealing Ring
15. Oil Pump Cover Bolts
16. Oil Pump Cover
17. Sealing Ring
18. Dowel Sleeve
19. Coolant Neck Bolts
20. Coolant Neck
21. Gasket
22. Temperature Sensor
23. Sealing Ring
24. Cap Bolt
25. Cap
26. Gasket
27. Studs

PR1069900064000X

Fig. 7 Oil pump & coolant guide housing

fixing bore on housing, **Fig. 19.**
c. Ensure groove in camshaft faces outward toward cylinder head cover, **Fig. 20.**
d. Turn engine 90° on stand until (1–3) cylinder head bank is facing upward.
e. Install blocking device tool No. 9612, or equivalent, onto rear of cylinder head, **Fig. 21.**
f. Remove four camshaft sprocket bolts from front of camshaft.
g. Align camshafts by turning pretensioned center piece of blocking tool until sword bolt can be fitted into bearing bore of intake camshaft, **Fig. 22.**
h. Tighten camshaft sprocket to specification.
i. Remove blocking device.

54. Adjust camshaft timing for cylinder bank (4–6) as follows:
  a. Turn engine to installation position on support stand.
  b. Remove position pin from crankshaft pulley and turn crankshaft pulley 360° clockwise until pulley OT Zyl. 1 (TDC) mark is aligned with fixing bore on housing, **Fig. 19.**
  c. Ensure groove in camshaft faces outward toward cylinder head cover, **Fig. 20.**
  d. Turn engine 90° on stand until (4–6) cylinder head bank is facing upward.
  e. Install blocking device tool No. 9612, or equivalent, onto rear of cylinder head, **Fig. 21.**
  f. Remove four camshaft sprocket bolts from front of camshaft.
  g. Align camshafts by turning pretensioned center piece of blocking tool until sword bolt can be fitted into bearing bore of intake camshaft, **Fig. 22.**
  h. Tighten camshaft sprocket to specification.
  i. Remove blocking device.
55. Install (1–3) oil extraction pump, ensure direction arrow (1–3) faces crankcase, **Fig. 23.**
56. Install (4–6) oil extraction pump, ensure direction arrow (4–6) faces crankcase, **Fig. 24.**
57. Install drive belt tensioners and rollers.
58. Install drive belt in the following order:
  a. Coolant pump pulley.
  b. Alternator drive pulley.
  c. Deflection roller.
  d. Power steering pump drive pulley.
  e. A/C compressor pulley.
  f. Crankshaft pulley.
  g. Turn tensioning roller clockwise and install belt over roller.
59. Install intake distributor assembly, **Fig. 5.**

VALVE CLEARANCE SPECIFICATIONS

This engine uses hydraulic lifters. No adjustment is required.

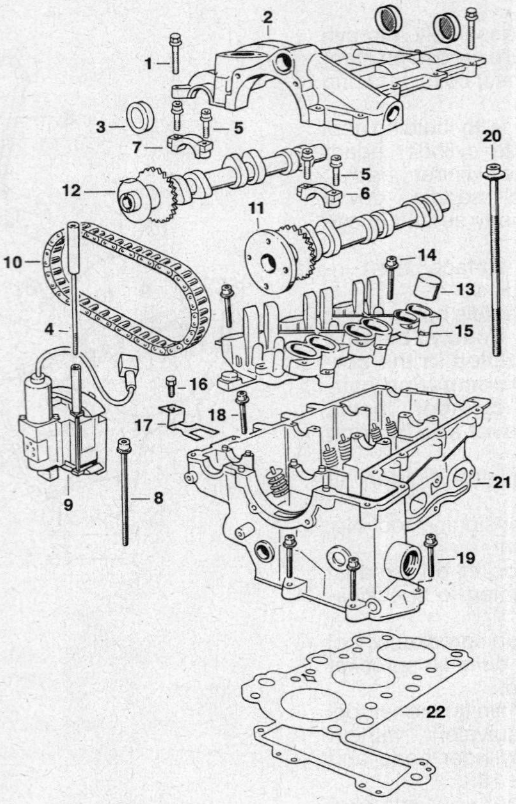

1. Cylinder Head Cover Bolts
2. Cylinder Head Cover
3. Camshaft Closure Cap
4. Tensioning Bolt
5. Camshaft Bearing Saddle Bolts
6. Exhaust Camshaft Bearing Saddle
7. Intake Camshaft Bearing Saddle
8. Tensioning Tool Bolt
9. Camshaft Tensioning Tool
10. Timing Chain
11. Exhaust Camshaft
12. Intake Camshaft
13. Valve Tappet
14. Valve Tappet Guide Bolts
15. Valve Tappet Guide
16. Cylinder Head Shield Bolt
17. Cylinder Head Shield (1-3)
18. Bolt w/Captive Washer
19. Bolt w/Captive Washer
20. Cylinder Head Bolts (Replace)
21. Cylinder Head Bolts (Can Reuse)
22. Cylinder Head Gasket

PR1069900062000X

Fig. 8 Cylinder head cover & camshaft drive

CRANKSHAFT SEAL

REPLACE

1. Remove air cleaner assembly collar screw, then disconnect oil filler neck.
2. Remove hose clamp from throttle body and disconnect mass air flow meter electrical connector.
3. Remove air cleaner assembly.
4. Rotate belt tensioner clockwise and remove drive belt.
5. Remove crankshaft pulley attaching bolt, using pulley holding tool No. 9593, or equivalent.
6. Insert suitable sheetmetal screw into seal.
7. Remove seal from opening using suitable prying lever.
8. Reverse procedure to install, noting the following:
  a. Coat seal with clean engine oil.
  b. Tighten crankshaft pulley to specification.

CRANKSHAFT REAR OIL SEAL

REPLACE

1. **On models equipped with automatic transmissions,** remove transmission as outlined in "Automatic Transmissions" section, then the flywheel.
2. **On models equipped with manual transmissions,** remove transmission as outlined in "Clutch & Manual Transmissions" section, then the driveplate.
3. **On all models,** pry sealing ring from crankshaft opening.
4. Reverse procedure to install, noting the following:

a. Coat new sealing ring and sealing surface with clean engine oil.
b. Install seal with seal installation tool No. 9609, or equivalent.

SERPENTINE DRIVE BELT

ROUTING

Refer to **Fig. 25** for serpentine drive belt routing.

REPLACEMENT

1. Remove air cleaner assembly.
2. Turn tensioning pulley clockwise to relieve tension from belt.
3. Remove belt.
4. Reverse procedure to install.

COOLING SYSTEM BLEED

The engine cooling system is factory filled with a lifetime engine coolant. This engine coolant must not be mixed or replaced with other coolants. Use only original Porsche coolant, or equivalent, when changing or topping up the engine coolant.

1. Ensure there is no pressure in system and remove fill cap.
2. Lift bow on bleeder valve.
3. **On models equipped with automatic transmission,** proceed as follows:
   a. Ensure pneumatically triggered coolant shutoff valve (flat seat valve) is open.
   b. Electric switch over valve must be switched off.
   c. In normal operation this occurs with ignition switched on or with engine running at engine temperature of 185°F or higher.
   d. Triggering can be performed either with a Porsche System Tester or equivalent, or by pulling transmission control module fuse B1, **Fig. 26. Ensure ignition switch is off before pulling fuse.**
4. **On all models,** ensure coolant shutoff valve is open.
5. Fill coolant until level is at bottom edge of filler neck.
6. Run engine at idle speed, then add coolant until no more coolant can be added.
7. Close regulator and run engine at 2500 RPM until it reaches operating temperature (approximately 10 minutes).
8. Turn on both coolant fans as follows:
   a. Remove coolant fan relays from relay carrier located behind left-hand side kick panel.
   b. Insert jumper tool No. 964.610, or equivalent, into relay sockets.
9. Run engine at 2500 RPM for an additional five minutes, during this time rev engine to 5000 RPM every 30 seconds. **Ensure coolant level stays above "MIN" mark of reservoir during bleed procedure.**
10. Remove jumper from coolant fan relay sockets.

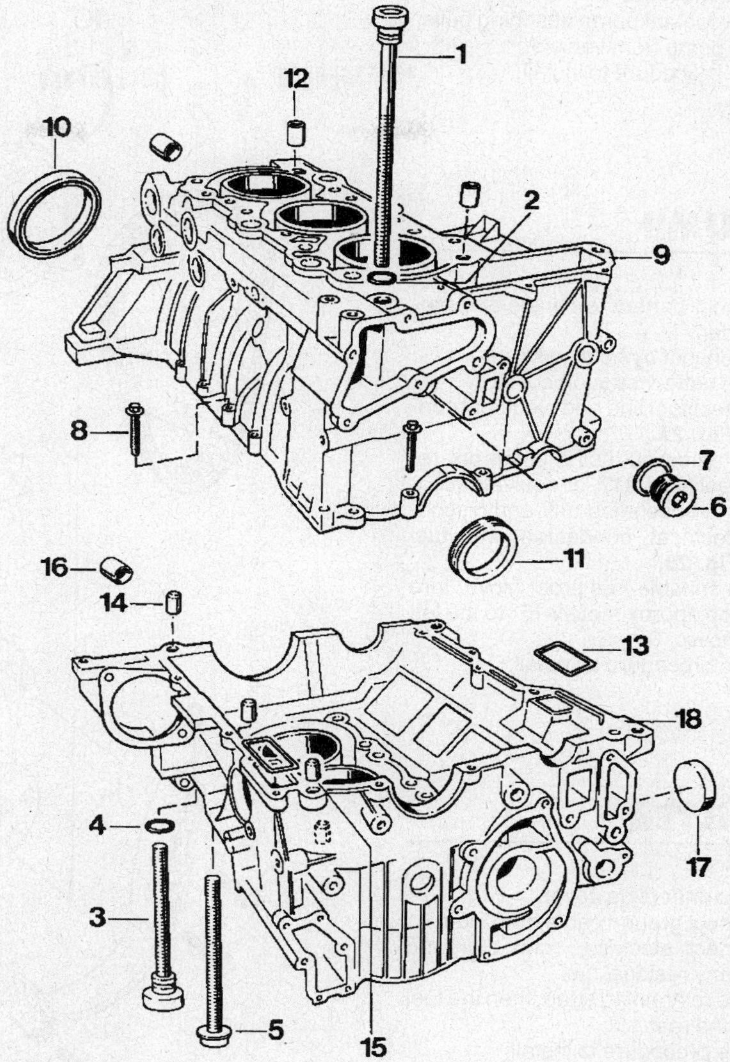

1. Bearing Housing Bolt
2. O-ring
3. Bearing Housing Bolt
4. O-ring
5. Bearing Housing Bolt
6. Piston Pin Assembly Bore Plug
7. Sealing Ring
8. Crankcase Half Bolts
9. Crankcase Half (4-6)
10. Sealing Ring
11. Sealing Ring
12. Dowel Sleeve
13. Gasket
14. Cylindrical Pin
15. Dowel Sleeve
16. Dowel Sleeve
17. Cap
18. Crankcase Half (1-3)

PR1069900065000X

Fig. 9 Crankcase halves

11. Allow engine to cool completely (approximately 25 minutes).
12. Carefully open reservoir cap and add coolant until level reaches "MAX" level mark.
13. Reposition bow of bleeder valve.
14. **On models equipped with automatic transmission,** reactivate ATF shutoff valve.

WATER PUMP

REPLACE

1. Drain coolant into a suitable container.
2. Clamp shut coolant hoses with hose clamp tool No. 3093, or equivalent.
3. Remove air cleaner assembly.
4. Remove accessory drive belt.
5. Disconnect engine stabilizer by removing both bearing blocks.
6. Fasten support bridge tool No. 9624/1, or equivalent, at take up points on bearing blocks.
7. Screw in pressure screw until pressure disc contacts with crankcase under slight pressure.
8. Remove bracket for catalytic converter.

9. Undo engine carrier.
10. Remove coolant pump attaching bolts, then the pump from vehicle.
11. Reverse procedure to install.

FUEL PUMP

REPLACE

1. Disconnect battery terminals and battery holder.
2. Lift battery out by holding strap.
3. Remove battery support cover.
4. Disconnect fuel line and electrical connector, **Fig. 27.**
5. Loosen union nut using union nut remover tool No. 3217, or equivalent.
6. Lift fuel tank sending unit and disconnect electrical connector and fuel pipes, **Fig. 28.**
7. Using a suitable fuel proof glove, turn fuel pump approximately 15° to the left and remove.
8. Reverse procedure to install.

FUEL FILTER

REPLACE

1. Remove underside cover.
2. Disconnect ground cable from filter.
3. Disconnect electrical connector and collect any residual fuel.
4. Remove restraining strap, then the fuel filter to the rear.
5. Reverse procedure to install.

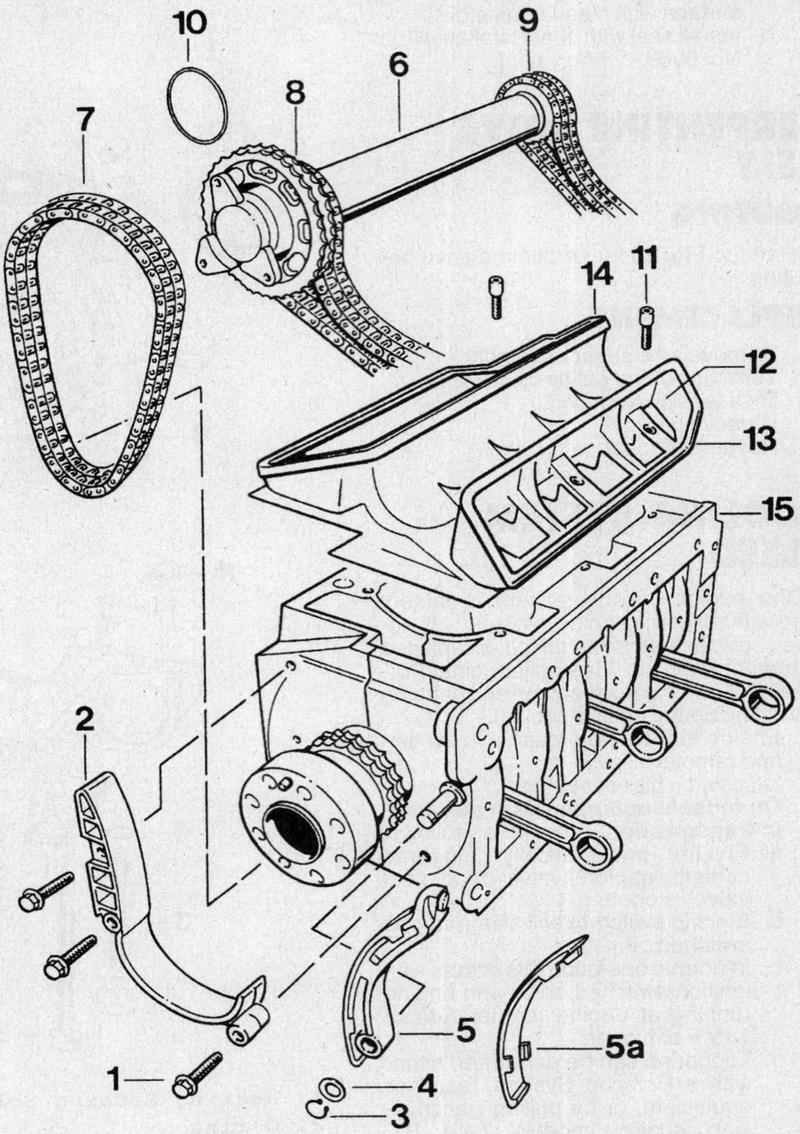

1. Slide Rail Bolts
2. Slide Rail
3. Circlip
4. Washer
5. Tensioning Rail
5a. Tensioning Rail Lining
6. Intermediate Shaft
7. Intermediate Shaft Chain
8. Camshaft Drive Chain
9. Camshaft Drive Chain
10. O-ring
11. Oil Separator Bolts
12. Gasket
13. Gasket
14. Oil Separator
15. Bearing Housing

PR1069900066000X

Fig. 10 Intermediate shaft & bearing housing

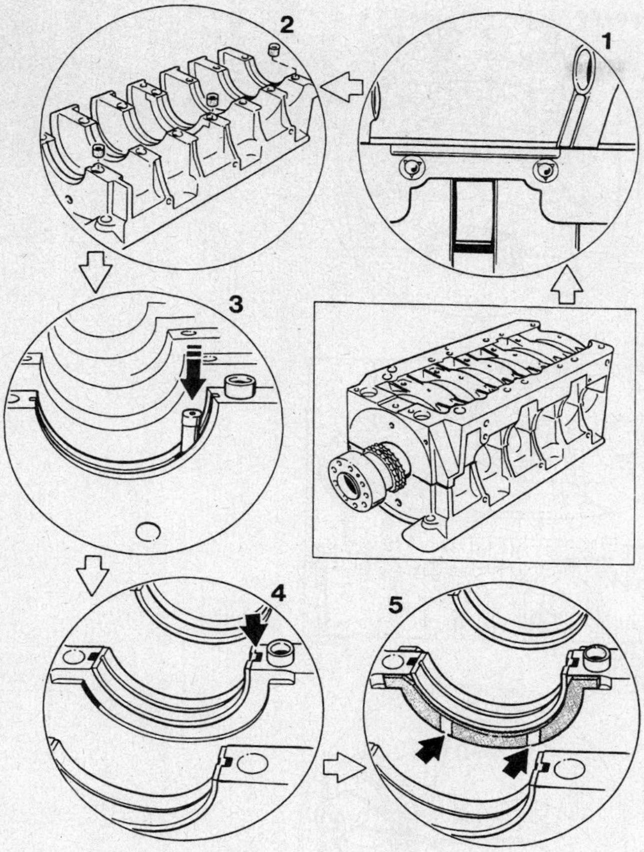

1. Sealing Balls
2. Dowel Sleeves
3. Piston Spray Nozzles
4. Crankshaft Bearing Shells
5. Intalling Thrust Plates

PR1069900067010X

Fig. 11 Crankshaft & bearing housing assembly (Part 1 of 2)

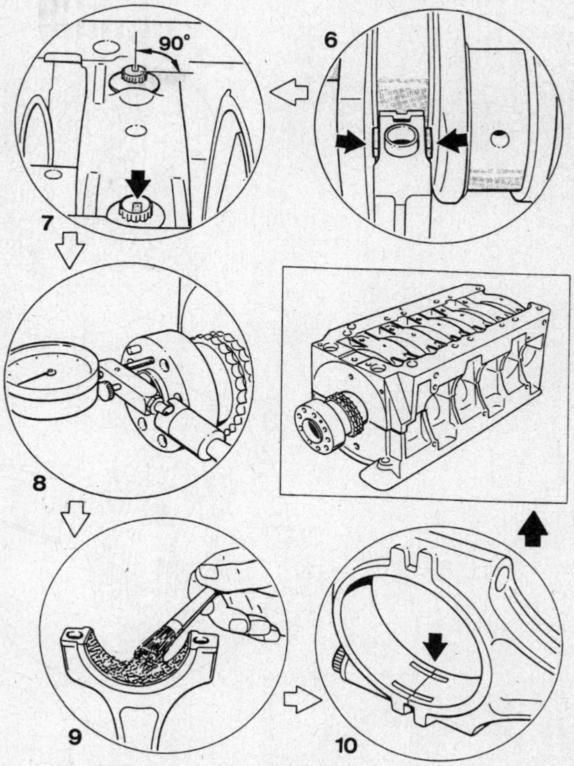

6. Checking Thrust Plates
7. Thrust Bearing Bolts
8. Checking Crankshaft Endplay
9. Connecting Rod Bearing Shells
10. Completed Connecting Rod

PR1069900067020X

Fig. 11 Crankshaft & bearing housing assembly (Part 2 of 2)

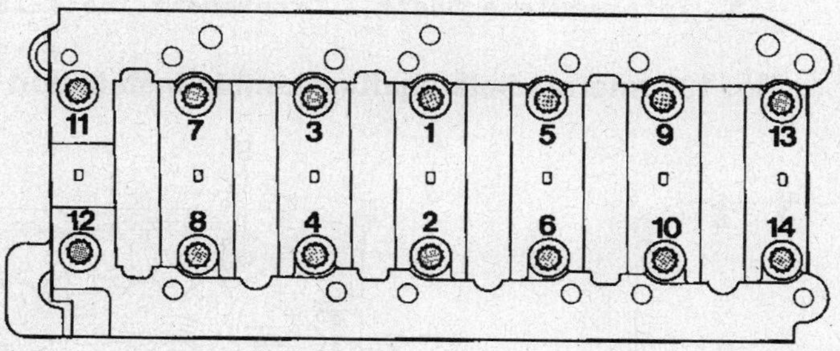

PR1069900068000X

Fig. 12 Thrust bearing bolt tightening sequence

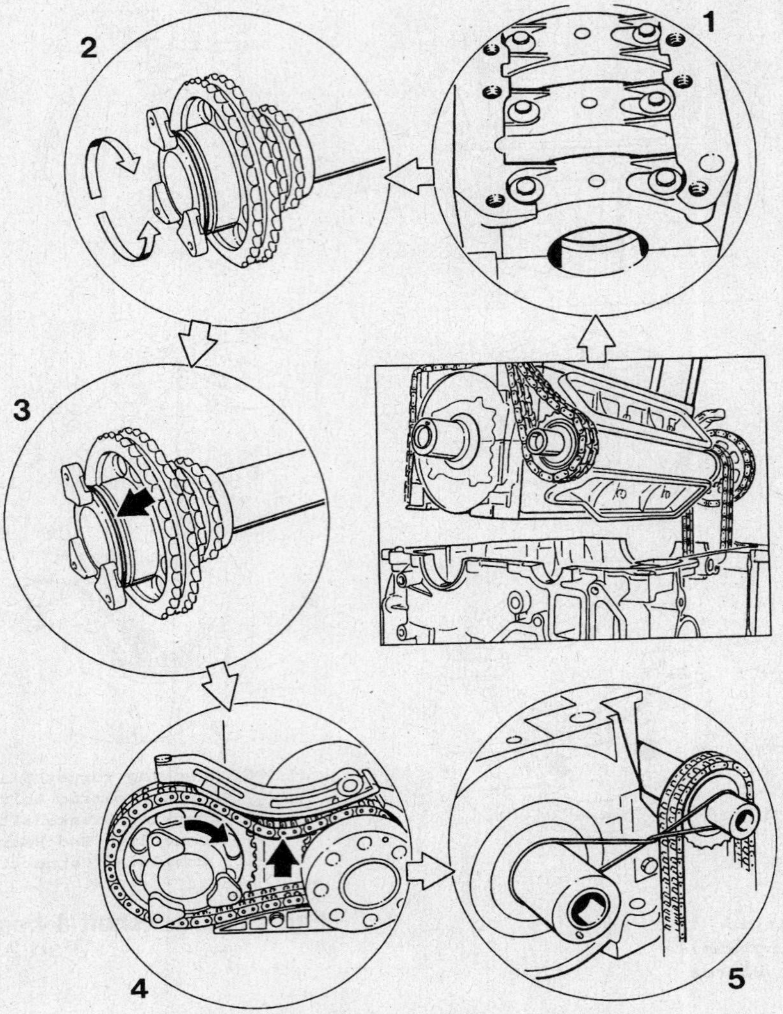

1. Bearing Housing Sealing Surface
2. Intermediate Shaft Flange Bearing
3. O-ring
4. Intermediate Shaft Chain
5. Intermediate Shaft & Crankshaft Installation

PR1069900069000X

Fig. 13 Intermediate shaft assembly installation

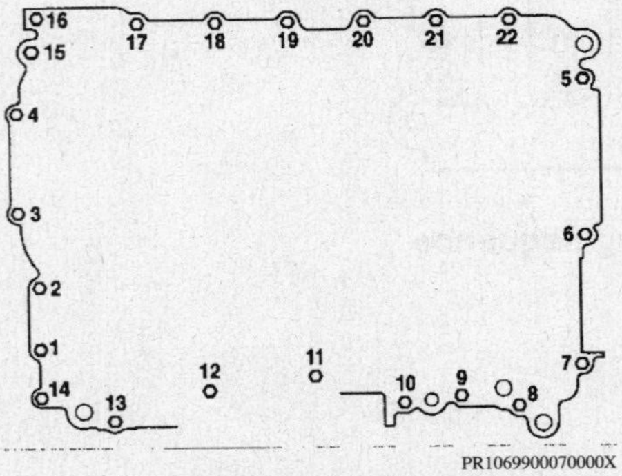

Fig. 14 Crankcase half bolt tightening sequence

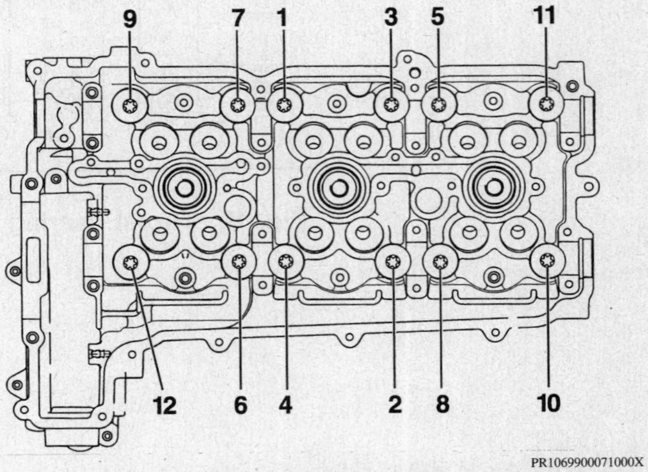

Fig. 15 Cylinder head bolt tightening sequence

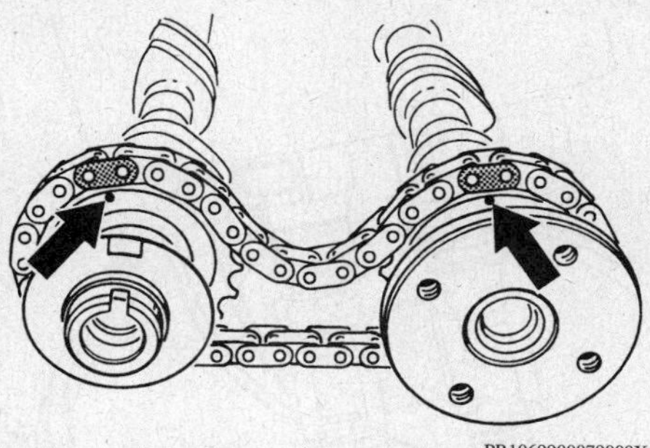

Fig. 16 Camshaft sprocket & chain alignment

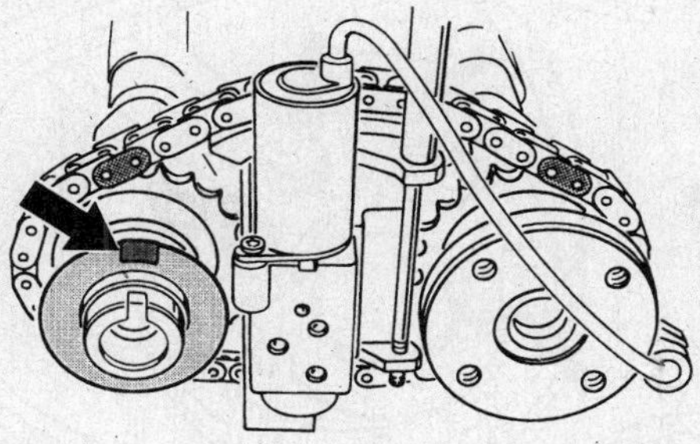

Fig. 17 Camshaft chain tensioning tool installation

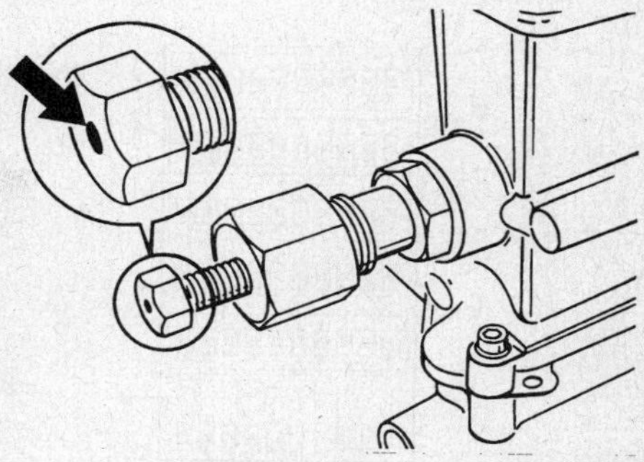

Fig. 18 Auxiliary chain tensioner installation

A – Fastening screw with star knob on cylinder head lug. Pull back centring piece (B) and sword bolt (C) when tightening.

B – Centring piece in groove of the exhaust camshaft. Pull sword bolt (C) back when tightening.

C – Sword bolt

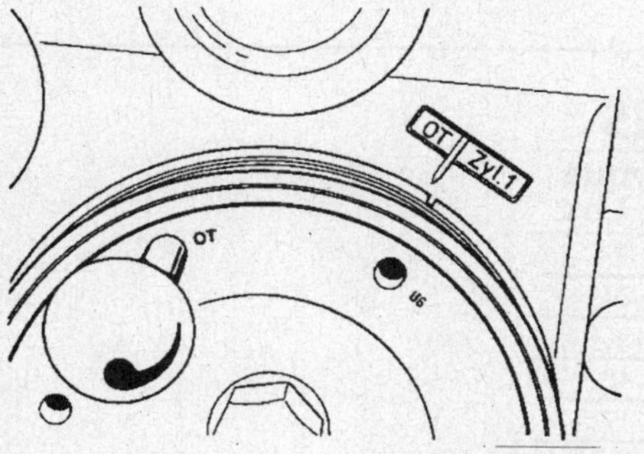

Fig. 19 Crankshaft pulley alignment

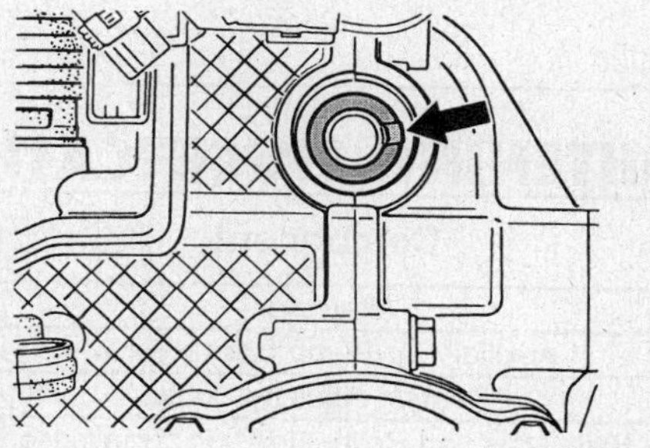

Fig. 20 Camshaft groove alignment

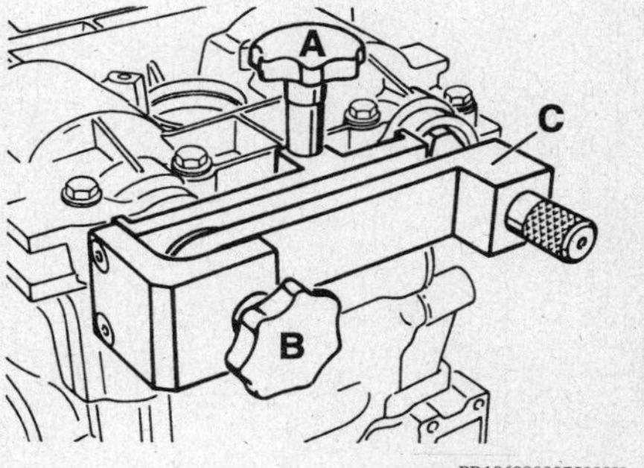

Fig. 21 Blocking device tool installation

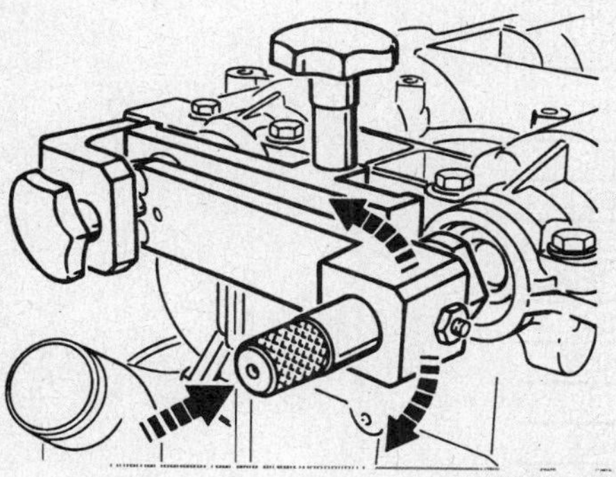

Fig. 22 Camshaft alignment

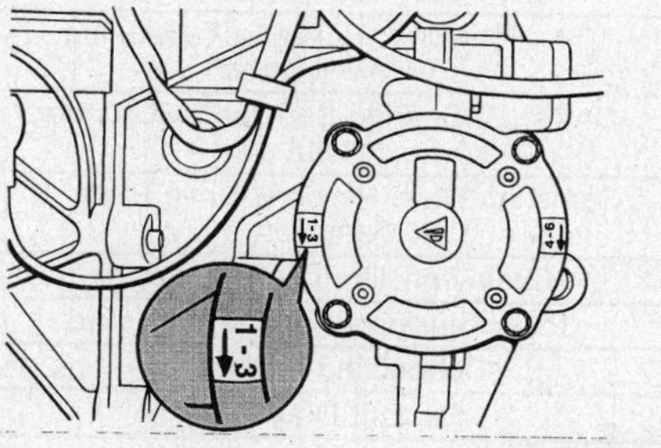

Fig. 23 Cylinder head (1-3) oil extraction pump installation

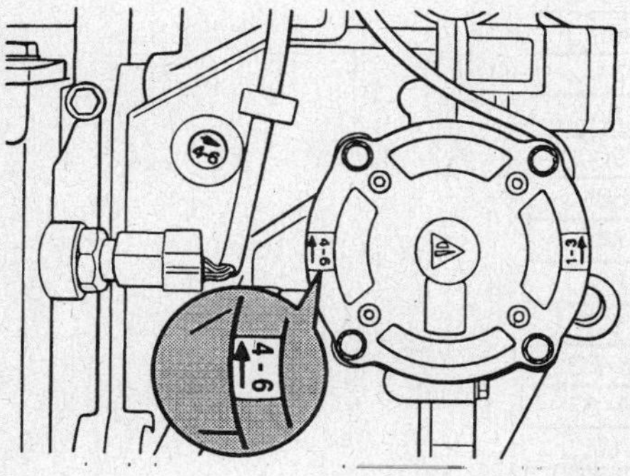

Fig. 24 Cylinder head (4-6) oil extraction pump installation

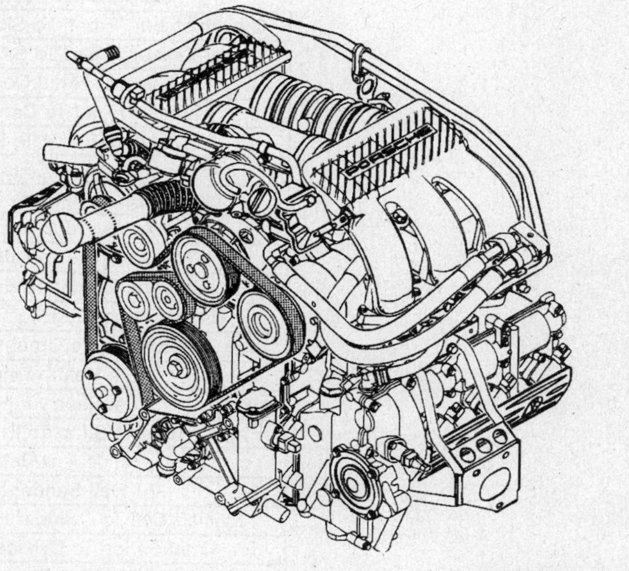

Fig. 25 Serpentine drive belt routing

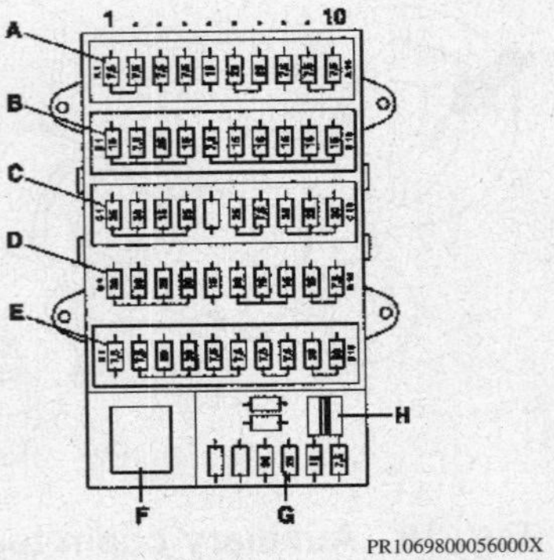

Fig. 26 B1 fuse location

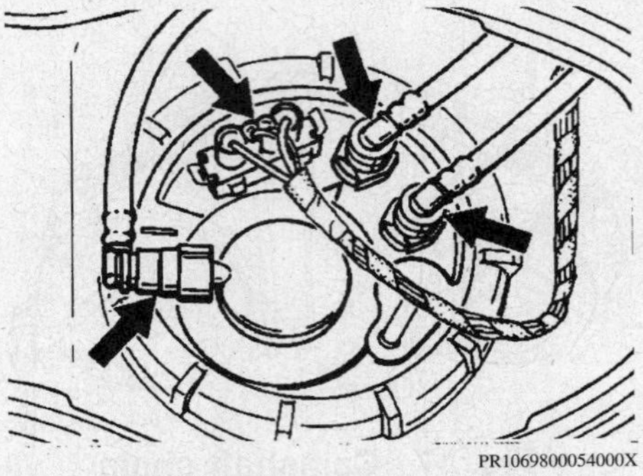

Fig. 27 Sending unit connections

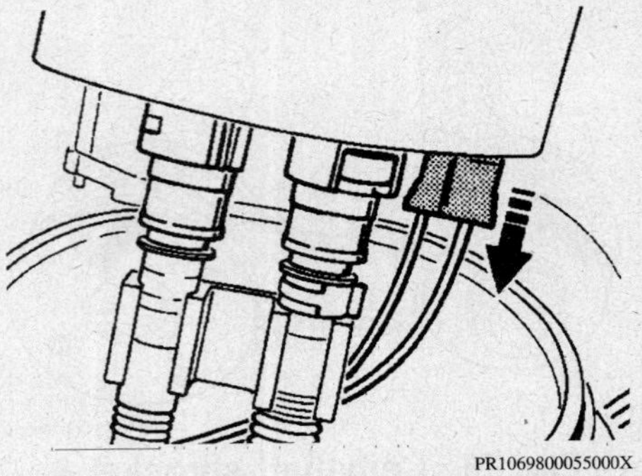

Fig. 28 Fuel pump connections

TIGHTENING SPECIFICATIONS

Year	Component	Torque, Ft. Lbs.
1998–2001	Alternator	33
	Auxiliary Air Pump Check Valve	24
	Bearing Housing Bolts	19②
	Belt Deflection Roller No. 1 To Crankcase	48
	Belt Deflection Roller No. 2 To Bracket	17
	Belt Pulley To Alternator	45–51
	Belt Pulley To Hydraulic Pump	17
	Belt Tensioner Roller To Tensioning Element Lever	44
	Camshaft Bearing Saddles To Cylinder Head	90①
	Camshaft Drive Pinion & Drive Plate To Camshaft	11
	Chain Tensioner To Crankcase	59
	Chain Tensioner To Cylinder Head	59
	Connecting Rod Bolts	15②
	Coolant Drain Plug	60–120①
	Coolant Guide Housing To Crankcase	33
	Coolant Pump To Crankcase	90②
	Crankcase Half Attaching Bolts	③
	Crankshaft Pulley	37②
	Crossmember (Front) To Side Of Carrier	48
	Crossmember (Rear) To Side Of Carrier	74
	Cylinder Head Cover	10
	Cylinder Head To Crankcase	④
	Diagonal Brace To Body	48
	Diagonal Brace To Crossmember	74
	Diagonal Brace To Side Of Carrier	17
	Driveplate To Crankshaft	19②
	Driveshaft To Transmission	60
	Engine Carrier To Engine	34
	Engine Mount To Engine Carrier	63
	Flywheel To Crankshaft	19②
	Fuel Return Line	16–22
	Fuel Supply Line	19–25
	Ground Strap To Engine	17
	Guide Rail Bolt	90①
	Hall Sender	84–96①
	Ignition Coil To Cylinder Head Cover	90①
	Intake Pipe To Cylinder Head	84①
	Intermediate Shaft Flange Locknut	10

Continued

TIGHTENING SPECIFICATIONS—Continued

Year	Component	Torque, Ft. Lbs.
1998–2001	Intermediate Shaft Flange To Crankcase	90①
	Knock Sensor	14–16
	NTC Coolant Temperature	16–22
	Oil Deflector To Bearing Housing	90①
	Oil Drain Plug	37
	Oil Filter To Crankcase	18–20
	Oil Level Sender To Crankcase	15
	Oil Pan To Crankcase	90①
	Oil Pressure Plug To Cylinder Head	90①
	Oil Pressure Switch	16–22
	Oil Relief Valve	19
	Oil Reservoir To Power Steering Pump	17
	Oil Return Pump To Cylinder Head	90①
	Oil Suction Pipe To Crankcase	90①
	Oxygen Sensor To Catalytic Converter	38–44
	Piston Pin Plug For Assembly Bore	59
	Power Steering Pressure Line	22
	Power Steering Pump To Bracket	17
	Power Steering Return Line	30
	Spark Plugs	20
	Speed Sender	84–96①
	Stabilizer To Stabilizer Mount	34
	Starter	33
	Thrust Plate To Flywheel	17
	Transmission Support To Body	48
	Valve Tappet Housing To Cylinder Head	90①
	Water Pump To Crankcase	90①
	Wheel To Wheel Hub	96

① — Inch lbs.

② — Turn an additional 90.°

③ — M6 bolts, 10 ft. lbs., M9 bolts, 16 ft. lbs.

④ — Refer to "Engine Assemble" for tightening procedure and sequence.

3.6L Engine

NOTE: On Air Bag Equipped Models, Refer To "Air Bag System Precautions" Located In The Front Of This Manual For System Disarming & Arming Procedures.

NOTE: Prior To Performing Any Service Operations Listed In This Section, Consult The "Technical Service Bulletins" Section For Related Information.

INDEX

	Page No.
Belt Tension Data	6-33
Camshaft, Replace	6-31
Compression Pressure	6-26
Crankshaft Seal, Replace	6-32
Install	6-32
Removal	6-32
Cylinder Head, Replace	6-27
Installation	6-27
Removal	6-27
Engine Rebuilding Specifications	6-109
Engine, Replace	6-26
Engine Assemble	6-28
Camshaft Housing	6-29
Crankcase	6-28
Cylinders	6-28
Engine Disassemble	6-27
Camshaft Housing	6-27
Crankshaft	6-28
Lefthand Crankcase	6-27
Righthand Crankcase	6-27
Fuel Filter, Replace	6-33
Hydraulic Lifters, Replace	6-29
Piston & Rod Assembly	6-32
Connecting Rod	6-32
Piston	6-32
Pistons, Pins & Rings	6-32
Installation	6-32
Removal	6-32
Precautions	6-26
Air Bag Systems	6-26
Battery Ground Cable	6-26
Rocker Arms	6-29
Tightening Specifications	6-34
Timing Chain, Replace	6-30
Adjustment	6-30
Camshaft Timing Chain	6-30
Chain Sprocket Parallelity	6-30
Timing Chain Tensioner, Replace	6-31
Turbocharger, Replace	6-33
Valve Clearance Specifications	6-29
Valve Guides	6-29
Installation	6-29
Removal	6-29

PRECAUTIONS

AIR BAG SYSTEMS

Refer to "Air Bag System Precautions" in the front of this manual for system disarming and arming procedures.

BATTERY GROUND CABLE

Prior to service, disconnect battery ground cable and isolate as required.

COMPRESSION PRESSURE

1. Perform compression pressure check with engine at normal operating temperature, spark plugs removed and throttle wide open.
2. Compression should be 142–184 psi with a minimum of 107 psi on any cylinder. Pressure should not vary more than 22 psi between cylinders.

ENGINE

REPLACE

1. Raise and support vehicle. Cover protruding engine compartment cover upper lock section with protective cover to prevent injury.
2. Remove A/C compressor bracket attaching bolts and position compressor aside. **Do not disconnect refrigerant lines.**
3. Remove hot air blower and air cleaner assembly.
4. Remove crankcase/oil tank vent hoses.

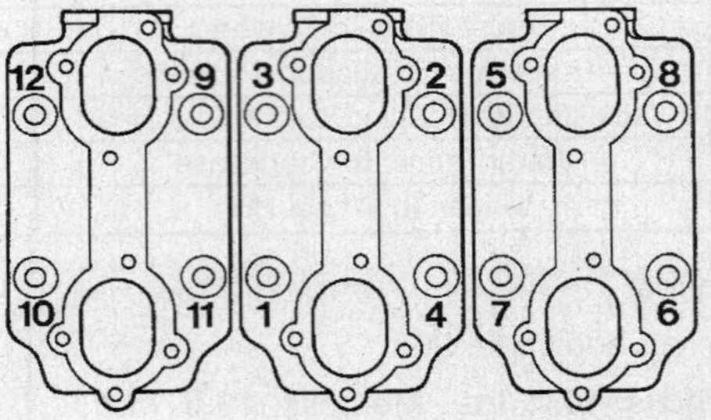

Fig. 1 Cylinder head tightening sequence

5. Remove cylinder No. 4 and 5 spark plug cables, place suitable container under hydraulic pump, disconnect power steering pump hoses and catch oil. Plug pump hoses and openings.
6. Remove intake rail plug.
7. Remove lefthand front engine compartment connectors for carbon canister, brake booster, cylinder No. 3 temperature sensor II, knock sensor, cruise control and reference mark sender.
8. Remove engine compartment electrical system cover and carefully remove connectors.
9. Remove righthand cover next to air conditioning compressor, unlatch and disconnect oxygen sensor connector.
10. Remove fuel return and supply lines.
11. Remove throttle cable from pedal return lever, back locknut off and remove ball joint.
12. Raise and support vehicle.
13. Remove engine/transmission guard and rear underbody panel.
14. Release ball clamps and remove rear muffler tailpipes.
15. Remove rear mufflers.
16. Remove drive shafts from transmission flange, protect with hose sections and place on subframe side sections.
17. Remove mounting bolt and pull selector rod coupling off internal shift rod.
18. Remove hot-air hoses and pipers, then the front crosslink.
19. Remove stabilizer bar.
20. Loosen toe arm outer mounting, mark inner mounting (toe eccentric) with scriber and highlight with color dot.
21. Remove toe eccentric and toe arm.
22. Mark rear crossmember position and remove mounting bolts.
23. Remove transmission oil pipe.
24. Release righthand sill cover and catch thermostat housing engine oil in suitable container.
25. Disconnect ground strap on body.
26. Disconnect electrical connectors and cables from starter motor.
27. Loosen clutch cable retainer.
28. Remove clutch release lever and spring.
29. Remove positioning lever and spring.
30. Remove release lever from release lever shaft.
31. Remove driveshaft from differential flange.
32. Suspend left driveshaft from vehicle using a suitable piece of wire.
33. Remove rear cowl panel attaching screws, then the rear cowl panel.
34. Support transmission assembly with a suitable jack.
35. Loosen transmission carrier attaching bolts.

36. Loosen engine carrier attaching bolts.
37. Lower support jack slightly, then disconnect electrical connector from shock absorber crossmember as well as plug on air flow sensor.
38. Lower jack with engine/transmission carefully and roll out toward rear of vehicle. **If vehicle has to be moved after removal of engine/transmission assembly, suspend driveshafts from vehicle in a horizontal position.**
39. Reverse procedure to install.

CYLINDER HEAD

REPLACE

REMOVAL

1. Remove camshaft housing as outlined under "Engine Disassemble."
2. Remove cylinder head retaining nuts.
3. Remove cylinder heads.

INSTALLATION

1. Apply thin coat of Optimoly HT, or equivalent copper paste, to stud threads.
2. Fit cylinder heads.
3. Apply thin coat of suitable copper paste to head nuts.
4. **On non-turbocharged models,** using sequence shown in **Fig. 1, torque** cylinder head nuts to 18 ft. lbs., then an additional 90.°
5. **On models equipped with turbocharged engine,** using sequence shown in **Fig. 1,** tighten cylinder head bolts as follows:
   a. **Torque** nuts to 18 ft. lbs.
   b. Loosen all bolts completely in reverse sequence.
   c. **Torque** nuts to 84 inch lbs.
   d. Tighten bolts an additional 120.°

ENGINE DISASSEMBLE

CAMSHAFT HOUSING

1. Remove inner and outer cylinder bolts (M 8 X 55) and (M 8 X 30), **Fig. 2.**
2. Remove self-locking (M 6 X 28) bolt and O-ring.
3. Remove cover attaching bolts, then the cover.
4. Remove intake rocker arm shaft attaching bolts, then the rocker arm shafts, rocker arms and valve lifters.
5. Remove exhaust rocker arm shaft attaching bolts, then the rocker arm shafts, rocker arms and valve lifters.
6. Remove timing chain and camshaft sprocket as outlined under "Timing Chain, Replace."
7. Remove camshaft, then the camshaft housing.

LEFTHAND CRANKCASE

Refer to **Fig. 3** when servicing lefthand crankcase.

1. Remove cylinder head as previously outlined.
2. Remove mounting bolt, washer and sensor bracket, then the mounting bolt and retainer.

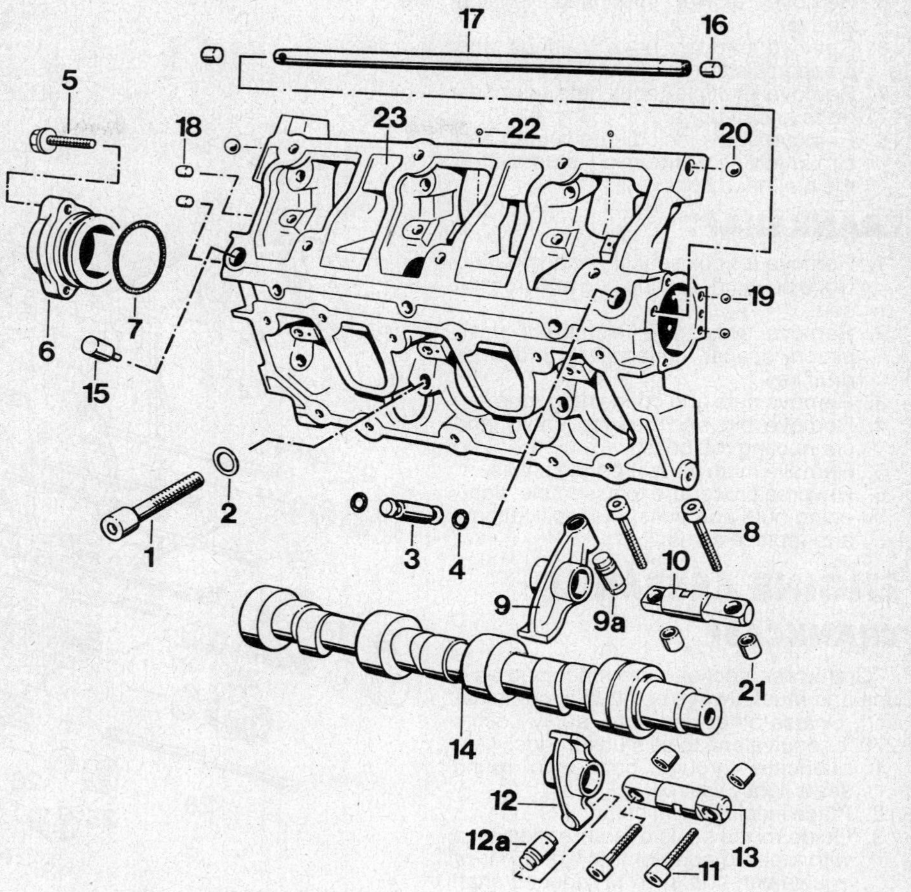

1. Cylinder Bolts
2. Washer
3. Flange
4. O-ring
5. Bolt w/Permanent Washer
6. Cover
7. O-ring
8. Cylinder Bolt
9. Intake Rocker Arm
9a. Valve Lifter
10. Rocker Arm Shafts
11. Cylinder Bolt
12. Exhaust Rocker Arm
13. Rocker Arm Shafts
14. Camshaft
15. Plug w/Positioning Tip
16. Plug
17. Spray Tube
18. Plug
19. Ball
20. Ball
21. Adapter Sleeve
22. Ball

PR1069300081000X

Fig. 2 Camshaft housing assembly

3. Remove mounting nuts, washers, retainer, ventilation cover, gasket and stud.
4. Remove drain plug, seal and threaded insert.
5. Remove oil pressure release valve plug, seal, thrust spring and piston.
6. Remove oil return flange and seal. Screw-in flange area may have to be heated.
7. Remove multiple-tooth nut, stepped discs and O-rings.
8. Remove main bearing saddle VII nut and washer.
9. Drill a .1969 inch pilot hole .0787 inch deep into piston cooling oil spray jets, and remove cover, spring and ball.
10. Heat surrounding area, inset a M 5 tap (finishing tap No. 3) and remove jet remains. M6 tap (taper tap No. 1) may have to be used.
11. Heat area and remove studs, then the stud, adapter sleeve and distributor stud.

RIGHTHAND CRANKCASE

Refer to **Fig. 4** when servicing righthand crankcase.

1. Remove oil pressure sender, temperature gauge sender, seals, mounting nut, washer, cover, O-ring and studs.
2. Remove plug and seal, then the oil inlet flange and seal.
3. Remove mounting bolt, washer cover and O-ring.
4. Remove oil pressure relief valve plug, piston, thrust spring, spring guide sleeve, seal and spacer ring.

5. Remove blower mounting tension sleeve.
6. Remove through bolts, O-rings and stepped discs.
7. Remove multiple-tooth nuts, stepped discs and O-rings.
8. Remove studs including oil pump and circumferential mounting studs, then the hex head bolts.

CRANKSHAFT

1. Remove rear oil seal, then the bearing No. 8 bushing, sealing ring and front oil seal.
2. Remove snap ring, distributor drive pinion, spacer, timing gear and woodruff key.
3. Remove nuts and connecting rods.
4. Remove big end bearing shells and connecting rod bolts.
5. Remove main thrust bearing shells.
6. Reverse procedure to assemble, tightening nuts and bolts to specifications, and replace seals.

ENGINE ASSEMBLE

CRANKCASE

Crankcase sections are machined as a unit and must always be fitted in combination. Unless otherwise note, apply Loctite 270, or equivalent, to all stud threads.

1. Lubricate through bolts and round seals lightly with oil.
2. Place insulators on bolts.
3. Guide round seals over threaded area with tapered adapter tool No. 9511, or equivalent, and slide to reduced shaft head end. **O-ring must not be used on bolt collar.**
4. Coat lefthand crankcase mating surfaces and bearing seats lightly with Loctite No. 574, or equivalent.
5. Assembly sections and tighten outer crankcase M8 nuts until mating surfaces contact.
6. Install prepared bolts into righthand crankcase from below against metal stop.
7. Slide tapered adapter with mounted and lubricated round seals on threaded end.
8. Slide round seal off adapter carefully with thin wall end of cylinder sleeve.
9. Remove tapered adapter and slide round seal into final position with thick wall end of cylindrical sleeve while counter holding bolt.
10. Install insulators dry and press on lightly with thick wall cylindrical sleeve.
11. Install thread lubricated, multiple-tooth nuts finger tight.
12. Install righthand crankcase studs near bearing No. 1.
13. Install M10 nut and spring washer on stud with rounded side face nut.
14. Tighten bolts to specifications in sequence shown in **Fig. 5.** Have helper counter hold while tightening.
15. Tighten outer crankcase bolts to specifications.
16. Reverse process outlined under "Engine Dissemble" to continue assembly, noting the following:
   a. Bond piston cooling spray jets in place with Loctite 639, or equivalent. Bore must be free of bonding material.
   b. New spray jets are installed with balls pointing toward saddle.
   c. Bond oil return flange in place with Loctite 270, or equivalent.
   d. Coat both sides of ventilation cover gasket with Loctite 574, or equivalent.

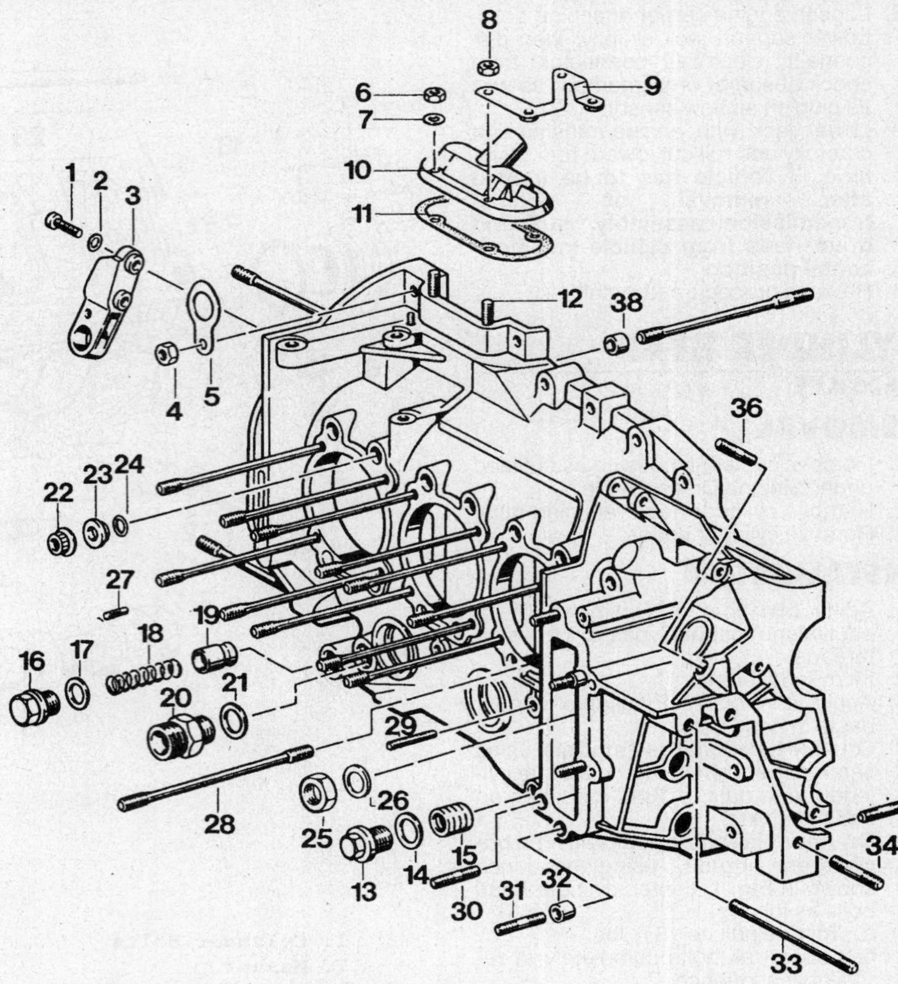

1-Mounting bolt
2-Washer
3-Sensor bracket
4-Mounting bolt
5-Retainer
6-Mounting nut
7-Washers
8-Mounting nut
9-Retainer
10-Ventilation cover
11-Gasket
12-Stud
13-Drain plug
14-Seal
15-Threaded insert
16-Oil pressure valve plug
17-Seal
18-Thrust spring
19-Piston
20-Oil return flange
21-Seal
22-Multi-tooth nut
23-Stepped disc
24-O-rings
25-VII nut
26-Washer
27-Jet
28-Stud
29-Stud
30-Stud
31-Stud
34-Adapter sleeve
36-Distributor stud

PR1069300036000X

Fig. 3 Lefthand crankcase

CYLINDERS

Cylinder are stamped opposite the knock sensor bridge mounting lug with cylinder bore tolerance group, and cylinder height tolerance group (in triangle), **Fig. 6.**

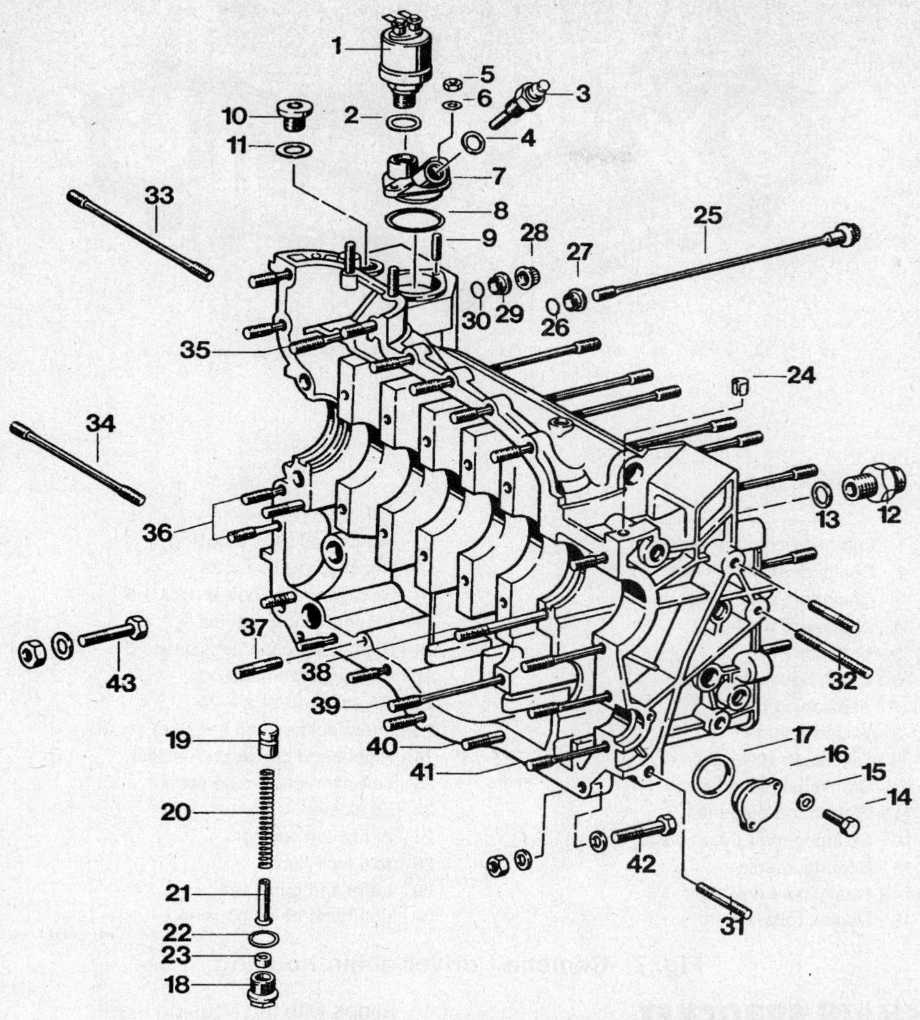

1-Oil pressure sender
2-Seal
3-Temperature sender
4-Seal
5-Self-locking nut
6-Washer
7-Cover
8-O-ring
9-Stud
10-Plug
11-Seal
12-Screw-in flange
13-Seal
14-Head bolt
15-Washer
16-Cover
17-O-ring
18-Plug
19-Piston
20-Thrust spring
21-Spring guide sleeve
22-Seal
23-Spacer ring
24-Tension sleeve
25-Through bolt
26-O-ring
27-Stepped disc
28-Multi-tooth nut
29-Stepped disc
30-O-ring
31-Stud
32-Stud
33-Stud
34-Stud
35-Stud
36-Stud
37-Stud
38-Stud
39-Stud
40-Stud
41-Stud
42-Head bolt
43-Head bolt

PR1069300037000X

Fig. 4 Righthand crankcase

Cylinder on same side of engine must be from the same height group.

CAMSHAFT HOUSING

1. Install camshaft housing, then the camshaft, **Fig. 2.**
2. Install timing chain and camshaft sprocket as outlined under "Timing Chain, Replace."
3. Install exhaust valve lifters, rocker arms, rocker arm shafts and rocker arm shaft attaching bolts.
4. Install intake valve lifters, rocker arms, rocker arm shafts and rocker arm shaft attaching bolts.
5. Install cover, then the cover attaching bolts.
6. Install O-ring and self-locking bolt (M 6 X 28).
7. Install inner and outer cylinder bolts (M 8 X 55) and (M 8 X 30).

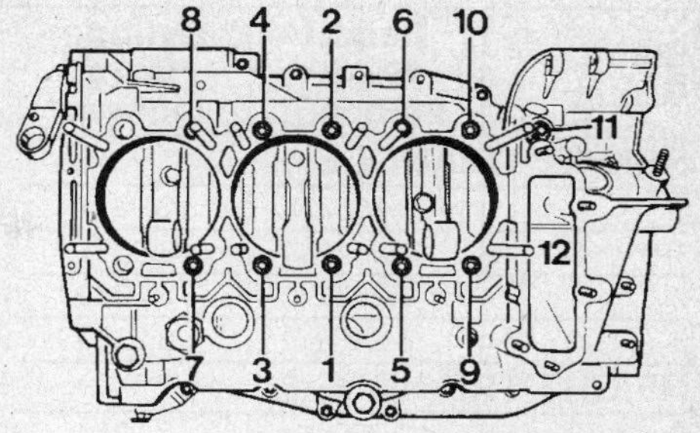

PR1069300038000X

Fig. 5 Crankcase tightening sequence

VALVE CLEARANCE SPECIFICATIONS

This engine uses hydraulic lifters. No adjustment is required.

ROCKER ARMS

Intake rocker arms have valve lifter bore drilled, plugged with cover and punched.

Exhaust rocker arms valve lifter bores are not drilled.

VALVE GUIDES

REMOVAL

1. Work from camshaft side and machine off protruding sections with spot facer until guides are flush with head.
2. Loosen guide with sharp hammer blows.
3. Press out remainder of guide toward combustion chamber.

INSTALLATION

1. Measure valve guide bores.
2. Machine oversize valve guides according to bore measurements. Press fit must be .0024–.0031 inch.
3. Coat guides with suitable powder and fit into head with suitable drift working from camshaft side.
4. Use broach or precision boring equipment to bore inner diameter to .3150–.3156 inch.
5. Inspect sealing pattern and recut valve seats as required.

HYDRAULIC LIFTERS

REPLACE

Refer to procedure as outlined under "Camshaft, Replace."

Stamp Group	Height Size, Inches①	Cylinder Bore, Inches②
HEIGHT TRIANGLE 5		
0	3.2582	3.9374
1	3.2582	3.9377
2	3.2582	3.9380
3	3.2582	3.9382
HEIGHT TRIANGLE 6		
0	3.2590	3.9374
1	3.2590	3.9377
2	3.2590	3.9380
3	3.2590	3.9382

① — Height -.0008 inch.
② — Bore +. 0003 inch.

Fig. 6 Cylinder identification

TIMING CHAIN

REPLACE

CAMSHAFT TIMING CHAIN

Refer to **Figs. 7 and 8** when replacing camshaft timing chains.

1. Set cylinder No. 1 to TDC (overlapping cylinder No. 4 TDC). Camshaft punch marks should face up.
2. Remove locknuts, washers, cover, gasket and chain tensioner.
3. Remove screws, washers, support bracket, roller pin and adapter sleeves.
4. Use suitable locking device and remove bolt.
5. Remove washer and straight pin using puller tool No. 212, or equivalent.
6. Remove chain, then the sprocket, sprocket flange, woodruff key, shims and thrust washer.
7. Remove mounting bolts, washers, end cover, O-ring and gasket.
8. Remove retaining stub, seal and guide rail, then the retaining stub, seal and tensioning rail.
9. Remove locknuts, washers and gasket from chain housing.
10. Remove collar pins and studs.
11. Remove locknuts, washers, flange, seal, sleeve seals and stud.
12. Reverse procedure to install, noting following:
    a. Bond studs with Loctite 270, or equivalent.
    b. Coat both sides of gaskets with Loctite 574, or equivalent.
    c. Replace all seals, gaskets and O-rings.
    d. Thinly coat sprocket bolt with Optimoly HT, or equivalent.
    e. Install chain tensioner. On righthand side, oil supply bore pointing down; on lefthand side, oil supply bore points up. Spring retainers are marked "oben" for top, "unten rechts" for bottom right and "unten links" for bottom left.
    f. Adjust chain sprocket parallelity as outlined under "Chain Sprocket Parallelity."
    g. Tighten nuts and bolts to specifications.

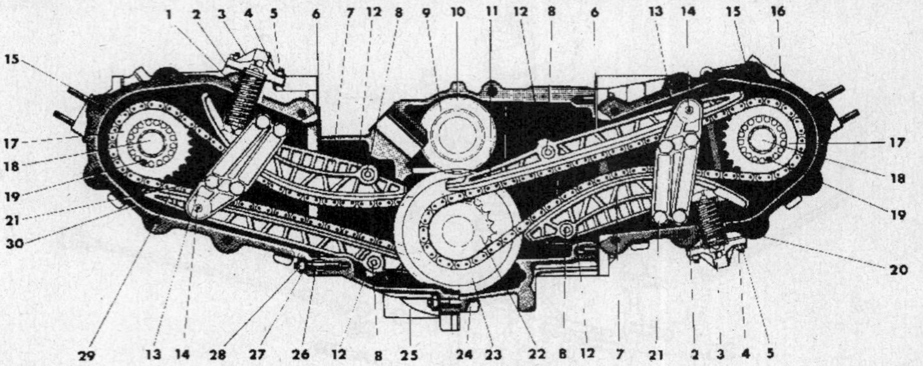

1 - Left-hand chain tensioner
2 - Chain tensioner gasket
3 - Chain tensioner cover
4 - Aluminum washer
5 - M 6 lock nut
6 - Chain housing gasket
7 - Tensioning rail
8 - Support stud
9 - Distributor drive gear
10 - Crankshaft sprocket z = 35
11 - Right-hand guide rail
12 - Spring-loaded thrust piece
13 - Bearing saddle
14 - Heavy type dowel pin
15 - Duplex roller chain
16 - Right-hand chain housing
17 - Chain sprocket z = 28
18 - Hexagon head bolt M 12 x 1.5
19 - Straight pin, 6 mm dia.
20 - Right-hand chain tensioner
21 - M 6 hexagon-head bolt
22 - Chain sprocket z = 24
23 - Intermediate shaft sprocket z = 60
24 - Right-hand crankcase section
25 - Left-hand crankcase section
26 - Fit sleeve
27 - Aluminum washer
28 - M 8 lock nut
29 - Left-hand guide rail
30 - Left-hand chain housing

PR1069300040000X

Fig. 7 Camshaft driver chain housing

CHAIN SPROCKET PARALLELITY

Offset parallelity between drive sprockets on intermediate shaft must not be more than ±.0098 inch.

1. Move intermediate shaft toward flywheel and ensure bearing support collar is seated correctly.
2. Insert or remove .0197 inch shims to adjust sprockets.
3. Lefthand side for cylinders No. 1–3 usually requires three shims.
4. Righthand side for cylinders No. 4–6 usually requires four shims.
5. Use camshaft locking tools No. 8551 or 9552, or equivalents, to tighten bolt to specification.
6. Measure distance between intermediate shaft face to crankcase front edge.
7. This measurement plus designed measurement equal sprocket positions on camshafts.
8. Designed measurement for rear intermediate shaft sprocket (cylinders No. 1–3) front face is 3.8614 inches.
9. Designed measurement for front intermediate shaft sprocket (cylinders No. 4–6) front face is 1.7037 inches.

ADJUSTMENT

1. Rotate crankshaft pulley until mark aligns with fan housing mark.
2. Remove bolt and pulley using helper lock and retaining wrench tool No. 9548, or equivalent.
3. Remove intermediate shaft access hole cover.
4. Install locking tool No. 9553, or equivalent.
5. Turn both camshafts until punch marks face up. If mark is missing, woodruff key grove must point up. Camshafts may be aligned and rotated from flywheel end using locking devices No. 9551 or 9552, or equivalents.
6. Ensure pulley Z1 mark aligns with seam and camshaft punch marks point up. This is TDC for cylinder No. 1 and overlap TDC for cylinder No. 4.
7. Install auxiliary chain tensioner tool No. 9401, or equivalent, **Fig. 9.** Plunger recess must be barely visible for correct preload.
8. Install locking device tool No. 9551, or equivalent, on lefthand camshaft and locking device tool No. 9552, or equivalent, on righthand camshaft.
9. Adjustment is correct when one sprocket hole lines up exactly with one sprocket flange hole.
10. Thinly coat bolts with Optimoly HT, or

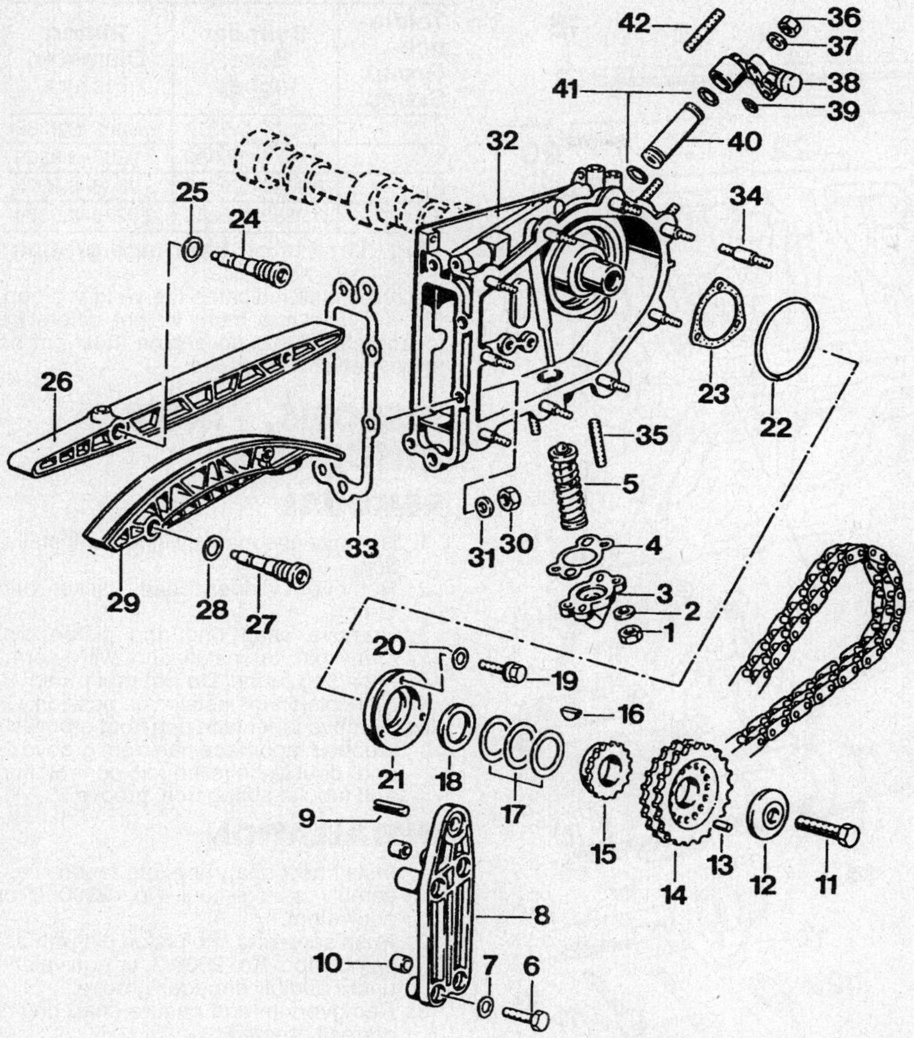

1-Lock nut
2-Washer
3-Cover
4-Gasket
5-Chain tensioner
6-Head screw
7-Washer
8-Support Bracket
9-Roll pin
10-Adapter sleeve
11-Head bolt
12-Washer
13-Straight pin
14-Sprocket
15-Sprocket flange
16-Woodruff key
17-Shim
18-Thrust washer
19-Head bolt
20-Washer
21-End cover
22-O-ring
23-Gasket
24-Retaining stud
25-Seal
26-Guide rail
27-Retaining stud
28-Seal
29-Tensioning nut
30-Lock nut
31-Washer
32-Chain housing
33-Gasket
34-Collar pin
35-Stud
36-Lock nut
37-Washer
38-Flange
39-Seal
40-Sleeve
41-Seal
42-Stud

PR1069300041000X

Fig. 8 Cylinders 4–6 camshaft chain drive

equivalent, and tighten bolts to specifications.

11. Remove auxiliary chain tensioner tool and install chain tensioners. On righthand side, oil supply bore pointing down; on lefthand side, oil supply bore points up. Spring retainers are marked "oben" for top, "unten rechts" for bottom right and "unten links" for bottom left.

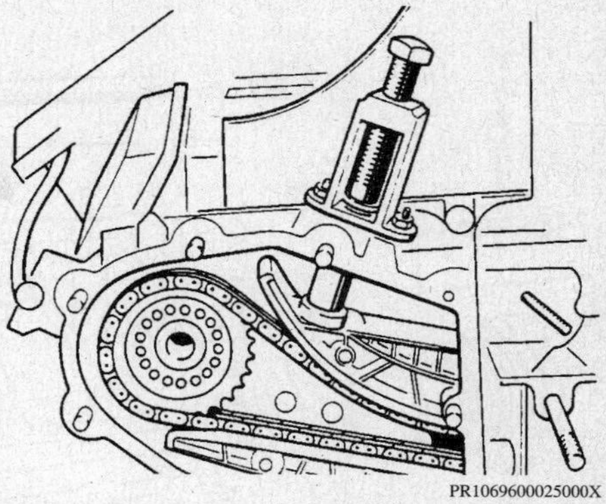

PR1069600025000X

Fig. 9 Auxiliary chain tensioner installation, lefthand side

TIMING CHAIN TENSIONER

REPLACE

Refer to procedure as outlined under "Timing Chain, Replace."

CAMSHAFT

REPLACE

Refer to **Fig. 10** when removing and installing camshaft.

1. Remove mounting bolts and washers, then the camshaft housing.
2. Remove flange and O-rings.
3. Remove mounting bolt, cover and O-ring.
4. Remove cylinder bolts, intake rocker arms, valve lifters and rocker arm shafts.
5. Remove cylinder bolts, exhaust rocker arms, valve lifters and rocker arm shafts.
6. Remove camshaft.
7. If there is bearing damage or engine is being rebuilt, spray tubes must be removed as follows:
   a. Drill positioning tip plug and lateral plug with .1969 inch bit approximately .3544 inch deep.
   b. Tap in M6 thread with bottoming tap.
   c. Install M6 screw, and remove plugs and spacer sleeve.
   d. Remove spray tube.
   e. If bearings are damaged, remove plug and balls.
   f. Thoroughly clean spray tubes.
   g. Clean lateral oil ducts.
8. Reverse procedure to install, noting the following:
   a. If spray tubes were removed, turn plug to .4882 inch diameter. Tap M5 thread into plug and install M5 X 35 screw. Push spray tube into camshaft housing and position with tool made from old plug. Coat new plug with Optimoly HT, or equivalent, and push in flush. Ensure sealing balls have been installed.
   b. Unless otherwise noted, coat all

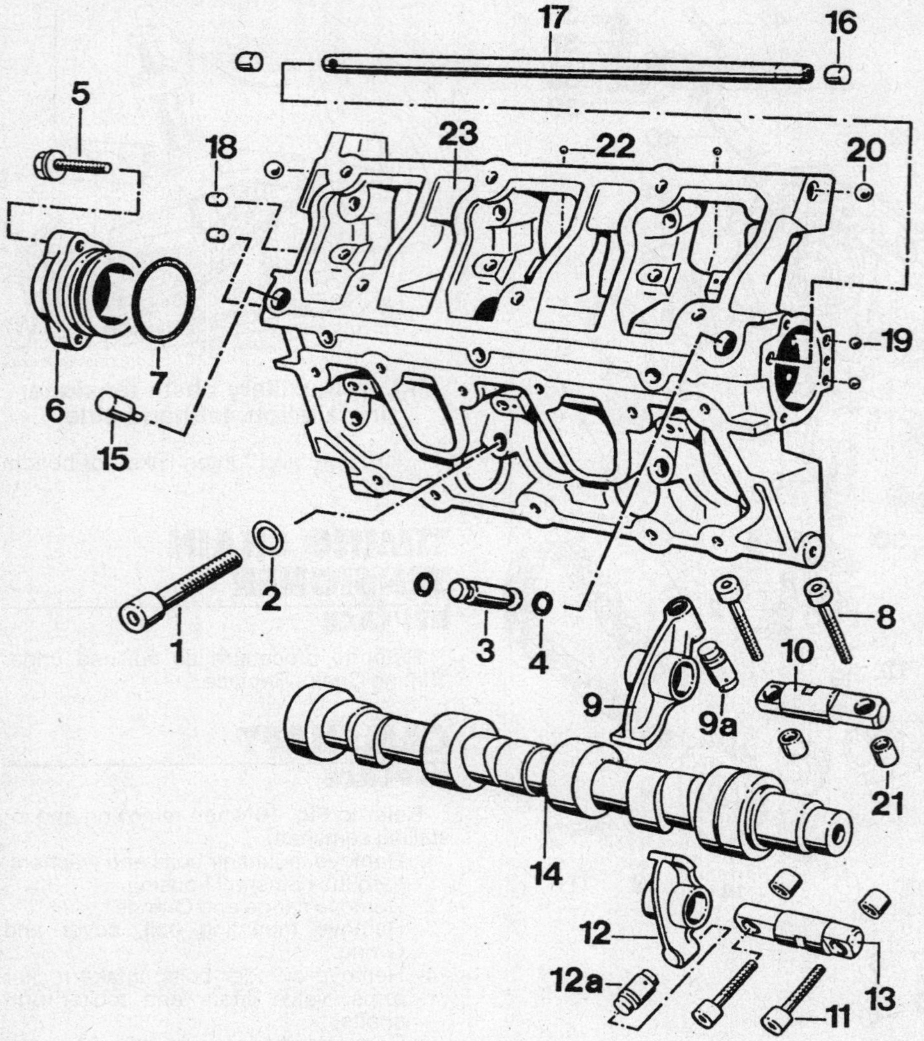

1-Mounting bolts
2-Washers
3-Flange
4-O-rings
5-Mounting bolt
6-Cover
7-O-ring
8-Cylinder bolts
9-Intake rocker arms
9a-Valve lifters
10-Rocker arm shafts
11-Cylinder bolts
12-Exhaust rocker arms
12a-Valve lifters
13-Rocker arm shafts
14-Camshaft
15-Tip plug
16-Lateral plug
17-Spray tube
18-Plug
19-Ball
20-Ball
22-Ball

PR1069300039000X

Fig. 10 Lefthand camshaft replacement

aluminum plugs with Optimoly HT, or equivalent copper paste, and press flush. Do not use any other lubricant.

c. Install camshaft with punch mark pointing up and hold in place with locking device tool No. 9551, or equivalent.
d. Lightly oil bearing surfaces.
e. Install new valve lifters and O-rings.
f. Coat outer and inner cylinder bolt threads with Loctite 574, or equivalent.
g. Tighten bolts to specifications.

PISTON & ROD ASSEMBLY

PISTON

Pistons are stamped on the upper crown section with "E" toward intake, change lever ID to right, tolerance group to left of "E," **Fig. 11** and weight class next to tolerance group.

CONNECTING ROD

Connecting rods are divided into several weight groups. The final digit engraved on the rod shank indicates the weight group, **Fig. 12.** The maximum weight difference for rods fitted into an engine must not be more than .2777 ounces.

Tolerance Group Stamp	Cylinder Bore, Inches	Piston Diameter, Inches
0	3.9374–3.9377	3.9362–3.9388
1	3.9377–3.9380	3.9365–3.9369
2	3.9380–3.9382	3.9368–3.9372
3	3.9382–3.9385	3.9370–3.9374

Fig. 11 Piston tolerance groups

PISTONS, PINS & RINGS

REMOVAL

1. Remove and mark cylinder for installation.
2. Remove cylinder head gasket and O-ring.
3. Remove snap ring and piston pin. Mark pin to installation with corresponding piston. **Do not mix pins.**
4. Mark piston for installation position.
5. Remove taper face ring from groove 1, stepped taper face ring from groove 2, and double-bevelled oil control ring and tubular spring from groove 3.

INSTALLATION

1. Install new snap ring into tapered assembly sleeve tool No. 9500/2, or equivalent.
2. Push snap ring into piston pin with assembly tool No. 9500/3, or equivalent, until it audibly engages groove.
3. Remove tool and ensure snap ring is correctly seated.
4. Pre-assemble pistons and cylinders on a suitable plastic or wooden support.
5. Place pre-assembled cylinder on studs with tapered assembly sleeve in piston pin bore.
6. Insert plunger into tapered assembly sleeve on piston pin bore.
7. Press piston pin in until snap ring engages with an audible click.

CRANKSHAFT SEAL

REPLACE

REMOVAL

1. Deform oil seat at crankcase cutout with a suitable drift or crosscut chisel.
2. Lever seal out with suitable screwdriver.

INSTALL

1. Inspect running surface sealing lip.
2. Clean surface in crankcase. Use a suitable scraper to deburr.
3. Coat sealing lip running surface with oil.
4. Install new seal with thrust piece tool part No. 9517 and installation tool No. 9517/1, or equivalents.

Weight, Ounces		Weight Group	Rod ID
From	To		
17.92	18.13	1	50
18.13	18.34	2	51
18.34	18.55	3	52
18.55	18.76	4	53
18.76	18.98	5	54
18.98	19.17	6	55
19.17	19.40	7	56

Fig. 12 Connecting rod weight groups

5. Press in until oil seal is .0787 inch below crankcase flange.

BELT TENSION DATA

This procedure has been revised by a Technical Service Bulletin.

Belt	Cold, Lbs.①	Hot, Lbs.①
A/C	33–51	44–62
Alternator	33–51	44–62
Cooling Fan	33–51	44–62

① — Measure w/belt tension tester tool No. 9574, or equivalent.

FUEL FILTER

REPLACE

1. Remove air cleaner cover and filter.
2. Remove air cleaner housing from air rail and disconnect air flow sensor, then the air cleaner housing. **Do not lose air flow sensor O-ring.**
3. Wrap fuel filter with suitable rag and place suitable container under lines to catch spilling fuel.
4. Disconnect fuel lines using suitable second wrench to lock lines.
5. Remove clamp and fuel filter
6. Reverse procedure to install noting fuel flow direction arrow.

TURBOCHARGER

REPLACE

1. Remove screen retaining nuts and the screen, **Fig. 13.**
2. Remove sheetmetal screw and the light assembly.
3. Remove closing panel bracket attaching screws, then the bracket and closing panel.
4. Remove spoiler assembly oval-head sheetmetal screws.
5. Remove combination screws, seal and the spoiler assembly.
6. Remove heat shield retaining nuts and the heat shield.

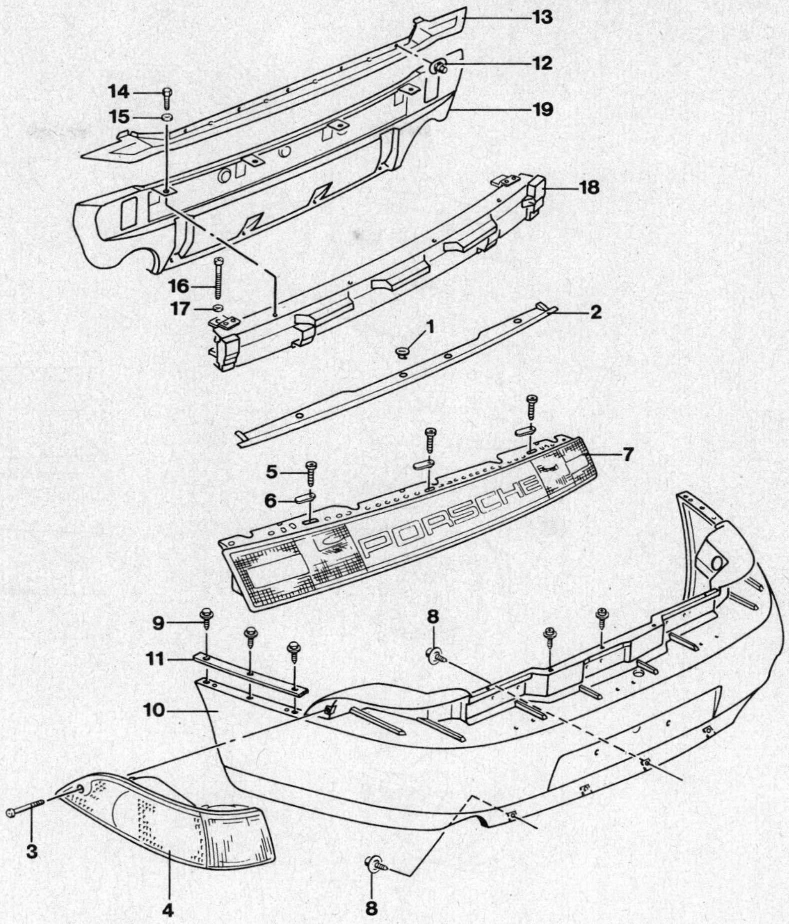

1. Screen
2. Nut
3. Sheetmetal Screw
4. Light Assembly
5. Pan Head Screw
6. Bracket
7. Closing Panel
8. Oval-Headed Sheetmetal Screw
9. Combination Screw
10. Rear Spoiler
11. Seal
12. Nut
13. Closing Panel Heat Shield
14. Sheetmetal Screw
15. Washer
16. Pan Head Screw
17. Washer
18. Bumper Support

PR1069500082000X

Fig. 13 Rear spoiler & bumper assembly

7. Remove bumper support sheetmetal and pan head screws.
8. Remove bumper support and bumper.
9. Remove A/C compressor mounting bolts, then position compressor aside.
10. Remove pressure hose between charge air cooler and turbocharger, **Fig. 14.** Plug opening to prevent any foreign substances from entering system.
11. Disconnect oxygen sensor electrical connectors.
12. Remove heat shields from catalytic converter and turbocharger.
13. Remove turbocharger mounting bolts, then disconnect hose and oil supply line from turbocharger.
14. Cut control hose from bypass flap vacuum control unit, then remove turbocharger assembly.
15. Reverse procedure to install.

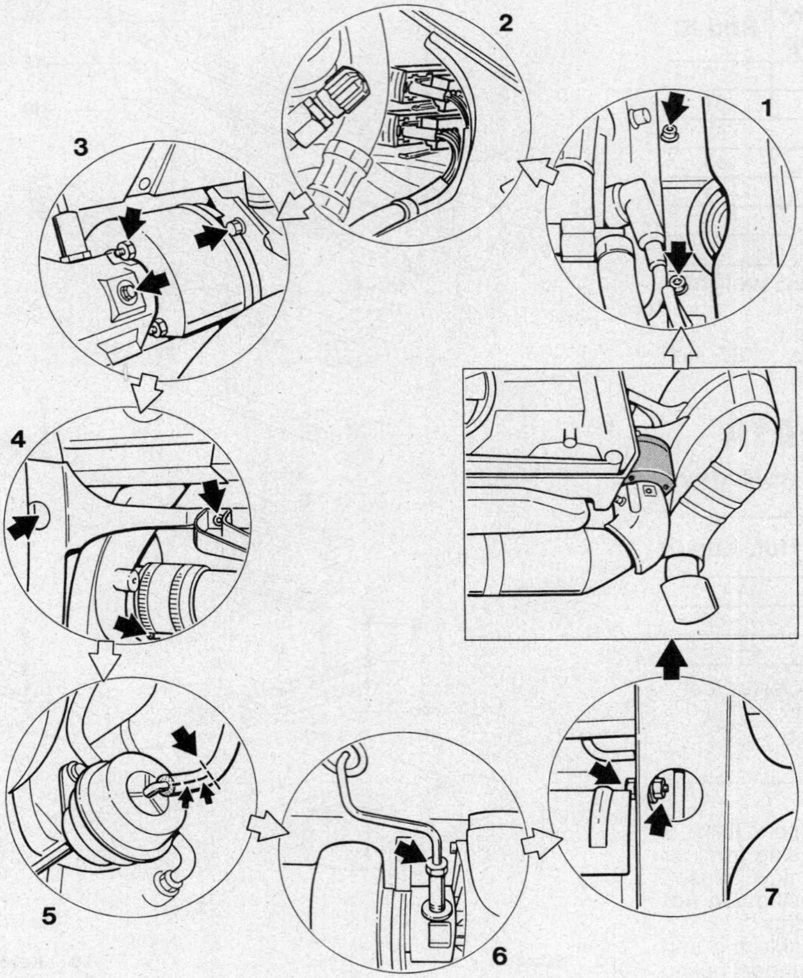

1. Turbocharger Carrier
2. Oxygen Sensor Connectors
3. Heat Shields
4. Turbocharger Mounting
5. Bypass Flap Vacuum Control Unit
6. Oil Supply Line
7. Turbocharger Mounting

PR1069500083000X

Fig. 14 Turbocharger replacement

TIGHTENING SPECIFICATIONS

Year	Component	Torque, Ft. Lbs.
1998–2001	Air Injection Lines	18
	Alternator Pulley	33–41
	Belt Monitor	84③
	Belt Monitor Bracket	11–15
	Camshaft Housing	17
	Catalytic Converter	18–22
	Central Shaft Clamping Sleeve	22–30
	Connecting Rod Bolt	22②
	Control Arm To Crossmember	63
	Control Arm To Wheel Carrier	63
	Crankcase Hex Head Bolts & Nuts	17
	Crankcase Through Bolts	37
	Crossmember, Front	48
	Crossmember, Rear	88

Continued

TIGHTENING SPECIFICATIONS—Continued

Year	Component	Torque, Ft. Lbs.
1998–2001	Crossmember Link	63
	Cylinder Head	①
	Drive Plate	66
	Driveshaft To Transmission Flange	60
	Engine Carrier	63
	Engine Support To Engine Mount	63
	Fan Pulley	10–11
	Fan Tensioning Strap	72③
	Flywheel, Dual Mass	63
	Fuel Return Line	26
	Fuel Supply Line	26
	Fuel Tank Sender	22
	Heat Exchanger	17
	Idler Pulley	84③
	Knock Sensor	11–19
	Knock Sensor Bridge	84③
	Muffler Strap	15
	NTC to Cylinder Head Three	84–108③
	Oil Feed Flange, Righthand	66
	Oil Pan Drain Plug	37
	Oil Pan Thermostat Housing	37
	Oil Pump	17
	Oil Return Neck, Lefthand	52
	Oxygen Sensor	37–44
	Power Steering Pump Gear	88
	Pressure Plate	17
	Pressure Relief Plug	44
	Rocker Arm Shaft	11
	Selector Rod	13
	Shift Rod	17
	Spark Plugs	15–22
	Stabilizer Bar	17
	Starter To Transmission	34
	Tailpipe	18–22
	Thermostat Housing Drain Plug	33–41
	Timing Chain Bearing Saddle	84③
	Timing Chain Cover	84③
	Timing Chain Housing To Crankcase	17
	Timing Chain Sprocket To Camshaft	15②
	Timing Gear Flange Stud	22
	Timing Gear Sprocket	88
	Track Rod	63
	Transmission Carrier	34
	Transmission Mount To Body	34
	Valve Cover	84③
	V-Belt Pulley	125
	Wheel To Wheel Hub	96

① — Refer to “Cylinder Head, Replace” for tightening sequence and procedure.

② — Plus an additional 90.°

③ — Inch lbs.

Clutch & Manual Transmission

INDEX

	Page No.
Adjustments	6-36
Clutch	6-36
Intermediate Lever	6-36
Shift Lever	6-36
Clutch, Replace	6-37
Boxster	6-37
911	6-37
Differential, Replace	6-38
Hydraulic System Service	6-36
Clutch Slave Cylinder, Replace	6-36
Clutch System Bleed	6-36
Maintenance	6-36
Fluid Change	6-36
Fluid Check	6-36
Tightening Specifications	6-38
Transmission, Replace	6-37
Boxster	6-37
911	6-37

MAINTENANCE

FLUID CHECK

1. Raise and support vehicle.
2. Remove filler screw located on side of transmission.
3. Ensure oil is up to the bottom edge of oil filler opening. Refer to "Specifications" for fluid type and amount.
4. **Torque** filler bolt to 22 ft. lbs.

FLUID CHANGE

1. Raise and support vehicle.
2. Remove oil filler bolt located on side of transmission.
3. Remove drain plug located at bottom of transmission.
4. Drain transmission oil into a suitable container.
5. Clean drain plug and fill plug.
6. Install drain plug and **torque** to 22 ft. lbs.
7. Fill transmission to bottom edge of oil filler opening. Refer to "Specifications" for fluid type and amount.
8. Install fill plug and **torque** to 22 ft. lbs.

ADJUSTMENTS

CLUTCH

Boxster

Because the clutch master cylinder has internal stop, the system has an automatic hydraulic adjustment and clutch free travel cannot be measured at the pedal. Adjust the clutch pedal position by pulling pedal back with spring scale. A minimum force of 22 ft. lbs. should return pedal to home position. If pedal yields, adjust Allen screw to obtain balance between return effect and pedal force boost.

911

Because the clutch master cylinder has internal stop, the system has automatic hydraulic adjustment and clutch free travel cannot be measured at the pedal. Adjust the clutch pedal position by pulling pedal back with spring scale. A minimum force of 22 ft. lbs. should return pedal to home position. If pedal yields, adjust Allen screw to obtain balance between return effect and pedal force boost.

1. Disconnect clutch cable or loosen completely at holder.

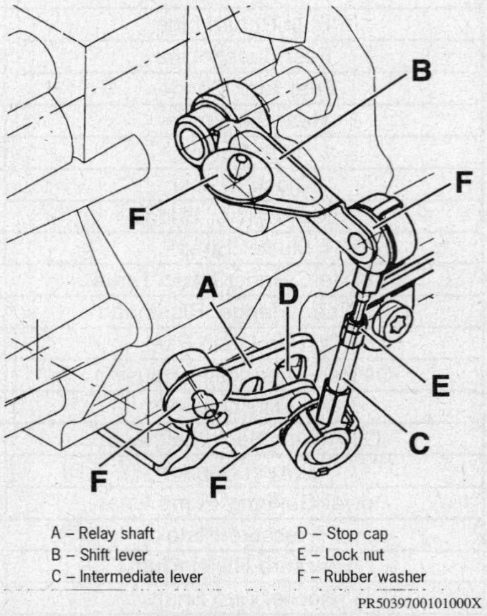

Fig. 1 Intermediate lever & shift lever assembly. Boxster

2. Using a feeler gauge, adjust clutch play to .0472 inch and lock adjusting screw.
3. Reconnect clutch cable.
4. Tighten clutch cable until clutch play is .0393 inch.

SHIFT LEVER

911

1. Remove access cover from shift rod tunnel in front of rear seats.
2. Loosen shift rod clamp and turn shift rod for selector shaft to right in neutral position.
3. Move shift lever in neutral to point where lower part of shift lever is positioned vertically and touching left stop.
4. Lightly tighten shift rod clamp.
5. Ensure travel is equal in gears 1 through 4, and 5th and reverse gears can be easily engaged, adjusting as necessary.
6. Tighten clamp nut to specifications.
7. Shift into 5th gear. With dust boot at shift rod coupling pushed back, ensure rotational play is evident at selector shaft.

INTERMEDIATE LEVER

Boxster

1. Move shift lever to the Neutral position.
2. Raise and support vehicle, then disconnect shift cables at transmission.
3. Disconnect intermediate lever end piece from shift lever, **Fig. 1.**
4. Turn relay shaft counterclockwise until it rests against upper stop, then attach a suitable weight to hold in place, **Fig. 2.**
5. Turn shift lever counterclockwise to upper stop, then insert a bolt 4.33 inches long as shown in **Fig. 3,** to hold shift lever in position.
6. Adjust intermediate lever length by turning lever until end piece of lever will press onto the upper ball without tension.
7. Ensure intermediate lever end piece is at right angle to axis of ball pin, **Fig. 4.**
8. Tighten locknut and press shift cables onto ball pins.
9. Check shifting function.

HYDRAULIC SYSTEM SERVICE

CLUTCH SLAVE CYLINDER, REPLACE

1999–2001 911

1. Raise and support vehicle, then remove rear axle crossmember.
2. Disconnect hydraulic line from clutch slave cylinder, **Fig. 5.**
3. Remove transmission side cover to hydraulic line clip retaining bolts.
4. Remove slave cylinder attaching bolts, then the slave cylinder.
5. Reverse procedure to install. Bleed system as outlined under "Clutch System Bleed."

CLUTCH SYSTEM BLEED

This bleed procedure uses a pressure bleeder.

1. Fill tank to upper edge with brake fluid and remove restrictor sleeve.
2. Connect bleeder.
3. Switch on bleeder and open bleeder screw on clutch slave cylinder until escaping fluid is without air bubbles. Operate clutch pedal several times during this step.

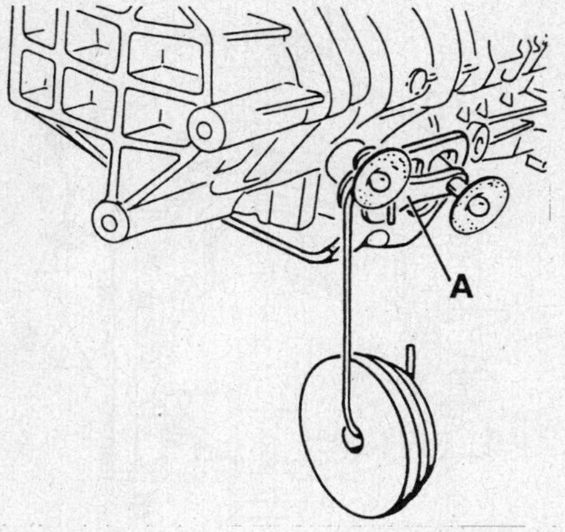

Fig. 2 Relay shaft positioning. Boxster

4. Switch bleeder off.
5. If necessary, unscrew slave cylinder on clutch housing, push rod against stop in slave cylinder and release. **Never operate clutch pedal with slave cylinder removed.**

CLUTCH

REPLACE

BOXSTER

1. Remove transmission as outlined under "Transmission, Replace."
2. Remove release lever and bearing, then the retaining spring.
3. Remove mounting bolts in crosswise pattern, in several steps.
4. Remove thrust plate and drive plates.
5. Remove mounting bolts and flywheel, then the needle bushing.
6. Reverse procedure to install, noting the following:
   a. Ensure centering pin is centered.
   b. Tighten flywheel in a crisscross pattern to specification.

911

This procedure has been revised by a Technical Service Bulletin.

1. Remove engine/transmission assembly as outlined under "3.6L Engine."
2. Separate transmission from engine as outlined under "Transmission, Replace."
3. Loosen clutch attaching bolts in star pattern no more than two turns per time until spring tension is relieved.
4. Remove clutch assembly.
5. Reverse procedure to install using new bolts and tighten to specifications.

TRANSMISSION

REPLACE

BOXSTER

1. Support engine using transport carrier with support bridge tool No. 10-22A and support feet tools No. 9591/a, or equivalents.

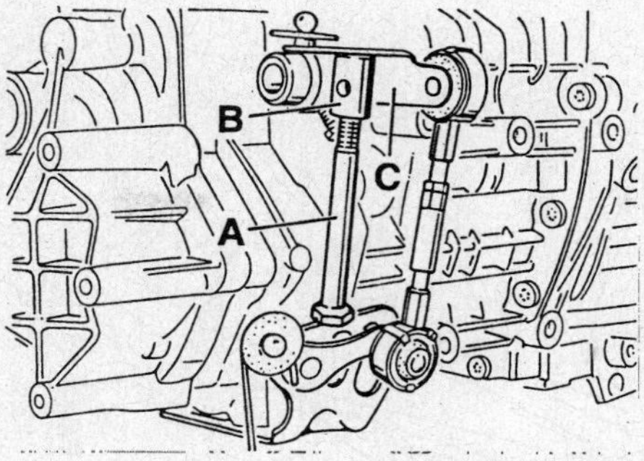

Fig. 3 Intermediate shaft adjustment. Boxster

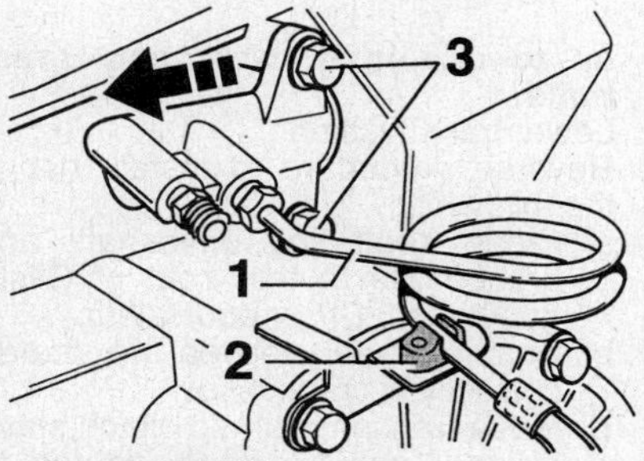

1. Hydraulic Line
2. Hydraulic Line Clip
3. Clutch Slave Cylinder Bolts

PR5039900105000X

Fig. 5 Clutch slave cylinder replacement. 1999–2001 911

2. Remove diagonal braces and transverse strut member, then the stabilizer bar.
3. Remove muffler with catalytic converters, then the rear crossmember and muffler mount.
4. Remove drive shafts and protect with scrap 1.181 inches diameter hose.
5. Remove back-up lamp connector.
6. Remove clutch slave cylinder mounting bolts and hang cylinder at side with hose attached. **Attach note to vehicle, warning against operating clutch pedal while slave cylinder is detached.**
7. Remove retaining clip, unclip joint rod, remove securing screw, remove shift and selector cable ball head retaining clips.
8. Press tabs and carefully pull sleeves from support bracket.
9. Place suitable transmission jack under transmission and secure with retaining strap.
10. Remove transmission support with left and righthand hydraulic mounts. **Do not loosen nut C, Fig. 6,** otherwise transmission prop will be damage.
11. Remove transmission to engine mounting bolts.
12. Pull transmission to rear, lower and remove.
13. Reverse procedure to install, noting the following:
    a. Clean drive shaft teeth and lubricate with thin coat of Olista Longtime 3 EP, or equivalent grease.

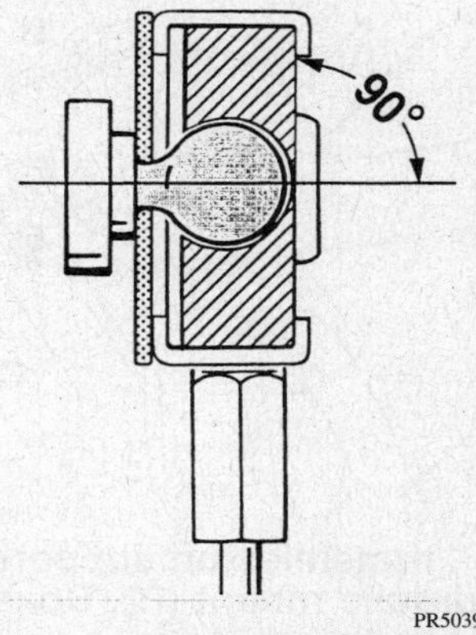

Fig. 4 Checking intermediate lever position. Boxster

   b. Ensure dowel sleeves are properly seated.
   c. Tighten bolts to specifications.
   d. Bleed clutch system.

911

1998

Removal

1. Remove engine/transmission assembly as outlined under "3.6L Engine."
2. Remove starter and reverse lamp switch wires.
3. Remove M6X16 bolt, bracket and mount cover.
4. Pull out release shaft using M6X40 bolt.
5. Remove mounting nuts and separate transmission from engine.

Installation

1. For corrosion protection, apply very thin coat of Olista Longtime 3 EP, or equivalent, to input shaft splines.
2. Engage release fork in release bearing and secure with suitable adhesive tape.
3. Connect transmission to engine.
4. Engage release shaft with seals into release fork and remove locating tape.
5. Fit needle-roller bearing, mount cover and bracket.
6. Tighten bolt to specifications.

1999–2001

1. Raise and support vehicle.
2. Remove middle and rear under body panels.
3. Remove crossmember from under transmission.
4. Secure engine in installation position with engine holding fixture tool No. 9624/1, or equivalent, as follows:
   a. Remove mounting for stabilizer.
   b. Swivel stabilizer forward and screw on engine holding fixture tool.
   c. Screw in pressure screw until pressure disc has contact with crankcase.
5. Remove driveshafts at transmission. **Use a scrap piece of hose on splines to prevent damage.**
6. Disconnect reverse light switch connector.

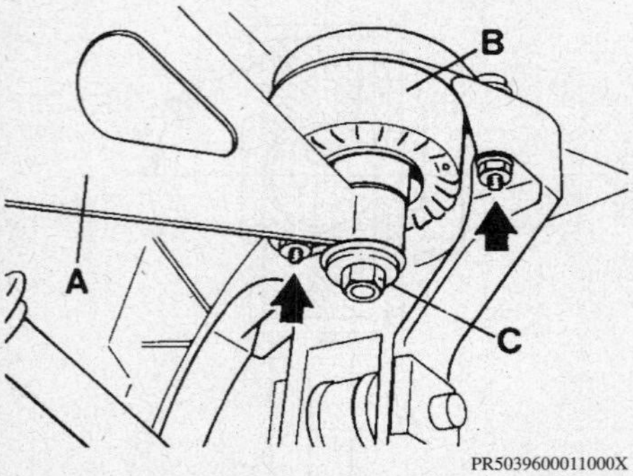

Fig. 6 transmission support (A) & hydraulic mount (B). Boxster

7. Unclip hydraulic line for clutch slave cylinder at side of transmission case cover.
8. Unscrew clutch slave cylinder and secure at side of body. **Clutch pedal must not be pressed after slave cylinder has been remove or damage will occur.**
9. Disengage shift and selector cables on transmission. **Do not bend or kink cables.**
10. Place a suitable transmission jack under transmission and fasten a suitable fixing strap.
11. Remove transmission holder and transmission support, **Fig. 7.**
12. Remove eight transmission to engine bolts, **Fig. 8. Engine can be lowered up to one inch to access upper bolts.**
13. Lower transmission.
14. Reverse procedure to install, noting the following:
    a. Clean teeth of driveshaft and grease with a thin coat of Olista Longtime 3 EP, or equivalent.
    b. Ensure dowel sleeves are seated correctly in crankcase.
    c. Move transmission so clutch slave cylinder can be fitted, tighten to specification, then move transmission further inward and fasten to engine.
    d. Tighten bolts to specification.

Fig. 7 Transmission support. 1999–2001 911

DIFFERENTIAL

REPLACE

1. Remove flanged shaft and snap ring.
2. Remove mounting bolts and final drive cover.
3. Remove differential.
4. Remove speedometer drive gear, RPM sensor and oroidal sealing ring.
5. Reverse procedure to install. Use new snap ring and tighten bolts to specifications.

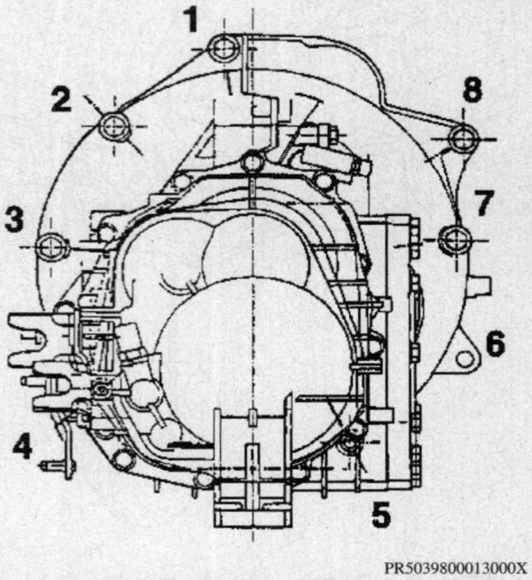

Fig. 8 Transmission to engine bolt locations

TIGHTENING SPECIFICATIONS

Year	Component	Torque, Ft. Lbs.
BOXSTER		
1998–2001	Back-Up Lamp Retaining Plate	18
	Back-Up Lamp Switch	84①
	Clutch Slave Cylinder	17
	Differential Crown Wheel	②
	Drain Plug	18
	Drive Shaft	29
	Fifth/Reverse Interlock	84①
	Final Drive Cover	18
	Flywheel	18③
	Hydraulic Mount	18
	Interlock Switch	18
	Relay Shaft	29
	Release Bearing Guide Sleeve	26
	Reverse Idler Shaft	26
	Reverse Lever Ball Journal	18
	Rocker Holder	17
	Shift Cable Bracket	33
	Shift Lever	17
	Shift Rod Cover	15
	Transmission Case Cover	18

Continued

TIGHTENING SPECIFICATIONS—Continued

Year	Component	Torque, Ft. Lbs.
BOXSTER		
1998–2001	Transmission Mount (M10)	33
	Transmission Mount (M12)	63
	Transmission Support	48
911		
1998	Bleeder In Case	26
	Clamping Plate	84①
	Clutch Plate	17
	Return Gear II Collar	26
	Front Cover	17
	Guide Tube	84①
	Halfshaft Flange	32
	Input Shaft (M22X1.5)	103
	Input Shaft (M30X1.5)	184
	Longitudinal Mount	63
	Longitudinal Mount Locknut	22
	Oil Cup	48①
	Oil Drain Plug	22
	Oil Filler Plug	22
	Output Shaft	184
	Ring Gear	148
	Reversing Lamp Switch	26
	Selector Gate	84①
	Side Cover	17
	Shift Rod Clamp	18
	Shift Fork	17
	Tensioning Plate	17
	Transmission Mount	34
	Transmission Mount Locknut	63
	Vent	26
1999–2001	Cross Member To Carrier Side Member	48
	Clutch Slave Cylinder To Transmission	17
	Drive Shaft To Transmission	60
	Stabilizer To Rear Axle Cross Member Side	17
	Transmission Carrier To Body	48
	Transmission Support To Body	48
	Transmission Support/Transmission Carrier To Transmission Bearing	48
	Transmission To Engine Bolts (M 10)	33
	Transmission To Engine Bolts (M 12)	63

① — Inch lbs.

② — Torque to 45 ft. lbs. and finally tighten additional 45.°

③ — Plus an additional 90.°

Rear Axle & Suspension

INDEX

	Page No.
Coil Spring, Replace	6-44
Hub & Bearing, Replace	6-40
911	6-40
Maintenance	6-40
Axle Fluid Change	6-40
Rear Axle Shaft, Replace	6-40
911	6-40
Rear Suspension, Replace	6-40
911	6-40
Strut, Replace	6-41
Boxster	6-41
911	6-42
Strut Service	6-42
Boxster	6-42
911	6-43
Tightening Specifications	6-44
Trailing Arm Service	6-44
911	6-44

MAINTENANCE

AXLE FLUID CHANGE

Automatic transmission

There is no drain plug on the final drive.

1. Remove oil filler plug.
2. Remove oil using a suitable suction hand pump. **Ensure transmission is warm to thin oil.**
3. Fill axle to specification using axle fill tool No. 1924 or equivalent.
4. Filling must be carried out very slowly due to a baffle plate in cover of axle.
5. Replace sealing ring for filler plug, install and **torque** to 22 ft. lbs.

REAR AXLE SHAFT

REPLACE

911

1. Raise and support vehicle.
2. Remove rear wheels, then the engine guard and rear underbody panel.
3. Remove cotter pin, then the hub castle nut while applying brakes.
4. Remove Allen bolts from axle flanges.
5. Remove axle shaft.
6. Reverse procedure to install. Tighten axle shaft and halfshaft castle nut to specifications.

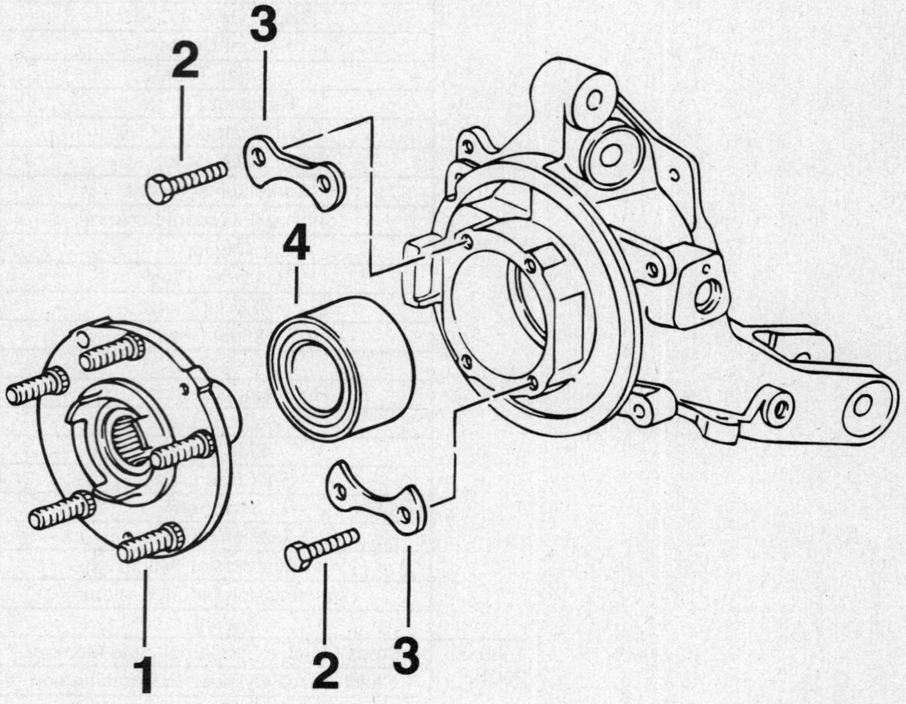

Fig. 1 Wheel hub & bearing assembly. 1998 911

HUB & BEARING

REPLACE

911

1998

1. Remove wheel bearing housing assembly as outlined under "Rear Suspension, Replace."
2. Press wheel hub off of wheel bearing housing assembly using a suitable hydraulic press and pressing tool No. P 297, or equivalent, **Fig. 1.**
3. Remove bearing retainer plates attaching bolts, then the retainer plates.
4. Heat wheel bearing housing assembly to 212°F, then press wheel bearing out of housing with tool No. VW 415 A, or equivalent.
5. Reverse procedure to install, noting the following:
   a. Heat wheel bearing housing assembly to 212°F and press bearing into housing with logo facing wheel hub.
   b. Press wheel hub into housing with pressure piece tool No. P 297 A, or equivalent.

REAR SUSPENSION

REPLACE

911

1998

1. Raise and support vehicle.
2. Remove rear wheels, then the engine guard and rear underbody panel.
3. While pressing on brakes, remove driveshaft locknut, **Fig. 2.**
4. Push driveshaft out of wheel hub using a suitable wheel hub puller tool.
5. Remove control arm cover.
6. Remove RPM sensor connector attaching bolt, then disconnect sensor connector.
7. Separate RPM sensor wires from wheel carrier clip, then remove sensor from wheel carrier.
8. Remove brake caliper assembly from wheel carrier, and suspend caliper inside wheel housing.
9. Remove stabilizer mount from stabilizer bar, then the stabilizer clamp.
10. Lower vehicle and remove cassette box and hand brake lever cover from center column.
11. Remove hand brake locknut and adjustment nut, **Fig. 3.**
12. Remove retainer, then the hand brake lever support pin.
13. Remove hand brake lever with pull rod.
14. Remove hand brake cable retaining nut upper and lower tab washers.
15. Pull hand brake cable out of guide. **If**

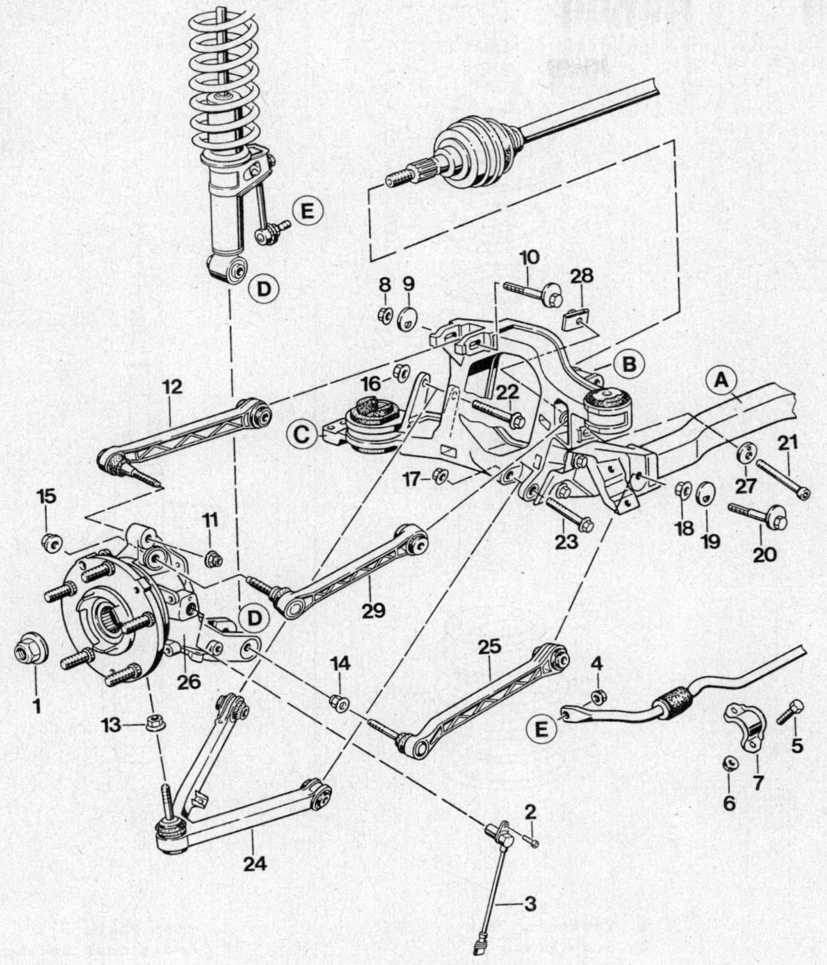

1. Driveshaft Locknut
2. Pan Head Screws
3. RPM Sensor
4. Stabilizer Locknut
5. Bolts
6. Stabilizer Bracket Locknut
7. Retaining Bracket
8. Camber Eccenctric Locknut
9. Eccentric Washer
10. Camber Eccentric
11. Control Arm 3 Locknut
12. Control Arm 3
13. Control Arm 1/5 Locknut
14. Control Arm 2 Locknut
15. Control Arm 4 Locknut
16. Locknut
17. Locknut
18. Toe Eccentric Locknut
19. Eccentric Washer
20. Toe Eccentric
21. Eccentric Bolt
22. Bolt
23. Bolt
24. Control Arm 1/5
25. Control Arm 2
26. Wheel Carrier
27. Eccentric Washer
28. Retaining Nut
29. Control Arm 4

PR20395000f0000X

Fig. 2 Rear suspension. 1998 911

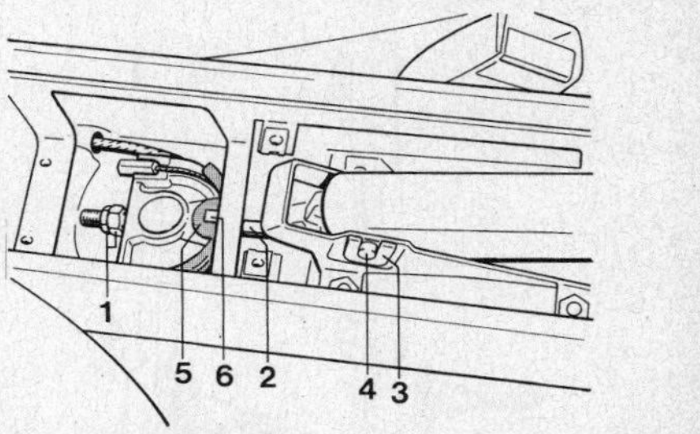

1. Adjustment Nut
2. Tie Rod
3. Retainer
4. Support Pin
5. Tab Washer
6. Retaining Lug

PR2039500011000X

Fig. 3 Hand brake lever assembly. 1998 911

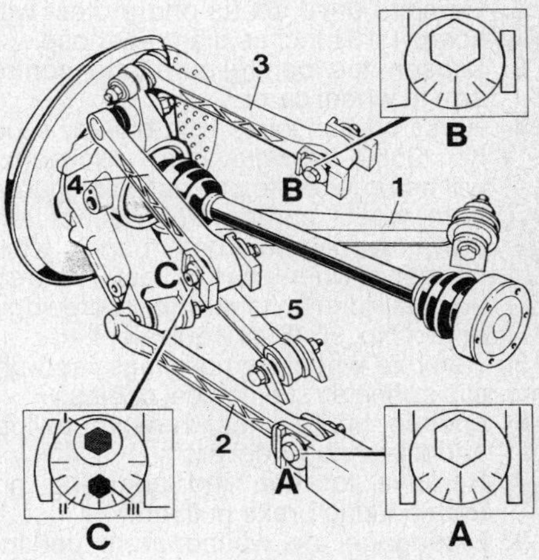

A. Toe Eccentric
B. Camber Eccentric
C. Camber Eccentric
1. Control Arm 1
2. Control Arm 2
3. Control Arm 3

PR2039500012000X

Fig. 4 Rear suspension eccentric bolts. 1998 911

only replacing wheel bearing, wheel carrier or wheel hub, the hand brake cable does not have to be disconnected from the lever assembly.

16. Mark position of eccentric bolts (A), (B) and (C), **Fig. 4. Eccentric bolts (A) and (B) are identical, therefore they must be marked in a way that they can be installed in the correct control arm.**
17. Remove control arm No. 3 to wheel carrier locknut, then press control arm ball joint from wheel carrier with pressing tool No. 9546, or equivalent.
18. Loosen all control arm to wheel carrier locknuts. **Do not remove locknuts at this time.**
19. Press 1/5 control arm (lower) ball joint out of wheel carrier, using pressing tool No. 9560, or equivalent.
20. Remove eccentric bolt from control arm 2 (toe control arm) and pivot arm out of crossmember in a downward direction.
21. Press ball joint of control arm (4) off of wheel carrier with pressing tool No. 9546, or equivalent. Do not remove control arm at this time.
22. Remove control arm 1/5 (lower).
23. Remove control arms 2 (toe control arm) and 4 from wheel carrier.
24. Reverse procedure to install, noting the following:
    a. Dacromet-type bolt unions (aluminum color) must not be greased.
    b. Refer to **Fig. 5** for control arm identification.
    c. Align rear suspension as outlined in "Wheel Alignment" section.

STRUT

REPLACE

BOXSTER

1. Raise and support vehicle. Remove wheel.

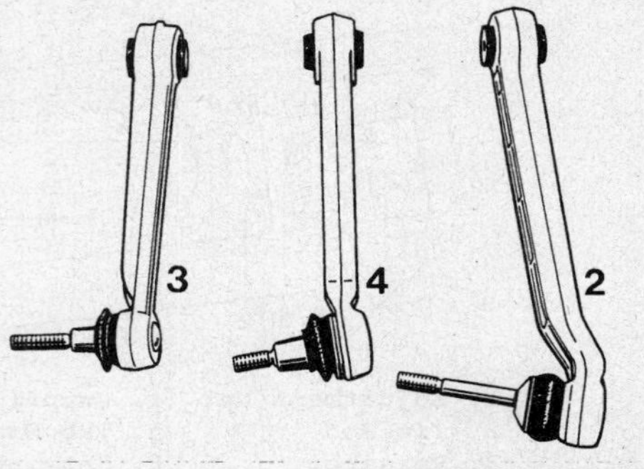

PR2039500013000X

Fig. 5 Control arm identification. 1998 911

2. Remove drive shafts and protect with scrap 1.181 inches diameter hose.
3. Loosen toe control arm and control arm at wheel carrier.
4. Press off ball joints with ball joint tool No. 9560, or equivalent. Assistance will be required to pull ball joint journal from wheel carrier. Pull control arm down evenly with both hands while swinging wheel carrier out. Counter hold ball joint bolts with Torx screwdriver tool No. 9546, or equivalent.
5. Remove wheel carrier plugs, and unclip spring strut electrical cables.
6. Loosen brake lines, remove caliper and attach to wheel arch.
7. Remove locknut and adjusting nut from parking brake pull rod.
8. Disengage tab washer from parking brake cable, remove cable and pull to guide rear.
9. Mark spring strut mount position for installation and remove mounting nuts.
10. Remove spring strut with wheel carrier. **Be careful to not damage ball joint and drive shaft boots. Ensure mount back-up ring is not shifted out of position with recesses between collars.**
11. Loose stabilizer mount clamp and remove spring strut.
12. Reverse procedure to install. Tighten nuts and bolts to specifications.

911

1998

1. Raise and support vehicle.
2. Remove rear wheel, engine guard and rear underside panel.
3. Disconnect stabilizer mount from stabilizer. Leave stabilizer mount attached to strut assembly.
4. Loosen control arm 2 (toe control arm), **Fig. 2. Do not remove at this time.**
5. Mark position of eccentric bolt (A), **Fig. 4.**
6. Remove eccentric bolt (A), then swing control arm 2 out from below crossmember.
7. Place a protective tube over driveshaft assembly.
8. Remove left spring strut upper retaining nuts.
9. Remove control arm No. 2 completely, then the strut assembly.

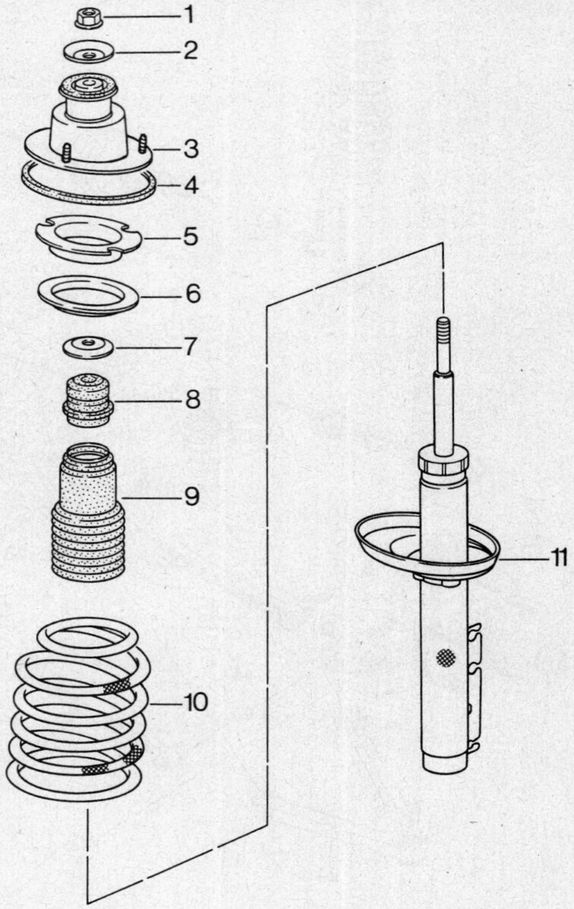

1. Fastening Nut
2. Stop Plate
3. Spring Strut Mount
4. Sealing Ring
5. Back-Up Ring
6. Spring Plate (Compensation Part)
7. Stop Plate
8. Additional Spring
9. Bellows
10. Coil Spring
11. Vibration Damper

PR2039700016000X

Fig. 6 Exploded view of strut assembly. Boxster

10. Reverse procedure to install, noting the following:
    a. Ensure correct strut assembly is installed, do not mix left and right strut assembles (marked on top of strut assembly).
    b. Check grade of eccentric bolt (grade is marked on top of bolt). If grade is 8.8, replace with grade 10.9 bolt and transfer reference mark to new bolt.
    c. Tighten eccentric bolt in its reference position. Control arm 2 and rear crossmember must form a horizontal line, if necessary raise wheel carrier with a suitable jack before tightening eccentric bolt.
    d. Check wheel alignment as outlined in "Wheel Alignment" section.

1999-2001

1. Raise and support vehicle.
2. Mark installed position of three collar nuts that support top of strut. **Spring strut mount is located in vehicle interior.**
3. Remove fastening nuts from upper strut mount.
4. Loosen stabilizer mount and stabilizer.
5. Remove bolt attaching spring strut to wheel carrier and pull out strut.
6. Reverse procedure to install.

STRUT SERVICE

BOXSTER

1. Compress strut assembly with a suitable spring compressor.
2. Remove upper strut assembly fastening nut, **Fig. 6.**
3. Remove stop plate, spring strut mount, sealing ring and back-up ring.
4. Remove spring plate (compensation part), stop plate, additional spring, protective bellows and coil spring.
5. Reverse procedure to assemble, noting the following:
    a. There are two different spring plate (compensation part) sizes. To determine which spring plate to use, check color coding on the coil spring (1 green line = 6.5 mm spring

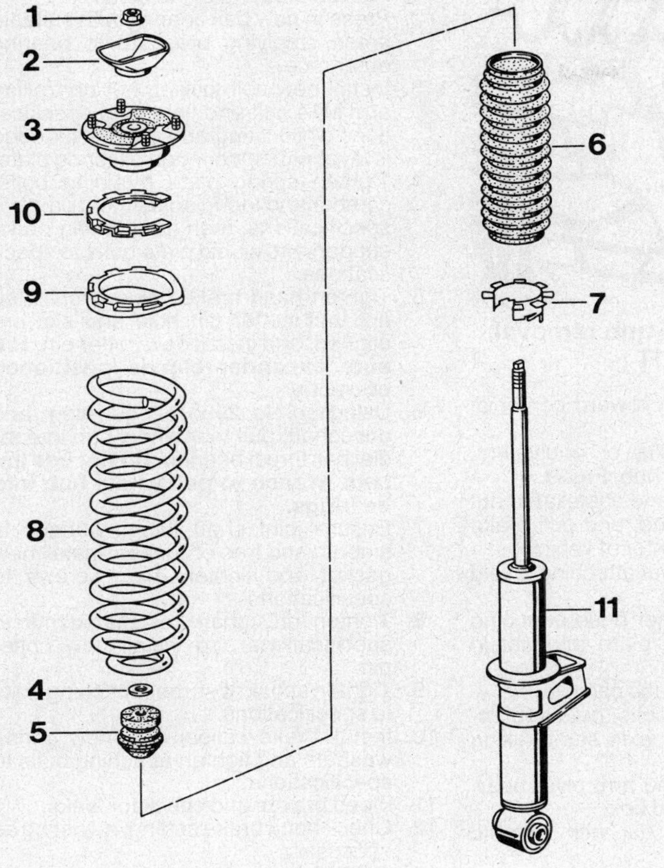

1. Fastening Nut
2. Stop Plate
3. Spring Strut Mount
4. Washer
5. Helper Spring
6. Bellows
7. Support Clip Mount
8. Coil Spring
9. Spring Support
10. Intermediate Section
11. Shock Absorber

PR2039500017000X

Fig. 7 Exploded view of strut assembly. 1998 911

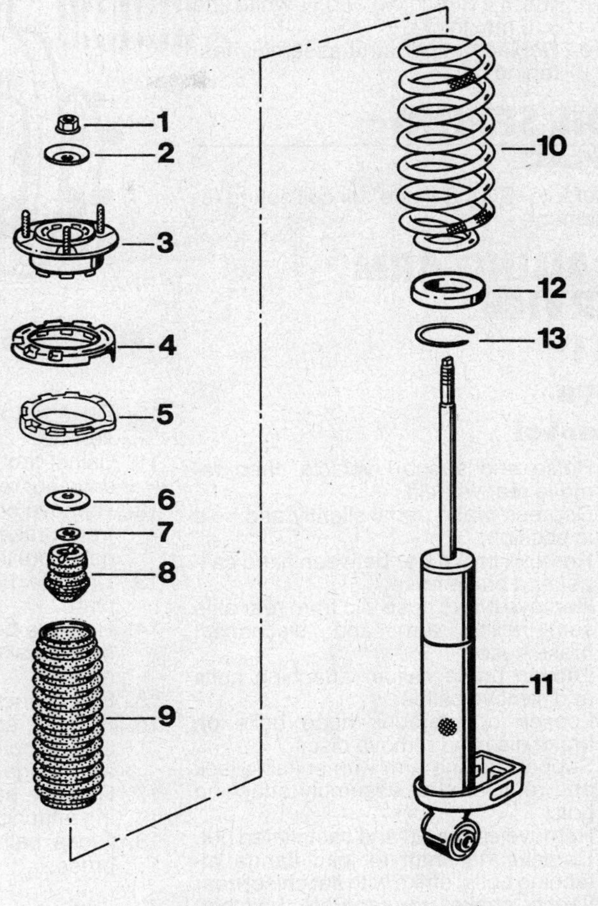

1. Fastening Nut
2. Stop Plate
3. Spring Strut Mount
4. Intermediate Part (Compensation Part)
5. Spring Plate
6. Stop Plate
7. Washer
8. Additional Spring
9. Bellows
10. Coil Spring
11. Damper
12. Spring Plate
13. Snap Ring

PR2039900015000X

Fig. 8 Exploded view of strut assembly. 1999–2001 911

plate) and (1 white line = 3 mm spring plate).

b. These vehicles are equipped with two types of dampers depending on which suspension is being used. To identify the damper assembly, check color coding on the damper assembly (blue dot = standard suspension) and (red dot = sport type suspension).
c. Tighten fastening nut to specification with a suitable torque wrench. **Never use an impact type wrench to tighten fastening nut.**

911

1998

1. Compress strut assembly with a suitable spring compressor.
2. Remove upper strut assembly fastening nut, **Fig. 7.**
3. Remove stop plate, spring strut mount, intermediate section, spring support and coil spring.
4. Remove washer, helper spring, bellows and mount.
5. Reverse procedure to assemble, noting the following:
   a. Coil springs must be replaced in pairs.
   b. If new coil springs are installed, it may be necessary to use a new intermediate section. Intermediate sections are available in three different thicknesses (3 mm, 5.5 mm and 8 mm). Match intermediate section with number of color coded lines on spring assembly (1 line = 8 mm section, 2 lines = 5.5 mm section, 3 lines = 3 mm section).
   c. Replace upper strut assembly fastening nut.

1999–2001

1. Compress strut assembly with a suitable spring compressor.
2. Remove upper strut assembly fastening nut, **Fig. 8.**
3. Remove stop plate, spring strut mount, intermediate plate and spring plate.
4. Remove stop plate, washer, additional spring and bellows.
5. Remove coil spring, vibration damper, bottom spring plate and snap ring.
6. Reverse procedure to assemble, noting the following:
   a. Coil springs should be replaced in pairs.
   b. Select correct intermediate plate by matching color coded lines on spring assembly with plate (1 green

line = 4 mm thick) and (1 white line =. 5 mm thick).

c. Replace upper strut assembly fastening nut.

COIL SPRING

REPLACE

Refer to "Strut Service" for coil spring replacement.

TRAILING ARM SERVICE

911

1998

Removal

1. Raise and support vehicle, then remove rear wheels.
2. Depress brake pedal slightly and hold in position.
3. Remove brake line between fixed caliper and brake hose.
4. Remove brake hose clip from rear axle semi-trailing arm and disconnect brake hose.
5. Loosen brake caliper attaching bolts and remove caliper.
6. Loosen countersunk head bolts on brake disc and remove disc.
7. Support trailing arm with suitable jack and remove strut assembly attaching bolt.
8. Remove cotter pin and castellated nut.
9. Remove halfshaft to joint flange attaching bolts, strike with flat chisel near flange gasket to separate halfshaft from joint flange, and remove halfshaft.

Fig. 9 Rear wheel hub removal. 1998 911

10. Drive out axle shaft toward center of vehicle.
11. Using tool No. 297a, or equivalent, drive out rear wheel hub, **Fig. 9.**
12. Remove cotter pin and castellated nut from brake cable end, and pull brake cable out toward center of vehicle.
13. Unscrew hexagon nut attaching shield plate.
14. Remove brake carrier plate attaching nuts, brake carrier plate and shield plate.
15. Disconnect hand brake cable guide.
16. Remove attaching bolts, nuts and eccentric bolts of rear axle semi-trailing arm flange.
17. Remove semi-trailing arm pivot bearing attaching nut and bolt.
18. Press ball bearing out with suitable press.

Installation

1. Do not grease Dacroment-type (aluminum colored) nuts and bolts.
2. Press in new ball bearing with suitable press, applying pressure to bearing outer race.
3. Install new self locking nut on trailing arm M14 bolt and tighten to specifications while lifting arm until lower edge is level with upper edge of spring plate.
4. Tighten spring plate retaining bolts, camber and toe-in adjustment cams to specifications, then the parking brake support and shield plate bolts to specifications.
5. Tighten hand brake cable castellated nut until cotter pin hole and slot are aligned, and install new cotter pin. **Ensure expander clip is positioned correctly.**
6. Using tool No. 298b, or equivalent, and driveshaft, pull rear wheel hub into radial ball thrust bearing. **Do not use impact wrench to pull wheel hub into bearings.**
7. Ensure joint shaft flange surface is smooth and free of grease, install new gasket and tighten Allen screws to specifications.
8. Tighten driveshaft castellated nut to specifications and install new cotter pin.
9. Tighten shock absorber attaching bolts to specifications.
10. Install brake caliper with new spring washers and tighten attaching bolts to specifications.
11. Bleed brakes and check for leaks.
12. Check hand brake setting, adjusting as necessary.
13. Adjust toe-in and camber.

TIGHTENING SPECIFICATIONS

Year	Component	Torque, Ft. Lbs.
BOXSTER		
1998–2001	Brake Caliper	63
	Brake Cover Plate	84①
	Brake Disc	84①
	Camber Eccentric	81
	Carrier Side Section	48
	Carrier Side Section Stud	15
	Control Arm To Wheel Carrier	55
	Crossmember	48
	Diagonal Arm	117
	Diagonal Brace	48
	Driveshaft To Transmission	29
	Driveshaft To Wheel Hub	339
	Engine Bracket	34
	Engine Carrier	48
	Engine Carrier Stud	15
	Engine Mount	48
	Hydraulic Mount To Carrier Side Section	24
	Hydraulic Mount To transmission Bracket	63
	Shock Absorber Piston Rod Fastening Nut	44

Continued

TIGHTENING SPECIFICATIONS—Continued

Year	Component	Torque, Ft. Lbs.
BOXSTER		
1998–2001	Speed Sensor	84①
	Spring Strut To Body	27
	Spring Strut To Wheel Carrier	63
	Stabilizer To Carrier Side Section	17
	Stabilizer To Wheel Carrier	63
	Strut Panel To Carrier Side Section	48
	Strut Panel To Crossmember	34
	Toe Control Arm	55
	Toe Eccentric	81
	Transmission Bracket	48
	Transverse Strut Rear	48
	V-Brace	48
	Wheel Bearing To Wheel Carrier	27
	Wheel To Hub	96
911		
1998	Adjusting Lever To Spring Strut	185
	Brake Disc To Hub	48①
	Brake Disc To Wheel	63
	Brake Protection Plate	84①
	Camber Adjustment Cam	43
	Camber Eccentric Bolts	45
	Caster Link To Subframe	63
	Caster Link To Wheel Carrier	55
	Crossmember, Center	48
	Crossmember, Side	63
	Crossmember, Side Front	88
	Crossmember, Side Rear	48
	Damper To Mount	43
	Drive Shaft To transmission	60
	Drive Shaft To Wheel Hub	339
	Joint Shaft Flange (M10)	60
	Joint Shaft Flange (M8)	30
	Lower Link To Subframe (M12)	63
	Lower Link To Subframe (M14)	147
	Lower Link to Wheel Carrier	55
	Parking Brake Shield Plate	18
	Parking Brake Support Plate	18
	Radius Arm	65
	Radius Arm Bearing Cap	35
	Rear Axle Control Arm	87
	Rear Halfshaft Castellated Nut	217–253
	Shock Absorber Hex Nut	55
	Spring Plate	68
	Spring Strut To Body	24
	Spring Strut To Wheel Carrier	63
	Stabilizer Bar To Crossmember	17
	Stabilizer Bar Mount	34
	Subframe	88
	Toe Link	63
	Toe-In Adjustment Cam	43
	Tracking Eccentric Bolts	36

Continued

TIGHTENING SPECIFICATIONS—Continued

Year	Component	Torque, Ft. Lbs.
911		
1998	Trailing Arm Self Locking Nut	43
	Wheel Bearing	17
	Wheel Hub To Rear Wheel Shaft	339
	Wheel Nuts	96
	Wheel Sensor	84①
1999–2001	Brake Caliper To Wheel Carrier	63
	Brake Cover Plate	90①
	Brake Disc To Wheel Hub	90①
	Brake Hose Holder To Carrier Side Section	90①
	Carrier Side Section To Body Nut	74
	Carrier Side Section To Body Stud	34
	Clutch Hydraulic Line	22
	Combination Wire Retainer To Wheel Carrier	90①
	Control Arm 2 (Toe Control Arm) To Wheel Carrier	56
	Control Arm 2 (Toe Control Arm) To Crossmember (Toe Eccentric)	74
	Cross Member To Carrier Side Section (Front)	48
	Cross Member To Carrier Side Section (Rear)	74
	Diagonal Brace To Body	48
	Diagonal Brace To Crossmember	74
	Diagonal Brace To Carrier Side Section	17
	Diagonal Control Arm To Carrier Side Section	133
	Diagonal Control Arm To Control Arm	118
	Driveshaft To Transmission	60
	Driveshaft To Wheel Hub	339
	Engine Carrier To Engine	34
	Engine Mount To Body	17
	Engine Mount To Engine Carrier	34
	Longitudinal Support To Body	48
	Longitudinal Support To Mount	48
	Lower Control Arm To Carrier Side Section	74
	Lower Control Arm To Wheel Carrier	56
	Power Steering Pressure Line	22
	Power Steering Return Line	30
	Speed Sensor To Wheel Carrier	90①
	Stabilizer Mount To Spring Strut	34
	Stabilizer To Carrier Side Section	17
	Stabilizer To Stabilizer Mount	34
	Strut Assembly Piston Rod Fastening Nut	43
	Strut To Body	34
	Strut To Wheel Carrier	74
	Transmission Support To Body Nut	48
	Transmission Support To Body Stud	15
	Upper Control Arms To Carrier Side Section	74
	Upper Control Arms To Wheel Carrier	74
	Wheel Bearing To Wheel Carrier	27
	Wheel To Wheel Hub	96

① — Inch lbs.

Front Suspension & Steering

NOTE: On Air Bag Equipped Models, Refer To "Air Bag System Precautions" Located In The Front Of This Manual For System Disarming & Arming Procedures.

NOTE: Prior To Performing Any Service Operations Listed In This Section, Consult The "Technical Service Bulletins" Section For Related Information.

INDEX

	Page No.
Ball Joint, Replace	6-48
Boxster & 1999–2001 911	6-48
1998 911	6-48
Ball Joint Inspection	6-48
Coil Spring & Strut Service	6-48
Boxster & 1999–2001 911	6-48
1998 911	6-49
Control Arm, Replace	6-49
Boxster & 1999–2001 911	6-49
1998 911	6-49
Driveshaft, Replace	6-47
1998	6-47
Power Steering Gear, Replace	6-49
Boxster & 1999–2001 911	6-49
1998 911	6-49
Precautions	6-47
Air Bag Systems	6-47
Battery Ground Cable	6-47
Stabilizer Bar, Replace	6-49
1998 911	6-49
Strut, Replace	6-48
Boxster & 1999–2001 911	6-48
1998 911	6-48
Technical Service Bulletins	6-50
Front Suspension Creaking Or Grinding	6-50
Tie Rod End, Replace	6-49
Boxster & 2001 911	6-49
1998 911	6-49
Tightening Specifications	6-52
Wheel Bearing, Replace	6-47
Wheel Carrier, Replace	6-47
Boxster & 1999–2001 911	6-47
1998 911	6-47

PRECAUTIONS

AIR BAG SYSTEMS

Refer to "Air Bag System Precautions" in the front of this manual for system disarming and arming procedures.

BATTERY GROUND CABLE

Prior to service, disconnect battery ground cable and isolate as required.

WHEEL BEARING

REPLACE

1. Raise and support vehicle, then remove wheel and tire assembly.
2. Remove wheel hub bearing retaining nut while applying brakes.
3. Remove wheel carrier assembly as outlined under "Wheel Carrier, Replace."
4. Press wheel hub from wheel carrier with pressure piece tool No. P 297, or equivalent, and a suitable hydraulic press.
5. Remove bearing retainer plate attaching bolts, then the retainer plate, **Figs. 1 and 2.**
6. Heat wheel bearing housing to approximately 212°F, then press wheel bearing from wheel carrier using pressure piece tool No. P 297, or equivalent, and a suitable press.
7. Press inner wheel bearing race from wheel carrier with pressure piece tool No. P 297a, or equivalent.
8. Reverse procedure to assemble, noting the following:
   a. Clean wheel bearing housing bore with a polishing cloth.
   b. Heat bearing housing to approximately 212°F, then press new bearing assembly into bearing housing with pressure piece tool No. P 297, or equivalent, and a suitable press.

WHEEL CARRIER

REPLACE

BOXSTER & 1999–2001 911

1. Raise and support vehicle, then remove wheel and tire assembly.
2. Remove RPM sensor retaining screw, then the RPM sensor from wheel carrier.
3. Remove brake caliper mounting bolts.
4. Remove brake caliper assembly and suspend aside with suitable wire. **Do not disconnect brake hydraulic line.**
5. Remove ball joint to wheel carrier retaining nut, then separate ball joint from wheel carrier with ball joint remover tool No. 9560, or equivalent.
6. Remove track rod (tie rod end) to wheel carrier retaining nut, then separate track rod (tie rod end) from wheel carrier with ball joint remover tool No. 9560, or equivalent.
7. Loosen strut assembly to wheel carrier clamped connection, then remove strut from wheel carrier mounting bolts.
8. Remove wheel carrier assembly from front of vehicle.
9. Reverse procedure to install.

1998 911

1. Raise and support vehicle, then remove wheel and tire assembly.
2. Remove RPM sensor retaining screw, then the RPM sensor from wheel carrier, **Fig. 3.**
3. Remove air guide attaching locknut and screw, then the air guide.
4. Remove stabilizer to wheel carrier retaining bolt.
5. Remove ball joint to wheel carrier retaining nut, then separate ball joint from wheel carrier as outlined under "Ball Joint, Replace."
6. Remove tie rod end to wheel carrier retaining nut, then separate tie rod end from wheel carrier.
7. Remove lower strut to wheel carrier mounting bolts.
8. Remove brake line from strut mounted bracket.
9. Remove brake caliper assembly from wheel carrier and suspend aside.
10. **On all wheel drive models,** separate driveshaft from wheel carrier as outlined under "Driveshaft, Replace."
11. **On all models,** remove wheel carrier assembly from front of vehicle.
12. Reverse procedure to install.

DRIVESHAFT

REPLACE

1998

1. Loosen driveshaft to wheel hub retaining nut while applying brakes.
2. Raise and support vehicle, then remove wheel and tire assembly.
3. Remove underside panel, then the brake cooling duct from control arm.
4. Remove stabilizer arm from wheel carrier.
5. Separate ball joint from wheel carrier as outlined under "Ball Joint, Replace."
6. Remove driveshaft to transmission flange attaching bolts.
7. Separate driveshaft from wheel carrier assembly, then remove driveshaft from vehicle.

8. Reverse procedure to install.

BALL JOINT INSPECTION

1. Raise and support vehicle.
2. Grasp tire at top and bottom.
3. Shake tire in a side to side motion and check for any ball joint movement.
4. Replace ball joint if any movement is noticed.

BALL JOINT

REPLACE

BOXSTER & 1999-2001 911

The ball joint is part of the control arm assembly. Refer to "Control Arm, Replace" for ball joint replacement.

1998 911

1. Raise and support vehicle, then remove wheel and tire assembly.
2. Remove ball joint to wheel carrier assembly retaining nut,
3. Separate ball joint from wheel carrier with ball joint separator tool No. 9560, or equivalent.
4. Remove ball joint to control arm attaching bolts.
5. Remove ball joint from control arm.
6. Reverse procedure to install.

STRUT

REPLACE

BOXSTER & 1999-2001 911

1. Raise and support vehicle, then remove front wheel.
2. Loosen stabilizer mount at stabilizer, then the track rod (tie rod end) and control arm at wheel carrier.
3. Press off ball joints with ball joint remover tool No. 9560, or equivalent. Counter hold ball joint bolts with Torx screwdriver tool No. 9546, or equivalent.
4. Disconnect wheel carrier plugs, loosen connections and remove cables at spring strut.
5. Mark spring strut mounting for installation and remove mounting nuts.
6. Remove strut with wheel carrier.
7. Loosen spring strut to wheel carrier clamp and separate strut from carrier.
8. Reverse procedure to install. Tighten nuts and bolts to specifications, and inspect front wheel alignment.

1998 911

1. Raise and support vehicle, then remove front wheel and underside panel.
2. Open wiring harness retainer on strut assembly, then remove wiring harness from retainer.
3. Disconnect wheel speed sensor connector, then remove sensor retaining bolt and the sensor.
4. Holding brake pedal down to prevent brake fluid from leaking from reservoir, disconnect brake hose at strut and remove caliper attaching bolts.
5. Cover or plug brake hose and pipe, then remove brake hose retaining spring.
6. Remove brake cooling duct and stabilizer mount.
7. Separate tie rod and ball joint from wheel carrier assembly as outlined under "Tie Rod, Replace" and "Ball Joint, Replace."
8. Remove strut-to-wheel carrier bolt, then the strut and wheel carrier.
9. Remove strut to wheel carrier attaching bolts, then lower vehicle.
10. Remove strut collar locknuts, then raise and support vehicle.
11. Separate strut from wheel carrier and remove from vehicle.
12. Reverse procedure to install, noting following:
    a. Do not grease Dacroment-type (aluminum colored) nuts and bolts.
    b. Use Torx screwdriver part No. 9546, or equivalent, when tightening locknuts.
    c. Spring strut mount red dot must point forward in strut dome because mount is not symmetrical.
    d. Ride height and alignment must be checked completely.

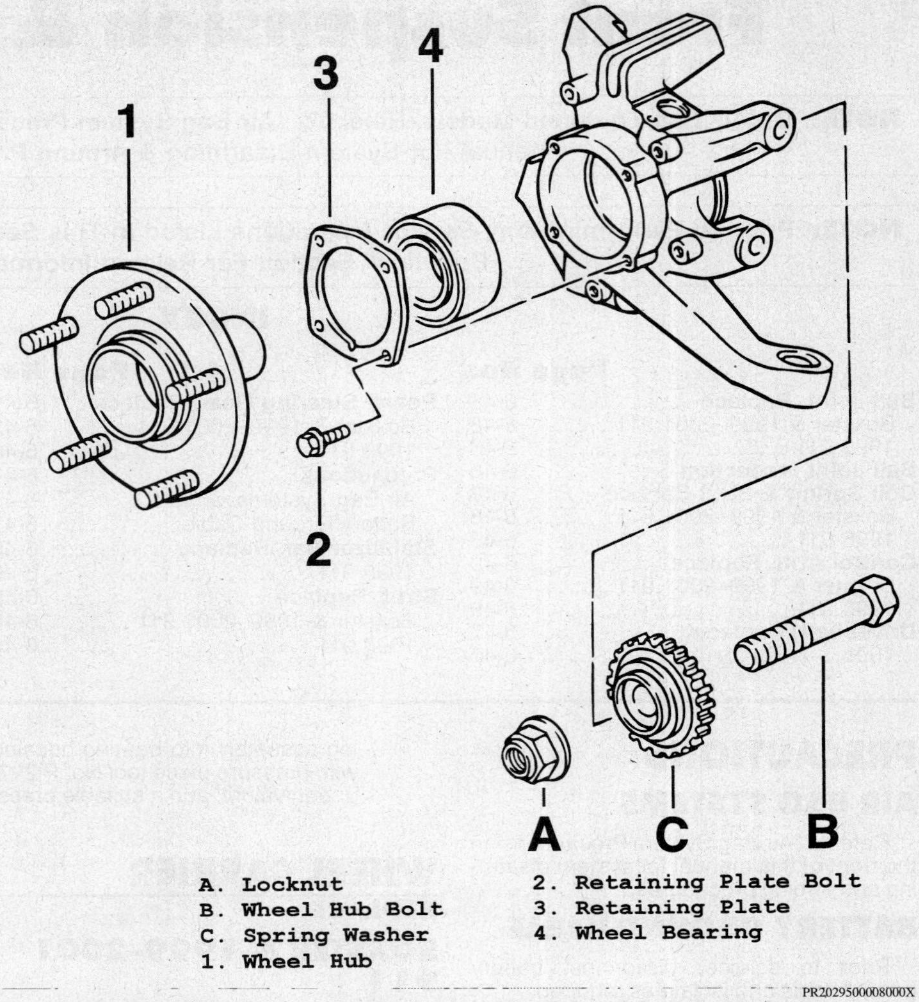

Fig. 1 Wheel carrier & wheel bearing assembly. 1998 911

COIL SPRING & STRUT SERVICE

BOXSTER & 1999-2001 911

1. Compress coil spring with suitable spring compressor.
2. Holding piston rod with a suitable 7 mm Allen wrench, remove piston rod fastening nut. **Never use an impact type wrench to remove fastening nut.**
3. Remove stop plate, spring strut mount, stop plate, mount and back-up plate, **Fig. 4.**
4. Remove spring plate (compensation part), cup washer, additional spring, bellows and coil spring.
5. Reverse procedure to assemble, noting the following:
    a. Select correct spring plate (compensation part) by matching color coded lines on spring assembly with plate (1 green line = 6.5 mm thick) and (1 white line = 3 mm thick).
    b. Tighten piston rod fastening nut to

specifications. **Do not use impact wrench to tighten fastening nut.**

1998 911

1. Compress coil spring with suitable spring compressor.
2. Holding piston rod with a suitable 7 mm Allen wrench, remove piston rod fastening nut.
3. Remove collar, washer, mount, additional spring and bellows, **Fig. 5.**
4. Remove coil spring and lower spring mounting plate.
5. Mark position of adjustment nut to shock absorber, then remove adjustment nut.
6. Reverse procedure to assemble, noting the following:
   a. Apply Optimoly TA, or equivalent, lubricant to threads of adjustment nut.
   b. Position adjustment nut in same position on new damper as on old damper.
   c. Tighten piston rod fastening nut to specifications. **Do not use impact wrench to tighten fastening nut.**

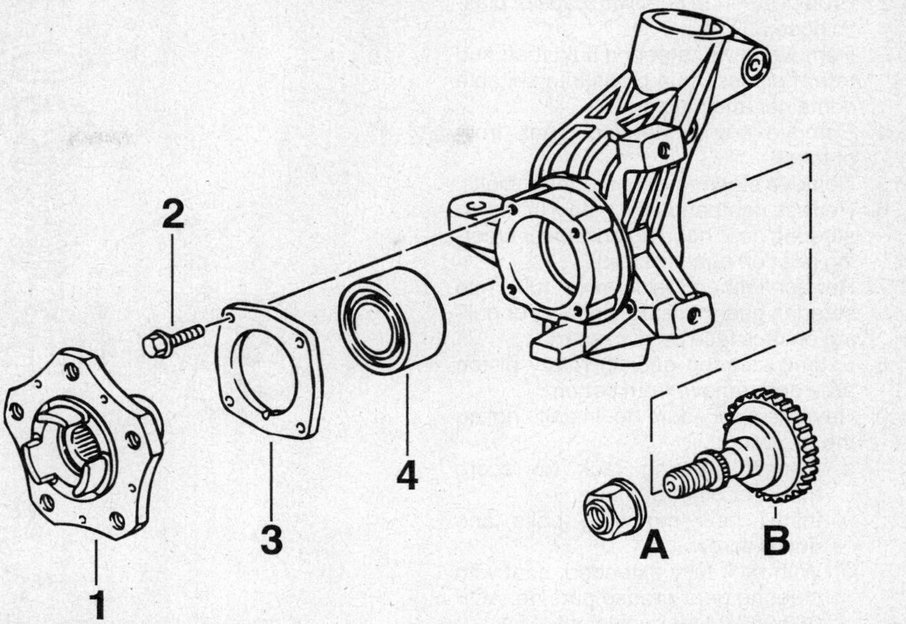

Fig. 2 Wheel carrier & wheel bearing assembly. Boxster & 1999–2001 911

CONTROL ARM

REPLACE

BOXSTER & 1999–2001 911

1. Remove ball joint to wheel carrier retaining nut, then separate ball joint from wheel carrier with ball joint remover tool No. 9560, or equivalent.
2. Remove control arm to side member attaching bolt.
3. Remove control arm to diagonal arm attaching bolt, then the control arm from vehicle.
4. Reverse procedure to install.

1998 911

1. Raise and support vehicle, then remove wheel and tire assembly.
2. Mark position of caster eccentric bolt.
3. Remove caster eccentric bolt and knurled bolt locknuts, then separate control arm from ball joint.
4. Remove control arm to side member flange bolts, then the control arm from vehicle.
5. Reverse procedure to install.

STABILIZER BAR

REPLACE

1998 911

1. Separate stabilizer bar from stabilizer mount.
2. Remove stabilizer bar to wheel carrier attaching bolts.
3. Remove stabilizer bar bracket attaching bolts, then the brackets and stabilizer bar from vehicle.
4. Reverse procedure to install.

TIE ROD END

REPLACE

BOXSTER & 2001 911

1. Raise and support vehicle.
2. Position steering wheel and road wheels in a straight ahead position.
3. Remove tie rod end (track rod) to wheel carrier retaining nut.
4. Press tie rod end (track rod) ball joint out of wheel carrier with ball joint remover tool No. 9560, or equivalent.
5. Remove tie rod end (track rod) from steering gear.
6. Reverse procedure to install, noting the following:
   a. Tighten bolts and nuts to specifications.
   b. Inspect toe-in and adjust as outlined in "Wheel Alignment" section.

1998 911

1. Raise and support vehicle.
2. Position steering wheel and road wheels in a straight ahead position.
3. Remove tie rod end to wheel carrier retaining nut.
4. Press tie rod end ball joint out of wheel carrier with ball joint remover tool No. 9560, or equivalent.
5. Remove tie rod end from steering gear.
6. Reverse procedure to install, noting the following:
   a. Tighten bolts and nuts to specifications.
   b. Inspect toe-in and adjust as outlined in "Wheel Alignment" section.

POWER STEERING GEAR

REPLACE

BOXSTER & 1999–2001 911

1. Remove underside panel.
2. Position steering with front wheels aligned straight ahead.
3. Loosen steering shaft universal joint at steering gear.
4. Remove track rods (tie rod ends) from wheel carrier as outlined in "Tie Rod End, Replace."
5. Remove feed and return fluid pipes from steering gear. Plug pipes to prevent contamination.
6. Remove steering gear mounting bolts.
7. Extend steering gear to left.
8. If necessary, remove right and left track rods (tie rod ends) from steering gear.
9. Reverse procedure to install. Coat extended rack with VW No. AOF 063 000 04, or equivalent grease. Tighten nuts and bolts to specifications.

1998 911

1. Remove tie rod ends from steering gear as outlined in "Tie Rod End, Replace."

2. Protect steering gear with caps or plastic hose.
3. Remove power steering fluid feed and return pipes. Drain pipes into suitable container and plug ends.
4. Remove power steering pipes from bracket.
5. Remove steering gear mounting bolts.
6. Retract righthand side rack fully into steering gear housing and lower steering gear on righthand side.
7. Retract lefthand side rack fully into steering gear housing, pushing or pulling on rack face as necessary.
8. Extend steering gear in rotary piston area and remove from bottom.
9. Reverse procedure to install, noting the following:
   a. Inspect steering rack for score marks or other damage.
   b. Install new mounting bolts and dowel screw.
   c. With rack fully extended, coat with steering gear grease part No. AOF 063 000 04, or equivalent.
   d. Tighten bolts and nuts to specifications.
   e. If slider has been pulled off shaft, roll pin must face tooth cutout when installing.
   f. Inspect toe-in and adjust as outlined in "Wheel Alignment" section.

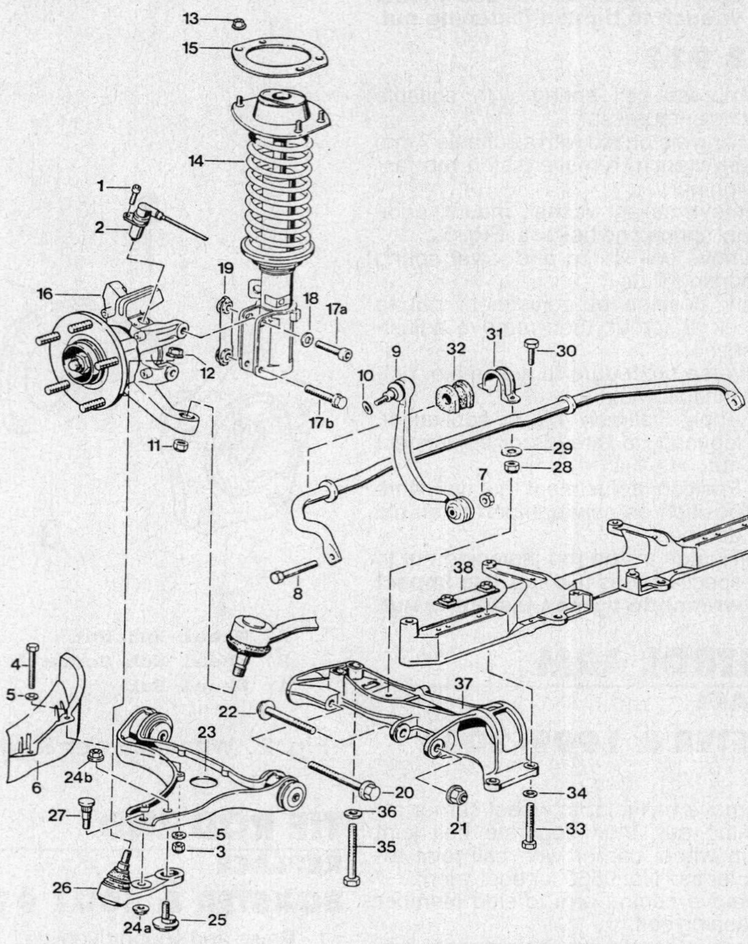

1. RPM Sensor Bolt
2. RPM Sensor
3. Air Guide Locknut
4. Air Guide Bolt
5. Washer
6. Air Guide
7. Stabilizer Bar Locknut
8. Stabilizer Bar Bolt
9. Stabilizer Mount
10. Washer
11. Tie Rod End Locknut
12. Ball Joint Locknut
13. Strut Collar Locknut
14. Strut Assembly
15. Gasket
16. Wheel Carrier
17a. Lower Strut Bolt
17b. Lower Strut Bolt
18. Washer
19. Cage w/Collar Nuts
20. Control Arm Flange Bolt
21. Control Arm Collar Nut
22. Control Arm Flange Bolt
23. Control Arm
24a. Knurled Bolt Locknut
24b. Caster Eccentric Locknut
25. Caster Eccentric Bolt
26. Ball Joint
27. Knurled Bolt
28. Stabilizer Bar Bracket Locknut
29. Washer
30. Stabilizer Bar Bracket Bolt
31. Stabilizer Bar Bracket
32. Stabilizer Bar Mount
33. Side Member Rear Bolt
34. Washer
35. Side Member Front Bolt
36. Washer
37. Side Mount
38. Threaded Plate

PR2029500007000X

Fig. 3 Exploded view of front suspension. 1998 911

TECHNICAL SERVICE BULLETINS

FRONT SUSPENSION CREAKING OR GRINDING

1998 911

On some of these models built before Coupe VIN WPOAA2 99 7 SS 32 3709 or Cabriolet VIN WPOCA2 99 7 99 7 SS 34 2592, the front suspension may creak or grind, especially during cold and wet weather.

To correct this condition, replace stabilizer rubber mounts. Coat mounting surface with Vaseline before installation.

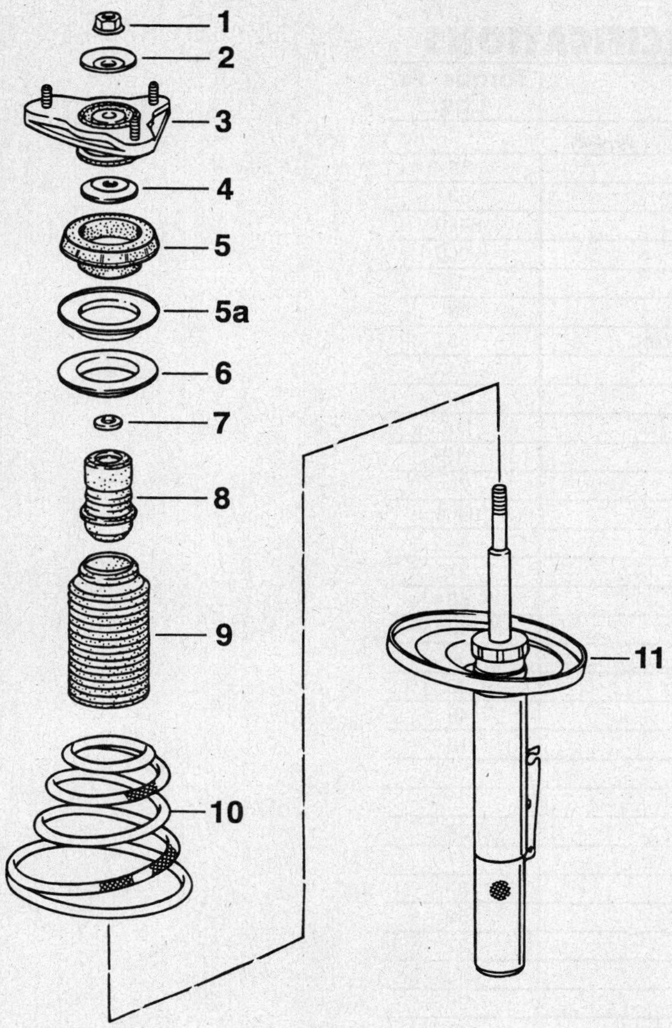

1. Piston Rod Fastening Nut
2. Stop Plate
3. Spring Strut Mount
4. Stop Plate
5. Mount
5a. Back-Up Ring
6. Spring Plate (Compensation Part)
7. Cup Washer
8. Additional Spring
9. Bellows
10. Coil Spring
11. Damper

PR2029700011000X

Fig. 4 Strut assembly. Boxster & 1999–2001 911

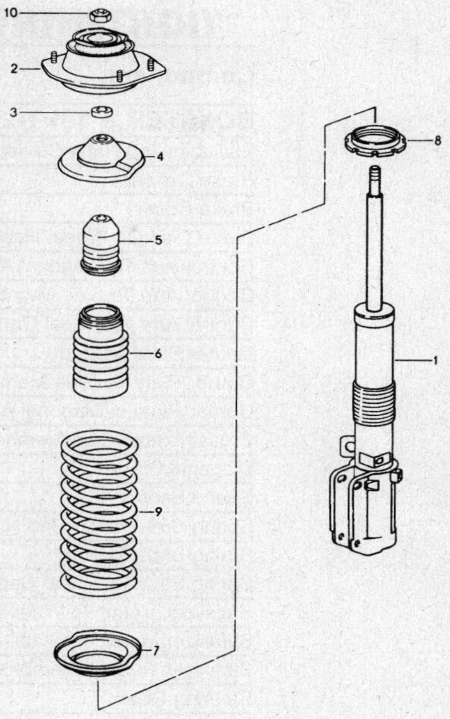

1. Damper Assembly
2. Collar
3. Washer
4. Upper Mount
5. Additional Spring
6. Bellows
7. Lower Mounting Plate
8. Adjustment Nut
9. Coil Spring
10. Piston Rod Fastening Nut

PR2029500009000X

Fig. 5 Strut assembly. 1998 911

TIGHTENING SPECIFICATIONS

Component	Torque, Ft. Lbs.
BOXSTER & 1999–2001 911	
Ball Joint To Wheel Carrier Nut	55
Brake Caliper	63
Brake Cover	84①
Brake Disc On Wheel Hub	90①
Control Arm To Diagonal Arm	118
Control Arm To Side Member	88
Control Arm To Wheel Carrier (Ball Joint)	55
Corner Plate To Body	74
Corner Plate To Side Member	48
Corner Plate w/Diagonal Arm	118
Crossmember/Side Member To Body	118
Diagonal Brace	74
Speed Sensor	84①
Spring Strut Piston Rod Nut	44
Spring Strut To Body	27
Spring Strut To Wheel Carrier	63
Stabilizer Mount To Wheel Carrier	63
Stabilizer Mount To Stabilizer	34
Stabilizer To Side Member	48
Steering Gear	48
Steering Gear Fluid Pipes	15
Steering Lock	10
Steering Outer Tub, Bottom	22
Steering Outer Tub, Top	34
Steering Shaft Universal Joint	17
Track Rod To Wheel Carrier Nut	37
Track Rod To Steering Gear	59
Wheel Bearing Retainer Plate	27
Wheel Hub To Wheel Carrier	339
Wheel Lug Nuts	96
1998 911	
Ball Joint To Control Arm Mounting Bolt	88
Ball Joint To Wheel Carrier	55
Brake Air Duct	84①
Brake Caliper	63
Brake Protect Plate	84①
Caster Eccentric Bolt	48
Control Arm To Sidemember (Front)	81
Control Arm To Sidemember (Rear)	63
Crossmember (Inner)	35
Crossmember (Outer)	77
Crossmember To Body	66
Driveshaft To Wheel Hub	340
Front Axle Driveshaft To Transmission②	29
Front Axle Driveshaft To Wheel Hub②	340
Power Steering Pressure Line	15
Power Steering Return Line	15
RPM Sensor	84①
Stabilizer Bar Mount	34
Stabilizer Bar To Side Member	17
Steering Gear To Crossmember	33
Steering Shaft U-Joint	17
Strut Mount To Body	24
Strut To Wheel Carrier (Lower)	147

Continued

TIGHTENING SPECIFICATIONS—Continued

Component	Torque, Ft. Lbs.
1998 911	
Strut To Wheel Carrier (Upper, Camber Adjustment)	88
Strut Piston Rod Fastening Nut	59
Tie Rod End Ball Joint	55
Tie Rod End To Steering Gear	52
Wheel Bearing Retaining Plate	27
Wheel Hub To Wheel Carrier	339
Wheel Lug Nuts	96

① — Inch lbs.
② — Carrera 4.

Wheel Alignment

INDEX

	Page No.
Front Wheel Alignment	6-54
Boxster & 1999–2001 911	6-54
1998 911	6-54
Preliminary Inspection	6-54
Rear Wheel Alignment	6-54
Boxster	6-54
911	6-54
Vehicle Ride Height	6-55
Boxster	6-55
911	6-55
Wheel Alignment Specifications	6-2
Front	6-2
Rear	6-3

PRELIMINARY INSPECTION

Ensure tire pressures are at their specified values, fuel tank is full, spare tire is in place, and a weight approximately the same as the driver, positioned on the driver's seat.

FRONT WHEEL ALIGNMENT

Accurate front axle height adjustment is critical to toe-in, camber, and caster adjustments.

BOXSTER & 1999–2001 911

Inspect and adjust rear wheel alignment first.

Camber Adjustment

1. Loosen spring strut mount to body mounting nuts.
2. Remove piston rod cap.
3. Move strut transversely to adjust.
4. **Torque** mounting nuts to 27 ft. lbs.

Toe-In Adjustment

1. Turn front wheels to straight ahead position and center steering wheel.
2. Adjust front wheel alignment until driver (1) pin (2) and steering gear housing (4) lug are aligned (3), **Fig. 1.** If necessary, reposition steering wheel.
3. Clamp steering wheel into centered position.
4. Loosen locknut and adjust toe with track rod (tie rod end) nuts.

Caster Adjustment

Caster is not adjustable on models with factory equipped control arms. Control arms with a caster eccentric are available if adjustment is necessary.

1998 911

Camber Adjustment

1. Loosen lower strut to wheel carrier fastening bolts, **Fig. 2.** Use special tool 9265/1, or equivalent, with torque wrench to loosen upper fastening bolt.
2. Place eccentric insert part tool No. 9265, or equivalent, on upper bolt head and turn to adjust.

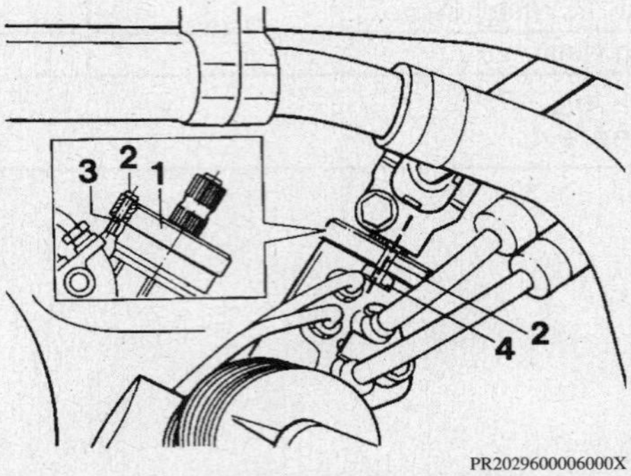

Fig. 1 Center steering. Boxster & 1999–2001 911

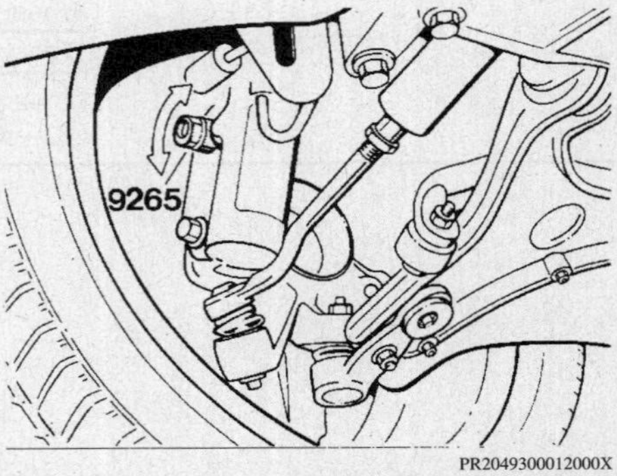

Fig. 2 Camber adjustment. 1998 911

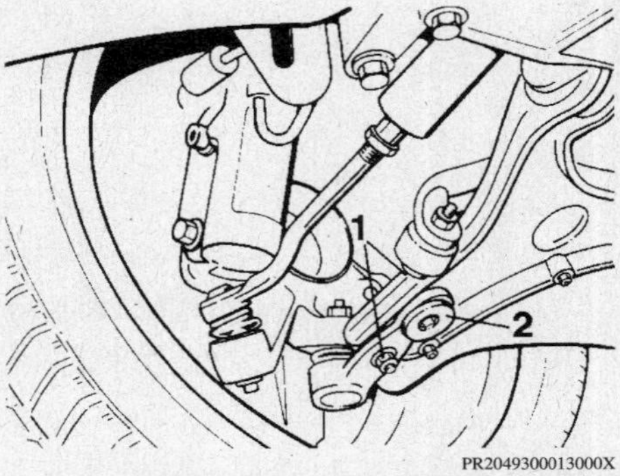

Fig. 3 Caster adjustment. 1998 911

Caster Adjustment

1. Loosen control arm ball joint carrier (1), **Fig. 3.**
2. Turn caster eccentric (2), moving ball joint carrier forward or backward.

Toe-In Adjustment

1. Inspect steering wheel offset.
2. If steering wheel is not centered, remove underside paneling, then center steering gear using special tool No. 9116, or equivalent.
3. Clamp steering wheel in centered position.
4. Loosen tie rod end locknut (1), **Fig. 4.**
5. Adjust toe-in at tie rods.
6. Ensure bellows are not damaged or twisted.
7. Tow difference angle cannot be adjusted. It can only be modified by replacing steering arms.

REAR WHEEL ALIGNMENT

BOXSTER

Toe-In Adjustment

Loosen locknut and adjust toe eccentric (A), **Fig. 5.**

Camber Adjustment

Loosen locknut and adjust camber eccentric (B), **Fig. 5.**

911

1998

Adjust rear wheel alignment in the following order: toe-in, camber and kinematic toe-in change.

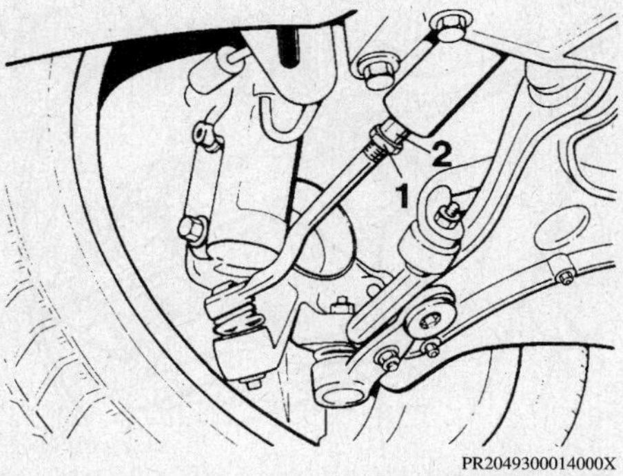

Fig. 4 Toe-in adjustment. 1998 911

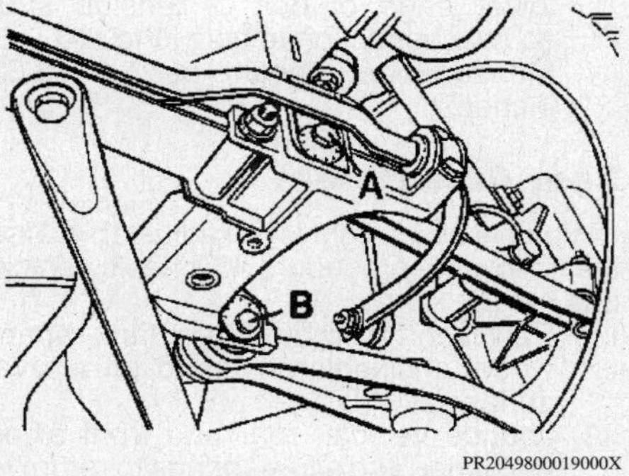

Fig. 7 Rear camber and toe adjustments. 1999–2001 911

Toe-In Adjustment

1. Remove underbody panel.
2. Turn eccentric (A) as required, **Fig. 6.**
3. If only toe-in is being corrected, kinematic toe-in change will not have to be checked.

Camber Adjustment

1. Remove bottom control arm (1 and 5), **Fig. 6.**
2. Use torque wrench with insert tool No. 9558, or equivalent, to release locknut.
3. Rotate eccentric (B) to adjust camber.
4. Use retaining wrench tool No. 9557, or equivalent, to lock eccentric (B).
5. When tightening locknut with insert tool No. 9558, or equivalent, **torque** of 63 ft. lbs. at locknut equals **torque** of 48 ft. lbs. at torque wrench.
6. If camber setting has been corrected, kinematic toe-in will have to be checked.

Kinematic Toe-In Change Adjustment

Angular measuring instrument tool No. 9549 and 9550, or equivalents, are required for measuring left and righthand sides.

With tool No. 9549, negative measurements are read on long end of tool pointing toward transmission.

With tool No. 9550, the upper scale is for the lefthand side, while the lower scale is for the righthand side.

1. Inspect control arm (2), **Fig. 6,** cover for correct fit. Cover should move less than. 3937 inch left or right with light

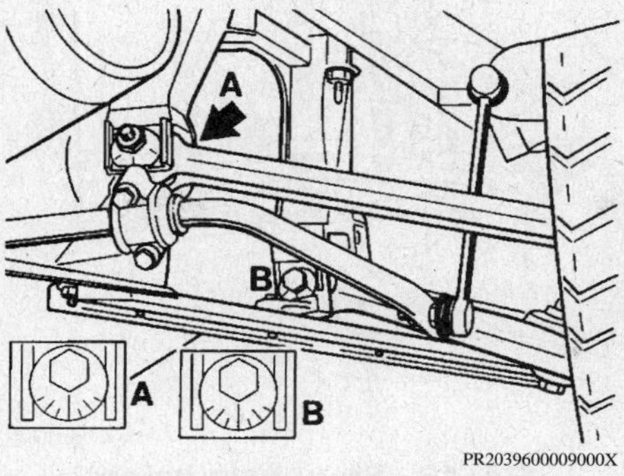

Fig. 5 Rear suspension alignment. Boxster

force. Trapezoidal cover end should point toward wheel.
2. Clean measuring surfaces of all dirt.
3. Center cover and mount tool 9550 on control arm (2). Cover cutouts help locate tool. Ensure measuring arms at either end of tool contact control arm.
4. Ensure mounting surface is free of grease and mount tool 9549 to control arm (5) with long end of tool pointing toward transmission. Place tool against wheel side support lug. Inner measuring arm must contact control arm.
5. Read both tool measurements at center of bubble level. Measurements may vary by not more than 1.5 scale units.
6. Kinematic toe-in change is correct when both bubble level numerical values align.
7. To adjust control arm (4), loosen fastening bolt and turn eccentric washer (C).
8. Ensure camber values remain within range.
9. When one side kinematic tow-in change is correct, switch tools to other side. Tool 9549 must be switched over, while tool 9550 maintains its orientation.

1999–2001

Rear Toe Adjustment

1. Using locknut remover tool No. 9626, or equivalent, loosen locknut and turn eccentric A, **Fig. 7.**
2. Refer to "Specifications" for proper alignment specification.

Rear Camber Adjustment

1. Using locknut remover tool No. 9626, or equivalent, loosen locknut and turn eccentric B, **Fig. 7.**
2. Refer to "Specifications" for proper alignment specification.

VEHICLE RIDE HEIGHT

BOXSTER

Front Axle Height Adjustment

Vehicle axle height is not adjustable. To inspect height, proceed as follows:

1. Place vehicle with full fuel tank, and spare wheel and tools installed, on level surface.

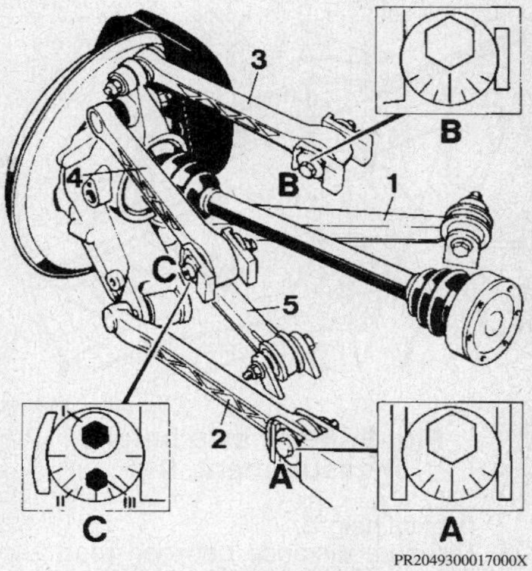

Fig. 6 Rear wheel alignment adjustment. 911

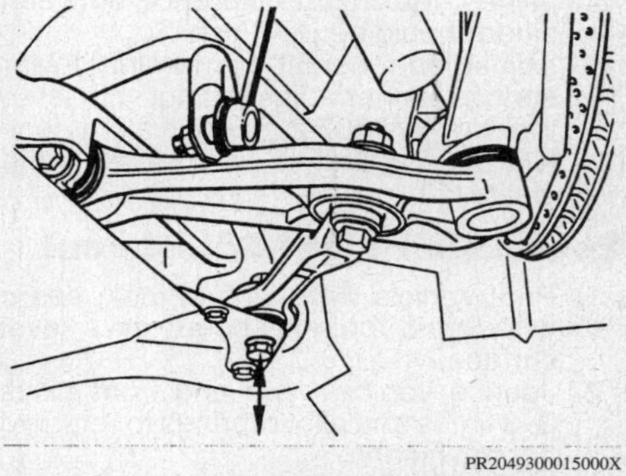

Fig. 8 Front axle height measurement. 1998 911

2. Joust vehicle approximately . 984 inches, 2–3 times and allow to spring back freely.
3. Measure distance from tension-strut bolt lower edge to ground.
4. Standard measurement should be 5.59–6.38 inches.

Rear Axle Height Adjustment

Vehicle axle height is not adjustable. To inspect height, proceed as follows:

1. Place vehicle with full fuel tank, and spare wheel and tools installed, on level surface.
2. Joust vehicle approximately .984 inches, 2–3 times and allow to spring back freely.
3. Measure distance from control arm diagonal brace mounting point's lowest surface to ground.
4. Standard measurement should be 5.35–6.14 inches.

911

1998

Front Axle Height Adjustment

1. Park vehicle with full fuel tank, spare wheel and tools on board on a level surface.
2. Jounce vehicle, rear and front axles 2–3 times and allow springs to return to

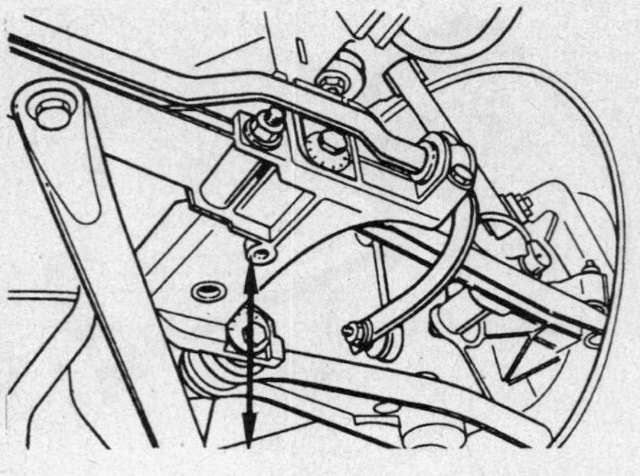

Fig. 9 Rear axle height measurement. 911

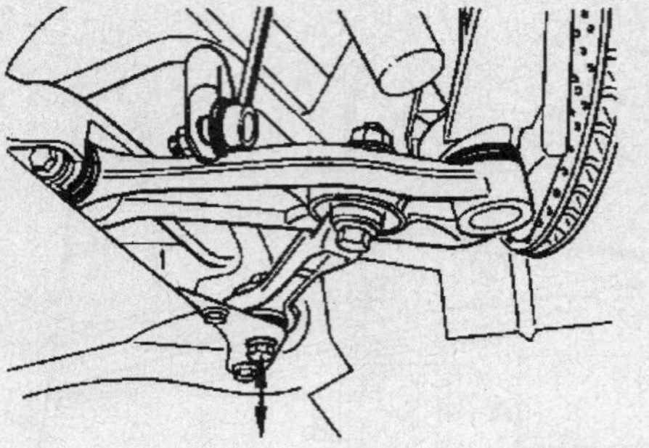

Fig. 10 Front axle height location. 1999–2001 911

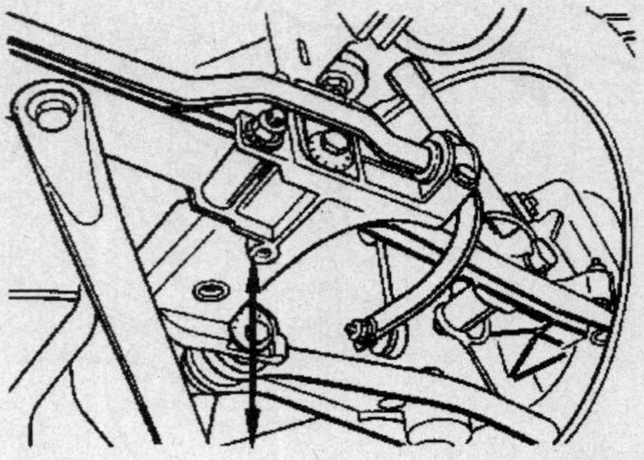

Fig. 11 Rear axle height location. 1999–2001 911

normal height.
3. Measure distance between road and bottom of outer crossmember-to-body bolt connection bolt head, **Fig. 8.**
4. Measurement should be 6.457–7.245 inches. Maximum difference between sides should be .197 inch.
5. Adjust ride height by turning lower spring retainer adjusting nut with lever tool No. VW 637/2, or equivalent hook wrench. Turning to right, raises vehicle; to left, lowers.

Rear Axle Height Adjustment

1. Park vehicle with full fuel tank, spare wheel and tools on board on a level surface.
2. Jounce vehicle, rear and front axles 2–3 times and allow springs to return to normal height.
3. Measure distance between road contact surface an suspension subframe bottom mating face, **Fig. 9.**
4. Measurement should be 5.788–6.575 inches. Maximum difference between sides should be .197 inch.
5. Adjust height by correcting spacer thickness at upper spring retainers. Struts must be remove.

1999–2001

Front Axle Height

Vehicle ride height is not adjustable. Use the following procedure to check vehicle ride height.

1. Park vehicle with full fuel tank, spare wheel and tools on board on a level surface.
2. Jounce vehicle, rear and front axles 2–3 times and allow springs to return to normal height.
3. Measure from road contact surface to lower edge of bolt of tension strut screw connection to body, **Fig. 10**
4. Measurement should be 5.83–6.62 inches.

Rear Axle Height

Vehicle ride height is not adjustable. Use the following procedure to check vehicle ride height.

1. Park vehicle with full fuel tank, spare wheel and tools on board on a level surface.
2. Jounce vehicle, rear and front axles 2–3 times and allow springs to return to normal height.
3. Measure from road contact surface to locating bore in rear axle side section between toe and camber eccentrics, **Fig. 11.**
4. Measurement should be 5.83–6.62 inches.

Air Conditioning

INDEX

	Page No.
A/C Specifications	6-57
Discharging System	6-57
Refrigerant Recovery Procedure	6-57
Oil Charge	6-57
Boxster & 1999–2001 911	6-57
1998 911	6-57
Oil Level Check	6-57
Precautions	6-57
Battery Ground Cable	6-57
Product Compatibility	6-57

PRECAUTIONS

PRODUCT COMPATIBILITY

Before replenishing refrigerant or refrigerant oil, ensure product is compatible with the system being serviced. Refer to "A/C Specifications."

BATTERY GROUND CABLE

Prior to service, disconnect battery ground cable and isolate as required.

DISCHARGING SYSTEM

REFRIGERANT RECOVERY PROCEDURE

The use of refrigerant recovery and recycling stations allows the recovery and reuse of refrigerant after contaminants and moisture have been removed. When servicing systems using R-134a refrigerant, use of specialized recycling equipment is required.

When using a recovery or recycling station, follow the manufacturer's operating instructions, noting the following:

1. **Use extreme caution and observe all safety and service precautions related to use of refrigerants.**
2. Connect refrigerant recycling station hoses to vehicle A/C service ports and recovery station inlet fitting. Hoses used should have shutoff devices or check valve within 12 inches of hose ends to minimize introduction of air into recycling station and to minimize amount of refrigerant release when hoses are disconnected.
3. Turn recycling station On to start recovery process. Allow recycling station to pump refrigerant from A/C system until station pressure gauge indicates vacuum.
4. After vehicle A/C system has been evacuated, close station inlet valve, if equipped.
5. Turn station Off. On some stations pump will automatically be turned Off by a low pressure switch.
6. Allow vehicle A/C system to remain closed for approximately two minutes. Observe vacuum level indicated on gauge. If pressure does not rise, disconnect recycling station hoses.
7. If system pressure rises, repeat steps 3 through 6 until vacuum level remains stable for two minutes.
8. Service A/C system as necessary, then evacuate and recharge A/C system.

OIL CHARGE

BOXSTER & 1999–2001 911

New compressors are pre-charged with the proper amount of lubricant needed for the entire refrigerant system. If a new compressor is installed and no additional oil has been lost from the system, drain approximately 2.70 ounces of oil from compressor, leaving approximately 4.06 ounces in compressor.

When replacing system components, add the following quantities of refrigerant oil to the compressor: condenser, 1.35 ounce; evaporator, .67 ounces; lines 1.01 ounces.

1998 911

New compressors are pre-charged with the proper amount of lubricant needed for the entire refrigerant system. If a new compressor is installed and no additional oil has been lost from the system, drain approximately 2.05 ounces of oil from compressor, leaving approximately 3.00 ounces in the compressor.

When replacing system components, add the following quantities of refrigerant oil to the compressor: condenser, .67 ounce; evaporator, 1.01 ounces; lines 1.35 ounces.

OIL LEVEL CHECK

No provision is made for checking oil on these vehicles. Oil is added according to component(s) being replaced. Refer to "Oil Charge."

A/C SPECIFICATIONS

Model	Refrigerant Capacity, Lbs.	Refrigerant Type	Refrigerant Oil		Charging Valve Locations	
			Viscosity	Total System Capacity, Ounces	High Pressure	Low Pressure
1998						
Boxster	1.87	R134a	①	6.09–7.10	On High Pressure Line	On Low Pressure Line
911	1.97	R134a	①	4.06–5.41	On High Pressure Line	On Low Pressure Line
1999–2001						
Boxster	1.87	R134a	①	6.09–7.10	On High Pressure Line	On Low Pressure Line
911	1.97	R134a	①	6.08–7.09	On High Pressure Line	On Low Pressure Line

① — Nippondenso oil ND8, or equivalent.

Cooling Fans

NOTE: "Electrical Symbol & Wire Color Code Identification" Located In The Front Of This Manual May Be Used As An Aid When Using Wiring Circuits Found In This Section.

INDEX

	Page No.
Component Replacement	6-58
Cooling Fan	6-58
Description	6-58
Boxster & 1999–2001 911	6-58
Precautions	6-58
Air Bag Systems	6-58
Battery Ground Cable	6-58
System Diagnosis & Testing	6-58

PRECAUTIONS

AIR BAG SYSTEMS

Refer to "Air Bag System Precautions" in the front of this manual for system disarming and arming procedures.

BATTERY GROUND CABLE

Prior to service, disconnect battery ground cable and isolate as required.

DESCRIPTION

BOXSTER & 1999-2001 911

There are two electric cooling fans. The fans are mounted on the rear of the radiators which are located on the front left and right sides of the front compartment. The cooling fans are operated by two coolant fan relays (High and Low), the relays are located on relay support No. 1. The relays are operated by the Engine Control Module (ECM) which receives an engine temperature signal from the Engine Coolant Temperature (ECT) sensor.

SYSTEM DIAGNOSIS & TESTING

Refer to **Fig. 1** for cooling fan relay location and **Figs. 2 and 3** cooling fan system wiring diagrams.

COMPONENT REPLACEMENT

COOLING FAN

1. Raise and support vehicle.
2. Remove front wheel and wheel housing liner.
3. Disconnect fan motor electrical connector.
4. Remove cooling fan assembly to radiator attaching bolts, then the cooling fan from radiator.
5. Reverse procedure to install.

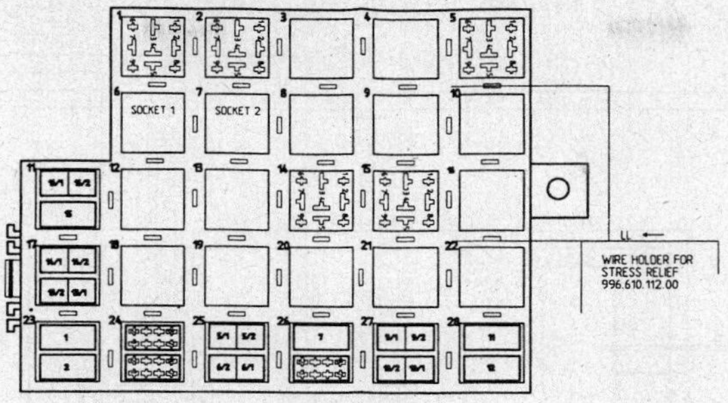

RELAY

PLUG POSITION	DESIGNATION	PORSCHE-NUMBER	M-NO.	NOTE
1	--- --- --- --	--- --- --- --		
2	--- --- --- --	--- --- --- --		
3	FLASHER	1H0.953.227		
4	REAR WINDOW DEFOGGER / MIRROR	996.615.117.00		
5	--- --- --- --	--- --- --- --		
6	CU DAYTIME RUNNING LIGHT	996.615.111.00	M 113	DOUBLE RELAY
7	CU DAYTIME RUNNING LIGHT	--- --- --- --		
8	CU HEADLIGHT WASHING	996.618.113.00	M 288	
9	TERM.XE	141.951.253.B		
10	TWO-TONE HORNS	141.951.253.B		
12	FOG LIGHT USA / JAPAN	431.951.253.G	M 193 M 553	
13	FUEL PUMP	996.615.101.00		
14	--- --- --- --	--- --- --- --		
15	--- --- --- --	--- --- --- --		
16	WIPER INTERMITTENT CONTROL	996.615.103.00		
18	ACTUATION HEATING	141.951.253.B		
19	RADIATOR FAN 1 STAGE 1	141.951.253.B		
20	RADIATOR FAN 1 STAGE 2	141.951.253.B		
21	RADIATOR FAN 2 STAGE 1	141.951.253.B		
22	RADIATOR FAN 2 STAGE 2	141.951.253.B		

POTENTIAL DISTRIBUTOR BRIDGE PLUG

PLUG POSITION	NAME	COLOR	POTENTIAL	NAME	COLOR	POTENTIAL	NOTE
11	BS. 16/1	BK/BR	TERM.15 SI B 8	BS. 16/2	BK/OR	TERM.15 SI B 5	
11	BS. 15	GR/RE	TERM.58d LED		————		8 PINS
17	BS. 13/1	OR	TERM.86S SI E 1	BS. 13/2	NOT USED		
17	BS. 14/1	BK/YE	TERM.X WIPER	BS. 14/2	BK	TERM.15 STOP LIGHT FUSE INPUT	
23	BS. 1/1	GR/PK	TERM. SPEEDOMETER A		————		8 PINS
23	BS. 2/1	BK/RE	TERM.15 SI B 10	BS. 2/2	NOT USED		
24	BS. 3/1	NOT USED		BS. 3/2	NOT USED		
24	BS. 4/1	NOT USED		BS. 4/2	NOT USED		
25	BS. 5/1	WT	TERM.56a	BS. 5/2	GR/BL/BR	TERM.31d LED	
25	BS. 6/1	BR/YE	SIGNAL PARKING BRAKE	BS. 6/2	BK/OR	TERM.54 STOP LIGHT	
26	BS. 7	RE/BK	CONSUMER SWITCHED OFF		————		8 PINS
26	BS. 8	NOT USED			NOT USED		
27	BS. 9/1	RE/BR	TERM.30 CLS	BS. 9/2	RE/BK	TERM.30 SI B 1	
27	BS. 10/1	GR	TERM.58 SI A 5	BS. 10/2	YE	TERM.56 RIGHT	
28	BS. 11	BR	TERM.31 GP 4		————		8 PINS
28	BS. 12	BR	TERM.31 GP 3		————		8 PINS

PR1089500003000X

Fig. 1 Relay support No. 1

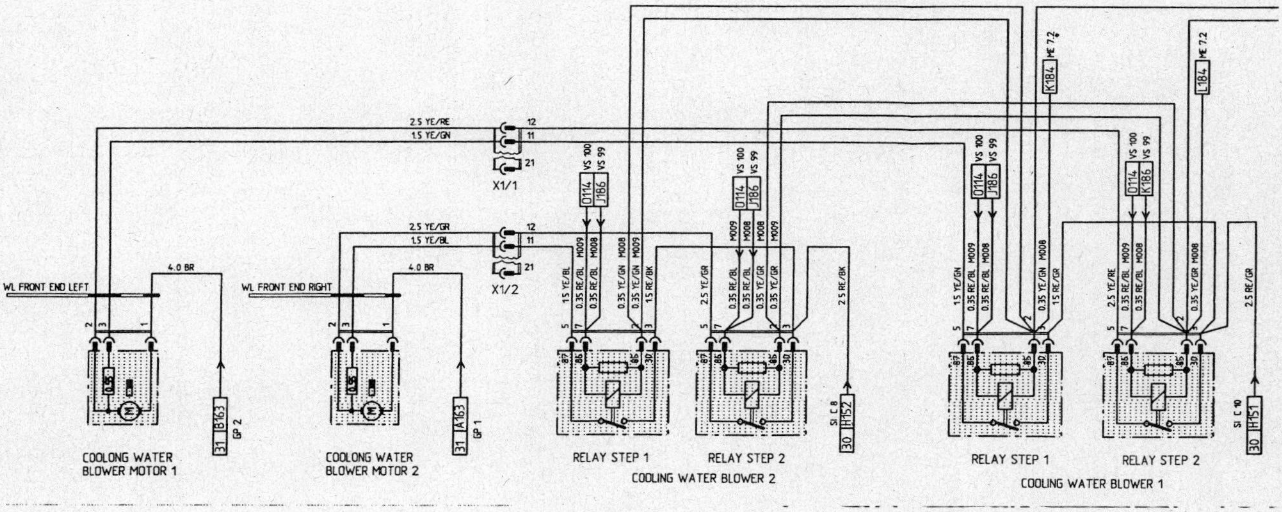

PR1089500004000X

Fig. 2 Cooling fan wiring circuit. Boxster

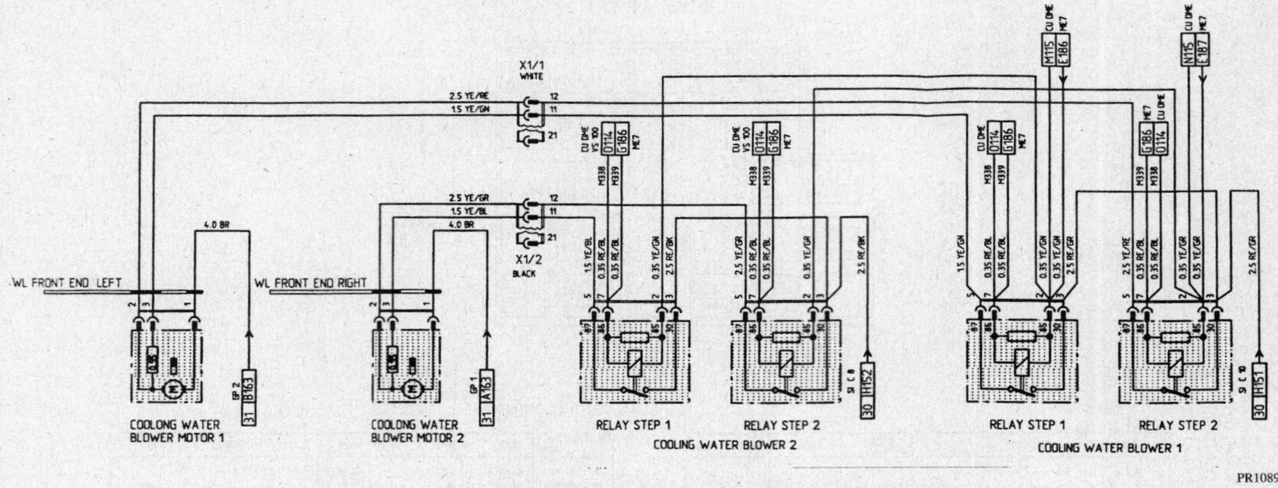

PR1089500005000X

Fig. 3 Cooling fan wiring circuit. 911

Dash Gauges

NOTE: Refer To The "Dash Panel Service" Section For Dash Panel Removal Procedures.

INDEX

	Page No.
Gauges	6-61
Precautions	6-61
Air Bag Systems	6-61
Battery Ground Cable	6-61

PRECAUTIONS

AIR BAG SYSTEMS

Refer to "Air Bag System Precautions" in the front of this manual for system disarming and arming procedures.

BATTERY GROUND CABLE

Prior to service, disconnect battery ground cable and isolate as required.

GAUGES

Refer to **Figs. 1 through 3** fog instrument cluster and gauge assembly wiring diagrams.

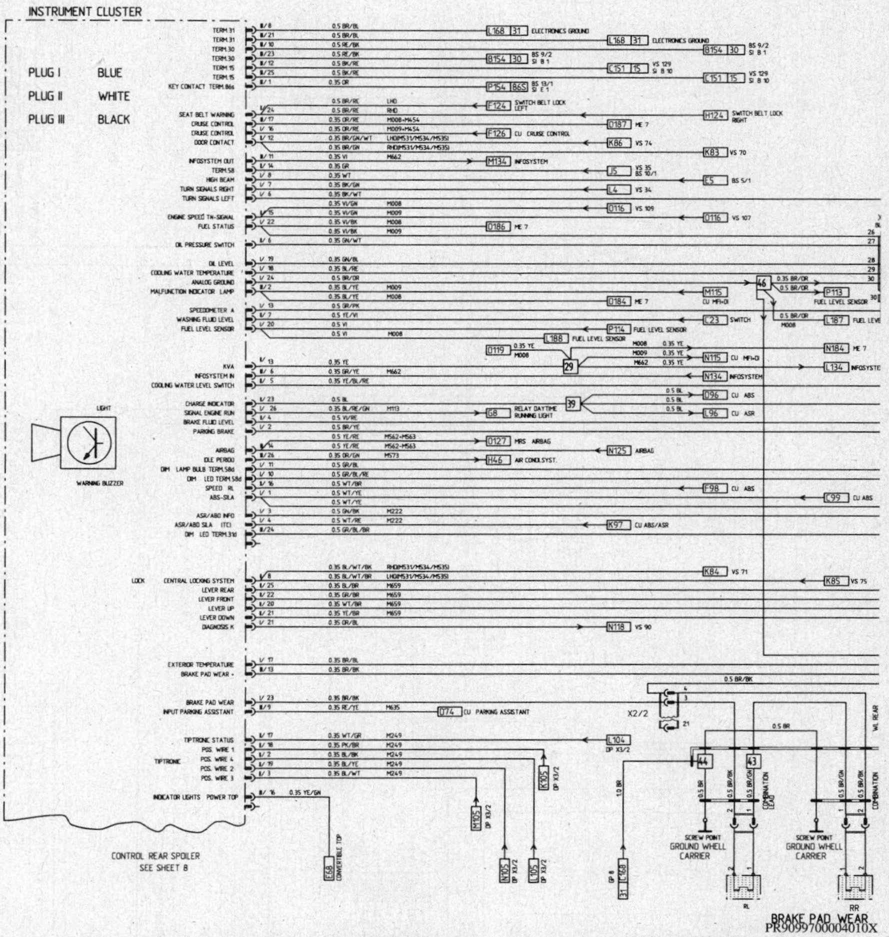

Fig. 1 Instrument cluster & gauge assembly wiring diagram (Part 1 of 3). Boxster

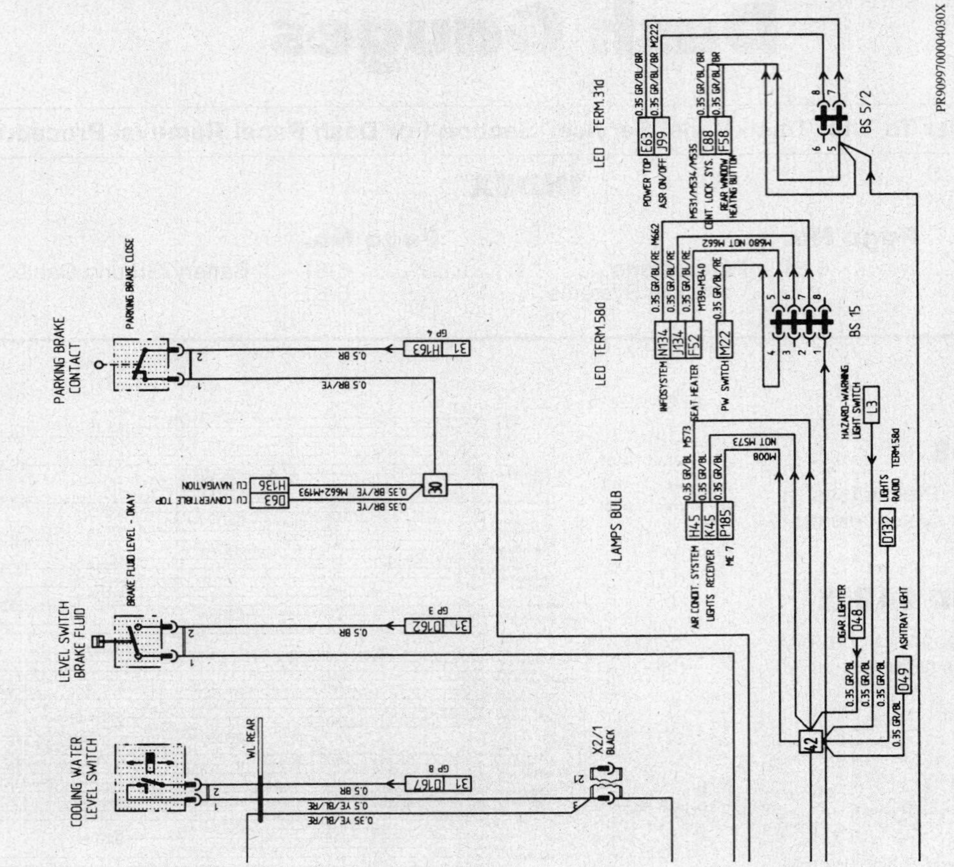

Fig. 1 Instrument cluster & gauge assembly wiring diagram (Part 3 of 3). Boxster

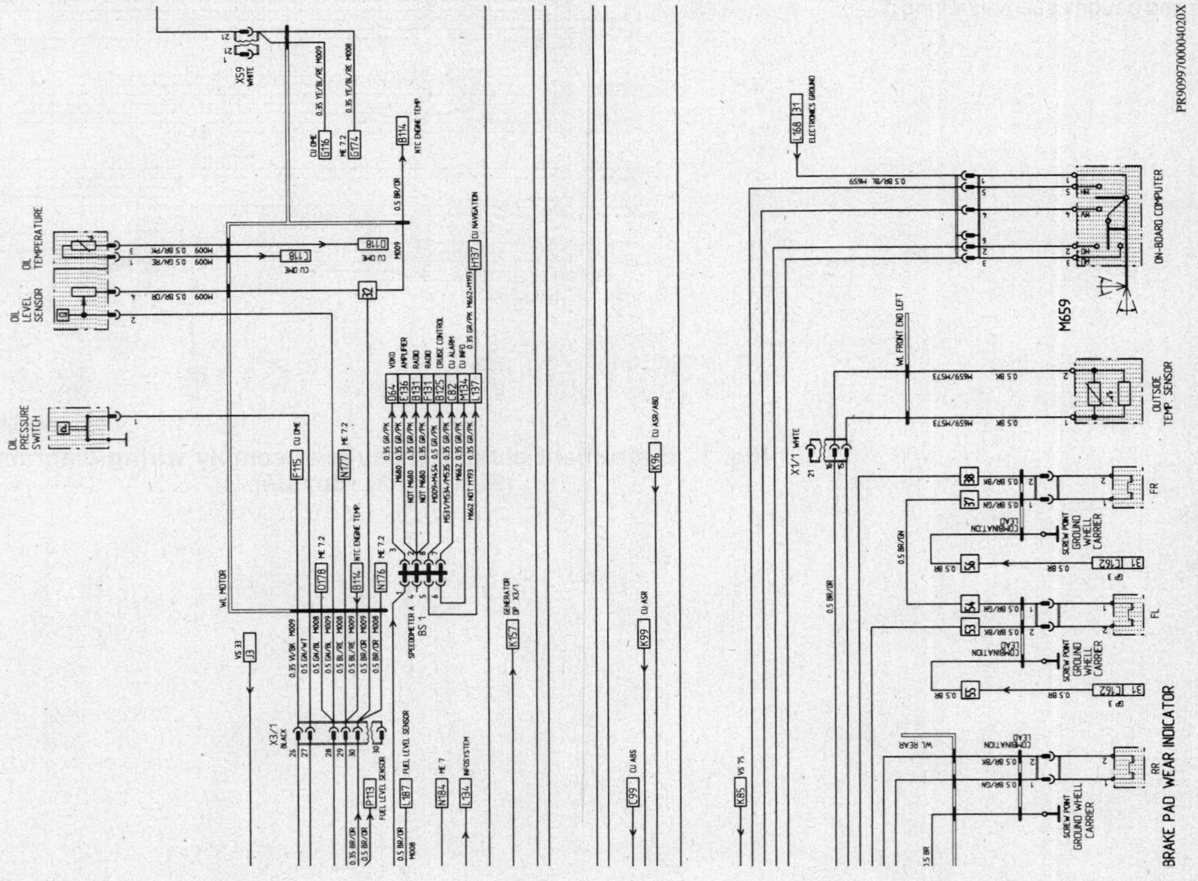

Fig. 1 Instrument cluster & gauge assembly wiring diagram (Part 2 of 3). Boxster

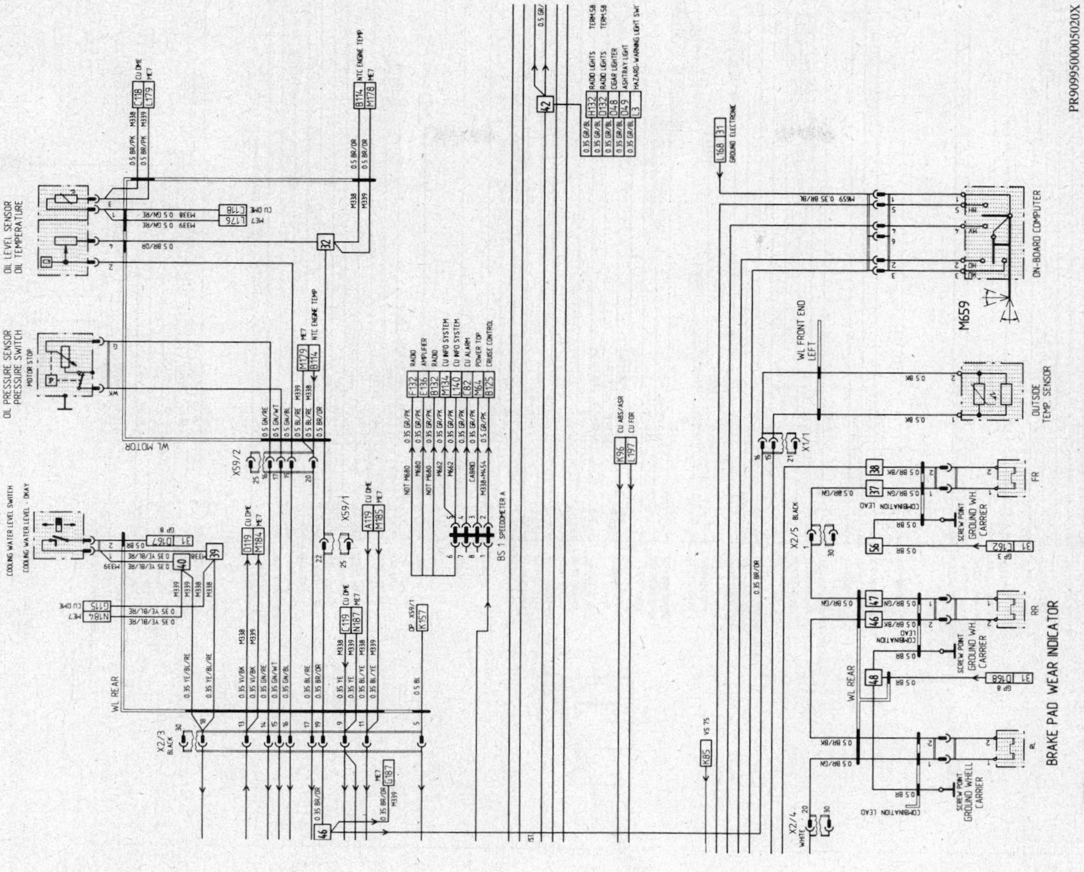

Fig. 2 Instrument cluster & gauge assembly wiring diagram (Part 2 of 3). 1998 911

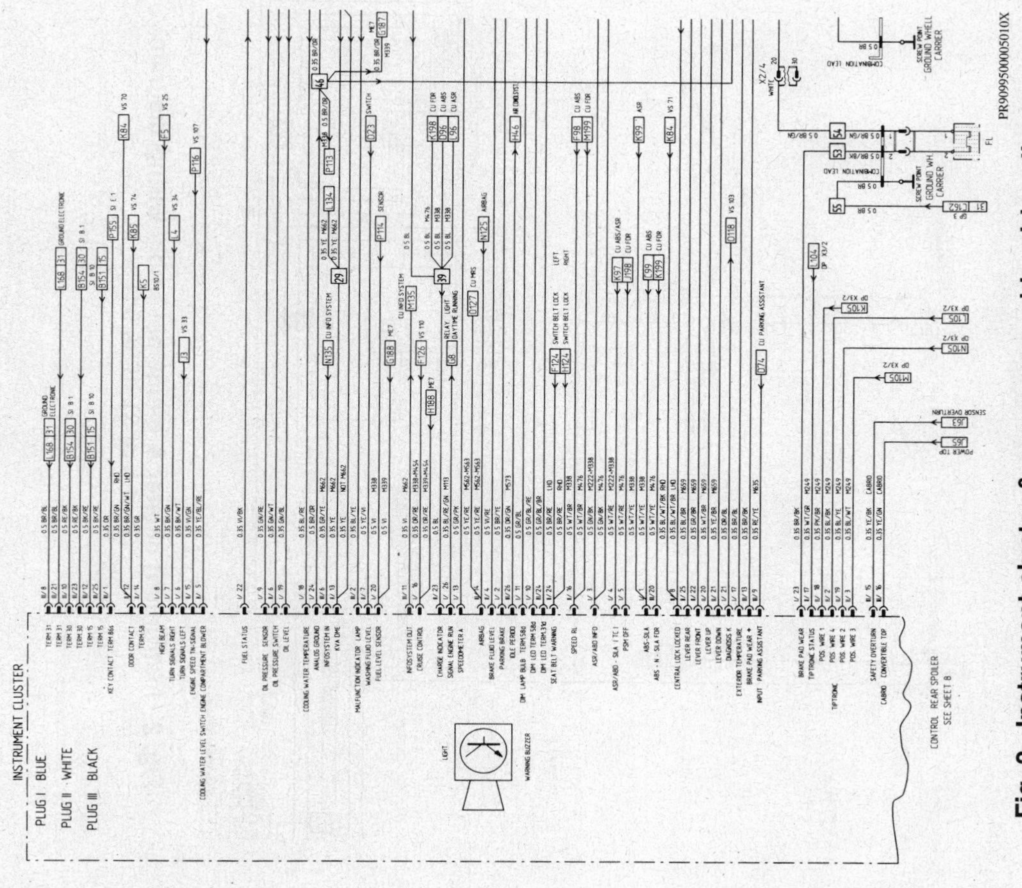

Fig. 2 Instrument cluster & gauge assembly wiring diagram (Part 1 of 3). 1998 911

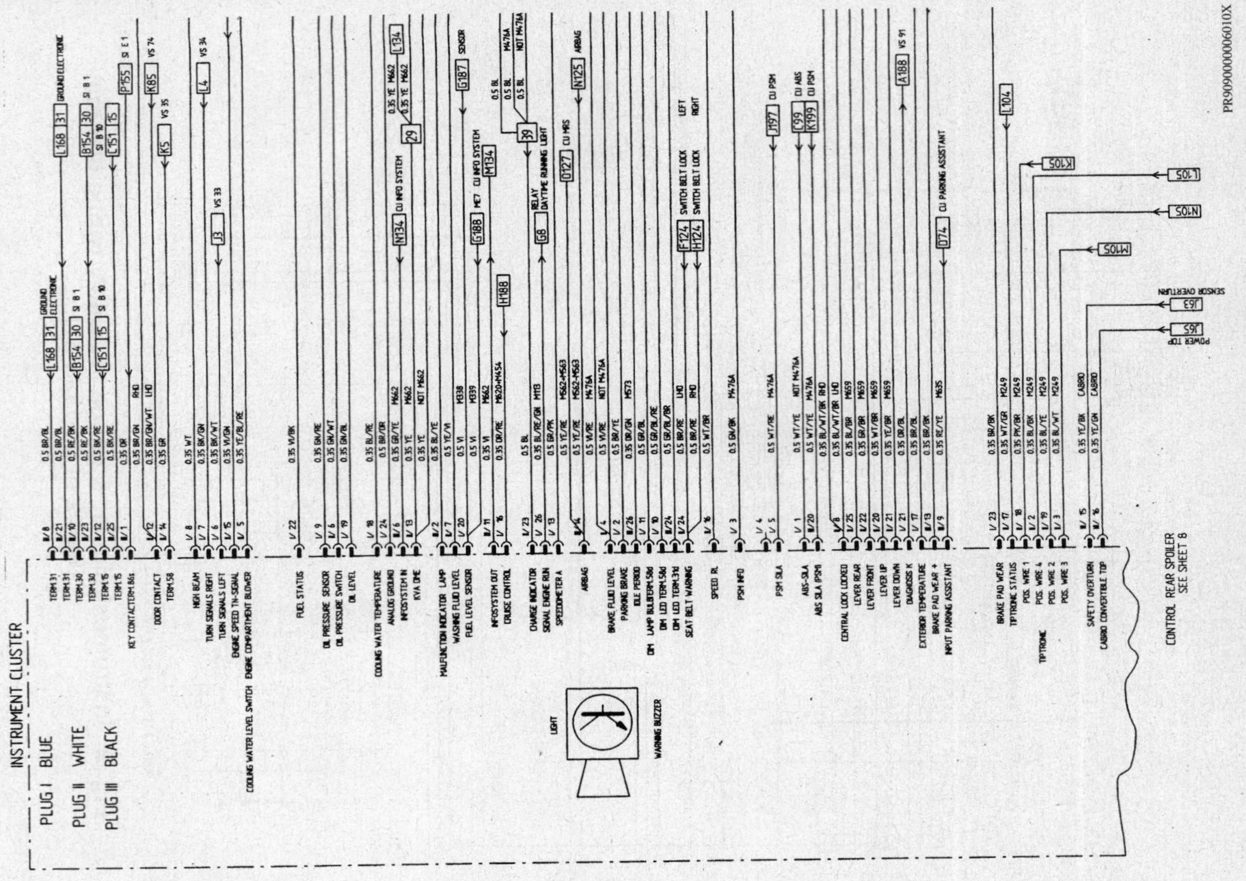

Fig. 3 Instrument cluster & gauge assembly wiring diagram (Part 1 of 3). 1999–2001 911

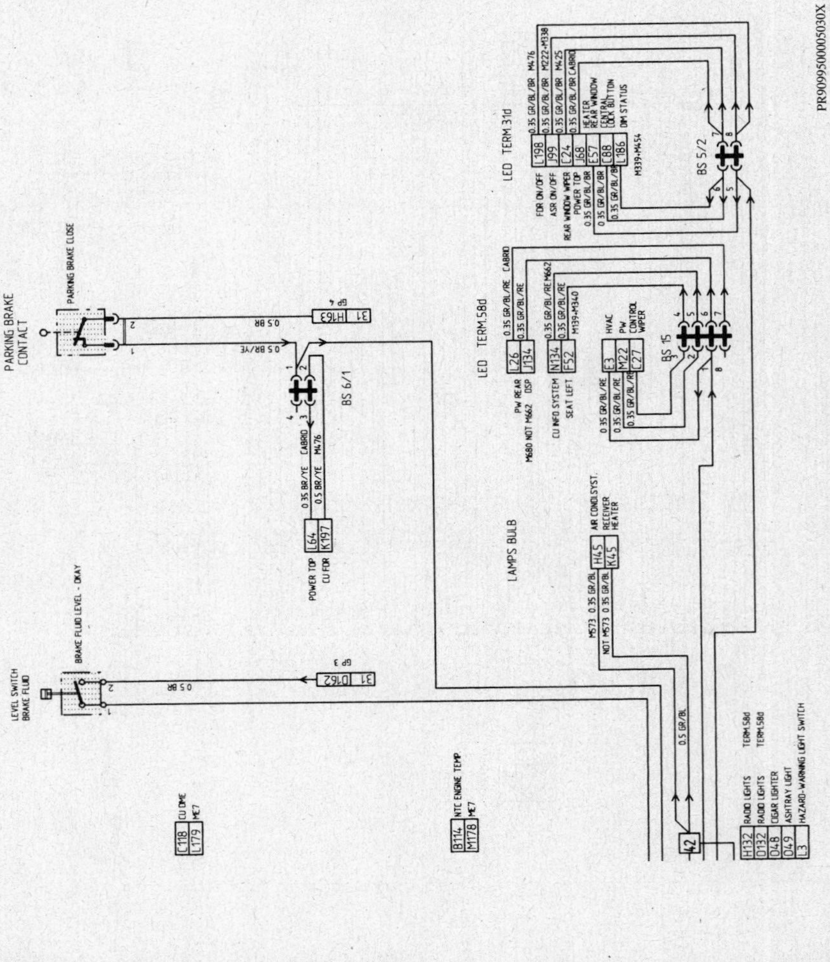

Fig. 2 Instrument cluster & gauge assembly wiring diagram (Part 3 of 3). 1998 911

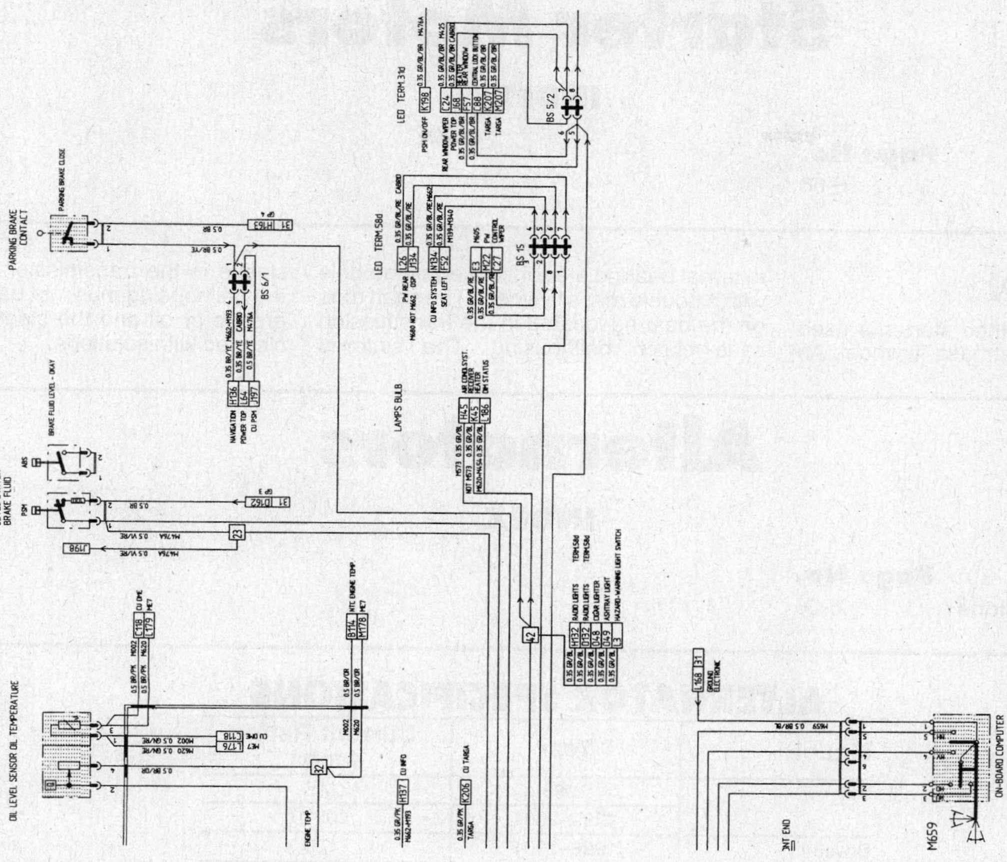

Fig. 3 Instrument cluster & gauge assembly wiring diagram (Part 3 of 3). 1999–2001 911

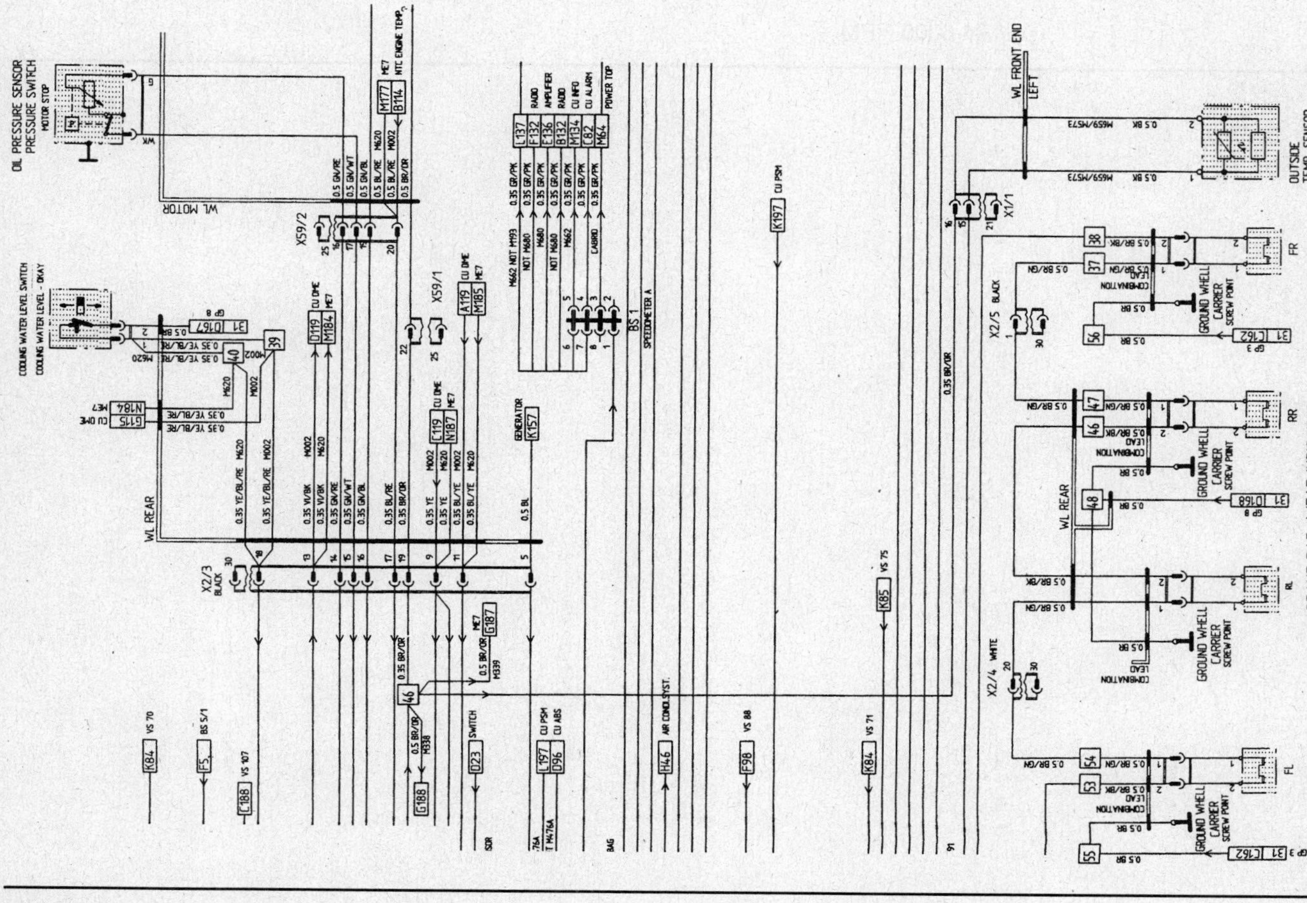

Fig. 3 Instrument cluster & gauge assembly wiring diagram (Part 2 of 3). 1999–2001 911

Starter Motors

INDEX

Page No.
Description 6-66

DESCRIPTION

A countershaft mouthed starter is used on models less double mass flywheel. An external bearing starter is used on models with a double mass flywheel. The shaft runs on the bearing located in the transmission case clutch bellhousing. The sintered sleeve in the transmission case, close to the bellhousing must not be lubricated with grease or oil and the sleeve must not be cleaned with solutions.

Alternators

INDEX

Page No.
Alternator Specifications 6-66

ALTERNATOR SPECIFICATIONS

Model	Year	Current Rating Amps.
911	1998	115
	1999–2001	105①
Boxster	1998–2001	120

① — At 6000 RPM.

Speed Control Systems

NOTE: On Air Bag Equipped Models, Refer To "Air Bag System Precautions" Located In The Front Of This Manual For System Disarming & Arming Procedures.

INDEX

	Page No.
Adjustments	6-67
Cable	6-67
Component Replacement	6-67
Control Unit	6-67
Description	6-67
Precautions	6-67
Air Bag Systems	6-67
Battery Ground Cable	6-67
System Diagnosis & Testing	6-67

DESCRIPTION

The cruise control system (Tempostat E) is an electrically controlled system. On Boxster models, the cruise control unit is mounted to the pedal bearing block above the accelerator. On 911 models, the cruise control unit is located below the center instrument panel, near the radio. The electric connection is made with a 14-pin connector and an additional coding connector, the assembly is covered by a cap. On 911 models, the electric drive servo is located on the lefthand side of the engine compartment. The electric drive connection is made with a six-pin connector. A cable is used as a mechanical connection between the drive and throttle valve.

PRECAUTIONS

AIR BAG SYSTEMS

Refer to "Air Bag System Precautions" in the front of this manual for system disarming and arming procedures.

BATTERY GROUND CABLE

Prior to service, disconnect battery ground cable and isolate as required.

ADJUSTMENTS

CABLE

Boxster

1. Loosen snap ring and push threaded part along cable.
2. Engage cable on control unit and clip on adjusting piece.
3. Unscrew threaded part until accelerator plate is pulled.
4. Pull accelerator plate back firmly against idle stop.
5. Push snap ring back.
6. Make final adjustment by turning threaded portion.

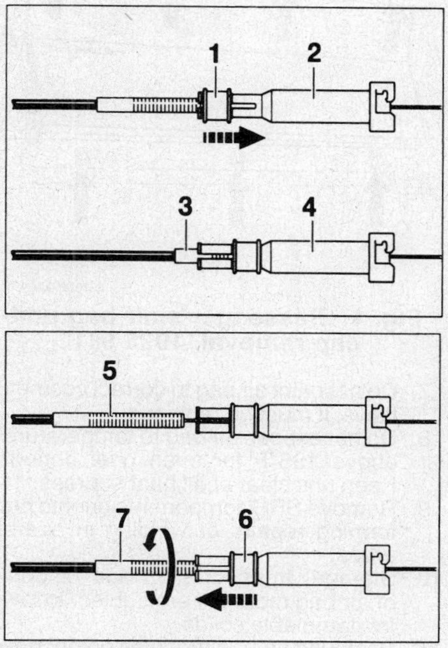

1. SNAP RING
2. ADJUSTING PIECE
3. THREADED END
4. ADJUSTING PIECE
5. THREADED ROD
6. SNAP RING
7. THREADED ROD

PR0149500001000X

Fig. 1 Cruise control cable adjustment. 911

7. Proper play is 0–.0397 inch.

911

1. Loosen snap ring at adjusting piece, **Fig. 1.**
2. Push threaded part and cable through adjuster.
3. Loosen threaded part until accelerator plate is noticeably pulled.
4. Pull accelerator back firmly against its stop.
5. Make final adjustment using threaded rod, specified play is 0–.39 inch.

SYSTEM DIAGNOSIS & TESTING

Information not available from the manufacturer.

COMPONENT REPLACEMENT

CONTROL UNIT

Boxster

1. Remove heat and air conditioning air guide, and footwell air vent.
2. Remove brake lamp switch.
3. Loosen cruise control unit mounting bolts.
4. Move control unit to rear and to side.
5. Disconnect electrical connector.
6. Loosen adjusting piece snap ring and push threaded part along cable.
7. Loosen adjusting piece bayonet lock and remove cable.

911

1. Remove air guide and A/C and heater footwell air vent.
2. Remove brake light switch from pedal bearing block.
3. Pull cruise control actuator towards the rear and disconnect electrical connectors.
4. Loosen snap ring at adjusting piece, then push threaded part and cable out of actuator.
5. Remove actuator from bearing block.
6. Reverse procedure to install.

Air Bag System

INDEX

	Page No.
Air Bag System Disarming & Arming	6-68
Arming	6-68
Disarming	6-68
Collision Inspection	6-68
Component Service	6-68
Air Bag Assembly Disposal	6-70
Contact Unit, Replace	6-69
Control Unit Programming	6-69
Control Unit, Replace	6-69
Front Crash Sensors, Replace	6-69
Passenger's Air Bag Module, Replace	6-68
Diagnosis & Testing	6-68
Precautions	6-68
Scheduled Maintenance	6-68
Tightening Specifications	6-70

AIR BAG SYSTEM DISARMING & ARMING

DISARMING

1. Place ignition switch in Off position.
2. Disconnect and isolate battery ground cable.
3. Wait at least 1 minute before beginning diagnosis or repairs. This is necessary to allow the air bag's back-up power supply to discharge.

ARMING

1. Place ignition switch in Off position.
2. Connect battery ground cable.
3. Turn ignition On and note air bag warning lamp operation.
4. **On Boxster models,** lamp should light for approximately three seconds, then go off.
5. **On 911 models,** lamp should light for approximately four seconds, then go off.
6. **On all models,** if lamp fails to light, remains illuminated or comes on again, refer to "Diagnosis & Testing."

PRECAUTIONS

The air bag/Supplemental Restraint System (SRS) must be disarmed prior to disconnecting any system electrical connectors or servicing any components located near an SRS electrical connector. Refer to "Air Bag System Disarming & Arming."

Always observe the following safety measures when working on the SRS:

1. SRS components must not be opened or repaired. Always install new components.
2. If air bag module, crash sensor or control unit have been dropped from a height of 18 inches or more, they must be replaced.
3. Always replace SRS components which have been damaged.
4. Do not leave an undeployed air bag module unattended if work is interrupted. Install into vehicle as soon as it is removed from packaging.
5. Always place a removed air bag module so pad is facing upwards.
6. Air bag must not be exposed to oil, grease, or cleaning solutions.

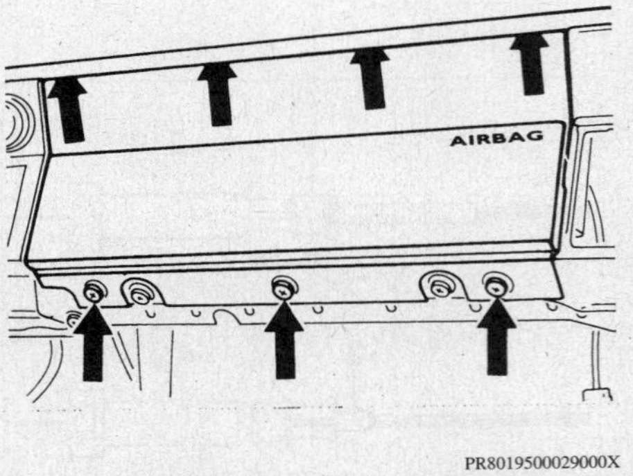

Fig. 1 Passenger's air bag unit cap removal. 1998 911

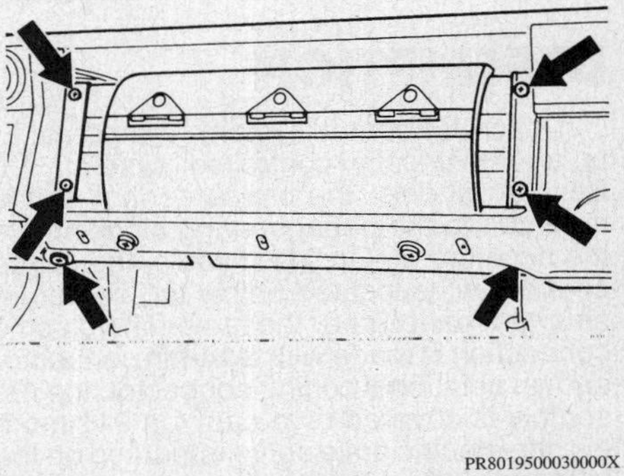

Fig. 2 Passenger's air bag unit mounting bolt locations. 1998 911

7. Do not paint air bag to correct cosmetic flaws. It must be replaced.
8. Do not expose air bag to temperatures above 195°F for even brief periods. Keep unit clear of all heat sources.
9. Remove SRS components prior to performing repairs or welding in nearby areas.
10. Storage, transportation and disposal of air bag modules are subject to laws for flammable solids.
11. Deployed air bag modules do not have to be disposed of as hazardous waste. They may be discarded with automotive metal scrap for recycling.
12. Wash hands thoroughly after handling a deployed air bag module.

SCHEDULED MAINTENANCE

The SRS must be inspected at four, eight and 10 year intervals after date of vehicle manufacture, then every two years thereafter. The manufacture date is listed on the safety compliance decal.

Inspect the SRS as follows:

1. Inspect SRS for stored Diagnostic Trouble Codes (DTCs).
2. Ensure no decals, stickers or other items have been affixed to air bag pads.
3. Inspect condition of SRS components and wiring, replace as necessary.
4. Determine whether modifications have been made to SRS, and that additional electrical equipment has not been connected to system wiring.

DIAGNOSIS & TESTING

Refer to **MOTOR's "Air Bag Manual"** for complete diagnosis and testing information.

COLLISION INSPECTION

On vehicles which have experienced an SRS deployment, certain system components must be replaced.

To ensure proper SRS operation on any vehicle involved in a collision, perform procedures outlined under "Diagnosis & Testing." All SRS components should be inspected for dents, cracks, exposure to excessive heat and other damage. All SRS wiring should be inspected for chafing and interference with other vehicle components. The air bag modules, control unit, both crash sensors and contact unit should be replaced with new components if SRS deployment was experienced. On models with passenger's air bag, the instrument panel should also be inspected. When repairing the vehicle, the SRS should be disarmed as outlined under "Air Bag System Disarming & Arming." When performing service procedures, do not expose components or wiring to heat guns, welding or spray guns.

COMPONENT SERVICE

PASSENGER'S AIR BAG MODULE, REPLACE

Boxster & 1999–2001 911

1. Disarm SRS as outlined under "Air Bag

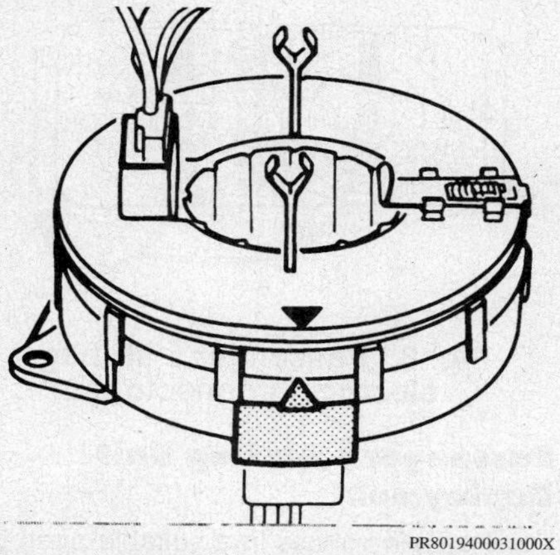

Fig. 3 Contact unit arrow mark alignment

System Disarming & Arming."
2. Remove air guide from bottom right-hand side of instrument panel, then the air bag unit mounting bolts.
3. Disconnect air bag igniter circuit electrical connector.
4. Remove air bag unit from instrument panel, then the hinge pin and cover from air bag module.
5. Reverse procedure to install. Use new mounting bolts and screws, then tighten to specifications.

1998 911

1. Disarm SRS as outlined under "Air Bag System Disarming & Arming."
2. Remove left and righthand side nozzles, then the radio, mounting bracket and ashtray.
3. Remove HVAC control and mounting bracket, then the knee bolster.
4. Disconnect air bag unit connector.
5. Remove lower, then the upper air bag cap retaining screws, **Fig. 1.** After removing screws, press flap forward and pull out from below to disengage stay.
6. Remove air bag unit mounting bolts, **Fig. 2.**
7. Remove air bag unit from instrument panel.
8. Reverse procedure to install. Use new mounting bolts and screws, and tighten to specifications.

CONTACT UNIT, REPLACE

1. Place front wheels in straight ahead position.
2. Disarm SRS as outlined under "Air Bag System Disarming & Arming."
3. Remove driver's air bag as described under "Driver's Air Bag Module, Replace."
4. Remove steering wheel retaining nuts.
5. Place alignment marks on steering wheel hub and steering column shaft for use during installation.
6. Using suitable puller remove steering wheel.
7. Remove steering column upper trim panel.
8. Remove contact unit attaching screws.
9. **On 911 models,** remove HVAC control, then the release tie wraps from connectors.

Fig. 4 Control unit electrical connector latch release. 911

10. **On all models,** disconnect electrical connector and remove contact unit.
11. Contact unit is automatically locked in position when steering wheel is removed.
12. Reverse procedure to install, noting the following:
    a. Prior to installation, ensure front wheels are in straight ahead position.
    b. New contact units are locked in center position. **Do not remove lock until after contact unit has been installed.**
    c. Contact unit's two arrow marks should be aligned when unit is centered, **Fig. 3.**

CONTROL UNIT, REPLACE

Boxster

Never remove control unit without first disarming air bag system and disconnecting connector.

1. Disarm SRS as outlined under "Air Bag System Disarming & Arming."
2. Remove front cover of center console.
3. Unlatch control unit electrical connector safety latch, then rotate latch and disconnect connector.
4. Remove shear nuts retaining control unit using serrated socket tool No. 925, or equivalent.
5. Remove remaining mounting nuts, then the control unit from vehicle.
6. Reverse procedure to install, noting the following:
    a. Tighten to specification.
    b. Prior to installation, ensure control mounting contact surface is down to bare metal.
    c. Use a ¼ inch socket to tighten shear-off nuts.
    d. If a replacement control unit was installed it must be programmed as outlined under "Control Unit, Programming."

911

Never remove control unit without first disarming air bag system, then disconnecting connector.

1. Disarm SRS as outlined under "Air Bag System Disarming & Arming."
2. Pull control unit electrical connector clamp open from under passenger's side of instrument panel and disconnect connector, **Fig. 4.**
3. Using serrated socket tool No. 925, or equivalent, remove shear nuts retaining control unit. Access nuts from driver's side.
4. Remove remaining mounting nuts, then the control unit from vehicle.
5. Reverse procedure to install, noting the following:
    a. Tighten to specification.
    b. Prior to installation, ensure control mounting contact surface is down to bare metal.
    c. Use a ¼ inch socket to tighten shear-off nuts.
    d. If a replacement control unit was installed it must be programmed as outlined under "Control Unit, Programming."

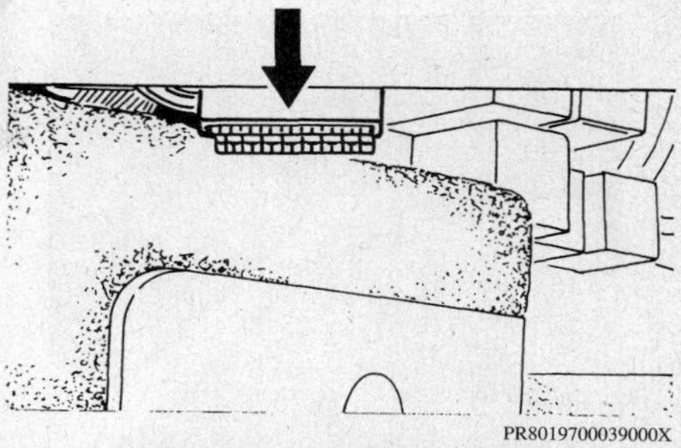

Fig. 5 Diagnostic link connector. Boxster

CONTROL UNIT PROGRAMMING

1. Turn ignition Off.
2. Connect Porsche System Tester 2, or equivalent scan tool, to vehicle DLC, **Figs. 5 and 6.**
3. Select "Driver's/Passenger's Air Bag" on scan tool display.
4. Select vehicle type. **Once selected vehicle type cannot be changed.**
5. Select "Locking." After a short period of time, scan tool should display "Air Bag Was Locked."
6. If a fault is present in SRS, control unit cannot be locked.
7. To check coding, under scan tool menu select "Checking The Coding."
8. To change coding, under scan tool menu select "Changing The Coding." The following equipment features can be changed:
    a. Driver's/Passenger's Air Bag.
    b. Seat Belt Buckle (detects whether seat belt is fastened).
    c. Seat Occupancy (Passenger's).
    d. Child Seat Occupancy (Passenger).

FRONT CRASH SENSORS, REPLACE

1. Disarm air bag system as described under "Air Bag System Disarming & Arming."
2. Disconnect sensor electrical connector.
3. Remove sensor mounting nuts, then the sensor using tool No. 9259, or equivalent.

Fig. 6 Diagnostic link connector. 911

4. Reverse procedure to install, noting the following:
   a. Prior to installation, ensure sensor mounting contact surface is bare down to metal.
   b. Use a ¼ inch socket to tighten shear-off bolts.

AIR BAG ASSEMBLY DISPOSAL

A face shield and rubber gloves should be worn when handling a deployed air bag assembly. Vehicle interior and HVAC ducts should be vacuumed. If sinus or throat irritation is encountered during air bag removal, exit vehicle and breathe fresh air. If skin irritation is encountered, flush affected area with cool water. If any type of irritation continues, consult a physician. Wash hands and rinse thoroughly with water after handling a deployed air bag assembly.

A deployed air bag should be removed as outlined under "Driver's Air Bag Module, Replace," or "Passenger's Air Bag Module, Replace." Place tape over exhaust vents prior to removing a deployed air bag assembly. After unit has been removed, it should be placed in a heavy duty plastic bag, sealed securely, then placed with automotive scrap.

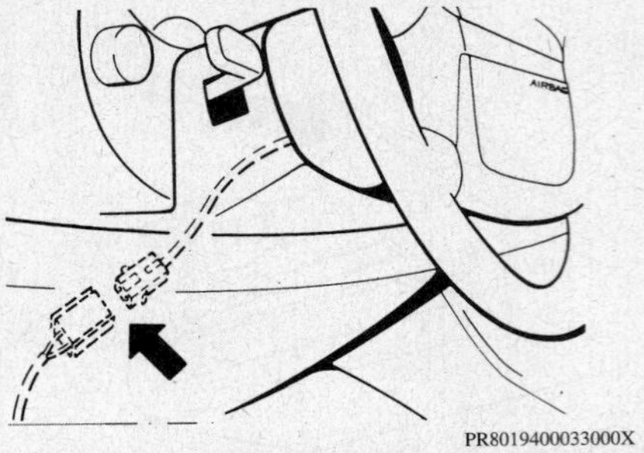

Fig. 7 Contact reel electrical connector

If vehicle is to be scrapped, the air bag unit must be deployed as outlined under "Driver's Air Bag Unit Deployment."

Driver's Air Bag Unit Deployment

1. Position vehicle in a suitable open location with no strong winds or breezes.
2. Disarm SRS as outlined under "Air Bag System Disarming & Arming."
3. Disconnect two-terminal contact unit electrical connector from under steering column, **Fig. 7**
4. Connect air bag deployment tool No. 9257, or equivalent, to contact reel electrical connector.
5. Ensure no loose objects are in vehicle.
6. Open side windows and rear hatch.
7. Close vehicle doors.
8. Position a fully charged 12 volt battery approximately 33 ft. from front of vehicle.
9. Extend deployment tool's wiring to full length to reach battery.
10. Connect tool to battery.
11. Ensure no people, animals or objects are in area of vehicle.
12. To deploy air bag unit, depress tool button. **After unit has deployed, wait at least 30 minutes prior to handling components.**
13. **If air bag unit fails to deploy,** do not approach vehicle for at least three minutes. Contact Porsche for disposal procedures.

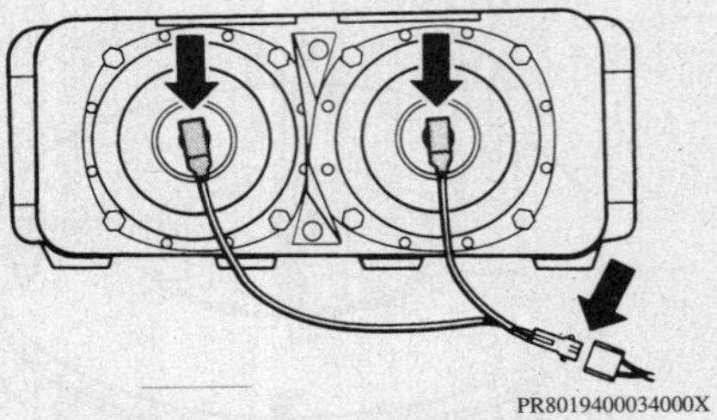

Fig. 8 Passenger's air bag electrical connectors

Passenger's Air Bag Unit Deployment

1. Position vehicle in a suitable open location with no strong winds or breezes.
2. Disarm SRS as outlined under "Air Bag System Disarming & Arming."
3. Disconnect electrical connector from passenger's air bag unit.
4. Connect air bag deployment tool harness No. 9257/1 to both air bag unit terminals, **Fig. 8.** Connect harness No. 9257/1 to air bag unit deployment tool No. 9257, or equivalent.
5. Ensure no loose objects are in vehicle.
6. Open side windows and rear hatch.
7. Close vehicle doors.
8. Position a fully charged 12 volt battery approximately 33 ft. from front of vehicle.
9. Extend deployment tool's wiring to full length to reach battery.
10. Connect tool to battery.
11. Ensure no people, animals or objects are in area of vehicle.
12. To deploy air bag unit, depress tool button. **After unit has deployed, wait at least 30 minutes prior to handling components. Ensure both air bag unit generators have ignited.** This will be indicated by burn marks on both ignition harness 9257/1 connector terminals.
13. **If unit fails to deploy,** do not approach vehicle for at least three minutes. Contact Porsche for disposal procedures.

TIGHTENING SPECIFICATIONS

Year	Component	Torque, Ft. Lbs.
BOXSTER		
1998–2001	Control Unit	84①
	Driver's Air Bag Bracket	48①
	Driver's Air Bag T30 Torx	84①
	Passenger's Air Bag	15
	Steering Wheel	34
911		
1998–2001	Control Unit	84①
	Driver's Air Bag Bracket	48①
	Driver's Air Bag T30 Torx	84①
	Passenger Side Air Bag	48①
	Steering Wheel	34

① — Inch lbs.

Dash Panel Service

NOTE: On Air Bag Equipped Models, Refer To "Air Bag System Precautions" Located In The Front Of This Manual For System Disarming & Arming Procedures.

NOTE: Refer To "Dash Gauges" Section For Related Information.

INDEX

	Page No.
Dash Panel, Replace	6-71
911	6-71
Boxster	6-71
Precautions	6-71
Air Bag Systems	6-71
Battery Ground Cable	6-71

PRECAUTIONS

AIR BAG SYSTEMS

Refer to "Air Bag System Precautions" in the front of this manual for system disarming and arming procedures.

BATTERY GROUND CABLE

Prior to service, disconnect battery ground cable and isolate as required.

DASH PANEL

REPLACE

BOXSTER

1. Remove mounting combination screws, sheet metal nuts, bolts and Torx screws.
2. Remove dash panel.
3. Remove mounting bolts and knee protector.
4. Remove mounting nuts and panel holder.
5. Remove mounting nuts and cover.
6. Remove mounting bolts, washers and balancing element.
7. Remove threaded plate and support frame.
8. Reverse procedure to install.

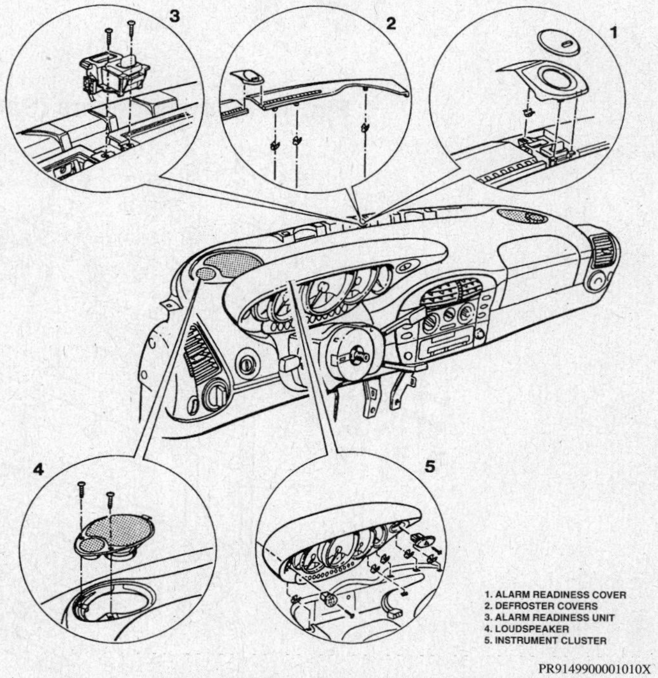

Fig. 1 I/P components (Part 1 of 2). 911

911

1. Remove alarm readiness cover, then the defroster covers, **Fig. 1.**
2. Remove alarm readiness unit Torx screws, then the alarm readiness unit.
3. Remove loudspeakers Torx screws and the loudspeakers.
4. Remove hazard warning switch button from instrument cluster by inserting two narrow screwdrivers on each side of switch and pulling outward.
5. Remove hazard warning switch by pressing locking hook on right side of switch inward, then grip switch with a pair of suitable pliers and pull out of cluster.
6. Remove plug from lefthand side of instrument cluster and remove instrument cluster Torx screws.
7. Pull cluster out of instrument panel and disconnect electrical connectors.
8. Remove light switch control button by pulling button outward, then pressing in locking device on bottom of button with a small screwdriver.
9. Remove lefthand side nozzle Torx screws, then pull nozzle from instrument panel and disconnect electrical connectors.
10. Remove steering column switch attaching screws.
11. Disconnect electrical connector and remove steering column switch.
12. Remove steering column cover Torx screws, then the cover from steering column.
13. Remove switch covers from center of instrument panel.
14. Remove A/C and heater control panel Torx screws, then the control panel from instrument panel.
15. Remove instrument panel Torx screws from A/C and heater control panel opening.
16. Remove blower panel to instrument panel Torx screws, then unclip and disconnect Bowden cables.
17. Disconnect blower panel electrical connector and remove panel from instrument panel.
18. Remove instrument panel Torx screws from blower panel opening.
19. Remove instrument panel attaching screws, bolt and nuts, **Fig. 2.**
20. Remove instrument panel from vehicle.
21. Reverse procedure to install.

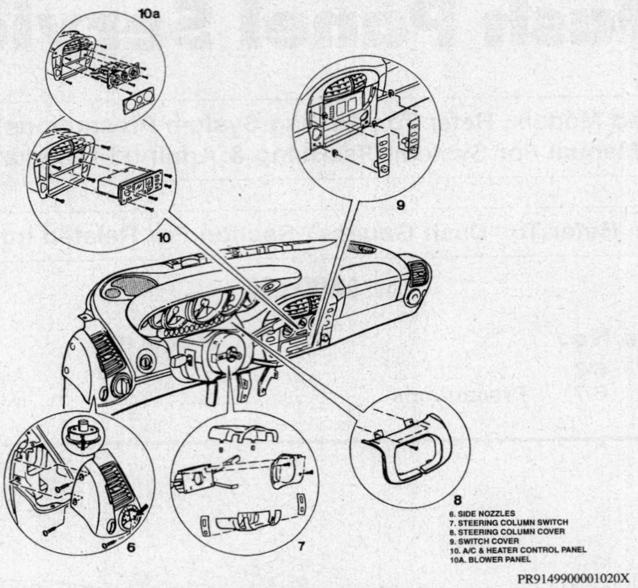

Fig. 1 I/P components (Part 2 of 2). 911

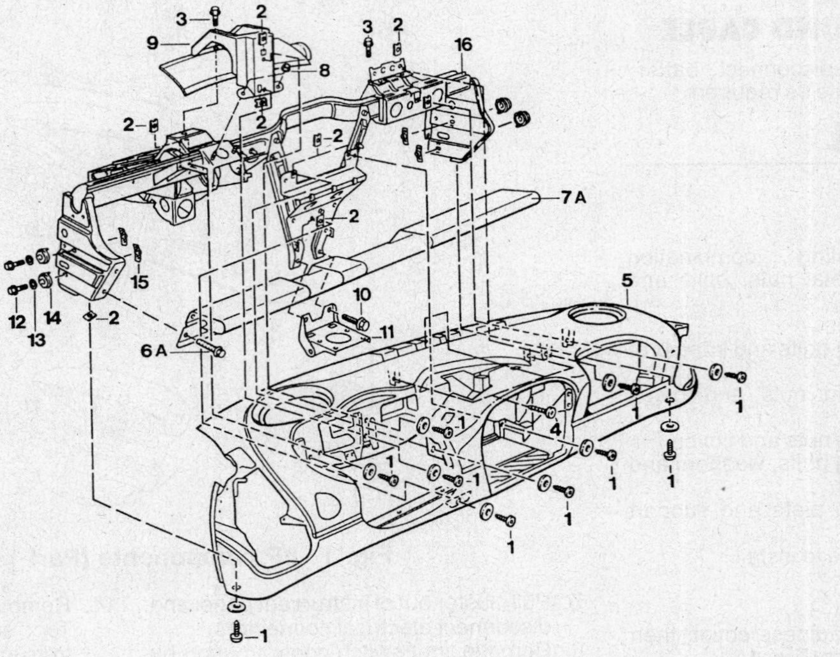

1. Combination screw
2. Sheetmetal nut
3. Hexagon head bolt
4. Torx screw
5. Instrument panel
6. Heaxagon head bolt
7. Knee protector
8. Collar nut
9. Holder
10. Hexagon head bolt
11. Cover panel
12. Hexagon head bolt
13. Washer
14. Compensating element
15. Threaded plate
16. Support frame

Fig. 2 Exploded view of I/P. 911

Disc Brakes

INDEX

	Page No.
Brake Pad Service	6-73
Boxster	6-73
911	6-73
Caliper Service	6-73
911	6-73
Disc Brake Specifications	6-74
Parking Brake Service	6-73
Adjustment	6-73
Replace	6-74
Precautions	6-73
Air Bag Systems	6-73
Battery Ground Cable	6-73
Tightening Specifications	6-75

PRECAUTIONS

AIR BAG SYSTEMS

Refer to "Air Bag System Precautions" in the front of this manual for system disarming and arming procedures.

BATTERY GROUND CABLE

Prior to service, disconnect battery ground cable and isolate as required.

BRAKE PAD SERVICE

BOXSTER

1. Raise and support vehicle. Remove wheels.
2. Remove retainer and retainer pin.
3. Lift warning contact line and remove warning contacts from plates. Warning contact may be reused if there are no scrape marks on plastic part or line wear.
4. Remove some brake fluid from reservoir.
5. Set pads as far back as possible with suitable piston reset fixture.
6. Use suitable puller to remove pads.
7. Reverse procedure to install. Grease rear pad backing plates.

911

1. Raise and support vehicle, then remove wheels.
2. Remove retainer and retainer pin.
3. Lift warning contact line and remove warning contacts from plates. Warning contact may be reused if there are no scrape marks on plastic part or line wear.
4. Remove some brake fluid from reservoir.
5. Set pads as far back as possible with suitable piston reset fixture.
6. Remove pads using a suitable puller.
7. Reverse procedure to install, noting the following:
   a. Replace vibration damper, expanding spring, retaining pin and retainer bracket.
   b. **New brake pads require a bedding in period of approximately 125 miles. During this time, the brakes should be subjected to full stress only in emergencies when traveling at high speeds.**

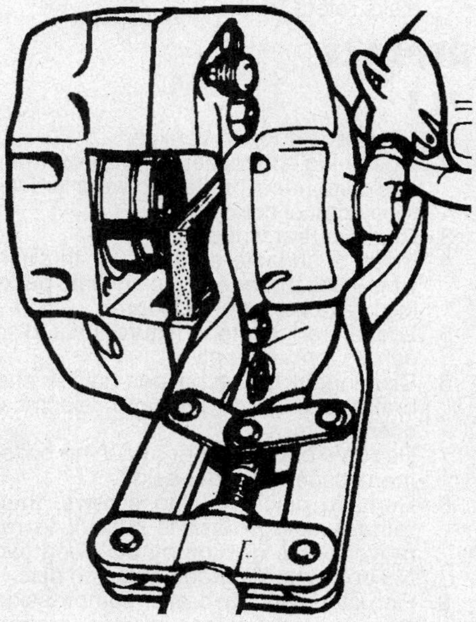

Fig. 1 Brake caliper piston removal. 1998 911

CALIPER SERVICE

911

1998

1. Raise and support vehicle.
2. Remove wheels and brake pads.
3. Disconnect brake hydraulic line. **Using a suitable device, depress and hold brake pedal to restrict flow of brake fluid from reservoir.**
4. Remove caliper retaining bolts, caliper, and metal shield.
5. Loosen bleeder valve and carefully blow hydraulic fluid out of caliper. **Recommended air pressure for fluid removal is 14 psi.**
6. Position caliper in a soft jaw vise, and remove clamping ring and dust boot.
7. Depress one caliper piston with tool No. 83, or equivalent, and position a wood block approximately ⅓ inches thick between tool arm and piston being removed, **Fig. 1.**
8. Apply pressure. **Start with 29 psi, and raise pressure as necessary. Keep fingers clear of caliper slot. Repair cylinders one at a time since pressure cannot be built up with one removed.**
9. Remove piston seal with plastic pin to prevent damage to cylinder bore groove.
10. Clean parts in alcohol. **Disassemble calipers only if O-rings which seal fluid passages between both caliper halves are defective and leak.**
11. Check cylinder bore, piston, and slot surfaces for damage.
12. Coat cylinder bore, piston, and piston seal with ATE brake paste, or equivalent.
13. Install piston seal into cylinder bore groove.
14. Position piston into caliper cylinder using aligning tool No. 84, or equivalent, **Fig. 2.**
15. Remove brake cylinder paste from piston ridge and install dust covers.
16. Install caliper and bleed system.

1999–2001

Calipers are not serviceable. Replace as an assembly.

PARKING BRAKE SERVICE

ADJUSTMENT

Boxster

1. Raise and support vehicle, then remove rear wheels.
2. Release parking brake lever and push rear brake pads back until brake disc rotates freely.
3. Open tray behind handbrake lever, then remove rubber inlay and insert.
4. Loosen turnbuckle until cables are without pretension.
5. Insert screwdriver into threaded wheel bolt hole.
6. Rotate parking brake adjustment sprocket until disc cannot be rotated by hand.
7. Loosen adjuster by five notches until wheel can be turned, then another four notches.
8. Pull parking bake lever up two notches and turn turnbuckle adjusting nut until both wheels can just barely be turned by hand.
9. Release parking brake and ensure disks rotate freely.

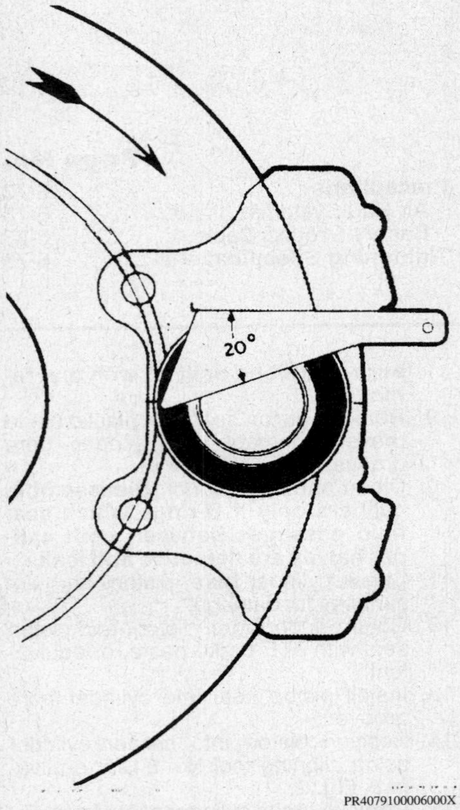

Fig. 2 Piston in caliper cylinder alignment. 1998 911

911

1. Raise and support vehicle, then remove rear wheels.
2. Release parking brake lever and push rear brake pads back until brake disc rotates freely.
3. Open access panel behind parking brake lever and loosen turnbuckle adjusting nut until cable has no tension.
4. Insert a suitable screwdriver through a threaded wheel bolt hole and into adjustment fixture, then rotate adjustment fixture until disc cannot be rotated.
5. Tighten adjustment fixture five more notches, then release approximately three notches until disc can be turned freely
6. Loosen adjuster another two notches.
7. Pull parking bake lever up two notches and turn turnbuckle adjusting nut until both wheels can just barely be turned by hand.
8. Release parking brake and ensure disks rotate freely.

REPLACE

911

1. Raise and support vehicle.
2. Open plug connection on wheel carrier and disconnect brake pad wear indicator electrical connector.
3. Remove rear wheel.
4. Insert a suitable screwdriver through wheel bolt threaded hole and into parking brake adjustment fixture.
5. Loosen adjustment fixture until disc can be rotated freely.
6. Disconnect brake caliper holder and brake pad wear indicator electrical connectors.
7. Remove brake caliper attaching bolts, then suspend caliper aside.
8. Remove disc retaining screws, then remove disc. If disc is difficult to remove, press disc off by installing two M8 bolts into threaded holes on disc.
9. Remove parking brake compression springs, adjustment device, return spring and parking brake shoes, **Fig. 3**.
10. Reverse procedure to install, noting the following:
    a. Apply a light coat of grease to adjustment device, actuating lever pins and parking brake shoe sliding surfaces.
    b. Ensure curved end of upper compression spring is pointing upward and curved end of lower compression spring is pointed downward.
    c. Adjust parking brake as previously outlined.

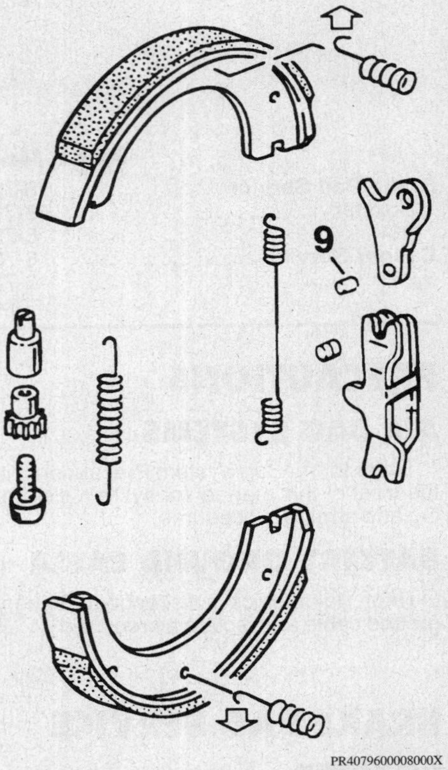

Fig. 3 Parking brake assembly. 911

DISC BRAKE SPECIFICATIONS

Model	Front Disc Brake				Rear Disc Brake			
	Nominal Thickness, Inch	Minimum Refinish Thickness, Inch	Thickness Variation Parallelism, Inch	Lateral Run-Out (T.I.R.), Inch	Nominal Thickness, Inch	Minimum Refinish Thickness, Inch	Thickness Variation Parallelism, Inch	Lateral Run-Out (T.I.R.), Inch
1998								
Boxster	.945	.890	.0008	.002	.787	.732	.0008	.002
911 Carrera, Carrera 4 & Targa	1.103	1.025	.0008	.002	.945	.890	.0008	.002
911 Carrera 4S & Turbo	1.260	1.205	.0008	.002	1.102	1.047	.0008	.002
1999–2001								
Boxster	.945	.890	.0008	.002	.787	.732	.0008	.002
911 Carrera	1.103	1.025	.0008	.002	.945	.867	.0008	.002
911 Turbo	1.340	1.261	.0008	.002	1.103	1.025	.0008	.002

TIGHTENING SPECIFICATIONS

Component	Torque, Ft. Lbs.
BOXSTER	
Brake Unit	17
Caliper	63
Cover Plate	84①
Disc	84①
Parking Brake Console	17
Reversing Box	84①
Speed Sensor	84①
Wheel To Hub	96
1998 911	
Ball Joint To Brake Push-Rod	13
Caliper To Axle	63
Caliper To Rear Axle Arm	43
Caliper To Steering Knuckle	51
Cover Plate To Axle	84①
Disc To Hub	48①
Disc To Hub Bolt	17
Guard & Backplate To Rear Axle Arm	18
Guard To Backplate	18
Guard To Knuckle	84①
Sensor To Axles	84①
Steering Knuckle	11
Wheel To Hub	96
1999–2001 911	
Brake Unit	17
Brake Unit Support	17
Caliper To Axle	63
Cover Plate To Axle	90①
Disc To Hub	90
Parking Brake Console	17
Sensor To Axles	90
Wheel To Hub	96

① — Inch lbs.

Hydraulic Brake Systems

INDEX

	Page No.
Brake System Bleed	6-76
Component Replacement	6-76
Master Cylinder	6-76
Tightening Specifications	6-76

COMPONENT REPLACEMENT

MASTER CYLINDER

911

1. Remove operating rod lockpin.
2. Remove master cylinder mounting bolt located inside on luggage compartment floor plate.
3. Drain brake fluid reservoir with suitable siphon.
4. Disconnect stop light switches, vacuum hose clamp and brake lines.
5. Remove upper bolt from booster body and booster base retaining nuts.
6. Reverse procedure to install.

BRAKE SYSTEM BLEED

Brake fluid is extremely damaging to paint. If fluid should accidentally touch painted surface, immediately wipe fluid from paint and clean painted surface.

1. Fill reservoir to rim with brake fluid and remove filter insert.
2. Attach pressure bleeder to reservoir and turn On.
3. First bleed clutch, then master cylinder if master cylinder or brake fluid tank has been removed.
4. Operate brake pedal firmly several times during bleeding procedure in order to remove all air bubbles in master cylinder.
5. Open bleeder valve of each wheel until escaping brake fluid is without air bubbles.
6. Check for leaks in system after bleeding procedure is completed.

TIGHTENING SPECIFICATIONS

Year	Component	Torque, Ft. Lbs.
1998–2001	Bleeder Screw	72–108①
	Brake Unit	17
	Caliper Pipe	108①
	Caliper Pressure Hose	10
	Damper To Pump	11①
	Hydraulic Unit	84①
	Long Pressure Line Connector	10–12①
	Master Cylinder	36①
	Press Pipe Fittings (M10)	10
	Press Pipe Fittings (M12)	15
	Proportion Valve Pipe	10
	Pump To Brace Bolts	88–114①②
	Short Pressure Line Connector	10–11③

①— Inch lbs.

②— 911.

③— Boxster.

Power Brake Units

INDEX

	Page No.
Power Brake Unit Service	6-77
Brake Booster, Replace	6-77

POWER BRAKE UNIT SERVICE

BRAKE BOOSTER, REPLACE

911

1. Remove brake booster operating rod lockpin.
2. Remove master cylinder attaching bolt from luggage compartment floor plate.
3. Drain brake fluid reservoir.
4. Disconnect electrical connectors for stop light switch, then the vacuum hose at brake booster and brake lines at master cylinder.
5. Remove brake booster brace upper mounting bolt and booster base attaching nuts, then the master cylinder and booster as an assembly. **Brace and operating rod do not have to be disconnected at pedal assembly to remove brake booster.**
6. Reverse procedure to install, noting the following:
   a. Clevis for operating rod must be installed so that clevis clip can be installed from above. **Operating rod must be attached when brake pedal is at its rest position without any force applied to operating lever. Play set at factory must not be changed.**
   b. **Torque** booster base nuts and master cylinder bolt to 17 ft. lbs.
   c. **Torque** support to rod bolt to 25 ft. lbs.
   d. Pull brake pedal back to stop.
   e. Loosen nuts on operating rod and adjust rod until lockpin for operating lever can be installed without tension.
   f. Tighten nuts on operating rod and bleed brake system.
   g. Check operating rod play at brake pedal by manual operation with engine off. Play must be at least .4 inch.

Anti-Lock Brakes

TABLE OF CONTENTS

	Page No.
ABS 5 & ABS 5/ABD	6-78
ABS 5.3 & ABS/TC 5.3	6-84
APPLICATION CHART	6-77

Application Chart

Model	Year	System
Boxster	1998–2001	ABS 5.3 & ABS TC/5.3
911	1998	ABS 5 & ABS 5/ABD
	1999–2001	ABS 5.3 & ABS TC/5.3

ABS 5 & ABS 5/ABD

NOTE: On Air Bag Equipped Models, Refer To "Air Bag System Precautions" Located In The Front Of This Manual For System Disarming & Arming Procedures.

INDEX

	Page No.
Description	6-78
Diagnosis & Testing	6-78
Accessing Diagnostic Trouble Codes	6-78
Connector Pin Identification	6-78
Diagnostic Tests	6-78
Test 1, Control Unit Faulty (Code 11)	6-78
Test 2, Stop Light Switch (Code 12)	6-78
Test 3, Incorrect Gearwheel (Code 13)	6-79
Test 4, Intake Valve (Code 14)	6-79
Test 5, Switch-Over Valve (Code 15)	6-79
Test 6, Throttle Information (Code 17)	6-79
Tests 7–10, Speed Sensor Signal Implausible (Codes 21–24)	6-79
Tests 11–14, Speed Sensor Open/Short Circuit (Codes 25–28)	6-80
Tests 15–22, ABS Inlet & Exhaust Valves (Codes 31–38)	6-80
Test 23, Solenoid Valve Relay (Code 39)	6-80
Test 24, Return Pump Relay Open/Short Circuit (Code 40)	6-80
Diagnostic Trouble Code (DTC) Interpretation	6-78
Wiring Diagrams	6-78
Precautions	6-78
Air Bag Systems	6-78
Battery Ground Cable	6-78
System Service	6-81
Brake System Bleed	6-81
Component Replacement	6-81
Electronic Control Unit	6-81
Hydraulic Unit	6-81
Wheel Sensors	6-81
Troubleshooting	6-78

PRECAUTIONS

AIR BAG SYSTEMS

Refer to "Air Bag System Precautions" in the front of this manual for system disarming and arming procedures.

BATTERY GROUND CABLE

Prior to service, disconnect battery ground cable and isolate as required.

DESCRIPTION

The ABS 5 anti-lock braking system **Fig. 1**, prevents the wheels from locking in an emergency stop, until shortly before the vehicle comes to halt, thus assuring full steerability and directional stability. In addition, the system optimizes the braking distance corresponding to the varying degree of grip between the wheel and road surface. The four channel ABS system has a speed sensor at each wheel to detect wheel spin. If a sensor detects a wheel locking condition, the control unit will activate the solenoid for that wheel and limit the amount of hydraulic pressure to that wheel.

On 911 Carrera 4, Carrera 4S and Turbo models, the four-channel ABS system also incorporates a separate Automatic Brake Differential (ABD) system. The ABD system uses the brake hydraulic system as a traction aid. If the wheel speed sensor detects excessive wheel spin, the control unit will activate the hydraulic solenoid for that wheel to slow the wheel spin.

TROUBLESHOOTING

Refer to "Diagnosis & Testing" for troubleshooting procedures.

DIAGNOSIS & TESTING

After any work on the braking system which did not affect parts directly involved in the ABS, a function test check is required. The pilot lamp in the instrument cluster will go out when the engine is started if the ABS system is intact. Repairs include replacing brake pads, brake hoses, brake discs, brake unit, tandem master cylinder, brake cables and parts of the parking brake lines not connected to the hydraulic unit.

If work is performed on the hydraulic unit, electronic control unit, wheel speed sensors or the lines or if units are replaced, a function test must be performed with the ABS tester.

Accessing Diagnostic Trouble Codes

Connect Porsche system tester tool No. 9288 with adapter lead tool No. 9288/1, or equivalents, per manufacturer's instructions.

Diagnostic Trouble Code (DTC) Interpretation

Refer to **Fig. 2** for DTC identification and description.

Wiring Diagrams

Refer to **Fig. 3** for ABS system wiring diagram.

Connector Pin Identification

Refer to **Fig. 4** for ABS/ABD control unit identification.

Diagnostic Tests

TEST 1, CONTROL UNIT FAULTY (CODE 11)

The control unit must be replaced to correct this code. Check the following items prior to replacing the control unit.

1. Inspect control unit connector for loose or damaged terminals.
2. Check control unit ground connections to pin Nos. 28 and 29 (located in the luggage compartment).
3. Check other important ground connections, such as the transmission ground and from starter to body.

TEST 2, STOP LIGHT SWITCH (CODE 12)

1. Using tester 9288, or equivalent, check values by pressing brake pedal, values should indicate an open and then closed circuit.
2. Disconnect stop light switch electrical connector and check switch contacts with a suitable multi-meter.
3. Check stop light switch adjustment.
4. Inspect wiring circuit for open or short circuit.
5. If wiring and connectors are satisfactory, replace switch.

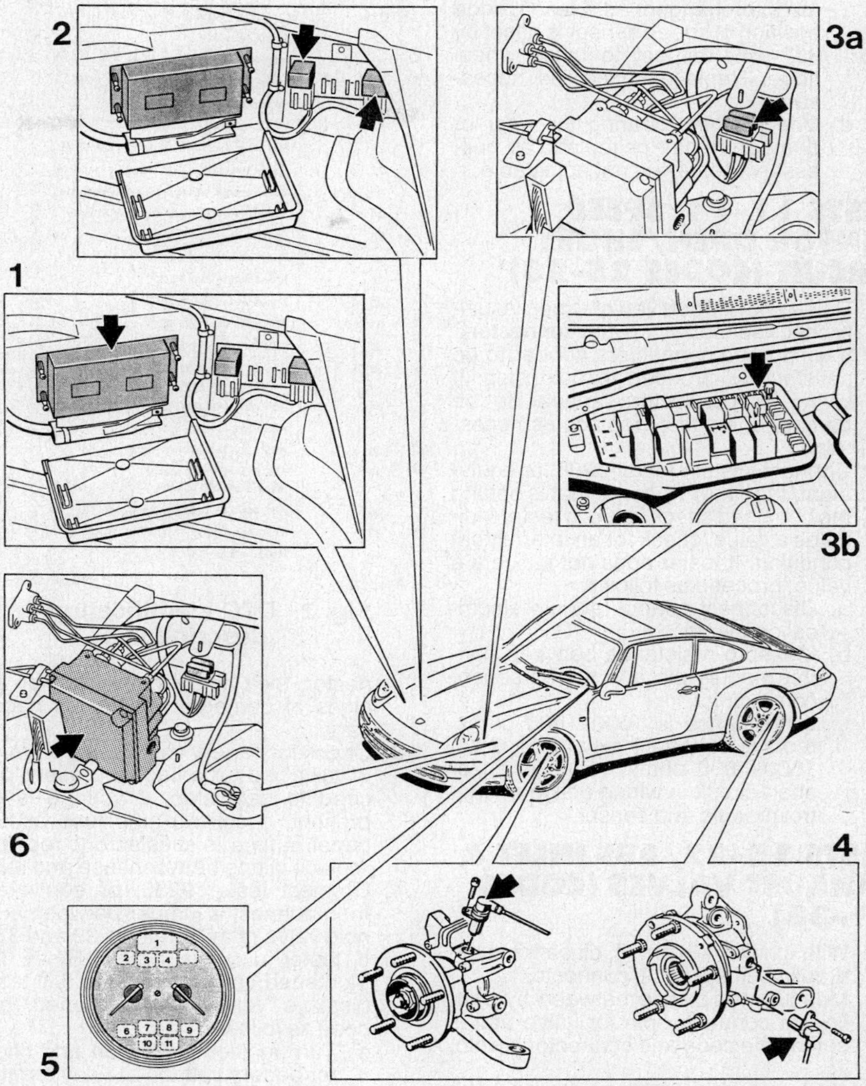

1. ABS/ABD Control Unit
2. Solenoid & Pump Relays
3a. Fuses
3b. 60 Amp Maxi-Fuse
4. Speed Sensor
5. Warning & Info Lamps
6. Hydraulic Unit

PR4029500001000X

Fig. 1 ABS 5 & ABS 5/ABD anti-lock brake system

TEST 3, INCORRECT GEARWHEEL (CODE 13)

This condition is usually caused by an incorrect number of teeth on the gearwheel.

1. Remove front wheel and count the number of teeth on the gearwheel.
2. **On models less all wheel drive,** there should be 48 teeth.
3. **On models with all wheel drive,** there should be 45 teeth.
4. **On all models,** if number of teeth is as specified, proceed to next step. If number of teeth is not as specified, replace gearwheel.
5. Check tires and wheels, extreme differences in size could cause this code to set, replace as necessary.

TEST 4, INTAKE VALVE (CODE 14)

1. Check wiring circuit between control unit connector pin and intake valve. If wiring circuit is satisfactory, proceed to next step. If wiring circuit is not satisfactory, repair or replace as necessary.
2. Check intake valve electrical connector. If connector is satisfactory, proceed to next step. If connector is not satisfactory, repair or replace as necessary.
3. Using system tester 9288, or equivalent, operate valve. If valve will not operate, replace valve. If valve operates, check control unit.

TEST 5, SWITCH-OVER VALVE (CODE 15)

1. Check wiring circuit between control unit connector pin and switch-over valve. If wiring circuit is satisfactory, proceed to next step. If wiring circuit is not satisfactory, repair or replace as necessary.
2. Check switch-over electrical connector. If connector is satisfactory, proceed to next step. If connector is not satisfactory, repair or replace as necessary.
3. Using system tester 9288, or equivalent, operate valve. If valve will not operate, replace valve. If valve operates, check control unit.

TEST 6, THROTTLE INFORMATION (CODE 17)

This code is the result of the ABS/ABD control unit not receiving any throttle information from the DME control unit.

1. Check throttle (TP) signal to DME control unit, using tester 9288, or equivalent.
2. If throttle signal is present at DME control unit, proceed to step 3. If throttle signal is not present at DME control unit, proceed as follows:
   a. Check wiring and TP sensor connector between DME control unit and sensor, repair or replace as necessary.
   b. If wiring and connector are satisfactory, check TP sensor using tester actual values menu. If sensor is satisfactory, check control unit. If sensor is not satisfactory, replace sensor.
3. Check wiring circuit and connectors between DME and ABS/ABD control units. If wiring circuit and connectors are satisfactory, check ABS/ABD control unit. If wiring circuit or connectors are not satisfactory, repair or replace as necessary.

TESTS 7-10, SPEED SENSOR SIGNAL IMPLAUSIBLE (CODES 21-24)

These code are caused by the control unit receiving incorrect or unrealistic speed sensor signals.

1. Connect system tester 9288, or equivalent, and display all four wheels.
2. Drive vehicle forward at 1.5–2.5 mph.
3. If wheel speed is within .65 mph at all wheels, check ABS/ABD control unit. If wheel speed is not within .65 mph at all wheels, proceed as follows:
   a. Check air gap between sensor and pulse wheel. Gap could be too large due to wear or a broken sensor tip. Check installation and repair as necessary.
   b. Check pulse wheel for wear or damage, repair or replace as necessary.

c. Speed sensors for front and rear are interchanged. As a result, edge position of speed sensor is offset by 90° with respect to pulse wheel edge. Replace sensor as necessary.
d. Check wheel bearing for wear or damage, repair or replace as necessary. Bearing is not adjustable.

TESTS 11-14, SPEED SENSOR OPEN/SHORT CIRCUIT (CODES 25-28)

1. Raise and support vehicle, then visually check sensor wiring and connectors. If wiring and connectors appear to be satisfactory, proceed to next step. If wiring or connectors appear to be damaged, repair or replace as necessary.
2. Connect system tester 9288, or equivalent, then turn wheel(s) that is setting the code and check value. If tester indicates a value, check for an intermittent condition. If tester does not indicate a value, proceed as follows:
   a. Disconnect control module electrical connector.
   b. Measure resistance between control module pin and speed sensor connector.
   c. If resistance is 1600–1800 ohms, replace sensor. If resistance is not 1600–1800 ohms, repair open or short circuit in wiring between control module and sensor.

TESTS 15-22, ABS INLET & EXHAUST VALVES (CODES 31-38)

1. With ignition switch off, disconnect hydraulic unit electrical connector.
2. Measure resistance between hydraulic unit connector pin for valve that is setting the code and connector pin No. 15.
3. **On inlet valves,** resistance should be 9–10 ohms.
4. **On exhaust valves,** resistance should be 4–5 ohms.
5. **On all valves,** if resistance is within specifications, proceed to next step. If resistance is not within specifications, replace hydraulic unit.
6. With ignition switch off, disconnect control unit electrical connector.
7. Check for continuity between control unit connector pin for valve that is setting the code and hydraulic unit connector pin. If continuity exists, proceed to next step. If continuity does not exist, repair open or short circuit between control unit and hydraulic unit.
8. Check ABS/ABD control unit.

TEST 23, SOLENOID VALVE RELAY (CODE 39)

1. Remove relay bracket from inner fender by pressing out attaching rivet, **Fig. 5.**
2. Disconnect solenoid valve relay connector, then check connector for any signs of damage, replace as necessary.
3. Check for battery voltage at pin No. 30 of valve relay. If voltage is present, proceed to next step. If voltage is not present, check 60 amp fuse at fuse panel. If fuse is satisfactory, repair or replace wiring between fuse and relay.
4. Connect tester 9288, or equivalent, then connect a jumper between solenoid valve relay terminals 30 and 37.
5. If tester displays "Valve Relay Not Tightened," proceed to step 6. If tester displays "Valve Relay Tightened," proceed as follows:
   a. Turn ignition switch on and check for battery voltage at relay terminal No. 86.
   b. If battery voltage is present, replace relay.
   c. If battery voltage is not present, check wiring circuit between control unit and relay.
   d. If wiring circuit is satisfactory, check ABS/ABD control unit. If wiring circuit is not satisfactory, repair or replace as necessary.
6. Disconnect hydraulic unit electrical connector.
7. Check wiring circuit between hydraulic unit connector pin No. 15 and relay terminal No. 87. If circuit is satisfactory, proceed to next step. If circuit is not satisfactory, repair or replace as necessary.
8. **On models less ABD,** proceed as follows:
   a. Measure resistance between relay terminal No. 87 and control unit pin Nos. 5, 53 and 54. If resistance is 9–12 ohms, proceed to next step. If resistance is not 9–12 ohms, check wiring between control unit and hydraulic unit, repair or replace if necessary. If wiring is satisfactory, replace control unit.
   b. Measure resistance between relay terminal No. 87 and control unit pin Nos. 25, 26 and 33. If resistance is 4–7 ohms, proceed to step 10. If resistance is not 4–7 ohms, check wiring between control unit and hydraulic unit, repair or replace if necessary. If wiring is satisfactory, replace control unit.
9. **On models with ABD,** proceed as follows:
   a. Measure resistance between relay terminal No. 87 and control unit terminal Nos. 3, 4, 5, 6, 53 and 54. If resistance is 9–12 ohms, proceed to next step. If resistance is not 9–12 ohms, check wiring between control unit and hydraulic unit, repair or replace if necessary. If wiring is satisfactory, replace control unit.
   b. Measure resistance between relay terminal No. 87 and control unit pin Nos. 25, 26, 33 and 34. If resistance is 4–7 ohms, proceed to step 11. If resistance is not 4–7 ohms, check wiring between control unit and hydraulic unit, repair or replace if necessary. If wiring is satisfactory, replace control unit.
10. **On models less ABD,** proceed as follows:
    a. Measure resistance between hydraulic unit connector pin Nos. 7, 8, 10 and No. 15. If resistance is 9–10 ohms in each measurement, proceed to next step. If resistance is not 9–10 ohms in each measurement, replace hydraulic unit.
    b. Measure resistance between hydraulic unit pin Nos. 5, 6, 11 and pin No. 15. If resistance is 4–5 ohms in each measurement, replace control unit. If resistance is not 4–5 ohms in each measurement, replace hydraulic unit.
11. **On models with ABD,** proceed as follows:
    a. Measure resistance between hydraulic unit connector pin Nos. 1, 2, 7, 8, 9, 10 and No. 15. If resistance is 9–10 ohms in each measurement, proceed to next step. If resistance is not 9–10 ohms in each measurement, replace hydraulic unit.
    b. Measure resistance between hydraulic unit pin Nos. 5, 6, 11, 13 and pin No. 15. If resistance is 4–5 ohms in each measurement, replace control unit. If resistance is not 4–5 ohms in each measurement, replace hydraulic unit.

Fault code	Fault display
11	Control unit faults
12	Stop light switch
13	Incorrect gearwheel
14*	Intake valve
15*	Switch-over valve
17*	TP information
21	Speed sensor front left (Signal unplausible)
22	Speed sensor front right (Signal unplausible)
23	Speed sensor rear right (Signal unplausible)
24	Speed sensor rear left (Signal unplausible)
25	Speed sensor front left***
26	Speed sensor front right***
27	Speed sensor rear right***
28	Speed sensor rear left***
31	ABS valve Inlet front left
32	ABS valve Inlet front right
33**	ABS valve Inlet rear or rear left on ABD vehicles
34*	ABS valve Inlet rear right
35	ABS valve Exhaust front left
36	ABS valve Exhaust front right
37**	ABS valve Exhaust rear or rear left on ABD vehicles
38*	ABS valve Exhaust rear right
39	Valve relay
40	Return pump

PR4029500002000X

Fig. 2 DTC identification & description

TEST 24, RETURN PUMP RELAY OPEN/SHORT CIRCUIT (CODE 40)

1. Remove relay bracket from inner fender by pressing out attaching rivet.

2. Disconnect return pump relay connector, then check connector for any signs of damage, replace as necessary.
3. Check for battery voltage at pin No. 30 of valve relay. If voltage is present, proceed to next step. If voltage is not present, check 60 amp fuse at fuse panel. If fuse is satisfactory, repair or replace wiring between fuse and relay.
4. Connect a jumper between terminal Nos. 30 and 87 of relay base. If return pump does not run, proceed to next step. If return pump runs, replace relay.
5. Check ground cable between return pump and battery ground. If ground is satisfactory, proceed to next step. If ground is not satisfactory, repair or replace as necessary.
6. Check wiring circuit between relay and hydraulic unit. If wiring is satisfactory, proceed to next step. If wiring is not satisfactory, repair or replace as necessary.
7. Disconnect control unit electrical connector.
8. Check wiring circuit between control unit pump motor monitor terminal and control unit pin No. 9. If wiring is not satisfactory, repair or replace as necessary. If wiring is satisfactory, replace control unit.

SYSTEM SERVICE

Brake System Bleed

Refer to "Hydraulic Brake System" for bleeding procedure.

Component Replacement

HYDRAULIC UNIT

These components are non-serviceable and must be replaced as a unit.

1. Mark wheel hub for reassembly and remove right front wheel assembly.
2. Remove wheel arch inner panel.
3. Disconnect all brake lines.
4. Disconnect ground wire and remove mounting bolts from hydraulic-unit holder.
5. Move hydraulic unit and holder out slightly to gain access to strain relief for 12-pole connector, and disconnect strain relief and remove connector.
6. Unclip ABS wire harness from hydraulic-unit holder and remove hydraulic unit with holder.
7. Reverse procedure to install and bleed brake system.

ELECTRONIC CONTROL UNIT

The ABS/ABD control unit is located on the right front corner of the luggage compartment.

1. Disengage retaining spring lock and disconnect connector from electrical control unit.
2. Unscrew retaining nuts and remove electronic control unit from holder.
3. Reverse procedure to install.

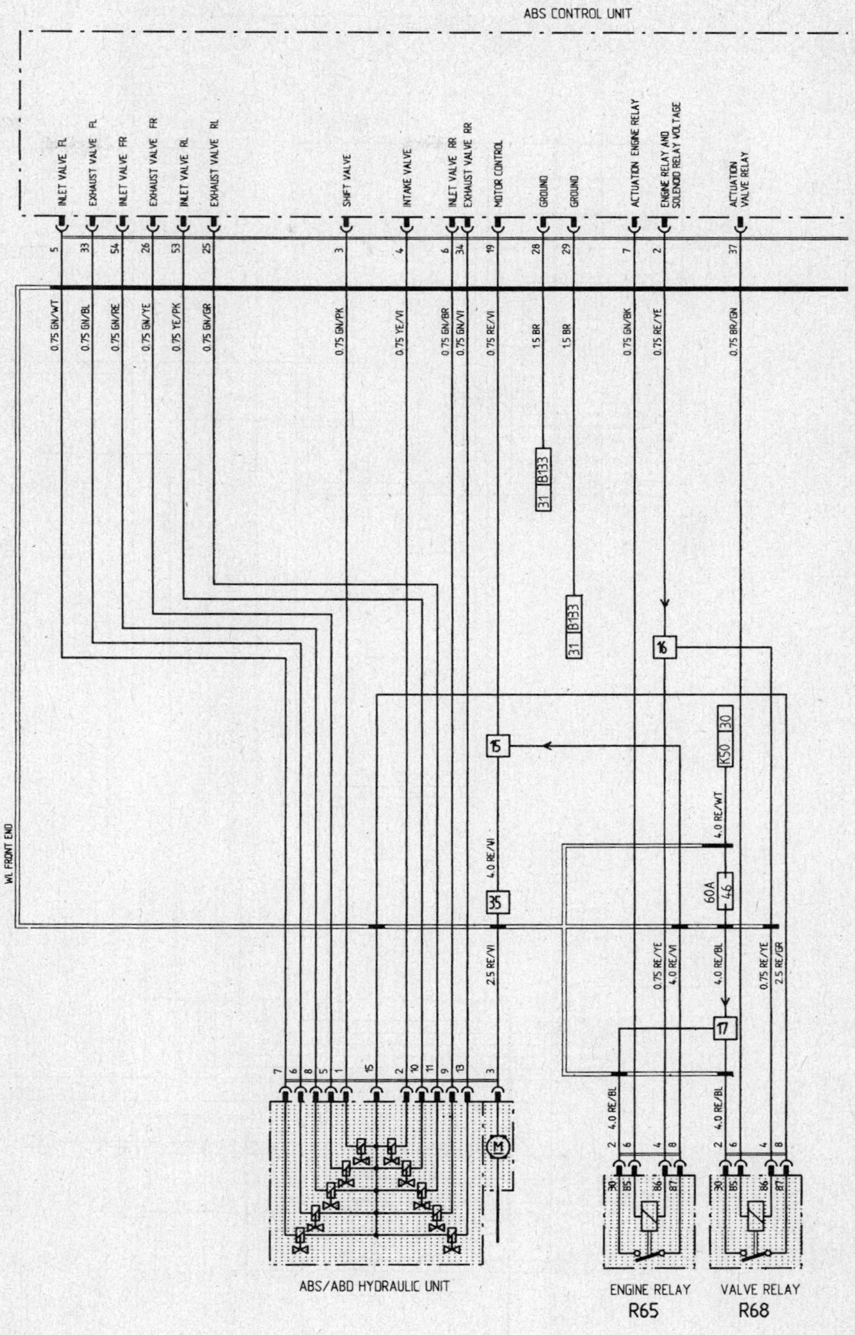

Fig. 3 ABS 5 wiring diagram (Part 1 of 3)

WHEEL SENSORS

Wheel sensors are installed without O-rings and coated with Molycote Longterm 2, or equivalent grease. On some models, front axle sensors use toothed wheels, while rear axle drive shaft sensors are pulse wheels. Number of teeth or pulse lands vary with application, therefore ensure proper replacement parts are ordered and installed.

1. Turn ignition switch to Off position.
2. Open combination connector connection and remove speed sensor connector.
3. Remove mounting nut and sensor.
4. Reverse procedure to install, ensuring there are no metal chips at magnetic edge. **Torque** mounting bolt to 7 ft. lbs.

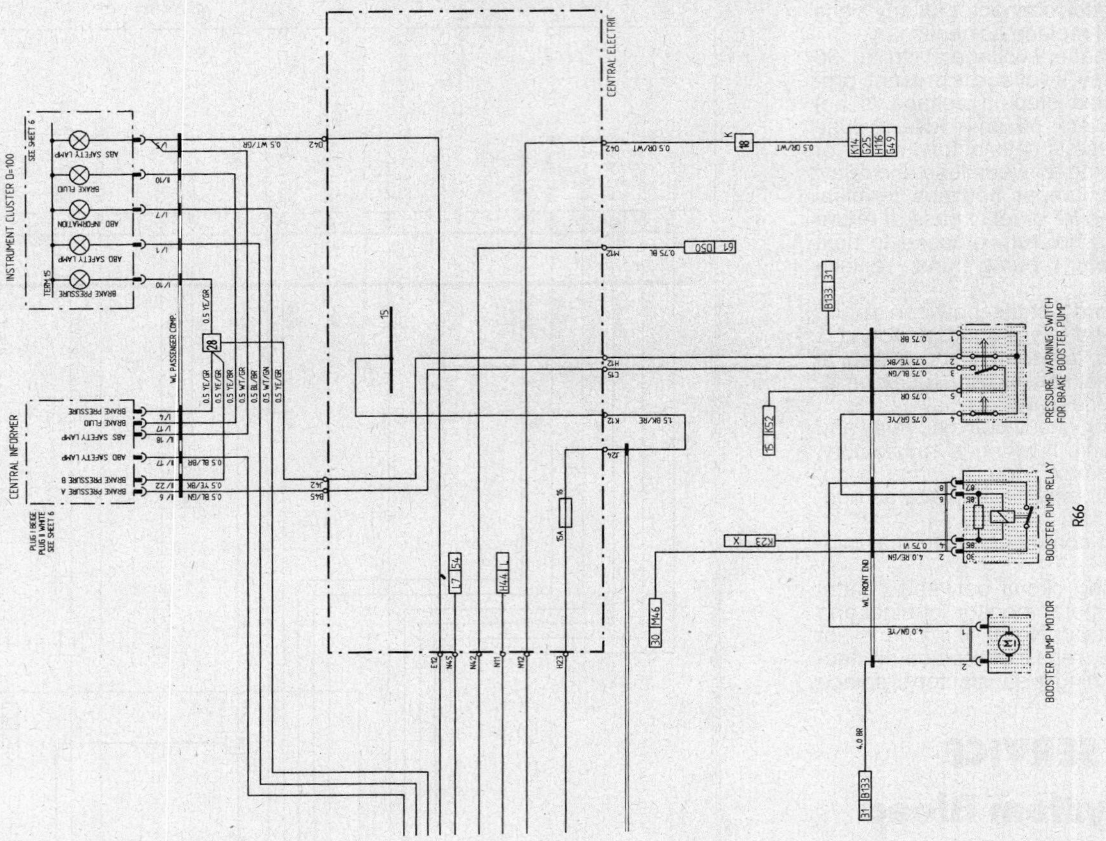

PR4029500003030X

Fig. 3 ABS 5 wiring diagram (Part 3 of 3)

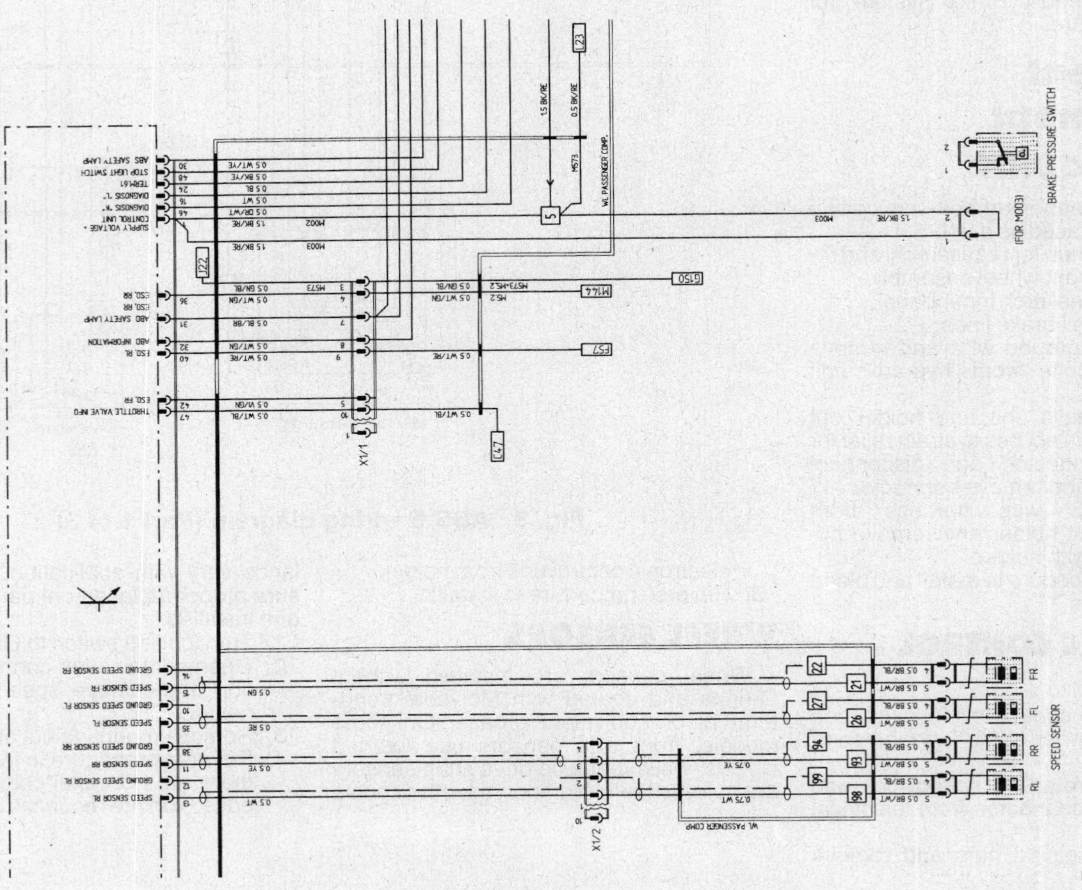

PR4029500003020X

Fig. 3 ABS 5 wiring diagram (Part 2 of 3)

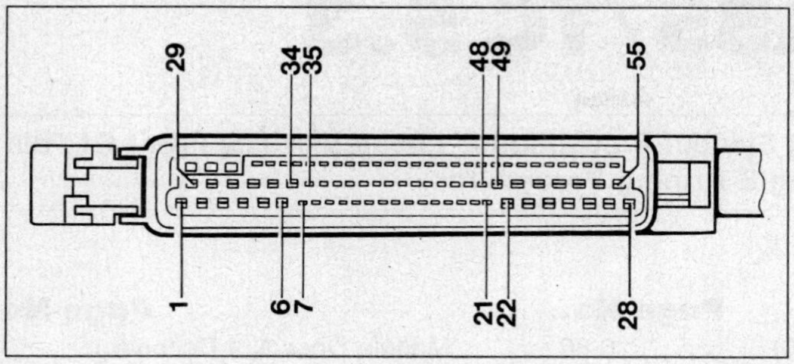

1 - Control unit voltage supply (Terminal 15 / from fuse No. 16)

2 - Voltage for return pump relay and valve relay

3 - With solo ABS = Not used

3 - With ABS / ABD = Switchover solenoid triggering (ground)

4 - With solo ABS =Not used

4 - With ABS / ABD = Intake solenoid triggering (ground)

5 - Triggering of front left inlet valve (ground)

6 - With solo ABS = Not used

6 - With ABS / ABD =Triggering of rear right inlet solenoid valve (ground)

7 - Return pump relay triggering (ground)

8 - Not used

9 - **Up to MY '95 = Not used** with Tiptronic vehicles **as of MY '96** = Output signal (Front left rpm sensor) **to** Tiptronic control unit

10 - Front left speed sensor ground

11 - Signal from rear right speed sensor

12 - Rear left speed sensor ground

13 - With solo ABS = Output signal (Rear left speed sensor) to Central Information System (speedometer signal)

13 - With ABS / ABD = Signal from rear left speed sensor

14 - Front right speed sensor ground

15 - Signal from front right speed sensor

16 - L wire from diagnosis

17 - 18 Not used

PR4029500004010X

Fig. 4 ABS/ABD control unit connector pin identification (Part 1 of 2)

19 - Engine monitor (Return pump)

20 - 23 Not used

24 - D+ , terminal 61

25 - With solo ABS = Triggering of rear axle outlet solenoid (ground)

25 - With ABS / ABD = Triggering of rear left outlet solenoid (ground)

26 - Triggering of front right outlet solenoid (ground)

27 - Not used

28 - Ground

29 - Ground

30 - Triggering of ABS warning lamp (ground)

31 - With solo ABS = Not used

31 - With ABS / ABD = Triggering of ABD warning lamp (ground)

32 - With solo ABS = Not used

32 - With ABS / ABD = Triggering of ABD information lamp (ground)

33 - Triggering of front left outlet solenoid (ground)

34 - With solo ABS = Not used

34 - With ABS / ABD = Triggering of rear right outlet solenoid (ground)

35 - With **ABS / ABD (RWD and 4WD)** = Signal from front left speed sensor

36 - With **solo ABS** = Signal from front left speed sensor

37 - Solenoid relay triggering (ground)

38 - Rear right speed sensor ground

39 - Not used

40 - With solo ABS = Signal from rear left speed sensor

40 - With ABS / ABD = Output signal (rear left speed sensor) to Central Information System (speedometer signal)

41 - Not used

42 - With manual transmission vehicles = Not used

42 - With Tiptronic vehicles = Output signal (front right speed sensor) **to** Tiptronic control unit

43 - 45 Not used

46 - Diagnosis K wire

47 - With solo ABS = Not used

47 - With ABS / ABD = Throttle information signal **from** DME control unit. Required for ABD control

48 - Stop light switch signal (system voltage when brakes are actuated)

49 - 52 Not used

53 - With solo ABS = Triggering of rear-axle inlet solenoid (ground)

53 - With ABS / ABD = Triggering of rear left inlet solenoid (ground)

54 - Triggering of front right inlet solenoid (ground)

55 - Not used

PR4029500004020X

Fig. 4 ABS/ABD control unit connector pin identification (Part 2 of 2)

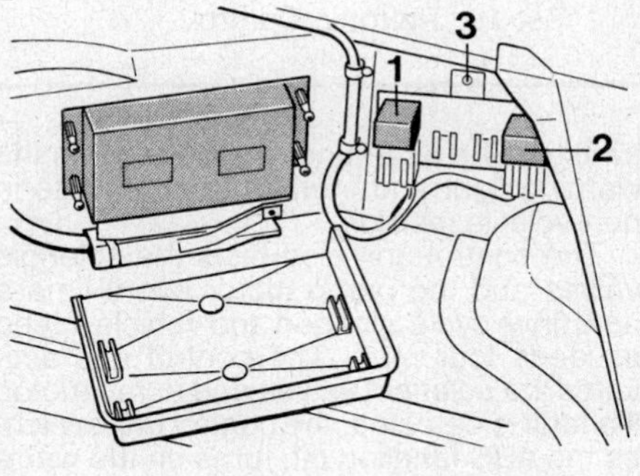

1. Return Pump Relay
2. Solenoid Valve Relay
3. Relay Bracket

PR4029500005000X

Fig. 5 Relay valve & bracket

ABS 5.3 & ABS/TC 5.3

NOTE: On Air Bag Equipped Models, Refer To "Air Bag System Precautions" Located In The Front Of This Manual For System Disarming & Arming Procedures.

INDEX

	Page No.
Description	6-84
ABS 5.3 (3-Channel)	6-84
ABS/TC 5.3 (4-Channel)	6-84
Diagnosis & Testing	6-84
Accessing Diagnostic Trouble Codes	6-84
Clearing Diagnostic Trouble Codes	6-88
Connector Pin Identification	6-85
Diagnostic Tests	6-85
Test 1, Control Module Faulty (Code 4607)	6-85
Test 2, Front Left Speed Sensor/Signal Implausible (Code 4206)	6-85
Test 3, Front Right Speed Sensor/Signal Implausible (Code 4201)	6-85
Test 4, Rear Right Speed Sensor/Signal Implausible (Code 4211)	6-85
Test 5, Rear Left Speed Sensor/Signal Implausible (Code 4216)	6-86
Test 6, Front Left Speed Sensor/Open Or Short Circuit (Code 4205)	6-86
Test 7, Front Right Speed Sensor/Open Or Short Circuit (Code 4200)	6-86
Test 8, Rear Right Speed Sensor/Open Or Short Circuit (Code 4210)	6-86
Test 9, Rear Left Speed Sensor/Open Or Short Circuit (Code 4215)	6-86
Test 10, ABS Solenoid Valve Faulty (Codes 4226, 4231, 4236, 4241, 4246, 4251, 4256 & 4261)	6-87
Test 11, Valve Supply Voltage (Code 4276)	6-87
Test 12, Return Pump Fault (Code 4266)	6-87
Test 13, Stop Lamp Switch (Code 4340)	6-87
Test 14, Wrong Gear Wheel (Code 4225)	6-87
Test 15, Control Module/ Hydraulic Unit Voltage Too Low (Code 4802)	6-87
Test 16, Intake Valve (Code 5260)	6-87
Test 17, Switch-Over Valve (Code 5265)	6-88
Test 18, Wrong Version Coding (Code 5281)	6-88
Test 19, Tiptronic Control Module Does Not Receive Signal From ABS/TC Control Module (Code 5282)	6-88
Test 20, Engine RPM Information Missing (Code 5283)	6-88
Test 21, ABS/TC Control Module Does Not Receive Signal From DME Control Module (Code 5284)	6-88
Test 22, ABS/TC Control Module Does Not Receive Signal From DME Control Module (Code 5285)	6-88
Test 23, Fault Stored In DME Control Module (Code 5286)	6-88
Diagnostic Trouble Code Interpretation	6-85
Intermittents	6-88
Wiring Circuits	6-85
Precautions	6-84
Air Bag Systems	6-84
Battery Ground Cable	6-84
System Service	6-88
Brake System Bleed	6-88
Component Replacement	6-88
Troubleshooting	6-84

PRECAUTIONS

AIR BAG SYSTEMS

Refer to "Air Bag System Precautions" in the front of this manual for system disarming and arming procedures.

BATTERY GROUND CABLE

Prior to service, disconnect battery ground cable and isolate as required.

DESCRIPTION

ABS 5.3 (3-CHANNEL)

This anti-lock brake system, **Fig. 1,** prevents wheel lockup by controlling hydraulic pressure to the two front brake calipers and the rear wheel circuit.

If any lockup is detected by the individual wheel speed sensors, the inlet valve for that wheel is closed to prevent any further increase in brake pressure. If wheel continues to lockup, the outlet valve is opened and brake fluid is pumped back to the brake master cylinder through the return pump until wheel begins to turn again.

The function and input signals are continuously monitored by the ABS control unit. If a fault is detected, the control unit switches the ABS function off, turns on the warning light and stores the fault code in non-volatile memory.

The control unit also tests the solenoid valves and the pump motor every time a new drive cycle is begun and vehicle speed exceeds four mph. The control unit activates the solenoid valves and pump motor, if a fault is detected, the control unit switches the ABS function off, turns on the warning light and stores the fault code.

ABS/TC 5.3 (4-CHANNEL)

This anti-lock brake and traction control system, **Fig. 2,** prevents wheel lockup by controlling hydraulic pressure to all four brake calipers individually.

If any lockup is detected by the individual wheel speed sensors, the inlet valve for that wheel is closed to prevent any further increase in brake pressure. If wheel continues to lockup, the outlet valve is opened and brake fluid is pumped back to the brake master cylinder through the return pump until wheel begins to turn again.

If any excessive wheel spin is detected, the Traction Control (TC) part of the system reduces engine power to that wheel. The ABS part of the system also increases hydraulic pressure to that wheel.

The function and input signals are continuously monitored by the ABS control unit. If a fault is detected, the control unit switches the ABS function off, turns on the warning light and stores the fault code in non-volatile memory.

The control unit also tests the solenoid valves and the pump motor every time a new drive cycle is begun and vehicle speed exceeds four mph. The control unit activates the solenoid valves and pump motor, if a fault is detected, the control unit switches the ABS/TC functions off, turns on the warning light and stores the fault code.

TROUBLESHOOTING

Refer to "Diagnosis & Testing" for system troubleshooting.

DIAGNOSIS & TESTING

Accessing Diagnostic Trouble Codes

Connect Porsche System Tester 2, or equivalent, scan tool to the Diagnostic Link Connector (DLC), then follow scan tool instructions to access ABS diagnostic codes. The DLC is located under the lefthand side

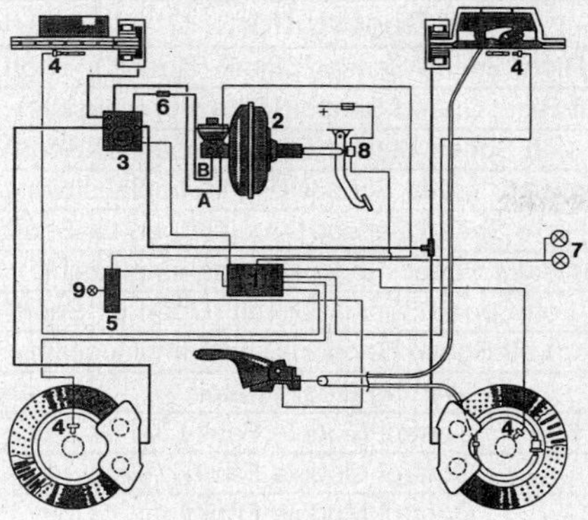

1 ABS control module *
2 Brake unit (brake booster with tandem master brake cylinder)
3 ABS hydraulic unit * (**3** hydraulic outputs)
4 ABS speed sensors
5 Instrument cluster
6 Brake proportioning valve (**1x**)
7 Brake light
8 Stop-light switch
9 ABS MIL (yellow)
A Front-axle braking circuit
B Rear-axle braking circuit

* Control module, hydraulic unit, pump-motor relay and valve relay form a unit, which is located next to the master brake cylinder.

PR4029700016000X

Fig. 1 Anti-lock brake system. ABS 5.3 w/3-channels

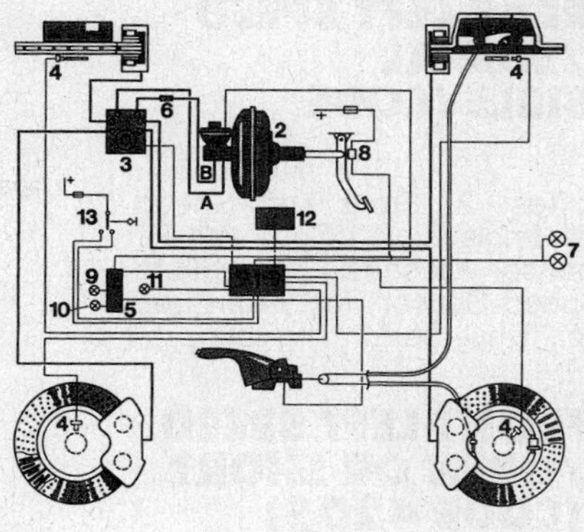

1 ABS/TC control module *
2 Brake unit (brake booster with tandem master brake cylinder)
3 **ABS/TC** hydraulic unit * (**4** hydraulic outputs)
4 ABS speed sensors
5 Instrument cluster
6 Brake proportioning valve (**1x**)
7 Brake light
8 Stop-light switch
9 ABS MIL (yellow)
10 TC MIL (TC/yellow)
11 TC function light (yellow/ or green on some vehicles of the initial production run)
12 **DME control module**
13 TC rocker switch (see Page 45 - D 10)
A Front-axle braking circuit
B Rear-axle braking circuit

* Control module, hydraulic unit, pump-motor relay and valve relay form a unit, which is located next to the master brake cylinder.

PR4029700017000X

Fig. 2 Anti-lock brake system. ABS/TC 5.3 w/4-channels

of the instrument panel, left of the steering column, **Fig. 3**.

Diagnostic Trouble Code Interpretation

Refer to **Fig. 4** for diagnostic trouble code identification and description.

Wiring Circuits

Refer to **Figs. 5 through 8** for system wiring circuits.

Connector Pin Identification

Refer to **Fig. 9** for ABS control module connector pin identification.

Diagnostic Tests

TEST 1, CONTROL MODULE FAULTY (CODE 4607)

1. Check for other codes. If code 4226, 4231, 4236, 4241, 4246, 4251, 4256 or 4261 is displayed along with code 4607, refer to "Test 10, ABS Solenoid Valve Faulty (Codes 4226, 4231, 4236, 4241, 4246, 4251, 4256 & 4261)."
2. Check control module ground circuits. If ground circuits are satisfactory, proceed to step 3. If ground circuits are not satisfactory, repair as necessary.

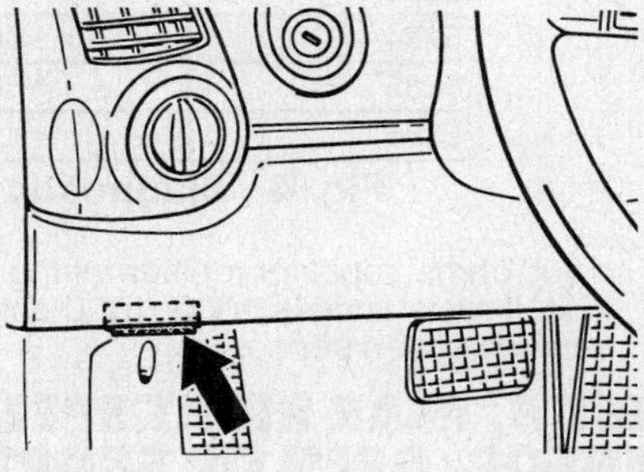

PR4029700018000X

Fig. 3 DLC connector

3. Check for battery voltage at pin Nos. 17 and 18 of the control module connector. If battery voltage is present, replace control module/hydraulic unit. If battery voltage is not present, repair circuit as necessary.

TEST 2, FRONT LEFT SPEED SENSOR/SIGNAL IMPLAUSIBLE (CODE 4206)

1. With Porsche Tester 2, or equivalent, scan tool connected to DLC, drive vehicle at 1–2 mph.
2. Activate tester "Actual Values" menu and compare speed sensor readings from speed sensors.
3. If speed sensor readings are all within. 62 mph, sensor readings are satisfactory, check for intermittent problem. If speed sensor readings are not within. 62 mph, proceed as follows:
   a. Check speed sensor for damage and correct installation, repair or replace as necessary.
   b. Check pulse wheel for damage or corrosion, replace as necessary.
   c. Check for wheel bearing damage, replace as necessary.
   d. Check speed sensor to control module wiring circuit for open or short circuit.
   e. If all related parts and wiring circuits are satisfactory, replace speed sensor.

TEST 3, FRONT RIGHT SPEED SENSOR/SIGNAL IMPLAUSIBLE (CODE 4201)

Refer to "Test 2, Front Left Speed Sensor/Signal Implausible (Code 4206)" for speed sensor diagnosis, Substitute "Front Right Speed Sensor" for "Front Left Speed Sensor" while performing test procedure.

TEST 4, REAR RIGHT SPEED SENSOR/SIGNAL IMPLAUSIBLE (CODE 4211)

Refer to "Test 2, Front Left Speed Sensor/Signal Implausible (Code 4206)" for speed sensor diagnosis, Substitute "Rear Right Speed Sensor" for "Front Left Speed Sensor" while performing test procedure.

TEST 5, REAR LEFT SPEED SENSOR/SIGNAL IMPLAUSIBLE (CODE 4216)

Refer to "Test 2, Front Left Speed Sensor/Signal Implausible (Code 4206)" for speed sensor diagnosis, Substitute "Rear Left Speed Sensor" for "Front Left Speed Sensor" while performing test procedure.

TEST 6, FRONT LEFT SPEED SENSOR/OPEN OR SHORT CIRCUIT (CODE 4205)

1. Disconnect speed sensor electrical connector and check connector for damage. If connector is satisfactory, proceed to step 2. If connector is not satisfactory, repair or replace as necessary.
2. Connect speed sensor connector, then with Porsche Tester 2, or equivalent, scan tool connected to DLC, turn front left wheel and check for signal.
3. If there is no speed signal detected, proceed to next step. If a signal is detected, check for an intermittent condition (loose connection or sensor) that may be causing this code.
4. Check wiring circuit between control module and speed sensor. If wiring circuit is satisfactory, proceed to next step. If wiring circuit is not satisfactory, repair or replace as necessary.
5. Disconnect control module electrical connector, then measure resistance between control module connector pin Nos. 6 and 7. If resistance is not 1600–1800 ohms, repair or replace wiring circuit. If resistance is 1600–1800 ohms, replace speed sensor.

TEST 7, FRONT RIGHT SPEED SENSOR/OPEN OR SHORT CIRCUIT (CODE 4200)

1. Disconnect speed sensor electrical connector and check connector for damage. If connector is satisfactory, proceed to step 2. If connector is not satisfactory, repair or replace as necessary.
2. Connect speed sensor connector, then with Porsche Tester 2, or equivalent, scan tool connected to DLC, turn front right wheel and check for signal.
3. If there is no speed signal detected, proceed to next step. If a signal is detected, check for an intermittent condition (loose connection or sensor) that may be causing this code.
4. Check wiring circuit between control module and speed sensor. If wiring circuit is satisfactory, proceed to next step. If wiring circuit is not satisfactory, repair or replace as necessary.
5. Disconnect control module electrical connector, then measure resistance between control module connector pin Nos. 4 and 5. If resistance is not 1600–1800 ohms, repair or replace wiring circuit. If resistance is 1600–1800 ohms, replace speed sensor.

Code	Description
4200	Front Right Speed Sensor Circuit (Open Or Short)
4201	Front Right Speed Sensor (Signal Implausible)
4205	Front Left Speed Sensor Circuit (Open Or Short)
4206	Front Left Speed Sensor (Signal Implausible)
4210	Rear Right Speed Sensor Circuit (Open Or Short)
4211	Rear Right Speed Sensor (Signal Implausible)
4215	Rear Left Speed Sensor Circuit (Open Or Short)
4216	Rear Left Speed Sensor (Signal Implausible)
4225	Wrong Gear Wheel
4226	Control Module Faulty
4231	Control Module Faulty
4236	Control Module Faulty
4241	Control Module Faulty
4246	Control Module Faulty
4251	Control Module Faulty
4256	Control Module Faulty
4261	Control Module Faulty
4266	Return Pump Fault
4276	Valve Supply Voltage
4340	Stop Lamp Switch
4607	Control Module Faulty
4802	Under Voltage
5260	Intake Valve
5265	Switch-Over Valve
5281	Version Coding
5282	ABS/TC To Transmission Control Circuit
5283	Engine RPM Information Missing
5284	ABS/TC To DME Control Unit Circuit
5285	ABS/TC To DME Control Unit Circuit
5286	DME Control Module

Fig. 4 Diagnostic trouble code interpretation

TEST 8, REAR RIGHT SPEED SENSOR/OPEN OR SHORT CIRCUIT (CODE 4210)

1. Disconnect speed sensor electrical connector and check connector for damage. If connector is satisfactory, proceed to step 2. If connector is not satisfactory, repair or replace as necessary.
2. Connect speed sensor connector, then with Porsche Tester 2, or equivalent, scan tool connected to DLC, turn rear right wheel and check for signal.
3. If there is no speed signal detected, proceed to next step. If a signal is detected, check for an intermittent condition (loose connection or sensor) that may be causing this code.
4. Check wiring circuit between control module and speed sensor. If wiring circuit is satisfactory, proceed to next step. If wiring circuit is not satisfactory, repair or replace as necessary.
5. Disconnect control module electrical connector, then measure resistance between control module connector pin Nos. 1 and 2. If resistance is not 1600–1800 ohms, repair or replace wiring circuit. If resistance is 1600–1800 ohms, replace speed sensor.

TEST 9, REAR LEFT SPEED SENSOR/OPEN OR SHORT CIRCUIT (CODE 4215)

1. Disconnect speed sensor electrical connector and check connector for damage. If connector is satisfactory, proceed to step 2. If connector is not satisfactory, repair or replace as necessary.
2. Connect speed sensor connector, then with Porsche Tester 2, or equivalent, scan tool connected to DLC, turn rear left wheel and check for signal.
3. If there is no speed signal detected, proceed to next step. If a signal is detected, check for an intermittent condition (loose connection or sensor) that may be causing this code.
4. Check wiring circuit between control module and speed sensor. If wiring circuit is satisfactory, proceed to next step. If wiring circuit is not satisfactory, repair or replace as necessary.
5. Disconnect control module electrical connector, then measure resistance between control module connector pin Nos. 8 and 9. If resistance is not 1600–1800 ohms, repair or replace wiring circuit. If resistance is 1600–1800 ohms, replace speed sensor.

1800 ohms, repair or replace wiring circuit. If resistance is 1600–1800 ohms, replace speed sensor.

TEST 10, ABS SOLENOID VALVE FAULTY (CODES 4226, 4231, 4236, 4241, 4246, 4251, 4256 & 4261)

1. Disconnect control module connector and check control unit ground connections for continuity to ground. If ground circuits are satisfactory, proceed to step 2. If ground circuits are not satisfactory, repair or replace as necessary.
2. Check for battery voltage at connector pin Nos. 17 and 18. If battery voltage is present, proceed to step 3. If battery voltage is not present, repair or replace voltage circuit as necessary.
3. Connect Porsche Tester 2, or equivalent, to DLC, then operate solenoid valve(s) with scan tool. Wheel should alternately lockup and rotate freely. If valve operates as specified, check for an intermittent problem. If valve fails to operate as specified, proceed as follows:
   a. Check wiring circuit between solenoid valve and control unit, repair or replace as necessary.
   b. If different solenoid operates then one being tested, check for crossed hydraulic lines, repair as necessary.
   c. If wiring circuit and hydraulic lines are satisfactory, replace control module/hydraulic unit.

TEST 11, VALVE SUPPLY VOLTAGE (CODE 4276)

1. Connect Porsche Tester 2, or equivalent, scan tool to DLC connector.
2. Follow scan tool instructions and observe valve relay operation.
3. If scan tool indicates "Valve relay picked up," check for an intermittent problem. If scan tool does not indicate "Valve relay picked up," proceed as follows:
   a. Check control unit ground circuits, repair or replace as necessary.
   b. Check for battery voltage at pin Nos. 17 and 18 of the control module connector. If battery voltage is present, replace control module/hydraulic unit. If battery voltage is not present, repair circuit as necessary.

TEST 12, RETURN PUMP FAULT (CODE 4266)

1. Connect Porsche Tester 2, or equivalent, scan tool to DLC connector.
2. Follow scan tool instructions to activate return pump. If pump runs, check for an intermittent problem. If pump does run, proceed as follows:
   a. Check control unit ground circuits, repair or replace as necessary.
   b. Check for battery voltage at pin

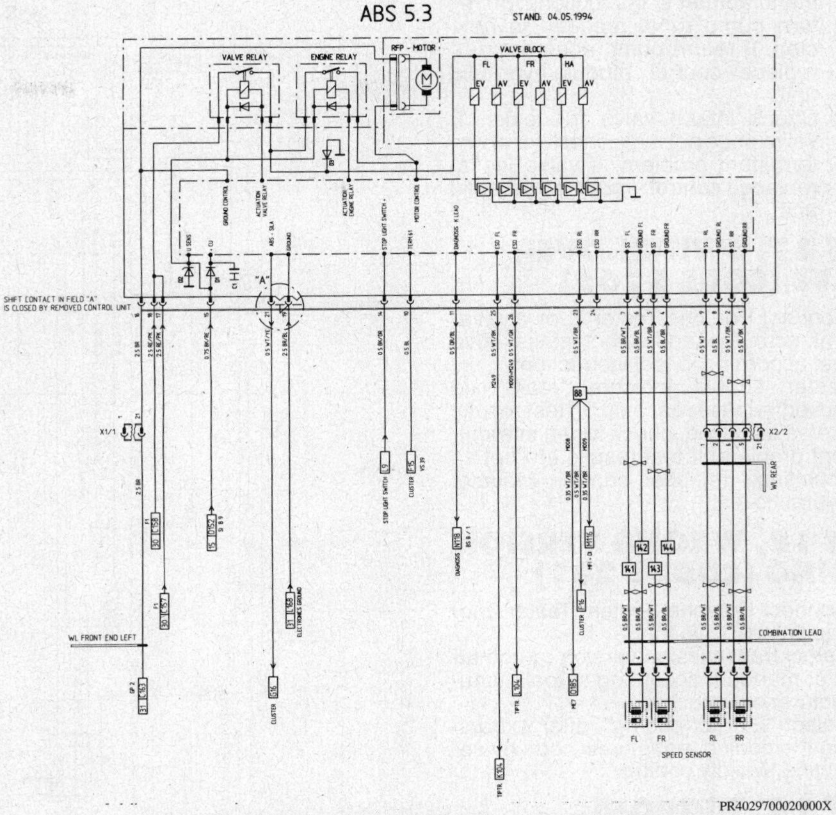

Fig. 5 ABS 5.3 wiring circuit. Boxster

Nos. 17 and 18 of the control module connector. If battery voltage is present, replace control module/hydraulic unit. If battery voltage is not present, repair circuit as necessary.

TEST 13, STOP LAMP SWITCH (CODE 4340)

1. Connect Porsche Tester 2, or equivalent, scan tool to DLC connector.
2. Follow scan tool instructions and observe stop lamp switch operation.
3. While pressing on brake pedal scan tool should indicate switch "actuated" and "not actuated." If switch operates as specified, check for an intermittent problem. If switch does operate as specified, proceed as follows:
   a. Disconnect stop lamp switch electrical connector.
   b. Apply battery voltage to switch and check switch operation. If switch operates, check wiring circuit between switch and control unit. If switch does not operate, replace switch.

TEST 14, WRONG GEAR WHEEL (CODE 4225)

1. Check ABS gear wheels (clamping pins on front axle and pulse strip on rear axle) for dirt or damage. Clean or replace as necessary.
2. Check wheel and tire sizes, extreme differences is size could cause this code.

TEST 15, CONTROL MODULE/HYDRAULIC UNIT VOLTAGE TOO LOW (CODE 4802)

1. Check vehicle battery for proper charge.
2. Disconnect control module/hydraulic unit electrical connector.
3. Measure voltage between pin Nos. 15 and 19. If battery voltage is present, check for intermittent problem. If battery voltage is not present, check wiring circuit and system grounds, repair or replace as necessary.

TEST 16, INTAKE VALVE (CODE 5260)

1. Connect Porsche Tester 2, or equivalent, scan tool and select intake valve test according to tool instructions.
2. Tester should indicate "rear axle locked/rear axle still locked/release rear axle." If test results are as specified, check for an intermittent problem. If test results are not as specified, check the following:
   a. Ensure hydraulic circuit is properly bled.
   b. Check pump operation by selecting "return pump" according to tool

manufacturer's instructions. If return pump runs, proceed to next step. If return pump does not run, replace control module/hydraulic unit.

c. Check intake valve for leaks. If valve does not leak, check for an intermittent problem. If valve leaks, replace control module/hydraulic unit.

TEST 17, SWITCH-OVER VALVE (CODE 5265)

1. Connect Porsche Tester 2, or equivalent, scan tool and select intake valve test according to tool instructions.
2. Tester should indicate "rear axle locked/release rear axle." If test results are as specified, check for an intermittent problem. If test results are not as specified, replace control module/hydraulic unit.

TEST 18, WRONG VERSION CODING (CODE 5281)

1. Connect Porsche System Tester 2, or equivalent, scan tool.
2. Select transmission version (automatic or manual), according to tool manufacturer's instructions.
3. Select "Extract coding", after extracting the coding, adapt new code by selecting "Modify coding."

TEST 19, TIPTRONIC CONTROL MODULE DOES NOT RECEIVE SIGNAL FROM ABS/TC CONTROL MODULE (CODE 5282)

1. Check wiring circuit between pin No. 28 of ABS control module and pin No. 19 of Tiptronic (transmission) control module for open or short.
2. If wiring circuit is satisfactory, check for an intermittent problem. If wiring circuit is not satisfactory, repair or replace as necessary.

TEST 20, ENGINE RPM INFORMATION MISSING (CODE 5283)

1. Connect Porsche System Tester 2, or equivalent, scan tool.
2. Check RPM signal at control module/hydraulic unit according to tool manufacturer's instructions. If there is no signal present, proceed to next step. If signal is present, check for an intermittent problem.
3. Check RPM signal at DME control module unit according to tool manufacturer's instructions. If signal is not present, proceed to next step. If signal is present, repair or replace wiring circuit between DME control module and ABS control module/hydraulic unit.
4. Check RPM sensor to DME control module wiring circuit and connector, repair or replace as necessary. If wiring circuit is satisfactory, replace RPM sensor.

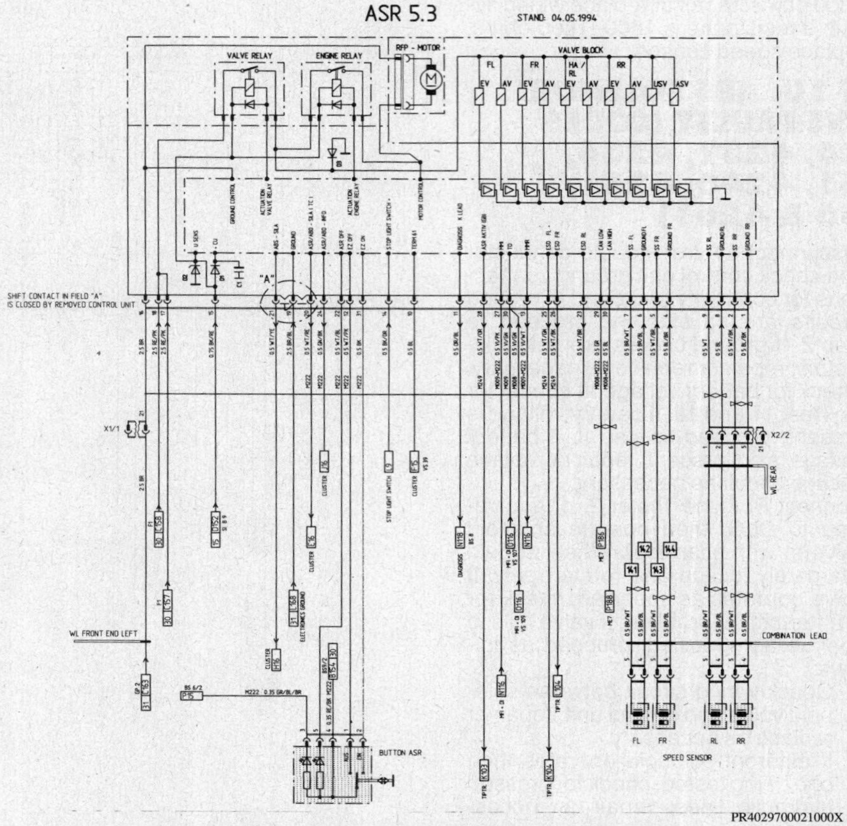

Fig. 6 ABS/TC 5.3 wiring circuit. Boxster

TEST 21, ABS/TC CONTROL MODULE DOES NOT RECEIVE SIGNAL FROM DME CONTROL MODULE (CODE 5284)

1. Check wiring circuit between pin No. 27 of ABS control module and pin No. 29 of DME control module for open or short.
2. If wiring circuit is satisfactory, check for an intermittent problem. If wiring circuit is not satisfactory, repair or replace as necessary.

TEST 22, ABS/TC CONTROL MODULE DOES NOT RECEIVE SIGNAL FROM DME CONTROL MODULE (CODE 5285)

1. Check wiring circuit between pin No. 13 of ABS control module and pin No. 48 of DME control module for open or short.
2. If wiring circuit is satisfactory, check for an intermittent problem. If wiring circuit is not satisfactory, repair or replace as necessary.

TEST 23, FAULT STORED IN DME CONTROL MODULE (CODE 5286)

Diagnose DME control module using Porsche System Tester 2, or equivalent.

Intermittents

Intermittent problems are usually caused by loose or damaged electrical connectors and wiring. To properly diagnose an intermittent condition, visually check entire wiring circuit and electrical connectors related to the condition. Physically moving the wiring circuit and connectors related to the problem can sometimes help recreate an intermittent condition.

Clearing Diagnostic Trouble Codes

Connect Porsche System Tester 2, or equivalent, scan tool to the Diagnostic Link Connector (DLC), then follow scan tool instructions to clear ABS diagnostic codes.

SYSTEM SERVICE

Brake System Bleed

Refer to "Hydraulic Brake System" for bleeding procedure.

Component Replacement

Refer to **Figs. 10 and 11** for component location.

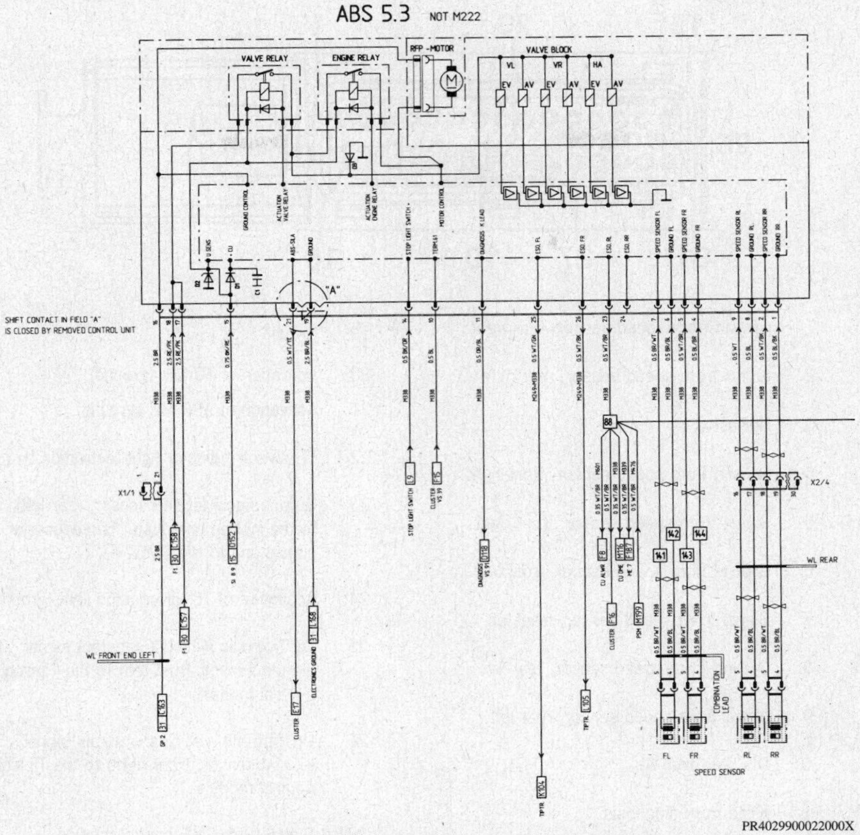

Fig. 7 ABS 5.3 wiring circuit. 911

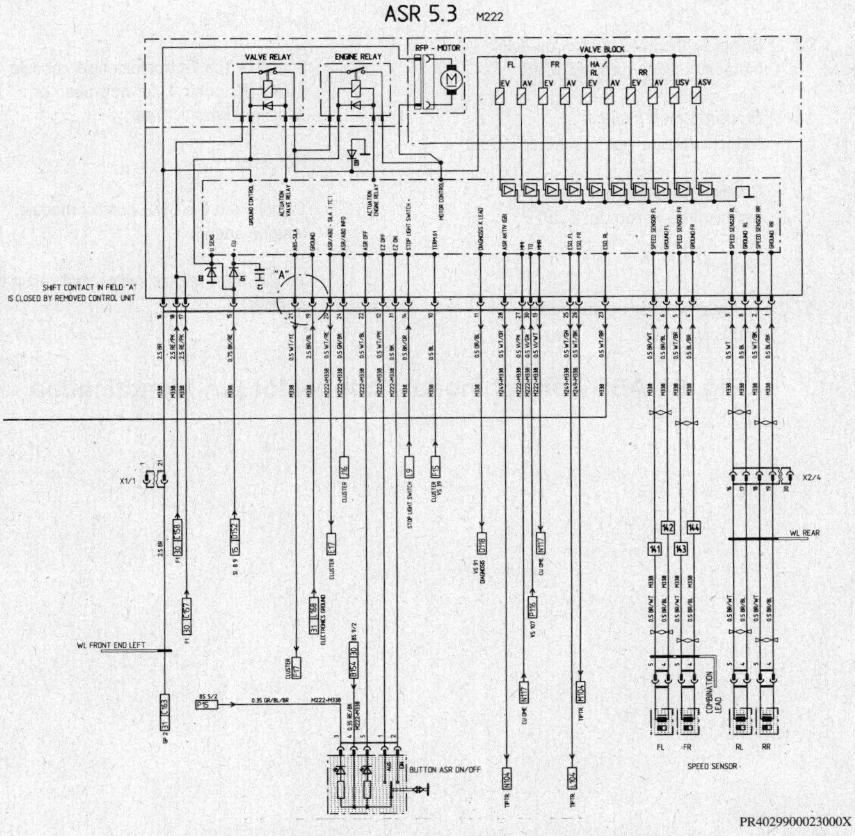

Fig. 8 ABS/TC 5.3 wiring circuit. 911

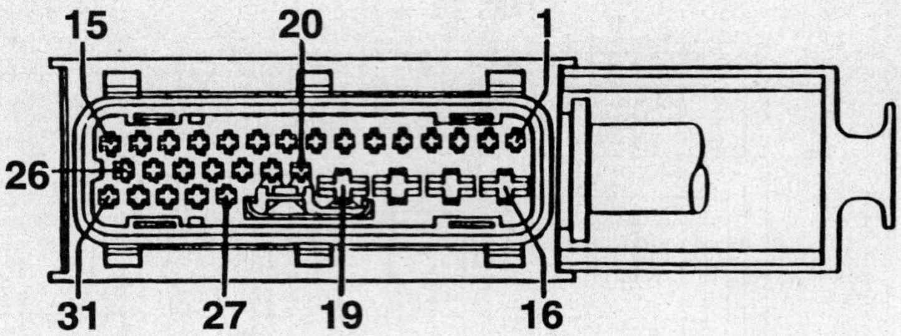

1 Ground from speed sensor, rear right

2 Signal from speed sensor, rear right

3 Not used

4 Ground from speed sensor, front right

5 Signal from speed sensor, front right

6 Ground from speed sensor, front left

7 Signal from speed sensor, front left

8 Ground from speed sensor, rear left

9 Signal from speed sensor, rear left

10 D +, terminal 61

11 K-line from diagnosis

12 TC OFF from rocker switch (activation by positive)

13 Signal to the DME control module (setpoint engine torque / MMR)

14 Stop-light switch signal (vehicle voltage when brake actuated)

15 Control module power supply (terminal 15 / from fuse B9)

16 Ground

17/18 Voltage for return pump relay and valve relay

19 Ground

20 Activation of TC MIL (ground)

21 Activation of ABS MIL (ground)

22 TC switch indicator light (activation by ground)

23 Output signal (speed sensor, rear left) to the instrument cluster (speedometer signal) and to the DME

24 Activation of TC information light (ground)

25 On Tiptronic vehicles = output signal (speed sensor, front left) **to** the Tiptronic control module

26 On Tiptronic vehicles = output signal (speed sensor, front right) **to** the Tiptronic control module

27* Signal from DME control module (actual engine

torque / MMI)

28* Signal **to** the Tiptronic-control module during TC control, for activation of a specific Tiptronic map

29 Not used

30* Signal from the DME control module (engine speed)

31* TC ON from rocker switch (activation by positive)

PR4029700024000X

Fig. 9 ABS control module connector pin identification

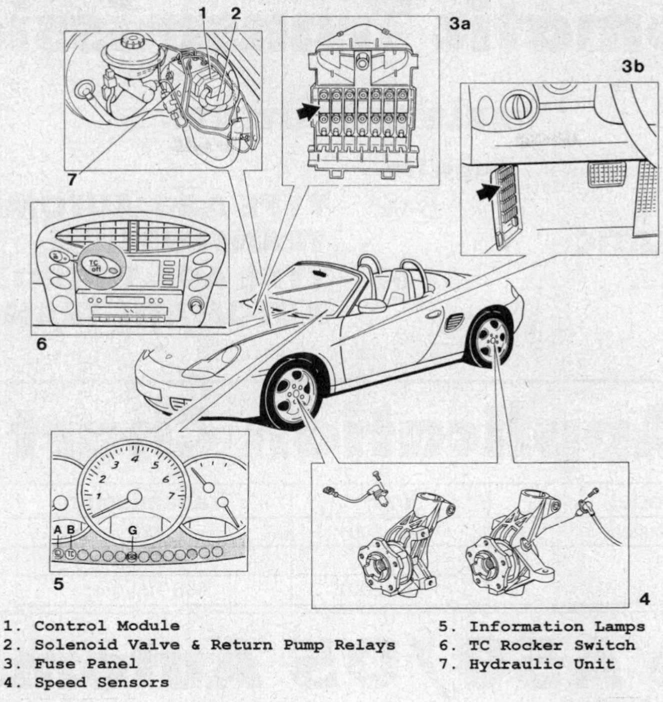

1. Control Module
2. Solenoid Valve & Return Pump Relays
3. Fuse Panel
4. Speed Sensors
5. Information Lamps
6. TC Rocker Switch
7. Hydraulic Unit

Fig. 10 ABS & ABS/TC component locations. Boxster

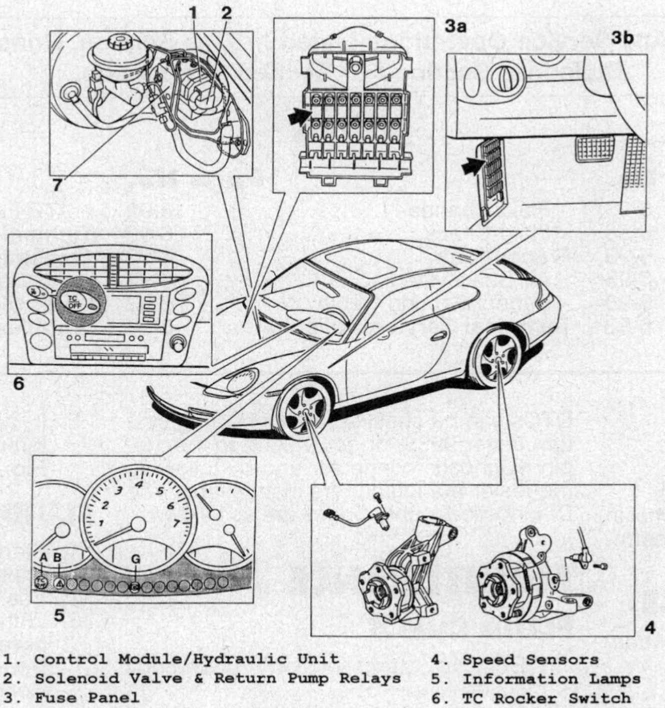

1. Control Module/Hydraulic Unit
2. Solenoid Valve & Return Pump Relays
3. Fuse Panel
4. Speed Sensors
5. Information Lamps
6. TC Rocker Switch

Fig. 11 ABS & ABS/TC component locations. 911

Automatic Transmissions

TABLE OF CONTENTS

	Page No.
APPLICATION CHART	6-92
TYPE A50/05 AUTOMATIC TRANSMISSION	6-92
TYPE A86 AUTOMATIC TRANSMISSION	6-102
TYPE A96 TIPTRONIC AUTOMATIC TRANSMISSION	6-95

Application Chart

Model	Year	Transmission
Boxster	1998–2001	A86
911	1998	A50/05
	1999–2001	A96 Tiptronic

Type A50/05 Automatic Transmission

NOTE: Prior To Performing Any Service Operations Listed In This Section, Consult The "Technical Service Bulletins" Section For Related Information.

INDEX

	Page No.
Adjustments	6-93
Selector Cable	6-93
In-Vehicle Repairs	6-93
Hydraulic Control Unit, Replace	6-93
Position Switch, Replace	6-93
Maintenance	6-92
Fluid Change	6-92
Fluid Check	6-92
Precautions	6-92
Air Bag Systems	6-92
Battery Ground Cable	6-92
Technical Service Bulletins	6-93
ATF Flow Noises	6-93
Tightening Specifications	6-94
Transmission, Replace	6-93
Installation	6-93
Removal	6-93
Troubleshooting	6-92

PRECAUTIONS

AIR BAG SYSTEMS

Refer to "Air Bag System Precautions" in the front of this manual for system disarming and arming procedures.

BATTERY GROUND CABLE

Prior to service, disconnect battery ground cable and isolate as required.

TROUBLESHOOTING

The Tiptronic A50/05 automatic transmission is electronically controlled and equipped with a diagnosis system. Detected faults in monitored components are stored in the control unit memory. The control unit will evaluate the information and differentiate between 26 Diagnostic Trouble Codes (DTC), **Fig. 1.** These detected DTCs can be checked by connecting system tester 9288, or equivalent, to the 19–pin diagnostic connector and by following the tester manufacturers instructions. The Diagnostic Trouble Codes are as follows:

MAINTENANCE

FLUID CHECK

1. Remove transmission underbody cover.
2. Operate vehicle until transmission fluid temperature is approximately 176°F.
3. With vehicle on a level surface, place transmission selector lever in Park and apply parking brake. Engine should be operating at idle speed.
4. Transmission fluid level should be between 176°F Min. and Max. markings on transmission fluid level indicator, **Fig. 2**
5. If necessary, add Dexron IID ATF through transmission quick fill device, **Fig. 3.**

FLUID CHANGE

1. Start engine, allow to reach normal operating temperature.
2. Position vehicle on level surface.
3. With engine Off, raise and support vehicle.
4. Remove drain screw from transmission and allow fluid to drain.
5. Remove transmission oil pan, then the strainer using a Torx T 27 bit.
6. Clean oil pan and strainer.
7. Position strainer on transmission with new O-ring and install.
8. Place two magnets into pan grooves, position transmission oil pan to case with new seal and install.
9. Fill transmission with Dexron IID type ATF, through quick fill device to 86°F

Code	Fault
1	Control Unit Voltage
2	Drive Links Voltage
3	Sensors Voltage
4	DME Control Unit Speed Signal
5	DME Control Unit Load Signal
6	Throttle Plate Potentiometer
7	Change Of Dwell Angle
8	Solenoid Valve 1
9	Solenoid Valve 2
10	Torque Converter Clutch Solenoid Valve
11	Pressure Regulator
12	Transaxle Selector Switch
13	Speed Sensor
14	Transaxle Temperature Sensor
15	Transaxle Selector Switch
16	Faulty Control Unit
17	Faulty Control Unit
18	Faulty Control Unit
19	Downshift Fault
20	Rev. Limiter
21	Manual Program Switch
22	Tip Switch, Up And/Or Downshifting
23	Kickdown Switch
24	Transverse Accel. Sensor
25	Speed Signal 1, ABS Control Unit
26	Oil Cooler Blower Relay

Fig. 1 Diagnostic Trouble Codes

level, **Figs. 2 and 3.**

10. Start engine and check fluid as described under "Fluid Check."

ADJUSTMENTS

SELECTOR CABLE

1. Place transmission selector lever in 1 position.
2. Position multi-function switch operating lever to 1 position.
3. Push cable forward and adjust cable fork by aligning holes on cable fork head with holes in operating lever, **Fig. 4.** After aligning cable fork and operating lever holes, thread cable fork an additional two turns onto cable threads.
4. Ensure adjustment by shifting transmission through all ranges.

IN-VEHICLE REPAIRS

POSITION SWITCH, REPLACE

1. Set parking brake and place transmission selector lever in Neutral position.
2. Remove transmission underbody cover.
3. Disconnect transmission selector cable from selector lever, **Fig. 4.**
4. Remove nut and washer, then the selector lever from shaft.
5. Unlatch switch electrical connector holder and disconnect switch electrical connector.
6. Remove attaching screws and switch.
7. Reverse procedure to install. After completing installation, check selector cable adjustment, as describer under "Selector Cable, Adjust."

HYDRAULIC CONTROL UNIT, REPLACE

1. Remove transmission underbody cover.
2. Remove transmission oil pan drain screw and allow transmission fluid to drain.
3. Remove transmission oil pan and using a Torx T27 bit, remove the transmission oil strainer.
4. Remove speed sensor holder and sensor, then the sensor wiring harness from retainers.
5. Remove hydraulic control unit retaining screws using a Torx T27 bit. Note location of retaining screws, as screw lengths of 2.559, 3.150 and 4.528 inches are used.
6. Remove control unit from transmission, using care not to place tension on wiring harness.
7. Tag wiring harness push on sleeves prior to disconnecting from solenoids. Disconnect push on sleeves from solenoid valves.
8. Remove wiring harness from retaining clamps, then the valve body from vehicle.
9. Reverse procedure to install noting the following:
   a. Ensure wiring harness push on sleeves are properly seated on solenoid valves.
   b. When mounting hydraulic control

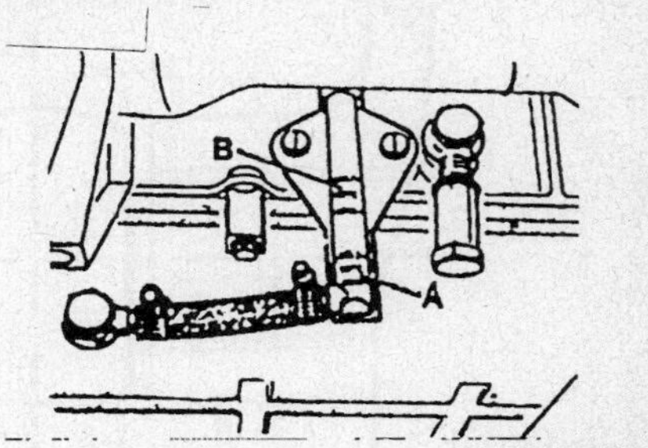

Fig. 2 Transmission fluid level indicator, A: Fluid level range at 86°F. B: Fluid level range at 176°F

   unit, ensure pin of notched disc projects into recess of selector slide.
   c. Use care to install hydraulic control unit retaining screws in same locations as removed.
   d. Position control unit by placing notched disc to position 1 (1st gear) and push control unit back unit it rests against notched disc.

TRANSMISSION

REPLACE

REMOVAL

1. Remove engine/transmission assembly as outlined under "3.6L Engine."
2. Remove starter and reverse lamp switch wires.
3. Remove M6X16 bolt, bracket and mount cover.
4. Pull out release shaft using M6X40 bolt.
5. Remove mounting nuts and separate transmission from engine.

INSTALLATION

1. For corrosion protection, apply very thin coat of Olista Longtime 3 EP, or equivalent, to input shaft splines.
2. Engage release fork in release bearing and secure with suitable adhesive tape.
3. Connect transmission to engine.
4. Engage release shaft with seals into release fork and remove locating tape.
5. Fit needle-roller bearing, mount cover and bracket.
6. Tighten bolt to specifications.

TECHNICAL SERVICE BULLETINS

ATF FLOW NOISES

911 w/Tiptronic Transmission

On these models there may be automatic transmission fluid noises in cold conditions or when driving a scraping noise may be heard. To correct this condition, proceed as follows:

1. Increase ATF level in transmission by .590 inch at 176°F.
2. Increase clearance of ATF lines near transmission to at least .787 inch by bending line outward.

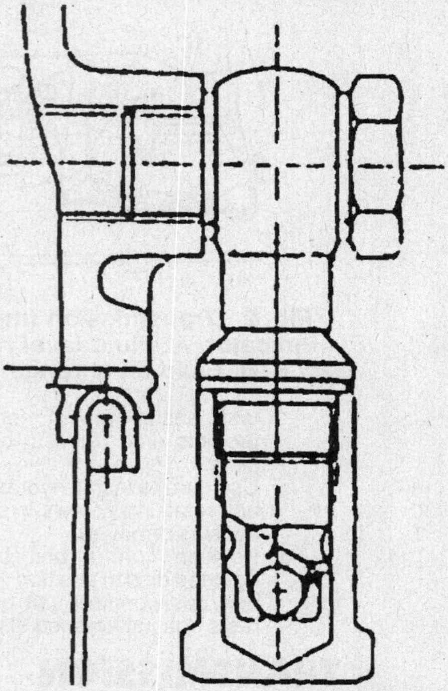

Fig. 3 Transmission quick fill device

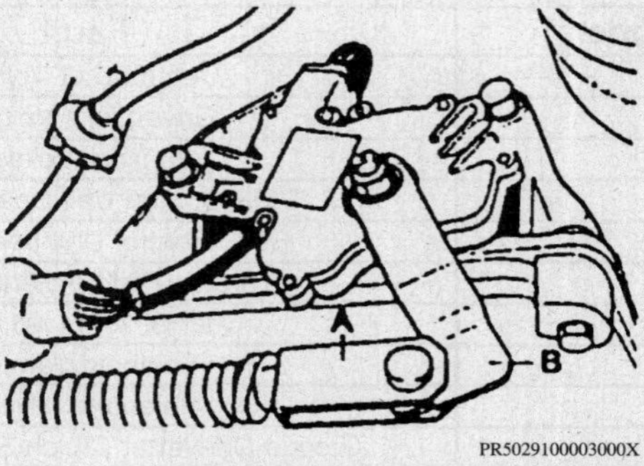

Fig. 4 Selector cable & actuating lever, A: Cable fork. B: Actuating lever

TIGHTENING SPECIFICATIONS

Year	Component	Torque, Ft. Lbs.
1998–2001	Actuator Shaft	11
	Control Unit	72①
	Oil Level Pipe	29
	Oil Pan	48①
	Plug	29
	Position Switch	84①
	Strainer	72①

① — Inch lbs.

Type A96 Tiptronic Automatic Transmission

NOTE: On Air Bag Equipped Models, Refer To "Air Bag System Precautions" Located In The Front Of This Manual For System Disarming & Arming Procedures.

NOTE: Refer To "Computer Relearn Procedures" Located In The Front Of This Manual When Battery Power To The Computer Has Been Interrupted.

INDEX

	Page No.
Adjustments	6-96
Selector Lever Cable	6-96
Description	6-95
In-Vehicle Service	6-96
ATF Cooler, Replace	6-96
ATF Filter, Replace	6-96
Differential, Replace	6-96
Final Drive/Transmission Housing Double Sealing Ring, Replace	6-96
Hydraulic Control Unit, Replace	6-97
Inner Oil Tube, Replace	6-97
Input Speed Sensor, Replace	6-97
Long Flanged Shaft Sealing Ring, Replace	6-97
Long Flanged Shaft, Replace	6-97
Multi-Function Switch, Replace	6-97
Selector Knob, Replace	6-98
Selector Lever Cable, Replace	6-98
Selector Lever Support, Replace	6-98
Selector Shaft Sealing Ring, Replace	6-99
Shiftlock Solenoid, Replace	6-99
Short Flanged Shaft Sealing Ring, Replace	6-98
Transmission Speed Sensor, Replace	6-99
Wiring Harness, Replace	6-99
Maintenance	6-95
Final Drive Oil Change	6-96
Fluid Change	6-95
Fluid Check	6-95
Tightening Specifications	6-101
Transmission Identification	6-95
Transmission, Replace	6-99

TRANSMISSION IDENTIFICATION

The manufacturers code and transmission number are located on the lefthand side of transmission, on the attached tag, **Fig. 1.**

DESCRIPTION

The Tiptronic automatic transmission, **Fig. 2,** is a fully automatic 5 speed transmission. This transmission allows the driver the choice of allowing the transmission to shift through the gears automatically or manually shifting up and down with the steering wheel mounted switches.

The transmission has five forward gears with closer gear spacing than previous transmissions. Fourth gear is a direct 1:1 drive while fifth is an overdrive for reduced fuel consumption and noise while cruising. Leaving the selector in "D" allows the transmission to operate like other automatic transmissions, while moving the lever to "M" allows steering mounted switches to control upshifts and downshifts according to driving style and conditions.

When left in the fully automatic drive setting, the transmission bases it's gear changes on input from the throttle potentiometer, ABS wheel sensors, flywheel speed sensor and the ECU.

MAINTENANCE

FLUID CHANGE

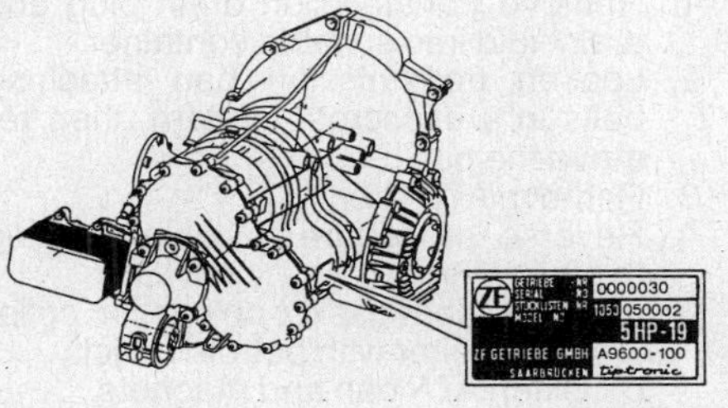

PR5029900007000X

Fig. 1 Transmission identification

1. Remove ATF drain plug, **Fig. 3,** and drain fluid into suitable container.
2. Replace sealing ring for drain plug and tighten plug to specification.
3. Remove ATF filler screw, **Fig. 3,** and fill with ATF until surplus fluid escapes at hole of ATF filler screw.
4. Move selector lever to "P" and allow engine to idle.
5. With engine running, add ATF again until excess emerges from bore of ATF filler screw.
6. With brake pedal pressed, move gear selector through all lever positions, remaining in each position for approximately 10 seconds.
7. Check ATF level again and add fluid if necessary.

FLUID CHECK

1. To properly check fluid level the following conditions must be met:
   a. Transmission must not be in reduced driving program.
   b. ATF temperature must be between 30–45°C.
   c. Selector lever in "P" position and engine idling.
   d. Air conditioning and heater must be switched Off.
   e. Vehicle must be parked on level ground.
2. Attach filled ATF container tool No. V.A.G. 1924, or equivalent, as high up on the vehicle as possible.
3. Place a suitable drain pan under transmission.
4. Wearing protective goggles, remove ATF filler screw (2), **Fig. 3.** If fluid flows from filler screw hole and if fluid temperature is 86–104°F, fluid level is normal.
5. Install filler screw and tighten to specification.
6. Filler screw must be installed before fluid temperature reaches 45°C.
7. If fluid does not flow from filler screw opening with fluid temperature between 86–104°F, fluid must be added.
8. Add fluid with ATF container tool No.

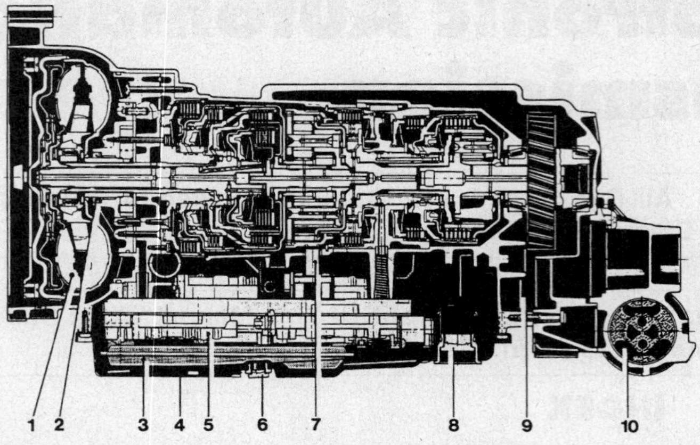

1 – Torque converter
2 – Sealing ring for torque converter
3 – ATF filter
4 – ATF pan
5 – Hydraulic control unit
6 – ATF drain plug
7 – Transmission input speed sensor
8 – ATF filler screw
9 – Gasket for spur gear
10 – Transmission bearing

PR5029900024000X

Fig. 2 Tiptronic A96 Transmission

V.A.G. 1924, or equivalent, until surplus fluid flows from filler hole.

FINAL DRIVE OIL CHANGE

There is no oil drain plug on the final drive assembly.

1. Remove oil filler drain plug, then drain fluid by suction using a suitable hand pump, while fluid is warm.
2. Fill final drive slowly with suitable transmission oil. Refer to "Lubricant Data" for fluid amount and type.
3. Replace sealing ring for oil filler plug and tighten to specification.

ADJUSTMENTS

SELECTOR LEVER CABLE

1. Move selector lever to "P" position.
2. Remove cable from transmission.
3. Slide locking sleeve (1) forward and turn it clockwise to removal position, **Fig. 4.**
4. Check installation dimension of end piece, **Fig. 5.** Dimension must be .46–49 inch.
5. Using a suitable pair of pliers, press end piece onto transmission.
6. Install cable onto selector support and into open adjuster (1), then close adjuster (3). Locking sleeve must move to end position automatically, **Fig. 4.**
7. Select all gears and ensure correct gear is indicated in righthand instrument cluster.
8. Move selector from "D" to "M," ensure movement is straight and selector does not stick.
9. If necessary, minor corrections can be made on the cable end piece.

IN-VEHICLE SERVICE

ATF COOLER, REPLACE

1. Clamp coolant hoses with tool No. 3094, or equivalent.
2. Remove selector lever cable from transmission lever and cooler bracket.
3. Place suitable oil drain pan under transmission.
4. Remove ATF cooler attaching screws with a T30 Torx bit.
5. Reverse procedure to install, noting the following:
   a. Replace toroidal sealing rings.
   b. Check coolant level.
   c. Tighten fasteners to specification.

ATF FILTER, REPLACE

1. Remove transmission drain plug and drain fluid into suitable container.
2. Loosen transmission pan attaching bolts in a crisscross pattern, then remove the pan.
3. Remove ATF filter.
4. Reverse procedure to install, noting the following:
   a. Thinly coat gasket on suction collar of ATF filter with petroleum jelly.
   b. Clean ATF pan and magnets.
   c. Place magnets in seams of ATF pan. Magnets must lie flat over entire surface.
   d. Install new pan seal and tighten screws to specification in a crisscross pattern.
   e. Replace sealing ring on ATF drain plug.

DIFFERENTIAL, REPLACE

1. Remove left rear wheel.
2. Remove diagonal braces and rear axle carrier.
3. Remove left drive shaft from transmission.
4. Remove left stabilizer connecting rod.
5. Place suitable drain pan under transmission.
6. Remove flanged shaft attaching screw, then pull out flange, **Fig. 6.**
7. Remove cover screws, then the cover.
8. Remove tapered roller bearing outer ring and adjusting shim from transmission housing. **Do not lose tapered**

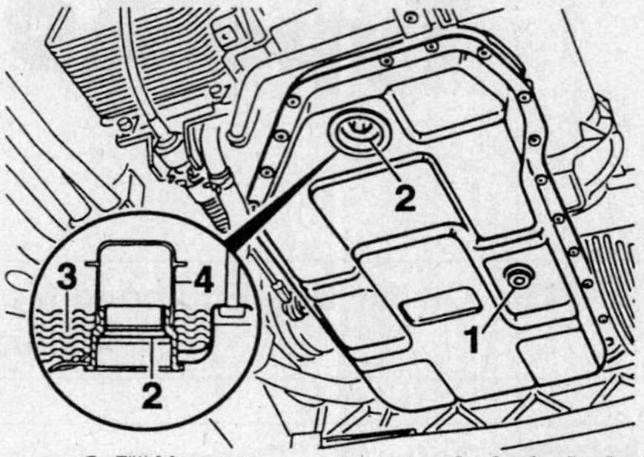

PR5029900008000X

Fig. 3 Oil plugs

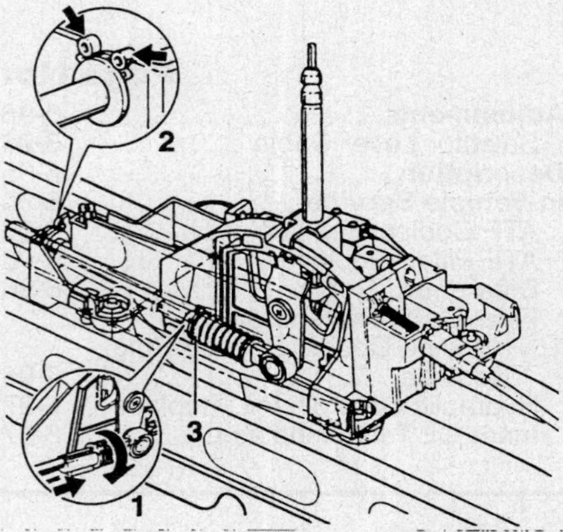

PR5029900009000X

Fig. 4 Selector lever cable removal

roller bearing outer ring and adjusting shim. Adjusting shim is calibrated and cannot be replaced by another shim.

9. Reverse procedure to install, noting the following:
   a. Install new toroidal sealing ring untwisted and coat with transmission oil.
   b. Tighten cover screws in a diagonally opposite sequence and in several steps to specification.
   c. Add transmission oil for final drive.

FINAL DRIVE/ TRANSMISSION HOUSING DOUBLE SEALING RING, REPLACE

A defective double sealing ring allows ATF or transmission oil to escape through the middle vent opening of the shaft seal (between the two sealing lips) into the converter bell housing. A defective double sealing ring can also allow ATF to enter the differential.

1. Remove rear wheels.
2. Remove differential and long flanged shaft.
3. Remove bearing outer race and adjusting shim by hand. **Adjusting shim is calibrated and cannot be exchanged for a different shim.**
4. Carefully pull out gasket with hook tool No. VW 681, or equivalent. **Hook tool must be applied behind the two**

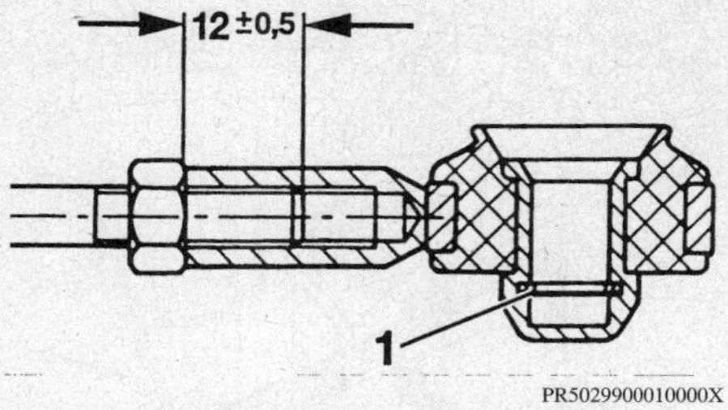

Fig. 5 Selector lever cable dimension

sealing lips of the sealing ring. Do not apply to outer circumference of sealing ring or damage to contact area will occur.

5. Inspect seat of sealing ring in transmission housing for damage.
6. Thinly coat outer circumference and sealing lip of sealing ring with petroleum jelly.
7. Push sealing ring onto tool No. 3383, or equivalent, so that projecting sealing lip faces tool.
8. Drive sealing ring into stop.

HYDRAULIC CONTROL UNIT, REPLACE

1. Remove fluid drain plug and drain fluid into suitable container.
2. Loosen fluid pan attaching screws in a crisscross pattern, then remove fluid pan.
3. Remove filter.
4. Disconnect transmission speed sensor and solenoid valve electrical connectors.
5. Remove hydraulic control unit attaching bolts, **Fig. 7.**
6. Disconnect pressure regulator and transmission input speed sensor electrical connectors from rear of hydraulic control unit, then the cables from housing.
7. Reverse procedure to install, noting the following:
   a. Insert pin of detent disc (1) into groove of selector valve (2), **Fig. 8.**
   b. Tighten hydraulic unit attaching screws to specification, working from inner screws to outer screws.
   c. Thinly coat gasket on suction collar of ATF filter with petroleum jelly.
   d. Replace gasket for ATF pan, clean all four magnets in beads of pan and ensure there is full contact over full area of ATF pan.
   e. Tighten screws of ATF pan to specification, in diagonally opposite sequence in several steps.

INNER OIL TUBE, REPLACE

Defective toroidal sealing rings at the inner oil tube allow fluid to enter the differential. The differential eventually becomes overfilled, and oil exhausts from the differential vent. Removed oil tubes should always be replaced with new components.

1. Remove hydraulic control unit as previously outlined.
2. Pry out oil tube with suitable screwdriver or pry bar.

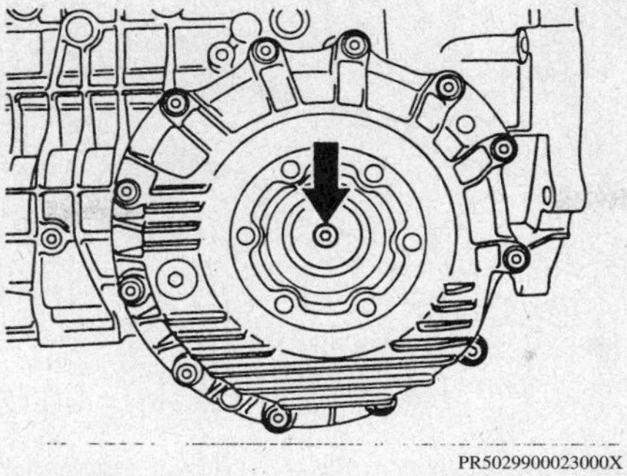

Fig. 6 Flanged shaft removal

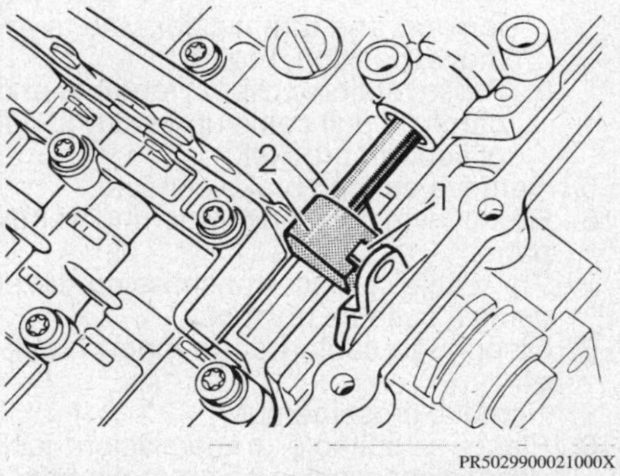

Fig. 8 Hydraulic control valve detent disc

3. Reverse procedure to install, noting the following:
   a. Coat toroidal sealing rings of new oil tube with petroleum jelly.
   b. Insert oil tube into tool No. 3381, or equivalent, and push into transmission housing as far as the stop on the tool will allow. **Do not attempt to install oil tube without using installation tool No. 3381, or equivalent, leakage due to bending of tube may occur.**
   c. Open side of tool should face outer wall of transmission.
   d. **Do not tilt oil tube, drive in both tube ends equally.**

INPUT SPEED SENSOR, REPLACE

1. Remove hydraulic control unit as previously outlined.
2. Remove sensor.
3. Install new sensor with two space sleeves and tighten to specification. **Do not reuse sensors that have been dropped.**

LONG FLANGED SHAFT, REPLACE

1. Remove right rear wheel.
2. Drain rear axle oil. **Suction removal of rear oil prevents rear axle oil from entering the ATF.**
3. Disconnect right drive shaft from transmission.
4. Remove three mounting screws for mounting saddle.
5. Reverse procedure to install, noting the following:
   a. Replace square sealing ring in

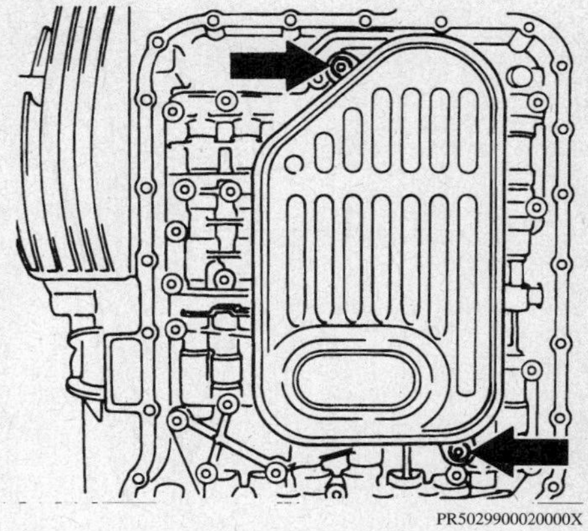

Fig. 7 Hydraulic control unit removal

mounting saddle.

   b. Remove any burrs or sharp edges from flanged shaft.
   c. Carefully insert flange into transmission. Flange shaft must be guided by hand to prevent damage to double sealing ring in transmission.
   d. Refill rear axle oil.

MULTI-FUNCTION SWITCH, REPLACE

1. Unclip, release and disconnect cable connection to multi-function switch.
2. Remove ATF line, drain fluid from line into suitable container.
3. Unscrew fastening screws and pull switch off the selector shaft.
4. Reverse procedure to install, noting the following:
   a. Put multi-function switch on the selector shaft. Flat point on serrations in switch must lie against the flat point on the selector shaft.
   b. Do not force or tilt switch during installation, damage to switch contacts may occur.
   c. Turn switch until fitting bore on switch housing can be put on dowel pin on transmission housing.
   d. Replace seal rings for ATF line, then install the line.
   e. Tighten all fasteners to specification.

LONG FLANGED SHAFT SEALING RING, REPLACE

1. Remove long flanged shaft.
2. Remove snap ring for ball bearing.
3. Press flanged shaft out of mounting saddle.
4. Pry sealing ring out of saddle with a large screwdriver.
5. Install new sealing ring up to stop with tool No. 9615, or equivalent.
6. Press mounting saddle with ball bearing onto flanged shaft.
7. Insert snap ring.
8. Install flanged shaft, check transmission oil in final drive and fill as necessary.

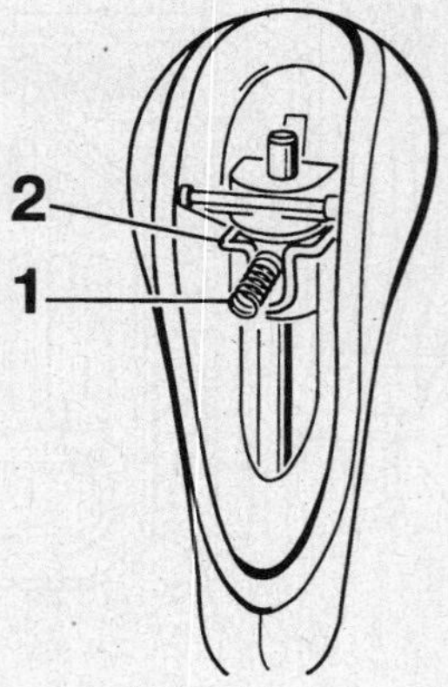

1 – Compression spring
(conical as of 12.10.98)
2 – Spring clip

PR5029900011000X

Fig. 9 Selector knob removal

SHORT FLANGED SHAFT SEALING RING, REPLACE

1. Remove left rear wheel.
2. Disconnect left drive shaft from transmission.
3. Place suitable oil drain pan under transmission.
4. Remove flanged shaft attaching bolt, **Fig. 6.**
5. Pull out flanged shaft.
6. Remove sealing ring with tool No. VW 681, or equivalent.
7. Thinly coat new sealing ring and outer circumference of sealing ring with petroleum jelly.
8. Install sealing ring with tool No. 3384, or equivalent, up to stop ring.
9. Sealing ring must fit in housing at same depth all around.
10. Check transmission oil in final drive and add fluid if necessary.

SELECTOR KNOB, REPLACE

1. Pry off locking button with an angled pry bar or other suitable tool.
2. Turn ignition key to "1" position, press locking button to allow tool to be inserted between shift lever and locking button.
3. Remove compression spring (1) and spring clip (2), then pull off selector knob, **Fig. 9.**
4. Reverse procedure to install.

SELECTOR LEVER CABLE, REPLACE

Use care to ensure selector cable does not become excessively bent or kinked during removal or installation.

Removal

1. Move selector lever to "P" position.
2. Remove selector knob as previously outlined.
3. Remove center console.
4. Disconnect selector lever cable at selector lever support as follows:
   a. Slide locking sleeve of adjuster (1)

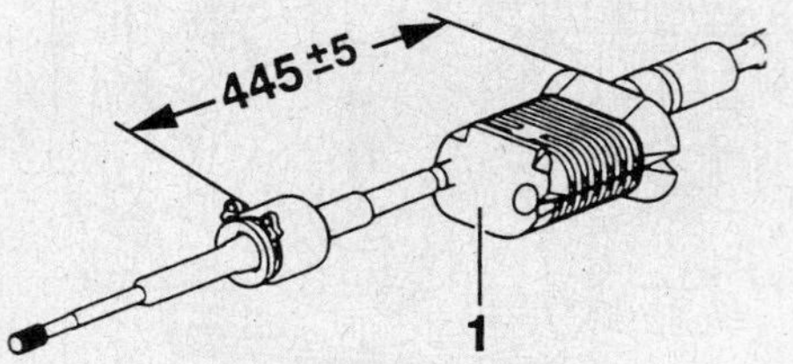

PR5029900014000X

Fig. 10 Rubber sleeve placement

   forward and turn it clockwise to removal position, **Fig. 4.**
   b. Press retaining clip (2) together and carefully pull cable upward and out of support bracket.
5. Remove parking brake console.
6. Remove middle and rear underbody panel.
7. Pry cable off of transmission lever using a suitable pry tool.
8. Disengage cable from support bracket.
9. Remove crossmember.
10. Place a suitable transmission jack under transmission and remove transmission support.
11. From passenger compartment, press rubber sleeve out to rear and pull wire out of slotted sleeve.

Installation

1. Install cable end piece, **Fig. 5.**
2. Position rubber sleeve, **Fig. 10.**
3. Apply a generous coating of suitable lubricant on rubber sleeve and wire in the area of the body opening.
4. Install cable through body opening from behind.
5. Insert wire into slot of rubber sleeve and carefully press sleeve into body opening.
6. Fasten cable into support bracket.
7. Press cable end piece onto transmission lever using a suitable pliers.
8. Install transmission support and cross member.
9. Install parking brake console, then route cable as illustrated, **Fig. 11,** noting that "A" indicates where cable runs next to console, and "B" indicates where cable runs below console.
10. Attach cable to support bracket.
11. Move selector lever to "P" position, then insert cable into open adjuster (1), **Fig. 4,** and close the adjuster.
12. Locking sleeve must move to end position automatically.
13. Check adjustment of selector cable, then adjust parking brake.
14. Install center console and selector knob.
15. Install underbody panels.

SELECTOR LEVER SUPPORT, REPLACE

Removal

1. Remove selector knob as outlined previously.

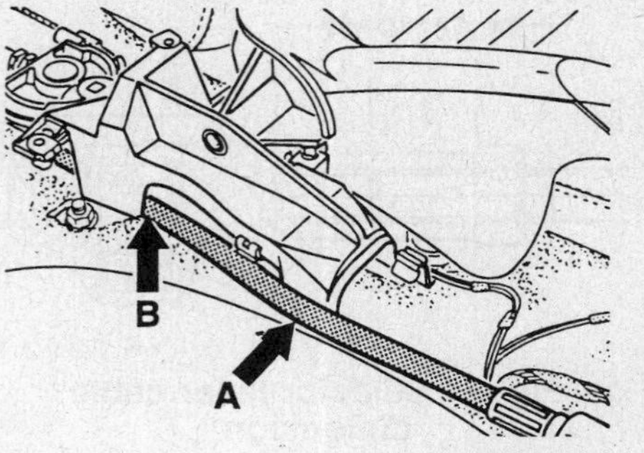

PR5029900015000X

Fig. 11 Selector lever cable routing

2. Remove center console.
3. Move selector lever to "D" position.
4. Open adjuster (3) by pressing unlocking button (7), **Fig. 12.**
5. Press retaining clip (4) together and carefully pull adjuster (3) upward and out of support bracket.
6. Disengage cable nipple (1) from keylock lever (2).
7. Slide locking sleeve of adjuster forward and turn it clockwise to removal position (8).
8. Press retaining clip (10) together and carefully pull cable upward and out of support bracket.
9. Disconnect electrical connector.
10. Remove attaching nuts (11).

Installation

1. Tighten attaching nuts (11) to specification.
2. Press cable into support bracket until retaining clip engages into housing (10).
3. Press cable into open adjuster (8) and close adjuster (9). Locking sleeve must move to end position automatically (9).
4. Turn ignition key to "1" position (ignition On) and move selector lever to "D" position.
5. Open adjuster (3).
6. Engage cable nipple (1) onto keylock lever (2).
7. Press housing for adjuster (3) into support bracket until retaining clip (4) engages.
8. Move selector lever to "P" position and turn ignition key to position "0" (removal position).
9. Press cable sleeve (5) toward selector support.
10. Release cable and press locking button (7) until it engages.
11. Turn ignition key to position "1" (ignition On).
12. Move selector lever from "P" position to "D" position and turn ignition key counterclockwise. Ignition key should not be allowed to turn to the Removal position.
13. Release ignition key again and position selector lever in the "P" position.
14. It should now be possible to move the ignition key to the removal position and locking button must be locked.
15. Fit rotary pusher into correct position

and install center console, **Fig. 13.**

SELECTOR SHAFT SEALING RING, REPLACE

1. Remove multi-function switch console.
2. Disconnect selector lever cable at transmission selector lever.
3. Drive out roll pin until selector lever can be removed from shaft.
4. Pierce sealing ring with small screwdriver and pull out.
5. Apply a thin coat of petroleum jelly to outer circumference and sealing lip of new sealing ring.
6. Using tool No. 3385, or equivalent, drive in sealing ring as far as the mounting face.

SHIFTLOCK SOLENOID, REPLACE

1. Remove center console.
2. Remove selector lever support as previously outlined.
3. Remove cover plate on selector lever support, **Fig. 14.**
4. Pull cable off of manual switch, then unclip holder for electrical connector and remove cable from cable guides.
5. Pull solenoid holding clip far enough away to access solenoid to be removed. Do not overstretch the holding clip.
6. Reverse procedure to install.

TRANSMISSION SPEED SENSOR, REPLACE

1. Remove ATF oil pan.
2. Remove sensor.
3. Install new sensor and tighten to specification.

WIRING HARNESS, REPLACE

The ATF temperature sensor is integrated in the transmission wiring harness. If damaged, the complete transmission wiring harness must be replaced.

1. Disconnect transmission wiring harness electrical connector by turning it counterclockwise, then pulling straight off.
2. Remove retaining clip.
3. Remove hydraulic control unit, then disconnect the wiring harness.
4. Replace sealing rings for socket, coat rings thinly with petroleum jelly and insert wiring harness socket into correct position. Lug "A," must point towards spur gear, **Fig. 15.**
5. Install retaining clip.
6. Connect socket into correct position and lock by turning in a clockwise direction.

TRANSMISSION

REPLACE

1. Raise and support vehicle. Ensure attaching bolts of diagonal braces are accessible.
2. Remove multi-function switch console.
3. Secure crankshaft using tool No. 9595/1 (short), or equivalent. Turn crankshaft until one of the bores U4, U5 or U6 in pulley is aligned with centering bore in crankcase, then insert tool.
4. Hold torque converter in position using tool No. 9595/1 (long), or equivalent.
5. Install tool No. 9596, or equivalent, then two of six converter attaching bolt using a 6mm wrench, **Fig. 16.**
6. For remaining four attaching bolts, remove tool No. 9591/1, rotate crankshaft 120° (to pulley mark U4, U5 or U6) and secure again.
7. Remove underbody covers and side covers.
8. Pull off vacuum pipe at switch over valve.
9. Remove stabilizer at side parts of rear axle support.
10. Remove cross member (9A), diagonal braces (B) and rear axle support (C), **Fig. 17.**
11. Remove lower fastening screws on transmission bell housing.
12. Secure engine in installation position with holding device. Attach tool No. 9624/1, or equivalent with four screws and turn thrust screw until pressure disc is in contact with crankcase.
13. Disconnect left and right drive shafts from transmission.
14. Place suitable drain pan under transmission.
15. Clamp coolant hoses with tool No. 3094, or equivalent, then release spring clamps and remove hoses.
16. Pry cable off of transmission lever.
17. Disconnect cable from support bracket.

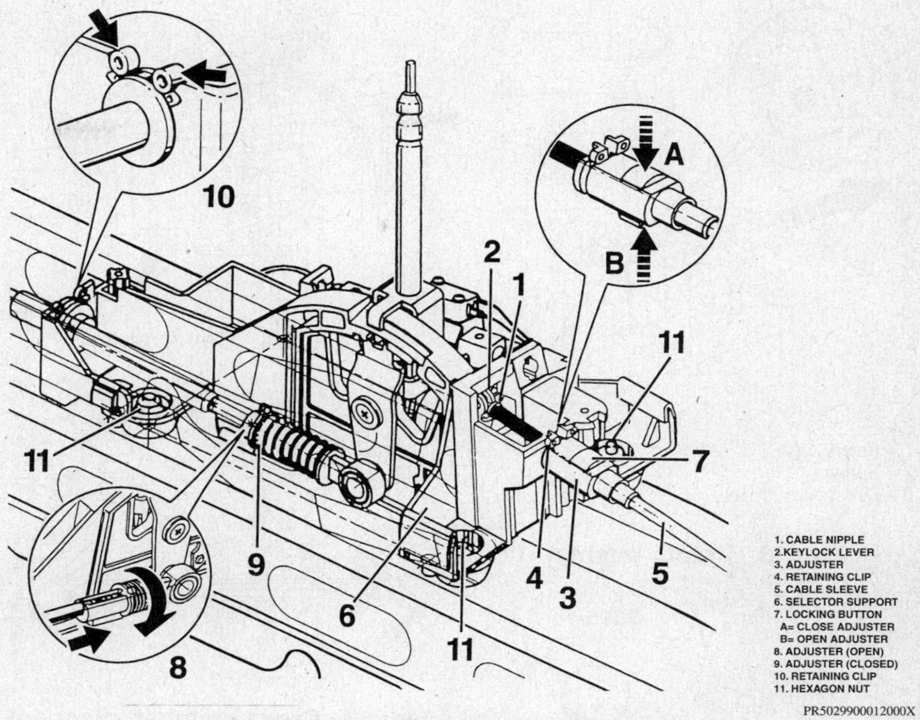

Fig. 12 Selector lever support

18. Disconnect multi-function switch electrical connector.
19. Turn round connector (bayonet lock) counterclockwise and disconnect from transmission.
20. Place suitable transmission jack under transmission and attach with fixing strap.
21. Remove transmission holder and transmission support.
22. Remove transmission/engine fastening screws. Engine may be lowered by up to one inch to access upper screws.
23. Pull transmission to front and lower it carefully.
24. Reverse procedure to install, noting the following:
    a. Ensure dowel sleeves are fully seated in crankcase.
    b. Secure converter in installation position with tool No. 9595/1 (long).
    c. Lubricate converter bearing journal with a thin coat of Olista Longtime 3 EP, or equivalent.
    d. Move transmission into position and fasten to engine.
    e. Tighten all fasteners to specifications, **Fig. 18.**
    f. Push vacuum pipe onto switch-over valve.
    g. Press end piece of selector lever cable onto transmission lever using a suitable pair of pliers. Ensure cable end fully engages.
    h. Check adjustment of selector lever cable.
    i. Check coolant level.
    j. Tighten all remaining fasteners to specification.

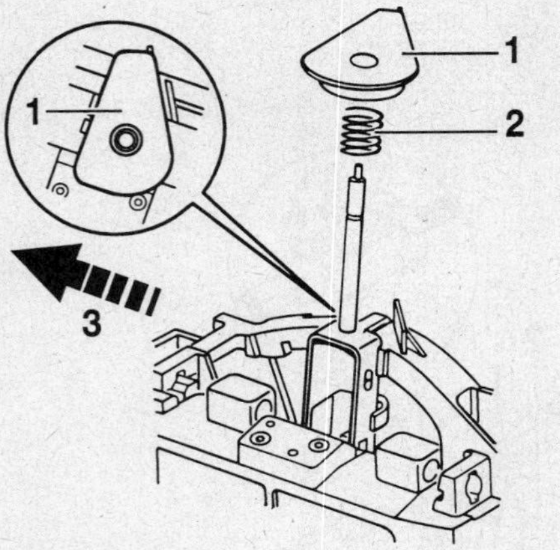

1 – Rotary valve
2 – Spring
3 – Direction of travel

PR5029900013000X

Fig. 13 Rotary pusher

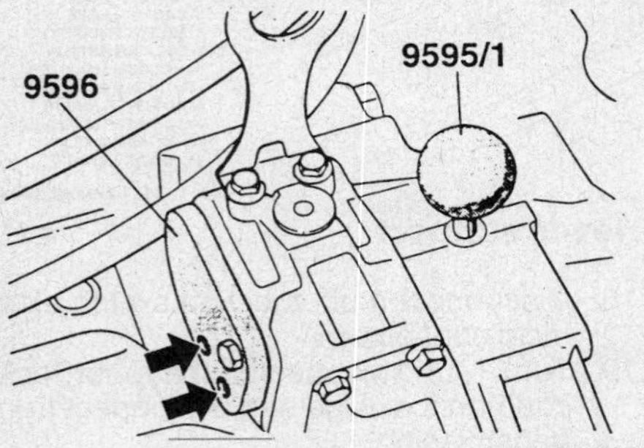

PR5029900017000X

Fig. 16 Tool Nos. 9595/1 & 9596 installation

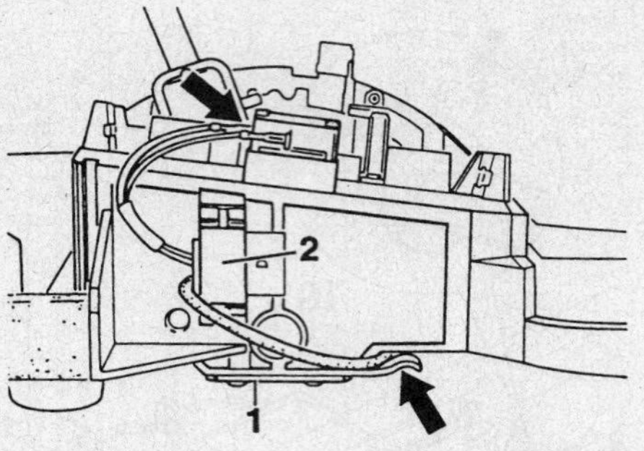

PR5029900016000X

Fig. 14 Cover plate

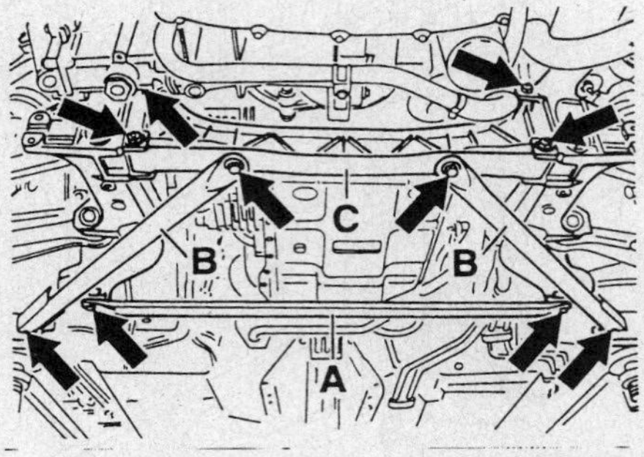

PR5029900018000X

Fig. 17 Cross member, diagonal braces & rear axle support

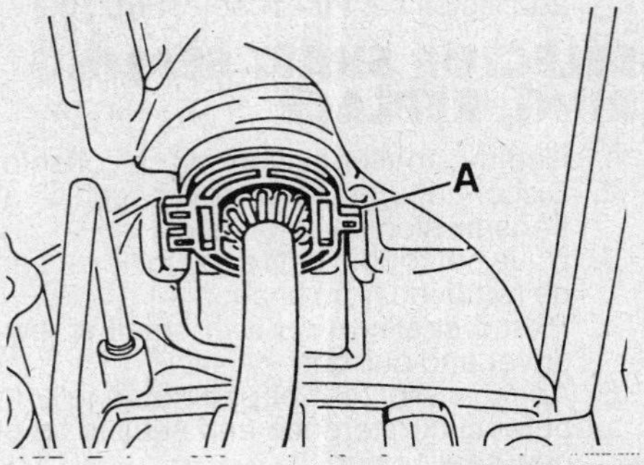

PR5029900022000X

Fig. 15 Socket lug "A" position

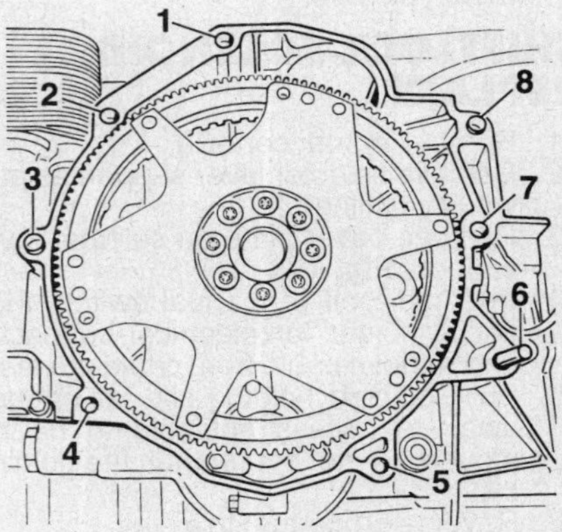

No.	Screw/nut	Nm (ftlb.)
1	M12 x 70	85 (63)
2	M12 x 100	85 (63)
3	M12 x 100	85 (63)
4*	M10 x 50	45 (33)
5	M10 x 50	45 (33)
6**	M12	85 (63)
7	M12 x 70	85 (63)
8	M12 x 70	85 (63)

* Multiple-tooth nut
**Hexagon nut
(fastening point omitted as of 5.5.98)

PR5029900019010X

Fig. 18 Transmission to engine bolt location & torque specifications

TIGHTENING SPECIFICATIONS

Year	Component	Torque, Ft. Lbs.
1999–2001	Bracket For ATF Lines To Transmission	17
	Carrier To Transmission Bearing	48
	Connecting Rod To Spring Strut	34
	Converter To Drive Plate	29
	Cooler Mounting	96①
	Crossmember To Carrier Side Member	48
	Diagonal Braces Carrier Side Member	17
	Diagonal Braces To Body	48
	Diagonal Braces To Cross Member	74
	Drain Plug	30
	Drive Shaft To Flanged Shaft	60
	Driveshaft To Transmission	60
	Filler Plug	59
	Filter To Control Unit	54①
	Final Drive Oil Fill Plug	22
	Flange Shaft Mounting Saddle	17
	Hydraulic Control Unit To Transmission	72①
	Input Sensor	48①
	Multi-Function Switch To Transmission	72①
	Oil Pan	96①
	Parking Brake Console Mounting	17
	Rear Axle Carrier To Carrier Side Member	74
	Selector Support Mounting Nuts	96①
	Short Flanged Shaft To Transmission	18
	Speed Sensor	48①
	Transmission Carrier To Body	48
	Transmission Support To Body	48
	Transmission Support/Transmission Carrier To Transmission Mount	48
	Wheel Mounting	96

① — Inch lbs.

Type A86 Automatic Transmission

INDEX

	Page No.
Adjustments	6-102
Selector Lever Cable	6-102
Differential, Replace	6-103
In-Vehicle Repairs	6-102
Hydraulic Control Unit, Replace	6-103
Inner Oil Tube, Replace	6-102
Multi-Function Switch, Replace	6-102
Oil Cooler, Replace	6-103
Selector Shaft Sealing Ring, Replace	6-103
Spur Gear Cover Gasket, Replace	6-102
Maintenance	6-102
Fluid Change	6-102
Fluid Check	6-102
Tightening Specifications	6-104
Transmission, Replace	6-103

MAINTENANCE

FLUID CHECK

1. Park vehicle on level area with air condition and heater off.
2. Attach filled ATF container tool No. VAG 1924, or equivalent, as high as possible on vehicle, **Fig. 1.**
3. Place suitable container under transmission.
4. Connect Porsche System Tester 2 and call up ATF temperature. ATF temperature must not be higher than 96°F at inspection start.
5. Ensure selector lever is in P position and allow engine to run at idle.
6. Wearing protective goggles, remove ATF filler screw (2), **Fig. 1.** If ATF temperature is 56–96°F and ATF escapes from filler hole, ATF level is correct.
7. Use ATF container tool No. VAG 1924 to fill transmission until fluid runs out of filler hole. **Filler hook must be carefully inserted in ATF thrower cap (4) on filler hole because oil guard cap (4) can spring off.**
8. Filler screw must be installed with new seal before ATF temperature reaches 113°F. Tighten screw to specifications.

FLUID CHANGE

1. Remove transverse strut panel and place suitable container under transmission.
2. Remove drain plug (1), **Fig. 1,** and drain ATF. **Vehicle cannot be started or towed without ATF.**
3. Replace seal, install drain plug and tighten to specifications.
4. Remove filler screw (2) and fill transmission with ATF (3) until fluid runs out of filler hole.
5. Move transmission selector to P position, start engine and allow to idle.
6. Again fill transmission with ATF until fluid runs out of filler hole.
7. With brake pedal applied, move transmission selector through each gear, remaining in each gear for approximately 10 seconds.
8. Again fill transmission with ATF until fluid runs out of filler hole.
9. Install filler screw with new seal and tighten to specifications.

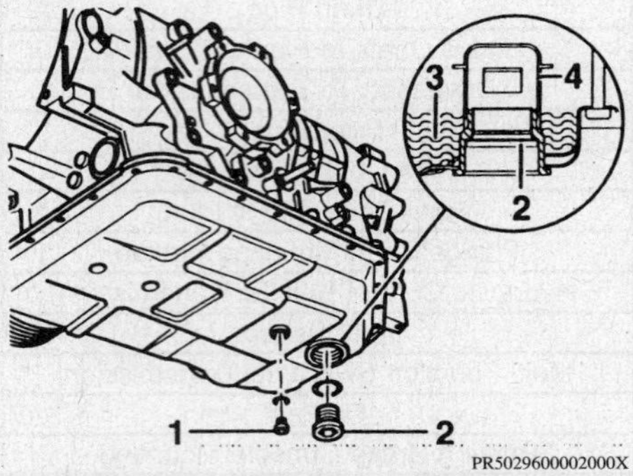

Fig. 1 ATF fluid check & replacement. Boxster

ADJUSTMENTS

SELECTOR LEVER CABLE

1. Move selector lever and transmission selector shaft to P position.
2. Adjust cable length at mounting head to be free of tension.
3. Select all gears and ensure proper gear indicated.

IN-VEHICLE REPAIRS

INNER OIL TUBE, REPLACE

Defective inner oil tube toroidal seals allow ATF to enter differential and overflow from differential vent.

1. Remove hydraulic control unit as outlined under "Hydraulic Control Unit, Replace."
2. Use suitable screwdriver to lever out oil tube.
3. Install new toroidal sealing rings coated thinly with Vaseline.
4. Install tube in insert air tool No. 3381, or equivalent.
5. With open side of tool facing transmission outer wall, push tube into housing to tool's stop without tilting tube. Install with equal force on both ends.

MULTI-FUNCTION SWITCH, REPLACE

1. Support engine using transport carrier with support bridge tool No. 10-22A and support feet tools No. 9591/a, or equivalents.
2. Remove lefthand catalytic converter.

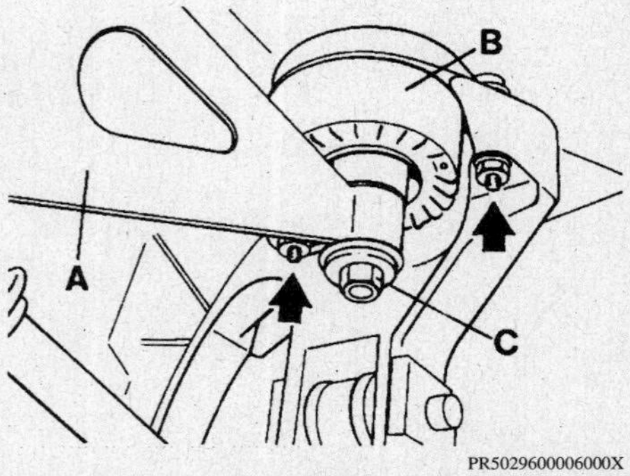

Fig. 2 Transmission support (A) and hydraulic mount (B). Boxster

3. Remove selector lever cable from deflection lever and transmission support.
4. Support transmission with suitable transmission jack and remove lefthand transmission support with hydraulic mount. **Do not loosen nut C, Fig. 2,** otherwise transmission prop will be damage.
5. Release and disconnect multi-function switch cable.
6. Remove mounting bolts and switch.
7. Reverse procedure to install. Do not tilt or force switch onto shaft. Tighten bolts to specifications.

SPUR GEAR COVER GASKET, REPLACE

1. Remove mufflers and muffler transmission mount.
2. Clamp flow side coolant hose shut and remove port plate.
3. Place suitable container under transmission and remove spur gear cover mounting screws.
4. Slowly and carefully remove cover to prevent spur gears from falling out. **If spur gears fall onto floor they must be replaced.**
5. Reverse procedure to install, noting the following:
   a. If spur gears were remove, replace with markings face away from transmission.
   b. Ensure faultless dowel sleeve seating.
   c. Install two centering pin tools No. 9312, or equivalent, into housing.
   d. Install gasket and fit cover.

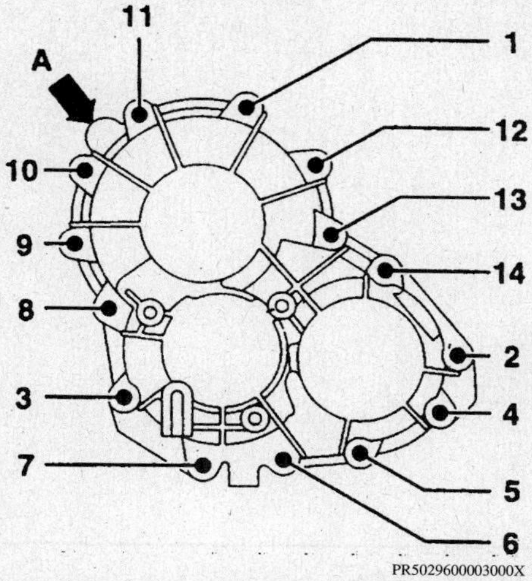

Fig. 3 Spur gear cover tightening sequence. Boxster

e. Tighten bolts 1–3 by hand and ensure gap between cover and housing is equal.
f. Tighten bolts to specifications following sequence show in **Fig. 3.**

SELECTOR SHAFT SEALING RING, REPLACE

1. Remove multi-function switch as outlined under "Multi-Function Switch,"
2. Remove selector lever push rod.
3. Drive out roll pin and remove selector lever from shaft.
4. Remove sealing ring with suitable small screwdriver.
5. Reverse procedure to install, driving Vaseline coated sealing ring over thinly coated sealing lip with driving tool No. 3385, or equivalent.

HYDRAULIC CONTROL UNIT, REPLACE

Do not run engine with transmission pan removed or without ATF.

1. Remove transverse member panel and place suitable container under transmission.
2. Remove drain screw and drain fluid.
3. Remove pan loosening bolts in crosswise pattern.
4. Remove oil filter.
5. Remove wiring harness and speed sensor connectors.
6. Remove mounting screws marked in **Fig. 4.**
7. Remove control unit. **Do not rest unit on transmission input speed sensor.**
8. Reverse procedure to install, noting the following:
   a. Thinly coat sealing rings with Vaseline.
   b. Install control unit and install detent disc pin into selector valve groove.
   c. Hand tighten mounting bolts and final tighten to specifications.

OIL COOLER, REPLACE

1. Clamp coolant hoses shut and remove righthand catalytic converter.
2. Place suitable container under transmission.
3. Remove cooler mounting bolts. Mirror may be required to remove top bolts.
4. Reverse procedure to install using new sealing rings.

TRANSMISSION

REPLACE

1. Remove starter as outlined under "Electrical."
2. Remove passenger compartment rear wall.
3. Turn crankshaft until pulley bores U4, U5 or U6 aligned with crankcase center bore.
4. Install dowel pin tool No. 9595, or equivalent, to hold converter in installation position.
5. Install assembly aid tool No. 9596, or equivalent, and remove two converter mounting bolts.
6. Remove dowel pin, turn crankshaft to next bore, install dowel pin and remove two more converter mounting bolts. Repeat until all eight mounting bolts have been removed.
7. Remove switch over valve vacuum line.
8. Support engine using transport carrier with support bridge tool No. 10-22A and support feet tools No. 9591/a, or equivalents.
9. Remove diagonal braces and crossmember panel, then the stabilizer bar.
10. Remove mufflers and catalytic converters, then the rear crossmember.
11. Remove front crossmember.
12. Remove drive shafts and protect with scrap 1.181 inches diameter hose.
13. Clamp coolant hoses shut and place suitable container under transmission.
14. Release clamps, and pull cooler hoses off flow and return sides.
15. Disconnect multi-function switch connector.
16. Turn transmission socket plug counterclockwise and remove.
17. Remove selector lever cable at deflection lever and transmission support.
18. Place suitable transmission jack under transmission and secure with retaining strap.
19. Remove transmission support with left and righthand hydraulic mounts. **Do not loosen nut C, Fig. 2,** otherwise transmission prop will be damage.
20. Remove transmission to engine mounting bolts.
21. Pull transmission to rear, lower and remove.
22. Reverse procedure to install, noting the following:
    a. Ensure dowel sleeves are properly seated.
    b. Tighten bolts to specifications.

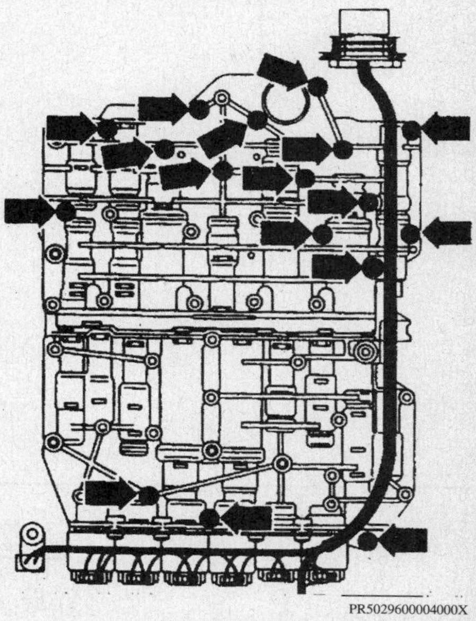

Fig. 4 Hydraulic control unit removable bolts. Boxster

DIFFERENTIAL

REPLACE

1. Support engine using transport carrier with support bridge tool No. 10-22A and support feet tools No. 9591/a, or equivalents.
2. Remove righthand rear wheel, diagonal braces and crossmember panel, then the righthand catalytic converter.
3. Remove drive shafts and protect with scrap 1.181 inches diameter hose.
4. Remove stabilizer mount ball joint, toe control arm and control arm from wheel carrier.
5. Place suitable container under transmission.
6. Remove flanged shaft mounting bolts and secure from turning with suitable mandrel.
7. Remove transmission support with hydraulic mount. **Do not loosen nut C, Fig. 2,** otherwise transmission prop will be damage.
8. Clamp coolant return side hose shut, and unscrew hose at ATF cooler and final drive.
9. Remove cover screws in reverse order of tightening, **Fig. 5.**
10. Remove differential, bearing outer race and adjusting shims.
11. Reverse procedure to install, noting the following:
    a. Adjusting shims are calibrated and cannot be exchanged for approximate substitute.
    b. Tighten bolts 1–3 by hand and ensure gap between cover and housing is equal.
    c. Tighten bolts to specifications following sequence show in **Fig. 5.**

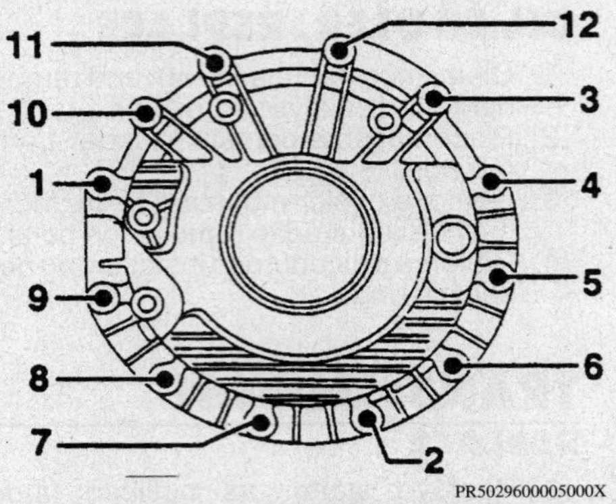

Fig. 5 Differential cover tightening sequence. Boxster

TIGHTENING SPECIFICATIONS

Year	Component	Torque, Ft. Lbs.
1998–2001	Drain Plug	29
	Filler Screw	59
	Final Drive Cover	17
	Final Drive Cover Plug	22
	Hydraulic Control Unit	72①
	Hydraulic Mount	17
	Input Sensor	48①
	Long Flanged Shaft Mounting Saddle	17
	Multi-Function Switch	72①
	Pan	84①
	RPM Sensor	48①
	Short Flanged Shaft	18
	Solenoid Valves	48①
	Spur Gear Housing	17
	Strainer	48①
	Transmission Mount To Engine (M10)	33
	Transmission Mount To Engine (M12)	63
	Transmission Prop	48

① — Inch lbs.

All-Wheel Drive Systems

INDEX

	Page No.
Description	6-105
Precautions	6-105
Air Bag Systems	6-105
Battery Ground Cable	6-105

PRECAUTIONS

AIR BAG SYSTEMS

Refer to "Air Bag System Precautions" in the front of this manual for system disarming and arming procedures.

BATTERY GROUND CABLE

Prior to service, disconnect battery ground cable and isolate as required.

DESCRIPTION

The 911 Carrera 4, Carrera 4S and Turbo models are equipped with an electronically controlled four wheel drive system with limited slip differential and automatic brake differential (ABD) traction system. Front wheels are driven by a transfer box and a driveshaft running in the central pipe. The four wheel drive system has a permanent division of 31% of the drive torque to the front axle and 69% to the rear axle. The static axle load distribution is 60% to the rear axle and 40% to the front axle. The transverse lock is applied to reduce over-steer while driving the car in curves. The interaxle lock stabilizes the vehicle when accelerating out of a curve, sends more drive torque to the slower turning axle by locking the transfer. The locking effect is increased until equal wheel speeds are restored.

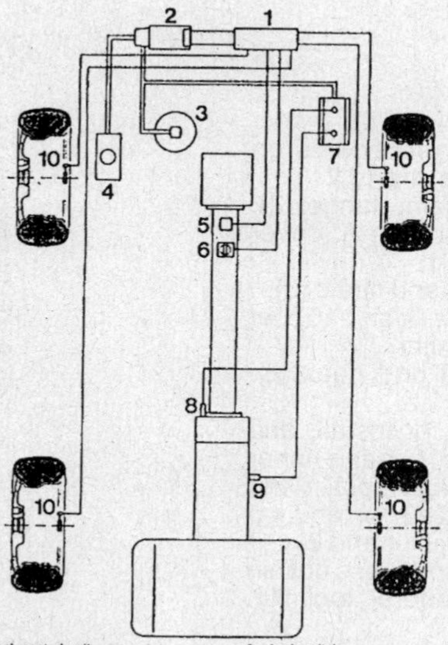

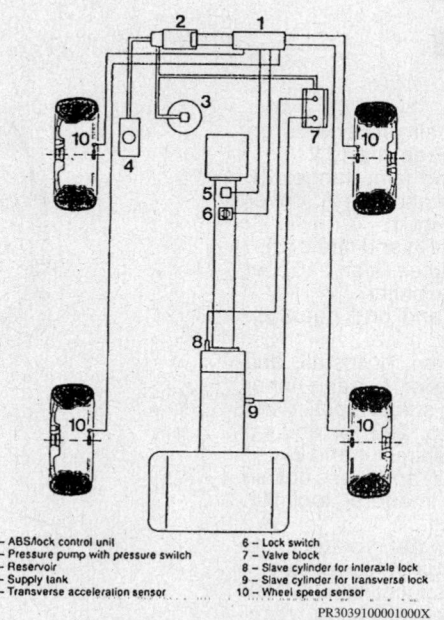

1 – ABS/lock control unit
2 – Pressure pump with pressure switch
3 – Reservoir
4 – Supply tank
5 – Transverse acceleration sensor
6 – Lock switch
7 – Valve block
8 – Slave cylinder for interaxle lock
9 – Slave cylinder for transverse lock
10 – Wheel speed sensor

PR3039100001000X

Fig. 1 AWD component locations

Refer to **Fig. 1,** for all wheel drive component locations.

Drive Axles

INDEX

	Page No.
Adjustments	6-106
911	6-106
Assemble	6-106
911	6-106
Disassemble	6-106
911	6-106
Tightening Specifications	6-108

DISASSEMBLE

911

When performing repair procedures on this differential, refer to **Figs. 1 and 2.**

1. Remove bolt (1) and joint flange (2), then the nuts (3), washers (4), cover (5) and O-ring (6), **Fig. 1.**
2. Remove differential (7) and seals (8).
3. Pull bearing outer races (9 and 10) out with suitable internal puller.
4. Remove bolts (1) and ring gear (2), **Fig. 2.**
5. Mark adjusting shims for install, and remove tapered roller bearing inner races (3 and 5) with suitable puller and thrust piece tool No. 263, or equivalent, and adjusting shims (4 and 6).
6. Remove spiral pin (7) and press out pin (8) with centering mandrel tool No. 9289, or equivalent.
7. Use centering mandrel, rotate bevel pinion (9) to housing (14) opening.
8. lift bevel pinions, spacer sleeve (10) and needle roller sleeves (11) out carefully, taking care not to lose any of individual needle rollers.
9. Remove the shaft bevel gears (12) and threaded pieces (13).

ASSEMBLE

911

1. Install differential gears (12), pressed-in threaded washers (13) across differential housing (14) large opening, then position with halfshaft flanges, **Fig. 2.**
2. Assemble stiff gears bevel pinion (9) and needle rollers (11), using centering mandrel tool No. 9289, or equivalent, and spacer sleeve (10), then install across housing opening.
3. Assemble second bevel pinion with needle rollers, then carefully push onto centering mandrel. **Do not lose needle rollers.**
4. Rotate bevel pinion with centering mandrel until housing bores align.
5. Press differential pin (8) into position, remove centering mandrel and install lock pin (7) as outlined under "Adjustments."
6. Install adjusting shim, determine thickness as outlined under "Adjustments."
7. Press on tapered roller bearing inner races with thrust piece tool No. 264b, or equivalent.
8. Ensure bolts and holes are dry and grease free, then install ring gear (7) with ribbed seating surface bolts (1). Tighten bolts to specifications.
9. Press in bearing outer races (9) and (10) with suitable thrust piece, **Fig. 1.**
10. Pack space between dust and sealing lips with Optimol HT2 + 2 EP grease, or equivalent.
11. Press seals (8) in until they are seated against stop, with thrust piece tool No. 9252, or equivalent.
12. Install differential (7).
13. Apply a light coat of oil to O-ring, then install O-ring and cover (5). **Do not twist O-ring.**
14. Install washers and nuts, then tighten to specifications.
15. Install joint flanges (2) and tighten bolts (1) to specifications.

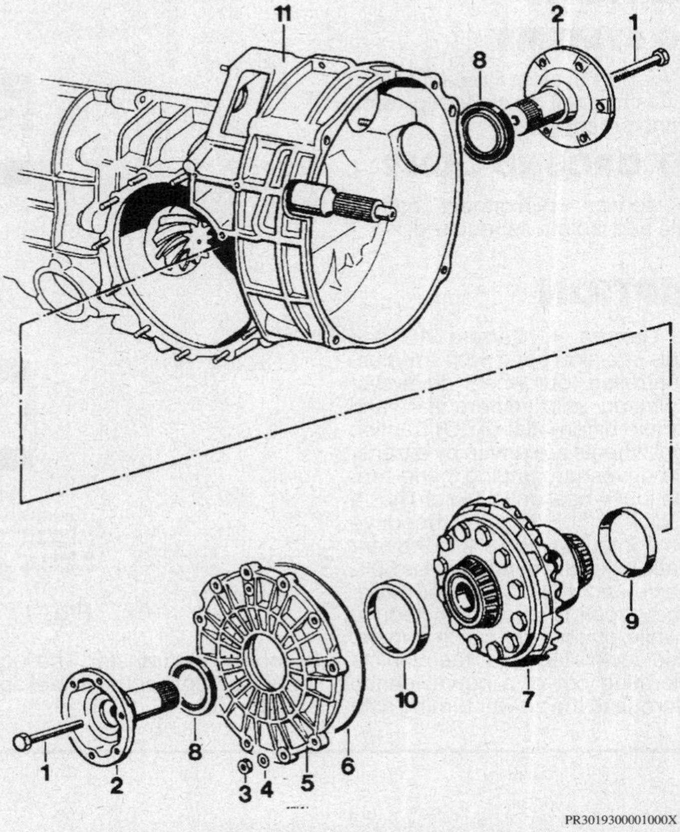

Fig. 1 Differential replacement. 911

ADJUSTMENTS

911

1. If it is necessary, adjust drive pinion and ring gear as follows:
   a. Determine total ring gear shim thickness for specified tapered roller bearings/differential preload.
   b. Determine drive pinion shim thickness.
   c. Split total shim thickness into individual spacers to obtain specified circumferential backlash.
2. Refer to shim replacement chart, **Fig. 3,** for available adjustment shims.

Drive Set

Matching numbers are stamped on the end of the drive pinion and the side of ring gear. The ring gear matching number is followed by the backlash measurement and setting value. Setting value is the sum of designed dimension (2.402 inches) and deviation allowed to obtain prescribed tooth backlash. For example, a ring gear embossed 09 F0,16 E61,43 has matching

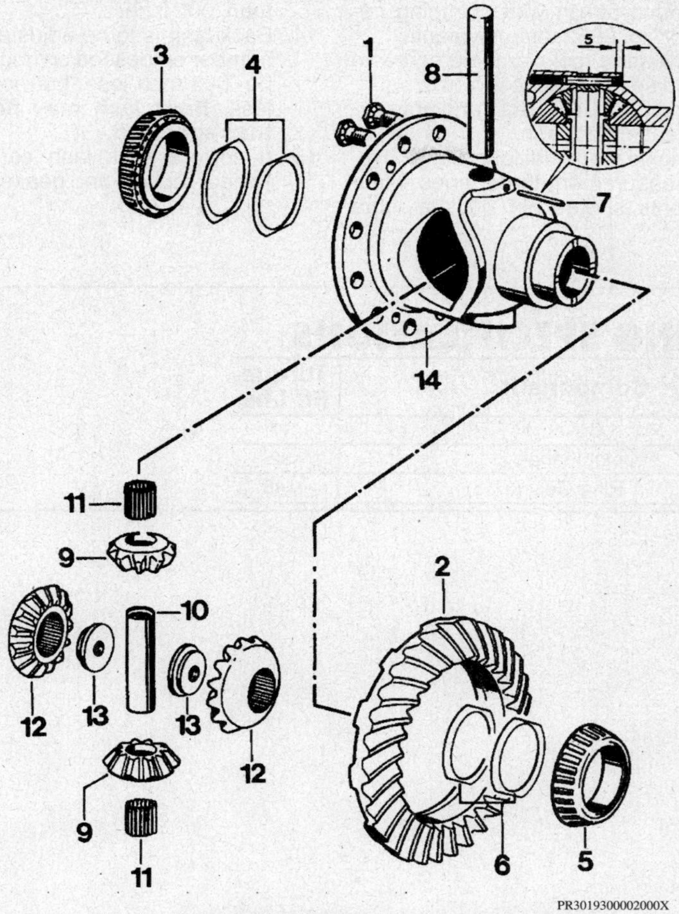

Fig. 2 Exploded view of differential. 911

Component Replaced	Ring Gear Shims	Drive Pinion Shim
Differential Housing	X	—
Differential Roller Bearing	X	—
Drive Set	X	X
Lateral Transaxle Cover	X	—
Large Cylindrical Roller Bearing & Drive Pinion Four-Point Bearing	X	X
Transaxle Case	X	X

Fig. 3 Shim replacement chart. 911

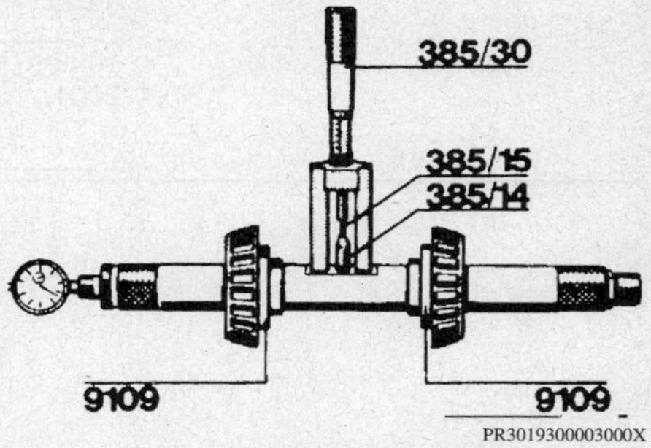

Fig. 4 Install mandrel measurement. 911

number 09, back lash of .16mm (.0063 inch) and setting value of 61.43 mm (2.4187 inches).

Drive Pinion

1. Note setting valve embossed on ring gear.
2. Install complete gear set without ring gear shims and **torque** tensioning plate nuts to 17 ft. lbs.
3. Fit gear housing and engage sixth gear.
4. Block input shaft with holder tool No. 9253, or equivalent, and **torque** drive pinion collar nut to 184 ft. lbs.
5. Set adjusting ring on measuring mandrel tool No. VW 385/1, or equivalent, to approximately 2.5593 inches.
6. Assembly measuring mandrel with centering disk tool No. 9109, tapered roller bearing, gauge plunger tool No. VW 385/14 and dial gauge extension tool No. VW 385/15, or equivalents, **Fig. 4.**
7. Set measuring mandrel with master gauge tool No. VW 385/30, to setting value.
8. Set suitable. 1181 inch measuring range dial gauge to zero with .0397 inch preload
9. Set gauge block plate tool No. 9281, or equivalent, on drive pinion head and install measuring mandrel into transmission case with dial gauge extension located in gauge block plate area.
10. Install lateral transmission cover less O-ring and tighten four nuts crosswise. **Do not hammer cover into place.**
11. Pull second centering disk with spindle towards outside until measuring mandrel can just be hand turned.
12. Turn measuring mandrel until dial gauge extension is vertical to drive pinion head face, and read and record measurement.
13. Measured value always deviated from set dimension clockwise with dial gauge smaller pointer between one and two. Large point will indicate shim thickness. Round up or down to nearest .0020 inch. For example, .0146 inches becomes .0140 inches.
14. Install necessary shims and check setting value, again. Deviation of ±.0012 inch is allowed.

Ring Gear

Drive pinion must be removed to determine differential tapered roller bearing preload.

1. Ensure tapered roller bearing outer races are well seated in case or cover.
2. Install one .0984 inch spacer ring on ring gear side and opposite side of differential.
3. Install differential into case and rotate several times.
4. Install lateral cover less seal and **torque** nuts to 17 ft. lbs.
5. Put gauge block plate tool No. VW 385/17, or equivalent, on differential collar.
6. Install universal dial gauge tool No. VW 387, or equivalent, with suitable dial gauge and 1.181–1.575 inches extension to case and set zero with .0787 inch preload. **Do not turn differential while measuring back lash.**
7. Calculate ring gear shim thickness value by adding fitted shim thickness to measured value plus tapered roller bearing pressure fit (.0157 inch).
8. Remove differential and pull both tapered roller bearings off.
9. Split calculated value and increase thickness of one shim and decrease thickness by .0276 inch as starting point. Calculated shim thickness must be rounded up or down to reasonable dimensions that do not alter total thickness.
10. Measure shims with micrometer in several places and ensure a deviation of no more than .0008 inch. Also inspect for burrs and damage.

Circumferential Backlash

1. Mount gear set with shims determined under "Drive Pinion."
2. Ensure drive pinion collar nut is **torqued** to 183 ft. lbs.
3. Install differential with tapered roller bearing and shims into housing.
4. Instal lateral cover and **torque** nuts to 17 ft. lbs.
5. Ensure there is some backlash. **Never allow drive pinion to seize.**
6. Assemble measuring lever tool No, VW 388, adjusting device tool No. VW

521/4, or equivalents, and 3.149 inch plunger.
7. Install adjusting device tool No. 9145, or equivalent, into differential and clamp firmly.
8. Rotate differential in both directions several times to settle tapered roller bearings.
9. Install universal dial gauge holder to produce a 90° angle between dial gauge and lever.
10. Block drive pinion with clamping device tool No. 9562, or equivalent.
11. Turn adjusting tool clamping screw to stop and set dial gauge to zero.
12. Turn ring gear back, read and note circumferential backlash.
13. Turn ring gear an additional 90° and repeat measurement three times. Measurements should not deviate more than .002 inch.
14. Back lash is to be adjusted to second number embossed on ring gear. It may be .002 inch less, but not .0039 inch less. **Back lash may not be more than specified.**
15. If correct back lash cannot be obtained, replace ring gear spacers.

TIGHTENING SPECIFICATIONS

Year	Component	Torque, Ft. Lbs.
1998–2001	Cover	17
	Joint Flange	32
	Ring Gear	148

Engine Rebuilding Specifications

INDEX

	Page No.
Camshaft	6-109
Crankshaft, Bearings & Rods	6-110
Cylinder Block	6-110
Cylinder Head, Valve Guide & Valve Seats	6-109
Pistons, Pins & Rings	6-110
Valve Springs	6-109
Valves	6-109

CYLINDER HEAD, VALVE GUIDE & VALVE SEATS

All Measurements Given In Inches, Unless Otherwise Specified.

Engine Liter	Year	Cylinder Head Warpage Limit①	Valve Guides			Valve Seats		
			Standard Inside Diameter	Stem To Guide Clearance		Seat Angle Degrees	Seat Width	
				Intake	Exhaust		Intake	Exhaust
2.5L	1998–2001	.0006	—	—	—	—	—	—

① — Maximum.

VALVE SPRINGS

Engine Liter	Year	Valve Spring			
		Free Length	Installed Height	Pressure @ Installed Height	Out Of Square Limit
2.5L	1998–2001	—	—	—	—
3.6L	1998	—	①	—	—

① — Intake valve: 1.4450 inch +.0118 inch; Exhaust valve: 1.4057 inch +.0118 inch.

VALVES

All Measurements Given In Inches, Unless Otherwise Specified.

Engine Liter	Year	Valves					Valve Clearance	
		Stem Diameter		Face Angle	Valve Spring Installed Height		Intake	Exhaust
		Intake	Exhaust		Intake	Exhaust		
2.5L	1998–2001	—	—	—	—	—	—	—
3.6L	1998	.3138	②	45	1.4332–1.4568	1.3938–1.4175	①	①

① — Equipped w/hydraulic valve lash adjusters.

② — Tappers from .3130 to .3138 inch.

CAMSHAFT

All Measurements Given In Inches, Unless Otherwise Specified.

Engine Liter	Year	Camshaft Journal Diameter	Maximum Journal Runout	Camshaft Endplay	Lifter Bore Diameter	Lifter Diameter
2.5L	1998–2001	—	—	—	—	—
3.6L	1998	1.8470–1.8480	.0008	.0060–.0080	—	—

CRANKSHAFT, BEARINGS & RODS

All Measurements Given In Inches, Unless Otherwise Specified.

Engine Liter	Year	Crankshaft Std. Journal Dia.		Bearing Clearance		Endplay	
		Main Bearing	Crank Pin	Main Bearing	Connecting Rod Bearing	Crankshaft	Connecting Rod
2.5L	1998–2001	—	—	—	—	—	—
3.6L	1998	2.3613–2.3620	2.1642–2.1650	—	—	—	—

PISTONS, PINS & RINGS

All Measurements Given In Inches, Unless Otherwise Specified.

Engine Liter	Year	Piston Diameter (Std.)	Piston Clearance	Piston Pin Diameter	Piston Ring End Gap		Piston Ring Side Clearance	
					Comp.	Oil	Comp.	Oil
2.5L	1998–2001	—	—	—	—	—	—	—
3.6L	1998	3.93579–3.93619	—	.866	.00039–.0079	.0059–.0120	①	.0008–.0019

① — Top ring .0030–.0040 inch, 2nd ring .0020–.0030 inch.

CYLINDER BLOCK

All Measurements Given In Inches, Unless Otherwise Specified.

Engine Liter	Year	Cylinder Bore Diameter (Std.)	Cylinder Bore Out of Round Max.
2.5L	1998–2001	—	—
3.6L	1998	3.94	.0016

SAAB

INDEX OF SERVICE OPERATIONS

	Page No.
AIR BAG SYSTEM PRECAUTIONS	0-12
AIR QUALITY STANDARDS	0-23
AUTOMATIC TRANSAXLES	7-153
BRAKES	
Anti-Lock Brakes	7-98
Disc Brakes	7-90
Hydraulic Brake Systems	7-95
Power Brakes Units	7-97
CLUTCH & MANUAL TRANSAXLE	
Adjustments	7-26
Clutch, Replace	7-27
Hydraulic System Service	7-26
Precautions	7-26
Tightening Specifications	7-29
Transaxle, Replace	7-28
COMPUTER RELEARN PROCEDURE	0-10
ELECTRICAL	
Air Bags	7-69
Air Conditioning	7-45
Alternators	7-63
Alternator, Replace	7-6
Blower Motor, Replace	7-9
Coil Pack, Replace	7-6
Cooling Fans	7-46
Cruise Controls	7-65
Dash Panel	7-82
Dash Gauges	7-59
Distributor, Replace	7-6
Evaporator Core, Replace	7-10
Fuel Pump Relay Location	7-5
Fuse Panel & Flasher Location	7-5
Heater Core, Replace	7-10
Ignition Lock, Replace	7-7
Ignition Switch, Replace	7-7
Instrument Cluster, Replace	7-8
Neutral Safety Switch, Replace	7-7
Passive Restraints	7-69
Precautions	7-5
Radio, Replace	7-8
Relay Center Location	7-6
Speed Controls	7-65
Starter Motors	7-61
Starter, Replace	7-6
Steering Columns	7-85
Steering Wheel, Replace	7-8
Turn Signal Switch, Replace	7-8
Wiper Motor, Replace	7-8
Wiper Switch, Replace	7-9
Wiper Transmission, Replace	7-9
ELECTRICAL SYMBOL IDENTIFICATION	0-33
ENGINE	
Belt Tension Data	7-22
Camshaft, Replace	7-20
Cooling System Bleed	7-22
Crankshaft Seal, Replace	7-20
Cylinder Head, Replace	7-16
Engine Rebuilding Specifications	7-206
Engine, Replace	7-12
Front Cover Seal, Replace	7-18
Fuel Pump, Replace	7-22
Intake Air Heat Plates, Replace	7-16
Intake Manifold, Replace	7-15
Main & Rod Bearings	7-20
Oil Pan, Replace	7-21
Oil Pump, Replace	7-21
Pistons, Pins & Rings	7-20
Precautions	7-12
Serpentine Drive Belt	7-22
Tightening Specifications	7-24
Timing Belt, Replace	7-19
Timing Chain, Replace	7-19
Turbocharger, Replace	7-23
Valve Adjustment	7-18
Valve Clearance Specifications	7-18
Valve Guides	7-18
Valve Seats	7-18
Water Pump, Replace	7-22
FRONT SUSPENSION & STEERING	
Ball Joint, Replace	7-36
Coil Spring, Replace	7-36
Control Arm, Replace	7-37
Hub & Bearing, Replace	7-36
Power Steering	7-88
Power Steering Gear, Replace	7-38
Power Steering Pump, Replace	7-39
Power Steering System Bleed	7-40
Precautions	7-36
Shock Absorber, Replace	7-36
Tightening Specifications	7-41
FRONT WHEEL DRIVE AXLES	7-169
REAR AXLE & SUSPENSION	
Coil Spring, Replace	7-33
Hub & Bearing, Replace	7-32
Longitudinal Link, Replace	7-34
Lower Transverse Link, Replace	7-33
Panhard Rod & Bushing, Replace	7-34
Rear Axle, Replace	7-31
Rear Suspension Subframe, Replace	7-31
Roll Bar, Replace	7-34
Shock Absorber, Replace	7-32
Spring Linkage, Replace	7-33
Tightening Specifications	7-35
Torque Arm, Replace	7-33
Transverse Link Ball Joint, Replace	7-34
Upper Transverse Link, Replace	7-33
SPECIFICATIONS	
Fluid Capacities & Cooling System Data	7-3
Front Wheel Alignment Specifications	7-3
General Engine Specifications	7-2
Lubricant Data	7-4
Rear Wheel Alignment Specifications	7-3
Tune Up Specifications	7-2
TRACTION CONTROL SYSTEMS	7-180
VEHICLE IDENTIFICATION	0-3
VEHICLE LIFT POINTS	0-24
VEHICLE MAINTENANCE SCHEDULES	0-45
WHEEL ALIGNMENT	
Front Wheel Alignment	7-43
Preliminary Inspection	7-43
Rear Wheel Alignment	7-43
Vehicle Ride Height	7-44
Wheel Alignment Specifications	7-3
WIRE COLOR CODE IDENTIFICATION	0-33

Specifications

GENERAL ENGINE SPECIFICATIONS

Year	Model, Engine/ Liters	Fuel System	Bore X Stroke, Inches (mm)	Comp. Ratio	Maximum Brake H.P. @ RPM	Maximum Torque Ft. Lbs. @ RPM	Normal Oil Pressure, psi①
1998	900 w/2.0L	Saab Trionic System	3.54 X 3.07 (90 X 78)	9.2	185 @ 5500	195 @ 2100	39
	900 w/2.3L	Saab Trionic System	3.54 X 3.54 (90 X 90)	10.5	150 @ 5700	155 @ 4300	39
	9000 w/2.3L	Saab Trionic System	3.54 X 3.54 (90 X 90)	9.25	225 @ 5500	253 @ 1800	39
1999	9-3 w/2.0L③	Saab Trionic System	3.54 X 3.07 (90 X 78)	9.2	185 @ 5500	195 @ 2100	39
	9-3 w/2.0L②	Saab Trionic System	3.54 X 3.07 (90 X 78)	9.2	200 @ 5500	209 @ 2300	39
	9-5 w/2.3L	Saab Trionic System	3.54 X 3.54 (90 X 90)	9.3	170 @ 5500	207 @ 1800	37
	9-5 w/3.0L	Saab Trionic System	3.38 X 3.35 (90 X 90)	9.5	200 @ 5000	229 @ 2500	46
2000–01	9-3 w/2.0L③	Saab Trionic System	3.54 X 3.07 (90 X 78)	9.2	185 @ 5500	195 @ 2100	39
	9-3 w/2.0L②	Saab Trionic System	3.54 X 3.07 (90 X 78)	9.2	205 @ 5500	209 @ 2300	39
	9-3 w/2.3L②	Saab Trionic System	3.54 X 3.07 (90 X 90)	—	230 @ 5500	258 @ 2500	39
	9-5 w/2.3L③	Saab Trionic System	3.54 X 3.07 (90 X 78)	9.2	185 @ 5500	207 @ 2100	39
	9-5 w/2.3L②	Saab Trionic System	3.54 X 3.07 (90 X 90)	—	230 @ 5500	258 @ 2500	39
	9-5 w/3.0L	Saab Trionic System	3.38 X 3.35 (90 X 90)	9.5	200 @ 5000	229 @ 2500	46

① — At 2000 RPM.

② — High output turbocharged engine.

③ — Turbocharged engine.

TUNE UP SPECIFICATIONS

Year & Engine	Spark Plug Gap, Inch	Ignition Timing			Curb Idle Speed		Fast Idle Speed		Fuel Pressure, psi	Valve Lash, Inch	
		Firing Order Fig.②	Timing, °BTDC	Timing Mark Fig.	Man. Trans.	Auto. Trans.③	Man. Trans.	Auto. Trans.		Intake	Exhaust
1998											
2.0L Turbo	.040	⑥	⑤	—	⑤	⑤	⑤	⑤	43	①	①
2.3L	.023	⑦	⑤	—	⑤	⑤	⑤	⑤	43	①	①
2.3L Turbo	.040	⑥	⑤	—	⑤	⑤	⑤	⑤	43	①	①
1999–2001											
2.0L	.040	⑥	⑤	—	⑤	⑤	⑤	⑤	43	①	①
2.0L High Output Turbo	.040	⑥	⑤	—	⑤	⑤	⑤	⑤	43	①	①
2.3L	.040	⑥	⑤	—	⑤	⑤	⑤	⑤	43	①	①
3.0L	.040	④	⑤	—	⑤	⑤	⑤	⑤	43	①	①

BTDC — Before Top Dead Center
N — Neutral
① — Equipped w/hydraulic valve lash adjusters.
② — Before disconnecting spark plug wires from distributor cap, determine location of No. 1 wire in cap, as distributor position may have been altered from that shown.
③ — When adjusting idle speed, set parking brake & chock drive wheels.
④ — Firing order 1-2-3-4-5-6.
⑤ — Controlled by electronic control unit.
⑥ — Firing order, 1–3-4-2, direct ignition system (DIS) Trionic system, **Fig. B.**
⑦ — Firing order 1-3-4–2, **Fig. A.**

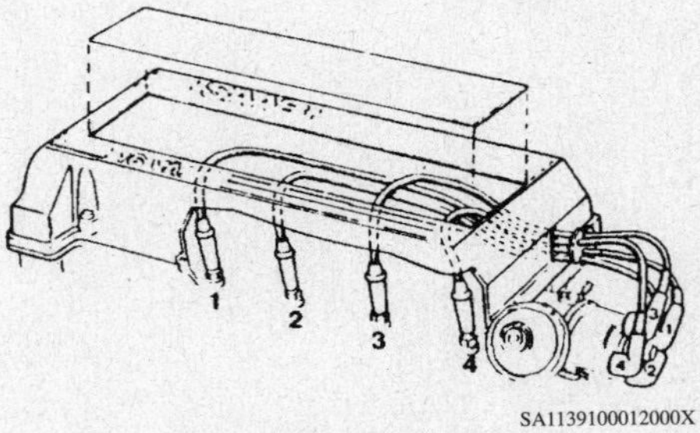

Fig. A

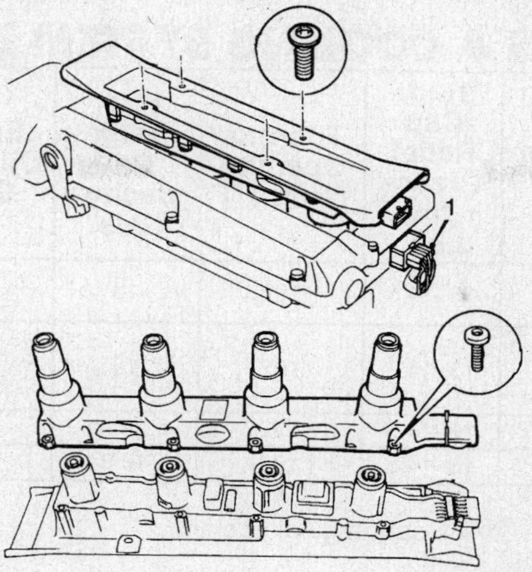

Fig. B

FRONT WHEEL ALIGNMENT SPECIFICATIONS

Year	Model	Caster Angle, Degrees		Camber Angle, Degrees		Toe-In, Inch	Toe-Out On Turns, Degrees		Ball Joint Inspection	
		Limits	Desired	Limits	Desired		Inner Wheel	Outer Wheel	Upper	Lower
1998	900	+1.6 to +2.6	+2.10	0 to –1	–.5	.06	21	20	①	①
	9000	+1.15 to +2.15	+1.65	–1.15 to -.15	–.65	.06	21	20	①	①
1999–2001	9-3	+1.6 to +2.6	+2.10	0 to –1	–.5	.06	21	20	①	①
	9-5	+2.4 to +3.4	+2.9	–1.30 to –.30	–.80	.14	21.25	20	①	①

① — Axial play, .08 inch; radial play, .04 inch.

REAR WHEEL ALIGNMENT SPECIFICATIONS

Year	Model	Camber Angle, Degrees		Toe-In, Inch
		Limits	Desired	
1998	900	–2 to –1.40	–1.70	.04
	9000	–.50 to 0	–.25	.10
1999–2001	9-3	–2 to –1.40	–1.70	.04
	9-5	–1.05 to –.55	–.80	.21

FLUID CAPACITIES & COOLING SYSTEM DATA

Year	Model, Engine	Coolant System Capacity, Qts.	Coolant Type	Rad. Cap Relief Pressure, Lbs.	Thermo. Opening Temp., °F	Fuel Tank Capacity, Gals.	Engine Oil Refill, Qts.①	Transaxle Oil		
								Man. Trans., Pts.	Auto. Trans., Qts.	
									Drain & Refill	Total Capacity
1998	900 2.0L Turbo	8.7	②	13–14.5	192	18	4.2	4	3.4	7.6
	900 2.3L	8.7	②	13–14.5	192	18	4.2	4	3.4	7.6
	9000 2.3L	9.5	②	13–14.5	192	17.4	5	4	3.7	9.2

Continued

FLUID CAPACITIES & COOLING SYSTEM DATA—Continued

Year	Model, Engine	Coolant System Capacity, Qts.	Coolant Type	Rad. Cap Relief Pressure, Lbs.	Thermo. Opening Temp., °F	Fuel Tank Capacity, Gals.	Engine Oil Refill, Qts.①	Transaxle Oil		
								Man. Trans., Pts.	Auto. Trans., Qts.	
									Drain & Refill	Total Capacity
1999–2001	9-3 2.0L Turbo	8.9	②	13–14.5	192	18	4.2	3.8	3.4	7.6
	9-3 2.0L High Output Turbo	8.9	②	13–14.5	192	18	4.2	3.8	3.4	7.6
	9-5 2.3L	7.8	②	13–14.5	192	19.8	5.7	4	3.4	7.6
	9-5 3.0L	7.6	②	13–14.5	192	19.8	5.3	—	3.4	7.6

① — Includes oil for filter change.

② — Saab original coolant.

LUBRICANT DATA

Year	Model	Lubricant Type			
		Transmission		Power Steering	Brake System
		Manual	Automatic		
1998	900	SF CC/CD 10W-30/10W-40 Motor Oil①	Dexron II	③	DOT 4
	9000	SF CC/CD 10W-30/10W-40 Motor Oil①	Dexron II	④	DOT 4
1999–2001	9-3	Saab Synthetic Manual Gearbox Oil No. 400 108 247①	Dexron III	②	DOT 4
	9-5	Saab Synthetic Manual Gearbox Oil No. 400 108 247①	Dexron III	②	DOT 4

① — Synthetic motor oil must not be used.

② — Saab power steering fluid part No. 30 32 380.

③ — Saab power steering fluid part No. (45) 30 09 800.

④ — Saab power steering fluid 1890, Part No. (45) 3002995.

Electrical

NOTE: On Air Bag Equipped Models, Refer To "Air Bag System Precautions" Located In The Front Of This Manual For System Disarming & Arming Procedures.

INDEX

	Page No.
Air Bags	7-69
Air Conditioning	7-45
Alternator, Replace	7-6
9-5	7-6
Alternators	7-63
Blower Motor, Replace	7-9
9-3 & 900	7-9
9-5	7-9
9000	7-10
Coil Pack, Replace	7-6
Less Direct Ignition System (DIS)	7-6
With Direct Ignition System (DIS)	7-7
Cooling Fans	7-46
Cruise Controls	7-65
Dash Gauges	7-59
Dash Panels	7-82
Distributor, Replace	7-6
Evaporator Core, Replace	7-10
9-3 & 900	7-10
9-5	7-10
9000	7-11
Fuel Pump Relay Location	7-5
9-3 & 9-5	7-5
9000	7-6
900	7-6
Fuse Panel & Flasher Location	7-5
9-3 & 9-5	7-5
9000	7-5
900	7-5
Heater Core, Replace	7-10
9-3 & 900	7-10
9-5	7-10
9000	7-10
Ignition Lock, Replace	7-7
Ignition Switch, Replace	7-7
9-3 & 900	7-7
9-5 & 9000	7-7
Instrument Cluster, Replace	7-8
9-3 & 900	7-8
9-5 & 9000	7-8
Neutral Safety Switch, Replace	7-7
Passive Restraints	7-69
Precautions	7-5
Air Bag Systems	7-5
Battery Ground Cable	7-5
Radio Anti-Theft Lock	7-5
Radio, Replace	7-8
9-3 & 9-5	7-8
9000	7-8
900	7-8
Relay Center Location	7-6
9-3 & 9-5	7-6
9000	7-6
900	7-6
Speed Controls	7-65
Starter Motors	7-61
Starter, Replace	7-6
9-5	7-6
9-3 & 900	7-6
9000	7-6
Steering Columns	7-85
Steering Wheel, Replace	7-8
9-3 & 900	7-8
9-5 & 9000	7-8
Turn Signal Switch, Replace	7-8
Wiper Motor, Replace	7-8
9-3 & 900	7-8
9-5	7-9
9000	7-9
Wiper Switch, Replace	7-9
9-3, 900 & 9000	7-9
9-5	7-9
Wiper Transmission, Replace	7-9
9-3 & 900	7-9
9-5 & 9000	7-9

PRECAUTIONS

AIR BAG SYSTEMS

Refer to "Air Bag System Precautions" in the front of this manual for system disarming and arming procedures.

BATTERY GROUND CABLE

Prior to service, disconnect battery ground cable and isolate as required.

RADIO ANTI-THEFT LOCK

9000

The Radio and cassette player are equipped with an electronic four-digit anti-theft lock. This four-digit code is programmed at manufacturing and cannot be changed. If the battery is disconnected for more than three minutes, if unit is removed or if otherwise cut off from power, the four-digit code must be entered with the quick-selection buttons as follows:

1. Turn radio on, then, when display shows "Code In," enter four-digit code with quick-selection buttons. If code is correct, last-tuned radio frequency is shown on display. If wrong digit has been entered by mistake, all four digits must be entered again. If code is wrong it stays on display.
2. If incorrect four-digit code has been entered, press Band button for more than three seconds to clear display. Display shows "Code In" and new attempt to enter correct code can be made.
3. If wrong code has been used three times in succession, four dashes appear on display and you must wait an hour with radio switched on before trying again.
4. To try again, hold Band button for at least three seconds. "Code In" should appear on display.
5. Correct code must be entered at first attempt, otherwise you must wait another hour with unit switched on before trying again.

FUSE PANEL & FLASHER LOCATION

9-3 & 9-5

The fuse panel is located behind the lefthand side of the instrument panel, above the lefthand side kick panel. There are two engine compartment fuse panels. The main engine compartment fuse panel is located on the rear lefthand side of the engine compartment. The maxi engine compartment fuse panel is located on the front lefthand side of the engine compartment, next to the battery.

Flasher operation is controlled by the Dashboard Integrated Central Electronics (DICE) module. The DICE module is located behind the lefthand side of the instrument panel, left of the steering column, above the instrument panel main relay panel.

900

The fuse panel is located on the lefthand side of the vehicle, between the door and the instrument panel. Two additional fuse panels are located in the engine compartment. One fuse panel is located at the far left of the engine bay below the windshield and the other (Maxi fuse box) is located between the battery and the lefthand strut tower. The Integrated Central Electrics (ICE) control module is located on the lefthand side of the vehicle, between the door and the instrument panel.

9000

The fuse panel and flasher are located behind the glove compartment. An additional fuse/relay panel is located in the engine compartment.

FUEL PUMP RELAY LOCATION

9-3 & 9-5

The fuel pump relay is located in the instrument panel main relay box. The instrument panel main relay box is located behind the lefthand side of the instrument panel, left of the steering column.

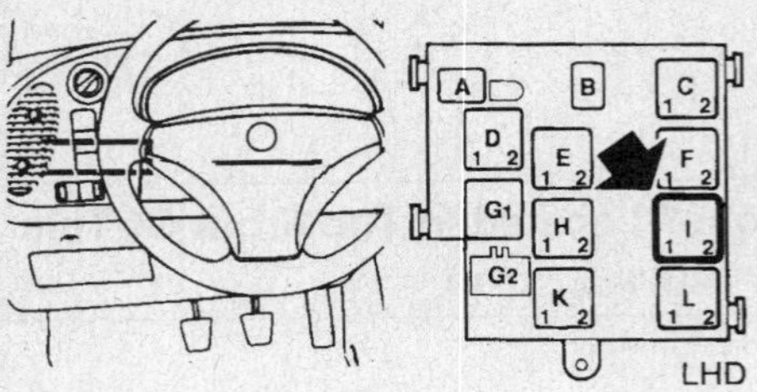

Fig. 1 Fuel pump relay location. 900 w/Motronic 4.1 fuel system

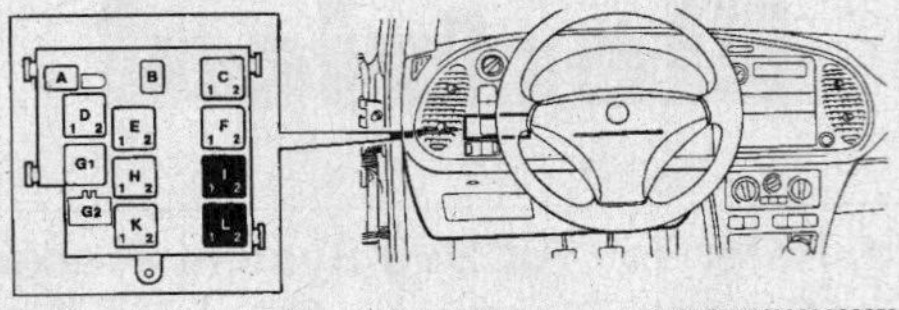

Fig. 2 Fuel pump relay location. 900 w/Motronic 5.2 fuel system

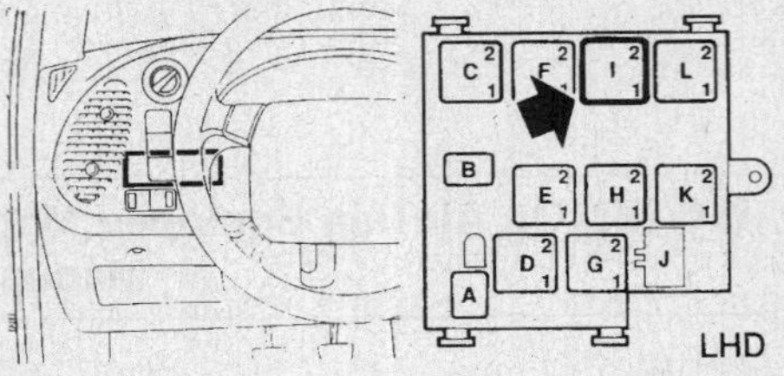

Fig. 3 Fuel pump relay location. 900 w/Trionic fuel system

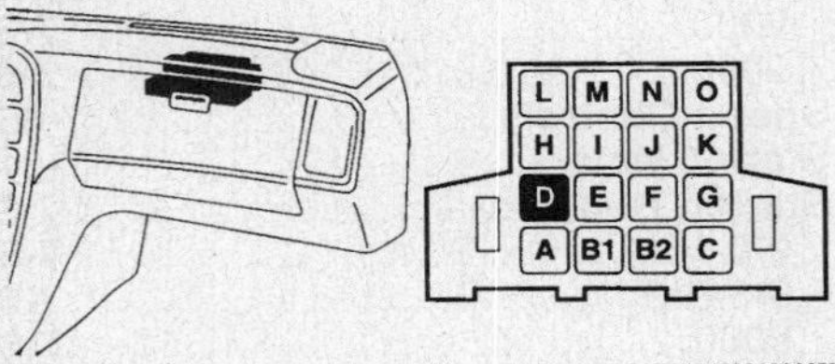

Fig. 4 Fuel pump relay location. 9000 w/Trionic fuel system

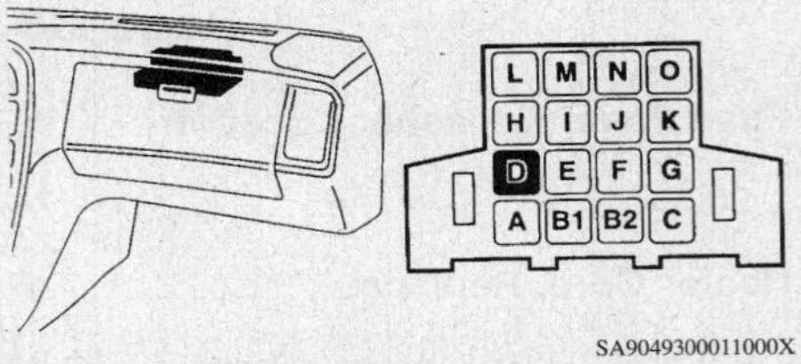

Fig. 5 Fuel pump relay location. 9000 w/Motronic 2.8 fuel system

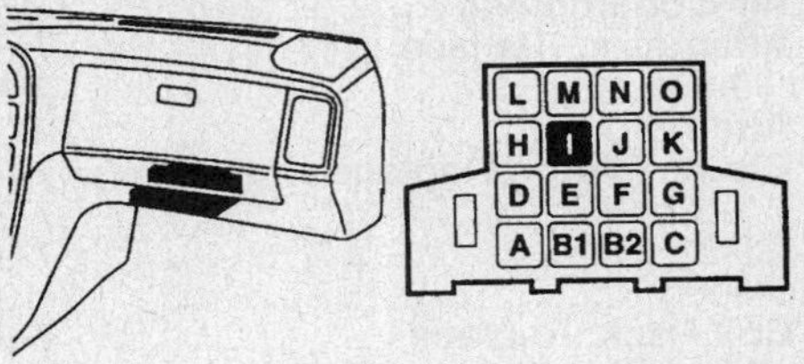

Fig. 6 Fuel pump relay location. 9000 w/Motronic 5.2 fuel system

900

Refer to **Figs. 1 through 3** for fuel pump relay location.

9000

The fuel pump relay is located on the righthand upper instrument panel behind the glove box, **Figs. 4 through 6.**

RELAY CENTER LOCATION

9-3 & 9-5

The engine compartment relay panel is located on the rear lefthand side of the engine compartment. The instrument panel main relay box is located behind the lefthand side of the instrument panel, left of the steering column. On convertible models, there is a relay panel mounted left of the rear seat, behind the trim panel.

900

The fuse/relay panel is located in the engine compartment. Some relays are also located in the fuse panel behind the glove compartment.

9000

The fuse/relay panel is located in the engine compartment. Some relays are also located in the fuse panel behind the glove compartment and in the ABS/TCS fuse box behind the brake fluid reservoir.

STARTER

REPLACE

9.3 & 900

2.0L & 2.3L Engines

1. Remove upper attaching bolt.
2. Raise and support vehicle, then disconnect starter motor cables.
3. Remove lower attaching bolt.
4. Twist exhaust pipe slightly to one side and lift out starter motor.
5. Reverse procedure to install.

9-5

1. Remove battery cover and intake manifold shield.
2. Remove starter motor upper retaining bolt.
3. Disconnect starter motor electrical connectors.
4. Raise and support vehicle.
5. Cut strap from around solenoid.
6. Remove starter motor lower retaining bolt, then the starter.
7. Reverse procedure to install.

9000

1. Obtain radio anti-theft code as outlined under "Precautions."
2. Disconnect starter motor electrical connectors.
3. Loosen starter motor bracket bar upper attaching bolt. Do not remove bolt.
4. Remove both starter motor to engine block attaching bolts.
5. Remove starter motor from vehicle.
6. Reverse procedure to install.

ALTERNATOR

REPLACE

9-5

1. Remove battery cover and intake manifold shield.
2. Remove crankcase ventilation solenoid and constant pressure valves.
3. Release serpentine belt tension with belt tensioner tool No. 83 95 254, or equivalent, then remove belt.
4. Remove upper alternator attaching bolt.
5. Mark position of righthand engine mount, then loosen mount retaining bolt. Lubricate mount so that it will slide.
6. Raise and support vehicle, then remove the front exhaust pipe.
7. Loosen alternator rear mounting bolt, then remove hose between oil trap and oil sump.
8. Disconnect wire terminals from rear of alternator.
9. Remove lower alternator attaching bolt.
10. Lower alternator between steering gear and intermediate shaft, then remove alternator between transaxle and subframe.
11. Reverse procedure to install, noting the following:
    a. **Torque** belt tensioner bolt to 33 ft. lbs.
    b. **Torque** engine mount bolt to 37 ft. lbs.
    c. **Torque** alternator rear mounting bolt to 19 ft. lbs.

DISTRIBUTOR

REPLACE

1. **On 9000 models,** obtain radio anti-theft code as outlined under "Precautions."
2. **On all models,** disconnect high tension leads from distributor cap.
3. Disconnect Hall sensor and vacuum hose.
4. Remove distributor cap from distributor body.
5. Pry back on distributor retaining clip, then remove distributor.
6. Reverse procedure to install.

COIL PACK

REPLACE

LESS DIRECT IGNITION SYSTEM (DIS)

900

1. Remove engine covers (1), then unplug ignition coil pack electrical connector (2).
2. Remove coil pack mounting bolts (3), then coil pack, **Fig. 7.**

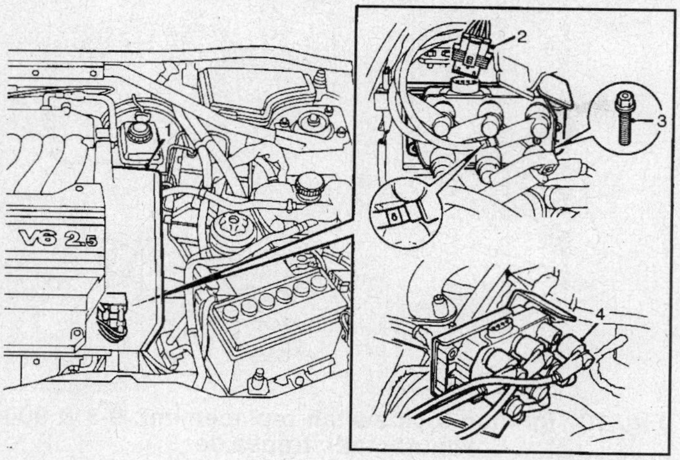

SA1119500001000X

Fig. 7 Coil pack replacement. 900 less DIS

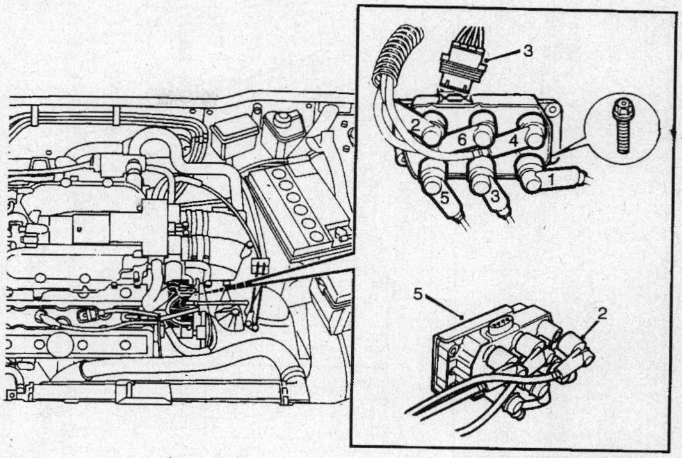

SA1119500003000X

Fig. 8 Coil pack replacement. 9000 less DIS

3. Disconnect spark plug wires (4), record position for installation reference.
4. Reverse procedure to install.

9000

1. Remove intake duct and resonating chamber.
2. Disconnect spark plug wires (2).
3. Disconnect ignition coil pack top electrical connector (3).
4. Remove coil pack mounting bolts, then coil pack (5), **Fig. 8.**
5. Reverse procedure to install.

WITH DIRECT IGNITION SYSTEM (DIS)

1. Disconnect DIS coil pack electrical connector (1), **Fig. 9.**
2. Remove DIS coil pack mounting bolts and coil pack from top of cylinder head.
3. Reverse procedure to install.

IGNITION LOCK

REPLACE

Refer to "Ignition Switch, Replace" for procedure.

IGNITION SWITCH

REPLACE

9-3 & 900

Automatic Transaxle

1. Place selector lever in P position and remove key.
2. Release indicator plate and rubber seal from selector lever housing, then turn it to one side.
3. Release selector lever wire clip.
4. Remove ignition lock switch (4), then the ignition lock (5), **Fig. 10.**
5. Reverse procedure to install, then check play in parking lock.

Manual Transaxle

1. Remove lefthand front seat, middle console side covers and middle console.
2. Remove air duct, then engage transaxle in 4th gear.
3. Remove plastic plug on gearbox, then insert locking pin with ring in uppermost position.
4. Remove clamp holding gear rod in linkage.
5. Engage 3rd gear so gear rod and linkage separate, then remove screws holding gear lever housing.
6. Lift up housing and turn, then remove two clamps holding ignition lock cables in gear lever housing.
7. Disconnect terminal on ignition lock, then pull backward and lift out gear lever housing with gear rod.
8. Remove locking plate holder, then the spring securing locking plate (3), **Fig. 11.**
9. Using screwdriver, click up on rider controlled by ignition lock, then lift up locking plate and plastic fastener (4).
10. Remove ignition lock switch (5), then the ignition lock (6).
11. Reverse procedure to install, noting the following:
    a. Adjust position of locking plate with screw on plate holder. Locking plate should be level with heel in gear lever housing. **Stop should not touch locking plate during adjustment.**
    b. **Torque** gear rod to linkage clamp nut to 16 ft. lbs.

9-5 & 9000

1. Obtain radio anti-theft code as outlined under "Precautions."
2. Remove steering wheel as outlined under "Steering Wheel, Replace."
3. Remove wiper/washer and turn signal switch covers.
4. Remove upper section of instrument panel.
5. Remove air ducts both in and above steering column.
6. Cut off clip securing wiring harness and flexible ducts to steering column.
7. Disconnect wiper/washer and turn signal electrical connectors. Disconnect horn switch and ignition switch leads.
8. Remove upper joint pinch bolt. Loosen remaining bolt and withdraw universal joint from steering column shaft splines.
9. Remove steering wheel adjustment assembly as follows:
    a. Using hammer and drift, tap out tubular dowel.
    b. Remove nut and washer.
    c. Withdraw shaft from clamp.
    d. Lift off upper section of steering wheel adjustment assembly.
10. Remove three attaching screws, then lift off turn signal switch.
11. Remove rubber bushing from housing, then the upper section of the steering column.
12. Remove washer and steering column bearing.
13. Loosen attaching screws, then remove ignition switch.
14. Turn ignition switch key to position 1, then press in locking tab and withdraw lock cylinder.
15. Reverse procedure to install.

NEUTRAL SAFETY SWITCH

REPLACE

1. **On 9-5 and 9000 models,** obtain radio anti-theft code as outlined under "Precautions."
2. **On all models,** loosen locknut and remove shift knob and shift indicator plate.
3. Disconnect indicator lamp, then remove top cover.
4. Pull carpet back from shifter cover assembly.
5. Remove rear ashtray and five screws securing center rear console.
6. Disconnect wiring harness connectors and remove console.
7. Disconnect wiring harness connectors to switch assembly.
8. Remove screws securing switch to shifter assembly, then the switch.
9. Place transaxle selector in neutral and install switch with screws finger tight.
10. Rotate switch until line on switch is aligned with lever and secure switch.
11. Reconnect wiring harness connectors

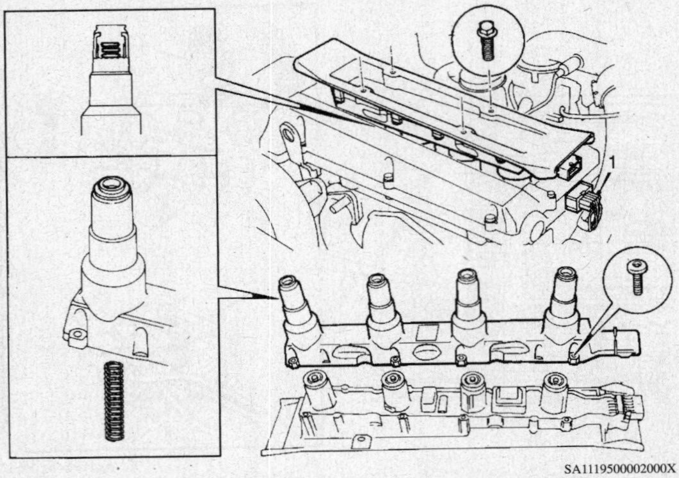

Fig. 9 Coil pack replacement. With DIS

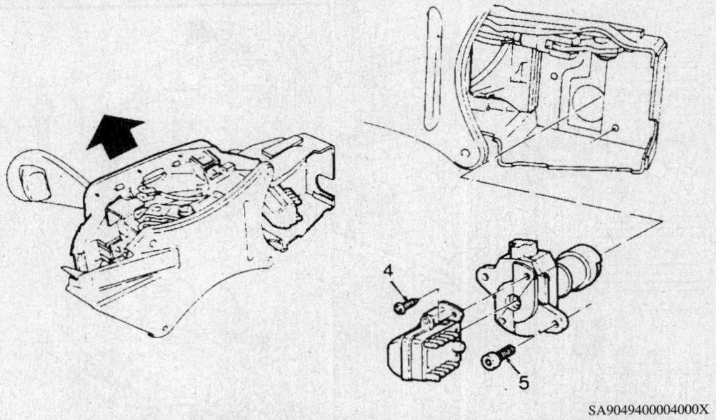

Fig. 10 Ignition lock switch replacement. 9-3 & 900 w/automatic transaxle

and reverse procedure to install remaining components.

TURN SIGNAL SWITCH

REPLACE

Switches for direction indicator lights and the wiper/washer system are fitted in a panel mounted on the steering wheel bearing support. The panel can be removed after the cover beneath the support is removed.

STEERING WHEEL

REPLACE

9-3 & 900

1. Remove air bag module retaining screws from underside of steering wheel, then disconnect electrical connector and remove air bag module.
2. Disconnect horn connector, then set wheels in straight ahead position.
3. Loosen steering column, then rock steering wheel loose and remove.
4. Reverse procedure to install.

9-5 & 9000

1. Position wheels in straight ahead position, then remove two horn pad/air bag module retaining screws from rear of steering wheel.
2. Disconnect horn pad/air bag module electrical connectors, then remove from vehicle.
3. Place match marks on steering shaft and steering wheel, then remove steering wheel nut.
4. Using puller, gently ease steering wheel off of shaft so air bag clock spring is not damaged.
5. Reverse procedure to install, noting the following:
   a. Set wheels in straight ahead position.
   b. Rotate clock spring clockwise until it stops, then rotate counterclockwise 3 ½ turns.
   c. Hold clock spring in position, then thread air bag module and horn wiring through hole in steering wheel.
   d. Align match marks on shaft and steering wheel, then align clock spring with hole in wheel.
   e. **Torque** steering wheel nut to 24–32 ft. lbs.

INSTRUMENT CLUSTER

REPLACE

9-3 & 900

1. Remove steering wheel covers.
2. Remove all switches, SID module and audio system from fascia.
3. Mark all connectors for installation reference.
4. Remove nine screws holding front panel.
5. Fold front plate out toward interior.
6. Remove four instrument housing screws.
7. Remove connector(s) from back.
8. Reverse procedure to install.

9-5 & 9000

1. Obtain radio anti-theft code as outlined under "Precautions."
2. Remove both speaker grilles on either side of instrument panel.
3. Remove instrument panel attaching screws, then the panel and duct.
4. Disconnect vacuum hose from turbocharger pressure gauge, then the speedometer cable and all connectors from instrument cluster.
5. Remove instrument cluster attaching screw, then the instrument cluster.
6. Reverse procedure to install.

RADIO

REPLACE

9-3 & 9-5

A Tech 2, or equivalent, scan tool is necessary to remove the radio from this vehicle.

1. Connect scan tool to diagnostic connector, then follow scan tool instructions to "divorce" radio from vehicle. The diagnostic connector is located under the lefthand side of the instrument panel.
2. Insert radio removal tool No. 84 71 161, or equivalent, into access holes on each side of radio.
3. Remove radio from instrument panel, then disconnect antenna and electrical connectors.
4. Reverse procedure to install. Follow scan tool instructions to "marry" radio to vehicle.

900

1. Remove radio knobs and face plate retaining nuts and washers.
2. Remove face plate and radio, then the rear radio support bracket if installed.
3. Remove antenna cable and electrical connections.
4. Reverse procedure to install.

9000

1. Obtain radio anti-theft code as outlined under "Precautions."
2. Bend puller arms of radio puller tool No. 8471 161, or equivalent, to a 90° angle and insert into two holes on front of radio unit, **Fig. 12.**
3. Holding puller tool horizontal, pull out radio unit, then disconnect connections.
4. Connect connections, then insert radio unit into dash.

WIPER MOTOR

REPLACE

9-3 & 900

1. Pry off protective cap at base of wiper arms with screwdriver, then remove nut and lift off arm.
2. Disconnect washer hose for hood from protective cover space between bulkhead partitions.
3. Remove rubber sealing strip from partition.
4. Remove clip for protective cover over space between bulkhead partitions.
5. Raise cover slightly and disconnect washer hose from underside, then remove cover.

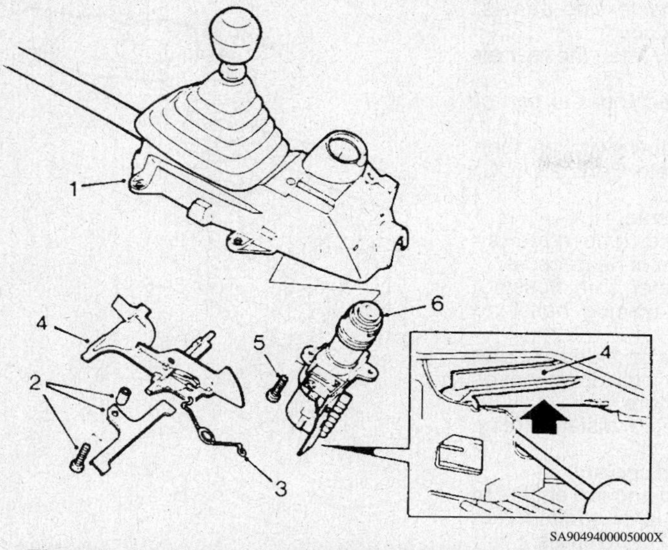

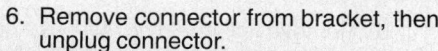

Fig. 11 Ignition lock switch removal. 9-3 & 900 w/manual transaxle

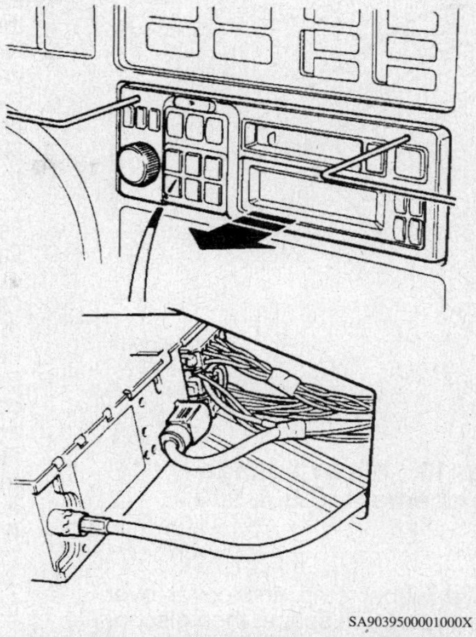

Fig. 12 Radio removal. 9000

6. Remove connector from bracket, then unplug connector.
7. Remove spindle guide covers, then the three bolts securing wiper mechanism.
8. Lift out entire wiper unit, then remove linkages from bracket and motor, **Fig. 13.**
9. Remove three bolts securing motor to bracket and separate motor and bracket, **Fig. 14.**
10. Reverse procedure to install.

9-5

1. Remove wiper arm retaining nuts, then the wiper arms from spindles.
2. Remove protective cover retaining screws and rubber seals from spindles.
3. Loosen rubber molding along edge of bulkhead.
4. Remove cover from bulkhead panel, then lift cover off of center spindle and climate housing.
5. Disconnect wiper motor electrical connectors.
6. Remove wiper assembly attaching bolts, then lift entire assembly out of vehicle.
7. Separate wiper motor from wiper assembly.
8. Reverse procedure to install.

9000

1. Obtain radio anti-theft code as outlined under "Precautions."
2. Remove wiper arms by lifting covers and removing attaching nuts.
3. Remove rubber grommets from spindles.
4. Remove four bulkhead panel bolts from underneath hood.
5. Remove bulkhead for access to wiper motor.
6. Disconnect wiper motor electrical connectors.
7. Remove spindle nuts.
8. Remove four securing bolts for wiper motor bracket.
9. Push down and pull forward lefthand wiper pushrod.
10. Remove wiper motor with bracket and linkage. **To ease removal, hold electrical connectors under wiper motor bracket as wiper motor is removed.**
11. Remove bracket and linkage from wiper motor.
12. Reverse procedure to install.

WIPER SWITCH

REPLACE

9-3, 900 & 9000

Refer to "Turn Signal Switch, Replace" when replacing wiper switch.

9-5

1. Pull steering wheel out as far as possible.
2. Remove upper and lower covers from top of steering column.
3. Pull switch out of steering column and disconnect electrical connector.
4. Reverse procedure to install.

WIPER TRANSMISSION

REPLACE

9-3 & 900

The wiper assembly is an integral unit mounted on the bulkhead in the engine compartment. Power from the motor is transferred to the spindles by the transmission. The transmission is an integral part of the motor. Refer to "Wiper Motor, Replace" for wiper transmission replacement procedure.

9-5 & 9000

Refer to "Wiper Motor, Replace" for wiper transmission and motor replacement.

BLOWER MOTOR

REPLACE

9-3 & 900

1. Pry off protective cap at base of wiper arms with screwdriver, then remove nuts and lift off arms.
2. Remove cover over bulkhead, then disconnect washer hose to hood from protective cover over space between bulkhead partitions.
3. Remove rubber sealing strip from partition.
4. Remove protective cover clip from space between bulkhead partitions.
5. Raise cover slightly, then disconnect washer hose from underside and lift off cover.
6. Remove connector from bracket, then disconnect connector.
7. Remove cover for spindle guides, then the three wiper mechanism attaching bolts and windshield wiper unit.
8. Remove fresh-air filter, then disconnect ventilator fan electrical connector.
9. Remove screw holding electrical connection, then the ventilation fan screws and the ventilation fan.
10. Reverse procedure to install.

9-5

1. Remove wiper assembly as outlined under "Wiper Motor, Replace."
2. Remove frame from around blower motor.
3. Remove wiper arm bracket from top of blower motor.
4. Remove wire harness clips from blower motor case, then position wire harness aside.
5. Remove blower motor cover attaching screws and the cover.
6. Remove blower motor, cut cable tie and disconnect blower motor electrical connector.
7. Reverse procedure to install.

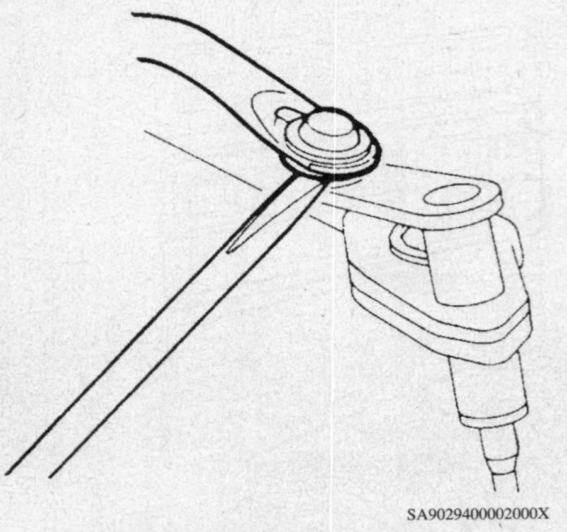

Fig. 13 Wiper linkage replacement. 9-3 & 900

9000

1. Remove rubber strip and cover over bulkhead partition space, then disconnect washer hose.
2. Free righthand shield plates, then open brace over A/C lines.
3. Remove evaporator casing screws, then lift evaporator casing forward to gain access to servo motor screws.
4. Remove servo motor screws, then disconnect motor electrical connector and motor.
5. Position motor, then place evaporator casing in position. **Ensure drainage hose is not kinked and water can freely run out of evaporator casing and down drainage hose.**
6. Secure evaporator casing, then plug servo motor connector.
7. Lower brace over A/C lines, then install shield plates.
8. Connect washer hose to cover and secure cover and rubber strip over bulkhead partition space.
9. Calibrate system by pressing Auto and Vent buttons at same time. **When calibrating, all previous diagnostic trouble codes are erased. All stored diagnostic trouble codes should be read before calibration.**

HEATER CORE

REPLACE

9-3 & 900

1. Install hose clips on hoses by heater core, then remove hoses from heater core.
2. Empty coolant from core using compressed air.
3. Remove glove compartment as follows:
   a. Open glove compartment, then the covers to expose retaining screws.
   b. Remove all retaining screws, retaining bolt and expanding rivet in front edge, then the catch from bulkhead bracket.
   c. Remove glove compartment and disconnect glove compartment lamp connector.
4. Remove center console side panels, then the ignition lock cover.
5. Remove rear ashtray, then the rear air vents and cover.
6. Remove screws attaching rear part of center console.
7. Remove power window switches, then the Automatic Climate Control (ACC) control unit.
8. Remove center console.
9. Cut off cable ties and remove rear air ducts on floor in front of heater core.
10. Open cover on heater core housing, then remove clips holding hoses to heater core.
11. Remove toggle clips on side of heater core housing, then pull down hoses and remove heater core.
12. Reverse procedure to install, noting the following:
    a. Refill system with coolant.
    b. Refit pressure lid and run engine at varying speeds until radiator fan has started three more times.
    c. Switch off engine and top off to MAX level.

9-5

1. Drain coolant into a suitable container.
2. Blow compressed air into cylinder head hose connection to remove any coolant remaining in heater core.
3. Remove glove compartment from under righthand side or instrument panel.
4. Remove trim panel from righthand side of center console.
5. Disconnect air outlet hose from air duct.
6. Remove pad connector holding heater core tubes to heater core.
7. Remove heater core to heater core housing attaching bolts.
8. Reverse procedure to install.

9000

1. Obtain radio anti-theft code as outlined under "Precautions."
2. Drain cooling system.
3. Remove blower motor as outlined under "Blower Motor, Replace."
4. Release clips and disconnect heater hoses from heater core.
5. Remove heater core from housing.
6. Reverse procedure to install. Use new O-rings when connecting heater hoses.

EVAPORATOR CORE

REPLACE

9-3 & 900

If the evaporator has one-piece pipes between the evaporator and the lead-through in the bulkhead wall, the pipes must be cut before removal and a new evaporator installed.

1. Drain refrigerant into an approved recovery/recycling device compatible with refrigerant type.
2. Remove glove compartment as follows:
   a. Open glove compartment, then the covers to expose retaining screws.

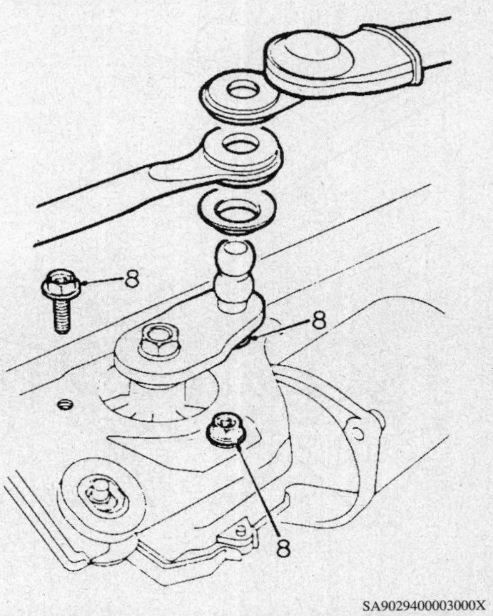

Fig. 14 Wiper motor replacement. 9-3 & 900

   b. Remove all retaining screws, retaining bolt and expanding rivet in front edge, then the catch from bulkhead bracket.
   c. Remove glove compartment and disconnect glove compartment lamp connector.
3. Remove center console side panel, then the knee guard.
4. Remove air duct in floor, then the air duct to panel's side vent.
5. **On models equipped with automatic transaxle,** remove gearbox control unit from bracket on bulkhead wall and let hang on its cables.
6. **On all models,** remove evaporator bracket, then disconnect cables. Open cable ties and turn cables to one side.
7. Turn down carpet and remove protective cover.
8. **On models equipped with Automatic Climate Control (ACC),** remove fan control unit attaching screws.
9. **On models equipped with 2.3L engine,** remove screw holding A/C hoses PAD connection to expansion valve. Screw is accessible from engine compartment.
10. **On all models,** disconnect electrical connectors, then remove anti-frost thermostat.
11. Cut pipes with plate sheers and pull out evaporator from climate control.
12. Reverse procedure to install. **Torque** expansion valve screws 4 ft. lbs. or block screws 15 ft. lbs.

9-5

1. Discharge A/C system refrigerant as outlined in "Air Conditioning" section.
2. Remove glove compartment from under righthand side of instrument panel.
3. Cut cable ties holding wiring harness and cooler hose to evaporator core service cover.
4. Remove service cover and fresh air filter.

5. Remove blower motor as outlined under "Blower Motor, Replace."
6. **On models with jointless refrigerant pipes,** access pipes through the air recirculation flap in the engine compartment and cut pipes with a sheet metal cutter or air-driven jigsaw.
7. **On models with jointed refrigerant pipes,** disconnect pipes from evaporator core.
8. **On all models,** remove evaporator core and disconnect temperature sensor.
9. Remove two Allen screws attaching expansion valve to evaporator core, then the valve from evaporator core.
10. Reverse procedure to install.

9000

1. Obtain radio anti-theft code as outlined under "Precautions."
2. Discharge refrigerant into an approved recovery/recycling device compatible with refrigerant type.
3. Remove false bulkhead panel in engine compartment and top bolt from oil filler pipe support.
4. Disconnect refrigerant lines from receiver inlet and evaporator outlet. Plug lines and open fittings.
5. Remove plastic bushing from panel and secure refrigerant lines aside.
6. Remove vacuum pump for cruise control system.
7. Disconnect electrical connectors from fan control unit, air recirculation valve motor, thermostat and pressure switch.
8. Remove bolts securing engine mount bracket and insert rubber mallet between brace and engine.
9. Remove bolts securing evaporator housing.
10. Lift up on end of housing, move assembly toward center, then remove housing assembly from vehicle.
11. Remove fresh air filter and receiver mounting screw.
12. Remove insulation, clip and sensor body, then disconnect capillary tube and expansion valve from evaporator.
13. Remove receiver and expansion valve as an assembly. Plug all open fittings.
14. Remove thermostat assembly and actuating motor for air recirculation valve.
15. Separate housing and remove evaporator.
16. Reverse procedure to install.

Engine

NOTE: On Air Bag Equipped Models, Refer To "Air Bag System Precautions" Located In The Front Of This Manual For System Disarming & Arming Procedures.

INDEX

	Page No.
Belt Tension Data	7-22
Camshaft, Replace	7-20
Cooling System Bleed	7-22
2.0L & 2.3L Engines	7-22
3.0L Engine	7-22
Crankshaft Seal, Replace	7-20
9-3 & 900	7-20
9000	7-21
Cylinder Head, Replace	7-16
9-3 & 900	7-16
9000	7-16
Engine Rebuilding Specifications	7-206
Engine, Replace	7-12
9-3 & 900	7-12
9000	7-13
Front Cover Seal, Replace	7-18
9-3 & 900	7-18
9000	7-18
Fuel Pump, Replace	7-22
9-3 & 900	7-22
9000	7-22
Intake Air Heat Plates, Replace	7-16
9-3 & 900	7-16
Intake Manifold, Replace	7-15
9-3 & 900	7-15
9000	7-15
Main & Rod Bearings	7-20
Oil Pan, Replace	7-21
9-3 & 900	7-21
9000	7-21
Oil Pump, Replace	7-21
9-3 & 900	7-21
9000	7-21
Pistons, Pins & Rings	7-20
Precautions	7-12
Air Bag Systems	7-12
Battery Ground Cable	7-12
Radio Anti-Theft Lock	7-12
Serpentine Drive Belt	7-22
Inspection	7-22
Routing	7-22
Tightening Specifications	7-24
9-3 & 900	7-24
9000	7-24
Timing Belt, Replace	7-19
3.0L Engine	7-19
Timing Chain, Replace	7-19
2.0L & 2.3L Engines	7-19
Turbocharger, Replace	7-23
9-3 & 900	7-23
9000	7-23
Valve Adjustment	7-18
Valve Clearance Specifications	7-18
Valve Guides	7-18
Valve Seats	7-18
Water Pump, Replace	7-22
9-3 & 900	7-22
9000	7-22

PRECAUTIONS

AIR BAG SYSTEMS

Refer to "Air Bag System Precautions" in the front of this manual for system disarming and arming procedures.

BATTERY GROUND CABLE

Prior to service, disconnect battery ground cable and isolate as required.

RADIO ANTI-THEFT LOCK

Radio and cassette player are equipped with an electronic four-digit anti-theft lock. This four-digit code is programmed at manufacturing and cannot be changed. If the battery is disconnected for more than three minutes, if unit is removed or if otherwise cut off from power, the four-digit code must be entered with the quick-selection buttons as follows:

1. Turn radio on, then, when display shows "Code In," enter four-digit code with quick-selection buttons. If code is correct, last-tuned radio frequency is shown on display. If wrong digit has been entered by mistake, all four digits must be entered again. If code is wrong it stays on display.
2. If incorrect four-digit code has been entered, press Band button for more than three seconds to clear display. Display shows "Code In" and new attempt to enter correct code can be made.
3. If wrong code has been used three times in succession, four dashes appear on display and you must wait an hour with radio switched on before trying again.
4. To try again, hold Band button for at least three seconds. "Code In" should appear on display.
5. Correct code must be entered at first attempt, otherwise you must wait another hour with unit switched on before trying again.

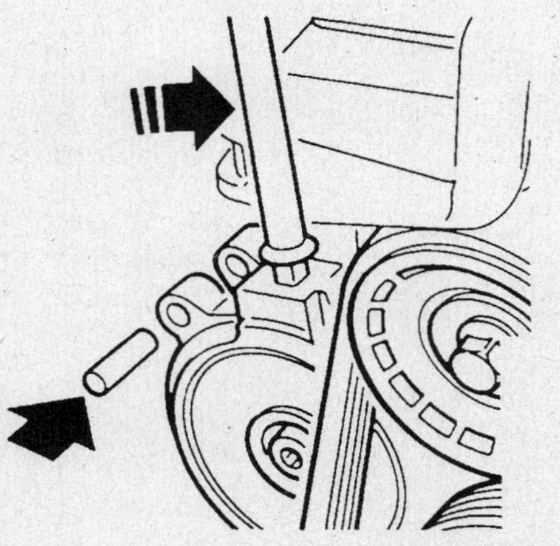

Fig. 1 Belt tensioner loosening. 9-3 & 900 w/2.0L & 2.3L engines

ENGINE

REPLACE

9-3 & 900

1. Remove battery, then drain coolant. Remove filler cap on expansion tank to speed draining.
2. Remove air cleaner with hoses, then the cover or resonator.
3. Detach throttle cable and position aside.
4. Remove cruise control unit with cable as follows:
   a. Disconnect cruise control cable from throttle body, then disconnect electrical connector.
   b. Remove cruise control retaining bolts.
   c. Remove cruise control and cable from vehicle.
5. Disconnect fuel hoses using fuel line separator tool No. 83 94 702, or equivalent.
6. Disconnect tank breather hose and position aside.
7. **On turbocharged models,** remove pressure sensor and place it on engine.
8. **On all models,** disconnect secondary injection vacuum hose, then the brake servo vacuum hose from intake manifold.
9. **On turbocharged models,** remove boost pressure control and place it on engine.
10. **On all models,** loosen belt tensioner using ratchet handle extension and 6 mm drill, **Fig. 1. Use care to ensure belt tensioner does not break at its end position.**
11. Remove servo pump from bracket and set aside.
12. **On turbocharged models,** remove pressure pipe between charge air cooler and throttle body.

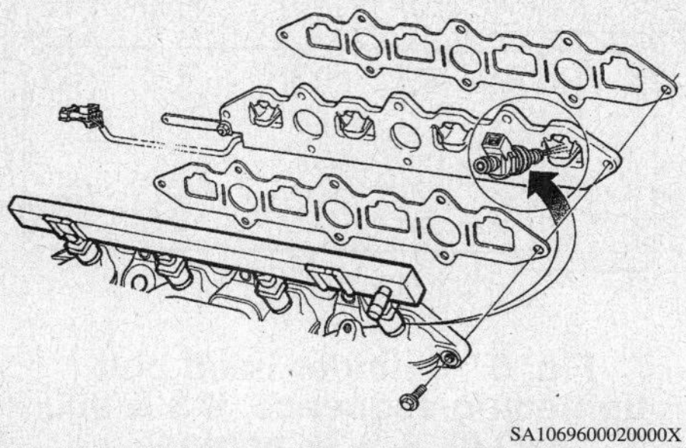

Fig. 2 Intake air heat plate replacement. 9-3 & 900

13. **On all models,** remove coolant hoses, then the secondary air injection hose.
14. Disconnect A/C compressor connector and remove compressor upper retaining bolts.
15. Disconnect positive lead from positive terminal block on engine, then the ground cable from gearbox.
16. **On models equipped with B206i and B234i engines,** remove ignition cable and electrical leads from ignition coil.
17. **On all models,** disconnect gearbox electrical connectors and place on engine.
18. Disconnect oxygen sensor lead and catalytic converter temperature warning lead.
19. **On models equipped with automatic transaxle,** remove breather hose from gearbox, then the selector lever cable.
20. **On models equipped with manual transaxle or Sensonic,** separate selector rod, then the clutch cable or clutch pipe and plug.
21. **On all models,** remove glove compartment.
22. Pull back carpet and unplug central locking system control module, then remove engine wiring.
23. Pull wiring through grommet into engine bay and place on engine. **On turbocharged models, do not forget lead running to BPC.**
24. Loosen hub nuts on both sides of vehicle, then raise and support vehicle.
25. Remove front wheels, then remove hub nuts.
26. Remove brake calipers and hang from suspension struts.
27. Remove end piece nut, then the steering swivel member nuts.
28. Remove wheel housing covers and spoiler sections.
29. Disconnect front pipe and intermediate pipe, then remove front exhaust pipe from exhaust manifold or turbocharger.
30. Remove catalytic converter from bracket and take down exhaust pipe.
31. **On models equipped with automatic transaxle,** disconnect oil hoses from gearbox and position aside. Plug holes.
32. **On turbocharged models,** remove pipe between turbocharger and charge air cooler, then disconnect oil hoses from oil cooler. Plug hoses.
33. **On all models,** position suitable lifting table under vehicle so table supports are directly under front engine mountings and gearbox.
34. Remove bolts retaining subframe and front engine mountings, then slightly lower table along with powertrain and sub-frame.
35. Disconnect end pieces and driveshafts on both sides.
36. Remove A/C compressor and hang from tow rope attachment eye.
37. Lower lifting table fully and remove rear engine mounting from gearbox and remove subframe.
38. Reverse procedure to install. Fill cooling system and check for leaks.

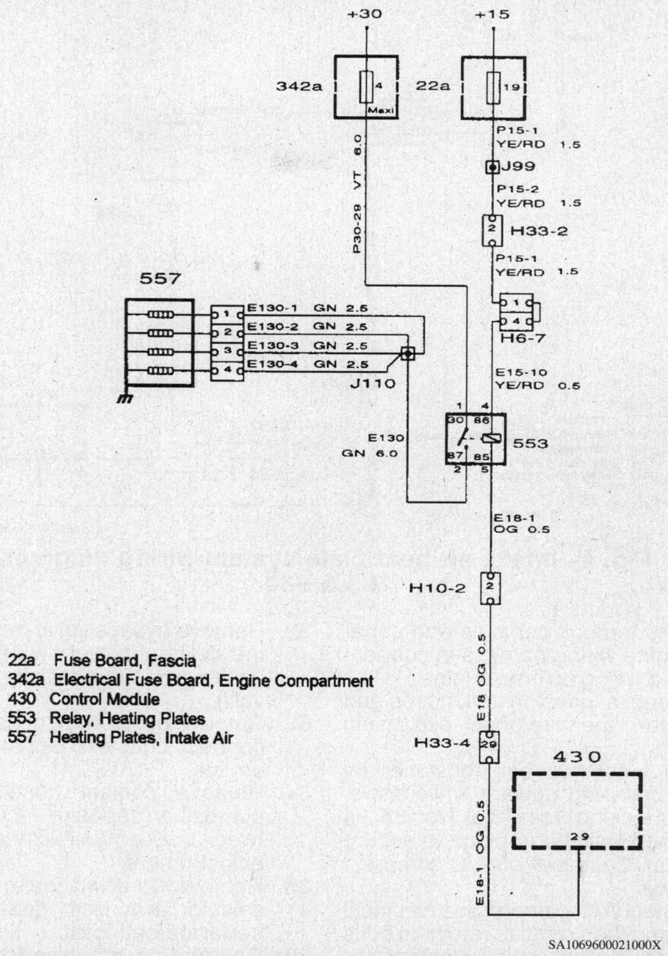

Fig. 3 Intake air heat plate system wiring diagram. 9-3 & 900

9000

2.3L Engine

1. Raise and support vehicle, then remove front wheels.
2. Remove wheel housing trim molding and righthand side front wing liner.
3. Remove middle fill panel from under spoiler.
4. Remove radiator drain plug and drain coolant. Lower vehicle and remove filler cap from expansion tank to speed drainage.
5. Remove throttle cable retaining clip and position cable aside.
6. Remove front main fuse box, then the positive cable terminal block.
7. Obtain radio anti-theft code as outlined under "Precautions."
8. Disconnect positive cable, then remove clamp from tray.
9. Disconnect ABS control module electrical connector, then remove battery tray.
10. Disconnect negative cable from gearbox grounding point.
11. Disconnect windshield washer hose and remove bulkhead space cover and rubber molding from bulkhead partition.
12. Remove clamp securing engine wiring harness to bulkhead partition, then disconnect connector.
13. Disconnect pressure sensor electric lead, then place sensor on engine.
14. Remove bulkhead partition, then snip through cable on righthand side.
15. Disconnect pressure sensor cable, then position aside.
16. Remove ABS relay box and brake fluid reservoirs from holders.
17. Snip through cable tie on lefthand side, then disconnect two engine wiring harness connectors.
18. Disconnect control module connector,

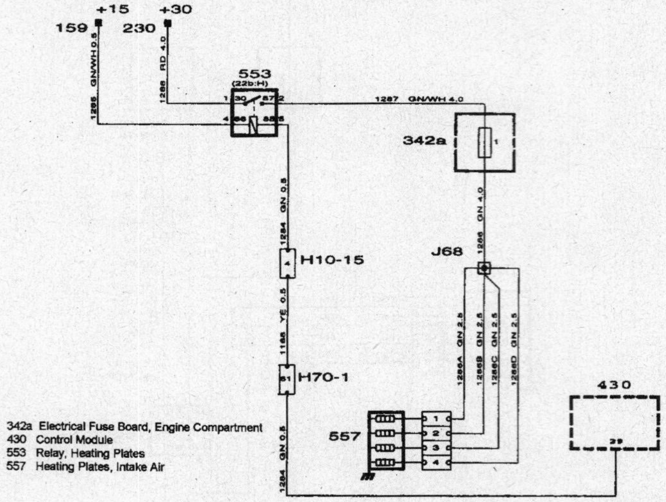

SA1069600022000X

Fig. 4 Intake air heat plate system wiring diagram. 9-3 & 900

then snip through cable tie and separate engine wiring harness in connector. Bend wiring up onto engine.

19. Disconnect expansion tank hoses and connector, then remove expansion tank.
20. Loosen automatic belt tensioner by pulling belt hard upward while assistant fits locking yoke tool No. 83 94 448, or equivalent, in place to secure tensioner. Ease belt off A/C compressor pulley.
21. Disconnect A/C compressor electrical connector, then remove retaining bolts and rest compressor on radiator crossmember.
22. Disconnect return fuel hose from fuel pressure sensor and bend hose up against bulkhead partition.
23. Disconnect fuel delivery hose from fuel rail and vacuum hose from evaporative emission canister on intake manifold, then the brake servo hose. Position hose aside.
24. Disconnect interference suppressor cable (ground) from torque arm bracket.
25. Snip through cable ties holding hoses and wiring at upper torque arm, then remove torque arm.
26. Remove torque arm bracket, then disconnect oxygen sensor electrical connector below intake manifold.
27. Disconnect oxygen sensor cable, then remove power steering fluid reservoir. Lower reservoir and siphon off fluid.
28. Disconnect power steering pump suction hose from reservoir and bend it under intake manifold. Stand reservoir on bulkhead.
29. Disconnect solenoid valve connector, then remove solenoid valve from holder and position valve up against engine.
30. Remove intake hose between air cleaner and turbo, then the filter insert from air cleaner.
31. Remove delivery pipe between turbocharger and charge air cooler.
32. Remove bypass valve from hose, then the delivery pipe between charge air cooler and throttle body with bypass valve.
33. Remove upper coolant hose, then disconnect heat exchanger hoses from engine.
34. Remove coolant hose from water pump, then separate vacuum hose between intake manifold and turbocharger instrument.
35. Remove kickdown cable, then the gear selector arm from gearbox **Do not separate ball joint.**
36. **On models equipped with manual transaxle,** separate gear selector rod by moving tapered pin.
37. **On all models,** press out gear selector cable rubber bushing from gearbox casing bracket.
38. **On models equipped with manual transaxle,** separate clutch pipe.
39. **On all models,** disconnect oil cooler hoses from gearbox, then remove front exhaust pipe and bolts securing front exhaust pipe to exhaust manifold.
40. Remove catalytic converter top mounting bolt, then raise and support vehicle.
41. Remove catalytic converter mounting bolt, then the front exhaust pipe rear connecting flange bolts. Carefully lower front exhaust pipe, being sure not to damage oxygen sensor.
42. Disconnect two oil cooler hoses from engine, then the power steering pump delivery hose from pump. Plug hose.
43. Remove clips around rubber gaiters secured to driveshaft joints.
44. Remove two strut electric leads, then the brake hoses.
45. Remove bottom strut bolts from steering swivel members.
46. Pull out steering swivel members to separate driveshaft joints. Fit protective caps over both halves of driveshaft joints.
47. Remove radiator fan lower retaining bolt, then lower vehicle and remove radiator fan upper retaining bolts.

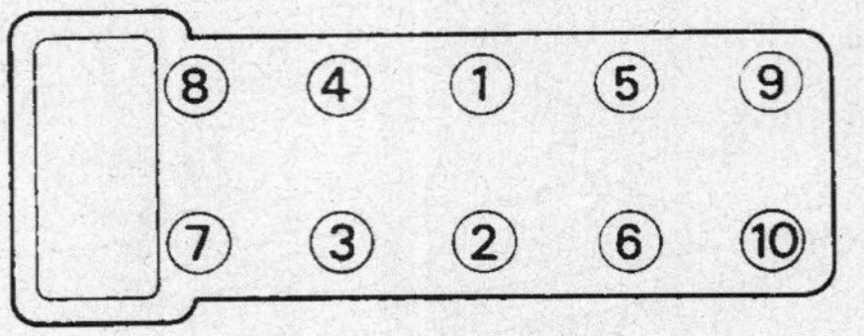

SA1069100002000X

Fig. 5 Cylinder head bolt tightening sequence. 9-3 & 900 w/2.0L & 2.3L engines

48. Disconnect radiator fan wiring harness and remove fan.
49. Remove three engine mounting bolts, then the gas springs from hood. Fit gas spring extension tool No. 83 94 439, or equivalent, on springs.
50. Hook suitable engine lifting yoke to engine lifting eyes and raise engine slightly. Ensure engine is suspended in balance. If it is not, lower engine again and rebalance upper lifting yoke.
51. Reverse procedure to install, noting the following:
    a. **On models equipped with manual transaxle,** insert tapered pin, then install clutch pipes and bleed system.
    b. **On all models,** tighten fasteners to specifications.
    c. **Ensure gearbox is grounded. Failure to ground gearbox could cause fire.**
    d. After refilling cooling system, check for leaks.

3.0L Engine

1. Obtain radio anti-theft code as outlined under "Precautions."
2. Remove battery.
3. Disconnect front electrical distribution box from battery shelf, then remove distribution box.
4. Disconnect cruise control cable from lever.
5. Remove positive terminal block from battery shelf and take off clamp for positive lead.
6. Pull vacuum hose from battery shelf clamps, then remove cable conduit fastenings and battery shelf bolts.
7. Slightly raise battery shelf and disconnect cruise control electrical connector, then remove battery shelf with cruise control module and cable.
8. Release throttle cable from bracket, then snap out control rod and fold bracket to one side.
9. Remove pipes complete with resonator as follows:
    a. Disconnect hose clamps between inlet pipes and intake manifold.
    b. Disconnect hose clamps between resonator and mass air flow sensor.
    c. Raise pipes and disconnect vacuum hoses and electrical connectors.
10. Disconnect secondary air injection hoses from check valves and cut cable tie at resonator bracket.
11. Remove bulkhead plate seal, then the cover, disconnecting washer hoses.

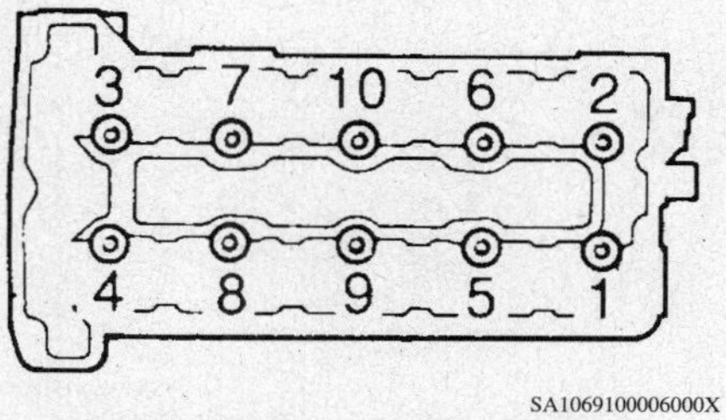

SA1069100006000X

Fig. 6 Cylinder head bolt loosening sequence. 9000 w/2.3L engine

12. Disconnect fuel pipe clamps from bulkhead plate, then remove bulkhead plate bolts and raise plate.
13. Disconnect Motronic control module electrical connector and separate engine wiring harness, pulling wiring through engine compartment and removing bulkhead plate.
14. Disconnect torque arm engine mounting lead, then remove power steering servo oil reservoir and torque arm.
15. Turn power steering belt tensioner pulley forward to release load from tensioner, then move belt to one side.
16. Disconnect power steering servo pump and remove clamp from servo pipe, then position pump and reservoir aside.
17. **On models equipped with automatic transaxle,** disconnect gear selector cable.
18. **On all models,** disconnect rear oxygen sensor and release electrical connectors from bracket.
19. **On models equipped with automatic transaxle,** disconnect oil hoses from transaxle. Plug hoses and install bolts into transaxle.
20. **On all models,** disconnect fuel hoses, then ease expansion tank lid.
21. Slightly raise and support vehicle, then remove both front wheels.
22. Disconnect steering knuckle housings from MacPherson struts and remove clamps around inner universal joint gaiters. Pull universal joints apart and install covers over halves.
23. Raise vehicle further and support, then remove oxygen sensor, knock sensor and crankshaft position sensor lead clamp from cylinder block.
24. Disconnect oxygen sensor, knock sensor and crankshaft position sensor electrical connectors, then remove from bracket.
25. Separate exhaust pipe at front joint, then remove exhaust manifold to front exhaust pipe nuts and remove front exhaust pipe.
26. Remove center air shield, then drain engine coolant into suitable container.
27. Loosen A/C compressor lower and upper bolts. **These bolts can be accessed from under A/C system but cannot be removed in this position.**
28. **On models equipped with automatic transaxle,** pull transaxle oil hoses forward.
29. **On all models,** lower vehicle and disconnect upper, then the lower radiator hoses from engine. Pull lower radiator hoses forward.

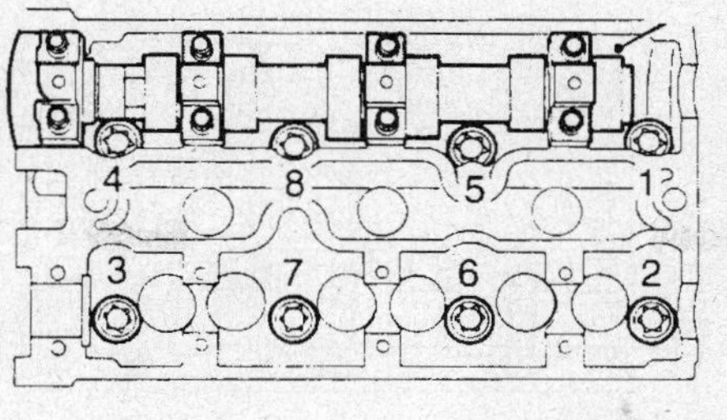

SA1069500014000X

Fig. 7 Front cylinder head bolt removal sequence. 9000 w/3.0L engine

30. Disconnect heat exchanger hoses, then the expansion tank hose.
31. Raise power steering servo pump and oil reservoir, then the brake servo vacuum hose from intake manifold.
32. Disconnect positive lead from positive terminal block, then the grounding lead from gearbox.
33. Remove A/C compressor bolts, then the compressor.
34. Disconnect rear and righthand engine mounting and install extender tool No. 83 94 439, or equivalent, on engine hood gas springs.
35. Install lifting yoke tool No. 83 92 409, or equivalent, on suitable engine lift and engine, then remove lefthand engine mounting.
36. Lift engine slightly, then remove resonator bracket.
37. Remove engine from vehicle.
38. Reverse procedure to install, noting the following:
    a. Adjust throttle cable adjusting screw so stops on throttle body are no more than .0118 inch from end position, as checked with suitable feeler gauge. Adjusting screw is on front underside of throttle cable control bracket.
    b. Fill cooling system with suitable coolant as specified.
    c. Fill engine with suitable engine oil as specified.
    d. Bleed cooling system as outlined under "Cooling System Bleed," then test drive vehicle.

INTAKE MANIFOLD

REPLACE

9-3 & 900

1. **On turbocharged models,** remove cowl.
2. **On non-turbocharged models,** remove resonator.
3. **On all models,** remove crankcase breather hose and idle adjusting valve.
4. Disconnect pressure and return fuel lines from fuel injection manifold using fuel line separator tool No. 83 94 702, or equivalent.
5. Remove four fuel injection manifold retaining bolts (two at each end), then the two protective covers.

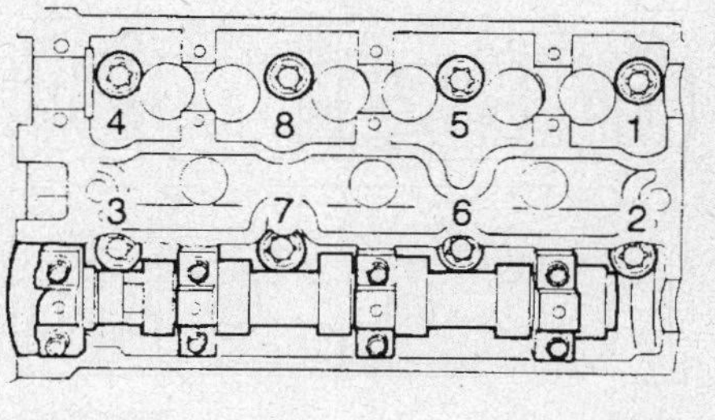

SA1069500015000X

Fig. 8 Rear cylinder head bolt removal sequence. 9000 w/3.0L engine

6. Disconnect injector electrical leads, then carefully remove fuel injection manifold.
7. Remove injector to injection manifold locking clips, then the injector.
8. **On turbocharged models equipped with intake air heat plates,** remove heat plate assembly as outlined under "Intake Air Heat Plates, Replace."
9. **On all models,** reverse procedure to install. Lubricate all O-rings with petroleum jelly before installing.

9000

2.3L Engine

1. Obtain radio anti-theft code as outlined under "Precautions."
2. Disconnect battery positive cable.
3. Drain coolant from engine.
4. Disconnect throttle cable.
5. Disconnect pre-heater hose from throttle body.
6. Remove oil filler pipe from intake manifold.
7. Disconnect hoses from signal converter and distributor assembly.
8. Disconnect hose and tee piece from brake servo outlet from intake manifold.
9. Disconnect fuel pressure regulator and pressure transmitter tee hoses.
10. Relieve fuel system pressure by loosening banjo coupling on fuel filter. Hold a cloth or shop towel round the coupling while doing this to soak up escaping fuel.
11. Disconnect fuel hose from fuel injection manifold. Do not allow fuel to drip onto starter motor assembly.
12. Disconnect fuel return line from fuel pressure regulator outlet.
13. Disconnect turbocharger pressure pipe from throttle body.
14. Disconnect throttle switch, auxiliary air valve, temperature sensor (NTC resistor) and injection valve electrical connectors.
15. Loosen intake manifold to throttle body attaching bracket bar bolts.
16. Disconnect breather hose from camshaft cover.
17. Loosen intake manifold attaching bolts, then lift intake manifold assembly from engine.
18. Reverse procedure to install. Tighten intake manifold bolts to specifications.

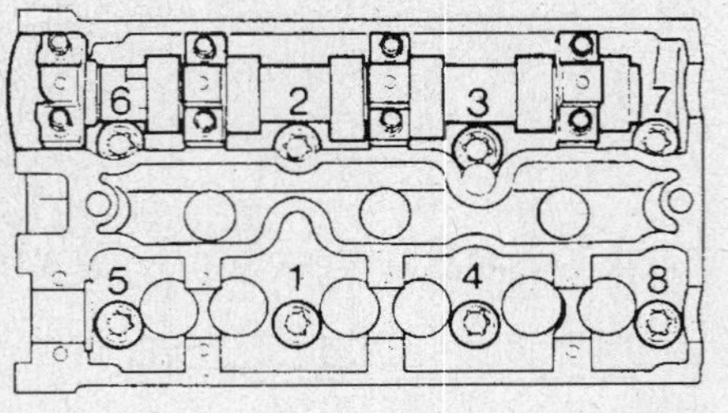

Fig. 9 Front cylinder head bolt tightening sequence. 9000 w/3.0L engine

3.0L Engine

For intake manifold replacement, refer to "Cylinder Head, Replace."

INTAKE AIR HEAT PLATES

REPLACE

9-3 & 900

On the low emission version of the turbocharged equipped engine, intake air heat plates have been added to further minimize exhaust emission, **Fig. 2.** The four intake air heat plates are integrated in one assembly, mounted between the intake manifold and cylinder head. During warm-up, the intake air heat plates vaporize injected fuel. This vaporization of fuel reduces the need for fuel enrichment, thereby reducing exhaust emissions. Heating of the intake air heat plates begins upon start-up and ceases when engine temperature reaches 185°F or four minutes after start-up.

There are no diagnostic trouble codes for the intake air heat plate system. When troubleshooting intake air heat plate assembly electrical circuits, refer to **Figs. 3 and 4.**

1. Drain engine coolant.
2. Remove charge air bypass hose, turbocharger delivery pipe and charge air cooler. Plug charge air cooler to prevent dirt contamination.
3. Remove oil dipstick tube, then crankcase ventilation and vacuum hoses from camshaft cover.
4. Remove engine lift brackets and disconnect electrical connectors.
5. Remove throttle body preheating hoses.
6. Remove engine coolant manifold to thermostat housing bolts.
7. Disconnect engine temperature sensor electrical connector at intake manifold.
8. Remove intake manifold bolts, then intake manifold and intake air heat plates.
9. Reverse procedure to install, noting the following:
   a. Align intake air heat plates with intake manifold and new gaskets.
   b. Install air heat plate assembly and bolts, then tighten assembly bolts to specifications.
   c. Check and fill engine coolant to proper level.

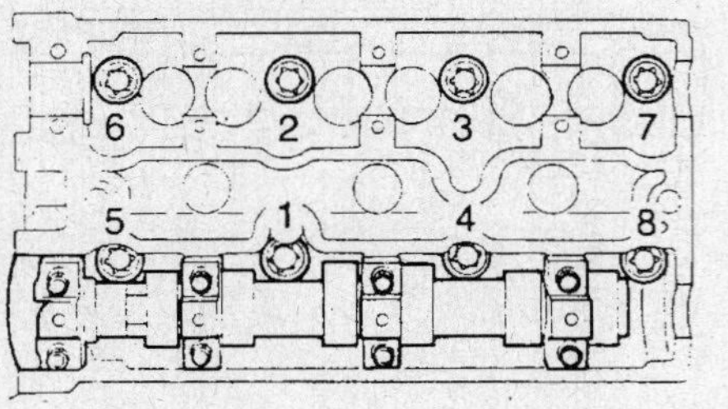

Fig. 10 Rear cylinder head bolt tightening sequence. 9000 w/3.0L engine

CYLINDER HEAD

REPLACE

9-3 & 900

1. Drain coolant.
2. **On B206i and B234i engines,** disconnect mass air flow sensor and inlet hose.
3. **On all engines,** remove air cleaner.
4. **On turbocharged models,** remove bypass hose and inlet hose. Plug inlet pipe.
5. **On all models,** remove cover or resonator.
6. **On turbocharged models,** remove pressure pipe between charge air cooler and throttle body. Plug hose at charge air cooler end.
7. **On all models,** loosen belt tensioner using ratchet handle extension and 6 mm drill bit, **Fig. 1.** Remove belt.
8. Disconnect servo pump and position aside.
9. **On turbocharged models,** proceed as follows:
   a. Remove crankcase breather valve and inlet pipe.
   b. Remove turbocharger nuts and washers, then the turbocharger steady bar bolts.
   c. Disconnect coolant hoses from cylinder head and remove water pipe for cooling turbocharger from cylinder head.
   d. Disconnect ignition discharge module connector.
10. **On non-turbocharged models,** remove exhaust manifold.
11. **On all models,** remove bracket for dipstick tube and remove tube.
12. Disconnect crankcase breather and vacuum hoses from camshaft cover, then remove lifting eyes at intake manifold and move bracket for electrical connections to one side.
13. Disconnect throttle body preheating hose and bolts securing water pipe to thermostat housing cover.
14. Disconnect throttle body preheating hose, then remove water pipe to thermostat housing cover bolts.
15. Disconnect temperature sensor electrical connector, located next to intake manifold.
16. Remove intake manifold steady bar bolts, then the intake manifold.
17. **On turbocharged models equipped with intake air heat plates,** remove intake air heat plates as outlined under "Intake Air Heat Plates, Replace" procedures.
18. **On B206i and B234i engines,** remove cover plate, ignition cables and distributor cap.
19. **On all engines,** remove spark plugs, then the camshaft cover. Line up 0° mark on flywheel with timing mark and ensure timing marks on camshafts are also in line.
20. Remove chain tensioner, then the camshaft sprockets. Position chain so it will not obstruct cylinder head removal.
21. Remove cylinder head by starting with timing cover bolts and continuing in **reverse** order of tightening, **Fig. 5.**
22. Ensure timing chain does not obstruct removal, then remove cylinder head.
23. Reverse procedure to install. When installing cylinder head and tightening cylinder head bolts, **torque** bolts in sequence, **Fig. 5,** first to 44 ft. lbs., then to 59 ft. lbs. and finally an additional 90.°

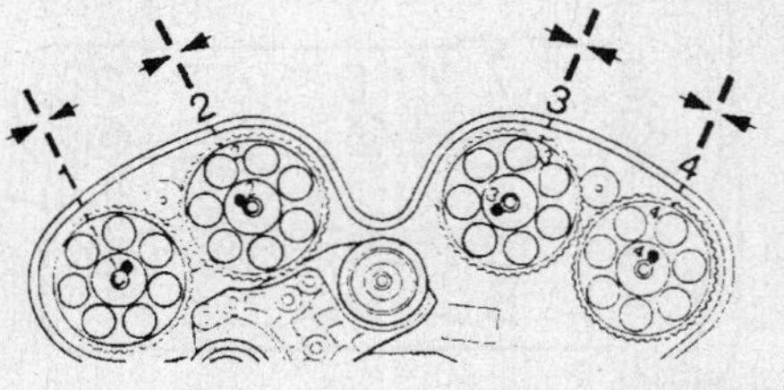

Fig. 11 Camshaft sprocket alignment. 9000 w/3.0L engine

9000

2.3L Engine

1. Raise and support vehicle, then drain engine coolant. Lower vehicle and remove filler cap to speed drainage.
2. Obtain radio anti-theft code as outlined under "Precautions."
3. Remove throttle control retaining clip, then bend up lever and remove control.
4. Disconnect coolant level sensor connector, then remove coolant tank. Disconnect coolant hoses so they are with tank.
5. Remove belt.
6. Disconnect A/C compressor electrical connector, then remove retaining bolts and rest compressor on radiator crossmember.
7. Remove A/C compressor bracket.
8. Snip through cable ties holding hoses and wiring at upper torque arm, then remove interference suppressor cable (ground), torque arm and two cylinder head upper bolts.
9. Disconnect ignition discharge module connector, then the temperature sensor connector.
10. **On turbocharged models,** remove turbocharger pressure pipe between charge air cooler and throttle body.
11. **On all models,** remove radiator hose from throttle body, then the upper radiator hose from cylinder head.

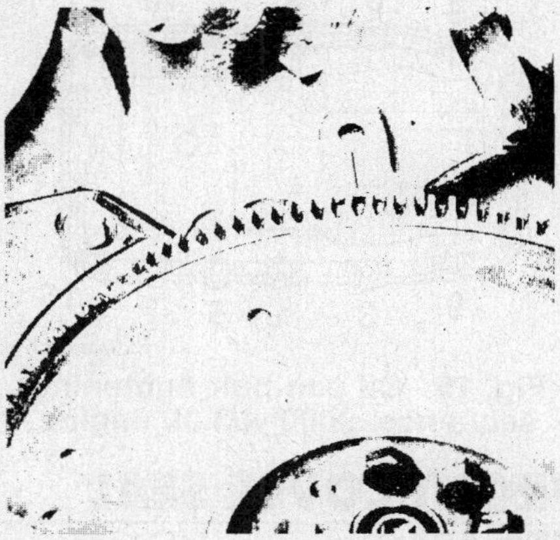

SA1069100007000X

Fig. 12 Flywheel timing mark alignment. 2.0L & 2.3L Engines

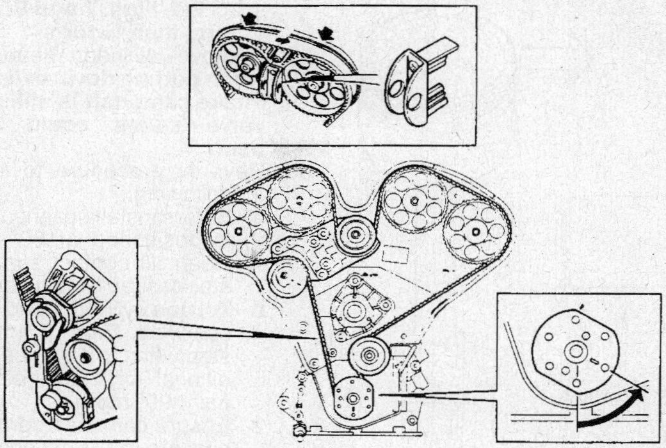

SA1069500019000X

Fig. 13 Camshaft & crankshaft alignment for timing belt removal. 3.0L engine

12. Disconnect heat exchanger hose and water temperature sensor connector from cylinder head.
13. Disconnect crankcase breather and vacuum hoses from camshaft cover.
14. **On turbocharged models,** remove turbocharged intake hose.
15. **On all models,** disconnect solenoid valve connector, then remove solenoid valve from holder and bend valve up against engine.
16. Remove vacuum hose at bypass valve and remove bypass valve.
17. Remove bolts securing front exhaust pipe to exhaust manifold, then the bolt from bracket on top of catalytic converter using suitable extension bar.
18. Raise and support vehicle, then remove bolt from catalytic converter bracket.
19. Remove front exhaust pipe rear connecting flange bolts, then disconnect oxygen sensor cable at exhaust pipe and feed it into engine bay.
20. Carefully lower front exhaust pipe, then remove oil drain pipe.
21. Lower vehicle.
22. **On turbocharged models,** remove coolant pipe between turbocharger and cylinder head, then the turbocharger oil delivery pipe and coolant pipe between turbocharger and water pump.
23. **On all models,** remove oil return pipe.
24. **On turbocharged models,** remove two hoses between solenoid valve and turbo, then the delivery pipe between turbocharger and charge air cooler.
25. **On all models,** remove seven bolts and five washers securing manifold to cylinder head.
26. Remove manifold and turbocharger unit.
27. Remove gasket, then the intake manifold from cylinder head as follows:
    a. Remove lifting eye, then the oil filler pipe bracket.
    b. Remove fuel rail retaining bolts, then the fuel rail with nozzles.
    c. Remove intake manifold retaining bolts, then the gasket.
    d. Remove water pipe bracket on thermostat housing, then the intake manifold.
    e. Remove ignition discharge module and spark plugs.
28. Remove camshaft cover, then line up crankshaft with 0° mark and ensure timing marks on camshafts are also in alignment.
29. Remove power steering fluid reservoir, then the chain tensioner.
30. Unscrew camshaft sprocket bolts and remove sprockets from camshafts.
31. Hold up chain and lower chain guide to middle of engine.
32. Remove two timing cover to cylinder head bolts.
33. Unscrew cylinder head bolts in sequence, **Fig. 6.**
34. Reverse procedure to install. **Torque** cylinder head bolts in sequence, **Fig. 5,** first to 44 ft. lbs., then to 59 ft. lbs. Then **torque** bolts an additional 90.°

3.0L Engine

The camshafts must not be rotated because the valves could touch the pistons or each other, causing damage. The crankshaft may only be turned between 0° and 60° Before Top Dead Center (BTDC) when the camshafts of both cylinder heads are locked with suitable locking tools.

1. Obtain radio anti-theft code as outlined under "Precautions."
2. Raise and support vehicle, then remove rear exhaust pipe to exhaust manifold nuts.
3. Remove center air shield, then drain engine coolant into suitable container.
4. Lower vehicle and remove engine covers, then disconnect cruise control cable.
5. Disconnect throttle cable from throttle cable bracket, then disconnect control rod and bracket. Position bracket aside. Disconnect inlet pipe to intake manifold and resonator and mass air flow sensor hose clamps, then slightly raise inlet pipes.
6. Disconnect vacuum hoses and electrical connectors, then remove pipes complete with resonator.
7. Remove intake manifold bolts, then disconnect throttle body preheater hoses, crankcase ventilation hose and vacuum hoses from intake manifold. **Note where hoses are connected.**
8. Disconnect IAC valve electrical connector, then the fuel pressure regulator hose and remove wiring harness conduit from under throttle body.
9. Disconnect throttle position indicator electrical connector and ignition coil, then the TCS throttle body electrical connector.
10. Lift off intake manifold. Plug openings with paper.
11. Disconnect injector electrical connector, then the camshaft position sensor.
12. Disconnect fuel lines and plug openings, then remove center intake manifold bolts. Secure center intake manifold with fuel rail aside.
13. Mark position of lower part of intake manifold and remove. Plug openings with paper.
14. Remove coolant bridge and bend aside.
15. When removing rear cylinder head, proceed as follows:
    a. Disconnect ignition leads 1–3–5.
    b. Remove oxygen sensor from holder, then the crankcase ventilation housing. Plug all openings with paper.
16. When removing front cylinder head, proceed as follows:
    a. Disconnect ignition leads 2–4–6, then the ignition coil. Bend coil aside and remove ignition coil bracket.
    b. Remove lifting eye and heat shield over exhaust manifold.
17. Remove power steering servo oil reservoir, then disconnect torque arm engine mounting lead and remove torque arm.
18. Remove servo line clamp from torque arm engine mounting, then the engine mounting.
19. Disconnect expansion tank upper hose, then the upper part of generator air intake.

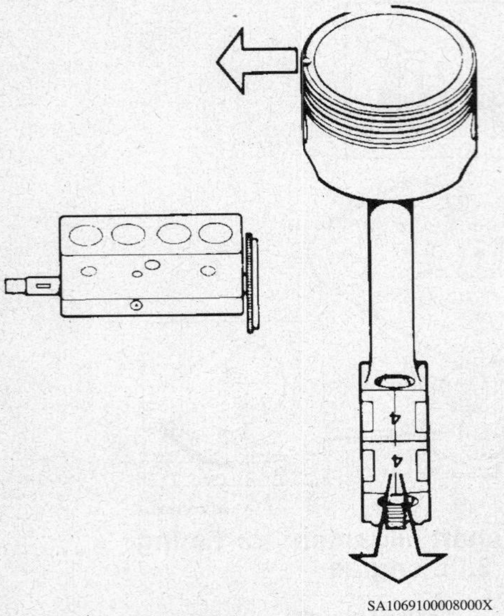

Fig. 14 Piston & connecting rod installation

20. Slightly loosen pulley bolts, then remove power steering belt, belt tensioner, power steering servo pump, coolant pump pulley and timing cover.
21. Remove six crankshaft pulley outer bolts, then the pulley. **Do not remove center bolt.**
22. Zero engine, then insert suitable locking tool for camshaft sprocket on cylinder head. **Markings on camshaft sprocket and timing cover should align, as should marking on crankshaft.**
23. Mark toothed belt direction of rotation, then release belt from tension and remove belt. **For easier installation, mark belt at both camshaft marking and crankshaft marking.**
24. Remove adjuster pulley bolts, then turn crankshaft back to 60° BTDC and remove bracket holding upper adjuster and tensioner pulleys.
25. Remove timing cover. **Ensure O-rings are in position and do not fall into engine.**
26. Remove cylinder head camshaft sprockets, then the timing cover bolts in cylinder head, noting the following:
    a. On rear cylinder head, camshaft sprockets are marked "1" and "2."
    b. On front cylinder head, camshaft sprockets are marked "3" and "4."
    c. **On both cylinder heads, ensure open-ended wrench used as holding tool to remove camshaft sprockets does not have jaws which are too long. There is a risk of damaging casting, causing tappet to lock.**
27. Remove exhaust camshaft bearing caps, noting the following:
    a. **It is important to finish removal at bearing cap where valve depressors are compressed.**
    b. Note marking on bearing caps.
    c. Remove bolts in stages of ½ to one turn and lift out camshaft.
28. Remove cylinder head bolts in order specified, **Figs. 7 and 8. First loosen ¼ turn, then ½ turn.**
29. Remove cylinder head. **Use care when putting down cylinder head as intake camshaft is still in place and valve stems could accidentally bend.**
30. Reverse procedure to install, noting the following:
    a. Before installing, ensure crankshaft is positioned at 60° BTDC, then clean all contact surfaces and install gasket. Note guides for gasket.
    b. **Torque** cylinder head bolts in order specified, **Figs. 9 and 10,** in four steps: first to 19 ft. lbs., next an additional 90°, then another 90° and finally, 90° more.
    c. Ensure camshaft sprocket locating pins are in correct position. If locating pins are hollow, change them for solid pins. Fit camshaft sprockets in correct relation to locating pins, **Fig. 11.**
    d. Adjust kickdown and throttle cables.
    e. Fill radiator with suitable coolant according to specifications and check system for leaks.
    f. Check oil and fluid levels and adjust as necessary, then bleed cooling system as outlined under "Cooling System Bleed."
    g. Test drive vehicle.

VALVE CLEARANCE SPECIFICATIONS

Hydraulic valve lifters are used on all engines and no adjustment is required.

VALVE ADJUSTMENT

Hydraulic valve lifters are used on all engines and no adjustment is required.

VALVE GUIDES

Before removing valve guide, flush cylinder head with hot water. Remove guide using jackscrew and pull rod tool No. 83 93 811 with spacer No. 8393829 and nut No. 8393845, or equivalents. Install guide from top after flushing cylinder head with hot water and cooling guide with cold water. Install guide using jackscrew and pull rod tool No. 83 93 811 with stop No. 8393837, centering sleeve No. 8390379 and nut No. 8393845, or equivalents. Center tool in valve seat and draw guide into position using tool.

VALVE SEATS

Machine valve seats as necessary using a 60 milling cutter. Width of intake valve seat should measure 1–1.5 mm and width of exhaust valve seat should measure 1.5–2 mm.

Only a limited amount of material can be removed from exhaust valve face, since the stellite coating must be preserved as much as possible. Consequently, if valve is badly pitted or worn, it should be replaced.

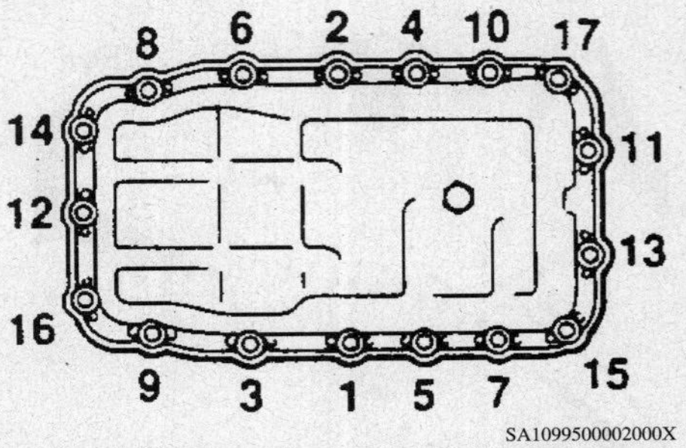

Fig. 15 Oil pan bolt tightening sequence. 9000 w/3.0L engine

FRONT COVER SEAL

REPLACE

9-3 & 900

1. Remove air cleaner and mass air flow sensor.
2. Slightly loosen pulley bolts, then remove drive belt, tensioner, power steering pump pulley, water pump pulley and cover.
3. Remove front righthand wheel and cover in wheel housing.
4. Remove crankshaft pulley. Loosen six bolts, but do not remove center bolt.
5. Position No. 1 cylinder in compression position. Markings on camshaft sprockets and timing cover should be in alignment as well as marking on crankshaft. Insert suitable locking tools for camshaft sprockets on cylinder heads.
6. Before removing belt, mark direction of rotation at camshaft markings and crankshaft marking.
7. Remove tensioning roller and two adjusting rollers, then the belt.
8. Turn crankshaft back 60° Before Top Dead Center (BTDC).
9. Raise and support vehicle and remove protective plate for flywheel.
10. Install flywheel stop, then remove crankshaft pulley and spacer ring.
11. Pry out seal, using care not to damage crankshaft sealing surface.
12. Fit inner part of crankshaft seal assembly tool No. 83 94 942, or equivalent, on crankshaft, then lubricate seal and fit onto shaft. Tap seal into place using outer part of tool.
13. Install spacer ring and crankshaft pulley. Tighten crankshaft pulley to specifications.
14. Install cover in wheel housing, then the front righthand wheel. Tighten wheel bolt to specifications.
15. Install cover, water pump pulley, power steering pump pulley, belt tensioner and multigroove drive belt.
16. Install air cleaner and mass air flow sensor.

9000

1. Raise and support front of vehicle.
2. Remove front fender inner liner.
3. Loosen accessory attaching bolts, then remove drive belts.
4. Using clamp tool No. 83 93 993, or equivalent, secure crankshaft from

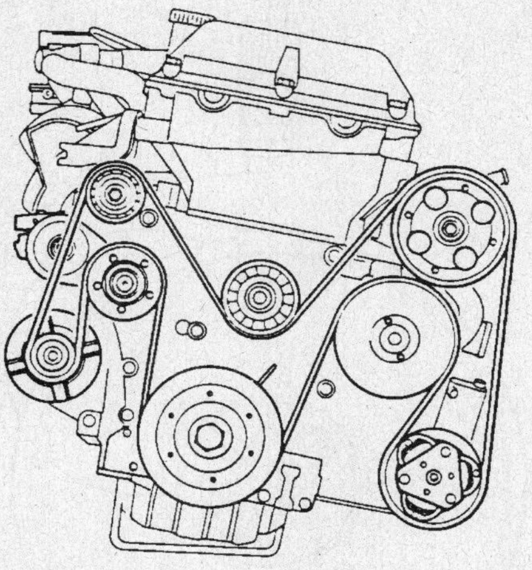

SA1069400010000X

Fig. 16 Serpentine drive belt routing. 9-3 & 900 w/2.0L & 2.3L engines

turning, then remove crankshaft pulley attaching bolt.
5. Remove crankshaft pulley.
6. Using screwdriver, pry out old front seal from crankshaft.
7. Using installer tool No. 83 93 349, or equivalent, install new front seal onto crankshaft.
8. Install crankshaft pulley and tighten pulley attaching bolt to specifications.
9. Install and tension drive belts.
10. Install fender liner and wheel, then tighten attaching bolts and lower vehicle.

TIMING CHAIN

REPLACE

2.0L & 2.3L ENGINES

The camshaft timing mechanism is comprised of a chain and sprockets. The chain has two guides, one fixed and one pivoting. The pivoting guide maintains tension in the chain aided by a hydraulic chain tensioner.

1. Remove engine from vehicle as outlined in "Engine, Replace."
2. Remove breather hose for crankcase ventilation from valve cover.
3. Disconnect vacuum hose and Hall transducer from distributor, then remove distributor cap with ignition wires.
4. Remove spark plug inspection cover and clips for plug wires.
5. Remove valve cover.
6. Rotate engine until (0) mark on flywheel is aligned with pointer, **Fig. 12. Ensure camshaft timing marks are also correctly aligned.**
7. Remove chain tensioner.
8. Remove camshaft sprockets.
9. Remove crankshaft pulley, then the belt tensioner.
10. Remove water pump pipe.
11. Remove oil pipes, then the water pump pulley.
12. Remove water pump and three bolts in block.
13. Remove oil pump.
14. Remove timing cover.
15. Remove pivoting chain guide. **Do not remove fixed chain guide.**
16. Remove timing chain and sprocket with oil pump drive dog. **Do not rotate camshafts or crankshaft with timing chain removed.**
17. Reverse procedure to install, noting the following:
    a. Install timing chain around crankshaft sprocket, then install chain and sprocket on exhaust valve camshaft. **Ensure chain is taut between crankshaft and exhaust valve camshaft sprockets.**
    b. Install chain and sprocket on intake valve camshaft. **Maintain chain tension between camshaft sprockets while installing.**
    c. Set chain tensioner by pushing and turning adjuster simultaneously, then install chain tensioner. **Ensure copper gasket is in good condition and sealing surface is clean and free of burrs.**
    d. Using wrench, release chain tensioner by pressing pivoting chain guide against tensioner, then press pivoting guide against chain to give basic tension. **Ensure chain is correctly positioned in guides.**
    e. Ensure chain tensioner maintains tension on chain when pressure on chain guide is released and that basic setting stop for tensioner holds chain guide tight against chain. **A limited amount of play will be present until hydraulic pressure develops with engine running.**
    f. Rotate engine two complete turns, ensuring crankshaft and camshafts are properly aligned.

TIMING BELT

REPLACE

3.0L ENGINE

With the timing belt removed, avoid turning the camshaft or crankshaft. If movement is required, exercise extreme caution to avoid valve damage caused by piston contact.

Removal

Each cylinder head has twin overhead camshafts with a large-diameter base circle, providing a large amount of lift with little stress. All four camshafts are driven by an internally-cogged belt with self-adjusting belt tensioner. The belt assembly also includes two adjuster rollers.

1. Lift power steering servo oil reservoir and free lead from torque arm engine mounting, then remove torque arm.
2. Remove servo line clamp from torque arm engine mounting and remove engine mounting.
3. Slightly loosen power steering pump pulley bolts, then release load from belt tensioner by turning belt tensioner pulley screw forward in vehicle.
4. Remove belt from coolant pump pulley and carefully release belt tensioner.

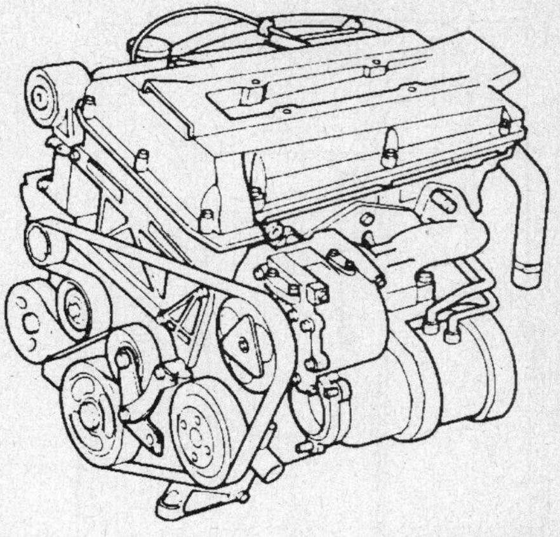

SA1069100012000X

Fig. 17 Serpentine drive belt routing. 9000

5. Disconnect expansion tank hoses, then remove coolant pump pulley.
6. Remove upper portion of generator air intake, then the belt tensioner and power steering servo pump.
7. Remove timing cover.
8. Remove six crankshaft pulley bolts, then the pulley. **Do not remove center bolt.**
9. Zero engine, noting the following:
    a. Marks on camshaft sprockets and timing cover should align, **Fig. 13.**
    b. Markings on crankshaft and timing cover should align, **Fig. 13.**
    c. Install locking tool Nos. KM-800-1 and KM-800-2, or equivalents, for camshaft sprockets on cylinder heads and locking tool No. KM-800-10, or equivalent, for crankshaft.
10. Release belt from tension and remove, then remove adjuster pulley bolts. **Before removing belt, mark direction of rotation. Markings can be made at both camshaft and crankshaft.**

Installation

1. Install toothed belt in marked direction of rotation as follows:
    a. Holding belt in position, lightly adjust tensioner roller by hand so belt does not disengage. Adjust counter clockwise.
    b. Install piece of toothed belt and belt tension meter tool No. 83 93 985, or equivalent, to measure belt tension.
    c. Lightly turn center bolt on adjuster rollers.
    d. Adjust lower roller counter clockwise to tension of 62–67 lbs. **This belt tension adjustment is only preparatory measure and must not be used as check when belt is finally adjusted.**
2. Adjust tensioning pulley with suitable Allen wrench until two marks are aligned. Tighten tensioning pulley to specifications.
3. Remove locking tool for camshaft sprockets 1 and 2, then adjust upper adjusting roller counterclockwise until No. 2 sprocket moves .039–.079 inch

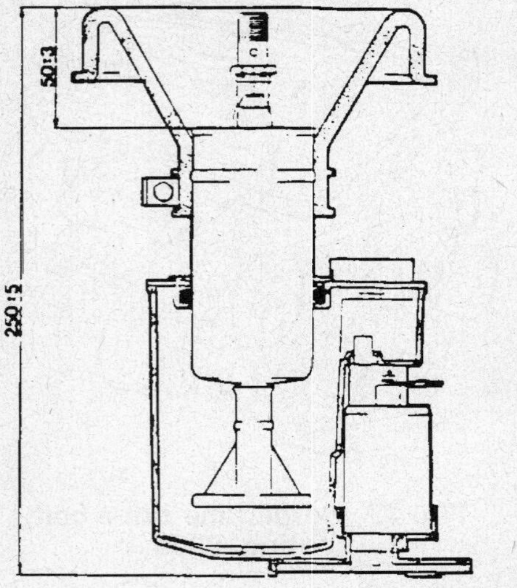

SA1029100001000X

Fig. 18 Fuel pump installation. 9000 w/Bosch non-ejector type pump

clockwise. Tighten sprockets to specifications, then remove upper locking tool.

4. Turn engine two revolutions to just before zero marking and install suitable locking tool to crankshaft.
5. Carefully turn crankshaft in direction of engine rotation until arm is against coolant pump flange. Tighten crankshaft.
6. Position tool No. KM-800-20, or equivalent and ensure markings on camshaft sprocket are aligned with markings on tool and edge of belt meets edge of sprocket. Also ensure tensioning roller marks are aligned.
7. Install crankshaft pulley, then the timing cover.
8. Install power steering servo pump, then the belt tensioner.
9. Install upper portion of generator air intake.
10. Install coolant pump pulley, then connect upper hose to expansion tank.
11. Relieve load from belt tensioner by turning belt tensioner pulley locking bolt forward in vehicle.
12. Fit belt on coolant pump pulley and check other pulleys, then carefully release belt tensioner.
13. Install torque arm engine mounting, then the servo line clamp.
14. Install torque arm, then bolt lead to torque arm engine mounting and install power steering servo oil reservoir.

CAMSHAFT

REPLACE

1. Remove breather hose for crankcase ventilation from valve cover.
2. Disconnect vacuum hose and Hall transducer from distributor, then remove distributor cap with ignition wires.
3. Remove spark plug inspection cover and clips for plug wires.
4. Remove valve cover.
5. Rotate engine until (0) mark on flywheel is aligned with pointer. **Ensure camshaft timing marks are also correctly aligned.**
6. Remove distributor.
7. Remove camshaft sprockets with chain.
8. Remove oil pipes, then the camshaft bearing caps and camshafts.
9. Reverse procedure to install.

PISTONS, PINS & RINGS

The type pistons used varies with the engine compression ratio. Either Mahle or Karl Schmidt pistons may be fitted to the engine, but pistons of different makes should not be installed in the same engine as an imbalance condition may be created.

Pistons and rings are available in standard, .020 inch (.5 mm) oversize and .040 inch (1 mm) oversize. Standard size pistons are supplied in 3 different size classes and all pistons and cylinder bores should be measured prior to installation. Pistons should be measured at right angles to the piston pin hole at a point .63 inch (16 mm) above lower edge of skirt for Mahle pistons or 1.03 inches (26 mm) above edge of skirt for Schmidt pistons.

Measure piston installation clearance using a spring gauge and feeler gauges ½ inch wide. Clearance should be measured with piston installed in a lightly oiled bore, without rings, at right angle to piston pin bore. When indication on spring gauge used to pull feeler gauge between piston and bore is 1.8–2.6 lbs., piston clearance is equal to the thickness of the feeler gauge used.

Piston ring gap should be measured in the finished bore, using feeler gauges. Push each ring into bore using an inverted piston to properly position rings. New rings fitted to a worn cylinder bore should be checked at the bottom of the piston travel, as the cylinder will be narrowest at this point.

Install piston and rod assemblies with FRONT mark or notch pointing toward timing cover, **Fig. 14.** Piston and rod should be assembled so reference stampings on connecting rod, **Fig. 14,** face exhaust side of engine. Use a piston ring installation tool to position the lower compression ring with the side marked "top" uppermost. Rotate compression rings so that gaps in alternate rings are 180° in relation to each other, positioned over the ends of the piston pins. Make sure that the ring gaps of the top and bottom rings in the three piece scraper ring are staggered.

MAIN & ROD BEARINGS

Rod and main bearings are available in standard size and under sizes of .010 inch (.25 mm), .020 inch (.5 mm), .030 inch (.75 mm) and. 040 inch (1 mm).

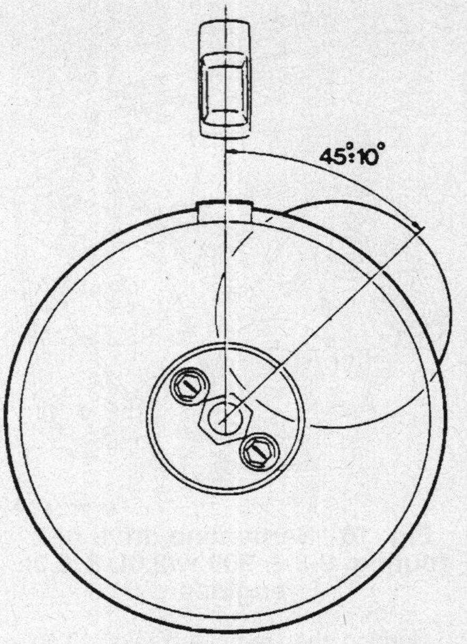

SA1029100002000X

Fig. 19 Fuel pump relief valve positioning. 9000 w/Bosch non-ejector type pump

CRANKSHAFT SEAL

REPLACE

9-3 & 900

2.0L & 2.3L Engines

1. Loosen belt tensioner using ratchet handle extension and 6 mm drill bit, **Fig. 1. Use care to ensure belt tensioner does not break at its end position.**
2. Raise and support vehicle, then remove front righthand wheel and cover.
3. Remove protective plate and fit flywheel locking segment tool No. 83 94 868, or equivalent, on flywheel ring gear.
4. Remove crankshaft pulley, then use screwdriver to break off old seal.
5. Fit new seal using assembly tool No. 83 94 876, or equivalent.
6. Install crankshaft pulley. Tighten to specifications.
7. Install drive belt and check position of belt on all pulleys, then install cover.
8. Install wheel, then lower vehicle and tighten wheel nuts to specifications.
9. Loosen belt tensioner as outlined earlier.
10. Run engine at idle speed, then turn off and check if drive belt is correctly positioned.

2.5L Engine

1. Remove transaxle.
2. **On models equipped with manual transaxle,** remove clutch, pressure plate and flywheel.
3. **On models equipped with automatic transaxle,** remove driver disc.
4. **On all models,** pry seal out using care not to damage sealing surface.
5. Lubricate sealing lips.

6. Insert rear crankshaft seal assembly kit tool No. 83 94 934, or equivalent, to tap seal into place. Ensure sealing lips fit correctly on crankshaft.
7. **On models equipped with manual transaxle,** install flywheel, then the clutch and gearbox.
8. **On models equipped with automatic transaxle,** install driver disc, then the transaxle.

9000

1. Remove transaxle, clutch and flywheel.
2. Using screwdriver, pry out old oil seal.
3. Before installing, lubricate lip of new seal with engine oil, then install seal using installer tool No. 83 92 540, or equivalent.
4. Reinstall transaxle, clutch and flywheel, tighten flywheel bolts to specifications.

OIL PAN

REPLACE

9-3 & 900

The engine oil pan is an integral part of engine case. To remove the oil pan, remove the engine and transaxle assembly as outlined in "Engine, Replace."

2.0L & 2.3L Engines

1. Remove dipstick and stuff cloth into end of dipstick tube, then raise engine slightly with suitable lift.
2. Disconnect oxygen sensor leads, then disconnect cable clamp and remove clip.
3. Raise and support vehicle, then drain oil and position suitable lifting table under engine.
4. Remove front wheels and spoiler sections, then disconnect joint between front exhaust pipe and intermediate pipe.
5. Remove exhaust pipe from turbocharger or exhaust manifold.
6. Remove catalytic converter from its bracket, then the exhaust pipe.
7. Remove steering swivel member end pieces, then the rear engine mounting.
8. Raise lifting table, then remove other bolts and subframe.
9. Disconnect oil level sensor connector and pull cable out of its clamps.
10. Remove protective plate and oil pan. Do not remove guide sleeve from cylinder block.
11. Reverse procedure to install, noting the following:
    a. Make sure there are no impurities or foreign matter in pan, then thoroughly clean flange with benzine.
    b. Apply even bead of Loctite 518, or equivalent, along flange before installing pan.

9000

2.3L Engine

1. Obtain radio anti-theft code as outlined under "Precautions."

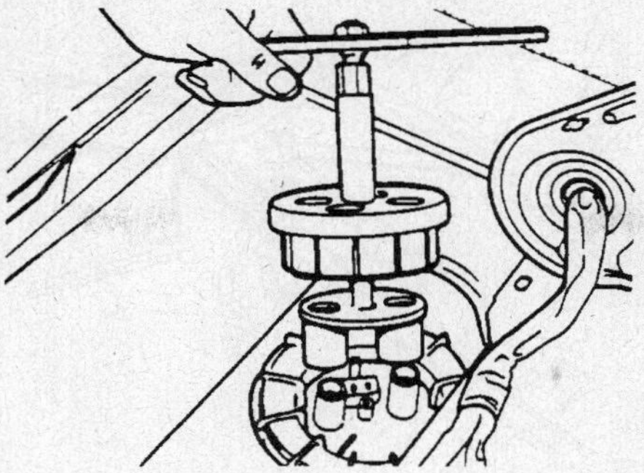

Fig. 20 Tool No. 83-94-397 installation. 9000 w/Walbro ejector type pump

2. Raise and support vehicle.
3. Remove front righthand wheel, then the righthand wheel housing trim molding.
4. Remove righthand front fender liner.
5. Loosen automatic belt tensioner by pulling belt hard upward while an assistant secures tensioner with locking yoke tool No. 83 94 448, or equivalent.
6. **On turbocharged models,** remove three bolts securing exhaust pipe to turbo.
7. **On all models,** disconnect oxygen sensor connector and cable, then remove front exhaust pipe.
8. Drain oil from oil pan, then disconnect oil level sensor connector and remove sensor cable from pan.
9. Remove bolts from rear engine mounting and righthand engine mounting.
10. Remove five oil pan front retaining bolts, then remove clip around rubber gaiter on righthand driveshaft universal joint.
11. Remove two electric leads, brake hose and strut lower bolts from steering swivel member.
12. Pull away steering swivel member to separate driveshaft joint. Install protective caps.
13. Remove driver bracket retaining bolts from engine, then the driver.
14. Remove crankcase breather hose, ground cable from torque arm, then the torque arm.
15. Move lifting eye from rear position to front position.
16. Lift engine and remove protective plate from gearbox.
17. Raise vehicle and remove remaining bolts from pan, then the pan.
18. Reverse procedure to install. Apply sealing compound Loctite 518, or equivalent, to joint surfaces of pan and cylinder block.

3.0L Engine

1. Raise and support vehicle, then drain engine oil into suitable container.
2. Remove front exhaust pipe from both exhaust manifolds, then pull front exhaust pipe down a little.
3. Remove cover plate.
4. Remove oil pan bolts, then the oil pan.
5. Reverse procedure to install, noting the following:
    a. Apply suitable sealant to oil pan bolts.
    b. Using sequence shown, **Fig. 15,** tighten oil pan bolts to specifications.

OIL PUMP

REPLACE

9-3 & 900

2.0L & 2.3L Engines

1. Disconnect air cleaner and position aside.
2. Loosen belt tensioner with ratchet handle extension and 6 mm drill, **Fig. 1.**
3. Raise and support vehicle, then remove front righthand wheel.
4. Remove crankshaft pulley and oil pump circlip.
5. Remove pump cover using large pair of slip-joint pliers, then the pump gears.
6. Reverse procedure to install, noting the following:
    a. Ensure marking on oil pump ring gear faces outward.
    b. Insert pump gears and place pump cover correctly with aid of arrows.
    c. Tighten crankshaft pulleys and wheel bolts to specifications.

9000

2.3L Engine

1. Raise and support vehicle, then remove front righthand wheel.
2. Remove wheel housing trim molding and front fender liner.
3. Loosen automatic belt tensioner by pulling belt hard upward while an assistant secures tensioner with locking yoke tool No. 83 94 488, or equivalent.
4. Remove protective plate from gearbox, then lock flywheel with flywheel holder tool No. 83 94 868, or equivalent.
5. Lift belt off crankshaft pulley, then remove crankshaft pulley.
6. If replacing crankshaft seal, pry out seal with screwdriver.
7. Remove retaining ring with chamfer facing outward.
8. Note markings on oil pump, then remove pump.
9. Reverse procedure to install. Ensure oil pump arrows are opposite each other.

3.0L Engine

1. Remove timing belt as outlined under "Timing Belt, Replace."
2. Remove bracket holding upper adjuster pulley and tensioner pulley.
3. Remove coolant pump, then lock camshaft sprockets with locking tool Nos. KM-800-1 and KM-800-2, or equivalents and remove camshaft sprockets.
4. Remove rear timing cover.
5. Raise and support vehicle, then disconnect front exhaust pipe from both exhaust manifolds.
6. Remove protective plate, then install holder tool No. 83 95 063, or equivalent and remove crankshaft pulley.

7. Remove alternator, then the A/C compressor. Hang A/C compressor aside.
8. Drain engine oil, then remove oil pan and strainer.
9. Disconnect oil pressure switch cable, then lower vehicle and place suitable wood block under front edge of engine block.
10. Remove A/C compressor bracket, then the oil pump housing.
11. Remove cover, then the two impellers.
12. Check oil pressure release valve and oil pressure control valve
13. Reverse procedure to install.

BELT TENSION DATA

Model	Belt	New Lbs.	Used Lbs.
9-3 & 900	A/C	110–130	75–85
	Alt.(2)	110–130	75–85
	Alt.(3)	110–130(4)	(5)
	Power Steer.	90–110	65–75
9000(1)	A/C	110–130	75–85
	Alt.	170–190	110–130

(1) — 4-cylinder engine, less balancer shafts.
(2) — Single belt.
(3) — Double belt.
(4) — Check belts separately.
(5) — When checking one belt, 65–75 ft. lbs.; when checking both belts together, 140–150 ft. lbs.

SERPENTINE DRIVE BELT

ROUTING

Refer to **Figs. 16 through 17** for routing of serpentine drive belt.

INSPECTION

Check performance of belt tensioner by pressing and pulling belt. Belt should return smoothly to tensioned position. Tension of belt should be a minimum of 40 ft. lbs.

COOLING SYSTEM BLEED

2.0L & 2.3L ENGINES

These engines do not require a specific bleed procedure. After filling cooling system, run engine to operating temperature with the radiator/pressure cap off. Air will then be automatically bled through cap opening.

3.0L ENGINE

1. Fill system to MAX level, then fit pressure lid.
2. Start engine and run warm, preferably at varying speeds, until radiator fan starts.
3. Remove pressure lid and top up to MAX level.
4. Refit pressure lid and run engine at varying speeds until radiator fan starts three more times.
5. Switch off engine and top up to MAX level if necessary.

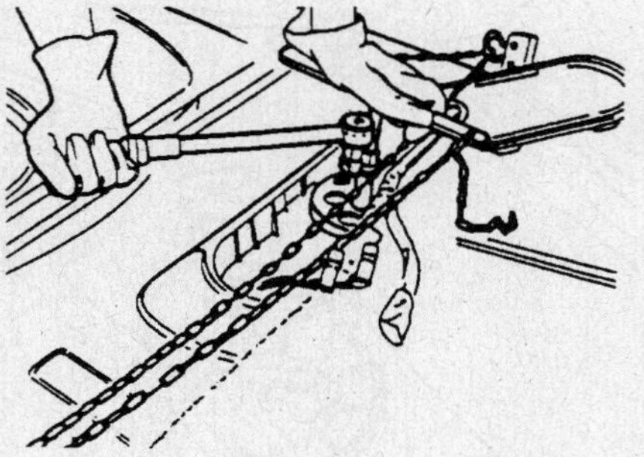

SA1029100004000X

Fig. 21 Load securing chain installation. 9000 w/Walbro ejector type pump

WATER PUMP

REPLACE

9-3 & 900

1. Drain coolant, then remove air cleaner. Open expansion tank lid to speed drainage.
2. **On turbocharged models,** disconnect intake hose and plug pipe, then remove bypass hose and pressure pipe between charge air cooler and throttle body.
3. **On all models,** loosen belt tensioner with ratchet extension and 6 mm drill, **Fig. 1.**
4. Disconnect steering servo pump with console and hang on radiator crossmember.
5. Disconnect coolant hoses and pipes from pump, then remove screw holding coolant pipe to front lefthand corner of engine.
6. Remove hose connecting throttle body to coolant pipe, then remove screws on thermostat housing. Move pipes to one side.
7. **On turbocharged models,** remove boost pressure control valve and move to one side.
8. **On all models,** remove coolant pipe.
9. Remove sleeve with O-rings, then the coolant pump from pump housing.
10. Reverse procedure to install.

9000

1. Raise and support vehicle, then remove righthand wheel.
2. Remove front wheelwell liner for access to water pump.
3. Drain coolant.
4. Loosen drive belt and remove water pump pulley.
5. Remove belt tensioner pulley.
6. Remove clips securing oil lines.
7. Remove clip securing water pipe to block.
8. Disconnect hoses from pump and remove pump attaching bolts, then the pump.
9. Reverse procedure to install, tighten bolts and refill cooling system to specifications.

FUEL PUMP

REPLACE

The fuel system on models with fuel injection is under constant pressure. Exercise caution when disconnecting fuel lines to release pressure slowly and prevent fuel from spraying.

9-3 & 900

1. Using suitable tank draining unit, drain fuel tank through fuel filler pipe.
2. Raise and support vehicle. Ensure righthand rear support is positioned as far out as possible so it won't obstruct work.
3. Remove rubber hoses from tank and plug tank.
4. Remove clamp securing fuel filter.
5. Support tank with suitable pillar lift, then remove metal strap nuts and straps.
6. Carefully lower tank, righthand side first, until top becomes visible.
7. Disconnect fuel pump connectors, then the fuel pump pressure and return lines.
8. Lower tank to convenient working height, then use fuel pump tool No. 83 94 462, or equivalent, to remove screw ring from top of fuel pump.
9. Lift pump until top of it is about 50 mm above tank, then turn pump clockwise about 80.° Carefully remove pump.
10. Reverse procedure to install. Tighten fasteners to specifications.

9000

Bosch Non-Ejector Type Pump

1. Obtain radio anti-theft code as outlined under "Precautions."
2. Disconnect and tape battery positive cable.
3. Lift up rear section of luggage compartment floor, then remove two floor to panel attaching screws and lift out floor panel.
4. Using an Allen wrench, loosen two bayonet attaching screws, then remove fuel pump cover.
5. Disconnect electrical connectors from fuel pump, feed pump and fuel gauge transmitter.
6. Loosen, then remove fuel pipe banjo coupling. Retain washers.
7. Remove fuel pump rubber collar clip.
8. Remove fuel pump and suction reservoir.
9. Reverse procedure to install, noting the following:
   a. Install fuel pump in rubber collar so lip of collar is 1.97 inches (50 mm) above top edge of pump as shown, **Fig. 18.**
   b. Ensure relief valve on reservoir is turned 35–55° from mark, **Fig. 19.**
   c. Adjust overall length of fuel pump to 9.84 inches (250 mm), **Fig. 18.**

Walbro Ejector Type Pump

1. Obtain radio anti-theft code as outlined

under "Precautions."
2. Disconnect and tape battery positive cable.
3. Lift up rear section of luggage compartment floor, then remove two floor to panel attaching screws and lift out floor panel.
4. Remove pump cover, then disconnect wiring harness.
5. Disconnect fuel lines. Position lines aside.
6. Install tool No. 83 94 397, or equivalent, **Fig. 20.**
7. Install chain through load securing eyes, **Fig. 21,** then tighten chain.
8. Loosen screw top, then remove tool.
9. Remove screw top, then the seal.
10. Remove fuel pump from fuel tank, tilting top to right.
11. Reverse procedure to install, noting the following:
    a. Ensure bottom of pump is between ribs on bottom of tank.
    b. Ensure mark on top of pump aligns with mark on top of tank.
    c. Using tool No. 83 94 397, or equivalent, **torque** screw top to 40 ft. lbs. Do not allow pump to turn when tightening screw top.

TURBOCHARGER

REPLACE

9-3 & 900

1. Drain coolant. Remove expansion tank lid to speed drainage.
2. Raise and support vehicle, then remove air pipe and hose between turbocharger and charge air cooler.
3. Disconnect joint between front exhaust pipe and intermediate pipe, then loosen screw holding exhaust pipe to engine.
4. Remove front exhaust pipe from turbocharger and hang pipe to oxygen sensor cable is not damaged.
5. Break seal and remove wastegate locking ring.
6. Remove turbocharger stay, then the oil return pipe. Plug pipe with rag.
7. Disconnect oil pipe on oil filter, then lower vehicle.
8. Remove hoses to boost pressure control valve, noting their positions.
9. Remove intake hose with bypass hose.
10. Remove wastegate diaphragm nuts, then the intake pipe together with crankcase ventilation pipe.
11. Remove oil pipe to turbocharger, then the lower coolant pipe.
12. Remove upper coolant pipe screw from turbocharger, then the turbocharger.
13. Reverse procedure to install, noting the following:
    a. Lubricate three pin screws on turbocharger with Molycote 1000, or equivalent, before installing front exhaust pipe.
    b. Tighten turbocharger to specifications.
    c. Ensure turbocharger system is working properly.

9000

1. Loosen A/C compressor belt tensioner, then remove A/C compressor drive belt.
2. Disconnect upper pipe coupling on oil cooler, then remove clips attaching pipe to radiator.
3. Remove A/C compressor mounting bolts, then insert piece of sheet metal to protect oil cooler and position A/C compressor aside.
4. Disconnect solenoid valve electrical connector, then remove solenoid valve from mounting on radiator.
5. Disconnect radiator cooling fan electrical connector, then remove mounting bolts and radiator cooling fan.
6. Disconnect air mass meter electrical connector and remove clips securing air mass meter to air cleaner cover, then pull rubber socket connector off turbocharger and position air mass meter aside.
7. Disconnect pressure pipe from turbocharger.
8. Remove bolts securing oil pipe to turbocharger, then unbolt clutch slave cylinder and remove clip securing oil pipe to cylinder head.
9. Disconnect oil pipe banjo coupling from engine block, then remove clip on intake manifold.
10. Disconnect exhaust pipe from turbocharger.
11. Disconnect exhaust pipe front rubber hangers.
12. Remove support bracket between oil pan and turbocharger.
13. Remove attaching bolts for oil return pipe at engine block. **Cover exposed hole to prevent nuts or washers from exhaust manifold entering engine during removal.**
14. Remove nuts and washers securing exhaust manifold to cylinder head.
15. Lower exhaust manifold until clear of studs, then remove exhaust manifold and turbocharger unit as an assembly.
16. Mount assembly in vise and remove nuts attaching turbocharger and exhaust manifold.
17. Separate turbocharger from exhaust manifold.
18. Reverse procedure to install, noting the following:
    a. Install new locknuts attaching turbocharger to exhaust manifold with locking flanges turned inward, then tighten to specifications.
    b. Tighten exhaust manifold nuts to specifications.
    c. Adjust A/C drive belt tension.

TIGHTENING SPECIFICATIONS

9-3 & 900

Year	Component	Torque, Ft. Lbs.
2.0L & 2.3L ENGINES		
1998–2001	Camshaft Cover Bolts	11
	Camshaft Sprocket Bolts	47
	Chain Tensioner	47
	Chain Tensioner Pushrod & Spring	16
	Cover Plate	21
	Crankshaft Pulley	130
	Cylinder Head Bolts	①
	Front Engine Mounting Bolts	54
	Front Exhaust Pipe Nuts	16
	Front Subframe Retaining Bolts	85
	Fuel Pump Screw Ring	55
	Gearbox Oil Hoses	19
	Ignition Discharge Module	21
	Intake Manifold	16
	Middle Subframe Retaining Bolts	141
	Oil Cooler	13
	Oil Pan Bolts	16
	Rear Subframe Retaining Bolts	81②
	Selector Lever Cable	16
	Selector Rod	16
	Spark Plugs	21
	Timing Cover To Cylinder Head Cover Bolts	16
	Turbocharger	16
	Turbocharger Nuts	16

① — Refer to "Cylinder Head, Replace" for procedure.

② — Plus an additional 75.°

9000

Year	Component	Torque, Ft. Lbs.
2.0L & 2.3L ENGINES		
1998–99	Balance Shaft Idler Wheel Sprocket	17
	Balance Shaft Sprockets	47
	Big-End Bearings②	41
	Big-End Bearings③	15④
	Camshaft Bearing Caps	11
	Camshaft Cover Attaching Bolts	11
	Camshaft Sprocket Bolts	47
	Crankshaft Pulley②	129
	Crankshaft Pulley③	129
	Cylinder Head Bolts	①
	Distributor Bolt②	13
	Engine Mounting Bolts⑤	29
	Engine To Transaxle Bolts	40-75
	Exhaust Manifold Nuts (Non-Turbo)	13
	Exhaust Manifold Nuts (Turbo)②	19
	Exhaust Manifold Nuts (Turbo)③	18
	Flywheel Bolts (17 mm Bolt)	44
	Flywheel Bolts (19 mm Bolt)	63
	Intake Manifold Attaching Bolts	16
	Main Bearings②	81
	Main Bearings③	15④

Continued

9000—Continued

Year	Component	Torque, Ft. Lbs.
2.0L & 2.3L ENGINES		
1998–99	Oil Pan Bolts	16
	Oil Pan Drain Plug	19
	Oil Pump Bolts	72⑦
	Spark Plugs	21
	Thermostat Housing	16
	Throttle Housing	16
	Timing Chain Tensioner	47
	Timing Cover②	18
	Timing Cover③	15
	Valve Cover Bolts	11
	Water Pump Pulley Bolts	72⑦
	Water Pump Retaining Bolts	15
3.0L ENGINE		
1998	Belt Tensioning Pulley	15
	Camshaft Bearing Cap Bolts	72⑦
	Camshaft Sprocket	37⑤
	Center Intake Manifold Bolts	16
	Coolant Bridge Bolts	22
	Crankshaft Pulley	15
	Cylinder Head Bolts	①
	Engine Mounting Bolts	29
	Intake Manifold Bolts	15
	Lower Intake Manifold Bolts	15
	Lower Roller Counter	30
	Oil Pan Bolts	11
	Oil Pump Housing Bolts	60⑦
	Oil Pump Housing Lid Bolts	60⑦
	Oil Pressure Release Valve	⑥
	Power Steering Pump Belt Tensioner	30
	Spark Plugs	19
	Steering Swivel Member To MacPherson Struts	68
	Tensioning Pulley	15

① — Refer to "Cylinder Head, Replace" for procedure.
② — Less balancer shafts.
③ — With balancer shafts.
④ — Tighten an additional 70.°
⑤ — Tighten an additional 60.°
⑥ — Aluminum grommet, 15 ft. lbs.; copper grommet, 21 ft. lbs.
⑦ — Inch lbs.

Clutch & Manual Transaxle

INDEX

	Page No.
Adjustments	7-26
Clutch Pedal	7-26
Shift Linkage	7-26
Clutch, Replace	7-27
9-3 & 900	7-27
9-5	7-27
9000	7-27
Hydraulic System Service	7-26
Clutch System Bleed	7-27
Master Cylinder, Replace	7-26
Slave Cylinder Bleed	7-27
Slave Cylinder, Replace	7-26
Precautions	7-26
Air Bag Systems	7-26
Battery Ground Cable	7-26
Tightening Specifications	7-29
Transaxle, Replace	7-28
9-3 & 900	7-28
9-5	7-28
9000	7-29

PRECAUTIONS

AIR BAG SYSTEMS

Refer to "Air Bag System Precautions" in the front of this manual for system disarming and arming procedures.

BATTERY GROUND CABLE

Prior to service, disconnect battery ground cable and isolate as required.

ADJUSTMENTS

CLUTCH PEDAL

No adjustment is necessary since clutch adjustment is automatic. On hydraulic clutches, the sliding lock ring on the slave cylinder moves along the piston to compensate for clutch disc wear.

SHIFT LINKAGE

9-3 & 900

1. Place gear lever in 4th gear.
2. Remove gearbox plastic plug and fit locking pin tool No. 87 92 335, or equivalent, so 4th gear is fixed in gearbox. Locking pin ring should be all the way up.
3. Remove gaiter on gear lever and ensure locking pin tool can be inserted into hole in lever housing. locking pin ring should be down in the hole. If it is not possible to insert locking pin, continue this procedure to adjust lever. If no adjustment is necessary, remove locking pin tool.
4. Remove clamp holding gear rod in linkage on gearbox, then ensure gear lever is in 4th gear.
5. Insert locking pin tool in gear lever housing. locking pin ring should be down in hole.
6. Tighten gear rod to linkage clamp nut to specifications.
7. Remove locking pin from gearbox, then install plastic plug.
8. Remove locking pin from gear lever housing and install gaiter.
9. Test shift linkage by changing gears.

9000

1. Pry out and lift rubber boot from console.
2. Place gear shift lever in reverse by inserting a .16 inch (4 mm) drill through fixing holes in gear lever housing.
3. Connect selector rod to selector rod joint, then tighten pinch bolt to specifications.
4. Remove drill, then reinstall rubber boot.

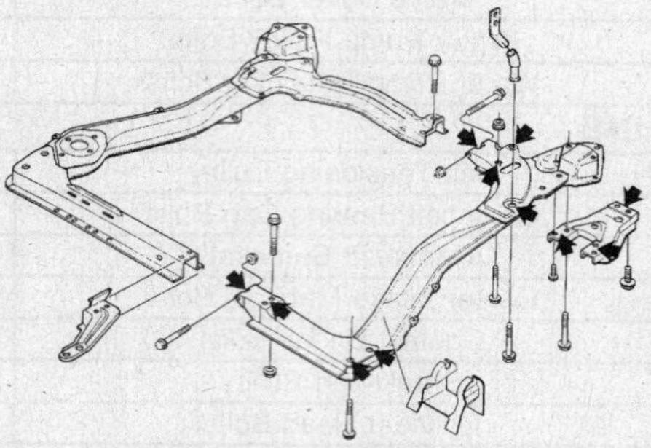

Fig. 1 Subframe mounting bolts. 9000

HYDRAULIC SYSTEM SERVICE

SLAVE CYLINDER, REPLACE

9-3, 900 & 9000

1. Remove transaxle as outlined in "Transaxle, Replace."
2. Remove release bearing from slave cylinder.
3. Disconnect pressure pipe and remove bleed nipple.
4. Remove three slave cylinder retaining bolts, then the slave cylinder.
5. Reverse procedure to install, noting the following:
   a. Use new O-rings.
   b. Bleed clutch hydraulic system as outlined in "Clutch System Bleed."

9-5

1. Remove transaxle as outlined under "Transaxle, Replace."
2. Disconnect fluid delivery pipe from slave cylinder.
3. Remove slave cylinder retaining bolts, then the slave cylinder.
4. Reverse procedure to install, noting the following:
   a. Apply Loctite 577, or equivalent, sealant to slave cylinder retaining bolts, then tighten to specification.
   b. Before installing transaxle, bleed slave cylinder as outlined under "Slave Cylinder Bleed."
   c. Bleed clutch hydraulic system as outlined under "Clutch System Bleed."

MASTER CYLINDER, REPLACE

9-3 & 900

1. Remove clip securing hydraulic tube from master cylinder, then disconnect tube from cylinder.
2. Remove knee shield from under left-hand side of instrument panel.
3. Remove clevis pin connecting pushrod to clutch pedal.
4. Remove master cylinder retaining nuts from inside of bulkhead, then the master cylinder from engine compartment side.
5. Disconnect hydraulic supply hose from master cylinder and secure it in a raised position so that fluid will not runout.
6. Reverse procedure to install. Bleed clutch hydraulic system as outlined in "Clutch System Bleed."

9-5

1. Remove trim panel from under left-hand side of instrument panel.
2. Lift spring from clutch pedal.
3. Remove clip and pin from clutch pedal.
4. Lift up engine compartment fuse and relay panel.
5. Remove fuse and relay panel bracket attaching screw, then position panel aside.
6. Remove intake manifold cover.
7. Remove crankcase ventilation valve and bracket.
8. Drain fluid from master cylinder reservoir, then disconnect supply hose and fluid delivery pipe.
9. Remove master cylinder retaining nuts, then the master cylinder.
10. Reverse procedure to install, noting the following:
    a. Lubricate clutch pedal pin with Nynas Alexol L 12, or equivalent.
    b. Bleed clutch hydraulic system as outlined under "Clutch System Bleed."

9000

1. Remove trim panel from under left-hand side of instrument panel.
2. Remove clip, then the clevis pin connecting clutch pedal to master cylinder pushrod.
3. Place sheet of cardboard under clutch pedal to prevent hydraulic fluid from dripping on carpet.
4. Disconnect supply hose from cylinder and plug end of hose.
5. Disconnect hydraulic hose from cylinder, then remove retaining bolts and cylinder.
6. Reverse procedure to install. Bleed clutch hydraulic system as outlined in "Clutch System Bleed."

CLUTCH SYSTEM BLEED

9-3, 900 & 9000

1. Attach clear vinyl hose to bleed nipple of slave cylinder, then place opposite end of hose into a clear container.
2. Fill fluid reservoir and open bleed nipple ½ turn.
3. Attach suitable cooling system pressure tester to the fluid reservoir.
4. Pump pressure tester until all air bubbles are gone from system.
5. Close bleed nipple, refill reservoir and ensure clutch operates properly.

9-5

A brake pressure bleeder tool No. 88 19 096, or equivalent, is necessary to perform this bleed procedure.

1. Disconnect bleed nipple on top of transaxle.
2. Connect brake pressure bleeder tool No. 88 19 096, or equivalent, to bleed nipple.
3. Connect compressed air to bleed tool, then bleed clutch until clear fluid runs from nipple.
4. Remove tool from bleed nipple and refill brake fluid.

SLAVE CYLINDER BLEED

9-5

The transaxle must be removed to perform this bleed procedure.

1. Connect an 18 x .3 inch piece of clear plastic hose to slave cylinder delivery pipe connection.
2. Connect pressure/vacuum pump tool No. 30 14 883, or equivalent, to plastic hose.
3. Pump up pressure until slave cylinder seal move out and brake fluid runs down into cylinder. Pressure increases when seal is fully out.
4. Remove pressure/vacuum pump and carefully press release bearing to its stop. Check tube for bubbles.
5. Repeat steps 3 and 4 until there are no air bubbles in tube.
6. After bleed procedure is complete, leave slave cylinder seal in its innermost position, then drain and remove plastic hose.

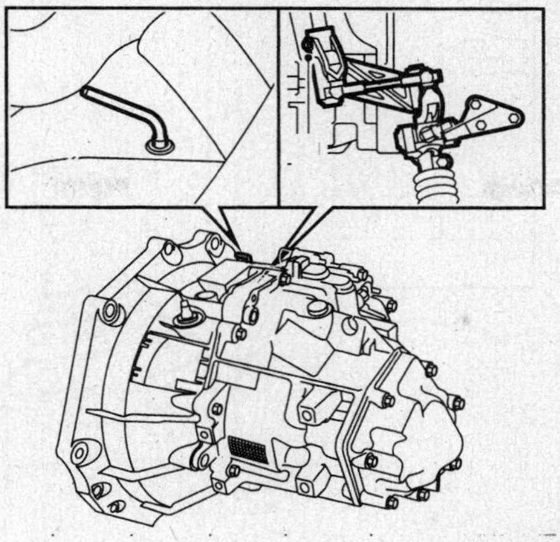

SA5039900029000X

Fig. 2 Transaxle lock pin installation. 9-5

CLUTCH

REPLACE

9-3 & 900

1. Remove transaxle as outlined under, "Transaxle, Replace."
2. Install flywheel holder tool No. 83 94 868, or equivalent, to lock flywheel.
3. Remove pressure plate screws, then the clutch.
4. Inspect clutch as follows:
   a. Check clutch plate contact surface in flywheel. If surface is blue annealed and has small cracks, it is satisfactory. If there are deep scratches, flywheel should be turned in lathe or replaced.
   b. Check pressure plate in spring unit for any scratches or deformity. Replace pressure plate if surfaces are uneven.
   c. Check wear on clutch plate and replace as necessary.
5. Place plate and pressure plate on flywheel and loosely attach screws.
6. Center plate with centering drift tool No. 87 92 327, or equivalent. Tighten screws alternately to specifications.
7. Install manual transaxle as outlined under "Transaxle, Replace."

9-5

1. Remove transaxle as outlined under "Transaxle, Replace."
2. Position flywheel locking attachment tool No. 83 94 868, or equivalent, to secure flywheel.
3. Remove pressure plate attaching bolts in several steps, then the pressure plate and clutch from flywheel.
4. Reverse procedure to install, noting the following:
   a. Inspect flywheel driven plate for cracks. If there are minor cracks or bluing, the surface is satisfactory. If there are major cracks, replace flywheel.
   b. Check pressure plate for cracks or distortion. If uneven, replace plate.
   c. Check release bearing for noise or excessive wear. Replace as necessary.

9000

An inspection opening has been included in the clutch housing to check clutch wear.

1. Perform clutch inspection as follows:
   a. Remove plug from inspection opening in clutch cover.
   b. Depress and release clutch pedal and ensure release bearing is in contact with pressure plate fingers.
   c. Measure clearance between front edge of plastic sleeve and edge of release bearing.
   d. Clearance should be .08–.35 inch. If clearance is less than .08 inch, clutch should be replaced.
2. Raise and support front of vehicle.
3. Obtain radio anti-theft code as outlined under "Precautions."
4. Remove battery.
5. Remove washer fluid reservoir, then disconnect positive lead from terminal block.
6. Remove fuel filter, terminal block, then the battery shelf.
7. Disconnect electrical connector from air mass meter, then remove meter.
8. Remove air cleaner intake duct, then disconnect Hall transmitter lead from distributor.
9. Remove cover and filter element from air cleaner, then the air cleaner body.
10. Remove turbocharger pressure pipe, then disconnect battery ground lead and back-up lamp switch from gearbox.
11. Attach clamp to hose in slave cylinder pressure line, then tighten clamp securely and disconnect pressure line between pipe and hose. Remove oil supply pipe clamp.
12. Disconnect lefthand engine mount, then support engine using engine lifting tool No. 83 93 977, or equivalent.
13. Remove lefthand front wheel and wing insert panel, then separate suspension arm from lower ball joint.
14. Disconnect speedometer cable, then carefully remove cable as not to allow drive to fall into transaxle.
15. Separate selector rod joint halves, then remove clip from dust cover on intermediate driveshaft.
16. Disconnect intake manifold brace, then remove starter motor attaching bolts and starter.
17. Remove engine to transaxle attaching bolts, except bolt positioned at top flange between engine and transaxle. Insert locating dowel tools No. 8392128, or equivalents, in bolt holes.
18. Loosen two subframe pivot mountings, then remove four attaching bolts, **Fig. 1.**
19. Remove attaching bolts and screws from subframe attaching point, then remove wheel arch bracket lower attaching point attaching bolts, allowing subframe to hang from anti-roll bar.
20. Remove rubber boot to U-joint retaining clip, then the driveshaft and install protective covers on open ends of boot and driver cup.
21. Attach lifting sling to transaxle, then remove last attaching bolt. Withdraw

transaxle and allow to hang from sling.
22. Install flywheel lock tool No. 86 92 987, or equivalent, to top of locating dowel, then lift off clutch assembly and remove driven plate.
23. Reverse procedure to install. Tighten bolts to specifications.

TRANSAXLE

REPLACE

9-3 & 900

1. Place vehicle on ramp and engage 4th gear.
2. Remove battery.
3. Disconnect battery ground cable from gearbox.
4. **On models equipped with 2.3L engine,** disconnect front clamp holding positive cable.
5. **On all models,** disconnect terminal to rear light switch.
6. Disconnect clutch wire from clutch lever, then release clutch wire rubber damper from fastener on gearbox.
7. **On models equipped with 2.3L engines,** remove oxygen sensor, then push out rubber bushing from lefthand lifting eye. Push out rubber bushing from lefthand lifting eye.
8. **On all models,** place yoke tool No. 83 93 850, or equivalent, on wheel housings. Ensure yoke is in close contact with fender edges.
9. Take up load of engine and gearbox.
10. Remove plastic plug on gearbox and install locking pin tool No. 87 92 335, or equivalent, with ring facing upward, to secure gear position.
11. Disconnect clamp holding gear rod in linkage on gearbox.
12. Engage 3rd gear so gear rod is released from linkage, then install locking pin. locking pin ring should be down in hole.
13. Raise and support vehicle, then remove front wheels.
14. Remove front exhaust pipe, then the lefthand and righthand spoilers below bumper.
15. Remove plastic seal at bottom of righthand inner fender.
16. Remove ball bolts on both sides, then place mobile jack tool No. 83 94 793, or equivalent, with mother fixture tool No. 83 94 801, or equivalent, under vehicle.
17. Place front holder tool No. 83 94 819, or equivalent, in mother fixture and fit guide pins.
18. Place rear holders tool No. 83 94 827, or equivalent, on mother fixture and install small bosses.
19. Fit mobile jack up against carrying frame, then remove two rear engine support nuts.
20. Remove carrying frame screws, then place washer under two rear screws in safe place.
21. Lower mobile jack with carrying frame.
22. Remove oil drain plug and drain oil from gearbox, then install plug using thread-sealing liquid. Tighten drain plug to specifications.
23. Remove lefthand driveshaft using removal tool No. 89 96 654, or equivalent, then suspend shaft using securing straps.
24. Fit cover tool No. 87 92 244, or equivalent, to gearbox, then pull out righthand driveshaft from intermediate shaft with removal tool. Suspend shaft with securing straps.
25. **On models equipped with 2.3L engine,** remove two intermediate shaft bearing to bearing bracket screws, then pull out shaft.
26. **On all models,** install sealing cover No. 8792244, or equivalent, to gearbox.
27. Remove splash plate behind flywheel, then the two engine bracket screws.
28. Remove three gearbox bracket screws from gearbox.
29. Remove engine/gearbox parting surface screws, accessible from outside.
30. **On models equipped with 2.3L engine,** remove bottom starter motor nut.
31. **On all models,** lower vehicle, then remove two outer gearbox screws so gearbox hangs on middle screw.
32. Fit lifting bracket tool No. 87 92 368 and wire tool No. 87 92 251, or equivalents, on gearbox parting surface, then connect suitable engine hoist.
33. Lower entire powertrain about 1.97 inches, then remove last screw.
34. Pull out and lower gearbox, then remove rear engine bracket console.
35. Reverse procedure to install. Ensure rear engine bracket console and its linkage has been installed, if removed.

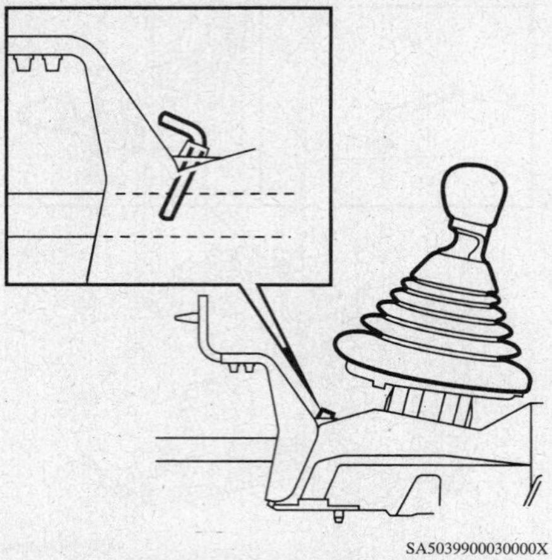

Fig. 3 Shift lever lock pin installation. 9-5

9-5

1. Remove grille and intake manifold cover.
2. Remove battery and battery tray.
3. Place transaxle shift lever in 4th gear, then remove plastic plug from top of transaxle and insert lock pin tool No. 87 92 335, or equivalent, into transaxle to secure transaxle in 4th gear, **Fig. 2.**
4. Lift shifter boot, then position shifter into 3rd gear so selector rod disengages from linkage. Insert locking pin tool No. 87 92 335, or equivalent, into gear lever housing, **Fig. 3.**
5. Remove clip from slave cylinder, then disconnect hydraulic fluid delivery pipe and reinstall clip.
6. Disconnect back-up switch electrical connector and engine harness positive leads.
7. Remove three upper transaxle attaching bolts.
8. Disconnect gear linkage from transaxle.
9. Remove rear engine mount retaining nut.
10. Loosen three rear engine mount attaching bolts.
11. Support engine and transaxle assembly with lifting beam tool No. 83 93 850, or equivalent.
12. Remove torque arm to subframe attaching bolts.
13. Raise and support vehicle, then remove front wheels.
14. Remove front cover from under bumper.
15. Remove front exhaust pipe from flange on turbocharger assembly.
16. Remove front exhaust pipe from rear bracket, then from the vehicle. **Do not damage bellows or oxygen sensors.**
17. Remove rear engine mounting and bracket, transaxle gear linkage should separate from transaxle at this time.
18. Remove steering gear attaching bolts.
19. Remove power steering fluid delivery pipe clamps from subframe.
20. Disconnect air cleaner from subframe.
21. Detach A/C pipes from subframe plastic clips.
22. Remove engine oil cooler to charge air cooler attaching screws, then the oil cooler from air cooler.
23. Secure radiator in place with suitable tape.
24. Remove three lower ball joint to link arm attaching bolts.
25. Remove roll bar to strut retaining nuts from both struts.
26. Remove cover plate from behind flywheel.
27. Remove rear support attaching bolts.
28. Place support tool No. 83 94 793, or equivalent, under subframe.
29. Remove power steering delivery pipe brackets from subframe.
30. Remove subframe attaching bolts, then the subframe from vehicle.
31. Drain transaxle fluid.
32. Separate lefthand driveshaft from transaxle with removal tool No. 87 92 616, or equivalent. Suspend shaft aside using cable ties.
33. Lower vehicle and mark position of left engine mount.
34. Remove left engine mount attaching bolts, then the left engine mount.
35. Disconnect ground wire from transaxle.
36. Remove transaxle mount attaching bolts and the transaxle mount.
37. Lower transaxle until it is free from structural support.
38. Raise and support vehicle, then attach transaxle jack tool No. MKM 886 87 96 608, or equivalent to transaxle.
39. Remove two remaining transaxle to engine attaching bolts.

40. Lower transaxle assembly from vehicle.
41. Reverse procedure to install.

9000

2.0L Engine

1. Raise and support front of vehicle.
2. Remove battery.
3. Disconnect air intake duct from inside fender wheel housing.
4. Remove washer fluid reservoir, then disconnect positive cable from terminal block.
5. Remove fuel filter, terminal block, then the battery shelf.
6. Disconnect air mass meter electrical connector, then remove mass meter. **Handle mass meter very carefully.**
7. Disconnect bayonet coupling at air intake duct, then remove air intake duct from air cleaner.
8. Disconnect Hall sensor cable from distributor.
9. Remove air cleaner assembly, then the turbocharger delivery pipe.
10. Disconnect ground cable and back-up light switch wire connector from transaxle.
11. Attach suitable clamp around clutch slave cylinder hydraulic line and tighten enough to prevent fluid loss. Disconnect hydraulic line from slave cylinder and remove support clip.
12. Remove lefthand side engine mounting nut and bolt.
13. Position lifting beam tool No. 83 93 977, or equivalent, on fender edges, then attach to engine for support.
14. Remove lefthand front wheel and fender insert panel.
15. Separate lefthand front lower control arm from lower ball joint.
16. Disconnect speedometer cable. **Use caution when removing cable not to drop pinion into gearbox.**
17. Disconnect shift linkage from selector rod joint.
18. Remove intermediate driveshaft dust cover clamp.
19. Remove steady bar to intake manifold attaching bolt, remove starter motor, then push steady bar aside. Allow starter motor to hang by electrical leads.
20. Remove all but top flywheel housing to engine block attaching bolts, installing locating dowels tool No. 83 92 128, or equivalent.
21. Loosen subframe pivot mounting nuts, then remove front, then rear subframe mounting.
22. Remove wheel arch bracket lower mounting to subframe attaching bolt and allow subframe to hang from stabilizer bar.
23. Loosen stabilizer bar to lower control arm attaching nut and allow lower control arm to hang, then remove lefthand side stabilizer bar bracket from subframe.
24. Loosen inboard universal joint boot clamp, then remove driveshaft and universal joint from drive cup. Cover drive cup and universal joint to prevent contamination.
25. Attach suitable lifting device to transaxle and remove remaining engine to transaxle attaching bolt.
26. Pull transaxle away from engine and lower to ground.
27. Reverse procedure to install. Tighten bolts to specifications.

2.3L Engine

1. Remove battery.
2. Remove washer fluid container.
3. Remove holder with connectors, terminal blocks and positive battery cable.
4. Release stay for ABS hydraulic unit.
5. Remove battery tray, then bolts for cover over bulkhead.
6. Remove rubber strip, then lift cover and disconnect washer hoses from nozzle, then remove cover.
7. Separate speedometer cable connector, then pull speedometer cable and washer hose through rubber grommet.
8. Disconnect electrical connectors from air mass meter and air intake temperature sensor, then disconnect hose on air delivery pipe from bypass valve.
9. Remove delivery pipe between throttle housing and intercooler.
10. Remove starter motor retaining nuts, then secure starter motor to steering gear.
11. Separate selector rod universal joint, then the selector rod.
12. Pinch slave cylinder pressure hose using suitable clamping tongs, then separate pressure line.
13. Remove upper bolts for stay at wheel housing, then release lefthand engine mount.
14. Position lifting beam tool No. 83 93 977, or equivalent, on fender edges, then attach to engine for support.
15. Disconnect negative battery cable from battery and reversing light switch connector from gearbox.
16. Separate suspension arm from ball joint, then remove anti-roll bar.
17. Remove lower bolt for stay at wheel housing, then the three bottom bolts from joint between engine and gearbox.
18. Remove center and lefthand skirts from spoiler.
19. Separate subframe at front and rear, then lower, using suitable jack.
20. Remove universal joint, then lower vehicle.
21. Attach suitable lifting device to transaxle and remove remaining engine to transaxle attaching bolt.
22. Pull transaxle away from engine and lower to ground.
23. Reverse procedure to install. Tighten bolts to specifications.

TIGHTENING SPECIFICATIONS

Year	Component	Torque, Ft. Lbs.
9-3 & 900		
1998–2001	Ball Joint To Link Arm Nuts	55
	Clutch Plate Screws	16
	Engine Bracket Screws	54
	Engine/Gearbox Parting Surface Screws	50
	Front Carrying Frame	85
	Gearbox Bracket Screws	30
	Gearbox Parting Surface Screw	16
	Gear Rod To Linkage Clamp Nut	16
	Intermediate Shaft Bearing Screws	15
	Middle Carrying Frame	141
	Rear Carrying Frame	81
	Transaxle Drain Plug	37
	Wheel Lug Nuts	100

Continued

TIGHTENING SPECIFICATIONS—Continued

Year	Component	Torque, Ft. Lbs.
9-5		
1999–2001	Drain Plug	37
	Engine To Transaxle	50
	Left Engine Mount	33
	Lower Ball To Link Arm	22
	Master Cylinder	15
	Rear Engine Mount To Body	18
	Rear Engine Mount To Transaxle	50
	Slave Cylinder	84①
	Slave Cylinder Delivery Pipe	16
	Subframe	74
	Support Plate	44
	Transaxle Mount To Transaxle	30
	Wheel Lug Nuts	88
9000		
1998	Control Arm To Lower Ball Joint	15–20
	Engine Mount Bolts	52
	Flywheel (17 mm Bolts)	44
	Flywheel (19 mm Bolts)	63
	Front Sway Bar Pinch-Bolt	30–40
	Master Cylinder Pressure Line	11–14
	Pressure Line Clamp Bolt	13–20
	Reverse Light Switch	15–17
	Selector Rod Joint Pinch Bolt	22–25
	Slave Cylinder Mounting Bolts	72–96①
	Slave Cylinder Pressure Line	11–14
	Starter Motor Attaching Bolts	28–35
	Subframe Attaching Bolts	32–42
	Sway Bar	30–40
	Transaxle Drain Plug	30–44
	Transaxle To Engine Bolts	40–75
	Wheel Lug Nuts	100

① — Inch lbs.

Rear Axle & Suspension

INDEX

	Page No.
Coil Spring, Replace	7-33
9-3 & 900	7-33
9-5	7-33
9000	7-33
Hub & Bearing, Replace	7-32
9-3, 9-5 & 900	7-32
9000	7-32
Longitudinal Link, Replace	7-34
9-5	7-34
Lower Transverse Link, Replace	7-33
9-5	7-33
Panhard Rod & Bushing, Replace	7-34
Rear Axle, Replace	7-31
9-3 & 900	7-31
9000	7-31
Rear Suspension Subframe, Replace	7-31
9-5	7-31
Roll Bar, Replace	7-34
9-3 & 900	7-34
9-5	7-34
9000	7-34
Shock Absorber, Replace	7-32
9-3 & 900	7-32
9-5	7-32
9000	7-32
Spring Linkage, Replace	7-33
9-3 & 900	7-33
9000	7-33
Tightening Specifications	7-35
Torque Arm, Replace	7-33
Transverse Link Ball Joint, Replace	7-34
Lower	7-34
Upper	7-34
Upper Transverse Link, Replace	7-33
9-5	7-33

REAR AXLE

REPLACE

9-3 & 900

1. Use brake clamp to hold brake pedal in depressed position.
2. Raise and support vehicle, then remove rear wheels.
3. Disconnect speed sensor connectors and cables from spring link.
4. Remove return springs from levers on both sides, then the lefthand parking brake cable from lever, holder and equalizing sleeve.
5. Remove righthand parking brake cable from lever and holder.
6. Remove rear silencer, then the anti-roll bar. Collect nut washers.
7. Remove lefthand and righthand rear brake pipes, **Fig. 1.** Plug brake calipers and hose connections.
8. Remove retaining clips for brake hose connections and press them out of holder.
9. Use suitable high-lift jack to slightly press up spring link on one side.
10. Remove damper lower retaining bolt, then the jack.
11. Carefully force spring link down using crowbar, then remove coil spring and spacer.
12. Remove four hub assembly retaining nuts, then the hub assembly and spacer, **Fig. 1.**
13. Place jack under spring link on other side of vehicle, then slightly press up spring link.
14. Remove damper lower retaining bolt.
15. Carefully release and lower spring link, then remove coil spring and spacer.
16. Remove four hub assembly retaining nuts, then the hub assembly with spacer.
17. Position jack under rear axle, then remove rear axle retaining bolts.
18. Lower rear axle, then place on workbench.
19. Remove inner anti-roll bar and bushing.

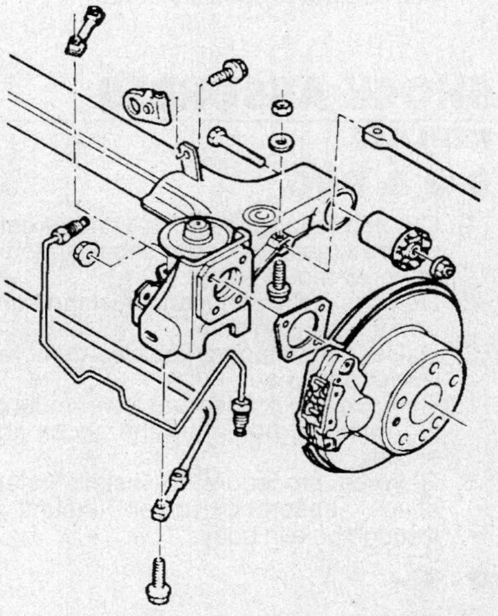

Fig. 1 Rear axle components. 9-3 & 900

20. Remove brake hose and brake cable holder.
21. Reverse procedure to install, noting the following:
    a. Install new bushings.
    b. Using jack, raise spring link to about 14.55 inches (37 cm) between edge of wheel arch and upper edge of hub center, then tighten bolts to specifications.
    c. Ensure marking on coil spring faces rearward.

9000

1. Raise and support vehicle, then disconnect hand brake cables from levers on brake calipers.
2. Unscrew clips attaching cables to spring links.
3. Remove or disconnect righthand side components as follows:
    a. Remove ABS sensor from hub and release ABS lead from clips on spring link.
    b. Remove screw plug from over adjusting screw and slightly back off adjusting screw.
    c. Remove brake caliper and disc backplate mounting bolts, then brake caliper. Hang caliper on torque arm.
    d. Disconnect panhard rod from rear axle. Position rod aside.
    e. Position jack under spring link and raise link enough to relieve load on mountings.
    f. Remove bolt from spring link rear mounting, then lower jack under spring link and remove coil spring.
4. Repeat previous step for lefthand side components.
5. Disconnect torque arms from rear axle, then place jack under middle of rear axle. Slightly raise rear axle.
6. Disconnect lower mountings for dampers and anti-roll bar.
7. Lower rear axle from vehicle.
8. Reverse procedure to install.

REAR SUSPENSION SUBFRAME

REPLACE

9-5

1. Raise and support vehicle, then remove rear wheels.
2. Disconnect center and rear exhaust hangers. Support exhaust system so that not too much strain is on front hangers or flexible section.
3. Place a suitable jack under rear subframe.
4. Remove upper and lower transverse links from longitudinal links on both side of vehicle, **Fig. 2.**
5. Remove anti-roll bar to longitudinal links attaching bolts, then disconnect anti-roll bars from both sides.
6. Remove subframe attaching bolts, then lower subframe with anti-roll bar and transverse links attached from vehicle.

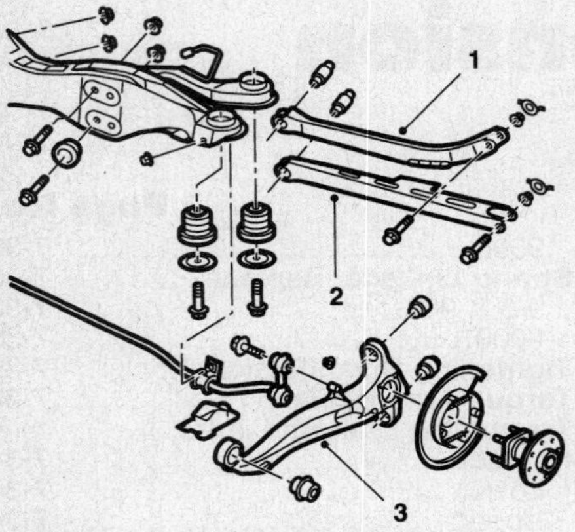

Fig. 2 Rear suspension. 9-5

7. Remove anti-roll bar and transverse links from subframe.
8. Reverse procedure to install, noting the following:
   a. **Ensure transverse attaching bolts fitted with protective sleeves are installed in their original position. These sleeves were designed to protect the fuel tank and fuel lines in the event of a collision.**
   b. Do not tighten bolts to specification until wheels are on the ground.
   c. Check rear wheel alignment as outlined in "Wheel Alignment" section.

HUB & BEARING

REPLACE

9-3, 9-5 & 900

The wheel bearings are incorporated in the hub and are not part of a shaft or subaxle assembly. The bearings are of double-row, angular contact type which are permanently lubricated and maintenance free. They cannot be replaced individually.

1. Raise and support vehicle, then press back brake pistons using slip joint pliers.
2. Remove two brake caliper retaining bolts, then disconnect brake pipe if necessary. Suspend brake caliper aside with cable tie.
3. Back off brake shoe adjusting screw.
4. Remove lever return spring, then disconnect parking brake cable from lever.
5. Remove brake disc retaining bolts, then the brake disc.
6. Disconnect speed sensor connector, then remove four wheel hub retaining bolts.
7. Remove wheel hub, back plate and spacer, then separate wheel hub from back plate.
8. Reverse procedure to install, noting the following:
   a. Clean contact surfaces with wire brush.
   b. Secure brake disc locking screw with Loctite, or equivalent.

9000

1. Raise rear of vehicle and support at frame.
2. Remove rear wheels, then disconnect hand brake cable from caliper.
3. Disconnect wheel sensor from hub and release lead from bracket on trailing end of spring link.
4. Remove screw plug, then slightly unscrew adjusting screw in caliper.
5. Remove caliper from mounting. Hang caliper from torque arm.
6. Remove brake disc, dust cap, locknut and washer.
7. Remove hub assembly, using puller if necessary. **Hub, bearing and seals are an integral unit and must be serviced as an assembly.**
8. Reverse procedure to install. Tighten bolt and nut to specifications.

SHOCK ABSORBER

REPLACE

9-3 & 900

1. Cut flap in luggage compartment carpeting to gain access to shock absorber upper mounting.
2. Remove nut, washer and bushing from upper mounting point.
3. Raise and support vehicle, then remove rear wheel.
4. Remove shock absorber lower mounting retaining bolt, then the shock absorber.
5. Reverse procedure to install. Insert shock absorber upper mounting through hole in body.

9-5

1. Raise and support vehicle, then remove rear wheel.
2. Remove lower spring bracket bolts and loosen upper spring bracket bolts, **Fig. 3.**
3. Remove shock absorber lower retaining bolt, then the shock absorber and spring assembly.
4. Disassemble shock and coil spring assembly as follows:
   a. Loosen shock absorber locknut. **Do not remove locknut at this time.**
   b. Compress coil spring with spring compressor tool No. 88 18 791, or equivalent.
   c. Remove shock absorber locknut, spring and spacer ring.
5. Reverse procedure to install, noting the following:
   a. Ensure end of spring is fitted into spacer ring recess.
   b. When tightening shock absorber locknut grip shock absorber piston rod to prevent it from turning.

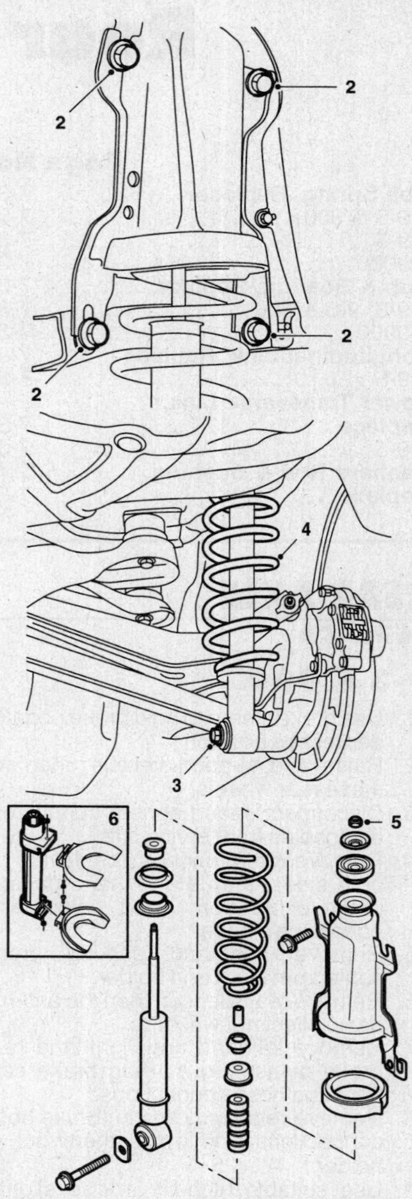

Fig. 3 Shock absorber removal. 9-5

9000

1. Raise vehicle at rear jacking point.
2. Support using jackstands placed under rear mountings of spring links.
3. Raise vehicle enough to relieve load on shocks and sway bar.
4. Remove rear wheels.
5. Remove lower shock mounting bolts.
6. From inside vehicle, remove panel

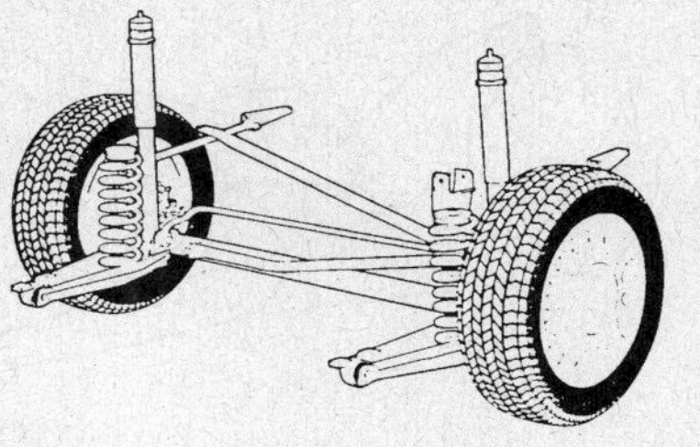

Fig. 4 Rear suspension assembly. 9000

over spare tire, then fold back carpet.
7. Remove nut, cap and bushing from top of shocks, then remove shocks.
8. Reverse procedure to install.

COIL SPRING

REPLACE

9-3 & 900

1. Raise and support vehicle, then remove wheel.
2. Place jack under spring link, then remove jack.
3. Place crowbar or other suitable tool in damper mounting bracket and carefully lever spring link downward.
4. Remove coil spring.
5. Reverse procedure to install, noting the following:
   a. Press spring link down and position coil spring with spring support on it.
   b. Marking on coil spring should face rearward.
   c. Tighten damper lower mounting bolt and wheel bolts to specifications.

9-5

Refer to "Shock Absorber, Replace" for coil spring replacement.

9000

1. Raise and support vehicle.
2. Remove rear wheel and position jack under spring link, **Fig. 4.**
3. Remove parking brake cable bracket from spring link.
4. **On models with anti-lock brakes,** release ABS lead from clips.
5. **On all models,** remove bolt attaching rear of spring link to rear axle.
6. Lower spring link, then remove spring.
7. Reverse procedure to install.

SPRING LINKAGE

REPLACE

9-3 & 900

1. Remove coil spring as outlined under "Coil Spring, Replace."
2. **On vehicles with anti-roll bar,** remove spring link front mounting bolt and anti-roll bar.
3. **On all models,** remove two bolts attaching front spring link mounting bracket to body, then the spring link.
4. Remove front bushing by pressing out using a sleeve applied to tube of bushing.
5. Remove rear bushing using bushing remover No. 89-96-274, or equivalent.
6. Reverse procedure to install. Lubricate new bushings with petroleum jelly.

9000

Spring Links

1. Remove coil spring as outlined under "Coil Spring, Replace."
2. Remove spring link front bracket mounting bolts, then the link.
3. Reverse procedure to install.

Spring Link Front Bushing

1. Remove rear wheel and position jack under spring link.
2. Disconnect spring link from bushing and bracket.
3. Remove bracket from underside of body.
4. Install new bushing and bracket onto spring link, then the spring link to underside of body.

Spring Link Rear Bushing

1. Remove coil spring as outlined under "Coil Spring, Replace."
2. Clean bushing and surrounding area, then apply petroleum jelly to all visible parts of bushing.
3. Position bushing remover tool No. 89 96 506, or equivalent, as shown, **Fig. 5.**
4. Press out bushings.
5. Reverse procedure to install.

TORQUE ARM

REPLACE

1. Raise and support vehicle
2. Remove torque arm mounting nuts, then the torque arm.
3. Press out rear bushing using 24 mm socket as support and 14 mm socket applied to inner spacer.
4. Press out front bushings using 30 mm socket and tool No. 89 96 464, or equivalent, as support.
5. Reverse procedure to install.

LOWER TRANSVERSE LINK

REPLACE

9-5

1. Raise and support vehicle, then remove rear wheel.
2. Disconnect center and rear exhaust hangers. Support exhaust system so that not too much strain is on front hangers or flexible section.
3. Remove upper and lower transverse link to longitudinal link attaching bolts, **Fig. 2.**
4. Remove anti-roll bar to longitudinal link attaching bolt.
5. Remove subframe attaching bolts on side that transverse link is being replaced, then loosen subframe attaching bolts on opposite side.

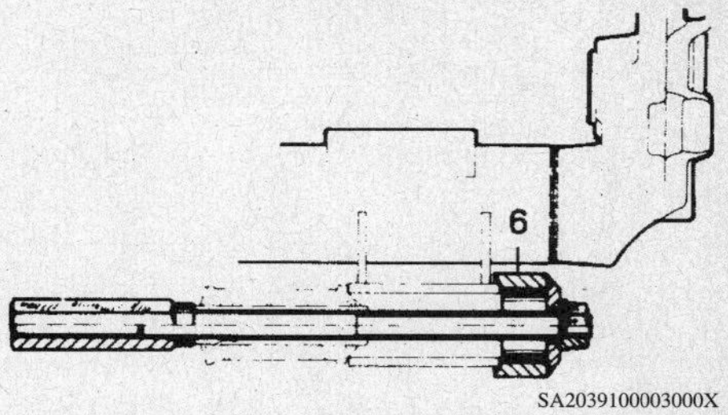

Fig. 5 Spring link rear bushing installation. 9000

6. Remove transverse link to subframe attaching bolts, then the transverse link from vehicle.
7. Reverse procedure to install, noting the following:
   a. **Ensure transverse attaching bolts fitted with protective sleeves are installed in their original position. These sleeves were designed to protect the fuel tank and fuel lines in the event of a collision.**
   b. Do not tighten bolts to specification until wheels are on the ground.
   c. Check rear wheel alignment as outlined in "Wheel Alignment" section.

UPPER TRANSVERSE LINK

REPLACE

9-5

1. Raise and support vehicle, then remove rear wheel.
2. Disconnect center and rear exhaust hangers. Support exhaust system so that not too much strain is on front hangers or flexible section.
3. Remove upper and lower transverse link to longitudinal link attaching bolts, **Fig. 2.**
4. Remove anti-roll bar to longitudinal link attaching bolt.
5. Remove subframe attaching bolts on side that transverse link is being replaced, then loosen subframe attaching bolts on opposite side.
6. Remove lower transverse link to subframe attaching bolts.
7. Remove upper transverse link to subframe attaching bolts, then the transverse link from vehicle.
8. Reverse procedure to install, noting the following:
   a. **Ensure transverse attaching bolts fitted with protective sleeves are installed in their original position. These sleeves were designed to protect the fuel tank and fuel lines in the event of a collision.**
   b. Do not tighten bolts to specification until wheels are on the ground.
   c. Check rear wheel alignment as outlined in "Wheel Alignment" section.

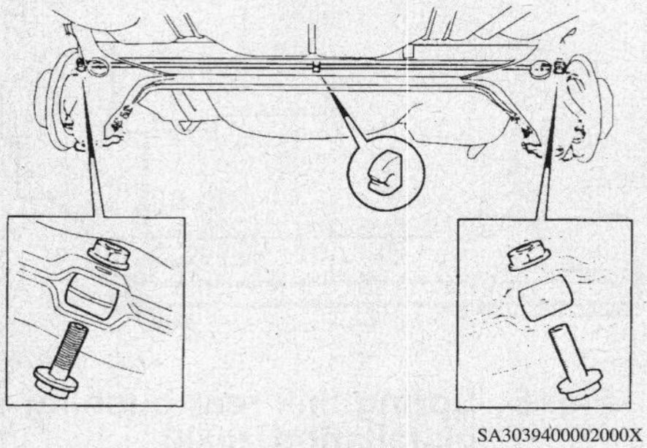

Fig. 6 Rear inner roll bar replacement. 9-3 & 900

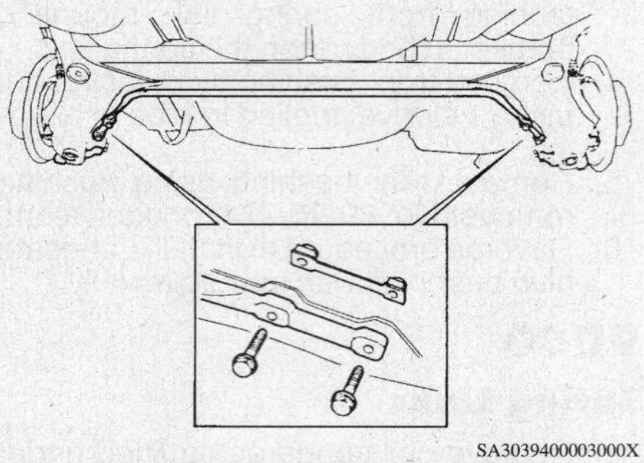

Fig. 7 Rear outer roll bar replacement. 9-3 & 900

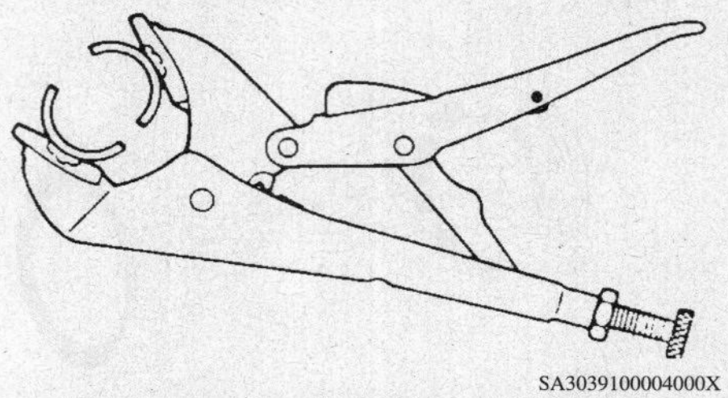

Fig. 8 Anti-roll bar bushing installer fabrication. 9000

TRANSVERSE LINK BALL JOINT

REPLACE

LOWER

9-5

1. Raise and support vehicle, then remove rear wheel.
2. Remove lower transverse link to longitudinal link attaching bolt, then place a spacer between upper and lower transverse links.
3. Remove brake caliper assembly and position aside.
4. Disconnect ABS sensor electrical connector.
5. Remove wheel hub attaching bolts.
6. Disconnect handbrake return spring and remove hub with brake disc.
7. Press ball joint out of transverse link with pressing tool No. 89 96 761, or equivalent.
8. Reverse procedure to install.

UPPER

9-5

1. Raise and support vehicle, then remove rear wheel.
2. Remove upper transverse link to longitudinal link attaching bolt, then place a spacer between upper and lower transverse links.
3. Press ball joint out of transverse link with pressing tool No. 89 96 761, or equivalent.
4. Reverse procedure to install.

LONGITUDINAL LINK

REPLACE

9-5

1. Raise and support vehicle, then remove rear wheel.
2. Remove brake caliper and position aside.
3. Remove brake line bracket from longitudinal link.
4. Disconnect ABS sensor electrical connector.
5. Remove lower shock absorber attaching bolt.
6. Remove lower transverse link to longitudinal link attaching bolt.
7. Remove handbrake cable bracket from longitudinal link.
8. Disconnect handbrake cable return spring and remove cable.
9. Remove anti-roll bar to longitudinal link attaching bolt.
10. Remove longitudinal link to body attaching bolts.
11. Remove longitudinal link to rear wheel hub attaching bolts, then the longitudinal link from vehicle.
12. Reverse procedure to install.

ROLL BAR

REPLACE

9-3 & 900

Inner

1. Raise and support vehicle, then remove one of rear wheels.
2. Remove inner anti-roll bar retaining bolts, **Fig. 6.**
3. Remove anti-roll bar from vehicle.
4. Coat anti-roll bar with thin coat of grease, then slide into rear axle.
5. Install retaining bolts. Tighten to specifications.
6. Ensure rubber block is properly positioned in center of bar, **Fig. 6.**
7. Install wheel, then lower vehicle.

Outer

1. Raise and support vehicle, then remove four outer anti-roll bar bolts, **Fig. 7.**
2. Lower outer anti-roll bar.
3. Position anti-roll bar on vehicle.
4. Install anti-roll bar bolts. Tighten to specifications.
5. Lower vehicle.

9-5

1. Raise and support vehicle, then remove rear wheels.
2. Remove anti-roll bar attaching bolts and nuts.
3. Remove anti-roll bar from rear suspension.
4. Reverse procedure to install.

9000

1. Raise and support vehicle.
2. Place jack under rear axle, then slightly lift rear axle.
3. Remove outboard mountings of anti-roll bar.
4. Disconnect anti-roll bar from link arms, then remove bar.
5. Remove U clamps from anti-roll bar.
6. Remove bushings using bushing remover tool No. 89 96 274, or equivalent.
7. To install bushings fabricate tool as follows:
   a. Parts necessary to fabricate tool: self grip pliers with jaw opening of at least 35 mm and 20 mm length of water pipe with inside diameter of 27 mm and thickness of 3–4 mm.
   b. Cut piece of pipe into two equal halves.
   c. Position two halves in jaws of pliers so they are flush with edges of jaws on one side.
   d. Weld two halves to jaws, **Fig. 8.**
8. Lubricate bushing and seating surface of anti-roll bar.
9. Assemble tool complete with bushings, bolt, sleeve and nut, then press bushing into place. Remove tool.
10. Install U clamps to anti-roll bar.
11. Connect anti-roll bar to link arms, then install outboard mountings. Tighten fasteners to specifications.
12. Slowly lower rear axle, then the vehicle.

PANHARD ROD & BUSHING

REPLACE

1. Raise and support vehicle.
2. Disconnect panhard rod from rear axle and body.
3. **On 9-3 and 900 models,** press out bushing using suitable sleeve and base.
4. **On 9000 models,** press out bushing using a 14 mm socket and tool No. 89 96 464, or equivalent, as a support.
5. **On all models,** reverse procedure to install.

TIGHTENING SPECIFICATIONS

Year	Component	Torque, Ft. Lbs.
9-3, 900 & 9000		
1998–2001	Axle Nut	207–221
	Caliper Mount Bolts	52–81
	Hub Nut	207–221
	Rear Inner Anti-Roll Bar Retaining Bolts	44
	Rear Outer Anti-Roll Bar Retaining Bolts	18
	Shock Absorber Lower Mounting Bolts	46
	Shock Absorber Upper Nut	7–15
	Spring Link Front Mounting Bracket	30–47
	Spring Link To Mounting Bracket	30–40
	Spring Link To Rear Axle Mount	30–47
	Tie Down Bracket Bolt	18
	Wheel Lug Bolts	78–92
	Wheel Lug Nuts	66–81
9-5		
1999–2001	Anti-Roll Bar To Longitudinal Link	40
	Anti-Roll Bar To Subframe	40
	Longitudinal Link Bushing To Body Bracket	70①
	Longitudinal Link Mounting To Body	70②
	Lower Transverse Link To Longitudinal Link	70①
	Lower Transverse Link To Subframe	70①
	Shock Absorber Lower Mounting Bolt	140
	Shock Absorber Upper Mount	15
	Spring Bracket To Body	40
	Subframe To Body	70①
	Upper Transverse Link To Longitudinal Link	70①
	Upper Transverse Link To Subframe	70①
	Wheel Lug Nut	88

① — Plus an additional 60.°
② — Plus an additional 30.°

Front Suspension & Steering

NOTE: On Air Bag Equipped Models, Refer To "Air Bag System Precautions" Located In The Front Of This Manual For System Disarming & Arming Procedures.

INDEX

	Page No.
Ball Joint, Replace	7-36
9-3 & 900	7-36
9-5 & 9000	7-36
Coil Spring, Replace	7-36
9-3 & 900	7-36
9-5 & 9000	7-36
Control Arm, Replace	7-37
Lower	7-37
Upper	7-37
Hub & Bearing, Replace	7-36
9-3 & 900	7-36
9-5 & 9000	7-36
Power Steering	7-
Power Steering Gear, Replace	7-38
9-3 & 900	7-38
9-5	7-39
9000	7-39
Power Steering Pump, Replace	7-39
9-3 & 900	7-39
9-5	7-40
9000	7-40
Power Steering System Bleed	7-40
Precautions	7-36
Air Bag Systems	7-36
Shock Absorber, Replace	7-36
9-3 & 900	7-36
9-5 & 9000	7-37
Tightening Specifications	7-41
9-3 & 900	7-41
9-5	7-41
9000	7-42

PRECAUTIONS

AIR BAG SYSTEMS

Refer to "Air Bag System Precautions" in the front of this manual for system disarming and arming procedures.

HUB & BEARING

REPLACE

9-3 & 900

The wheel bearings are incorporated in the hub and are not part of a shaft or subaxle assembly. The bearings are of double-row, angular contact type which are permanently lubricated and maintenance free. They cannot be replaced individually.

1. Remove shock absorber as outlined under "Shock Absorber, Replace."
2. Place two pieces of flat or square bar under shock absorber.
3. Press front wheel hub off wheel bearing using front wheel bearing drift tool No. 89 96 704, or equivalent.
4. Remove circlips from shock absorber.
5. Remove wheel bearing from steering swivel member using wheel bearing drift tool No. 89 96 704, or equivalent.
6. Install outer circlip on steering swivel member. Opening in circlip should face downward.
7. Press wheel bearing in until it abuts circlip, using front wheel bearing drift tool No. 89 96 704, or equivalent.
8. Lubricate baring seat and outside of bearing with suitable grease.
9. Install inner circlip on steering swivel member. Opening in circlip should face downward.
10. Install hub in wheel bearing using front wheel bearing drift tool No. 89 96 704, or equivalent.
11. Install shock absorber as outlined under "Shock Absorber, Replace."

9-5 & 9000

1. Loosen hub center nut and wheel attaching bolts.

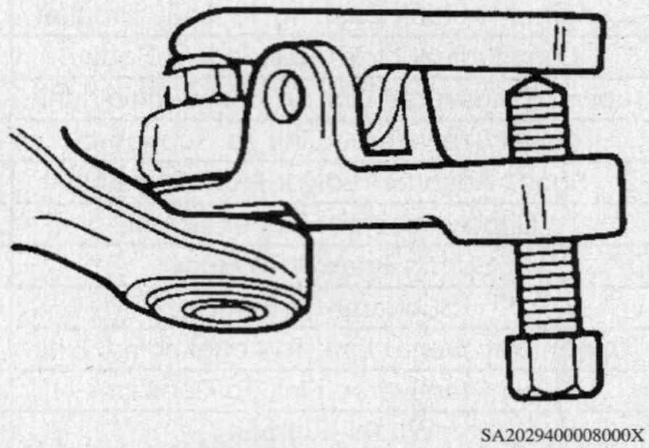

Fig. 1 Ball joint removal. 9-3 & 900

2. Raise and support front of vehicle, then remove wheel.
3. Remove hub center nut and thrust washer.
4. Remove brake hose from retaining clip, then the caliper. Position aside.
5. Remove locating stud, then the brake rotor.
6. Gently push in on driveshaft, then remove four hub-to-steering spindle attaching bolts.
7. Remove hub and backing plate. **Wheel bearings are an integral part of hub assembly. If the wheel bearings are defective, hub assembly must be replaced.**
8. Reverse procedure to install, noting the following:
   a. Ensure slot in hub faces upward.
   b. Tighten hub to steering spindle bolts to specifications.
   c. Tighten caliper bolts to specifications.
   d. Tighten hub center nut to specifications.

BALL JOINT

REPLACE

9-3 & 900

1. Raise and support vehicle, then remove wheels.
2. Remove anti-roll bar nut.
3. Use puller tool No. 89 96 696, or equivalent, to press ball joint stud out of swivel member, **Fig. 1.**
4. Remove ball joint nut, then bend support arm/suspension arm down.
5. Remove locking ring securing rubber gaiter, then the gaiter.
6. Reverse procedure to install, noting the following:
   a. Pack new rubber gaiter with suitable grease.
   b. Tighten ball joint nut and anti-roll bar nut to specifications.

9-5 & 9000

1. Raise and support vehicle, then remove wheels.
2. Remove ball joint spindle to steering knuckle retaining bolt.
3. Remove bolts attaching ball joint to lower control arm.
4. Remove ball joint.
5. Reverse procedure to install. Tighten ball joint to spindle nut to specifications.

COIL SPRING

REPLACE

9-3 & 900

Refer to "Shock Absorber, Replace" for front spring replacement.

9-5 & 9000

Refer to "Shock Absorber, Replace" for front spring replacement.

SHOCK ABSORBER

REPLACE

9-3 & 900

1. Slightly loosen hub center nut when all four wheels are on ground.
2. Raise and support vehicle, then remove five wheel bolts and wheel.

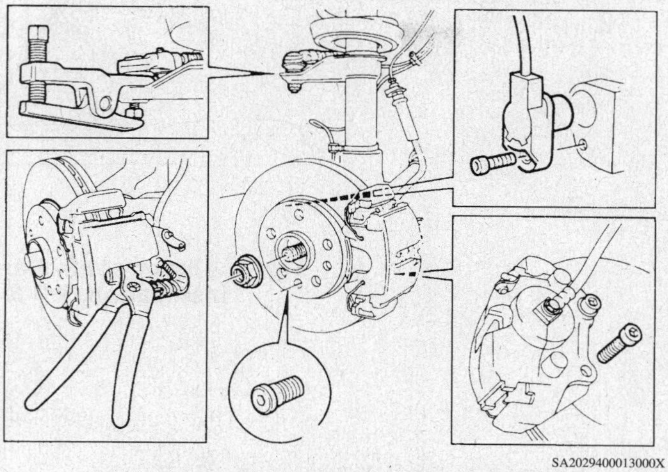

Fig. 2 Front suspension. 9-3 & 900

3. Remove hub center nut, then the wheel sensor, **Fig. 2.**
4. Press back brake piston using slip-joint pliers, **Fig. 2.**
5. Remove caliper from steering swivel member, **Fig. 2,** then suspend in wheel housing with cable tie.
6. Remove brake disc and back plate, **Fig. 2,** then slightly loosen tie rod end nut.
7. Press out tie rod end nut using puller tool No. 89 96 696, or equivalent.
8. Remove nut and tie rod end bolt, then the anti-roll bar to swinging arm nut.
9. Remove outer ball joint nut.
10. Press ball joint out of steering swivel member using puller tool No. 89 96 696, or equivalent, installed on spring link.
11. Remove nut and discard. **Do not reuse self-locking nut.**
12. Remove three upper strut mounting nuts, then the strut.
13. Clamp strut in vice.
14. Compress spring using spring compressor tool No. 88 18 791 and holder tool No. 88 18 809, or equivalents.
15. Hold piston rod and remove nut using strut socket tool No. 89 96 662, or equivalent. **This is a self-locking nut and must not be reused.**
16. Remove mounting and top spring seat, then the coil spring, gaiter and compression stop.
17. Unscrew damper using wrench tool No. 89 96 670, or equivalent, then remove damper from strut.
18. Reverse procedure to install, noting the following:
    a. Screw damper in place using wrench tool No. 89 96 670, or equivalent.
    b. Lower end of coil spring should abut against stop in bottom of spring cup.
    c. Position strut on vehicle and install three retaining nuts on top mounting. Tighten nuts alternately, according to specifications.
    d. Always use new hub center nut with self-locking threads.

9-5 & 9000

1. Raise and support vehicle.
2. Remove brake line from strut.
3. Remove bolts attaching strut to spindle, **Fig. 3.**
4. Remove three bolts attaching top of strut, then the strut assembly from vehicle.
5. Compress spring.
6. Remove top nut, then the upper fixture and spring cup.
7. Remove spring and lower spring cup.
8. Remove compression stop and boot.
9. Remove strut damper assembly. **Damper is an integral part of strut, not an insert and therefore cannot be replaced separately.**
10. Reverse procedure to install, noting the following:
    a. Distance between boot and lower spring cup should be approximately .5 inch (12 mm).
    b. Rotate boot until mark at bottom of boot is aligned with kingpin mounting and groove in spring cap.
    c. Install top spring cup with notch aligned with mark on boot. **Ensure marks are aligned with kingpin mounting.**
    d. Tighten three top nuts to specifications.
    e. Tighten top nut securing spring to specifications.
    f. Tighten bolts securing strut to spindle to specifications.

CONTROL ARM

REPLACE

UPPER

9-3 & 900

1. If lefthand control arm is to be replaced, remove engine and transaxle assembly.
2. Remove top shock absorber nut.
3. Raise and support vehicle.
4. Remove wheel and shock absorber.
5. Compress coil spring using spring compressor tool No. 89 95 839, or equivalent.
6. Remove bolts securing upper ball joint to control arm. **Support steering knuckle to prevent brake lines from being damaged.**
7. Remove bolts securing control arm bearings, **Fig. 4,** then the control arm and spring.
8. Remove nuts securing bearings to control arm, then the bearings and rubber bushings.
9. Press new bushings into bearings using press tool No. 78 41 331, or equivalent. **Do not use oil or grease to ease installation. If lubrication is necessary, use a soap and water solution.**
10. Reinstall bearing assemblies. Tighten nuts to specifications, noting proper angle between control arm and bearing, **Fig. 5.**
11. Reverse procedure to install. Road test vehicle, then check alignment.

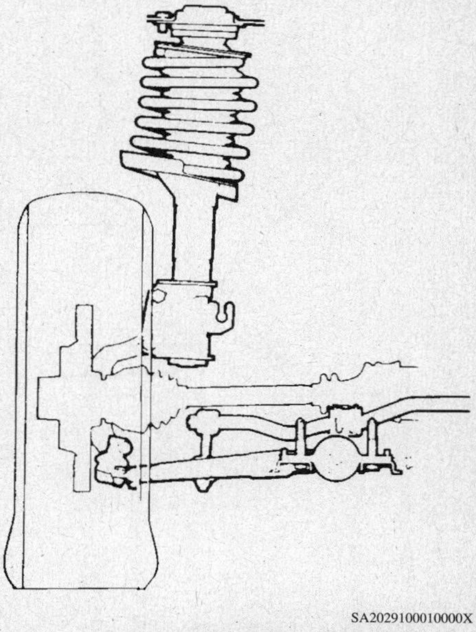

Fig. 3 Front suspension. 9-5 & 9000

LOWER

9-3 & 900

1. Raise vehicle and remove appropriate front wheel.
2. Remove anti-roll bar nut.
3. Loosen ball joint nut, then install puller tool No. 89 96 696, or equivalent, to press out ball joint, **Fig. 1.**
4. Remove ball joint nut, then the support arm to suspension arm nut, **Fig. 6.**
5. Reverse procedure to install. When replacing suspension arm, new self-locking nut must be installed.

9-5

Removal

1. Raise and support vehicle, then remove front wheel.
2. Remove control arm to subframe attaching bolts.
3. Remove ball joint from steering knuckle as outlined under "Ball Joint, Replace."

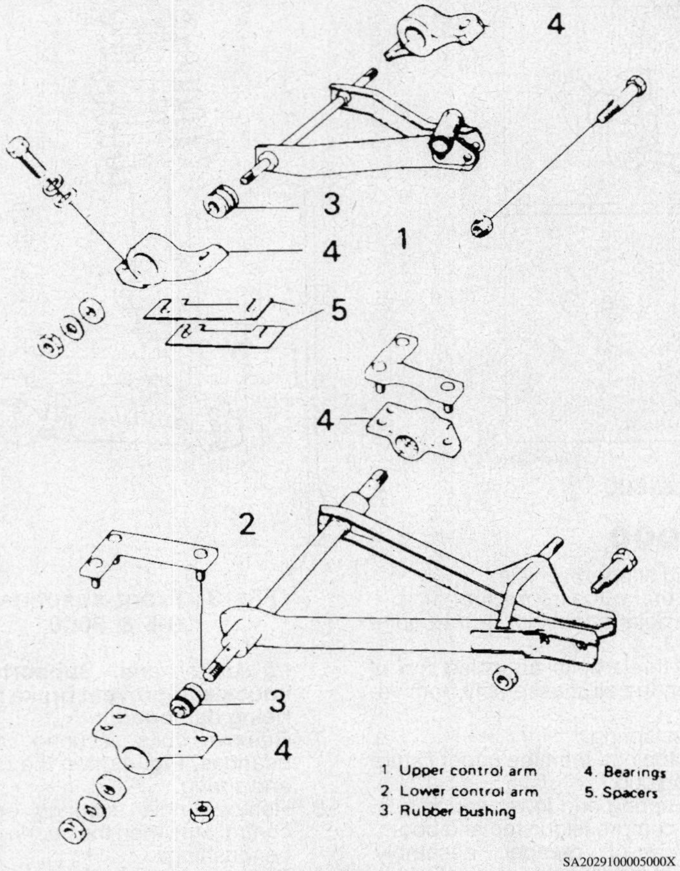

Fig. 4 Exploded view of control arm assemblies. 9-3 & 900

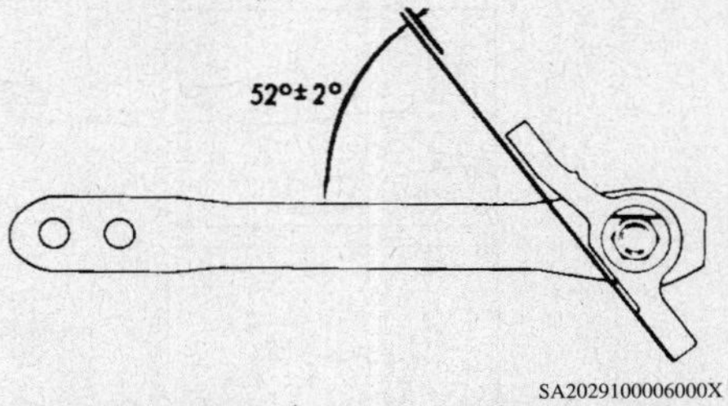

Fig. 5 Upper control arm bearing installation. 9-3 & 900

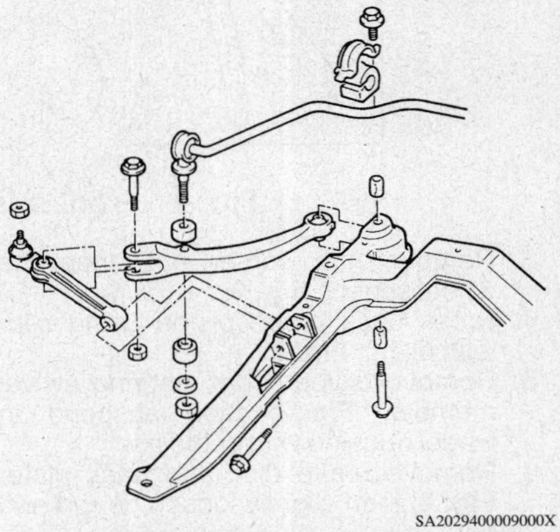

Fig. 6 Exploded view of suspension arm. 9-3 & 900

4. Remove control arm to ball joint attaching bolts.

Installation

1. Install ball joint onto new control arm and tighten to specifications.
2. Install ball joint onto steering knuckle. **Do not tighten retaining nut at this time.**
3. Install rear control arm to subframe attaching bolts. **Do not tighten bolts at this time.**
4. Place a suitable high-lift jack under the ball joint, then raise the jack until the control arm is 1° below the horizontal line. Tighten ball joint nut and rear control arm bolts to specification.
5. Remove jack and install wheel.
6. Check wheel alignment as outlined in "Wheel Alignment" section.

9000

1. Raise and support vehicle, then remove wheel.
2. Remove nut securing sway bar link to control arm, **Fig. 3,** then the upper securing bolt for sway bar link.
3. Press down on control arm and remove sway bar link.
4. Remove two nuts at front of control arm securing arm to frame.
5. Remove two rear bolts securing reinforcement member to frame.
6. Remove two bolts securing control arm rear pivot to frame, then the control arm.
7. Reverse procedure to install, noting the following:
   a. To facilitate control arm installation, leave nuts for bushing in rear pivot loose until arm is installed, **Fig. 7.**
8. Road test vehicle, then check alignment.

POWER STEERING GEAR

REPLACE

9-3 & 900

1. Remove hose connected to return pipe on steering system, then plug hose.
2. Fit length of hose onto pipe and place other end in suitable container that will hold at least .53 quarts (.5 liters).
3. Turn steering wheel to full left lock and full right lock until all fluid has runout of steering system.
4. Remove length of hose from return pipe and refit return hose.
5. Remove main fuse box.
6. Remove lower lefthand section of instrument panel, then the bolt from steering column shaft joint, **Fig. 8.**
7. Turn steering wheel to straight ahead position. **Fix steering wheel so it will not move out of straight-ahead position to avoid twisting and breaking coil spring. Tape steering wheel to instrument panel with suitable heavy-duty adhesive fabric type tape.**
8. Separate joint on steering column shaft from steering gear, then remove tie rod from steering gear.
9. Raise and support vehicle, then remove front lefthand wheel.
10. Remove tie rod from MacPherson strut using puller tool No. 89 96 696, or equivalent, then press out ball joint, **Fig. 1.**
11. Remove tie rod and lower vehicle to floor.
12. Remove fixing clamps on lefthand and righthand sides.
13. Disconnect power steering gear delivery and return pipes using steering system hydraulic pipe wrench tool No. 87 91 287, or equivalent. Plug pipes and connections on valve body.
14. Disconnect internal pipe connections from valve body and bend upward. Plug pipes and connections.
15. Remove steering gear through lefthand wheel housing.
16. Reverse procedure to install, noting the following:
    a. Move bulkhead seal and rubber bushings on righthand and lefthand sides away from valve body, then disconnect internal pipes from steering gear and plug them.
    b. If steering wheel has moved, coil

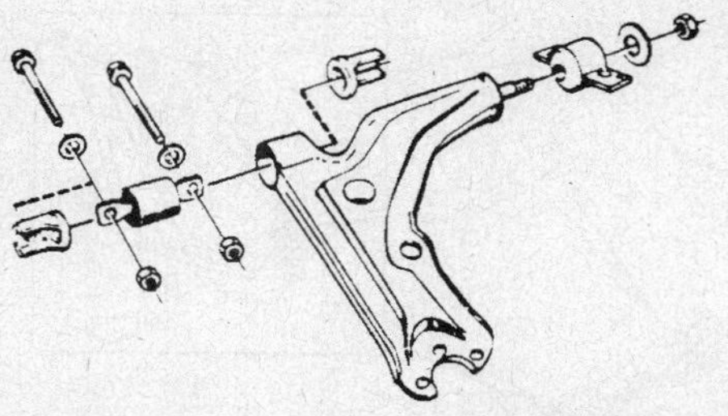

SA2029100011000X

Fig. 7 Exploded view of lower control arm assembly. 9000

spring must be readjusted as outlined in "Air Bag Systems."

9-5

1. Drain power steering fluid reservoir.
2. Remove fluid reservoir and position aside.
3. Disconnect return hose from reservoir.
4. Place end of return hose into a container that will hold at lease one quart of fluid.
5. Raise front of vehicle until wheels are clear of the ground.
6. Start and run engine, turn steering wheel from right full lock to left full lock. Turn engine off when flow of fluid diminishes. **Do not allow pump to run dry.**
7. Attach return hose to reservoir.
8. Turn steering wheel to the straight ahead position, then secure steering wheel in place with heavy-duty adhesive tape.
9. Remove steering column shaft to steering gear retaining bolt. Bolt is accessible from under the instrument panel.
10. Push steering column shaft upwards to separate shaft from steering gear.
11. Remove intake manifold cover.
12. Remove rear engine cushion to subframe attaching bolts, then the engine cushion to engine mounting retaining nut.
13. Attach engine lifting device tool No. 83 94 850, or equivalent, to engine rear lifting eye bolt.
14. Raise and support engine.
15. Loosen outer tie rod end locknut.
16. Remove tie rod end ball joint to steering knuckle retaining nut, then separate tie rod end from steering knuckle.
17. Remove tie rod end from steering gear, count the number of turns it takes for installation reference.
18. Remove rear subframe support assembly.
19. Separate exhaust system between catalytic converter and silencer.
20. Remove subframe center attaching bolts, then lower rear of subframe and remove engine cushion.
21. Disconnect power steering delivery and return pipes, then cut plastic line retaining ties.
22. Remove steering gear to subframe attaching bolts.
23. Remove steering gear through passenger side wheelhouse.
24. Reverse procedure to install.

9000

1. Remove steering column lower clamp attaching bolt, then loosen upper clamp attaching bolt and remove intermediate shaft.
2. From inside vehicle, remove floor panel covering, then the cover plate, gasket, seal and plastic bushing.
3. Raise and support front of vehicle, then remove wheel assemblies.
4. Remove lefthand fender rear undercover.
5. Remove tie rod ends from steering arms, using puller tool No. 89 95 409, or equivalent.
6. Clean surfaces of hydraulic line connectors at pump reservoir, then drain reservoir fluid.
7. Disconnect servo pump hoses, then the reservoir return hose. **Cap all line and reservoir openings to prevent entry of foreign material.**
8. Remove steering gear attaching bolts, then the vertical brace between engine and body subframe.
9. Remove steering gear through lefthand wheelwell, using care not to damage brake components, gear unit or surrounding components.
10. Reverse procedure to install, noting the following:
    a. Check fluid level and toe setting, adjusting as necessary.
    b. Bleed power steering system by turning steering wheel from lock to lock several times with engine running at idle.

POWER STEERING PUMP

REPLACE

9-3 & 900

1. Remove hose connected to return pipe on steering system, then plug hose.
2. Fit length of hose onto pipe and replace other end in suitable container that will hold at least .53 quarts.
3. Turn steering wheel to full left lock and full right lock until all fluid has runout of steering system.
4. Remove hose from return pipe and install return hose.
5. Remove main fuse box.
6. Remove lower section of lefthand dashboard.
7. Remove bolt from joint on steering column shaft (1), **Fig. 9,** then turn steering wheel to straight-ahead position.
8. Fix steering wheel so it will not move out of this position. If steering wheel moves, coil spring may twist and break. One method is to tape steering wheel to dashboard with suitable heavy-duty fabric adhesive tape.
9. Separate joint on steering column shaft from steering gear, then remove track rod from steering gear (2).
10. Raise and support vehicle, then remove front lefthand wheel.
11. Remove track rod from MacPherson strut using puller tool No. 89 96 696, or equivalent, to press out ball joint (3).

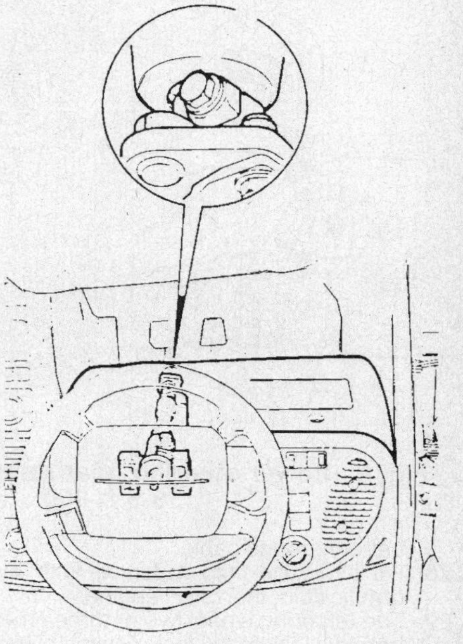

SA6039100001000X

Fig. 8 Steering column shaft joint. 9-3 & 900

12. Lift out track rod and lower vehicle to floor.
13. Remove fixing clamps from both sides (4).
14. Disconnect delivery and return pipes from steering gear (5), using steering system hydraulic pipe wrench tool No. 87 91 287, or equivalent. Plug pipes and connections on valve body and note cable holder on righthand side.
15. Disconnect both internal pipe connections from valve body and bend upward. Plug pipes and connections.
16. Remove steering gear through lefthand wheel housing.
17. Move bulkhead seal and rubber bushes on both sides away from valve body if installing new steering gear.
18. Disconnect internal pipes from steering gear and plug them if installing new steering gear.
19. Lift steering gear into place through lefthand wheel housing.
20. Remove plugs and connect pipes to valve body.
21. Remove plugs and connect delivery and return pipes using steering system hydraulic wrench tool No. 87 91 287, or equivalent.
22. Mount fixing clamps on both sides. Note cable holder on righthand side.
23. Install track rod to steering swivel member, then **torque** connection to 44 ft. lbs.
24. Install both track rods to steering gear and **torque** connections to 68 ft. lbs.
25. Install steering column shaft joint to steering gear, then remove tape holding steering wheel in position. **If steering wheel has moved, coil spring must be readjusted. Refer to "Passive Restraints."**
26. Install lower lefthand section of dashboard.
27. Install main fuse box, then connect

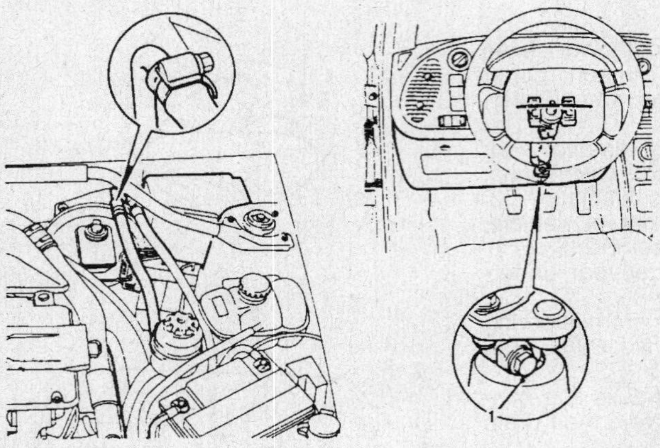

Fig. 9 Power steering gear removal (Part 1 of 2). 9-3 & 900

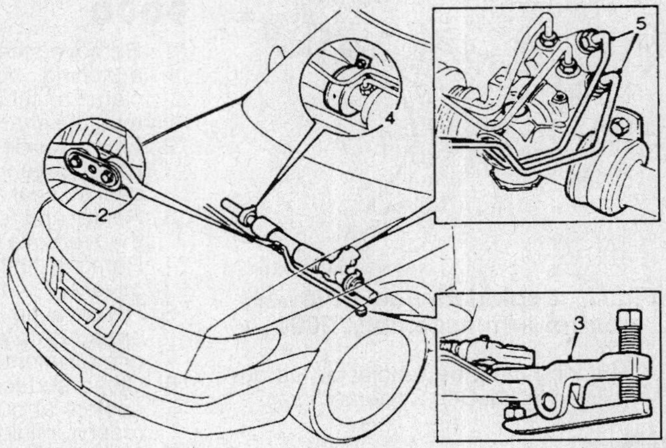

Fig. 9 Power steering gear removal (Part 2 of 2). 9-3 & 900

battery ground cable.

28. Fill hydraulic fluid reservoir with hydraulic fluid, then start engine.
29. Turn steering wheel two or three times from full lock to full lock. Switch off engine and top off fluid reservoir.
30. Install wheel, then lower vehicle.
31. Check toe-in and adjust if necessary.

9-5

1. Siphon power steering fluid from reservoir.
2. Remove fluid reservoir and position aside.
3. Disconnect return hose from reservoir.
4. Place end of return hose into a container that will hold at lease one quart of fluid.
5. Raise front of vehicle until wheels are clear of the ground.
6. Start and run engine, turn steering wheel from right full lock to left full lock. Turn engine off when flow of fluid diminishes. **Do not allow pump to run dry.**
7. Attach return hose to reservoir, then position reservoir back into place.
8. Disconnect air intake hose and position aside.
9. Relieve tension from belt tensioner and remove belt.
10. Disconnect suction and delivery hoses from pump.
11. Remove pump attaching bolts, then the pump.
12. Reverse procedure to install.

9000

1. Siphon power steering fluid from reservoir.
2. Obtain radio anti-theft code as outlined under "Precautions."
3. Raise and support vehicle, then remove righthand front wheel and inner fender liner.
4. Loosen, then remove drive belt.
5. Remove bracket for engine oil filler pipe.
6. Remove engine support.
7. Clean area around hose connections, then disconnect hoses and cap openings.
8. Remove power steering pump. **One of pump attaching bolts is located behind pulley and is accessible through hole in pulley.**
9. Using puller tool No. 899 64 23, or equivalent, remove pump pulley from shaft.
10. Reverse procedure to install, noting the following:
    a. Press pulley onto pump shaft using installer tool No. 899 64 15, or equivalent. **Ensure distance between end plate of pump body and outer pulley rim is 4.23 inches (107.5 mm).**
    b. Adjust drive belt tension to specifications.
    c. Bleed power steering system
    d. Refill system to full mark on dipstick.

POWER STEERING SYSTEM BLEED

1. Fill pump reservoir with power steering fluid, then start and run engine at idle speed.
2. Turn steering wheel two or three times from full lock to full lock position.
3. Check reservoir fluid level.

TIGHTENING SPECIFICATIONS

9-3 & 900

Year	Component	Torque, Ft. Lbs.
1998–2001	Anti-Roll Bar Nut	84②
	Axle Nut	214
	Ball Joint Nut	55
	Damper	159
	Driveshaft Nut	214
	Hub Center Nut	214
	Steering Arm To Subframe Bolt	85
	Strut Top Mounting Retaining Nuts	13
	Support Arm To Subframe Bolt	74①
	Support Arm To Suspension Arm Bolt	68
	Tie Rod To Steering Gear Bolts	68
	Wheel Lug Nuts	78–96

① — Tighten an additional 82.°
② — Inch lbs.

9-5

Year	Component	Torque, Ft. Lbs.
1999–2001	Anti-Roll Bar Link Bolt	65
	Anti-Roll Bar To Subframe Clamp Bolts	20
	Axle Nut	215
	Ball Joint Spindle To Steering Knuckle Bolt	65
	Ball Joint To Control Arm	25
	Caliper Bolts	81
	Control Arm To Subframe	70
	Driveshaft Nut	215
	Hub Center Nut	215
	Power Steering Pump	20
	Power Steering Pump Delivery Pipe	25
	Steering Column Shaft To Steering Gear	20
	Steering Gear Attaching Bolts	70
	Steering Gear Delivery Pipe	25
	Steering Gear Return Pipe	25
	Strut Lower Mounting Bolts	65
	Strut Upper Mounting Nut	55
	Strut Upper Mounting Bolts	20
	Subframe Reinforcement Bolts	50
	Tie Rod End Locknuts	45
	Tie Rod End To Steering Knuckle	45
	Wheel Lug Nuts	88

TIGHTENING SPECIFICATIONS

9000

Year	Component	Torque, Ft. Lbs.
1998	Anti-Roll Bar Anchor Bolt	15–19
	Anti-Roll Bar Retainer Clamp Bolts	15–19
	Axle Nut	194–208
	Ball Joint Lower Bolt	15–19
	Ball Joint To Spindle Nut	32–41
	Ball Joint Upper Bolt	31–41
	Caliper Bolts	51–79
	Driveshaft Nut	195–208
	Hub Center Nut	195–208
	Hub To Steering Spindle	40–43
	Hydraulic Line Couplings	14–26
	Lower Control Arm Bushing Bolt	51–69
	Shock Absorber Tower Nut	49–59
	Shock Absorber Upper Nuts	16–21
	Steering Gear Attaching Bolts	46–56
	Steering Shaft Clamp Bolts	27–32
	Strut Lower Mounting Bolts	56–76
	Strut To Spindle Bolts	56–75
	Strut Tower Cap Nut	49–59
	Strut Upper Mounting Bolts	29–39
	Tie Rod End Locknuts	46–56
	Tie Rod End To Steering Arm Nuts	36–46
	Wheel Bolts	65–79

Wheel Alignment

INDEX

	Page No.
Front Wheel Alignment	7-43
Camber	7-43
Caster	7-43
Kingpin Inclination	7-43
Swivel-Pin Inclination	7-43
Toe-In	7-43
Preliminary Inspection	7-43
Rear Wheel Alignment	7-43
Camber	7-43
Toe-In	7-43
Vehicle Ride Height	7-44
9000	7-44
Wheel Alignment Specifications	7-3

PRELIMINARY INSPECTION

1. Ensure tires are inflated to correct pressure and check for uneven wear.
2. Check front wheel bearings, suspension arm bearing, ball joints and track rods for damage. Replace components as necessary.
3. Check rack and pinion steering gear and adjust as necessary.
4. Check shock absorbers for damage. Replace as necessary.
5. Rock vehicle backward and forward, then bounce it upward and downward to settle it prior to alignment.
6. Ensure vehicle is unloaded and on an alignment rack according to manufacturer's instructions. **When measuring equipment is attached directly to outer end of driveshaft and front wheels are on turntables, apply brake to prevent improper vehicle movement.**

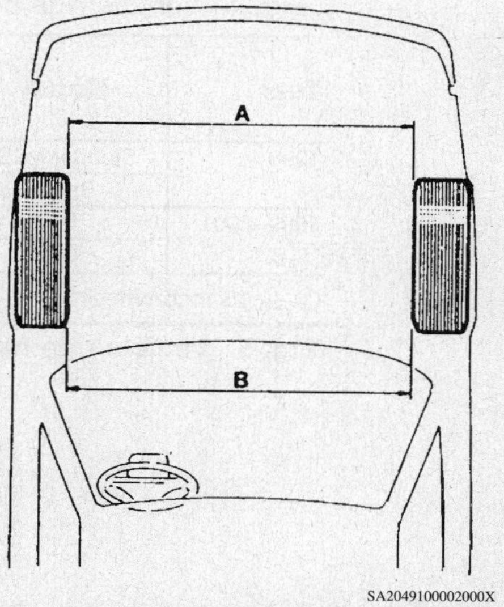

Fig. 1 Toe-in adjustment vehicle position. 9-3, 900 & 9000

FRONT WHEEL ALIGNMENT

CAMBER

Camber is preset during production and is not adjustable. If front camber is not within specified limits, check and replace defective components.

CASTER

Caster cannot be adjusted. If setting is not within specified limits, defective components must be replaced.

TOE-IN

9-3, 900 & 9000

1. Roll vehicle straight forward on level floor and stop without using brakes.
2. Take reading at dimension "A," **Fig. 1,** using toe-in gauge between the front wheel rims level with axle. Mark measurement parts with chalk.
3. Roll vehicle forward until chalk marks are level with, but behind, axles and take reading of B, **Fig. 1.** Any necessary adjustment is made by altering length of tie rod.
4. Remove rubber bellows to track rod retaining clip.
5. Push rubber bellows toward steering gear housing to expose groove in which bellows seals.
6. Measure distance A, **Fig. 2.** Distance A should not exceed 2.03 inches (52 mm) on 9-3 and 900 models or 5.51 inches (140 mm) on 9000 models.
7. Perform steps 4 through 6 on opposite side of vehicle, then compare measurements calculated at each side of vehicle. **Difference between measurements must not exceed .079 inch (2 mm) on 9000 or .114 inch (3 mm) on 9-3 and 900 models.**
8. If necessary to adjust, loosen nut on outer end of tie rod, then rotate tie rod until distance A, is as specified.
9. **Torque** tie rod end locknuts to 46–56 ft. lbs.

9-5

1. Adjust rear wheel toe-in.
2. Position steering wheel in a straight ahead position, then secure steering wheel in place.
3. Loosen tie rod end locknut.
4. Turn tie rod end clockwise to reduce toe-in and counterclockwise to increase toe-in.
5. Adjust toe-in to specification, then **torque** locknut to 55 ft. lbs.
6. Check tie rod length by measuring distance A, **Fig. 2.**

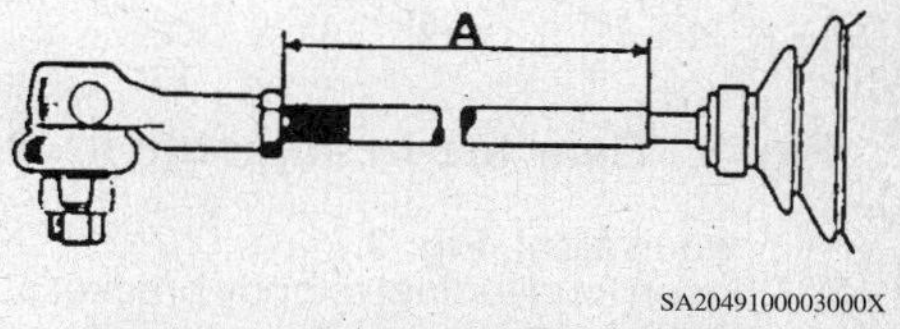

Fig. 2 Toe-in adjustment

7. Distance A cannot exceed 8.27 inches, if distance is greater than specified, adjust tie rod as necessary.
8. Compare distance A measurements from both tie rods, the maximum difference between sides cannot exceed .28 inch. If difference is greater than specified, adjust tie rod ends as necessary.

KINGPIN INCLINATION

Kingpin inclination is preset and not adjustable. If kingpin inclination is incorrect, but camber is satisfactory, check for a faulty steering swivel member. Replace if necessary.

SWIVEL-PIN INCLINATION

Swivel-pin inclination is preset and not adjustable. If swivel-pin inclination is incorrect, but camber is satisfactory, replace steering knuckle.

REAR WHEEL ALIGNMENT

CAMBER

Camber cannot be adjusted. If setting is not within specified limits, defective components must be replaced.

TOE-IN

9-3, 900 & 9000

Rear toe-in is not adjustable. If setting is not within specified limits, check and replace defective components.

9-5

1. Raise and support vehicle on a 4-pillar lift so that wheels and suspension are under load.
2. Secure longitudinal link on one side of the vehicle with jig tool No. 89 96 795,

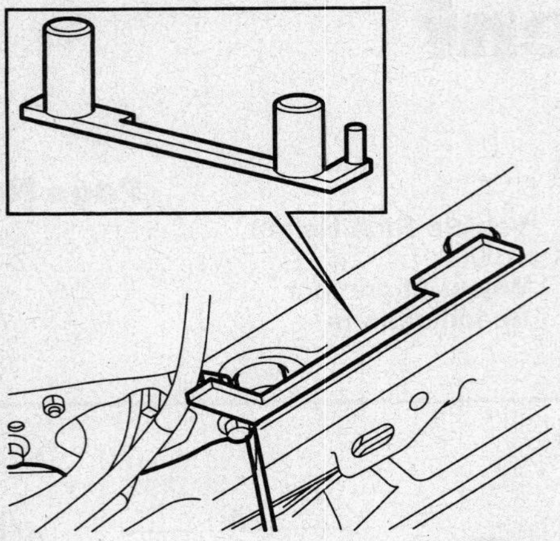

Fig. 3 Rear toe-in adjustment. 9-5

or equivalent, **Fig. 3.**

3. Loosen longitudinal to body bracket attaching bolts.
4. Insert a suitable pry bar between outer mounting of body attaching bracket and body.
5. To increase toe-in, pry bracket inward.
6. **Torque** body bracket attaching bolts to 70 ft. lbs.
7. Repeat steps 2–5 on the opposite side.

VEHICLE RIDE HEIGHT

9000

When measuring vehicle ride height, refer to vehicle ride height dimension and measurement chart, **Figs. 4 and 5.**

1. Roll vehicle forward, then backward approximately 3 feet.
2. Depress front of vehicle, then release.
3. Measure height and record results.
4. Repeat step 1.
5. Pull up on front of vehicle, then release.
6. Measure height and record results.
7. Calculate an average of the two measurements. Maximum tolerance for variation is .393 inch.

Fig. 4 Vehicle ride height dimension. 9-5 & 9000

Year	Model	Vehicle Ride Height, Inches	
		Front	Rear
1998	Standard CS	23.4	22.7
	Sport	23.4	22.9
1999–2001	①	22.5–24.8	22.1–24.4
	②	22.9–25.2	22.5–25.2

① — 15 inch wheels. ② — 16 inch wheels.

Fig. 5 Vehicle ride height measurement. 9-5 & 9000

Air Conditioning

NOTE: On Air Bag Equipped Models, Refer To "Air Bag System Precautions" Located In The Front Of This Manual For System Disarming & Arming Procedures.

INDEX

	Page No.
A/C Specifications	7-46
Belt Tension	7-46
Oil Charge	7-45
Performance Test	7-45
Pressure Reading	7-45
Temperature Readings	7-45
Precautions	7-45
Air Bag Systems	7-45
Battery Ground Cable	7-45
R134a Systems	7-45
Refrigerant Recovery	7-45

PRECAUTIONS

AIR BAG SYSTEMS

Refer to "Air Bag System Precautions" in the front of this manual for system disarming and arming procedures.

R134A SYSTEMS

Avoid breathing A/C refrigerant and lubricant vapor or mist. Exposure may irritate eyes, nose and/or throat. Wear eye protection when servicing the refrigerant system. Serious eye injury can result from eye contact with refrigerant.

Do not expose refrigerant to open flame. Poisonous gas is created when refrigerant is burned. An electronic type leak detector is recommended.

If accidental system discharge occurs, ventilate work area before resuming service. Large amounts of refrigerant released in a closed work area will displace the oxygen and cause suffocation.

The evaporation rate of R-134a refrigerant at average temperature and altitude is extremely high. As a result, anything that comes in contact with the refrigerant will freeze. Always protect skin or delicate objects from direct contact with refrigerant.

Liquid refrigerant is corrosive to metal surfaces. Follow operating instructions supplied with equipment being used.

BATTERY GROUND CABLE

Prior to service, disconnect battery ground cable and isolate as required.

PERFORMANCE TEST

TEMPERATURE READINGS

1. Ensure doors and windows are closed and engine speed is between 1500–2000 RPM.
2. Ensure all vent panels are open.
3. **On models with Automatic Climate Control,** select Lo position on ACC control unit and max fan speed.
4. **On models with manual A/C,** set fan speed to position 4, air distribution to Vent position and recirculation to On position.
5. **On all models,** measure temperature 4 inches inside center panel outlet. Take reading after five minutes.
6. Temperature should be between 43–54°F. Difference between turn on and turn off temperature should be 33–39°F.

PRESSURE READING

1. Ensure both valves for the low pressure hose and valve for the high pressure hose on gauge stank are closed.
2. Connect hoses to compressor, then open valves on both snap-on couplings.
3. Start engine.
4. With an engine speed of 1500–2000 RPM and ambient temperature of 68°F, pressure reading should be as follows:
   a. Low-pressure side should read, 14.5–43.5 psi.
   b. High-pressure side should read, 174–239 psi.

REFRIGERANT RECOVERY

Using refrigerant recovery and recycling stations allows the recovery and reuse of refrigerant after moisture and contaminants have been removed.

When using a recovery or recycling station, follow the manufacturers operating instructions, noting the following:

1. **Use extreme caution and observe all safety and service precautions related to use of refrigerants.**
2. Connect refrigerant recycling station hose(s) to vehicle A/C service port(s) and recovery station inlet fitting. Hoses used should have shutoff devices or check valve within 12 inches of hose ends to minimize introduction of air into recycling station and to limit amount of refrigerant release when hose(s) is disconnected.
3. Turn recycling station on to start recovery process. Allow recycling station to pump refrigerant from A/C system until pressure gauge indicates vacuum.
4. After vehicle A/C system has been evacuated, close station inlet valve, if equipped.
5. Turn station off. On some stations the pump will automatically be turned off by a low pressure switch.
6. Allow vehicle A/C system to remain closed for approximately two minutes. Observe vacuum level indicated on gauge. If pressure does not rise, disconnect recycling station hose(s).
7. If system pressure rises, start recovery process again and continue until vacuum level remains stable for two minutes.
8. Service A/C system as necessary, then evacuate and recharge A/C system.

OIL CHARGE

New compressors are pre-charged with the proper amount of lubricant needed for the entire refrigerant system. If a new compressor is installed and no additional oil has been lost from the system, drain 4.4 ounces from new compressor.

When servicing A/C system, add refrigerant oil as follows: purging refrigerant,. 67 ounce, burst A/C hose, 1.35 ounces, A/C hose replacement,. 67 ounce, condenser, 1.35 ounces, evaporator, 1.35 ounces, receiver-drier, 1.35 ounces, expansion valve,. 67 ounce.

A/C SPECIFICATIONS

		Refrigerant		Refrigerant Oil			Charging Valve Locations	
Year	Model	Capacity, Lbs.	Type	Viscosity	Total System Capacity, Ounces	Compressor Oil Level Check, Inches	High Press.	Low Press.
1998	900	1.6	R-134a	500	6.76①	②	③	③
	9000	2.1	R-134a	500	6.76①	②	③	③
1999–2001	9-3	1.6	R-134a	500	6.76①	②	③	③
	9-5	2.1	R-134a	500	4.93⑥	②	④	⑤

① — Suniso 5GS, or equivalent.
② — Oil level inches cannot be checked.
③ — On accumulator.
④ — On high pressure line.
⑤ — On low pressure line.
⑥ — ND8 SK-20, or equivalent.

BELT TENSION

Use a suitable tension gauge to measure and adjust belt tension. If a new belt is installed, tension should be adjusted to 110–130 lbs. If adjusting a used belt, tension should be 75–85 lbs.

Cooling Fans

NOTE: On Air Bag Equipped Models, Refer To "Air Bag System Precautions" Located In The Front Of This Manual For System Disarming & Arming Procedures.

NOTE: "Electrical Symbol & Wire Color Code Identification" Located In The Front Of This Manual May Be Used As An Aid When Using Wiring Circuits Found In This Section.

INDEX

	Page No.
Component Replacement	7-51
Electric Cooling Fan, Replace	7-51
Description	7-47
9-3	7-47
9-5	7-47
9000	7-48
900	7-47
Precautions	7-46
ACC Air Flap Stepper Motor Calibration	7-46
Air Bag Systems	7-46
Battery Ground Cable	7-46
Battery Ground Cable	7-47
Radio Anti-Theft Lock	7-46
System Diagnosis & Testing	7-48
9-3	7-48
9-5	7-48
900	7-50
Troubleshooting	7-48
9000	7-48

PRECAUTIONS

AIR BAG SYSTEMS

Refer to "Air Bag System Precautions" in the front of this manual for system disarming and arming procedures.

BATTERY GROUND CABLE

Prior to service, disconnect battery ground cable and isolate as required.

RADIO ANTI-THEFT LOCK

Radio and cassette player are equipped with an electronic four-digit anti-theft lock. This four-digit code is programmed at manufacturing and cannot be changed. If the battery is disconnected for more than three minutes, if unit is removed or if otherwise cut off from power, the four-digit code must be entered with the quick-selection buttons as follows:

1. Turn radio on, then, when display shows "Code In," enter four-digit code with quick-selection buttons. If code is correct, last-tuned radio frequency is shown on display. If wrong digit has been entered by mistake, all four digits must be entered again. If code is wrong it stays on display.
2. If incorrect four-digit code has been entered, press Band button for more than three seconds to clear display. Display shows "Code In" and new attempt to enter correct code can be made.
3. If wrong code has been used three times in succession, four dashes appear on display and you must wait an hour with radio switched on before trying again.
4. To try again, hold Band button for at least three seconds. "Code In" should appear on display.
5. Correct code must be entered at first attempt, otherwise you must wait another hour with unit switched on before trying again.

ACC AIR FLAP STEPPER MOTOR CALIBRATION

The ACC stepper motors do not have a feedback function. Whenever power to the ACC control module is interrupted or a stepper motor is serviced, it is necessary to calibrate the flap stepper motors to their end position. This calibration may be accomplished using the ISAT or other suitable scan tool or by placing the system into a self-test mode.

ISAT Method

Connect the ISAT or suitable scan tool to the green connector found under the left seat using the correct interface cable. Start vehicle to maintain correct system voltage during calibration procedure. Select "ACC" mode, then select "Calibrate" from menu. Follow ISAT menu steps to calibrate stepper motors by entering ISAT diagnostic trouble code 900.

ACC Control Panel Method

Retrieve any stored diagnostic trouble codes from memory. Refer to "System Diagnosis and Testing."

Start vehicle to ensure correct system voltage during calibration. Press and hold the "Auto" and "Vent" buttons for approximately one second. This puts the system into self-test mode. The system will check for any current diagnostic trouble codes and display them while cycling flap motors to their calibration positions. The vehicle must remain running for at least 35 seconds for a complete sequence to occur.

Turn off engine and wait at least 30 seconds before turning ignition switch to On position or restarting vehicle.

BATTERY GROUND CABLE

Prior to service, disconnect battery ground cable and isolate as required.

DESCRIPTION

9-3

These vehicles are equipped with one two-speed coolant fan. The fan is controlled by the DICE module. The DICE module turns the coolant fan on and off using a signal from the coolant temperature sensor.

The DICE module uses two (low and high) relays to turn on the coolant fans. When coolant temperature reaches approximately 212°F, the DICE module will turn on the coolant fan by supplying a ground circuit to the low speed fan relay. Low speed operation is maintained because the system current is reduced by a series resistor. The module will also operate the coolant fan at low speed when the A/C is turned on and outside temperature is above 72°F or if vehicle speed is below 24 mph and A/C pressure is between 130–261 psi.

When coolant temperature reaches approximately 235°F, the module will operate the fan at high speed by supplying a ground circuit to the high speed relay. The module will also operate the fan at high speed anytime the A/C is turned on and A/C pressure is above 261 psi.

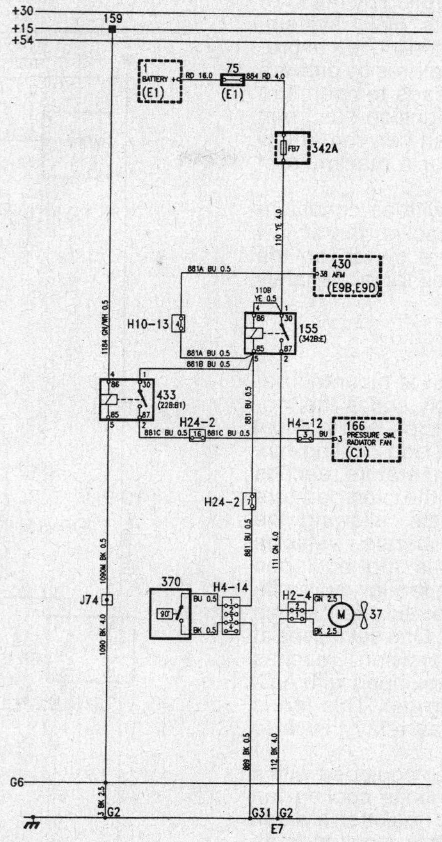

G2. Engine Harness Ground, LH Wheelhouse
G31. Engine Harness Ground, Near RH Healamp
H2-4. Cooling Fan Motor Connector
H4-12. Harness Conector, RH Wheelhouse
H4-14. Temperature Switch Connector
H10-13. Engine Harness Connector, Near Wiper Motor
37. Cooing Fan Motor
75. Distribution Block
166. Cooling Fan Pressure Switch
342A. Fuse Holder
430. AFM Control Unit
433. Cooing Fan Relay

SA1089300004000X

Fig. 1 Cooling fan wiring circuit. 9000 w/single-speed fan

9-5

Less A/C

These vehicles are equipped with one two-speed coolant fan. The fan is controlled by the DICE module. The DICE module turns the coolant fan on and off using a signal from the coolant temperature sensor.

The DICE module uses two (low and high) relays to turn on the coolant fans. When coolant temperature reaches approximately 212°F, the DICE module will turn the coolant fan by supplying a ground circuit to the low speed fan relay. Low speed operation is maintained because system current is reduced by a series resistor.

When coolant temperature reaches approximately 235°F, the module will operate the fan at high speed by supplying a ground circuit to the high speed relay.

With A/C

These vehicles are equipped with two two-speed coolant fans. The fans are controlled by the DICE module. The DICE module operates the fans with three relays using signals from the coolant temperature, A/C pressure, vehicle speed and ambient temperature sensors.

When coolant temperature reaches approximately 212°F, the module will operate the fan at low speed by providing a ground circuit to the low speed relay. Low speed operation is continued because system current is reduced as a result of the fans being connected in a series. The module will also operate the coolant fans at low speed when the A/C is turned on and outside temperature is above 72°F or if vehicle speed is below 24 mph and A/C pressure is between 130–261 psi.

When coolant temperature reaches approximately 235°F, the module will operate the fans at high speed by providing power directly and separately to both coolant fans. When the fans are being run at high speed they are connected in parallel. The module will also operate the fans at high speed anytime the A/C is turned on and A/C pressure is above 261 psi.

900

Vehicles are equipped with either a one- or two-speed cooling fan, which is located behind the radiator and is powered by an electric motor. A relay in relay position G in the distribution center of the engine compartment is used for the one-speed cooling fan and also for the two-speed fan when it is running at low speed. In relay position I in the distribution center of the engine compartment, is the relay used for the two-speed fan when it is operated at high speed.

The cooling fan is controlled by the Integrated Central Electronics (ICE) system. ICE starts and stops the cooling fan at programmed coolant temperatures by grounding the relay. The ICE reads temperature for 20 minutes after the ignition has been turned off. The cooling fan can run at low speed during that time for a maximum of three minutes.

On models equipped with air conditioning, the ICE starts the cooling fan at low speed when the pressure switch on the desiccant container closes (approximately 240 psi).

9000

The electric cooling fan is mounted behind the radiator assembly and is thermostatically controlled. Vehicles with manual transaxles have a one-speed cooling fan. When engine coolant temperature reaches about 90°C (194°F), the temperature switch closes its contacts, allowing the electric cooling fan to operate. Vehicles with automatic transaxles are equipped with a two-speed cooling fan for more efficient cooling. The temperature fan switch has two pairs of contacts. One set closes at 90°C (194°F) and the other when it reaches 110°C (230°F). Models equipped with A/C, have an auxiliary cooling fan. This fan is controlled by a time-delay relay that also turns on the compressor.

These vehicles are also equipped with a time-delay relay, which limits cooling fan running time after engine has been shutoff. The relay that controls this function is always energized when the engine is running. When the engine is switched off, the supply to the relay coil will be interrupted. After about 10 minutes, the relay will trip the supply to the fan motor, even if temperature switch is still closed.

TROUBLESHOOTING

9000

When checking these systems refer to wiring circuits **Figs. 1 and 2.**

1. Check cooling fan fuse and ensure supply to it is live.
2. Check for voltage at temperature switch.
3. Check radiator fan operation by connecting jumper wire across temperature switch terminals.
4. Run engine until it reaches normal operating temperature and ensure temperature switch turns fan on.
5. Check connectors, cable harnesses and ground connections.

SYSTEM DIAGNOSIS & TESTING

9-3

When performing diagnostic procedures on these systems refer to wiring circuit, **Fig. 3** and component locations, **Fig. 4.**

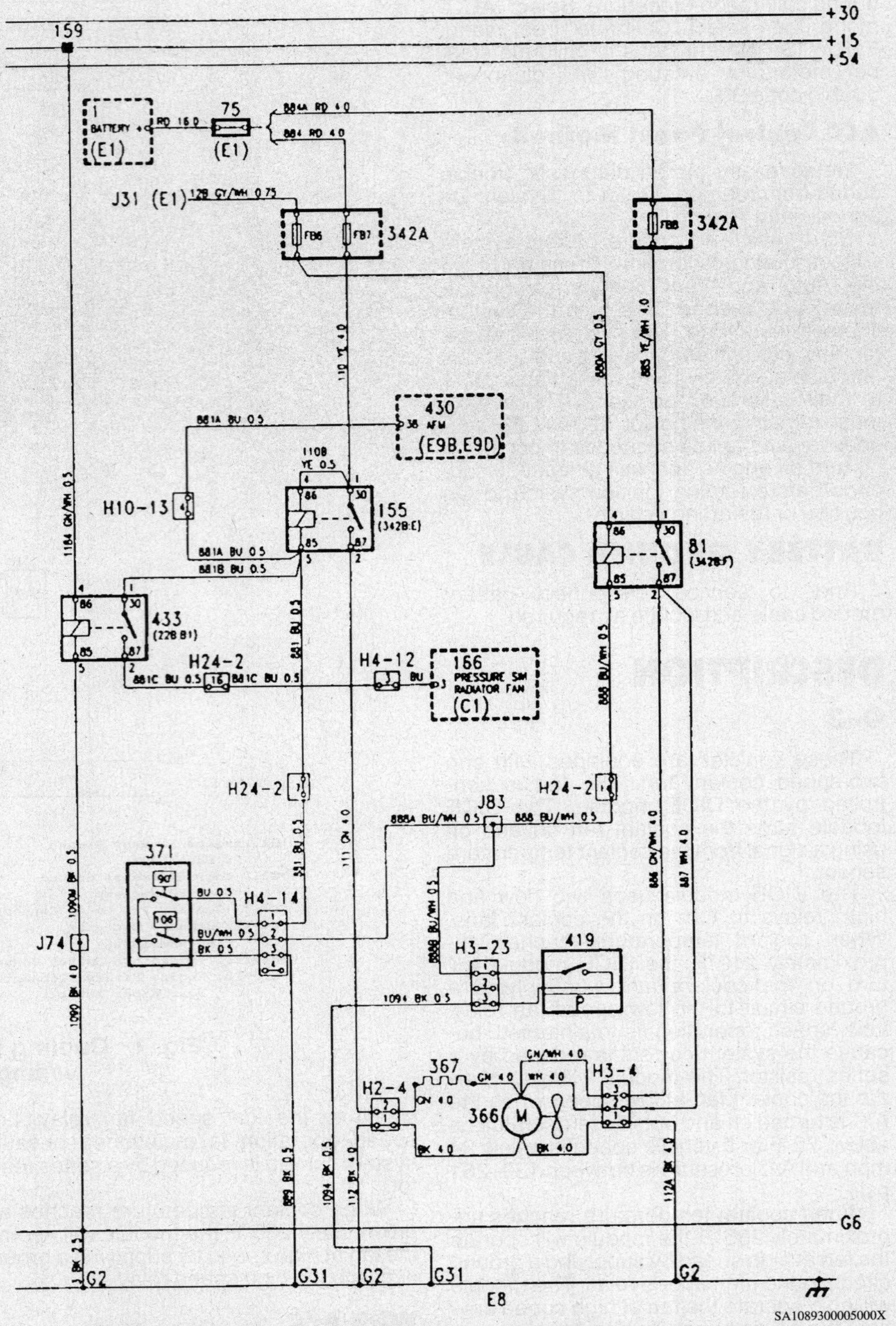

Fig. 2 Cooling fan wiring circuit. 9000 w/two-speed fan

9-5

WIRING DIAGRAMS & COMPONENT LOCATIONS

When performing diagnostic procedures on these systems refer to wiring circuit, **Figs. 5 and 6** and component locations, **Fig. 7.**

SYSTEM TESTING, MODELS LESS A/C

Low Speed Not Working

1. Remove high speed relay from relay holder.
2. Connect a suitable jumper wire between relay holder terminal Nos. 1 and 3.

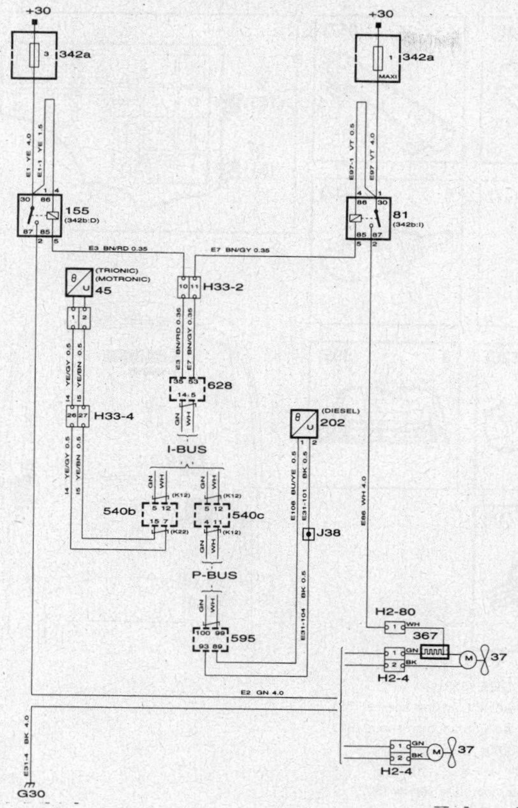

Components

No.	Name and location
37	Motor, radiator fan; on radiator
45	Temperature sensor, engine coolant, instrument; on left-hand side of engine
81	Relay, 2-speed radiator fan, high-speed; on main relay board in engine bay
155	Relay, 2-speed radiator fan, low-speed; on main relay board in engine bay
202	Temperature sensor, engine coolant, engine management system **petrol:** on intake manifold flange between cylinders 3 and 4 **diesel:** on thermostat housing
342a	Main fuse board, engine bay; on left-hand side of engine bay below windscreen
367	Resistor, 2-speed radiator fan; on radiator fan cowling
540b	Main instrument unit; in front of driver in dashboard
540c	Main instrument unit, diesel; in front of driver in dashboard
595A	Control module, EDC15, connector A; on right-hand side of compartment below the A-pillar
595B	Control module, EDC 15, connector B; on right-hand side of cabin below A-pillar
628	Control module, DICE **LHD:** above main relay board in dashboard **RHD:** behind main relay board in dashboard

2-pin connectors

No.	Location
H2-4	Black connector by the radiator fan motor
H2-80	Grey connector by the radiator fan motor

33-pin connector

No.	Location
H33-2	Black connector on bracket below left-hand A-pillar
H33-4	LHD: Black connector on bulkhead behind glove box RHD: Black connector under the engine control module

Crimped connections

No.	Location
J38	Approx 50 mm from control module branching point towards the 33-pin connectors

Grounding points

No.	Location
G30	Grounding point left-hand structural member; in engine bay on side plate in front of left-hand wheel housing

SA1089900023000X

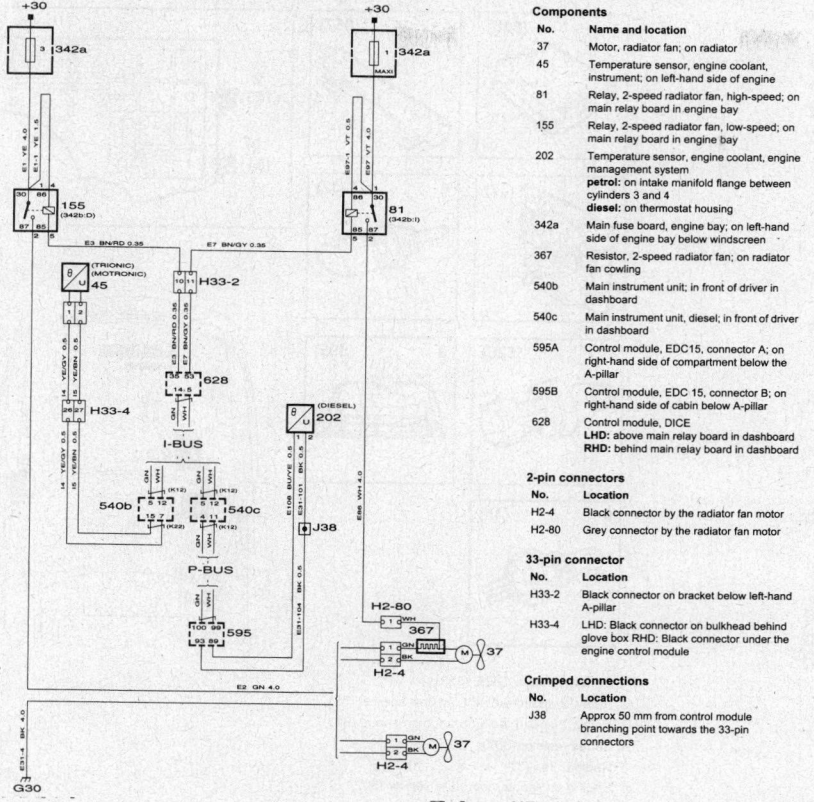

Fig. 3 Cooling fan wiring circuit. 9-3

3. Turn ignition to the ON position.
4. Connect a suitable scan tool to Data Link Connector (DLC) connector located below lefthand side of instrument panel and activate low speed coolant fan with scan tool.
5. If coolant fan runs at low speed, replace high speed relay.
6. If coolant fan does not run, locate and repair open circuit in wire to terminal No. 3 of relay holder.

High Speed Not Working

1. Connect a suitable scan tool to DLC connector located under the lefthand side of the instrument panel.
2. Turn ignition switch to the ON position.
3. Remove high speed relay from relay holder.
4. Connect a suitable jumper wire between terminal Nos. 1 and 2 of relay holder.
5. Activate cooling fan low speed with scan tool.
6. If fan runs at high speed, replace high speed relay.
7. If fan does not run, locate and repair open circuit in wire to terminal No. 2 of relay holder.

High & Low Speed Not Working

1. Remove low speed coolant fan relay from relay holder.
2. Connect a suitable jumper wire between relay holder terminal Nos. 1 and 2.
3. If coolant fan runs at low speed, replace low speed coolant fan relay.
4. If coolant fan does not run, remove high speed coolant fan relay.
5. Turn ignition switch to the ON position, then connect a suitable can tool to DLC connector.
6. Connect a suitable jumper wire between terminal Nos. 1 and 3 of high speed relay holder.
7. Activate coolant fan low speed with scan tool.
8. If coolant fan runs at low speed, replace high speed relay.
9. If coolant fan does not run, disconnect lefthand cooling fan electrical connector.
10. Connect a suitable jumper wire between pin No. 1 of the female connector and terminal No. 1 of the relay holder.
11. Connect another jumper wire between pin No. 2 of the female connector and the motor bracket.
12. If coolant fan runs at high speed, locate and repair open circuit between terminal No. 2 of low speed coolant fan relay holder and terminal No. 1 of high speed coolant fan relay holder.
13. If coolant fan does not run at high speed, replace lefthand fan motor.

Low Speed Operates At High Speed, High Speed Working

1. Remove high speed relay.
2. Connect a suitable jumper wire between terminal Nos. 1 and 3 of the relay holder.
3. Connect a suitable scan tool to DLC connector, then turn ignition switch to the ON position.
4. Activate low speed coolant fan with scan tool.
5. If fan runs at low speed, replace high speed relay.
6. If fan does not run, locate and repair open circuit between terminal No. 3 of high speed relay holder and pin No. 1 of fan resistor female connector.

SYSTEM TESTING, MODELS WITH A/C

Low Speed Malfunction, High Speed Operates

1. Connect a suitable scan tool to Data Link Connector (DLC) located under lefthand side of instrument panel.
2. Turn ignition switch to the ON position, then remove left fan high speed relay.
3. Connect a suitable jumper wire between terminal Nos. 1 and 3 of relay holder.
4. Activate coolant fan low speed with scan tool.

5. If coolant fan runs at low speed, replace high speed relay.
6. If coolant fan does not run, locate and repair open circuit between high speed relay holder terminal No. 3 and terminal No. 2 of righthand coolant fan relay.

Low Speed & Left Fan High Speed Malfunction

1. Remove low speed radiator fan relay.
2. Connect a suitable jumper wire between terminal Nos. 1 and 2 of low speed fan relay holder.
3. If fan runs, replace low speed relay.
4. If fan does not run, remove left fan high speed relay.
5. Connect a suitable jumper wire between terminal Nos. 1 and 3 of high speed relay holder.
6. Activate coolant fan low speed with scan tool.
7. If coolant fan runs at low speed, replace high speed relay.
8. If coolant fan does not run, locate and repair open circuit between low speed relay holder terminal No. 2 high speed relay holder terminal No. 1.

Low Speed & Right Fan High Speed Malfunction

1. Disconnect right coolant fan electrical connector.
2. Connect a suitable test lamp between No. 1 and No. 2 terminals of female side of connector.
3. Connect a suitable scan tool to Data Link Connector (DLC) located under lefthand side of instrument panel.
4. Activate right coolant fan high speed with scan tool.
5. If lamp illuminates, replace right side radiator fan.
6. If lamp does not illuminate, locate and repair open circuit between terminal No. 2 of right coolant fan relay holder and coolant fan connector.

Low & High Speed Malfunction

Locate and repair open circuit between connector "J3" and ground "G30."

Low Speed Operates & Left Fan High Speed Malfunction

1. Remove left fan high speed relay.
2. Connect a suitable jumper wire between terminal Nos. 1 and 2 of high speed relay holder.
3. Connect a suitable scan tool to Data Link Connector (DLC) located under lefthand side of instrument panel.
4. Turn ignition switch to the ON position, then activate low speed coolant fan with scan tool.
5. If right coolant fan runs at high speed, replace left high speed relay.
6. If right coolant fan does not run at high speed, locate and repair open circuit between terminal No. 2 of right coolant fan relay and ground connector "J3."

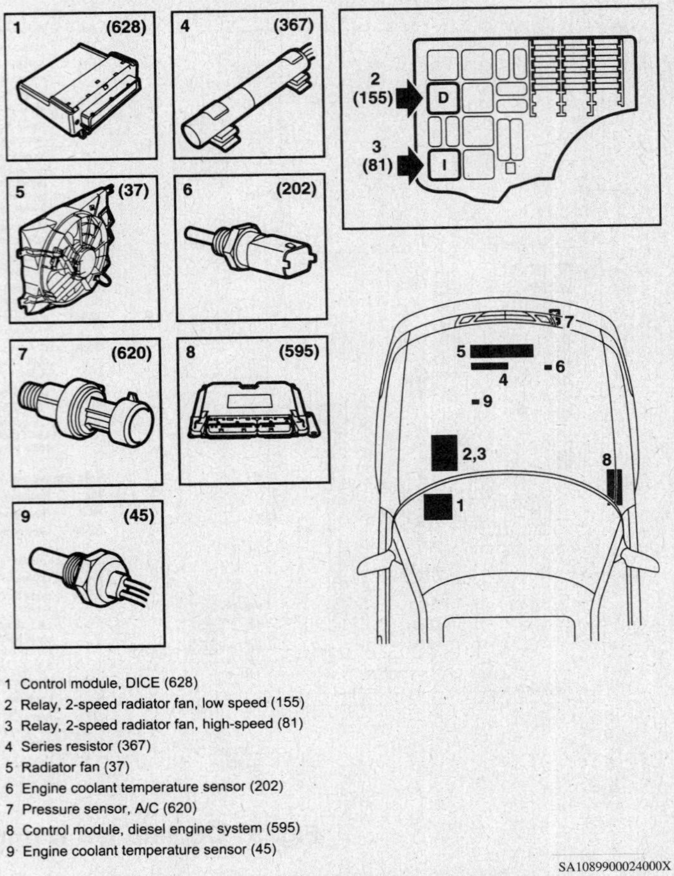

Fig. 4 Component location. 9-3

Low Speed Operates & Right Fan High Speed Malfunction

1. Disconnect right coolant fan electrical connector.
2. Replace fuse No. 6, then connect a suitable test lamp between battery positive terminal and pin No. 1 of connector.
3. If test lamp illuminates, locate and repair open circuit between pin No. 1 of connector and terminal No. 2 of high speed relay connector.
4. If test lamp does not illuminate, replace right cooling fan.

Left Fan Operates At High Speed & Right Fan High Speed Malfunction

Locate and repair short to ground in circuit between left high speed relay holder terminal No. 2 and left coolant fan electrical connector.

900

Refer to **Fig. 8** for cooling fan wiring circuit and **Figs. 9 and 10** for connector view and terminal identification.

For diagnostic testing, refer to **Figs. 11 through 18.** Follow equipment manufacturer's instructions for using test equipment.

1. **Never remove ICE signal ground on A pillar without first disconnecting battery, as the control module could be seriously damaged.**
2. SDA MkII should never be connected to ISAT scan tool.
3. Data link connector is located by steering column under fascia.
4. During diagnosis, ignition key should always be in drive position.
5. If it is not possible to connect ISAT and cooling system, first ensure fuse Nos. 3 or 4 in engine compartment distribution center is intact and is receiving power, then check cable between ICE control module connection No. 60 and data link connector pin No. 8.
6. Ensure there is power and correct ground in data link connector and connector pins are undamaged and securely fitted.
7. To avoid damage to control module and components, always ensure ignition is switched off before connector(s) is disconnected.
8. Check for correct control module ground connection and power supply.
9. If necessary, remove connectors and ensure connections and pins are undamaged and securely fitted. Reconnect connectors and erase all diagnostic trouble codes. If possible, start vehicle and check if faults are still there.
10. All signals around 12-volt level are proportional to battery voltage and levels should only be used as a guide.
11. The 0-volt signals designate ground,

but could give indication of measurable voltage on sensitive multimeter.
12. Never switch from one unit of measurement to another without first disconnecting instrument measuring cables.
13. After performing function check, always erase fault memory with "CLEAR DIAGNOSTIC TROUBLE CODES" command.

COMPONENT REPLACEMENT

ELECTRIC COOLING FAN, REPLACE

9-3 & 900

1. Remove battery.
2. **On models equipped with Sensonic,** remove battery shelf.
3. **On all models,** separate radiator fan electrical connections.
4. Disconnect servo pump oil pipes and radiator breather hose clips from radiator crossmember. Turn oil pipe to one side.
5. Remove two radiator fan cover screws, then the cover.
6. Remove radiator fan to fan cover screws.
7. **On models equipped with two-speed cooling fan,** disconnect resistor.
8. **On all models,** disconnect fan cover contacts, then remove fan.
9. Reverse procedure to install.

9000

Main Fan

Do not attempt to remove the electric cooling fan with engine hot. The electric cooling fan operates in conjunction with engine coolant operating temperatures. Ensure engine coolant temperature drops enough to safely permit electric cooling fan removal.

1. Obtain radio anti-theft code as outlined under "Precautions."
2. Disconnect electric cooling fan and thermoswitch electrical connectors.
3. Remove electric cooling fan-to-radiator attaching bolts. **If necessary, loosen radiator attaching bolts and move radiator back to allow sufficient clearance for fan removal. On some models it also may be necessary to disconnect radiator hose(s) to allow sufficient clearance for fan removal.**
4. Remove electric cooling fan from vehicle.
5. Reverse procedure to install.

Auxiliary Fan

1. Obtain radio anti-theft code as outlined under "Precautions."
2. Remove front spoiler and grill.
3. Remove screws from tops of radiator support member bars, then the lower radiator support member attaching screws.
4. Remove light cluster retaining screw and pull light forward slightly.
5. Remove headlights, then ignition coil attaching screws. Position coil out of the way.
6. Remove cooler battery to radiator support attaching screw.
7. Remove radiator support attaching bolts, then unplug horn electrical connectors.
8. Lift out radiator support and position aside.
9. Remove cooling fan retaining nut and screws.
10. Reverse procedure to install.

9-5

2.3L Engine

1. Remove bypass pipe and valve.
2. Disconnect radiator fan electrical connectors.
3. Loosen cooling system vent hose clip.
4. **On models with automatic transaxle,** remove pipe mounting from fan cowling.
5. **On all models,** remove upper radiator fan attaching bolts.
6. Unhook radiator fan lower retaining hooks, then raise fan slightly.
7. Remove fan assembly from vehicle.
8. Reverse procedure to install. **Torque** bypass pipe, bypass hose clip and radiator fan bolts to 70 inch lbs.

3.0L Engine

1. Remove upper engine cover.
2. Remove turbo pressure hose, bypass pipe, valve, then disconnect vacuum hose from turbo bypass valve.
3. Remove mass air flow sensor and hose.
4. Remove turbo intake pipe.
5. Disconnect cooling fan electrical connectors.
6. Remove radiator fan assembly retaining bolts, then the radiator fan assembly.
7. Reverse procedure to install, noting the following:
   a. **Torque,** radiator fan assembly attaching bolts to 70 inch lbs.
   b. **Torque,** turbo intake pipe V-clamp to 28 inch lbs.
   c. **Torque,** crankcase breather pipe to 18 ft. lbs.
   d. **Torque,** bypass pipe and bypass hose clip to 70 inch lbs.

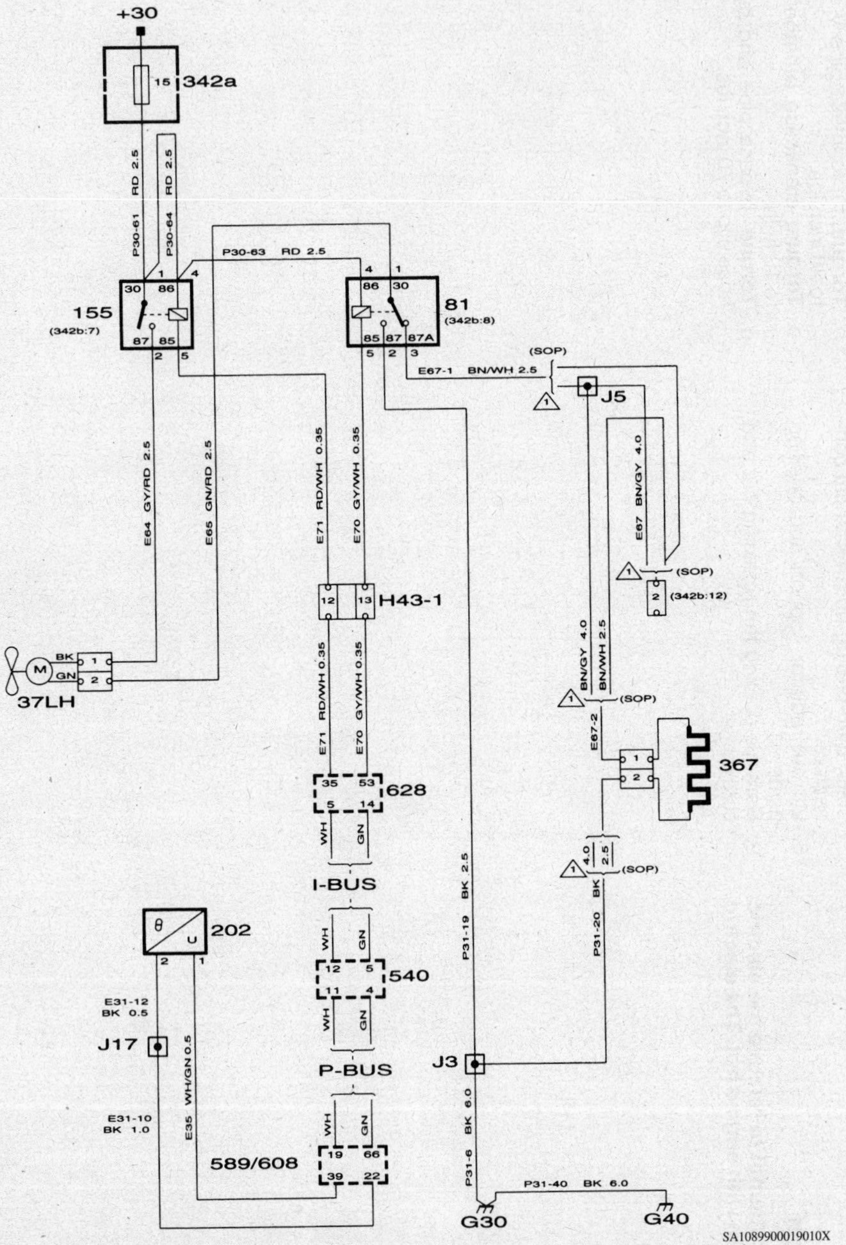

Fig. 5 Cooling fan wiring circuit (Part 1 of 2). 9-5 less A/C

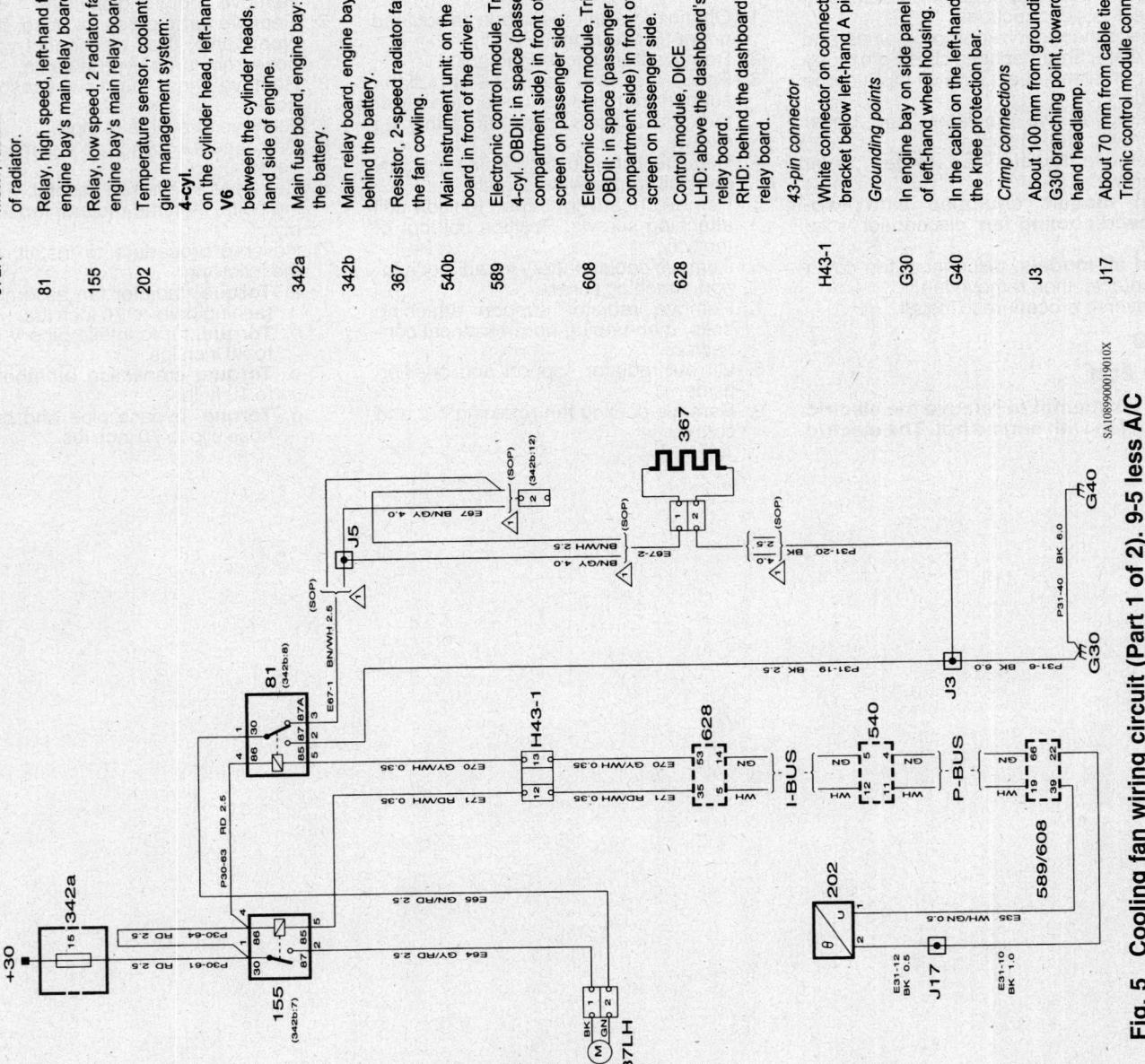

37LH	Motor, radiator fan: On left-hand side of radiator.
81	Relay, high speed, left-hand fan: on engine bay's main relay board.
155	Relay, low speed, 2 radiator fans: on engine bay's main relay board.
202	Temperature sensor, coolant, engine management system: **4-cyl.** on the cylinder head, left-hand end. **V6** between the cylinder heads, on left-hand side of engine.
342a	Main fuse board, engine bay: behind the battery.
342b	Main relay board, engine bay: behind the battery.
367	Resistor, 2-speed radiator fan: on the fan cowling.
540b	Main instrument unit: on the dashboard in front of the driver.
589	Electronic control module, Trionic 4-cyl. OBDII; in space (passenger compartment side) in front of windscreen on passenger side.
608	Electronic control module, Trionic V6 OBDII; in space (passenger compartment side) in front of windscreen on passenger side.
628	Control module, DICE LHD: above the dashboard's main relay board. RHD: behind the dashboard's main relay board.
	43-pin connector
H43-1	White connector on connector bracket below left-hand A pillar.
	Grounding points
G30	In engine bay on side panel in front of left-hand wheel housing.
G40	In the cabin on the left-hand side of the knee protection bar.
	Crimp connections
J3	About 100 mm from grounding point G30 branching point, towards left-hand headlamp.
J17	About 70 mm from cable tie on Trionic control module connector.

SA1089900019020X

Fig. 5 Cooling fan wiring circuit (Part 2 of 2). 9-5 less A/C

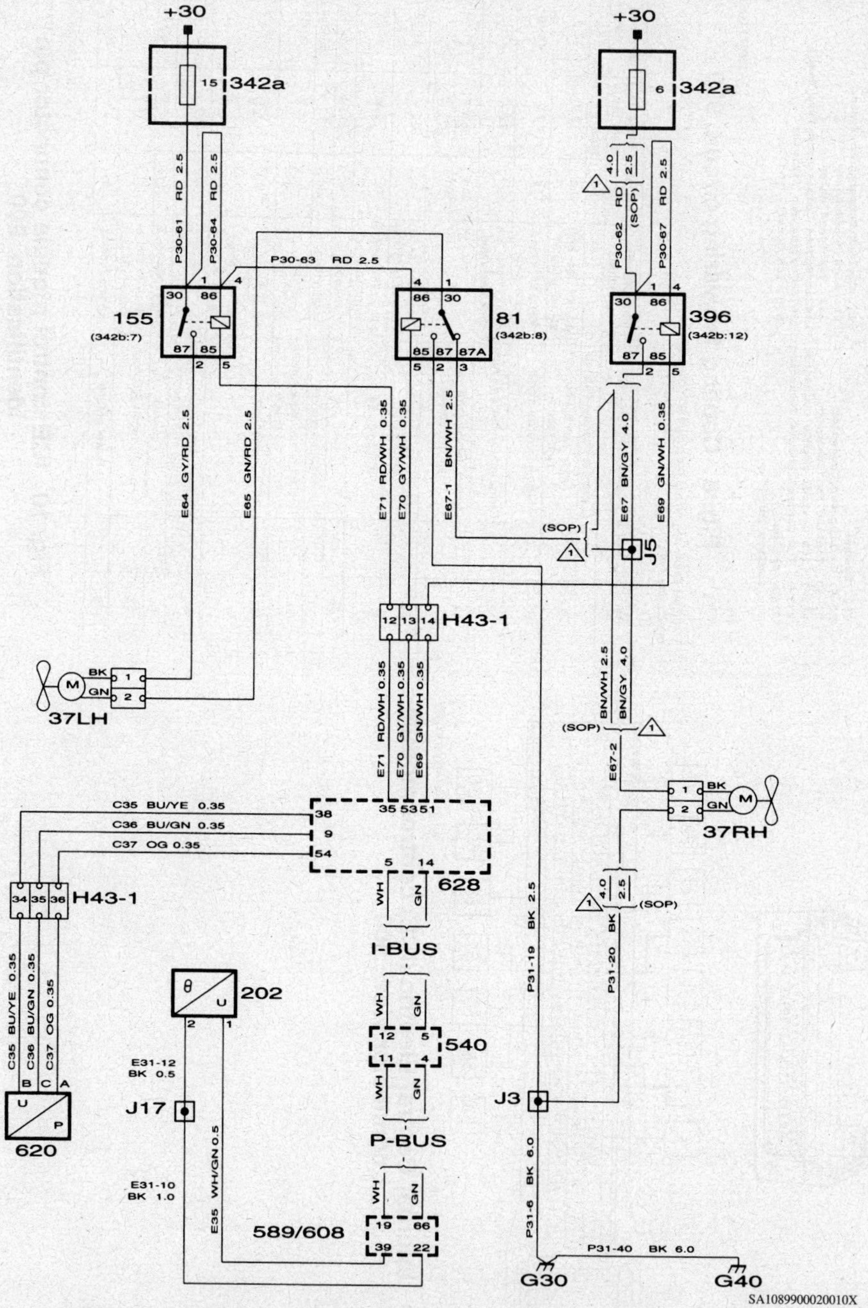

Fig. 6 Cooling fan wiring circuit (Part 1 of 2). 9-5 with A/C

37LH	Motor, radiator fan: On left-hand side of radiator.
37RH	Motor, radiator fan: on right-hand side of radiator.
81	Relay, high speed, left-hand fan: on engine bay's main relay board.
155	Relay, low speed, 2 radiator fans: on engine bay's main relay board.
202	Temperature sensor, coolant, engine management system: **4-cyl.** on the cylinder head, left-hand end. **V6** between the cylinder heads, on left-hand side of engine.
342a	Main fuse board, engine bay: behind the battery.
342b	Main relay board, engine bay: behind the battery.
396	Relay, high speed, right-hand radiator fan: in the engine bay's main fuse box.
540b	Main instrument unit: on the dashboard in front of the driver.
589	Electronic control module, Trionic 4-cyl. OBDII; in space (passenger compartment side) in front of windscreen on passenger side.
608	Electronic control module, Trionic V6 OBDII; in space (passenger compartment side) in front of windscreen on passenger side.
620	Pressure sensor, A/C; down below on right-hand side of evaporator.
628	Control module, DICE LHD: above the dashboard's main relay board. RHD: behind the dashboard's main relay board.

43-pin connector

H43-1	White connector on connector bracket below left-hand A pillar.

Grounding points

G30	In engine bay on side panel in front of left-hand wheel housing.
G40	In the cabin on the left-hand side of the knee protection bar.

Crimp connections

J3	About 100 mm from grounding point G30 branching point, towards left-hand headlamp.
J17	About 70 mm from cable tie on Trionic control module connector.

SA1089900020020X

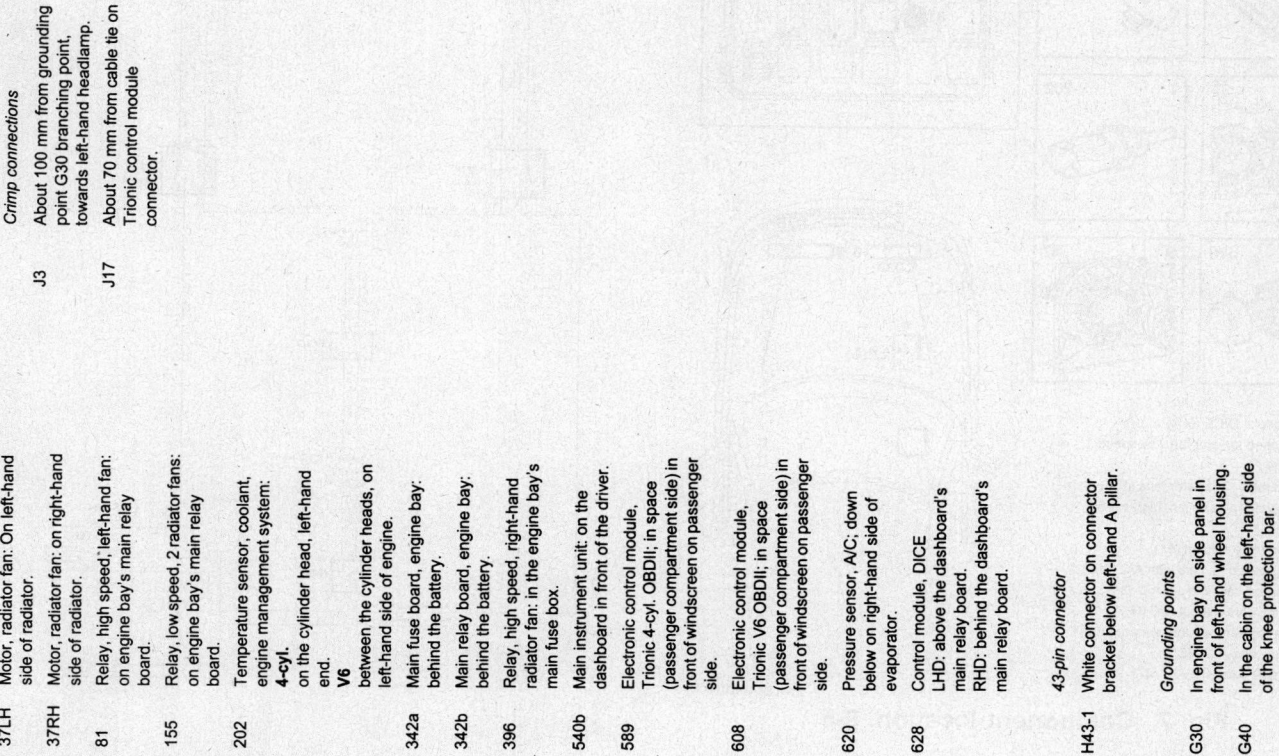

Fig. 6 Cooling fan wiring circuit (Part 2 of 2). 9-5 with A/C

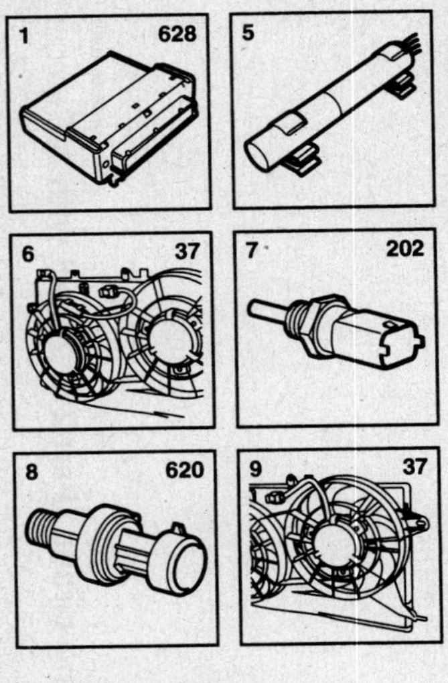

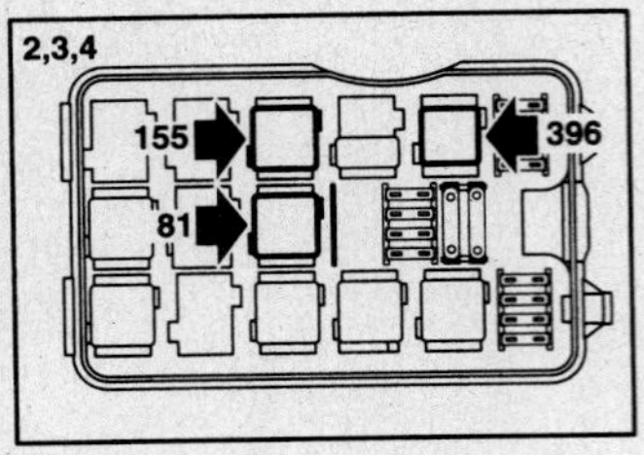

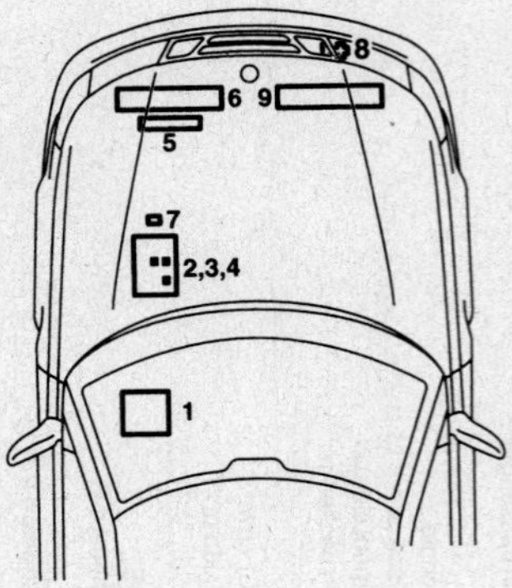

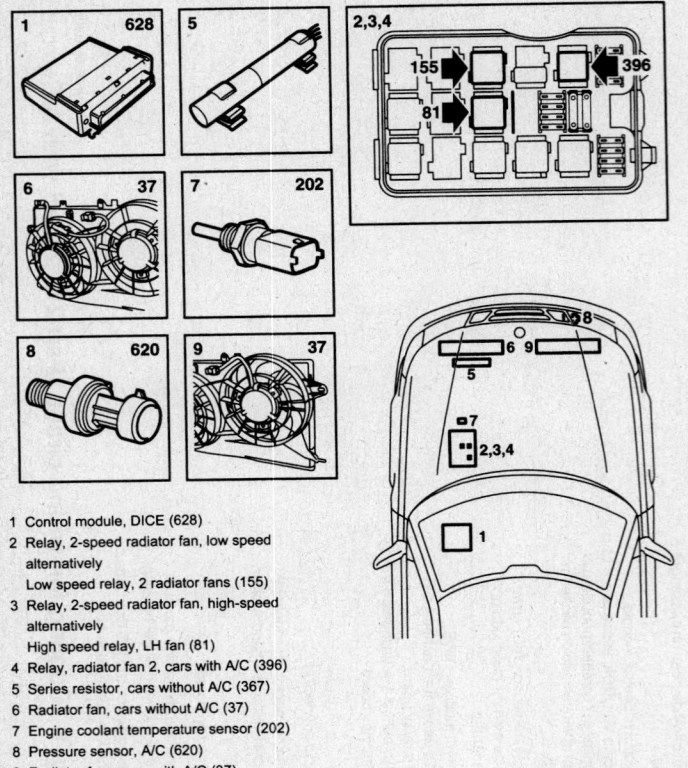

1. Control module, DICE (628)
2. Relay, 2-speed radiator fan, low speed alternatively
   Low speed relay, 2 radiator fans (155)
3. Relay, 2-speed radiator fan, high-speed alternatively
   High speed relay, LH fan (81)
4. Relay, radiator fan 2, cars with A/C (396)
5. Series resistor, cars without A/C (367)
6. Radiator fan, cars without A/C (37)
7. Engine coolant temperature sensor (202)
8. Pressure sensor, A/C (620)
9. Radiator fans, cars with A/C (37)

SA1089900021000X

Fig. 7 Component location. 9-5

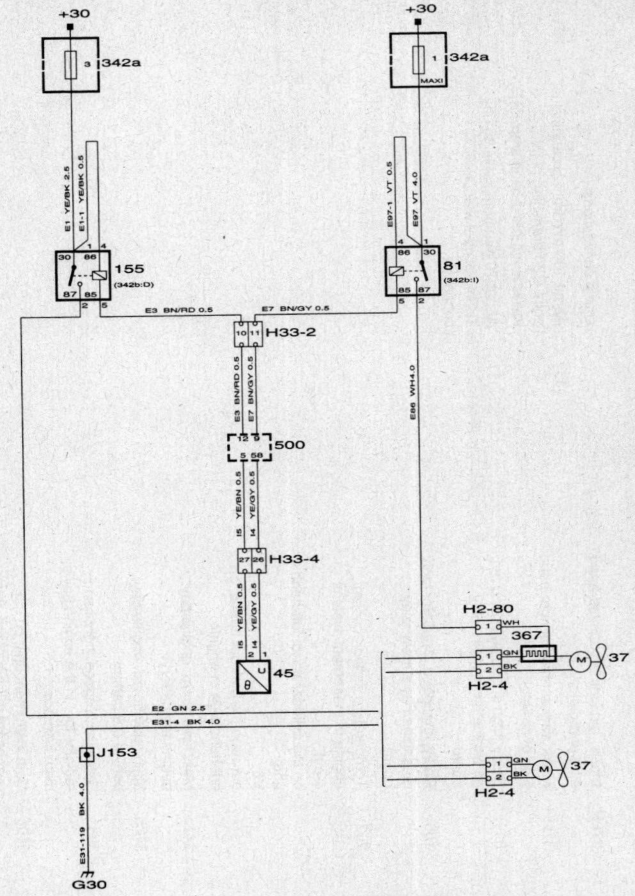

G30. Ground
H2-4. Cooling Fan Connector
H2-80. Cooling Fan Connector
H33-2. ICE Control Module Connector
H33-4. ICE Control Module Connector
J153. Splice
37. Cooling Fan
45. Coolant Temperature Sensor
81. High Speed Relay
155. Low Speed Relay
342a. Engine Compartment Fuse Panel
367. Cooling Fan Resistor
500. ICE Control Module

SA1089400006000X

Fig. 8 Cooling fan wiring circuit. 900

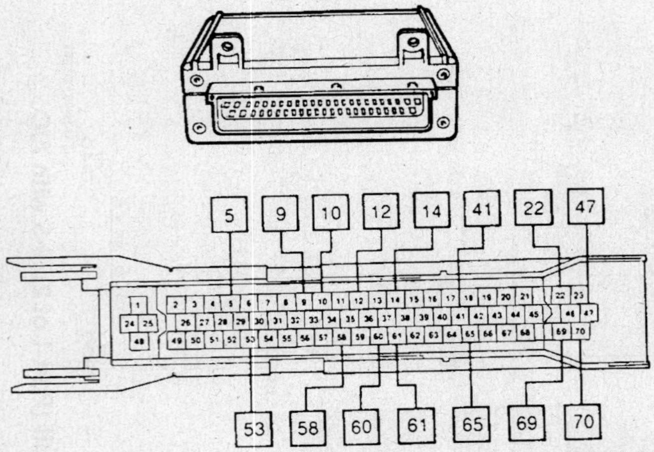

SA1089400007000X

Fig. 9 Internal Central Electric (ICE) control module connector view. 900

The table below only shows the pins which concern the cooling system.

Pin	Colour	Component/function	Measurement conditions	In/Out	Measure-ment result	Between X-Y
5		Coolant temperature sensor		In	about 0-12 V	5-58
9		Relay, radiator fan high speed	Radiator fan high speed activated	Out	12 V	47-9
10		Idling increase signal	Idling increase activated	Out	12 V	47-10
12		Relay, radiator fan low speed	Radiator fan low speed activated	Out	12 V	47-12
14		Coolant temperature signal (main instrument 2)		Out/ PWM	about 122 Hz 8-92 %duty	14-70
22		Pressure switch radiator fan A/C	If pressure switch is closed (>15 bar)	In	12 V	47-22
41		Supply +54	Ignition key in drive position	In	12 V	41-70
47		Power +30	Always	In	<0.5 V	B+-47
53		Signal ground	Engine running	In	<0.1 V	53-Batt-
58		Coolant temperature sensor, ground side	Always	In	12 V	47-58
60		Diagnosis	ISAT not connected ISAT connected + contact with ICE	In/Out	0 V 12 V	60-70
61		Coolant temperature signal (main instrument 1)		Out	500 Hz 8-92%duty	61-70
65		Power B	Key in position B	In	12 V	65-70
69		Pressure switch A/C cool	Pressure switch closed (>22 bar)	In	12 V	47-69
70		Power ground	Engine running	In	<0.1 V	70-Batt-

SA1089400008000X

Fig. 10 ICE control module connector pin identification. 900

Diag-nostic trouble code	Faulty function/component	Test on the ISAT display
B1102	Relay, radiator fan high speed	FAULT XX P/I B1102 RAD FAN HIGH SPEED RELAY SHORT TO BATTERY +
B1103	Relay, radiator fan high speed	FAULT XX P/I B1103 RAD FAN HIGH SPEED RELAY SHORT TO GR/BREAK
B1104	Relay, radiator fan low speed	FAULT XX P/I B1104 RAD FAN LOW SPEED RELAY SHORT TO BATTERY +
B1105	Relay, radiator fan low speed	FAULT XX P/I B1105 RAD FAN LOW SPEED RELAY SHORT TO GR/BREAK
B1311	Temperature sensor, coolant	FAULT XX P/I B1311 COOLANT TEMP SENSOR OUTSIDE LIMIT
B1412	Idling increase function	FAULT XX P/I B1412 IDLING INCREASE SHORT TO BATTERY
B1417	Temperature gauge, coolant	FAULT XX P/I B1417 COOLANT TEMP GAUGE SIGNAL SHORT TO BATTERY
B1422	Temperature gauge, coolant	FAULT XX P/I B1422 COOLANT TEMP GAUGE SIGNAL SHORT TO BATTERY

SA1089400009000X

Fig. 11 Diagnostic trouble codes. 900

Diagnostic trouble code	Reason for fault	Fault symptom
B1102	Short to battery +	Radiator fan does not work.
B1103	Short to ground, open circuit.	Radiator fan running continuously at high speed even when ignition is switched off.
B1104	Short to battery +	Radiator fan does not work.
B1105	Short to ground, open circuit	Radiator fan running continuously at low speed even when the ignition is switched off, or does not work.
B1311		Radiator fan running all the time.
B1412	Short to battery +	No increase in idling speed when radiator fan starts.
B1417	Short to battery +	Temperature gauge always shows cold engine.
B1422	Short to battery +	Temperature gauge always shows cold engine.

SA1089400010000X

Fig. 12 Diagnostic trouble code symptoms. 900

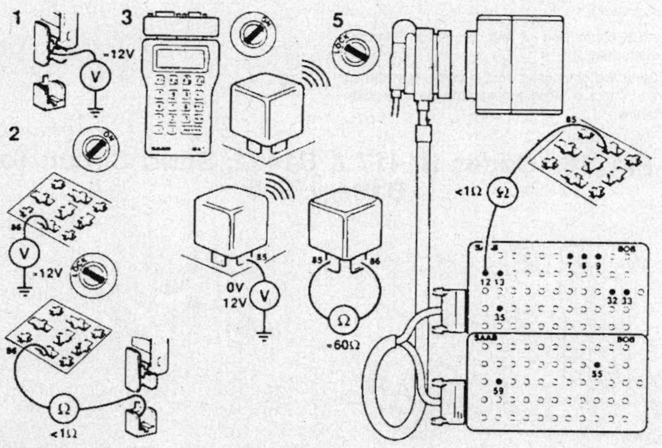

Measures

1. Check that fuses 3 (1-speed radiator fan or 2-speed radiator fan, low speed) and 4 (2-speed radiator fan, high speed) in the engine compartment's distribution centre are intact and that there is power to the fuses.
2. With the ignition key in drive position, check that there is power to the control coil on relay connection 86. The relay for the 1-speed radiator fan and the 2-speed radiator fan low speed position is situated in relay position G in the engine compartment. There is a relay for the 2-speed radiator fan high speed position in relay position I in the engine compartment.

   If there is no power, check the wiring between the fuse and the relay for any open circuits/short circuits.
3. Connect ISAT and select "ACTIVATE RELAY" on the menu. Depending upon which relay is to be checked, select the next activation command like "RADIATOR LOW".

   Check connection 85 on the relay with a voltmeter, i.e the relay should be in place but slightly raised. Repeat point 3 and read the voltmeter as follows:

   Relay activated— 0 V

   Relay not activated—12 V

   If the voltages are not correct, remove the relay and check that the resistance between pins 85 and 86 is 50-100 Ohm.

   If this is not the case, fit a new relay.
4. If the resistance is correct, check that the pins for each connection in the relay holder are securely fitted and that the relay is properly pressed down.
5. When the ignition is switched off, a BOB can be connected to the ICE wiring (control module disconnected). Check the cable between the ICE control module's connection 9 (2-speed radiator fan, high speed) or 12 (1-speed radiator fan and 2-speed radiator fan, low speed) and the relay holder's connection 85 as regards an open circuit/short circuit to ground.

   Attend to any faulty wiring or connector.

SA1089400011000X

Fig. 13 Codes B1102–1105: Radiator Fan Does Not Work Or Radiator Fan Is Running Continuously At High Or Low Speed When Ignition Is Switched Off. 900

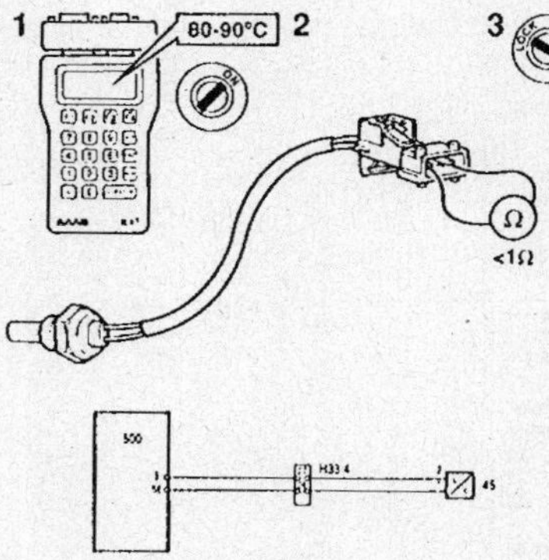

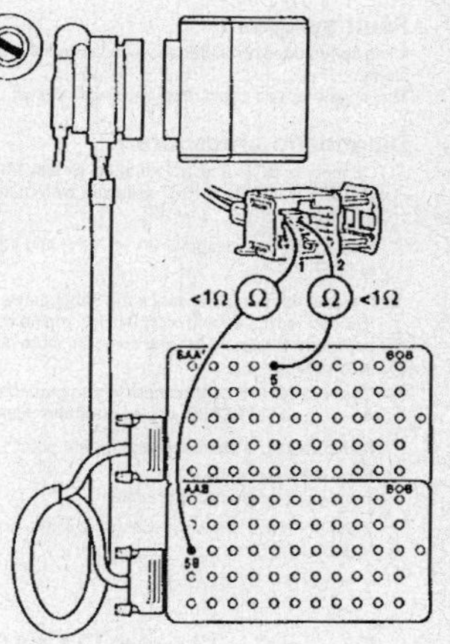

Fault symptom

Radiator fan running all the time

Diagnostic procedure

1. Select "OBTAIN READOUTS" on the ISAT menu followed by "COOLANT TEMP.". Read the result on ISAT.

   The coolant temperature should be 80-90°C (176-194°F) when the engine is warm. If there is a fault in the circuit, ISAT will show 215°C (419°F).
2. Check the resistance on the coolant temperature sensor's connector and compare with the table.

   If the resistance is not correct, the fault is in the temperature sensor. Fit a new temperature sensor.

   If the resistance is correct, connect a BOB and check the cable between ICE connections 5 and 58 respectively and coolant temperature sensor connections 2 and 1 respectively as regards open circuits/short circuits.

°C	°F	Resistance kOhm
-30	-22	24
20	68	2
30	86	1.6
50	122	0.8
85	185	0.3
110	230	0.14
130	266	0.1

SA1089400012000X

Fig. 14 Code B1311: Cooling Temperature Lower Than -76°F Or Higher Than 320°F. 900

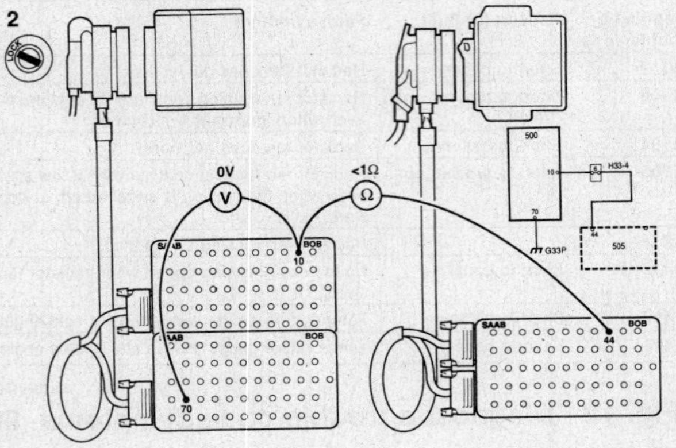

Fault symptom

Idling speed does not increase when the radiator fan starts.
The engine speed could drop causing it to stall.

Diagnostic procedure

1 Connect a BOB and a voltmeter. Select "ACT OTHER FUNCT" on ISAT followed by "IDLING INCREASE".

Check that the voltage is 0 V at "ON" and 12 V at "OFF".

2 If that is not the case, check the cable between ICE connection 10 and MOTRONIC engine control module's pin 44 for any short circuit to positive voltage.

3 Connect the ICE control module and ground pin 44 on the MOTRONIC engine control module.

Measure with a voltmeter and repeat point 1.

4 If the voltmeter shows 0 V, fault in the engine control system.

If the voltmeter shows a voltage which is not 0 V, fault in ICE

SA1089400013000X

Fig. 15 Code B1412: Idling Speed Increase Short-Circuited To Battery. 900

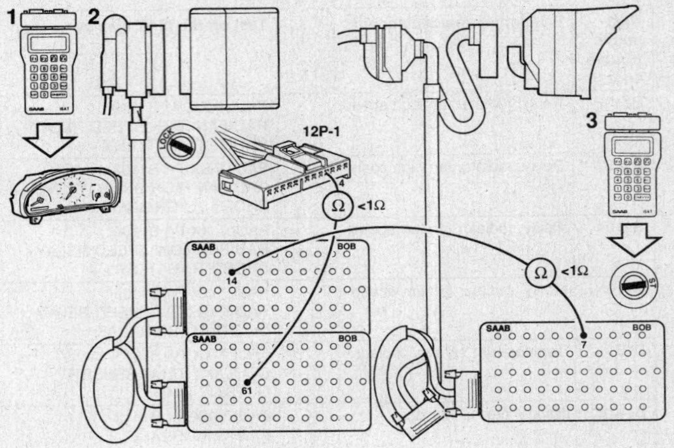

Fault symptom

Temperature gauge always shows cold engine.

Diagnostic procedure

1 Check that there are no diagnostic trouble codes stored in the main instrument. If there are diagnostic trouble codes, fault in main instrument

2 Connect a BOB and check the wiring for any short circuit to positive voltage between:

- ICE connection 61 and connection 4 in main instrument 1.

- ICE connection 14 and connection 7 in main instrument 2.

3 Clear the diagnostic trouble code, start the car and check if the diagnostic trouble code reappears.

SA1089400014000X

Fig. 16 Codes B1417 & B1422: Short Circuit To Battery. 900

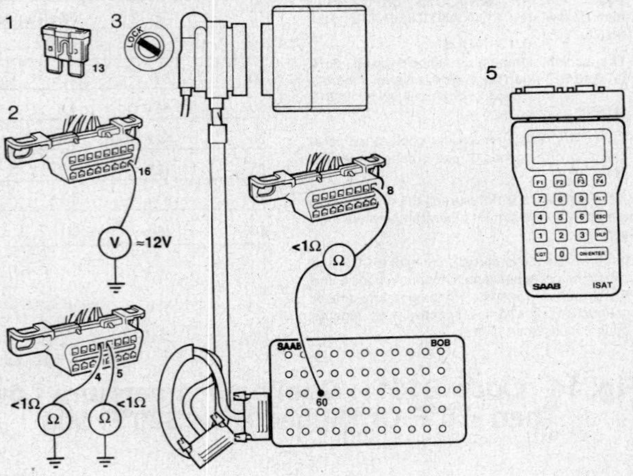

Fault symptom

Contact cannot be established with ISAT

Diagnostic procedure

1 Check that fuse 13 is intact and that there is power to the fuse.

2 Check that there is 12 V between connection 16 in the data link connector and a safe grounding point.

Also check the grounding in connections 4 and 5.

3 Check the wiring between the data link connector and the ICE control module for open circuits/ short circuits.

4 Check ISAT, SDA and the wiring for ISAT by testing with another ISAT.

SA1089400015000X

Fig. 17 Data Link Connector Functional Check. 900

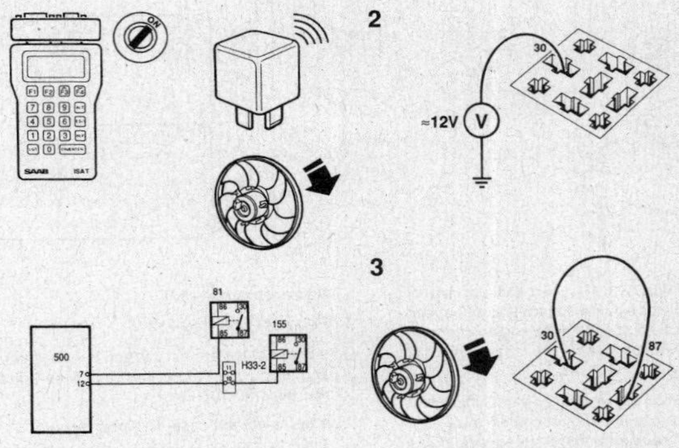

Radiator fan

1 Connect ISAT and select "READ FAULT CODES" on the menu.

2 To start the radiator fan, select "ACTIVATE RELAY" on the menu followed by "RADIATOR FAN, LOW".

If the car is equipped with a 2-speed radiator fan, select "ACTIVATE RELAY" followed by "RADIATOR FAN, LOW".

If the radiator fan does not work, check that there is 12 V on connection 30 on the relay holder for each radiator fan relay.

3 Strap between connections 30 and 87 in the relay holder.

If the radiator fan works, the fault is in the relay. Fit a a new relay.

If the radiator fan does not work, continue with point 4.

SA1089400016010X

Fig. 18 Cooling System Functional Check (Part 1 of 8). 900

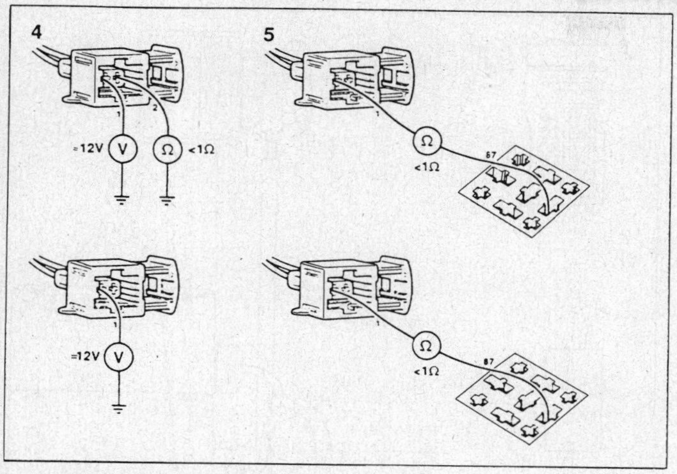

4 Disconnect the radiator fan's connector and check that there is:

-12 V between pin 1 and a safe grounding point.

-a resistance which is less than 1 Ohm between pin 2 and a safe grounding point.

5 If that is not the case, check the wiring for short circuits open circuits between the connection87 on the relay holder and connector 1 on the radiator fan.

6 If the fan does not work in spite of these checks, fit a new radiator fan.

SA1089400016020X

Fig. 18 Cooling System Functional Check (Part 2 of 8). 900

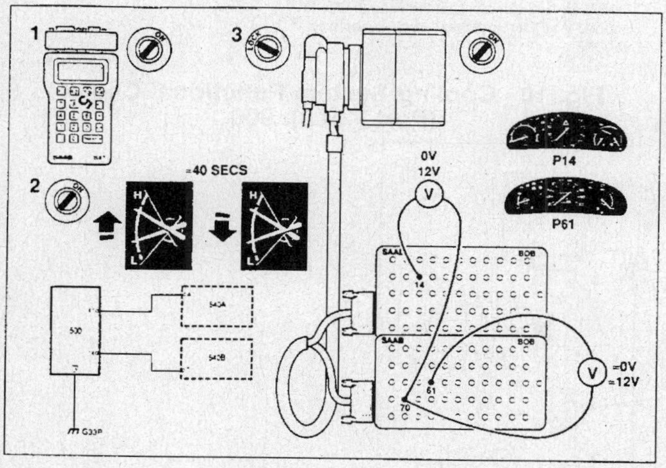

The temperature in the cooling system

1 Connect ISAT and select "READ FAULT CODES" on the menu.

2 Check the temperature gauge in the main instrument by first selecting "ACT INSTR FUNCT" followed by "SIM.COOL.TEMP. 2" or "SIM.COOL.TEMP. 1". The ICE will now simulate a temperature in the cooling system between -30 and +130°C (-22 and—+266°F) for 40 seconds.

Read the temperature gauge in the car.

3 Connect a BOB and connect a voltmeter between connections 70 and 61 for main instrument 1 or between connections 70 and 14 for main instrument 2. Then select "ACT INSTR FUNCT" followed by "TEMP.GAUGE.OUT. 1" or "TEMP.GAUGE.OUT. 2". The measured voltage should be

- about 0 V at "ON"
- about 12 V at "OFF"

SA1089400016040X

Fig. 18 Cooling System Functional Check (Part 4 of 8). 900

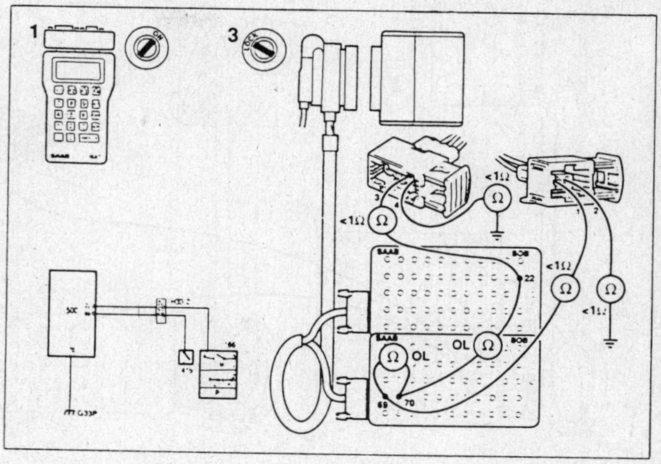

Pressure switch A C

1 Connect ISAT and select " OBTAIN READ-OUTS " followed by " PRESS SWITCH 1 AC ". For certain markets the car is equipped with an extra pressure switch in which case select "PRESS SWITCH 2 AC ".

"OPEN" → The fan should not be activated

"CLOSED" → The fan should be activated

2 If this is not correct, disconnect the pressure switch and clamp between the connectors pins and repeat point 1.

3 If this does not work, connect a BOB and check the wiring for any open circuits short circuits as follows:

Pressure switch 1

- between connection 22 on the ICE and connection 3 on the pressure switch.
- between connection 4 on the pressure switch and a safe grounding point.

Pressure switch 2

- between connection 69 on the ICE and connection 1 on the pressure switch.
- between connection 2 on the pressure switch and a safe grounding point.

4 If there is no fault in the wiring, replace the pressure switch.

SA1089400016030X

Fig. 18 Cooling System Functional Check (Part 3 of 8). 900

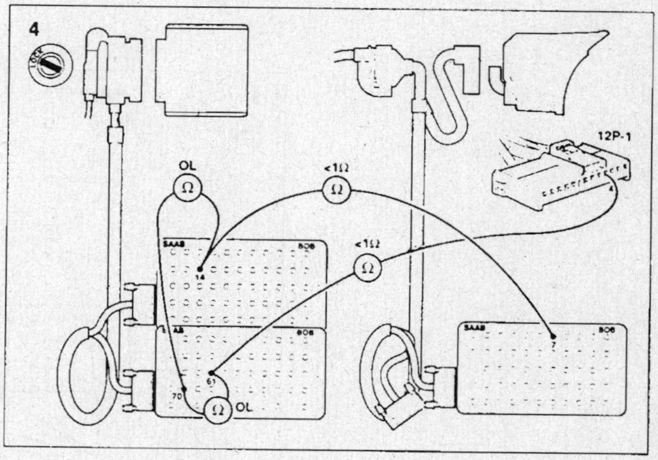

4 If the voltage is not correct, check the wiring for any open circuits/short circuits as follows:

- between connection 61 on the ICE and connection 4 on the main instrument (main instrument 1)
- between connection 14 on the ICE and connection 7 on the main instrument (main instrument 2).

SA1089400016050X

Fig. 18 Cooling System Functional Check (Part 5 of 8). 900

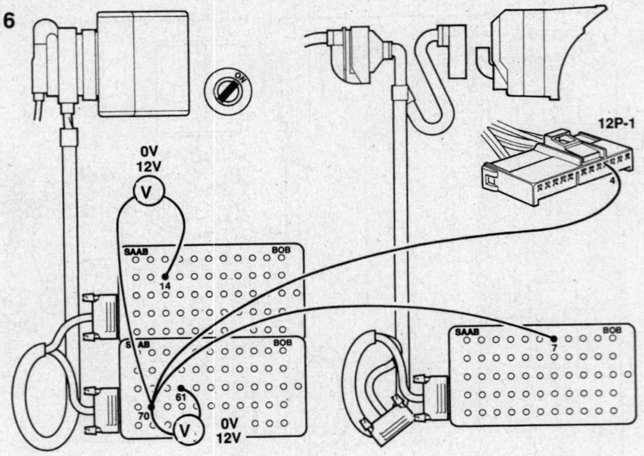

5 If the wiring is intact, the fault is probably in one of the electronic control modules.

6 Connect the ICE electronic control module and repeat points 2 and 3 and at the same time ground pin 4 in the connector (12p-1 main instrument 1) or pin 7 in the connector (main instrument 2).

Measured voltage should be 0 V at "ON" and 12 V at "OFF".

If the voltage is correct, the fault is probably in the main instrument, go to page 192for fault diagnosis in the main instrument.

If the voltage is wrong, continue

SA1089400016060X

Fig. 18 Cooling System Functional Check (Part 6 of 8). 900

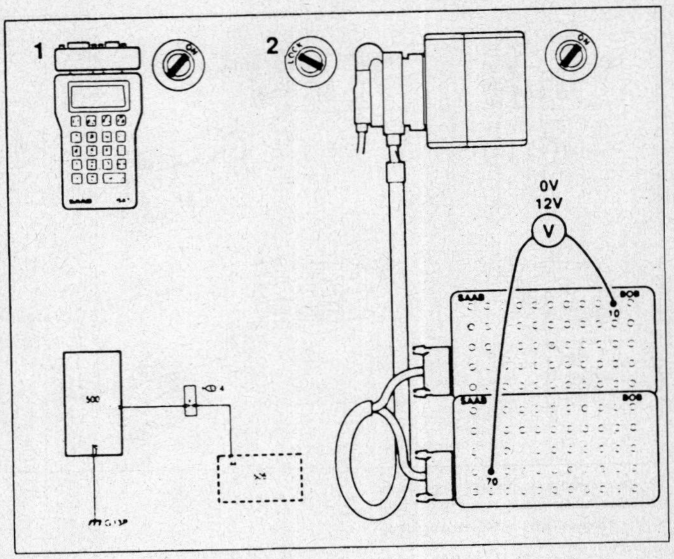

Checking the idling speed increase (only in MOTRONIC 2.10.2)

1 Connect ISAT and select "READ FAULT CODES" on the menu.

2 Connect a BOB and measure with a voltmeter between connections 10 and 70. Check the idling speed increase function by selecting "ACT OTHER FUNCT" on the menu followed by "IDLING INCREASE".

Check on the voltmeter that the voltage falls to about 0 V at "ON" and that it rises to about 12 V at "OFF".

SA1089400016070X

Fig. 18 Cooling System Functional Check (Part 7 of 8). 900

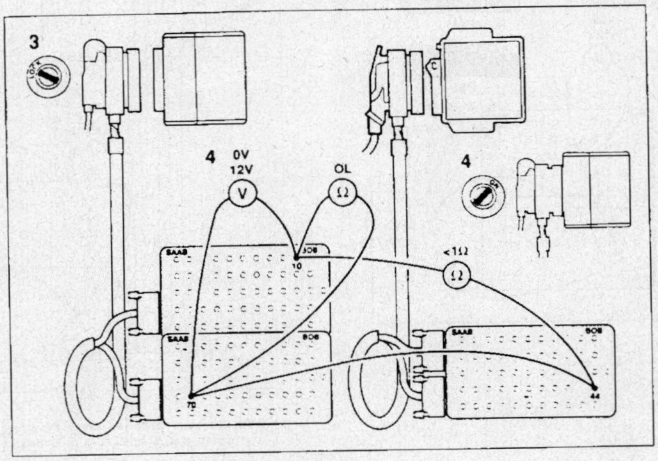

3 If it does not work, check the wiring between the ICE control module and the engine control system's control module (both control modules disconnected) for any open circuits/short circuits.

4 Connect the engine control system's control module and repeat point 2.

The voltage should be 0 V at "ON" and 12 V at "OFF".

If the voltage is correct, the fault is in the engine control system

SA1089400016080X

Fig. 18 Cooling System Functional Check (Part 8 of 8). 900

Dash Gauges

NOTE: On Air Bag Equipped Models, Refer To "Air Bag System Precautions" Located In The Front Of This Manual For System Disarming & Arming Procedures.

NOTE: Refer To "Dash Panel Service" Section For Dash Panel Removal Procedures.

INDEX

	Page No.
Gauges	7-59
Fuel	7-59
Temperature	7-59
Precautions	7-59
Air Bag Systems	7-59
Battery Ground Cable	7-59

PRECAUTIONS

AIR BAG SYSTEMS

Refer to "Air Bag System Precautions" in the front of this manual for system disarming and arming procedures.

BATTERY GROUND CABLE

Prior to service, disconnect battery ground cable and isolate as required.

GAUGES

FUEL

9-3 & 900

The fuel gauge is operative when the ignition switch is in drive position.

1. Disconnect connector to fuel level transmitter, located under cover in rear seat.
2. Measure resistance between connector pins. Resistance should be 2–4.5 ohms. If resistance is outside this range, there is a fault in transmitter or its connecting cable. If resistance is correct, continue this procedure.
3. Check wiring between fuel level transmitter and main instrument. Disconnect main instrument and three connectors.
4. Connect connector to fuel level transmitter. Measure between pin 6 (black 12-pin connector) and pin 1 (14-pin connector) in connectors to instrument for any open or short circuits. Resistance should be 2-4.5 ohms. If resistance is outside range, there is fault in wiring. If resistance is correct, continue this procedure.
5. Check foil circuits at back of main instrument by measuring between terminal 6 (12p-2) and screw marked "F SIG" and between terminal 1 (14p) and screw marked "GND" behind fuel gauge on main instrument for any open circuits.
6. If circuits are intact and fuel gauge does not work, fault is probably in fuel gauge. Install new main instrument. If there is an open circuit, change foil.

9-5

The fuel level sensor has a variable resistance, the value of this resistance corresponds to the sensor's float level in the tank. The resistance increases with higher fuel level. The sensor is directly connected to pin No. 9 of the Main Instrument Unit (MIU) control module where it is supplied with battery voltage and grounded through pin No. 8. The control module detects the sensor's resistance and controls the current to the fuel gauge so that the position of the meter needle corresponds to the resistance of the sensor.

1. If fuel gauge is not working at all, proceed as follows:
   a. Disconnect fuel level sensor electrical connector.
   b. Connect a suitable test lamp between battery positive terminal and pin No. 3 of sensor's male connector. If test lamp illuminates, proceed to next step. If test lamp does not illuminate, locate and repair open circuit between pin No. 8 of MIU control module and pin No. 3 of sensor connector.
   c. Connect a suitable scan tool to Data Link Connector (DLC) located under lefthand side of instrument panel, then follow scan tool instructions to contact MIU control module.
   d. Read fuel level sensor value. If value is approximately 5 volts, proceed to next step. If value is not approximately 5 volts, locate and repair open or short circuit between fuel level sensor connector pin No. 4 and MIU control module pin No. 9.
   e. Connect a suitable jumper wire between fuel level sensor male connector pin Nos. 3 and 4. If scan tool indicates voltage is zero, replace fuel level sensor. If scan tool indicates voltage is not zero, locate and repair open or short circuit between fuel level sensor connector pin No. 4 and MIU control module pin No. 9.
2. If fuel gauge is not working correctly, adjust gauge as follows:
   a. Connect a suitable scan tool to Data Link Connector (DLC) located under lefthand side of instrument panel, then follow scan tool instructions to contact MIU control module.
   b. Drain fuel tank and read scan tool value. If value indicated is zero, proceed to next step. If value indicated is not zero, adjust "Tank Offset" with scan tool until value indicated is zero, then proceed to next step.
   c. Add 2.6 gallons of fuel to tank, then adjust "Tank Offset" with scan tool until value indicated is "Tank Reserve," this breakpoint is when reserve lamp illuminates. Ensure gauge reading is correct, then proceed to next step.
   d. Add 2.4 gallons of fuel to tank, then adjust "Tank Offset" with scan tool until value indicated is "Tank ¼." Ensure gauge reading is correct, then proceed to next step.
   e. Add 5 gallons of fuel to tank, then adjust "Tank Offset" with scan tool until value indicated is "Tank ½." Ensure gauge reading is correct, then proceed to next step.
   f. Add 5.2 gallons of fuel to tank, then adjust "Tank Offset" with scan tool until value indicated is "Tank ¾." Ensure gauge reading is correct, then proceed to next step.
   g. Disconnect scan tool and check fuel gauge operation.

9000

The fuel gauge is monitored by the EDU 1/2 trip computer. In the event of a fault "Err" may light up on the computer display.

1. Check fuse 13 and that power is supplied to it.
2. Ensure fuel gauge terminals have power supplied to them.
3. Check connectors, cable harnesses and ground connections.
4. Resistance of fuel level transmitter are as follows:
   a. With fuel tank full, 350 ohms.
   b. With fuel tank empty, 35 ohms.

TEMPERATURE

9-3 & 900

1. Check foil circuits at back of instrument by measuring between terminal 4

(12p-1) and screw marked "T-SIG" in main instrument for any open circuits.

2. If cables are intact and temperature gauge does not work, fault is in temperature gauge. Install new main instrument.
3. If there is an open circuit, change foil.

9-5

The coolant temperature gauge is supplied with current and controlled by the Main Instrument Unit (MIU) control module. The engine control module continuously sends coolant temperature information on the bus. Using this information, the MIU inserts breaks at certain temperatures to give a stable display at normal coolant temperatures.

If the temperature gauge is not working or not working properly, check coolant sensor wiring and wiring connectors. If wiring and connectors are satisfactory, replace coolant sensor.

Starter Motors

INDEX

	Page No.		Page No.		Page No.
Description	7-61	Bench	7-62	Starter Specifications	7-62
Diagnosis & Testing	7-61	In-Vehicle	7-61		

DESCRIPTION

The starter motor used is a gear reduction starter. This starter, **Fig. 1**, uses six permanent magnets in place of conventional wound field magnets to reduce electrical and starting resistance. The gear reduction system uses a planetary gear train to transmit armature rotation to the pinion shaft.

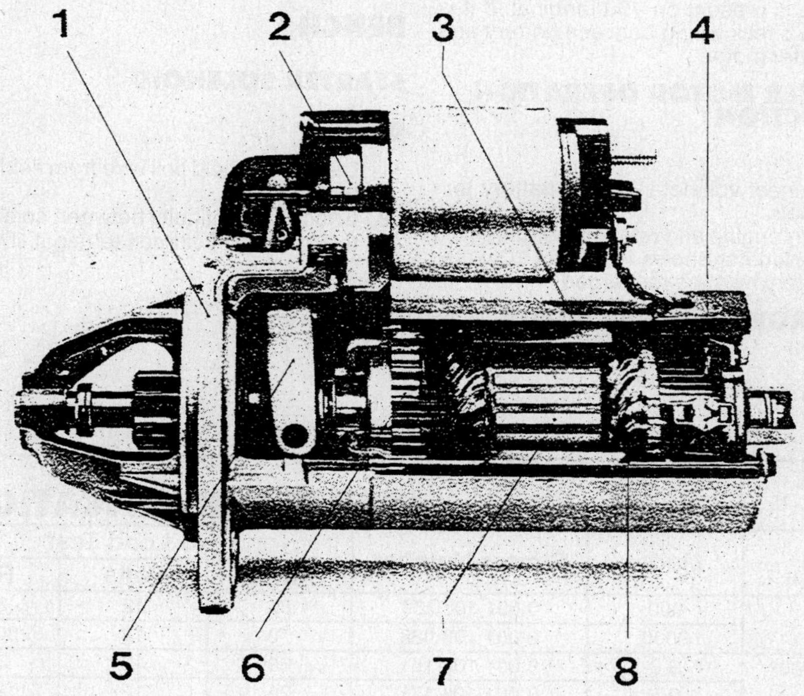

1 Pinion bracket assembly
2 Solenoid
3 Permanent magnets
4 Brush-holder assembly
5 Pinion-engaging lever
6 Planetary gear train
7 Armature
8 Stator frame

SA1129100001000X

Fig. 1 Cross-sectional view of starter motor

DIAGNOSIS & TESTING

IN-VEHICLE

Before beginning any tests, ensure battery is fully charged and that all connections are satisfactory.

AMPERAGE DRAW TEST

9000

1. Run engine until it reaches normal operating temperature, then turn engine off.
2. Connect suitable battery-starter tester according to manufacturer's instructions.
3. Turn battery-starter tester control knob to OFF position.
4. Turn voltmeter selector knob to "16 Volt" position.
5. Turn battery-starter function selector to STARTER TEST (0–500 amp scale).
6. Connect red positive ammeter lead to positive battery terminal and black negative ammeter lead to negative battery terminal.
7. Connect red positive voltmeter lead to positive battery terminal and black negative voltmeter lead to negative terminal.
8. Connect remote starter switch according to manufacturer's instructions. **Do not crank engine excessively during testing.**
9. Disconnect coil wire from distributor cap and secure it to good ground.
10. Crank engine and observe voltmeter reading, then stop cranking engine.
11. Turn tester control knob clockwise until voltmeter reading is the same as when engine was being cranked. Ammeter should read between 105–210 amps.

STARTER RESISTANCE TEST

9000

1. Disconnect positive battery cable and connect 0–300 scale ammeter between disconnected lead and terminal post.
2. Connect voltmeter between positive post on battery and starter relay terminal on starter solenoid.
3. Crank engine while observing readings on voltmeter and ammeter. A voltage reading exceeding. 3 volts indicates a high resistance caused by loose circuit connections, faulty cable, burned starter relay or solenoid switch contacts. High current combined with slow cranking speed indicates a need for starter repair.
4. Reconnect positive battery lead.

GROUND TEST

1. Connect voltmeter positive lead to starter through bolt and negative voltmeter lead to battery negative post.
2. Crank engine with remote starter switch and observe voltmeter reading.
3. If voltmeter reading exceeds. 2 volt, isolate points of excessive voltage loss by leaving negative lead connected to negative battery post and repeating test at the following locations:
   a. Voltmeter positive lead to starter drive housing.
   b. Voltmeter positive lead to ground terminal at engine.
   c. Voltmeter positive lead to cable clamp at battery.
4. Small changes in voltmeter reading should occur every time lead position is changed. A large change in voltage reading would indicates last part eliminated in test is at fault.

STARTER SOLENOID TEST

9000

1. Connect heavy jumper wire on starter relay between battery and solenoid terminals.
2. If engine cranks, perform "Starter Relay Test."
3. If engine does not crank or solenoid chatters, check wiring and connectors

from relay to starter solenoid.

BASIC INSPECTION

900

1. Use voltmeter to ensure at least 12 volts is present directly across battery terminals. If it is not, test battery.
2. Use voltmeter to ensure at least 12 volts is present across terminal 30 on starter motor and negative battery terminal.
3. Use voltmeter to ensure operating voltage is present on +50 terminal. If it is not, check wiring between battery and starter motor.

STARTER MOTOR OPERATION INSPECTION

900

1. Connect voltmeter across battery terminals.
2. Start engine and read off instrument.
3. If voltmeter shows less than 10 volts, battery must be recharged.

VOLTAGE DROP IN CIRCUIT

900

1. Connect voltmeter across the following:
   a. Positive battery terminal and terminal 30 on starter motor.
   b. Positive battery terminal and terminal 50 on starter motor (voltage in starting position only).
   c. Negative battery terminal and starter motor casing.
2. Start engine and read off voltmeter. Reading should not exceed .2–.3 volts.
3. If circuit shows higher reading it should be checked to determine reason for excessive voltage drop.

BENCH

STARTER SOLENOID

9000

1. Disconnect field coil wire from field coil terminal.
2. Check for continuity between solenoid terminal and field coil terminal. There should be continuity.
3. Check for continuity between solenoid terminal and solenoid housing. There should be continuity.
4. If continuity does not exist in either test, replace solenoid assembly.

STARTER RELAY TEST

9000

1. Place transaxle in neutral and apply parking brake.
2. Check for battery voltage between starter relay battery terminal and ground.
3. Connect jumper wire on starter relay between battery and ignition terminals.
4. If engine does not crank, connect second jumper wire to starter relay between ground terminal and good ground, repeat test.
5. If engine now cranks, transaxle linkage is improperly adjusted or neutral switch is defective.
6. If engine does not crank now, starter relay is defective.

STARTER SPECIFICATIONS

Year	Model	Starter Number	No Load Test			Load Test		
			Amps	Volts	RPM	Amps	Volts	RPM
1998	900	0 001 108 151	80	12	3000	310	9	1630
	9000	0 001 108 038	70	12	3000①	315	9	1700①
1999–2001	9-3	0 001 108 151	80	12	3000	310	9	1630
	9-5	0 001 108 171	70	12	2550	310	9	1390

① — Minimum.

Alternators

INDEX

	Page No.
Alternator Specifications	7-64
Diagnosis & Testing	7-63
In-Vehicle	7-63
Troubleshooting	7-63
Alternator Not Charging	7-63
Current Too High	7-63
Insufficient Or Irregular Power Supply	7-63
Noisy Alternator	7-63

TROUBLESHOOTING

ALTERNATOR NOT CHARGING

1. Drive belt slipping.
2. Open in charging or ground circuits.
3. Defective brushes, regulator or diodes.
4. Broken excitation circuit or rotor winding.
5. Open stator ground circuit.

INSUFFICIENT OR IRREGULAR POWER SUPPLY

1. Drive belt slipping.
2. Defective brushes, regulator or diode rectifiers.
3. Partial short circuit in rotor.
4. Poor stator to ground connection.

CURRENT TOO HIGH

1. Defective regulator.
2. Poor contact between regulator and alternator.

NOISY ALTERNATOR

1. Worn drive belt.
2. Pulley fitted incorrectly.
3. Loose alternator brackets.
4. Alternator and crankshaft pulleys misaligned.
5. Worn or defective bearings.
6. Short circuit in diode rectifier.

DIAGNOSIS & TESTING

IN-VEHICLE

9-3 & 900

Never start the engine while carrying out this test procedure, as the alternator could be permanently damaged.

1. If lamp fails to light up when ignition is switched on, ground D terminal on alternator while ignition is still switched on.
2. If lamp lights up, electrical system is satisfactory and alternator is faulty.
3. Connect voltmeter across battery terminals.
4. Run engine at medium-high RPM for several minutes and read voltmeter. Reading should be 13.5–14 volts.
5. Connect ammeter to alternator output circuit (B) or use clip-on ammeter.
6. Run engine at about 2500 RPM.
7. Apply maximum electrical load to alternator either by connecting special carbon film resistor to it or by switching on all of vehicle's electrical equipment.
8. Read ammeter. Reading should be 45–90 amps.
9. Connect voltmeter across battery positive terminal and alternator B terminal.
10. Run engine at 2500 RPM and apply electrical load to alternator by switching on all lights.
11. Read instrument, then connect voltmeter across battery negative terminal and alternator B- terminal (ground).
12. Run engine at 2500 RPM and apply electrical load again. Read instrument.
13. Readings taken above should not exceed .5 volts. If higher reading is obtained, check relevant circuit for shorting or continuity.

9-5

1. Check the following:
   a. Battery terminals are tight and clean.
   b. Battery ground and power connections are clean and tight.
   c. Alternator connectors are clean and tight.
   d. Drive belt is in good condition and properly tensioned.
2. Connect test leads of a suitable voltmeter to battery terminals.
3. Start and run engine at 2500 RPM. If voltage is 13.5–14.5 volts, proceed to next step. If voltage is not 13.5–14.5 volts, repair or replace alternator.
4. Connect a suitable ammeter between battery positive and alternator.
5. Turn all accessories and lights on, then run engine at 1800 RPM and compare readings with those listed in "Alternator Specifications" chart. If output is satisfactory, proceed to next step, If readings are not satisfactory, repair or replace alternator as necessary.
6. Connect a voltmeter to battery positive terminal and alternator positive connection, then turn on headlamps. If voltage drop is less than .5 volts when headlamps are turned on, proceed to next step. If voltage drop is more than .5 volts when headlamps are turned on, repair wiring circuit between battery positive terminal and alternator.
7. Connect a voltmeter to battery negative terminal and alternator negative connection, then turn on headlamps. If voltage drop is less than .5 volts when headlamps are turned on, alternator is functioning correctly. If voltage drop is more than .5 volts when headlamps are turned on, repair wiring circuit between battery negative terminal and alternator.

9000

When measuring charging current, never disconnect battery leads with engine running. Avoid applying any mechanical stress where leads extend from the diode holder, do not bend or apply pressure to wire where it is joined to the terminal.

1. Connect a volt/amp meter to system following manufacturers' instructions. **Alternator output voltage should be checked between battery positive post and alternator ground.**
2. Connect a tachometer to engine, start and run engine until it reaches normal operating temperature.
3. Apply current load to alternator and set engine to run at following speeds:
   a. 55 amp alternator, 900 RPM.
   b. 65 amp alternator, 950 RPM.
   c. 70 amp Motorola alternator, 800 RPM.
   d. 70 amp Bosch alternator, 850 RPM.
   e. 80 amp alternator, 800 RPM.
4. Compare output readings with those listed in "Alternator Specifications" chart.
5. If output is not within specifications, check drive belt, feed and ground circuits. Repair as required.
6. If wiring and drive belt are satisfactory, repair or replace alternator as necessary.

ALTERNATOR SPECIFICATIONS

Year	Model	Alternator Model	Rated Hot Output Amps	Rated Hot Output Volts	Output @ 14 Volts Amps @ RPM	Output @ 14 Volts Amps @ RPM	Regulator
1998	900	Bosch KC-14V 70A	70	14	40 @ 1800	70 @ 6000	Integral
		Bosch KC-14V 90A	90	14	45 @ 1800	90 @ 6000	Integral
		Bosch NC-14V 120A	120	14	60 @ 1800	120 @ 6000	Integral
	9000	Bosch K1-14V 70A	70	14	27 @ 1500	46 @ 2000	Integral
		Bosch N1-14V 80A	80	14	36 @ 1500	54 @ 1900	Integral
		Bosch N1-14V 115A	115	14	40 @ 1500	62 @ 1900	Integral
1999–2001	9-3	Bosch KC-14V 70A	70	14	40 @ 1800	70 @ 6000	Integral
		Bosch KC-14V 90A	90	14	45 @ 1800	90 @ 6000	Integral
		Bosch NC-14V 120A	120	14	60 @ 1800	120 @ 6000	Integral
	9-5	Bosch KC 14V 45-90A	90	14	45 @ 1800	90 @ 6000	Integral
		Bosch NC 14V 65-130A	130	14	65 @ 1800	130 @ 6000	Integral

Speed Control Systems

NOTE: "Electrical Symbol & Wire Color Code Identification" Located In The Front Of This Manual May Be Used As An Aid When Using Wiring Circuits Found In This Section.

INDEX

	Page No.
Description	7-65
Precautions	7-65
Air Bag Systems	7-65
Battery Ground Cable	7-65
System Diagnosis & Testing	7-65
9-3 & 9-5	7-65
9000	7-65
900	7-65

DESCRIPTION

The cruise control system uses the cruise control module, cruise control switches, brake pedal switch and clutch pedal switch to control vehicle speed.

The driver sets the speed control system using the switch on the combination switch. The system will disengage automatically when either the clutch pedal or brake pedal is pressed, when the switch is moved to the Off or Tip position, when the selector lever is in the N position or when the traction control system is activated.

The control module incorporates an electric stepping motor which mechanically regulates the cruise control cable connected to the throttle body, either retracting it or extending it according to the speed of the vehicle.

PRECAUTIONS

AIR BAG SYSTEMS

Refer to "Air Bag System Precautions" in the front of this manual for system disarming and arming procedures.

BATTERY GROUND CABLE

Prior to service, disconnect battery ground cable and isolate as required.

SYSTEM DIAGNOSIS & TESTING

9-3 & 9-5

These cruise control systems are part of the "Trionic Engine Control System." Refer to the "Saab Engine Performance" chapter for diagnosis and testing procedures on these systems.

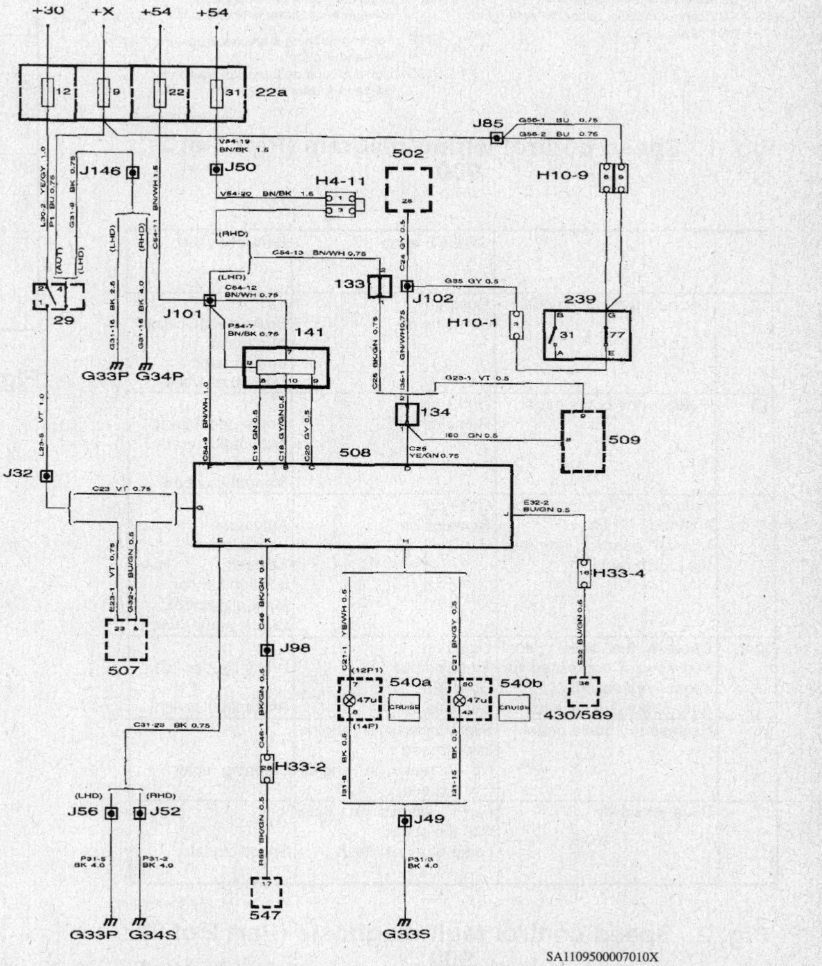

Fig. 1 Speed control wiring diagram (Part 1 of 2). 900

900

Refer to wiring diagram **Fig. 1** and speed control fault diagnosis **Figs. 2 and 3** when testing the speed control system.

9000

Refer to wiring diagram **Fig. 4** and speed control fault diagnosis **Figs. 5 and 6** when testing the speed control system.

22A Fuse holder in the dashboard
29 Brake lights switch on the pedal assembly
30 Brake light bulbs, right-hand and left-hand rear light clusters
47U CRUISE indicator lamp in main instrument display
76 Switch, idling speed increase, in selector lever position sensor 239 on the transmission.
133 Clutch switch, Cruise Control, on the clutch pedal
134 Brake pedal switch, on the brake pedal
141 Cruise Control switch, on the lights switch, on the left-hand side of the steering column
239 Selector lever position sensor, on the transmission
430 Trionic control module, in the cabin, below the right-hand A pillar
500 ICE control module, on top of relay holder 22B, under the dashboard adjacent to the steering wheel
502 TCM control module, on the bulkhead partition, behind the glove box
507 TCS control module, under the right-hand front seat
508 Cruise Control system control module, on a bracket in the false bulkhead space, in the engine bay on the right-hand side
540 Main instrument display panel on the dashboard
540A Main instrument display 1, without rev counter (tachometer), on the dashboard
540B Main instrument display 2, with rev counter (tachometer), on the dashboard
547 ABS control module, on the brake unit in the engine bay

10-pin connectors

H10-1 On a bracket behind the battery in the engine bay
H10-3 On a bracket behind the battery in the engine bay

33-pin connectors

H33-1 Blue 33-pin connector on a bracket below the left-hand A pillar
H33-2 Black 33-pin connector on a bracket below the left-hand A pillar
H33-4 On a bracket on the bulkhead partition behind the glove bo҂
G3 Grounding point in the luggage compartment on the left-hand side
G33P Power ground on a bracket below the left-hand A pillar
G33S Signal ground on a bracket below the left-hand A pillar

SA1109500007020X

Fig. 1 Speed control wiring diagram (Part 2 of 2). 900

		CRUISE lamp	Item checked
1	Engine switched off and handbrake applied		
2	Automatic transmission: selector lever in position N (P, R) Manual gearbox: clutch pedal depressed		
3	Move the switch to the TIP position and hold it there while the engine starts.		
	The CRUISE lamp should light up to confirm that you are in diagnosis mode.	Lights up Remains out	
4	Release the TIP button	Goes out Remains on	 TIP function
5	Press the SET button	Lights up Remains out	 SET function
	Release the SET button	Goes out Remains on	 SET function
7	Move the switch to the RES/— position	Lights up Remains out	 RESUME function
8	Release RES/—	Goes out Remains on	 RESUME function
9	Move the switch to the ON/OFF position	Lights up Remains out	 ON/OFF function
10	Release ON/OFF	Goes out Remains on	 ON/OFF function
11	Automatic transmission: shift to D (3, 2, 1) Manual gearbox: release the clutch pedal	Lights up Remains out	 Automatic transmission: Selector lever position sensor Manual gearbox: Clutch pedal switch

SA1109400005010X

Fig. 2 Speed control fault diagnosis (Part 1 of 2). 900

		CRUISE lamp	Item checked
12	Depress the brake pedal	Goes out Remains on	 Brake pedal switch Automatic transmission Manual gearbox
13	Release the brake pedal	Lights up Remains out	 Brake pedal switch Automatic transmission Manual gearbox
14	Automatic transmission: shift to N (P, R) Manual gearbox: depress the clutch pedal	Goes out Remains on	 Automatic transmission: Selector lever position sensor Manual gearbox: Clutch pedal switch
15	Depress the brake pedal and keep it depressed for about five seconds. After about five seconds	Lights up Remains out Goes out Remains on	 Brake light switch Brake light switch
16	Release the brake pedal	Slight increase in engine idling speed No increase in engine idling speed	 Stepping motor
17	Drive off slowly	Lamp flashes in time with the speed Lamp does not flash	 Speed signal

SA1109400005020X

Fig. 2 Speed control fault diagnosis (Part 2 of 2). 900

Pin	Colour	Component/function	Test conditions	Input/ Output	Test value	Across X—Y
1 (A)	Green	Switch	Switch held in ON/OFF position Ignition switched on	Input	12 V	1-5
2 (B)	Grey/ green	Switch	Switch held in ON/OFF position Ignition switched on	Input	12 V	2-5
3 (C)	Grey	Switch	Switch held in ON/OFF position Ignition switched on	Input	12 V	3-5
4 (D)	Yellow/ green	Pedal switches				
		Brake switch	Automatic transmission D, 1, 2, 3 Pedal not depressed Pedal depressed	Input	12 V 0 V	4-5
			Manual gearbox Pedal not depressed Pedal depressed	Input	12 V 0 V	4-5
		Clutch pedal switch	Manual gearbox Pedal not depressed Pedal depressed	Input	12 V 0 V	4-5
5 (E)	Black	Power ground		Input	12 V	5-batt+
6 (F)	Brown/ white	Ignition +54	Ignition switched on	input	12 V	6-5
7 (G)	Violet or Blue/ green	Brake light switch	Brake pedal depressed Brake pedal not depressed	Input	12 V 0 V	7-5
8 (H)	Brown/ yellow or Yellow/ white	CRUISE lamp	Lamp out Lamp on	Output	0 V 12 V	8-5
9 (J)	Blue/ green	Communication with other systems	In diagnosis mode ON/OFF SET RESUME	Output	12 V	9-5
10 (K)	Black/ green	Speed signal	Left-hand front wheel spinning 1/2 rev/sec	Input	approx. 15 Hz	10-5

SA1109400006000X

Fig. 3 Speed control module connector test values. 900

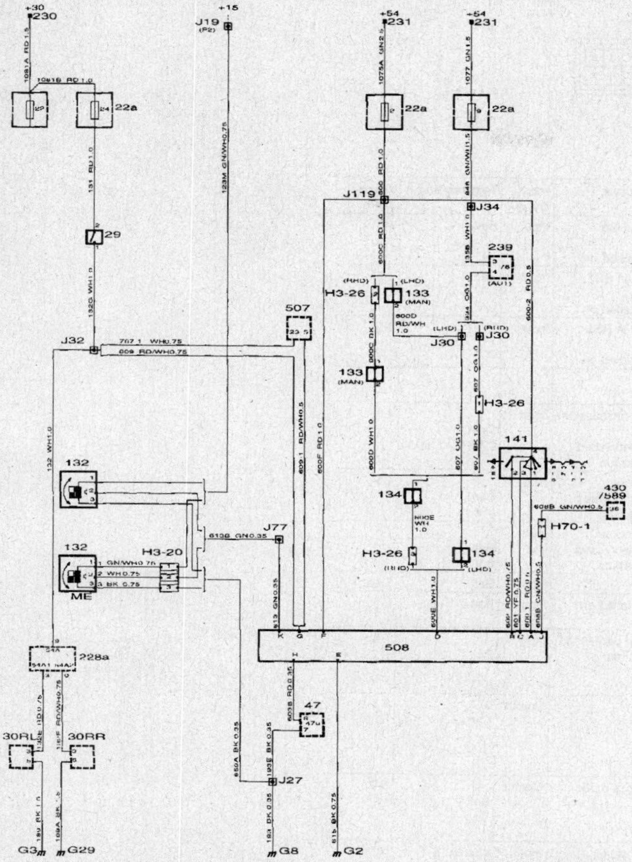

SA1109500008010X

Fig. 4 Speed control wiring diagram (Part 1 of 2). 9000

	Action	CRUISE lamp	Item checked
1	Engine switched off and hand-brake applied.		
2	Automatic transmission: selector lever in position N (P, R). Manual gearbox: clutch pedal depressed.		
3	Press the SET and RES buttons simultaneously and keep them depressed while the engine starts.		
	The CRUISE lamp should light up to confirm that you are in diagnostics mode.	Lights up Remains out	On function SET function RESUME function Cruise lamp
4	First release the SET button and then the RES button.	Goes out Remains on	SET function RESUME function
5	Press the SET button.	Lights up Remains out	SET function
	Release the SET button.	Goes out Remains on	SET function
7	Move the switch to the RES/- position.	Lights up Remains out	RESUME function
8	Release RES/-.	Goes out Remains on	RESUME function
9	Move the switch to the TIP/OFF position.	Lights up Remains out	TIP/OFF function
10	Release TIP/OFF.	Goes out Remains on	TIP/OFF function
11	Automatic transmission: shift to D (3, 2, 1). Manual gearbox: release the clutch pedal.	Lights up Remains out	Automatic transmission: Selector lever position sensor Manual gearbox: Clutch pedal switch

SA1109500009010X

Fig. 5 Speed control fault diagnosis (Part 1 of 2). 9000

- 22A Fuse holder in the dashboard
- 29 Brake lights switch on the pedal assembly
- 30 Brake light bulbs, right-hand and left-hand rear light clusters
- 47U CRUISE indicator lamp in the main instrument display
- 228A Filament monitor
- 133 Clutch switch, Cruise Control, on the clutch pedal
- 134 Brake pedal switch, on the brake pedal
- 141 Cruise Control switch, on the lights stalk, on the left-hand side of the steering column
- 239 Selector lever position sensor, under the selector lever
- 430 TRIONIC control module, in the cabin, below the right-hand A pillar
- 132 Speedometer, in the main instrument display
- 507 TCS control module, under the left-hand front seat
- 508 Cruise Control system control module, on a bracket in the engine bay
- H10-1 10-pin connector, mounted on a bracket behind the battery in the engine bay
- H10-3 10-pin connector, mounted on a bracket behind the battery in the engine bay
- H3-20 3-pin connector, behind the main instrument display adjacent to the speedometer (ME)
- H70-1 70-pin connector, in the false bulkhead space
- H3-26 3-pin connector, above the pedal assembly adjacent to the pedal switches
- G3 Grounding point, luggage compartment
- G8 Grounding point, dashboard
- G2 Grounding point, battery tray
- G29 Grounding point, right-hand rear light cluster

SA1109500008020X

Fig. 4 Speed control wiring diagram (Part 2 of 2). 9000

	Action	CRUISE lamp	Item checked
12	Depress the brake pedal.	Goes out Remains on	Brake pedal switch Automatic transmission Manual gearbox
13	Release the brake pedal.	Lights up Remains out	Brake pedal switch Automatic transmission Manual gearbox
14	Automatic transmission: shift to N (P, R). Manual gearbox: depress the clutch pedal.	Goes out Remains on	Automatic transmission: Selector lever position sensor Manual gearbox: Clutch pedal switch
15	Depress the brake pedal and keep it depressed for about five seconds. After about five seconds:	Lights up Remains out Goes out Remains on	Brake lights switch Control module
16	Release the brake pedal.	Slight increase in engine idling speed No increase in engine idling speed	Stepping motor/ cable
17	Drive off slowly.	Lamp flashes in time with the speed. Lamp does not flash.	Speed signal

SA1109500009020X

Fig. 5 Speed control fault diagnosis (Part 2 of 2). 9000

Pin	Colour	Component/function	Test conditions	Input/ Output	Test reading	Across X—Y
1 (A)	Green	Switches	Switch set to ON position Ignition switched on	Input	Batt+	1-5
2 (B)	Grey/ green	Switches	Switch held in SET position Ignition switched on	Input	Batt+	2-5
3 (C)	Grey	Switches	Switch held in RES position Ignition switched on	Input	Batt+	3-5
4 (D)	Yellow/ green	Pedal switches				
		Brake pedal switch	Automatic transmission D, 1, 2, 3 Pedal not depressed Pedal depressed	Input	Batt+ 0 V	4-5
			Manual gearbox Pedal not depressed Pedal depressed	Input	Batt+ 0 V	4-5
		Clutch pedal switch	Manual gearbox Pedal not depressed Pedal depressed	Input	Batt+ 0 V	4-5
5 (E)	Black	Power ground		Input	Batt+	5-batt+
6 (F)	Brown/ white	Ignition +54	Ignition switched on	Input	Batt+	6-5
7 (G)	Violet or Blue/ green	Brake lights switch	Brake pedal depressed Brake pedal not depressed	Input	Batt+ 0 V	7-5
8 (H)	Brown/ yellow or Yellow/ white	CRUISE indicator lamp	Lamp out Lamp on	Output	0 V Batt+	8-5
9 (J)	Blue/ green	Communication with Tronic	In diagnostics mode ON/OFF SET RESUME	Output	Batt+	6-9
10 (K)	Black/ green	Speed signal	Car driven slowly forward	Input	approx. 6 V	10-5

SA1109500010000X

Fig. 6 Speed control module connector test values. 9000

Air Bag System

NOTE: Prior To Performing Any Service Operations Listed In This Section, Consult The "Technical Service Bulletins" Section For Related Information.

INDEX

	Page No.
Air Bag System Disarming & Arming	7-69
Arming	7-69
Disarming	7-69
Collision Inspection	7-72
9-3 & 9-5	7-72
900 & 9000	7-72
Component Locations	7-72
Component Service	7-73
Air Bag Module, Replace	7-73
Driver	7-73
Passenger	7-73
Side	7-74
Air Bag Or Seat Belt Pretensioner Assembly Disposal	7-77
Air Bag Deployment	7-78
Seat Belt Pretensioner Deployment	7-78
Side Air Bag Deployment	7-79
Contact Roller Unit, Replace	7-75
9-3	7-75
9-5	7-75
Contact Unit, Replace	7-74
9000	7-75
900	7-74
Control Module, Replace	7-76
9-3 & 900	7-76
9-5	7-76
9000	7-76
Front Sensors, Replace	7-75
9000	7-75
Seat Belt Pretensioner, Replace	7-76
9-3	7-76
9-5	7-77
900 & 9000	7-77
Side Impact Sensor, Replace	7-77
9-3	7-77
9-5	7-77
Description & Operation	7-69
Components	7-69
Air Bag Module	7-70
Contact Roller Unit	7-70
Contact Unit	7-70
Control Module	7-69
Front Sensors	7-69
Pyrotechnical Seat Belt Pretensioner	7-70
SRS Warning Lamp	7-71
System	7-69
9-3 & 9-5	7-69
900 & 9000	7-69
Diagnosis & Testing	7-72
Precautions	7-71
Air Bag Systems	7-71
Battery Ground Cable	7-72
Scheduled Maintenance	7-72
9-3 & 9-5	7-72
900 & 9000	7-72
Tightening Specifications	7-81
Wire Harness & Connector Repair	7-72

AIR BAG SYSTEM DISARMING & ARMING

DISARMING

1. Disconnect battery ground cable.
2. Prior to performing any service or diagnostic procedure, wait at least 20 minutes for back up power supply to deplete.

ARMING

1. Connect battery ground cable. **Ensure no one is inside vehicle when connecting battery ground cable.**
2. Turn ignition On and note SRS warning lamp operation. The SRS warning lamp should light for about six seconds and then go off. If lamp remains illuminated or fails to light, refer to "Diagnosis and Testing."

DESCRIPTION & OPERATION

System

900 & 9000

This system consists of a safety sensor, control module, driver and passenger air bag modules and pyrotechnical seat belt pretensioners, **Fig. 1.**

The air bag(s) and pyrotechnical seat belt pretensioner(s) will activate when the safety sensor is subjected to a force equivalent to a frontal collision at approximately 15 mph.

9-3 & 9-5

The SRS components are shown in **Figs. 2 and 3.** They include the control module (1), side impact sensor (2), driver's air bag module (3), passenger's air bag module (4), side air bags (5), seat belt tensioners (6), and driver's and passenger's knee shields (7 and 8).

The air bags and pyrotechnical seat belt tensioners will deploy when the SRS control module and/or sensors determine that an impact of sufficient force has occurred.

Components

FRONT SENSORS

9000

The front sensor consist of a contact roller which is held in position by a spring, **Fig. 4.** When the roller is subjected to a force in excess of 16g, the roller will move forward and close the circuit. **It is extremely important that the sensor be installed in the proper direction to avoid accidental deployment.**

CONTROL MODULE

900 & 9000

The control module contains the safety sensor, a capacitor pack and the diagnostic unit. **It is important that the control module be mounted facing in proper direction.**

The diagnostic unit continuously monitors the air bag system. If a system fault or condition should occur, the SRS warning lamp will light. The symbol will flash for about 10 minutes, then the lamp will remain On steadily until the ignition is turned Off. If a condition is still present the next time the ignition is turned On, the SRS lamp will again flash for approximately 10 minutes. Condition indications are stored as DTCs in the diagnostic unit memory.

9-3 & 9-5

The control module contains an accelerometer, a microprocessor and voltage converter, an electromechanical magnetic reed type safety sensor and back-up power supplies. **It is important that the control module be mounted facing in the proper direction.**

The diagnostic unit continuously monitors the air bag system. If a system fault condition should occur, the SRS warning lamp will light. Condition indications are stored as Diagnostic Trouble Codes (DTCs) in the diagnostic unit memory.

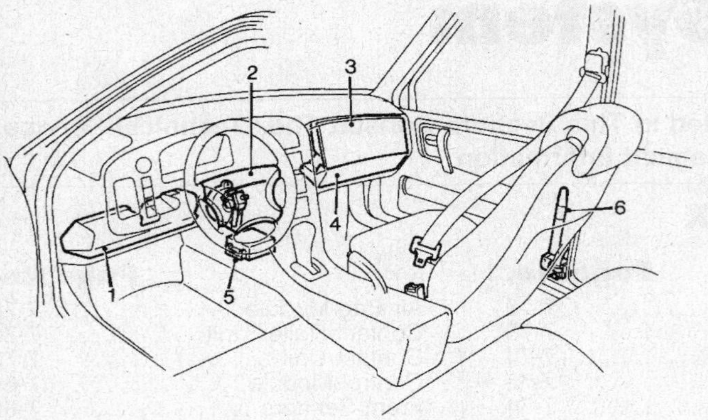

Fig. 1 SRS components. 900 & 9000

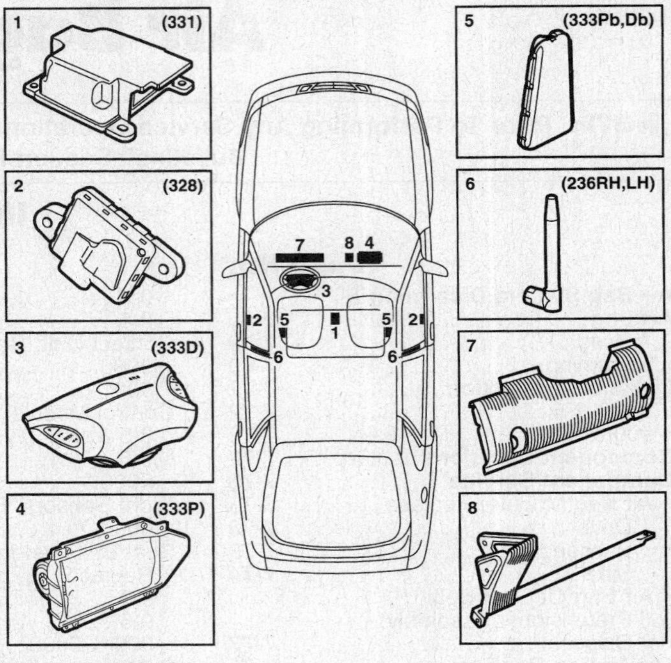

1 Control Module
2 Side Impact Sensor
3 Driver's Air Bag Module
4 Passenger's Air Bag module
5 Side Impact Air Bag
6 Seat Belt Tensioner
7 Knee Shield

SA8019900065000X

Fig. 2 SRS components. 9-3

AIR BAG MODULE

DRIVER

900 & 9000

The driver air bag module, located in the steering wheel pad, contains the gas generator and air bag, **Fig. 5.** The gas generator consists of an aluminum case with a center compartment and two annular compartments, **Fig. 6.** The center compartment has an electric detonator and an explosive charge and communicates with the inner annular compartment.

9-3 & 9-5

The driver's air bag module, located in the center of the steering wheel, **Fig. 7,** consists of the air bag module proper and a gas generator with its detonator. When the air bag module receives an "active" command, the control module sends a current pulse along to the detonator to ignite the explosive charge. The combustion process generates a gas. An internal filter cools the gas and removes particles before it passes into the air bag.

PASSENGER

900 & 9000

The passenger air bag module, located under a panel in the instrument panel pad above the glove compartment, contains the gas generator and air bag, **Fig. 5.** The gas generator consists of an aluminum case with a center compartment and two annular compartments, **Fig. 6.** The center compartment has an electric detonator and an explosive charge and communicates with the inner annular compartment.

9-3 & 9-5

The passenger's air bag module, **Fig. 8,** located in the instrument panel pad above the glove compartment, contains a gas generator and air bag proper. The air bag stays in place with a plastic cover with fracture lines. Corresponding fracture lines are also found in the instrument panel pad. When the air bag module receives an "active" command, the control module sends a current pulse along to the detonator to ignite the explosive charge. The combustion process generates a gas. An internal filter cools the gas and removes particles before it passes into the air bag.

SIDE

The side air bag modules, **Fig. 9,** are hidden under the front seats' backrest upholstery fabric. They enhance crash protection if an impact occurs. The inflation provides a cushion between the occupant's upper body and the sides of the doors. On activation, the control module sends a current pulse to the side air bag module's detonator, triggering the charge's combustion. The pressure vessel's seal gives way from the pressure and the bag inflates.

PYROTECHNICAL SEAT BELT PRETENSIONER

The pyrotechnical seat belt pretensioner is located in the seat belt retractor units found in the vehicle "B" pillar. The unit contains a gas generator and piston, which in a collision will automatically tighten the seat belt and shoulder harness.

CONTACT UNIT

900 & 9000

The contact unit, **Fig. 10,** is located between the steering wheel and the steering column bracket. The contact unit is used to transmit testing and firing signals to the air bag unit. It also supplies current to the horn and turn signal switches. The unit consists of a fixed and moving part. A coiled plastic strip with four conductors is located between the fixed and movable parts. The movable part can be rotated the number of turns listed on the label in either direction from the center position. If the movable part is rotated beyond these limits, the plastic coil strip may break, rendering the air bag system inoperative.

CONTACT ROLLER UNIT

9-3 & 9-5

The contact roller unit, **Fig. 11,** is located between the steering wheel and the steering column bracket. The contact roller unit is used to transmit testing and firing signals to the air bag unit. It also supplies current to the horn and audio system. The unit consists of a fixed and moving part. A coiled plastic strip with four conductors is located between the fixed and movable parts. On 9-3 models, the movable part can be rotated approximately two turns in either direction from the center position. On 9-5 models, the movable part can be rotated

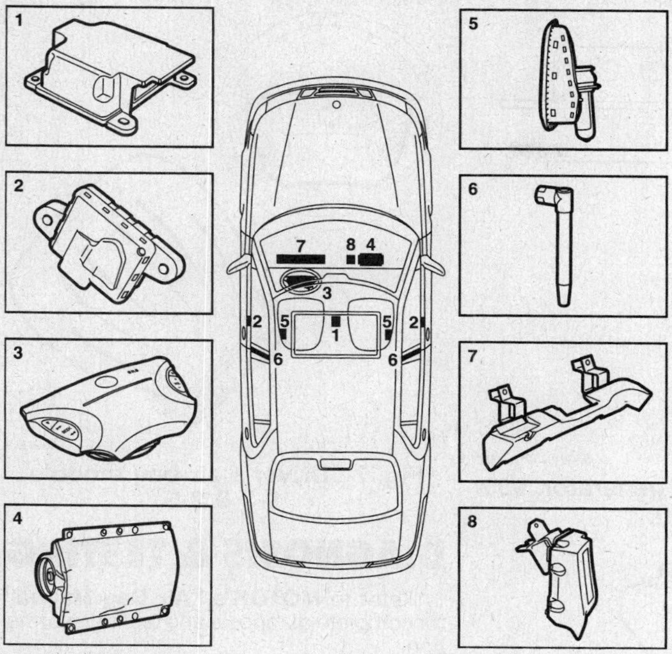

1 Control Module
2 Side Impact Sensor
3 Driver's Air Bag Module
4 Passenger's Air Bag module
5 Side Impact Air Bag
6 Seat Belt Tensioner
7 Knee Shield

SA8019900088000X

Fig. 3 SRS components. 9-5

approximately 2½ turns in either direction from the center position. On all models, if the movable part is rotated beyond these limits, the plastic coil strip may break, rendering the air bag system inoperative.

SRS WARNING LAMP

900 & 9000

The warning lamp is located in the combined instrument panel on 900 models and in the pictogram on 9000 models. This lamp will light for approximately six seconds when the ignition is turned on and will go out if there are no SRS conditions.

9-3 & 9-5

This warning lamp is located in the instrument cluster. It will light for approximately 3–4 seconds when the ignition is turned On then go out if there are no SRS fault conditions. If an air bag module or seat belt tensioner deploys the air bag warning lamp will light and stay lit.

PRECAUTIONS

AIR BAG SYSTEMS

900 & 9000

The SRS must be disarmed prior to disconnecting any SRS electrical connectors or servicing any system components located near them. Refer to "Air Bag System Disarming & Arming."

1. SRS components must not be opened or repaired. Always install new components.
2. Always replace SRS system components which have been damaged.
3. SRS wiring cannot be repaired or spliced. If damaged, replace the wiring harness.
4. When performing body work or welding repairs, always disconnect the driver's air bag and seat belt pretensioner electrical connectors.
5. The air bag must not be stored at temperatures higher than 158°F. There is a risk of self-detonation at temperatures above 275°F.
6. Do not paint air bag unit cover to correct cosmetic flaws. It must be replaced.
7. The contact unit must not be turned more than number of turns listed on the label in either direction from center as contact unit damage may result.
8. Do not leave an undeployed air bag module or seat belt pretensioner unattended if work is interrupted. Install into vehicle as soon as unit is removed from packaging.
9. The SRS must be inspected every 10 years.
10. Handle air bag module carefully so that it is not exposed to impacts or vibrations.
11. Air bag must be stored and carried with its metal case facing downward to prevent injury in event of accidental detonation.
12. Do not store air bag together with petroleum products or other flammable materials.
13. Wear safety goggles and protective gloves during removal of a deployed air bag and place it in a tightly sealed plastic bag. The surface may contain deposits of sodium hydroxide, a by-product of the gas generated during deployment. Because sodium hydroxide is irritating to the skin, wash your hands in a mild soap and lukewarm water solution after handling a deployed air bag.
14. Use care when handling control module as it is sensitive to static electricity. Do not touch or allow foreign objects to come into contact with connector pins.

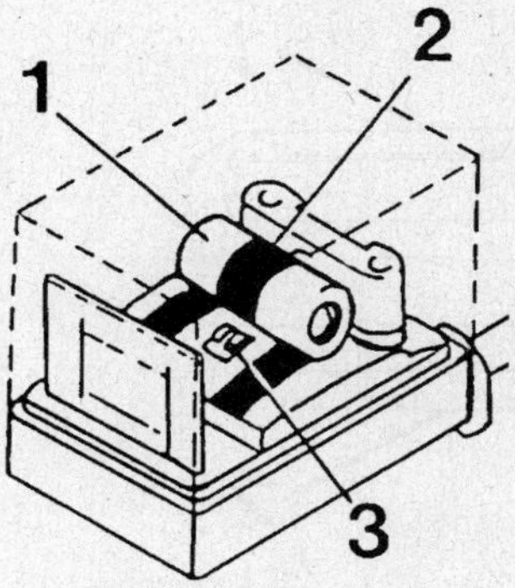

1 Contact roller
2 Contact surface
3 Contact

SA8019400034000X

Fig. 4 Front sensor assembly. 9000

9-3 & 9-5

The SRS must be disarmed prior to disconnecting any SRS electrical connectors or servicing any system components located near them. Refer to "Air Bag System Disarming & Arming."

1. SRS components must not be opened or repaired. Always install new components.
2. Always replace SRS system components which have been damaged.
3. SRS wiring cannot be repaired or spliced. If damaged, replace wiring harness.
4. When performing body work or welding repairs, always disconnect driver's air bag and seat belt tensioner electrical connectors.
5. The air bag must be stored at room temperature. There is a risk of self-detonation at temperatures above 212°F.
6. Never expose seat belt tensioners to temperatures above 212°F.
7. Seat belt tensioners that have been dropped onto a hard surface from a height of 16 inches or higher must not be used.
8. Do not paint air bag unit cover to correct cosmetic flaws. It must be replaced.
9. The contact roller unit must not be

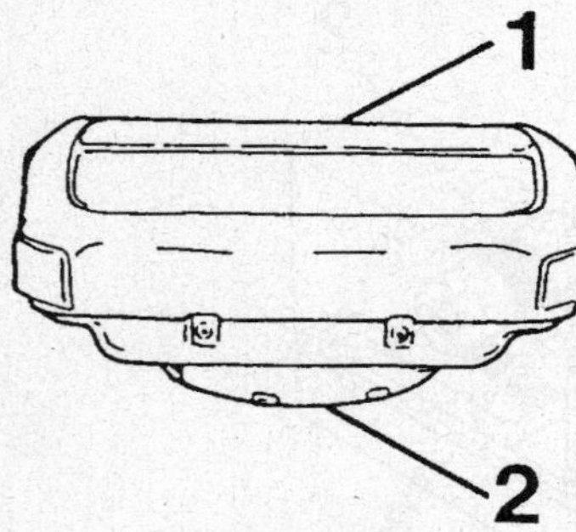

SA8019400035000X

Fig. 5 Air bag module. 900 & 9000

turned more than number of turns listed on label in either direction from center or contact roller unit damage may result.

10. Do not leave an undeployed air bag module or seat belt tensioner unattended if work is interrupted. Install into vehicle as soon as unit is removed from packaging.
11. The SRS must be inspected every 10 years.
12. Handle air bag module carefully so that it is not exposed to impacts or vibrations.
13. Air bag must be stored and carried with its metal case facing downward to prevent injury in event of accidental detonation.
14. Do not store air bag together with petroleum products or other flammable materials.
15. Wear safety goggles and protective gloves during removal of a deployed air bag, and place it in a tightly sealed plastic bag. The surface may contain deposits of sodium hydroxide, a by-product of the gas generated during deployment. Because sodium hydroxide is irritating to skin, wash your hands in a mild soap and lukewarm water solution after handling a deployed air bag.
16. Use care when handling control module as it is sensitive to static electricity. Do not touch or allow foreign objects to come into contact with connector pins.

BATTERY GROUND CABLE

Prior to service, disconnect battery ground cable and isolate as required.

SCHEDULED MAINTENANCE

900 & 9000

The SRS must be inspected every 10 years. The SRS should be inspected for stored DTCs. Refer to "Diagnosis and Testing." The air bag module, steering wheel, contact unit, control module, front sensors and brackets, wiring harnesses and seat belt pretensioner(s), if equipped, should be inspected for wear and damage and replaced as necessary. Refer to "Component Service" for replacement procedures.

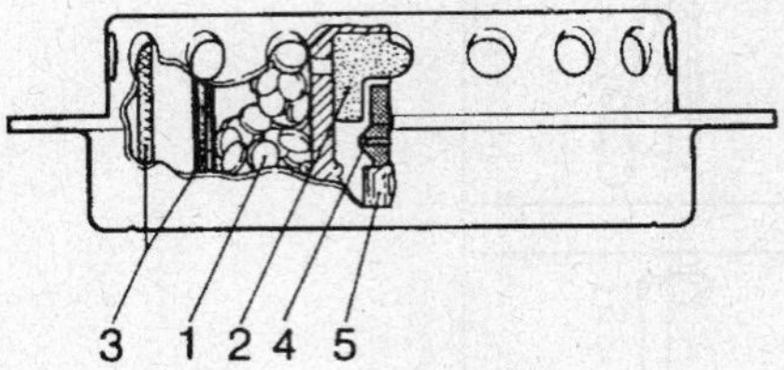

1 Fuel
2 Explosive charge
3 Filter
4 Electric detonator
5 Electrical connection

SA8019400036000X

Fig. 6 Air bag gas generator. 900 & 9000

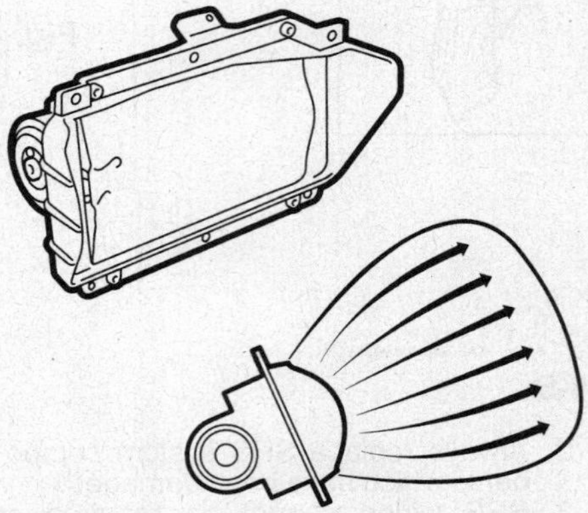

SA8019900067000X

Fig. 8 Passenger's air bag module. 9-3 & 9-5

9-3 & 9-5

The SRS must be inspected every 10 years. The SRS should be inspected for stored DTCs. Refer to "Diagnosis & Testing." The air bag module, steering wheel, contact roller unit, control module, and brackets, wiring harnesses and seat belt tensioner(s), if equipped, should be inspected for wear and damage and replaced as necessary. Refer to "Component Service" for replacement procedures.

WIRE HARNESS & CONNECTOR REPAIR

The SRS wiring harness should not be spliced. If wiring harness insulation is damaged, but the copper conductor is in satisfactory condition, the insulation may be replaced.

COMPONENT LOCATIONS

Refer to **Figs. 1 through 3,** for SRS component locations.

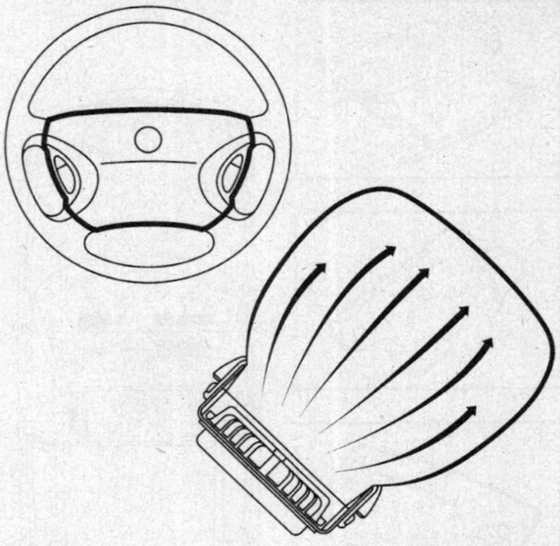

SA8019900066000X

Fig. 7 Driver's air bag module. 9-3 & 9-5

DIAGNOSIS & TESTING

Refer to **MOTOR's "Air Bag Manual"** for complete diagnosis and testing information.

COLLISION INSPECTION

900 & 9000

If SRS deployment has occurred, the air bag module, contact unit, control module or control module, front sensors and seat belt pre-tensioner(s), if equipped, must be replaced. Refer to "Component Service" for replacement procedures. The SRS wiring circuit, sensor brackets, steering wheel, steering column bracket, steering shaft, knee bolster and cable should be inspected for damage and replaced as necessary.

Wear safety goggles and protective gloves during removal of a deployed air bag. Place air bag in a tightly sealed plastic bag. The sealed plastic bag should then be placed with automotive scrap. Vehicle interior and A/C, vent, defroster and heater ducts should be vacuumed.

The air bag surface may contain deposits of sodium hydroxide, a by-product of the gas generated during deployment. Because sodium hydroxide is irritating to the skin, wash your hands in mild soap solution and lukewarm water after handling a detonated air bag. If sinus or throat irritation is encountered during air bag removal, exit vehicle and breathe fresh air. If skin irritation is encountered, flush effected area with cool water. If sinus, throat, skin or any other type of irritation continues, consult a physician.

9-3 & 9-5

On vehicles which have experienced an air bag system deployment, certain SRS components must be replaced. To determine which SRS components require replacement, refer to the "General Information" section located at the front of this manual.

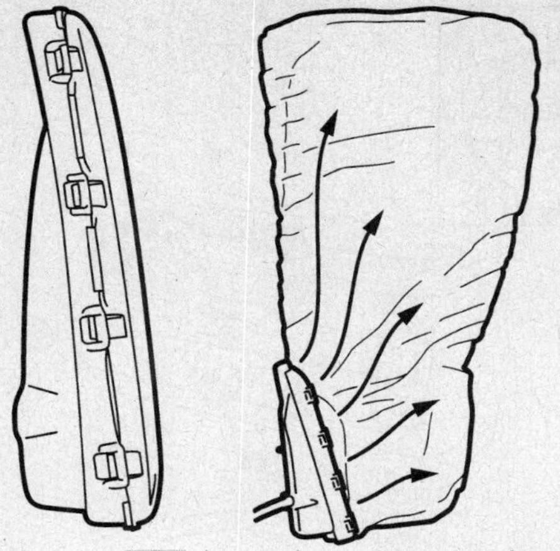

SA8019900068000X

Fig. 9 Side air bag module. 9-3 & 9-5

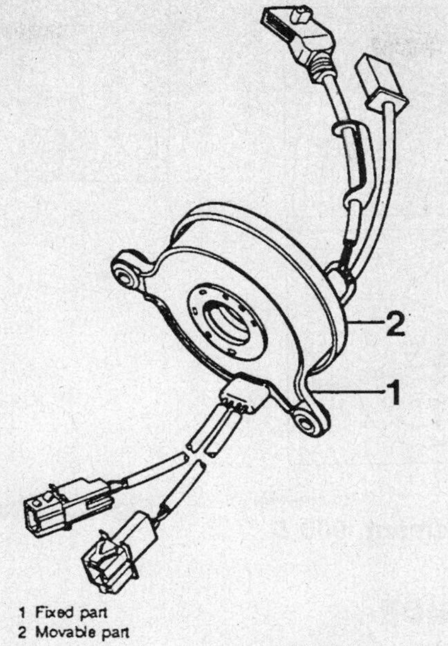

SA8019400037000X

Fig. 10 Contact unit. 900 & 9000

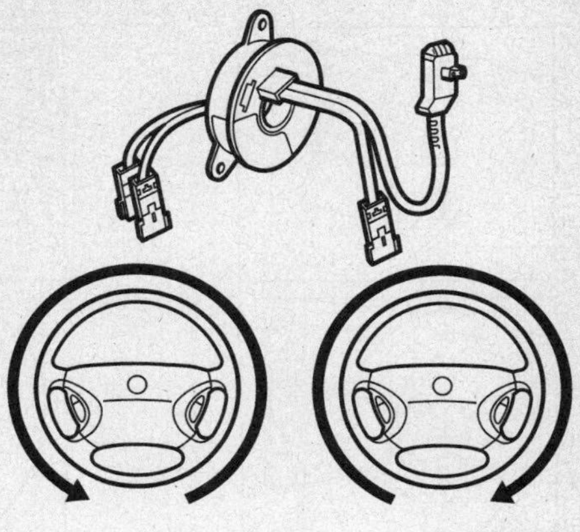

SA8019900069000X

Fig. 11 Contact roller unit. 9-3 & 9-5

The SRS wiring circuit, sensors and brackets, steering wheel, steering column bracket, steering shaft, knee bolster, seat belt tensioners and cable should be inspected for damage and replaced as necessary.

Wear safety goggles and protective gloves during removal of a deployed air bag. Place it in a tightly sealed plastic bag, then discard with automotive scrap. Vehicle interior and HVAC ducts should be vacuumed.

The air bag surface may contain deposits of sodium hydroxide, a by-product of the gas generated during deployment. Wash your hands in a mild soap and lukewarm water solution after handling a detonated air bag because sodium hydroxide is irritating to the skin. If sinus or throat irritation is encountered during air bag removal, exit vehicle and breathe fresh air. If skin irritation is encountered, flush affected area with cool water. Consult a physician if sinus, throat, skin or any other type of irritation continues.

After air bags have deployed, there are several other components which must also be replaced. Refer to **Figs. 2 and 3** for component locations. These include the steering wheel and column assembly with the driver's air bag module, the contact roller unit, the control module, all front seat belts which include tensioners, all rear seat belts which were in use when the impact occurred, and the side air bags with their sensor and backrest upholstery cover which deployed during the impact. If the passenger's air bag module has deployed the instrument panel must also be replaced.

If the seat belt tensioners have deployed, replace all front seat belts which include tensioners and all rear seat belts which were in use when the impact occurred.

The SRS control module can be used up to three times after the side air bags have been deployed, but the side impact sensor and backrest upholstery covers must be replaced.

Inspect the knee shield, SRS wiring harness and windshield for deformities and burn damage.

COMPONENT SERVICE

Prior to performing any service procedures, disarm SRS system as outlined under "Air Bag System Disarming & Arming." After a component has been replaced it may be necessary to clear the diagnostic trouble code from the control module memory.

It may be necessary to clear the DTCs from the control module memory after component has been installed.

Air Bag Module, Replace

DRIVER

900 & 9000

1. Disarm SRS as outlined under "Air Bag System Disarming & Arming."
2. Remove air bag module to steering wheel retaining screws, **Fig. 12.**
3. Disconnect air bag connector, then remove air bag module.
4. Reverse procedure to install. Tighten retaining screws to specifications.

9-3 & 9-5

1. Disarm SRS as outlined under "Air Bag System Disarming & Arming."
2. Remove round plugs on sides of steering wheel to reveal air bag module retaining screws.
3. Remove air bag module retaining screws, then lift module clear of steering wheel.
4. Disconnect air bag electrical connector, then remove air bag module.
5. Reverse procedure to install, noting the following:
   a. Tighten retaining screws to specifications.
   b. Turn ignition On and connect Tech2 or equivalent scan tool to DLC.
   c. Clear any DTCs that may be present.
   d. Turn ignition Off, then On again and wait at least 10 seconds.
   e. Diagnose any DTCs that may be present.

PASSENGER

9-3

1. Disarm SRS as outlined under "Air Bag System Disarming & Arming."
2. Remove glove compartment and disconnect glove box lamp.
3. Remove console side panel retaining screw, then the side panel.
4. Remove knee shield retaining screws, then the knee shield.
5. Remove floor and side air ducts.
6. Disconnect air bag electrical connector.
7. Remove safety band to steering wheel beam screw.
8. Remove six nuts holding air bag to instrument panel.
9. Carefully lift passenger's air bag module from instrument panel.
10. Reverse procedures to install, noting the following:
    a. Ensure no foreign objects are lodged between air bag module and instrument panel before placing module into position.
    b. Route all wiring to avoid chafing and pinching.
    c. Tighten all fasteners to specifications.
    d. Turn ignition On and connect Tech2 or equivalent scan tool to DLC.
    e. Clear any DTCs that may be present.
    f. Turn ignition Off, then On again and wait at least 10 seconds.
    g. Diagnose any DTCs that may be present.

9-5

1. Disarm SRS as outlined under "Air Bag System Disarming & Arming."
2. Remove instrument panel as outlined under "Instrument Panel, Replace."
3. Remove passenger's air bag module to instrument panel retaining nuts.

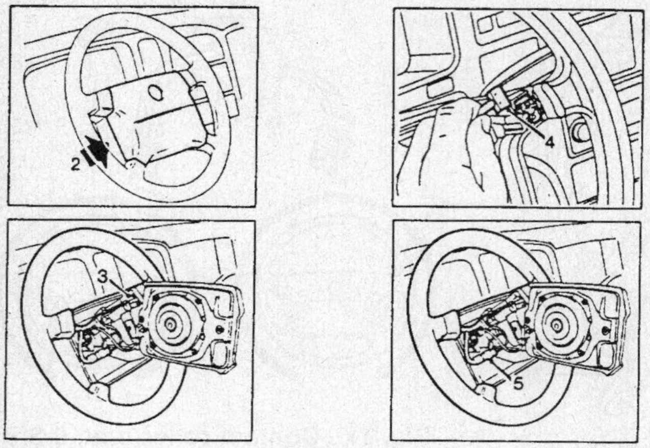

SA8019400049000X

Fig. 12 Driver air bag module replacement. 900 & 9000

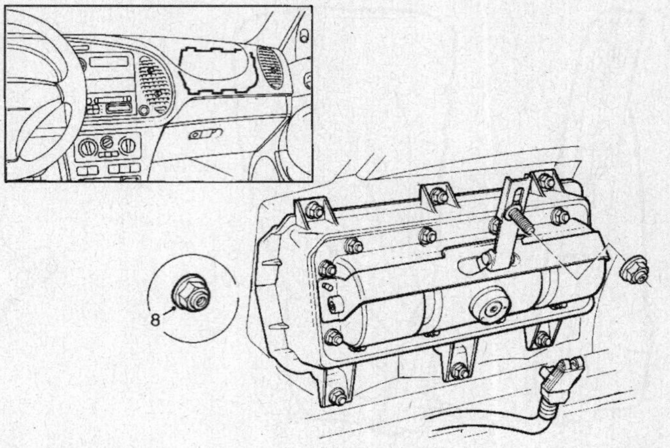

SA8019400050000X

Fig. 13 Passenger air bag module replacement. 900

4. Carefully separate air bag module from panel.
5. Reverse procedure to install, noting the following:
   a. Tighten fasteners to specifications.
   b. Turn ignition On and connect Tech2 or equivalent scan tool to DLC.
   c. Clear any DTCs that may be present.
   d. Turn ignition Off, then On again and wait at least 10 seconds.
   e. Diagnose any DTCs that may be present.

900

1. Disarm SRS as outlined under "Air Bag System Disarming & Arming."
2. Remove glove box lid, then remove and disconnect clove box lamp.
3. Remove screws and push clips retaining glove box, then remove glove box.
4. Disconnect air bag connector **Fig 13.**
5. Remove nut retaining air bag stay to support member, then remove nuts holding air bag to instrument panel.
6. Reverse procedures to install, noting the following:
   a. Tighten nuts to specifications.
   b. Use a suitable sealing compound on right upper and left lower nuts.

9000

1. Disarm air bag system as outlined under "Air Bag System Disarming & Arming."
2. Remove trim caps and retaining screws for lower cover, **Fig. 14.**
3. Pry out lower cover clips using trim tool No. 82 92 997, or equivalent, then remove cover.
4. Disconnect air bag connector.
5. Remove air bag mounting screws, then grasp air bag at rear and pull assembly from instrument panel. Trim panel also has mounting clips.
6. Reverse procedures to install, noting the following:
   a. Ensure all trim clips are firmly seated.
   b. Tighten screws to specifications.

SIDE

9-3 & 9-5

Removal

1. Move seat as far forward as possible, then remove two seat track rear retaining bolts.
2. Move seat as far rearward as possible, then remove two seat track front retaining bolts.
3. Disarm SRS as outlined under "Air Bag System Disarming & Arming."
4. Tilt seat back, cut cable tie and disconnect 29-pin electrical connector under seat.
5. Lift seat assembly out of vehicle.
6. Remove lower upholstery retaining batten.
7. Remove stiffening board from backrest upholstery.
8. **On 9-3 models,** proceed as follows:
   a. Disconnect air bag electrical connector from 29-pin electrical connector
   b. Note routing details of under seat wiring, then cut cable tie.
   c. Fold rear portion of seat backrest cover off to sides.
   d. Remove lumbar support adjuster.
9. **On all models,** fold rear edge portion of seat backrest frame off to sides.
10. Disconnect two wire rods which retain front lining at lower rear edge.
11. Unhook felt cover on air bag side of backrest hinge.
12. Remove upholstery retaining strip along edge of rear of backrest frame.
13. **On 9-3 models,** remove plastic coated resistance spring.
14. **On all models,** note routing details of side air bag wiring, then remove three side air bag retaining nuts.
15. Carefully remove side air bag module from seat assembly.

Installation

1. Carefully install side air bag module into seat assembly, ensuring wiring is properly routed. Tighten three nuts to specifications.
2. **On 9-3 models,** note remaining plastic coated resistance spring's installation details, then install its opposite in proper fashion.
3. **On all models,** follow removal procedure in reverse order to assemble seatback.
4. Carefully install seat assembly into vehicle.
5. Tighten seat track mounting bolts to specifications.
6. Turn ignition On and connect Tech2 or equivalent scan tool to DLC.
7. Clear any DTCs that may be present.
8. Turn ignition Off, then On again and wait at least 10 seconds.
9. Diagnose any DTCs that may be present.

Contact Unit, Replace

900

REMOVAL

1. Disarm SRS as outlined under "Air Bag System Disarming & Arming."
2. Remove air bag module as outlined under "Air Bag Module, Replace."
3. Position front wheels in straight-ahead position, then disconnect horn connector.
4. Remove steering wheel, then both steering column covers.
5. Disconnect connectors for horn and contact unit, **Fig. 15.**
6. Remove contact unit retaining screws.
7. Remove contact unit.

INSTALLATION

1. Remove transit safety, if any, from contact unit.
2. Install contact unit on bracket, then connect electrical connectors.
3. Install and tighten mounting screws to specifications.
4. Install both steering column covers.
5. Set contact unit to center position as follows:
   a. Ensure front wheels are in straight-ahead position.
   b. Turn contact unit clockwise as far

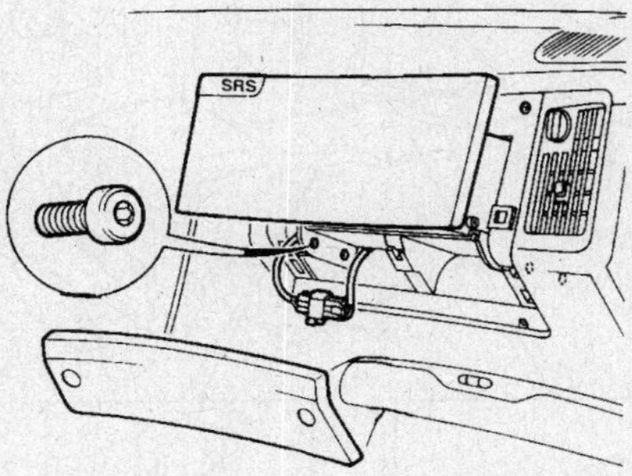

SA8019400051000X

Fig. 14 Passenger air bag module replacement. 9000

as possible, then turn counterclockwise two and one half turns.

6. Install steering wheel. **Torque** nut to 24–32 ft. lbs.
7. Connect horn connector.
8. Install air bag module as outlined under "Air Bag Module, Replace."
9. Arm SRS as outlined under "Air Bag System Disarming & Arming."

9000

1. Disarm SRS as outlined under "Air Bag System Disarming & Arming."
2. Remove air bag module as outlined under "Air Bag Module."
3. Position front wheels in straight-ahead position, then disconnect horn connector.
4. Remove steering wheel, then steering column covers.
5. Disconnect horn connector, then cut strap and disconnect contact unit connector.
6. Remove contact unit mounting screws, then the contact unit, **Fig. 15.**
7. Reverse procedure to install. Adjust contact unit (coil spring) as follows:
   a. Ensure front wheels are in straight-ahead position.
   b. Rotate contact unit clockwise to end position, then rotate counterclockwise then number of turns listed on label.

Contact Roller Unit, Replace

9-3

REMOVAL

1. Ensure front wheels are in straight-ahead position.
2. Disarm SRS as outlined under "Air Bag System Disarming & Arming."
3. Remove driver's air bag module as outlined under "Air Bag Module, Replace."
4. Ensure front wheels are still in straight-ahead position.
5. **Steering wheel tends to separate quickly from tapered shaft. Prevent contact roller unit and leads from catching on wheel.**
6. Loosen steering wheel retaining nut up to last outer threads, then pull wheel up to that point.
7. Remove steering wheel retaining nut, then carefully lift off steering wheel.
8. Remove steering column upper and lower covers.
9. Remove two coil spring attaching screws.
10. Disconnect leads from hook and connectors.
11. Remove contact roller unit.

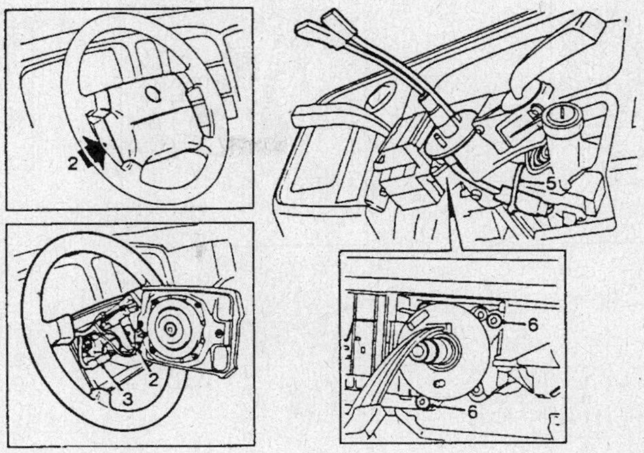

SA8019400052000X

Fig. 15 Contact roller unit replacement. 900

INSTALLATION

1. Install contact roller unit into position, then connect electrical connectors.
2. Install and tighten mounting screws.
3. Install both steering column covers.
4. New contact roller units are already centered and held in place with a safety catch, but an old unit being installed again will require centering as follows:
   a. Ensure front wheels are still in straight-ahead position.
   b. Turn contact roller unit clockwise until sluggish resistance is apparent.
   c. Turn counterclockwise two turns, plus distance remaining until electrical leads are at 12 o'clock position.
5. Ensure electrical connectors and wiring are secure but not pinched.
6. Install steering wheel. Tighten retaining nut to specifications.
7. Install air bag module as outlined under "Air Bag Module, Replace."
8. Arm SRS as outlined under "Air Bag System Disarming & Arming."

9-5

1. Disarm SRS as outlined under "Air Bag System Disarming & Arming."
2. Ensure ignition is turned Off.
3. Remove center console as follows:
   a. **On models equipped with manual transaxle,** pry up console shift boot.
   b. **On all models,** remove shift lever surround panel.
   c. Disconnect central locking switch electrical connector.
   d. Disconnect electrical connectors at seat heater switches and lighter.
   e. Remove rear portion of console by lifting straight up, then disconnect all related electrical connectors.
   f. Apply parking brake, place manual transaxle in Reverse or automatic transaxle in Park, then remove ignition key.
   g. Remove theft deterrent cover from ignition lock, then disconnect electrical connector.
   h. Place key in ignition and transaxle in Neutral.
   i. Disconnect power window switch electrical connectors.
   j. Remove upper portion of console retaining screws, then the upper portion.
   k. Fold back carpeting and remove two front console to floor retaining screws. These are located on sides of console.
   l. Remove two rear console to floor retaining screws.
   m. Carefully lift console out of vehicle.
4. Disconnect control module electrical connector.
5. Remove control module attaching nuts, then the control module.
6. Reverse procedure to install.

Front Sensors, Replace

9000

1. Disarm SRS as outlined under "Air Bag System Disarming & Arming."
2. **On lefthand side,** position electrical distribution box aside.
3. **On both sides,** cut retaining strap and disconnect connector.
4. Using Torx bit 84 71 120, or equivalent, remove sensor, **Fig. 16.**
5. Reverse procedure to install, noting the following:
   a. Ensure a good ground is obtained for sensor.
   b. Lubricate threads of new mounting screw with silicone dielectric compound or other suitable lubricant

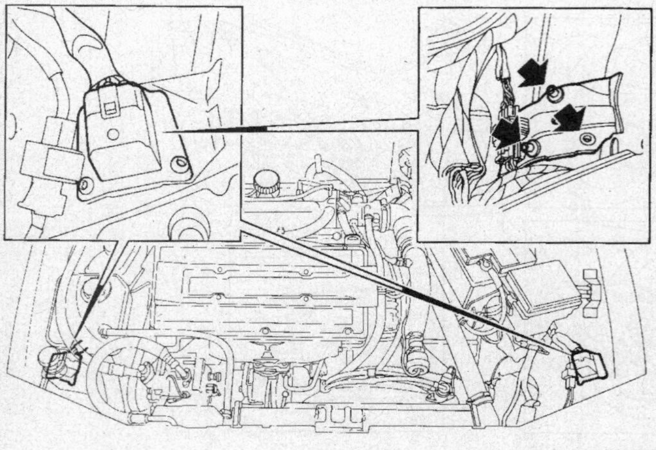

Fig. 16 Front sensor replacement. 9000

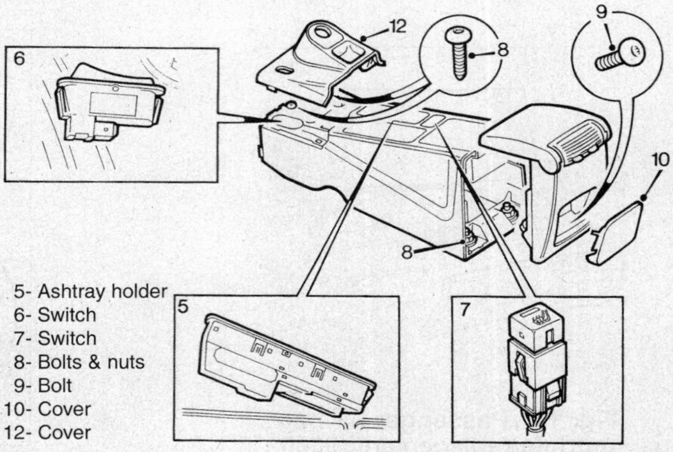

Fig. 17 Center console replacement. 9-3 & 900

having good conductivity and high viscosity.

c. Install sensor with arrow markings on sensor pointing forward.
d. Tighten attaching screws to specifications.

Control Module, Replace

Use care when handling control module as it is sensitive to static electricity. Do not touch or allow foreign objects to come in contact with connector pins.

9-3 & 900

REMOVAL

1. Disarm SRS as outlined under "Air Bag System Disarming & Arming."
2. Apply parking brake.
3. Remove center console as follows:
   a. Remove immobilizing unit from console and disconnect its electrical connector.
   b. Remove ignition switch cover by loosening rear edge first, next the front, then disengaging the front, **Fig. 17.**
   c. Disconnect ignition switch lamp electrical connector.
   d. Remove console retaining screws.
   e. Remove rear ashtray and cover plate.
   f. Remove rear cover screw and rear cover.
   g. Remove rear retaining nuts, then loosen center console by lifting and pulling back slightly.
   h. Disconnect all electrical connectors for interior lamps, heated seats and power windows.
   i. Lift out center console.
4. Disconnect SRS control module electrical connector (14), **Fig. 18.** and ground connections.
5. Remove control module bracket mounting screws (15), then carefully lift module out of vehicle.

INSTALLATION

1. Ensure arrow markings on control module face forward.
2. Tighten attaching fasteners securely.
3. If a new module has been installed it will require programming. Proceed as follows:
   a. Connect Tech2 or an equivalent scan tool to DLC.
   b. Select proper model and year of vehicle.
   c. Advance to SRS DIRECTORY and select PROGRAMMING.
   d. Read control module configuration with respect to passenger's air bag module.
   e. Adjust settings as required.
   f. Turn ignition On and record any DTCs.

9-5

1. Disarm SRS as outlined under "Air Bag System Disarming & Arming."
2. Ensure ignition is turned Off.
3. **On models equipped with manual transaxle,** pry up console shift boot.
4. **On all models,** remove shift lever surround panel.
5. Disconnect central locking switch electrical connector.
6. Disconnect electrical connectors at seat heater switches and lighter.
7. Remove rear portion of console by lifting straight up, then disconnect all related electrical connectors.
8. Apply parking brake, place manual transaxle in Reverse or automatic transaxle in Park, then remove ignition key.
9. Remove theft deterrent cover from ignition lock, then disconnect electrical connector.
10. Place key in ignition and transaxle in Neutral.
11. Disconnect power window switch electrical connectors.
12. Remove upper portion of console retaining screws, then the upper portion.
13. Fold back carpeting and remove two front console to floor retaining screws. These are located on sides of console.
14. Remove two rear console to floor retaining screws.
15. Carefully lift console out of vehicle.
16. Disconnect control module electrical connector.
17. Remove control module attaching nuts, then the control module.
18. Reverse procedure to install.

9000

1. Disarm SRS as outlined under "Air Bag System Disarming & Arming."
2. Remove carpet panel from passenger side of center console, **Fig. 19.**
3. Disconnect connector from control module.
4. Remove control module attaching screws, then the control module.
5. Reverse procedure to install. Tighten attaching screws to specifications.

Seat Belt Pretensioner, Replace

9-3

1. Position front seat forward, then position seat backrest forward.
2. Disarm SRS as outlined under "Air Bag System Disarming & Arming."
3. Disengage front and rear door scuff plate clips, then remove the scuff plates.
4. Remove B-pillar door seals.
5. Disengage clip retaining seat belt to front seat. A bent screwdriver can be inserted into the retainer hole to depress the clip.
6. Disengage air vent grille clips, then remove air vent grille.
7. Remove upper B-pillar trim, then detract belt from trim. Grip top edge of trim and carefully pull downward while bending fasteners with a suitable tool.
8. Detach lower B-pillar trim clips, then remove trim.
9. Detach upper outer pillar trim clips, then the trim.
10. Remove belt adjuster plate upper retaining bolt, then guide plate out from lower edge.
11. Remove belt link.
12. Disconnect seat belt tensioner electrical connector.
13. Remove the seat belt inertia reel screw.
14. Remove the belt roller and tensioner.

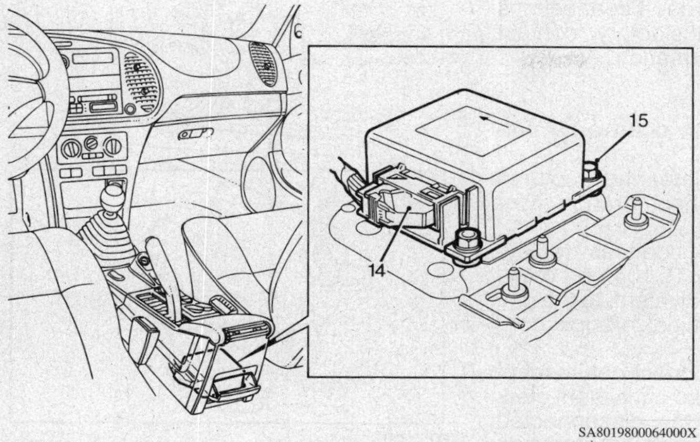

SA8019800064000X

Fig. 18 Control module replacement. 9-3 & 900

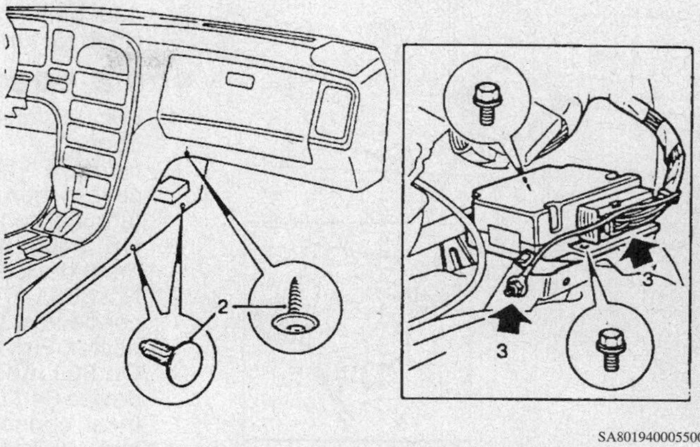

SA8019400055000X

Fig. 19 Control module replacement. 9000

15. Reverse procedure to install, noting the following:
    a. After new belt and tensioner are securely installed, turn ignition On and connect Tech2 or equivalent scan tool to DLC.
    b. Clear any DTCs that may be present.
    c. Turn ignition Off, then On again and wait at least 10 seconds.
    d. Diagnose any DTCs that may be present.
    e. Tighten all fasteners to specifications.

9-5

1. Position front seat forward, then position seat backrest forward.
2. Disarm SRS as outlined under "Air Bag System Disarming & Arming."
3. Pull B-pillar trim away and lift out of air duct.
4. Disconnect seat belt bracket in front seat by pushing catch inward using a suitable angled screwdriver.
5. Remove seat belt guide, then pass belt through B-pillar trim.
6. Disconnect electrical connector at seat belt tensioner.
7. Remove seat belt tensioner retaining screws, then the tensioner.
8. Reverse procedure to install. Tighten attaching bolts to specifications.

900 & 9000

1. Disarm SRS as outlined under "Air Bag System Disarming & Arming."
2. Position front seat forward, then position the seat backrest forward.
3. Remove door sill plate.
4. Release bottom edge of seat belt guide cover, then remove guide cover.
5. Remove seat belt guide from B-pillar.
6. Remove seat belt guide from B-pillar, then remove trim panel.
7. Remove cover from seat belt pretensioner.
8. Disconnect connector at seat belt pretensioner.
9. Remove seat belt reel attaching bolts, then remove seat belt reel.
10. Reverse procedure to install, noting the following:
    a. Tighten attaching bolts to specifications.

Side Impact Sensor, Replace

9-3

REMOVAL

1. Disarm SRS as outlined under "Air Bag System Disarming & Arming."
2. Remove door inner trim panel.
3. Carefully remove door water shield.
4. Drill out sensor retaining rivets (4), **Fig. 20,** then clean away all metal chips and shavings.
5. Lift side impact sensor (5) out of door, then disconnect electrical connector (6).

INSTALLATION

1. Clean away any remaining metal chips and shavings.
2. Plug electrical connector into side impact sensor.
3. Mount sensor into position and secure with pop rivets.
4. Install door water shield.
5. Install door inner trim panel.
6. Turn ignition On and connect Tech2 or equivalent scan tool to DLC.
7. Clear any DTCs that may be present.
8. Turn ignition Off, then On again and wait at least 10 seconds.
9. Diagnose any DTCs that may be present.

9-5

REMOVAL

1. Disarm SRS as outlined under "Air Bag System Disarming & Arming."
2. Remove door trim molding clips, then the molding.
3. Disconnect door mirror electrical connector.
4. Remove door inside handle, cover piece and retaining screw.
5. Remove door inner trim panel. Use caution when lifting it off lock buttons.
6. Remove door lamp from trim panel.
7. **On driver's door,** disconnect tailgate release and fuel filler cap release electrical connectors.
8. Carefully remove door water shield (7), **Fig. 21.**
9. Drive out sensor retaining rivet center pins (8) with a hammer and pin punch.
10. Drill out rivets, then clean away all metal chips and shavings.
11. Lift side impact sensor (10) out of door, then disconnect electrical connector (11).

INSTALLATION

1. Clean away any remaining metal chips and shavings.
2. Plug electrical connector into side impact sensor.
3. Mount sensor into position and secure with pop rivets.
4. Install door water shield.
5. Install door inner trim panel.
6. Turn ignition On and connect Tech2 or equivalent scan tool to DLC.
7. Clear any DTCs that may be present.
8. Turn ignition Off, then On again and wait at least 10 seconds.
9. Diagnose any DTCs that may be present.

Air Bag Or Seat Belt Pretensioner Assembly Disposal

In the event an air bag assembly or seat belt pretensioner must be discarded, it is recommended that the unit be triggered without removing the system from the vehicle.

Wear ear protection, safety goggles and protective gloves during deploying and removal of a deployed air bag or tensioner. Place deployed components in a tightly sealed plastic bag, then discard with automotive scrap. Vehicle interior and all HVAC ducts should be vacuumed.

The air bag surface may contain deposits of sodium hydroxide, a by-product of the gas generated during deployment. Because sodium hydroxide is irritating to the skin, wash your hands in a mild soap and lukewarm water solution after handling a detonated air bag or tensioner. If sinus or throat irritation is encountered during air bag removal, exit vehicle and breathe fresh air. If skin irritation is encountered, flush affected area with cool water. If any type of irritation continues, consult a physician.

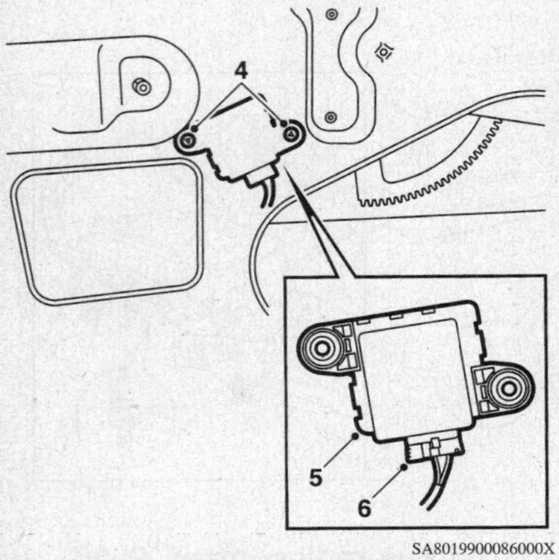

Fig. 20 Side impact sensor. 9-3

An air bag unit that has not been deployed must be deployed prior to disposal.

AIR BAG DEPLOYMENT

9-3 & 9-5

1. Locate vehicle in an open area outdoors.
2. Disconnect battery ground cable.
3. For driver's air bag proceed as follows:
   a. Remove bottom steering column cover, then disconnect orange two-terminal air bag electrical connector.
   b. Connect deployment tool No. 84 71 104 and cable No. 86 11 477, or equivalents, to disconnected driver's air bag electrical connector, **Figs. 22 and 23.**
4. For passenger's air bag proceed as follows:
   a. **On 9-3 models,** remove glove compartment, then disconnect passenger's air bag module electrical connector.
   b. **On 9-5 models,** remove lower instrument panel section with air ducts.
   c. **On all models,** disconnect passenger's air bag electrical connector.
   d. Connect deployment harness tool No. 86 11 469 and deployment tool No. 84 71 104, or equivalents to passenger's air bag electrical connector.
5. Route leads through door opening.
6. Ensure all vehicle windows and doors are closed after connecting deployment tool.
7. Connect deployment tool to a fully charged 12 volt battery positioned approximately 30 ft. from vehicle. **Ensure no people, animals or objects are within 30 feet of vehicle.**
8. Press deployment tool button to detonate air bag. When air bag detonation occurs, an explosion will be heard and white smoke will be visible in passenger compartment. **After air bag has detonated, allow SRS system components 30 minutes to cool before handling.**
9. If air bag fails to detonate, disconnect deployment tool from battery and carefully inspect connections. Also inspect battery state of charge. If connections and battery are satisfactory, contact Saab for further information.

900 & 9000

1. Locate vehicle in an open area outdoors.
2. Remove bottom steering column cover, then disconnect orange two-terminal connector.
3. **On 9000 models,** connect deployment device No. 84 71 104 and cable No. 86 11 477, or equivalent, to the disconnected two terminal orange connector, **Fig. 24.**
4. **On 900 models,** connect deployment device 84 71 104 or an equivalent electrical connector to the disconnected two terminal orange connector, **Fig. 24.**
5. **On all models,** ensure all vehicle windows and doors are closed after connecting deployment device.
6. Connect deployment device to a fully charged 12 volt battery positioned approximately 30 ft. from vehicle. **Ensure no people, animals or objects are within 30 feet of the vehicle.**
7. Press deployment tool button to detonate air bag. When air bag detonation occurs, an explosion will be heard and white smoke will be visible in passenger compartment. **After air bag has detonated, allow SRS system components 30 minutes to cool before handling.**
8. If air bag fails to detonate, disconnect deployment device from battery and carefully inspect connections. Also inspect battery state of charge. If connections and battery are satisfactory, contact Saab for further information.

SEAT BELT PRETENSIONER DEPLOYMENT

9-3 & 9-5

1. Locate vehicle in an open area outdoors.
2. Position front seat forward, then position seat backrest forward.
3. Disconnect battery ground cable.
4. Remove B-pillar interior trim panel using a suitable screwdriver, then position panel aside.
5. Disconnect electrical connector at tensioner.
6. Connect deployment harness (A) No. 86 11 469, and deployment tool (B) No. 84 71 104, or equivalents to tensioner, **Fig. 25.**
7. Place B-pillar trim panel against B-pillar.
8. Ensure seat belt runs freely through guide and can be taken up approximately seven inches without causing damage.
9. Ensure all doors and windows are closed.
10. Route outer end of deployment tool harness to a fully charged 12 volt battery.
11. **Ensure no people, animals or objects are within 30 feet of vehicle.**
12. Depress deployment tool button.
13. Disconnect deployment tool from vehicle battery. **After seat belt tensioner has detonated, allow SRS system components 30 minutes to cool before handling.**
14. If tensioner fails to detonate, disconnect deployment tool from battery and carefully inspect connections. Also inspect battery state of charge. If connections and battery are satisfactory, contact Saab for further information.

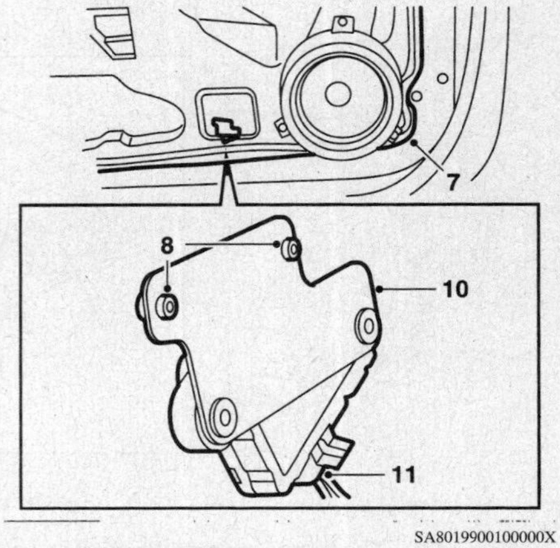

Fig. 21 Side impact sensor. 9-5

900 & 9000

1. Locate vehicle in an open area outdoors.
2. Position front seat forward, then position seat backrest forward.
3. Remove door sill plate.
4. Release bottom edge of seat belt guide cover, then remove guide cover.
5. Remove seat belt guide from B-pillar.
6. Remove seat belt guide from B-pillar, then remove trim panel.
7. Remove cover from seat belt pretensioner.
8. Disconnect connector at pretensioner.
9. **On 9000 models,** connect deployment device No. 84 71 104 and cable No. 86 11 469 to tensioner, **Fig. 26.**
10. **On all other models,** connect deployment device harness No. 85 80 052, or equivalent, to tensioner, **Fig. 26.**
11. Position upper seat belt guide on mounting. Ensure seat belt runs freely through guide and can be taken up approximately seven inches without causing damage.
12. Route outer end of deployment device harness No. 85 80 052, or equivalent, to engine compartment.
13. Ensure all doors and windows are closed.
14. Connect deployment device harness to vehicle battery. Ensure vehicle battery is sufficiently charged and that nobody is inside vehicle.
15. While standing in front of vehicle, depress deployment device button.
16. Disconnect deployment device from vehicle battery. **After seat belt pretensioner has detonated, allow SRS system components 30 minutes to cool before handling.**

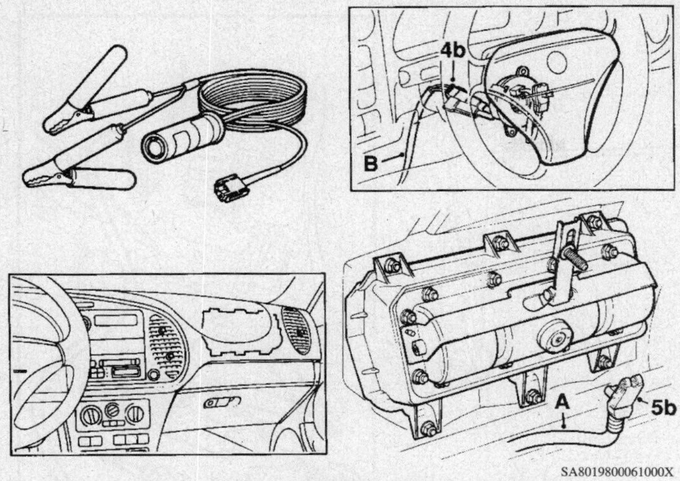

Fig. 22 Deployment tool & harness to air bag connections. 9-3

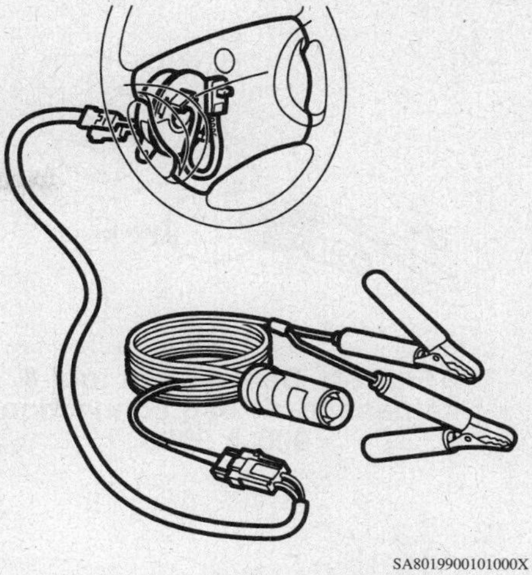

Fig. 23 Deployment tool & harness to air bag connections. 9-5

SIDE AIR BAG DEPLOYMENT

9-3

1. Locate vehicle in an open area outdoors.
2. Remove seat track mounting bolts.
3. Disconnect battery ground cable.
4. Ensure ignition is turned Off.
5. Rock seat back and forth.
6. Disconnect 29-pin electrical connector under seat.
7. Connect cable tool No. 86 12 343, or equivalent to 29-pin electrical connector.
8. Install seat track mounting bolts.
9. Connect cable tool No. 86 12 343 to deployment tool No. 84 71 104, or equivalents.
10. Run leads through door opening.
11. Ensure all vehicle windows and doors are closed after connecting deployment tool.
12. Connect deployment tool to a fully charged 12 volt battery positioned approximately 30 ft. from vehicle. **Ensure no people, animals or objects are within 30 feet of vehicle.**
13. Press deployment tool button to detonate air bag. When air bag detonation occurs, an explosion will be heard and white smoke will be visible in passenger compartment. **After air bag has detonated, allow SRS system components 30 minutes to cool before handling.**
14. If air bag fails to detonate, disconnect deployment tool from battery and carefully inspect connections. Also inspect battery state of charge. If connections and battery are satisfactory, contact Saab for further information.

9-5

1. Locate vehicle in an open area outdoors.
2. Disconnect battery ground cable.
3. Ensure ignition is turned Off.
4. Slice open seat backrest upholstery fabric.
5. Remove cardboard sheet located between fabric layers.
6. Continue slicing to access and disconnect side air bag electrical connector.
7. Connect cable tool No. 86 12 103, or equivalent to side air bag electrical connector.
8. Connect deployment tool No. 84 71 104 into cable tool No. 86 12 103, or equivalents.
9. Run leads through door opening.
10. Ensure all vehicle windows and doors are closed after connecting deployment tool.
11. Connect deployment tool to a fully charged 12 volt battery positioned approximately 30 ft. from vehicle. **Ensure no people, animals or objects are within 30 feet of vehicle.**
12. Press deployment tool button to detonate air bag. When detonation occurs, an explosion will be heard in passenger compartment. **After air bag has detonated, allow SRS system components 30 minutes to cool before handling.**
13. If air bag fails to detonate, disconnect deployment tool from battery and carefully inspect connections. Also inspect battery state of charge. If connections and battery are satisfactory, contact Saab for further information.

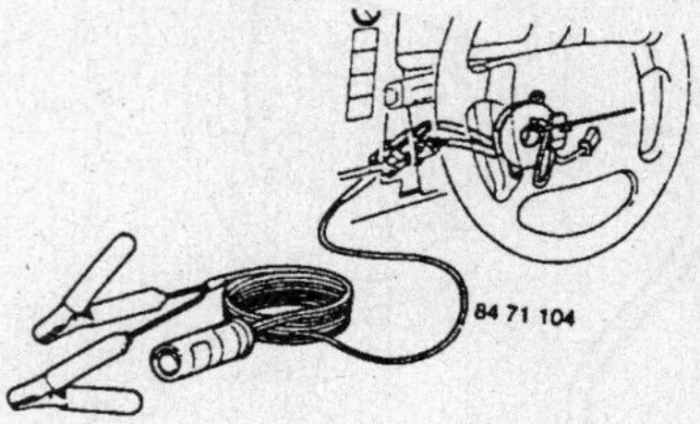

SA8019400056000X

Fig. 24 Deployment tool & harness to air bag connection. 900 & 9000

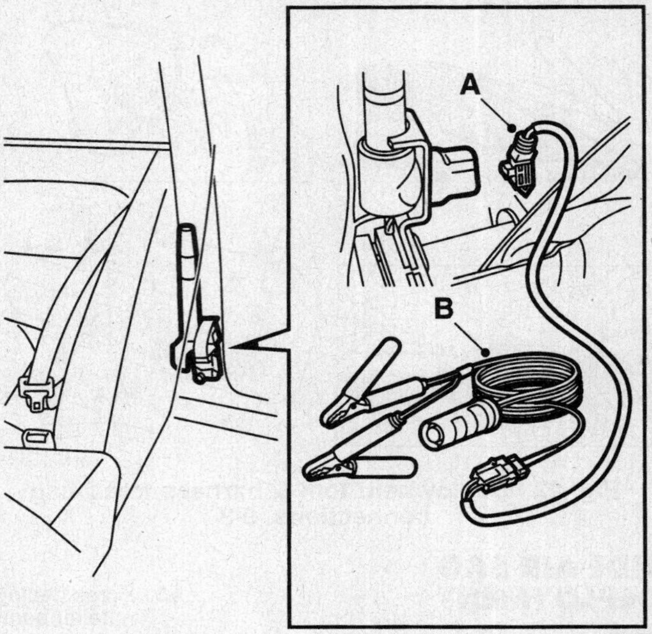

SA8019800063000X

Fig. 25 Deployment tool & harness connections for seat belt tensioner. 9-3 & 9-5

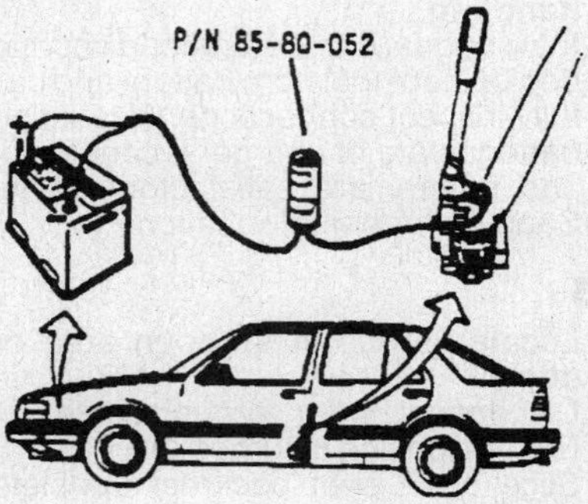

SA8019400057000X

Fig. 26 Deployment tool & harness to seat belt pretensioner connection. 900 & 9000

TIGHTENING SPECIFICATIONS

Year	Component	Torque/Ft. Lbs.
9-3		
1999–2001	Passenger's Front Air Bag Module Nuts	79①
	Safety Band To Steering Wheel Beam Screw	79①
	Seat Belt Adjusting Plate Bolt	18
	Seat Belt Inertia Reel Retaining Screws	33
	Seat Belt Tensioner Slide Rail Screws	33
	Seat Track To Floor Bolts	18
	Side Air Bag Module Nuts	57①
	Steering Wheel Retaining Nut	28
9-5		
1999–2001	Control Module Nuts	79①
	Driver's Front Air Bag Module Screws	63①
	Passenger's Front Air Bag Module Nuts	79①
	Seat Belt Guide At B-Pillar	33
	Seat Belt Reel Retaining Bolt	33
	Steering Column Lower Retaining Bolt	20
	Steering Column Pinch Bolt	25
	Steering Column Upper Retaining Bolts	20
	Steering Wheel Retaining Nut	29
900		
1998	Air Bag Module Retaining Screws	48–60①
	Control Module	60–72①
	Front Sensor	60–72①
	Steering Wheel Retaining Nut	24–32
9000		
1998	Air Bag Module Retaining Screws	48–60①
	Control Module	84①
	Front Sensor	72①
	Steering Wheel Retaining Nut	22
	Seat Belt Reel Retaining Bolt	19–50
	Seat Belt Guide At B-Pillar	18–29
	Seat Belt Anchor Point At Seat	19–50

① — Inch lbs.

Dash Panel Service

NOTE: On Air Bag Equipped Models, Refer To "Air Bag System Precautions" Located In The Front Of This Manual For System Disarming & Arming Procedures.

NOTE: Refer To "Dash Gauges" Section For Dash Panel Related Information.

INDEX

	Page No.
Dash Panel, Replace	7-82
9-3 & 900	7-82
9-5	7-83
9000	7-84
Precautions	7-82
Air Bag Systems	7-82
Battery Ground Cable	7-82
Radio Anti-Theft Lock	7-82

PRECAUTIONS

AIR BAG SYSTEMS

Refer to "Air Bag System Precautions" in the front of this manual for system Disarming and arming procedures.

RADIO ANTI-THEFT LOCK

Radio and cassette player are equipped with an electronic four-digit anti-theft lock. This four-digit code is programmed at manufacturing and cannot be changed. If the battery is disconnected for more than three minutes, if unit is removed or if otherwise cut off from power, the four-digit code must be entered with the quick-selection buttons as follows:

1. Turn radio on, then, when display shows "Code In," enter four-digit code with quick-selection buttons. If code is correct, last-tuned radio frequency is shown on display. If wrong digit has been entered by mistake, all four digits must be entered again. If code is wrong it stays on display.
2. If incorrect four-digit code has been entered, press Band button for more than three seconds to clear display. Display shows "Code In" and new attempt to enter correct code can be made.
3. If wrong code has been used three times in succession, four dashes appear on display and you must wait an hour with radio switched on before trying again.
4. To try again, hold Band button for at least three seconds. "Code In" should appear on display.
5. Correct code must be entered at first attempt, otherwise you must wait another hour with unit switched on before trying again.

BATTERY GROUND CABLE

Prior to service, disconnect battery ground cable and isolate as required.

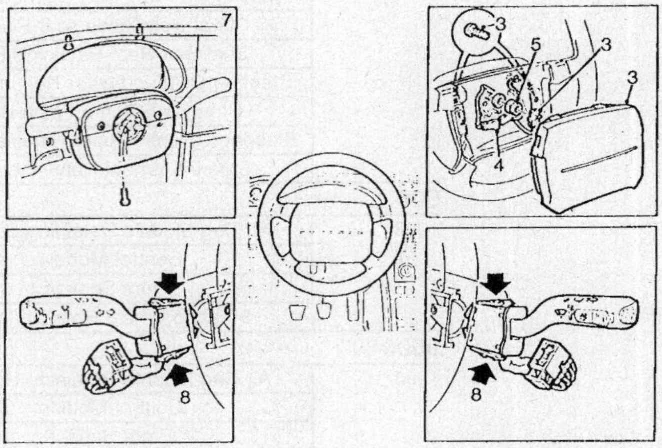

SA9149400002010X

Fig. 1 Instrument panel removal (Part 1 of 4). 9-3 & 900

DASH PANEL

REPLACE

9-3 & 900

1. Pull back steering wheel to full extent.
2. Remove air bag module screws from under side of steering wheel, then disconnect connector and remove module (3), **Fig. 1.**
3. Disconnect horn connector (4), then turn steering wheel so front wheels point straight ahead.
4. Loosen steering column nut (5) but do not remove.
5. Rock steering wheel loose, then pull out connectors and unscrew steering column nut.
6. Remove screws securing upper and lower sections of cowl, then the cowl (7).
7. Press in two clips on each mounting (8), then pull steering column controls straight out. Disconnect electrical connectors.
8. Remove diagnostic socket (9) located under lefthand side of dashboard.
9. Remove screws securing lower dashboard section (10), then the expanding rivets in front edge. To remove expanding rivets, press center pin further into rivet.
10. Release radio with forks (11), then remove.
11. Remove storage compartment (12), then the radio contact box (13), using screwdriver.
12. Remove auxiliary instrument panel (SID unit) with suitable extraction screws (14). Disconnect connector.
13. Remove light switch and headlamp beam control switch (15) by pressing out from behind.
14. Remove instrument panel retaining screws.
15. Loosen top of instrument panel. Ensure short side clips release and go clear.
16. Lift out panel, then disconnect all instrument panel electrical connectors.
17. Open glove compartment, then open

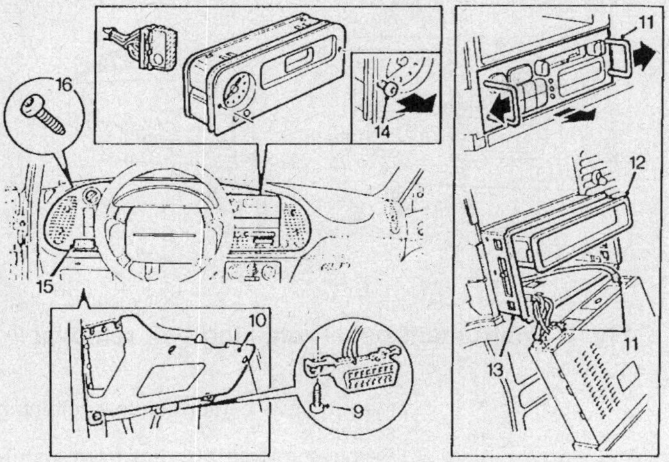

SA9149400002020X

Fig. 1 Instrument panel removal (Part 2 of 4). 9-3 & 900

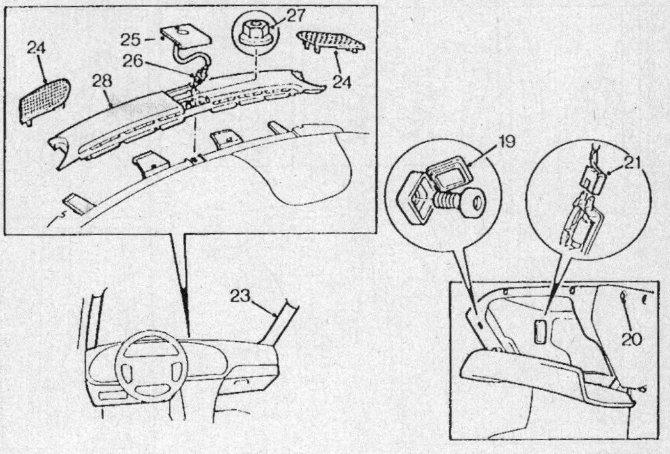

SA9149400002030X

Fig. 1 Instrument panel removal (Part 3 of 4). 9-3 & 900

covers to remove retaining screws (19).

18. Remove other glove compartment retaining screws (20), retaining bolt and expanding rivet in front edge and remove catch from bulkhead bracket.
19. Remove glove compartment and disconnect electrical connector for glove compartment lamp (21).
20. Pull A-pillar rubber moldings away and remove pillar trim (3).
21. Remove lefthand and righthand speaker grilles (24) using screwdriver.
22. Pull sun sensor surround (25) slightly rearward, then lift to remove.
23. **On models equipped with ACC and/or alarm,** disconnect sun sensor and/or alarm electrical connector (26).
24. **On all models,** remove defroster cover retaining nut (27), then the defroster by lifting rear edge straight up, then move sideways to clear lugs on dashboard.
25. Remove main instrument panel retaining screws (29), then pull straight out. Disconnect electrical connector (30).
26. Snip cable ties to release wiring harness underneath dashboard (31). Cable tie on passenger side can be opened.
27. Remove lefthand floor duct, then the two fuse holder retaining screws and fuse holder. Let fuse holder hang down.
28. Remove dashboard retaining bolts from A pillar (34).
29. Press out heating control panel (35) and remove expanding rivets securing dashboard to center console. Press about 3 mm into center pin, then remove.
30. Disconnect passenger side air bag electrical connector and nut securing stay (36).
31. Remove righthand and center air vent ducts.
32. Disconnect cable ties holding speaker wiring on righthand side, then the speaker connectors.
33. Remove retaining bolts from each side of speakers (39), then carefully remove dashboard.
34. Reverse procedure to install, noting the following:
    a. **Torque** passenger side air bag stay nut to 15 ft. lbs.
    b. When installing steering wheel, turn contact unit (coil spring) counterclockwise to end position, then back 2.5 turns.

9-5

1. Ensure front wheels are in straight-ahead position.
2. Disarm SRS as outlined under "Air Bag System Disarming & Arming."
3. Ensure ignition is turned Off.
4. Remove speaker grille retaining clips, then the speaker grilles.
5. Disconnect speaker electrical connectors, then carefully remove speakers.
6. Remove instrument panel front center cover.
7. **On models equipped with automatic climate control or theft deterrent system,** disconnect their electrical connectors and push sensor down through instrument panel.
8. **On all models,** remove glove compartment.
9. Remove air duct.
10. Ensure front wheels are in straight-ahead position.
11. Remove driver's front air bag module from steering wheel.
12. Disconnect electrical connectors at horn, speed control and radio controls.
13. Remove steering wheel retaining nut.
14. Carefully remove steering wheel.
15. Keep contact roller in alignment with steering column using suitable tape.
16. Remove DLC retaining screws, then the DLC.
17. Remove driver's side lower instrument panel and air duct retaining screws, then the panel.
18. Remove lower instrument panel foot lamp.
19. **On models equipped with manual transaxle,** pry up console shift boot panel.
20. **On all models,** remove console compartment or ashtray.
21. Remove two screws now visible at front of console shift boot panel.
22. Disconnect central locking switch electrical connector.
23. Lift up transaxle shift lever cover, then disconnect electrical connectors at seat heater switches and lighter.
24. Remove switch panel.
25. Remove fuse panel retaining screws, then the fuse panel.
26. Remove steering column closeout panel retaining screws, then the panel.
27. Remove instrument cluster retaining screws, then the cluster.
28. Remove driver's side air duct.
29. Disconnect passenger's front air bag module electrical connector.
30. Remove air bag retaining strap screw, then the strap.
31. Remove passenger's side front sill plate.
32. Fold back carpet, then remove protective plate in front of lower instrument panel mounting.
33. Remove rear portion of floor console by lifting it straight up, then disconnect all related electrical connectors.
34. Apply parking brake, place manual transaxle in Reverse or automatic transaxle in Park, then remove ignition key.
35. Remove theft deterrent cover from ignition lock, then disconnect electrical connector.
36. Place key in ignition and transaxle in Neutral.
37. Disconnect power window switch electrical connector.
38. Remove upper portion of console retaining screws, then the upper portion.
39. Using a suitable pencil, make alignment marks on metal console with alignment pin where it meets floor.
40. Loosen metal console retaining screws.
41. Remove two instrument panel upper retaining screws, then loosen the center nut.
42. Remove two instrument panel lower edge retaining screws.
43. Lift up on instrument panel and pull outward.

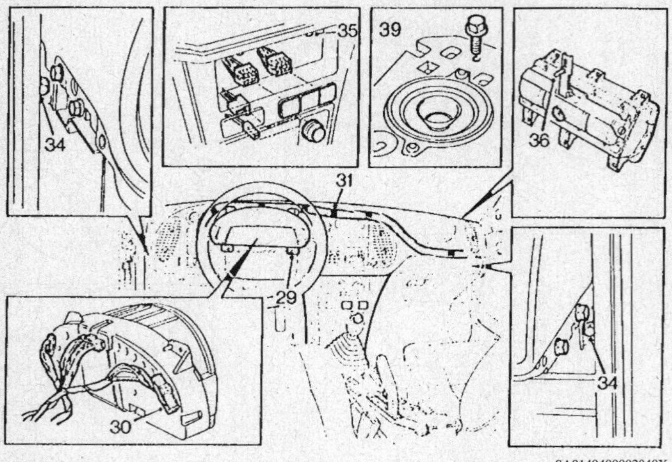

Fig. 1 Instrument panel removal (Part 4 of 4). 9-3 & 900

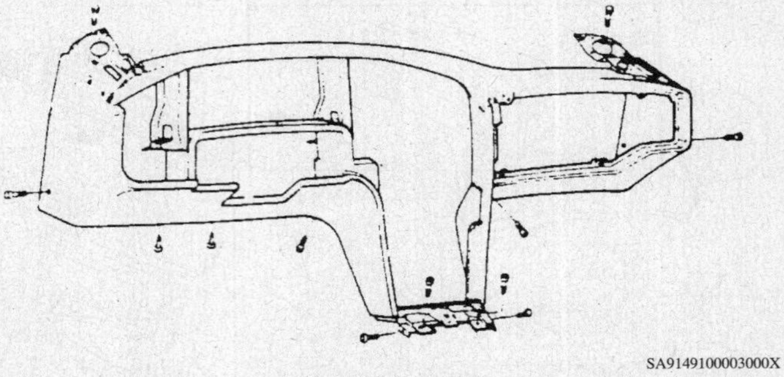

Fig. 2 Instrument panel retaining bolt removal. 9000

44. Carefully remove instrument panel from vehicle.
45. Reverse procedure to install, noting the following:
    a. Ensure no electrical connectors or wiring are pinched.
    b. Ensure no wiring or electrical connectors are trapped or resting on knee protection beam.
    c. Lift instrument panel into position at windshield.
    d. Ensure passenger's air bag module retaining strap passes over front of cross bar.
    e. **On models equipped with manual transaxle,** ensure shift boot is not trapped on pinched.
    f. **On all models,** tighten fasteners to specifications.
    g. Turn ignition On and connect Tech2, or equivalent, scan tool to DLC.
    h. Clear any DTCs that may be present.
    i. Turn ignition Off, then On again and wait at least 10 seconds.
    j. Diagnose any DTCs that may be present.

9000

1. Obtain radio anti-theft code as outlined under "Precautions."
2. Remove speaker grilles, then instrument panel top trim panel.
3. Remove glove compartment, then the air vent.
4. Remove fuse panel retaining screws, then pull it forward.
5. Remove ashtray and ashtray housing.
6. Remove steering column trim covers, then instrument panel attaching bolts located behind steering wheel.
7. Lift rubber insulator around gearshift, then remove center console retaining screws.
8. Remove middle air vent from instrument panel.
9. **On models with standard A/C,** remove control panel as follows:
    a. Press in four control panel retaining clips.
    b. Pull panel out of instrument panel.
    c. Disconnect ball joint and link rod for air distribution.
    d. Remove gear housing for temperature control valve and disconnect all electrical connectors.
10. **On models with automatic climate control,** pull rearward on climate control unit. Remove panel vent and disconnect electrical connectors.
11. **On all models,** remove steering wheel.
12. Remove instrument panel to instrument cluster attaching screws.
13. Remove trim from under instrument panel.
14. Remove all instrument panel retaining screws, **Fig. 2.**
15. Remove instrument panel from vehicle.

Steering Columns

NOTE: On Air Bag Equipped Models, Refer To "Air Bag System Precautions" Located In The Front Of This Manual For System Disarming & Arming Procedures.

INDEX

	Page No.
Precautions	7-85
Air Bag Systems	7-85
Battery Ground Cable	7-85
Radio Anti-Theft Lock	7-85
Steering Column, Replace	7-85
9-3 & 900	7-85
9-5	7-85
9000	7-86
Steering Column Service	7-87
9-3 & 900	7-87
9000	7-87

PRECAUTIONS

AIR BAG SYSTEMS

Refer to "Air Bag System Precautions" in the front of this manual for system disarming and arming procedures.

RADIO ANTI-THEFT LOCK

Radio and cassette player are equipped with an electronic four-digit anti-theft lock. This four-digit code is programmed at manufacturing and cannot be changed. If the battery is disconnected for more than three minutes, if unit is removed or if otherwise cut off from power, the four-digit code must be entered with the quick-selection buttons as follows:

1. Turn radio on, then, when display shows "Code In," enter four-digit code with quick-selection buttons. If code is correct, last-tuned radio frequency is shown on display. If wrong digit has been entered by mistake, all four digits must be entered again. If code is wrong it stays on display.
2. If incorrect four-digit code has been entered, press Band button for more than three seconds to clear display. Display shows "Code In" and new attempt to enter correct code can be made.
3. If wrong code has been used three times in succession, four dashes appear on display and you must wait an hour with radio switched on before trying again.
4. To try again, hold Band button for at least three seconds. "Code In" should appear on display.
5. Correct code must be entered at first attempt, otherwise you must wait another hour with unit switched on before trying again.

BATTERY GROUND CABLE

Prior to service, disconnect battery ground cable and isolate as required.

STEERING COLUMN

REPLACE

9-3 & 900

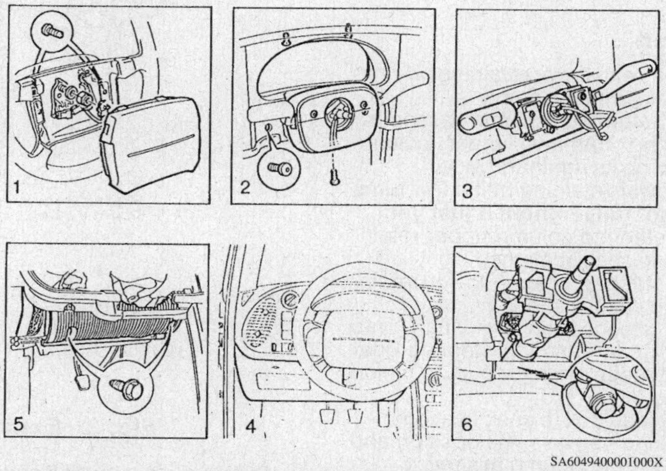

Fig. 1 Steering column replacement. 9-3 & 900

1. Remove steering wheel (1) as outlined under "Steering Wheel, Replace" under "Electrical."
2. Remove upper and lower sections of steering wheel cowling (2), then the coil spring and two retaining screws (3), **Fig. 1.** Disconnect electrical connectors.
3. Remove all switches from steering column as well as the fixing cable from bearing housing.
4. Remove lower part of dashboard (4), then the two knee protection member retaining bolts and member (5).
5. Remove locking bolt from steering column shaft joint and lift joint off pinion shaft (6).
6. Remove steering column assembly retaining bolt above ventilation duct, then the retaining nuts under instrument panel.
7. Remove steering column assembly.
8. Reverse procedure to install, noting the following:
   a. After fitting steering column shaft joint onto pinion shaft, lock adjusting lever.
   b. **Torque** steering wheel nut to 22 ft. lbs.

9-5

Removal

1. Place front wheels in straight-ahead position.
2. Disarm SRS as outlined under "Air Bag System Disarming & Arming."
3. Remove driver's front air bag module as outlined under "Driver's Air Bag Module, Replace."
4. Remove steering wheel retaining nut, then carefully remove wheel.
5. Release steering wheel adjustment lever.
6. Remove steering column upper and lower covers.
7. Remove multi-function switches and disconnect their electrical connectors.
8. Disconnect contact roller unit electrical connectors.
9. Remove contact roller unit and multi-function switch retainer.
10. Remove driver's side lower portion of instrument panel.
11. Remove steering column shaft to steering gear pinch bolt.
12. Press steering shaft upward, then extract it from steering gear. **Do not separate steering column shaft.**
13. Remove all wiring harness cable ties, then position harness aside.
14. Slide dust boot over steering wheel adjustment lever to allow the lever to come out same opening as steering column shaft.
15. Remove steering column assembly's upper mounting bolts.

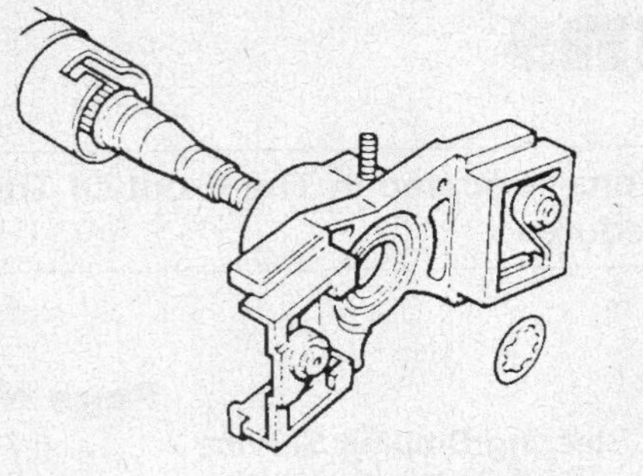

Fig. 2 Bearing housing & bolt replacement. 9-3 & 900

16. Carefully lift steering column out of vehicle.

Installation

1. Partially thread lower retaining bolt into steering column assembly.
2. Position steering column assembly with wiring harness under column shaft and on its righthand side.
3. Rotate lower retaining bolt a few turns **but do not fully tighten it just yet.**
4. Tighten steering column upper retaining bolts to specifications.
5. Tighten steering column lower retaining bolt to specifications.
6. Position steering column shaft onto steering gear, ensuring steering gear bolt fits properly into groove on pinion shaft.
7. Tighten pinch bolt to specifications.
8. Place wiring harness into position and tie it to steering column assembly.
9. Route dust boot over steering wheel adjustment lever, allowing lever to protrude from hole in boot.
10. Install contact roller unit and multi-function switch retainer with its groove facing upward.
11. Connect contact roller unit electrical connector.
12. Connect multi-function switch electrical connectors, then install switches.
13. Install steering upper and lower column covers.
14. Align contact roller unit as outlined under "Contact Roller Unit, Replace."
15. Install steering wheel with locating groove properly aligned. Tighten retaining nut to specifications.
16. Install driver's front air bag module.
17. Install lower portion of instrument panel.
18. Arm SRS as outlined under "Air Bag System Disarming & Arming."
19. Turn ignition On and connect Tech2 or equivalent scan tool to DLC.
20. Clear any DTCs that may be present.
21. Turn ignition Off, then On again and wait at least 10 seconds.
22. Diagnose any DTCs that may be present.

9000

Removal

1. Remove left front door sill plate, then, using ignition switch, stop wipers at straight up position.
2. Obtain radio anti-theft code as outlined under "Precautions."
3. Remove A pillar trim.
4. Remove speaker grilles, then disconnect burglar alarm LED connector.
5. Disconnect sun sensor connector, located in the right speaker grille, then remove gaskets.
6. Remove eight screws from top of dash panel. One screw is located behind rubber plug inside glove compartment door.
7. Remove glove compartment as follows:
   a. Drop glove compartment door to its lower position by prying out hinge arms to release stop cleats.
   b. Remove glove compartment retaining screws.
   c. Pull out glove compartment together with right ventilation air outlet. Pry outlet out carefully with screwdriver. Note positions of clips. Disconnect cable from glove compartment light and light switch.
8. Remove electrical distribution box mounting screw, then position box aside.
9. Remove ashtray, then bend down two locking tabs at top of ashtray holding. Pull out holder and disconnect electrical connectors.
10. Remove lower radio basket and disconnect electrical connections.
11. Remove upper radio basket and disconnect antenna cable and electrical connections.
12. Press out ACC control unit and disconnect connectors.
13. Remove steering wheel center pad (air bag module) mounting screws, then disconnect air bag electrical connector and remove center pad.
14. Position wheels in straight ahead position, then disconnect horn connector.
15. Remove steering wheel, then the top and bottom steering column covers.
16. Remove cover plates over interior temperature sensor and unused openings.
17. Carefully pry at edges of interior temperature sensor while pressing it inward.
18. Press out all switches and disconnect connectors.
19. Remove clock/DCC instrument, then disconnect connectors.
20. Remove direction indicator/light switch upper connector, then the washer/wiper switch connector. Remove stalk switches, then the two remaining direction indicator/light switch connectors.
21. Remove instrument panel as follows:
   a. Remove five instrument panel retaining screws, then the cover plate around gearshaft lever. One instrument panel screw is located under the rubber cover at gearshaft lever.
   b. Pull out instrument panel slightly, then carefully pry up plastic catches

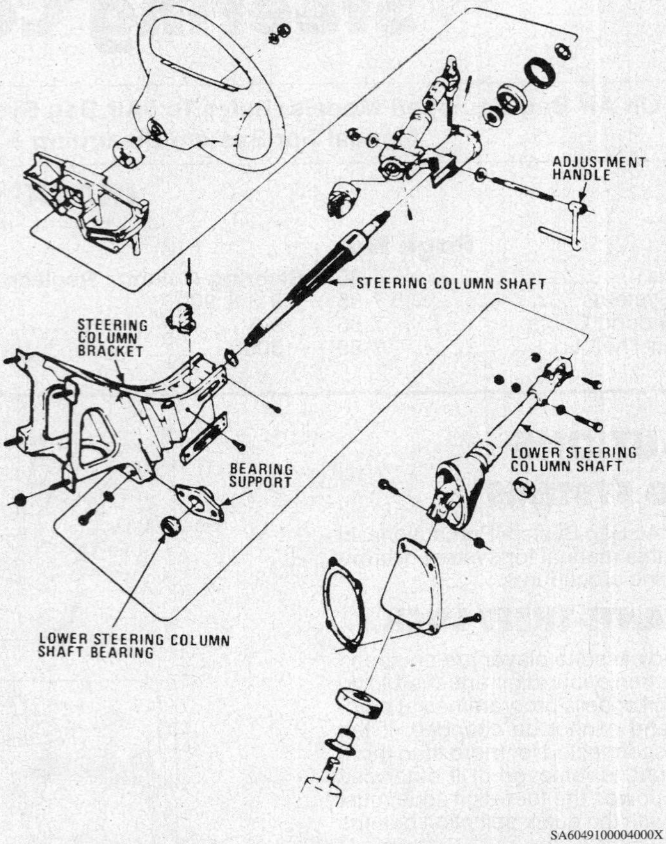

Fig. 3 Exploded view of steering column. 9000

locking panel to middle ventilation air outlet.
   c. Lift out panel in middle and pull it out of bracket at outer side.
22. Cut straps and separate connectors from horn and contact unit (coil spring).
23. Remove contact unit mounting screws, then the contact unit.
24. Remove stalk switch holder.
25. Remove instrument cluster (combined instrument) as follows:
   a. Remove cluster mounting screws.
   b. Remove hose to boost pressure gauge and turn cluster so its glass faces windshield.
   c. Remove connectors and rubber supports from cluster and lift out.
26. Remove left and right sound baffles, floor ducts and carpeted center console panels.
27. Remove screws holding side defroster outlets to dash panel, then disconnect speaker leads.
28. Remove burglar alarm control unit from panel and leave it hanging by its cables.
29. Remove dash panel retaining screws. Two screws are located under plastic cover on center console. Cut straps holding safety cable to panel.
30. Place gearshift lever in reverse position and carefully move lower part of dash panel. Move gearshift lever forward and lift dash panel out of vehicle.
31. Cut strap and remove left air duct, then the left ventilation air outlet.
32. Remove inner part of left ventilation air outlet.
33. Remove defroster outlet for left of windshield, then position wiring harness on left side of steering column aside.
34. Disconnect connector from ignition switch and remove strap securing cable. Remove strap securing wiring harness to right side of steering column.
35. Disconnect clamped joint and remove screw between universal joint and intermediate shaft.
36. Remove safety cable from bracket on tunnel. Detach cable from retainer on other side.
37. Remove holder for wiring harness, then the metal clips between steering column and dash panel crossmember. These clips do not have to be reinstalled.
38. Remove two screws holding electronic holder on steering column.
39. From engine compartment, remove cover from left portion of firewall space.
40. Lift plastic casing and remove clip holding ABS control unit. Remove strap and cable, then position control unit aside.
41. Position ABS electrical distribution box aside. Remove ABS control unit mounting bracket and position LH control unit aside.
42. Pry off plastic bushing that holds link rod to left wiper spindle, then remove steering column mounting nuts.
43. Disengage vacuum hose from steering column and lift column out of vehicle. Note location of washers.

Installation

Reverse removal procedure to install, noting the following:

1. **Torque** standard steering column nuts to 15–20 ft. lbs. and green chromated nuts to 11–16 ft. lbs.
2. Adjust clearance between upper intermediate shaft universal joint and steering column .118–.197 inch (3–5 mm), then **torque** universal joint bolt to 17–22 ft. lbs.
3. **Torque** safety cable to 1 ft. lbs.
4. Adjust contact unit (coil spring) as follows:
   a. Ensure front wheels are in straight ahead position.
   b. Rotate contact unit counterclockwise to end position. Then rotate it clockwise about 3½ turns.
5. **Torque** steering wheel nut to 22 ft. lbs.
6. **Torque** air bag module to 4–5 ft. lbs.
7. Start vehicle. Ensure SRS lamp illuminates for approximately 6 seconds then goes out. For vehicles with electronic unit part No. 9124074, then engine must be allowed to idle for about 15 minutes. Then ensure SRS lamp does not flash.

STEERING COLUMN SERVICE

9-3 & 900

1. Remove steering wheel as outlined under "Steering Wheel, Replace" under "Electrical."
2. Remove upper and lower sections of steering wheel cowling, then the coil spring and two retaining screws.
3. Remove locking ring.
4. Remove bearing housing bolt, then the bearing housing, **Fig. 2.**
5. Reverse procedure to install.

9000

The two sections of steering column shaft are matched and must not be pulled apart under any circumstances.

1. Remove transverse bolt together with spacer and washers, then detach universal joint from steering column shaft, **Fig. 3.**
2. Remove circlip at lower end of column shaft.
3. Press column shaft together so it comes out of lower bearing, then remove complete steering column shaft with ignition switch.
4. Remove slide rails from bracket, then drill out blind rivets and remove holder for dash panel.
5. Remove electronic holder mounting brackets, then the steering column shaft bearing housing and clip for vacuum tube.
6. Drill out blind rivets that hold knee guard, then remove knee guard with safety cable.
7. Reverse procedure to assemble, noting the following:
   a. **Torque** universal joint to 17–22 ft. lbs.
   b. **Torque** transverse bolt to 15 ft. lbs.

Power Steering

NOTE: On Air Bag Equipped Models, Refer To "Air Bag System Precautions" Located In The Front Of This Manual For System Disarming & Arming Procedures.

INDEX

	Page No.
Power Steering System Service	7-88
Power Steering Gear Service	7-88
Precautions	7-88
Air Bag Systems	7-88
Battery Ground Cable	7-88

PRECAUTIONS

AIR BAG SYSTEMS

Refer to "Air Bag System Precautions" in the front of this manual for system disarming and arming procedures.

BATTERY GROUND CABLE

Prior to service, disconnect battery ground cable and isolate as required.

POWER STEERING SYSTEM SERVICE

POWER STEERING GEAR SERVICE

9000

1. Thoroughly clean rack and pinion gear.
2. Loosen locknuts, then remove tie rod ends.
3. Remove boots and pressure equalizing pipe, **Fig. 1.**
4. Disconnect and cap all hydraulic lines.
5. Loosen rack radial adjuster locknut, then remove plunger and spring.
6. Tap rack and pinion gear gently to free plunger. Plunger may also be removed using snap ring pliers.
7. Remove cover from valve bottom.
8. Remove nut from shaft. **Use an 9/16 inch open end wrench to hold valve shaft.**
9. Remove snap ring from upper end of valve.
10. Using sleeve and support tools Nos. 8790644 and 8391849, or equivalents, press out control valve. **Do not attempt to remove valve by tapping or knocking it out.**
11. Remove righthand side inner ball joint as follows:
    a. Clamp rack into vise.
    b. Slide back thrust washer from ball joint flats.
    c. Using crow's foot wrench tool No. 89966480, or equivalent, loosen ball joint. **Never hold pinion when loosening or tightening ball joint.**
12. Remove snap ring from hydraulic cylinder end, using drift to depress snap ring.
13. Remove lefthand side inner ball joint in same manner.

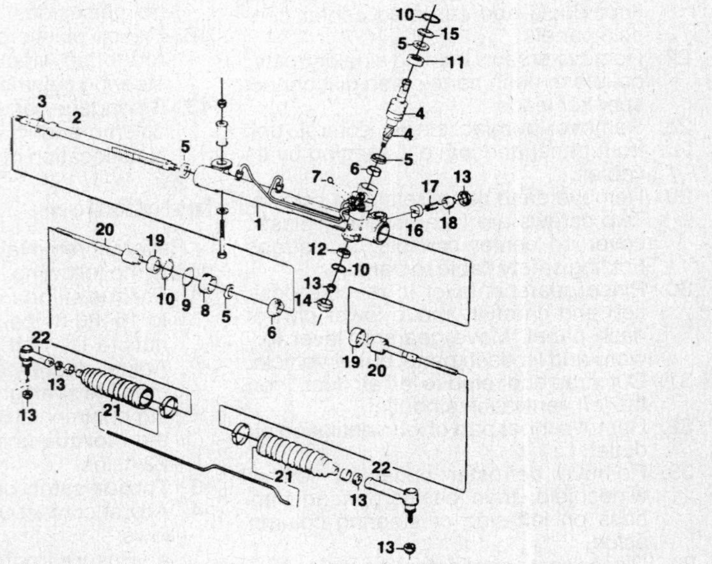

1 Rack-and-pinion gear assembly
2 Rack with piston
3 Piston ring
4a Pinion
4b Valve
5 Hydraulic seal
6 Bush
7 O ring
8 Seal retainer
9 O ring
10 Circlip
11 Needle bearing and race
12 Ball bearing
13 Locknut
14 End cap
15 Dust cap
16 Plunger
17 Spring
18 Adjuster
19 Thrust washer (end stop)
20 Inner ball joint with track rod
21 Gaiter
22 Track-rod end

SA6029100004000X

Fig. 1 Exploded view of power steering gear assembly. 9000

14. Withdraw rack completely with hydraulic seal and bushing attached.
15. Using seal removal tool No. 8996399, or equivalent and drift, remove inner hydraulic seal.
16. Remove snap ring and lower pinion bearing.
17. Remove sealing ring and bushing from other end of pinion. **Lubricate pinion, rack teeth, bearing and dust seal with 2.1 oz. (60 grams) of lithium grease equivalent, to Shell EP, B2, Code 71303. Lubricate hydraulic components using Saginaw hydraulic fluid, or equivalent.**
18. Install lower pinion bearing.
19. Using sleeve tool No. 8996407, or equivalent, install upper bushing and hydraulic seal. **Do not exceed force of 118 lbs., when install bushing and hydraulic seal.**
20. Using sleeve tool No. 8995938, or equivalent, install inner hydraulic seal into rack. **Use caution not to damage sealing lip.**
21. Install rack into housing and press inner hydraulic seal into position using rack piston. **Do not exceed force of 100 lbs. when installing rack. If excessive force is used, piston may separate from rack assembly. Ensure not to withdraw rack too far after the inner seal has been installed or damage to inner sealing ring will result.**
22. Install new O-ring onto seal retainer and check hydraulic seal, then install seal if it is free of defects. If seal is to be replaced, install using sleeve tool No. 8996407, or equivalent.
23. Install seal retainer onto rack. **Use caution not to damage sealing lip.**
24. Insert rack so equal length protrudes at either end. Twist rack until pinion teeth mesh with those on rack.
25. Install control valve as follows:

a. Hold valve body with slot in end of strut pointing to left as teeth are enmeshed.
b. Insert pinion and rotate valve body so slot in end of the shaft is pointing forward when shaft is inserted.

26. Install locknut and cover. **Torque** locknut to 21–32 ft. lbs.
27. Install bearing race and needle bearing, hydraulic seal, duct cap and snap ring onto upper end of control valve.
28. Install plunger, spring, adjusting screw and locknut onto radial adjuster.
29. Adjust adjusting screw as follows:
    a. Turn adjusting screw completely inward.
    b. Back off adjusting screw 40–60.°
    c. Tighten adjusting screw locknut.

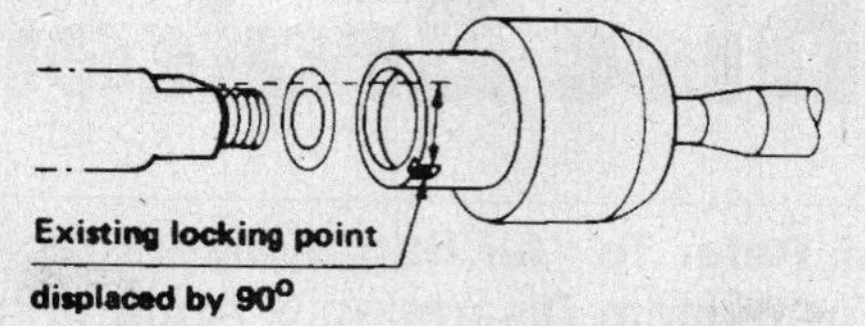

Fig. 2 Positioning locking mark on inner ball joint. 9000

    d. **Torque** locknut to 47–54 ft. lbs.

30. Clamp rack assembly into vise, then slide thrust washers into position and install inner ball joints complete with track rods. Clamp toothed end of rack into vise.
31. When installing ball joints, special washer must be installed which will move slot through 90°, **Fig. 2.**
32. Using crowsfoot wrench tool No. 8996480, or equivalent and torque wrench, **torque** ball joint to 58–73 ft. lbs.
33. Secure inner ball joints by tapping tabs against two flats on rack.
34. Install snap ring seal retainer at end of hydraulic cylinder.
35. Install rubber boots and ventilation pipe.
36. Connect hydraulic lines between control valve and hydraulic cylinder.
37. **Torque** line fittings to 15–21 ft. lbs.
38. Install locknuts and tie rod ends. **Torque** locknuts to 46–56 ft. lbs.

Disc Brakes

NOTE: On Air Bag Equipped Models, Refer To "Air Bag System Precautions" Located In The Front Of This Manual For System Disarming & Arming Procedures.

INDEX

	Page No.
Adjustments	7-92
Parking Brake Cable Equalization	7-93
Parking Brake Lever	7-92
Parking Brake Shoes	7-93
Brake Pad Service	7-90
Front	7-90
Rear	7-91
Caliper Service	7-91
Caliper Overhaul	7-92
Caliper, Replace	7-91
Disc Brake Specifications	7-93
Precautions	7-90
Air Bag Systems	7-90
Battery Ground Cable	7-90
Radio Anti-Theft Lock	7-90
Tightening Specifications	7-94

PRECAUTIONS

AIR BAG SYSTEMS

Refer to "Air Bag System Precautions" in the front of this manual for system disarming and arming procedures.

RADIO ANTI-THEFT LOCK

Radio and cassette player are equipped with an electronic four-digit anti-theft lock. This four-digit code is programmed at manufacturing and cannot be changed. If the battery is disconnected for more than three minutes, if unit is removed or if otherwise cut off from power, the four-digit code must be entered with the quick-selection buttons as follows:

1. Turn radio on, then, when display shows "Code In," enter four-digit code with quick-selection buttons. If code is correct, last-tuned radio frequency is shown on display. If wrong digit has been entered by mistake, all four digits must be entered again. If code is wrong it stays on display.
2. If incorrect four-digit code has been entered, press Band button for more than three seconds to clear display. Display shows "Code In" and new attempt to enter correct code can be made.
3. If wrong code has been used three times in succession, four dashes appear on display and you must wait an hour with radio switched on before trying again.
4. To try again, hold Band button for at least three seconds. "Code In" should appear on display.
5. Correct code must be entered at first attempt, otherwise you must wait another hour with unit switched on before trying again.

BATTERY GROUND CABLE

Prior to service, disconnect battery ground cable and isolate as required.

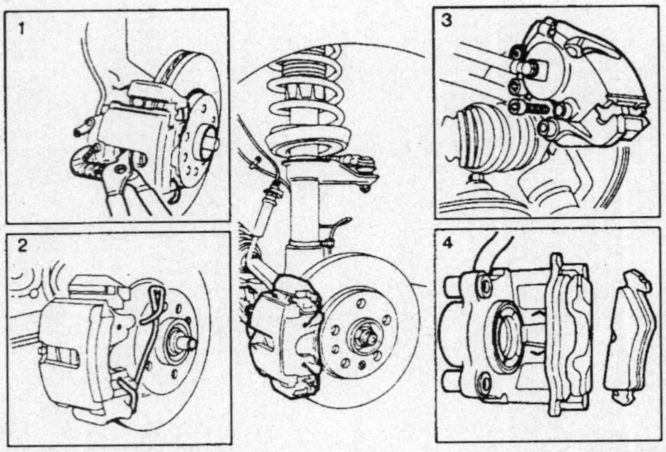

SA4079400002000X

Fig. 1 Front brake pad replacement. 9-3, 9-5 & 900

BRAKE PAD SERVICE

FRONT

9-3, 9-5 & 900

Because the brakes are self-adjusting, it is impossible to tell from the brake pedal stroke whether the linings are worn. The lining thickness should be checked at specified intervals as outlined in "Vehicle Maintenance Schedule" section.

When vehicle is serviced, the brake pads must be replaced before lining thickness falls below .2 inches (5 mm).

1. Raise and support vehicle, then remove wheel.
2. Press piston back with suitable pliers (1), then remove clip from caliper (2), **Fig. 1.**
3. Remove dust caps from guide pins, then the guide pins (3).
4. Lift brake caliper off brake disc and bind it in spring strut with tie.
5. Remove brake pads (4).
6. Reverse procedure to install, noting the following:
   a. Clean inside of brake caliper with soft metal brush and check dust covers.
   b. Tighten guide brake caliper pins and wheel studs to specifications.
   c. After lowering vehicle, press out brake pads by depressing brake pedal.
   d. Check brake fluid and correct if necessary.

9000

1. Raise and support vehicle, then remove front wheels.
2. Remove dust caps, **Fig. 2,** then both guide pin bolts, using a 7 mm Allen wrench or hex bit adapter.
3. Remove pad retainer, then the caliper and pads.
4. Reverse procedure to install brake pads, noting the following:
   a. Clean surfaces between pads and carrier.
   b. Press pistons fully into bores, taking care not to damage dust boots.
   c. Ensure guide pins slide freely and dust covers are in good condition.
   d. Pump brake pedal to move pads to operating positions. **Do not move**

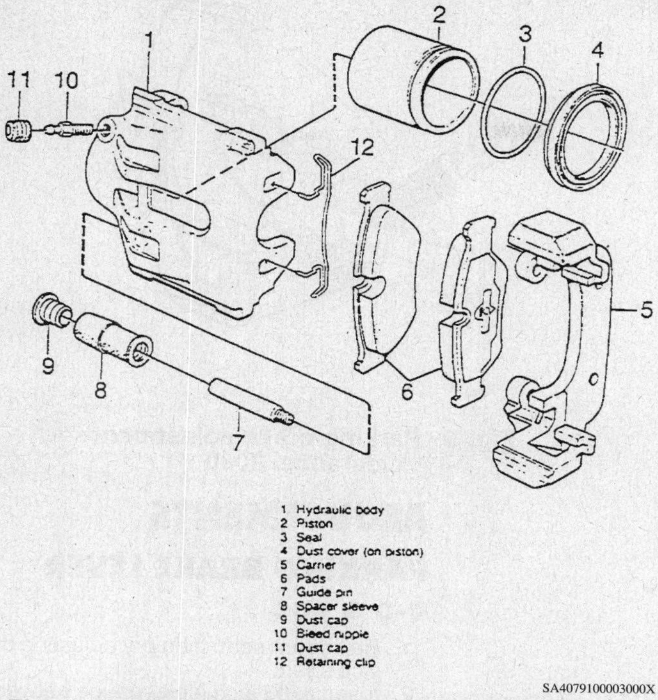

Fig. 2 Exploded view of front disc brake caliper. 9000

vehicle until brakes are operating properly.

REAR

9-3, 9-5 & 900

Because the brakes are self-adjusting, it is impossible to tell from the brake pedal stroke if the linings are worn. The lining thickness should be checked at specified intervals as outlined in "Vehicle Maintenance Schedule" section.

When vehicle is serviced, the brake pads must be replaced before lining thickness falls below .2 inches (5 mm).

Refer to **Fig. 3** when replacing rear brake pads.

1. Raise and support vehicle, then remove wheel.
2. Press pistons back with suitable pliers (1), then remove pins and keep lock spring (2).
3. Remove brake pads. If pads are jammed, use brake pad remover tool No. 89 95 771, or equivalent (3), to remove.
4. Reverse procedure to install, noting the following:
   a. Clean surfaces where brake pads are in contact with brake caliper using soft metal brush, then check dust covers.
   b. Tighten wheel studs to specifications.
   c. Adjust brake pad clearance by fully depressing brake pedal several times.
   d. Check brake fluid level and correct if necessary.

9000

1. Raise and support vehicle, then remove rear wheels.
2. Ensure parking brake is released, then remove pad retainer, **Fig. 4.**
3. Remove parking brake cable from lever.
4. Remove both guide pin bolts.
5. Remove caliper, then the brake pads.
6. Reverse procedure to install, noting the following:
   a. Clean surfaces between pads and carrier.
   b. Remove plug from adjusting screw and retract piston by turning adjusting screw.
   c. Ensure guide pins slide freely and dust covers are in good condition.
   d. Turn adjusting screw in until rotor is locked, then back off adjusting screw ¼–½ turn. **Ensure rotor turns freely.**
   e. Ensure clearance between parking brake lever and stop is .02–.06 inch (.5–1.5 mm).
   f. Adjust parking brake as necessary.

CALIPER SERVICE

CALIPER, REPLACE

FRONT

9-3, 9-5 & 900

1. Remove brake pads as outlined previously.
2. Loosen brake hose at caliper.

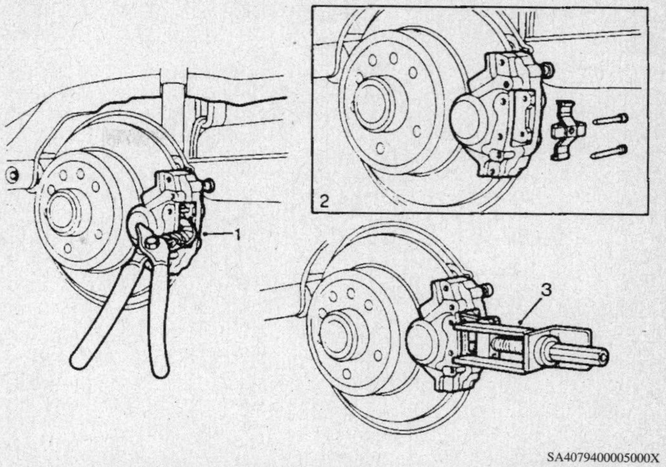

Fig. 3 Rear brake pad removal. 9-3, 9-5 & 900

3. Press brake pedal fully to floor and secure in that position.
4. Remove upper guide pin bolt, then disconnect brake hose at caliper and plug hose and fitting.
5. Remove caliper.
6. Reverse procedure to install and bleed brake system.

9000

1. Remove brake pads as outlined previously.
2. Loosen brake hose at caliper.
3. Press brake pedal fully to the floor and secure in that position.
4. Disconnect brake hose at caliper and plug hose and fitting.
5. Remove caliper.
6. Reverse procedure to install. Bleed brake system.

REAR

9-3, 9-5 & 900

1. Raise and support vehicle, then remove wheel.
2. Press out brake pistons with suitable pliers.
3. Depress brake pedal with brake clamp.
4. Disconnect brake pipe from brake caliper, then plug pipes and brake caliper.
5. Remove pins and locking spring, then the brake pads.
6. Remove two brake caliper securing bolts, then the caliper.
7. Reverse procedure to install, noting the following:
   a. Bleed brake system as outlined under "Hydraulic Brake Systems."
   b. Tighten wheel studs to specifications.

9000

1. Remove brake pads as outlined previously.
2. Disconnect brake hose at caliper and plug hose and fitting.
3. Remove caliper.

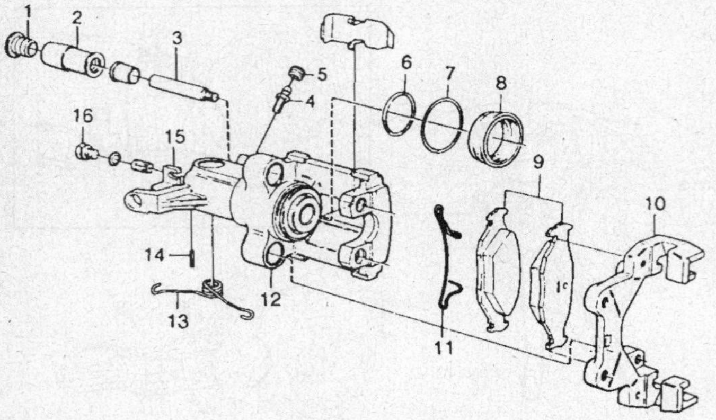

1 Dust cap
2 Spacer sleeve
3 Guide pin
4 Bleed nipple
5 Dust cap
6 Piston seal
7 Retaining ring
8 Dust cover
9 Brake pads
10 Carrier
11 Pad retaining clip
12 Hydraulic body
13 Return spring
14 Stop pin
15 Lever
16 Screw plug (over adjusting screw)

SA4079100004000X

Fig. 4 Exploded view of rear disc brake caliper. 9000

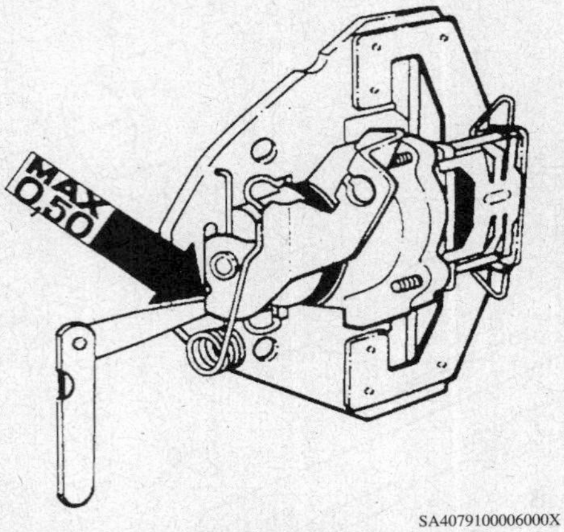

SA4079100006000X

Fig. 5 Parking brake adjustment clearance. 9000

4. Reverse procedure to install, noting the following:
   a. Bleed brake system.
   b. Adjust parking brake as necessary.

CALIPER OVERHAUL

FRONT

9-3, 9-5 & 900

1. Remove brake caliper as outlined previously.
2. Remove brake pads, then clean hydraulic body.
3. Force piston out with compressed air through hose connection.
4. Remove dust cover and piston seal.
5. Check for damage due to wear.
6. Lubricate piston seal with grease supplied in kit, then fill dust cover with grease.
7. Position new piston seal in groove on brake cylinder, then slip dust cover onto piston.
8. Press dust cover collar into brake cylinder groove.
9. Press piston into brake cylinder and install brake pads.
10. Install caliper as outlined previously.

9000

Front and rear calipers are the same except for the parking brake mechanism incorporated in the rear caliper. Refer to "Rear" for service procedure.

REAR

9-3, 9-5 & 900

1. Remove brake caliper as outlined previously.
2. Clean caliper with degreasing agent, then remove two dust covers.
3. Remove plugs and press out piston using compressed air and rear brake piston removal tool No. 89 96 712, or equivalent, as a dolly.
4. Remove seals in cylinder bores and check for damage due to wear.
5. Lubricate piston seals with grease supplied in kit, then fill dust covers with grease.
6. Install piston seals into cylinder bores, then the pistons into cylinders.
7. Install dust covers.
8. Install caliper as outlined previously.

9000

1. Remove caliper and clean housing.
2. Remove dust caps and bushings.
3. Remove spring from parking brake lever.
4. Remove dust cover retainer, then the dust cover.
5. Remove plug for adjusting screw, then the piston adjusting screw.
6. Remove piston seal.
7. Wash parts in solvent, then rinse with clean brake fluid and blow dry with compressed air.
8. Replace any components found defective.
9. Reverse procedure to assemble, noting the following:
   a. Prior to installing piston seal, lubricate seal with grease included in seal kit and pack dust cover with grease.
   b. Ensure dust cover is correctly installed in groove in cylinder.
   c. Install caliper, then turn adjusting screw in until rotor is locked. Back off adjusting screw ¼–½ turn. **Ensure rotor turns freely.**
   d. Ensure clearance between parking brake lever and stop is .02–.06 inch.
   e. Bleed brake system, then adjust parking brake as necessary.

ADJUSTMENTS

PARKING BRAKE LEVER

9-3 & 900

1. Raise rear seat, then pry adjusting device apart.
2. Insert a. 08 inch feeler gauge between parking brake lever and stop on brake caliper.
3. Screw locknut against adjusting sleeve until feeler gauge drops out.
4. Apply and release parking brake lever a few times to settle adjusting device.
5. Ensure clearance between lever and stop is .02–.08 inch.
6. Lower rear seat.

9-5

1. Apply parking brake two notches, then raise and support vehicle so rear wheels can spin freely.
2. Tighten parking brake lever adjusting nut through center console access hole until brakes just begin to take effect.
3. Release parking brake lever and apply it again.
4. Rear wheels should lock between the third and sixth notch of the parking brake lever.
5. If wheels do not lock, repeat adjustment procedure.

9000

1. Release parking brake.
2. Remove screw plug from adjusting screw on back side of rear caliper, **Fig. 5.**
3. Tighten adjusting screw, then back off ¼–½ turn. **Ensure rotor turns freely.**
4. Ensure clearance between parking brake lever and stop is .02–.06 inch. (.5–1.5 mm).
5. If clearance is not as specified, proceed as follows:
   a. Remove brush seal from parking brake lever inside vehicle.
   b. Remove plastic locking plate from adjusting nuts.
   c. Insert a .04 inch (1 mm) feeler gauge between parking brake lever and stop on caliper.

d. Turn adjusting nut at parking brake lever (inside vehicle) until feeler gauge drops out.
e. Ensure clearance is correct, then install locking plate and brush plate to parking brake lever inside vehicle.

6. Refit screw plug at caliper.

PARKING BRAKE SHOES

9-3, 9-5 & 900

1. Raise and support vehicle, then remove rear wheels.
2. Unscrew adjustment until brake disc is blocked.
3. Screw adjustment back until brake disc drags slightly but can be turned.
4. Carry out same method on other rear wheel, then install rear wheels.
5. Pull parking brake to sixth notch and ensure both wheels are locked.
6. Check parking brake as well, then adjust cable equalization if necessary as outlined under "Parking Brake Cable Equalization."

PARKING BRAKE CABLE EQUALIZATION

1. Set parking brake at notch 2.
2. Raise and support vehicle, then tighten adjusting nut on link rod (wire equalization) until brake starts to act.
3. Lower vehicle slightly, then release parking brake and tighten again. Wheels must be locked at sixth notch.

DISC BRAKE SPECIFICATIONS

Year	Model	Nominal Thickness	Minimum Refinish Thickness	Thickness Variation (Parallelism)	Lateral Runout (TIR)	Caliper Bore Diameter, Inches
FRONT						
1998	900	.930	.850	.0006	.003	2.13
	9000	.980	.910	.0006	.003	2.24
1999–2001	9-3	.930	.850	.0006	.003	2.13
	9-5	.980	.910	.0006	.003	2.24
REAR						
1998	900	.350	.320	.0006	.003	1.30
	9000	.350	.290	.0006	.003	1.26
1999–2001	9-3	.350	.320	.0006	.003	1.30
	9-5	.390	.330	.0006	.003	1.50

TIGHTENING SPECIFICATIONS

Year	Component	Torque, Ft. Lbs.
9-3 & 900		
1998–2001	Caliper Mounting Bolts①	52–81
	Caliper Mounting Bolts②	30–40
	Hub Carrier To Hub	51–80
	Hub Nut①	195–208
	Hub Nut②	207–221
	Guide Pin①	22–26
	Guide Pin②	18–22
	Wheel Lug Nuts	66–81
	Brake Caliper Guide Pins	78
	Wheel Studs	87
9000		
1998	Caliper Mounting Bolts①	52–81
	Caliper Mounting Bolts②	52–67
	Hub Carrier To Hub	51–80
	Hub Nut①	195–208
	Hub Nut②	207–221
	Wheel Lug Bolts	78–92
9-5		
1999–2001	Brake Disc Locking Screw①	36③
	Brake Disc Locking Screw②	89③
	Brake Hose①	33
	Brake Hydraulic Line②	12
	Caliper Bleed Fitting①	97③
	Caliper Bleed Fitting①	53③
	Caliper Guide Pins①	21
	Caliper Mounting Bolts①	81
	Caliper Mounting Bolts②	59
	Wheel Hub Retaining Bolts ②	37
	Wheel Lug Nuts	88

① — Front brakes.
② — Rear brakes.
③ — Inch lbs.

Hydraulic Brake Systems

INDEX

	Page No.
Brake System Bleed	7-96
9-3 & 900	7-96
9-5	7-96
9000	7-96
Component Replacement	7-95
Master Cylinder, Replace	7-95
Component Service	7-95
Master Cylinder Overhaul	7-95
Description	7-95

DESCRIPTION

When the brake pedal is depressed, pedal pressure assisted by power from the servo unit pushes the input rod into the master cylinder. The input rod pushes the primary plunger up the bore which closes the cutoff port to the fluid reservoir. This creates pressure ahead of the primary plunger. This pressure also acts on the secondary plunger, pushing it up the bore and closing the cutoff port from the secondary chamber. The pressure in both circuits increases and, because the plungers are the same size, pressure in each circuit is the same. Fluid pressure is directed to the brake system, which advances the piston in each individual caliper. When the pedal is released, the plungers in the master cylinder retract and cutoff ports are opened. The pressure is exhausted and the piston seal in each caliper returns the piston to its retracted position.

If there is a fluid leak in the primary circuit, the input rod pushes the primary plunger up the bore until it acts mechanically on the secondary plunger. The secondary plunger closes the cutoff port, allowing hydraulic pressure to build up in the secondary circuit. If a leak should occur in the secondary circuit, the secondary plunger will be pushed right up the bore until it reaches the end of the cylinder. In either case, greater pedal movement will be required to achieve desired braking effect.

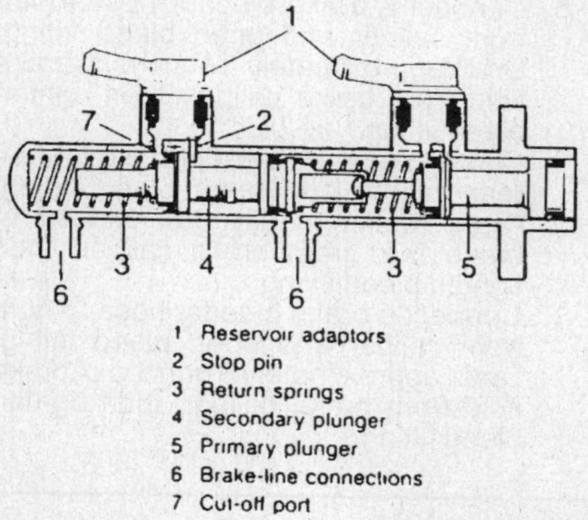

Fig. 1 Internal view of master cylinder

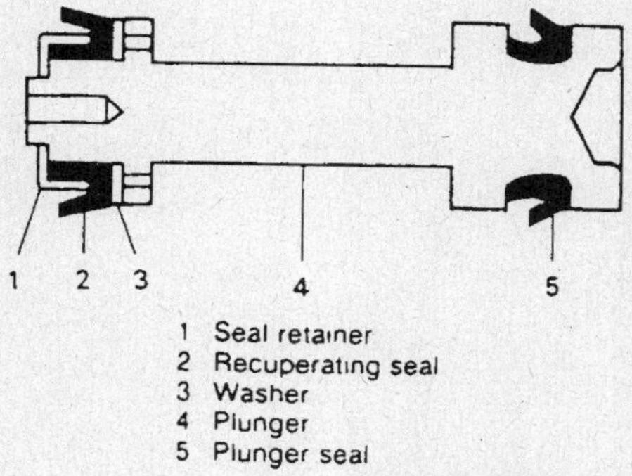

Fig. 2 Secondary plunger seal installation

COMPONENT REPLACEMENT

MASTER CYLINDER, REPLACE

9-3 & 900

1. Drain brake fluid from fluid reservoir.
2. Disconnect hydraulic lines from cylinder.
3. Temporarily plug these lines to avoid loss of fluid.
4. Disconnect brake/warning switch connector on filler cap.
5. Remove the two nuts connecting cylinder to brake booster, then the master cylinder.
6. Reverse procedure to install, then bleed brake system.

9-5

1. Remove maxi fuse holder and engine compartment main fuse panel, then disconnect anti-theft alarm switch connector.
2. Remove fuse panel bracket.
3. Disconnect brake fluid level sensor connector.
4. Drain brake fluid from reservoir with brake system bleeder tool No. 88 19 096, or equivalent.
5. Place a clean shop rag under master cylinder.
6. **On models with manual transaxle,** disconnect hydraulic hose from clutch master cylinder.
7. **On all models,** remove reservoir from master cylinder by lifting straight upward.
8. Disconnect brake hydraulic lines from master cylinder.
9. Remove master cylinder retaining nuts, then the master cylinder.
10. Reverse procedure to install. Bleed brake hydraulic system.

9000

1. Obtain anti-theft code as outlined under "Precautions."
2. Remove battery.
3. Disconnect fuel filter mounting and move to one side.
4. Drain brake fluid reservoir, then remove lines with adapters from master cylinder and move toward reservoir.
5. Disconnect brake lines.
6. Remove attaching nuts and master cylinder.
7. Reverse procedure to install, then bleed brake system.

COMPONENT SERVICE

MASTER CYLINDER OVERHAUL

When working on any hydraulic brake components it is extremely important to keep the work area clean. Clean any parts that are to be reused with new brake fluid or a cleaning fluid specifically designed for hydraulic components. Wipe all parts dry using clean lint-free paper or cloth. Gaskets, seals, O-rings and rubber components should not be reused. Prior to assembly, all components should be generously lubricated with clean brake fluid.

Disassemble

1. Clamp master cylinder in soft-jaw vice.
2. Remove rubber seals from brake hose connections.
3. Carefully push primary plunger up bore at bulkhead end and remove stop pin from secondary plunger, **Fig. 1.**
4. Remove plunger assemblies and loose plastic bleed cup from cylinder bore.

Assemble

1. Fit new seals to secondary plunger, **Fig. 2. Because the primary assembly is fitted with captive plastic bleed cup, if a seal is worn the entire plunger assembly must be replaced.**
2. Install spring and spring retainer onto secondary plunger.
3. Lubricate seals and cylinder bore with brake fluid, then install secondary plunger plastic bleed cup.
4. Insert secondary plunger, then the primary plunger into cylinder bore, taking care not to damage seals.

5. Push primary plunger up bore and install secondary plunger stop pin.
6. Install master cylinder and bleed brake system.

BRAKE SYSTEM BLEED

9-3 & 900

1. Unscrew cover of brake fluid reservoir and top off with brake fluid.
2. Connect topping-off fitting from brake bleeding unit kit tool No. 88 19 096, or equivalent, to brake fluid reservoir.
3. Position hose with one end on topping-off fitting and other end in bottle filled with clean brake fluid.
4. Raise and support vehicle, then connect brake bleeder hose to front left wheel and open nipple. Draw off approximately. 1 quart brake fluid. Repeat at front right wheel.
5. Move brake bleeder to rear left wheel and open nipple. Draw off approximately .05 quart brake fluid. Repeat at rear right wheel.
6. Lower vehicle, then check brake operation. Depress brake pedal and ensure it does not drop.
7. Remove topping-off fitting, hose and bottle.
8. Adjust brake fluid level.

9-5

1. Ensure fluid reservoir is full.
2. Connect fluid filler tunnel from brake system bleeder kit tool No. 88 19 096, or equivalent, to brake fluid reservoir.
3. Place one end of a clear plastic tube into filler funnel and other end in a bottle of clean brake fluid.
4. Raise and support vehicle.
5. Connect a brake bleeder hose to left front caliper and open bleed fitting. Drain approximately 3 ounces of brake fluid from brake caliper, then tighten bleed fitting.
6. Connect a brake bleeder hose to right rear caliper and open bleed fitting. Drain approximately 1.5 ounces of brake fluid from brake caliper, then tighten bleed fitting.
7. Connect a brake bleeder hose to right front caliper and open bleed fitting. Drain approximately 3 ounces of brake fluid from brake caliper, then tighten bleed fitting.
8. Connect a brake bleeder hose to left rear caliper and open bleed fitting. Drain approximately 1.5 ounces of brake fluid from brake caliper, then tighten bleed fitting.
9. Lower vehicle and check brake operation.
10. Remove filler funnel, plastic hose and bottle.
11. Refill brake fluid reservoir.

9000

1. Ensure brake fluid reservoir is full.
2. Connect transparent hose to bleed nipple of brake caliper.
3. Place other end of hose into clear container.
4. Depress brake pedal, then open bleed nipple. Close nipple as soon as pedal reaches floor. Repeat this until no air bubbles are visible in fluid.
5. Repeat previous step at each brake caliper, then refill fluid reservoir. **Front calipers must be bled before rear calipers.**

Power Brake Units

NOTE: "Electrical Symbol & Wire Color Code Identification" Located In The Front Of This Manual May Be Used As An Aid When Using Wiring Circuits Found In This Section.

INDEX

	Page No.		Page No.		Page No.
Description	7-97	Power Brake Unit Service	7-97	Replacement	7-97

DESCRIPTION

The servo (booster) unit, **Fig. 1,** provides power assistance to the pedal effort applied. The servo obtains its power from vacuum created in the engine inlet manifold and provides assistance in a ratio of about 4 to 1. Should a vacuum failure occur, the two pushrods will act as a single rod, allowing brakes to work conventionally but with a much greater pedal effort.

When the brake pedal is depressed, then input rod pushes the control piston and diaphragm forward, closing the vacuum port. As the input rod continues to move forward, the control piston opens the atmospheric port, allowing atmospheric pressure to enter through the filter and into the rear shell behind the diaphragm. Since vacuum is still present at the front of the diaphragm, the pressure assists the input rod in pushing the diaphragm forward and the output rod to actuate the master cylinder.

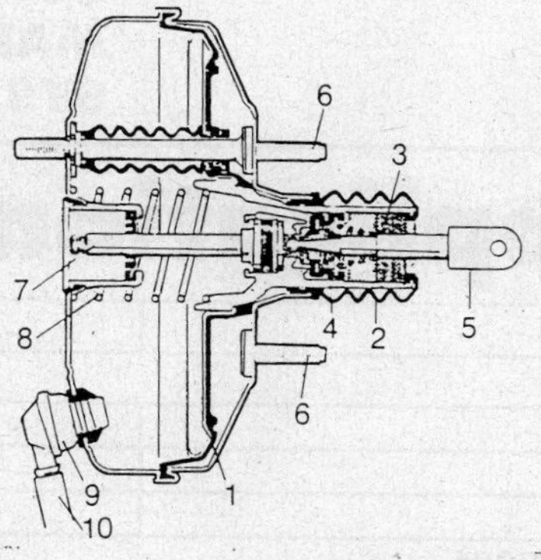

Fig. 1 Power brake booster (servo)

POWER BRAKE UNIT SERVICE

REPLACEMENT

9-3 & 900

1. Remove bar fixed between spring struts, then the air canister over throttle body.
2. Remove master cylinder as outlined under "Hydraulic Brake Systems."
3. Remove brake servo vacuum hose.
4. Disconnect electrical distribution box and move aside.
5. Remove four brake servo retaining nuts from bracket.
6. Remove rubber gaiter from bulkhead partition and pull it toward servo container.
7. Disconnect pushrod clip, then the brake servo container.
8. Reverse procedure to install. Ensure brake pipe connections do not leak.

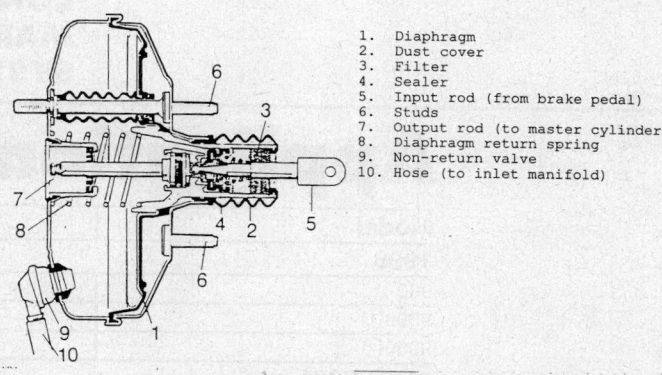

9-5

1. Remove master cylinder as outlined under "Hydraulic Brake Systems."
2. Remove master cylinder rear brake line from ABS hydraulic unit.
3. Disconnect vacuum hose from booster.
4. Remove booster unit retaining nuts from bracket.
5. Remove brake pedal pushrod to booster pushrod retaining clip.
6. Remove booster from vehicle.
7. Reverse procedure to install, noting the following:
   a. Connect brake pedal and booster pushrod together.
   b. After installing booster assembly, depress brake pedal to lock pedal pushrod into booster pushrod retaining clip.

9000

1. Remove master cylinder as outlined under "Hydraulic Brake Systems."
2. Remove vacuum hose from booster.
3. Remove trim panel for access to brake pedal mounting.
4. Remove retaining clip and pin from linkage between brake pedal and pushrod to booster.
5. Remove four bolts securing booster to pedal mounting, then the booster.
6. Reverse procedure to install, then bleed brake system as outlined in "Hydraulic Brake Systems."

Anti-lock Brakes

TABLE OF CONTENTS

	Page No.
APPLICATION CHART	7-98
BOSCH 5.3 ANTI-LOCK BRAKE SYSTEM	7-128
BOSCH 5.4 ANTI-LOCK BRAKE SYSTEM	7-145
MARK II ANTI-LOCK BRAKE SYSTEM LESS TRACTION CONTROL	7-99
MARK II ANTI-LOCK BRAKE SYSTEM w/TRACTION CONTROL	7-108
MARK IV ANTI-LOCK BRAKE SYSTEM	7-119

Application Chart

Model	Type
1998	
900	Bosch 5.3
9000①	Mark II
9000②	Mark IV
1999–2001	
9-3	Bosch 5.4
9-5	Bosch 5.4

① — Turbo models w/traction control and manual transaxle.
② — Except turbo models w/traction control and manual transaxle.

Mark II Anti-Lock Brake System Less Traction Control

NOTE: On Air Bag Equipped Models, Refer To "Air Bag System Precautions" Located In The Front Of This Manual For System Disarming & Arming Procedures.

NOTE: "Electrical Symbol & Wire Color Code Identification" Located In The Front Of This Manual May Be Used As An Aid When Using Wiring Circuits Found In This Section.

INDEX

	Page No.
Description	7-99
Components	7-99
System	7-99
Diagnosis & Testing	7-100
Accessing Diagnostic Trouble Codes	7-100
Diagnostic Trouble Code Interpretation	7-104
Precautions	7-99
Air Bag Systems	7-99
Battery Ground Cable	7-99
Radio Anti-Theft Lock	7-99
System Service	7-105
Brake System Bleed	7-105
Component Replacement	7-106
Accumulator	7-106
Brake Fluid Reservoir	7-106
ECU	7-107
Hydraulic Unit	7-106
Pressure Switch	7-106
Pump & Motor Unit	7-107
Pump Delivery Line	7-106
System Pressure Relief	7-106
Valve Block	7-107
Wheel Sensors	7-107
Troubleshooting	7-100

PRECAUTIONS

AIR BAG SYSTEMS

Refer to "Air Bag System Precautions" in the front of this manual for system disarming and arming procedures.

RADIO ANTI-THEFT LOCK

Radio and cassette player are equipped with an electronic four-digit anti-theft lock. This four-digit code is programmed at manufacturing and cannot be changed. If the battery is disconnected for more than three minutes, if unit is removed or if otherwise cut off from power, the four-digit code must be entered with the quick-selection buttons as follows:

1. Turn radio on, then, when display shows "Code In," enter four-digit code with quick-selection buttons. If code is correct, last-tuned radio frequency is shown on display. If wrong digit has been entered by mistake, all four digits must be entered again. If code is wrong it stays on display.
2. If incorrect four-digit code has been entered, press Band button for more than three seconds to clear display. Display shows "Code In" and new attempt to enter correct code can be made.
3. If wrong code has been used three times in succession, four dashes appear on display and you must wait an hour with radio switched on before trying again.
4. To try again, hold Band button for at least three seconds. "Code In" should appear on display.
5. Correct code must be entered at first attempt, otherwise you must wait another hour with unit switched on before trying again.

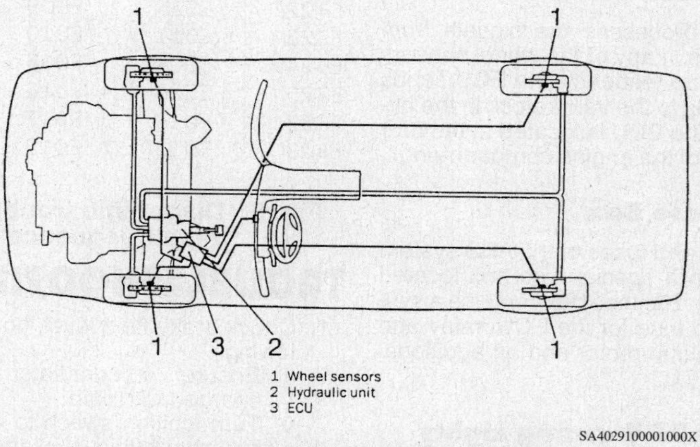

Fig. 1 Anti-lock brake system

BATTERY GROUND CABLE

Prior to service, disconnect battery ground cable and isolate as required.

DESCRIPTION

SYSTEM

This Anti-Lock Brake System (ABS), **Fig. 1,** is a triple-circuit system, with split circuits and individual monitoring and control for each front wheel and for the two rear wheels together.

Signals from the four wheel sensors are sent to the ECU, which continuously monitors the speed, acceleration and deceleration of the wheels, road speed and tire slip. If a wheel is about to lock up, the ECU sends signals to the solenoid valves for the wheel that is slipping. This signal modulates the amount of hydraulic brake pressure sent to that wheel. By preventing lock up, the ABS system provides the shortest possible stopping distance without losing steering control.

COMPONENTS

Hydraulic Unit

The hydraulic unit replaces the conventional master cylinder and vacuum-operated servo. This unit is comprised of a master cylinder, hydraulic servo cylinder, brake fluid reservoir, independent pump for hydraulic pressure and a valve block which modulates pressure to the individual calipers. The valve block contains six solenoid valves, three inlet and three outlet, this gives each brake circuit one inlet and one outlet valve.

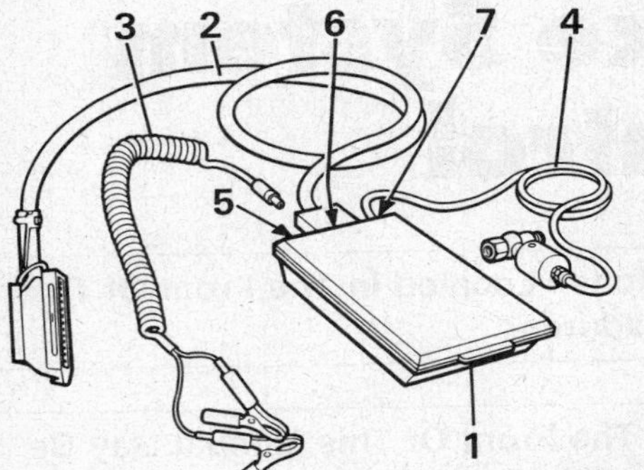

1 Tester unit
2 Test lead with two-way 35-pin connector
3 Power supply lead
4 Pressure sensor with connecting lead
5 Port for power supply
6 Port for test lead
7 Port for pressure-sensor lead

SA4029100002000X

Fig. 2 ABS system tester

If the ABS system should become inoperative for any reason, all the solenoid valves will be de-energized and the brake system will operate in the same way as a conventional braking system.

Electronic Control Unit (ECU)

The ECU processes the signals from wheel sensors. If any of the wheel sensors detect a lock up tendency, the ECU sends signals directly to the valve block in the hydraulic unit. The ECU is located at the rear lefthand side of the engine compartment.

Relay & Fuse Box

The relays and fuses of the ABS system are housed in a special fuse box located near the ECU. The fuse box contains a system relay and fuse for the ECU, relay and fuse for the pump motor and an additional fuse for the ECU.

Brake & ABS Warning Lights

As on cars with conventional brakes, the brake warning light will come on if level in the fluid reservoir falls below the MIN mark. However, if there is a pressure drop in the accumulator both the brake warning and the ABS warning lights will come on. The ABS warning light will also come on if there is an additional drop of fluid in the reservoir, a malfunction in the ECU, an open circuit in the electrical system or a weak signal being received from the wheel sensors. The ABS system is inoperative when the ABS warning light is on.

Wheel Sensors

The wheel sensors are mounted near a toothed sensor wheel at each wheel. Each time a tooth on the sensor wheel passes the sensor, it distorts a magnetic field, which causes a signal to be sent to the ECU. Although the sensors are mounted differently in the front (radially) and rear (axially), they operate exactly the same.

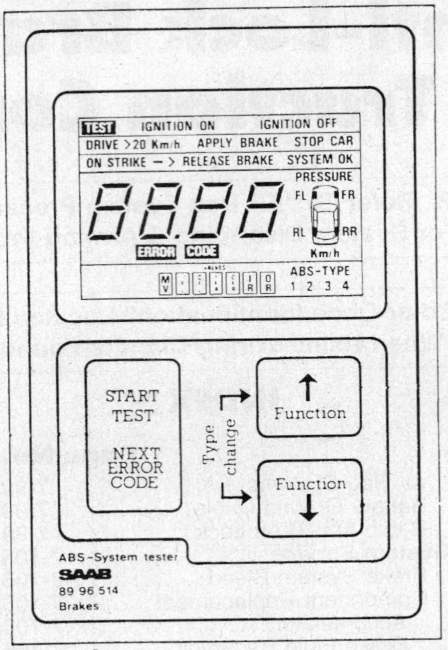

SA4029100003000X

Fig. 3 ABS tester display

E002	EE24	E001	E033
E422	EE25	E009	E034
E523	E011	E010	E035
E624	E008	E015	E132
E725	E320	E016	PRES
EE22	E014	E017	
EE23	E032	E018	

SA4029100005000X

Fig. 5 Diagnostic trouble code repair sequence

TROUBLESHOOTING

1. Check brake fluid level, noting the following:
   a. Ensure accumulator is fully charged with fluid.
   b. Turn ignition switch to On position and check fluid level after hydraulic pump cuts out.
   c. Fill as necessary with DOT 4 brake fluid to bring level to MAX mark on side of reservoir.
2. Inspect all fuses in fuse panel adjacent to ABS system ECU.
3. Ensure relays for ECU and pump motor have been properly installed.
4. Check all electrical connectors and ensure sensor lead connectors are making good contact.
5. Check all ground points.

DIAGNOSIS & TESTING

ACCESSING DIAGNOSTIC TROUBLE CODES

To access diagnostic trouble codes and perform system service, a SAAB ABS system tester will be required. The tester, **Fig. 2,** can perform three different sets of tests. These tests include; automatic testing of each wheel sensor and hydraulic pressure (Test Mode), manual valve testing (Valve Test Mode) and manual testing of each wheel sensor and hydraulic pressure (Monitor Mode).

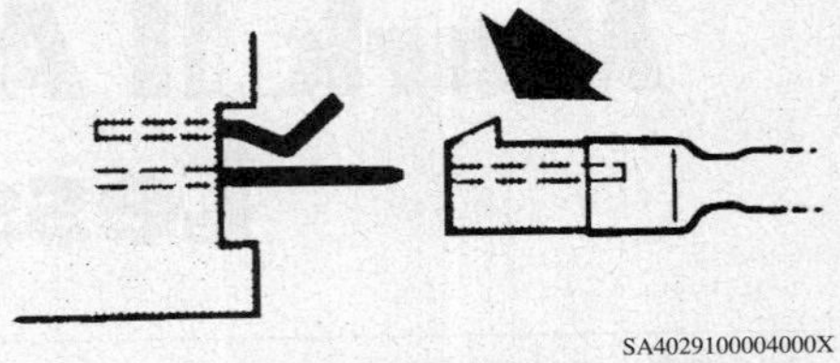

SA4029100004000X

Fig. 4 Tester power lead connection

The tester display, **Fig. 3,** is divided into three zones; test prompts; measured values and diagnostic trouble codes, with overview of test items; valve and ABS-version monitor. The test prompts display, displays driving instructions for the operator during testing. The measured values and diagnostic trouble codes display, shows instantaneous values for wheel speed, wheel sensor signal amplitude, sensor-wheel eccentricity and which wheel the values refer to. A check is also made of the relays, accumulator pressure if pressure sensor is connected and the diagnostic trouble codes are displayed at the end of the run. The valve monitoring display, shows which valves are operating during test whenever ABS-system version is selected.

The tester control panel has three buttons to control the function of the ABS tester. Button A is used to start the test cycle and to run through the diagnostic trouble codes. Button B is used to select the program that measures wheel sensor signal strength, tests the operation of wheel sensors and measures accumulator pressure (if pressure sensor is connected). Button C is used to select the program that measures sensor wheel eccentricity, test the operation of the wheel sensors and to measure accumulator pressure (if pressure sensor is connected). Buttons B and C can be pressed simultaneously to select ABS-system version.

CONNECTING ABS-SYSTEM TESTER

1. Perform system checks as outlined under "Troubleshooting."
2. Switch ignition off, then remove ECU cover located at rear lefthand corner of engine compartment.
3. Release ECU retaining clips, then disconnect ECU.
4. Connect tester lead between ECU and ABS wiring harness connector using a two-way 35-pin connector.
5. Support ECU and connectors using vinyl ties, then run tester electrical lead through driver window.
6. Connect power supply lead to battery negative terminal, then the positive terminal.
7. Run power lead through the window and connect it to the tester, **Fig. 4. Ensure connector is installed correctly at the tester, if connector is installed upside down, tester circuitry may be burnt out.**

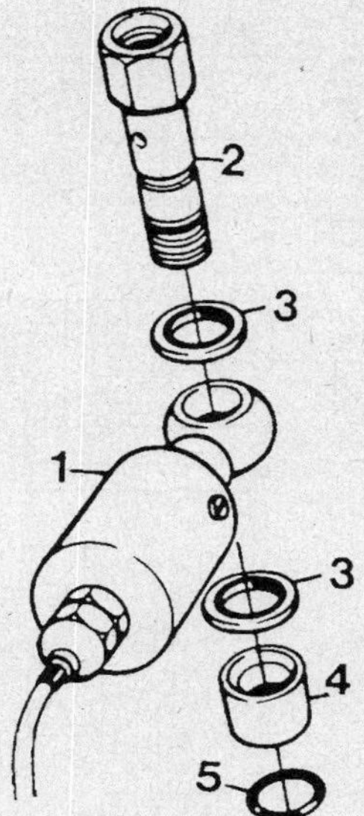

1 Pressure sensor
2 Fitting with groove for 'O' ring
3 Washer
4 Sleeve
5 'O' ring

SA4029100006000X

Fig. 6 Pressure sensor connection

8. Tester will now automatically select ABS-type 1. **Always switch off the ignition before unplugging test lead connector from the ECU. Failure to do so can result in ECU circuitry being burnt out.**

Test Mode

1. Ensure tester is in "Monitor Mode." **This is the mode the tester enters automatically after "ABS-System Version" has been selected.**
2. Drive the vehicle at about 6 mph and press START TEST button.
3. The word TEST will now start to flash on the display, indicating that "TEST MODE" has been started.
4. If tester will not enter TEST MODE, remain in MONITOR MODE and check wheel sensor signal strength for each wheel as outlined in "Monitor Mode."
5. Drive vehicle for at least three minutes at a speed of approximately 42 mph. **Test results will not be affected by the vehicle stopping and starting.**
6. Test cycle for each wheel takes about two seconds.
7. Tester will beep each time a fault is detected, testing will continue until tester is switched off or START TEST button is pressed for approximately three seconds.
8. To read test results, proceed as follows:
   a. Stop vehicle but do not turn off the ignition switch, wait until display indicates FR, FL, RL or RR and press START TEST button.
   b. If no faults have been detected, display will read SYSTEM OK.
   c. If any faults have been detected, ERROR will appear on the display followed by a figure indicating the number of faults found.
   d. To read diagnostic trouble codes, press NEXT ERROR CODE button and diagnostic trouble codes will be displayed. Press button again to read each successive diagnostic trouble code.
   e. If several diagnostic trouble codes are displayed together they must be investigated and repaired in the order, **Fig. 5.**
9. To diagnose and repair diagnostic trouble codes, refer to "Diagnostic Trouble Code Interpretation."
10. To return to MONITOR MODE, press one of the function buttons.

Error code	ECU pin no	Malfunction indicated
E001	1	No earth connection
E002	2	Battery voltage low or absent
E320	3, 20	System relay function
E422	4, 22	No signal from right rear wheel sensor
E523	5, 23	No signal from front left wheel sensor
E624	6, 24	No signal from left rear wheel sensor
E725	7, 25	No signal from right front wheel sensor
E008	8	Systemrelay-controlsignalmissing
E009	9	Brake fluid level low: hydraulic pressure low
E010	10	ECU defective
E011	11	No earth connection
E014	14	Pump relay/pressure switch defective
E015	15	Right front inlet valve
E016	16	Rear outlet valve
E017	17	Rear inlet valve
E018	18	Main valve
EE22	Sensor	Right rear sensor wheel runout
EE23	Sensor	Left front sensor wheel runout
EE24	Sensor	Left rear sensor wheel runout
EE25	Sensor	Right front sensor wheel runout
E032	32	Pump relay defective
E132	1, 32	Pump running continuously
E033	33	Left front outlet valve
E034	34	Right front outlet valve
E035	35	Left front inlet valve
PRES	ext	Low accumulator pressure

SA4029100007000X

Fig. 7 Diagnostic trouble code & ECU pin identification. 900

Valve Test Mode

During this test you will need to stop the vehicle abruptly several times. Use roads that are lightly traveled or deserted.

1. Ensure tester is in MONITOR MODE, vehicle is not moving and engine at idle speed.
2. Press one of the function buttons to enter VALVE TEST MODE. The ABS warning light on the instrument panel will come on and stay on during the test sequence.
3. Press START TEST button, TEST will now flash on the display, indicating test sequence has begun.
4. Tester will beep each time a fault is detected.
5. Inlet valves will be tested in this order; IFL-Inlet Front Left, IFR-Inlet Front Right, IR-Inlet Rear. **When rear inlet valve is to be tested, choose a place to stop the vehicle where it can remain parked while the remaining valves are tested.**
6. To test inlet valves, proceed as follows:
   a. System prompt DRIVE 20km/h, drive vehicle between 13–19 mph.
   b. System prompt STOP CAR & RELEASE BRAKE, take foot off accelerator and let car coast. **Do not touch brake pedal. Use the parking brake or depress clutch pedal several times to slow vehicle down.**
   c. When the vehicle reaches 11 mph, APPLY BRAKE prompt will appear on the screen. Press down hard on the brake pedal as soon as the prompt appears. Test will now measure the wheel retardation as the vehicle slows down.
   d. System prompt RELEASE BRAKE, release brake pedal as soon as the vehicle has stopped. **Do not touch brake pedal again.**
   e. After test sequence for inlet valves has been completed, tester will automatically continue the next test sequence.
7. Outlet valves will be tested in this order; OR-Outlet Rear, OFR-Outlet Front Right, OFL-Outlet Front Left, MV-Main Valve. **During the test for the main valve, the brake pedal will pulsate strongly.**
8. To test outlet valves and main valve, proceed as follows:
   a. Ensure vehicle is parked and engine off.
   b. System prompt IGNITION ON, turn key to DRIVE position.
   c. System prompt RELEASE BRAKE. **Do not touch brake pedal.** After approximately five seconds, pump will have raised pressure in accumulator to 2610 psi and RELEASE BRAKE will disappear from screen.
   d. System prompt APPLY BRAKE, press down hard on the brake pedal as soon as the prompt appears.
   e. System prompt ON STRIKE- & IGNITION OFF, brake pedal should pulsate or there should be excessive pedal travel when pedal is depressed. If pedal responds as outlined, turn ignition switch off

Error code	ECU pin no	Malfunction indicated
E001	1	No earth connection
E002	2	Battery voltage low
E008	8	No control signal to system relay
E009	9	Brake fluid level or hydraulic pressure low
E010	10	ECU defective
E011	11	No earth connection
E014	14	Pump relay/pressure switch defective
E015	15	Right front inlet valve
E016	33	Rear outlet valve
E017	17	Rear inlet valve
E018	18	Main valve
E032	32	Pump relay defective
E033	16	Left front outlet valve
E034	34	Right front outlet valve
E035	35	Left front inlet valve
E132	1, 32	Pump running continuously
E320	3, 20	System relay defective
E422	4, 22	No signal from right rear wheel sensor
E523	5, 23	No signal from front left wheel sensor
E624	6, 24	No signal from left rear wheel sensor
E725	7, 25	No signal from right front wheel sensor
EE22	Sensor	Right rear sensor wheel runout
EE23	Sensor	Left front sensor wheel runout
EE24	Sensor	Left rear sensor wheel runout
EE25	Sensor	Right front sensor wheel runout
PRES	ext	Hydraulic pressure to pressure switch low

SA4029100008000X

Fig. 8 Diagnostic trouble code & ECU pin identification. 9000

within 10 seconds to send acknowledgment to the tester. **If brake pedal does not respond as outlined, do not turn off ignition at this time.** Wait approximately 20 seconds for system prompt RELEASE BRAKE to appear on the screen.

9. If system does not detect any faults, display will read SYSTEM OK.
10. If any faults have been detected, ERROR will appear on the display followed by a figure indicating the number of faults found.
11. To read diagnostic trouble codes, press NEXT ERROR CODE button and diagnostic trouble codes will be displayed. Press button again to read each successive diagnostic trouble code.
12. If several diagnostic trouble codes are displayed together they must be investigated and repaired in the order, **Fig. 5.**
13. To diagnose and repair diagnostic trouble codes, refer to "Diagnostic Trouble Codes."
14. To return to MONITOR MODE, press one of the function buttons.

Monitor Mode

1. After tester has been powered up and ABS-System Version selected, tester will automatically enter MONITOR MODE.
2. MONITOR MODE can be used to test wheel speed, wheel signal strength, sensor wheel eccentricity (out-of-round) and accumulator pressure (if pressure sensor is connected).
3. Tester will beep each time a fault is found.
4. To test Road-Wheel speed, proceed as follows:
   a. Drive vehicle at a steady speed.
   b. Km/h will appear on display together with a number, indicating speed of wheel.
   c. The tester will begin the test with the FR (front right) wheel, which will be indicated on the display screen.
   d. To test speed of other wheels, press top FUNCTION button, wheels will now be tested in a counterclockwise sequence.
   e. Values for wheel speed should be approximately the same.
5. To test accumulator pressure, connect pressure sensor as outlined in "Connecting Pressure Sensor." Working pressure of the accumulator will be displayed in bar. **Some of the valve segments may flash during this test, this is quite normal and can be disregarded.**
6. To test Wheel-Sensor signal strength, proceed as follows:
   a. Drive vehicle at a steady speed, then press top FUNCTION button for about three seconds.
   b. The letter "A" will be displayed along with a value proportional to signal voltage.
   c. The tester will begin the test with the FR (front right) wheel, which will be indicated on the display screen.

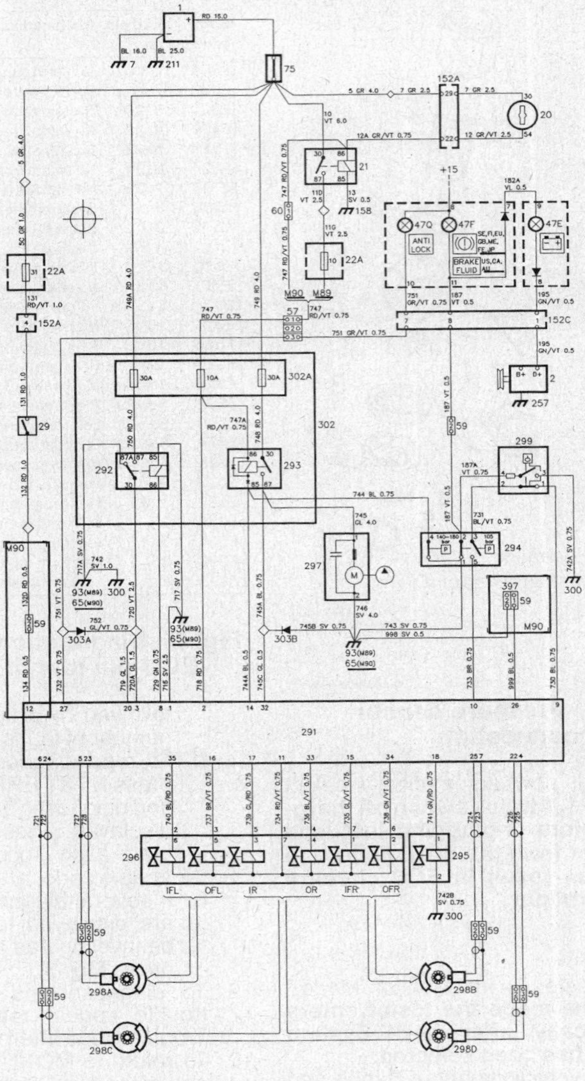

1. Battery
2. Alternator
7. Ground-Radiator Support
20. Ignition Switch
21. Ignition Switch Relay
22A. Fuse Holder
47E. Charging Warning Lamp
47F. Brake Warning Lamp
47K. Shift Up Warning Lamp
47Q. ABS Warning Lamp
47T. SRS Warning Lamp
57. Connector, 3-pin
58. Connector, 12-pin
59. Connector, 2-pin
60. Connector, 1-pin
65. Ground, Rear Seat
75. Power Distribution Block
93. Ground, Left Wheelhouse
98. Connector, 10-pin
123. Connector, 4-pin
152A. Connector, 29-pin White
152B. Connector, 29-pin Red
152C. Connector, 29-pin Black
158. Negative Distribution Terminal
211. Ground, Transaxle
257. Ground, Alternator Bracket
291. ABS Control Unit
292. ABS System Relay
293. ABS Pump Relay
294. ABS Pressure Switch
295. ABS Master Valve
296. ABS Valve Block
297. ABS Hydraulic Pump Motor
298A. LH Front Wheel Sensor
298B. RH Front Wheel Sensor
298C. LH Rear Wheel Sensor
298D. RH Rear Wheel Sensor
299. ABS Fluid Level Sensor
300. Ground, Hydraulic Unit
302. ABS Electrical Distribution Box
302A. ABS Fuse Holder
303A. ABS Diode
303B. ABS Diode

SA4029100009000X

Fig. 9 ABS system wiring circuit. 900

   d. To test speed of other wheels, press top FUNCTION button, wheels will now be tested in a counterclockwise sequence.
   e. The voltage values for the wheels should be within 20 percent of each other.
7. To test Sensor-Wheel eccentricity (out-of-round), proceed as follows:
   a. Drive vehicle at a speed of 25–30 mph for a minimum period of sixty seconds, then press bottom function button for three seconds to start test.
   b. The letter "E" will appear on the display together with a number indicating ratio of amplitude variation to maximum amplitude during one revolution of the wheel. **This value should not be higher than 6.**
   c. The front right wheel sensor will the first one tested, to test the other

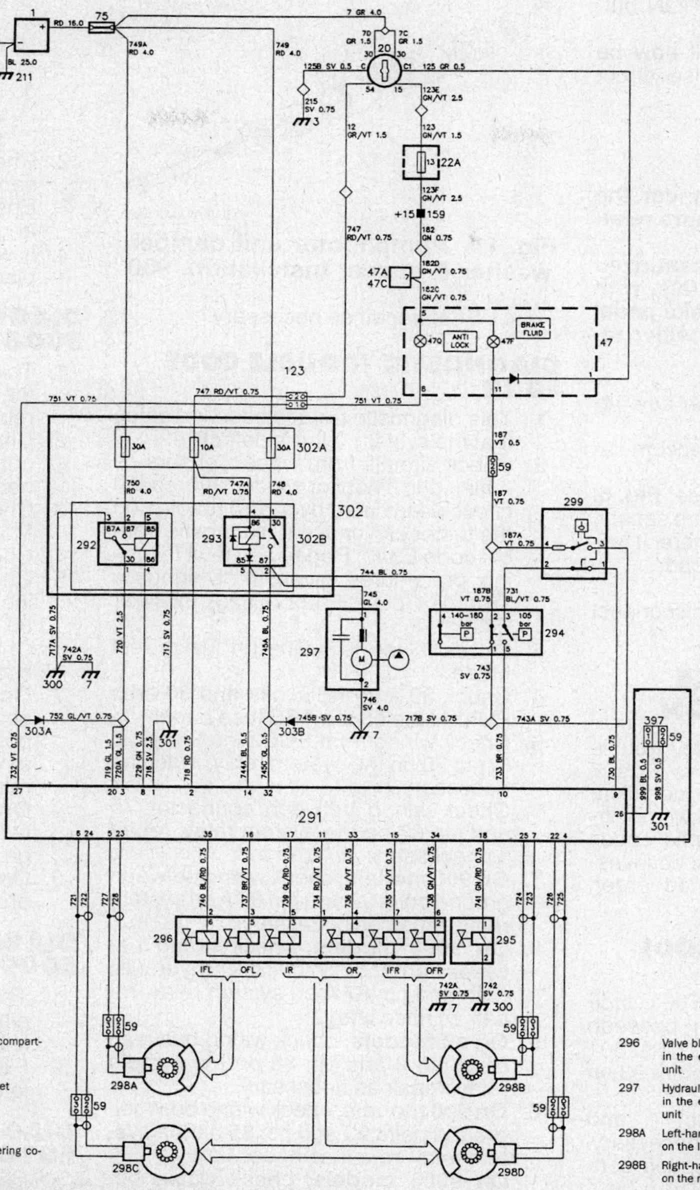

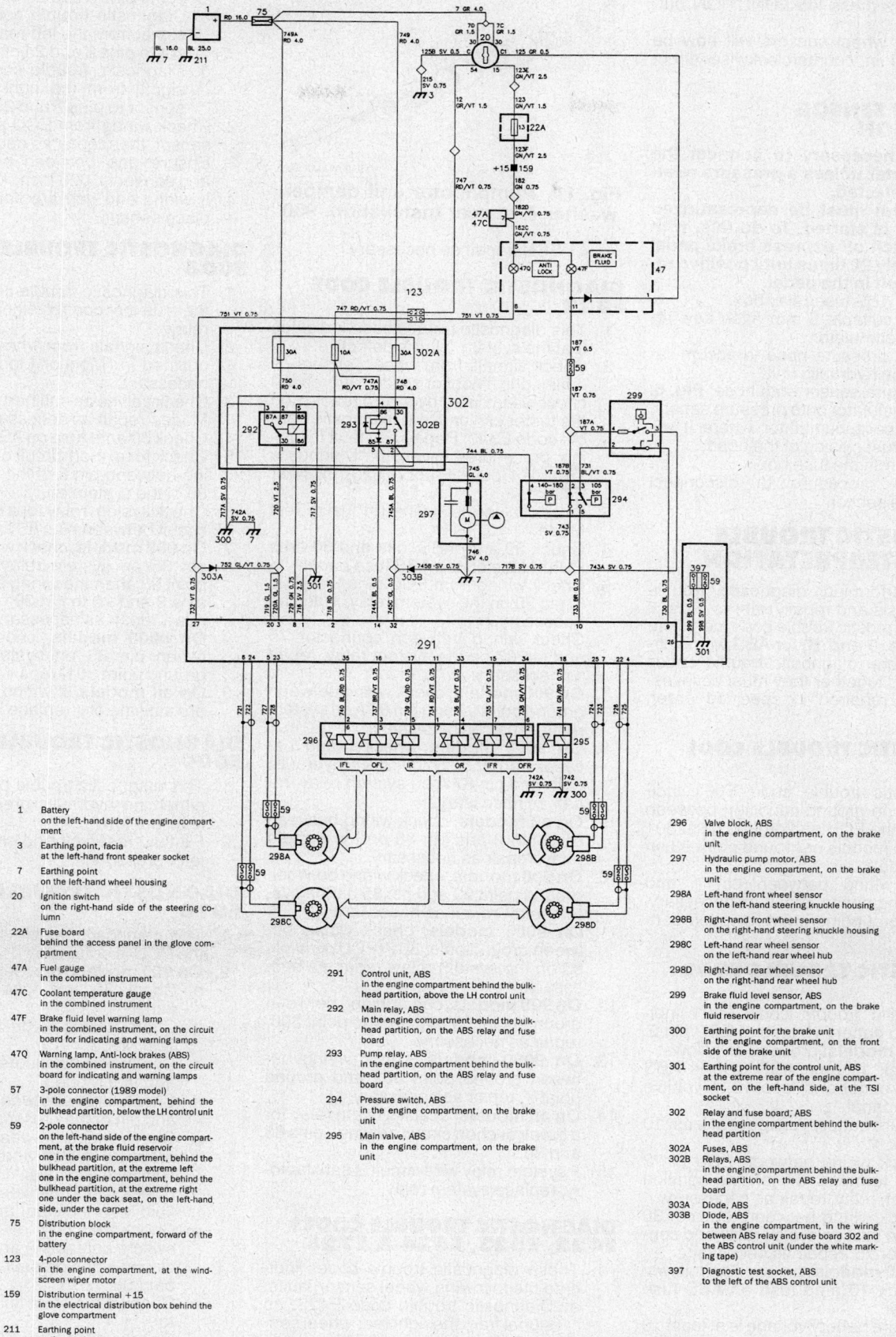

1 Battery
on the left-hand side of the engine compartment

3 Earthing point, facia
at the left-hand front speaker socket

7 Earthing point
on the left-hand wheel housing

20 Ignition switch
on the right-hand side of the steering column

22A Fuse board
behind the access panel in the glove compartment

47A Fuel gauge
in the combined instrument

47C Coolant temperature gauge
in the combined instrument

47F Brake fluid level warning lamp
in the combined instrument, on the circuit board for indicating and warning lamps

47Q Warning lamp, Anti-lock brakes (ABS)
in the combined instrument, on the circuit board for indicating and warning lamps

57 3-pole connector (1989 model)
in the engine compartment, behind the bulkhead partition, below the LH control unit

59 2-pole connector
on the left-hand side of the engine compartment, at the brake fluid reservoir
one in the engine compartment, behind the bulkhead partition, at the extreme left
one in the engine compartment, behind the bulkhead partition, at the extreme right
one under the back seat, on the left-hand side, under the carpet

75 Distribution block
in the engine compartment, forward of the battery

123 4-pole connector
in the engine compartment, at the windscreen wiper motor

159 Distribution terminal +15
in the electrical distribution box behind the glove compartment

211 Earthing point
on the gearbox

291 Control unit, ABS
in the engine compartment behind the bulkhead partition, above the LH control unit

292 Main relay, ABS
in the engine compartment behind the bulkhead partition, on the ABS relay and fuse board

293 Pump relay, ABS
in the engine compartment behind the bulkhead partition, on the ABS relay and fuse board

294 Pressure switch, ABS
in the engine compartment, on the brake unit

295 Main valve, ABS
in the engine compartment, on the brake unit

296 Valve block, ABS
in the engine compartment, on the brake unit

297 Hydraulic pump motor, ABS
in the engine compartment, on the brake unit

298A Left-hand front wheel sensor
on the left-hand steering knuckle housing

298B Right-hand front wheel sensor
on the right-hand steering knuckle housing

298C Left-hand rear wheel sensor
on the left-hand rear wheel hub

298D Right-hand rear wheel sensor
on the right-hand rear wheel hub

299 Brake fluid level sensor, ABS
in the engine compartment, on the brake fluid reservoir

300 Earthing point for the brake unit
in the engine compartment, on the front side of the brake unit

301 Earthing point for the control unit, ABS
at the extreme rear of the engine compartment, on the left-hand side, at the TSI socket

302 Relay and fuse board, ABS
in the engine compartment behind the bulkhead partition

302A Fuses, ABS
302B Relays, ABS
in the engine compartment behind the bulkhead partition, on the ABS relay and fuse board

303A Diode, ABS
303B Diode, ABS
in the engine compartment, in the wiring between ABS relay and fuse board 302 and the ABS control unit (under the white marking tape)

397 Diagnostic test socket, ABS
to the left of the ABS control unit

SA4029100010000X

Fig. 10 ABS system wiring circuit. 9000

wheels press top FUNCTION button.
d. Other wheel sensors will now be tested in counterclockwise direction.

PRESSURE SENSOR CONNECTION

It is not necessary to connect the pressure tester unless a pressure related fault is detected.

The system must be depressurized before work is started. To do this, with ignition switch off depress brake pedal approximately 20 times until positive resistance is felt in the pedal.

1. Remove ABS fuse/relay box.
2. Using a suitable 8 mm Allen key, remove accumulator.
3. Connect pressure hose to accumulator port on hydraulic unit.
4. Fit pressure sensor onto hose, **Fig. 6.**
5. Set accumulator onto pressure sensor, then place accumulator where it will not obstruct closing of the hood.
6. Loosely refit the fuse box.
7. Reverse procedure to disconnect pressure sensor.

DIAGNOSTIC TROUBLE CODE INTERPRETATION

When performing diagnostic trouble code diagnosis and repair, refer to **Figs. 7 and 8** for diagnostic trouble code identification and **Figs. 9 and 10** for ABS wiring circuits. If several diagnostic trouble codes are displayed together they must be investigated and repaired in specified order, **Fig. 5.**

DIAGNOSTIC TROUBLE CODE E001

1. Diagnostic trouble code E001 indicates a no ground condition between pin 1 of the ECU and ground point 301 on 9000 models or ground point 93 on 900 models.
2. Check wiring between pin 1 and grounding points, repair as necessary.
3. Check grounding point for good contact.

DIAGNOSTIC TROUBLE CODE E002

1. Diagnostic trouble code E001 indicates no battery voltage at ECU pin 2.
2. **On 900 models,** proceed as follows:
   a. Check 10 amp ABS fuse in ABS fuse panel and fuse 10 in vehicle fuse panel.
   b. Ensure battery voltage is at least 10 volts.
   c. Check wiring between ECU pin 2 and terminal 87 of the ignition switch relay, repair as necessary.
   d. Check wiring between terminal 30 of the ignition switch relay and connector 75, repair as necessary.
3. **On 9000 models,** proceed as follows:
   a. Check 10 amp fuse on ABS fuse panel.
   b. Ensure battery voltage is at least 10 volts.
   c. Check wiring between terminal 54 of the ignition switch and pin 2 of the

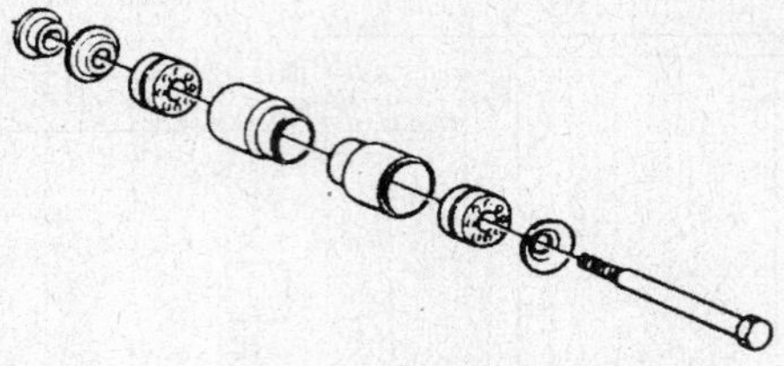

SA4029100011000X

Fig. 11 Pump/motor unit damper, washer & spacer installation. 900

ECU, repair as necessary.

DIAGNOSTIC TROUBLE CODE E320

1. This diagnostic trouble code indicates that the system relay is defective.
2. Check signals from wheel sensors as outlined in "Monitor Mode." A break in circuitry indicated by a zero reading on the tester can cause a diagnostic trouble code E320. Repair any fault following procedures given in "Diagnostic Trouble Codes E422, E523, E624 or E725."
3. Check valves as outlined in "Valve Test Mode."
4. Check 30 amp ABS fuse and 30 amp PUMP fuse on the ABS fuse panel.
5. Check wiring from ECU pins 3 and 20 to pin 30 on the system relay, repair as necessary.
6. Check wiring between connector 75 and pin 87 on the system relay, repair as necessary.
7. **On 900 models,** check wiring between ground point 93 and pin 87 A on system relay, repair as necessary.
8. **On 9000 models,** check wiring between ground point 300 (hydraulic unit) and pin 87 A on system relay, repair as necessary.
9. **On all models,** check wiring between ECU pin 8 and pin 86 on the system relay, repair as necessary.
10. **On 900 models,** check wiring between ground point 93 and pin 85 on the system relay, repair as necessary.
11. **On 9000 models,** check wiring between ground point 301 (ECU) and pin 85 on the system relay, repair as necessary.
12. **On 900 models,** check wiring between ground point 93 and ground point 300, repair as necessary.
13. **On 9000 models,** check wiring between ground point 301 and ground point 7, repair as necessary.
14. **On all models,** check system relay for a break or short circuit between pins 85 and 86.
15. If system relay wire circuit is satisfactory, replace system relay.

DIAGNOSTIC TROUBLE CODES E422, E523, E624 & E725

1. These diagnostic trouble codes indicate the following wheel sensor faults:
   a. Diagnostic trouble code E422, no signal from the right rear wheel sensor to pins 4 and 22 of ECU.
   b. Diagnostic trouble code E523, no signal from the left front wheel sensor to pins 5 and 23 of ECU.
   c. Diagnostic trouble code E624, no signal from the left rear wheel sensor to pins 6 and 24 of ECU.
   d. Diagnostic trouble code E725, no signal from the right front wheel sensor to pins 7 and 25 of ECU.
2. Check wiring from ECU pins to wheel sensor, then repair as necessary.
3. Ensure gap between sensor wheel and sensor is. 026 inch.
4. If wiring and gap are satisfactory, replace sensor.

DIAGNOSTIC TROUBLE CODE E008

1. This diagnostic trouble code indicates there is no control signal to system relay.
2. Check signals from wheel sensors as outlined in "Monitor Mode," repair as necessary.
3. Check valves as outlined in "Valve Test Mode," repair as necessary.
4. Check 30 amp fuse on ABS fuse panel.
5. Check for a short circuit or break in wiring between pin 8 of the ECU and pin 86 of the system relay.
6. Check system relay for a break or short circuit between pins 85 and 86.
7. **On 900 models,** check wiring between pin 85 on system relay and ground point 93, then the wiring between ECU pins 3 and 20 to pin 30 on the system relay, repair as necessary.
8. **On 9000 models,** check wiring between pin 85 on system relay and ground point 301, repair as necessary.
9. **On all models,** if wiring and grounds are satisfactory, replace ECU.

DIAGNOSTIC TROUBLE CODE E009

1. This diagnostic trouble code indicates either the hydraulic pressure or fluid level are low.
2. Fill fluid reservoir and check accumulator pressure.

DIAGNOSTIC TROUBLE CODE E010

1. This diagnostic trouble code indicates the ECU is defective.
2. **On 900 models,** proceed as follows:
   a. Check 30 amp fuse in ABS fuse panel.
   b. Check valves as outlined in "Valve Test Mode."
   c. Check wheel sensors as outlined in "Monitor Mode."
   d. Check wiring between ECU pin 10 and pin of the pressure switch.
   e. Check wiring between pin 3 of the pressure switch and pin 2 on the fluid level indicator.
   f. Check wiring between pin 1 of the fluid level indicator and ECU pin 9.
   g. Check function of the pressure switch, contacts 3 and 5 should be closed when pressure is above 105 bar (1523 psi).
   h. Check function of fluid level indicator.
   i. Check wiring from ECU pins 3 and 20 to pin 30 on the system relay.
   j. Check wiring between connector

75 and pin 87 on the system relay.
  k. Check wiring between ECU pin 8 and pin 86 on system relay.
  l. Check for break or short circuit between pins 85 and 86 on the system relay.
  m. Check wiring between pin 85 of system relay and ground point 93.
  n. If fuses and wiring are satisfactory, replace ECU.
3. **On 9000 models,** proceed as follows:
  a. Check wiring between pin 10 of the ECU and pin 5 of the pressure switch.
  b. Check wiring between pin 3 of the pressure switch and pin 2 of the fluid level indicator.
  c. Check wiring between pin 1 of the fluid level indicator and pin 9 of the ECU.
  d. Check function of the pressure switch, contacts 3 and 5 should be closed if pressure is above 105 bar (1523 psi).
  e. Check function of fluid level indicator.
  f. If pressure switch, fluid level indicator and wiring are satisfactory, replace ECU.

DIAGNOSTIC TROUBLE CODE E011

1. This diagnostic trouble code indicates there is a break in continuity between pin 11 of the ECU and pin 1 on the valve block connector.
2. Check wiring between ECU pin 11 and pin 1 of valve block connector, repair as necessary.
3. Ensure ground point 300 of the hydraulic unit is secure.

DIAGNOSTIC TROUBLE CODE E014

1. This diagnostic trouble code indicates a defective pump relay or pressure switch, this diagnostic trouble code is tripped if terminal 14 of the ECU has sensed continuous pump operation for more than 90 seconds during testing.
2. **On 900 models,** check 10 amp ABS fuse on ABS fuse panel and 10 amp fuse on main fuse panel.
3. **On 9000 models,** check 10 amp ABS fuse on ABS fuse panel.
4. **On all models,** if pressure is below 140 bar (2030 psi), ensure switch between terminals 1 and 4 on the pressure switch is closed.
5. **On 900 models,** check wiring between connector 75 and pin 86 on the pump relay.
6. **On 9000 models,** check wiring between 54 terminal of the ignition switch and pin 86 on the pump relay.
7. **On all models,** check wiring between pin 85 on the pump relay and pin 4 on the pressure switch.
8. **On 900 models,** check wiring between pin 1 on the pressure switch and ground point 93.
9. **On 9000 models,** check wiring between pin 1 on the pressure switch and ground point 7.
10. **On all models,** check wiring between pin 85 on the pump relay and pin 14 on the ECU.
11. If wiring is satisfactory, replace pump relay.

DIAGNOSTIC TROUBLE CODES E015, E016, E017, E018, E033, E034 & E035

1. These diagnostic trouble codes indicate the following inlet and outlet valve faults:
  a. Diagnostic trouble code E015, right front inlet valve is defective.
  b. Diagnostic trouble code E016, rear outlet valve is defective.
  c. Diagnostic trouble code E017, rear inlet valve is defective.
  d. Diagnostic trouble code E018, main valve is defective.
  e. Diagnostic trouble code E033, front left outlet valve is defective.
  f. Diagnostic trouble code E034, front right outlet valve is defective.
  g. Diagnostic trouble code E035, front left inlet valve is defective.
2. Check wiring as follows:
  a. Diagnostic trouble code E015, check between pin 7 of the valve block connector and pin 15 of the ECU.
  b. Diagnostic trouble code E016, check between pin 4 of the valve block connector and pin 33 of the ECU.
  c. Diagnostic trouble code E017, check between pin 5 of the valve block connector and pin 17 of the ECU.
  d. Diagnostic trouble code E018, check between main valve connector and pin 18 of the ECU.
  e. Diagnostic trouble code E033, check between pin 3 of the valve block connector and pin 16 of the ECU.
  f. Diagnostic trouble code E034, check between pin 6 of the valve block connector and pin 34 of the ECU.
  g. Diagnostic trouble code E034, check between pin 2 of the valve block connector and pin 35 of the ECU.
3. If wiring is satisfactory, replace valve block.

DIAGNOSTIC TROUBLE CODES EE22, EE23, EE24 & EE25

1. These error codes indicate sensor wheel runout, replace sensor wheel as follows:
  a. Diagnostic trouble code EE22, right rear sensor wheel.
  b. Diagnostic trouble code EE23, left front sensor wheel.
  c. Diagnostic trouble code EE24, left rear sensor wheel.
  d. Diagnostic trouble code EE25, right front sensor wheel.

DIAGNOSTIC TROUBLE CODE E032

1. This diagnostic trouble code indicates a defective pump relay. This diagnostic trouble code is triggered if signal level at pins 14 and 32 of the ECU has been the same for more than 40 seconds.
2. Check 30 amp fuse of the ABS fuse panel.
3. Check wiring between connector 75 and pin 30 on the pump relay.
4. Check wiring between pin 32 of the ECU and pin 87 on the pump relay.
5. Check wiring between pin 87 on the pump relay and pin 1 on the pump motor.
6. Check for break in circuit continuity or short circuit between pins 85 and 86 of the pump relay.
7. **On 900 models,** check wiring between pin 2 on pump motor and ground point 93.
8. **On 9000 models,** check wiring between pin 2 on pump motor and ground point 7.
9. **On all models,** if wiring is satisfactory, replace pump relay.

DIAGNOSTIC TROUBLE CODE E132

1. This diagnostic trouble code indicates hydraulic pump is running continuously. This diagnostic trouble code can be triggered only if ECU terminal 32 has been energized for more than 90 seconds during testing.
2. Check wiring between pin 14 on the ECU and pin 85 on the pump relay.
3. Check wiring between pin 85 on the pump relay and pin 4 on the pressure switch.
4. If hydraulic pressure is higher than 180 bar (2610 psi), check if switch between pins 1 and 4 on the pressure switch is open.
5. If switch is not open and wiring is satisfactory, replace pump relay.

DIAGNOSTIC TROUBLE CODE PRES

1. This diagnostic trouble code indicates hydraulic pressure to pressure switch is low.
2. Ensure pressure switch connections are satisfactory.
3. Check level in brake fluid reservoir.
4. **On 900 models,** check wiring between pin 1 on the pump and ground point 93.
5. **On 9000 models,** check wiring between pin 1 on the pump and ground point 7.
6. **On all models,** if pressure switch connections, brake fluid level and wiring are satisfactory, replace pump.

SYSTEM SERVICE

Brake System Bleed

Front brake calipers must be bled first.

1. Fill fluid reservoir to the top.
2. Connect a length of transparent hose to right front caliper bleed nipple and place other end of hose into a clear container.
3. While depressing brake pedal, open bleed nipple. Repeat until there are no more air bubbles visible in hose.
4. Connect hose to left front caliper and repeat bleed process.

5. Connect hose to rear caliper, switch on ignition and repeat bleed process. **Pump motor must not run for more than two minutes at a time. After motor has been running, let it cool for approximately 10 minutes.** Repeat on the other rear caliper, then fill fluid reservoir.

Component Replacement

SYSTEM PRESSURE RELIEF

Prior to beginning work, system must be depressurized. To depressurize the system, turn ignition switch off and press brake pedal down about 20 times until positive resistance is felt in the pedal. The hydraulic unit and its connections must also be thoroughly cleaned, to prevent dirt from entering the hydraulic system.

BRAKE FLUID RESERVOIR

1. Remove accumulator as outlined in "Accumulator, Replace."
2. Remove hydraulic unit as outlined in "Hydraulic Unit, Replace."
3. Disconnect pump inlet hose from brake fluid reservoir, then remove reservoir to hydraulic unit attaching screw.
4. Lift reservoir off hydraulic unit, then remove rubber bushings from hydraulic unit. **Take care not to lose spacer and O-ring on rear connection.**
5. Reverse procedure to install, noting the following:
   a. Install two new rubber bushings into hydraulic unit.
   b. Bleed brake system as outlined in "Brake System Bleed."
   c. Switch ignition on and ensure brake-warning and ABS-warning lights go off.

HYDRAULIC UNIT

900

1. Remove lower trim panel from under the steering wheel.
2. Remove heater duct, sound insulation from behind brake pedal, disconnect lefthand side defroster hose.
3. Remove hydraulic pushrod pin retaining clip, then the pin from the pushrod.
4. Remove air intake hose and coolant tank retaining bolts, then position coolant tank aside.
5. Disconnect hydraulic unit electrical connectors.
6. Remove retaining bolt from bracket between hydraulic unit and front assembly, then move bracket and electrical leads out of the way.
7. Siphon as much fluid as possible from reservoir.
8. **On models with manual transaxle,** disconnect and plug hose for clutch cylinder.
9. **On all models,** unplug electrical connector for the pump motor at the hydraulic unit.
10. Label brake hydraulic pipes and large bore return pipe.
11. Disconnect brake pipes from valve block, then plug all pipes to prevent dirt from entering system.
12. Remove hydraulic unit retaining nuts, then the hydraulic unit.
13. Reverse procedure to install, noting the following:
    a. **Torque** hydraulic unit retaining nuts to 16–22 ft. lbs.
    b. Switch ignition on and ensure pump is operating.
    c. Bleed brake system as outlined in "Brake System Bleed."

9000

1. Remove lower trim panel from under the steering wheel.
2. Remove hydraulic pushrod pin retaining clip, then the pin from the pushrod.
3. To gain access to the hydraulic unit, remove the following:
   a. Remove battery.
   b. Two clips for positive battery lead at bottom of battery shelf.
   c. Terminal block with leads from battery shelf.
   d. Bracket and connector at rear of battery shelf.
   e. Fuel filter from battery shelf, then the battery shelf.
4. Remove steady bar between fender and subframe.
5. Position fuel filter aside, then siphon as much fluid as possible from reservoir.
6. Remove lefthand front wheel and wheelwell liner.
7. Remove steady bar between fender and subframe.
8. Disconnect hydraulic unit electrical connectors.
9. Remove ground lead retaining clip and ground lead.
10. **On models with manual transaxle,** disconnect and plug hose for clutch cylinder.
11. **On all models,** label brake hydraulic pipes, then disconnect brake pipes from valve block.
12. Plug all pipes to prevent dirt from entering system.
13. Remove accumulator from hydraulic unit, then the hydraulic unit retaining nuts and hydraulic unit from bulkhead.
14. Reverse procedure to install, noting the following:
    a. **Torque** hydraulic unit retaining nuts to 16–22 ft. lbs.
    b. **Torque** accumulator to hydraulic unit retaining nuts to 2B4 ft. lbs.
    c. Switch ignition on and ensure pump is operating.
    d. Bleed brake system as outlined in "Brake System Bleed."

ACCUMULATOR

900

1. Depressurize system as outlined in "Hydraulic Unit, Replace," prior to beginning work.
2. Using a suitable 8 mm Allen key, remove accumulator retaining bolt.
3. Remove accumulator from vehicle.
4. Reverse procedure to install, noting the following:
   a. Install new O-ring.
   b. **Torque** accumulator attaching bolt to 2B4 ft. lbs.
   c. Turn ignition switch on and ensure brake and ABS warning lights go off.

9000

1. Depressurize system as outlined in "Hydraulic Unit, Replace," prior to beginning work.
2. Remove battery.
3. Remove fuel filter from battery shelf, then position aside.
4. Remove accumulator from vehicle.
5. Reverse procedure to install, noting the following:
   a. Install new O-ring.
   b. **Torque** accumulator attaching bolt to 2B4 ft. lbs.
   c. Turn ignition switch on and ensure brake and ABS warning lights go off.

PRESSURE SWITCH

900

1. Depressurize system as outlined in "Hydraulic Unit, Replace," prior to beginning work.
2. Remove rubber damper from pump delivery pipe.
3. Disconnect pressure switch electrical connector.
4. Using socket tool No. 89 96 571, or equivalent, remove pressure switch.
5. Reverse procedure to install, noting the following:
   a. Fit new O-ring onto pressure switch.
   b. **Torque** pressure switch to 15–19 ft. lbs.
   c. Switch ignition on to ensure brake and ABS warning lights go off.

9000

1. Depressurize system as outlined in "Hydraulic Unit, Replace," prior to beginning work.
2. Remove rubber covering from delivery pipe.
3. Disconnect pressure switch electrical connector.
4. Using socket tool No. 89 96 571, or equivalent, remove pressure switch.
5. Reverse procedure to install, noting the following:
   a. Fit new O-ring onto pressure switch.
   b. **Torque** pressure switch to 15–19 ft. lbs.
   c. Switch ignition on to ensure brake and ABS warning lights go off.

PUMP DELIVERY LINE

900

1. **Depressurize system as outlined in "Hydraulic Unit, Replacement," prior to beginning work.**
2. Remove air intake, then remove coolant expansion tank retaining bolt and position tank aside.
3. Siphon hydraulic fluid from the fluid reservoir.
4. Disconnect electrical connector for fluid level indicator.
5. **On models equipped with manual**

transaxle, disconnect and plug end of hose for clutch cylinder.
6. **On all models,** remove reservoir retaining screw, then lift reservoir off of hydraulic unit.
7. Disconnect rear brake pipe on the hydraulic unit to gain access to pump delivery pipe coupling.
8. Remove pump delivery pipe, plug two openings for pipe unit.
9. Reverse procedure to install, bleed brake system as outlined in "Brake System Bleed."

9000

1. Remove hydraulic unit as outlined in "Hydraulic Unit, Replace."
2. Remove pump delivery pipe from hydraulic unit and plug both openings.
3. Reverse procedure to install, bleed brake system as outlined in "Brake System Bleed."

PUMP & MOTOR UNIT

900

1. Remove hydraulic unit as outlined in "Hydraulic Unit, Replace."
2. Remove pump delivery pipe from pump unit.
3. Pry back catch and unplug motor electrical connector.
4. Disconnect inlet hose from pump unit, then remove screw at front of pump unit.
5. Remove dampers, spacers and washers.
6. Remove pump and motor from rear mounting, then the pressure switch.
7. Reverse procedure to install, noting the following:
   a. Install a new O-ring on the pressure switch.
   b. Assemble dampers, washers and spacers, **Fig. 11,** then install front securing screw.
   c. Bleed brake system as outlined in "Brake System Bleed."

9000

1. Remove hydraulic unit as outlined in "Hydraulic Unit, Replace."
2. Remove pump delivery pipe from pump, then plug port in pump unit.
3. Release catch and unplug electrical connector.
4. Disconnect pump inlet hose from pump.
5. Remove securing bolt from front of pump unit. **When removing washers, note their position for assembly reference.**
6. Lift pump unit out of rear mounting, then remove pressure switch.
7. Reverse procedure to install, noting the following:
   a. Install a new O-ring, then **torque** pressure switch to 15–19 ft. lbs.
   b. Position washers in order they were removed, then install securing bolt.
   c. Bleed brake system as outlined in "Brake System Bleed."
   d. Switch ignition on to ensure brake and ABS warning lights go off.

VALVE BLOCK

900

1. **Depressurize system as outlined in "Hydraulic Unit, Replace," prior to beginning work.**
2. Remove air intake, then remove coolant expansion tank retaining bolt and position tank aside.
3. Siphon hydraulic fluid from the fluid reservoir.
4. Disconnect electrical connector on valve block.
5. Disconnect brake hydraulic pipes from underside of valve block.
6. Disconnect remaining brake hydraulic pipes and large bore return pipe from valve block.
7. Loosen nut on cover underneath brake hydraulic pipes.
8. Pull brake pipes and return pipe away from valve body, then plug ends of pipes.
9. Cut tie that secures wiring harness to valve block.
10. Remove three retaining nuts and remove valve block.
11. Reverse procedure to install, bleed brake system as outlined in "Brake System Bleed," then switch ignition on to ensure brake and ABS warning lights go off.

ECU

1. **On 9000 models,** remove cover from rear lefthand side of engine compartment.
2. **On all models,** remove ECU attaching bolts.
3. Disconnect ECU electrical connector, then remove ECU.
4. Reverse procedure to install.

WHEEL SENSORS

900

Front

1. Disconnect sensor lead connector for each wheel, lead connectors are located in the engine compartment.
2. Raise and support front of vehicle, then remove wheel.
3. Pull sensor lead from guide and rubber grommet on wheelwell.
4. Remove sensor retaining screw from caliper, then the sensor.
5. Reverse procedure to install, bleed brake system as outlined in "Brake System Bleed," then switch ignition on to ensure brake and ABS warning lights go off.

Rear

1. Disconnect sensor lead located under the rear seat.
2. Raise and support rear of vehicle, then remove wheel.
3. Pull sensor lead through rubber grommet on floor.
4. Remove parking brake cable to suspension arm securing clip.
5. Release sensor lead from guide on back of suspension arm.
6. Remove sensor retaining screw from caliper, then the sensor.
7. Reverse procedure to install, bleed brake system as outlined in "Brake System Bleed," then switch ignition on to ensure brake and ABS warning lights go off.

9000

Front

1. Disconnect sensor lead connector for each wheel, lead connectors are located in the engine compartment.
2. Remove cover over space behind false bulkhead panel at rear lefthand side of engine compartment.
3. Lift rubber molding on false bulkhead panel and remove plastic clip on the panel.
4. Remove cover from fresh air filter at false bulkhead panel on the rear righthand side of engine compartment.
5. Undo pipe clips for A/C flow and return pipes, then raise A/C pipes and pull sensor lead through.
6. Loosen bolt securing false bulkhead panel and raise panel enough to allow sensor lead to be pulled under the panel.
7. Raise and support vehicle, then remove wheel assembly.
8. Remove wheelwell liner rear section, then cut through tie holding sensor lead to top bracket.
9. Pull sensor lead through rubber grommet on wheelwell.
10. Remove sensor retaining bolt and sensor.
11. Reverse procedure to install.

Rear

1. Tilt rear seat forward and remove cover.
2. Disconnect sensor lead connector.
3. Raise and support rear of vehicle, then remove rear wheel.
4. Undo clip and pull sensor lead through rubber grommet on floor.
5. Remove sensor retaining bolt and sensor.
6. Reverse procedure to install.

Mark II Anti-Lock Brake System w/Traction Control

NOTE: On Air Bag Equipped Models, Refer To "Air Bag System Precautions" Located In The Front Of This Manual For System Disarming & Arming Procedures.

NOTE: "Electrical Symbol & Wire Color Code Identification" Located In The Front Of This Manual May Be Used As An Aid When Using Wiring Circuits Found In This Section.

INDEX

	Page No.
Description	7-108
Components	7-109
System	7-108
Diagnosis & Testing	7-110
Accessing Diagnostic Trouble Codes	7-110
Diagnostic Trouble Code Interpretation	7-110
TC/ABS Control Unit Pin Inspection	7-117
Precautions	7-108
Air Bag Systems	7-108
Battery Ground Cable	7-108
Radio Anti-Theft Lock	7-108
System Service	7-117
Brake System Bleed	7-118
Component Replacement	7-118
Control Valve For Turbo Bypass Valve	7-118
Non-Return Valve	7-118
Safety Valve	7-118
TC/ABS ECU	7-118
TC/ABS Hydraulic Unit	7-118
ETS ECU Calibration	7-117
Troubleshooting	7-109

PRECAUTIONS

AIR BAG SYSTEMS

Refer to "Air Bag System Precautions" in the front of this manual for system disarming and arming procedures.

RADIO ANTI-THEFT LOCK

Radio and cassette player are equipped with an electronic four-digit anti-theft lock. This four-digit code is programmed at manufacturing and cannot be changed. If the battery is disconnected for more than three minutes, if unit is removed or if otherwise cut off from power, the four-digit code must be entered with the quick-selection buttons as follows:

1. Turn radio on, then, when display shows "Code In," enter four-digit code with quick-selection buttons. If code is correct, last-tuned radio frequency is shown on display. If wrong digit has been entered by mistake, all four digits must be entered again. If code is wrong it stays on display.
2. If incorrect four-digit code has been entered, press Band button for more than three seconds to clear display. Display shows "Code In" and new attempt to enter correct code can be made.
3. If wrong code has been used three times in succession, four dashes appear on display and you must wait an hour with radio switched on before trying again.
4. To try again, hold Band button for at least three seconds. "Code In" should appear on display.
5. Correct code must be entered at first attempt, otherwise you must wait another hour with unit switched on before trying again.

BATTERY GROUND CABLE

Prior to service, disconnect battery ground cable and isolate as required.

DESCRIPTION

SYSTEM

Traction Control System (TCS) prevents wheel spin when the vehicle is accelerating on a slippery surface.

The TCS system for manual transaxles consists of two subsystems, Anti-Lock Braking System (ABS) and Electronic Throttle System (ETS).

The TCS system utilizes many of the components in the ABS system. The major difference is the addition of the Electronic Throttle System. Refer to "Traction Control System" section for ETS information.

The Manual transaxle TCS has the capability to apply the front brakes independently during low speed wheel spin and also the ability to close the throttle butterfly to reduce wheel spin at any speed.

TRACTION CONTROL SYSTEM OPERATION

This system uses the speed of the rear wheels as a reference speed against the speed of each front wheel. If the speed of a front wheel exceeds that of the reference speed from the rear wheels, the condition is known as wheel spin. The magnitude of the spin together with the speed of the vehicle determine how the system operates.

To enable the vehicle to achieve maximum traction, a certain amount of wheel spin, which varies depending on the speed of the car, is allowed.

Low Speed Operating Mode

The front wheel having the poorer grip (lower friction) starts to spin first.

When wheel spin has reached a speed of just under 10 mph, TCS control is initiated and the TC/ABS system applies the brake for that wheel. As brake is applied to the wheel, additional torque is transferred to the other wheel, which still is maintaining good traction. If the road surface is very slippery, the other wheel may also start to spin, if it does, once it is spinning at a speed of about 4 mph, the amount of throttle is reduced electronically, inhibiting further wheel spin.

So the system is able to provide the optimum combination of traction and steering precision with the same traction or mobility as that provided by a conventional limited-slip differential.

The upper limit for the amount of wheel spin allowed before the TCS takes over is gradually reduced up to a speed of about 12 mph, after which it remains constant regardless of how much throttle is used, although the upper limit for braking will then be increased.

High Speed Operating Mode (Over 25 mph)

Once the vehicle reaches a speed of about 25 mph, the system switches mode and initiates throttle control when the first wheel starts spinning. Traction control by application of the brake will be initiated for the other wheel if the amount of wheel spin is great enough.

Up to a speed of about 37 mph, wheel spin of up to just under 2 mph is allowed, after which an increase of about 5 percent relative to the increased speed of the vehicle will be allowed.

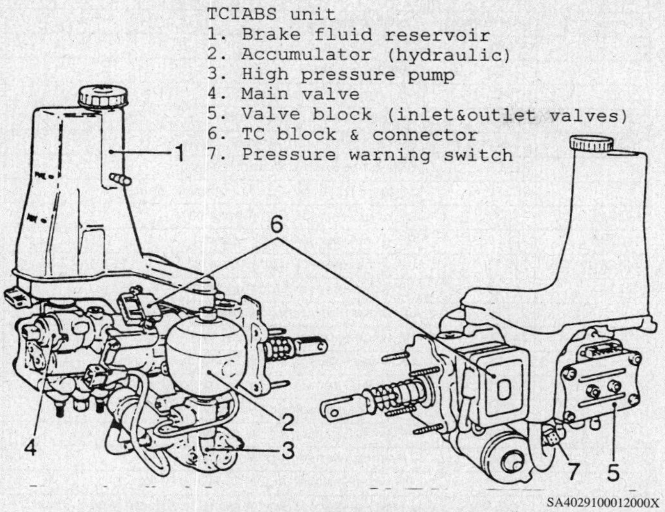

Fig. 1 Hydraulic unit components

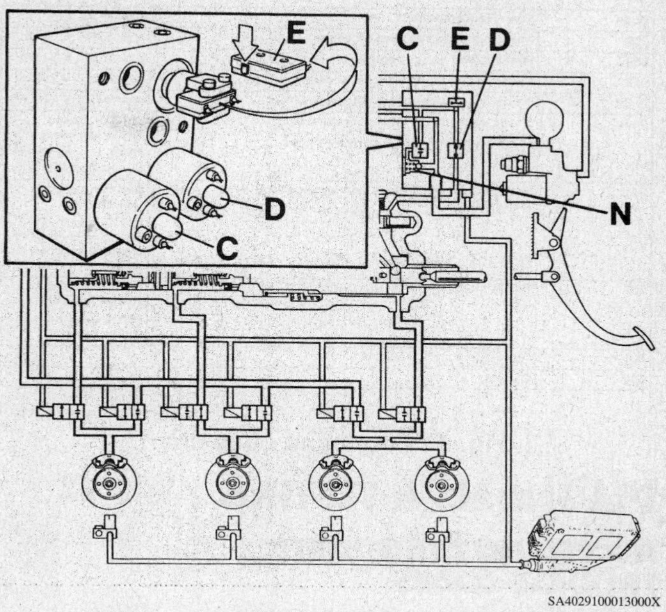

Fig. 2 TCS valve block components

So at speed of 87 mph, for instance, wheel spin of approximately 4.4 mph will be allowed before electronic control of the throttle is initiated.

System Interaction

Conventional operation of the ABS system is the same as before, but an additional valve block (TC block) for the anti-spin function has been added onto the hydraulic unit.

The TC block, together with the main valve, wheel sensors and inlet and outlet valves are the main components of the TC/ABS system. The system is equipped with indicator/warning lights for monitoring and checking of the system. These warning lights indicate when the system is operating and provide a warning if a fault should occur.

The wheel sensors send wheel speed information to the ABS ECU. Using the average speed of the rear wheels as a reference value, the ECU continuously monitors the amount of wheel spin in the front wheels (speed above reference value for rear wheels).

When the system detects a tendency for wheel spin and the TCS calls for braking of the front wheel concerned, pressure is directed from the accumulator through the TC block and main valve to the front wheel circuits. The inlet and outlet valves then control the TCS initiated braking.

COMPONENTS

ELECTRONIC CONTROL UNIT (TC/ABS ECU)

The ECU is programmed to detect both permanent and intermittent faults. Faults detected by the ECU are stored in an EEPROM chip, so the diagnostic trouble codes remain in memory even when power supply is switched off or interrupted.

TC/ABS HYDRAULIC UNIT

The main components of the hydraulic unit, **Fig. 1,** are the brake fluid reservoir, fluid level switch, accumulator and a pressure warning switch.

TCS VALVE BLOCK

In contrast to the conventional ABS unit. the TC/ABS unit has a separate valve block (TC block), **Fig. 2,** to direct accumulator pressure for TC controlled braking to the appropriate wheel.

The pressure is directed to the front wheel circuits through the main valve and is modulated by the inlet and outlet valves for the front wheel indicating spin.

The TC block, **Fig. 2,** includes two control valves (C and D), a pressure reducing valve (N) and a pressure switch (E). The function of the control valve is to direct hydraulic pressure as required, depending on whether braking is TCS controlled or required for modulation in conjunction with ABS control.

TROUBLESHOOTING

1. The diagnostic socket (green) is located below the righthand front seat.
2. During fault diagnosis, the ignition switch must always be in the On position.
3. The ISAT system number for the TC/ABS system is number 3.
4. Always read off and note down all stored diagnostic trouble codes before disconnecting the battery or ECU.
5. If communication cannot be established between ISAT and the ECU, check the leads between ECU pins 23 and 42 and the diagnostic socket. Also ensure the power feed and ground circuits to the diagnostic socket are good and the connector pins are not damaged.
6. Once diagnostic trouble codes stored in the systems's ECU have been transferred to ISAT, the diagnosis function is finished. The technician should next enter any command codes which apply to the problem which exists. It is sometimes quite helpful to enter All command codes to check the status of certain signals and components before proceeding with the detailed diagnostic procedure.
7. To avoid doing damage to the ECU, ensure the ignition is off before unplugging the connector.
8. Before tracing faults on a vehicle's electronic systems, always start by checking that the grounding circuits for the ECU concerned are good and that all nominal voltage levels are correct.
9. Unplug connectors and plugs to check the pins are undamaged and not loose. After checking, plug in all connectors and clear all diagnostic trouble codes. Start engine or drive vehicle again to ensure the fault or faults persist.
10. When first detected, a fault will be assigned a permanent diagnostic trouble code. If the fault later disappears, the fault will be classified as intermittent.
11. All signals around the 12 volt level are proportional to battery voltage. These levels must therefore be taken only as a rough guide.
12. Zero voltage signal levels indicate ground, although a sensitive multimeter may indicate a value slightly above zero volts.
13. When ISAT command codes are being used to test the system while the vehicle is being driven, communication between ISAT and the ECU will be broken if the speed of the vehicle exceeds 12 mph.
14. If no diagnostic trouble codes can be read from the system even though the warning lights are On, start by checking the safety circuit (pin 8 and 51).
15. Never use the breakout box when vehicle is being driven.

Code	Function/Component	Display Text
259	Reads speed signal from LF wheel sensor	e.g. 80020 = 20 km/h
25A	Reads speed signal from RF wheel sensor	e.g. 80020 = 20 km/h
25B	Reads speed signal from LR wheel sensor	e.g. 80020 = 20 km/h
25C	Reads speed signal from RR wheel sensor	e.g. 80020 = 20 km/h
200	Shows status of TC-block pressure switch (Manual transmission TCS version only)	8B100 = closed (brake released) 8B000 = open (brake applied)
201	Shows status of pressure and level-warning switch (safety circuit)	8B100 = closed (system OK) 8B000 = open (low fluid level or low pressure or open circuit)
202	Shows status of brake-light switch	8B100 = closed (brake applied) 8B000 = open (brake released)
800	Terminate communications	
900	Clear all fault codes	

SA4029100014000X

Fig. 3 Command code chart

Permanent	Intermittent	Component/signal
	775B1	ECU fault
	775B2	ECU fault (RAM)
E7061	F7061	No communication with ETS
32251	22251	System-relay function faulty
35321	25321	Brake-light switch function faulty
	36521	Pressure switch function faulty
	36522	Safety circuit, pins 8-51, open or shorted
44221	24221	LF wheel-sensor signal absent
44222	24222	RF wheel-sensor signal absent
44223	24223	LR wheel-sensor signal absent
44224	24224	RR wheel-sensor signal absent
	2422A	LF wheel-sensor signal faulty (>40 km h)
	2422B	RF wheel-sensor signal faulty (>40 km h)
	2422C	LR wheel-sensor signal faulty (>40 km h)
	2422D	RR wheel-sensor signal faulty (>40 km h)
	24291	LF wheel-sensor signal faulty (<40 km h)
	24292	RF wheel-sensor signal faulty (<40 km h)
	24293	LR wheel-sensor signal faulty (<40 km h)
	24294	RR wheel-sensor signal faulty (<40 km h)
	24251	LF wheel-sensor signal faulty (compare wheel speed)
	24252	RF wheel-sensor signal faulty (compare wheel speed)
	24253	LR wheel-sensor signal faulty (compare wheel speed)
	24254	RR wheel-sensor signal faulty (compare wheel speed)
53427	33427	Main valve fault
53428	33428	NC TC-block valve fault
53429	33429	NO TC-block valve fault
53421	33421	LF inlet valve fault
53422	33422	LF outlet valve fault
53423	33423	RF inlet valve fault
53424	33424	RF outlet valve fault
53425	33425	Rear inlet valve fault
53426	33426	Rear outlet valve fault
	234B1	LF outlet valve hydraulic fault
	234B2	RF outlet valve hydraulic fault
	234B3	Rear outlet valve hydraulic fault
	234B4	Rear outlet valve hydraulic fault
		Warning light diagnostics

SA4029100015000X

Fig. 4 TC/ABS diagnostic trouble code chart

DIAGNOSIS & TESTING

ACCESSING DIAGNOSTIC TROUBLE CODES

Command codes instruct the ECU to perform certain functions while diagnosing diagnostic trouble codes.

Refer to **Fig. 3** for ISAT command codes.

The ECU connector on the wiring loom is in the form of a molded plug, test probes cannot be connected to the back of the connector.

Use breakout box 8611006 with test lead set 8611030, which should be connected between the ECU and the connector.

All measurements on the system must be made with breakout box connected.

To access diagnostic trouble codes, connect ISAT tester to diagnostic socket (green), located under righthand front seat, then follow instructions included with tester.

DIAGNOSTIC TROUBLE CODE INTERPRETATION

Refer to **Fig. 4** for diagnostic trouble code identification and **Fig. 5 and Fig. 6,** for system wiring diagram.

DIAGNOSTIC TROUBLE CODE 3/22251

If another diagnostic trouble code other than 32251 or 22251 exists, diagnose that diagnostic trouble code(s) first.

1. Ensure battery voltage is present at pins 3, 33 and 35.
   a. If no voltage is present at all pins, check ABS 30A fuse for the 30 feed (fuse box at bulkhead), RD lead from fuse to system relay and to terminal block on battery shelf.
   b. If voltage is present at one of the pins, check lead from ECU pin to system relay.
   c. If voltage is present at pin 35 only, check system relay operating circuit and that no other diagnostic trouble codes exist for faults that could cause exciter circuit to be open.
2. If no voltage is present at pins 34, 3 and 33, check 10A fuse (ABS).
   a. If fuse is good, check live feed to pin 53. If no voltage is present at pin 53, go to step e.
   b. If voltage is present at pin 53, check GN lead between pin 86 on system relay and ECU pin 34.
   c. Ensure voltage is present at system relay pin 85. If not, go to step f.
   d. If voltage exists, try a new system relay.
   e. If no voltage exits at pin 53, check RD/WH lead as far as the fuse, and the feed in the lead from pin 54 of ignition switch to the live side of ABS fuse.
   f. Check BK lead from pin 85 on system relay through pump relay to 10A fuse.
3. If there is battery voltage at pin 34 but not at pins 3 and 33, operating circuit is satisfactory but ECU has failed to ground the circuit because of another fault in ABS system.
4. If battery voltage is reaching pin 34 but diagnostic trouble code 3/22251 is still being generated, check resistance across relay pins 85 and 86. Resistance should be approximately 75 ohms.

DIAGNOSTIC TROUBLE CODE 36522

There are three different conditions associated with diagnostic trouble code 36522 and the safety circuit. For complete test procedure of this circuit, follow the fault tracing procedure for all three conditions.

Short To 12V

1. With ignition in Drive position, enter ISAT command code 201. If display shows 8B100, it indicates continuity from pin 8 to pin 51. If display shows 8B000, it indicates an open circuit.
2. With ignition in Off position, remove ECU and connect breakout box. With ignition in Drive position, ensure voltage exists across pin 8 and ground and across pin 51 and ground.
   a. If voltage exists, check circuit between pins 8 and 51 for short to 12V.
   b. If voltage does not exist, turn ignition to Off position, fit and connect ECU, then clear diagnostic trouble code and see if it is regenerated.
3. If diagnostic trouble code 36522 is regenerated, continue with "Short To

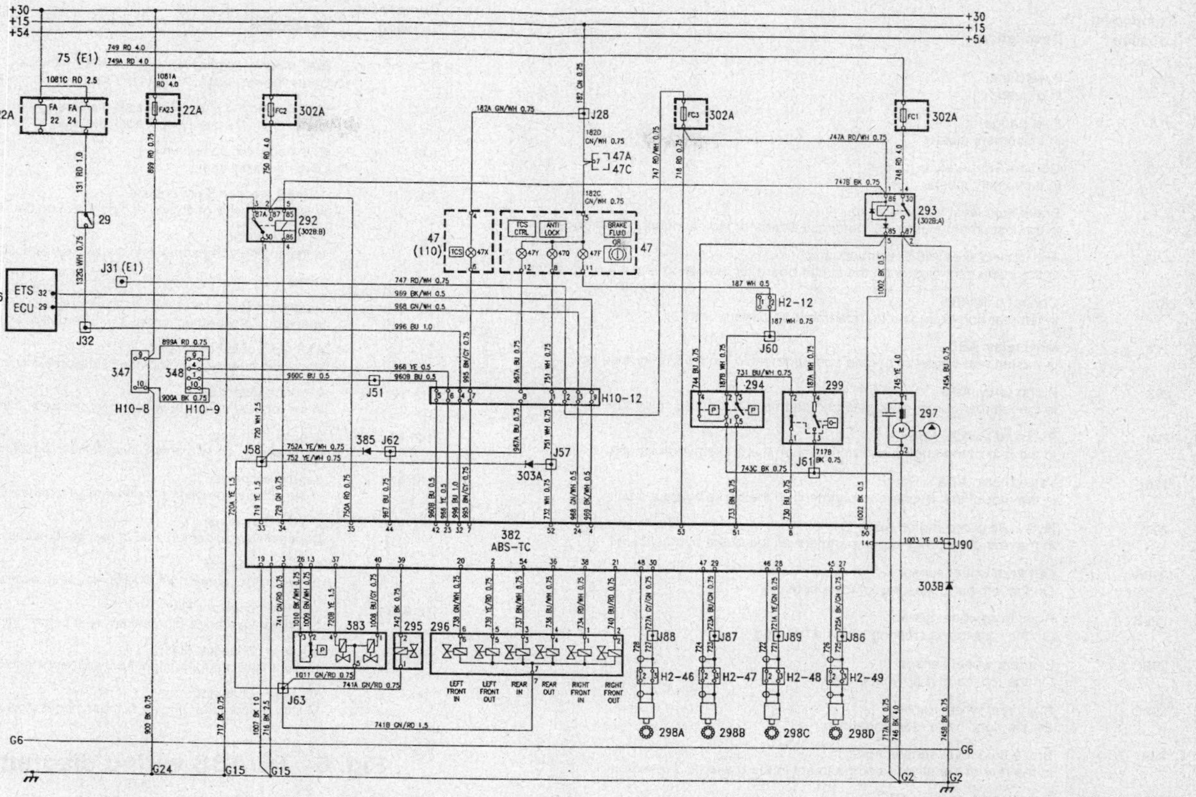

SA4029100016030X

Fig. 5 TC/ABS wiring diagram (Part 1 of 3)

Ground" test procedure. If no other faults are found after test procedure is completed, replace ECU.

Short To Ground

1. With ignition in Drive position, enter ISAT command code 201. If display shows 8B100, it indicates continuity from pin 8 to pin 51. If display shows 8B000, it indicates an open circuit.
2. Turn ignition to Off position, remove ECU and connect breakout box.
3. Measure resistance across pin 8 and ground and across pin 51 and ground. Resistance should be infinity.
4. If resistance is not infinity, check leads and connections for short to ground.

Open Circuit

1. With ignition in On position, ensure pump is running and check brake fluid level.
   a. If brake fluid level is low, check system for leaks. Add brake fluid if necessary to bring to correct level.
   b. If pump is not running or pressure is below 1522 psi, check fuse for pump (ABS 30A) and pump relay operating circuit (ABS 10A).
   c. If fluid level, pump and pressure are satisfactory, go to next step and check safety circuit.
2. With ignition in Drive position, enter ISAT command code 201. If display shows 8B100, it indicates circuit continuity. If display shows 8B000, it indicates an open circuit. With ignition in Off position, connect breakout box. Measure resistance across pins 8 and 51 to determine whether circuit has continuity or is open.
3. If circuit is open, check circuit continuity as follows:
   a. Between ECU pin 8 and pin 1 on reservoir switch.
   b. Between pins 1 and 2 on reservoir switch.
   c. Between pin 2 at reservoir and pin 3 on pressure-warning switch.
   d. Between pins 3 and 5 on pressure-warning switch.
   e. Between pin 5 on pressure-warning switch and ECU pin 51.
4. Discharge accumulator, then with ignition in On position, check for battery voltage at pin 14 (pump relay operation).
   a. If voltage does not exist, go to step 6.
   b. If voltage exists, switch ignition to Off position, check motor winding by measuring resistance across pin 14 and ground.
   c. Resistance should be approximately 10 ohms. If not, check resistance across pins 1 and 2 on motor.
   d. If resistance is as specified, check YE lead between pin 1 on motor and pin 87 on pump relay, then BK lead between pin 2 on motor and grounding point G2.
   e. Check diode circuit between pin 87 on pump relay and ground by removing relay and disconnecting pump connector before measuring resistance.
   f. Ensure diode has continuity in one direction and no continuity in the other direction.
5. If the fault has not been found at this point of diagnosis, replace pump.
6. With ignition in On position and pump not running, ensure battery voltage is reaching ECU pin 50. If not, ensure voltage is reaching pins 85 and 86 on pump relay and the 10-A fuse. Ensure circuit continuity in leads from pin 86 on pump relay via fuse holder to pin 54 on ignition switch.
7. If voltage exists at pin 86 but not at pin 85, replace pump relay.
8. If battery voltage exists at pin 50, exciter circuit is satisfactory but is not being grounded by pressure-warning switch.
   a. With ignition in Off position, accumulator discharged and ECU connector disconnected, ensure pressure-warning switch is closed by measuring circuit continuity between pin 50 and ground.
   b. If a fault is found in circuit, check BU lead between pump relay pin 85 and pin 4 on pressure-warning switch, between pins 4 and 1 on switch, then check BK lead between pin 1 on switch and ground.
9. If continuity does not exist between pins 1 and 4 on pressure-warning

Component Location	Description
22A	Fuse panel In glovebox
47A	Fuel gauge In instrument cluster
47C	Coolant temperature gauge In instrument cluster
47F	Brake fluid level warning lamp In the instrument cluster on the circuit board for indicating and warning lamps
47Q	Anti-lock brakes (ABS) warning lamp In the instrument cluster on the circuit board for indicating and warning lamps
291	Control unit, ABS In left rear corner engine compartment on battery bracket
292	Main relay, ABS In the left rear corner of engine compartment in the ABS relay/fuse box
293	Pump relay, ABS In the left rear corner of engine compartment in the ABS relay/fuse box
294	Pressure switch, ABS In the rear of the engine compartment on the brake hydraulic unit
296	Valve block, ABS In the rear of the engine compartment on the brake hydraulic unit
297	Hydraulic pump motor, ABS In the rear of the engine compartment on the brake hydraulic unit
298A	Left front wheel sensor On the left-hand steering knuckle housing
298B	Right front wheel sensor On the right-hand steering knuckle housing
298C	Left rear wheel sensor On the left-hand rear wheel hub
298D	Right rear wheel sensor On the right-hand rear wheel hub
299	Brake fluid level sensor, ABS In the rear of the engine compartment in the brake fluid reservoir
302A	Relay and fuse box, ABS In the left rear corner of the engine compartment on the false bulkhead
303A, 303B	Diode, ABS Inside the ABS relay/fuse box under the relay/fuse holders

SA4029100016010X

Fig. 6 TC/ABS wiring diagram (Part 2 of 3)

Component Location	Description
347	ISAT diagnostic plug for engine systems (black) Under forward edge of right front seat behind trim plate
348	ISAT diagnostic plug for chassis systems (green) Under forward edge of right front seat behind trim plate
376	ETS electronic control unit Under left front seat
382	TC/ABS electronic control unit In left rear corner of engine compartment on battery bracket
383	TC valve block In the engine compartment on the brake hydraulic unit
385	Diode
397	Diagnostic test socket, ABS (1990 model) In engine compartment under the false bulkhead to the left of the ABS control unit
414	ASR electronic control unit Under left front seat on top of ETS electronic control unit
H2-12	2-pole connector In the left rear corner of engine compartment to the left of the brake fluid reservoir
H2-46	2-pole connector In the engine compartment under false bulkhead to the extreme left
H2-47	2-pole connector In the engine compartment under false bulkhead to the extreme right
H2-48	2-pole connector Beneath floor under left side of rear seat, access through foam plug
H2-49	2-pole connector Beneath floor under right side of rear seat, access through foam plug
H10-8	10-pole connector (347) Under forward edge of right front seat behind trim plate (black)
H10-9	10-pole connector (348) Under forward edge of right front seat behind trim plate (green)
H10-12	10-pole connector In left rear corner of engine compartment below ABS fuse/relay box

SA4029100016020X

Fig. 6 TC/ABS wiring diagram (Part 3 of 3)

switch connector, replace switch.

DIAGNOSTIC TROUBLE CODES 4/24221, 2422A, 24251 & 24291

1. Raise and support vehicle.
2. With ignition in Drive position, enter ISAT command code 259. The diagnostic trouble code displayed will be between 80002 and 80020 (0–20 km/h), depending on whether wheel is stationary or being rotated by hand.
3. With AC range selected on multimeter, signal can also be measured by connecting probes across pins 30 and 48. Voltage should be approximately .1–.5V AC as wheel is rotated by hand.
4. With ignition in Off position and ECU connector disconnected, check sensor winding for continuity by measuring resistance across pins 30 and 48. Resistance should be approximately 1100 ohms.
5. Check leads between sensor and pins 30 and 48 on TC/ABS-system ECU for shorting. Check for poor contact in connectors. Resistance should be as follows:
   a. Pin 30 and ground: infinity.
   b. Pin 48 and ground: infinity.
6. When testing for short to 12V, voltage should be as follows:
   a. Pin 30 and ground: 0V DC (indicates no short to 12V).
   b. Pin 48 and ground: 0V DC (indicates no short to 12V).
7. Ensure left front wheel sensor is properly installed.
8. Ensure sensor wheel is not damaged and is properly installed. Check for play in wheel bearings.
9. Check clearance between sensor and sensor wheel.
10. Ensure ECU pins 1 and 19 are properly grounded.
11. If no fault has been found, test drive vehicle to see if diagnostic trouble code is regenerated. If so, try a known good ECU.

DIAGNOSTIC TROUBLE CODES 4/24222, 2422B, 24252 & 24292

1. Raise and support vehicle.
2. With ignition in Drive position, enter ISAT command code 25A. The code displayed will be between 80002 and 80030 (0–20 km/h), depending on whether wheel is stationary or being rotated by hand.
3. With AC range selected on multimeter, signal can also be measured by connecting probes across pins 29 and 47.
4. With ignition in Off position and ECU connector disconnected, check sensor winding for continuity by measuring resistance across pins 29 and 47. Resistance should be approximately 1100 ohms.
5. Check leads between sensor and pins 29 and 47 on TC/ABS-system ECU for shorting. Check for poor contact in connectors. Resistance should be as follows:
   a. Across pin 29 and ground: infinity.
   b. Across pin 47 and ground: infinity.
6. When testing for short to 12V, voltage should be as follows:
   a. Across pin 29 and ground: 0V DC (indicates no short to 12V).
   b. Across pin 47 and ground: 0V DC (indicates no short to 12V).
7. Ensure right front wheel sensor is properly installed.
8. Ensure sensor wheel is not damaged and is properly installed. Check for play in wheel bearings.
9. Check clearance between sensor and sensor wheel. Clearance should be 0.45–1.55 mm.
10. Ensure ECU pins 1 and 19 are properly grounded.
11. If no fault has been found, test drive vehicle to see if diagnostic trouble code is regenerated. If so, try a known good ECU.

DIAGNOSTIC TROUBLE CODES 4/24223, 2422C, 24253 & 24293

1. Raise and support vehicle.
2. With ignition in Drive position, enter ISAT command code 25B. The code displayed will be between 80002 and 80020 (0–20 km/h), depending on whether wheel is stationary or being rotated by hand.
3. With AC range selected on multimeter,

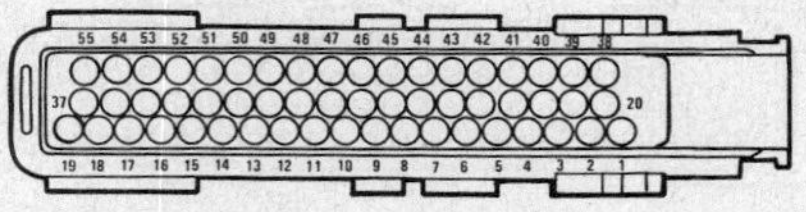

Voltage Checks

The following signals must be tested with the breakout box connected, all system components connected and the ignition switched on. All tests should be made at the breakout box.

Pin#	Circuit/Function	Wire Color	Test
1	Ground	Black	Check voltage drop to ground should be less than 0.1 volts (Ignition must be on to check voltage drop).
2	Left front outlet valve (ECU energizes valve by providing ground)	Yellow/Red	See resistance testing procedure
3	Power in from system relay	Green/Red –or– Yellow/White	System operational (relay activated) = battery volts Relay de–energizes (fault in system) = less than 2 volts
4*	Communication between TC/ABS and ETS (digital signal to ETS pin #32)	Black/White	Engine running = approx. 5 volts D.C. (A reading close to 0 or close to 10 volts indicates a problem in this wire/circuit.) A logic probe should also indicate a continuous 'PULSE' signal.
5	Not used		
6	Not used		
7*	TCS indicator light (ECU provides ground for bulb when system is operating in TCS mode)	Brown/Red	Light off = approx. battery volts Light on = approx. 0 volts
8	Pressure/fluid safety circuit (with pin #51)	Blue	System O.K. (switches closed) = 5 to 10 volts Fault (switch open) = 0 volts

* Manual Transmission TCS Version Only
‡ Automatic Transmission TCS Version Only

SA4029100017010X

Fig. 7 TC/ABS control unit pin voltage inspection (Part 1 of 5)

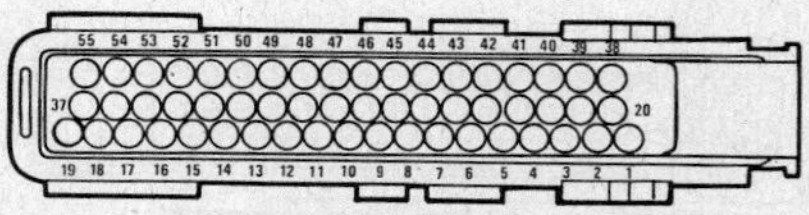

Voltage Checks

The following signals must be tested with the breakout box connected, all system components connected and the ignition switched on. All tests should be made at the breakout box.

Pin#	Circuit/Function	Wire Color	Test
9‡	RR wheel speed signal (digital output to ASR ECU)	Green	Using a Logic Probe: –You should find a steady 'PULSE' at each wire with the ignition ON and the wheel NOT turning (this is a test pulse). –The frequency of the 'PULSE' should increase as the speed of each wheel increases.
10‡	LF wheel speed signal (digital output to ASR ECU)	Yellow	
11‡	RF wheel speed signal (digital output to ASR ECU)	Blue	
12‡	LR wheel speed signal (digital output to ASR ECU)	Grey	
13*	TC block pressure switch (voltage signal into switch)	Brown/White	Brake off = approx. 8 volts (switch closed) Brake applied = approx. 10 volts (switch open)
14	Pump relay pin 87 (monitors the status of relay contacts)	Yellow	Pump relay energizes = battery volts Pump relay de–energizes = 0 volts
15	Not used		
16	Not used		
17	Not used		
18	Not used		
19	Ground	Black	Check voltage drop to ground. Should be less than 0.1 volt (ignition must be on to check voltage drop).
20	Left front inlet valve (ECU energizes valve by providing ground)	Green/White	See resistance testing procedure
21	Right front outlet valve (ECU energizes valve by providing ground)	Blue/Red	See resistance testing procedure

* Manual Transmission TCS Version Only
‡ Automatic Transmission TCS Version Only

SA4029100017020X

Fig. 7 TC/ABS control unit pin voltage inspection (Part 2 of 5)

signal can also be measured by connecting probes across pins 28 and 46. Voltage should be approximately 0.1–0.5V AC as wheel is rotated by hand.

4. With ignition in Off position and ECU connector disconnected, check sensor winding for continuity by measuring resistance across pins 28 and 46. Resistance should be approximately 1100 ohms.
5. Check leads between sensor and pins 28 and 46 on TC/ABS-system ECU for shorting. Check for poor contact in connectors. Resistance should be as follows:
   a. Across pin 28 and ground: infinity.
   b. Across pin 46 and ground: infinity.
6. When testing for short to 12V, voltage should be as follows:
   a. Across pin 28 and ground: 0V DC (indicates no short to 12V).
   b. Across pin 46 and ground: 0V DC (indicates no short to 12V).
7. Ensure left rear wheel sensor is properly installed.
8. Ensure sensor wheel is not damaged and is properly installed.
9. Check clearance between sensor and sensor wheel. Clearance should be 0.45–1.55 mm.
10. Ensure ECU pins 1 and 19 are properly grounded.
11. If no fault has been found, test drive vehicle to see if diagnostic trouble code is regenerated. If so, try a known good ECU.

DIAGNOSTIC TROUBLE CODES 4/24224, 2422D, 24254 & 24294

1. Raise and support vehicle.
2. With ignition in Drive position, enter ISAT command code 25C. The code displayed will be between 80002 and 80020 (0–20 km/h), depending on whether wheel is stationary or being rotated by hand.
3. With AC range selected on multimeter, signal can also be measured by connecting probes across pins 27 and 45. Voltage should be approximately 0.1–0.5V AC as wheel is rotated by hand.
4. With ignition in Off position and ECU connector disconnected, check sensor winding for continuity by measuring resistance across pins 27 and 45. Resistance should be approximately 1100 ohms.
5. Check leads between sensor and pins 27 and 45 on TC/ABS-system ECU for shorting. Check for poor contact in connectors. Resistance should be as follows:
   a. Across pin 27 and ground: infinity.
   b. Across pin 45 and ground: infinity.
6. When testing for short to 12V, voltage should be as follows:
   a. Across pin 27 and ground: 0V DC (indicates no short to 12V).
   b. Across pin 45 and ground: 0V DC (indicates no short to 12V).
7. Ensure right rear wheel sensor is properly installed.
8. Ensure sensor wheel is not damaged and is properly installed.
9. Check clearance between sensor and sensor wheel. Clearance should be 0.45–1.55 mm.
10. Ensure ECU pins 1 and 19 are properly grounded.
11. If no fault has been found, test drive vehicle to see if diagnostic trouble code is regenerated. If so, try a known good ECU.

DIAGNOSTIC TROUBLE CODE B3421

1. With ECU connector disconnected, check resistance in circuit between pin 3 and pin 20 of TC/ABS-system ECU using breakout box. Resistance should be 5–7 ohms.
   a. If circuit is good, clear diagnostic trouble code and test drive vehicle to see if diagnostic trouble code is regenerated. If so, try a known good ECU.
   b. If circuit is faulty, continue to next step.
2. Check for continuity in left front inlet valve winding by measuring resistance across pins 6 and 7 on valve body. Resistance should be 5–7 ohms. If not, replace hydraulic unit.
3. Check lead between pin 6 on valve connector and pin 20 on TC/ABS-system ECU for a broken or short circuit.
4. Check lead between pin 7 on valve connector and pin 30 on system relay for a broken or short circuit.

DIAGNOSTIC TROUBLE CODE B3422

1. With ECU connector disconnected,

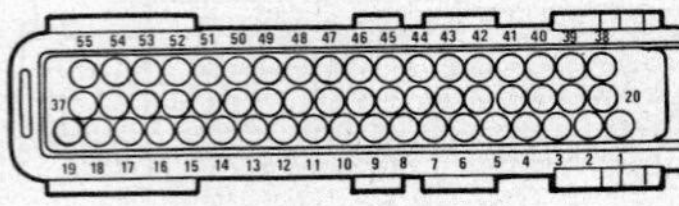

Voltage Checks

The following signals must be tested with the breakout box connected, all system components connected and the ignition switched on. All tests should be made at the breakout box.

Pin#	Circuit/Function	Wire Color	Test
22	Not used		
23	Diagnostic "L" lead (request from ISAT to the ECU)	Yellow	
24*	Communication between TC/ABS and ETS (digital signal to ETS pin #29)	Green/White	Engine running – approx. 5 volts D.C. (A reading of close to 0 or close to 10 volts indicated a problem in this wire/circuit.) A logic probe should also show a continuous 'PULSE' signal.
25	Not used		
26*	TC block pressure switch (voltage signal from switch)	Black/White	Brake off = approx. 8 volts (switch closed) Brake applied = 0 volt (switch open)
27	Shield, RR wheel sensor	Black/Green	Connect A.C. voltmeter between pin 27 and 45. With wheel rotating one revolution per second, sensor should produce approximately 0.1 to 0.5 volts A.C.
28	Shield, LR wheel sensor	Yellow/Green	Connect A.C. voltmeter between pin 28 and 46. With wheel rotating one revolution per second, sensor should produce approximately 0.1 to 0.5 volts A.C.
29	Shield, RF wheel sensor	Blue/Green	Connect A.C. voltmeter between pin 29 and 47. With wheel rotating one revolution per second, sensor should produce approximately 0.1 to 0.5 volts A.C.
30	Shield, LF wheel sensor	Gray/Green	Connect A.C. voltmeter between pin 30 and 48. With wheel rotating one revolution per second, sensor should produce approximately 0.1 to 0.5 volts A.C.
31	Not used		

* Manual Transmission TCS Version Only

SA4029100017030X

Fig. 7 TC/ABS control unit pin voltage inspection (Part 3 of 5)

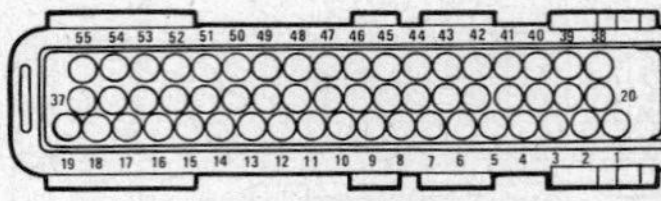

Voltage Checks

The following signals must be tested with the breakout box connected, all system components connected and the ignition switched on. All tests should be made at the breakout box.

Pin#	Circuit/Function	Wire Color	Test
32	Brake light signal (from brake light switch)	Blue	Brake off – 0 volts Brake applied = Battery volts
33	Power in from system relay	Yellow	System operation (relay activated) = battery volts Relay de-energizes (fault in system) = less than 2 volts
34	System relay control signal (ECU energizes relay by providing ground)	Green	Relay de-energizes = approx. battery volts Relay energizes = approx. 1.0 volt or less
35*	+30 Constant power	Red	Battery voltage all the time
36	Rear outlet valve (ECU energizes valve by providing ground)	Blue/White	See resistance testing procedure
37*	TC block normally open valve (ECU energizes valve by providing ground)	Yellow	See resistance testing procedure
38	Right front inlet valve (ECU energizes valve by providing ground)	Red/White	See resistance testing procedure
39	Main valve (ECU energizes valve by providing ground)	Black	See resistance testing procedure
40*	TC block normally closed valve (ECU energizes valve by providing ground)	Blue/Gray	See resistance testing procedure
41	Not used		
42	Diagnostic "K" lead (reply from control unit to ISAT)	Blue	
43	Not used		
44*	TCS control warning light	Blue	Light off = approx. battery volts Light on = less than 2 volts

* Manual Transmission TCS Version Only

SA4029100017040X

Fig. 7 TC/ABS control unit pin voltage inspection (Part 4 of 5)

check resistance in circuit between pin 3 and pin 2 of TC/ABS-system ECU using breakout box. Resistance should be 3–4 ohms.
   a. If circuit is good, clear diagnostic trouble code and test drive vehicle to see if diagnostic trouble code is regenerated. If so, try a known good ECU.
   b. If circuit is faulty, go to step 2.
2. Check for continuity in left front outlet valve winding by measuring resistance across pins 5 and 7 on valve body. Resistance should be 3–4 ohms. If not, replace hydraulic unit.
3. Check lead between pin 5 on valve connector and pin 2 on TC/ABS-system ECU for a broken or short circuit.
4. Check lead between pin 7 on valve connector and pin 30 on system relay for a broken or short circuit.

DIAGNOSTIC TROUBLE CODE B3423

1. With ECU connector disconnected, check resistance in circuit between pin 3 and pin 38 of TC/ABS-system ECU using breakout box. Resistance should be 5–7 ohms.
   a. If circuit is good, clear diagnostic trouble code and test drive vehicle to see if diagnostic trouble code is regenerated. If so, try a known good ECU.
   b. If circuit is faulty, go to step 2.
2. Check for continuity in right front inlet valve winding by measuring resistance across pins 1 and 7 on valve body. Resistance should be 5–7 ohms. If not, replace hydraulic unit.
3. Check lead between pin 1 on valve connector and pin 38 on TC/ABS-system ECU for a broken or short circuit.
4. Check lead between pin 7 on valve connector and pin 30 on system relay for a broken or short circuit.

DIAGNOSTIC TROUBLE CODE B3424

1. With ECU connector disconnected, check resistance in circuit between pin 3 and pin 21 of TC/ABS-system ECU using breakout box. Resistance should be 3–4 ohms.
   a. If circuit is good, clear diagnostic trouble code and test drive vehicle to see if diagnostic trouble code is regenerated. If so, try a known good ECU.
   b. If circuit is faulty, go to step 2.
2. Check for continuity in right front outlet valve winding by measuring resistance across pins 2 and 7 on valve body. Resistance should be 3–4 ohms. If not, replace hydraulic unit.
3. Check lead between pin 2 on valve connector and pin 21 on TC/ABS-system ECU for a broken or short circuit.
4. Check lead between pin 7 on valve connector and pin 30 on system relay for a broken or short circuit.

DIAGNOSTIC TROUBLE CODE B3425

1. With ECU connector disconnected, check resistance in circuit between pin 3 and pin 54 of TC/ABS-system ECU using breakout box. Resistance should be 5–7 ohms.
   a. If circuit is good, clear diagnostic trouble code and test drive vehicle to see if diagnostic trouble code is regenerated. If so, try a known good ECU.
   b. If circuit is faulty, go to step 2.
2. Check for continuity in rear inlet valve winding by measuring resistance across pins 3 and 7 on valve body. Resistance should be 5–7 ohms. If not, replace hydraulic unit.
3. Check lead between pin 3 on valve connector and pin 54 on TC/ABS-system ECU for a broken or short circuit.
4. Check lead between pin 7 on valve connector and pin 30 on system relay for a broken or short circuit.

DIAGNOSTIC TROUBLE CODE B3426

1. With ECU connector disconnected, check resistance in circuit between pin 3 and pin 36 of TC/ABS-system ECU using breakout box. Resistance should be 3–4 ohms.
   a. If circuit is good, clear diagnostic trouble code and test drive vehicle to see if diagnostic trouble code is

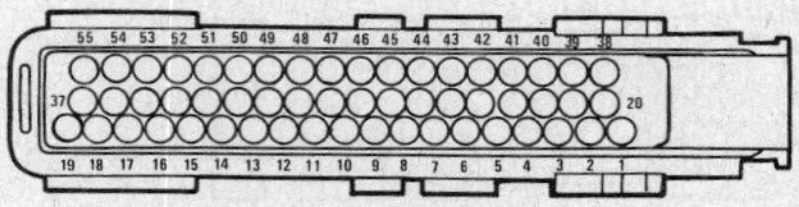

Voltage Checks

The following signals must be tested with the breakout box connected, all system components connected and the ignition switched on. All tests should be made at the breakout box.

Pin#	Circuit/Function	Wire Color	Test
45	Right rear wheel sensor signal	Green	Connect A.C. voltmeter between pin 45 and 27. With wheel rotating one revolution per second, sensor should produce approximately 0.1 to 0.5 volts A.C.
46	Left rear wheel sensor signal	Green	Connect A.C. voltmeter between pin 46 and 28. With wheel rotating one revolution per second, sensor should produce approximately 0.1 to 0.5 volts A.C.
47	Right front wheel sensor signal	Green	Connect A.C. voltmeter between pin 47 and 29. With wheel rotating one revolution per second, sensor should produce approximately 0.1 to 0.5 volts A.C.
48	Left front wheel sensor signal	Green	Connect A.C. voltmeter between pin 48 and 30. With wheel rotating one revolution per second, sensor should produce approximately 0.1 to 0.5 volts A.C.
49	Not used		
50	Pump relay pin 85 (monitors the status of relay "pull-down")	Black	Relay "pulldown" circuit de-energized (pressure switch open) = approx battery volts Relay "pulldown" circuit energizes (pressure switch closed) = less than 1 volt
51	Pressure/fluid safety circuit (with pin #8)	Brown	System O.K. (switches closed) = 5 to 10 volts Fault (switch open) = approx. 1.5 volts
52	Anti-lock warning light	White	Light off = approx. battery volts Light on = less than 2 volts
53	+54 Switched power input	Red	Battery volts with ign. in "Run" pos. only.
54	Rear inlet valve (ECU energizes valve by providing ground)	Brown/White	See resistance testing procedure page.
55	Not used		

* Manual Transmission TCS Version Only

SA4029100017050X

Fig. 7 TC/ABS control unit pin voltage inspection (Part 5 of 5)

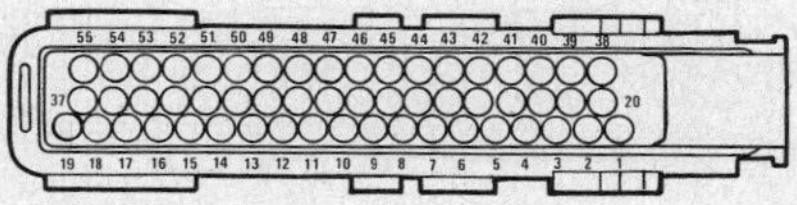

Resistance Checks

The following resistance values must be tested with the breakout box connected, the ECU **DISCONNECTED** and the ignition switched **OFF**. All tests should be made at the breakout box.

Pin#	Circuit/Function	Wire Color	Test
1	Ground	Black	Less than 1 ohm resistance to battery negative.
2	Left front outlet valve (ECU energizes valve by providing ground)	Yellow/Red	Resistance from ECU pin 2 to ECU pin 3 should be 3 - 4 ohms.
3	Power in from system relay	Green/Red -or- Yellow/White	Check for continuity to system relay pin 30.
4*	Communication between TC/ABS and ETS (digital signal to ETS pin #32)	Black/White	Check for: -Continuity to ETS Pin #32 -No continuity to ground
5	Not used		
6	Not used		
7*	TCS indicator light (ECU provides ground for bulb when system is operating in TCS mode)	Brown/Red	See voltage test procedure.
8	Pressure/fluid safety circuit (with pin #51)	Blue	Check for continuity between ECU pin 8 and ECU pin 51 with accumulator charged.
9‡	RR wheel speed signal (digital output to ASR ECU)	Green	See voltage test procedure.
10‡	LF wheel speed signal (digital output to ASR ECU)	Yellow	See voltage test procedure.
11‡	RF wheel speed signal (digital output to ASR ECU)	Blue	See voltage test procedure.
12‡	LR wheel speed signal (digital output to ASR ECU)	Grey	See voltage test procedure.

* Manual Transmission TCS Version Only
‡ Automatic Transmission TCS Version Only

SA4029100018010X

Fig. 8 TC/ABS control unit pin resistance inspection (Part 1 of 4)

regenerated. If so, try a known good ECU.

b. If circuit is faulty, go to step 2.

2. Check for continuity in rear outlet valve winding by measuring resistance across pins 4 and 7 on valve body. Resistance should be 3–4 ohms. If not, replace hydraulic unit.
3. Check lead between pin 4 on valve connector and pin 36 on TC/ABS-system ECU for a broken or short circuit.
4. Check lead between pin 7 on valve connector and pin 30 on system relay for a broken or short circuit.

DIAGNOSTIC TROUBLE CODE B3427

1. With ECU connector disconnected, check resistance in circuit between pin 3 and pin 39 of TC/ABS-system ECU using breakout box. Resistance should be 4–5 ohms.
   a. If circuit is good, clear diagnostic trouble code and test drive vehicle to see if diagnostic trouble code is regenerated. If so, try a known good ECU.
   b. If circuit is faulty, go to step 2.
2. Check for continuity in main-valve winding by measuring resistance across pins 1 and 2 on valve body. Resistance should be 4–5 ohms. If not, replace hydraulic unit.
3. Check GN/RD lead between pin 1 on main valve and pin 3 on TC/ABS-system ECU for a broken or short circuit.
4. Check BK lead between pin 2 on main valve and pin 39 on TC/ABS-system ECU for a broken or short circuit.

DIAGNOSTIC TROUBLE CODE B3428

1. With ECU connector disconnected, check resistance in circuit between pin 3 and pin 40 of TC/ABS-system ECU using breakout box. Resistance should be 6–8 ohms.
   a. If circuit is good, clear diagnostic trouble code and test drive vehicle to see if diagnostic trouble code is regenerated. If so, try a known good ECU.
   b. If circuit is faulty, go to step 2.
2. Check for continuity in TC-valve (NC) winding by measuring resistance across pins 1 and 5 on valve connector. Resistance should be 6–8 ohms. If not, replace hydraulic unit.
3. Check lead between pin 1 on TC block and pin 40 on TC/ABS-system ECU for a broken or short circuit.
4. Check lead between pin 5 on TC block and pin 3 on TC/ABS-system ECU for a broken or short circuit.

DIAGNOSTIC TROUBLE CODE B3429

1. With ECU connector disconnected, check resistance in circuit between pin 3 and pin 37 of TC/ABS-system ECU using breakout box. Resistance should be 6–8 ohms.
   a. If circuit is good, clear diagnostic trouble code and test drive vehicle to see if diagnostic trouble code is regenerated. If so, try a known good ECU.
   b. If circuit is faulty, go to step 2.
2. Check for continuity in TC-valve (NC) winding by measuring resistance across pins 4 and 5 on valve-block connector. Resistance should be 6–8 ohms.
3. Check lead between pin 4 on TC block and pin 37 on TC/ABS-system ECU for a broken or short circuit.
4. Check lead between pin 5 on TC block and pin 3 on TC/ABS-system ECU for a broken or short circuit.

DIAGNOSTIC TROUBLE CODES 234B1, 234B2, 234B3 & 234B4

1. Perform diagnosis for any other diagnostic trouble codes first.
2. Check wheel sensors. Refer to wheel sensor diagnostic trouble code diagnosis.
3. Replace hydraulic unit.

DIAGNOSTIC TROUBLE CODE 775B1

1. Clear diagnostic trouble code and test drive vehicle to see if diagnostic trouble code is regenerated.
2. If diagnostic trouble code is regenerated, check grounding circuits to pin 1 and pin 19 of ECU. Ensure ground G15

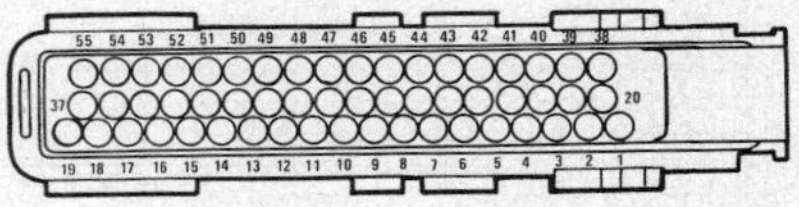

Resistance Checks

The following resistance values must be tested with the breakout box connected, the ECU **DISCONNECTED** and the ignition switched **OFF**. All tests should be made at the breakout box.

Pin #	Circuit/Function	Wire Color	Test
13*	TC block pressure switch (voltage signal **into** switch)	Brown/White	Check for continuity from ECU pin 13 to ECU pin 26 with brake pedal released.
14	Pump relay pin 87 (monitors the status of relay contacts)	Yellow	Check for continuity to pump relay pin #87.
15	Not used		
16	Not used		
17	Not used		
18	Not used		
19	Ground	Black	Less than 1 ohm resistance to battery negative.
20	Left front inlet valve (ECU energizes valve by providing ground)	Green/White	Resistance from ECU pin 20 to ECU pin 3 should be 5 – 7 ohms.
21	Right front outlet valve (ECU energizes valve by providing ground)	Blue/Red	Resistance from ECU pin 21 to ECU pin 3 should be 3 – 4 ohms.
22	Not used		
23	Diagnostic "L" lead (request from ISAT to control unit)	Yellow	
24*	Communication between TC/ABS and ETS (digital signal to ETS pin #29)	Green/White	Check for: –Continuity to ETS pin #29 –No continuity to ground
25	Not used		

* Manual Transmission TCS Version Only
‡ Automatic Transmission TCS Version Only

SA4029100018020X

Fig. 8 TC/ABS control unit pin resistance inspection (Part 2 of 4)

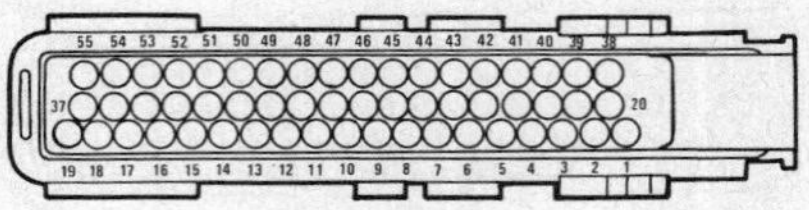

Resistance Checks

The following resistance values must be tested with the breakout box connected, the ECU **DISCONNECTED** and the ignition switched **OFF**. All tests should be made at the breakout box.

Pin#	Circuit/Function	Wire Color	Test
26*	TC block pressure switch (voltage signal **from** switch)	Black/White	Check for continuity from ECU pin 26 to ECU pin 13 with brake pedal released.
27	Shield, RR wheel sensor	Black/Green	Resistance from ECU pin 27 to ECU pin 45 should be approx. 1100 ohms.
28	Shield, LR wheel sensor	Yellow/Green	Resistance from ECU pin 28 to ECU pin 46 should be approx. 1100 ohms.
29	Shield, RF wheel sensor	Blue/Green	Resistance from ECU pin 29 to ECU pin 47 should be approx. 1100 ohms.
30	Shield, LF wheel sensor	Gray/Green	Resistance from ECU pin 30 to ECU pin 48 should be approx. 1100 ohms.
31	Not used		
32	Brake light signal (from brake light switch)	Blue	See voltage test procedure.
33	Power in from system relay	Yellow	Check for continuity to system relay pin 30.
34	System relay control signal (ECU energized relay by providing ground)	Green	Check for continuity with system relay pin 86.
35*	+30 Constant power	Red	See voltage test procedure.
36	Rear outlet valve (ECU energizes valve by providing ground)	Blue/White	Resistance from ECU pin 36 to ECU pin 3 should be 3 – 4 ohms.
37*	TC block normally open valve (ECU energizes valve by providing ground)	Yellow	Resistance from ECU pin 37 to ECU pin 3 should be 6 – 8 ohms.
38	Right front inlet valve (ECU energizes valve by providing ground)	Red/White	Resistance from ECU pin 38 to ECU pin 3 should be 5 – 7 ohms.
39	Main valve (ECU energized valve by providing ground)	Black	Resistance from ECU pin 39 to ECU pin 3 should be 4 – 5 ohms.

* Manual Transmission TCS Version Only

SA4029100018030X

Fig. 8 TC/ABS control unit pin resistance inspection (Part 3 of 4)

grounding point is making good connection.

3. Try a known good ECU.

DIAGNOSTIC TROUBLE CODE 775B2

1. Clear diagnostic trouble code and test drive vehicle to see if diagnostic trouble code is regenerated.
2. If diagnostic trouble code is regenerated, try a known good ECU.

DIAGNOSTIC TROUBLE CODE E/F7061

This diagnostic trouble code is usually generated by the presence of another fault. Perform diagnosis for any other codes first.

1. Disconnect ETS-system connector.
2. With ignition in On position and engine not running, check reference voltage from pin 4 of TC/ABS-system ECU to pin 32 of ETS connector. Voltage should be approximately 10V DC
   a. If voltage is as specified, go to step 3.
   b. If voltage is close to 0, check for a short to ground in the wire.
   c. If no shorts are found, try a new TC/ABS ECU.
   d. If voltage is as specified at TC/ABS ECU but no voltage exists at ETS connector, check for an open circuit in the wire.
3. With ignition in Off position, connect ETS ECU and start engine. Check communication signal with a DC voltmeter or a Logic Probe. Voltage should be approximately 5V DC or Logic Probe reading should be a continuous "pulse."
4. If voltage was as specified in step 2 but not in step 3, try a new ETS ECU. Ensure no other diagnostic trouble codes were present in either the ETS system or the TC/ABS system.
5. With ignition in Off position, disconnect TC/ABS-system ECU.
6. With ignition in On position and engine not running, check reference voltage from pin 29 of ETS-system ECU to pin 24 of TC/ABS connector. Voltage should be approximately 10V DC.
   a. If voltage is as specified, go to step 7.
   b. If voltage is close to 0, check for a short to ground in the wire.
   c. If no shorts are found, try a new ETS ECU.
   d. If voltage is as specified at ETS ECU but no voltage exists at TC/ABS connector, check for an open circuit in the wire.
7. With ignition in Off position, connect TC/ABS ECU and start engine. Check communication signal with a DC voltmeter or a Logic Probe. Voltage should be approximately 5V DC or Logic Probe reading should be a continuous "Pulse."
8. If voltage was as specified in step 6 but not in step 7, try a new TC/ABS ECU. Ensure no other diagnostic trouble codes were present in either the ETS system or the TC/ABS system.

DIAGNOSTIC TROUBLE CODE 3/25321

This fault may also be generated if the pressure switch in the TC block is faulty. Refer to TC block test procedure.

1. With ignition in Drive position, enter ISAT command code 202. When brake pedal is applied, ISAT should display 85100; with foot off pedal, ISAT should display 8B000. Measure voltage at pin 32: this should be battery voltage when the pedal is applied and 0V with foot off. If not voltage is reaching the pin, go to step 2. If signal is correct, perform test procedure for pressure switch in TC block.
2. Check fuse No. 24. Ensure brake lights are working properly.
   a. Ensure voltage is reaching brake light switch.
   b. If voltage is not reaching brake light switch, check RD lead between switch and fuse holder.
3. Check lead between ECU connector pin 32 and brake light switch.
4. Perform test procedure for pressure switch in TC block as outlined under "Diagnostic Trouble Code 36521."
5. Replace brake light switch.

DIAGNOSTIC TROUBLE CODE 36521

With ISAT Tester

1. With ignition in Drive position, enter ISAT command code 200.

2. With brake pedal applied, pressure switch should be open, indicated on ISAT display by 8D000.
3. With brake pedal released, switch should be closed, indicated by 8B100.
4. If signal is correct, perform test procedure for brake light switch.

Less ISAT Tester

1. Switch on ignition and wait for pump to build up pressure in the accumulator. After system has pressurized, switch off ignition and unplug ECU connector.
2. Using a multimeter, ensure circuit across pins 13 and 26 is closed, and that it opens when the brake pedal is applied. If circuit is not as specified, check the following:
   a. BN/WH lead between pin 13 on ECU connector and pin 2 on TC block connector.
   b. BK/WH lead between ECU pin 26 and TC block connector pin 3.
3. If pressure switch on TC block is faulty, replace hydraulic unit.
4. Perform brake light test procedure.
5. If not faults are found, replace ECU.

WARNING & INDICATOR LIGHTS

Anti-Lock Light

1. With ECU connector plugged in and ignition in Drive position, ensure battery voltage at pin 52 exists. If not, check bulb and lead between ECU pin 52 and pin 8 on main instrument panel (H10-12).
2. With ignition Off and connectors for ECU and system relay unplugged, check circuit between ECU pin 52 and ECU pin 33. Ensure diode prevents current flow toward pin 52.

TCS CTRL Light

1. With ignition in Drive position, ensure battery voltage at pin 52 exists. If not, check bulb and lead between ECU pin 44 and pin 12 on main instrument panel (H10-12).
2. With ignition Off and connectors for ECU and system relay unplugged, check circuit between ECU pin 52 and ECU pin 33. Ensure diode prevents current flow towards pin 44.

Brake Fluid Light

1. Ensure light is working by turning ignition to a point between Start and Drive positions. If light does not illuminate, check bulb in panel.
2. If light fails to illuminate when pressure is low, proceed as follows:
   a. With pressure warning switch connector (294) unplugged and ignition in Drive position, ensure battery voltage is at pin 2 of pressure switch connector. If not, check WH lead between pin 2 on connector and pin 11 on instrument panel.
   b. If voltage is at pin 2, switch off ignition and depressurize system.
   c. Check resistance across pins 1 and 2 on pressure warning switch. Reading should indicate circuit

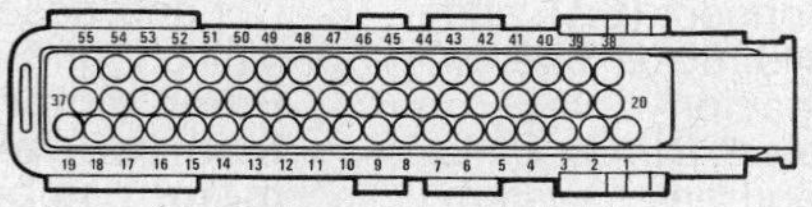

Resistance Checks

The following resistance values must be tested with the breakout box connected, the ECU **DISCONNECTED** and the ignition switched **OFF**. All tests should be made at the breakout box.

Pin#	Circuit/Function	Wire Color	Test
40*	TC block normally closed valve (ECU energized valve by providing ground)	Blue/Gray	Resistance from ECU pin 40 to ECU pin 3 should be 6 – 8 ohms.
41	Not used		
42	Diagnostic "K" lead (reply from control unit to ISAT)	Blue	
43	Not used		
44*	TCS control warning light	Blue	See voltage test procedure.
45	Right rear wheel sensor output signal	Green	Resistance from ECU pin 45 to ECU pin 27 should be approx. 1100 ohms.
46	Left rear wheel sensor output signal	Green	Resistance from ECU pin 46 to ECU pin 28 should be approx. 1100 ohms.
47	Right front wheel sensor output signal	Green	Resistance from ECU pin 47 to ECU pin 29 should be approx. 1100 ohms.
48	Left front wheel sensor output signal	Green	Resistance from ECU pin 48 to ECU pin 30 should be approx. 1100 ohms.
49	Not used		
50	Pump relay pin 85 (monitors the status of relay "pull–down")	Black	Check for continuity to pump relay pin 85. Also should have continuity to ground with pressure switch closed (accumulator discharged).
51	Pressure/fluid safety circuit (with pin #8)	Brown	Check for continuity between ECU pin 8 and ECU pin 51 with accumulator charged.
52	Anti-lock warning light	White	See voltage test procedure.
53	+54 Switched power input	Red	See voltage test procedure.
54	Rear inlet valve (ECU energizes valve by providing ground)	Yellow/Red	Resistance from ECU pin 54 to ECU pin 3 should be 5 – 7 ohms
55	Not used		

* Manual Transmission TCS Version Only

SA4029100018040X

Fig. 8 TC/ABS control unit pin resistance inspection (Part 4 of 4)

continuity. If not, replace switch.
   d. If switch is satisfactory, check BK lead between pin 1 of pressure switch connector and ground.
3. If light fails to illuminate when fluid level is low, proceed as follows:
   a. With connector for level warning switch (299) unplugged and ignition in Drive position, ensure battery voltage is at pin 4 of reservoir switch connector. If not, check WH lead between pin 4 on connector and pin 11 on instrument panel. If voltage exists at pin 4, switch off ignition and proceed to step b.
   b. Check level switch by verifying that circuit is closed when the float is pressed down and that the circuit is open when the float is up. If values are unsatisfactory, replace reservoir. If values are satisfactory, proceed to step c.
   c. Check BK lead by measuring resistance across pin 3 of reservoir switch connector and ground.

TCS Light

1. With ignition in Drive position, ensure battery voltage is at ECU pin 7. If battery voltage does not exist, proceed as follows:
   a. Ensure bulb is good.
   b. Circuit continuity exists in BN/GY lead between ECU pin 7 and pin 6 on tachometer connector.
   c. Ensure there is a live feed to pin 4 on rev counter.
2. If TCS light fails to illuminate when the system is operating and no other warning lights are on, replace ECU.

TC/ABS CONTROL UNIT PIN INSPECTION

VOLTAGE INSPECTION

Refer to **Fig. 7** for voltage checks.

RESISTANCE INSPECTION

When an intermittent fault is suspected, wiggle wires and connectors related to the pin being tested.

In cases where resistance specifications indicate a range such as "3–4 ohms," good judgement must be used before condemning a circuit which indicates 4.1 ohms for example.

Refer to **Fig. 8,** for resistance checks.

SYSTEM SERVICE

ETS ECU CALIBRATION

Calibration must be carried out after replacing any major system component, such as ETS ECU, TC/ABS ECU, pedal potentiometer or throttle housing.

1. Start and run engine until normal operating temperature is reached. If the engine will not run correctly during warm up cycle, establish ISAT communications and enter command code 974 in order to enter basic data and enable warm up to be completed.

2. Switch off engine. Connect ISAT and capacitor lead, part No. 86-11-048, to Black diagnostic connector.
3. Turn ignition On, select DIAG, ONE system from menu and enter system number 3. Check if any diagnostic trouble codes are stored in memory. If diagnostic trouble codes are present, repair as necessary, then erase diagnostic trouble codes before proceeding.
4. To enter the base line setting, enter command code 971. ISAT will display 8A971. After several seconds, the display will change to 8D971, indicating that the basic setting has been made and the system is ready for calibration.
5. With ignition On, engine Off, enter command code 973.
   a. Once the TCS CTRL light illuminates, start engine. **Do not touch pedals.**
   b. Wait for idle to stabilize at approximately 850 RPM.
   c. The ECU will raise engine speed to approximately 3000 RPM.
6. The calibration procedure will be discontinued if a pedal is depressed or vehicle starts to roll.
7. When calibration process is complete, the TCS CTRL light will shutoff. Terminate ISAT communications and shutoff engine. Check if any diagnostic trouble codes were stored during calibration procedure.

Brake System Bleed

Front brake calipers must be bled first.

1. Fill fluid reservoir to the top.
2. Connect a length of transparent hose to right front caliper bleed nipple and place other end of hose into a clear container.
3. While depressing brake pedal, open bleed nipple.
4. Repeat step 3 until there are no more air bubbles visible in the hose.
5. Connect hose to left front caliper and repeat steps 3 and 4.
6. Connect hose to rear caliper, switch on ignition and repeat steps 3 and 4. **Pump motor must not run for more than two minutes at a time. After motor has been running, let it cool for approximately 10 minutes.**
7. Repeat step 6 on the other rear caliper, then fill fluid reservoir.

Component Replacement

TC/ABS ECU

1. Obtain radio anti-theft code as outlined under "Precautions."
2. Remove two mounting screws, then lift out ECU and disconnect connector.
3. Reverse procedure to install.

CONTROL VALVE FOR TURBO BYPASS VALVE

This valve is located inside the engine compartment, on the lefthand inner fender.

1. Remove two mounting nuts.
2. Unplug electrical connector, then disconnect three signal hoses. Keep color coded rings on valve ports when hoses are disconnected.
3. Reverse procedure to install.

SAFETY VALVE

This valve is mounted on the false bulkhead panel on right side of car.

1. Remove two mounting nuts.
2. Unplug connector, then disconnect vacuum hoses. Keep color coded rings on valve ports when hoses are disconnected.
3. Reverse procedure to install.

NON-RETURN VALVE

This valve is installed in the vacuum hose between the safety valve and inlet manifold.

1. Disconnect vacuum hoses.
2. To install, reconnect vacuum hoses. Ensure white end of valve is pointed towards the safety valve.

TC/ABS HYDRAULIC UNIT

Before beginning this procedure, depressurize accumulator in the TC/ABS hydraulic unit by repeatedly depressing the brake pedal until a dramatic increase in resistance is felt (at least 20 times). Failure to perform this step could result in serious injury.

1. Remove lower dash panel to gain access to top of pedal assembly.
2. Remove pin retaining clip, then withdraw pin from hydraulic unit pushrod.
3. Obtain radio anti-theft code as outlined under "Precautions."
4. Remove battery.
5. Remove clips securing positive lead to battery shelf, then the terminal block (with leads) from battery shelf.
6. Remove connectors at rear of battery shelf, then nuts for the brace.
7. Position TC/ABS ECU aside.
8. Remove battery shelf, then release ABS fuse/relay panel. Position panel aside.
9. Siphon fluid from reservoir, then remove lefthand front wheel and fender liner.
10. Remove brace between engine subframe and wheel housing.
11. Cut tie strap and disconnect all electrical leads from hydraulic unit.
12. Remove mount for battery shelf at hydraulic unit.
13. Disconnect hose for clutch cylinder, then plug end of hose. Do not spill any brake fluid as this could allow air to get into clutch system.
14. Disconnect and plug brake lines from valve block, then remove accumulator.
15. Remove four hydraulic unit mounting nuts, located on bulkhead behind pedal assembly.
16. Remove hydraulic unit.
17. Reverse procedure to install, noting the following:
    a. **Torque** hydraulic unit mounting nuts to 19 ft. lbs.
    b. **Torque** accumulator to 28 ft. lbs.

Mark IV Anti-Lock Brake System

NOTE: On Air Bag Equipped Models, Refer To "Air Bag System Precautions" Located In The Front Of This Manual For System Disarming & Arming Procedures.

NOTE: "Electrical Symbol & Wire Color Code Identification" Located In The Front Of This Manual May Be Used As An Aid When Using Wiring Circuits Found In This Section.

INDEX

	Page No.
Description	7-119
Components	7-119
System	7-119
Diagnosis & Testing	7-121
Accessing Diagnostic Trouble Codes	7-121
Component Testing	7-126
Diagnostic Trouble Code Interpretation	7-121
Precautions	7-119
Air Bag Systems	7-119
Battery Ground Cable	7-119
Radio Anti-Theft Lock	7-119
System Service	7-126
Brake System Bleed	7-126
Component Replacement	7-126
ABS Electronic Control Unit (ECU)	7-127
Front Wheel Sensors	7-127
Hydraulic Unit	7-126
Master Cylinder	7-126
Rear Wheel Sensors	7-127
Travel Sensor	7-127
Vacuum Operated Servo	7-127
Fluid Change	7-126
Troubleshooting	7-120

PRECAUTIONS

AIR BAG SYSTEMS

Refer to "Air Bag System Precautions" in the front of this manual for system disarming and arming procedures.

RADIO ANTI-THEFT LOCK

Radio and cassette player are equipped with an electronic four-digit anti-theft lock. This four-digit code is programmed at manufacturing and cannot be changed. If the battery is disconnected for more than three minutes, if unit is removed or if otherwise cut off from power, the four-digit code must be entered with the quick-selection buttons as follows:

1. Turn radio on, then, when display shows "Code In," enter four-digit code with quick-selection buttons. If code is correct, last-tuned radio frequency is shown on display. If wrong digit has been entered by mistake, all four digits must be entered again. If code is wrong it stays on display.
2. If incorrect four-digit code has been entered, press Band button for more than three seconds to clear display. Display shows "Code In" and new attempt to enter correct code can be made.
3. If wrong code has been used three times in succession, four dashes appear on display and you must wait an hour with radio switched on before trying again.
4. To try again, hold Band button for at least three seconds. "Code In" should appear on display.
5. Correct code must be entered at first attempt, otherwise you must wait another hour with unit switched on before trying again.

BATTERY GROUND CABLE

Prior to service, disconnect battery ground cable and isolate as required.

DESCRIPTION

SYSTEM

The Anti-Lock Brake System (ABS), **Fig. 1,** has been developed to provide optimum braking, with no loss of directional stability, under widely varying conditions. The braking system is divided into two separate diagonal brake circuits. One circuit comprises the right front wheel and left rear wheel (primary circuit), while the other comprises the left front wheel and right rear wheel (secondary circuit).

COMPONENTS

HYDRAULIC UNIT

The hydraulic unit consists of a valve block, master cylinder, hydraulic pump and electric motor in one unit. The hydraulic unit is secured in a vacuum-operated servo (brake pressure booster). The brake fluid reservoir is separate from the hydraulic unit.

Electric Motor

The electric motor, part of the hydraulic unit, drives the hydraulic pump is a direct current motor with a built-in speed sensor so the ECU can receive information that the pump motor is running. The motor can be replaced only as a complete unit with pump and valve block.

Hydraulic Pump

The pump unit, part of the hydraulic unit, delivers brake fluid under ABS control to the brake circuits. Pressure of the brake fluid is determined by brake pressure in the master cylinder, which in turn is proportional to the pedal force applied. The hydraulic pump can be replaced only as a complete unit with motor and valve block.

Master Cylinder

The master cylinder, part of the hydraulic unit, consists of a tandem cylinder made of aluminum. Two central valves open the port to the brake fluid reservoir in the brakes Off position so that the sealing rings are not damaged during braking when ABS is activated. These central valves replace cutoff ports to prevent damage to the sealing ring when ABS is activated. The central valves are made of steel to withstand the high pressure in the master cylinder.

Valve Block

The valve block, part of the hydraulic unit, modulates the pressure to the brake calipers when the ABS system is operative. The valve block contains eight solenoid valves: four inlet valves and four outlet valves. Each brake circuit has one inlet and one outlet valve per wheel.

BRAKE FLUID RESERVOIR

The reservoir contains five chambers. One chamber for the clutch (manual transmission only). On vehicles with automatic transmission this chamber is plugged. Two chambers for the primary circuit. One for master cylinder and one to supply the hydraulic pump. Two chambers for the secondary circuit. One for the master cylinder and one to supply the hydraulic pump.

A safety function is incorporated in the design of the chambers. In the event of a leak in one of the circuits, sufficient brake fluid will always remain for the other circuit and full braking effect will be maintained.

TRAVEL SENSOR

The travel sensor is mounted on the vacuum servo and consists of a set of resistors connected in series which are read by a

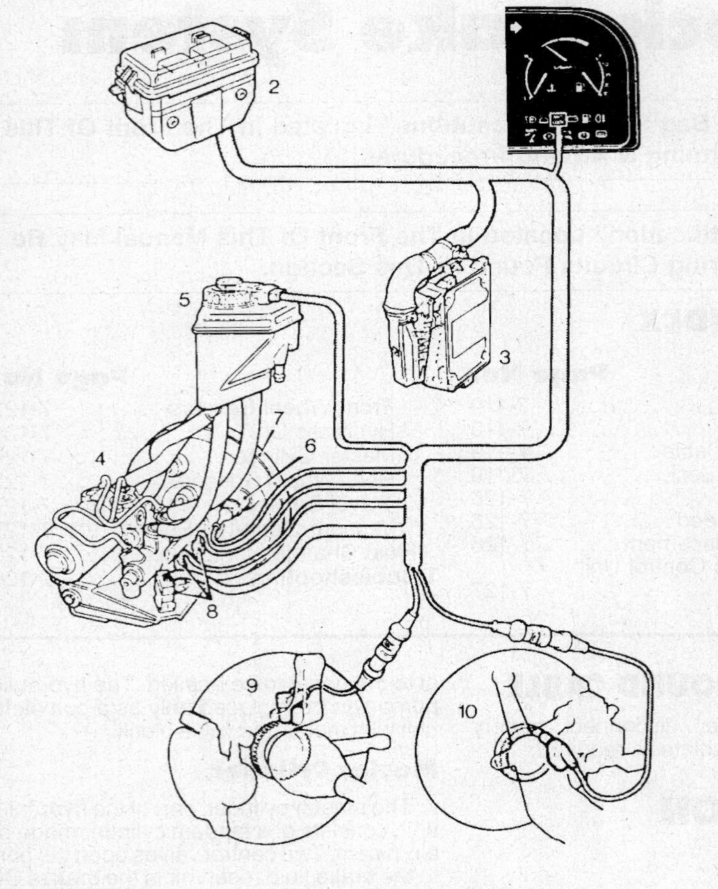

1 ABS warning lights
2 ABS relay box
3 ECU
4 Hydraulic unit
5 Brake fluid reservoir
6 Travel sensor
7 Vacuum-operated servo
8 ABS connectors
9 Wheel sensor, front wheel
10 Wheel sensor, back wheel

SA4029100019000X

Fig. 1 Anti-lock brake system components

ABS command codes

Code	Function/component	Display text
100	Reads all stored trouble codes	
201	Travel sensor	8B X00 (X = 1-7)
202	Brake light switch	8B 000/100 (100 = Closed, 000 = Open)
259	Left front wheel speed	8B 0XX (XX = km/h)
25A	Right front wheel speed	8B 0XX
25B	Left rear wheel speed	8B 0XX
25C	Right rear wheel speed	8B 0XX
800	Communication completed	
900	Clear all trouble codes	11111

SA4029100020000X

Fig. 2 ISAT command codes

sliding contact. This enables the travel sensor to detect a total of seven pedal position points for evaluation by the ECU.

A pump test begins every time the car exceeds 19 mph after starting. The pump then runs for around 300 msec.

If the pedal has reached the seventh position of the travel sensor, the pump will be started regardless of whether braking requires ABS or not. If the ECU does not modulate the pedal to the preceding position, the ABS warning light will come On. If the ECU then detects a defect in the power supply, the ABS will be completely inoperative.

ELECTRONIC CONTROL UNIT (ECU)

The ECU processes the signals from the wheel sensors and, on detecting any lock-up tendency in one or more wheels, sends signals to the solenoid valves in the valve block. the pump starts and stops as required. The ECU is located in the engine compartment on the side of the battery tray.

BRAKE WARNING & ABS WARNING LIGHTS

The brake warning light will come On if the level in the fluid reservoir falls below the MIN mark.

The ABS warning light will come On under the following conditions: malfunction in the ECU, break in circuit continuity or weak signals being received from the wheel sensors. The ABS is always inoperative when the ABS warning light is On and the vehicle will then have standard power assisted brakes.

FRONT WHEEL SENSOR & SENSOR WHEELS

The front wheel sensors are mounted radially relative to the trigger wheel and operate on the same principle as a generator. Each time a tooth on the rotating sensor wheel passes the sensor, it distorts a magnetic field, causing a signal to be sent to the ECU, which processes the signals to produce the control information it requires, such as wheel speed, retardation and slip.

REAR WHEEL SENSORS & SENSOR WHEELS

The rear wheel sensors are mounted axially relative to the trigger wheel: the trigger wheels are therefore of a different design to those for the front wheels, although they operate in exactly the same way.

TROUBLESHOOTING

1. The diagnostic socket (green) is located below the righthand front seat.
2. During fault diagnosis, the ignition switch must always be in the On position.
3. The ISAT system number for the ABS system is number 3.
4. Always read off and note down all stored diagnostic trouble codes before disconnecting the battery or ECU.
5. If communication cannot be established between ISAT and the ECU, check the leads between ECU pins 23 and 42 and the diagnostic socket. Also ensure the power feed and ground circuits to the diagnostic socket are good and the connector pins are not damaged.
6. Once diagnostic trouble codes stored in the systems's ECU have been transferred to ISAT, the diagnosis function is finished. The faults are now available in the form of five-figure trouble codes.
7. To avoid doing damage to the ECU, ensure the ignition is off before unplugging the connector.
8. Before tracing faults on a vehicle's electronic systems, always start by checking that the grounding circuits for the ECU concerned are good and that all nominal voltage levels are correct.
9. Unplug connectors and plugs to check the pins are undamaged and not loose. After checking, plug in all connectors and clear all diagnostic trouble codes. Start engine or drive car again to ensure the fault or faults persist.
10. When first detected, a fault will be assigned a continuous diagnostic trouble code. If the fault later disappears, the fault will be classified as intermittent.
11. All signals around the 12 volt level are proportional to battery voltage. These levels must therefore be taken only as a rough guide.
12. Zero voltage signal levels indicate

ground, although a sensitive multimeter may indicate a value slightly above zero volts.

13. When ISAT command codes are being used to test the system while the car is being driven, communication between ISAT and the ECU will be broken if the speed of the car exceeds 12 mph.
14. Never use the breakout box when car is being driven.

ABS trouble codes

Continuous	Intermittent	Component/Signal
	775B1	ECU fault
	775B2	ECU fault, RAM
42251	22251	System relay, defective
44221	24221	No signal from front left wheel sensor
44222	24222	No signal from right front wheel sensor
44223	24223	No signal from left rear wheel sensor
44224	24224	No signal from right rear wheel sensor
	2422A	Incorrect signal from left front wheel sensor (>40 km/h)
	2422B	Incorrect signal from right front wheel sensor (>40 km/h)
	2422C	Incorrect signal from left rear wheel sensor (>40 km/h)
	2422D	Incorrect signal from right rear wheel sensor (>40 km/h)
	24291	Incorrect signal from left front wheel sensor (<40 km/h)
	24292	Incorrect signal from right front wheel sensor (<40 km/h>
	24293	Incorrect signal from left rear wheel sensor (<40 km/h)
	24294	Incorrect signal from right rear wheel sensor (<40 km/h)
	24251	Incorrect signal from left front wheel sensor (compare wheel speed)
	24252	Incorrect signal from right front wheel sensor (compare wheel speed)
	24253	Incorrect signal from left rear wheel sensor (compare wheel speed)
	24254	Incorrect signal from right rear wheel sensor (compare wheel speed)
53421	33421	Left front inlet valve inoperative
53422	33422	Left front outlet valve inoperative
53423	33423	Right front inlet valve inoperative
53424	33424	Right front outlet valve inoperative
53425	33425	Left rear inlet valve inoperative
53426	33426	Left rear outlet valve inoperative
53427	33427	Right rear inlet valve inoperative
53428	33428	Right rear outlet valve inoperative
	334B1	Left front outlet valve hydraulic fault
	334B2	Right front outlet valve, hydraulic fault
	334B3	Left rear outlet valve, hydraulic fault
	334B4	Right rear outlet valve, hydraulic fault
45721	25721	Travel sensor fault
	24791	Pump fault. Does not operate despite control signal
44792	24792	Pump fault. Operates without control signal
E75B1		Hydraulic fault

SA4029100021000X

Fig. 3 ABS diagnostic trouble codes

DIAGNOSIS & TESTING

ACCESSING DIAGNOSTIC TROUBLE CODES

Command codes instruct the ECU to perform certain functions while accessing diagnostic trouble codes.

Refer to **Fig. 2** for ISAT command codes.

The ECU connector on the wiring loom is in the form of a molded plug, test probes cannot be connected to the back of the connector.

Use breakout box 8611006 with test lead set 8611030, which should be connected between the ECU and the connector.

All measurements on the system must be made with breakout box connected.

To access diagnostic trouble codes, connect ISAT tester to diagnostic socket (green), located under righthand front seat, then follow instructions included with tester.

DIAGNOSTIC TROUBLE CODE INTERPRETATION

Refer to **Fig. 3** for diagnostic trouble codes identification and **Figs. 4 and 5** for system wiring diagram.

DIAGNOSTIC TROUBLE CODE 4/22251

If another diagnostic trouble code other than 42251 exists, diagnose this diagnostic trouble code first.

1. Ensure battery voltage is present at pins 3 and 33.
   a. If no voltage is present at either pin, check ABS 30A fuse for the +30 supply in main fuse box on bulkhead and red wire from fuse to main relay and to distribution block on battery tray.
2. If there is no voltage at any pins, check wire from ECU to main relay from pin concerned.
3. With 0 volts on pin 34 and no voltage at pins 3 and 33, ensure 10A ABS fuse is intact.
   a. If fuse is satisfactory, check power supply to pin 53. If there is no voltage, proceed to step e.
   b. If there is voltage at pin 53, check green wire between pin 85 of system relay and pin 34 of ECU.
   c. Check there is voltage at pin 86 of system relay. If voltage is no present, proceed to step f.
   d. If there is voltage, install new system relay.
   e. If there is no voltage at pin 53 either, check red and white wire as far as fuse. Also ensure power is supplied from pin 54 of ignition switch in grey and white wire as far as supply side of ABS fuse.
   f. Check red and white wire between 86 on system relay via pump relay to 10A fuse.
4. If there is battery voltage on pin 34 but no voltage on pins 3 and 33, the control circuit is correct but the ECU has not grounded the circuit due to a different fault in the ABS system.

DIAGNOSTIC TROUBLE CODES 4/24221, 2422A, 24251 & 24291

1. Raise and support vehicle.
2. With ignition in Drive position, enter command code 259 on ISAT. 8B OXX will show on display.
3. With a multimeter set to AC, take reading across pins 30 and 48. Reading should be 150–700 mV.
4. With ignition turned off and connector of ECU removed, check sensor winding for breaks in continuity by measuring resistance between pins 30 and 48. Resistance must be approximately 1000 ohms.
5. Check wires between sensor and pins 30 and 48 of ABS ECU for short circuits and for poor contact in connector as follows:
   a. Between pin 30 and ground. Resistance should be infinity and voltage should be 0 volts.
   b. Between pin 48 and ground. Resistance should be infinity and voltage should be 0 volts.
6. Ensure left front wheel sensor is firmly in position.
7. Check sensor wheel is not damaged and is firmly in position. Also ensure there is no bearing clearance.
8. Ensure gap between sensor and sensor wheel is .0255 inch (.65 mm).
9. Ensure ECU has a satisfactory ground connection at pin 1 and pin 19.
10. If no fault is discovered, test drive vehicle and check if diagnostic trouble code is triggered again. If diagnostic trouble code persists, proceed to "Guidelines for ECU replacement."

DIAGNOSTIC TROUBLE CODES 4/24222, 2422B, 24252 & 24292

1. Raise and support vehicle.
2. With ignition in Drive position, enter command code 25A on ISAT. 8B OXX will show on display.
3. With a multimeter set to AC, take reading across pins 29 and 47. Reading should be 150–700 mV.
4. With ignition turned off and connector of ECU removed, check sensor winding for breaks in continuity by measuring resistance between pins 29 and 47. Resistance must be approximately 1000 ohms.
5. Check wires between sensor and pins 29 and 47 of ABS ECU for short circuits and for poor contact in connector as follows:
   a. Between pin 29 and ground. Resistance should be infinity and voltage

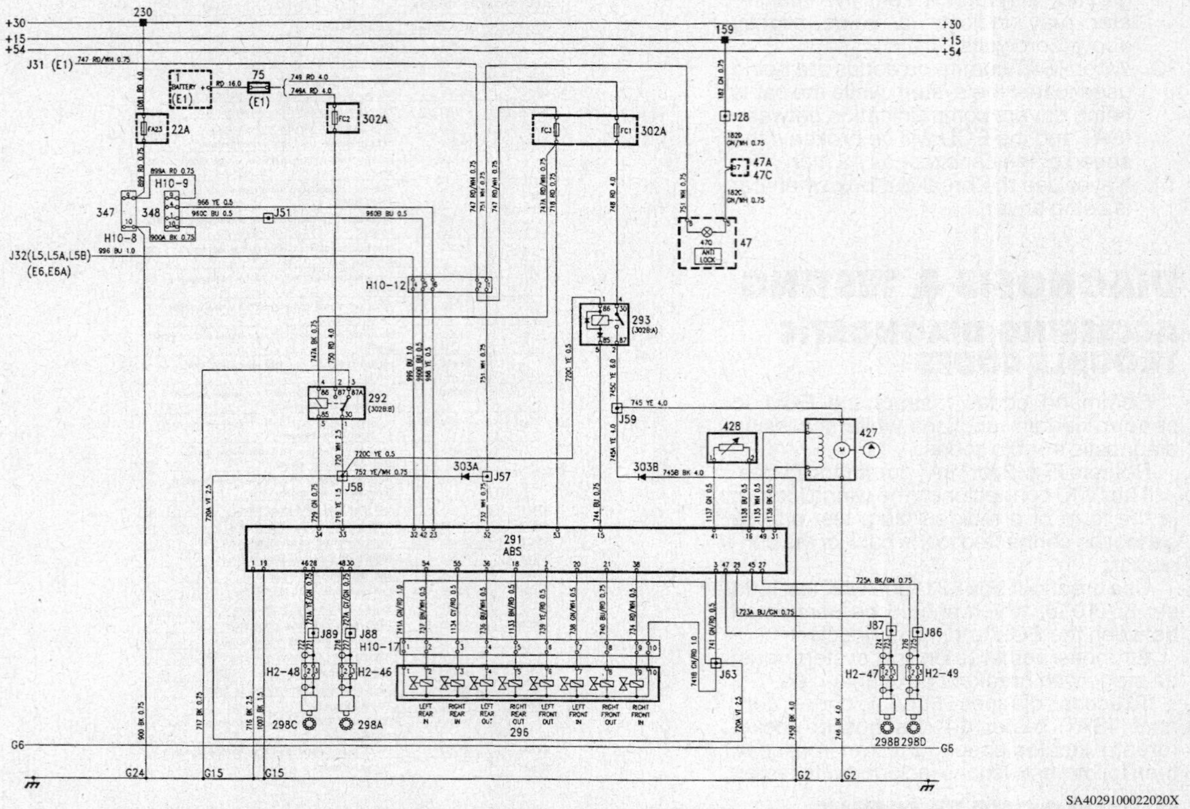

Fig. 4 ABS wiring diagram (Part 1 of 2). Less automatic slip reduction

should be 0 volts.

b. Between pin 47 and ground. Resistance should be infinity and voltage should be 0 volts.

6. Ensure right front wheel sensor is firmly in position.
7. Check sensor wheel is not damaged and is firmly in position. Also ensure there is no bearing clearance.
8. Ensure gap between sensor and sensor wheel is .0255 inch (.65 mm).
9. Ensure ECU has a satisfactory ground connection at pin 1 and pin 19.
10. If no fault is discovered, test drive vehicle and check if diagnostic trouble code is triggered again. If diagnostic trouble code persists, proceed to "Guidelines for ECU replacement."

DIAGNOSTIC TROUBLE CODES 4/24223, 2422C, 24253 & 24293

1. Raise and support vehicle.
2. With ignition in Drive position, enter command code 25B on ISAT. 8B OXX will show on display.
3. With a multimeter set to AC, take reading across pins 28 and 46. Reading should be 150–700 mV.
4. With ignition turned off and connector of ECU removed, check sensor winding for breaks in continuity by measuring resistance between pins 28 and 46. Resistance must be approximately 1000 ohms.
5. Check wires between sensor and pins 28 and 46 of ABS ECU for short circuits and for poor contact in connector as follows:
   a. Between pin 28 and ground. Resistance should be infinity and voltage should be 0 volts.
   b. Between pin 46 and ground. Resistance should be infinity and voltage should be 0 volts.
6. Ensure left rear wheel sensor is firmly in position.
7. Check sensor wheel is not damaged and is firmly in position. Also ensure there is no bearing clearance.
8. Ensure gap between sensor and sensor wheel is .0255 inch (.65 mm).
9. Ensure ECU has a satisfactory ground connection at pin 1 and pin 19.
10. If no fault is discovered, test drive vehicle and check if diagnostic trouble code is triggered again. If diagnostic trouble code persists, proceed to "Guidelines for ECU replacement."

DIAGNOSTIC TROUBLE CODES 4/24224, 2422D, 24254 & 24294

1. Raise and support vehicle.
2. With ignition in Drive position, enter command code 25C on ISAT. 8B OXX will show on display.
3. With a multimeter set to AC, take reading across pins 27 and 45. Reading should be 150–700 mV.
4. With ignition turned off and connector of ECU removed, check sensor winding for breaks in continuity by measuring resistance between pins 27 and 45. Resistance must be approximately 1000 ohms.
5. Check wires between sensor and pins 27 and 45 of ABS ECU for short circuits and for poor contact in connector as follows:
   a. Between pin 27 and ground. Resistance should be infinity and voltage should be 0 volts.
   b. Between pin 45 and ground. Resistance should be infinity and voltage should be 0 volts.
6. Ensure right rear wheel sensor is firmly in position.
7. Check sensor wheel is not damaged and is firmly in position. Also ensure there is no bearing clearance.
8. Ensure gap between sensor and sensor wheel is .0255 inch (.65 mm).
9. Ensure ECU has a satisfactory ground connection at pin 1 and pin 19.
10. If no fault is discovered, test drive vehicle and check if diagnostic trouble code is triggered again. If diagnostic trouble code persists, proceed to "Guidelines for ECU replacement."

DIAGNOSTIC TROUBLE CODE B3421

1. With ECU disconnected, check circuit between pin 20 and pin 3 of ABS ECU. Resistance should be approximately 7 ohms. If circuit is satisfactory, clear diagnostic trouble code and test drive vehicle. Check if diagnostic trouble code is triggered again. If diagnostic trouble code persists, proceed to "Guidelines for ECU replacement." If

circuit is unsatisfactory, proceed to step 2.

2. Check winding of left front inlet valve is intact by measuring resistance between pins 7 and 10 or 1 on valve body. Resistance should be approximately 7 ohms. If resistance is not as specified, install new hydraulic unit. If resistance is now correct, fault is in the wiring harness, proceed to step 3.
3. Check green and white wire between pin 7 on connector of valve housing and pin 20 on ABS ECU for break in continuity.
4. Check green and white wire between pin 10 or 1 on connector of valve housing and pin 3 on ABS ECU for break in continuity.

DIAGNOSTIC TROUBLE CODES B3422 & 334B1

1. With ECU disconnected, check circuit between pin 2 and pin 3 of ABS ECU. Resistance should be 3–4 ohms. If circuit is satisfactory, clear diagnostic trouble code and test drive vehicle. Check if diagnostic trouble code is triggered again. If diagnostic trouble code persists, proceed to "Guidelines for ECU replacement." If circuit is unsatisfactory, proceed to following step.
2. Check winding of left front outlet valve is intact by measuring resistance between pins 6 and 10 or 1 on valve body. Resistance should be 3–4 ohms. If resistance is not as specified, install new hydraulic unit. If resistance is now correct, fault is in the wiring harness, proceed to following step.
3. Check yellow and red wire between pin 6 on connector of valve housing and pin 2 on ABS ECU for break in continuity.
4. Check wire between pin 10 or 1 on connector of valve housing and pin 3 on ABS ECU for break in continuity.

DIAGNOSTIC TROUBLE CODE B3423

1. With ECU disconnected, check circuit between pin 38 and pin 3 of ABS ECU. Resistance should be approximately 7 ohms. If circuit is satisfactory, clear diagnostic trouble code and test drive vehicle. Check if diagnostic trouble code is triggered again. If diagnostic trouble code persists, proceed to "Guidelines for ECU replacement." If circuit is unsatisfactory, proceed to step 2.
2. Check winding of right front inlet valve is intact by measuring resistance between pins 9 and 10 or 1 on valve body. Resistance should be approximately 7 ohms. If resistance is not as specified, install new hydraulic unit. If resistance is now correct, fault is in the wiring harness, proceed to step 3.
3. Check red and white wire between pin 1 on connector of valve housing and pin 38 on ABS ECU for break in continuity.
4. Check wire between pin 10 or 1 on connector of valve housing and pin 3 on ABS ECU for break in continuity.

1	Battery in the engine compartment
22A	Fuse holder behind the access panel in the glove box
47A	Fuel gauge
47C	Coolant temperature gauge
47Q	ABS/ABS-TCS warning lamp
75	Distribution block, positive battery supply, on the battery tray
159	Distribution terminal +15 in the electrical distribution box behind the glove box
230	Distribution terminal +30 in the electrical distribution box behind the glove box
291	ABS control unit on the battery tray
292	Main relay for ABS, in the engine compartment between the battery tray and the brake fluid reservoir, in the electrical distribution board (302B:B)
293	ABS pump relay, in the engine compartment in the electrical distribution box (302B:A)
296	Valve block, ABS
298A	Left-hand front wheel sensor, on the left-hand steering knuckle housing
298B	Right-hand front wheel sensor, on the left-hand steering knuckle housing
298C	Left-hand rear wheel sensor, on the left-hand rear wheel hub
298D	Right-hand rear wheel sensor, on the right-hand rear wheel hub
302A	ABS fuse holder in the engine compartment on the bulkhead partition
303A/ 303B	Diode, ABS, in the engine compartment, in the ABS electrical distribution box under the relay board, in the casing
347 (H10-8)	Diagnostic test socket, engine electronics, under the right-hand front seat (black)
348 (H10-9)	Diagnostic test socket, car electronics, under the right-hand front seat (green)
427	Motor for hydraulic pump (ABS/ ABS-ASR Mark IV) in the engine compartment on the brake unit
428	Pedal position transmistter (ABS/ ABS-ASR Mark IV) on the vacuum servo which is located on the bulkhead partition
	2-pole connector
H2-46	In the engine compartment behind the bulkhead partition on the extreme left
H2-47	In the engine compartment behind the bulkhead partition on the extreme right
H2-48	Under the rear seat on the left-hand side under the carpet
H2-49	Under the rear seat on the right-hand side under the carpet
	10-pole connector
H10-12	In the engine compartment on the left, below the ABS 302 electrical distribution box
H10-17	On the valve block
G2	Earthing point, battery tray, on left-hand wheel housing
G15	Earthing point, ABS, on the left-hand structuiral member, at the ABS control unit

SA4029100022010X

Fig. 4 ABS wiring diagram (Part 2 of 2). Less automatic slip reduction

DIAGNOSTIC TROUBLE CODES B3424 & 334B2

1. With ECU disconnected, check circuit between pin 21 and pin 3 of ABS ECU. Resistance should be 3–4 ohms. If circuit is satisfactory, clear diagnostic trouble code and test drive vehicle. Check if diagnostic trouble code is triggered again. If diagnostic trouble code persists, proceed to "Guidelines for ECU replacement." If circuit is unsatisfactory, proceed to step 2.
2. Check winding of right front outlet valve is intact by measuring resistance between pins 8 and 10 or 1 on valve body. Resistance should be 3–4 ohms. If resistance is not as specified, install new hydraulic unit. If resistance is now correct, fault is in the wiring harness, proceed to step 3.
3. Check blue and red wire between pin 8 on connector of valve housing and pin 2 on ABS ECU for break in continuity.
4. Check wire between pin 10 or 1 on connector of valve housing and pin 3 on ABS ECU for break in continuity.

DIAGNOSTIC TROUBLE CODE 3/53425

1. With ECU disconnected, check circuit between pin 54 and pin 3 of ABS ECU. Resistance should be approximately 7 ohms. If circuit is satisfactory, clear diagnostic trouble code and test drive vehicle. Check if diagnostic trouble code is triggered again. If diagnostic trouble code persists, proceed to "Guidelines for ECU replacement." If circuit is unsatisfactory, proceed to step 2.
2. Check winding of left rear inlet valve is intact by measuring resistance between pins 2 and 10 or 1 on valve body. Resistance should be approximately 7 ohms. If resistance is not as specified, install new hydraulic unit. If resistance is now correct, fault is in the wiring harness, proceed to step 3.
3. Check brown and white wire between pin 2 on connector of valve housing and pin 54 on ABS ECU for break in continuity.
4. Check wire between pin 10 or 1 on connector of valve housing and pin 3 on ABS ECU for break in continuity.

DIAGNOSTIC TROUBLE CODES B3426 & 334B3

1. With ECU disconnected, check circuit between pin 36 and pin 3 of ABS ECU. Resistance should be 3–4 ohms. If circuit is satisfactory, clear diagnostic trouble code and test drive vehicle. Check if diagnostic trouble code is triggered again. If diagnostic trouble code persists, proceed to "Guidelines for

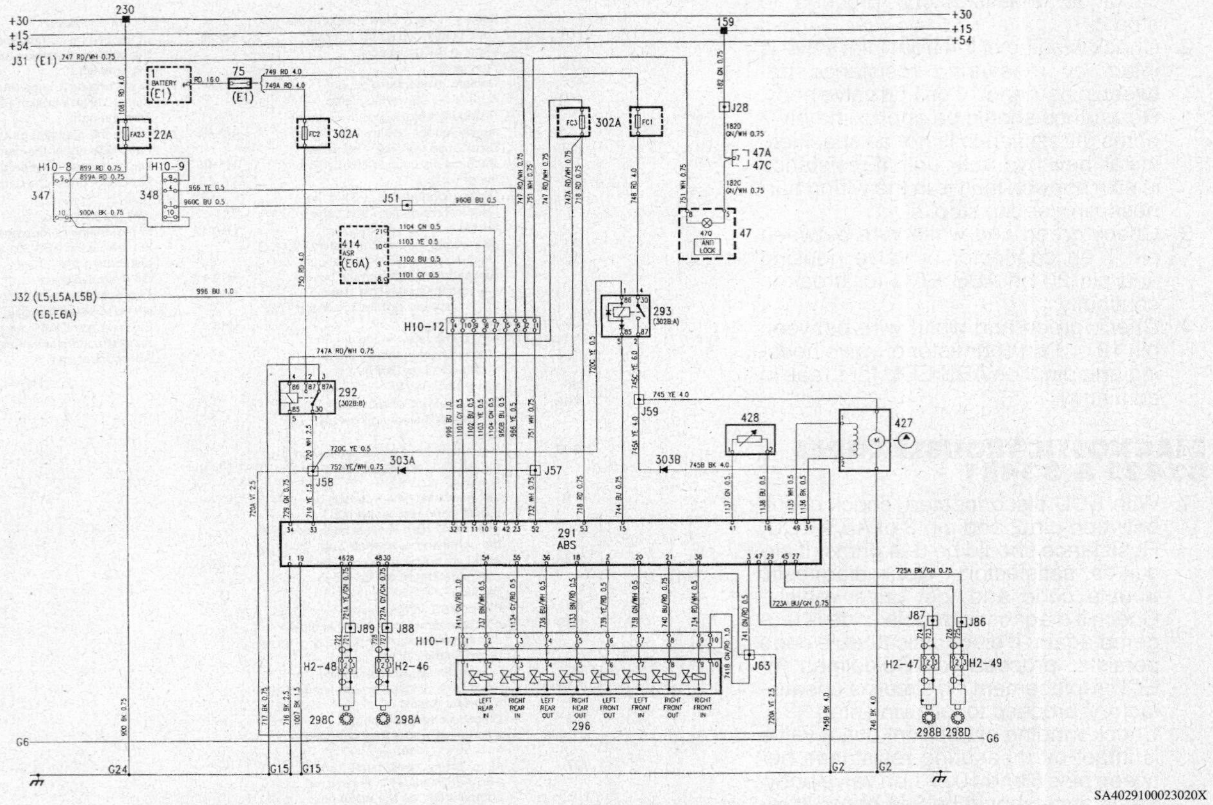

Fig. 5 ABS wiring diagram (Part 1 of 2). With automatic slip reduction

ECU replacement." If circuit is unsatisfactory, proceed to step 2.

2. Check winding of left rear outlet valve is intact by measuring resistance between pins 4 and 10 or 1 on valve body. Resistance should be 3–4 ohms. If resistance is not as specified, install new hydraulic unit. If resistance is now correct, fault is in the wiring harness, proceed to step 3.
3. Check blue and white wire between pin 4 on connector of valve housing and pin 36 on ABS ECU for break in continuity.
4. Check wire between pin 10 or 1 on connector of valve housing and pin 3 on ABS ECU for break in continuity.

DIAGNOSTIC TROUBLE CODE B3427

1. With ECU disconnected, check circuit between pin 55 and pin 3 of ABS ECU. Resistance should be approximately 7 ohms. If circuit is satisfactory, clear diagnostic trouble code and test drive vehicle. Check if diagnostic trouble code is triggered again. If diagnostic trouble code persists, proceed to "Guidelines for ECU replacement." If circuit is unsatisfactory, proceed to step 2.
2. Check winding of right rear inlet valve is intact by measuring resistance between pins 3 and 10 or 1 on valve body. Resistance should be approximately 7 ohms. If resistance is not as specified, install new hydraulic unit. If resistance is now correct, fault is in the wiring harness, proceed to step 3.
3. Check wire between pin 3 on connector of valve housing and pin 55 on ABS ECU for break in continuity.
4. Check black wire between pin 10 or 1 on connector of valve housing and pin 3 on ABS ECU for break in continuity.

DIAGNOSTIC TROUBLE CODES B3428 & 334B4

1. With ECU disconnected, check circuit between pin 18 and pin 3 of ABS ECU. Resistance should be 3–4 ohms. If circuit is satisfactory, clear diagnostic trouble code and test drive vehicle. Check if diagnostic trouble code is triggered again. If diagnostic trouble code persists, proceed to "Guidelines for ECU replacement." If circuit is unsatisfactory, proceed to step 2.
2. Check winding of right rear outlet valve is intact by measuring resistance between pins 5 and 10 or 1 on valve body. Resistance should be 3–4 ohms. If resistance is not as specified, install new hydraulic unit. If resistance is now correct, fault is in the wiring harness, proceed to step 3.
3. Check brown and white wire between pin 5 on connector of valve housing and pin 18 on ABS ECU for break in continuity.
4. Check wire between pin 10 or 1 on connector of valve housing and pin 3 on ABS ECU for break in continuity.

DIAGNOSTIC TROUBLE CODE 775B1

1. If diagnostic trouble code returns, check ground points of ECU at pins 1 and 19 and that grounding point, located near ABS control unit, is satisfactory.
2. Clear diagnostic trouble code and test drive vehicle. Check if diagnostic trouble code is triggered again. If diagnostic trouble code persists, proceed to "Guidelines for ECU replacement."

DIAGNOSTIC TROUBLE CODE 775B2

1. Clear diagnostic trouble code and test drive vehicle. Check if diagnostic trouble code is triggered again. If diagnostic trouble code persists, proceed to "Guidelines for ECU replacement."

DIAGNOSTIC TROUBLE CODES 45721 & 25721

1. Connect breakout box.
2. Check voltage between pins 41 and 16 as shown in **Fig. 6.**
3. Remove travel sensor. Check resistance as shown in **Fig. 6.**
4. If resistance is as specified, clear diagnostic trouble code and test drive vehicle. Check if diagnostic trouble code is triggered again. If diagnostic trouble code persists, proceed to "Guidelines for ECU replacement."

47A	Fuel gauge
47C	Coolant temperature gauge
47Q	ABS/ABS-TCS warning lamp
75	Distribution block, positive battery supply, on the battery tray
159	Distribution terminal +15 in the electrical distribution box behind the glove box
230	Distribution terminal +30 in the electrical distribution box behind the glove box
291	ABS control unit on the battery tray
292	Main relay for ABS, in the engine compartment between the battery tray and the brake fluid reservoir, in the electrical distribution board (302B:B)
293	ABS pump relay, in the engine compartment in the electrical distribution box (302B:A)
296	Valve block, ABS
298A	Left-hand front wheel sensor, on the left-hand steering knuckle housing
298B	Right-hand front wheel sensor, on the left-hand steering knuckle housing
298C	Left-hand rear wheel sensor, on the left-hand rear wheel hub
298D	Right-hand rear wheel sensor, on the right-hand rear wheel hub
302A	ABS fuse holder in the engine compartment on the bulkhead partition
303A/ 303B	Diode, ABS, in the engine compartment, in the ABS electrical distribution box under the relay board, in the casing
347 (H10-8)	Diagnostic test socket, engine electronics, under the right-hand front seat (black)
348 (H10-9)	Diagnostic test socket, car electronics, under the right-hand front seat (green)
427	Motor for hydraulic pump (ABS/ ABS-ASR Mark IV) in the engine compartment on the brake unit
428	Pedal position transmistter (ABS/ ABS-ASR Mark IV) on the vacuum servo which is located on the bulkhead partition

	2-pole connector
H2-46	In the engine compartment behind the bulkhead partition on the extreme left
H2-47	In the engine compartment behind the bulkhead partition on the extreme right
H2-48	Under the rear seat on the left-hand side under the carpet
H2-49	Under the rear seat on the right-hand side under the carpet
	10-pole connector
H10-12	In the engine compartment on the left, below the ABS 302 electrical distribution box
H10-17	On the valve block
G2	Earthing point, battery tray, on left-hand wheel housing
G15	Earthing point, ABS, on the left-hand structuiral member, at the ABS control unit
G24	Earthing point, on the right-hand front seat member

SA4029100023010X

Fig. 5 ABS wiring diagram (Part 2 of 2). With automatic slip reduction

Position of travel sensor	Resistance Ohms	Voltage Volts
1	250	1.0
2	437	1.7
3	564	2.3
4	691	2.8
5	817	3.3
6	1034	4.1
7	OL	10.0

SA4029100024000X

Fig. 6 Resistance & voltage specifications

DIAGNOSTIC TROUBLE CODE 24791

1. Connect breakout box to ECU connector, then inspect fuse FC 30A.
2. Ensure battery voltage is present at pin 30 of pump relay and 0 volts is present at pin 87.
3. Activate pump by connecting pins 1, 34 and 15 on breakout box for a maximum of 2 minutes. Ensure ABS pump relay clicks.
4. Check pins 49 and 31 on breakout box. With motor running reading should be approximately. 7 volt AC. With motor stationary reading should be 0 volt.
5. Check pin 2 with relay operated. If battery voltage is present, check ground. If ground is satisfactory, install new pump.

DIAGNOSTIC TROUBLE CODES 44792 & 24792

1. Unplug ECU and connect breakout box to its connector.
2. Ensure pump motor and speed sensor are operative. Refer to "Diagnostic Trouble Code 24791."
3. Check travel sensor.
4. Check voltage at pin 15 of breakout box. Battery voltage should be present. If voltage is not as specified, clear diagnostic trouble code and test drive vehicle. Check if diagnostic trouble code is triggered again. If diagnostic trouble code persists, proceed to "Guidelines for ECU replacement."

DIAGNOSTIC TROUBLE CODES E75B1

1. Ensure there is brake fluid in system and thickness of brake pads is within specification. Check master cylinder operation and all hoses for damage or swelling.
2. Check voltage between pins 41 and 16 as shown in **Fig. 6.**
3. Remove travel sensor. Check resistance as shown in **Fig. 6.**
4. If resistance is as specified, clear diagnostic trouble code and test drive vehicle. Check if diagnostic trouble code is triggered again. If diagnostic trouble code persists, proceed to "Guidelines for ECU replacement."

WARNING LIGHTS

Anti-Lock Light

1. With ECU connector connected and ignition switch in Drive position, check there is battery voltage at pin 52. If voltage is not present, check bulb is intact and white wire between pins 52 and 8 of main instrument display panel.
2. With ignition in Off position and ECU main relay disconnected, check circuit between pins 52 and 33.
3. Ensure diode is nonconducting to pin 52.

Brake Fluid Level Light

1. **If light comes on when car is started,** proceed as follows:
   a. With ignition On, check for battery voltage at pin 2 on brake fluid reservoir. If voltage is not present at 2, check pin 5 on combined instrument. If battery voltage is present at pin 5, there is no fault in power supply.
   b. Check light. If light is intact, install a new circuit.
   c. Ensure pin 1 is grounded. If not, check ground supply. If ground is found at supply, install new float.
   d. If no voltage is present at pin 5 on combined instrument, there is a fault in power supply.
2. **If light does not come on when care is started,** proceed as follows:
   a. Ensure lamp comes on when float is pressed down in reservoir.
   b. Check pin 1 of main instrument display panel. Test position of ignition switch equals 0 volt. If voltage reading is as specified, replace circuit board. If voltage is present, check ground on ignition switch. If switch is grounded, install new ignition switch. If switch is not grounded, check grounding path.

GUIDELINES FOR ECU REPLACEMENT

When all checks have been carried out according to diagnostic trouble code diagnosis without any faults being discovered, it is logical to assume the ECU is defective. The following steps must therefore be carried out carefully before the ABS ECU is identified as the cause of the fault.

1. Check the following:
   a. Correct wheel size.
   b. All wheels are of the same height/ width.
   c. Correct air pressure in all wheels.
   d. No play in wheel bearings.
2. Ensure all steps in the diagnostic trouble code diagnosis have been carried out.
3. Study wiring diagram of the circuit concerned and familiarize yourself with how it works.
4. Inspect all ground points. Check power

Pin no.	Wire colour	Component/function	In-put	Out-put	Voltage (V)	Remarks
1	BK	Earth 1	X		0	G 15
2	YE/RD	Left front outlet valve		X	Pwm neg	Ref 12V
3	GN/RD	REF voltage	X		Batt.	
4						Not connected
5						Not connected
6						Not connected
7						Not connected
8						Not connected
9	GN	ASR right rear		X		To ASR
10	YE	ASR left front		X		To ASR
11	BU	ASR right front		X		To ASR
12	GY	ASR left rear		X		To ASR
13						Not connected
14						Not connected
15	BU	Pump relay Pin 85		X	0v	Relay earth Ref 12V (off)
16	BU	Travel sensor	X		1-10V	Depending on position
17						Not connected
18	BN/RD	Right rear outlet valve		X	Pwm neg	Ref 12V
19	BK	Earth 2	X		0	G 15
20	GN/WH	Left front inlet valve		X	Pwm neg	Ref 12V
21	BU/RD	Right front outlet valve		X	Pwm neg	Ref 12V
22						Not connected
23	YE	Diagnostic lead L	X			Pin 4
24						Not connected
25						Not connected
26						Not connected

SA4029100025010X

Fig. 7 ABS ECU voltage specifications (Part 1 of 2)

Pin no.	Wire colour	Component/function	In-put	Out-put	Voltage (V)	Remarks
27	BK/GN	Right rear wheel sensor		X	0V	Ref earth
28	YE/GN	Left front wheel sensor		X	0V	Ref earth
29	BU/GN	Right front wheel sensor		X	0V	Ref earth
30	GN/GY	Left front wheel sensor		X	0V	Ref earth
31	BK	Pump sensor		X	approx. 0.7 AC	Active
32	BU	Brake light switch	X		12V	0V off
33	YE	Power supply +30	X		12 V	Via main relay
34	GN	Main relay earth		X	0V	Ref 12V Pin 85
35						Not connected
36	BU/WH	Left rear outlet valve		X	Pwm neg	Ref 12V
37						Not connected
38	RD/WH	Right front inlet valve		X	Pwm neg	Ref 12V
39						No connection activated
40						Not connected
41	GN	Travel sensor		X	0V	Earth
42	BU	Diagnostic lead K		X		Pin 1
43						Not connected
44						Not connected
45	GN	Right rear wheel sensor	X		0.15-0.70	AC sine wave
46	GN	Left rear wheel sensor	X		0.15-0.70	AC sine wave
47	GN	Right front wheel sensor	X		0.15-0.70	AC sine wave
48	GN	Left front wheel sensor	X		0.15-0.70	AC sine wave
49	WH	Pump sensor	X		approx. 0.7 AC	Signal
50						Not connected
51						Not connected
52	WH	ANTI LOCK warning light earth		X	0V	Ref 12V off
53	RD	Power supply +54	X		12v	+54
54	BN/WH	Left rear inlet valve		X	Pwm neg	Ref 12V
55	GY/RD	Right rear inlet valve		X	Pwm neg	Ref 12V

SA4029100025020X

Fig. 7 ABS ECU voltage specifications (Part 2 of 2)

ground and signal ground are electrically separated.

5. Check power supply to ECU.
6. Clear diagnostic trouble code. Test drive vehicle again. If original diagnostic trouble code persists, The ABS ECU must be replaced.

COMPONENT TESTING

ABS ECU VOLTAGE TEST USING BREAKOUT BOX

Refer to **Fig. 7**, for voltage specifications.

SYSTEM SERVICE

Fluid Change

All brake fluid deteriorates after a time through oxidation and absorption of water. This lower the boiling point of the fluid, which may therefore vaporize during prolonged hard braking. The result can be sudden brake failure. It is therefore essential to change brake fluid at specified intervals.

1. Using bleeder unit tool No. 88 19 096, or equivalent, siphon off fluid from reservoir.
2. Fill reservoir with DOT 4 brake fluid.
3. Using bleeder unit to drain each individual wheel. The following quantities must be drained from each wheel:
   a. Right front wheel, 1 quart.
   b. Left rear wheel, .5 quart.
   c. Left front wheel, 1 quart.
   d. Right rear wheel, .5 quart.
4. Fill system with new brake fluid to bring level up to MAX mark on side of reservoir. Also change fluid in clutch system.

Brake System Bleed

Brake system must be bled when the hydraulic unit is replaced.

Brakes must be bled in the following sequence: right front, left rear, left front and right rear wheels.

1. Unscrew cover of brake fluid reservoir, then connect topping-up assembly (part of brake bleed unit kit part No. 88 19 096) to reservoir.
2. Disconnect ECU connector. Plug connector of breakout box into ABS connector for ECU.
3. Connect wiring loom 1, part No. 86 11 212, to pins 1, 34 and 15 of breakout box.
4. Connect wiring loom 2, part No. 86 11 212, to pins 18, 36, 21 and 2 of breakout box.
5. Connect pin 1 when ignition is switched On. Run pump for 1 minute. Connect battery terminal 20 seconds after pump has started to ensure outlet valves are opened.
6. Disconnect battery terminal after 20 seconds and pin 1, 60 seconds after pump has started.
7. Switch ignition Off.
8. Bleed system using bleeder unit tool No. No. 88 19 096, or equivalent.
9. After bleeding is complete, reconnect ECU connector.
10. Turn ignition switch to On position. Ensure ABS warning light goes Off.

Component Replacement

HYDRAULIC UNIT

1. Obtain radio anti-theft code as outlined under "Precautions."
2. Remove bolt securing battery to tray.
3. Remove battery, then disconnect main fuse box by lifting straight up.
4. Remove battery tray mounting bolts and screws, then the battery tray.
5. Unplug connector from ECU on side of battery tray, then disconnect ABS wiring loom clip.
6. Remove throttle cable from throttle housing, then the ABS main fuse box and brake fluid reservoir from their brackets.
7. Using brake bleeder unit part No. 88 19 096, or equivalent, siphon brake fluid out of reservoir.
8. **On models with manual transaxle,** disconnect clutch cylinder hose from reservoir.
9. **On all models,** mark and remove four brake pipes. Plug ends of valve block and brake pipes.
10. Disconnect hydraulic unit connectors, then the travel sensor connector.
11. Remove hydraulic unit mounting nuts, then the unit.
12. Reverse procedure to install. Bleed brake system as outlined under "Brake System Bleed."

MASTER CYLINDER

1. Clean around ends of brake pipes.
2. Obtain radio anti-theft code as outlined under "Precautions."
3. Remove bolt securing battery to tray.
4. Remove battery, then disconnect main fuse box by lifting straight up.
5. Remove battery tray mounting bolts and screws, then the battery tray.
6. Drain brake fluid reservoir, then disconnect brake pipes from master cylinder.

7. Remove securing bolt from below master cylinder.
8. Remove nuts mounting master cylinder to vacuum operated servo.
9. Remove master cylinder assembly, then disconnect hose from master cylinder.
10. Reverse procedure to install, then bleed brake system as outlined under "Brake System Bleed."

VACUUM OPERATED SERVO

1. Remove ABS hydraulic unit as outlined under "Hydraulic Unit, Replace."
2. Disconnect lower dash panel by pressing locking pins on 5 plastic clips with a flat head screwdriver.
3. Disconnect clip and pin from pushrod.
4. Remove vacuum servo mounting nuts, then disconnect vacuum hose and travel sensor connector from servo.
5. Remove servo unit. When changing vacuum servo unit, travel sensor must be transferred to new servo unit. Adjusting sleeve having same color as mark servo should be installed on travel sensor.
6. Reverse procedure to install.

ABS ELECTRONIC CONTROL UNIT (ECU)

1. Obtain radio anti-theft code as outlined under "Precautions."
2. Disconnect ABS wiring loom clip.
3. Disconnect ECU electrical connector.
4. Remove ECU mounting bolts, then the ECU.
5. Reverse procedure to install.

TRAVEL SENSOR

1. Remove rubber elbow from throttle housing.
2. Remove ABS main fuse box and brake fluid reservoir.
3. Disconnect connectors from hydraulic unit, then remove circlip below travel sensor.
4. Remove travel sensor, then the O-ring from sensor.
5. Reverse procedure to install. Adjusting sleeve should have same color as mark on vacuum servo.

FRONT WHEEL SENSORS

1. Disconnect sensor connector (one for each wheel) by pushing halves together to release catches:
    a. Lift rubber molding on bulkhead panel. Remove cover over space behind bulkhead panel. Remove plastic clip at panel.
    b. On right side, raise A/C pipes and pull sensor lead through.
2. Raise and support vehicle, then remove front wheel(s).
3. Remove rear section of wing liner.
4. Cut cable tie securing sensor lead to top bracket. Pull sensor lead through rubber grommet in wheel housing.
5. Remove sensor mounting bolt, then the sensor.
6. Reverse procedure to install. Turn steering wheel from lock to lock to ensure sensor lead cannot rub against any front assembly components.

REAR WHEEL SENSORS

1. Tilt rear seat forward and remove cover on left and/or right side of floor.
2. Unplug sensor connector from brackets by clipping tie on top bracket.
3. Raise and support vehicle, then remove rear wheel(s).
4. Disconnect clip and pull sensor lead through rubber grommet in floor.
5. Remove sensor mounting bolt, then the sensor.
6. Reverse procedure to install.

Bosch 5.3 Anti-Lock Brake System

NOTE: On Air Bag Equipped Models, Refer To "Air Bag System Precautions" Located In The Front Of This Manual For System Disarming & Arming Procedures.

NOTE: "Electrical Symbol & Wire Color Code Identification" Located In The Front Of This Manual May Be Used As An Aid When Using Wiring Circuits Found In This Section.

INDEX

	Page No.
Description	7-128
Components	7-128
System	7-128
Diagnosis & Testing	7-130
ABS Measured Data	7-130
Accessing Diagnostic Trouble Codes	7-130
Diagnostic Tests	7-130
Diagnostic Trouble Code Interpretation	7-130
Wiring Circuit	7-130
Diagnostic Chart Index	7-135
Precautions	7-128
Air Bag Systems	7-128
Battery Ground Cable	7-128
System Service	7-130
Brake System Bleed	7-130
Component Replacement	7-130
ABS Control Module	7-130
Hydraulic Unit	7-130
Wheel Sensors	7-131
Troubleshooting	7-129
Break In Continuity Inspection	7-129
Short-Circuit To Ground Inspection	7-130

PRECAUTIONS

AIR BAG SYSTEMS

Refer to "Air Bag System Precautions" in the front of this manual for system disarming and arming procedures.

BATTERY GROUND CABLE

Prior to service, disconnect battery ground cable and isolate as required.

DESCRIPTION

SYSTEM

The Anti-Lock Brake System (ABS) is a two-circuit, four-port brake system, **Fig. 1.**

Four wheel sensors at the wheels send signals to an electronic control unit, which continuously calculates on the basis of the wheel acceleration (speed increase), wheel deceleration (speed decrease), the speed of the vehicle and the slip of the wheels (degree of wheel lock-up). If any wheel approaches the limit for lock-up, the control unit passes signals to solenoid valves in the valve block for the wheel concerned. The pressure in the brake circuit for the wheel is controlled in this way so the maximum possible braking power is transmitted to the road surface at all times with no loss of steering ability.

Electronic Brake-Force Distribution (EBD), a built in function of the electronic control module, controls the rear electromagnetic intake valves to provide maximum braking power at the rear wheels without front wheel lock-up.

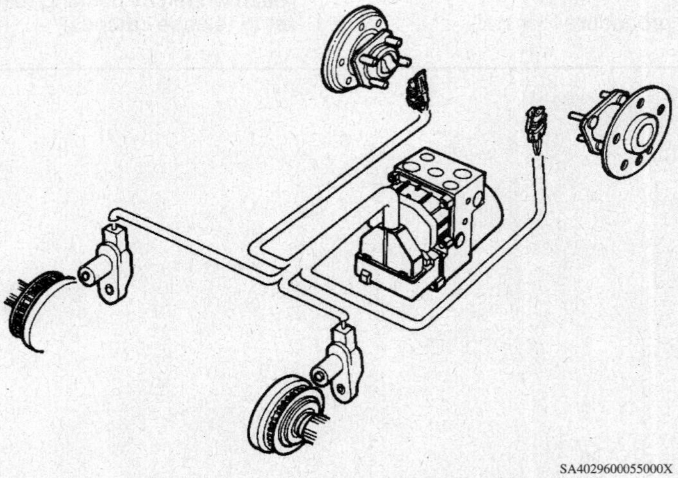

Fig. 1 Anti-lock brake system

COMPONENTS

HYDRAULIC UNIT

The hydraulic unit consists of the valve block with eight boost pressure control valves (1 intake and outlet valve for each wheel and an electronic control module with main and pump relays and return pump.

The master cylinder is separated from the hydraulic unit and is connected via two pipes from the primary and secondary circuits.

ELECTRONIC CONTROL MODULE

The electronic control module forms an integral unit with the ABS hydraulic unit and has a 26/31-pin connector.

The control module receives wheel speed information through input signals from the wheel sensors.

If any of the wheels has greater deceleration on braking than the others, the control module controls the solenoid valves so the hydraulic brake pressure can be kept constant or reduced to each wheel, while receiving maximum friction from the road surface.

WHEEL SENSORS

The wheel sensors are mounted near a toothed sensor wheel at each wheel. Each time a tooth on the sensor wheel passes the sensor, it interrupts a magnetic field, which causes a signal to be sent to the Electronic Control Unit (ECU).

The rear wheel sensor is designed differently than the front, in that it is less sensitive to wheel bearing play and starts to pass information to the control module at very low wheel speeds.

SOLENOID VALVES

Normal Position (Pressure Build-Up)

In normal position, **Fig. 2,** the solenoid valve is de-energized. The piston is pressed down toward the normal position of the return spring. The brake fluid is now able to flow freely from the master cylinder out through the solenoid valve to the wheel

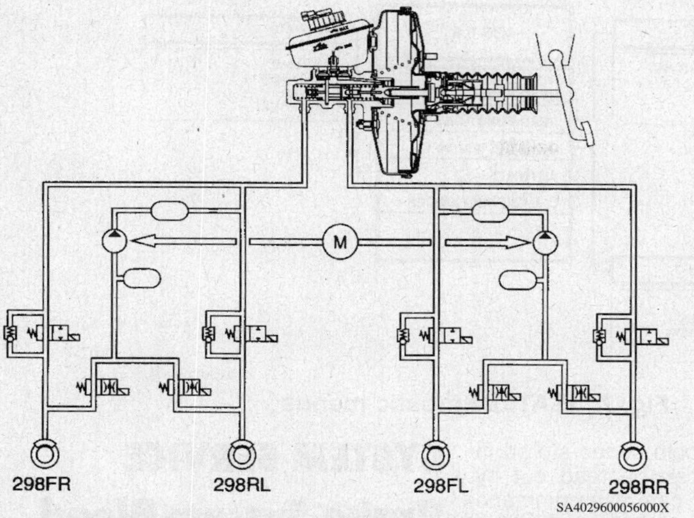

Fig. 2 Solenoid valve in normal position (pressure build-up)

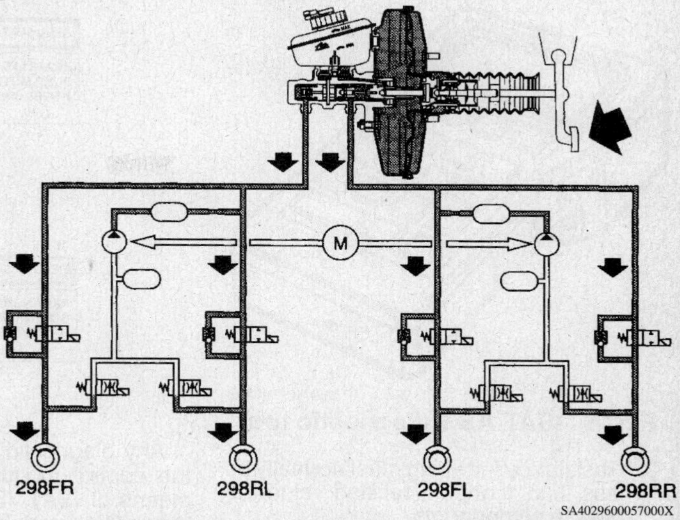

Fig. 3 Solenoid valve in pressure holding position

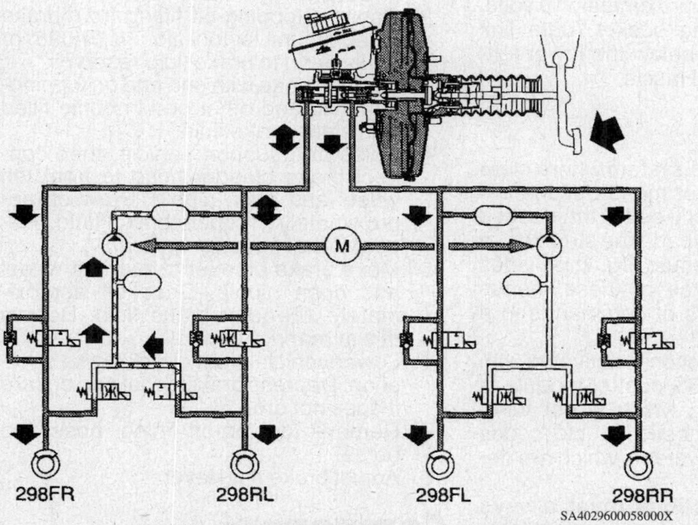

Fig. 4 Solenoid valve in pressure relief position

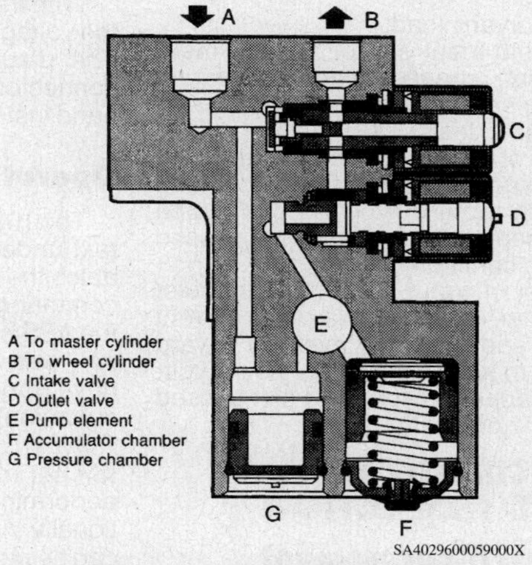

Fig. 5 Equalization valve replacement

cylinder. This position is the normal position in braking without ABS control and the pressure build-up position in ABS control.

Pressure Holding Position

In this position, **Fig. 3,** the solenoid valve has received around half the current from the ABS control module. The piston has moved into the pressure holding position by rising slightly and the passage from the master cylinder to the wheel cylinder is consequently closed.

This is one of the three positions with which the control module operates under ABS control.

Pressure Relief

In this position, **Fig. 4,** the solenoid valve obtains full current from the control module. The piston in the valve has risen to the pressure relief position and opens the channel from the wheel cylinder to the pressure accumulator which can quickly receive pressure from the wheel cylinder. The control module energizes the return pump and the pressure can be pumped back to the master cylinder.

EQUALIZATION VALVE

In addition to the solenoid valve, there is an equalization valve, **Fig. 5,** for the rear wheel circuit so both rear wheels can be operated with only one solenoid valve.

The equalization valve ensures both rear wheels receive the same brake pressure in ABS control. This means the vehicle has good directional stability.

In the case of ABS control of the rear wheels, the solenoid valve moves to the pressure holding position. The channel to the rear right wheel is now blocked. If the pressure from the master cylinder rises, a pressure difference develops below and above the piston (1). The piston is raised and the valve (2) closes the pressure to the rear left wheel. If the pressure to the rear right wheel drops (pressure relief), a greater pressure difference develops above and below the piston (1) and the piston is lifted further upward until the pressure for the right and left rear wheels has balanced out.

BRAKE LIGHT SWITCH

The control module receives voltage from the brake light switch, when the brake is activated. For example, the brake light switch is used if the surface is very slippery and the driver decides to apply the brake.

Every time the driver depresses the brake pedal, when power is fed to the ECU from the brake light switch, the ABS control restarts from its starting position.

TROUBLESHOOTING

BREAK IN CONTINUITY INSPECTION

Resistance Measurement

1. Ensure component or cable to be checked is not live.
2. With instrument set for resistance measurement, connect the measuring cables to each end of the component or cable to be checked.

Fig. 6 ISAT ABS diagnostic tool

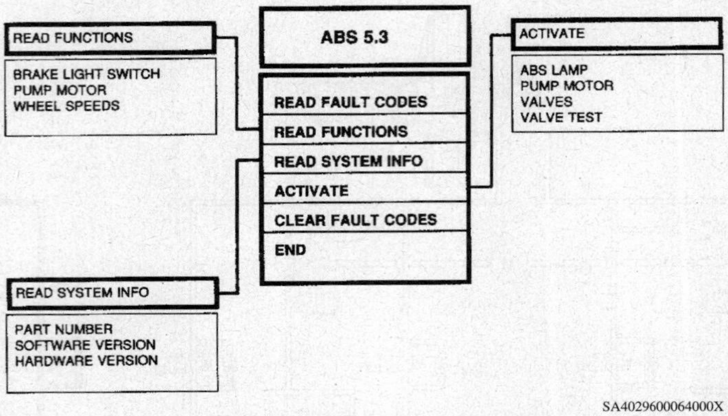

Fig. 7 ISAT diagnostic menus

3. Resistance for wiring must normally be less than 1 ohm. Specified value applies to components.

Voltage Measurement

1. Switch on any load.
2. With instrument set for voltage measurement, connect black measuring cable to safe ground and red measuring cable to lead side.
3. In case of output from control module/switch, measure away from these and gradually move out toward load. When load disappears, you have just passed break in continuity.
4. In case of input to control module/consumer, measure away from current source and gradually move in toward control module/consumer. When voltage disappears, you have just passed break in continuity.

SHORT-CIRCUIT TO GROUND INSPECTION

Resistance Measurement

1. Ensure lead to be checked is not live and that any load has been disconnected.
2. With instrument set for resistance measurement, connect one measuring cable to load side of lead and the other to safe ground.
3. Move carefully on wiring and check at same time that instrument shows infinite resistance the whole time.

DIAGNOSIS & TESTING

ABS MEASURED DATA

1. Several voltage levels must be regarded as guide values. Apply common sense in judging whether a measured value is correct or faulty.
2. If any measured value is faulty, refer to "Wiring Circuit" to find out which leads, connectors or components should be checked more closely.

ACCESSING DIAGNOSTIC TROUBLE CODES

The ABS control module communicates with ISAT, **Fig. 6,** through pin 11 and is bidirectional.

Any diagnostic trouble codes stored in the control module can be read out by means of ISAT. ISAT can also command the control module to control the solenoid valves or read the wheel speed.

With the ignition on and ISAT connected, the voltage on pin is approximately 10 volts. The diagnostic testing socket (data link connector) is located below the lower left-hand instrument panel fascia.

Operation

The ISAT features a system where clear text under a number of menu options enables the user to directly select the desired command with the keypad. The structure of the ABS command menus, **Fig. 7,** provides six main menus. Three of these menus have varying numbers of commands in a submenu.

When a system function is activated with ISAT, it means the ABS control module is performing something which is not functionally normal. diagnostic trouble codes can be put into other systems which are dependent on the ABS.

The Activate functions must always be used with caution. Always deactivate an activated function before proceeding in the ISAT menu. Always clear any diagnostic trouble codes recorded in ABS or any other system after work has been completed.

DIAGNOSTIC TROUBLE CODE INTERPRETATION

When performing diagnostic trouble code diagnosis and repair, refer to **Fig. 8** for diagnostic trouble code identification.

Refer to **Fig. 9** for valve test interpretation and **Fig. 10** for front left (FL) and front right (FR) valve test interpretation.

WIRING CIRCUIT

Refer to **Figs. 11 and 12** for connector and connector pin identification.

Refer to **Fig. 13,** for ABS system wiring circuit.

DIAGNOSTIC TESTS

Refer to **Figs. 14 through 32** for diagnostic trouble code diagnostic routines.

SYSTEM SERVICE

Brake System Bleed

1. Unscrew cover of brake fluid reservoir and top off with brake fluid.
2. Connect topping-off fitting from brake bleeding unit kit tool No. 88 19 096, or equivalent, to brake fluid reservoir.
3. Position hose with one end on topping-off fitting and other end in bottle filled with clean brake fluid.
4. Raise and support vehicle, then connect brake bleeder hose to front left wheel and open nipple. Draw off approximately .1 quart brake fluid. Repeat this at front right wheel.
5. Move brake bleeder to rear left wheel and open nipple. Draw off approximately .05 quart brake fluid. Repeat this at rear right wheel.
6. Lower vehicle, then check brake operation. Depress brake pedal and ensure it does not drop.
7. Remove topping-off fitting, hose and bottle.
8. Adjust brake fluid level.

Component Replacement

HYDRAULIC UNIT

1. Remove black plastic cover screw, then the cover, **Fig. 33.**
2. Disconnect electrical connector and electrical connection, then the ground cable.
3. Remove brake pipe connections and plug holes.
4. Remove two hydraulic unit to bracket bolts.
5. Remove hydraulic unit.
6. Reverse procedure to install. Bleed brake system as outlined under "Brake System Bleed."

ABS CONTROL MODULE

1. Remove hydraulic unit cover.
2. Remove electrical boot, then disconnect two-pole electrical connector.
3. Remove six control module securing bolts, then the control module from hydraulic unit. Leave washers on hydraulic unit.

Diagnostic Trouble Code	Function/component fault	ABS	ISAT display text
B1371	Wheel sensor front left, faulty signal	ON	FAULT XX B1371 WHEEL SENSOR FL SIGNAL FAULTY
B1372	Wheel sensor front left, Signal faulty (open-circuit)	ON	FAULT XX B1372 WHEEL SENSOR FL NO SIGNAL
B1376	Wheel sensor front right, signal faulty	ON	FAULT XX B1376 WHEEL SENSOR FR SIGNAL FAULTY
B1377	Wheel sensor front right, no signal (open-circuit)	ON	FAULT XX B1376 WHEEL SENSOR FR NO SIGNAL
B1381	Wheel sensor rear left, signal faulty	ON	FAULT XX B1381 WHEEL SENSOR RL SIGNAL FAULTY
B1382	Wheel sensor rear right, no signal (open-circuit)	ON	FAULT XX B1382 WHEEL SENSOR RL NO SIGNAL
B1386	Wheel sensor rear right, signal faulty	ON	FAULT XX B1386 WHEEL SENSOR RR SIGNAL FAULTY
B1387	Wheel sensor rear right, no signal (open-circuit)	ON	FAULT XX B1387 WHEEL SENSOR RR NO SIGNAL
B1390	Wheel sensor, incorrect teeth number at a wheel sensor	ON	FAULT XX B1390 WHEEL SENSOR WRONG NO. OF TEETH
B2415	Boost pressure control valve rear left, faulty	ON	FAULT XX B2415 SOLENOID VALVE RL FAULTY
B2450	Boost pressure control valve front left, faulty	ON	FAULT XX B2450 SOLENOID VALVE FL FAULTY
B2455	Boost pressure control valve front right, faulty	ON	FAULT XX B2455 SOLENOID VALVE FR FAULTY
B2485	Boost pressure control valve rear right, faulty	ON	FAULT XX B2485 SOLENOID VALVE RR FAULTY
B1540	Boost pressure control valve, no voltage supply (open-circuit)	ON	FAULT XX B1540 SOLENOID VALVES NO VOLTAGE

SA4029600065010X

Fig. 8 ABS diagnostic trouble codes (Part 1 of 2)

Diagnostic Trouble Code	Function/component fault	ABS	ISAT display text
B1605	Electronic control module fault	ON	FAULT XX B1605 CONTROL MODULE INTERNAL FAULT
B1532	Battery voltage, low voltage rating	ON	FAULT XX B1532 BATTERY VOLTAGE LOW
B2470	Brake light switch, no signal (open-circuit)	ON	FAULT XX B2470 BRAKE LIGHT SWITCH NO SIGNAL
B2465	Pump motor, faulty	ON	FAULT XX B2465 PUMP MOTOR FAULTY

SA4029600065020X

Fig. 8 ABS diagnostic trouble codes (Part 2 of 2)

ISAT DISPLAY 1

ACTIVATE
VALVE TEST FL
VALVE TEST FR
VALVE TEST RL
VALVE TEST RR

1 Select VALVE TEST in the ACTIVATE menu.

Caution

The test can only be started when the car is standing still.

ISAT DISPLAY 2

VALVE TEST FL
NORMAL POSITION
ROTATE WHEEL! OK?
YES NO

2 Rotate the wheel by hand. The wheel should rotate freely.
If you respond YES the intake valve and passage from the master cylinder to the wheel cylinder is closed.

ISAT DISPLAY 3

VALVE TEST FL
HOLDING PRESSURE
BRAKE AND HOLD!
PRESS ON/ENTER

3 The intake valve is closed. The valve has moved to HOLDING PRESSURE position. The passage is closed and there is no brake pressure to the wheels.

ISAT DISPLAY 4

VALVE TEST FL
HOLDING PRESSURE
ROTATE WHEEL! OK?
YES NO

4 The wheel should rotate freely.
If you respond YES the intake valve and passage are opened. Brake pressure can go to the wheels.

SA4029600066000X

Fig. 9 Valve Test Interpretation

4. Reverse procedure to install. Start vehicle and ensure warning lamps go out.

WHEEL SENSORS

Front

1. Raise and support vehicle.
2. Remove wheel, then clean around wheel sensor with soft steel brush.
3. Remove wheel sensor securing bolt and disconnect sensor.
4. Disconnect sensor cable from bracket in wheel arch, then disconnect connector.
5. Reverse procedure to install.

Rear

1. Raise and support vehicle, then remove wheel.
2. Force brake pistons back with suitable pliers, then depress brake pedal with brake clamp.
3. Remove two brake caliper securing bolts, then the brake pipe from clip. Bind brake caliper in tie.
4. Loosen brake shoe adjustment.
5. Remove lever return spring, then disconnect parking brake cable from lever.
6. Remove brake disc securing bolt, then the brake disc.
7. Disconnect speed sensor connector.
8. Remove four wheel hub retaining nuts, then the wheel hub, disc backing plate and spacer strip.
9. Remove wheel hub from disc backing plate
10. Reverse procedure to install. Tighten fasteners to specifications.

ISAT DISPLAY 5

VALVE TEST FL
NORMAL POSITION
WHEEL LOCKED?
YES NO

5 The wheel should be locked
If you respond with YES the outlet valve opens and the return pump starts. Brake fluid pressure returns from the wheel cylinder with the aid of the return pump.

ISAT DISPLAY 6

VALVE TEST FL
PRESSURE RELIEVED
ROTATE WHEELI OK?
YES NO

6 The wheel should rotate freely.

ISAT DISPLAY 7

TEST OK
PRESS ON/ENTER

7 The last display shows that the test is accomplished.

ISAT DISPLAY 8

VALVE TEST FL
FAULT IN TEST
SEE SERVICE MANUAL
PRESS ON/ENTER

8 If a fault arises when the test is in progress or you answer NO to any of the questions this display is shown.

SA4029600067000X

Fig. 10 Front Left & Front Right Valve Test Interpretation

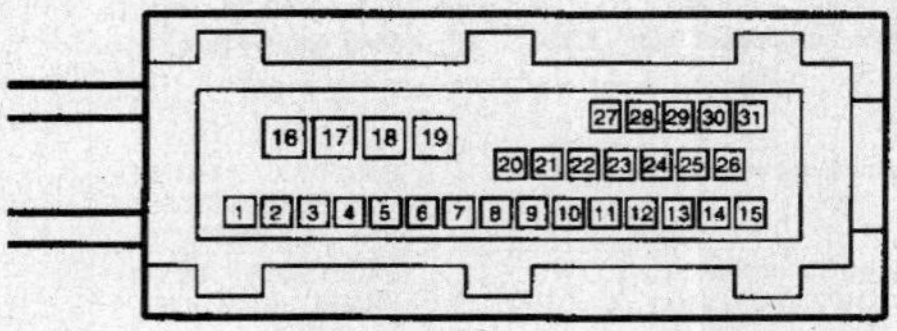

SA4029600060000X

Fig. 11 ABS control module connector view

Pin	Colour	Component/ Operation	In/Out	Measuring conditions	Test results	Be-tween X-Y
1	YE	Wheel sensor RR Reference ground	In	Rotate the wheel 1 turn/second	L100 mVac	1-2
2	BK	Wheel sensor RR Signal input	In	Rotate the wheel 1 turn/second	L100 mVac	2-1
3	BK	Wheel sensors FR reference ground	In	Rotate the wheel 1 turn/second	L100 mVac	3-5
4		No connection				
5	YE	Wheel sensor FR Signal input	In	Rotate the wheel 1 turn/second	L100 mVac	5-3
6	BK	Wheel sensor FL reference ground	In	Rotate the wheel 1 turn/second	L100 mVac	6-7
7	YE	Wheel sensors FL Signal input	In	Rotate the wheel 1 turn/second	L100 mVac	7-6
8	BK	Wheel sensor RL Reference ground	In	Rotate the wheel 1 turn/second	L100 mVac	8-9
9	YE	Wheel sensors RL Signal input	In	Rotate the wheel 1 turn/second	L100 mVac	9-8
10		No connection				
11	WH/BK	Data link	In/Out			
12		No connection				
13		No connection				
14	VT	Brake Light Switch	In	Brake activity	B+	14-16
15	YE/RD	+15 voltage	In	Ignition timing on	<0,5V	15-B+
16	BK	Power ground	In		B+	16-B+
17	RD	+30 voltage	In		<0,5V	17-B+
18	RD	+30 voltage	In		<0,5V	18-B+
19	BK	Ground	In		B+	19-B+
20		No connection				
21	GY/GN	Warning lamp ABS	In	Ignition timing on	<0,5V	21-B+

SA4029600061010X

Fig. 12 ABS control module connector pin identification (Part 1 of 2)

Pin	Colour	Component/ Operation	In/Out	Measuring conditions	Test results	Be-tween X-Y
22		No connection				
23	OG/WH	Wheel speed RL	Out	Slowly rotate the wheel Rotate the wheel 1 turn/second	0/approx. 12 V approx. 6 V	*)
24	YE/BN	Wheel speed RR	Out	See pin 23	See pin 23	*)
25	BK/GN	Wheel speed FL	Out	See pin 23	See pin 23	*)
26	PK/BK	Wheel speed FR	Out	See pin 23	See pin 23	*)

*) = Must be tested at the receiving components.

SA4029600061020X

Fig. 12 ABS control module connector pin identification (Part 2 of 2)

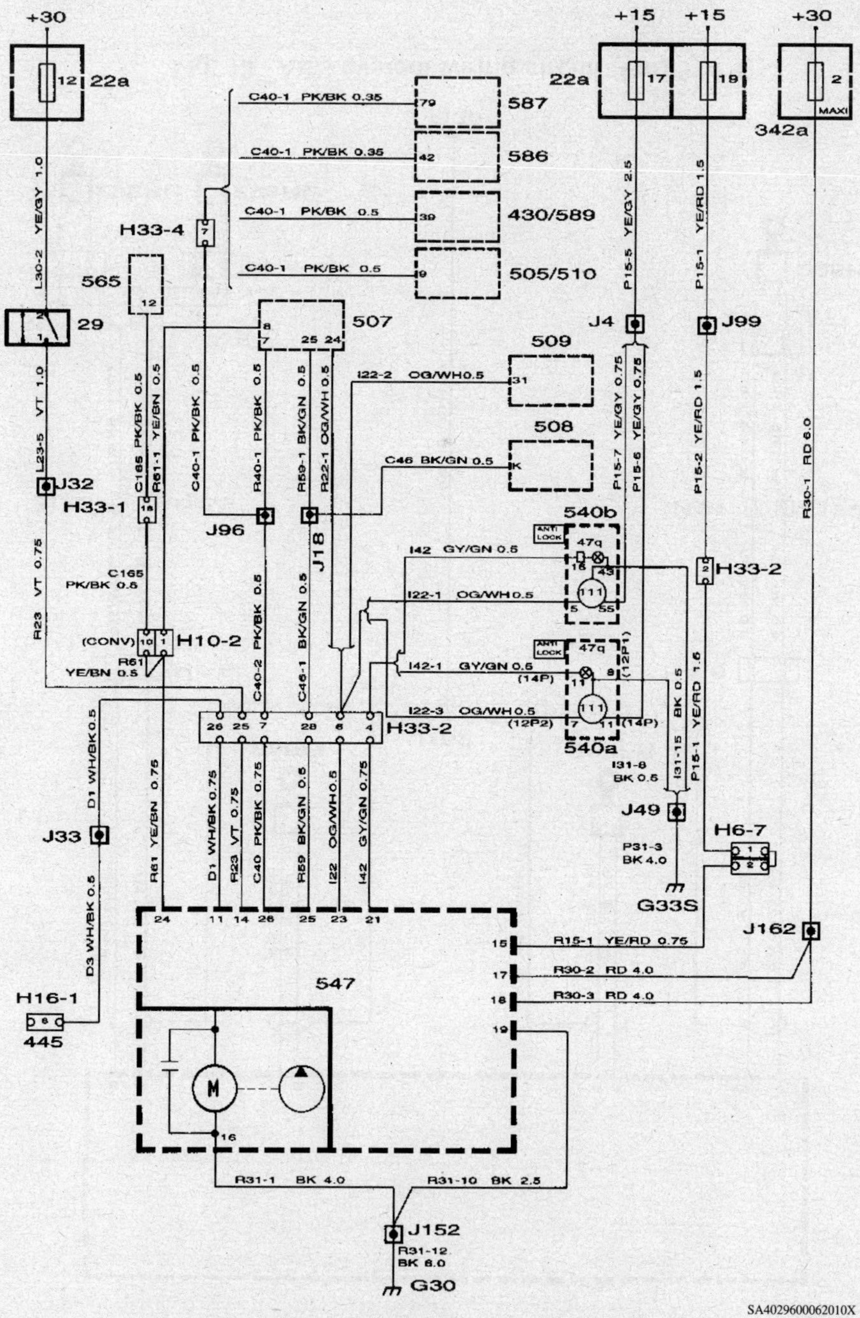

Fig. 13 ABS system wiring circuit (Part 1 of 4)

22a	Fuse board in electrical distribution box, facia
29	Brake light switch for brake pedal
47q	ABS Warning lamp in main instrument
111	Electronic speedometer
342a	Fuse board in electrical distribution box in engine compartment
430	Trionic electronic control module on the right side inside the side trim below the A-pillar
445	Data Link Connector, 16 pole, CARB
505	Motronic electronic control module M2.10.3 on the right side inside the side trim below the A-pillar
507	Electronic control module TCS V6
508	The electronic control module cruise control to the far right in the engine compartment below the windscreen.
509	Saab Sensonic electronic control module behind the glove compartment on the bulk head partition.
510	Electronic control module Motronic M2.8.1 on the right side inside the side trim under the A-pillar.
540a	Main instrument, low specification.
540b	Main instrument, high specification
547	ABS electronic control module integrated in hydraulic brake unit between the battery and the front electrical distribution box.
586	Motronic electronic control module 4.1 OBDII
587	Motronic electronic control module 5.2 OBDII
589	Electronic control module, Saab Trionic OBDII
H6-7	6 pole connectors
H10-2	10-pole connectors below the left A-pillar
H16-1	Data link connector under the facia at the steering column
H33-2	Black 33-pole connectors on the bracket below the left A-pillar
H33-4	33-pole connectors on the bulkhead partition at the back of the glove compartment

G30	Grounding point left structural member behind the battery
G33S	Signal ground connector bracket, below the left A-pillar on connector bracket.
J4	Crimp (LHD):Approx. 450 mm from the rheostat towards the main instrument (RHD):Approx. 240 mm from the rheostat towards the main instrument
J18	Crimp (LHD):Approx. 145 mm from the connectors H33-2 (RHD):Approx. 170 mm from the connectors H33-2 towards grounding point G33
J32	Crimp (LHD):Approx. 210 mm from the brake light switch towards the rheostat (RHD):Approx. 60 mm from branching rheostat towards the ICE electronic control module (CONV):Approx. 150 mm from branching electrically heated rear window towards the luggage compartment
J33	Crimp (LHD):Approx. 90 mm from the connectors H33-3 (RHD):Approx. 450 mm from the connectors H33-2 against SID
J49	Crimp (LHD):Approx. 390 mm from the rheostat against the connector bracket, left A-pillar (RHD):Approx. 150 mm from branching SID against the main instrument
J96	Crimp (LHD):Approx. 110 mm from branching ICE electronic control module against the brake light switch (RHD):Approx. 290 mm from the connectors H33-4 towards the grounding point G34
J99	Crimp (LHD):Approx. 270 mm from the grounding point G33 against the ICE (RHD):Approx. 340 mm from the connectors H33-4 against the grounding point G34
J152	Crimp approx. 60 mm from the branching washer fluid pump against the electrical distribution box
J162	Crimp approx. 250 mm from the ABS electronic control module

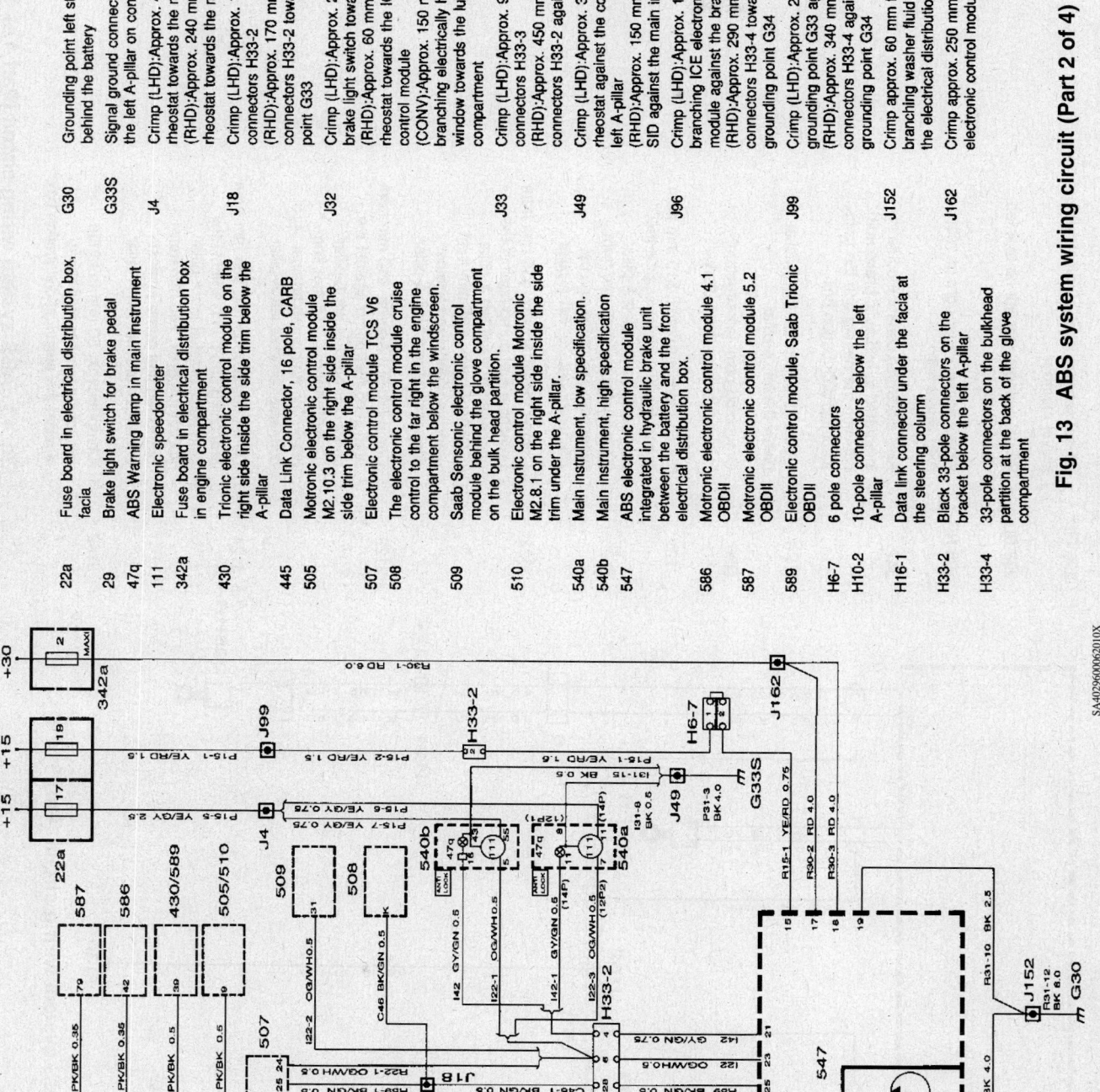

SA4029600062020X

Fig. 13 ABS system wiring circuit (Part 2 of 4)

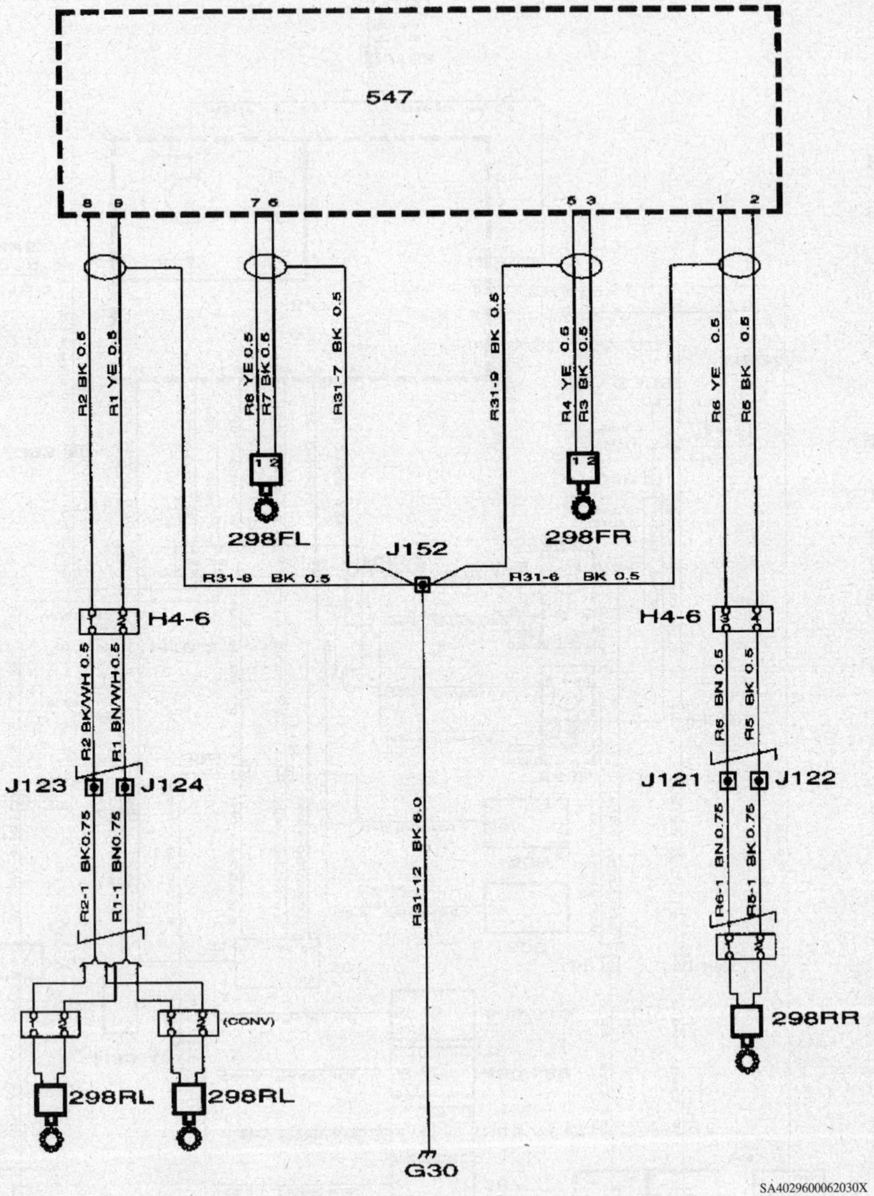

Fig. 13 ABS system wiring circuit (Part 3 of 4)

298 FR	Wheel sensor front right on steering swivel member
298 FL	Wheel sensors front left on steering swivel member
298 RL	Wheel sensors rear left on rear left wheel hub
298 RR	Wheel sensors rear right on rear right wheel hub
547	ABS electronic control module integrated in hydraulic brake unit between the battery and the front electrical distribution box
H4-6	4-pole connector on the bracket below the left A-pillar
G30	Grounding point left structural member behind the battery
J121	Crimp (3d/5D):Approx. 510 mm from branching fuel pump against the connector bracket left A-pillar (CONV):Approx. 640 mm from branching fuel pump against connector bracket left A-pillar
J122	Crimp (3d/5D):Approx. 535 mm from branching fuel pump against the connector bracket left A-pillar (CONV):Approx. 665 mm from branching fuel pump against connector bracket left A-pillar
J123	Crimp (3d/5D):Approx. 610 mm from branching fuel pump against the connector bracket left A-pillar (CONV):Approx. 715 mm from branching fuel pump against connector bracket left A-pillar
J124	Crimp (3d/5D):Approx. 585 mm from branching fuel pump against the connector bracket left A-pillar (CONV):Approx. 740 mm from branching fuel pump against connector bracket left A-pillar
J152	Crimp approx. 60 mm from the branching washer fluid pump against the electrical distribution box

SA4029600062040X

Fig. 13 ABS system wiring circuit (Part 4 of 4)

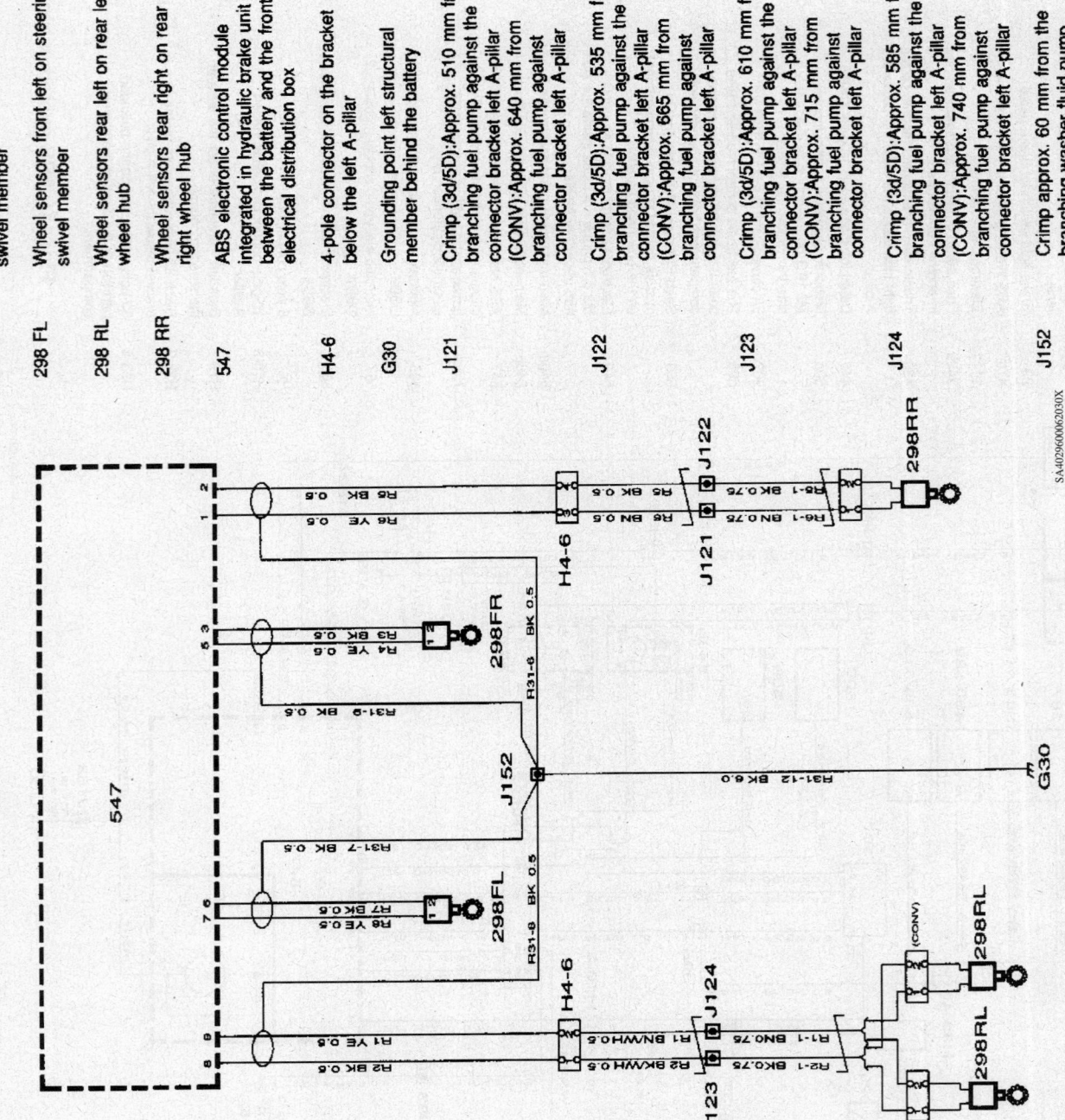

DIAGNOSTIC CHART INDEX

Code	Description	Page No.	Fig. No.
B1371	Wheel Sensor Front Left, Signal Faulty	7-136	14
B1372	Wheel Sensor Front Left, Signal Faulty Open Circuit	7-136	15
B1376	Wheel Sensor Front Right, Signal Faulty Or No Signal	7-137	16
B1377	Wheel Sensor Front Right, Signal Faulty Open Circuit	7-137	17
B1381	Wheel Sensor Rear Left, Signal Faulty Or No Signal	7-138	18
B1382	Wheel Sensor Rear Left, Signal Faulty Open Circuit	7-138	19
B1386	Wheel Sensor Rear Right, Signal Faulty	7-139	20
B1387	Wheel Sensor Rear Right, No Signal Open Circuit	7-139	21
B1390	Wheel Sensor, Wrong Number Of Teeth	7-140	22
B1532	Battery Voltage Low	7-141	25
B1540	Boost Pressure Control Valve, No Voltage Supply Open Circuit	7-140	23
B1605	Electronic Control Module Fault	7-140	24
B2415	Boost Pressure Control Valve Rear Left, Faulty	7-141	26
B2450	Boost Pressure Control Valve Rear Left, Faulty	7-141	26
B2455	Boost Pressure Control Valve Rear Left, Faulty	7-141	26
B2485	Boost Pressure Control Valve Rear Left, Faulty	7-141	26
B2470	Brake Light Switch No Signal Open Circuit	7-142	28
B2465	Pump Motor Faulty	7-141	27
—	ABS Lamp Not Operating	7-142	29
—	ABS Lamp On At All Times	7-143	30
—	No Wheel Speed Signal	7-143	31
—	Test Procedure Prior To ECM Replacement	7-144	32

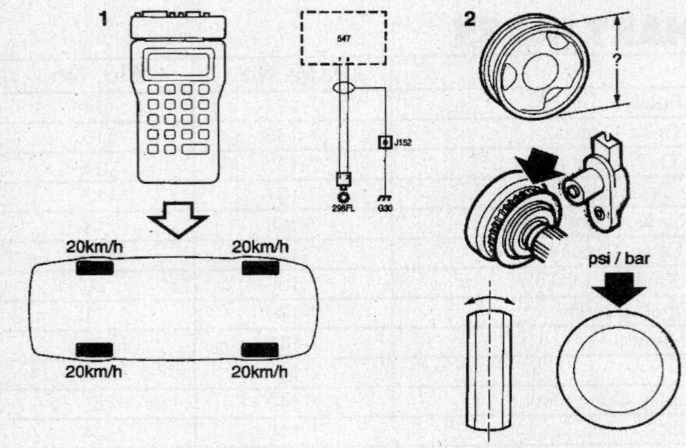

Fault symptom

ABS warning lamp on, no ABS function.

Condition

Fault registered as open-circuit with a speed of 40 km/h.

Diagnostic help

- The front left wheel sensor can be read by ISAT.
  - Select "READ FUNCTIONS"
  - Select "WHEEL SPEEDS"

The current wheel speed in km/h is displayed.

- If the front assembly of the vehicle is lifted the ISAT should display approx. 5 km/h if the left front wheel is rotated by hand at approx. 1 turn per second.

Diagnostic procedure

1 **Diagnostic Trouble Code inspection**
- Connect the ISAT Scan Tool.
- Start and test drive the car at an even speed. Read WHEEL SPEEDS in accordance with diagnostic help. Compare the four wheel speeds shown.

Does the front left wheel speed have a faulty rating?

YES Continue with point 2.

NO Continue with point 4.

2 **Mechanical size inspection.**
- Check that:

- wheel size and tyre pressure are correct.
- there is no wheel bearing play.
- the toothed wheel is not damaged.

Is the inspection OK?

YES Continue with point 3.

NO Rectify the fault

SA4029600068010X

Fig. 14 Code B1371: Wheel Sensor Front Left, Signal Faulty (Part 1 of 2)

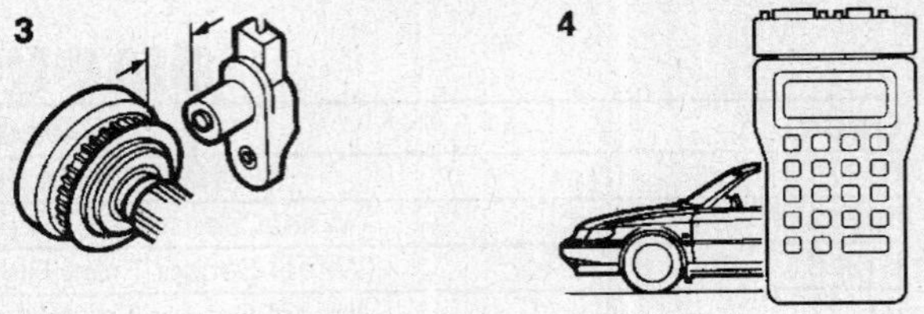

3 **Toothed wheel air gap inspection**
- Check that the air gap between the toothed wheel and the wheel sensor is 0.6±0.3 mm.

Is the air gap correct?

YES Continue with point 4.

NO Rectify the fault

4 **Final inspection**
- Erase the diagnostic trouble code.
- Carry out the driving cycle, drive the car with various load and engine speeds for 5 minutes.
- Read the diagnostic trouble code.

Is the diagnostic trouble code stored?

YES Continue With "Test Procedure Prior To Replacing ECM"

NO The diagnostic procedure performed is right or the fault is of intermittent character.

SA4029600068020X

Fig. 14 Code B1371: Wheel Sensor Front Left, Signal Faulty (Part 2 of 2)

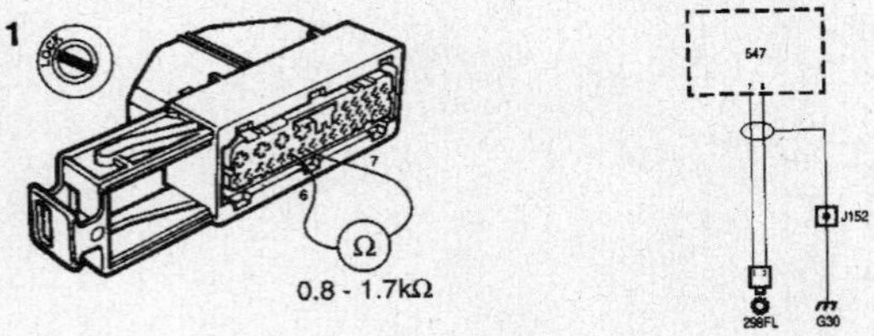

Fault symptom

ABS warning lamp on, no ABS function.

Condition

Fault registered as open-circuit

Diagnostic help

- The front left wheel sensor can be read by ISAT.
  - Select "READ FUNCTIONS"
  - Select "WHEEL SPEEDS"

The current wheel speed in km/h is displayed.

- If the front assembly of the vehicle is lifted the ISAT should display approx. 5 km/h if the left front wheel is rotated by hand at approx. 1 turn per second.

Diagnostic procedure

1 **Wheel sensor resistance check**
- Disconnect the electronic control module connector.
- Take a resistance reading from the electronic control module sensor connector between pin 6 and 7. The resistance should be 0.8-1.7 kOhm

Is the resistance correct?

YES Continue with point 3.

NO Continue with point 2.

SA4029600069010X

Fig. 15 Code B1372: Wheel Sensor Front Left, Signal Faulty Open Circuit (Part 1 of 2)

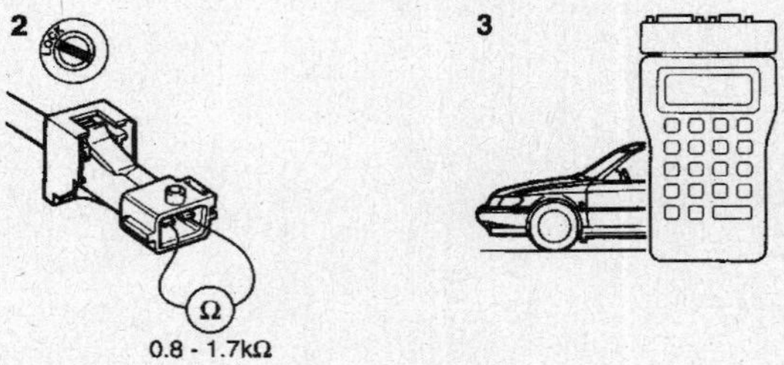

2 **Wheel sensor resistance check**
- Disconnect the wheel sensors connector (2 pin connector located at the left wheel house in the engine compartment).
- Take a resistance reading in the wheel sensor connector between the two connector pins. The resistance should be 0.8-1.7 kOhm

Is the resistance rating correct?

YES Check and rectify the wiring including the connection between the electronic control module and the wheel sensor connector.

NO Check and possibly rectify the wiring including the connector to the wheel sensor. If there is no relevant reason for the fault, change the wheel sensor.

3 **Final inspection**
- Erase the diagnostic trouble code.
- Perform the driving cycle, drive the car at varying loads and engines speeds for 5 minutes.
- Read diagnostic trouble codes.

Is the diagnostic trouble code stored?

YES Continue Test Procedure Prior To Replacing ECM

NO The diagnostic procedure taken is right.

SA4029600069020X

Fig. 15 Code B1372: Wheel Sensor Front Left, Signal Faulty Open Circuit (Part 2 of 2)

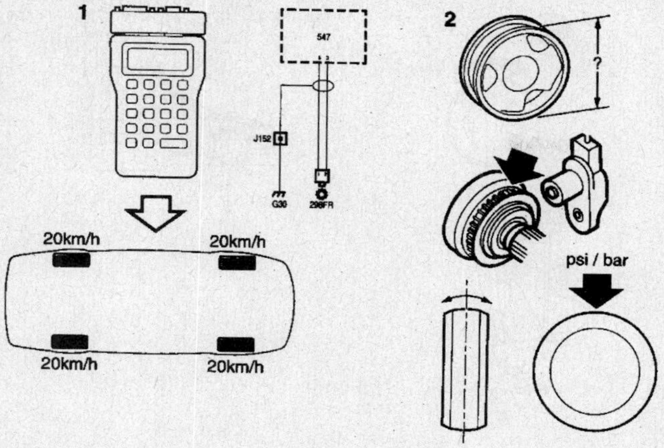

Fault symptom
ABS warning lamp on, no ABS function.

Condition
Fault registered as open-circuit with a speed of 40 km/h.

Diagnostic help

- The front right wheel sensor can be read by ISAT.
  - Select "READ FUNCTIONS"
  - Select "WHEEL SPEEDS"

The current wheel speed in km/h is displayed.

- If the front assembly of the vehicle is lifted the ISAT should display approx. 5 km/h if the right front wheel is rotated by hand at approx. 1 turn per second.

Diagnostic procedure

1 **Diagnostic Trouble Code inspection**
- Connect the ISAT Scan Tool.
- Start and test drive the car at an even speed. Read WHEEL SPEEDS in accordance with diagnostic help. Compare the four wheel speeds shown.

Does the front right wheel speed have a faulty rating?

YES Continue with point 2.
NO Continue with point 4.

2 **Mechanical size inspection.**
- Check that:

- wheel size and tyre pressure are correct.
- there is no wheel bearing play.
- the toothed wheel is not damaged.

Is the inspection OK?

YES Continue with point 3.
NO Rectify the fault

SA4029600070010X

Fig. 16 Code B1376: Wheel Sensor Front Right, Signal Faulty Or No Signal (Part 1 of 2)

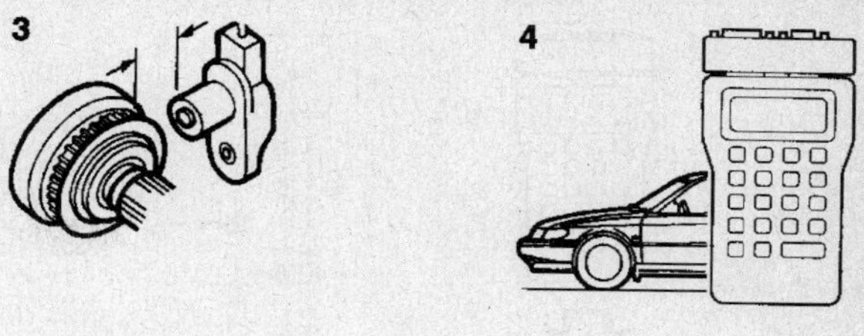

3 **Toothed wheel air gap inspection**
- Check that the air gap between the toothed wheel and the wheel sensor is 0.6±0.3 mm.

Is the air gap correct?

YES Continue with point 4.
NO Rectify the fault

4 **Final inspection**
- Erase the diagnostic trouble code.
- Carry out the driving cycle, drive the car with various load and engine speeds for 5 minutes.
- Read the diagnostic trouble code.

Is the diagnostic trouble code stored?

YES Continue With "Test Procedure Prior To Replacing ECM"
NO The diagnostic procedure performed is right or the fault is of intermittent character.

SA4029600070020X

Fig. 16 Code B1376: Wheel Sensor Front Right, Signal Faulty Or No Signal (Part 2 of 2)

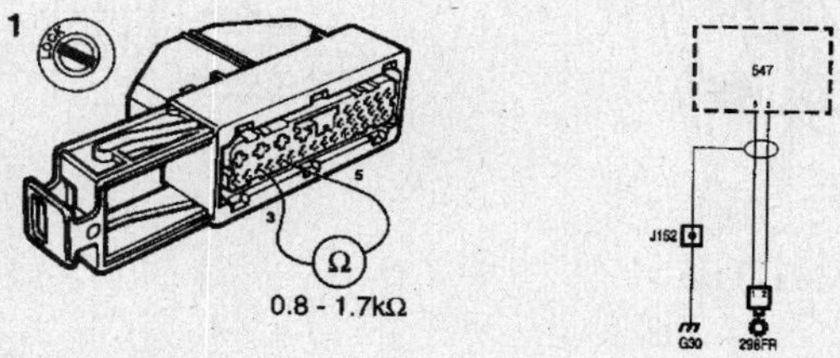

Fault symptom
ABS warning lamp on, no ABS function.

Condition
Fault registered as open-circuit

Diagnostic help

- The front right wheel sensor can be read by ISAT.
  - Select "READ FUNCTIONS"
  - Select "WHEEL SPEEDS"

The current wheel speed in km/h is displayed.

- If the front assembly of the vehicle is lifted the ISAT should display approx. 5 km/h if the right front wheel is rotated by hand at approx. 1 turn per second.

Diagnostic procedure

1 **Wheel sensor resistance check**
- Disconnect the electronic control module connector.
- Take a resistance reading at the electronic control module sensor connector between pin 3 and 5. The resistance should be 0.8-1.7 kOhm

Is the resistance correct?

YES Continue with point 3.
NO Continue with point 2.

SA4029600071010X

Fig. 17 Code B1377: Wheel Sensor Front Right, Signal Faulty Open Circuit (Part 1 of 2)

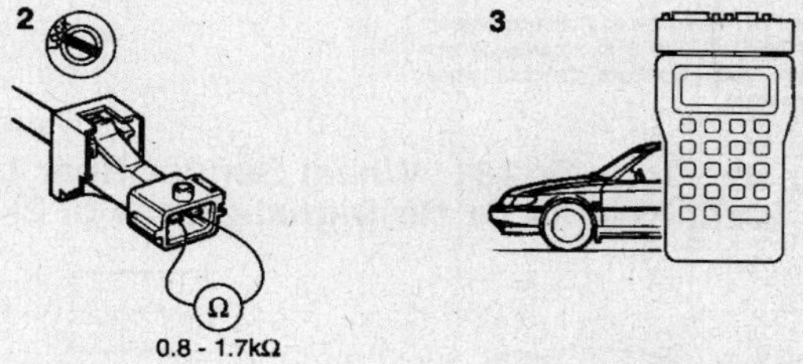

2 **Wheel sensor resistance check**

Remove the wheel sensor connector (2 pin connector located at the right of the wheel housing in the engine compartment).
- Take a resistance reading in the wheel sensor connector between the two connector pins. The resistance should be 0.8-1.7 kOhm

Is the resistance rating correct?

YES Check and rectify the wiring including the connection between the electronic control module and the wheel sensor connector.
NO Check and possibly rectify the wiring including the connector to the wheel sensor. If there is no relevant reason for the fault, change the wheel sensor.

3 **Final inspection**
- Erase the diagnostic trouble code.
- Perform the driving cycle, drive the car at varying loads and engines speeds for 5 minutes.
- Read diagnostic trouble codes.

Is the diagnostic trouble code stored?

YES Continue Test Procedure Prior To Replacing ECM
NO The diagnostic procedure taken is right.

SA4029600071020X

Fig. 17 Code B1377: Wheel Sensor Front Right, Signal Faulty Open Circuit (Part 2 of 2)

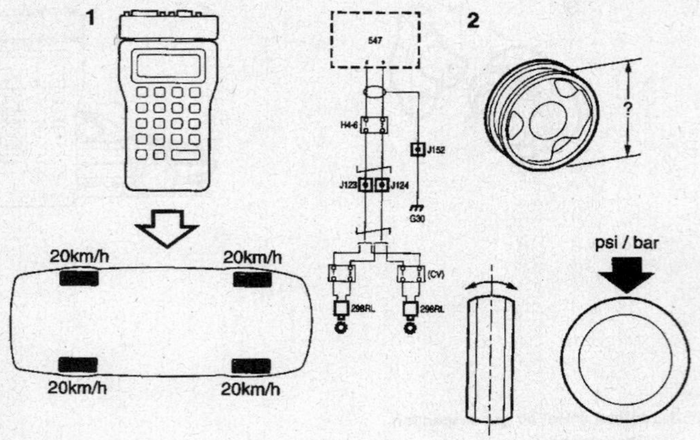

Fault symptom
ABS warning lamp on, no ABS function.

Condition
Fault registered at a speed of I10 km/h.

Diagnostic help

- The rear left wheel sensor can be read by ISAT.
  - Select "READ FUNCTIONS"
  - Select "WHEEL SPEEDS"

The current wheel speed in km/h is displayed.

- If the rear assembly of the vehicle is lifted the ISAT should display approx. 5 km/h if the left rear wheel is rotated by hand at approx. 1 turn per second.

Diagnostic procedure

1 **Diagnostic Trouble Code inspection**
- Connect the ISAT Scan Tool.
- Start and test drive the car at an even speed. Read WHEEL SPEEDS in accordance with diagnostic help. Compare the four wheel speeds shown.

Does the rear left wheel speed show a faulty rating?

YES Continue with point 2.
NO Continue with point 4.

2 **Mechanical size inspection.**
- Check that:

- wheel size and tyre pressure are correct.
- there is no wheel bearing play.

Is the inspection OK?

YES Continue with point 3.
NO Rectify the fault

SA4029600072010X

Fig. 18 Code B1381: Wheel Sensor Rear Left, Signal Faulty Or No Signal (Part 1 of 2)

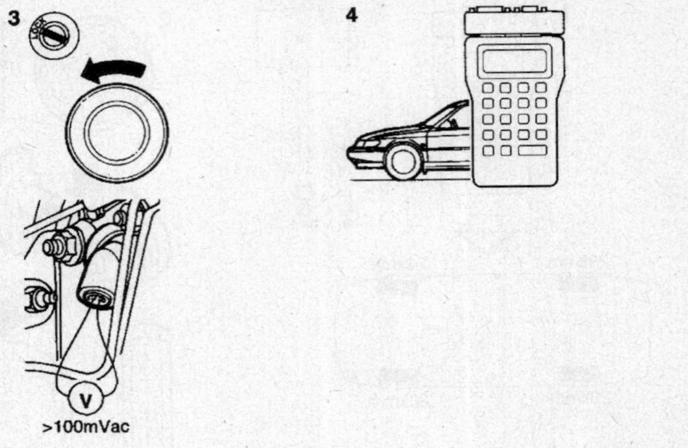

3 **Wheel sensor signal check**
- *Lift the rear suspension of the vehicle.*
- Take a voltage measurement, mVac, at the wheel sensors connector. Connect a voltmeter between the connector pins. Rotate the rear left wheel at approx. 1 turn per second. The wheel sensor voltage should be I100 mVac.

Is the voltage OK?

YES Continue with point 4.
NO Change wheel sensor.

4 **Final inspection**
- Erase the diagnostic trouble code.
- Carry out the driving cycle, drive the car with various load and engine speeds for 5 minutes.
- Read the diagnostic trouble code.

Is the diagnostic trouble code stored?

YES Continue With "Test Procedure Prior To Replacing ECM"
NO The diagnostic procedure performed is right or the fault is of intermittent character.

SA4029600072020X

Fig. 18 Code B1381: Wheel Sensor Rear Left, Signal Faulty Or No Signal (Part 2 of 2)

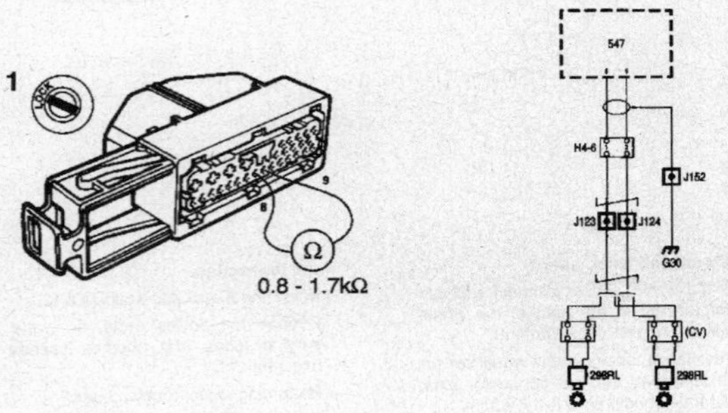

Fault symptom
ABS warning lamp on, no ABS function.

Condition
Fault registered as open-circuit

Diagnostic help

- The rear left wheel sensor can be read by ISAT.
  - Select "READ FUNCTIONS"
  - Select "WHEEL SPEEDS"

The current wheel speed in km/h is displayed.

- If the rear assembly of the vehicle is lifted the ISAT should display approx. 5 km/h if the left rear wheel is rotated by hand at approx. 1 turn per second.

Diagnostic procedure

1 **Wheel sensor resistance check**
- Disconnect the electronic control module connector.
- Take a resistance reading at the electronic control module sensor connector between pin 8 and pin 9. The resistance should be 0.8-1.7 kOhm.

Is the resistance rating correct?

YES Continue with point 3.
NO Continue with point 2.

SA4029600073010X

Fig. 19 Code B1382: Wheel Sensor Rear Left, Signal Faulty Open Circuit (Part 1 of 2)

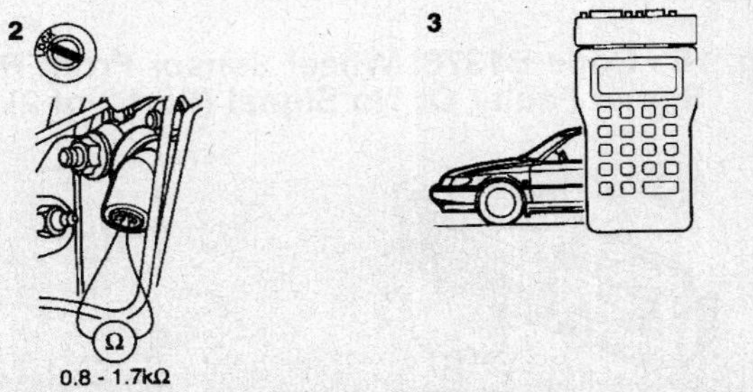

2 **Wheel sensor resistance check (cont.)**
- Remove the wheel sensor connector. The connector is integrated into the wheel sensor, against the wheel bearing rear side.
- Take a resistance reading at the wheel sensor switch between two connector pins. The resistance should be 0.8-1.7 kOhm.

Is the resistance rating correct?

YES Check and rectify the wiring including the connection between the electronic control module and the wheel sensor.
NO Inspect the wheel sensor connector for damp and corrosion. If there is no obvious fault cause, change the wheel sensor.

3 **Final inspection**
- Erase the diagnostic trouble code.
- Carry out the driving cycle, drive the car with various load and engine speeds for 5 minutes.
- Read the diagnostic trouble code.

Is the diagnostic trouble code stored?

YES Continue With "Test Procedure Prior To Replacing ECM"
NO The diagnostic procedure taken is right.

SA4029600073020X

Fig. 19 Code B1382: Wheel Sensor Rear Left, Signal Faulty Open Circuit (Part 2 of 2)

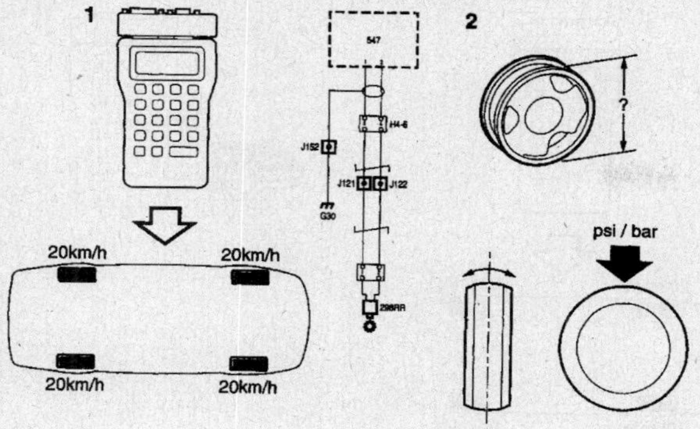

Fault symptom
ABS warning lamp on, no ABS function.

Condition
Fault registered at a speed of I10 km/h.

Diagnostic help

- The rear right wheel sensor can be read by ISAT.
  - Select "READ FUNCTIONS"
  - Select "WHEEL SPEEDS"

The current wheel speed in km/h is displayed.

- If the rear assembly of the vehicle is lifted the ISAT should display approx. 5 km/h if the right rear wheel is rotated by hand at approx. 1 turn per second.

Diagnostic procedure

1 **Diagnostic Trouble Code inspection**
- Connect the ISAT Scan Tool.
- Start and test drive the car at an even speed. Read WHEEL SPEEDS in accordance with diagnostic help. Compare the four wheel speeds shown.

Does the rear right wheel speed have an incorrect reading?

YES Continue with point 2.
NO Continue with point 4.

2 **Mechanical size inspection.**
- Check that:

- wheel size and tyre pressure are correct.
- there is no wheel bearing play.

Is the inspection OK?

YES Continue with point 3.
NO Rectify the fault

SA4029600074010X

Fig. 20 Code B1386: Wheel Sensor Rear Right, Signal Faulty (Part 1 of 2)

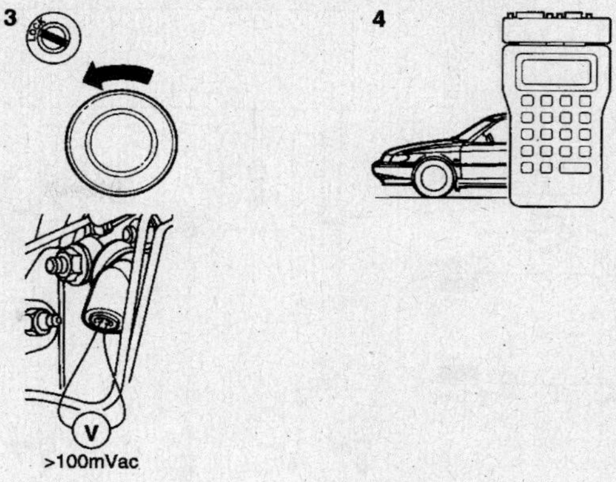

3 **Wheel sensor signal check**
- Lift the rear suspension of the vehicle.
- Take a voltage reading, mVac, at the wheel sensor connector. Connect a voltmeter between the connector pins. Rotate the rear right wheel at approx. 1 turn per second. The wheel sensor voltage should be I100 mVac.

Is the voltage OK?

YES Continue with point 4.
NO Change wheel sensor.

4 **Final inspection**
- Erase the diagnostic trouble code.
- Carry out the driving cycle, drive the car with various load and engine speeds for 5 minutes.
- Read the diagnostic trouble code.

Is the diagnostic trouble code stored?

YES Continue With "Test Procedure Prior To Replacing ECM"
NO The diagnostic procedure performed is right or the fault is of intermittent character.

SA4029600074020X

Fig. 20 Code B1386: Wheel Sensor Rear Right, Signal Faulty (Part 2 of 2)

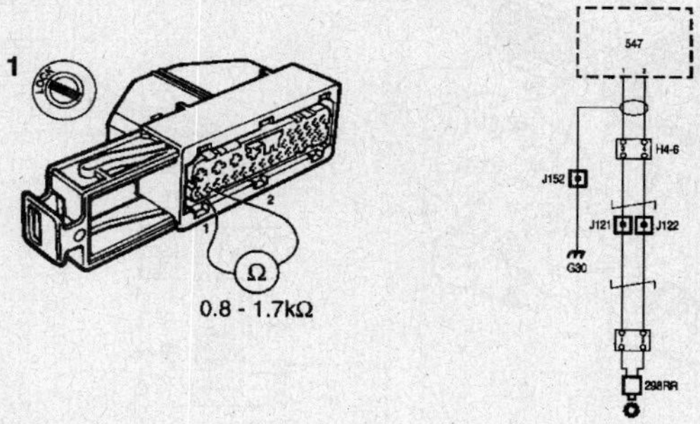

Fault symptom
ABS warning lamp on, no ABS function.

Condition
Fault registered as open-circuit

Diagnostic help

- The rear right wheel sensor can be read by ISAT.
  - Select "READ FUNCTIONS"
  - Select "WHEEL SPEEDS"

The current wheel speed in km/h is displayed.

- If the rear assembly of the vehicle is lifted the ISAT should display approx. 5 km/h if the right rear wheel is rotated by hand at approx. 1 turn per second.

Diagnostic procedure

1 **Wheel sensor resistance check**
- Disconnect the electronic control module connector.
- Take a resistance reading at the electronic control module sensor connector between pins 1 and 2. The resistance should be 0.8-1.7 kOhm.

Is the resistance rating correct?

YES Continue with point 3.
NO Continue with point 2.

SA4029600075010X

Fig. 21 Codes B1387: Wheel Sensor Rear Right, No Signal Open Circuit (Part 1 of 2)

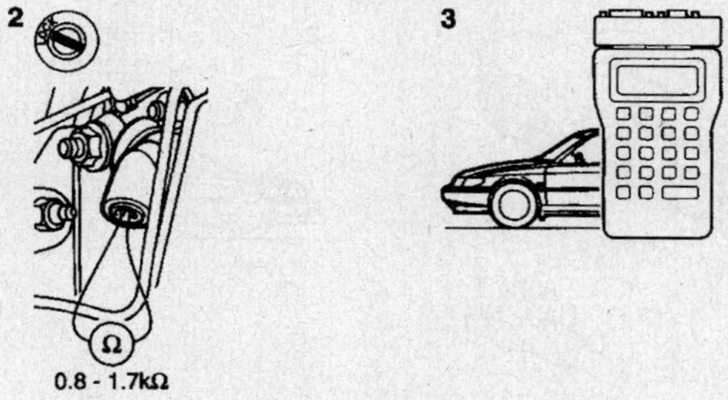

2 **Wheel sensor resistance check (cont.)**
- Remove the wheel sensor connector. The sensor connector is integrated in the wheel sensor against the rear side of the wheel sensor.
- Take a resistance reading at the wheel sensor switch between two connector pins. The resistance should be 0.8-1.7 kOhm.

Is the resistance rating correct?

YES Check and rectify the wiring including the connection between the electronic control module and the wheel sensor.
NO Inspect the wheel sensor connector for damp and corrosion. If there is no obvious fault cause, change the wheel sensor.

3 **Final inspection**
- Erase the diagnostic trouble code.
- Carry out the driving cycle, drive the car with various load and engine speeds for 5 minutes.
- Read the diagnostic trouble code.

Is the diagnostic trouble code stored?

YES Continue With "Test Procedure Prior To Replacing ECM"
NO The diagnostic procedure taken is right.

SA4029600075020X

Fig. 21 Codes B1387: Wheel Sensor Rear Right, No Signal Open Circuit (Part 2 of 2)

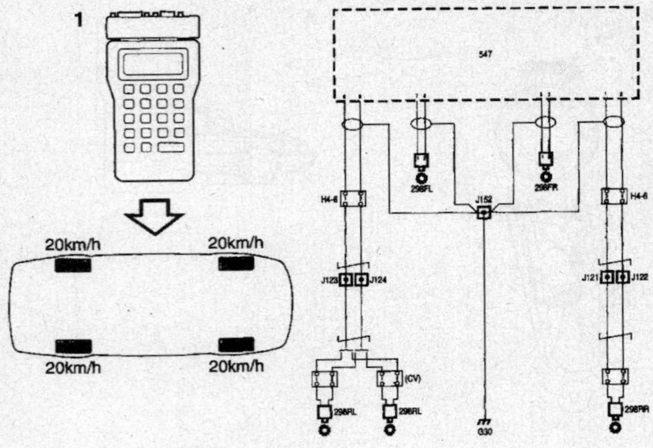

Fault symptom
ABS warning lamp on, no ABS function.

Condition
The wheel speed is compared to a reference speed (= filtrated mean value of all wheel speeds).

- a wheel speed l25% higher than the reference speed for 20 seconds.
- Two wheel speeds l6% higher than the reference speed for 80 seconds.
- A wheel speed <6% lower than the reference speed for 20 seconds, or two wheel speeds for 10 seconds.
- Continual ABS modulation for more than 60 seconds.

Diagnostic help

- Any particular wheel speed sensor can be read by the ISAT Scan Tool.
  - Select "READ FUNCTIONS"
  - Select "WHEEL SPEEDS"

The current wheel speed in km/h is displayed.

SA4029600076010X

Fig. 22 Code B1390: Wheel Sensor, Wrong Number Of Teeth (Part 1 of 2)

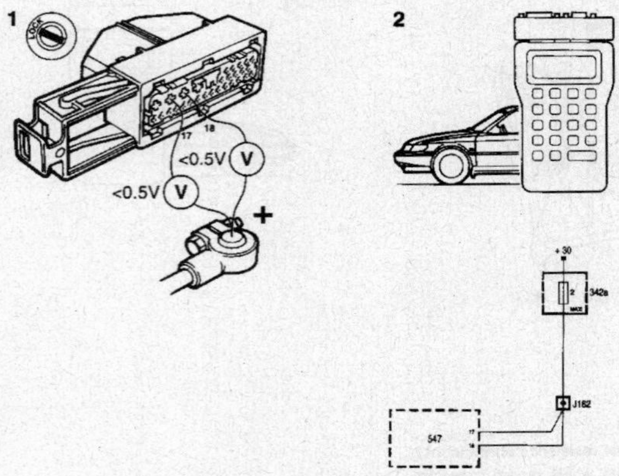

Fault symptom
ABS warning lamp on, no ABS function.

Condition

- If three or more valves lack voltage supply.
- If the internal voltage relay is out of order.
- The electronic control module lacks a +30-voltage supply (connector pins 17 and 18).

Diagnostic procedure

1 **+30 voltage supply check**
- Remove the electronic control module connector. Take a voltage measurement at the electronic control module sensor connector. Connect the voltmeter
- between pin 17 and B+ = < 0.5 V
- between pin 18 and B+ = < 0.5 V.

Are the voltage ratings OK?

YES Continue with point 2.

NO Check and possibly rectify the wiring between pin 17 and 18 of the electronic control module and the MAXI 2 fuse. If the wiring is correct, continue fault diagnosis in Service Manual 3:2 Electrical system, power supply +30.

2 **Final inspection**
- Erase the diagnostic trouble code.
- Carry out the driving cycle, drive the car with various load and engine speeds for 5 minutes.
- Read the diagnostic trouble code.

Is the diagnostic trouble code stored?

YES "Test Procedure Prior To Replacing ECM"

NO The diagnostic procedure performed is right or the fault is of intermittent character.

SA4029600078000X

Fig. 23 Code B1540: Boost Pressure Control Valve, No Voltage Supply Open Circuit

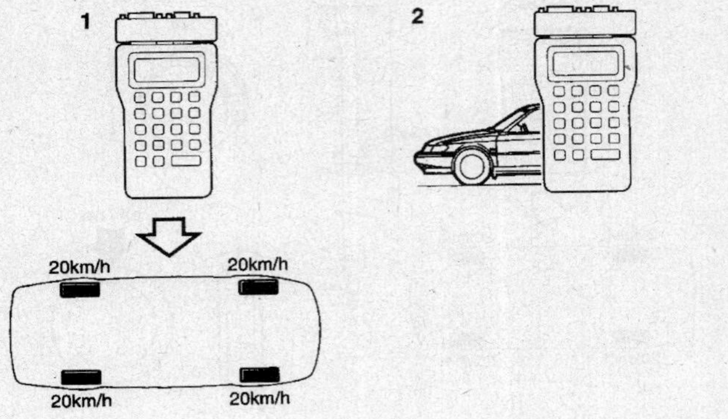

Diagnostic procedure

1 **Diagnostic Trouble Code inspection**
- Connect the ISAT Scan Tool.
- Start and test drive the car at an even speed. Read WHEEL SPEEDS according to the Diagnostic help. Compare the four displayed wheel speeds. All wheel speed ratings should be the same.

Does the ISAT display the correct rating?

YES Continue with point 2.

NO Displays FL faulty reading, continue fault diagnosis according to B1371
Displays FR faulty reading, continue fault diagnosis according to B1376
Displays RL faulty reading, continue fault diagnosis according to B1381
Displays RR faulty reading, continue fault diagnosis according to B1386.

2 **Final inspection**
- Erase the diagnostic trouble code.
- Carry out the driving cycle, drive the car with various load and engine speeds for 5 minutes.
- Read the diagnostic trouble code.

Is the diagnostic trouble code stored?

YES Continue on Test Procedure Prior To Replacing ECM

NO The diagnostic procedure performed is right or the fault is of intermittent character.

SA4029600076020X

Fig. 22 Code B1390: Wheel Sensor, Wrong Number Of Teeth (Part 2 of 2)

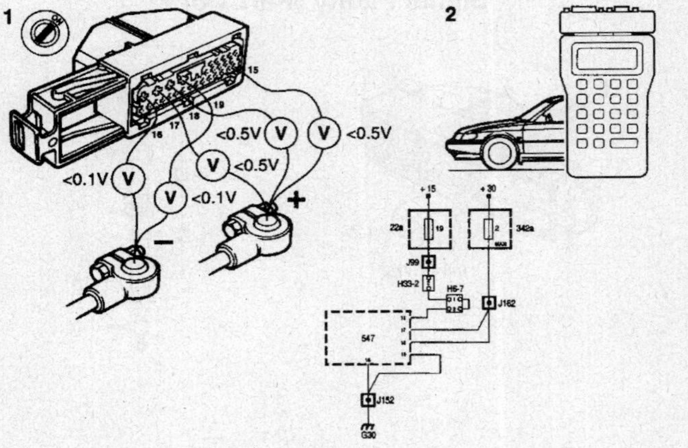

Fault symptom
ABS warning lamp on, no ABS function.

Condition
Fault registered as an internal program fault.

Diagnostic procedure

1 **Electronic control module ground and voltage supply check**
- Disconnect the electronic control module connector.
The ignition timing is in the On position.
Take a voltage reading at the electronic control module sensor connector. Connect the voltmeter,
- between pin 15 and B+ = <0.5V
- between pin 17 and B+ = <0.5V
- between pin 18 and B+ = <0.5V
- between pin 16 and B- = <0.1V
- between pin 19 and B- = <0.1V

Are the voltage ratings OK?

YES Continue with point 2.

NO Check and rectify the wiring including the connector and grounding points.

2 **Final inspection**
- Erase the diagnostic trouble code.
- Carry out the driving cycle, drive the car with various load and engine speeds for 5 minutes.
- Read the diagnostic trouble code.

Is the diagnostic trouble code stored?

YES

NO The diagnostic procedure performed is right or the fault is of intermittent character.

SA4029600079000X

Fig. 24 Code B1605: Electronic Control Module Fault

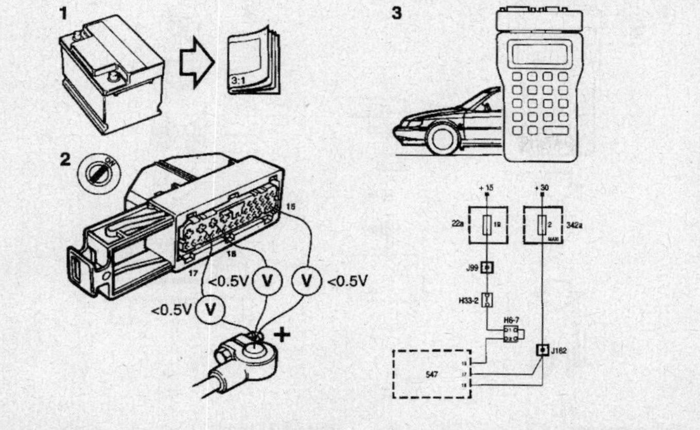

Fault symptom
ABS warning lamp on, no ABS function.

Condition

- Battery voltage <9V for more than 0.5 seconds.
- Wheel speeds over 6 km/h.

Diagnostic procedure

1 **Battery check**

- Check the condition of the battery.

Is the condition of the battery OK?

YES Continue with point 2.

NO Rectify the fault

2 **Electronic control module voltage supply check**

- Remove the electronic control module connector. The ignition should be in the ON position. Take a voltage measurement at the sensor connector. Connect the voltmeter

- between pin 17 and B+ = <0.5V
- between pin 18 and B+ = <0.5V
- between pin 15 and B+ = <0.5V

Are the voltage ratings OK?

YES Continue with point 3.

NO Check and rectify the wiring including the connector.

3 **Final inspection**

- Erase the diagnostic trouble code.
- Carry out the driving cycle, drive the car with various load and engine speeds for 5 minutes.
- Read the diagnostic trouble code.

Is the diagnostic trouble code stored?

YES Continue "Test Procedure Prior To Replacing ECM"

NO The diagnostic procedure performed is right or the fault is of intermittent character.

SA4029600080000X

Fig. 25 Code B1532: Battery Voltage Low

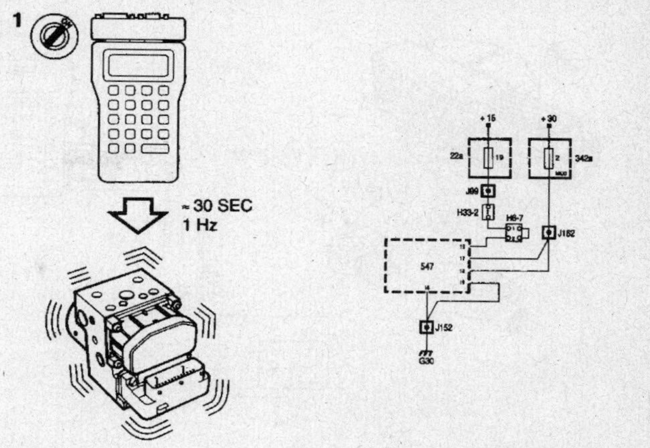

Fault symptom
ABS warning lamp on, no ABS function.

Condition

- The ignition timing is in the On position.
- The electronic control module makes a boost pressure control valve connection test.

Diagnostic help
The boost pressure control valves can be activated with the ISAT Scan Tool.

- Select "ACTIVATE"
- Select "VALVES"

Particular valves can be identified in the sub menu. The selected valve is activated within approx. 30 seconds with a frequency of 1 Hz.

Diagnostic procedure

1 **Valve check**

- Connect the ISAT Scan Tool. The ignition timing is in the ON position
- First activate the "INTAKE" and then after the activation period is over activate the "OUTLET" Listen if the valves click.

Do the valves click?

YES Continue with point 3.

NO Continue with point 2.

SA4029600077010X

Fig. 26 Codes B2415, 2450, 2455 & 2485: Boost Pressure Control Valve Rear Left, Faulty (Part 1 of 2)

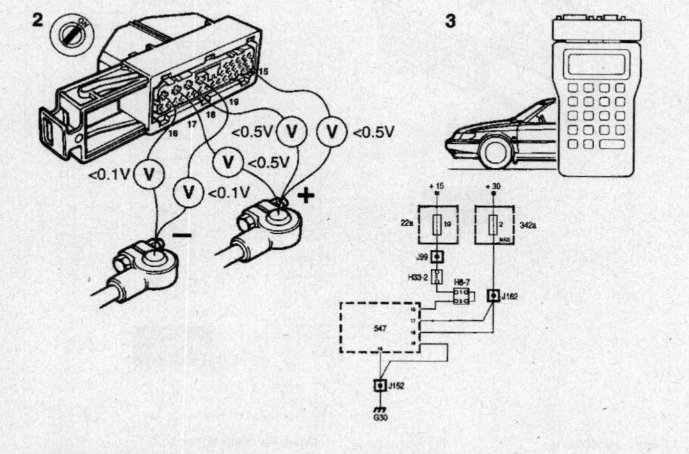

2 **Electronic control module ground and voltage supply check**

- Disconnect the electronic control module connector. The ignition timing is in the On position. Take a voltage reading at the electronic control module sensor connector. Connect the voltmeter,

- between B+ and pin 15 = <0.5V
- between B+ and pin 17 = <0.5V
- between B+ and pin 18 = <0.5V
- between pin 16 and B- = <0.1V
- between pin 19 and B- = <0.1V

Are the voltage ratings OK?

YES Continue with point 3.

NO Check and rectify the wiring including the connector and grounding points.

3 **Final inspection**

- Erase the diagnostic trouble code.
- Carry out the driving cycle, drive the car with various load and engine speeds for 5 minutes.
- Read the diagnostic trouble code.

Is the diagnostic trouble code stored?

YES Continue on Test Procedure Prior To Replacing ECM

NO The diagnostic procedure performed is right or the fault is of intermittent character.

SA4029600077020X

Fig. 26 Codes B2415, 2450, 2455 & 2485: Boost Pressure Control Valve Rear Left, Faulty (Part 2 of 2)

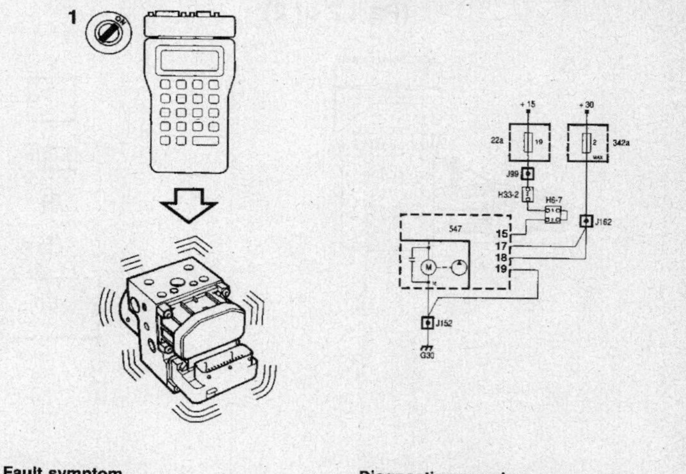

Fault symptom
ABS warning lamp on, no ABS function.

Condition

- The pump motor is tested after the car has started and the wheels start to rotate (VI6 km/h). Then observe it continually.

Diagnostic help
The pump motor can be rotated with the ISAT Scan Tool.

- Select "ACTIVATE"
- Select "PUMP MOTOR"

- If the ABS electronic control module has no ground connection (connector pin 16) a diagnostic trouble code is registered.

Diagnostic procedure

1 **Pump motor inspection**

- Connect the ISAT Scan Tool. The ignition timing is in the ON position
- Activate the pump motor in accordance with Diagnostic help. Listen if the motor comes on/off.

Does the pump motor work?

YES Continue with point 3.

NO Inspect the 2 pole sensor connector for any open-circuit. If the conductors are correct continue with point 2.

SA4029600082010X

Fig. 27 Code B2465: Pump Motor Faulty (Part 1 of 2)

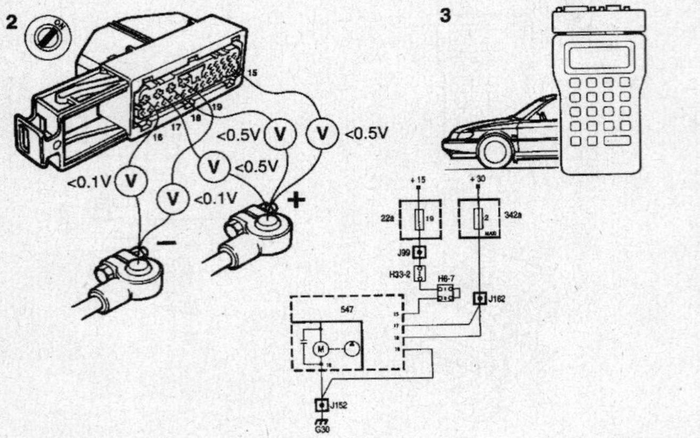

2 **Electronic control module ground and voltage supply check**

- Disconnect the electronic control module connector.
  The ignition timing is in the On position.
  Take a voltage reading at the electronic control module sensor connector. Connect the voltmeter,

- between B+ and pin 15 = <0.5V
- between B+ and pin 17 = <0.5V
- between B+ and pin 18 = <0.5V
- between pin 16 and B- = <0.1V
- between pin 19 and B- = <0.1V

Are the voltage ratings OK?

YES Continue with point 3.

NO Check and rectify the wiring including the connector and grounding points.

3 **Final inspection**

- Erase the diagnostic trouble code.
- Carry out the driving cycle, drive the car with various load and engine speeds for 5 minutes.
- Read the diagnostic trouble code.

Is the diagnostic trouble code stored?

YES Test Procedure Prior To Replacing ECM

NO The diagnostic procedure performed is right or the fault is of intermittent character.

SA4029600082020X

Fig. 27 Code B2465: Pump Motor Faulty (Part 2 of 2)

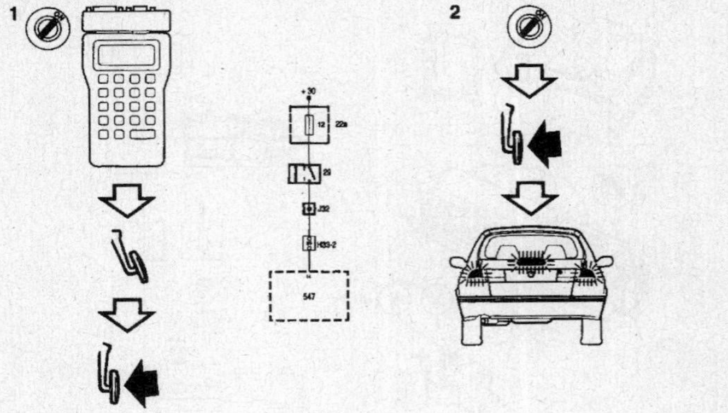

Fault symptom
No sumptoms.

Condition
Fault registered with open circuit for longer than 1 second.

Diagnostic help
Brake light switch position ON/OFF, can be read with the ISAT Scan Tool.

- Select "READ FUNCTIONS"
- Select "BRAKE LIGHT SWITCH"

Diagnostic procedure

1 **Brake light switch inspection.**

- Connect the ISAT Scan Tool.
  The ignition timing is in the ON position
- Check the brake light switch in accordance with Diagnostic help and depress and release the brake pedal.

Does the ISAT display the correct rating?

YES Continue with point 3.

NO Continue with point 2.

2 **Brake lights inspection.**

- Check that the brake light functions when the brake pedal is depressed.

Does the brake light function?

YES Check and rectify the cable including the connector between pin 14 of the electronic control module and brake light switch.

NO Continue the fault diagnosis

SA4029600081010X

Fig. 28 Code B2470: Brake Light Switch No Signal Open Circuit (Part 1 of 2)

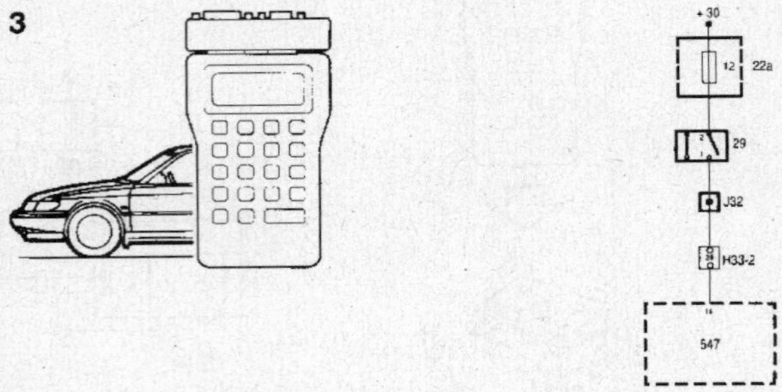

3 **Final inspection**

- Erase the diagnostic trouble code.
- Perform a driving cycle, drive the car with varying loads and engine speed and use the brake pedal.
- Read the diagnostic trouble code.

Is the diagnostic trouble code stored?

YES With "Test Procedure Prior To Replacing ECM"

NO The diagnostic procedure performed is right or the fault is of intermittent character.

SA4029600081020X

Fig. 28 Code B2470: Brake Light Switch No Signal Open Circuit (Part 2 of 2)

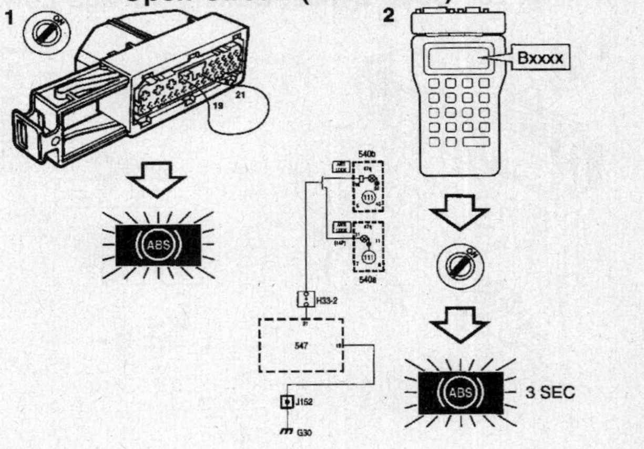

Fault symptom
The lamp test is carried out with the ignition timing on.
ABS-lamp should be on for approx. 3 seconds.
ABS lamps fails to come on.

Condition

- Open-circuit in the electrical circuit.

Diagnostic help
ABS lamp can be activated with the ISAT Scan Tool
Select "ACTIVATE"
Select "ABS LAMP"

Diagnostic procedure

1 **ABS lamp operation check**

- Remove electronic control module connector
  The ignition timing is in the ON position.
- Interconnect a loop between pin 21 and pin 19 in the electronic control module sensor connector.
  The ABS lamp should come on.

Does the lamp come on?

YES Check the electronic control module connector for damp, corrosion and dislodged contact pins. Continue with point 2..

NO Inspect the cable between pin 21 of the ABS electronic control module and pin 16 of the main instrument. If the cable is not faulty, continue the fault diagnosis

2 **Final inspection**

- Make a operations check of the ABS lamp with the ignition timing switched on.

Does the lamp come on?

YES The diagnostic procedure taken is right.

NO on Test Procedure Prior To Replacing ECM

SA4029600083000X

Fig. 29 ABS Lamp Not Operating

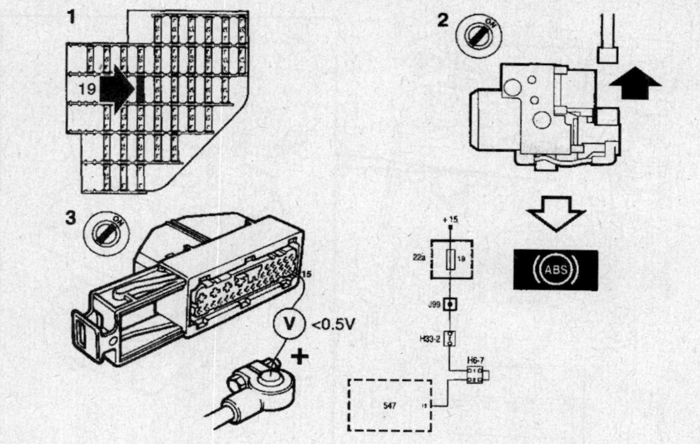

Fault symptom

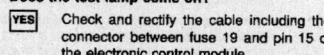

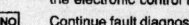

The ABS lamp is on constantly.

Condition

- Short circuit to ground in the electrical circuit.
- The ABS electronic control module faults +15 voltage (pin 15).

Diagnostic procedure

1 **Inspection of fuses**

- Check that fuse 19 is intact.

Is fuse 19 intact?

YES Continue with point 2.

NO Replace fuse.

2 **ABS lamp operation check**

- Disconnect the electronic control module connector.
  The ignition timing is in the On position.

Is the ABS lamp on?

YES Inspect the conductors between pin 21 of the electronic control module and pin 16 of the main instrument.
If the cable is not faulty, continue fault diagnosis

NO Continue with point 3.

3 **The electronic control module +15 voltage supply check.**

- The ignition timing is in the ON position.
  Take a voltage measurement between B+ and the electronic control module sensor connector, pin 15.
  The voltage should be <0.5V.

Is the voltage correct?

YES Continue with point 5.

NO Continue with point 4.

SA4029600084010X

Fig. 30 ABS Lamp On At All Times (Part 1 of 2)

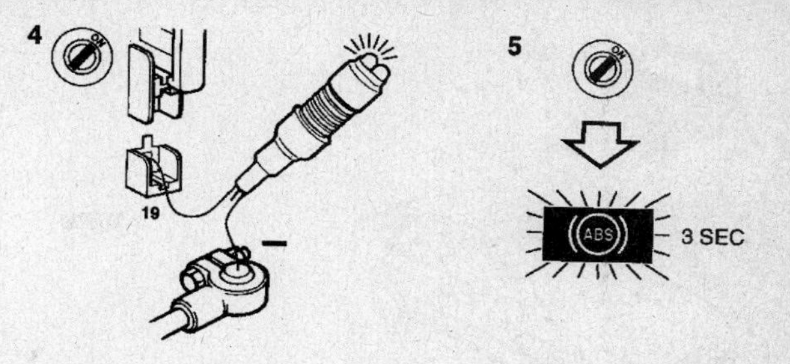

4 **Check the +15-voltage supply**

- Check that there is a +15-voltage at fuse 19.
  The ignition timing is in the ON position.
  Connect the test lamp between fuse 19 and a definite grounding point.

Does the test lamp come on?

YES Check and rectify the cable including the connector between fuse 19 and pin 15 of the electronic control module.

NO Continue fault diagnosis

5 **Final inspection**

- Make a operations check of the ABS lamp with the ignition timing switched on.

Does the ABS lamp operate correctly?

YES The diagnostic procedure taken was correct

NO Continue With "Test Procedure Prior To Replacing ECM"

SA4029600084020X

Fig. 30 ABS Lamp On At All Times (Part 2 of 2)

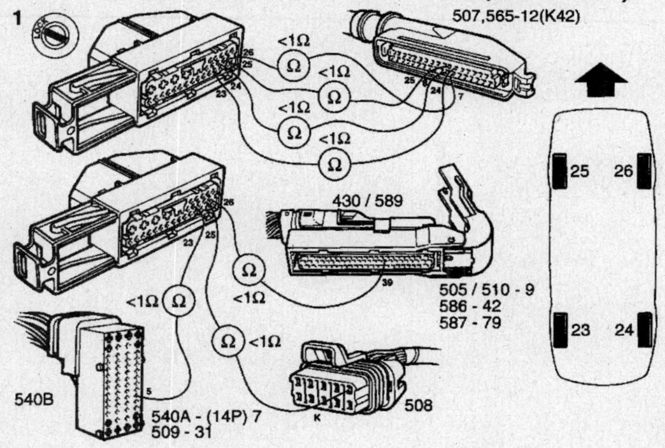

Fault symptom

The diagnostic trouble code for one of the other electronic systems in the car displays that there is no speed signal.

Condition

- Open/short-circuit in the electrical circuit.

Diagnostic procedure

1 **Cable inspection**

- Remove the electronic control module connector.
  Remove the connector to the electronic control module that detected the faulty wheel speed.
  Make a continuity test on the cables between the respective electronic control module.

Is the cable OK?

YES Continue with point 2.

NO Rectify the fault

SA4029600085010X

Fig. 31 No Wheel Speed Signal (Part 1 of 2)

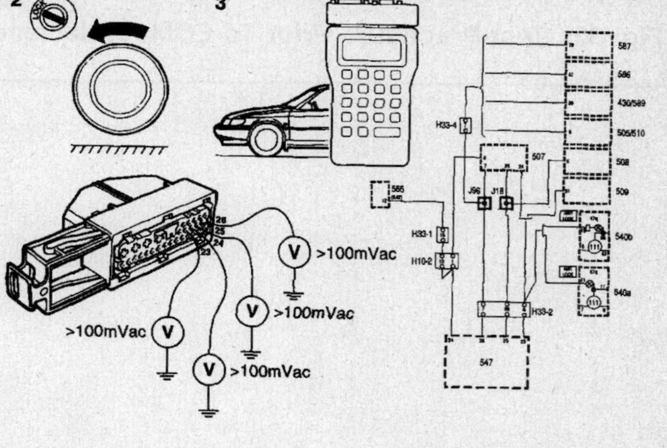

2 **Wheel speed signal check**

- Connect the ABS electronic control module
  Lift the car
  Take a voltage measurement, mVac, at the particular connector pin that detected the faulty wheel speed in the electronic control module.
  Rotate the wheel concerned by hand at 1 turn a second. The voltmeter should show a reading of l100 mVac.

Is the voltage OK?

YES Continue the fault diagnosis in the *appropriate service manual*

NO Continue with point 3.

3 **Final inspection**

- *Make an operation check.*

- Erase the diagnostic trouble code in the system concerned
- Drive the car with varying loads and engine speeds for approx. 5 minutes.
  - *Check if the fault symptom remains.*

Do the fault symptoms remain?

YES Continue With "Test Procedure Prior To Replacing ECM"

NO *The diagnostic procedure taken is right.*

SA4029600085020X

Fig. 31 No Wheel Speed Signal (Part 2 of 2)

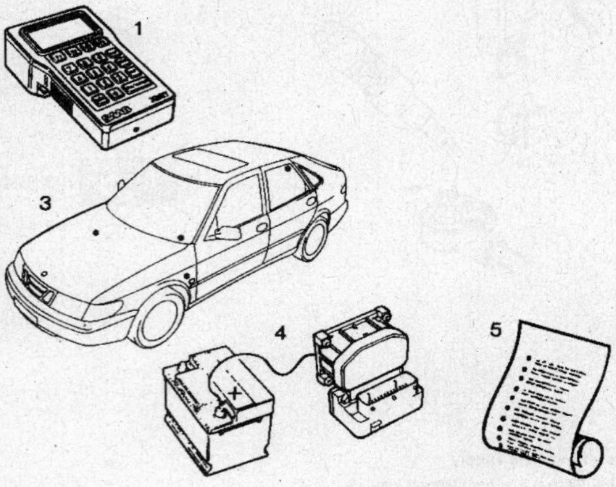

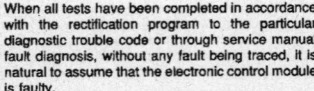

When all tests have been completed in accordance with the rectification program to the particular diagnostic trouble code or through service manual fault diagnosis, without any fault being traced, it is natural to assume that the electronic control module is faulty.
Observe the following points before you definitely identify the ABS electronic control module as the cause of the problem.

1 Check once again that all tests in the codes fault diagnostic scheme have been carried out.
2 Study the particular circuits wiring diagram and familiarise yourself with its operation.

wiring diagram.

3 When fitting or removing the electronic control module be aware of its sensitivity to electrostatic discharge.
4 Check all grounding points and the voltage supply to the electronic control module. If you have checked this before, check it once again.
5 If the suggested diagnostic procedure routine fails to correctly rectify the problem, attempt to trace the problem through testing and analyse "Test reading, electronic control module connections".
6

Be very reluctant to change the electronic control module.

Think through all likely fault reasons before replacing the electronic control module!

7 If the original fault remains, despite that, the ABS electronic control module must be changed.

SA4029600086000X

Fig. 32 Test Procedure Prior To ECM Replacement

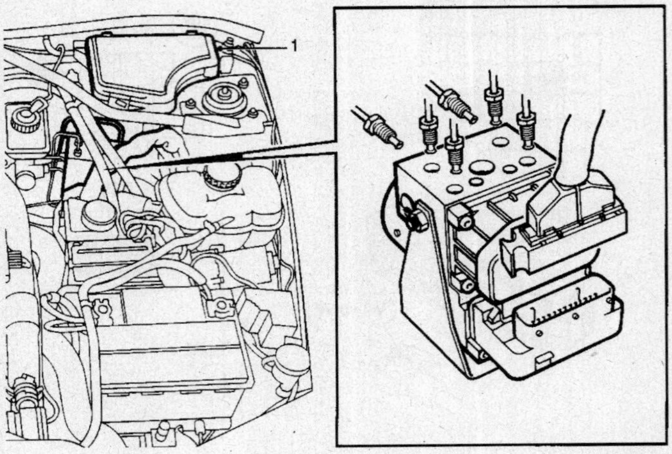

SA4029600087000X

Fig. 33 Hydraulic unit replacement

Bosch 5.4 Anti-Lock Brake System

NOTE: On Air Bag Equipped Models, Refer To "Air Bag System Precautions" Located In The Front Of This Manual For System Disarming & Arming Procedures.

NOTE: "Electrical Symbol & Wire Color Code Identification" Located In The Front Of This Manual May Be Used As An Aid When Using Wiring Circuits Found In This Section.

INDEX

	Page No.
Description	7-145
Components	7-145
System	7-145
Diagnosis & Testing	7-146
Accessing Diagnostic Trouble Codes	7-146
Clearing Trouble Codes	7-151
Diagnosis Before Changing Control Module	7-151
Diagnostic Tests	7-146
ABS Warning Lamp Not Operating	7-151
ABS Warning Lamp On Constantly	7-151
Code C1371, Front Left Wheel Sensor (Signal Incorrect)	7-146
Code C1372, Front Left Wheel Sensor (No Signal)	7-146
Code C1376, Front Right Wheel Sensor (Signal Incorrect)	7-146
Code C1377, Front Right Wheel Sensor (No Signal)	7-147
Code C1381, Rear Left Wheel Sensor (Signal Incorrect)	7-147
Code C1382, Rear Left Wheel Sensor (No Signal)	7-147
Code C1386, Rear Right Wheel Sensor (Signal Incorrect)	7-147
Code C1387, Rear Right Wheel Sensor (No Signal)	7-147
Code C1390, Wheel Sensor (Wrong Number Of Teeth)	7-150
Code C1532, Battery Voltage Too Low	7-150
Code C1540, Solenoids (Open Circuit)	7-150
Code C1605, Control Module	7-150
Code C2465, Pump Motor Incorrect	7-150
Code C2470, Brake Light Switch Open Circuit	7-151
Codes C2415, C2450, C2455 & C2485 Solenoid Valve Defective	7-150
No Wheel Speed Signal	7-151
Diagnostic Trouble Code Interpretation	7-146
Intermittents	7-151
Wiring Circuits	7-146
Precautions	7-145
Air Bag Systems	7-145
Battery Ground Cable	7-145
System Service	7-151
Brake System Bleed	7-151
Component Replacement	7-151
ABS Control Module/Hydraulic Unit	7-151
Front Wheel Sensor	7-152
Rear Wheel Sensor	7-152
Troubleshooting	7-146

PRECAUTIONS

AIR BAG SYSTEMS

Refer to "Air Bag System Precautions" in the front of this manual for system disarming and arming procedures.

BATTERY GROUND CABLE

Prior to service, disconnect battery ground cable and isolate as required.

DESCRIPTION

SYSTEM

The Bosch 5.4 Anti-Lock Brake System (ABS) is a dual circuit, four-port brake system, **Fig. 1.**

Four wheel sensors at the wheels send signals to an electronic control unit, which continuously calculates on the basis of the wheel acceleration (speed increase), wheel deceleration (speed decrease), the speed of the vehicle and the slip of the wheels (degree of wheel lock-up). If any wheel approaches the limit for lock-up, the control unit passes signals to solenoid valves in the valve block for the wheel. The pressure in the brake circuit for the wheel is controlled so the maximum possible braking power is transmitted to the road surface at all times with no loss of steering ability.

Electronic Brake-Force Distribution (EBD), a built in function of the electronic control module, controls the rear intake valves to provide maximum braking power at the rear wheels without front wheel lock-up.

COMPONENTS

Hydraulic Unit

The hydraulic unit consists of a valve block, an electronic control module with main and pump relays and a return pump.

The master cylinder is separated from the hydraulic unit and is connected via two pipes from the primary and secondary circuits.

Control Module

The control module receives wheel speed information through input signals from the wheel sensors.

If any of the wheels has greater deceleration on braking than the others, the control module controls the solenoid valves and return pump so hydraulic brake pressure can be kept constant or reduced to each wheel.

Wheel Sensors

The front wheel sensors consist of a hub-mounted toothed wheel and a inductive sensor. The rear wheel sensors are integrated with the wheel hub and consist of a inductive sensor with 29 teeth.

The inductive sensors work like small alternators, the sine-wave voltage of the sensor increases with increasing wheel speed. The sine-wave voltage alternates between negative and positive polarity, which is achieved by alternate teeth and gaps on the toothed wheel. The control module uses this polarity reversal as a pulse generator. The frequency of the pulse increases with wheel speed.

The rear wheel sensor is designed differently than the front, in that it is less sensitive to wheel bearing play and starts to pass information to the control module at very low wheel speeds.

Valve Block

The valve block is an integral part of the hydraulic unit and controls brake hydraulic pressure to the caliper assemblies during ABS controlled braking.

The valve block has eight boost pressure control valves (1 intake and outlet valve for each wheel). In the rest position, the inlet valve is open and the outlet valve is closed.

Each inlet and outlet valve is equipped with an accumulator chamber and pressure chamber. The accumulator chamber, located between the outlet valve and return pump, accumulates brake fluid until the return pump begins to run. The pressure chamber, located between the return pump and the master cylinder, is used to dampen

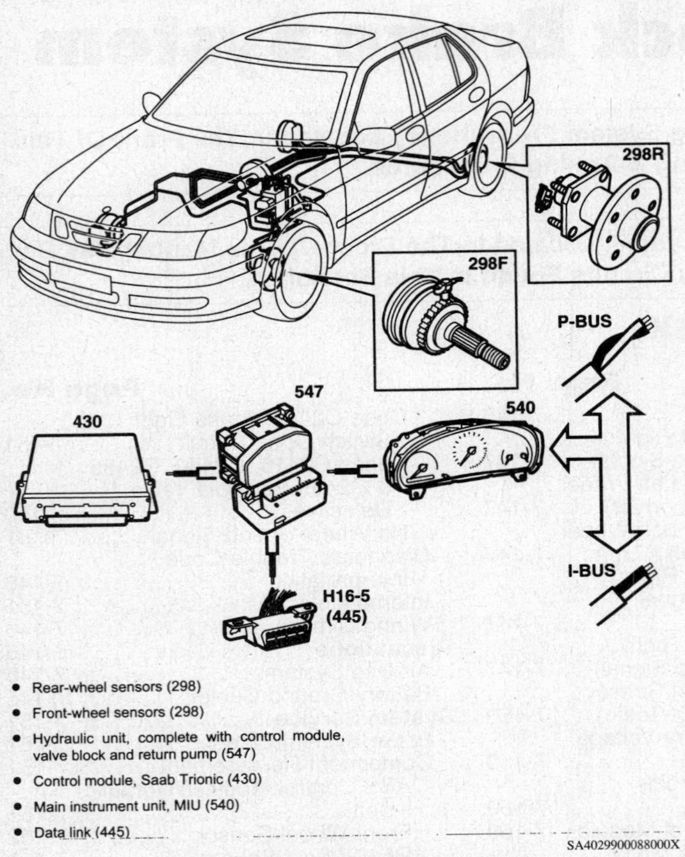

Fig. 1 Anti-lock brake system

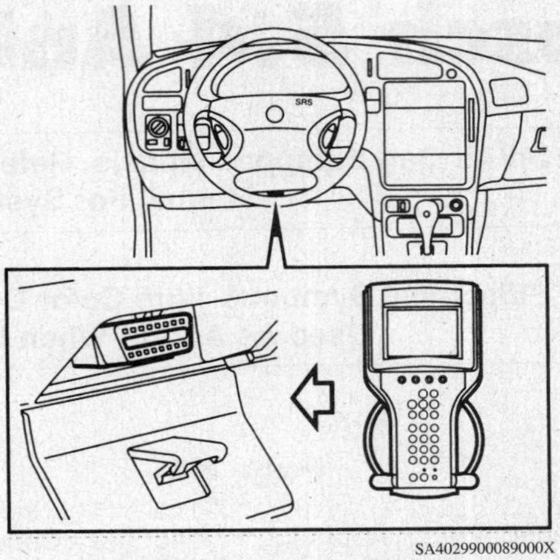

Fig. 2 DLC connector

the noise and pressure fluctuations when the return pump is running.

Brake Light Switch

Each time the brake pedal is depressed the control module receives voltage signal from the brake light switch. The control module uses this voltage signal during pump-motor testing and ABS modulation.

Return Pump

The return pump, an integral part of the hydraulic unit, is equipped with a D.C. motor. The motor activates a hydraulic pump which returns surplus brake fluid to the master cylinder. The pump is only activated when an outlet valve is open.

TROUBLESHOOTING DIAGNOSIS & TESTING

Accessing Diagnostic Trouble Codes

Connect a suitable scan tool to the Data Link Connector (DLC) located under the lefthand side of the instrument panel, under the steering column, **Fig. 2.**

Diagnostic Trouble Code Interpretation

When performing diagnostic trouble code diagnosis and repair, refer to **Fig. 3** for diagnostic trouble code identification.

Wiring Circuits

Refer to **Figs. 4 and 5,** for ABS system wiring circuit.

Diagnostic Tests

CODE C1371, FRONT LEFT WHEEL SENSOR (SIGNAL INCORRECT)

1. With scan tool connected to DLC connector, drive vehicle at a steady speed and read front left wheel speed with scan tool.
2. If wheel speed matches vehicle speed, proceed to step 3. If wheel speed does not match vehicle speed, proceed as follows:
   a. Check tire pressure, wheel size, bearing play and toothed wheel. If satisfactory, proceed to next step. If not satisfactory, repair or replace as necessary.
   b. Check gap between toothed wheel and sensor. If gap is between .0118–.0472 inch, proceed to step 3. If gap is not between .0118–.0472 inch, replace toothed wheel or sensor.
3. Clear diagnostic trouble codes.
4. Test drive vehicle varying engine speeds for approximately five minutes. If diagnostic trouble code does not return, refer to "Intermittents." If diagnostic trouble code returns, refer to "Diagnosis Before Changing Control Module."

CODE C1372, FRONT LEFT WHEEL SENSOR (NO SIGNAL)

1. Disconnect front left wheel sensor electrical connector.
2. Turn ignition key to the RUN position.
3. Measure voltage at terminal No. 1 on the harness side of the sensor connector. If voltage is approximately 4.7 volts, proceed to next step. If voltage is not approximately 4.7 volts, locate and repair open circuit between control module and sensor connector terminal No. 1. Proceed to step 5.
4. Measure voltage between terminal No. 2 on the harness side of the sensor connector and battery positive terminal. If battery voltage is indicated, replace speed sensor and proceed to step 5. If battery voltage is not indicated, locate and repair open circuit between control module and sensor connector terminal No. 2, then proceed to step 5.
5. Test drive vehicle varying engine speeds for approximately five minutes. If diagnostic trouble code does not return, refer to "Intermittents." If diagnostic trouble code returns, refer to "Diagnosis Before Changing Control Module."

CODE C1376, FRONT RIGHT WHEEL SENSOR (SIGNAL INCORRECT)

1. With scan tool connected to DLC connector, drive vehicle at a steady speed and read front right wheel speed with scan tool.
2. If wheel speed matches vehicle speed, proceed to step 3. If wheel speed does not match vehicle speed, proceed as follows:
   a. Check tire pressure, wheel size, bearing play and toothed wheel. If satisfactory, proceed to next step. If

not satisfactory, repair or replace as necessary.

b. Check gap between toothed wheel and sensor. If gap is between .0118–.0472 inch, proceed to step 3. If gap is not between .0118–.0472 inch, replace toothed wheel or sensor and proceed to step 3.

3. Clear diagnostic trouble codes.
4. Test drive vehicle varying engine speeds for approximately five minutes. If diagnostic trouble code does not return, refer to "Intermittents." If diagnostic trouble code returns, refer to "Diagnosis Before Changing Control Module."

CODE C1377, FRONT RIGHT WHEEL SENSOR (NO SIGNAL)

1. Disconnect front right wheel sensor electrical connector.
2. Turn ignition key to the RUN position.
3. Measure voltage at terminal No. 1 on the harness side of the sensor connector. If voltage is approximately 4.7 volts, proceed to next step. If voltage is not approximately 4.7 volts, locate and repair open circuit between control module and sensor connector terminal No. 1. Proceed to step 5.
4. Measure voltage between terminal No. 2 on the harness side of the sensor connector and battery positive terminal. If battery voltage is indicated, replace speed sensor and proceed to step 5. If battery voltage is not indicated, locate and repair open circuit between control module and sensor connector terminal No. 2, then proceed to step 5.
5. Test drive vehicle varying engine speeds for approximately five minutes. If diagnostic trouble code does not return, refer to "Intermittents." If diagnostic trouble code returns, refer to "Diagnosis Before Changing Control Module."

CODE C1381, REAR LEFT WHEEL SENSOR (SIGNAL INCORRECT)

1. With scan tool connected to DLC connector, drive vehicle at a steady speed and read rear left wheel speed with scan tool.
2. If wheel speed matches vehicle speed, proceed to step 3. If wheel speed does not match vehicle speed, check tire pressure, wheel size and wheel bearing play. If satisfactory, proceed to next step. If not satisfactory, repair or replace as necessary and proceed to step 3.
3. Clear diagnostic trouble codes.
4. Test drive vehicle varying engine speeds for approximately five minutes. If diagnostic trouble code does not return, refer to "Intermittents." If diagnostic trouble code returns, refer to "Diagnosis Before Changing Control Module."

Type	DTC	Faulty function/component
C	1371	Wheel Sensor Front Left. Signal Incorrect
C	1372	Wheel Sensor Front Left. No Signal
C	1376	Wheel Sensor Front Right. Signal Incorrect
C	1377	Wheel Sensor Front Right. No Signal
C	1381	Wheel Sensor Rear Left. Signal Incorrect
C	1382	Wheel Sensor Rear Left. No Signal
C	1386	Wheel Sensor Rear Right. Signal Incorrect
C	1387	Wheel Sensor Rear Right. No Signal
C	1390	Wheel Sensor. Wrong Number of Teeth
C	1532	Battery Voltage. Too Low
C	1540	Solenoids. Open Circuit.
C	1605	Control module - ECU fault
C	2415	Solenoid valves, rear left, defective
C	2450	Solenoid valves, front left, defective
C	2455	.Solenoid valves, front right, defective
C	2485	Solenoid valves, rear right, defective
C	2465	Pump Motor. Incorrect
C	2470	Brake Light Switch. Open Circuit.

SA4029900090000X

Fig. 3 Diagnostic trouble coder interpretation

CODE C1382, REAR LEFT WHEEL SENSOR (NO SIGNAL)

1. Disconnect rear left wheel sensor electrical connector.
2. Turn ignition key to the RUN position.
3. Measure voltage at terminal "A" on the harness side of the sensor connector. If voltage is approximately 4.7 volts, proceed to next step. If voltage is not approximately 4.7 volts, locate and repair open circuit between control module and sensor connector terminal "A," then proceed to step 5.
4. Measure voltage between terminal "B" on the harness side of the sensor connector and battery positive terminal. If battery voltage is indicated, replace speed sensor and proceed to step 5. If battery voltage is not indicated, locate and repair open circuit between control module and sensor connector terminal "B," then proceed to step 5.
5. Test drive vehicle varying engine speeds for approximately five minutes. If diagnostic trouble code does not return, refer to "Intermittents." If diagnostic trouble code returns, refer to "Diagnosis Before Changing Control Module."

CODE C1386, REAR RIGHT WHEEL SENSOR (SIGNAL INCORRECT)

1. With scan tool connected to DLC connector, drive vehicle at a steady speed and read rear right wheel speed with scan tool.
2. If wheel speed matches vehicle speed, proceed to step 3. If wheel speed does not match vehicle speed, check tire pressure, wheel size and wheel bearing play. If satisfactory, proceed to next step. If not satisfactory, repair or replace as necessary and proceed to step 3.
3. Clear diagnostic trouble codes.
4. Test drive vehicle varying engine speeds for approximately five minutes. If diagnostic trouble code does not return, refer to "Intermittents." If diagnostic trouble code returns, refer to "Diagnosis Before Changing Control Module."

CODE C1387, REAR RIGHT WHEEL SENSOR (NO SIGNAL)

1. Disconnect rear right wheel sensor electrical connector.
2. Turn ignition key to the RUN position.
3. Measure voltage at terminal "A" on the harness side of the sensor connector. If voltage is approximately 4.7 volts, proceed to next step. If voltage is not approximately 4.7 volts, locate and repair open circuit between control module and sensor connector terminal "A," then proceed to step 5.
4. Measure voltage between terminal "B" on the harness side of the sensor connector and battery positive terminal. If battery voltage is indicated, replace speed sensor and proceed to step 5. If battery voltage is not indicated, locate and repair open circuit between control module and sensor connector terminal "B," then proceed to step 5.
5. Test drive vehicle varying engine

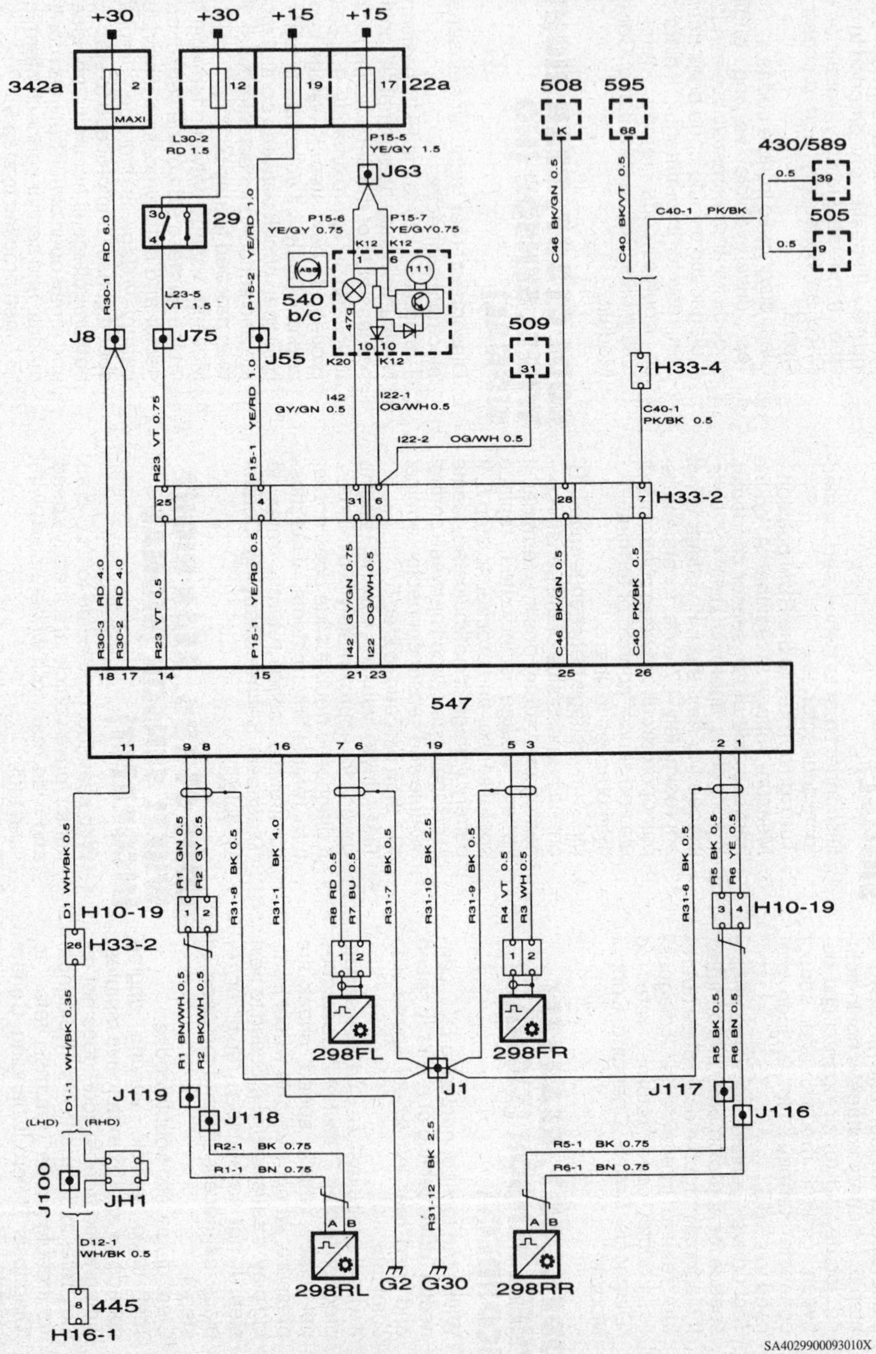

SA4029900093010X

Fig. 4 ABS system wiring circuit (Part 1 of 2). 9-3

SMS	Components
22a	Main fuse board, instrument panel
29	Brake-light switch
47q	Warning lamp, ABS
298FL	Wheel speed sensor, front left
298FR	Wheel speed sensor, front right
298RL	Wheel speed sensor, rear left
298RR	Wheel speed sensor, rear right
342a	Main fuse board, engine bay
430	Control module, Saab Trionic
505	Control module, Motronic 2.10.3. In the cabin on the right-hand side below the A pillar.
508	Control module, cruise control, on the right in the engine bay below the windscreen.
509	Control module, Saab Sensonic, in the cabin on the right-hand side of the bulkhead partition.
445	Data link connector, 16-pin, CARB
540	Main instrument unit
547	Control module, ABS
589	Control module, Trionic OBDII, in the cabin on the right-hand side behind the side trim below the A pillar.
595A	Control module, EDC15, contact A, in the cabin on the right-hand side below the A pillar.
595B	Control module, EDC15, contact B, in the cabin on the right-hand side below the A pillar.

Connector

H10-19	In the engine bay beside the pedal position sensor.
H16-1	Under the instrument panel adjacent to the steering column.
H33-2	Black connector on the bracket below the left-hand A pillar.
H33-4	LHD: Black connector on the bulkhead partition behind the glove box. RHD: Black connector under the engine control module.

Crimp connections

J1	About 60 mm from the washer fluid pump branching point, towards the main fuse box.
J8	About 250 mm from the ABS control module.
J55	**LHD:** About 170 mm from the G33 grounding point branch, towards the DICE control module. **RHD:** About 80 mm from the G34 grounding point branch, towards connector H33-4.
J63	**LHD:** About 200 mm from the MIU branching point, towards the SID. **RHD:** About 50 mm from the rheostat branching point, towards the lights switch.
J75	**LHD:** About 200 mm from the G33 grounding point branch, towards the DICE control module. **RHD:** About 70 mm from the main relay board.
J100	**LHD:** About 100 mm from the MIU branching point, towards the SID. **RHD:**--
J116	**3D/5D:** About 510 mm from the fuel tank branching point, towards the left-hand door. **CONV:** About 125 mm from the branching point for the fuel tank/rear wheel sensors, towards the control module.
J117	**3D/5D:** About 535 mm from the fuel tank branching point, towards the left-hand door. **CONV:** About 150 mm from the branching point for the fuel tank/rear wheel sensors, towards the control module.
J118	**3D/5D:** About 610 mm from the fuel tank branching point, towards the left-hand door. **CONV:** About 200 mm from the branching point for the fuel tank/rear wheel sensors, towards the control module.
J119	**3D/5D:** About 585 mm from the fuel tank branching point, towards the left-hand door. **CONV:** About 275 mm from the branching point for the fuel tank/rear wheel sensors, towards the control module.

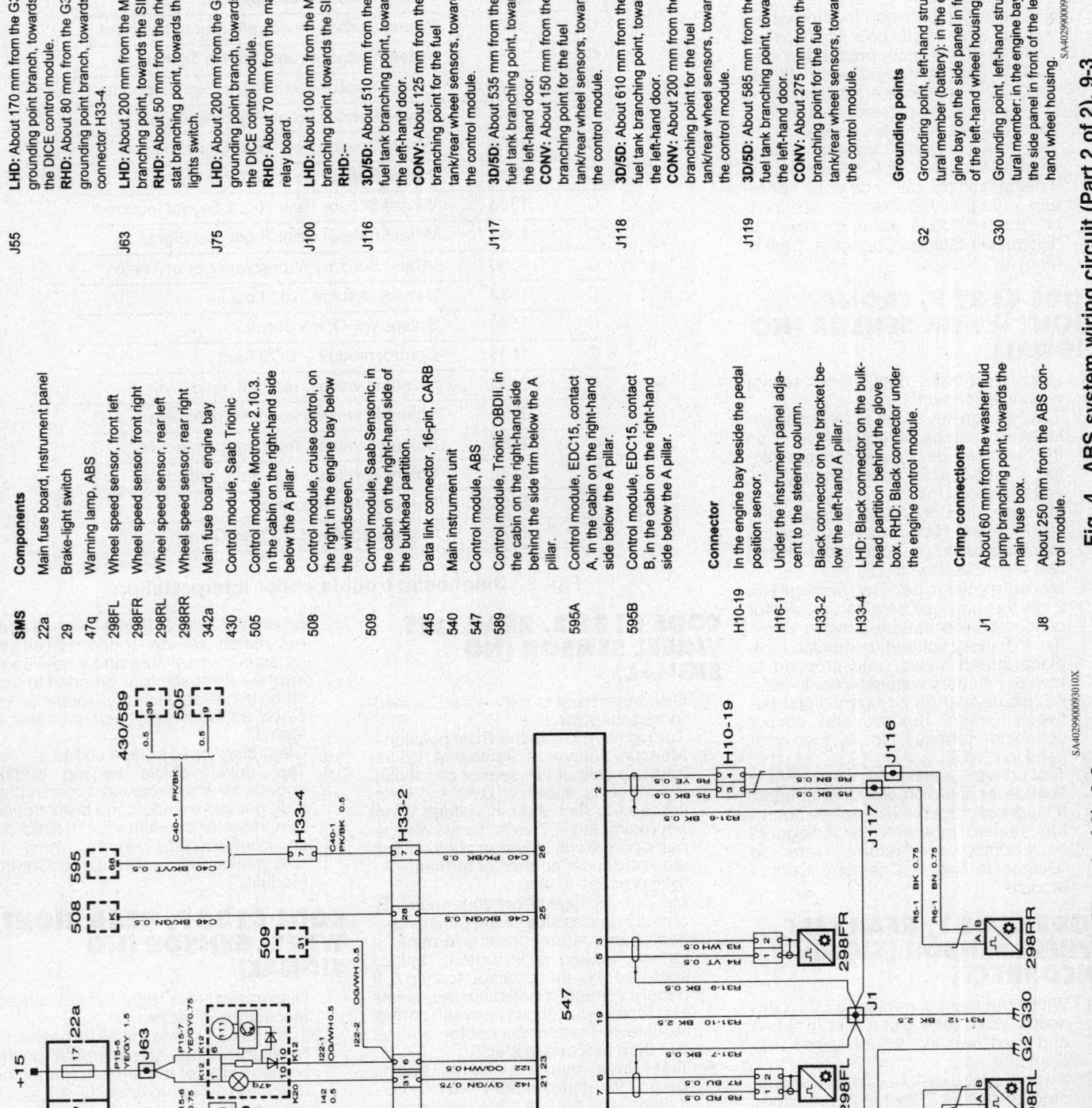

Grounding points

G2	Grounding point, left-hand structural member (battery): in the engine bay on the side panel in front of the left-hand wheel housing.
G30	Grounding point, left-hand structural member: in the engine bay on the side panel in front of the left-hand wheel housing.

SA4029900093020X

Fig. 4 ABS system wiring circuit (Part 2 of 2). 9-3

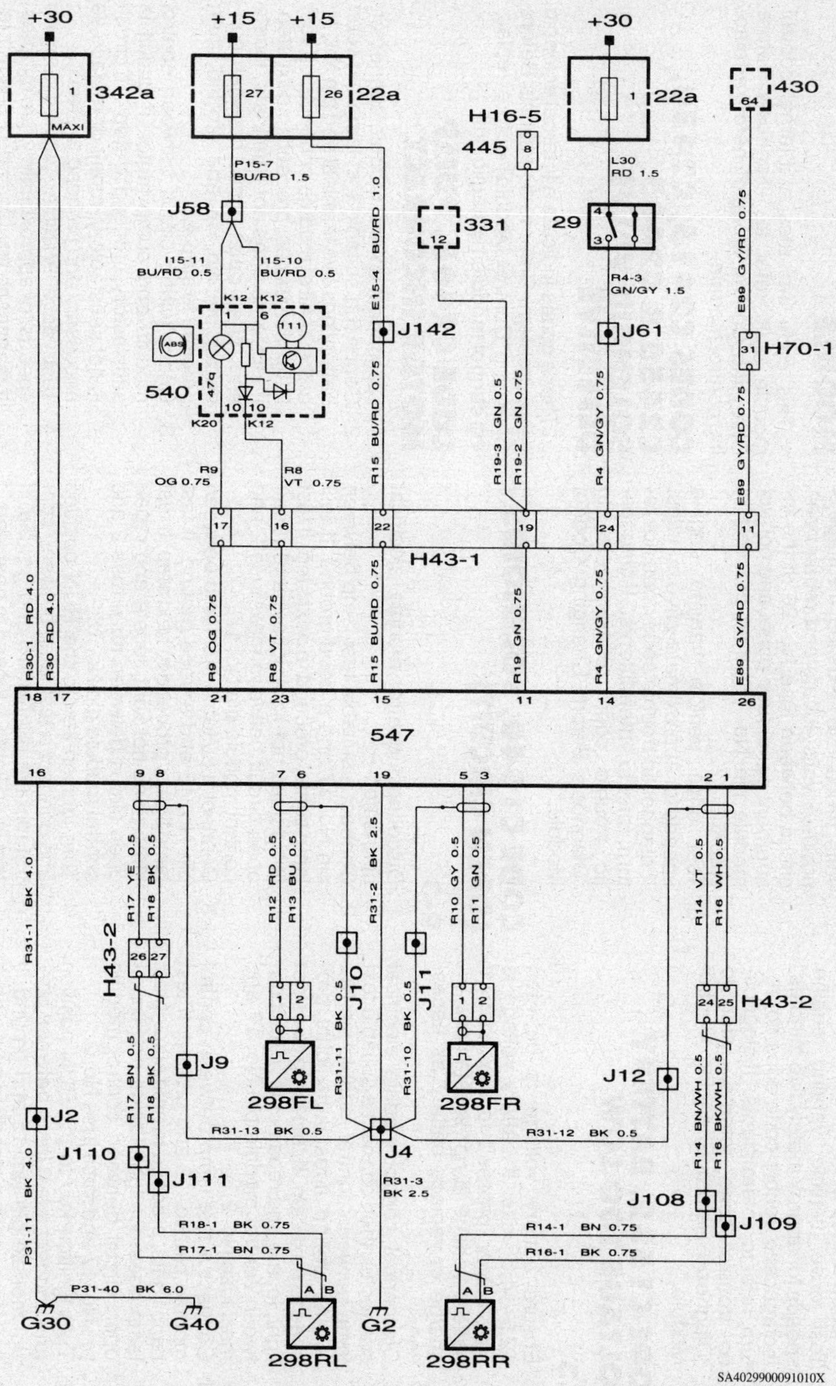

Fig. 5 ABS system wiring circuit (Part 1 of 2). 9-5

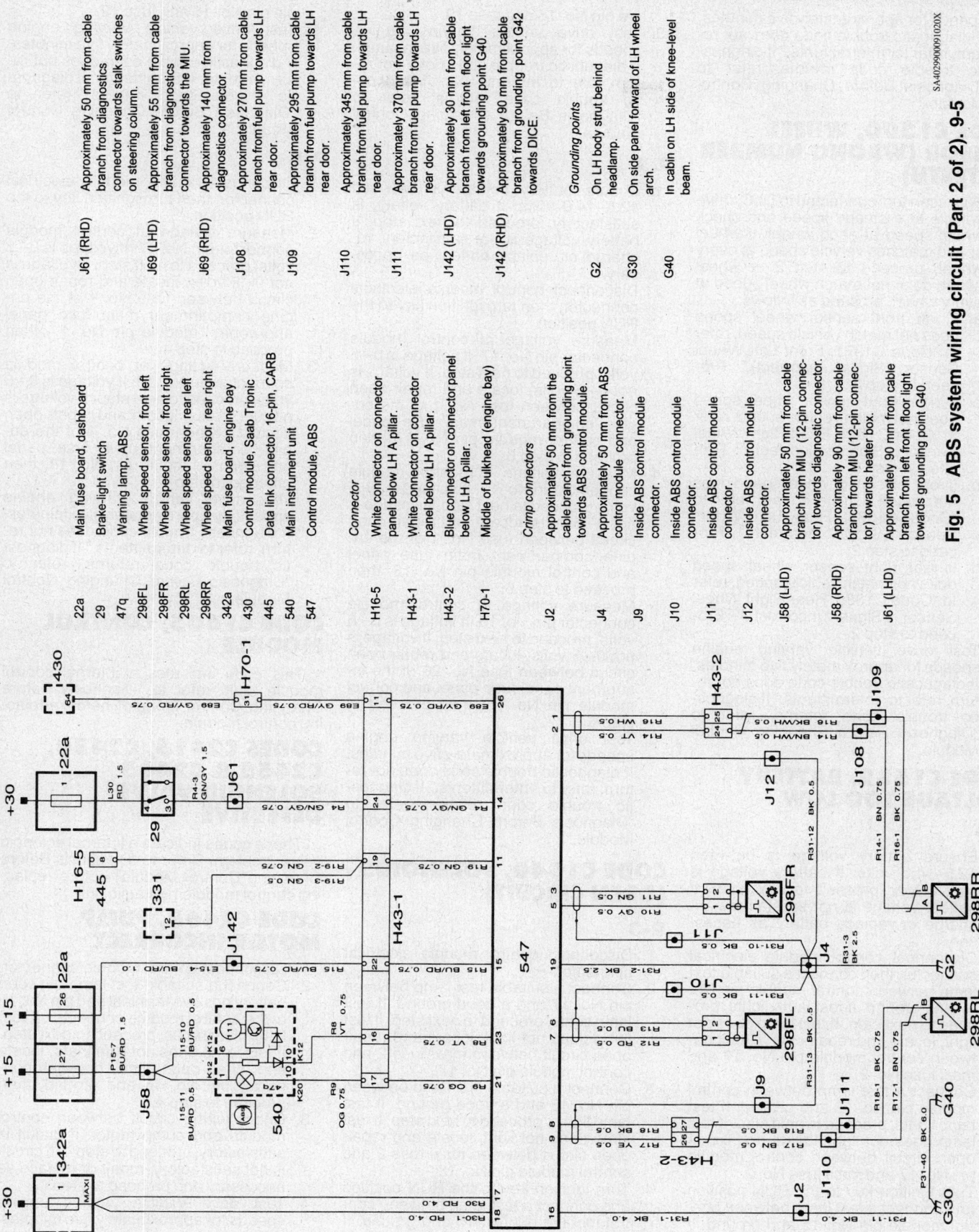

22a	Main fuse board, dashboard
29	Brake-light switch
47q	Warning lamp, ABS
298FL	Wheel speed sensor, front left
298FR	Wheel speed sensor, front right
298RL	Wheel speed sensor, rear left
298RR	Wheel speed sensor, rear right
342a	Main fuse board, engine bay
430	Control module, Saab Trionic
445	Data link connector, 16-pin, CARB
540	Main instrument unit
547	Control module, ABS

Connector

H16-5	White connector on connector panel below LH A pillar.
H43-1	White connector on connector panel below LH A pillar.
H43-2	Blue connector on connector panel below LH A pillar.
H70-1	Middle of bulkhead (engine bay)

Crimp connectors

J2	Approximately 50 mm from the cable branch from grounding point towards ABS control module.
J4	Approximately 50 mm from ABS control module connector.
J9	Inside ABS control module connector.
J10	Inside ABS control module connector.
J11	Inside ABS control module connector.
J12	Inside ABS control module connector.
J58 (LHD)	Approximately 50 mm from cable branch from MIU (12-pin connector) towards diagnostic connector.
J58 (RHD)	Approximately 90 mm from cable branch from MIU (12-pin connector) towards heater box.
J61 (LHD)	Approximately 90 mm from cable branch from left front floor light towards grounding point G40.
J61 (RHD)	Approximately 50 mm from cable branch from diagnostics connector towards stalk switches on steering column.
J69 (LHD)	Approximately 55 mm from cable branch from diagnostics connector towards the MIU.
J69 (RHD)	Approximately 140 mm from diagnostics connector.
J108	Approximately 270 mm from cable branch from fuel pump towards LH rear door.
J109	Approximately 295 mm from cable branch from fuel pump towards LH rear door.
J110	Approximately 345 mm from cable branch from fuel pump towards LH rear door.
J111	Approximately 370 mm from cable branch from fuel pump towards LH rear door.
J142 (LHD)	Approximately 30 mm from cable branch from left front floor light towards grounding point G40.
J142 (RHD)	Approximately 90 mm from cable branch from grounding point G42 towards DICE.

Grounding points

G2	On LH body strut behind headlamp.
G30	On side panel forward of LH wheel arch.
G40	In cabin on LH side of knee-level beam.

SA4029900091020X

Fig. 5 ABS system wiring circuit (Part 2 of 2). 9-5

speeds for approximately five minutes. If diagnostic trouble code does not return, refer to "Intermittents." If diagnostic trouble code returns, refer to "Diagnosis Before Changing Control Module."

CODE C1390, WHEEL SENSOR (WRONG NUMBER OF TEETH)

1. With scan tool connected to DLC, drive vehicle at a steady speed and check wheel speed at each wheel. If wheel speed matches vehicle speed at every wheel, proceed to step 2. If wheel speed does not match wheel speed at every wheel, proceed as follows:
   a. If left front sensor wheel speed does not match vehicle speed, refer to "Code C1371, Front Left Wheel Sensor (Signal Incorrect)." Proceed to step 2.
   b. If right front sensor wheel speed does not match vehicle speed, refer to "Code C1376, Front Right Wheel Sensor (Signal Incorrect)." Proceed to step 2.
   c. If rear left sensor wheel speed does not match vehicle speed, refer to "Code C1381, Rear Left Wheel Sensor (Signal Incorrect)." Proceed to step 2.
   d. If rear right sensor wheel speed does not match vehicle speed, refer to "Code C1386, Rear Right Wheel Sensor (Signal Incorrect)." Proceed to step 2.
2. Test drive vehicle varying engine speeds for approximately five minutes. If diagnostic trouble code does not return, refer to "Intermittents." If diagnostic trouble code returns, refer to "Diagnosis Before Changing Control Module."

CODE C1532, BATTERY VOLTAGE TOO LOW

9.3

1. Ensure battery voltage is between 12.5–14.0 volts. If battery voltage is satisfactory, proceed to next step. If battery voltage is not satisfactory, recharge or replace battery as necessary.
2. Disconnect control module electrical connector, then connect a suitable test lamp between control module pin No. 17 and ground. If test lamp lights, proceed to next step. If test lamp does not light, locate and repair open circuit between control module pin No. 17 and maxi fuse No. 2.
3. Connect a test lamp between control module pin No. 18 and ground. If test lamp lights, proceed to next step. If test lamp does not light, locate and repair open circuit between control module pin No. 17 and maxi fuse No. 2.
4. Turn ignition key to the RUN position and connect a test lamp between control module pin No. 15 and ground. If test lamp lights, proceed to next step. If test lamp does not light, locate and repair open circuit between control module pin No. 15 and fuse 19.
5. Test drive vehicle varying engine speeds for approximately five minutes. If diagnostic trouble code does not return, refer to "Intermittents." If diagnostic trouble code returns, refer to "Diagnosis Before Changing Control Module."

9.5

1. Ensure battery voltage is between 12.5–14.0 volts. If battery voltage is satisfactory, proceed to next step. If battery voltage is not satisfactory, recharge or replace battery as necessary.
2. Disconnect control module electrical connector, then turn ignition key to the RUN position.
3. Measure voltage at control module connector pin No. 17. If voltage is 0–.5 volts, proceed to next step. If voltage is not 0–.5 volts, locate and repair open circuit between fuse No. 1 of the engine compartment main fuse panel and control module pin No. 17, then proceed to step 6.
4. Measure voltage at control module connector pin No. 18. If voltage is 0–.5 volts, proceed to next step. If voltage is not 0–.5 volts, locate and repair open circuit between fuse No. 1 of the engine compartment main fuse panel and control module pin No. 18, then proceed to step 6.
5. Measure voltage at control module connector pin No. 15. If voltage is 0–.5 volts, proceed to next step. If voltage is not 0–.5 volts, locate and repair open circuit between fuse No. 26 of the instrument panel fuse panel and control module pin No. 15, then proceed to step 6.
6. Test drive vehicle varying engine speeds for approximately five minutes. If diagnostic trouble code does not return, refer to "Intermittents." If diagnostic trouble code returns, refer to "Diagnosis Before Changing Control Module."

CODE C1540, SOLENOIDS (OPEN CIRCUIT)

9-3

1. Disconnect control module electrical connector.
2. Connect a suitable test lamp between pin No. 17 and a good ground. If test lamp lights, proceed to next step. If test lamp does not light, locate and repair open circuit between maxi fuse 2 and control module pin No. 17.
3. Connect a suitable test lamp between pin No. 18 and a good ground. If test lamp lights, proceed to next step. If test lamp does not light, locate and repair open circuit between maxi fuse 2 and control module pin No. 18.
4. Turn ignition key to the RUN position and connect a test lamp between control module pin No. 15 and ground. If test lamp lights, proceed to next step. If test lamp does not light, locate and repair open circuit between control module pin No. 15 and fuse 19.
5. Test drive vehicle varying engine speeds for approximately five minutes. If diagnostic trouble code does not return, refer to "Intermittents." If diagnostic trouble code returns, refer to "Diagnosis Before Changing Control Module."

9-5

1. Disconnect control module electrical connector, then turn ignition key to the RUN position.
2. Measure voltage at control module connector pin No. 17. If voltage is 0–.5 volts, proceed to next step. If voltage is not 0–.5 volts, locate and repair open circuit between fuse No. 1 of the engine compartment main fuse panel and control module pin No. 17, then proceed to step 4.
3. Measure voltage at control module connector pin No. 18. If voltage is 0–.5 volts, proceed to next step. If voltage is not 0–.5 volts, locate and repair open circuit between fuse No. 1 of the engine compartment main fuse panel and control module pin No. 18, then proceed to step 4.
4. Test drive vehicle varying engine speeds for approximately five minutes. If diagnostic trouble code does not return, refer to "Intermittents." If diagnostic trouble code returns, refer to "Diagnosis Before Changing Control Module."

CODE C1605, CONTROL MODULE

This code indicates a internal control module fault, refer to "Diagnosis Before Changing Control Module" before replacing control module.

CODES C2415, C2450, C2455 & C2485 SOLENOID VALVE DEFECTIVE

These codes indicate a internal solenoid valve problem. Refer to "Diagnosis Before Changing Control Module" before replacing control module/hydraulic unit.

CODE C2465, PUMP MOTOR INCORRECT

1. Disconnect control module connector.
2. Connect a suitable test lamp between battery positive terminal and pin No. 16 of the control module connector. If test lamp illuminates, proceed to next step. If test lamp does not illuminate, locate and repair open circuit between connector pin No. 16 and ground, then proceed to step 4.
3. Check wiring circuit between control module and pump motor. If circuit is satisfactory, proceed to step 4. If circuit is not satisfactory, repair or replace as necessary and proceed to step 4.
4. Test drive vehicle varying engine speeds for approximately five minutes. If diagnostic trouble code does not return, refer to "Intermittents." If diagnostic trouble code returns, refer to

"Diagnosis Before Changing Control Module."

CODE C2470, BRAKE LIGHT SWITCH OPEN CIRCUIT

9-3

1. Check brake light operation.
2. If brake light operation is not satisfactory, replace brake light switch and proceed to next step. If brake light operation is satisfactory, locate and repair open circuit between control module pin No. 14 and brake light switch pin No. 4, then proceed to next step.
3. Test drive vehicle varying engine speeds for approximately five minutes. If diagnostic trouble code does not return, refer to "Intermittents." If diagnostic trouble code returns, refer to "Diagnosis Before Changing Control Module."

9-5

1. Check brake light operation.
2. If brake light operation is not satisfactory, replace brake light switch and proceed to next step. If brake light operation is satisfactory, locate and repair open circuit between control module pin No. 14 and brake light switch pin No. 3, then proceed to next step.
3. Test drive vehicle varying engine speeds for approximately five minutes. If diagnostic trouble code does not return, refer to "Intermittents." If diagnostic trouble code returns, refer to "Diagnosis Before Changing Control Module."

ABS WARNING LAMP NOT OPERATING

1. Disconnect control module electrical connector.
2. Connect a suitable jumper wire between connector terminal Nos. 19 and 21. If ABS warning lamp does not illuminate, proceed to next step. If ABS warning lamp illuminates, check control module connector for moisture, corrosion or misplaced pins. If connector is satisfactory, proceed to step 4.
3. Check wiring circuit between control module connector pin No. 21 and Main Instrument Unit (MIU) pin No. 10. If wiring is satisfactory, proceed to next step. If wiring is not satisfactory, repair or replace as necessary.
4. Before replacing control module, refer to "Diagnosis Before Changing Control Module."

ABS WARNING LAMP ON CONSTANTLY

1. Disconnect control module electrical connector.
2. Break ABS warning lamp contact strip on connector. If lamp goes out, proceed to next step. If lamp does not go out, proceed to step 4.
3. Visually check contact strip breaker pin to ensure it is working properly. If contact strip is working properly, proceed to next step. If contact strip is not working properly, replace it and proceed to next step.
4. Before replacing control module, refer to "Diagnosis Before Changing Control Module."

NO WHEEL SPEED SIGNAL

9-3

1. Disconnect control module electrical connector.
2. Check for continuity between control module pin No. 23 and Main Instrument Unit (MIU) pin No. 10. If continuity exists, proceed to next step. If continuity does not exist, locate and repair open circuit between control module and MIU.
3. Check for continuity between control module pin No. 26 and Trionic control module pin No. 39. If continuity exists, proceed to next step. If continuity does not exist, locate and repair open circuit between control module and Trionic control module.
4. Before replacing control module, refer to "Diagnosis Before Changing Control"

9-5

1. Disconnect control module electrical connector.
2. Check for continuity between control module pin No. 23 and Main Instrument Unit (MIU) pin No. 10. If continuity exists, proceed to next step. If continuity does not exist, locate and repair open circuit between control module and MIU.
3. Check for continuity between control module pin No. 26 and Trionic control module pin No. 63. If continuity exists, proceed to next step. If continuity does not exist, locate and repair open circuit between control module and Trionic control module.
4. Before replacing control module, refer to "Diagnosis Before Changing Control Module."

Diagnosis Before Changing Control Module

1. Check the following items before replacing the ABS control module/hydraulic unit:
   a. Ensure all system ground points and control module power supply circuits are clean and tight.
   b. Using a suitable scan tool, ensure all readings are plausible and all activated functions are working.
2. If problem persists replace control module/hydraulic unit. **Always replace control module/hydraulic unit as an assembly.**

Intermittents

Intermittent problems are usually caused by faulty electrical connections or wiring. Before replacing any components, visually check related wiring harnesses for improperly mated connector halves, damaged terminals or poor wire to terminal connections

Clearing Trouble Codes

Follow scan tool instructions to clear trouble codes from control module memory.

SYSTEM SERVICE

Brake System Bleed

1. Unscrew cover of brake fluid reservoir and top off with brake fluid.
2. Connect topping-off fitting from brake bleeding unit kit tool No. 88 19 096, or equivalent, to brake fluid reservoir.
3. Position hose with one end on topping-off fitting and other end in bottle filled with clean brake fluid.
4. Raise and support vehicle, then connect brake bleeder hose to front left wheel and open nipple. Draw off approximately 3 ounces of brake fluid. Repeat this at front right wheel.
5. Move brake bleeder to rear left wheel and open nipple. Draw off approximately 1.5 ounces of brake fluid. Repeat this at rear right wheel.
6. Lower vehicle, then check brake operation. Depress brake pedal and ensure it does not drop.
7. Remove topping-off fitting, hose and bottle.
8. Adjust brake fluid level.

Component Replacement

ABS CONTROL MODULE/ HYDRAULIC UNIT

1. Release engine compartment maxi-fuse panel retainer.
2. Disconnect anti-theft alarm electrical connector.
3. Cut and remove positive battery cable ties from maxi-fuse panel.
4. Remove maxi-fuse panel retaining nuts, then position panel aside.
5. Prevent brake fluid escaping from master cylinder by depressing brake pedal approximately two inches, then use a suitable clamp to hold pedal in position.
6. Disconnect control module electrical connector.
7. Remove brake hydraulic pipes from hydraulic unit.
8. Remove control module/hydraulic unit retaining nuts.
9. Lift control module/hydraulic unit from engine compartment.
10. Reverse procedure to install, noting the following:
    a. **Torque** retaining nuts to 15 ft. lbs.
    b. Bleed brake system as outlined under "Brake System Bleed."

FRONT WHEEL SENSOR

1. **On left front wheel sensor,** disconnect sensor electrical connector located on lefthand side of engine compartment.
2. **On right front wheel sensor,** disconnect sensor electrical connector located on righthand side of engine compartment.
3. **On all sensors,** raise and support vehicle.
4. Remove wheel, then clean around wheel sensor with soft steel brush.
5. Remove wheel sensor securing bolt, then the sensor from steering knuckle.
6. Remove grommet, then the sensor and sensor wiring harness.
7. Reverse procedure to install.

REAR WHEEL SENSOR

1. Raise and support vehicle, then remove wheel.
2. Force brake pistons back with suitable pliers, then depress brake pedal with brake clamp.
3. Remove two brake caliper securing bolts, then the brake hydraulic pipe from clip. Position caliper assembly aside and secure with a suitable tie.
4. Back off parking brake adjustment, the parking brake adjuster is accessible through a hole in brake disc.
5. Remove brake disc securing bolt, then the brake disc.
6. Disconnect speed sensor connector.
7. Remove four wheel hub retaining nuts, then the wheel hub and disc backing plate.
8. Reverse procedure to install.

Automatic Transaxles

TABLE OF CONTENTS

	Page No.
AISIN-WARNER 50-40LE AUTOMATIC TRANSAXLE	7-153
AISIN-WARNER 50-42LE AUTOMATIC TRANSAXLE	7-158
APPLICATION CHART	7-153
ZF 4-HP-18 AUTOMATIC TRANSAXLE	7-165

Application Chart

Year	Model	Transaxle
1998	900	Aisin-Warner 50-40 LE
	9000	ZF 4-HP-18
1999–2001	9-3	Aisin-Warner 50-40 LE (FA44)
	9-5	Aisin-Warner 50-42 LE (FA47)

Aisin-Warner 50-40LE Automatic Transaxle

INDEX

	Page No.
Adjustments	7-154
Kickdown Function..............	7-154
Shift-Lock Solenoid	7-154
Transaxle Range Switch	7-154
Description	7-153
Sport Switch....................	7-153
Winter Switch...................	7-153
In-Vehicle Repairs	7-154
Solenoid........................	7-155
Valve Housing	7-154
Maintenance	7-153
Fluid Change	7-154
Fluid Check....................	7-153
Precautions......................	7-153
Air Bag Systems................	7-153
Battery Ground Cable...........	7-153
Shift Lock System	7-156
Diagnosis & Testing............	7-156
Solenoid, Replace	7-156
Tightening Specifications	7-157
Transaxle, Replace	7-155

PRECAUTIONS

AIR BAG SYSTEMS

Refer to "Air Bag System Precautions" in the front of this manual for system disarming and arming procedures.

BATTERY GROUND CABLE

Prior to service, disconnect battery ground cable and isolate as required.

DESCRIPTION

The Aisin-Warner 50-40LE automatic transaxle is electronically-controlled with 4 speeds. The transaxle is controlled by a Transaxle Control Module (TCM), which is fed with digital and analog signals. The TCM uses this information to control the transaxle hydraulic system by means of electronic control signals.

These transaxles have many advantages compared to conventional hydraulically-controlled transaxles. These transaxles have better quality of gear shifting and softer gear shifting since torque is reduced during gear shifting. The driving program is designed to optimize fuel consumption. The driver can choose from NORMAL, SPORT OR WINTER driving programs for optimum performance. There is also reduced mechanical stresses on the entire transaxle and it has the ability of self-diagnosis and to store diagnostic codes.

SPORT SWITCH

A spring-loaded switch in the selector knob allows the driver to switch between NORMAL and SPORT gear shifting programs. NORMAL is always connected from the start. The SPORT program means the transaxle stays longer in each gear than normal and the gear shifting points are adapted for performance.

When the SPORT program is selected, the SPORT indicator lamp comes on in the main instrument.

WINTER SWITCH

A spring-loaded switch in the selector lever's console enables the driver to select the WINTER gear shifting program. This aids the vehicle when starting on slippery roads. When activated, the transaxle is automatically prevented from engaging in first and second gears. The vehicle is started in third gear.

MAINTENANCE

FLUID CHECK

1. Place vehicle on level surface and apply parking brake.
2. Transaxle fluid should be at operating temperature (176°F or 80°C). This is reached after driving about 12.4 miles.
3. Clean fluid dipstick with lint-free cloth, then reinsert.
4. Fluid level should read between MIN and MAX markings on side of oil dipstick marked °C.
5. If necessary, top off fluid with Dexron II type automatic transaxle fluid through pipe in dipstick. Distance between

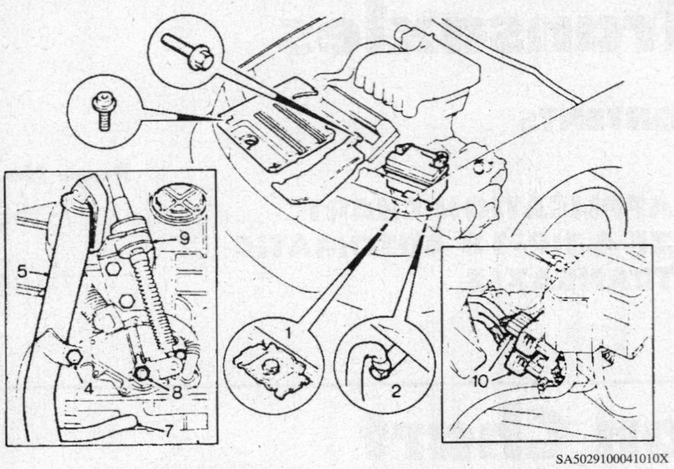

Fig. 1 Transaxle removal (Part 1 of 5)

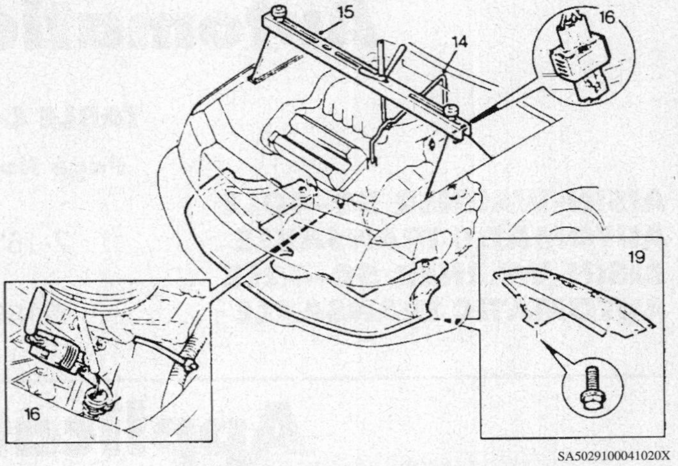

Fig. 1 Transaxle removal (Part 2 of 5)

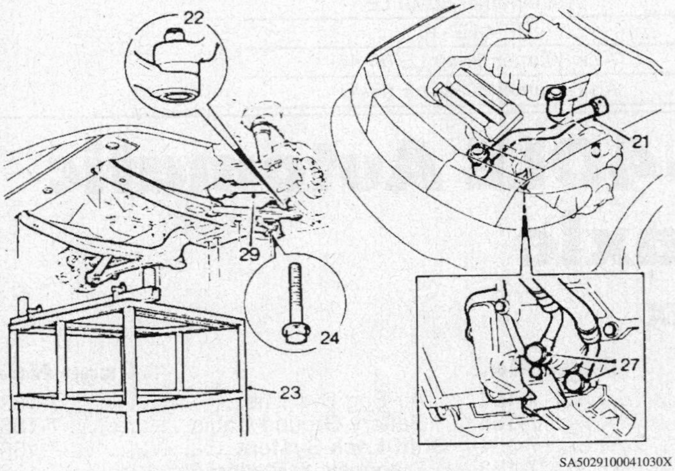

Fig. 1 Transaxle removal (Part 3 of 5)

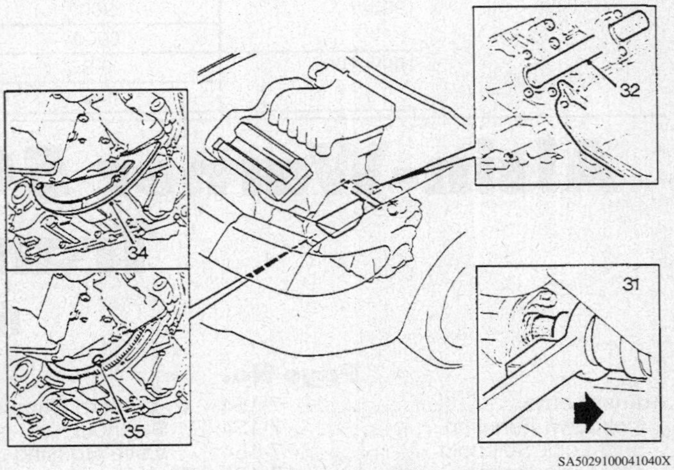

Fig. 1 Transaxle removal (Part 4 of 5)

markings corresponds to volume of about. 42 quarts.

6. When outdoor temperature is low (below 32°F), a temperature of 176°F (80°C) is never reached. Read fluid level on side of dipstick marked °C.

FLUID CHANGE

1. Raise and support vehicle.
2. Remove hose connector for oil cooler return from front of transaxle. Place a suitable drain pan under vehicle to collect oil.
3. When fluid has stopped draining, reinstall oil cooler return hose.
4. Add recommended fluid to transaxle pan through filler tube.
5. Refer to "Fluid Check," for final fluid level check.

ADJUSTMENTS

TRANSAXLE RANGE SWITCH

If arrow on transaxle lever does not correspond to marking on transaxle range switch, adjust the switch.

1. Remove dipstick from lever.
2. Loosen transaxle range switch screw.
3. Turn switch so marking corresponds to arrow on lever, then tighten screw to specifications.
4. Install dipstick to lever.

SHIFT-LOCK SOLENOID

1. Remove floor and center consoles.
2. Release wiring by cutting cable tie.
3. Loosen solenoid screws.
4. When hook is in bottom position, distance to pin should be 1–2 mm.
5. Tighten solenoid screws to specification, then install floor and center consoles.

KICKDOWN FUNCTION

1. **On models equipped with 2.3L engine,** remove resonator.
2. **On all models,** press down on accelerator pedal so it exactly reaches kickdown switch.
3. Ensure it is easy to press pedal to kickdown switch. If it is not, throttle cable may be improperly adjusted.
4. Ensure throttle is fully open. If not, continue this procedure to adjust throttle cable.
5. Release accelerator pedal and check for slack in throttle cable. If there is no slack, remove lower part of fascia and adjust with help of accelerator pedal setting screw on upper part of pedal.
6. Start vehicle and check idling speed.
7. Install lower part of fascia, then the resonator.

IN-VEHICLE REPAIRS

VALVE HOUSING

1. Remove transaxle venting hose.
2. Install suitable lift to engine, then raise and support vehicle.
3. Remove spoiler shields, then the engine mounting securing bolts.
4. Remove grounding cable and engine console securing bolts.
5. Place oil pan under transaxle, then remove cooling hoses. Plug hoses and turn to one side.
6. Remove transaxle temperature sensor to valve housing cover bolt.
7. Remove eight remaining bolts.
8. Remove valve housing cover and turn it to right of engine mounting. Use rubber mallet to knock out cover.
9. Remove nine valve housing securing

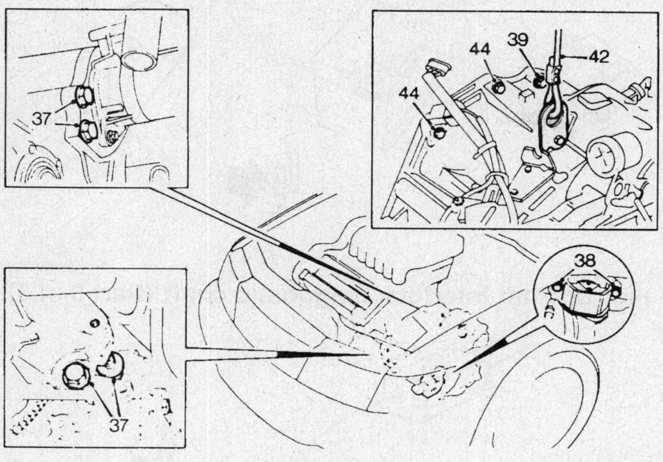

SA5029100041050X

Fig. 1 Transaxle removal (Part 5 of 5)

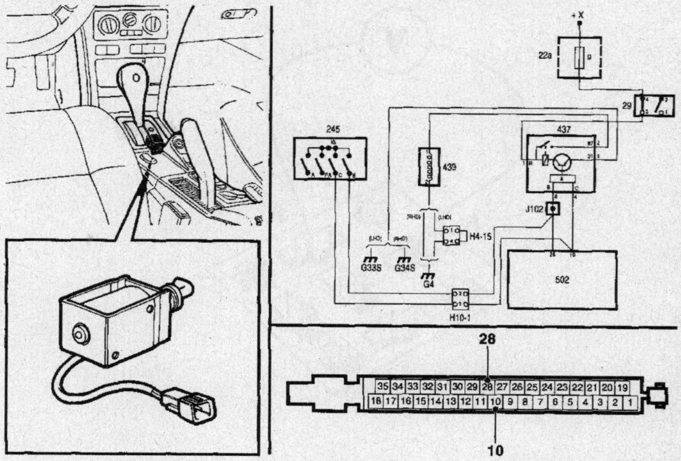

SA5029600070010X

Fig. 2 Shift interlock diagnostic chart (Part 1 of 6)

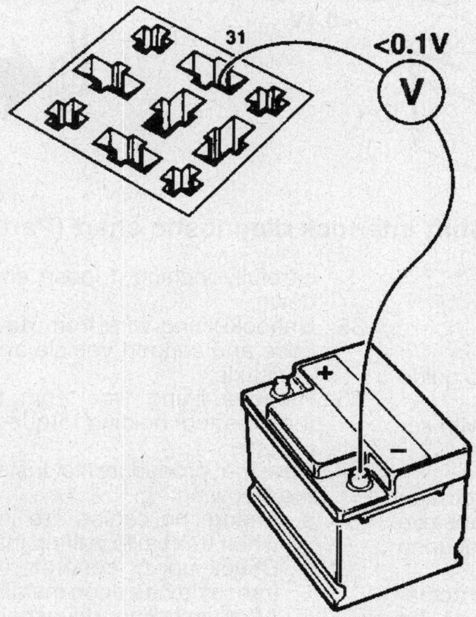

SA5029600070020X

Fig. 2 Shift interlock diagnostic chart (Part 2 of 6)

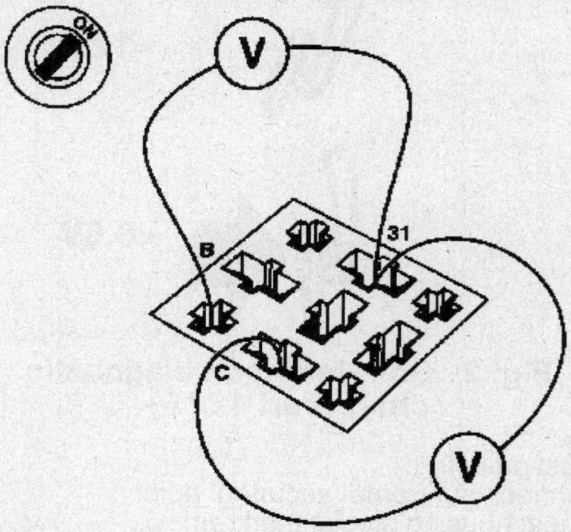

SA5029600070030X

Fig. 2 Shift interlock diagnostic chart (Part 3 of 6)

screws. **Start with two screws at bottom left holding cover for oil channels. Save two upper screws for last.**

10. Carefully remove selector lever manual valve from lifting eye.
11. Carefully remove valve housing. **Ensure two O-rings from inside valve housing do not fall out.**
12. Reverse procedure to install, noting the following:
    a. Clean any old sealant residue from contact surfaces of valve housing cover and transaxle. Place string of sealant on transaxle contact surface.
    b. Ensure all oil is removed from surface so sealant will adhere in thin and even layer. If transaxle has been removed, sealant can be applied to contact surface of cover.

SOLENOID

1. Remove valve housing cover as outlined under "Valve Housing."
2. Disconnect solenoid electrical connector.
3. Remove solenoid screw, then the solenoid with screwdriver.
4. Reverse procedure to install. Tighten solenoid screw to specifications.

TRANSAXLE

REPLACE

1. Remove battery negative cable secured to automatic transaxle valve housing. Negative cable securing bolt also secures valve housing.
2. **On models equipped with 2.3L engine,** remove cable securing point from dipstick.
3. **On all models,** remove dipstick securing screw (4), then pull dipstick and dipstick sleeve straight up (5), **Fig. 1.** Plug dipstick hole on transaxle.
4. Remove venting hose (7), then the selector lever arm (8) from transaxle.
5. Remove wire from transaxle securing point (9), then move wire to one side.
6. Disconnect transaxle electrical connectors (one gray and one black,10).
7. Disconnect straps holding cables on transaxle.
8. **On models equipped with 2.3L engine,** remove engine air filter housing.
9. **On all models,** remove engine lifting eye rubber bushings.
10. Install lifting beam tool No. 83 948 50, or equivalent (14).
11. Disconnect heated oxygen sensor connector (16).
12. Raise and support vehicle, then remove both front wheels.
13. Remove spoiler shields and middle spoiler shield in front right wheel housing secured by three screws (19).
14. **On models equipped with 2.3L engine,** remove heated oxygen sensor cable securing point from front end of engine.
15. **On all models,** remove front part of

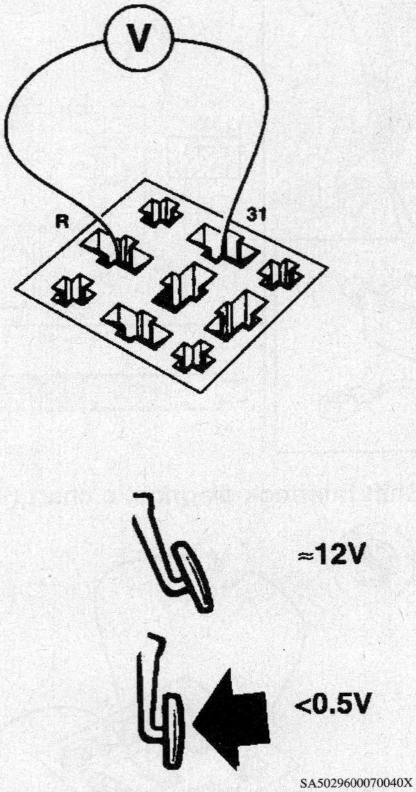

Fig. 2 **Shift interlock diagnostic chart (Part 4 of 6)**

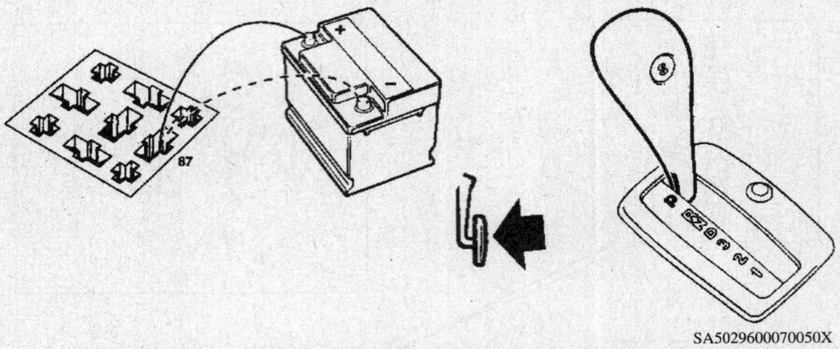

Fig. 2 **Shift interlock diagnostic chart (Part 5 of 6)**

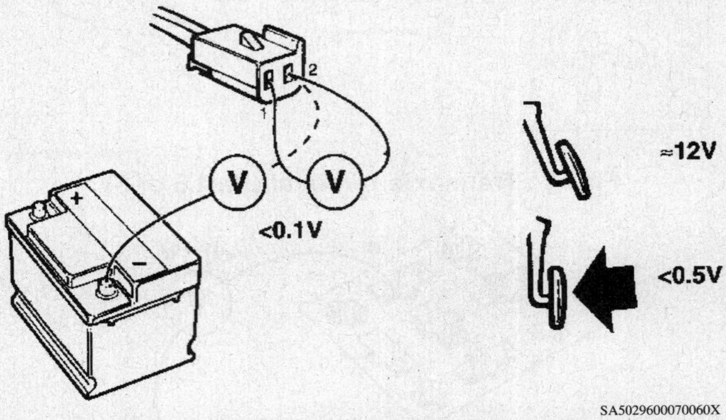

Fig. 2 **Shift interlock diagnostic chart (Part 6 of 6)**

exhaust pipe (21).

16. Disconnect subframe securing point for wheel housing pivots, then remove two subframe securing points on engine (22).
17. Install suitable lifting device under subframe (23), then remove six remaining subframe securing screws (24).
18. Lower lifting device about 2 cm, then release frame from pivots and remove.
19. Remove transaxle oil cooler inlet and outlet hoses (27). Plug inlet and outlet holes on transaxle. Plug hoses and turn upward.
20. Remove left driveshaft (29) from transaxle by releasing from splines and carefully pulling straight out from splines by hand. Plug driveshaft inlet hole on transaxle with plastic plug.
21. Secure driveshaft to vehicle body so it does not hang in way to be damaged when vehicle is lowered.
22. Separate right driveshaft from intermediate shaft securing point in engine, including spacers (31). **Right driveshaft is connected to intermediate with splines and is disconnected and secured to vehicle body the same way as the left driveshaft.**
23. Remove intermediate shaft securing point in engine (32) as follows:
    a. Release lower generator bolt, then remove three securing point screws.
    b. Turn generator upward and force out securing point to free two guide pins.
    c. Pull out intermediate shaft with securing point.
24. Plug inlet hole with plastic plug.
25. Remove two screws, then the actuator cover between engine and transaxle (34) to free torque converter securing point on actuator.
26. Remove six torque converter to actuator screws (35). **Engine must be turned to reach all screws.**
27. Install special tool to hold torque converter in place while removing transaxle. Using torque converter fixing tool No. 87 92 277, or equivalent.
28. Remove lower transaxle to engine securing bolts (37).
29. Remove front engine mounting bolts (38), then the rear bolt from three upper securing bolts (39).
30. Lower vehicle.
31. Lower engine and transaxle with lifting beam to create gap of about 10 cm between vehicle body and transaxle front mounting. Gap can be seen from front lefthand wheel housing.
32. Install lifting wire tool No. 87 92 251, or equivalent, to transaxle rear securing holes (42), then the wire to lifting device.
33. Tighten with lifting device, then remove remaining two upper securing bolts (44).
34. Remove transaxle from engine by carefully inching it loose and lifting it down.
35. Unhook lifting wire from device, then raise and support vehicle and pull out transaxle.
36. Remove lifting wire from transaxle, then the tool holding torque converter in place.
37. Reverse procedure to install, noting the following:
    a. Ensure no cables are in the way when transaxle is lifted into vehicle.
    b. Check upper generator bolt after transaxle has been installed.
    c. After installing driveshaft, ensure spline connections has "clicked in" by pulling at wheel housing.
    d. Ensure oxygen sensor cable is pulled behind lower water pipe so cable cannot move forward onto exhaust pipe.

SHIFT LOCK SYSTEM

DIAGNOSIS & TESTING

When performing diagnosis and testing of shift lock system, refer to **Fig. 2.**

SOLENOID, REPLACE

1. Remove floor center console.
2. Remove shift lock solenoid, **Fig. 3.**
3. Reverse procedure to install noting the following:
    a. Measure distance between hook and pin when hook is in bottom position. Distance should be 1–2 mm.
    b. Install solenoid and consoles.

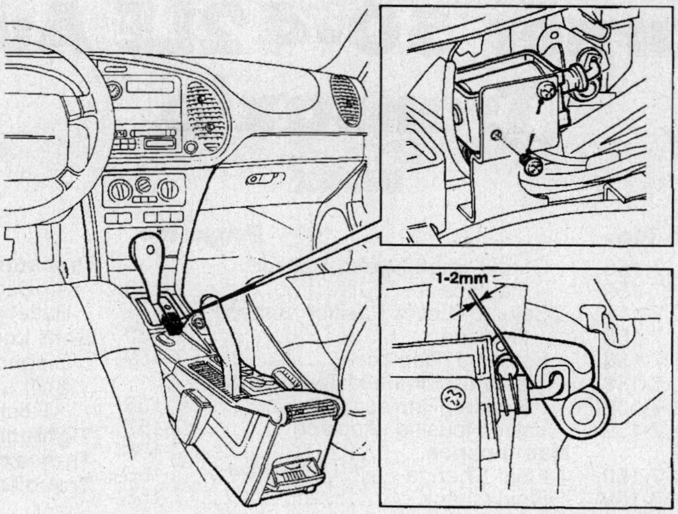

SA5029600071000X

Fig. 3 Shift interlock solenoid replacement

TIGHTENING SPECIFICATIONS

Year	Component	Torque, Ft. Lbs.
1998–2001	Input Shaft To Speed Sensor Screw	60①
	Output Speed Shaft Sensor	60①
	Solenoid Screw	60①
	Torque Converter Cover To Actuator Screws	60①
	Torque Converter To Actuator Screws	37
	Transaxle Fluid Temperature Sensor Cover Screw	19
	Transaxle Fluid Temperature Sensor Screw	19
	Transaxle Range Switch	19
	Transaxle To Oil Cooler Hose	16
	Transaxle Upper Securing Bolts	55
	Valve Housing Cover Screws	19
	Valve Housing Screws	60①

① — Inch lbs.

Aisin-Warner 50-42LE Automatic Transaxle

INDEX

	Page No.
Adjustments	7-158
Selector Lever Cable	7-159
Selector Lever Position Sensor	7-158
Description	7-158
Sport Switch	7-158
Winter Switch	7-158
Identification	7-158
In-Vehicle Repairs	7-159
Input Shaft Speed Sensor, Replace	7-160
Left Driveshaft Seal, Replace	7-159
Output Shaft Speed Sensor, Replace	7-160
Selector Lever Position Sensor, Replace	7-160
Solenoid, Replace	7-159
Transmission Fluid Temperature Sensor, Replace	7-160
Valve Housing, Replace	7-159
Maintenance	7-158
Fluid Change	7-158
Fluid Check	7-158
Precautions	7-158
Air Bag Systems	7-158
Battery Ground Cable	7-158
Shift Lock System	7-161
Diagnosis & Testing	7-161
Shift Lock Electromagnet, Replace	7-161
Tightening Specifications	7-164
Transaxle, Replace	7-160
Troubleshooting	7-158

PRECAUTIONS

AIR BAG SYSTEMS

Refer to "Air Bag System Precautions" in the front of this manual for system disarming and arming procedures.

BATTERY GROUND CABLE

Prior to service, disconnect battery ground cable and isolate as required.

IDENTIFICATION

Refer to **Fig. 1** for transaxle identification.

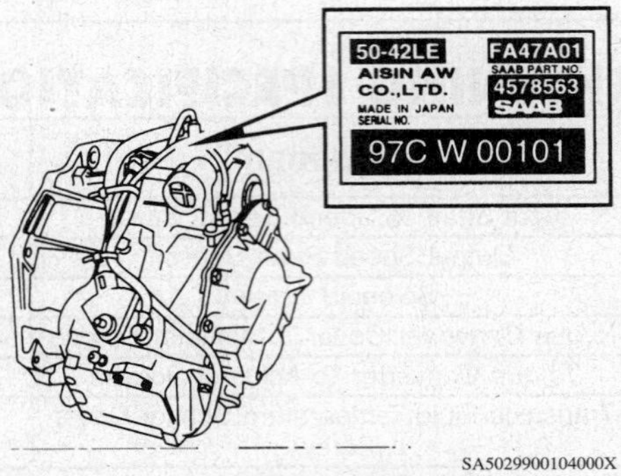

Fig. 1 Transaxle Identification plate

DESCRIPTION

The Aisin-Warner 50-42LE is an electronically-controlled 4-speed automatic transaxle with a lock-up function. The transaxle is controlled by a Transaxle Control Module (TCM), which continuously processes information from its own sensors and from other control modules. The TCM uses this information to control the transaxle hydraulic system.

SPORT SWITCH

A spring-loaded switch in the selector knob allows the driver to switch between NORMAL and SPORT gear shifting programs. NORMAL is always connected from the start. The SPORT program means the transaxle stays longer in each gear than normal and the gear shifting points are adapted for performance.

When the SPORT program is selected, the SPORT indicator lamp comes on in the main instrument.

WINTER SWITCH

A spring-loaded switch in the selector lever's console enables the driver to select the WINTER gear shifting program. This aids the vehicle when starting on slippery roads. When activated, the transaxle is automatically prevented from engaging in first and second gears. The vehicle is started in third gear.

TROUBLESHOOTING

Refer to **Fig. 2** for transaxle troubleshooting chart.

MAINTENANCE

FLUID CHECK

1. Place vehicle on level surface and apply parking brake.
2. Transaxle fluid should be at operating temperature (176°F or 80°C). This temperature should be reached after driving approximately 12 miles.
3. With engine at idle speed, apply brake pedal and shift transaxle to D position and hold for 15 seconds, then shift transaxle to R position and hold for another 15 seconds, repeat in P position.
4. Clean fluid dipstick with a lint-free cloth, then reinsert.
5. Fluid level should read between MIN and MAX markings on side of oil dipstick marked +80°C.
6. If necessary, add Dexron type III automatic transaxle fluid through pipe in dipstick. Distance between markings corresponds to volume of about .42 quarts.

FLUID CHANGE

1. Raise and support vehicle.
2. Remove hose connector for oil cooler return from front of transaxle. Place a suitable drain pan under vehicle to collect oil.
3. When fluid has stopped draining, reinstall oil cooler return hose.
4. Add recommended fluid to transaxle pan through filler tube.
5. Refer to "Fluid Check," for final fluid level check.

ADJUSTMENTS

SELECTOR LEVER POSITION SENSOR

1. Remove battery cover, battery and battery tray.
2. Move selector lever to position No. 1, then loosen selector lever retaining nut.
3. Move selector lever to the N position, then remove selector lever cable retaining nut and the lever cable from position sensor.
4. Install sensor alignment tool No. 87 92 467, or equivalent, onto position sensor, then check if line on position sensor is visible in center of alignment tool notch, **Fig. 3.**
5. If position sensor line is visible, proceed to step 6. If position sensor line is not visible, proceed as follows:
   a. Clean area around fluid filler pipe where it enters transaxle, then remove fluid filler pipe retaining nut and filler pipe from transaxle.
   b. Loosen position sensor attaching bolts.
   c. Turn sensor until line is visible in center of alignment tool notch, **Fig. 3.**
   d. Tighten sensor bolts to specification.

Fault	Possible causes	Diagnostic procedure
Engine cannot be started.	Selector lever not in position P or N. Selector lever position sensor out of adjustment.	Adjust the selector lever position sensor.
Car cannot be driven in selector lever positions D, 3, 2, 1 or else slippage or jerkiness occurs.	The transmission fluid level is too low. The filter strainer beside the oil pump inlet is choked. The oil pump is blocked. Loss of fluid in clutch C1 or in the fluid system. Loss of fluid in brake band B4's fluid system. Free-wheel F2 defective. Free-wheel F3 defective. Loss of fluid in brake B3 or in the fluid system. Valve housing defective. The torque converter is blocked.	Correct the transmission fluid level. Change the transmission.
Car cannot be driven in selector lever position R.	The transmission fluid level is too low. The filter strainer beside the oil pump inlet is choked. The oil pump is blocked. The 1-2/3-4 shift solenoid (S1) or shifting valve in the valve housing is blocked. Loss of fluid in clutch C2 or the fluid system. Loss of fluid in brake B3 or in the fluid system. Loss of fluid in brake band B4's fluid system. Loss of fluid in clutch C3 or the fluid system. The torque converter is blocked. The valve housing is defective.	Correct the transmission fluid level. Change the transmission.
No 1-2 upshifting.	Selector lever in position 1. Selector lever position sensor out of adjustment. The 1-2/3-4 shift solenoid (S1) or shifting valve in the valve housing is blocked. Loss of fluid in brake B1 or in the fluid system. Loss of fluid in brake B2 or in the fluid system. Free-wheel F1 defective. Valve housing defective.	Adjust the selector lever position sensor. Change the shift solenoid (S1). Change the transmission.
No 2-3 upshifting.	Loss of fluid in clutch C3 or the fluid system. The 2-3 shift solenoid (S2) or shifting valve in the valve housing is blocked.	Change the shift solenoid (S2). Change the transmission.
No 3-4 upshifting in selector lever position D.	Loss of fluid in clutch C3 or the fluid system. The 1-2/3-4 shift solenoid (S1) or shifting valve in the valve housing is blocked. Transmission fluid temperature sensor defective.	Change the shift solenoid (S1). Change the transmission fluid temperature sensor. Change the transmission.
No 4-3 downshifting on kickdown.	Kickdown function defective. Loss of fluid in clutch C2 or the fluid system. The 1-2/3-4 shift solenoid (S1) or shifting valve in the valve housing is blocked. Free-wheel F1 defective. Throttle cable out of adjustment.	Check the throttle cable setting. Change the shift solenoid (S1). Change the transmission. Adjust the throttle cable.
No 3-2 downshifting on kickdown.	Kickdown function defective. The 2-3 shift solenoid (S2) or shifting valve in the valve housing is blocked. Loss of fluid in brake B4. Free-wheel F3 defective. Throttle cable out of adjustment.	Check the throttle cable setting. Change the shift solenoid (S2). Change the transmission. Adjust the throttle cable.
No 2-1 downshifting on kickdown.	Kickdown function defective. The 1-2/3-4 shift solenoid (S1) or shifting valve in the valve housing is blocked. Free-wheel F2 defective. Throttle cable out of adjustment.	Check the throttle cable setting. Change the shift solenoid (S1). Change the transmission. Adjust the throttle cable.
Engine braking in selector lever position 1 ineffective.	Loss of fluid in brake B3 or the shifting valve. The 1-2/3-4 shift solenoid (S1) or shifting valve in the valve housing is blocked.	Change the shift solenoid (S1). Change the transmission.

SA5029900100010X

Fig. 2 Transaxle troubleshooting chart (Part 1 of 2)

Engine braking in selector lever position 2 ineffective.	Loss of fluid in brake band B4's fluid system. Loss of fluid in brake B1 or the shifting valve. The 2-3 shift solenoid (S2) or shifting valve in the valve housing is blocked.	Change the shift solenoid (S2). Change the transmission.
Engine braking in selector lever position 3 ineffective.	Loss of fluid in brake B1 or in the fluid system. Loss of fluid in clutch C3 or the fluid system. The 1-2/3-4 shift solenoid (S1) or shifting valve in the valve housing is blocked.	Change the shift solenoid (S1). Change the transmission.
Rough N-D shifting.	Valve housing defective. Clutch C1's pressure chamber defective. Loss of fluid in clutch C1 or the fluid system. Loss of fluid in brake band B4's fluid system. Free-wheel F2 defective. Free-wheel F3 defective.	Change the transmission.
Rough N-R shifting.	Valve housing defective. Clutch C2's pressure chamber defective. Loss of fluid in clutch C2 or the fluid system. Loss of fluid in brake B3 or in the fluid system. Loss of fluid in brake band B4's fluid system.	Change the transmission.
Rough shifting in all gears.	Valve housing defective. Pressure chamber defective. Loss of fluid in clutches or brakes or the fluid system.	Change the transmission.
Torque converter clutch does not engage.	Solenoid valve for the torque converter clutch defective. Valve housing defective. Torque converter defective.	Change the LOCK-UP solenoid valve (SL). Change the transmission.

SA5029900100020X

Fig. 2 Transaxle troubleshooting chart (Part 2 of 2)

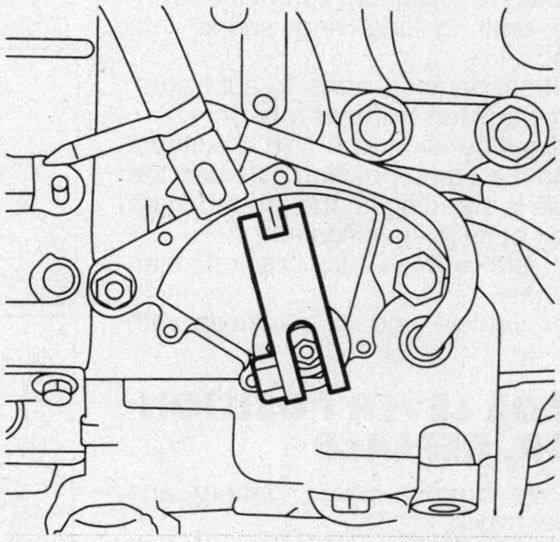

SA5029900094000X

Fig. 3 Selector lever position sensor alignment

e. Lubricate fluid filler pipe O-ring with petroleum jelly and install into transaxle.
6. Remove alignment tool and install selector lever cable.
7. Move selector lever to the P position, then install lever cable retaining nut and tighten to specification.
8. Install battery tray, battery and battery cover.
9. Ensure engine starts in Park or Neutral and does not start in any other shifter position.

SELECTOR LEVER CABLE

Check shifter play in Neutral and D positions. If shifter play is the same in N or D, shifter lever does not need adjustment. If shifter play is different in N or D, use the following procedure to adjust lever cable.

1. Move shifter to the Neutral position.
2. Lift up cable adjusting yoke, using two angle screwdrivers, **Fig. 4.**
3. Move shifter to the Park position, then the selector lever on transaxle to Park position.
4. Roll the vehicle until P interlock locks.
5. Press adjusting yoke down until it secures cable.
6. Check shifter play in N and D positions.

IN-VEHICLE REPAIRS

VALVE HOUSING, REPLACE

1. Remove torque arm from subframe, then raise and support vehicle.
2. Remove ground cable and torque arm with bracket.
3. Place a suitable drain pan under transaxle, then remove oil cooler lines from transaxle.
4. Remove temperature sensor cover attaching bolt, then the sensor cover.
5. Remove valve housing cover attaching bolts.
6. Knock valve housing cover loose with a suitable rubber mallet, then remove cover.
7. Disconnect solenoid electrical connectors. **Valve housing bolts are three different lengths, mark bolts for installation reference.**
8. Remove manual valve from selector lever and out of retaining eye.
9. Carefully remove valve housing from transaxle.
10. Reverse procedure to install.

SOLENOID, REPLACE

1. Remove valve housing cover as outlined under "Valve Housing."
2. Disconnect solenoid electrical connector.
3. Remove solenoid screw, then the solenoid with screwdriver. **Do not remove solenoid ST which controls system pressure.**
4. Reverse procedure to install.

LEFT DRIVESHAFT SEAL, REPLACE

Removal

1. Raise and support vehicle, then remove left front wheel.
2. Remove brake hose retaining clip from bottom of strut.
3. Remove suspension arm to subframe attaching bolts, then lower suspension arms from subframe.
4. Remove left driveshaft from transaxle, using puller tool No. 87 92 616, or equivalent.
5. Remove seal, using puller tool No. 87 92 350, or equivalent.

Installation

1. Tap new seal into place with seal installation tool No. 83 90 122, or equivalent.
2. Fit protective collar tool No. 83 95 162, or equivalent, into sealing ring.

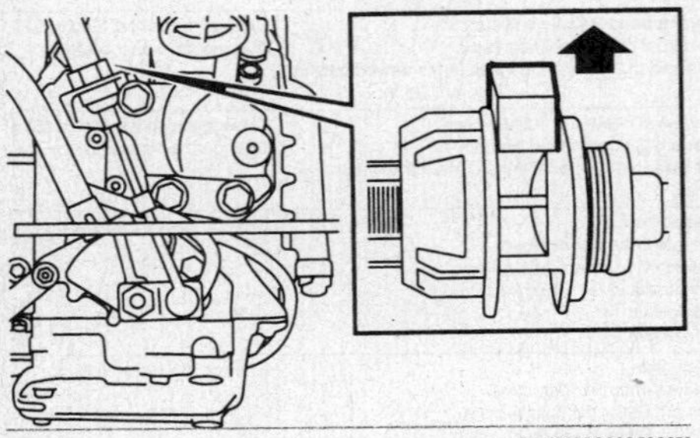

SA5029900095000X

Fig. 4 Selector lever cable adjustment

3. Slide driveshaft into transaxle until all but two inches of the shaft is in the transaxle, then remove sealing ring protective collar.
4. Continue to install driveshaft into transaxle until locking ring snaps into place.
5. Install suspension arms to subframe. **Do not tighten bolts at this time.**
6. Raise suspension arm with a suitable jack to the same position as when the vehicle is standing on the ground, then tighten bolts to specification.
7. Install brake hose into bracket, then the wheel.
8. Lower vehicle and fill transaxle with fluid.

SELECTOR LEVER POSITION SENSOR, REPLACE

1. Remove battery cover, battery and battery tray.
2. Move selector lever to position No. 1, then remove selector lever retaining nut and lever cable from position sensor.
3. Remove position sensor attaching bolts and nut.
4. Disconnect position sensor electrical connector, then remove position sensor.
5. Reverse procedure to install. Check position sensor adjustment as outlined under "Adjustments."

INPUT SHAFT SPEED SENSOR, REPLACE

1. Remove battery cover, battery and battery tray.
2. Remove input shaft speed sensor retaining bolt, **Fig. 5.**
3. Raise and support vehicle, then remove left front wheel.
4. Remove sensor from transaxle and disconnect electrical connector.
5. Reverse procedure to install.

OUTPUT SHAFT SPEED SENSOR, REPLACE

1. Lift up engine compartment main fuse panel and position aside.
2. Remove sensor retaining bolt and the sensor, **Fig. 6.**
3. Disconnect sensor electrical connector.
4. Reverse procedure to install.

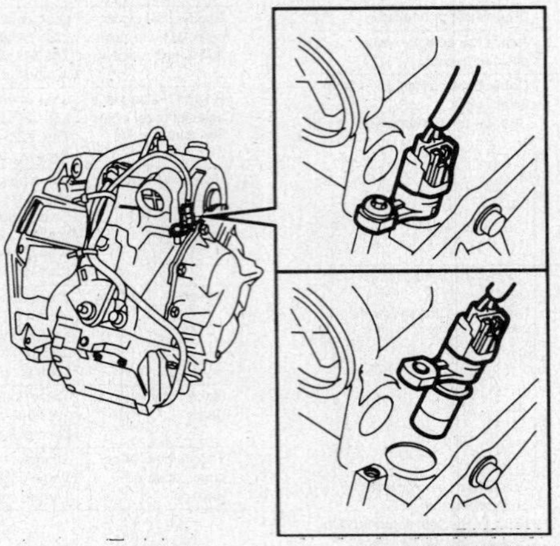

SA5029900096000X

Fig. 5 Input shaft speed sensor replacement

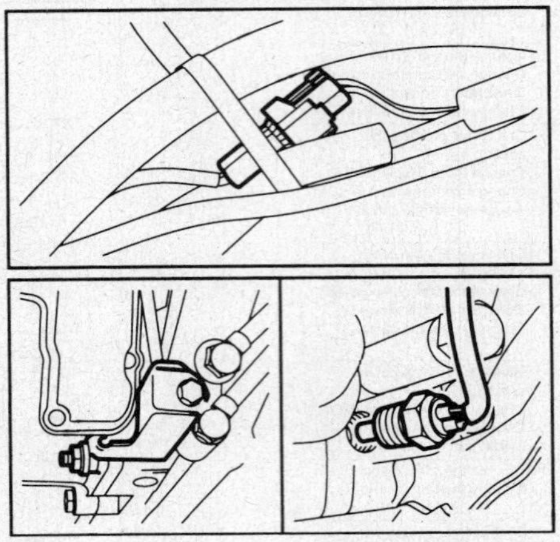

SA5029900098000X

Fig. 7 Transmission fluid temperature sensor replacement

TRANSMISSION FLUID TEMPERATURE SENSOR, REPLACE

1. Remove battery cover, battery and battery tray.
2. Disconnect fluid temperature sensor electrical connector, **Fig. 7.**
3. Raise and support vehicle.
4. Remove two fluid temperature sensor cover attaching bolts, then the cover.
5. Place a suitable oil drain pan under transaxle.
6. Remove sensor from transaxle.
7. Reverse procedure to install. Fill transaxle fluid.

TRANSAXLE

REPLACE

1. Remove front grille and intake manifold cover.
2. Remove battery cover, battery and battery tray.
3. Disconnect 10-pin and 16-pin electrical connectors from transaxle.
4. Remove breather hose from transaxle.
5. Position shift lever in the Neutral position, then disconnect shift lever arm from shift position sensor.

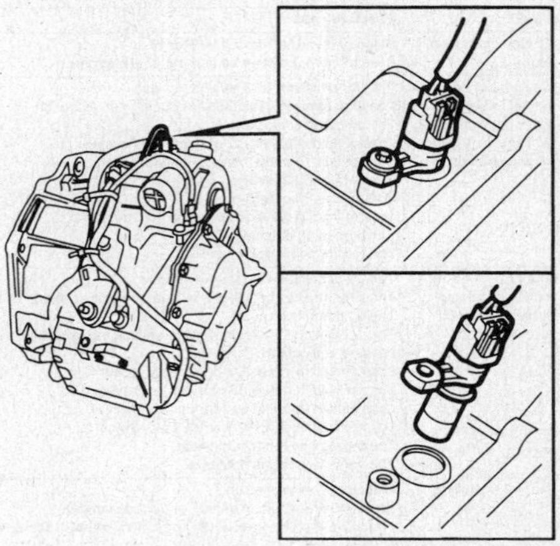

SA5029900097000X

Fig. 6 Output shaft speed sensor replacement

6. Remove shift lever cable clamp and press out cable, using a suitable screwdriver.
7. Remove battery positive cable's clamp.
8. Remove three upper transaxle to engine attaching bolts.
9. Remove transaxle dipstick tube. Plug opening to prevent contamination.
10. Disconnect oxygen sensor electrical connector.
11. Remove rear engine mount nut, then loosen three engine mount retaining bolts. Leave bolts in place.
12. Support engine with lifting device tool No. 83 93 850, or equivalent.
13. Remove torque arm from subframe.
14. Raise and support vehicle, then remove front wheels.
15. Remove engine lower cover.
16. Remove front exhaust pipe, then the rear engine mount and mount cushion.
17. Remove steering gear attaching bolts, then the two clamps holding power steering fluid delivery pipes to subframe, **Fig. 8.**
18. Remove A/C pipes from clips on subframe, then the air cleaner casing from subframe.
19. Remove oil cooler from charge air cooler.
20. Place holding strap tool No. 83 95 212, or equivalent, around radiator core and radiator crossmember.
21. Remove ball joint to steering knuckle retaining bolts from both sides.
22. Remove anti-roll bar upper ball joints.
23. Remove rear engine support plate.
24. Position a suitable lifting table under subframe.
25. Remove remaining subframe attaching bolts.
26. Lower subframe approximately two inches, then remove two power steering fluid delivery pipe clamps from subframe.
27. Lower subframe onto lifting table and remove from vehicle.
28. Remove two driveplate cover attaching bolts and the cover.
29. Remove six torque converter to driveplate attaching bolts.
30. Install torque converter holding tool

No. 87 92 574, or equivalent, to hold torque converter in place during transaxle removal.
31. Remove ground cable from side of transaxle.
32. Remove torque arm with bracket.
33. Place a suitable drain pan under transaxle, then remove drain plug and drain transaxle fluid.
34. Disconnect oil cooler inlet and outlet hoses. Plug openings to prevent contamination.
35. Remove lefthand driveshaft with prying tool No. 87 92 616, or equivalent. Suspend shaft with a suitable cable tie.
36. Lower vehicle.
37. Mark position of left engine mount, then remove mount
38. Lower engine and transaxle assembly approximately four inches until transaxle clears structural member.
39. Remove transaxle bracket from transaxle.
40. Raise and support vehicle.
41. Connect transaxle lifting tool No. MKM-886, or equivalent, and suitable transmission jack to transaxle.
42. Remove remaining transaxle to engine attaching bolts.
43. Lower transaxle from vehicle.
44. Reverse procedure to install.

SHIFT LOCK SYSTEM

DIAGNOSIS & TESTING

1. Check brake light operation. If brake light is working properly, proceed to step 2. If brake light is not working properly, check the following:
   a. Brake light fuse in instrument panel fuse panel, replace as necessary.
   b. Brake light switch, replace as necessary.
   c. Brake light switch wiring circuit, repair or replace as necessary, **Fig. 9.**
2. Disconnect H6-4 connector located next to selector lever.
3. Connect a suitable test lamp between pin No. 5 of the female side of the connector and ground. then depress brake pedal. If test lamp illuminates, proceed to next step. If test lamp does not illuminate, locate and repair open circuit between pin No. 5 and brake light switch.
4. Connect a suitable test lamp between pin No. 6 of the female side of the connector and battery positive. If test lamp illuminates, replace shift lock electromagnet. If test lamp does not illuminate, locate and repair open circuit between pin No. 6 and ground.

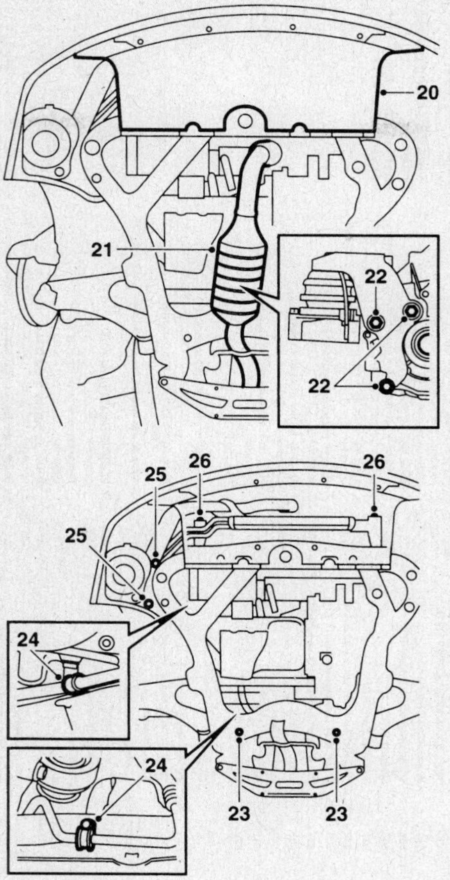

20. Engine Undercover
21. Exhaust System
22. Rear Engine Mount Bolts
23. Steering Gear Bolts
24. A/C & Power Steering Pipe Clamps
25. Air Cleaner Casing
26. Oil Cooler

SA5029900099000X

Fig. 8 Subframe removal

SHIFT LOCK ELECTROMAGNET, REPLACE

1. Remove shift lever surround panel.
2. Disconnect central locking switch electrical connector.
3. Disconnect electrical connectors at seat heater switches and lighter.
4. Remove rear portion of console by lifting straight up, then disconnect all related electrical connectors.
5. Apply parking brake, place transaxle in Park, then remove ignition key.
6. Remove theft deterrent cover from ignition lock, then disconnect electrical connector.
7. Place key in ignition and transaxle in Neutral.
8. Disconnect power window switch electrical connectors.
9. Remove console upper portion retaining screws, then the console upper portion.
10. Fold back carpeting and remove two front console to floor retaining screws. These are located on sides of console.
11. Remove two rear console to floor retaining screws.
12. Carefully lift console out of vehicle.
13. Remove shift lever circlip, **Fig. 10.**
14. Drive selector lever pin while removing end of cable from ball.
15. Remove selector lever attaching bolts, then disconnect selector lever electrical connector.
16. Lift selector lever housing upward and disconnect ignition switch electrical connector.
17. Remove clamp from locking catches.
18. Carefully press locking catches toward each other and remove lever cable from bracket.
19. Remove selector lever housing from vehicle.
20. Place selector lever in Neutral or D.
21. Remove screw from front part of selector lever casing, then the casing from selector lever.
22. Press sport button upward and unsolder sport button electrical connection.
23. Remove clip and pull up detent button together with rear part of selector lever casing.
24. Cut cable tie holding wiring harness for console lighting in place, **Fig. 11.**
25. Cut cable ties holding selector lever wiring harness in place.
26. Pull shift-lock electromagnet pins from selector lever connector pin Nos. 5 and 6.
27. Drill out cover rivets with a three millimeter drill bit.
28. Separate upper and lower parts of selector lever housing.
29. Remove screws near electromagnet, then the cover from top of electromagnet.
30. Remove electromagnet from vehicle.
31. Reverse procedure to install.

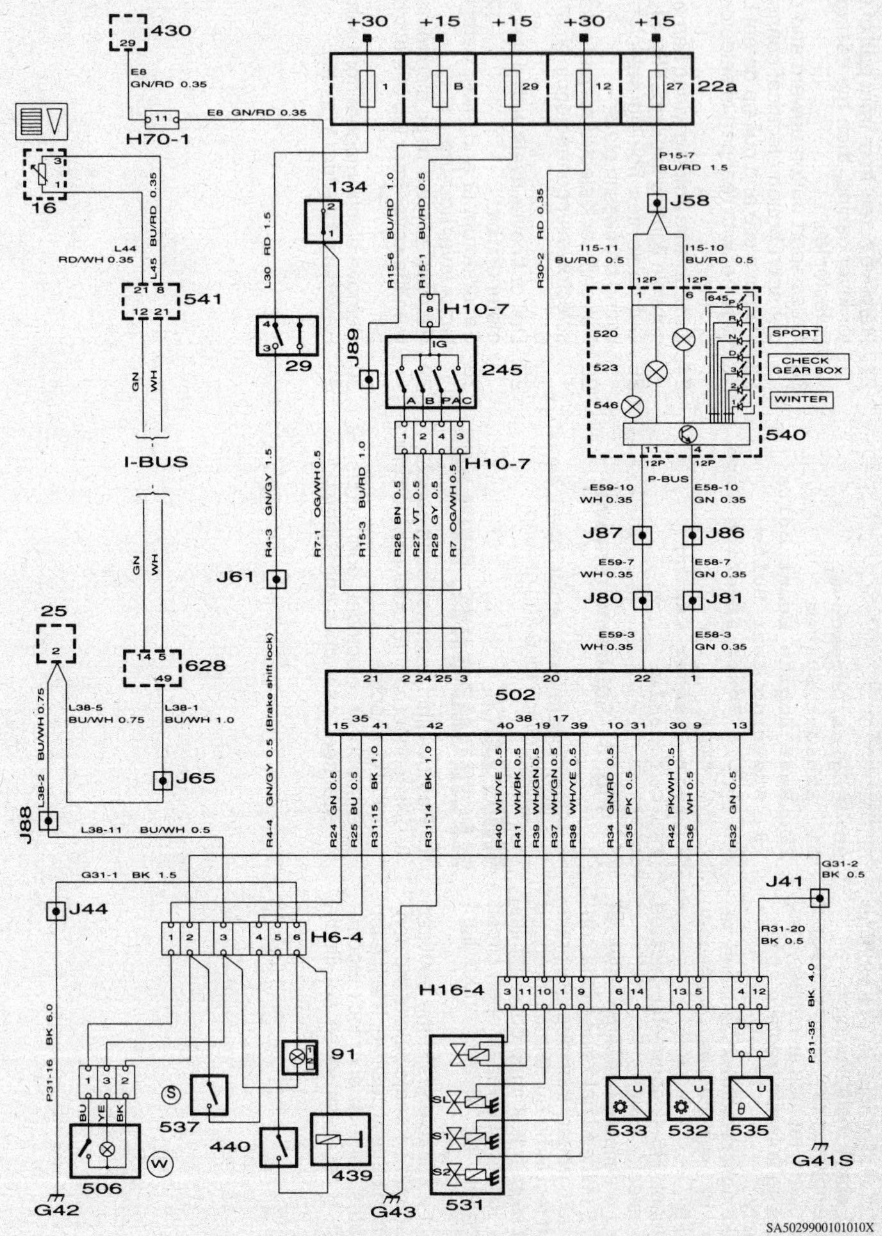

Fig. 9 Transaxle wiring circuit (Part 1 of 2)

Components

16	Rheostat, instrument lighting
22a	Main fuse board, dashboard
29	Brake lights switch
91	Lamp, selector lever position indicator lighting
134	Switch, brake, cruise control
245	Selector lever position switch 1, automatic transmission
430/589	Control module, Saab Trionic
439	Solenoid, selector lever, SHIFT LOCK
440	Microswitch, selector lever
502	Transmission control module, TCM
506	Switch, WINTER
531	Solenoid valves, TCM
532	Input shaft speed sensor, transmission
533	Output shaft speed sensor, transmission
535	Transmission fluid temperature sensor
537	Switch, SPORT
540	Main instrument unit
541	SID
628	Control module, DICE

Connectors

H6-4	6-pin connector Selector lever, automatic transmission
H10-7	10-pin connector Automatic transmission
H16-4	16-pin connector Automatic transmission
H70-1	70-pin connector Engine

Crimp connections

J41 (LHD)	About 200 from the SID branching point, towards the MIU
J41 (RHD)	About 90 mm from the grounding point G41S branching point, towards the MIU
J44 (LHD)	About 140 mm from the SID branching point, towards grounding point G42
J44 (RHD)	About 150 mm from the SID branching point, towards the ignition switch
J58 (LHD)	About 50 mm from the MIU (12-pin connector) branching point, towards the data link connector
J58 (RHD)	About 90 mm from the MIU (12-pin connector) branching point, towards the heater housing
J61 (LHD)	About 90 mm from the left-hand front floor lamp branching point, towards grounding point G40
J61 (RHD)	About 90 mm from the data link connector branching point, towards the steering column switches
J65 (LHD)	About 40 mm from the MIU (20-pin connector) branching point, towards its 12-pin connector
J65 (RHD)	About 120 mm from the MIU (12-pin connector) branching point, towards the radio connector
J72 (LHD)	About 50 mm from the MIU's 12-pin connector
J72 (RHD)	About 50 mm from the MIU's 12-pin connector
J73 (LHD)	About 50 mm from the MIU's 12-pin connector
J73 (RHD)	About 50 mm from the MIU's 12-pin connector
J76 (LHD)	About 50 mm from the SID's connector
J76 (RHD)	About 50 mm from the SID's connector
J77 (LHD)	About 50 mm from the SID's connector
J77 RHD)	About 50 mm from the SID's connector
J80 (LHD)	Beside the cable tie on the TCM's connector
J80 (RHD)	Beside the cable tie on the TCM's connector
J81 (LHD)	Beside the cable tie on the TCM's connector
J81 (RHD)	Beside the cable tie on the TCM's connector
J86 (LHD)	About 50 mm from the MIU's 12-pin connector
J86 (RHD)	About 50 mm from the MIU's 12-pin connector
J87 (LHD)	About 50 mm from the MIU's 12-pin connector
J87 (RHD)	About 50 mm from the MIU's 12-pin connector
J88 (LHD)	About 40 mm from the grounding point G41S branching point, towards the SID
J88 (RHD)	About 160 mm from the grounding point G41S branching point, towards the MIU
J89 (LHD)	About 70 mm from the grounding point G41S branching point, towards the MIU
J89 (RHD)	About 145 mm from the grounding point G41S branching point, towards the radio

Grounding points

G41S	Centre grounding bolt on the knee member's left-hand side (inside the cabin)
G42	In the cabin on the knee member's left-hand side
G43	Right-hand grounding bolt in the centre of the knee member (inside the cabin)

SA5029900101020X

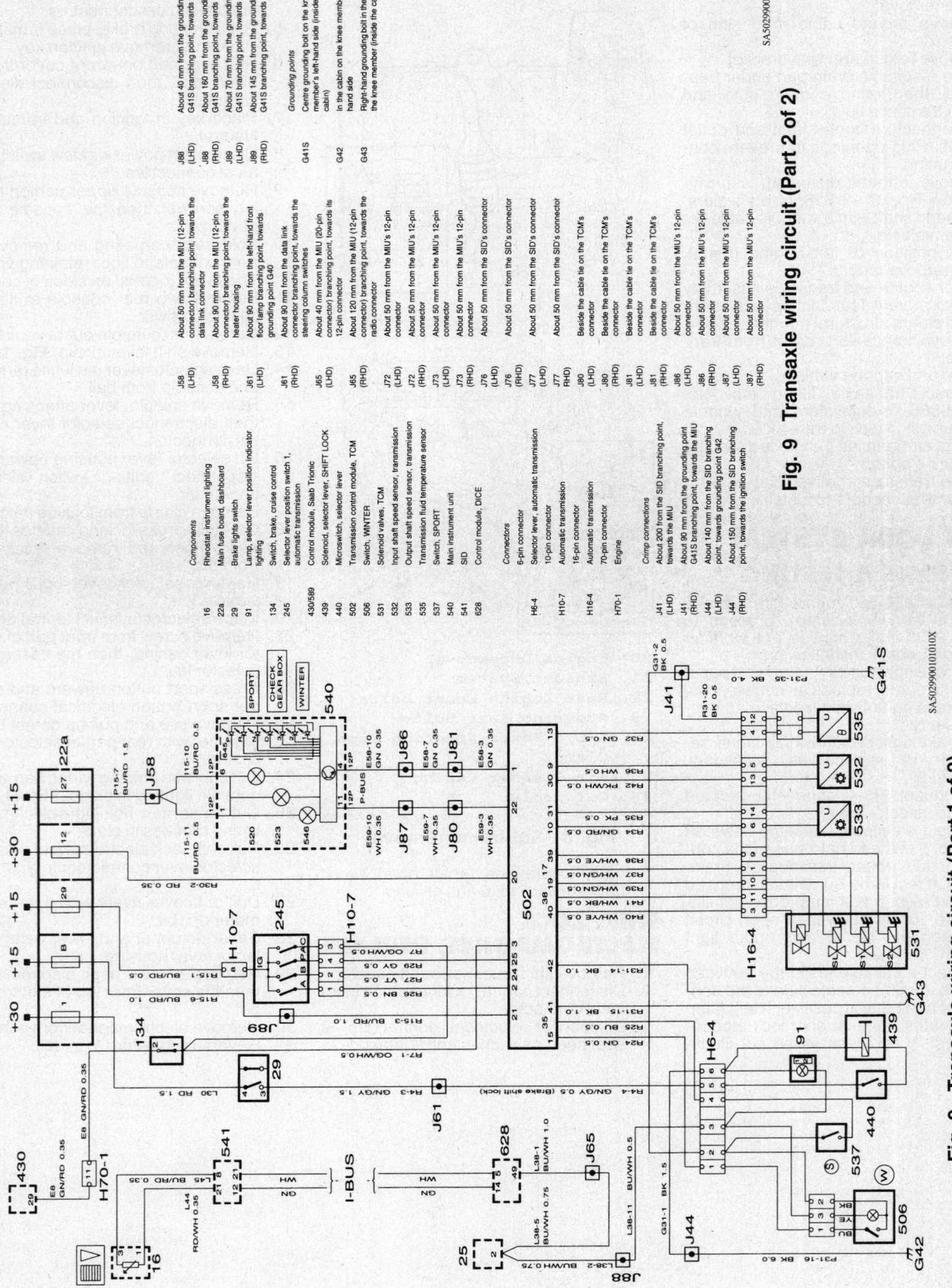

Fig. 9 Transaxle wiring circuit (Part 2 of 2)

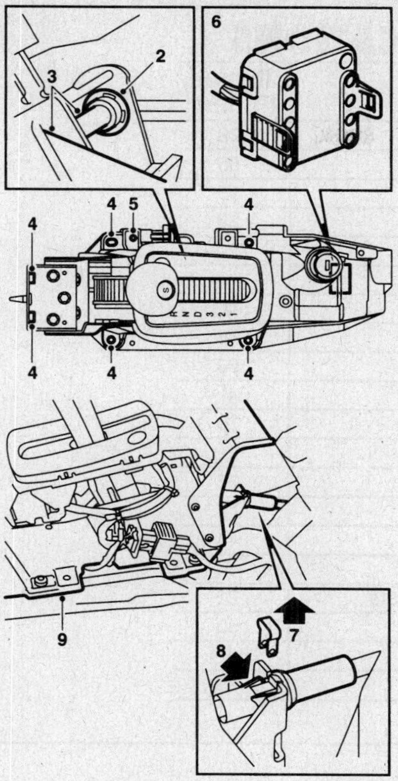

2. Circlip
3. Pin
4. Selector Lever Housing Bolts
5. Selector Lever Housing Connector
6. Ignition Switch Connector
7. Clamp
8. Locking Catches
9. Selector Lever Housing

SA5029900102000X

Fig. 10 Selector lever housing removal

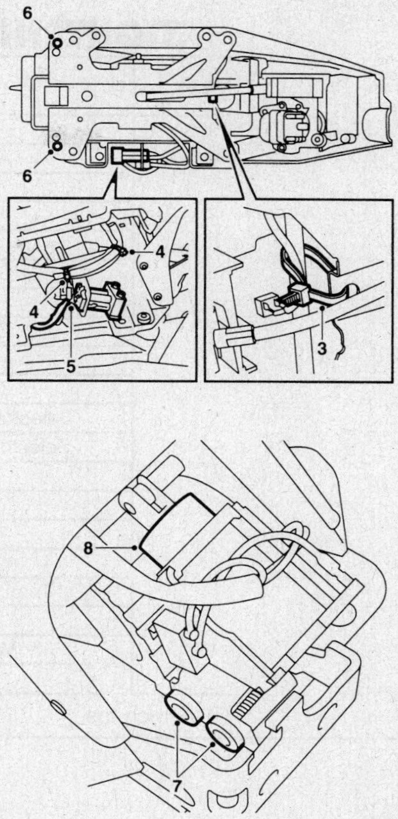

3. Light Harness Cable Tie
4. Selector Harness Cable Ties
5. Selector Lever Housing Connector
6. Cover Rivets
8. Shift Electromagnet

SA5029900103000X

Fig. 11 Shift-lock electromagnet replacement

TIGHTENING SPECIFICATIONS

Year	Component	Torque, Ft. Lbs.
1999–2001	Alternator	29
	Anti-Roll Bar Ball Joint	55
	Banjo Bolt	16
	Bearing Bracket	29
	Driveplate Cover	72①
	Fluid Temperature Sensor	19
	Input Speed Sensor	54①
	Oil Pipes To Transaxle	16
	Outer Ball Joints	63
	Output Speed Sensor	54①
	Selector Lever Position Sensor Bolt	19
	Selector Lever Position Sensor Nut	72①
	Steering Gear	66
	Subframe	74
	Support Plates	44
	Tie Rod End	44
	Torque Converter To Driveplate	22
	Transaxle To Engine	52
	Valve Housing Solenoid	60①
	Wheel Bolts	89

① — Inch lbs.

ZF 4-HP-18 Automatic Transaxle

INDEX

	Page No.
Adjustments	7-167
Brake Band Mechanism	7-167
Selector Lever	7-167
Throttle Cable	7-167
Identification	7-165
In-Vehicle Repairs	7-167
Governor Assembly	7-167
Valve Body	7-167
Maintenance	7-167
Fluid Change	7-167
Fluid Check	7-167
Precautions	7-165
Air Bag Systems	7-165
Battery Ground Cable	7-165
Radio Anti-Theft Lock	7-165
Tightening Specifications	7-168
Transaxle, Replace	7-167
Troubleshooting	7-165
Car Pulls Away In Neutral Position	7-166
Downshift Too Harsh	7-166
Engine Cannot Be Started	7-165
Engine Speed Flares On 4-3 Downshift	7-166
Engine Speed Flares Up On 4-3 Downshift At Part Throttle	7-166
Erratic Or Hard Shifts	7-165
Full Throttle Kickdown Shifting Too Harsh	7-166
Full Throttle Kickdown Shifting Too Slow	7-166
Harsh Jerk When Selector Lever Is Moved From N To D	7-166
Harsh Jerk When Selector Lever Moved From P To R	7-166
High Shift Point	7-166
Incorrect Full Throttle Shift Points	7-166
Incorrect Shifting Speed On Roll Out	7-166
Leakage Between Gearbox & Converter Housing	7-167
Manual Downshift Inoperative	7-166
No 1-2 Upshift	7-166
No 1-2/2-1 Shift	7-166
No 2-3 Upshift	7-166
No 2-3/3-2 Shift	7-166
No 3-4 Upshift	7-166
No 3-4/4-3 Shift	7-166
No Drive	7-166
No Electrical Fault But Reversing Lights Do Not Light Up	7-166
No Forward/Reverse Drive, Loud Noise	7-166
No Kickdown Shift	7-166
Noise In All Selector Lever Positions	7-167
Oil Dripping From Converter Housing	7-167
Parking Pawl Does Not Engage Or Slips	7-165
Reverse Gear Does Not Engage	7-166
Slipping Or Shuddering When Pulling Away	7-166
Slipping Or Vibrations When Pulling Away	7-166
Speed Dependent Noise	7-167
Throttle Cable Jams	7-166
Transaxle Binding Can Only Be Driven In Locked 1st Position	7-166
Vehicle Pulls Away In 2nd Gear	7-166
Vehicle Pulls Away In 3rd Gear	7-166

PRECAUTIONS

AIR BAG SYSTEMS

Refer to "Air Bag System Precautions" in the front of this manual for system disarming and arming procedures.

BATTERY GROUND CABLE

Prior to service, disconnect battery ground cable and isolate as required.

RADIO ANTI-THEFT LOCK

Radio and cassette player are equipped with an electronic four-digit anti-theft lock. This four-digit code is programmed at manufacturing and cannot be changed. If the battery is disconnected for more than three minutes, if unit is removed or if otherwise cut off from power, the four-digit code must be entered with the quick-selection buttons as follows:

1. Turn radio on, then, when display shows "Code In," enter four-digit code with quick-selection buttons. If code is correct, last-tuned radio frequency is shown on display. If wrong digit has been entered by mistake, all four digits must be entered again. If code is wrong it stays on display.
2. If incorrect four-digit code has been entered, press Band button for more than three seconds to clear display. Display shows "Code In" and new attempt to enter correct code can be made.
3. If wrong code has been used three times in succession, four dashes appear on display and you must wait an hour with radio switched on before trying again.
4. To try again, hold Band button for at least three seconds. "Code In" should appear on display.
5. Correct code must be entered at first attempt, otherwise you must wait another hour with unit switched on before trying again.

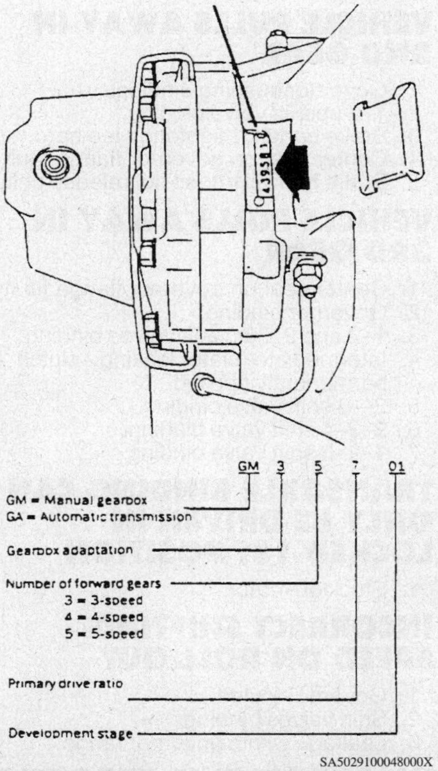

Fig. 1 Transaxle identification

IDENTIFICATION

Refer to **Fig. 1** for transaxle identification.

TROUBLESHOOTING

ERRATIC OR HARD SHIFTS

A transaxle that exhibits erratic or hard shifts, noise when shifting, particularly on 2–3 upshift and/or clutch slipping tendencies, may indicate a radiator oil cooler failure. Refer to "Valve Body" in "In-Vehicle Repairs" section to inspect for antifreeze contamination of the transaxle.

PARKING PAWL DOES NOT ENGAGE OR SLIPS

1. Selector control or cable in correctly adjusted.
2. Excessive play at parking pawl washer.
3. Segment incorrectly fitted.
4. Excessive friction in the parking pawl mechanism.

ENGINE CANNOT BE STARTED

1. Start inhibitor switch faulty.
2. Excessive play in selector lever shaft.

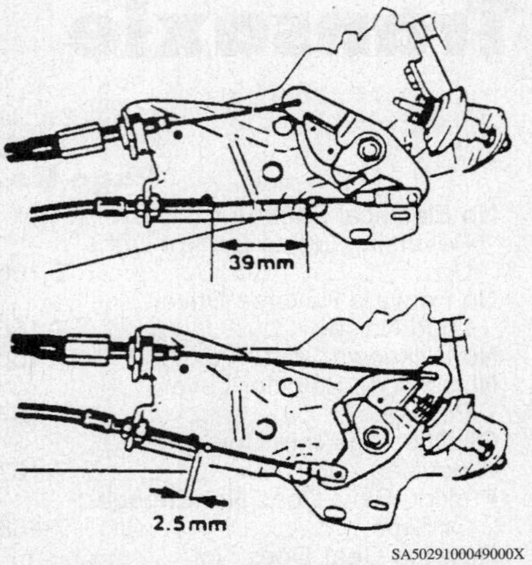

Fig. 2 Throttle cable adjustment

REVERSE GEAR DOES NOT ENGAGE

1. Selector control or selector cable between selector lever and transaxle incorrectly adjusted.
2. Oil filter clogged.
3. Clutch B faulty.
4. Brake D faulty. No back-off braking will be obtained in position 1.
5. Binding governor.
6. Inhibitor valve 1 and R binding.

SLIPPING OR VIBRATIONS WHEN PULLING AWAY

1. Clutch B or brake D damaged.
2. Oil supply circuit to clutch B leaking.

HARSH JERK WHEN SELECTOR LEVER MOVED FROM P TO R

1. Accumulator D faulty.

NO ELECTRICAL FAULT BUT REVERSING LIGHTS DO NOT LIGHT UP

1. Start inhibitor switch is faulty.

CAR PULLS AWAY IN NEUTRAL POSITION

1. Selector control or cable incorrectly adjusted.

NO DRIVE

1. Selector control or cable incorrectly adjusted.
2. Oil filter clogged.
3. 3–4 shift timing valve binding.
4. Converter relief valve binding.
5. Clutch A defective.
6. 1st Gear one-way clutch slipping.

SLIPPING OR SHUDDERING WHEN PULLING AWAY

1. Clutch A damaged.
2. Seal on turbine shaft damaged.
3. O-ring of clutch A piston damaged.

HARSH JERK WHEN SELECTOR LEVER IS MOVED FROM N TO D

1. Accumulator A binding or spring failed.
2. Ball in 3–4 shift timing valve leaking.
3. Clutch A damaged.

NO 1-2/2-1 SHIFT

1. Governor binding.
2. 1–2 Upshift valve binding.

NO 1-2 UPSHIFT

1. Brake C or band C1 damaged.

NO 2-3/3-2 SHIFT

1. Governor binding.
2. 2–3 upshift valve binding.

NO 2-3 UPSHIFT

1. Clutch E damaged.
2. Seal on engine or turbine shaft leaking.
3. Oil supply to clutch E leaking.

NO 3-4/4-3 SHIFT

1. Governor binding.
2. 3–4 upshift valve binding.

NO 3-4 UPSHIFT

1. Brake band C1 defective and 1–2 upshift also faulty.
2. Brake band C1 is not preloaded.
3. 2–3–4 shift valve binding.
4. Position 3 valve binding.

VEHICLE PULLS AWAY IN 2ND GEAR

1. Governor bushing binding.
2. 1–2 upshift valve binding.
3. Brake band C1 tightened too hard.
4. Center seal on governor flange faulty.
5. Brake band C1 does not release unit.

VEHICLE PULLS AWAY IN 3RD GEAR

1. Center seal on governor flange faulty.
2. Governor binding.
3. 1–2 and 2–3 upshift valves binding.
4. Intermediate plate leaking, clutch B permanently applied.
5. 2—3 shift valve binding.
6. 2–3–4 shift valve binding.
7. 1–2–3 shift valve binding.

TRANSAXLE BINDING CAN ONLY BE DRIVEN IN LOCKED 1ST POSITION

1. Stuck governor.

INCORRECT SHIFTING SPEED ON ROLL OUT

1. Governor fouled.
2. Shift valves binding.
3. Leakage within governor range.

INCORRECT FULL THROTTLE SHIFT POINTS

1. Throttle cable incorrectly adjusted.

NO KICKDOWN SHIFT

1. Throttle cable incorrectly adjusted.

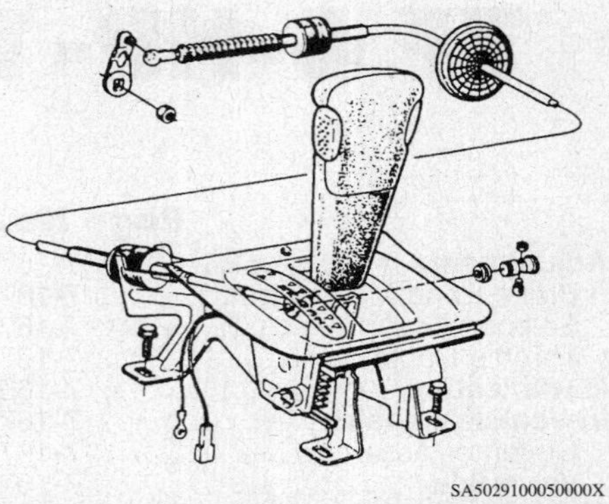

Fig. 3 Selector lever adjustment

HIGH SHIFT POINT

1. Governor unbalance.

DOWNSHIFT TOO HARSH

1. Accumulator function faulty.
2. Modulation pressure too high.
3. Clutch plates damaged.

FULL THROTTLE KICKDOWN SHIFTING TOO SLOW

1. Accumulator function faulty.
2. Modulation pressure too low.
3. Clutch plates damaged.

FULL THROTTLE KICKDOWN SHIFTING TOO HARSH

1. Incorrect modulation pressure.
2. Accumulator function faulty.

ENGINE SPEED FLARES UP ON 4-3 DOWNSHIFT AT PART THROTTLE

1. Throttle cable incorrectly adjusted.
2. Transaxle does not disengage.
3. Orifice control valve binding in the braking position.
4. 3-4 shift timing valve binding.
5. Brake band incorrectly adjusted.

ENGINE SPEED FLARES ON 4-3 DOWNSHIFT

1. Improper operation of timing valve and 4-3 downshift valve.
2. Clutch "A" damaged.
3. Accumulator function for clutch "A" and 4–3 shift timing valve defective.
4. Boost pressure supply incorrect.

MANUAL DOWNSHIFT INOPERATIVE

1. Inhibitor valve 2 binding.
2. Governor binding.

THROTTLE CABLE JAMS

1. Nipple in throttle cam unhooked.
2. Throttle cam deformed.
3. Throttle cam spring broken.
4. High friction in throttle cable sheath.
5. Kickdown valve binding.

NO FORWARD/REVERSE DRIVE, LOUD NOISE

1. Driveplate between converter and flywheel damaged.

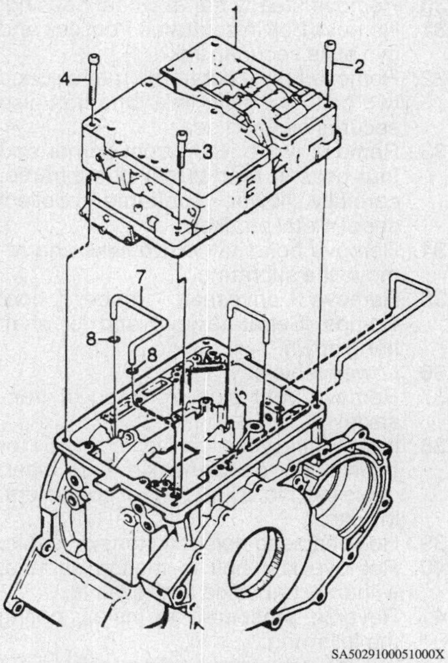

Fig. 4 Valve body assembly

2. Pump drive failure.

OIL DRIPPING FROM CONVERTER HOUSING

1. Seal in converter housing damaged.
2. Converter leaking at welded joint.

LEAKAGE BETWEEN GEARBOX & CONVERTER HOUSING

1. Converter housing retaining bolts loose.

NOISE IN ALL SELECTOR LEVER POSITIONS

1. Oil level too low.
2. Valve body leaking.
3. Oil filter clogged.

SPEED DEPENDENT NOISE

1. Bearing adjustment of the intermediate gear has changed or is incorrect.
2. Bearing setting of the differential has changed or is incorrect.

MAINTENANCE

FLUID CHECK

1. Ensure vehicle is on level surface.
2. Apply parking brake firmly.
3. Start engine and allow to reach normal operating temperature.
4. Shift selector lever through all positions, then place lever in park position. Do not shutdown engine during fluid level checks.
5. Clean all dirt and from dipstick cap before removing dipstick from filler tube.
6. Pull dipstick from tube, wipe clean and replace completely back in tube.
7. Remove transaxle dipstick to check fluid level, add specified fluid to raise level to full mark on dipstick. Do not overfill.

FLUID CHANGE

1. Raise and support vehicle.
2. Remove hose connector for oil cooler return from front of transaxle. Place a suitable drain pan under vehicle to collect oil.
3. When fluid has stopped draining, reinstall oil cooler return hose.
4. Add recommended fluid to transaxle pan through filler tube.
5. Refer to "Fluid Check," for final fluid level check.

ADJUSTMENTS

THROTTLE CABLE

1. Verify crimp is correctly positioned by opening throttle to point where kickdown cam in transaxle begins to engage.
2. Measure from end of cable housing to crimp, distance should be 1.53 inches or (39 mm), **Fig. 2.**
3. If distance is incorrect, move crimp.
4. Close throttle and measure same clearance again.
5. Distance should be .098 inch or (2.5 mm).
6. If incorrect, dimension can be brought within specification by adjusting two nuts which lock cable assembly to throttle housing bracket.

BRAKE BAND MECHANISM

1. Fit O-ring to parallel pin and fit pin into gearbox.
2. Screw in adjusting screw and tighten to specification.
3. Make a mark on adjusting screw and gearbox.
4. Back off adjusting screw two turns.
5. Hold adjusting screw and tighten locknut to specification.

SELECTOR LEVER

1. Loosen nut on adjustment mechanism in front of selector lever, **Fig. 3.**
2. Place lever on transaxle to N position.
3. Place selector lever in N position.
4. Tighten nut to specification.

IN-VEHICLE REPAIRS

GOVERNOR ASSEMBLY

1. Remove lefthand front wheel and wing liner assembly.
2. Remove side cover attaching bolts, then the side cover and gasket.
3. Remove screw on pinion shaft. **The parking pawl must be engaged.**
4. Remove gearwheel with inner race of taper roller bearing from pinion shaft.
5. Remove outer race of taper bearing, heat may be required.
6. Remove governor and governor housing as an assembly.
7. Reverse procedure to install noting the following:

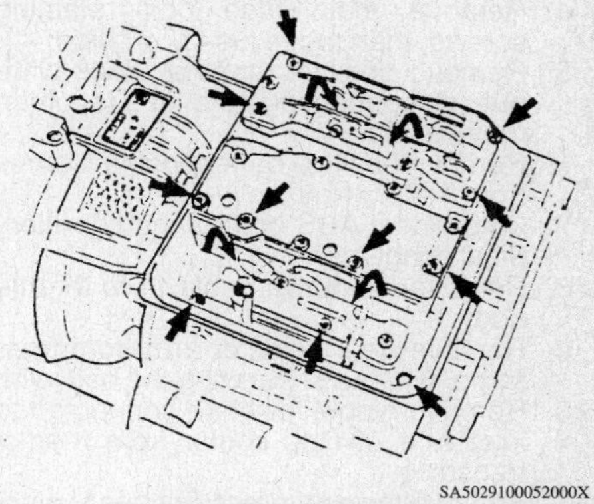

Fig. 5 Valve body contamination locations

   a. Apply petroleum jelly to seals before installing governor.
   b. Tighten bolt on pinion shaft to specification.
   c. Tighten side cover bolts to specification.

VALVE BODY

The following procedure has been revised by a Technical Service Bulletin:

1. Obtain radio anti-theft code as outlined under "Precautions."
2. Remove battery and shelf.
3. Remove oil dipstick.
4. Remove valve body cover retaining screws, then the valve body cover, **Fig. 4.**
5. Inspect valve body for antifreeze contamination. Inspect for any of the following indications:
   a. Separated droplets of antifreeze or pink, milky emulsion in the recesses of the valve body assembly, screw heads or main case, **Fig. 5.** Probing and stirring may be necessary to provide a complete inspection.
   b. Rust formation and/or sludge accumulation on old style metal vent.
   c. Rust formation and/or sludge accumulation on underside of valve body cover.
   d. Rust formation on steel separator plates of valve body assembly.
6. Remove valve body retaining screws.
7. Remove oil tubes, then the valve body.
8. Reverse procedure to install noting the following:
   a. Set selector mechanism in position 1.
   b. Set selector rod in valve body to position 1, fully inserted.
   c. Tighten valve body retaining screws to specification.
   d. Replace all oil tube O-rings.

TRANSAXLE

REPLACE

1. Obtain radio anti-theft code as outlined under "Precautions."
2. Remove battery.
3. Remove throttle cable retaining clip and cable, then move cable aside.

4. Remove main fuse box retaining screws, then move fuse box aside.
5. Remove positive terminal block without disconnecting the leads, then move aside.
6. Remove positive battery cable clamps from battery tray.
7. Disconnect ABS control module electrical connector.
8. Remove kickdown cable from throttle body.
9. Remove gear selector arm from transaxle, without separating the ball joint.
10. Remove nipple for hose connected to inlet side of fluid cooler from rear of transaxle.
11. Remove nut and press out gear selector cable rubber bushing from mounting on transaxle casing.
12. Using a suitable container, place container under vehicle to collect fluid.
13. Remove nipple for hose connected to outlet side of fluid cooler from front of transaxle and plug hole.
14. Disconnect battery ground cable from transaxle.
15. Unplug connector on speedometer sensor cable.
16. Remove mating surface attaching bolts. These are only accessible from the top, except the front bolt. One bolt is also an attaching bolt for the starter motor.
17. Remove bolts securing upper end of steady bar in wheel housing.
18. Place engine lifting beam tool No. 83 93 977, or equivalent, on wheel housings, making sure that the beam abuts against edges of fenders. Install hook in engine's lifting eyebolt and loosely tighten the wing nut.
19. Raise and support vehicle, then remove lefthand front wheel.
20. Remove wheel housing trim molding and front part of fender liner.
21. Remove lefthand and center spoiler sections.
22. Remove transaxle protective plate.
23. Remove bolts securing torque converter to driver disc. To gain access to bolts it will be necessary to turn the engine.
24. Install holder tool No. 87 92 293, or equivalent, to hold torque converter in place when transaxle is removed. Holder is secured with M10 bolts.
25. Remove remaining bolts in the mating surface from underneath.
26. Remove three bolts securing ball joint to suspension arm.
27. Remove nut from anti-roll bar mounting in suspension arm.
28. Remove two bolts securing anti-roll bar bearing.
29. Remove attaching nut and washers from front engine mount.
30. Remove steady bar at wheel housing.
31. Remove bolt in subframe front link and two bolts securing link
32. Remove bolt in subframe rear link and two bolts securing link. One bolt also secures steering gear.
33. Remove two bolts in front corner and four bolts in rear corner of subframe. carefully lower subframe. Collect sheet metal bracket.
34. Remove bolts in the two links and remove the subframe.
35. Remove driveshaft rubber boot clamps. Separate joint and let shaft hang down.
36. Lower vehicle.
37. Remove vent plug from top of transaxle.
38. Install lifting yoke tool No. 87 91 451, or equivalent, on transaxle and insert cable tool No. 87 92 251, or equivalent, in yoke.
39. Hook cable to hoist and tension cable.
40. Remove last bolt in mating surface, withdraw transaxle and lower it.
41. Reverse procedure to install, noting the following:
    a. Use converter holding tool No. 87 92 293, or equivalent, to hold torque converter in place when installing transaxle.

TIGHTENING SPECIFICATIONS

Year	Component	Torque, Ft. Lbs.
1998–2001	Anti-Roll Bar Bearing Bolts	30–40
	Anti-Roll Bar To Suspension Arm Nut	30–40
	Ball Joint To Suspension Arm Bolts	19–25
	Brake Band Adjusting Screw	84①
	Brake Band Adjusting Screw Locknut	59
	Engine Mount Bolt	35–65
	Pinion Shaft Bolt	110
	Selector Lever Nut	48–84①
	Side Cover Bolts	84①
	Steady Bar To Wheel Housing	32–42
	Subframe Front Mounting Bolts	32–42
	Subframe Rear Mounting Bolts	36–47
	Torque Converter	37–49
	Valve Body Retaining Screws	84①
	Wheel Housing Steady Bar To Subframe Bolts	32–42

① — Inch lbs.

Front Wheel Drive Axles

INDEX

	Page No.
Driveshaft, Replace	7-169
9-3 & 900	7-169
9-5	7-169
9000	7-170
Driveshaft Service	7-170
9-3 & 900	7-170
9-5	7-170
9000	7-170
Precautions	7-169
Air Bag Systems	7-169
Battery Ground Cable	7-169

PRECAUTIONS

AIR BAG SYSTEMS

Refer to "Air Bag System Precautions" in the front of this manual for system disarming and arming procedures.

BATTERY GROUND CABLE

Prior to service, disconnect battery ground cable and isolate as required.

DRIVESHAFT

REPLACE

9-3 & 900

1. Remove dust cap and loosen hub center nut (1), **Fig. 1. Do not completely remove nut.**
2. Raise and support vehicle, then remove wheel.
3. Remove hub center nut (1), then the ball joint nut (2).
4. Remove ball joint using ball joint tool No. 89 96 696, or equivalent.
5. Remove anti-roll bar nut (4) and collect washer and rubber bushing.
6. Press spring link down.
7. Tap driveshaft out of hub using rubber mallet, then move MacPherson strut aside and pull out driveshaft. Use care to avoid stretching brake hoses and sensor cables.
8. Remove driveshaft joint from intermediate shaft using driveshaft dismantling tool No. 89 96 654, or equivalent.
9. Reverse procedure to install, noting the following:
   a. **Torque** ball joint to 55 ft. lbs.
   b. **Torque** anti-roll bar nut to 7 ft. lbs.
   c. **Torque** wheel bolts to 87 ft. lbs.
   d. Install new hub center nut and **torque** to 214 ft. lbs. It is self-locking and should not be reused.

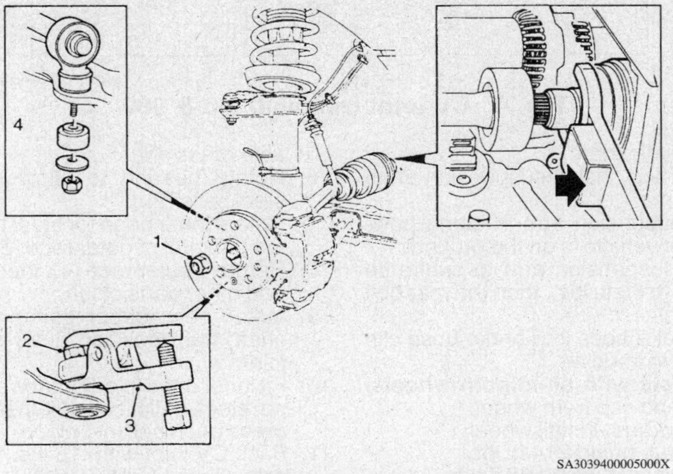

Fig. 1 Driveshaft removal. 9-3 & 900

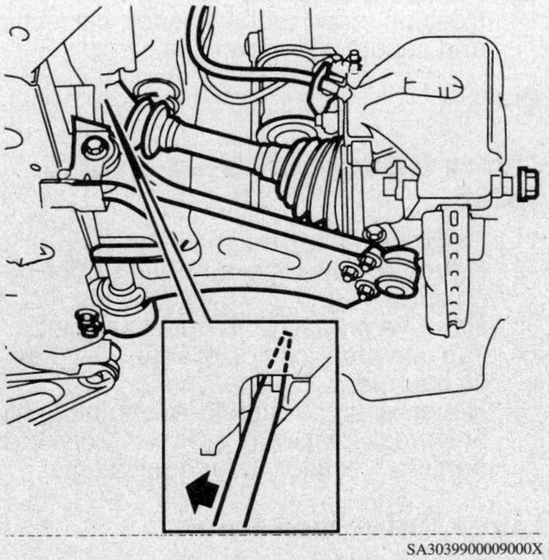

Fig. 2 Driveshaft removal. 9-5

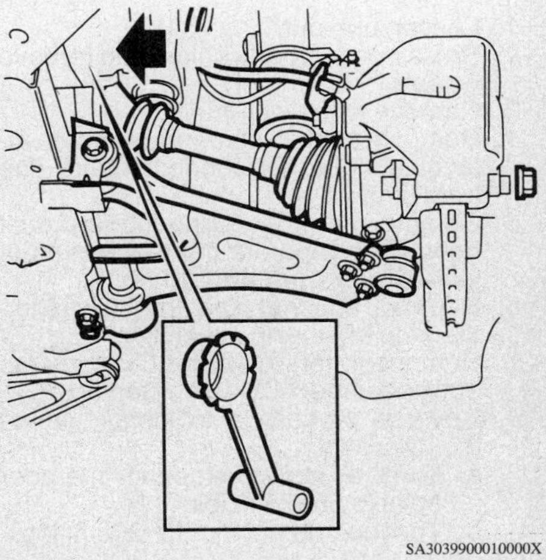

Fig. 3 Lefthand side driveshaft installation. 9-5

9-5

Removal

1. Raise and support vehicle, then remove wheel.
2. Remove center hub nut, **Fig. 2.**
3. **On lefthand side,** separate driveshaft from transaxle with prying tool No. 87 92 616, or equivalent.
4. **On righthand side,** separate driveshaft from intermediate shaft with a suitable brass drift and hammer.
5. **On all sides,** remove brake hose retaining clip.
6. Remove suspension arm front and rear brackets from subframe.
7. Fold suspension arms downward.
8. Pull strut outward and remove driveshaft from transaxle or intermediate shaft.
9. Tap driveshaft from hub with a plastic hammer.

Installation

1. Install driveshaft into hub, then the center nut loosely. **Do not tighten nut at this time.**
2. **On lefthand side,** install driveshaft as follows:
   a. Install protective collar tool No. 83 95 162, or equivalent, into seal ring, **Fig. 3**
   b. Install driveshaft into transaxle until about .8 inch of shaft remains, remove protective collar tool from transaxle.
   c. Slide driveshaft into transaxle until circlip clicks in.
3. **On righthand side,** pull strut assembly outward, then slide driveshaft into

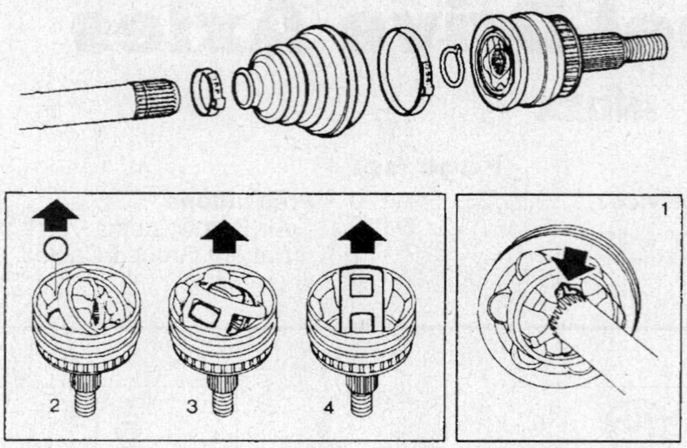

SA3039400008000X

Fig. 4 CV joint removal. 9-3 & 900

intermediate shaft.

4. **On all sides,** install suspension arms to subframe.
5. Place suspension arm in same position when vehicle is on the ground.
6. **Torque** suspension arm to subframe front bolt to 66 ft. lbs., then the rear bolt to 66 ft. lbs.
7. Install brake hose into brake hose clip on steering knuckle.
8. **On models with aluminum wheels,** remove hub cap from wheel.
9. **On all models,** install wheel.
10. **Torque** hub nut to 214 ft. lbs.
11. **Torque** wheel bolts to 88 ft. lbs.

9000

1. Loosen hub nut.
2. Raise and support vehicle and remove wheels.
3. Remove wheelwell liners.
4. Remove strut-to-steering member attaching bolts. Disconnect brake line from strut.
5. Remove clamp securing inboard dust boot, then separate the two halves of joint. **Cover boot and driver.**
6. Remove hub nut and thrust washer, then the drive axle assembly.
7. Remove inner and outer CV joints as outlined under "CV Joint, Replace."
8. Reverse procedure to install, noting the following:
   a. **Torque** strut-to-steering member bolts to 56–75 ft. lbs.
   b. **Torque** hub nut to 195–208 ft. lbs.

DRIVESHAFT SERVICE

9-3 & 900

1. Remove driveshaft assembly as outlined under "Driveshaft, Replace."
2. Ensure driveshaft and gaiter are clean, then clamp driveshaft in vice.
3. Unfasten gaiter clips on CV joint and slide gaiter along shaft.
4. Remove all grease from CV joint.
5. Open circlip (1), **Fig. 4,** and tap CV joint off shaft using hammer and suitable brass drift.
6. Rotate bearing to allow removal of steel balls (2).
7. Rotate inner cage for steel balls to permit removal of outer race (3).
8. Remove outer race (4), then wipe balls and other parts clean.
9. Install new rubber gaiter onto driveshaft, then position outer race in CV joint.
10. Fit inner cage in outer race and rotate it so steel balls can be inserted, then press each ball into place.
11. Pack CV joint with. 18 lbs. fresh Molycote Rapid G VN24612C grease, or equivalent.
12. Press driveshaft into CV joint.
13. Position new rubber gaiter correctly and secure with new clips.

9-5

Outer Driveshaft Universal Joint

1. Place driveshaft into suitable vise.
2. Remove joint clips and push boot up on shaft, **Fig. 5.**
3. Remove grease from universal joint.
4. Tap universal joint off of shaft with plastic hammer.
5. Reverse procedure to assemble. Fill universal joint with grease, Molykote part No. VN 2461 C, or equivalent.

Inner Universal Joint

1. Remove boot retaining clips, then slide boot off of tripod assembly, **Fig. 6.**
2. Remove circlip, then the tripod from shaft with a suitable 3-arm puller.
3. Remove boot from driveshaft.
4. Remove grease from universal joint, tripod and driveshaft.
5. Reverse procedure to assemble. Fill universal joint with Shell grease part No. SL0233, or equivalent.

9000

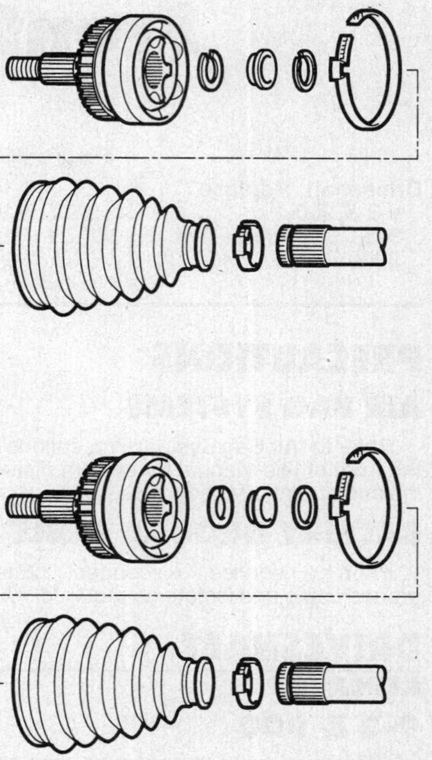

SA3039900011000X

Fig. 5 Exploded view of outer driveshaft universal joint. 9-5

1. Remove drive axle assembly as outlined under "Driveshaft, Replace." **Inner driver is retained in differential bearing carrier with a snap ring. If replacement is necessary, bearing carrier must be removed and differential clearances must be checked during reassembly.**
2. Remove outer joint from shaft as follows:
   a. Release clamp securing boot to outer joint and slide boot toward center of shaft.
   b. Open retaining clip, **Fig. 7,** and remove joint from end of shaft.
3. Rubber boots can be removed, if necessary, by sliding off outer end of shaft.
4. To remove inner joint spider assembly, remove retaining clip and press spider from shaft, using a spacer. **The intermediate shaft uses a tapered shoulder as an inner stop for the spider, replacing the lock ring previously used. Only the conforming type spider can be fitted to the tapered shaft. However, this type spider assembly can be fitted to early type shaft previously used, Fig. 8.**
5. Reverse procedure to install, pack joints and needle bearings with grease, and install rubber boots.
6. Clean inner driver and pack with grease. Reverse procedure to install drive axle assembly.

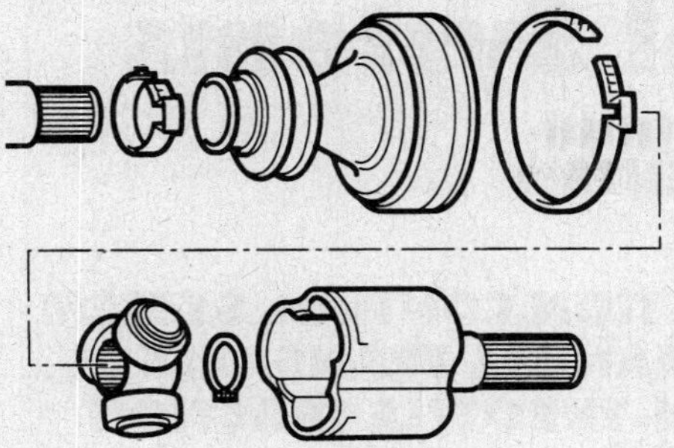

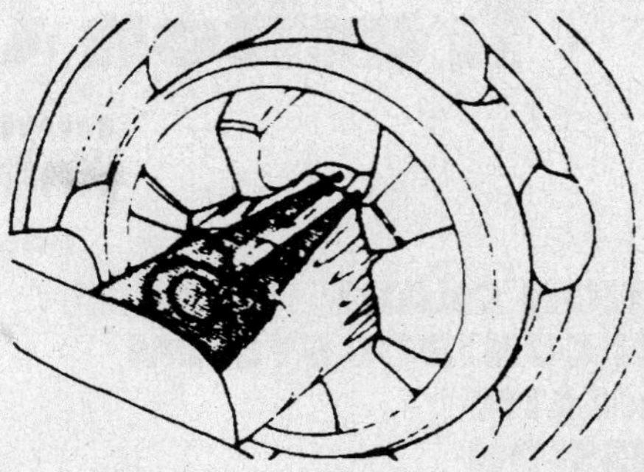

Fig. 7 Outer CV joint removal. 9000

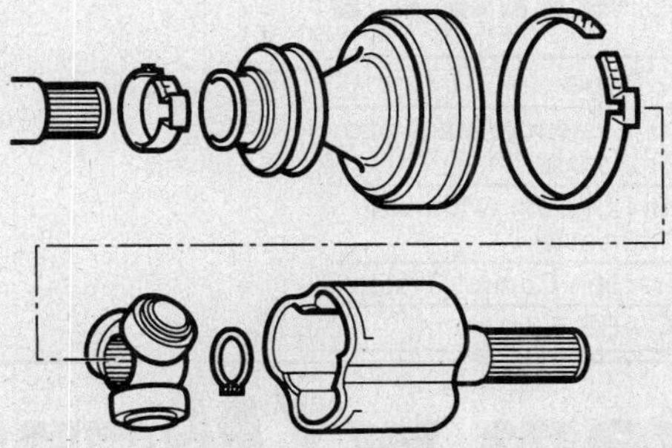

Fig. 6 Exploded view of inner driveshaft universal joint. 9-5

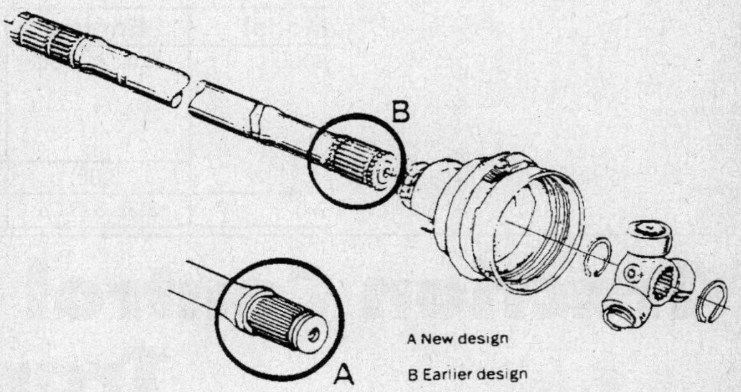

Fig. 8 Inner driveshaft & CV joint spider identification. 9000

Traction Control Systems

TABLE OF CONTENTS

	Page No.
APPLICATION CHART	7-172
TRACTION CONTROL SYSTEM W/AUTOMATIC TRANSMISSION	7-180
TRACTION CONTROL SYSTEM W/MANUAL TRANSAXLE	7-172
TWIN-THROTTLE TRACTION CONTROL SYSTEM	7-187

Application Chart

Model	Engine	Type
9000	2.0L & 2.3L	Traction Control System w/Automatic Transaxle
		Traction Control System w/Manual Transaxle
	3.0L	Twin-Throttle Traction Control System
9-5	2.3L & 3.0L	TC/ABS 5.3

Traction Control System w/Manual Transaxle

NOTE: On Air Bag Equipped Models, Refer To "Air Bag System Precautions" Located In The Front Of This Manual For System Disarming & Arming Procedures.

INDEX

	Page No.
Description	7-173
Anti-Lock Brake System Component Description	7-174
Electronic Throttle System Component Description	7-174
Subsystem	7-173
System	7-173
Traction Control System Operation	7-173
Diagnosis & Testing	7-176
Electronic Throttle System (ETS)	7-176
Traction Control/Anti-Lock Brake System (TC/ABS)	7-176
Precautions	7-172
Air Bag Systems	7-172
Battery Ground Cable	7-172
Battery Ground Cable	7-173
Radio Anti-Theft Lock	7-172
System Service	7-176
Component Replacement	7-177
ETS ECU Calibration	7-176
Troubleshooting	7-175
Anti-Lock Brake System	7-175
Electronic Throttle System	7-175

PRECAUTIONS

AIR BAG SYSTEMS

Refer to "Air Bag System Precautions" in the front of this manual for system disarming and arming procedures.

BATTERY GROUND CABLE

Prior to service, disconnect battery ground cable and isolate as required.

RADIO ANTI-THEFT LOCK

Radio and cassette player are equipped with an electronic four-digit anti-theft lock. This four-digit code is programmed at manufacturing and cannot be changed. If the battery is disconnected for more than three minutes, if unit is removed or if otherwise cut off from power, the four-digit code must be entered with the quick-selection buttons as follows:

1. Turn radio on, then, when display shows "Code In," enter four-digit code with quick-selection buttons. If code is correct, last-tuned radio frequency is shown on display. If wrong digit has been entered by mistake, all four digits must be entered again. If code is wrong it stays on display.
2. If incorrect four-digit code has been entered, press Band button for more than three seconds to clear display. Display shows "Code In" and new attempt to enter correct code can be made.
3. If wrong code has been used three times in succession, four dashes appear on display and you must wait an hour with radio switched on before trying again.
4. To try again, hold Band button for at least three seconds. "Code In" should appear on display.
5. Correct code must be entered at first

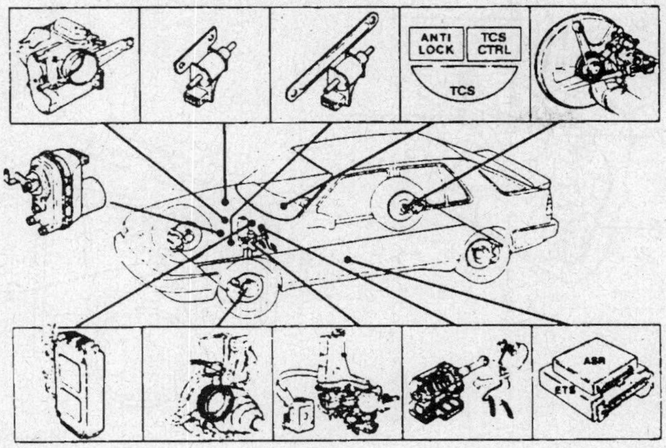

Fig. 1 Traction control system components

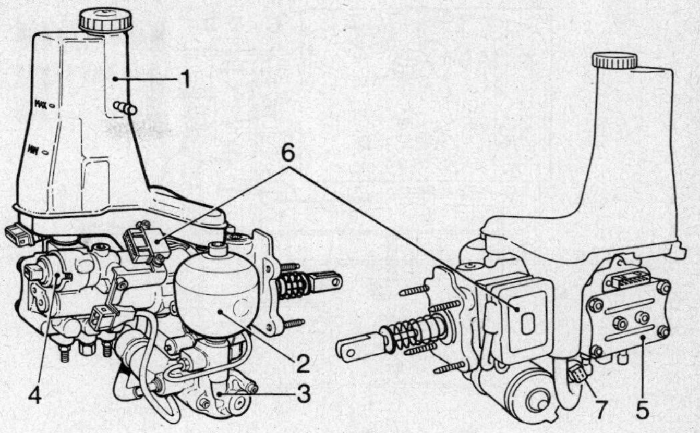

TC/ABS unit
1. Brake fluid reservoir
2. Accumulator (hydraulic)
3. High pressure pump
4. Main valve
5. Valve block (inlet & outlet valves)
6. TC block & connector
7. Pressure warning switch

SA5039100017000X

Fig. 2 Hydraulic unit components

attempt, otherwise you must wait another hour with unit switched on before trying again.

BATTERY GROUND CABLE

Prior to service, disconnect battery ground cable and isolate as required.

DESCRIPTION

SYSTEM

Traction Control System (TCS), used on 9000 models, **Fig. 1,** is used to prevent wheel spin when the car is accelerating on a slippery surface.

The TCS system for manual transmissions consists of two subsystems, the Antilock Braking System (ABS) and Electronic Throttle System (ETS).

TCS utilizes many of the components in the ABS system. The major addition to the system is the Electronic Throttle System.

Manual transmission TCS has the capability to apply the front brakes independently during low speed wheel spin and also the ability to close the throttle butterfly to reduce wheel spin at any speed.

SUBSYSTEM

ELECTRONIC THROTTLE SYSTEM (ETS)

The main purpose of the ETS system is to electronically control the position of the throttle butterfly.

The throttle housing is equipped with an actuating motor for the throttle butterfly, a vacuum unit, a throttle potentiometer and a safety cutout switch. Connected to the accelerator pedal is a pedal sensor with associated solenoid valves and a non-return valve fitted on the bulkhead. For additional safety, a parallel system using a throttle cable is provided, which will take over in the limp-home mode.

Automatic Idling Control (AIC)

The ETS eliminates the need for separate components for Automatic Idling Control (AIC) and load related control over the entire working range of the engine.

Smooth Response To Heavy-Footed Use Of Accelerator

If the driver depresses or releases the accelerator abruptly, the throttle butterfly will be operated in two steps within a period of just a few milliseconds. This allows the car responding smoothly on both acceleration and deceleration.

Integral Cruise Control Function

The ETS system incorporates a cruise control function. Since operation of the cruise control system is based on acceleration control, maximum engine performance is available under all conditions, unlike some previous systems which reverted to basic boost when cruise control was operating.

Intelligent System

The ETS is an intelligent or adaptive system, which means that it adapts itself automatically to changes in air pressure, humidity and variations due to wear in components.

The ETS also incorporates an AIC function for the warm-up phase, governed by time and coolant temperature.

The system continuously processes data from the speedometer, direct ignition system, ABS system, LH system and temperature sensor. It also monitors the position of the throttle butterfly and accelerator.

On the basis of this input data, the ECU controls the actuating motor for the throttle butterfly.

TRACTION CONTROL SYSTEM OPERATION

This system uses the speed of the rear wheels as a reference speed against the speed of each front wheel. If the speed of a front wheel exceeds that of the reference speed from the rear wheels, the condition is known as wheel spin. The magnitude of the spin together with the speed of the car determine how the system operates.

To enable the car to achieve maximum traction, a certain amount of wheel spin, which varies depending on the speed of the car, is allowed.

LOW SPEED OPERATING MODE

The front wheel having the poorer grip (lower friction) starts to spin first.

When wheel spin has reached a speed of just under 10 mph, TCS control is initiated and the TC/ABS system applies the brake for that wheel. As brake is applied to the wheel, additional torque is transferred to the other wheel, which still is maintaining good traction. If the road surface is very slippery, the other wheel may also start to spin, if it does, once it is spinning at a speed of about 4 mph, the amount of throttle is reduced electronically, inhibiting further wheel spin.

So the system is able to provide the optimum combination of traction and steering precision with the same traction or mobility as that provided by a conventional limited-slip differential.

The upper limit for the amount of wheel spin allowed before the TCS takes over is gradually reduced up to a speed of about 12 mph, after which it remains constant regardless of how much throttle is used, although the upper limit for braking will then be increased.

HIGH SPEED OPERATING MODE (OVER 25 MPH)

Once the car reaches a speed of about 25 mph, the system switches mode and initiates throttle control when the first wheel

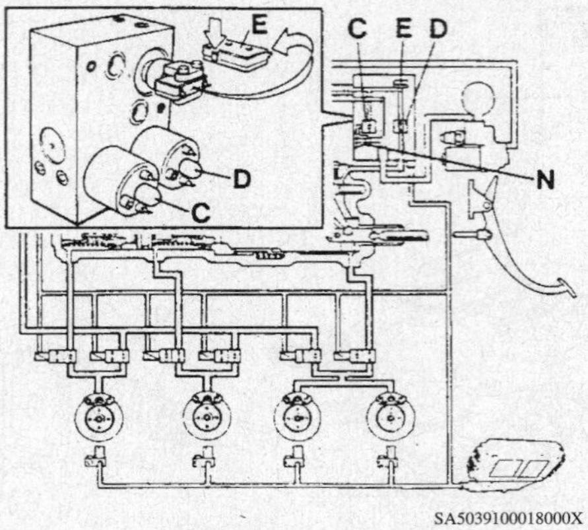

Fig. 3 TC valve block components

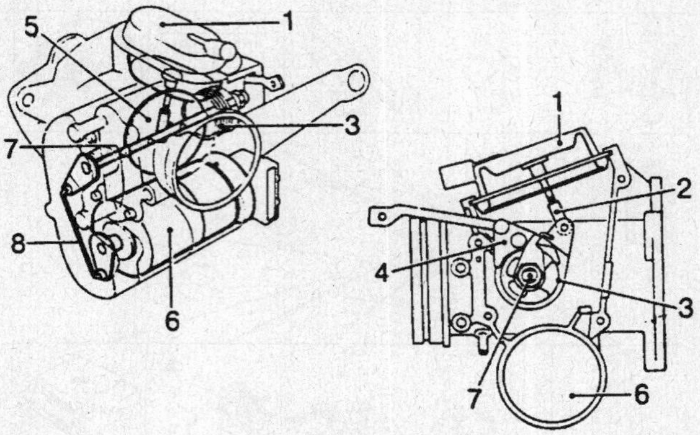

Fig. 4 Throttle housing components

starts spinning. Traction control by application of the brake will be initiated for the other wheel if the amount of wheel spin is great enough.

Up to a speed of about 37 mph, wheel spin of up to just under 2 mph is allowed, after which an increase of about 5 percent relative to the increased speed of the car will be allowed.

So at speed of 87 mph, for instance, wheel spin of approximately 4.4 mph will be allowed before electronic control of the throttle is initiated.

SYSTEM INTERACTION

Conventional operation of the ABS system is the same as before, but an additional valve block (TC block) for the anti-spin function has been added onto the hydraulic unit.

The TC block, together with the main valve, wheel sensors and inlet and outlet valves are the main components of the TC/ABS system. The system is equipped with indicator/warning lights for monitoring and checking of the system. These warning lights indicate when the system is operating and provide a warning if a fault should occur.

The wheel sensors send wheel speed information to the ABS ECU. Using the average speed of the rear wheels as a reference value, the ECU continuously monitors the amount of wheel spin in the front wheels (speed above reference value for rear wheels).

When the system detects a tendency for wheel spin and the TCS calls for braking of the front wheel concerned, pressure is directed from the accumulator through the TC block and main valve to the front wheel circuits. The inlet and outlet valves then control the TCS initiated braking.

ANTI-LOCK BRAKE SYSTEM COMPONENT DESCRIPTION

TRACTION CONTROL/ ANTI-LOCK BRAKE SYSTEM ELECTRONIC CONTROL UNIT (TC/ABS ECU)

The ECU is programmed to detect both permanent and intermittent faults. Faults detected by the ECU are stored in an EEPROM chip, so the diagnostic trouble codes remain in memory even when power supply is switched off or interrupted.

TC/ABS HYDRAULIC UNIT

The main components of the hydraulic unit, **Fig. 2,** are the brake fluid reservoir, fluid level switch, accumulator and a pressure warning switch.

TC VALVE BLOCK

In contrast to the conventional ABS unit. the TC/ABS unit has a separate valve block (TC block), **Fig. 3,** to direct accumulator pressure for TC controlled braking of the appropriate wheel.

The pressure is directed to the front wheel circuits through the main valve and is modulated by the inlet and outlet valves for the front wheel indicating spin.

The TC block, **Fig. 3,** includes two control valves (C and D), a pressure reducing valve (N) and a pressure switch (E). The function of the control valve is to direct hydraulic pressure as required, depending on whether braking is TCS controlled or required for modulation in conjunction with ABS control.

ELECTRONIC THROTTLE SYSTEM COMPONENT DESCRIPTION

ELECTRONIC CONTROL UNIT (ETS ECU)

The ETS ECU receives information on a variety of engine parameters, which it processes before sending appropriate control signals to the throttle housing.

The ECU has an integral self-diagnostics function which is activated every time the ignition is switched off. On power off, automatic testing takes place of all functions and the latest adaptive values are added to memory.

The ECU monitors operation of the system continuously and if a fault is detected that could affect safety, immediately switches to the limp-home function.

THROTTLE HOUSING

The throttle housing, **Fig. 4,** controls the amount of air supplied to the engine, but the position of the throttle butterfly is controlled by means of a pulse width modulated motor.

A throttle cable is connected in parallel, for use in emergency limp-home mode.

Normal Mode

Refer to **Fig. 4** for component locations.

When the engine is started, a vacuum is raised in the vacuum unit (1). This causes the diaphragm (2) and lever assembly to move upwards, which tensions the spring (3). This action also causes the throttle cable attachment lever (4) to turn, slackening the cable and allowing the throttle butterfly (5) to be controlled over idling to full throttle range by the motor (6). The motor actuates the throttle spindle (7) through a link rod (8) attached at either end to levers on the motor and spindle.

Limp-Home Mode

If a fault should occur anywhere in the system, a safety valve on the bulkhead immediately exhausts the vacuum in the vacuum unit.

The diaphragm rod and lever assembly moves down, tensioning the spring, to bring full spring force to bear on the throttle spindle. Since the motor is not powerful enough to overcome the force of the spring to operate the throttle butterfly, the throttle can only be operated by the throttle cable.

The car is now in the limp-home mode, which is clearly evident by both the additionally force required to move the accelerator and the fact that the TCS CTRL light has come on.

AUTOMATIC IDLING CONTROL (AIC)

Because the mass of air that the AIC valve admitted through the throttle housing to compensate idling speed for A/C cut-in etc. varies depending on pressure and temperature, the compensation it provides also tends to vary to some extent with ambient conditions.

However, because the AIC function in the ETS is adaptive, continuous compensation related to pressure and temperature takes place, which means that the opening duration and throttle angle will always be exactly right to admit the precise mass of air

Code	Command function	ISAT Display Text
27A	Accelerator travel, %	e.g. 80033 = 33%
100	Display all fault codes to ISAT	–
101	Display 1st fault code + counter	e.g. 58351 80255 = Fault code 58351 generated 255 times
102	Display 2nd fault code + counter	
103	Display 3rd fault code + counter	
104	Display 4th fault code + counter	
105	Display 5th fault code + counter	

SA5039100021010X

Fig. 5 ETS command code chart (Part 1 of 2)

required for correct idling speed compensation. This means that ETS compensates for cut-in of power consumers not just on idling but throughout the engine speed range (except at full throttle).

CRUISE CONTROL

Cruise control function is incorporated in the ETS and is controlled by the ratio between torque and engine speed at any given instant, in accordance with the map curve in the ECU.

The throttle is adjusted to maintain the selected speed at any given moment and under all driving conditions (engine load conditions).

The system operation is automatically terminated if either the brake or clutch pedal is depressed or the switch is moved to the Off position.

Code	Command function	ISAT Display Text
200	Current status of AC request	8B100 = Activated (AC on) 8B000 = Not activated
202	Cruise-control status, ON/OFF switch	8B102 = ON (Cruise switch "on") 8B002 = OFF
203	Cruise control: SET status	8B103 = ON (SET switch depressed) 8B003 = OFF
204	Cruise control: RESUME status	8B104 = ON (RESUME switch depressed) 8B004 = OFF
205	Status of brake & clutch-pedal switches	8B105 = ON (either pedal depressed) 8B005 = OFF (both pedals released)
206	Status of brake-light switch	8B106 = ON (brake lights on) 8B006 = OFF (brake lights off)
249	Engine rpm	803500 = 3500 rpm
250	Coolant temperature, °C	Last 3 digits indicate temperature example: 800 + 20 = +20°C 800 – 10 = –10°C, 800 >+ 50 = above +50°C 800 >–30 = below –30°C
279	Throttle-butterfly angle %	e.g. 80030 = 30%
280	Road speed (from speedometer)	80110 = 110 km/h
281	Load signal, Tq (pulse width in μs) (check that the signal changes)	Idling = Approx. 80025 (25 μs) Full throttle = Approx. 80500 (500 μs)
380	EPROM serial no.	80xxxxxx
382	ETS-system ECU part no.	80yyyyyy
383	ETS-system ECU serial no.	80zzzzzz
550	Excite AC relay, 0.2 Hz	8A550 (AC must be switched on)
551	Activate safety valve (1 Hz)	8A551
552	Activate valve for turbo bypass	8A552
553	Activate TCS CTRL light (1 Hz)	8A553
800	Terminate communications	–
900	Clear fault codes and set adaptive values to nominal values	11111
930	Reset adaptive values	11011
971*	Base-line setting	8A971 = In progress 8D971 = Finished
973*	Calibration: warm engine	8A973
974*	Base-line setting for idling	8A974
975	Display engine variant	See codes 977 & 97A
977	Store data for B234 Turbo M.T.	802.3TS
97A	Store data for B234 Turbo A.T.	802.3TA

SA5039100021020X

Fig. 5 ETS command code chart (Part 2 of 2)

TROUBLESHOOTING

ANTI-LOCK BRAKE SYSTEM

1. The diagnostic socket (green) is located below the righthand front seat.
2. During Diagnosis, the ignition switch must always be in the On position.
3. The ISAT system number for the TC/ABS system is number 3.
4. Always read off and note down all stored diagnostic trouble codes before disconnecting the battery or ECU.
5. If communication cannot be established between ISAT and the ECU, check the leads between ECU pins 23 and 42 and the diagnostic socket. Also ensure the power feed and ground circuits to the diagnostic socket are good and the connector pins are not damaged.
6. Once diagnostic trouble codes stored in the systems's ECU have been transferred to ISAT, the diagnosis function is finished. The technician should next enter any command codes which apply to the problem which exists. It is sometimes quite helpful to enter All command codes to check the status of certain signals and components before proceeding with the detailed diagnostic procedure.
7. To avoid doing damage to the ECU, ensure the ignition is off before unplugging the connector.
8. Before tracing faults on a vehicle's electronic systems, always start by checking that the grounding circuits for the ECU concerned are good and that all nominal voltage levels are correct.
9. Unplug connectors and plugs to check the pins are undamaged and not loose. After checking, plug in all connectors and clear all diagnostic trouble codes. Start engine or drive car again to ensure the fault or faults persist.
10. When first detected, a fault will be assigned a permanent diagnostic trouble code. If the fault later disappears, the fault will be classified as intermittent.
11. All signals around the 12 volt level are proportional to battery voltage. These levels must therefore be taken only as a rough guide.
12. Zero voltage signal levels indicate ground, although a sensitive multimeter may indicate a value slightly above zero volts.
13. When ISAT command codes are being used to test the system while the car is being driven, communication between ISAT and the ECU will be broken if the speed of the car exceeds 12 mph.
14. If no diagnostic trouble codes can be read from the system even though the warning lights are On, start by checking the safety circuit (pin 8 and 51).
15. Never use the breakout box when car is being driven.

ELECTRONIC THROTTLE SYSTEM

1. The diagnostics socket (black) is located below the righthand front seat.
2. During fault diagnosis, the ignition switch must always be in Drive position.
3. The ISAT system number for the ETS system is number 3.
4. Always read off and note down all stored diagnostic trouble codes before disconnecting the battery or ECU.
5. If communication cannot be established between ISAT and the ECU, check leads between ECU pins 9 and 34 and the diagnostics socket. Also check the power feed and ground circuits to the diagnostics socket and the ECU are good and the connector pins are not damaged.
6. Once diagnostic trouble codes stored in the systems's ECU have been transferred to ISAT, the diagnosis function is finished. The technician should next enter any command codes which apply to the problem which exists. It is sometimes quite helpful to enter All command codes to check the status of certain signals and components before proceeding with the detailed diagnostic procedure.
7. To avoid damaging the ECU, ensure the ignition is off before disconnecting the connector.
8. Prior to tracing faults on a vehicle's electronic systems, always checking that the grounding circuits for the ECU concerned are good and that all nominal voltage levels are correct.
9. Disconnect connectors and plugs to check the pins are undamaged and not loose. After checking, plug in all connectors and clear all diagnostic trouble codes. Start engine or drive car again to ensure the fault or faults persist.
10. When first detected, a fault will be assigned a permanent diagnostic trouble code. If the fault later disappears, the fault will be classified as intermittent.

Permanent	Intermittent	Malfunction indicated
42220	22220	No voltage to pin 22 and/or pin 13
42241	22241	Battery voltage high: >18 V
42252	22252	Battery voltage low: <6 V
42320	22320	+15 signal absent despite Td (while ignition pulses detected)
43691	23691	Setting motor KDW, wire drawn to much
43692	23692	Setting motor KDW, wire drawn too little
44020	24020	Communication with TC/ABS disabled
44021	24021	No communication with TC/ABS
44090	24090	Faulty signal from TC/ABS
44221	24221	RPM signal absent
44260	24260	Speed signal from TC/ABS absent
44261	24261	Speedometer signal absent
44262	24262	No signal from wheel sensors/ABS system ECU
44290	24290	Speedometer signal corrupted
44291	24291	Speedometer signal faulty re TC/ABS
44295	24295	No signal from wheel sensor, LF
44296	24296	No signal from wheel sensor, RF
44297	24297	No signal from wheel sensor, LR
44298	24298	No signal from wheel sensor, RR
44390	24390	Td signal indicating speed >7000 rpm
44391	24391	Td–signal–increase too rapid
44420	24420	Load signal, Tq, absent
44490	24490	Tq signal corrupted/high during deceleration
44690	24690	Td/Tq ratio faulty
44691	24691	Engine revs signal missing
45240	25240	Throttle potentiometer signal high
45241	25241	Pedal potentiometer signal high
45242	25242	Throttle potentiometer signal ground high
45243	25243	Pedal potentiometer signal ground high
45244	25244	KDW potentiometer, signal ground too high
45245	25245	KDW potentiometer, signal voltage too high
45250	25250	Throttle potentiometer signal low
45251	25251	Pedal potentiometer signal low
45252	25252	Throttle potentiometer signal ground low
45253	25253	Pedal potentiometer signal ground low
45254	25254	KDW potentiometer, signal ground too low

SA5039100020010X

Fig. 6 ETS diagnostic trouble code chart (Part 1 of 3)

Permanent	Intermittent	Malfunction indicated
45255	25255	KDW potentiometer, signal ground too low
45290	25290	Throttle potentiometer signal faulty
45291	25291	Pedal potentiometer signal faulty
45292	25292	Deviations in signals from ETS throttle and pedal potentiometers
45360	25360	Pedal switch faulty
45391	25391	No 'DRIVE' signal with ignition on and road speed above 3 km/hr.
45720	25720	Throttle switch constantly off
45721	25721	Pedal switch constantly off
45722	25722	Brake/clutch–pedal switch faulty
45723	25723	Brake signal from ETS but not from TC
45724	25724	Brake signal from TC but not from ETS
45770	25770	Throttle switch constantly on
45771	25771	Pedal switch constantly on
45780	25780	Throttle switch voltage high
45781	25781	Pedal switch voltage high
45791	25791	Kickdown point not detected
457B1	257B1	Kickdown wire not connected
457B2	257B2	Kickdown wire adjustment incorrect
46221	26221	Temperature sensor: temperature low
46271	26271	Temperature sensor: temperature high
53240	33240	System relay current high
53250	33250	System relay current low
53270	33270	System relay constantly activated
53440	33440	Safety valve current high
53450	33450	Safety valve current low
53630	33630	Idling control not operating
55780	35780	Throttle switch voltage low
55781	35781	Pedal switch voltage low
58341	38341	Idling speed low
58351	38351	Idling speed high

SA5039100020020X

Fig. 6 ETS diagnostic trouble code chart (Part 2 of 3)

11. All signals around the 12 volt level are proportional to battery voltage. These levels must therefore be taken only as a rough guide.
12. Zero voltage signal levels indicate ground, although a sensitive multimeter may indicate a value slightly above zero volts.
13. If a system fault occurs, the system relay cuts off power supply to the ECU and other components.
14. All diagnostic trouble codes starting with a 4 or 5 denote permanent faults; a 2 or 3 at the beginning indicates an intermittent fault.

DIAGNOSIS & TESTING

TRACTION CONTROL/ ANTI-LOCK BRAKE SYSTEM (TC/ABS)

For diagnostic information, refer to "Anti-Lock Brake System" section of this chapter.

ELECTRONIC THROTTLE SYSTEM (ETS)

ACCESSING DIAGNOSTIC TROUBLE CODES

All diagnostic trouble codes starting with a 4 or 5 indicate permanent faults. All diagnostic trouble codes starting with a 2 or 3 indicate intermittent faults.

To access diagnostic trouble codes, connect ISAT tester to diagnostics socket (black), located under righthand front seat, then follow instructions included with tester.

Command Codes

Command codes instruct the ECU to perform certain functions.

When the vehicle is being driven with ISAT connected, it is normal for the TCS CTRL light to be on, for idling to be rough and for the cruise control to be disabled.

All ISAT command codes beginning with the numeral 2 can be used with the engine is running. Use the following procedure to initiate command codes.

1. Connect ISAT and capacitor lead, part No. 86-11-048, to Black diagnostic connector.
2. Turn ignition key to Drive position. Do not start engine.
3. Establish communications between ISAT and EST ECU.
4. Enter desired command code (starting with 2xx), **Fig. 5.**
5. Start vehicle, then perform test. ISAT response to a command code is constantly shown on the display.
6. To enter a new command code, terminate communications, shut off engine and repeat this procedure.

DIAGNOSTIC TROUBLE CODE INTERPRETATION

Refer to **Fig. 6** for diagnostic trouble code interpretation.

ETS CONTROL UNIT PIN INSPECTION

Refer to **Fig. 7** for ETS control unit pin function tests.

SYSTEM SERVICE

ETS ECU CALIBRATION

Calibration must be carried out after replacing any major system component, such as ETS ECU, TC/ABS ECU, pedal potentiometer, throttle housing.

Permanent	Intermittent	Malfunction indicated
62490	72940	ECU fault: PID regulator
67190	77190	ECU fault: RAM fault
67191	77191	ECU fault: ROM fault
67192	77192	ECU fault: EEPROM fault
67193	77193	ECU fault: EEPROM fault
67196	77196	ECU fault: time function
67290	77290	ECU fault: D/A converter fault
672B1	772B1	ECU error, D/A convertor for KDW motor
67390	77390	ECU fault: speed control <20 km/h
67391	77391	ECU fault: speed control >48 km/h
67590	77590	Internal monitoring (Watchdog 1)
67591	77591	ECU fault: reset function
67592	77592	Internal monitoring (Watchdog 2)
67593	77593	ECU fault: safety switch 30
67594	77594	ECU fault: safety switch 31
67595	77595	ECU fault: safety switch 32
675B0	–	ECU fault–calibration not completed
675B1	–	ECU fault–calibration impossible
675B2	–	ECU fault–engine variant not specified
675B3	775B3	ECU error, EEPROM
675B4	775B4	ECU error, monitoring (watchdog)
675B5	775B5	ECU error, ROM
68170	78170	Software fault: system relay
68331	78331	Short circuit in output stage of KDW motor
68340	78340	ECU fault: transistor for system relay
68341	78341	ECU fault: safety valve
68342	78342	ECU fault: TCS CTRL light
68390	78390	ECU fault: throttle control faulty
68391	78391	ECU fault: GR flip–flop
683B0	783B0	ECU fault–throttle control
683B1	783B1	KDW motor, output stage incorrect function
E7590	D7590	Safety system activated
E75B1	D75B1	Communication error, serial interface
E75B2	D75B2	Communication error, communication interrupted
E75B3	D75B3	Communication error, communication cannot be reinstated

SA5039100020030X

Fig. 6 ETS diagnostic trouble code chart (Part 3 of 3)

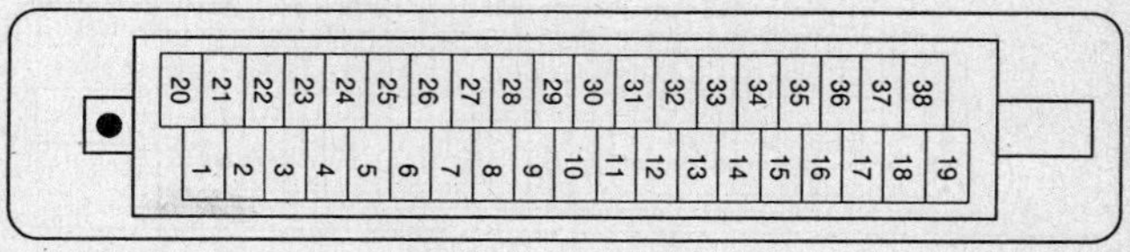

The following signals may be tested at the back of the ETS ECU connector with all components connected and the ignition switched on.

Pin#	Circuit/Function	Wire Color	Test
1	Ground	Black	Check voltage drop to ground. Should be less than 0.1 volts (Ignition must be on to check voltage drop).
2	Pedal potentiometer reference voltage	Yellow/Red	Approximately 5 volts
3	Throttle potentiometer reference voltage	Yellow/White	Approximately 5 volts
4	Pedal potentiometer common	Yellow	Approximately 0.1 to 0.2 volts
5	Throttle potentiometer common	White	Approximately 0.1 to 0.2 volts
6	Bypass valve control signal	Gray	Not actuated = approx. battery volts Actuated = approx. 0 volts
7	Not used		
8	Not used		
9	Diagnostic "L" line (request from ISAT to ECU)	Yellow/White	Approximately 12 volts with ignition on
10	Speedometer signal input (Hall effect switch signal)	Green/Red	Should switch from approximately 0 volts to approximately 10 – 12 volts as transmission is turned slowly by hand.
11	Not used		
12	RPM	Orange	At least 2.0 volts A.C. while cranking. Approx. 3.0 volts at idle. Voltage may increase slightly as RPM increases.
13	System relay control (energizes system relay pulldown circuit when grounded. ECU internally grounds this circuit when it receives a +15 signal provided that there are no faults in the ETS system)	Blue	Not activated = approx battery volts Activated = less than 1.5 volt

SA5039100022010X

Fig. 7 ETS control unit pin inspection (Part 1 of 4)

1. Start and run engine until normal operating temperature is reached. If the engine will not run correctly during warm up cycle, establish ISAT communications and enter command code 974 in order to enter basic data and enable warm up to be completed.
2. Switch off engine. Connect ISAT and capacitor lead, part No. 86-11-048, to Black diagnostic connector.
3. Turn ignition On, select DIAG, ONE system from menu and enter system number 3. Check if any diagnostic trouble codes are stored in memory. If diagnostic trouble codes are present, repair as necessary, then erase diagnostic trouble codes before proceeding.
4. To enter the base line setting, enter command code 971. ISAT will display 8A971. After several seconds, the display will change to 8D971, indicating that the basic setting has been made and the system is ready for calibration.
5. With ignition On, engine Off, enter command code 973.
    a. Once the TCS CTRL light illuminates, start engine. **Do not touch pedals.**
    b. Wait for idle to stabilize at approximately 850 RPM.
    c. The ECU will raise engine speed to approximately 3000 RPM.
6. The calibration procedure will be discontinued if a pedal is depressed or vehicle starts to roll.
7. When calibration process is complete, the TCS CTRL light will shutoff. Terminate ISAT communications and shutoff engine. Check if any diagnostic trouble codes were stored during calibration procedure.

COMPONENT REPLACEMENT

TC/ABS ECU

1. Obtain radio anti-theft code as outlined under "Precautions."
2. Remove two mounting screws, then lift out ECU and disconnect connector.
3. Reverse procedure to install.

Control Valve For Turbo Bypass Valve

This valve is located inside the engine compartment, on the lefthand inner fender.

1. Remove two mounting nuts.
2. Unplug electrical connector, then disconnect three signal hoses. Keep color coded rings on valve ports when hoses are disconnected.
3. Reverse procedure to install.

Safety Valve

This valve is mounted on the false bulkhead panel on right side of car.

1. Remove two mounting nuts.
2. Unplug connector, then disconnect vacuum hoses. Keep color coded rings on valve ports when hoses are disconnected.
3. Reverse procedure to install.

Non-Return Valve

This valve is installed in the vacuum hose between the safety valve and inlet manifold.

1. Disconnect vacuum hoses.
2. To install, reconnect vacuum hoses. Ensure white end of valve is pointed towards the safety valve.

Pedal Sensor

1. Remove lower dash panel and carpeting from driver side of center console.
2. Unplug connector from pedal sensor.
3. Remove clip, then disconnect sensor linkage from accelerator.
4. Remove sensor.
5. Reverse procedure to install.

ETS ECU

The replacement ETS ECU must be recalibrated.

1. Move driver seat to fully forward position with backrest also angled forward.
2. Obtain radio anti-theft code as outlined under "Precautions."

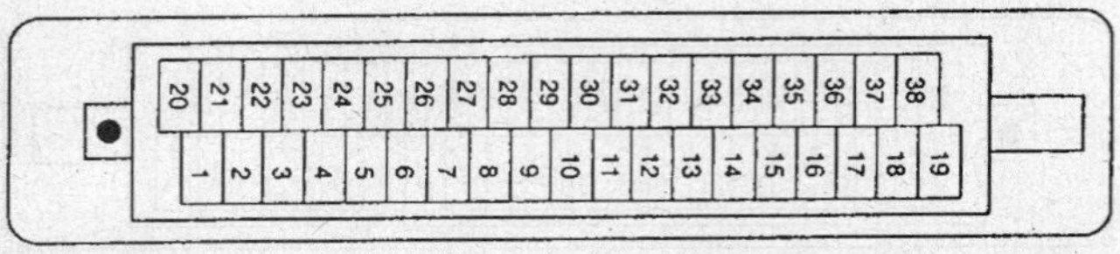

The following signals may be tested at the back of the ETS ECU connector with all components connected and the ignition switched on.

Pin #	Circuit/Function	Wire Color	Test
14	Accelerator pedal safety switch	Gray/White	Pedal released = approx. 1.0 volt Pedal depressed = approx 7–9 volts (halfway)
15	Brake light switch	White	Brakes released = 0 volts Brakes applied = approx. battery volts
16	Throttle potentiometer position signal	Blue/White	Approx. 4.0 volts at idle – decreases to – Approx. 0.1 volts at full throttle Throttle butterfly must be held in the full open position by hand.
17	Pedal potentiometer position signal	Green/Yellow	Approx. 0.1 volts at idle – increases to – Approx. 4.0 volts at full throttle
18	Cruise control: "RESUME"	Yellow	"Resume" switch depressed = battery volts "Resume" switch released = 0 volts
19	Cruise control: "SET"	Red/White	"Set" switch depressed = battery volts "Set" switch released = 0 volts
20	Throttle motor	Green	
21	Throttle motor	Green/White	
22	Power in from system relay	Blue/Red	System relay energized = approx. battery volts System relay de-energized = approx. 0 volts
23	TCS-CTRL Warning light	Violet/White	Light on = less than 2 volts Light off = approx battery volts
24	Not used		
25	+15 (switched power in)	Green/White	Ignition on = approx. battery volts Ignition off = approx. 0 volts

SA5039100022020X

Fig. 7 ETS control unit pin inspection (Part 2 of 4)

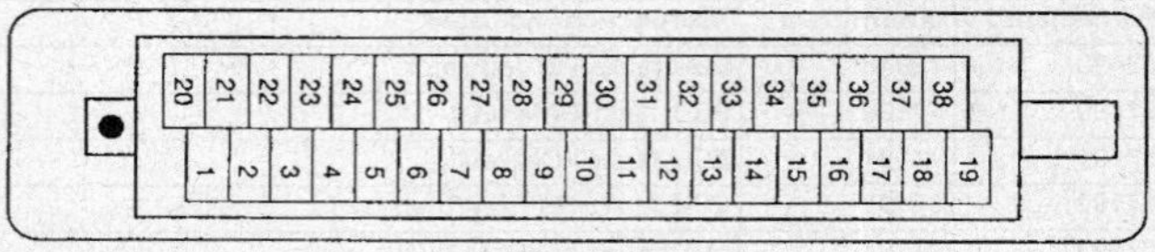

The following signals may be tested at the back of the ETS ECU connector with all components connected and the ignition switched on.

Pin#	Circuit/Function	Wire Color	Test
26	Throttle angle output signal to LH & DI (TK)	Yellow	Use ISAT pulsemeter to check that pulse width changes with throttle opening. (Frequency may change also)
27	Load signal (TQ)	White	Use ISAT pulsemeter to check that pulse frequency changes with engine load. (Pulse width may change also)
28	Throttle safety switch	Black/White	Throttle closed = approx. 1.0 volt Throttle open = 7–10 volts (half throttle or more)
29	Communications signal • Connected to TC/ABS pin 24 on manual transmission cars. • Connected to ASR pin 14 on automatic transmission cars.	Green/White	With engine idling and vehicle stationary = approx. 5 volts D.C. (A reading close to 0 or close to 10 volts indicates a problem in this wire/circuit) A logic probe should also indicate a continuous 'PULSE' signal.
30	Not used		
31	Cruise control: "ON" or "OFF"	Red	Cruise switch "ON" = approx. battery volts Cruise switch "OFF" = approx. 0 volts
32	Communications signal • Connected to TC/ABS pin 4 on manual transmission cars. • Connected to ASR pin 2 on automatic transmission cars.	Black/White	With engine idling and vehicle stationary = approx 5 volts D.C. (A reading close to 0 or close to 10 volts indicates a problem in this wire/circuit) A logic probe should also indicate a continuous 'PULSE' signal.
33	Coolant temperature sensor	Yellow	Voltage varies with coolant temperature Approx. 4.0 volts at –20°C (–4°F) Approx. 2.3 volts at +20°C (68°F) Approx. 0.5 volts at 80°C (176°F)

SA5039100022030X

Fig. 7 ETS control unit pin inspection (Part 3 of 4)

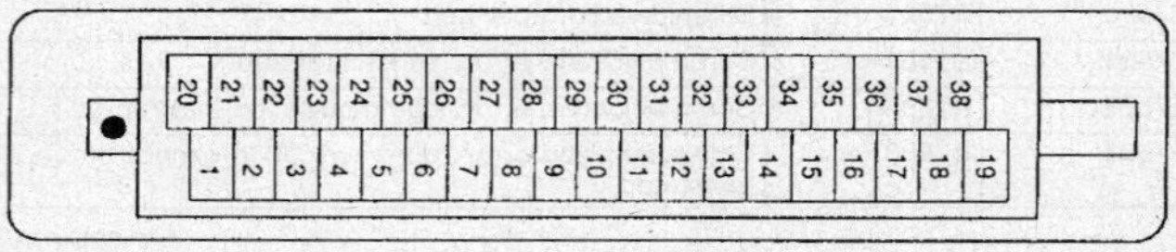

The following signals may be tested at the back of the ETS ECU connector with all components connected and the ignition switched on.

Pin#	Circuit/Function	Wire Color	Test
34	Diagnostic "K" lead (reply from ECU to ISAT)	Blue/White	
35	Safety valve control signal	Brown/White	System operational (safety valve energized) = approx. 1.0 volt System deactivated (safety valve de-energized) = 0 volt (possible battery voltage if system relay stayed energized)
36	Brake and clutch switches	White	Both pedals released = approx. battery volts Either pedal depressed = less than 1.0 volt
37	A.C. Request (power signal to ECU when A.C. switch is on, or when A.C.C. is requesting A.C)	Yellow	A.C. Switched on (or A.C.C. in air conditioning mode) = approx. 10–12 volts A.C. Switched off (or A.C.C. in econ. mode; or pressure switches open) = 0 volts
38	A.C. Relay control signal (ETS control unit provides ground for A.C. relay to operate compressor)	Black	A.C. Relay energized = approx. 1.0 volt A.C. Relay de-energized (with request signal present) = approx. 10–12 volts A.C. Relay de-energized (with A.C. switched off) = 0 volts

SA5039100022040X

Fig. 7 ETS control unit pin inspection (Part 4 of 4)

3. Loosen two clips and fold carpet up under seat.
4. Remove protecting plate mounting screw. Position plate aside.
5. Remove control unit from under spring tensioned bracket. Disconnect connector housing from ECU.
6. Remove cover plate. Lift out ECU and disconnect connector.
7. Reverse procedure to install. Calibrate new ECU as outlined under "System Service."

Throttle Housing

1. Drain enough coolant to lower level in system to below throttle housing.
2. Disconnect two coolant hoses from housing.
3. Disconnect rubber elbow for air intake. Position aside.
4. Disconnect two vacuum hoses.
5. Remove two clips, then disconnect throttle cable from throttle housing.
6. Unplug connector, then remove nut at bottom of throttle housing.
7. Remove bolt at bottom of throttle housing, then position brace aside.
8. Remove throttle housing mounting nuts, then the housing. Save O-ring.
9. Reverse procedure to install. Recalibrate system as outlined under "System Service."

TC/ABS Hydraulic Unit

Before beginning this procedure, depressurize accumulator in the TC/ABS hydraulic unit by repeatedly depressing the brake pedal until a dramatic increase in resistance is felt (at least 20 times). Failure to perform this step could result in serious injury.

1. Remove lower dash panel to gain access to top of pedal assembly.
2. Remove pin retaining clip, then withdraw pin from hydraulic unit pushrod.
3. Obtain radio anti-theft code as outlined under "Precautions."
4. Remove battery.
5. Remove clips securing positive lead to battery shelf, then the terminal block (with leads) from battery shelf.
6. Remove connectors at rear of battery shelf, then nuts for the brace.
7. Position TC/ABS ECU aside.
8. Remove battery shelf, then release ABS fuse/relay panel. Position panel aside.
9. Siphon fluid from reservoir, then remove lefthand front wheel and fender liner.

10. Remove brace between engine subframe and wheel housing.
11. Cut tie strap and disconnect all electrical leads from hydraulic unit.
12. Remove mount for battery shelf at hydraulic unit.
13. Disconnect hose for clutch cylinder, then plug end of hose. Do not spill any brake fluid as this could allow air to get into clutch system.
14. Disconnect and plug brake lines from valve block, then remove accumulator.
15. Remove four hydraulic unit mounting nuts, located on bulkhead behind pedal assembly.
16. Remove hydraulic unit.
17. Reverse procedure to install, noting the following:
    a. **Torque** hydraulic unit mounting nuts to 19 ft. lbs.
    b. **Torque** accumulator to 28 ft. lbs.

Traction Control System w/Automatic Transmission

INDEX

	Page No.
Description	7-180
Automatic Slip Reduction (ASR) Component Description	7-181
Electronic Throttle System Component Description	7-181
Subsystem	7-180
System	7-180
Diagnosis & Testing	7-183
Electronic Throttle System (ETS)	7-183
Traction Control/Anti-Lock Brake System (TC/ABS)	7-183
Precautions	7-180
Air Bag Systems	7-180
Battery Ground Cable	7-180
Radio Anti-Theft Lock	7-180
System Service	7-183
ASR System Calibration	7-183
Component Replacement	7-184
Troubleshooting	7-182
Electronic Throttle System	7-182

PRECAUTIONS

AIR BAG SYSTEMS

Refer to "Air Bag System Precautions" in the front of this manual for system disarming and arming procedures.

BATTERY GROUND CABLE

Prior to service, disconnect battery ground cable and isolate as required.

RADIO ANTI-THEFT LOCK

9000

Radio and cassette player are equipped with an electronic four-digit anti-theft lock. This four-digit code is programmed at manufacturing and cannot be changed. If the battery is disconnected for more than three minutes, if unit is removed or if otherwise cut off from power, the four-digit code must be entered with the quick-selection buttons as follows:

1. Turn radio on, then, when display shows "Code In," enter four-digit code with quick-selection buttons. If code is correct, last-tuned radio frequency is shown on display. If wrong digit has been entered by mistake, all four digits must be entered again. If code is wrong it stays on display.
2. If incorrect four-digit code has been entered, press Band button for more than three seconds to clear display. Display shows "Code In" and new attempt to enter correct code can be made.
3. If wrong code has been used three times in succession, four dashes appear on display and you must wait an hour with radio switched on before trying again.
4. To try again, hold Band button for at least three seconds. "Code In" should appear on display.
5. Correct code must be entered at first attempt, otherwise you must wait another hour with unit switched on before trying again.

DESCRIPTION

SYSTEM

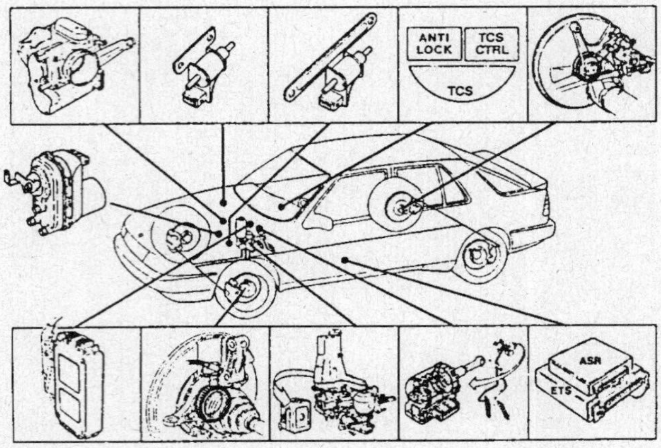

SA5029100053000X

Fig. 1 Traction control system components

Traction Control System (TCS), used on 9000 models, **Fig. 1,** is used to prevent wheel spin when the car is accelerating on a slippery surface.

The TCS system for automatic transmissions consists of two subsystems, the Electronic Throttle System (ETS) and Automatic Slip Reduction (ASR).

TCS utilizes many of the components in the ABS system. The major addition to the system is the Electronic Throttle System.

Automatic transmission TCS does not have the capability to apply the brakes during wheel spin conditions, however this system does control the operation of the transmission kickdown cable in addition to controlling the throttle butterfly.

SUBSYSTEM

ELECTRONIC THROTTLE SYSTEM (ETS)

The main purpose of the ETS system is to electronically control the position of the throttle butterfly.

The throttle housing is equipped with an actuating motor for the throttle butterfly, a vacuum unit, a throttle potentiometer and a safety cutout switch. Connected to the accelerator pedal is a pedal sensor with associated solenoid valves and a non-return valve fitted on the bulkhead. For additional safety, a parallel system using a throttle cable is provided, which will take over in the limp-home mode.

Automatic Idling Control (AIC)

The ETS eliminates the need for separate components for Automatic Idling Control (AIC) and load related control over the entire working range of the engine.

Smooth Response To Heavy-Footed Use Of Accelerator

If the driver depresses or releases the accelerator abruptly, the throttle butterfly will be operated in two steps within a period of just a few milliseconds. This allows the car responding smoothly on both acceleration and deceleration.

Integral Cruise Control Function

The ETS system incorporates a cruise control function. Since operation of the cruise control system is based on acceleration control, maximum engine performance is available under all conditions, unlike some previous systems which reverted to basic boost when cruise control was operating.

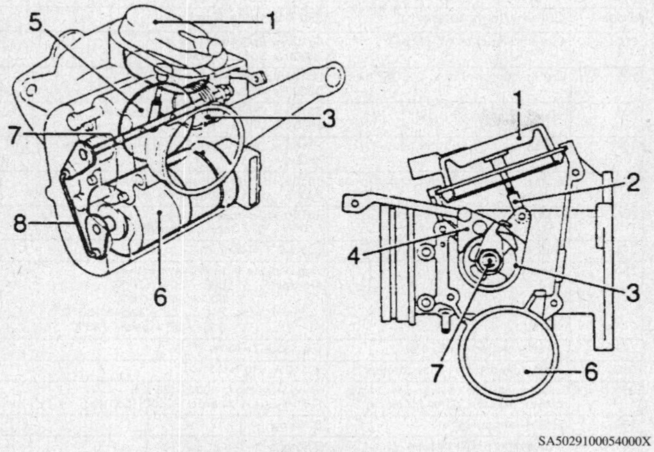

Fig. 2 Throttle housing components

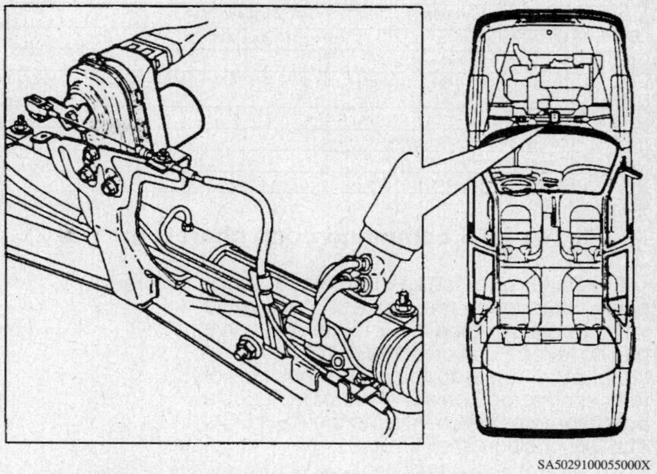

Fig. 3 Kickdown wire & motor assembly

Intelligent System

The ETS is an intelligent or adaptive system, which means that it adapts itself automatically to changes in air pressure, humidity and variations due to wear in components.

The ETS also incorporates an AIC function for the warm-up phase, governed by time and coolant temperature.

The system continuously processes data from the speedometer, direct ignition system, ABS system, LH system and temperature sensor. It also monitors the position of the throttle butterfly and accelerator.

On the basis of this input data, the ECU controls the actuating motor for the throttle butterfly.

AUTOMATIC SLIP REDUCTION (ASR)

Vehicles with automatic transmissions utilize only the throttle butterfly for traction control. With the addition of a kickdown cable control, the ASR system can be described separately even though ASR is an integral part of the Electronic Throttle System (ETS).

Automatic transmission vehicles with traction control utilize another control unit to assist in operation of the kickdown wire (KDW). This additional ECU is on top of the ETS ECU which is fitting since the ASR ECU and the ETS ECU are basically one control unit.

ELECTRONIC THROTTLE SYSTEM COMPONENT DESCRIPTION

ELECTRONIC CONTROL UNIT (ETS ECU)

The ETS ECU receives information on a variety of engine parameters, which it processes before sending appropriate control signals to the throttle housing.

The ECU has an integral self-diagnostics function which is activated every time the ignition is switched off. On power off, automatic testing takes place of all functions and the latest adaptive values are added to memory.

The ECU monitors operation of the system continuously and if a fault is detected that could affect safety, immediately switches to the limp-home function.

THROTTLE HOUSING

The throttle housing, **Fig. 2,** controls the amount of air supplied to the engine, but the position of the throttle butterfly is controlled by means of a pulse width modulated motor.

A throttle cable is connected in parallel, for use in emergency limp-home mode.

Normal Mode

Refer to **Fig. 2** for component locations.

When the engine is started, a vacuum is raised in the vacuum unit (1). This causes the diaphragm (2) and lever assembly to move upwards, which tensions the spring (3). This action also causes the throttle cable attachment lever (4) to turn, slackening the cable and allowing the throttle butterfly (5) to be controlled over idling to full throttle range by the motor (6). The motor actuates the throttle spindle (7) through a link rod (8) attached at either end to levers on the motor and spindle.

Limp-Home Mode

If a fault should occur anywhere in the system, a safety valve on the bulkhead immediately exhausts the vacuum in the vacuum unit.

The diaphragm rod and lever assembly moves down, tensioning the spring, to bring full spring force to bear on the throttle spindle. Since the motor is not powerful enough to overcome the force of the spring to operate the throttle butterfly, the throttle can only be operated by the throttle cable.

The car is now in the limp-home mode, which is clearly evident by both the additionally force required to move the accelerator and the fact that the TCS CTRL light has come on.

AUTOMATIC IDLING CONTROL (AIC)

Because the mass of air that the AIC valve admitted through the throttle housing to compensate idling speed for A/C cut-in etc. varies depending on pressure and temperature, the compensation it provides also tends to vary to some extent with ambient conditions.

However, because the AIC function in the ETS is adaptive, continuous compensation related to pressure and temperature takes place, which means that the opening duration and throttle angle will always be exactly right to admit the precise mass of air required for correct idling speed compensation. This means that ETS compensates for cut-in of power consumers not just on idling but throughout the engine speed range (except at full throttle).

CRUISE CONTROL

Cruise control function is incorporated in the ETS and is controlled by the ratio between torque and engine speed at any given instant, in accordance with the map curve in the ECU.

The throttle is adjusted to maintain the selected speed at any given moment and under all driving conditions (engine load conditions).

The system operation is automatically terminated if either the brake or clutch pedal is depressed or the switch is moved to the Off position.

AUTOMATIC SLIP REDUCTION (ASR) COMPONENT DESCRIPTION

ELECTRONIC CONTROL UNIT (ASR ECU)

The ASR ECU has two functions; deciding when traction control mode is needed and operating the kickdown wire motor.

The ASR ECU is an addition to the ETS ECU. Both ECUs can be found below the driver seat fixed to a mounting bracket. Several wires from the ASR ECU are connected to the ETS ECU, since the two units share many of the same signals.

KICKDOWN WIRE SETTING MOTOR

The kickdown wire (KDW) motor that controls the kickdown cable is located on a separate bracket on the engine frame adjacent to the steering rack, **Fig. 3.**

Code	Command function	ISAT Display Text
27A	Accelerator travel, %	e.g. 80033 = 33%
100	Display all fault codes to ISAT	-
101	Display 1st fault code + counter	e.g. 58351 80255 = Fault code 58351 generated 255 times
102	Display 2nd fault code + counter	
103	Display 3rd fault code + counter	
104	Display 4th fault code + counter	
105	Display 5th fault code + counter	

SA5029100057010X

Fig. 4 ETS command code chart (Part 1 of 2)

Code	Command function	ISAT Display Text
200	Current status of AC request	88100 = Activated (AC on) 88000 = Not activated
202	Cruise-control status, ON/OFF switch	88102 = ON (Cruise switch "on") 88002 = OFF
203	Cruise control: SET status	88103 = ON (SET switch depressed) 88003 = OFF
204	Cruise control: RESUME status	88104 = ON (RESUME switch depressed) 88004 = OFF
205	Status of brake & clutch-pedal switches	88105 = ON (either pedal depressed) 88005 = OFF (both pedals released)
206	Status of brake-light switch	88106 = ON (brake lights on) 88006 = OFF (brake lights off)
249	Engine rpm	803500 = 3500 rpm
250	Coolant temperature, °C	Last 3 digits indicate temperature example: 800 + 20 = +20°C 800 - 10 = -10°C. 800 >+ 50 = above +50°C 800 >-30 = below -30°C
279	Throttle-butterfly angle %	e.g. 80030 = 30%
280	Road speed (from speedometer)	80110 = 110 km/h
281	Load signal, Tq (pulse width in µs) (check that the signal changes)	Idling = Approx. 80025 (25 µs) Full throttle = Approx. 80500 (500 µs)
380	EPROM serial no.	80xxxxxx
382	ETS-system ECU part no.	80yyyyyy
383	ETS-system ECU serial no.	80zzzzzz
550	Excite AC relay, 0.2 Hz	8A550 (AC must be switched on)
551	Activate safety valve (1 Hz)	8A551
552	Activate valve for turbo bypass	8A552
553	Activate TCS CTRL light (1 Hz)	8A553
800	Terminate communications	-
900	Clear fault codes and set adaptive values to nominal values	11111
930	Reset adaptive values	11011
971*	Base-line setting	8A971 = In progress 8D971 = Finished
973*	Calibration: warm engine	8A973
974*	Base-line setting for idling	8A974
975	Display engine variant	See codes 977 & 97A
977	Store data for B234 Turbo M.T.	802.3TS
97A	Store data for B234 Turbo A.T.	802.3TA

* Consult complete calibration procedures

SA5029100057020X

Fig. 4 ETS command code chart (Part 2 of 2)

The main purpose of the motor is to replace the lever on the conventional throttle valve housing, since the ETS throttle valve has no lever. Position of the KDW is proportional at all times to the actual position of the accelerator. The KDW motor includes a potentiometer which informs the ASR ECU of KDW position at all times.

Limp-Home Mode—Kickdown Wire

If a fault occurs in the ASR system or in the ETS system which is critical to the operation of Traction Control, the system will revert to the limp-home mode.

In the limp-home mode, the kickdown wire is set to a fixed position of approximately 40 percent of full travel. At the same time, engine torque is limited to a maximum of 85 percent of normal through control of the throttle valve opening position.

This torque limitation combined with the fixed position of the kickdown wire help prevent any transmission slippage.

PEDAL & THROTTLE POTENTIOMETERS

The ASR ECU constantly compares the signal at pin 1 (pedal potentiometer position) with the signal at pin 3 (throttle potentiometer position). If there is an abnormal deviation between the two signals, the system will revert to the limp-home position.

WHEEL SPEED SIGNALS

The ASR ECU receives wheel speed information from the Anti-Lock Brake System Electronic Control Unit (ABS ECU). The ABS ECU receives and AC voltage from each wheel speed sensor and converts the AC voltage to a digital square wave. As the speed of the wheel increases, the frequency of the AC voltage increases, so the ABS ECU increases the frequency of the digital square wave. Test pulses are generated by the ABS ECU so that the ASR ECU can check for continuity of the signal wires even when the car is stationary.

If there is a deviation in the speed of either front wheel when compared with the reference speed (average rear wheel speed), the ASR ECU sends a signal to the ETS ECU to decrease the throttle opening to stop the wheel spin.

GEAR SELECTOR SIGNAL

The ASR ECU receives information from the gear selector switch regarding gear selector position. When the gear selector is in Park or Neutral there is no signal (zero volts). When the gear selector is placed in any driving position, the ASR ECU receives a 12 volt signal. The ASR ECU then sends a signal to the ETS ECU for idle compensation.

TROUBLESHOOTING

ELECTRONIC THROTTLE SYSTEM

1. The diagnostics socket (black) is located below the righthand front seat.
2. During fault diagnosis, the ignition switch must always be in Drive position.
3. The ISAT system number for the ETS system is number 3.
4. Always read off and note down all stored diagnostic trouble codes before disconnecting the battery or ECU.
5. If communication cannot be established between ISAT and the ECU, check leads between ECU pins 9 and 34 and the diagnostics socket. Also check the power feed and ground circuits to the diagnostics socket and the ECU are good and the connector pins are not damaged.
6. Once diagnostic trouble codes stored in the systems's ECU have been transferred to ISAT, the diagnosis function is finished. The technician should next enter any command codes which apply to the problem which exists. It is sometimes quite helpful to enter All command codes to check the status of certain signals and components before proceeding with the detailed diagnostic procedure.
7. To avoid damaging the ECU, ensure the ignition is off before disconnecting the connector.
8. Prior to tracing faults on a vehicle's electronic systems, always ensure the grounding circuits for the ECU concerned are good and that all nominal voltage levels are correct.
9. Disconnect connectors and plugs to ensure the pins are undamaged and not loose. After checking, plug in all connectors and clear all diagnostic trouble codes. Start engine or drive car again to ensure the fault or faults persist.
10. When first detected, a fault will be assigned a permanent diagnostic trouble code. If the fault later disappears, the fault will be classified as intermittent.
11. All signals around the 12 volt level are proportional to battery voltage. These levels must therefore be taken only as a rough guide.
12. Zero voltage signal levels indicate ground, although a sensitive multimeter may indicate a value slightly above zero volts.
13. If a system fault occurs, the system relay cuts off power supply to the ECU and other components.
14. All diagnostic trouble codes starting

Permanent	Intermittent	Malfunction Indicated
675B0	–	ECU fault-calibration not completed
675B1	–	ECU fault-calibration impossible
675B2	–	ECU fault-engine variant not specified
683B0	783B0	ECU fault-throttle control
E7590	D7590	Safety system activated
42220	22220	No voltage to pin 22 and/or pin 13
42241	22241	Battery voltage high: >18 V
42252	22252	Battery voltage low: <6 V
42320	22320	+15 signal absent (while ignition pulses detected)
44020	24020	Communication with TC/ABS disabled
44021	24021	No communication with TC/ABS
44090	24090	Faulty signal from TC/ABS
44221	24221	RPM signal absent
44260	24260	Speed signal from TC/ABS absent
44261	24261	Speedometer signal absent
44290	24290	Speedometer signal corrupted
44291	24291	Speedometer signal faulty re TC/ABS
44390	24390	Td signal indicating speed >7000 rpm
44391	24391	Td-signal-increase too rapid
44420	24420	Load signal, Tq, absent
44490	24490	Tq signal corrupted/high during deceleration
44690	24690	Td/Tq ratio faulty
45240	25240	Throttle potentiometer signal high
45241	25241	Pedal potentiometer signal high
45242	25242	Throttle potentiometer signal ground high
45243	25243	Pedal potentiometer signal ground high
45250	25250	Throttle potentiometer signal low
45251	25251	Pedal potentiometer signal low
45252	25252	Throttle potentiometer signal ground low
45253	25253	Pedal potentiometer signal ground low
45290	25290	Throttle potentiometer signal faulty

SA5029100056010X

Fig. 5 ETS diagnostic trouble code chart (Part 1 of 3)

Permanent	Intermittent	Malfunction Indicated
45291	25291	Pedal potentiometer signal faulty
45360	25360	Pedal switch faulty
45720	25720	Throttle switch constantly off
45721	25721	Pedal switch constantly off
45722	25722	Brake/clutch-pedal switch faulty
45723	25723	Brake signal from ETS but not from TC
45724	25724	Brake signal from TC but not from ETS
45770	25770	Throttle switch constantly on
45771	25771	Pedal switch constantly on
45780	25780	Throttle switch voltage high
45781	25781	Pedal switch voltage high
46221	26221	Temperature sensor: temperature low
46271	26271	Temperature sensor: temperature high
53240	33240	System relay current high
53250	33250	System relay current low
53270	33270	System relay constantly activated
53440	33440	Safety valve current high
53450	33450	Safety valve current low
53630	33630	Idling control not operating
55780	35780	Throttle switch voltage low
55781	35781	Pedal switch voltage low
58341	38341	Idling speed low
58351	38351	Idling speed high

SA5029100056020X

Fig. 5 ETS diagnostic trouble code chart (Part 2 of 3)

with a 4 or 5 denote permanent faults; a 2 or 3 at the beginning indicates an intermittent fault.

DIAGNOSIS & TESTING

TRACTION CONTROL/ ANTI-LOCK BRAKE SYSTEM (TC/ABS)

For diagnostic information, refer to "Anti-Lock Brake System" section of this chapter.

ELECTRONIC THROTTLE SYSTEM (ETS)

DIAGNOSTIC TROUBLE CODES

All diagnostic trouble codes starting with a 4 or 5 indicate permanent faults. All diagnostic trouble codes starting with a 2 or 3 indicate intermittent faults.

To access diagnostic trouble codes, connect ISAT tester to diagnostics socket (black), located under righthand front seat, then follow instructions included with tester.

Command Codes

Command codes instruct the ECU to perform certain functions.

When the vehicle is being driven with ISAT connected, it is normal for the TCS CTRL light to be on, for idling to be rough and for the cruise control to be disabled.

All ISAT command codes beginning with the numeral 2 can be used with the engine is running. Use the following procedure to initiate command codes.

1. Connect ISAT and capacitor lead, tool No. 86-11-048, or equivalent, to Black diagnostic connector.
2. Turn ignition key to Drive position. Do not start engine.
3. Establish communications between ISAT and EST ECU.
4. Enter desired command code (starting with 2xx), **Fig. 4.**
5. Start vehicle, then perform test. ISAT response to a command code is constantly shown on the display.
6. To enter a new command code, terminate communications, shutoff engine and repeat this procedure.

DIAGNOSTIC TROUBLE CODES INTERPRETATION

Refer to **Fig. 5** for automatic transmission diagnostic trouble codes.

ETS CONTROL UNIT PIN INSPECTION

Refer to **Fig. 6** for ETS control unit pin function tests.

AUTOMATIC SLIP REDUCTION (ARS) CONTROL UNIT PIN VOLTAGE INSPECTION

Refer to **Fig. 7** for ASR control unit pin function voltage checks.

SYSTEM SERVICE

ASR SYSTEM CALIBRATION

Calibration must be carried out after replacing any major system component, such as ETS ECU, ASR ECU, pedal potentiometer, throttle housing, kickdown wire motor.

1. Before calibration is done, the kickdown cable should be adjusted as follows:
   a. Loosen clamp on cable sheath. Leave kickdown cable attached to lever.
   b. Move lever to fully extended position (right side of vehicle) against the mechanical stop. Hold lever in this position until step D is complete.
   c. Pull kickdown cable sheath past kickdown position to full throttle mechanical stop in transmission.
   d. Tighten kickdown cable sheath clamp to specifications, while holding full throttle position.
2. Start and run engine until normal operating temperature is reached. If engine will not run correctly during warm up cycle, establish ISAT communications and enter command code 974 in order to enter basic data and enable warm up to be completed.
3. Switch off engine. Connect ISAT and capacitor lead part No. 86-11-048 to the Black diagnostic connector.
4. Turn ignition On, select DIAG, ONE system from menu and enter system number 3. Check if any diagnostic trouble codes are stored in memory. If diagnostic trouble codes are present, repair as necessary, then erase diagnostic trouble codes before proceeding.
5. With ignition On, engine Off, enter command code 971:
   a. Several seconds after entering command code 971, ISAT will terminate communications.
   b. Wait 30 seconds (ASR and ETS will store base line settings at this time.
6. Establish communication with ISAT. With ignition On, engine Off, enter

Permanent	Intermittent	Malfunction indicated
62490	72940	ECU fault: PID regulator
67190	77190	ECU fault: RAM fault
67191	77191	ECU fault: ROM fault
67192	77192	ECU fault: EEPROM fault
67193	77193	ECU fault: EEPROM fault
67196	77196	ECU fault: time function
67290	77290	ECU fault: D/A converter fault
67390	77390	ECU fault: speed control <20 km/h
67391	77391	ECU fault: speed control >48 km/h
67590	77590	Internal monitoring (Watchdog 1)
67591	77591	ECU fault: reset function
67592	77592	Internal monitoring (Watchdog 2)
67593	77593	ECU fault: safety switch 30
67594	77594	ECU fault: safety switch 31
67595	77595	ECU fault: safety switch 32
68170	78170	Software fault: system relay
68340	78340	ECU fault: transistor for system relay
68341	78341	ECU fault: safety valve
68342	78342	ECU fault: TCS CTRL light
68390	78390	ECU fault: throttle control faulty
68391	78391	ECU fault: GR flip-flop

SA5029100056030X

Fig. 5 ETS diagnostic trouble code chart (Part 3 of 3)

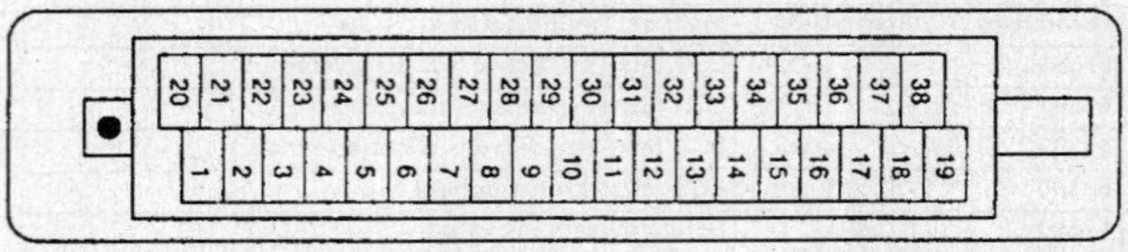

The following signals may be tested at the back of the ETS ECU connector with all components connected and the ignition switched on.

Pin#	Circuit/Function	Wire Color	Test
1	Ground	Black	Check voltage drop to ground. Should be less than 0.1 volts (Ignition must be on to check voltage drop).
2	Pedal potentiometer reference voltage	Yellow/Red	Approximately 5 volts
3	Throttle potentiometer reference voltage	Yellow/White	Approximately 5 volts
4	Pedal potentiometer common	Yellow	Approximately 0.1 to 0.2 volts
5	Throttle potentiometer common	White	Approximately 0.1 to 0.2 volts
6	Bypass valve control signal	Gray	Not actuated = approx. battery volts Actuated = approx. 0 volts
7	Not used		
8	Not used		
9	Diagnostic "L" line (request from ISAT to ECU)	Yellow/White	Approximately 12 volts with ignition on
10	Speedometer signal input (Hall effect switch signal)	Green/Red	Should switch from approximately 0 volts to approximately 10 – 12 volts as transmission is turned slowly by hand.
11	Not used		
12	RPM	Orange	At least 2.0 volts A.C. while cranking. Approx. 3.0 volts at idle. Voltage may increase slightly as RPM increases.
13	System relay control (energizes system relay pulldown circuit when grounded. ECU internally grounds this circuit when it receives a +15 signal provided that there are no faults in the ETS system)	Blue	Not activated = approx battery volts Activated = less than 1.5 volt

SA5029100058010X

Fig. 6 ETS control unit pin inspection (Part 1 of 4)

command code 973:

a. Once TCS CTRL light illuminates, start engine. Do not touch pedals.
b. Wait for idle to stabilize at approximately 850 RPM.
c. When TCS CTRL light starts to flash, press and hold cruise control Set Speed button within 10 seconds. Keep button depressed until calibration process is complete (TCS CTRL light will shutoff when calibration is complete).
d. The ECU will pull kickdown wire to its maximum position and idle position. The ECU will also increase engine speed to approximately 3000 RPM.

7. Calibration procedure will be discontinued if any of the following occur:
   a. Set button is not depressed within 10 seconds of TCS CTRL light beginning to flash.
   b. Set button is depressed before the TCS CTRL light starts to flash.
   c. Set button is released before calibration process is completed.
   d. Set button is inoperative.
   e. A pedal is depressed.
   f. Vehicle starts to roll.
   g. Gear selector position is changed.
8. When calibration process is complete, the TCS CTRL light will shutoff. Terminate ISAT communications and shutoff engine. Check if any diagnostic trouble codes were stored during calibration procedure.

COMPONENT REPLACEMENT

TURBO BYPASS VALVE CONTROL VALVE

This valve is located inside the engine compartment, on the lefthand inner fender.

1. Remove two mounting nuts.
2. Unplug electrical connector, then disconnect three signal hoses. Keep color coded rings on valve ports when hoses are disconnected.
3. Reverse procedure to install.

SAFETY VALVE

This valve is mounted on the false bulkhead panel on right side of car.

1. Remove two mounting nuts.
2. Unplug connector, then disconnect vacuum hoses. Keep color coded rings on valve ports when hoses are disconnected.
3. Reverse procedure to install.

NON-RETURN VALVE

This valve is installed in the vacuum hose between the safety valve and inlet manifold.

1. Disconnect vacuum hoses.
2. To install, reconnect vacuum hoses. Ensure white end of valve is pointed towards the safety valve.

PEDAL SENSOR

1. Remove lower dash panel and carpeting from driver side of center console.
2. Unplug connector from pedal sensor.
3. Remove clip, then disconnect sensor linkage from accelerator.
4. Remove sensor.
5. Reverse procedure to install.

THROTTLE HOUSING

1. Drain enough coolant to lower level in system to below throttle housing.
2. Disconnect two coolant hoses from housing.
3. Disconnect rubber elbow for intake air. Position aside.
4. Disconnect two vacuum hoses.
5. Remove two clips, then disconnect throttle cable from throttle housing.
6. Unplug connector, then remove nut at bottom of throttle housing.
7. Remove bolt at bottom of throttle housing, then position brace aside.
8. Remove throttle housing mounting nuts, then the housing. Save O-ring.
9. Reverse procedure to install. Recalibrate system as outlined under "System Service."

ASR ECU

The replacement ASR ECU must be recalibrated.

1. Move driver seat to fully forward position with backrest also angled forward.
2. Obtain radio anti-theft code as outlined under "Precautions."
3. Loosen two clips and fold carpet up under seat.
4. Remove protecting plate attaching screws. Position plate aside.
5. Remove control unit from under spring tensioned bracket, then the connector housing from ECU. Release connector housing by pressing down on locking tab.

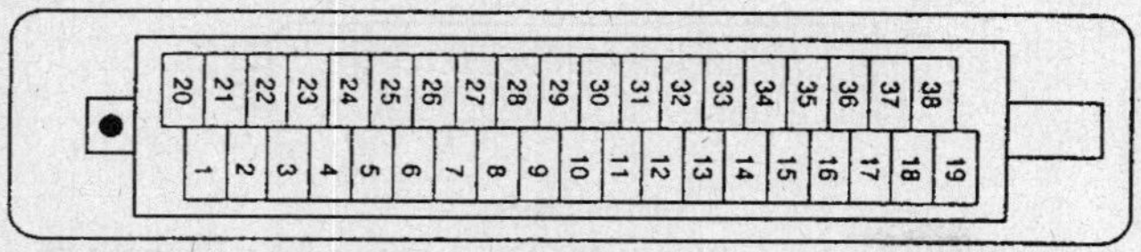

The following signals may be tested at the back of the ETS ECU connector with all components connected and the ignition switched on.

Pin #	Circuit/Function	Wire Color	Test
14	Accelerator pedal safety switch	Gray/White	Pedal released = approx. 1.0 volt Pedal depressed = approx 7–9 volts (halfway)
15	Brake light switch	White	Brakes released = 0 volts Brakes applied = approx. battery volts
16	Throttle potentiometer position signal	Blue/White	Approx. 4.0 volts at idle – decreases to – Approx. 0.1 volts at full throttle Throttle butterfly must be held in the full open position by hand.
17	Pedal potentiometer position signal	Green/Yellow	Approx. 0.1 volts at idle – increases to – Approx. 4.0 volts at full throttle
18	Cruise control: "RESUME"	Yellow	"Resume" switch depressed = battery volts "Resume" switch released = 0 volts
19	Cruise control: "SET"	Red/White	"Set" switch depressed = battery volts "Set" switch released = 0 volts
20	Throttle motor	Green	
21	Throttle motor	Green/White	
22	Power in from system relay	Blue/Red	System relay energized = approx. battery volts System relay de-energized = approx. 0 volts
23	TCS-CTRL Warning light	Violet/White	Light on = less than 2 volts Light off = approx battery volts
24	Not used		
25	+15 (switched power in)	Green/White	Ignition on = approx. battery volts Ignition off = approx. 0 volts

SA5029100058020X

Fig. 6 ETS control unit pin inspection (Part 2 of 4)

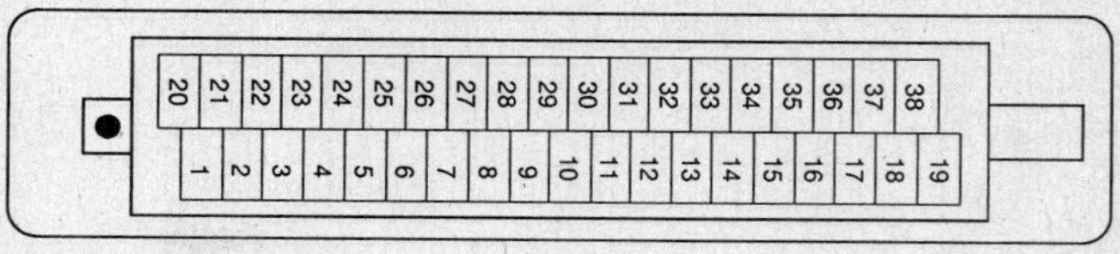

The following signals may be tested at the back of the ETS ECU connector with all components connected and the ignition switched on.

Pin#	Circuit/Function	Wire Color	Test
26	Throttle angle output signal to LH & DI (TK)	Yellow	Use ISAT pulsemeter to check that pulse width changes with throttle opening. (Frequency may change also)
27	Load signal (TQ)	White	Use ISAT pulsemeter to check that pulse frequency changes with engine load. (Pulse width may change also)
28	Throttle safety switch	Black/White	Throttle closed = approx. 1.0 volt Throttle open = 7–10 volts (half throttle or more)
29	Communications signal • Connected to TC/ABS pin 24 on manual transmission cars. • Connected to ASR pin 14 on automatic transmission cars.	Green/White	With engine idling and vehicle stationary = approx. 5 volts D.C. (A reading close to 0 or close to 10 volts indicates a problem in this wire/circuit) A logic probe should also indicate a continuous 'PULSE' signal.
30	Not used		
31	Cruise control: "ON" or "OFF"	Red	Cruise switch "ON" = approx. battery volts Cruise switch "OFF" = approx. 0 volts
32	Communications signal • Connected to TC/ABS pin 4 on manual transmission cars. • Connected to ASR pin 2 on automatic transmission cars.	Black/White	With engine idling and vehicle stationary = approx 5 volts D.C. (A reading close to 0 or close to 10 volts indicates a problem in this wire/circuit) A logic probe should also indicate a continuous 'PULSE' signal.
33	Coolant temperature sensor	Yellow	Voltage varies with coolant temperature Approx. 4.0 volts at –20°C (–4°F) Approx. 2.3 volts at +20°C (68°F) Approx. 0.5 volts at 80°C (176°F)

SA5029100058030X

Fig. 6 ETS control unit pin inspection (Part 3 of 4)

6. Reverse procedure to install.
7. Program correct motor type with ISAT as follows:
   a. **On models with manual transaxle,** enter ISAT command code 977. ISAT should now display 802.3TS.
   b. **On models with automatic transaxle,** enter ISAT command code 97A. ISAT should now display 802.3TA.
8. Calibrate ASR system as outlined under "System Service."

KICKDOWN WIRE ACTUATING MOTOR

1. Remove clip, then disconnect cable from motor lever.
2. Unplug electrical connector.
3. Loosen mounting screws slightly. Remove motor by sliding it up into the slotted holes in bracket and rotating it back towards firewall.
4. Reverse procedure to install. ASR system must be calibrated, including basic kickdown cable setting. Recalibrate ASR system as outlined under "System Service."

KICKDOWN WIRE ACTUATING MOTOR BRACKET

1. Remove nut for cable sheath clamp.
2. Remove actuating motor as outlined under "Kickdown Wire Actuating Motor."
3. Remove tie strap from bracket.
4. Remove two steering rack bolts and push rack to the rear.
5. Remove bracket mounting bolts, then the bracket.
6. Reverse procedure to install, noting the following:
   a. **Torque** steering rack mounting bolts to 44–59 ft. lbs.
   b. ASR system must be calibrated, including basic kickdown cable setting. Recalibrate ASR system as outlined under "System Service."

KICKDOWN CABLE

Removal

1. Obtain radio anti-theft code as outlined under "Precautions."
2. Remove battery.
3. Remove ABS control unit, then disconnect connectors from battery shelf.
4. Remove battery cable clamps, then disconnect cables from terminal block.
5. Lift out relay and fuse box.
6. Remove battery shelf four retaining bolts, then lift out battery shelf.
7. Clean area around kickdown cable, then disconnect electrical connector to air mass meter.
8. Remove transmission dipstick, then the transmission valve body cover.
9. Move gear selector lever fully to rear (position 1).
10. Using oil pipe remover No. 87-91-360, or equivalent, remove oil pipe from valve body. Ensure O-rings are removed.
11. Remove valve body assembly.
12. Remove clip, then disconnect cable from lever on kickdown wire motor.
13. Remove nut from cable sheath clamp, then the cable from clamp by first pulling it upwards, then loosening it at bottom.
14. Lift cable off throttle cam, then disconnect cable from cam.
15. Disconnect sheathing from transmission housing. Do not lose rubber seal.

Installation

1. Apply grease to O-ring on cable sheath and fit cable into transmission.
2. Fasten cable end to throttle cam, then place cable in groove of cam.
3. Fasten cable into holder by inserting it at bottom, then pressing cable downward from above.
4. Install cable into clamp on motor bracket. Do not tighten nut.
5. Push shift selector slide completely into valve body (selector lever position 1).
6. Install valve body assembly. **Torque** screw to 5–6 ft lbs.
7. Using oil pipe installer No. 87-91-782, or equivalent, mount oil pipe in valve body. Replace O-ring as necessary.
8. Install valve body cover. **Torque** cover bolts to 4 ft. lbs.
9. Install dipstick and connect electrical connector on air mass meter.
10. Set basic position of kickdown cable as follows:
    a. Ensure lever is against stop in fully

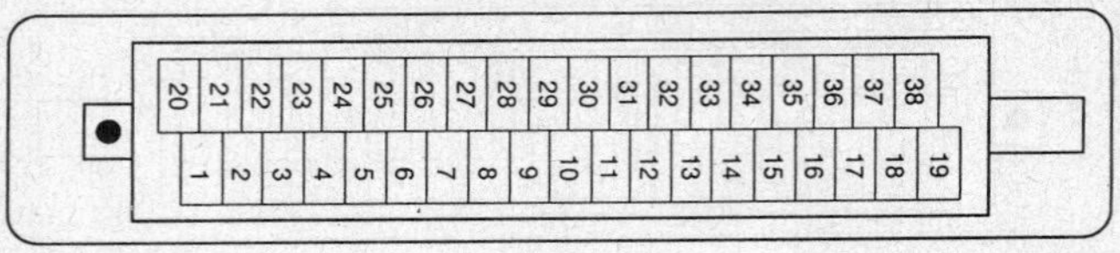

The following signals may be tested at the back of the ETS ECU connector with all components connected and the ignition switched on.

Pin#	Circuit/Function	Wire Color	Test
34	Diagnostic "K" lead (reply from ECU to ISAT)	Blue/White	
35	Safety valve control signal	Brown/White	System operational (safety valve energized) = approx. 1.0 volt System deactivated (safety valve de-energized) = 0 volt (possible battery voltage if system relay stayed energized)
36	Brake and clutch switches	White	Both pedals released = approx. battery volts Either pedal depressed = less than 1.0 volt
37	A.C. Request (power signal to ECU when A.C. switch is on, or when A.C.C. is requesting A.C)	Yellow	A.C. Switched on (or A.C.C. in air conditioning mode) = approx. 10-12 volts A.C. Switched off (or A.C.C. in econ. mode; or pressure switches open) = 0 volts
38	A.C. Relay control signal (ETS control unit provides ground for A.C. relay to operate compressor)	Black	A.C. Relay energized = approx. 1.0 volt A.C. Relay de-energized (with request signal present) = approx. 10-12 volts A.C. Relay de-energized (with A.C. switched off) = 0 volts

SA5029100058040X

Fig. 6 ETS control unit pin inspection (Part 4 of 4)

Voltage Checks

The following signals may be tested at the back of the ASR ECU connector with all components connected and the ignition switched on.

Pin#	Circuit/Function	Wire Color	Test
1	Pedal potentiometer position signal (connected to ETS pin 17)	Gray/Green	Approx. 0.1 volts at idle – increases to – Approx. 4.0 volts at full throttle
2	Communication with ETS (connected to ETS pin 32)	Black/White	With engine idling and vehicle stationary = approx. 5 volts D.C. (A reading close to 0 or close to 10 volts indicates a problem in this wire/circuit) A logic probe should also indicate a continuous 'PULSE' signal.
3	Throttle potentiometer position signal (connected to ETS pin 16)	Blue/White	Approx. 4.0 volts at idle – decreases to – Approx. 0.1 volts at full throttle
4	Not used		
5	Not used		
6	Not used	Yellow/Red	
7	Pedal potentiometer reference voltage (connected to ETS pin 2)	Yellow/Red	Approximately 5 volts
8	LR wheel speed signal (digital input signal from ABS ECU pin 12)	Gray	Using a Logic Probe:
9	RF wheel speed signal (digital input signal from ABS ECU pin 11)	Blue	–You should find a steady 'PULSE' at each wire with the ignition ON and the wheel NOT turning (this is a test pulse).
10	LF wheel speed signal (digital input signal from ABS ECU pin 10)	Yellow	–The frequency of the 'PULSE' should increase as the speed of each wheel increases.
11	KDW potentiometer reference voltage	Yellow/Red	Approximately 5 volts

SA5029100069010X

Fig. 7 ASR control unit pin voltage inspection (Part 1 of 3)

Voltage Checks

The following signals may be tested at the back of the ASR ECU connector with all components connected and the ignition switched on.

Pin#	Circuit/Function	Wire Color	Test
12	+15 Switched power in (connected to ETS pin 25)	Green/White	Ignition on = Approx. battery volts Ignition off = Approx. 0 volts
13	Ground	Black	Check voltage drop to ground. Should be less than 0.1 volts (ignition must be on to check voltage drop)
14	Communication with ETS (connected to ETS pin 29)	Yellow	With engine idling and vehicle stationary = Approx. 5 volts D.C. (A reading close to 0 or close to 10 volts indicates a problem in this wire/circuit) A logic probe should also indicate a continuous 'PULSE' signal.
15	KDW Potentiometer Common	Red	Approx. 0.1 to 0.2 volts
16	"Drive" signal	Orange	With selector in R,D,3,2,1 = Approx. battery volts With selector in N,P = Approx. 0 volts
17	Not used		
18	RPM	Orange	At least 2.0 volts A.C. while cranking. Approx. 3 volts A.C. at idle Voltage may increase slightly as engine speed increases.
19	TCS indicator light (ECU provides ground for bulb when system is operating in TCS mode)	Brown/White	Light off = approx. battery volts Light on = approx. 0 volts
20	Throttle potentiometer reference voltage (connected to ETS pin 3)	Yellow/White	Approximately 5 volts

SA5029100069020X

Fig. 7 ASR control unit pin voltage inspection (Part 2 of 3)

Voltage Checks

The following signals may be tested at the back of the ASR ECU connector with all components connected and the ignition switched on.

Pin#	Circuit/Function	Wire Color	Test
21	RR wheel speed signal (digital input signal from ABS ECU pin 9)	Green	See test procedure for pins 8, 9 and 10.
22	KDW potentiometer position signal	Blue/Red	With the ignition ON and the engine not running, the KDW motor is in a fixed position approximately half way through its travel. The voltage reading at this point should be approx. 2.5 volts.
23	KDW motor	Blue/White	See test procedure page 212 – 213 .
24	KDW motor	White	
25	Power in from system relay	Blue/Red	System relay energized = approx. battery volts System relay de-energized = approx. 0 volts

SA5029100069030X

Fig. 7 ASR control unit pin voltage inspection (Part 3 of 3)

extended position (toward right side of car).

b. Hold this position until completed step D.
c. Pull kickdown cable sheath past kickdown position to full throttle mechanical stop in transmission.
d. Tighten kickdown cable sheath clamp to specification, while holding full throttle position.

11. Mount battery shelf, connect cables to terminal block, then install battery cable clamps.
12. Install ABS control unit and ABS relay/fuse box.
13. Install battery and connect cables.
14. Enter radio anti-theft code as outlined under "Precautions."
15. Recalibrate ASR system as outlined under "System Service."

Twin-Throttle Traction Control System

INDEX

	Page No.
Description	7-187
Components	7-187
Operation	7-187
System	7-187
Diagnosis & Testing	7-188
Accessing Diagnostic Trouble Codes	7-188
Diagnostic Tests	7-189
Diagnostic Trouble Code Interpretation	7-189
Wiring Circuits	7-189
Diagnostic Chart Index	7-194
Precautions	7-187
Air Bag Systems	7-187
Battery Ground Cable	7-187
System Service	7-205
TCS Control Module Programming	7-205
TCS Control Module, Replace	7-205
TCS Throttle Body, Replace	7-205
Troubleshooting	7-188
Quick Test	7-188

PRECAUTIONS

AIR BAG SYSTEMS

Refer to "Air Bag System Precautions" in the front of this manual for system disarming and arming procedures.

BATTERY GROUND CABLE

Prior to service, disconnect battery ground cable and isolate as required.

DESCRIPTION

SYSTEM

The Traction Control System (TCS), used on 9000 models equipped with the 3.0L engine, prevents uncontrolled wheel spin during heavy acceleration and on icy or slippery road surfaces.

This system is based on the use of two throttle butterflies. The system adjusts engine torque by regulating the throttle butterfly in the extra throttle body which forms part of the system.

The extra TCS throttle body is mounted after the regular cable-operated throttle body. When the vehicle is in motion, the TCS throttle follows the regular throttle under the control of the TCS control module.

As soon as the maximum permissible wheel spin is exceeded, the opening angle of the TCS butterfly is reduced in relation to that of the regular throttle butterfly. This reduces engine torque until wheel spin is no longer excessive.

The control module's most important information is obtained from the four wheel sensors via the ABS control module, but the TCS system does not affect the brake system at all. To compensate for normal changes in the circumference of the wheels, the system is adaptive in regard to tire wear.

OPERATION

PERMISSIBLE WHEEL SPIN

900

When starting on a slippery road surface, the TCS permits a certain amount of wheel spin to a maximum of 3 mph. The upper limit for permissible wheel spin successively drops to about 1 mph at 21 mph, corresponding to a slip of about 4.5 percent.

Permissible wheel spin then remains constant up to 62 mph, where the wheel spin to road speed relationship drops to 1.5 percent.

Permissible wheel spin remains constant from 62 mph to 112 mph, then stays at a constant above 112 mph.

9000

When starting on a slippery road surface, the TCS permits a certain amount of wheel spin to a maximum of 2 mph. The upper limit for permissible wheel spin successively drops to about 1 mph at 22 mph, corresponding to a slip of about 4.5 percent.

Permissible wheel spin then remains constant up to 62 mph, where the wheel spin to road speed relationship drops to 1.8 percent.

Permissible wheel spin remains constant from 62 mph to 124 mph, then stays at a constant above 124 mph.

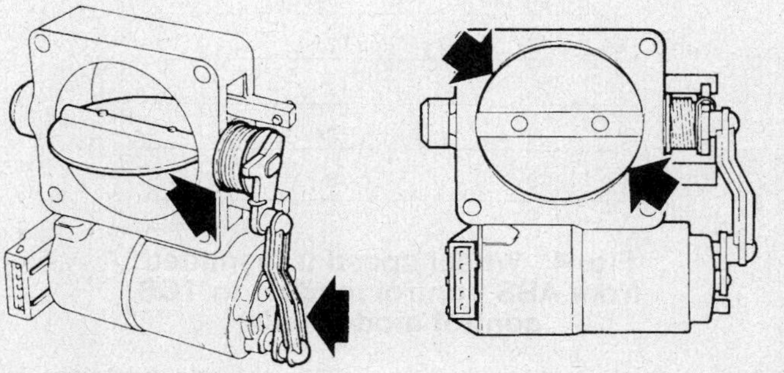

Fig. 1 Throttle butterfly operation. 900

THROTTLE BUTTERFLY OPERATION

The control module contains a special program for checking the TCS throttle butterfly and synchronizing it with the regular throttle butterfly. The program includes calibration of the butterfly's full throttle (wide open) and idling (fully closed) positions, **Figs. 1 and 2,** checking the operation and force of the spring which returns the butterfly to the wide open position and also checking that the butterfly runs freely without binding.

COMPONENTS

TCS CONTROL MODULE

The 35-pin Traction Control System (TCS) control module is located under the righthand front seat, **Fig. 3.**

When power is not supplied to the TCS throttle actuator motor, the throttle butterfly is held by a spring in the open position. When the ignition switch is turned to Drive position, the actuator motor rotates the butterfly toward the wide open position for 128 ms, ensuring it is wide open. Then the actuator motor switches off. After another 128 ms, the signal from the butterfly position sensor is stored as "wide open butterfly" in the control module. As soon as the speed exceeds 2.41 mph and the engine speed exceeds 600 RPM, the TCS throttle butterfly is synchronized with the regular throttle butterfly as long as the system is not manually switched off and wheel spin does not occur.

TCS INDICATOR LAMP

Whenever wheel spin requires engine torque to be reduced by more than 7 percent, the indicator lamp lights up after a

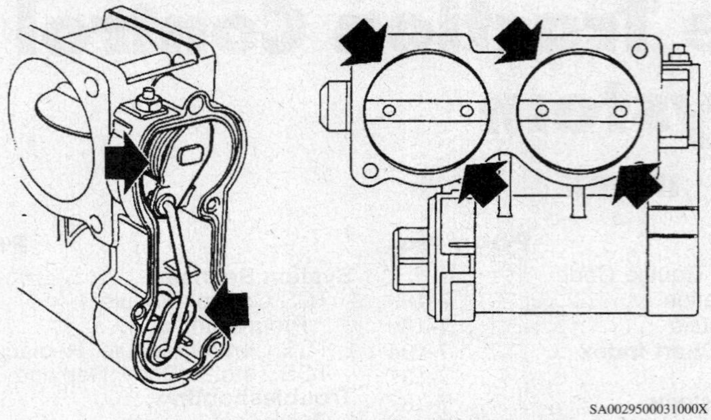

SA0029500031000X

Fig. 2 Throttle body operation. 9000

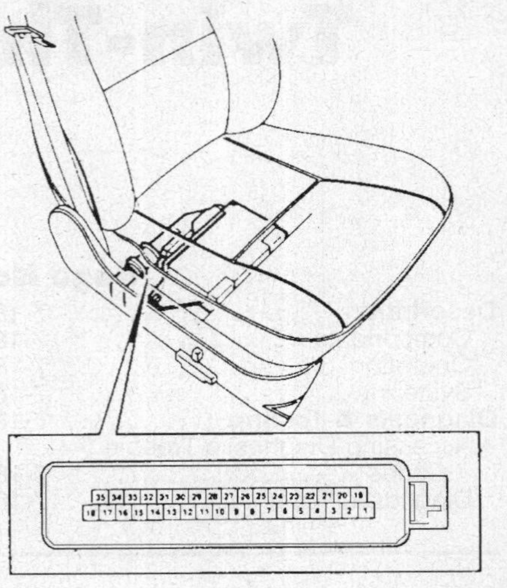

SA0029100002000X

Fig. 3 Traction Control System (TCS) module

Wheel	ABS control module pin	TCS control module pin
FL	17	25
FR	7	7
RL	22	24
RR	19	8

SA0029100003000X

Fig. 4 Wheel speed transmitted from ABS control module to TCS control module. 900

Wheel	Pin on ABS control module	Pin on TCS control module
FL	10	25
FR	11	7
RL	12	24
RR	9	8

SA0029500032000X

Fig. 5 Wheel speed transmitted from ABS control module to TCS control module. 9000

slight delay (360 ms). In case of torque reduction of more than 30 percent, the lamp lights up at once. It always stays lit for at least one second.

TCS OFF WARNING LAMP

When the ignition switch is turned to Drive position, the warning lamp lights up for three seconds.

If there is a system fault, the lamp will remain on. The warning lamp also lights up when the system is disconnected manually. The system can be disengaged at speeds lower than 37 mph by pressing the TCS switch. The system can be engaged at any speed by pressing the TCS switch. The system is always engaged automatically when ignition switch is turned to the On position when starting the vehicle.

ON/OFF SWITCH

The spring-loaded on/off switch is located on the lefthand side of the center console. The on/off switch can be used to switch off the system at speeds lower than 37 mph or to engage the system at any speed.

TCS THROTTLE BODY

900

The TCS throttle body consists of a body, butterfly, electric motor and linkage. It is mounted after the regular throttle body and cannot be fitted the wrong way around.

In limp-home mode, there is no extra cable to regulate the TCS throttle butterfly. The electric motor power supply is switched off and the spring sets the butterfly to the wide open position.

The throttle butterfly is not adjustable.

9000

The TCS throttle body is mounted beside the ordinary throttle body and consists of the body, butterfly, electric motor and link arm. If the TCS Off mode, the current is cut and the throttle is opened by a spring.

The TCS throttle is not adjustable. The TCS system is self-calibrating.

SPEED SIGNALS

To determine whether wheel spin occurs at any of the drive wheels, the control module receives front wheel speed information. Since the speed of the rear wheels is used as a reference value, this information is also received by the control module. The speed of each wheel is obtained by the ABS control module, **Figs. 4 and 5.**

ENGINE SPEED

Current engine speed information is obtained from the Motronic control module. Engine speed information allows the control module, together with information on the positions of the main throttle butterfly and the TCS throttle butterfly, to calculate engine torque. Also, the control module with the speed signals from the wheels, calculate the appropriate gear.

CRUISE CONTROL

900

As soon as the TCS is activated, the cruise control system is disengaged.

FULL-LOAD ENRICHMENT

If the TCS is activated at full throttle, the Motronic system's normal full-load enrichment must be inhibited. This is because the TCS now controls the engine load through the TCS throttle butterfly and because the input from the main throttle butterfly to the Motronic control module no longer provides correct information.

TROUBLESHOOTING

QUICK TEST

Refer to **Figs. 6 and 7** for TCS quick test.

DIAGNOSIS & TESTING

ACCESSING DIAGNOSTIC TROUBLE CODES

The TCS control module communicates with ISAT through pin 9. Any diagnostic trouble codes stored in the control module can be read out by means of the ISAT. The diagnostic testing socket is located below the lower lefthand instrument panel fascia.

Operation

The ISAT features a system where clear text under a number of menu options enables the user to directly select the desired command with the keypad. The structure of

Unless otherwise stated, the ignition switch should be in the ON position. All figures are approximate.

Pin	Component/Function	In/Out	Test conditions	Test reading	Across X-Y
1	TCS ON/OFF	In	TCS switch ON (depressed)	Battery +	32—1
			TCS switch OFF (not depressed)	0 V	
2	Not connected				
3	Position sensor, TCS butterfly, reference voltage	Out		approx. 5 V	3—13
4	Position signal, TCS throttle butterfly	Out	Activate with ISAT: BUTTERFLY CLOSING ON	1.6 V 122 Hz 13%(+) 1.1 ms (+)	4—13
			Activate with ISAT: BUTTERFLY CLOSING OFF	8.5-11 V 122 Hz 70-92%(+) 5.7-7.5ms (+)	
5	Disengagement of Cruise Control	Out	Activate with ISAT: ON	Battery +	5—13
			Activate with ISAT: OFF	0 V	
6	Engine speed	In	Idling	40 Hz	6—13
			2500 rpm	125 Hz	
7	Wheel speed, FR	In	Rotate FR wheel about 1/2 rev/s	15 Hz	7—13
8	Wheel speed, RR	In	Rotate RR wheel approx. 1/2 rev/s	15 Hz	8—13
9	Diagnostic lead K	In/Out	ISAT connected	Battery +	9—13
			ISAT not connected	0 V	
10	Not connected				
11	Position signal, main throttle butterfly (from MOTRONIC) Engine temperature signal (from MOTRONIC)	In	Idling	1.2 V 100 Hz 9%(+) 0.9 ms (+)	11—13
			2500 rpm	2 V 100 Hz 15%(+) 1.5 ms (+)	
			Ignition ON, starter motor in operation	0.25-1.0 V 100 Hz 2-8.2%(+) 0.2-0.82ms (+)	

SA0029100005010X

Fig. 6 Quick test (Part 1 of 3). 900

Pin	Component/Function	In Out	Test conditions	Test reading	Across X-Y
12	TCS lamp	Out	Activate with ISAT: ON	Battery +	32—12
			Activate with ISAT: OFF	0 V	
13	Ground	In		< 0.1 V	13—B negative
14	Not connected				
15	Not connected				
16	Not connected				
17	Not connected				
18	Throttle motor Important Clear any diagnostic trouble codes after this test	Out	Activate with ISAT: BUTTERFLY CLOSING ON	3.5 V 500 Hz 35%(+) 0.7 ms (+)	18—13
			As above + open butterfly by hand (max. 5 sec)	8-11 V	
			As above + close butterfly **additionally** by hand (max. 5 sec)	minus 8 to minus 11 V	
19	Not connected				
20	Position sensor, TCS throttle butterfly, ground	Out		Battery +	32—20
21	Disconnection of full-load enrichment	Out		6 V 31 Hz 50%(+) 16 ms (+)	21—13
			TCS activated	6 V 62 Hz 50%(+) 8 ms (+)	
22	Not connected				
23	Brake light switch	In	Brakes applied	Battery +	23—13
			Brakes not applied	0 V	
24	Wheel speed, RL	In	Rotate RL wheel approx. 1/2 rev/s	15 Hz	24—13
25	Wheel speed, FL	In	Rotate FL wheel approx. 1/2 rev/s	15 Hz	25—13

SA0029100005020X

Fig. 6 Quick test (Part 2 of 3). 900

the TCS command menus, **Fig. 8,** provides seven main menus. Three of these menus have varying numbers of commands in a submenu.

When a system function is activated with ISAT, it means the TCS control module is performing something which is not functionally normal. diagnostic trouble codes can be put into other systems which are dependent on the TCS.

Refer to **Fig. 9** for Obtain Readouts command menu.

Refer to **Fig. 10** for Activate command menu. **The Activate functions must always be used with caution. Always deactivate an activated function before proceeding in the ISAT menu. Always clear any diagnostic trouble codes recorded in TCS or any other system after work has been completed.**

Diagnostic Schedule

Use the following guidelines when diagnosing faults in each individual case:

1. Always begin by using ISAT to obtain readout of diagnostic trouble codes, if any.
2. In some fault diagnosis procedures, electric wiring is disconnected while ignition is switched on or TCS throttle butterfly is moved out of its normal position. This causes other diagnostic trouble codes. When work is finished, always clear any such trouble codes that may have been created.
3. Check fuses 19 and 28, then inspect connectors, especially H16-2. Check for corrosion on pins and contact surfaces, excessive play, looseness or anything else which may cause poor contact or reduced conductivity. If problems due to poor contact are suspected, spray CONTACT 61, or equivalent, on female connectors.
4. Before connecting BOB into circuit, first check voltage supply to pins 28 and 32 and ensure pins 13 and 30 are properly grounded.
5. Always start diagnosis in ABS system if ANTI LOCK lamp is lit.
6. With ignition switch turned off, ensure throttle butterfly can be moved to closed position without obstruction or binding and spring returns it to open position with ease.

DIAGNOSTIC TROUBLE CODE INTERPRETATION

Refer to **Fig. 11** for diagnostic trouble code table.

WIRING CIRCUITS

Refer to **Figs. 12 and 13** for TCS wiring circuit.

DIAGNOSTIC TESTS

900

Refer to **Figs. 14 through 29** for diagnostic trouble code diagnostic routines. Prior to replacing the control module, refer to **Fig. 30.**

9000

Refer to **Fig. 21** and **Figs. 31 through 42** for diagnostic trouble code diagnostic routines. Prior to replacing the control module, refer to **Fig. 30.**

Pin	Component/Function	In Out	Test conditions	Test reading	Across X-Y
26	TCS OFF lamp	Out	Turn off TCS with switch: lamp ON	Battery +	32—26
			Activate TCS with switch: lamp OUT	0 V	
27	Position sensor, TCS throttle butterfly, position signal	In	Activate with ISAT: BUTTERFLY CLOSING ON	approx. 1.1 V	27—13
			Activate with ISAT: BUTTERFLY CLOSING OFF	approx. 4.4 V	
28	+15 voltage	In		< 0.5 Volt	B positive - 28
			Ignition OFF	Battery +	
29	Not connected				
30	Ground	In		< 0.1 V	30—B.negative
31	Not connected				
32	Supply voltage	In		<0.5 V	B.positive-32
33	Not connected				
34	Not connected				
35	Throttle motor	Out	See pin 18		35—18

SA0029100005030X

Fig. 6 Quick test (Part 3 of 3). 900

Pin	Color	Component/Function	In/ Out	Measuring conditions	Measured value	Between X-Y
11	YE	Position signal, main butterfly (from MOTRONIC) Engine temp. signal (from MOTRONIC)	In	Idling	1.2 Volt 100 Hz 9% (+) 0.9 ms (+) (LP LO HI)	11 — 13
				Ignition ON, starter motor running	0.25-1.0 V 100 Hz 2-8.2% (+) 0.2-0.82ms (+) (LP LO HI)	
12	BN/WH	TCS lamp	Out	Activate with ISAT: ON	Batt+	32 — 12
				Activate with ISAT: OFF	0 Volt	
13	BK	Ground	In		< 0.1 V	13 — B minus
14		No connection				
15		No connection				
16		No connection				
17		No connection				
18	GN/WH	Throttle motor Important Erase any trouble codes after this test.	Out	Activate with ISAT: BUTTERFLY CLOSING ON	3.5 Volt 500 Hz 35% (+) 0.7 ms (+) (LP LO HI)	18 — 35
				As above + manually open throttle (max. 5 secs)	8-11 Volts	
				As above + close butterfly additionally by hand (max 5 secs)	minus 8 to minus 11 V	
19		No connection				
20	WH	Position sensor, butterfly TCS, ground	Out		Batt+	32 — 20
21	GY	Disengaging full-load enrichment system	Out		6 Volt 31 Hz 50% (+) 16 ms (+) (LP Hip LOp)	21 — 13
				TCS function activated	6 Volt 62 Hz 50% (+) 8 ms (+) (LP HI LO)	
22		No connection				

SA0029500033020X

Fig. 7 Quick test (Part 2 of 3). 9000

Pin	Color	Component/Function	In/ Out	Measuring conditions	Measured value	Between X-Y
1	BK/WH	TCS OFF/ON	In	TCS switch ON (pushed in)	Batt+	32 — 1
				TCS switch OFF (not pushed in)	0 Volt	
2		No connection				
3	YE/WH	Position sensor, TCS throttle, reference voltage	Out		approx. 5 Volts	3 — 13
4		No connection				
5	RD/WH	Disengaging cruise control	Out	Activate with ISAT: ON	Batt+	5 — 13
				Activate with ISAT: OFF	0 Volt	
6	OG	Engine speed	In	Idling	40 Hz (LP LO HI)	6 — 13
7	BU	Wheel speed FR	In		14.25 Hz (LP HI LOp)	
				Rotate FR wheel approx. 1/2 turn/s	46 Hz (LP HI LOp)	7 — 13
8	GN	Wheel speed RR	In		14.25 Hz (LP HI LOp)	
				Rotate RR wheel approx. 1/2 turn/s	46 Hz (LP HI LOp)	8 — 13
9	BU/WH	Diagnostics lead K	In/ Out	ISAT connected	Batt+	9 — 13
				ISAT not connected	0 Volt	
10		No connection				

SA0029500033010X

Fig. 7 Quick test (Part 1 of 3). 9000

Pin	Color	Component/Function	In/ Out	Measuring conditions	Measured value	Between X-Y
11	YE	Position signal, main butterfly (from MOTRONIC) Engine temp. signal (from MOTRONIC)	In	Idling	1.2 Volt 100 Hz 9% (+) 0.9 ms (+) (LP LO HI)	11 — 13
				Ignition ON, starter motor running	0.25-1.0 V 100 Hz 2-8.2% (+) 0.2-0.82ms (+) (LP LO HI)	
12	BN/WH	TCS lamp	Out	Activate with ISAT: ON	Batt+	32 — 12
				Activate with ISAT: OFF	0 Volt	
13	BK	Ground	In		< 0.1 V	13 — B minus
14		No connection				
15		No connection				
16		No connection				
17		No connection				
18	GN/WH	Throttle motor Important Erase any trouble codes after this test.	Out	Activate with ISAT: BUTTERFLY CLOSING ON	3.5 Volt 500 Hz 35% (+) 0.7 ms (+) (LP LO HI)	18 — 35
				As above + manually open throttle (max. 5 secs)	8-11 Volts	
				As above + close butterfly additionally by hand (max 5 secs)	minus 8 to minus 11 V	
19		No connection				
20	WH	Position sensor, butterfly TCS, ground	Out		Batt+	32 — 20
21	GY	Disengaging full-load enrichment system	Out		6 Volt 31 Hz 50% (+) 16 ms (+) (LP Hip LOp)	21 — 13
				TCS function activated	6 Volt 62 Hz 50% (+) 8 ms (+) (LP HI LO)	
22		No connection				

SA0029500033030X

Fig. 7 Quick test (Part 3 of 3). 9000

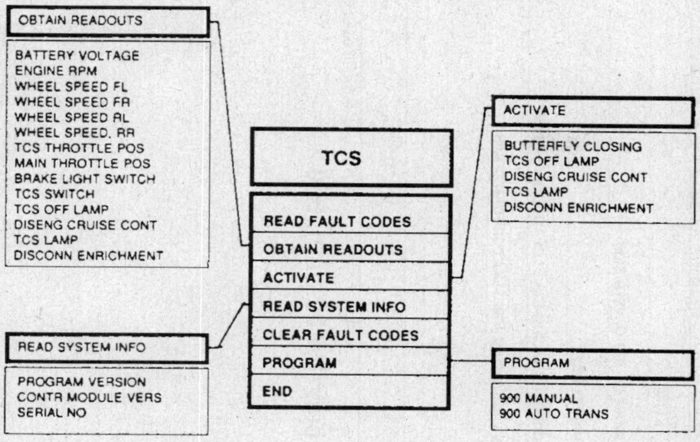

SA0029100007000X

Fig. 8 ISAT diagnostic menus

	ISAT display	Function
1	THROTTLE CLOSING ON/OFF	The TCS control module closes the TCS throttle almost completely
2	TCS OFF LAMP FUNCTION ON/OUT	The TCS control module activates the TCS OFF lamp
3	DISENG CRUISE CONT FUNCTION ON/OFF	The TCS control module disengages the Cruise Control system
4	TCS—LAMP FUNCTION ON/OFF	The TCS control module activates the TCS lamp and the TCS program in the TCM control module
5	DISCONN ENRICHMENT FUNCTION ON/OFF	The TCS control module sends battery + via the cable to the MOTRONIC control unit for disconnection of full-load enrichment. The MOTRONIC control module interprets this as fuel shut-off and the engine stops (used only as a wiring check).

SA0029100009000X

Fig. 10 "Activate" command menu

	ISAT display	Function
1	BATTERY VOLTAGE XX.X V	Shows control module's supply voltage
2	ENGINE RPM XXXX rpm	Engine rpm (shows 450 rpm as lowest speed)
3	WHEEL SPEED FL XXX km/h	Wheel speed FL (shows 3 km/h as lowest speed)
4	WHEEL SPEED FR XXX km/h	Wheel speed FR (shows 3 km/h as lowest speed)
5	WHEEL SPEED RL km/h	Wheel speed RL (shows 3 km/h as lowest speed)
6	WHEEL SPEED RR XXX km/h	Wheel speed RR (shows 3 km/h as lowest speed)
7	TCS THROTTLE POS XX %	This figure is the pulse ratio of the TCS throttle butterfly position signal from the TCS control module to the TCM control module (9-92%)
8	MAIN THROTTLE POS XX %	This figure is the pulse ratio of the main throttle butterfly position signal from the MOTRONIC control module to the TCS contro module (9-92%)
9	BRAKE LIGHT SWITCH ON/OFF	Shows status of brake light switch
10	TCS SWITCH ACTIVE/NOT ACTIVE	Shows status of TCS switch ("ACTIVE" only when the switch is pressed continuously)
11	TCS OFF LAMP ON/OUT	Shows whether the TCS control module turns on the TCS OFF lamp
12	DISENG CRUISE CONT ON/OFF	Shows whether the TCS control module disengages the Cruise Control system
13	TCS LAMP ON/OUT	Shows whether the TCS control module turns on the TCS lamp and whether the TCS control module activates the TCS function in the TCM control module
14	DISCONN ENRICHMENT ON/OFF	Shows whether the TCS control module sends the "disconnect full-load enrichment" signal to the MOTRONIC control module (the ISAT display alternates between ON and OFF when the function is activated)

SA0029100008000X

Fig. 9 "Obtain Readouts" command menu

Engine running or ignition switched on

Diagnostic trouble code	Defective function/component	TCS-OFF	Text in ISAT display
B1192	TCS switch, shorting to ground	ON	FAULT XX P/I B1192 TCS SWITCH SHORTING TO GROUND
B1302	Position sensor TCS throttle butterfly, shorting to ground/break	ON	FAULT XX P/I B1302 TCS THROTTLE SENSOR SHORT TO GR/BREAK
B1303	Position sensor TCS throttle butterfly, shorting to B+/break	ON	FAULT XX P/I B1303 TCS THROTTLE SENSOR SHORT BATT+/BREAK
B1371	Wheel speed FL, no signal	ON	FAULT XX P/I B1371 WHEEL SPEED FL FAULTY SIG/NO SIG
B1376	Wheel speed, FR, no signal	ON	FAULT XX P/I b1376 WHEEL SPEED FR FAULTY SIG/NO SIG
B1381	Wheel speed RL, no signal	ON	FAULT XX P/I B1381 WHEEL SPEED RL FAULTY SIG/NO SIG
B1386	Wheel speed RR, no signal	ON	FAULT XX P/I B1386 WHEEL SPEED RR FAULTY SIG/NO SIG
B1406	Position signal, main throttle butterfly, incorrect	ON	FAULT XX P/I B1406 MAIN THROTTLE POS SIGNAL INCORRECT
B1407	Position signal, main throttle butterfly, shorting to ground	ON	FAULT XX P/I B 1407 MAIN THROTTLE POS SHORT TO GROUND
B1408	Position signal, main throttle butterfly, shorting to battery +/no continuity	ON	FAULT XX P/I B1408 MAIN THROTTLE POS SHORT BATT+/BREAK
B1605	TCS control module, control module fault	ON	FAULT XX P/I B1605 CONTROL MODULE INTERNAL FAULT
B1610	Control module not programmed	ON	FAULT XX P/I B1610 CONTROL MODULE NOT PROGRAMMED
B1710	Engine speed, no signal	ON	FAULT XX P/I B1710 ENGINE RPM SIGNAL FAULTY SIG/NO SIG
B2433	TCS throttle body, shorting to battery + or ground	ON	FAULT XX P/I B 2433 THROTTLE MOTOR SHORT BATT+/GROUND
B2434	TCS throttle body, no continuity/mechanical fault	ON	FAULT XX P/I B2434 THROTTLE BODY/MOTOR BREAK/MECH FAULT

SA0029100010000X

Fig. 11 TCS diagnostic trouble codes

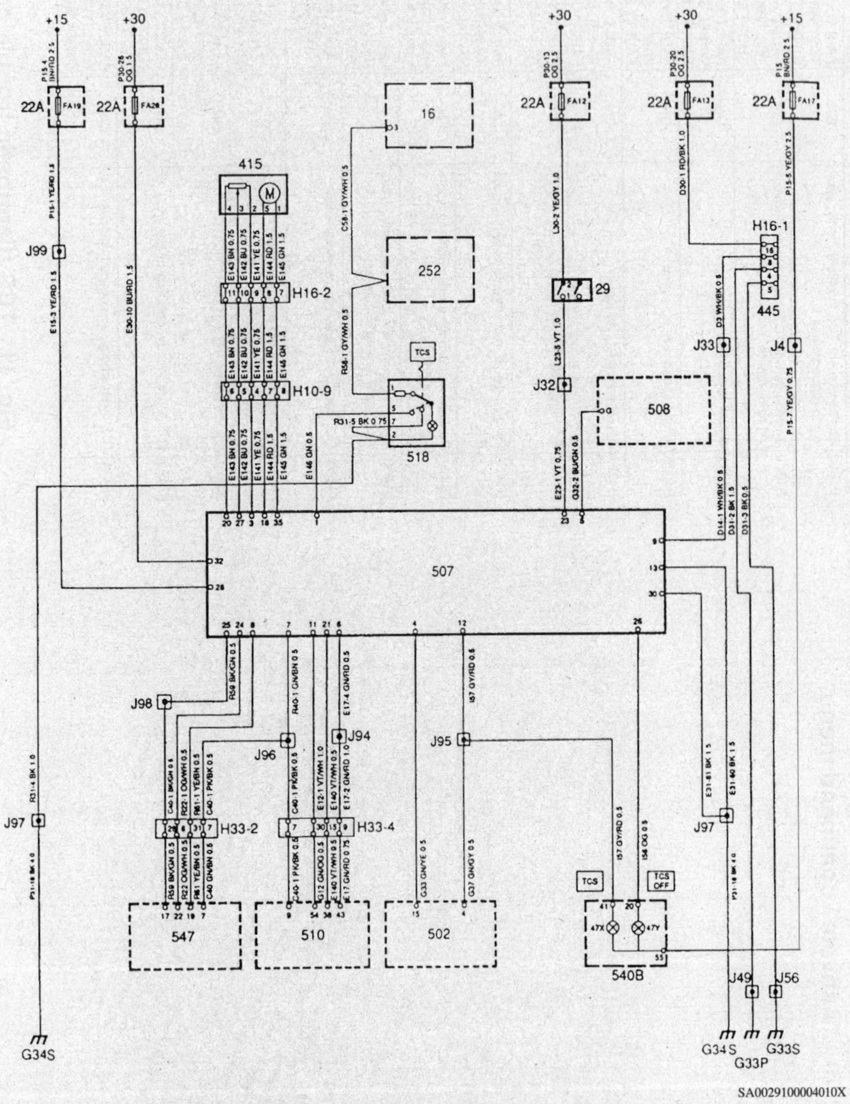

Fig. 12 TCS wiring circuit (Part 1 of 2). 900

List of components

29	Brake light switch at brake pedal
415	TCS actuator motor on throttle body
502	TCM control module behind the glove box
507	TCS control module under right-hand front seat
508	Cruise control module
510	MOTRONIC control module M2.8.1 below right-hand A pillar
518	TCS switch on centre console
540B	Main instrument 2 in instrument panel
547	ABS control module integrated in brake unit
H33-2	33-pin black connector below left-hand A pillar
H33-4	33-pin connector on bracket at the MOTRONIC ECM
H10-9	10-pin connector on bracket at the MOTRONIC ECM
H16-1	16-pin Data Link Connector under instrument panel on the drivers side
,6-2	16-pin connector adjacent to inlet manifold in engine bay
J33	(LC 3) approx. 210 mm from the blue 33-pin connector facing the TCS control module
J32	(CC 68) approx. 320 mm from the brake light switch facing the TCS control module
G34S	Grounding points below the right-hand A pillar
47 X	TCS indicator lamp
47 Y	TCS OFF warning lamp

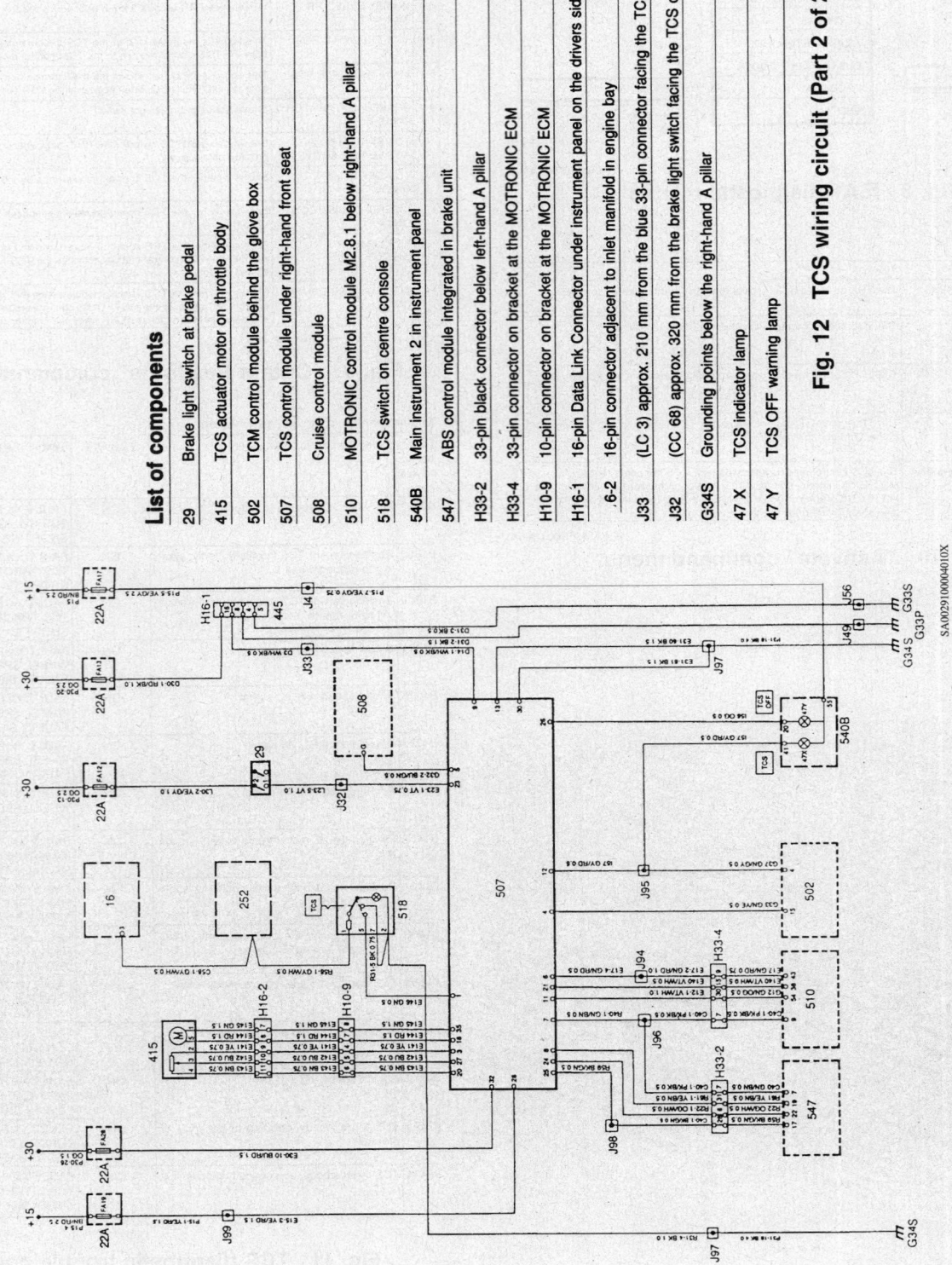

SA0029100004020X

Fig. 12 TCS wiring circuit (Part 2 of 2). 900

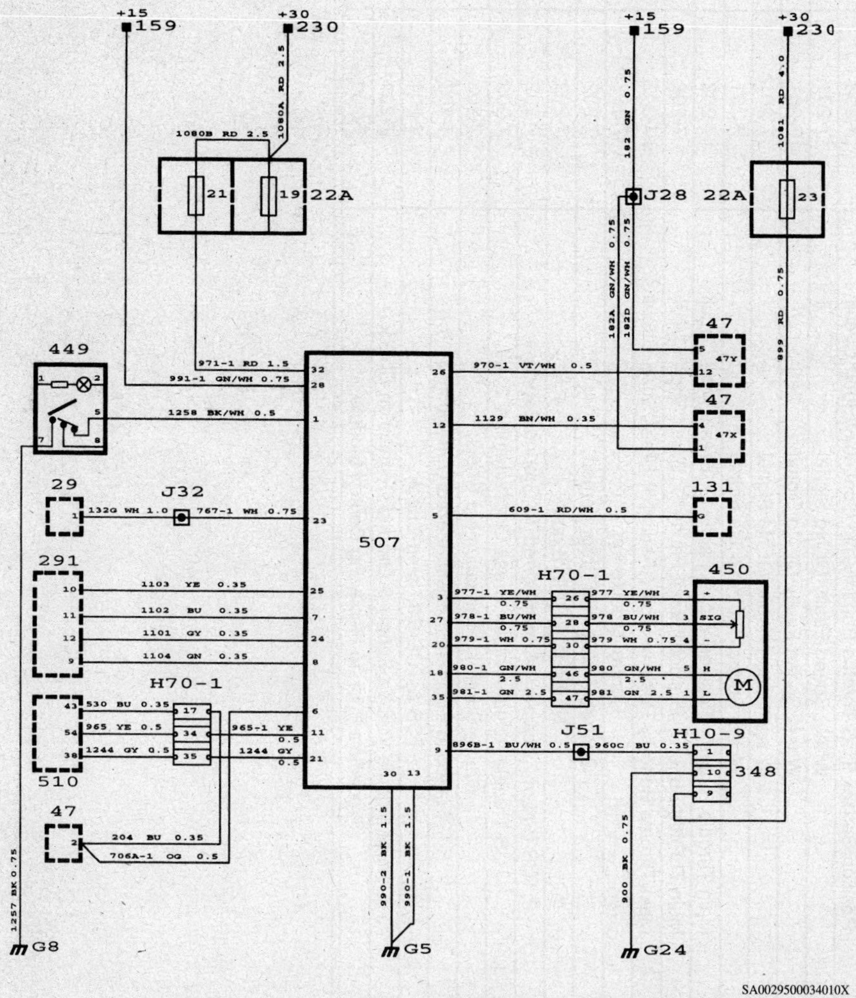

Fig. 13 TCS wiring circuit (Part 1 of 2). 9000

List of components

29	Brake light switch on the pedal bracket
131	Control module, cruise control behind battery on battery shelf
159	Distribution terminal, +15 in the electrical distribution box
230	Distribution terminal, +30 in the electrical distribution box
291	Control module, ABS on the battery shelf behind the battery
47	Combined instrument on the facia behind the steering wheel
450	Actuator motor, TTS
449	TCS switch on the facia
507	TCS control module under the left-hand front seat
510	Motronic control module 2.8.1 in the bulkhead space
H70-1	70 pin connector, engine/main grid
G8	Grounding point, facia
G5	Grounding point, rear seat
G24	Grounding point, right-hand front seat member
H10-9 (348)	Diagnostic data link connector, under right-hand seat (green)
J32	Crimped connector (LHD): Approx. 190 mm from the brake light connector facing the central console (main grid). Crimped connector (RHD): Approx. 190 mm from the brake light connector facing the central console (main grid)
J51	Crimped connector approx. 275 mm from the diagnostic data link terminal under the right-hand front seat (main grid).
J28	Crimped connector (LHD): Approx. 310 mm from the EDU (main grid) Crimped connector (RHD): Approx. 230 mm from the EDU (main grid)
22A	Central fuse box in the glove compartment (or under the passenger airbag)

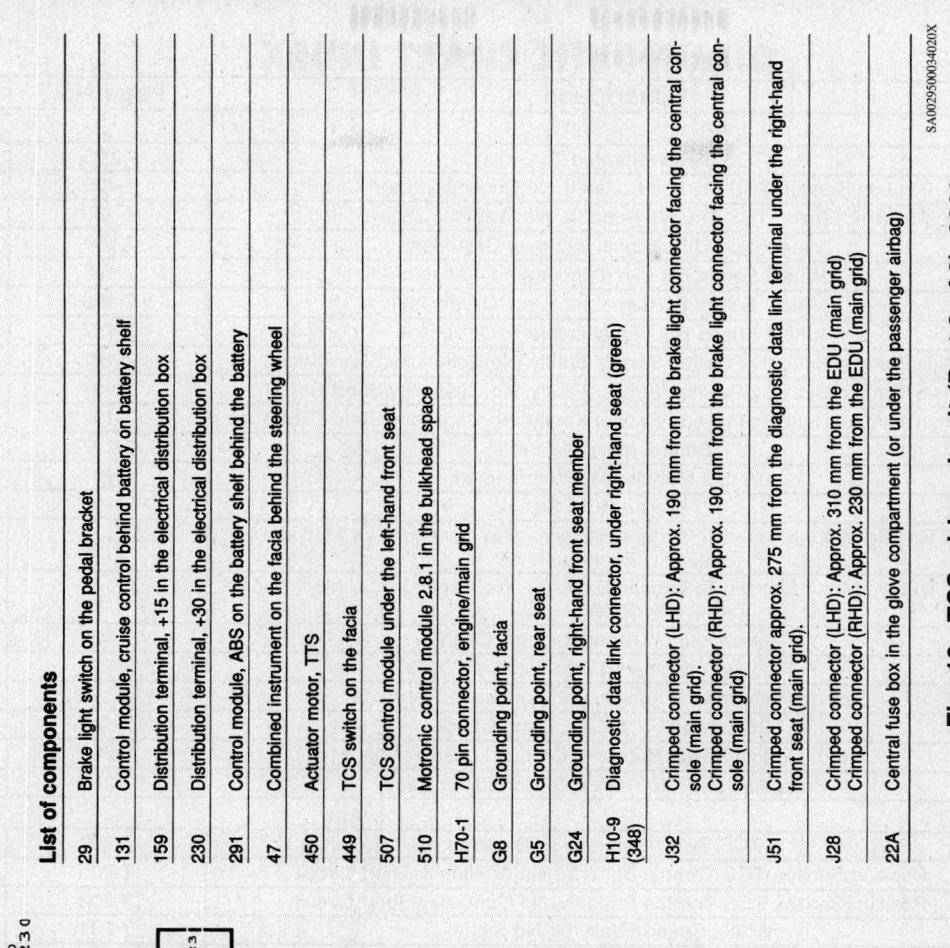

SA0029500034020X

Fig. 13 TCS wiring circuit (Part 2 of 2). 9000

DIAGNOSTIC CHART INDEX

Code	Description	Page No.	Fig. No.
900			
B1192	TCS Switch Shorted To Ground	7-195	14
B1302	Position Sensor, TCS Throttle Butterfly, No Continuity/Short Circuit.	7-195	15
B1303	Position Sensor, TCS Throttle Butterfly, No Continuity/Short Circuit	7-195	15
B1371	Wheel Speed FL Signal Incorrect Or Absent	7-196	16
B1376	Wheel Speed FR Signal Incorrect Or Absent	7-196	17
B1381	Wheel Speed RL Signal Incorrect Or Absent	7-196	18
B1386	Wheel Speed RR Signal Incorrect Or Absent	7-197	19
B1406	Main Throttle Butterfly Position Sensor Faulty, No Continuity/Short Circuit	7-197	20
B1407	Main Throttle Butterfly Position Sensor Faulty, No Continuity/Short Circuit	7-197	20
B1408	Main Throttle Butterfly Position Sensor Faulty, No Continuity/Short Circuit	7-197	20
B1605	Control Module Fault	7-197	21
B1610	Control Module Not Programmed	7-197	22
B1710	No Engine RPM Signal	7-198	23
B2433	TCS Throttle Motor Shorted To Ground/Battery +, No Continuity Or Mechanical Fault	7-198	24
B2434	TCS Throttle Motor Shorted To Ground/Battery +, No Continuity Or Mechanical Fault	7-198	24
—	Cruise Control Disengagement Check	7-199	25
—	Full-Load Enrichment Disconnection Check	7-199	26
—	Shifting Performance Adjustment. Automatic Transaxle	7-199	27
—	TCS Lamp & TCS OFF Lamp Check	7-199	28
—	Control Module Power Supply & Ground Location Check	7-200	29
—	Procedure Prior To Replacing Control Module	7-200	30
9000			
B1192	TCS Switch Shorted To Ground	7-200	31
B1302	Position Sensor, TCS Throttle Butterfly, No Continuity/Short Circuit	7-200	32
B1303	Position Sensor, TCS Throttle Butterfly, No Continuity/Short Circuit	7-200	32
B1371	Wheel Speed Faulty Or No Signal	7-201	33
B1376	Wheel Speed Faulty Or No Signal	7-201	33
B1381	Wheel Speed Faulty Or No Signal	7-201	33
B1386	Wheel Speed Faulty Or No Signal	7-201	33
B1406	Main Throttle Butterfly Position Signal Faulty Or Break/Short Circuit	7-202	34
B1407	Main Throttle Butterfly Position Signal Faulty Or Break/Short Circuit	7-202	34
B1408	Main Throttle Butterfly Position Signal Faulty Or Break/Short Circuit	7-202	34
B1605	Control Module Fault	7-197	21
B1610	Control Module Not Programmed	7-202	35
B1710	No Engine RPM Signal	7-202	36
B2433	TCS Butterfly Actuator Motor Shorted To Ground/Battery +	7-202	37
B2434	TCS Throttle Actuator Motor Break Or Mechanical Fault	7-203	38
—	Cruise Control Disengagement Check	7-203	39
—	Full-Load Enrichment Disconnection Check	7-203	40
—	TCS & TCS Off Lamp Check	7-204	41
—	Control Module Voltage Supply & Ground Connection Check	7-204	42
—	Procedure Prior To Replacing Control Module	7-200	30

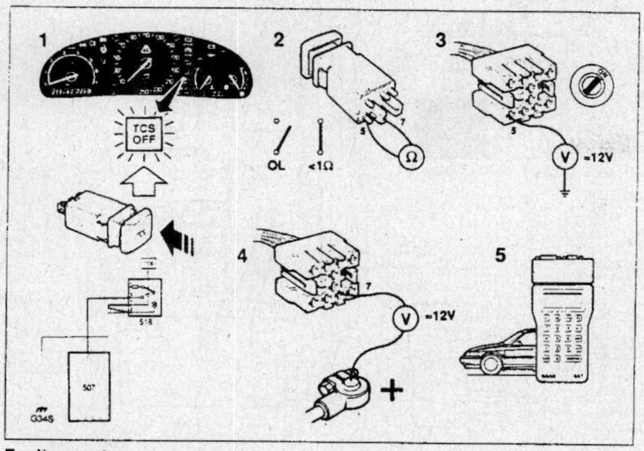

Fault symptom

TCS system cannot be turned off with the switch.

Condition

Control module pin 1 shorted to ground for longer than 10 seconds, or switch pressed continuously for more than 10 seconds.

Diagnostic procedure

1 On repeated depression of the TCS switch the TCS OFF-lamp should come on and go out alternately.

If this is OK, clear the trouble code and drive the car to check whether the code is generated afresh.

2 Remove the TCS switch from the dash. Unplug the connector from the switch and check that the resistance across pins 5 and 7 of the switch is <1 ohm when the switch is depressed and infinite (OL) when it is released.

If the readings are incorrect, fit a replacement switch.

3 With the ignition switch turned to the Drive position, check that battery + is present across pin 5 of the switch connector and a good ground.

If it is not, check the cable between pin 5 of the connector and pin 1 of the TCS control module for continuity/shorting to ground.

4 Check that battery + is present across pin 7 of the switch connector and B positive (+).

If it is not, check the cable between pin 7 of the connector and grounding point G34S for continuity.

5 Clear the trouble code. Start the car and drive it to check whether the code is generated afresh.

If it is, go to "Procedure Prior To Replacing Control Module" figure.

SA0029100018000A

Fig. 14 Code B1192: TCS Switch Shorted To Ground. 900

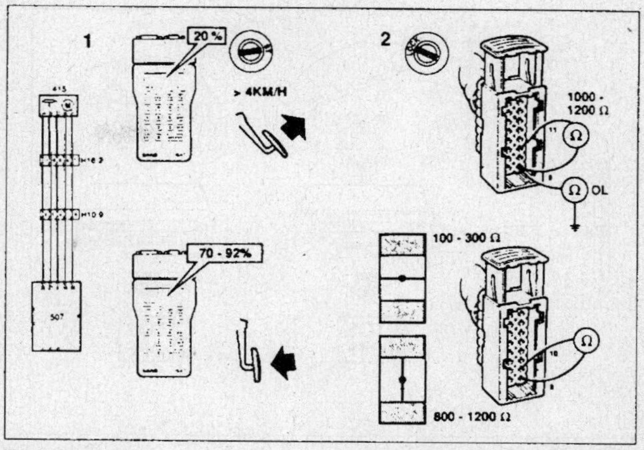

Fault symptom

TCS OFF lamp on, TCS system inoperative

Condition

For trouble code B1302: Control module output pin 3 shorted to ground or no continuity. Alternatively, control module input pin 27 shorted to ground.

For trouble code B1303: Control module output pin 20 shorted to B+ or no continuity. Alternatively, control module input pn 27 shorted to B+.

Note:

B1302 and B1303 can be generated in connection with fault diagnosis when wiring to the throttle body is disconnected and the ignition switch is turned to the Drive position.

Diagnostic procedure

1 Connect an ISAT and select "TCS THROTTLE POS" in the "OBTAIN READINGS" menu. Drive the car at >4 km/h. On releasing the accelerator the ISAT should show a reading of about 20%. This should then successively rise to 70-92%at full throttle. (Note that the TCS throttle opens fully at speeds <4 km/h.)

If the readings are correct, clear the trouble code, drive the car on the road and check whether the trouble code is generated afresh.

If the readings are incorrect or if the trouble code is generated afresh, proceed with point 2.

2 Switch off the ignition.

Unplug connector H16-2 and measure the resistance in the TCS throttle position sensor across pins 9 and 11 of the female connector.

The correct resistance is approx. 1000-1200 ohms.

Also measure the resistance across pins 9 and 10 of the female connector while slowly closing the throttle butterfly by hand. The resistance should now rise smoothly from about 100-300 ohms to about 800-1200 ohms.

SA0029100012010X

Fig. 15 Codes B1302 & B1303: Position Sensor, TCS Throttle Butterfly, No Continuity/Short Circuit (Part 1 of 3). 900

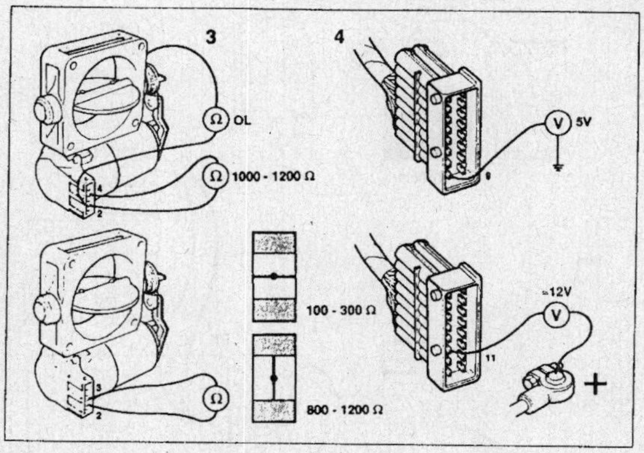

Also check that the resistance across pin 9 and a good ground is infinite (OL).

If the resistance is OK, the fault lies between connector H16-2 and the control module. Continue with point 4.

If it is not, the fault lies between connector H16-2 and the throttle body or in the throttle body. Proceed to point 3.

3 Remove the TCS throttle body.

Carry out checking as described in point 2 above, directly on throttle body pins 2, 3 and 4.

If the measurements produce correct readings, remedy the defective wiring between the throttle body and connector H16- 2.

Should the measurements produce incorrect readings, on the other hand, fit a replacement TCS throttle body.

4 Turn the ignition switch to the drive position. Measure the voltage across pin 9 of the male connector (H16-2) and B negative (-).

The correct voltage is about 5 V.

Also check that pin 11 of the male connector is correctly grounded by measuring the voltage to B positive (+).

The correct voltage is battery +.

If the readings are correct, the supply from control module output pins 3 and 20 is correct and the fault lies between pin 27 of the control module and pin 10 of the male connector (H16-2). Continue with point 5.

If the readings are incorrect, the fault lies between pin 20 of the control module and pin 11 of the male connector or between pin 3 of the control module and pin 9 of the male connector. Proceed to point 6.

SA0029100012020X

Fig. 15 Codes B1302 & B1303: Position Sensor, TCS Throttle Butterfly, No Continuity/Short Circuit (Part 2 of 3). 900

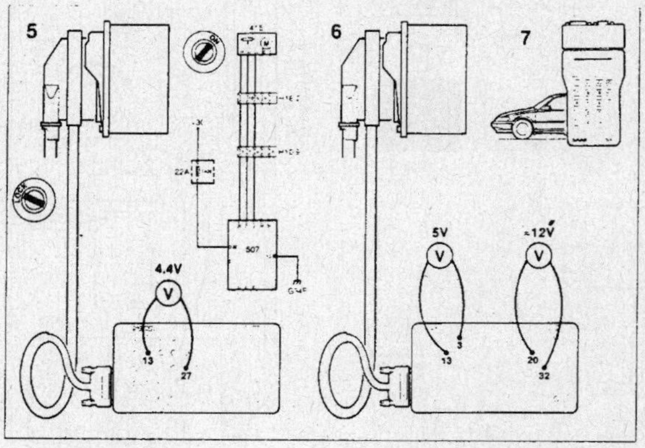

5 Switch off the ignition

Remove the right-hand front seat, withdraw the TCS control module and plug in a BOB.

With the ignition switch in the drive position, check the cable for the input from the TCS throttle butterfly's position sensor by measuring the voltage across pins 27 and 13 of the TCS control module.

The correct voltage is about 4.4 V.

If this is not obtained, remedy the cable between pin 27 of the control module and pin 10 of the male connector (H16-2).

6 Switch off the ignition.

Remove the right-hand front seat, withdraw the TCS control module and plug the BOB into the control module connector (control module disconnected).

Check the cable between pin 3 of the control module and pin 9 of the male connector (H16-2) and also the cable between pin 20 of the control module and pin 11 of the male connector for continuity/shorting.

Remedy any defective wiring.

Plug in connector H16-2, connect the control module and turn the ignition switch to the Drive position. Check that the control module is correctly grounded on pin 20 by measuring the voltage across pins 20 and 32.

Correct voltage is battery +.

Also check that there is a voltage of about 5 V on pin 3 of the control module by measuring the voltage across pins 3 and 13.

7 Clear the trouble codes. Start the car and drive it to check whether the trouble code is generated afresh.

If it is, go to "Procedure Prior To Replacing Control Module" figure.

SA0029100012030A

Fig. 15 Codes B1302 & B1303: Position Sensor, TCS Throttle Butterfly, No Continuity/Short Circuit (Part 3 of 3). 900

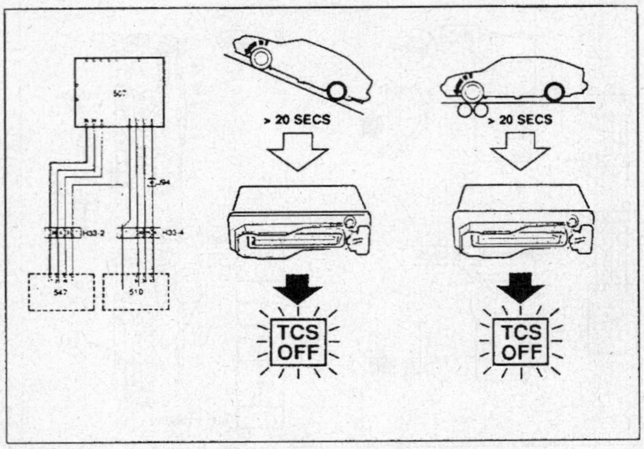

Fault symptom

TCS OFF lamp on, TCS system inoperative.

Condition

Wheel speed signal incorrect or absent, or indicates a speed higher than 280 km/h.

Note:

The trouble code for wheel speed signals can be generated when the brakes are tested (in connection with annual vehicle inspection, for instance) or if the car is started on a slippery uphill gradient so that the front wheels spin and the rear wheels remain stationary.

If only one wheel spins and the other three remain stationary, the control module cannot tell whether the speed signals from the three stationary wheels are correct or false. In such case, trouble codes are generated for the three stationary wheels. These trouble codes are cleared automatically, however, as soon as the signals return.

If wheelspin continues for more than 20 seconds while one of the wheels remains stationary the whole time, the TCS system will be disconnected and the TCS OFF lamp will come on. To restore the TCS function, the ignition must be turned off and then on again.

SA0029100014010X

Fig. 16 Code B1371: Wheel Speed FL, Signal Incorrect Or Absent (Part 1 of 2). 900

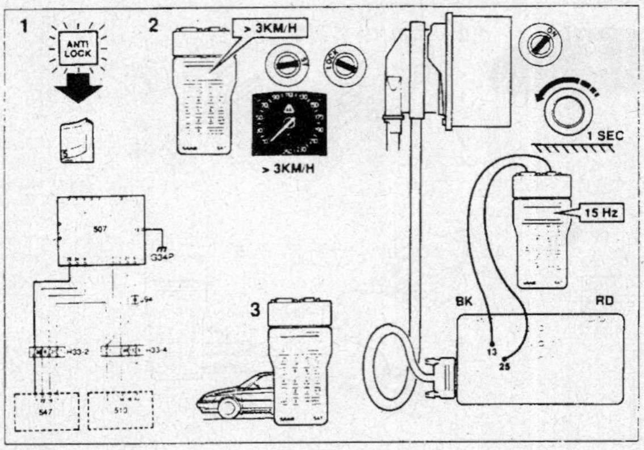

Diagnostic procedure

1 If the ANTI LOCK lamp also lights up, obtain readings of any trouble codes in the ABS system and take the necessary remedial action

2 Connect the ISAT. Drive the car slowly (but at least 3 km/h) and select WHEEL SPEED FL in the "OBTAIN READINGS" menu to check whether wheel speed is displayed.

If it is not, connect a BOB and check whether a wheel speed signal is present on pin 25 when the LH front wheel is rotated at a speed of about 1/2 revolution per second. The correct reading is about 15 Hz.

If the reading is not correct, check the cable between pin 25 of the TCS control module and pin 17 of the ABS control module for continuity/shorting.

Remedy any defective cable.

3 Clear the trouble code. Start the car and drive it to check whether the code is generated afresh.

If it is, go to "Procedure Prior To Replacing Control Module" figure.

SA0029100014020A

Fig. 16 Code B1371: Wheel Speed FL, Signal Incorrect Or Absent (Part 2 of 2). 900

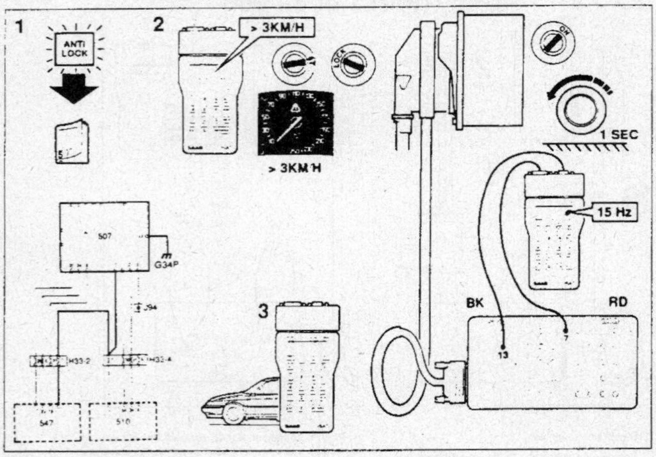

Fault symptom

TCS OFF lamp on, TCS system inoperative

Condition

Wheel speed signal incorrect or absent, or indicates a speed higher than 280 km/h.

Note:

See under diagnoostic trouble code B1371.

Diagnostic procedure

1 If the ANTI LOCK lamp also lights up, obtain readings of any trouble codes in the ABS system and take the necessary remedial action

2 Connect the ISAT. Drive the car slowly (but at least 3 km/h) and select WHEEL SPEED FR in the "OBTAIN READINGS" menu to check whether wheel speed is displayed.

If it is not, connect a BOB and check whether a wheel speed signal is present on pin 7 when the RH front wheel is rotated at a speed of about 1/2 revolution per second. The correct reading is about 15 Hz.

If the reading is not correct, check the cable between pin 7 of the TCS control module and pin 7 of the ABS control module for continuity/ shorting.

Remedy any defective cable.

3 Clear the trouble code. Start the car and drive it to check whether the code is generated afresh.

If it is, go to "Procedure Prior To Replacing Control Module" figure.

SA0029500015000A

Fig. 17 Code B1376: Wheel Speed FR, Signal Incorrect Or Absent. 900

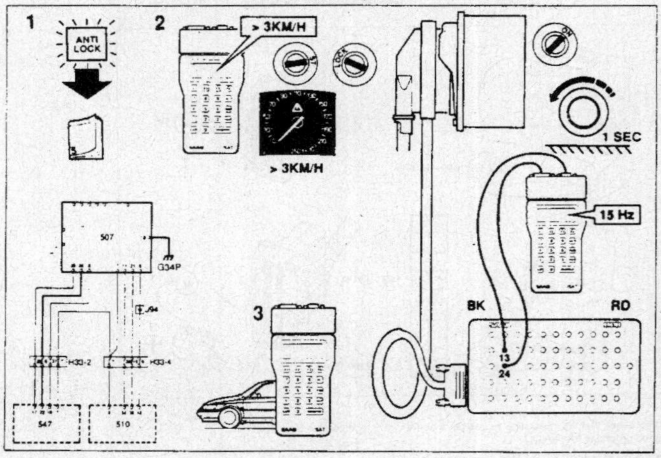

Fault symptom

TCS OFF lamp on, TCS system inoperative

Condition

Wheel speed signal incorrect or absent, or indicates a speed higher than 280 km/h.

Note:

See under diagnostic trouble code B1371.

Diagnostic procedure

1 If the ANTI LOCK lamp also lights up, obtain readings of any trouble codes in the ABS system and take the necessary remedial action

2 Connect the ISAT. Drive the car slowly (but at least 3 km/h) and select WHEEL SPEED RL in the "OBTAIN READINGS" menu to check whether wheel speed is displayed.

If it is not, connect a BOB and check whether a wheel speed signal is present on pin 24 when the LH rear wheel is rotated at a speed of about 1/2 revolution per second. The correct reading is about 15 Hz.

If the reading is not correct, check the cable between pin 24 of the TCS control module and pin 22 of the ABS control module for continuity/ shorting.

Remedy any defective cable.

3 Clear the trouble code. Start the car and drive it to check whether the code is generated afresh.

If it is, go to "Procedure Prior To Replacing Control Module" figure.

SA0009200016000A

Fig. 18 Code B1381: Wheel Speed RL, Signal Incorrect Or Absent. 900

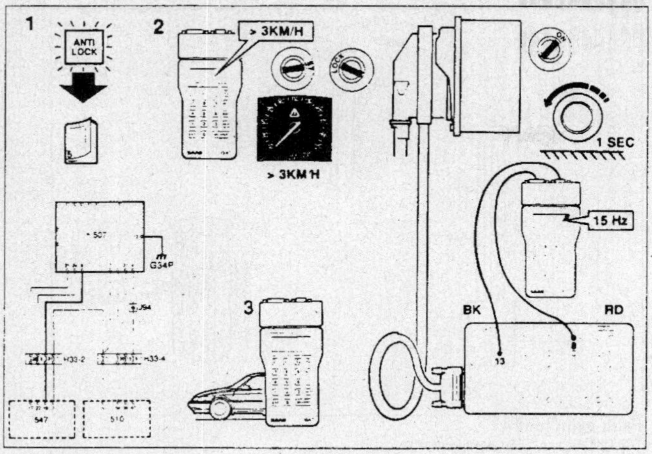

Fault symptom

TCS OFF lamp on, TCS system inoperative.

Condition

Wheel speed signal incorrect or absent, or indicates a speed higher than 280 km/h.

Note:

See under diagnostic trouble code B1371.

Diagnostic procedure

1 If the ANTI LOCK lamp also lights up, obtain readings of any trouble codes in the ABS system and take the necessary remedial action

2 Connect the ISAT. Drive the car slowly (but at least 3 km/h) and select WHEEL SPEED RR in the "OBTAIN READINGS" menu to check whether wheel speed is displayed.

If it is not, connect a BOB and check whether a wheel speed signal is present on pin 8 when the RH front wheel is rotated at a speed of about 1/2 revolution per second. The correct reading is about 15 Hz.

If the reading is not correct, check the cable between pin 8 of the TCS control module and pin 19 of the ABS control module for continuity/shorting.

Remedy any defective cable.

3 Clear the trouble code. Start the car and drive it to check whether the code is generated afresh.

If it is, go to "Procedure Prior To Replacing Control Module" figure.

SA0029100017000A

Fig. 19 Code B1386: Wheel Speed RR, Signal Incorrect Or Absent. 900

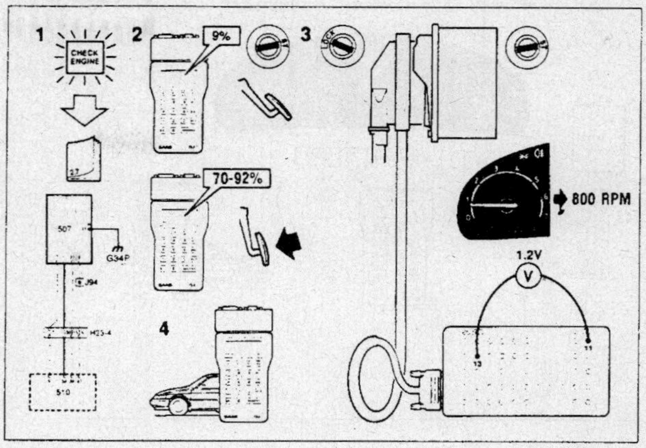

Fault symptom

TCS OFF lamp on, TCS system inoperative and possibly trouble codes in MOTRONIC.

Condition

For trouble code B1406: Main throttle butterfly position signal from pin 54 of the MOTRONIC control module to pin 11 of the TCS control module incorrect.

For trouble code B1407: Main throttle butterfly position signal from pin 54 of the MOTRONIC control module to pin 11 of the TCS control module shorted to ground.

For trouble code B1408: Main throttle butterfly position signal from pin 54 of the MOTRONIC control module to pin 11 of the TCS control module shorted to battery + or no continuity.

Diagnostic procedure

1 If the CHECK ENGINE lamp (MIL) is also on, obtain a reading of the trouble codes in the MOTRONIC system.

2 Connect the ISAT and select "MAIN THROTTLE POS" in the "OBTAIN READOUTS" menu. Drive the car and check that the ISAT shows about 9% at idling speed and about 70-92% at full throttle.

3 If it does not, switch off the ignition and connect a BOB to the TCS control module. Start the engine and check whether the main throttle butterfly's position signal is present on pin 11 so that a reading can be obtained.

Correct readings are about 1.2 V when idling and about 2 V at 2500 rpm.

If the readings are incorrect, check the cable between pin 11 of the TCS control module and pin 54 of the MOTRONIC control module for continuity/shorting.

Remedy any defective cable.

4 Clear the trouble codes, if any. Start the car and drive it to check whether the code is generated afresh.

If it is, go to "Procedure Prior To Replacing Control Module" figure.

SA0029100019000A

Fig. 20 Codes B1406, B1407 & B1408: Position Sensor, Main Throttle Butterfly, Faulty, No Continuity/Short Circuit. 900

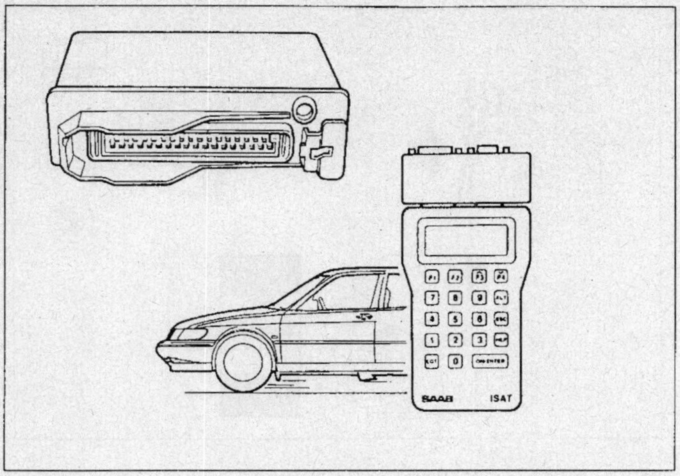

Fault symptom

TCS OFF lamp on, TCS symptom inoperative

Condition

Internal fault in control module

Diagnostic procedure

1 Clear the trouble code. Start the car and drive it to check whether the code is generated afresh.

SA0029100011000X

Fig. 21 Code B1605: Control Module Fault

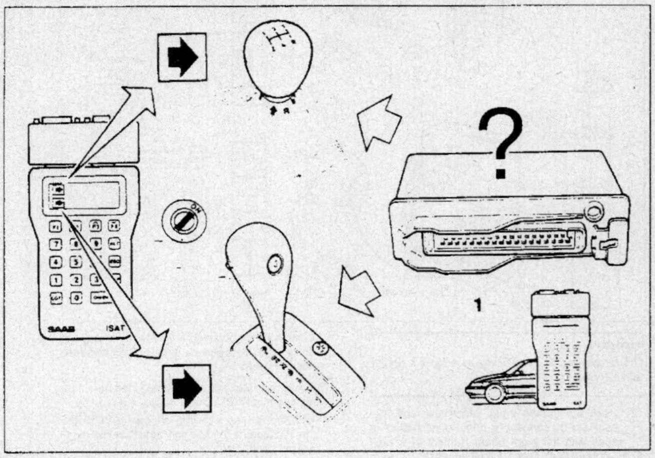

Fault symptom

TCS OFF lamp on, TCS system inoperative.

Condition

Contro module not programed.

Diagnostic procedure

Program the control module by means of an ISAT. For the M94 TCS control module there are only two variants, one for the Saab 900 with manual gearbox and one for the Saab 900 with automatic transmission.

1 Clear the trouble codes. Start the car and drive it to check whether the code is generated afresh.

SA0029100021000A

Fig. 22 Code B1610: Control Module Not Programmed. 900

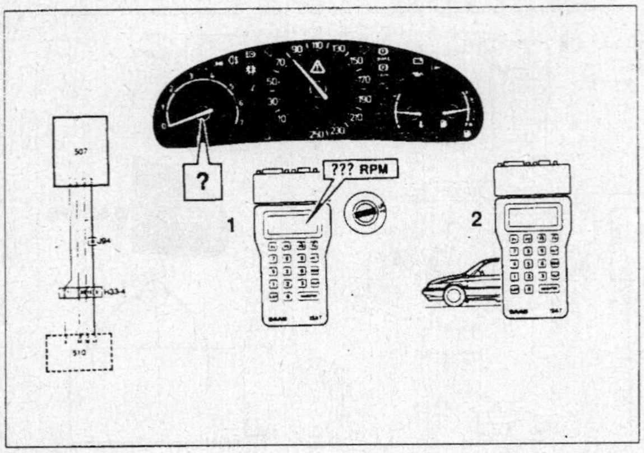

Fault symptom

TCS OFF lamp on, TCS system inoperative.

Condition

No engine rpm signal and car driven at speeds above 60 km/h.

Diagnostic procedure

Note:

If the tachometer (rev counter) does not work, the problem is probably a short circuit in one of the systems where the rpm signal is used.

1 With the engine running, check that engine speed is correct when ENGINE RPM is selected in the "OBTAIN READINGS" menu on the ISAT.

If it is not, check the cable between pin 6 of the control menu and pin 43 of the MOTRONIC control module.

2 Clear the trouble code. Start the car and drive it to check whether the code is generated afresh.

If it is, go to "Procedure Prior To Replacing Control Module" figure.

SA0029100013000A

Fig. 23 Code B1710: No Engine RPM Signal. 900

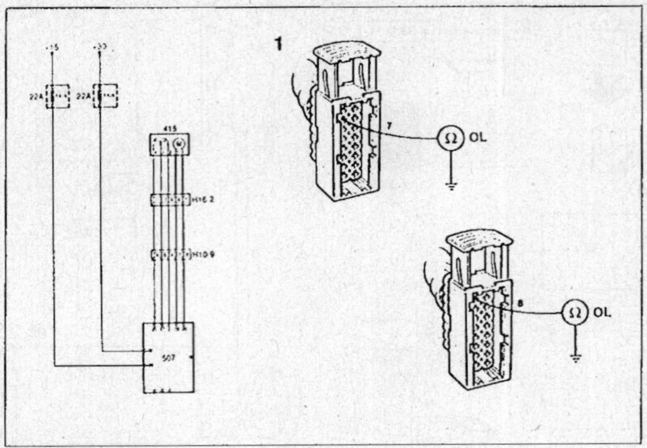

Fault symptom

TCS OFF lamp on, TCS system inoperative

Condition

B2433: Control module output pin 18 shorted to ground, battery + or pin 35.

Control module output pin 35 shorted to ground, battery + or pin 18.

B2434: Control module output pin 18, no continuity.

Control module output pin 35, no continuity.

Control module input pin 27, no continuity.

Throttle butterfly mechanism or motor binding.

Note:

B2434 is generated when the butterfly's "ACTUAL" value does not coincide with its "REFERENCE" value. This means that the butterfly cannot assume a position calculated by the control module or that the control module cannot calculate the position of the butterfly. This could be due to any of three reasons:

- A mechanical fault, such as a binding throttle butterfly.
- An electrical fault, such as a break in the wiring, which prevents the throttle motor from working.
- No information received by the control module from the throttle body about the position of the butterfly, such as no continuity on pin 27 of the control module input.

B2434 can be generated in connection with fault diagnosis when the throttle body wiring is disconnected and the ignition switch is turned to the Drive position.

Diagnostic procedure - B2433

1 With the ignition switched off, unplug connector H16-2 and check that the engine is not shorted to ground by measuring the resistance across ground and pin 7 of the female connector and also across ground and pin 8 of the female connector.

In both cases the resistance should be infinite (OL).

SA0029100020010X

Fig. 24 Codes B2433 & B2434: TCS Throttle Motor Shorted To Ground/Battery +, No Continuity Or Mechanical Fault (Part 1 of 3). 900

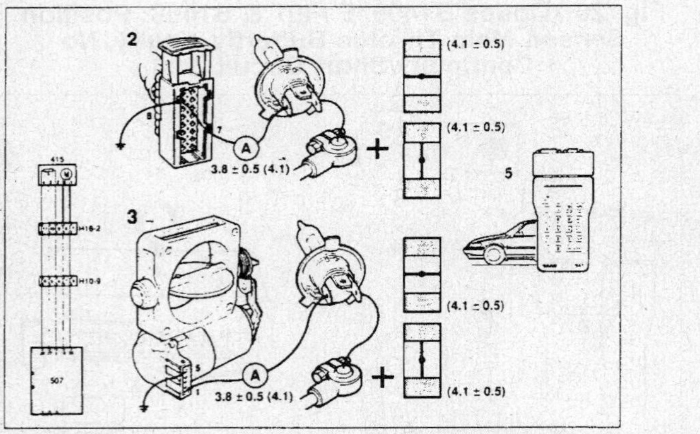

Important

The throttle motor must never be supplied directly with 12 V.

2 Check the throttle motor electrically and mechanically by connecting it to the car battery in series with the high- beam filament of a 12V/60W bulb (H4). Using a multimeter set for measuring current in the 10A range, a reading of 3.8 ± 0.5 A should be obtained. Slowly change the position of the butterfly by hand from open to closed. The meter reading should now vary by a maximum of ± 0.5 A from the reading first obtained.

Also check that it is noticeably harder to close the butterfly when the throttle motor is supplied with current.

If the above checks out OK, proceed to point 4. If not, continue with point 3.

3 Remove the TCS throttle body

Repeat the checking procedure described in points 1 and 2, but now directly on pins 1 and 5 of the throttle motor.

If the readings obtained are correct, remedy the faulty wiring between the throttle motor and connector H16-2.

If incorrect readings are also obtained here, fit a replacement TCS throttle body.

4 With the ignition switched off, plug a BOB into the TCS control module connector (control module not connected).

Check the cable between pin 18 of the control module connector and pin 8 of the male connector (H16-2) for continuity/shorting.

Also check the cable between pin 35 of the control module connector and pin 7 of the male connector for continuity/shorting.

5 Clear the trouble code. Start the car and drive it to check whether the code is generated afresh.

SA0029100020020A

Fig. 24 Codes B2433 & B2434: TCS Throttle Motor Shorted To Ground/Battery +, No Continuity Or Mechanical Fault (Part 2 of 3). 900

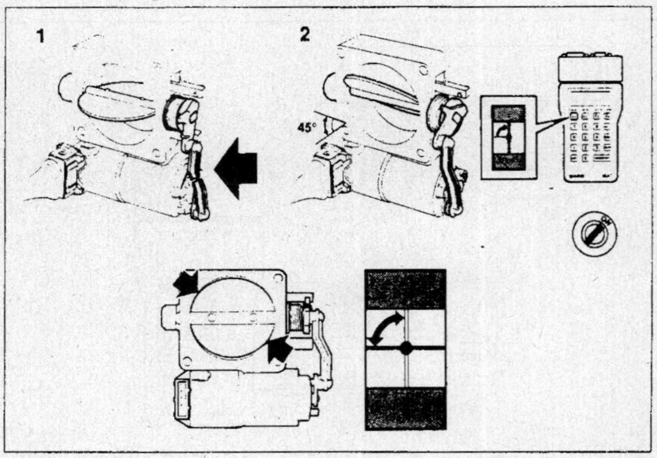

Diagnostic procedure - B2434

1 With the ignition switched off, check that the throttle butterfly can easily be moved to the closed position by hand and that no binding occurs. The force of the spring should also return it to the open position with ease.

If it is in proper working order, proceed to point 2. If it is not, remedy the fault if possible or fit a replacement throttle body.

2 Connect the ISAT.

With the ignition in the Drive position, open the TCS throttle butterfly halfway by hand. Then select "BUTTERFLY CLOSING ON" in the "ACTIVATE" menu.

Note:

If the actuator motor rotates the TCS throttle butterfly towards the open position when "BUTTERFLY CLOSING ON" is activated, it is because the control module receives no information about the position of the butterfly on input pin 27.

If the butterfly **either** closes or opens, proceed to point 4.

If it does not, continue with point 3.

3 Carry out the measures described under diagnostic trouble code B2433

4 Carry out the measures described under diagnostic trouble codes B1302 and B1303

SA0029100020030A

Fig. 24 Codes B2433 & B2434: TCS Throttle Motor Shorted To Ground/Battery +, No Continuity Or Mechanical Fault (Part 3 of 3). 900

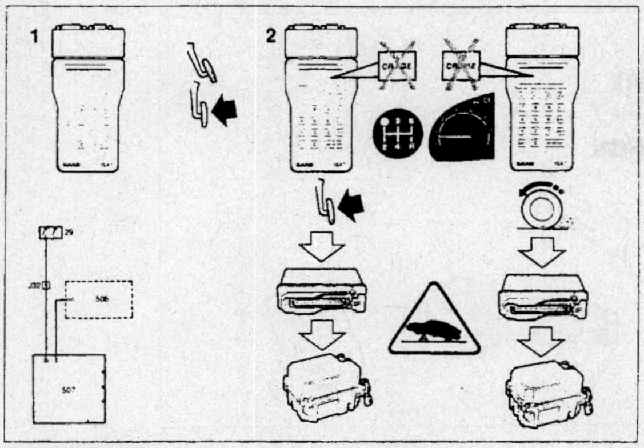

Fault symptom

The Cruise Control does not disengage when the TCS function is activated or the brakes are applied.

Diagnostic procedure

1 Connect the ISAT and select "BRAKE LIGHT SWITCH" in the "OBTAIN READOUTS" menu. Check that the switch is in proper working order. If it is, proceed to point 2.

If it is not, check the operation of the brake light switch

WARNING

The car can be jacked up to activate the TCS function. Proceed with the outmost caution if this method is chosen. If only the front of the car is raised and supported on stands, the handbrake must always be applied and nobody should stand in front of the car or beside the front wheels while the test is in progress. Speed should be restricted to the minimum possible above 4 km/h.

2 Select "DISENG CRUISE CONT" in the "OBTAIN READOUTS" menu and check that the Cruise Control system is disengaged when the TCS function is activated or the brakes are applied.

Note

The TCS lamp comes on about one second before disengagement takes place.

If the Cruise Control disengages correctly, check the cable between pin 5 of the TCS control module and pin G of the Cruise Control for continuity/shorting.

SA0029100022000A

Fig. 25 Cruise Control Disengagement Check. 900

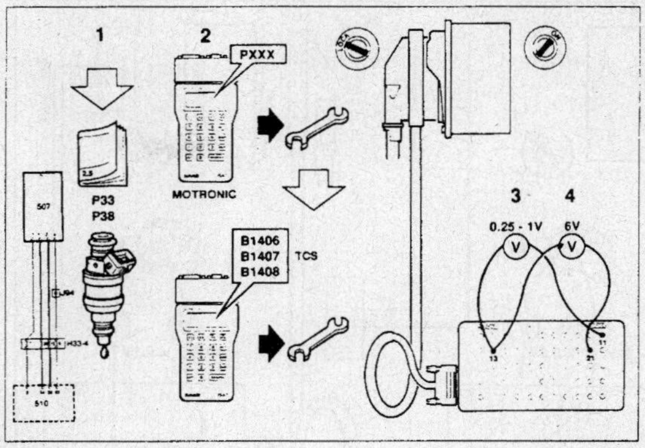

Fault symptom

Diagnostic trouble codes generated in the MOTRONIC.

Diagnostic procedure

1 Study what is described in "Disconnection of full-load enrichment"

2 If **other** diagnostic trouble codes have been generated in the MOTRONIC, or if any of the trouble codes B1406, B1407 or B1408 have been generated in the TCS, deal with them first. If no trouble codes have been generated, continue with point 3.

Drive the car on the road and check whether any trouble codes are generated afresh in the MOTRONIC. If they are, proceed as follows:

3 With the ignition switched off, connect a BOB to the TCS. While the engine is still hot and switched off, and with the ignition switch in the Drive position, check whether a 100 Hz PWM signal (0.2-0.82 ms (+), 2-8.2 % (+), 0.25-1.0 V) is present on pin 11.

If it is not, the fault is in the MOTRONIC system.

If the signal is OK, continue with point 4.

4 With the engine still hot and switched off, and with the ignition switch in the Drive position, check whether a 31 Hz PWM signal is present on pin 21. The signal should be about 6 V.

If the signal is OK, check the cable to pin 38 of the MOTRONIC control module for continuity.

If the signal is not OK, check the cable to pin 38 of the MOTRONIC control module for shorting to ground.

5 If the cable to pin 38 of the MOTRONIC control module is OK and there is still no signal on pin 21 of the TCS control module,
go to "Procedure Prior To Replacing Control Module" figure.

SA0029100023000A

Fig. 26 Full-Load Enrichment Disconnection Check. 900

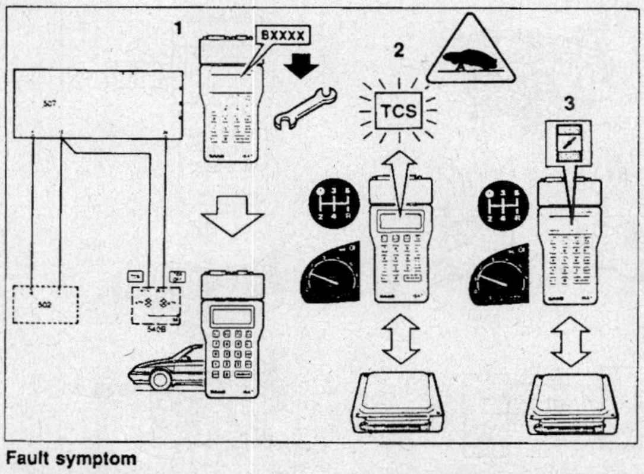

Fault symptom

Diagnostic trouble codes P1786, P1787 or P1788 generated in the TCM system.

Hard shifting when the TCS is activated.

Diagnostic procedure

1 If diagnostic trouble codes have been generated in the TCS system, deal with them first. If no trouble codes have been generated, proceed as follows.

Drive the car on the road and check whether trouble codes are generated afresh in the TCM system. If they are, proceed as follows.

WARNING

To activate the TCS function, the car can be raised on a garage lift. Proceed with the outmost caution if this method is chosen. If only the front of the car is raised and supported on stands, the handbrake must always be applied and nobody should stand in front of the car or beside the front wheels while the test is in progress. Speed should be restricted to the minimum possible above 4 km/h.

2 Use the ISAT to communicate with the TCM system and select "TCS ACTIVE" in the "READ ON/OFF" menu.

Activate the TCS by engaging a gear and driving the front wheels while the front assembly of the car is raised. Check whether the ISAT display text changes from TCS OFF to TCS ON at the same time as the TCS lamp lights up.

If it does not, check the cable between pin 12 of the TCS control module and pin 4 of the TCM control module for continuity/shorting.

3 Use the ISAT to communicate with the TCM system and select "TCS THROTTLE POSITION" in the "READ FUNCTIONS" menu.

Check that the throttle position is about 70-92%when the wheels are stationary and that it changes to a much lower figure when the speed of the front wheels exceeds 4 km/h.

If it does not, check the cable between pin 4 of the TCS control module and pin 15 of the TCM control module for continuity/shorting.

SA0029100024000X

Fig. 27 Shifting Performance Adjustment. Automatic Transaxle. 900

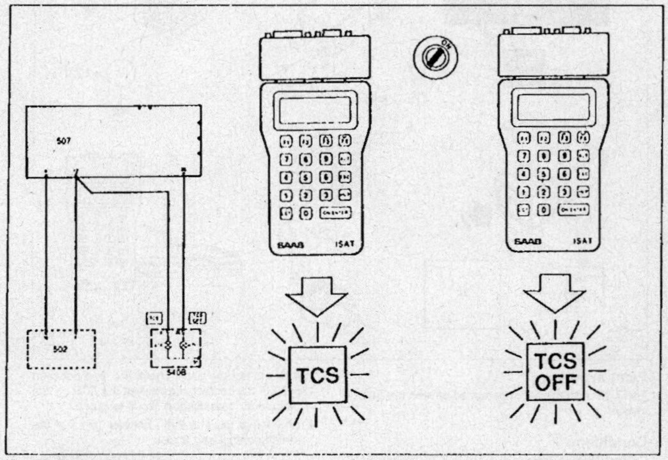

Fault symptom

The lamps do not light up or remain alight continuously but no trouble code is generated. (Note that the lamps are tested for three seconds when the ignition is switched on.)

Diagnostic procedure

1 Activate the lamps by means of the ISAT's "ACTIVATE" menu.

If the lamps do not work, first check whether the bulbs are intact.

If the bulbs are OK, check the cable for the TCS lamp between pin 12 of the control module and pin 41 of the instrument, or the cable for the TCS OFF lamp between pin 26 of the control module and pin 20 of the instrument, for continuity or shorting.

Remedy any defective cable.

SA0029100025000X

Fig. 28 TCS Lamp & TCS OFF Lamp Check. 900

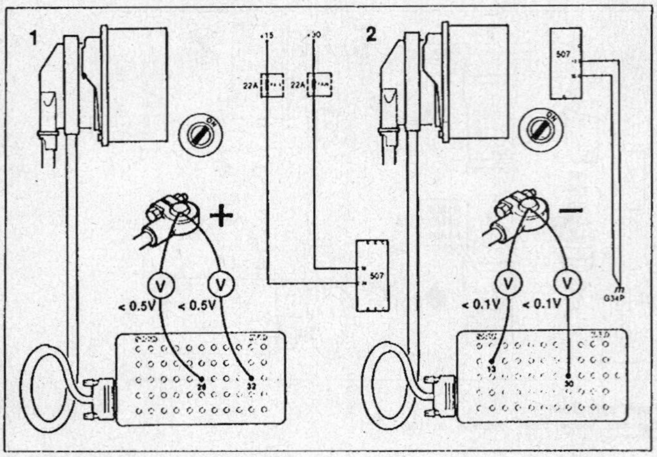

Fault symptom

Alternative I: TCS OFF lamp on, TCS inoperative.

Alternative II: TCS OFF lamp and TCS lamp both fail to light up when ignition turned ON.

Alternative II: Malfunctioning.

Diagnostic procedure

When a BOB is connected in conjunction with fault diagnosis, the voltage supply and ground connections should always be checked first, as follows:

Ignition switch in Drive position

1. Battery positive—pin 32 <0.5 V
2. Battery positive—pin 28 <0.5 V
3. Pin 30—Battery negative <0.1 V
4. Pin 13—Battery negative <0.1 V

SA0029100026000X

Fig. 29 Control Module Power Supply & Ground Location Check. 900

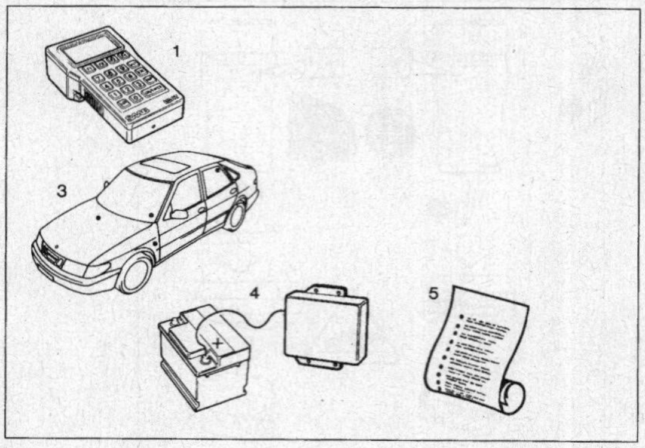

If it has not been possible to find any fault after everything has been checked in accordance with the diagnostic procedure for the relevant diagnostic trouble code, and separate checking of component operation has also been carried out, it is natural to assume that the control module is defective.

In view of the fact that the control module is manufactured to extremely exacting standards of quality, and also because it is a rather expensive component, every effort should be made to ensure that the diagnosis is as accurate as possible.

Therefore, run through the following points before definitely settling on the TCS control module as the cause of the fault.

1. Check once again that all points in the relevant diagnostic procedure have been carried out correctly.
2. Study the schematic diagram of the relevant circuit until you understand how it works. If necessary, consult appropriate parts of the technical description
3. Check the control module's ground connections once again and also check that the relevant grounding points are good and correct.
4. Check the control module's voltage supply.
5. check that nothing has been forgotten or overlooked.
6. If the original fault still persists, the TCS control module will have to be changed.

Do not forget to program the control module for the car variant in question.

SA0029100027000A

Fig. 30 Procedure Prior To Replacing Control Module

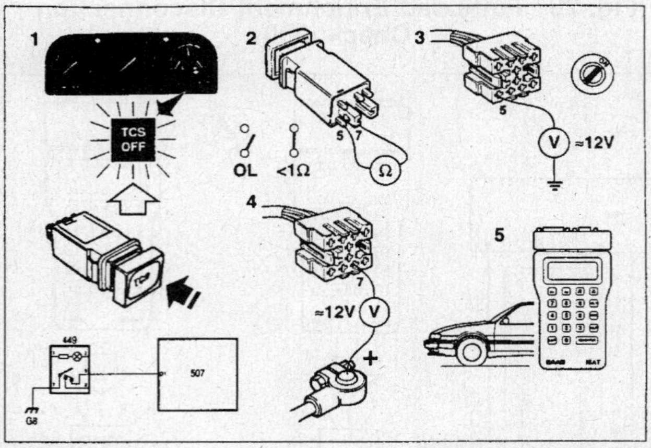

Fault symptom

The TCS system cannot be turned off with the TCS switch

Conditions

Control module input pin 1 shorted to ground for more than 10 seconds, or switch held depressed for more than 10 seconds.

Action

Check the function of the switch.

Ignition in ON position.

1. If the TCS switch is pressed repeatedly, the TCS OFF lamp should alternately go on and off.

   If this is OK, proceed to point 5.
   If the function is faulty, proceed to point 2.
2. Remove the TCS switch from the facia. Unplug the connector from the switch and check that the resistance across pins 5 and 7 of the switch is <1 Ohm when the switch is depressed and infinite (OL) when the switch is not depressed.

   If values are incorrect, change the switch
3. With the ignition in the drive position, check that there is Batt+ across pin 5 of the switch contact and a safe grounding point.

   If this is not the case, check the lead between pin 5 of the contact and pin 1 of the TCS control module for breaks/short circuit to ground.
4. Check that there is Batt+ between pin 7 of the switch contact and B plus.

   If this is not the case, check for breaks in the lead between pin 7 on the connector and grounding point G8.
5. Erase the diagnostic trouble code, test-drive the car and see if the diagnostic trouble code is re-registered.

   If it is, go to "Procedure Prior To Replacing Control Module" figure.
   If the diagnostic trouble code is not registered, the action taken was correct or the fault was of the intermittent type.

SA0029500038000X

Fig. 31 Code B1192: TCS Switch Shorted To Ground. 9000

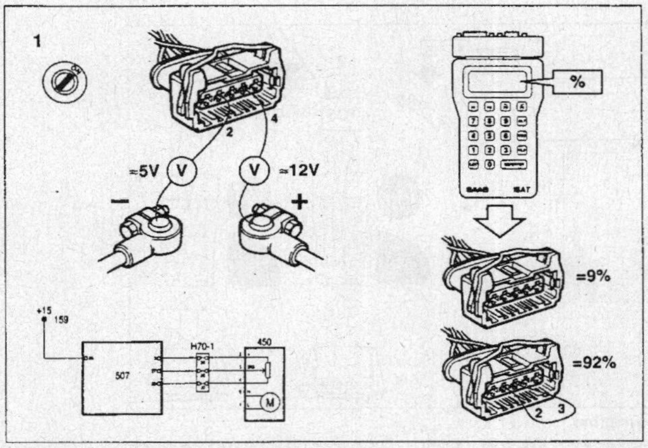

Fault symptom

TCS OFF lamp lit, TCS system not functioning

Conditions

For diagnostic trouble code B1302: Control module output pin 3 broken or shorted to ground, or control module input pin 27 shorted to ground

For diagnostic trouble code B1303: Control module output pin 20 broken or shorted to battery+, or control module input pin 27 shorted to battery+.

Important

B1302 and B1303 can be registered during fault diagnosis when connectors to the throttle body and unplugged and the ignition is placed in the drive position.

Action

Check the cable assembly to the control module:

1. Unplug the 5 pin connector from the throttle body.

   Ignition in ON position.

   Measure voltage supply in the female connector:

   - pin 2 to Batt- ________ approx. 5V
   - Batt+ to pin 4 ________ approx 12V

   Connect the ISAT and select the command "TCS THROTTLE POS" in the "OBTAIN READOUTS" menu.

   - ISAT should show approx 9%

   Bridge between pins 2 and 3 in the female connector.

   - ISAT should now show approx 92%.

   If all measured values are correct, change the throttle body.
   If any of the values is incorrect, proceed to point 2.

SA0029500035010X

Fig. 32 Codes B1302 & B1303: Position Sensor, TCS Throttle Butterfly, No Continuity/Short Circuit (Part 1 of 2). 9000

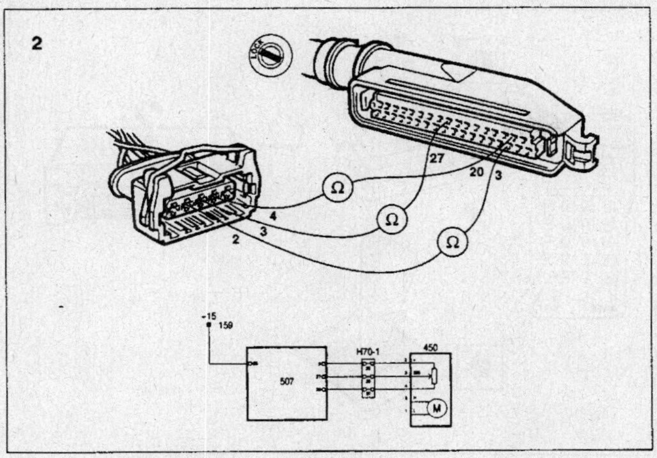

2 Conduct continuity tests on the leads between pins 2,3,4 in the female connector and associated control module connector for breaks, shorts and any bypasses.
If the values are correct, proceed to point 3.

3 Erase the diagnostic trouble code, test-drive the car and see if the diagnostic trouble code is re-registered.
If it is, go to "Procedure Prior To Replacing Control Module" figure.
If the diagnostic trouble code is not registered, the action taken was correct or the fault was of the intermittent type.

SA0029500035020X

Fig. 32 Codes B1302 & B1303: Position Sensor, TCS Throttle Butterfly, No Continuity/Short Circuit (Part 2 of 2). 9000

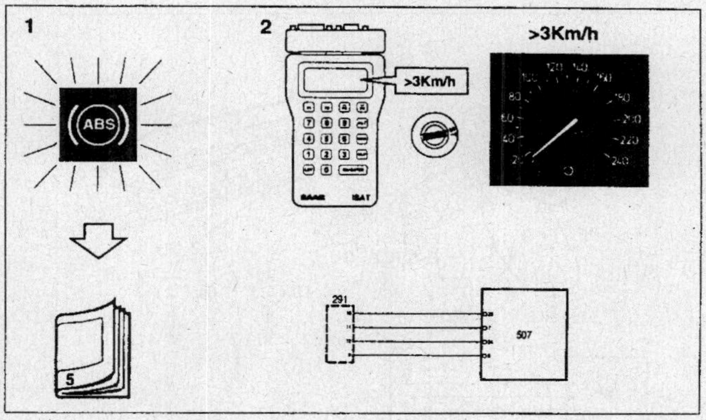

Action

1 If the ANTI LOCK lamp also lights while driving, obtain readings and act on diagnostic trouble codes in the ABS system

Ensure that there is no wheel speed signal:

2 Ignition in ON position.
Connect the ISAT and select the "WHEEL SPEED" command in the "OBTAIN READOUTS" menu.
Check by driving the car or by rotating each wheel that all four wheel speed signals are functioning.
Note that the lowest display on the ISAT is 3km/h
If all values are correct, proceed to point 4.
If any value is incorrect, proceed to point 3.

SA0029500037020X

Fig. 33 Codes B1371, B1376, B1381 & B1386: Wheel Speed Faulty Or No Signal (Part 2 of 3). 9000

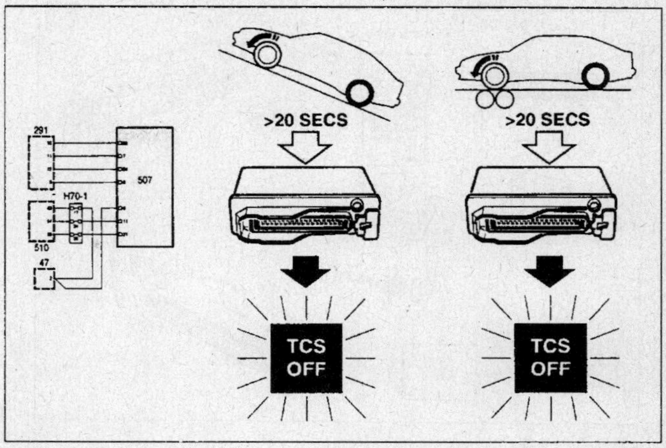

Fault symptom

TCS OFF lamp lit, TCS system not functioning.

Conditions

Wheel speed signal incorrect or absent, or indicates a speed higher than 280 km/h

Important

The diagnostic trouble code for wheel signals can be generated when the brakes are tested or if the car is started on a slippery uphill gradient, when the front wheels spin and the rear wheels remain stationary.

If only one wheel spins and the other three remain stationary, the control module cannot tell whether the speed signals from the three stationary wheels are correct or false. In this case, trouble codes are generated for the three stationary wheels. The trouble codes are however automatically erased as soon as the signals return.

If wheelspin continues for more than 20 seconds, while one of the wheels remains stationary, The TCS system is disconnected and the TCS OFF lamp lights. To restore the TCS function, the ignition must be switched off and back on again.

SA0029500037010X

Fig. 33 Codes B1371, B1376, B1381 & B1386: Wheel Speed Faulty Or No Signal (Part 1 of 3). 9000

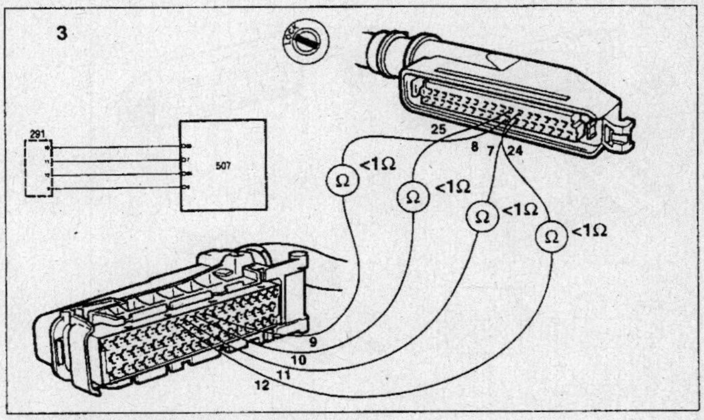

3 Conduct continuity measurements on the lead for the wheel speed signal in question. Check between the ABS control module and the TCS control module for breaks, shorts and bypasses.
If the values are correct, proceed to point 4.

Wheel	Pin on ABS control module	Pin on TCS control module
FL	10	25
FR	11	7
RL	12	24
RR	9	8

4 Erase the diagnostic trouble code, test-drive the car and see if the diagnostic trouble code is re-registered. If it is, go to "Procedure Prior To Replacing Control Module" figure.

If the diagnostic trouble code is not registered, the action taken was correct or the fault was of the intermittent type.

SA0029500037030X

Fig. 33 Codes B1371, B1376, B1381 & B1386: Wheel Speed Faulty Or No Signal (Part 3 of 3). 9000

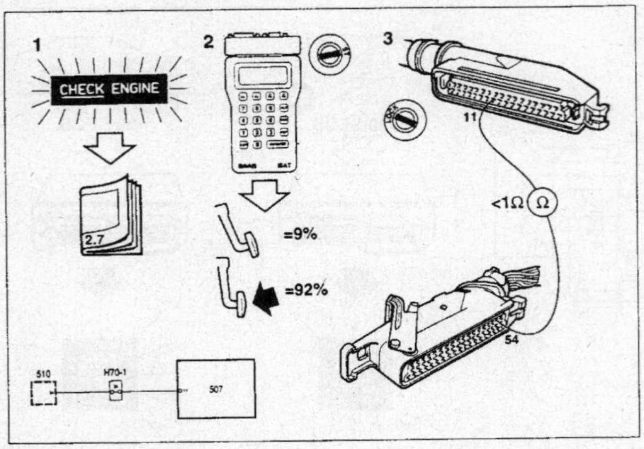

Fault symptom

TCS OFF lamp lit, TCS system not functioning and possibility of diagnostic trouble codes in the MOTRONIC

Conditions

For diagnostic trouble code B1406: Main butterfly position signal from pin 54 in the MOTRONIC control module to pin 11 in the TCS control module is faulty

For diagnostic trouble code B1407: Main butterfly position signal from pin 54 in the MOTRONIC control module to pin 11 in the TCS control module is shorted to ground

For diagnostic trouble code B1408: Main butterfly position signal from pin 54 in the MOTRONIC control module to pin 11 in the TCS control module is shorted to Batt+/broken

Action

1 If the CHECK ENGINE lamp is also lit when driving, read and act on diagnostic trouble codes in the MOTRONIC.

2 Start the engine.
Connect the ISAT and select the "MAIN THROTTLE POS" command in the OBTAIN READOUTS" menu.

- The ISAT should show approx. 9% when idling and approx. 92% at wide open throttle.
  If the values are correct, proceed to point 4.
  If the values are incorrect, proceed to point 3.

3 Conduct continuity test on the lead between pin 54 of the MOTRONIC control module and pin 11 of the TCS control module for breaks, shorts and bypasses.
If the value is correct, proceed to point 4.

4 Erase the diagnostic trouble code, test-drive the car and see if the diagnostic trouble code is re-registered.

If the diagnostic trouble code is not registered, the action taken was correct or the fault was of the intermittent type.

SA0029500039000X

Fig. 34 Codes B1406, B1407 & B1408: Main Throttle Butterfly Position Signal Faulty Or Break/ Short Circuit. 9000

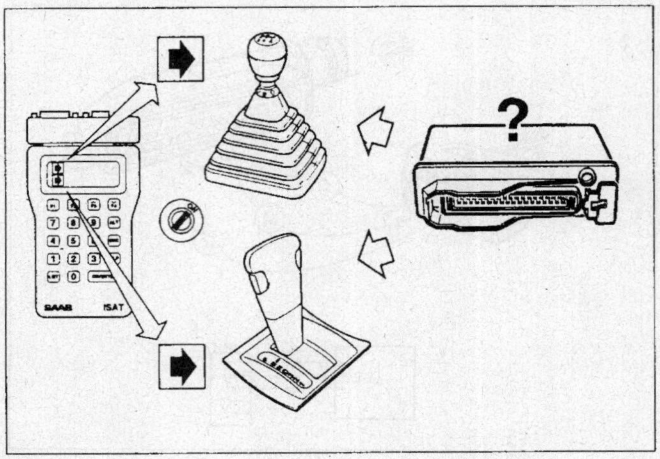

Fault symptom

TCS OFF lamp lit, TCS system not functioning

Conditions

Control module not programmed

Action

1 Program the control module using the ISAT.
Select "9000 MANUAL" or "9000 AUTO TRANS".

2 Erase diagnostic trouble code.
Test-drive the car to see if the diagnostic trouble code is regenerated.
If the diagnostic trouble code is not regenerated, the action taken was correct.

SA0029500042000X

Fig. 35 Code B1610: Control Module Not Programmed. 9000

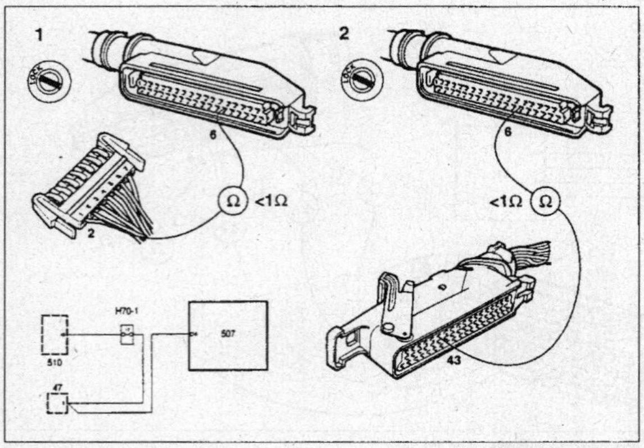

Fault symptom

TCS OFF lamp lit, TCS system not functioning

Conditions

No engine speed signal and the car is travelling at over 60 km/h.

Action

Check the lead between the MOTRONIC control module and the TCS control module:

1 **If the tachometer is working,** conduct continuity test on the lead between speedometer pin 2 and TCS control module pin 6 for breaks.

2 **If the tachometer is not working,** conduct a continuity test between pin 43 on the MOTRONIC control module via pin 2 on the speedometer to pin 6 on the TCS control module for breaks, shorts and bypasses.

3 Erase the diagnostic trouble code, test-drive the car and see if the diagnostic trouble code is re-registered.

If the diagnostic trouble code is not registered, the action taken was correct or the fault was of the intermittent type.

SA0029500036000X

Fig. 36 Code B1710: No Engine RPM Signal. 9000

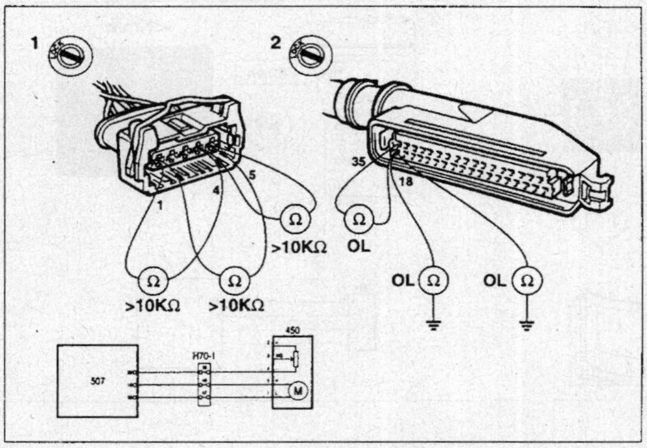

Fault symptom

TCS OFF lamp lit, TCS system not functioning

Conditions

Control module output pin 18 shorted to ground, Batt+ or to pin 35.

Control module output pin 35 shorted to ground, Batt+ or to pin 18.

Action

Check the leads to the throttle actuator motor for shorts:

1 Ignition in OFF position.
Unplug the throttle body connector. Check the resistance in the female connector.

- pin 4 (ground) to pin 1 ______________ >10 kΩ
- pin 4 (ground) to pin 5 ______________ >10 kΩ
- pin 1 to pin 5 ______________ >10 kΩ

If the values are correct, change the throttle body.
If the values are incorrect, proceed to point 2.

2 Unplug the throttle body connector.
Conduct a continuity test on the two leads from control module outputs 18 and 35 for shorting to ground, to Batt+ or between the leads.
If the values are correct, proceed to point 3.

3 Erase the diagnostic trouble code, test-drive the car and see if the diagnostic trouble code is re-registered.

If the diagnostic trouble code is not registered, the action taken was correct or the fault was of the intermittent type.

If it is, go to "Procedure Prior To Replacing Control Module" figure.

SA0029500040000X

Fig. 37 Code B2433: TCS Butterfly Actuator Motor Shorted To Ground/Battery +. 9000

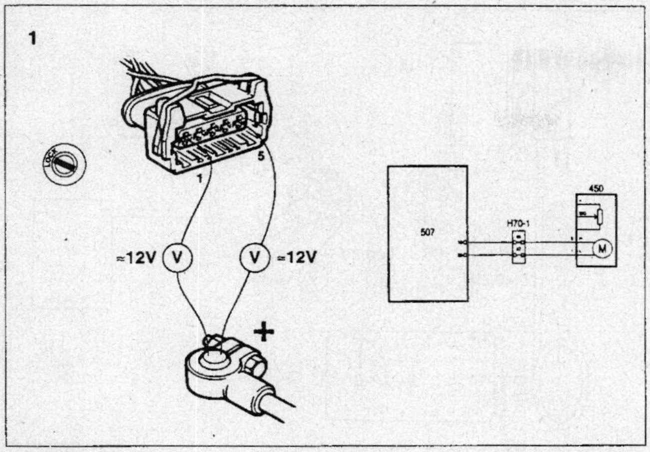

Fault symptom
TCS OFF lamp lit, TCS system not functioning

Conditions
Control module output pin 18, break.
Control module output pin 35, break.
Throttle mechanism or motor seizing.
Linkage or return spring faulty.

Important
B2434 is generated when the throttle's "ACTUAL" value does not coincide with its "REFERENCE" value. This means that the throttle cannot assume a position calculated by the control module. This could be due to one of two reasons.

- Mechanical fault, for example seized butterfly.
- An electrical fault such as a break which prevents the throttle motor from working.
  If there is another diagnostic trouble code in the TCS system, remedy that first.

Action
Check the leads to the throttle motor for breaks.

1 Ignition in the OFF position.
Unplug the connector from the throttle body.
Check the voltage supply in the female connector.

- pin 1 to Batt+ ________________approx. 12V
- pin 5 to Batt+ ________________approx. 12V
  If the values are correct, proceed to point 2.
  If the values are incorrect, proceed to point 3.

SA0029500041010X

Fig. 38 Code B2434: TCS Throttle Actuator Motor Break Or Mechanical Fault (Part 1 of 2). 9000

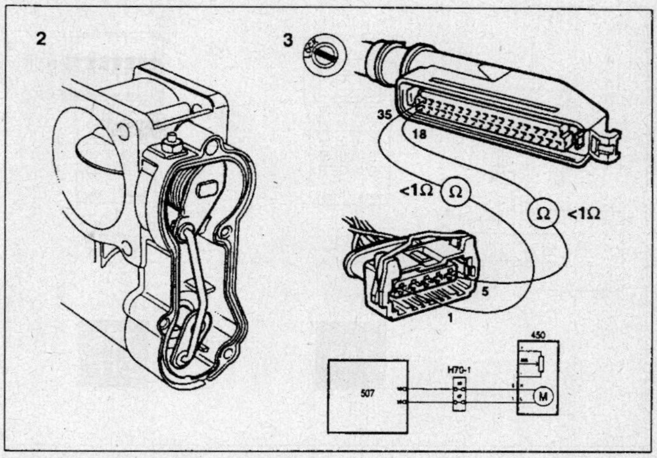

2 Remove the cover from the throttle body linkage.
With the ignition turned off, check that the butterfly can easily be closed against the stop screw without siezing.
The butterfly should also easily return to the fully open position under spring force.
If the function is OK, change the throttle body.
If the function is not correct, remedy the fault if possible or change the throttle body.

3 Conduct continuity tests on the two leads from control module outputs 18 and 35 for breaks.
If the values are correct, proceed to point 4.

4 Erase the diagnostic trouble code, test-drive the car and see if the diagnostic trouble code is re-registered.

If the diagnostic trouble code is not registered, the action taken was correct or the fault was of the intermittent type.

If it is, go to "Procedure Prior To Replacing Control Module" figure.

SA0029500041020X

Fig. 38 Code B2434: TCS Throttle Actuator Motor Break Or Mechanical Fault (Part 2 of 2). 9000

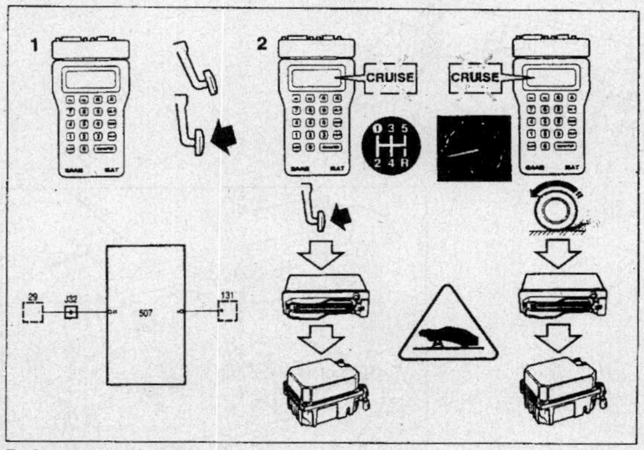

Fault symptom
The cruise control does not disengage when the TCS function is activated

Action

1 Connect the ISAT and select the "BRAKE LIGHT SWITCH" command in the "OBTAIN READOUTS" menu.
Check that the brake light switch is in working order.
If it is, proceed to point 2.
If it is faulty, check the operation of the brake light switch as described in Service Manual 3:2.
Also check for breaks in the leads between crimped connector J32 and TCS control module pin 23.

> ⚠ **WARNING**
> The car can be jacked up to activate the TCS function. If this method is used, proceed with extreme care. If only the front of the car is raised and supported on stands, the hand-brake must always be applied and personnel should never stand in front of the car or beside the front wheels while the test is in progress. Speed should be restricted to the minimum possible above 4 km/h.

2 Select "DISENG CRUISE CONT" in the "OBTAIN READOUTS" menu and check that the operation is correct when the TCS function is activated or the brakes are applied.

Important
The TCS lamp lights for about 1 second before disengagement.

If this functions correctly, check for breaks and shorts in the lead from TCS control module pin 5 to cruise control pin G.

If it does not, go to "Procedure Prior To Replacing Control Module" figure.

SA0029500043000X

Fig. 39 Cruise Control Disengagement Check. 9000

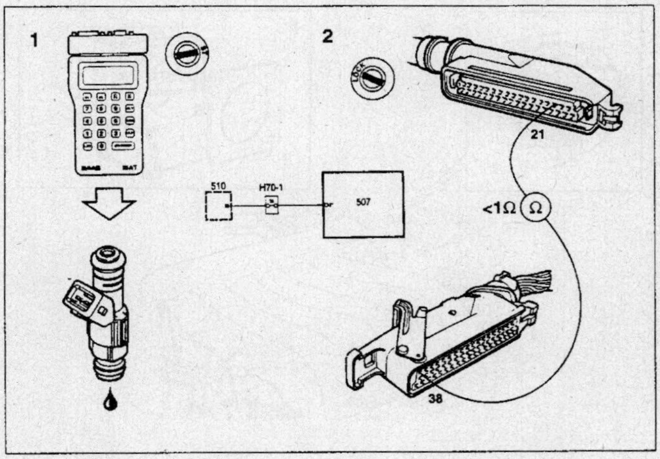

Fault symptom
Diagnostic trouble codes generated in the MOTRONIC (P1630, P1631).

Action

1 Start the engine and let it idle.
Connect the ISAT and select "DISCONN ENRICHMENT" in the "ACTIVATE" menu.
When the ISAT function is activated, the engine should stop.
If this works OK, the diagnostic trouble code (if any) in the MOTRONIC can be left without action.
If the function is faulty, proceed to point 2.

2 Conduct continuity test on the lead between TCS control module pin 21 and MOTRONIC connector pin 38, looking for breaks or shorts.

If values are correct, go to "Procedure Prior To Replacing Control Module" figure.

SA0029500044000X

Fig. 40 Full-Load Enrichment Disconnection Check. 9000

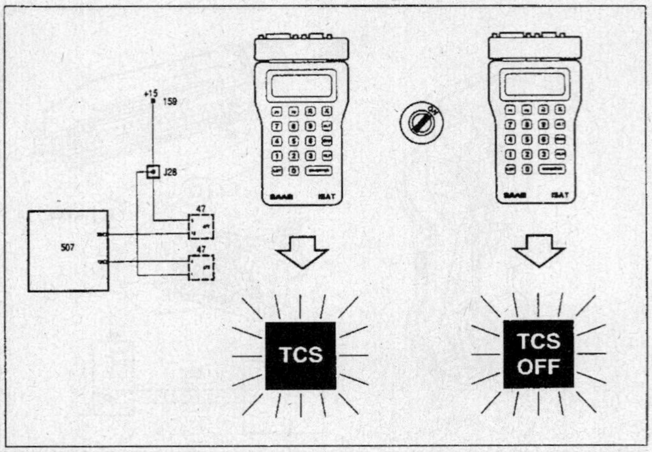

Fault symptom

The lamps do not light or stay lit without a diagnostic trouble code being generated. (Note that the lamps are tested for 3 seconds when the ignition is switched on)

Action

1. Activate the lamps using the ISAT "ACTIVATE" menu.

   If the lamps do not work, first check that the lamps are not broken.

   If the lamps are intact, check the TCS lamp lead for breaks or shorts between control module pin 12 and pin 4 on the instrument. Alternatively check the TCS OFF lamp lead for breaks or shorts between control module pin 26 and pin 12 on the instrument.

   Remedy any faulty lead.

SA0029500045000X

Fig. 41 TCS & TCS Off Lamp Check. 9000

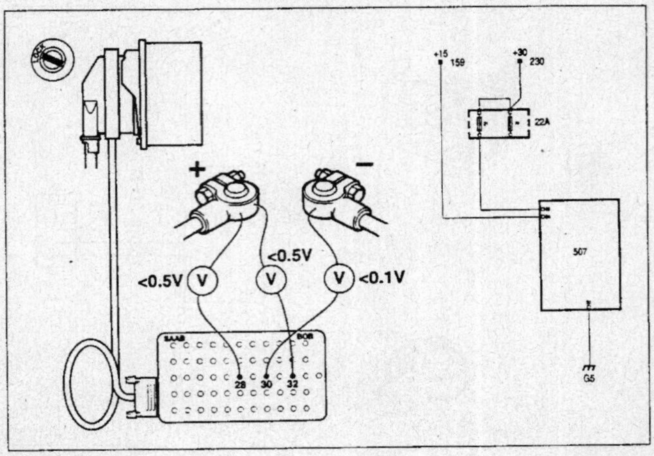

Fault symptom

Alternative I: TCS OFF lamp on, TCS inoperative

Alternative II: TCS OFF lamp and TCS lamp both fail to light when the ignition is turned ON

Alternative III: Malfunctions

Action

When a BOB is connected during trouble diagnosis, the voltage supply and ground connections should always be connected first, as follows:

Ignition in ON position

1. Battery positive — pin 32 ________ <0.5 Volts
2. Battery positive — pin 28 ________ <0.5 Volts
3. Pin 30 — Battery negative ________ <0.1 Volts
4. Pin 13 — Battery negative ________ <0.1 Volts

SA0029500046000X

Fig. 42 Control Module Voltage Supply & Ground Connection Check. 9000

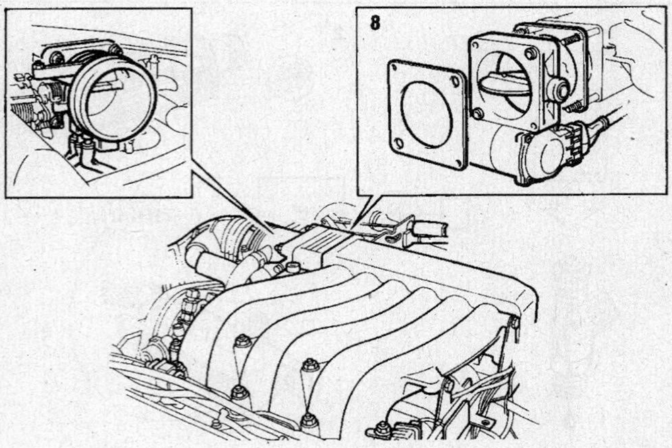

To remove (contd.)

7. Remove the four retaining nuts for the main throttle and TCS throttle.

   Withdraw the main throttle, remove the vacuum hoses and then move the main throttle to one side.
8. Unplug the TCS throttle body connector.

   Lift away the TCS throttle body with the two gaskets. Pay attention to the orientation of the pattern of holes in the outer gasket.
9. Remove the old gasket from the mating surfaces of the inlet manifold.

SA0029100028000A

Fig. 43 TCS throttle body replacement. 900

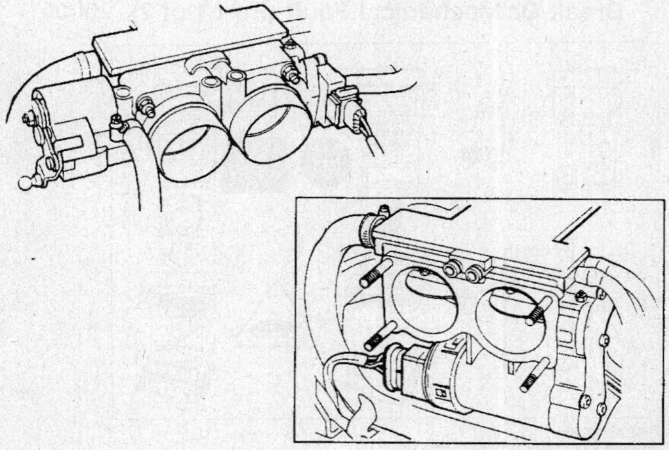

SA0029500047000X

Fig. 44 TCS throttle body replacement. 9000

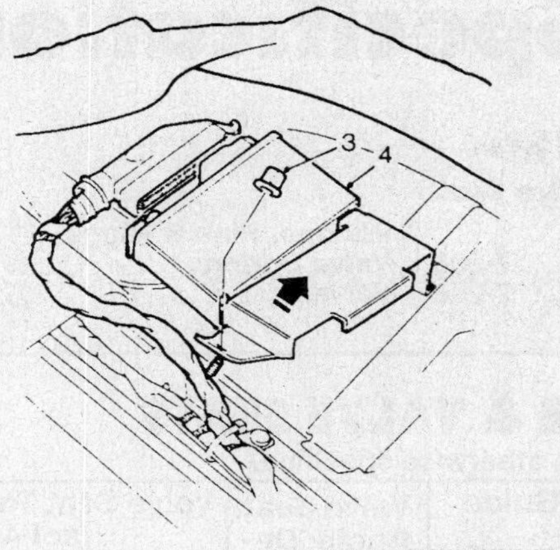

SA0029100029000X

Fig. 45 TCS control module replacement. 900

READ SYSTEM INFO

	ISAT display	Function
1	PROGRAM VERSION	Shows current program version in the TCS control module
2	CONTR MODULE VERS	Shows the control module version number
3	SERIAL NO.	Shows the serial number of the control module

PROGRAM

	ISAT display	Function
1	PROGRAMMED FOR 900 AUTO TRANS 900 MANUAL CHANGE/OK	Shows the gearbox variant for which the TCS control module is programmed
2	TYPE OF GEARBOX 900 AUTO TRANS 900 MANUAL	Enables the control module to be programmed for the type of gearbox concerned

SA0029100030000X

Fig. 46 TCS control module programming

SYSTEM SERVICE

TCS THROTTLE BODY, REPLACE

900

1. Remove engine covers, then the seven bolts retaining upper half of intake manifold.
2. Open hose clip on rubber spigot, then disconnect IAC valve hose.
3. Remove rear knock sensor connector from rubber spigot, then the spigot.
4. Disconnect accelerator and cruise control cables from butterfly lever and bracket.
5. Remove intake manifold mounting strut by removing upper screw and loosening lower one.
6. Remove cable conduit and disconnect vacuum hose from nipple on bottom of manifold on lefthand side.
7. Lift upper half of intake manifold and rest it on one of studs in lower half of intake manifold or support it with rubber mallet, or equivalent.
8. Remove four main throttle and TCS throttle retaining nuts, **Fig. 43.**
9. Remove main throttle, then the vacuum hoses.
10. Disconnect TCS throttle body connector, **Fig. 43,** then remove throttle body with two gaskets.
11. Remove old gasket from mating surfaces of intake manifold.
12. Reverse procedure to install, noting the following:
    a. Clean contact surfaces between main throttle body and intake manifold. Remove any gasket residue and clean mating surfaces of inlet manifold.
    b. Install new gaskets.
    c. **Torque** four main throttle body retaining nuts to 6 ft. lbs.
    d. **Torque** inlet manifold retaining bolts to 15 ft. lbs.
    e. **Torque** rear intake manifold mounting strut to 15 ft. lbs.

9000

1. Remove engine covers, then disconnect control rod from throttle.
2. Release control plate bracket fastenings, then remove control plate bracket.
3. Disconnect mass air flow sensor to resonator box hose clamp, then open two snap locks between mass air flow sensor and air cleaner.
4. Disconnect mass air flow electrical connectors, then remove sensor.
5. Remove idle air control valve hose from inlet manifold, then the hose clamps between inlet manifold and throttle body.
6. Remove manifold complete with resonance box, then disconnect vacuum hoses from vacuum tank and outer throttle control valve and control valve electrical connectors.
7. Remove intake manifold and resonance box.
8. Remove main throttle and TCS throttle nuts, **Fig. 44,** then pull out main throttle and disconnect hoses.
9. Disconnect crankcase ventilation hoses, then the throttle body electrical connectors.
10. Carefully lift vacuum plate, then remove throttle body.
11. Reverse procedure to install, noting the following:
    a. Clean contact surfaces between main throttle body and intake manifold. Remove any gasket residue and clean mating surfaces of inlet manifold.
    b. Install new gaskets.
    c. **Torque** throttle cable nuts to 6 ft. lbs.
    d. Adjust throttle cable and kick-down cable, then test drive and ensure TCS is working properly.

TCS CONTROL MODULE, REPLACE

900

The TCS control module is located under the righthand front seat behind the crossmember. It is secured with a fixing clamp.

1. Remove four righthand front seat bolts.
2. Disconnect righthand front seat heating/adjustment/belt warning connector, then place seat on rear seat.
3. Remove sill scuff plate and fold back carpet.
4. Remove clamp to scuff plate plastic nut, then press in shank and fold up console.
5. Note position of wiring and remove control module, **Fig. 45.**
6. Reverse procedure to install, noting the following:
    a. Ensure wiring is properly positioned.
    b. Program module for appropriate gearbox as outlined under "TCS Control Module Programming."

9000

The TCS control module is located under the lefthand front seat.

1. Raise seat and push it as far forward as possible, then remove carpet clips and fold back carpet.
2. Remove rear control module attachment screws, then the cover cap.
3. Remove control module attachment nuts.
4. Lift up control module attachment, then disconnect control module electrical connector and remove control module.
5. Reverse procedure to install, noting the following:
    a. Ensure wiring is properly positioned.
    b. Program module for appropriate gearbox as outlined under "TCS Control Module Programming."

TCS CONTROL MODULE PROGRAMMING

Refer to **Fig. 46** to program new TCS control module.

Engine Rebuilding Specifications

INDEX

	Page No.		Page No.		Page No.
Camshaft	7-207	Cylinder Head, Valve Guide & Valve Seats	7-206	Pistons, Pins & Rings	7-207
Crankshaft, Bearings & Rods	7-207	Oil Pump	7-208	Valve Springs	7-206
Cylinder Block	7-208			Valves	7-206

CYLINDER HEAD, VALVE GUIDE & VALVE SEATS

All measurements given in inches, unless otherwise specified.

Year	Engine Liter	Cylinder Head Height		Valve Stem To Guide Clearance①		Valve Seat Angle, Degrees	Valve Seat To Face Contact Area	
		Nominal	Minimum	Intake	Exhaust		Intake	Exhaust
1998	2.0L	5.490	5.470	.0200	.0200	44.5	.06–.08	.04–.06
	2.3L	5.490	5.470	.0200	.0200	44.5	.06–.08	.04–.06
	3.0L	5.280	5.270	—	—	45.3	.04–.06	.06–.07
1999–2001	2.0L	5.496	5.477	.0067	.0071	45.0	.04–.06	.06–.08
	2.3L	5.496	5.477	.0067	.0071	45.0	.04–.06	.06–.08
	3.0L	5.280	5.270	—	—	45.3	.04–.06	.06–.07

① — Measured w/valve guide head raised. 12 inch above seat.

VALVE SPRINGS

All measurements given in inches, unless otherwise specified.

Year	Engine Liter	Valve Springs		
		Free Length	Installed Height	Compressed Pressure, Pounds @ Inches
1998	2.0L	1.73–1.85	1.46	138–150 @ 1.12
	2.3L	1.73–1.85	1.46	139–144 @ 1.12
	3.0L	1.65	1.34	141—153 @.95
1999–2001	2.0L	2.25–2.37	1.48	—
	2.3L	2.25–2.37	1.48	—
	3.0L	1.65	1.34	141–153 @.95

VALVES

All measurements given in inches, unless otherwise specified.

Year	Engine Liter	Valves			
		Stem Diameter		Face Angle, Degrees	Valve Clearance
		Intake	Exhaust		
1998	2.0L	.2742–.2748	.2750–.2756	44.5	①
	2.3L	.2742–.2748	.2750–.2756	44.5	①
	3.0L	.2346–.2352	.2342–.2348	45.3	①
1999–2001	2.0L	.1958–.1964	.1956–.1962	45.0	①
	2.3L	.1958–.1964	.1956–.1962	45.0	①
	3.0L	.2346–.2352	.2342–.2348	45.3	①

① — Not adjustable.

CAMSHAFT

All measurements given in inches, unless otherwise specified.

Year	Engine Liter	Camshaft		Cam Follower		
		Bearing Diameter	Endplay	Cam Follower Height	Cam Follower Diameter	Cam Follower Bore In Cylinder Head
1999–2001	2.0L	1.1395–1.1400	.003–.014	1.02	1.2976–1.2992	1.3002–1.3008
	2.3L	1.1395–1.1400	.003–.014	1.02	1.2976–1.2992	1.3002–1.3008
	3.0L	1.1008–1.1016	.002–.006	—	—	—

CRANKSHAFT, BEARINGS & RODS

All measurements given in inches, unless otherwise specified.

Year	Engine Liter	Crankshaft					Bearing Clearance		Connecting Rod Pin Bushing Bore Diameter
		Standard Journal Diameter		Out of Round	Taper	Endplay	Main Bearings	Connecting Rod Bearings	
		Main Bearing	Crank Pin						
1998	2.0L	2.2845–2.2952	2.0481–2.0488	.0002	.0002	.0020–.0120	.0006–.0024	—	.9458–.9460
	2.3L	2.2845–2.282	2.0481–2.0488	.0002	.0002	.0020–.0120	.0006–.0024	—	.9458–.9460
	3.0L	2.6764–2.6770	1.9280–1.9286	.0001	—	.0039–.0299	.0006–.0017	.0005–.0024	—
1999–2001	2.0L	2.2845–2.2952	2.0481–2.0488	.0004	.0002	.0032–.0134	.0006–.0024	—	.9458–.9460
	2.3L	2.2845–2.2952	2.0481–2.0488	.0004	.0002	.0032–.0134	.0006–.0024	—	.9458–.9460
	3.0L	2.6764–2.6770	1.9280–1.9286	.0001	—	.0039–.0299	.0006–.0017	.0005–.0024	—

PISTONS, PINS & RINGS

All measurements given in inches, unless otherwise specified.

Year	Engine Liter	Piston Diameter (Standard)	Piston Clearance	Piston Pin Diameter	Piston Pin To Piston Clearance	Piston Ring End Gap①		Piston Ring Side Clearance	
						Comp.	Oil	Comp.	Oil
1998	2.0L②	③④	.0004–.0014	.9448	.0002–.0006	⑤	.015	.002–.003	—
	2.0L⑥	④⑦	.0002–.0012	.9448	.0002–.0006	⑤	.015	.002–.003	—
	2.3L	④⑧	.0004–.0015	.9448		.0350	⑩	—	—
	3.0L	⑫	.0010–.0020	.8264—.8267	—	.0118–.0197	.0157–.0551	—	—
1999–2001	2.0L	④⑦	.0002–.0012	.9448	.0002–.0006	⑤	.015	.002–.003	—
	2.3L	④⑬	.0012–.0027	.9454–.9456	.0005–.0008	.0118–.0197	.0102–.0401	⑭	—
	3.0L	⑨⑪	.0010–.0018	.8272–.8274	—	.0118–.0197	.0158–.0551	—	—

① — Minimum.
② — Except Turbo.
③ — Piston class A, 3.5451–3.5454 inches; piston class AB, 3.5454–3.5456 inches; piston class B, 3.5456–3.5460 inches; piston class C, 3.5460–3.5466 inches.
④ — Piston class is stamped on piston crown.
⑤ — Top ring, .014 inch; 2nd ring, .012 inch.
⑥ — Turbo.
⑦ — Piston class A, 3.5451–3.5455 inches; piston class AB, 3.5455–3.5458 inches; piston class B, 3.5458–3.5462 inches; piston class C, 3.5462–3.5468 inches.
⑧ — Piston class A, 3.5028–3.5425 inches; piston class AB, 3.5425–3.5429 inches; piston class B, 3.5429–3.5433 inches; piston class C, 3.5433–3.5438 inches.
⑨ — Oversize 7+0.5, 3.4055–3.4059 inches; oversize 8+0.5, 3.4059–3.4063 inches; oversize 9+.05, 3.4063–3.4067 inches; oversize 0+.05, 3.4067–3.4071 inches.
⑩ — Top ring, .0012–.020 inch; 2nd ring, .0059–.0256 inch.
⑪ — Piston class 8, 3.3862–3.3866 inches; piston class 99, 3.3866–3.3870 inches; piston class 00, 3.3870–3.3874 inches; piston class 01, 3.3874–3.3878 inches; piston class 02, 3.3878–3.3882 inches.
⑫ — Piston class 8, 3.3835–3.3839 inches; piston class 99, 3.3839–3.3843 inches; piston class 00, 3.3843–3.38465 inches; piston class 01, 3.3847–3.3850 inches; piston class 02, 3.3850–3.3854 inches.
⑬ — Piston class A, 3.5441–3.4778; piston class B, 3.5449–3.5456; 1st oversize, 3.5638–3.5645; 2nd oversize, 3.5835–3.5842.
⑭ — Top ring, .0008–.0026; 2nd ring, .0016–.0029.

CYLINDER BLOCK

All measurements given in inches, unless otherwise specified.

Year	Engine Liter	Cylinder Bore Diameter (Standard)⑦
1998	2.0L③	⑤
	2.0L④	⑥
	2.3L	⑥
	3.0L	①
1999–2001	2.0L	⑥
	2.3L	⑥
	3.0L	②⑧

① — Cylinder class 8, 3.38484–3.38524 inches; cylinder class 99, 3.38524–3.38563 inches; cylinder class 00, 3.38563–3.38602 inches; cylinder class 01, 3.38602–3.38642 inches; class 02, 3.38642–3.38681 inches.
② — Oversize 7+0.5, 3.4067–3.4071 inches; oversize 8+0.5, 3.4071–3.4075 inches; oversize 9+0.5, 3.4075–3.4079 inches; oversize 0+0.5, 3.4079–3.4083 inches.
③ — Less twin balance shafts.
④ — With twin balance shafts.
⑤ — Cylinder class A, 3.5460–3.5464 inches; cylinder class B, 3.5464–3.5468 inches.
⑥ — Cylinder class A, 3.5460–3.5465 inches; cylinder class B, 3.5461–3.5468 inches; 1st oversize, 3.5657–3.5665 inches; 2nd oversize, 3.5854–3.5862 inches.
⑦ — Cylinder class is stamped on cylinder plane.
⑧ — Cylinder class 8, 3.3874–3.3878 inches; cylinder class 99, 3.3878–3.3882 inches; cylinder class 00, 3.3882–3.3886 inches; cylinder class 01, 3.3886–3.3890 inches; class 02, 3.3890–3.3894 inches.

OIL PUMP

All measurements given in inches, unless otherwise specified.

Year	Engine Liter	Gear To Body Clearance	Relief Valve Opening Pressure, psi	Engine Oil Pressure @ 2000 RPM①	Engine To Oil Cooler Thermostat Opening Temperature °F
1998	2.0L②	.0012–.0031	52–75	39	194
	2.0L③	.0012–.0031	44	39	225
	2.3L④	—	55	39	176
	2.3L⑤	.0012–.0031	44	39	225
	3.0L	—	64	—	—
1999–2001	2.0L	.0012–.0031	55	36	225
	2.3L	.0012–.0031	55	36	225
	3.0L	—	65	—	—

① — At engine temperature of 176°F, using 10W-30 engine oil.
② — Less twin balance shafts.
③ — With twin balance shafts.
④ — 900.
⑤ — 9000.

VOLKSWAGEN

INDEX OF SERVICE OPERATIONS

	Page No.
AIR BAG SYSTEM PRECAUTIONS	0-12
AIR QUALITY STANDARDS	0-23
AUTOMATIC TRANSAXLES	8-165
BRAKES	
Anti-Lock Brakes	8-134
Disc Brakes	8-123
Drum Brakes	8-130
Hydraulic Brake Systems	8-132
Power Brake Units	8-133
CLUTCH & MANUAL TRANSAXLE	
Adjustments	8-65
Clutch, Replace	8-66
Hydraulic System Service	8-66
Precautions	8-65
Tightening Specifications	8-68
Transaxle, Replace	8-66
COMPUTER RELEARN PROCEDURE	0-10
ELECTRICAL	
Air Bags	8-99
Air Conditioning	8-81
Alternator, Replace	8-10
Alternators	8-87
Blower Motor, Replace	8-14
Coil Pack, Replace	8-11
Combination Switch, Replace	8-12
Cooling Fans	8-83
Cruise Controls	8-89
Dash Panels	8-117
Distributor, Replace	8-10
Evaporator Core, Replace	8-15
Fuel Pump Relay Location	8-9
Fuse Panel & Flasher Location	8-9
Headlamp Switch, Replace	8-12
Heater Core, Replace	8-15
Ignition Lock, Replace	8-11
Ignition Switch, Replace	8-12
Instrument Cluster, Replace	8-13
Neutral Safety Switch, Replace	8-12
Passive Restraints	8-99
Precautions	8-9
Radio, Replace	8-13
Relay Center Location	8-10
Speed Controls	8-89
Starter Motors	8-86
Starter, Replace	8-10
Steering Columns	8-120
Steering Wheel, Replace	8-12
Stop Light Switch, Replace	8-12
Turn Signal Switch, Replace	8-12
Wiper Motor, Replace	8-13
Wiper Switch, Replace	8-14
Wiper Transmission, Replace	8-14
ELECTRICAL SYMBOL IDENTIFICATION	0-33
FRONT SUSPENSION & STEERING	
Ball Joint, Replace	8-77
Ball Joint Inspection	8-76
Coil Spring, Replace	8-77
Control Arm, Replace	8-78
Description	8-75
Hub & Bearing, Replace	8-76
Manual Steering Gear, Replace	8-78
Power Steering	8-121
Power Steering Gear, Replace	8-78
Precautions	8-75
Strut, Replace	8-77
Strut Service	8-77
Swing Arm/Wheel Bearing Housing, Replace	8-75
Tightening Specifications	8-79
Wheel Bearing Housing, Replace	8-76
FRONT WHEEL DRIVE AXLES	8-180
REAR AXLE & SUSPENSION	
Coil Spring & Shock Absorber, Replace	8-72
Hub & Bearing, Replace	8-71
Precautions	8-70
Rear Axle, Replace	8-70
Strut, Replace	8-72
Strut Service	8-72
Tightening Specifications	8-74
Wheel Bearing, Adjust	8-72
SERVICE REMINDER & WARNING LAMP RESET PROCEDURES	0-14
SPECIFICATIONS	
Diesel Engine Performance Specifications	8-5
Engine Application Chart	8-3
Fluid Capacities & Cooling System Data	8-7
Front Wheel Alignment Specifications	8-6
General Engine Specifications	8-4
Lubricant Data	8-8
Rear Wheel Alignment Specifications	8-6
Tune Up Specifications	8-5
VEHICLE IDENTIFICATION	0-3
VEHICLE LIFT POINTS	0-24
VEHICLE MAINTENANCE SCHEDULES	0-45
WHEEL ALIGNMENT	
Front Wheel Alignment	8-80
Preliminary Inspection	8-80
Rear Wheel Alignment	8-80
Wheel Alignment Specifications	8-6
WIRE COLOR CODE IDENTIFICATION	0-33
1.8L TURBOCHARGED GASOLINE ENGINE	
Camshaft, Replace	8-20
Compression Pressure	8-17
Cooling System Bleed	8-22
Cylinder Head, Replace	8-18
Engine Rebuilding Specifications	8-185
Engine, Replace	8-17
Exhaust Manifold, Replace	8-18
Front Main Bearing Oil Seal, Replace	8-21
Fuel Pump, Replace	8-24
Hydraulic Lifter Inspection	8-18
Hydraulic Lifters, Replace	8-19
Intake Manifold, Replace	8-18
Main & Rod Bearings	8-21
Oil Pump, Replace	8-21
Piston & Rod Assembly	8-21
Pistons, Pins & Rings	8-21
Precautions	8-17
Radiator, Replace	8-23
Serpentine Drive Belt	8-22
Tightening Specifications	8-25
Timing Belt, Replace	8-19
Turbocharger, Replace	8-24
Valve Adjustment	8-18
Valve Guides	8-19
Water Pump, Replace	8-22
1.9L TURBOCHARGED DIRECT INJECTION (TDI) DIESEL ENGINE	
Camshaft, Replace	8-33
Compression Pressure	8-26
Cooling System Bleed	8-33
Crankshaft Rear Oil Seal, Replace	8-33
Cylinder Head, Replace	8-27
Engine Mount, Replace	8-27
Engine Rebuilding Specifications	8-185
Engine, Replace	8-27
Front Main Bearing Oil Seal, Replace	8-33
Fuel Filter, Replace	8-35
Glow Plug System	8-37
Hydraulic Lifter Inspection	8-28
Hydraulic Lifter, Replace	8-28
Idle Speed, Adjust	8-36
Injection Pump, Replace	8-34
Injection Pump Timing	8-35
Main & Rod Bearings	8-33
Oil Pan, Replace	8-33
Oil Pump, Replace	8-33
Oil Pump Service	8-33
Piston & Rod Assembly	8-33
Precautions	8-26
Radiator, Replace	8-34
Tightening Specifications	8-37
Timing Belt, Replace	8-29
Turbocharger, Replace	8-34
Valve Adjustment	8-28
Valve Clearance Specifications	8-28
Valve Guides	8-28
Water Pump, Replace	8-34
2.0L GASOLINE ENGINE	
Camshaft, Replace	8-45
Compression Pressure	8-39
Cooling System Bleed	8-47
Crankshaft Rear Oil Seal, Replace	8-46
Cylinder Head, Replace	8-42
Engine Mount, Replace	8-39
Engine Rebuilding Specifications	8-185
Engine, Replace	8-39

Page No.

Exhaust Manifold, Replace 8-41
Front Main Bearing Oil Seal, Replace 8-47
Fuel Pump, Replace 8-48
Hydraulic Lifter Inspection 8-43
Hydraulic Lifters, Replace 8-44
Intake Manifold, Replace 8-41
Main & Rod Bearings 8-46
Oil Pan, Replace 8-47
Piston & Rod Assembly 8-46
Pistons, Pins & Rings 8-46
Precautions 8-39
Radiator, Replace 8-48
Serpentine Drive Belt 8-47
Tightening Specifications 8-50
Timing Belt, Replace 8-44
Valve Adjustment 8-43
Valve Guides 8-43
Water Pump, Replace 8-47

2.8L V6 GASOLINE ENGINE

Camshaft, Replace 8-61
Compression Pressure 8-59
Cooling System Bleed 8-62
Cylinder Head, Replace 8-60
Engine Rebuilding Specifications 8-185
Engine, Replace 8-59
Front Main Bearing Oil Seal, Replace 8-62
Fuel Pump, Replace 8-63
Hydraulic Lifter Inspection 8-60
Main & Rod Bearings 8-62
Oil Pan, Replace 8-62
Piston & Rod Assembly 8-62
Precautions 8-59
Radiator, Replace 8-62
Serpentine Drive Belt 8-62
Tightening Specifications 8-64
Timing Belt, Replace 8-61
Valve Adjustment 8-60
Valve Guides 8-61
Water Pump, Replace 8-62

2.8L VR6 GASOLINE ENGINE

Camshaft, Replace 8-55
Compression Pressure 8-52
Cooling System Bleed 8-56
Crankshaft Rear Oil Seal, Replace 8-55
Crankshaft Seal, Replace 8-55
Cylinder Head, Replace 8-53
Engine Mount, Replace 8-52
Engine Rebuilding Specifications 8-185
Engine, Replace 8-53
Fuel Pump, Replace 8-56
Oil Pan, Replace 8-56
Oil Pump, Replace 8-56
Piston & Rod Assembly 8-55
Precautions 8-52
Radiator, Replace 8-56
Tightening Specifications 8-58
Timing Chain, Replace 8-54
Valve Adjustment 8-54
Valve Clearance Specifications 8-54
Valve Guides 8-54
Water Pump, Replace 8-56

Specifications

ENGINE APPLICATION CHART

Year	Model	Engine Liter	Engine Code
1998	Cabrio	2.0L	ABA
	Golf	2.0L	ABA
	GTI	2.8L	AAA
	Jetta	1.9L TDI	1Z
		2.0L	ABA
		2.8L	AAA
	New Beetle	1.8L	APH
		1.9L TDI	ALH
		2.0L	AEG
	Passat	1.8L	AEB
		2.8L	AHA
1999	Cabrio	2.0L	AEG
	EuroVan	2.8L	—
	Golf	1.9L TDI	ALH
		2.0L	AEG
	GTI	2.0L	AEG
		2.8L	AFP
	Jetta	1.9L TDI	ALH
		2.0L	AEG
		2.8L	AFP
	New Beetle	1.8L	APH
		1.9L TDI	ALH
		2.0L	AEG
	Passat	1.8L	AEB
		2.8L	AHA
2000	Cabrio	2.0L	ABA
	EuroVan	2.8L	—
	Golf	1.9L TDI	ALH
		2.0L	AEG
	GTI	1.8L	AWD
		2.8L	AFP
	Jetta	1.9L TDI	ALH
		2.0L	AEG
		2.8L	AFP
	New Beetle	1.8L	APH
		1.9L TDI	ALH
		2.0L	AEG
	Passat	1.8L	ATW
		2.8L	ATQ
2001	Cabrio	2.0L	ABA
	EuroVan	2.8L	—
	Golf	1.8L	AWD
		1.9L TDI	ALH
		2.0L	AEG
	GTI	1.8L	AWD
		2.8L	AFP
	Jetta	1.8L	AWD
		1.9L TDI	ALH
		2.0L	AEG
		2.8L	AFP
	New Beetle	1.8L	APH
		1.9L TDI	ALH
		2.0L	AEG
	Passat	1.8L	ATW
		2.8L	ATQ

TDI — Turbocharged Direct Injection diesel.

GENERAL ENGINE SPECIFICATIONS

Year	Engine Liter	Engine Code	Fuel System	Bore & Stroke, Inches	Comp. Ratio	Horsepower @ RPM	Torque Ft. Lbs. @ RPM
1998	1.8L	AEB & APH	Motronic	3.19 x 3.40	9.5	150 @ 5700	155 @ 1750
	1.9L TDI	1Z	Mechanical Direct Injection	3.13 x 3.76	19.5	90 @ 4000	149 @ 1900
		AHH	Mechanical Direct Injection	3.13 x 3.76	19.5	90 @ 3750	149 @ 1900
	2.0L	ABA	CIS-E Motronic	3.25 x 3.65	10.0	115 @ 5400	122 @ 3200
		AEG	Motronic	3.25 x 3.65	10.0	115 @ 5400	122 @ 3200
	2.8L	AAA	Motronic	3.19 x 3.56	10.0	172 @ 5800	173 @ 4200
		AHA	Motronic	3.19 x 3.56	10.6	190 @ 6000	206 @ 3200
1999	1.8L	AEB & APH	Motronic	3.19 x 3.40	9.5	150 @ 5700	155 @ 1750
	1.9L TDI	AHH	Mechanical Direct Injection	3.13 x 3.76	19.5	90 @ 3750	155 @ 1900
		ALH	Mechanical Direct Injection	3.13 x 3.76	19.5	90 @ 3750	155 @ 1900
	2.0L	AEG	Motronic	3.25 x 3.65	10.0	115 @ 5400	122 @ 3200
	2.8L	AES	Motronic	3.25 x 3.65	10.0	140 @ 4500	177 @ 3000
		AFP	Motronic	3.19 x 3.56	10.0	174 @ 5800	181 @ 3200
		AHA	Motronic	3.19 x 3.56	10.6	190 @ 6000	206 @ 3200
2000	1.8L	APH	Motronic	3.19 x 3.40	9.5	150 @ 5800	162 @ 2200
	1.9L TDI	ALH	Mechanical Direct Injection	3.13 x 3.76	19.5	90 @ 3750	155 @ 1900
	2.0L	ABA	Motronic	3.25 x 3.65	10.0	115 @ 5400	122 @ 3200
		AEG	Motronic	3.25 x 3.65	10.0	115 @ 5200	122 @ 2600
	2.8L	AES	Motronic	3.19 x 3.54	10.0	140 @ 4500	177 @ 3000
		AFP	Motronic	3.19 x 3.56	10.0	174 @ 5800	181 @ 3200
		ATQ	Motronic	3.25 x 3.40	10.6	190 @ 6000	206 @ 3200
2001	1.8L	APH	Motronic	3.19 x 3.40	9.5	150 @ 5800	162 @ 2200
		AWD	Motronic	3.19 x 3.40	9.5	150 @ 5700	155 @ 1950
	1.9L TDI	ALH	Mechanical Direct Injection	3.13 x 3.76	19.5	90 @ 3750	155 @ 1900
	2.0L	ABA & AEG	Motronic	3.25 x 3.65	10.0	115 @ 5200	122 @ 2600
	2.8L	AFP	Motronic	3.19 x 3.56	10.0	174 @ 5800	181 @ 3200
		ATQ	Motronic	3.25 x 3.40	10.6	190 @ 6000	206 @ 3200
		①	Motronic	3.19 x 3.54	10.0	201 @ 6200	181 @ 2500

TDI — Turbocharged Direct Injection diesel.

① — EuroVan.

TUNE UP SPECIFICATIONS

Year & Engine, Liter	Spark Plug Gap, Inch	Ignition Timing			Curb Idle Speed, RPM		Fuel System Pressure, psi	Valve Lash	
		Firing Order	Timing, °BTDC	Timing Mark Fig.	Man. Trans.	Auto. Trans.		Intake	Exhaust
1998									
1.8L⑦	.039	1-3-4-2	①	—	820–900②	820–900N②	36	③	③
2.0L⑧	.039	1-3-4-2	①	—	760–880②	760–880N②	51.45	③	③
2.0L⑨	.032	1-3-4-2	12①	—	800–880②	800–880N②⑤	36	③	③
2.8L⑩	.028	1-5-3-6-2-4	6 ①	—	650–750②④	650–750N②④	36	③	③
2.8L⑪	.063	1-4-3-6-2-5	①	—	⑥	⑥	51.45	③	③
1999									
1.8L⑦	.039	1-3-4-2	①	—	820–920②	820–920N②	36	③	③
2.0L	.039	1-3-4-2	①	—	740–820②	740–820N②	51.45	③	③
2.8L⑩	.028	1-5-3-6-2-4	①	—	680–720②④	680–720N②④	36	③	③
2.8L⑪	.063	1-4-3-6-2-5	①	—	⑥	⑥	51.45	③	③
2000–01									
1.8L⑦	.031	1-3-4-2	①	—	700–820②	640–760②	36	③	③
2.0L	.035–.043	1-3-4-2	①	—	740–820②	740–820②	36	③	③
2.8L⑩	.028	1-5-3-6-2-4	①	—	680–720②	680–720②	36	③	③
2.8L⑪	.063	1-4-3-6-2-5	①	—	⑥	⑥	51.45	③	③

BTDC — Before Top Dead Center
D — Drive
N — Neutral
① — Non-adjustable, controlled by ECM.
② — Not adjustable.
③ — Equipped w/hydraulic valve lash adjusters. No adjustment required.
④ — When battery voltage drops below 10.5 volts, idle speed will be raised to 900 RPM by ECM.
⑤ — 640–720D.
⑥ — FWD, 740–860 RPM; AWD, 620–740 RPM.
⑦ — Turbo.
⑧ — New Beetle.
⑨ — Cabrio, Golf & Jetta.
⑩ — Two-valve engine: Cabrio, EuroVan, Golf & Jetta.
⑪ — Five-valve engine: Passat.

DIESEL ENGINE PERFORMANCE SPECIFICATIONS

Engine Liter	Firing Order	Injection Pump Timing	Cylinder Compression			Fuel Injectors		Idle Speed	Max. Speed @ Zero Load, RPM	Valve Lash
			Cranking Pressure, psi	Limit. psi	Maximum Variation	Spray Test, psi	Leak Test, psi③			
1998–2001										
1.9L	1-3-4-2	①②	363–450	276	73	3191–3396④	2176	②	②	②

① — Refer to "Injection Pump Timing" procedure in "4 Cylinder Diesel Engine Performance."
② — Computer controlled.
③ — Maintain pressure for 10 seconds w/no fuel leakage.
④ — Opening pressure new, wear limit 2901 psi.

FRONT WHEEL ALIGNMENT SPECIFICATIONS

EXCEPT EUROVAN

Year	Model	Caster Angle, Deg.		Camber Angle, Deg.		Toe Per Wheel, Deg.	Total Toe, Deg.①
		Limits	Desired	Limits	Desired		
1998	Cabrio	+1 1/3 to +2 1/3	+1 5/6	–11/12 to –1/4	–1/2	—	–1/6 to +1/6
	Golf III & Jetta III 2.0L	+1 1/3 to +2 1/3	+1 5/6	–11/12 to –1/4	–7/12	—	–1/6 to +1/6
	GTI-VR6 & Jetta III GLX 2.8L	+2 3/5 to +3 23/30	+3 4/15	–5/6 to –1/6	–1/2	—	–1/6 to +1/6
1998–2001	New Beetle②	+7 1/6 to +8 1/6	+7 2/3	–1 to 0	–1/2	—	–1/6 to +1/6
	New Beetle③	+7 1/3 to +8 1/3	+7 5/6	–1 1/20 to –1/20	–11/20	—	–1/6 to +1/6
	Passat②	—	—	–5/6 to 0	–5/12	+2/15 to +1/5	—
	Passat③	—	—	–1 1/12 to –1/4	–2/3	+2/15 to +1/5	—
	Passat④	—	—	–2/3 to +1/6	–1/4	+2/15 to +1/5	—
1999–2001	Golf & Jetta②	+7 1/6 to +8 1/6	+7 2/3	–1 to 0	–1/2	—	—
	Golf & Jetta③	+7 1/3 to +8 1/3	+7 5/6	–1 1/20 to –1/20	–11/20	—	—

① — Toe-in (+); toe-out (–).
② — Standard suspension.
③ — Sport suspension.
④ — Heavy duty suspension.

EUROVAN

Year	Group No.①	Caster Angle, Deg.②			Camber Angle, Deg.③			Total Toe, Deg.③		
		Empty	Half Load	Full Load	Empty	Half Load	Full Load	Empty	Half Load	Full Load
1999–2001	Groups 1 & 2	+3 1/6	+3 1/3	+3 1/2	–5/12	–2/3	–5/6	+1/3	0	–1/3
	Group 3	+3 1/6	+3 1/3	+3 1/2	–7/12	–3/4	–5/6	+1/6	0	–1/3
	Group 4	+3 1/6	+3 1/3	+3 1/2	–3/4	–5/6	–11/12	0	–1/6	–1/3

① — The vehicle group number sticker is located on lefthand side A-pillar. Group number is located after term Grund or Kom. Early vehicles not equipped with a group number sticker are considered to be group 1.
② — Plus or minus 1/2°.
③ — Plus or minus 1/3°.

REAR WHEEL ALIGNMENT SPECIFICATIONS

EXCEPT EUROVAN

Year	Model	Camber Angle, Deg.		Toe Per Wheel, Deg.	Total Toe, Deg.①
		Limits	Desired		
1998	Cabrio	–1 2/3 to –1 1/3	–1 1/2	—	+1/6 to +1/2⑤
	Golf III, GTI-VR6, Jetta III & Jetta III GLX	–1 2/3 to –1 1/3	–1 1/2	—	+1/6 to +1/2⑤
1998–2001	New Beetle②	–1 37/60 to –1 17/60	–1 9/20	—	+1/6 to +1/2
	New Beetle③	–1 37/60 to –1 17/60	–1 9/20	—	+1/4 to +7/12
	Passat FWD②	–1 5/6 to –1 1/6	–1 1/2	—	+1/6 to +7/12
	Passat FWD③	–1 5/6 to –1 1/6	–1 1/2	—	+3/10 to +43/60
	Passat FWD ④	–1 5/6 to –1 1/6	–1 1/2	—	+1/60 to +13/30
	Passat AWD	–1 1/6 to –1/6	–2/3	+1/20 to +13/60	+1/10 to +13/30
1999–2001	Golf & Jetta②	–1 37/60 to –1 17/60	–1 3/10	—	+1/6 to +1/2
	Golf & Jetta③	–1 37/60 to –1 17/60	–1 3/10	—	+1/4 to +7/12

① — Toe-in (+); toe-out (–).
② — Standard suspension.
③ — Sport suspension.
④ — Heavy duty suspension.
⑤ — On models which experience abnormal rear tire wear (cupping or feathered edge), a specially machined stub axle can be installed to decrease positive toe. Inspect rear wheel alignment before installing stub axle. Too much positive toe on rear axle must be present for vehicle to require installation of stub axle. Installation on vehicle w/negative toe reading can compound rear tire wear. Stub axle will change total toe by minus 1/6 degree. Stub axle must only be installed on left rear. For Cabrio, Golf, GTI, Jetta & Jetta GLX, use Part No. 191-501-117C

for models w/rear drum brakes less ABS; Part No. 191-501-117G for models w/rear drum brakes & ABS; Part No. 191-501-117F for models w/rear disc brakes less ABS; Part No. 191-501-117H for models w/rear disc brake & ABS. For Passat, use Part No. 357-501-117D for models w/rear drum brakes less ABS; Part No. 357-501-117C for models w/rear drum brakes & ABS; Part No. 357-501-117B for models w/rear disc brakes.

EUROVAN

Year	Group No.①	Camber Angle, Deg.②			Total Toe, Deg.③		
		Empty	Half Load	Full Load	Empty	Half Load	Full Load
1998–2001	Group 1	$-\frac{1}{2}$	$-1\frac{1}{6}$	$-1\frac{7}{12}$	$+\frac{1}{3}$	$+\frac{2}{3}$	+1
	Group 2	0	$-\frac{2}{3}$	$-1\frac{1}{6}$	$+\frac{1}{10}$	$+\frac{2}{5}$	$+\frac{2}{3}$
	Group 3	$-\frac{1}{2}$	$-1\frac{1}{6}$	$-1\frac{7}{12}$	$+\frac{1}{3}$	$+\frac{2}{3}$	+1
	Group 4	$-\frac{2}{3}$	$-1\frac{1}{6}$	$-1\frac{1}{6}$	$+\frac{2}{5}$	$+\frac{11}{15}$	$+\frac{9}{10}$

① — The vehicle group number sticker is located on lefthand side A-pillar. Group number is located after term Grund or Kom. Early vehicles not equipped w/a group number sticker are considered to be group 1.

② — Plus or minus ½°.

③ — Plus or minus ⅓°.

FLUID CAPACITIES & COOLING SYSTEM DATA

Year	Model	Cooling System Capacity Qts.	Recommended Engine Coolant Type	Radiator Cap Relief Pressure Lbs.	Thermo. Opening Temp. °F	Fuel Tank Capacity Gals.	Engine Oil Refill Qts.①	Transaxle Capacity		
								Manual, Pts.	Auto. Trans. Qts.	
									Trans.②	Final Drive Pts.
1998–2001	Cabrio	6.7	⑧	19–23	188	14.5	4	4.2	5.9	—
	EuroVan	③	⑧	20–23	188	21.1	6	5.4	6.5	2.44
	Golf & Jetta 1.9L Diesel	6.3	⑧	20–23	185	14.5	4.75	4.2	⑤	—
	Golf & Jetta 2.0L	5.3	⑧	20–23	—	14.5	4.2	4.2	⑤	—
	Golf & Jetta 2.8L	9.5	⑧	20–30	187	14.5	6.4	4.2	⑤	—
	New Beetle 1.8L Turbo	5.3	⑧	—	185	14.5	3.7	4.2	⑤	1.6
	New Beetle 1.9L Diesel	6.3	⑧	20.3–23.2	185	14.5	4.75	4.2	⑤	1.6
	New Beetle 2.0L	5.3	⑧	20.3–23.2	—	14.5	4.2	4.2	⑤	1.6
	Passat 1.8L Turbo	6.2	⑧	20.3–23.2	185	16.4	3.7	4.8	④	⑥
	Passat 2.8L	10.4	⑧	20–30	187	16.4	6⑦	4.8	④	⑥

① — Includes filter.

② — Approximate. Make final inspection w/dipstick.

③ — Models w/1 heat exchanger, 9.5 qts.; w/2 exchangers, 11.4 qts.; w/2 exchangers & water heater, 17.8 qts.

④ — Model 01N trans. fluid change 3.7 qts., complete refill 5.7 qts.; model 01V trans. fluid change 2.7 qts., complete refill 9.5 qts.

⑤ — Fluid change 3.2 qts.; complete refill 5.6 qts.

⑥ — Models w/01N trans. 1.4 pts.; models w/01V trans. 1.6 pts.

⑦ — Third generation engine, 6.3 qts.

⑧ — Use Volkswagen coolant G 012 A8D A1, or equivalent. This coolant is red in color.

LUBRICANT DATA

Year	Model	Lubricant Type					
		Engine	Transaxle			Power Steering	Brake System
			Manual	Automatic			
1998–2001	All	③	G-50 SAE 75W/90 Synthetic	①	G-50 SAE 75W/90 Synthetic	②	DOT 4

TDI — Turbocharged Direct Injection diesel.

① — 096 transaxle, use Dexron; 01M transaxle, use VW part No. G 052 162 A2 transaxle oil, or equivalent.

② — Hydraulic oil, Volkswagen part No. G 002 000, G 002 012, or equivalent.

③ — Gasoline engine, API service SG, SH, or equivalent; Diesel engine, API service CD, or equivalent

Electrical

NOTE: On Air Bag Equipped Models, Refer To "Air Bag System Precautions" Located In The Front Of This Manual For System Disarming & Arming Procedures.

NOTE: Refer To "Computer Relearn Procedures" Located In The Front Of This Manual When Battery Power To The Computer Has Been Interrupted.

INDEX

	Page No.
Air Bags	8-99
Air Conditioning	8-81
Alternator, Replace	8-10
Alternators	8-87
Blower Motor, Replace	8-14
Cabrio & 1998 Golf, GTI & Jetta	8-14
New Beetle & 1999–2001 Golf, GTI & Jetta	8-14
Passat	8-14
Coil Pack, Replace	8-11
Combination Switch, Replace	8-12
Cooling Fans	8-83
Cruise Controls	8-89
Dash Panels	8-117
Distributor, Replace	8-10
Installation	8-11
Removal	8-10
Evaporator Core, Replace	8-15
Cabrio & 1998 Golf, GTI & Jetta	8-15
New Beetle & 1999–2001 Golf, GTI & Jetta	8-15
Passat	8-15
Fuel Pump Relay Location	8-9
Cabrio & 1998 Golf, GTI & Jetta	8-9
New Beetle & 1999–2001 Golf, GTI & Jetta	8-9
Passat	8-9
Fuse Panel & Flasher Location	8-9
Headlamp Switch, Replace	8-12
Cabrio & 1998 Golf, GTI & Jetta	8-12
New Beetle, Passat & 1999–2001 Golf, GTI & Jetta	8-12
Heater Core, Replace	8-15
Cabrio & 1998 Golf, GTI & Jetta	8-15
New Beetle & 1999–2001 Golf, GTI & Jetta	8-15
Passat	8-15
Ignition Lock, Replace	8-11
Cabrio & 1998 Golf, GTI, Jetta	8-11
New Beetle & Passat	8-11
1999–2001 Golf, GTI & Jetta	8-11
Ignition Switch, Replace	8-12
Cabrio & 1998 Golf, GTI, Jetta	8-12
New Beetle & Passat	8-12
1999–2001 Golf, GTI & Jetta	8-12
Instrument Cluster, Replace	8-13
Cabrio & 1998 Golf, GTI & Jetta	8-13
New Beetle & 1999–2001 Golf, GTI & Jetta	8-13
Passat	8-13
Neutral Safety Switch, Replace	8-12
Passive Restraints	8-99
Precautions	8-9
Air Bag Systems	8-9
Audio Coded Anti-Theft System	8-9
Battery Ground Cable	8-9
Radio, Replace	8-13
Relay Center Location	8-10
Speed Controls	8-89
Starter Motors	8-86
Starter, Replace	8-10
Cabrio, Golf, GTI & Jetta	8-10
New Beetle	8-10
Passat	8-10
Steering Columns	8-120
Steering Wheel, Replace	8-12
Stop Light Switch, Replace	8-12
Installation	8-12
Removal	8-12
Turn Signal Switch, Replace	8-12
Wiper Motor, Replace	8-13
Front	8-13
Rear	8-13
Wiper Switch, Replace	8-14
Wiper Transmission, Replace	8-14
Front	8-14
Rear	8-14

PRECAUTIONS

AIR BAG SYSTEMS

Do not use computer memory saver tool on air bag equipped models. Using the tool will keep the air bag system charged and may cause accidental activation of the air bag unit.

Refer to "Air Bag System Precautions" in the front of this manual for system disarming and arming procedures.

BATTERY GROUND CABLE

Prior to disconnecting the battery negative cable, obtain the radio security code. After service has been completed and the battery negative cable has been reconnected, use security code to activate the radio. Prior to service, disconnect battery ground cable and isolate as required.

AUDIO CODED ANTI-THEFT SYSTEM

Some models are equipped with a radio anti-theft system that will disable the system when battery power is interrupted, unless the system is reset the radio will not operate.

1. Turn radio to On position, SAFE and 1000 should be displayed.
2. Enter radio code using first four program station buttons. Security code will appear on display.
3. Depress and hold righthand side of radio right or left blocker until anti-theft coding is activated indicated by a brief signal sound.
4. If code number has been entered correctly, when ignition key is removed a diode on front of radio will flash.

FUSE PANEL & FLASHER LOCATION

The fuse/relay panel is located on the lefthand end of instrument panel. The flasher relays are located at the fuse panel.

FUEL PUMP RELAY LOCATION

CABRIO & 1998 GOLF, GTI & JETTA

The fuel pump relay is located behind the lefthand side of the instrument panel on the fuse/relay panel.

PASSAT

The fuel pump relay is located behind the lefthand side of the instrument panel on the 13-position auxiliary relay panel.

NEW BEETLE & 1999-2001 GOLF, GTI & JETTA

The fuel pump relay is located behind the lefthand side of the instrument panel on the 13-position auxiliary relay panel.

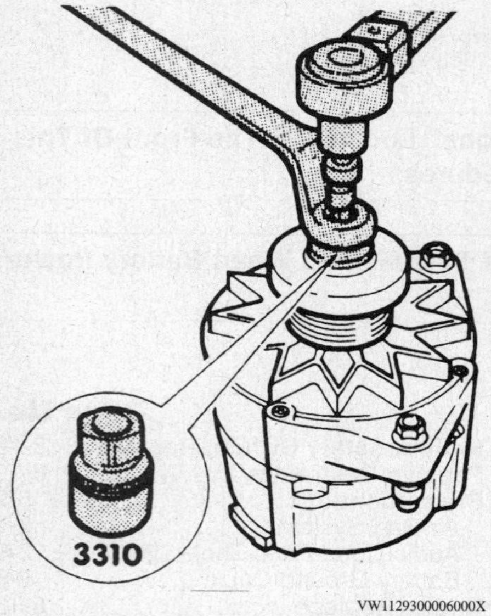

Fig. 1 Serpentine belt pulley removal

RELAY CENTER LOCATION

The relay panels are located on the left-hand side end of the instrument panel.

STARTER

REPLACE

CABRIO, GOLF, GTI & JETTA

1998

1. Remove black plastic cap, then disconnect solenoid electrical connectors.
2. Remove nut securing battery wire to solenoid.
3. Remove dipstick tube bracket retaining nut from stud.
4. **On models equipped with 1.8L, 1.9L and 2.0L engines,** remove starter to front console attaching bolt.
5. **On all models,** remove starter motor attaching nut and bolt, then the starter.
6. Reverse procedure to install, noting the following:
   a. **Torque** starter motor attaching nut and bolt to 44 ft. lbs.
   b. **On models equipped with 1.8L, 1.9L and 2.0L engines, torque** starter motor to front console bolt to 33 ft. lbs.
   c. **On all models, torque** dipstick tube bracket nut to 84 inch lbs.
   d. **Torque** battery wire terminal nut to 10 ft. lbs.

1999–2001

1. Remove battery cover, battery and battery base plate.
2. Disconnect engine harness connector and pull harness out of bracket.
3. Unclip engine harness connector from starter solenoid.

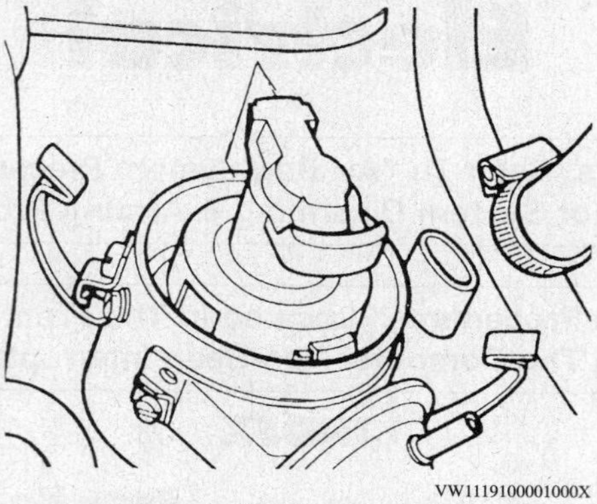

Fig. 2 Distributor rotor alignment

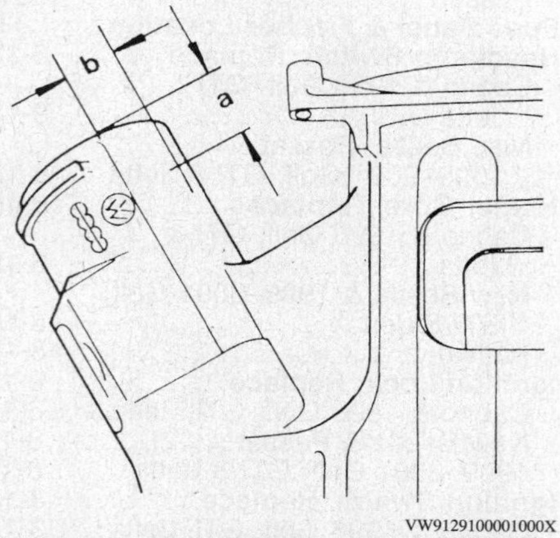

Fig. 4 Ignition lock cylinder drilling dimensions

4. Remove retaining nut, then disconnect battery terminal connector from starter solenoid.
5. Remove starter motor upper attaching bolt.
6. Raise and support vehicle.
7. Remove engine center insulator cover attaching bolts, then the cover.
8. Remove engine lefthand insulator cover retaining clips, then the cover.
9. Remove power steering pressure hose bracket and position hose aside.
10. Remove starter motor lower attaching bolt, then the starter.
11. Reverse procedure to install, noting the following:
    a. **Torque** starter motor attaching bolts to 48 ft. lbs.
    b. **Torque** battery terminal connector retaining nut to 10 ft. lbs.

PASSAT

1. Unclip engine harness connector from starter solenoid.
2. Remove retaining nut, then disconnect battery terminal connector from starter solenoid.
3. Remove starter motor retaining bracket nuts, then the bracket.
4. Remove starter motor upper attaching bolt.
5. Remove starter motor attaching bolts, then the starter.
6. Reverse procedure to install, noting the following:

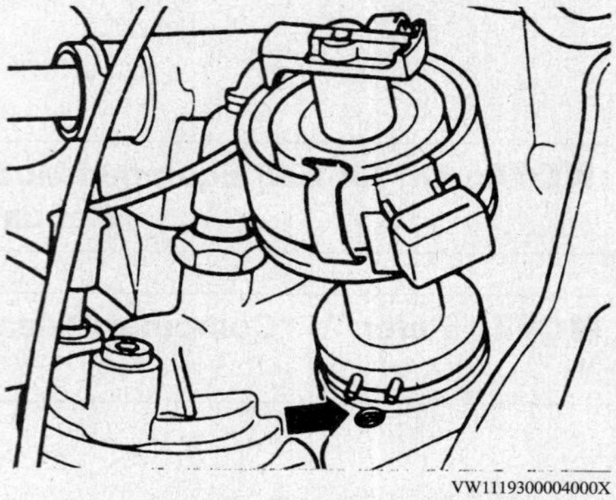

Fig. 3 Distributor alignment

   a. **Torque** starter motor attaching bolts to 48 ft. lbs.
   b. **Torque** battery terminal connector retaining nut to 10 ft. lbs.
   c. **Torque** starter motor retaining bracket nuts to 16 ft. lbs.

NEW BEETLE

1. Cut and discard cable ties used to secure wiring for starter.
2. Disconnect electrical connectors from solenoid.
3. Remove nut securing hose support bracket to starter.
4. Remove 12 mm bolt securing starter to engine support, if required.
5. Remove upper and lower starter mounting bolts, then the starter motor.
6. Reverse procedure to install, noting the following:
   a. **Torque** starter solenoid nut to 10 ft. lbs.
   b. **Torque** starter mounting bolts to 44 ft. lbs.
   c. **Torque** 8 mm nut for hose support bracket to 84 inch lbs.
   d. **Torque** 12 mm mounting bolt to 33 ft. lbs, if removed.

ALTERNATOR

REPLACE

1. Disconnect wiring connectors from alternator.
2. Remove serpentine drive belt as outlined in the appropriate engine section.
3. Remove alternator mounting bolts, then the alternator.
4. Remove serpentine belt pulley using holder tool No. 3310, or equivalent, **Fig. 1.**
5. Reverse procedure to install, noting the following:
   a. **Torque** drive belt pulley to 45–51 ft. lbs.
   b. **Torque** alternator mounting bolts to 18 ft. lbs.
   c. Tension drive belt as outlined in the appropriate engine section.

DISTRIBUTOR

REPLACE

REMOVAL

1. Disconnect electrical connector from distributor, then remove distributor cap.

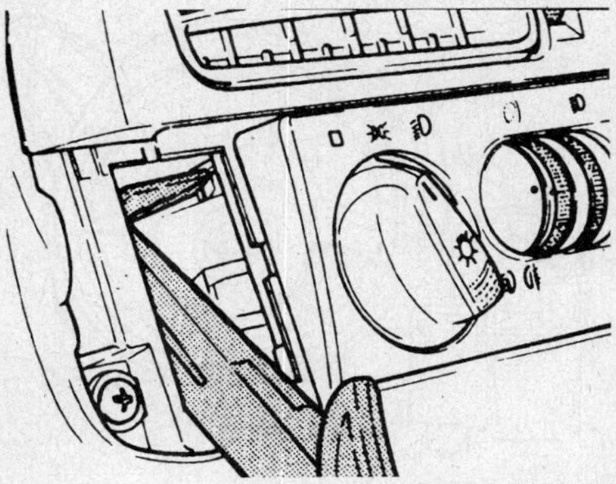

VW9019300001000X

Fig. 5 Headlamp switch replacement. Cabrio & 1998 Golf, GTI & Jetta

2. Set engine to Top Dead Center (TDC) compression stroke, rotating engine in normal direction of rotation only.
3. Ensure center of rotor tip is aligned with centering mark on distributor housing, **Fig. 2.**
4. If alignment cannot be achieved, engine re-timing may be required as outlined under "2.0L Gasoline Engine" section.
5. Remove distributor clamp bolt, then the distributor. Due to helical gears of distributor drive, rotor will turn slightly during removal. Note this position for later assembly.

INSTALLATION

1. Ensure engine is set to TDC compression stroke.
2. Replace distributor base sealing gasket or O-ring as necessary.
3. Rotate distributor shaft and rotor so that tip center is slightly to right of centering mark on distributor body (about width of rotor tip), **Fig. 2.**
4. Using a suitable long screwdriver, align oil pump drive slot so it is parallel to the crankshaft.
5. Insert distributor into engine, then ensure oil pump drive is fully engaged, rotor and centering mark are aligned and locating pins on distributor body are centered over mounting bolt hole, **Fig. 3.**
6. If alignment cannot be achieved, remove timing belt from intermediate shaft sprocket as outlined under "2.0L Gasoline Engine" section.
7. Turn intermediate shaft until alignment of crankshaft TDC, rotor tip centering and distributor locating pin can be achieved.
8. Install timing belt as outlined under "2.0L Gasoline Engine" section.
9. Install distributor hold-down clamp and bolt, **torque** to 18 ft. lbs.
10. Install wiring connectors and distributor cap.
11. Check ignition timing. Refer to "Specifications" for data.

COIL PACK

REPLACE

1. Note position of spark plug wires for installation reference.

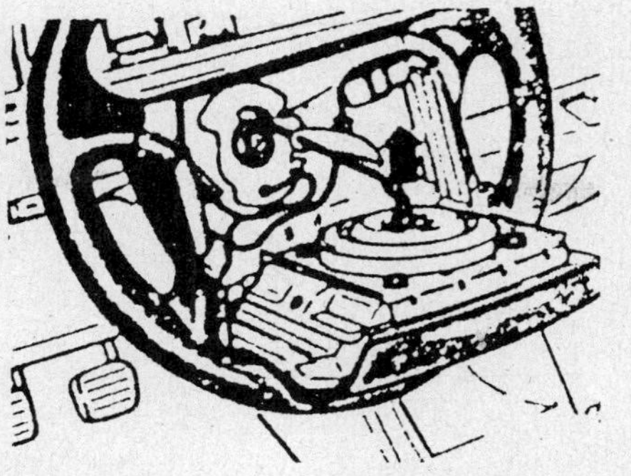

VW9049100001000X

Fig. 6 Air bag unit electrical connector

2. Disconnect spark plug wires from coil pack.
3. Disconnect electrical connector from coil pack.
4. Remove mounting bolts, then coil pack.
5. Reverse procedure to install. **Torque** mounting bolts to 84 inch lbs.

IGNITION LOCK

REPLACE

CABRIO & 1998 GOLF, GTI, JETTA

1. Remove combination switch as outlined under "Combination Switch, Replace."
2. Remove spacer or spring and locking washer, as equipped, from steering shaft using suitable tools, as outlined in "Steering Columns" section.
3. Remove steering column shrouds, it may be necessary to remove upper shroud later with lock assembly.
4. Using suitable tools, clamp or block steering shaft so it will not slide down into steering column.
5. **On models equipped with shifter lock cable,** disconnect shifter lock cable from ignition lock.
6. **On all models,** using a suitable drill, drill head of ignition lock to steering column shear head bolt.
7. Ensure body of shear head bolt is either drilled out or backed out sufficiently to clear mounting tab of steering column during lock removal.
8. Unlock steering lock from column with ignition key. If ignition key is not available or key tumbler will not move, remove complete steering column, as outlined in "Steering Columns" section, then remove key lock tumbler as follows:
   a. Insert ignition key into ignition lock cylinder.
   b. Using ⅛ inch drill bit, drill hole in lock housing approximately ⅛ inch deep as shown in **Fig. 4.** Dimension A =. 47 inch, dimension B =. 39 inch.
   c. Using a suitable drift punch, remove lock cylinder with key by

VW9039300001000X

Fig. 7 Radio removal tool No. VW160

   pressing in check spring using hole previously drilled.
   d. When installing lock tumbler, ensure tumbler and lock assembly are in Off position.
9. Slide ignition lock, with upper trim if necessary, off steering column. Heat lock body with hot air blower if necessary.
10. Reverse procedure to install, noting the following:
   a. Position ignition lock on column for proper clearance of slip ring contacts and trim shroud alignment.
   b. Tighten shear bolt until head breaks off.
   c. **On models equipped with shifter lock cable,** adjust shifter lock cable as outlined in "Automatic Transaxles" section.

1999–2001 GOLF, GTI & JETTA

1. Remove air bag.
2. Ensure front wheels are in straight ahead position.
3. Remove steering wheel nut, then the steering wheel.
4. Remove tilt lever, then the upper and lower steering column switch trim.
5. Disconnect steering column switch electrical connector, then disengage locking lugs and remove return ring and collector.
6. Loosen locking screw, then remove steering column switch.
7. Insert ignition key into lock cylinder and turn to "Drive" position.
8. Insert a wire (approximately. 047 inch diameter) into lock release hole on face of lock cylinder.
9. Press wire into hole to release lock lever and remove lock cylinder from housing.
10. Reverse procedure to install.

NEW BEETLE & PASSAT

1. Remove upper and lower steering column covers.
2. Insert ignition key into lock cylinder and turn to "Drive" position.
3. Insert a wire (approximately. 047 inch diameter) into lock release hole on face of lock cylinder.
4. Press wire into hole to release lock

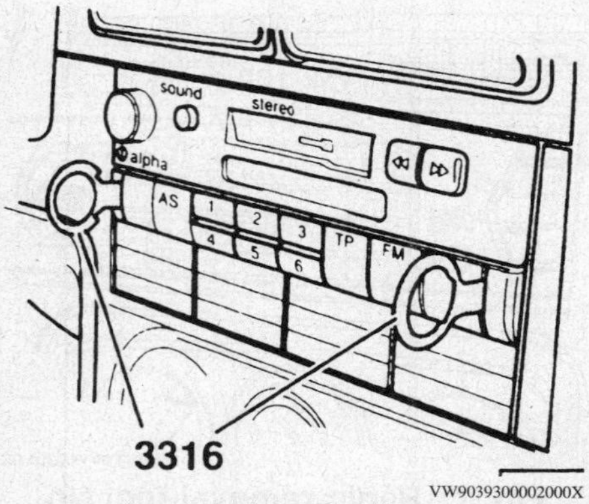

VW9039300002000X

Fig. 8 Radio removal tool No. 3316

lever and remove lock cylinder from housing.
5. Reverse procedure to install.

IGNITION SWITCH

REPLACE

CABRIO & 1998 GOLF, GTI, JETTA

1. Remove ignition lock housing as outlined under "Ignition Lock, Replace."
2. Disconnect ignition switch electrical connector.
3. Remove screw attaching ignition switch to lock housing assembly, then ignition switch.
4. Reverse procedure to install.

1999–2001 GOLF, GTI & JETTA

1. Remove steering column switch as outlined under "Ignition Lock, Replace."
2. Disconnect electrical connector from ignition switch.
3. Remove locking fluid from threaded holes of attaching screws.
4. Loosen two attaching screws and pull ignition switch out from steering lock housing.
5. Reverse procedure to install.

NEW BEETLE & PASSAT

1. Remove upper and lower steering column switch trim.
2. Disconnect electrical connector from ignition switch.
3. Remove locking fluid from threaded holes of attaching screws.
4. Loosen two attaching screws and pull ignition switch out from steering lock housing.
5. Reverse procedure to install.

NEUTRAL SAFETY SWITCH

REPLACE

The neutral safety switch is a part of the multi-function transaxle range switch. Refer to the appropriate transaxle section for procedures.

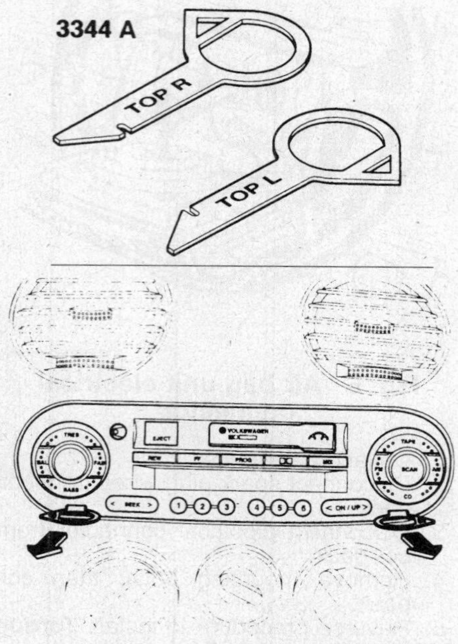

VW9039900003000X

Fig. 9 Radio removal tool No. 3344A

HEADLAMP SWITCH

REPLACE

CABRIO & 1998 GOLF, GTI & JETTA

1. Using a suitable flat tool, pry out trim plate to left of switch.
2. Using a suitable blunt pointed tool with a 90° bend, reach above and behind switch, in line with knob, and press in on release button, **Fig. 5.**
3. Pull switch from dash, then disconnect electrical connector.
4. Reverse procedure to install.

NEW BEETLE, PASSAT & 1999–2001 GOLF, GTI & JETTA

1. Turn rotary knob switch to "0" position.
2. Press rotary knob inward and turn slightly to right, holding knob in this position, pull rearward on knob to remove lamp switch from instrument panel.
3. Disconnect lamp switch electrical connector.
4. Reverse procedure to install.

STOP LIGHT SWITCH

REPLACE

REMOVAL

1. Remove left underdash panels as necessary to access switch, then disconnect electrical connector from brake lamp switch.
2. Turn brake lamp switch 90° clockwise, then remove switch.

INSTALLATION

1. Pull switch plunger to its fullest extension.

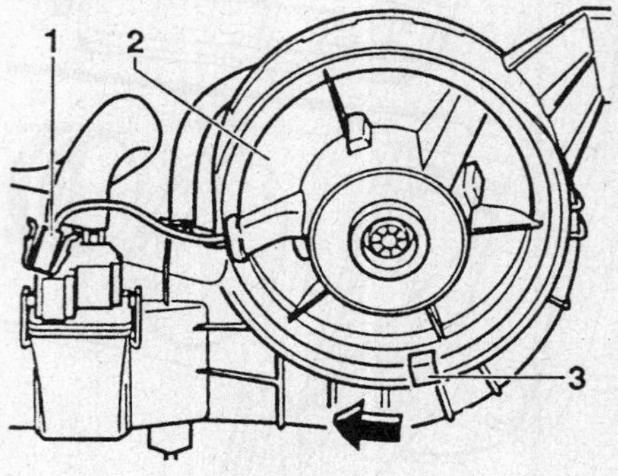

1. Electrical Connector
2. Blower Motor
3. Retaining Clip

VW7029600053000X

Fig. 10 Blower motor removal. Cabrio & 1998 Golf, GTI & Jetta less A/C

2. Hold brake pedal down, then install new switch and turn 90° counterclockwise to fasten.
3. Pull brake pedal fully to rear to allow switch to auto adjust.
4. Connect electrical connector, then test brake lamp operation.

COMBINATION SWITCH

REPLACE

1. Remove steering wheel as outlined under "Steering Wheel, Replace."
2. Remove lower and upper trim cover attaching screws, then trim covers, as necessary.
3. Remove socket head bolt from switch at top of column.
4. Disconnect electrical harness connectors from steering column switches.
5. Remove steering column switches.
6. Reverse procedure to install. Lubricate turn signal cancelling ring with multipurpose grease.

TURN SIGNAL SWITCH

REPLACE

1. Remove combination switch as outlined under "Combination Switch, Replace."
2. Carefully pry clips holding wiper switch and turn signal switch together, then separate switches.
3. Reverse procedure to install.

STEERING WHEEL

REPLACE

1. Place front wheels in straight ahead position.
2. **Wait 20 minutes after disconnecting battery ground cable, before working on steering wheel to allow air bag system capacitor to discharge.**
3. Remove Torx screws from rear of horn pad.
4. Carefully detach air bag unit from steering wheel, then tilt downward. **Gently pry horn pad buttons from**

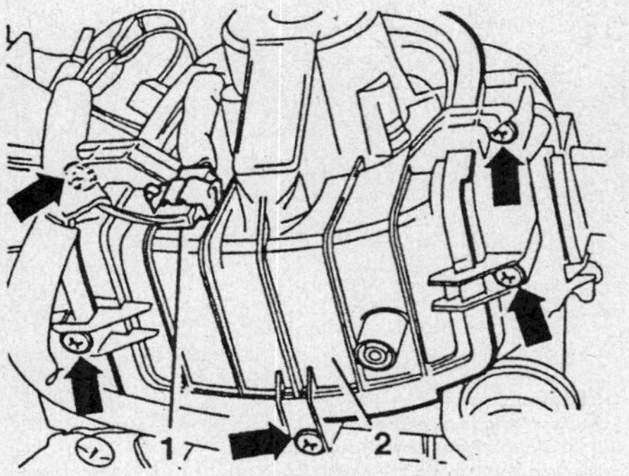

1. Electrical Connector
2. Mounting Screws

VW7029600054000X

Fig. 11 Blower motor removal. Cabrio & 1998 Golf, GTI & Jetta with A/C

front of horn pad, if equipped, then disconnect electrical connectors.

5. Disconnect electrical connector from air bag unit, **Fig. 6,** then remove air bag unit. **Do not place air bag unit on its vinyl horn pad side. Always place unit on its metal housing.**
6. Remove steering wheel retaining nut and spring washer.
7. Remove lower steering column shroud, then disconnect connector from spiral spring assembly.
8. Mark steering wheel in relation to steering spindle.
9. Remove steering wheel. **Do not turn or release spiral spring assembly while steering wheel is removed.**
10. Reverse procedure to install, noting the following:
    a. Ensure wheels are in straight ahead position prior to installing wheel.
    b. Align index marks made during removal.
    c. Spiral spring assembly must be seated.
    d. **Torque** steering wheel retaining nut to 36 ft. lbs.

INSTRUMENT CLUSTER

REPLACE

CABRIO & 1998 GOLF, GTI & JETTA

1. Remove headlamp switch as outlined under "Headlamp Switch, Replace."
2. Remove trim panel from dash at right lower corner of instrument cluster.
3. Remove screws from lower steering column trim cover, then steering column upper cover.
4. Remove instrument cluster trim cover mounting screws.
5. Release instrument cluster trim cover side retainers by pulling firmly at top, then remove instrument cluster trim cover.
6. Remove instrument cluster mounting screws.
7. Tilt instrument cluster downward and disconnect electrical connectors from back of instrument cluster.
8. Remove instrument cluster.
9. Reverse procedure to install.

NEW BEETLE & 1999-2001 GOLF, GTI & JETTA

1. Release steering wheel position lock, pull steering wheel out completely and lock again in lowest position.
2. Remove trim ring by pulling rearward to disengage mounting clips.
3. Remove two cluster mounting screws.
4. Tilt cluster slightly toward passenger compartment and disconnect electrical connectors from rear of cluster.
5. Remove cluster from instrument panel.
6. Reverse procedure to install.

PASSAT

1. Remove steering wheel as outlined under "Steering Wheel, Replace."
2. Remove combination switch as outlined under "Combination Switch, Replace."
3. Remove two driver's side kick panel attaching screws, then unclip panel.
4. Unclip instrument panel side cover.
5. Remove lower dash panel attaching screws.
6. Unclip and remove lower dash panel, then disconnect lamp switch electrical connector.
7. Slide trim around base of steering column upwards and hold in place by wedging screwdriver handle.
8. Remove four screws then cover from steering column.
9. Remove two screws from instrument cluster, then slide cluster rearward.
10. Disconnect cluster electrical connectors and remove cluster.
11. Reverse procedure to install.

RADIO

REPLACE

Factory supplied radios use three distinct types of mountings and face plates, requiring three different removal tools. Refer to **Figs. 7 through 9** to determine, by the type of face plate, which tool will be required.

1. Determine removal tool required.
2. Insert tools as shown in **Figs. 7 through 9** until they are felt to be seated.
3. **On models using tool No. VW160, or equivalent,** after tool is inserted, press outward on tools while pulling radio out.
4. **On models using tool No. 3316, or equivalent,** after tool is inserted, pull straight out with no up/down, twist or side movements.
5. **On models using too No. 3344A, or equivalent,** after tool is inserted, pull straight out on grip rings with no up/down, twist or side movements.
6. **On all models,** disconnect wiring connectors and antenna lead.
7. Release tool from radio by pressing in on radio mounting tabs while pulling on tool.

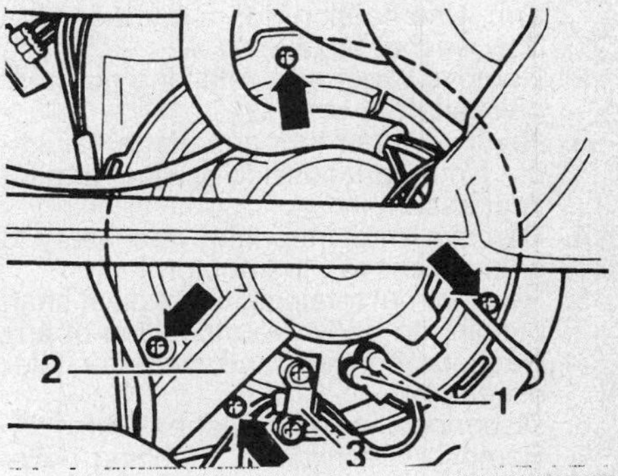

Fig. 12 Blower motor removal

8. Reverse procedure to install, noting the following:
    a. While installing radio, ensure wiring will not be pinched and rear mounting post will be engaged.

WIPER MOTOR

REPLACE

FRONT

1. Open hood and remove any panels necessary to gain access to cowl area where wiper motor and linkage are mounted.
2. Disconnect wiper motor electrical connector.
3. Note Park position of wiper arms for later assembly.
4. **On models equipped with wiper motor mounting bolts/nuts accessible through cowl,** disconnect wiper linkage rods from crank arm on motor, then remove mounting bolts/nuts and motor.
5. **On models where wiper motor mounting bolts/nuts are not accessible through cowl,** proceed as follows:
    a. Remove wiper assembly as outlined under "Wiper Transmission, Replace."
    b. Place assembly on suitable workspace.
    c. Disconnect wiper linkage rods from crank arm on motor.
    d. Remove mounting bolts/nuts and motor.
6. **On all models,** reverse procedure to install, noting the following:
    a. Prior to installing motor, connect motor to vehicle electrical connector, turn ignition on, then turn wiper on and off to ensure motor is in Park position.
    b. Turn ignition off, then disconnect electrical connector.
    c. Ensure wiper linkage is in Park position. If necessary, remove and position crank arm on motor to correct alignment.
    d. Install motor and mounting bolts/nuts, then **torque** to 14 ft. lbs.

REAR

1. Remove cap or cover at base of wiper

arm. Use caution not to damage window washer nozzle.

2. Remove wiper arm retaining nut from pivot shaft.
3. Remove wiper arm and blade assembly. Note Park position of wiper arm for later assembly.
4. Remove any trim panels necessary to gain access to wiper motor.
5. Remove nut retaining wiper pivot shaft bushing to body. Note position of any washers, spacers and seals for later assembly.
6. Disconnect window washer hose.
7. Remove wiper motor attaching bolts/nuts, then disconnect electrical connector.
8. Remove wiper motor assembly, with brackets if equipped, from liftgate.
9. Use caution not to damage seals when withdrawing pivot bushing.
10. Remove mounting bolts, then wiper motor from brackets, if equipped.
11. Reverse procedure to install, noting the following:
    a. Prior to installing motor, connect motor to vehicle electrical connector and turn ignition on.
    b. Turn wiper on and off to ensure motor is in Park position, then turn ignition off.
    c. **Torque** wiper motor mounting bolts/nuts to 44 inch lbs.
    d. **Torque** wiper pivot shaft bushing mounting nut to 62 inch lbs.
    e. **Torque** wiper arm mounting nut to 12 ft. lbs.

WIPER SWITCH

REPLACE

1. Remove combination switch as outlined under "Combination Switch, Replace."
2. Carefully pry clips holding wiper switch and turn signal switch together, then separate switches.
3. Reverse procedure to install.

WIPER TRANSMISSION

REPLACE

FRONT

1. Remove cap or cover at base of wiper arms, then remove wiper arm retaining nuts from pivot shafts.
2. Remove wiper arm and blade assemblies. Note Park position of wiper arms for later assembly.
3. Open hood and remove any panels necessary to gain access to cowl area where wiper motor and linkage are mounted.
4. Disconnect wiper motor electrical connector.
5. Remove nuts retaining wiper pivot shaft bushing to panel. Note position of any washers, spacers and seals for later assembly.
6. Remove any bolts/nuts retaining wiper frame assembly.
7. Remove wiper assembly from vehicle. Use caution not to damage seals when withdrawing pivot bushing.

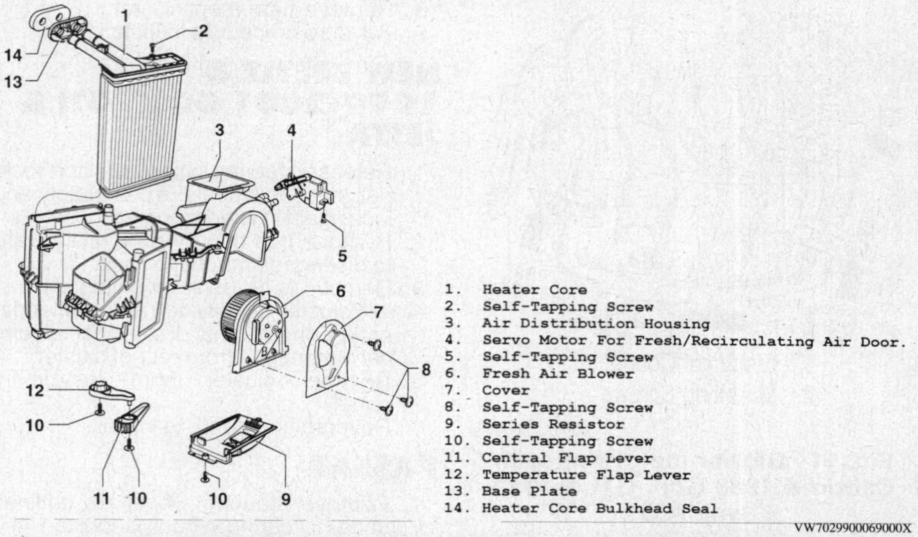

Fig. 13 Blower motor removal. New Beetle & 1999–2001 Golf, GTI & Jetta

8. Disconnect wiper linkage from motor crank arm and wiper pivot shafts.
9. Noting position of O-rings and washers, remove C-clip from pivot shaft, then slide pivot shaft out of bushings.
10. Reverse procedure to install, noting the following:
    a. Ensure wiper linkage is in Park position. If necessary, remove and position crank arm on motor to correct alignment.
    b. **Torque** wiper pivot shaft bushing mounting nut to 62 inch lbs.
    c. **Torque** wiper arm mounting nut to 12 ft. lbs.

REAR

1. Remove cap or cover at base of wiper arms, then remove wiper arm retaining nuts from pivot shafts.
2. Remove wiper arm and blade assemblies. Note Park position of wiper arms for later assembly.
3. Remove trim panels necessary to access rear wiper assembly.
4. Disconnect wiper motor electrical connector.
5. Remove nuts retaining wiper pivot shaft bushing to panel. Note position of any washers, spacers and seals for later assembly.
6. Remove any bolts/nuts retaining wiper frame assembly.
7. Remove wiper assembly from vehicle. Use caution not to damage seals when withdrawing pivot bushing.
8. Disconnect wiper linkage from motor crank arm and wiper pivot shafts.
9. Noting position of O-rings and washers, remove C-clip from pivot shaft, then slide pivot shaft out of bushings.
10. Reverse procedure to install, noting the following:
    a. Ensure wiper linkage is in Park position. If necessary, remove and position crank arm on motor to correct alignment.
    b. **Torque** wiper pivot shaft bushing mounting nut to 62 inch lbs.
    c. **Torque** wiper arm mounting nut to 12 ft. lbs.

BLOWER MOTOR

REPLACE

CABRIO & 1998 GOLF, GTI & JETTA

Less Air Conditioning

1. Remove glove compartment assembly to gain access to blower motor.
2. Disconnect electrical connector, then the blower motor retaining lug, **Fig. 10.**
3. Turn motor clockwise, then pull from housing.
4. Reverse procedure to install.

With Air Conditioning

1. Remove glove compartment assembly to gain access to blower motor.
2. Disconnect electrical connector, then remove screws retaining blower assembly to housing, **Fig. 11.**
3. Pull blower assembly downward to remove.
4. Reverse procedure to install.

PASSAT

1. Remove righthand lower shelf.
2. Remove glove compartment, then disconnect wiring connectors, **Fig. 12.**
3. Remove cable clamp, then the four mounting screws.
4. Pull blower unit out of housing, then remove downward.
5. Reverse procedure to install.

NEW BEETLE & 1999–2001 GOLF, GTI & JETTA

1. Remove glove box.
2. Remove three blower motor cover screws and cover, **Fig. 13.**
3. Remove one lower cover screw and

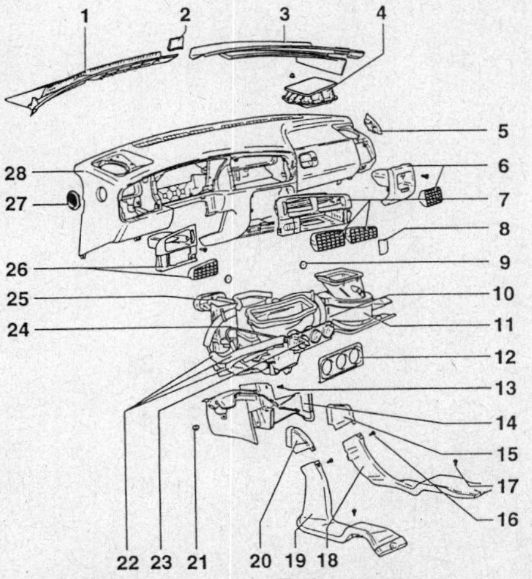

1. Left Plenum Cover
2. Connecting Clip
3. Right Plenum Cover
4. Air Intake Adapter
5. Side Window Air Outlet
6. Right Air Outlet
7. Center Air Outlet
8. Trim Cover
9. Nut
10. Blower Resistor w/Fuse
11. Blower
12. Trim Plate
13. Screw
14. Footwell Air Outlet
15. Right Rear Footwell Air Duct Connector
16. Screw
17. Screw
18. Right Rear Footwell Air Duct
19. Left Rear Footwell Air Duct
20. Left Rear Footwell Air Duct Connector
21. Clip
22. Control Cables
23. Heating & A/C Control
24. Heater & Evaporator Housing
25. Heater Core
26. Left Air Outlet
27. Side Window Air Outlet
28. Dash Panel

VW7029600057000X

Fig. 14 Heater box removal. Cabrio & 1998 Golf, GTI & Jetta

cover, then disconnect series resistor and blower motor electrical connectors.
4. Remove blower motor series resistor.
5. Slide blower motor downwards and out of fresh air assembly.
6. Reverse procedure to install.

HEATER CORE

REPLACE

CABRIO & 1998 GOLF, GTI & JETTA

1. **On models equipped with A/C,** recover refrigerant as outlined under "Air Conditioning."
2. **On all models,** drain cooling system into suitable container.
3. Remove instrument panel as outlined under "Dash Panel Service."
4. **On models equipped with A/C,** disconnect A/C lines at expansion valve and cap openings.
5. **On all models,** remove heater housing fasteners in engine compartment, then the instrument panel bracket.
6. Remove evaporator housing water drain valve, then the heater housing assembly, **Fig. 14.**
7. Remove heater core from housing, **Fig. 15.**
8. Reverse procedure to install, noting the following:
   a. **On models equipped with A/C,** replace seal at evaporator core inlet/outlet pipes on firewall.
   b. **On all models,** replace seal at heater core inlet/outlet pipes, and other seals/gaskets, if necessary.

PASSAT

1. Remove instrument panel as outlined in "Dash Panel Service" section.
2. **On models equipped with A/C,** recover refrigerant as outlined in "Air Conditioning" section.
3. **On models equipped with A/C,** disconnect refrigerant lines from evaporator, then plug and cap lines and fittings.
4. **On all models,** remove Instrument panel as outlined in "Dash Panel Service" section.
5. Remove heater core from heating unit, **Fig. 16.**
6. Reverse procedure to install.

NEW BEETLE & 1999-2001 GOLF, GTI & JETTA

1. Remove instrument panel as outlined in "Dash Panel Service" section.
2. **On models equipped with A/C,** recover refrigerant as outlined in "Air Conditioning" section.
3. **On models equipped with A/C,** disconnect refrigerant lines from evaporator, then plug and cap lines and fittings.
4. **On all models,** remove heater core from heating unit, **Fig. 17.**
5. Reverse procedure to install.

EVAPORATOR CORE

REPLACE

CABRIO & 1998 GOLF, GTI & JETTA

1. Remove heater and evaporator assembly as outlined under "Heater Core, Replace."
2. Separate heater housing assembly and evaporator/blower assembly, **Fig. 18,** then remove blower motor.
3. Pry off retaining clips for evaporator housing halves using a screwdriver, then remove seal at A/C inlet/outlet pipes.
4. Remove air distribution case from housing, then the air intake duct.
5. Remove remaining housing retaining clips, then the evaporator capillary tube.

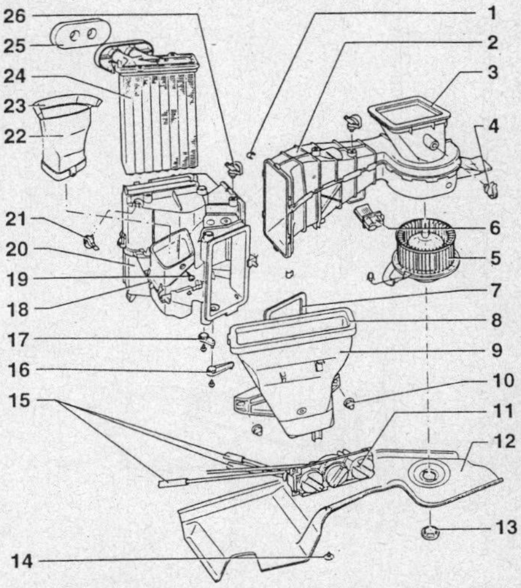

1. Clip
2. Air Duct w/Main Shut Off Flap (wHeater Only)
3. Gasket
4. Wire Clip
5. Blower
6. Blower Resistor w/Fuse
7. Gasket
8. Gasket
9. Air Duct
10. Nut
11. Air & Heat Controls
12. Cover
13. Plug
14. Clip
15. Control Cables
16. Central Air Flap Lever
17. Temperature Flap Lever
18. Footwell/Defrost Flap Lever
19. Screw
20. Air Distribution Housing
21. Wire Clip
22. Air Duct Connector
23. Gasket
24. Heater Core
25. Gasket
26. Wire Clip

VW7029600058000X

Fig. 15 Heater core removal. Cabrio & 1998 Golf, GTI & Jetta

6. Separate housing halves, then remove evaporator core.
7. Reverse procedure to install, noting the following:
   a. Install new seals at A/C inlet/outlet lines at evaporator and heater cores, air intake duct, air distribution case and other locations as necessary.
   b. Apply silicone sealer to mating surfaces of fresh air blower housing, air intake duct and upper evaporator housing.
   c. Recover and recharge A/C system as outlined in "General Service" section.

PASSAT

Refer to "Heater Core, Replace" for HVAC unit removal, then separate case halves and remove evaporator.

NEW BEETLE & 1999-2001 GOLF, GTI & JETTA

Refer to "Heater Core, Replace" for HVAC unit removal, then separate case halves and remove evaporator.

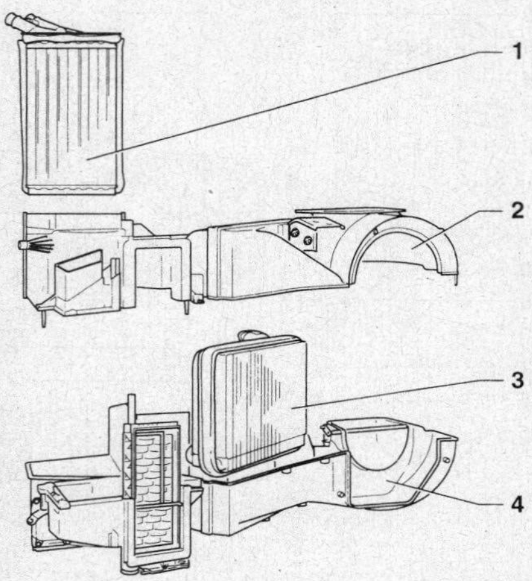

1. Heater Core
2. Housing, Upper Part
3. Evaporator
4. Housing, Lower Part

VW7029900070000X

Fig. 16 Heater & evaporator core removal. Passat

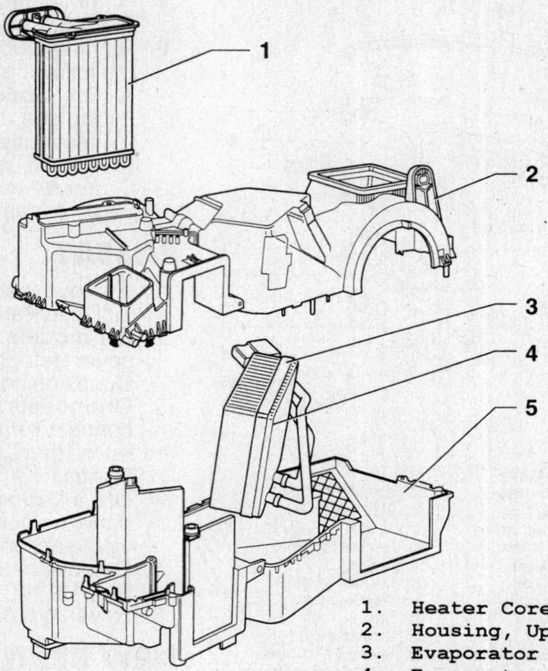

1. Heater Core
2. Housing, Upper Part
3. Evaporator Seal
4. Evaporator
5. Housing, Lower Part

VW7029900071000X

Fig. 17 Heater core removal. New Beetle & 1999–2001 Golf, GTI & Jetta

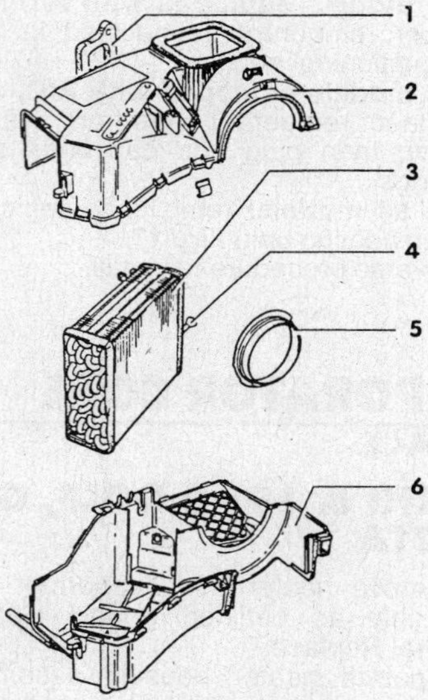

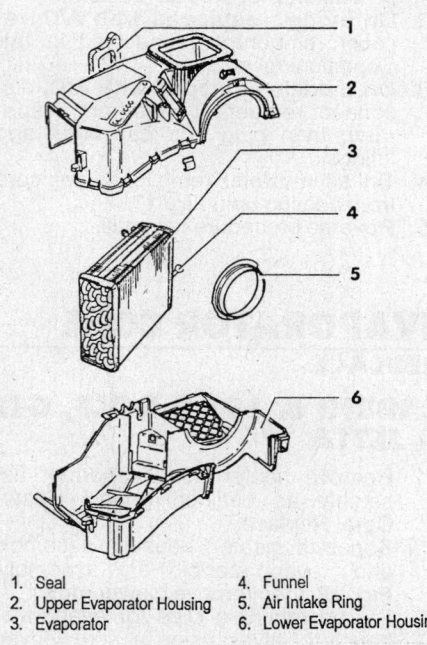

1. Seal
2. Upper Evaporator Housing
3. Evaporator
4. Funnel
5. Air Intake Ring
6. Lower Evaporator Housing

VW7029600056000X

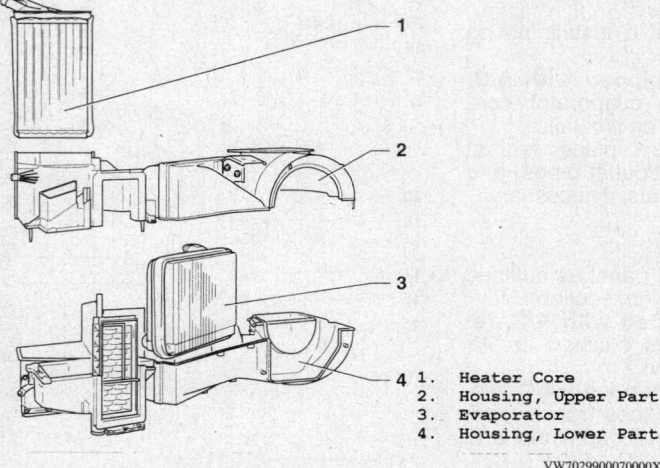

Fig. 18 Evaporator removal. Cabrio & 1998 Golf, GTI & Jetta

1.8L Turbocharged Gasoline Engine

NOTE: On Air Bag Equipped Models, Refer To "Air Bag System Precautions" Located In The Front Of This Manual For System Disarming & Arming Procedures.

NOTE: Refer To "Computer Relearn Procedures" Located In The Front Of This Manual When Battery Power To The Computer Has Been Interrupted.

INDEX

	Page No.
Camshaft, Replace	8-20
Compression Pressure	8-17
Cooling System Bleed	8-22
Cylinder Head, Replace	8-18
Engine Rebuilding Specifications	8-185
Engine, Replace	8-17
Exhaust Manifold, Replace	8-18
Front Main Bearing Oil Seal, Replace	8-21
Installation	8-21
Removal	8-21
Fuel Pump, Replace	8-24
Golf, GTI, Jetta & New Beetle	8-24
Passat	8-24
Hydraulic Lifter Inspection	8-18
Hydraulic Lifters, Replace	8-19
Intake Manifold, Replace	8-18
Main & Rod Bearings	8-21
Oil Pump, Replace	8-21
Golf, GTI, Jetta & New Beetle	8-21
Passat	8-21
Piston & Rod Assembly	8-21
Pistons, Pins & Rings	8-21
Precautions	8-17
Air Bag Systems	8-17
Audio Coded Anti-Theft System	8-17
Battery Ground Cable	8-17
Radiator, Replace	8-23
Golf, GTI & Jetta	8-23
New Beetle	8-23
Passat	8-23
Serpentine Drive Belt	8-22
Golf, GTI, Jetta & New Beetle	8-22
Passat	8-22
Tightening Specifications	8-25
Timing Belt, Replace	8-19
Golf, GTI, Jetta & New Beetle	8-19
Passat	8-20
Turbocharger, Replace	8-24
Valve Adjustment	8-18
Valve Guides	8-19
Inspection	8-19
Replacement	8-19
Water Pump, Replace	8-22
Golf, GTI, Jetta & New Beetle	8-22
Passat	8-22

PRECAUTIONS

AIR BAG SYSTEMS

Do not use computer memory saver tool on air bag equipped models. Using the tool will keep the air bag system charged and may cause accidental activation of the air bag unit. Refer to "Air Bag System Precautions" in the front of this manual for system disarming and arming procedures.

BATTERY GROUND CABLE

Prior to disconnecting the battery negative cable, obtain the radio security code. After service has been completed and the battery negative cable has been reconnected, use security code to activate the radio. Prior to service, disconnect battery ground cable and isolate as required.

AUDIO CODED ANTI-THEFT SYSTEM

Some models are equipped with a radio anti-theft system that will disable the system when battery power is interrupted, unless the system is reset the radio will not operate.

1. Turn radio to On position, SAFE and 1000 should be displayed.
2. Enter radio code using first four program station buttons. Security code will appear on display.
3. Depress and hold righthand side of radio right or left blocker until anti-theft coding is activated indicated by a brief signal sound.
4. If code number has been entered correctly, when ignition key is removed a diode on front of radio will flash.

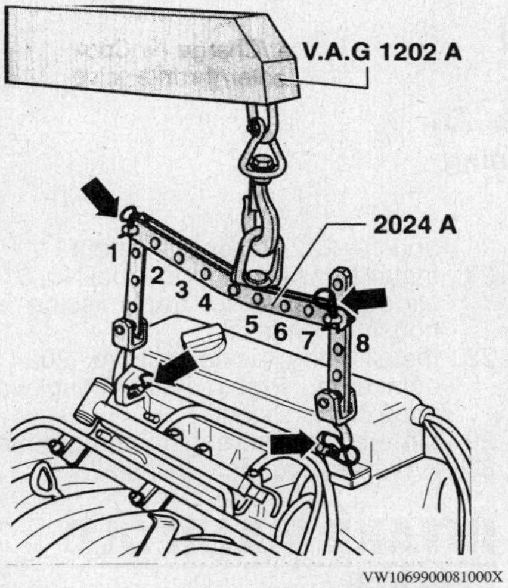

Fig. 1 Engine lift installation

COMPRESSION PRESSURE

1. Perform compression test with engine at operating temperature, spark plugs removed, engine oil temperature must be at least 86°F and throttle plate completely open.
2. Disconnect ignition coil connectors and remove ignition coils.
3. Remove spark plugs.
4. Connect compression tester tool No. VAG 1381/VAG 1763, or equivalent, per manufacturer's instructions. Then crank engine until compression tester shows no further increase in pressure.
5. Compression should be 145–188.5 psi with a maximum difference between highest and lowest cylinder of 43.5 psi. Minimum compression should be 101.5 psi.

ENGINE

REPLACE

1. Remove insulation tray.
2. Remove front bumper.
3. Drain cooling system.
4. Remove power steering cooler line attaching bolt.
5. Remove hood lock assembly with attachments.
6. Remove turbocharger air cooler, air cleaner and throttle valve control module.
7. Remove serpentine drive belt.
8. Remove power steering pump mounting bolts from bracket and position pump aside.
9. Remove retaining clamps from A/C refrigerant lines.
10. Remove A/C compressor, then secure aside with tie strap.
11. Remove starter motor.
12. Disconnect front exhaust pipe from exhaust manifold.
13. Disconnect front exhaust pipe from catalytic converter.
14. Remove catalytic converter from turbocharger.
15. Remove air cleaner.
16. Disconnect throttle cable at throttle

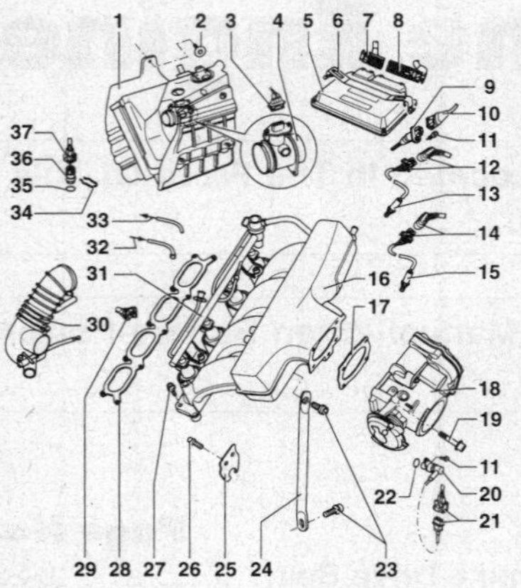

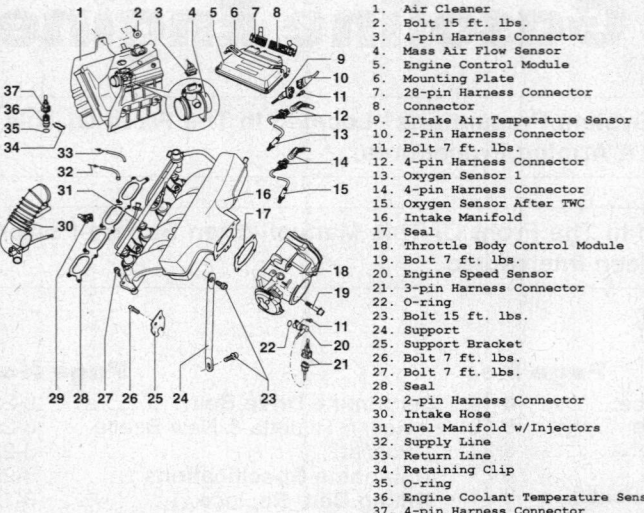

1. Air Cleaner
2. Bolt 15 ft. lbs.
3. 4-pin Harness Connector
4. Mass Air Flow Sensor
5. Engine Control Module
6. Mounting Plate
7. 28-pin Harness Connector
8. Connector
9. Intake Air Temperature Sensor
10. 2-Pin Harness Connector
11. Bolt 7 ft. lbs.
12. 4-pin Harness Connector
13. Oxygen Sensor 1
14. 4-pin Harness Connector
15. Oxygen Sensor After TWC
16. Intake Manifold
17. Seal
18. Throttle Body Control Module
19. Bolt 7 ft. lbs.
20. Engine Speed Sensor
21. 3-pin Harness Connector
22. O-ring
23. Bolt 15 ft. lbs.
24. Support
25. Support Bracket
26. Bolt 7 ft. lbs.
27. Bolt 7 ft. lbs.
28. Seal
29. 2-pin Harness Connector
30. Intake Hose
31. Fuel Manifold w/Injectors
32. Supply Line
33. Return Line
34. Retaining Clip
35. O-ring
36. Engine Coolant Temperature Sensor
37. 4-pin Harness Connector

VW1059900005000X

Fig. 2 Exploded view of intake manifold

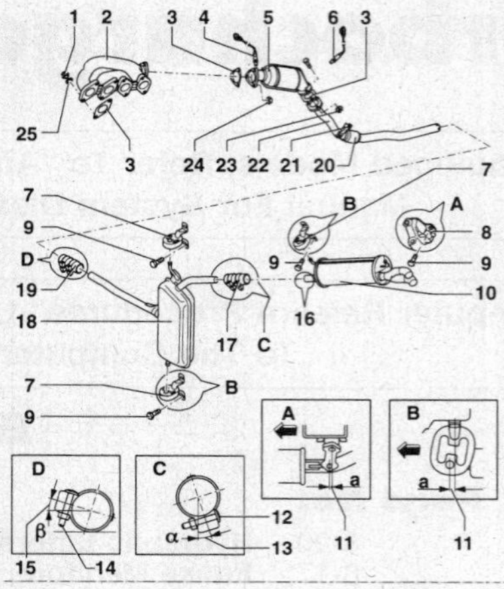

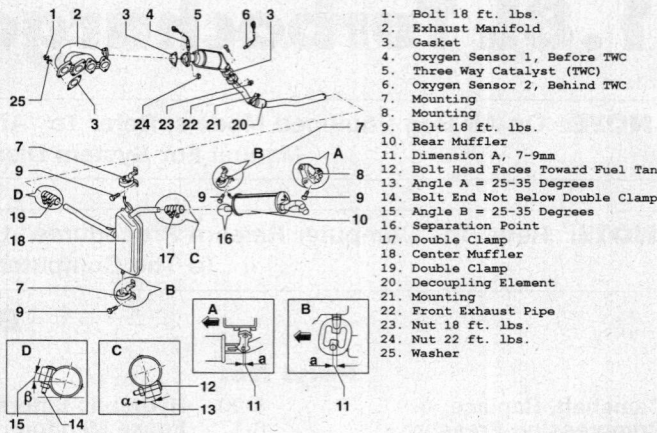

1. Bolt 18 ft. lbs.
2. Exhaust Manifold
3. Gasket
4. Oxygen Sensor 1, Before TWC
5. Three Way Catalyst (TWC)
6. Oxygen Sensor 2, Behind TWC
7. Mounting
8. Mounting
9. Bolt 18 ft. lbs.
10. Rear Muffler
11. Dimension A, 7-9mm
12. Bolt Head Faces Toward Fuel Tank
13. Angle A = 25-35 Degrees
14. Bolt End Not Below Double Clamp
15. Angle B = 25-35 Degrees
16. Separation Point
17. Double Clamp
18. Center Muffler
19. Double Clamp
20. Decoupling Element
21. Mounting
22. Front Exhaust Pipe
23. Nut 18 ft. lbs.
24. Nut 22 ft. lbs.
25. Washer

VW1079900008000X

Fig. 3 Exploded view of exhaust manifold

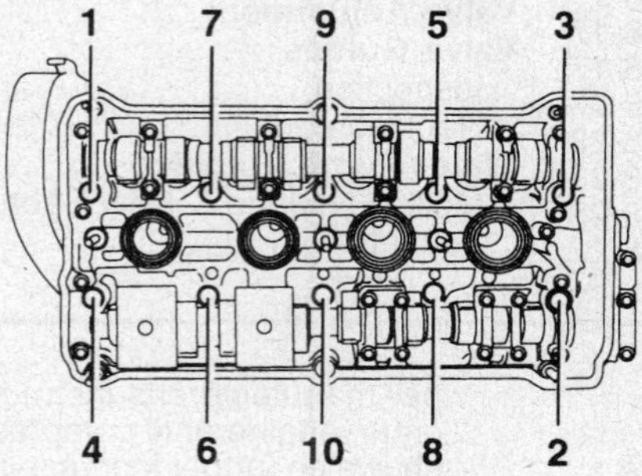

VW1069900082000X

Fig. 4 Cylinder head loosening sequence

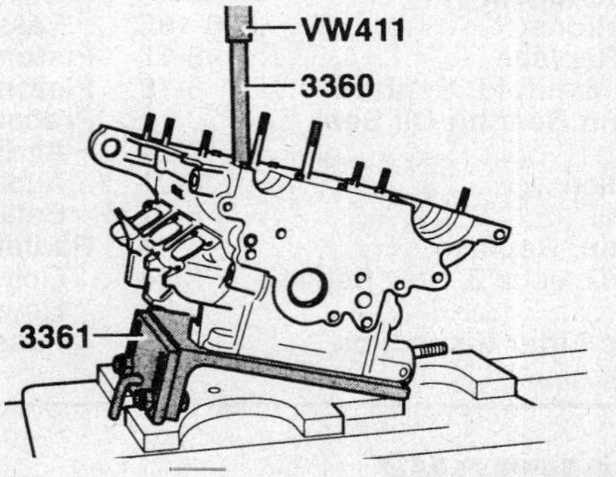

VW1060100123000X

Fig. 5 Valve guide removal

valve control module cable disc and support bracket.

17. Remove intake manifold cover.
18. Disconnect fuel supply and return lines at fuel rail.
19. Disconnect all coolant hoses from engine.
20. Remove all vacuum and intake hoses from engine and turbocharger.
21. Remove coolant system expansion reservoir, then set aside.
22. Remove upper engine/transaxle mounting bolts.
23. Remove left and right engine mount upper mounting bolts.
24. **On models equipped with automatic transaxle,** proceed as follows:
    a. Remove three torque converter to drive plate attaching nuts. **Secure torque converter, to ensure that it does not fall out after engine removal.**
    b. Lift engine and transaxle slightly using a suitable workshop crane, then remove lower engine to transaxle connecting bolts.
25. **On models equipped with manual transaxle,** remove lower engine to transaxle connecting bolts.
26. **On all models** install engine support bracket and hooks tool Nos. 10–222A and 10–222A/2, or equivalent.
27. Install transaxle support tool No. 3147, or equivalent, to transmission bell housing bolt hole.
28. Install lifting tackle tool No. 2024, or equivalent, **Fig. 1,** while lifting workshop crane slightly.
29. Lift engine from engine compartment.
30. Reverse procedure to install.

INTAKE MANIFOLD

REPLACE

Refer to **Fig. 2** for intake manifold replacement.

EXHAUST MANIFOLD

REPLACE

Refer to **Fig. 3** for exhaust manifold replacement.

CYLINDER HEAD

REPLACE

1. Drain engine coolant.
2. Separate fuel supply and return lines at fuel rail connection. **Seal off lines to prevent contamination.**
3. Disconnect front exhaust pipe or catalyst from exhaust manifold.
4. Remove upper timing belt guard.
5. Release belt tensioner and remove toothed belt from camshaft sprocket.
6. Remove valve cover.
7. Loosen socket head bolts in sequence **Fig. 4,** then remove head.
8. Reverse procedure to install noting the following:
    a. Clean cylinder head, cylinder block and bolt holes.
    b. Install all cylinder head bolts hand tight.
    c. Reverse sequence shown in **Fig. 4** and tighten bolts in four steps. First step, **torque** bolts to 30 ft. lbs.; second step, **torque** bolts to 44 ft. lbs.; third step, tighten bolts an additional 90°; fourth step, tighten bolts an additional 90.°

VALVE ADJUSTMENT

All engines are equipped with hydraulic lifters. No adjustment provision is provided.

HYDRAULIC LIFTER INSPECTION

Hydraulic valve lifters are non-adjustable. Noisy lifters may be replaced after the following check.

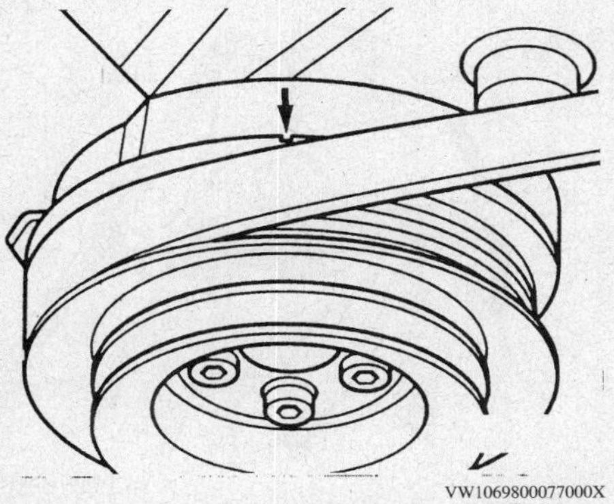

Fig. 6 Crankshaft pulley TDC mark alignment

1. Run engine until radiator fan comes on at least once.
2. Raise engine speed to 2500 RPM, for two minutes.
3. If lifter(s) is still noisy, proceed as follows:
   a. Remove upper intake manifold.
   b. Remove cylinder head cover.
   c. Turn crankshaft pulley bolt clockwise until cam lobes of cylinder point upward. Inspect for damage.
   d. Press down lightly against valve lifter with a wooden stick. If lifter can be pushed down more than. 004 inch, replace as outlined under "Hydraulic Lifter, Replace."

VALVE GUIDES

INSPECTION

1. Remove all carbon deposits from valve guide.
2. Set up a dial indicator on cylinder head to check suspected guide.
3. Insert new valve into valve guide. End of valve stem must be flush with valve guide end.
4. Rock valve back and forth against dial indicator.
5. Maximum for intake valves is. 039 inch. Maximum for exhaust valves is. 051 inch. Replace guide(s) if reading is beyond limit.

REPLACEMENT

1. Worn valve guides can be removed using support tool No. 3361, or equivalent.
2. Press guides out from camshaft side using drift tool No. 3360, or equivalent, **Fig. 5.**
3. Coat new guides with engine oil, then press into cold cylinder head from camshaft side.
4. Press guides in as far as they will go. Once valve guide shoulder is seated, do not use more than one ton of pressure or guide shoulder may break. Ream guides by hand using tool No. 3363, or equivalent, and a proper cutting lubricant.
5. Machine valve seats.

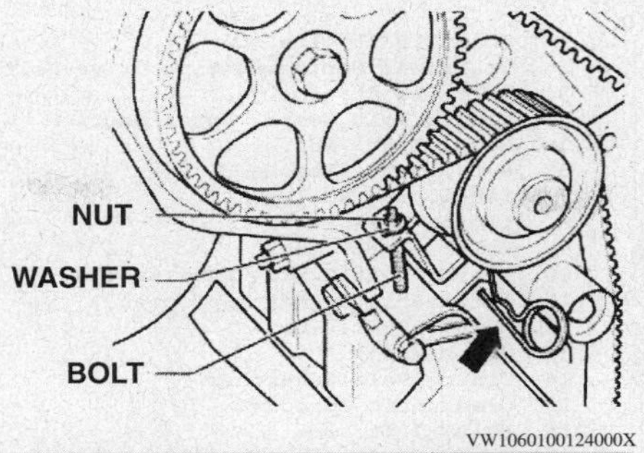

Fig. 7 Timing belt tension relief. Golf, GTI, Jetta & New Beetle

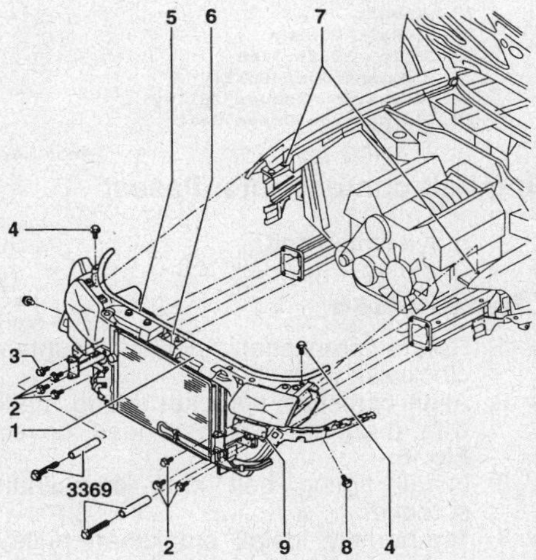

1. Lock carrier w/attachments
2. Bolt (37 ft. lbs.)
3. Bolt (37 ft. lbs.)
4. Bolt (71 inch lbs.)
5. Seal
6. Bowden cable
7. Hole in side panel
8. Bolt
9. Hole for special tool

Fig. 9 Header panel mounting. Passat

HYDRAULIC LIFTERS

REPLACE

After replacing hydraulic lifters, do not run engine for 30 minutes. This will allow lifters time to bleed down to proper adjustment.

1. Remove camshaft as outlined under "Camshaft, Replace."
2. Replace defective lifter(s).
3. Install camshaft as outlined under "Camshaft, Replace."

TIMING BELT

REPLACE

Avoid turning the camshaft or crankshaft when the timing belt has been removed. If movement is required, use extreme caution to avoid valve damage from piston contact.

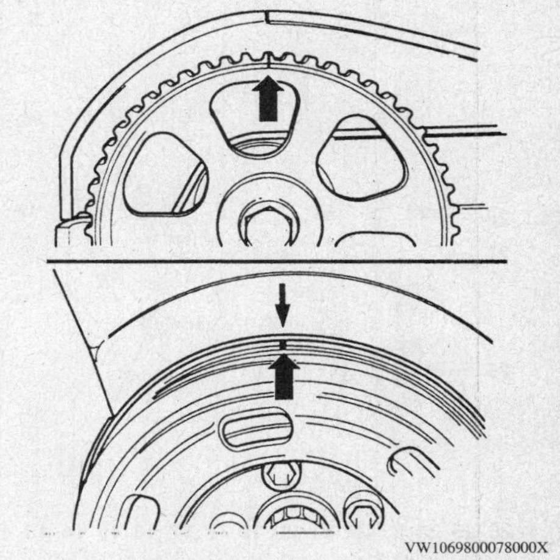

Fig. 8 Camshaft sprocket TDC mark alignment

GOLF, GTI, JETTA & NEW BEETLE

Removal

1. **On Golf, GTI and Jetta models,** remove lower noise insulation pan, then the right headlight.
2. **On New Beetle models,** remove right-hand insulation tray.
3. **On all models,** remove engine cover, then the air tube between turbocharger and charge air cooler.
4. Remove serpentine drive belt, then the tensioner.
5. Set No. 1 cylinder to TDC, **Fig. 6.**
6. Remove coolant overflow tank screws, then position tank aside.
7. Remove power steering fluid reservoir screws, then position reservoir aside.
8. Disconnect vacuum line at EVAP canister and throttle valve supports.
9. Remove upper timing belt guide.
10. Install engine support bridge tool No. 10-222A and bracket tool No. 10-222A-1, or equivalents.
11. Install retainer tool No. 3180, or equivalent at right lifting eye bolt on cylinder head, then lift engine slightly to relieve tension from engine mount.
12. Remove subframe mount bolts, then the subframe mount.
13. Remove harmonic balancer pulley, then the lower timing belt cover.
14. Mark direction of engine rotation on timing belt.
15. Release tension on timing belt using a M5x55 threaded bolt with nut and large washer installed on belt tensioner, **Fig. 7.**
16. Relieve timing belt tension just enough to install suitable drift into hole in tensioner and housing.
17. Remove timing belt.

Installation

1. Align mark on camshaft with mark on cylinder head cover, **Fig. 8. When turning camshaft , crankshaft must not be at TDC on any cylinder.**
2. Install timing belt on crankshaft sprocket.

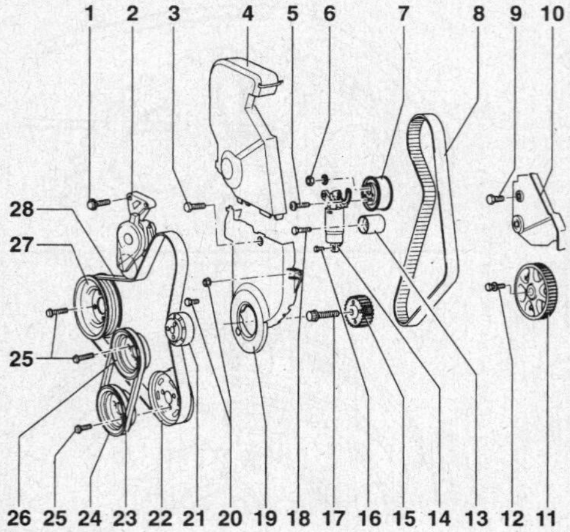

1. Bolt, 18 ft. lbs.
2. Tensioner For Serpentine Drive Belt
3. Bolt, 15 ft. lbs.
4. Timing Belt Guard, Upper Section
5. Bolt, 7 ft. lbs.
6. Nut, 15 ft. lbs.
7. Tensioning Roller
8. Timing Belt
9. Bolt, 15 ft. lbs.
10. Timing Belt Guard, Rear Section
11. Intermediate Shaft Sprocket
12. Bolt, 59 ft. lbs.
13. Idler Wheel
14. Timing Belt Tensioner
15. Crankshaft Sprocket
16. Bolt, 7 ft. lbs.
17. Bolt, 65 ft. lbs. + 1/4 turn
18. Bolt, 18 ft. lbs.
19. Timing Belt Guard, Lower Section
20. Bolt & Nut, 7 ft. lbs.
21. Viscous Fan Pulley
22. Power Steering Pump Pulley
23. V-Belt
24. V-Belt Pulley
25. Bolt, 18 ft. lbs.
26. Coolant Pump Pulley
27. Vibration Damper Pulley
28. Serpentine Drive Belt

VW1069900084000X

Fig. 10 Exploded view of timing belt components. Passat

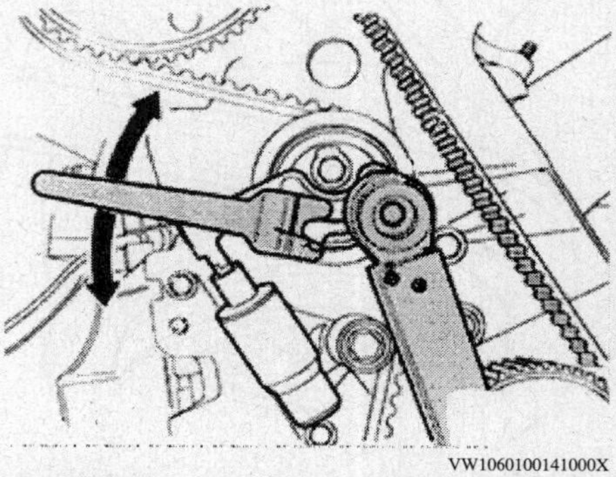

VW1060100141000X

Fig. 11 Timing belt tension adjustment. Passat

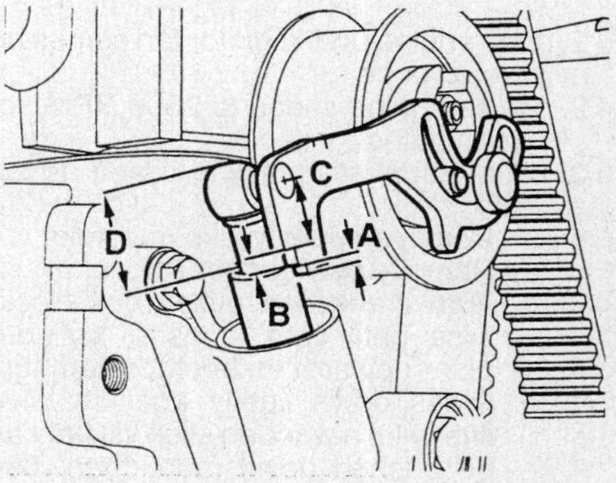

VW1069800080000X

Fig. 12 Timing belt tension inspection. Passat

3. Install subframe mount, then the lower timing belt cover.
4. Install harmonic balancer pulley, then set No. 1 cylinder at TDC.
5. Install timing belt on water pump, tensioner pulley and camshaft sprocket.
6. Remove drift and threaded bolt from timing belt tensioner.
7. Rotate crankshaft twice, then verify timing marks.
8. Install upper timing belt cover.
9. Install serpentine belt tensioner, then the serpentine belt.
10. Remove engine support tools.
11. Connect EVAP canister and throttle valve support vacuum lines.
12. Install power steering fluid reservoir, then the coolant overflow jug.
13. Install turbocharger air tube.
14. **On Golf, GTI and Jetta models,** install lower noise insulation pan, then the right headlight.
15. **On New Beetle model,** install right-hand insulation tray.
16. **On all models,** install lower noise insulation pan, then the engine cover.

PASSAT

Removal

1. Remove front bumper.
2. Remove air guide between header panel and air cleaner.
3. Remove bolts, **Fig. 9,** then thread in VW tool No. 3369, or equivalent, into lefthand and righthand long members.
4. Remove header panel bolts, then pull header panel forward.
5. Mark belt running direction, then rotate engine accessory drive belt tensioner clockwise and lock it with pin VW tool No. 3204, or equivalent.
6. Remove accessory drive belt and tensioner, **Fig. 10**
7. Rotate crankshaft pulley until No. 1 cylinder reaches TDC, **Fig. 6.**
8. Remove crankshaft pulley using a suitable puller.
9. Remove timing belt lower cover.
10. Loosen timing belt tensioner, then remove timing belt.

Installation

1. Rotate crankshaft slightly counterclockwise.
2. Align camshaft sprocket timing mark with mark on cylinder head cover, **Fig. 8.**
3. Install timing belt onto crankshaft sprocket.
4. Temporarily install crankshaft pulley and secure it with one bolt.
5. Rotate crankshaft slightly clockwise until No. 1 cylinder reaches TDC, **Fig. 6.**
6. Route timing belt onto tensioner roller and camshaft sprocket.
7. Adjust timing belt tension by rotating tensioner **Fig. 11** clockwise with pin wrench VW tool No. V159, or equivalent, until piston is fully extended and piston lifts approximately. 039 inch.
8. Tighten tensioner mounting bolt to specifications.
9. Rotate crankshaft pulley two turns clockwise and ensure timing marks are properly aligned.
10. Inspect timing belt tension as follows:
    a. Ensure area "A,"**Fig. 12** aligns with piston's upper edge or dimension "D" is. 98–1.14 inch.
    b. Dimension "A" indicates adjustment is satisfactory.
    c. Dimension "B" indicates wear area.
    d. Dimension "C" indicates a need to inspect timing belt tensioner for wear or adjust belt tension once again.
11. Remove crankshaft pulley.
12. Install timing belt lower cover.
13. Install crankshaft pulley, then tighten bolts to specifications.
14. Install timing belt upper cover.
15. Install engine accessory drive belt tensioner.
16. Install accessory drive belt. Note running direction of belt.
17. Tighten accessory drive belt tensioner bolt to specifications.
18. Position header panel, **Fig. 9** and **torque** bolts (2 and 3) to 37 ft. lbs., and bolts (4) to 71 inch lbs. Ensure hoses and wiring are not kinked or pinched.
19. Install air guide.
20. Install front bumper.
21. Start engine to ensure proper operation.

CAMSHAFT

REPLACE

1. Remove upper timing belt guard.
2. Set camshaft sprockets to TDC No. 1 cylinder by turning crankshaft. Mark on camshaft sprocket must align with mark on cylinder head cover, **Fig. 13.**
3. Remove cylinder head cover.
4. Release tensioner and remove toothed belt from camshaft sprocket.
5. Turn crankshaft back slightly.
6. Remove camshaft sprocket, **Fig. 14.** When loosening camshaft sprocket bolt, counter hold with holder tool No. 3036 or equivalent.
7. Remove woodruff key from camshaft.
8. Remove camshaft position sensor housing.
9. Remove washer and hood for camshaft position sensor.
10. Clean drive chain and camshaft chain sprocket in area of arrows on bearing caps and mark installation position.
11. Secure chain tensioner with retainer tool No. 3366 or equivalent.
12. Remove intake and exhaust cam third and fifth bearing caps.
13. Remove double bearing cap.

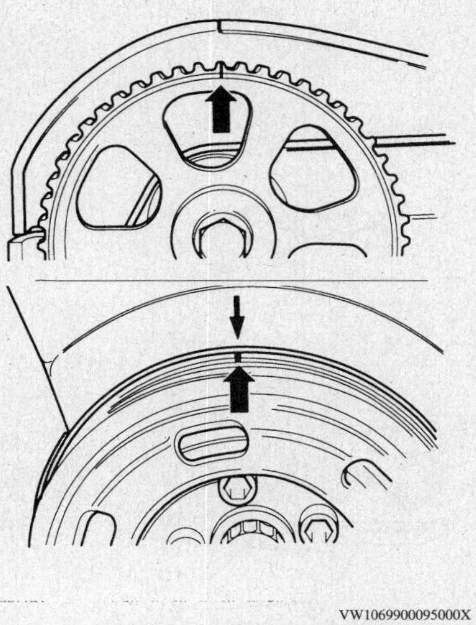

Fig. 13 Setting to TDC

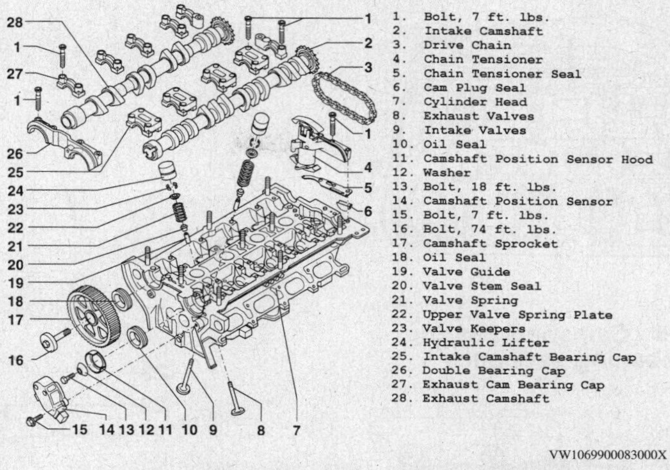

Fig. 14 Exploded view of cylinder head components

14. Remove both bearing caps at chain sprockets on intake and exhaust camshafts.
15. Remove chain tensioner securing bolts.
16. Remove intake and exhaust camshaft 2nd and 4th bearing caps using alternate and cross-over sequence, **Fig. 15.**
17. Remove intake and exhaust camshafts with chain tensioner and retainer for tool.
18. Reverse procedure to install, noting the following:
    a. When installing camshafts, cam lobes for cylinder No. 1 must face upwards.
    b. When installing bearing caps, ensure cap markings can be read from inside of cylinder head.
    c. Replace chain tensioner gasket and coat shaded area with sealant, part no. D 454 300 A2 or equivalent.
    d. Slide chain tensioner between drive chain.
    e. Apply oil to running surfaces of both camshafts.
    f. Tighten intake and exhaust camshaft second and fourth bearing caps using alternate and cross-over sequence to specifications.
    g. Install both bearing caps at chain sprockets for intake and exhaust camshafts. Ensure camshafts are positioned correctly.
    h. Apply oil to hatched area of double bearing cap with sealant, part No. D 454 300 A2 or equivalent.
    i. Ensure camshaft position of camshaft marks are aligned, **Fig. 16.**

PISTON & ROD ASSEMBLY

Assemble the piston to the rod with the arrow on the piston crown pointing toward the front of the engine and the casting marks on the rod facing the intermediate shaft.

PISTONS, PINS & RINGS

Pistons and rings are available in. 010 inch,. 020 inch and. 040 inch oversizes. Oversize piston pins are not available.

MAIN & ROD BEARINGS

Main and connecting rod bearings are available in. 010 inch,. 020 inch and. 030 inch undersizes.

FRONT MAIN BEARING OIL SEAL

REPLACE

REMOVAL

1. Remove accessory drive belt and timing belt.
2. Remove crankshaft sprocket, by counter-holding sprocket with leverage tool No. 3099, or equivalent.
3. Screw bolt from oil seal installation tool No. 3083, or equivalent, fully into crankshaft, to guide oil seal extractor.
4. Loosen inner part of oil seal extractor tool two turns out of outer section, then tighten lock screw.
5. Lubricate threaded head of oil seal extractor, then place into position and exert firm pressure while screwing as far into seal as possible.
6. Loosen lock screw and turn inner part against crankshaft until oil seal is removed.

INSTALLATION

1. Lightly oil sealing lip of oil seal.
2. Place guide sleeve from oil seal installation tool No. 3083, or equivalent, onto crankshaft journal.
3. Slide oil seal over guide sleeve.
4. Press oil seal in onto stop with press sleeve from seal installation tool.
5. Install crankshaft sprocket and lock in position with counter-hold tool No. 3099 or equivalent.
6. Install timing belt, then accessory drive belt.

OIL PUMP

REPLACE

GOLF, GTI, JETTA & NEW BEETLE

1. Refer to **Fig. 17** for oil pump removal.
2. Reverse procedure to install.

PASSAT

1. Place lock carrier into service position.
2. Drain engine oil into a suitable container.
3. Mark direction of engine rotation on timing belt.
4. Remove accessory drive belt.
5. Remove A/C compressor drive belt tensioning roller complete.
6. Remove A/C compressor drive belt.
7. Secure viscous fan coupling belt pulley with a suitable punch.
8. Remove viscous fan coupling securing bolt, then fan coupling with belt pulley.
9. Remove torque rod bracket bolts.
10. Using suitable cutting tool, cut starter wiring retainer cable ties.
11. Remove support between sump and intake manifold.
12. Disconnect left upper engine mounting.
13. Mark installation position of threaded connection and lower locating sleeve on lefthand and righthand engine mountings.
14. Slide lock carrier to rear, then bolt top on.
15. Attach engine support bracket tool No. 10–222A or equivalent.
16. Support engine at front lifting eyelet with lifting device.
17. Lift engine with spindle of lifting device until air hose to throttle valve part touches bulkhead.
18. Take out left engine mounting.
19. Support subframe with workshop crane.
20. First remove front subframe bolts from

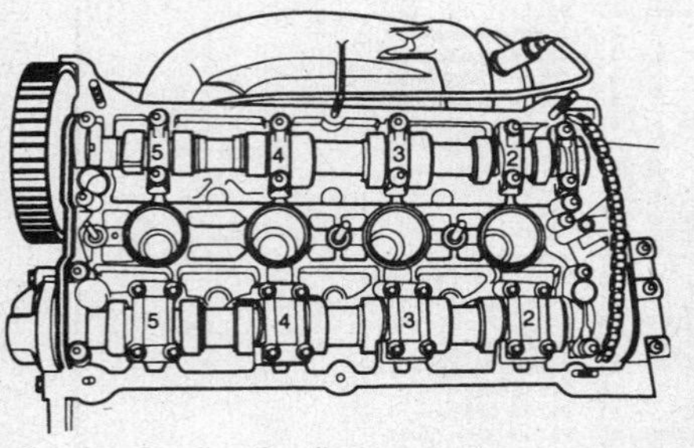

VW1069900096000X

Fig. 15 Camshaft bearing loosening sequence

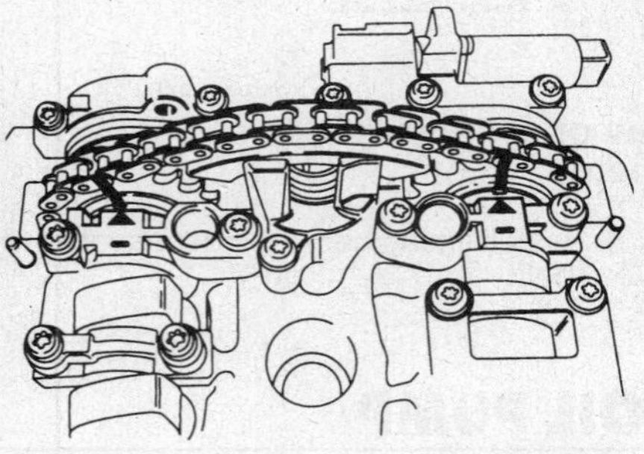

VW1069900097000X

Fig. 16 Camshaft alignment marks

lefthand and righthand sides, then remove rear bolt. To avoid measuring wheel alignment, subframe must only be loosened or lowered at front end.

21. Loosen rear right gearbox mounting rear bolt several turns then remove right gearbox mounting front bolt.
22. Loosen nut for lefthand gearbox mounting until it aligns with the lower edge of bolt.
23. Lower subframe slowly with workshop crane.
24. Remove workshop crane, then swing anti-roll bar down.
25. Remove oil pump. It may be necessary to tap on oil pump using a suitable rubber hammer.
26. Reverse procedure to install.

SERPENTINE DRIVE BELT

GOLF, GTI, JETTA & NEW BEETLE

1. Mark rotation of drive belt.
2. Move tensioner in direction of arrow to release tension on drive belt, **Fig. 18.**
3. Lock belt tensioner using suitable drift.
4. Remove noise insulation pan, then the serpentine drive belt.
5. Reverse procedure to install.
6. Start engine and inspect belt for proper operation.

PASSAT

1. Put lock carrier into service position.
2. Mark direction of engine rotation on belt.
3. Slacken belt by turning tensioner in direction of arrow.
4. Lock tensioning device with pin tool No. 3204, or equivalent.
5. Remove belt.
6. Reverse procedure to install belt.
7. Start engine and inspect belt for proper operation.

COOLING SYSTEM BLEED

1. After filling cooling system, start engine and maintain an engine speed of about 2000 RPM for approximately three minutes.
2. Allow engine to idle until lower radiator hose becomes hot.
3. Check coolant level and add coolant as necessary. **Engine coolant level in reservoir should be at "Max" mark when warm and at "Min" mark when cold.**

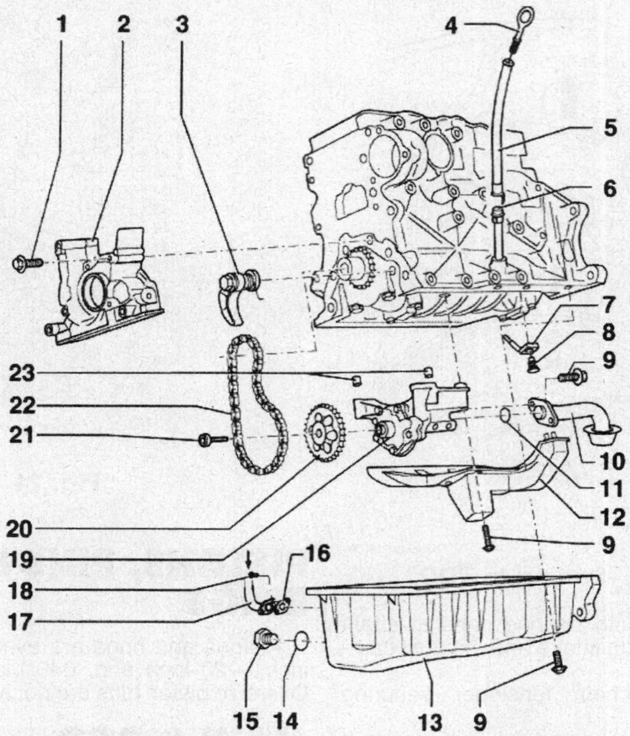

1. Bolt 11 ft. lbs.
2. Sealing Flange
3. Chain Tensioner
4. Dipstick
5. Guide
6. Guide Tube
7. Oil Spray Jet
8. Pressure Relief Valve 20 ft. lbs.
9. Bolt 11 ft. lbs.
12. Baffle Plate
13. Sump
14. Seal
15. Oil Drain Plug 22 ft. lbs.
16. Gasket
17. Oil Return Pipe
18. Bolt 84 inch lbs.
19. Oil Pump
20. Chain Sprocket
21. Bolt 18 ft. lbs.
22. Chain
23. Dowels

VW1060100126000X

Fig. 17 Oil pump removal. Golf, GTI, Jetta & New Beetle

WATER PUMP

REPLACE

GOLF, GTI, JETTA & NEW BEETLE

1. Drain coolant into suitable container, then remove serpentine drive belt.
2. Remove upper and middle timing belt guard.
3. Remove timing belt from water pump sprocket as outlined under "Timing Belt, Replace.".
4. Remove water pump bolts, then the water pump.
5. Reverse procedure to install.

PASSAT

1. Refer to **Figs. 19 and 20** when removing or installing water pump.
2. Tighten water pump assembly bracket to cylinder block in lettered sequence, **Fig. 21.**

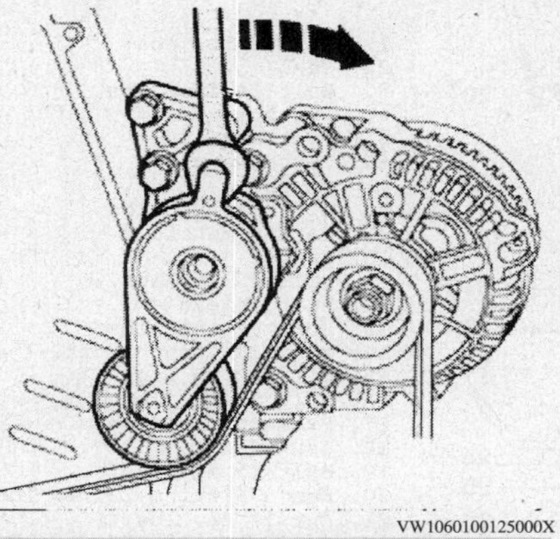

Fig. 18 Serpentine drive belt removal. Golf, GTI, Jetta & New Beetle

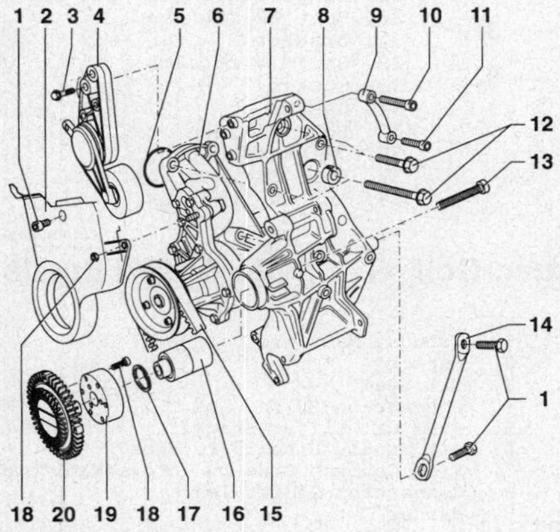

1. Bolt
2. Belt Guard
3. Bolt
4. Belt Tensioner
5. O-ring
6. Coolant Pump
7. Assembly Bracket
8. Bushing
9. Bolt
10. Bolt
11. Bolt
12. Bolt
13. Bolt
14. Assembly Bracket Support
15. V-Belt
16. Bushing
17. Circlip
18. Bolt
19. Belt Pulley
20. Viscous Fan Coupling

VW1089900011000X

Fig. 21 Assembly bracket tightening sequence. Passat

RADIATOR

REPLACE

GOLF, GTI & JETTA

1. Drain coolant into suitable container, then remove front bumper.
2. Remove radiator hoses from radiator.
3. Disconnect electrical connector from thermal switch.
4. Remove bowden cable on lock.
5. Remove one bolt from each longitudi-

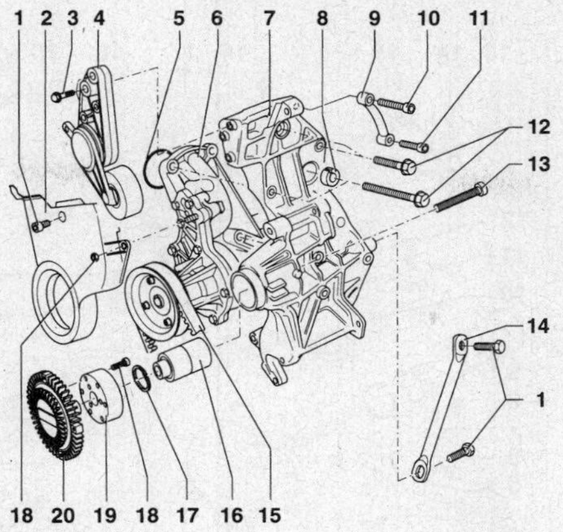

1. Bolt
2. Belt Guard
3. Bolt
4. Belt Tensioner
5. O-ring
6. Coolant Pump
7. Assembly Bracket
8. Bushing
9. Bolt
10. Bolt
11. Bolt
12. Bolt
13. Bolt
14. Assembly Bracket Support
15. V-Belt
16. Bushing
17. Circlip
18. Bolt
19. Belt Pulley
20. Viscous Fan Coupling

VW1089900010000X

Fig. 19 Water pump & bracket removal. Passat

nal member, then install guide rods, tool No. 3411, or equivalent, **Fig. 22.**

6. **On models equipped with A/C,** remove condenser from radiator and secure to lock carrier.
7. **On all models,** remove radiator bolts, then the radiator.
8. Reverse procedure to install.

NEW BEETLE

1. Drain coolant into suitable container, then remove front bumper.
2. Remove radiator hoses from radiator.
3. Disconnect thermo switch and radiator fan electrical connectors.
4. Remove tensioning element for serpentine drive belt.
5. **On models equipped with A/C,** remove condenser from radiator and secure to lock carrier.
6. **On all models,** remove radiator bolts, then the radiator.
7. Reverse procedure to install.

PASSAT

1. Drain engine coolant into a suitable container.
2. Remove front bumper.
3. Remove upper and lower radiator hoses.
4. Disconnect thermo switch harness connector.
5. **On models equipped with automatic transaxle,** disconnect transaxle fluid lines from radiator.

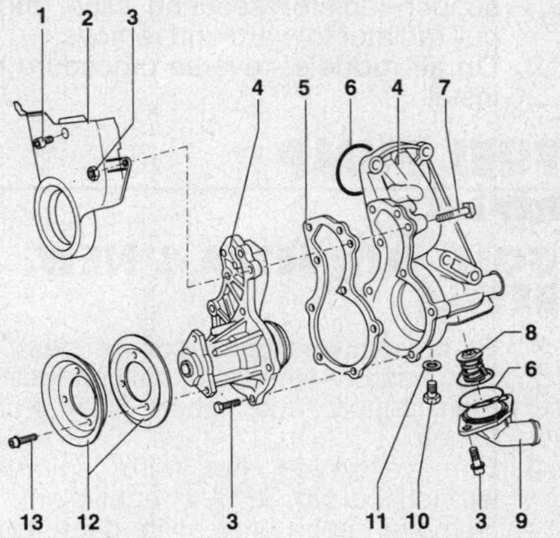

1. Bolt
2. Belt Guard
3. Nut
4. Coolant Pump
5. Gasket
6. O-ring
7. Hammer Head Bolt
8. Thermostat
9. Connecting Pipe
10. Drain Plug
11. Oil Seal
12. Belt Bulley
13. Bolt

VW1089900012000X

Fig. 20 Exploded view of water pump. Passat

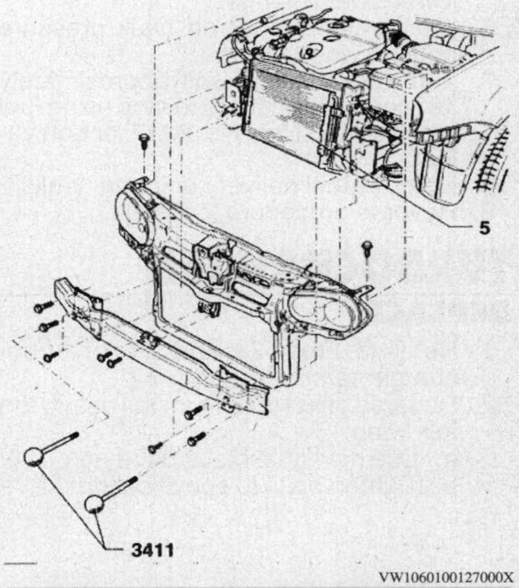

Fig. 22 Lock carrier in service position. Golf, GTI & Jetta

6. **On all models,** disconnect power steering hydraulic oil cooling pipe bracket.
7. **On models equipped with A/C,** proceed as follows:
   a. Remove retaining clamps from refrigerant lines.
   b. Remove condenser from radiator and pull forward as far as possible.
   c. Secure condenser to body so refrigerant lines are not stressed.
   d. Pull radiator out between condenser and lock carrier.
8. **On models less A/C,** disconnect

supper radiator securing clips, then pull radiator forward and remove.

9. **On all models,** reverse procedure to install.

FUEL PUMP

REPLACE

GOLF, GTI, JETTA & NEW BEETLE

1. Remove cover from under rear seat.
2. Disconnect 4–pin electrical connector, then supply and return lines from flange.
3. Remove union nut with spanner wrench tool No. 3217, or equivalent.
4. Remove fuel pump with seal from opening in fuel tank.
5. Reverse procedure to install ensuring mark on flange is aligned with mark on fuel tank.

PASSAT

1. Pull back cover from trunk floor and remove floor cover.
2. Disconnect 4–pin electrical connector, then supply and return lines from flange.
3. Remove union nut with spanner wrench tool No. 3217, or equivalent.
4. Pull flange and seal out of opening in fuel tank.
5. Pull fuel lines and connector from lower side of flange.
6. Unclip fuel sender on back pressure housing and remove.
7. Turn fuel delivery unit approximately 15° counterclockwise to stop using fuel pump wrench tool No. 3217, or equivalent.
8. Remove fuel delivery unit from tank.
9. Reverse procedure to install.

TURBOCHARGER

REPLACE

1. Refer to **Figs. 23 and 24** for turbocharger removal.
2. Reverse procedure to install noting the following:
   a. Use new gaskets and O-rings.
   b. Tighten bolts to specifications.

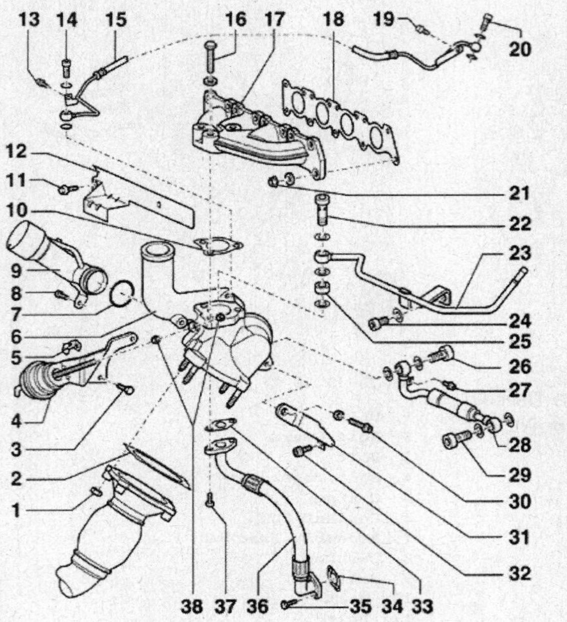

1. Nut 30 ft. lbs.
2. Seal
3. Bolt 84 inch lbs.
4. Pressure Unit
5. Locking Clip
6. Turbocharger
7. O-ring
8. Bolt 84 inch lbs.
9. Intake Manifold
10. Gasket
11. Bolt 15 ft. lbs.
12. Heat Shield
13. Bolt 84 inch lbs.
14. Banjo Fitting 22 ft. lbs.
15. Oil Supply Line
16. Bolt 22 ft. lbs.
17. Exhaust Manifold
18. Gasket
19. Bolt 15 ft. lbs.
20. Banjo Fitting 22 ft. lbs.
21. Nut 18 ft. lbs.
22. Banjo Fitting 26 ft. lbs.
23. Coolant Return Line
24. Bolt 18 ft. lbs.
25. Spacer Sleeve
26. Banjo Fitting 26 ft. lbs.
27. Bolt 84 inch lbs.
28. Coolant Supply Line
29. Banjo Fitting 26 ft. lbs.
30. Bolt 22 ft. lbs.
31. Bracket
32. Bolt 18 ft. lbs.
33. Gasket
34. Gasket
35. Bolt 84 inch lbs.
36. Oil Return Line
37. Bolt 84 inch lbs.
38. Nut 84 inch lbs.

VW1060100128000X

Fig. 23 Exploded view of turbocharger. Golf, GTI, Jetta & New Beetle

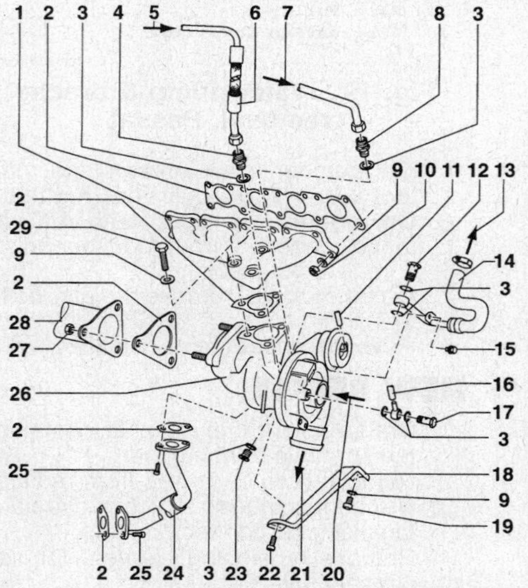

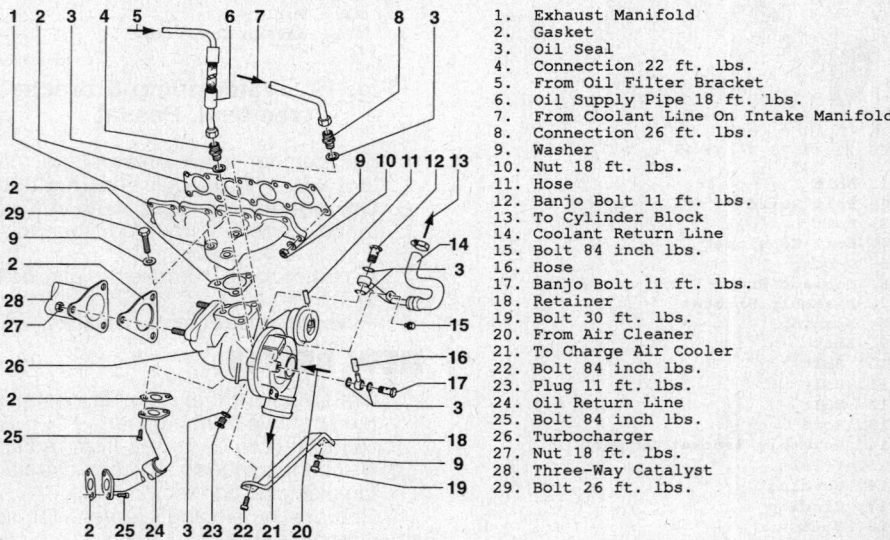

1. Exhaust Manifold
2. Gasket
3. Oil Seal
4. Connection 22 ft. lbs.
5. From Oil Filter Bracket
6. Oil Supply Pipe 18 ft. lbs.
7. From Coolant Line On Intake Manifold
8. Connection 26 ft. lbs.
9. Washer
10. Nut 18 ft. lbs.
11. Hose
12. Banjo Bolt 11 ft. lbs.
13. To Cylinder Block
14. Coolant Return Line
15. Bolt 84 inch lbs.
16. Hose
17. Banjo Bolt 11 ft. lbs.
18. Retainer
19. Bolt 30 ft. lbs.
20. From Air Cleaner
21. To Charge Air Cooler
22. Bolt 84 inch lbs.
23. Plug 11 ft. lbs.
24. Oil Return Line
25. Bolt 84 inch lbs.
26. Turbocharger
27. Nut 18 ft. lbs.
28. Three-Way Catalyst
29. Bolt 26 ft. lbs.

VW1060100129000X

Fig. 24 Exploded view of turbocharger. Passat

TIGHTENING SPECIFICATIONS

Year	Component	Torque, Ft. Lbs.
1998–2001	Accessory Drive Belt Tensioner Bolt	18
	Assembly Bracket (Alternator & Power Steering Pump)	22
	Camshaft Bearing Caps	84②
	Camshaft Position Sensor	84②
	Camshaft Sprocket	74
	Chain Tensioner	84②
	Compact Bracket To Cylinder Block	22
	Crankshaft Pulley Bolts	18
	Crankshaft Sprocket	74
	Cylinder Head Bolts	①
	Driveplate	30③
	Engine Mounting To Engine Support	18
	Engine Mounting To Sub-Frame	18
	Engine Speed Sensor Sender Wheel	84②③
	Exhaust Manifold	18
	Exhaust Pipe To Turbocharger	30
	Flywheel	30③
	Intake Manifold Bracket	18
	Intermediate Plate Nut	84②
	Intermediate Shaft Sprocket	59
	Knock Sensor	15
	Lefthand Engine Bracket	22
	Main Bearing Cap	48③
	Oil Cooler Nut	18
	Oil Pan	11
	Oil Pan Drain Plug	22
	Oil Pump Cover	18
	Oil Return Pipe From Turbocharger	84②
	Oxygen Sensor	37
	Pressure Relief Valve	20
	Rear Timing Belt Cover	15
	Righthand Engine Bracket	22
	Rod Bearing Cap	22③
	Sealing Flange	18
	Support Bracket (Turbocharger & Cylinder Block)	22
	Tensioner Mounting Bolt	18
	Timing Belt Cover	15
	Timing Belt Tensioner	84②
	Torque Rod Bracket To Engine	18
	Transaxle Mount To Sub-Frame	18
	Transaxle Support To Transaxle Mount	30
	Turbocharger To Exhaust Manifold	22
	Union Nut	44
	Valve Cover	84②
	Viscous Fan Coupling	33
	Water Pump	84②
	Water Pump Pulley	18

① — Refer to "Cylinder Head, Replace" for tightening specification.
② — Inch lbs.
③ — Plus an additional 90.°

1.9L Turbocharged Direct Injection (TDI) Diesel Engine

NOTE: On Air Bag Equipped Models, Refer To "Air Bag System Precautions" Located In The Front Of This Manual For System Disarming & Arming Procedures.

NOTE: Refer To "Computer Relearn Procedures" Located In The Front Of This Manual When Battery Power To The Computer Has Been Interrupted.

INDEX

	Page No.
Camshaft, Replace	8-33
Compression Pressure	8-26
Cooling System Bleed	8-33
Crankshaft Rear Oil Seal, Replace	8-33
Cylinder Head, Replace	8-27
New Beetle	8-27
Passat & 1998 Jetta	8-28
1999–2001 Golf & Jetta	8-27
Engine Mount, Replace	8-27
Engine Rebuilding Specifications	8-185
Engine, Replace	8-27
Front Main Bearing Oil Seal, Replace	8-33
Fuel Filter, Replace	8-35
Golf, Jetta & New Beetle	8-35
Passat	8-35
Glow Plug System	8-37
Testing	8-37
Hydraulic Lifter Inspection	8-28
Hydraulic Lifter, Replace	8-28
Idle Speed, Adjust	8-36
Injection Pump, Replace	8-34
New Beetle, Passat & 1999–2001 Golf & Jetta	8-35
1998 Jetta	8-34
Injection Pump Timing	8-35
New Beetle, Passat & 1999–2001 Golf & Jetta	8-36
1998 Jetta	8-35
Main & Rod Bearings	8-33
Oil Pan, Replace	8-33
Oil Pump, Replace	8-33
Oil Pump Service	8-33
Piston & Rod Assembly	8-33
Precautions	8-26
Air Bag Systems	8-26
Audio Coded Anti-Theft System	8-26
Battery Ground Cable	8-26
Radiator, Replace	8-34
Tightening Specifications	8-37
Timing Belt, Replace	8-29
New Beetle	8-31
Passat	8-32
1998 Jetta	8-29
1999–2001 Golf & Jetta	8-29
Turbocharger, Replace	8-34
Valve Adjustment	8-28
Valve Clearance Specifications	8-28
Valve Guides	8-28
Inspection	8-28
Replacement	8-28
Water Pump, Replace	8-34

PRECAUTIONS

AIR BAG SYSTEMS

Do not use computer memory saver tool on air bag equipped models. Using the tool will keep the air bag system charged and may cause accidental activation of the air bag unit. Refer to "Air Bag System Precautions" in the front of this manual for system disarming and arming procedures.

BATTERY GROUND CABLE

Prior to disconnecting the battery negative cable, obtain the radio security code. After service has been completed and the battery negative cable has been reconnected, use security code to activate the radio. Prior to service, disconnect battery ground cable and isolate as required.

AUDIO CODED ANTI-THEFT SYSTEM

Some models are equipped with a radio anti-theft system that will disable the system when battery power is interrupted, unless the system is reset the radio will not operate.

1. Turn radio to On position, SAFE and 1000 should be displayed.

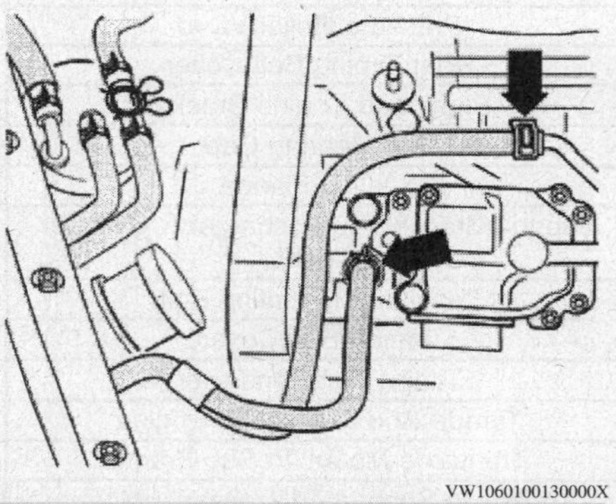

Fig. 1 Injection pump fuel lines. New Beetle & 1999–2001 Golf & Jetta

2. Enter radio code using first four program station buttons. Security code will appear on display.
3. Depress and hold righthand side of radio right or left blocker until anti-theft coding is activated indicated by a brief signal sound.
4. If code number has been entered correctly, when ignition key is removed a diode on front of radio will flash.

COMPRESSION PRESSURE

1. Perform compression test with engine oil temperature at least 86°.
2. Disconnect fuel cut-off valve and quantity adjuster electrical connector on injection pump.
3. Disconnect glow plug electrical connectors.
4. Remove glow plugs using flexible wrench tool No. 3220, or equivalent.
5. Install adapter tool No. VAG 1381/12, or equivalent in place of glow plugs.
6. Check compression using compression tester tool No. VAG 1763, or equivalent.
7. Operate starter until display on tester shows no further increase in pressure.
8. Correct compression should be 362.5–449.5 psi with a maximum difference between highest and lowest cylinder of 72.5 psi. Minimum compression is 275.5 psi.
9. Remove compression tester and adapters, then install glow plugs tightening to specifications.
10. Connect quantity adjuster electrical

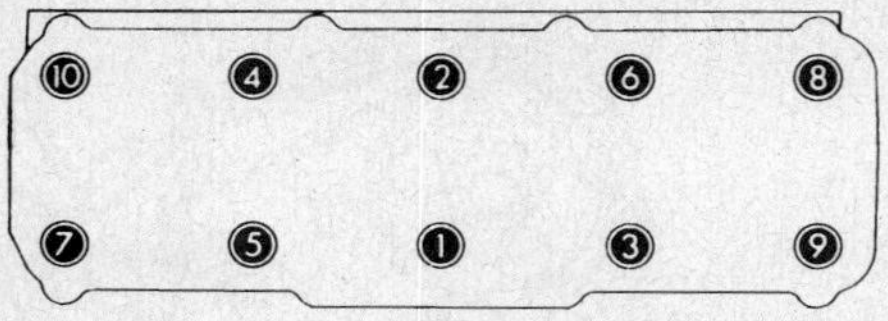

Fig. 2 Cylinder head bolt tightening sequence

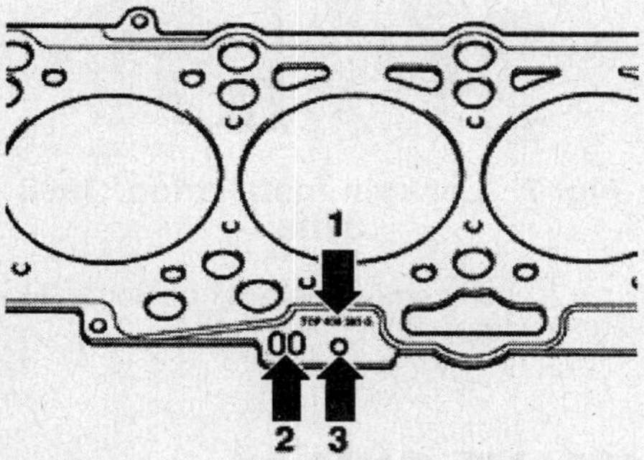

Fig. 3 Cylinder head gasket identification. New Beetle & 1999–2001 Golf & Jetta

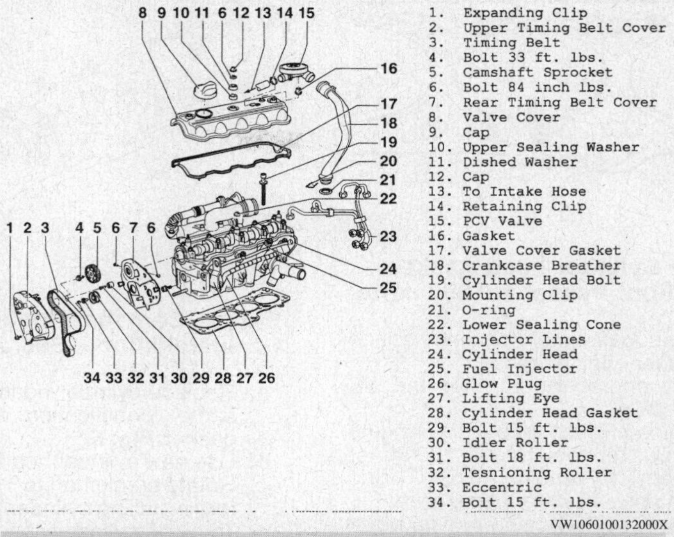

Fig. 4 Cylinder head removal. Passat & 1998 Jetta

connector, then the fuel cut-off valve.

11. Clear any stored DTCs due to injection pump harness being disconnected.

ENGINE MOUNT

REPLACE

Refer to "2.0L Gasoline Engine" section for replacement procedures.

ENGINE

REPLACE

Refer to "2.0L Gasoline Engine" section for replacement procedures.

CYLINDER HEAD

REPLACE

1999–2001 GOLF & JETTA

1. Ensure no pistons are at TDC.
2. Remove engine cover, then the air cleaner.
3. Drain coolant into suitable container, then remove refrigerant hoses at cylinder head using suitable spring clamp pliers.
4. Remove serpentine drive belt, then the front exhaust pipe with catalytic converter.
5. Disconnect fuel pressure and return lines at fuel injection pump, **Fig. 1.**
6. Disconnect vacuum and ventilation lines from cylinder head.
7. Disconnect glow plug connectors.
8. Disconnect electrical connectors from cylinder head and position aside.
9. Remove oil pressure and oil return line for turbocharger and cylinder head.
10. Remove fuel injectors lines using wrench tool No. 3035, or equivalent.
11. Remove brake booster vacuum pump, then the timing belt upper cover.
12. Remove valve cover, then the timing belt from camshaft sprocket as outlined under "Timing Belt, Replace."
13. Slightly rotate crankshaft counterclockwise
14. Loosen center bolt on camshaft sprocket one turn using holding tool No. 3036, or equivalent.
15. Remove camshaft sprocket and tensioner using two arm puller tool No. T40001, or equivalent.
16. Remove belt cover bolts at rear of cylinder head.
17. Loosen and remove cylinder head bolts in reverse order of tightening sequence, **Fig. 2.**
18. Carefully remove cylinder guiding bolt for tensioner through rear of belt cover.
19. Reverse procedure to install noting the following:
    a. Replace cylinder head gasket with same identification as removed gasket, **Fig. 3.**
    b. Use new cylinder head bolts.
    c. Rotate crankshaft to TDC mark before installing cylinder head.
    d. To aid in cylinder head and gasket alignment install threaded guide pins tool No. 3079/9 into outer holes on injection pump side.
    e. Install cylinder head, then thread in eight remaining head bolts tightening by hand.
    f. Remove guide pins using removal tool No. 3070, or equivalent, then install two remaining cylinder head bolts.
    g. Using tightening sequence, **Fig. 2, torque** cylinder head bolts in four steps as follows: first, to 30 ft. lbs.; second, to 44 ft. lbs.; third, tighten an additional 90°; and finally, tighten an additional 90.°

NEW BEETLE

1. Ensure no pistons are at TDC.
2. Remove engine cover, then the air cleaner.
3. Remove connecting pipe between charge air cooler and intake manifold/EGR vacuum regulator solenoid valve.
4. Remove sound dampening tray, then drain coolant into suitable container.
5. Disconnect fuel supply and return lines at fuel filter, **Fig. 1.**
6. Remove front exhaust pipe, then the serpentine drive belt.
7. Remove wiper arms.
8. Pull center dash panel cover forward and remove.
9. Lift and remove both dash panel plenum covers.
10. Remove close out panel bolts, then the close out panels from dash panel.
11. Remove fuel filter with bracket.
12. Disconnect all coolant, vacuum and breather hoses from engine.
13. Disconnect electrical connectors from alternator, starter and transaxle, then position aside.
14. Remove coolant reservoir bolt, then position reservoir aside.
15. Remove upper timing belt cover, then the valve cover.
16. Remove brake booster vacuum pump.
17. Disconnect turbocharger oil return line at cylinder block.
18. Disconnect oil supply line at turbocharger.
19. Remove injection lines as a set using offset tubing wrench tool No. 3035, or equivalent.
20. Remove return line from injector jets/injection pump.
21. Remove glow plug harness connector.
22. Install engine support bracket tool No. 10–222A with legs tool No. 10–222A/1, or equivalents.

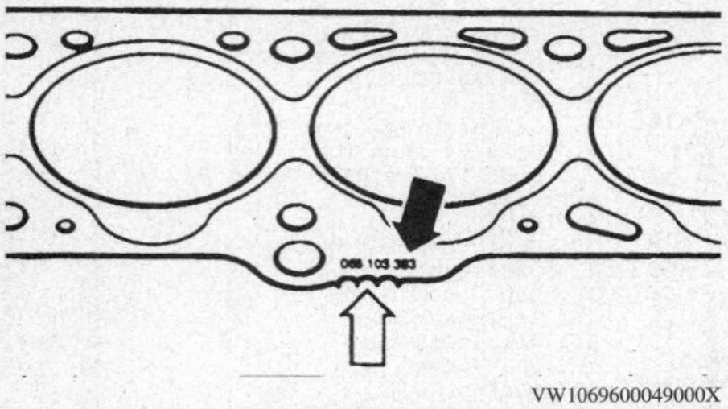

Fig. 5 Cylinder head gasket identification. Passat & 1998 Jetta

23. Loosen subassembly on engine side from upper engine bracket.
24. Remove engine mount, then the engine bracket.
25. Lift engine slightly, then install engine lifting bracket tool No. T 10014, or equivalent to engine block using threaded hole in water pump area.
26. Lift engine slightly using engine block lifting bracket to relieve tension on cylinder head lifting rod, then remove rod.
27. Position engine at TDC with camshaft sprocket loosened and timing belt removed from camshaft sprocket.
28. Remove tension roller, then the camshaft sprocket.
29. Remove upper timing belt cover rear bolt.
30. Remove cylinder head bolts in reverse order of tightening sequence, **Fig. 2.**
31. Carefully remove cylinder head from engine.
32. Reverse procedure to install noting the following:
    a. Replace cylinder head gasket with same identification as removed gasket, **Fig. 3.**
    b. Use new cylinder head bolts.
    c. Rotate crankshaft to TDC mark before installing cylinder head.
    d. To aid in cylinder head and gasket alignment install threaded guide pins tool No. 3079/9 into outer holes on injection pump side.
    e. Install cylinder head, then thread in eight remaining head bolts tightening by hand.
    f. Remove guide pins using removal tool No. 3070, or equivalent, then install two remaining cylinder head bolts.
    g. Using tightening sequence, **Fig. 2, torque** cylinder head bolts in four steps as follows: first, to 30 ft. lbs.; second, to 44 ft. lbs.; third, tighten an additional 90°; and finally, tighten an additional 90.°

PASSAT & 1998 JETTA

1. Refer to **Fig. 4** for cylinder head removal noting the following:
    a. Drive off camshaft taper using suitable hammer and drift through timing belt cover openings.
    b. Remove injector lines using wrench tool No. 3035, or equivalent.
    c. Remove cylinder head bolts in reverse order of tightening sequence, **Fig. 2.**
2. Reverse procedure to install noting the following:

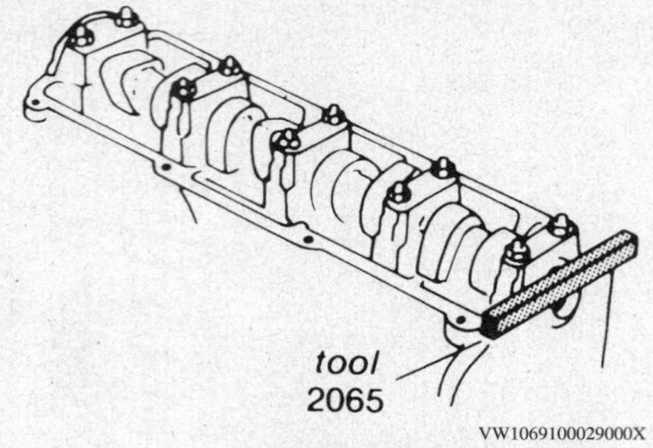

Fig. 6 Camshaft locking tool installation. 1998 Jetta

    a. Replace cylinder head gasket with same identification as removed gasket, **Fig. 5.**
    b. Use new cylinder head bolts.
    c. Rotate crankshaft to TDC mark before installing cylinder head.
    d. To aid in cylinder head and gasket alignment install threaded guide pins tool No. 3079/9 into outer holes on injection pump side.
    e. Install cylinder head, then thread in eight remaining head bolts tightening by hand.
    f. Remove guide pins using removal tool No. 3070, or equivalent, then install two remaining cylinder head bolts.
    g. Using tightening sequence, **Fig. 2, torque** cylinder head bolts in four steps as follows: first, to 30 ft. lbs.; second, to 44 ft. lbs.; third, tighten an additional 90°; and finally, tighten an additional 90.°

VALVE CLEARANCE SPECIFICATIONS

These engines are equipped with hydraulic lifters. No procedure for adjustment is provided.

VALVE ADJUSTMENT

These engines are equipped with hydraulic lifters. No procedure for adjustment is provided.

HYDRAULIC LIFTER INSPECTION

Hydraulic valve lifters are non-adjustable. Noisy lifters may be replaced after the following check.

1. Run engine until radiator fan comes on at least once.
2. Raise engine speed to 2500 RPM, for two minutes.
3. If lifter(s) is still noisy, proceed as follows:
    a. Remove cylinder head cover.
    b. Turn crankshaft pulley bolt clockwise until cam lobes of cylinder to be checked, point upward.
    c. Press down lightly against valve lifter with a wooden stick. If lifter can be pushed down more than. 004 inch, replace as outlined under "Hydraulic Lifter, Replace."

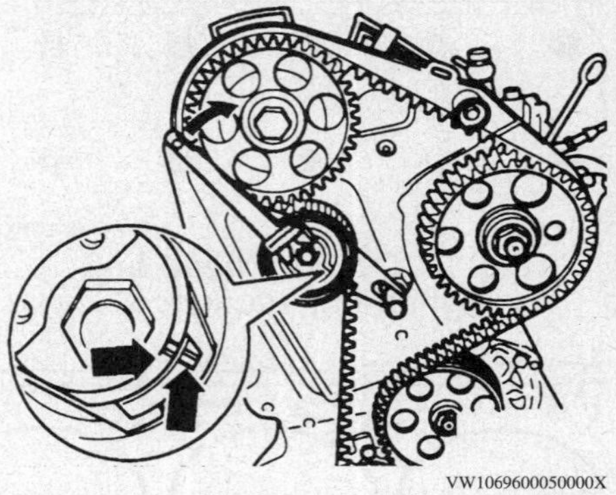

Fig. 7 Lockpin installation. 1998 Jetta

VALVE GUIDES

INSPECTION

1. Remove all carbon deposits from valve guide.
2. Set up a dial indicator on cylinder head to check suspected guide.
3. Insert new valve into valve guide. End of valve stem must be flush with valve guide end.
4. Rock valve back and forth against dial indicator.
5. Maximum is. 051 inch for all valves. Replace guide(s) if reading is beyond limit.

REPLACEMENT

1. Worn valve guides can be removed using drift tool No. 3121, or equivalent.
2. Press guides with collar out from combustion chamber side of cylinder head and worn guides out from camshaft side of cylinder head.
3. Coat new guides with engine oil, then press into cold cylinder head from camshaft side.
4. Press guides in as far as they will go. Once valve guide shoulder is seated, do not use more than one ton of pressure, or guide shoulder may break. Ream guides by hand using reamer tool No. 3120, or equivalent, and a proper cutting lubricant.
5. Machine valve seats.

HYDRAULIC LIFTER

REPLACE

After replacing hydraulic lifters, do not run engine for 30 minutes. This will allow lifters time to bleed down to proper adjustment.

1. Remove camshaft as outlined under "Camshaft, Replace."
2. Replace defective lifter.
3. Install camshaft as outlined under "Camshaft, Replace."

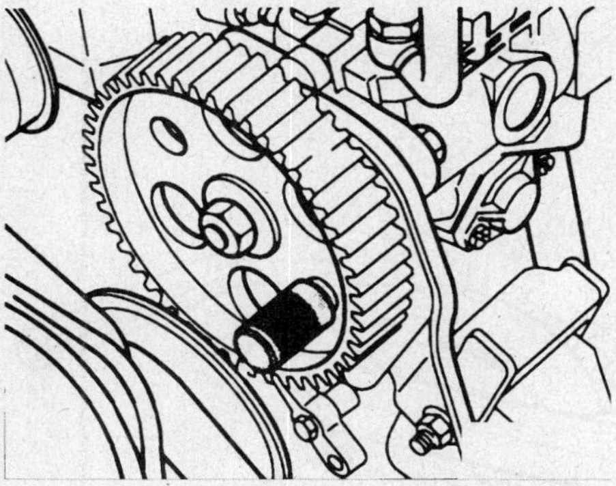

VW1069600051000X

Fig. 8 Timing belt tensioning. 1998 Jetta

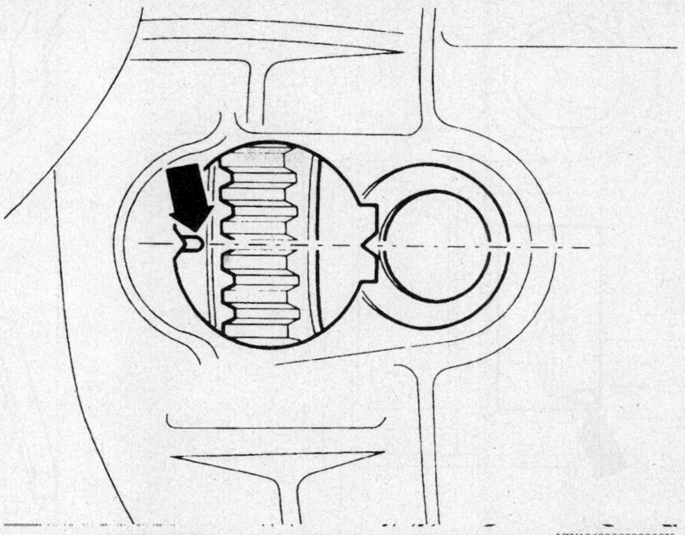

VW1069900088000X

Fig. 9 M/T flywheel timing mark alignment. New Beetle, Passat & 1999–2001 Golf & Jetta

TIMING BELT

REPLACE

1998 JETTA

This procedure has been revised by a Technical Service Bulletin.

The timing belt and tensioner must be replaced at 60,000 mile intervals.

With the timing belt removed, avoid turning the camshaft or crankshaft. If movement is required, exercise extreme caution to avoid valve damage caused by piston contact.

1. Remove drive belts to allow access to crankshaft pulley.
2. Remove upper timing belt cover, then the cylinder head cover.
3. **Do not rotate engine opposite normal direction of rotation (counterclockwise) using crankshaft center bolt, as torque setting may be disturbed allowing sprocket to loosen.**
4. Rotate crankshaft until cylinder No. 1 is at TDC compression stroke, then lock camshaft using setting bar tool No. 2065A, or equivalent, **Fig. 6,** on rear of camshaft. Align setting bar as follows:
   a. Turn camshaft until one end of setting bar touches cylinder head.
   b. Measure gap at other end of setting bar with a feeler gauge.
   c. Take half of measurement and insert a shim of this thickness between setting bar and cylinder head.
   d. Turn camshaft so that setting bar rests on shim.
   e. Insert a second shim of same thickness between other end of setting bar and cylinder head.
5. Insert locking pin No. 2064, or equivalent, into injector pump sprocket, **Fig. 7.** Ensure marks on sprocket, pump and bracket are properly aligned. Refer to "Injection Pump Timing."
6. Remove water pump pulley and crankshaft pulley. Note position of offset bolt hole for crankshaft pulley mounting to crankshaft sprocket.
7. Remove lower timing belt covers, then, if equipped, any timing belt guides.
8. Loosen timing belt tensioner and remove belt. **Do not rotate camshaft or crankshaft with belt removed, as engine damage will result.**
9. Prior to installation, ensure all timing marks are properly aligned and injection pump mounting bolts are centered in elongated holes of mounting bracket.
10. Loosen camshaft sprocket retaining bolt ½ turn and loosen sprocket on taper shaft by tapping with a hammer.
11. Install timing belt, tighten camshaft sprocket retaining bolt to specifications, then remove camshaft locking bar.
12. Remove locking pin from injection pump sprocket.
13. Adjust belt tension by turning tensioner until marks are aligned, **Fig. 8,** then tighten retaining nut to specifications.
14. Ensure injection pump timing is within specifications as outlined under "Injection Pump Timing," then reverse procedure to complete installation.

1999–2001 GOLF & JETTA

Avoid turning the camshaft or crankshaft when the timing belt has been removed. If movement is required, use extreme caution to avoid valve damage from piston contact.

Removal

1. Remove upper engine cover.
2. Remove fuel supply and return lines from fuel filter. Plug lines to prevent dirt entry.
3. Remove righthand headlamp assembly.
4. Remove charge air cooler to intake manifold connecting pipe.
5. Remove righthand sound damper cover.
6. Mark engine accessory drive belt's running direction.
7. Using a suitable 16 mm box wrench, rotate accessory drive belt tensioner clockwise.
8. **On models less A/C,** start removing drive belt at alternator, then proceed from there.
9. **On models equipped with A/C,** start removing drive belt at idler pulley, then proceed from there.
10. **On all models,** remove engine accessory drive belt tensioner mounting fasteners, then tensioner.
11. Remove brake booster vacuum pump.
12. Remove timing belt upper cover.
13. Remove all connectors, hoses and tubing from valve cover.
14. Remove valve cover bolts, then the cover.
15. Rotate engine in normal running direction until M/T flywheel or A/T flexplate timing marks are properly aligned, **Figs. 9 and 10.**
16. Lock camshaft in place using VW setting bar tool No. 3418, or equivalent, **Fig. 11,** then ensure setting bar is centered as follows:
    a. Rotate camshaft so that one end of setting bar contacts cylinder head.
    b. Measure gap at setting bar's opposite end with a suitable feeler gauge.
    c. Insert a feeler gauge of ½ of gap between setting bar and head.
    d. Rotate camshaft until setting bar contacts feeler gauge.
    e. Insert a second feeler gauge of same thickness at other end between setting bar and head.
17. Lock injection pump sprocket into place using VW pin tool No. 3359, or equivalent, **Fig. 12.**
18. Loosen injection pump sprocket bolts, **Fig. 12. Do not loosen hub nut, as pump basic setting will be altered and special equipment will be required to reset pump.**
19. Install VW engine support tool No. 10-222A with legs tool No. 10-222A/1, or their equivalents.
20. Position coolant expansion tank aside, but leave hoses intact.

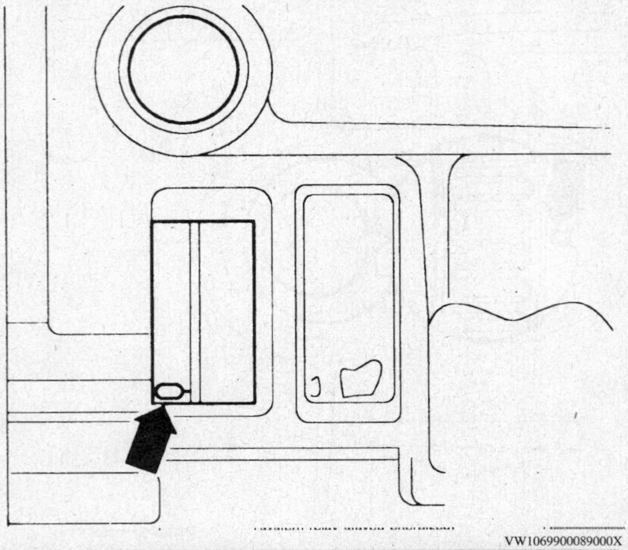

Fig. 10 A/T flexplate timing mark alignment. New Beetle, Passat & 1999–2001 Golf & Jetta

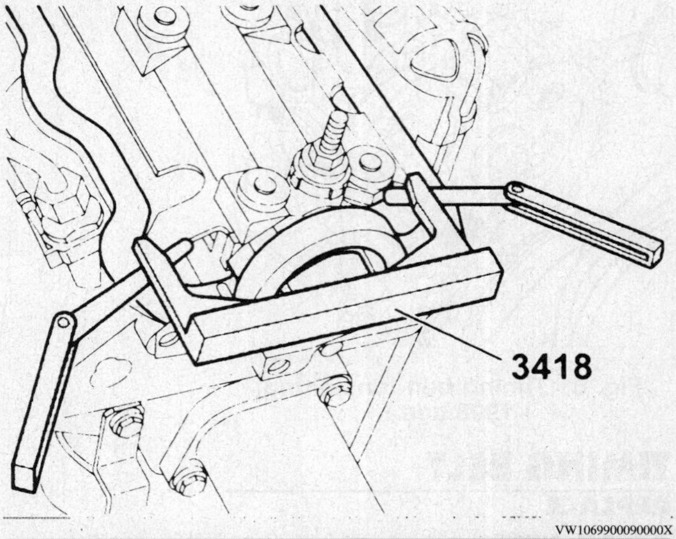

Fig. 11 Camshaft locked into place. New Beetle, Passat & 1999–2001 Golf & Jetta

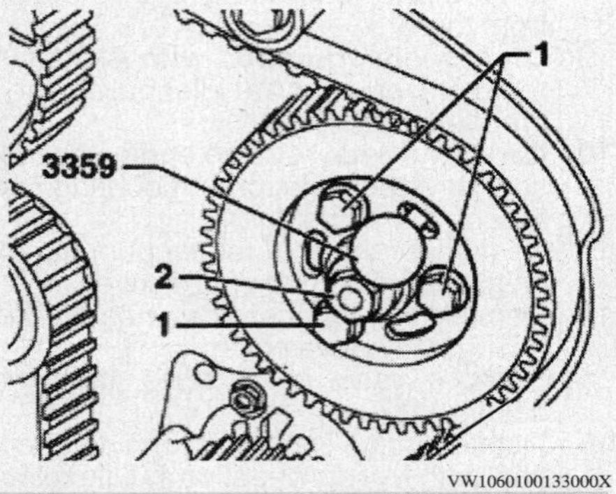

Fig. 12 Injection pump locked into place

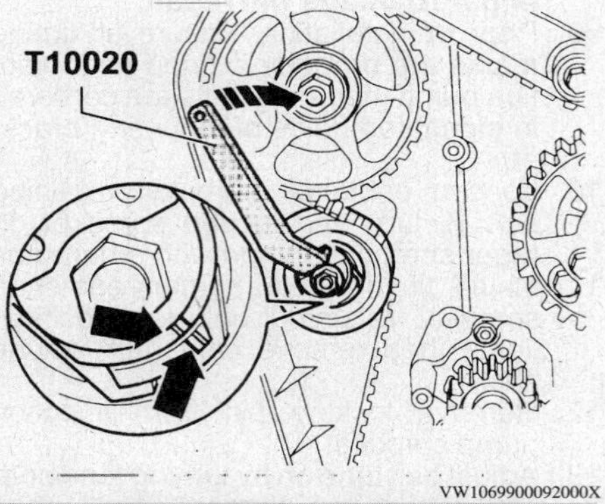

Fig. 13 Adjusting tensioner. 1999–2001 Golf & Jetta w/manual transaxle

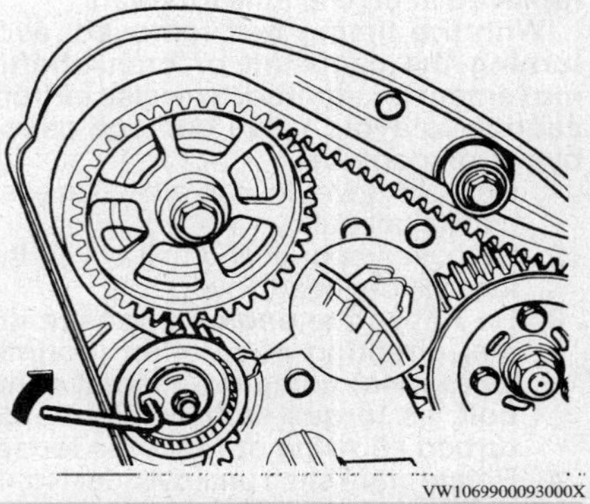

Fig. 14 Adjusting tensioner. 1999–2001 Golf & Jetta w/automatic transaxle

21. Position power steering fluid reservoir aside, but leave hoses intact.
22. Remove six side engine support mounting bolts, then the mount.
23. Remove crankshaft pulley retaining bolts, then the pulley.
24. Remove timing belt center and lower covers.
25. Remove three engine mount bracket bolts, then the bracket.
26. Release tension on the timing belt, then remove belt.

Installation

1. Inspect water pump and all nearby seals for leakage or damage. Replace as required.
2. Ensure flywheel or flexplate timing marks are still properly aligned.
3. Hold camshaft sprocket in position using holding tool No. 3036, or equivalent, loosen camshaft sprocket bolt one turn.
4. Remove camshaft sprocket using VW puller 40001, or equivalent. Use a suitable open end wrench to counter hold puller when removing camshaft sprocket.
5. Install new timing belt, starting at crankshaft sprocket, onto idler pulley, then around injection pump, water pump and tensioner roller.
6. Adjust injection pump sprocket on mount so that mounting slots are centered.
7. Install camshaft sprocket with timing belt and position with sprocket mounting bolt. Do not fully tighten mounting bolt. Camshaft sprocket should still turn.
8. **On models equipped with manual transaxle,** using VW pin wrench tool No. T10020, or equivalent, rotate tensioner clockwise until notch and raised mark align, **Fig. 13.**
9. **On models equipped with automatic transaxle,** using a suitable hex wrench, rotate tensioner clockwise until notch and pointer align, **Fig. 14.**
10. **On all models,** tighten tensioner roller locknut to specifications. Ensure roller is properly located into timing belt rear cover, **Fig. 15.**
11. Ensure flywheel or flexplate timing marks are still properly aligned.
12. Hold camshaft sprocket in position using holding tool No. 3036, or equivalent, tighten camshaft sprocket bolt to specifications.
13. Install new injection pump sprocket mounting bolts, then tighten to specifications, **Fig. 12. Do not disturb hub nut, as pump basic setting will be altered and special equipment will be required to reset pump.**
14. Remove setting bar tool from camshaft.
15. Remove injection pump locking pin tool.
16. Rotate engine two turns in running direction, then ensure all timing marks align.
17. Install engine mount bolts into bracket holes, then fit bracket to block.

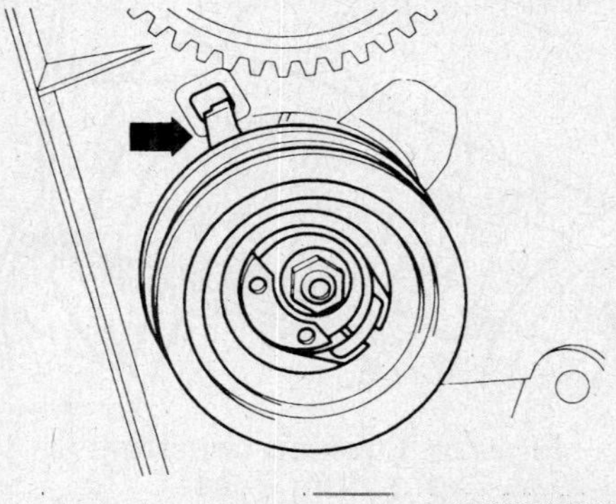

VW1069900094000X

Fig. 15 Tensioner roller installation into belt cover. 1999–2001 Golf & Jetta

18. Install timing belt lower and center covers.
19. Install crankshaft pulley. Tighten bolts to specifications.
20. Install engine mount assembly with new bolts as follows:
    a. Tighten mount to body bolts to specifications, then rotate an additional 90 degrees.
    b. Tighten mount and bracket to body bolt to specifications.
    c. Tighten mount to engine bracket bolt to specifications, then rotate an additional 90 degrees.
21. Install power steering fluid reservoir, then the coolant expansion tank.
22. Install valve cover. Tighten bolts to specifications.
23. Install brake booster vacuum pump.
24. Install engine accessory drive belt tensioner. Tighten bolts to specifications.
25. **On models less A/C,** install engine accessory drive belt, starting at alternator, then proceeding from there.
26. **On models equipped with A/C,** install engine accessory drive belt, starting at idler pulley, then proceeding from there.
27. **On all models,** install righthand sound damper cover.
28. Install charge air cooler to intake manifold connecting pipe.
29. Install righthand headlamp assembly.
30. Connect fuel supply and return lines at fuel filter.
31. Install upper engine cover.
32. Inspect diesel injection pump start of injection as outlined under "Injection Pump Timing."

NEW BEETLE

Avoid turning the camshaft or crankshaft when the timing belt has been removed. If movement is required, use extreme caution to avoid valve damage from piston contact.

Removal

1. Remove tube between charge air cooler and air intake pipe.
2. Disconnect fuel supply and return lines at fuel filter.
3. Remove fuel filter from its bracket.

VW1069500075000X

Fig. 16 Timing belt tension inspection. New Beetle & Passat w/semi-automatic tensioner

4. Remove timing belt upper cover, then the valve cover.
5. Remove brake booster vacuum pump.
6. Remove pipe between charge air cooler and turbocharger.
7. Remove righthand side insulation tray.
8. Mark engine accessory drive belt's running direction.
9. Using a suitable 15 mm box wrench, rotate accessory drive belt tensioner clockwise, then remove accessory drive belt.
10. Remove engine accessory drive belt tensioner mounting fasteners, then the tensioner.
11. Remove timing belt upper cover.
12. Remove PCV valve and valve cover.
13. Rotate crankshaft until No. 1 cylinder is at TDC, **Figs. 9 and 10.**
14. Lock camshaft using VW setting bar tool No. 3418, or equivalent, **Fig. 11.**
15. Rotate camshaft, with locking bar in place, until one end of bar touches cylinder head.
16. Measure gap at other end of setting bar with a feeler gauge.
17. Select a feeler gauge that is half that of measured gap, then temporarily install it between setting bar and cylinder head.
18. Rotate camshaft so setting bar rests against feeler gauge, then insert a feeler gauge of identical halved thickness at other end between setting bar and cylinder head.
19. Lock injection pump sprocket with VW lockpin tool No. 3359, or equivalent, **Fig. 12.**
20. Loosen injection pump sprocket bolts, **Fig. 12. Do not loosen hub nut, as pump basic setting will be altered and special equipment will be required to reset pump.**
21. Loosen timing belt tensioner mounting bolt to release tension on timing belt.
22. Install VW engine support tool No. 10-222A and legs tool No. 10-222A/1, or their equivalents.
23. Ensure engine is securely supported.
24. Remove engine mount attaching bolts, then the mount.
25. Remove vibration damper and crankshaft pulley.
26. Remove timing belt center and lower covers.
27. Remove timing belt.

Installation

1. Ensure timing marks are all properly aligned.
2. Loosen camshaft sprocket mounting bolt ½ turn.
3. Loosen sprocket from camshaft's cone by tapping carefully and lightly with a mandrel through hole in timing belt rear cover.
4. Note timing belt's running direction, then install it, beginning at crankshaft sprocket, next to intermediate pulley, then onto injection pump sprocket, camshaft sprocket and tension roller. Leave lockpin installed in injection pump sprocket.
5. Turn tension roller to right with a suitable wrench until notch and raised portion, **Fig. 16,** are aligned. Ensure angled retainer is securely located in cylinder head cutout.
6. Tighten tension roller clamp nut to specifications.
7. Ensure all timing marks are still properly aligned.
8. Tighten camshaft sprocket mounting bolt to specifications.
9. Install new injection pump sprocket mounting bolts, then tighten to specifications, **Fig. 12. Do not disturb hub nut, as pump basic setting will be altered and special equipment will be required to reset pump.**
10. Remove feeler gauges and locking bar tools.
11. Remove injection pump lockpin.

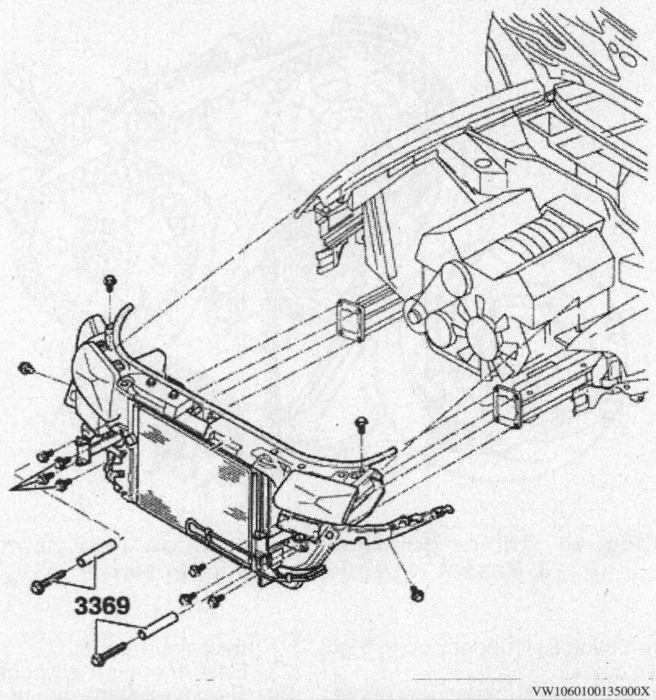

Fig. 17 Header panel mounting. Passat

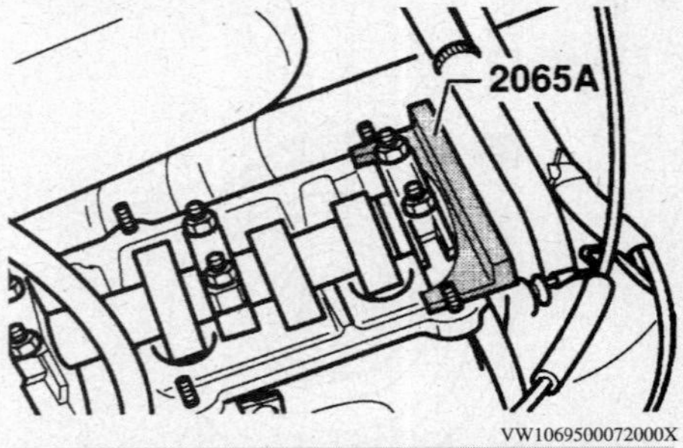

Fig. 18 Locking camshaft in position. Passat

12. Rotate crankshaft two turns in normal running direction and ensure all timing marks align.
13. Install engine mount bracket to block with new bolts.
14. Tighten mount to body bolts to specifications, then rotate an additional 90 degrees.
15. Install the engine mount onto the bracket with new bolts. Tighten to specifications, then rotate an additional 90 degrees.
16. Tighten engine mount to body bolt to specifications.
17. Install timing belt lower cover.
18. Install crankshaft pulley and vibration damper. Tighten pulley mounting bolts to specifications, then rotate an additional 90 degrees.
19. Install water pump pulley and drive belt, noting its running direction. Tighten pulley mounting bolts to specifications.
20. Install power steering pump pulley and drive belt, noting its running direction. Tighten pulley mounting bolts to specifications.
21. Install valve cover and PCV valve. Tighten valve cover to specifications.
22. Install timing belt upper cover.
23. Tighten alternator mounting bolts to specifications.
24. Install righthand side insulation tray.
25. Install pipe between charge air cooler and turbocharger.
26. Install brake booster vacuum pump.
27. Install timing belt upper cover.
28. Install fuel filter into its bracket.
29. Connect fuel return and supply lines at fuel filter.
30. Install tube between charge air cooler and air intake pipe.
31. Adjust engine accessory drive belt tension using the proper VW lever tool.
32. Inspect diesel injection pump start of injection as outlined under "Injection Pump Timing."

PASSAT

Removal

1. Remove front bumper.
2. Remove air guide between header panel and air cleaner.
3. Remove bolts, **Fig. 17,** then thread in VW tool No. 3369, or equivalent into lefthand and righthand long members.
4. Remove bolts, then pull header panel forward. This allows for an easier access to timing belt components.
5. Mark running direction on accessory drive belt.
6. Release tension from accessory drive belt tensioner using VW lever tool No. 3297, or equivalent, then remove drive belt.
7. Rotate crankshaft until the No. 1 cylinder is at TDC, **Figs. 9 and 10.**
8. Remove timing belt upper cover, then the valve cover.
9. Ensure the No. 1 cylinder is at TDC, **Figs. 9 and 10.**
10. Install VW camshaft locking bar tool No. 2065A, or equivalent, **Fig. 18,** into camshaft end slot. Locking bar must slide into slot without resistance.
11. Rotate camshaft, with locking bar in place, until one end of bar touches cylinder head.
12. Measure gap at other end of setting bar with a feeler gauge.
13. Select a feeler gauge that is half that of measured gap, then temporarily install it between setting bar and cylinder head.
14. Rotate camshaft so setting bar rests against feeler gauge, then insert a feeler gauge of identical halved thickness at other end between setting bar and cylinder head.
15. Remove idler roller.
16. Lock injection pump sprocket with VW lockpin tool No. 3359, or equivalent, **Fig. 12.**
17. Remove vibration damper and crankshaft pulley.
18. Remove timing belt center and lower covers.
19. Loosen timing belt tensioner mounting bolt to release tension on timing belt.
20. Remove timing belt.

Installation

1. Ensure timing marks are all properly aligned.
2. Loosen camshaft sprocket mounting bolt ½ turn. Loosen sprocket from camshaft's cone by tapping carefully and lightly with a mandrel through hole in timing belt rear cover.
3. Install idler roller.
4. Note timing belt's running direction, then install it, beginning at crankshaft sprocket, next to intermediate pulley, then onto injection pump sprocket, camshaft sprocket and tension roller.
5. Remove lockpin installed in injection pump sprocket.
6. Turn tension roller to the right with a suitable wrench until notch and raised portion, **Fig. 16,** are aligned. Ensure angled retainer is securely located in cylinder head cutout.
7. Tighten tension roller clamp nut to specifications.
8. Ensure all timing marks are still properly aligned.
9. Tighten camshaft sprocket mounting bolt to specifications.
10. Remove feeler gauges and locking bar tools.
11. Rotate crankshaft two turns in normal running direction and ensure all timing marks align as they should.
12. Install timing belt lower cover.
13. Install crankshaft pulley and vibration damper. Tighten pulley mounting bolts to specifications.
14. Install valve cover. Tighten nuts to specifications.
15. Install timing belt upper cover.

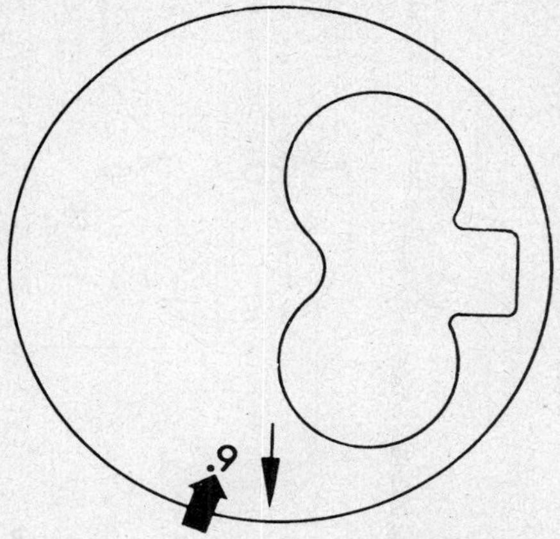

VW1069100031000X

Fig. 19 Piston marked ".9" in direction of installation

16. Adjust engine accessory drive belt tension using proper VW lever tool.
17. Ensure no hoses or wiring are kinked or pinched when positioning header panel to main body. Tighten bolts to specifications.
18. Install air guide, then the front bumper.
19. Inspect diesel injection pump start of injection as outlined under "Injection Pump Timing."

CAMSHAFT

REPLACE

1. Remove timing belt as outlined under "Timing Belt, Replace."
2. Remove bearing caps 1, 3 and 5, then diagonally loosen caps 2 and 4.
3. Remove bearing caps 2 and 4, then the camshaft.
4. Install new camshaft with lobes for cylinder No. 1 facing upwards, then oil bearing surfaces.
5. Install bearing caps 2 and 4, noting offset and tighten to specifications diagonally.
6. Install bearing caps 1, 3 and 5. Locate bearing cap 5 by tapping lightly on end of camshaft.
7. Tighten bearing caps 1, 3 and 5 to specifications, then reinstall timing belt as outlined under "Timing Belt, Replace."

PISTON & ROD ASSEMBLY

1. Prior to removal, mark pistons and rods to match cylinder number.
2. Remove circlips from piston, press pin out by hand and separate assembly. **If pin is too tight in bore, heat piston to approximately 140°F.**
3. Check piston to cylinder wall clearance at right angles to piston pin, ⅜ inch from top and bottom and in center of travel.
4. Check ring gap by installing ring approximately 9⁄16 inch from top of cylinder and centering with an inverted piston. End gap for compression rings should be. 007–.016 inch, oil ring end gap should be. 010–.020 inch.
5. Assemble piston and rod combinations with casting marks on rod and markings on piston crown, **Fig. 19,** facing timing belt. **If piston pin is tight in pin bore, heat piston to approximately 140°F to aid installation. Ensure pin attaching locks are properly seated.**
6. Pistons marked with 1/2 are for cylinder Nos. 1 and 2, pistons marked with 3/4 are for cylinder Nos. 3 and 4.
7. Install piston rings with TOP markings facing piston crown. Side clearance for compression rings should measure. 002–.004 inch on upper rings and. 002–.003 inch on lower rings and must not exceed. 008 inch. Side clearance for oil rings should measure. 001–.002 inch and must not exceed. 006 inch.
8. Install assemblies with piston marking facing timing belt, using a ring compressor. Ensure connecting rod side clearance is less than. 004 inch. **Ensure "stretch" type connecting rod bolts are used. Bolts are not reusable, and must be replaced during assembly. During installation, tighten nuts to specified value, then turn each nut an additional ½ turn to obtain proper stretch.**

MAIN & ROD BEARINGS

Main and connecting rod bearings are available in. 010 inch,. 020 inch and. 030 inch undersizes.

CRANKSHAFT REAR OIL SEAL

REPLACE

1. **On models equipped with manual transaxle,** remove transaxle, flywheel, pressure plate, clutch disc and intermediate plate as outlined under "Clutch & Manual Transaxle."
2. **On models equipped with automatic transaxle,** remove transaxle, torque converter and torque converter driveplate as outlined under "Automatic Transaxles."
3. **On all models,** pry oil seal out of oil seal flange using a screwdriver, or equivalent.
4. Lubricate new seal, center seal in seal flange and press until fully seated.
5. Reverse procedure to complete installation.

FRONT MAIN BEARING OIL SEAL

REPLACE

1. Remove timing belt as outlined under "Timing Belt, Replace."
2. Remove crankshaft sprocket retaining bolt, then sprocket. **Do not allow crankshaft to turn as piston valve contact will occur.**
3. Using a suitable tool, remove oil seal.

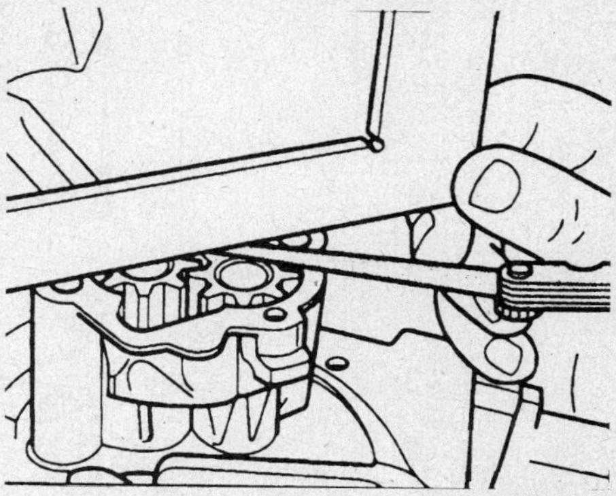

VW1069600052000X

Fig. 20 Oil pump wear inspection

4. Lightly lubricate sealing lip and outer edge of new oil seal.
5. Place suitable guide sleeve onto crankshaft, then push oil seal over guide sleeve.
6. Using a suitable tool, press oil seal in until it reaches stop.
7. Reverse procedure to install. Tighten to specifications.

OIL PAN

REPLACE

1. Remove oil pan drain plug and drain engine oil.
2. Disconnect oil return line from turbocharger.
3. Remove oil pan to engine attaching bolts, then the oil pan, discarding gasket.
4. Reverse procedure to install, using new sealing washers. Tighten to specification.

OIL PUMP

REPLACE

1. Remove oil pan as outlined under "Oil Pan, Replace."
2. Remove oil pump pick-up tube retaining bolts.
3. Remove oil pump mounting bolts, then pump.
4. Reverse procedure to install, noting the following
   a. Tighten to specifications.
   b. Ensure oil pump driveshaft is properly engaged into vacuum pump drive.

OIL PUMP SERVICE

1. Remove oil pump cover plate and inspect plate for excessive wear.
2. Using a suitable feeler gauge, **Fig. 20,** check oil pump for gear backlash and endplay.
3. Maximum backlash should be. 009 inch, maximum end clearance should be. 006 inch.

COOLING SYSTEM BLEED

1. Slowly fill coolant expansion tank to Max mark, then install expansion tank cap.

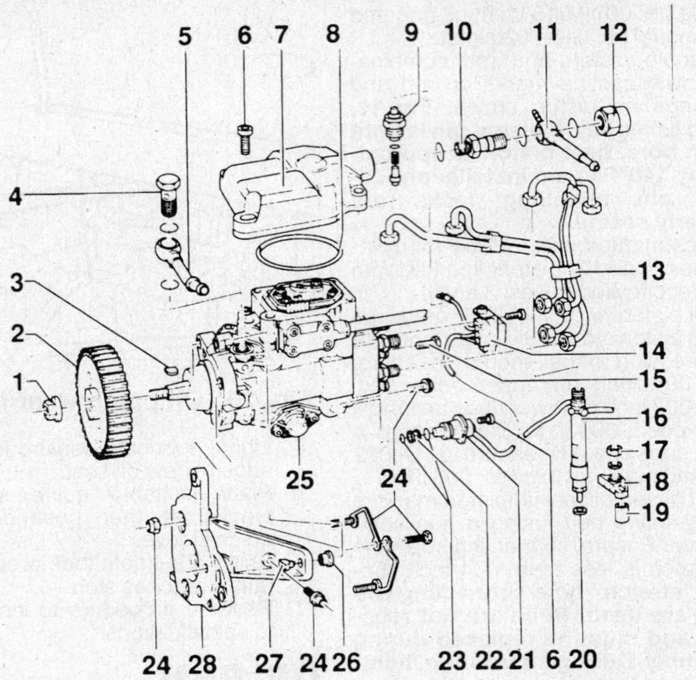

1-Sprocket Nut
2-Sprocket
3-Woodruff Key
4-Banjo Bolt Fuel Inlet
5-Fuel Inlet Line
6-Pump Cover Bolt
7-Pump Cover
8-Gasket
9-Fuel Shut Off Valve
10-Union/Reducer
11-Fuel Return Line
12-Cap Nut Fuel Return
13-Fuel Injector Pipe Set
14-Connector
15-Bolt
16-Fuel Injector
17-Nut
18-Injector Retainer
19-Spacer
20-Injector Heat Shield
21-Cold Start Injector
22-Strainer
23-O-ring
24-Bolt
25-Timing Control Cover
26-Tapered Sleeve
27-Tapered Nut
28-Pump Mount

VW1029600069000X

Fig. 21 Injection system components. 1998 Jetta

2. Run engine until cooling fan comes on, then check coolant level.
3. Coolant level should be at or slightly above Max mark with engine at normal operating temperature, and between Min and Max marks with engine cold.
4. If necessary, add coolant to specified marking.

WATER PUMP

REPLACE

Refer to "2.0L Gasoline Engine" section for replacement procedure.

RADIATOR

REPLACE

Refer to "1.8L Turbocharged Gasoline Engine" section for replacement procedures.

TURBOCHARGER

REPLACE

This procedure has been revised by a Technical Service Bulletin.

1. Remove exhaust pipe from turbocharger.
2. Disconnect oil supply line and mounting clamp, then remove air hose between intake manifold/turbocharger and turbocharger/intercooler.
3. Disconnect oil return line from oil pan and support bracket on cylinder block, then remove mounting bolts and turbocharger from top.
4. Reverse procedure to install, noting the following:
   a. Tighten nuts and bolts to specifications.
   b. Prior to connecting oil supply line, fill connection on turbocharger with engine oil.
   c. After installing turbocharger, let en-

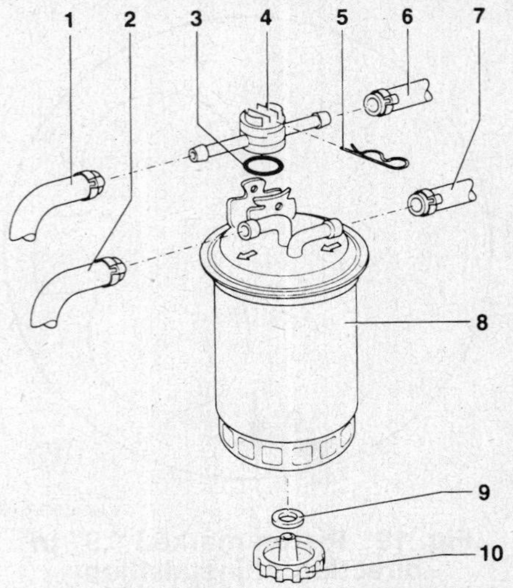

1-Fuel Return Line
2-Fuel Supply Line
3-O-Ring
4-Control Valve
5-Securing Clip
6-Fuel Return Line
7-Fuel Supply Line
8-Filter Element
9-Water Drain Gasket
10-Water Drain Plug

VW1029600070000X

Fig. 22 Fuel filter replacement. Golf, Jetta & New Beetle

gine idle for approximately one minute.

INJECTION PUMP

REPLACE

1998 JETTA

1. Remove timing belt as outlined under "Timing Belt, Replace."
2. Loosen injection pump sprocket retaining bolt slightly, **Fig. 21.**
3. Install puller tool No. VW203b, or equivalent, so that jaws are at 90° angle to crossbar and facing direction of spindle rotation.
4. Carefully apply pressure to sprocket and tap puller spindle with a light hammer until sprocket is released from shaft taper. **Do not apply excessive force with puller, as sprocket at pump shaft will be damaged.**
5. Remove puller, retaining bolt and sprocket.
6. Disconnect fuel pipe assembly from pump and plug lines and open fittings.
7. Disconnect wiring connections from pump.
8. Remove lower bolt securing pump mounting plate, bolts securing pump to mounting plate and braces (if equipped) and remove pump. **Do not loosen bolts on fuel distributor head, as distributor will be damaged.**
9. Install pump on mounting bracket with marks on pump and bracket aligned. Tighten bolts to specifications.
10. Install pump sprocket and tighten retaining bolt to specifications. Align mark on pump sprocket with marks on pump and bracket and lock position with pin 2064.
11. Install timing belt as outlined under "Timing Belt, Replace." Check injection

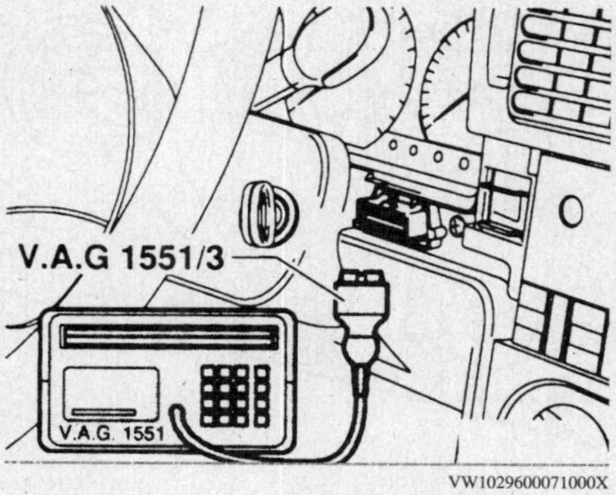

Fig. 23 Scan tool connection. 1998 Jetta

timing as outlined under "Injection Pump Timing."

12. Reverse procedure to complete installation.

NEW BEETLE, PASSAT & 1999-2001 GOLF & JETTA

Removal

1. Remove engine cover.
2. Disconnect fuel supply and return lines at injection pump, then plug open lines.
3. Remove injector lines together using wrench tool No. 3035, or equivalent.
4. Remove right headlight, then the connecting line between charge air cooler and intake manifold.
5. Remove upper timing belt cover, then the valve cover.
6. Remove brake servo vacuum pump.
7. Rotate engine in normal running direction until M/T flywheel or A/T flexplate timing marks are properly aligned, **Figs. 9 and 10.**
8. Lock camshaft using setting bar tool No. 3418, or equivalent.
9. Rotate camshaft so that one end of setting bar contacts cylinder head.
10. Measure gap at setting bar's opposite end with a suitable feeler gauge.
11. Insert a feeler gauge of ½ of gap between setting bar and head.
12. Rotate camshaft until setting bar contacts feeler gauge.
13. Insert a second feeler gauge of same thickness at other end between setting bar and head.
14. Lock injection pump sprocket using pin tool No. 3359, or equivalent, then remove injection pump sprocket bolts. **Do not loosen hub nut, as pump basic setting will be altered and special equipment will be required to reset pump.**
15. Remove timing belt tensioner bolt, then relieve tension on timing belt.
16. Remove camshaft and injection pump sprockets.
17. Disconnect injection pump metering unit electrical connector.
18. Remove injection pump bolts, then the injection pump.

Installation

1. Install injection pump on bracket, then tighten rear bolt to specifications.
2. Install front injection pump bolts, then tighten to specifications.
3. Install injection pump using new bolts, do not tighten bolts at this time.
4. Lock injection pump sprocket using pin tool No. 3359, or equivalent.
5. Align injection pump sprocket to central position in elongated holes.
6. Hold camshaft sprocket using counter holder tool No. 3036, or equivalent, then loosen camshaft bolt by one turn.
7. Remove camshaft sprocket using two arm puller tool No. T-40001, or equivalent.
8. Ensure timing mark on flywheel is at TDC.
9. Place timing belt on injection pump sprocket and tensioner.
10. Install camshaft sprocket with timing belt.
11. **On models equipped with manual transaxle,** apply tension to timing belt using two hole pin spanner tool No. T10020, or equivalent on eccentric. Turn clockwise until notch and raised mark align.
12. **On models equipped with automatic transaxle,** apply tension to timing belt by turning eccentric clockwise using suitable hex key until notch and indicator align.
13. **On all models,** ensure tensioning roller seats correctly in rear timing belt cover, then tighten lock nut to specifications.
14. Install camshaft sprocket with timing belt, then tighten injection pump bolts to specifications.
15. Hold camshaft sprocket with counter hold tool No. 3036 and tighten bolt to specifications.
16. Turn crankshaft two revolutions in direction of engine rotation until crankshaft is set to TDC on cylinder No. 1.
17. Connect fuel injection lines, then the fuel supply line.
18. Connect injection pump metering unit electrical connector.
19. Thread adapter tool No. VAG 1318/10, or equivalent into return hole in injection pump.
20. Connect hand vacuum pump tool No. VAG 1390, or equivalent to adapter using suitable clear plastic hose.
21. Operate vacuum pump until fuel flows out of return supply opening. Do not draw fuel into vacuum pump.
22. Remove adapter, then connect return supply line.
23. Install brake servo vacuum pump, then the valve cover. Tighten valve cover bolts to specifications.
24. Install headlight.
25. Install upper timing belt cover, then check start of injection as outlined under "Injection Pump Timing."

FUEL FILTER

REPLACE

GOLF, JETTA & NEW BEETLE

The filter element should be replaced at normal maintenance intervals to ensure reliable operation of the pump and injectors.

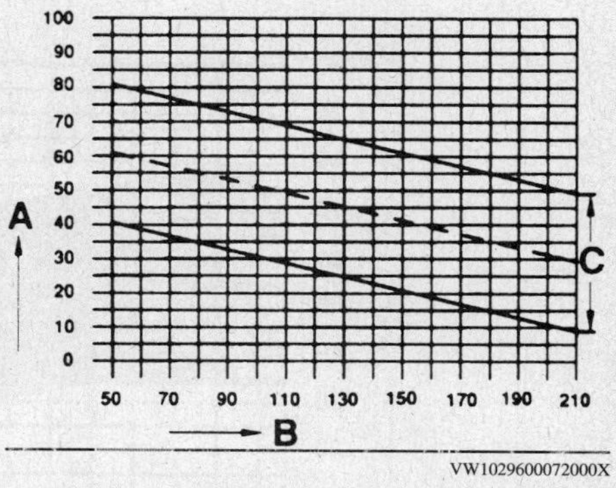

Fig. 24 Temperature correction table for injection pump timing. 1998 Jetta

1. Remove securing clip, **Fig. 22,** then remove fuel return control valve from filter. Discard sealing O-ring.
2. Disconnect fuel supply lines from filter.
3. Fill new filter with clean diesel fuel (no further priming should be necessary when filter is full of fuel), replace filter.
4. Install new fuel return control valve O-ring, then valve and securing clip.
5. Connect and properly clamp fuel supply lines to filter.
6. Start engine, allow to idle until air self bleeds from filter, then check for fuel leaks at connections.

PASSAT

1. Loosen bleeder screw, then drain diesel fuel from filter.
2. Remove filter using suitable strap wrench.
3. Fill new filter with clean diesel fuel.
4. Install filter and tighten by hand.

INJECTION PUMP TIMING

1998 JETTA

Basic

1. Remove upper belt cover.
2. Set engine to TDC compression stroke as outlined under "Timing Belt, Replace."
3. Ensure marks on pump body and on pump sprocket are aligned with marks on pump bracket.
4. Ensure pump mounting bolts are centered in elongated slots in pump mounting bracket.
5. If required, adjust basic timing as outlined under "Injection Pump, Replace."
6. Proceed to "Dynamic Injection Pump Timing."

Dynamic

1. Connect scan tool No. VAG1551 or VAG 1552, or equivalents, to the Diagnostic Link Connector (DCL) found to right of steering column, under left-hand side of instrument panel, **Fig. 23.**
2. With engine running at closed throttle idle, select "Engine Electronics" with "Address Word 01," on scan tool.

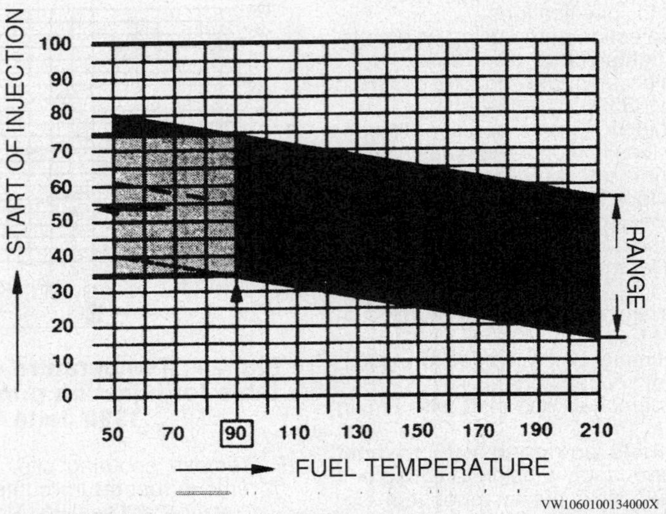

Fig. 25 Start of injection graph. New Beetle, Passat & 1999–2001 Golf & Jetta

3. Select function 04, "Introduction Of Basic Setting," then 00, "Display Group 00."
4. Read output figures from scan tool channel 2 (injection timing) and channel 9 (fuel temperature).
5. Injection timing is dependent on fuel temperature. Refer to table in **Fig. 24,** in which "A" equals injection timing and "B" equals fuel temperature. Zone "C" of table is acceptable range with no adjustment required.
6. If adjustment is required, proceed as follows:
   a. Shut off engine.
   b. Remove upper timing belt cover.
   c. Loosen injection pump mounting bolts until pump can be moved.
   d. If timing was retarded move pump against direction of engine rotation. If advanced, move in direction of rotation.
   e. Secure injection pump, then check timing. If necessary, repeat above steps until mean value of zone "C," **Fig. 24,** is reached.
   f. Tighten pump mounting bolts to specifications.
7. Install upper belt cover, then remove scan tool.

NEW BEETLE, PASSAT & 1999–2001 GOLF & JETTA

1. Inspect diesel injection pump start of injection, dynamic checking as follows:
   a. Connect VW scan tool 1551/1552, or equivalent, to data link connector located under lefthand side of instrument panel.
   b. Start engine and operate at idle speed.
   c. Select scan tool function 0 and 1 to access engine electronic.
   d. Press 0 and 4 to select basic setting, then press Q to confirm entry.
   e. Press O button three times, then press Q to confirm entry.
   f. Check coolant temperature indicated in display 7 on scan tool screen. Coolant temperature indication should be less than 73 (which is equal to 85°C). Continue check procedure only when engine coolant temperature is obtained.
   g. Start of injection is displayed in scan tool display field 2 and is dependent on fuel temperature, which is indicated under display field 9, **Fig. 25.** Referring to chart, **Fig. 25,** if numerical value for fuel temperature is 90, start of injection should be within specified range of 34–73.
2. If start of injection is within range for specified fuel temperature, proceed as follows:
   a. Press arrow button on scan tool.
   b. Press scan tool buttons 0 and 6 to end output, then press Q button to enter input.
   c. With scan tool Erase DTC memory and set readiness code.
   d. Remove connecting line between charge air cooler and intake manifold.
   e. Remove upper timing belt cover.
   f. Tighten injection pump sprocket mounting bolts an additional 90°, **Fig. 12. Do not disturb hub nut, as pump basic setting will be altered and special equipment will be required to reset pump.**
   g. Install upper timing belt cover and connecting line.
3. If start of injection is not within range for specified fuel temperature, proceed as follows:
   a. Remove connecting line between charge air cooler and intake manifold.
   b. Remove upper timing belt cover.
   c. Loosen two of three injection pump sprocket mounting bolts, **Fig. 12. Do not disturb hub nut, as pump basic setting will be altered and special equipment will be required to reset pump.**
   d. Place a 22 mm box wrench onto injection pump hub nut, **Fig. 12,** to counter hold pump shaft, then loosen third injection pump sprocket mounting bolt. **Do not disturb hub nut, as pump basic setting will be altered and special equipment will be required to reset pump.**
   e. To advance start of injection timing, slightly turn pump shaft to left. To retard start of injection pump timing, slight turn pump shaft to right. Start of injection pump timing should be set to mean value of specified start of injection range.
   f. Tighten injection pump sprocket mounting bolts to specifications.
   g. Using scan tool, check start of injection setting and re-adjust as necessary.
   h. Press scan tool buttons 0 and 6 to end output, then press Q button to enter input.
   i. Press arrow button on scan tool.
   j. Press scan tool buttons 0 and 6 to end output, then press Q button to enter input.
   k. With scan tool Erase DTC memory and set readiness code.
   l. After start of injection setting has been properly set, ensure injection pump sprocket mounting bolts are tightened to specifications. Tighten the injection pump sprocket mounting bolts an additional 90°.
   m. Install upper timing belt cover and connecting line.
   n. Loosen fuel injection lines at injection pump, then tighten lines to specifications. This will relieve any strain on lines which may have occurred during adjustment procedure.

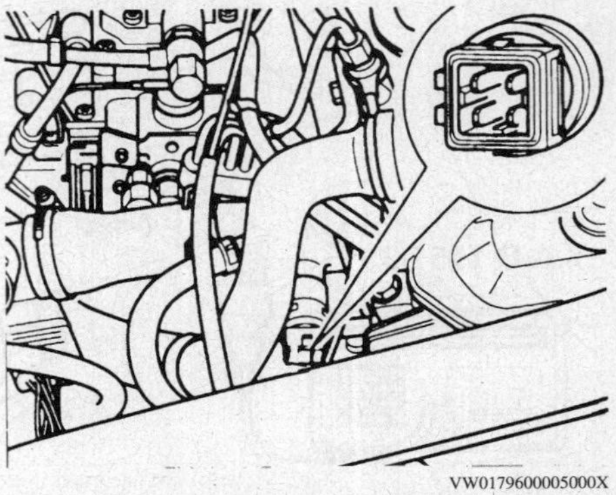

Fig. 26 Glow plug temperature sensor

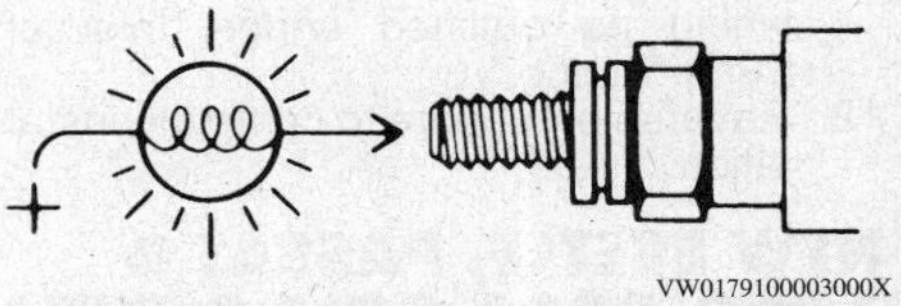

Fig. 27 Glow plug continuity inspection

IDLE SPEED

ADJUST

Engine idle speed is computer controlled and cannot be adjusted.

GLOW PLUG SYSTEM

During cold starts, diesel compression heat is dissipated rapidly through the cold engine so that a preheating provision is necessary to ensure compression ignition. The glow plugs are threaded into the cylinder head so they project into each combustion chamber. A heating element in each plug gets red hot whenever current is applied to the plug terminals.

Current is supplied to the glow plugs directly from the battery by a relay that is controlled by the Turbocharged Direct Injection (TDI) diesel Engine Control Module (ECM). A temperature sensor connected to the ECM controls preheating time. The colder the temperature, the longer the preheating time. The glow plug light is on when the plugs are being heated and goes off when the engine is ready to start.

Defective glow plugs cause hard starting and rough running during warm-up. Carbon deposits can build up and insulate the heating element. If the system seems satisfactory, but the engine is hard to start, the glow plugs should be removed for cleaning.

Most problems in the preheat system can be found with a test light. Glow plugs can also be checked with an ohmmeter. The resistance value is about. 25 ohms.

TESTING

1. With ignition switch in Off position, disconnect engine coolant temperature sensor on water outlet housing, **Fig. 26,** to simulate cold engine, then remove glow plug connectors.
2. Connect test light clip to ground and touch test light probe to any glow plug connection, turn on ignition switch.
3. Test light should light up for about 20 seconds if system is working properly.
4. Connect test light clip to battery positive post and probe to each glow plug connection. Test light should light up each time if heating elements are satisfactory, **Fig. 27.**

TIGHTENING SPECIFICATIONS

Year	Component	Torque, Ft. Lbs.
1998	Camshaft Bearing Cap To Cylinder Head Nuts	15
	Camshaft Sprocket To Camshaft Bolt	33
	Connecting Rod Nuts	22①
	Crankshaft Timing Belt Sprocket To Crankshaft Bolt	66①
	Cylinder Head Bolts	③
	Cylinder Head Cover To Cylinder Head Bolts	84⑤
	Exhaust Pipe To Turbocharger Nuts	18
	Front Main Oil Seal Housing To Block Bolts	15
	Glow Plugs To Cylinder Head	11
	Injection Pump Bolts	18
	Injection Pump Bracket To Injection Pump Bolts	18
	Injection Pump Sprocket To Injection Pump Nut	41
	Injector Pipe Nuts To Injector	14
	Injector Retainer Nuts To Cylinder Head	15
	Intermediate Shaft Oil Seal Flange To Block Bolts	18
	Lower Header Panel Bolts	37
	Main Bearing Cap Bolts	48
	Oil Pan Drain Plug To Oil Pan	22
	Oil Pan To Block Bolts	15
	Oil Pressure Switch To Oil Filter Bracket	18
	Oil Pump Cover To Oil Pump Housing Bolts	84⑤
	Oil Pump Pickup To Pump Bolts	84⑤
	Oil Pump To Block Bolts	15
	Oil Return Line To Pan Bolt	37
	Oil Return Line To Turbocharger Nut	30
	Oil Spray Nozzle To Block Bolt	84④⑤
	Pulley to Crankshaft Timing Belt Sprocket Bolt	15
	Timing Belt Tensioner Nut	33
	Turbocharger To Exhaust Manifold Bolts	33②
	Upper Header Panel Bolts	71⑤
	Water Pump Pulley To Water Pump Bolts	15
	Water Pump To Water Pump Housing Bolts	84⑤

Continued

TIGHTENING SPECIFICATIONS—Continued

Year	Component	Torque, Ft. Lbs.
1999–2001	Alternator Bolts	18
	Camshaft Bearing Cap Bolts	15
	Camshaft Sprocket Bolt	33
	Connecting Rod Bolts	22①
	Crankshaft Pulley	84①⑤
	Cylinder Head Bolts	③
	Engine Mount To Body Bolt	30①
	Engine Mount To Bracket	44
	Exhaust Manifold/Turbocharger To Intake	18
	Exhaust Pipe To Turbocharger	18
	Front Sealing Flange Bolts	11
	Fuel Injection Lines	18
	Glow Plugs To Cylinder Head	11
	Injection Pump Bolts	18
	Injection Pump Sprocket Bolts	15
	Lower Header Panel Bolts	37
	Main Bearing Cap Bolts	48①
	Oil Pan Drain Plug	22
	Oil Pan To Engine Block	11–15
	Oil Pan To Transaxle Bolts	33
	Oil Pump To Engine Block	11
	Power Steering Pump Pulley	18
	Tension Roller Clamp Nut	15
	Timing Belt Tensioner Lock Nut	15
	Upper Header Panel Bolts	71⑤
	Valve Cover	84⑤
	Water Pump Pulley	18

① — Plus an additional 1/4 (90°) turn.
② — Coat threads & head contact surface w/sealant No. G 000 500, or equivalent.
③ — Refer to "Cylinder Head, Replace."
④ — Coat threads w/sealant No. AMV 188 100 02, or equivalent.
⑤ — Inch lbs.

2.0L Gasoline Engine

NOTE: On Air Bag Equipped Models, Refer To "Air Bag System Precautions" Located In The Front Of This Manual For System Disarming & Arming Procedures.

NOTE: Refer To "Computer Relearn Procedures" Located In The Front Of This Manual When Battery Power To The Computer Has Been Interrupted.

INDEX

	Page No.
Camshaft, Replace	8-45
Compression Pressure	8-39
Cooling System Bleed	8-47
Crankshaft Rear Oil Seal, Replace	8-46
Cylinder Head, Replace	8-42
Cabrio & 1998 Golf & Jetta	8-42
New Beetle	8-42
1999–2001 Golf & Jetta	8-43
Engine Mount, Replace	8-39
Engine Rebuilding Specifications	8-185
Engine, Replace	8-39
Cabrio & 1998 Golf & Jetta	8-39
New Beetle & 1999–2001 Golf & Jetta	8-40
Exhaust Manifold, Replace	8-41
Cabrio & 1998 Golf & Jetta	8-41
New Beetle	8-41
1999–2001 Golf & Jetta	8-41
Front Main Bearing Oil Seal, Replace	8-47
Fuel Pump, Replace	8-48
Except In Tank	8-48
In Tank	8-48
Hydraulic Lifter Inspection	8-43
Hydraulic Lifters, Replace	8-44
Intake Manifold, Replace	8-41
Main & Rod Bearings	8-46
Oil Pan, Replace	8-47
Piston & Rod Assembly	8-46
Pistons, Pins & Rings	8-46
Precautions	8-39
Air Bag Systems	8-39
Audio Coded Anti-Theft System	8-39
Battery Ground Cable	8-39
Radiator, Replace	8-48
Cabrio & 1998 Golf & Jetta	8-48
New Beetle & 1999–2001 Golf & Jetta	8-48
Serpentine Drive Belt	8-47
Replacement	8-47
Routing	8-47
Tightening Specifications	8-50
Timing Belt, Replace	8-44
Cabrio & 1998 Golf & Jetta	8-44
New Beetle & 1999–2001 Golf & Jetta	8-44
Valve Adjustment	8-43
Valve Guides	8-43
Inspection	8-43
Replacement	8-44
Water Pump, Replace	8-47
Cabrio & 1998 Golf & Jetta	8-47
New Beetle & 1999–2001 Golf & Jetta	8-48

PRECAUTIONS

AIR BAG SYSTEMS

Do not use computer memory saver tool on air bag equipped models. Using the tool will keep the air bag system charged and may cause accidental activation of the air bag unit. Refer to "Air Bag System Precautions" in the front of this manual for system disarming and arming procedures.

BATTERY GROUND CABLE

Prior to disconnecting the battery negative cable, obtain the radio security code. After service has been completed and the battery negative cable has been reconnected, use security code to activate the radio. Prior to service, disconnect battery ground cable and isolate as required.

AUDIO CODED ANTI-THEFT SYSTEM

Some models are equipped with a radio anti-theft system that will disable the system when battery power is interrupted, unless the system is reset the radio will not operate.

1. Turn radio to On position, SAFE and 1000 should be displayed.
2. Enter radio code using first four program station buttons. Security code will appear on display.
3. Depress and hold righthand side of radio right or left blocker until anti-theft coding is activated indicated by a brief signal sound.
4. If code number has been entered correctly, when ignition key is removed a diode on front of radio will flash.

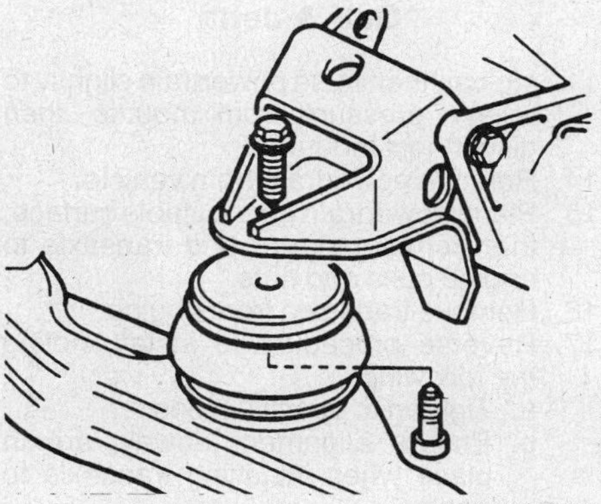

Fig. 1 Front engine & transaxle mount

COMPRESSION PRESSURE

1. Perform compression test with engine at operating temperature, spark plugs removed, coolant temperature at least 176°F and throttle plate completely open.
2. Disconnect power output stage of ignition coil high tension wire from distributor cap and connect to suitable ground.
3. Connect compression tester tool No. VAG 1763, or equivalent, per manufacturer's instructions, then crank engine until compression tester shows no further increase in pressure.
4. Compression should be 140.5–188.5 psi with a maximum difference between highest and lowest cylinder of 43.5 psi. Minimum compression should be 108.75 psi.

ENGINE MOUNT

REPLACE

1. Attach a suitable engine lifting tool to engine, positioned to relieve pressure from mount to be replaced, then loosen engine mount center mounting bolt, **Figs. 1 through 7.**
2. Raise engine and transaxle assembly until weight is off mount, then remove center bolt from mount.
3. Remove remaining engine mount and subframe mounting bolts, then engine mount.
4. Reverse procedure to install.

ENGINE

REPLACE

CABRIO & 1998 GOLF & JETTA

1. Drain cooling system.

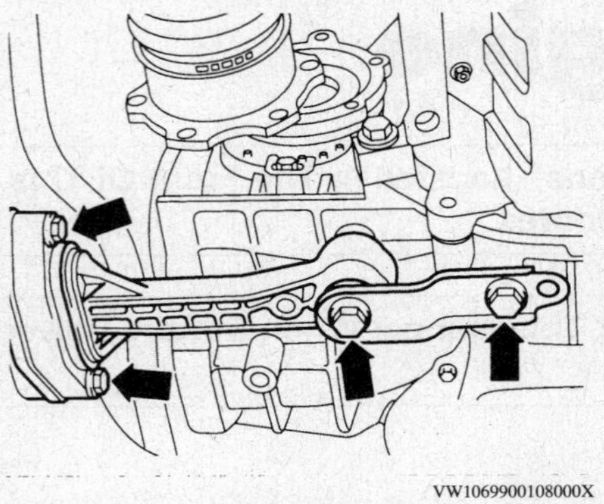

Fig. 2 Pendulum engine support

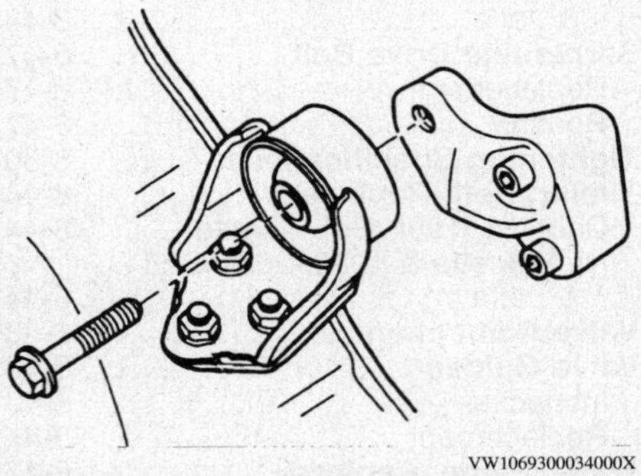

Fig. 5 Right engine & transaxle mount. Cabrio

2. Remove air cleaner and ducting as necessary.
3. Raise and support vehicle, then disconnect drive axles from transaxle and support them aside.
4. Disconnect exhaust system and position aside.
5. Disconnect necessary lines, electrical connectors, clamps, cables, components and hoses to allow removal of lock carrier, **Fig. 8.**
6. **On models equipped with A/C,** disconnect components necessary to allow condenser with radiator and fans, receiver drier and compressor to be removed and supported aside without disconnecting lines, **Fig. 9.**
7. **On models equipped with power steering,** disconnect any additional components necessary to allow pump and lines to be removed and supported aside without disconnecting lines.
8. **On all models,** remove lock carrier, **Fig. 8** then radiator, supporting aside A/C and power steering components, if equipped, **Fig. 9**
9. Remove any additional drive belts and components needed for removal clearance.
10. Disconnect clutch cable and gearshift mechanism.
11. Disconnect any remaining lines, cables, electrical connectors, hoses or components necessary to allow powertrain removal.
12. Connect lifting bar tool No. 2024A, or equivalent, **Figs. 10 and 11,** suitably adjusted to keep powertrain unit balanced during removal of engine.
13. Attach suitable lifting equipment to lifting bar, then raise powertrain slightly to relieve pressure from mounts, then disconnect mounts.

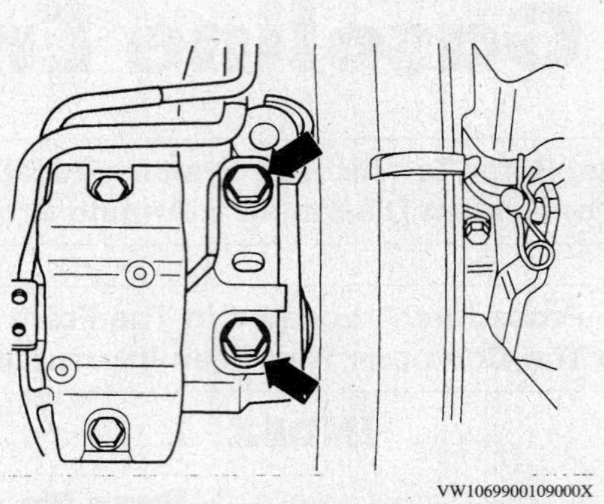

Fig. 3 Right engine & transaxle mount. New Beetle & 1999–2001 Golf & Jetta

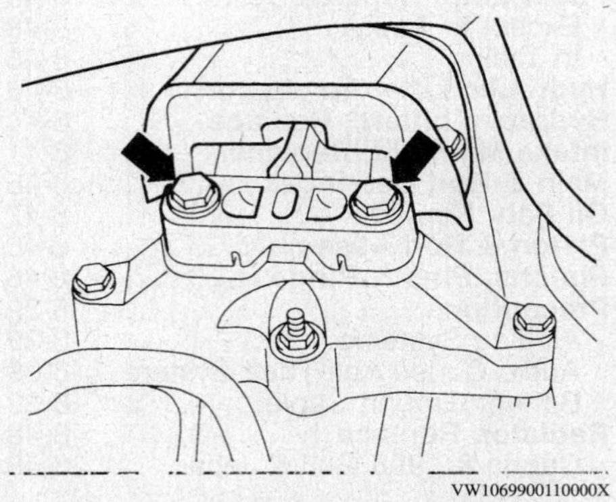

Fig. 6 Right engine & transaxle mount. New Beetle & 1999–2001 Golf & Jetta

14. Remove powertrain from vehicle.
15. Place powertrain on a suitable surface, then remove starter and transaxle to engine bolts and nuts.
16. Remove transaxle from engine.
17. Reverse procedure to install, noting the following:
    a. Tighten to specifications.
    b. Ensure alignment dowels are in place when installing transaxle to engine.
    c. **Note type of coolant, do not allow red coolant to be mixed with any other type.**
    d. Lubricate transaxle input shaft splines, and if equipped, release bearing guide sleeve with a suitable grease.
    e. Ensure drive axles are properly positioned during powertrain installation.
    f. Ensure locating tabs of right rear and front motor mounts are engaged into recesses of mount brackets, **Fig. 12.**
    g. Prior to tightening motor mount bolts, shake powertrain unit to relieve any stresses.
    h. Ensure correct adjustment of headlamps.

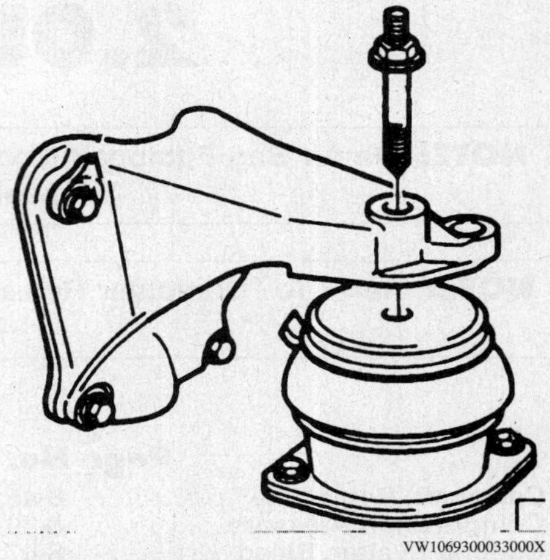

Fig. 4 Right engine & transaxle mount. Except Cabrio, New Beetle & 1999–2001 Golf & Jetta

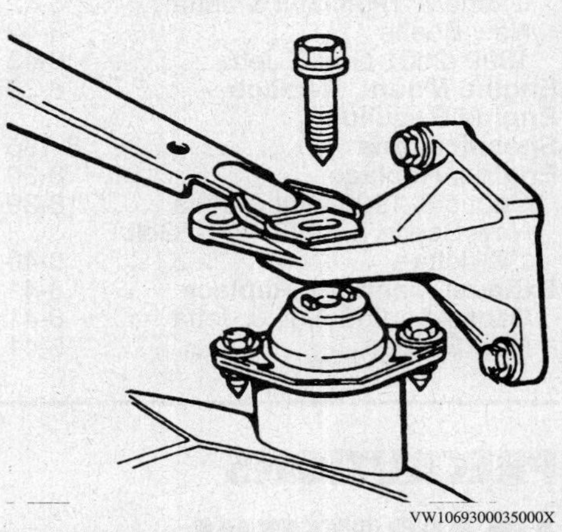

Fig. 7 Left engine & transaxle mount. Cabrio & 1998 Golf & Jetta

    i. Ensure correct adjustment of all cables.
    j. Replace any cable ties cut during powertrain removal with suitable equivalents.

NEW BEETLE & 1999–2001 GOLF & JETTA

1. Remove engine cover.
2. Remove power steering reservoir and position aside. Do not remove hoses from reservoir.
3. Remove battery, then the battery bracket.
4. Disconnect fuel lines from fuel rail. Plug all open lines.
5. Remove air cleaner.
6. **On models equipped with manual transaxle,** proceed as follows:
    a. Disconnect transaxle range selector from transaxle.
    b. Remove hydraulic clutch slave cylinder.
7. **On models equipped with automatic transaxle,** remove range selector lever cable.
8. **On all models,** remove sound dampener tray.
9. Drain coolant into suitable container, then remove serpentine drive belt.

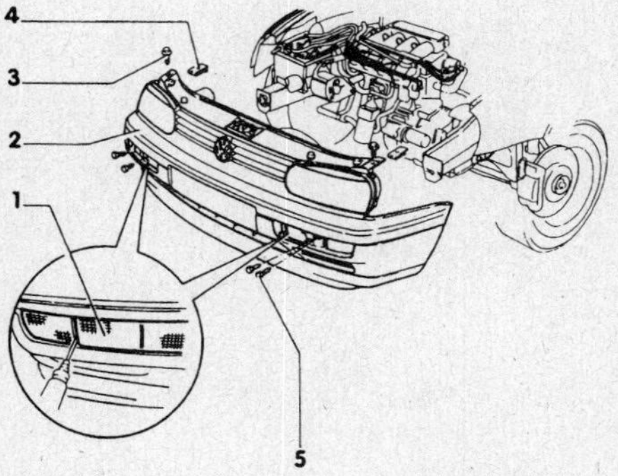

Fig. 8 Lock carrier removal. Cabrio & 1998 Golf & Jetta

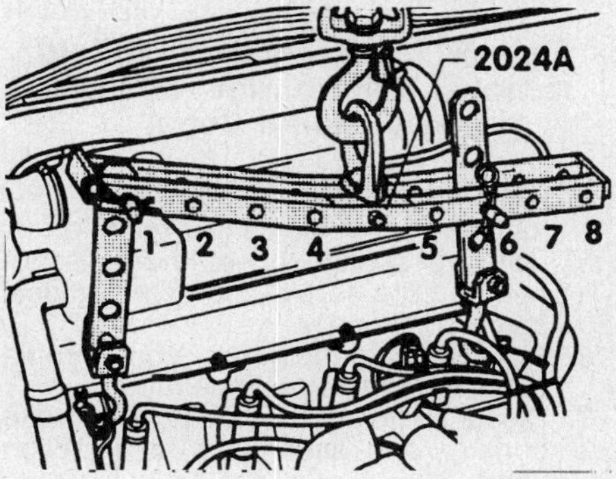

Fig. 11 Lifting bar connection. Automatic transaxle

10. Remove righthand auxiliary cooling fan.
11. Remove mounting clamps for power steering pressure lines.
12. Remove power steering pump with bracket and position aside. Do not remove power steering lines.
13. **On models equipped with A/C,** remove A/C compressor and position aside. Do not remove lines from compressor.
14. **On all models,** remove interconnecting coolant, vacuum and intake hoses from engine.
15. Remove secondary air injection pump from bracket.
16. Disconnect electrical connectors from alternator, starter and transaxle.
17. Disconnect electrical connectors from engine and position aside.
18. Remove pendulum support bolts, then the righthand inner CV joint boot.
19. Remove righthand driveshaft, then disconnect lefthand driveshaft at transaxle as outlined in "Front Wheel Drive Axles" section.
20. Remove exhaust pipe from exhaust manifold.
21. Install engine bracket tool No. 3396, or equivalent into engine/transaxle jack tool No. VAG 1383A, or equivalent.
22. Remove bracket for coolant hose under engine block.

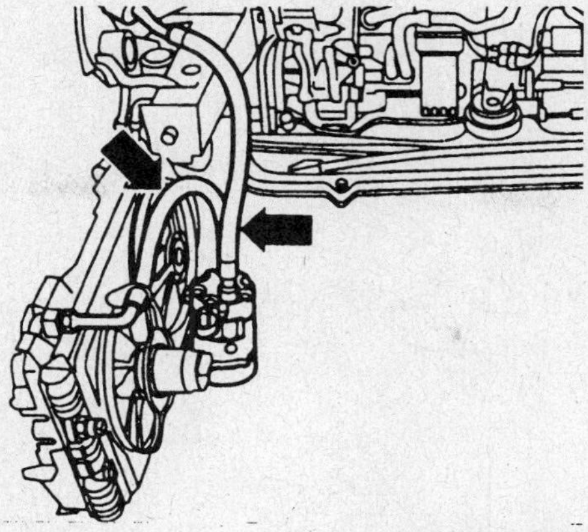

Fig. 9 A/C component position. Cabrio & 1998 Golf & Jetta

23. Mount engine bracket tool No. T 100 12 to bottom of engine.
24. Carefully lift engine and transaxle using engine/transaxle jack.
25. Remove engine mount bolts from engine.
26. Remove transaxle mount bolts from transaxle.
27. Carefully lower engine/transaxle assembly and remove from vehicle.
28. Support transaxle on suitable work bench, then remove engine from transaxle.
29. Reverse procedure to install noting the following:
    a. Ensure engine/transaxle centering dowels are installed in engine block.
    b. Lubricate transaxle input shaft splines and release bearing guide sleeve with suitable grease.
    c. Tighten bolts to specifications.

INTAKE MANIFOLD

REPLACE

Refer to **Figs. 13 through 16** for component locations during removal procedures.

EXHAUST MANIFOLD

REPLACE

CABRIO & 1998 GOLF & JETTA

Removal

Refer to **Fig. 17** for component locations during removal procedures.

Installation

When tightening exhaust pipe to manifold nuts refer to **Fig. 18** for sequence.

NEW BEETLE

1. Remove engine cover, then the intake hose.
2. Remove pressure and vacuum hoses from combi-valve.

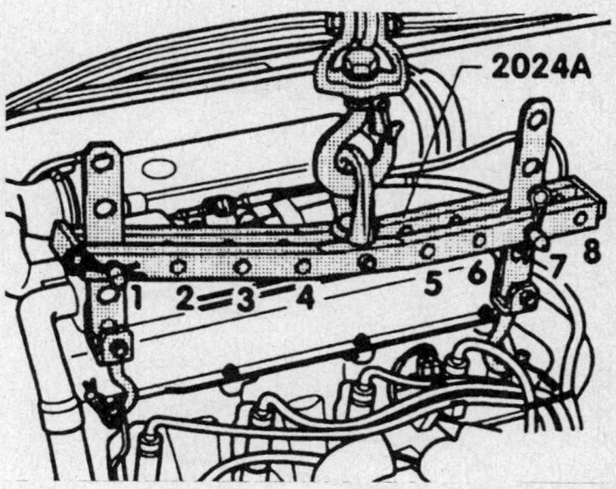

Fig. 10 Lifting bar connection. Manual transaxle

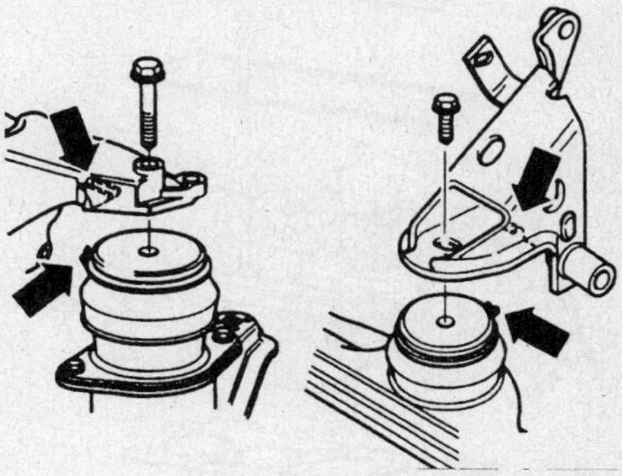

Fig. 12 Motor mount tab alignment

3. Loosen combi-valve connector pipe, then the heat shield.
4. Remove righthand inner CV joint protection cover.
5. Raise and secure righthand driveshaft.
6. Remove exhaust pipe from manifold.
7. Remove vibration damper pulley.
8. Remove exhaust manifold nuts, then the manifold.
9. Reverse procedure to install noting the following:
    a. Replace all seals and self-locking nuts.
    b. Tighten bolts to specifications.

1999–2001 GOLF & JETTA

1. Remove engine cover, then the intake hose.
2. Remove pressure and vacuum hoses from combi-valve.
3. Remove connector pipe from combi-valve and exhaust manifold.
4. Remove warm air collector plate, then the righthand inner CV joint protective cover.
5. Disconnect righthand driveshaft from transaxle.
6. Remove protective cover, then disconnect oxygen sensor electrical connectors.
7. Remove front exhaust pipe with bracket.
8. Remove exhaust manifold bolts, then the manifold.

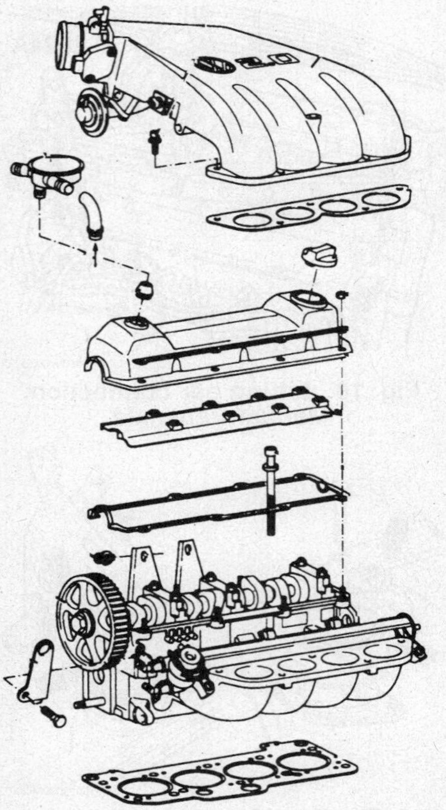

Fig. 13 Upper intake manifold removal. Cabrio & 1998 Golf & Jetta

9. Reverse procedure to install noting the following:
   a. Replace all seals and self-locking nuts.
   b. Tighten bolts to specifications.

CYLINDER HEAD

REPLACE

CABRIO & 1998 GOLF & JETTA

This procedure has been revised by a Technical Service Bulletin.

1. Drain cooling system.
2. Remove upper intake manifold attaching bolts, then manifold as shown in "Intake Manifold, Replace."
3. Loosen alternator adjusting bolt or drive belt tensioner as equipped, then remove alternator drive belt.
4. Remove any alternator mounting brackets and/or alternator that may interfere with cylinder head removal.
5. Disconnect all hoses, cables and wires that will interfere with cylinder head removal.
6. Disconnect exhaust manifold from exhaust pipe.
7. Remove timing belt as outlined under "Timing Belt, Replace."
8. Remove valve cover to cylinder head attaching nuts, then valve cover and gasket.
9. Loosen cylinder head bolts in reverse order, **Fig. 19.**
10. Remove bolts and the cylinder head, note whether engine is supplied with a metal or a fiber head gasket.
11. Reverse procedure to install, noting the following:
    a. Ensure gasket surfaces are clean and free of damage.
    b. **On models equipped with a metal type head gasket,** ensure head bolts have three raised dots (bolt B), **Fig. 20. Do not substitute any other type bolt.**
    c. **On models equipped with a fiber type head gasket,** ensure head bolts do not have three raised dots (bolt A), **Fig. 20. Do not substitute any other type bolt.**
    d. **On all models,** insert bolts 8 and 10 first to align cylinder head and gasket, then tighten all bolts hand tight.
    e. Using sequence, **Fig.19 torque,** cylinder head bolts in four stages: first to 30 ft. lbs.; then to 44 ft. lbs.; next tighten 1/4 (90°) turn; and finally, tighten an additional 1/4 (90°) turn.

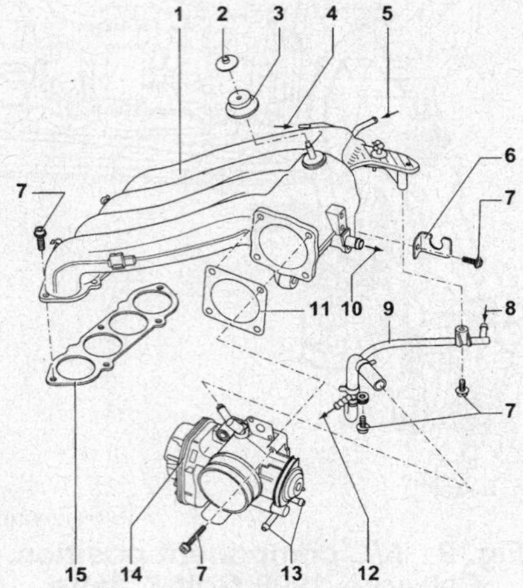

1. Upper Intake Manifold
2. Nut 53 inch lbs.
3. Rubber Bushing
4. From Fuel Pressure Regulator
5. From Leak Detection Pump
6. Support Bracket
7. Bolt 84 inch lbs.
8. From EVAP Canister Purge Valve
9. Connecting Pipe
10. To Brake Servo Vacuum Pipe
11. Gasket
12. To Intake Hose
13. Connections For Coolant Hoses
14. Throttle Valve Control Module
15. Gasket

VW1060100136000X

Fig. 14 Upper intake manifold removal. New Beetle & 1999–2001 Golf & Jetta

NEW BEETLE

1. Remove engine cover, then drain coolant into suitable container.
2. Disconnect fuel lines at fuel rail, then plug open lines.
3. Disconnect LDP pump vacuum line at fuel rail.
4. Remove air cleaner, then the accelerator cable to throttle control module.
5. Remove suction hose, then disconnect throttle control module electrical connector.
6. Remove coolant hoses from throttle control module to cylinder head.
7. Disconnect vacuum hoses from brake booster and secondary air injection valve.
8. Remove intake manifold bolts, then the vent line.
9. Remove warm air deflector bolts.
10. Disconnect fuel pressure regulator vacuum hose.
11. Remove fuel supply and return lines from fuel pressure regulator.
12. Remove secondary air injection pump intake and pressure lines.
13. Disconnect camshaft position sensor, fuel injector and secondary air injection pump electrical connectors.
14. Remove spark plug wires, then the serpentine drive belt tensioner.
15. Remove timing belt upper cover.
16. Release tensioning roller, then remove timing belt from camshaft sprocket.
17. Remove upper bolt from rear timing belt cover.
18. Remove front exhaust pipe from exhaust manifold, then the valve cover.
19. Remove cylinder head bolts in reverse of tightening sequence, **Fig. 21.**
20. Carefully lift and remove cylinder head.
21. Reverse procedure to install noting the following:
    a. Use new cylinder head bolts.
    b. Position No. 1 cylinder to TDC, then turn crankshaft back slightly.
    c. Center guide pins tool No. 3450/2A, or equivalent into head bolt holes.
    d. Install cylinder head gasket with part number facing upward.
    e. Remove guide pins through bolt holes using pin driver tool No. 3450/3, or equivalent by turning it counterclockwise.

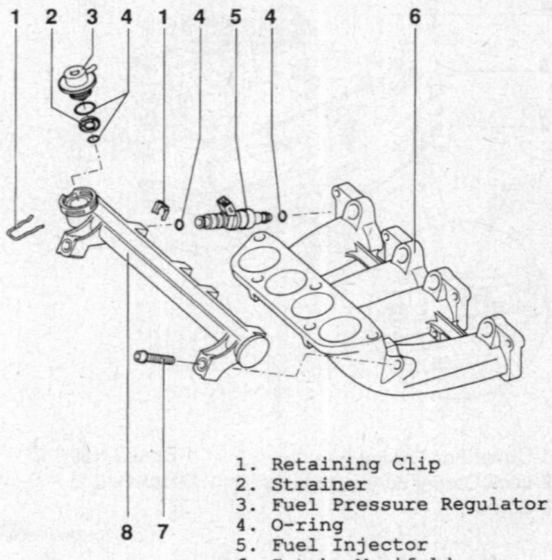

1. Retaining Clip
2. Strainer
3. Fuel Pressure Regulator
4. O-ring
5. Fuel Injector
6. Intake Manifold
7. Bolt 84 inch lbs.
8. Fuel Rail

VW1060100138000X

Fig. 15 Lower intake manifold removal. Cabrio, New Beetle & 1998 Golf & Jetta

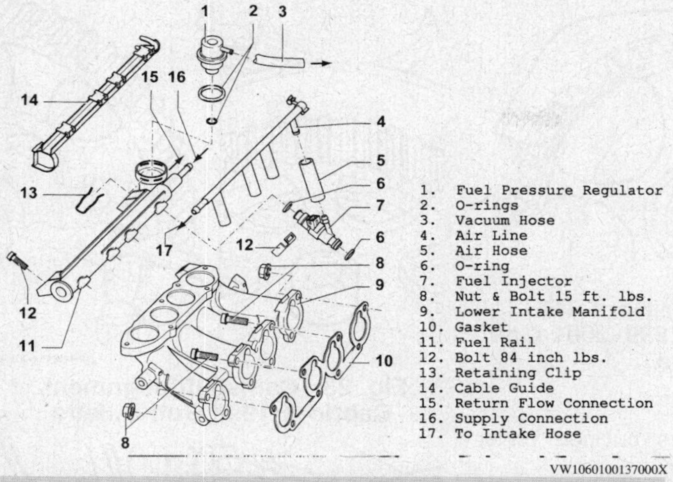

Fig. 16 Lower intake manifold removal. 1999–2001 Golf & Jetta

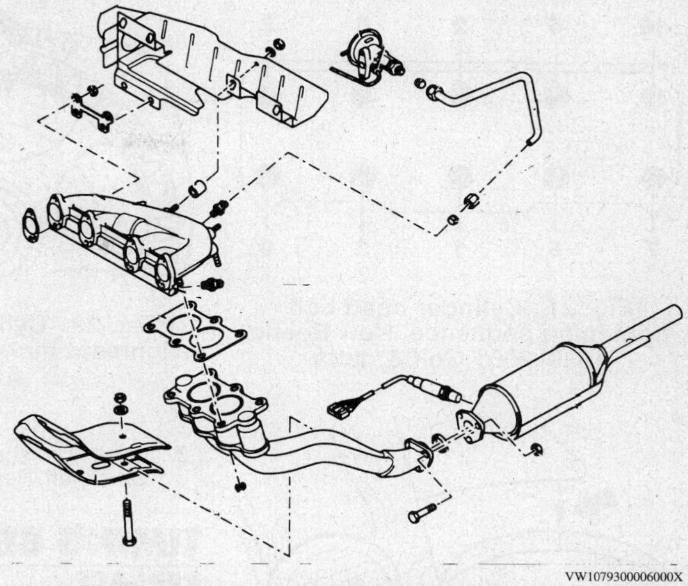

Fig. 17 Exhaust manifold removal. Cabrio & 1998 Golf & Jetta

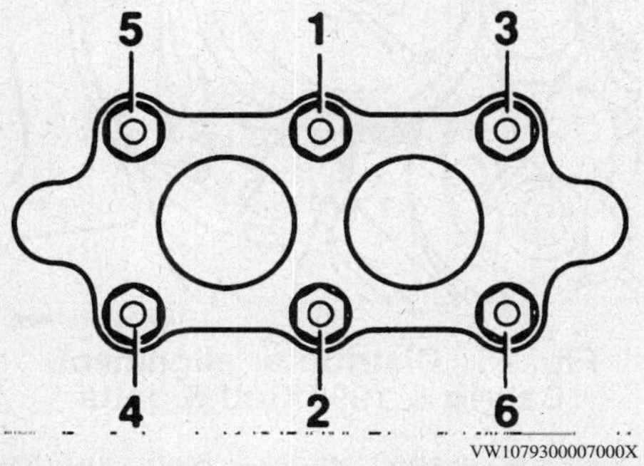

Fig. 18 Exhaust manifold to pipe tightening sequence. Cabrio & 1998 Golf & Jetta

f. **Torque** cylinder head bolts in sequence, **Fig. 21** using three steps, first to 30 ft. lbs., then turn 90° and finally an additional 90°.

1999–2001 GOLF & JETTA

1. Remove upper intake manifold as outlined under "Intake Manifold, Replace."
2. Drain coolant into suitable container, then remove hoses from cylinder head.
3. Disconnect fuel lines from fuel rail, then plug open lines.
4. Remove front exhaust pipe from manifold.
5. Remove serpentine drive belt.
6. Remove serpentine drive belt tensioner with bracket.
7. Remove timing belt upper cover.
8. Turn engine until No. 1 cylinder is at TDC, **Fig. 22.**
9. Release tensioning roller, then remove timing belt from camshaft sprocket.
10. Turn camshaft back slightly, then remove valve cover.
11. Remove upper bolt from rear timing belt cover.
12. Remove cylinder head bolts in reverse of tightening sequence, **Fig. 21.**

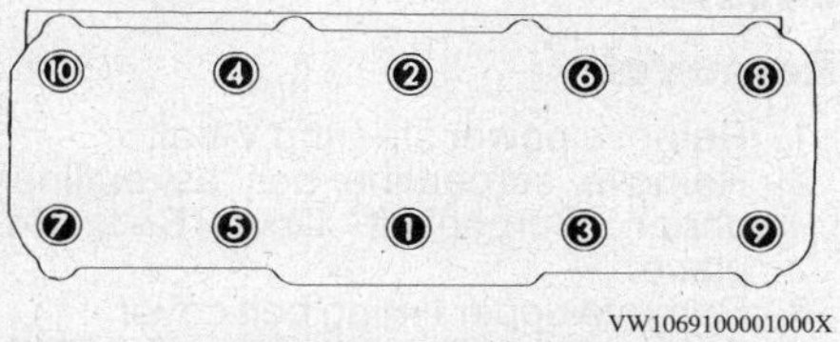

Fig. 19 Cylinder head bolt tightening sequence

13. Carefully lift and remove cylinder head.
14. Reverse procedure to install noting the following:
    a. Use new cylinder head bolts.
    b. Position No. 1 cylinder to TDC, then turn crankshaft back slightly.
    c. Center guide pins tool No. 3450/2A, or equivalent into head bolt holes.
    d. Install cylinder head gasket with part number facing upward.
    e. Remove guide pins through bolt holes using pin driver tool No. 3450/3, or equivalent by turning it counterclockwise.
    f. **Torque** cylinder head bolts in sequence, **Fig. 21** using three steps, first to 30 ft. lbs., then turn 90° and finally an additional 90°.

VALVE ADJUSTMENT

All engines are equipped with hydraulic lifters. No adjustment provision is provided.

HYDRAULIC LIFTER INSPECTION

Hydraulic valve lifters are non-adjustable. Noisy lifters may be replaced after the following check.

1. Run engine until radiator fan comes on at least once.

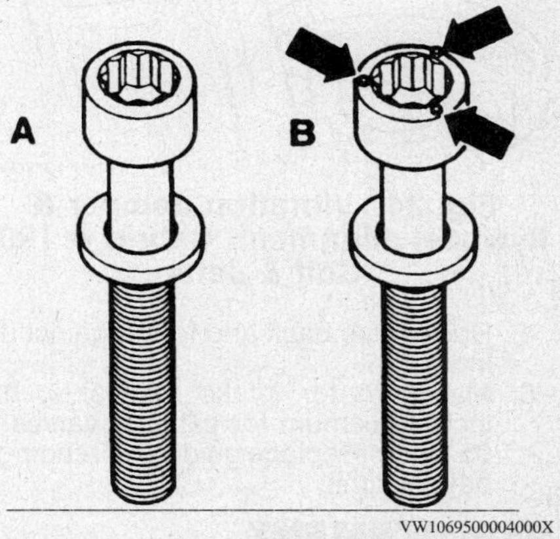

Fig. 20 Head bolt identification

2. Raise engine speed to 2500 RPM, for two minutes.
3. If lifter(s) is still noisy, proceed as follows:
    a. Remove upper intake manifold.
    b. Remove cylinder head cover.
    c. Turn crankshaft pulley bolt clockwise until cam lobes of cylinder point upward. Inspect for damage.
    d. Press down lightly against valve lifter with a wooden stick. If lifter can be pushed down more than. 004 inch, replace as outlined under "Hydraulic Lifter, Replace."

VALVE GUIDES

INSPECTION

1. Remove all carbon deposits from valve guide.
2. Set up a dial indicator on cylinder head to check suspected guide.
3. Insert new valve into valve guide. End of valve stem must be flush with valve guide end.

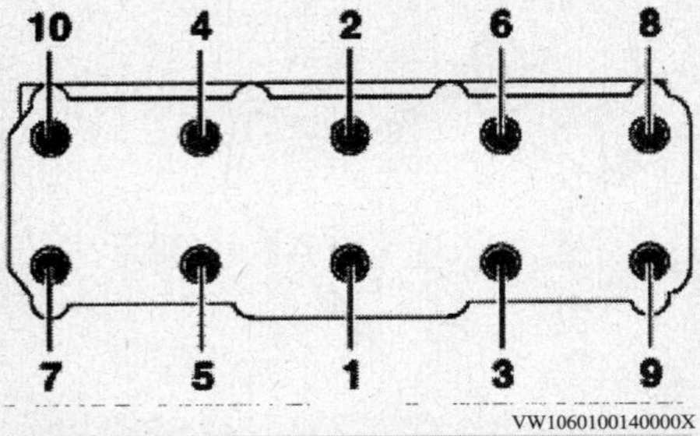

Fig. 21 Cylinder head bolt tightening sequence. New Beetle 1999–2001 Golf & Jetta

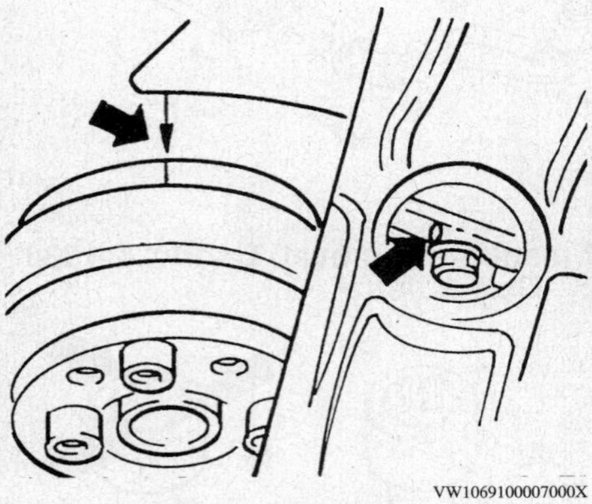

Fig. 24 Vibration damper & flywheel alignment. Cabrio & 1998 Golf & Jetta

4. Rock valve back and forth against dial indicator.
5. Maximum for intake valves is. 039 inch. Maximum for exhaust valves is. 051 inch. Replace guide(s) if reading is beyond limit.

REPLACEMENT

1. Worn valve guides can be removed using rod tool No. 3121, or equivalent.
2. Press guides with collar out from combustion chamber side of cylinder head and cracked guides out from camshaft side of cylinder head.
3. Coat new guides with engine oil, then press into cold cylinder head from camshaft side.
4. Press guides in as far as they will go. Once valve guide shoulder is seated, do not use more than one ton of pressure or guide shoulder may break. Ream guides by hand using tool No. 3120, or equivalent, and a proper cutting lubricant.
5. Machine valve seats.

HYDRAULIC LIFTERS

REPLACE

After replacing hydraulic lifters, do not run engine for 30 minutes. This will allow lifters time to bleed down to proper adjustment.

1. Remove camshaft as outlined under "Camshaft, Replace."
2. Replace defective lifter(s).

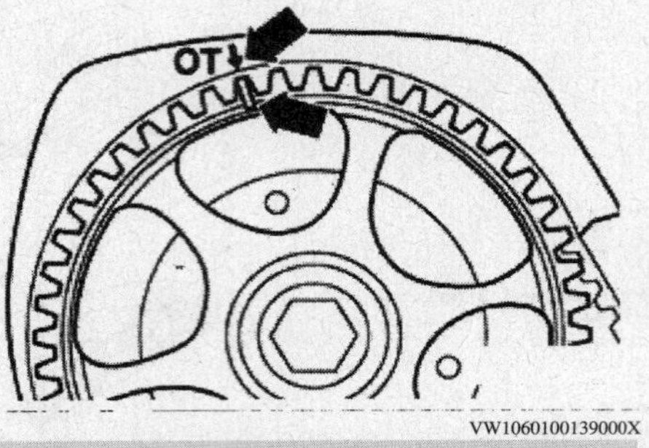

Fig. 22 Cylinder No. 1 TDC alignment marks. 1999–2001 Golf & Jetta

3. Install camshaft as outlined under "Camshaft, Replace."

TIMING BELT

REPLACE

CABRIO & 1998 GOLF & JETTA

Removal

1. Remove power steering V-belt.
2. Remove serpentine belt as outlined under "Serpentine Drive Belt, Replace."
3. Remove upper timing belt cover.
4. Set engine to Top Dead Center (TDC) compression stroke using timing marks, **Figs. 23 and 24.**
5. Loosen belt tensioner, then remove timing belt from camshaft drive sprocket.
6. Remove crankshaft vibration damper/pulley. Note installed position for later assembly.
7. If timing belt is to be reused, mark with direction of rotation.
8. Remove lower timing belt cover, then belt.

Installation

1. Install the timing belt on crankshaft and intermediate shaft sprockets. **If a used belt is being installed, note direction of rotation mark made during removal.**
2. Install lower drive belt cover, then water pump pulley.
3. Install crankshaft vibration damper. Note offset mounting bolt holes for alignment of pulley to crankshaft.
4. Align mark on front of camshaft sprocket with arrow on valve cover, **Fig. 23.** If valve cover has been removed, align mark on rear of sprocket with cylinder head.
5. Align crankshaft and intermediate shaft as follows:
   a. With engine removed, align TDC mark on vibration damper with arrow on drive belt cover, **Fig. 24.**
   b. With engine installed, align TDC mark on flywheel with mark on clutch housing, **Fig. 24.**
   c. Remove distributor cap.
   d. While allowing belt to slip over crankshaft sprocket teeth, turn intermediate shaft sprocket to align rotor tip to mark on distributor body, **Fig. 25.**

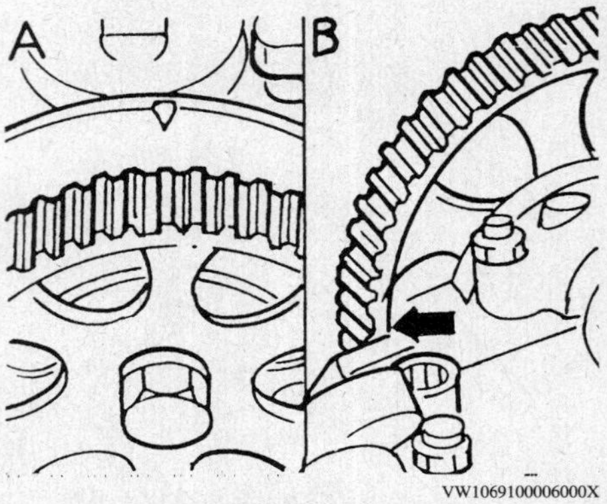

Fig. 23 Camshaft alignment. Cabrio & 1998 Golf & Jetta

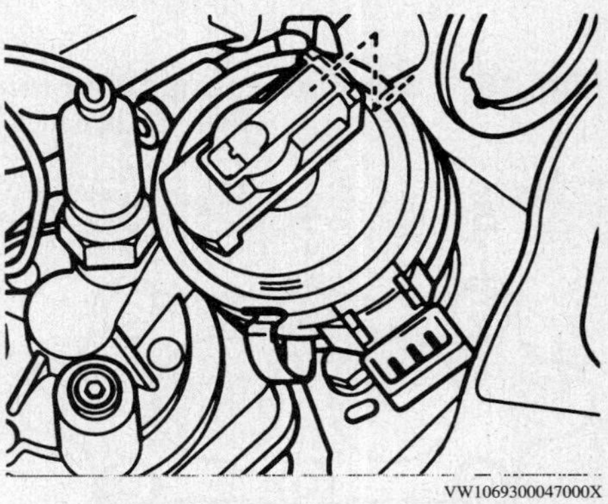

Fig. 25 Distributor alignment. Cabrio & 1998 Golf & Jetta

6. Mount drive belt on camshaft drive sprocket and over tensioner pulley.
7. Tighten belt tensioner eccentric adjuster by turning clockwise until belt can just be twisted 90° at mid-point between cam sprocket and intermediate shaft sprocket, **Fig. 26.**
8. Tighten tensioner locknut to specifications.
9. Rotate crankshaft twice in normal direction of rotation, then check tension adjustment. If adjustment is incorrect, repeat steps above. If adjustment is correct, proceed to next step.
10. Install upper drive belt cover, then drive belts.

NEW BEETLE & 1999–2001 GOLF & JETTA

Removal

With the timing belt removed, avoid turning the camshaft or crankshaft. If movement is required, exercise extreme caution to avoid valve damage caused by piston contact.

1. Remove engine appearance cover.
2. Remove righthand insulation tray.
3. Rotate engine accessory drive belt tensioner clockwise.
4. Lock tensioner with VW locking tool

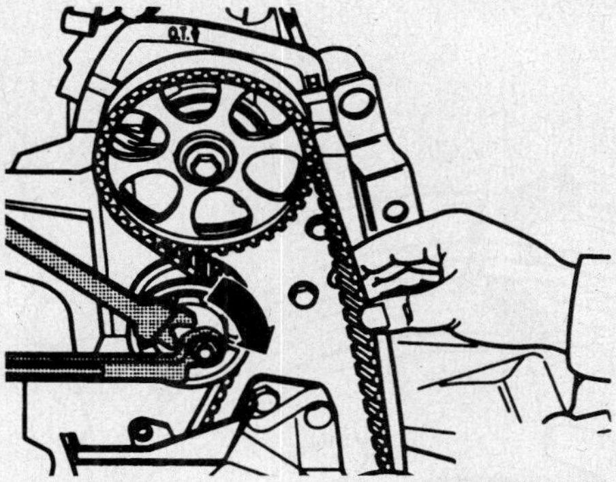

VW1069300048000X

Fig. 26 Timing belt tension. Cabrio & 1998 Golf & Jetta

No. 3090, or a 5⁄16 diameter pin approximately 2⅛ inch long. **An assistant may be required for this step.**

5. Note running direction, then remove accessory drive belt.
6. Remove accessory drive belt tensioner mounting bolts, then the tensioner.
7. **On Golf and Jetta models equipped with manual transaxle,** rotate crankshaft in normal running direction until the No. 1 cylinder reaches TDC on its compression stroke and flywheel timing marks are properly aligned, **Fig. 27.**
8. **On Golf and Jetta models equipped with automatic transaxle,** rotate crankshaft in normal running direction until No. 1 cylinder reaches TDC on its compression stroke and flexplate timing marks are properly aligned, **Fig. 28.**
9. **On New Beetle models,** rotate crankshaft in normal running direction until No. 1 cylinder reaches TDC on its compression stroke and crankshaft pulley timing marks are properly aligned, **Fig. 29.**
10. **On all models,** remove timing belt upper cover.
11. Ensure camshaft sprocket timing marks are properly aligned, **Fig. 30.**
12. **On Golf and Jetta models,** install VW engine support tool No. 10-222A with legs tool No. 10-222A/1, or their equivalents.
13. **On New Beetle models,** install VW engine support tool No. 10-222A with legs tool No. 10-222A/1, and adapter tool No. 10-222 A/8, or their equivalents. **It will be necessary to drill a 12.5 mm hole in 10-222 A/21 guide approximately 7.9 inches in from hole opposite slotted end before adapter can be used.**
14. **On Golf and Jetta models,** proceed as follows:
    a. Position coolant expansion tank aside, but leave hoses intact.
    b. Position power steering fluid reservoir aside, but leave hoses intact.
    c. Remove six side engine support mounting bolts, then the mount.
15. **On New Beetle models,** remove four engine mount bolts, **Fig. 31,** then loosen, but do not remove, bolt "A."
16. **On all models,** remove crankshaft pulley retaining bolts, then the pulley.

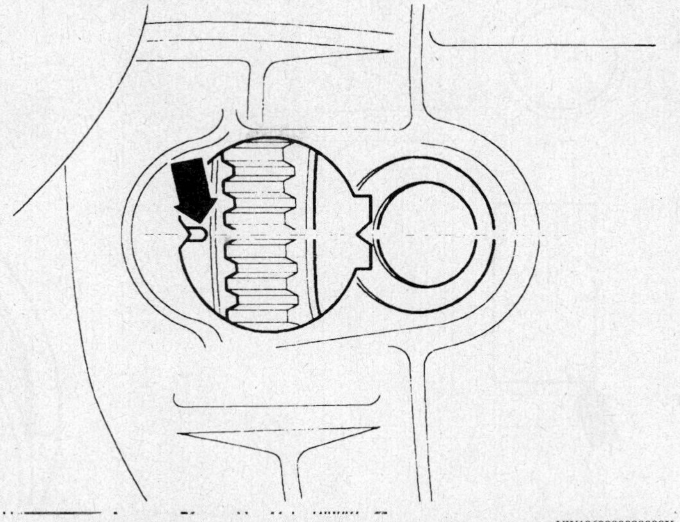

VW1069900098000X

Fig. 27 M/T flywheel alignment marks. 1999–2001 Golf & Jetta

17. Remove timing belt center and lower covers.
18. Remove three engine mount bracket bolts, then the bracket. It may be necessary to raise engine slightly to loosen retaining bolts.
19. Using VW wrench tool No. T 10020, or equivalent, rotate timing belt tensioner counterclockwise to release timing belt tension, then remove the belt.

Installation

1. Inspect water pump and all nearby seals for leakage or damage. Replace as required.
2. Ensure all timing marks are still properly aligned, **Figs. 27 through 30. If alignment of camshaft sprocket timing marks is required, turn crankshaft back slightly. If piston is at TDC, valve could strike piston when aligning camshaft sprocket timing marks. After aligning camshaft sprocket timing marks, align crankshaft timing marks.**
3. **Wait until engine has cooled down before installing timing belt.**
4. Install timing belt onto crankshaft sprocket and water pump.
5. Insert engine mount bracket retaining bolts into bracket, then install bracket onto engine block.
6. Install timing belt lower and center covers.
7. Install crankshaft pulley.
8. Ensure crankshaft pulley timing marks are properly aligned, **Fig. 29.**
9. Install engine mount with new bolts.
10. **On Golf and Jetta models,** ensure mount is properly aligned **Fig. 32,** bolt heads must align with edge of mount.
11. **On New Beetle models,** tighten engine mount bolts to specifications.
12. **On all models,** remove engine support tools.
13. Ensure all timing marks are still properly aligned, **Figs. 27 through 30. If alignment of camshaft sprocket timing marks is required, turn crankshaft back slightly. If piston is at TDC, valve could strike piston when aligning camshaft sprocket timing marks. After aligning camshaft sprocket timing marks, align crankshaft timing marks.**
14. Loop timing belt around camshaft sprocket and tensioner roller.
15. Using VW wrench tool No. T 10020, or equivalent, rotate timing belt tensioner counterclockwise until notch and indicator are aligned, **Fig. 33. Use a suitable mirror for this inspection. Angled retainer must also be securely located in cylinder head cutout.**
16. Rotate crankshaft two turns in normal running direction. Timing belt tensioner notch and indicator must move back into proper alignment, **Fig. 33,** It is important that last ⅛ turn of rotation is made without interruption.
17. Install timing belt upper cover.
18. Install engine accessory drive belt tensioner, then tighten bolts to specifications
19. Lock tensioner with VW locking tool No. 3090, or a 5⁄16 diameter pin approximately 2⅛ inch long. **An assistant may be required for this step.**
20. Install accessory drive belt, then the righthand insulation tray.
21. Install engine appearance cover.
22. Start engine and ensure it operates properly.

CAMSHAFT

REPLACE

1. Remove valve cover to cylinder head attaching bolts, then the valve cover.
2. Remove timing belt as outlined under "Timing Belt, Replace."
3. Remove camshaft sprocket attaching bolt and the camshaft sprocket.

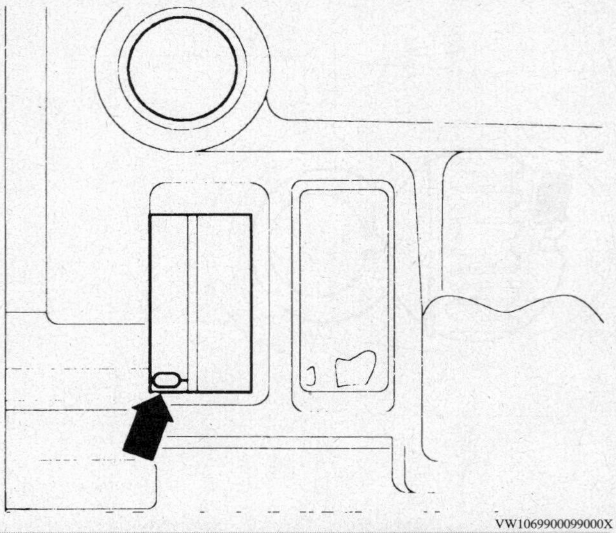

Fig. 28 A/T flywheel alignment marks. 1999–2001 Golf & Jetta

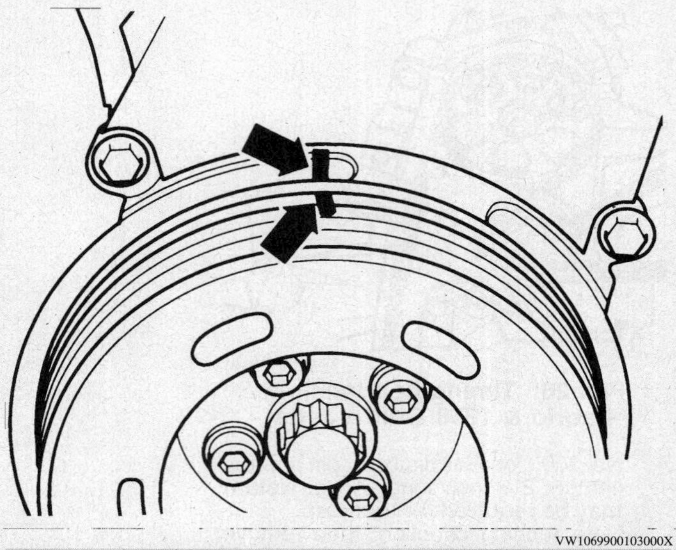

Fig. 29 Crankshaft pulley alignment marks. New Beetle, 1999–2001 Golf & Jetta

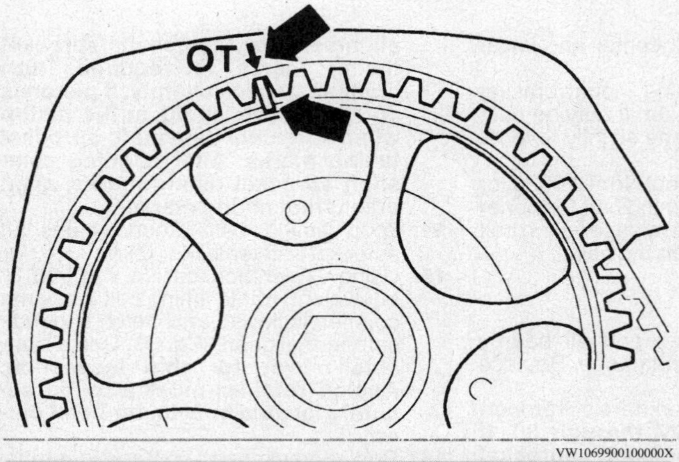

Fig. 30 Camshaft sprocket alignment marks. New Beetle & 1999–2001 Golf & Jetta

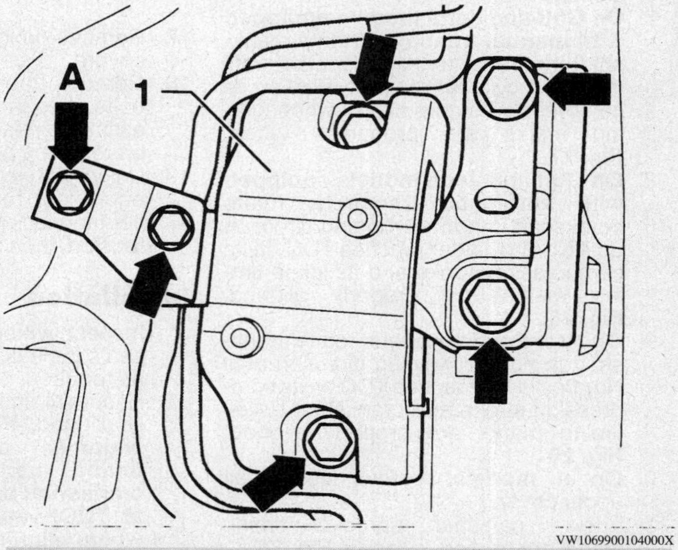

Fig. 31 Engine mount bolt removal. New Beetle

4. Working from front of engine, remove Nos. 5, 1 and 3 bearing caps.
5. Diagonally loosen, then remove, Nos. 2 and 4 bearing caps. **Numbered from front to rear.**
6. Remove camshaft from cylinder head.
7. Lubricate bearing shells, journals and contact surface of bearing caps with engine oil.
8. Position camshaft onto bearing saddles and install new camshaft oil seal.
9. Install bearing caps and ensure caps align correctly, **Fig. 34.**
10. Lightly tighten Nos. 2 and 4 bearing caps diagonally, then tighten all caps to specifications.
11. Install camshaft sprocket onto camshaft and tighten attaching bolt to specifications.
12. Align timing marks, then install timing belt, timing cover and valve cover.

PISTON & ROD ASSEMBLY

Assemble the piston to the rod with the arrow on the piston crown pointing toward the front of the engine and the casting marks on the rod facing the intermediate shaft.

PISTONS, PINS & RINGS

Pistons and rings are available in. 010 inch,. 020 inch and. 040 inch oversizes. Oversize piston pins are not available.

MAIN & ROD BEARINGS

Main and connecting rod bearings are available in. 010 inch,. 020 inch and. 030 inch undersizes.

CRANKSHAFT REAR OIL SEAL

REPLACE

1. **On models equipped with manual transaxle,** remove transaxle, flywheel, pressure plate, clutch disc and intermediate plate as outlined under "Clutch & Manual Transaxle."

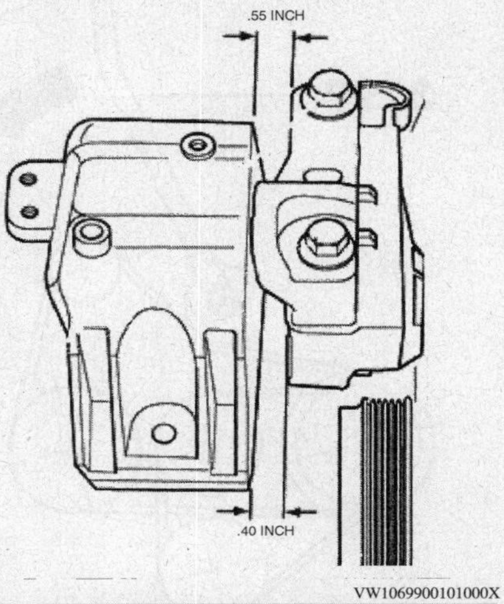

Fig. 32 Engine mount alignment. 1999–2001 Golf & Jetta

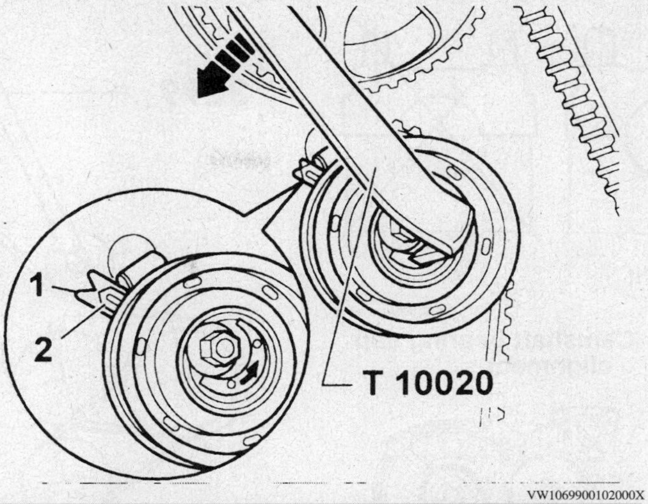

Fig. 33 Timing belt tensioner alignment. New Beetle & 1999–2001 Golf & Jetta

2. **On models equipped with automatic transaxle,** remove transaxle, torque converter and torque converter driveplate as outlined under "Automatic Transaxles."
3. **On all models,** pry oil seal out of oil seal flange using a screwdriver, or equivalent.
4. Lubricate new seal, center seal in seal flange and press until fully seated.
5. Reverse procedure to complete installation.

FRONT MAIN BEARING OIL SEAL

REPLACE

1. Remove timing belt as outlined under "Timing Belt, Replace."
2. Remove crankshaft sprocket retaining bolt, then sprocket. **On 16-valve engines, do not allow crankshaft to turn as piston valve contact will occur.**
3. Using a suitable tool remove oil seal.
4. Lightly lubricate sealing lip and outer edge of new oil seal.
5. Place suitable guide sleeve onto crankshaft, then push oil seal over guide sleeve.
6. Using a suitable tool, press oil seal in until it reaches stop.
7. Reverse procedure to install. Use a suitable Loctite on crankshaft sprocket bolt and tighten to specifications.

OIL PAN

REPLACE

1. Remove oil pan drain plug and drain engine oil.
2. Remove oil pan to engine attaching bolts and the oil pan.
3. Reverse procedure to install. Tighten to specifications.

SERPENTINE DRIVE BELT

ROUTING

Refer to **Figs. 35 through 38** for serpentine drive belt routing and tensioner release tool placement.

REPLACEMENT

1. Loosen power steering pump adjustment bolts, then remove V-belt.
2. Mark running direction of serpentine drive belt if it is to be reused.
3. Insert tensioner tool No. 3299, or equivalent, onto belt tensioner.
4. Rotate tensioner clockwise to release tension, then remove belt from alternator pulley.
5. Remove belt from remaining pulleys.
6. Reverse procedure to install. Note running direction of used belts.

COOLING SYSTEM BLEED

Note type of coolant, do not allow red coolant to be mixed with any other type.

1. Slowly fill coolant expansion tank to Max mark, then install expansion tank cap.
2. Run engine until cooling fan comes on, then check coolant level.
3. Coolant level should be at or slightly above Max mark with engine at normal operating temperature, and between Min and Max marks with engine cold.
4. If necessary, add coolant to specified marking.

WATER PUMP

REPLACE

CABRIO & 1998 GOLF & JETTA

1. Drain cooling system into suitable container.
2. **On models equipped with A/C,** remove A/C drive belt.
3. **On models less A/C,** loosen alternator drive belt.
4. **On all models,** remove water pump pulley retaining bolts, then the pulley.
5. Remove upper timing belt cover retaining bolts, then the cover.
6. Set engine to Top Dead Center (TDC) compression stroke, **Fig. 39. Do not turn engine counterclockwise using sprocket retaining bolt, as this may slightly loosen bolt.**
7. Remove crankshaft pulley, then lower timing belt cover.
8. Remove timing belt guide, if equipped.
9. If belt is to be reused, mark direction of rotation.
10. Loosen timing belt tensioner adjusting nut, then remove timing belt.
11. Remove intermediate shaft sprocket.
12. Remove water pump to housing attaching bolts, then discard bolts.
13. Remove water pump and gasket.
14. Reverse procedure to install , noting the following:
    a. Ensure crankshaft pulley notch is aligned with intermediate sprocket mark at TDC pointer, **Fig. 39.**
    b. Ensure camshaft sprocket mark is aligned with valve cover flange, **Fig. 39.**
    c. Install timing belt onto sprockets, then tighten belt tensioner adjuster clockwise until belt can just be twisted 90° at mid-point between cam sprocket and intermediate shaft sprocket.
    d. Tighten adjuster retaining nut.
    e. Install timing belt guide, if equipped, then the lower timing belt cover.
    f. Install crankshaft and water pump pulleys, then upper timing belt cover.
    g. **Note type of coolant, do not allow red coolant to be mixed with any other type.**
    h. Install and tension drive belts.

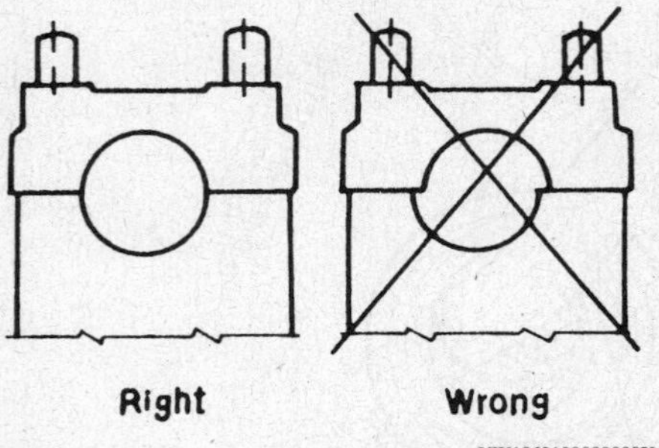

Fig. 34 Camshaft bearing cap alignment

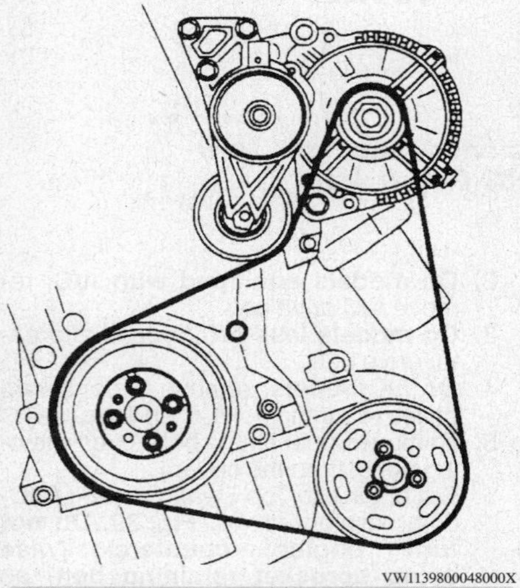

Fig. 37 Drive belt routing. New Beetle & 1999–2001 Golf & Jetta less A/C

NEW BEETLE & 1999–2001 GOLF & JETTA

1. Drain coolant into suitable container, then remove serpentine drive belt as outlined under "Serpentine Drive Belt."
2. Remove serpentine drive belt tensioner, then the upper timing belt cover.
3. Remove timing belt from water pump sprocket as outlined under "Timing Belt, Replace."
4. Remove water pump bolts, then the water pump.
5. Reverse procedure to install. Tighten bolts to specifications.

RADIATOR

REPLACE

CABRIO & 1998 GOLF & JETTA

1. Drain cooling system.
2. Remove radiator cover and radiator mounting shroud.
3. Disconnect upper and lower radiator hoses.
4. Disconnect coolant expansion tank tube from radiator.

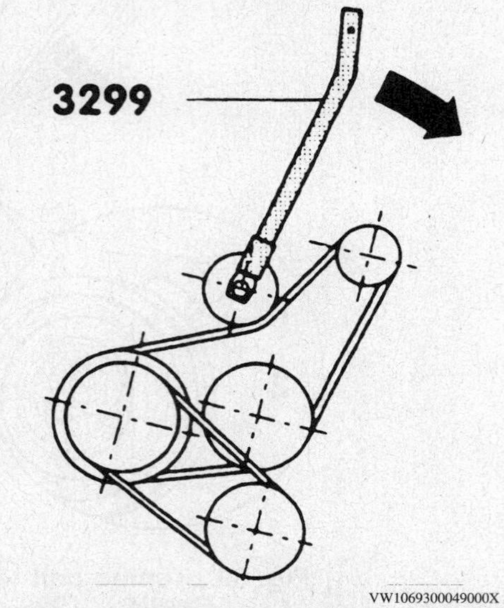

Fig. 35 Drive belt routing. Cabrio & 1998 Golf & Jetta less A/C

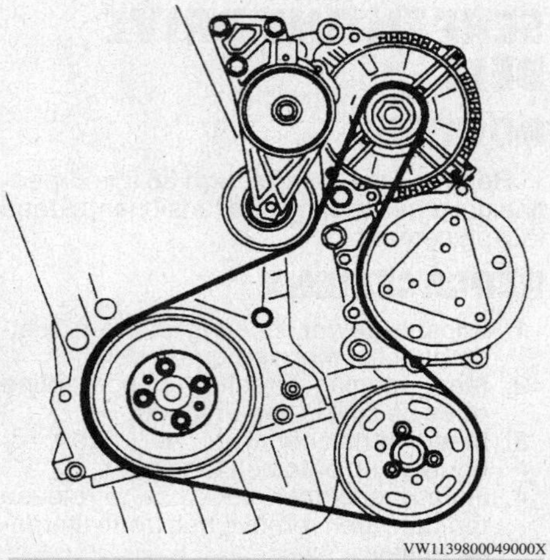

Fig. 38 Drive belt routing. New Beetle & 1999–2001 Golf & Jetta with A/C

5. Remove cooling fan cowl with cooling fan(s).
6. **On models equipped with automatic transaxle,** disconnect oil cooler hose.
7. **On all models,** remove thermo switch from radiator.
8. Remove radiator.
9. Reverse procedure to install, **note type of coolant, do not allow red coolant to be mixed with any other type.**

NEW BEETLE & 1999–2001 GOLF & JETTA

Refer to "1.8L Turbocharged Engine" for replacement procedures.

FUEL PUMP

REPLACE

The fuel system is designed to retain a residual fuel pressure. When disconnecting lines use precautions to prevent any fuel spillage.

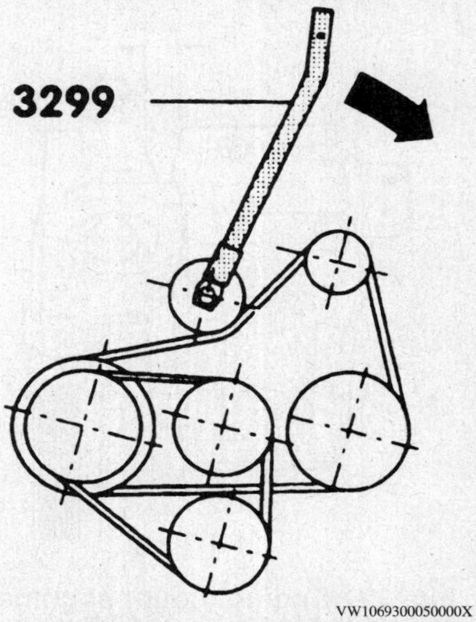

Fig. 36 Drive belt routing. Cabrio & 1998 Golf & Jetta with A/C

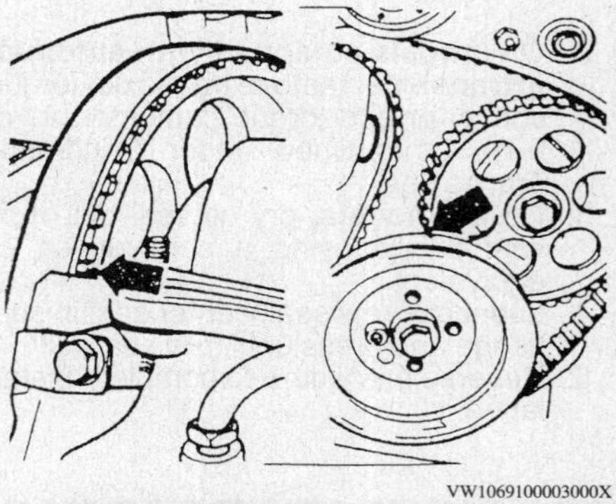

Fig. 39 Timing mark alignment. Cabrio & 1998 Golf & Jetta

EXCEPT IN TANK

1. Remove fuel cap to release fuel vapor pressure.
2. Disconnect fuel lines from pump. Use a suitable clamping device on pump inlet line to prevent fuel siphon.
3. Disconnect mounting bracket from underbody, then the electrical connector from fuel pump.
4. Remove fuel pump from bracket.
5. Reverse procedure to install.

IN TANK

1. Remove fuel tank cap to relieve tank pressure.
2. Locate fuel pump access port from inside vehicle luggage compartment.
3. Remove screws, then pry up cover.
4. Clean fuel pump and fuel line unions thoroughly to prevent entry of dirt into fuel system.
5. Disconnect fuel lines and electrical connections from pump.
6. Place match marks on fuel pump flange and tank for later assembly.
7. Remove fuel pump flange retaining

ring nut using wrench tool No. 3217, or equivalent.

8. Remove flange and seal.
9. Turn fuel pump module to left to disengage, then lift from tank. Use caution not to damage fuel level sender float arm.
10. Separate pump from module.
11. Reverse procedure to install, noting the following:
    a. **On Cabrio and 1998 Golf and Jetta models,** when installing fuel pump module, float arm will point to front of vehicle, offset to the left 5°.

TIGHTENING SPECIFICATIONS

Year	Component	Torque, Ft. Lbs.
1998–2001	Axle Shaft To Transaxle Flange Bolts	33
	Axle Nut	195
	Ball Joint To Suspension Arm Bolts	26
	Camshaft Bearing Cap To Cylinder Head Nuts	15
	Camshaft Sprocket To Camshaft Bolt	74
	Clutch Pressure Plate (Driveplate) To Crankshaft	44①⑥
	Clutch Slave Cylinder	18⑤
	Connecting Rod Nuts	22①
	Crankshaft Pulley	④
	Crankshaft Timing Belt Sprocket To Crankshaft Bolt	66①
	Cylinder Head Cover To Cylinder Head Bolts	84⑦
	Cylinder Head Bolts	②
	Engine To Transaxle Bolts, M10	33
	Engine To Transaxle Bolts, M12	59
	Exhaust Pipe To Exhaust Manifold Bolts	30
	Front Main Oil Seal Housing To Block Bolts	15
	Front Engine Mount Bracket To Body	18
	Front Engine Mount To Body	30①
	Front Engine Mount To Engine Bracket	44①
	Flywheel To Crankshaft Bolts	44①⑤
	Flywheel To Pressure Plate (Driveplate) Bolts	15⑥
	Intermediate Shaft Oil Seal Flange To Block Bolts	18
	Intermediate Shaft Sprocket To Intermediate Shaft Bolt	48
	Hub Nut	195
	Lower Timing Belt Cover Bolts	84⑦
	Main Bearing Cap Bolts	48①
	Oil Cooler To Oil Filter Bracket Nut	18
	Oil Pan Drain Plug To Oil Pan	22
	Oil Pan To Block Bolts	15
	Oil Pressure Switch To Oil Filter Bracket	18
	Oil Pump Cover To Oil Pump Housing Bolts	84⑦
	Oil Pump Pickup To Pump Bolts	84⑦
	Oil Pump To Block Bolts	15
	Oil Spray Nozzle To Block Bolt	84⑤⑦
	Pendulum Support To Engine	15①
	Pendulum Support To Transaxle	30①
	Power Steering Pump To Mounting Bracket Bolts	18
	Pressure Plate (Driveplate) To Crankshaft	44①⑥
	Pressure Plate To Flywheel	15⑤
	Radiator Mounting Bolts	84⑦
	Rear Engine Mount To Body	18
	Rear Engine Mount To Transaxle	44①
	Rear Main Oil Seal Housing To Block Bolts	15
	Rear Timing Belt Cover To Block Bolts	22
	Rear Timing Belt Cover To Block Threaded Bolt	22③
	Thermostat Flange Bolts	84⑦
	Timing Belt Tensioner Nut	33
	Upper Intake Manifold Bolts	15

Continued

TIGHTENING SPECIFICATIONS—Continued

Year	Component	Torque, Ft. Lbs.
1998–2001	Upper Timing Belt Cover Bolts	48⑦
	Vibration Damper (Pulley) To Crankshaft Timing Belt Sprocket Bolt	74
	Water Pump Housing To Block Bolts	15
	Water Pump Pulley To Water Pump Bolts	15
	Water Pump To Water Pump Housing Bolts	84⑦

① — Plus an additional 1/4 (90°) turn.
② — Refer to "Cylinder Head, Replace."
③ — Coat threads with D6 locking compound, or equivalent.
④ — Golf & Jetta; 30 ft. lbs., New Beetle 18 ft. lbs.
⑤ — Models w/02A transaxle.
⑥ — Models w/020 transaxle.
⑦ — Inch lbs.

2.8L VR6 Gasoline Engine

NOTE: On Air Bag Equipped Models, Refer To "Air Bag System Precautions" Located In The Front Of This Manual For System Disarming & Arming Procedures.

NOTE: Refer To "Computer Relearn Procedures" Located In The Front Of This Manual When Battery Power To The Computer Has Been Interrupted.

INDEX

	Page No.
Camshaft, Replace	8-55
Installation	8-55
Removal	8-55
Compression Pressure	8-52
1998	8-52
1999–2001	8-52
Cooling System Bleed	8-56
Crankshaft Rear Oil Seal, Replace	8-55
Crankshaft Seal, Replace	8-55
Cylinder Head, Replace	8-53
1998	8-53
1999–2001	8-53
Engine Mount, Replace	8-52
Front	8-52
Left	8-52
Right	8-52
Engine Rebuilding Specifications	8-185
Engine, Replace	8-53
1998	8-53
1999–2001	8-53
Fuel Pump, Replace	8-56
Oil Pan, Replace	8-56
Oil Pump, Replace	8-56
Piston & Rod Assembly	8-55
Precautions	8-52
Air Bag Systems	8-52
Audio Coded Anti-Theft System	8-52
Battery Ground Cable	8-52
Radiator, Replace	8-56
1998	8-56
1999–2001	8-56
Tightening Specifications	8-58
Timing Chain, Replace	8-54
Valve Adjustment	8-54
Valve Clearance Specifications	8-54
Valve Guides	8-54
Inspection	8-54
Replacement	8-54
Water Pump, Replace	8-56
1998	8-56
1999–2001	8-56

PRECAUTIONS

AIR BAG SYSTEMS

Do not use computer memory saver tool on air bag equipped models. Using the tool will keep the air bag system charged and may cause accidental activation of the air bag unit. Refer to "Air Bag System Precautions" in the front of this manual for system disarming and arming procedures.

BATTERY GROUND CABLE

Prior to disconnecting the battery negative cable, obtain the radio security code. After service has been completed and the battery negative cable has been reconnected, use security code to activate the radio. Prior to service, disconnect battery ground cable and isolate as required.

AUDIO CODED ANTI-THEFT SYSTEM

Some models are equipped with a radio anti-theft system that will disable the system when battery power is interrupted, unless the system is reset the radio will not operate.

1. Turn radio to On position, SAFE and 1000 should be displayed.
2. Enter radio code using first four program station buttons. Security code will appear on display.
3. Depress and hold righthand side of radio right or left blocker until anti-theft coding is activated indicated by a brief signal sound.
4. If code number has been entered correctly, when ignition key is removed a diode on front of radio will flash.

COMPRESSION PRESSURE

1998

1. Perform compression test with engine oil temperature at a minimum of 86°F and throttle plate completely open.
2. Disconnect 5-pin connector from ignition coil.
3. Connect compression tester tool No. VAG 1763, or equivalent. Crank engine until compression tester shows no further pressure increase.
4. Compression pressure should be 145–189 psi with a maximum difference between cylinders of 44 psi. Minimum pressure is 109 psi.

1999–2001

1. Perform compression test with engine oil temperature at a minimum of 86°F and throttle plate completely open.
2. Disconnect electrical connector from heating resistor.
3. Remove intake hose between upper half of air filter and throttle control unit together with crankcase purge valve.
4. Remove spark plug wires, then the spark plugs.
5. Remove engine cover, then disconnect 5-way electrical connector from ignition coil.
6. Remove fuse No. 32 from fuse block.
7. Connect compression tester tool No. 1763, or equivalent. Crank engine until tester no longer shows an increase in pressure.
8. Compression pressure should be 145–189 psi with a maximum difference between cylinders of 43.5 psi. Minimum pressure is 109 psi.

ENGINE MOUNT

REPLACE

FRONT

1. Attach engine lifting tool No. 2024A, or equivalent, and loosen front engine mount center mounting bolt.
2. Raise engine and transaxle assembly until weight is off mount, then remove center bolt.
3. Remove center engine mount bolt, then remove subframe mounting bolts and engine mount.
4. Reverse procedure to install.

LEFT

1. Attach engine lifting tool No. 2024A, or equivalent, and loosen engine/transaxle center mount mounting bolt.
2. Raise engine and transaxle assembly until weight is off mount, then remove center mounting bolt.
3. Remove engine mount bolts from subframe, then engine mount.
4. Reverse procedure to install.

RIGHT

1. Attach engine lifting tool No. 2024A, or equivalent, and loosen center engine mount mounting bolt.
2. Raise engine and transaxle assembly until weight is off mount, then remove center mounting bolt.
3. Remove engine mount bolts from subframe, then engine mount.
4. Reverse procedure to install.

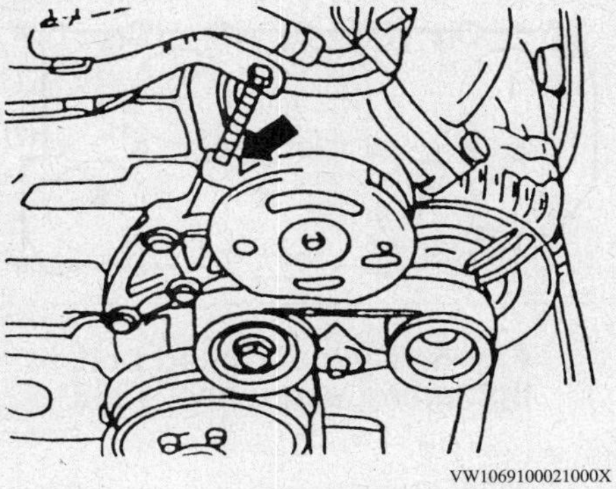

Fig. 1 Belt tension release

ENGINE

REPLACE

1998

1. Ensure ignition switch is in Off position, then remove air cleaner housing.
2. Drain cooling system, then remove radiator.
3. **On models equipped with manual transaxle,** unbolt and disconnect slave cylinder, then disconnect shift cable and support bracket.
4. **On models equipped with automatic transaxle,** unclip and disconnect selector lever cable.
5. **On all models,** thread an 8 mm x 80 mm bolt into threaded hole on tensioner, **Fig. 1,** to release belt tension. **Thread in bolt only far enough to release tension on belt, otherwise, damage to tensioner may occur.**
6. Remove belt from power steering pump and A/C compressor, then the A/C compressor and secure to body or frame. **Do not disconnect or kink A/C refrigerant lines.**
7. Remove power steering pump from bracket and secure to body or frame. **Do not disconnect or kink power steering hoses.**
8. Remove ignition wire guides and ignition wires, then the distributor cap.
9. Remove cylinder head cover trim covers, then disconnect accelerator cable at throttle body and cable guide.
10. Disconnect 42-point electrical connector from engine electrical harness, then all other engine and transaxle electrical wiring as necessary, and position aside.
11. Disconnect all coolant, vacuum and intake hoses from engine, then the inlet and return fuel lines at fuel distributor. **Cap all open fuel lines.**
12. Disconnect oxygen sensor and front exhaust pipe, then the axle shafts and secure to body or frame.
13. Attach engine sling as shown in **Fig. 2,** then relieve engine weight using a suitable lift.
14. Unbolt engine from engine mounts, carefully guide engine and transaxle assembly from vehicle, then separate engine from transaxle.
15. Reverse procedure to install, noting the following:
    a. Ensure recesses on front and rear engine brackets fit into mounting tabs of rubber bushings.
    b. Hand tighten mount bolts, lightly rock or shake engine to adjust position, then tighten mount bolts to specifications.
    c. **Note type of coolant, do not allow red coolant to be mixed with any other type.**

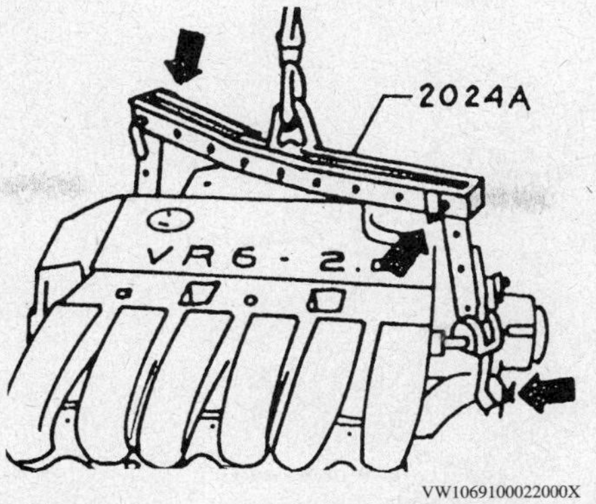

Fig. 2 Engine sling installation

1999–2001

Engine is removed together with transaxle from below.

1. Remove spark plug wires, then the engine cover.
2. Remove battery and battery tray, then the air filter assembly.
3. Disconnect fuel supply and return lines from fuel rail.
4. Remove lower sound insulation panels.
5. Remove serpentine drive belt.
6. Remove power steering pump and position aside. Do not disconnect lines from pump.
7. Remove mounting bracket for power steering pressure line.
8. **On models equipped with A/C,** remove compressor and position aside. Do not disconnect A/C lines.
9. **On models equipped with manual transaxle,** disconnect shift linkage, then remove clutch slave cylinder.
10. **On models equipped with automatic transaxle,** remove selector cable from transaxle.
11. **On all models,** remove front bumper cover.
12. Disconnect hood release cable.
13. Remove one bolt on each longitudinal member, then install guide rods tool No. 3411, or equivalent.
14. Remove remaining bolts, then pull lock carrier forward onto guide rods.
15. Remove intake pipe, then disconnect vacuum and vent hoses from engine.
16. Disconnect electrical connectors from alternator, starter motor and transaxle.
17. Disconnect electrical connectors from ignition transformer, coolant servo pump, injection valves, coolant temperature sensor, engine speed sensor, knock sensor and oxygen sensor.
18. Drain coolant into suitable container, then disconnect radiator hoses from engine.
19. Remove front exhaust pipe, then the righthand CV joint dust boot from engine.
20. Remove drive axles as outlined in "Front Wheel Drive Axles" section.
21. Remove rocker bracket, **Fig. 3.**
22. Install engine bracket tool No. 3395, or equivalent into engine/transaxle jack tool No. VAG 1383 A or equivalent.
23. Attach engine bracket to engine block, then raise engine and transaxle slightly.
24. Remove engine and transaxle mounts.
25. Carefully lower engine and transaxle together from vehicle.
26. Reverse procedure to install. Tighten bolts to specifications.

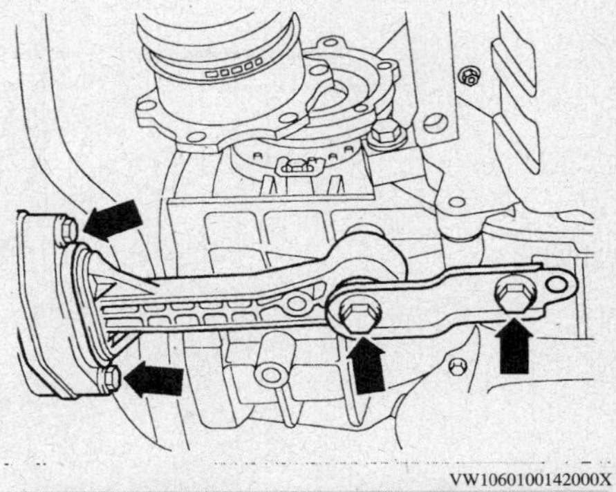

Fig. 3 Rocker bracket removal. 1999–2001

CYLINDER HEAD

REPLACE

1998

Prior to removing drive chains, mark direction of rotation with paint.

Refer to **Fig. 4** for cylinder head replacement, noting the following:

1. Adjust valve timing.
2. Install new cylinder head bolts hand tight.
3. **Torque** cylinder head bolts, **Fig. 5** to 29 ft. lbs., then to 43 ft. lbs., and finally an additional ½ (180°) turn.
4. **Note type of coolant, do not allow red coolant to be mixed with any other type.**

1999–2001

1. Remove spark plug wires, then the engine cover.
2. Disconnect heating resistor electrical connector.
3. Remove inlet hose between air flow sensor and throttle control unit.
4. Disconnect electrical connector and ground connection from throttle control unit.
5. Open and close balancing reservoir sealing cover to allow pressure to escape from cooling system.
6. Remove coolant hoses from throttle control unit, then plug openings.
7. Unclip fuel lines from cylinder head, then disconnect vacuum hoses from intake manifold.
8. Unclip secondary air pump inlet line

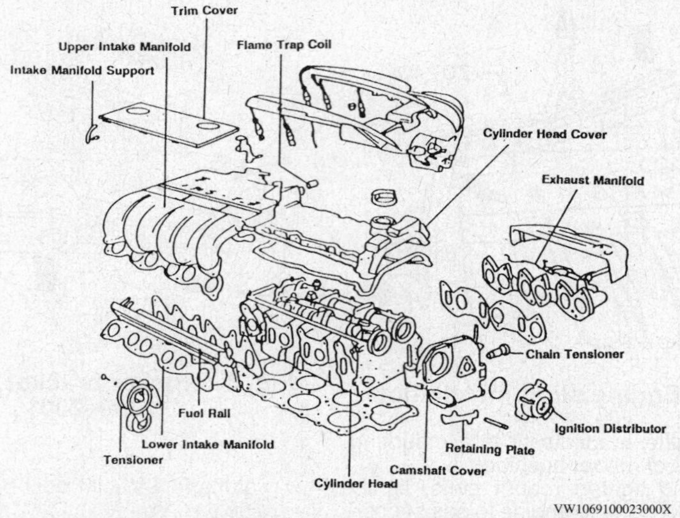

VW1069100023000X

Fig. 4 Exploded view of cylinder head. 1998

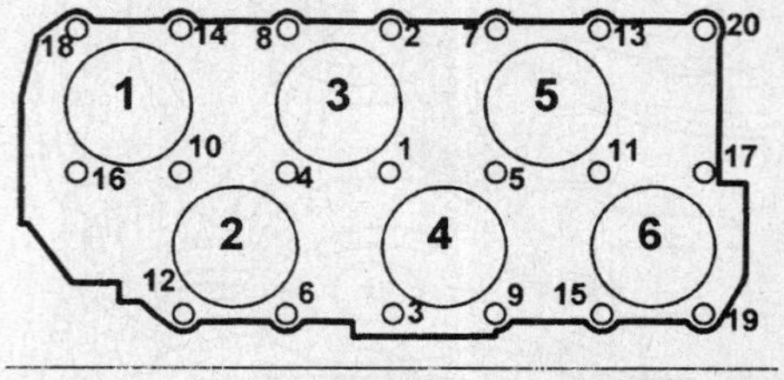

VW1060100146000X

Fig. 5 Cylinder head bolt tightening sequence. 1998

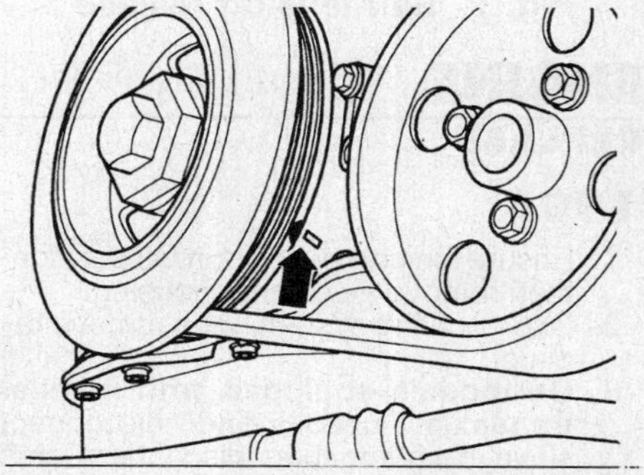

VW1060100143000X

Fig. 6 Cylinder No. 1 TDC alignment. 1999–2001

and all other lines out of brackets at upper intake manifold.

9. Remove dipstick duct from upper intake manifold.
10. Remove two intake manifold support screws.
11. Disconnect fuel supply and return lines from fuel rail, then plug openings.
12. Remove lower sound insulation panels.
13. Remove front bumper cover, then disconnect hood release cable.
14. Remove one bolt on each longitudinal member, then install guide rods tool No. 3411, or equivalent.
15. Remove remaining bolts, then pull lock carrier forward onto guide rods.
16. **On models equipped with A/C,** remove serpentine drive belt, then the A/C compressor. Do not open A/C lines.
17. **On all models,** remove combination valve.
18. Remove upper intake manifold bolts, then the upper intake manifold.
19. Remove valve cover bolts, then the valve cover.
20. Disconnect high voltage line and ground strap from ignition coil.
21. Set crankshaft damper pulley to TDC on cylinder No. 1, **Fig. 6.**
22. Disconnect injector valve connector, then the vacuum hose from fuel pressure regulator.
23. Remove thermostat housing, then the electrical coolant return pump.
24. Disconnect three wire alternator sensor electrical connector.
25. Remove ignition coil, then the camshaft roller chain tensioner.
26. Loosen camshaft sprocket bolts while holding camshafts in place using fork wrench tool No. SW24, or equivalent.
27. Remove camshaft sprocket, then the roller chain track.
28. Disconnect exhaust pipe from exhaust manifold.
29. Remove cylinder head bolts in sequence, **Fig. 7.**
30. Remove cylinder head using suitable shop crane.
31. Reverse procedure to install noting the following:
    a. Ensure cylinder head dowels are installed on engine block.
    b. Install cylinder head gasket with part number facing upward.
    c. Hold camshafts in place using ruler tool No. 3268, or equivalent.
    d. Fill. 12 inch holes in cylinder head gasket with sealant AMV 188 001 02, or equivalent, then coat sealing surfaces on cover and sealing flange with sealant, **Fig. 8.**
    e. **Torque** cylinder head bolts in sequence, **Fig. 5** to 37 ft. lbs., then an additional 90° and finally an additional 90°

VALVE CLEARANCE SPECIFICATIONS

These engine are equipped with hydraulic lifters and no specifications are available.

VALVE ADJUSTMENT

1. Rotate engine until piston for cylinder No. 1 is at TDC.
2. Align casting on sealing flange with TDC marking on flywheel, then remove ignition wire guides.
3. Remove upper intake manifold, then the valve cover.
4. Install and align camshaft guide tool No. 3268, or equivalent, onto cylinder head studs with both camshafts positioned snug in guide indentations, **Fig. 9. This alignment is only possible every second engine revolution.**

VALVE GUIDES

INSPECTION

1. Remove all carbon deposits from valve guide.
2. Position a dial indicator on cylinder head to check guides.
3. Insert new valve into valve guide. End of valve stem must be flush with valve guide end.
4. Rock valve back and forth against dial indicator.
5. Maximum clearance is. 039 inch for intake valves and. 051 inch for exhaust valves. Replace guide(s) if reading is not within specifications.

REPLACEMENT

1. Worn valve guides can be removed using rod tool No. 3121, or equivalent.
2. Lay cylinder head flat on work bench, then press guides out from combustion chamber side.
3. Coat new guides with engine oil, then press into cold cylinder head from camshaft side.
4. Press guides in as far as they will go. Once valve guide shoulder is seated, do not use more than one ton of pressure, or guide shoulder may break. Ream guides by hand using reamer tool No. 3120, or equivalent, and a proper cutting lubricant.
5. Machine valve seats.

TIMING CHAIN

REPLACE

Before removing timing chains, mark running direction using a felt tip pen, **Fig. 10.**

1. Remove timing chain covers and valve cover.
2. Loosen all chain tensioners and remove, then sliding rail.

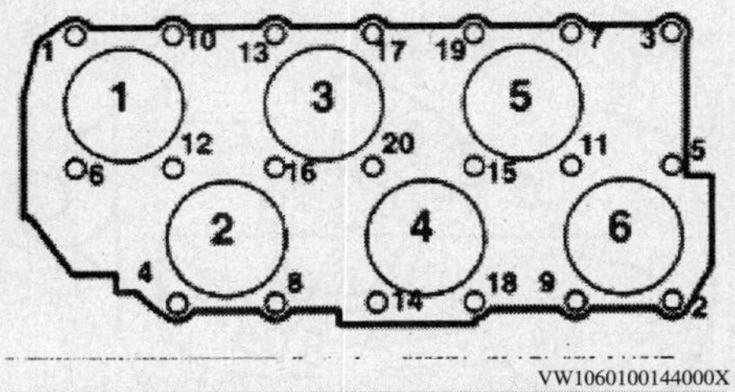

Fig. 7 Cylinder head bolt removal sequence. 1999–2001

3. Remove camshaft sprockets, then timing chains.
4. Reverse procedure to install, tightening chain tensioners and sliding rail bolts to specifications.

CAMSHAFT

REPLACE

REMOVAL

1998

1. Remove ignition cable guide, then remove upper intake manifold. **Cover intake channels with a clean shop towel to avoid contamination.**
2. Set crankshaft to TDC on cylinder No. 1, then remove ignition coil.
3. Remove cylinder head cover and chain tensioner.
4. Remove camshaft sprocket cover, then the camshaft sprocket bolts.
5. **Before removing double chains, mark direction of rotation with touch-up paint.**
6. On cylinder Nos. 1, 3 & 5, proceed as follows:
   a. Remove bearing caps 1 and 7, **Fig. 11.**
   b. Remove bearing caps 3 and 5 alternately and diagonally.
7. On cylinder Nos. 2, 4 and 6 proceed as follows:
   a. Remove bearing cap 4.
   b. Loosen caps 2 and 6 alternately and diagonally.

1999–2001

1. Set crankshaft damper to TDC on cylinder No. 1, **Fig. 6.**
2. Remove ignition coil, then the camshaft roller chain tensioner.
3. Remove valve cover.
4. Loosen camshaft sprocket bolts while holding camshafts in place using fork wrench tool No. SW24, or equivalent.
5. Remove camshaft sprockets.
6. On cylinder Nos. 1, 3 and 5, proceed as follows:
   a. Remove bearing caps 1 and 7, **Fig. 11.**
   b. Remove bearing caps 3 and 5 alternately and diagonally.
7. On cylinder Nos. 2, 4 and 6 proceed as follows:
   a. Remove bearing cap 4.
   b. Loosen caps 2 and 6 alternately and diagonally.

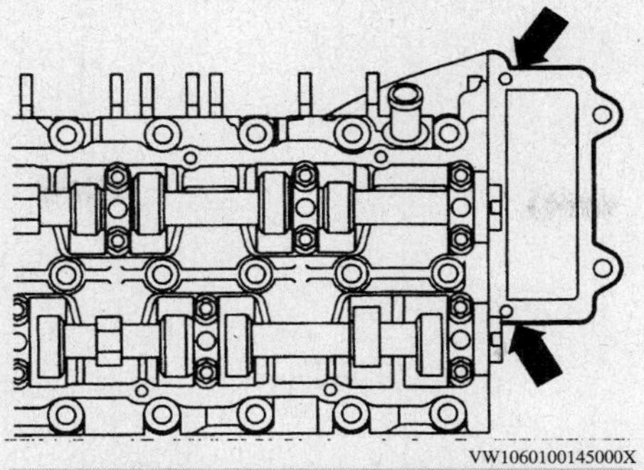

Fig. 8 Sealant location. 1999–2001

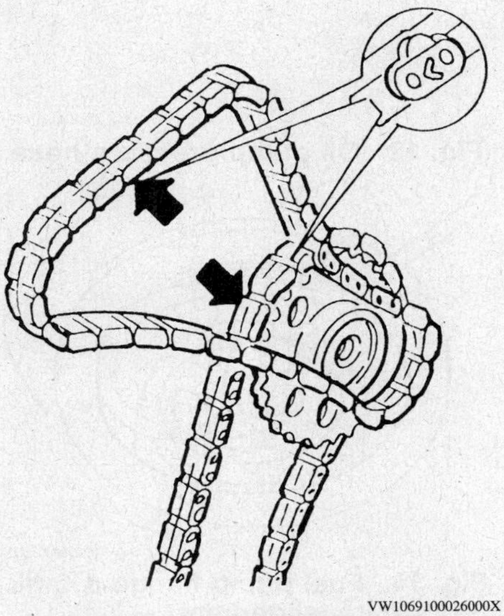

Fig. 10 Running direction marking

INSTALLATION

1. Install bearing caps ensuring marking can be read from exhaust manifold side and arrow points to vibration damper.
2. Install bearing caps 3 and 5 alternately and diagonally, then tighten to specifications.
3. Install bearing caps 1 and 7, then tighten to specifications.
4. Install bearing caps 2 and 6 alternately and diagonally, then tighten to specifications, then cap 4, and tighten to specifications.
5. Adjust valve timing following procedure described under "Valve Timing, Adjust," then clean camshaft sprocket cover sealing surface.
6. Clean old sealant from holes in cylinder head gasket, then fill holes with sealant No. AMV 188 001 02, or equivalent.
7. Clean sealing surfaces of cover and coat with sealant No. AMV 188 001 02, or equivalent, then replace O-ring.
8. Install valve cover and tighten to specifications.
9. Install chain tensioner and tighten to specifications.

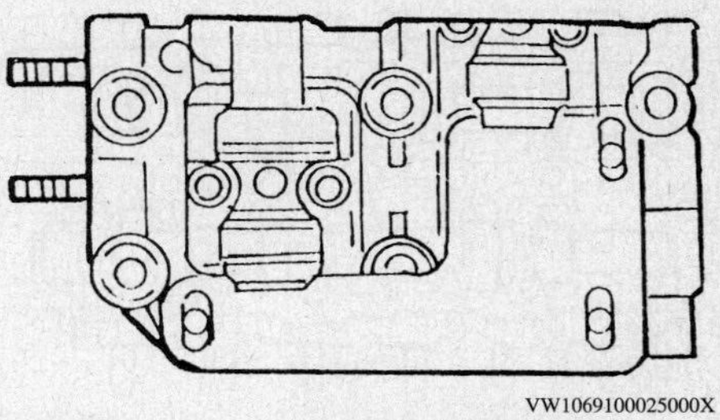

Fig. 9 Camshaft guide tool

PISTON & ROD ASSEMBLY

Mark installation portion and cylinder number. Install piston and rod assembly with highest side of piston crown facing center of cylinder block.

CRANKSHAFT SEAL

REPLACE

1. Remove ribbed belt, then using support bracket tool No. 3406, or equivalent, remove vibration dampener.
2. Unscrew inner portion of oil seal extractor tool No. 3203, or equivalent, three turns out of outer portion (approximately. 16 inch) and lock in position with knurled screw.
3. Lubricate threaded head of oil seal extractor, place in position and push into seal as far as possible.
4. Loosen knurled screw, then turn inner part against crankshaft until oil seal is pulled out.
5. Clamp extractor in a vise and remove oil seal using pliers.
6. Lightly lubricate sealing lip and outer edge of new oil seal, then place guide sleeve from tool No. 3266-1, or equivalent, onto crankshaft pin and push oil seal over guide sleeve.
7. Press oil seal in with sleeve tool No. 3266, or equivalent, until stop using vibration dampener securing bolt.
8. Install vibration dampener using support bracket and tighten to specifications.
9. Install ribbed belt.

CRANKSHAFT REAR OIL SEAL

REPLACE

1. Raise and support vehicle then remove transaxle and clutch following procedure described under "Clutch, Replace."
2. Use flywheel holding tool No. 58, or equivalent, remove flywheel bolts, then remove flywheel.
3. **On models equipped with automatic transaxle,** remove torque converter.
4. **On all models,** using seal puller tool No. 2086, or equivalent, remove crankshaft seal.
5. Lightly lubricate new seal lip and outer edge, then install with pull sleeves tool

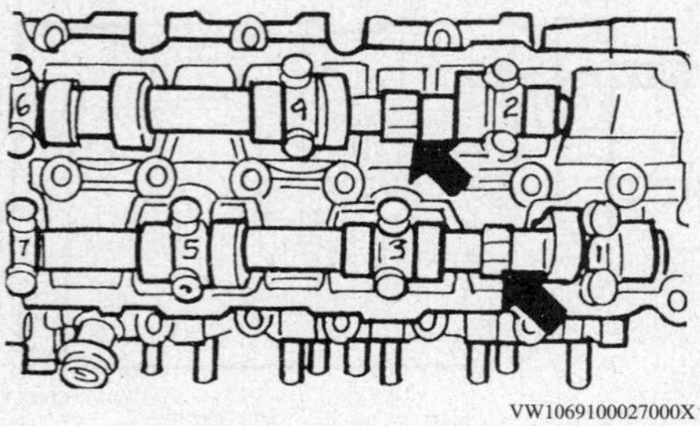

Fig. 11 Camshaft bearing caps

No. 2003-2A, or equivalent, and press in seal to stop using tool No. 2003-1, or equivalent.

6. Reverse procedure to complete repair.

OIL PAN

REPLACE

1. Raise and support vehicle, then drain engine oil.
2. Remove oil pan attaching nuts, then oil pan.
3. Reverse procedure to install.

OIL PUMP

REPLACE

1. Raise and support vehicle, then drain engine oil.
2. Remove oil pan following procedure described under "Oil Pan, Replace."
3. Remove attaching bolts from oil pressure hose to crankcase housing, **Fig. 12.**
4. Remove attaching bolts from oil pump to crankcase housing, then lower oil pump.
5. Reverse procedure to install.

COOLING SYSTEM BLEED

Note type of coolant, do not allow red coolant to be mixed with any other type.

1. Slowly fill coolant expansion tank to Max mark, then install expansion tank cap.
2. Run engine until cooling fan comes on, then check coolant level.
3. Coolant level should be slightly above Max mark with engine at normal operating temperature, and between Min and Max marks with engine cold.
4. If necessary, add coolant to specified marking.

WATER PUMP

REPLACE

1998

1. Drain cooling system, then disconnect front exhaust pipe at flange to catalyst.
2. Remove ribbed belt, then disconnect engine with bracket from front and rear rubber engine mounts.
3. Disconnect transaxle with bracket from rear transaxle rubber mount, then remove ignition cable guide.
4. Attach engine sling as shown in **Fig. 2,**

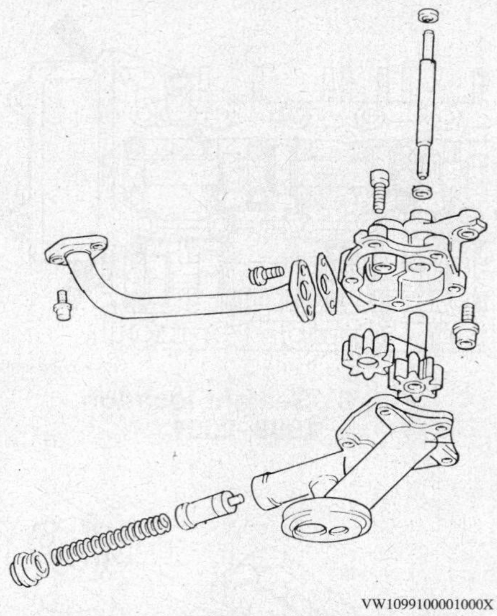

Fig. 12 Oil pump pressure hose

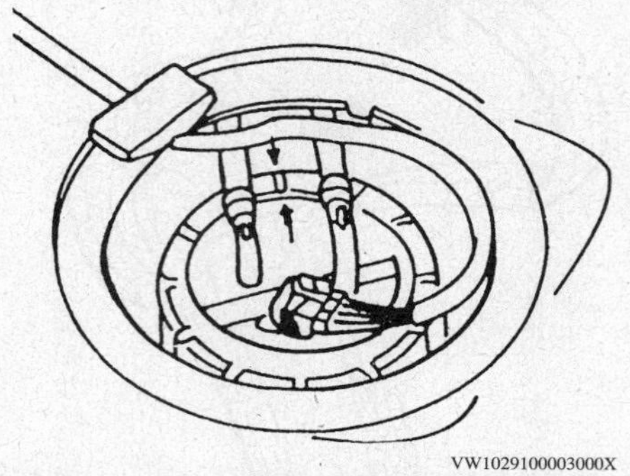

Fig. 14 Fuel pump flange & tank alignment

then lift engine with transaxle using a suitable lift, to gain access to water pump.

5. Using water pump wrench tool No. VAG 1590, or equivalent, remove water pump pulley.
6. Remove water pump bolts, then push engine/transaxle assembly slightly to the left by hand to gain clearance for removal of pump.
7. Reverse procedure to install, noting the following:
   a. Ensure recesses on front and rear engine brackets fit into mounting tabs of rubber bushings.
   b. Hand tighten mount bolts, lightly rock or shake engine to adjust position, then tighten mount bolts to specifications.
   c. Bleed cooling system as outlined under "Cooling System Bleed."

1999–2001

1. Drain coolant into suitable container, then remove serpentine drive belt.
2. Remove water pump pulley bolts using face pin spanner wrench tool No. 3387, or equivalent to hold pulley.
3. Remove water pump bolts, then the water pump.
4. Reverse procedure to install, noting the following:
   a. Install water pump with sealing plug pointing downward.
   b. Tighten bolts to specifications.
   c. Bleed cooling system as outlined under "Cooling System Bleed."

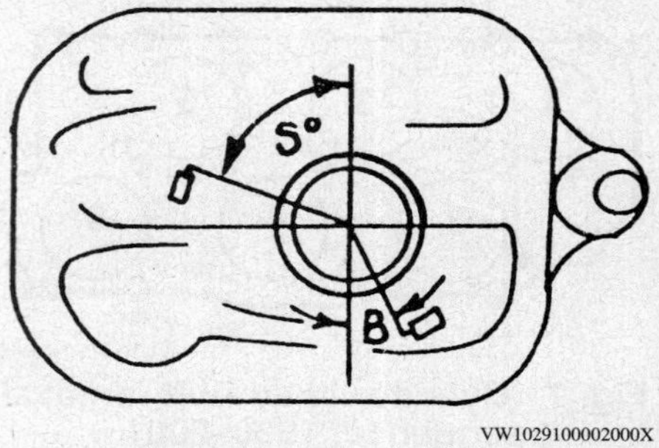

Fig. 13 Fuel pump installation

RADIATOR

REPLACE

1998

1. Turn ignition switch off and wait at least 20 seconds for platinum hot-wire in air mass sensor to burn itself clean.
2. Remove battery.
3. Drain engine coolant.
4. Disconnect coolant hoses from radiator.
5. Disconnect thermo switch and cooling fan.
6. Remove radiator mounting bolts.
7. Remove front bumper.
8. Remove hood lock support.
9. **On models equipped with A/C,** separate condenser from radiator and pull forward as far as possible.
10. **On all models,** remove radiator from top.
11. Reverse procedure to install. Bleed cooling system as outlined under "Cooling System Bleed."

1999–2001

1. Drain coolant into suitable container, then remove front bumper.
2. Pull quick coupler off radiator.
3. Disconnect thermo switch and cooling fan electrical connectors.
4. Remove one bolt on each longitudinal member, then install guide rods tool No. 3411, or equivalent.
5. Remove remaining bolts, then pull lock carrier forward onto guide rods.
6. **On models equipped with A/C,** separate condenser from radiator and secure to lock carrier.
7. **On all models,** remove radiator bolts, then remove radiator and cooling fan from vehicle.
8. Reverse procedure to install. Bleed cooling system as outlined under "Cooling System Bleed."

FUEL PUMP

REPLACE

Wait at least 20 seconds after switching off ignition before disconnecting battery. This will allow the platinum hot wire in air mass sensor to burn itself clean.

Ensure the ignition switch is in the Off position whenever disconnecting or connecting battery or any part of Motronic ignition wiring system to prevent damage to Motronic control unit.

1. Remove cover plate in luggage compartment floor, then disconnect electrical connector and fuel lines from flange.
2. Unscrew flange nut using spanner tool No. 3217, or equivalent, then withdraw flange and O-ring from fuel tank.
3. Reverse procedure to install, noting the following:
   a. Ensure sender is not bent when installing.
   b. Fuel pump assembly is correctly installed when sender float angle from direction of travel A, **Fig. 13,** is 5.°
   c. Coat flange O-ring with fuel, then install flange with mark on flange aligned with mark on fuel tank, **Fig. 14.**

TIGHTENING SPECIFICATIONS

Year	Component	Torque, Ft. Lbs.
1998–2001	Camshaft Sprocket Bolts	74
	Camshaft Sprocket Cover Bolts	18
	Connecting Rod Bolts	22③
	Cylinder Head Bolts	②
	Cylinder Head Cover Nuts	84④
	Double Drive Chain Sprocket Bolt	74
	Driveshaft To Flange Bolts	33
	Engine Mounts To Engine Bolts	44
	Engine Mounts To Engine Rubber Mounts Bolt	44
	Engine Rubber Mount To Bracket Bolt, Front	41
	Engine Rubber Mount To Bracket Bolts, Right	18
	Engine Support To Body Bolts	37
	Engine To Transaxle Bolts, M10	44
	Engine To Transaxle Bolts, M12	59
	Flywheel Bolts	44③
	Front Crankshaft Seal Flange Bolts	84④
	Front Crankshaft Seal Mounting Flange Bolts	18
	Front Exhaust Pipe To Catalytic Converter Bolts	18
	Front Exhaust Pipe To Exhaust Manifold Bolts	30
	Intermediate Shaft Guide Ring Bolts	84④
	Main Bearing Cap Bolts	22①
	Oil Cooler Cover Bolt	18
	Oil Drain Plug	22
	Oil Filter Housing Bolt	18
	Oil Injection Nozzle Bolts	87④
	Oil Pan Bolts	11
	Oil Pump Drive Cover Bolts	84④
	Oil Pump To Block Bolts	18
	Oil Pressure Relief Valve To Block	44④
	Oil Pressure Switch	18
	Oil Temperature Sender	84④
	Pressure Plate To Flywheel Bolts	15
	Rear Crankshaft Seal Flange Bolts	84④
	Ribbed Belt Tension Roller Bolts	18
	Speed/Reference Sender Bolt	84④
	Thermostat Housing Bolts	84④
	Timing Chain Guide Rail Bolts	15
	Timing Chain Locating Pin w/Collar	18
	Timing Chain Pivot Pin	18
	Timing Chain Tensioner Bolt	22
	Timing Chain Tensioner w/Plate Bolts	84④
	Transaxle Mount To Transaxle Bolts	18
	Transaxle Mount To Transaxle Rubber Mount Bolts	44
	Transaxle Rubber Mount To Bracket Bolts	22
	Upper Intake Manifold Bolts	18
	Vibration Dampener Bolt	74③
	Water Pump Bolts	11
	Water Pump Pulley To Water Pump Nuts	18

① — Plus an additional ½ (180°) turn.
② — Refer to "Cylinder Head, Replace" for tightening procedure.
③ — Plus an additional ¼ (90°) turn.
④ — Inch lbs.

2.8L V6 Gasoline Engine

NOTE: On Air Bag Equipped Models, Refer To "Air Bag System Precautions" Located In The Front Of This Manual For System Disarming & Arming Procedures.

NOTE: Refer To "Computer Relearn Procedures" Located In The Front Of This Manual For Computer Relearn Procedures.

INDEX

	Page No.
Camshaft, Replace	8-61
Compression Pressure	8-59
Cooling System Bleed	8-62
Cylinder Head, Replace	8-60
Engine Rebuilding Specifications	8-185
Engine, Replace	8-59
Front Main Bearing Oil Seal, Replace	8-62
Fuel Pump, Replace	8-63
Hydraulic Lifter Inspection	8-60
Main & Rod Bearings	8-62
Oil Pan, Replace	8-62
Piston & Rod Assembly	8-62
Precautions	8-59
Air Bag Systems	8-59
Audio Coded Anti-Theft System	8-59
Battery Ground Cable	8-59
Radiator, Replace	8-62
Serpentine Drive Belt	8-62
Replacement	8-62
Routing	8-62
Tightening Specifications	8-64
Timing Belt, Replace	8-61
Valve Adjustment	8-60
Valve Guides	8-61
Inspection	8-61
Replacement	8-61
Water Pump, Replace	8-62

PRECAUTIONS

AIR BAG SYSTEMS

Do not use computer memory saver tool on air bag equipped models. Using the tool will keep the air bag system charged and may cause accidental activation of the air bag unit. Refer to "Air Bag System Precautions" in the front of this manual for system disarming and arming procedures.

BATTERY GROUND CABLE

Prior to disconnecting the battery negative cable, obtain the radio security code. After service has been completed and the battery negative cable has been reconnected, use security code to activate the radio. Prior to service, disconnect battery ground cable and isolate as required.

AUDIO CODED ANTI-THEFT SYSTEM

Some models are equipped with a radio anti-theft system that will disable the system when battery power is interrupted, unless the system is reset the radio will not operate.

1. Turn radio to On position, SAFE and 1000 should be displayed.
2. Enter radio code using first four program station buttons. Security code will appear on display.
3. Depress and hold righthand side of radio right or left blocker until anti-theft coding is activated indicated by a brief signal sound.
4. If code number has been entered correctly, when ignition key is removed a diode on front of radio will flash.

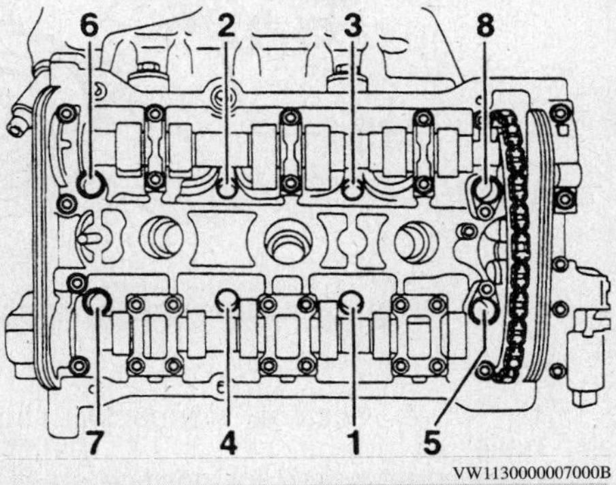

Fig. 1 Cylinder head bolt tightening sequence

COMPRESSION PRESSURE

1. Perform compression test with engine oil temperature at a minimum of 86°F and throttle plate completely open.
2. Remove engine cover, then the spark plug wires.
3. Remove spark plugs, then disconnect 5-pin electrical connector from ignition coil.
4. Remove fuse No. 28 for fuel pump or disconnect all fuel injector electrical connectors.
5. Connect compression tester tool No. 1763, or equivalent. Crank engine until tester no longer shows an increase in pressure.
6. Compression pressure should be 130–203 psi with a maximum difference between cylinders of 43 psi. Minimum pressure should be 108 psi.

ENGINE

REPLACE

The engine is removed forward without transaxle.

1. Remove front noise insulation panel, then the front bumper.
2. Drain coolant into suitable container, then remove radiator hoses.
3. Remove power steering oil cooling line. Do not open line.
4. Remove lower noise insulation panels, then the turn signals.
5. Disconnect hood release cable, then the electrical connector.
6. Remove front bumper, then the side mounted guide from fender.
7. Remove A/C condenser, then the oil cooler from lock carrier.
8. Remove bolts, then the lock carrier.
9. Remove serpentine drive belt as outlined under "Serpentine Drive Belt."
10. **On models equipped with A/C,** remove A/C compressor and position aside. Do not disconnect refrigerant lines.
11. **On all models,** remove exhaust pipe from manifolds.
12. Remove upper air cleaner, then the intake manifold cover.
13. Remove cruise control vacuum module.
14. Disconnect accelerator pedal cable at throttle valve control module cable disc and support bracket.
15. Disconnect fuel supply and return lines at fuel rail.
16. Remove coolant, intake and vacuum hoses from engine.

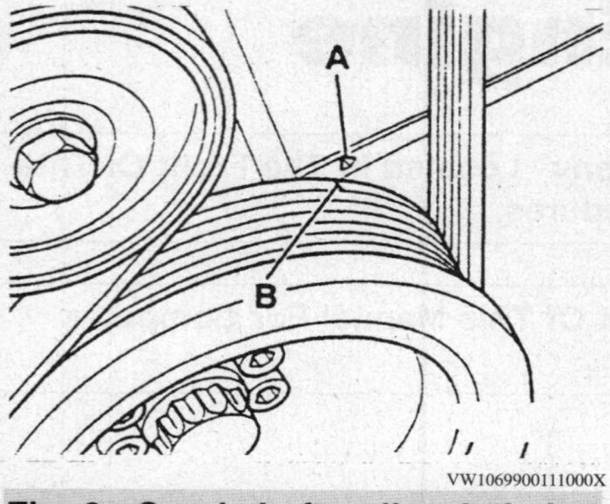

Fig. 2 Crankshaft pulley & timing belt cover timing marks

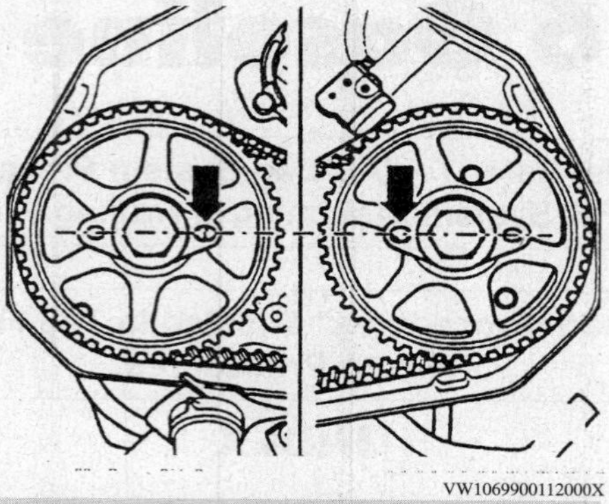

Fig. 3 Camshaft sprocket alignment

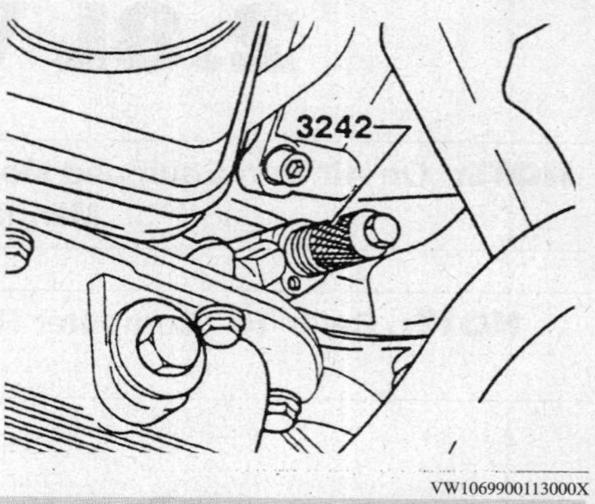

Fig. 4 Crankshaft locking tool installation

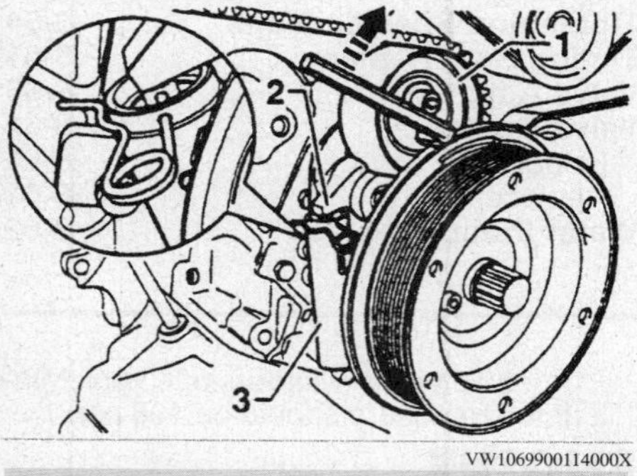

Fig. 5 Securing timing belt tensioner

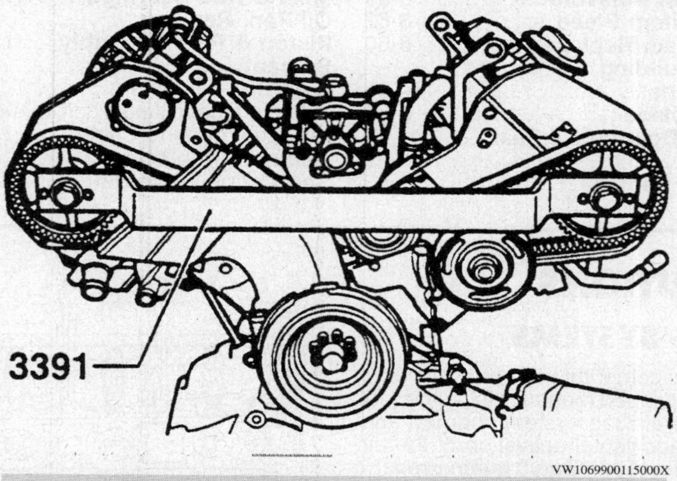

Fig. 6 Camshaft sprocket holder tool installation

17. Remove coolant overflow reservoir and position aside.
18. Disconnect all necessary electrical connectors from engine.
19. Remove starter motor, then the intake elbow.
20. Remove upper engine to transaxle bolts, then the engine mount bolts.
21. **On models equipped with automatic transaxle,** remove three torque converter bolts, then lift engine using suitable jack.
22. **On all models,** remove lower engine to transaxle bolts.
23. Install engine support bridge tool No. 10-222A, or equivalent, then attach support adapter tool No. 3147, or equivalent to transaxle bell housing.
24. Install engine sling tool No. 2024A, or equivalent, then attach sling to workshop crane tool No. VAG 1201A, or equivalent.
25. Lift engine and remove toward front of vehicle.
26. Reverse procedure to install. Tighten bolts to specifications.

CYLINDER HEAD

REPLACE

1. Ensure pistons are not at TDC.
2. Remove engine cover, then the front noise insulation panel.
3. Drain coolant into suitable container.
4. Remove air duct pipe, then the air elbow between mass air flow sensor and throttle valve control module.
5. Disconnect accelerator pedal cable, then the EVAP canister purge regulator valve electrical connector and hose.
6. Disconnect hoses for positive crankcase breather on valve cover.
7. Disconnect electrical connectors from the following:
   a. Intake Manifold Tuning (IMT) valve.
   b. Secondary Air Injection (AIR) solenoid valve.
   c. Intake Air Temperature (IAT) sensor.
   d. Throttle valve control module.
   e. Ignition coil power output stage.
   f. Camshaft adjustment valves.
   g. Camshaft Position (CMP) sensor.
   h. Engine Coolant Temperature (ECT) sensor.
8. Disconnect fuel pressure regulator hose.
9. Disconnect vacuum pipes at combivalves.
10. Remove retaining plate for IMT valve and AIR solenoid valve.
11. Remove timing belt as outlined under "Timing Belt, Replace."
12. Remove exhaust pipe from exhaust manifold.
13. Disconnect fuel injector electrical connectors.
14. Remove fuel rail bolts, then the fuel rail with injectors positioning aside.
15. Remove ignition coils with bracket.
16. Remove intake manifold bolts, then the intake manifold.
17. Remove connecting pipe, then the rear coolant pipe.
18. Remove timing belt rear cover, then the front coolant pipe.
19. Remove valve cover bolts, then the valve cover.
20. Remove cylinder head bolts in reverse order of tightening sequence, **Fig. 1.**
21. Carefully remove cylinder head from vehicle.
22. Reverse procedure to install, noting the following:
   a. Set No. 3 cylinder to TDC, then turn crankshaft back slightly.
   b. Install cylinder head gasket with part number facing upward.
   c. **Torque** new cylinder head bolts in sequence, **Fig. 1** to 44 ft. lbs, then turn an additional 90° and finally turn an additional 90°.

VALVE ADJUSTMENT

All engines are equipped with hydraulic lifters. No adjustment provision is provided.

HYDRAULIC LIFTER INSPECTION

Hydraulic valve lifters are non-adjustable. Noisy lifters may be replaced after the following check.

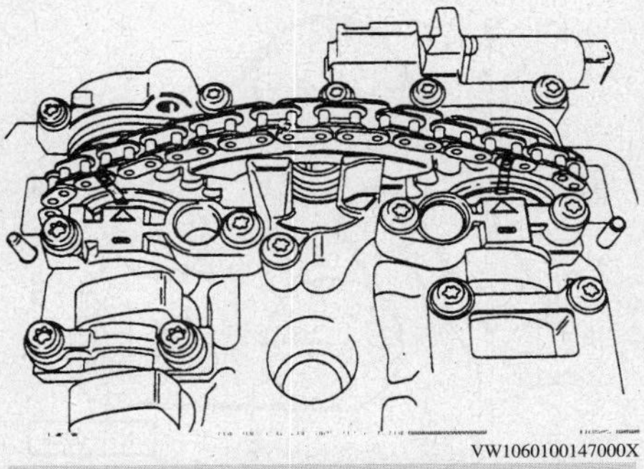

Fig. 7 Camshaft drive chain reference marks

1. Run engine until radiator fan comes on at least once.
2. Raise engine speed to 2500 RPM, for two minutes.
3. If lifter(s) is still noisy, proceed as follows:
   a. Remove valve cover.
   b. Turn crankshaft pulley bolt clockwise until camshaft lobe of lifter to be checked is pointing upward. Inspect for damage.
   c. Replace lifter if clearance between camshaft and lifter is more than. 008 inch.
   d. If clearance is less than. 004 inch or no clearance, go to step e.
   e. Press down lightly against valve lifter with a wooden stick. If. 008 inch feeler gauge can be inserted between camshaft and lifter, replace lifter.

VALVE GUIDES

INSPECTION

1. Remove all carbon deposits from valve guide.
2. Set up a dial indicator on cylinder head to check suspected guide.
3. Insert new valve into valve guide. End of valve stem must be flush with valve guide end.
4. Rock valve back and forth against dial indicator.
5. Maximum side to side play is. 031 inch. Replace guide(s) if reading is beyond limit.

REPLACEMENT

1. Worn valve guides can be removed using rod tool No. 3360, or equivalent.
2. Press valve guides out from camshaft side.
3. Coat new guides with engine oil, then press into cold cylinder head from camshaft side.
4. Press guides in as far as they will go. Once valve guide shoulder is seated, do not use more than one ton of pressure or guide shoulder may break. Ream guides by hand using tool No. 3363, or equivalent, and a proper cutting lubricant.
5. Machine valve seats.

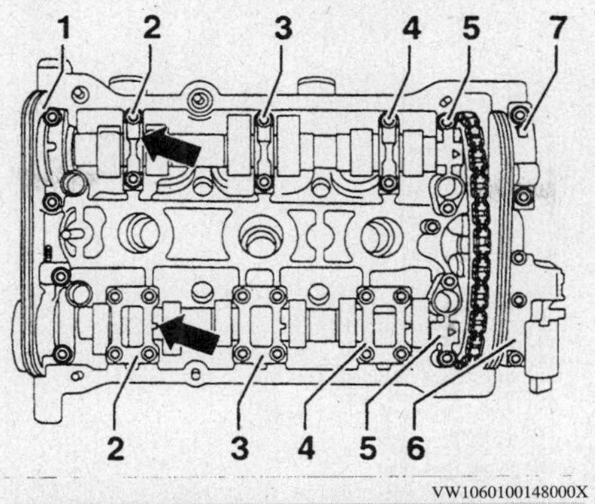

Fig. 8 Camshaft bearing cap locations

TIMING BELT

REPLACE

With the timing belt removed, avoid turning the camshaft or crankshaft. If movement is required, exercise extreme caution to avoid valve damage caused by piston contact.

1. Remove serpentine drive belt as outlined under "Serpentine Drive Belt."
2. Rotate engine in its normal running direction until **No. 3** cylinder reaches TDC on its compression stroke, **Fig. 2.**
3. Ensure camshaft sprockets are properly aligned, **Fig. 3. Larger holes must align opposite one another on inside. If they are positioned to outside, rotate crankshaft one more turn.**
4. Remove sealing plug from lefthand side of engine block, then ensure TDC drilling is visible or at least can be felt.
5. Thread VW crankshaft holder tool No. 3242, or equivalent, into sealing plug hole, **Fig. 4.** This will lock crankshaft and prevent it from turning.
6. Remove serpentine belt tensioner mounting bolts, then the tensioner.
7. Remove timing belt center and righthand covers.
8. Using a suitable 8 mm hex wrench, rotate timing belt tensioner roller clockwise.
9. While holding hex wrench, **Fig. 5,** use 2 mm diameter spring pin from VW tool No. 2024A, or an equivalent, to secure tensioner so holes in piston and housing are both aligned. Tensioner is oil dampened and might take a while to compress.
10. Remove crankshaft harmonic balancer.
11. Remove fan retainer and timing belt sprocket cover.
12. Remove timing belt.
13. Reverse procedure to install noting the following:
    a. Ensure all the timing marks are properly aligned, **Figs. 2 and 3.**
    b. Hold camshaft sprockets in place using camshaft sprocket holder tool No. 3391, or equivalent, **Fig. 6.**
    c. Tighten bolts to specifications. **Fan clutch bolts have lefthand threads.**

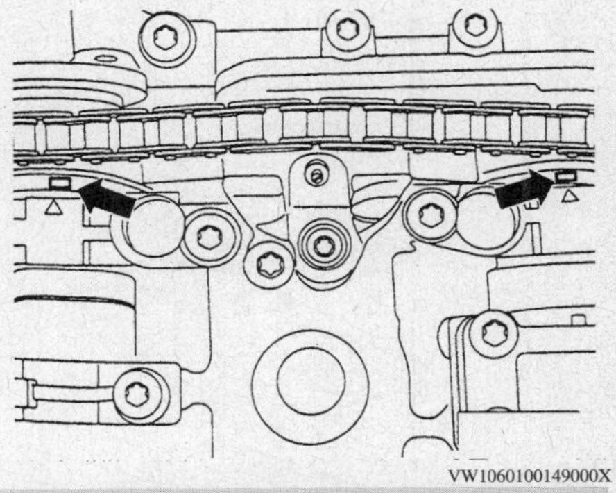

Fig. 9 Camshaft to bearing cap alignment

CAMSHAFT

REPLACE

1. Remove timing belt as outlined under "Timing Belt, Replace."
2. Turn crankshaft back slightly, then remove camshaft sprocket.
3. Remove rear timing belt cover, then the valve cover.
4. Remove camshaft position sensor and shutter.
5. Clean drive chain and camshaft chain sprockets between bearing caps, then mark chain for reference during installation **Fig. 7.** Distance between marks should be 16 rollers on drive chain.
6. Compress camshaft adjuster using retainer tool No. 3366, or equivalent.
7. Remove camshaft adjuster.
8. Remove bearing caps one, three, five and seven, **Fig. 8** then place them in correct order on a clean surface.
9. Loosen bearing caps two and four, **Fig. 8** alternately and diagonally.
10. Lift out camshafts together with camshaft adjuster.
11. Reverse procedure to install, noting the following:
    a. Pistons must not be positioned at TDC.
    b. Install chain sprockets and camshafts using reference marks made during removal.
    c. Oil camshaft contact surfaces.
    d. Install bearing caps two and four with casting for intake camshaft toward chain and casting for exhaust camshaft toward exhaust manifold.
    e. Tighten bearing caps two and four alternately and diagonally to specifications.
    f. Lightly coat contact surfaces of bearing caps one and seven with sealant AMV 174 004 01, or equivalent.
    g. Tighten bearing caps one, three, five and seven to specifications.
    h. Ensure arrows on bearing caps align with cut outs on camshaft, **Fig. 9,** if necessary move one camshaft onto markings.
    i. Check valve timing.

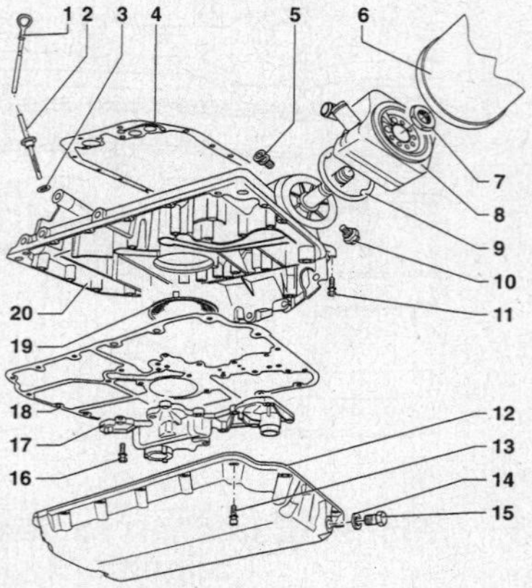

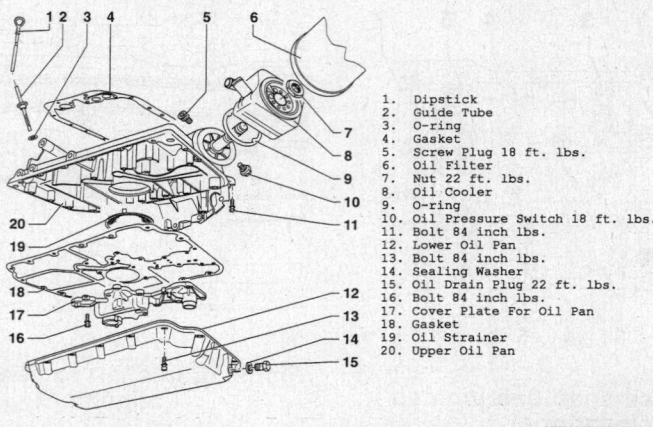

1. Dipstick
2. Guide Tube
3. O-ring
4. Gasket
5. Screw Plug 18 ft. lbs.
6. Oil Filter
7. Nut 22 ft. lbs.
8. Oil Cooler
9. O-ring
10. Oil Pressure Switch 18 ft. lbs.
11. Bolt 84 inch lbs.
12. Lower Oil Pan
13. Bolt 84 inch lbs.
14. Sealing Washer
15. Oil Drain Plug 22 ft. lbs.
16. Bolt 84 inch lbs.
17. Cover Plate For Oil Pan
18. Gasket
19. Oil Strainer
20. Upper Oil Pan

VW1060100150000X

Fig. 10 Oil pan removal

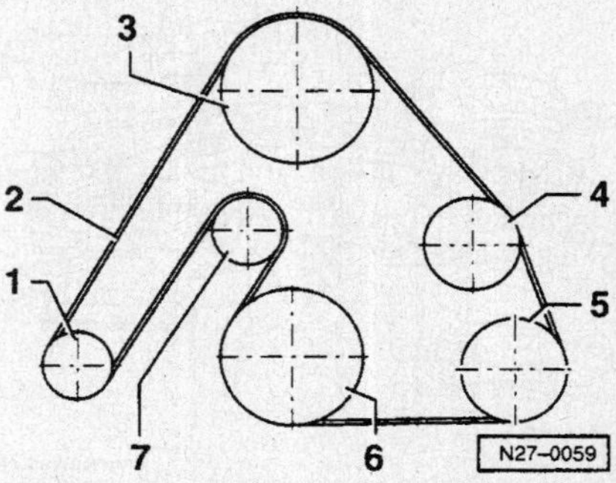

1 - Generator
2 - Ribbed belt
3 - Power steering pump
4 - Viscous fan
5 - Air conditioner compressor
6 - Crankshaft
7 - Tensioning roller

VW1139800050000X

Fig. 11 Serpentine drive belt routing with A/C

PISTON & ROD ASSEMBLY

Assemble the piston to the rod with the arrow on piston crown pointing toward front of engine and the casting marks on the rod facing toward front of engine for cylinders 1–3 and toward rear of engine for cylinders 4–6.

MAIN & ROD BEARINGS

Main and connecting rod bearings are available in. 010 inch,. 020 inch and. 030 inch undersizes.

FRONT MAIN BEARING OIL SEAL

REPLACE

1. Remove timing belt as outlined under "Timing Belt, Replace."
2. Remove cylinder block lefthand sealing plug, then set No. 3 cylinder at TDC.
3. Secure crankshaft using crankshaft holder tool No. 3242, or equivalent.
4. Remove timing belt crankshaft sprocket.
5. Unscrew inner part of seal remover tool No. 3203, or equivalent two turns approximately. 118 inch out of outer part, then lock with knurled screw.
6. Lubricate threaded head of oil seal removal tool, then install while applying firm pressure screw it as far as possible into oil seal.
7. Loosen knurled screw, then turn inner part against crankshaft until oil seal is pulled out.
8. Reverse procedure to install, noting the following:
   a. Slide dry seal over guide sleeve tool No. 3202/1, or equivalent.
   b. Press oil seal in flush using seal installer tool No. 3265, or equivalent.

OIL PAN

REPLACE

Refer to **Fig. 10** for oil pan removal.

SERPENTINE DRIVE BELT

REPLACEMENT

1. Using VW wrench tool No. 3212, or equivalent, counterhold fan pulley.
2. Using VW wrench tool No. 3312, or equivalent, loosen fan clutch pulley retaining bolts. **These bolts have left-hand threads, so they must be loosened by turning clockwise.**
3. Rotate serpentine belt tensioner retaining bolt clockwise until both tensioner alignment holes align.
4. Insert VW drift tool No. 3204, or equivalent, into holes to keep tension off belt.
5. Note routing, then remove serpentine belt.
6. Reverse procedure to install.

ROUTING

Refer to **Figs. 11 and 12** for serpentine drive belt routing.

COOLING SYSTEM BLEED

1. Set heater controls to maximum heat.
2. Run engine at 2000 RPM for approximately three minutes.
3. Allow engine to run at idle until lower radiator hose becomes hot, then check coolant level.
4. Coolant level should be at Max mark with engine at normal operating temperature, and between Min and Max marks with engine cold.
5. If necessary, add coolant to specified mark.

WATER PUMP

REPLACE

1. Drain coolant into suitable container, then remove front bumper.
2. Remove air guide between lock carrier and air cleaner.
3. Remove lock carrier bolts, then install guide rods tool No. 3369, or equivalent.
4. Pull lock carrier forward onto guide rods.
5. Remove viscous fan clutch, then the serpentine drive belt as outlined under "Serpentine Drive Belt."
6. Remove timing belt as outlined under "Timing Belt, Replace."
7. Remove viscous fan clutch bracket.
8. Remove water pump bolts, then the water pump.
9. Reverse procedure to install. Tighten bolts to specifications.

RADIATOR

REPLACE

1. Drain coolant into suitable container, then remove front bumper.
2. Remove radiator hoses, then disconnect cooling fan control thermal switch electrical connector.
3. **On models equipped with automatic transaxle,** remove transaxle fluid cooler lines from radiator.
4. **On all models,** remove power steering oil cooling pipe from radiator.
5. **On models equipped with A/C,** remove condenser from radiator and secure to body.

6. **On all models,** remove upper radiator securing clips, then the radiator.
7. Reverse procedure to install.

FUEL PUMP

REPLACE

1. Remove luggage compartment floor cover.
2. Disconnect 4-pin electrical connector, then the fuel supply and return lines from fuel pump.
3. Remove union nut using ring nut spanner tool No. 3217, or equivalent.
4. Remove fuel pump from vehicle.
5. Reverse procedure to install. Mark on fuel pump module must align with mark on fuel tank.

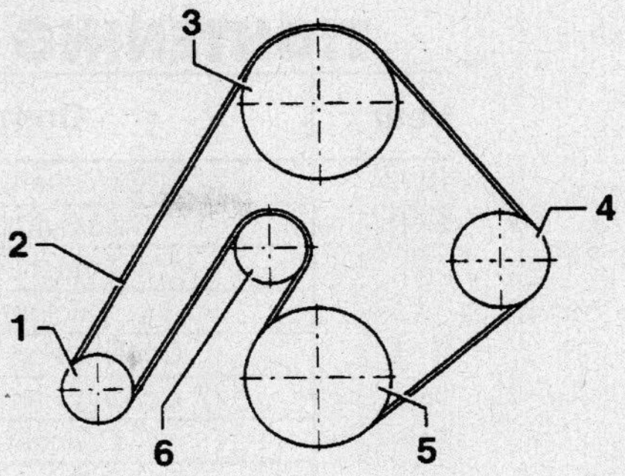

1 - Generator
2 - Ribbed belt
3 - Power steering pump
4 - Viscous fan
5 - Crankshaft
6 - Tensioning roller

VW1139800051000X

Fig. 12 Serpentine drive belt routing less A/C

TIGHTENING SPECIFICATIONS

Year	Component	Torque Ft. Lbs.
1998–2001	Camshaft Bearing Caps	84②
	Camshaft Sprocket Bolts	41
	Connecting Rod Bolts	22
	Coolant Drain Plug	15
	Cooling Fan Pulley Bolt (M6)	84②
	Cooling Fan Pulley Bolt (M8)	18
	Cylinder Head Bolts	①
	Drive Plate Bolt	44③
	Engine To Transaxle Bolts (M6)	84②
	Engine To Transaxle Bolts (M8)	15
	Engine To Transaxle Bolts (M10)	33
	Engine To Transaxle Bolts (M12)	44
	Exhaust Manifold Bolts	18
	Exhaust Pipe To Exhaust Manifold	18
	Fan Clutch Bolts	30
	Flywheel Bolt	44④
	Intake Manifold Bolts	84②
	Main Bearing Cap Bolt	44③
	Oil Check Valve	18
	Oil Cooler Nut	22
	Oil Pan Bolts	84②
	Oil Pan Cover Plate	84②
	Oil Pan Drain Plug	22
	Oil Pressure Switch	18
	Serpentine Belt Tensioner Bolt	41
	Starter Motor To Transaxle	48
	Timing Belt Cover Bolts (M6)	84④
	Timing Belt Cover Bolts (M8)	18
	Timing Belt Idler Pulley Bolt	33
	Timing Belt Tensioner Bolt	18
	Valve Cover Nut	84②
	Vibration Damper Bolt	18
	Viscous Fan Clutch	30
	Water Pump Bolts	84②

① — Refer to "Cylinder Head, Replace."
② — Inch lbs.
③ — Plus an additional 90°.
④ — Plus an additional 180°

Clutch & Manual Transaxle

NOTE: On Air Bag Equipped Models, Refer To "Air Bag System Precautions" Located In The Front Of This Manual For System Disarming & Arming Procedures.

NOTE: Refer To "Computer Relearn Procedures" Located In The Front Of This Manual When Battery Power To The Computer Has Been Interrupted.

INDEX

	Page No.
Adjustments	8-65
Hydraulically Operated Clutch	8-65
Shift Lever	8-65
Clutch, Replace	8-66
012 Transaxle	8-66
02J Transaxle	8-66
Hydraulic System Service	8-66
Clutch System Bleed	8-66
Precautions	8-65
Air Bag Systems	8-65
Audio Coded Anti-Theft System	8-65
Battery Ground Cable	8-65
Tightening Specifications	8-68
Transaxle, Replace	8-66
Golf, GTI, Jetta & New Beetle	8-66
Passat	8-67

PRECAUTIONS

AIR BAG SYSTEMS

Do not use computer memory saver tool on air bag equipped models. Using the tool will keep the air bag system charged and may cause accidental activation of the air bag unit. Refer to "Air Bag System Precautions" in the front of this manual for system disarming and arming procedures.

BATTERY GROUND CABLE

Prior to disconnecting the battery negative cable, obtain the radio security code. After service has been completed and the battery negative cable has been reconnected, use security code to activate the radio. Prior to service, disconnect battery ground cable and isolate as required.

AUDIO CODED ANTI-THEFT SYSTEM

Some models are equipped with a radio anti-theft system that will disable the system when battery power is interrupted, unless the system is reset the radio will not operate.

1. Turn radio to On position, SAFE and 1000 should be displayed.
2. Enter radio code using first four program station buttons. Security code will appear on display.
3. Depress and hold righthand side of radio right or left blocker until anti-theft coding is activated indicated by a brief signal sound.
4. If code number has been entered correctly, when ignition key is removed a diode on front of radio will flash.

ADJUSTMENTS

HYDRAULICALLY OPERATED CLUTCH

The clutch operating system used on these vehicles is self adjusting.

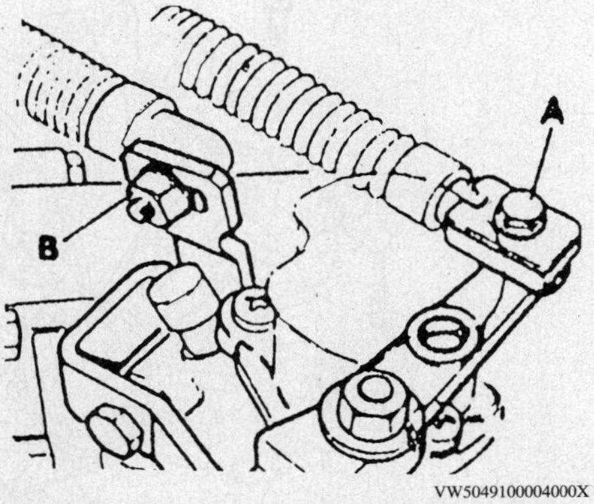

Fig. 1 Gearshift lever operating cables

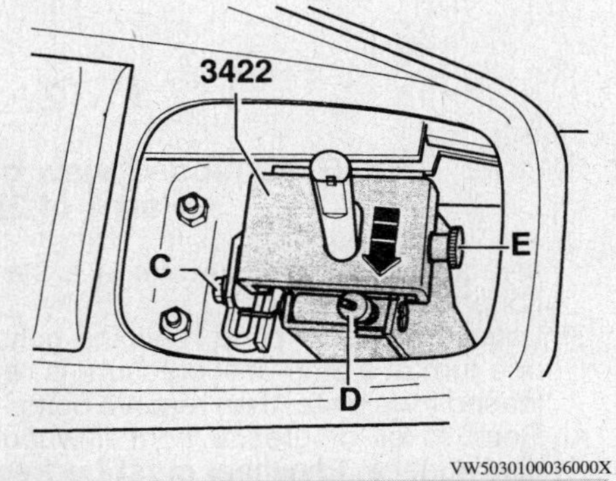

Fig. 2 Shift lever gauge installation

SHIFT LEVER

To obtain a correct gearshift adjustment, shift linkage should be operating satisfactorily, shift/selector cable mounting components and cable boots should be in satisfactory condition, shift cables should be operating smoothly and transaxle and clutch should be in satisfactory condition.

1. Place gearshift lever in Neutral position, then remove the gearshift lever knob and shift boot.
2. Loosen bolt A and nut B until operating cables move freely in centering holes, **Fig. 1.**
3. Loosen bolt C, then install shift lever gauge tool No. 3193, or equivalent, **Fig. 2.**
4. Pivot locating pin (for attaching gauge) under bearing plate, then tighten nut D.
5. Press gearshift lever into left detent of slide, then press gearshift lever with slide to left stop (toward driver side), and tighten bolt E.
6. Move gearshift lever to right detent (toward passenger side), then tighten bolt C.
7. Install wedge and locating pin tool No. 3192-1, or equivalent, **Fig. 3,** then push wedge between gearshift lever and cover, until no play is present. **Wedge must not raise transaxle gearshift lever.**
8. Attach operating cables in this position, then check position of the wedge.
9. Remove wedge and pin, then the shift lever gauge.
10. **On Passat models,** start engine and depress clutch pedal, wait approximately three to six seconds until transaxle input shaft comes to a standstill, then shift into all gears several times. Notice effectiveness of reverse gear pawl.
11. **On all models,** if any gear binds or drags, check transaxle rod travel as follows:
    a. Shift into first gear.
    b. Press shift lever to left, up to stop, then release.
    c. Have an assistant watch shift rod on transaxle. Rod must travel approximately 3⁄64 inch in direction of arrow, **Fig. 4,** when activating shift lever.
12. If rod travel is not within specifications:
    a. Shift out of first gear, then loosen nut A at selector cable mounting

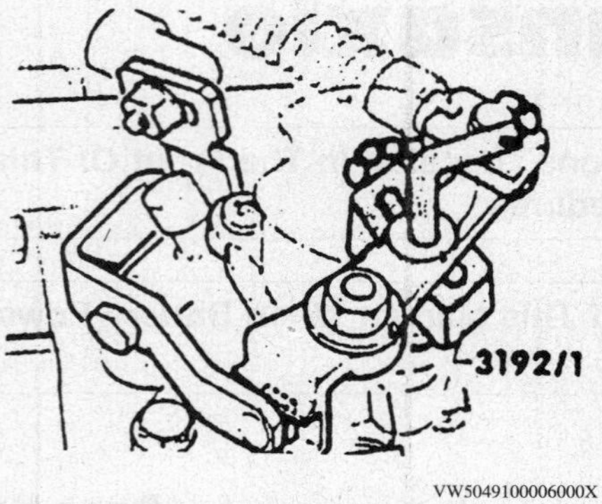

Fig. 3 Wedge & locating pin installation

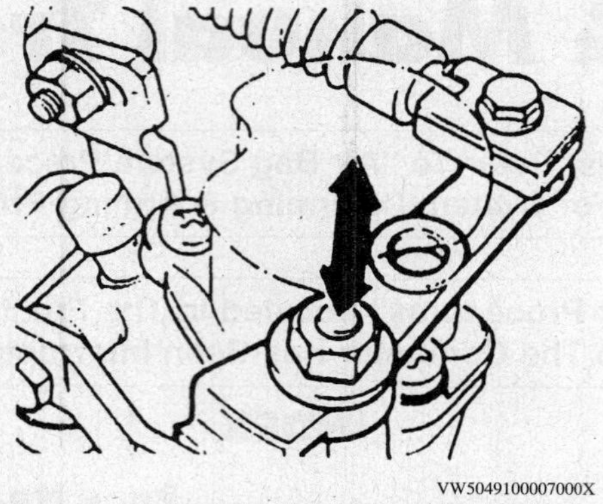

Fig. 4 Transaxle rod travel check

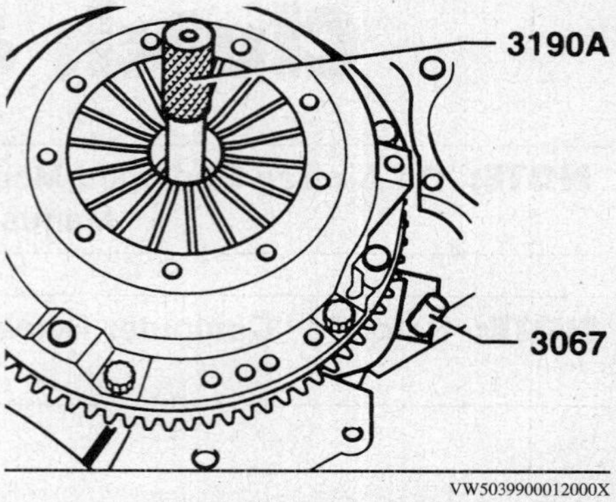

Fig. 5 Clutch plate removal. 02J transaxle

lug. **Minimal cable play at lug is normal.**

b. Reposition cable/lug slightly toward instrument panel to increase cable play and away from instrument panel to decrease cable play, then tighten nut.

HYDRAULIC SYSTEM SERVICE

CLUTCH SYSTEM BLEED

Obtain a suitable brake pressure bleeder to bleed clutch hydraulic system. Follow manufacturer's instructions for bleeding procedures. Maximum working pressure should be 36 psi. Bleed master cylinder first, then clutch slave cylinder.

CLUTCH

REPLACE

012 TRANSAXLE

1. Remove transaxle assembly as outlined under "Transaxle, Replace."
2. Using suitable tool, lock flywheel to prevent turning.
3. Loosen clutch cover attaching bolts evenly in diagonal pattern.
4. Remove cover and pressure plate.
5. Remove flywheel attaching bolt, then remove.
6. Inspect clutch lining for damaged rivets, burnt, split, oiled, loosened, or if worn to rivet heads.
7. Replace springs if rusted solid, broken, cracked or loose.
8. Replace clutch hub if rusted or grooves are damaged.
9. Replace torsion damper if torsion guide spring is broken, damaged cover, torsion spring loose or broken or damper is grooved.
10. Reverse procedure to install, noting that pressure plate must make complete contact with flywheel before installing attaching bolts.

02J TRANSAXLE

1. Remove transaxle as described in "Transaxle, Replace."
2. Using flywheel retainer tool No. 3067, or equivalent, lock flywheel in a stationary position, **Fig. 5.**
3. Loosen pressure plate retaining bolts one turn at a time until pressure is released from plate, then remove bolts.
4. Remove oil or grease from flywheel disc surface. **Flywheel must be free of grooves and/or pitting.** Resurface or replace as necessary.
5. Install new clutch disc, then the clutch pilot tool No. 3190A, or equivalent, into flywheel.
6. Install pressure plate assembly, then tighten bolts one or two turns at a time until bolts bottom out in flywheel. Tighten pressure plate retaining bolts to specifications.
7. Remove corrosion and grease from input shaft splines, then lightly apply grease part No. G 000 100, or equivalent, to input shaft splines. **Excess grease must be removed.**
8. Move release bearing back and forth until movement is free, **Fig. 6.**
9. Install transaxle assembly.

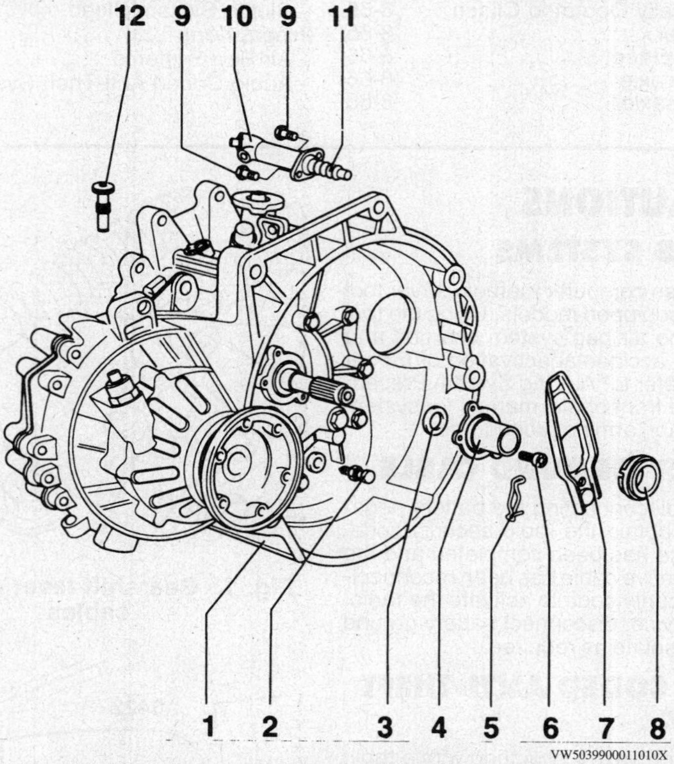

Fig. 6 Exploded view of clutch release mechanism (Part 1 of 2). 02J transaxle

TRANSAXLE

REPLACE

GOLF, GTI, JETTA & NEW BEETLE

1. Drain fluid from transaxle.
2. Remove power steering reservoir from battery bracket, but do not loosen hoses.
3. Tie reservoir up to upper radiator support.
4. Disconnect battery cable and remove battery and battery carrier.
5. Remove intake hose and connector from air mass meter.

1. Transmission
2. Ball Stud
3. Input Shaft Oil Seal
4. Guide Sleeve
5. Retaining Spring
6. Bolt
7. Clutch Release Lever
8. Release Bearing
9. Bolt
10. Slave Cylinder
11. Plunger
12. Assembly Bolt

VW5039900011020X

Fig. 6 Exploded view of clutch release mechanism (Part 2 of 2). 02J transaxle

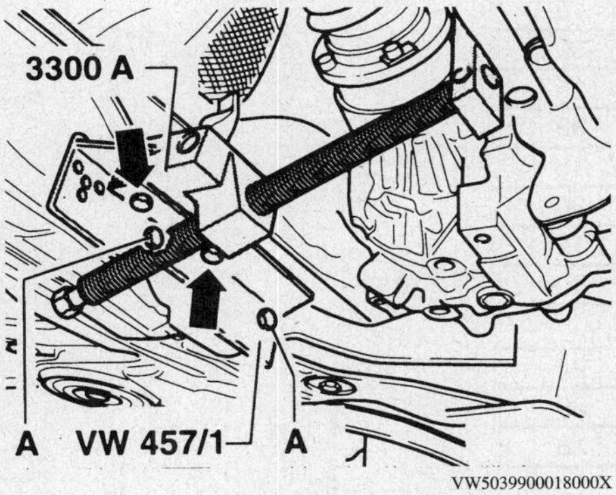

Fig. 9 Transaxle support installation

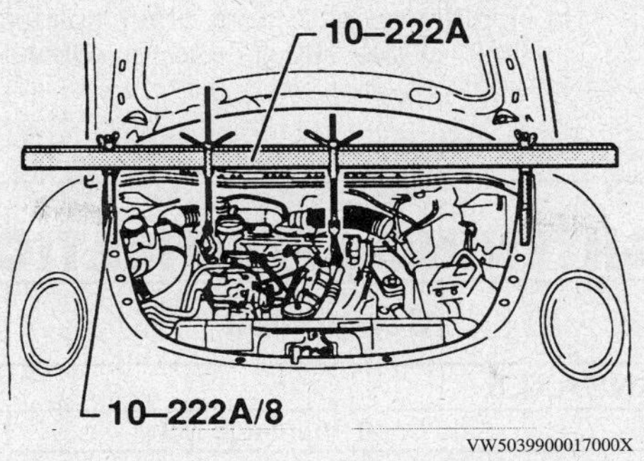

Fig. 7 Engine support installation. Golf, GTI, Jetta & New Beetle

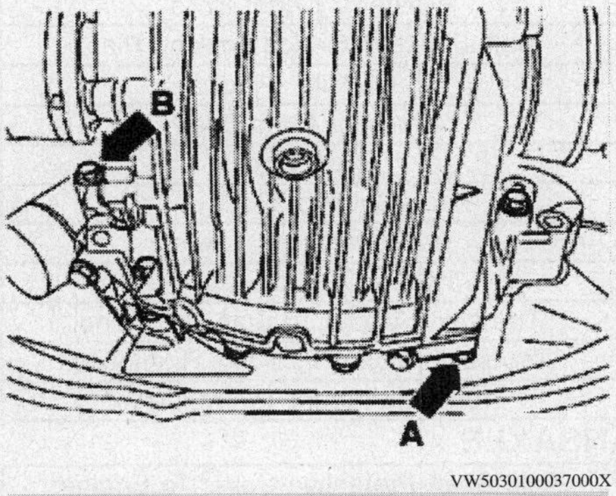

Fig. 10 Lower transaxle bolt removal. Passat

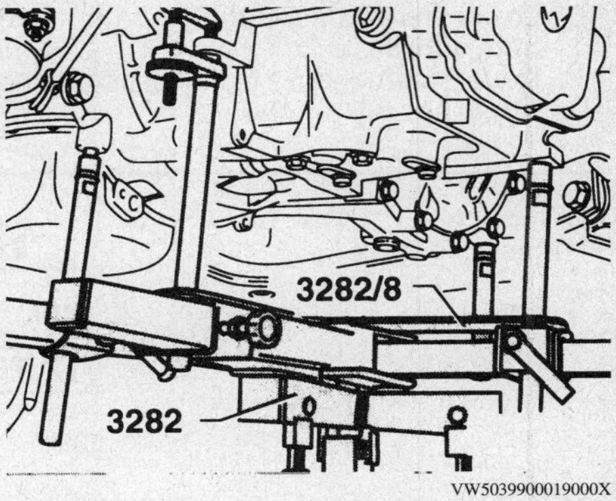

Fig. 8 Transaxle jack installation. Golf, GTI, Jetta & New Beetle

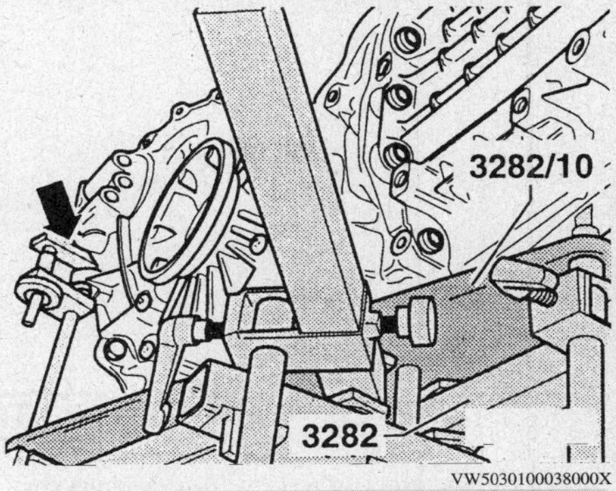

Fig. 11 Transaxle safety support. Passat

6. Remove air cleaner housing attaching bolts and housing.
7. Disconnect all electrical connectors and wiring from transaxle.
8. Remove gearshift cable from gearshift lever, then the selector cable with linkage lever from the transaxle.
9. Remove cable support from transaxle.
10. Remove clutch slave cylinder and position aside. **Do not open hydraulic lines.**
11. Remove cable retainer on starter.
12. Remove ground strap at engine/transaxle upper securing bolt.
13. Remove hoses and wiring connections in area of engine mount eye, if necessary.
14. Install engine support bar tool No. 10-222 A, or equivalent and bases tool No. 10-222 A/1, or equivalent, **Fig. 7. New holes may need to be drilled in support bridge and rails to adapt to this vehicle.**
15. Slightly tighten engine/transaxle support to take weight off of engine/transaxle assembly.
16. Remove sound insulation tray.
17. Remove power steering line from starter and transaxle mounts.
18. Remove starter.
19. Remove inner right constant velocity joint heat shield, then the axle shafts from the flanges. Wire axle shafts out of the way.
20. Remove pendulum support bolts.
21. Remove transaxle support and left assembly mounting bolts.
22. Lower engine/transaxle assembly slightly using spindle on support bar.
23. Assemble transaxle jack with transaxle support tool No. 3282 and adjustment plate tool No. 3282/8, or equivalents for 02A transaxle.
24. Remove gear carrier housing cover bolts and cover, position a transaxle jack under transaxle **Fig. 8,** then remove lower engine/transaxle attachment bolt.
25. Carefully pry transaxle from bushings and lower from vehicle.
26. Reverse procedure to install, noting the following:
    a. Press clutch release lever toward transaxle housing, then secure by mounting pin or M8 X 22 bolt. **Remove pin after transaxle is installed.**
    b. Install transaxle support with bolts and spacers tool Nos. 3300 A and VW 457/1, or equivalents when mounting transaxle, **Fig. 9.**
    c. Adjust shift linkage as previously described.
    d. Tighten nuts and bolts to specifications.
    e. Fill transaxle with suitable fluid. Refer to "Lubrication Data & Maintenance Charts" for fluid type and capacity.

PASSAT

1. Remove coolant overflow reservoir and position aside.
2. Remove intake air hose, then the upper transaxle bolts.
3. Remove righthand wheel, then the transaxle undertray.
4. Remove undertray bracket, then the front exhaust system with catalytic converter.
5. Remove cover plate over righthand axle shaft flange, then the cover above lefthand axle shaft.
6. Disconnect axle shafts from transaxle flanges, then carefully tie shafts up as high as possible.
7. Remove starter and secure aside.
8. Remove selector rod, then the push rod from transaxle.
9. Disconnect all electrical connectors and ground wires from transaxle.
10. Remove lower transaxle bolts except for bolts A and B, **Fig. 10.**
11. Install transaxle support tool No. 3282 and adjustment plate tool No. 3282/10, or equivalents, then support transaxle using transaxle jack tool No. VAG 1383A, or equivalent.
12. Align adjustment plate parallel to transaxle, then lock safety support on transaxle, **Fig. 11.**
13. Remove remaining transaxle bolts.
14. Remove transaxle from dowel sleeves and lower until clutch slave cylinder is accessible.
15. Remove clutch slave cylinder and secure aside with suitable wire. **Do not disconnect hydraulic lines.**

16. Lower transaxle carefully and remove from vehicle.
17. Reverse procedure to install noting the following:
    a. Lightly grease input shaft splines with G 000 100 grease, or equivalent.
    b. Ensure dowel sleeves are installed on cylinder block.
    c. Tighten bolts to specifications.

TIGHTENING SPECIFICATIONS

Year	Component	Torque, Ft. Lbs.
012 TRANSAXLE		
1998–2001	Axle Shaft To Flange M8	33
	Axle Shaft To Flange M10	59
	Clutch Slave Cylinder	18
	Cover Plate	15
	Master Cylinder Bolts	15
	Multi-Function Switch Locking Plate	18
	Oil Filler Plug	18
	Pressure Plate Bolts	18
	Push Rod	30
	Selector Rod	15
	Transaxle Bolts, Lower	33
	Transaxle Bolts, Upper	48
	Transaxle Mount To Body, Lefthand	30
	Transaxle Mount To Body, Righthand	15
	Transaxle Mount To Transaxle	30
02J TRANSAXLE		
1998–2001	Axle Shaft Protective Cover To Engine	24
	Axle Shaft To Flange Shaft	30
	Balance Weight Bolt	18
	Clutch Pressure Plate Bolts (Single Piece Flywheel)	15
	Clutch Pressure Plate Bolts (Two Part Flywheel)	10
	Clutch Release Lever Ball Stud	18
	Clutch Release Lever Bolt	15
	Cover Plate Bolt	18①
	Cross Support To Body Bolts	18
	Differential Ring Gear Nut & Bolt	52

Continued

TIGHTENING SPECIFICATIONS—Continued

Year	Component	Torque, Ft. Lbs.
02J TRANSAXLE		
1998–2001	5th Gear Selector Fork Bolts	18
	5th Gear Selector Jaw Bolt	18
	5th Gear & Synchronizer Torx Head bolts	59
	Filler Plug	18
	Flange Shaft Cone Head Bolt	18
	Gear Lever Housing To Body Nuts	18
	Gear Lever Fulcrum Pin Bolt	11
	Gear Lever Mounting Plate Nuts	15
	Gear Selector Lever Nut	18
	Guide Sleeve Bold	15
	Master Cylinder Nuts	18
	Pendulum Support Base Bolts	15②
	Pendulum Support Bracket Bolts	30②
	Pivot Pin Bolts	18
	Relay Lever Nut	11
	Relay lever To Actuating Arm Nut & Bolt	11
	Reverse Gear Selector Fork Bolt	18
	Reverse Shaft Support Bolts	22
	Reverse Shaft Support Torx Bolt	22
	Selector Cable Support Bracket Bolts	18
	Selector Fork Bolt	18
	Selector Mechanism Cover Lock Bolt	30
	Selector Shaft End Nut	18
	Shift Cover Plate Bolts	18
	Slave Cylinder Bolts	18
	Speedometer Drive Gear Nut	22
	Support Bearing Nuts	18②
	Torx Socket Head Bolt	59
	Transaxle Housing Bolts	18②
	Transaxle Housing Cover Bolts	84③
	Transaxle Mount To Transaxle Bolts	30②
	Transaxle To Body Mount Bolts	44②
	Transaxle To Body Support Rod Bolts	18
	Transaxle To Engine Bolts	18②
	Transaxle To Engine M7x12 Bolts	84③
	Transaxle To Engine M10x50 Bolts	33
	Transaxle To Engine M10x60 Bolts	30
	Transaxle To Engine M12x55 Bolts	59
	Transaxle To Engine M12x65 Bolts	59
	Transaxle To Engine M12x150 Bolts	59

① — Loosen & tighten diagonally.
② — Tighten an additional 90.° This may be done in several steps.
③ — Inch lbs.

Rear Axle & Suspension

NOTE: On Air Bag Equipped Models, Refer To "Air Bag System Precautions" Located In The Front Of This Manual For System Disarming & Arming Procedures.

INDEX

	Page No.
Coil Spring & Shock Absorber, Replace	8-72
Hub & Bearing, Replace	8-71
New Beetle & 1999–2001 Golf & Jetta	8-71
Passat	8-71
Precautions	8-70
Air Bag Systems	8-70
Audio Coded Anti-Theft System	8-70
Battery Ground Cable	8-70
Rear Axle, Replace	8-70
Cabrio & 1998 Golf, GTI & Jetta	8-70
New Beetle & 1999–2001 Golf, GTI & Jetta	8-70
Passat	8-71
Strut, Replace	8-72
1998 Cabrio, Golf, GTI & Jetta	8-72
Passat	8-72
Strut Service	8-72
Tightening Specifications	8-74
Wheel Bearing, Adjust	8-72
1998 Golf, GTI & Jetta	8-72
New Beetle, Passat & 1999–2001 Golf & Jetta	8-72

PRECAUTIONS

AIR BAG SYSTEMS

Do not use computer memory saver tool on air bag equipped models. Using the tool will keep the air bag system charged and may cause accidental activation of the air bag unit. Refer to "Air Bag System Precautions" in the front of this manual for system disarming and arming procedures.

BATTERY GROUND CABLE

Prior to disconnecting the battery negative cable, obtain the radio security code. After service has been completed and the battery negative cable has been reconnected, use security code to activate the radio. Prior to service, disconnect battery ground cable and isolate as required.

AUDIO CODED ANTI-THEFT SYSTEM

Some models are equipped with a radio anti-theft system that will disable the system when battery power is interrupted, unless the system is reset the radio will not operate.

1. Turn radio to On position, SAFE and 1000 should be displayed.
2. Enter radio code using first four program station buttons. Security code will appear on display.
3. Depress and hold righthand side of radio right or left blocker until anti-theft coding is activated indicated by a brief signal sound.
4. If code number has been entered correctly, when ignition key is removed a diode on front of radio will flash.

REAR AXLE

REPLACE

CABRIO & 1998 GOLF, GTI & JETTA

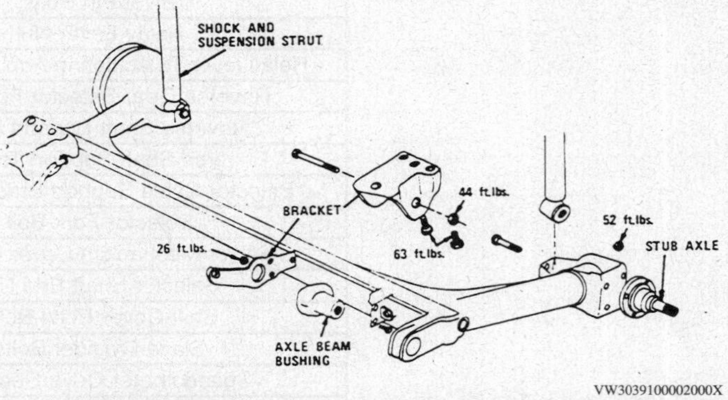

Fig. 1 Rear axle assembly. Cabrio & 1998 Golf, GTI & Jetta

1. Raise and support vehicle, then remove wheels.
2. Disconnect rear brake pressure regulator spring, **Fig. 1.**
3. Remove rear brakes as outlined under "Drum Brakes."
4. **On models equipped with ABS,** disconnect wheel speed sensors.
5. **On all models,** disconnect brake fluid lines from wheel cylinders, then remove backing plates and spindles.
6. Disconnect and remove electrical cables, parking brake cables and brake fluid lines from rear axle.
7. Support rear axle at rear, then remove struts or coil springs and shocks. Refer to "Strut, Replace" or "Shock Absorber, Replace" as required.
8. Support rear axle at front, then disconnect from mounting bracket.
9. Remove axle from vehicle.
10. Reverse procedure to install, noting the following:
    a. Tighten to specifications.
    b. Bleed brakes as outlined under "Hydraulic Brake Systems."
    c. Adjust rear brake pressure, if equipped, with a rear brake pressure regulator, as outlined under "Hydraulic Brake Systems."
    d. Ensure mounting pads for spindles are clean and free of rust and scale.

NEW BEETLE & 1999-2001 GOLF, GTI & JETTA

1. Remove upper shock mount retaining bolts with vehicle standing on wheels. **It may be necessary to raise vehicle until bolts are accessible.**
2. Raise vehicle to relieve pressure on coil spring, then remove rear wheels.
3. Unclip brake line from rear axle.
4. Remove brake caliper, then hang from body using suitable wire. **Do not allow caliper to hang by brake hose.**
5. **On models equipped with ABS,** disconnect wheel speed sensor electrical connector.
6. **On models less ABS,** remove brake pressure regulator bolts.
7. **On all models,** support rear axle using suitable transaxle jack.
8. Remove rear axle bearing bracket bolts **Fig. 2**, then the rear axle.
9. Reverse procedure to install noting the following:
    a. Tighten bolts to specifications using new mounting bracket bolts.
    b. Bleed brakes as outlined in "Hydraulic Brake Systems" section.
    c. Ensure steering wheel is in straight ahead position while driving.

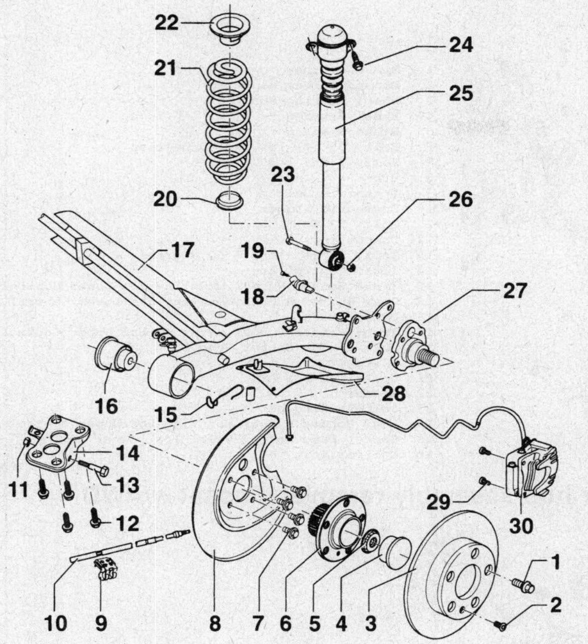

1. Wheel Bolts 89 ft. lbs.
2. Screw 35 inch lbs.
3. Brake Disc
4. Dust Cap
5. Self-locking Nut
6. Wheel Bearing/Hub Unit & ABS Speed Sensor Rotor
7. Hex Bolt
8. Splash Shield
9. Parking Brake Cable Bracket
10. Parking Brake Cable
11. Self-Locking Hex Nut
12. Hex Bolt 55 ft. lbs.
13. Hex Bolt 59 ft. lbs.
14. Rear Axle Mounting Bracket
15. Parking Brake Cable Bracket
16. Bonded Rubber Bushing
17. Axle Beam
18. ABS Wheel Speed Sensor
19. Socket-head Bolt 71 inch lbs.
20. Spacer Bushing
21. Coil Spring
22. Spring Seat
23. Hex Bolt 44 ft. lbs.
24. Hex Bolt 55 ft. lbs.
25. Shock Absorber
26. Hex Nut
27. Stub Axle
28. Stone Protection Plate
29. Socket-Head Bolts
30. Brake Caliper

VW3039900025000X

Fig. 2 Rear axle assembly. New Beetle & 1999–2001 Golf, GTI & Jetta

PASSAT

1. Remove upper shock mount retaining bolts with vehicle standing on wheels. **It may be necessary to raise vehicle until bolts are accessible.**
2. Raise vehicle to relieve pressure on coil spring.
3. Pull rear axle down and remove coil spring, **Fig. 3.**
4. Remove rear wheels, then the cover.
5. Remove parking brake cable retainers.
6. Remove ABS wheel speed sensor.
7. Unclip wheel speed sensor wiring from retainer.
8. Unclip brake line.
9. Unbolt brake caliper and hang from body using suitable wire.
10. Remove brake line retainer.
11. Loosen left mounting bracket bolts.
12. Support rear axle.
13. Mark installed position of mounting bracket on longitudinal member.
14. Remove rear axle bushing bolts on both sides then lower rear axle from vehicle.
15. Reverse procedure to install noting to tighten to specifications.

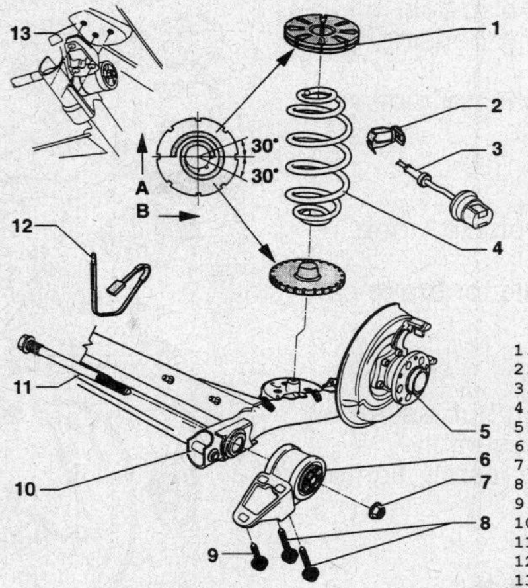

1. Spring Support
2. Wheel Speed Sensor Retainer
3. Wheel Speed Sensor
4. Coil Spring
5. Wheel Bearing
6. Mounting Bracket
7. Nut
8. Bolt, 81 ft. lbs. + 90 Degrees
9. Bolt, 81 ft. lbs. + 90 Degrees
10. Axle Beam
11. Bolt, 89 ft. lbs. + 90 Degrees
12. Retaining Strap
13. Threads In Longitudinal Member

VW2039900003000X

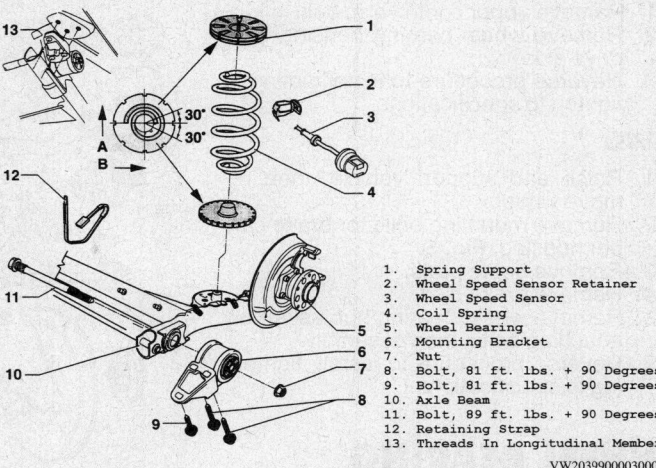

Fig. 3 Rear axle removal. Passat

HUB & BEARING

REPLACE

NEW BEETLE & 1999–2001 GOLF & JETTA

1. Raise and support vehicle, then remove rear wheel.
2. Remove dust cap.
3. **On models equipped with rear disc brakes,** proceed as follows:
   a. Remove brake caliper attaching bolts, then the brake caliper, suspend caliper assembly aside.
   b. Remove brake rotor attaching bolts, then the brake rotor.
4. **On models equipped with drum brakes,** remove brake drum.
5. **On all models,** pull wheel bearing and hub assembly off of stub axle with puller tool Kuko No. 20/2, or equivalent.
6. Pull bearing inner race off of stub axle with puller tool and leg clamp Kuko No. 204-2, or equivalent.
7. Reverse procedure to install.

PASSAT

AWD

1. Raise and support vehicle, then remove wheel.
2. Remove brake caliper mounting bolts **Fig. 4,** then the brake caliper, suspend caliper assembly aside.
3. Remove brake rotor.
4. Remove splash shield attaching bolts, then splash shield.
5. Remove wheel bearing and hub unit attaching bolts, then the wheel bearing and hub unit.
6. Remove ABS wheel speed sensor from wheel bearing housing.
7. Remove connecting link bolt, then link.
8. Remove track rod bolt, then track rod.
9. Mark installed position of eccentric washer for lower control arm bolt.
10. Remove lower control arm bolt.

11. Remove upper control arm bolt.
12. Remove wheel bearing housing from drive axle.
13. Reverse procedure to install noting to tighten to specifications.

FWD

1. Raise and support vehicle, then remove wheel.
2. Remove mounting bolts for brake caliper housing, **Fig. 5.**
3. Remove brake pads.
4. Remove brake disc.
5. Remove wheel bearing/hub assembly attaching bolts, then assembly.
6. Reverse procedure to install, tightening to specifications.

WHEEL BEARING

ADJUST

1998 GOLF, GTI & JETTA

1. Raise and support rear of vehicle, then remove the wheel/tire assembly.
2. Remove grease cap, then the cotter pin and locknut.
3. Tighten adjusting nut while turning wheel to settle bearings.
4. Loosen, then retighten adjusting nut, until thrust washer can be moved slightly with screwdriver.
5. Install locknut and new cotter pin, then the grease cap.
6. Install wheel/tire assembly and lower vehicle to ground.

NEW BEETLE, PASSAT & 1999–2001 GOLF & JETTA

Wheel bearings cannot be adjusted on these vehicles.

STRUT

REPLACE

1998 CABRIO, GOLF, GTI & JETTA

Whenever replacing struts, always remove then install one strut at a time to prevent personal injury and/or damage to vehicle.

1. Raise and support vehicle, then loosen but do not remove lower strut mounting bolts, **Fig. 1.**
2. Support axle beam at rear ends with struts in fully extended position.
3. Locate and disconnect upper strut mounting for one side. **Remove and install struts one side at a time.**
4. Remove lower strut mounting bolt, then strut.
5. Reverse procedure to install. Tighten to specifications.

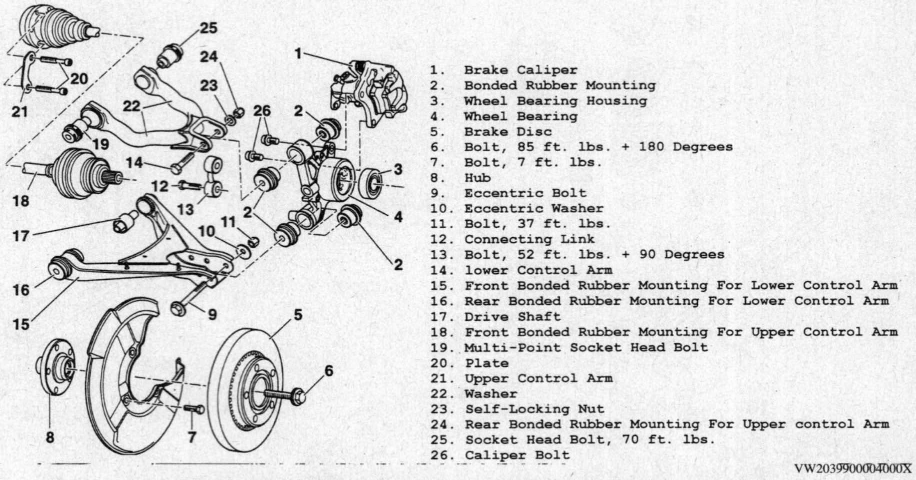

Fig. 4 Rear hub assembly removal. Passat w/AWD

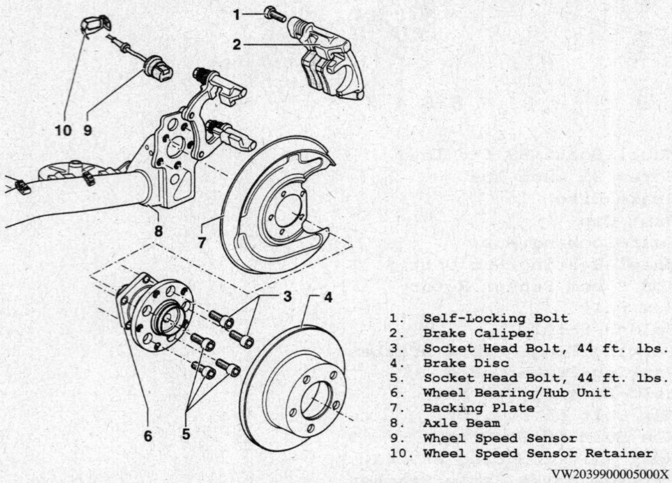

Fig. 5 Rear hub assembly removal. Passat w/FWD

PASSAT

1. Remove brake caliper mounting bolts, then the stabilizer bar clamp.
2. Remove connecting link from stabilizer bar, then the control arm bolt.
3. Remove strut bolts, then the strut.
4. Reverse procedure to install. Tighten bolts to specifications.

STRUT SERVICE

Refer to **Figs. 6 and 7** for component location locations during strut service.

1. Remove strut from vehicle as outlined under "Strut, Replace."
2. Secure strut/coil spring assembly in a suitable coil spring compressor, remove nut, then spring and components.
3. Assemble spring and components to new strut.
4. Reverse procedure to complete installation.

COIL SPRING & SHOCK ABSORBER

REPLACE

1. Remove upper shock absorber attaching bolts with vehicle standing on its wheels.
2. Raise vehicle further to relieve coil spring pressure.
3. Remove lower shock absorber attaching bolt.
4. Remove shock absorber.
5. Remove coil spring retaining clamps, then coil spring.
6. Reverse procedure to install. Tighten to specifications.

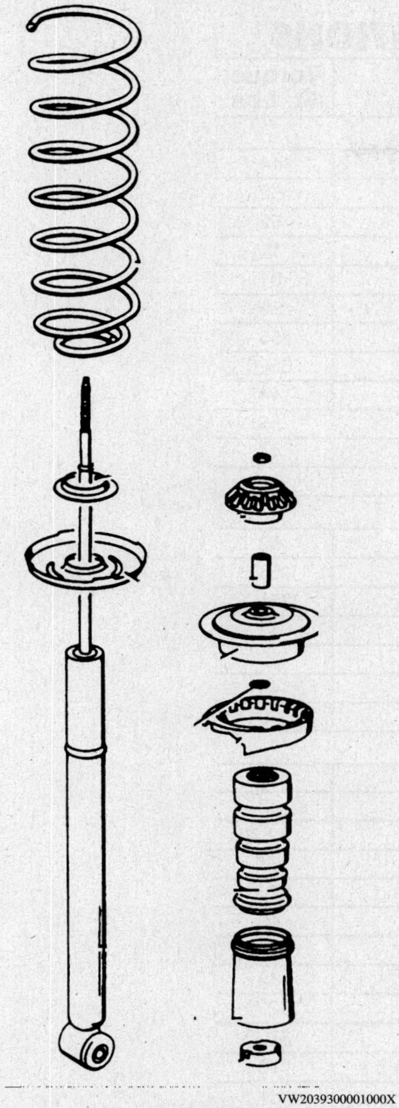

Fig. 6 Exploded view of rear strut. Cabrio, Golf, GTI & Jetta

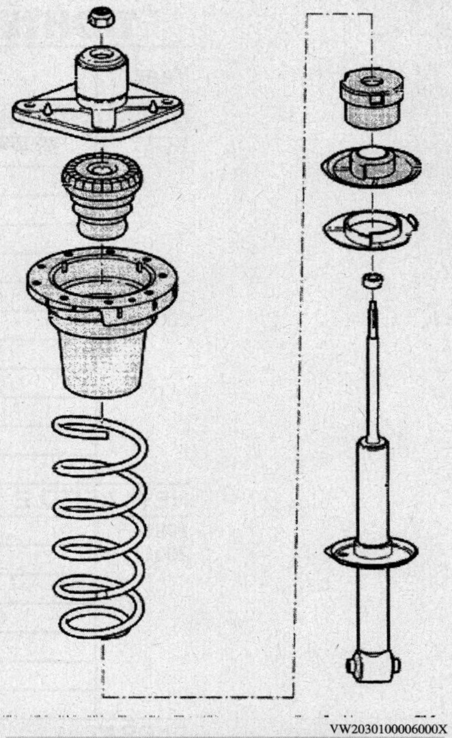

Fig. 7 Exploded view of rear strut. Passat

TIGHTENING SPECIFICATIONS

Year	Component	Torque, Ft. Lbs.
GOLF, GTI & JETTA		
1998	Axle To Axle Bracket Bolts	44
	Axle Bracket To Body Bolts	52
	Lower Strut To Axle Bolts	52
	Upper Strut To Body Nuts	11
	Wheel Lug Nuts	81
1999–2001	Axle To Axle Bracket Bolts	59
	Axle Bracket To Body Bolts	55
	Disc To Hub Screw	35①
	Shock Absorber To Rear Axle	44
	Shock Absorber To Body	55
	Splash Shield Bolt	44
	Wheel Bolts	89
NEW BEETLE		
1998–2001	Axle To Axle Bracket Bolts	59
	Axle Bracket To Body Bolts	55
	Disc To Hub Screw	35①
	Shock Absorber To Rear Axle	44
	Shock Absorber To Body	55
	Splash Shield Bolt	44
	Wheel Bolts	89
PASSAT		
1998–2001	Axle Beam To Body	81②
	Brake Caliper To Bracket	22
	Bushing To Rear Axle	89②
	Connecting Link To Stabilizer Bar	37
	Control Arm To Wheel Bearing Housing	52②
	Driveshaft To Final Drive	40
	Mounting Bracket To Body	81②
	Shock Absorber To Body	33
	Shock Absorber To Control Arm	52②
	Shock Absorber To Rear Axle	37②
	Stabilizer Bar Clamp To Axle Beam	18
	Wheel Lug Nuts	81

① — Inch lbs.
② — Plus an additional 90.°

Front Suspension & Steering

NOTE: On Air Bag Equipped Models, Refer To "Air Bag System Precautions" Located In The Front Of This Manual For System Disarming & Arming Procedures.

INDEX

	Page No.
Ball Joint, Replace	8-77
Ball Joint Inspection	8-76
Coil Spring, Replace	8-77
Control Arm, Replace	8-78
Description	8-75
Hub & Bearing, Replace	8-76
Installation	8-76
Removal	8-76
Manual Steering Gear, Replace	8-78
Power Steering	8-121
Power Steering Gear, Replace	8-78
Precautions	8-75
Air Bag Systems	8-75
Audio Coded Anti-Theft System	8-75
Battery Ground Cable	8-75
Strut, Replace	8-77
Strut Service	8-77
Swing Arm/Wheel Bearing Housing, Replace	8-75
Passat	8-75
Tightening Specifications	8-79
Wheel Bearing Housing, Replace	8-76
Installation	8-76
Removal	8-76

PRECAUTIONS

AIR BAG SYSTEMS

Do not use computer memory saver tool on air bag equipped models. Using the tool will keep the air bag system charged and may cause accidental activation of the air bag unit. Refer to "Air Bag System Precautions" in the front of this manual for system disarming and arming procedures.

BATTERY GROUND CABLE

Prior to disconnecting the battery negative cable, obtain the radio security code. After service has been completed and the battery negative cable has been reconnected, use security code to activate the radio. Prior to service, disconnect battery ground cable and isolate as required.

AUDIO CODED ANTI-THEFT SYSTEM

Some models are equipped with a radio anti-theft system that will disable the system when battery power is interrupted, unless the system is reset the radio will not operate.

1. Turn radio to On position, SAFE and 1000 should be displayed.
2. Enter radio code using first four program station buttons. Security code will appear on display.
3. Depress and hold righthand side of radio right or left blocker until anti-theft coding is activated indicated by a brief signal sound.
4. If code number has been entered correctly, when ignition key is removed a diode on front of radio will flash.

DESCRIPTION

These vehicles use a McPherson strut type front suspension. The upper part of strut is attached to the upper fender reinforcement. The strut and wheel bearing housing are separate and distinct parts, with the strut attached to the housing with through bolts. The assembly is attached to the lower control arm through a ball joint, **Figs. 1 through 3.** During steering maneuvers, the strut and housing rotate as an assembly.

The axle shafts are attached inboard to the transaxle output drive flanges and outboard to the driven wheel hub.

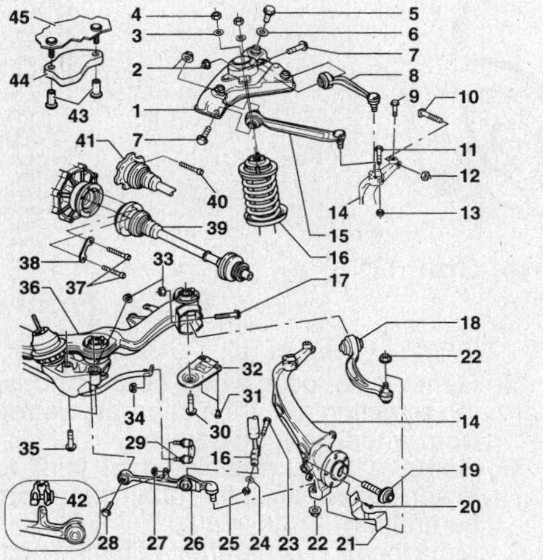

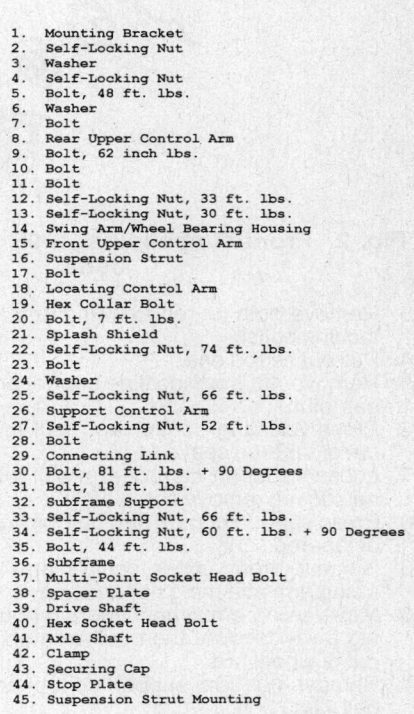

1. Mounting Bracket
2. Self-Locking Nut
3. Washer
4. Self-Locking Nut
5. Bolt, 48 ft. lbs.
6. Washer
7. Bolt
8. Rear Upper Control Arm
9. Bolt, 62 inch lbs.
10. Bolt
11. Bolt
12. Self-Locking Nut, 33 ft. lbs.
13. Self-Locking Nut, 30 ft. lbs.
14. Swing Arm/Wheel Bearing Housing
15. Front Upper Control Arm
16. Suspension Strut
17. Bolt
18. Locating Control Arm
19. Hex Collar Bolt
20. Bolt, 7 ft. lbs.
21. Splash Shield
22. Self-Locking Nut, 74 ft. lbs.
23. Bolt
24. Washer
25. Self-Locking Nut, 66 ft. lbs.
26. Support Control Arm
27. Self-Locking Nut, 52 ft. lbs.
28. Bolt
29. Connecting Link
30. Bolt, 81 ft. lbs. + 90 Degrees
31. Bolt, 18 ft. lbs.
32. Subframe Support
33. Self-Locking Nut, 66 ft. lbs.
34. Self-Locking Nut, 60 ft. lbs. + 90 Degrees
35. Bolt, 44 ft. lbs.
36. Subframe
37. Multi-Point Socket Head Bolt
38. Spacer Plate
39. Drive Shaft
40. Hex Socket Head Bolt
41. Axle Shaft
42. Clamp
43. Securing Cap
44. Stop Plate
45. Suspension Strut Mounting

VW2029900014000X

Fig. 1 Front suspension. Passat

SWING ARM/WHEEL BEARING HOUSING

REPLACE

PASSAT

1. Remove axle shaft bolt.
2. Remove wheel.
3. Remove bolts for brake caliper, then remove brake caliper.
4. Secure brake caliper to body with wire.
5. Pull ABS wheel speed sensor wiring out of retainer on brake caliper.
6. Remove brake disc.
7. Remove bolts for splash plate.
8. Pull ABS wheel speed sensor from swing arm/wheel bearing housing.
9. Remove nuts 2 and 3.
10. Pull out rubber grommet and separate connector 2.
11. Pull ABS wheel speed sensor wiring from retainers.
12. Guide wiring out through opening in swing arm/wheel bearing housing, then remove.

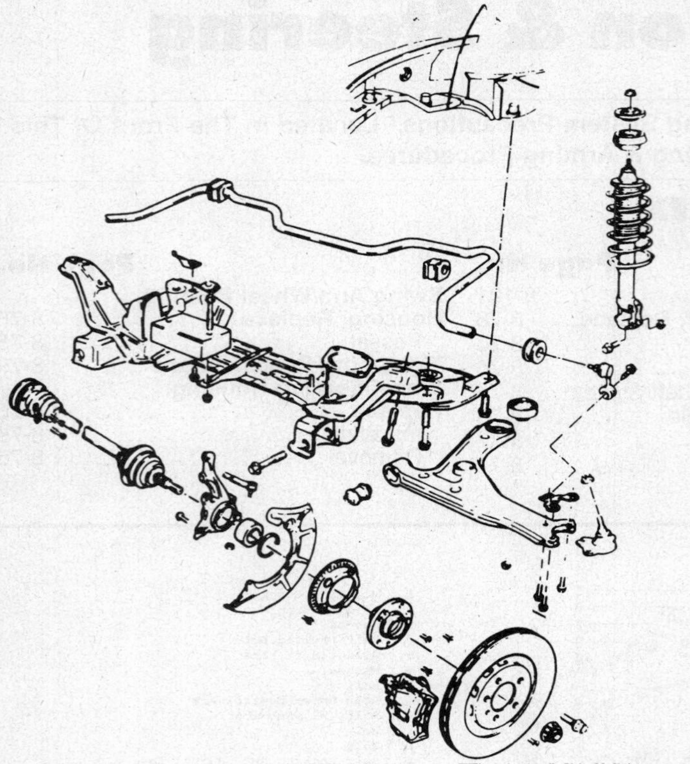

VW2029100002000A

Fig. 2 Front suspension. 1998 Cabrio, Golf, GTI, Jetta

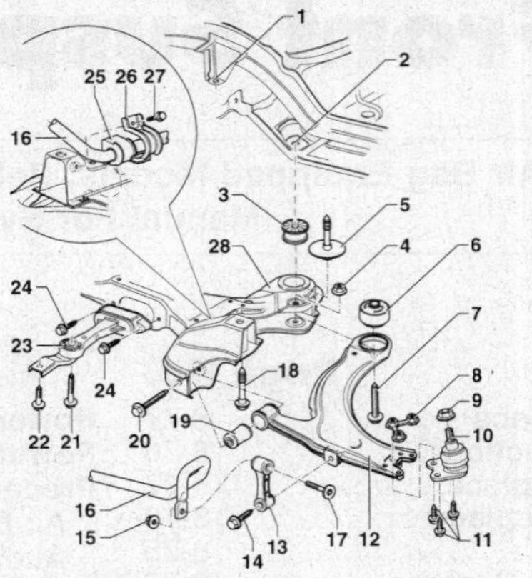

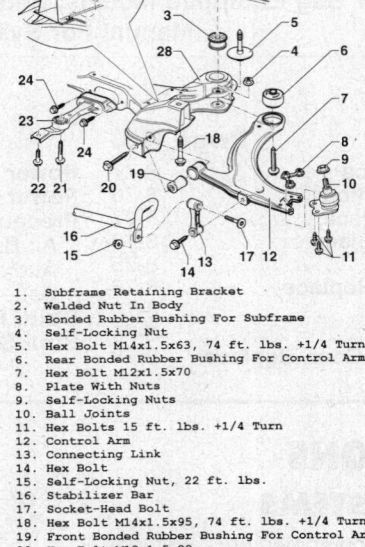

1. Subframe Retaining Bracket
2. Welded Nut In Body
3. Bonded Rubber Bushing For Subframe
4. Self-Locking Nut
5. Hex Bolt M14x1.5x63, 74 ft. lbs. +1/4 Turn
6. Rear Bonded Rubber Bushing For Control Arm
7. Hex Bolt M12x1.5x70
8. Plate With Nuts
9. Self-Locking Nuts
10. Ball Joints
11. Hex Bolts 15 ft. lbs. +1/4 Turn
12. Control Arm
13. Connecting Link
14. Hex Bolt
15. Self-Locking Nut, 22 ft. lbs.
16. Stabilizer Bar
17. Socket-Head Bolt
18. Hex Bolt M14x1.5x95, 74 ft. lbs. +1/4 Turn
19. Front Bonded Rubber Bushing For Control Arm
20. Hex Bolt M12x1.5x82
21. Hex Bolt M10x70, 30 ft. lbs. +1/4 Turn
22. Hex Bolt M10x30, 30 ft. lbs. +1/4 Turn
23. Transmission Support
24. Hex Bolts, 15 ft. lbs. +1/4 Turn
25. Stabilizer Bar Bushing
26. Mounting Bracket
27. Hex Bolt, 18 ft. lbs.
28. Subframe

VW2029900012000X

Fig. 3 Front suspension. New Beetle & 1999–2001 Golf & Jetta

13. Remove both tie rod to swing arm attaching bolts.
14. Pull out tie rod end.
15. Remove nut from locating control arm ball joint.
16. Press Locating control arm ball joint out of tapered seat.
17. Loosen support control arm ball joint nut, do not remove completely.
18. Press support control arm ball joint out of tapered seat.
19. Remove front upper control arm to swing arm attaching nut and bolt.
20. Move swing arm/wheel bearing housing away to side, then pull axle shaft out of wheel hub.
21. Remove nut from support control arm ball joint.
22. Remove swing arm/wheel bearing housing.
23. Reverse procedure to install.

WHEEL BEARING HOUSING

REPLACE

Refer to **Fig. 4** to aid in removal and installation of wheel bearing housing.

REMOVAL

1. Remove axle shaft to hub retaining nut.
2. Raise and support vehicle. Remove wheel assembly.
3. Remove brake caliper and support using a length of wire.
4. Remove brake rotor.
5. Remove tie rod to wheel bearing housing retaining nut, then separate tie rod from wheel bearing housing.
6. Remove bolts retaining ball joint to lower control arm, then ball joint from control arm.
7. Mark location of camber adjusting bolt, if installed, then remove the bolts, **Fig. 4**.
8. Support axle shaft, pull housing from strut and remove housing from vehicle.

INSTALLATION

1. Insert axle shaft into hub, then install wheel bearing housing onto strut bracket. Install cam bolts, if installed, and through bolts. Align reference marks on cam bolt and tighten through bolt to specifications.
2. Install ball to control arm, then tighten bolts to specifications.
3. Connect tie rod to wheel bearing housing and tighten retaining nut to specifications. Install new cotter pin.
4. Install brake rotor and caliper.
5. Install wheel and axle shaft to hub retaining nut, then lower vehicle and tighten to specifications.

HUB & BEARING

REPLACE

REMOVAL

Damage will occur to the wheel bearing as hub is pressed from the housing. Therefore, it will be necessary to install a new bearing.

1. Remove wheel bearing housing as outlined under "Wheel Bearing Housing, Replace."
2. Press hub from wheel bearing housing.
3. Using a suitable puller, remove wheel bearing inner race from hub.
4. Remove brake dust shield from wheel bearing housing.
5. Remove retaining clips, then press bearing from wheel bearing housing.

INSTALLATION

1. Install outer retaining clip, then press new bearing into housing. Ensure press tool bears only against outer race of bearing assembly.
2. Install inner retaining clip.
3. Install brake dust shield on wheel bearing housing.
4. Press hub assembly into wheel bearing housing. Ensure press tool properly supports inner bearing races of bearing assembly.
5. Install strut or wheel bearing housing.

BALL JOINT INSPECTION

1. Raise and support vehicle.
2. Check ball joint axial play by forcing ball joint up and down.
3. Check ball joint radial play by moving lower part of tire inward and outward.
4. If there is any noticeable axial or radial play, replace ball joint.

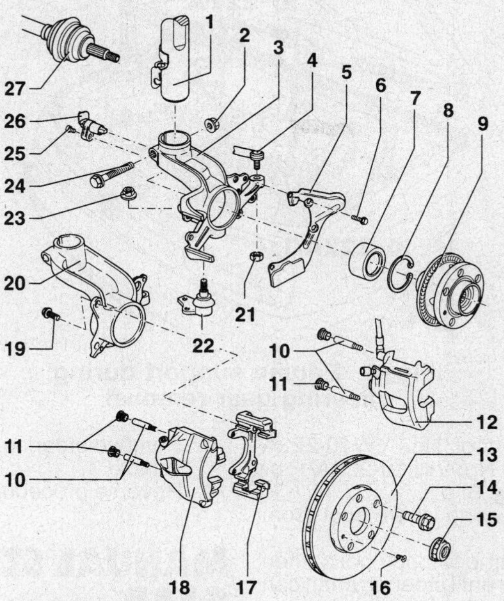

1. Suspension Strut
2. Self-Locking Nut, 37 ft. lbs. +1/4 Turn
3. Wheel Bearing Housing
4. Tie Rod End
5. Splash Plate
6. Hex Bolt 7 ft. lbs.
7. Wheel Bearing
8. Circlip
9. Wheel Hub w/ABS Wheel Speed Sensor Rotor
10. Guide Pins, 20 ft. lbs.
11. Protective Cap
12. Brake Caliper
13. Ventilated Brake Disc
14. Wheel Bolts, 89 ft. lbs.
15. Self-Locking Nut
16. Screw, 35 Inch lbs.
17. Brake Carrier
18. Brake Caliper
19. Self-Locking Bolt, 92 ft. lbs.
20. Wheel Bearing Housing
21. Self-Locking Nut, 33 ft. lbs.
22. Ball Joint
23. Self-Locking Nut, 33 ft. lbs.
24. Hex Bolt
25. Socket-Head Bolt, 71 inch lbs.
26. ABS Wheel Speed Sensor
27. Drive Axle

VW2029900013000X

Fig. 4 Wheel bearing housing and hub assembly. New Beetle & 1999–2001 Golf & Jetta

BALL JOINT

REPLACE

1. Raise and support vehicle, then remove front wheel.
2. **On Passat models,** remove ball joint to wheel bearing housing clamp bolt, then separate ball joint from housing.
3. **On all models except Passat,** remove ball joint nut, then using a suitable tool, separate taper shaft from wheel bearing housing.
4. **On all models,** mark position of ball joint in control arm for later assembly.
5. Remove bolts, then ball joint from control arm
6. Position new ball joint to control arm and install retaining bolts, spring washers and nuts and tighten to specifications.
7. Reverse procedure to complete installation.

COIL SPRING

REPLACE

1. Remove strut assembly as outlined under "Strut, Replace." **Mark position of upper mount in relation to strut. Scribe mark on upper mount to aid installation.**
2. Compress coil spring, using suitable spring compressor tool.
3. Hold shock absorber shaft with hex key, then remove attaching nut.
4. Carefully release tension on spring compressor, then remove retainer, end collar and mount, rubber damper, bearing, upper spring seat and the coil spring.
5. Inspect rubber components for deterioration, retainers and seats for cracks or distortion and bearing for binding. Replace if necessary.
6. Position coil spring onto strut and compress, using suitable spring compressor.
7. Install upper spring seat, bearing rubber damper, end collar and mount, then the retainer and nut. Tighten nut to specifications.
8. Remove spring compressor.

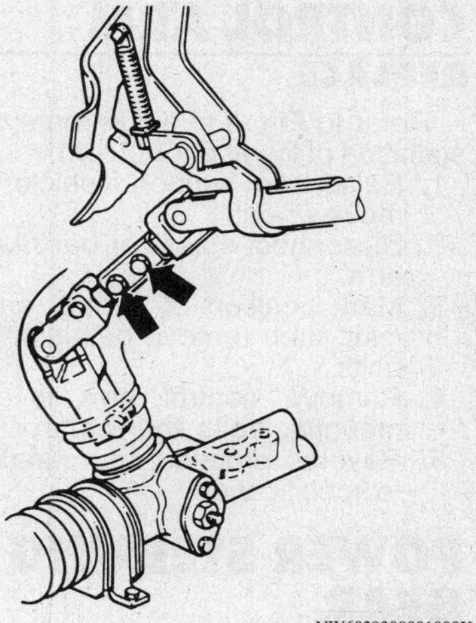

VW6029300001000X

Fig. 5 Steering shaft bolts removal

STRUT

REPLACE

Mark position of strut to hub cam bolt, if installed, to aid installation.

1. Raise and support vehicle, then remove front wheels.
2. Disconnect caliper brake hose from brake line support on strut.
3. Mark position of strut to wheel bearing housing.
4. Support control arm and wheel bearing housing assembly with a suitable jack, then remove strut to wheel bearing housing bolts.
5. Lower wheel bearing housing assembly and disconnect from strut.
6. Remove the upper nut and stop plate.
7. Remove the strut assembly.
8. Reverse procedure to install. Tighten to specifications.

STRUT SERVICE

These vehicles incorporate an integral, non-serviceable shock absorber cartridge built into the strut assembly.

1. Remove coil spring as outlined under "Coil Spring, Replace."
2. Secure strut assembly in a vise, then remove the strut tube threaded cap.
3. Remove strut cartridge from strut assembly.
4. Reverse procedure to install. Tighten strut tube threaded cap to specifications.

CONTROL ARM

REPLACE

Refer to **Fig. 3** to aid in removal and installation of lower control arm.

1. Raise and support vehicle, then remove wheel.
2. Disconnect stabilizer bar from control arm.
3. Mark position of control arm to ball joint, then remove ball joint mounting bolts.
4. Remove control arm to subframe mounting bolts, then control arm.
5. Reverse procedure to install. Tighten to specification.

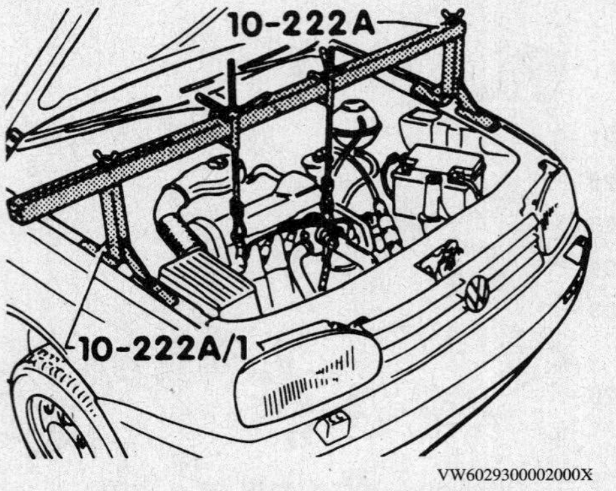

Fig. 6 Engine support during steering gear removal

POWER STEERING GEAR

REPLACE

1. Raise and support vehicle, then disconnect tie rod ends from steering arms.
2. From under lefthand side of instrument panel, remove connecting bolts from steering shaft, **Fig. 5.**
3. Drain oil from steering system at suction line of pump.
4. Support engine and transaxle using support frame tool No. VW10-222A and leg set tool No. VW 10-222A/1, or equivalents, **Fig. 6.**
5. Disconnect steering shaft boot from steering gear.
6. Remove subframe to body bolts, then lower assembly until steering shaft can be separated.
7. Disconnect fluid lines from steering gear, cap or plug all lines or fittings.
8. Remove steering gear mounting bolts. Note that bolts will stay in subframe.
9. Remove steering gear towards rear of vehicle.
10. Reverse procedure to install.

MANUAL STEERING GEAR

REPLACE

Follow procedure described under "Power Steering Gear, Replace."

TIGHTENING SPECIFICATIONS

Year	Component	Torque, Ft. Lbs.
1998–2001	Axle Shaft To Hub Nuts	195
	Axle Shaft Bolts M14	85②
	Axle Shaft Bolts M16	140②
	Ball Joint To Control Arm Nuts, Golf, GTI & Jetta	25
	Ball Joint To Control Arm Nuts, Passat	25
	Ball Joint To Wheel Bearing Housing Nuts	37
	Control Arm To Subframe Bolts	96
	Control Arm To Swing Arm Supports	74
	Control Arm To Swing Arm Joints	30
	Hub Nut	195
	Stabilizer Bar Link Rod To Control Arm Nuts	18
	Steering Gear To Subframe Bolts	22
	Steering Shaft Bolts	18
	Strut Assembly Nut	30
	Strut To Wheel Bearing Housing Nut	70
	Strut To Wheel Bearing Housing Nut, New Beetle & 1999–2001 Golf & Jetta	37①
	Subframe To Body Bolts	52①
	Subframe Rear Bracket	48
	Tie Rod Bolt	62
	Tie Rod Self-Locking Nut	33
	Tie Rod End To Power Steering Gear Assembly Nuts	59
	Tie Rod End To Wheel Bearing Housing Nuts	26
	Wheel Lug Nuts, Except New Beetle & 1999–2001 Golf & Jetta	81
	Wheel Bolts, New Beetle & 1999–2001 Golf & Jetta	89

① — Tighten an additional 90.°
② — Tighten an additional 180.°

Wheel Alignment

INDEX

	Page No.
Front Wheel Alignment	8-80
Camber Adjustment	8-80
Caster Adjustment	8-80
Toe Adjustment	8-80
Preliminary Inspection	8-80
Rear Wheel Alignment	8-80
Camber Adjustment	8-80
Toe Adjustment	8-80
Wheel Alignment Specifications	8-6

PRELIMINARY INSPECTION

1. Ensure tires are inflated to correct pressure, inspect tires for uneven wear.
2. Inspect suspension arms and ball joints for damage, replace as necessary.
3. Inspect steering gear and tie rod ends for damage, replace as necessary.
4. Inspect strut and coil springs for damage or leakage, replace as necessary.

FRONT WHEEL ALIGNMENT

CASTER ADJUSTMENT

The caster angle on these vehicles cannot be adjusted.

CAMBER ADJUSTMENT

1998 Cabrio, Golf, GTI & Jetta w/2.0L Gasoline Engine

Camber should never be adjusted by moving position of ball joint in control arm.

1. Loosen bolts securing suspension strut to wheel bearing housing.
2. Move top of wheel/tire in or out to achieve proper camber.
3. **Torque** bolts to 59 ft. lbs., then recheck camber.
4. If camber is out of specified range, use replacement bolt, part No. N 101 740.01, or equivalent. This will allow 1° of camber adjustment.
5. Using original bolt in lower position, pivot top of wheel/tire in or out to achieve proper camber.
6. If more movement is required for specified camber, replace original bolt with part No. N 101 740.01, or equivalent.
7. **Torque** bolts to 59 ft. lbs., then recheck camber.

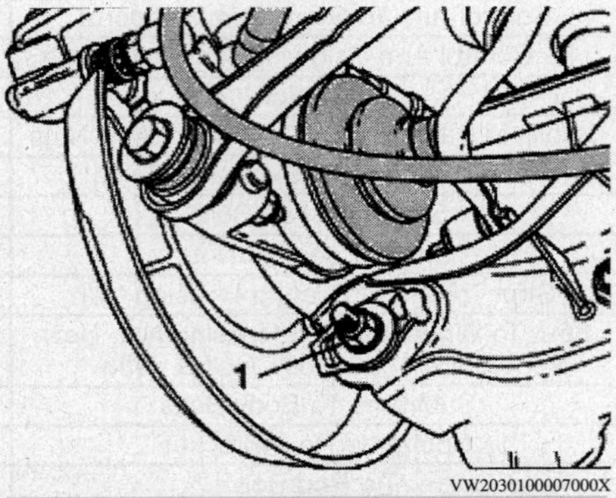

Fig. 1 Rear wheel camber eccentric bolt. Passat w/AWD

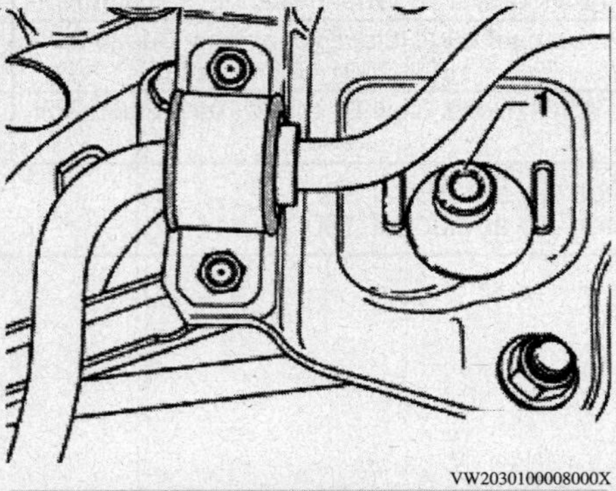

Fig. 2 Rear wheel toe eccentric bolt. Passat w/AWD

New Beetle & 1999-2001 Golf, GTI & Jetta

The camber on these vehicles cannot be adjusted.

Passat

1. Remove noise dampening panel.
2. Install alignment tool No. VAG 1941, or equivalent, then loosen subframe bolts.
3. Adjust camber by turning bolt on alignment tool.
4. Remove alignment tool, then **torque** front subframe bolts to 44 ft. lbs. and rear bolts to 81 ft. lbs. plus an additional 90°

TOE ADJUSTMENT

1. Loosen clamps on tie rod boot at tie rod and if necessary, at steering box if equipped.
2. Loosen jam nut at tie rod end.
3. Turn tie rod to perform adjustments. Use caution not to twist boot.
4. Tighten tie rod jam nut and if equipped, boot clamps.

REAR WHEEL ALIGNMENT

CAMBER ADJUSTMENT

Except Passat w/AWD

Camber on rear axle assembly is not adjustable.

Passat w/AWD

Camber can be adjusted by turning eccentric bolt, **Fig. 1.**

TOE ADJUSTMENT

Except Passat w/AWD

Rear axle assembly toe is not adjustable.

Passat w/AWD

Rear wheel toe can be adjusted by turning eccentric bolt, **Fig. 2.**

Air Conditioning

INDEX

	Page No.
A/C Specifications	8-82
Charging System	8-82
Discharging System	8-82
Leak Test	8-81
Oil Charge	8-82
Performance Test	8-81
Test Conditions & Preparations	8-81
Precautions	8-81
A/C System	8-81
Air Bag Systems	8-81
Audio Coded Anti-Theft System	8-81
Battery Ground Cable	8-81
System Evacuation	8-82

PRECAUTIONS

AIR BAG SYSTEMS

Do not use computer memory saver tool on air bag equipped models. Using the tool will keep the air bag system charged and may cause accidental air bag unit activation.

Refer to "Air Bag System Precautions" in the front of this manual for system disarming and arming procedures.

BATTERY GROUND CABLE

Prior to service, disconnect battery ground cable and isolate as required.

AUDIO CODED ANTI-THEFT SYSTEM

Some models are equipped with a radio anti-theft system that will disable the system when battery power is interrupted. Unless the system is reset the radio will not operate.

1. Turn radio On. SAFE and 1000 should be displayed.
2. Enter radio code using first four program station buttons. Security code will appear on display.
3. Depress and hold righthand side of radio righthand or lefthand blocker until anti-theft coding is activated indicated by a brief signal sound.
4. If code number has been entered properly, a diode on front of radio will flash when ignition key is removed.

A/C SYSTEM

Do not add any other type of refrigerant to a R-134a system. Use only specified synthetic oil Polyalkylene Glycol/PAG on these systems. If refrigerants or oils are mixed, total system contamination may occur and compressor failure may result.

R-134a refrigerant system oil (PAG oil) absorbs moisture very rapidly. Moisture combines with the refrigerant to form acids which will damage the system. Use only the specified oil from a sealed container and always reseal oil container immediately after use. **Do not use oil that has been contaminated with moisture. Immediately plug open connections on A/C components to prevent dirt and moisture contamination.**

Test 1 Temperature from center air vent*	Test 2 High pressure	Test 3 Low pressure	Possible causes of incorrect readings	Corrective measures
Normal	Normal	Normal	None	—
Too high	Normal	Normal	Temperature flap position incorrect	Adjust temperature flap cable
Too high	Too low	Normal	Compressor	Replace compressor
Normal	Too low	Normal	Compressor	Replace compressor
Normal	Normal	Too high or too low	Expansion valve or compressor	Replace expansion valve or compressor
Too high	Normal	Too high or too low	Expansion valve or compressor	Replace expansion valve or compressor
Normal	Too high or too low	Too high or too low	Expansion valve or compressor	Replace expansion valve or compressor

* Normal air outlet temperature approx. 43°F (6°C).

VW7029300035000X

Fig. 1 A/C performance test diagnostic table

PERFORMANCE TEST

TEST CONDITIONS & PREPARATIONS

1. Ambient temperature is between 68–86°F, vehicle in shade.
2. Ensure condenser and radiator are clean.
3. Drive belt is properly tensioned and in good condition.
4. Air ducts are properly installed and all cables properly adjusted.
5. A/C compressor clutch functions properly.
6. Connect pressure gauge set to service valves, then open all dash air outlets.
7. Close windows and doors.

Test 1, Temperature From Center Vent

1. Start engine, warm to operating temperature and allow to idle.
2. Set air distribution to instrument panel outlets.
3. Set temperature control to Full Cold.
4. Set Blower to second speed (2nd position).
5. Place suitable thermometer in center air outlet.
6. Switch A/C On with NORM A/C button.
7. Raise engine speed to 1500 RPM, maintain during test.
8. Outlet air temperature should drop to below 50°F in less than one minute.
9. If results are not as expected, perform "Test 2" and "Test 3," then compare results with **Fig. 1.**

Test 2, High Pressure Inspection

1. Connect suitable High/Low pressure gauge set to service valves if not previously connected.
2. Disconnect electrical connector to radiator cooling fans.
3. Set air distribution to footwell.
4. Set temperature control to Full Hot.
5. Set Blower to high speed (4th position).
6. Start engine, then turn On A/C with MAX A/C button.
7. Raise engine speed to 1500 RPM, maintain during test.
8. System high pressure should rise to about 232 psi in less than 30 seconds.
9. If results are not as expected, perform "Test 1" and "Test 3," then compare results with **Fig. 1.**

Test 3, Low Pressure Inspection

1. Connect suitable High/Low pressure gauge set to service valves if not previously connected.
2. Set air distribution to instrument panel outlets.
3. Set temperature control to Full Cold.
4. Set Blower to low speed (1st position).
5. Start engine, then turn On A/C with NORM A/C button.
6. Raise engine speed to 1500 RPM, maintain during test.
7. System low pressure should drop to about 22–36 psi in less than 30 seconds.
8. If results are not as expected, perform "Test 1" and "Test 2," then compare results with **Fig. 1.**

LEAK TEST

Use halogen leak detector Hitec HI400A-TEL or equivalent to inspect for refrigerant leaks.

Refrigerant gas dissipates very quickly. Avoid drafty or windy areas when inspecting for leaks. If the refrigerant system is empty, charge system with approximately 3.5 oz. of refrigerant in order to inspect for leaks. Inspect A/C systems for leaks following the leak detector manufacturer's instructions.

DISCHARGING SYSTEM

Ensure initial setup had been performed on the refrigerant recovery/recycling/recharging unit before discharging A/C system.

1. Connect red high pressure hose of recovery/recycling unit to high side fitting on vehicle and open coupler valve.
2. Connect blue low pressure hose of refrigerant recovery/recycling unit to low side fitting on vehicle and open coupler valve.
3. Recover refrigerant following refrigerant recovery/recycling/recharging unit manufacturer's instructions.
4. Close manifold gauge valves when refrigerant is fully recovered.
5. Disconnect power supply from A/C clutch to prevent accidental compressor operation with A/C discharged.

SYSTEM EVACUATION

Automotive refrigerant containing CFCs is hazardous to the earth's atmosphere. To protect our environment, use an Underwriter's Laboratory (UL) approved refrigerant recovery/recycling unit such as Kent-Moore ACR4 or equivalent whenever discharging an A/C system.

The A/C system should be serviced only by trained personnel familiar with equipment use, related safety precautions and regulations governing the discharging/handling/disposal of automotive refrigerants.

Always wear safety goggles when charging or discharging system. Use caution so that refrigerant does not come in contact with your skin or eyes. If refrigerant comes in contact with skin or eyes, do not rub. Flush immediately with cool water, then seek medical attention. Keep refrigerant away from open flames, refrigerant exposure to open flame may produce poisonous gas.

1. Close both valves on A/C manifold gauge set, then connect hose from low pressure gauge to low pressure service valve.
2. Connect hose from high pressure gauge to high pressure service valve, then the manifold gauge hose to inlet connection on refrigerant recovery/recycling unit.
3. Follow refrigerant recovery/recycling unit manufacturer's instructions to recover refrigerant.
4. Close manifold gauge valves when refrigerant is fully recovered.
5. Disconnect power supply from compressor clutch to prevent damage to system if compressor is accidentally switched on with refrigerant system discharged.

CHARGING SYSTEM

Follow refrigerant recharging unit manufacturer's instructions for evacuating and recharging the A/C system. After system recharge, manually rotate A/C compressor 10 turns before starting the engine. Start engine with A/C off and allow to idle for at least two minutes with A/C on before raising engine speed.

OIL CHARGE

See "A/C Specifications" chart for oil charge amount on each model.

A/C SPECIFICATIONS

Year	Refrigerant Capacity, Lbs.	Refrigerant Type	Compressor Oil Viscosity	Total System Oil Capacity, Oz.	Compressor Clutch Air Gap, Inch
CABRIO					
1998–2001	1.76	R-134a	④	3.90	.028
EUROVAN					
1999	②	R-134a	③	⑥	—
GOLF, GTI & JETTA					
1998	1.76	R-134a	④	3.90	.028
1999–2001	1.63	R-134a	⑦	4.56	.015–.023
NEW BEETLE					
1998–2001	1.54	R-134a	④	4.56	.015–.023
PASSAT					
1998–2001	1.43	R-134a	⑤	8.50	①

① — Models w/Denso 7SB-16C compressor,. 015–.023 inch; models w/Zexel DCW-17D compressor,. 011–.023 inch.
② — Models w/one evaporator, 2.09 lbs.; models w/two evaporators, 2.98 lbs.
③ — Sanden SP-20, or equivalent.
④ — Sanden SP-10, or equivalent.
⑤ — Models w/Denso 7SB-16C compressor, part No. G 052 300 A2, or equivalent; models w/Zexel DCW-17D compressor, part No. G 052 154 A2 or G 052 200 A2, or equivalent.
⑥ — Models w/one evaporator, 4.60 oz.; models w/two evaporators, 8.10 oz.
⑦ — Part No. G 052 154 A2.

Cooling Fans

INDEX

	Page No.
Component Replacement	8-83
Description	8-83
Less A/C	8-83
With A/C	8-83
Precautions	8-83
Air Bag Systems	8-83
Audio Coded Anti-Theft System	8-83
Battery Ground Cable	8-83

PRECAUTIONS

AIR BAG SYSTEMS

Do not use computer memory saver tool on air bag equipped models. Using the tool will keep the air bag system charged and may cause accidental air bag unit activation.

Refer to "Air Bag System Precautions" in the front of this manual for system disarming and arming procedures.

BATTERY GROUND CABLE

Prior to service, disconnect battery ground cable and isolate as required.

AUDIO CODED ANTI-THEFT SYSTEM

Some models are equipped with a radio anti-theft system that will disable the system when battery power is interrupted. Unless the system is reset the radio will not operate.

1. Turn radio On. SAFE and 1000 should be displayed.
2. Enter radio code using first four program station buttons. Security code will appear on display.
3. Depress and hold righthand side of radio righthand or lefthand blocker until anti-theft coding is activated indicated by a brief signal sound.
4. If code number has been entered properly, a diode on front of radio will flash when ignition key is removed.

DESCRIPTION

LESS A/C

The electric cooling fan uses a thermoswitch to control fan motor operation. The fan operates at low speed when engine coolant temperature is 197–205°F. The fan operates at high speed when coolant temperature is 210–221°F.

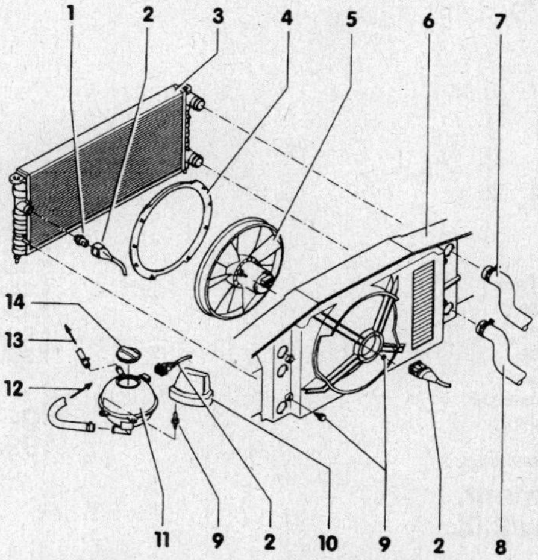

Fig. 1 Cooling fan replacement. 1998 Golf & Jetta w/1.9L TDI engine

WITH A/C

The three speed electric cooling fan is controlled by the cooling fan control module through a coolant temperature sensor mounted in the radiator and a second thermo sensor mounted in the coolant manifold and by the A/C control system and the after run control module, if equipped. Various fan speeds are chosen dependent on coolant temperature and refrigerant pressure when the A/C system is On. The coolant fan can also be switched on after the ignition is switched Off if coolant temperature rises above 198°F by the after run control module to prevent hot soak starting problems.

Fan speeds will be: 1st (low) speed when engine coolant temperature is 198–207°F, 2nd (medium) speed when coolant temperature is 210–221°F and 3rd (high) speed when coolant temperature is 234°F. The fan will run at 1st (low) speed whenever the A/C is turned On and at 2nd (medium) speed whenever refrigerant pressure rises above 232 psi regardless of coolant temperature.

COMPONENT REPLACEMENT

Refer to **Figs. 1 through 9** for cooling fan replacement.

1. Disconnect fan electrical connector.
2. **On models equipped with A/C,** disconnect resistor connector and fan relay.
3. **On all models,** remove shroud from radiator, then the fan and shroud from the vehicle.
4. Remove nuts securing fan motor to shroud.
5. Remove fan motor.
6. Reverse procedure to install.

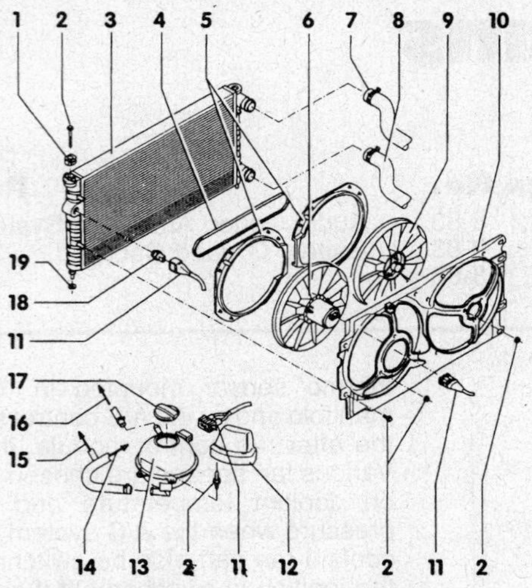

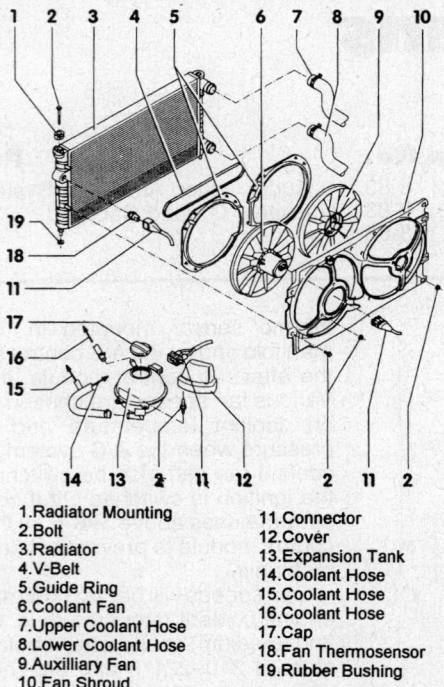

1.Radiator Mounting
2.Bolt
3.Radiator
4.V-Belt
5.Guide Ring
6.Coolant Fan
7.Upper Coolant Hose
8.Lower Coolant Hose
9.Auxilliary Fan
10.Fan Shroud
11.Connector
12.Cover
13.Expansion Tank
14.Coolant Hose
15.Coolant Hose
16.Coolant Hose
17.Cap
18.Fan Thermosensor
19.Rubber Bushing

VW1089300008000X

Fig. 2 Cooling fan replacement. Cabrio & 1998 Golf & Jetta w/2.0L engine

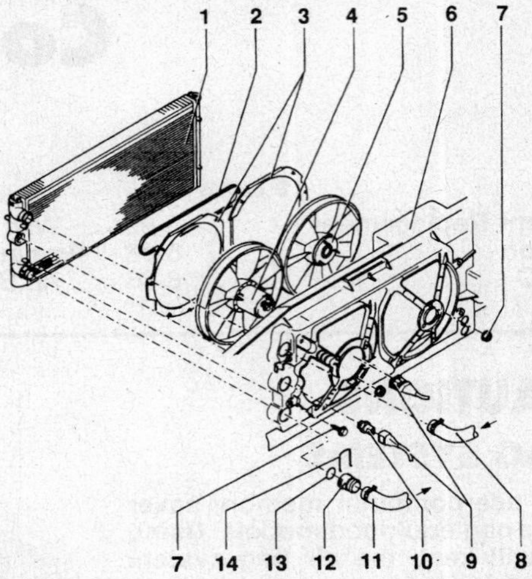

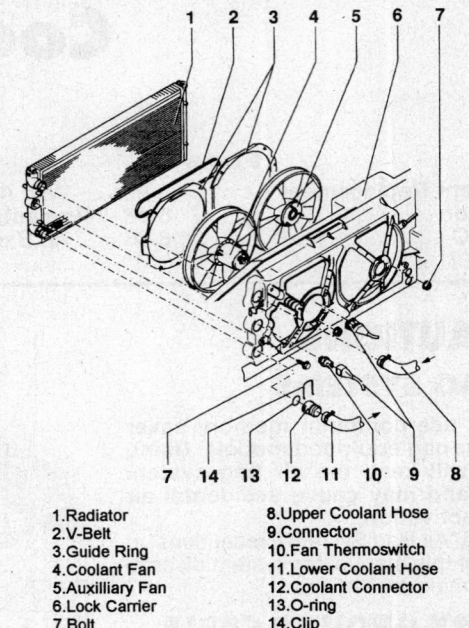

1.Radiator
2.V-Belt
3.Guide Ring
4.Coolant Fan
5.Auxilliary Fan
6.Lock Carrier
7.Bolt
8.Upper Coolant Hose
9.Connector
10.Fan Thermoswitch
11.Lower Coolant Hose
12.Coolant Connector
13.O-ring
14.Clip

VW1089500009000X

Fig. 3 Cooling fan replacement. 1998 GTI & Jetta w/2.8L engine

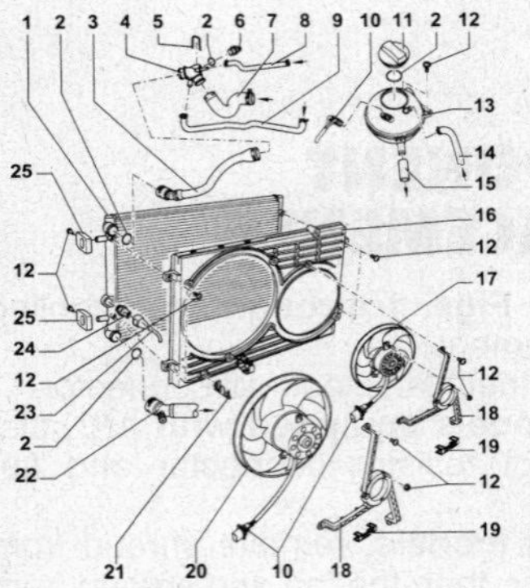

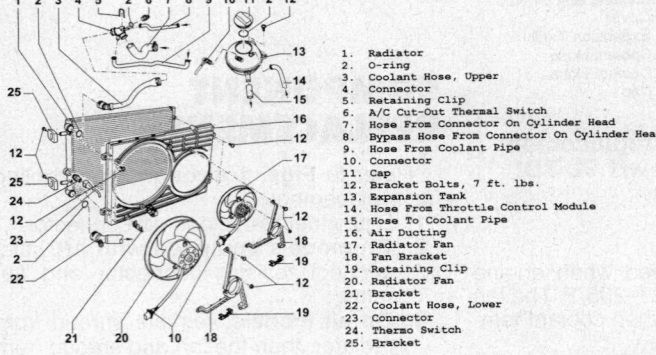

1. Radiator
2. O-ring
3. Coolant Hose, Upper
4. Connector
5. Retaining Clip
6. A/C Cut-Out Thermal Switch
7. Hose From Connector On Cylinder Head
8. Bypass Hose From Connector On Cylinder Head
9. Hose From Coolant Pipe
10. Connector
11. Cap
12. Bracket Bolts, 7 ft. lbs.
13. Expansion Tank
14. Hose From Throttle Control Module
15. Hose To Coolant Pipe
16. Air Ducting
17. Radiator Fan
18. Fan Bracket
19. Retaining Clip
20. Radiator Fan
21. Bracket
22. Coolant Hose, Lower
23. Connector
24. Thermo Switch
25. Bracket

VW1089900015000X

Fig. 4 Cooling fan replacement. 1999–2001 Golf & Jetta w/1.9L TDI & 2.0L engines

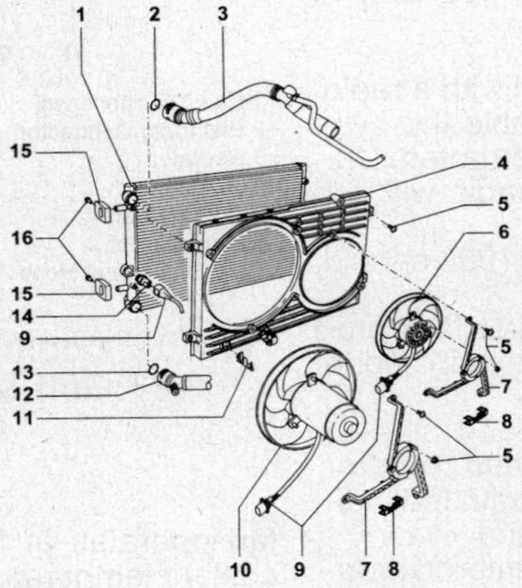

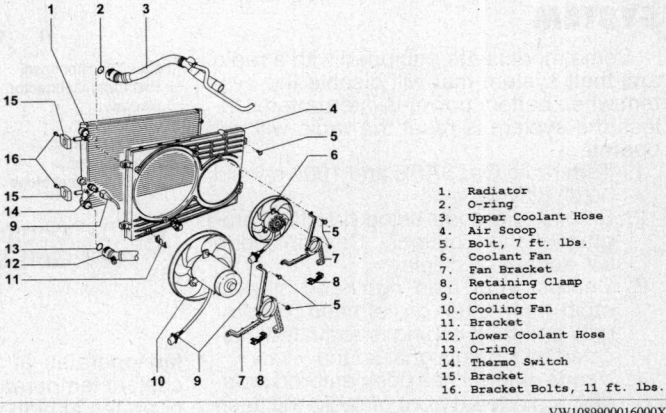

1. Radiator
2. O-ring
3. Upper Coolant Hose
4. Air Scoop
5. Bolt, 7 ft. lbs.
6. Coolant Fan
7. Fan Bracket
8. Retaining Clamp
9. Connector
10. Cooling Fan
11. Bracket
12. Lower Coolant Hose
13. O-ring
14. Thermo Switch
15. Bracket
16. Bracket Bolts, 11 ft. lbs.

VW1089900016000X

Fig. 5 Cooling fan replacement. 1999–2001 GTI & Jetta w/2.8L engine & 2001 Golf, GTI & Jetta w/1.8L turbocharged engine

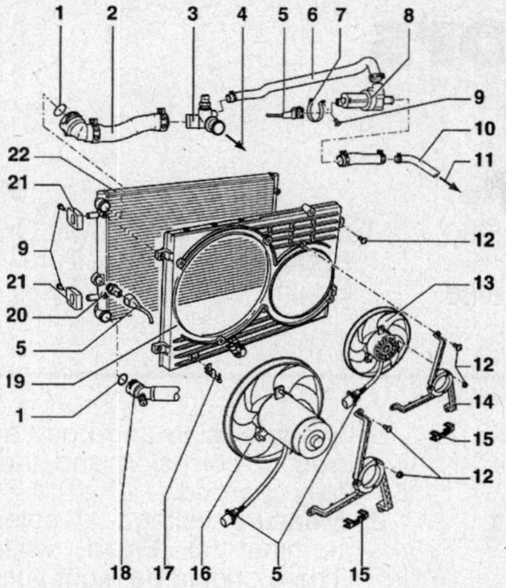

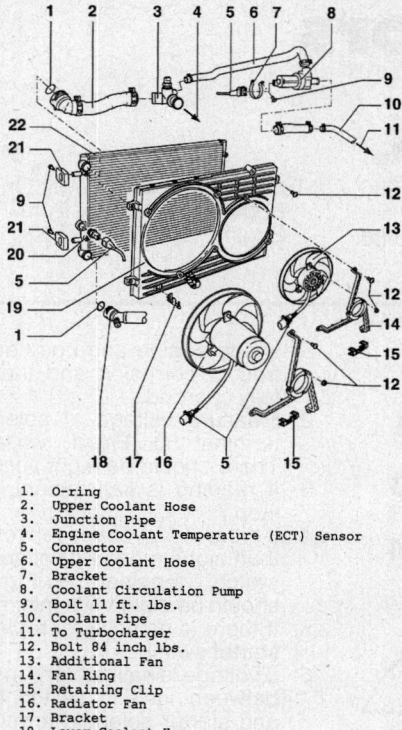

1. O-ring
2. Upper Coolant Hose
3. Junction Pipe
4. Engine Coolant Temperature (ECT) Sensor
5. Connector
6. Upper Coolant Hose
7. Bracket
8. Coolant Circulation Pump
9. Bolt 11 ft. lbs.
10. Coolant Pipe
11. To Turbocharger
12. Bolt 84 inch lbs.
13. Additional Fan
14. Fan Ring
15. Retaining Clip
16. Radiator Fan
17. Bracket
18. Lower Coolant Hose
19. Air Duct
20. Thermo Switch
21. Bracket
22. Radiator

VW1080100019000X

Fig. 6 Cooling fan replacement. New Beetle w/1.8L turbocharged engine

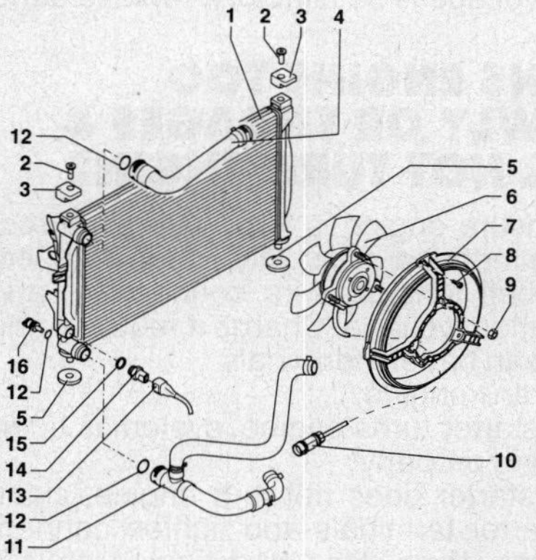

1. Radiator
2. Securing Clip
3. Securing Rubber
4. Radiator Hose, Upper
5. Rubber Washer
6. Radiator Fan
7. Fan Ring
8. Locking Bolt
9. Nut, 7 ft. lbs.
10. 2-pin Harness Connector
11. Radiator Hose, Lower
12. O-ring
13. 3-Pin Harness Connector
14. Coolant Fan Control Thermal Switch
15. Oil Seal
16. Drain Screw

VW1089900013000X

Fig. 8 Cooling fan replacement. Passat w/1.8L turbocharged & 1.9L TDI engines

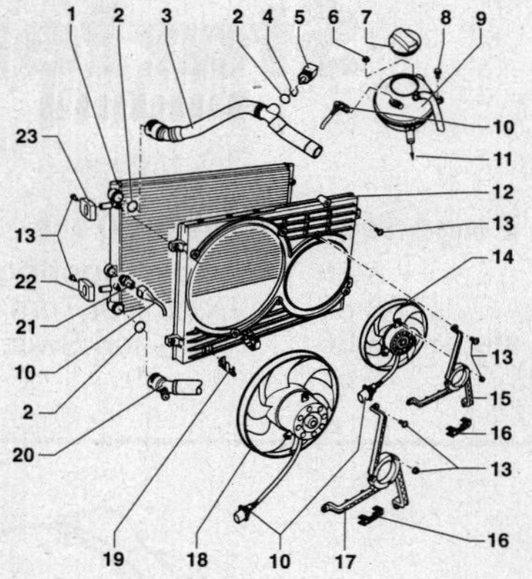

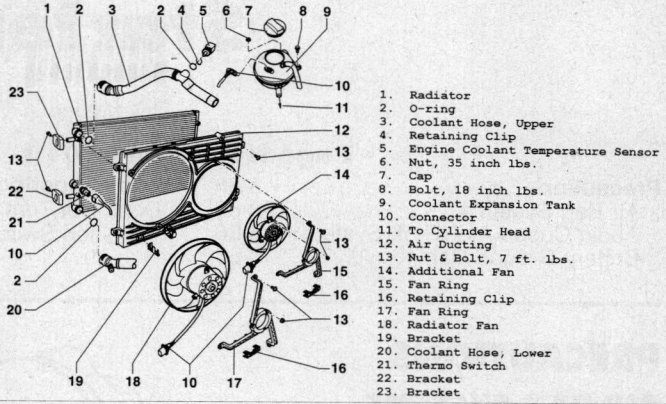

1. Radiator
2. O-ring
3. Coolant Hose, Upper
4. Retaining Clip
5. Engine Coolant Temperature Sensor
6. Nut, 35 inch lbs.
7. Cap
8. Bolt, 18 inch lbs.
9. Coolant Expansion Tank
10. Connector
11. To Cylinder Head
12. Air Ducting
13. Nut & Bolt, 7 ft. lbs.
14. Additional Fan
15. Fan Ring
16. Retaining Clip
17. Fan Ring
18. Radiator Fan
19. Bracket
20. Coolant Hose, Lower
21. Thermo Switch
22. Bracket
23. Bracket

VW1089900014000X

Fig. 7 Cooling fan replacement. New Beetle w/1.9L TDI & 2.0L engines

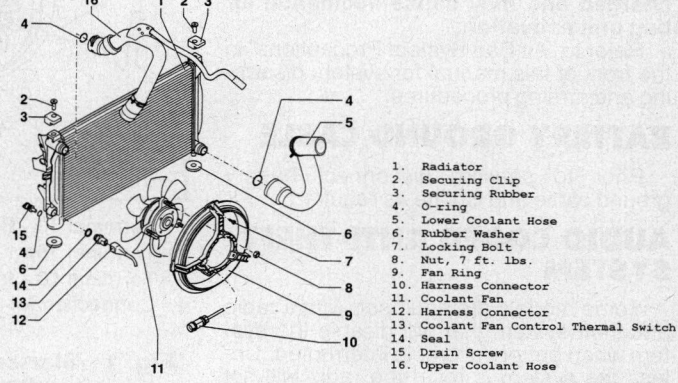

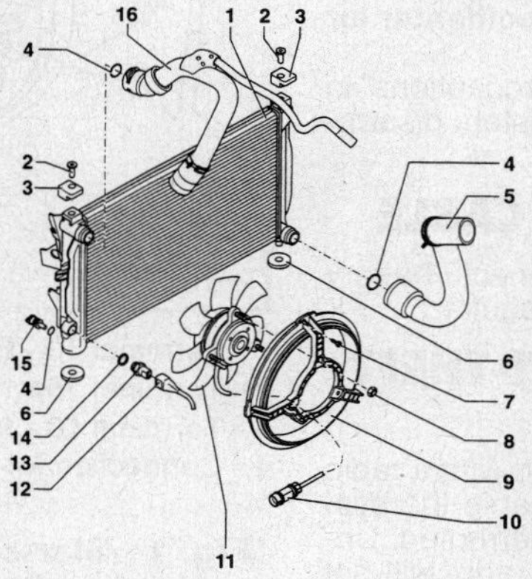

1. Radiator
2. Securing Clip
3. Securing Rubber
4. O-ring
5. Lower Coolant Hose
6. Rubber Washer
7. Locking Bolt
8. Nut, 7 ft. lbs.
9. Fan Ring
10. Harness Connector
11. Coolant Fan
12. Harness Connector
13. Coolant Fan Control Thermal Switch
14. Seal
15. Drain Screw
16. Upper Coolant Hose

VW1089900017000X

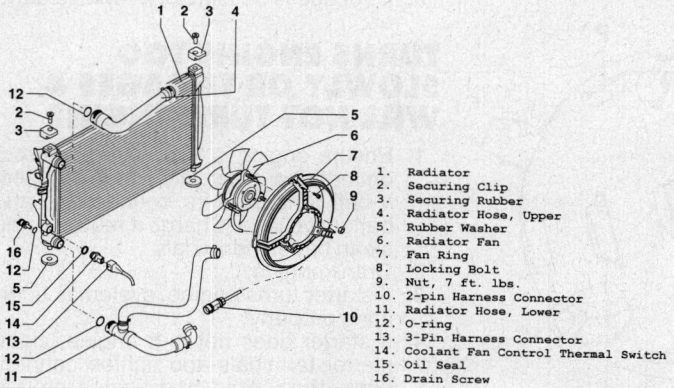

Fig. 9 Cooling fan replacement. Passat w/2.8L engine

Starter Motors

INDEX

	Page No.
Precautions	8-86
Air Bag Systems	8-86
Audio Coded Anti-Theft System	8-86
Battery Ground Cable	8-86
Troubleshooting	8-86
Does Not Turn Engine When Ignition Switch Is Operated	8-86
Turns Engine Too Slowly Or Engages & Will Not Turn Engine	8-86

PRECAUTIONS

AIR BAG SYSTEMS

Do not use computer memory saver tool on air bag equipped models. Using the tool will keep the air bag system charged and may cause accidental air bag unit activation.

Refer to "Air Bag System Precautions" in the front of this manual for system disarming and arming procedures.

BATTERY GROUND CABLE

Prior to service, disconnect battery ground cable and isolate as required.

AUDIO CODED ANTI-THEFT SYSTEM

Some models are equipped with a radio anti-theft system that will disable the system when battery power is interrupted. Unless the system is reset the radio will not operate.

1. Turn radio On. SAFE and 1000 should be displayed.
2. Enter radio code using first four program station buttons. Security code will appear on display.
3. Depress and hold righthand side of radio righthand or lefthand blocker until anti-theft coding is activated indicated by a brief signal sound.
4. If code number has been entered properly, a diode on front of radio will flash when ignition key is removed.

TROUBLESHOOTING

DOES NOT TURN ENGINE WHEN IGNITION SWITCH IS OPERATED

Use SUN VAT-40 or SUN VAT-60, or equivalents, for measurements.

1. Ensure solenoid switch connections are satisfactory, ground straps between engine and body are tight and free of corrosion and that battery is fully charged.
2. Measure voltage at solenoid switch terminal 50, **Fig. 1,** while cranking. There should be eight volts minimum.
3. If reading is satisfactory, proceed to step 7.
4. If there is no voltage, or voltage is less than eight, measure voltage at ignition switch terminal 50,**Fig. 2.** There should be eight volts minimum.
5. If there is no voltage, replace ignition/starter switch.
6. If voltage is satisfactory, inspect wiring between ignition switch terminal 50 and starter solenoid terminal 50. Repair or replace as required.
7. If reading is satisfactory from step 3, measure voltage at connection 4, **Fig.1,** for field winding on solenoid switch. There should be eight volts minimum.
8. If there is no voltage, replace solenoid switch.
9. If voltage is satisfactory, replace starter.

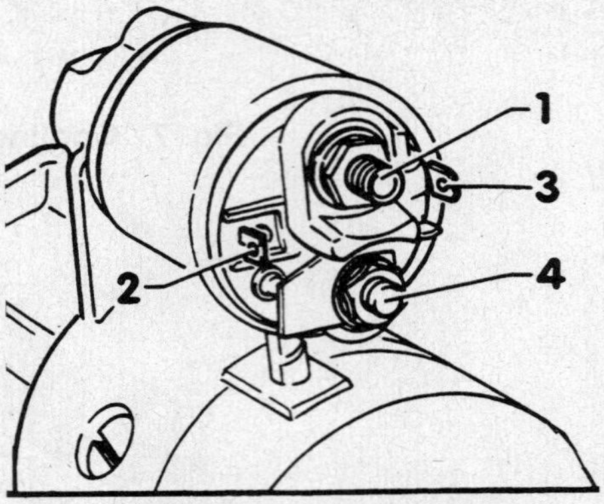

1 - Terminal **30** - **B+**, from battery
2 - Terminal **15a**
3 - Terminal **50** - from starter switch
4 - Connection for field windings

VW1129100001000A

Fig. 1 Starter solenoid terminal identification

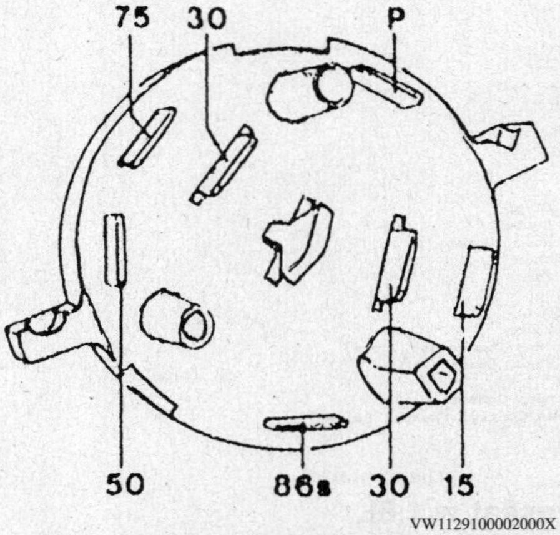

VW1129100002000X

Fig. 2 Ignition switch terminal identification

TURNS ENGINE TOO SLOWLY OR ENGAGES & WILL NOT TURN ENGINE

1. Ensure engine is filled with oil of recommended viscosity, then inspect V-belt tension, wire connections and battery voltage. Charge if required and clean battery terminals.
2. Crank engine.
3. If starter turns engine, system is operating properly.
4. If starter does not turn engine, clean starter terminals and tighten connections, then clean and tighten ground strap connections between transaxle and body at transaxle.
5. Crank engine.
6. If starter turns engine, system is operating properly.
7. If starter does not turn engine, starter is faulty. Replace starter.

Alternators

INDEX

	Page No.
Alternator Specifications	8-88
Diagnosis & Testing	8-87
Exciter Circuit	8-87
Output Test	8-87
Precautions	8-87
Air Bag Systems	8-87
Audio Coded Anti-Theft System	8-87
Battery Ground Cable	8-87
Troubleshooting	8-87
Indicator Lamp Does Not Light	8-87
Lamp Does Not Go Out When RPM Increases	8-87
Lamp Lit w/Ignition Off	8-87

PRECAUTIONS

AIR BAG SYSTEMS

Do not use computer memory saver tool on air bag equipped models. Using the tool will keep the air bag system charged and may cause accidental air bag unit activation.

Refer to "Air Bag System Precautions" in the front of this manual for system disarming and arming procedures.

BATTERY GROUND CABLE

Prior to service, disconnect battery ground cable and isolate as required.

AUDIO CODED ANTI-THEFT SYSTEM

Some models are equipped with a radio anti-theft system that will disable the system when battery power is interrupted. Unless the system is reset the radio will not operate.

1. Turn radio On. SAFE and 1000 should be displayed.
2. Enter radio code using first four program station buttons. Security code will appear on display.
3. Depress and hold righthand side of radio righthand or lefthand blocker until anti-theft coding is activated indicated by a brief signal sound.
4. If code number has been entered properly, a diode on front of radio will flash when ignition key is removed.

TROUBLESHOOTING

INDICATOR LAMP DOES NOT LIGHT

Possible open circuit between alternator D+ and indicator lamp.

1. Remove alternator cover, then disconnect D+ wire from alternator.
2. Connect a jumper wire between D+ and ground, then turn ignition On.
3. If indicator lamp lights, proceed as follows:
   a. Inspect for improper alternator ground, worn carbon brushes, faulty voltage regulator or rotor.
   b. If alternator grounding and brushes are faulty, make required corrections. If lamp now lights, system is operating properly.
   c. If alternator grounding and brushes are satisfactory, replace voltage regulator. If lamp still fails to light, replace alternator.
4. If indicator lamp does not light, proceed as follows:
   a. Indicator bulb is burned out.
   b. Replace bulb, connect ground cable and turn ignition On.
   c. If indicator lamp lights, system is operating properly.
   d. If indicator lamp does not light, wiring between alternator D+ and indicator lamp is open. Repair as required.

LAMP LIT w/IGNITION OFF

Alternator diode faulty. Replace alternator. Possible short in wiring between alternator D+ and indicator. Repair as required.

LAMP DOES NOT GO OUT WHEN RPM INCREASES

Inspect for slipping fan belt, short to ground between alternator D+ and indicator lamp or alternator is faulty. Replace as required.

DIAGNOSIS & TESTING

OUTPUT TEST

Use SUN VAT-40 or SUN VAT-60 or their equivalents for test.

1. Connect black clamp from VAT to battery ground cable, then red clamp from VAT to battery positive cable.
2. Connect green clamp from VAT (inductive pickup) to alternator D+ either at alternator or battery.
3. Start engine, raise speed and hold at 2000 RPM.
4. Slowly adjust load control of VAT until highest possible reading is obtained. Reading must be within 10% of manufacturer's specifications. **Test must be performed and completed within 15 seconds to avoid overloading and damaging electrical system.**

EXCITER CIRCUIT

Inspection

If a "battery isn't being charged" comment is received even though warning lamp lights when ignition is switched On and goes out when ignition is turned Off, inspect exciter circuit as follows:

1. Ensure battery voltage is approximately 12 volts minimum, then charge if required.
2. Disconnect blue wire from alternator terminal 61.
3. Switch multimeter tool No. US 1119, or equivalent, to 200 mA range.
4. Connect multimeter between disconnected blue wire and terminal 61.
5. Turn ignition On.
6. Current must fall between 150 and 185 mA.
7. If reading is lower than 150 mA, inspect blue wire between alternator and instrument panel or replace printed circuit in instrument cluster as required.

Resistance Inspection

If a "battery isn't being charged" comment is received even though warning lamp lights when ignition is switched On and goes out when ignition is turned Off, inspect exciter circuit resistance as follows:

1. Disconnect blue wire (D+/61) from back of alternator.
2. Switch multimeter US 1119 or equivalent to 200 ohm range.
3. Connect multimeter between disconnected blue wire and battery positive terminal.
4. Turn ignition On.
5. Reading should be 140–160 ohms.
6. If reading is infinite, reverse probes and inspect again.
7. If reading is still infinite, printed circuit must be replaced.

ALTERNATOR SPECIFICATIONS

Year	Model	Alternator Type	Rated Hot Output	
			Amps	Volts
1998–2001	Cabrio	Bosch	90	14
	EuroVan	Bosch	②	14
	Golf/GTI	Bosch	①	14
	Golf TDI	Bosch	120	14
	Jetta	Bosch	①	14
	Jetta TDI	Bosch	①	14
	New Beetle	Bosch	90	14
	Passat	Bosch	90	14
	Passat TDI	Bosch	120	14
	Passat Wagon GLS V6	Bosch	120	14

① — Less A/C, 70 amps; with A/C, 90 amps.

② — Except Camper, 150 amps; Camper, 120 amps.

Speed Control Systems

NOTE: "Electrical Symbol & Wire Color Code Identification" Located In The Front Of This Manual May Be Used As An Aid When Using Wiring Circuits Found In This Section.

INDEX

	Page No.
Adjustments	8-90
Vacuum Servo Rod	8-90
Component Replacement	8-91
Cruise Control Switch	8-91
Engine Control Module (ECM)	8-91
Speed Control Vacuum Pump	8-91
Throttle Control Element	8-91
Vent Valves	8-91
Description	8-89
Except TDI Engine & 1998–99 New Beetle & 1999 Golf & Jetta	8-89
New Beetle & 1999–2001 Golf & Jetta	8-89
With TDI Engine	8-89
Precautions	8-89
Air Bag Systems	8-89
Audio Coded Anti-Theft System	8-89
Battery Ground Cable	8-89
System Diagnosis & Testing	8-90
Accessing Diagnostic Trouble Codes	8-90
Clearing Diagnostic Trouble Codes	8-90
Component Testing	8-90
Diagnostic Trouble Code Interpretation	8-90
Troubleshooting	8-89
Except TDI Engine	8-89

DESCRIPTION

EXCEPT TDI ENGINE & 1998-99 NEW BEETLE & 1999 GOLF & JETTA

The speed control system on these engines is controlled by a separate electronic control unit. The control unit operates a vacuum pump and vacuum vent valve, which control throttle position with a vacuum actuator, **Fig. 1.**

WITH TDI ENGINE

The speed control system on this engine is a function of the Engine Control Module (ECM) and the fuel control unit of the fuel injection pump.

The ECM controls vehicle speed using inputs from the cruise control switch, brake pedal and clutch pedal. The ECM then sends output signals to the fuel control unit, which controls fuel flow to the injectors.

NEW BEETLE & 1999-2001 GOLF & JETTA

On these models, the cruise control system function is controlled by the ECM.

PRECAUTIONS

AIR BAG SYSTEMS

Do not use computer memory saver tool on air bag equipped models. Using the tool will keep the air bag system charged and may cause accidental air bag unit activation.

Refer to "Air Bag System Precautions" in the front of this manual for system disarming and arming procedures.

BATTERY GROUND CABLE

Prior to service, disconnect battery ground cable and isolate as required.

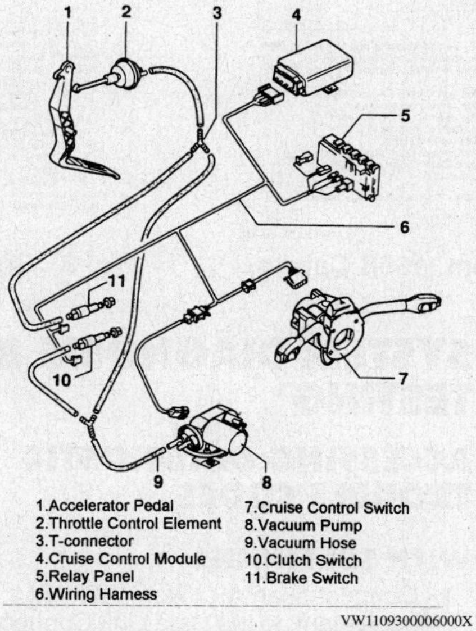

Fig. 1 Speed control system components. Except TDI engine & 1998–99 New Beetle & 1999 Golf & Jetta

AUDIO CODED ANTI-THEFT SYSTEM

Some models are equipped with a radio anti-theft system that will disable the system when battery power is interrupted. Unless the system is reset the radio will not operate.

1. Turn radio On. SAFE and 1000 should be displayed.
2. Enter radio code using first four program station buttons. Security code will appear on display.
3. Depress and hold righthand side of radio righthand or lefthand blocker until anti-theft coding is activated indicated by a brief signal sound.
4. If code number has been entered properly, a diode on front of radio will flash when ignition key is removed.

TROUBLESHOOTING

EXCEPT TDI ENGINE

Vacuum System Leak Test

Refer to component identification diagram, **Fig. 1,** when testing for vacuum leaks.

1. Remove trim panels and covers required to access throttle control element.
2. Disconnect vacuum line at pump and plug.
3. Hold down brake pedal to open vacuum vent valve.
4. Push in throttle control element diaphragm in and hold while releasing brake pedal to close vacuum vent valve.
5. Release throttle control element diaphragm, element must not move.
6. If element moves, repeat above test after isolating each component and circuit until leak is located.

Electrical Component Testing

During troubleshooting procedures, refer to wiring diagrams, **Figs. 2 through 19,** and component identification diagram, **Fig. 1.**

1. Ensure vacuum system is in good condition. Perform "Vacuum System Leak Test" if required.
2. Inspect fuse 14 (10A) for condition.
3. **On models equipped with automatic transaxle,** inspect fuse 51 (5A) for condition.
4. **On all models,** ensure lefthand brake lamp is functioning.
5. Ensure ignition is in Off position.
6. Remove cruise control system control module from behind center console, then disconnect connector.
7. Connect adapter tool No. 1466/8, or equivalent, then tester tool No. 1466 to adapter.
8. **On models equipped with automatic transaxle,** to supply voltage to

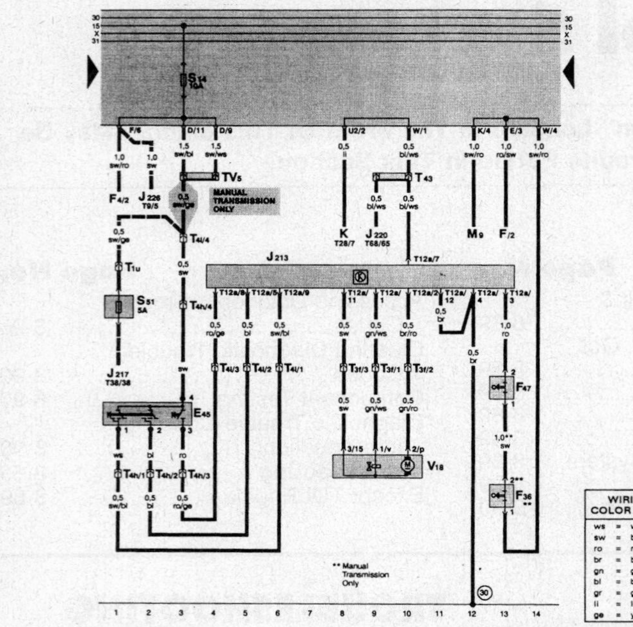

E45 - Cruise Control Switch
F - Brake Light Switch
F4 - Back-Up Light Switch
F36 - Cruise Control Clutch Pedal Position Switch
F47 - Cruise Control Brake Pedal Position Switch
J213 - Cruise Control Module
J217 - Transmission Control Module (TCM)
J220 - Motronic Engine Control Module (ECM)
J226 - Park/Neutral Position (PNP) Relay
K - Instrument Cluster
M9 - Brake Light, Left
S51 - Fuse
V18 - Cruise Control Vacuum Pump
T1u - Connector, Single, behind fuse/relay panel
T3f - Connector, 3 Pin, below left side of dash
T4h - Connector, 4 Pin, behind steering column switch trim
T4l - Connector, 4 Pin, behind fuse/relay panel
T9 - Connector, 9 Pin, on Park/Neutral Position (PNP) Relay
T12a - Connector, 12 Pin, on Cruise Control Module
T28 - Connector, 28 Pin, instrument cluster
T38 - Connector, 38 Pin, below right front seat, on Transmission Control Module (TCM)
T43 - Connector, vehicle speed signal
T68 - Connector, 68 Pin, under right side of hood, on Motronic Engine Control Module (ECM)
TV5 - Connector, terminal 15a
(30) - Ground connection - beside fuse/relay panel
- - - Automatic transmission only

VW1109300004000X

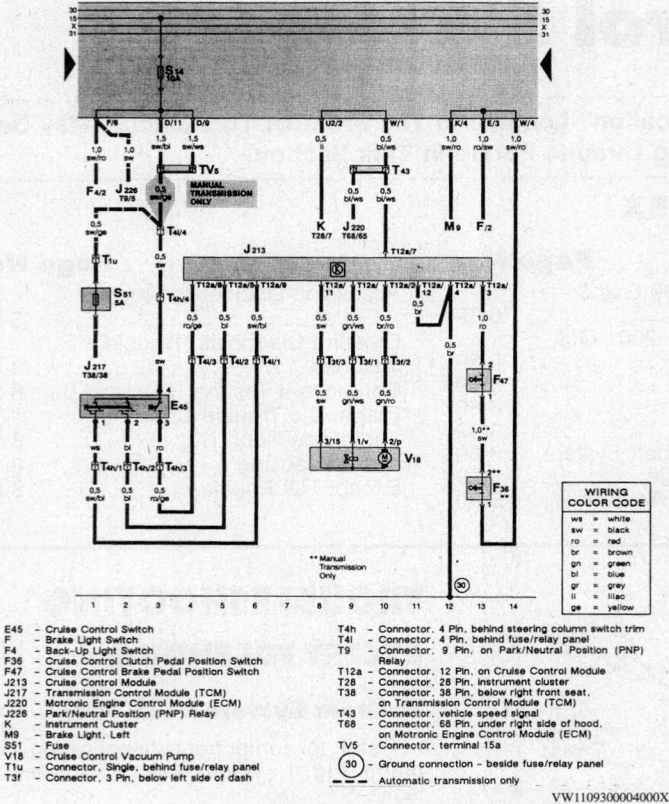

Fig. 2 Speed control wiring diagram. 1998 Cabrio, Golf III & GTI

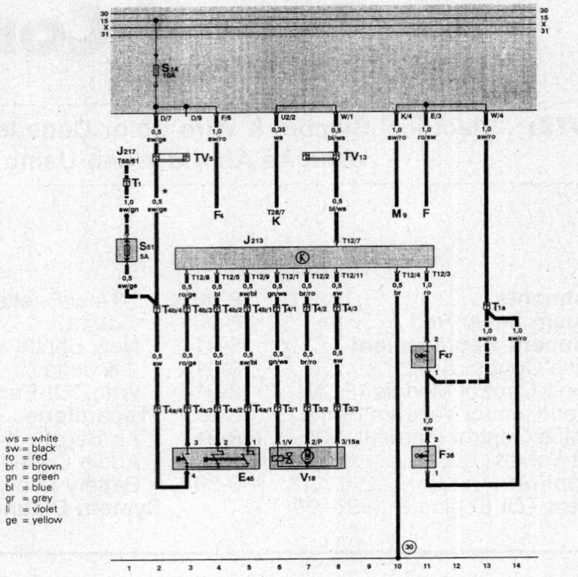

E45 - Cruise Control Switch
F - Brake Light Switch
F4 - Back-Up Light Switch
F36 - Clutch Vacuum Vent Valve Switch
F47 - Brake Pedal Cruise Control Switch
J104 - ABS Control Module
J213 - Cruise Control, Control Module
J217 - Transmission Control Module
K - Instrument Cluster
M9 - Left Brake Light
S51 - Fuse (Only Automatic Transmission)
T1 - Single Connector, behind fuse/relay panel
T1a - Single Connector, behind fuse/relay panel
T3 - 3-Pin Connector, behind fuse/relay panel
T4 - 4-Pin Connector, behind fuse/relay panel
T4a - 4-Pin Connector
T4b - 4-Pin Connector
T8 - 8-Pin Connector, on Radio
T12 - 12-Pin Conenctor
T28 - 28-Pin Connector
T68 - 68-Pin Connector, on Transmission Control Module
T55 - 68-Pin Connector, on ABS Control Module
TV5 - Terminal 15a Wire Connector
TV13 - Vehicle Speed Signal Wire Connector
V18 - Cruise Control Vacuum Pump
(30) - Ground connection, -1-, beside fuse/relay panel
- - - Only for vehicles with automatic transmission
* - Only for vehicles with standard transmission

VW9040000335000X

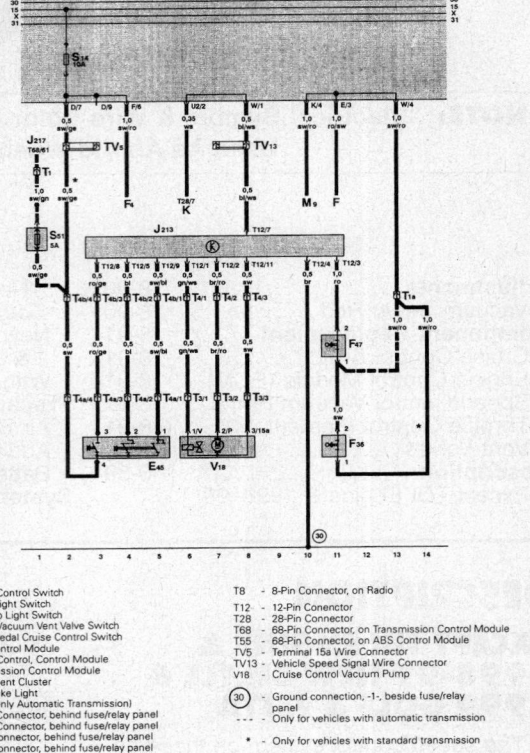

Fig. 3 Speed control wiring diagram. 1999–2001 Cabrio

cruise control module for testing, proceed as follows:

a. Separate connector T1 from behind fuse panel.
b. Connect one end of a suitable extension wire to disconnected lead, then the other end to a suitable 12 volt source that is hot with key on only.

9. **On all models,** refer to troubleshooting table, **Fig. 20,** and wiring diagrams, **Figs. 2 through 19.** Follow steps one through nine.
10. Perform each step, do not advance to next step until specified value is obtained.
11. If specified value is obtained on all steps, replace speed control module.

ADJUSTMENTS

VACUUM SERVO ROD

Passat

1. Turn rod in onto stop, then turn back one turn.
2. Play between rod and vacuum servo linkage should be. 019–.030 inch.
3. Secure servo linkage to keep from turning.

SYSTEM DIAGNOSIS & TESTING

ACCESSING DIAGNOSTIC TROUBLE CODES

WITH TDI ENGINE

1. Connect scan tool No. VAG 1551, or equivalent, to the Data Link Connector (DLC), located on the lefthand lower side of the instrument panel to right of the steering column.
2. Follow scan tool manufacturer's instructions to access Engine Electronics, then function two (02), Accessing Diagnostic Trouble Codes (DTCs).
3. If diagnostic trouble codes are accessed, refer to "Diagnostic Trouble Code Interpretation" for possible fault.

DIAGNOSTIC TROUBLE CODE INTERPRETATION

WITH TDI ENGINE

1. Refer to "Speed Control Diagnosis Trouble Code Table," **Fig. 21,** for information and possible repair procedures on any speed control diagnostic trouble code accessed.

CLEARING DIAGNOSTIC TROUBLE CODES

WITH TDI ENGINE

Diagnostic trouble codes must be accessed before the ECM will allow them to be cleared.

1. Follow scan tool manufacturer's instructions to access Engine Electronics, then function two (02), Accessing Diagnostic Trouble Codes.
2. Access any diagnostic codes that may be stored.
3. Follow scan tool manufacturer's instructions to access function five (05), Clearing Diagnostic Trouble Codes.
4. Select code clearing command, then select End Data Output.

COMPONENT TESTING

SPEED CONTROL SWITCH

With TDI Engine

In the event a display value of 255 is shown in Display Field 4 of the scan tool during the following procedure, refer to "Activate Speed Control."

1. Connect scan tool No. VAG 1551, or equivalent, to the Data Link Connector (DLC), located on the lefthand lower side of the instrument panel to right of the steering column.

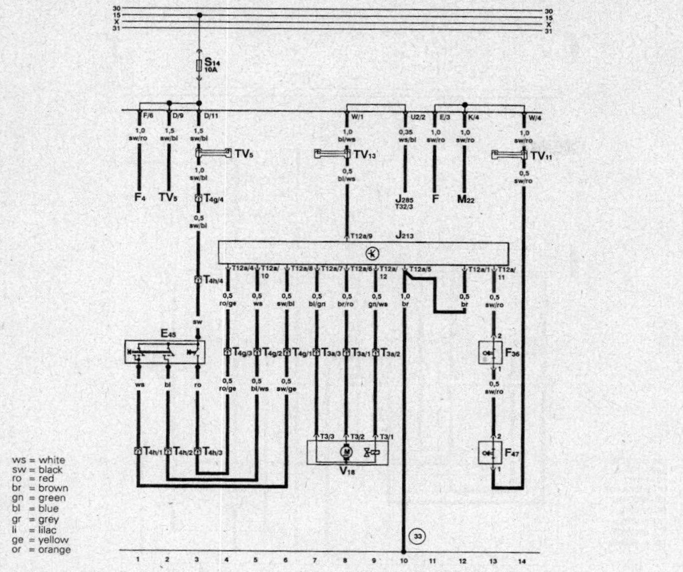

E45 - Cruise Control Switch
F - Brake Light Switch
F4 - Back-Up Light Switch
F36 - Clutch Vacuum Vent Valve Switch
F47 - Brake Vacuum Vent Valve Switch for cruise control
J213 - Cruise Control, Control Module, behind instrument panel, right
J285 - Control module with indicator unit in instrument panel insert
M22 - Right Brake/Tail Light
T3 - 3-Pin Connector
T3a - 3-Pin Connector, behind fuse/relay panel
T4g - 4-Pin Connector, behind fuse/relay panel
T4h - 4-Pin Connector, behind steering column switch cover
T12a - 12-Pin Connector
T32 - 32-Pin Connector, blue
TV5 - Terminal 15a Wire Connector, green, 4-Pin and 8-Pin
TV11 - Terminal 54 Wire Connector, orange
TV13 - Vehicle Speed Signal Wire Connector
V18 - Cruise Control Vacuum Pump
(33) - Ground connection, behind instrument panel, right

VW1100100024000X

Fig. 4 Speed control wiring diagram. 2000 EuroVan w/manual transaxle

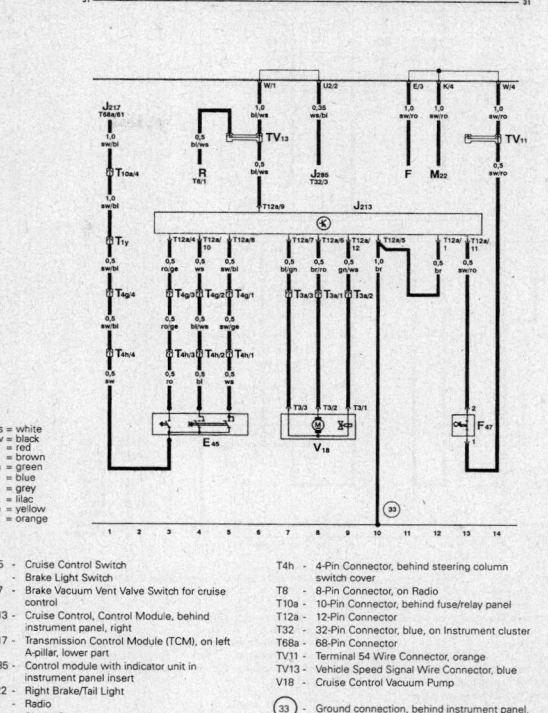

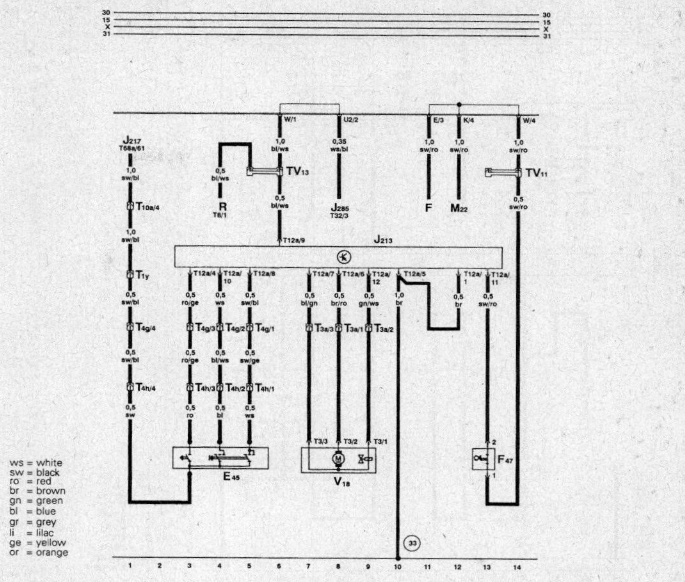

E45 - Cruise Control Switch
F - Brake Light Switch
F47 - Brake Vacuum Vent Valve Switch for cruise control
J213 - Cruise Control, Control Module, behind instrument panel, right
J217 - Transmission Control Module (TCM), on left A-pillar, lower part
J285 - Control module with indicator unit in instrument panel insert
M22 - Right Brake/Tail Light
R - Radio
T1y - Single Connector, behind fuse/relay panel
T3 - 3-Pin Connector
T3a - 3-Pin Connector, behind fuse/relay panel
T4g - 4-Pin Connector, behind fuse/relay panel
T4h - 4-Pin Connector, behind steering column switch cover
T8 - 8-Pin Connector, on Radio
T10a - 10-Pin Connector, behind fuse/relay panel
T12a - 12-Pin Connector
T32 - 32-Pin Connector, blue, on Instrument cluster
T68a - 68-Pin Connector
TV11 - Terminal 54 Wire Connector, orange
TV13 - Vehicle Speed Signal Wire Connector, blue
V18 - Cruise Control Vacuum Pump
(33) - Ground connection, behind instrument panel, right

VW1100100025000X

Fig. 5 Speed control wiring diagram. 2000 EuroVan w/automatic transaxle

2. Follow scan tool manufacturer's instructions to access "Engine Electronics."
3. Follow scan tool manufacturer's instructions to access "Read Measuring Block Value" and "Display Group 06."
4. Refer to **Fig. 22** for scan tool display values for each test condition and their possible fault correction procedures.

COMPONENT REPLACEMENT

CRUISE CONTROL SWITCH

Refer to "Combination Switch, Replace" in "Electrical" section for procedure.

THROTTLE CONTROL ELEMENT

Except TDI Engine

1. Remove lower instrument panel covers.
2. Disconnect vacuum line from element.
3. Disconnect actuator rod from pedal.
4. Remove element mounting nut, then element.
5. Reverse procedure to install. Adjust element as outlined under "Adjustments."

VENT VALVES

Except TDI Engine

To prevent trapping vacuum in throttle control element and inadvertent racing of engine, ensure throttle pedal is fully returned before connecting vacuum line to vent valve.

1. Remove lower instrument panel covers.
2. Disconnect vacuum line and electrical connectors from valve.
3. Unscrew valve from bracket.
4. Reverse procedure to install. Ensure pedal for valve is fully returned to stop after valve is installed.

SPEED CONTROL VACUUM PUMP

Except TDI Engine

1. Obtain audio coded anti-theft code and disarm as outlined under "Precautions."
2. Remove battery, then, if required, the windshield washer bottle.
3. Disconnect wiring connector and vacuum line.
4. Disconnect pump from mounting, then remove pump.
5. Reverse procedure to install.

ENGINE CONTROL MODULE (ECM)

In the event that the speed control function has been blocked in the Engine Control Module (ECM) or a new ECM is installed, use the following procedure to activate the speed control system.

1. Connect scan tool No. VAG 1551, or equivalent, to the Data Link Connector (DLC), located under the lefthand side of the instrument panel.
2. Follow scan tool manufacturer's instructions to access "Engine Electronics" and "Log In."
3. Enter code 11463 to encode "Activate Speed Control" into ECU.
4. After encoding "Activate Speed Control" into ECU, disconnect scan tool and road test vehicle for speed control functions.

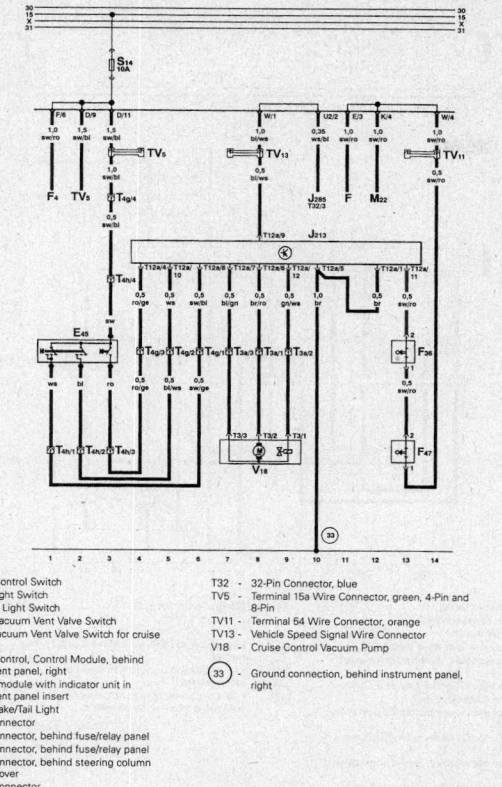

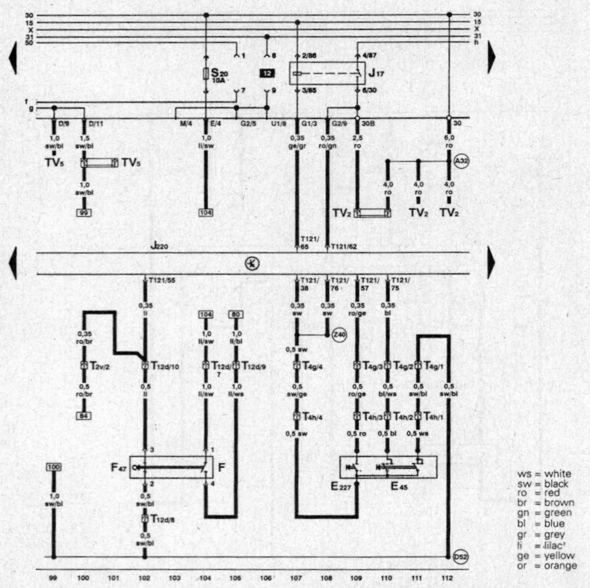

E45 - Cruise Control Switch
E227 - Button for cruise control (set)
F - Brake Light Switch
F47 - Brake Vacuum Vent Valve Switch for cruise control
J17 - Fuel Pump (FP) Relay
J220 - Motronic Engine Control Module (ECM), in engine compartment, left
T2v - Double Connector, behind fuse/relay panel
T4g - 4-Pin Connector, behind fuse/relay panel
T4h - 4-Pin Connector, near steering column
T12d - 12-Pin Connector, behind fuse/relay panel
T121 - 121-Pin Connector
TV2 - Terminal 30 (B+) Wire Connector, red, each 6 points
TV5 - Terminal 15a Wire Connector, green, 4-Pin and 8-Pin
(A32) - Plus connection (30), in instrument panel wiring harness
(D52) - Plus connection (15a), in engine compartment wiring harness
(Z40) - Plus connection (15), in cruise control wiring harness

VW1100100026000X

Fig. 6 Speed control wiring diagram. 2001 EuroVan

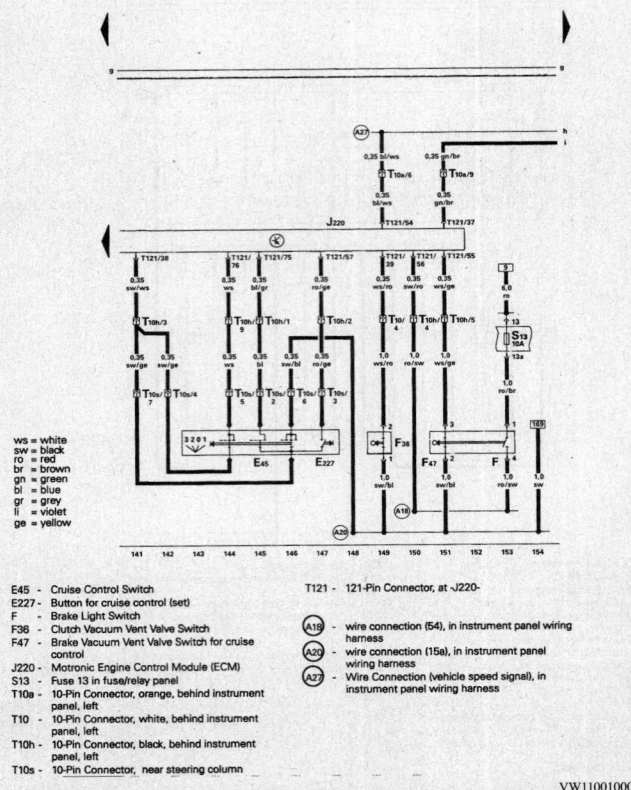

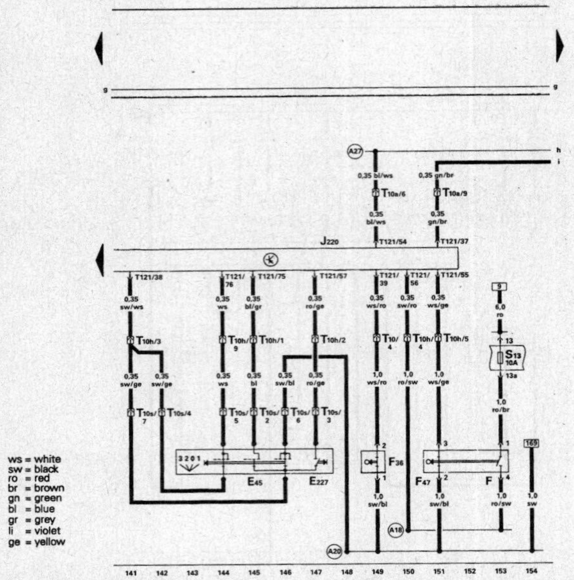

E45 - Cruise Control Switch
E227 - Button for cruise control (set)
F - Brake Light Switch
F36 - Clutch Vacuum Vent Valve Switch
F47 - Brake Vacuum Vent Valve Switch for cruise control
J220 - Motronic Engine Control Module (ECM)
S13 - Fuse 13 in fuse/relay panel
T10a - 10-Pin Connector, orange, behind instrument panel, left
T10 - 10-Pin Connector, white, behind instrument panel, left
T10h - 10-Pin Connector, black, behind instrument panel, left
T10s - 10-Pin Connector, near steering column
T121 - 121-Pin Connector, at J220-
(A18) - wire connection (54), in instrument panel wiring harness
(A20) - wire connection (15a), in instrument panel wiring harness
(A27) - Wire Connection (vehicle speed signal), in instrument panel wiring harness

VW1100100018010X

Fig. 7 Speed control wiring diagram (Part 1 of 4). New Beetle w/1.8L engine

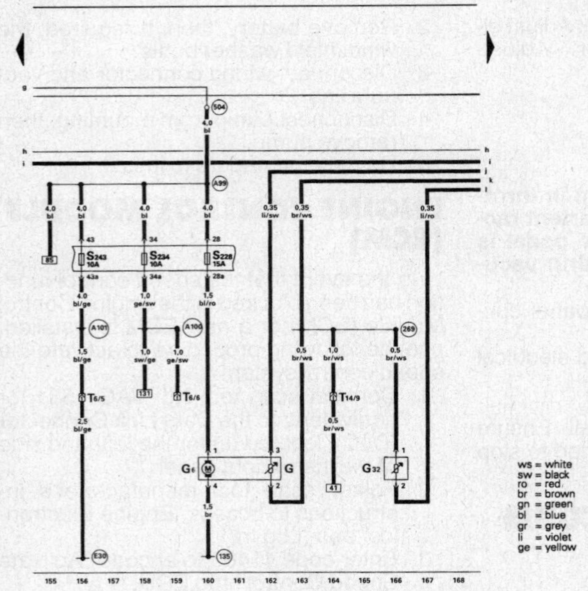

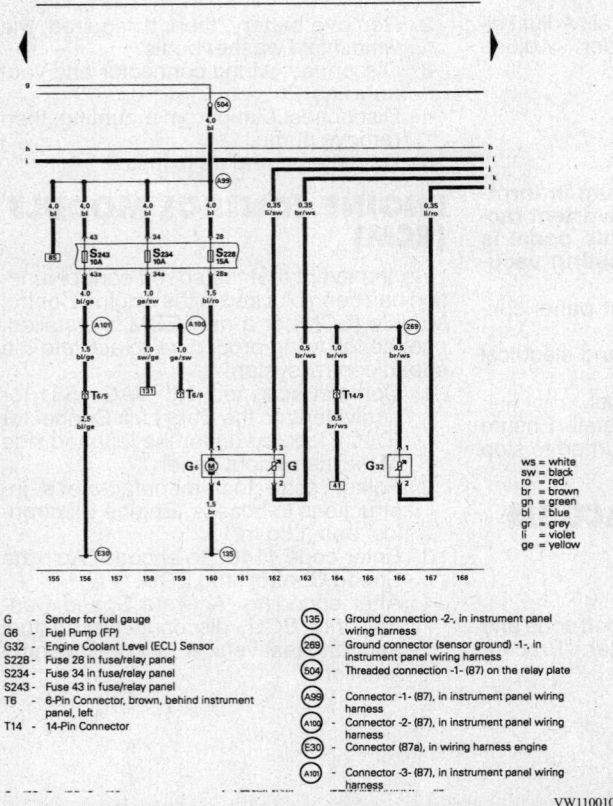

G - Sender for fuel gauge
G6 - Fuel Pump (FP)
G32 - Engine Coolant Level (ECL) Sensor
S228 - Fuse 28 in fuse/relay panel
S234 - Fuse 34 in fuse/relay panel
S243 - Fuse 43 in fuse/relay panel
T6 - 6-Pin Connector, brown, behind instrument panel, left
T14 - 14-Pin Connector
(135) - Ground connection -2-, in instrument panel wiring harness
(269) - Ground connector (sensor ground) -1-, in instrument panel wiring harness
(504) - Threaded connection -1- (87) on the relay plate
(A99) - Connector -1- (87), in instrument panel wiring harness
(A100) - Connector -2- (87), in instrument panel wiring harness
(E30) - Connector (87a), in wiring harness engine
(A101) - Connector -3- (87), in instrument panel wiring harness

VW1100100018020X

Fig. 7 Speed control wiring diagram (Part 2 of 4). New Beetle w/1.8L engine

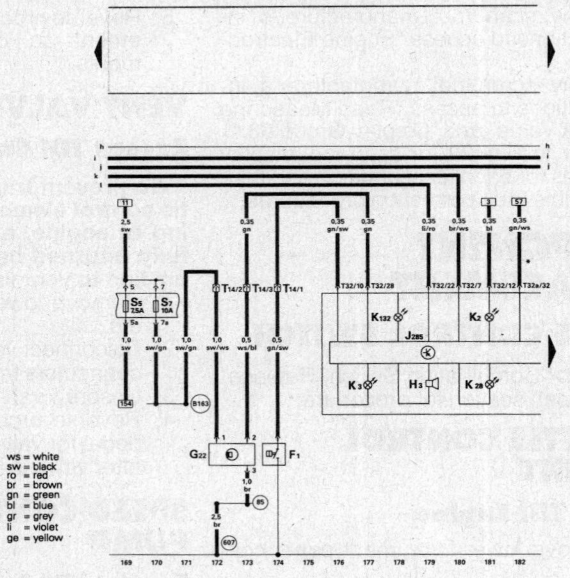

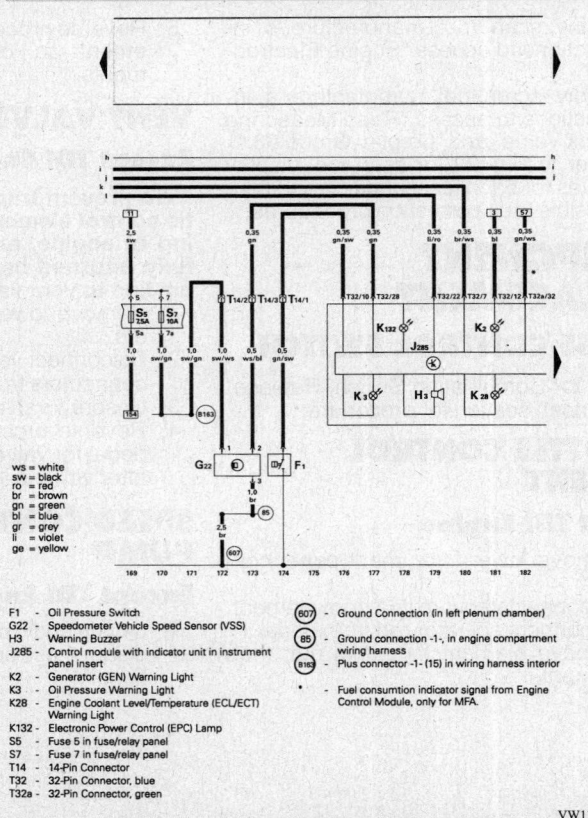

F1 - Oil Pressure Switch
G22 - Speedometer Vehicle Speed Sensor (VSS)
H3 - Warning Buzzer
J285 - Control module with indicator unit in instrument panel insert
K2 - Generator (GEN) Warning Light
K3 - Oil Pressure Warning Light
K28 - Engine Coolant Level/Temperature (ECL/ECT) Warning Light
K132 - Electronic Power Control (EPC) Lamp
S5 - Fuse 5 in fuse/relay panel
S7 - Fuse 7 in fuse/relay panel
T14 - 14-Pin Connector
T32 - 32-Pin Connector, blue
T32a - 32-Pin Connector, green
(607) - Ground Connection (in left plenum chamber)
(85) - Ground connection -1-, in engine compartment wiring harness
(B163) - Plus connector -1- (15) in wiring harness interior
* - Fuel consumtion indicator signal from Engine Control Module, only for MFA.

VW1100100018030X

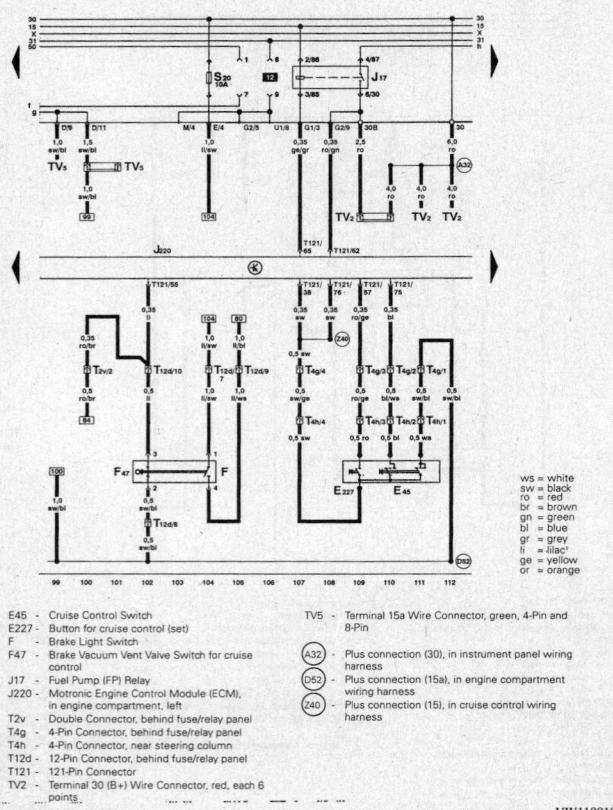

Fig. 7 Speed control wiring diagram (Part 3 of 4). New Beetle w/1.8L engine

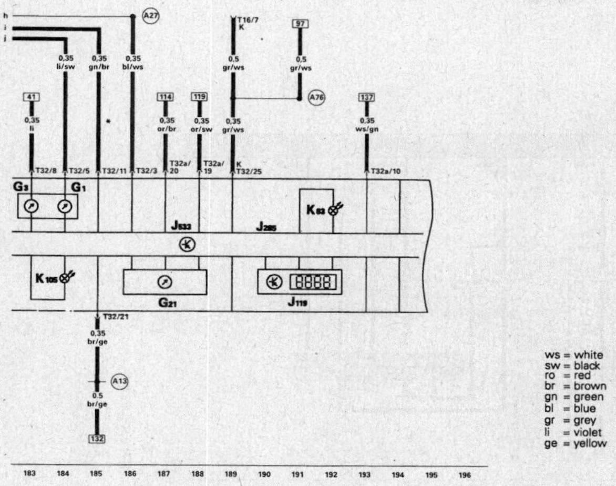

G1 - Fuel Gauge
G3 - Engine Coolant Temperature (ECT) Gauge
G21 - Speedometer
J119 - Multi-function Indicator (MFA)
J285 - Control module with indicator unit in instrument panel insert
J533 - Data Bus On Board Diagnostic Interface
K83 - Malfunction Indicator lamp (MIL)
K105 - Low Fuel Level Warning Light
T16 - 16-Pin Connector, Data link Connector (DLC), below steering column, left
T32 - 32-Pin Connector, blue
T32a - 32-Pin Connector, green

(A13) - wire connection (door contact switch) in instrument panel wiring harness
(A27) - Wire Connection (vehicle speed signal), in instrument panel wiring harness
(A76) - Connector (K-diagnosis wire) in instrument panel wiring harness
* - Engine Speed signal from ECM

VW1100100018040X

Fig. 7 Speed control wiring diagram (Part 4 of 4). New Beetle w/1.8L engine

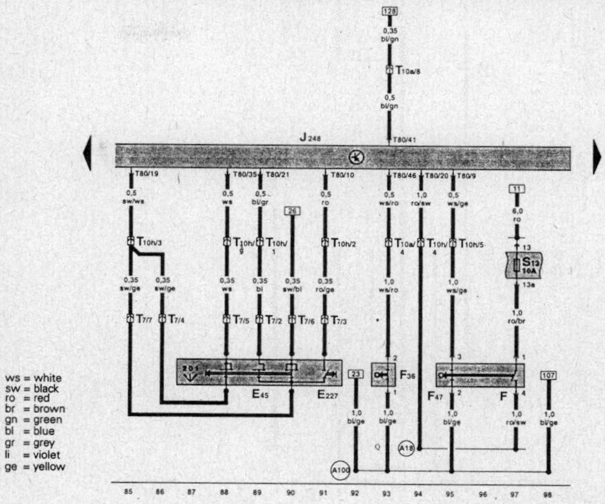

E45 - Cruise Control Switch (if equipped)
E227 - Button for cruise control (set), (if equipped)
F - Brake Light Switch
F36 - Clutch Vacuum vent Valve Switch
F47 - Brake Vacuum Vent Valve Switch for cruise control/diesel fuel injection (DFI)
J248 - Diesel Direct Fuel Injection (DFI) Engine Control Module (ECM), behind instrument panel, left
S13 - Fuse 13 in fuse holder
T7 - 7-Pin Connector, near steering column
T10a - 10-Pin Connector, orange, behind instrument panel, left
T10h - 10-Pin Connector, black, behind instrument panel, left
T80 - Connector, 80 point

(A18) - wire connection (54), in instrument panel wiring harness
(A100) - Connector -2- (87), in instrument panel wiring harness
* - manual transmission only

VW1109900011010X

Fig. 8 Speed control wiring diagram (Part 1 of 2). New Beetle w/1.9L TDI engine

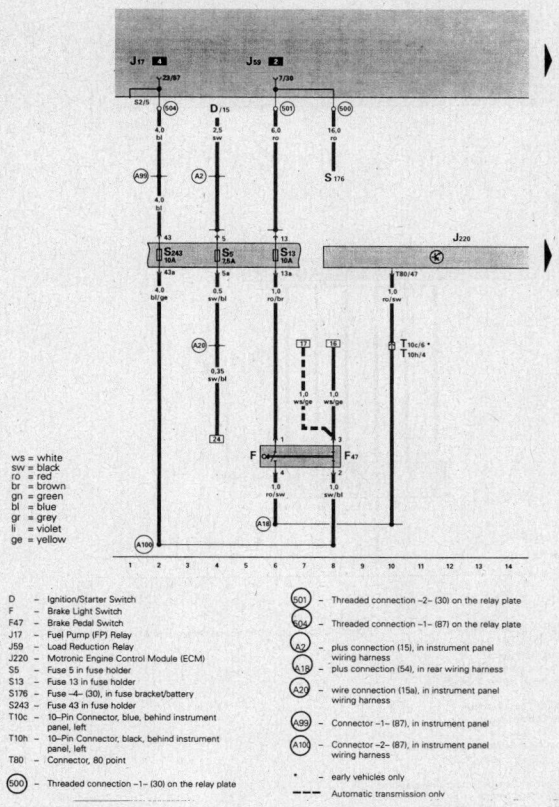

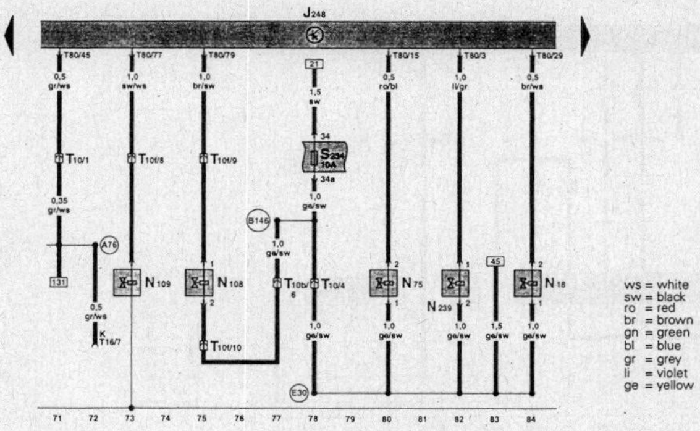

J248 - Diesel Direct Fuel Injection (DFI) Engine Control Module (ECM), in plenum chamber, left
N18 - EGR Vacuum Regulator Solenoid Valve
N75 - Wastegate Bypass Regulator Valve
N108 - Cold Start Injector
N109 - Fuel Cut-off Valve
N239 - Change-over valve for intake manifold flap
S234 - Fuse 34 in fuse holder
T10 - 10-Pin Connector, white, behind instrument panel, left
T10b - 10-Pin Connector, in engine compartment, left
T10f - 10-Pin Connector, on engine, front
T16 - 16-Pin Connector, Data Link Connector (DLC), below steering column
T80 - Connector, 80 point

(A76) - Connector (K-diagnosis wire), in instrument panel wiring harness
(B146) - Plus connector -1- (87), in wiring harness interior
(E30) - Connector (87a), in wiring harness engine

VW1109900011020X

Fig. 8 Speed control wiring diagram (Part 2 of 2). New Beetle w/1.9L TDI engine

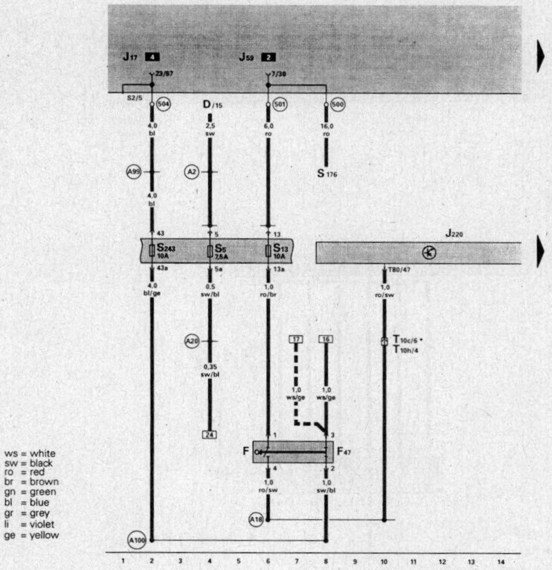

D - Ignition/Starter Switch
F - Brake Light Switch
F47 - Brake Pedal Switch
J17 - Fuel Pump (FP) Relay
J59 - Load Reduction Relay
J220 - Motronic Engine Control Module (ECM)
S5 - Fuse 5 in fuse holder
S13 - Fuse 13 in fuse holder
S176 - Fuse -4- (30), in fuse bracket/battery
S243 - Fuse 43 in fuse holder
T10c - 10-Pin Connector, blue, behind instrument panel, left
T10h - 10-Pin Connector, black, behind instrument panel, left
T80 - Connector, 80 point
(500) - Threaded connection -1- (30) on the relay plate

(501) - Threaded connection -2- (30) on the relay plate
(504) - Threaded connection -1- (87) on the relay plate
(A2) - plus connection (15), in instrument panel wiring harness
(A18) - plus connection (54), in rear wiring harness
(A20) - wire connection (15a), in instrument panel wiring harness
(A99) - Connector -1- (87), in instrument panel
(A100) - Connector -2- (87), in instrument panel wiring harness
* - early vehicles only
--- Automatic transmission only

VW1109900012010X

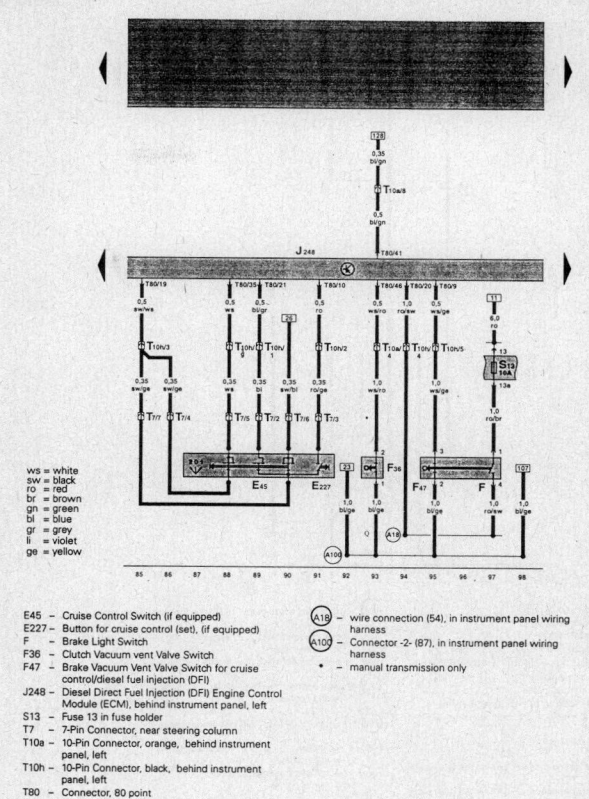

Fig. 9 Speed control wiring diagram (From 1/98, Part 1 of 3). New Beetle w/2.0L engine

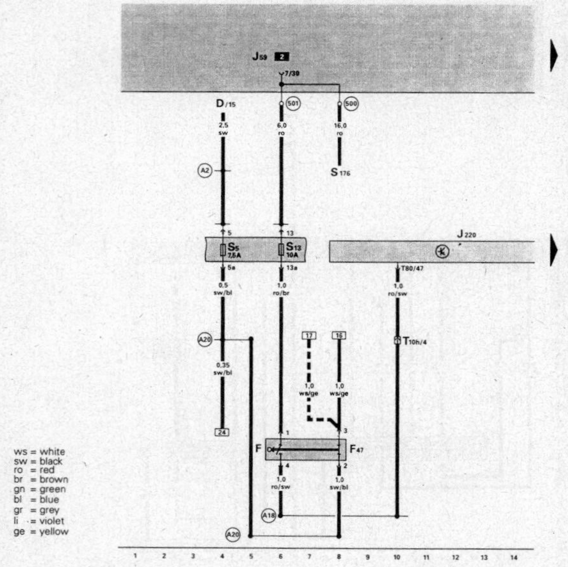

D – Ignition/Starter Switch
F – Brake Light Switch
F47 – Brake Pedal Switch
J59 – Load Reduction Relay
J220 – Motronic Engine Control Module (ECM)
S5 – Fuse 5 in fuse holder
S13 – Fuse 13 in fuse holder
S176 – Fuse -4- (30), in fuse bracket/battery
T10h – 10-Pin Connector, black, behind instrument panel, left
T80 – Connector, 80 point
(500) – Threaded connection -1- (30) on the relay plate
(501) – Threaded connection -2- (30) on the relay plate
(504) – Threaded connection -1- (87) on the relay plate
(A2) – plus connection (15), in instrument panel wiring harness
(A18) – plus connection (54), in rear wiring harness
(A20) – wire connection (15a), in instrument panel wiring harness
(A99) – Connector -1- (87), in instrument panel
(A100) – Connector -2- (87), in instrument panel wiring harness
- - - Automatic transmission only

VW1109900012020X

Fig. 9 Speed control wiring diagram (From 8/98, Part 1 of 3). New Beetle w/2.0L engine

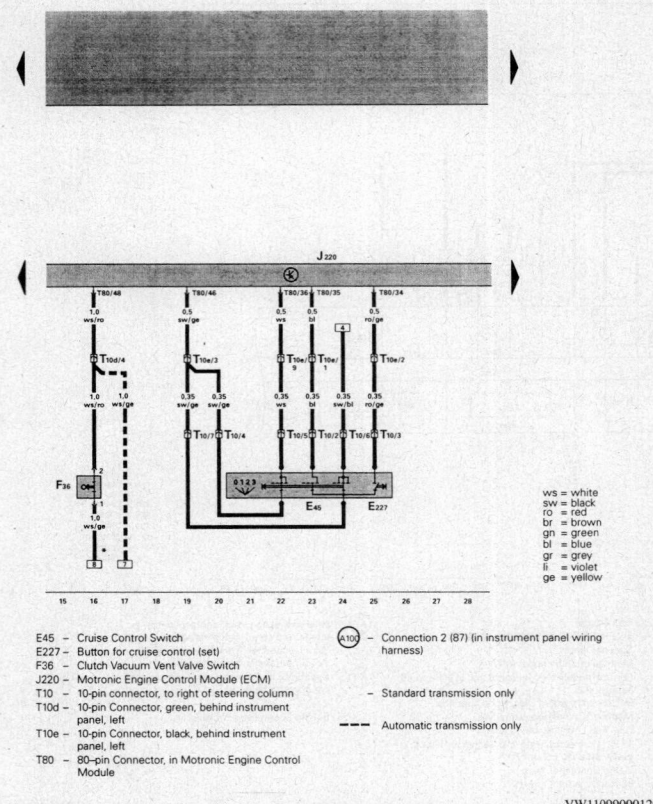

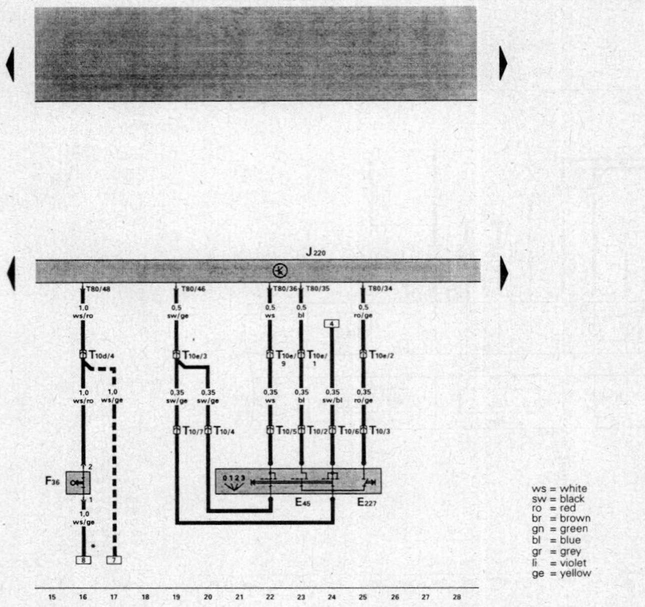

E45 – Cruise Control Switch
E227 – Button for cruise control (set)
F36 – Clutch Vacuum Vent Valve Switch
J220 – Motronic Engine Control Module (ECM)
T10 – 10-pin connector, to right of steering column
T10d – 10-pin Connector, green, behind instrument panel, left
T10e – 10-pin Connector, black, behind instrument panel, left
T80 – 80-pin Connector, in Motronic Engine Control Module
(A100) – Connection 2 (87) (in instrument panel wiring harness)
— Standard transmission only
- - - Automatic transmission only

VW1109900012030X

Fig. 9 Speed control wiring diagram (Part 2 of 3). New Beetle w/2.0L engine

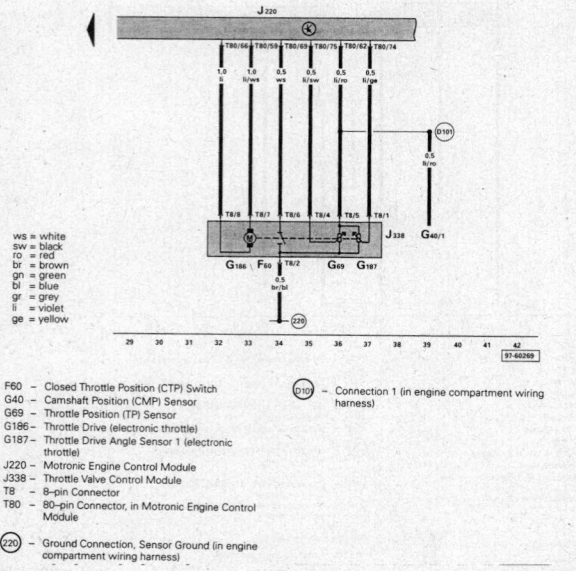

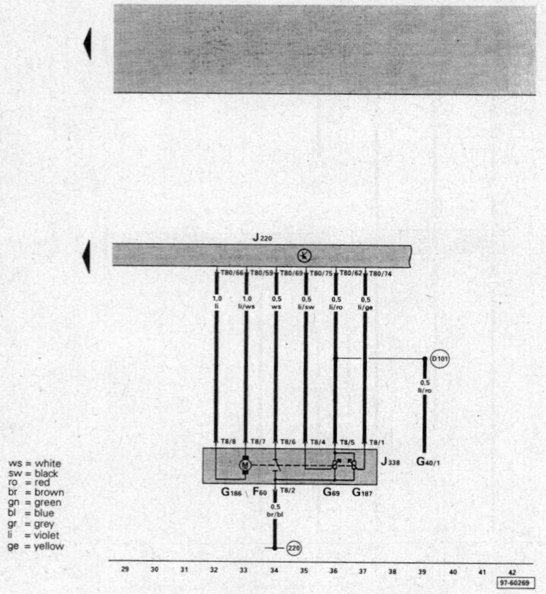

F60 – Closed Throttle Position (CTP) Switch
G40 – Camshaft Position (CMP) Sensor
G69 – Throttle Position (TP) Sensor
G186 – Throttle Drive (electronic throttle)
G187 – Throttle Drive Angle Sensor 1 (electronic throttle)
J220 – Motronic Engine Control Module
J338 – Throttle Valve Control Module
T8 – 8-pin Connector
T80 – 80-pin Connector, in Motronic Engine Control Module
(220) – Ground Connection, Sensor Ground (in engine compartment wiring harness)
(D101) – Connection 1 (in engine compartment wiring harness)

VW1109900012040X

Fig. 9 Speed control wiring diagram (Part 3 of 3). New Beetle w/2.0L engine

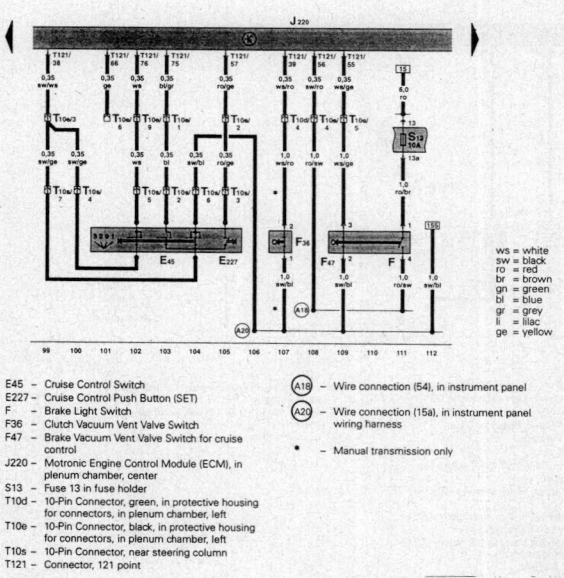

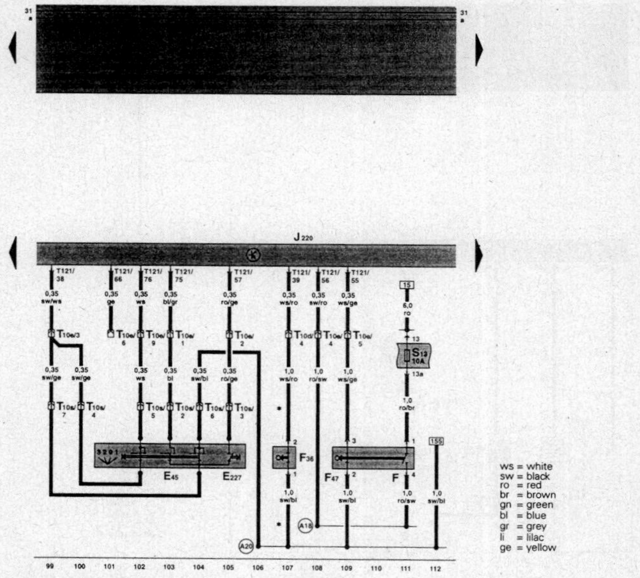

E45 – Cruise Control Switch
E227 – Cruise Control Push Button (SET)
F – Brake Light Switch
F36 – Clutch Vacuum Vent Valve Switch
F47 – Brake Vacuum Vent Valve Switch for cruise control
J220 – Motronic Engine Control Module (ECM), in plenum chamber, center
S13 – Fuse 13 in fuse holder
T10d – 10-Pin Connector, green, in protective housing for connectors, in plenum chamber, left
T10e – 10-Pin Connector, black, in protective housing for connectors, in plenum chamber, left
T10s – 10-Pin Connector, near steering column
T121 – Connector, 121 point
(A18) – Wire connection (54), in instrument panel
(A20) – Wire connection (15a), in instrument panel wiring harness
* – Manual transmission only

VW1109900013000X

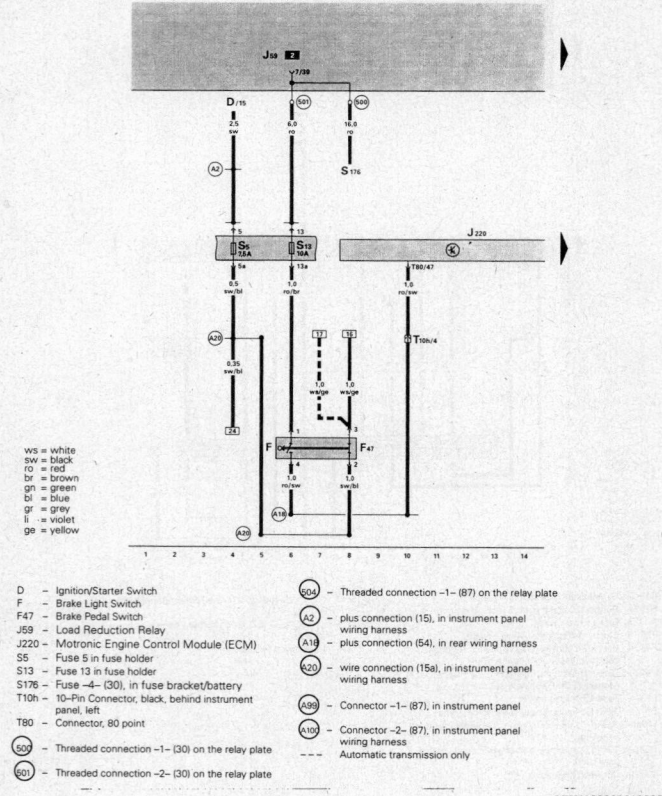

Fig. 10 Speed control wiring diagram. 1999–2001 Golf & Jetta w/2.8L engine

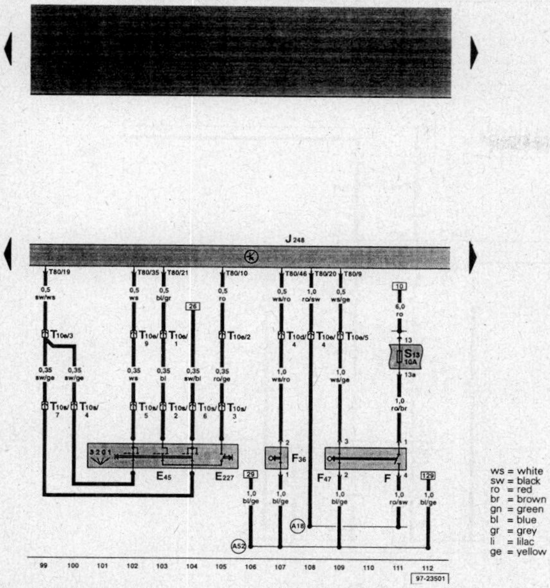

E45 – Cruise Control Switch**
E227 – Cruise Control Push Button (SET)**
F – Brake Light Switch
F36 – Clutch Vacuum Vent Valve Switch
F47 – Brake Vacuum Vent Valve Switch for cruise control/diesel
J248 – Diesel Direct Fuel Injection (DFI) Engine Control Module (ECM), in plenum chamber, center
S13 – Fuse 13 in fuse holder
T10d – 10-Pin Connector, green, in protective housing for connectors, in plenum chamber, left
T10e – 10-Pin Connector, black, in protective housing for connectors, in plenum chamber, left
T10s – 10-Pin Connector, near steering column**
T80 – Connector, 80 point

(A18) – Wire connection (54), in instrument panel wiring harness
(A52) – Plus connection (30), in instrument panel wiring harness

** – Vehicles with cruise control only

VW1109900014000X

Fig. 11 Speed control wiring diagram. 1999 Golf & Jetta w/1.9L engine & manual transaxle

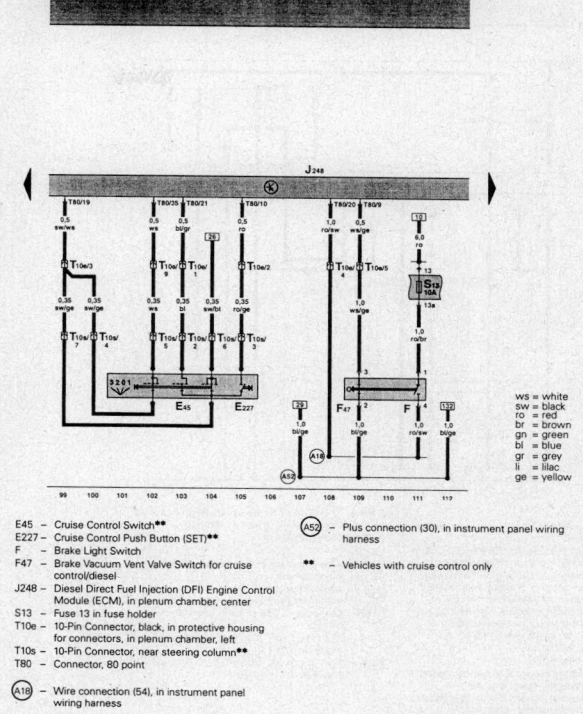

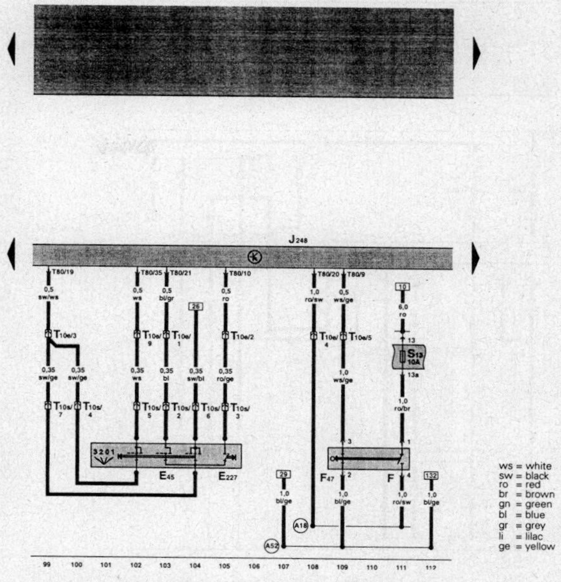

E45 – Cruise Control Switch**
E227 – Cruise Control Push Button (SET)**
F – Brake Light Switch
F47 – Brake Vacuum Vent Valve Switch for cruise control/diesel
J248 – Diesel Direct Fuel Injection (DFI) Engine Control Module (ECM), in plenum chamber, center
S13 – Fuse 13 in fuse holder
T10e – 10-Pin Connector, black, in protective housing for connectors, in plenum chamber, left
T10s – 10-Pin Connector, near steering column**
T80 – Connector, 80 point

(A18) – Wire connection (54), in instrument panel wiring harness

(A52) – Plus connection (30), in instrument panel wiring harness

** – Vehicles with cruise control only

VW1109900015000X

Fig. 12 Speed control wiring diagram. 1999 Golf & Jetta w/1.9L engine & automatic transaxle

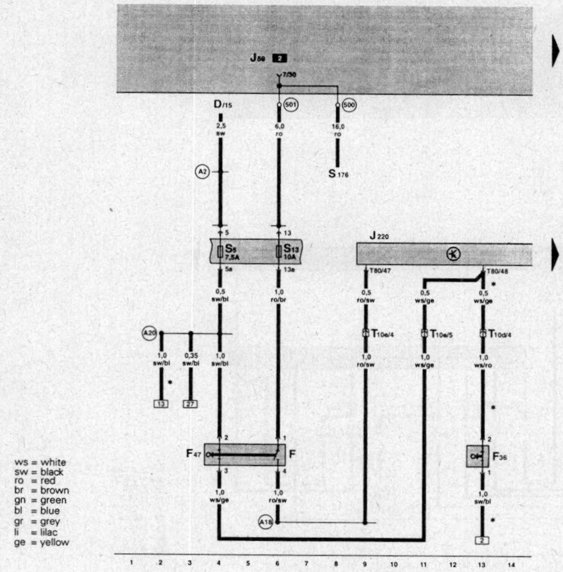

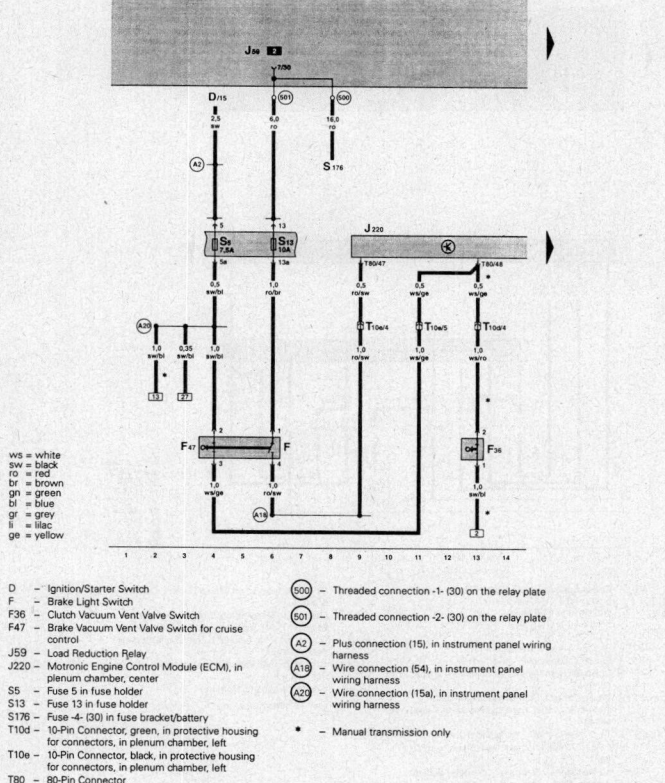

D – Ignition/Starter Switch
F – Brake Light Switch
F36 – Clutch Vacuum Vent Valve Switch
F47 – Brake Vacuum Vent Valve Switch for cruise control
J59 – Load Reduction Relay
J220 – Motronic Engine Control Module (ECM), in plenum chamber, center
S5 – Fuse 5 in fuse holder
S13 – Fuse 13 in fuse holder
S176 – Fuse -4- (30) in fuse bracket/battery
T10d – 10-Pin Connector, green, in protective housing for connectors, in plenum chamber, left
T10e – 10-Pin Connector, black, in protective housing for connectors, in plenum chamber, left
T80 – 80-Pin Connector

(500) – Threaded connection -1- (30) on the relay plate
(501) – Threaded connection -2- (30) on the relay plate
(A2) – Plus connection (15), in instrument panel wiring harness
(A18) – Wire connection (54), in instrument panel wiring harness
(A20) – Wire connection (15a), in instrument panel wiring harness

* – Manual transmission only

VW1109900016010X

Fig. 13 Speed control wiring diagram (Part 1 of 2). 1999–2001 Golf & Jetta w/2.0L engine

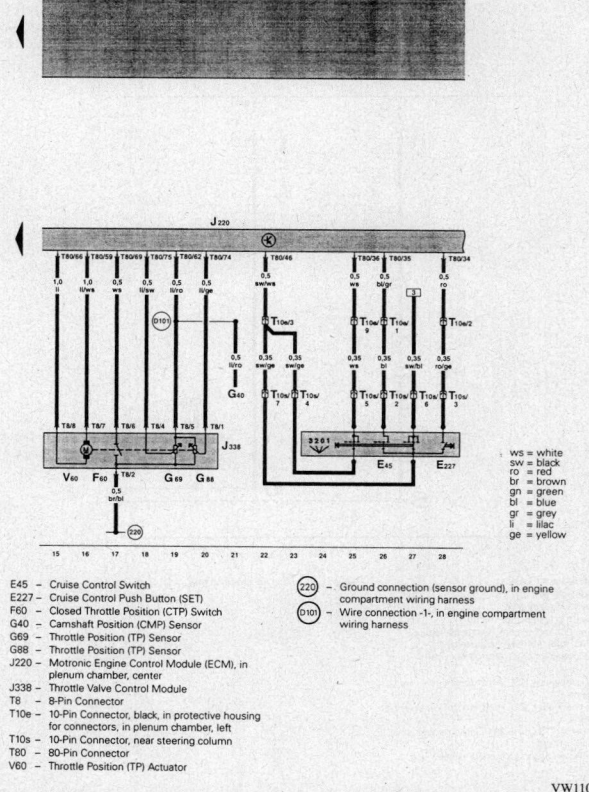

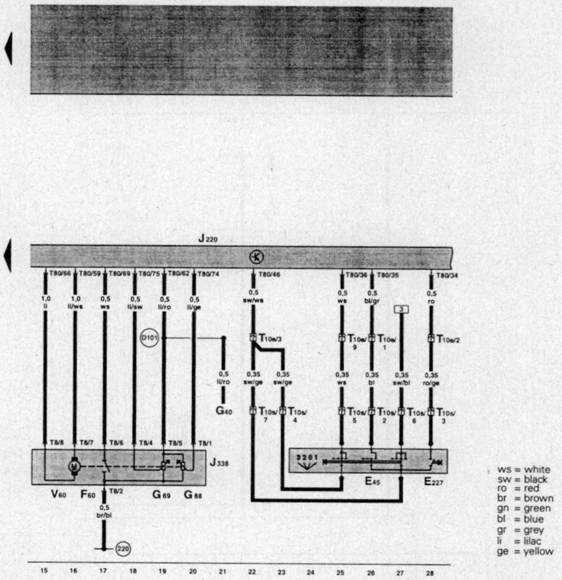

E45 – Cruise Control Switch
E227 – Cruise Control Push Button (SET)
F60 – Closed Throttle Position (CTP) Switch
G40 – Camshaft Position (CMP) Sensor
G69 – Throttle Position (TP) Sensor
G88 – Throttle Position (TP) Sensor
J220 – Motronic Engine Control Module (ECM), in plenum chamber, center
J338 – Throttle Valve Control Module
T8 – 8-Pin Connector
T10e – 10-Pin Connector, black, in protective housing for connectors, in plenum chamber, left
T10s – 10-Pin Connector, near steering column
T80 – 80-Pin Connector
V60 – Throttle Position (TP) Actuator

(220) – Ground connection (sensor ground), in engine compartment wiring harness
(D101) – Wire connection -1-, in engine compartment wiring harness

VW1109900016020X

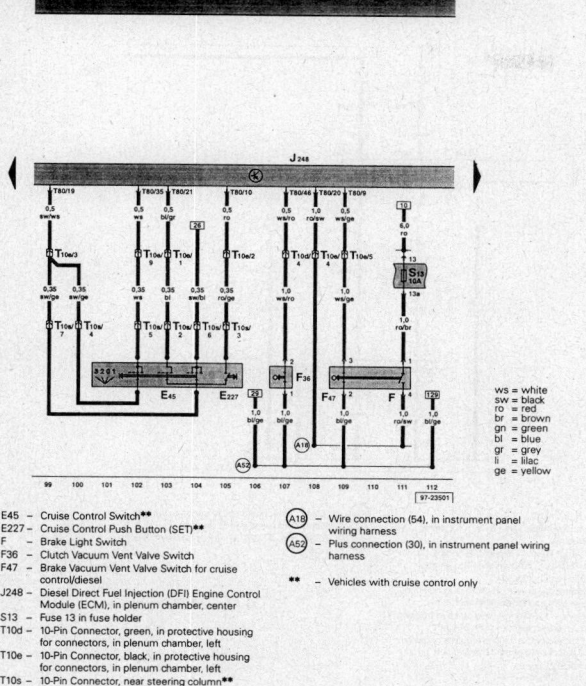

Fig. 13 Speed control wiring diagram (Part 2 of 2). 1999–2001 Golf & Jetta w/2.0L engine

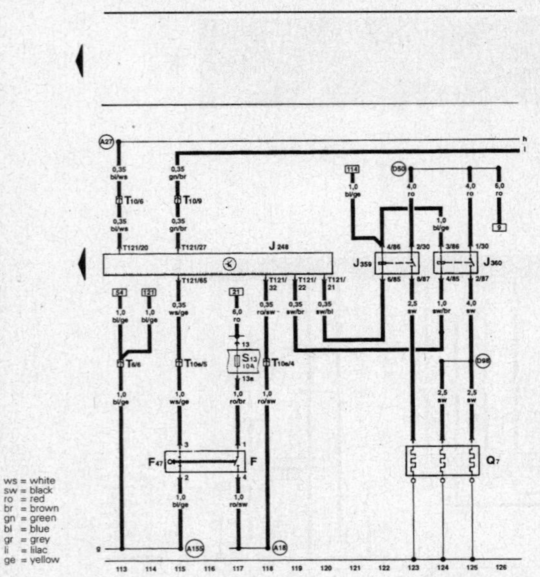

F – Brake Light Switch
F47 – Brake Vacuum Vent Valve Switch for cruise control/diesel
J248 – Diesel Direct Fuel Injection (DFI) Engine Control Module (ECM), in plenum chamber, center
J359 – Relay for preheating coolant, low heat output, in protective housing, in engine compartment, left, production control number (53)
J360 – Relay for preheating coolant, high heat output, in protective housing, in engine compartment, left, production control number (53)
Q7 – Glow plugs (coolant)
S13 – Fuse 13 in fuse holder
T6 – 6-Pin Connector, brown, in protective housing for connectors, in plenum chamber, left
T10 – 10-Pin Connector, orange, in protective housing for connectors, in plenum chamber, left
T10e – 10-Pin Connector, black, in protective housing for connectors, in plenum chamber, left
T121 – Connector, 121 point
(A18) – Wire connection (54), in instrument panel wiring harness
(A27) – Wire Connection (vehicle speed signal), in instrument panel wiring harness
(A155) – Connector -2- (86), in instrument panel wiring harness
(D50) – Plus connection (30), in engine compartment wiring harness
(D98) – Wire connection (glow plugs), in engine compartment wiring harness

VW1100100019000X

Fig. 14 Speed control wiring diagram. 2000–01 Golf & Jetta w/1.9L TDI engine

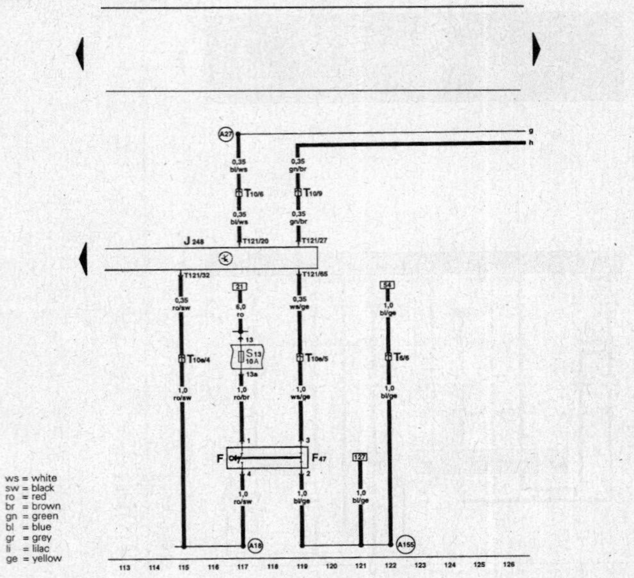

F – Brake Light Switch
F47 – Brake Vacuum Vent Valve Switch for cruise control/diesel
J248 – Diesel Direct Fuel Injection (DFI) Engine Control Module (ECM), in plenum chamber, center
S13 – Fuse 13 in fuse holder
T6 – 6-Pin Connector, brown, in protective housing for connectors, in plenum chamber, left
T10 – 10-Pin Connector, orange, in protective housing for connectors, in plenum chamber, left
T10e – 10-Pin Connector, black, in protective housing for connectors, in plenum chamber, left
T121 – Connector, 121 point
(A18) – Wire connection (54), in instrument panel wiring harness
(A27) – Wire Connection (vehicle speed signal), in instrument panel wiring harness
(A155) – Connector -2- (86), in instrument panel wiring harness

VW1100100020000X

Fig. 15 Speed control wiring diagram. 2000–01 Golf & Jetta w/1.9L TDI engine

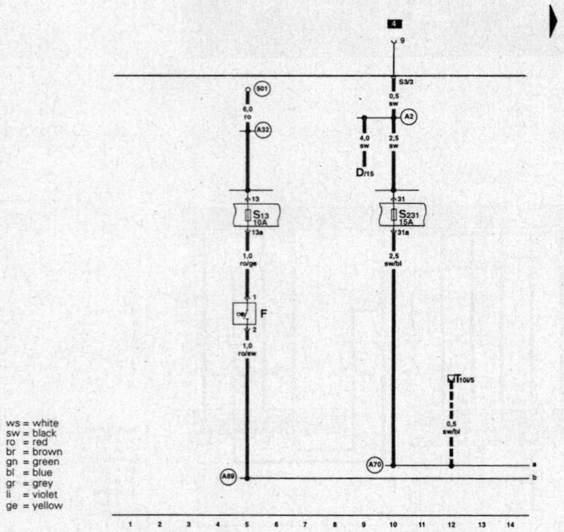

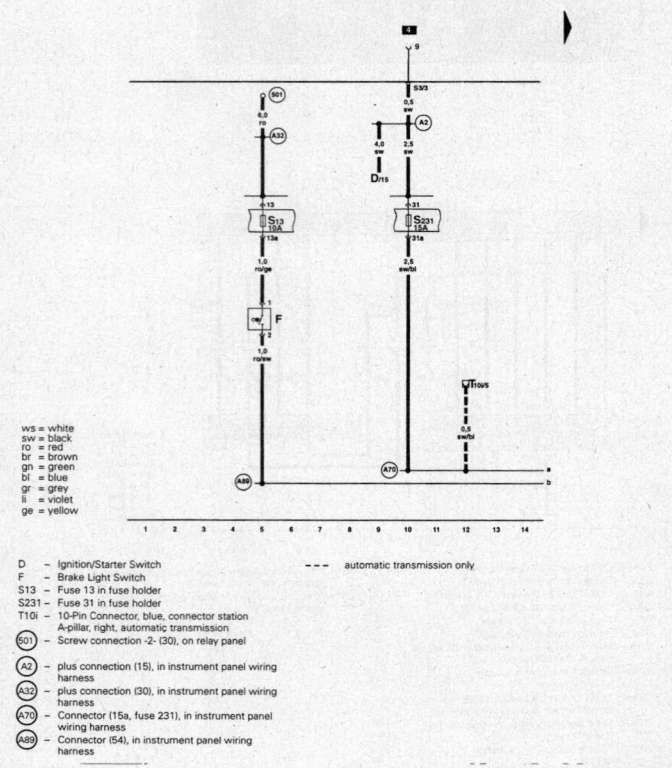

D – Ignition/Starter Switch
F – Brake Light Switch
S13 – Fuse 13 in fuse holder
S231 – Fuse 31 in fuse holder
T10i – 10-Pin Connector, blue, connector station A-pillar, right, automatic transmission
(501) – Screw connection -2- (30), on relay panel
(A2) – plus connection (15), in instrument panel wiring harness
(A32) – plus connection (30), in instrument panel wiring harness
(A70) – Connector (15a, fuse 231), in instrument panel wiring harness
(A89) – Connector (54), in instrument panel wiring harness
--- automatic transmission only

VW1109900017010X

Fig. 16 Speed control wiring diagram (Part 1 of 3). 1998–99 Passat

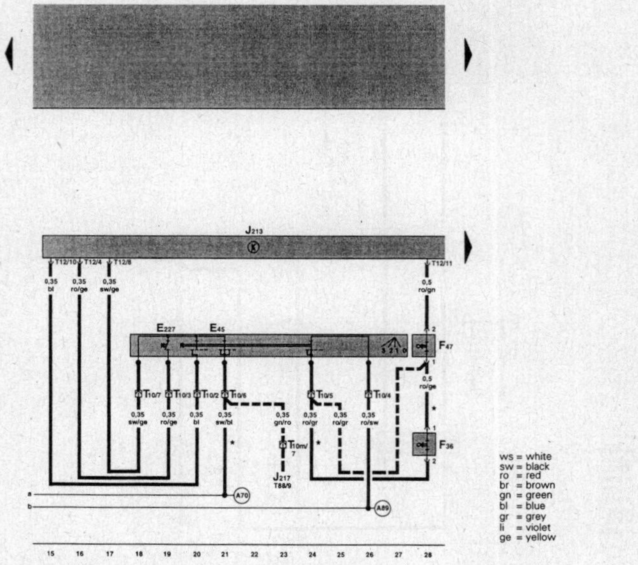

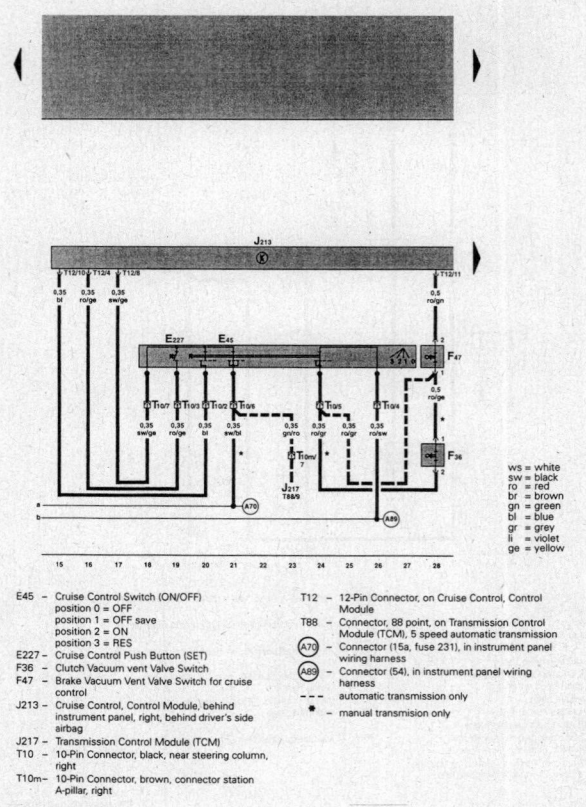

E45 – Cruise Control Switch (ON/OFF)
position 0 = OFF
position 1 = OFF save
position 2 = ON
position 3 = RES
E227 – Cruise Control Push Button (SET)
F36 – Clutch Vacuum vent Valve Switch
F47 – Brake Vacuum Vent Valve Switch for cruise control
J213 – Cruise Control, Control Module, behind instrument panel, right, behind driver's side airbag
J217 – Transmission Control Module (TCM)
T10 – 10-Pin Connector, black, near steering column, right
T10m – 10-Pin Connector, brown, connector station A-pillar, right
T12 – 12-Pin Connector, on Cruise Control, Control Module
T88 – Connector, 88 point, on Transmission Control Module (TCM), 5 speed automatic transmission
(A70) – Connector (15a, fuse 231), in instrument panel wiring harness
(A89) – Connector (54), in instrument panel wiring harness
--- automatic transmission only
* – manual transmision only

VW1109900017020X

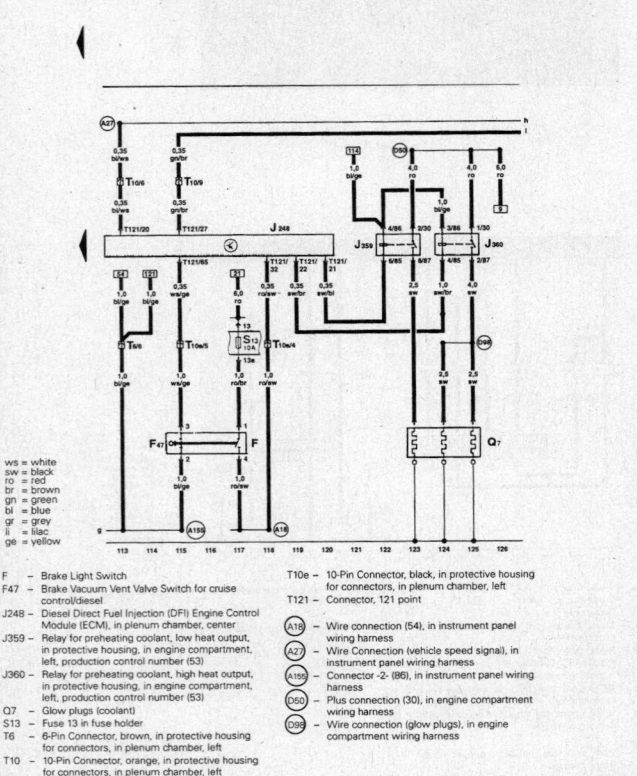

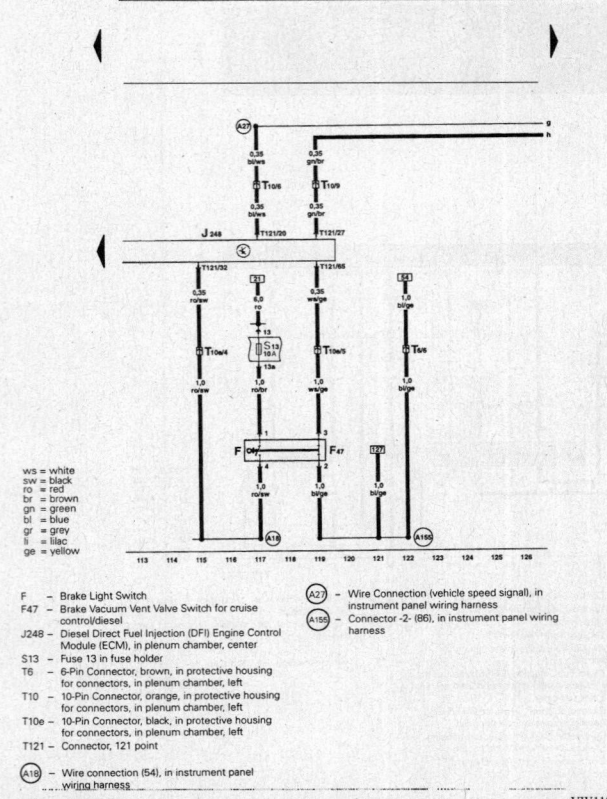

Fig. 16 Speed control wiring diagram (Part 2 of 3). 1998–99 Passat

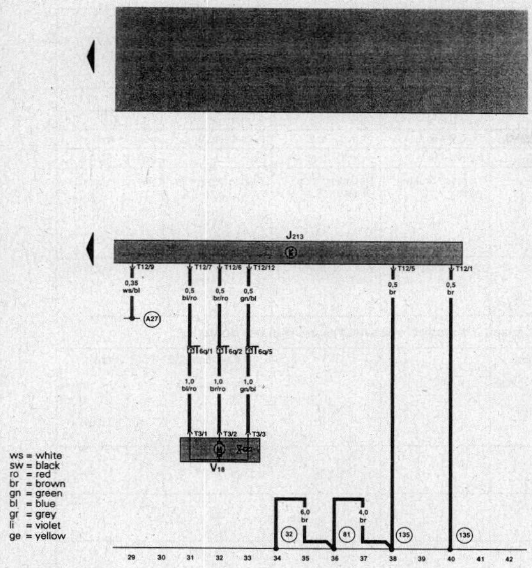

- J213 – Cruise Control, Control Module, behind instrument panel, right, behind driver's side airbag
- T3 – 3-Pin Connector
- T6q – 6-Pin Connector, black, connector station A-pillar, left
- T12 – 12-Pin Connector, on Cruise Control, Control Module
- V18 – Cruise Control Vacuum pump
- (32) – Ground connection, behind instrument panel, left
- (81) – Ground connection -1-, in instrument panel wiring harness
- (135) – Ground connection -2-, in instrument panel wiring harness
- (A27) – wire Connection (vehicle speed signal), in instrument panel wiring harness

VW1109900017030X

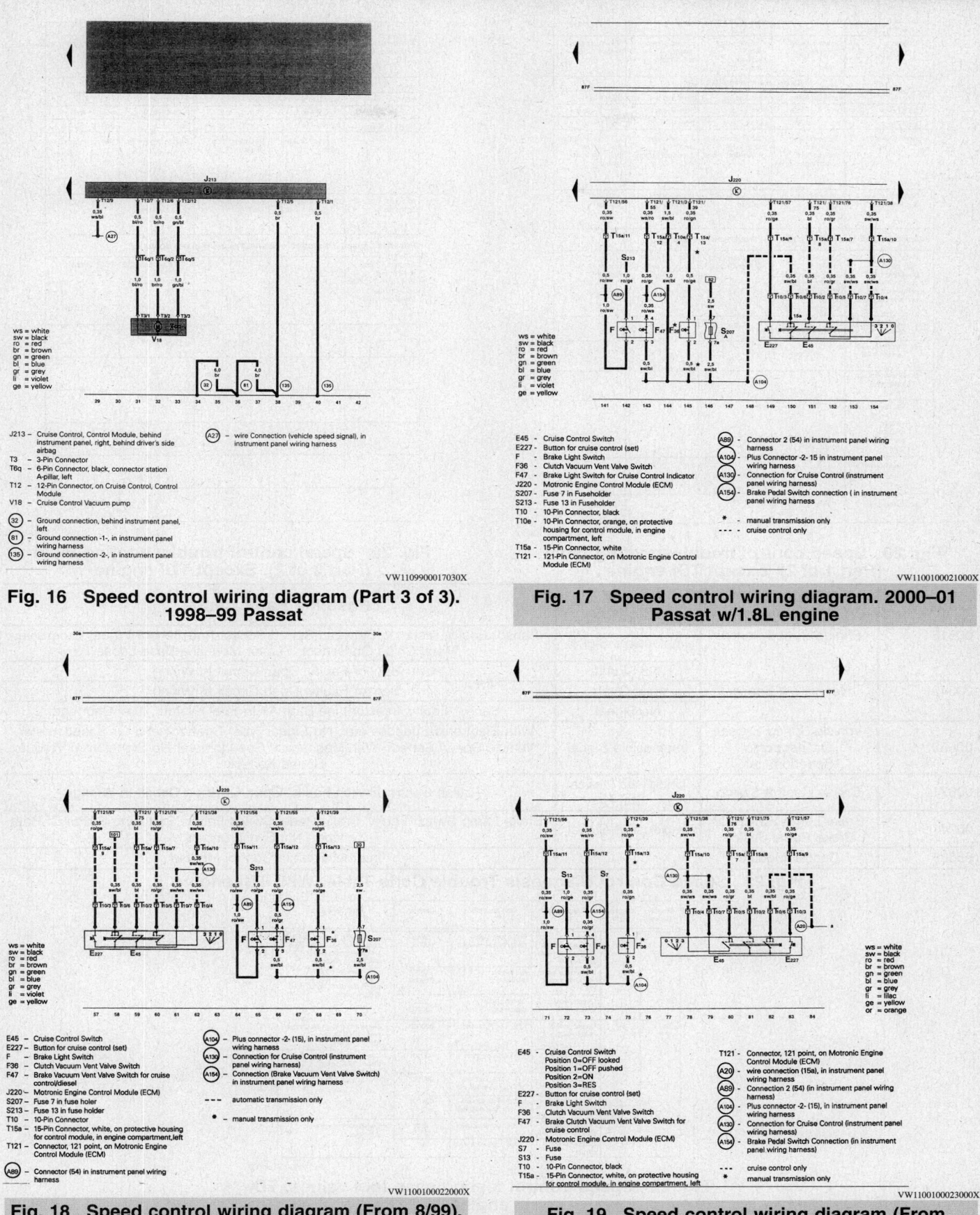

Fig. 16 Speed control wiring diagram (Part 3 of 3). 1998–99 Passat

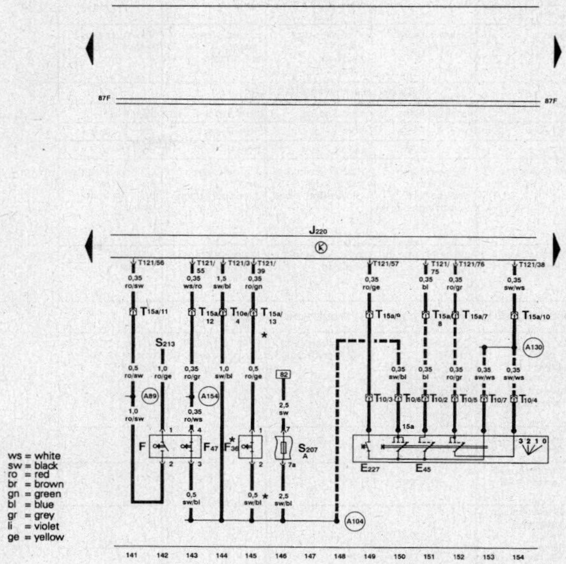

- E45 - Cruise Control Switch
- E227 - Button for cruise control (set)
- F - Brake Light Switch
- F36 - Clutch Vacuum Vent Valve Switch
- F47 - Brake Light Switch for Cruise Control Indicator
- J220 - Motronic Engine Control Module (ECM)
- S207 - Fuse 7 in Fuseholder
- S213 - Fuse 13 in Fuseholder
- T10 - 10-Pin Connector, black
- T10e - 10-Pin Connector, orange, on protective housing for control module, in engine compartment, left
- T15a - 15-Pin Connector, white
- T121 - 121-Pin Connector, on Motronic Engine Control Module (ECM)
- (A89) - Connector 2 (54) in instrument panel wiring harness
- (A104) - Plus Connector -2- 15 in instrument panel wiring harness
- (A130) - Connection for Cruise Control (instrument panel wiring harness)
- (A154) - Brake Pedal Switch connection (in instrument panel wiring harness
- * - manual transmission only
- - - - cruise control only

VW1100100021000X

Fig. 17 Speed control wiring diagram. 2000–01 Passat w/1.8L engine

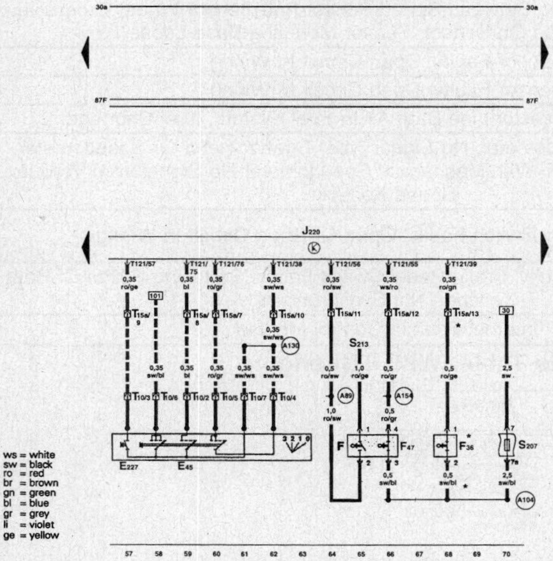

- E45 – Cruise Control Switch
- E227 – Button for cruise control (set)
- F – Brake Light Switch
- F36 – Clutch Vacuum Vent Valve Switch
- F47 – Brake Vacuum Vent Valve Switch for cruise control/diesel
- J220 – Motronic Engine Control Module (ECM)
- S207 – Fuse 7 in fuse holer
- S213 – Fuse 13 in fuse holder
- T10 – 10-Pin Connector
- T15a – 15-Pin Connector, white, on protective housing for control module, in engine compartment,left
- T121 – Connector, 121 point, on Motronic Engine Control Module (ECM)
- (A89) – Connector (54) in instrument panel wiring harness
- (A104) – Plus connector -2- (15), in instrument panel wiring harness
- (A130) – Connection for Cruise Control (instrument panel wiring harness)
- (A154) – Connection (Brake Vacuum Vent Valve Switch) in instrument panel wiring harness
- - - - automatic transmission only
- • – manual transmission only

VW1100100022000X

Fig. 18 Speed control wiring diagram (From 8/99). 2000–01 Passat w/2.8L engine

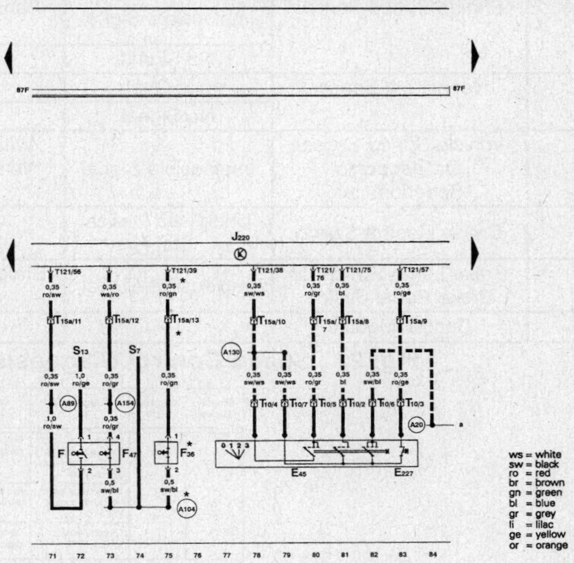

- E45 - Cruise Control Switch
  - Position 0=OFF looked
  - Position 1=OFF pushed
  - Position 2=ON
  - Position 3=RES
- E227 - Button for cruise control (set)
- F - Brake Light Switch
- F36 - Clutch Vacuum Vent Valve Switch
- F47 - Brake Clutch Vacuum Vent Valve Switch for cruise control
- J220 - Motronic Engine Control Module (ECM)
- S7 - Fuse
- S13 - Fuse
- T10 - 10-Pin Connector, black
- T15a - 15-Pin Connector, white, on protective housing for control module, in engine compartment, left
- T121 - Connector, 121 point, on Motronic Engine Control Module (ECM)
- (A20) - wire connection (15a), in instrument panel wiring harness
- (A89) - Connection 2 (54) (in instrument panel wiring harness)
- (A104) - Plus connector -2- (15), in instrument panel wiring harness
- (A130) - Connection for Cruise Control (instrument panel wiring harness)
- (A154) - Brake Pedal Switch Connection (in instrument panel wiring harness)
- - - - cruise control only
- * manual transmission only

VW1100100023000X

Fig. 19 Speed control wiring diagram (From 10/2000). 2000–01 Passat w/2.8L engine

Checking step:	1	2	3	4
Check:	Power supply (terminal 15)	Cruise control switch position "reset"	Cruise control switch set button	Vehicle speed sensor (VSS)
Connector assignment VAG 1466:				
red wire	from 9 to S+	from 5 to S+	from 8 to S+	from 9 to S+
black wire	from S− to L+	from S− to L+	from S− to L+	from S− to D+
blue wire	from L− to 4	from L− to 4	from L− to 4	from D− to 7
Additional steps:	Cruise control switch into position "on" Switch ingnition on	Push cruise control switch to left into position "reset"	Cruise control switch press set button	Lift front of vehicle and turn or push left front wheel
Specified value/ test result:	Indicator lamp (L) lights up	Indicator lamp (L) lights up	Indicator lamp (L) lights up	LED (D) flashes

Possible causes if specified value/test result was not obtained:

Wiring relay panel/ component or component/ component or component/ground	S 51 or D/11 to E 45 or E 45, contact 1 to J 213, contact 12/9 or J 213, contact 12/4 to ground	E45, contact 2 to J 213, contact 12/5	E 45, contact 3 to J 213, contact 12/8	W/1 to J 213, contact 12/7 or U2/2 to K
or Cruise control switch	X	X	X	--
or Vehicle speed sensor (VSS)	--	--	--	X
or Brake vacuum vent valve switch	--	--	--	--
or Clutch vacuum vent valve switch manual transmission only	--	--	--	--
or Cruise control vacuum pump	--	--	--	--
or Relay panel	X	--	--	X

VW1109500010010X

Fig. 20 Speed control troubleshooting table (Part 1 of 2). Except TDI engine

	5	6	7	8	9
Check:	Brake vacuum vent valve switch,	Brake vacuum vent valve switch,	Clutch vacuum vent valve switch,	Cruise control vacuum pump	Cruise control vacuum pump
Connector assignment VAG 1466:					
red wire	from 9 to S+	from 9 to S+	from 9 to S+	from 9 to S+	from 1 to 9
black wire	from S− to L+	from S− to L+	from S− to L+	from S− to 2	from 11 to D+
blue wire	from L− to 3	from L− to 3	from L− to 3	from 11 to 4	from D− to 4
Additional steps:	--	Depress brake pedal	Depress clutch pedal	Switch on ignition	Switch on ignition
Specified value/ test result:	Indicator lamp (L) lights up	Indicator lamp (L) goes out	Indicator lamp (L) goes out	Cruise control vacuum pump V 18 runs	LED (D) lights up

Possible causes if specified value/test result was not obtained:

Wiring	Contact 12/3 to F 47 or F 47 to W/4 (or F 47 to F 36 with manual transmission)	--	--	J 213, contact 12/2 to V 18 or J 213, contact 12/1 to V 18	J 213, contact 12/11 to V 18
or Cruise control switch	--	--	--	--	--
or Vehicle speed sensor (VSS)	--	--	--	--	--
or Brake vacuum vent valve switch	X	X	--	--	--
or Clutch vacuum vent valve switch manual transmission only	--	--	X	X	X
or Cruise control vacuum pump	--	--	X	--	X
or Relay panel	X	--	X	X	--

VW1109500010020X

Fig. 20 Speed control troubleshooting table (Part 2 of 2). Except TDI engine

Code	Related Component	Fault Indication	Possible Fault Cause
00513	Engine Speed Sensor	Implausible Signal	Sensor Faulty, Distance Between Speed Sensor And Sensor Wheel Excessive, Metal Chips On Sensor, Sensor Mounting Base Loose
		No Signal	Sensor Faulty, Open Circuit In Wiring
00542	Needle Lift Sensor	Inlet Open	Sensor Faulty, Open Circuit In Wiring
		No Signal	Sensor Faulty, Injector Line Bad, Air In Fuel System, Fuel Shortage
00652	Vehicle Speed Sensor Or Electronic Speedometer	Implausible Signal	With Electronic Speedometer, No Signal From Speedometer Or Speedometer Vehicle Speed Sensor. With Mechanical Speedometer No Signal from Vehicle Speed Sensor
00671	Cruise Control Switch	Undefined Switch State	Cruise Control Switch Faulty, Open Or Short Circuit In Wiring
00741	Brake Lamp Switch Or Brake Pedal Switch	Implausible Signal	Brake Lamp Switch Faulty, Brake Pedal Switch Faulty, Switching Points Of Both Switches Not Synchronized
65535	Control Module	—	Internal Fault In Control Module

Fig. 21 Speed Control Diagnosis Trouble Code Table. With TDI engine

Display Group	Display Field	Designation	Test conditions	Display	Fault correction
06	2 3	Brake pedal switch for cruise control (F47), clutch pedal switch (F36)	Brake and clutch pedal in rest position	000 000000	– Check wiring to brake pedal switch for cruise control (F47) and clutch pedal switch (F36) using wiring diagram – Check electrical function of cruise control switch (F47) and clutch pedal switch (F36) at brake pedal
		Brake pedal switch for cruise control (F47)	Brake pedal depressed	011 010000	
		Clutch pedal switch (F36)	Clutch pedal depressed	100 100000	
06	3	Cruise control switch (E45)	E45 in OFF position	000000	– Check wiring to cruise control switch (E45) using wiring diagram
		Cruise control switch (E45)	E45 in ON position	000001	– Check wiring to cruise control switch (E45) using wiring diagram
		Cruise control switch (E45)	E45 in ON position, SET button pressed	000101	
		Cruise control switch (E45)	E45 pushed toward left into RES position	001001	
	4	Cruise control status	Cruise control blocked	255	– Cruise control system activated
		Cruise control status	Cruise control activated	0	

VW1109300008000X

Fig. 22 Speed control testing scan tool values. TDI engine

Air Bag System

NOTE: "Electrical Symbol & Wire Color Code Identification" Located In The Front Of This Manual May Be Used As An Aid When Using Wiring Circuits Found In This Section.

NOTE: Prior To Performing Any Service Operations Listed In This Section, Consult The "Technical Service Bulletins" Section For Related Information.

INDEX

	Page No.
Air Bag System Disarming & Arming	8-99
Arming	8-99
Disarming	8-99
Collision Inspection	8-100
Air Bag System	8-101
Seat Belt Tensioning System	8-101
Component Locations	8-100
Component Service	8-101
Air Bag Assembly Disposal	8-107
Coding Control Module	8-101
Control Module Replace	8-104
Driver's Air Bag Module, Replace	8-102
Passenger's Air Bag Module, Replace	8-102
Seat Belt Tensioner Disposal	8-107
Seat Belt Tensioner, Replace	8-106
Side Impact Air Bag Module, Replace	8-103
Side Impact Air Bag Sensor, Replace	8-105
Spiral Spring, Replace	8-104
Description & Operation	8-99
Air Bag System	8-99
Seat Belt Tensioning System	8-99
Diagnosis & Testing	8-100
Precautions	8-99
Scheduled Maintenance	8-100
Air Bag System	8-100
Seat Belt Tensioning System	8-100
Technical Service Bulletins	8-107
Air Bag Control Module Coding Revisions	8-107
Use Of Stabilant 22A On Electrical Connections	8-107
Tightening Specifications	8-116
Wiring Diagrams	8-100

AIR BAG SYSTEM DISARMING & ARMING

Disarming

Do not use the computer memory saver tool on air bag equipped models. Using this tool will keep the system charged and may cause unwanted air bag unit activation. Obtain the radio security code prior to disconnecting the battery ground cable. After service has been completed and the cable connected, use this code to activate the radio.

To disarm air bag system, disconnect and isolate battery ground cable.

Arming

1. **Ensure nobody is in vehicle, then connect battery ground cable.**
2. Turn ignition On and note air bag warning lamp operation. Lamp should light for approximately three to eight seconds, then go off. If lamp fails to light or remains lit after eight seconds, refer to "Diagnosis & Testing."

DESCRIPTION & OPERATION

AIR BAG SYSTEM

The Supplemental Restraint System (SRS) is designed to supplement protection offered by seat belts in a frontal impact collision.

The SRS incorporates an on-board diagnostic feature. System faults or Diagnostic Trouble Codes (DTCs) detected are stored in the control unit memory. DTCs can be extracted from the memory using a scan tool No. VAG 1551, or equivalent.

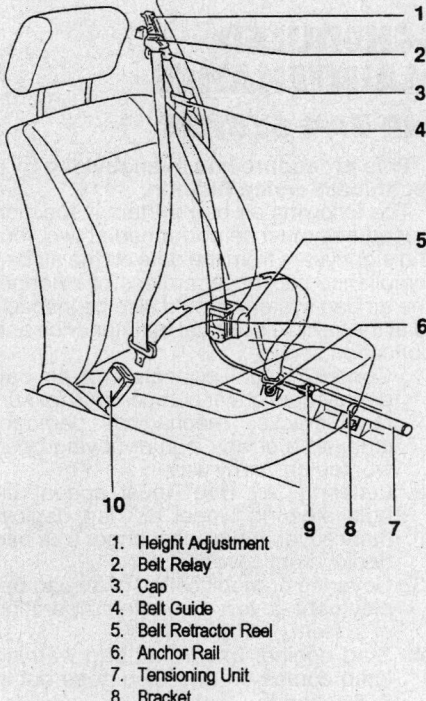

The Golf, New Beetle and Passat models are also equipped with a side air bag system. This system consist of an air bag module mounted to the outboard side of each front seat and two side impact sensors located under the passenger's and driver's front seats. The side air bag modules will deploy when a side impact of sufficient force is encountered.

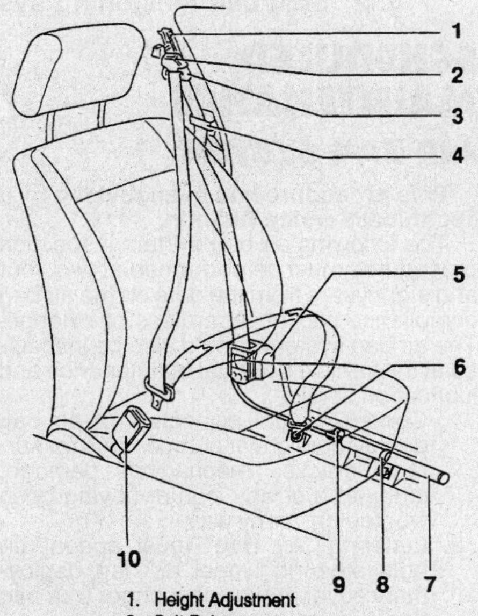

Fig. 1 Seat belt tensioning system components. Cabrio

SEAT BELT TENSIONING SYSTEM

Cabrio

The seat belt tensioning system is designed to remove slack from the seat belt system when a collision of sufficient force occurs, **Fig. 1.** The system uses inertia-fired pyrotechnic cylinders operating on the seat belts through a cable.

Golf, GTI & Jetta

On these models the seat belt tensioning system will remove seat belt system slack if a collision of sufficient force occurs. Inertia-fired pyrotechnic devices act upon the belt retractors, **Fig. 2.**

New Beetle & Passat

The seat belt tensioners will be activated when the vehicle is involved in a collision of sufficient force.

PRECAUTIONS

1. SRS must be disarmed prior to disconnecting any system electrical connectors, servicing any system components or other items located near any system electrical connectors. Refer to "Air Bag System Disarming & Arming."

2. Seat belt tensioning system must be removed from vehicle before performing any welding, body disassembly, straightening or other bodywork.
3. **Do not use impact-driven or hammer-action tools when servicing seat belt tensioning system components.**
4. Obtain radio security code prior to disconnecting battery ground cable. After service has been completed and cable connected, use this code to activate radio. Reset clock at this time.
5. Air bag units must be inspected on regular basis. Refer to "Scheduled Maintenance" for inspection procedure.
6. SRS inspection is never conducted with test lamp, voltmeter or analog ohmmeter. Use scan tool No. VAG 1551, or equivalent, and inspect system in installed condition.
7. SRS or seat belt tensioning components must not be opened or repaired. Always use new components.
8. If air bag unit, seat belt tensioning unit or triggering unit has been dropped 18 inches or more, do not install component into vehicle. These units must be replaced.
9. Always replace SRS or seat belt tensioning components that have been mechanically damaged (i.e., bubbles, cracks, cigarette burns, dents, webbing tears, etc.).
10. Do not use computer memory saver tool on air bag equipped models. Using this tool will keep system charged and may cause accidental unit activation.
11. Do not leave undeployed air bag or seat belt tensioning unit unattended if work is interrupted. Install component into vehicle as soon as unit is removed from packaging.
12. Always place removed air bag unit so it rests on its metal housing and pad faces upward.
13. Air bag or seat belt tensioning units must not be exposed to grease, or cleaned with any type of cleaning agent.
14. Do not paint air bag units to correct cosmetic flaws. They must be replaced.
15. Do not expose air bag or seat belt tensioning units to temperatures of more than 194°F for even brief periods. Keep units clear of all heat sources.
16. Deployed air bag or seat belt tensioning units do not have to be disposed of as hazardous waste, but may be discarded with other automotive scrap for recycling.
17. Triggering units contain mercury switch and must be disposed of in approved manner.
18. To avoid electrostatic discharge damage to air bag system and other system components, always touch suitable metal component prior to handling component.
19. Do not install non-original or aftermarket seat upholstery or trim. Use only manufacturer's original equipment. Any other type may cause interference with side impact air bag system.

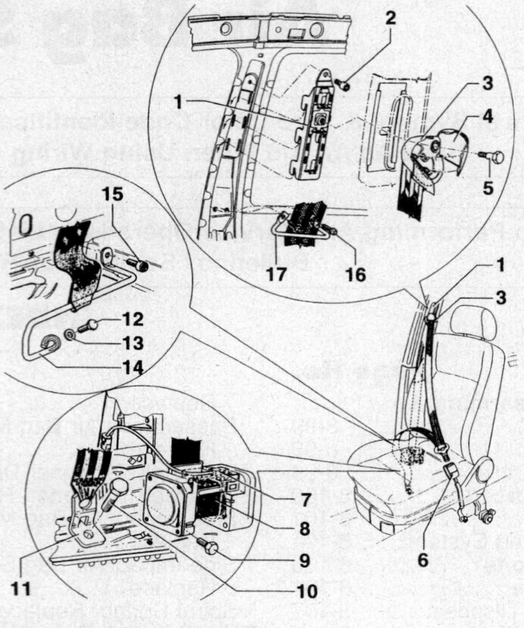

(1-belt height adjuster; 2-bolt; 3-belt relay; 4-guide cover cap; 5-bolt; 6-belt lock; 7-electrical connector; 8-belt; 9 & 10-bolts; 11-lower belt mount [4-door models]; 12-bolt [2-door models]; 13-washer [2-door models]; 14-belt guide [2-door models]; 15-cap screw [4-door models]; 16-guide screws; 17-belt guide)

VW8019900052000X

Fig. 2 Seat belt tensioning system components. Golf, GTI & Jetta

SCHEDULED MAINTENANCE

AIR BAG SYSTEM

This procedure has been revised by a Technical Service Bulletin.

The following air bag system inspection procedures must be performed at two, four and eight years from the date on the air bag compliance sticker regardless of mileage. The air bag system should also be inspected at the vehicle's annual maintenance and lubrication service.

1. Conduct visual inspection of air bag deployment cover components for surface cracks, mechanical damage, glue, tape or any sign of having been worked on in any way.
2. Lettering "Air Bag" must appear on both steering wheel air bag deployment cover and on passenger's air bag deployment cover.
3. Covering or modification of air bag deployment covers can affect operation of system.
4. Start engine. Ensure air bag warning lamp comes on and then goes out in 3–8 seconds.
5. Road test vehicle. Ensure air bag warning lamp does not come on or flicker.
6. Inspect air bag control module to ensure it is properly mounted.

SEAT BELT TENSIONING SYSTEM

Do not use impact-driven or hammer-action tools when servicing seat belt tensioning system components.

The pyrotechnic seat belt tensioner propellent has no expiration date and requires no scheduled maintenance.

A visual inspection of gas generator tube, tensioning cable and belts for damage should be performed on a regular basis.

WIRING DIAGRAMS

Refer to **Figs. 3 through 14** for SRS wiring diagrams.

COMPONENT LOCATIONS

Refer to **Figs. 15 through 17** for SRS and seat belt tensioning system component locations.

DIAGNOSIS & TESTING

Refer to **MOTOR'S "Air Bag Manual"** for complete diagnosis and testing information.

COLLISION INSPECTION

On vehicles which have experienced an air bag system or seat belt tensioning system deployment, certain system

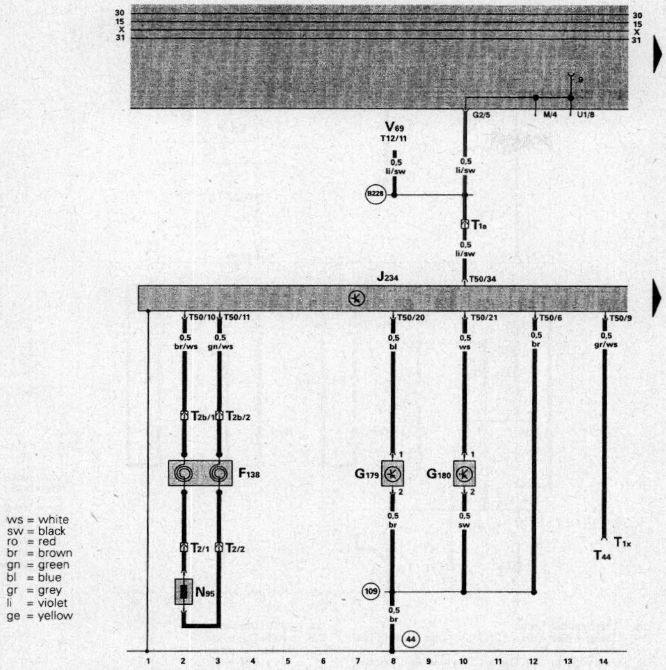

F138 - Airbag Spiral Spring/Return Spring w. Slip Ring
G179 - Crash sensor for side airbag, driver's side
G180 - Crash sensor for side airbag, passenger side
J234 - Airbag Control Module
N 95 - Driver's Side Airbag Igniter
T1a - Single Connector
T1x - Single Connector
T2 - 2-Pin Connector
T2b - 2-Pin Connector, near steering column
T50 - 50-Pin Connector
T44 - Junction Box for Data Link Connector (DLC), above fuse/relay panel
V69 - Central Locking System Pump and Control Module
(44) - Ground connection, on left A-pillar, lower part
(109) - Ground connection, in airbag wiring harness
(B228) - Connection (Crash-Signal) (interior wiring harness)

VW9040000331010X

Fig. 3 SRS wiring diagram (Part 1 of 2). Cabrio from August 1998

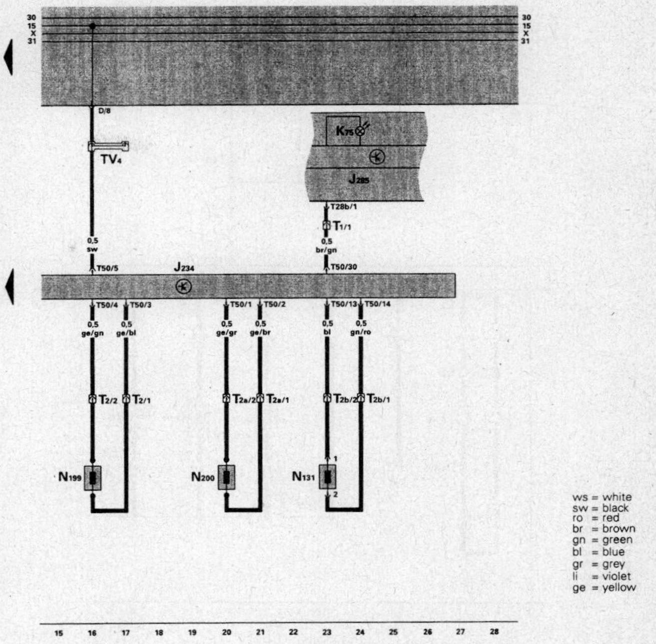

J234 - Airbag Control Module
J285 - Control module with indicator unit in instrument panel insert
K75 - Airbag Malfunction Indicator Lamp (MIL)
N131 - Passenger's Side Airbag Igniter 1
N199 - Igniter for side airbag, driver's side
N200 - Igniter for side airbag, passenger side
T1 - Single connector
T2 - 2-Pin Connector
T2a - 2-Pin Connector
T2b - 2-Pin Connector
T28b - 28-Pin Connector, on instrument panel insert
T50 - 50-Pin Connector
TV4 - Terminal 15 Wire Connector

VW9040000331020X

Fig. 3 SRS wiring diagram (Part 2 of 2). Cabrio from August 1998

components must be replaced. To determine which components require replacement, refer to the "General Information" section located at the front of this manual.

AIR BAG SYSTEM

To ensure proper system operation on any vehicle involved in a collision, perform procedures outlined under "Diagnosis & Testing." All system components should be inspected for dents, cracks, exposure to excessive heat and other damage. All air bag system wiring should be inspected for chafing and interference with other vehicle components. The instrument panel should also be inspected. The system should be disarmed as outlined under "Air Bag System Disarming & Arming" when repairing the vehicle. Do not expose components or wiring to heat guns, welding or spray guns when performing service procedures.

SEAT BELT TENSIONING SYSTEM

To ensure proper system operation on any vehicle involved in a collision both seat belts must be replaced if one or both belts were activated during an accident.

If tensioners were not activated, system components should be inspected for damage.

COMPONENT SERVICE

The air bag system must be disarmed prior to disconnecting any air bag system electrical connectors or servicing any system components or other components located near any air bag system electrical connectors. Refer to "Air Bag System Arming & Disarming."

Do not use a computer memory saver tool on air bag equipped models. Using this tool will keep the air bag system charged and may cause accidental unit activation.

Obtain the radio security code prior to disconnecting the battery ground cable. After service has been completed and the cable connected, use this code to activate the radio.

CODING CONTROL MODULE

If the air bag module is not coded, the Malfunction Indicator Lamp (MIL) will remain lit continuously. When the on-board diagnosis program is actuated, the scan tool will display an improper coding for the air bag system installed on the vehicle. This procedure must also be performed when installing a replacement air bag module.

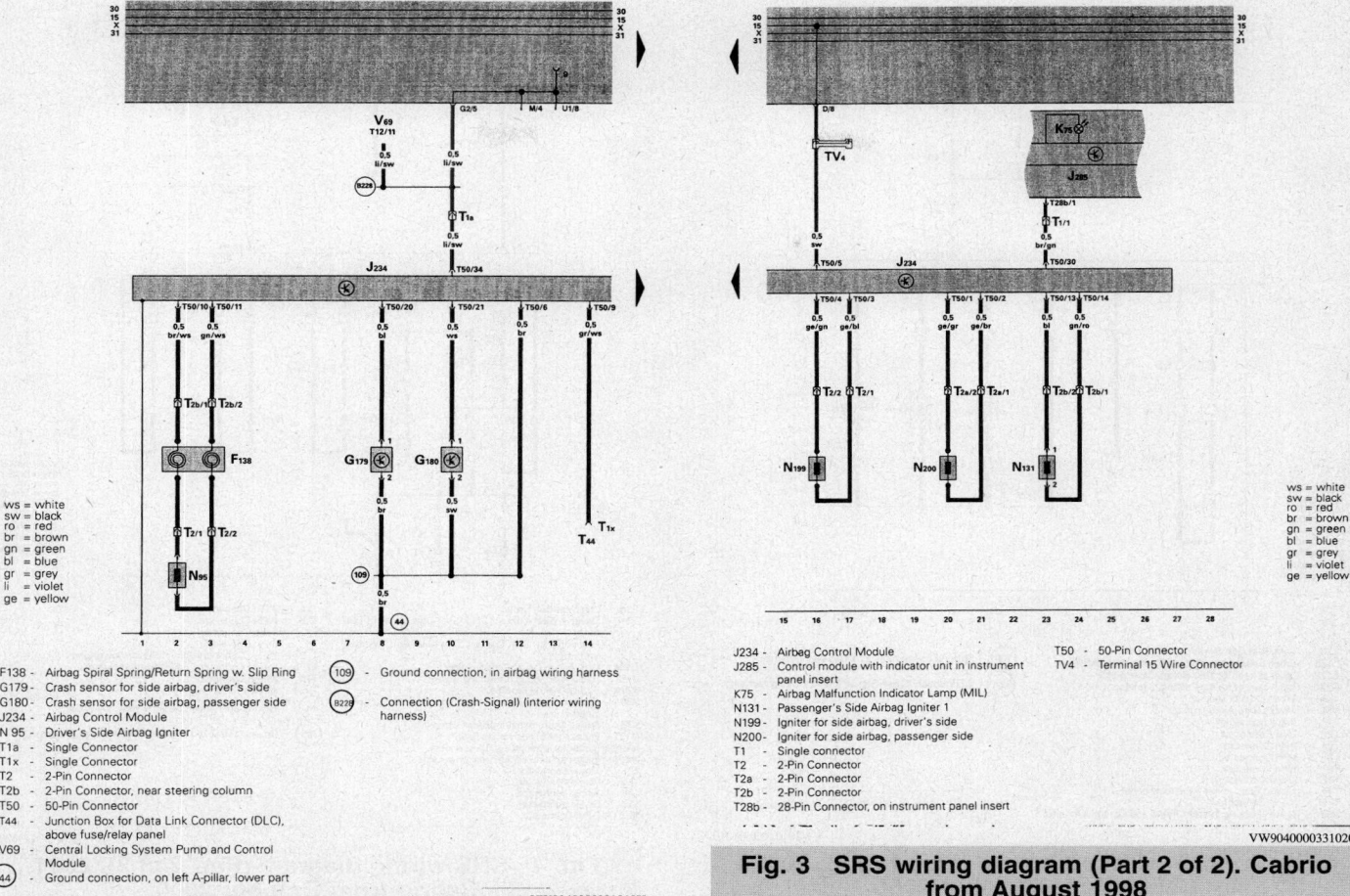

1. Turn ignition On, then depress scan tool button 1 to access Rapid Data Transfer.
2. Press scan tool buttons 1 and 5 to insert address word air bag, then press button Q to enter data.
3. After five seconds, the air bag control module number will appear on the display.
4. Press scan tool button with arrow symbol inscription.
5. Press scan tool buttons 0 and 7 to select code control module, then press button Q to enter data.
6. Scan tool will indicate code control module enter code number.
7. Index letters are same as part number suffixes. For example, part No. 1J0 909 608 AQ has index of AQ.
8. Enter code, **Fig. 18,** using key pad.
9. Press scan tool button Q to confirm input.
10. Control module serial No. and code number should be displayed on scan tool.
11. Inspect and clear DTC memory.
12. Depress scan tool buttons 0 and 6 to select end output function 06, then depress Q button to confirm input. The

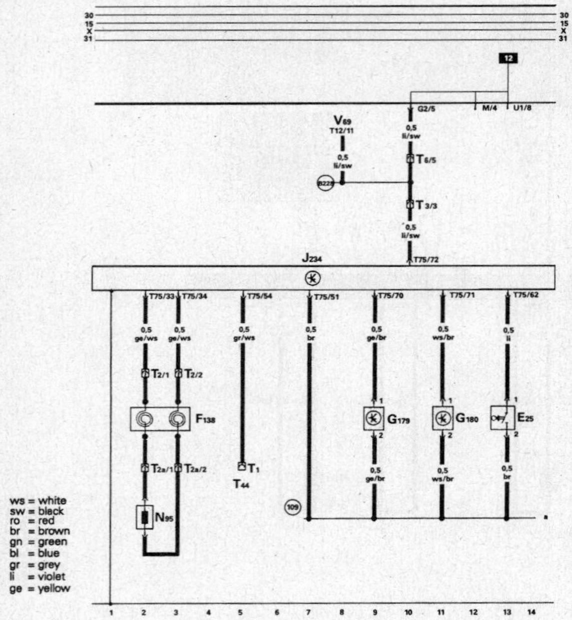

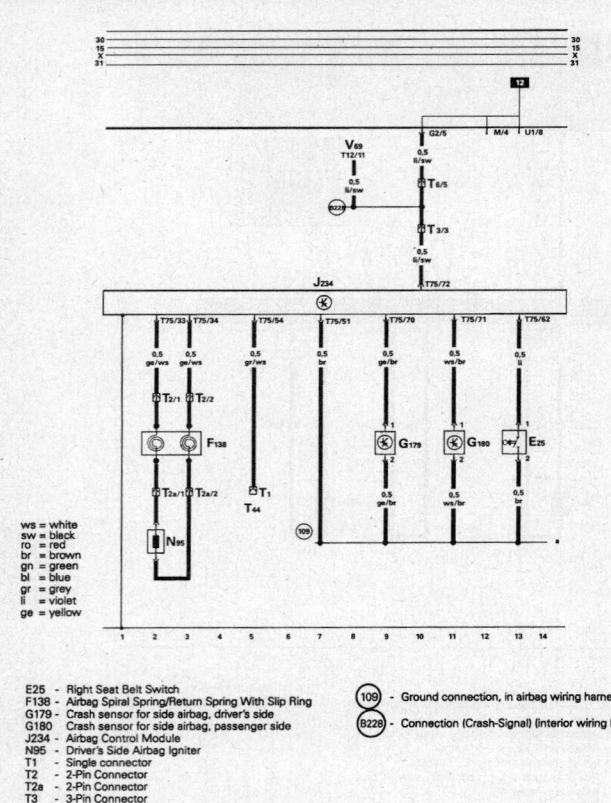

E25 - Right Seat Belt Switch
F138 - Airbag Spiral Spring/Return Spring With Slip Ring
G179 - Crash sensor for side airbag, driver's side
G180 Crash sensor for side airbag, passenger side
J234 - Airbag Control Module
N95 - Driver's Side Airbag Igniter
T1 - Single connector
T2 - 2-Pin Connector
T2a - 2-Pin Connector
T3 - 3-Pin Connector
T6 - 6-Pin Connector
T12 - 12-Pin Connector
T44 - Juntion Box , above fuse/relay panel
T75 - 75-Pin Connector
V69 - Central Locking System Pump and Control Module

(109) - Ground connection, in airbag wiring harness
(B228) - Connection (Crash-Signal) (interior wiring harness)

VW8010100079010X

Fig. 4 SRS wiring diagram (Part 1 of 2). 2001 Cabrio from October 2000

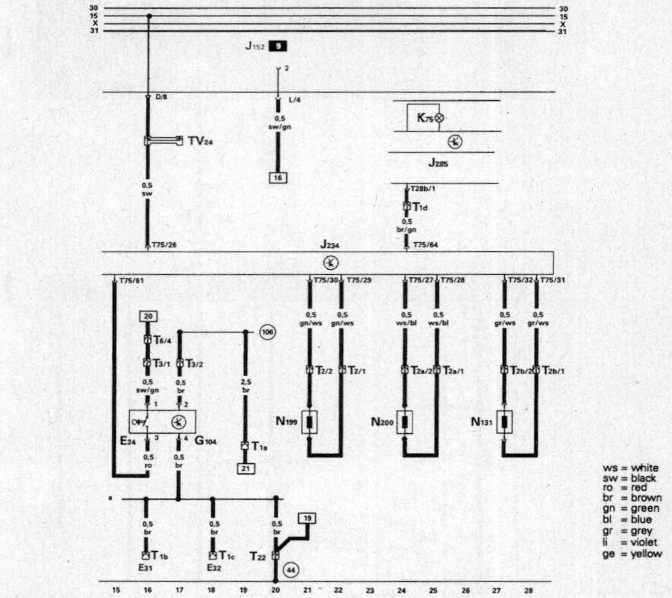

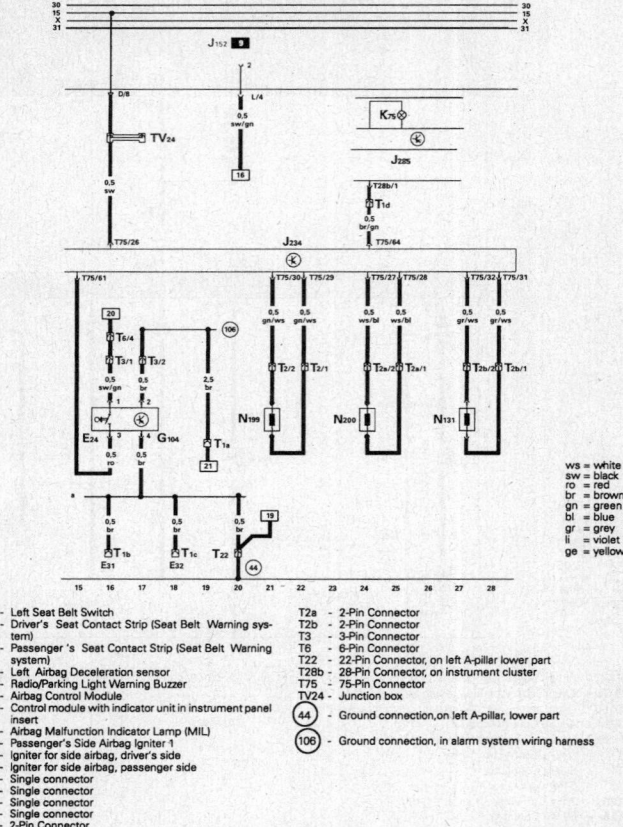

E24 - Left Seat Belt Switch
E31 - Driver's Seat Contact Strip (Seat Belt Warning system)
E32 - Passenger 's Seat Contact Strip (Seat Belt Warning system)
G104 - Left Airbag Deceleration sensor
J152 - Radio/Parking Light Warning Buzzer
J234 - Airbag Control Module
J285 - Control module with indicator unit in instrument panel insert
K75 - Airbag Malfunction Indicator Lamp (MIL)
N131 - Passenger's Side Airbag Igniter 1
N199 - Igniter for side airbag, driver's side
N200 - Igniter for side airbag, passenger side
T1a - Single connector
b - Single connector
c - Single connector
T1d - Single connector
T2 - 2-Pin Connector
T2a - 2-Pin Connector
T2b - 2-Pin Connector
T3 - 3-Pin Connector
T6 - 6-Pin Connector
T22 - 22-Pin Connector, on left A-pillar lower part
T28b - 28-Pin Connector, on instrument cluster
T75 - 75-Pin Connector
TV24 - Junction box

(44) - Ground connection,on left A-pillar, lower part
(106) - Ground connection, in alarm system wiring harness

VW8010100079020X

Fig. 4 SRS wiring diagram (Part 2 of 2). 2001 Cabrio from October 2000

scan tool should return to Basic.

DRIVER'S AIR BAG MODULE, REPLACE

CABRIO, EUROVAN & 1998 GOLF, GTI & JETTA

Removal

1. Disarm air bag system as outlined under "Air Bag System Disarming & Arming."
2. Ensure front wheels are in straight-ahead position.
3. Remove socket-head bolts, then carefully lift air bag unit from wheel, **Fig. 19.**
4. Disconnect red connector from air bag unit.
5. **Place air bag unit so it rests on its metal housing with horn pad facing upward.**

Installation

1. Connect electrical connector to air bag unit, then position unit to steering wheel.
2. Install fasteners and tighten bolts to specifications.
3. Arm SRS as outlined under "Air Bag System Disarming & Arming."

NEW BEETLE, PASSAT & 1999–2001 GOLF, GTI & JETTA

Removal

On models equipped with four-spoke steering wheel, the wheel and air bag module are of two different designs. One type has rectangular retaining studs to mount the modules. The other mounts with stepped pins. The stud type air bag module cannot be installed on a stepped pin wheel and vice versa. Ensure the components are compatible.

1. Disarm SRS as outlined under "Air Bag System Disarming & Arming."
2. Release steering column height adjustment.
3. Rotate steering wheel until spokes are in vertical position.
4. Pull steering column out completely, press into lowest position and lock into place.
5. Pry upward to release clip and locking lug by inserting suitable screwdriver approximately 1 ¾ inches into rear side of steering wheel, **Fig. 20.**
6. Rotate steering wheel 180° in opposite direction until spokes are in vertical position.
7. Release clip and locking lug by inserting suitable screwdriver into opposite side.
8. Rotate steering wheel into straight-ahead position.
9. Disconnect driver's air bag module electrical connector.
10. Remove driver's air bag module from steering wheel.

Installation

1. Connect electrical connector to air bag module.
2. Push air bag module into steering wheel until tabs lock securely into position.
3. Adjust steering column settings.
4. Arm SRS as outlined under "Air Bag System Disarming & Arming."

PASSENGER'S AIR BAG MODULE, REPLACE

CABRIO & 1998 GOLF, GTI & JETTA

1. Disarm SRS as outlined under "Air Bag System Disarming & Arming."
2. Remove screws, upper tabs and right-hand knee bar, then screws and air vent housing.
3. Remove hex bolts, then slide air bag cover to right and remove, **Fig. 21.**
4. Remove hex bolts, then lift air bag module and disconnect electrical connector.
5. Reverse procedure to install, tightening bolts to specifications. Arm SRS as

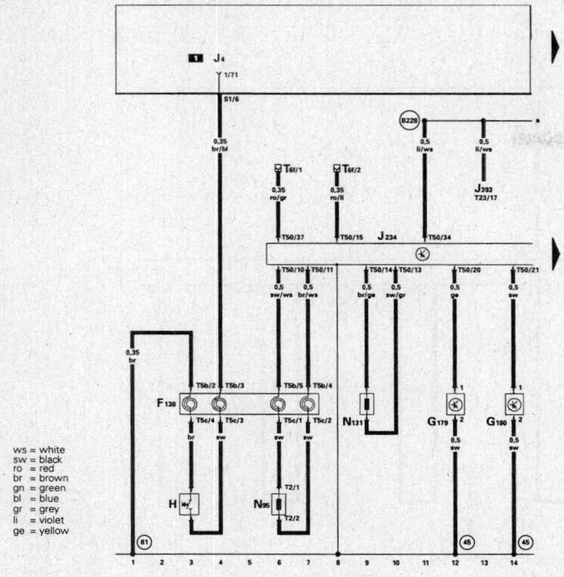

F138 – Airbag Spiral Spring/Return Spring With Slip Ring
G179 – Crash sensor for side airbag, driver's side
G180 – Crash sensor for side airbag, passenger side
H – Horn Button
J4 – Dual Horn Relay
J234 – Airbag Control Module, behind console
J393 – Central control module for comfort system
N95 – Driver's Side Airbag Igniter
N131 – Passenger's Side Airbag Igniter 1
T2 – Double Connector, yellow, on Airbag Igniter
T5b – 5-Pin Connector, yellow, near steering column on Airbag Spiral Spring/Return Spring
T5c – 5-Pin Connector, black, near steering column on Airbag Spiral Spring/Return Spring
T6f – 6-Pin Connector, below passenger's seat, red
T23 – 23-Pin Connector, on Central control module for comfort system
T50 – 50-Pin Connector
(45) – Ground connection, behind instrument panel, center
(81) – Ground connection -1-, in instrument panel wiring harness
(B228) – wire connection (crash), in instrument panel wiring harness

VW8019800037010X

Fig. 5 SRS wiring diagram (Part 1 of 2). 1998–99 New Beetle

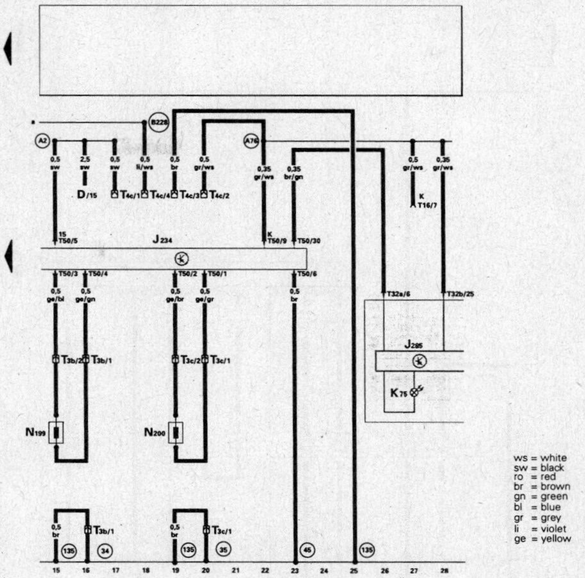

D – Ignition/Starter Switch
J234 – Airbag Control Module, behind console
J285 – Control module with indicator unit in instrument panel insert
K75 – Airbag Malfunction Indicator Lamp (MIL)
N199 – Igniter for side airbag, driver's side
N200 – Igniter for side airbag, passenger side
T3b – 3 –Pin Connector
T3c – 3 –Pin Connector
T4c – 4-Pin Connector
T16 – 16-Pin Connector, Data Link Connector (DLC) below steering column
T32a – 32-Pin Connector, blue, on instrument cluster
T32b – 32-Pin Connector, green, on instrument cluster
T50 – 50-Pin Connector
(34) – Ground connection below driver's seat
(35) – Ground connection, below passenger's side
(45) – Ground connection, behind instrument panel, center
(135) – Ground connection -2-, in instrument panel wiring harness
(A2) – plus connection (15), in instrument panel wiring harness
(A76) – Connector (K-diagnosis wire), in instrument panel wiring harness
(B228) – wire connection (crash), in instrument panel wiring harness

VW8019800037020X

Fig. 5 SRS wiring diagram (Part 2 of 2). 1998–99 New Beetle

outlined under "Air Bag System Disarming & Arming."

EUROVAN

1. Disarm SRS as outlined under "Air Bag System Disarming & Arming."
2. Carefully remove air vent grille using needle nose pliers.
3. Remove air vent grille housing retaining screw, then the housing.
4. Remove trim panel or radio from instrument panel.
5. Remove passenger's air bag module retaining bolts through radio and air vent grille openings, **Fig. 22.**
6. Disconnect passenger's air bag module electrical connector, then remove the module.
7. Reverse procedure to install, noting the following:
   a. Ensure wiring and connectors are properly routed to avoid pinching.
   b. Tighten mounting bolts and nuts to specifications.
   c. Arm SRS as outlined under "Air Bag System Disarming & Arming."

1999–2001 GOLF, GTI & JETTA

1. Disarm SRS as outlined under "Air Bag System Disarming & Arming."
2. Pull up passenger's air bag module cover and remove mounting nuts, **Fig. 23.**
3. Remove mounting bolts and air bag module from supports.
4. Disconnect air bag module electrical connector.
5. Remove passenger's air bag module from instrument panel.
6. Reverse procedure to install, noting the following:
   a. Push in air bag module cover until it fits flush with instrument panel.
   b. Tighten mounting bolts and nuts to specifications.
   c. Arm SRS as outlined under "Air Bag System Disarming & Arming."

NEW BEETLE & PASSAT

1. Disarm SRS as outlined under "Air Bag System Disarming & Arming."
2. Disengage passenger's air bag cover from retaining clips and lift up.
3. **On Passat models,** remove two passenger's air bag cover retaining nuts, then the cover.
4. **On all models,** remove passenger's air bag module retaining bolts.
5. Disconnect passenger's air bag module electrical connector, then the air bag module.
6. Reverse procedure to install, noting the following:
   a. Ensure wiring and connectors are properly routed to avoid pinching.
   b. Tighten mounting bolts and nuts to specifications.
   c. Arm SRS as outlined under "Air Bag System Disarming & Arming."

SIDE IMPACT AIR BAG MODULE, REPLACE

GOLF, GTI & JETTA

1. Disarm SRS as outlined under "Air Bag System Disarming & Arming."
2. Position front seat forward.
3. Remove cover and tunnel side track cover mounting screw, **Fig. 24.**
4. Lift up rear of cover and slide it to rear.
5. Remove mounting screw, cover and rocker panel side mounting screw.
6. Lift up rear of cover and slide it to rear.
7. Slide seat to rear and remove seat mounting bolts.
8. Slide seat back out of guide rails.
9. Disconnect side impact air bag system ignition and ground wire.
10. Disconnect side impact air bag module and seat electrical accessories electrical connectors, **Fig. 25.**
11. Insert air bag adapter tool No. VAS 5094, or equivalent, into connector housing.
12. Disconnect electrical connectors at seatback frame.
13. Separate seat backrest frame from base.
14. Remove side impact air bag module mounting bolts.
15. Disconnect side impact air bag module electrical connector.
16. Remove side impact air bag module.
17. Reverse procedure to install, noting the following:

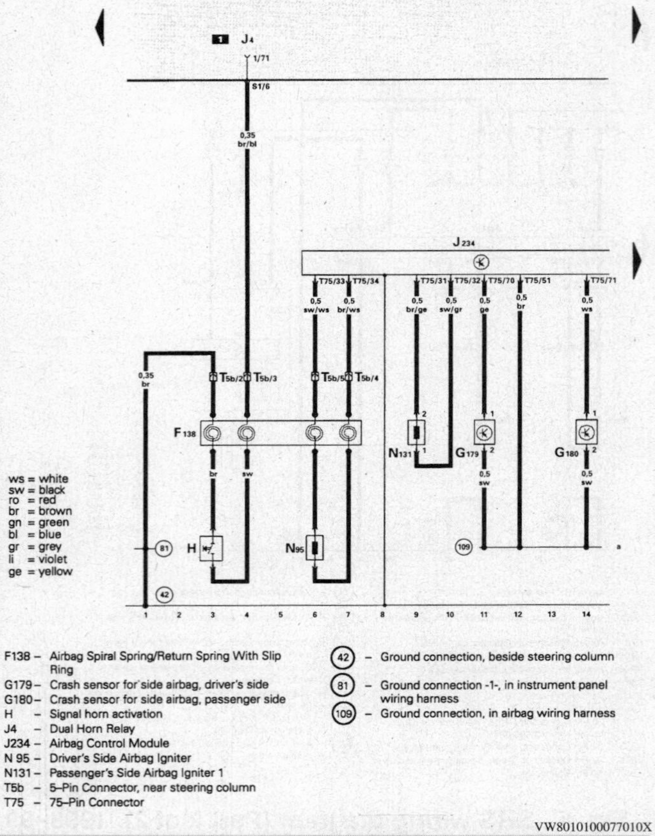

Fig. 6 SRS wiring diagram (Part 1 of 3). 2000–01 New Beetle from June 1999

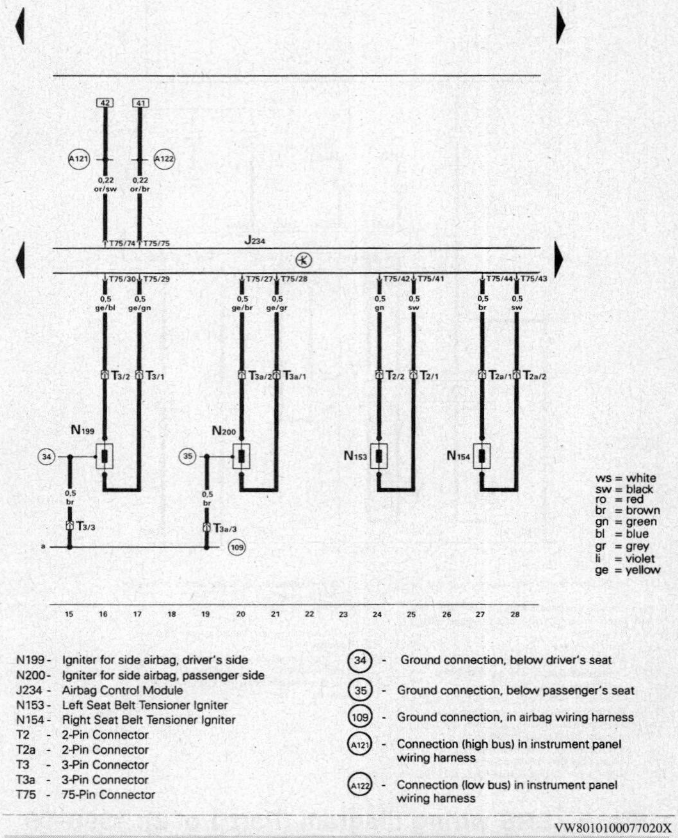

Fig. 6 SRS wiring diagram (Part 2 of 3). 2000–01 New Beetle from June 1999

a. Ensure wiring and connectors are properly routed to avoid pinching.
b. Tighten mounting bolts and nuts to specifications.
c. Arm SRS as outlined under "Air Bag System Disarming & Arming."

NEW BEETLE & PASSAT

1. Disarm SRS as outlined under "Air Bag System Disarming & Arming."
2. Position front seat forward, then unclip cover from inner and outer seat rail.
3. Slide seat to rear and remove front mounting bolts.
4. Slide seat back out of guide rails.
5. Disconnect side impact air bag system ignition and ground wire.
6. Disconnect seat heating and adjustment electrical connectors, as required.
7. Remove front seat.
8. Remove seat belt buckle.
9. Press off seat adjustment knob from side of seat.
10. Press four spreader pins inward and remove set adjustment lever.
11. Remove seat lower side trim cover from inboard side of seat.
12. Remove two mounting screws and seat outboard lower trim cover.
13. Disconnect seat backrest heater wiring.
14. Remove bolts from side of seat and seat backrest.
15. Release seat backrest cover in area of side impact air bag module.
16. Remove two side impact air bag module to seat frame mounting bolts, **Fig. 26.**
17. Disconnect electrical connector and remove side impact air bag module from seatback frame.
18. Reverse procedure to install, noting the following:
    a. Tighten mounting bolts to specifications.
    b. Arm SRS as outlined under "Air Bag System Disarming & Arming."

SPIRAL SPRING, REPLACE

1. Place steering wheel in straight-ahead position.
2. Disarm SRS as outlined under "Air Bag System Disarming & Arming."
3. Remove driver's air bag module as outlined under "Driver's Air Bag Module, Replace."
4. Place alignment marks on steering wheel hub and steering shaft for installation alignment.
5. Remove lower steering column trim, then pull foam tube off, as required, and disconnect electrical connectors.
6. Remove mount nut, washer and steering wheel using suitable steering wheel puller tool.
7. Remove horn connector from air bag spiral spring.
8. Remove mounting screws and air bag spiral spring.
9. Reverse procedure to install, noting the following:
    a. Ensure steering wheel is in straight-ahead position.
    b. New replacement air bag spiral springs are secured in neutral position with cable ties.
    c. Tighten mounting bolts, nuts and screws to specifications.
    d. Arm SRS as outlined under "Air Bag System Disarming & Arming."

CONTROL MODULE REPLACE

When the air bag control module is replaced, it must be coded. Refer to "Coding Control Module" under "Component Service" for procedure.

CABRIO & 1998 GOLF, GTI & JETTA

1. Disarm SRS as outlined under "Air Bag System Disarming & Arming."
2. Remove center console and footwell air outlet.
3. Cut carpeting and insulation in module mounting bracket area, if required.
4. Move connector lock and remove connector from module.
5. Remove nuts and module.
6. Reverse procedure to install, noting the following:

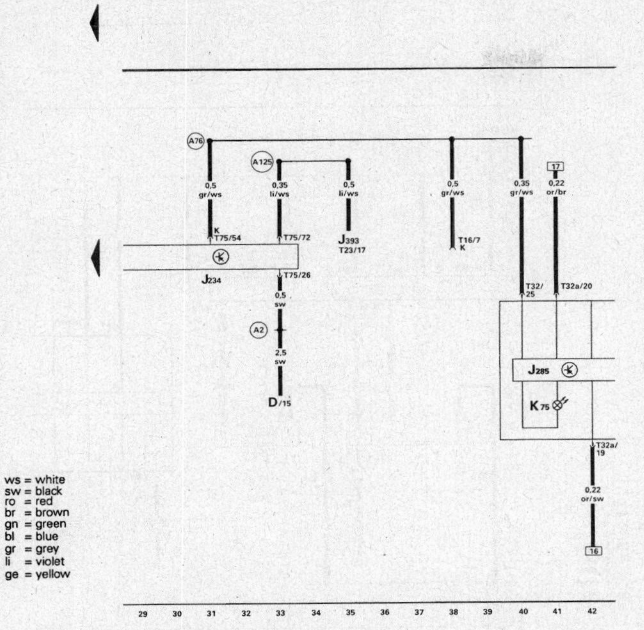

D - Ignition/Starter Switch
J234 - Airbag Control Module
J285 - Control module with indicator unit in instrument panel insert
J393 - Central control module for comfort system
K75 - Airbag Malfunction Indicator Lamp (MIL)
T16 - 16-Pin Connector, Data Link Connector (DLC), below steering column, left
T23 - 23-Pin Connector
T32 - 32-Pin Connector, blue, on instrument cluster
T32a - 32-Pin Connector, green, on instrument cluster

(A2) - plus connection (15), in instrument panel wiring harness
(A76) - Connection (K-diagnosis wire) in instrument
(A125) - Connection (crash signal) in instrument panel wiring harness

VW8010100077030X

Fig. 6 SRS wiring diagram (Part 3 of 3). 2000–01 New Beetle from June 1999

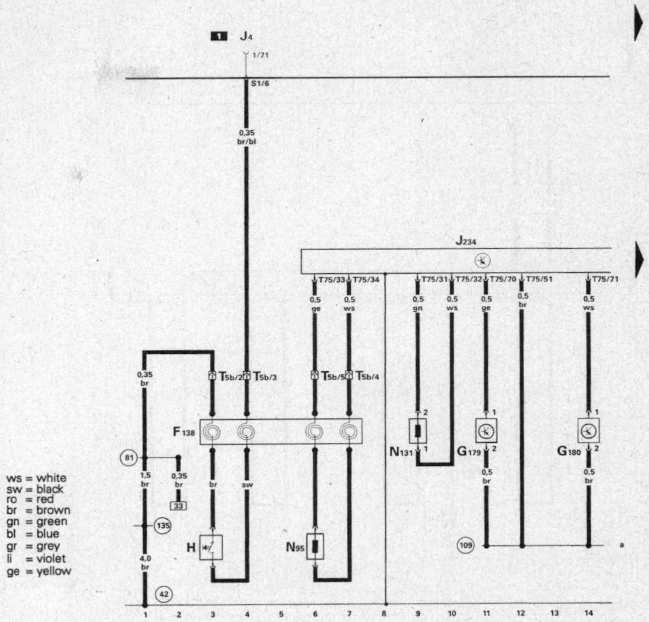

F138 - Airbag Spiral Spring/Return Spring With Slip Ring
G179 - Crash sensor for side airbag, driver's side
G180 - Crash sensor for side airbag, passenger side
H - Signal horn activation
J4 - Dual Horn Relay
J234 - Airbag Control Module
N 95 - Driver's Side Airbag Igniter
N131 - Passenger's Side Airbag Igniter 1
T5b - 5-Pin Connector, near steering column
T75 - 75-Pin Connector

(42) - Ground connection, beside steering column
(81) - Ground connection -1-, in instrument panel wiring harness
(109) - Ground connection, in airbag wiring harness
(135) - Ground connection -2-, in instrument panel wiring harness

VW8010100078010X

Fig. 7 SRS wiring diagram (Part 1 of 3). 2000–01 New Beetle from October 2000

a. Ensure wiring and connectors are properly routed to avoid pinching.
b. Tighten mounting bolts and nuts to specifications.
c. Arm SRS as outlined under "Air Bag System Disarming & Arming."

EUROVAN

1. Disarm SRS as outlined under "Air Bag System Disarming & Arming."
2. Remove center lower instrument panel trim and footwell air outlet.
3. Move connector lock and remove connector from module.
4. Remove nuts and module.
5. Reverse procedure to install. Tighten bolts to specifications. Arm SRS as outlined under "Air Bag System Disarming & Arming."

1999–2001 GOLF, GTI & JETTA

1. Disarm SRS as outlined under "Air Bag System Disarming & Arming."
2. Remove floor console lefthand side footwell trim.
3. Pull out in opposite direction of arrow on electrical connector locking bar, then disconnect connector from control module.
4. Remove mounting nuts and pull control module off its studs.
5. Reverse procedure to install, noting the following:
   a. Ensure wiring is properly routed to avoid pinching.
   b. Tighten mounting bolts and nuts to specifications.
   c. Arm SRS as outlined under "Air Bag System Disarming & Arming."

NEW BEETLE & PASSAT

1. Disarm SRS as outlined under "Air Bag System Disarming & Arming."
2. Remove center console and instrument panel center cover.
3. Move connector lock and remove connector from module.
4. Remove nuts and module.
5. Reverse procedure to install. Tighten bolts to specifications. Arm SRS as outlined under "Air Bag System Disarming & Arming."

SIDE IMPACT AIR BAG SENSOR, REPLACE

1999–2001 GOLF, GTI & JETTA

1. Disarm SRS as outlined under "Air Bag System Disarming & Arming."
2. Disconnect side impact air bag system igniter and ground wire.
3. Remove front seat and install adapter tool No. VAG 5061, No. VAS 5094, or equivalents into electrical connector housing.
4. Roll back carpet and insulation in area near side impact air bag sensor, as required.
5. Disconnect sensor electrical connector.
6. Remove mounting bolts and side impact air bag sensor.
7. Reverse procedure to install, noting the following:
   a. Ensure wiring is properly routed to avoid pinching.
   b. Tighten mounting bolts and nuts to specifications.
   c. Arm SRS as outlined under "Air Bag System Disarming & Arming."

NEW BEETLE & PASSAT

1. Disarm SRS as outlined under "Air Bag System Disarming & Arming."
2. Position front seat forward, then unclip cover from inner, then outer seat rail.
3. Slide seat to rear, then remove front seat attaching bolts.
4. Slide seatback out of guide rails.
5. Disconnect side air bag system ignition and ground wire. **To avoid electrostatic discharge damage to air bag system and other system components, technician should touch a suitable metal component prior to**

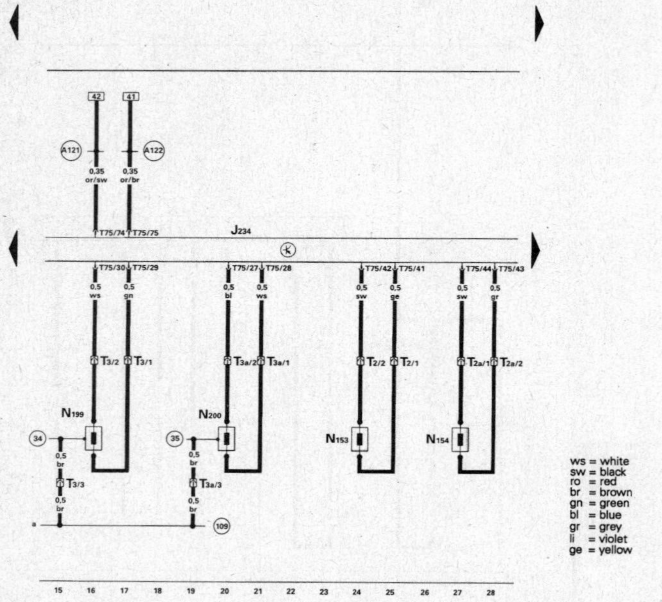

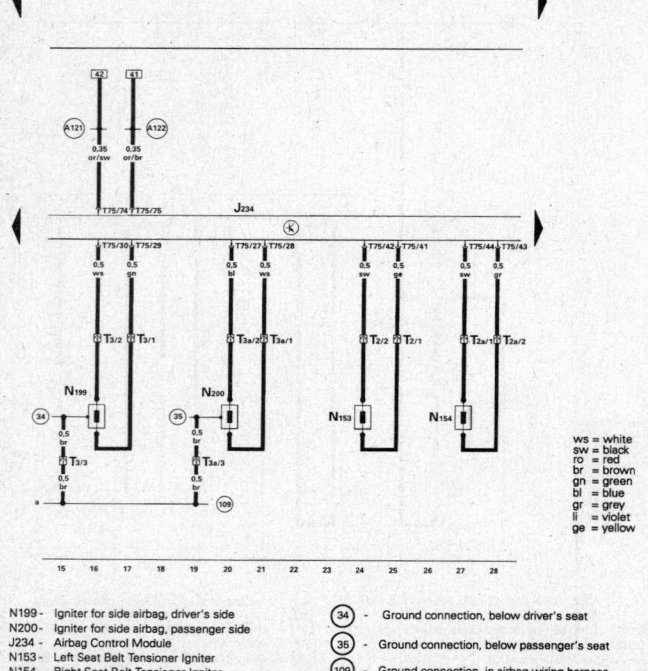

N199 - Igniter for side airbag, driver's side
N200 - Igniter for side airbag, passenger side
J234 - Airbag Control Module
N153 - Left Seat Belt Tensioner Igniter
N154 - Right Seat Belt Tensioner Igniter
T2 - 2-Pin Connector
T2a - 2-Pin Connector
T3 - 3-Pin Connector
T3a - 3-Pin Connector
T75 - 75-Pin Connector

(34) - Ground connection, below driver's seat
(35) - Ground connection, below passenger's seat
(109) - Ground connection, in airbag wiring harness
(A121) - Connection (high bus) in instrument panel wiring harness
(A122) - Connection (low bus) in instrument panel wiring harness

VW8010100078020X

Fig. 7 SRS wiring diagram (Part 2 of 3). 2000–01 New Beetle from October 2000

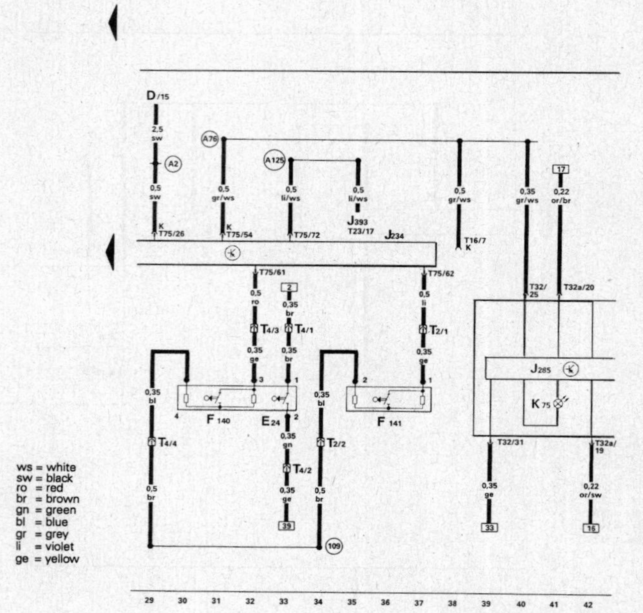

D - Ignition/Starter Switch
E24 - Left Seat Belt Switch
F140 - Left front seat belt micro switch
F141 - Right front seat belt micro switch
J234 - Airbag Control Module
J285 - Control module with indicator unit in instrument panel insert
J393 - Central control module for comfort system
K75 - Airbag Malfunction Indicator Lamp (MIL)
T2 - 2-Pin Connector
T4 - 4-Pin Connector
T16 - 16- Pin Connector, Data Link Connector (DLC), below steering column, left
T23 - 23-Pin Connector
T32 - 32-Pin Connector, blue, on instrument cluster
T32a - 32-Pin Connector, green, on instrument cluster
T75 - 75-Pin Connector

(A2) - plus connection (15), in instrument panel wiring harness
(A76) - Connection (K-diagnosis wire) in instrument
(A125) - Connection (crash signal) in instrument panel wiring harness
(109) - Ground connection, in airbag wiring harness

VW8010100078030X

Fig. 7 SRS wiring diagram (Part 3 of 3). 2000–01 New Beetle from October 2000

separating ignition and ground wire.

6. Disconnect seat heating and adjustment electrical connectors, if equipped.
7. Remove front seat from vehicle.
8. Connect adapter tool No. VAG 5061, or equivalent, to side air bag electrical connector.
9. Release carpet and insulation mat in area of side air bag sensor, **Fig. 27.**
10. Disconnect side air bag sensor electrical connector.
11. Remove side air bag sensor retaining screws, then the side air bag sensor.

SEAT BELT TENSIONER, REPLACE

CABRIO

1. Disarm SRS as outlined under "Air Bag System Disarming & Arming."
2. **On two-door models,** remove rear seat and rear quarter trim.
3. **On four-door models,** remove interior B-pillar trim and tensioner unit gas generator tube mounting nut.
4. **On all models,** disconnect anchor rail.
5. Disconnect upper belt mounting and guide.
6. Remove belt reel mounting bolt, unclip gas generator tube and lift assembly.
7. Reverse procedure to install, noting the following:
   a. Tighten mounting bolts to specifications.
   b. Arm SRS as outlined under "Air Bag System Disarming & Arming."

GOLF, GTI & JETTA

1. Disarm SRS as outlined under "Air Bag System Disarming & Arming."
2. Remove upper B-pillar trim.
3. Remove seat belt height adjuster.
4. Remove seat belt relay, **Fig. 2.**
5. Remove cover cap and belt guide bolt.
6. Disconnect seat belt tensioner electrical connector.
7. Remove lower B-pillar trim and sill panel trim.
8. Remove mounting bolts and tensioner.
9. Reverse procedure to install, noting the following:
   a. Ensure wiring is properly routed to avoid pinching.
   b. Tighten mounting bolts to specifications.
   c. Arm SRS as outlined under "Air Bag System Disarming & Arming."

NEW BEETLE & PASSAT

Front

1. Disarm SRS as outlined under "Air Bag System Disarming & Arming."
2. Remove upper B-pillar trim.
3. Remove seat belt relay, **Fig. 28.**
4. Remove seat belt guide.
5. Remove lower B Pillar trim and sill panel trim.
6. Remove lugs determining position of seat belt retractor.
7. Remove seat belt retractor mounting bolt, noting the following:
   a. **Loosening seat belt tensioner mounting bolts makes belt tensioner safe.**
   b. **Tightening seat belt tensioner mounting bolts makes tensioner functional.**
8. Remove seat belt and tensioner.
9. Reverse procedure to install, noting the following:
   a. Tighten mounting bolts to specifications.
   b. Arm SRS as outlined under "Air Bag System Disarming & Arming."

Rear

1. Disarm SRS as outlined under "Air Bag System Disarming & Arming."
2. Release rear seat backrest and fold forward.
3. Loosen nut and striker bolt.
4. Pull upper area of padding out of clip, press lower locking lug to rear and pull up.

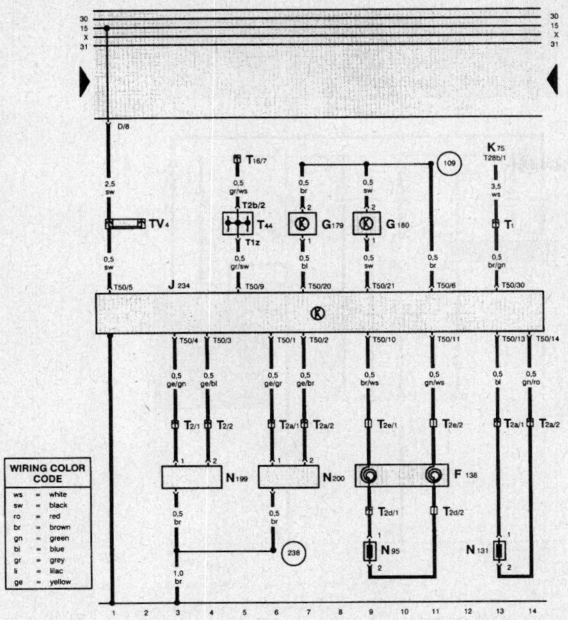

F138 – Airbag Spiral Spring /Return Spring with Slip Ring
G179 – Crash Sensor for Side Airbag, Driver's Side
G180 – Crash Sensor for Side Airbag, Passenger's Side
J234 – Airbag Control Module
K75 – Airbag Malfunction Indicator Light (MIL), in Instrument Cluster
N95 – Driver's Side Airbag Igniter
N131 – Passenger's Side Airbag Igniter 1
N199 – Igniter for Side Airbag, Driver's Side
N200 – Igniter for Side Airbag, Passenger's Side
T1 – Single Connector, behind instrument panel, center
T1z – Single Connector, next to fuse/relay panel
T2 – Double Connector, on airbag wiring harness
T2a – Double Connector, on airbag wiring harness
T2b – Double Connector, next to fuse/relay panel
T2c – Double Connector, on airbag wiring harness
T2d – Double Connector, on airbag wiring harness
T2e – Double Connector, on airbag wiring harness
T16 – Data Link Connector, behind center of dash
T44 – Junction Block for On-board Diagnosis, next to fuse/relay panel
T50 – 50-Pin Connector, on Airbag Control Module
TV4 – Terminal 15 Wire Connector (Black), next to fuse/relay panel
(109) – Ground connection, in airbag wiring harness
(283) – Ground connection, in airbag wiring harness

VW8019700031000X

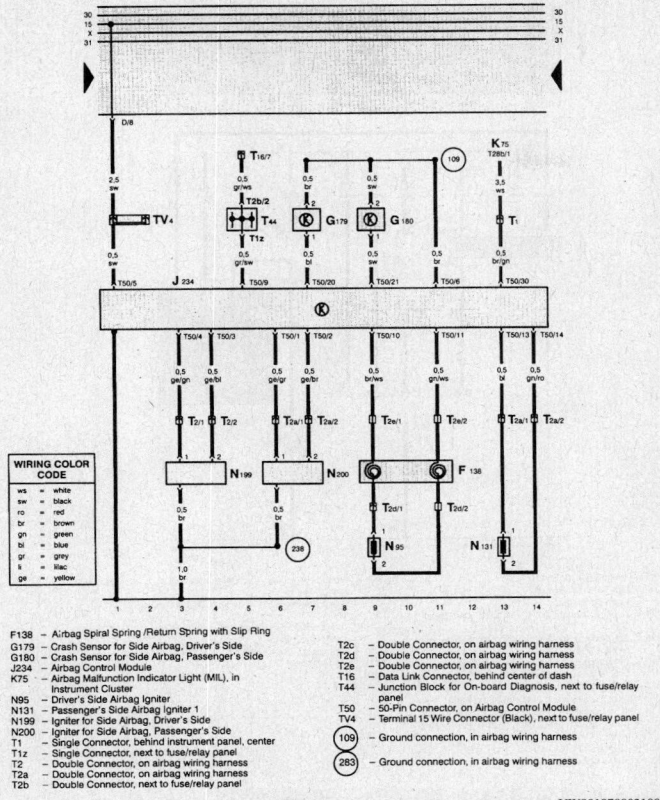

Fig. 8 SRS wiring diagram. 1998 Golf, GTI & Jetta

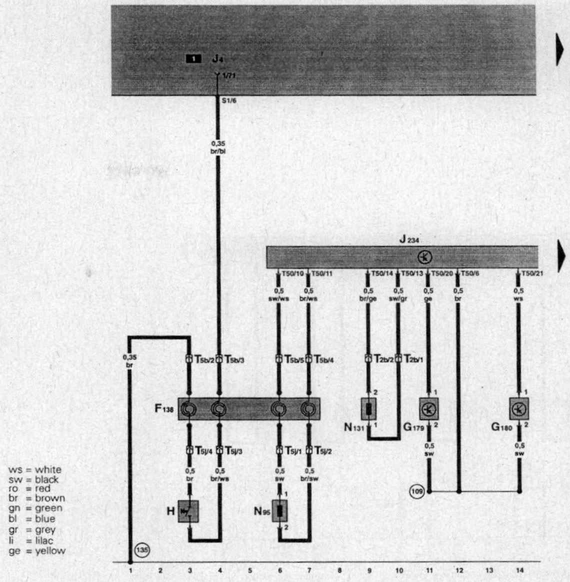

F138 – Airbag Spiral Spring/Return Spring With Slip Ring
G179 – Crash sensor for side airbag, driver's side
G180 – Crash sensor for side airbag, passenger side
H – Signal horn activation
J4 – Dual Horn Relay
J234 – Airbag Control Module, behind console, lower part
N95 – Driver's Side Airbag Igniter
N131 – Passenger's Side Airbag Igniter 1
T2b – 2–Pin Connector, on passenger's side airbag igniter 1
T5b – 5-Pin Connector, beside steering column
T5j – 5-Pin Connector, behind driver's airbag
T50 – 50-Pin Connector
(109) – Ground connection, in airbag wiring harness
(135) – Ground connection -2-, in instrument panel wiring harness

VW9040000355010X

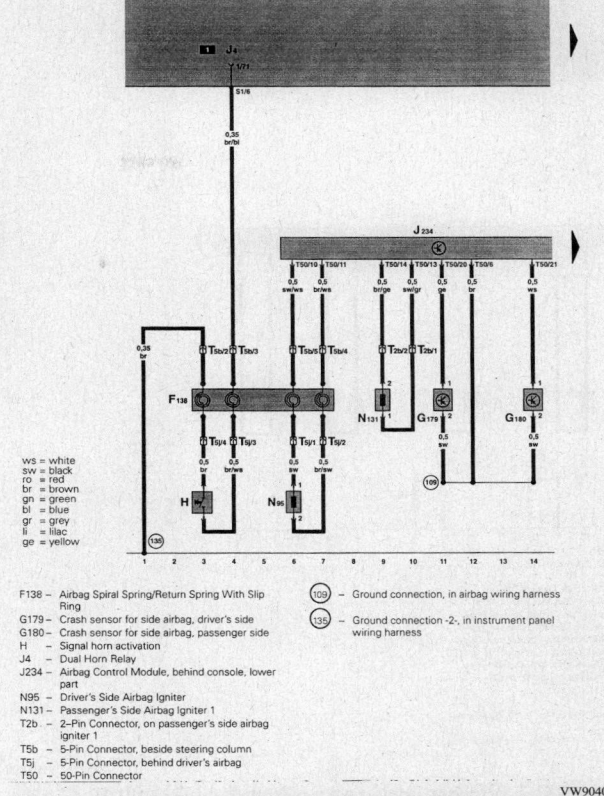

Fig. 9 SRS wiring diagram (Part 1 of 3). 1999 Golf, GTI & Jetta

5. Remove seat belt tensioner bolt, **Fig. 29,** noting the following:
   a. **Loosening seat belt tensioner mounting bolt makes belt tensioner safe.**
   b. **Tightening seat belt tensioner mounting bolts makes tensioner functional.**
6. Unhook seat belt with tensioner.
7. Open seat belt guide.
8. Remove anchor bolt, seat belt and tensioner.
9. Reverse procedure to install, noting the following:
   a. Tighten mounting bolts to specifications.
   b. Arm SRS as outlined under "Air Bag System Disarming & Arming."

AIR BAG ASSEMBLY DISPOSAL

When handling a deployed air bag assembly, a face shield and rubber gloves should be worn. Vehicle interior and all HVAC ducts should be vacuumed. If sinus or throat irritation is encountered during air bag removal, exit vehicle and breathe fresh air. If skin irritation is encountered, flush affected area with cool water. If any type of irritation continues, consult a physician. Wash hands and rinse thoroughly with water after handling a deployed air bag assembly.

DEPLOYED AIR BAG MODULE

A deployed air bag should be removed as outlined under "Air Bag Module, Replace." Prior to removing a deployed air bag assembly, place tape over air bag exhaust vents. After unit has been removed, it should be placed in a heavy duty plastic bag, sealed securely, then placed with automotive scrap.

Air bag units that have not been deployed must be deployed prior to scrapping. Refer to "Undeployed Air Bag Module."

UNDEPLOYED AIR BAG MODULE

Contact Volkswagen for air bag module disposal procedure.

SEAT BELT TENSIONER DISPOSAL

DEPLOYED SEAT BELT TENSIONER

Deployed seat belt tensioner may be placed with normal automotive scrap.

UNDEPLOYED SEAT BELT TENSIONER

Contact Volkswagen for seat belt tensioner disposal procedure.

TECHNICAL SERVICE BULLETINS

USE OF STABILANT 22A ON ELECTRICAL CONNECTIONS

On these models, always use Stabilant 22A contact enhancer on all SRS wiring connections and terminals whenever these are replaced or separated.

Stabilant 22A should also be used whenever a harness replacement is performed.

AIR BAG CONTROL MODULE CODING REVISIONS

1998–99 Cabrio, EuroVan, Golf, GTI, Jetta, New Beetle & Passat

On these models, there are revised air bag control module codings, **Fig. 30.**

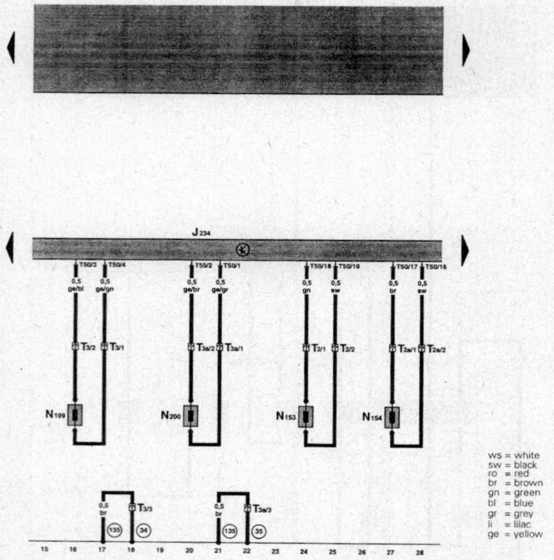

J234 – Airbag Control Module, behind console, lower part
N153 – Left Seat Belt Tensioner Igniter
N154 – Right Seat Belt Tensioner Igniter
N199 – Igniter for side airbag, driver's side
N200 – Igniter for side airbag, passenger side
T2 – Double Connector, below driver's seat
T2a – Double Connector, below driver's seat
T3 – 3-Pin Connector, below driver's seat
T3a – 3-Pin Connector, below passenger's seat
T50 – 50-Pin Connector
(34) – Ground connection, below driver's seat
(35) – Ground connection, below passenger's seat
(135) – Ground connection -2-, in instrument panel wiring harness

VW9040000355020X

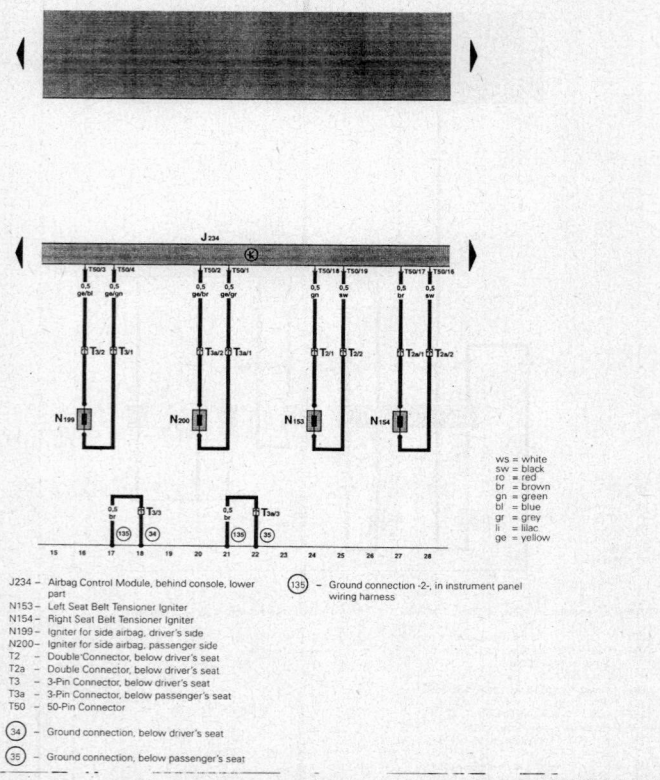

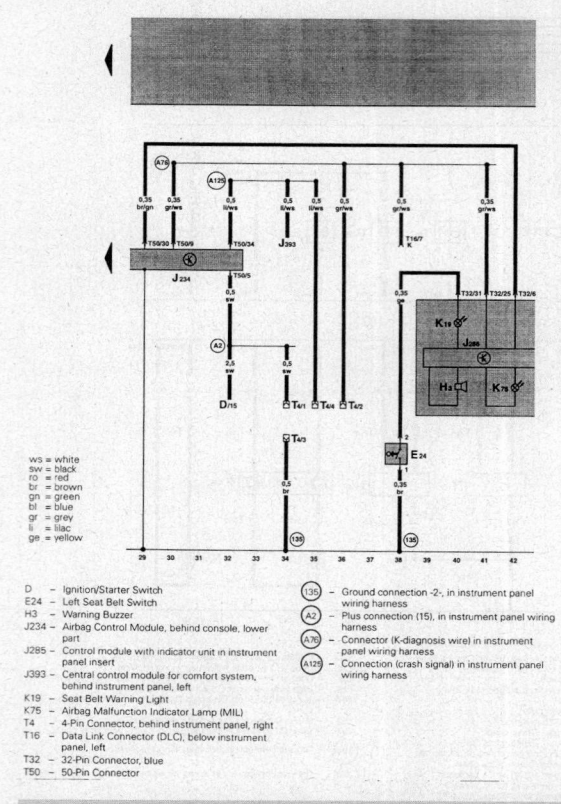

Fig. 9 SRS wiring diagram (Part 2 of 3). 1999 Golf, GTI & Jetta

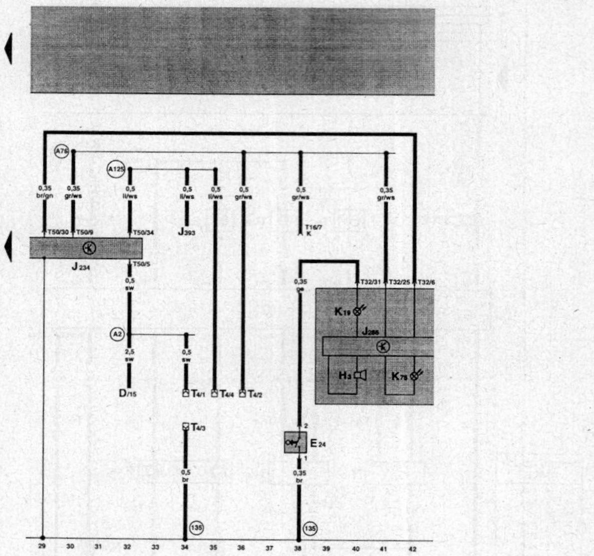

D – Ignition/Starter Switch
E24 – Left Seat Belt Switch
H3 – Warning Buzzer
J234 – Airbag Control Module, behind console, lower part
J285 – Control module with indicator unit in instrument panel insert
J393 – Central control module for comfort system, behind instrument panel, left
K19 – Seat Belt Warning Light
K75 – Airbag Malfunction Indicator Lamp (MIL)
T4 – 4-Pin Connector, behind instrument panel, right
T16 – Data Link Connector (DLC), below instrument panel, left
T32 – 32-Pin Connector, blue
T50 – 50-Pin Connector
(135) – Ground connection -2-, in instrument panel wiring harness
(A2) – Plus connection (15), in instrument panel wiring harness
(A76) – Connector (K-diagnosis wire) in instrument panel wiring harness
(A125) – Connection (crash signal) in instrument panel wiring harness

VW9040000355030X

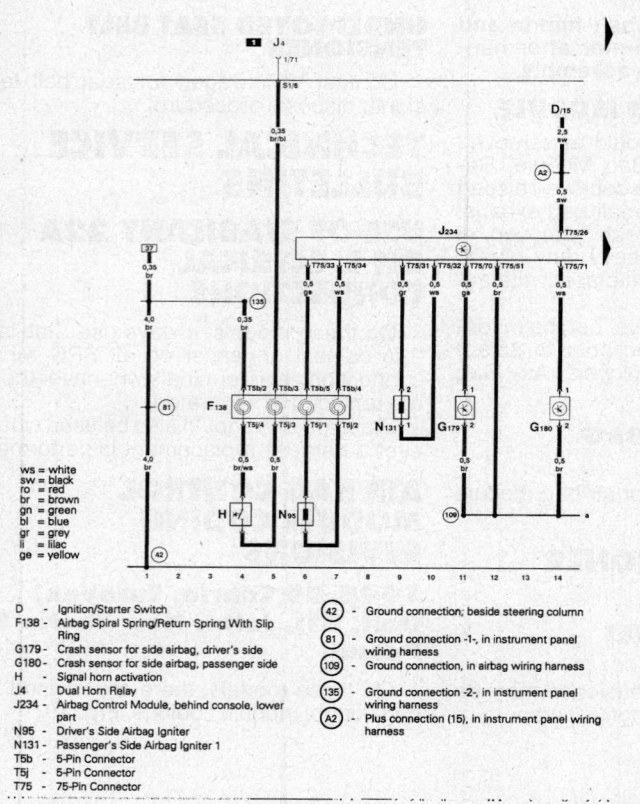

Fig. 9 SRS wiring diagram (Part 3 of 3). 1999 Golf, GTI & Jetta

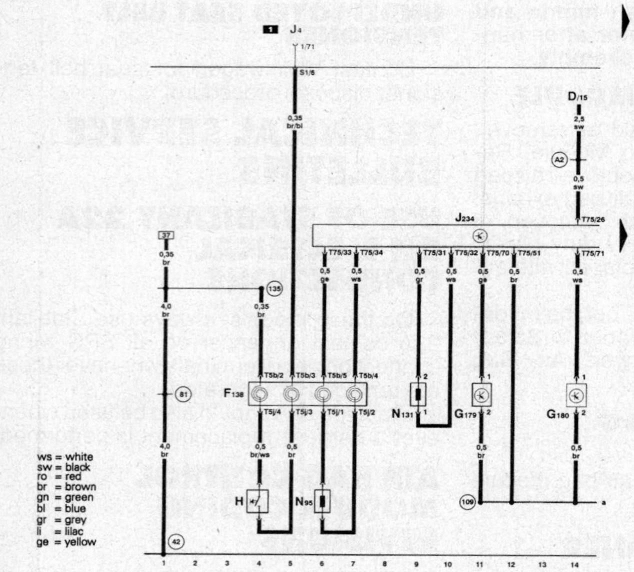

D – Ignition/Starter Switch
F138 – Airbag Spiral Spring/Return Spring With Slip Ring
G179 – Crash sensor for side airbag, driver's side
G180 – Crash sensor for side airbag, passenger side
H – Signal horn activation
J4 – Dual Horn Relay
J234 – Airbag Control Module, behind console, lower part
N95 – Driver's Side Airbag Igniter
N131 – Passenger's Side Airbag Igniter 1
T5b – 5-Pin Connector
T5j – 5-Pin Connector
T75 – 75-Pin Connector
(42) – Ground connection, beside steering column
(81) – Ground connection -1-, in instrument panel wiring harness
(109) – Ground connection, in airbag wiring harness
(135) – Ground connection -2-, in instrument panel wiring harness
(A2) – Plus connection (15), in instrument panel wiring harness

VW8010100082010X

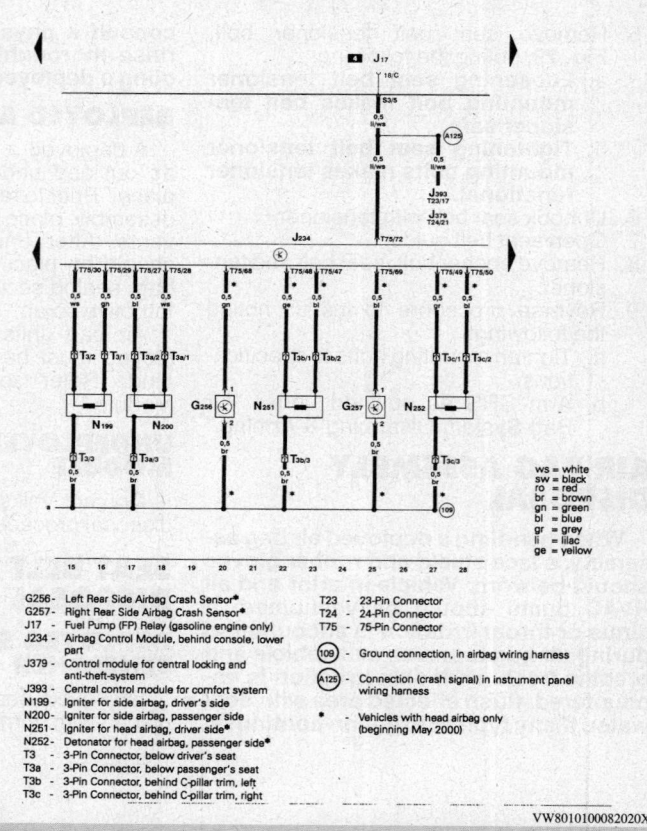

Fig. 10 SRS wiring diagram (Part 1 of 3). 2000–01 Golf, GTI & Jetta from May 1999

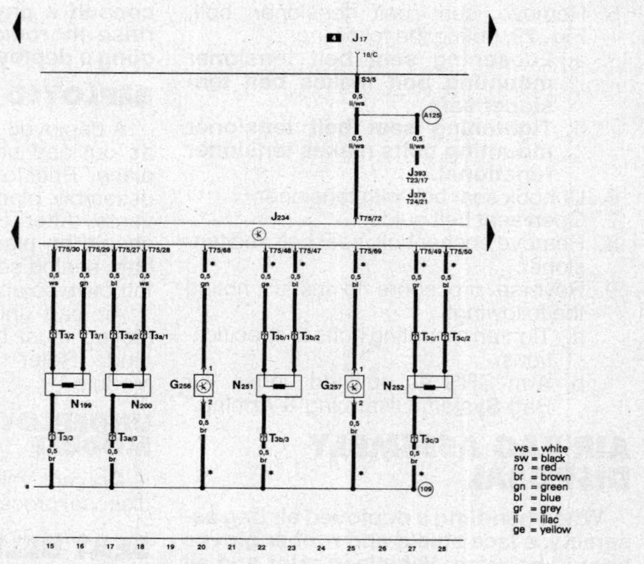

G256 – Left Rear Side Airbag Crash Sensor*
G257 – Right Rear Side Airbag Crash Sensor*
J17 – Fuel Pump (FP) Relay (gasoline engine only)
J234 – Airbag Control Module, behind console, lower part
J379 – Control module for central locking and anti-theft-system
J393 – Central control module for comfort system
N199 – Igniter for side airbag, driver's side
N200 – Igniter for side airbag, passenger side
N251 – Igniter for head airbag, driver side*
N252 – Detonator for head airbag, passenger side*
T3 – 3-Pin Connector, below driver's seat
T3a – 3-Pin Connector, below passenger's seat
T3b – 3-Pin Connector, behind C-pillar trim, left
T3c – 3-Pin Connector, behind C-pillar trim, right
T23 – 23-Pin Connector
T24 – 24-Pin Connector
T75 – 75-Pin Connector
(109) – Ground connection, in airbag wiring harness
(A125) – Connection (crash signal) in instrument panel wiring harness
* – Vehicles with head airbag only (beginning May 2000)

VW8010100082020X

Fig. 10 SRS wiring diagram (Part 2 of 3). 2000–01 Golf, GTI & Jetta from May 1999

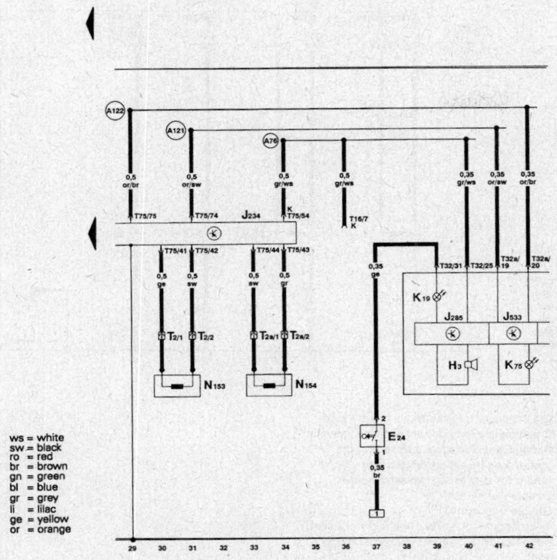

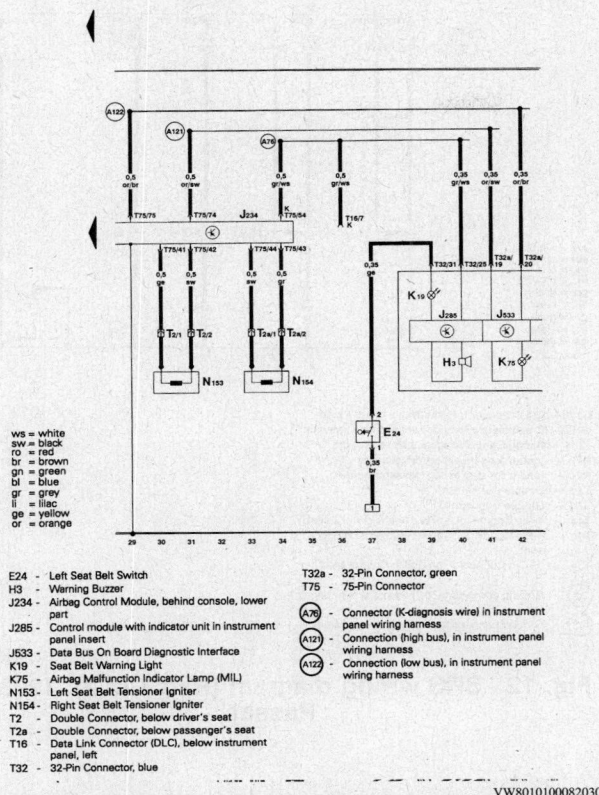

E24 - Left Seat Belt Switch
H3 - Warning Buzzer
J234 - Airbag Control Module, behind console, lower part
J285 - Control module with indicator unit in instrument panel insert
J533 - Data Bus On Board Diagnostic Interface
K19 - Seat Belt Warning Light
K75 - Airbag Malfunction Indicator Lamp (MIL)
N153 - Left Seat Belt Tensioner Igniter
N154 - Right Seat Belt Tensioner Igniter
T2 - Double Connector, below driver's seat
T2a - Double Connector, below passenger's seat
T16 - Data Link Connector (DLC), below instrument panel, left
T32 - 32-Pin Connector, blue
T32a - 32-Pin Connector, green
T75 - 75-Pin Connector
(A76) - Connector (K-diagnosis wire) in instrument panel wiring harness
(A121) - Connection (high bus), in instrument panel wiring harness
(A122) - Connection (low bus), in instrument panel wiring harness

VW8010100082030X

Fig. 10 SRS wiring diagram (Part 3 of 3). 2000–01 Golf, GTI & Jetta from May 1999

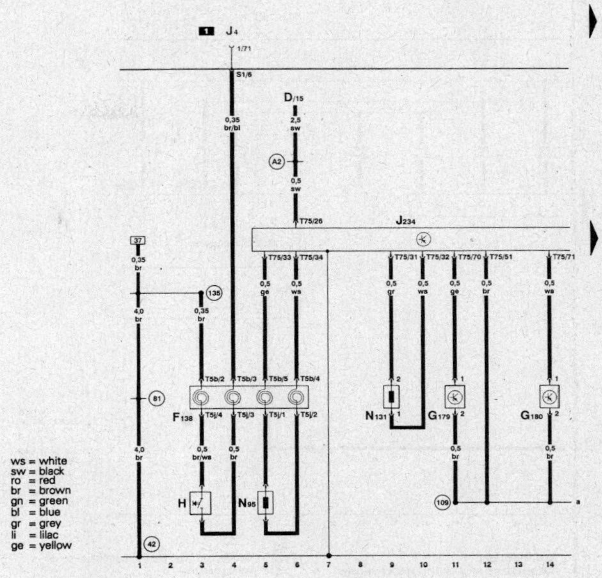

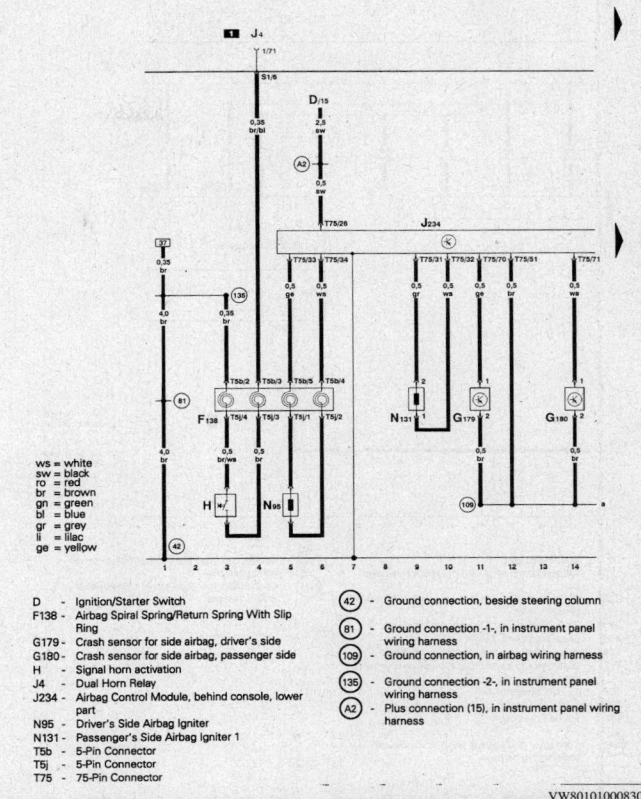

D - Ignition/Starter Switch
F138 - Airbag Spiral Spring/Return Spring With Slip Ring
G179 - Crash sensor for side airbag, driver's side
G180 - Crash sensor for side airbag, passenger side
H - Signal horn activation
J4 - Dual Horn Relay
J234 - Airbag Control Module, behind console, lower part
N95 - Driver's Side Airbag Igniter
N131 - Passenger's Side Airbag Igniter 1
T5b - 5-Pin Connector
T5j - 5-Pin Connector
T75 - 75-Pin Connector
(42) - Ground connection, beside steering column
(81) - Ground connection -1-, in instrument panel wiring harness
(109) - Ground connection, in airbag wiring harness
(135) - Ground connection -2-, in instrument panel wiring harness
(A2) - Plus connection (15), in instrument panel wiring harness

VW8010100083010X

Fig. 11 SRS wiring diagram (Part 1 of 4). 2001 Golf, GTI & Jetta from October 2000

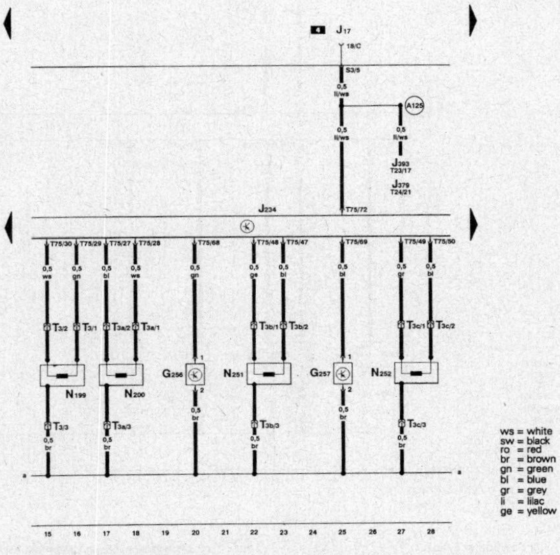

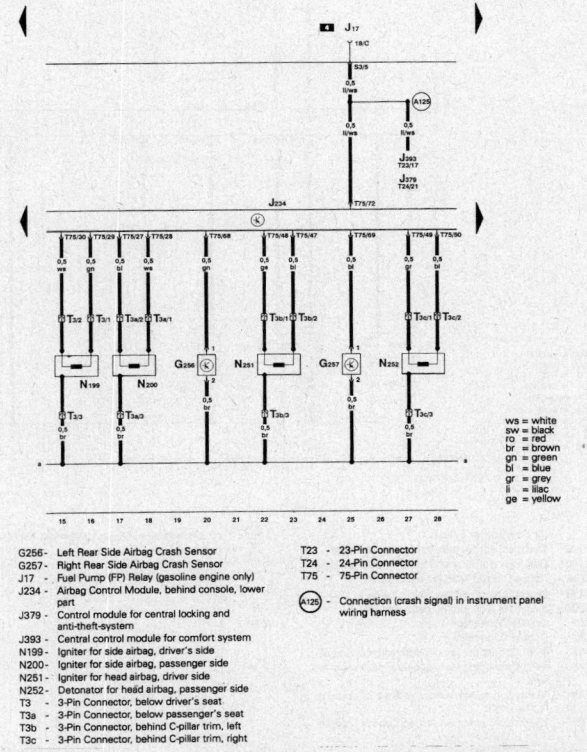

G256 - Left Rear Side Airbag Crash Sensor
G257 - Right Rear Side Airbag Crash Sensor
J17 - Fuel Pump (FP) Relay (gasoline engine only)
J234 - Airbag Control Module, behind console, lower part
J379 - Control module for central locking and anti-theft-system
J393 - Central control module for comfort system
N199 - Igniter for side airbag, driver's side
N200 - Igniter for side airbag, passenger side
N251 - Igniter for head airbag, driver side
N252 - Detonator for head airbag, passenger side
T3 - 3-Pin Connector, below driver's seat
T3a - 3-Pin Connector, below passenger's seat
T3b - 3-Pin Connector, behind C-pillar trim, left
T3c - 3-Pin Connector, behind C-pillar trim, right
T23 - 23-Pin Connector
T24 - 24-Pin Connector
T75 - 75-Pin Connector
(A125) - Connection (crash signal) in instrument panel wiring harness

VW8010100083020X

Fig. 11 SRS wiring diagram (Part 2 of 4). 2001 Golf, GTI & Jetta from October 2000

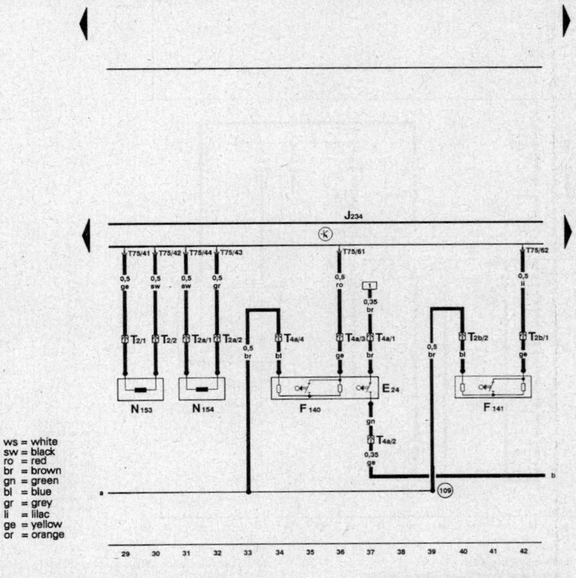

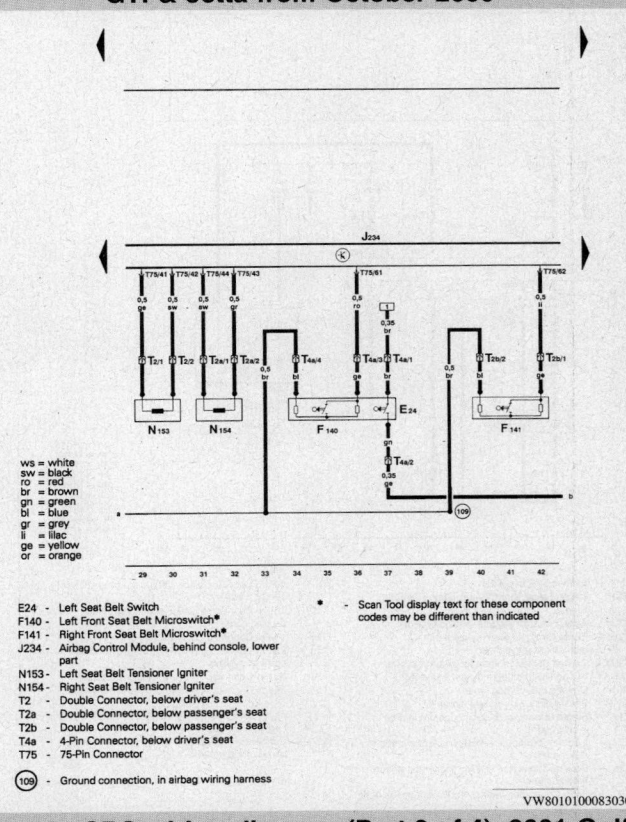

E24 - Left Seat Belt Switch
F140 - Left Front Seat Belt Microswitch*
F141 - Right Front Seat Belt Microswitch*
J234 - Airbag Control Module, behind console, lower part
N153 - Left Seat Belt Tensioner Igniter
N154 - Right Seat Belt Tensioner Igniter
T2 - Double Connector, below driver's seat
T2a - Double Connector, below passenger's seat
T2b - Double Connector, below passenger's seat
T4a - 4-Pin Connector, below driver's seat
T75 - 75-Pin Connector
(109) - Ground connection, in airbag wiring harness

* - Scan Tool display text for these component codes may be different than indicated

VW8010100083030X

Fig. 11 SRS wiring diagram (Part 3 of 4). 2001 Golf, GTI & Jetta from October 2000

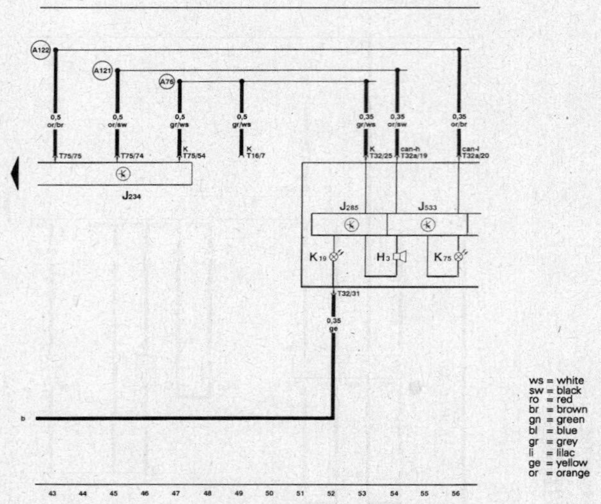

H3 - Warning Buzzer
J234 - Airbag Control Module, behind console, lower part
J285 - Control module with indicator unit in instrument panel insert
J533 - Data Bus On Board Diagnostic Interface
K19 - Seat Belt Warning Light
K75 - Airbag Malfunction Indicator Lamp (MIL)
T16 - Data Link Connector (DLC), below instrument panel, left
T32 - 32-Pin Connector, blue
T32a - 32-Pin Connector, green
T75 - 75-Pin Connector

(A76) - Connector (K-diagnosis wire) in instrument panel wiring harness

(A121) - Connection (high bus), in instrument panel wiring harness
(A122) - Connection (low bus), in instrument panel wiring harness

VW8010100083040X

Fig. 11 SRS wiring diagram (Part 4 of 4). 2001 Golf, GTI & Jetta from October 2000

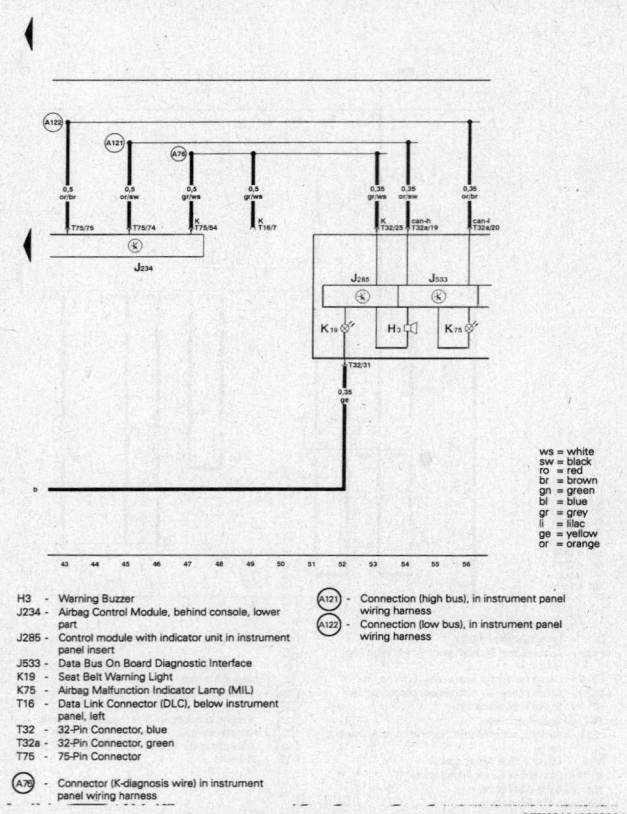

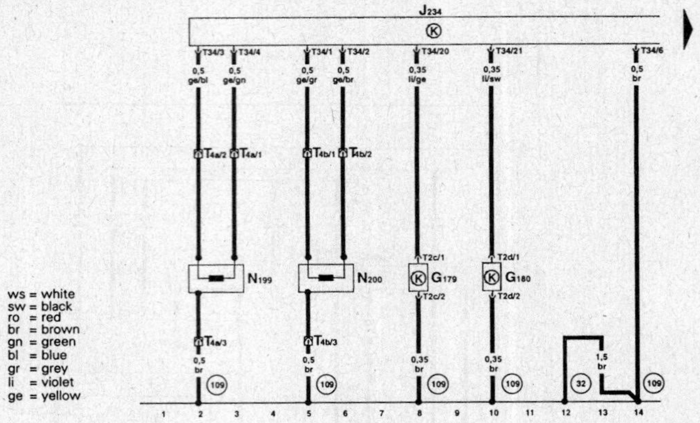

G179– Crash sensor for side airbag, driver's side
G180– Crash sensor for side airbag, passenger side
J234 – Airbag Control Module, behind console
N199– Igniter for side airbag, driver's side
N200– Igniter for side airbag, passenger side
T2c – Double Connector
T2d – Double Connector
T4a – 4-Pin Connector, yellow, below driver's seat
T4b – 4-Pin Connector, yellow, below passenger's seat
T34 – 34-Pin Connector, on Airbag Control Module

(32) – Ground connection, behind instrument panel, left
(109) – Ground connection, in airbag wiring harness

VW8019800036010X

Fig. 12 SRS wiring diagram (Part 1 of 2). 1998–99 Passat

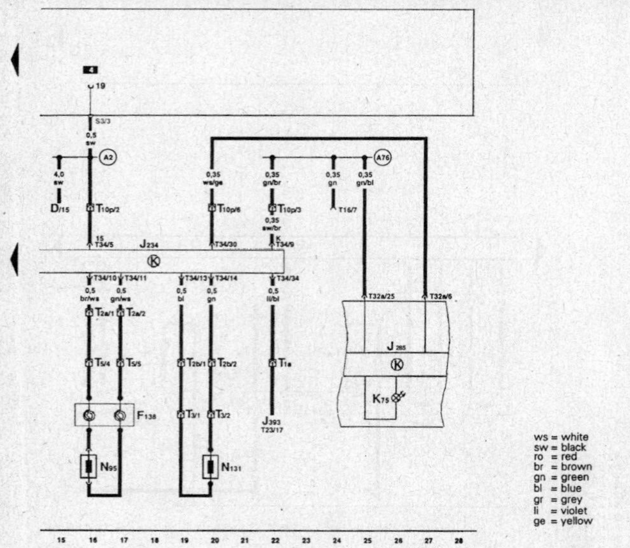

D – Ignition/Starter Switch
F138 – Airbag Spiral Spring/Return Spring With Slip Ring
J234 – Airbag Control Module, behind console
J285 – Control module with indicator unit in instrument panel insert
J393 – Central control module for comfort system
K75 – Airbag Malfunction Indicator Lamp (MIL)
N95 – Driver's Side Airbag Igniter
N131 – Passenger's Side Airbag Igniter 1
T1a – Single Connector, black, connector station A-pillar, right
T2a – Double Connector, yellow, connector station A-pillar, left
T2b – Double Connector, yellow, connector station A-pillar, right
T3 – 3-Pin Connector, behind instrument panel, right
T5 – 5-Pin Connector, black, behind steering column switch cover
T10p – 10-Pin Connector, green, connector station A-pillar, right
T16 – 16-Pin Connector, near parking brake lever
T23 – 23-Pin Connector, on central control module for comfort system
T32a – 32-Pin Connector, blue, on instrument cluster
T34 – 34-Pin Connector, on airbag control module

(A2) – plus connection (15), in instrument panel wiring harness
(A76) – Connector (K-diagnosis wire) in instrument panel wiring harness

VW8019800036020X

Fig. 12 SRS wiring diagram (Part 2 of 2). 1998–99 Passat

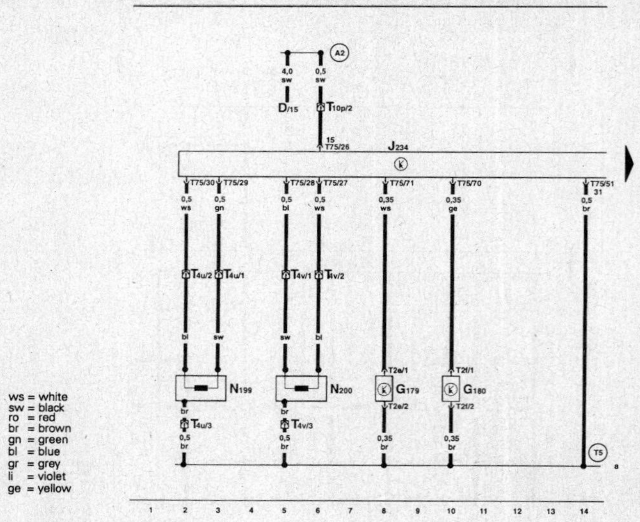

D – Ignition/Starter Switch
G179– Crash sensor for side airbag, driver's side
G180– Crash sensor for side airbag, passenger side
J234 – Airbag Control Module, behind console
N199– Igniter for side airbag, driver's side
N200– Igniter for side airbag, passenger side
T2e – Double Connector
T2f – Double Connector
T4u – 4-Pin Connector, yellow, below driver's seat
T4v – 4-Pin Connector, yellow, below passenger's seat
T10p – 10-Pin Connector, yellow, connector station A-pillar, right
T75 – 75-Pin Connector, on Airbag Control Module

(A2) – plus connection (15), in instrument panel wiring harness
(T5) – wire connection -2-, in airbag wiring harness

VW8010100080010X

Fig. 13 SRS wiring diagram (Part 1 of 3). 2000–01 Passat from August 1999

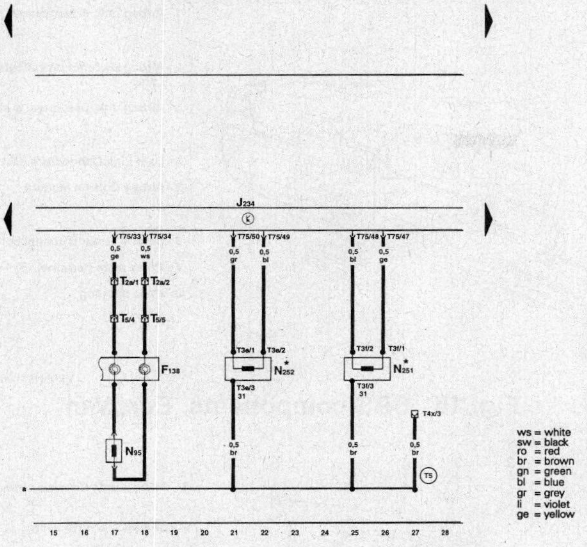

F138 - Airbag Spiral Spring/Return Spring With Slip Ring
J234 - Airbag Control Module, behind console
N95 - Driver's Side Airbag Igniter
N251 - Igniter for head airbag, rear, driver side
N252 - Igniter for head airbag, rear, passenger side
T2a - Double Connector, yellow, connector station A-pillar, left
T3e - 3-Pin Connector
T3f - 3-Pin Connector
T4x - 4-Pin Connector, yellow, connector station A-pillar, right
T5 - 5-Pin Connector, yellow, behind steering column switch cover
T75 - 75-Pin Connector, on Airbag Control Module

(T5) - wire connection -2-, in airbag wiring harness
* - vehicles with head airbag only

VW8010100080020X

Fig. 13 SRS wiring diagram (Part 2 of 3). 2000–01 Passat from August 1999

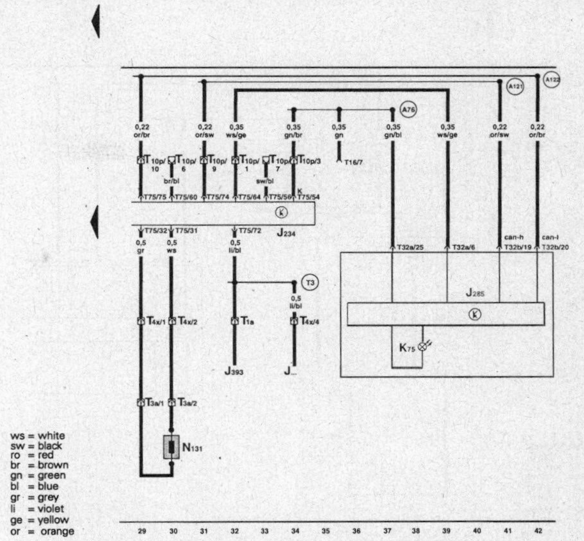

J... - Engine Control Modules (ECM)
J234 - Airbag Control Module, behind console
J285 - Control module with indicator unit in instrument panel insert
J393 - Central control module for comfort system
K75 - Airbag Malfunction Indicator Lamp (MIL)
N131 - Passenger's Side Airbag Igniter 1
T1a - Single Connector, black, connector station A-pillar, right
T3a - 3-Pin Connector, behind instrument panel, right
T4x - 4-Pin Connector, yellow, connector station A-pillar, right
T10p - 10-Pin Connector, yellow, connector station A-pillar, right
T16 - 16-Pin Connector, Data Link Connector (DLC), below instrument panel, left
T32a - 32-Pin Connector, blue, on instrument cluster
T32b - 32-Pin Connector, green, on instrument cluster
T75 - 75-Pin Connector, on airbag control module

(A76) - Connector (K-diagnosis wire) in instrument panel wiring harness
(A121) - Connector (high bus) in instrument panel wiring harness
(A122) - Connector (low bus) in instrument panel wiring harness
(T3) - wire connection, in airbag wiring harness

VW8010100080030X

Fig. 13 SRS wiring diagram (Part 3 of 3). 2000–01 Passat from August 1999

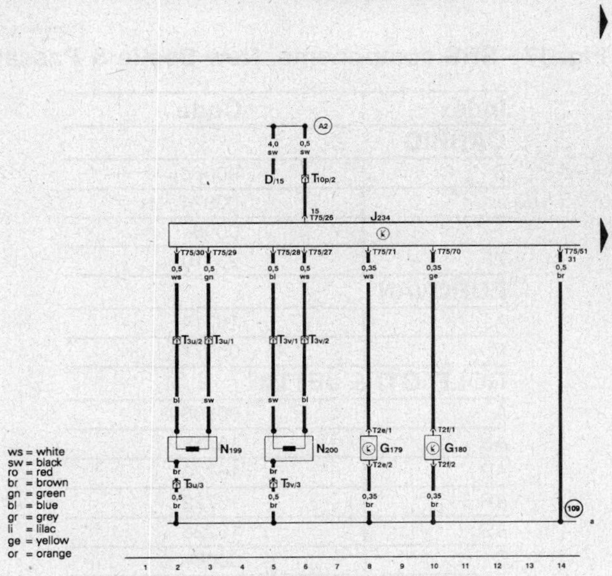

D - Ignition/Starter Switch
G179 - Crash sensor for side airbag, driver's side
G180 - Crash sensor for side airbag, passenger side
J234 - Airbag Control Module
N199 - Igniter for side airbag, driver's side
N200 - Igniter for side airbag, passenger side
T2e - Double Connector
T2f - Double Connector
T3u - 3-Pin Connector, yellow, below driver's seat
T3v - 3-Pin Connector, yellow, below passenger's seat
T10p - 10-Pin Connector, yellow, connector station A-pillar, right
T75 - 75-Pin Connector, on Airbag Control Module

(A2) - plus connection (15), in instrument panel wiring harness
(109) - Ground connection, in airbag wiring harness

VW8010100081010X

Fig. 14 SRS wiring diagram (Part 1 of 3). 2001 Passat from October 2000

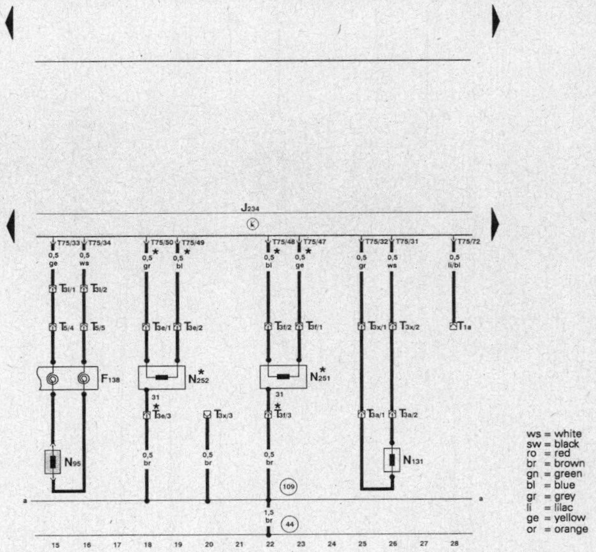

F138 - Airbag Spiral Spring/Return Spring With Slip Ring
J234 - Airbag Control Module, behind console
N95 - Driver's Side Airbag Igniter
N131 - Passenger's Side Airbag Igniter 1
N251 - Igniter for head airbag, rear, driver side
N252 - Front Passenger Head Airbag Igniter
T1a - Single Connector, black, connector station A-pillar, right
T3a - 3-Pin Connector, behind instrument panel, right
T3e - 3-Pin Connector
T3f - 3-Pin Connector
T3l - 3-Pin Connector, yellow, connector station A-pillar, left
T3x - 3-Pin Connector, yellow, connector station A-pillar, right
T5 - 5-Pin Connector, yellow, behind steering column switch cover
T75 - 75-Pin Connector, on Airbag Control Module

(44) - Ground connection, on left A-pillar, lower part
(109) - Ground connection, in airbag wiring harness
* - vehicles with head airbag only

VW8010100081020X

Fig. 14 SRS wiring diagram (Part 2 of 3). 2001 Passat from October 2000

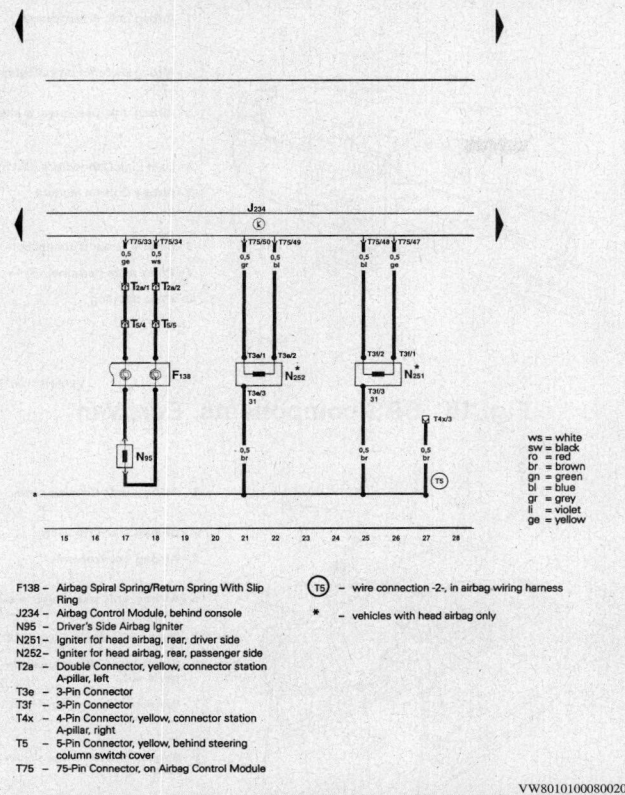

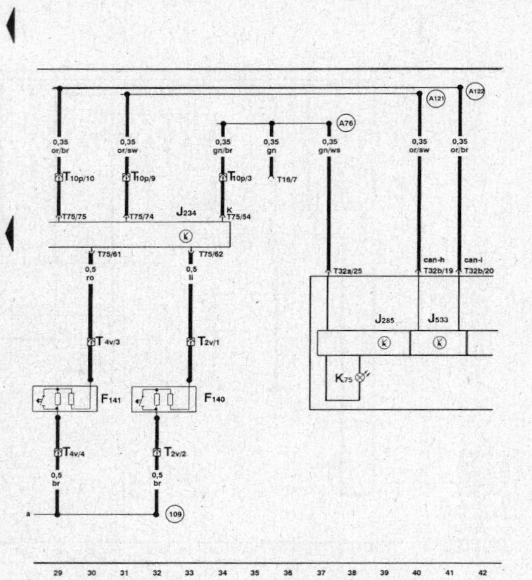

ws = white
sw = black
ro = red
br = brown
gn = green
bl = blue
gr = grey
li = lilac
ge = yellow
or = orange

F140 - Left Front Seat Belt Microswitch*
F141 - Right Front Seat Belt Microswitch*
J234 - Airbag Control Module, behind console
J285 - Control module with indicator unit in instrument panel insert
J533 - Data Bus On Board Diagnostic Interface
K75 - Airbag Malfunction Indicator Lamp (MIL)
T10p - 10-Pin Connector, yellow, connector station A-pillar, right
T2v - Double Connector
T4v - 4-Pin Connector
T16 - 16-Pin Connector, Data Link Connector (DLC) below instrument panel, left
T32a - 32-Pin Connector, blue, on instrument cluster
T32b - 32-Pin Connector, green, on instrument cluster
T75 - 75-Pin Connector, on Airbag Control Module

(109) - Ground connection, in airbag wiring harness
(A76) - Connector (K-diagnosis wire) in instrument panel wiring harness
(A121) - Connection (high bus) in instrument panel wiring harness
(A122) - Connection (low bus) in instrument panel wiring harness
* - Scan Tool display text for these component codes may be different than indicated

VW8010100081030X

Fig. 14 SRS wiring diagram (Part 3 of 3). 2001 Passat from October 2000

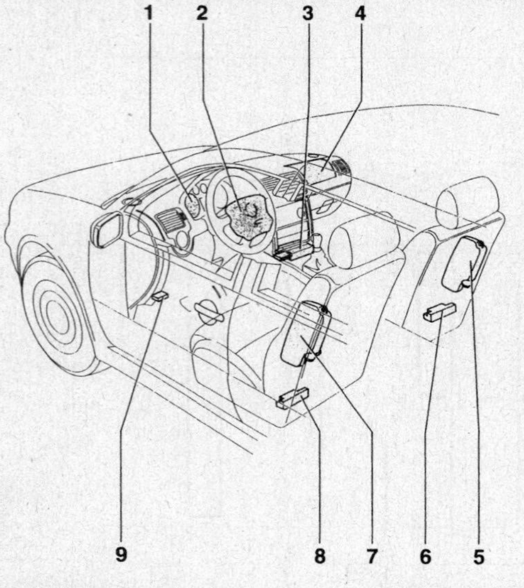

1 - **Airbag Malfunction Indicator Lamp (MIL) -K75**
2 - **Airbag unit driver's side (with Airbag igniter, driver's side -N95)**
3 - **Airbag Control Module -J234**
4 - **Airbag unit passenger's side (with Airbag igniter 1, passenger's side -N131)**
5 - **Side airbag, front passenger's side (with Side airbag igniter, passenger's side -N200)**
6 - **Side airbag crash sensor, passenger's side -G180**
7 - **Side airbag, front driver's side (with Side airbag igniter, driver's side -N199)**
8 - **Side airbag crash sensor, driver's side -G179**
9 - **Data Link Connector (DLC)**

VW8019900054000X

Fig. 16 SRS components. Golf, GTI & Jetta

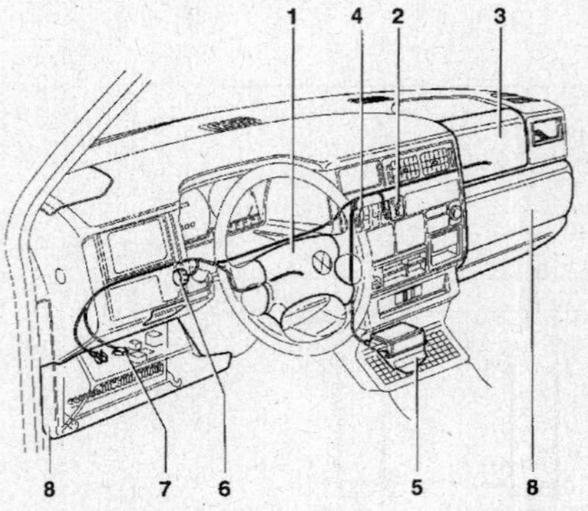

1 - **Airbag unit, driver's side**
2 - **Airbag Malfunction Indicator (MIL) Lamp**
3 - **Airbag unit, passenger's side**
4 - **Data Link Connectors (DLC)**
5 - **Airbag Control Module**
6 - **Central Ground connection**
7 - **Relay plate (terminal 15)**
8 - **Knee padding**

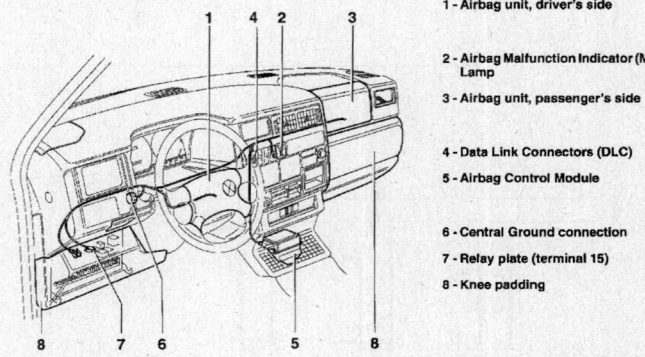

VW8019800038000X

Fig. 15 SRS components. EuroVan

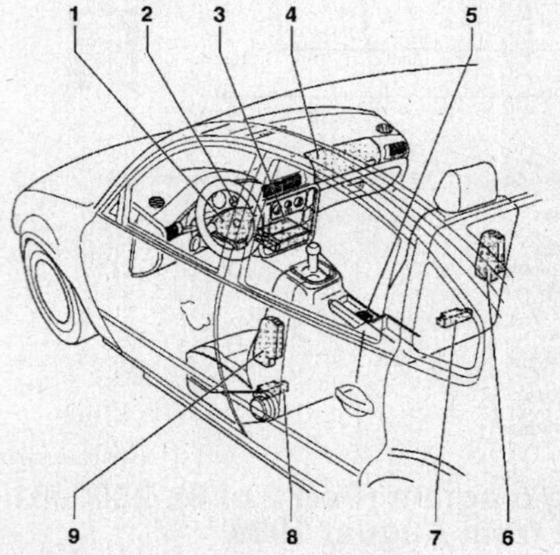

1 - **Airbag unit driver's side**
2 - **Airbag warning lamp**
3 - **Airbag control unit**
4 - **Airbag unit passenger's side**
5 - **Data Link Connector (DLC)**
6 - **Side airbag, front passenger's side**
7 - **Sensor (side airbag, front passenger)**
8 - **Sensor (side airbag, driver's side)**
9 - **Side airbag, driver's side**

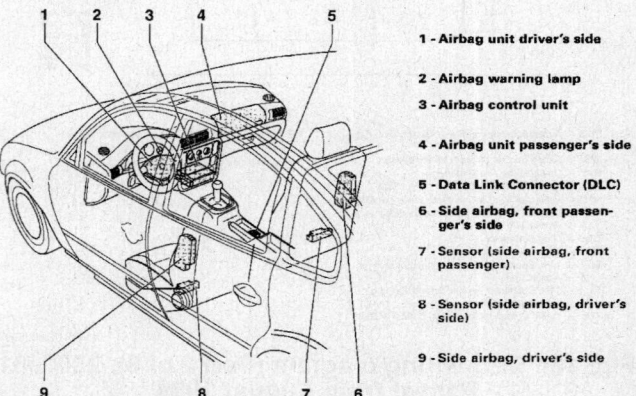

VW8019800039000X

Fig. 17 SRS components. New Beetle & Passat

Index	Code
CABRIO	
D	00068
J	00074
T	00084
ZF	23110
EUROVAN	
AJ	16714
M	00077
GOLF, GTI & JETTA	
A	00065
AN	16718
AP	16720
AR	16722
AS	16723
B	00066
C	00067
J	00074
NEW BEETLE	
AQ	16721
F	00070
PASSAT	
B	00066
G	00071

Fig. 18 Control module codes

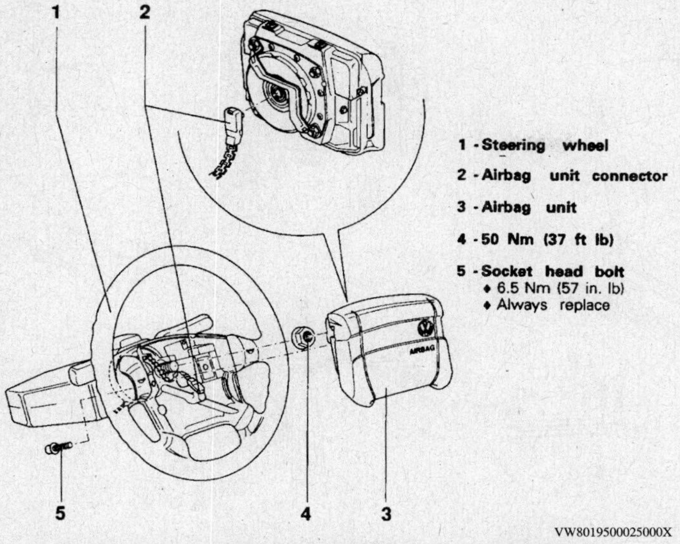

Fig. 19 Driver's air bag module replacement

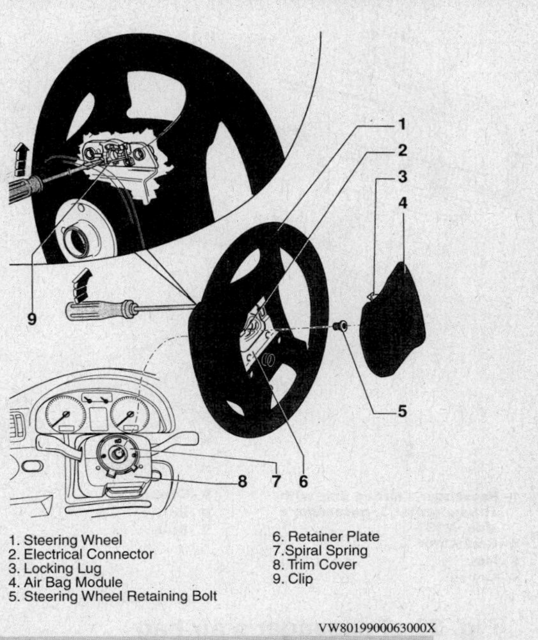

Fig. 20 Driver's air bag module replacement. Golf, GTI, Jetta, New Beetle & Passat

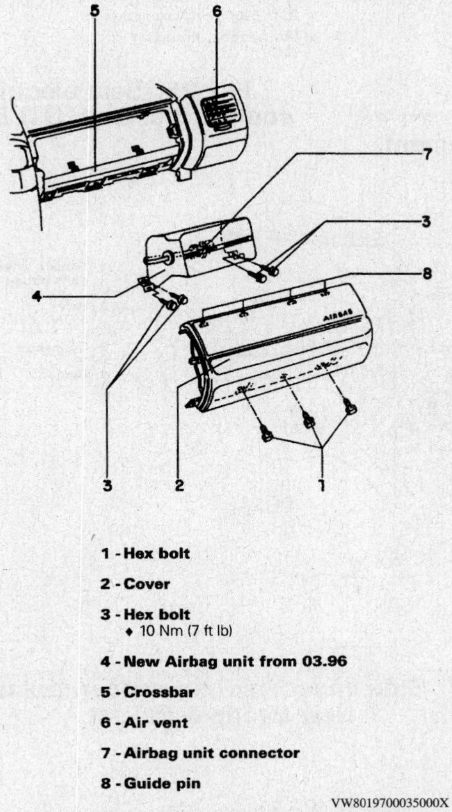

Fig. 21 Passenger's air bag module replacement. Cabrio, Golf, GTI & Jetta

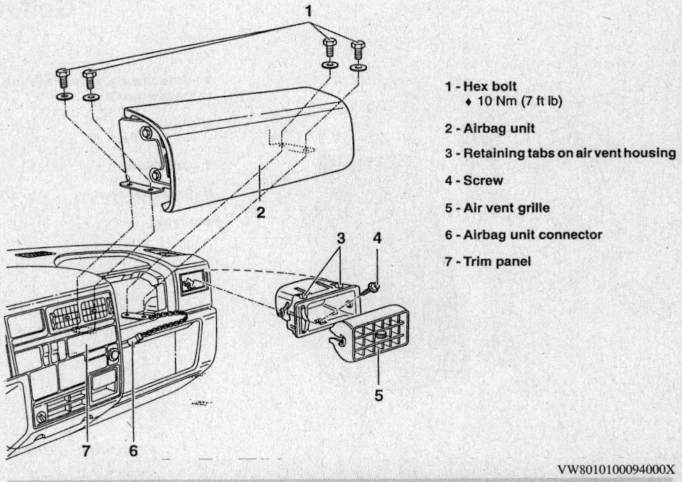

Fig. 22 Passenger's air bag module replacement. EuroVan

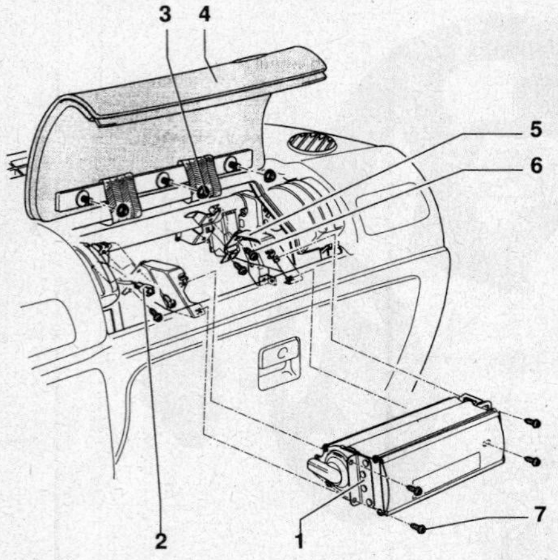

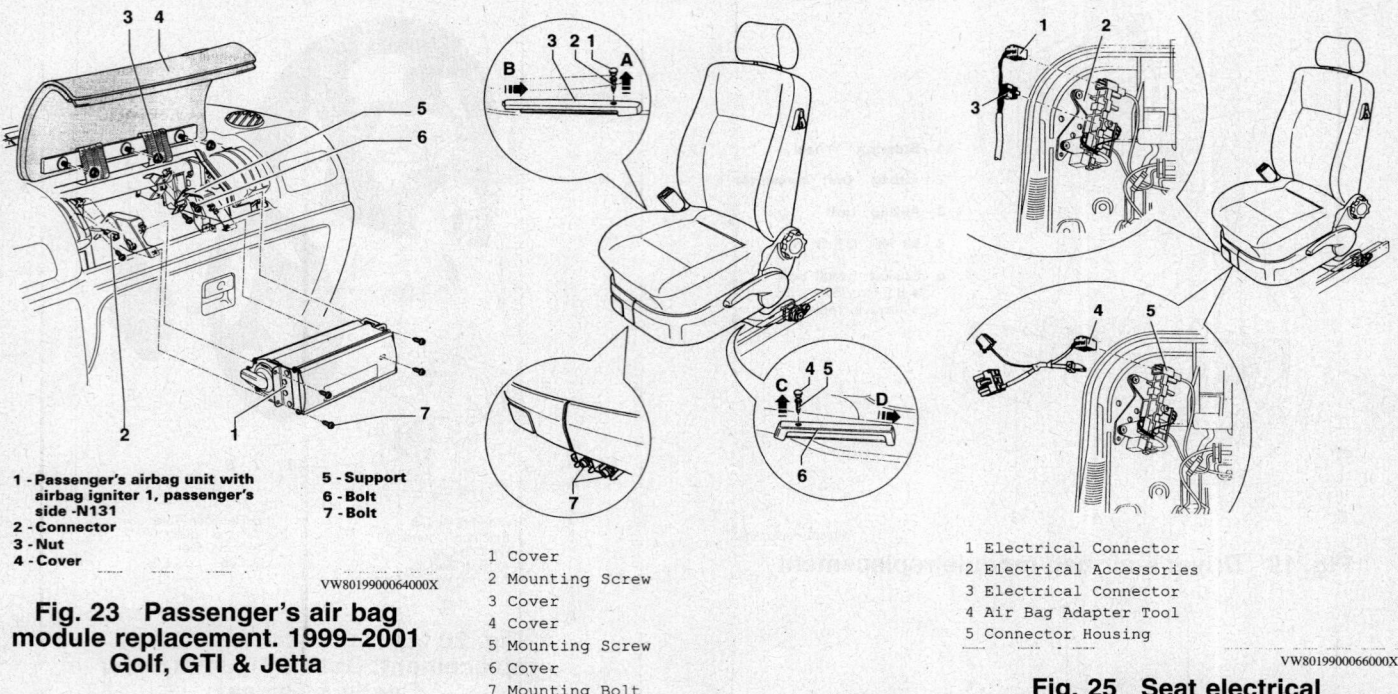

1 - Passenger's airbag unit with airbag igniter 1, passenger's side -N131
2 - Connector
3 - Nut
4 - Cover
5 - Support
6 - Bolt
7 - Bolt

VW8019900064000X

Fig. 23 Passenger's air bag module replacement. 1999–2001 Golf, GTI & Jetta

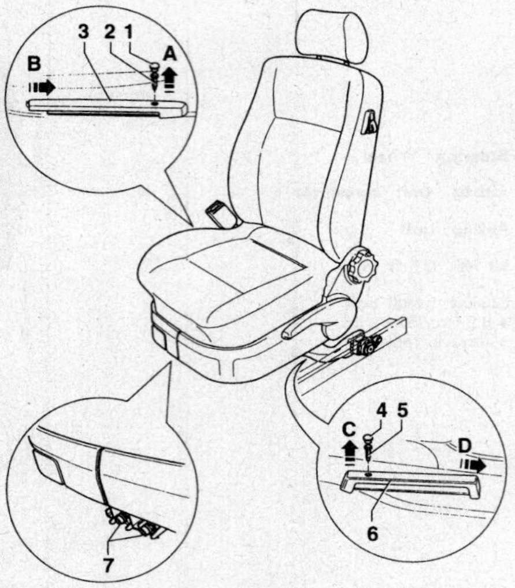

1 Cover
2 Mounting Screw
3 Cover
4 Cover
5 Mounting Screw
6 Cover
7 Mounting Bolt

VW8019900065000X

Fig. 24 Front seat replacement. Golf, GTI & Jetta

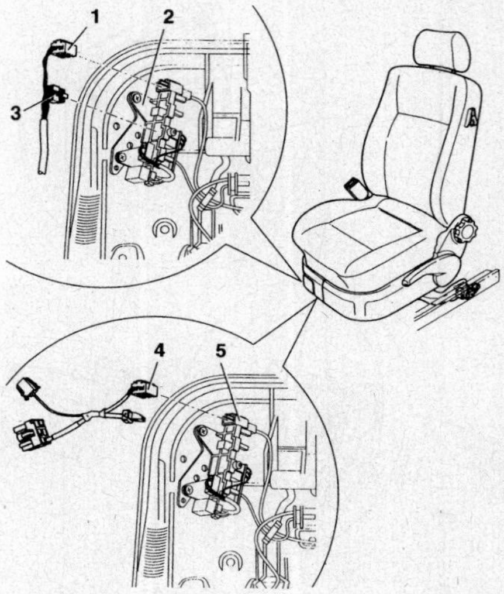

1 Electrical Connector
2 Electrical Accessories
3 Electrical Connector
4 Air Bag Adapter Tool
5 Connector Housing

VW8019900066000X

Fig. 25 Seat electrical connectors. Golf, GTI & Jetta

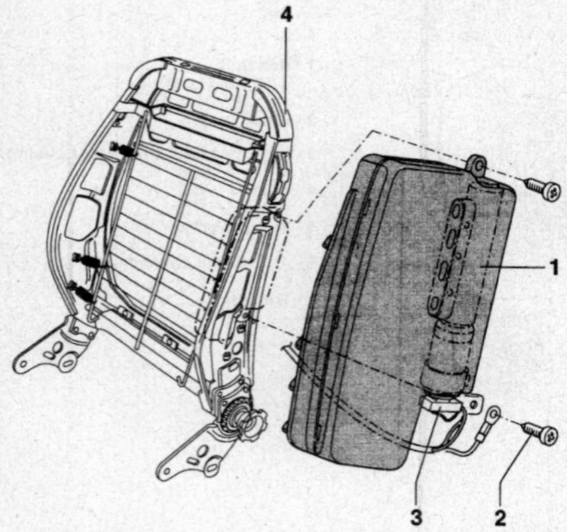

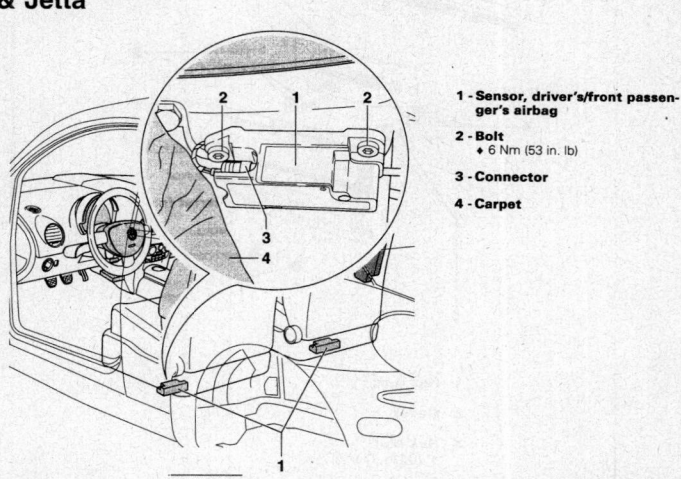

1 - Side airbag, driver's/front passenger's
2 - Bolt
◆ 7 Nm (62 in. lb)
3 - Connector
4 - Backrest frame
Removing

VW8010100095000X

Fig. 26 Side impact air bag module replacement. New Beetle & Passat

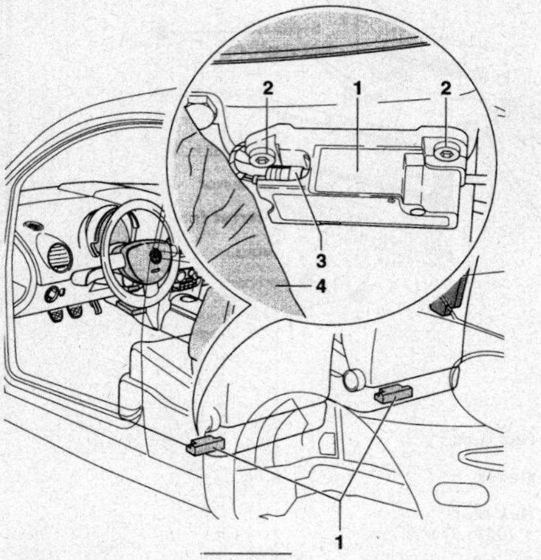

1 - Sensor, driver's/front passenger's airbag
2 - Bolt
◆ 6 Nm (53 in. lb)
3 - Connector
4 - Carpet

VW8010100096000X

Fig. 27 Side impact air bag sensor replacement. New Beetle & Passat

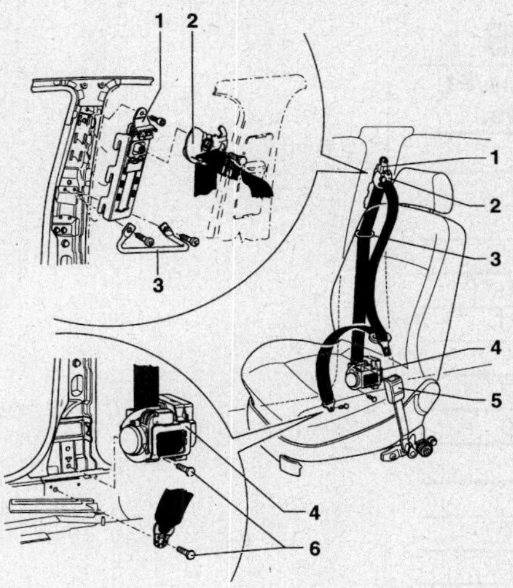

1 Seat Belt Height Adjuster
2 Seat Belt Relay
3 Seat Belt Guide
4 Seat Belt w/Tensioner
5 Front Belt Lock
6 Mounting Bolt

VW8019800050000X

Fig. 28 Front seat belt & retractor replacement. New Beetle & Passat

1 Mounting Bolt
2 Anchor

VW8019800051000X

Fig. 29 Rear seat belt and retractor replacement. Passat

Vehicle	Index*	Coding
A3 Golf / Jetta	D	00068
	J	00074
	T	00084
A3 Cabrio	D	00068
	J	00074
	T	00084
	ZF	23110
A4 Golf / Jetta	C	00067
	J	00074
B4 Passat	G	00071
B5 Passat	B	00066
NB New Beetle	F	00070
	AQ	16721
T4 Eurovan	M	00077
	AJ	16714
A2 Corrado (Canada)	C	00067

VWA089900001000X

Fig. 30 Control module coding revisions. 1998–99 Cabrio, EuroVan, Golf, GTI, Jetta New Beetle & Passat

TIGHTENING SPECIFICATIONS

Component	Torque/Ft. Lbs.
CABRIO & 1998 GOLF, GTI & JETTA	
Air Bag Control Module	80①
Air Bag Module, Driver's	58①
Air Bag Module, Passenger's	58①
Knee Bolster	12–15①
Seat Belt Reel Unit	30
Seat Belt Tensioning Unit Locknut	17
Steering Wheel Nut	37
Upper Belt Mounting	30
EUROVAN	
Air Bag Control Module	84①
Air Bag Module, Driver's	58①
Air Bag Module, Passenger's	84①
1999–2001 GOLF, GTI & JETTA	
Air Bag Control Module	35–53①
Air Bag Module Cover, Passenger's	35①
Air Bag Module, Driver's	44
Air Bag Module, Passenger's	35①
Air Bag Module, Side Impact	62①
Air Bag Module Support, Passenger's	35①
Air Bag Sensor, Side Impact	53①
Front Seat Backrest	15②
Front Seat Belt Guide	13①
Front Seat Belt Height Adjuster	17
Front Seat Belt Relay	30
Front Seat Belt Tensioner	30
Front Seat Track	17
Steering Wheel Bolt	44
Steering Wheel Retainer Plate Bolts	44①
NEW BEETLE	
Air Bag Control Module	70①
Air Bag Cover, Passenger's	35①
Air Bag Module, Driver's	44①
Air Bag Module, Passenger's	108①
Air Bag Module, Side Impact	62①
Side Impact Air Bag Sensor	53①
Steering Wheel Bolt	44
Upper Belt Mounting	30
PASSAT	
Air Bag Control Module	35①
Air Bag Module, Driver's	44①
Air Bag Module, Passenger's	35①
Air Bag Module, Side Impact	62①
Steering Wheel, Multi-Point Socket Head Type Bolt	44

① — Inch lbs.
② — Use VW locking fluid part No. D 000 600 A2, or equivalent, when installing these bolts.

Dash Panel Service

NOTE: On Air Bag Equipped Models, Refer To "Air Bag System Precautions" Located In The Front Of This Manual For System Disarming & Arming Procedures.

INDEX

	Page No.
Dash Panel, Replace	8-117
1999–2001 Golf & Jetta	8-118
Cabrio & 1998 Golf, GTI & Jetta	8-117
Eurovan	8-117
New Beetle	8-118
Passat	8-119
Precautions	8-117
Air Bag Systems	8-117
Audio Coded Anti-Theft System	8-117
Battery Ground Cable	8-117

PRECAUTIONS

AIR BAG SYSTEMS

Do not use computer memory saver tool on air bag equipped models. Using the tool will keep the air bag system charged and may cause accidental air bag unit activation.

Refer to "Air Bag System Precautions" in the front of this manual for system disarming and arming procedures.

BATTERY GROUND CABLE

Prior to service, disconnect battery ground cable and isolate as required.

AUDIO CODED ANTI-THEFT SYSTEM

Some models are equipped with a radio anti-theft system that will disable the system when battery power is interrupted. Unless the system is reset the radio will not operate.

1. Turn radio On. SAFE and 1000 should be displayed.
2. Enter radio code using first four program station buttons. Security code will appear on display.
3. Depress and hold righthand side of radio righthand or lefthand blocker until anti-theft coding is activated indicated by a brief signal sound.
4. If code number has been entered properly, a diode on front of radio will flash when ignition key is removed.

DASH PANEL

REPLACE

CABRIO & 1998 GOLF, GTI & JETTA

1. **On models equipped with air bag systems,** remove Torx screws from rear of horn pad and disconnect electrical connectors.
2. **On all models,** remove steering wheel nut, then steering wheel.
3. Remove cap plugs from sides of console extension, then the screws.
4. Pull out and disconnect rear lid opening switch connector.
5. Remove shift knob and trim.
6. Remove floor console.
7. Remove combination switch and radio assembly.
8. Remove relay cover, then the lefthand side of lower dash cover.
9. Remove tray from lower righthand side of instrument panel.
10. Remove passenger side air bag assembly from instrument panel.
11. Pull off temperature control trim plate, remove temperature control unit mounting screws, then push into dash (control unit remains in vehicle when dash removed).
12. Remove and disconnect any switches from instrument panel trim plate as required.
13. Remove instrument panel trim plate screws, then the trim plate.
14. Remove instrument cluster assembly.
15. Remove mounting screws from lower edge of dash panel, then the mounting nuts from air inlet plenum from under hood. Note position of all sealing washers.
16. Partially remove dash panel, then disconnect any remaining electrical connectors and cables.
17. Remove instrument panel from vehicle, **Fig. 1.**
18. Reverse procedure to install.

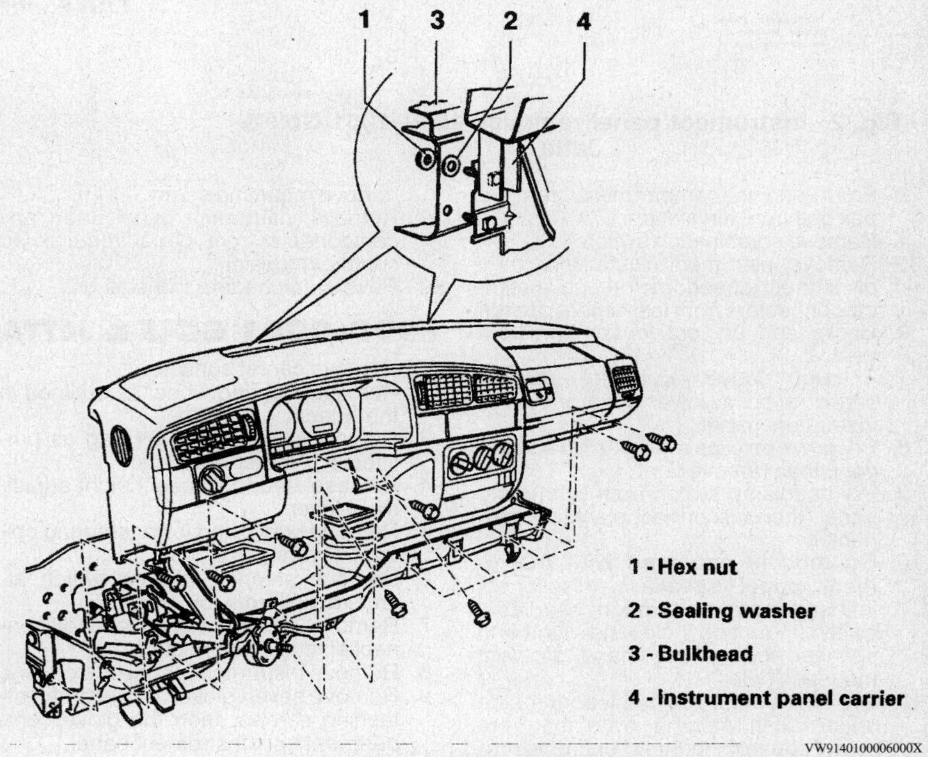

Fig. 1 Instrument panel removal. Cabrio

EUROVAN

1. Ensure steering wheel is in straight-ahead position.
2. Remove steering wheel nut, then the steering wheel.

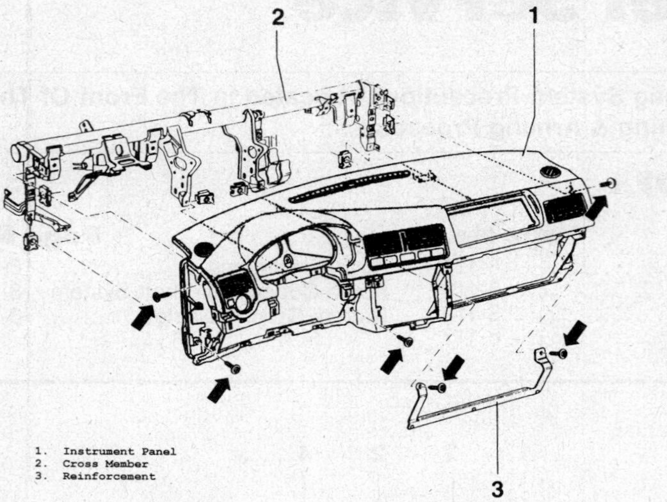

Fig. 2 Instrument panel removal. 1999–2001 Golf & Jetta

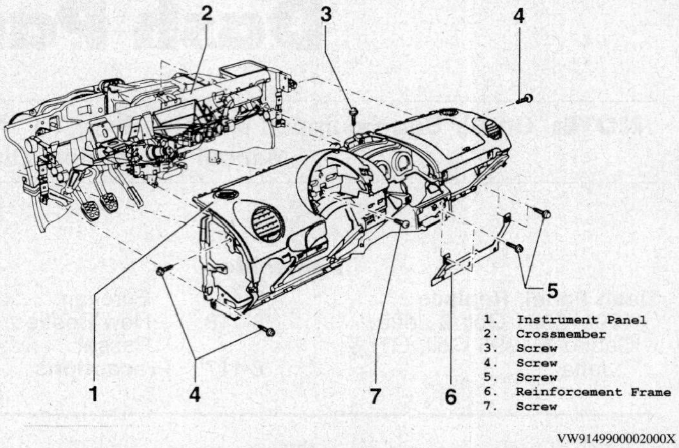

Fig. 3 Instrument panel removal. New Beetle

3. From engine compartment, remove hex bolt from air inlet duct.
4. Remove combination switch.
5. Remove instrument cluster trim, then disconnect speedometer and electrical connectors from instrument cluster.
6. Unclip and pry out louver unit from vent.
7. Through louver opening, remove screw retaining lower edge of vent to instrument panel.
8. Pry down on clips retaining top edge of vent, then remove vent.
9. Pry headlamp switch from instrument panel, then disconnect electrical connector.
10. **On models equipped with instrument panel speakers,** disconnect lefthand speaker through headlamp switch mounting hole and righthand speaker through righthand air vent mounting hole.
11. **On all models,** remove lefthand side under dash storage tray, then pry screw cap from lefthand end of instrument panel and remove mounting screw.
12. Pry out and disconnect any dash mounted switches.
13. Remove heater and A/C knobs by pulling straight out of control unit.
14. Pry heater and A/C control unit trim from instrument panel, then disconnect heater blower switch.
15. Remove radio by inserting suitable extraction tools through faceplate to release latches, then pull from dash.
16. Remove screws retaining front edge of heater and A/C control unit to instrument panel (control unit remains in vehicle when dash is removed).
17. **On models equipped with center footwell air duct,** remove console, then remove mounting screws from lower edge of instrument panel.
18. **On all models,** remove glove compartment, then pry screw cap from righthand end of instrument panel and remove mounting screw.
19. Remove instrument panel, then any components from panel required to complete repair.
20. Reverse procedure to install.

1999–2001 GOLF & JETTA

1. Remove center console.
2. Remove steering wheel as outlined in the "Electrical" section.
3. Remove passenger's air bag as outlined in "Air Bag Systems."
4. Release steering wheel height adjustment lever.
5. Remove upper and lower steering column covers.
6. Remove steering column switch attaching bolt from top of column.
7. Remove column switch and disconnect electrical connectors.
8. Remove instrument panel end covers.
9. Remove seven glove compartment attaching screws, then the glove compartment from instrument panel.
10. Remove driver's side lower knee bolster and console trim panel.
11. Remove data link connector.
12. Remove six driver's side sound damper panel attaching screws, then panel.
13. Remove radio as outlined in the "Electrical" section.
14. Unclip and remove all instrument panel switches.
15. Unclip and remove trim for climate control.
16. Remove climate control attaching screws, then slide out climate control and disconnect electrical connectors.
17. Remove five climate control and radio reinforcement frame attaching screws, then frame from instrument panel.
18. Remove three instrument panel driver's side footwell panel attaching screws, then panel.
19. Remove two gage cluster attaching screws, then slide out cluster and disconnect electrical connectors.
20. Unclip photo sensor from center defrost vent, then disconnect electrical connector.
21. Press lamp switch in, then turn clockwise, pull out and disconnect electrical connector.
22. Unclip instrument panel lamp dimmer switch, then disconnect electrical connector.
23. Remove instrument panel reinforcement, then pull instrument panel off of crossmember, **Fig. 2.**
24. Reverse procedure to install.

NEW BEETLE

1. Remove steering wheel as outlined in "Electrical" section.
2. Remove passenger's air bag as outlined in "Air Bag Systems."
3. Release steering wheel height adjustment lever.
4. Remove upper and lower steering column covers.
5. Remove steering column switch attaching bolt from top of column.
6. Remove column switch and disconnect electrical connectors.
7. Remove driver's side footwell cover.
8. Remove instrument panel end covers.
9. Remove end caps from switch panel under climate control.
10. Remove switch panel from instrument panel, then disconnect electrical connectors.
11. Remove radio as outlined in "Electrical" section.
12. Remove center instrument panel trim.
13. Remove four climate control attaching screws, then push control into panel and out of bottom of instrument panel.
14. Disconnect climate control electrical connectors.
15. Remove six glove compartment attaching screws, then the glove compartment.
16. Press lamp switch in, then turn clockwise, pull out and disconnect electrical connector.
17. Remove lighting control switch, then disconnect electrical connector.
18. Remove knee bolster panel.
19. Slide center instrument panel cover forward and out of retainer, then remove cover from instrument panel.

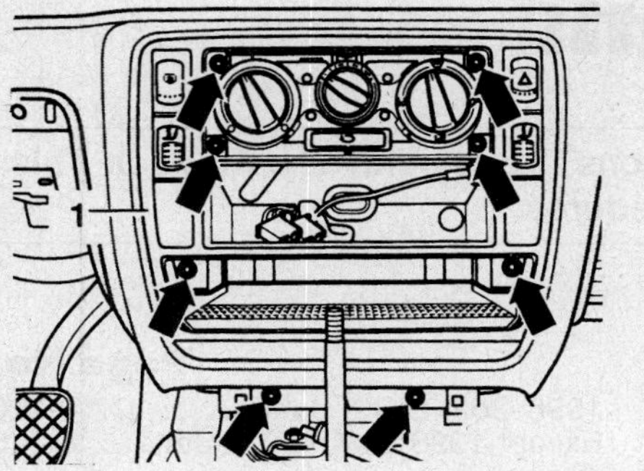

Fig. 4 Instrument panel center screw locations. Passat

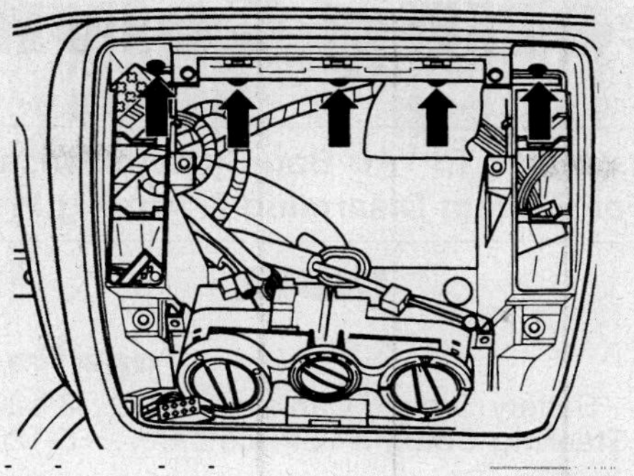

Fig. 5 Center mounting screw locations. Passat

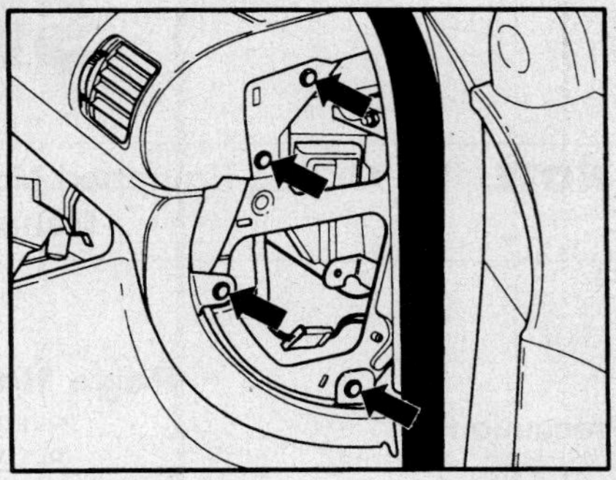

Fig. 6 Instrument panel end screw locations. Passat

20. Remove three screws from top center of instrument panel.
21. Lift lefthand plenum pane cover and remove from clips at front and rear edge.
22. Remove lefthand plenum pane cover by pulling cover toward center of instrument panel and out of retainer in A-pillar.
23. Lift righthand plenum pane cover and remove from clips at front and rear edge.
24. Remove righthand plenum pane cover by pulling cover toward center of instrument panel and out of retainer in A-pillar.
25. Unclip instrument cluster hood trim.
26. Remove instrument cluster attaching screws, then cluster.
27. Disconnect instrument cluster electrical connector.
28. Remove air duct from center instrument panel.
29. Remove reinforcement frame.
30. Remove instrument panel attaching screws, **Fig. 3.**
31. Lift and remove instrument panel from crossmember.
32. Reverse procedure to install. Reset audio coded anti-theft system as outlined under "Precautions."

PASSAT

1. Remove steering wheel as outlined in "Electrical" section.
2. Remove passenger's air bag as outlined in "Air Bag Systems."
3. Release steering wheel height adjustment lever.
4. Remove upper and lower steering column covers.
5. Remove steering column switch attaching bolt from top of column.
6. Remove column switch and disconnect electrical connectors.
7. Remove footwell side kick panels.
8. Remove instrument panel end covers.
9. Slide column trim ring up, then place a screwdriver or equivalent between trim ring and column to secure.
10. Remove four trim ring attaching screws, then the trim ring.
11. Remove two instrument panel insert attaching screws, then insert from instrument panel.
12. Remove two steering column support bolts.
13. Remove radio as outlined in the "Electrical" section.
14. Unclip climate control face trim, then remove eight screws, **Fig. 4.**
15. Remove instrument panel center cover and disconnect electrical connectors.
16. Remove five screws, **Fig. 5.**
17. Remove instrument panel center support to floor attaching screw.
18. Remove glove compartment attaching screws as follows:
    a. With glove compartment closed, remove screws from lower lefthand and righthand corners.
    b. With glove compartment open, remove five attaching screws around the edge of the glove compartment opening.
19. Pry out glove compartment lamp, then disconnect electrical connector.
20. Remove glove compartment from instrument panel.
21. Remove four instrument panel to crossmember attaching screws from each end of instrument panel, **Fig. 6.**
22. Remove instrument panel from vehicle.
23. Reverse procedure to install.

Steering Columns

NOTE: On Air Bag Equipped Models, Refer To "Air Bag System Precautions" Located In The Front Of This Manual For System Disarming & Arming Procedures.

INDEX

	Page No.
Precautions	8-120
Air Bag Systems	8-120
Audio Coded Anti-Theft System	8-120
Battery Ground Cable	8-120
Steering Column Service	8-120
1998 Golf, GTI & Jetta	8-120
Except 1998 Golf, GTI & Jetta	8-120

PRECAUTIONS

AIR BAG SYSTEMS

Do not use computer memory saver tool on air bag equipped models. Using the tool will keep the air bag system charged and may cause accidental air bag unit activation.

Refer to "Air Bag System Precautions" in the front of this manual for system disarming and arming procedures.

BATTERY GROUND CABLE

Prior to service, disconnect battery ground cable and isolate as required.

AUDIO CODED ANTI-THEFT SYSTEM

Some models are equipped with a radio anti-theft system that will disable the system when battery power is interrupted. Unless the system is reset the radio will not operate.

1. Turn radio On. SAFE and 1000 should be displayed.
2. Enter radio code using first four program station buttons. Security code will appear on display.
3. Depress and hold righthand side of radio righthand or lefthand blocker until anti-theft coding is activated indicated by a brief signal sound.
4. If code number has been entered properly, a diode on front of radio will flash when ignition key is removed.

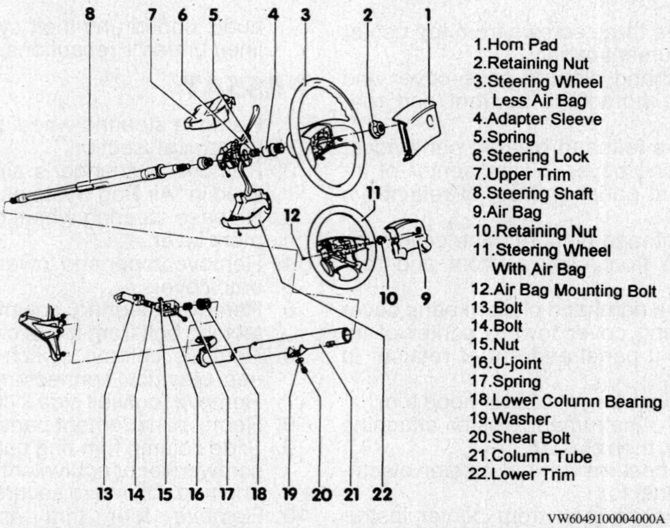

Fig. 1 Exploded view of steering column assembly. 1998 Golf, GTI & Jetta

STEERING COLUMN SERVICE

1998 GOLF, GTI & JETTA

Prior to removing steering column, ensure proper shear head bolts are available. If shear bolts are not replaced with proper components, steering column collapse functions may be impaired.

For steering column service, refer to **Fig. 1** for component locations. Refer also to ignition lock procedures found in the "Electrical" section.

EXCEPT 1998 GOLF, GTI & JETTA

On these models, the steering column is not serviceable and must be replaced as a unit.

Power Steering

INDEX

	Page No.
Diagnosis & Testing	8-122
Pump Pressure Inspection	8-122
System Pressure Inspection	8-122
Power Steering Pressure Specifications	8-121
Power Steering System Service	8-122
Adjustments	8-122
Rack Preload	8-122
Component Service	8-122
Power Steering System Bleed	8-122
Precautions	8-121
Air Bag Systems	8-121
Audio Coded Anti-Theft System	8-121
Battery Ground Cable	8-121
Troubleshooting	8-121
Hydraulic Oil In Fluid Reservoir Had To Be Replaced A Second Time	8-122
Hydraulic Oil In Fluid Reservoir Milky Or Foamy	8-122
Hydraulic Oil Level In Fluid Reservoir Too Low	8-121
Hydraulic Oil Spray In Engine Compartment	8-122
No Hydraulic Oil In Fluid Reservoir	8-121
Oil Spotting Under Vehicle	8-121
Steering Difficult/Insufficient Power Assist	8-122
Steering Effort Occasionally High	8-122
Steering In Center Position Difficult/Poor Straight Line Driving	8-122
Steering Wheel Jerks At Full Lock	8-122
Steering Wheel Vibrates/Shakes While Driving	8-122

POWER STEERING PRESSURE SPECIFICATIONS

Year/Model	System/Pump Pressure, psi①
EuroVan	1310–1595
New Beetle	②
Passat	1595–1740
1998 Cabrio, Golf, GTI & Jetta	1233–1378
1999–2001, Golf & Jetta	②

①— Install pressure gauge in high pressure line. Shut flow off no more than 5 seconds while reading maximum pressure.

②— Diesel engine, 1392–1523 psi.; gasoline engines, 1233–1378 psi.

PRECAUTIONS

AIR BAG SYSTEMS

Do not use computer memory saver tool on air bag equipped models. Using the tool will keep the air bag system charged and may cause accidental air bag unit activation.

Refer to “Air Bag System Precautions” in the front of this manual for system disarming and arming procedures.

BATTERY GROUND CABLE

Prior to service, disconnect battery ground cable and isolate as required.

AUDIO CODED ANTI-THEFT SYSTEM

Some models are equipped with a radio anti-theft system that will disable the system when battery power is interrupted. Unless the system is reset the radio will not operate.

1. Turn radio On. SAFE and 1000 should be displayed.
2. Enter radio code using first four program station buttons. Security code will appear on display.
3. Depress and hold righthand side of radio righthand or lefthand blocker until anti-theft coding is activated indicated by a brief signal sound.
4. If code number has been entered properly, a diode on front of radio will flash when ignition key is removed.

TROUBLESHOOTING

OIL SPOTTING UNDER VEHICLE

1. Excessive leakage at steering gear (oil in boot). Replace steering gear.
2. Excessive leakage at power steering pump (intake connection). Replace power steering pump.
3. Leak at fluid reservoir. Replace reservoir.
4. Hydraulic oil hose/line faulty. Replace hydraulic oil hose/line.
5. Leak at hydraulic oil hose/line. Tighten hose/line connections.
6. Fluid reservoir overflowing. Fill reservoir level to between MIN/MAX marks.

NO HYDRAULIC OIL IN FLUID RESERVOIR

1. Excessive leakage at steering gear (oil in boot). Replace steering gear.
2. Excessive leakage at power steering pump (intake connection). Replace power steering pump.
3. Leak at fluid reservoir. Replace reservoir.
4. Hydraulic oil hose/line faulty. Replace hydraulic oil hose/line.
5. Leak at hydraulic oil hose/line. Tighten hose/line connections.

HYDRAULIC OIL LEVEL IN FLUID RESERVOIR TOO LOW

1. Excessive leakage at steering gear (oil in boot). Replace steering gear.
2. Excessive leakage at power steering pump (intake connection). Replace power steering pump.
3. Leak at fluid reservoir. Replace reservoir.
4. Hydraulic oil hose/line faulty. Replace hydraulic oil hose/line.
5. Leak at hydraulic oil hose/line. Tighten

hose/line connections.

HYDRAULIC OIL IN FLUID RESERVOIR HAD TO BE REPLACED A SECOND TIME

1. Hydraulic oil hose/line faulty. Replace hydraulic oil hose/line.
2. Leak at hydraulic oil hose/line. Tighten hose/line connections.

HYDRAULIC OIL SPRAY IN ENGINE COMPARTMENT

1. Leak at fluid reservoir. Replace reservoir.
2. Hydraulic oil hose/line faulty. Replace hydraulic oil hose/line.
3. Leak at hydraulic oil hose/line. Tighten hose/line connections.
4. Fluid reservoir overflowing. Fill reservoir level to between MIN/MAX marks.

HYDRAULIC OIL IN FLUID RESERVOIR MILKY OR FOAMY

1. Leak at hydraulic oil hose/line. Tighten hose/line connections.
2. Air leak in system. Inspect and tighten hose connections, then add hydraulic oil.

STEERING DIFFICULT/ INSUFFICIENT POWER ASSIST

1. Hydraulic oil level too low/oil loss. Inspect system for leaks and repair, then fill fluid reservoir to "MAX."
2. Power steering pump faulty. Measure feed pressure. Replace pump if required.
3. Steering gear faulty. Measure system pressure. Replace steering gear if required.
4. Air in hydraulic system, hose connections loose. Tighten hose connections.
5. Improper front end alignment. Align front end to specifications.
6. Improper power steering belt tension. Adjust drive belt tension and inspect belt/pulley for damage.
7. Front wheel/wheel assembly out of balance. Correct imbalance.
8. Steering gear mounting loose. Tighten steering gear mounting.
9. Bearing in steering column switch faulty. Replace bearing.

STEERING EFFORT OCCASIONALLY HIGH

1. Hydraulic oil level too low/oil loss. Inspect system for leaks and repair. Fill fluid reservoir to "MAX."
2. Power steering belt tension improper. Adjust drive belt tension, inspect belt/ pulley for damage.
3. Power steering pump faulty. Measure feed pressure. Replace pump if required.
4. Steering gear faulty. Measure system pressure. Replace steering gear if required.
5. Air in hydraulic system, hose connections loose. Tighten hose connections.
6. Steering gear mounting loose. Tighten steering gear mounting.

STEERING WHEEL JERKS AT FULL LOCK

1. Hydraulic oil level too low/oil loss. Inspect system for leaks and repair, fill fluid reservoir to "MAX."
2. Power steering belt tension improper. Adjust drive belt tension, inspect belt/ pulley for damage.
3. Power steering pump faulty. Measure feed pressure. Replace pump if required.
4. Steering gear faulty. Measure system pressure. Replace steering gear if required.
5. Air in hydraulic system, hose connections loose. Tighten hose connections.
6. Tire pressure too low. Inspect and adjust.
7. Steering gear mounting loose. Tighten steering gear mounting.
8. Steering gear mounted under tension. Loosen and tighten steering column mounting bolts.

STEERING IN CENTER POSITION DIFFICULT/ POOR STRAIGHT LINE DRIVING

1. Power steering pump faulty. Measure feed pressure. Replace pump if required.
2. Steering gear faulty. Measure system pressure. Replace steering gear if required.
3. Air in hydraulic system, hose connections loose. Tighten hose connections.
4. Front end alignment improper. Align front end to specifications.
5. Front wheel/wheel assembly out of balance. Correct imbalance.
6. Tire pressure too low. Inspect and adjust.
7. Bearing in steering column switch faulty. Replace bearing.

STEERING WHEEL VIBRATES/SHAKES WHILE DRIVING

1. Insufficient wheel clearance, wide tires/rims. Locate and correct insufficient wheel clearance.
2. Front wheel/wheel assembly out of balance. Correct imbalance.

DIAGNOSIS & TESTING

PUMP PRESSURE INSPECTION

1. Disconnect pressure line from pump, then install adapters VW 1402/1A, VW 1402/2 and US 1074/4 A, as required, and pressure gauge US 1074B, or equivalents. Ensure valve on pressure gauge is in open position.
2. Start engine, and if required, fill up fluid in reservoir.
3. With engine running at idle, close valve on gauge and inspect pressure. **Do not leave valve closed for longer than five seconds or system damage may occur.**
4. If pressure is not within specifications. Replace power steering pump.

SYSTEM PRESSURE INSPECTION

1. Disconnect pressure line from pump, then install adapters VW 1402 1A and US 1074/4 A and pressure gauge US 1074B, or equivalents. Ensure valve on pressure gauge is in open position.
2. Start engine, and if required, fill fluid in reservoir.
3. With engine running at idle close valve open, rotate steering wheel from lock to lock and hold to inspect pressure in each position. **Do not hold against stop longer than five seconds or system damage may occur.**
4. If pressure is not within specifications, replace power steering gear assembly.

POWER STEERING SYSTEM SERVICE

Power Steering System Bleed

Replacement power steering pumps must be filled with part No. G002-000 hydraulic oil, or equivalent, and rotated by hand to prevent possible damage.

Fill system with a suitable hydraulic oil, start engine and allow to idle. Turn steering wheel lock to lock several times to release trapped air from system. If fluid becomes aerated, allow to settle before adjusting level.

Component Service

On these models, the power steering gear should be replaced as a unit.

Adjustments

RACK PRELOAD

Two technicians are required to perform the following adjustment.

1. Ensure ignition is Off, vehicle is on ground and wheels are in straight-ahead position.
2. Move steering wheel back and forth approximately 30° from center position while listening for rattling and/or popping noises from steering gear.
3. Have second technician turn adjusting screw clockwise until rattling and/or popping noises are no longer heard from inside vehicle.
4. Test drive vehicle and adjust if required. Ensure steering returns to straight-ahead position on its own after turning.

Disc Brakes

TABLE OF CONTENTS

	Page No.
APPLICATION CHART	8-123
GIRLING/LUCAS SINGLE PISTON w/DUAL MOUNTING BOLTS, FRONT	8-124
SINGLE PISTON REAR DISC BRAKE	8-128
TEVES/ATE SINGLE PISTON w/DUAL MOUNTING BOLTS, FRONT	8-126

Application Chart

Year	Model	Application	Rotor, Inch
FRONT			
1998–2001	Cabrio, Golf, Jetta, GTI & Passat w/1.9L TDI & 2.0L Engine	Girling/Lucas Single Piston w/Dual Mounting Bolts, 10.1 Inch Rotor	10.1
	GTI VR6, Jetta GLX & Passat w/2.8L Engine	Teves/Ate Single Piston w/Dual Mounting Bolt	11.3
	EuroVan	Girling/Lucas Single Piston w/Dual Mounting Bolts	10.1
REAR			
1998–2001	All	Single Piston Disc Brake	—

Girling/Lucas Single Piston w/Dual Mounting Bolts, Front

INDEX

	Page No.
Brake Pad Service	8-124
Brake Rotor, Replace	8-124
Caliper Service	8-124
Overhaul	8-124
Disc Brake Specifications	8-125
Precautions	8-124
Air Bag Systems	8-124
Audio Coded Anti-Theft System	8-124
Battery Ground Cable	8-124
Tightening Specifications	8-125

PRECAUTIONS

AIR BAG SYSTEMS

Do not use computer memory saver tool on air bag equipped models. Using the tool will keep the air bag system charged and may cause accidental air bag unit activation.

Refer to "Air Bag System Precautions" in the front of this manual for system disarming and arming procedures.

BATTERY GROUND CABLE

Prior to service, disconnect battery ground cable and isolate as required.

AUDIO CODED ANTI-THEFT SYSTEM

Some models are equipped with a radio anti-theft system that will disable the system when battery power is interrupted. Unless the system is reset the radio will not operate.

1. Turn radio On. SAFE and 1000 should be displayed.
2. Enter radio code using first four program station buttons. Security code will appear on display.
3. Depress and hold righthand side of radio righthand or lefthand blocker until anti-theft coding is activated indicated by a brief signal sound.
4. If code number has been entered properly, a diode on front of radio will flash when ignition key is removed.

BRAKE PAD SERVICE

Always remove some brake fluid from master cylinder reservoir prior to installing new pads. When caliper piston is pushed back, fluid is forced out of caliper and into reservoir. After pads are installed and seated, fill reservoir to MAX mark.

1. Raise and support vehicle, then remove front wheels.
2. Using open end wrench to hold guide pin head, **Fig. 1,** remove lower caliper mounting bolt.

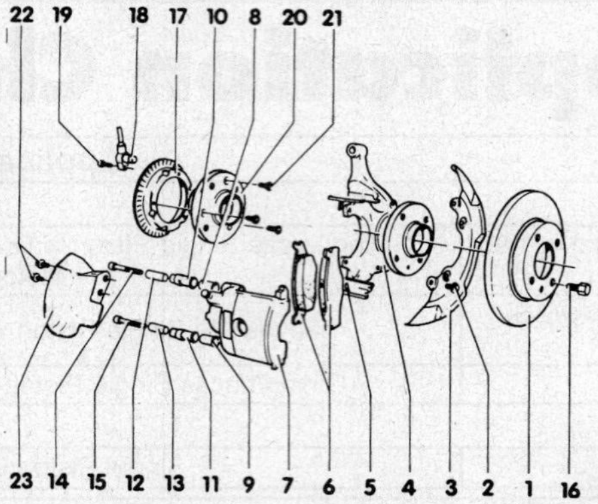

1.Brake Disc
2.Bolt
3.Disc Shield
4.Hub & Knuckle
5.Pad Retaining Spring
6.Brake Pad
7.Caliper
8.Upper Sleeve
9.Lower Sleeve
10.Upper Bushing
11.Lower Bushing
12.Upper Spacer Sleeve
13.Lower Spacer Sleeve
14.Upper Mountig Bolt
15.Lower Mounting Bolt
16.Lug Bolt
17.Brake Disc
18.ABS Speed Sensor
19.Bolt
20.Hub
21.Screw
22.Bolt
23.Air Deflector

VW4079300005000X

Fig. 1 Front brake components

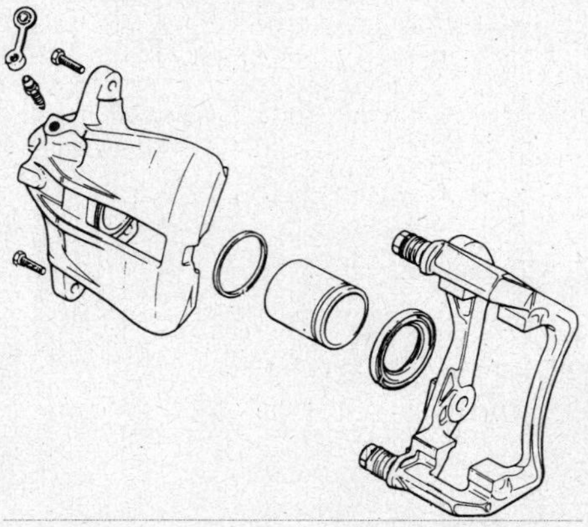

VW4079300006000X

Fig. 2 Exploded view of caliper

3. Swing caliper upward, then remove brake pads.
4. Push piston back into caliper housing.
5. Install brake pads and heat shield with shield facing piston, then swing caliper downward and install "new" lower self-locking mounting bolt. Use an open end wrench to hold guide pin in position when tightening lower mounting bolt. Tighten bolt to specifications.
6. Depress brake pedal several times to position caliper piston and seat brake pads.
7. Reverse remaining procedure. Tighten bolts and nuts to specifications.

CALIPER SERVICE

OVERHAUL

Refer to **Fig. 2** when servicing caliper.

1. Place wooden block between caliper piston and caliper housing, then apply compressed air to brake line bore to force piston from housing.
2. Remove piston seal from caliper piston bore using a plastic rod. **If either caliper piston or caliper piston bore is corroded, pitted or scored, affected part must be replaced.**
3. Slide dust cap onto piston, then lubricate piston and caliper piston bore lightly with a suitable brake cylinder paste.
4. Install piston into caliper bore and insert inner lip of dust cap into groove on caliper.
5. Open bleeder screw, then press caliper piston into caliper as far as possible, ensuring outer lip of dust cap slips into groove in piston.

BRAKE ROTOR

REPLACE

1. Raise and support vehicle, then remove front wheels.
2. Remove brake caliper, then remove brake disc securing screw.
3. Remove brake disc.
4. Reverse procedure to instal. Tighten bolts and nuts to specifications.

DISC BRAKE SPECIFICATIONS

Model	Year	Brake Lining Wear Limit Inch	Rotor Nominal Thickness Inch	Rotor Min. Refinish Thickness Inch	Rotor Discard Thickness Inch⑨	Rotor Thickness Variation Parallelism Inch	Rotor Lateral Run Out (T.I.R.) Inch
Cabrio	1998–99	.276②	④	—	①	.0004	.0012
	2000–01	.276②	.866	—	.787	—	—
EuroVan	1998–2001	.078	⑤	—	⑥	—	.003
Golf & Jetta 4 Cylinder	1998	.276②	④	—	①	—	—
	1999–2001	.276②	.866	—	.787	—	—
Golf, GTI & Jetta VR6	1998–2001	.276②	.984	—	.866	—	—
New Beetle 1.8L	1998–2001	.276②	.984	—	.955	—	—
New Beetle 1.9L & 2.0L	1998–2001	.276②	.866	—	.787	—	—
Passat	1998–2001	③	⑦	—	⑧	.0004	.012

① — Solid rotor. 394 inch; vented rotor. 709 inch.
② — Includes backing plate.
③ — Teves/ATE brake,. 080 inch; Lucas brake,. 078 inch.
④ — Solid rotor. 472 inch; vented rotor,. 787 inch.
⑤ — Vented rotor,. 945 inch; solid rotor,. 709 inch.
⑥ — Vented rotor,. 787 inch; solid rotor,. 591 inch.
⑦ — Teves-ATE rotor,. 984 inch; Lucas rotor,. 866 inch.
⑧ — Teves-ATE rotor,. 906 inch; Lucas rotor,. 787 inch.
⑨ — Stamped on rotor.

TIGHTENING SPECIFICATIONS

Year	Component	Torque, Ft. Lbs.
1998–2001	Brake Pad Carrier Lower & Upper Bolts	26
	Brake Pad Carrier Center Bolt	92
	Splash Shield Bolts	89①
	Wheel Lug Nut	89
	Wheel Speed Sensor Bolt	89①

① — Inch lbs.

Teves/Ate Single Piston w/Dual Mounting Bolts, Front

INDEX

	Page No.
Brake Pad Service	8-126
Brake Rotor, Replace	8-126
Caliper Service	8-126
Overhaul	8-126
Disc Brake Specifications	8-127
Tightening Specifications	8-127

BRAKE PAD SERVICE

Brake pads used in this caliper are directional, if pads are to be reinstalled mark them for location prior to removal.

Always remove some brake fluid from master cylinder reservoir prior to installing new pads. When caliper piston is pushed back, fluid is forced out of caliper and into reservoir. After pads are installed and seated, fill reservoir to MAX mark.

1. Raise and support vehicle, then remove front wheels.
2. Pry off brake pad retaining spring using a suitable pry bar, **Fig. 1.**
3. Remove protective caps from caliper guide pin bushings.
4. Remove upper and lower guide pins from caliper and bushing using a suitable hex wrench.
5. Pull caliper from frame and support aside without placing brake fluid hose under a strain.
6. Remove pads from caliper frame and/or caliper housing.
7. Clean rust, scale and old adhesive from caliper, frame and slider surfaces, then lubricate slider surfaces and guide pins using a suitable brake grease.
8. Push piston back into caliper housing using a suitable piston compressor.
9. Install brake pads. Inner pad is installed to caliper, outer pad is installed to frame.
10. **Arrow marked on each pad must be pointed downward, Fig. 2.**
11. Remove foil backing on outer brake pad only.
12. Place caliper in place onto frame, install caliper guide pins, then tighten to specifications.
13. Depress brake pedal several times to position caliper piston and seat brake pads.
14. Reverse remaining procedure. Tighten bolts and nuts to specifications.

CALIPER SERVICE

OVERHAUL

Refer to **Fig. 3** when servicing caliper.

1. Place wooden block between caliper

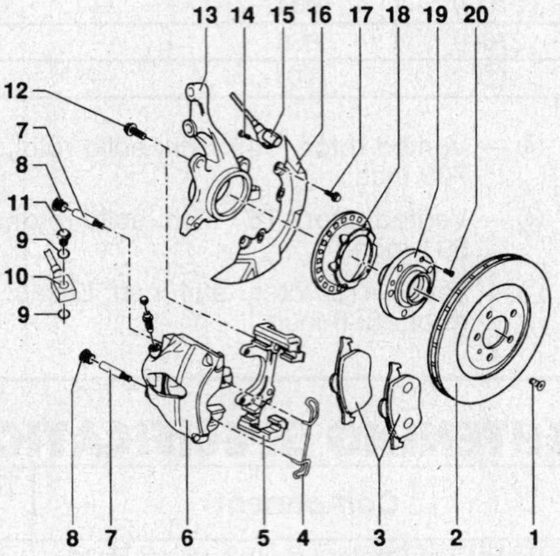

Fig. 1 Front brake components

piston and caliper housing, then apply compressed air to brake line bore to force piston from housing.

2. Remove piston seal from caliper piston bore using a plastic rod. **If either caliper piston or caliper piston bore is corroded, pitted or scored, affected part must be replaced.**
3. Slide dust cap onto piston, then lubricate piston and caliper piston bore lightly with a suitable brake cylinder paste.
4. Install piston into caliper bore and insert inner lip of dust cap into groove on caliper.
5. Open bleeder screw, then press caliper piston into caliper as far as possible, ensuring outer lip of dust cap slips into groove in piston.

BRAKE ROTOR

REPLACE

1. Raise and support vehicle, then re-

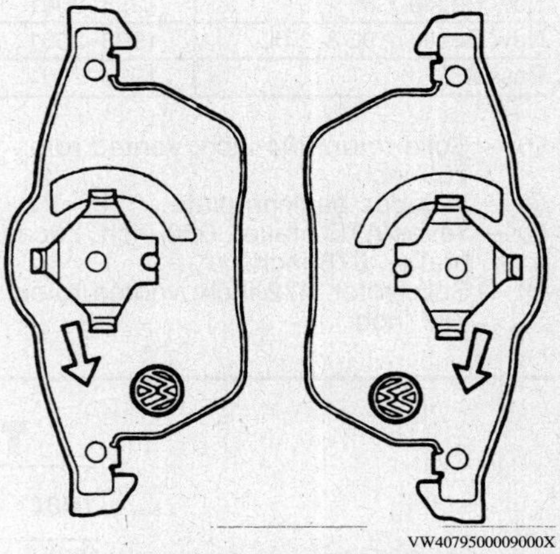

Fig. 2 Brake pad installation direction

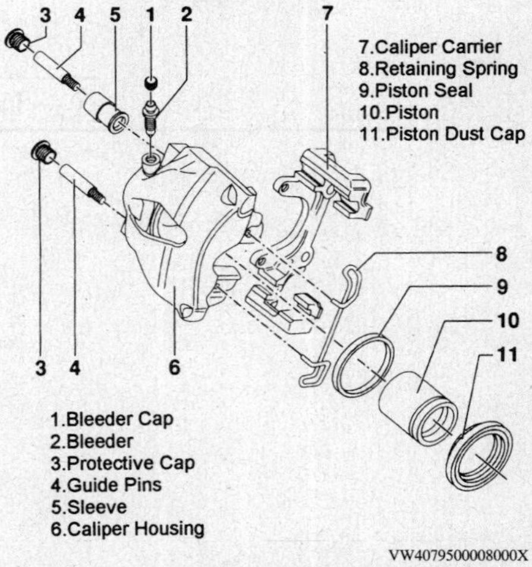

Fig. 3 Exploded view of caliper

move front wheels.

2. Remove brake caliper, then remove brake disc securing screw.
3. Remove brake disc.
4. Reverse procedure to instal. Tighten bolts and nuts to specifications.

DISC BRAKE SPECIFICATIONS

Model	Year	Brake Lining Wear	Rotor Nominal Thickness Inch	Rotor Min. Refinish Thickness Inch	Rotor Discard Thickness Inch⑦	Rotor Thickness Variation Parallelism Inch	Rotor Lateral Run Out (T.I.R.) Inch
Golf & Jetta 4 Cylinder	1998	.276②	④	—	①	—	—
	1999–2001	.276②	.866	—	.787	—	—
Golf, GTI & Jetta VR6	1998–2001	.276②	.984	—	.866	—	—
Passat	1998–2001	③	⑤	—	⑥	.0004	.012

① — Solid rotor. 394 inch; vented rotor. 709 inch.
② — Includes backing plate.
③ — Teves/ATE brake,. 080 inch; Lucas brake,. 078 inch.
④ — Solid rotor. 472 inch; vented rotor,. 787 inch.
⑤ — Teves-ATE rotor,. 984 inch; Lucas rotor,. 866 inch.
⑥ — Teves-ATE rotor,. 906 inch; Lucas rotor,. 787 inch.
⑦ — Stamped on rotor.

TIGHTENING SPECIFICATIONS

Year	Component	Torque, Ft. Lbs.
1998–2001	Caliper Guide Pins	18
	Brake Hose Banjo Bolt	22
	Caliper Assembly Mounting Bolts	92
	Rotor To Hub Screw	48①
	Splash Shield Bolts	89①
	Wheel Lug Nut	89
	Wheel Speed Sensor Bolt	89①

① — Inch lbs.

Single Piston Rear Disc Brake

INDEX

	Page No.
Adjustments	8-128
Parking Brake	8-128
Brake Caliper Pre-Bleeding	8-128
Brake Pad Service	8-128
Brake Rotor, Replace	8-128
Caliper Service	8-128
Overhaul	8-128
Disc Brake Specifications	8-129
Tightening Specifications	8-129

BRAKE PAD SERVICE

This caliper uses an internal screw type parking brake self adjusting mechanism. If the caliper piston is pushed back into caliper this mechanism will be destroyed. Always return piston by rotating it clockwise using a suitable tool.

Always remove some brake fluid from master cylinder reservoir prior to installing new pads. When caliper piston is pushed back, fluid is forced out of caliper and into reservoir. After pads are installed and seated, fill reservoir to MAX mark.

1. Raise and support vehicle, then remove rear wheels.
2. Disconnect parking cables from caliper, **Fig. 1.**
3. Remove mounting bolts, then the caliper.
4. Screw piston into housing using caliper piston seating tool No. 3272, or equivalent, **Fig. 2,** by turning clockwise and pushing firmly.
5. Install brake pads onto carrier, then the caliper and "new" self-locking mounting bolts. Tighten mounting bolts to specifications.
6. Connect parking brake cable, then adjust parking brake as outlined under "Parking Brake, Adjust."

CALIPER SERVICE

OVERHAUL

Refer to **Fig. 3** when servicing caliper.

1. Secure caliper in a suitable soft-jawed vise, then remove piston from bore by turning counterclockwise with caliper piston seating tool No. 3272, or equivalent, **Fig. 2.**
2. Pry piston seals from groove being careful not to score the piston bore.
3. Slide outer dust boot onto piston.
4. Lubricate piston and cylinder bore lightly with a suitable brake cylinder paste.
5. Insert inner lip of dust boot into groove of brake cylinder.
6. Press piston down, while turning clockwise. Turn piston in as far as possible. Outer lip of dust cap must slip into groove of piston.

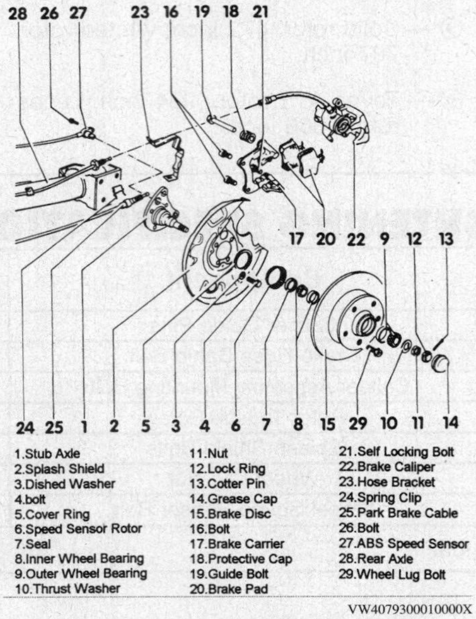

Fig. 1 Rear brake components

ADJUSTMENTS

PARKING BRAKE

1. Ensure parking brake lever is in Off position, then tighten adjusting nut until levers on calipers just move off their stops. **Maximum permissible distance from stop is. 059 inch.**
2. Apply and release parking brake and ensure both wheels rotate freely.

BRAKE ROTOR

REPLACE

1. Raise and support vehicle, then remove front wheels.
2. Remove brake caliper, then remove brake disc securing screw.
3. Remove brake disc.

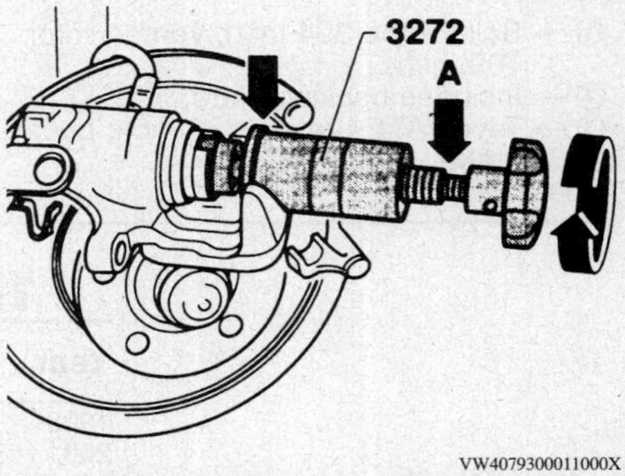

Fig. 2 Caliper piston installation

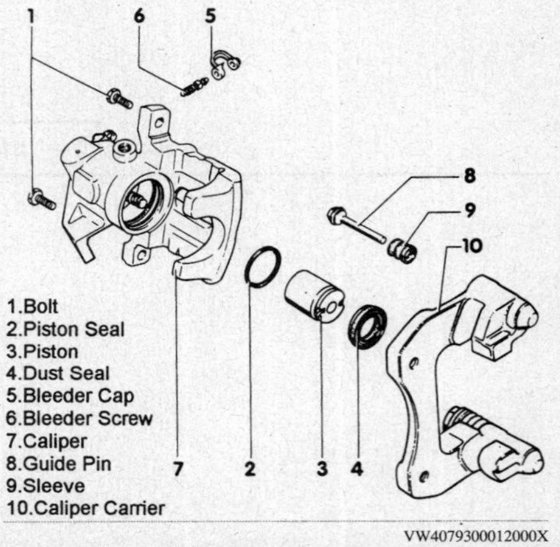

Fig. 3 Exploded view of caliper

4. Reverse procedure to install. Tighten bolts and nuts to specifications.

BRAKE CALIPER PRE-BLEEDING

1. Place caliper so that piston bore is facing downward.
2. Open bleeder valve, then connect a suitable hose and fill with brake fluid through bleeder valve until fluid flows out from brake hose connection.

DISC BRAKE SPECIFICATIONS

Model	Year	Brake Lining Wear Limit Inch	Rotor Nominal Thickness Inch	Rotor Min. Re- finish Thickness Inch	Rotor Discard Thickness Inch②	Thickness Variation Parallelism Inch	Rotor Lateral Runout (T.I.R.) Inch
Cabrio	1998	.276①	.394	—	.315	—	—
	2000–01	.295①	.354	—	.276	—	—
EuroVan	1998–2001	.078	.472	—	.394	—	—
Golf & Jetta 4 Cylinder	1998	.276①	.394	—	.315	—	.002
	1999–2001	.295①	.354	—	.315	—	—
Golf & Jetta VR6	1998	.276①	.394	—	.315	—	.002
	1999–2001	.295①	.393	—	.276	—	—
New Beetle 1.8L	1998–2001	.295①	.354	—	.275	—	—
New Beetle 1.9L & 2.0L	1998–2001	.295①	.354	—	.275	—	—
Passat	1998–99	.078	.393	—	.314	—	—

① — Includes backing plate. ② — Stamped on rotor.

TIGHTENING SPECIFICATIONS

Year	Component	Torque, Ft. Lbs.
1998–2001	Disc Brake Shield Bolts	89①
	Rear Brake Pad Carrier Bolts	41
	Rear Carrier To Brake Pad Carrier Bolts	21
	Wheel Lug Nuts	89

① — Inch lbs.

Drum Brakes

INDEX

	Page No.
Adjustments	8-130
Parking Brake Cable	8-130
Brake Service	8-130
Shoes, Replace	8-130
Wheel Cylinder Overhaul	8-130
Drum Brake Specifications	8-131
Tightening Specifications	8-131

BRAKE SERVICE

SHOES, REPLACE

Failure to follow outlined procedures may lead to a reduction in parking brake efficiency.

1. Remove one wheel bolt, then push self adjusting wedge upwards with a suitable screwdriver through wheel bolt hole to back off brake shoes, **Fig. 1**.
2. Install wheel bolt and tighten to specifications, then remove grease cap with puller tool No. VW 637/2, or equivalent.
3. Remove cotter pin and axle nut, then pull off brake drum.
4. Remove spring retainer by pressing it against spring and turning ¼ turn.
5. Disconnect brake shoes from anchor pins, then remove return spring.
6. Disconnect parking brake cable from lever, then the spring for adjusting wedge and upper return spring using suitable pliers.
7. Remove brake shoes.
8. Install pushrod and brake shoe in a suitable soft jaw vise, then disconnect tensioning spring.
9. Install "new" brake shoe in vise, slide on pushrod, then connect tensioning spring on pushrod and brake shoe.
10. Insert adjusting wedge. Lug on adjusting wedge faces backing plate and must be in initial position.
11. Attach other brake shoe with lever to pushrod, then install upper return spring.
12. Connect parking brake cable onto lever, then place brake shoes onto brake cylinder pistons.
13. Connect lower return spring onto brake shoes, then mount brake shoes onto retaining pins.
14. Connect spring for adjusting wedge onto adjusting wedge and brake shoe, then install retaining springs and spring retainers.
15. Install brake drum and adjust wheel bearings as outlined in "Rear Axle & Suspension" section.
16. Apply brake pedal firmly once to set self-adjusting mechanism.

WHEEL CYLINDER OVERHAUL

Refer to **Fig. 2** to aid in overhaul of wheel cylinder.

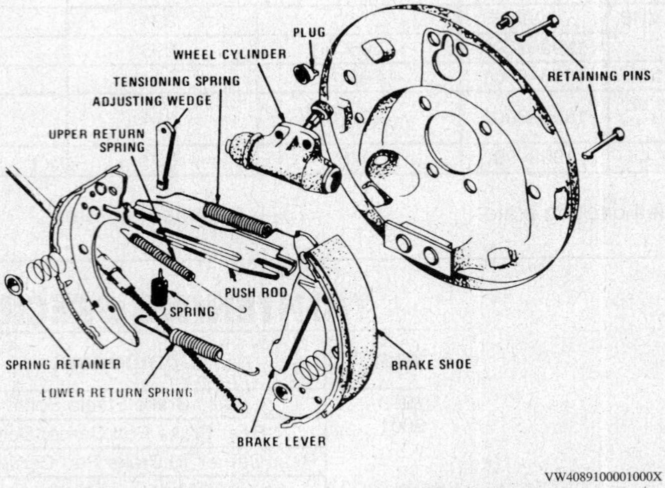

Fig. 1 Exploded view of brake assembly

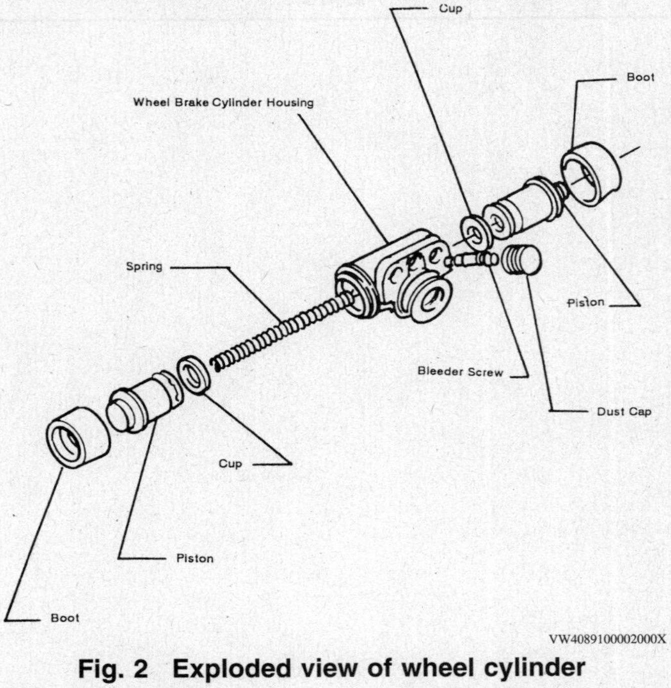

Fig. 2 Exploded view of wheel cylinder

ADJUSTMENTS

PARKING BRAKE CABLE

1. Apply brake pedal firmly once, then pull parking brake lever to fourth tooth.
2. Tighten adjusting nuts until both wheels can just be turned by hand.
3. Release parking brake and ensure wheels rotate freely, then tighten locknuts.

DRUM BRAKE SPECIFICATIONS

Model	Year	Brake Lining Wear Limit, Inch②	Brake Drum Inside Diameter, Inches			Drum Runout Limit, Inch	Drum Maximum Out Of Roundness, Inch
			Nominal	Maximum Refinish	Maximum Inside Diameter (Discard Limit)①		
Cabrio	1998	.098	7.874	7.893	7.913	—	—
Golf & Jetta	1998	.098	7.874	—	7.913	—	—
New Beetle	1998–2001	.098	9.055	—	9.094	—	—

① — Maximum brake drum inside diameter (discard limit) is stamped on drum.

② — Above rivet head or shoe. Original equipment type brake linings.

TIGHTENING SPECIFICATIONS

Year	Component	Torque, Ft. Lbs.
1998–2001	Brake Cylinder Mounting Bolts	89①
	Brake Assembly To Axle Mounting Bolt	44
	Wheel Lug Nuts	89

① — Inch lbs.

Hydraulic Brake Systems

INDEX

	Page No.		Page No.		Page No.
Adjustments	8-132	Conventional Bleed	8-132	**Component Replacement**	8-132
Brake Pressure Regulator	8-132	Pressure Bleed	8-132	Master Cylinder	8-132
Brake System Bleed	8-132	Scan Tool Bleed	8-133		

ADJUSTMENTS

BRAKE PRESSURE REGULATOR

Except EuroVan

The brake pressure regulator is mounted on a bracket and operates by a spring attached to the rear axle.

Inspect with vehicle empty of occupants and the fuel tank full.

1. Firmly depress brake pedal once, with vehicle on the ground.
2. Release pedal suddenly and ensure lever on pressure regulator lever moves.
3. Raise and support vehicle.
4. Remove bleeder screw on lefthand front caliper and connect gauge tool No. US 1016, or equivalent.
5. Remove bleeder screw on righthand rear wheel cylinder or caliper and connect gauge tool.
6. Bleed both hoses and gauges with bleeding screws on gauges, then lower vehicle and bounce rear of vehicle several times.
7. **On Golf, GTI & Jetta models,** depress brake pedal until gauge of lefthand front caliper reads 1015 psi. Gauge of rear axle should read 522–609 psi.
8. **On Golf, GTI & Jetta models,** increase pressure to brake pedal until gauge of lefthand front caliper reads 1450 psi. Gauge of rear axle should read 710–798 psi.
9. **On New Beetle models,** proceed as follows:
   a. Depress brake pedal until gauge of lefthand front caliper reads 1015 psi.
   b. Gauge of rear axle should read 551–638 psi. on models with drum brakes and 478–565 on models with rear disc brakes.
   c. Increase pressure to brake pedal until gauge of lefthand front caliper reads 1450 psi. Gauge of rear axle should read 740–827 psi on models with drum brakes and 609–696 psi on models with rear disc brakes.
10. **On all models,** release brake pedal.
11. Adjust regulator spring tension.
12. If test pressure is too high, decrease spring tension.
13. If test pressure is too low, increase spring tension.
14. Inspect regulator pressures and adjust if required.
15. Disconnect pressure gauges and bleed brakes as outlined under "Brake System Bleed."

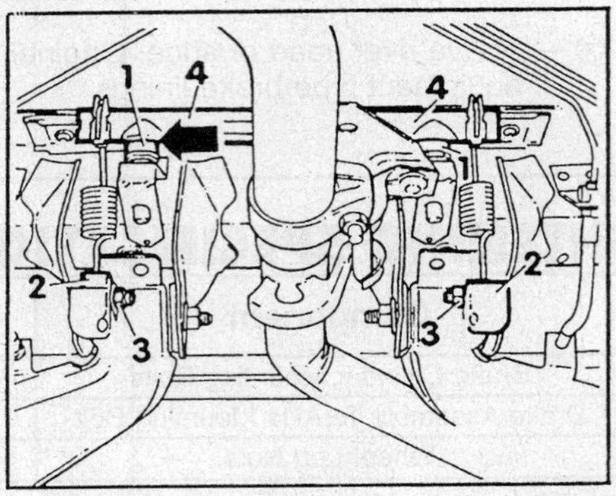

VW4099100001010X

Fig. 1 Brake pressure regulator adjustment (Part 1 of 2). EuroVan

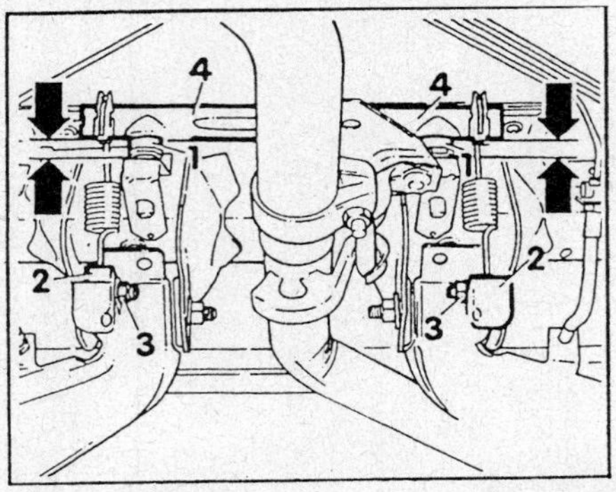

VW4099100001020X

Fig. 1 Brake pressure regulator adjustment (Part 2 of 2). EuroVan

EuroVan

1. Connect pressure gauge tool No. VAG 1310, or equivalent, to righthand front caliper and lefthand rear wheel cylinder.
2. Bleed both gauges, then depress brake pedal and obtain specified pressure at front axle and read measured pressure at rear axle. Front should be 725 psi and rear axle should be 290–319 psi.
3. Refer to **Fig. 1** during the following adjustment procedures:
   a. Screw back both buffer stops **1.**
   b. Mark position of mounting **2** on trailing arm, then loosen bolts **3** and slide mounting **2.**
   c. Sliding mounting **2** downward increases pressure. Upward decreases pressure.
4. Adjustment of second sliding mount **2** is only required if horizontal beam **4** is more than. 157 inches from horizontal beam (arrows). A. 039 inch adjustment upward or downward of sliding mounting **2** will alter rear axle pressure by approximately 58 psi.
5. Correct pressure regulator setting at second mounting **2.**
6. Counter hold and tighten bolt **3.**

COMPONENT REPLACEMENT

MASTER CYLINDER

1. Siphon brake fluid from reservoir, then disconnect brake lines from master cylinder and electrical connectors from brake lamp switches.
2. Remove master cylinder to firewall or brake booster attaching nuts, then the master cylinder and seal.
3. Position new master cylinder and seal to firewall or brake booster, then install attaching nuts.
4. Transfer brake lamp switches to new master cylinder, then connect brake lines and electrical connectors.
5. Fill fluid reservoir with clean brake fluid and bleed brake system.

BRAKE SYSTEM BLEED

CONVENTIONAL BLEED

1. Connect suitable bottle with transparent hose to each wheel.
2. Pump brake pedal several times, then hold.
3. Open and close bleeder screw, then release pedal.
4. Bleed brake system using the following sequence:
   a. Righthand rear caliper/wheel cylinder.
   b. Lefthand rear caliper/wheel cylinder.
   c. Righthand front caliper.
   d. Lefthand front caliper.
5. Repeat procedure until brake fluid flows without air bubbles.

PRESSURE BLEED

1. Connect brake filling and bleeding unit tool No. US 1116, or equivalent.
2. **On models equipped with brake pressure regulator,** press regulator toward rear of vehicle when bleeding brakes.

3. **On all models,** open bleeder screw and bleed brakes using the following sequence:
   a. Righthand rear.
   b. Lefthand rear.
   c. Righthand front.
   d. Lefthand front.

SCAN TOOL BLEED

1. Connect a suitable scan tool to the Diagnostic Link Connector (DLC) as outlined under "Diagnosis & Testing."
2. Connect a suitable pressure brake bleeder following pressure bleeder manufacturer's instructions.
3. Access "Brake Electronics," then "Basic Settings" using scan tool.
4. Follow step by step procedure of scan tool to bleed brakes.

Power Brake Units

INDEX

Page No.		Page No.		Page No.	
Power Brake Unit Service	8-133	Brake Booster Inspection	8-133	Brake Booster, Replace	8-133

POWER BRAKE UNIT SERVICE

BRAKE BOOSTER, REPLACE

1. Remove master cylinder as outlined in this section.
2. Disconnect vacuum line(s) from booster.
3. Remove brake booster attaching bolts.
4. Disconnect booster pushrod from brake pedal.
5. Reverse procedure to install.

BRAKE BOOSTER INSPECTION

1. Depress brake pedal firmly approximately 20 times with engine Off.
2. Depress brake pedal and hold.
3. Start engine. If brake booster is working properly, pedal will fall slightly and then hold.

Anti-Lock Brakes

INDEX

	Page No.
Description	8-134
Diagnosis & Testing	8-134
Accessing Diagnostic Trouble Codes	8-134
Clearing Diagnostic Trouble Codes	8-135
Diagnostic Tests	8-135
Bosch 5.3	8-135
Bosch 5	8-135
ITT Mark 20 IE	8-135
Teves Type 04	8-135
Teves Type 20	8-135
Diagnostic Trouble Code Interpretation	8-135
Testing	8-135
Diagnostic Chart Index	8-137
Precautions	8-134
Air Bag Systems	8-134
Audio Coded Anti-Theft System	8-134
Battery Ground Cable	8-134
Brake Fluid	8-134
System Service	8-163
Brake System Bleed	8-163
Component Replacement	8-163
Coding Control Module	8-163
Control Module	8-164
Hydraulic Modulator	8-163
Troubleshooting	8-134

PRECAUTIONS

AIR BAG SYSTEMS

Do not use computer memory saver tool on air bag equipped models. Using the tool will keep the air bag system charged and may cause accidental air bag unit activation.

Refer to "Air Bag System Precautions" in the front of this manual for system disarming and arming procedures.

BATTERY GROUND CABLE

Prior to service, disconnect battery ground cable and isolate as required.

AUDIO CODED ANTI-THEFT SYSTEM

Some models are equipped with a radio anti-theft system that will disable the system when battery power is interrupted. Unless the system is reset the radio will not operate.

1. Turn radio On. SAFE and 1000 should be displayed.
2. Enter radio code using first four program station buttons. Security code will appear on display.
3. Depress and hold righthand side of radio righthand or lefthand blocker until anti-theft coding is activated indicated by a brief signal sound.
4. If code number has been entered properly, when ignition key is removed a diode on front of radio will flash.

BRAKE FLUID

Do not allow brake fluid to come in contact with painted surfaces.

Brake fluid absorbs moisture from the air and should therefore be replaced every two years.

Do not use silicone based brake fluid (DOT 5). Even the smallest traces may cause corrosion in the brake system.

DESCRIPTION

Refer to **Figs. 1 through 6** to identify ABS system components and type.

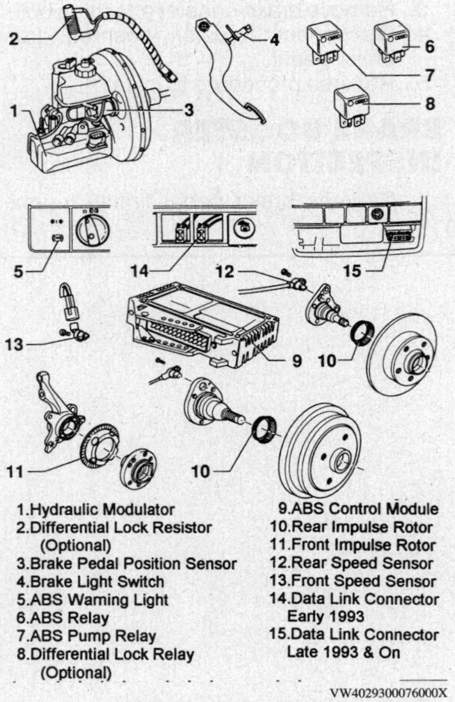

Fig. 1 ABS components. Cabrio, Golf III, GTI & Jetta III w/Teves type 04

TROUBLESHOOTING

Refer to "Diagnosis & Testing" for ABS troubleshooting.

DIAGNOSIS & TESTING

Accessing Diagnostic Trouble Codes

The ABS control unit has a permanent fault memory. If fault conditions occur at electrically monitored sensors or components they are stored in memory.

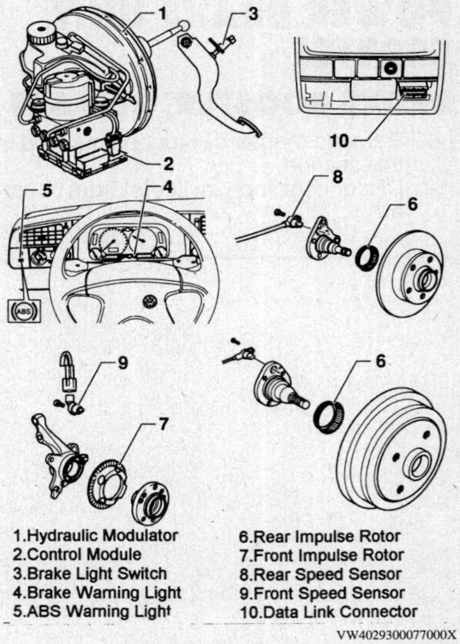

Fig. 2 ABS components. Cabrio, Golf III, GTI & Jetta III w/Teves type 20

Faults are stored with varying priorities. Solenoid faults have the highest priority and are displayed first. Faults which occur occasionally or sporadic faults have the lowest priority and are displayed last.

Do not drive vehicle with VAG 1551 or equivalent scan tool connected.

1. Connect a suitable scan tool to the Diagnostic Link Connector (DLC). Refer to **Figs. 7 through 11** for DLC locations and types.
2. Follow scan tool manufacturer's instructions to access Anti-Lock Brake System (ABS) Electronic Control Unit (ECU) Diagnostic Trouble Codes (DTCs).
3. Record all DTCs, then refer to "Diagnostic Chart Index" to locate proper DTC tables for vehicle.

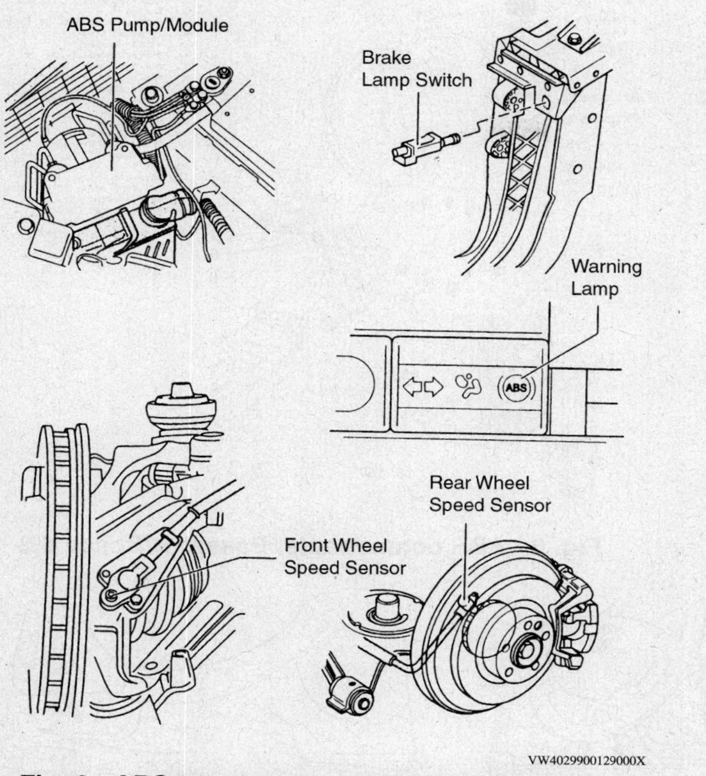

Fig. 3 ABS components. EuroVan w/Bosch 5

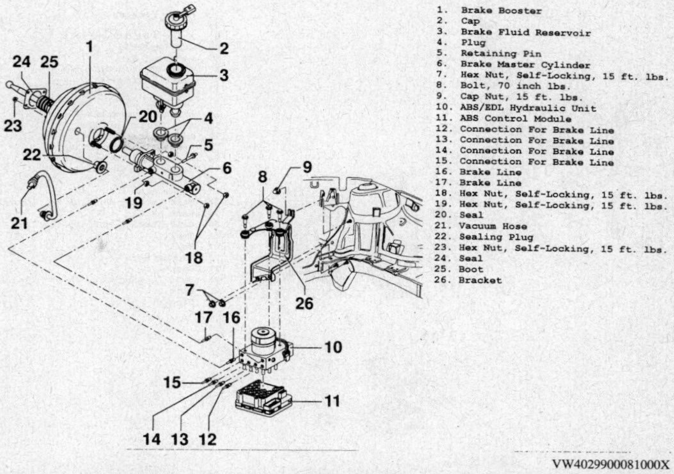

Fig. 4 ABS components. Golf & Jetta w/ITT Mark 20 IE

Refer to the "Diagnostic Chart Index" for DTC identification and location.

Diagnostic Trouble Code Interpretation

Refer to the "Diagnostic Chart Index" for diagnostic trouble code identification.

Diagnostic Tests

BOSCH 5

Refer to **Figs. 12 through 24** for DTC diagnosis.

BOSCH 5.3

Refer to **Figs. 25 through 40** for DTC diagnosis.

ITT MARK 20 IE

Refer to **Figs. 41 through 48** for DTC diagnosis.

TEVES TYPE 04

Refer to **Figs. 49 through 61** for DTC diagnosis.

TEVES TYPE 20

Teves model 20 ABS control modules are coded to the vehicle. If a DTC is accessed that requires coding of control module, refer to "Coding Teves Type 20 Control Module" for procedures.

Refer to **Figs. 62 through 67** for DTC diagnosis.

Clearing Diagnostic Trouble Codes

Follow scan tool manufacturer's instructions to clear DTCs.

Testing

Obtain the following test equipment: pin-out test box tool No. VAG 1598, **Fig. 68,** adapter tool No. VAG 1598/3, test kit connector tool No. VAG 1594 and multimeter tool No. US 1119, or equivalents.

Connect ABS control unit multi-pin electrical connector to pin-out tester tool No. VAG 1598 using adapter tool No. VAG 1598/3, test kit connector tool No. VAG 1594, or equivalents. **The terminal numbering on the pin-out tester tool No. VAG 1598 test box is identical to the numbering of the control unit.**

When using these tests in conjunction with a scan tool, perform only those tests recommended in the DTC tables.

When using these tests without a scan tool or on vehicles for which the self-diagnosis feature does not determine the problem source, perform all steps in sequence.

Ensure fuses and ground wires for control unit are in satisfactory condition, and that ignition switch remains in Off position during all test steps.

When performing electrical testing, refer to wiring diagrams, **Figs. 69 through 79,** and test steps, **Figs. 80 and 81.**

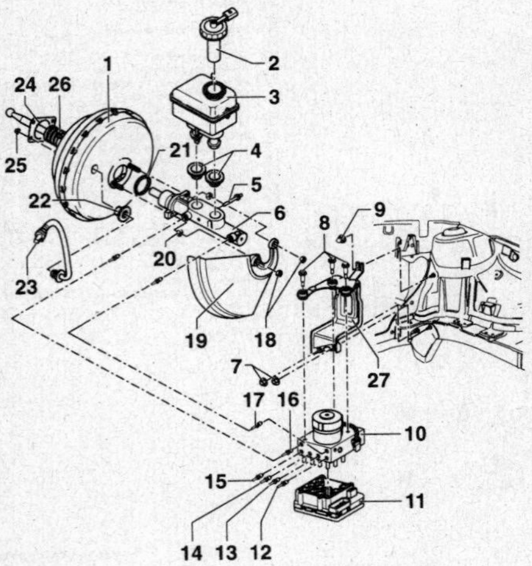

Fig. 5 ABS components. New Beetle w/ITT Mark 20 IE

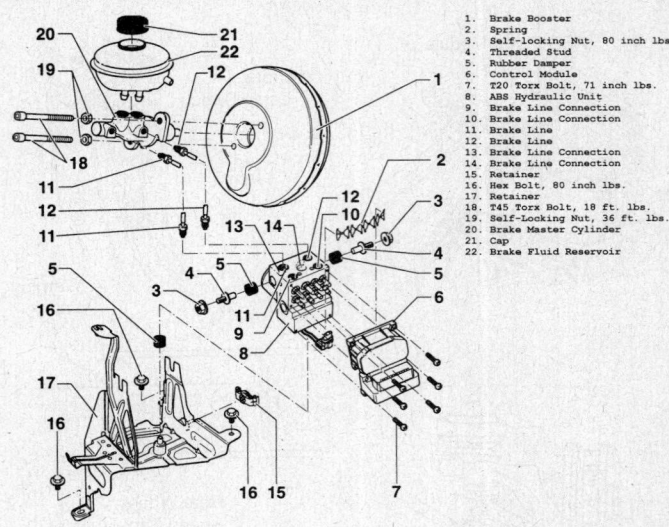

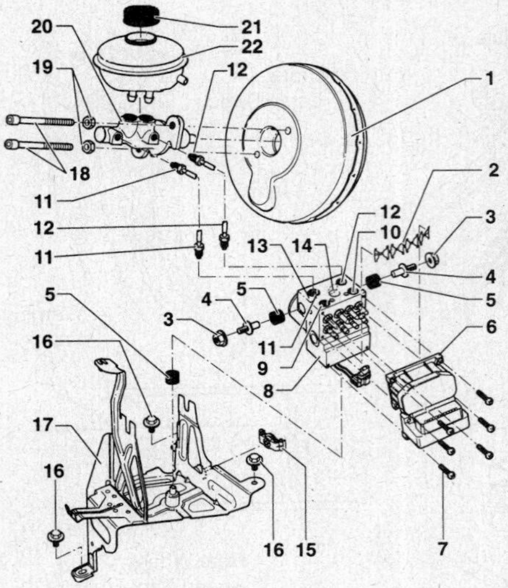

Fig. 6 ABS components. Passat w/Bosch 5.3

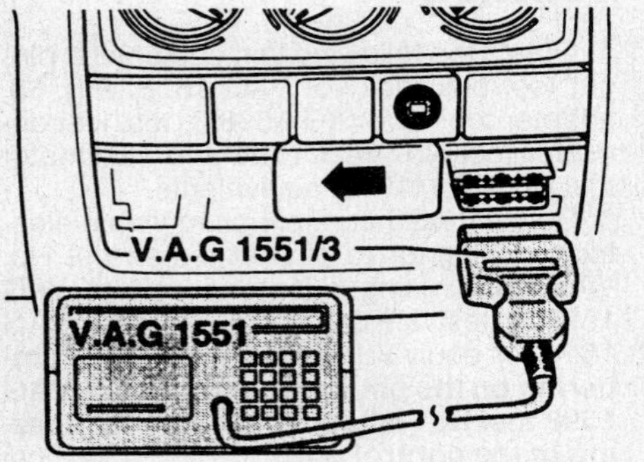

Fig. 7 Diagnostic Link Connectors (DLC). Cabrio & 1998 Golf III, GTI & Jetta III

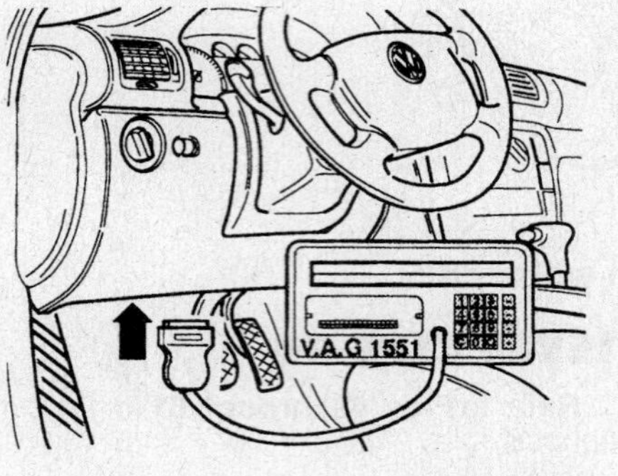

Fig. 8 Diagnostic Link Connectors (DLC). Passat

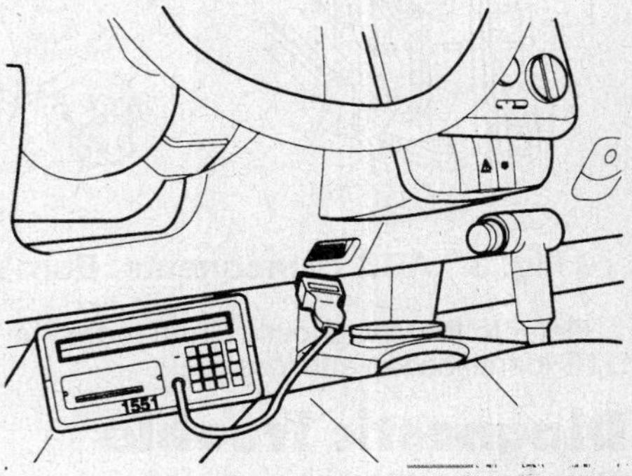

Fig. 9 Diagnostic Link Connectors (DLC). New Beetle

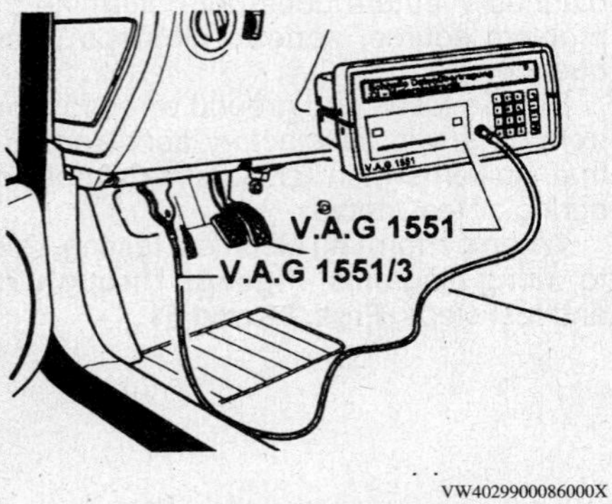

Fig. 10 Diagnostic Link Connectors (DLC). 1999–2001 Golf & Jetta

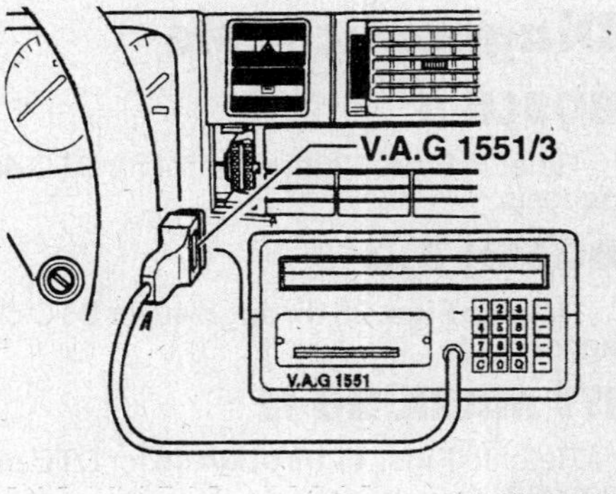

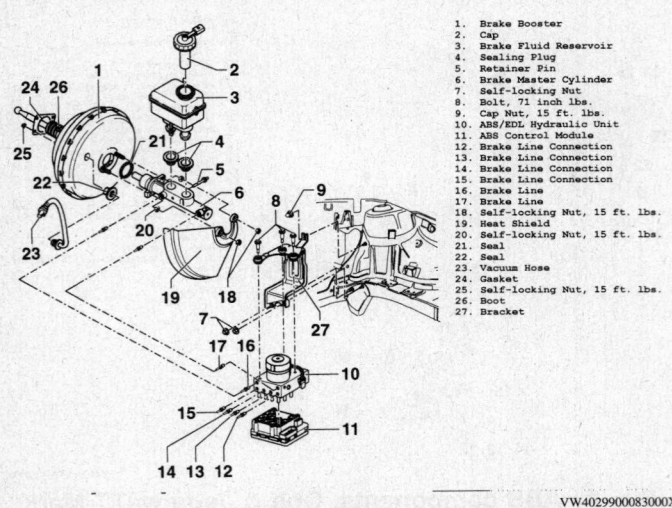

Fig. 11 Diagnostic Link Connectors (DLC). EuroVan

DIAGNOSTIC CHART INDEX

Code	Description	Page No.	Fig. No.
CABRIO & 1998 GOLF III, GTI & JETTA III w/TEVES TYPE 04			
00000, 00257 & 00259/1112, 1114 & 4444	No DTC Recognized & Inlet Valves	8-144	49
00257	No DTC Recognized & Inlet Valves	8-144	49
00259/1112	No DTC Recognized & Inlet Valves	8-144	49
1114	No DTC Recognized & Inlet Valves	8-144	49
4444	No DTC Recognized & Inlet Valves	8-144	49
00265	Inlet & Outlet Valves	8-144	50
00267	Inlet & Outlet Valves	8-144	50
00273	Inlet & Outlet Valves	8-144	50
00274/1132	Inlet & Outlet Valves	8-144	50
1134	Inlet & Outlet Valves	8-144	50
1211	Inlet & Outlet Valves	8-144	50
1212	Inlet & Outlet Valves	8-144	50
00275	Differential Lock & Outlet Valves	8-144	51
00276	Differential Lock & Outlet Valves	8-144	51
00279	Differential Lock & Outlet Valves	8-144	51
00280/1213	Differential Lock & Outlet Valves	8-144	51
1214	Differential Lock & Outlet Valves	8-144	51
1223	Differential Lock & Outlet Valves	8-144	51
1224	Differential Lock & Outlet Valves	8-144	51
00283/1233	Front Lefthand Wheel Speed Sensor	8-145	52
00285/1241	Front Righthand Wheel Speed Sensor	8-145	53
00287/1243	Rear Righthand Wheel Speed Sensor	8-145	54
00290/1311	Rear Lefthand Wheel Speed Sensor	8-145	55
00292	Hydraulic Energy Supply & Battery Supply Voltage	8-145	56
00532/1313	Hydraulic Energy Supply & Battery Supply Voltage	8-145	56
2234	Hydraulic Energy Supply & Battery Supply Voltage	8-145	56
00547/2133	ABS Pressure Control Switch	8-145	57
005994	Plausibility Pressure/Brake Lamp Switch	8-145	58
00634	Series Resistance	8-145	59
00793/3231	Brake Pedal Position Sensor	8-146	60
01276	Hydraulic Pump & Control Module Malfunction	8-146	61
65535/1111	Hydraulic Pump & Control Module Malfunction	8-146	61
4133	Hydraulic Pump & Control Module Malfunction	8-146	61
CABRIO & 1998 GOLF III, GTI & JETTA III w/TEVES TYPE 20			
00000	No DTC Recognized	8-146	62
00283	Front Lefthand Wheel Speed Sensor	8-146	63
00285	Front Righthand Wheel Speed Sensor	8-146	64
00287	Rear Righthand Speed Sensor	8-146	65
00290	Front Lefthand Speed Sensor, Battery Supply Voltage & Control Module Coding	8-146	66
00668	Front Lefthand Speed Sensor, Battery Supply Voltage & Control Module Coding	8-146	66
01044	Front Lefthand Speed Sensor, Battery Supply Voltage & Control Module Coding	8-146	66
01130	ABS Operation, ABS Hydraulic Pump & Control Module Malfunction	8-146	67
01276	ABS Operation, ABS Hydraulic Pump & Control Module Malfunction	8-146	67
65535	ABS Operation, ABS Hydraulic Pump & Control Module Malfunction	8-146	67
EUROVAN			
01200	ABS Valves Supply Voltage & ABS Pump Supply Voltage Or No DTC Recognized	8-139	12
01201	ABS Valves Supply Voltage & ABS Pump Supply Voltage Or No DTC Recognized	8-139	12
00301	ABS Return Flow Pump, ABS Operation Signal Outside Tolerance & Control Module	8-139	13
01130	ABS Return Flow Pump, ABS Operation Signal Outside Tolerance & Control Module	8-139	13
65535	ABS Return Flow Pump, ABS Operation Signal Outside Tolerance & Control Module	8-139	13
00526	Brake Lamp Switch F Open Circuit & Voltage Supply Signal Low	8-139	14
00532	Brake Lamp Switch F Open Circuit & Voltage Supply Signal Low	8-139	14

Continued

DIAGNOSTIC CHART INDEX—Continued

Code	Description	Page No.	Fig. No.
EUROVAN			
00283	Lefthand Front, ABS Wheel Speed Sensor	8-139	15
00285	Righthand Front ABS Wheel Speed Sensor	8-139	16
00290	Lefthand Rear ABS Wheel Speed Sensor	8-139	17
00287	Righthand Rear ABS Wheel Speed Sensor	8-139	18
00257	Front Lefthand Or Righthand ABS Inlet Valve	8-139	19
00259	Front Lefthand Or Righthand ABS Inlet Valve	8-139	19
00273	Rear Lefthand Or Righthand ABS Inlet Valve	8-140	20
00274	Rear Lefthand Or Righthand ABS Inlet Valve	8-140	20
00265	Front Lefthand & Righthand ABS Outlet Valve	8-140	21
00267	Front Lefthand & Righthand ABS Outlet Valve	8-140	21
00276	Rear Lefthand & Righthand ABS Outlet Valve	8-140	22
00275	Rear Lefthand & Righthand ABS Outlet Valve	8-140	22
00642	Front Lefthand & Righthand EDL Switch-Over Valve	8-140	23
00644	Front Lefthand & Righthand EDL Switch-Over Valve	8-140	23
00643	Front Lefthand & Righthand EDL Outlet Valve	8-140	24
00645	Front Lefthand & Righthand EDL Outlet Valve	8-140	24
NEW BEETLE & 1999–2001 GOLF & JETTA			
—	No DTC Recognized	8-142	41
00283	Lefthand Front ABS Wheel Speed Sensor	8-142	42
00285	Righthand Front Wheel Speed Sensor	8-143	43
00287	Righthand Rear Wheel Speed Sensor	8-143	44
00290	Lefthand Rear ABS Wheel Speed Sensor	8-143	45
00668	Vehicle Voltage Terminal 30, Signal Outside Of Tolerance & Control Module Improperly Coded	8-144	46
01044	Vehicle Voltage Terminal 30, Signal Outside Of Tolerance & Control Module Improperly Coded	8-144	46
01130	ABS Operation	8-144	47
01276	ABS Hydraulic Pump & Control Module Fault	8-144	48
65535	ABS Hydraulic Pump & Control Module Fault	8-144	48
PASSAT			
—	No DTC Recognized	8-140	25
00283	Lefthand Front ABS Wheel Speed Sensor	8-140	26
00285	Righthand Front ABS Wheel Speed Sensor	8-140	27
00287	Righthand Rear ABS Wheel Speed Sensor	8-141	28
00290	Lefthand Rear ABS Wheel Speed Sensor	8-141	29
00301	ABS Return Flow Pump & Brake Lamp Switch Open Circuit	8-141	30
00526	ABS Return Flow Pump & Brake Lamp Switch Open Circuit	8-141	30
00529	Speed Information Missing No Signal	8-141	31
00532	Supply Voltage Signal Too Low	8-141	32
00597	Different Wheel Speed Impulses	8-141	33
00623	ABS/Transaxle Electrical Connection	8-141	34
00646	ABS-TCS Motor Electrical Connection 1	8-141	35
00647	ABS-TCS Engine Electrical Connection 2	8-142	36
00761	Fault Stored In Engine Control Module & ABS Operation Implausible Signal	8-142	37
01130	Fault Stored In Engine Control Module & ABS Operation Implausible Signal	8-142	37
01200	Voltage Supply For ABS Valves	8-142	38
01201	ABS Return Flow Pump Supply Voltage	8-142	39
01203	ABS/Instrument Cluster Electrical Connection Open Circuit Or Short To Ground & ABS Control Module Faulty	8-142	40
65535	ABS/Instrument Cluster Electrical Connection Open Circuit Or Short To Ground & ABS Control Module Faulty	8-142	40

VAG 1551 print-out	Possible cause	Malfunction elimination
No DTC recognized	If "No DTC" appears after repairing, On Board Diagnostic (OBD) is ended. If, despite "No DTC recognized" display, ABS system does not operate properly, proceed as follows: 1. Perform road test exceeding 30 km/h (19 mph), 2. Check DTC memory again and repair. 3. If no DTCs are indicated continue checking without OBD and work through complete Electrical checks	
01201 ABS pump supply voltage	Fuse S53 inoperative	– Check fuses, wiring, connections and voltage supply to control module
01200 ABS valves supply voltage	Fuse S54 inoperative	– Replace fuse S54 – Check wiring harness wiring

VW4029900112000X

Fig. 12 Codes 01200, 01201 Or No DTC Recognized: ABS Valves Supply Voltage & ABS Pump Supply Voltage Or No DTC Recognized. EuroVan

VAG 1551 scan tool print-out	Possible cause	Repairing malfunction
00526 Brake light switch F Open circuit	♦ Both brake lights -M9-, -M10- or control module -J104- inoperative ♦ open circuit or short circuit to positive/Ground in wiring between brake light switch and control module -J104-. ♦ Brake light switch inoperative.	– Locate open circuit or short circuit – Check brake light switch, "Read measuring value block"
00532 Voltage supply Signal low	♦ Transfer resistance in voltage supply to control module -J104- (terminal 4). ♦ Voltage dip in vehicle electrical system. ♦ Battery inoperative.	– Locate open circuit or transfer resistance – Check alternator and voltage regulator

VW4029900114000X

Fig. 14 Codes 00526 & 00532: Brake Lamp Switch F Open Circuit & Voltage Supply Signal Low. EuroVan

VAG 1551 scan tool print-out	Possible cause	Repairing malfunction
00285		
ABS Wheel Speed Sensor, RF -G45-	Open circuit or loose connection in: ♦ ABS wheel speed sensor wire ♦ Connector ♦ ABS wheel speed sensor winding Wheel speed sensor electrical short circuit	– Check wiring, connectors, ABS wheel speed sensor, and ground to control module:
Mechanical malfunction[1]	Excessive air gap between ABS wheel speed sensor and impulse rotor (signal not OK)	– Check installation of ABS wheel speed sensor and impulse rotor – Function 08, read measuring value block
Signal outside tolerance[1]	Impulse rotor and ABS wheel speed sensor dirty or damaged	

[1] This malfunction can only be recognized above 30 km/h (19 mph).

VW4029900116000X

Fig. 16 Code 00285: Righthand Front ABS Wheel Speed Sensor. EuroVan

VAG 1551 scan tool print-out	Possible cause	Repairing malfunction
00287		
ABS Wheel Speed Sensor, RR -G44-	Open circuit or loose connection in: ♦ ABS wheel speed sensor wire ♦ Connector ♦ ABS wheel speed sensor winding ABS wheel speed sensor electrical short circuit	– Check wiring, connectors, ABS wheel speed sensor, and ground to control module:
Mechanical fault[1]	Excessive air gap between ABS wheel speed sensor and impulse rotor (signal not OK)	– Check installation of ABS wheel speed sensor and impulse rotor – Function 08, read measuring value block
Signal outside tolerance[1]	Impulse rotor or ABS wheel speed sensor dirty or damaged	

[1] This malfunction can only be recognized above 30 km/h (19 mph).

VW4029900118000X

Fig. 18 Code 00287: Righthand Rear ABS Wheel Speed Sensor. EuroVan

VAG 1551 scan tool print-out	Possible cause	Repairing malfunction
00301 ABS Return Flow Pump -V39-	♦ Open circuit or transfer resistance in ground connections or voltage supply to return flow pump -V39-. ♦ Fuse S53 inoperative ♦ Return flow pump -V39- or hydraulic unit inoperative.	– Locate open circuit or transfer resistance according to "Electrical Wiring Diagrams Troubleshooting & Component Locations" binder and repair. – Locate open circuit or short circuit according to "Electrical Wiring Diagrams Troubleshooting & Component Locations" binder and repair. – Check return flow pump -V39- and ABS hydraulic unit -N55-, Perform Electrical tests
01130 ABS operation Signal outside tolerance[1]	Electrical interference from external sources (high frequency radiation, e.g. non-insulated ignition cable)	Sequence: – Check all wiring and connections for short to positive or ground – Erase DTC memory – Perform test drive exceeding 30 km/h (19 mph) – Check DTC memory again
65535 Control module	Control module inoperative	– Replace control module

[1] This malfunction can only be recognized above 30 km/h (19 mph).

VW4029900113000X

Fig. 13 Codes 00301, 01130 & 65535: ABS Return Flow Pump, ABS Operation Signal Outside Tolerance & Control Module. EuroVan

VAG 1551 scan tool print-out	Possible cause	Repairing malfunction
00283		
ABS Wheel Speed Sensor, LF -G47-	Open circuit or loose connection in: ♦ ABS wheel speed sensor wire ♦ Connector ♦ ABS wheel speed sensor winding ABS wheel speed sensor electrical short circuit	– Check wiring, connectors, ABS wheel speed sensor and ground to control module:
Mechanical malfunction[1]	Excessive air gap between speed sensor and impulse rotor (signal not OK)	– Check installation of ABS wheel speed sensor and impulse rotor – Function 08, read measuring value block
Signal outside tolerance[1]	Impulse rotor and ABS wheel speed sensor dirty or damaged	

[1] This malfunction can only be recognized above 30 km/h (19 mph).

VW4029900115000X

Fig. 15 Code 00283: Lefthand Front, ABS Wheel Speed Sensor. EuroVan

VAG 1551 scan tool print-out	Possible cause	Repairing malfunction
00290		
ABS Wheel Speed Sensor, LR -G46-	Open circuit or loose connection in: ♦ ABS wheel speed sensor wire ♦ Connector ♦ ABS wheel speed sensor winding ABS wheel speed sensor electrical short circuit	– Check wiring, connectors, ABS wheel speed sensor, and ground to control module:
Mechanical malfunction[1]	Excessive air gap between ABS wheel speed sensor and impulse rotor (signal not OK)	– Check installation of ABS wheel speed sensor and impulse rotor – Function 08, read measuring value block
Signal outside tolerance[1]	Impulse rotor and ABS wheel speed sensor dirty or damaged	

[1] This malfunction can only be recognized above 30 km/h (19 mph).

VW4029900117000X

Fig. 17 Code 00290: Lefthand Rear ABS Wheel Speed Sensor. EuroVan

VAG 1551 scan tool print-out	Possible cause	Repairing malfunction
00257 ABS Inlet Valve, LF -N101-	♦ Open circuit, short circuit to positive/Ground. ♦ ABS inlet valve -N101- inoperative.	– Perform "Electrical test" – If after performing electrical tests no cause can be found, check wiring and connectors for loose connections. – If none of the mentioned measures correct the malfunction, replace control module.
00259 ABS Inlet Valve, RF -N99-	♦ Open circuit, short circuit to positive/Ground. ♦ ABS inlet valve -N99- inoperative.	– Perform "Electrical test" – If after performing electrical tests no malfunctions can be found, check wiring and connectors for loose connections. – If these measures do not correct malfunction, replace control module.

VW4029900119000X

Fig. 19 Codes 00257 & 00259: Front Lefthand Or Righthand ABS Inlet Valve. EuroVan

VAG 1551 scan tool print-out	Possible cause	Repairing malfunction
00274 ABS Inlet Valve, LR -N134-	♦ Open circuit, short circuit to positive/Ground. ♦ ABS inlet valve -N134- inoperative.	– Perform "Electrical test" – If after performing electrical tests no cause can be found, check wiring and connectors for loose connections. – If these measures do not correct malfunction, replace control module.
00273 ABS Inlet Valve, RR -N133-	♦ Open circuit, short circuit to positive/Ground. ♦ ABS inlet valve -N133- inoperative.	– Perform "Electrical test" – If after performing electrical tests no cause can be found, check wiring and connectors for loose connections. – If these measures do not correct malfunction, replace control module.

VW4029900120000X

Fig. 20 Codes 00273 & 00274: Rear Lefthand Or Righthand ABS Inlet Valve. EuroVan

VAG 1551 scan tool print-out	Possible cause	Repairing malfunction
00276 ABS Outlet Valve, LR -N136-	♦ Open circuit, short circuit to positive/Ground. ♦ ABS outlet valve -N136- inoperative.	– Perform "Electrical test" – If after performing electrical tests no cause can be found, check wiring and connectors for loose connections. – If these measures do not correct malfunction, replace control module.
00275 ABS Outlet Valve, RR -N135-	♦ Open circuit, short circuit to positive/Ground. ♦ ABS outlet valve -N135- inoperative.	– Perform "Electrical test" – If after performing electrical tests no cause can be found, check wiring and connectors for loose connections. – If these measures do not correct malfunction, replace control module.

VW4029900122000X

Fig. 22 Codes 00276 & 00275: Rear Lefthand & Righthand ABS Outlet Valve. EuroVan

VAG 1551 scan tool print-out	Possible cause	Repairing malfunction
00645 EDL Outlet Valve, LF -N169-	♦ Open circuit, short circuit to positive/Ground. ♦ EDL outlet valve -N169- inoperative. EDS -ASV1-	– Perform "Electrical test" – If after performing electrical tests no cause can be found, check wiring and connectors for loose connections. – If these measures do not correct malfunction, replace control module.
00643 EDL Outlet Valve, RF -N167-	♦ Open circuit, short circuit to positive/Ground. ♦ EDL outlet valve -N167- inoperative. -ASV2-	– Perform "Electrical test" – If after performing electrical tests no cause can be found, check wiring and connectors for loose connections. – If these measures do not correct malfunction, replace control module.

VW4029900124000X

Fig. 24 Codes 00643 & 00645: Front Lefthand & Righthand EDL Outlet Valve. EuroVan

VAG 1551 scan tool printout	Possible cause of malfunction	Repairing malfunction
00283 ABS Wheel Speed Sensor, LF -G47-[1)] or:	♦ Sensor not installed correctly ♦ Impulse rotor dirty or damaged ♦ Wheel bearing play excessive ♦ ABS wheel speed sensor -G47- faulty ♦ Short to Ground (GND)	– Check ABS wheel speed sensor installation position. – Check, clean or replace impulse rotor. – Replace wheel bearing. – Check ABS wheel speed sensor, "Read measured value block" – Test step No. 5
ABS Wheel Speed Sensor, LF -G47- Open circuit/short to positive	♦ Wiring open circuit, short to positive in wiring between ABS wheel speed sensor -G47- and ABS control module -J104-	– If there is no display during function "Read measured value block" and no malfunctions can be localized in wheel speed sensor wiring and connections, replace hydraulic unit.

1) This type of malfunction will be recognized when driving at a minimum of 60 Km/h (37 mph) for 30 seconds

VW4029900097000X

Fig. 26 Code 00283: Lefthand Front ABS Wheel Speed Sensor. Passat

VAG 1551 scan tool print-out	Possible cause	Repairing malfunction
00265 ABS Outlet Valve, LF -N102-	♦ Open circuit, short circuit to positive/Ground. ♦ ABS outlet valve -N102- inoperative.	– Perform "Electrical test" – If after performing electrical tests no cause can be found, check wiring and connectors for loose connections. – If these measures do not correct malfunction, replace control module.
00267 ABS Outlet Valve, RF -N100-	♦ Open circuit, short circuit to positive/Ground. ♦ ABS outlet valve -N100- inoperative.	– Perform "Electrical test" – If after performing electrical tests no cause can be found, check wiring and connectors for loose connections. – If these measures do not correct malfunction, replace control module.

VW4029900121000X

Fig. 21 Codes 00265 & 00267: Front Lefthand & Righthand ABS Outlet Valve. EuroVan

VAG 1551 scan tool print-out	Possible cause	Repairing malfunction
00644 EDL Switch-Over Valve, LF -N168-	♦ Open circuit, short circuit to positive/Ground. ♦ EDL Switch-Over Valve -N168- inoperative. -USV1-	– Perform "Electrical test" – If after performing electrical tests no cause can be found, check wiring and connectors for loose connections. – If these measures do not correct malfunction, replace control module.
00642 EDL Switch-Over Valve, RF -N166-	♦ Open circuit, short circuit to positive/Ground. ♦ EDL Switch-over Valve -N166- inoperative. -USV2-	– Perform "Electrical test" – If after performing electrical tests no cause can be found, check wiring and connectors for loose connections. – If these measures do not correct malfunction, replace control module.

VW4029900123000X

Fig. 23 Codes 00642 & 00644: Front Lefthand & Righthand EDL Switch-Over Valve. EuroVan

VAG 1551 scan tool printout	Possible cause of malfunction	Repairing malfunction
No DTC recognized	If "No DTC recognized" appears after carrying out repairs, On Board Diagnostic (OBD) program sequence has ended. If, despite "No DTC recognized" being displayed, the ABS system does not operate properly, then proceed as follows: 1. Carry out test drive, maintaining at least 60 Km/h (37 mph) for 30 seconds; 2. Again check DTC memory. If there is still no malfunction stored; 3. Troubleshoot without On Board Diagnostic (OBD) and work through the complete Electrical check	

VW4029900096000X

Fig. 25 No DTC Recognized. Passat

VAG 1551 scan tool printout	Possible cause of malfunction	Repairing malfunction
00285 ABS Wheel Speed Sensor, RF -G45-[1)] or:	♦ Sensor not installed correctly ♦ Impulse rotor dirty or damaged ♦ Wheel bearing play excessive ♦ ABS wheel speed sensor -G45- faulty ♦ Short to Ground (GND).	– Check ABS wheel speed sensor installation position. – Check, clean or replace impulse rotor. – Replace wheel bearing. – Check ABS wheel speed sensor – Test step No. 4
ABS Wheel Speed Sensor, RF -G45- Open circuit/short to positive	♦ ABS control module identification not correct. ♦ Wiring open circuit, short to positive in wiring between ABS wheel speed sensor -G45- and ABS control module -J104-	– Check ABS control module identification – If there is no display during function "Read measured value block" and no malfunctions can be localized in wheel speed sensor wiring and connections, replace hydraulic unit.

1) This type of malfunction will be recognized when driving at a minimum of 60 Km/h (37 mph) for 30 seconds

VW4029900098000X

Fig. 27 Code 00285: Righthand Front ABS Wheel Speed Sensor. Passat

VAG 1551 scan tool printout	Possible cause of malfunction	Repairing malfunction
00287		
ABS Wheel Speed Sensor, RR -G44-[1)] or:	♦ Sensor not installed correctly ♦ Impulse rotor dirty or damaged ♦ Wheel bearing play excessive ♦ ABS wheel speed sensor -G44- faulty ♦ Short to Ground (GND)	– Check ABS wheel speed sensor installation position. – Check, clean or replace impulse rotor. – Replace wheel bearing. – Check ABS wheel speed sensor, "Read measured value block" – Test step No. 6
ABS Wheel Speed Sensor, RR -G44- Open circuit/short to positive	♦ ABS control module identification not correct. ♦ Wiring open circuit, short to positive in wiring between ABS wheel speed sensor -G44- and ABS control module -J104-	– Check ABS control module identification, – If there is no display during function "Read measured value block" and no malfunctions can be localized in wheel speed sensor wiring and connections, replace hydraulic unit.

[1)] This type of malfunction will be recognized when driving at a minimum of 60 Km/h (37 mph) for 30 seconds

VW4029900099000X

Fig. 28 Code 00287: Righthand Rear ABS Wheel Speed Sensor. Passat

VAG 1551 scan tool printout	Possible cause of malfunction	Repairing malfunction
00301		
ABS return flow pump -V39-	♦ Malfunction in hydraulic unit	– Erase DTC memory 05 – End output 06 – Switch ignition off – Switch ignition on – If the malfunction occurs again the hydraulic unit must be replaced.
00526		
Brake light switch -F-		
Open circuit	♦ Brake light switch -F- faulty, or incorrectly adjusted. ♦ Both brake lights -M9-, -M10- faulty ♦ Wiring from brake lights to control module faulty ♦ ABS control module -J104- faulty	– Check brake light switch -F-, "Read measured value block" – If necessary adjust brake light switch -F- – Locate and eliminate wiring open or short circuit. – Replace bulbs.

VW4029900101000X

Fig. 30 Codes 00301 & 00526: ABS Return Flow Pump & Brake Lamp Switch Open Circuit. Passat

VAG 1551 printout	Possible cause of malfunction	Repairing malfunction
00532		
Supply voltage signal too low Note: ♦ This malfunction refers to the control module voltage supply. ♦ This malfunction will only be stored if it occurs at a vehicle speed in excess of 6 km/h (approx. 4 mph).	♦ Wiring open circuit or excessive transfer resistance in the voltage supply from terminal 15 to hydraulic unit, contact 15. ♦ Voltage interruptions in vehicle electrical system.	– Locate wiring open circuit in voltage supply and repair – Check battery, Generator and voltage regulator As soon as the vehicle electrical system voltage is greater than 10 volts the ABS, ABS/EDL or TCS (ASR) system(s) switch on and the warning lights go out. – Check Ground (GND) connections
	♦ Malfunction in hydraulic unit	– If no malfunction can be found in the voltage supply, the hydraulic unit must be replaced

VW4029900103000X

Fig. 32 Code 00532: Supply Voltage Signal Too Low. Passat

VAG 1551 scan tool printout	Possible cause of malfunction	Repairing malfunction
00623		
ABS/transmission electrical connection Note: Vehicles with TCS	**Manual transmission** ♦ ABS/EDL/TCS control module -J104- incorrectly coded. ♦ Short to positive	– Check ABS/EDL/TCS control module -J104- coding – Locate and repair short circuit.
	Automatic transmission ♦ ABS/EDL/TCS control module -J104- incorrectly coded. ♦ Wiring open circuit or short to Ground (GND) between ABS/EDL/TCS control module -J104- and transmission control module -J217-	– Check ABS/EDL/TCS control module -J104- coding – Locate and repair wiring open circuit or short circuit.

VW4029900105000X

Fig. 34 Code 00623: ABS/Transaxle Electrical Connection. Passat

VAG 1551 scan tool printout	Possible cause of malfunction	Repairing malfunction
00290		
ABS Wheel Speed Sensor, LR -G46-[1)] or:	♦ ABS wheel speed sensor -G46- not installed correctly ♦ Impulse rotor dirty or damaged ♦ Wheel bearing play excessive ♦ ABS wheel speed sensor -G46- faulty ♦ Short to Ground (GND)	– Check ABS wheel speed sensor installation position. – Check, clean or replace impulse rotor. – Replace wheel bearing. – Check ABS wheel speed sensor, "Read measured value block" – Test step No. 7
ABS Wheel Speed Sensor, LR -G46- Open circuit/short to positive	♦ Wiring open circuit, short to positive in wiring between ABS wheel speed sensor -G46- and control module -J104-	– If there is no display during function "Read measured value block" and no malfunctions can be localized in wheel speed sensor wiring and connections, replace hydraulic unit.

[1)] This type of malfunction will be recognized when driving at a minimum of 60 Km/h (37 mph) for 30 seconds

VW4029900100000X

Fig. 29 Code 00290: Lefthand Rear ABS Wheel Speed Sensor. Passat

VAG 1551 scan tool printout	Possible cause of malfunction	Repairing malfunction
00529		
Speed information missing No signal	♦ Wiring open circuit or short to positive/Ground in wiring between ABS control module -J104- and engine control module	– Locate and repair wiring open circuit or short circuit. – Check engine speed, "Read measured value block"
Note: Vehicles with TCS.	♦ Engine control module faulty	– If tachometer in instrument cluster is faulty and no malfunctions can be located in wiring, engine control module is faulty.
	♦ ABS control module -J104- faulty	– If tachometer in instrument cluster is not functioning and no malfunctions can be found in wiring, ABS control module -J104- is faulty.

VW4029900102000X

Fig. 31 Code 00529: Speed Information Missing No Signal. Passat

VAG 1551 scan tool printout	Possible cause of malfunction	Repairing malfunction
00597		
Different wheel speed impulses	♦ Different wheels and tire sizes on vehicle	– Check wheel and tire sizes
	♦ Impulse rotor dirty or damaged	– Check impulse rotor and replace if necessary
	♦ Wheel bearing play excessive	– Check wheel bearing
	♦ Wheel speed sensors -G44, -G45, -G46, -G47 not correctly installed ♦ Wheel speed sensors -G44, -G45, -G46, -G47	– Check wheel speed sensors

VW4029900104000X

Fig. 33 Code 00597: Different Wheel Speed Impulses. Passat

VAG 1551 scan tool printout	Possible cause of malfunction	Repairing malfunction
00646		
ABS-TCS motor electrical connection 1 Note: Vehicles with TCS – Following signals are sent via this connection:	♦ Wiring open circuit or short to positive/Ground in the wiring between ABS control module -J104- and engine control module	– Locate and repair wiring open circuit or short circuit.
♦ MOD signal (Mask Override Diagnosis) for On board diagnostic (OBD) ♦ SET signal (Specified Engine Torque) ♦ EBC signal (Engine Braking Control)	♦ ABS control module -J104- faulty	– Replace ABS/EDL/TCS hydraulic unit.
The transfer is from ABS control module -J104- to engine control module	♦ Engine control module	– Replace engine control module.

VW4029900106000X

Fig. 35 Code 00646: ABS-TCS Motor Electrical Connection 1. Passat

VAG 1551 scan tool printout	Possible cause of malfunction	Repairing malfunction
00647		
ABS-TCS engine electrical connection 2	♦ Wiring open circuit or short to positive/Ground in wiring between ABS control module -J104- and engine control module	– Locate and repair wiring open circuit or short circuit – Check Actual Engine Torque (AET), "Read measured value block"
Note: Vehicles with TCS – Following signals are sent via this connection:		
♦ AET signal (Actual Engine Torque)	♦ Engine control module faulty	– Replace engine control module
The transfer is from ABS/EDL/TCS control module -J104- to engine control module	♦ ABS/EDL/TCS control module -J104- faulty	– ABS/EDL/TCS hydraulic unit.

VW4029900107000X

Fig. 36 Code 00647: ABS-TCS Engine Electrical Connection 2. Passat

VAG 1551 scan tool printout	Possible cause of malfunction	Repairing malfunction
01200		
Voltage supply for ABS valves Note: This malfunction refers to the voltage supply for ABS hydraulic unit -N55- and the ABS return flow pump -V39-	♦ Wiring open circuit or excessive transfer resistance in the voltage supply from terminal 30 to hydraulic unit, contact 17 and 18. ♦ Voltage interruptions in vehicle electrical system.	– Locate and repair voltage supply wiring open circuit. – Check battery, Generator and voltage regulator.
	♦ malfunction in hydraulic unit	– No malfunction can be found in voltage supply system

VW4029900109000X

Fig. 38 Code 01200: Voltage Supply For ABS Valves. Passat

VAG 1551 scan tool printout	Possible cause of malfunction	Repairing malfunction
01203		
ABS/instrument cluster electrical connection	♦ Wiring open circuit between instrument cluster and hydraulic unit contact 10.	– Locate and repair wiring open circuit
Open circuit/short to Ground	♦ Malfunction in instrument cluster	– Check stationary period, "Read measured value block"
Note: Only vehicles with EDL		– Check instrument cluster
65535		
ABS control module faulty	ABS control module faulty	– Replace hydraulic unit

VW4029900111000X

Fig. 40 Code 01203 & 65535: ABS/Instrument Cluster Electrical Connection Open Circuit Or Short To Ground & ABS Control Module Faulty. Passat

VAG 1551 Scan tool print-out	Possible cause	Corrective action
00283		
Left front ABS wheel speed sensor -G47-	♦ Open circuit, short to positive or ground, loose connection in wiring between left front wheel speed sensor -G47- and Control Module -J104- ♦ Wheel speed sensor winding (coil) ♦ Damage to rotor or wheel speed sensor ♦ Control module malfunction	– Check wiring, connectors, and wheel speed sensor – Check wheel speed sensor and rotor for damage. – Replace damaged rotor or wheel speed sensor. If DTC occurs again: – Replace Control Module

1) Type of DTC, this DTC is only recognized above 20 km/h (13 mph) (perform test drive).

VW4029900089010X

Fig. 42 Code 00283: Lefthand Front ABS Wheel Speed Sensor (Part 1 of 3). New Beetle & 1999–2001 Golf & Jetta

VAG 1551 scan tool printout	Possible cause of malfunction	Repairing malfunction
00761		
Malfunction stored in engine control module Note: Vehicles with TCS.	♦ A malfunction has been stored in the engine control module. The engine control module cannot reduce the engine torque.	– Repair malfunction in engine management according to appropriate engine Repair Manual and erase malfunction stored in engine control module Diagnostic Trouble Code (DTC) memory
01130		Sequence:
ABS operation Implausible signal 1)	Electrical interference from external interference sources (high frequency radiation, e.g. non-insulated ignition cable)	– Check all wiring and connections for short to positive or Ground (GND) – Erase DTC memory – Carry out a test drive at a minimum speed of 60 km/h (37 mph) for 30 seconds – Check DTC memory again

1) This type of malfunction will be recognized when driving at a minimum of 60 Km/h (37 mph) for 30 seconds

VW4029900108000X

Fig. 37 Codes 00761 & 01130: Fault Stored In Engine Control Module & ABS Operation Implausible Signal. Passat

VAG 1551 scan tool printout	Possible cause of malfunction	Repairing malfunction
01201		
ABS return flow pump -V39- supply voltage Note: This malfunction refers to the grounding of the ABS return flow pump -V39-	♦ Wiring open circuit or excessive transfer resistance in the hydraulic unit grounding, contact 16.	⇒ Test step No. 2 – Locate and repair wiring open circuit in Ground (GND) wiring. – Check voltage at ABS return flow pump -V39-, "Read measured value block"
	♦ Malfunction in hydraulic unit	– If no malfunction can be found in voltage supply system:

VW4029900110000X

Fig. 39 Code 01201: ABS Return Flow Pump Supply Voltage. Passat

VAG 1551 scan tool print-out	Possible cause	Corrective action
No DTC recognized	If "No DTC recognized" appears after performing repairs, On-Board Diagnostic (OBD) is ended. If, despite "No DTC recognized" appears on display, ABS system does not operate properly, proceed as follows: 1. Perform road test exceeding 20 km/h (13 mph), 2. Check DTC memory, if no DTC stored, 3. Continue diagnosis through complete Electrical checks	

VW4029900088000X

Fig. 41 No DTC Recognized. New Beetle & 1999–2001 Golf & Jetta

VAG 1551 Scan tool print-out	Possible cause	Corrective action
00283		
Left front ABS wheel speed sensor -G47- Signal out of tolerance 1)	♦ Open circuit, short to positive or ground, loose connection in wiring between left front wheel speed sensor -G47- and Control Module -J104- ♦ Outside electrical interference (high frequency interference) ♦ Air gap too large between speed sensor and rotor (bad signal) ♦ Damage to rotor or wheel speed sensor ♦ Wheel speed sensor winding (coil) damaged	– Check wiring, connectors, and wheel speed sensor – Function -08-, Read Measured Value Block – Check wheel speed sensor and rotor for damage. – Replace damaged rotor/wheel speed sensor.

1) Type of DTC, this DTC is only recognized above 20 km/h (13 mph) (perform test drive).

VW4029900089020X

Fig. 42 Code 00283: Lefthand Front ABS Wheel Speed Sensor (Part 2 of 3). New Beetle & 1999–2001 Golf & Jetta

VAG 1551 Scan tool print-out	Possible cause	Corrective action
00283		
Left front ABS wheel speed sensor -G47- Mechanical malfunction[1]	♦ Air gap too large between wheel speed sensor and rotor (bad signal) ♦ Malfunction in hydraulic unit outlet valves	– Check wheel speed sensor and rotor installation – Function -08-, Read Measured Value Block – Check function -03- Output Diagnostic Test mode (DTM) If DTC occurs again: – Replace hydraulic unit

[1] Type of DTC, this DTC is only recognized above 20 km/h (13 mph) (perform test drive).

VW4029900089030X

Fig. 42 Code 00283: Lefthand Front ABS Wheel Speed Sensor (Part 3 of 3). New Beetle & 1999–2001 Golf & Jetta

VAG 1551 Scan tool print-out	Possible cause	Corrective action
00285		
Right front ABS wheel speed sensor -G45- Signal out of tolerance[1]	♦ Open circuit, short to positive or ground, loose connection in wiring between left front wheel speed sensor -G45- and Control Module -J104- ♦ Outside electrical interference (high frequency interference) ♦ Air gap too large between speed sensor and rotor (bad signal) ♦ Damage to rotor or wheel speed sensor ♦ Wheel speed sensor coil damaged	– Check wiring, connectors, and wheel speed sensor – Function -08-, Read Measured Value Block – Check wheel speed sensor and rotor for damage. – Replace damaged rotor/wheel speed sensor.

[1] Type of DTC, this DTC is only recognized above 20 km/h (13 mph) (perform test drive).

VW4029900090020X

Fig. 43 Code 00285: Righthand Front Wheel Speed Sensor (Part 2 of 3). New Beetle & 1999–2001 Golf & Jetta

VAG 1551 Scan tool print-out	Possible cause	Corrective action
00287		
Right rear wheel speed sensor -G44-	♦ Open circuit, short to positive or ground, loose connection in wiring between left front wheel speed sensor -G44- and Control Module -J104- ♦ Wheel speed sensor coil damaged ♦ Rotor and/or speed sensor damaged ♦ Control module (on hydraulic unit) malfunction	– Check wiring, connectors, and wheel speed sensor – Check wheel speed sensor and rotor for damage – Replace wheel speed sensor/rotor If DTC occurs again: – Replace control module (on hydraulic unit)

[1] Type of DTC, this DTC is only recognized above 20 km/h (13 mph) (perform test drive).

VW4029900091010X

Fig. 44 Code 00287: Righthand Rear Wheel Speed Sensor (Part 1 of 3). New Beetle & 1999–2001 Golf & Jetta

VAG 1551 Scan tool print-out	Possible cause	Corrective action
00287		
Right rear ABS wheel speed sensor -G44- Mechanical malfunction[1]	♦ Air gap too large between wheel speed sensor and rotor (bad signal) ♦ Malfunction in hydraulic unit outlet valves	– Check wheel speed sensor and rotor installation – Function -03-, Read Measured Value Block – Check function -03- Output Diagnostic Test mode (DTM) If DTC occurs again: – Replace hydraulic unit

[1] Type of DTC, this DTC is only recognized above 20 km/h (13 mph) (perform test drive).

VW4029900091030X

Fig. 44 Code 00287: Righthand Rear Wheel Speed Sensor (Part 3 of 3). New Beetle & 1999–2001 Golf & Jetta

VAG 1551 Scan tool print-out	Possible cause	Corrective action
00285		
Right front wheel speed sensor -G45-	♦ Open circuit, short to positive or ground, loose connection in wiring between left front wheel speed sensor -G45- and Control Module -J104- ♦ Wheel speed sensor coil damaged ♦ Rotor and/or speed sensor damaged ♦ Control module (on hydraulic unit) malfunction	– Check wiring, connectors, and wheel speed sensor – Check wheel speed sensor and rotor for damage – Replace wheel speed sensor/rotor If DTC occurs again: – Replace control module (on hydraulic unit)

[1] Type of DTC, this DTC is only recognized above 20 km/h (13 mph) (perform test drive).

VW4029900090010X

Fig. 43 Code 00285: Righthand Front Wheel Speed Sensor (Part 1 of 3). New Beetle & 1999–2001 Golf & Jetta

VAG 1551 Scan tool print-out	Possible cause	Corrective action
00285		
Right front ABS wheel speed sensor -G45- Mechanical malfunction[1]	♦ Air gap too large between wheel speed sensor and rotor (bad signal) ♦ Malfunction in hydraulic unit outlet valves	– Check wheel speed sensor and rotor installation – Function -08-, read measured value block – Check function -03- Output Diagnostic Test mode (DTM) If DTC occurs again: – Replace hydraulic unit

[1] Type of DTC, this DTC is only recognized above 20 km/h (13 mph) (perform test drive).

VW4029900090030X

Fig. 43 Code 00285: Righthand Front Wheel Speed Sensor (Part 3 of 3). New Beetle & 1999–2001 Golf & Jetta

VAG 1551 Scan tool print-out	Possible cause	Corrective action
00287		
Right rear ABS wheel speed sensor -G44- Signal out of tolerance[1]	♦ Open circuit, short to positive or ground, loose connection in wiring between left front wheel speed sensor -G44- and Control Module -J104- ♦ Outside electrical interference (high frequency interference) ♦ Air gap too large between speed sensor and rotor (bad signal) ♦ Damage to rotor or wheel speed sensor ♦ Wheel speed sensor coil damaged	– Check wiring, connectors, and wheel speed sensor ⇒ Test step 7 and 11 – Function -08-, read measured value block – Check wheel speed sensor and rotor for damage. – Replace damaged rotor/wheel speed sensor.

[1] Type of DTC, this DTC is only recognized above 20 km/h (13 mph) (perform test drive).

VW4029900091020X

Fig. 44 Code 00287: Righthand Rear Wheel Speed Sensor (Part 2 of 3). New Beetle & 1999–2001 Golf & Jetta

VAG 1551 Scan tool print-out	Possible cause	Corrective action
00290		
Left rear wheel speed sensor -G46-	♦ Open circuit, short to positive or ground, loose connection in wiring between left front wheel speed sensor -G46- and Control Module -J104- ♦ Wheel speed sensor coil damaged ♦ Rotor and/or speed sensor damaged ♦ Control module (on hydraulic unit) malfunction	– Check wiring, connectors, and wheel speed sensor – Check wheel speed sensor and rotor for damage – Replace wheel speed sensor/rotor If DTC occurs again: – Replace control module (on hydraulic unit)

[1] Type of DTC, this DTC is only recognized above 20 km/h (13 mph) (perform test drive).

VW4029900092010X

Fig. 45 Code 00290: Lefthand Rear ABS Wheel Speed Sensor (Part 1 of 3). New Beetle & 1999–2001 Golf & Jetta

VAG 1551 Scan tool print-out	Possible cause	Corrective action
00290		
Left rear ABS wheel speed sensor -G46- Signal out of tolerance[1]	♦ Open circuit, short to positive or ground, loose connection in wiring between left front wheel speed sensor -G46- and Control Module -J104- ♦ Outside electrical interference (high frequency interference) ♦ Air gap too large between speed sensor and rotor (bad signal) ♦ Damage to rotor or wheel speed sensor ♦ Wheel speed sensor coil damaged	– Check wiring, connectors, and wheel speed sensor – Function -08-, read measured value block – Check wheel speed sensor and rotor for damage. – Replace damaged rotor/wheel speed sensor.

[1] Type of DTC, this DTC is only recognized above 20 km/h (13 mph) (perform test drive).

VW4029900092020X

Fig. 45 Code 00290: Lefthand Rear ABS Wheel Speed Sensor (Part 2 of 3). New Beetle & 1999–2001 Golf & Jetta

VAG 1551 Scan tool print-out	Possible cause	Corrective action
00290		
Left rear ABS wheel speed sensor -G46- Mechanical malfunction[1]	♦ Air gap too large between wheel speed sensor and rotor (bad signal) ♦ Malfunction in hydraulic unit outlet valves	– Check wheel speed sensor and rotor installation – Function -08-, read measured value block – Check function 03 Output Diagnostic Test mode (DTM) If DTC occurs again: – Replace hydraulic unit

[1] Type of DTC, this DTC is only recognized above 20 km/h (13 mph) (perform test drive).

VW4029900092030X

Fig. 45 Code 00290: Lefthand Rear ABS Wheel Speed Sensor (Part 3 of 3). New Beetle & 1999–2001 Golf & Jetta

VAG 1551 Scan tool print-out	Possible cause	Corrective action
00668		
Vehicle voltage terminal 30, signal outside tolerance	♦ Open circuit in wiring, short to positive or ground ♦ Voltage supply malfunction, fuses S178 and S179	– Check fuses, wires, connections as well as voltage supply to Control Module: – Check wiring in wiring harness
01044		
Control Module incorrectly coded	♦ Incorrect code number was entered in VAG 1551. ♦ Open or short circuit in bridge in wiring harness from terminal 3 to terminal 14. Vehicles with navigation system: ♦ Short in wire to navigation system terminal 6 or 23 ♦ Malfunction in navigation system	– Check Control Module code – Check fuses, wires, connections as well as voltage supply to Control Module: – Check wiring in wiring harness – Check wiring in wiring harness – Replace navigation system Control Module

VW4029900093000X

Fig. 46 Codes 00668 & 01044: Vehicle Voltage Terminal 30, signal outside of tolerance & Control Module Improperly Coded. New Beetle & 1999–2001 Golf & Jetta

VAG 1551 Scan tool print-out	Possible cause	Corrective action
01130		sequence:
ABS operation Implausible signal[1]	♦ External electrical interference (high frequency radiation, e.g. non-insulated ignition cable) ♦ Open circuit, short to positive or ground, loose connection in wiring.	– Check all wiring and connections for short to positive or ground – Erase DTC memory – Test drive exceeding 20 km/h (13 mph) – Check DTC memory again If DTC occurs again: – Replace Control Module

[1] This DTC is only recognized above 20 km/h (13 mph) (perform test drive).

VW4029900094000X

Fig. 47 Code 01130: ABS Operation. New Beetle & 1999–2001 Golf & Jetta

VAG 1551 Scan tool print-out	Possible cause	Corrective action
01276		
ABS hydraulic pump -V64- Signal out of tolerance[1]	♦ Connection of electric motor to control module ♦ Short to positive or ground ♦ Open circuit ♦ Pump motor malfunction	– Check fuses wiring and terminals – If pump runs DTC free when performing test step 18, replace control module
65535		
Control Module malfunction	Control Module malfunction	– Replace control module

VW4029900095000X

Fig. 48 Codes 01276 & 65535: ABS Hydraulic Pump & Control Module Fault. New Beetle & 1999–2001 Golf & Jetta

00000 4444		
No DTC recognized	If "No DTC recognized" is displayed after carrying out repairs, On Board Diagnostic (OBD) program sequence has ended. If, despite "No DTC recognized" being displayed, the ABS system does not operate properly, then proceed as follows: 1. Carry out road test exceeding 40 km/h (24 mph). 2. Again check DTC memory. If there is still no DTC stored: 3. Troubleshoot without On Board Diagnostic (OBD) and work through the complete electrical test	
00257 1112		
ABS Inlet Valve,LF –N101	Faulty wire, connector or valve winding	– Check wiring, connectors and valve winding Test steps 17 and 37[1]
00259 1114		
ABS Inlet Valve,RF –N99	Faulty wire, connector or valve winding	– Check wiring, connectors and valve winding Test steps 18 and 38[1]

[1] Electrical test

VW4029300035000X

Fig. 49 Codes 00000, 00257 & 00259/1112, 1114 & 4444: No DTC Recognized & Inlet Valves. Cabrio & 1998 Golf III, GTI & Jetta III w/Teves Type 04

00265 1132		
ABS Outlet Valve,LF –N102	Faulty wire, connector or valve winding	– Check wiring, connectors and valve winding Test steps 21 and 37[1]
00267 1134		
ABS Outlet Valve,RF –N100	Faulty wire, connector or valve winding	– Check wiring, connectors and valve winding Test steps 22 and 38[1]
00273 1211		
ABS Inlet Valve,RR –N133	Faulty wire, connector or valve winding	– Check wiring, connectors and valve winding Test steps 20 and 40[1]
00274 1212		
ABS Inlet Valve,LR –N134	Faulty wire, connector or valve winding	– Check wiring, connectors and valve winding Test steps 19 and 39[1]

[1] Electrical test

VW4029300023000X

Fig. 50 Codes 00265, 00267, 00273 & 00274/1132, 1134, 1211 & 1212: Inlet & Outlet Valves. Cabrio & 1998 Golf III, GTI & Jetta III w/Teves Type 04

00275 1213		
ABS Outlet Valve,RR –N135	Faulty wire, connector or valve winding	– Check wiring, connectors and valve winding Test steps 24 and 40[1]
00276 1214		
ABS Outlet Valve,LR –N136	Faulty wire, connector or valve winding	– Check wiring, connectors and valve winding Test steps 23 and 39[1]
00279 1223		
Differential Lock Valve 1–N125	Faulty wire, connector or valve winding	– Check wiring, connectors and valve winding Test steps 25 and 41[1]
00280 1224		
Differential Lock Valve 2–N126	Faulty wire, connector or valve winding	– Check wiring, connectors and valve winding Test steps 26 and 41[1]

[1] Electrical test

VW4029300024000X

Fig. 51 Codes 00275, 00276, 00279 & 00280/1213, 1214, 1223 & 1224: Differential Lock & Outlet Valves. Cabrio & 1998 Golf III, GTI & Jetta III w/Teves Type 04

00283 1233		
ABS Wheel Speed Sensor,LF–G47	Open circuit, short circuit or loose connection in: ♦ ABS wheel speed sensor wire ♦ Connector ♦ ABS wheel speed sensor winding	– Check wiring, connectors, ABS wheel speed sensor, Ground (GND) wiring to ABS control module and also capacitor for correct Ground (GND) connection Test steps 7, 11 and 34[1]
Mechanical malfunction[2]	Excessive or insufficient air gap between ABS wheel speed sensor and impulse rotor (signal not OK)	– Check installation of ABS wheel speed sensor and impulse rotor; clean if necessary
Signal outside tolerances[2]	Impulse rotor and ABS wheel speed sensor dirty or damaged	

[1] Electrical test

[2] Type of malfunction.

VW4029300025000X

Fig. 52 Codes 00283/1233: Front Lefthand Wheel Speed Sensor. Cabrio & 1998 Golf III, GTI & Jetta III w/Teves Type 04

00285 1241		
ABS Wheel Speed Sensor,RF–G45	Open circuit, short circuit or loose connection in: ♦ ABS wheel speed sensor wire ♦ Connector ♦ ABS wheel speed sensor winding	– Check wiring, connectors, ABS wheel speed sensor, Ground (GND) wiring to ABS control module and also capacitor for correct Ground (GND) connection Test steps 6, 10 and 33[1]
Mechanical malfunction[2]	Excessive or insufficient air gap between ABS wheel speed sensor and impulse rotor (signal not OK)	– Check installation of ABS wheel speed sensor and impulse rotor; clean if necessary
Signal outside tolerances[2]	Impulse rotor and ABS wheel speed sensor dirty or damaged	

[1] Electrical test

[2] Type of malfunction.

VW4029300026000X

Fig. 53 Codes 00285/1241: Front Righthand Wheel Speed Sensor. Cabrio & 1998 Golf III, GTI & Jetta III w/Teves Type 04

00287 1243		
ABS Wheel Speed Sensor,RR–G44	Open circuit, short circuit or loose connection in: ♦ ABS wheel speed sensor wire ♦ Connector ♦ ABS wheel speed sensor winding	– Check wiring, connectors, ABS wheel speed sensor, Ground (GND) wiring to ABS control module and also capacitor for correct Ground (GND) connection Test steps 8, 12 and 31[1]
Mechanical malfunction[2]	Excessive or insufficient air gap between ABS wheel speed sensor and impulse rotor (signal not OK)	– Check installation of ABS wheel speed sensor and impulse rotor; clean if necessary
Signal outside tolerances[2]	Impulse rotor and ABS wheel speed sensor dirty or damaged	

[1] Electrical test

[2] Type of malfunction.

VW4029300027000X

Fig. 54 Codes 00287/1243: Rear Righthand Wheel Speed Sensor. Cabrio & 1998 Golf III, GTI & Jetta III w/Teves Type 04

00290 1311		
ABS Wheel Speed Sensor,LR–G46	Open circuit, short circuit or loose connection in: ♦ ABS wheel speed sensor wire ♦ Connector ♦ ABS wheel speed sensor winding	– Check wiring, connectors, ABS wheel speed sensor, Ground (GND) wiring to ABS control module and also capacitor for correct Ground (GND) connection Test steps 9, 13 and 32[1]
Mechanical malfunction[2]	Excessive or insufficient air gap between ABS wheel speed sensor and impulse rotor (signal not OK)	– Check installation of ABS wheel speed sensor and impulse rotor; clean if necessary
Signal outside tolerances[2]	Impulse rotor and ABS wheel speed sensor dirty or damaged	

[1] Electrical test

[2] Type of malfunction.

VW4029300028000X

Fig. 55 Codes 00290/1311: Rear Lefthand Wheel Speed Sensor. Cabrio & 1998 Golf III, GTI & Jetta III w/Teves Type 04

00292 1313		
Hydraulic Energy Supply Pressure Level	Pressure loss through leaks or air in the hydraulic unit and brake system	– Bleed brake system
Mechanical malfunction[2]	ABS hydraulic pump -V64- not producing sufficient pressure	– If necessary, replace ABS hydraulic unit and tandem master cylinder – After repairs, erase DTC memory with VAG 1551 scan tool
00532 2234		
Supply Voltage (B+)	Faulty wiring, connectors, fuse -S4-, ABS valves fuse -S54- or ABS relay -J102-	– Check fuses, wiring, connectors, Ground (GND) wiring and the voltage supply to ABS control module Test steps 1–4, 14 and 30[1]

[1] Electrical test

[2] Type of malfunction.

VW4029300029000X

Fig. 56 Codes 00292 & 00532/1313 & 2234: Hydraulic Energy Supply & Battery Supply Voltage. Cabrio & 1998 Golf III, GTI & Jetta III w/Teves Type 04

VAG 1551 scan tool printout	Possible cause of malfunction	Repairing malfunction
00547 2133		
ABS Pressure Control Switch–F137[2]	Wire between terminal 13 and terminal 26 of ABS control module -J104- with ABS pressure control switch -F137- has connection to battery + or battery –	– Visual check of wiring between terminal 13 and terminal 26 – Disconnect multi-pin connector from ABS control module, connect to test box and use multimeter to measure voltage between terminals: 13 and 1 = max. 0.1 V 26 and 1 = max. 0.1 V Test step 29[1]

[1] Electrical test

[2] Applies to ABS control module 1H0 907 379A only.

VW4029300030000X

Fig. 57 Codes 00547/2133: ABS Pressure Control Switch. Cabrio & 1998 Golf III, GTI & Jetta III w/Teves Type 04

00599		
Plausibility Pressure/ Brake Light Switch	Faulty wiring, connectors, ABS pressure control switch -F137-, fuse -S20- or brake light switch -F-	– Visual check of wire routing from brake light switch -F-, ABS pressure control switch -F137- and fuse -S20- Test steps 5 and 29[1]
	Time delay between brake light switch signal and pressure control switch signal excessive	– Ensure that the brake light switch signal enters the ABS control module before the pressure control switch signal, if necessary adjust brake light switch

[1] Electrical test

VW4029300031000X

Fig. 58 Code 005994: Plausibility Pressure/Brake Lamp Switch. Cabrio & 1998 Golf III, GTI & Jetta III w/Teves Type 04

00634		
Series Resistance –N159	Faulty wiring, connectors, EDL relay -J310- or EDL series resistance -N159-	– Check wiring, connectors, EDL relay -J310- and EDL series resistance -N159- Test steps 15, 35 and 36[1] – Check EDL series resistance -N159- for continuity (using connector test kit and multimeter in 200 ohm resistance range); Specification: max. 2 Ω, replace if necessary

[1] Electrical test

VW4029300032000X

Fig. 59 Code 00634: Series Resistance. Cabrio & 1998 Golf III, GTI & Jetta III w/Teves Type 04

00793 3231		
Brake Pedal Pos. Sensor–G100 Mechanical malfunction²⁾	Faulty wiring, connectors, brake pedal position sensor -G100- or short to battery positive (B+) or Ground	– Check wiring, connectors and brake pedal position sensor -G100- Test steps 28¹⁾ – Unplug multi-pin connector from ABS control module, connect to test box with adapter and use multimeter to measure voltage between the terminals: 16 and 1 = max. 0.1 V 41 and 1 = max. 0.1 V

[1] Electrical test

[2] Type of malfunction.

VW4029300033000X

Fig. 60 Codes 00793/3231: Brake Pedal Position Sensor. Cabrio & 1998 Golf III, GTI & Jetta III w/Teves Type 04

00000	
No DTC recognized	If "No DTC recognized" is displayed after carrying out repairs, On Board Diagnostic (OBD) program sequence has ended. If, despite "No DTC recognized" being displayed, the ABS system does not operate properly, then proceed as follows: 1. Carry out road test exceeding 20 km/h (12 mph). 2. Again check DTC memory. If there is still no DTC stored: 3. Troubleshoot without On Board Diagnostic (OBD) and work through the complete electrical test

VW4029300036000X

Fig. 62 Code 00000: No DTC Recognized. Cabrio & 1998 Golf III, GTI & Jetta III w/Teves Type 20

00285		
ABS Wheel Speed Sensor,LF–G47	Open circuit, short circuit or loose connection in: ♦ ABS wheel speed sensor wire ♦ Connector ♦ ABS wheel speed sensor winding	– Check wiring, connectors, ABS wheel speed sensor and Ground (GND) wiring to ABS control module
	Short circuit in ABS wheel speed sensor	Test steps 5 and 9¹⁾
Mechanical malfunction²⁾	Excessive air gap between ABS wheel speed sensor and impulse rotor (signal not OK)	– Check installation of ABS wheel speed sensor and impulse rotor; clean if necessary Read measuring value block, function 08. Display field 2
Signal outside tolerances²⁾	Impulse rotor and ABS wheel speed sensor dirty or damaged	

[1] Electrical test.

[2] Type of malfunction; this malfunction is only recognized above 20 km/h (12 mph); test drive.

VW4029300038000X

Fig. 64 Code 00285: Front Righthand Wheel Speed Sensor. Cabrio & 1998 Golf III, GTI & Jetta III w/Teves Type 20

00290		
ABS Wheel Speed Sensor,LF–G47	Open circuit, short circuit or loose connection in: ♦ ABS wheel speed sensor wire ♦ Connector ♦ ABS wheel speed sensor winding	– Check wiring, connectors, ABS wheel speed sensor and Ground (GND) wiring to ABS control module
	Short circuit in ABS wheel speed sensor	Test steps 8 and 12¹⁾
Mechanical malfunction²⁾	Excessive air gap between ABS wheel speed sensor and impulse rotor (signal not OK)	– Check installation of ABS wheel speed sensor and impulse rotor; clean if necessary Read measuring value block, function 08. Display field 2
Signal outside tolerances²⁾	Impulse rotor and ABS wheel speed sensor dirty or damaged	
00668		
Battery Positive Voltage (B+) Term.30	Faulty voltage supply wires, connections, fuses 1 and/or 2 for control module–ABS, -S123- and/or -S124-	– Check fuses, wires, connections as well as battery positive voltage (B+) supply to ABS control module Test step 2¹⁾
01044		
Control Module incorrectly coded	An incorrect code number has been entered via VAG 1551 scan tool	– Check ABS control module coding
	Open or short circuit in wiring harness between terminals 15 and terminal 21	– Check wiring in harness Test step 13¹⁾

[1] Electrical test.

[2] Type of malfunction; this malfunction is only recognized above 20 km/h (12 mph); test drive.

VW4029300040000X

Fig. 66 Codes 00290, 00668 & 01044: Front Lefthand Speed Sensor, Battery Supply Voltage & Control Module Coding. Cabrio & 1998 Golf III, GTI & Jetta III w/Teves Type 20

01276 4133		
ABS Hydraulic Pump–V64 Signal outside tolerances²⁾	Faulty wiring, connectors, ABS hydraulic pump relay -J185-, ABS hydraulic pump -V64- or hydraulic pump sender -G101-	– Check wiring, connectors, ABS hydraulic pump relay -J185-, ABS hydraulic pump -V64- and hydraulic pump sender -G101- Test steps 15, 27, 35 and 36¹⁾
65535 1111		
Control Module Malfunctioning	Electrical malfunctions caused by outside interference, poor Ground (GND) connections, poor positive connections to ABS control module -J104-	– Check wiring, connectors and Ground (GND) wires to ABS control module and voltage supply Test steps 1–4, 14 and 30¹⁾
	ABS control module faulty	– Replace ABS control module if necessary

[1] Electrical test

[2] Type of malfunction.

VW4029300034000X

Fig. 61 Code 01276 & 65535/1111 & 4133: Hydraulic Pump & Control Module Malfunction. Cabrio & 1998 Golf III, GTI & Jetta III w/Teves Type 04

00283		
ABS Wheel Speed Sensor,LF–G47	Open circuit, short circuit or loose connection in: ♦ ABS wheel speed sensor wire ♦ Connector ♦ ABS wheel speed sensor winding	– Check wiring, connectors, ABS wheel speed sensor and Ground (GND) wiring to ABS control module
	Short circuit in ABS wheel speed sensor	Test steps 6 and 10¹⁾
Mechanical malfunction²⁾	Excessive air gap between ABS wheel speed sensor and impulse rotor (signal not OK)	– Check installation of ABS wheel speed sensor and impulse rotor; clean if necessary Read measuring value block, function 08. Display field 2
Signal outside tolerances²⁾	Impulse rotor and ABS wheel speed sensor dirty or damaged	

[1] Electrical test

[2] Type of malfunction; this malfunction is only recognized above 20 km/h (12 mph); test drive.

VW4029300037000X

Fig. 63 Code 00283: Front Lefthand Wheel Speed Sensor. Cabrio & 1998 Golf III, GTI & Jetta III w/Teves Type 20

00287		
ABS Wheel Speed Sensor,LF–G47	Open circuit, short circuit or loose connection in: ♦ ABS wheel speed sensor wire ♦ Connector ♦ ABS wheel speed sensor winding	– Check wiring, connectors, ABS wheel speed sensor and Ground (GND) wiring to ABS control module
	Short circuit in ABS wheel speed sensor	Test steps 7 and 11¹⁾
Mechanical malfunction²⁾	Excessive air gap between ABS wheel speed sensor and impulse rotor (signal not OK)	– Check installation of ABS wheel speed sensor and impulse rotor; clean if necessary ⇒ Read measuring value block, function 08. Display field 2
Signal outside tolerances²⁾	Impulse rotor and ABS wheel speed sensor dirty or damaged	

[1] Electrical test

[2] Type of malfunction; this malfunction is only recognized above 20 km/h (12 mph); test drive.

VW4029300039000X

Fig. 65 Code 00287 : Rear Righthand Speed Sensor. Cabrio & 1998 Golf III, GTI & Jetta III w/Teves Type 20

01130		
ABS operation Signal outside tolerance²⁾	Electrical interference from external sources (high frequency radiation; e.g. non-insulated ignition cable)	Sequence: – Check all wiring and connections for short to positive or Ground (GND) – Erase DTC memory – Carry out a test drive exceeding 20 km/h (12 mph) – Check DTC memory again
01276		
ABS hydraulic pump–V64 Signal outside tolerance ²⁾	♦ Connection electric motor to ABS control module ♦ Short to positive or Ground (GND) or open circuit ♦ Pump motor faulty	– Check wiring, connections ⇒ output Diagnostic Test Mode (DTM), function 03.
65535		
Control Module Malfunctioning	ABS control module faulty	– Replace ABS control module

[1] Electrical test.

[2] Type of malfunction; this malfunction is only recognized above 20 km/h (12 mph); test drive.

VW4029300041000X

Fig. 67 Codes 01130, 01276 & 65535: ABS Operation, ABS Hydraulic Pump & Control Module Malfunction. Cabrio & 1998 Golf III, GTI & Jetta III w/Teves Type 20

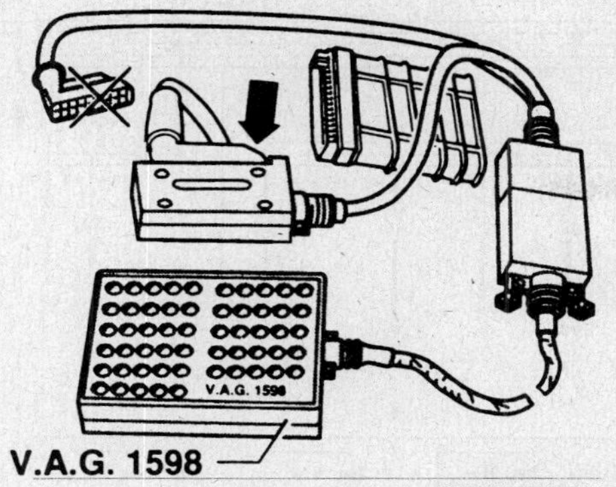

VW4029300069000X

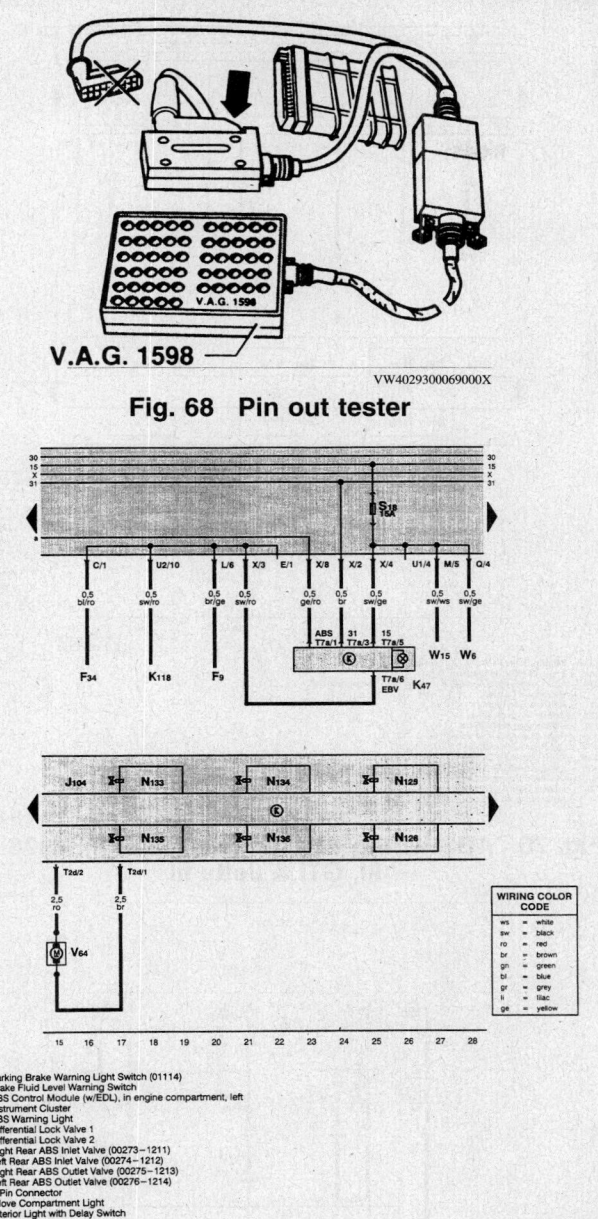

Fig. 68 Pin out tester

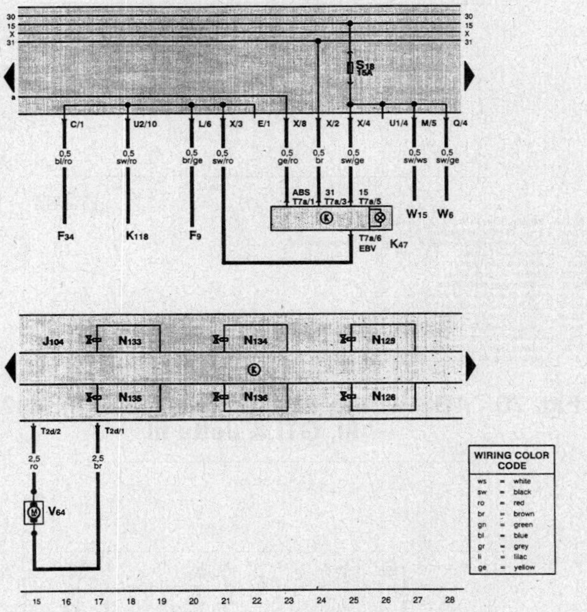

F9 – Parking Brake Warning Light Switch (01114)
F34 – Brake Fluid Level Warning Switch
J104 – ABS Control Module (w/EDL), in engine compartment, left
K – Instrument Cluster
K47 – ABS Warning Light
N125 – Differential Lock Valve 1
N126 – Differential Lock Valve 2
N133 – Right Rear ABS Inlet Valve (00273–1211)
N134 – Left Rear ABS Inlet Valve (00274–1212)
N135 – Right Rear ABS Outlet Valve (00275–1213)
N136 – Left Rear ABS Outlet Valve (00276–1214)
T7a – 7-Pin Connector
W6 – Glove Compartment Light
W15 – Interior Light with Delay Switch
V64 – ABS Hydraulic Pump

VW4029500065020X

Fig. 69 ABS wiring diagram (Part 2 of 3). Cabrio

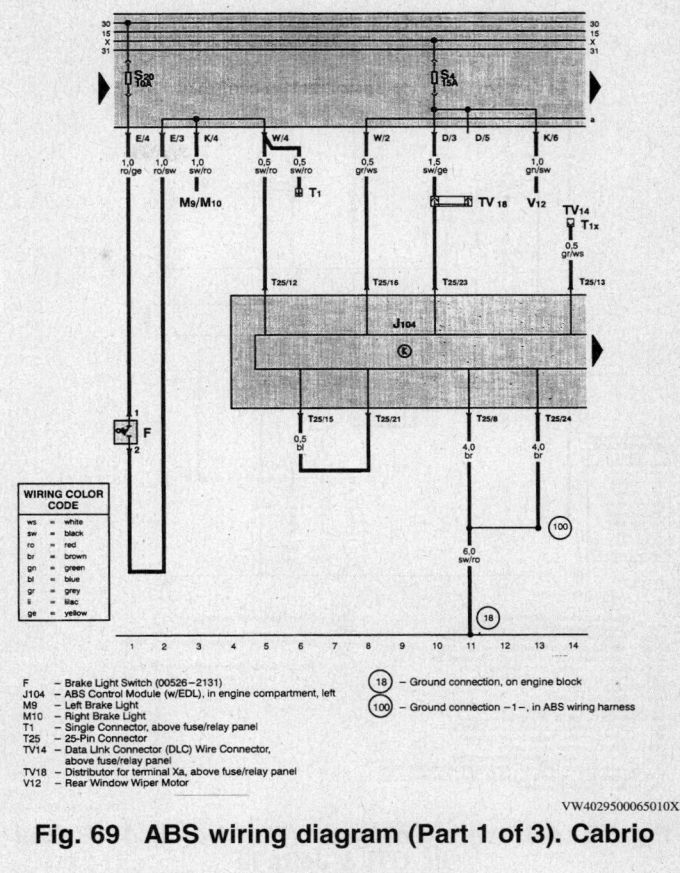

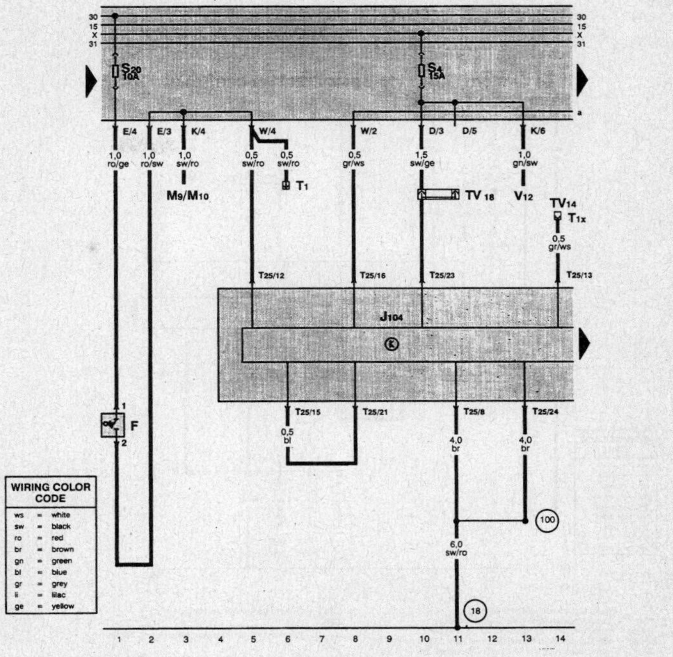

F – Brake Light Switch (00526–2131)
J104 – ABS Control Module (w/EDL), in engine compartment, left
M9 – Left Brake Light
M10 – Right Brake Light
T1 – Single Connector, above fuse/relay panel
T25 – 25-Pin Connector
TV14 – Data Link Connector (DLC) Wire Connector, above fuse/relay panel
TV18 – Distributor for terminal Xa, above fuse/relay panel
V12 – Rear Window Wiper Motor

(18) – Ground connection, on engine block
(100) – Ground connection –1–, in ABS wiring harness

VW4029500065010X

Fig. 69 ABS wiring diagram (Part 1 of 3). Cabrio

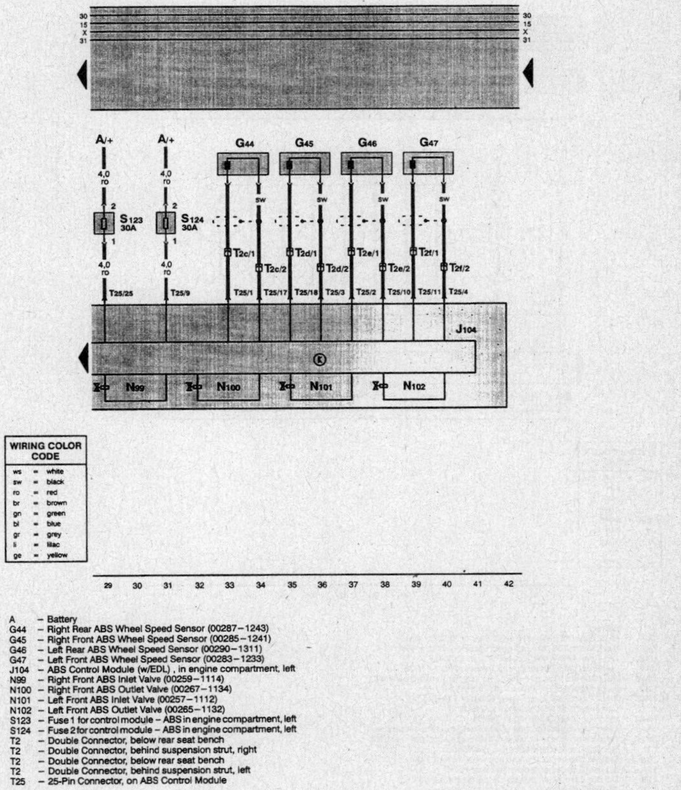

A – Battery
G44 – Right Rear ABS Wheel Speed Sensor (00287–1243)
G45 – Right Front ABS Wheel Speed Sensor (00285–1241)
G46 – Left Rear ABS Wheel Speed Sensor (00290–1311)
G47 – Left Front ABS Wheel Speed Sensor (00283–1233)
J104 – ABS Control Module (w/EDL), in engine compartment, left
N99 – Right Front ABS Inlet Valve (00259–1114)
N100 – Right Front ABS Outlet Valve (00267–1134)
N101 – Left Front ABS Inlet Valve (00257–1112)
N102 – Left Front ABS Outlet Valve (00265–1132)
S123 – Fuse 1 for control module – ABS in engine compartment, left
S124 – Fuse 2 for control module – ABS in engine compartment, left
T2 – Double Connector, below rear seat bench
T2 – Double Connector, behind suspension strut, right
T2 – Double Connector, below rear seat bench
T2 – Double Connector, behind suspension strut, left
T25 – 25-Pin Connector, on ABS Control Module

VW4029500065030X

Fig. 69 ABS wiring diagram (Part 3 of 3). Cabrio

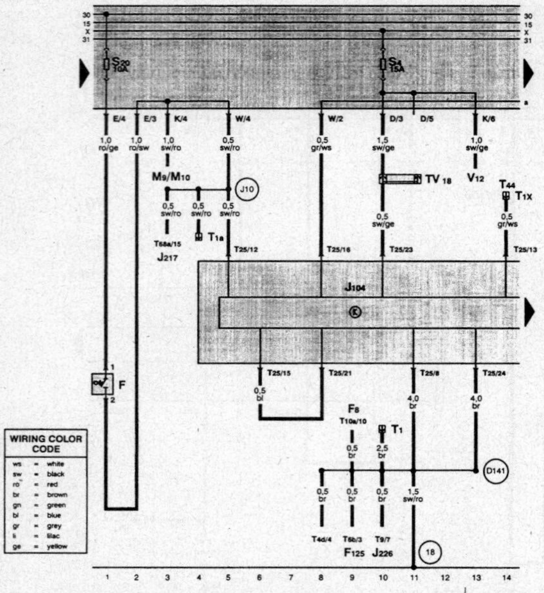

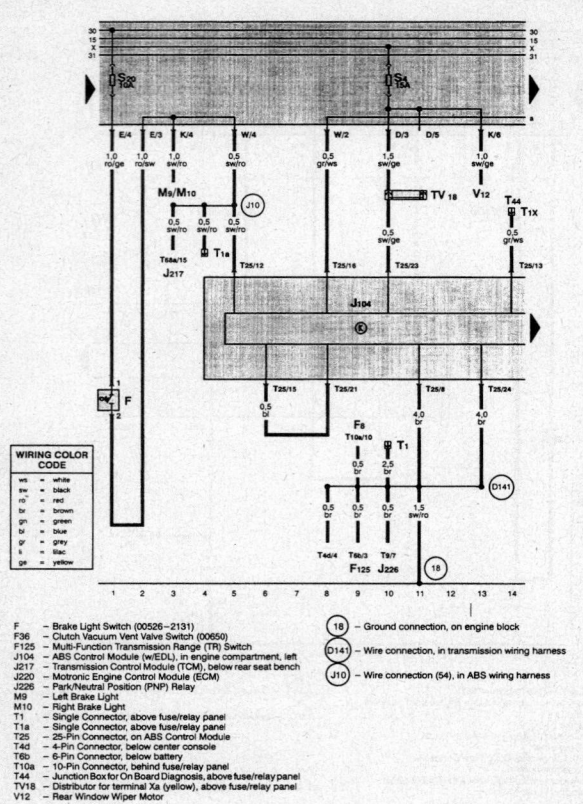

F – Brake Light Switch (00526–2131)
F36 – Clutch Vacuum Vent Valve Switch (00650)
F125 – Multi-Function Transmission Range (TR) Switch
J104 – ABS Control Module (w/EDL), in engine compartment, left
J217 – Transmission Control Module (TCM), below rear seat bench
J220 – Motronic Engine Control Module (ECM)
J226 – Park/Neutral Position (PNP) Relay
M9 – Left Brake Light
M10 – Right Brake Light
T1 – Single Connector, above fuse/relay panel
T1a – Single Connector, above fuse/relay panel
T25 – 25-Pin Connector, on ABS Control Module
T4d – 4-Pin Connector, below center console
T6b – 6-Pin Connector, below battery
T10a – 10-Pin Connector, behind fuse/relay panel
T44 – Junction Box for On Board Diagnosis, above fuse/relay panel
TV18 – Distributor for terminal Xa (yellow), above fuse/relay panel
V12 – Rear Window Wiper Motor

(18) – Ground connection, on engine block
(D141) – Wire connection, in transmission wiring harness
(J10) – Wire connection (54), in ABS wiring harness

VW4029600067010X

Fig. 70 ABS wiring diagram (Part 1 of 3). 1998 Golf III, GTI & Jetta III

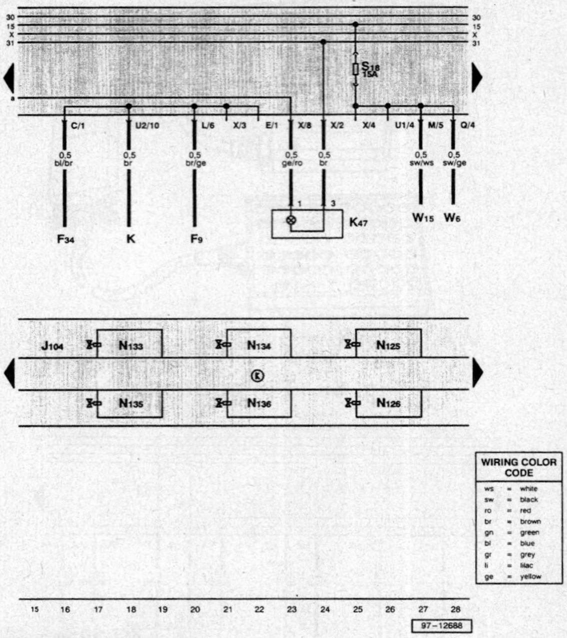

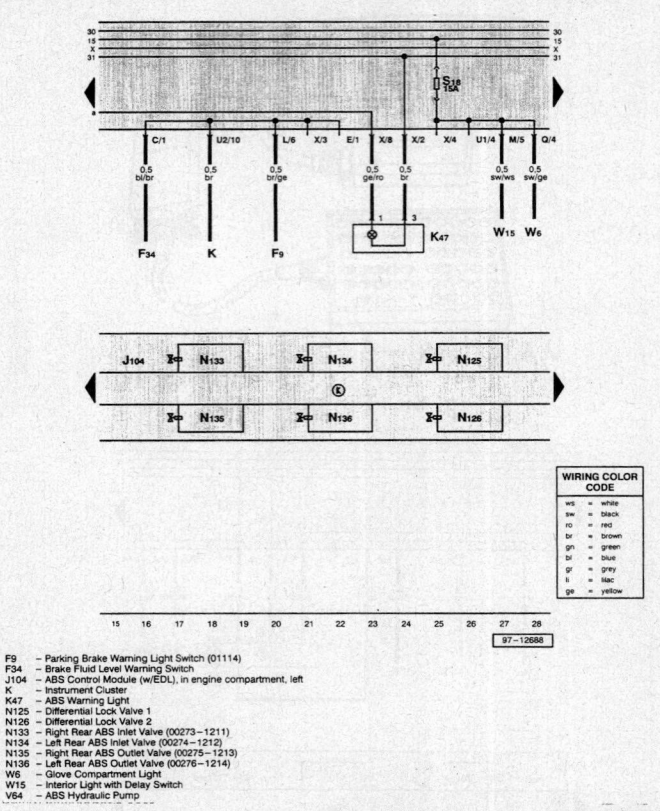

F9 – Parking Brake Warning Light Switch (01114)
F34 – Brake Fluid Level Warning Switch
J104 – ABS Control Module (w/EDL), in engine compartment, left
K – Instrument Cluster
K47 – ABS Warning Light
N125 – Differential Lock Valve 1
N126 – Differential Lock Valve 2
N133 – Right Rear ABS Inlet Valve (00273–1211)
N134 – Left Rear ABS Inlet Valve (00274–1212)
N135 – Right Rear ABS Outlet Valve (00275–1213)
N136 – Left Rear ABS Outlet Valve (00276–1214)
W6 – Glove Compartment Light
W15 – Interior Light with Delay Switch
V64 – ABS Hydraulic Pump

VW4029600067020X

Fig. 70 ABS wiring diagram (Part 2 of 3). 1998 Golf III, GTI & Jetta III

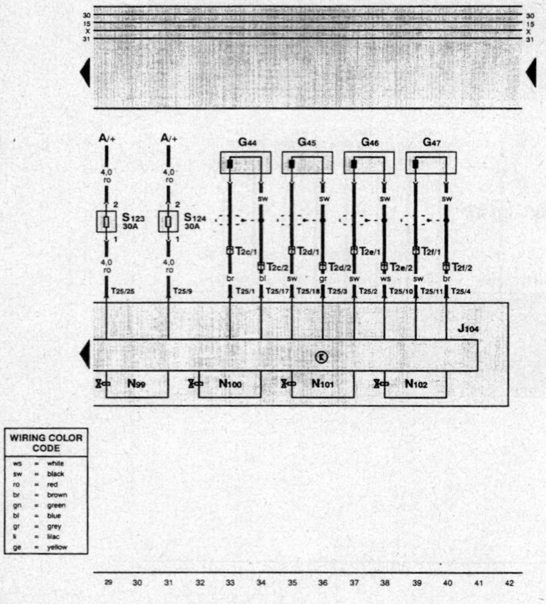

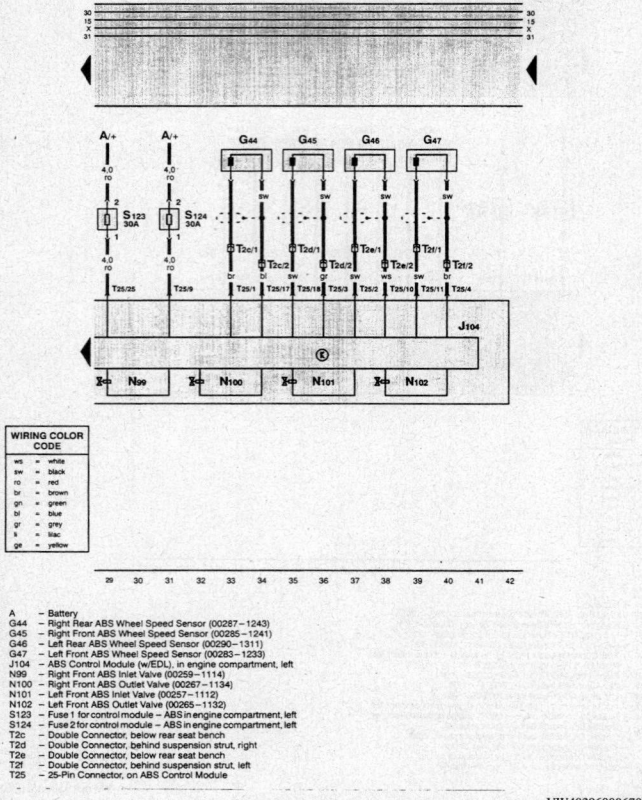

A – Battery
G44 – Right Rear ABS Wheel Speed Sensor (00287–1243)
G45 – Right Front ABS Wheel Speed Sensor (00285–1241)
G46 – Left Rear ABS Wheel Speed Sensor (00290–1311)
G47 – Left Front ABS Wheel Speed Sensor (00283–1233)
J104 – ABS Control Module (w/EDL), in engine compartment, left
N99 – Right Front ABS Inlet Valve (00259–1114)
N100 – Right Front ABS Outlet Valve (00267–1134)
N101 – Left Front ABS Inlet Valve (00257–1112)
N102 – Left Front ABS Outlet Valve (00265–1132)
S123 – Fuse 1 for control module – ABS in engine compartment, left
S124 – Fuse 2 for control module – ABS in engine compartment, left
T2c – Double Connector, below rear seat bench
T2d – Double Connector, behind suspension strut, right
T2e – Double Connector, below rear seat bench
T2f – Double Connector, behind suspension strut, left
T25 – 25-Pin Connector, on ABS Control Module

VW4029600067030X

Fig. 70 ABS wiring diagram (Part 3 of 3). 1998 Golf III, GTI & Jetta III

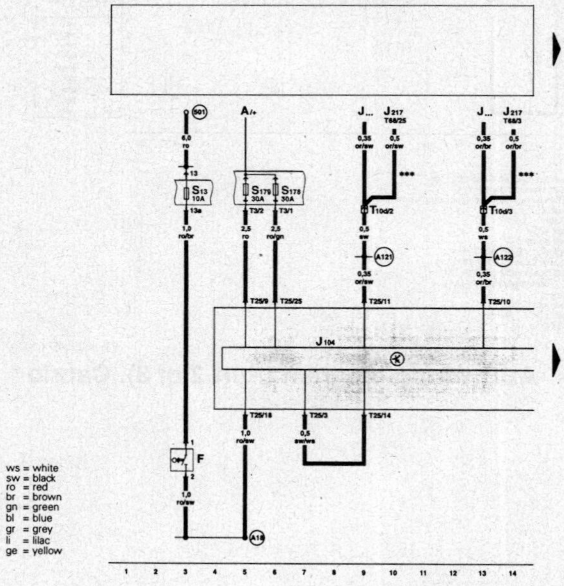

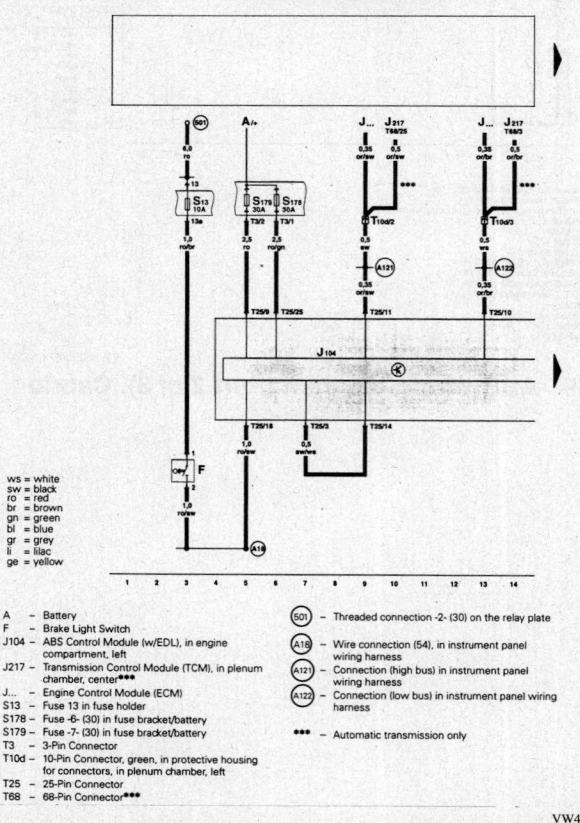

A – Battery
F – Brake Light Switch
J104 – ABS Control Module (w/EDL), in engine compartment, left
J217 – Transmission Control Module (TCM), in plenum chamber, center***
J... – Engine Control Module (ECM)
S13 – Fuse 13 in fuse holder
S178 – Fuse -6- (30) in fuse bracket/battery
S179 – Fuse -7- (30) in fuse bracket/battery
T3 – 3-Pin Connector
T10d – 10-Pin Connector, green, in protective housing for connectors, in plenum chamber, left
T25 – 25-Pin Connector
T68 – 68-Pin Connector***

(501) – Threaded connection -2- (30) on the relay plate
(A18) – Wire connection (54), in instrument panel wiring harness
(A121) – Connection (high bus) in instrument panel wiring harness
(A122) – Connection (low bus) in instrument panel wiring harness

*** – Automatic transmission only

VW4029900126010X

Fig. 71 ABS wiring diagram (Part 1 of 4). 1999–2001 Golf & Jetta

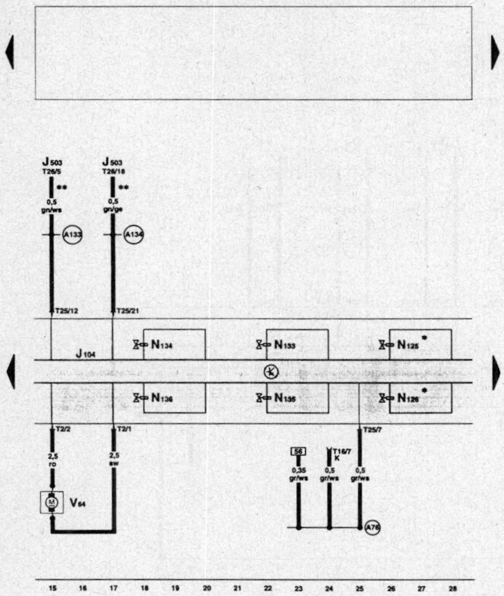

J104 – ABS Control Module (w/EDL), in engine compartment, left
J503 – Control Module with display unit for radio/navigation**
N125 – Differential lock valve 1*
N126 – Differential Lock Valve 2*
N133 – Right Rear ABS Inlet Valve
N134 – Left Rear ABS Inlet Valve
N135 – Right Rear ABS Outlet Valve
N136 – Left Rear ABS Outlet Valve
T2 – Double Connector
T16 – Data Link Connector (DLC), below instrument panel, left
T25 – 25-Pin Connector
T26 – 26-Pin Connector, on Control Module with display unit for radio/navigation**
V64 – ABS Hydraulic Pump
(A76) – Connector (K-diagnosis wire) in instrument panel wiring harness
(A133) – Connection (ABS-signal left) in instrument panel wiring harness
(A134) – Connection (ABS-signal right) in instrument panel wiring harness
* – Vehicles with Electronic Differential Lock (EDL) or Anti-Slip Control (ASC) only
** – Vehicles with navigation only

VW4029900126020X

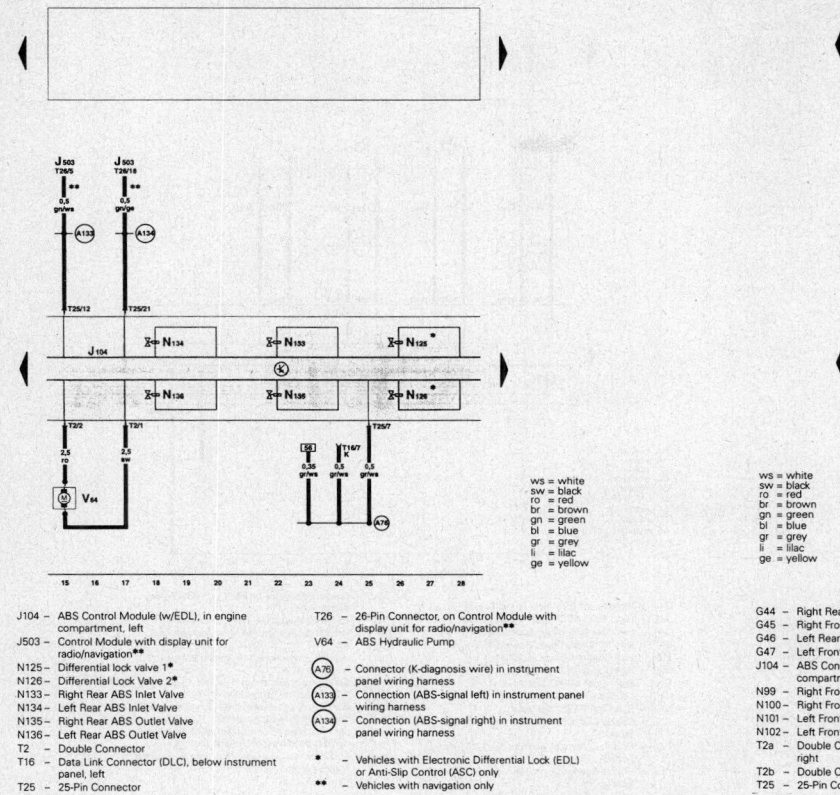

Fig. 71 ABS wiring diagram (Part 2 of 4). 1999–2001 Golf & Jetta

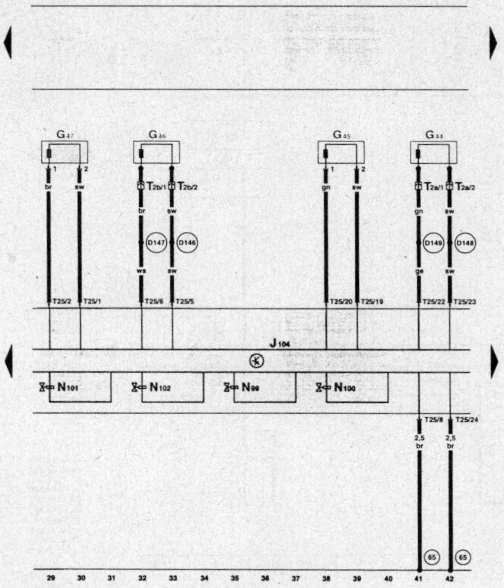

G44 – Right Rear ABS Wheel Speed Sensor
G45 – Right Front ABS Wheel Speed Sensor
G46 – Left Rear ABS Wheel Speed Sensor
G47 – Left Front ABS Wheel Speed Sensor
J104 – ABS Control Module (w/EDL), in engine compartment, left
N99 – Right Front ABS Inlet Valve
N100 – Right Front ABS Outlet Valve
N101 – Left Front ABS Inlet Valve
N102 – Left Front ABS Outlet Valve
T2a – Double Connector, near speed sensor rear, right
T2b – Double Connector, near speed sensor rear, left
T25 – 25-Pin Connector
(65) – Ground connection, on chassis side member, front left
(D146) – Connector (speed sensor rear, left +), in wiring harness engine compartment
(D147) – Connector (speed sensor rear, left -), in wiring harness engine compartment
(D148) – Connector (speed sensor rear, right +), in wiring harness engine compartment
(D149) – Connector (speed sensor rear, right -), in wiring harness engine compartment

VW4029900126030X

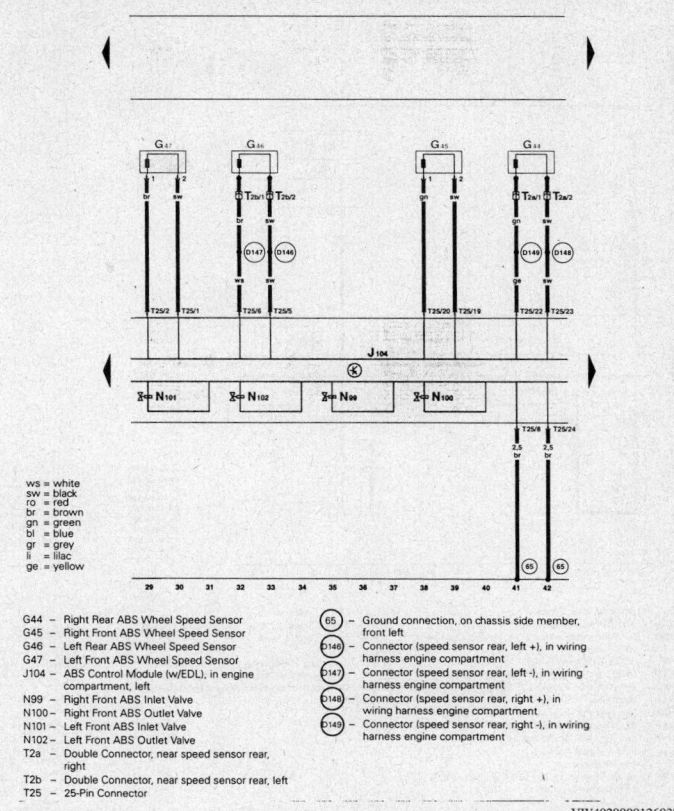

Fig. 71 ABS wiring diagram (Part 3 of 4). 1999–2001 Golf & Jetta

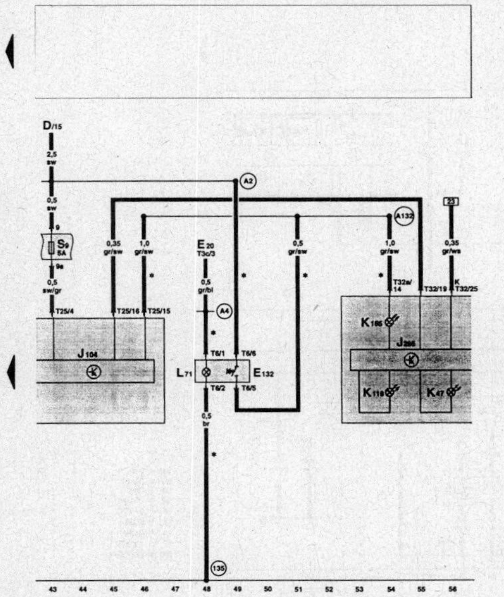

D – Ignition/Starter Switch
E20 – Instrument Panel Light Dimmer Switch
E132 – Anti-Slip Control Switch*
J104 – ABS Control Module (w/EDL), in engine compartment, left
J285 – Control module with indicator unit in instrument panel insert
K47 – ABS Warning Light
K118 – Warning light for brake system
K155 – Warning light for Anti-Slip Control (ASC)*
L71 – Anti-Slip Control Switch Illumination*
S9 – Fuse 9 in fuse holder
T3c – 3-Pin Connector
T6 – 6-Pin Connector*
T25 – 25-Pin Connector
T32 – 32-Pin Connector, blue
T32a – 32-Pin Connector, green
(135) – Ground connection -2-, in instrument panel wiring harness
(A2) – Plus connection (15), in instrument panel wiring harness
(A4) – Plus connection (58b), in instrument panel wiring harness
(A132) – Connection (ASC), in instrument panel wiring harness
* – Vehicles with Anti-Slip Control (ASC) only

VW4029900126040X

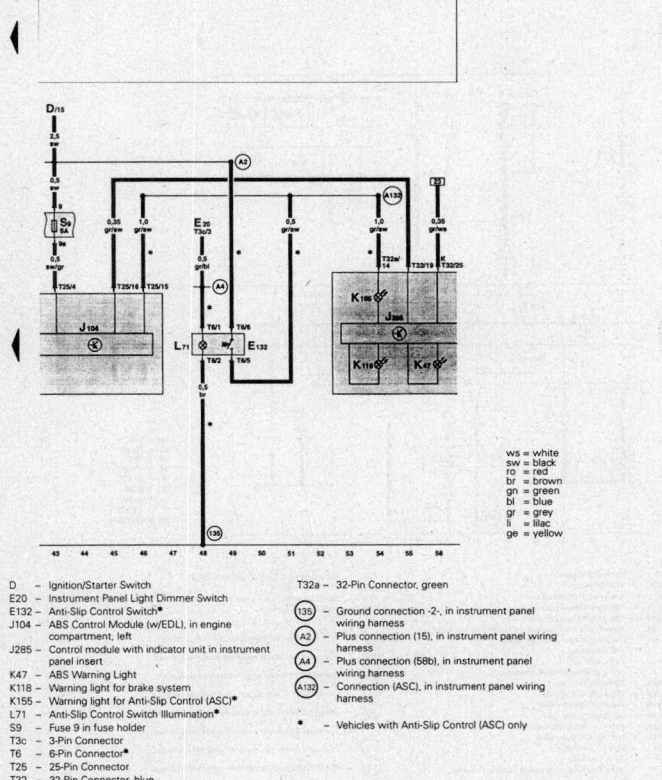

Fig. 71 ABS wiring diagram (Part 4 of 4). 1999–2001 Golf & Jetta

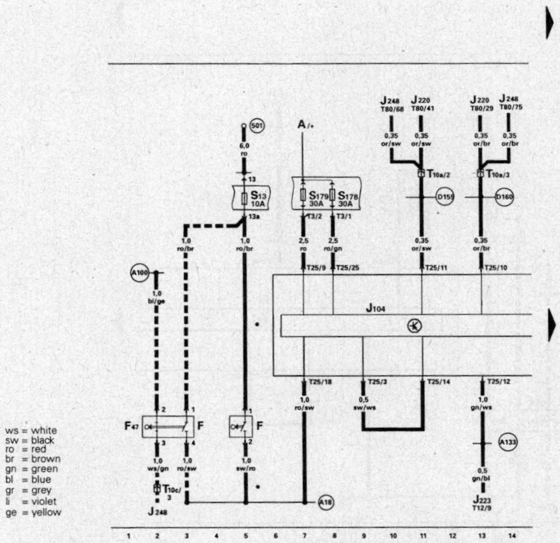

A – Battery
F – Brake Light Switch
F47 – Brake Vacuum Vent Valve Switch for cruise control/diesel fuel injection (DFI)
J104 – ABS Control Module (w/EDL)
J220 – Motronic Engine Control Module (TCM)
J223 – Rear Spoiler Control Module
J248 – Diesel Direct Fuel Injection (DFI) Engine Control Module (ECM)
S13 – Fuse 13 in fuse holder
S178 – Fuse -6- (30), in fuse bracket/battery
S179 – Fuse -7- (30), in fuse bracket/battery
T3 – 3-Pin Connector,
T10a – 10-Pin Connector, orange, behind instrument panel,left
T10c – 10-Pin Connector, blue, behind instrument panel, left
T12 – 12–pin Connector
T25 – 25-Pin Connector
T80 – 80-Pin Connector, on Control Module
(A18) – wire connection (54) , in instrument panel wiring harness
(A100) – Connector -2- (87) in instrument panel wiring harness
(A133) – Connection (ABS–signal left) in instrument panel wiring harness
(501) – Threaded connection -2- (30) on the relay plate
(D159) – CAN - bus High, in engine wiring harness
(D160) – CAN - bus Low, in engine wiring harness
- - - Diesel only
• – Gasoline only

VW4029900125010X

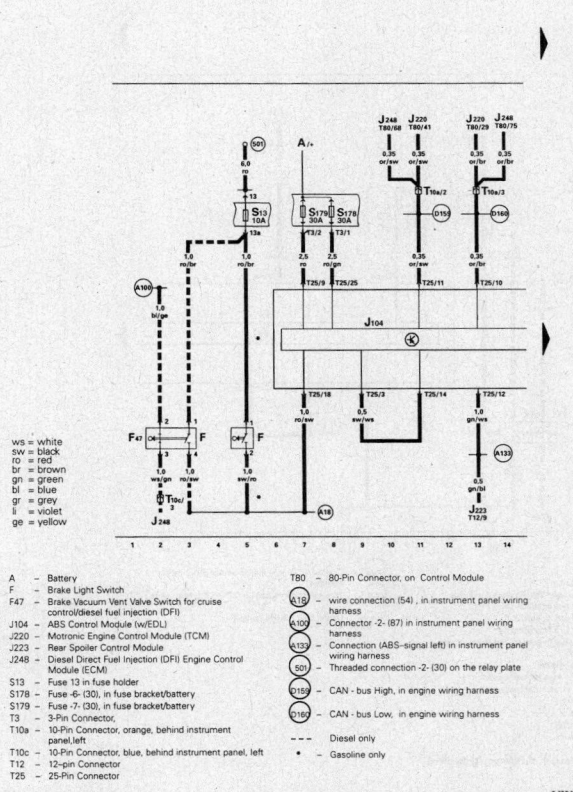

Fig. 72 ABS wiring diagram (Part 1 of 3). 1998–99 New Beetle

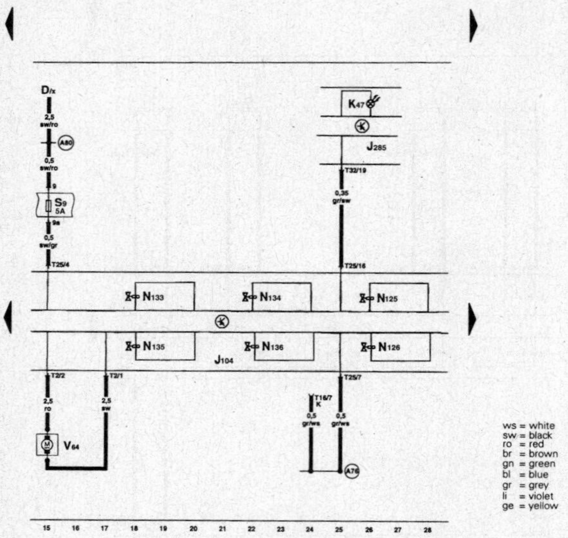

D – Ignition/Starter Switch
J104 – ABS Control Module (w/EDL)
J285 – Control module with indicator unit in instrument panel insert
K47 – ABS Warning Light
N125 – Differential Lock Valve 1
N126 – Differential Lock Valve 2
N133 – Right Rear ABS Inlet Valve
N134 – Left Rear ABS Inlet Valve
N135 – Right Rear ABS Outlet Valve
N136 – Left Rear ABS Outlet Valve
S9 – Fuse 9 in fuse holder
T2 – Double Connector
T16 – 16-Pin Connector, Data Link Connector (DLC) below steering column
T25 – 25-Pin Connector
T32 – 32-Pin Connector, blue, on instrument cluster
V64 – ABS Hydraulic Pump
(A76) – Connector (K-diagnosis wire), in instrument panel wiring harness
(A80) – Connector -1- (X), in instrument panel wiring harness

VW4029900125020X

Fig. 72 ABS wiring diagram (Part 2 of 3). 1998–99 New Beetle

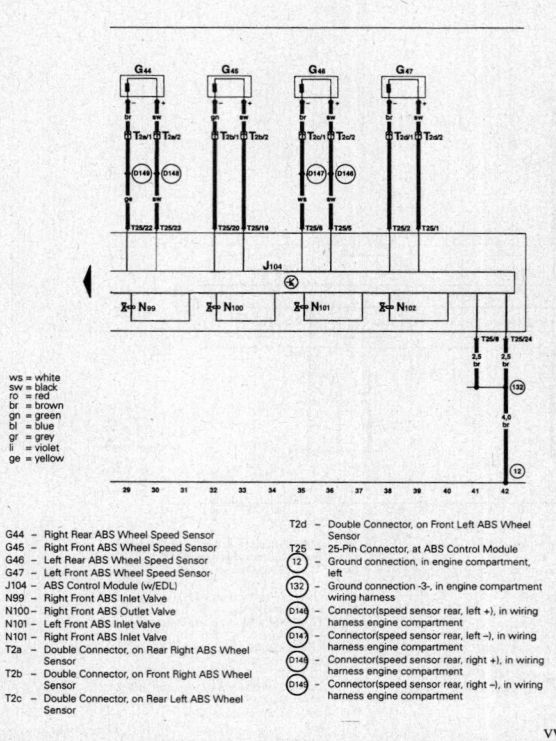

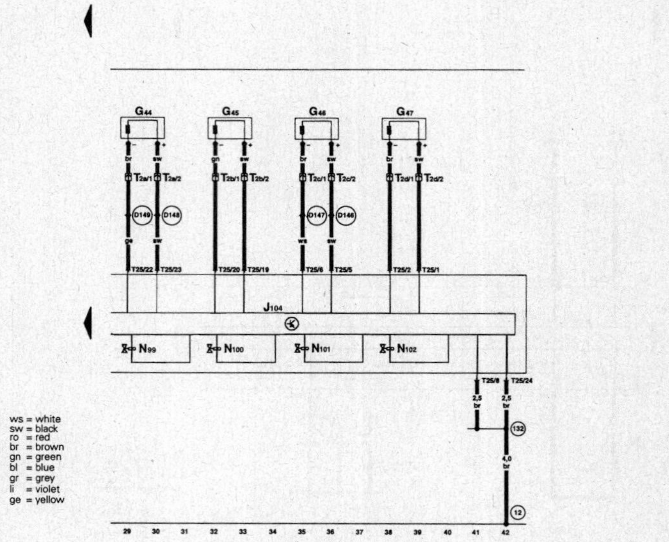

G44 – Right Rear ABS Wheel Speed Sensor
G45 – Right Front ABS Wheel Speed Sensor
G46 – Left Rear ABS Wheel Speed Sensor
G47 – Left Front ABS Wheel Speed Sensor
J104 – ABS Control Module (w/EDL)
N99 – Right Front ABS Inlet Valve
N100 – Right Front ABS Outlet Valve
N101 – Left Front ABS Inlet Valve
N101 – Right Front ABS Inlet Valve
T2a – Double Connector, on Rear Right ABS Wheel Sensor
T2b – Double Connector, on Front Right ABS Wheel Sensor
T2c – Double Connector, on Rear Left ABS Wheel Sensor
T2d – Double Connector, on Front Left ABS Wheel Sensor
T25 – 25-Pin Connector, at ABS Control Module
(12) – Ground connection, in engine compartment, left
(132) – Ground connection -3-, in engine compartment wiring harness
(D146) – Connector(speed sensor rear, left +), in wiring harness engine compartment
(D147) – Connector(speed sensor rear, left –), in wiring harness engine compartment
(D148) – Connector(speed sensor rear, right +), in wiring harness engine compartment
(D149) – Connector(speed sensor rear, right –), in wiring harness engine compartment

VW4029900125030X

Fig. 72 ABS wiring diagram (Part 3 of 3). 1998–99 New Beetle

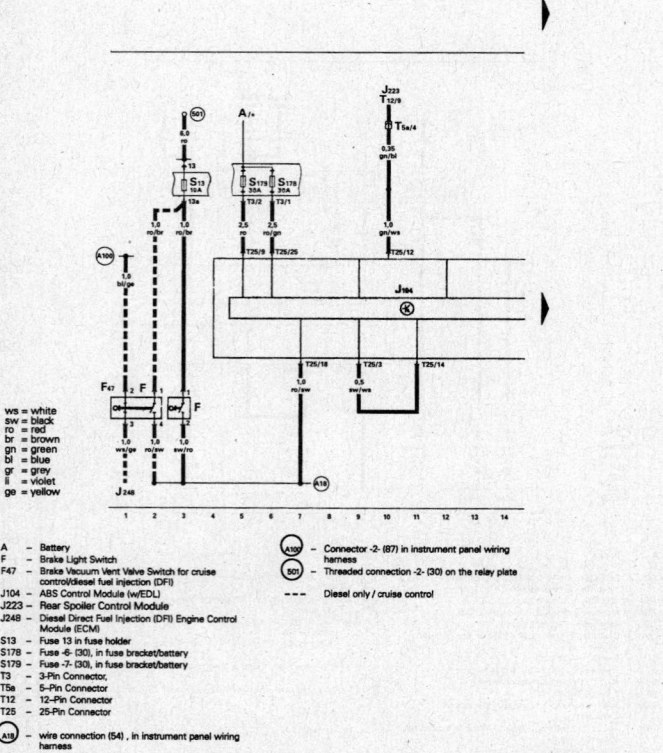

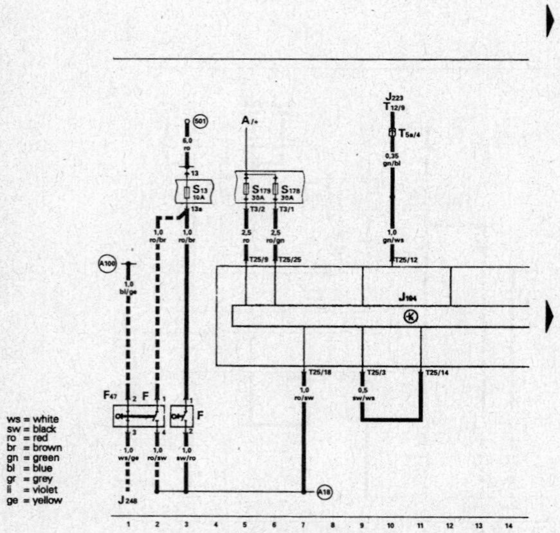

A – Battery
F – Brake Light Switch
F47 – Brake Vacuum Vent Valve Switch for cruise control/diesel fuel injection (DFI)
J104 – ABS Control Module (w/EDL)
J223 – Rear Spoiler Control Module
J248 – Diesel Direct Fuel Injection (DFI) Engine Control Module (ECM)
S13 – Fuse 13 in fuse holder
S178 – Fuse -6- (30), in fuse bracket/battery
S179 – Fuse -7- (30), in fuse bracket/battery
T3 – 3-Pin Connector,
T5a – 5–Pin Connector
T12 – 12–Pin Connector
T25 – 25-Pin Connector
(A18) – wire connection (54) , in instrument panel wiring harness
(A100) – Connector -2- (87) in instrument panel wiring harness
(501) – Threaded connection -2- (30) on the relay plate
--- Diesel only / cruise control

VW4020100132010X

Fig. 73 ABS wiring diagram (Part 1 of 3). 2000–01 New Beetle from June 1999

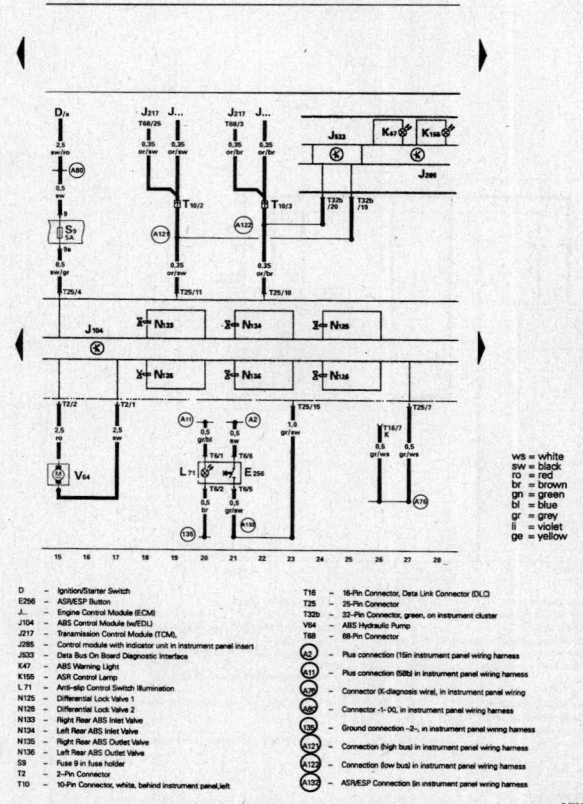

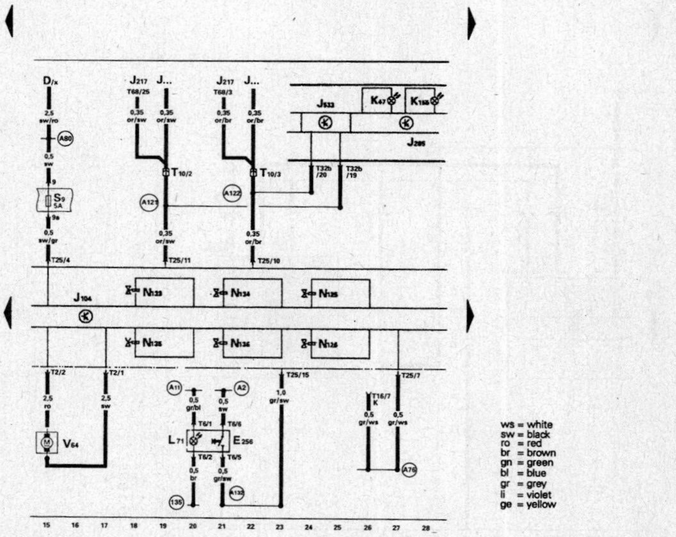

D – Ignition/Starter Switch
E256 – ASR/ESP Button
J... – Engine Control Module (ECM)
J104 – ABS Control Module (w/EDL)
J217 – Transmission Control Module (TCM),
J285 – Control module with indicator unit in instrument panel insert
J533 – Data Bus On Board Diagnostic Interface
K47 – ABS Warning Light
K155 – ASR Control Lamp
L 71 – Anti–slip Control Switch Illumination
N125 – Differential Lock Valve 1
N126 – Differential Lock Valve 2
N133 – Right Rear ABS Inlet Valve
N134 – Left Rear ABS Inlet Valve
N135 – Right Rear ABS Outlet Valve
N136 – Left Rear ABS Outlet Valve
S9 – Fuse 9 in fuse holder
T2 – 2–Pin Connector
T10 – 10-Pin Connector, white, behind instrument panel,left
T16 – 16-Pin Connector, Data Link Connector (DLC)
T25 – 25-Pin Connector
T32b – 32–Pin Connector, green, on instrument cluster
V64 – ABS Hydraulic Pump
T68 – 68-Pin Connector
(A2) – Plus connection (15in instrument panel wiring harness
(A11) – Plus connection (58b) in instrument panel wiring harness
(A76) – Connector (K-diagnosis wire), in instrument panel wiring
(A80) – Connector -1- (X), in instrument panel wiring harness
(135) – Ground connection –2–, in instrument panel wiring harness
(A121) – Connection (high bus) in instrument panel wiring harness
(A122) – Connection (low bus) in instrument panel wiring harness
(A132) – ASR/ESP Connection (in instrument panel wiring harness

VW4020100132020X

Fig. 73 ABS wiring diagram (Part 2 of 3). 2000–01 New Beetle from June 1999

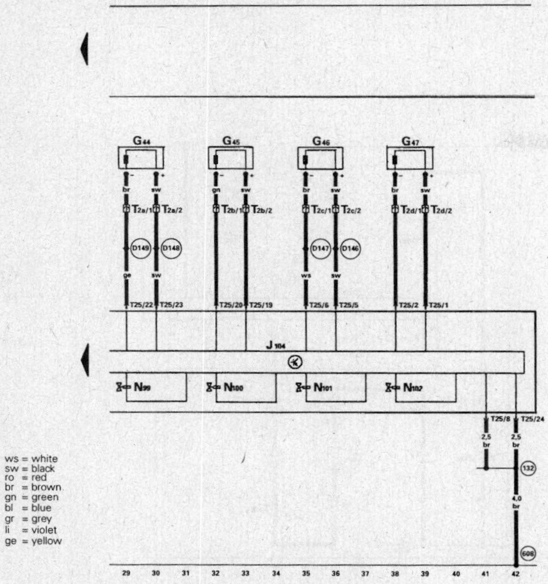

G44 – Right Rear ABS Wheel Speed Sensor
G45 – Right Front ABS Wheel Speed Sensor
G46 – Left Rear ABS Wheel Speed Sensor
G47 – Left Front ABS Wheel Speed Sensor
J104 – ABS Control Module (w/EDL)
N99 – Right Front ABS Inlet Valve
N100 – Right Front ABS Outlet Valve
N101 – Left Front ABS Inlet Valve
N102 – Right Front ABS Inlet Valve
T2a – Double Connector, on Rear Right ABS Wheel Sensor
T2b – Double Connector, on Front Right ABS Wheel Sensor
T2c – Double Connector, on Rear Left ABS Wheel Sensor
T2d – Double Connector, on Front Left ABS Wheel Sensor
T25 – 25-Pin Connector, at ABS Control Module

(132) – Ground connection -3-, in engine compartment wiring harness
(606) – Ground Connection (in center plenum chamber)
(D146) – Connector(speed sensor rear, left +), in wiring harness engine compartment
(D147) – Connector(speed sensor rear, left –), in wiring harness engine compartment
(D148) – Connector(speed sensor rear, right +), in wiring harness engine compartment
(D149) – Connector(speed sensor rear, right –), in wiring harness engine compartment

VW4020100132030X

Fig. 73 ABS wiring diagram (Part 3 of 3). 2000–01 New Beetle from June 1999

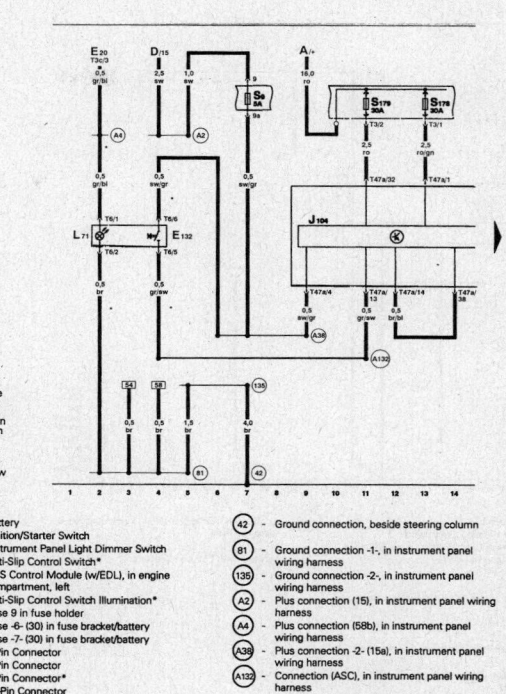

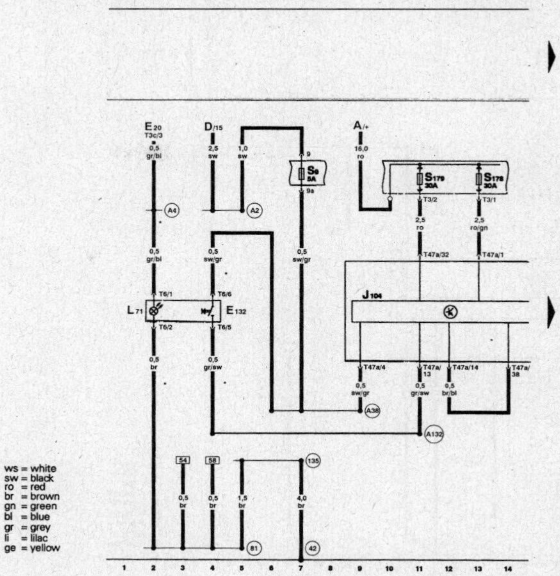

A - Battery
D - Ignition/Starter Switch
E20 - Instrument Panel Light Dimmer Switch
E132 - Anti-Slip Control Switch*
J104 - ABS Control Module (w/EDL), in engine compartment, left
L71 - Anti-Slip Control Switch Illumination*
S9 - Fuse 9 in fuse holder
S178 - Fuse -6- (30) in fuse bracket/battery
S179 - Fuse -7- (30) in fuse bracket/battery
T3 - 3-Pin Connector
T3c - 3-Pin Connector
T6 - 6-Pin Connector*
T47a - 47-Pin Connector

(42) - Ground connection, beside steering column
(81) - Ground connection -1-, in instrument panel wiring harness
(135) - Ground connection -2-, in instrument panel wiring harness
(A2) - Plus connection (15), in instrument panel wiring harness
(A4) - Plus connection (58b), in instrument panel wiring harness
(A38) - Plus connection -2- (15a), in instrument panel wiring harness
(A132) - Connection (ASC), in instrument panel wiring harness

* - Vehicles with Anti-Slip Control (ASC) only

VW4020100133010X

Fig. 74 ABS wiring diagram (Part 1 of 5). 2001 New Beetle from October 2000

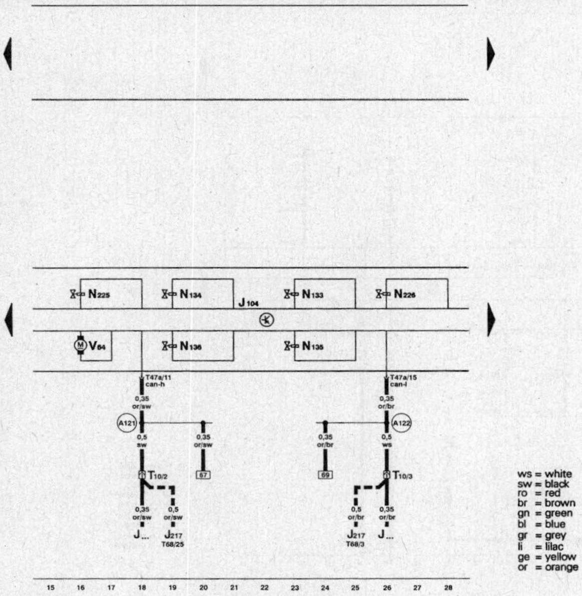

J104 - ABS Control Module (w/EDL), in engine compartment, left
J217 - Transmission Control Module (TCM), in plenum chamber, center
J... - Engine Control Module (ECM)
N133 - Right Rear ABS Inlet Valve
N134 - Left Rear ABS Inlet Valve
N135 - Right Rear ABS Outlet Valve
N136 - Left Rear ABS Outlet Valve
N225 - Pilot valve -1- traction control
N226 - Pilot valve -2- traction control
T10 - 10-Pin Connector, white, in protective housing for connectors, in plenum chamber, left
T47a - 47-Pin Connector
T68 - 68-Pin Connector, on Transmission Control Module (TCM)
V64 - ABS Hydraulic Pump

(A121) - Connection (high bus), in instrument panel wiring harness
(A122) - Connection (low bus), in instrument panel wiring harness

--- Automatic transmission only

VW4020100133020X

Fig. 74 ABS wiring diagram (Part 2 of 5). 2001 New Beetle from October 2000

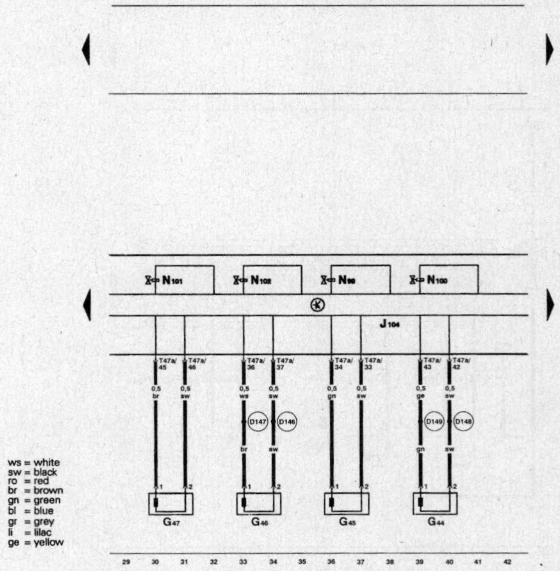

G44 - Right Rear ABS Wheel Speed Sensor
G45 - Right Front ABS Wheel Speed Sensor
G46 - Left Rear ABS Wheel Speed Sensor
G47 - Left Front ABS Wheel Speed Sensor
J104 - ABS Control Module (w/EDL), in engine compartment, left
N99 - Right Front ABS Inlet Valve
N100 - Right Front ABS Outlet Valve
N101 - Left Front ABS Inlet Valve
N102 - Left Front ABS Outlet Valve
T47a - 47-Pin Connector

(D146) - Connector (speed sensor rear, left +), in wiring harness engine compartment
(D147) - Connector (speed sensor rear, left -), in wiring harness engine compartment
(D148) - Connector (speed sensor rear, right +), in wiring harness engine compartment
(D149) - Connector (speed sensor rear, right -), in wiring harness engine compartment

VW4020100133030X

Fig. 74 ABS wiring diagram (Part 3 of 5). 2001 New Beetle from October 2000

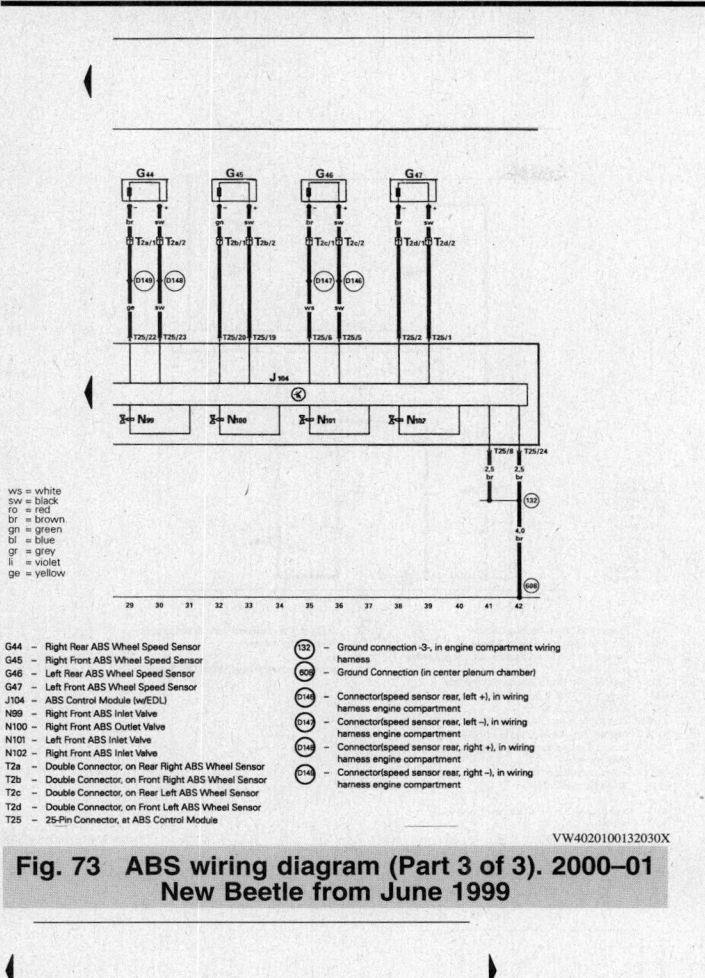

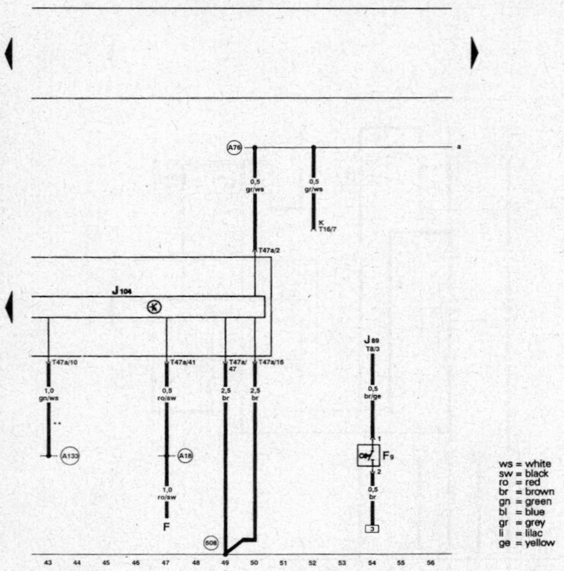

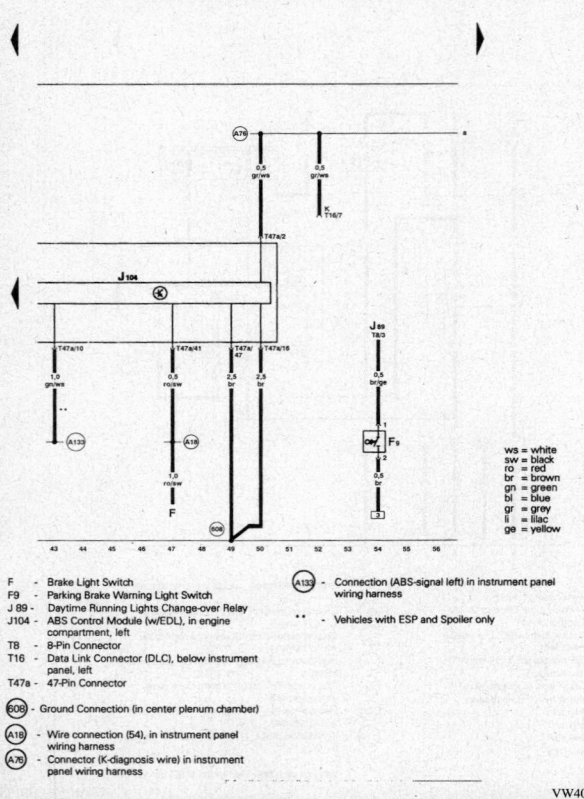

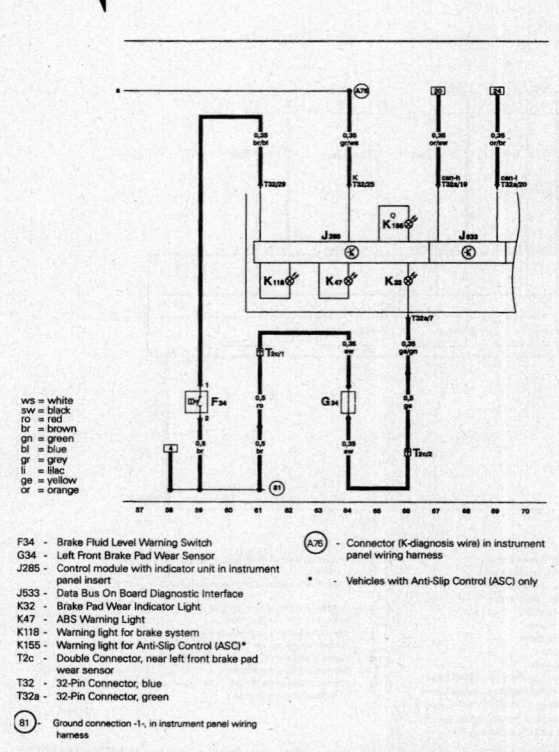

F - Brake Light Switch
F9 - Parking Brake Warning Light Switch
J 89 - Daytime Running Lights Change-over Relay
J104 - ABS Control Module (w/EDL), in engine compartment, left
T8 - 8-Pin Connector
T16 - Data Link Connector (DLC), below instrument panel, left
T47a - 47-Pin Connector
(608) - Ground Connection (in center plenum chamber)
(A18) - Wire connection (54), in instrument panel wiring harness
(A76) - Connector (K-diagnosis wire) in instrument panel wiring harness
(A133) - Connection (ABS-signal left) in instrument panel wiring harness
** - Vehicles with ESP and Spoiler only

VW4020100133040X

Fig. 74 ABS wiring diagram (Part 4 of 5). 2001 New Beetle from October 2000

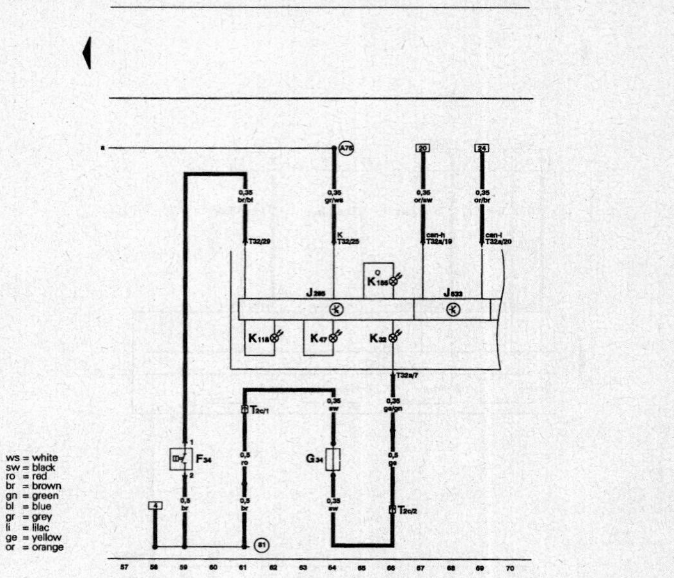

F34 - Brake Fluid Level Warning Switch
G34 - Left Front Brake Pad Wear Sensor
J285 - Control module with indicator unit in instrument panel insert
J533 - Data Bus On Board Diagnostic Interface
K32 - Brake Pad Wear Indicator Light
K47 - ABS Warning Light
K118 - Warning light for brake system
K155 - Warning light for Anti-Slip Control (ASC)*
T2c - Double Connector, near left front brake pad wear sensor
T32 - 32-Pin Connector, blue
T32a - 32-Pin Connector, green
(81) - Ground connection -1-, in instrument panel wiring harness
(A76) - Connector (K-diagnosis wire) in instrument panel wiring harness
* - Vehicles with Anti-Slip Control (ASC) only

VW4020100133050X

Fig. 74 ABS wiring diagram (Part 5 of 5). 2001 New Beetle from October 2000

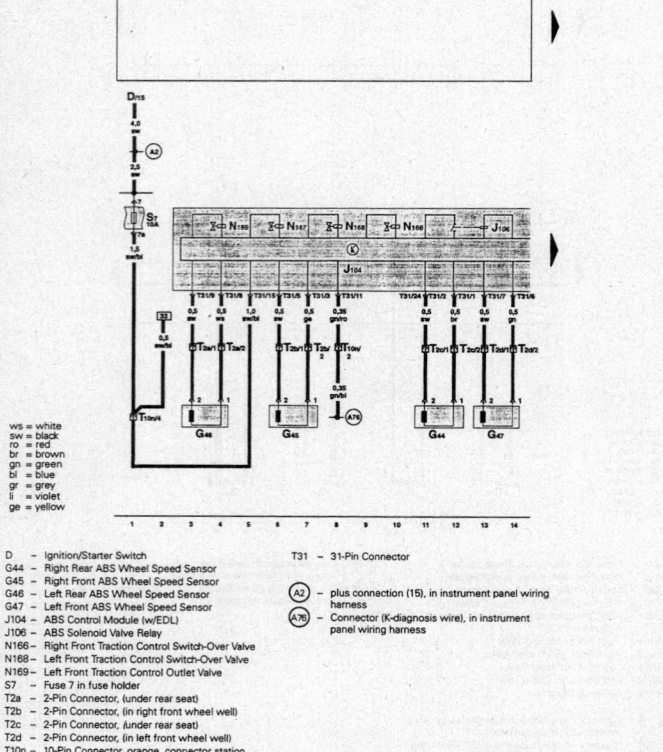

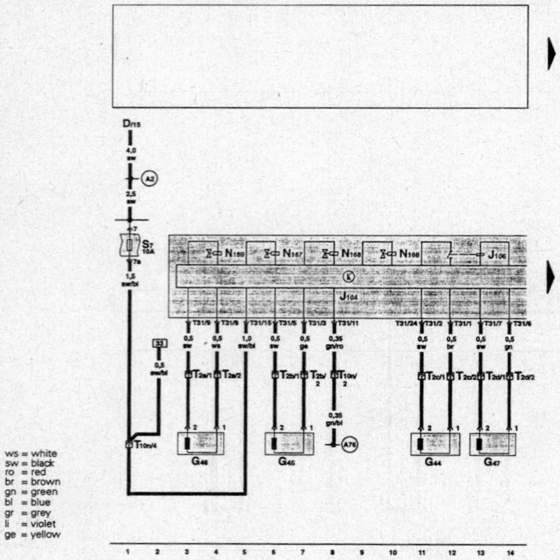

D – Ignition/Starter Switch
G44 – Right Rear ABS Wheel Speed Sensor
G45 – Right Front ABS Wheel Speed Sensor
G46 – Left Rear ABS Wheel Speed Sensor
G47 – Left Front ABS Wheel Speed Sensor
J104 – ABS Control Module (w/EDL)
J106 – ABS Solenoid Valve Relay
N166 – Right Front Traction Control Switch-Over Valve
N168 – Left Front Traction Control Switch-Over Valve
N169 – Left Front Traction Control Outlet Valve
S7 – Fuse 7 in fuse holder
T2a – 2-Pin Connector, (under rear seat)
T2b – 2-Pin Connector, (in right front wheel well)
T2c – 2-Pin Connector, (under rear seat)
T2d – 2-Pin Connector, (in left front wheel well)
T10n – 10-Pin Connector, orange, connector station A-pillar, left
T31 – 31-Pin Connector
(A2) – plus connection (15), in instrument panel wiring harness
(A76) – Connector (K-diagnosis wire), in instrument panel wiring harness

VW4029900127010X

Fig. 75 ABS wiring diagram (Part 1 of 3). Passat FWD w/EDL & ASR

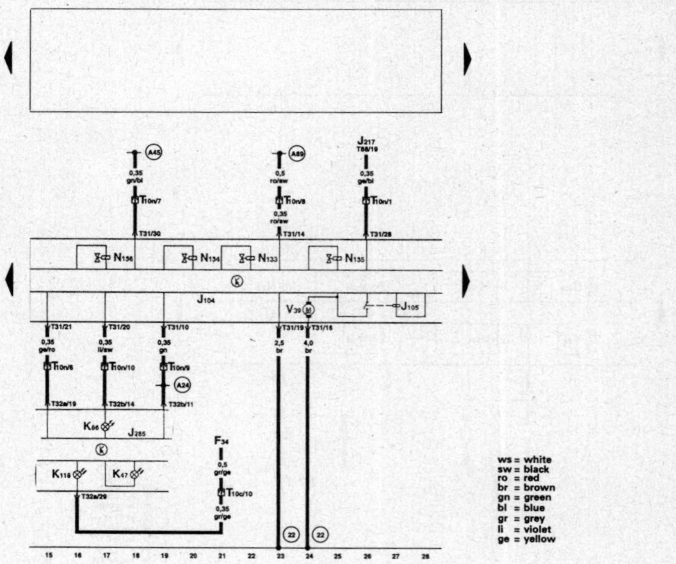

F34 – Brake Fluid Level Warning Switch
J104 – ABS Control Module (w/EDL)
J105 – ABS Return Flow Pump Relay
J217 – Transmission Control Module (TCM)
J285 – Control module with indicator unit in instrument panel insert
K47 – ABS Warning Light
K86 – Traction Control Indicator Light
K118 – Warning light for brake system
N133 – Right Rear ABS Inlet Valve
N134 – Left Rear ABS Inlet Valve
N135 – Right Rear ABS Outlet Valve
N136 – Left Rear ABS Outlet Valve
T10c – 10-Pin Connector, violet, connector station A-pillar, left
T10n – 10-Pin Connector, orange, connector station A-pillar, left
T31 – 31-Pin Connector
T32a – 32-Pin Connector, blue, on instrument cluster
T32b – 32-Pin Connector, green, on instrument cluster
V39 – ABS Return Flow Pump
T88 – Connector, 88 point, on Transmission Control Module (TCM)
(22) – Ground connection, on hydraulic unit
(A24) – wire connection (brake system monitoring), in instrument panel wiring harness
(A45) – wire connection (RPM-signal), in instrument panel wiring harness
(A89) – Connector (54), in instrument panel wiring harness

VW4029900127020X

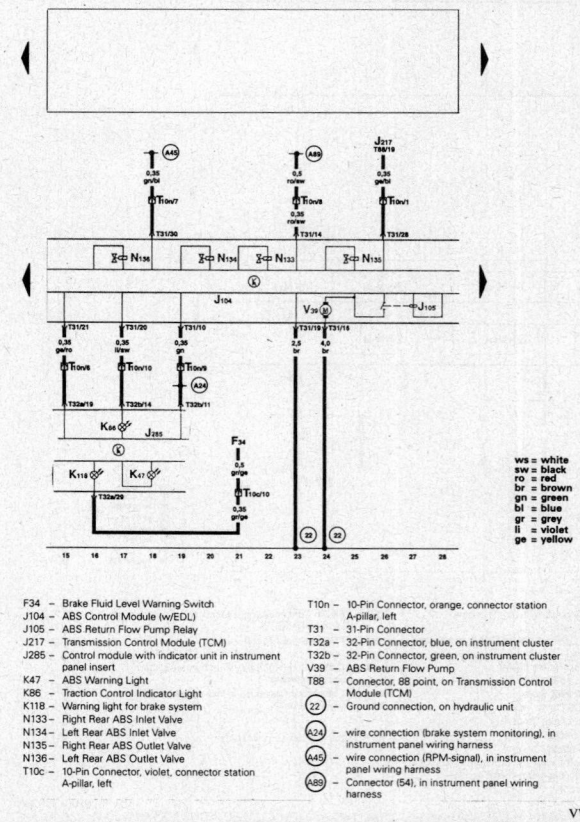

Fig. 75 ABS wiring diagram (Part 2 of 3). Passat FWD w/EDL & ASR

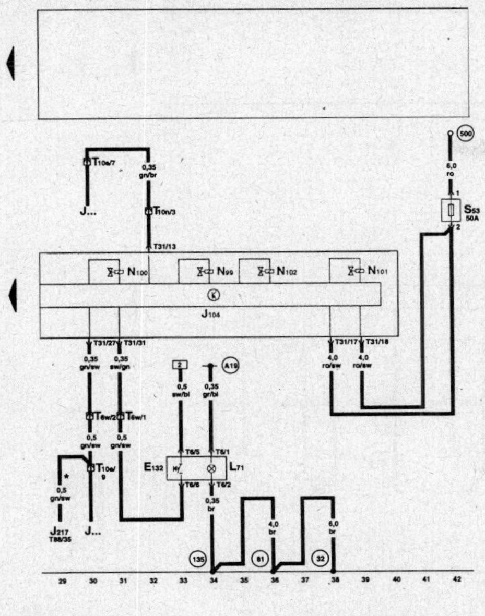

E132 – Anti-Slip Control Switch
J... – Engine Control Module
J104 – ABS Control Module (w/EDL)
J217 – Transmission Control Module (TCM)
L71 – Anti-slip Control Switch Illumination
N99 – Right Front ABS Inlet Valve
N100 – Right Front ABS Outlet Valve
N101 – Left Front ABS Inlet Valve
N102 – Left Front ABS Outlet Valve
S53 – ABS Hydraulic Pump Fuse, on the thirteenfold auxiliray relay panel, above relay panel
T6 – 6-Pin Connector, black
T6w – 6-Pin Connector, grey, connector station A-pillar, right
T10e – 10-Pin Connector, yellow, on protective housing for control module, in engine compartment, left
T10n – 10-Pin Connector, orange, connector station A-pillar, left
T31 – 31-Pin Connector
T88 – Connector, 88 point, on Transmission Control Module (TCM)
(32) – Ground connection, behind instrument panel, left
(81) – Ground connection -1-, in instrument panel wiring harness
(135) – Ground connection -2-, in instrument panel wiring harness
(500) – Screw connection -1- (30), on relay panel
(A19) – wire connection (58d), in instrument panel wiring harness
* – automatic transmission only

VW4029900127030X

Fig. 75 ABS wiring diagram (Part 3 of 3). Passat FWD w/EDL & ASR

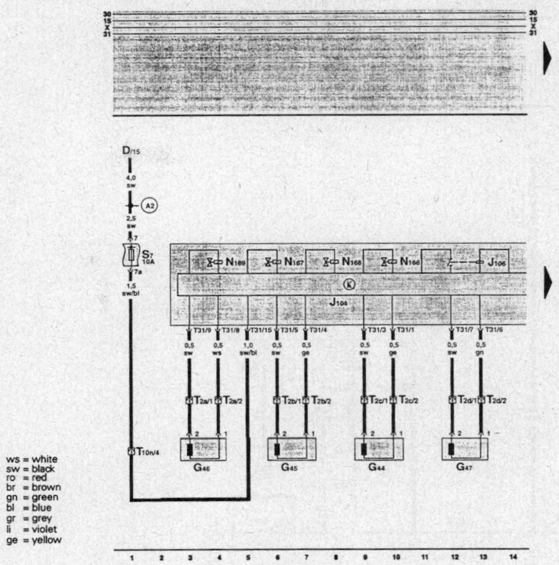

D – Ignition/Starter Switch
G44 – Right Rear ABS Wheel Speed Sensor
G45 – Right Front ABS Wheel Speed Sensor
G46 – Left Rear ABS Wheel Speed Sensor
G47 – Left Front ABS Wheel Speed Sensor
J104 – ABS Control Module (w/EDL)
J106 – ABS Solenoid Valve Relay
N166 – Right Front Traction Control Switch-Over Valve
N167 – Right Front Traction Control Outlet Valve
N168 – Left Front Traction Control Switch-Over Valve
N169 – Left Front Traction Control Outlet Valve
S7 – Fuse 7 in fuse holder
T2a – 2-Pin Connector (under rear seat)
T2b – 2-Pin Connector, (in right front wheel well)
T2c – 2-Pin Connector, (under rear seat)
T2d – 2-Pin Connector, (in left front wheel well)
T10n – 10-Pin Connector, orange, connector station A-pillar, left
T31 – 31-Pin Connector, on ABS Control Module (w/EDL)
(A2) – plus connection (15), in instrument panel wiring harness

VW4029900128010X

Fig. 76 ABS wiring diagram (Part 1 of 3). Passat FWD & AWD w/EDL

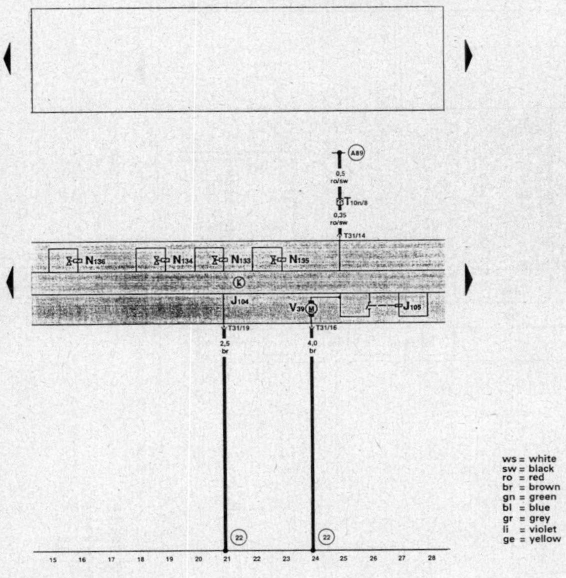

J104 – ABS Control Module (w/EDL)
J105 – ABS Return Flow Pump Relay
N133 – Right Rear ABS Inlet Valve
N134 – Left Rear ABS Inlet Valve
N135 – Right Rear ABS Outlet Valve
N136 – Left Rear ABS Outlet Valve
T10n – 10-Pin Connector, orange, connector station A-pillar, left
T31 – 31-Pin Connector, on ABS Control Module (w/EDL)
V39 – ABS Return Flow Pump
(22) – Ground connection, on hydraulic unit
(A89) – Connector (54), in instrument panel wiring harness

VW4029900128020X

Fig. 76 ABS wiring diagram (Part 2 of 3). Passat FWD & AWD w/EDL

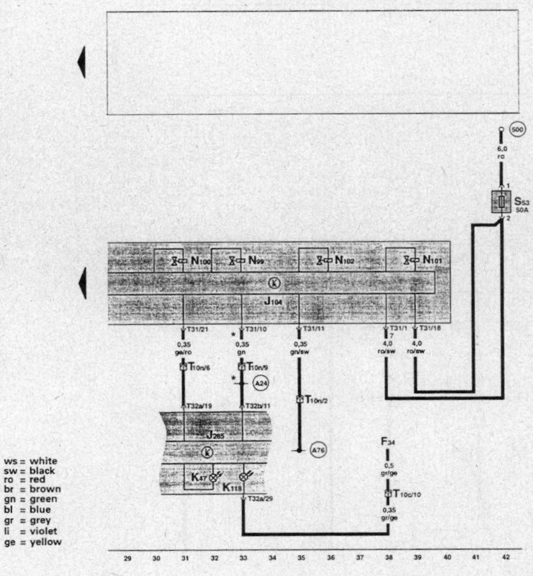

F34 – Brake Fluid Level Warning Switch
J104 – ABS Control Module (w/EDL)
J285 – Control module with indicator unit in instrument panel insert
K47 – ABS Warning Light
K118 – Warning light for brake system
N99 – Right Front ABS Inlet Valve
N100 – Right Front ABS Outlet Valve
N101 – Left Front ABS Inlet Valve
N102 – Left Front ABS Outlet Valve
S53 – ABS Hydraulic Pump Fuse, on the thirteenfold auxiliary relay panel, above relay panel
T10c – 10-Pin Connector, violet, connector station A-pillar, left
T10n – 10-Pin Connector, orange, connector station A-pillar, left
T31 – 31-Pin Connector, on ABS Control Module (w/EDL)
T32a – 32-Pin Connector, blue, on instrument cluster
T32b – 32-Pin Connector, green, on instrument cluster
(500) – Screw connection -1- (30), on relay panel
(A24) – wire connection (brake system monitoring), in instrument panel wiring harness
(A76) – Connector (K-diagnosis wire), in instrument panel wiring harness
* – with EDL only

VW4029900128030X

Fig. 76 ABS wiring diagram (Part 3 of 3). Passat FWD & AWD w/EDL

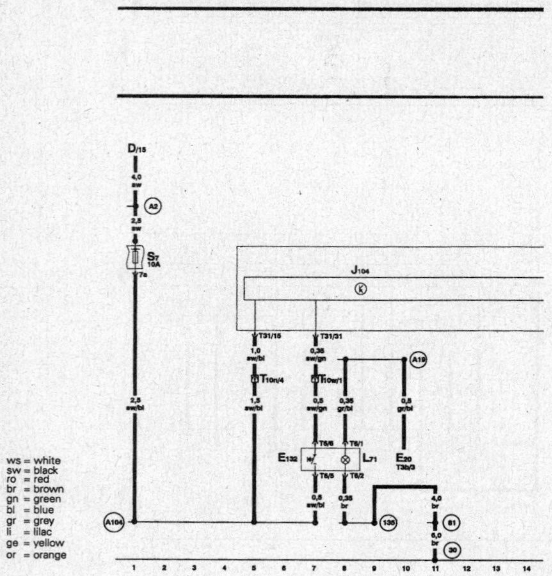

D - Ignition/Starter Switch
E20 - Instrument Panel Light Dimmer Switch
E132 - Anti-Slip Control Switch
J104 - ABS Control Module (w/EDL)
L71 - Anti-slip Control Switch Illumination
S7 - Fuse
T3b - 3-Pin Connector, black on Instrument Panel Light Dimmer Switch
T6 - 6-Pin Connector, black
T10n - 10-Pin Connector, orange, connector station A-pillar, left
T10w - 10-Pin Connector, grey, connector station A-pillar, right
T31 - 31-Pin Connector

(30) - Ground connection, -1-, beside fuse/relay panel
(81) - Ground connection -1-, in instrument panel wiring harness
(135) - Ground connection -2-, in instrument panel wiring harness
(A2) - plus connection (15), in instrument panel wiring harness
(A19) - wire connection (58d), in instrument panel wiring harness
(A104) - Plus connector -2- (15), in instrument panel wiring harness

VW4020100134010X

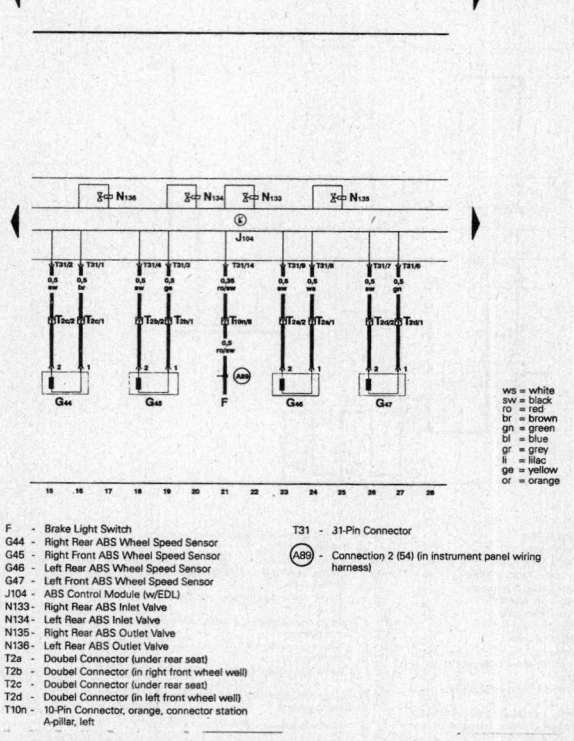

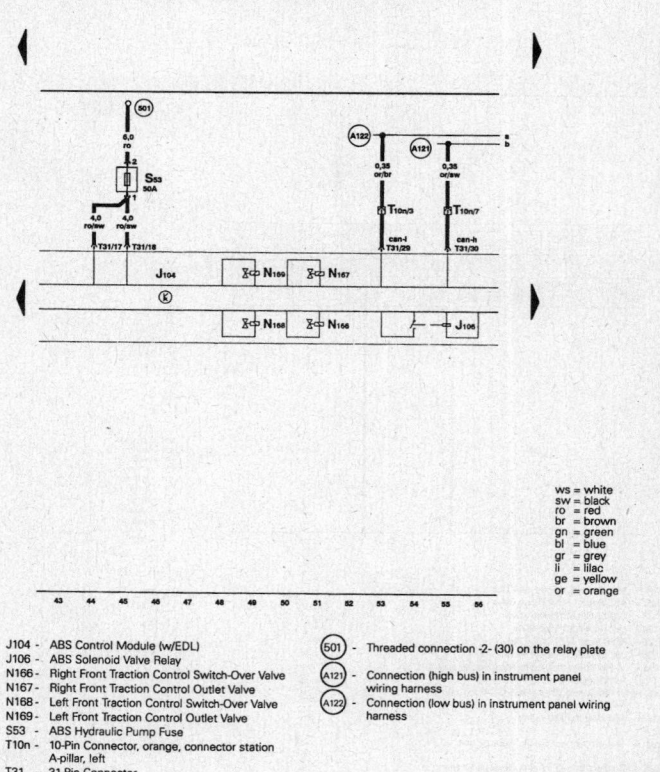

Fig. 77 ABS wiring diagram (Part 1 of 5). 2001 Passat FWD w/EDL & ASC

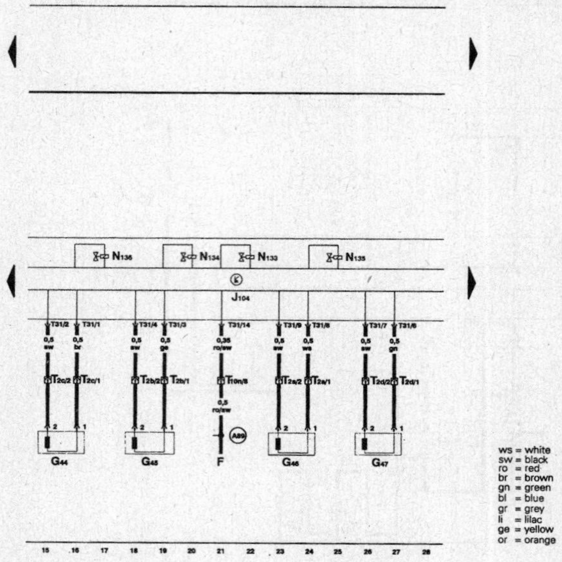

F - Brake Light Switch
G44 - Right Rear ABS Wheel Speed Sensor
G45 - Right Front ABS Wheel Speed Sensor
G46 - Left Rear ABS Wheel Speed Sensor
G47 - Left Front ABS Wheel Speed Sensor
J104 - ABS Control Module (w/EDL)
N133 - Right Rear ABS Inlet Valve
N134 - Left Rear ABS Inlet Valve
N135 - Right Rear ABS Outlet Valve
N136 - Left Rear ABS Outlet Valve
T2a - Doubel Connector (under rear seat)
T2b - Doubel Connector (in right front wheel well)
T2c - Doubel Connector (under rear seat)
T2d - Doubel Connector (in left front wheel well)
T10n - 10-Pin Connector, orange, connector station A-pillar, left
T31 - 31-Pin Connector

(A89) - Connection 2 (54) (in instrument panel wiring harness)

VW4020100134020X

Fig. 77 ABS wiring diagram (Part 2 of 5). 2001 Passat FWD w/EDL & ASC

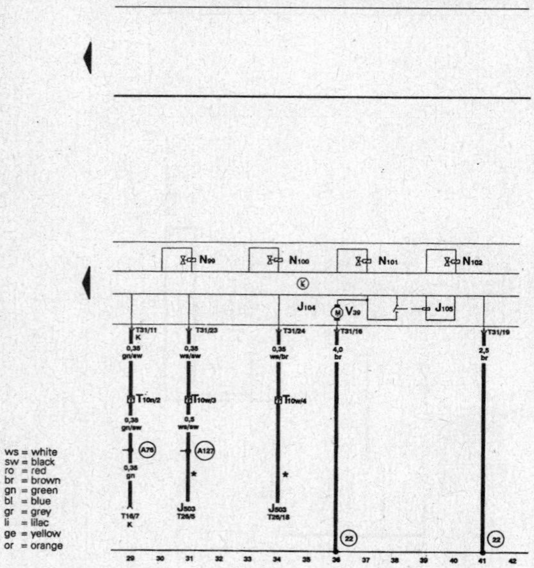

J104 - ABS Control Module (w/EDL)
J105 - ABS Return Flow Pump Relay
J503 - Radio/Navigation Display Control Module
N99 - Right Front ABS Inlet Valve
N100 - Right Front ABS Outlet Valve
N101 - Left Front ABS Inlet Valve
N102 - Left Front ABS Outlet Valve
T10n - 10-Pin Connector, orange, connector station A-pillar, left
T10w - 10-Pin Connector, grey, connector station A-pillar, right
T16 - 16-Pin Connector, Data Link Connector(DLC), below instrument panel, left
T26 - 26-Pin Connector, on Radio/Navigation Display Control Module
T31 - 31-Pin Connector

V39 - ABS Return Flow Pump
(22) - Ground connection, on hydraulic unit
(A76) - Connector (K-diagnosis wire) in instrument panel wiring harness
(A127) - Connector (left rear speed sensor) in instrument panel wiring harness
* Navigation only

VW4020100134030X

Fig. 77 ABS wiring diagram (Part 3 of 5). 2001 Passat FWD w/EDL & ASC

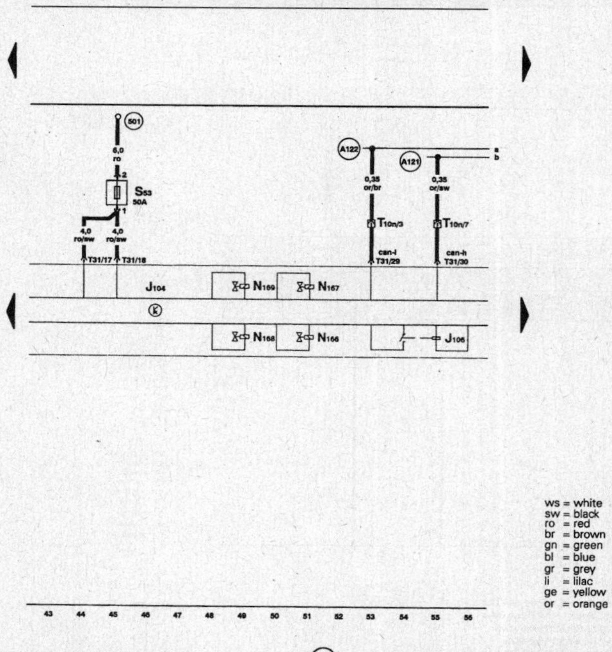

J104 - ABS Control Module (w/EDL)
J106 - ABS Solenoid Valve Relay
N166 - Right Front Traction Control Switch-Over Valve
N167 - Right Front Traction Control Outlet Valve
N168 - Left Front Traction Control Switch-Over Valve
N169 - Left Front Traction Control Outlet Valve
S53 - ABS Hydraulic Pump Fuse
T10n - 10-Pin Connector, orange, connector station A-pillar, left
T31 - 31-Pin Connector

(501) - Threaded connection -2- (30) on the relay plate
(A121) - Connection (high bus) in instrument panel wiring harness
(A122) - Connection (low bus) in instrument panel wiring harness

VW4020100134040X

Fig. 77 ABS wiring diagram (Part 4 of 5). 2001 Passat FWD w/EDL & ASC

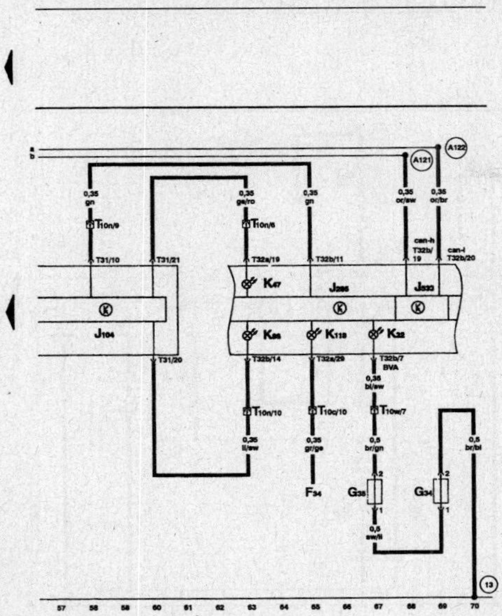

ws = white
sw = black
ro = red
br = brown
gn = green
bl = blue
gr = grey
li = lilac
ge = yellow
or = orange

F34 - Brake Fluid Level Warning Switch
G34 - Left Front Brake Pad Wear Sensor
G35 - Right Front Brake Pad Wear Sensor
J104 - ABS Control Module (w/EDL)
J285 - Control module with indicator unit in instrument panel insert
J533 - Data Bus On Board Diagnostic Interface
K32 - Brake Pad Wear Indicator Light
K47 - ABS Warning Light
K86 - Traction Control Indicator Light
K118 - Warning light for brake system
T10c - 10-Pin Connector, lilac, connector station A-pillar, left
T10n - 10-Pin Connector, orange, connector station A-pillar, left
T10w - 10-Pin Connector, grey, connector station A-pillar, right
T31 - 31-Pin Connector
T32a - 32-Pin Connector, blue, on instrument cluster
T32b - 32-Pin Connector, green, on instrument cluster
(13) - Ground connection, in engine compartment, right
(A121) - Connection (high bus) in instrument panel wiring harness
(A122) - Connection (low bus) in instrument panel wiring harness

VW4020100134050X

Fig. 77 ABS wiring diagram (Part 5 of 5). 2001 Passat FWD w/EDL & ASC

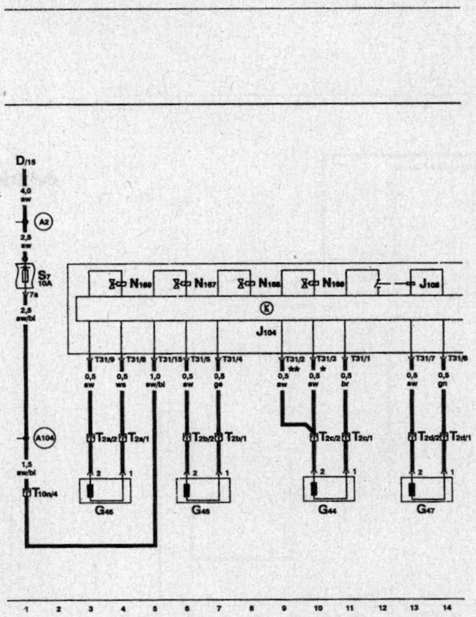

ws = white
sw = black
ro = red
br = brown
gn = green
bl = blue
gr = grey
li = lilac
ge = yellow
or = orange

D - Ignition/Starter Switch
G44 - Right Rear ABS Wheel Speed Sensor
G45 - Right Front ABS Wheel Speed Sensor
G46 - Left Rear ABS Wheel Speed Sensor
G47 - Left Front ABS Wheel Speed Sensor
J104 - ABS Control Module (w/EDL)
J106 - ABS Solenoid Valve Relay
N166 - Right Front Traction Control Switch-Over Valve
N167 - Right Front Traction Control Outlet Valve
N168 - Left Front Traction Control Switch-Over Valve
N169 - Left Front Traction Control Outlet Valve
S7 - Fuse
T2a - Doubel Connector (under rear seat)
T2b - Doubel Connector (in right front wheel well)
T2c - Doubel Connector (under rear seat)
T2d - Doubel Connector (in left front wheel well)
T10n - 10-Pin Connector, orange, connector station A-pillar, left
T31 - 31-Pin Connector
(A2) - plus connection (15), in instrument panel wiring harness
(A104) - Plus connector -2- (15), in instrument panel wiring harness
* front wheel drive only
** 4-Motion only

VW4020100135010X

Fig. 78 ABS wiring diagram (Part 1 of 4). 2001 Passat w/EDL

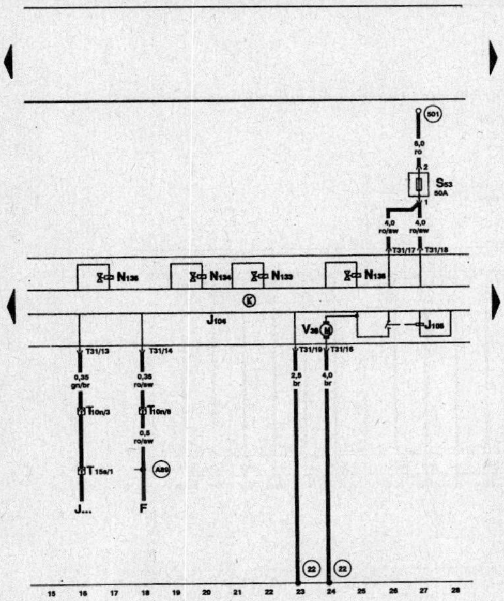

ws = white
sw = black
ro = red
br = brown
gn = green
bl = blue
gr = grey
li = lilac
ge = yellow
or = orange

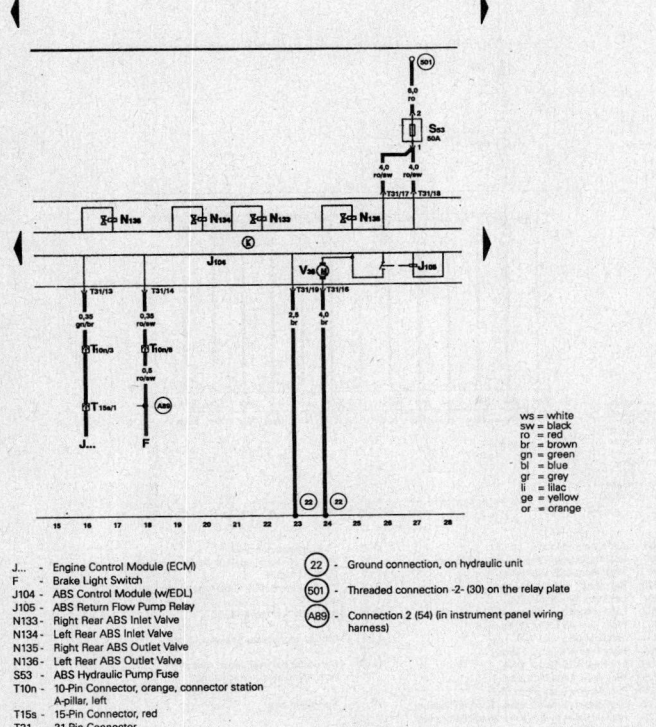

J... - Engine Control Module (ECM)
F - Brake Light Switch
J104 - ABS Control Module (w/EDL)
J105 - ABS Return Flow Pump Relay
N133 - Right Rear ABS Inlet Valve
N134 - Left Rear ABS Inlet Valve
N135 - Right Rear ABS Outlet Valve
N136 - Left Rear ABS Outlet Valve
S53 - ABS Hydraulic Pump Fuse
T10n - 10-Pin Connector, orange, connector station A-pillar, left
T15s - 15-Pin Connector, red
T31 - 31-Pin Connector
V39 - ABS Return Flow Pump
(22) - Ground connection, on hydraulic unit
(501) - Threaded connection -2- (30) on the relay plate
(A89) - Connection 2 (54) (in instrument panel wiring harness)

VW4020100135020X

Fig. 78 ABS wiring diagram (Part 2 of 4). 2001 Passat w/EDL

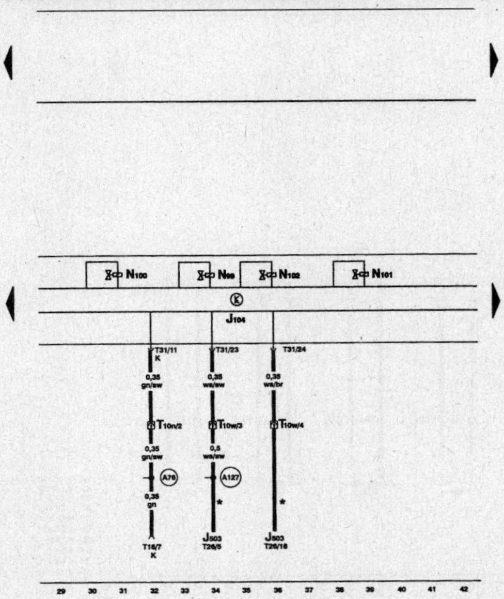

ws = white
sw = black
ro = red
br = brown
gn = green
bl = blue
gr = grey
li = lilac
ge = yellow
or = orange

J104 - ABS Control Module (w/EDL)
J503 - Radio/Navigation Display Control Module
N99 - Right Front ABS Inlet Valve
N100 - Right Front ABS Outlet Valve
N101 - Left Front ABS Inlet Valve
N102 - Left Front ABS Outlet Valve
T10n - 10-Pin Connector, orange, connector station A-pillar, left
T10w - 10-Pin Connector, grey, connector station A-pillar, right
T16 - 16-Pin Connector, Data Link Connector(DLC), below instrument panel, left
T26 - 26-Pin Connector, on Radio/Navigation Display Control Module
T31 - 31-Pin Connector
(A76) - Connector (K-diagnosis wire) in instrument panel wiring harness
(A127) - Connector (left rear speed sensor) in instrument panel wiring harness
* Navigation only

VW4020100135030X

Fig. 78 ABS wiring diagram (Part 3 of 4). 2001 Passat w/EDL

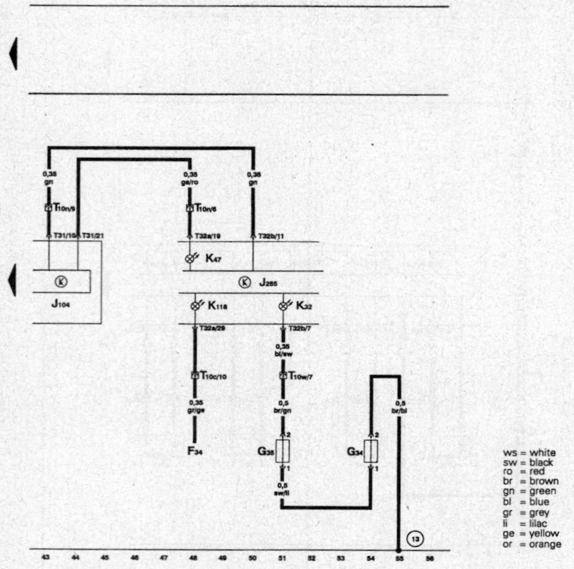

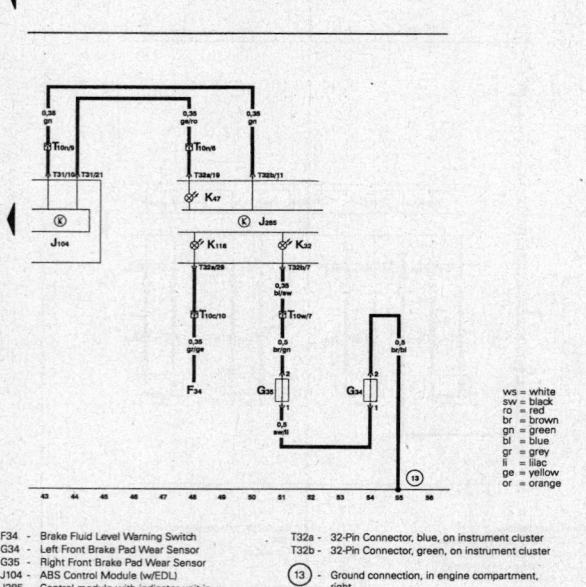

F34 - Brake Fluid Level Warning Switch
G34 - Left Front Brake Pad Wear Sensor
G35 - Right Front Brake Pad Wear Sensor
J104 - ABS Control Module (w/EDL)
J285 - Control module with indicator unit in instrument panel insert
K32 - Brake Pad Wear Indicator Light
K47 - ABS Warning Light
K118 - Warning light for brake system
T10c - 10-Pin Connector, lilac, connector station A-pillar, left
T10n - 10-Pin Connector, orange, connector station A-pillar, left
T10w - 10-Pin Connector, grey, connector station A-pillar, right
T31 - 31-Pin Connector
T32a - 32-Pin Connector, blue, on instrument cluster
T32b - 32-Pin Connector, green, on instrument cluster
(13) - Ground connection, in engine compartment, right

VW4020100135040X

Fig. 78 ABS wiring diagram (Part 4 of 4). 2001 Passat w/EDL

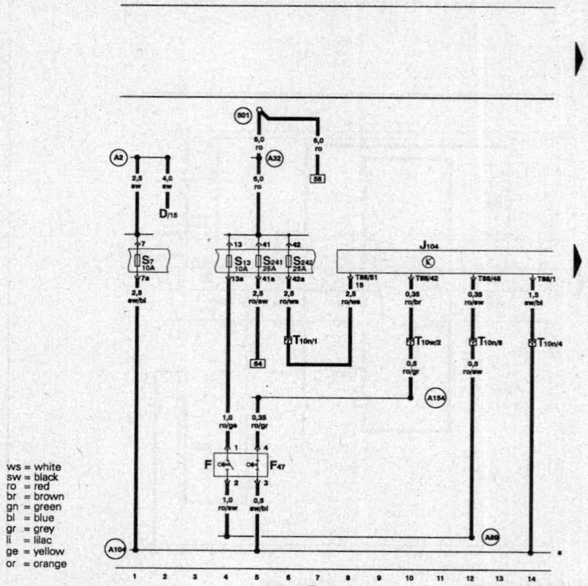

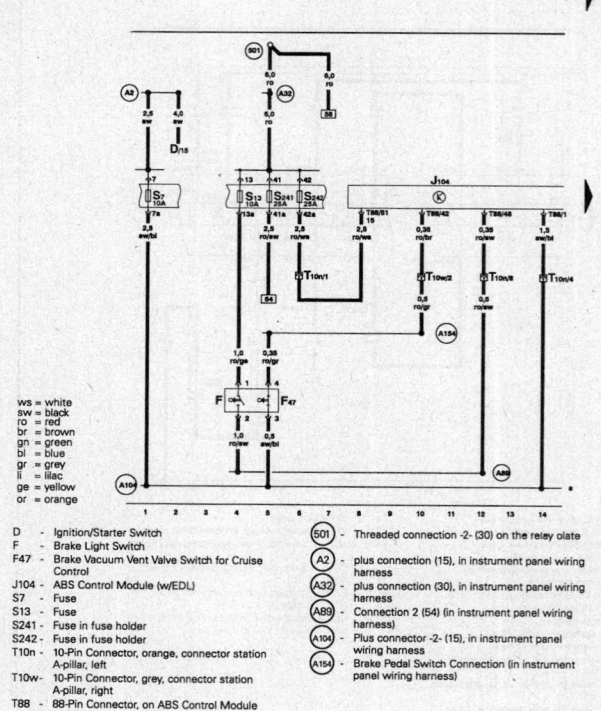

D - Ignition/Starter Switch
F - Brake Light Switch
F47 - Brake Vacuum Vent Valve Switch for Cruise Control
J104 - ABS Control Module (w/EDL)
S7 - Fuse
S13 - Fuse
S241 - Fuse in fuse holder
S242 - Fuse in fuse holder
T10n - 10-Pin Connector, orange, connector station A-pillar, left
T10w - 10-Pin Connector, grey, connector station A-pillar, right
T88 - 88-Pin Connector, on ABS Control Module (w/EDL)
(501) - Threaded connection -2- (30) on the relay olate
(A2) - plus connection (15), in instrument panel wiring harness
(A32) - plus connection (30), in instrument panel wiring harness
(A89) - Connection 2 (54) (in instrument panel wiring harness)
(A104) - Plus connector -2- (15), in instrument panel wiring harness
(A154) - Brake Pedal Switch Connection (in instrument panel wiring harness)

VW4020100136010X

Fig. 79 ABS wiring diagram (Part 1 of 6). 2001 Passat w/EDL, ASC & ESP

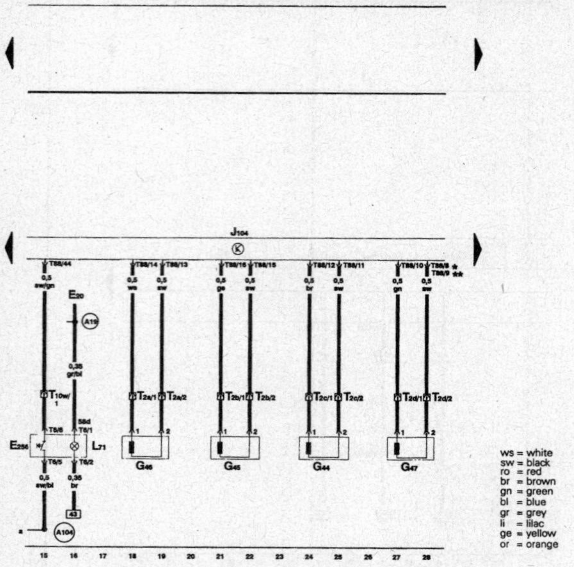

E20 - Instrument Panel Light Dimmer Switch
E256 - ASR/ESP Button
G44 - Right Rear ABS Wheel Speed Sensor
G45 - Right Front ABS Wheel Speed Sensor
G46 - Left Rear ABS Wheel Speed Sensor
G47 - Left Front ABS Wheel Speed Sensor
J104 - ABS Control Module (w/EDL)
L71 - Anti-slip Control Switch Illumination
T2a - Doubel Connector (under rear seat)
T2b - Doubel Connector (in right front wheel well)
T2c - Doubel Connector (under rear seat)
T6 - 6-Pin Connector, red on ASR/ESP Button
T10w - 10-Pin Connector, grey, connector station A-pillar, right
T88 - 88-Pin Connector, on ABS Control Module (w/EDL)
(A19) - wire connection (58d), in instrument panel wiring harness
(A104) - Plus connector -2- (15), in instrument panel wiring harness
* - all wheel drive only
** - 4-Motion only

VW4020100136020X

Fig. 79 ABS wiring diagram (Part 2 of 6). 2001 Passat w/EDL, ASC & ESP

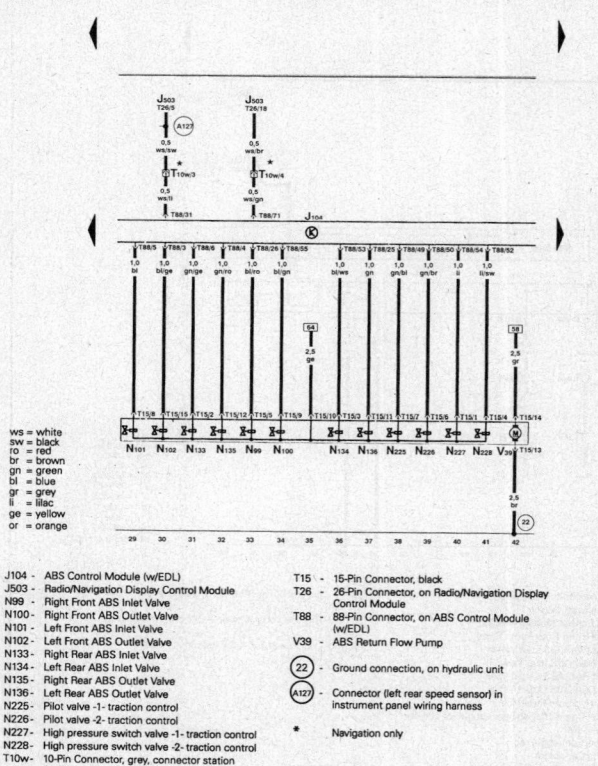

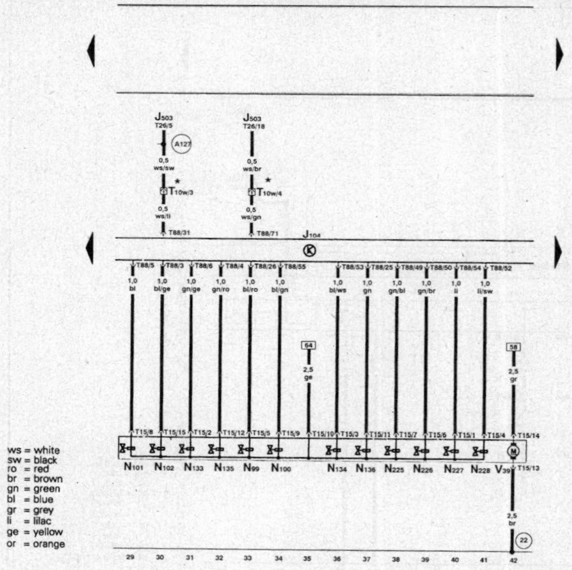

J104 - ABS Control Module (w/EDL)
J503 - Radio/Navigation Display Control Module
N99 - Right Front ABS Inlet Valve
N100 - Right Front ABS Outlet Valve
N101 - Left Front ABS Inlet Valve
N102 - Left Front ABS Outlet Valve
N133 - Right Rear ABS Inlet Valve
N134 - Left Rear ABS Inlet Valve
N135 - Right Rear ABS Outlet Valve
N136 - Left Rear ABS Outlet Valve
N225 - Pilot valve -1- traction control
N226 - Pilot valve -2- traction control
N227 - High pressure switch valve -1- traction control
N228 - High pressure switch valve -2- traction control
T10w - 10-Pin Connector, grey, connector station A-pillar, right
T15 - 15-Pin Connector, black
T26 - 26-Pin Connector, on Radio/Navigation Display Control Module
T88 - 88-Pin Connector, on ABS Control Module (w/EDL)
V39 - ABS Return Flow Pump
(22) - Ground connection, on hydraulic unit
(A127) - Connector (left rear speed sensor) in instrument panel wiring harness
* - Navigation only

VW4020100136030X

Fig. 79 ABS wiring diagram (Part 3 of 6). 2001 Passat w/EDL, ASC & ESP

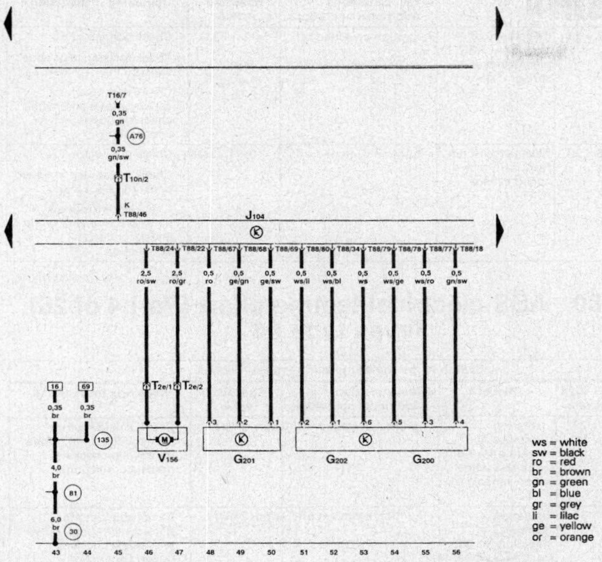

G200- Sensor for transverse acceleration
G201 - Sender 1 for brake booster
G202- Sender for rotation rate
J104 - ABS Control Module (w/EDL)
T2e - Double Connector, black
T10n - 10-Pin Connector, orange, connector station A-pillar, left
T16 - 16-Pin Connector, Data Link Connector(DLC), below instrument panel, left
T88 - 88-Pin Connector, on ABS Control Module (w/EDL)
V156 - Hydraulic pump for traction control

(30) - Ground connection, -1-, beside fuse/relay panel
(81) - Ground connection -1-, in instrument panel wiring harness
(135) - Ground connection -2-, in instrument panel wiring harness
(A76) - Connector (K-diagnosis wire) in instrument panel wiring harness

VW4020100136040X

Fig. 79 ABS wiring diagram (Part 4 of 6). 2001 Passat w/EDL, ASC & ESP

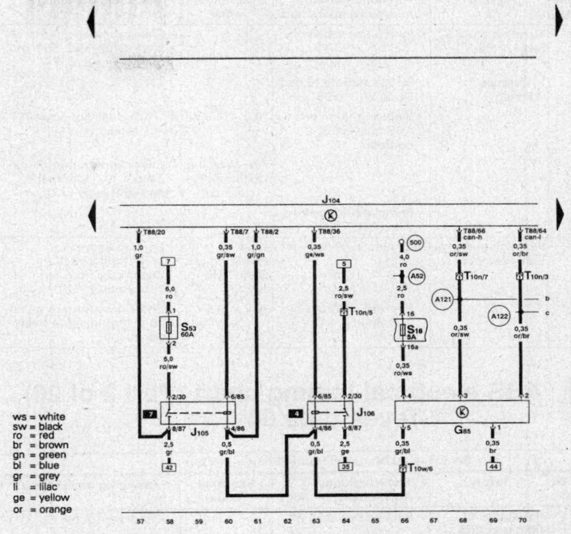

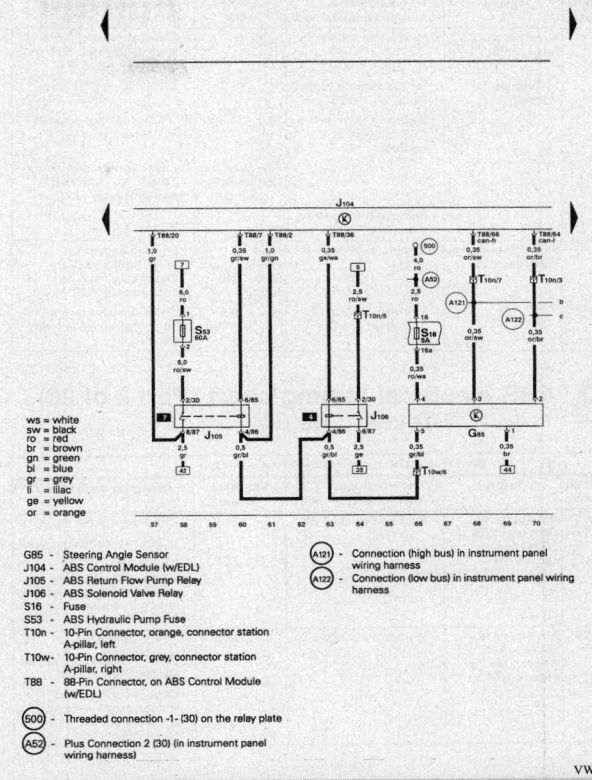

G85 - Steering Angle Sensor
J104 - ABS Control Module (w/EDL)
J105 - ABS Return Flow Pump Relay
J106 - ABS Solenoid Valve Relay
S16 - Fuse
S53 - ABS Hydraulic Pump Fuse
T10n - 10-Pin Connector, orange, connector station A-pillar, left
T10w- 10-Pin Connector, grey, connector station A-pillar, right
T88 - 88-Pin Connector, on ABS Control Module (w/EDL)

(500) - Threaded connection -1- (30) on the relay plate
(A52) - Plus Connection 2 (30) (in instrument panel wiring harness)
(A121) - Connection (high bus) in instrument panel wiring harness
(A122) - Connection (low bus) in instrument panel wiring harness

VW4020100136050X

Fig. 79 ABS wiring diagram (Part 5 of 6). 2001 Passat w/EDL, ASC & ESP

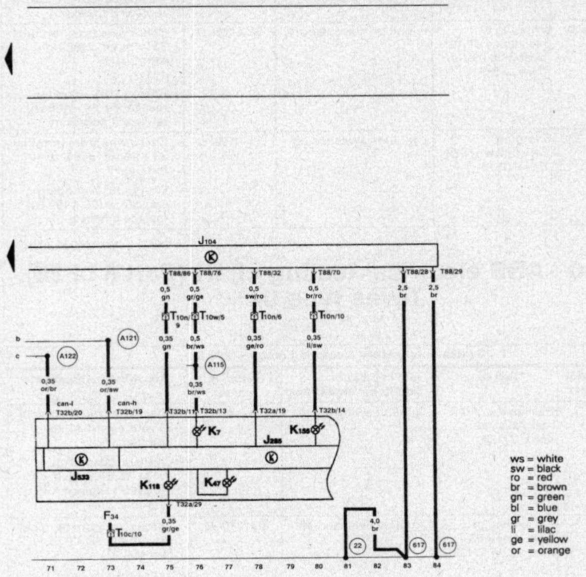

F34 - Brake Fluid Level Warning Switch
J104 - ABS Control Module (w/EDL)
J285 - Control module with indicator unit in instrument panel insert
J533 - Data Bus On Board Diagnostic Interface
K47 - ABS Warning Light
K118 - Warning light for brake system
T10c - 10-Pin Connector, lilac, connector station A-pillar, left
T10n - 10-Pin Connector, orange, connector station A-pillar, left
T10w- 10-Pin Connector, grey, connector station A-pillar, right
T32a - 32-Pin Connector, blue, on instrument cluster
T32b - 32-Pin Connector, green, on instrument cluster
T88 - 88-Pin Connector, on ABS Control Module (w/EDL)

(22) - Ground connection, on hydraulic unit
(617) - Ground Connection 2 (on right lower A-pillar)
(A115) - Connection (parking brake control) in instrument panel wiring harness
(A121) - Connection (high bus) in instrument panel wiring harness
(A122) - Connection (low bus) in instrument panel wiring harness

VW4020100136060X

Fig. 79 ABS wiring diagram (Part 6 of 6). 2001 Passat w/EDL, ASC & ESP

Switch to voltage measuring range — 20 V					
Test step	**VAG 1598 sockets**	**Test of**	**• Test conditions – Additional operations**	**Specified value**	**Repairing malfunction**
1 EDL	35 + 1	Voltage supply (terminal 30) at ABS control module -J104-	• Ignition switched off	10.0 – 14.5 V	– Check wire from terminal 1 to Ground (GND) point – Check wire from terminal 35 via ABS valves fuse -S54- to battery pos. (B+)
2	53 + 1	Voltage supply (terminal 15) at ABS control module -J104-	• Ignition switched off	10.0 – 14.5 V	– Check wire from terminal 1 to Ground (GND) point – Check wire from terminal 53 to terminal D/7 (relay panel)

VW4029300070010X

Fig. 80 ABS electrical testing chart (Part 1 of 26). Teves type 04

Switch to voltage measuring range — 20 V					
Test step	**VAG 1598 sockets**	**Test of**	**• Test conditions – Additional operations**	**Specified value**	**Repairing malfunction**
3	33 + 1	♦ Function of ABS relay -J102- ♦ Voltage supply at ABS control module -J104-	• Ignition switched off – Bridge sockets 19 and 34 on VAG 1598 – Switch ignition on: ABS relay -J102- operates – Remove bridge after check	 10.0 – 14.5 V ABS warning light -K47- goes out	– Check wire from terminal 1 to Ground (GND) point – Check wire from terminal 33 via -J102- and -S54- to battery positive (B+) If ABS relay -J102- does not operate, check activation: – Check wire from terminal 34 to -J102- terminal 4 and -J102-

VW4029300070020X

Fig. 80 ABS electrical testing chart (Part 2 of 26). Teves type 04

Switch to voltage measuring range — 20 V					
Test step	VAG 1598 sockets	Test of	• Test conditions – Additional operations	Specified value	Repairing malfunction
4	3 + 1	Function of ABS relay -J102-	• Ignition switched off		– Check wire from terminal 3 via -J102- and -S54- to battery positive (B+)
		(Reference voltage)	– Bridge sockets 19 and 34 on VAG 1598		
			– Switch ignition on: ABS relay -J102- operates	10.0 – 14.5 V	If -J102- does not operate, check activation:
				ABS warning light -K47- goes out	– Check wire from terminal 34 to -J102- terminal 4 and ABS relay -J102-
			– Remove bridge after the check		
5	32 + 1	Function of brake light switch -F-	• Ignition switched off	After operating the brake light switch:	– Check fuse and brake light switch -F- – Check wire from terminal 1 to Ground (GND) point
			– Depress and hold brake pedal	10.0 – 14.5V	– Check wire from terminal 32 to terminal W/4 (relay panel)

VW4029300070030X

Fig. 80 ABS electrical testing chart (Part 3 of 26). Teves type 04

Switch to resistance measuring range — 2 kΩ					
Test step	VAG 1598 sockets	Test of	• Test conditions – Additional operations	Specified value	Repairing malfunction
6	47 + 29	Resistance of right front ABS wheel speed sensor -G45-	• Ignition switched off	1.0 – 1.3 kΩ	– Check connector T2 – Check resistance of speed sensor (1.0 – 1.2 kΩ) – Check wire to speed sensor, move wire while checking (loose connection)
7	48 + 30	Resistance of left front ABS wheel speed sensor -G47-	• Ignition switched off	1.0 – 1.3 kΩ	– Check connector T2 – Check resistance of speed sensor (1.0 – 1.2 kΩ) – Check wire to speed sensor, move wire while checking (loose connection)

VW4029300070040X

Fig. 80 ABS electrical testing chart (Part 4 of 26). Teves type 04

Switch to resistance measuring range — 2 kΩ					
Test step	VAG 1598 sockets	Test of	• Test conditions – Additional operations	Specified value	Repairing malfunction
8	45 + 27	Resistance of right rear ABS wheel speed sensor -G44-	• Ignition switched off	1.0 – 1.3 kΩ	– Check connector T2 – Check resistance of speed sensor (1.0 – 1.2 kΩ) – Check wire to speed sensor, move wire while checking (loose connection)
9	46 + 28	Resistance of left rear ABS wheel speed sensor -G46-	• Ignition switched off	1.0 – 1.3 kΩ	– Check connector T2 – Check resistance of speed sensor (1.0 – 1.2 kΩ) – Check wire to speed sensor, move wire while checking (loose connection)

VW4029300070050X

Fig. 80 ABS electrical testing chart (Part 5 of 26). Teves type 04

Switch to resistance measuring range — 2 MΩ					
Test step	VAG 1598 sockets	Test of	• Test conditions – Additional operations	Specified value	Repairing malfunction
10	1 + 29	Insulation resistance of shielding for right front ABS wheel speed sensor -G45-	• Ignition switched off	Min. 2 MΩ[2]	– Check shielding for damage (chafing), move wire while checking (loose connection)
11	1 + 30	Insulation resistance of shielding for left front ABS wheel speed sensor -G47-	• Ignition switched off	Min. 2 MΩ[2]	– Check shielding for damage (chafing), move wire while checking (loose connection)

[2] Multimeter (Fluke 83 or equivalent) indicating "1" signifies infinite resistance and is OK.

VW4029300070060X

Fig. 80 ABS electrical testing chart (Part 6 of 26). Teves type 04

Switch to resistance measuring range — 2 MΩ					
Test step	VAG 1598 sockets	Test of	• Test conditions – Additional operations	Specified value	Repairing malfunction
12	1 + 27	Insulation resistance of shielding for right rear ABS wheel speed sensor -G44-	• Ignition switched off	Min. 2 MΩ[2]	– Check shielding for damage (chafing), move wire while checking (loose connection)
13	1 + 28	Insulation resistance of shielding for left rear ABS wheel speed sensor -G46-	• Ignition switched off	Min. 2 MΩ[2]	– Check shielding for damage (chafing), move wire while checking (loose connection)

[2] If multimeter (Fluke 83 or equivalent) indicates "1", this signifies infinite resistance and is OK.

VW4029300070070X

Fig. 80 ABS electrical testing chart (Part 7 of 26). Teves type 04

Switch to resistance measuring range — 200 Ω					
Test step	VAG 1598 sockets	Test of	• Test conditions – Additional operations	Specified value	Repairing malfunction
14	53 + 34	Winding resistance of ABS relay -J102-	• Ignition switched off	50 – 100 Ω	– Check wire from terminal 53 without -J102- to terminal 34 – Check -J102- winding resistance (50 – 100 Ω), replace if necessary
15	15 + 33	Winding resistance of ABS hydraulic pump relay -J185-	• Ignition switched off	50 – 100 Ω	– Check wire from terminal 33 without -J185- to terminal 15 – Check -J185- winding resistance (50 – 100 Ω), replace if necessary
16 EDL	7 + 33	Winding resistance of EDL relay -J310-	• Ignition switched off	50 – 100 Ω	– Check wire from terminal 33 without -J185- to terminal 7 – Check -J310- winding resistance (50 – 100 Ω), replace if necessary

VW4029300070080X

Fig. 80 ABS electrical testing chart (Part 8 of 26). Teves type 04

Switch to resistance measuring range — 200 Ω					
Test step	VAG 1598 sockets	Test of	• Test conditions – Additional operations	Specified value	Repairing malfunction
17	20 + 3	Resistance of left front ABS inlet valve -N101-	• Ignition switched off	6.5 – 10 Ω	– Check wire from terminal 20 without -N101- to terminal 3 – Check resistance of -N101- (6.5 – 8 Ω), if necessary replace ABS hydraulic unit
18	38 + 3	Resistance of right front ABS inlet valve -N99-	• Ignition switched off	6.5 – 10 Ω	– Check wire from terminal 38 without -N99- to terminal 3 – Check resistance of -N99- (6.5 – 8 Ω), if necessary replace ABS hydraulic unit

VW4029300070090X

Fig. 80 ABS electrical testing chart (Part 9 of 26). Teves type 04

Switch to resistance measuring range — 200 Ω					
Test step	VAG 1598 sockets	Test of	• Test conditions – Additional operations	Specified value	Repairing malfunction
19	54 + 3	Resistance of left rear ABS inlet valve -N134-	• Ignition switched off	6.5 – 10 Ω	– Check wire from terminal 54 without -N134- to terminal 3 – Check resistance of -N134- (6.5 – 8 Ω), if necessary replace ABS hydraulic unit
20	55 + 3	Resistance of right rear ABS inlet valve -N133-	• Ignition switched off	6.5 – 10 Ω	– Check wire from terminal 55 without -N133- to terminal 3 – Check resistance of -N133- (6.5 – 8 Ω), if necessary replace ABS hydraulic unit

VW4029300070100X

Fig. 80 ABS electrical testing chart (Part 10 of 26). Teves type 04

Switch to resistance measuring range — 200 Ω					
Test step	VAG 1598 sockets	Test of	• Test conditions – Additional operations	Specified value	Repairing malfunction
21	2 + 3	Resistance of left front ABS outlet valve -N102-	• Ignition switched off	3 – 7 Ω	– Check wire from terminal 2 without -N102- to terminal 3 – Check resistance of -N102- (3 – 5 Ω), if necessary replace ABS hydraulic unit
22	21 + 3	Resistance of right front ABS outlet valve -N100-	• Ignition switched off	3 – 7 Ω	– Check wire from terminal 21 without -N100- to terminal 3 – Check resistance of -N100- (3 – 5 Ω), if necessary replace ABS hydraulic unit

VW4029300070110X

Fig. 80 ABS electrical testing chart (Part 11 of 26). Teves type 04

Switch to resistance measuring range — 200 Ω					
Test step	VAG 1598 sockets	Test of	• Test conditions – Additional operations	Specified value	Repairing malfunction
25 EDL	37 + 3	Resistance of differential lock valve 1 -N125-	• Ignition switched off	6 – 10 Ω	– Check wire from terminal 37 without -N125- to terminal 3 – Check resistance of -N125- (6 – 8 Ω), if necessary replace ABS hydraulic unit
26 EDL	40 + 3	Resistance of differential lock valve 2 -N126-	• Ignition switched off	6 – 10 Ω	– Check wire from terminal 40 without -N126- to terminal 3 – Check resistance of -N126- (6 – 8 Ω), if necessary replace ABS hydraulic unit

VW4029300070130X

Fig. 80 ABS electrical testing chart (Part 13 of 26). Teves type 04

Switch to resistance measuring range — 200 Ω					
Test step	VAG 1598 sockets	Test of	• Test conditions – Additional operations	Specified value	Repairing malfunction
28	16 + 41	Resistance of brake pedal position sensor -G100-	• Ignition switched off		– Check wire from terminal 16 without -G100- to terminal 41
			-G100- has variable resistance. The following resistance values are specified, depending on pedal position as the pedal is depressed from rest:		– Check resistance of -G100- (with adapter cable VW 1594/23), if faulty, replace brake pedal position sensor
			–Stage 1 (Rest position)	230 – 270 Ω	
			–Stage 2	410 – 460 Ω	
			–Stage 3	540 – 600 Ω	
			–Stage 4	650 – 730 Ω	
			–Stage 5	770 – 860 Ω	
			–Stage 6	980 –1100 Ω	
			–Stage 7	2)	

2) Stage 7 is only achieved if a malfunction exists (pressure loss); Specification: min. 2MΩ.

VW4029300070150X

Fig. 80 ABS electrical testing chart (Part 15 of 26). Teves type 04

Switch to voltage measuring range — 2 V					
Test step	VAG 1598 sockets	Test of	• Test conditions – Additional operations	Specified value	Repairing malfunction
31	45 + 27	Right rear ABS wheel speed sensor -G44- voltage signal	• Vehicle raised • Ignition switched off		– Check connector T2, installation of speed sensor and impulse wheel
			– Rotate rear right wheel at approx. 1 rev./sec.	Min. 65 mV alternating voltage	– Check whether speed sensor has been interchanged
32	46 + 28	Left rear ABS wheel speed sensor -G46- voltage signal	• Vehicle raised • Ignition switched off		– Check connector T2, installation of speed sensor and impulse wheel
			– Rotate rear left wheel at approx. 1 rev./sec.	Min. 65 mV alternating voltage	– Check whether speed sensor has been interchanged

VW4029300070170X

Fig. 80 ABS electrical testing chart (Part 17 of 26). Teves type 04

Switch to resistance measuring range — 200 Ω					
Test step	VAG 1598 sockets	Test of	• Test conditions – Additional operations	Specified value	Repairing malfunction
23	36 + 3	Resistance of left rear ABS outlet valve -N136-	• Ignition switched off	3 – 7 Ω	– Check wire from terminal 36 without -N136- to terminal 3 – Check resistance of -N136- (3 – 5 Ω), if necessary replace ABS hydraulic unit
24	18 + 3	Resistance of right rear ABS outlet valve -N135-	• Ignition switched off	3 – 7 Ω	– Check wire from terminal 18 without -N135- to terminal 3 – Check resistance of -N135- (3 – 5 Ω), if necessary replace ABS hydraulic unit

VW4029300070120X

Fig. 80 ABS electrical testing chart (Part 12 of 26). Teves type 04

Switch to resistance measuring range — 200 Ω					
Test step	VAG 1598 sockets	Test of	• Test conditions – Additional operations	Specified value	Repairing malfunction
27	31 + 49	Resistance of hydraulic pump sensor -G101-	• Ignition switched off	29 – 40 Ω	– Check wire from terminal 49 without -G101- to terminal 31 – Check resistance of -G101- (29 – 40 Ω), if necessary replace ABS hydraulic unit

VW4029300070140X

Fig. 80 ABS electrical testing chart (Part 14 of 26). Teves type 04

Switch to resistance measuring range — 200 Ω (Note change to 2 MΩ range during test step 29)					
Test step	VAG 1598 sockets	Test of	• Test conditions – Additional operations	Specified value	Repairing malfunction
29	13 + 26	Function of ABS pressure control switch -F137-3)	• Ignition switched off		– Check wire from terminal 13 without -F137- to terminal 26
EDL			• Brake pedal not depressed – Select (2 MΩ) measuring range on multimeter (Fluke 83 or equivalent)	Min. 1.5 Ω	– If resistance is not attained, replace ABS hydraulic unit
			– Depress brake pedal fully and hold	Min. 2 M Ω	
30	1 + 3 1 + 33	Resistance of ABS relay -J102-	• Ignition switched off	Max. 1.5 Ω	– Check wire from terminal 3 and terminal 33 without -J102- to Ground (GND)
	1 + 19	Resistance of Ground (GND) connections			– Check wire from terminal 1 and terminal 19 via Ground connections2) to battery – (GND)

VW4029300070160X

Fig. 80 ABS electrical testing chart (Part 16 of 26). Teves type 04

Switch to voltage measuring range — 2 V					
Test step	VAG 1598 sockets	Test of	• Test conditions – Additional operations	Specified value	Repairing malfunction
33	47 + 29	Right front ABS wheel speed sensor -G45- voltage signal	• Vehicle raised • Ignition switched off		– Check connector T2, installation of speed sensor and impulse wheel
			– Rotate front right wheel at approx. 1 rev./sec.	Min. 65 mV alternating voltage	– Check whether speed sensor has been interchanged
34	48 + 30	Left front ABS wheel speed sensor -G47- voltage signal	• Vehicle raised • Ignition switched off		– Check connector T2, installation of speed sensor and impulse wheel
			– Rotate front left wheel at approx. 1 rev./sec.	Min. 65 mV alternating voltage	– Check whether speed sensor has been interchanged

VW4029300070180X

Fig. 80 ABS electrical testing chart (Part 18 of 26). Teves type 04

Test step	VAG 1598 sockets	Test of	• Test conditions – Additional operations	Specified value	Repairing malfunction
Functional check: ABS hydraulic pump -V64-					
CAUTION!: On no account must the brake pedal be depressed during this check!					
35	Bridge: 19 = 34 19 = 15	Function of ABS hydraulic pump -V64-	• Ignition switched off	After switching ignition on:	– Check wire from battery positive (B+) via ABS hydraulic pump fuse -S53-, -J185- and -V64- to battery – (GND)
			– Switch ignition on for max. 30 sec. – Remove bridge after test	ABS hydraulic pump -V64- must run audibly	– If no open circuit, replace ABS hydraulic unit
36	Bridge: 19 = 34 19 = 7	EDL function of ABS hydraulic pump -V64-	• Ignition switched off	After switching ignition on:	– Check wire from battery positive (B+) via ABS hydraulic pump fuse -S53-, -J310-, -N159- and -V64- to battery – (GND)
EDL			– Switch ignition on for max. 30 sec. – Remove bridge after test	ABS hydraulic pump -V64- must run audibly	– If no open circuit, replace ABS hydraulic unit

VW4029300070190X

Fig. 80 ABS electrical testing chart (Part 19 of 26). Teves type 04

Test step	VAG 1598 sockets	Test of	• Test conditions – Additional operations	Specified value	Repairing malfunction
Functional check: Left front ABS inlet and outlet valves -N101-/-N102-					
37	Bridge: 19 = 34 19 = 20 19 = 2	Function of left front ABS inlet and outlet valves (-N101-/-N102-)	• Vehicle raised • Ignition switched off		– Check that brake lines are correctly connected
			– Depress brake pedal and hold	Left front wheel locks	– ABS hydraulic unit faulty; replace
			– Switch ignition on for max. 30 sec. – Depress brake pedal and hold	Left front wheel must rotate freely; pedal must not give	
			– Remove bridge after check		

VW4029300070200X

Fig. 80 ABS electrical testing chart (Part 20 of 26). Teves type 04

Test step	VAG 1598 sockets	Test of	• Test conditions – Additional operations	Specified value	Repairing malfunction
Functional check: Right front ABS inlet and outlet valves -N99-/-N100-					
38	Bridge: 19 = 34 19 = 21 19 = 38	Function of right front ABS inlet and outlet valves (-N99-/-N100-)	• Vehicle raised • Ignition switched off		– Check that brake lines are correctly connected
			– Depress brake pedal and hold	Right front wheel locks	– ABS hydraulic unit faulty, replace
			– Switch ignition on for max. 30 sec. – Depress brake pedal and hold	Right front wheel must rotate freely; pedal must not give	
			– Remove bridge after check		

VW4029300070210X

Fig. 80 ABS electrical testing chart (Part 21 of 26). Teves type 04

Test step	VAG 1598 sockets	Test of	• Test conditions – Additional operations	Specified value	Repairing malfunction
Functional check: Left rear ABS inlet and outlet valves -N134-/-N136-					
39	Bridge: 19 = 34 19 = 36 19 = 54	Function of left rear ABS inlet and outlet valves (-N134-/-N136-)	• Vehicle raised • Ignition switched off		– Check that brake lines are correctly connected
			– Depress brake pedal and hold	Left rear wheel locks	– ABS hydraulic unit faulty, replace
			– Switch ignition on for max. 30 sec. – Depress brake pedal and hold	Left rear wheel must rotate freely; pedal must not give	
			– Remove bridge after check		

VW4029300070220X

Fig. 80 ABS electrical testing chart (Part 22 of 26). Teves type 04

Test step	VAG 1598 sockets	Test of	• Test conditions – Additional operations	Specified value	Repairing malfunction
Functional check: Right rear ABS inlet and outlet valves -N133-/-N135-					
40	Bridge: 19 = 55 19 = 34 19 = 18	Function of rear right ABS inlet and outlet valves (-N133-/-N135-)	• Vehicle raised • Ignition switched off		– Check that brake lines are correctly connected
			– Operate brake pedal and hold	Right rear wheel locks	– ABS hydraulic unit faulty, replace
			– Switch ignition on for max. 30 sec. – Operate brake pedal and hold	Right rear wheel must rotate freely; pedal must not give	
			– Remove bridge after check		

VW4029300070230X

Fig. 80 ABS electrical testing chart (Part 23 of 26). Teves type 04

Test step	VAG 1598 sockets	Test of	• Test conditions – Additional operations	Specified value	Repairing malfunction
Functional check: Differential lock valves 1 + 2 -N125-/-N126-					
41	Bridge: 1 = 7 1 = 34 1 = 40 1 = 37	Functional check of differential lock valves 1, 2 (-N125-, -N126-)	• Vehicle raised		– ABS hydraulic unit faulty, replace
EDL			– Switch ignition on for max. 30 sec.	It must not be possible to turn front wheels	
			– Remove bridge after check		

VW4029300070240X

Fig. 80 ABS electrical testing chart (Part 24 of 26). Teves type 04

Switch to voltage measuring range 20 V in test step 42 Resistance measuring range (20 Ω) in test step 43					
Test step	**VAG 1598 sockets**	**Test of**	**• Test conditions – Additional operations**	**Specified value**	**Repairing malfunction**
42	–	Voltage supply for VAG 1551 scan tool, data link connector T16	– Connect multimeter (Fluke 83/equivalent) to T16 using adapter cables from VW 1594 connector test kit ♦ Terminal 4: Ground ♦ Terminal 16: positive (B+)	10.0 – 14.5 V	– Check wire from T16/4 to Ground (GND) – Check wire from T16/16 via -S22- to terminal 30
43	–	Resistance of K wire for OBD data link connector T16, terminal 7	• Ignition switched off – Connect multimeter (Fluke 83/equivalent) to VAG 1598 test box socket 42 and data link connector T16 terminal 7 using adapter cables from VW 1594 connector test kit	Max. 1.5 Ω	– Check wire from T2d to terminal 42 – Check wire from T16/7 via TV14 to terminal 42

VW4029300070250X

Fig. 80 ABS electrical testing chart (Part 25 of 26). Teves type 04

Switch to voltage measuring range — 20 V					
Test step	**VAG 1598/21 sockets**	**Test of**	**• Test conditions – Additional operations**	**Specified value**	**Repairing malfunction**
1	8 + 25	Voltage supply for ABS hydraulic pump motor (terminal 30) on ABS control module -J104-	• Ignition switched off	10.0 – 14.5 V	– Check wire from terminal 8 to Ground (GND) – Check wire from terminal 25 via fuse 1 for control module – ABS -S123- to battery positive (B+)
2	9 + 24	Voltage supply for the inlet and outlet solenoid valves (terminal 30) on ABS control module -J104-	• Ignition switched off	10.0 – 14.5 V	– Check wire from terminal 24 to Ground (GND) – Check wire from terminal 9 via fuse 2 for control module – ABS -S124- to battery positive (B+)

VW4029300071010X

Fig. 81 ABS electrical testing chart (Part 1 of 8). Teves type 20

Switch to resistance measuring range — 2 kΩ					
Test step	**VAG 1598/21 sockets**	**Test of**	**• Test conditions – Additional operations**	**Specified value**	**Repairing malfunction**
5	3 + 18	Resistance of right front ABS wheel speed sensor -G45-	• Ignition switched off	1.0 – 1.3 kΩ	– Check connector T2d – Check resistance of ABS wheel speed sensor (1.0 – 1.3 kΩ) – Check wire to ABS wheel speed sensor, move wire while checking (loose connection)
6	4 + 11	Resistance of left front ABS wheel speed sensor -G47-	• Ignition switched off	1.0 – 1.3 kΩ	– Check connector T2f – Check resistance of ABS wheel speed sensor (1.0 – 1.3 kΩ) – Check wire to ABS wheel speed sensor, move wire while checking (loose connection)

VW4029300071030X

Fig. 81 ABS electrical testing chart (Part 3 of 8). Teves type 20

Switch to voltage measuring range — 2 V					
Test step	**VAG 1598/21 sockets**	**Test of**	**• Test conditions – Additional operations**	**Specified value**	**Repairing malfunction**
9	3 + 18	Right front ABS wheel speed sensor -G45- voltage signal	• Vehicle raised • Ignition switched off – Rotate right rear wheel at approx. 1 rev./sec.	Min. 65 mV alternating voltage	– Check installation of ABS wheel speed sensor and impulse rotor – Check whether ABS wheel speed sensor has been interchanged Read measuring value block.
10	4 + 11	Left front ABS wheel speed sensor -G47- voltage signal	• Vehicle raised • Ignition switched off – Rotate left front wheel at approx. 1 rev./sec.	Min. 65 mV alternating voltage	– Check installation of ABS wheel speed sensor and impulse rotor – Check whether ABS wheel speed sensor has been interchanged · Reading measured value

VW4029300071050X

Fig. 81 ABS electrical testing chart (Part 5 of 8). Teves type 20

Functional check: ABS warning light -K47-					
Test step	**VAG 1598 sockets**	**Test of**	**• Test conditions – Additional operations**	**Specified value**	**Repairing malfunction**
44	–	Function of ABS warning light -K47-	• Ignition switched off		– Check wire from terminal W/2 (relay panel) via ABS relay -J102- (diode) to Ground (GND)
			– Switch ignition on	ABS warning light -K47- lights up	– Check wire from terminal X/8 (relay panel) via -K47- to terminal X/4 (relay panel), -K47- (12 V, 1,2 W) replace if necessary
			– Bridge VAG 1598 test box sockets 1 and 34 (-J102- operates) – Bridge sockets 1 and 52 on VAG 1598 – Remove bridge after check	ABS warning light -K47- goes out ABS warning light -K47- lights up	– Check wire from terminal 52 to terminal W/2 (relay panel)

VW4029300070260X

Fig. 80 ABS electrical testing chart (Part 26 of 26). Teves type 04

Switch to voltage measuring range — 20 V					
Test step	**VAG 1598/21 sockets**	**Test of**	**• Test conditions – Additional operations**	**Specified value**	**Repairing malfunction**
3	8 + 23	Voltage supply (terminal X) on ABS control module -J104-	• Ignition switched on	10.0 – 14.5 V	– Check wire from terminal 8 to Ground (GND) – Check wire from terminal 23 to terminal D/3 (relay panel)
4	8 + 12	Function of brake light switch -F-	• Ignition switched off – Brake pedal not depressed	0.0 – 0.5 V	– Check fuse -S20- and brake light switch -F-. – Check wire from terminal 8 to Ground (GND)
			– Depress brake pedal	10.0 – 14.5 V	– Check wire from terminal 12 to terminal W/4 (relay panel)

VW4029300071020X

Fig. 81 ABS electrical testing chart (Part 2 of 8). Teves type 20

Switch to resistance measuring range — 2 kΩ					
Test step	**VAG 1598/21 sockets**	**Test of**	**• Test conditions – Additional operations**	**Specified value**	**Repairing malfunction**
7	1 + 17	Resistance of right rear ABS wheel speed sensor -G44-	• Ignition switched off	1.0 – 1.3 kΩ	– Check connector T2c – Check resistance of ABS wheel speed sensor (1.0 – 1.3 kΩ) – Check wire to ABS wheel speed sensor, move wire while checking (loose connection)
8	2 + 10	Resistance of left rear ABS wheel speed -G46-	• Ignition switched off	1.0 – 1.3 kΩ	– Check connector T2e – Check resistance of ABS wheel speed sensor (1.0 – 1.3 kΩ) – Check wire to ABS wheel speed sensor, move wire while checking (loose connection)

VW4029300071040X

Fig. 81 ABS electrical testing chart (Part 4 of 8). Teves type 20

Switch to voltage measuring range — 2 V, Resistance measurement — 200 Ω for test step 13					
Test step	**VAG 1598/21 sockets**	**Test of**	**• Test conditions – Additional operations**	**Specified value**	**Repairing malfunction**
11	1 + 17	Right rear ABS wheel speed sensor -G44- voltage signal	• Vehicle raised • Ignition switched off – Rotate right front wheel at approx. 1 rev./sec.	190 mV to 1140 mV	– Check installation of ABS wheel speed sensor and impulse rotor – Check whether ABS wheel speed sensor has been interchanged ⇒ Read measuring value block
12	2 + 10	Left rear ABS wheel speed sensor -G46- voltage signal	• Vehicle raised • Ignition switched off – Rotate left front wheel at approx. 1 rev./sec.	190 mV to 1140 mV	– Check installation of ABS wheel speed sensor and impulse rotor – Check whether ABS wheel speed sensor has been interchanged ⇒ Read measuring value block,
13	15 + 21	Coding bridge	• Ignition switched off	0.0 –1.0 Ω	– Check wire and wiring connections in harness connector – Replace if value deviates from specifications

VW4029300071060X

Fig. 81 ABS electrical testing chart (Part 6 of 8). Teves type 20

Switch to voltage measuring range — 20 V for test step 14, Resistance measurement — 200 Ω for test step 15					
Test step	VAG 1598/21 sockets	Test of	• Test conditions – Additional operations	Specified value	Repairing malfunction
14	–	Voltage supply for VAG 1551 scan tool, data link connector T16	– Connect multimeter (Fluke 83/equivalent) to T16 (black) using adapter cables from VW 1594 connector test kit ♦ Terminal 4 : Ground ♦ Terminal 16 : positive (B+)	 10.0 – 14.5 V	– Check wire from T16/4 to Ground (GND) – Check wire from T16/16 via -S22- to terminal 30
15	–	Resistance of K wire for On Board Diagnostic (OBD) data link connector T16	• Ignition switched off – Connect multimeter (Fluke 83/equivalent) to VAG 1598/21 test box socket 6 and data link connector T16, terminal 7. using adapter cables from VW 1594 connector test kit	 Max. 1.5 Ω	– Check wire from TV14 to terminal 13 – Check wire from T16/7 via TV14 to terminal 13

VW4029300071070X

Fig. 81 ABS electrical testing chart (Part 7 of 8). Teves type 20

Functional check: ABS warning light -K47-					
Test step	VAG 1598/21 sockets	Test of	• Test conditions – Additional operations	Specified value	Repairing malfunction
16	–	Function of ABS warning light -K47-	• Ignition switched off – Switch ignition on	 Warning light -K47- lights up	– Check wire from terminal W/2 (relay panel) to Ground (GND) – Check wire from terminal X/8 (relay panel) via -K47- to terminal X/3 (relay panel), -K47- (12 V; 1.2 W) replace if necessary – Check wire from terminal 16 to terminal W/2 (relay panel)
17	–	Function of warning light for brake system -K118-	• Ignition switched off – Switch ignition on	 Warning light for brake system -K118- lights up	– Check wire from terminal U2/10 (replay plate) to Ground (GND) – Check wire from terminal U2/10 (relay panel) via -K47- to terminal W/2 – Check wire from terminal 16 to terminal W/2 (relay panel) – Check wire from terminal U2/10 to terminal 28/18 (instrument cluster connector)

VW4029300071080X

Fig. 81 ABS electrical testing chart (Part 8 of 8). Teves type 20

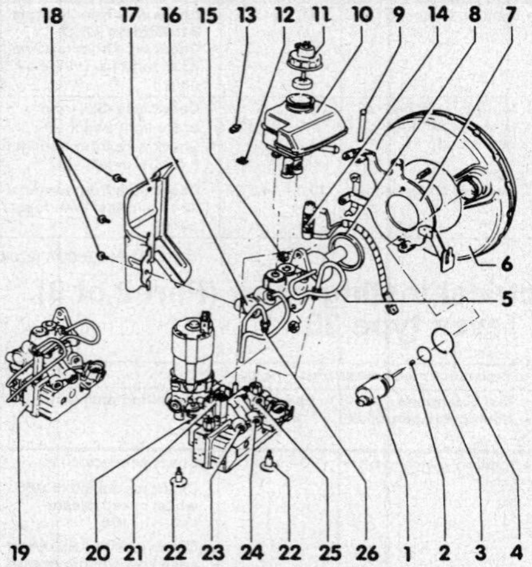

1. Pedal Position Sensor
2. Spacer Cap
3. O-ring
4. Cir-clip
5. Hydraulic Line
6. Brake Booster
7. Bracket
8. Seal
9. Pin
10. Reservoir
11. Cap
12. Clip
13. Screw
14. Diff. Lock Resistor (Optional)
15. Nut
16. Master Cylinder
17. Shield
18. Bolt
19. Hydraulic Modulator
20. Hydraulic Modulator w/Diff. Lock
21. Hydraulic Connection
22. Bolt□

VW4029300080000X

Fig. 82 Component view of hydraulic modulator. Teves type 04

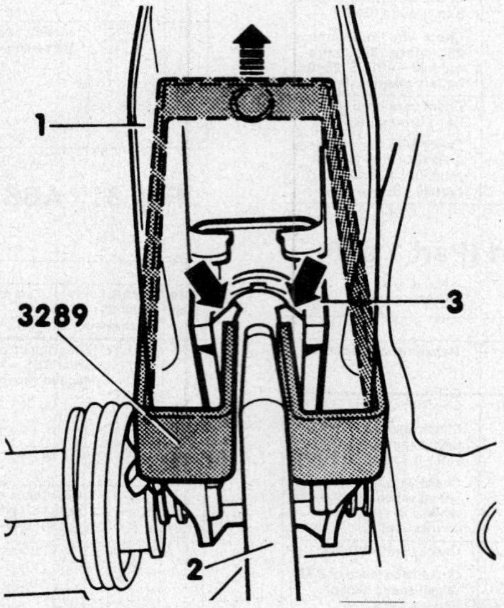

VW4029300079000X

Fig. 83 Booster from brake pedal disconnecting. Cabrio, Golf III, GTI & Jetta III w/Teves type 04

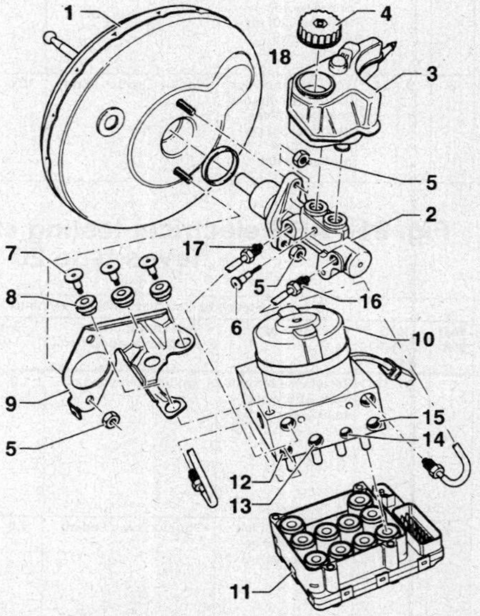

1. Brake Servo
2. Master Cylinder
3. Brake Fluid Reservoir
4. Cap
5. Self Locking Nut
6. Torx Bolt
7. Torx Bolt
8. Rubber Damper
9. Retainer
10. ABS Hydraulic Unit
11. ABS Control Module
12. Brake Line Connection
13. Brake Line Connection
14. Brake Line Connection
15. Brake Line Connection
16. Brake Line
17. Brake Line

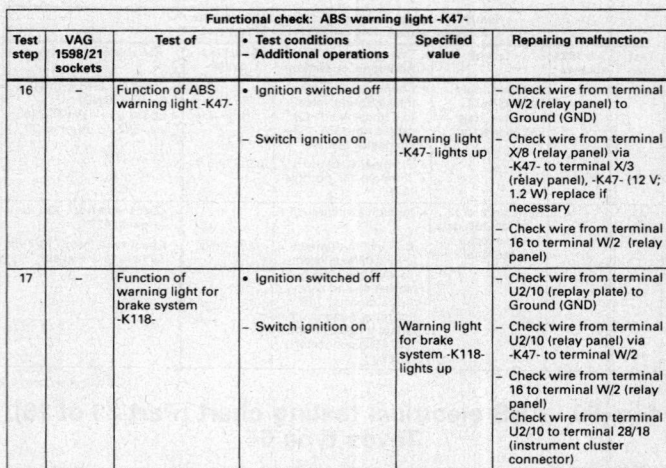

VW4029300081000X

Fig. 84 Component view of hydraulic modulator & control unit. Teves type 20

SYSTEM SERVICE

Brake System Bleed

Refer to "Hydraulic Brake Systems" for bleeding procedure.

Component Replacement

Bosch 5.3, ITT Mark 20 and Teves model 20 ABS control modules are coded to the vehicle. Replacement control modules must be coded after installation. Refer to "Coding Control Module" for procedures.

Prior to servicing the ABS system, always turn the ignition off.

The ABS control unit must never be exposed to temperatures greater than 185°F for more than two hours, or 203°F for even short time periods. The ABS control unit must be unplugged if an electric welder is to be used on the vehicle.

HYDRAULIC MODULATOR

When replacing hydraulic components, ensure all areas to be disassembled are clean before starting. Place all removed parts on a clean surface. Always cover and plug components if the repair cannot be completed immediately. Ensure all replacement parts are thoroughly cleaned before installation. Use care not to allow brake fluid to contact painted surfaces or electrical connectors.

Ensure all components and lines are connected in their original position. Do not allow lines to become crossed.

TEVES TYPE 04

For ease of service it is recommended that the modulator unit be removed and installed as an assembly with the brake vacuum booster.

1. Disconnect all electrical connectors from ABS hydraulic unit.
2. Remove brake fluid from reservoir.
3. Disconnect and plug fluid lines from ABS hydraulic unit, **Fig. 82.**
4. Remove any lefthand side under dash panels required to access brake pedal.
5. **On Cabrio, Golf III, GTI and Jetta III models,** disconnect brake booster pushrod from pedal as follows:
   a. Remove brake lamp switch as outlined in "Electrical" section.
   b. Push down on brake pedal and hold, then install pushrod disconnecting tool No. 3289, or equivalent, **Fig. 83.**
   c. Pull tool toward rear and into pedal socket until seated while holding pedal stationary.
   d. Pull tool and pedal together to rear until pedal pops off ball of booster pushrod.
6. **On Passat models,** disconnect clip from clevis pin, remove pin, then pull pedal from pushrod clevis.
7. **On all models,** remove nuts retaining booster to bulkhead, then remove assembly.

Code number	Engine code	Variant
03504	AEG	ABS
13504	AEG	ABS/EDL
03504	AFP	ABS
13504	AFP	ABS/EDL
03504	ALH	ABS
13504	ALH	ABS/EDL

VW4020100130000X

Fig. 85 Control module code table. Golf & Jetta w/ITT Mark 20 IE

Code number	Engine code	Variant
03504	AGU	ABS
13504	AGU	ABS/EDL
03504	AEG	ABS
13504	AEG	ABS/EDL
03504	ALH	ABS
13504	ALH	ABS/EDL

VW4020100131000X

Fig. 86 Control module code table. New Beetle w/ITT Mark 20 IE

8. Remove and install components from assembly as required to effect repair.
9. Install assembly to bulkhead, install mounting nuts, then **torque** nuts to 18 ft. lbs.
10. Install pedal to pushrod, align ball and socket, then push in until they pop together.
11. Reverse remaining procedures to install, then bleed brakes as outlined under "Hydraulic Brake Systems."

TEVES TYPE 20

In this system the ABS control module is mounted as an assembly with the ABS hydraulic modulator unit. **Use the highest standards of cleanliness when separating and assembling these components.**

The ABS hydraulic modulator unit may be shipped pre filled and pre-bled. If this is the case do not remove shipping plugs until connecting each line.

Teves model 20 ABS control modules are coded to the vehicle. Replacement control modules must be coded after installation. Refer to "Coding Control Module" for procedures.

1. Disconnect all electrical connectors from ABS hydraulic unit.
2. Disconnect coolant expansion tank and position aside.
3. Raise and support vehicle.
4. Connect a bleeder hose and bottle to lefthand front brake caliper bleeder screw, then open bleeder.
5. Depress brake pedal at least 2 3/8 inches, then block pedal to hold in this position.
6. Close bleeder screw on lefthand front caliper.
7. Remove heat shield from master cylinder, **Fig. 84.**
8. Remove fluid lines from master cylinder and hydraulic modulator. **Cap and plug all lines and fittings. Note position of all lines for later assembly.**
9. Remove "Torx" socket head bolts from ABS hydraulic unit mounting bracket, then remove hydraulic unit/control module assembly.
10. Disconnect hydraulic unit electrical connector from control module.
11. Maintain assembly in its installed position for the following procedures.
12. Remove nuts retaining control module to hydraulic unit.
13. **Pull control module straight off hydraulic unit so as not to damage or disturb solenoid assemblies.**
14. Keep control module covered with a lint free cloth until assembly.
15. Reverse procedure to install, noting the following:
    a. **Torque** mounting bracket "Torx" screws to 72 inch lbs.
    b. **Do not intermix brake fluid lines.**
    c. Bleed brakes as outlined under "Hydraulic Brake Systems."

ITT MARK 20 IE

Refer to **Control Module** in this section for hydraulic modulator replacement procedures.

BOSCH 5

Refer to **Control Module** in this section for hydraulic modulator replacement procedures.

BOSCH 5.3

Refer to **Control Module** in this section for hydraulic modulator replacement procedures.

CODING CONTROL MODULE

BOSCH 5.3

1. Connect a suitable scan tool as outlined under "Accessing Diagnostic Trouble Codes."
2. Follow manufacturer's instructions to access control module coding function of scan tool.
3. **On models equipped with manual transaxle,** enter code 00064.
4. **On models equipped with automatic transaxle,** enter code 00067.

ITT MARK 20 IE

1. Determine engine code and type of control module installed on vehicle.
2. Connect a suitable scan tool, as outlined under "Accessing Diagnostic Trouble Codes."
3. Follow scan tool manufacturer's instructions to access control module coding function.
4. Enter proper code from tables, **Figs. 85 and 86.**

TEVES TYPE 20

1. Connect a suitable scan tool as outlined under "Accessing Diagnostic Trouble Codes."
2. Follow scan tool manufacturer's instructions to access control module coding function.
3. Unless there is documentation with the

replacement control module, enter code 03604.

CONTROL MODULE

Always connect a suitable scan tool to ABS system and inspect for any stored Diagnostic Trouble Codes (DTC) before disconnecting control module.

Bosch 5.3, ITT Mark 20 and Teves model 20 ABS control modules are coded to the vehicle. Replacement control modules must be coded after installation. Refer to "Coding Control Module" for procedures.

CABRIO, GOLF, GTI, JETTA & NEW BEETLE

Teves Type 04

ABS control unit is located under the righthand side rear seat.

1. Pull outward on sheet metal straps near the control unit.
2. Pull control unit out.
3. Release connector latch, then disconnect connector.
4. Reverse procedure to install.

Teves Type 20

The Teves type 20 ABS control module is in unit with the hydraulic unit. Refer to "Hydraulic Modulator Replace" for procedures.

Teves model 20 ABS control modules are coded to the vehicle. Replacement control modules must be coded after installation. Refer to "Coding Teves Type 20 Control Module" for procedures.

ITT Mark 20 IE

1. Disconnect MAF sensor electrical connector.
2. Remove air filter attaching bolts, then position air filter aside.
3. **On models equipped w/diesel engine,** remove relay panel above brake booster.
4. **On all models,** remove as much brake fluid as possible from brake fluid reservoir using a suitable brake bleeder bottle.
5. Insert brake pedal depressor tool No. VAG 1869/2, or equivalent.
6. Activate brake pedal booster with brake pedal depressor.
7. Connect bleeder bottle hose to bleed screw of lefthand front brake caliper and open bleed screw.
8. Close lefthand front bleed screw.
9. Release ABS control module connector and remove.
10. Place plastic covering under control module and hydraulic unit.
11. Disconnect brake lines from hydraulic unit to brake master cylinder and suspend with suitable wire or rope.
12. Disconnect remaining brake lines from hydraulic unit.
13. Seal brake lines and threaded holes using plugs from repair kit part No. 1H0 698 311 A or equivalent.
14. Remove bolts from bracket for hydraulic unit.
15. Remove hydraulic unit with control module.
16. Disconnect hydraulic pump motor electrical connector from control module.
17. Remove four control module to hydraulic pump motor attaching screws, then separate control module from hydraulic pump motor.
18. Reverse procedure to install.

PASSAT

Bosch 5.3

1. Disconnect control module electrical connector.
2. Install brake pedal loading tool from tool No. VAG 1238 B, or equivalent.
3. Connect bleeder bottle hose to lefthand front brake caliper bleeder screw, then open screw.
4. Close lefthand front bleeder screw.
5. Place clean shop towels under control and hydraulic modules.
6. Remove brake lines from hydraulic unit.
7. Seal brake lines and threaded holes with plugs from repair set part No. 1H0 698 311 A, or equivalent.
8. Remove hex nuts on hydraulic unit bracket.
9. Remove hydraulic unit with control module.
10. Disconnect hydraulic pump motor electrical connector from control module.
11. Remove six control module to hydraulic pump motor attaching screws, then separate control module from hydraulic pump motor.
12. Reverse procedure to install.

EUROVAN

Bosch 5

1. Disconnect control module electrical connector.
2. Remove brake fluid from reservoir using a suitable suction bottle.
3. Position brake pedal loading device from tool No. VAG 1238 B, or equivalent.
4. Remove hydraulic unit ground wire.
5. Disconnect hydraulic unit brake lines, then plug openings.
6. Remove hydraulic unit by lifting up and out.
7. Remove control module to hydraulic pump motor attaching screws, then separate control module from hydraulic pump motor.
8. Reverse procedure to install.

Automatic Transaxles

TABLE OF CONTENTS

	Page No.
APPLICATION CHART	8-165
01M TRANSAXLE	8-165
01N TRANSAXLE	8-172
01V TRANSAXLE	8-175

APPLICATION CHART

Year	Model	Transaxle
1998–2001	Golf, GTI & Jetta	01M
	New Beetle	01M
	Passat	01N & 01V

01M Transaxle

INDEX

	Page No.
Adjustments	8-167
Ignition Lock Cable	8-168
Shift Lock Solenoid	8-168
Throttle Cable	8-167
Description	8-165
Identification	8-165
Maintenance	8-166
Final Drive Gear Oil Level Inspection	8-167
Fluid Inspection	8-166
Precautions	8-165
Air Bag Systems	8-165
Audio Coded Anti-Theft System	8-165
Battery Ground Cable	8-165
Tightening Specifications	8-171
Transaxle, Replace	8-168
1999–2001 Golf, GTI & Jetta	8-169
Cabrio & 1998 Golf, GTI & Jetta	8-168
New Beetle	8-169
Troubleshooting	8-165
Main Pressure	8-166
Shift Points	8-165
Stall Speed	8-165

PRECAUTIONS

AIR BAG SYSTEMS

Do not use computer memory saver tool on air bag equipped models. Using the tool will keep the air bag system charged and may cause accidental air bag unit activation.

Refer to "Air Bag System Precautions" in the front of this manual for system disarming and arming procedures.

BATTERY GROUND CABLE

Prior to service, disconnect battery ground cable and isolate as required.

AUDIO CODED ANTI-THEFT SYSTEM

Some models are equipped with a radio anti-theft system that will disable the system when battery power is interrupted. Unless the system is reset the radio will not operate.

1. Turn radio On. SAFE and 1000 should be displayed.
2. Enter radio code using first four program station buttons. Security code will appear on display.
3. Depress and hold righthand side of radio righthand or lefthand blocker until anti-theft coding is activated indicated by a brief signal sound.
4. If code number has been entered properly, a diode on front of radio will flash when ignition key is removed.

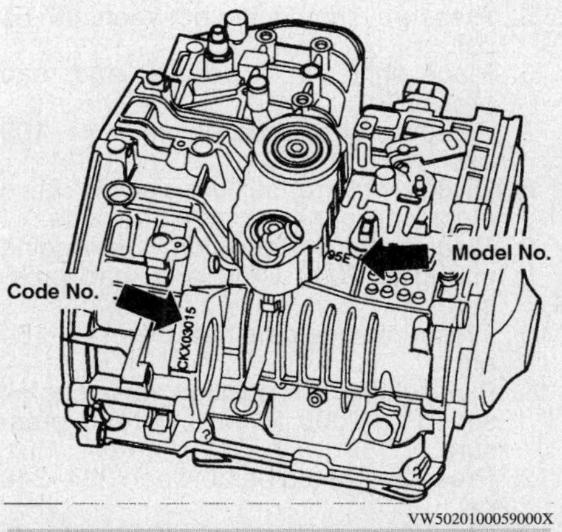

Fig. 1 Transaxle code & model number locations

IDENTIFICATION

The model identification numbers are located on the lefthand side of transaxle. Code letters are on the upper front part and type numbers are in the center.

Refer to **Fig. 1** to locate transaxle code and transaxle model numbers.

DESCRIPTION

The 01M transaxle is a fully automatic, four speed transaxle.

TROUBLESHOOTING

Refer to **Fig. 2** for troubleshooting procedures.

SHIFT POINTS

Locate transaxle code as outlined under "Identification," then refer to **Figs. 3 and 4** to locate shift point table that applies to vehicle being tested.

Note that the capitol letter following the shift (M or H) indicates whether the shift is to be performed (M) manually or (H) hydraulically.

Tables for transaxles with shift program selection built into the control module, (control module senses how fast accelerator pedal is depressed to choose between Sport or Economy modes) show only kickdown speeds.

STALL SPEED

Locate transaxle code as outlined under "Identification," then refer to **Fig. 5** to locate stall speed table that applies to vehicle being tested.

1. Connect a suitable engine tachometer to vehicle.

Condition	Possible cause	Correction
No. 1 Drive disc (drive plate) cracked	Engine/transmission centralizing bushes missing	– Replace engine/transmission centering bushings and drive plate
No. 2 Transmission oily	Transmission leaking	– Clean engine/transmission and determine where engine or transmission is leaking, if necessary use leak detector. – Seal or replace faulty components on leaky transmissions – Replace sealing rings, seals, screw connections or transmission housing (torque converter housing) ⇒ Repair automatic transmission 096 or 098
	ATF overfilled	– Clean transmission, check ATF level, if necessary extract ⇒ Repair automatic transmission 096 or 098; checking ATF level and topping up
	Gear oil overfilled	– Clean transmission, check gear oil level, if necessary extract ⇒ Repair automatic transmission 096 or 098; checking gear oil in final drive
No. 3 ATF leak in area of torque converter	Drive disc (drive plate) clearance dimension not OK	– Adjust drive plate clearance dimension
	Torque converter bushing faulty	– Replace torque converter ⇒ Repair automatic transmission 096 or 098; torque converter identification
	Torque converter oil seal faulty	– Replace torque converter oil seal, if bearing surface or torque converter is damaged then additionally replace torque converter ⇒ Repair automatic transmission 096 or 098; removing and installing torque converter oil seal
	ATF pump leaking	– Disassemble ATF pump, replace faulty components and then reassemble ⇒ Repair automatic transmission 096 or 098; disassembling and assembling planetary gearbox
No. 4 ATF in coolant or coolant in ATF	ATF cooler faulty	– Replace ATF cooler and coolant and replace ATF – If too much coolant is in ATF then the planetary gearbox as well as the clutches must be disassembled, cleaned and reassembled ⇒ Repair automatic transmission 096 or 098; disassembling and assembling planetary gearbox
No. 5 ATF and gear oil mixed	ATF level or gear oil level too low, no visible leaks on transmission exterior	– Correct ATF and gear oil levels – Carry out a longer test drive and again check ATF and gear oil levels, if levels have changed replace drive pinion oil seal and bearing support ring O–ring ⇒ Repair automatic transmission 096 or 098; removing and installing drive pinion

VW5029500004010X

Fig. 2 Transaxle troubleshooting (Part 1 of 4)

Condition	Possible cause	Correction
No. 6 Gear selector mechanism difficult to operate	Gear selector mechanism difficult (exterior to transmission) Gear selector mechanism difficult (within transmission)	– Remove selector lever cable at lever/selector shaft – If selector mechanism is stiff up to transmission exterior, then service stiff selector mechanism ⇒ Repair automatic transmission 096 or 098; servicing selector mechanism – Selector mechanism stiff within the transmission, disassemble and assemble parking lock ⇒ Repair automatic transmission 096 or 098; disassembling and assembling parking lock
No. 7 Selector lever position: 1 Automatic transmission will not select: 1st Gear (no drive)	1st to 3rd Gear clutch –K1– or reverse Gear brake –B1– faulty	– Service 1st to 3rd gear clutch –K1– or reverse gear –B1– ⇒ Repair automatic transmission 096 or 098; disassembling and assembling planetary gearbox
No. 8 Selector lever position: D, 3 or 2 Automatic transmission will not select: 1st Gear (no drive)	1st to 3rd Gear clutch –K1– or freewheel faulty	– Service 1st to 3rd gear clutch –K1– or freewheel ⇒ Repair automatic transmission 096 or 098; disassembling and assembling planetary gearbox
No. 9 Selector lever position: D, 3 or 2 Automatic transmission will not select: 2nd Gear	2nd and 4th Gear brake –B2– faulty	– Service 2nd and 4th gear brake –B2– ⇒ automatic transmission 096 or 098; disassembling and assembling planetary gearbox
No. 10 Selector lever position: D or 3 Automatic transmission will not select: 3rd Gear	Reverse Gear clutch –K2– faulty	– Service reverse gear clutch –K2– ⇒ Repair automatic transmission 096 or 098; disassembling and assembling planetary gearbox
No. 11 Selector lever position: D Automatic transmission will not select: 4th Gear	4th Gear (3rd and 4th Gear [1]) Clutch –K3– or 2nd and 4th Gear brake –B2– faulty	– Service 4th gear (3rd and 4th gear [1]) clutch or 2nd and 4th gear brake –B2– ⇒ Repair automatic transmission 096 or 098; disassembling and assembling planetary gearbox
No. 12 Selector lever position: R Automatic transmission will not select: Reverse gear	Reverse gear clutch –K2– faulty Reverse gear brake –B1– faulty	– Service reverse gear clutch –K2– or reverse gear brake –B1– ⇒ Repair automatic transmission 096 or 098; disassembling and assembling planetary gearbox

[1] Transmissions manufactured up to December 92 with program switch

VW5029500004020X

Fig. 2 Transaxle troubleshooting (Part 2 of 4)

2. Run engine until it is at normal operating temperature.
3. Block wheels and set parking brake.
4. Start engine, then while holding down on brake pedal, apply full throttle for no more than five seconds and read torque converter stall speed from the engine tachometer.
5. Compare reading with table.
   a. If stall speed reading is over 200 RPM high, inspect for a damaged forward clutch or one way clutch.
   b. If stall speed reading is up to 200 RPM low, inspect for poor engine performance.
   c. If stall speed reading is over 200 RPM low, inspect for a faulty torque converter.

MAIN PRESSURE

The following procedure will set a Diagnostic Trouble Code (DTC) into the control module memory. It will be required to have a suitable scan tool available to erase this DTC at completion of test.

Prior to performing the following procedure it is recommended that a suitable scan tool be connected to the vehicle as outlined under "Anti-Lock Brakes" in the "Diagnosis & Testing" section, then inspect for and repair any transaxle DTC. Inspect for other possible stored DTCs for other vehicle systems.

If possible, perform the following procedure on a chassis dynamometer.

If tests show pressure out of specification, the following areas should be inspected.

Engine idle too high or too low.
ATF pump faulty.
Sticking valve in valve body.

1. Connect a suitable transaxle pressure gauge to main pressure port on transaxle, **Fig. 6.**
2. Ensure transaxle oil is at normal operating temperature.
3. Start and idle engine.
4. Place shifter in D position and read pressure.
5. Pressure should be between 49–55 psi.
6. Place shifter in R position and read pressure.
7. Pressure should be between 94–109 psi.
8. Disconnect transaxle solenoid valve electrical connector from transaxle.
9. Place shifter in D position, raise engine speed to 2000 RPM and read pressure.
10. Pressure should be between 146–164 psi.
11. Place shifter in R position, raise engine speed to 2000 RPM and read pressure.
12. Pressure should be between 334–348 psi.
13. Stop engine, then remove pressure gauge.
14. Connect transaxle solenoid valve electrical connector to transaxle.
15. Connect a suitable scan tool to vehicle, then erase stored DTC.

MAINTENANCE

Use only ATF part No. VW G 052 162 A2, or equivalent, for filling up or replacing fluid on transaxle model 01M.

Note that Volkswagen original equipment transaxle oil is yellowish in color. It is not required to replace the transaxle fluid based on color alone.

FLUID INSPECTION

Use only ATF part No. VW G 052 162 A2, or equivalent, for filling up or replacing fluid.

1. Raise and support vehicle.
2. Connect a suitable scan tool to Data Link Connector (DLC) under lefthand side of dash panel, to right of steering column.
3. Follow scan tool manufacturer's instructions to access "Transaxle Electronics," then advance to transaxle oil temperature measurement.
4. Transaxle oil cannot be above 86° F to begin oil level test.
5. Remove ATF level plug from oil pan, **Fig. 7.** Discard seal. A small amount of fluid in tube should run out.
6. Run vehicle until transaxle temperature reaches 95–113° F. ATF should "drip" out of level overflow tube.
7. If fluid drips out, replace level plug with new gasket and tighten to specifications. Level inspection is complete.
8. If fluid does not drip out, proceed as follows:
   a. Pry securing cap off filler tube plug, **Fig. 8.** Discard securing cap. **Note that on some models a reusable securing cap with spring clip was used.**
   b. Remove filler tube plug, then fill transaxle with suitable ATF until fluid runs out of level plug hole.
   c. Install level tube plug using a new gasket.

Condition	Possible cause	Correction
No. 13 Selector lever position: D, 3, 2 or 1 No drive in all gears	1st to 3rd Gear clutch –K1– faulty Freewheel or reverse gear brake –B1– faulty	– Service 1st to 3rd gear clutch –K1– or freewheel or reverse gear brake –B1– ⇒ Repair automatic transmission 096 or 098; disassembling and assembling planetary gearbox
No. 14 Gear selections not taking place	Valves or solenoid valves in valve body stuck	– Replace valve body ⇒ Repair automatic transmission 096 or 098; removing and installing valve body
No. 15 Uncontrolled or harsh shifts	Short circuit between valve wiring or cable guide rail Valve in valve body or solenoid valve faulty	– Replace valve body ⇒ Repair automatic transmission 096 or 098; removing and installing valve body
No. 16 Shifts: When changing gear one shift is harsh	Check in which gear the harsh shifting occurs Relevant selector elements faulty	– Check selector element activation ⇒ Repair automatic transmission 096 or 098; transmission with selector elements – Replace selector element ⇒ Repair automatic transmission 096 or 098; disassembling and assembling planetary gearbox
No. 17 Transmission selects emergency running mode	Incorrect control module installed Conductor strip (cable guide rail) faulty valve in valve body stuck	– Select Control Module according to parts catalogue and if necessary replace – Carry out OBD and electrical check and then replace wiring or components if necessary ⇒ Repair automatic transmission 096 or 098; self–diagnosis or – Replace valve body ⇒ Repair automatic transmission 096 or 098; removing and installing valve body
No. 18 Parking lock will not engage	Selector lever cable defective or incorrectly adjusted Locking lever, parking lock wheel or locking lever mechanism faulty	– Replace selector lever cable and adjust ⇒ Repair automatic transmission 096 or 098; checking and adjusting selector lever cable – Service locking lever, parking lock wheel and locking lever mechanism ⇒ Repair automatic transmission 096 or 098; disassembling and assembling parking lock
No. 19 Noises in final drive	Taper roller bearing loud	– Replace taper roller bearing ⇒ Repair automatic transmission 096 or 098; disassembling and assembling final drive
	Drive pinion loud	– Replace drive pinion ⇒ Repair automatic transmission 096 or 098; removing and installing drive pinion
	Output gear loud	– Replace output gear ⇒ Repair automatic transmission 096 or 098; removing and installing drive pinion
	Input gear loud	– Replace input gear ⇒ Repair automatic transmission 096 or 098; removing and installing input gear
	Differential loud	– Replace differential ⇒ Repair automatic transmission 096 or 098; removing and installing differential

VW5029500004030X

Fig. 2 Transaxle troubleshooting (Part 3 of 4)

Transmission Code Letter	Shift	Kickdown km/h (mph)
CLB	1 H – 1 M	60 – 66 (37 – 41)
	1 M – 2 H	60 – 66 (37 – 41)
	2 H – 2 M	122 –128 (76 – 80)
	2 M – 3 H	122 –128 (76 – 80)
	3 H – 3 M	179 –185 (111 – 115)
	3 M – 4 H	179 –185 (111 –115)
	4 H – 4 M	179 –185 (111 – 115)
	4 M – 4 H	180 –174 (112 –108)
	4 H – 3 M	180 –174 (112 –108)
	3 M – 3 H	121 –115 (75 – 71)
	3 H – 2 M	121 –115 (75 –71)
	2 M – 2 H	121 –115 (75 – 71)
	2 H – 1 M	51 – 45 (32 – 28)
	1 M – 1 H	51 – 45 (32 – 28)

VW5029400008010X

Fig. 3 Shift point table (Part 1 of 2). 1998

Condition	Possible cause	Correction
No. 20 Poor driving characteristics (bucking or idling)	Throttle valve housing leaking (sometimes only when engine/transmission moves)	– Check throttle valve housing and air ducting for leaks
No. 21 Engine speed drops when selecting a driving range	Engine Control Module faulty	– Replace engine Control Module
No. 22 Vehicle will not start or starts in incorrect selector lever position	Park/Neutral position switch faulty	– Replace switch
No. 23 Selector lever can be moved from "N" or "P" or these positions are not blocked	Shiftlock solenoid –N110 faulty Transmission Control Module –J217 defective	– Replace shiftlock solenoid –N110 ⇒ Repair automatic transmission 096 or 098; disassembling and assembling selector mechanism – Replace TCM –J217 ⇒ Repair automatic transmission 096 or 098; On Board Diagnostic (OBD)
No. 24 Multifunction Transmission Range (TR) Switch –F125– contacts overheated	TR Switch faulty Wiring guide and connecters overheated Wiring as well as wiring guide seals faulty TR Switch contacts corroded	– Replace TR Switch ⇒ Repair automatic transmission 096 or 098; disassembling and assembling parking lock – Replace wiring and connections – The TR Switch contact assignment must be changed on transmissions 096 or 098 up to February 1994

VW5029500004040X

Fig. 2 Transaxle troubleshooting (Part 4 of 4)

Transmission Code Letter	Shift	Kickdown km/h (mph)
CLK	1 H – 1 M	49 – 55 (30 – 34)
	1 M – 2 H	49 – 55 (30 – 34)
	2 H – 2 M	98 –104 (61 – 65)
	2 M – 3 H	98 –104 (61 – 65)
	3 H – 3 M	137–143 (85 – 89)
	3 M – 4 H	137–143 (85 – 89)
	4 H – 4 M	137–143 (85 – 89)
	4 M – 4 H	139 –133 (86 – 83)
	4 H – 3 M	139 –133 (86 – 83
	3 M – 3 H	98 – 92 (61 – 57)
	3 H – 2 M	98 – 92 (61 – 57)
	2 M – 2 H	98 – 92 (61 – 57)
	2 H – 1 M	42 – 36 (26 – 22)
	1 M – 1 H	42 – 36 (26 – 22)
CKX	1 H – 1 M	46 – 52 (29 – 32)
	1 M – 2 H	46 – 52 (29 – 32)
	2 H – 2 M	90 – 96 (56 – 60)
	2 M – 3 H	90 – 96 (56 – 60)
	3 H – 3 M	105 –111 (65 – 69)
	3 M – 4 H	131 –137 (81 – 85)
	4 H – 4 M	131 –137 (81 – 85)
	4 M – 4 H	132 –126 (82 – 78)
	4 H – 3 M	132 –126 (82 – 78)
	3 M – 3 H	99 – 93 (61 – 58)
	3 H – 2 M	89 – 83 (55 – 51)
	2 M – 2 H	89 – 83 (55 – 51)
	2 H – 1 M	39 – 33 (24 – 20)
	1 M – 1 H	39 – 33 (24 – 20)

VW5029400008020X

Fig. 3 Shift point table (Part 2 of 2). 1998

d. Install filler plug, then the filler plug securing cap.

FINAL DRIVE GEAR OIL LEVEL INSPECTION

The oil level for the final drive gear is inspected with the transaxle installed.

1. Remove speedometer driveshaft from transaxle and wipe clean.
2. Install driveshaft into transaxle, then remove and inspect oil level on shaft.
3. Oil level must be between minimum and maximum marks on the shaft. If required add synthetic gear oil G50 SAE 75W90, or equivalent.

ADJUSTMENTS

THROTTLE CABLE

Cabrio & 1998 Golf, GTI & Jetta

1. Place spacer of. 60 inch between accelerator pedal and pedal stop.
2. Fully depress accelerator until it contacts spacer and hold in this position.
3. Open throttle by pulling on accelerator cable sleeve, then secure in this position using retainer clip.
4. Connect multimeter tool No. US 1119, or equivalent, to kickdown switch using adapter switch tool No. VW 1594, or equivalent. Switch must read infinite ohms.
5. Slowly depress accelerator pedal until full throttle is reached, after kickdown pressure point is reached resistance must drop to 0 ohms.
6. At this point accelerator pedal must be just short of the pedal stop.

New Beetle & 1999–2001 Golf & Jetta

1. Remove throttle cable retaining clip, then depress throttle pedal to wide open position.
2. Adjust throttle cable by moving retainer at support bracket so wide open throttle position is obtained at throttle control module.

Transmission Code Letter	Test conditions	Shift	Kickdown speed KPH (mph)
DYQ	Drive on a level road ATF temp. not above 140°C (284°F)	1H–2H	46-52 (29–33)
		2H–3H	84-90 (53-57)
		3H–3M	132-138 (83-86)
		3M–4H	132-138 (83-86)
		4H–4M	132-138 (83-86)
		4M–4H	131-125 (82-78)
		4H–3M	131-125 (82-78)
		3M–3H	101-95 (63-59)
		3H–2H	84-78 (53-49)
		2H–1H	43-37 (27-23)

VW5020100060000X

Fig. 4 Shift point table. 1999–2001

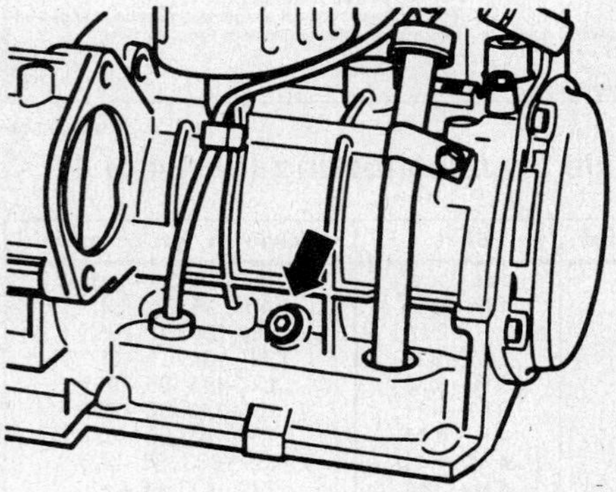

VW5029300011000X

Fig. 6 Transaxle main oil pressure port location

3. Release throttle pedal, then disconnect kickdown switch electrical connector on bulkhead.
4. Measure resistance of kickdown switch. Resistance should be infinite ohms.
5. Slowly depress throttle pedal toward wide open throttle. Resistance should decrease to 0 ohms before throttle pedal reaches stop bolt.
6. Inspect closed throttle and wide open throttle positions on throttle body after adjusting.

SHIFT LOCK SOLENOID

Adjustment

1. Access shift lock solenoid by removing console and shifter components as required.
2. Loosen solenoid mounting, then slide solenoid on elongated mounting slots and adjust as follows:
   a. Place selector lever in "N" position.
   b. Adjust position of solenoid until clearance of. 012 inch is achieved between rod and solenoid lever, **Fig. 9.**
3. Perform "Functional Inspection."

Functional Inspection

1. Ensure ignition cable lock is disengaged.
2. Place selector lever in "P" position.
3. Disconnect connector for solenoid, then connect solenoid to a suitable 12 volt source.
4. It must not be possible to move shifter into any gear position.
5. Disconnect 12 volt source, shifter must move to all gear positions.

Transmission Code Letter	Torque Converter Code Letter	Stall speed rpm
CLB	QCDV	2050 – 2350
CLK	QADB	2550 – 2850
CKX	QADB	2250 – 2550
CKZ	QCDB	...

VW5029400010000X

Fig. 5 Stall speed specifications

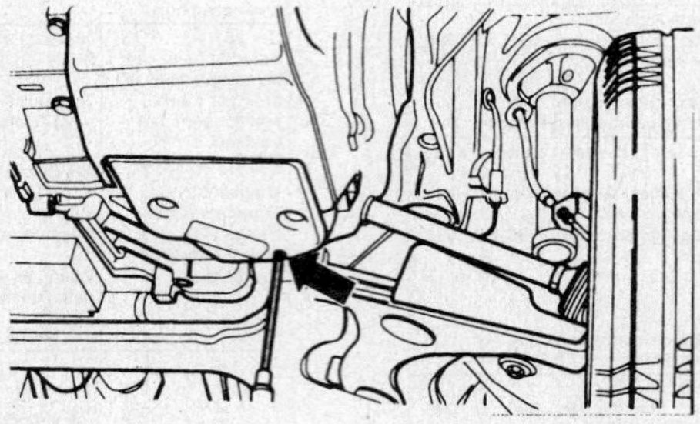

VW5029400012000X

Fig. 7 Level tube plug removal

6. Repeat above steps with lever in position "N."

IGNITION LOCK CABLE

Cabrio & 1998 Golf, GTI & Jetta

Ignition lock cable can only be adjusted after it has been completely installed.

1. Access ignition lock cable and lever by removing console and shifter components as required.
2. Place shift lever in "1" position, then release cable clamp bolt.
3. Turn ignition to Start, then release.
4. Adjust dimension between lever and locking pin to. 025–.030 inch, **Fig. 10.**
5. Tighten cable clamp bolt to specifications.
6. Place selector lever into "P" position and remove ignition key.
7. It must not be possible to remove ignition key with shift lever in any but "P" position.
8. It must not be possible to move shift lever from "P" position with ignition key removed.

New Beetle & 1999-2001 Golf, GTI & Jetta

1. Slide ignition lock cable sleeve forward, then release clip by pushing up.
2. Release shift plate retaining clips, then lift off.
3. Slide. 032 inch feeler gauge between locking lever and selector lever roller.
4. Pull outer sleeve of locking cable slightly forward in direction of travel, then push red clip down until it engages.
5. Push sleeve over clip, then inspect adjustment.

TRANSAXLE

REPLACE

CABRIO & 1998 GOLF, GTI & JETTA

1. Disconnect speedometer, then place selector in "P" position and remove selector cable from lever.
2. Disconnect electrical connectors from transaxle.
3. Remove Multi-Function Transaxle Range (TR) switch.
4. Pinch off coolant hoses at transaxle cooler using a suitable clamp, then remove hoses at cooler.
5. **On models equipped with 2.8L engines,** disconnect vacuum line (a) and electrical connector (b), **Fig. 11,** then the radiator fan electrical connector.
6. **On all models,** install a suitable engine support tool, **Fig. 12.**
7. Disconnect and remove front engine mount.
8. Dismount an position aside coolant expansion tank.
9. Remove complete lefthand engine mount.
10. **On models equipped with 2.8L engines,** remove drive belt cover for clearance when lowering engine.
11. **On all models,** remove starter, then the upper transaxle to engine bolts.
12. Remove protective plate for transaxle if equipped, then torque converter cover plate and torque converter mounting bolts.
13. Remove vibration weight from subframe, if equipped, then disconnect axle shafts at transaxle flange and raise and position righthand side shaft aside.
14. **On models equipped with tripod inner joint,** remove lefthand axle shaft from vehicle. Refer to "Front Wheel Drive Axles" for identification and procedure.
15. **On models less tripod inner joint,** mark, then loosen lower ball joint, then swing out to allow clearance.
16. **On all models,** remove bracket for power steering hose.
17. Place support device tool No. 3300A, or equivalent, into position, **Fig. 13,** then tilt engine forward.
18. Lower the engine and transaxle using

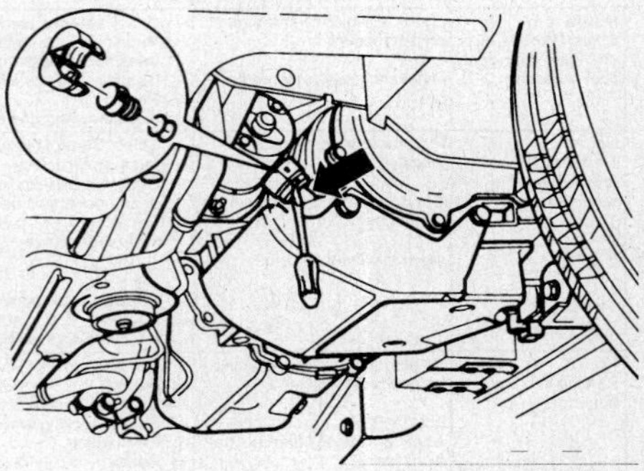

VW5029400013000X

Fig. 8 Filler tube cap removal. 01M transaxle

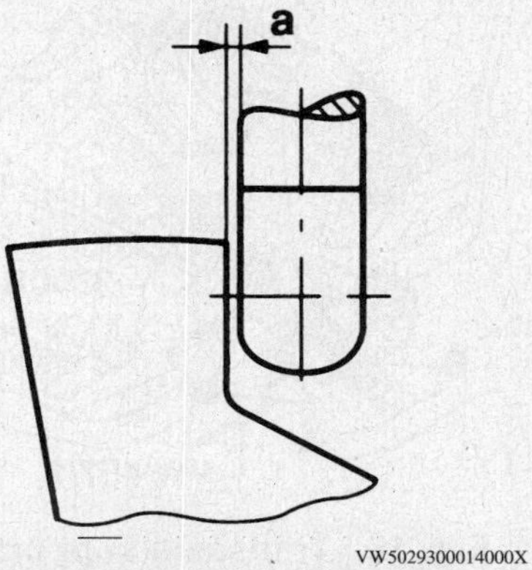

Fig. 9 Shift lock solenoid adjustment. Cabrio & 1998 Golf, GTI & Jetta

engine support unit until transaxle removal clearance is achieved

19. Position suitable transmission jack under transaxle.
20. Remove lower engine/transaxle bolts, separate transaxle from engine, then lower transaxle.
21. Reverse procedure to install, noting the following:
    a. Tighten nuts and bolts to specifications.
    b. Inspect and adjust selector cable if required.

1999–2001 GOLF, GTI & JETTA

1. Remove engine cover, then the battery and support bracket.
2. Remove air cleaner assembly, then the intake hose.
3. Disconnect electrical connector from MAF and transaxle.
4. Remove wiring harness from retainer on transaxle, then position aside.
5. Remove bracket for power steering hose with retainer for wiring harness.
6. Move shift lever to "P," then pry selector lever cable off selector shaft.
7. Remove circlip at selector lever cable support bracket, then the selector lever cable.
8. Remove ground cable from upper engine/transaxle bolt.
9. Disconnect electrical connectors from stater motor, then remove starter motor upper bolt.
10. Clamp off ATF cooler hoses using hose clamp tool No. 3094, or equivalent, then remove ATF cooler.
11. Remove upper engine/transaxle bolts.
12. Support engine and transaxle using support bar tool No. 10-222A with legs tool No. 10-222A/1, or equivalents.
13. Raise and support vehicle, then remove lefthand front wheel.
14. Remove noise insulation tray.
15. **On models equipped with 1.9L TDI engine,** remove line between charge air cooler and exhaust turbocharger.
16. **On all models,** remove ATF oil pan protective plate.

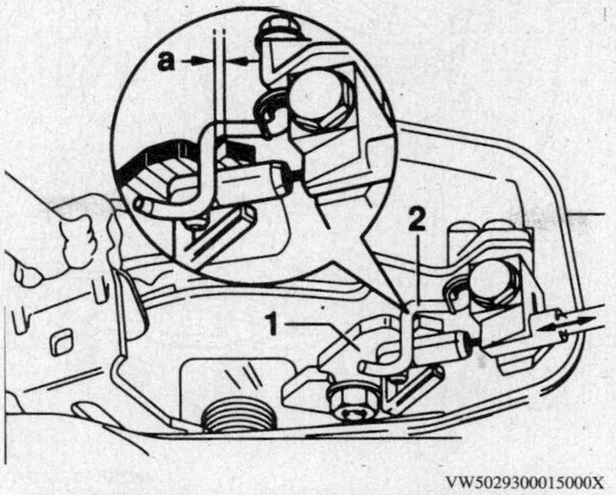

Fig. 10 Ignition lock cable adjustment. Cabrio & 1998 Golf, GTI & Jetta

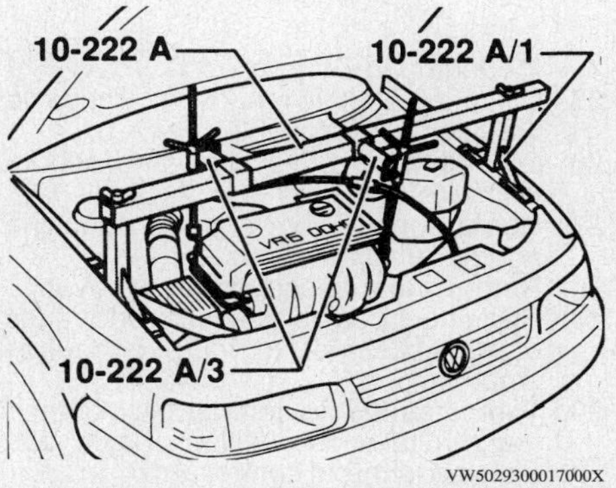

Fig. 12 Engine support tool installation. Cabrio & 1998 Golf, GTI & Jetta

17. Remove power steering pressure line bracket from lower starter bolt, then the starter motor.
18. Remove righthand inner CV joint protective cover from engine.
19. Disconnect axle shafts at transaxle, then raise righthand axle shaft and secure.
20. Remove pendulum support, **Fig. 14.**
21. Remove cap for torque converter nuts cover.
22. Remove torque converter bolts using socket tool No. V 175, or equivalent.
23. Turn steering to lefthand lock, then mark installation position of ball joint bolts on lefthand control arm and remove bolts.
24. Remove lefthand coupling rod from control arm, then turn rod upward.
25. Swing wheel bearing housing outward.
26. Remove lefthand axle shaft from transaxle, then fasten to suspension strut using suitable wire.
27. Remove bolts from lefthand assembly mount from lefthand console.
28. Carefully tilt engine and transaxle lowering lefthand spindle two inches on support bar to aid in removal.
29. Remove lefthand mount from transaxle, then separate exhaust system at exhaust pipe.
30. Bolt support rail tool No. 457/1, or equivalent, to securing holes on subframe, **Fig. 15,** then insert. 24 inch spacer between subframe and support rail.

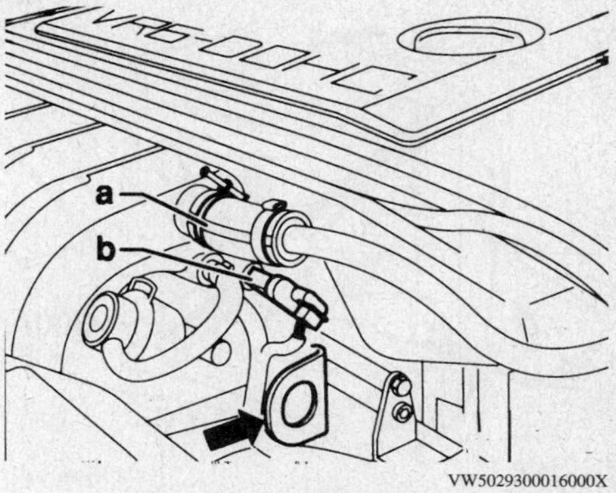

Fig. 11 Vacuum hose disconnection. 1998 GTI & Jetta w/2.8L engine

31. Install support tool No. 3300 A, or equivalent, **Fig. 15.**
32. Tilt transaxle forward using support tool.
33. Support transaxle using jack tool No. VAG 1383 and support tool No. 3282, or equivalents.
34. Place safety support pin on oil pan, then secure to transaxle housing.
35. **On models equipped with triple roller axle shaft,** turn transaxle flange to right until flat is vertical.
36. **On all models,** remove lower engine/transaxle connecting bolt.
37. Separate transaxle from engine while pushing torque converter out of drive plate.
38. Push torque converter against ATF pump, then lower transaxle slightly.
39. Carefully tilt and remove transaxle from vehicle, then secure torque converter to prevent it from falling.
40. Reverse procedure to install, noting the following:
    a. Ensure torque converter drive pins engage in ATF pump inner wheel recesses.
    b. Replace selector cable anchor lock washer.
    c. Replace transaxle mount bolts.
    d. Inspect and adjust selector cable if required.
    e. Tighten all bolts and nuts to specifications.

NEW BEETLE

1. Remove engine cover.
2. Remove power steering fluid reservoir from battery support, do not disconnect lines.
3. Remove battery, then the battery support bracket.
4. Remove air intake hose, then disconnect MAF sensor electrical connector.
5. Remove air cleaner assembly.
6. Disconnect electrical connector from vehicle speed sensor.

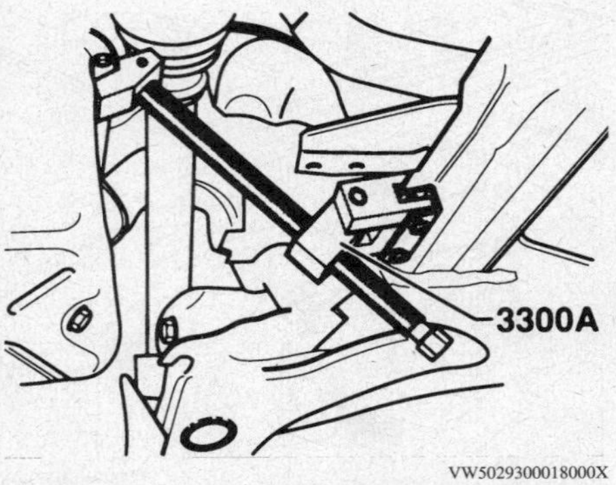

Fig. 13 Engine tilting forward w/support device. Cabrio & 1998 Golf, GTI & Jetta

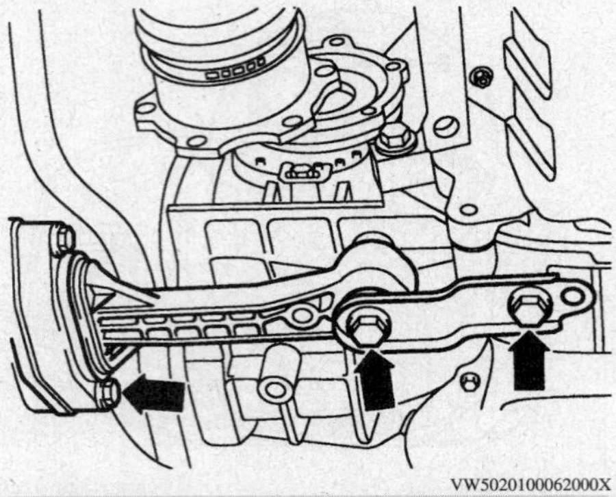

Fig. 14 Pendulum support. New Beetle, 1999–2001 Golf, GTI & Jetta

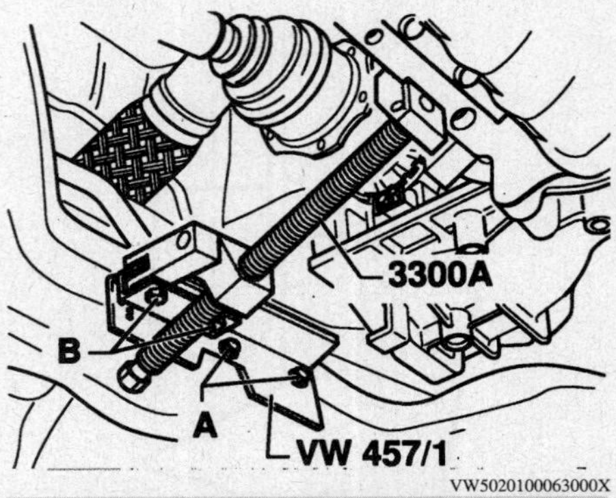

Fig. 15 Transaxle support tool installation. 1999–2001 Golf, GTI & Jetta

7. Disconnect electrical connectors from transaxle.
8. Remove wiring harness from retainer on transaxle and position aside.
9. Remove bracket for power steering hose with retainer for wiring harness from transaxle.
10. Move selector lever to P, then pry off selector lever cable off selector shaft.
11. Remove selector lever cable clip from support bracket, then the selector lever cable.
12. **On models equipped with 2.0L engine,** remove vehicle speed sensor, then the exhaust manifold heat shield.
13. **On all models,** disconnect ground cable from upper engine/transaxle bolt.
14. Disconnect starter motor electrical connectors, then the upper bolt.
15. Clamp off ATF cooler lines using hose clamp tool No. 3094, or equivalent, then seal open lines.
16. Remove upper engine/transaxle bolts.
17. Support engine using support bar tool No. 10-222 A with legs tool No. 10-222 A/1, or equivalent, then lift engine slightly.
18. Raise and support vehicle, then remove lefthand front wheel.
19. Remove center and lefthand noise insulation panels.
20. **On models equipped with 1.9L TDI engine,** remove intake air duct between intake air cooler and turbocharger.
21. **On all models,** remove righthand noise insulation panel.
22. Remove ATF pan protective cover, then the power steering pressure line from starter motor and transaxle.
23. Remove starter motor bolt, then the starter motor.
24. Remove protective cover from engine for righthand CV joint.
25. Disconnect drive shafts at transaxle flanges.
26. Lift righthand drive shaft and secure with wire.
27. Remove pendulum support, then the righthand auxiliary fan.
28. Remove torque converter nut cover.
29. Remove three torque converter nuts using socket tool No. V175, or equivalent.
30. Turn steering to lefthand lock, then mark installation position of axle joint bolts on lefthand control arm.
31. Remove axle joint bolts.
32. Remove lefthand coupling rod from control arm, then turn coupling rod upward.
33. Swing wheel bearing housing outwards, then guide lefthand drive shaft out between subframe and transaxle.
34. Lift drive shaft and secure to strut using suitable wire.
35. Remove pendulum support, **Fig. 14,** then the righthand auxiliary fan.
36. Remove torque converter nut cover, then the three torque converter nuts.
37. Turn steering to lefthand lock, then mark installation position of axle joint bolts on lefthand control arm and remove.
38. Remove lefthand coupling rod from control arm, then turn coupling rod upwards.
39. Swing wheel bearing housing outward, then guide lefthand drive shaft out between subframe and transaxle.
40. Lift drive shaft and secure to strut using suitable wire or rope.
41. Disconnect exhaust at front double clamp, then remove support if required.
42. Remove lefthand engine/transaxle support bolts, then tilt engine by lower lefthand spindle of support bar 2.3 inches.
43. Remove lefthand support from transaxle.
44. Install support rail tool No. VW457/1, or equivalent to both pendulum support bolt holes on subframe.
45. Insert spacers totaling 2.3 inches between subframe and support rail, then install engine support tool No. 3300 A, or equivalent.
46. Tilt transaxle forward using support tool.
47. Support transaxle using jack tool No. VAG 1383 and support tool No. 3282, or equivalents.
48. Place safety support pin on oil pan, then secure to transaxle housing.
49. Turn transaxle flange to right until flat is vertical, then remove lower engine/transaxle bolts.
50. Separate transaxle from engine while pushing torque converter out of drive plate against ATF pump.
51. Carefully lower and remove transaxle from vehicle. Secure torque converter to prevent it from falling out.
52. Reverse procedure to install, noting the following:
    a. Ensure torque converter drive pins engage in ATF pump inner wheel recesses.
    b. Replace selector cable anchor lock washer.
    c. Replace transaxle mount bolts.
    d. Inspect and adjust selector cable if required.
    e. Tighten all bolts and nuts to specifications.

TIGHTENING SPECIFICATIONS

Year	Component	Torque, Ft. Lbs.
1998–2001	Axle Nut (Cabrio & 1998 Golf & Jetta)	②
	Axle Nut (1999–2001 Golf & Jetta)	④
	Axle Nut (New Beetle)	⑤
	Axle Shaft To Transmission Flange Bolts	37
	Ball Join To Control Arm	26
	Cover Plate To Transmission Bolts	11
	Driveshaft Nut	②
	Fluid Level Plug	11
	Front Bracket To Mount Bolts	44
	Ignition Lock Cable Clamp Bolt	53①
	Lefthand Side Bracket To Transaxle Bolts	18
	Lefthand Side Mount To Transaxle Bolts	44
	Rear Transaxle Mount To Body	15③
	Rear Transaxle Mount To Transaxle	30③
	Starter To Transaxle	44
	Torque Converter To Drive Plate Bolts	44
	Transmission To Engine Bolts, M10	44
	Transmission To Engine Bolts, M12	59
	Wheel Lug Bolts	89

① — Inch lbs.
② — Cabrio, Golf III & Jetta III & Passat w/2.0L engine, 195 ft. lbs.; GTI–VR6, Jetta III GLX & Passat w/2.8L engine, 66 ft. lbs. plus an additional 45°.
③ — Plus an additional 90°.
④ — Use a new nut. Torque nut to 221 ft. lbs. Loosen 1 turn. Torque nut to 37 ft. lbs., then rotate nut an additional 30°.
⑤ — Use a new nut. Torque nut to 221 ft. lbs. Loosen ½ turn. Torque nut to 37 ft. lbs., then rotate nut an additional 30°.

01N Transaxle

INDEX

	Page No.
Adjustments	8-173
Ignition Locking Cable	8-173
Selector Lever Cable	8-173
Selector Lever Housing	8-173
Shift Lock Solenoid	8-173
Description	8-172
Identification	8-172
Maintenance	8-172
Transaxle Final Drive Differential	8-172
Transaxle Planetary Components	8-172
Precautions	8-172
Air Bag Systems	8-172
Audio Coded Anti-Theft System	8-172
Battery Ground Cable	8-172
Tightening Specifications	8-174
Transaxle, Replace	8-173

PRECAUTIONS

AIR BAG SYSTEMS

Refer to "Air Bag System Precautions" in the front of this manual for system disarming and arming procedures.

AUDIO CODED ANTI-THEFT SYSTEM

Some models are equipped with an audio anti-theft system that will disable the audio unit when battery power is interrupted. Unless the system is reset the audio unit will not operate.

1. Turn radio On. SAFE and 1000 should be displayed.
2. Enter radio code using first four program station buttons. Security code will appear on display.
3. Depress and hold righthand side of radio righthand or lefthand blocker until anti-theft coding is activated indicated by a brief signal sound.
4. If code number has been entered properly, a diode on front of radio will flash when ignition key is removed.

BATTERY GROUND CABLE

Prior to service, disconnect battery ground cable and isolate as required.

IDENTIFICATION

The manufacturer's code number and transaxle number are located on the top lefthand side of the transaxle, **Fig. 1.** The transaxle identification may also be found on the vehicle data plate.

Refer to **Fig. 2** for transaxle specifications.

DESCRIPTION

This fully automatic 4-speed transaxle is electronically controlled and has a lock-up torque converter. The Transmission Control Module (TCM) monitors signals from the valve body, vehicle speed sensor, malfunction switch, throttle position potentiometer, Engine Control Module (ECM), engine speed sensor, program switch, selector lever lock solenoid, Data Link Connector (DLC), cruise control switch, brake lamp switch, kickdown switch, starter lock-out relay and transmission range display. The TCM uses this information to determine transaxle shift points.

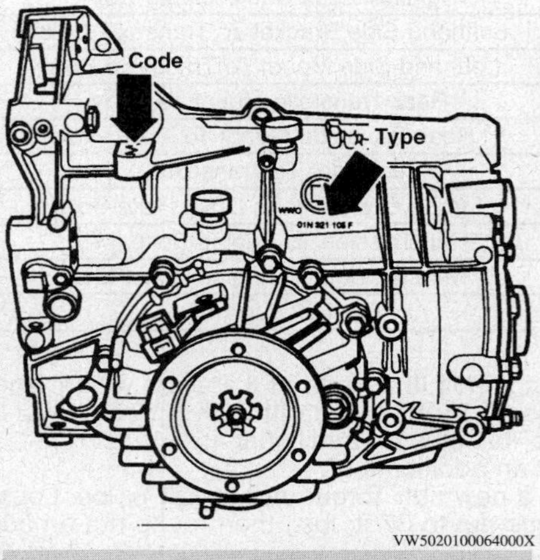

Fig. 1 Transaxle identification

An Emergency Running Mode (ERM) allows operation of the transaxle even when certain systems fail. If ERM is activated while vehicle is running with the shifter in D, 3 or 2, third gear will be hydraulically engaged until engine is stopped. If ERM is activated and the shifter is placed in position 1 or R the transaxle will operate hydraulically in that respective gear. All other transaxle related electronic functions will be disabled.

MAINTENANCE

TRANSAXLE PLANETARY COMPONENTS

Refer to "Lubricant Data & Maintenance Charts" for fluid amount and type.

Fluid Level Inspection

Do not inspect fluid level when transaxle is in emergency mode.

Transaxle fluid must be inspected at normal operating temperature to prevent over- or under-filling.

If fluid shows signs of foaming, allow vehicle to stand for at least 15 minutes, or until foaming subsides, prior to inspecting level.

1. Ensure level reaches at least 20°C mark on dipstick prior to driving vehicle to warm transaxle fluid to perform level inspection.
2. Inspect fluid for contamination. Correct as required.
3. Connect a suitable scan tool as outlined under "Accessing Diagnostic Trouble Codes."
4. Access scan tool function 08 as outlined under "Read Measuring Block Value," then display group 005 and display field 1 to read transaxle fluid temperature.
5. Operate vehicle to warm transaxle fluid to normal operating temperature of 95–113° F.
6. Place vehicle on a level surface with engine idling, apply parking brake, position shift lever in each gear position momentarily, then place in Park position.
7. Remove check plug in transaxle oil pan.
8. If fluid drips out of hole, level is satisfactory.
9. If fluid does not drip out of hole, adjust fluid level as required. Refer to "Lubricant Data Charts" for amount and type.

Fluid Change

1. Raise and support vehicle.
2. Disconnect filler tube from pan, then allow fluid to drain into a suitable container. Discard seal.
3. Remove pan mounting bolts, then the pan.
4. Remove strainer mounting bolts, then the strainer. Discard strainer O-ring seal.
5. Clean strainer and pan with a suitable cleaning fluid. Blow dry only.
6. Install strainer using a new O-ring seal.
7. Install oil pan using a new gasket.
8. Install filler tube to pan using a new gasket.
9. Install drain plug with a new gasket.
10. Fill transaxle with fluid. Refer to "Lubricant Data Charts" for fluid amounts and type, then to "Inspecting Fluid Level."

TRANSAXLE FINAL DRIVE DIFFERENTIAL

Inspecting Fluid Level

1. Raise and support vehicle.
2. Remove differential level check plug located on lefthand side of transaxle on differential housing.
3. Fluid level is proper when level is at bottom level of filler hole.
4. Refer to "Lubricant Data Charts" for fluid amount and type and add as required to proper level.

Automatic transmission			01N					
Transmission	Code letters		DFG		DFH		DFK	
	Manufactured	from to	12.95 12.96		12.95 12.96		02.96 12.96	
Torque converter	Code letters		LADC		LCDC		LCDC	
Valve body	Code letters		LCA		LCA		LCA	
	Manufactured	from to	12.95		12.95		02.96	
Number of plates			Inner	Outer	Inner	Outer	Inner	Outer
	Clutch -K1-		5	5	5	5	5	5
	Clutch -K2-		5	5	5	5	5	5
	Clutch -K3-		5	4	6	5	6	5
	Brake -B1-		5	5	5	5	6	6
	Brake -B2-		6	7	6	7	6	7
Application	Model		Passat 1998 ➤		Passat 1998 ➤		Passat 1998 ➤	
	Engine		1.6 ltr. - 74 kW 1.8 ltr. - 92 kW		1.9 ltr. TDI - 66 kW		1.9 ltr. TDI – 81 kW	

VW5020100065010X

Fig. 2 Transaxle specification table (Part 1 of 6)

Transmission	Code letters		DFG	DFH	DFK
Ratios	1st gear		2.714	2.714	2.714
	2nd gear		1.551	1.441	1.441
	3rd gear		1.000	1.000	1.000
	4th gear		0.679	0.742	0.742
	Reverse gear		2.111	2.884	2.884
Intermediate drive	No. of teeth	Input gear	51	51	51
		Output gear	44	44	44
	Ratio		0.863	0.863	0.863
Final drive	No. of teeth	Drive pinion	9	11	13
		Final drive gear	40	35	38
	Ratio		4.444	3.182	2.920
Drive shaft	Flange Dia. mm		108	108	108

VW5020100065020X

Fig. 2 Transaxle specification table (Part 2 of 6)

Automatic transmission			01N					
Transmission	Code letters		DFL		DFM		DMU	
	Manufactured	from to	01.97		01.97		10.96	
Torque converter	Code letters		LCDC		LCDC		LADC	
Valve body	Code letters		LCA		LCA		LEA	
	Manufactured	from to	12.95		12.95		10.96	
Number of plates			Inner	Outer	Inner	Outer	Inner	Outer
	Clutch -K1-		5	5	5	5	5	5
	Clutch -K2-		5	5	5	5	4	4
	Clutch -K3-		6	5	6	5	5	4
	Brake -B1-		5	5	6	5	5	5
	Brake -B2-		6	7	6	7	6	7
Application	Model		Passat 1998 ➤		Passat 1998 ➤		Passat 1998 ➤	
	Engine		2.6 ltr. - 110 kW (142 hp)		2.8 ltr. - 128 kW (171 hp)		1.6 ltr. - 74 kW (96 hp) 1.8 ltr. - 92 kW (119 hp)	

VW5020100065030X

Fig. 2 Transaxle specification table (Part 3 of 6)

Transmission	Code letters		DFL	DFM	DMU
Ratios	1st gear		2.714	2.714	2.714
	2nd gear		1.441	1.441	1.551
	3rd gear		1.000	1.000	1.000
	4th gear		0.742	0.742	0.679
	Reverse gear		2.884	2.884	2.111
Intermediate drive	No. of teeth	Input gear	51	51	51
		Output gear	44	44	44
	Ratio		0.863	0.863	0.863
Final drive	No. of teeth	Drive pinion	10	11	9
		Final drive gear	37	38	40
	Ratio		3.700	3.450	4.444
Drive shaft	Flange dia. mm (in.)		108 (4.25)	108 (4.25)	108 (4.25)

VW5020100065040X

Fig. 2 Transaxle specification table (Part 4 of 6)

5. Install differential level check plug.

Replacing Fluid

Differential fluid is of a permanent fill type and is not normally replaced, no provision has been made for draining.

Refer to "Lubricant Data Chart" for fluid amount and type.

ADJUSTMENTS

IGNITION LOCKING CABLE

1. Remove center console, then place selector lever in "N" position.
2. Remove bolts retaining locking cable to selector lever housing.
3. Loosen locking cable adjustment bolt, then turn ignition On.
4. Place a. 059 inch feeler gauge between locking flap and locking pin.
5. Adjust locking cable so that locking pin is pushed against feeler gauge, then tighten adjustment nut.
6. After operating several times, clearance between locking pin and locking flap should be. 047–.067 inch.
7. Move selector lever to "N" position, then install locking cable to selector lever housing. **Cable must be free of kinks.**
8. Install center console.
9. Ensure proper operation of locking cable.

SELECTOR LEVER CABLE

1. Raise and support vehicle, then remove components required to access shift cable.
2. Place selector lever in "P" position, then loosen nut at clamp for selector lever cable.
3. Move selector shaft lever at transaxle rearward as far as stop to "P" position. Ensure park pawl is engaged.
4. Tighten selector lever cable nut.
5. Turn ignition On, then depress and hold brake pedal.
6. Shift selector lever through all ranges and ensure selector lever position agrees with selector lever indicator on instrument cluster.

SELECTOR LEVER HOUSING

1. Place selector lever in Neutral position.
2. Install selector lever housing with nuts loosely secured.
3. Position selector lever housing so that selector lever travel is equal when moving from N to D and N to R.
4. Tighten selector lever housing nuts.

SHIFT LOCK SOLENOID

1. Place selector lever in R position.
2. Measure clearance between selector lever and solenoid using a feeler gauge.
3. Clearance should be. 024–.055 inch, adjust solenoid by loosening mounting screws and positioning for proper clearance.

TRANSAXLE

REPLACE

1. Remove engine cover, then assemble adapter tool No. 10-222 A/3, or equivalent, for front spindle on support bar.
2. Support engine and transaxle using support bar tool No. 10-222 A with legs tool No. 10-222 A/1, or equivalents.
3. Raise and support vehicle, then remove front wheels.
4. Remove noise insulation tray, then the bracket.
5. Disconnect electrical connectors from transaxle, then remove wiring harness clamp.
6. Disconnect speedometer connector at transaxle, then remove front exhaust pipe with catalytic convertor.
7. Remove righthand drive shaft and selector lever cable protective plates.
8. Remove righthand bonded rubber protective plate on transaxle.
9. Remove ATF lines and position aside.
10. Disconnect drive shafts at flanges and secure using suitable wire.
11. Remove starter motor bolts, then the starter motor.
12. Remove nut from torque converter, then the lower transaxle bolts.
13. Install transaxle mount tool No. 3282, or equivalent onto engine/transaxle jack tool No. VAG 1383A, or equivalent.
14. Support transaxle using jack and mount.

Automatic transmission			01N					
Transmission	Code letters		DMV		DMX			
	Manufactured	from to	01.97		10.96			
Torque converter	Code letters		LCDC		LCDC			
Valve body	Code letters		LEA		LEA			
	Manufactured	from to	10.96		10.96			
Number of plates			Inner	Outer	Inner	Outer	Inner	Outer
	Clutch -K1-		5	5	5	5		
	Clutch -K2-		5	5	5	5		
	Clutch -K3-		6	5	6	5		
	Brake -B1-		5	5	6	5		
	Brake -B2-		5	6	5	6		
Application	Model		Passat 1998 ➤		Passat 1998 ➤			
	Engine		1.9 ltr. TDI - 66 kW (85 hp)		1.9 ltr. TDI – 81 kW (105 hp)			

VW5020100065050X

Fig. 2 Transaxle specification table (Part 5 of 6)

Transmission	Code letters		DMV	DMX	
Ratios	1st gear		2.714	2.714	
	2nd gear		1.441	1.441	
	3rd gear		1.000	1.000	
	4th gear		0.742	0.742	
	Reverse gear		2.884	2.884	
Intermediate drive	No. of teeth	Input gear	51	51	
		Output gear	44	44	
	Ratio		0.863	0.863	
Final drive	No. of teeth	Drive pinion	11	13	
		Final drive gear	35	38	
	Ratio		3.180	2.920	
Drive shaft	Flange dia. mm (in.)		108 (42.5)	108 (42.5)	

VW5020100065060X

Fig. 2 Transaxle specification table (Part 6 of 6)

15. Align adjustment plate parallel to transaxle, then lock safety support on transaxle.
16. Move selector lever to Park position, then pull selector lever cable of selector lever shaft.
17. Remove bolt on selector lever cable support bracket, then the selector lever cable.
18. Remove righthand transaxle support with bonded rubber mount, then the lefthand bonded rubber mount.
19. Lower the rear of engine/transaxle assembly slightly, then remove upper transaxle bolts.
20. Separate transaxle from engine while pressing torque converter out of drive plate against ATF pump.
21. Carefully lower and remove transaxle from vehicle.
22. Secure torque converter to prevent it from falling.
23. Reverse procedure to install. Tighten bolts to specifications.

TIGHTENING SPECIFICATIONS

Year	Component	Torque, Ft. Lbs.
1998–2001	Crossmember To Body	18
	Differential Fluid Check Plug	18
	Driveshaft To Flange 8 mm Bolts	30
	Driveshaft To Flange 10 mm Bolts	57
	Driveshaft Heat Shield	18
	Filler Pipe	30
	Flanged Shaft Retaining Bolts	22
	Fluid Lines	18
	Fluid Pan	84①
	Selector Lever Cable	17
	Starter Motor	48
	Torque Converter To Drive Plate	63
	Transaxle Fluid Check Plug	11
	Transaxle Support to Body	82
	Transaxle To Engine 10 mm Bolts	33
	Transaxle To Engine 12 mm Bolts	48
	Transaxle Support To Transaxle	30
	Wheel Lug Bolts	89

① — Inch Lbs.

01V Transaxle

INDEX

	Page No.
Adjustments	8-176
Ignition Lock Cable	8-176
Propeller Shaft	8-176
Selector Lever Cable	8-176
Description	8-175
Identification	8-175
Maintenance	8-175
Fluid Change	8-176
Fluid Inspection	8-175
Precautions	8-175
Air Bag Systems	8-175
Audio Coded Anti-Theft System	8-175
Battery Ground Cable	8-175
Tightening Specifications	8-179
Transaxle, Replace	8-177
AWD Models	8-177
FWD Models	8-177

PRECAUTIONS

AIR BAG SYSTEMS

Refer to "Air Bag System Precautions" in the front of this manual for system disarming and arming procedures.

AUDIO CODED ANTI-THEFT SYSTEM

Some models are equipped with an audio anti-theft system that will disable the audio unit when battery power is interrupted. Unless the system is reset the audio unit will not operate.

1. Turn radio On. SAFE and 1000 should be displayed.
2. Enter radio code using first four program station buttons. Security code will appear on display.
3. Depress and hold righthand side of radio righthand or lefthand blocker until anti-theft coding is activated indicated by a brief signal sound.
4. If code number has been entered properly, a diode on front of radio will flash when ignition key is removed.

BATTERY GROUND CABLE

Prior to service, disconnect battery ground cable and isolate as required.

IDENTIFICATION

The transaxle identification code and serial number are located on a plate attached to the lower front of the transaxle, **Figs. 1 and 2.**

The model number and transaxle code may also be found on the vehicle data plate.

Refer to **Fig. 3** for transaxle specifications.

DESCRIPTION

This transaxle is an electronically controlled fully automatic 5 speed with a lock-up torque converter. The differential uses an electronically controlled clutch for traction control. The transaxle control electronics offer an adaptive program to suit various driving habits and conditions. The transaxle control system also interacts with the vehicle ABS system.

On AWD models, this transaxle has a permanently engaged Torsen third differential mounted to the rear of the transaxle in an attached housing. This differential is used to drive a rear axle differential.

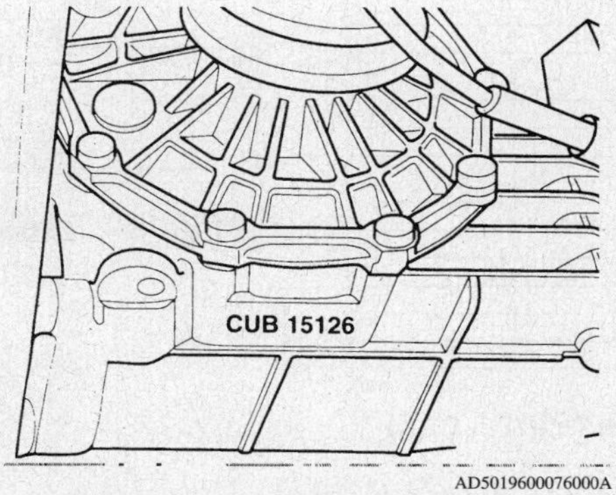

Fig. 1 Transaxle data plate location

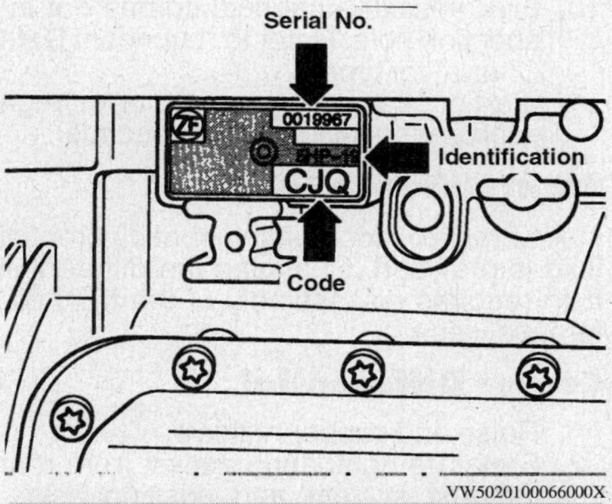

Fig. 2 Transaxle code location

An Emergency Running Mode (ERM) allows operation of the transaxle even when certain systems fail. When ERM is active the shift indicator segments in the instrument cluster will all be lit.

If ERM is activated while vehicle is running, fourth gear will be engaged. Park and neutral positions are available and reverse gear will function. All other transaxle related electronic functions will be disabled.

MAINTENANCE

This transaxle uses different lubricants in the planetary and differential sections. Care should be used to prevent intermixing of lubricants

Refer to "Lubricant Data & Maintenance Charts" for fluid amounts and types.

FLUID INSPECTION

Planetary

Do not inspect fluid level when transaxle is in emergency mode.

Transaxle fluid must be inspected at normal operating temperature to prevent over or under filling.

If fluid shows signs of foaming, allow vehicle to stand for at least 15 minutes or until foaming subsides prior to inspecting level.

1. Ensure sufficient fluid is in transaxle to prevent damage during inspection procedure.
2. Connect a suitable scan tool.
3. Access scan tool function 08 (transaxle electronics), then display group 04 and display field 1 to read transaxle fluid temperature.
4. Operate vehicle to warm transaxle fluid to normal operating temperature of 95–113° F.
5. Place vehicle on a level surface with engine idling, apply parking brake, position shift lever in each gear position momentarily, then place in Park position.
6. Remove transaxle pan inspection plug, **Fig. 4.**
7. If fluid level is proper, a small quantity will flow out.
8. Adjust fluid level as required as follows:
   a. Insert nozzle of a suitable fluid pump through inspection hole and through port of fluid deflector cap.
   b. Add fluid until fluid flows from inspection hole.
9. Refer to "Lubrication Data Charts" for fluid amount and type.
10. Install filler plug with a new sealing gasket.

Front Differential

1. Raise and support vehicle.
2. Remove filler plug from front differential case. Discard seal.
3. Fluid level should be level with bottom of filler hole.
4. Add suitable fluid as required. Refer to "Lubricant Data Charts" for fluid amount and type.
5. Install filler plug with a new seal ring.

Center Differential

1. Raise and support vehicle.

Automatic transmission			01V		
Transmission	Code letters		DDT		
	Manufactured	from to	04.97		
Torque converter	Code letters		M28		
Application	Model		Passat 1998 ➤		
	Engine		1.8 ltr. - 110 kW (148 hp)		
Ratios	1st gear		3.665		
	2nd gear		1.999		
	3rd gear		1.407		
	4th gear		1.000		
	5th gear		0.742		
	Reverse gear		4.096		

VW5020100067010X

Fig. 3 Transaxle specification table (Part 1 of 5)

Transmission	Code letters		DDT		
Intermediate drive	No. of teeth	Input gear	29		
		Output gear	35		
	Ratio		1.207		
Final drive	No. of teeth	Drive pinion	11		
		Crown wheel	34		
	Ratio		3.091		

VW5020100067020X

Fig. 3 Transaxle specification table (Part 2 of 5)

Automatic transmission			01V		
Transmission	Code letters		DRD		
	Manufactured	from to	08.97		
Torque converter	Code letters		F31		
Application	Model		Passat 1998 ➤		
	Engine		2.8 ltr. - 142 kW (190 hp)		
Ratios	1st gear		3.665		
	2nd gear		1.999		
	3rd gear		1.407		
	4th gear		1.000		
	5th gear		0.742		
	Reverse gear		4.096		

VW5020100067030X

Fig. 3 Transaxle specification table (Part 3 of 5)

Transmission	Code letters		DRD		
Intermediate drive	No. of teeth	Input gear	29		
		Output gear	35		
	Ratio		1.207		
Final drive	No. of teeth	Drive pinion	11		
		Crown wheel	30		
	Ratio		2.727		

VW5020100067040X

Fig. 3 Transaxle specification table (Part 4 of 5)

2. Separate righthand catalyst from rear exhaust system and position aside. Discard self locking bolts and nuts.
3. Remove filler plug from rear differential case. Discard filler plug.
4. Fluid level should be level with bottom of filler hole.
5. Add suitable fluid as required. Refer to "Lubricant Data Charts" for fluid amount and type.
6. Install new filler plug.
7. Install righthand catalyst to exhaust system using new self locking nuts and bolts.

FLUID CHANGE

Planetary

Transaxle fluid is considered lifetime fill under normal operating conditions. Fluid change is only recommended at 30,000 mile intervals when vehicle is operated under severe conditions such as under extremely high temperatures, trailer towing, continuous mountain driving or continuous stop and go driving.

Use only the recommended fluid or it's equivalent.

1. Raise and support vehicle.
2. Remove transaxle fluid pan drain plug, then allow fluid to drain into a suitable container. Discard seal.
3. Remove pan mounting bolts, then pan.
4. Remove strainer mounting bolts then strainer. Discard strainer O-ring seal.
5. Clean strainer and pan with a suitable cleaning fluid, blow dry only.
6. Install strainer with a new O-ring seal.
7. Install oil pan with a new gasket.
8. Install drain plug with a new gasket.
9. Remove inspection plug, then guide reservoir pump tool No. VAG 1924, or equivalent, through opening in deflector cap.
10. Fill transaxle until fluid comes out inspection hole. Refer to "Lubricant Data Charts" for type.
11. Start engine and shift selector through each gear position for 10 seconds.

Front Differential

No provision for draining front differential fluid is provided. Changing the differential fluid requires disassembly of the front differential case.

Center Differential

1. Raise and support vehicle.
2. Separate righthand catalyst from rear exhaust system and position aside. Discard self locking bolts and nuts.
3. Remove drain plug from rear differential case and allow fluid to drain into a suitable container. Discard drain plug.
4. Remove and discard filler plug, then install new drain plug.
5. Fill Center differential using suitable fluid until fluid is level with edge of filler hole. Refer to "Lubricant Data Charts" for fluid amount and type.
6. Install new filler plug.
7. Install righthand catalyst to exhaust system using new self locking nuts and bolts.
8. Road test vehicle to allow Torsen differential to fill, then inspect fluid level as outlined under "Inspecting Lubricant Levels."

ADJUSTMENTS

IGNITION LOCK CABLE

1. Ensure cable is properly attached at both ends and is routed free of stress.
2. Loosen mounting bolt until cable clamp can be moved back and forth in direction.
3. Install adjustment gauge tool No. 3352, or equivalent, between lever and cable eye.
4. Pull cable in direction of arrow, then tighten bolt.
5. Inspect function of locking system as follows:
   a. Turn ignition lock On. Shifter must move smoothly out of park with a force of 5.6 lbs. or less applied to gearshift button.
   b. It must not be possible to remove ignition key unless shift lever is in P position.
   c. With shifter in P position, ignition switch must turn freely to key withdrawal position and key must slide easily from ignition.
   d. With ignition key withdrawn it must not be possible to shift out of P position.

PROPELLER SHAFT

Refer to "Propeller Shaft, Replace" under "In-Vehicle Service" for procedures.

SELECTOR LEVER CABLE

1. Remove retaining clip from selector cable at selector shaft arm.
2. Disconnect cable from selector shaft arm.
3. Move selector lever from P position to 2 position, then back, lever must move smoothly.
4. Ensure selector shaft of transaxle is in park position (fully rearward, park pawl engaged).
5. Shift cable socket should fit free of stress onto ball of selector shaft arm.
6. Loosen cable securing plate mounting bolt at transaxle support as required.
7. Adjust cable for a stress free fit, then tighten securing plate mounting bolt.
8. Inspect gear selector system for free movement.

Automatic transmission		01V		
transmission	Code letters	DSJ	DSS	
	Manufactured from to	04.97	05.97	
Torque converter	Code letters	A33	F31	
application	Model	Passat 1998 ➤	Passat 1998 ➤	
	Engine	1.8 ltr. - 110 kW (150 hp)	2.3 ltr. - 110 kW (150 hp)	
Ratios	1st gear	3.665	3.665	
	2nd gear	1.999	1.999	
	3rd gear	1.407	1.407	
	4th gear	1.000	1.000	
	5th gear	0.742	0.742	
	Reverse gear	4.096	4.096	

VW5020100067050X

Fig. 3 Transaxle specification table (Part 5 of 5)

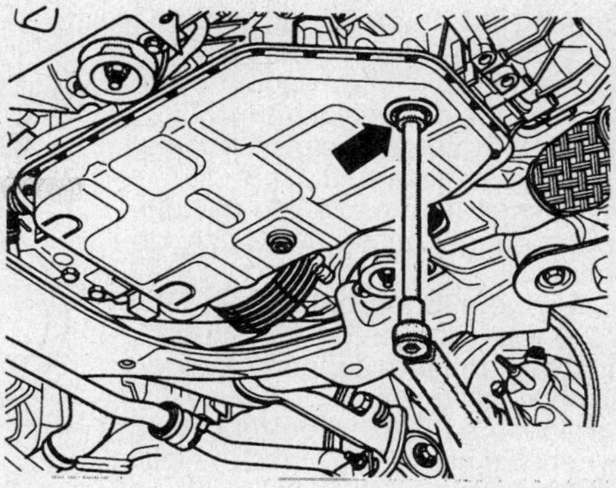

VW5020100068000X

Fig. 4 Transaxle inspection plug

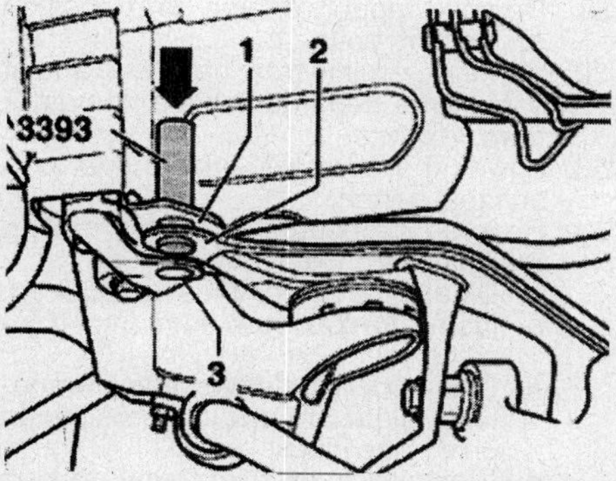

VW5029800069000X

Fig. 5 Mandrel tool No. 3393 installation. AWD Models

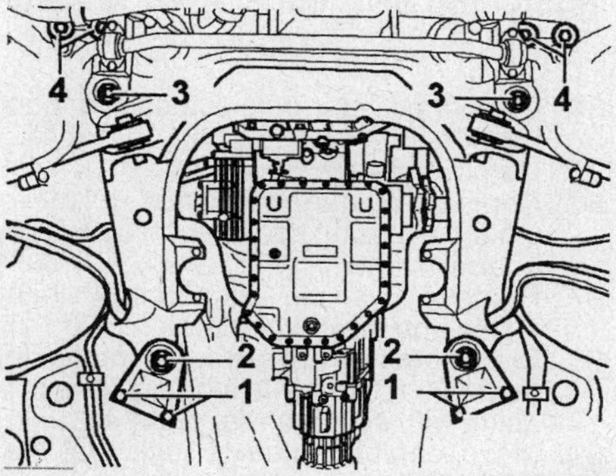

VW5029800070000X

Fig. 6 Subframe bolt removal sequence. AWD Models

TRANSAXLE

REPLACE

FWD Models

1. Remove engine cover.
2. Support engine and transaxle using support bar tool No. 10-222 A with legs tool No. 10-222 A/, or equivalents.
3. Raise and support vehicle, then remove front wheels.
4. Remove noise insulation tray, then the bracket.
5. Remove axle shaft noise insulation from wheelhousing.
6. Remove righthand axle shaft protective plate.
7. Remove driveshafts as outlined under "Front Wheel Drive Axles."
8. Disconnect electrical connectors from transaxle.
9. Disconnect speedometer connector at transaxle.
10. Mark position of selector lever cable support bracket to transaxle housing, then unbolt support bracket.
11. Remove front exhaust pipe.
12. Disconnect ATF lines from transaxle, then position aside. Plug all open lines.
13. Remove selector lever cable from selector shaft lever.
14. Remove starter motor bolts, then the starter motor.
15. Unbolt torque converter from drive plate using socket tool No. V175, or equivalent.
16. Remove lower transaxle bolts.
17. Support transaxle using support tool No. 3282 with adjusting plate tool No. 3282/19 and engine/transaxle jack tool No. VAG 1383, or equivalents.
18. Remove righthand bonded rubber mount protective plate, then the mount.
19. Remove lefthand transaxle support with bonded rubber mount.
20. Before loosening subframe, ensure holes align on both sides using mandrel tool No. 3393, or equivalent.
21. Remove rear and center bolts from subframe. **Do not remove front four bolts.**
22. Loosen front four bolts three full turns. **Rear of subframe will drop approximately six inches.**
23. Lower the rear of engine and transaxle slightly, then remove upper transaxle bolts.
24. Separate transaxle from engine while sliding torque converter against ATF pump.
25. Carefully lower transaxle and remove from vehicle.
26. Secure torque converter to prevent it from falling.
27. Reverse procedure to install, noting the following:
    a. Replace subframe to body and axle shaft bolts.
    b. Tighten all bolts and nuts to specifications.

AWD Models

1. Remove engine cover.
2. Remove air cleaner cover.
3. Remove air intake duct between lock carrier and air cleaner.
4. Disconnect EVAP canister purge regulator valve electrical connector and remove from bracket.
5. Disconnect MAF sensor electrical connector.
6. Remove intake hose from intake manifold.
7. Remove air cleaner upper section.
8. Remove cooling system expansion tank and position aside.

9. Disconnect HO_2S electrical connectors.
10. Remove lifting eye from engine sling tool No. 2024 A, or equivalent.
11. Install pin into center hole of engine sling and secure with split pin.
12. Insert lifting beam pin eye into spindle of support bridge tool No. 10-222 A, or equivalent.
13. Install engine support bridge tool No. 10-222 A with bracket tool No. 10-222 A/1 for engine and support engine/transaxle in this position.
14. Loosen drive axle to wheel hub bolt and wheel lug nuts while vehicle is still on the ground.
15. Raise and support vehicle.
16. Remove front tires and wheels.
17. Remove noise insulation panel and bracket.
18. Remove drive axle noise insulation from front wheelhousings.
19. Remove drive axle protective plates.
20. Remove drive axle assemblies.
21. Remove torque rod support mounting bolts.
22. Disconnect Vehicle Speed Sensor (VSS) electrical connector.
23. Remove engine speed (RPM) sensor from transaxle.
24. Disconnect electrical connector from multi-function switch.
25. Rotate locking lever and disconnect transaxle wiring harness electrical connector.
26. Loosen exhaust system clamps as required.
27. Remove front exhaust system together with Three Way Catalytic Converter (TWC).
28. Remove lower transaxle to engine bolts.
29. Remove alternator vent hose.
30. Remove ATF line bracket from engine oil pan.
31. Position a suitable drain pan below ATF cooler line fittings.
32. Disconnect ATF lines at cooler and remove bracket.
33. Remove starter mounting bolt on transaxle side.

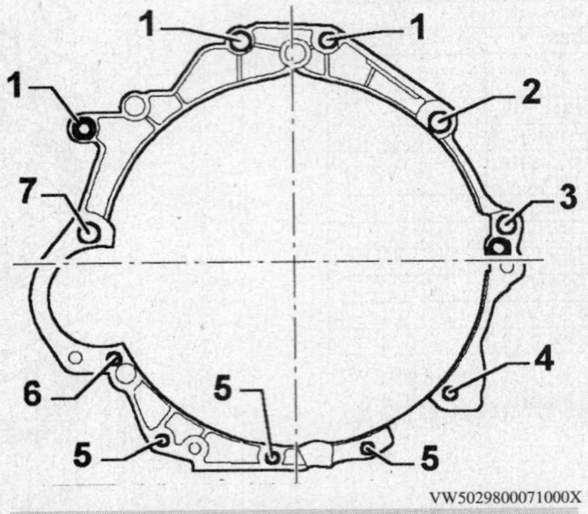

Fig. 7 Transaxle to engine bolt tightening sequence. AWD Models

34. Disconnect starter electrical connectors.
35. Remove starter.
36. Remove torque converter to drive plate bolts using socket tool No. V/175, or equivalent.
37. Remove vehicle underbody heat shield and the cover plate.
38. Disconnect driveshaft from transaxle, then push back to its stop and position aside with suitable wire or rope.
39. Move engine/transaxle jack tool No. VAG1383 A together with transaxle support tool No. 3282, or equivalents, under transaxle.
40. Remove righthand mount protective plate on transaxle support.
41. Remove righthand transaxle support together with mount.
42. Remove lefthand mount protective plate on transaxle support.
43. Remove lefthand transaxle support together with mount.
44. Remove selector lever cable protective plate.
45. Mark position of selector lever cable to transaxle housing support bracket.
46. Unbolt support bracket, then remove selector lever cable from selector shaft lever.
47. Ensure holes 1 and 2, **Fig. 5,** are aligned on both sides of vehicle before loosening subframe. Use mandrel tool No. 3393, or equivalent. If holes are not aligned, inspect wheel alignment after tightening subframe mounting bolts.
48. Remove and discard bolts 1 and 2, **Fig. 6,** at rear of subframe, then bolts 3 at front of subframe on both sides of vehicle.
49. Loosen bolts 4 on each side of vehicle three full turns. **Rear end of subframe will drop by approximately six inches when bolts are loosened.**
50. Lower the rear of engine/transaxle assembly slightly using jack.
51. Remove upper engine to transaxle connecting bolts.
52. Separate engine from transaxle and at same time separate torque converter from flexplate.
53. Lower the transaxle and move to a suitable bench.
54. Reverse procedure to install, noting the following:
    a. Clean ATF cooler lines as required.
    b. Install torque converter into transaxle.
    c. Ensure dowel sleeves and intermediate plate are properly positioned on engine block.
    d. Clean all locking material residue from threaded holes in drive flange at rear of transaxle using a suitable tap.
    e. Align transaxle to engine.
    f. Install upper transaxle to engine bolts.
    g. Tighten transaxle to engine bolts in sequence, **Fig. 7. Torque** bolts 1, 2, 3, 6 and 7 to 48 ft. lbs. **Torque** bolts 4 and 5 to 33 ft. lbs.
    h. Tighten all bolts and nuts to specifications.
    i. Bring engine and transaxle to operating temperature, then inspect ATF level and correct as required.

TIGHTENING SPECIFICATIONS

Year	Component	Torque, Ft. Lbs.
1998–2001	Bracket For Oil Lines	84①
	Bracket To Starter	84①
	Crossmember To Body	18
	Drive Axle To Drive Flange	57
	Drive Axle To Wheel Hub M14 Bolt	85③
	Drive Axle To Wheel Hub M16 Bolt	140③
	Driveshaft To Transaxle	59
	Engine Mount To Subframe	30
	Heat Shield For Driveshaft To Transaxle	18
	Heat Shield Under Multi-Function Switch	84①
	Multi-Function Switch	71
	Shield For Drive Axle	17
	Subframe To Body M8 Bolt	17
	Subframe To Body M10 Bolts	44
	Subframe To Body M12 Bolt	81②
	Torque Arm To Long Member	30
	Torque Converter To Flex Plate	63
	Transaxle Mount To Subframe	30
	Transaxle Support To Subframe	30
	Transaxle To Engine Bolts	④
	Wheel Lug Nuts	89

① — Inch lbs.
② — Rotate an additional 90°.
③ — Rotate an additional 180°.
④ — Refer to "Transaxle, Replace" for sequence & specifications.

Front Wheel Drive Axles

INDEX

	Page No.
Driveshaft, Replace	8-180
EuroVan & 1998 Golf, GTI & Jetta	8-180
New Beetle & 1999–2001 Golf, GTI & Jetta	8-180
Driveshaft Service	8-181
Constant Velocity Joint Boot	8-182
Inner Constant Velocity Joint	8-182
Outer Constant Velocity Joint	8-181
Tuned Absorber (Balance Weight), Replace	8-181
Precautions	8-180
Air Bag Systems	8-180
Audio Coded Anti-Theft System	8-180
Battery Ground Cable	8-180
Tightening Specifications	8-184

PRECAUTIONS

AIR BAG SYSTEMS

Do not use computer memory saver tool on air bag equipped models. Using the tool will keep the air bag system charged and may cause accidental air bag unit activation.

Refer to "Air Bag System Precautions" in the front of this manual for system disarming and arming procedures.

BATTERY GROUND CABLE

Prior to service, disconnect battery ground cable and isolate as required.

AUDIO CODED ANTI-THEFT SYSTEM

Some models are equipped with a radio anti-theft system that will disable the system when battery power is interrupted. Unless the system is reset the radio will not operate.

1. Turn radio On. SAFE and 1000 should be displayed.
2. Enter radio code using first four program station buttons. Security code will appear on display.
3. Depress and hold righthand side of radio righthand or lefthand blocker until anti-theft coding is activated indicated by a brief signal sound.
4. If code number has been entered properly, a diode on front of radio will flash when ignition key is removed.

DRIVESHAFT

REPLACE

EuroVan & 1998 Golf, GTI & Jetta

1. Remove drive axle retaining nut from wheel assembly while vehicle is still on ground.
2. Raise and support vehicle, then remove wheel.
3. Mark position of bolts attaching ball joints to control arms, then remove bolts and separate ball joint from control arm.
4. Remove drive axle to transaxle drive flange attaching bolts.
5. Mount puller tool No. 3283, or equivalent, onto hub assembly and press axle shaft out of hub. **Do not flex CV or tripod joints more than 25° from their original angles.**
6. Remove axle shaft from vehicle.
7. Reverse procedure to install, noting the following:
   a. **On models equipped with base suspension,** apply locking compound part No. D 185 400 A2, or equivalent to axle shaft splines in two 3 MM beads.
   b. **On all models,** tighten all bolts and nuts to specifications.

New Beetle & 1999-2001 Golf, GTI & Jetta

1. Remove drive axle retaining nut while vehicle is still on ground.
2. Raise and support vehicle, then remove tire and wheel.
3. **On New Beetle models,** proceed as follows:
   a. Remove noise insulator panel retainers, then the insulators.
   b. **On models equipped with 1.9L engine,** remove intake air duct between charge air cooler and turbocharger.
4. **On all models,** mark position of bolts attaching ball joints to control arms, then remove bolts and separate ball joint from control arm. Discard bolts.
5. Remove drive axle to transaxle drive flange attaching bolts.
6. Mount puller tool No. 3283, or equivalent, onto hub assembly and press axle shaft out of hub. **Do not flex CV or tripod joints more than 25° from their original angles.**
7. **On models equipped with automatic transaxle,** proceed as follows:
   a. Remove pendulum support mounting bolts, **Fig. 1.**
   b. Push engine and transaxle assembly forward using a suitable pry bar.
8. **On all models,** remove axle shaft from vehicle.
9. Reverse procedure to install, noting the following:
   a. Remove all paint residue and corrosion from outer joint splines.
   b. Coat outer joint splines, threads and hub splines with suitable oil.
   c. Coat hub nut contact surface and threads with suitable oil.
   d. Install axle shaft with outer joint as

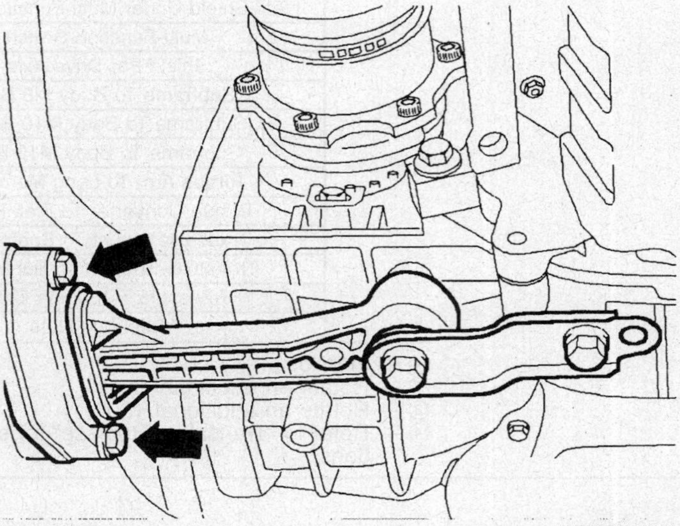

Fig. 1 Pendulum support mounting bolt removal. Models w/A/T

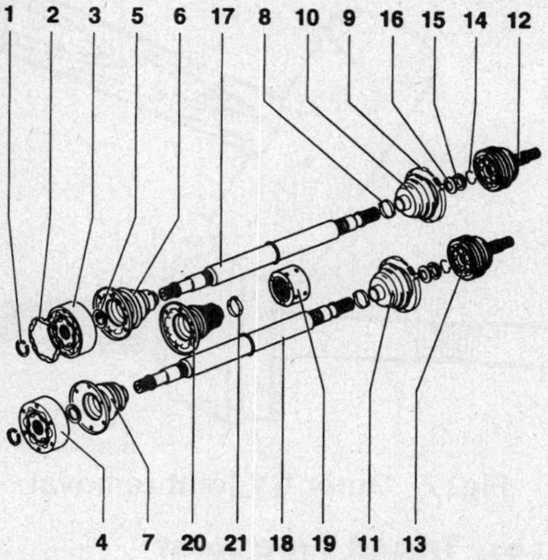

1. Circlip
2. Gasket
3. Inner CV Joint (100mm)
4. Inner CV Joint (94mm)
5. Dished Washer
6. Inner Boot (100mm)
7. Inner Boot (94mm)
8. Clamp
9. Clamp
10. Outer Boot (90mm)
11. Outer Boot (81mm)
12. Outer CV Joint (90mm)
13. Outer CV Joint (81mm)
14. Snap Ring
15. Thrust Washer
16. Dished Washer
17. Axle Shaft
18. Axle Shaft
19. Balance Weight
20. Inner Boot (100mm)
21. Clamp

VW3039300011000X

Fig. 2 Exploded view of driveshaft. 1998 Cabrio, Golf III, GTI & Jetta III

far inward as possible.

e. Connect ball joint to control arm with new bolts properly aligned with marks made during disassembly.
f. Tighten all bolts and nuts to specifications.

DRIVESHAFT SERVICE

When servicing driveshafts, refer to **Figs. 2 through 5** for component location and identification.

The surface of the axle shaft is covered with a special coating designed to prevent stress cracks from forming due to rust and abrasion. **Avoid damaging this surface while servicing unit.**

TUNED ABSORBER (BALANCE WEIGHT), REPLACE

1998 CABRIO, GOLF III, GTI & JETTA III

1. Raise and support vehicle.
2. Remove axle as outlined under "Driveshaft, Replace."
3. Remove drift pin securing both halves, then the absorber (weight).
4. Ensure axle shaft paint and friction tape on I.D. of weight are in good condition.
5. Refer to **Fig. 6,** then position and install balance weight so dimension (a) is 21.260–21.340 inches.
6. Reverse procedure to install. Tighten bolts and nuts to specifications.

OUTER CONSTANT VELOCITY JOINT

REPLACEMENT

1. Remove large boot clamp, then slide

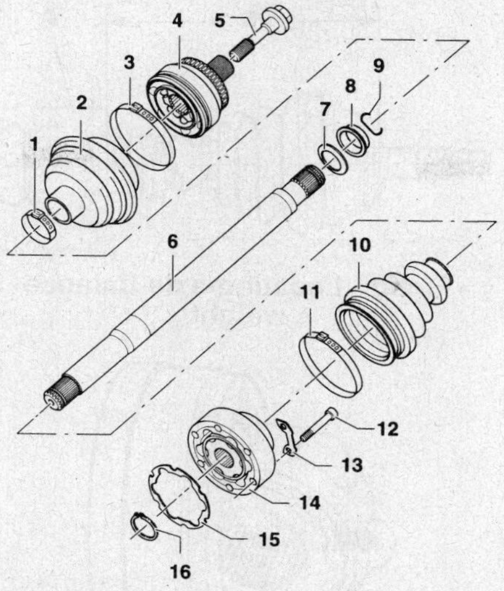

1. Hose Clip
2. Boot, Outer Constant Velocity Joint
3. Hose Clip
4. Outer Constant Velocity Joint
5. Hex Bolt
6. Drive Shaft
7. Dished Washer
8. Thrust Washer
9. Circlip
10. Inner Constant Velocity Joint Boot
11. Hose Clip
12. Allen Head Multi-Point Bolt, 59 ft. lbs.
13. Backing Plate
14. Inner Constant Velocity Joint
15. Gasket
16. Circlip

VW3039900026000X

Fig. 3 Exploded view of driveshaft. EuroVan

boot back from joint.

2. Clean area where shaft enters joint and determine whether joint has circlip or internal snap ring.
3. **On models using circlip joint retention,** proceed as follows:
   a. Clamp axle shaft into a suitable soft jaw vise.
   b. Expand and hold circlip using suitable circlip pliers.
   c. Tap on inner race of joint to start joint off axle spline using a suitable soft face hammer.
   d. Pull and tap to remove joint from shaft. Note position of dished washer and thrust washer for later assembly.
   e. Remove and discard circlip.
4. **On models using internal snap ring joint retention,** proceed as follows:
   a. Clamp axle shaft into a suitable soft jaw vise.
   b. Hold joint parallel to shaft, then strike body of joint, **Fig. 7,** with a suitable soft face hammer to unseat internal snap ring.
   c. Pull and tap to remove joint from shaft. Note position of dished washer and thrust washer for later assembly.
   d. Remove and discard snap ring from axle shaft.

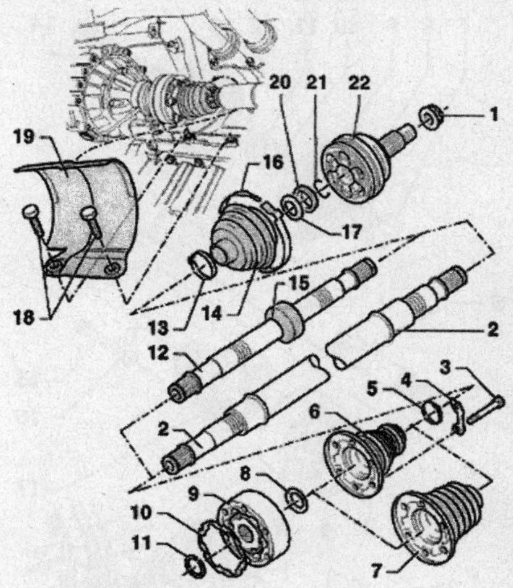

1. Hub nut
2. Tubular axle shaft
3. Plate bolt
4. Plate
5. Clamp
6. Polyelastomer inner boot (Less vent hole)
7. Rubber inner boot (w/vent hole)
8. Spring washer
9. Inner CV joint
10. Gasket
11. Circlip
12. Solid axle shaft
13. Clamp
14. CV joint boot
15. Vibration damper
16. Clamp
17. Spring washer
18. Bolt
19. Heat shield
20. Thrust washer
21. Circlip
22. Outer CV joint

VW3039900028000X

Fig. 4 Exploded view of driveshaft. New Beetle & 1999–2001 Cabrio, Golf, GTI & Jetta

5. **On all models,** reverse procedure to install, noting the following:
   a. Install new snap ring or circlip.
   b. Clean and inspect boot and shaft splines for damage.
   c. Ensure boot and joint are packed with proper quantity of suitable CV joint grease.

SERVICE

1. Clean joint thoroughly.
2. Mark position of ball hub in relation to cage and housing prior to disassembling.
3. Pivot and remove ball hub and cage, then remove balls, **Fig. 8. Do not interchange balls from one cage with balls from another.**
4. Turn cage until two rectangular openings are even with joint edge, **Fig. 9,** then remove cage from the hub.
5. Turn hub until one segment can be pushed into rectangular opening of cage, then tilt hub out of cage. Inspect housing, hub, cage and balls for pitting

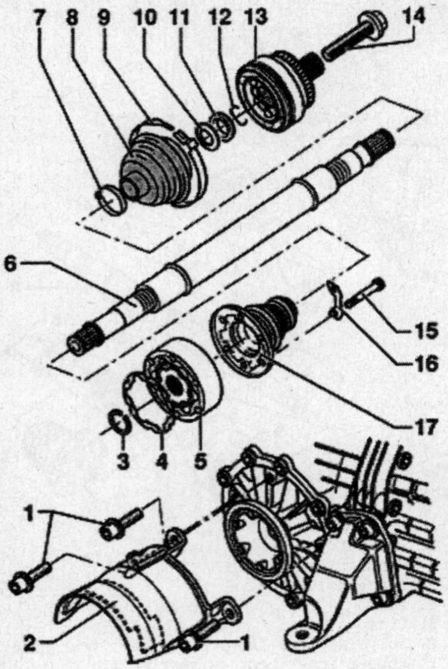

1. Hex head bolt
2. Heat shield
3. Circlip
4. Gasket
5. Inner CV joint
6. Tubular axle shaft
7. Clamp
8. Outer CV joint boot
9. Clamp
10. Dished washer
11. Thrust washer
12. Circlip
13. Outer CV joint
14. Hex bolt
15. Socket head bolt
16. Plate
17. Inner CV joint boot

VW3039800029000X

Fig. 5 Exploded view of driveshaft. Passat

or scoring. **Do not replace joint due to a polished appearance or because of visible ball track.**

6. Fill joint with approximately one pound of G6.2 grease (half of total amount).
7. Install cage with hub into housing. Balls must be installed from opposite side. **Marked position of hub, cage and housing must match.**
8. Install new snap ring on shaft or circlip into joint, then fill joint with remaining grease.

INNER CONSTANT VELOCITY JOINT

Some models may use a tripod type inner joint. Repair or replacement of tripod joint or boot can only be done as an assembly with axle shaft.

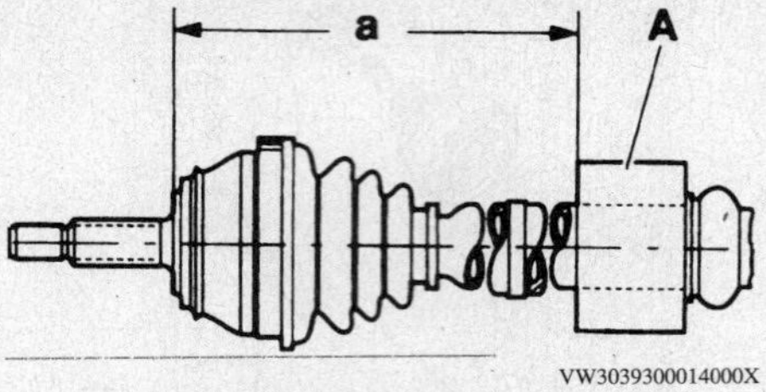

Fig. 6 Locating axle balance weight

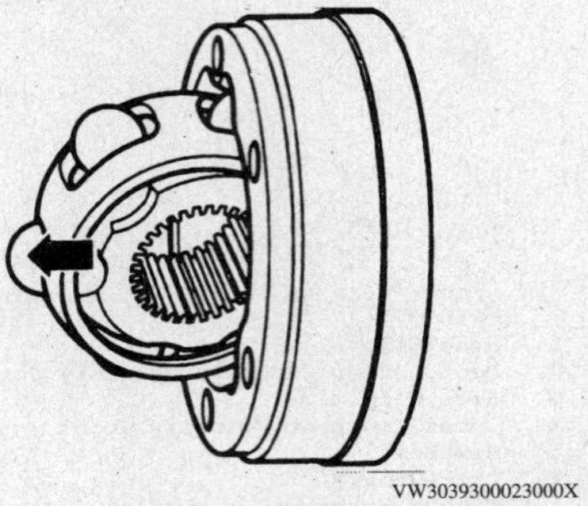

Fig. 8 Pivot ball hub & cage removal

REPLACEMENT

Tripod Type Joint

1. Remove outer CV joint as outlined under “Outer Constant Velocity Joint.”
2. Remove outer CV joint boot.
3. Reverse procedure to install.

Less Tripod Type Joint

1. Remove axle as outlined under “Driveshaft, Replace.”
2. Pull CV joint boot and shield back and away from joint.
3. Remove and discard circlip retaining joint to axle.
4. Place axle in a stable press, supporting inner race of joint on a suitable press plate.
5. Press shaft from inner race of joint.
6. Reverse procedure to install, noting the following:
   a. Clean and inspect boot and shaft splines for damage.
   b. Press joint onto axle using suitable press tools, **Fig. 10.**
   c. Install new circlip.
   d. Ensure boot and joint are packed with proper quantity of suitable CV joint grease.

SERVICE

Tripod Type Joint

The tripod type inner joint cannot yet be serviced in the field. Replacement of the joint with shaft is the only acceptable repair.

Fig. 7 Outer CV joint removal

Less Tripod Type Joint

1. Remove joint as outlined under “Inner Constant Velocity Joint.”
2. Service joint as outlined in “Outer Constant Velocity Joint.”

CONSTANT VELOCITY JOINT BOOT

REPLACEMENT

1. Remove constant velocity joint as outlined in this section.
2. Remove inner boot clamp, then the boot.
3. Position inner end of boot onto axle shaft as follows:
   a. Lefthand inner boot, **Fig. 11,** dimension (a) equals. 670 inch.
   b. Large diameter of righthand inner boot vent chamber “A,” **Fig. 12,** must fit on larger diameter of shaft. Air will vent through vent hole “B.”
   c. Lefthand outer boot on 27 MM driveshaft, **Fig. 13,** dimension (a) equals ½–1½ grooves visible.
   d. Lefthand outer boot on 22 MM driveshaft, **Fig. 14,** end of boot butts against shoulder.
   e. Righthand outer boot, **Fig. 15,** dimension (a) equals up to ½ groove visible.
4. Install constant velocity joint.
5. Install boot to joint, ensure boot is fully relaxed, then position clamps.
6. Crimp boot clamps, using a suitable torque wrench and crimping pliers tool No. VAG 1682, or equivalent, **Fig. 16.**
7. **Torque** crimping pliers drive bolt to 18 ft. lbs.

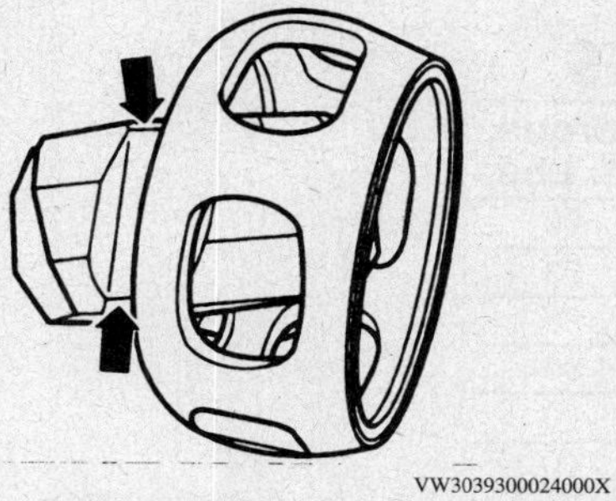

Fig. 9 CV joint hub from cage removal

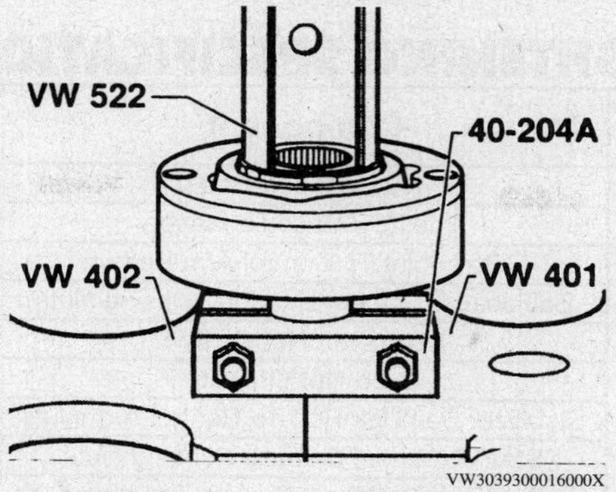

Fig. 10 Inner CV joint to shaft installation

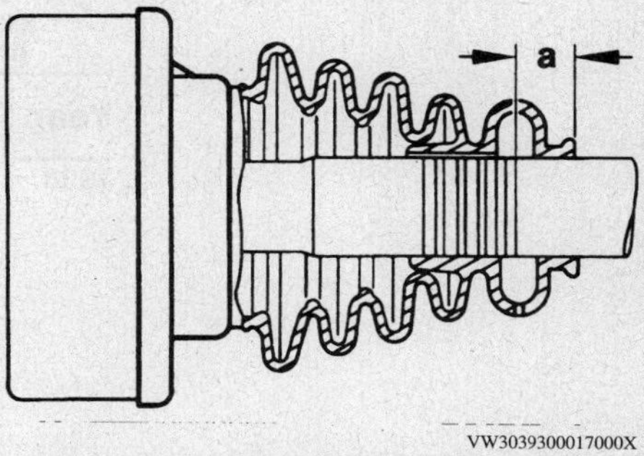

Fig. 11 Lefthand inner CV joint boot positioning

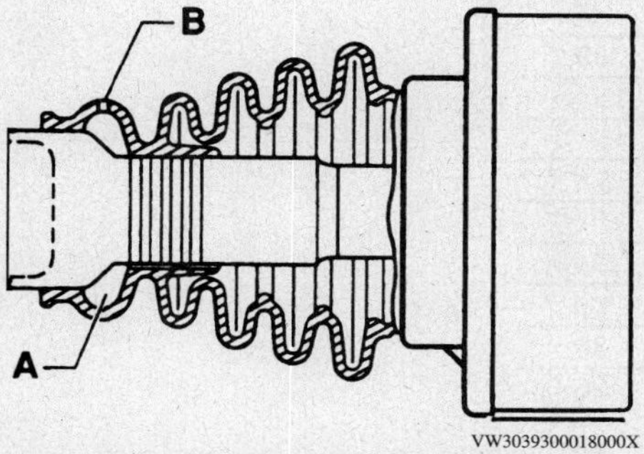

Fig. 12 Righthand inner CV joint boot positioning

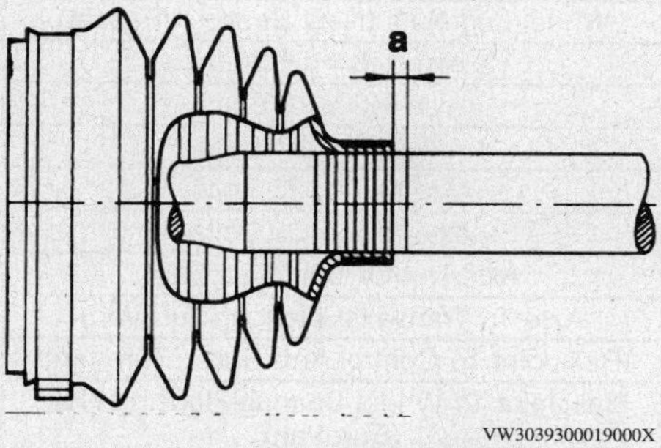

Fig. 13 Lefthand outer CV joint boot positioning. 27 MM axle shaft

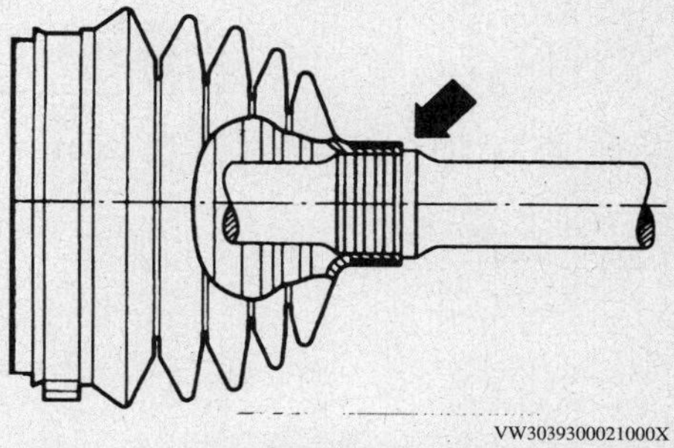

Fig. 14 Lefthand outer CV joint boot positioning. 22 MM axle shaft

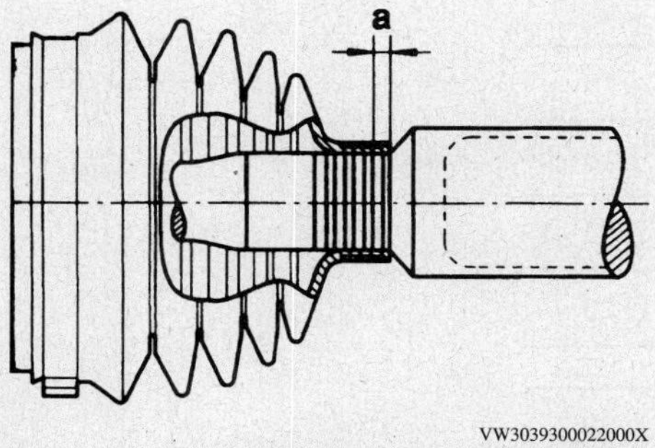

Fig. 15 Righthand outer CV joint boot positioning

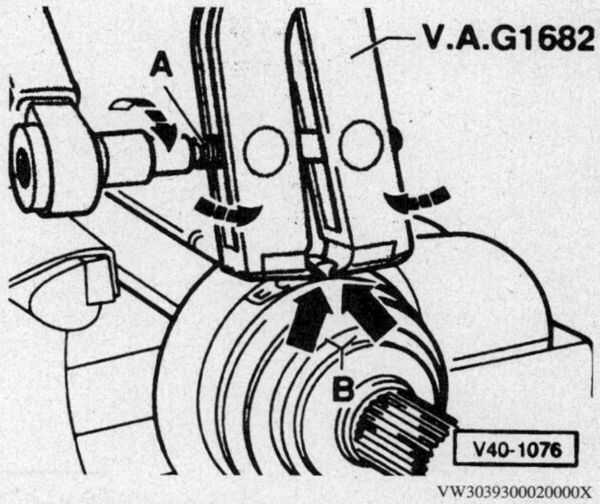

Fig. 16 CV joint boot clamp crimping

TIGHTENING SPECIFICATIONS

Year	Component	Torque, Ft. Lbs.
1998	Axle Nut Or Bolt	①
	Axle To Transaxle Flange	33
	Ball Joint To Control Arm Bolts	26
	Ball Joint To Wheel Bearing Housing Nuts	33
	Driveshaft Nut Or Bolt	①
	Hub Nut Or Bolt	①
	Stabilizer Bar Link Rod To Control Arm Nuts	18
	Strut To Wheel Bearing Housing Nuts	70
	Tie Rod End To Wheel Bearing Housing Nuts	26
	Wheel Lug Nuts (Cabrio, Golf & Jetta)	81
	Wheel Lug Nuts (EuroVan)	118
	Wheel Lug Nuts (New Beetle & Passat)	89
1999–2001	Axle M8 × 18 Bolts	15 ③
	Axle M8 × 28 Bolts	15 ③
	Axle M8 × 48 Bolts	15 ③
	Axle M10 × 23 Bolts	37 ④
	Axle M10 × 52 Bolts	37 ④
	Axle Nut Or Bolt (EuroVan)	111
	Axle To Transaxle Flange (EuroVan)	33
	Ball Joint To Control Arm Bolts (EuroVan)	26
	Ball Joint To Wheel Bearing Housing Nuts (EuroVan)	33
	Ball Joint To Control Arm Bolts & Nuts (Golf, GTI & Jetta)	15 ③
	Hub Nut (Golf, GTI, Jetta, New Beetle & Passat)	②
	Pendulum Support To Subframe Bolts (New Beetle)	18
	Stabilizer Bar Link Rod To Control Arm Nuts (EuroVan)	18
	Strut To Wheel Bearing Housing Nuts (EuroVan)	70
	Tie Rod End To Wheel Bearing Housing Nuts (EuroVan)	26
	Wheel Lug Nuts (EuroVan)	118
	Wheel Lug Nuts (Cabrio, Golf, GTI, Jetta, New Beetle & Passat)	89

① — Cabrio, Golf III & Jetta III, 195 ft. lbs.; GTI-VR6, Jetta III GLX, 66 ft. lbs. plus an additional 45°. 1998 Passat, M14 bolt 85 ft. lbs. plus an additional 180°, M16 bolt 140 ft. lbs. plus an additional 90°. EuroVan, 111 ft. lbs. New Beetle, torque nut to 148 ft. lbs., loosen and torque to 37 ft. lbs., then rotate an additional 60°.
② — Torque to 148 ft. lbs., loosen ½ turn, torque to 37 ft. lbs. & rotate an additional 60°.
③ — Tighten an additional 90 °.
② — Tighten an additional 45 °.

Engine Rebuilding Specifications

INDEX

	Page No.
Camshaft	8-185
Crankshaft, Bearings & Rods	8-186
Cylinder Block	8-186
Cylinder Head, Valve Guide & Valve Seats	8-185
Oil Pump	8-186
Pistons, Pins & Rings	8-186
Valves	8-185

CYLINDER HEAD, VALVE GUIDE & VALVE SEATS

Engine Liter	Year	Cylinder Head		Valve Stem To Guide Clearance②		Valve Seats		
		Warpage Limit	Minimum Height	Intake	Exhaust	Seat Angle, Degrees	Seat Width Intake	Seat Width Exhaust
1.8L	1998–2001	.004	—	.031	.031	45	.065	.071
1.9L TDI①	1998–2001	.004	—	.051	.051	45	.106	.087
2.0L	1998–2001	.004	—	.039	.051	45	.079	.094
2.8L	1998–2001	.004	—	.039	.051	45	.055	.079

① — Diesel.

② — Use dial indicator against head of valve to measure valve rock w/valve tip lifted flush with end of guide.

VALVES

Engine Liter	Year	Valve Stem Diameter		Valve Installed Height①		Valve Face Angle, Degrees	Valve Clearance	
		Intake	Exhaust	Intake	Exhaust		Intake	Exhaust
1.8L	1998–2001	.3140	.3130	—	—	45	②	②
1.9L TDI	1998–2001	.3140	.3130	1.409	1.421	45	②	②
2.0L	1998–2001	.3140	.3130	1.331	1.343	45	②	②
2.8L	1998–2001	.2744	.2736	1.336	1.343	45	②	②

① — Minimum allowable distance, measured from tip of valve stem to level of valve cover surface.

② — Hydraulic lifters, no adjustment required.

CAMSHAFT

Engine, Liter	Year	Camshaft Bearing Clearance	Camshaft Endplay
1.8L	1998–2001	.004	.006
1.9L TDI	1998–2001	.004	.006
2.0L	1998–2001	.004	.006
2.8L	1998–2001	.004	.006

CRANKSHAFT, BEARINGS & RODS

Engine Liter	Year	Crankshaft: Standard Journal Diameter: Main Bearing	Crankshaft: Standard Journal Diameter: Crank Pin	Crankshaft: End- play	Bearing Clearance: Main Bearings	Bearing Clearance: Connecting Rod Bearings	Connecting Rods: Piston Pin Bore Diameter	Connecting Rods: Side Clearance
1.8L (AEB, APH, AWD)	1998–2001	2.1251–2.1244	1.8810–1.8803	—	—	—	—	—
1.8L (ATW)	1998–2001	2.1245–2.1260	1.8803–1.8820	.0030–.0090	.0060(1)	.0004–.0020	—	—
1.9L TDI	1998–2001	2.1251–2.1244	1.8810–1.8803	.003–.007	.0012–.0031	.0031(1)	—	.0146(1)
2.0L	1998–2001	2.1053–2.1046	1.8633–1.8626	.003–.009	.0004–.0016	.0004–.0023	—	.002–.014
2.8L	1998–2001	2.3251–2.3259	2.1243–2.1251	—	—	—	—	—

(1) — Wear limit.

PISTONS, PINS & RINGS

Engine Liter	Year	Piston Diameter (Std.)	Piston Clearance	Piston Pin Diameter	Piston Ring End Gap: Comp.	Piston Ring End Gap: Oil	Piston Ring Side Clearance: Comp.	Piston Ring Side Clearance: Oil
1.8L (AEB, APH, AWD)	1998–2001	3.1875	.0018	—	.008–.016	.010–.020	.0024–.0035	.0012–.0024
1.8L (ATW)	2000–01	3.1180	.0023	—	.0078–.0157	.0098–.0197	(1)	.0011–.0023(2)
1.9L TDI	1998–2001	3.1291	.0012	1.020	.008–.016	.010–.020	(3)	.0012–.0024
2.0L	1998–2001	3.2179	.0018	.827	.008–.016	.010–.020	.0023–.0035	.0012–.0023
2.8L	1998–2001	3.1884	—	—	.008–.056	.010–.020	.0008–.0028	.0008–.0024

(1) — Upper compression ring,. 0023–.0035 inch, wear limit. 0078 inch; lower compression ring,. 0019–.0315 inch, wear limit. 0078 inch.

(2) — Wear limit. 0059 inch.

(3) — Top ring,. 0035–.0050; second ring,. 0020–.0031.

CYLINDER BLOCK

Engine, Liter	Year	Cylinder Bore Diameter (Std.)	Cylinder Bore Out Of Round (Max.)
1.8L (AEB, APH, AWD)	1998–2001	3.1594	.0031
1.8L (ATW)	2000–01	3.2484	.0031
1.9L TDI	1998–2001	3.1303	.0039
2.0L	1998–99	3.2179	.0015
2.8L	1998–2001	3.1893	.0015

OIL PUMP

Engine Liter	Year	Backlash: New	Backlash: Wear Limit	Axial Play
1.8L	1998–99	.002	.008	.006
	2000–01	—	—	—
1.9L TDI	1998–2001	.002	.006	.006
2.0L	1998–99	.002	.008	.006
	2000–01	—	—	—
2.8L	1998–2001	.002	.008	.006

VOLVO

INDEX OF SERVICE OPERATIONS

Page No.

AIR BAG SYSTEM PRECAUTIONS 0-12
AIR QUALITY STANDARDS 0-23
AUTOMATIC TRANSMISSIONS 9-116
BRAKES
- Anti-Lock Brakes 9-103
- Disc Brakes 9-99
- Hydraulic Brake Systems 9-101
- Power Brake Units 9-102

CLUTCH & MANUAL TRANSMISSION
- Adjustments 9-19
- Clutch, Replace 9-19
- Hydraulic System Service 9-19
- Precautions 9-19
- Tightening Specifications 9-21
- Transaxle, Replace 9-19

COMPUTER RELEARN PROCEDURES 0-10
DRIVE AXLES 9-127
ELECTRICAL
- Air Bags 9-77
- Air Conditioning 9-35
- Alternators 9-71
- Blower Motor, Replace 9-8
- Coil Pack, Replace 9-7
- Cooling Fans 9-42
- Cruise Controls 9-73
- Dash Gauges 9-47
- Dash Panels 9-96
- Distributor, Replace 9-7
- Evaporator Core, Replace 9-8
- Fuel Pump Relay Location 9-7
- Fuse Panel & Flasher Location 9-7
- Headlamp Switch, Replace 9-8
- Heater Core, Replace 9-8
- Ignition Switch, Replace 9-7
- Instrument Cluster, Replace 9-8
- Neutral Safety Switch, Replace 9-8
- Passive Restraints 9-77
- Precautions 9-7
- Relay Center Location 9-7
- Speed Controls 9-73
- Starter Motors 9-69
- Starter, Replace 9-7
- Steering Wheel, Replace 9-8
- Stop Light Switch, Replace 9-8
- Turn Signal Switch, Replace 9-8
- Wiper Motor, Replace 9-8
- Wiper Switch, Replace 9-8

ELECTRICAL SYMBOL IDENTIFICATION 0-33
ENGINE
- Belt Tension Data 9-16
- Camshaft, Replace 9-15
- Camshaft Oil Seal, Replace 9-15
- Compression Pressures 9-10
- Cooling System Bleed 9-16
- Crankshaft Seal, Replace 9-16
- Cylinder Head, Replace 9-12
- Engine Mount, Replace 9-10
- Engine Rebuilding Specifications 9-130
- Engine, Replace 9-10
- Exhaust Manifold, Replace 9-12
- Front Cover, Replace 9-14
- Fuel Filter, Replace 9-17
- Fuel Pump, Replace 9-17
- Intake Manifold, Replace 9-12
- Main & Rod Bearings 9-16
- Oil Pan, Replace 9-16
- Oil Pump, Replace 9-16
- Piston & Rod Assembly 9-16
- Pistons, Pins & Rings 9-16
- Precautions 9-10
- Radiator, Replace 9-16
- Serpentine Drive Belt 9-16
- Thermostat, Replace 9-16
- Tightening Specifications 9-18
- Timing Belt, Replace 9-15
- Valve Adjustment 9-14
- Valve Clearance Specifications 9-14
- Valve Guides 9-14
- Water Pump, Replace 9-16

FRONT SUSPENSION & STEERING
- Ball Joint, Replace 9-30
- Ball Joint Inspection 9-30
- Coil Spring, Replace 9-30
- Control Arm, Replace 9-31
- Control Arm Bushing, Replace 9-31
- Power Steering Gear, Replace 9-32
- Power Steering Pump, Replace 9-32
- Precautions 9-30
- Shock Absorber, Replace 9-30
- Stabilizer Bar, Replace 9-31
- Tightening Specifications 9-33
- Wheel Bearing, Adjust 9-30

REAR AXLE & SUSPENSION
- Application Chart 9-22
- Coil Spring, Replace 9-23
- Control Arm, Replace 9-24
- Differential Housing Bushings, Replace 9-26
- Hub & Bearing, Replace 9-23
- Rear Axle, Replace 9-22
- Rear Axle Link, Replace 9-27
- Rear Axle Shaft, Replace 9-23
- Shock Absorber, Replace 9-23
- Stabilizer Bar, Replace 9-25
- Support Arm, Replace 9-25
- Tightening Specifications 9-28
- Torque Rod & Bushings, Replace 9-23
- Track Rod, Replace 9-25
- Trailing Arm, Replace 9-24
- Transverse Arm Mount, Replace 9-26
- Upper Rear Axle Member Bushings, Replace 9-26

SERVICE REMINDER & WARNING LAMP RESET PROCEDURES 0-14
SPECIFICATIONS
- Fluid Capacities & Cooling System Data 9-5
- Front Wheel Alignment Specifications 9-4
- General Engine Specifications 9-2
- Lubricant Data 9-6
- Rear Wheel Alignment Specifications 9-4
- Tune Up Specifications 9-3

VEHICLE IDENTIFICATION 0-3
VEHICLE LIFT POINTS 0-24
VEHICLE MAINTENANCE SCHEDULES 0-45
WHEEL ALIGNMENT
- Front Wheel Alignment 9-34
- Preliminary Inspection 9-34
- Rear Wheel Alignment 9-34
- Wheel Alignment Specifications 9-4

WIRE COLOR CODE IDENTIFICATION 0-33

Specifications

GENERAL ENGINE SPECIFICATIONS

Year	Model	Engine Code/Liter	Fuel System	Bore & Stroke	Compression Ratio	Maximum Brake HP @ RPM	Maximum Torque Lbs. Ft. @ RPM	Normal Oil Pressure, psi
1998	S70 & V70	B5254S/2.4L	SFI	3.267 X 3.543 (83 X 90 mm)	10.3	168 @ 6100	162 @ 4700	14.50-50.75
		B5254T/2.5L	SFI	3.267 X 3.543 (83 X 90 mm)	9.0	190 @ 5100	199 @ 1800	14.50-50.75
		B5234T/2.3L	SFI	3.190 X 3.543 (81 X 90 mm)	8.5	236 @ 5100	243 @ 2100	14.50-50.75
	S90 & V90	B6304S/2.9L	SFI	3.267 X 3.543 (83 X 90 mm)	10.7	181 @ 5200	199 @ 4100	14.50-50.75
1999	S70 & V70	B5234T/2.3L	SFI	3.190 X 3.543 (81 X 90 mm)	8.5	236 @ 5100	244 @ 2100	—
		B5254S/2.4L	SFI	3.267 X 3.543 (83 X 90 mm)	10.3	162 @ 6100	162 @ 4700	—
		B5254T/2.5L	SFI	3.267 X 3.543 (83 X 90 mm)	9.0	190 @ 5100	199 @ 1800	—
	S80 2.9	B6304S/2.9L	SFI	3.267 X 3.543 (83 X 90 mm)	10.7	201 @ 6600	243 @ 4200	—
	S80 T6	B6284T/2.8L	SFI	3.190 X 3.543 (81 X 90 mm)	8.7	268 @ 5400	280 @ 2000	—
	C70 Coupe w/low pressure turbo	B5234T3/2.4L	SFI	3.267 X 3.543 (83 X 90 mm)	9.0	190 @ 5100	199 @ 1800	14.50-50.75
	C70 w/high pressure turbo	B5243T3/2.3L	SFI	3.190 X 3.543 (81 X 90 mm)	8.5	236 @ 5400	244 @ 2400	14.50-50.75
	C70 Conv.	B5234T3/2.4L	SFI	3.267 X 3.543 (83 X 90 mm)	9.0	190 @ 5100	199 @ 1800	14.50-50.75
2000–01	S40/V40	B4204T2/1.9L	SFI	3.267 X 3.543 (83 X 90 mm)	9.0	160 @ 5100	170 @ 4800	14.50-50.80
		B4204T3/1.9L	SFI	3.267 X 3.543 (83 X 90 mm)	9.0	162 @ 5250	177 @ 4200	14.50-50.80
	S70/V70	B5234T3/2.4L	SFI	3.190 X 3.540 (81 X 90 mm)	8.5	240 @ 5100	243 @ 5100	14.10-67.70
		B5244T/2.4L	SFI	3.260 X 3.540 (83 X 90)	9.0	190 @ 5100	199 @ 5000	14.10-67.70
	C70 Coupe w/low pressure turbo	B5234T3/2.4L	SFI	3.267 X 3.543 (83 X 90 mm)	9.0	190 @ 5100	199 @ 1800	14.50-50.75
	C70 w/high pressure turbo	B5243T3/2.3L	SFI	3.190 X 3.543 (81 X 90 mm)	8.5	236 @ 5400	244 @ 2400	14.50-50.75
	C70 Conv.	B5234T3/2.4L	SFI	3.267 X 3.543 (83 X 90 mm)	9.0	190 @ 5100	199 @ 1800	14.50-50.75
	S60	B5244T3/2.4L	SFI	3.270 X 3.540 (83 X 90)	9.0	197 @ 6000	210 @ 5000	14.00-67.70
		B5244S/2.4L	SFI	3.270 X 3.540 (83 X 90)	10.3	168 @ 5900	170 @ 4500	14.00-67.70
		B5234T3/2.3L	SFI	3.190 X 3.540 (81 X 90)	8.5	247 @ 5200	243 @ 5200	14.00-67.70
	S80 2.9	B6304S/2.9L	SFI	3.267 X 3.543 (83 X 90 mm)	10.7	201 @ 6600	243 @ 4200	—
	S80 T6	B6284T/2.8L	SFI	3.190 X 3.543 (81 X 90 mm)	8.7	268 @ 5400	280 @ 2000	—

TUNE UP SPECIFICATIONS

Year	Engine	Spark Plug Gap, Inch	Ignition Timing			Curb Idle Speed②		Fuel Pressure, psi	Valve Clearance Spec-ifications
			Firing Order	Timing, °BTDC	Timing Mark Fig.	Man. Trans.	Auto. Trans.		
1998	2.4L	.030	1-2-4-5-3	10	—	850③	850③	—	①
	2.4L Turbo (C70)	.030	1-2-4-5-3	6	—	850③	850③	—	①
	2.4L Turbo (S70/V70)	.030	1-2-4-5-3	5	—	850③	850③	—	①
	2.5L	.030	1-2-4-5-3	10	—	850③	850③	—	①
	2.9L	.030	1-5-3-6-2-4	9	—	750③	750③	—	①
1999	2.4L	.030	1-2-4-5-3	10	—	850③	850③	—	①
	2.4L Turbo (C70)	.030	1-2-4-5-3	8	—	850③	850③	—	①
	2.4L Turbo (S70/V70)	.030	1-2-4-5-3	5	—	850③	850③	—	①
	2.5L (C70)	.030	1-2-4-5-3	8	—	850③	850③	—	①
	2.5L (S70/V70)	.030	1-2-4-5-3	10	—	850③	850③	—	①
	2.8L	.030	1-5-3-6-2-4	10	—	650③	650③	—	①
	2.9L	.020	1-5-3-6-2-4	10	—	650③	650③	—	①
2000–01	1.9L	.030	1-3-4-2	0-15	—	775③	775③	58-72.5	.008
	2.3	.030	1–2–4–5–3	6	—	670③	670③	55	①
	2.4L	.030	1-2-4-5-3	10	—	850③	850③	—	①
	2.4L Turbo (C70)	.030	1-2-4-5-3	8	—	850③	850③	—	①
	2.4L Turbo (S70/V70)	.030	1-2-4-5-3	5	—	850③	850③	—	①
	2.5L (C70)	.030	1-2-4-5-3	8	—	850③	850③	—	①
	2.5L (S70/V70)	.030	1-2-4-5-3	10	—	850③	850③	—	①
	2.8L	.030	1-5-3-6-2-4	10	—	650③	650③	—	①
	2.9L	.020	1-5-3-6-2-4	10	—	650③	650③	—	①

① — Equipped w/hydraulic lash adjusters, no adjustment is required.

② — When adjusting idle speed, set parking brake and chock drive wheels.

③ — Controlled by Constant Idle Speed (CIS) system.

FRONT WHEEL ALIGNMENT SPECIFICATIONS

Model	Caster Angle, Degrees		Camber Angle, Degrees		Toe-In, Inch
	Limits	Desired	Limits	Desired	
1998					
C70	+2.35 to +4.35	+3.35	−1.50 to +0.50	−.50	①
S70/V70	+2.35 to +4.35	+3.35	−1.00 to +1.00	0	①
S90/V90	+5.50 to +6.50	+6.00	—	②	③
1999					
C70	+2.35 to +4.35	+3.35	−1.50 to +0.50	−.50	①
S70/V70	+2.35 to +4.35	+3.35	−1.00 to +1.00	0	①
S90/V90	+5.50 to +6.50	+6.00	—	②	③
S80	+3.00 to +5.00	+4.00	−.5 to +.5	0	+.2 to +.4
2000					
C70	+2.35 to +4.35	+3.35	−1.5 to +0.5	−.50	①
S70/V70	+2.35 to +4.35	+3.35	−1 to +1	0	①
S80	+3.00 to +5.00	+4.00	−.5 to +.5	0	+.2 to +.4
S40/V40	+2⅕ to +4⅕	+3⅕	−1 to +1	0	④
2001					
S80	+3.00 to +5.00	+4.00	−.5 to +.5	0	+.2 to +.4
S40/V40	+2⅕ to +4⅕	+3⅕	−1 to +1	0	④
S60	+3.00 to +5.00	+4.00	−1.05 to +.75	−.15	0 to +.2°
V70	+3.00 to +5.00	+4.00	−.5 to +.5	0	+.3°

① — Total toe +1/3°.

② — Models w/15 inch alloy rim, −.05°; models w/16 inch alloy rim, +.2°; models w/17 inch alloy +.5°.

③ — Total toe +3/10°.

④ — Total per wheel +3/20°.

REAR WHEEL ALIGNMENT SPECIFICATIONS

Model	Camber Angle, Degrees		Toe Degrees	
	Limits	Desired	Limits	Desired
1998				
C70, S70 & V70 FWD	−1.5 to −.5	−1	−.1 to +.3	+.1
S70 & V70 AWD	−1.25 to +.25	−.5	−.25 to +.25	0
1999				
C70, S70 & V70 FWD	−1.5 to −.5	−1	−.1 to +.3	+.1
S70 & V70 AWD	−1.25 to +.25	−.5	−.25 to +.25	0
S80	−.95 to +.55	−.2	0 to +.4	+.2
2000				
C70, S70 & V70 FWD	−1.5 to −.5	−1	−.1 to +.3	+.1
S70 & V70 AWD	−1.25 to +.25	−.5	−.25 to +.25	0
S80	−.95 to +.55	−.2	0 to +.4	+.2
S40/V40	−1⅒ to −⅒	−⅔	−⅒ to −⅕	−3/20
2001				
S80	−.95 to +.55	−.2	0 to +.4	+.2
S40/V40	−1⅒ to −⅒	−⅔	−⅒ to −⅕	−3/20
S60	−1 to +1	0	0 to +.4	+.2
V70	−.95 to +.55	−.2	0 to +.4	+.2

FLUID CAPACITIES & COOLING SYSTEM DATA

Model	Cooling Capacity, Qts.	Coolant Type	Radiator Cap Relief Pressure, Lbs.	Thermo Opening Temp., °F	Fuel Tank, Gals.	Engine Oil Refill, Qts.①	Transmission Oil	
							Man. Trans. Pts.	Auto. Trans, Qts.②
1998								
C70	7.6	Glycol	22	189	18.5	6.1	4.4	③
S70	7.6	Glycol	22	189	18.5	6.1	4.4	③
S70 Turbo	12.9	Glycol	22	189	18.5	6.1	4.4	③
V70	7.6	Glycol	22	189	18.5	6.1	4.4	③
V70 Turbo	12.9	Glycol	22	189	18.5	6.0	—	③
S90	10.5	Glycol	22	188	20.3	6.0	—	3.2
V90	10.5	Glycol	22	188	20.3	6.0	—	3.2
1999								
C70	7.6	Glycol	22	189	18.5	6.1	4.4	③
S70	7.6	Glycol	22	189	18.5	6.1	4.4	③
S70 Turbo	12.9	Glycol	22	189	18.5	6.1	4.4	③
V70	7.6	Glycol	22	189	18.5	6.1	4.4	③
V70 Turbo	12.9	Glycol	22	189	18.5	6.1	4.4	③
S80	9.3	Glycol	22	194	18.5	6.9	4.5	③
S80 Turbo	10.2	Glycol	22	194	21.1	6.0	—	③
S90	10.5	Glycol	22	188	20.3	6.0	—	3.2
V90	10.5	Glycol	22	188	20.3	6.0	—	3.2
2000								
S40/V40	6.0	Glycol	22	186	16.0	5.1	—	④
C70	7.0	Glycol	22	194	17.9	6.1	4.6	8.0
S70/V70	7.6	Glycol	22	194	18.0	6.1	4.6	8.0
S80	9.3	Glycol	22	194	21.1	7.3	—	7.9
S80 Turbo	10.2	Glycol	22	194	21.1	7.3	—	7.9
2001								
S40/V40	6.0	Glycol	22	186	16.0	5.7	—	8.0
S60	8.5	Glycol	22	194	18.5	5.8	4.4	7.9
S60 Turbo	9.3	Glycol	22	194	21.1	6.1	4.4	7.9
C70	7.4	Glycol	22	180	17.9	6.1	4.4	8.0
V70	7.6	Glycol	22	194	18.5	6.1	4.4	7.9
V70 Turbo	12.9	Glycol	22	194	21.1	6.1	4.4	7.9
S80	9.3	Glycol	22	194	21.1	7.3	—	13.4
S80 Turbo	10.2	Glycol	22	194	21.1	7.3	—	13.4

① — With filter change.
② — Approximate, make final check w/dipstick.
③ — Drain and refill 3.2 qts.; total capacity 8.1 qts.
④ — Drain and refill 6.9 qts,; total capacity 8.0 qts.

LUBRICANT DATA

Model	Lubricant Type						
	Transmission		Hydraulic Clutch Fluid	Transfer Case	Rear Axle	Power Steering	Brake System
	Manual	Automatic					
1998							
70 Series	①	Dexron IIE/III Mercon	DOT 4+	②	③	ATF Type F/G	DOT 4+
90 Series	④	Dexron IIE/III Mercon	DOT 4+	—	⑤	ATF Type F/G	DOT 4+
1999							
S80	④	Dexron III	—	—	—	ATF Type F/G, Dexron II/IIE/III	DOT 4+
70 Series	①	Dexron IIE/III Mercon	DOT 4+	②	③	ATF Type F/G	DOT 4+
90 Series	④	Dexron IIE/III Mercon	DOT 4+	—	⑤	ATF Type F/G	DOT 4+
2000							
C70	④	⑥	DOT 4+	—	—	Dexron III or Mercon	DOT 4+
S40/V40	—	Dexron III or Mercon	—	—	—	Dexron III or Mercon	DOT 4+
S70/V70	④	⑥	DOT 4+	—	—	Dexron III or Mercon	DOT 4+
S80	—	⑦	—	—	—	Dexron III or Mercon	DOT 4+
2001							
C70	④	⑧	DOT 4+	—	—	Dexron III or Mercon	DOT 4+
S40/V40	—	⑧	—	—	—	Dexron III or Mercon	DOT 4+
S70/V70	④	⑧	DOT 4+	—	—	Dexron III or Mercon	DOT 4+
S80	—	Dexron III	—	—	—	Dexron III or Mercon	DOT 4+

① — Models equipped w/M46 & M47 transaxles, use ATF F or G Volvo Thermo oil part No. 11 61 323, or equivalent. Models w/M90 transaxle, use Volvo synthetic oil part No. 11 61 423, or equivalent.

② — Type 1155 bevel gear, Volvo synthetic transmission oil part No. 11 61 513–5, or equivalent. Type 1165, Volvo transmission oil part No. 11 61 329–6, or equivalent.

③ — Below 14°F use SAE 80 GL-5/6; above 14°F use SAE 90 GL-5/6. Models equipped w/Dana differential brake require Volvo additive part No. 11 61 129, or equivalent; models w/Eaton automatic differential lock require Volvo additive part No. 11 61 329–6, or equivalent. Models less differential brake use low friction oil.

④ — Volvo synthetic oil part No. 11 61 423, or equivalent.

⑤ — G/L-5/6 low friction oil; models equipped w/Eaton differential lock require Volvo additive part No. 11 61 329–6, or equivalent.

⑥ — AW4 Trans use Dexron III or Mercon. AW5 type, Volvo gearbox oil parts No. 11 61 540–8, only.

⑦ — Geartronic type, Dexron III; AW5 type, Volvo gearbox oil part No. 11 61 540–8 only.

⑧ — AW5 type, Volvo Gearbox oil part No. 11 61 540–8 only.

Electrical

NOTE: On Air Bag Equipped Models, Refer To "Air Bag System Precautions" Located In The Front Of This Manual For System Disarming & Arming Procedures.

INDEX

	Page No.
Air Bags	9-77
Air Conditioning	9-35
Alternators	9-71
Blower Motor, Replace	9-8
Coil Pack, Replace	9-7
Cooling Fans	9-42
Cruise Controls	9-73
Dash Gauges	9-47
Dash Panels	9-96
Distributor, Replace	9-7
Evaporator Core, Replace	9-8
Fuel Pump Relay Location	9-7
Fuse Panel & Flasher Location	9-7
C70, S70 & V70	9-7
S40 & V40	9-7
S60 & S80	9-7
S90 & V90	9-7
Headlamp Switch, Replace	9-8
Heater Core, Replace	9-8
Ignition Switch, Replace	9-7
Instrument Cluster, Replace	9-8
Neutral Safety Switch, Replace	9-8
Passive Restraints	9-77
Precautions	9-7
Air Bag Systems	9-7
Battery Ground Cable	9-7
Microprocessor Radios	9-7
Relay Center Location	9-7
Speed Controls	9-73
Starter Motors	9-69
Starter, Replace	9-7
Steering Wheel, Replace	9-8
Stop Light Switch, Replace	9-8
Turn Signal Switch, Replace	9-8
Wiper Motor, Replace	9-8
Wiper Switch, Replace	9-8

PRECAUTIONS

AIR BAG SYSTEMS

Refer to "Air Bag System Precautions" in the front of this manual for system disarming and arming procedures.

BATTERY GROUND CABLE

Prior to service, disconnect battery ground cable and isolate as required.

MICROPROCESSOR RADIOS

On models equipped with microprocessor radios, always switch radio off before disconnecting or connecting battery ground cable to prevent damage to the radio.

FUSE PANEL & FLASHER LOCATION

C70, S70 & V70

These models are equipped with two separate fuse panels. One is located behind the lefthand corner of the instrument panel, the other is located near the left side shock tower in the engine compartment.

S60 & S80

These models are equipped with two separate fuse panels, one is located in the engine compartment, the other located in the left front instrument panel end cap. Additionally, there is an integrated relay/fusebox located in the rear cargo compartment.

S40 & V40

These models are equipped with two separate fuse panels, one is located in the engine compartment, the other located in the left front instrument panel end cap.

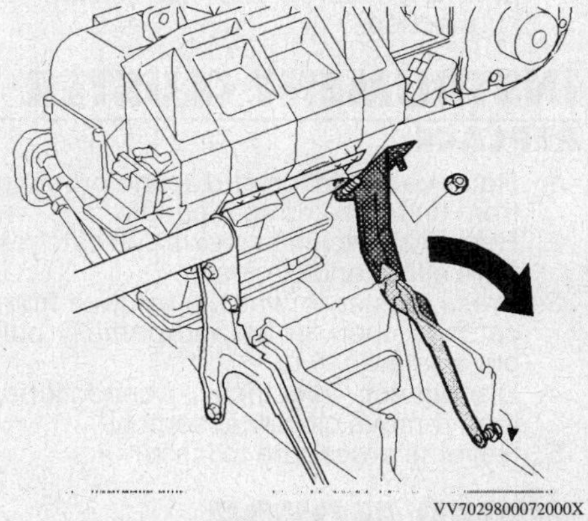

Fig. 1 A/C evaporator lower bracket removal. C70, S70 & V70

S90 & V90

These models are equipped with three separate fuse panels, one is located on either side of engine compartment, the other located in the left front instrument panel end cap.

FUEL PUMP RELAY LOCATION

The fuel pump relay is located in the fuse/relay box, under the lefthand side of the instrument panel.

RELAY CENTER LOCATION

The relay panel is located behind the left upper instrument panel. Additional relays are located in the underhood fuse panel.

STARTER

REPLACE

1. Remove hose and pipe for charge air cooler.
2. Remove splash guard.
3. Remove power cable and antenna from starter motor.
4. Remove starter motor retaining screws, then the starter motor.
5. Reverse procedure to install. **Torque** attaching screws to 37 ft. lbs.

DISTRIBUTOR

REPLACE

1. Remove distributor cap, then turn engine until rotor arm is aligned with timing mark on distributor housing.
2. Mark housing position in direction to cylinder block.
3. Loosen attaching bolts, then remove distributor.
4. Reverse procedure to install, noting the following:
   a. Turn rotor arm to position approximately 30° after mark.
   b. Mount distributor in position, ensure drive gears engage.
   c. Ensure rotor arm and housing are aligned with appropriate marks.

COIL PACK

REPLACE

1. Remove ignition coil cover screws and cover.
2. Mark positions of ignition coils, then remove coil retaining bolts.
3. Disconnect coil electrical connectors and remove coils.
4. Reverse procedure to install.

IGNITION SWITCH

REPLACE

1. Remove noise insulator panel below

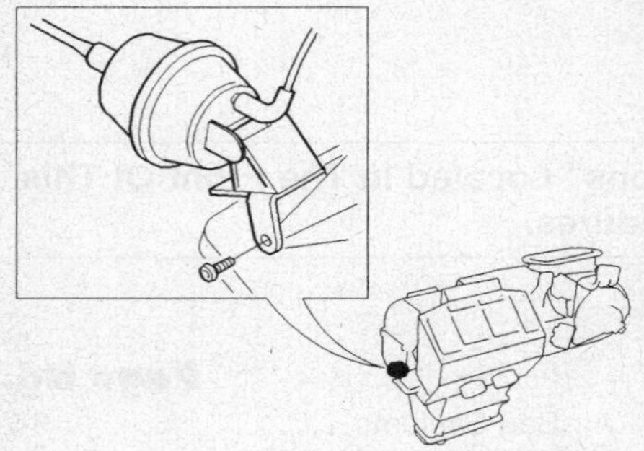

VV7029800073000X

Fig. 2 Cruise control vacuum control. C70, S70 & V70

instrument panel.
2. Remove upper steering column cover and casing around switch.
3. Loosen switch mounting screw, then install key and position in Start position.
4. Working through hole beneath holder, depress catch and remove switch from vehicle.
5. Reverse procedure to install.

NEUTRAL SAFETY SWITCH

REPLACE

The switch is located inside the passenger compartment and is mounted directly beneath the gear shift selector. Remove the selector cover and loosen the two retaining bolts to adjust or replace the switch.

HEADLAMP SWITCH

REPLACE

1. Remove trim panel under dashboard.
2. Remove switch retaining nut, then the switch.
3. Reverse procedure to install.

STOP LIGHT SWITCH

REPLACE

1. Disconnect switch wires.
2. Remove switch retaining nut, then the switch.
3. When installing switch, be sure that distance between brake pedal when fully released and thread bronze hub on switch is 4 mm (.008). If necessary, adjust by loosening bracket attaching screw and moving bracket.

TURN SIGNAL SWITCH

REPLACE

1. Remove screws holding upper and lower switch covers, then the covers.
2. Remove overdrive switch bracket.
3. Remove turn signal switch mounting screws, then the switch.
4. Reverse procedure to install.

STEERING WHEEL

REPLACE

1. Remove two Torx screws from rear of steering wheel, then disconnect electrical connector and remove air bag assembly.
2. Remove center attaching screw from steering wheel.
3. Loosen screw at end of plastic strap from Park position in steering wheel.
4. Place screw in pin on contact reel. Screw will now lock contact reel in zero position. **Be careful not to turn steering wheel. Otherwise it will shear head off lockpin.**
5. Remove steering wheel.
6. Remove upper and lower column casing attaching screws, then remove casings.
7. Reverse procedure to install, noting the following:
   a. Position steering wheel so contact reel pin is in center of hole in steering wheel.
   b. **Torque** center bolt to 24 ft. lbs.
   c. **Torque** Torx screws to 96 inch lbs.
   d. Ensure wires are not kinked or pinched.

INSTRUMENT CLUSTER

REPLACE

1. Remove insulation and sound proofing from under instrument panel.
2. Remove attaching screws and catches from either end of cluster.
3. Press cluster forward to remove from catches, then lift up and partially pull out cluster.
4. Disconnect electrical connections, then remove cluster assembly.
5. Reverse procedure to install.

WIPER MOTOR

REPLACE

1. Ensure wiper motor is in Park position.
2. Remove wiper arms from wiper mechanism.
3. Remove cover screws and fuse box cover, disconnect cover drain hoses, then remove cover.
4. Remove wiper linkage assembly screws, then the wiper assembly by pulling it out to release it from mounting pin.
5. Turn wiper linkage assembly over to access wiper motor mounting screws.
6. Mark wiper linkage where connected to wiper motor, then remove linkage nut and linkage.
7. Remove wiper motor mounting screws, then the motor.
8. Reverse procedure to install.

WIPER SWITCH

REPLACE

1. Position steering wheel straight ahead, turn ignition switch to off position.
2. Remove steering wheel cover screws, then the covers. Push upper cover off to one side.

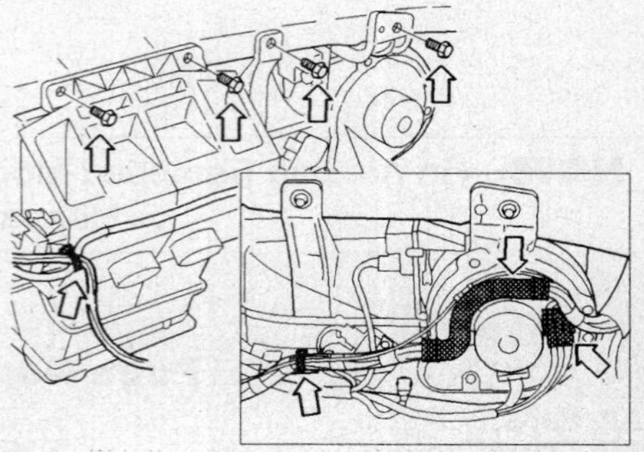

VV7029800074000X

Fig. 3 A/C evaporator mounting screws. C70, S70 & V70

3. Remove switch mounting screws and electrical connector, then the switch.
4. Reverse procedure to install.

BLOWER MOTOR

REPLACE

1. Turn ignition switch to Off position.
2. Remove glove compartment, soundproofing panels, and knee bolster/member.
3. Disconnect blower motor electrical connector.
4. Remove cable conduit and heater unit connector from blower motor, then remove motor.
5. Reverse procedure to install.

HEATER CORE

REPLACE

1. Clamp off heater coolant hoses with suitable clamps.
2. Remove right and left interior soundproofing panels.
3. Remove right and left carpet supports.
4. Remove RTI or booster bracket and knee bolster.
5. Remove drain hose and fold out of way.
6. Remove screws on heater unit cover on left and right hand sides.
7. Disconnect screws on heater unit pipe flange.
8. Remove heater unit with cover, then remove the heater core from the cover.
9. Reverse procedure to install.

EVAPORATOR CORE

REPLACE

1. Evacuate A/C system using a suitable A/C recovery station.
2. Clamp heater coolant hoses with suitable clamps.
3. Remove heater hoses from heater unit by pressing in hose connection and squeezing locking catches, then pull hose out.
4. Plug pipes to heater unit to prevent contamination.
5. Remove cover plate and rubber seal for lead-in.
6. Remove windshield wiper assembly.
7. Remove gutter, pollen filter and holder.
8. Remove screw holding pipe coupling

and receiver drier bracket in place to ease access to evaporator pipe.

9. Remove pipes from evaporator using removal tools No. 9995838 and No. 9995472, or equivalents.
10. Remove cover plate and rubber seal.
11. In the passenger compartment, perform the following:
    a. Remove ECC control module.
    b. Remove MCC control module.
    c. Remove instrument panel assembly.
    d. Remove support plates for carpeting.
    e. Remove cable tie straps to expose pipe for floor duct on passenger side.
    f. Remove pipes for floor ducts from A/C assembly.
    g. Remove bracket RTI or booster.
    h. Remove member for RTI.
    i. Remove knee bolster.
    j. Remove nuts and screws from evaporator mounting bracket, then the bracket, **Fig. 1.**
    k. Disconnect drain hose from floor.
    l. Remove vacuum control unit for cruise control, **Fig. 2.**
    m. Remove cable conduit from mounting on blower fan motor.
    n. Disconnect blower motor electrical connector, cable harness from bracket and cable harness from tie straps on air distribution housing.
    o. Remove mounting screws, then the A/C evaporator assembly, **Fig. 3.**
12. Remove recirculation damper motor and bracket.
13. Remove screws and clips from central module and evaporator cover, then remove evaporator from housing.
14. Reverse procedure to install.

Engine

NOTE: On Air Bag Equipped Models, Refer To "Air Bag System Precautions" Located In The Front Of This Manual For System Disarming & Arming Procedures.

INDEX

	Page No.
Belt Tension Data	9-16
Camshaft, Replace	9-15
2.3L/5, 2.4L & 2.9L Engines	9-15
Camshaft Oil Seal, Replace	9-15
2.3L/5, 2.4L & 2.9L Engines	9-15
Compression Pressures	9-10
Cooling System Bleed	9-16
2.3L/5, 2.4L & 2.9L Engines	9-16
Crankshaft Seal, Replace	9-16
Front	9-16
Rear	9-16
Cylinder Head, Replace	9-12
2.3L/5 & 2.4L Engines	9-12
2.9L Engine	9-13
Engine Mount, Replace	9-10
Engine Rebuilding Specifications	9-130
Engine, Replace	9-10
S70, V70, C70 & S80	9-10
S90 & V90	9-11
Exhaust Manifold, Replace	9-12
2.3L/5 & 2.4L Engines	9-12
2.9L Engine	9-12
Front Cover, Replace	9-14
2.3L/5 & 2.4L Engines	9-14
2.9L Engine	9-15
Fuel Filter, Replace	9-17
2.3L/5 & 2.4L Engines	9-17
2.9L Engine	9-17
Fuel Pump, Replace	9-17
2.3L/5 & 2.4L Engines	9-17
2.9L Engine	9-17
Intake Manifold, Replace	9-12
2.3L/5 & 2.4L Engines	9-12
2.9L Engine	9-12
Main & Rod Bearings	9-16
2.3L/5, 2.4L & 2.9L Engines	9-16
Oil Pan, Replace	9-16
2.3L/5, 2.4L & 2.9L Engines	9-16
Oil Pump, Replace	9-16
2.3L/5, 2.4L & 2.9L Engines	9-16
Piston & Rod Assembly	9-16
2.3L/5, 2.4L & 2.9L Engines	9-16
Pistons, Pins & Rings	9-16
2.3L/5, 2.4L & 2.9L Engines	9-16
Precautions	9-10
Air Bag Systems	9-10
Battery Ground Cable	9-10
Microprocessor Radios	9-10
Radiator, Replace	9-16
Serpentine Drive Belt	9-16
Belt Routing	9-16
Thermostat, Replace	9-16
Tightening Specifications	9-18
2.3L/5 & 2.4L Engines	9-18
2.9L Engine	9-18
Timing Belt, Replace	9-15
2.3L/5 & 2.4L Engines	9-15
2.9L Engine	9-15
Valve Adjustment	9-14
2.3L/5, 2.4L & 2.9L Engines	9-14
Valve Clearance Specifications	9-14
2.3L/5, 2.4L & 2.9L Engines	9-14
Valve Guides	9-14
2.3L/5, 2.4L & 2.9L Engines	9-14
Water Pump, Replace	9-16
2.3L/5, 2.4L & 2.9L Engines	9-16

PRECAUTIONS

AIR BAG SYSTEMS

Refer to "Air Bag System Precautions" in the front of this manual for system disarming and arming procedures.

MICROPROCESSOR RADIOS

On models equipped with microprocessor radios, always switch radio off before disconnecting or connecting battery ground cable to prevent damage to the radio.

BATTERY GROUND CABLE

Prior to service, disconnect battery ground cable and isolate as required.

COMPRESSION PRESSURES

1. Disconnect timing pick-up connector.
2. Remove ignition wiring cover.
3. Lock throttle in fully open position.
4. Remove spark plugs and connect starter switch (part No. 1158263, or equivalent) between alternator positive terminal and service socket of control unit box.
5. Measure compression in all cylinders using compression gauge tool No. 9689, or equivalent and extension sleeve part No. 1158540, or equivalent.
6. **On 1.9L engine,** compression pressure should measure 159–188 psi with engine hot.
7. **On 2.3L/5 turbocharged engine,** compression pressure should be 156–185 psi with engine hot.
8. **On 2.4L engine,** compression pressure should measure 188–218 psi with engine hot.
9. **On 2.9L engine,** compression pressure should measure 197–213 psi with engine hot.
10. **On all models,** the maximum difference between cylinder compression pressures should be 28 psi.

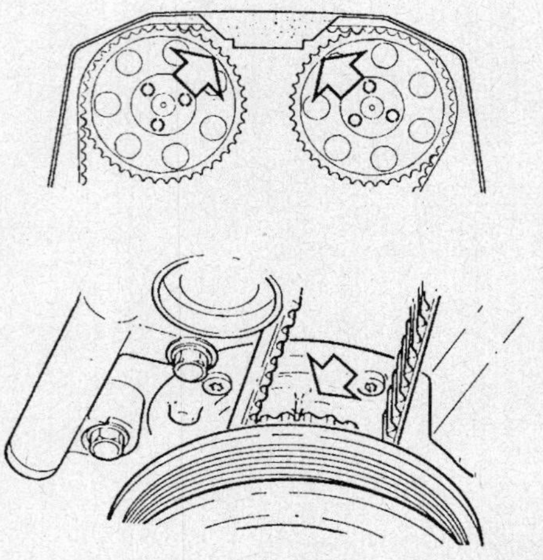
VV1069100008000X

Fig. 1 Timing mark alignment. 2.3L/5 & 2.4L engines

ENGINE MOUNT

REPLACE

1. **On models equipped w/turbocharged engines,** remove charge air pipe over engine.
2. **On all models,** remove upper camshaft belt cover.
3. Remove cover over ignition coils.
4. Remove attaching screw for torque rod.
5. Remove engine torque bracket.
6. Reverse procedure to install. Tighten to specifications.

ENGINE

REPLACE

S70, V70, C70 & S80

The engine and transmission are removed as an assembly.

1. Remove coolant expansion tank cap, then raise and support vehicle.
2. Remove splash guard and air baffle under engine, then open drain cocks on cylinder block and radiator and drain coolant.
3. Remove front wheel, disconnect steering arm/wheel spindle joints, then remove nuts securing ball joints to support arms.
4. Remove ABS lead and brake pipe/hose bracket retaining bolt, then the

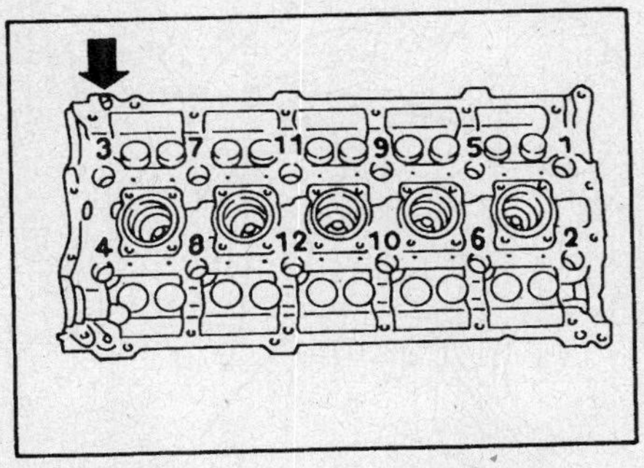

VV1069100009000X

Fig. 2 Cylinder head bolt loosening sequence. 2.3L/5 & 2.4L engines

lefthand driveshaft. **Use lever tool No. 5462, or equivalent, to free shaft.**

5. Disconnect thin black hoses from EVAP canister and white hose from vacuum reservoir.
6. Remove righthand driveshaft and intermediate bearing cap. **Place components carefully on steering servo pipes. Install sealing plugs No. 5488 in driveshaft holes.**
7. Disconnect wheel arch liner to gain access to righthand engine mount bolts, then remove mount bolts and torque arm bolt in transmission.
8. Remove front exhaust pipe nuts, springs and bolts and transmission/engine mounting shield bolt, then disconnect speedometer connector and lower vehicle.
9. Remove battery and battery shelf, fresh air hose between air intake and air cleaner housing, high tension lead between distributor and ignition coil and throttle pulley cover, then disconnect mass air flow sensor electrical connector and cruise control vacuum hose and electrical connector, if equipped.
10. Disconnect intake hose at throttle body and idle air control valve hose and vacuum hose and crankcase ventilation hose from intake hose.
11. Disconnect vacuum hoses and electrical connector from solenoid valve, heater hose and throttle cable from throttle pulley, then remove air cleaner housing and torque arm.
12. Disconnect heater hoses at firewall, brake servo hose and heated oxygen sensor connectors, then remove upper nut on rear engine mount.
13. Disconnect gear selector cables from mounting bracket on transmission, then remove rubber mounted section of cable bracket.
14. **On models equipped with automatic transmission,** disconnect connector, gear selector cables from transmission and oil cooler hoses from cooler.
15. **On all models,** remove clutch slave cylinder retaining ring, then disconnect slave cylinder from transmission, battery ground cable from engine and lower radiator hose at radiator.

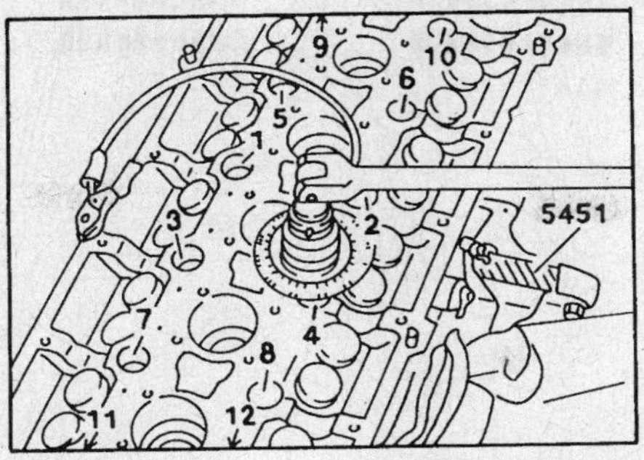

VV1069100010000X

Fig. 3 Cylinder head tightening sequence. 2.3L/5 & 2.4L engines

16. Remove rubber mount from air cleaner mounting bracket, withdraw clutch slave cylinder through front hole in bracket, then place bracket and cylinder aside.
17. Remove both relays from fan shroud, then disconnect electrical connectors and place wiring aside.
18. Remove control module box cooling air ducts, fan shroud screws from radiator, slide fan housing back slightly, then remove air intakes and fan assembly.
19. Remove long mounting bolts from A/C compressor. Leave compressor in position at this time.
20. Remove front engine mount nut and cable duct bracket mounting bolts, then the intake manifold and starter motor support brackets.
21. Disconnect upper radiator hose from thermostat housing, coolant hose between expansion tank and thermostat housing, expansion tank lower hose from engine and temperature sensor lead from bracket on servo pump.
22. Remove auxiliary drive belts, then the servo pump mounting bolts. Leave pump in position at this time.
23. Remove protective cover over fuel distribution manifold, upper and lower fuel pipe clips and fuel distribution manifold bolts, then disconnect braided ground strap from engine.
24. Secure injectors with holders tool No. 5465, or equivalent, then remove fuel distribution manifold complete with injectors and place aside.
25. Disconnect all electrical connectors from engine, then remove wiring harness.
26. Remove spark plug cover and attach lifting lugs tool No. 5459, or equivalent and tool No. 5464, or equivalent, then place servo pump and A/C compressor aside.
27. Remove engine and transmission assembly from vehicle using lifting yokes tool No. 2810, or equivalent and tool No. 5428, or equivalent.
28. Reverse procedure to install.

S90 & V90

The engine and transmission are removed as an assembly.

1. Drain cooling system and crankcase.

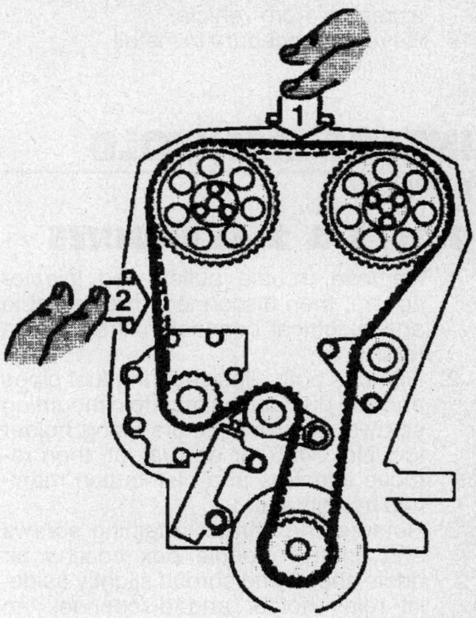

VV1069600023000X

Fig. 4 Timing belt installation. 2.3L/5 & 2.4L engines

2. Remove distributor cap, if necessary.
3. Remove preheating hose and fan shroud.
4. **On models equipped with turbocharged engine,** disconnect exhaust pipe at turbocharger assembly.
5. **On models equipped with power steering and A/C,** remove attaching bolts and position power steering pump and A/C compressor aside. **Do not disconnect lines and/or hoses.**
6. **On all models,** disconnect all electrical wires, hoses, lines and cables that will interfere will engine removal. Label all vacuum hoses to aid in installation.
7. Raise and support vehicle, then remove engine splash guard attaching screws and guard.
8. **On non-turbocharged models,** disconnect exhaust pipe from manifold.
9. **On all models,** remove engine mount to front crossmember attaching bolts.
10. Remove front exhaust pipe support from transmission.
11. **On models equipped with manual transmission,** disconnect clutch cable and remove gearshift lever.
12. **On models equipped with automatic transmission,** disconnect selector linkage from transmission.
13. **On all models,** disconnect speedometer cable, then remove driveshaft from transmission. On some models, the front U-joint is insulated for vibration with a rubber mount. Use care when separating joint from output flange to prevent damage to rubber mounting.
14. Support transmission with suitable jack, remove rear crossmember, then disconnect all electrical connectors from transmission.
15. Install lifting sling tool No. 5035 and lifting yoke tool No. 2810, or equivalents, then carefully lift engine/transmission

assembly from vehicle.
16. Reverse procedure to install.

INTAKE MANIFOLD

REPLACE

2.3L/5 & 2.4L ENGINES

1. Remove throttle pulley and injector covers, then disconnect throttle cable and electrical connectors from injectors.
2. Remove both clips securing fuel pipes and fuel distribution manifold mounting screws, secure injectors using holder tool No. 5465, or equivalent, then remove injectors and distribution manifold from intake.
3. Remove fan shroud retaining screws and control module box cooling air ducts, then bend shroud slightly aside, lift relay holder and disconnect fan electrical connectors.
4. Remove control module box and air cleaner intakes, then the fan assembly.
5. Disconnect idle air control valve and throttle position potentiometer electrical connectors, crankcase ventilation and EVAP canister hoses, servo reservoir and intake manifold vacuum servo hoses, then remove intake hose.
6. Remove upper intake manifold bolts, oil dipstick and bracket lower manifold bolts and manifold bracket bolts, then the intake manifold from cylinder head.
7. Reverse procedure to install. Tighten intake manifold bolts to specifications.

2.9L ENGINE

1. Disconnect electrical connector at air mass meter.
2. Disconnect idling valve electrical connector and air hose, then remove flame trap holder and intake hose.
3. Remove throttle pulley cover, then disconnect throttle switch electrical connector, throttle cable, cruise control vacuum servo, cable bracket at throttle pulley and vacuum hoses at throttle housing.
4. Remove injector cover plate and distribution manifold retaining bolts, then disconnect injector electrical connectors, pressure regulator vacuum hose and fuel line bracket and remove injector/distribution manifold assembly.
5. Remove air preheater inlet hose and manifold bottom mounting, then disconnect lefthand and righthand power stage connectors on bottom of manifold.
6. Disconnect vacuum hoses under manifold and brake servo vacuum hose, then cut away clamps securing rubber sleeves between manifold sections and discard.
7. Remove outer section of manifold, then the inner section of manifold.
8. Reverse procedure to install. Tighten intake manifold bolts to specifications.

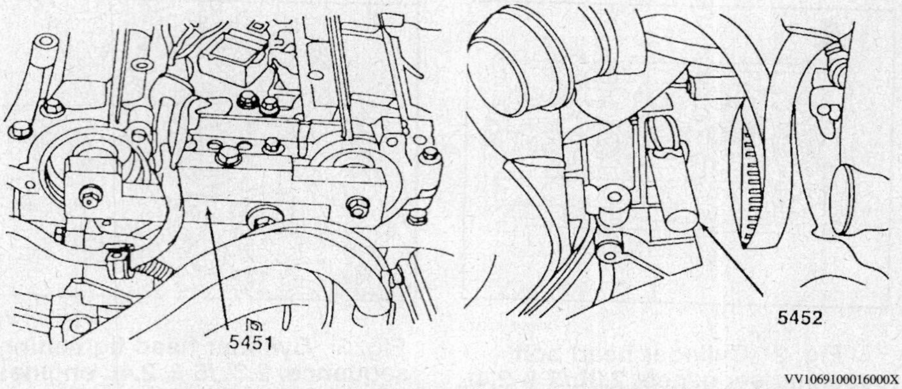

Fig. 5 Locking tool installation. 2.3L/5, 2.4L & 2.9L engines

EXHAUST MANIFOLD

REPLACE

2.3L/5 & 2.4L ENGINES

1. Disconnect front exhaust pipe, then remove heat shields from manifold.
2. Lift manifold off studs, turn 90° to right, then remove from vehicle.
3. Reverse procedure to install.

2.9L ENGINE

1. Disconnect front exhaust pipes, then remove heat shield from manifolds.
2. Remove manifolds from cylinder head.
3. Reverse procedure to install.

CYLINDER HEAD

REPLACE

2.3L/5 & 2.4L ENGINES

Removal

1. Remove coolant expansion tank cap and splash guard under engine.
2. Open drain cocks on cylinder block and radiator and drain coolant. Close drain cocks, then disconnect front exhaust pipe from exhaust manifold.
3. Remove exhaust manifold as outlined under "Exhaust Manifold, Replace," then the timing belt as follows:
   a. Remove spark plug cover, fuel line clips, coolant expansion tank, front timing belt cover and auxiliary drive belt.
   b. Remove righthand front wheel, arch liner and vibration damper guard, then turn crankshaft until all timing marks are aligned, **Fig. 1.**
   c. Place gauge tool No. 998 8500, or equivalent, between exhaust camshaft drive pulley and water pump and read gauge with aid of a mirror. If belt tension is correct, reading should be between 3.5 and 4.6 units. If tension is incorrect, replace tensioner.
   d. Remove tensioner upper mounting bolt and slacken lower mounting bolt, then twist tensioner to free pulley.
   e. Remove lower bolt, tensioner, upper timing belt cover and timing belt.
   f. Spin idler pulleys and check for bearing noise, check pulley surfaces that contact belt and ensure they are clean and smooth, ensure tensioner pulley arm has not seized, then check idler pulley mounting torques.
   g. Inspect tensioner for signs of leakage. Compress tensioner using tool No. 5456, or equivalent. Mount tensioner in tool and tighten center nut fully. Wait until compression has taken place and insert a 2 mm locking pin in plunger.
4. Remove intake manifold as outlined under "Intake Manifold, Replace," then disconnect braided ground straps from engine.
5. Disconnect upper radiator hose from thermostat housing, then mark and remove camshaft pulleys using counterhold tool No. 5199, or equivalent.
6. Remove inner timing belt cover bolt under exhaust camshaft pulley, air cleaner housing and hoses, camshaft position sensor and shutter, distributor cap, rotor and ignition lead clip, torque arm and brackets.
7. Remove bolts in upper half of cylinder head, starting at outer edge and working inward, then the upper half of cylinder head by tapping carefully upward with a copper mallet at parting lugs and at camshaft pulley end.
8. Mark and remove camshafts, then the coolant pipe bolts.
9. Remove cylinder head bolts starting at outer edge and working inward, **Fig. 2,** then the cylinder head and gasket.
10. Clean mating surfaces between exhaust manifold and cylinder head, cylinder block joint face, coolant pipe joint face and joint faces between top and bottom halves of cylinder head. **Do not use a metal scraper. Use a soft putty blade and gasket solvent No. 1 161 340-3.**

Installation

1. Remove starter motor and protective plug on block, then mount crankshaft locking tool No. 5451, or equivalent and turn crankshaft counterclockwise until stopped by tool.
2. Install lower half of cylinder head, then oil and install cylinder head bolts.

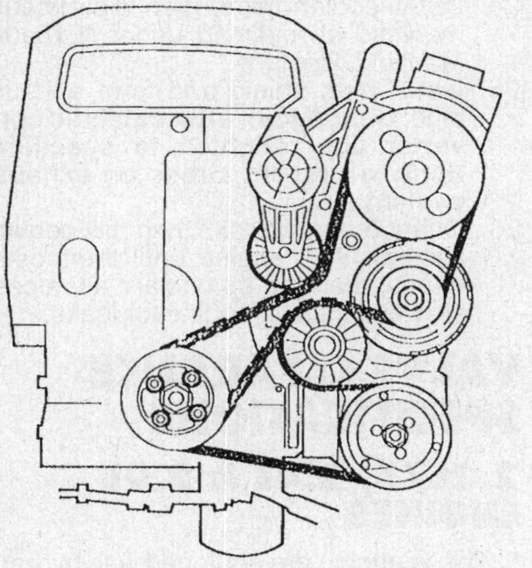

Fig. 6 Serpentine belt routing. 2.3L/5 & 2.4L engines

Torque cylinder head bolts starting inside and working outward, **Fig. 3,** to 15 ft. lbs., then to 44 ft. lbs. and finally another 130° using angle gauge tool No. 951 2050, or equivalent.

3. Install coolant pipe and new O-rings in spark plug wells, then remove No. 1 and 5 spark plugs.
4. Using a roller, apply liquid sealing compound tool No. 1 161 059-9, or equivalent, to upper section of cylinder head. Install camshafts and secure with front end holder tool No. 5453, or equivalent and rear end locking tool No. 5452, or equivalent. **Ensure sealing compound does not penetrate oil passages. A thin coating is sufficient.**
5. Position upper cylinder head and press onto lower section using press tool No. 5454, or equivalent. Tighten mounting bolts to specifications starting from inside and working outward. Remove press tool and camshaft front end holder.
6. Grease camshaft front seals, then tap into position using drift tool No. 5449, or equivalent.
7. Place upper timing belt cover in position, then mount camshaft pulleys and align timing marks. Insert two bolts in each pulley. Screw in bolts until they just contact pulleys, then remove upper timing belt cover.
8. Install timing belt tensioner and tighten bolts to specifications. Place timing belt over camshaft pulleys, around water pump and press over tensioner pulley. Loosen pulley bolts, then remove locking pin from tensioner.
9. Insert third bolt in each camshaft pulley, then tighten bolts to specifications. Install inner timing belt cover bolt below exhaust camshaft pulley and upper timing belt cover.
10. Remove crankshaft locking tool and install protective plug. Install starter motor, then remove camshaft locking tool.
11. Turn crankshaft through two revolutions and ensure timing marks on crankshaft and camshaft pulleys are

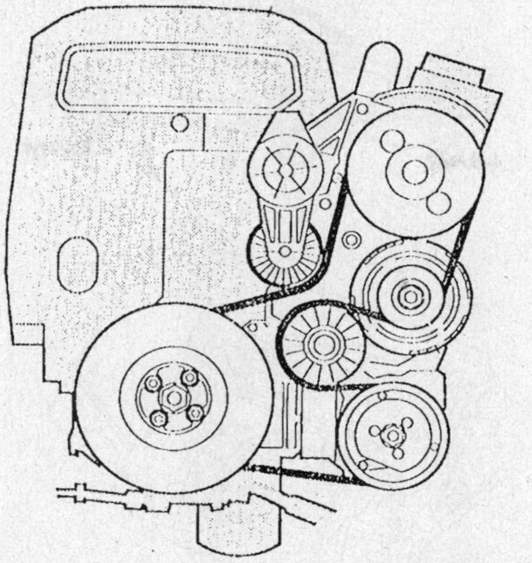

Fig. 7 Serpentine belt routing. 2.9L engine

correctly aligned, then install outer timing belt cover.

12. Grease camshaft rear seals, then press into position using drift tool No. 5450, or equivalent. **Seal is normally installed flush with inside edge of chamfer. If shaft is worn, seal may be located 2 mm further in by reversing tool.**
13. Install torque arm and switch brackets, distributor rotor and ignition lead clip, camshaft position sensor and shutter, spark plugs, distributor cap and ignition leads and air cleaner housing.
14. Install exhaust manifold as outlined under "Exhaust Manifold, Replace," intake manifold as outlined under "Intake Manifold, Replace," engine braided ground straps, exhaust pipe and splash guard under engine.
15. Change engine oil, then fill coolant system. Run engine until thermostat opens, then top up coolant as necessary and inspect engine for leaks.

2.9L ENGINE

Removal

1. Remove coolant expansion tank cap.
2. Open drain cock on righthand side of engine and drain coolant, then close drain cock.
3. Remove exhaust manifold as outlined under "Exhaust Manifold, Replace," then the coolant pipe bolts.
4. Remove timing belt and tensioner as follows:
   a. Remove auxiliary drive belt, front timing belt cover, splash guard under engine, vibration damper guard and ignition coil cover.
   b. Turn crankshaft clockwise until timing marks on camshaft pulleys/timing belt cover mounting plate and crankshaft pulley/oil pump housing are aligned, **Fig. 1,** then remove upper timing belt cover.
   c. Place gauge tool No. 998 8500, or equivalent, between exhaust camshaft drive pulley and water pump

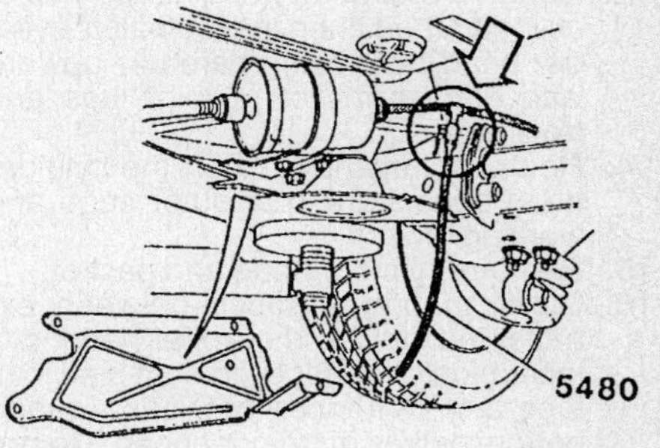

Fig. 8 Fuel filter location. 2.3L/5 & 2.4L engines

   and read gauge. If belt tension is correct, reading should be between 3.5 and 4.6 units. If tension is incorrect, replace tensioner.
   d. Remove tensioner upper mounting bolt and loosen lower mounting bolt, then twist tensioner to free plunger.
   e. Remove lower bolt, tensioner and timing belt.
   f. Spin idler pulleys and check for bearing noise, check pulley surfaces that contact belt and ensure they are clean and smooth, then check tensioner pulley arm and idler pulley mounting torques.
   g. Inspect tensioner for signs of leakage. Compress tensioner using tool No. 5456, or equivalent. Mount tensioner in tool and tighten center nut fully. Wait until compression has taken place and insert a 2 mm lock kingpin in plunger.
5. Remove timing belt cover mounting plate bolt, then disconnect electrical connector at air mass meter.
6. Disconnect idling valve electrical connector and air hose, then remove flame trap holder and intake hose.
7. Remove throttle pulley cover, then disconnect throttle switch electrical connector, throttle cable, cruise control vacuum servo, cable bracket at throttle pulley and vacuum hoses at throttle housing.
8. Remove injector cover plate and distribution manifold retaining bolts, then disconnect injector electrical connectors, pressure regulator vacuum hose and fuel line bracket and remove injector/distribution manifold assembly.
9. Cut away clamps securing rubber sleeves between manifold sections and discard, then remove outer section of intake manifold.
10. Remove coolant temperature sensor, then disconnect coolant hose from thermostat housing.
11. Mark positions and remove ignition coils, then the camshaft pulleys using counterhold tool No. 5199, or equivalent.
12. Remove camshaft position sensor, switch mounting bracket, ground terminals 1 and 2, temperature sensor connector and coolant hoses at rear of engine.

13. Remove mounting bolts for top half of cylinder head, then the top half of cylinder head by tapping carefully upward with copper mallet at joint lugs and front ends.
14. Remove camshafts, then the cylinder head bolts starting at outer edge and working inward.
15. Remove cylinder head and gasket.
16. Clean mating surfaces between exhaust manifold and cylinder head, cylinder block joint face, coolant pipe joint face and joint faces between top and bottom halves of cylinder head. **Do not use a metal scraper. Use a soft putty blade and gasket solvent No. 1 161 340-3.**

Installation

1. Remove starter motor and protective plug on block, then mount crankshaft locking tool No. 5451, or equivalent and turn crankshaft counterclockwise until stopped by tool.
2. Install lower half of cylinder head, then oil and install cylinder head bolts. **Torque** cylinder head bolts in sequence starting inside and working outward, to 15 ft. lbs., then to 44 ft. lbs. and finally another 130°.
3. Install new O-rings in spark plug wells, then oil camshaft bearing seats.
4. Using a roller, apply liquid sealing compound tool No. 1 161 059-9, or equivalent, to upper section of cylinder head. Install camshafts and secure with front end holder tool No. 5453, or equivalent and rear end locking tool No. 5452, or equivalent. **Ensure sealing compound does not penetrate oil passages. A thin coating is sufficient.**
5. Position upper cylinder head and press onto lower section using press tool No. 5454, or equivalent. Tighten mounting bolts to specifications starting from inside and working outward. Remove press tools and camshaft front end holder.
6. Grease camshaft front seals, then tap into position using drift tool No. 5449, or equivalent.
7. Place upper timing belt cover in position, then mount camshaft pulleys and align timing marks. Tighten each pulley with two bolts, then remove upper timing belt cover.
8. Install timing belt cover mounting plate bolt, then place timing belt around crankshaft and righthand idler. Place timing belt over camshaft pulleys, around water pump and press over tensioner pulley.
9. Install timing belt tensioner and tighten to specifications, then loosen camshaft pulley bolts and remove tensioner locking pin.
10. Insert third bolt in each camshaft pulley, then tighten bolts alternately to specifications.
11. Remove crankshaft locking tool and install protective plug. Install starter motor, then remove camshaft locking tool.
12. Install upper timing belt cover, then ensure timing marks on crankshaft and camshaft pulleys are correctly aligned.

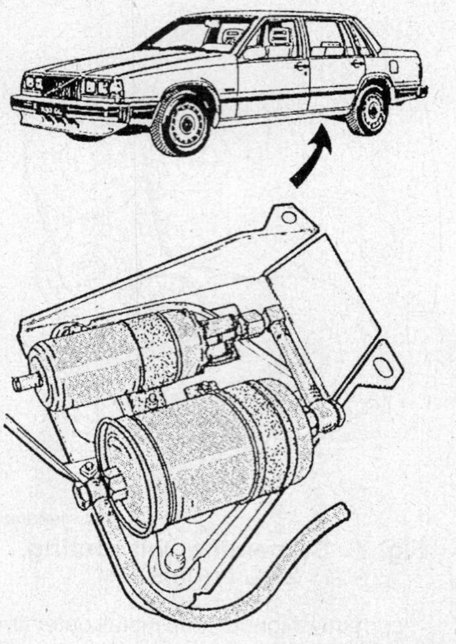

Fig. 9 Fuel filter location. 2.9L engine

13. Grease camshaft rear seals, then press into position using drift tool No. 5450, or equivalent. **Seal is normally installed flush with inside edge of chamfer. If shaft is worn, seal may be located 2 mm further in by reversing tool.**
14. Install temperature sensor connector, ground terminals 1 and 2, cover, switch mounting bracket, shutter, camshaft position sensor and coolant hoses at rear of engine.
15. Install ignition coils spark plug cover, front timing belt cover, auxiliary drive belt, vibration damper guard and splash guard under engine.
16. Pass wiring between 2nd and 3rd branches of inner intake manifold, then position outer section of intake manifold and crankcase ventilation hoses.
17. Insert manifold branches in rubber sleeves, then fit and secure with new Oetiker clamps.
18. Connect vacuum hoses and brake servo hose, then tighten manifold lower mounting.
19. Connect power stage connectors and air preheater hose, then inspect injector O-rings and lubricate with water-free vaseline.
20. Connect fuel pressure regulator vacuum hose, then press fuel distribution manifold into position and tighten manifold.
21. Connect injector electrical connectors and ECC vacuum hoses, then install injector cover.
22. Connect crankcase ventilation hoses, idling valve lead and air hose, air mass meter and throttle housing connector, then install cable bracket at throttle pulley.
23. Connect coolant hose to thermostat housing, then the coolant temperature sensor.
24. Install coolant pipe, then the exhaust manifold as outlined under "Exhaust Manifold, Replace."
25. Install heat shield and front exhaust pipe. **Unbolt joint after catalytic converter and retighten to specifications to prevent stress on exhaust system.**
26. Change engine oil, then fill coolant system. Run engine until thermostat opens, then top up coolant as necessary and inspect engine for leaks.

VALVE CLEARANCE SPECIFICATIONS

2.3L/5, 2.4L & 2.9L ENGINES

These engine are equipped with hydraulic valve lash adjusters and no adjustment is required.

VALVE ADJUSTMENT

2.3L/5, 2.4L & 2.9L ENGINES

No provision for adjustment is provided.

VALVE GUIDES

2.3L/5, 2.4L & 2.9L ENGINES

1. Mount cylinder head on fixture tool No. 5363, or equivalent. Adjust angle of inclination using holes at top of fixture ends. Clamp head to fixture using locating hole No. 2 on face. Use four sleeves as spacers for cylinder head bolts.
2. Using drift tool No. 5364, or equivalent, slowly press guide until drift bears against valve spring seat, then using drift tool No. 5365, or equivalent, slowly press guide until drift bears against valve seat. Remove valve guide and inspect upper section of guide bore.
3. Place new guide on drift tool No. 999 5505, or equivalent and slowly press guide into head until drift bears against valve spring seat. Top of guide should project by .50–.52 inch. **Press force must be at least 2025 lbs. If press force is lower, guide must be removed and reamed out for fitting oversized guide.**
4. Ream guide using reamer tool No. 999 5373, or equivalent, from combustion chamber side, then grind valve and seat after replacing guide.

FRONT COVER

REPLACE

2.3L/5 & 2.4L ENGINES

1. Remove spark plug cover, fuel line clips and coolant expansion tank, then the front timing belt cover.
2. Remove righthand front wheel, arch liner and vibration damper guard, then turn crankshaft until all timing marks are aligned, **Fig. 1.**

3. Remove upper timing belt cover.
4. Reverse procedure to install.

2.9L ENGINE

1. Remove auxiliary drive belt, front timing cover, splash guard under engine, vibration damper guard and ignition coil cover.
2. Turn crankshaft clockwise until timing marks on camshaft pulleys/timing belt cover mounting plate and crankshaft pulley/oil pump housing are aligned, **Fig. 1,** then remove upper timing cover.
3. Reverse procedure to install.

TIMING BELT

REPLACE

2.3L/5 & 2.4L ENGINES

With the timing belt removed, avoid turning the camshaft or crankshaft. If movement is required, exercise extreme caution to avoid valve damage caused by piston contact.

Removal

1. Remove spark plug cover, fuel line clips, coolant expansion tank, front timing belt cover and auxiliary drive belt.
2. Remove righthand front wheel, arch liner and vibration damper guard, then turn crankshaft until all timing marks are aligned, **Fig. 1.**
3. Place gauge tool No. 998 8500, or equivalent, between exhaust camshaft drive pulley and water pump and read gauge with aid of a mirror. If belt tension is correct, reading should be between 3.5 and 4.6 units. If tension is incorrect, replace tensioner.
4. Remove tensioner upper mounting bolt and slacken lower mounting bolt, then twist tensioner to free pulley.
5. Remove lower bolt, tensioner, upper timing belt cover and timing belt.
6. Spin idler pulleys and check for bearing noise, check pulley surfaces that contact belt and ensure they are clean and smooth, ensure tensioner pulley arm has not seized, then check idler pulley mounting torques.
7. Inspect tensioner for signs of leakage. Compress tensioner using tool No. 5456, or equivalent. Mount tensioner in tool and tighten center nut fully. Wait until compression has taken place and insert a 2 mm locking pin in plunger.

Installation

1. Install belt tensioner and tighten to specifications, then place belt around crankshaft pulley and righthand idler pulley, over camshaft pulleys, around water pump pulley and press over tensioner pulley, **Fig. 4.**
2. Remove locking pin from tensioner, install upper timing belt cover, then turn crankshaft through two revolutions and ensure timing marks on crankshaft and camshaft pulleys are correctly aligned.
3. Install fuel pipe clips, front timing belt cover, auxiliary drive belt, spark plug cover, coolant expansion tank, vibration damper guard and wheel arch liner.
4. Test run engine and check operation.

2.9L ENGINE

With the timing belt removed, avoid turning the camshaft or crankshaft. If movement is required, exercise extreme caution to avoid valve damage caused by piston contact.

Removal

1. Remove auxiliary drive belt, front timing belt cover, splash guard under engine, vibration damper guard and ignition coil cover.
2. Turn crankshaft clockwise until timing marks on camshaft pulleys/timing belt cover mounting plate and crankshaft pulley/oil pump housing are aligned, **Fig. 1,** then remove upper timing belt cover.
3. Place gauge No. 998 8500 between exhaust camshaft drive pulley and water pump and read gauge. If belt tension is correct, reading should be between 3.5 and 4.6 units. If tension is incorrect, replace tensioner.
4. Remove tensioner upper mounting bolt and loosen lower mounting bolt, then twist tensioner to free plunger.
5. Remove lower bolt, tensioner and timing belt.
6. Spin idler pulleys and check for bearing noise, check pulley surfaces that contact belt and ensure they are clean and smooth, then check tensioner pulley arm and idler pulley mounting torques.
7. Inspect tensioner for signs of leakage. Compress tensioner using tool No. 5456, or equivalent. Mount tensioner in tool and tighten center nut fully. Wait until compression has taken place and insert a 2 mm locking pin in plunger.

Installation

1. Place belt around crankshaft pulley and righthand idler pulley, over camshaft pulleys, around water pump pulley and press over tensioner pulley.
2. Install belt tensioner and tighten to specifications, remove locking pin from tensioner, install upper timing belt cover, then turn crankshaft through two revolutions and ensure timing marks on crankshaft and camshaft pulleys are correctly aligned.
3. Install ignition coil cover, front timing belt cover, auxiliary drive belt, vibration damper guard and splash guard under engine.
4. Test run engine and check operation.

CAMSHAFT

REPLACE

When camshaft is replaced due to wear, it is essential that the engine be flushed clean before installing new components. Replace engine oil and filter, run engine for approximately ten minutes, then drain engine oil and remove filter. After camshaft has been replaced, install new oil filter and fill engine with new oil.

2.3L/5, 2.4L & 2.9L ENGINES

1. Remove timing belt as outlined under "Timing Belt, Replace," then the camshaft pulleys using counterhold tool No. 5199, or equivalent.
2. Remove bolts from top half of cylinder head starting at outside and working inward, then the top half of cylinder head by tapping gently with a plastic mallet adjacent to lugs and front end of camshafts.
3. Remove camshafts by twisting and lifting simultaneously.
4. Reverse procedure to install, noting the following:
   a. Install top half of cylinder head using press tool No. 5454, or equivalent.
   b. Tighten fasteners to specifications.

CAMSHAFT OIL SEAL

REPLACE

2.3L/5, 2.4L & 2.9L ENGINES

1. Remove timing belt as outlined under "Timing Belt, Replace," then the camshaft pulleys using counterhold tool No. 5199, or equivalent.
2. Using a screwdriver, remove front camshaft seal(s). Ensure sealing surface is not damaged.
3. Coat new seal(s) with grease, then install seal(s) using drift tool No. 5449, or equivalent.
4. **If replacing rear seal(s) only,** proceed as follows:
   a. Remove camshaft position sensor and shutter.
   b. Using a screwdriver, remove rear camshaft seal(s). Ensure sealing surface is not damaged.
   c. Coat new seal(s) with grease, then install seal(s) using drift tool No. 5450, or equivalent. **Seal is normally installed flush with inside edge of chamfer. If shaft is worn, seal may be located .080 inch (2 mm) further in by reversing tool.**
5. **If front and rear seals or front seals only were replaced,** proceed as follows:
   a. **On 2.4L engine,** remove air cleaner housing and hoses, distributor cap, rotor and ignition lead clip and cooling fan.
   b. **On both engines,** remove camshaft position sensor and shutter and starter motor.
   c. Remove protective plug on block behind starter motor and mount crankshaft locking tool No. 5451, or equivalent, in position, **Fig. 5.** Turn crankshaft clockwise until stopped by tool, then mount camshaft locking tool No. 5452, or equivalent, at rear of camshafts.
   d. Install camshaft pulleys. Insert two

bolts in each pulley until just in contact with pulleys. **Ensure camshaft bolt holes are centered in pulley holes.**
e. Install timing belt as outlined under "Timing Belt, Replace."
f. Loosen two bolts in camshaft pulleys, install third bolt, then tighten bolts alternately to specifications using counterhold.
g. remove locking tools, then install upper timing cover.
h. Rotate crankshaft through two revolutions and ensure timing marks are still aligned.
i. Install camshaft position sensor and shutter, distributor rotor and cover, air cleaner housing and hoses, ignition coil cover, spark plug cover, starter motor, cooling fan, wheel arch and liner.

6. **On all models,** test run engine and check operation.

PISTON & ROD ASSEMBLY

2.3L/5, 2.4L & 2.9L ENGINES

Assemble connecting rods to pistons with arrow on piston crown facing forward and numerical designation stamp on connecting rod facing toward intake side of block.

PISTONS, PINS & RINGS

2.3L/5, 2.4L & 2.9L ENGINES

Pistons, pins and rings are not available in oversizes.

Oversize piston pins are not available. However, connecting rod bushing may be replaced if rod bore is worn.

MAIN & ROD BEARINGS

2.3L/5, 2.4L & 2.9L ENGINES

Main bearings are not available in undersizes.

Connecting rod bearings are available in .010 inch (.25 mm) and .020 inch (.50 mm) undersizes.

CRANKSHAFT SEAL

REPLACE

FRONT

2.3L/5, 2.4L & 2.9L Engines

1. Remove timing belt as outlined under "Timing Belt, Replace."
2. Remove guard plate, then the vibration damper using counterhold tool No. 5433, or equivalent.
3. Remove crankshaft belt pulley using a universal puller and two vibration damper bolts. **Finger tighten bolts as far as possible in pulley, then attach puller so that arms act on bolts, not on pulley.**
4. Use a screwdriver to pry out oil seal, then clean sealing face.
5. Grease oil seal, install seal on tool No. 5455, or equivalent, then press into place using crankshaft center nut.
6. Install timing belt as outlined under "Timing Belt, Replace," then the vibration damper. Tighten nut to specifications.

REAR

2.3L/5, 2.4L & 2.9L Engines

1. Remove transmission and if applicable, clutch assembly. Refer to "Clutch & Manual Transmission" or "Automatic Transmission" section for procedure.
2. Lock flywheel in place with gear sector No. 5112, then remove flywheel.
3. Use a screwdriver to pry out oil seal, being careful not to damage sealing surfaces on holder or crankshaft.
4. Inspect and clean sealing surfaces in holder and on crankshaft.
5. Oil lips of seal, install seal onto handle tool No. 1801 and drift tool No. 5430, or equivalents, then tap in seal until drift bottoms on crankshaft.
6. Install gear sector No. 5112 to lock flywheel, then tighten new flywheel bolts, coated with thread locking compound, to specifications and remove gear sector.
7. If applicable, install clutch assembly, refer to "Clutch & Manual Transmission" or "Automatic Transmission" section for procedure.

OIL PAN

REPLACE

2.3L/5, 2.4L & 2.9L ENGINES

1. Raise and support vehicle, then drain engine oil into suitable container.
2. Remove engine oil filter.
3. **On 2.9L engine,** disconnect flame trap return line.
4. **On all models,** remove oil pan retaining bolts.
5. Tap pan loose from engine block with a rubber mallet.
6. Clean old gasket material from oil pan and engine block mating surfaces.
7. Apply suitable liquid gasket to oil pan and install. Tighten oil pan bolts to specifications.

OIL PUMP

REPLACE

2.3L/5, 2.4L & 2.9L ENGINES

1. Remove crankshaft front seal as outlined under "Crankshaft Seal, Replace."
2. Remove oil pump.
3. Reverse procedure to install, noting the following:
   a. Use tool No. 5455, or equivalent and crankshaft center nut to press pump into place. Use bolts as guides.
   b. Tighten pump bolts to specifications.

BELT TENSION DATA

When belt tension is correct, belts may be depressed .20–.40 inch (5–10 mm) halfway between pulleys.

SERPENTINE DRIVE BELT

BELT ROUTING

Refer to **Figs. 6 and 7,** for proper belt routing.

COOLING SYSTEM BLEED

2.3L/5, 2.4L & 2.9L ENGINES

1. Fill system through coolant expansion tank.
2. Start engine and allow to reach normal operating temperatures.
3. Top up coolant as necessary.

THERMOSTAT

REPLACE

1. Drain coolant to below level of thermostat housing, then replace thermostat.
2. Refill coolant system.

WATER PUMP

REPLACE

2.3L/5, 2.4L & 2.9L ENGINES

1. Open drain cock on righthand side of engine block, remove coolant expansion tank cap and drain cooling system into suitable container.
2. Remove timing belt as outlined under "Timing Belt, Replace."
3. Remove water pump.
4. Reverse procedure to install.

RADIATOR

REPLACE

1. Remove expansion tank cap, then remove guard from under radiator.
2. Drain coolant into suitable container.
3. Remove electric cooling fan, then disconnect radiator hoses.
4. **On models equipped with A/C,** remove condenser to radiator mounting bolts, then the condenser.
5. **On all models,** remove radiator mounting bolts, then radiator.
6. Reverse procedure to install.

FUEL PUMP

REPLACE

2.3L/5 & 2.4L ENGINES

1. Drain fuel system as follows:
   a. Remove throttle pulley cover, fuel distribution manifold cover and shield over valve on fuel distribution manifold.
   b. Connect hose/union tool No. 999 5484, or equivalent, to fuel drainage unit tool Nos. 981 2270, 2273 and 2282, or equivalents and start fuel drainage unit.
   c. Connect union on fuel drainage unit to valve on fuel distribution manifold, then raise and support vehicle.
   d. Remove fuel filter cover and shield over valve at fuel filter, then use key tool No. 999 5480, or equivalent, to open vent cock upstream of fuel filter, **Fig. 8.**
2. Tilt righthand rear seat forward, then remove luggage compartment mat and cover over pump unit nut in tank.
3. Remove righthand luggage compartment panel, then disconnect fuel pump electrical connector.
4. Mark position, then disconnect quick release couplings on delivery and return lines using a screwdriver to lift outer sleeve carefully.
5. Remove pump unit nut using spanner tool No. 999 5485, or equivalent, then fabricate a tool to aid in pump removal by fitting two quick release couplings tool No. 3517 139-6, or equivalent, to a tube tool No. 1266 870-3, or equivalent.
6. Connect couplings to delivery and return lines, lift out pump unit and rubber seal, then reinstall pump unit nut on branch on tank.
7. Disconnect upper clip on fuel hose, then the electrical leads.
8. Twist lower section of unit to right, then pull pump base downward while working fuel hose downward.
9. Separate pump retaining halves, then remove spring and rubber spacer and disconnect fuel hose from pump.
10. Reverse procedure to install. Tighten fasteners to specifications.

2.9L ENGINE

The main fuel pump may be located on the lefthand side of the fuel tank or attached to a bracket underneath vehicle under the rear seat.

1. Clamp off the tank to pump hose with suitable pliers. Disconnect fuel lines from pump.
2. Disconnect wire connector from pump.
3. Remove pump retaining bolts, then the pump.
4. Reverse procedure to install. Tighten fasteners to specifications.

FUEL FILTER

REPLACE

2.3L/5 & 2.4L ENGINES

1. Drain fuel system as follows:
   a. Remove throttle pulley cover, fuel distribution manifold cover and shield over valve on fuel distribution manifold.
   b. Connect hose/union tool No. 999 5484, or equivalent, to fuel drainage unit tool Nos. 981 2270, 2273 and 2282, or equivalents and start fuel drainage unit.
   c. Connect union on fuel drainage unit to valve on fuel distribution manifold, then raise and support vehicle.
   d. Remove fuel filter cover and shield over valve at fuel filter, then use key tool No. 999 5480, or equivalent, to open vent cock upstream of fuel filter, **Fig. 8.**
2. Disconnect filter quick release couplings using an open spanner to push sleeves back, then remove screw securing filter clip.
3. Remove filter.
4. Reverse procedure to install.

2.9L ENGINE

Fuel filter is located next to fuel pump, **Fig. 9.** Disconnect filter couplings by pushing sleeves back with a 17 mm open end wrench.

TIGHTENING SPECIFICATIONS

2.3L/5 & 2.4L ENGINES

Year	Component	Torque, Ft. Lbs.
1998–2001	Camshaft Gear Bolts	15
	Carrier Plate Bolts	33①
	Connecting Rod Bearing Cap Nuts	15②
	Cylinder Head	③
	Engine Mounts (Front & Rear)	37
	Engine Mount (Righthand)	18
	Exhaust Manifold Bolts	17
	Flywheel Bolts	33④
	Fuel Distribution Manifold Bolts	84⑤⑦
	Intake Manifold Bolts	12
	Oil Pan Bolts	13
	Oil Pump Bolts	84⑦
	Oil Suction Line	15
	Oil Sump Bolts	13
	Oil Sump Plug	25
	Oil Trap	11
	Timing Belt Damper Unit Bolt	18
	Timing Belt Idler Pulley Bolt	18
	Timing Belt Tensioning Pulley Bolt	28
	Torque Arm Bolts	37
	Transmission To Engine Bolts	36
	Vibration Damper Flange Bolts	18⑥
	Vibration Damper Nut	132
	Water Pump Bolts	12

① — Tighten an additional 50.°
② — Tighten an additional 90.°
③ — Refer to "Cylinder Head, Replace."
④ — Tighten an additional 65.°
⑤ — Tighten an additional 75.°
⑥ — Tighten an additional 30.°
⑦ — Inch Lbs.

2.9L ENGINE

Year	Component	Torque, Ft. Lbs.
1998–2001	Camshaft Gear Bolt	15
	Carrier Plate Bolts	33①
	Connecting Rod Bearing Cap Nuts	15②
	Cylinder Head	③
	Engine Mount Nuts (Top)	37
	Flywheel Bolts	33①
	Fuel Distribution Manifold Bolts	84⑥④
	Intake Manifold Bolts	15
	Oil Pan Bolts	15
	Oil Suction Pipe	13
	Oil Sump Bolts	15
	Oil Sump Plug	28
	Oil Trap	11
	Timing Belt Damper Unit Bolt	18
	Timing Belt Idler Pulley Bolt	18
	Timing Belt Tensioning Pulley Bolt	29
	Vibration Damper Flange Bolts	26⑤
	Vibration Damper Nut	222
	Water Pump Bolts	13

① — Tighten an additional 50.°
② — Tighten an additional 90.°
③ — Refer to "Cylinder Head, Replace."
④ — Tighten an additional 75.°
⑤ — Tighten an additional 60.°
⑥ — Inch Lbs.

Clutch & Manual Transmission

NOTE: On Air Bag Equipped Models, Refer To "Air Bag System Precautions" Located In The Front Of This Manual For System Disarming & Arming Procedures.

INDEX

	Page No.
Adjustments	9-19
Clutch Pedal	9-19
Clutch, Replace	9-19
S70, V70, C70 & S80	9-19
Hydraulic System Service	9-19
Clutch Master Cylinder, Replace	9-19
Slave Cylinder, Replace	9-19
Precautions	9-19
Air Bag Systems	9-19
Battery Ground Cable	9-19
Microprocessor Radios	9-19
Tightening Specifications	9-21
Transaxle, Replace	9-19
S70, V70, C70 & S80	9-19
S90 & V90	9-20

PRECAUTIONS

AIR BAG SYSTEMS

Refer to "Air Bag System Precautions" in the front of this manual for system disarming and arming procedures.

BATTERY GROUND CABLE

Prior to service, disconnect battery ground cable and isolate as required.

MICROPROCESSOR RADIOS

On models equipped with microprocessor radios, always switch radio off before disconnecting or connecting battery ground cable to prevent damage to the radio.

ADJUSTMENTS

CLUTCH PEDAL

Mechanical Actuation

On vehicles with clutch pedal return spring mounted on the clutch pedal assembly, check clearance by pressing fork toward rear of vehicle. Clearance should be .039–.118 inch (1–3 mm). If necessary, adjust clearance using nut on cable.

On vehicles with clutch pedal return spring mounted on the clutch fork, check clearance by pressing fork forward. Clearance should be .039–.118 inch (1–3 mm). If necessary, adjust clearance using nuts on cable.

Hydraulic Actuation

This system is designed so clutch fork and throw-out bearing touch lightly on pressure plate. No provision for adjustment is provided.

HYDRAULIC SYSTEM SERVICE

CLUTCH MASTER CYLINDER, REPLACE

S70, V70, C70 & S80

1. Remove air cleaner, bracket retaining screws, then cable tie to drain hose and move to one side.
2. Place suitable shop towel under clutch master cylinder to protect paint.
3. Drain brake fluid from reservoir into suitable container, then disconnect brake line from clutch master cylinder.
4. Remove lower instrument panel, then the knee guard.
5. Fold carpeting back, remove clip securing clutch master cylinder pushrod to clutch pedal.
6. Remove nut and bolt securing clutch master cylinder to firewall, then clutch master cylinder.
7. Reverse procedure to install, noting the following:
   a. **Torque** clutch master cylinder attaching nuts to 18 ft. lbs.
   b. **Torque** knee guard to 15 ft. lbs.
   c. Bleed system using clutch bleeder unit tool No. 998 5876-3, or equivalent, following manufacturer's instructions.

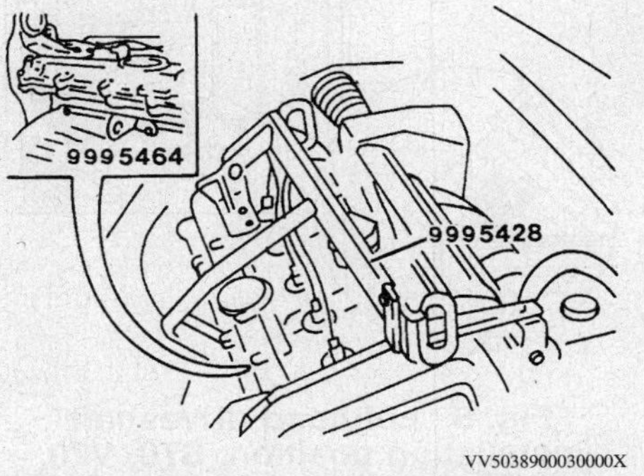

Fig. 1 Lifting lug & lifting yoke installation. S70, V70, C70 & S80

SLAVE CYLINDER, REPLACE

1. Disconnect hose from pipe and bracket.
2. Remove slave cylinder to bellhousing attaching bolts, then the slave cylinder.
3. Reverse procedure to install, then bleed hydraulic system.

CLUTCH

REPLACE

S70, V70, C70 & S80

1. Remove Transaxle as outlined under "Transaxle, Replace."
2. Hold clutch stationary using clutch tool No. 999 5112, or equivalent.
3. Remove pressure plate mounting bolts in a cross directional pattern, slowly backing off an equal amount on each bolt to prevent warpage.
4. Remove pressure plate and disc.
5. Remove throw out bearing from sleeve and fork.
6. Reverse procedure to install, noting the following:
   a. Tighten pressure plate mounting bolts in a cross directional pattern so clutch moves forward onto locating pin and lies flat against flywheel.
   b. **Torque** pressure plate attaching bolts to 18 ft. lbs.

TRANSAXLE

REPLACE

S70, V70, C70 & S80

1. Move steering wheel to highest position.
2. Place shift lever in neutral position, remove battery, air cleaner and air intake, battery shelf, then air cleaner bracket retaining screws.
3. Remove selector cables from bracket and levers, then selector link plate by tapping out pin.
4. Remove back-up light switch connector.
5. Remove cable tie from engine cable harness, then ground lead from transaxle.
6. Remove circlip from clutch slave cylinder to transaxle, then clutch slave cylinder.
7. Loosen nut on rear engine mounting/ splash guard, remove five bolts securing starter and transaxle, then remove

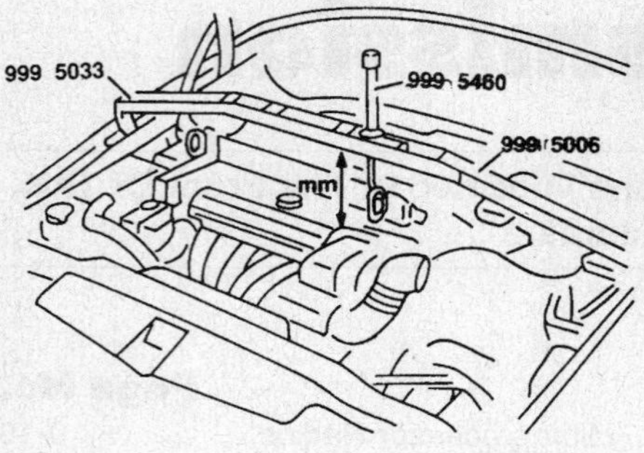

VV5038900031000X

Fig. 2 Supports, lifting beam & lifting hook installation. S70, V70, C70 & S80

cover over spark plug wires. Lift coolant expansion tank off bracket and place aside.

8. Remove tie bar between torque arm and engine, then disconnect ground lead from cable harness.
9. Install lifting tool No. 999 5459, or equivalent, on valve cover using two bolts from tie bar.
10. Install lifting lug tool No. 999 5464, or equivalent, with center bolt to manifold heat guard. Install lifting yoke tool No. 999 5428, or equivalent, then adjust lifting yoke to lifting lugs, **Fig. 1.**
11. Place support tool No. 999 5033, or equivalent, onto fender **Fig. 2.** Install lifting beam tool No. 999 5006, or equivalent, onto support. Place lifting beam directly above lugs on lifting yoke.
12. Install lifting hook tool No. 999 5460, or equivalent, as shown in **Fig. 2.** Extend hook approximately 5 mm to relieve the weight on engine mounting.
13. Raise and support vehicle, remove tire and wheels, then ABS sensor from lefthand outboard shaft.
14. Disconnect brake line and ABS cable brackets on both sides.
15. Remove fasteners from lefthand fenderwell.
16. Remove hub center nut locking device, then install tool No. 9995461, or equivalent and remove nut, **Fig. 3.**
17. Remove front splash guard bolts, push guard forward so locating pins on back come loose, then disconnect front of guard and remove.
18. Remove nuts attaching link arms and ball joints, then disconnect link arm and ball joints.
19. Remove roll bar, then any vacuum or electrical connectors as needed.
20. Remove steering gear line bracket, then two bolts securing the steady bar bracket to transaxle.
21. Drain transaxle into suitable container.
22. Remove righthand driveshaft bearing cap, driveshaft, then twist MacPherson strut out of way.
23. Loosen bolts holding steering gear to engine mounting one turn, remove nuts holding steering gear to subframe.
24. Position a jack tool No. 998 5972-0, or equivalent, under lefthand side of subframe, then gently tighten.

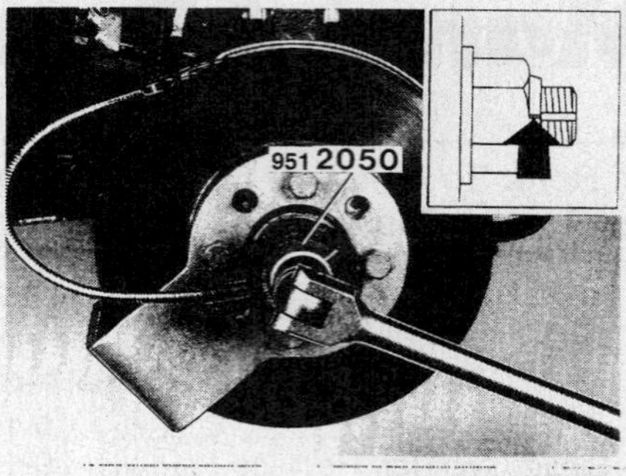

VV5038900032000X

Fig. 3 Hub attaching nut removal & installation. S70, V70, C70 & S80

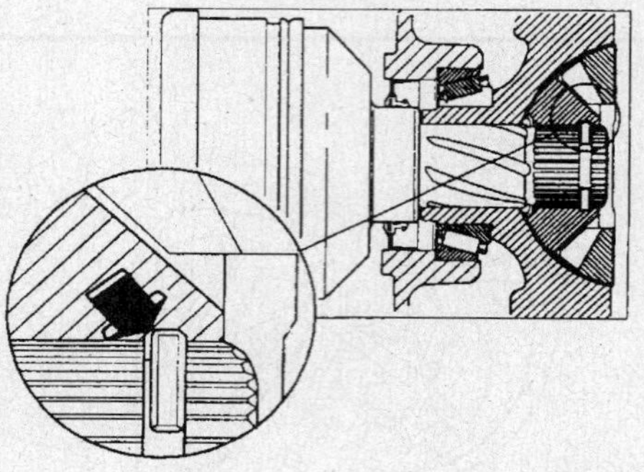

VV5038900029000X

Fig. 5 Lefthand driveshaft installation position. S70, V70, C70 & S80

25. Remove fixing bolts to subframe brackets on both sides, then unscrew two bolts holding subframe to body on righthand by 15 mm.
26. Lower subframe, let frame hang free from bolts on righthand side.
27. Remove bolts to engine mounting subframe and nut on top of engine mounting, then remove engine mounting. **Ensure steering gear is hanging properly on hook so that lower steering wheel shaft section does not slip out of steering column.**
28. Disconnect heated oxygen sensor cable terminals, then remove cover from rear engine mounting and rear mounting from transaxle.
29. Twist lefthand MacPherson strut and pull out. Tap lefthand driveshaft end with plastic mallet and pull shaft out of hub.
30. Using tool No. 999 5462, or equivalent, remove driveshaft from transaxle.
31. Lower engine and transaxle using lifting hook until approximately 130 mm of hook thread is clear.
32. Install universal tool No. 999 5972 and transaxle fixture 999 5463, or equivalents, then attach transaxle fixture to transaxle using fixing bolts from steady bar bracket. At same time position support plate 5463-2, or equivalent, on fixture, **Fig. 4.**
33. Raise engine, then remove seven remaining transaxle to engine attaching bolts.
34. Pull transaxle away from engine, then

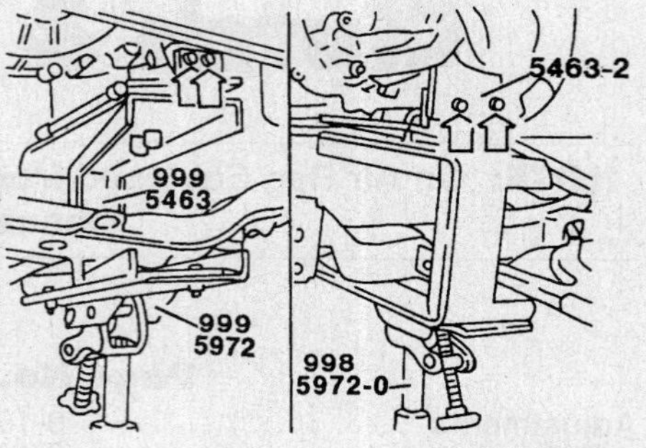

VV5038900033000X

Fig. 4 Transaxle jack installation. S70, V70, C70 & S80

lower jack and transaxle.

35. Reverse procedure to install, noting the following:
    a. **Torque** transaxle to engine bolts to 37 ft. lbs.
    b. **Torque** subframe and support plate attaching bolts to 77 ft. lbs. then an additional 120.°
    c. **Torque** frame bracket bolts to 37 ft. lbs.
    d. **Torque** righthand driveshaft bearing cap to 18 ft. lbs.
    e. When installing lefthand driveshaft, ensure driveshaft circlip snaps into place, **Fig. 5.**
    f. **Torque** lefthand hub nut using tool Nos. 999 5461 and protractor 951 2050, or equivalents to 80 ft. lbs. plus an additional 60° as shown in **Fig. 3.**
    g. **Torque** transaxle/starter motor bolts to 29 ft. lbs.

S90 & V90

1. **On models equipped with overdrive,** raise and support rear of vehicle. Start engine and engage 4th gear. Engage overdrive, then depress clutch pedal and stop engine.
2. **On all models,** support engine using support No. 5006, or equivalent.
3. Working under vehicle, disconnect selector lever from control rod.
4. From inside of vehicle, remove selector lever cover from floor.
5. Disconnect back-up light switch electrical connector.
6. Remove reverse detent plate, if equipped and selector lever.
7. Remove plastic bushing and rubber ring from selector lever mount.
8. Disconnect overdrive electrical connector, if equipped.
9. Disconnect speedometer cable, then driveshaft from transmission flange.
10. Remove starter bolts and position starter aside.
11. Remove slave cylinder from bellhousing and upper bolts securing bellhousing. Do not remove two lower bolts.
12. Loosen front exhaust pipe joint, then remove exhaust pipe bracket bolts and bracket.
13. Remove crossmember assembly from vehicle.
14. Lower hook of support tool No. 5006, or equivalent, until .4 inch clearance

remains between distributor cover and bulkhead.
15. Remove bellhousing to engine mount bolts.
16. Position a suitable jack under transmission.
17. Remove two lower bellhousing to engine bolts.
18. Separate bellhousing from engine, then lower transmission from vehicle.
19. Reverse procedure to install.

TIGHTENING SPECIFICATIONS

Year	Component	Torque, Ft. Lbs.
S70, V70, C70 & S80		
1998–2001	Anti-Roll Bar Link To Spring Strut	37
	Ball Joint To Control Arm	13②
	Ball Joint To Steering Knuckle	37
	Control Arm To Subframe	48②
	Power Steering Gear Center Mount Bolt	59
	Power Steering Gear Flange Lockbolt	15
	Power Steering Gear To Engine Pad	37
	Power Steering Pump Mounting Bolts	18
	Shock Absorber Upper Nuts	52
	Spring Strut To Steering Knuckle	48①
	Spring Strut Upper Mounting Nuts	18
	Subframe Bracket Bolts	37
	Subframe Mounting Bolts	77②
	Tie Rod End To Steering Knuckle	52
	Wheel Lug Nuts	81
S90 & V90		
1998	Anti-Roll Bar Link To Control Arm	63
	Ball Joint To Control Arm	44
	Ball Joint To Strut	22①
	Control Arm Strut Front Mount	70
	Control Arm Strut Rear Mount	63
	Power Steering Gear Flange Lockbolt	16
	Power Steering Gear Hose Screws	30
	Power Steering Gear Mounting Bolts	32
	Power Steering Pump Hose Screw	31
	Shock Absorber Upper Nut	111
	Spring Strut Upper Mounting Nuts	30
	Tie Rod End To Steering Arm	44
	Wheel Lug Nuts	63

① — Tighten an additional 90.°
② — Tighten an additional 120.°

Rear Axle & Suspension

INDEX

	Page No.
Application Chart	9-22
Coil Spring, Replace	9-23
Control Arm, Replace	9-24
Multi-Link Independent Suspension	9-24
Differential Housing Bushings, Replace	9-26
Multi-Link Independent Suspension	9-26
Hub & Bearing, Replace	9-23
Delta-Link Independent Suspension	9-23
Rear Axle, Replace	9-22
Constant-Track Live Axle	9-22
Multi-Link Independent Suspension	9-22
Rear Axle Link, Replace	9-27
Delta-Link Independent Suspension	9-27
Rear Axle Shaft, Replace	9-23
Constant-Track Live Axles	9-23
Shock Absorber, Replace	9-23
Delta-Link Independent Suspension	9-23
Stabilizer Bar, Replace	9-25
Constant-Track Live Axle	9-25
Delta-Link Independent Suspension	9-25
Support Arm, Replace	9-25
Multi-Link Independent Suspension	9-25
Tightening Specifications	9-28
Torque Rod & Bushings, Replace	9-23
Constant-Track Live Axle	9-23
Track Rod, Replace	9-25
Constant-Track Live Axles	9-25
Multi-Link Independent Suspension	9-25
Trailing Arm, Replace	9-24
Constant-Track Live Axle	9-24
Transverse Arm Mount, Replace	9-26
Delta-Link Independent Suspension	9-26
Upper Rear Axle Member Bushings, Replace	9-26
Multi-Link Independent Suspension	9-26

APPLICATION CHART

Model	Rear Suspension Type
S90 & V90	Multi-Link, Independent
S70 & V70	Delta Link, Semi-Independent
S80	Multi-Link, Independent
C70	Delta-Link, Semi-Independent

REAR AXLE

REPLACE

CONSTANT-TRACK LIVE AXLE

1. Raise and support vehicle, then remove rear wheels.
2. Remove brake caliper, then hang calipers from springs.
3. Remove brake discs and parking brake shoes, then disconnect parking brake cable from equalizing arms and clips on axle.
4. Loosen torque arms in frame, then disconnect torque arms from axle, **Fig. 1.**
5. Position support fixture tool No. 2714, or equivalent and a jack under axle and raise rear axle assembly slightly.
6. Remove exhaust pipe, if necessary, then disconnect track rod and speedometer cable.
7. Disconnect propeller shaft, upper torque arm, dampers from lower mountings in support arms, support arm front brackets, then pry support arms loose from front mountings.
8. Remove anti-roll bar, righthand and lefthand support arms, then the rear axle assembly.
9. Reverse procedure to install.

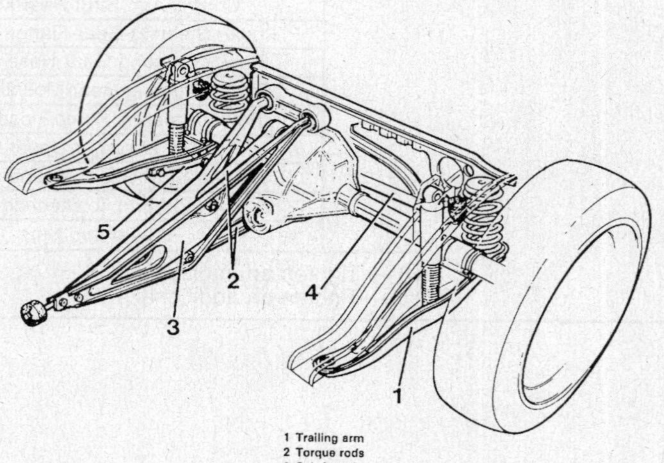

Fig. 1 Constant-track live axle rear suspension

MULTI-LINK INDEPENDENT SUSPENSION

1. Raise and support vehicle, then remove rear wheels, support arm guards and bolts securing support arms at front and rear, **Fig. 2.** Tap out rear end of support arms from wheel bearing housings.
2. Position support fixture tool No. 5972, or equivalent and a jack under support arms and lock support arms with fixture arms.
3. Slightly relieve tension on shock absorbers and remove bolts from upper shock mountings, then remove support arms complete with springs and shocks.
4. Remove calipers and secure with wire, then mark relation of propeller shaft to axle flange and disconnect propeller shaft.
5. Position support fixture tool No. 5972, or equivalent and a jack under axle, remove bolts securing axle to floor and lower axle slightly.
6. Disconnect speedometer cable from inspection cover, then remove screws securing cable to axle.
7. Disconnect parking brake cable, then remove rear axle assembly.
8. Reverse procedure to install.

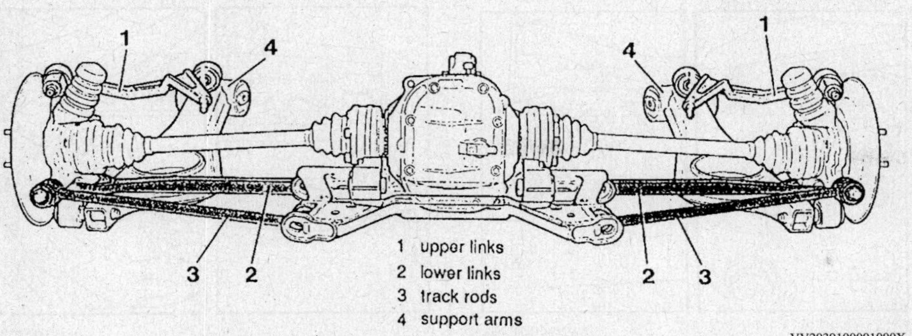

Fig. 2 Multi-Link Independent rear suspension

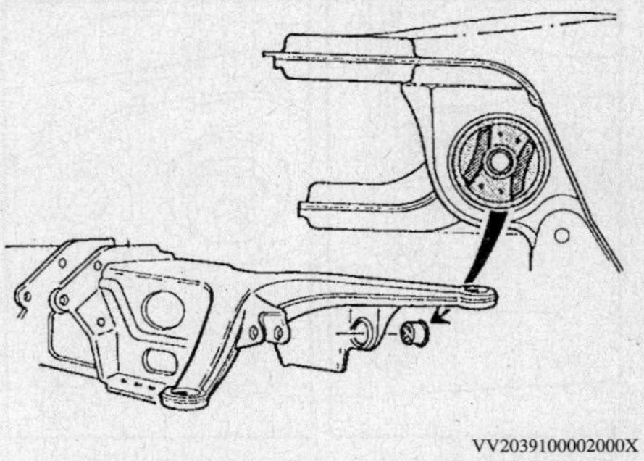

Fig. 3 Upper control arm bushing orientation. Multi-Link Independent rear suspension

REAR AXLE SHAFT

REPLACE

CONSTANT-TRACK LIVE AXLES

1. Raise and support vehicle, then remove rear wheel.
2. Remove brake caliper and secure to spring.
3. Remove brake disc and shoes.
4. Remove pressure plate bolts.
5. Invert brake disc and secure to axle with tapered end of lug nuts facing outward.
6. Remove axle shaft using brake disc to withdraw shaft.
7. Remove inner seal using a long screwdriver, then clean inside of rear axle tube.
8. Remove bearing and outer seal using press tool No. 5212, or equivalent and a hydraulic press.
9. Install bearing and outer seal using support tool No. 5010, or equivalent, standard handle tool No. 1801, or equivalent and a hydraulic press.
10. Install inner seal using drift tool No. 5243, or equivalent and standard handle tool No. 1801, or equivalent, then reverse removal steps to install axle shaft.

HUB & BEARING

REPLACE

DELTA-LINK INDEPENDENT SUSPENSION

1. Raise and support vehicle, then remove wheel.
2. Disconnect brake pipes from clip on rear axle, then the three way connector from lefthand trailing arm.
3. Remove caliper and hang from strut with wire, then disconnect parking brake shoe adjuster.
4. Remove guide pin, brake disc, protecting cover, hub nut and hub.
5. Remove ABS sensor, then the parking brake shoes.
6. Remove screw for brake wire in backing plate and bracket for wire's guide sleeve.
7. Remove screws on backing plate and brake shoe retaining springs, then the backing plate.
8. Pull guide sleeve forward on parking brake wire and disconnect wire from parking brake segment, then remove segment.
9. Remove bolts locating wheel axle end apiece, then the axle.
10. Reverse procedure to install, noting the following:
    a. Use a soft brush to clean ABS sensor before installing.
    b. If necessary to replace ABS toothed wheel, use mandrel tool No. 5351, spacer tool No. 5350, counterhold tool No. 5340, or equivalents and a hydraulic press to press wheel off hub. Use mandrel tool No. 5351, counterhold tool No. 2861, or equivalents and a hydraulic press to install wheel. **Ensure wheel sits square in hub.**
    c. Install hub protecting cover using mandrel tool No. 5225, or equivalent.
    d. Tighten all fasteners to specifications.

TORQUE ROD & BUSHINGS

REPLACE

CONSTANT-TRACK LIVE AXLE

1. Raise and support vehicle, then remove torque rod.
2. Replace bushings in large end using drift tool No. 5239, or equivalent, a V-block and a hydraulic press. **Press bushings in squarely.**
3. Replace bushings in small end using drift tool No. 5239, or equivalent, plate tool No. 5240, or equivalent, supported on a V-block and a hydraulic press.
4. Install torque rod and lower vehicle.

SHOCK ABSORBER

REPLACE

DELTA-LINK INDEPENDENT SUSPENSION

1. Fold rear seat backs forward, then undo luggage area carpet at front edge.
2. Remove cover plate under front edge of carpet, then undo righthand side panel at front edge and fold to one side. Remove seat back catch and panel attachment clip.
3. Raise rear of vehicle until wheels are off ground, remove upper shock absorber mounting bolts on righthand side, then disconnect electrical connector retainer and position wiring and connector away from shock mount.
4. Raise and support vehicle.
5. Remove load from shock absorber by pressing trailing arm upward. Use a jack placed against recess for spring mounting bolt.
6. Disconnect shock absorber from lower mount, then remove spring mounting nut and spring.
7. Lower vehicle, then lift out shock absorber with upper mount.
8. Place shock absorber mount in a vise, then remove nut using sleeve tool No. 5498, or equivalent and spanner tool No. 5499, or equivalent, for standard shock absorbers or sleeve tool No. 5500, or equivalent and spanner tool No. 5501, or equivalent, for Nivomat ride-height control shock absorbers.
9. Install new shock absorber in mount and tighten new nut to specifications, then install shock absorber and tighten upper mounting bolts a few turns.
10. Raise and support vehicle, then insert end of spring into trailing arm recess and attaching washer guide pin into hole in trailing arm. Tighten to specifications.
11. Press trailing arm upward using a jack placed against recess for spring mounting bolt, then connect shock absorber to lower mount and tighten to specifications.
12. Lower vehicle, then tighten upper shock absorber mounting bolts to specifications and connect electrical connector with a strip clamp.
13. Refit carpets and panels. Lock seat back catch plunger with locking fluid and tighten to specifications.

COIL SPRING

REPLACE

Refer to "Shock Absorber, Replace" for coil spring replacement.

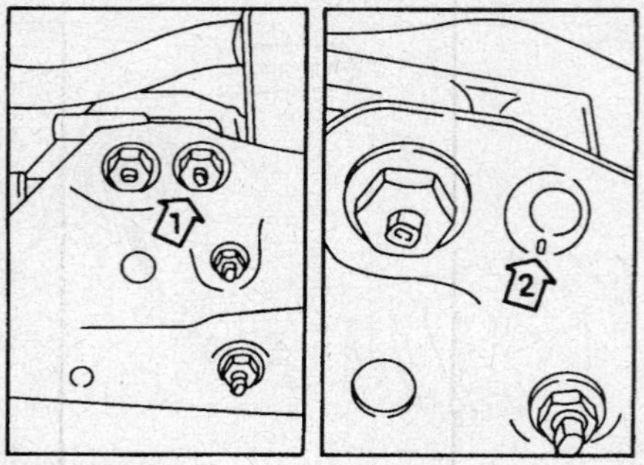

VV2039100003000X

Fig. 4 Transverse arm bolt removal. Delta-Link Independent rear suspension

CONTROL ARM

REPLACE

MULTI-LINK INDEPENDENT SUSPENSION

Upper

1. Raise and support vehicle, remove wheel, then the caliper and hang from spring with wire.
2. Disconnect support arm, lower control arm, track rod and upper control arm from wheel bearing housing. Use a small puller and a 12 mm x 50 mm bolt to disconnect track rod from housing. Retain spacers located between upper control arm and wheel bearing housing.
3. Remove nut securing control arm to rear axle member at rear, bolt and nut securing control arm to rear axle member at front, then the control arm.
4. Mount control arm in a vise, then use a chisel to pry up edge of outer bushing.
5. Mount control arm in a hydraulic press using two V-blocks as counterholds, then press out outer bushing using drift tool No. 5345, or equivalent.
6. Press in new outer bushing using drift tool No. 5090, or equivalent, counterhold tool No. 5087, or equivalent and a hydraulic press.
7. Mount control arm in a vise, then use a chisel to pry up edge of inner front bushing.
8. Mount control arm in a hydraulic press, then press out inner front bushing using drift tool No. 5345, or equivalent, counterhold tool No. 5343, or equivalent and drift tool No. 5347, or equivalent.
9. Press in new inner front bushing using drift tool No. 2731, or equivalent, counterhold tool No. 2904, or equivalent and a hydraulic press.
10. **If replacing lefthand inner rear bushing,** lower support arm slightly.
11. Press out inner rear bushing using press tool No. 5343, or equivalent.
12. Press in new inner rear bushing using press tool No. 5353, or equivalent. Note orientation of bushing, **Fig. 3.**
13. Install control arm, bolt and nut securing control arm to rear axle member, spacers between upper control arm and wheel bearing housing, then the nut securing control arm to wheel bearing housing.
14. Pull top of wheel bearing housing outward while tightening upper control arm nut to specifications.
15. Pull wheel bearing housing outward and insert lower control arm, then pull wheel bearing housing inward toward differential while tightening control arm nut to specifications.
16. Connect support arm and track rod, then install brake caliper and wheel.

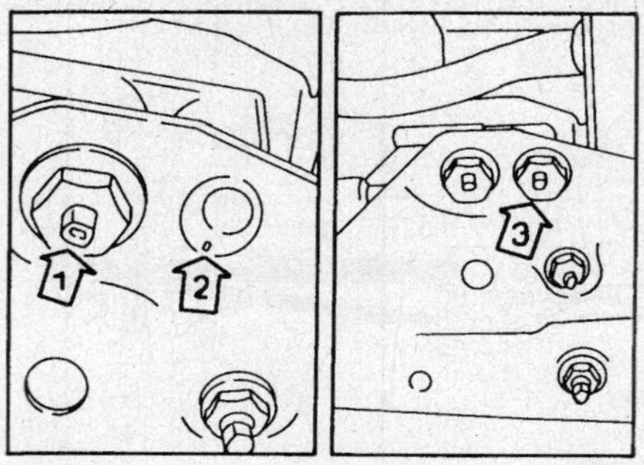

VV2039100004000X

Fig. 5 Transverse arm bolt installation. Delta-Link Independent rear suspension

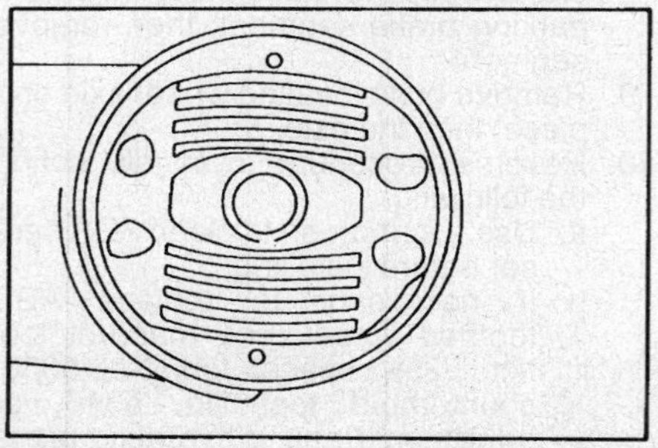

VV2029100001000X

Fig. 7 Support arm bushing orientation. Multi-Link Independent rear suspension

Lower

1. Raise and support vehicle, remove wheel, then the caliper and hang from spring with wire.
2. Remove brake disc and parking brake pads, then disconnect parking brake cable.
3. Disconnect support arm and lower control arm from wheel bearing housing and lower control arm from rear axle member, then remove lower control arm.
4. Use a small puller and a 12 mm x 50 mm bolt to disconnect track rod from housing.
5. Remove hub nut and nut securing upper support arm to wheel bearing housing, then the hub assembly. **Retain spacers between upper support arm and wheel bearing housing.**
6. Replace control rod bushing using a 1.318–1.358 inches (33.5–34.5 mm) outside diameter sleeve, counterhold tool No. 5090, or equivalent and a hydraulic press. **Bushing should project .40 inch (10 mm) on either side.**
7. Mount hub assembly in a vise, then chisel off bushing edges to provide a seat for counterhold.
8. Press out bushing using a 1.318–1.358 inches (33.5–34.5 mm) diameter sleeve, counterhold tool No. 5343, or equivalent and a hydraulic press.
9. Press in bushing using drift tool No. 5310, or equivalent, counterhold tool No. 5342, or equivalent and a hydraulic press.
10. Install hub assembly on halfshaft, hub nut, spacers between upper control arm and wheel bearing housing, wheel bearing housing on upper control arm, then the upper control arm nut and tighten to specifications while pulling outward on top of wheel bearing housing.
11. Pull wheel bearing housing outward and insert lower control arm, install a new lower control arm bolt and tighten to specifications while pulling inward toward differential.
12. Connect support arm, track rod and parking brake cable, then install parking brake pads, brake disc, brake caliper and wheel.
13. Lower vehicle then tighten hub nut to specifications.

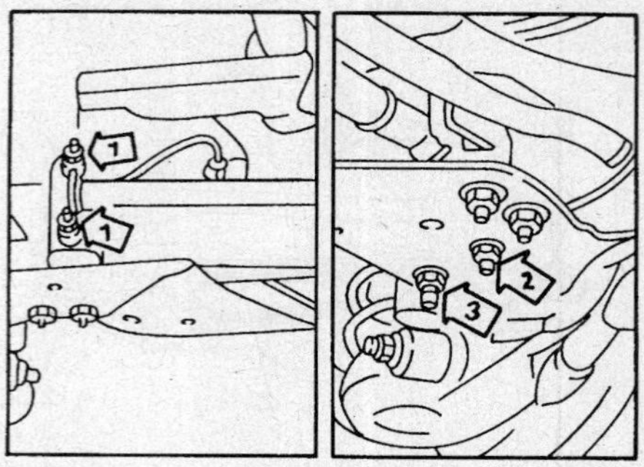

VV2039100005000X

Fig. 6 Transverse arm bolt tightening sequence. Delta-Link Independent rear suspension

TRAILING ARM

REPLACE

CONSTANT-TRACK LIVE AXLE

1. Raise and support vehicle, then remove wheel and caliper. Hang caliper from rear spring.
2. Scribe alignment marks on propeller shaft, remove rear flange bolts, then lower shaft slightly.
3. Support trailing arm on a jack stand, then remove bolts from both sides of anti-roll bar.
4. Remove shock absorber lower bolt and loosen bolt on opposite side.
5. Loosen bracket nuts crosswise, then remove bracket and rubber supports.
6. Remove bolts from front bracket, nut and bracket, then the trailing arm.

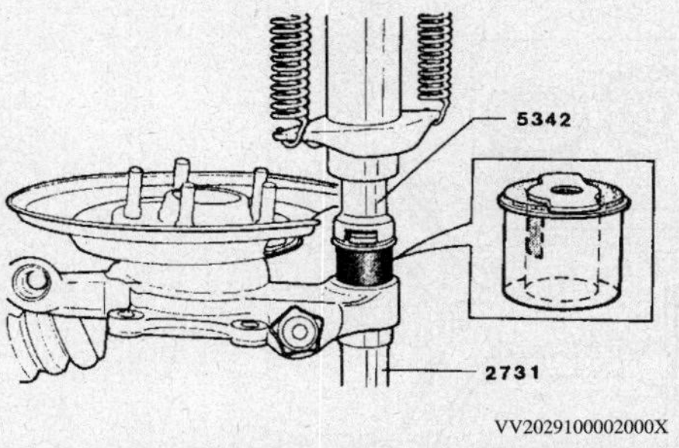

Fig. 8 Positioning support arm bushing in wheel bearing housing. Multi-Link Independent rear suspension

7. Replace bushing using drift tool No. 2704, or equivalent, support tool No. 5082, or equivalent and a hydraulic press. Bushing tapered hole should face upward and bushing must be evenly spaced in arm.
8. Reverse removal procedure to install. Tighten fasteners to specifications.

STABILIZER BAR

REPLACE

CONSTANT-TRACK LIVE AXLE

1. Raise and support vehicle, then use a jack stand to unload shock absorbers.
2. Remove nut from bracket, shock absorber lower bolt, then the anti-roll bar.
3. Reverse procedure to install. Tighten fasteners to specifications.

DELTA-LINK INDEPENDENT SUSPENSION

1. Raise and support vehicle, then remove lefthand rubber muffler support. Hang muffler with a strip clamp so that muffler is up as high as possible.
2. Remove outer nut (1) for transverse arm attachment, then the bolt, **Fig. 4.**
3. Mark position on righthand transverse arm attachment in relation to lefthand trailing arm's hole (2), **Fig. 4.** Center punch attachment at edge of hole, then remove attachments second bolt. **It is crucial that marking is correct, otherwise rear wheel toe-in will be incorrect.**
4. Remove anti-roll bar mounting bolts, then the anti-roll bar.
5. Reverse procedure to install, noting the following:
   a. Use new nuts and bolts.
   b. Install transverse arm attachment on trailing arm. Install inner bolt (1) and nut, **Fig. 5.** Adjust in anchorage according to previous marking (2). Tighten nut so that position may be fixed, then install nut and bolt (3).
   c. Tighten anti-roll bar attachment bolts, **Fig. 6,** to specifications.

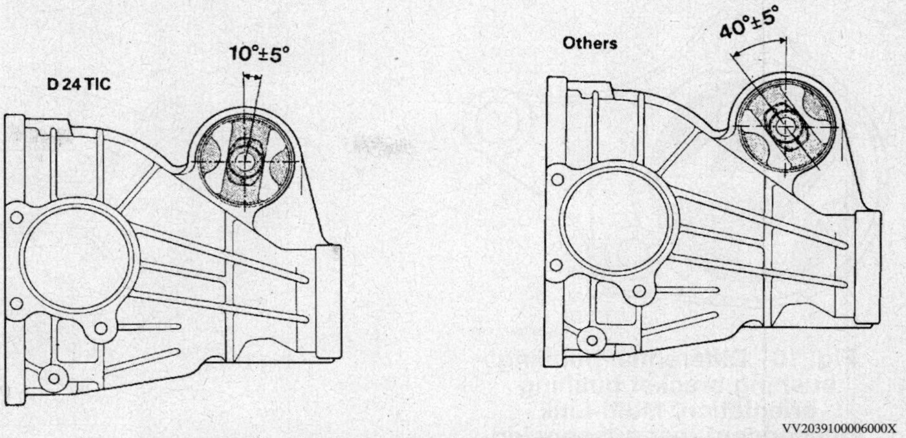

Fig. 9 Differential housing bushing orientation. Multi-Link Independent rear suspension

TRACK ROD

REPLACE

CONSTANT-TRACK LIVE AXLES

1. Raise and support vehicle, then remove track rod.
2. Replace axle side bushings using drift tool No. 2731, or equivalent, counterhold tool No. 2733, or equivalent and a hydraulic press. **Press in new bushing with counterhold inverted.**
3. Replace body side bushings using drift tool No. 2706, or equivalent, counterhold tool No. 2733, or equivalent and a hydraulic press. **Press in new bushing with counterhold inverted.**
4. Install track rod and lower vehicle.

MULTI-LINK INDEPENDENT SUSPENSION

1. Raise and support vehicle, remove wheel, then the track rod.
2. Replace bushings using drift tool No. 5345, or equivalent, counterhold tool No. 5349, or equivalent and a hydraulic press.
3. Install track rod and wheel, then lower vehicle.

SUPPORT ARM

REPLACE

MULTI-LINK INDEPENDENT SUSPENSION

1. Replace support arm assembly as follows:
   a. Perform steps 1 through 3 as outlined under "Rear Axle, Replace," then remove spring and rubber seats and shock absorber.
   b. Reverse step 1a to install.
2. Replace front support arm bushings as follows:
   a. Remove support arm, then the bracket at front of support arm.
   b. Note position of bushings, **Fig. 7,** then position spacer tool No. 5348, or equivalent, between bushings.
   c. Using drift tool No. 5347, or equivalent, handle tool No. 1801, or equivalent, counterhold tool No. 5346, or equivalent and a hydraulic press, remove one bushing at a time.
   d. Press in bushings from each side using drift, handle, counterhold and a hydraulic press. **Ensure bushings are orientated correctly.**
   e. Install bracket at front of support arm, then the support arm.
3. Replace rear support arm bushings as follows:
   a. Remove brake caliper and hang from spring with wire.
   b. Remove brake disc and brake pads, then disconnect parking brake cable at wheel bearing housing.
   c. Remove bolt and nut securing lower support arm and bolt securing track rod to wheel bearing housing, then use a small puller and a 12 mm x 50 mm bolt to disconnect track rod from housing.
   d. Remove hub nut and nut securing upper support arm to wheel bearing housing, then the hub assembly. **Retain spacers between upper support arm and wheel bearing housing.**
   e. Mount wheel bearing housing in a vise, remove brake shield mounting bolts, then chisel off bushing edges to provide a seat for counterhold.
   f. Remove bushing using 1.632–1.675 inches (41.45–42.55 mm) diameter sleeve, counterhold tool No. 5343, or equivalent and a hydraulic press.
   g. Install bushing using drift tool No. 5342, or equivalent, counterhold tool No. 2731, or equivalent and a hydraulic press. Bushing must be positioned with slot at top, **Fig. 8.**
   h. Install brake shield, hub assembly on halfshaft, hub nut, spacers between upper control arm and wheel bearing housing, then the nut at top of upper control arm and tighten to specifications while pulling outward on top of wheel bearing housing.
   i. Pull wheel bearing housing outward

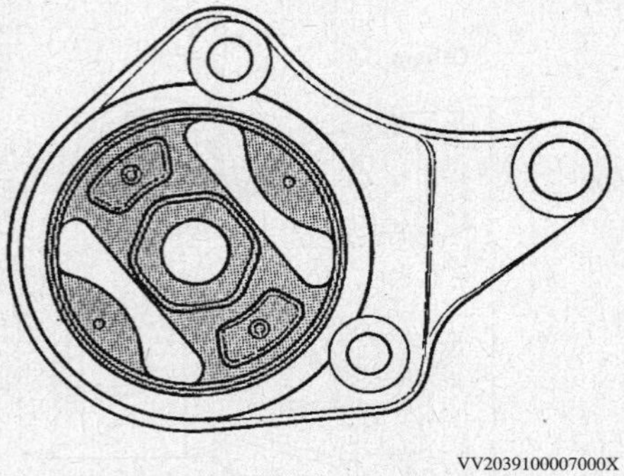

VV2039100007000X

Fig. 10 Differential housing bushing bracket bushing orientation. Multi-Link Independent rear suspension

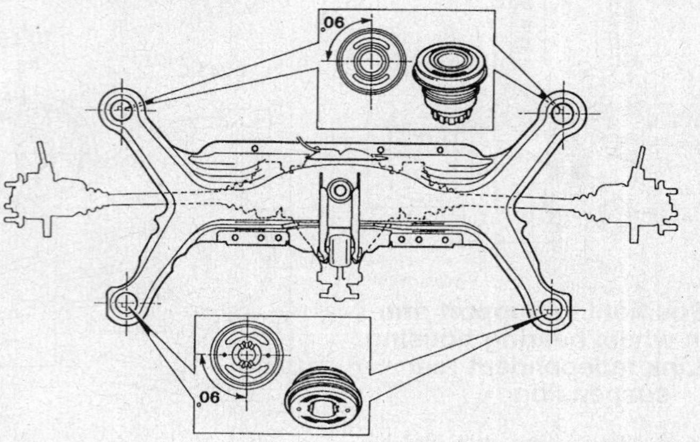

VV2039100008000X

Fig. 11 Upper rear axle member bushing orientation. Multi-Link Independent rear suspension

and insert lower control arm, install a new lower control arm bolt and tighten to specifications while pulling inward toward differential.

j. Connect parking brake cable to wheel bearing housing, then install brake pads, brake disc, brake caliper and track rod.

DIFFERENTIAL HOUSING BUSHINGS

REPLACE

MULTI-LINK INDEPENDENT SUSPENSION

1. Raise and support vehicle, then remove wheels and bolts attaching support arms to wheel bearing housings. Tap out arms.
2. Remove bolts and nuts securing lower control arms to wheel bearing housings, then the support arm bolt from one side.
3. Disconnect track rods from wheel bearing housings using a small puller and a 12 mm x 50 mm bolt to disconnect track rod from each housing.
4. Remove bolts securing upper and lower sections of rear axle member, then pull wheel bearing housings outward and remove lower section of rear axle member complete with track rods and control arms.
5. Remove bolts in propeller shaft/differential coupling, then place a jack and fixture tool No. 5972, or equivalent, under differential.
6. Remove three bolts securing differential to rear axle member, then lower differential slightly.
7. Replace upper bushing using press tool No. 5354, or equivalent. Note orientation of bushing, **Fig. 9.**
8. Remove lower bushing and bracket, then replace lower bushing using drift tool No. 5349, or equivalent, a V-block and a hydraulic press. Note orientation of bushing, **Fig. 10.**
9. Install lower bushing and bracket, then lift differential into position and tighten bolts attaching differential to rear axle member to specifications.
10. Install bolts in propeller shaft and tighten to specifications, then raise lower section of rear axle member and loosely install bolts securing upper and lower sections of rear axle member.
11. Install to 12 mm bolts or drifts into rear axle member centering holes, then tighten rear axle member assembly bolts to specifications.
12. Install bolts securing control arms to wheel bearing housings and tighten to specifications while pulling inward toward differential.
13. Install support arms, track rods and wheels.

UPPER REAR AXLE MEMBER BUSHINGS

REPLACE

MULTI-LINK INDEPENDENT SUSPENSION

1. Raise and support vehicle, remove wheels, then the caliper and hang from spring with wire.
2. Remove support arm guards, bolts and nuts at front of support arms and bolts at rear of support arms.
3. Disconnect support arms at rear, then the propeller shaft at differential.
4. Position fixture tool No. 5972, or equivalent and a jack underneath rear axle assembly, then remove bolts securing upper section of rear axle member to floor and lower rear axle slightly.
5. Replace front bushings using press tool No. 5344, or equivalent. Note orientation of bushings, **Fig. 11.**
6. Replace rear bushings using press tool No. 5352, or equivalent. Note orientation of bushings, **Fig. 11.**
7. Raise assembly and install lower attachment bolts and tighten to specifications.
8. Install propeller shaft bolts, then the front nuts and bolts in support arms. Tighten to specifications.
9. Tap in support arms at rear and tighten bolts to specifications, then install support arm guards, calipers and wheels.

TRANSVERSE ARM MOUNT

REPLACE

DELTA-LINK INDEPENDENT SUSPENSION

1. Fold rear seat back forward, then undo luggage area carpet at front edge.
2. Remove cover plate under front edge of carpet, then undo righthand side panel at front edge and fold to one side. Remove seat back catch and panel attachment clip.
3. Raise rear of vehicle until wheels are off ground, remove upper shock absorber mounting bolts on righthand side, then disconnect electrical connector retainer and position wiring and connector away from shock mount.
4. Raise and support vehicle.
5. Remove righthand wheel and protecting plate at bracket for rear axle link, then disconnect anti-roll bar mount at righthand side, **Fig. 12.**
6. Disconnect brake pipe bracket on righthand trailing arm, then the ABS pipe and brake pipe from clip on righthand trailing arm.
7. Remove load from shock absorber by pressing trailing arm upward. Use a jack placed against recess for spring mounting bolt.
8. Disconnect shock absorber from lower mount, then remove spring mounting nut and spring.
9. Reinstall shock absorber and tighten nut a few turns, then remove bolts A for transverse arm mounts on both sides, then bolts B and C on righthand side, **Fig. 13.**
10. Position a suitable jack under lefthand spring seat and raise seat a few centimeters, then disconnect trailing arm mount from body guide pin on righthand side.
11. Press out righthand trailing arm, lefthand trailing arm remains in position.
12. Install a new transverse arm mount for righthand trailing arm and tighten to specifications.

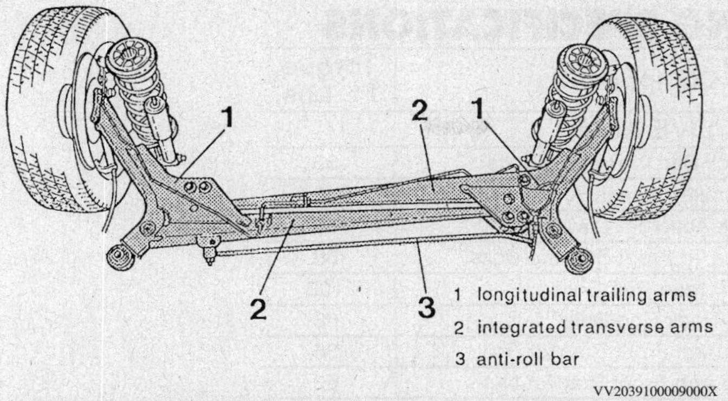

Fig. 12 Delta-Link Independent rear suspension

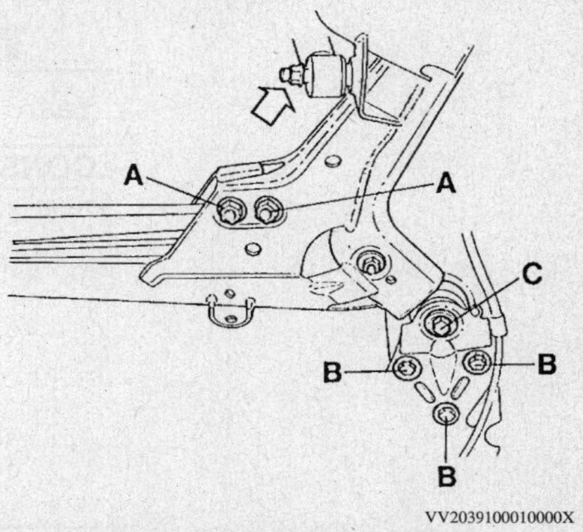

Fig. 13 Transverse arm anchorage bolt removal. Delta-Link Independent rear suspension

13. Align attachment with mount in lefthand trailing arm. Ensure trailing arm maintains same position relative to body, then tighten to specifications.
14. Adjust lefthand trailing arm position with jack, then install righthand transverse arm with attachment in its mount without inserting bolts.
15. Replace attachment for lefthand transverse arm and tighten to specifications.
16. Install transverse arm with attachment in its mount without inserting bolts, then connect righthand trailing arm to body guide pins using new bolts and tighten to specifications. Bolt C, which goes through rear axle link and bracket, should be tightened first then the brackets three bolts B, **Fig. 13.**
17. Install new bolts A for transverse arm attachments, then disconnect righthand shock absorber.
18. Install spring, then connect righthand shock absorber and tighten to nuts specifications.
19. Connect brake pipe and ABS cable to trailing arm attachment, brake pipe bracket to trailing arm attachment lug, then the anti-roll bar to trailing arm. Tighten to specifications.
20. Install protecting plate and wheel, the tighten lug nuts crosswise to specifications.
21. Tighten upper shock absorber mount to specifications, then connect electrical connector with a strip clamp.
22. Refit carpets and panels. Lock seat back catch plunger with locking fluid and tighten to specifications.

REAR AXLE LINK

REPLACE

DELTA-LINK INDEPENDENT SUSPENSION

1. Raise and support vehicle.
2. Remove nut attaching rear axle link to trailing arm, then knock out attachment bolt using a copper mallet.
3. Remove muffler bracket bolt and disconnect brake pipe from clips on lefthand side, then remove bolts retaining trailing arm bracket. Let bracket remain in place in brake cables attachment lug.
4. Raise righthand trailing arm a bit with a suitable jack, then force apart link on lefthand side from body guide pin using a lever. Ensure trailing arm link is free from guide pin in body.
5. Replace bushing in trailing arm using press tool No. 5497, or equivalent, then replace nut and bolt for rear axle link in trailing arm. **Do not tighten nut.**
6. Connect trailing arm to body guide pin, then install bolts for trailing arm bracket loosely.
7. Tighten rear axle link bracket through bolt, three bracket bolts and bolt passing through trailing arm rear axle link to specifications.
8. Connect brake pipe to clips, then install muffler bracket bolt.

TIGHTENING SPECIFICATIONS

Year	Component	Torque, Ft. Lbs.
CONSTANT-TRACK LIVE AXLE		
1998	Anti-Roll Bar To Bracket Bolts	33
	Brake Caliper Bolts	43
	Shock Absorber Lower Bolt	63
	Subframe To Front Bushing Bolts	63
	Torque Rod Bolts	103
	Track Rod Bolts	63
	Trailing Arm Front Bracket Bolt	35
	Trailing Arm Front Bracket Nut	63
	Wheel Lug Nuts	63
DELTA-LINK INDEPENDENT SUSPENSION		
1998–2001	ABS Sensor Screws	84⑥
	Anti-Roll Bar Nut 1	37
	Anti-Roll Bar Nut 2	37④
	Anti-Roll Bar Nut 3	66
	Anti-Roll Bar To Trailing Arm Nuts	37
	Brake Backing Plate Lower Screws	15
	Brake Backing Plate Upper Screws	18
	Brake Caliper Bolts	44
	Brake Disc Guide Pin	84⑥
	Lefthand Trailing Arm Mount	59
	Lefthand Transverse Arm Mount	59
	Rear Axle Link Bracket Bolts	48②
	Rear Axle Link Bracket Through Bolt	77③
	Rear Axle Link/Trailing Arm Through Bolt	48④
	Righthand Trailing Arm Bracket Bolts	48②
	Righthand Trailing Arm Bracket Through Bolt	77③
	Righthand Trailing Arm Mount	59
	Seat Back Catch Plunger	15
	Shock Absorber Lower Mounting Bolt	59
	Shock Absorber Upper Mounting Bolt	18
	Shock Absorber Upper Mount To Shock Absorber, Ride-Height Control	60
	Shock Absorber Upper Mount To Shock Absorber, Standard	30
	Transverse Arm Mount To Trailing Nuts & Bolts	37⑤
	Wheel Axle Bolts	26②
	Wheel Hub Nut	88①
	Wheel Lug Nuts	81

Continued

TIGHTENING SPECIFICATIONS—Continued

Year	Component	Torque, Ft. Lbs.
MULTI-LINK ACTIVE SUSPENSION		
1998–2001	Brake Caliper Bolts	44
	Differential/Propeller Shaft Bolts	37
	Rear Axle Damper Upper Mount	63
	Rear Axle Member Assembly Bolts	51①
	Rear Axle Member To Floor Bolts	52②
	Shock Absorber Lower Mounting Bolt	41
	Lower Control Arm Bolt	37③
	Support Arm Bracket Bolts	91④
	Support Arm Front Bolts	35
	Support Arm Front Large Nut	51③
	Support Arm Rear Bolt	44③
	Track Rod To Rear Axle Member Bolt	51
	Track Rod To Wheel Bearing Housing Bolt	62
	Upper Control Arm Inner Front Bolt & Nut	51②
	Upper Control Arm Inner Rear Nut	62
	Upper Control Arm Top Nut	84
	Wheel Hub Nut	102②
	Wheel Lug Nuts	62

① — Tighten an additional 30.°
② — Tighten an additional 60.°
③ — Tighten an additional 90.°
④ — Tighten an additional 120.°
⑤ — Tighten an additional 150.°
⑥ — Inch Lbs.

Front Suspension & Steering

NOTE: On Air Bag Equipped Models, Refer To "Air Bag System Precautions" Located In The Front Of This Manual For System Disarming & Arming Procedures.

INDEX

	Page No.
Ball Joint, Replace	9-30
S70, V70, C70 & S80	9-30
S90 & V90	9-30
Ball Joint Inspection	9-30
Coil Spring, Replace	9-30
Control Arm, Replace	9-31
S70, V70, C70 & S80	9-31
S90 & V90	9-31
Control Arm Bushing, Replace	9-31
S90 & V90	9-31
Power Steering Gear, Replace	9-32
S70, V70, C70 & S80	9-32
S90 & V90	9-32
Power Steering Pump, Replace	9-32
S70, V70, C70 & S80	9-32
S90 & V90	9-32
Precautions	9-30
Air Bag Systems	9-30
Battery Ground Cable	9-30
Microprocessor Radios	9-30
Shock Absorber, Replace	9-30
S70, V70, C70 & S80	9-30
S90 & V90	9-30
Stabilizer Bar, Replace	9-31
S70, V70, C70 & S80	9-31
S90 & V90	9-31
Tightening Specifications	9-33
Wheel Bearing, Adjust	9-30
S90 & V90	9-30

PRECAUTIONS

AIR BAG SYSTEMS

Refer to "Air Bag System Precautions" in the front of this manual for system disarming and arming procedures.

BATTERY GROUND CABLE

Prior to service, disconnect battery ground cable and isolate as required.

MICROPROCESSOR RADIOS

On models equipped with microprocessor radios, always switch radio off before disconnecting or connecting battery ground cable to prevent damage to the radio.

WHEEL BEARING

ADJUST

S90 & V90

Torque nut to 42 ft. lbs. while rotating wheel, then loosening nut ½ turn. Finger tighten nut and install cotter pin. If slot in nut does not align with hole in spindle, tighten nut to the next notch.

BALL JOINT INSPECTION

Measure ball joint radial and axial play, **Fig. 1.** If axial play exceeds .12 inch or radial play exceeds .02 inch, replace ball joint.

BALL JOINT

REPLACE

S70, V70, C70 & S80

1. Raise and support vehicle, then remove nuts securing ball joint to control arm.
2. Remove bolt between axle shaft and ball joint, then the ball joint.

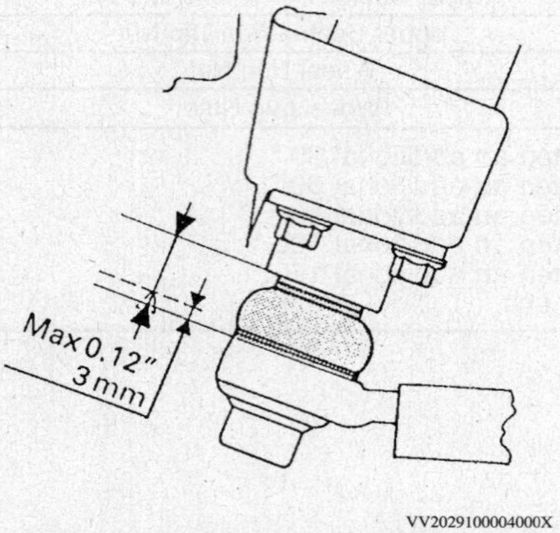

Fig. 1 Ball joint inspection

3. Reverse procedure to install. Tighten nuts and bolt to specifications.

S90 & V90

1. Raise and support vehicle.
2. Remove anti-roll bar link to control arm attaching bolt.
3. Remove ball joint stud cotter pin and nut.
4. Press ball joint out of control arm using ball joint replacement tool No. 5259, or equivalent.
5. Remove ball joint to strut attaching bolts, then press control arm down and remove ball joint.
6. Reverse procedure to install. Tighten to specifications.

COIL SPRING

REPLACE

Refer to "Shock Absorber, Replace" for coil spring replacement.

SHOCK ABSORBER

REPLACE

The following procedures allow servicing of the shock absorbers without removing the strut assembly from vehicle.

S70, V70, C70 & S80

1. Raise and support vehicle, then remove wheel.
2. Disconnect anti-roll bar link from spring strut, then remove ABS sensor lead from spring strut and brake bracket. **Do not disconnect connector.**
3. Install support tool No. 5466, or equivalent, under link arm to avoid damaging driveshaft.
4. Remove nuts securing spring strut to body, then the bolts securing spring strut to axle shaft.
5. Remove spring strut and clamp in a vise.
6. Compress spring using spring clamps tool No. 5407, or equivalent, then remove bolt and washer using socket tool No. 5467, or equivalent and counterhold tool No. 5468, or equivalent.
7. Remove bolt on shock absorber using socket tool No. 5469, or equivalent and counterhold tool No. 5468, or equivalent.
8. Remove spring seating, rubber bump stop with gaiter and spring.
9. Reverse procedure to assemble and install. Tighten fasteners to specifications.

S90 & V90

1. Raise and support front of vehicle and remove wheel.
2. Disconnect steering rod from steering arm.
3. Support control arm with a suitable jack, then disconnect anti-roll bar from link attachment.
4. Remove brake line bracket attaching bolt, then disconnect brake lines from retaining clips.
5. Remove rubber boot from upper strut nut, then disconnect high tension lead from ignition coil.
6. Loosen strut center nut.

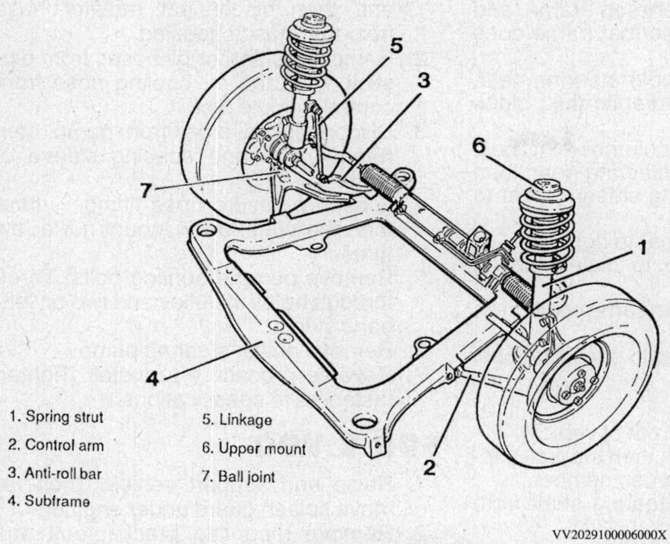

Fig. 2 Front suspension

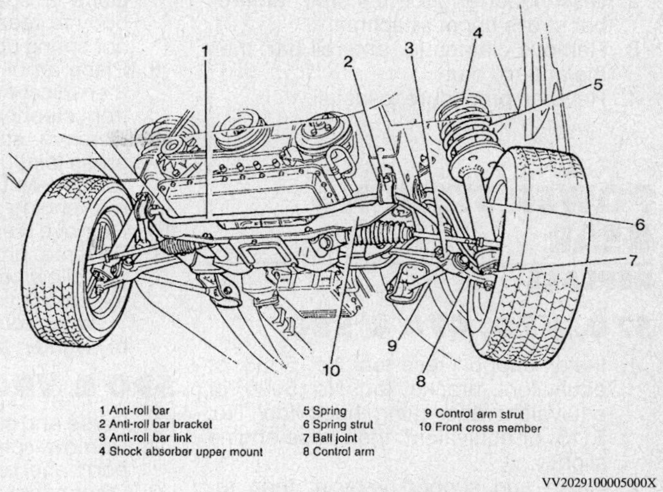

Fig. 3 Front suspension

7. Mark position of upper mount, then remove mount attaching nuts and washers.
8. Lower jack while supporting strut assembly to avoid damage to brake lines and fender. Attach retaining hook tool No. 5045, or equivalent, to strut and anti-roll bar.
9. Install two spring compressors tool No. 5040, or equivalents. Position compressors so that claws span three spring coils and compress each side alternately.
10. Remove strut center nut, then the upper mount, spring retainer, spring and rubber bumper or rubber bellows and disc on gas pressure shocks.
11. Remove shock absorber retaining nut, then the shock absorber.
12. Reverse procedure to install.

CONTROL ARM

REPLACE

S70, V70, C70 & S80

1. Raise and support vehicle, then remove nuts securing ball joint to control arm.
2. Remove control arm mounting bolts, then the control arm, **Fig. 2.**
3. Clean rust from bushing outer sleeves and note position of outer sleeves in relation to control arms.
4. Replace bushings using drift tool No. 5481, or equivalent, counterhold tool No. 5482, or equivalent and a hydraulic press.
5. Check position of bushings using gauge tool No. 5483, or equivalent.
6. Install control arm and control arm mounting bolts, then the ball joint to control arm nuts. Tighten nuts to specifications.
7. Lower vehicle and bounce up and down a few times, then tighten control arm bolts to specifications.

S90 & V90

1. Raise and support front of vehicle and remove wheel.
2. Remove ball joint stud cotter pin and nut.
3. Remove anti-roll bar link and control arm strut attaching bolt, **Fig. 3,** then drive out front bushing.
4. Press ball joint out of control arm using ball joint replacement tool No. 5259, or equivalent, then remove control arm from crossmember.
5. Secure control arm in a vise and press out bushing using press tool Nos. 5091 and 5240, or equivalents. Press in rear bushing using tools Nos. 2904 and 5240, or equivalents.
6. Align control arm strut with control arm, attach control arm to crossmember, then install retaining bolt. Do not tighten bolt at this time.
7. Install ball joint to control arm, then tighten attaching nut to specifications and install cotter pin.
8. Install control arm strut bushing, washer and retaining bolt. Tighten bolt to specifications.
9. Attach anti-roll bar link to control arm and tighten retaining bolt to specifications.
10. Lower vehicle, then bounce vehicle several times to allow control arm to set in position. Tighten control arm to crossmember retaining bolt to specifications.

CONTROL ARM BUSHING

REPLACE

S90 & V90

1. Raise and support front of vehicle and remove wheel.
2. Remove strut to control arm attaching bolt, then detach strut and remove bushing.
3. Remove strut rear mount attaching bolt, then remove strut from vehicle.
4. Press rear bushing out of strut.
5. Reverse procedure to install. Press rear bushing into strut using press tool No. 2731, or equivalent and a V-block. Tighten strut to control arm attaching bolt to specifications. Tighten rear mount attaching bolt to specifications.

STABILIZER BAR

REPLACE

S70, V70, C70 & S80

1. Install support rails tool No. 5033, or equivalent, bracket tool No. 5006, or equivalent and lifting hook tool No. 5115, or equivalent, then raise engine slightly.
2. Raise and support vehicle, then remove splash guard under engine and five nuts securing steering gear to subframe.
3. Disconnect hydraulic fluid line brackets from subframe at front and rear edges, then place a suitable jack under rear crossmember.
4. Remove four bolts securing subframe brackets to body on both sides, then the two bolts together with brackets and washers.
5. Loosen subframe front bolts approximately .60–.80 inch (15–20 mm), lower frame at rear edge and ensure steering gear bolts come away from frame.
6. Disconnect anti-roll bar from links, then remove anti-roll bar caps and the anti-roll bar.
7. Reverse procedure to install, noting the following:
   a. Press subframe up at rear edge using jack while installing steering gear mounting bolts into frame.
   b. Install new bolts on subframe loosely, move jack to front edge of frame, tighten bolts on lefthand side of frame to specifications, then the bolts on righthand side of frame to specifications.

S90 & V90

1. Raise and support vehicle, then remove splash guard under engine.

2. Disconnect anti-roll bar from anti-roll bar strut's upper attachment.
3. Remove clamps for anti-roll bar, then the anti-roll bar.
4. Reverse procedure to install.

POWER STEERING GEAR

REPLACE

S70, V70, C70 & S80

1. Install support rails tool No. 5033, or equivalent, bracket tool No. 5006, or equivalent and lifting hook tool No. 5115, or equivalent, then raise engine slightly.
2. Raise and support vehicle, then remove front wheels.
3. Disconnect tie rod ends using puller tool No. 5259, or equivalent, then measure length of tie rod on one side in relation to steering gear housing and record measurement.
4. Remove splash guard under engine, then disconnect bracket and clamps of hydraulic fluid pipes at front and rear edges.
5. Remove five nuts securing steering gear to subframe, then place a suitable jack under rear crossmember.
6. Remove four bolts securing subframe brackets to body on both sides, then the two bolts together with brackets and washers.
7. Loosen subframe front bolts approximately .60–.80 inch (15–20 mm), lower subframe at rear edge, then place a spacer between frame and body at rear edge so that frame does not spring up.
8. Place an oil pan under steering gear, then disconnect hydraulic fluid pipes from steering gear.
9. Remove steering column joint bolt, press joint up from steering gear, then remove bolt securing steering gear to rear engine pad.
10. Remove steering gear to right.
11. Reverse procedure to install, noting the following:
    a. Ensure tie rod is in same position as when removed.
    b. Tighten fasteners to specifications.

S90 & V90

1. Raise and support front of vehicle.
2. Remove splash pan, then the jack support panel on front crossmember.
3. Disconnect lower steering shaft from steering gear.
4. Remove snap rings from lower universal joint.
5. Loosen upper bolt and remove lower bolt from universal joint clamp, then slide joint up steering shaft.
6. Remove ball joint nut, then disconnect tie rods.
7. Disconnect oil lines from steering gear.
8. Remove steering gear attaching bolts, then the steering gear from vehicle.
9. Reverse procedure to install, tightening to specifications

POWER STEERING PUMP

REPLACE

S70, V70, C70 & S80

1. Drain approximately 3.2 quarts of coolant, then disconnect radiator hose from thermostat housing.
2. Remove holder for oil hoses from dipstick, then the air cooling hose from control module box.
3. Disconnect drive belt from pump, then remove bolt and spacing sleeve of plate.
4. Loosen pressure hose fitting ¼ turn, then the plate lower mount nut a few turns.
5. Remove pump mounting bolts. Three through holes in pulley and two on left-hand side.
6. Remove power steering pump.
7. Reverse procedure to install. Tighten fasteners to specifications.

S90 & V90

1. Raise and support vehicle, then remove splash guard under engine.
2. Remove mounting bracket bolt and nut, then loosen power steering belt.
3. Place a drip pan underneath pump, then remove hoses from pump.
4. Remove retaining bolts and drive belts, then lower pump slightly and disconnect filler hose.
5. Remove power steering pump.
6. Reverse procedure to install. Tighten fasteners to specifications.

TIGHTENING SPECIFICATIONS

Year	Component	Torque, Ft. Lbs.
S70, V70, C70 & S80		
1998–2001	Anti-Roll Bar Link To Spring Strut	37
	Ball Joint To Control Arm	13②
	Ball Joint To Steering Knuckle	37
	Control Arm To Subframe	48②
	Power Steering Gear Center Mount Bolt	59
	Power Steering Gear Flange Lockbolt	15
	Power Steering Gear To Engine Pad	37
	Power Steering Pump Mounting Bolts	18
	Shock Absorber Upper Nuts	52
	Spring Strut To Steering Knuckle	48①
	Spring Strut Upper Mounting Nuts	18
	Subframe Bracket Bolts	37
	Subframe Mounting Bolts	77②
	Tie Rod End To Steering Knuckle	52
	Wheel Lug Nuts	81
S90 & V90		
1998	Anti-Roll Bar Link To Control Arm	63
	Ball Joint To Control Arm	44
	Ball Joint To Strut	22①
	Control Arm Strut Front Mount	70
	Control Arm Strut Rear Mount	63
	Power Steering Gear Flange Lockbolt	16
	Power Steering Gear Hose Screws	30
	Power Steering Gear Mounting Bolts	32
	Power Steering Pump Hose Screw	31
	Shock Absorber Upper Nut	111
	Spring Strut Upper Mounting Nuts	30
	Tie Rod End To Steering Arm	44
	Wheel Lug Nuts	63

① — Tighten an additional 90.°
② — Tighten an additional 120.°

Wheel Alignment

INDEX

	Page No.
Front Wheel Alignment	9-34
Camber	9-34
Caster	9-34
Toe-In	9-34
Preliminary Inspection	9-34
Rear Wheel Alignment	9-34
S70, V70, C70 & S80	9-34
S90 & V90	9-34
Wheel Alignment Specifications	9-4

PRELIMINARY INSPECTION

1. Check tires for wear and proper inflation.
2. Check wheel runout.
3. Check front wheel bearings, front suspension, steering linkage and ball joints for wear or looseness.
4. Ensure front shock absorbers are functioning properly.

FRONT WHEEL ALIGNMENT

CASTER

Caster is not adjustable. If caster angle is not within specifications, check for damaged or worn suspension components and replace as needed.

CAMBER

Camber angle can be adjusted by modifying spring struts. To correct angle, proceed as follows:

1. Disconnect spring strut from steering knuckle, then drill out upper holes in shock absorber attachment to .55 inch (14 mm). Clean burrs from holes after drilling.
2. Install washer tool No. 3 546 451-0, or equivalent, with an old bolt and nut in lower hole. Do not tighten fully.
3. Install fixing plug tool No. 3 546 450-2, or equivalent, in upper hole, then drill a .16 inch (4 mm) hole through washer and shock absorber attachment. Drill at center of washer, then knock clamping pin tool No. 951 950-5, or equivalent, into hole.
4. Install spring strut using eccentric bolt tool No. 3 546 449-4, or equivalent, in upper hole and new bolt tool No. 977 267-4, or equivalent, in lower hole. Tighten bolts very lightly.
5. Adjust camber angle by turning upper bolt, then **torque** both nuts to 48 ft. lbs., plus an additional 90.°

TOE-IN

1. Loosen locknut on each tie rod.
2. Turn each tie rod to obtain proper toe-in. Length of tie rods may not differ more than .080 inch (2 mm), measured between edge of thread and locknut.
3. If after toe-in adjustment, steering wheel is not properly centered, proceed as follows:
   a. Place car on a level surface and ensure front wheels are straight, then disconnect battery ground cable and turn ignition switch to Off position.
   b. Remove Torx bolts at rear of steering wheel, disconnect air bag electrical connector, then remove air bag assembly.
   c. Connect special tool No. 998 8695, or equivalent, in place of air bag assembly so that vehicle may be driven without generating a fault code.
   d. Loosen, but do not remove nut in center of steering wheel, then check that steering wheel is straight.
   e. Connect battery ground cable, then drive vehicle straight ahead on a smooth surface to ensure front wheels are pointing perfectly straight ahead.
   f. Disconnect battery ground cable, remove special tool No. 998 8695, or equivalent and nut in center of wheel.
   g. Remove locking screw at end of plastic ribbon from its parking hole in steering wheel (leave screw in ribbon), then insert and tighten screw in contact reel.
   h. Lift off wheel and allow plastic ribbon and lead to pass through opening in wheel.
   i. Set contact reel to zero by turning contact reel fully to right, then turning back three turns to left. Ensure screw hole is at one o'clock, then lock contact reel in this position with screw in plastic ribbon. **Do not turn steering wheel or contact reel pin will be sheared off and whole contact reel will have to be replaced.**
   j. Pass contact reel lead through hole in steering wheel, install steering wheel nut finger tight, remove screw in end of plastic ribbon and install in parking hole in steering wheel, reconnect special tool No. 998 8695, or equivalent, then connect battery ground cable and drive vehicle on level ground and ensure steering wheel is straight.
   k. **Torque** wheel center nut 30 ft. lbs., ensure air bag warning lamp has gone out (no fault codes present), then disconnect battery ground cable and remove special tool No. 998 8695, or equivalent.
   l. Rest bottom of air bag assembly on steering wheel, connect electrical connector, place air bag assembly in position and **torque** righthand Torx bolt to 96 inch lbs., then the lefthand Torx bolt. **Ensure cable does not get pinched on reassembly.**
   m. Check that steering wheel turns easily and steering lock operates. Ensure air bag assembly is mounted securely.
   n. Turn ignition switch to On position, connect battery ground cable and check air bag lamp. If a fault code is displayed, refer to "Air Bag System" section for procedures to cancel fault code.

REAR WHEEL ALIGNMENT

S70, V70, C70 & S80

DELTA-LINK INDEPENDENT SUSPENSION

Camber

Camber angle cannot be adjusted. If angle is not within specifications, check trailing arms for damage.

Toe-In

If toe-in measurement is not within specifications, loosen nuts connecting transverse arms to trailing arms and adjust by moving transverse arms forward or rearward until correct value is obtained.

S90 & V90

MULTI-LINK INDEPENDENT SUSPENSION

Camber

Camber angle can be adjusted with eccentric bolts in lower inner link mountings. Using level scale tool Nos. 5493 or 8691, or equivalents, measure lower link angles to adjust camber as follows:

1. Loosen nut on lower link eccentric bolt so eccentric bolt can just be turned.
2. Use channel lock pliers to pull link inward, then turn eccentric bolt until bubble in level scale is centered.

Toe-In

1. Loosen nut for track rod eccentric bolt so bolt can just be turned. Turn bolt so smallest part of washer points inward.
2. Use channel lock pliers to pull rod inward, then turn eccentric bolt until toe-in is within specifications.

Air Conditioning

NOTE: On Air Bag Equipped Models, Refer To "Air Bag System Precautions" Located In The Front Of This Manual For System Disarming & Arming Procedures.

INDEX

	Page No.
A/C Specifications	9-41
Discharging System	9-35
Oil Charge	9-35
Performance Test	9-35
Automatic A/C	9-35
Manual A/C	9-35
Precautions	9-35
Air Bag Systems	9-35
Battery Ground Cable	9-35
Product Compatibility	9-35
Troubleshooting	9-35

PRECAUTIONS

AIR BAG SYSTEMS

Refer to "Air Bag System Precautions" in the front of this manual for system disarming and arming procedures.

PRODUCT COMPATIBILITY

Before replenishing refrigerant or refrigerant oil, ensure product is compatible with the system being serviced. Refer to "Specifications" in the front of this manual.

BATTERY GROUND CABLE

Prior to service, disconnect battery ground cable and isolate as required.

TROUBLESHOOTING

Refer to **Fig. 1,** for general troubleshooting, **Fig. 2,** for pressure testing troubleshooting and **Fig. 3,** for A/C system noise troubleshooting. Refer to **Figs. 4 and 5,** for system troubleshooting procedures.

PERFORMANCE TEST

AUTOMATIC A/C

1. Set temperature switch to full cooling, then set A/C switch to On position.
2. Set mode control switch to VENT, then the recirculation switch to REC.
3. Set blower speed to MAX speed, then close hood, doors and windows.
4. **On S70, V70, C70 & S80 models,** run engine at 1500–1600 RPM.
5. **On S90 & V90 models,** run engine at 2000 RPM.
6. **On all models,** place thermometer in center panel vent.
7. Allow system to stabilize at least eight minutes, then check temperature.

Refer to **Fig. 6,** for system operating specifications and diagnosis.

MANUAL A/C

S70, V70, C70 & S80

1. Set temperature switch to full cooling, then set A/C switch to On position.
2. Set mode control switch to Ventilation, then the recirculation switch to Recirculation.
3. Set fan switch to nearly full speed, then close hood, doors and windows.
4. Run engine at 1500–1600 RPM, then put thermometer in center panel vent.
5. Allow system to stabilize at least eight minutes, then check temperature in center panel vent. Refer to "Performance Test" as outlined under "Automatic Temperature Control System Diagnosis & Testing" for pressure and temperature specifications.

S90 & V90

1. Set temperature setting to maximum cooling.
2. Set A/C switch to On.
3. Set function selector to VENT and recirculation switch to REC.
4. Set blower speed to MAX.
5. Close hood and front doors and run engine at 2000 RPM.
6. Place thermometer in one of the center console valves.
7. Allow ventilation air temperature to stabilize.
8. Ensure the FC and compressor are operating normally.
9. Allow system to stabilize at least eight minutes, then check temperature in center panel vent. Refer to "Performance Test" as outlined under "Automatic Temperature Control System Diagnosis & Testing" for pressure and temperature specifications.

DISCHARGING SYSTEM

1. Block front wheels and set parking brake.
2. Connect low pressure hose of recovery station Part No. 9511000-3, or equivalent, to A/C system service valve.
3. Slowly open service valve to prevent oil from being drawn out of the compressor. Turn switch on recovery station to "Recovery."
4. Evacuation should take approximately 15–20 minutes.
5. When pressure gauges read zero, close valves.
6. Disconnect hose from service valve and install cap.
7. When the system is empty, the low pressure gauge should show a vacuum (less than zero).

OIL CHARGE

1. Discharge A/C system as described in "Discharging System."
2. After approximately five minutes the pressure in the recovery station will equalize.
3. Check recovery station drain valve for any oil that may have come out of the A/C system during system discharge.
4. Measure amount of oil in sight gauge and add an equal amount of oil to system.
5. To add oil directly to the A/C system, use valve extractor tool No. 981 1994 4, or equivalent, to remove Schraeder valve.
6. Using a clean syringe, measure how much oil needs to be added to the system, **Fig. 7.**
7. Add needed oil and replace Schrader valve.

Symptom: No cooling	Poor cooling	Intermittent cooling	Noise	Possible cause	Remedy
				Electrical faults:	
X				Blown fuse	Check fuses
X				Poor connection or short (compressor does not operate)	Check all cables
X				Compressor coupling burnt	Replace coupling
X				Fan motor (blower), does not operate	Check cables and motor
	X	X		Fan motor (blower), poor operation (loose or cracked motor)	Check/replace
		X	X	Broken or poor connection in compressor clutch winding (clutch moves in and out)	Replace clutch
			X	Fan motor screeches or contacts fan shroud	Check
				Mechanical faults	
X	X		X	Drive belt too loose or cracked	Tension or replace belt.
X	X			Heater control valve leaks in "COOL"	Check valve.
	X			Air ducts blocked	Check and clean
	X			Air inlet in front of windscreen/shield blocked	Check and clean
			X	Clutch bearing worn or off-centre	Replace bearing.
	X		X	Compressor worn or loose	Recondition compressor.
				System faults	
X				Evaporator thermostat does not disengage compressor.	Check/replace thermostat.
X				Expansion valve stuck in open position	Replace.
X				Leakage	Top-up system. Find leakage and repair.
X				Blocked hose or component	Check flow through each component
X				No refrigerant in system	Add refrigerant.
	X			Air flow through condenser blocked	Clean condenser
	X			Evaporator blocked on air cooling side	Clean off dirt etc.
	X			Evaporator thermostat incorrectly adjusted	Check thermostat.
	X		X	Insufficient refrigerant (whistling noise from evaporator near expansion valve, bubbles in sight glass)	Drain and refill system.
	X			Expansion valve capillary tube damaged.	Replace.
	X			Receiver/dryer blocked	Replace.
	X	X		Moisture in system. Cooling capacity good at start (few minutes) then poor. Or poor operation at high ambient temperatures	Drain system, replace receiver/dryer or drying agent, fill with refrigerant.
	X			Air in system (bubbles in sight glass)	Drain system, replace receiver/dryer or drying agent, fill with refrigerant.
		X		Ice on evaporator air cooling side (thermostat adjusted too low or fan not operating)	Check evaporator thermostat. Test with fan on
		X		Loose evaporator thermostat	Check/replace.
		X		Poor contact between expansion valve capillary tube and evaporator outlet or poor insulation	Check
		X		Too large a difference between off and on for evaporator thermostat	Replace.
			X	System overfull causes crashing noise or vibrations from high pressure lines, clicking noise from compressor. excessive compressor pressure and suction pressure, hissing noise from expansion valve, bubbles or vapour in sight glass. If compressor valves damaged by overfilling, compressor pressure will be too low	Drain System. Refill
			X	Moisture in system, can cause noise from expansion valve	Drain system, replace/receiver/dryer or drying agent, fill with refrigerant.

VV7029100022000X

Fig. 1 General troubleshooting

Low pressure side	High pressure side	Cause	Remedy
Low	Normal	1. Expansion valve blocked or seized in closed position. 2. Expansion valve capillary tube damage – liquid loss. 3. Moisture in system, causes ice in expansion valve.	*1. Remove blockage. Replace valve if necessary. *2. Replace expansion valve. 3. Drain system. Replace receiver/dryer. Evacuate system and fill.
Low	Low	1. Not enough refrigerant.	*1. Drain system, Evacuate and fill.
Low	High	1. Blockage in receiver/dryer or connecting pipes.	1. Replace. Remove blockage.
High	Normal	1. Expansion valve seized in open position. 2. Expansion valve coil against evaporator outlet, loose or poorly insulated. 3. Not enough refrigerant. Possibly bubbles in sight glass.	*1. Replace. 2. Secure coil and insulate. 3. Drain system. Evacuate and fill.
High	Low	1. Defective compressor.	1. Repair/replace. Replace receiver/dryer.
Normal – High	High	1. Too much refrigerant. 2. No cold air reaches condenser. 3. Blockage in high pressure side. 4. Engine radiator overheated. 5. Air in system. Poor evacuation and filling of refrigerant.	1. Drain system. Evacuate and fill. 2. Remove obstruction. Check cooling fan and belts. 3. Remove blockage. 4. Improve cooling. 5. Drain system. Replace receiver/dryer. Evacuate and fill according to instructions.
Normal	Normal	1. Moisture in system, occasional formation of ice. Low pressure side pressure varies. Cooling ability OK in cool conditions but poor or non existent in hot weather.	1. Drain system. Replace receiver/dryer. Evacuate and fill according to instructions.

*USA vehicles:
To conform with Warranty policy, the receiver/dryer must be replaced each time the system is opened.

VV7029100023000X

Fig. 2 Pressure testing troubleshooting

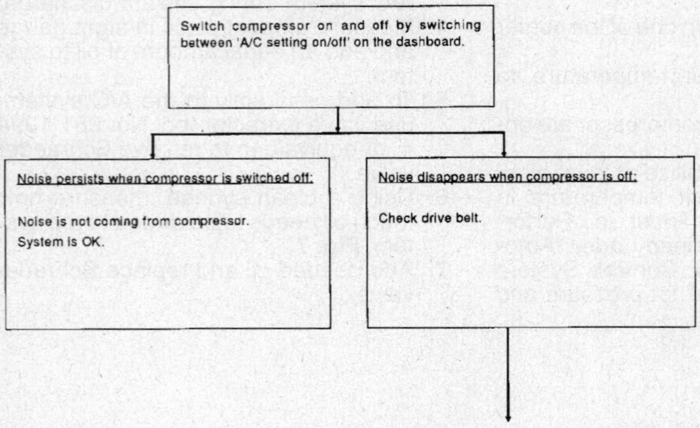

VV7029200030010X

Fig. 3 A/C noise troubleshooting (Part 1 of 4)

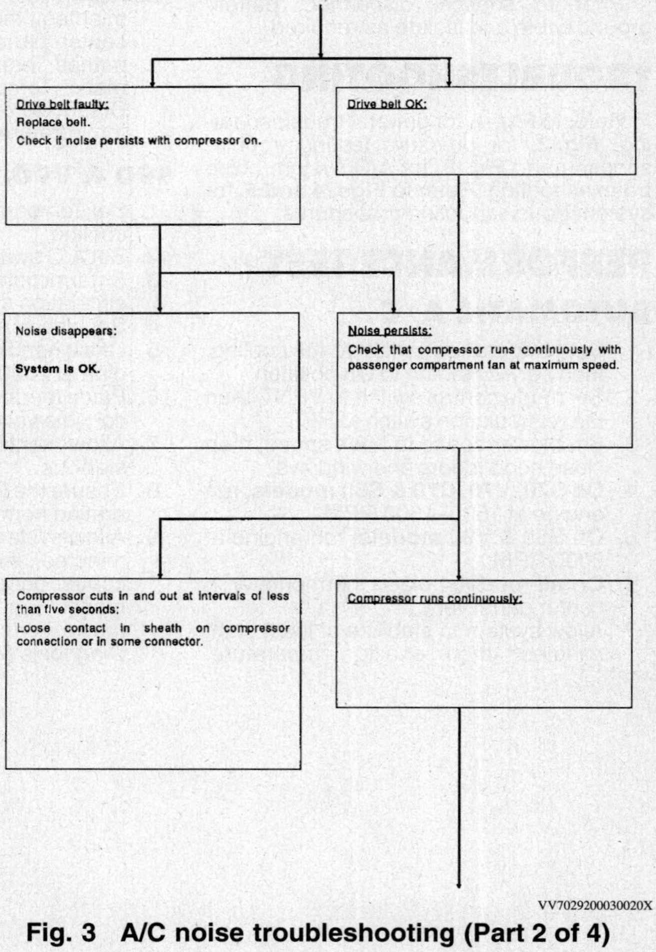

VV7029200030020X

Fig. 3 A/C noise troubleshooting (Part 2 of 4)

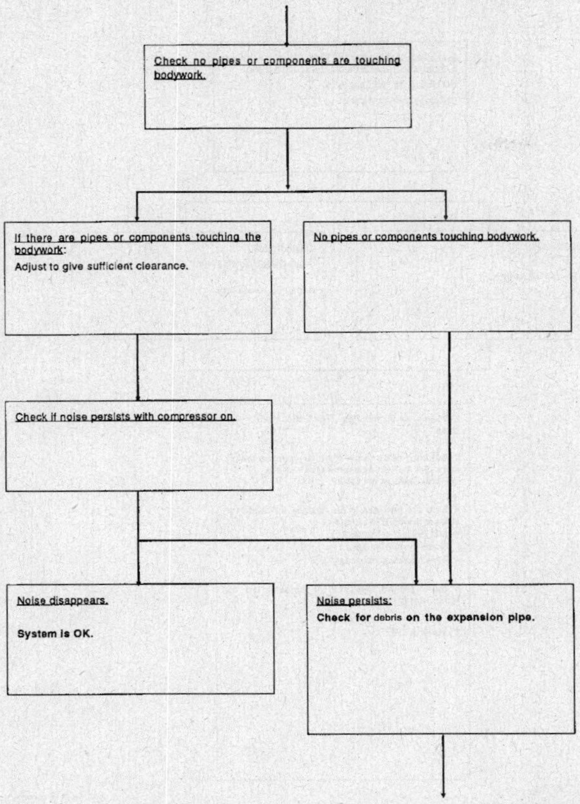

VV7029200030030X

Fig. 3 A/C noise troubleshooting (Part 3 of 4)

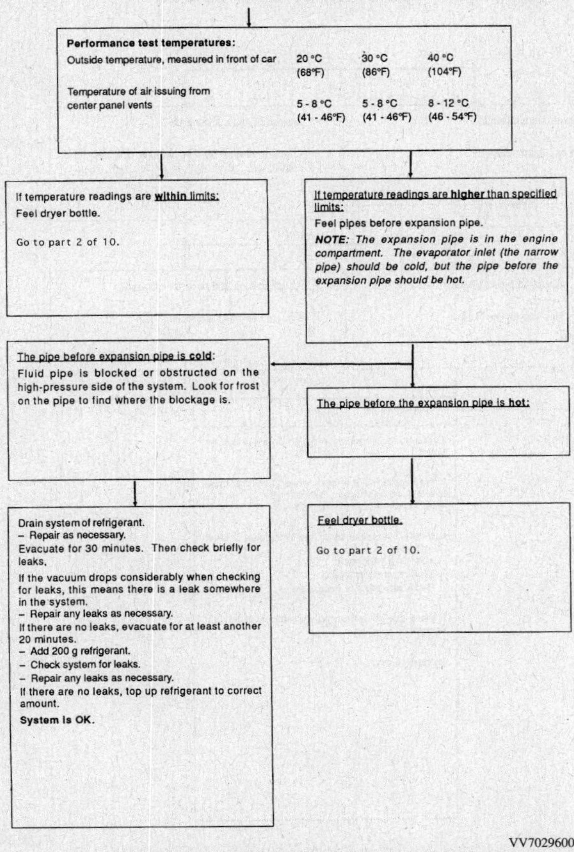

VV7029600043010X

Fig. 4 A/C system troubleshooting (Part 1 of 10). S70, V70, C70 & S80

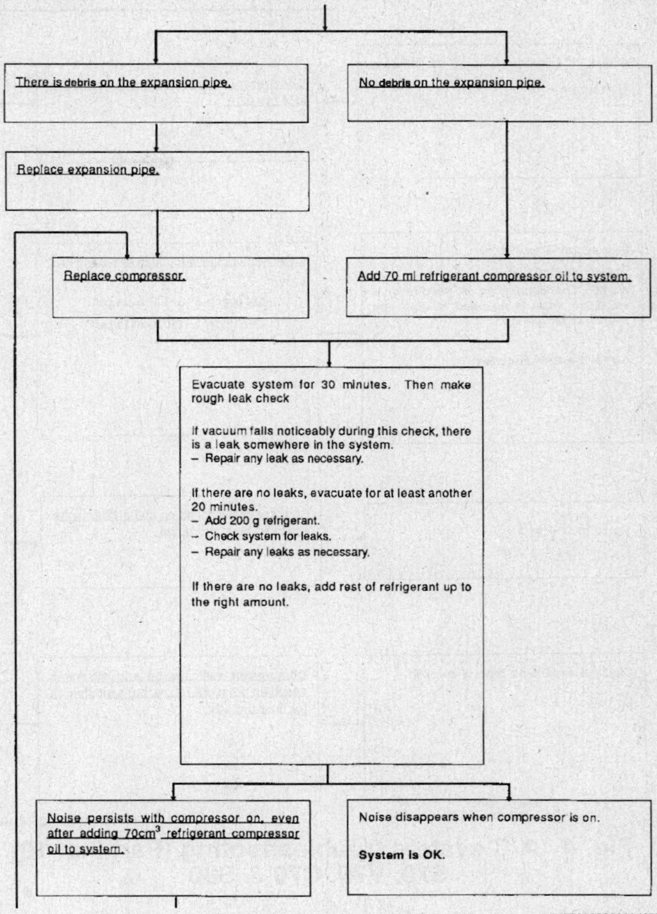

VV7029200030040X

Fig. 3 A/C noise troubleshooting (Part 4 of 4)

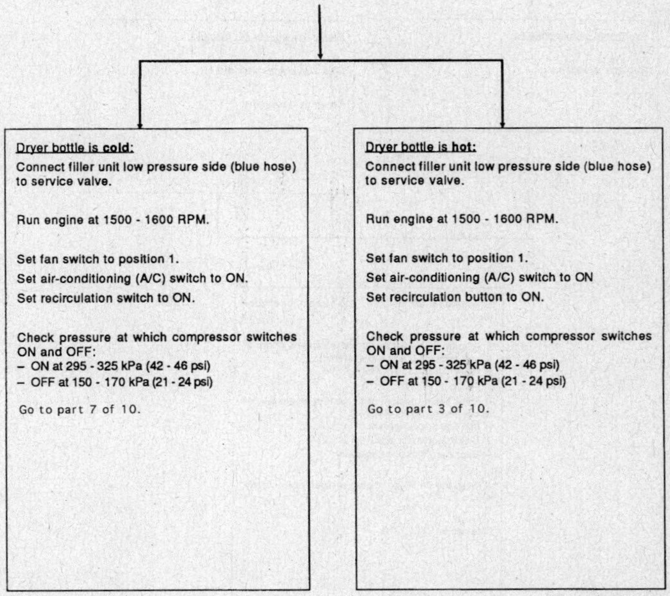

VV7029600043020X

Fig. 4 A/C system troubleshooting (Part 2 of 10). S70, V70, C70 & S80

Compressor runs constantly at over 325 kPa (46 psi):

Check if expansion pipe is missing

Go to part 6 of 10.

Compressor cuts in too high or out too low:

ON over 325 kPa (46 psi)

OFF under 150 kPa (21 psi)

Pressostat is faulty.

Replace pressostat.

NOTE: *The connection is fitted with a valve, so there is no need to drain the system of refrigerant.*

Go to "Performance test".

Compressor switches on and off within the specified pressure range.

Go to part 4 of 10.

Compressor switches on and off within specified pressure range, but switches off for long periods.

Check if expansion pipe is blocked.

Go to part 5 of 10.

VV7029600043030X

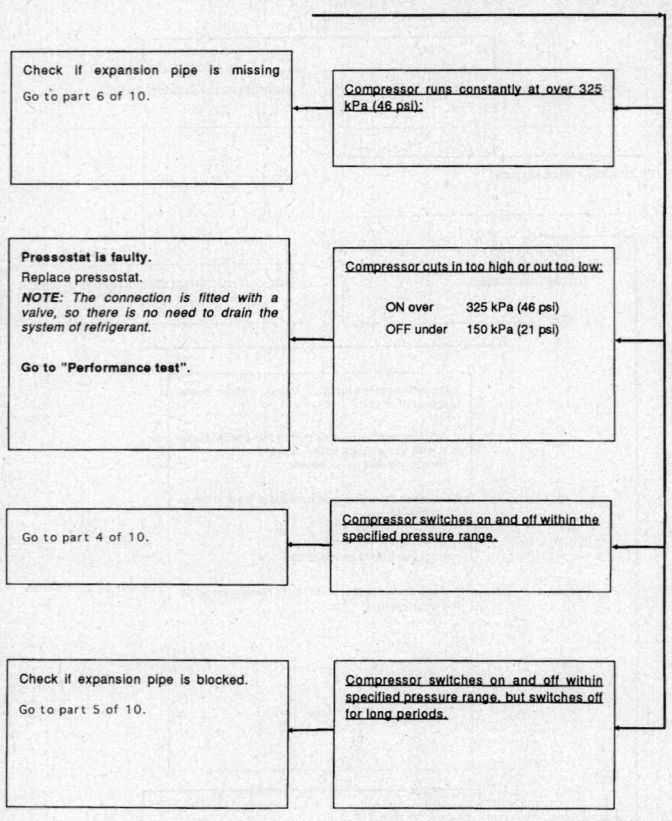

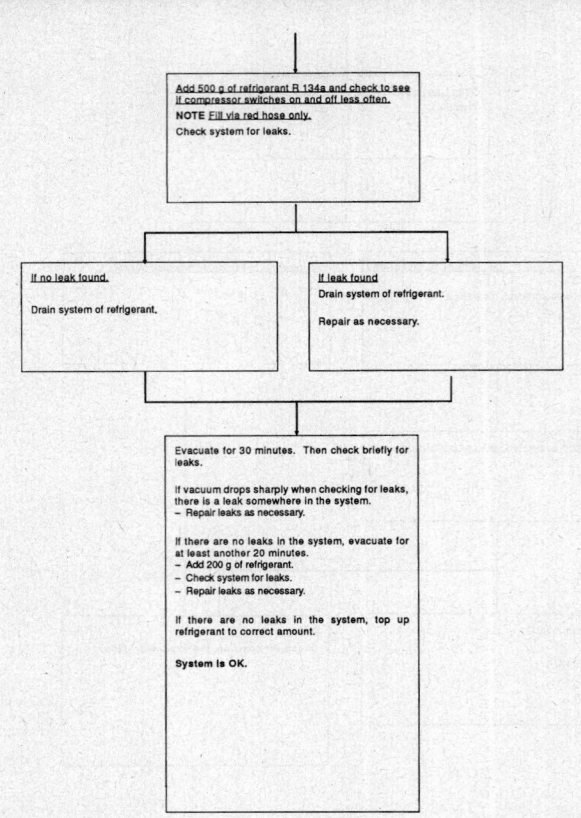

Fig. 4 A/C system troubleshooting (Part 3 of 10). S70, V70, C70 & S80

Add 500 g of refrigerant R 134a and check to see if compressor switches on and off less often.

NOTE Fill via red hose only.

Check system for leaks.

If no leak found.

Drain system of refrigerant.

If leak found

Drain system of refrigerant.

Repair as necessary.

Evacuate for 30 minutes. Then check briefly for leaks.

If vacuum drops sharply when checking for leaks, there is a leak somewhere in the system.
- Repair leaks as necessary.

If there are no leaks in the system, evacuate for at least another 20 minutes.
- Add 200 g of refrigerant.
- Check system for leaks.
- Repair leaks as necessary.

If there are no leaks in the system, top up refrigerant to correct amount.

System is OK.

VV7029600043040X

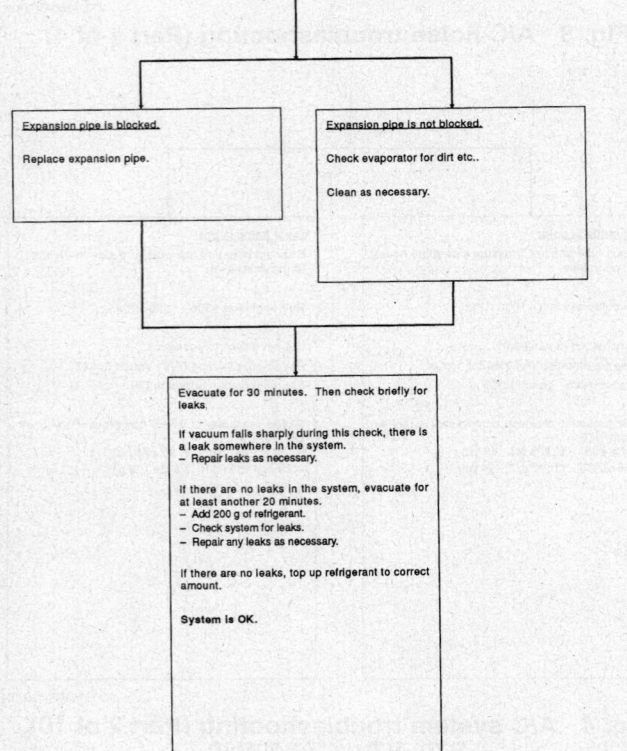

Fig. 4 A/C system troubleshooting (Part 4 of 10). S70, V70, C70 & S80

Expansion pipe is blocked.

Replace expansion pipe.

Expansion pipe is not blocked.

Check evaporator for dirt etc..

Clean as necessary.

Evacuate for 30 minutes. Then check briefly for leaks.

If vacuum falls sharply during this check, there is a leak somewhere in the system.
- Repair leaks as necessary.

If there are no leaks in the system, evacuate for at least another 20 minutes.
- Add 200 g of refrigerant.
- Check system for leaks.
- Repair any leaks as necessary.

If there are no leaks, top up refrigerant to correct amount.

System is OK.

VV7029600043050X

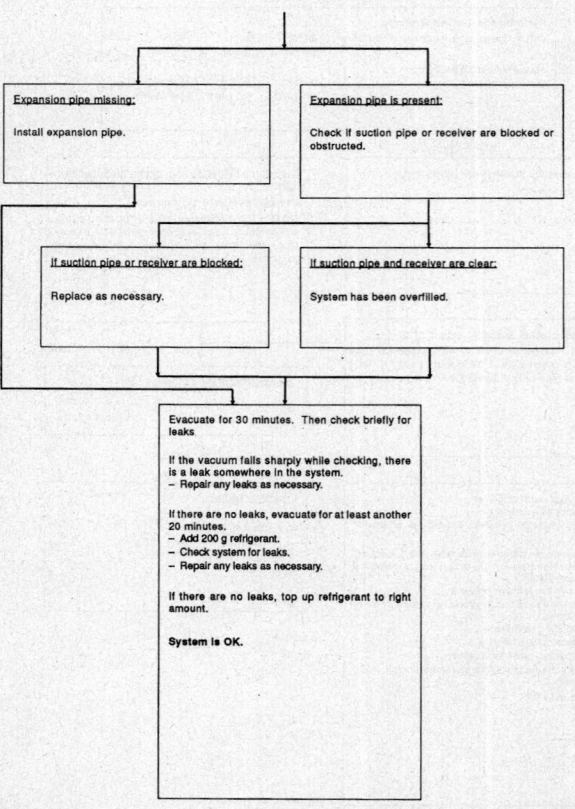

Fig. 4 A/C system troubleshooting (Part 5 of 10). S70, V70, C70 & S80

Expansion pipe missing:

Install expansion pipe.

Expansion pipe is present:

Check if suction pipe or receiver are blocked or obstructed.

If suction pipe or receiver are blocked:

Replace as necessary.

If suction pipe and receiver are clear:

System has been overfilled.

Evacuate for 30 minutes. Then check briefly for leaks

If the vacuum falls sharply while checking, there is a leak somewhere in the system.
- Repair any leaks as necessary.

If there are no leaks, evacuate for at least another 20 minutes.
- Add 200 g refrigerant.
- Check system for leaks.
- Repair any leaks as necessary.

If there are no leaks, top up refrigerant to right amount.

System is OK.

VV7029600043060X

Fig. 4 A/C system troubleshooting (Part 6 of 10). S70, V70, C70 & S80

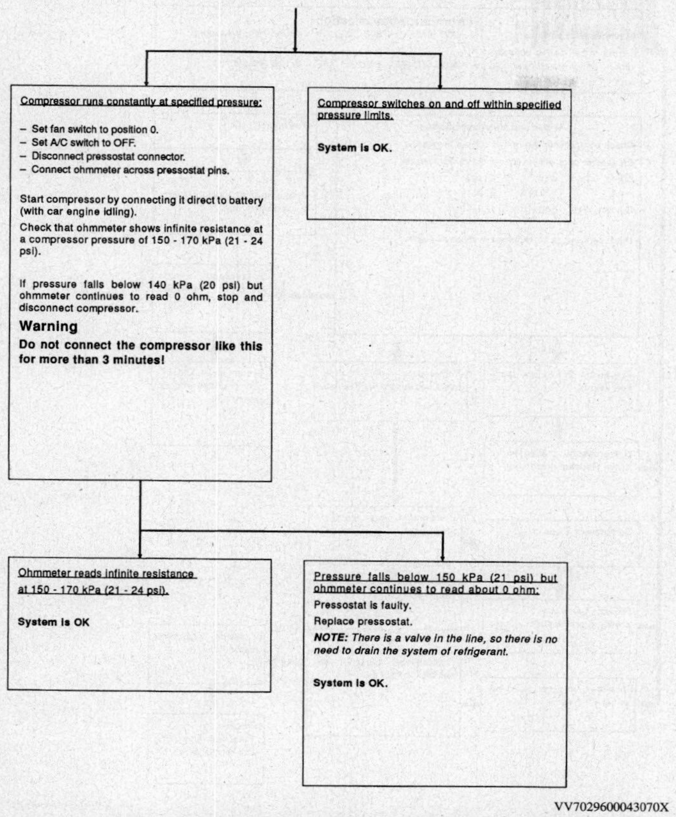

Compressor runs constantly at specified pressure:
– Set fan switch to position 0.
– Set A/C switch to OFF.
– Disconnect pressostat connector.
– Connect ohmmeter across pressostat pins.
Start compressor by connecting it direct to battery (with car engine idling).
Check that ohmmeter shows infinite resistance at a compressor pressure of 150 - 170 kPa (21 - 24 psi).
If pressure falls below 140 kPa (20 psi) but ohmmeter continues to read 0 ohm, stop and disconnect compressor.
Warning
Do not connect the compressor like this for more than 3 minutes!
Compressor switches on and off within specified pressure limits.
System is OK.
Ohmmeter reads infinite resistance at 150 - 170 kPa (21 - 24 psi).
System is OK
Pressure falls below 150 kPa (21 psi) but ohmmeter continues to read about 0 ohm:
Pressostat is faulty.
Replace pressostat.
NOTE: There is a valve in the line, so there is no need to drain the system of refrigerant.
System is OK.
VV7029600043070X

Fig. 4 A/C system troubleshooting (Part 7 of 10). S70, V70, C70 & S80

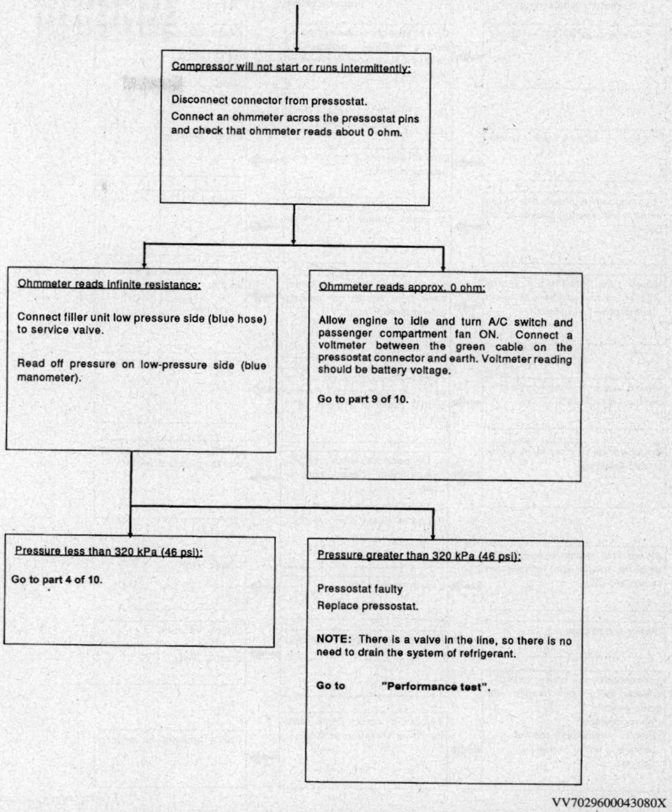

Compressor will not start or runs intermittently:
Disconnect connector from pressostat.
Connect an ohmmeter across the pressostat pins and check that ohmmeter reads about 0 ohm.
Ohmmeter reads infinite resistance:
Connect filler unit low pressure side (blue hose) to service valve.
Read off pressure on low-pressure side (blue manometer).
Ohmmeter reads approx. 0 ohm:
Allow engine to idle and turn A/C switch and passenger compartment fan ON. Connect a voltmeter between the green cable on the pressostat connector and earth. Voltmeter reading should be battery voltage.
Go to part 9 of 10.
Pressure less than 320 kPa (46 psi):
Go to part 4 of 10.
Pressure greater than 320 kPa (46 psi):
Pressostat faulty
Replace pressostat.
NOTE: There is a valve in the line, so there is no need to drain the system of refrigerant.
Go to "Performance test".
VV7029600043080X

Fig. 4 A/C system troubleshooting (Part 8 of 10). S70, V70, C70 & S80

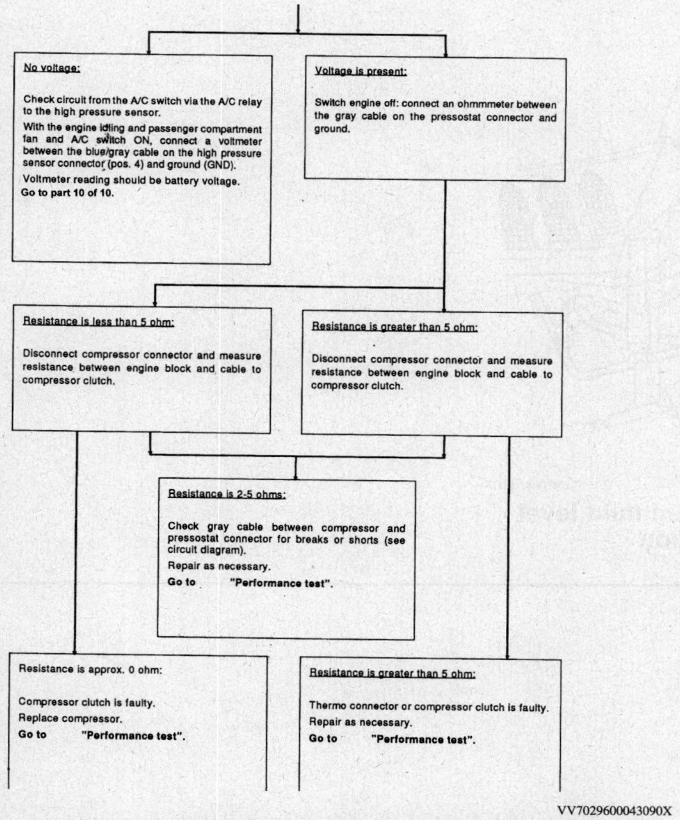

No voltage:
Check circuit from the A/C switch via the A/C relay to the high pressure sensor.
With the engine idling and passenger compartment fan and A/C switch ON, connect a voltmeter between the blue/gray cable on the high pressure sensor connector (pos. 4) and ground (GND).
Voltmeter reading should be battery voltage.
Go to part 10 of 10.
Voltage is present:
Switch engine off: connect an ohmmmeter between the gray cable on the pressostat connector and ground.
Resistance is less than 5 ohm:
Disconnect compressor connector and measure resistance between engine block and cable to compressor clutch.
Resistance is greater than 5 ohm:
Disconnect compressor connector and measure resistance between engine block and cable to compressor clutch.
Resistance is 2-5 ohms:
Check gray cable between compressor and pressostat connector for breaks or shorts (see circuit diagram).
Repair as necessary.
Go to "Performance test".
Resistance is approx. 0 ohm:
Compressor clutch is faulty.
Replace compressor.
Go to "Performance test".
Resistance is greater than 5 ohm:
Thermo connector or compressor clutch is faulty.
Repair as necessary.
Go to "Performance test".
VV7029600043090X

Fig. 4 A/C system troubleshooting (Part 9 of 10). S70, V70, C70 & S80

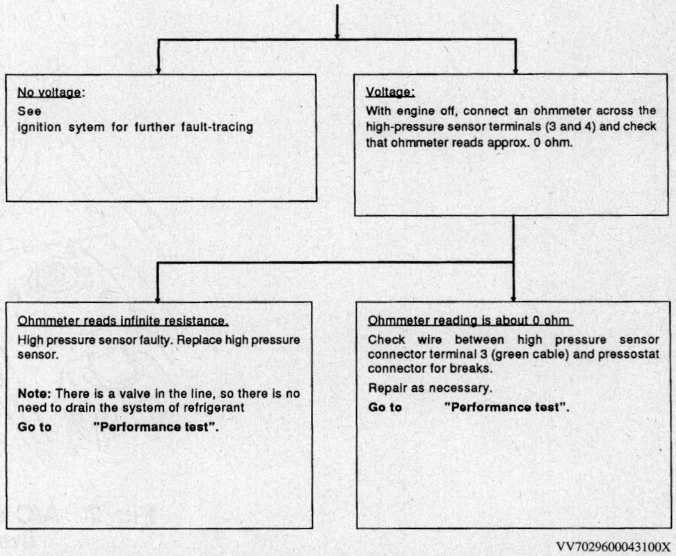

Fig. 4 A/C system troubleshooting (Part 10 of 10). S70, V70, C70 & S80

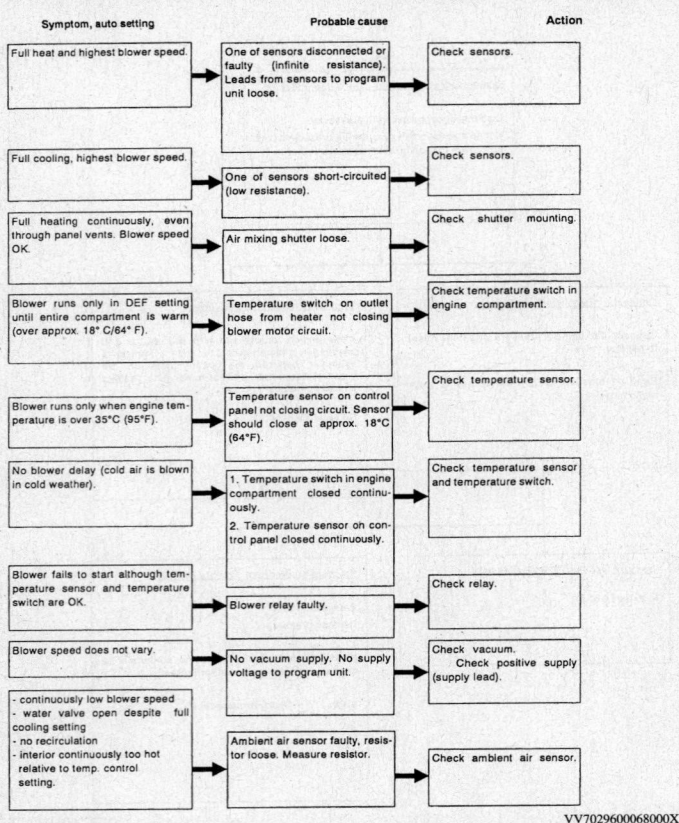

Symptom, auto setting	Probable cause	Action
Full heat and highest blower speed.	One of sensors disconnected or faulty (infinite resistance). Leads from sensors to program unit loose.	Check sensors.
Full cooling, highest blower speed.	One of sensors short-circuited (low resistance).	Check sensors.
Full heating continuously, even through panel vents. Blower speed OK.	Air mixing shutter loose.	Check shutter mounting.
Blower runs only in DEF setting until entire compartment is warm (over approx. 18° C/64° F).	Temperature switch on outlet hose from heater not closing blower motor circuit.	Check temperature switch in engine compartment.
Blower runs only when engine temperature is over 35°C (95°F).	Temperature sensor on control panel not closing circuit. Sensor should close at approx. 18°C (64°F).	Check temperature sensor.
No blower delay (cold air is blown in cold weather).	1. Temperature switch in engine compartment closed continuously. 2. Temperature sensor on control panel closed continuously.	Check temperature sensor and temperature switch.
Blower fails to start although temperature sensor and temperature switch are OK.	Blower relay faulty.	Check relay.
Blower speed does not vary.	No vacuum supply. No supply voltage to program unit.	Check vacuum. Check positive supply (supply lead).
- continuously low blower speed - water valve open despite full cooling setting - no recirculation - interior continuously too hot relative to temp. control setting.	Ambient air sensor faulty, resistor loose. Measure resistor.	Check ambient air sensor.

VV7029600068000X

Fig. 5 A/C system troubleshooting. S90 & V90

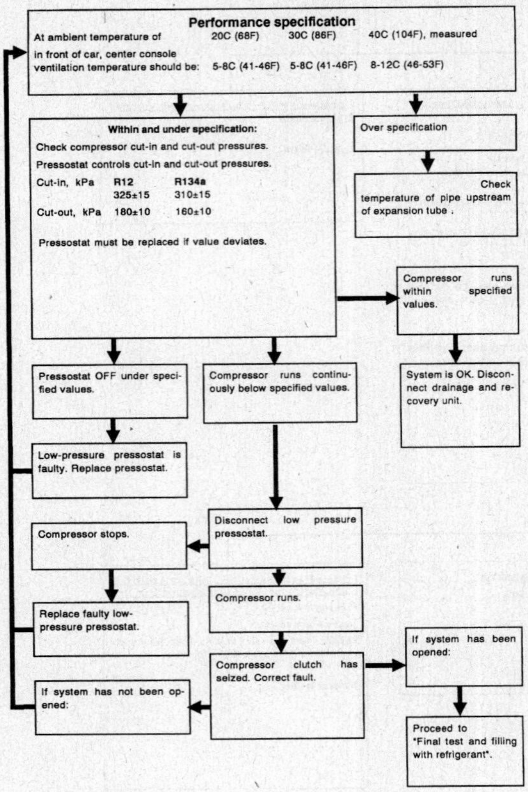

Performance specification
At ambient temperature of 20C (68F) 30C (86F) 40C (104F), measured in front of car, center console
ventilation temperature should be: 5-8C (41-46F) 5-8C (41-46F) 8-12C (46-53F)
Within and under specification:
Check compressor cut-in and cut-out pressures.
Pressostat controls cut-in and cut-out pressures.
Cut-in, kPa R12 325±15 R134a 310±15
Cut-out, kPa 180±10 160±10
Pressostat must be replaced if value deviates.
Over specification
Check temperature of pipe upstream of expansion tube .
Compressor runs within specified values.
System is OK. Disconnect drainage and recovery unit.
Pressostat OFF under specified values.
Compressor runs continuously below specified values.
Low-pressure pressostat is faulty. Replace pressostat.
Disconnect low pressure pressostat.
Compressor stops.
Compressor runs.
Replace faulty low-pressure pressostat.
Compressor clutch has seized. Correct fault.
If system has been opened:
If system has not been opened:
Proceed to "Final test and filling with refrigerant".

VV7029600046000X

Fig. 6 A/C system performance specifications & diagnosis

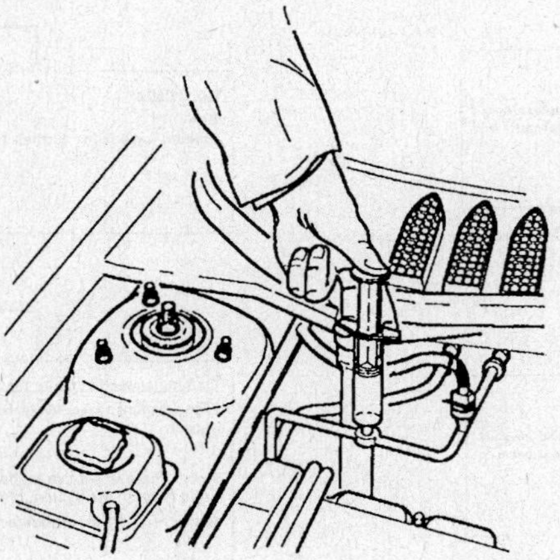

VV7029100026000X

Fig. 7 A/C system fluid level inspection

A/C SPECIFICATIONS

Model	Refrigerant Type	Refrigerant Capacity, Lbs.	Refrigerant Oil		Charging Valve Locations	
			Viscosity	Total System Capacity, Ounces	High Press.	Low Press.
1998						
S70 & V70	R134a	①	③	6.8	—	—
S90 & V90	R134a	2.2	②	8.1	—	—
1999						
C70	R134a	①	③	6.8	—	—
S70 & V70	R134a	—	—	—	—	—
S80	R134a	—	—	—	—	—
2000						
C70	R134a	①	③	6.8	—	—
S40	R134a					
S70 & V70	R134a	—	—	—	—	—
S80	R134a	—	—	—	—	—
2001						
C70	R134a	①	③	6.8	—	—
S40 & V40	R134a	—	—	—	—	—
S70 & V70	R134a	—	—	—	—	—
S80	R134a	—	—	—	—	—
V70	R134a	—	—	—	—	—

① — Cold climates, 1.8 lbs.; warm climates, 1.65 lbs.

② — Volvo part No. 1161425.

③ — Volvo part No. 1161407-0.

Cooling Fans

NOTE: On Air Bag Equipped Models, Refer To "Air Bag System Precautions" Located In The Front Of This Manual For System Disarming & Arming Procedures.

NOTE: "Electrical Symbol & Wire Color Code Identification" Located In The Front Of This Manual May Be Used As An Aid When Using Wiring Circuits Found In This Section.

INDEX

	Page No.
Component Replacement	9-43
Engine Cooling Fan	9-43
Precautions	9-42
Air Bag Systems	9-42
Battery Ground Cable	9-42
System Diagnosis & Testing	9-42
Less Motronic 4.4 Engine Control System	9-42
With Motronic 4.4 Engine Control System	9-42
Troubleshooting	9-42
Constant Half Speed	9-42
Constant High Speed	9-42
No High Speed	9-42
No Low Speed Or High Speed	9-42
No Low Speed	9-42

PRECAUTIONS

AIR BAG SYSTEMS

Refer to "Air Bag System Precautions" in the front of this manual for system disarming and arming procedures.

BATTERY GROUND CABLE

Prior to service, disconnect battery ground cable and isolate as required.

TROUBLESHOOTING

CONSTANT HALF SPEED

1. Short circuit to ground in low speed signal cable.
2. Defective engine cooling fan relay.

CONSTANT HIGH SPEED

1. Short circuit to ground in high speed signal cable.
2. Defective engine cooling fan relay.

NO LOW SPEED

1. Defective fan or cooling fan relay.

NO HIGH SPEED

1. Open circuit in high speed signal cable.
2. Defective engine cooling fan relay or cooling fan.

NO LOW SPEED OR HIGH SPEED

1. Open circuit in power cable to ground lead.
2. Defective engine cooling fan relay or cooling fan.

SYSTEM DIAGNOSIS & TESTING

When performing the following tests, refer to wiring circuits in **Figs. 1 through 4.**

LESS MOTRONIC 4.4 ENGINE CONTROL SYSTEM

Engine Cooling Fan & Relay

1. Turn ignition to ON position.
2. Connect a suitable jumper wire between thermal switch electrical connector terminals. **Do not disconnect electrical connector.**
3. With jumper wire properly installed, the engine cooling fan should activate.
4. If fan does not operate, visually check relay, wiring and electrical connector for open and/or short circuits, relay for correct installation, incorrectly grounded and/or damaged electrical connector. After conducting repairs on either the wiring, relay or electrical connector, repeat test.
5. If fan still does not operate, replace relay and repeat test procedure.

Micro-Switch

1. Connect a suitable test lamp between last terminal on switch and a 12 volt power supply.
2. Place a suitable feeler gauge between lower adjustment lower adjusting screw on switch lever and stop bracket.
3. With a .008 inch feeler gauge, test lamp should light.
4. With a .024 inch feeler gauge, test lamp should be off.
5. If necessary, place a .012 inch feeler gauge between lower adjustment screw and stop. Turn upper adjustment screw until test lamp lights and tighten adjustment screw.

Thermal Switch

1. Connect a suitable ohmmeter onto thermal switch terminals.
2. Place thermal switch into a container filled with oil. Submerge thermal switch in oil up to its flange. Do not completely submerge thermal switch. **When an oil bath solution is used to heat the thermal switch, ensure thermal switch does not come in contact with container bottom or its side or thermal switch damage will result.**
3. Place a suitable thermometer into the oil bath as close to the thermal switch as possible.
4. Heat the oil bath solution and observe both thermometer and ohmmeter readings.
5. The thermal switch should activate (as indicated by a small deflection by the ohmmeter needle) with oil bath solution heated to approximately 207–216°F.
6. Allow thermal switch to cool from approximately 207–198°F. At approximately 198°F, the thermal switch should deactivate (as indicated by a large deflection on ohmmeter needle).
7. If the thermal switch does not operate as specified in steps 5 and 6, replace thermal switch assembly.

Thermostat

Test thermostat in hot water. The maximum opening should be reached in two minutes in water at the opening temperature.

On models with marking of 87, thermostat opens at 187°F and is fully open at 216°F.

On models with marking of 90, thermostat opens 194°F and is fully open at 221°F.

WITH MOTRONIC 4.4 ENGINE CONTROL SYSTEM

High Speed Signal Cable Inspection

1. Connect test box and check ground terminals as follows:
   a. Turn ignition off and wait at least 3 minutes before disconnecting ECM.
   b. Connect adapter tool No. 9511351, or equivalent, into ECM connector, then connect test box (tool No.

9813190, or equivalent) to adapter, **Fig. 5.**

c. Turn off all lights and electrical accessories that use battery power.
d. Connect an ohmmeter between battery ground terminal and terminal A13 on test box and measure resistance.
e. Connect an ohmmeter between battery ground terminal and terminal A28 on test box and measure resistance.
f. Connect an ohmmeter between battery ground terminal and terminal A42 on test box and measure resistance.
g. Resistance should be approximately 0 ohms for all measurements.
h. If resistance is incorrect, check both ground terminals at rear of engine and their wires for an open circuit. Also check for open circuit in ground lead between engine and chassis.

2. Disconnect terminal B from engine cooling fan relay.
3. Connect an ohmmeter between coupling B connector No. 2, **Fig. 6,** and No. 22 (A22) on test box.
4. Resistance should be approximately 0 ohms.
5. If resistance is incorrect, check wire for open circuit between cooling fan relay terminal B2 and ECM.

Cooling Fan Motor High Speed Inspection

1. Turn ignition off.
2. Disconnect terminal C from cooling fan relay.
3. Connect an ohmmeter between terminal C2 and ground.
4. Resistance should be 0–10 ohms.
5. If resistance is within specifications but fan does not operate at high speed, replace cooling fan relay.
6. If resistance is not within specifications, replace cooling fan/motor.

Cooling Fan Motor Low Speed Inspection

1. Turn ignition off.
2. Disconnect terminal C from cooling fan relay.
3. Connect an ohmmeter between terminal C1 and ground.
4. Resistance should be 0–10 ohms.
5. If resistance is within specifications but fan does not operate at low speed, replace cooling fan relay.
6. If resistance is not within specifications, replace cooling fan/motor.

Cooling Fan Ground Inspection

1. Turn ignition off an disconnect cooling fan electrical connector (C/EA single pin ground lead), **Fig. 7.**
2. Connect an ohmmeter between single pin connector and ground.
3. Resistance should be approximately 0 ohms.
4. If resistance is within specifications but fan does not operate, perform cooling fan motor high speed and low speed inspections.
5. If resistance is not within specifications, replace cooling fan.

Cooling Fan Relay Low Speed Inspection

1. Turn ignition off and disconnect terminal B from engine cooling fan relay.
2. If cooling fan cuts out, check wire between relay terminal B1 and ECM terminal A7 for a short circuit.
3. If cooling fan does not cut out, replace cooling fan relay.

Cooling Fan Relay High Speed Inspection

1. Turn ignition off and disconnect terminal B from engine cooling fan relay.
2. If cooling fan cuts out, check wire between relay terminal B2 and ECM terminal A22 for a short circuit.
3. If cooling fan does not cut out, replace cooling fan relay.

COMPONENT REPLACEMENT

ENGINE COOLING FAN

S70, V70, C70 & S80

1. Remove fan shroud screws.
2. Bend shroud aside slightly, then lift relay holder and disconnect fan electrical connectors.
3. Remove control module box cooling air ducts and air cleaner housing.
4. Remove fan and shroud, then remove fan to shroud screws to separate fan and shroud.
5. Reverse procedure to install.

S90 & V90

1. Open hood.
2. Remove grille, if necessary.
3. Remove radiator, if necessary.
4. Disconnect electrical connectors from fan assembly.
5. Remove fan and fan shroud assembly.
6. Separate fan from fan shroud assembly.
7. Reverse procedure to install.

1/1	Battery
2/11	Relay, el. cooling fan
4/23	Control unit, LH-jetronic 2.4
6/29	Electric cooling fan
7/14	Thermostat, el. cooling fan
7/38	Low-speed pressure sensor, el. cooling fan
7/40	High-speed pressure sensor, el. cooling fan
31/1	Ground connection right front fender
31/2	Ground connection left front fender
31/64	Ground connection el. cooling fan

A	Connector at right suspension tower, 3-pin
*)	Fuse

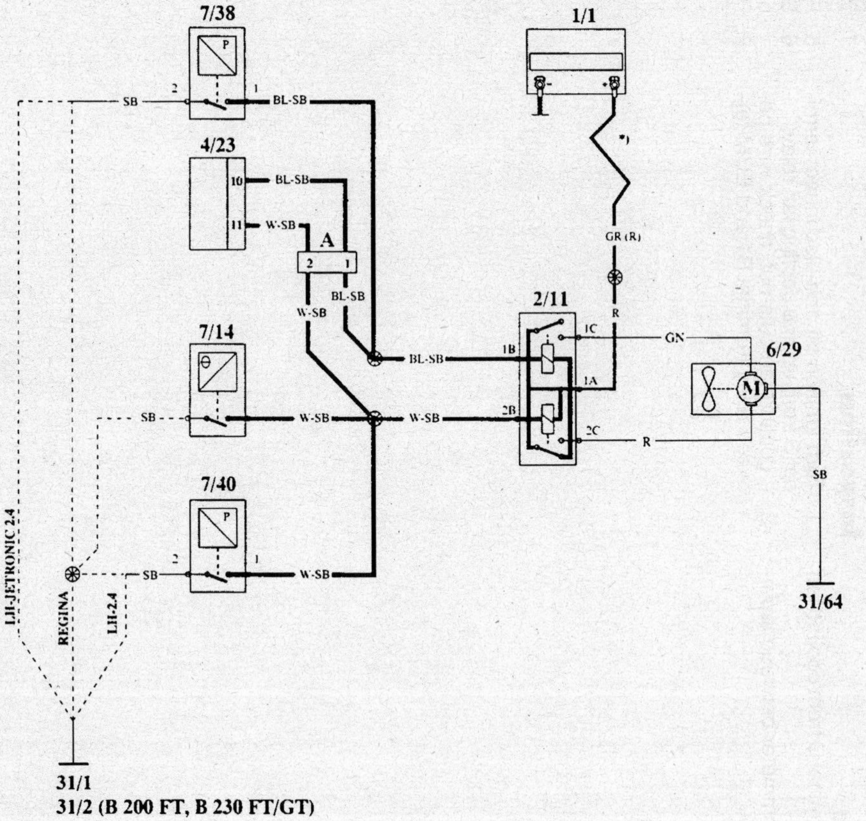

VV1089200001000X

Fig. 1 Electric cooling fan wiring circuit

1/1	Battery
2/11	Relay, electric cooling fan
4/12	Control unit, Motronic
6/29	Electric cooling fan
7/38	Low-speed pressure sensor, electric cooling fan
7/40	High-speed pressure sensor, electric cooling fan
31/1	Ground connection, right front wing
31/64	Ground connection, electric cooling fan

B	Connector, left A-post
C	Connector, right A-post
*)	Fuse-element (fuse)

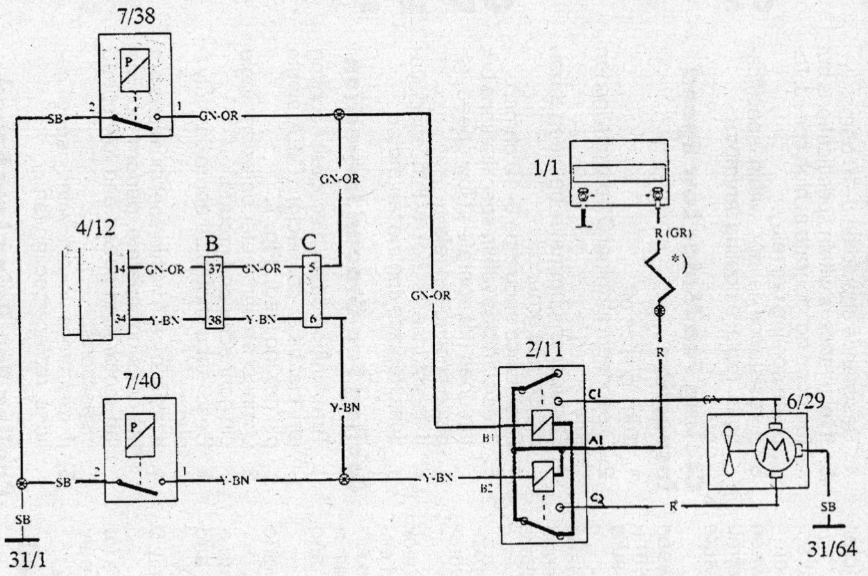

VV1089200002000X

Fig. 2 Electric cooling fan wiring circuit

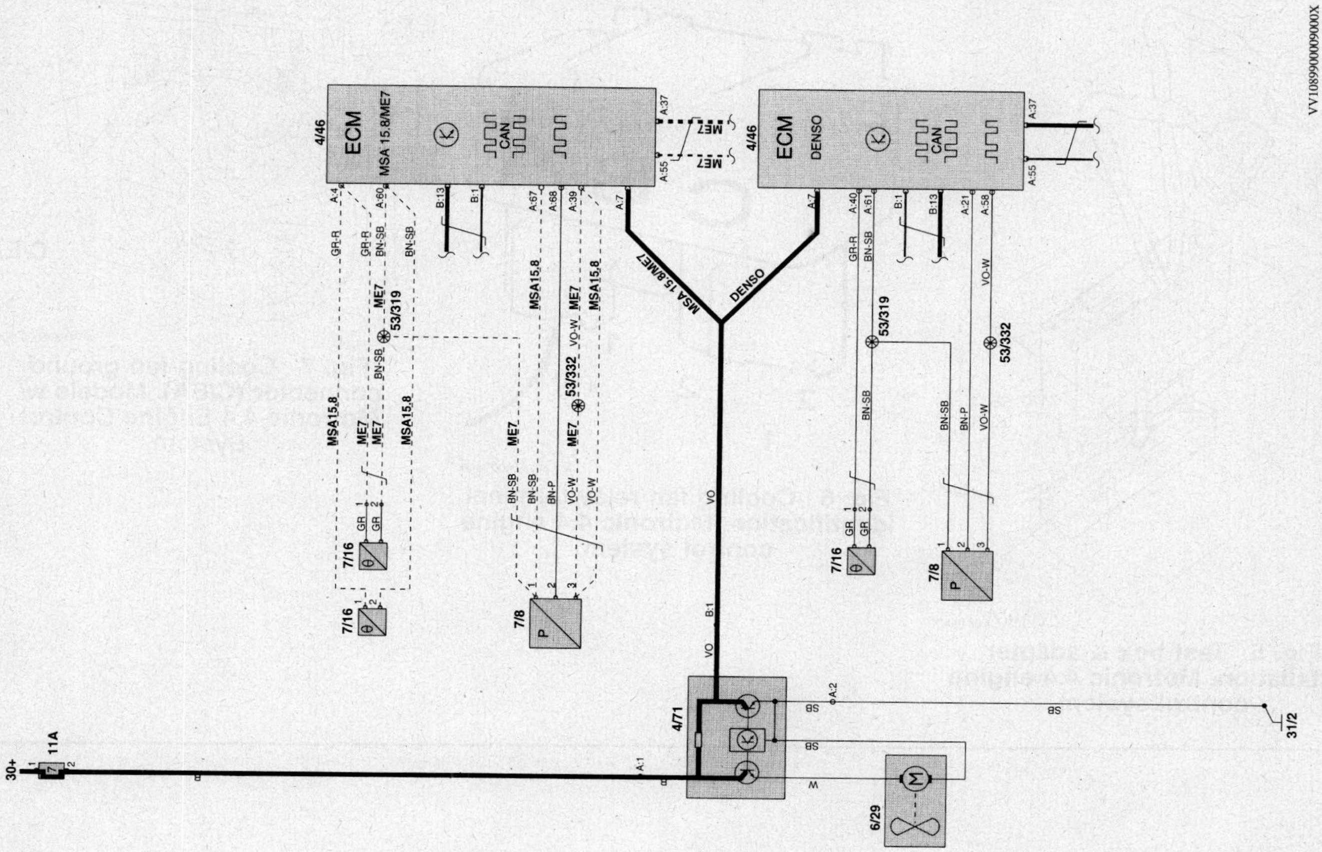

Fig. 4 Electric cooling fan wiring circuit. S80

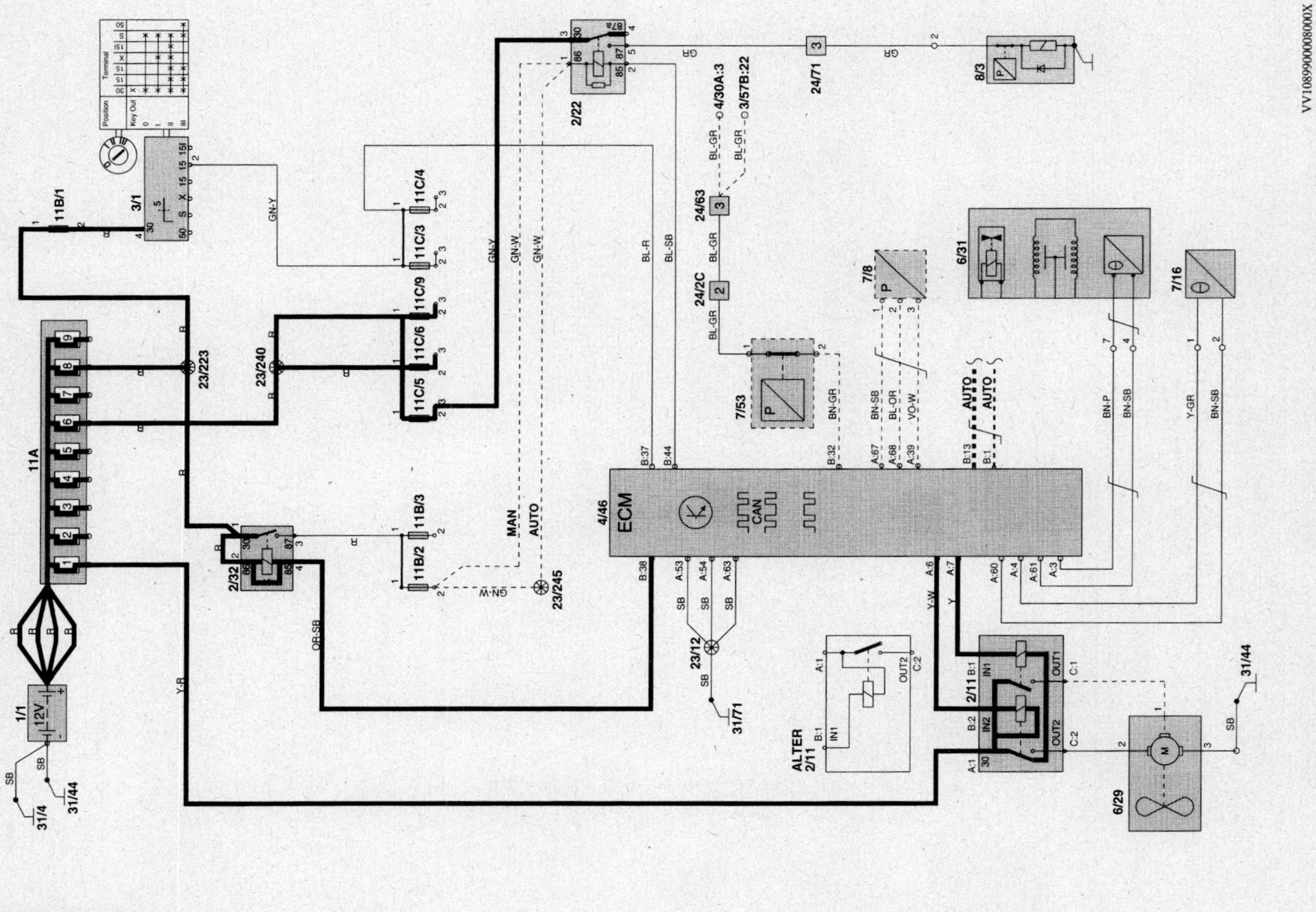

Fig. 3 Electric cooling fan wiring circuit. C70, S70 & V70

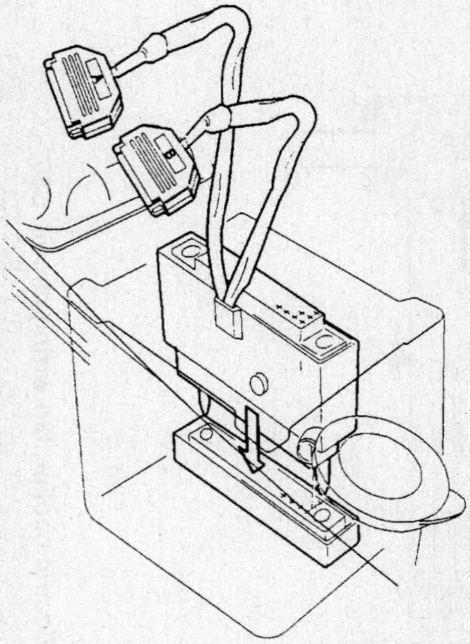

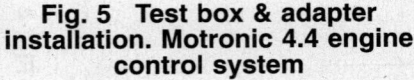

VV1089600004000X

Fig. 5 Test box & adapter installation. Motronic 4.4 engine control system

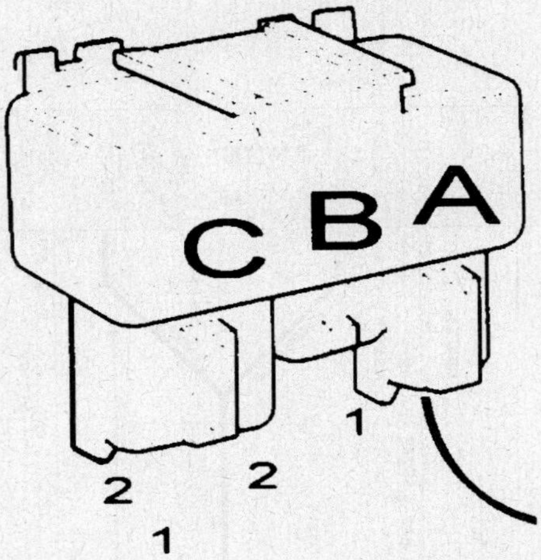

VV1089600005000X

Fig. 6 Cooling fan relay terminal identification. Motronic 4.4 engine control system

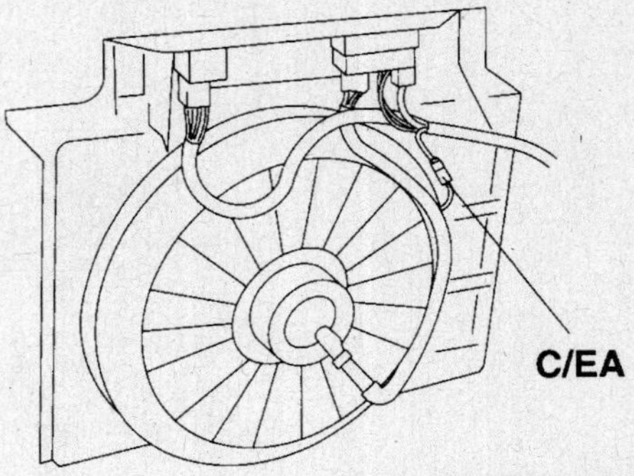

VV1089600007000X

Fig. 7 Cooling fan ground connector (C/EA). Models w/ Motronic 4.4 Engine Control System

Dash Gauges

NOTE: On Air Bag Equipped Models, Refer To "Air Bag System Precautions" Located In The Front Of This Manual For System Disarming & Arming Procedures.

NOTE: Refer To The "Dash Panel Service" Section For Dash Panel Removal Procedures.

INDEX

	Page No.
Gauges	9-47
Fuel	9-47
Tachometer	9-48
Temperature	9-47
Precautions	9-47
Air Bag Systems	9-47
Battery Ground Cable	9-47
Speedometer	9-48
Inspection	9-49
Troubleshooting	9-48
Wiring Diagram	9-47
Yazaki Combined Instrument Panel	9-49
Accessing Combined Instrument Panel Diagnostic Trouble Codes	9-50
Combined Instrument Panel Connector Views	9-50
Diagnostic Tests	9-50
Diagnostic Trouble Code Interpretation	9-50
Troubleshooting	9-49
Wiring Diagrams	9-49

PRECAUTIONS

AIR BAG SYSTEMS

Refer to "Air Bag System Precautions" in the front of this manual for system disarming and arming procedures.

BATTERY GROUND CABLE

Prior to service, disconnect battery ground cable and isolate as required.

WIRING DIAGRAM

Refer to **Fig. 1,** for instrument cluster wiring diagram.

GAUGES

FUEL

GAUGE NOT WORKING AT ALL

An inoperative fuel gauge may be caused by one or more of the following:

1. Open circuit in sensor ground connection.
2. Sensor ground connection shorted to battery potential.
3. Open circuit in sensor signal wiring.
4. Sensor signal wiring shorted to ground.
5. Open circuit in sensor.
6. Sensor short circuited.
7. Defective fuel gauge.
8. Sensor stuck in lowest position.

GAUGE READING INCORRECT

The fuel gauge may display an incorrect reading due to one or more of the following:

1. Sensor ground connection has incorrect ground potential.
2. Sensor is sticking.
3. Sensor at incorrect resistance.
4. Instrument cluster has incorrect ground potential.
5. Defective fuel gauge.

INSPECTION

Fuel Level Sensor Check

1. Turn ignition off.
2. Fold down righthand backrest on rear seat, then remove luggage compartment mat, **Fig. 2.**
3. Remove righthand luggage compartment panel.
4. Remove fuel pump and sensor plastic cover.
5. Remove fuel pump and sensor cover caps.
6. Disconnect electrical connectors and unscrew plastic nut from fuel level sensor, **Fig. 3.**
7. Lift up fuel level sensor while feeding wire through.
8. Connect an ohmmeter to sensor connector. Resistance should read 7–327 ohms depending on how much fuel is in the tank.
9. If resistance is within specifications, check sensor ground connection.
10. If resistance is not within specifications, replace sensor.

Sensor Ground Connection Check

1. Using an ohmmeter, measure resistance between sensor connector to harness (yellow/red) and ground.
2. Resistance should be approximately 0 ohms.
3. If resistance is correct, check sensor signal.
4. If resistance is incorrect, check for open circuits in wiring between connector (yellow/red) and 30-pole connector on instrument cluster (A4).

Sensor Signal Check

1. On connector leading to harness, connect a voltmeter between point 1 (yellow/gray) and ground.
2. Turn ignition switch on.
3. Voltmeter should read approximately 7 volts.
4. If voltmeter reads 0 volts, check wiring between connector point 1 (yellow/gray) and 30-pole connector on instrument cluster (A3) for open or short circuit.
5. If voltmeter reads battery voltage, check wiring between connector point 1 (yellow/gray) and 30-pole connector on instrument cluster (A5) for short circuit to battery potential.
6. If voltmeter reads 7 volts, replace instrument cluster.

TEMPERATURE

GAUGE NOT WORKING AT ALL

The coolant temperature gauge may become inoperative due to one or more of the following:

1. Fuel injection system not receiving any signal from temperature sensor.
2. Open circuit forwarding temperature signal from fuel system control module.
3. Temperature signal wiring from fuel system control module short circuit to ground or battery potential.
4. Defective temperature gauge.

GAUGE READING INCORRECT

The temperature gauge may give an incorrect reading due to the following:

1. Instrument cluster has defective ground potential.
2. Defective temperature sensor.
3. Defective temperature gauge.

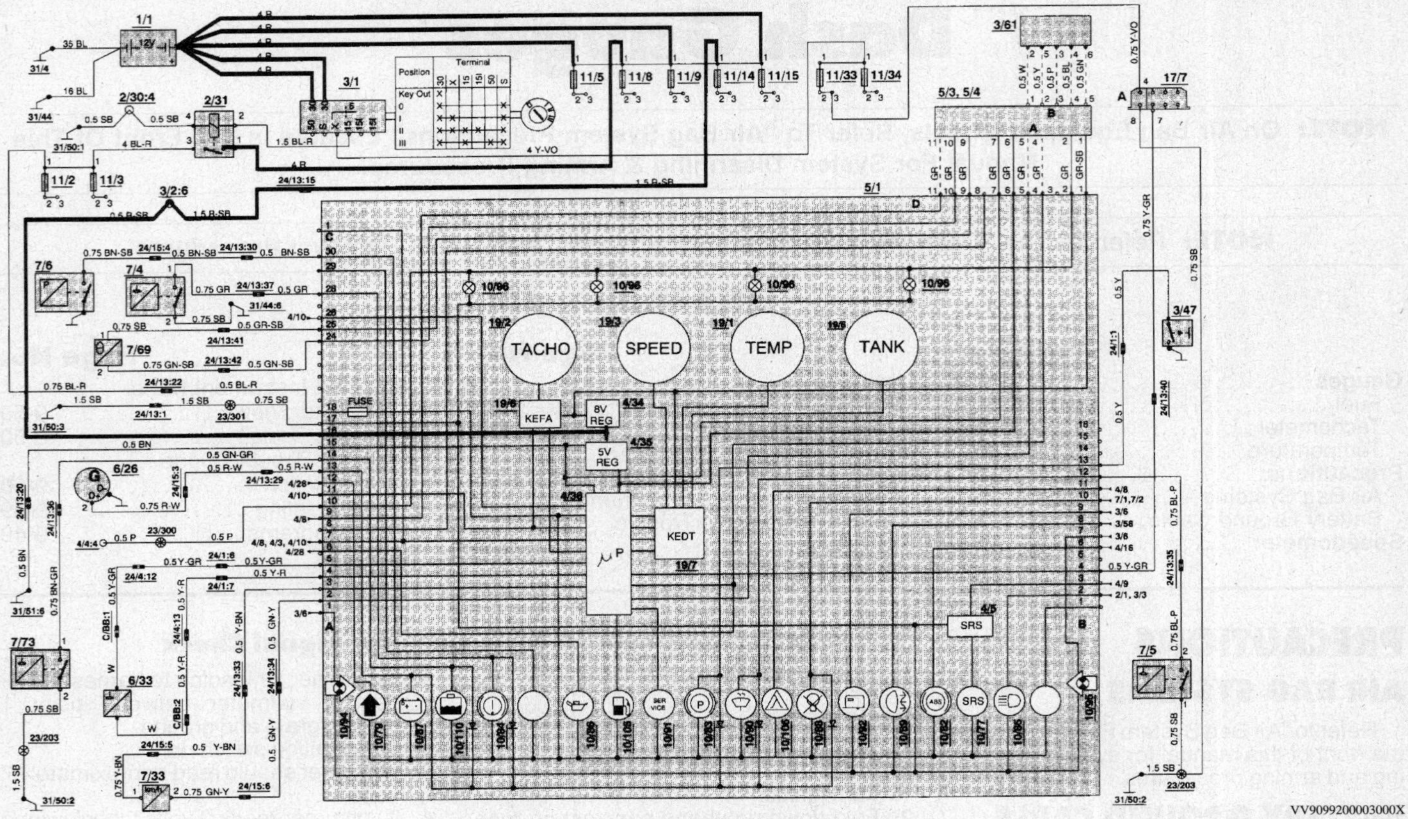

Fig. 1 Instrument cluster wiring diagram

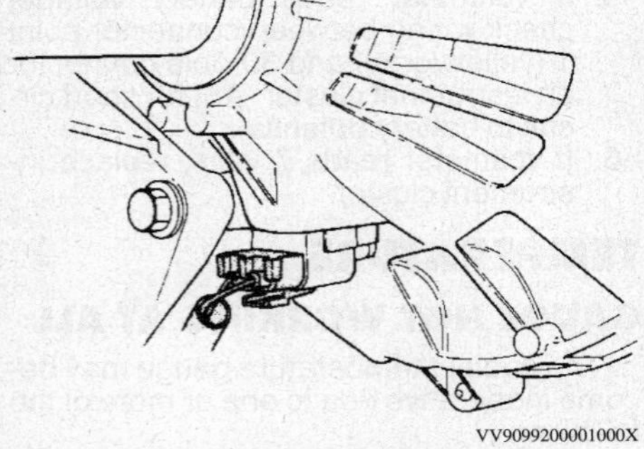

Fig. 2 Fuel level sensor access

TACHOMETER

TACHOMETER NOT WORKING AT ALL

The tachometer may become inoperative due to one or more of the following:

1. Open circuit in tachometer signal wiring from ignition control module.
2. Tachometer signal wiring from ignition control module short circuit to ground or battery potential.
3. Defective tachometer.
4. Defective ignition control module.

TACHOMETER READING INCORRECT

The temperature gauge may give an incorrect reading due to the following:

1. Instrument cluster has incorrect ground potential.
2. Defective tachometer.

INSPECTION

Gauge Check

1. If tachometer does not work at all, check wiring between 30-pole connector on instrument cluster A11 (white/black) and ignition control module connector B29 for short circuit.
2. If no short is found, replace instrument cluster.
3. If tachometer gives an inaccurate reading, check instrument cluster signal ground connection by inspecting wiring between 30-pin connector on instrument cluster (A15/brown) and ground point 31/51:6 on wiring diagram.

SPEEDOMETER

TROUBLESHOOTING

Speedometer Not Working At All

1. Open circuit in vehicle speed sensor ground connection.
2. Vehicle speed sensor ground connection short circuit to ground or battery potential.
3. Open circuit in speed sensor signal wiring.

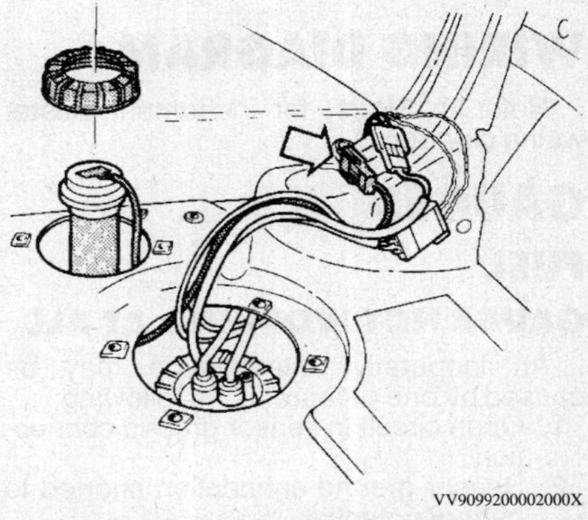

Fig. 3 Fuel level sensor connectors

4. Vehicle speed sensor signal wiring short circuit to ground or battery potential.
5. Open circuit in speed sensor.
6. Short circuit in speed sensor.
7. Speedometer defective.

Speedometer Reading Incorrect

1. Vehicle speed sensor position in relation to toothed wheel is incorrect.
2. Instrument cluster has incorrect ground potential.
3. Defective speedometer.

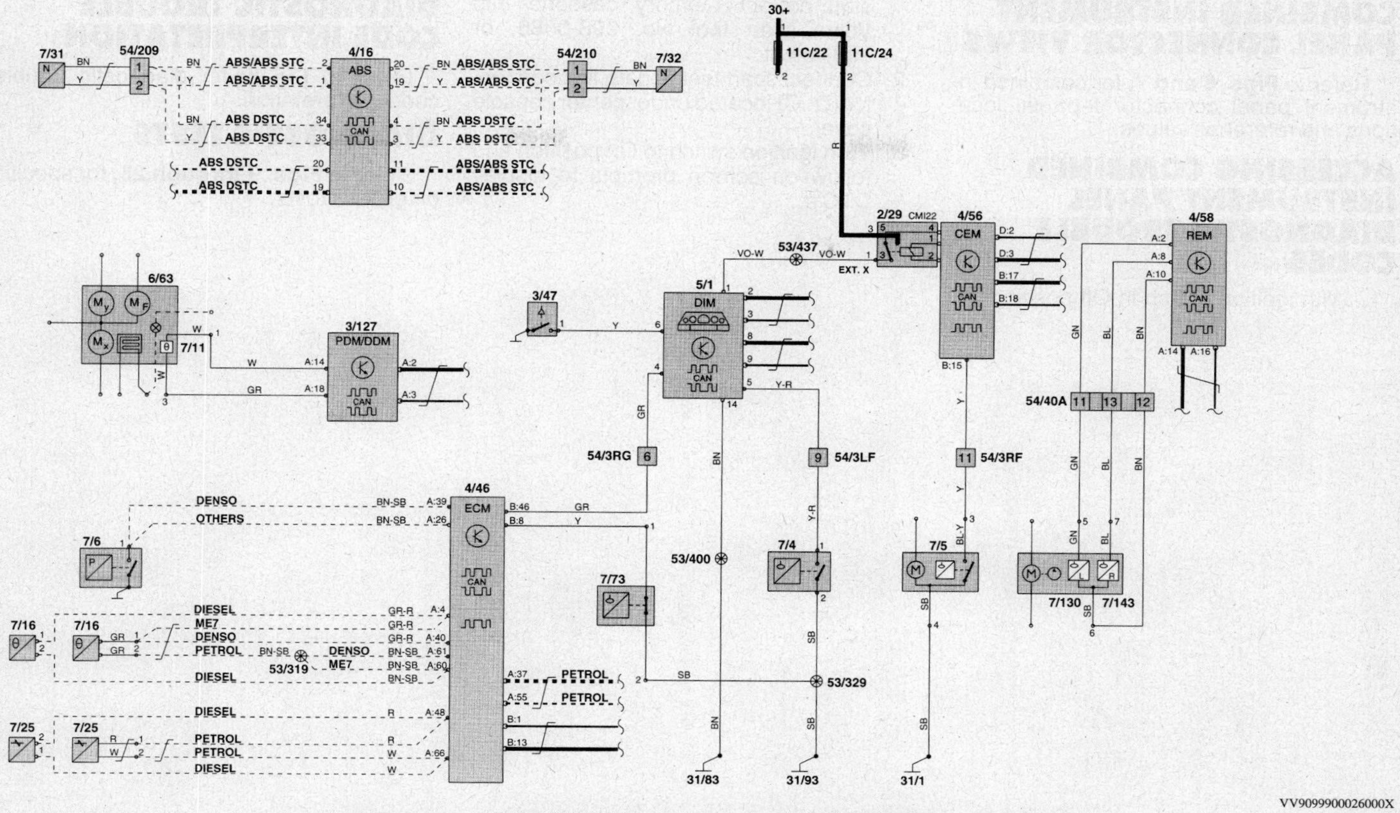

Fig. 4 Combined instrument panel wiring diagram. S80

4. Vehicle speed sensor ground connection has incorrect ground potential.

INSPECTION

Vehicle Speed Sensor Check

1. Turn ignition off and disconnect connector from vehicle speed sensor.
2. Connect an ohmmeter across sensor.
3. Resistance should be 640–1000 ohms.
4. If resistance is incorrect, replace vehicle speed sensor.
5. If resistance is within specifications, check sensor ground connection.

Sensor Ground Connection Check

1. Connect an ohmmeter between vehicle speed sensor connector 2 (green/yellow) and ground.
2. Resistance should be approximately 0 ohms.
3. If resistance is incorrect, check wiring between connector 2 (green/yellow) and 30-pole connector on instrument cluster (A2) for open circuits.

YAZAKI COMBINED INSTRUMENT PANEL

A combined instrument panel manufactured by the Yazaki corporation utilizes an onboard self diagnostic system which outputs diagnostic trouble codes (DTC) whenever an instrument malfunction occurs.

If the control module detects a fault it will store a DTC. At the same time the value of 17 predetermined parameters are frozen and stored. These are the frozen values. If the number of DTC's exceeds 5, the frozen values of the first two and the last three DTC's are displayed.

WIRING DIAGRAMS

Refer to **Figs. 4 and 5,** for combined instrument panel wiring diagrams.

TROUBLESHOOTING

NO GAUGES WORKING

If none of the combined instrument panel gauges are working, inspect for the following:

1. Blown fuse.
2. Open circuit in 15-supply.
3. Open circuit in signal ground terminal.
4. Internal fault in micro-processor.
5. Loose connections in connectors A or B.

INSTRUMENT LIGHTING NOT WORKING

If all combined instrument panel gauges are working and the lighting in the controls is working but the instrument lighting is not working, inspect for the following:

1. Open circuit in lighting ground.
2. Defective rheostat.
3. Defective bulbs.

TACHOMETER READING FAULTY

If there are no diagnostic trouble codes stored for the engine speed (RPM) signal in the fuel/ignition system or combined instrument panel, inspect for the following:

1. Defective tachometer.
2. Combined instrument panel is programmed for a different scale than the tachometer.

FUEL LEVEL WARNING LAMP LIGHTS AT THE WRONG LEVEL

If the fuel level warning lamp lights at a level other than approximately 2.1 gallons of fuel, inspect fuel level sensor calibration.

NO COMMUNICATION w/ COMBINED INSTRUMENT PANEL DIAGNOSTIC SYSTEM

If the gauges do not work, inspect for the following:

1. Open circuit in 15-supply.
2. Open circuit in 30-supply.
3. Open circuit in combined instrument panel signal to ground.
4. If the gauges are working, inspect for the following:
   a. Poor battery voltage.
   b. Open circuit, short circuit to ground or short circuit to supply voltage in cable to data link connector (DLC).
   c. Open circuit in data link connector supply voltage or ground.
   d. Defective scan tool, scan tool wiring.

COMBINED INSTRUMENT PANEL CONNECTOR VIEWS

Refer to **Figs. 6 and 7,** for combined instrument panel connector terminal locations and reference values.

ACCESSING COMBINED INSTRUMENT PANEL DIAGNOSTIC TROUBLE CODES

1. With ignition switch in Off position, install correct memory cassette into Volvo scan tool No. 998-8686, or equivalent.
2. Connect scan tool to data link connector (DLC) located under center console cover.
3. Turn ignition switch to On position and follow on screen prompts to display DTC's.

DIAGNOSTIC TROUBLE CODE INTERPRETATION

Refer to **Fig. 8,** for diagnostic trouble code interpretation.

DIAGNOSTIC TESTS

Refer to **Figs. 9 through 25,** for specific diagnostic tests.

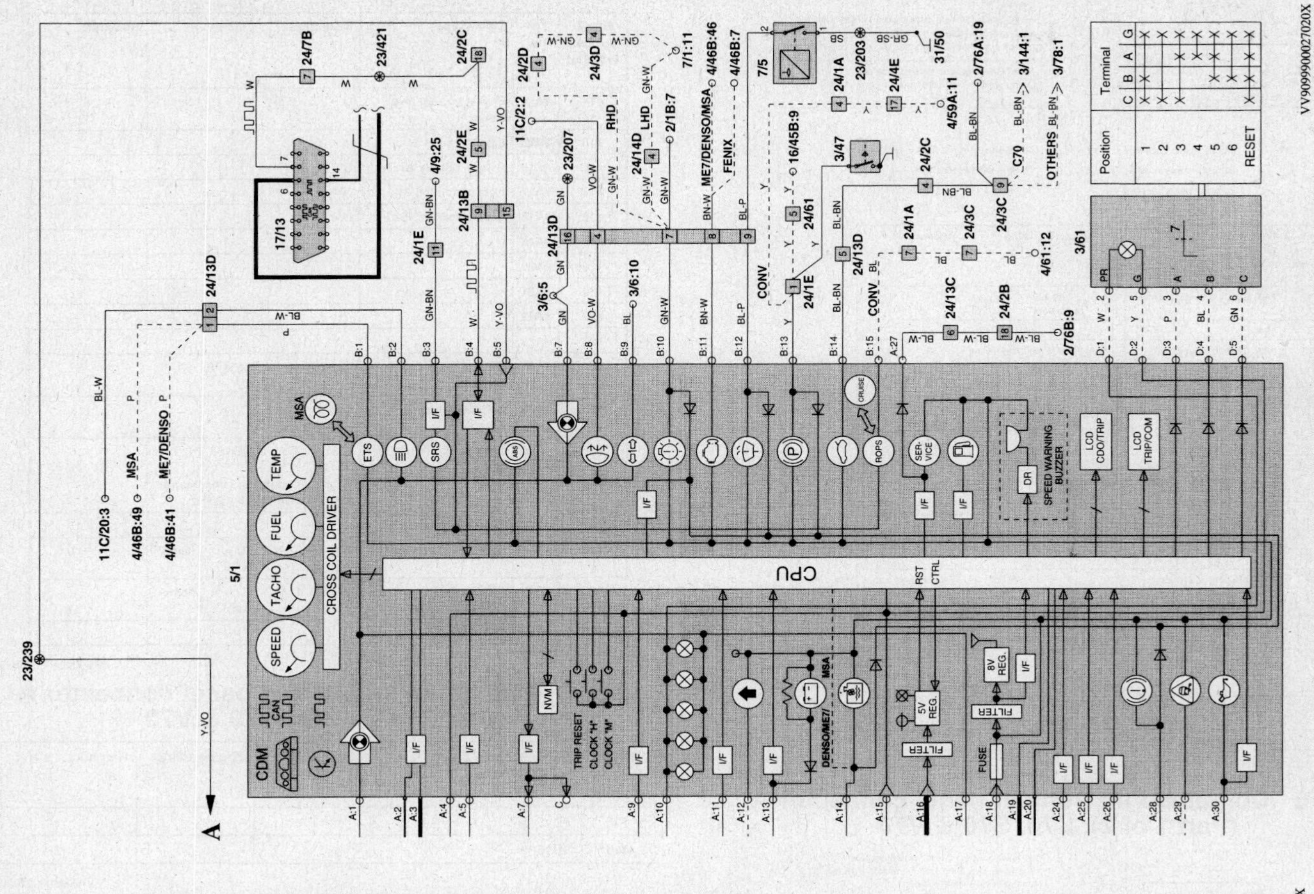

VV99999000270 20X

Fig. 5 Combined instrument panel wiring diagram (Part 2 of 2). C70, S70 & V70

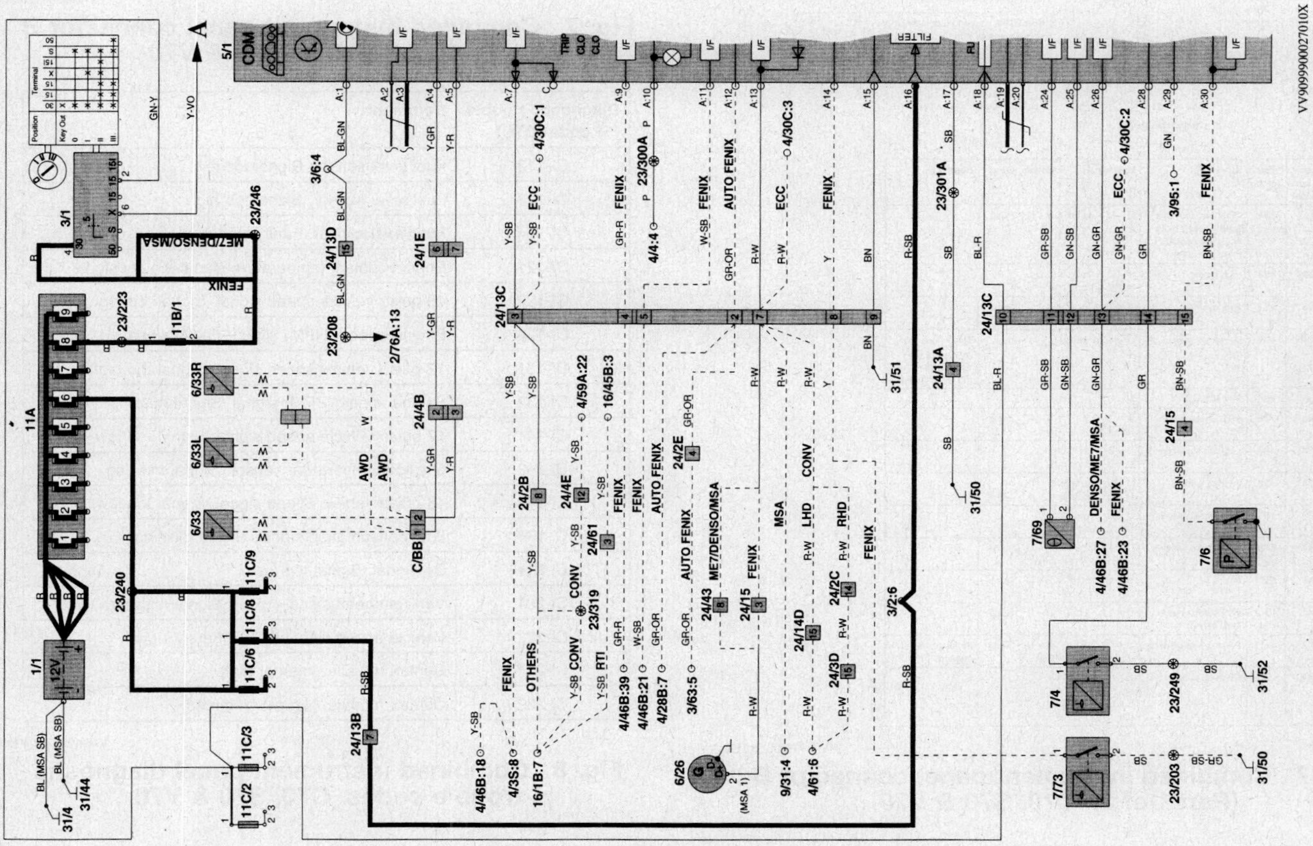

VV99999000270 10X

Fig. 5 Combined instrument panel wiring diagram (Part 1 of 2). C70, S70 & V70

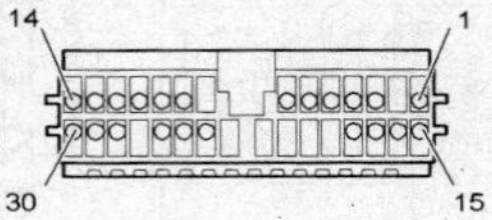

The following values are measured between the relevant terminal in column 1 and terminal # A15 (signal ground) unless otherwise stated.

Note! Check ground terminals before taking readings with the breakout box

U = DC voltage in volts (V)   f = frequency in Hertz (Hz)
U_{bat} = battery voltage in volts (V)   t = time in milliseconds (ms)
U_{low} = voltage approximately 0 V

Break-out box terminal	Ter-mi-nal	Signal type	Ignition on	Idling	Remarks
#1	#A1	Right turn signal lamp	$U \approx U_{low}$ (lamp off) $U \approx U_{bat}$ (lamp on)		
#2	#A2	-	-		-
#3	#A3	Speed input signal	$U \approx U_{low}$ or 6 V (oscillates when the front wheels are rotated slowly)		
#4	#A4	Fuel level sensor (-)	$U \approx U_{low}$		
#5	#A5	Fuel level sensor (+)	$U \approx$ 6-8 V (sensor disconnected) $U \approx$ Full fuel tank (sensor connected) $U \approx$ 5 V Empty fuel tank (sensor connected)		
#6	#A6	Speedometer output signal 48 pulses a revolution	$U \approx$ 0.5 V or U_{bat} -1 V (oscillates when the front wheels are rotated slowly)		
#7	#A7	Speedometer output signal 12 pulses a revolution	$U \approx$ 0.5 V or U_{bat} -1 V (oscillates when the front wheels are rotated slowly)		
#8	#A8	-	-		-
#9	#A9	Fuel consumption	$U \approx U_{bat}$	f ≈ 30 Hz	f increases with engine speed (RPM) and load
#10	#A10	Rheostat	$U \approx$ 0.5 - 1 V (rheostat min) $U \approx U_{bat}$ (rheostat max)		
#11	#A11	Engine speed (RPM) signal	$U \approx U_{bat}$	f ≈ 28 Hz	f increases with engine speed (RPM)
#12	#A12	Gear selector warning lamp	$U \approx U_{low}$ (lamp on) $U \approx U_{bat}$ (lamp off)		
#13	#A13	Generator signal D+	U≈0.5 - 2.5 V	$U \approx U_{bat}$	

VV9099900021010X

Fig. 6 Combined instrument panel connector A (Part 1 of 2). C70, S70 & V70

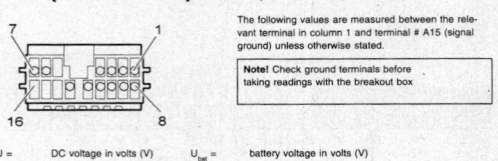

Break-out box terminal	Ter-mi-nal	Signal type	Ignition on	Idling	Remarks
#14	#A14	Engine coolant level sensor	$U \approx$ 1.5 - 2.5 V	$U \approx U_{bat}$ (lamp off)	
#15	#A15	Signal ground 31-	$U \approx U_{low}$		
#16	#A16	Supply voltage 30+	$U \approx U_{bat}$		
#17	#A17	Lighting ground 31-	$U \approx U_{low}$		
#18	#A18	Supply voltage 15+	$U \approx U_{bat}$		
#19	#A19	-	-	-	-
#20	#A20	-	-	-	-
#21	#A21	-	-	-	-
#22	#A22	-	-	-	-
#23	#A23	-	-	-	-
#24	#A24	Outside temperature gauge (+)	$U \approx$ 2 V at +20 °C (68 °F)		
#25	#A25	Outside temperature sensor (-)	$U \approx U_{low}$		
#26	#A26	Engine coolant temperature signal	Cold engine (+20 °C (68 °F)): f ≈ 40 Hz Engine at operating temperature (+90 °C (194 °F)): f ≈ 22 Hz		
#27	#A27	-	-	-	-
#28	#A28	Brake fluid level sensor	$U \approx$ 1.6 - 2.2 V	$U \approx U_{bat}$ (lamp off)	
#29	#A29	TRACS OFF warning	$U \approx$ 0.5 V (lamp on)	$U \approx U_{bat}$ (lamp off)	
#30	#A30	Oil pressure sensor	$U \approx U_{low}$	$U \approx U_{bat}$	

VV9099900021020X

Fig. 6 Combined instrument panel connector A (Part 2 of 2). C70, S70 & V70

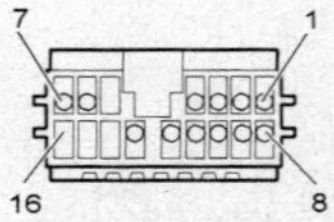

The following values are measured between the relevant terminal in column 1 and terminal # A15 (signal ground) unless otherwise stated.

Note! Check ground terminals before taking readings with the breakout box

U = DC voltage in volts (V) U_{bat} = battery voltage in volts (V)
U_{low} = voltage approximately 0 V

Break-out box terminal	Ter-minal	Signal type	Ignition on	Engine idling	Remarks
#31	#B1	Glow plug indicator lamp (Diesel) or Exhaust temperature (certain markets)	$U \approx U_{low}$ (lamp on)	$U \approx U_{bat}$ (lamp off)	-
#32	#B2	High beam	$U \approx U_{low}$ (lamp off) $U \approx U_{bat}$ (lamp on)		
#33	#B3	SRS system	$U \approx$ 7 - 8 V (lamp on)	$U \approx U_{low}$ (lamp off)	
#34	#B4	Diagnostic lead	$U \approx$ 1-2 V below U_{bat}		This voltage can vary when the Volvo Scan Tool (ST) is activated
#35	#B5	Power supply X	$U \approx U_{bat}$		
#36	#B6	ABS Brake system	$U \approx$ 7 - 8 V (lamp on)	$U \approx U_{low}$ (lamp off)	
#37	#B7	Left turn signal lamp	$U \approx U_{low}$ (lamp off) $U \approx U_{bat}$ (lamp on)		
#38	#B8	Fog tail lamps	$U \approx U_{low}$ (lamp off) $U \approx U_{bat}$ (lamp on)		
#39	#B9	Turn signal flasher, trailer	$U \approx U_{low}$ (lamp off) $U \approx U_{bat}$ (lamp on)		
#40	#B10	Bulb failure warning sensor	$U \approx$ 1.6 - 2.2 V (lamp on)	$U \approx U_{bat}$ (lamp off)	
#41	#B11	MIL	$U \approx$ 1 V (lamp on)	$U \approx U_{bat}$ (lamp off)	
#42	#B12	Windshield washer level sensor	$U \approx$ 1.6 - 2.2 V	$U \approx U_{bat}$ (lamp off)	
#43	#B13	Parking brake switch	$U \approx$ 1.6 - 2.2 V (lamp on)	$U \approx U_{bat}$ (lamp off)	Parking brake not engaged
#44	#B14	Open trunk lid switch	$U=U_{low}$ (lamp on) $U=U_{bat}$ (lamp off)	-	-

VV9099800022010X

Fig. 7 Combined instrument panel connector B (Part 1 of 2). C70, S70 & V70

Break-out box terminal	Ter-minal	Signal type	Ignition on	Engine idling	Remarks
#45	#B15	-	-	-	-
#46	#B16	-	-	-	-

VV9099800022020X

Fig. 7 Combined instrument panel connector B (Part 2 of 2). C70, S70 & V70

Diagnostic trouble code (DTC)	Comment
CI-112	Fuel level sensor. Signal too low.
CI-113	Fuel level sensor. Signal too high.
CI-114	Fuel level sensor. Faulty signal.
CI-121	Engine coolant temperature signal. Faulty signal.
CI-123	48 pulse vehicle speed signal. Signal too high.
CI-124	Engine speed (RPM) signal. Faulty signal.
CI-131	12 pulse vehicle speed signal. Signal too high.
CI-132	Engine speed (RPM) signal. Signal missing.
CI-141	12 pulse vehicle speed signal. Signal too low.
CI-142	Outside temperature sensor. Signal missing.
CI-143	48 pulse vehicle speed signal. Signal too low.
CI-174	Fuel consumption signal. Signal missing.
CI-211	D+ signal. Signal too low.
CI-221	Vehicle speed signal (VSS). Signal missing.
CI-222	Vehicle speed signal (VSS). Faulty signal.
CI-231	Control module. Internal fault.
CI-232	Control module. Not programmed.

VV9099800004000X

Fig. 8 Combined instrument panel diagnostic trouble codes. C70, S70 & V70

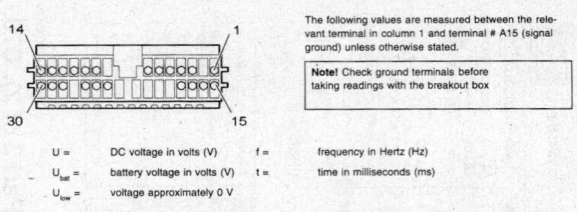

DIAGNOSTIC CHART INDEX

Code	Description	Page No.	Fig. No.
C70, S70 & V70			
CI-112	Fuel Level Sensor, Signal Too Low	9-53	9
CI-113	Fuel Level Sensor, Signal Too High	9-54	10
CI-114	Fuel Level Sensor, Faulty Signal	9-56	11
CI-121	Engine Coolant Temperature Sensor Signal, Faulty Signal	9-57	12
CI-123	48 Pulse Vehicle Speed Sensor, Signal Too High	9-58	13
CI-124	Engine Speed (RPM) Signal, Faulty Signal	9-59	14
CI-131	12 Pulse Vehicle Speed Sensor, Signal Too High	9-60	15
CI-132	Engine Speed (RPM) Signal, Signal Missing	9-60	16
CI-141	12 Pulse Vehicle Speed Sensor, Signal Too Low	9-62	17
CI-142	Outside Temperature Sensor Signal, Signal Missing	9-62	18
CI-143	48 Pulse Vehicle Speed Sensor	9-63	19
CI-174	Fuel Consumption Signal, Signal Missing	9-64	20
CI-211	D+ Signal, Signal Too Low	9-64	21
CI-221	Vehicle Speed Sensor Signal, Signal Missing	9-65	22
CI-222	Vehicle Speed Signal, Faulty Signal	9-66	23
CI-231	Control Module, Internal Fault	9-67	24
CI-232	Control Module, Not Programmed	9-68	25

A A. Diagnostic trouble code (DTC) information

Condition

– Resistance in fuel level sensor less than 2 Ω for more than 10 seconds.

Possible source

– Short-circuit in fuel level sensor.

– Short-circuit to ground in signal cable

– Fault in signal from combined instrument panel.

– Defective fuel level sensor.

Fault symptom(s)

– The fuel gauge displays an empty fuel tank continuously.

– The fuel gauge displays an empty fuel tank when the fuel tank is full, otherwise it displays the correct level.

• Start fault-tracing with AB. *Signal too low*

VV9099800005010X

Fig. 9 Code CI-112: Fuel Level Sensor, Signal Too Low (Part 1 of 5). C70, S70 & V70

AB1

Checking fuel level sensor resistance

Note! The Volvo All-wheel drive (AWD) has a different fuel tank with two fuel level sensors connected in series.

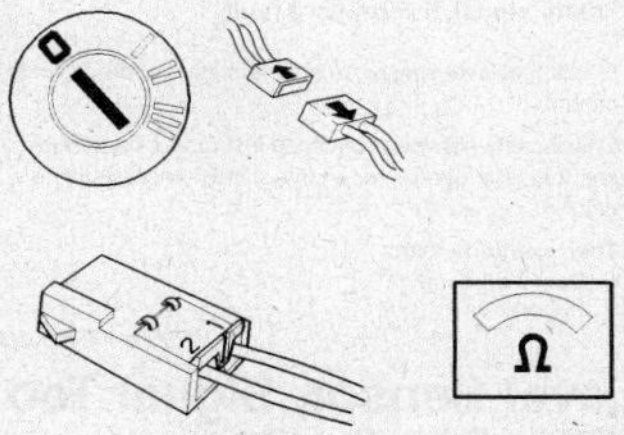

– Ignition off.

– Disconnect fuel level sensor connector

Connect an ohmmeter between terminals 1 and 2 in the fuel level sensor connector.

The ohmmeter should read 8-330 Ω, depending on fuel level.

If reading is OK:

• **AB3**

If reading is incorrect:

• **AB2**

AB2

Replacing component

Try a new fuel level sensor

Then continue with:

• **AB7**

VV9099800005020X

Fig. 9 Code CI-112: Fuel Level Sensor, Signal Too Low (Part 2 of 5). C70, S70 & V70

A B3

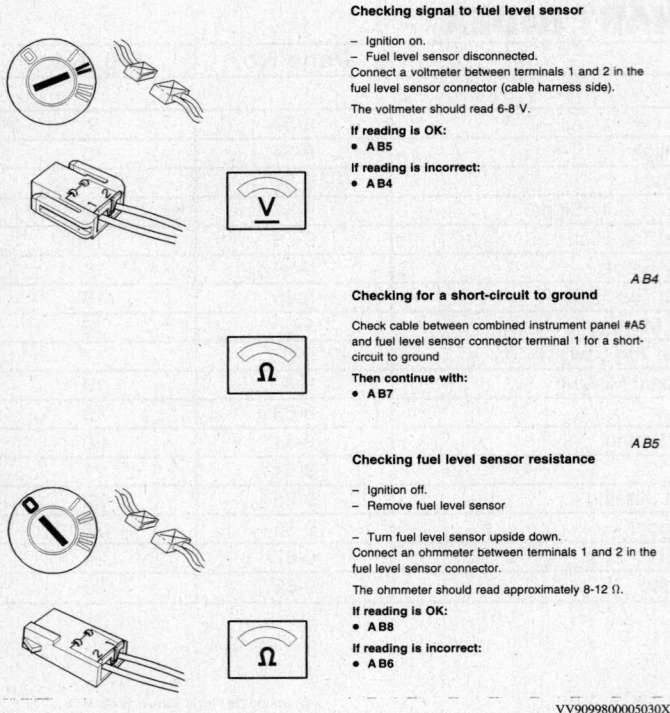

Checking signal to fuel level sensor

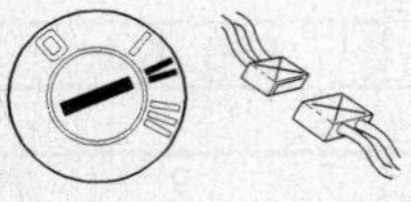

– Ignition on.
– Fuel level sensor disconnected.

Connect a voltmeter between terminals 1 and 2 in the fuel level sensor connector (cable harness side).

The voltmeter should read 6-8 V.

If reading is OK:
- A B5

If reading is incorrect:
- A B4

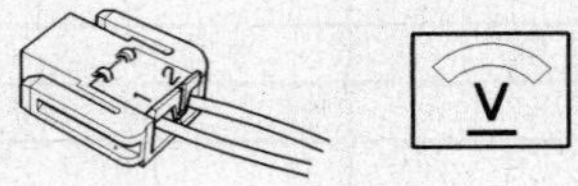

A B4

Checking for a short-circuit to ground

Check cable between combined instrument panel #A5 and fuel level sensor connector terminal 1 for a short-circuit to ground

Then continue with:
- A B7

A B5

Checking fuel level sensor resistance

– Ignition off.
– Remove fuel level sensor

– Turn fuel level sensor upside down.

Connect an ohmmeter between terminals 1 and 2 in the fuel level sensor connector.

The ohmmeter should read approximately 8-12 Ω.

If reading is OK:
- A B8

If reading is incorrect:
- A B6

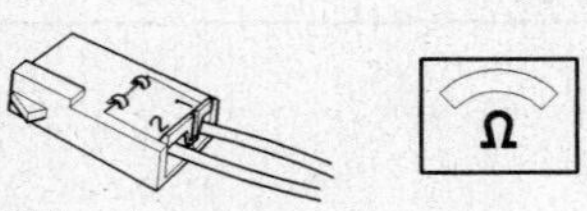

VV9099800005030X

Fig. 9 Code CI-112: Fuel Level Sensor, Signal Too Low (Part 3 of 5). C70, S70 & V70

A B6

Replacing component

Try a new fuel level sensor according to **DD L8**.

Then continue with:
- A B7

A B7

Verification

Hint: After carrying out the repair check that the fault has been remedied.

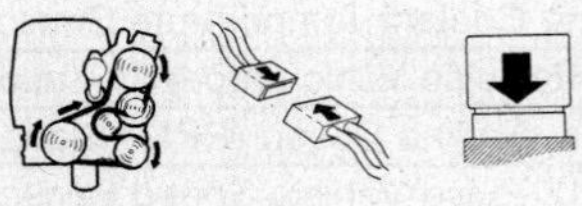

– Ignition off.
– Reconnect connectors, reinstall components.
– Connect combined instrument panel.
– Test drive the car at speeds above 20 km/h (12 mph), or lift up the front suspension and remove both front wheels.

> **Warning!** Test drive cars with AWD at a speed above 20 km/h (12 mph), or lift up the front and rear suspension and remove all wheels.

> **Note!** When the rear wheels are stationary and the front wheels rotate, diagnostic trouble codes (DTCs) may be stored in the ABS system. Erase any diagnostic trouble codes (DTCs) stored in the ABS system after fault-tracing.

> **Note!** Ensure that the front wheels are not rotating when the gear selector is moved.

– Ignition off.
– Disconnect the Volvo Scan Tool (ST) from the VADIS station. Use it as a stand alone tool and connect it to the data link connector (DLC) in the car.
– Ignition on.

Read off the diagnostic trouble code (DTC) counters.

Is counter value greater than 0?

Yes:
- Fault corrected

No:
- Fault not found

VV9099800005040X

Fig. 9 Code CI-112: Fuel Level Sensor, Signal Too Low (Part 4 of 5). C70, S70 & V70

A B8

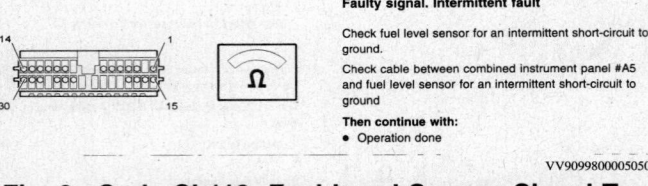

Faulty signal. Intermittent fault

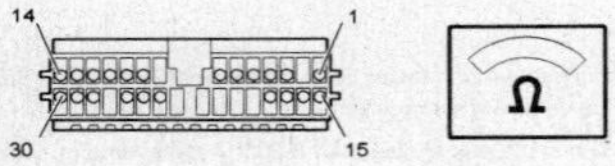

Check fuel level sensor for an intermittent short-circuit to ground.

Check cable between combined instrument panel #A5 and fuel level sensor for an intermittent short-circuit to ground

Then continue with:
- Operation done

VV9099800005050X

Fig. 9 Code CI-112: Fuel Level Sensor, Signal Too Low (Part 5 of 5). C70, S70 & V70

B A. Diagnostic trouble code (DTC) information

Condition

– The resistance in the fuel level sensor exceeds 335 Ω for more than 10 seconds.

Possible source

– Open-circuit in the fuel level sensor ground lead.
– Short-circuit to supply voltage in signal cable.
– Open-circuit in fuel level sensor signal cable.
– Fault in the signal to the combined instrument panel.
– Defective fuel level sensor.
– Large contact resistance.
– Loose connections.

Fault symptom(s)

– The fuel gauge displays an empty fuel tank continuously.

- Start fault-tracing with BB. *Signal too high*

VV9099800006010X

Fig. 10 Code CI-113: Fuel Level Sensor, Signal Too High (Part 1 of 8) C70, S70 & V70

B B. Signal too high

B B1

Checking fuel level sensor resistance

> **Note!** The Volvo All-wheel drive (AWD) has a different fuel tank with two fuel level sensors connected in series.

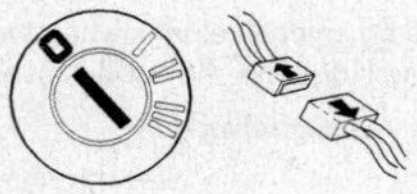

– Ignition off.
– Disconnect fuel level sensor connector according to **DD L1 - DD L2** for 4-door cars and **DD L4 - DD L5** for 5-door cars.

Connect an ohmmeter between terminals 1 and 2 in the fuel level sensor connector.

The ohmmeter should read 10-325 Ω, depending on fuel level.

If reading is OK:
- B B3

If reading is incorrect:
- B B2

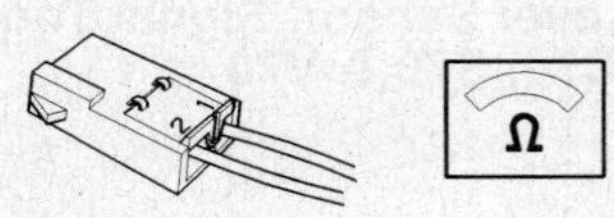

B B2

Replacing component

Try a new fuel level sensor

Then continue with:
- B B18

VV9099800006020X

Fig. 10 Code CI-113: Fuel Level Sensor, Signal Too High (Part 2 of 8) C70, S70 & V70

BB3

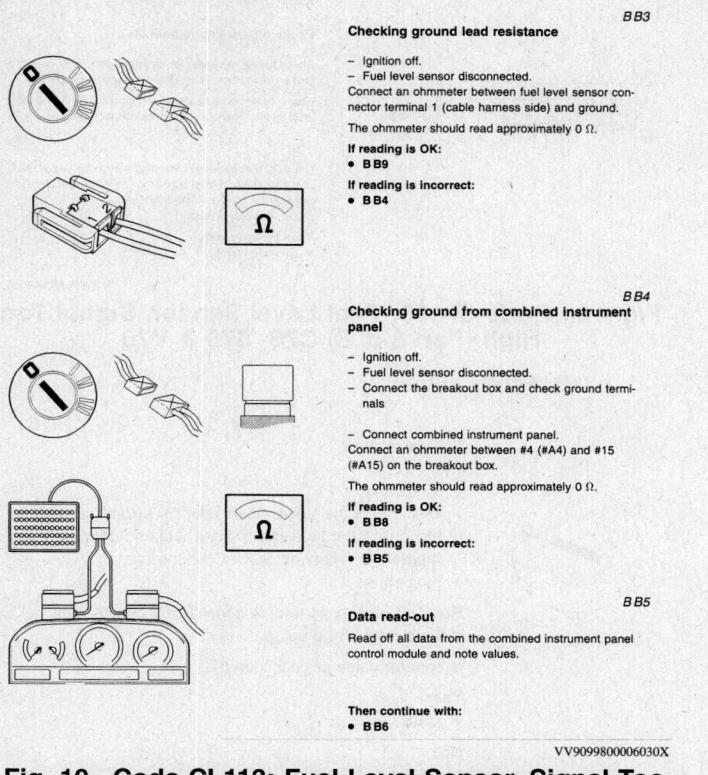

Checking ground lead resistance

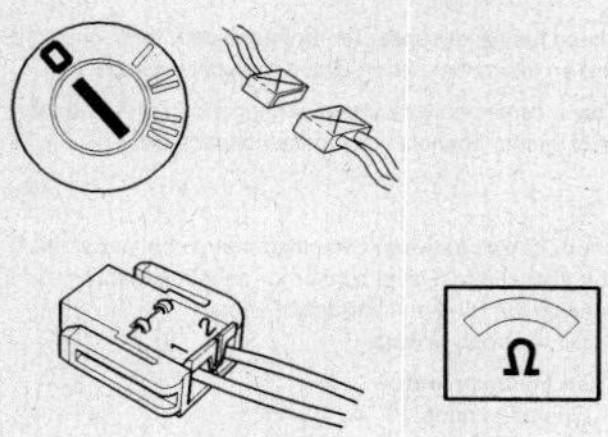

- Ignition off.
- Fuel level sensor disconnected.

Connect an ohmmeter between fuel level sensor connector terminal 1 (cable harness side) and ground.

The ohmmeter should read approximately 0 Ω.

If reading is OK:
- BB9

If reading is incorrect:
- BB4

BB4

Checking ground from combined instrument panel

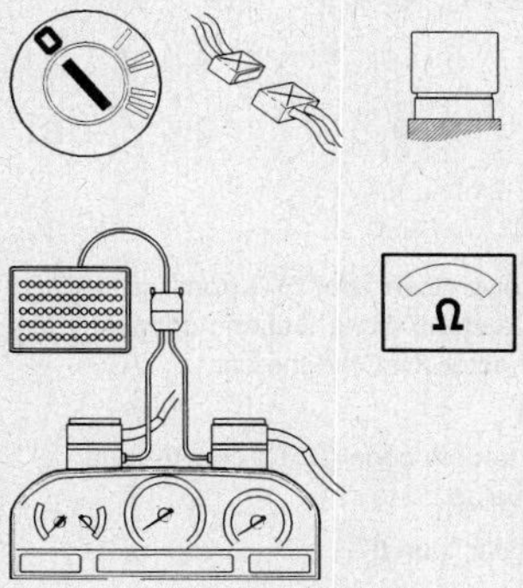

- Ignition off.
- Fuel level sensor disconnected.
- Connect the breakout box and check ground terminals

- Connect combined instrument panel.

Connect an ohmmeter between #4 (#A4) and #15 (#A15) on the breakout box.

The ohmmeter should read approximately 0 Ω.

If reading is OK:
- BB8

If reading is incorrect:
- BB5

BB5

Data read-out

Read off all data from the combined instrument panel control module and note values.

Then continue with:
- BB6

VV9099800006030X

Fig. 10 Code CI-113: Fuel Level Sensor, Signal Too High (Part 3 of 8) C70, S70 & V70

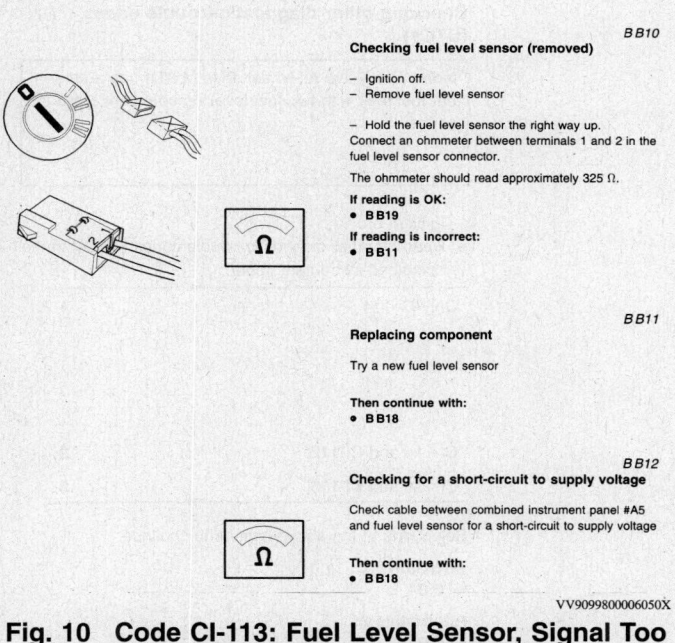

BB6

Replacing component

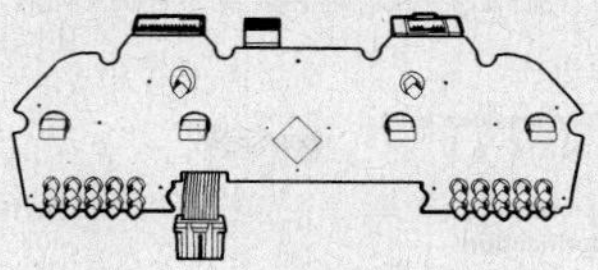

Try a new connection plate

Then continue with:
- BB7

BB7

Programming combined instrument panel

Program the control module with the values previously read off the combined instrument panel control module

Then continue with:
- BB18

BB8

Checking for an open-circuit

Check cable between combined instrument panel #A4 and fuel level sensor for an open-circuit

Then continue with:
- BB18

BB9

Checking signal to fuel level sensor

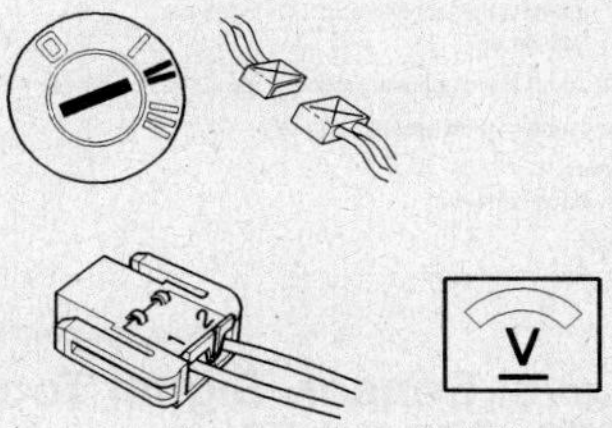

- Ignition on.
- Fuel level sensor disconnected.

Connect a voltmeter between connector terminals 1 and 2 (cable harness side).

The voltmeter should read 6-8 V.

If reading is OK:
- BB10

If value is higher:
- BB12

If value is lower:
- BB13

VV9099800006040X

Fig. 10 Code CI-113: Fuel Level Sensor, Signal Too High (Part 4 of 8) C70, S70 & V70

BB10

Checking fuel level sensor (removed)

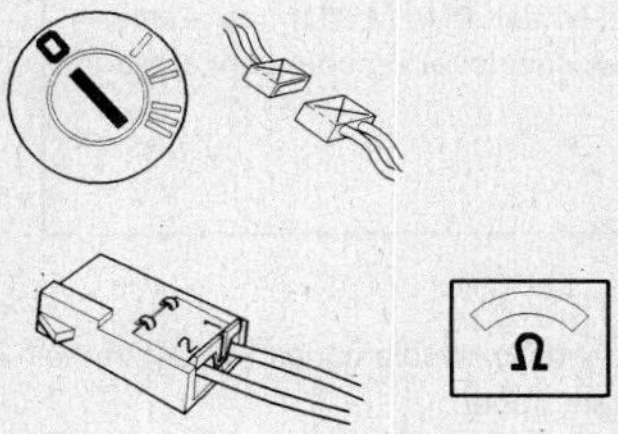

- Ignition off.
- Remove fuel level sensor

- Hold the fuel level sensor the right way up.

Connect an ohmmeter between terminals 1 and 2 in the fuel level sensor connector.

The ohmmeter should read approximately 325 Ω.

If reading is OK:
- BB19

If reading is incorrect:
- BB11

BB11

Replacing component

Try a new fuel level sensor

Then continue with:
- BB18

BB12

Checking for a short-circuit to supply voltage

Check cable between combined instrument panel #A5 and fuel level sensor for a short-circuit to supply voltage

Then continue with:
- BB18

VV9099800006050X

Fig. 10 Code CI-113: Fuel Level Sensor, Signal Too High (Part 5 of 8) C70, S70 & V70

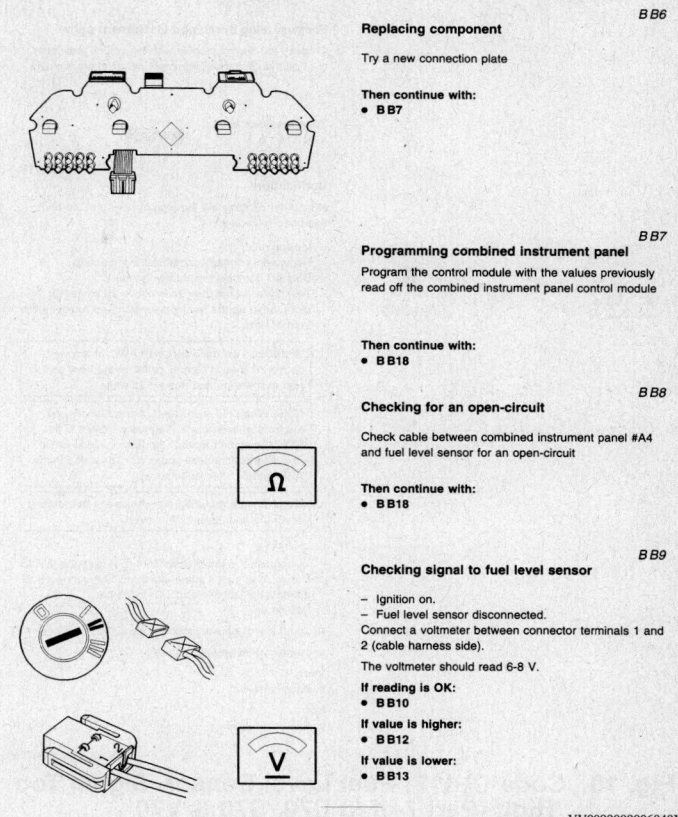

BB13

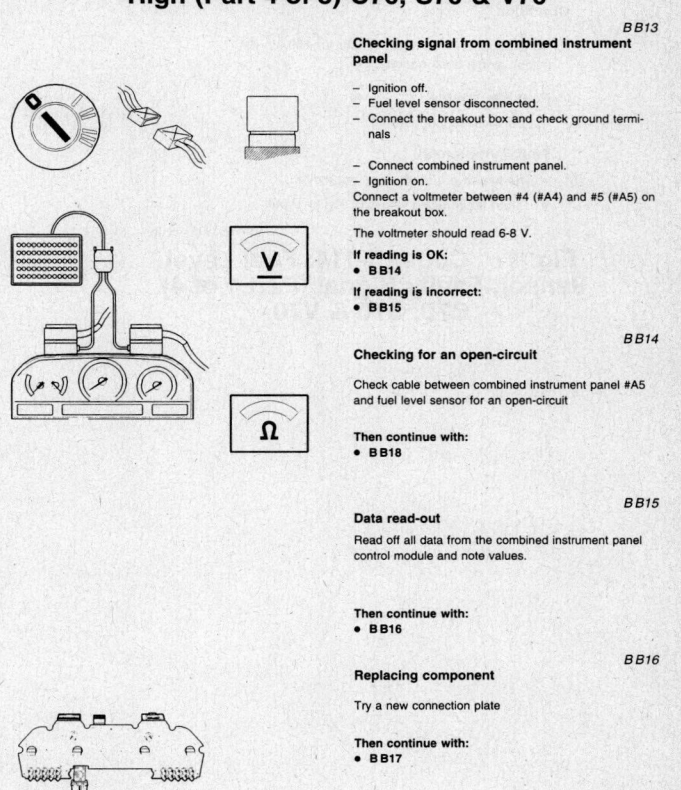

Checking signal from combined instrument panel

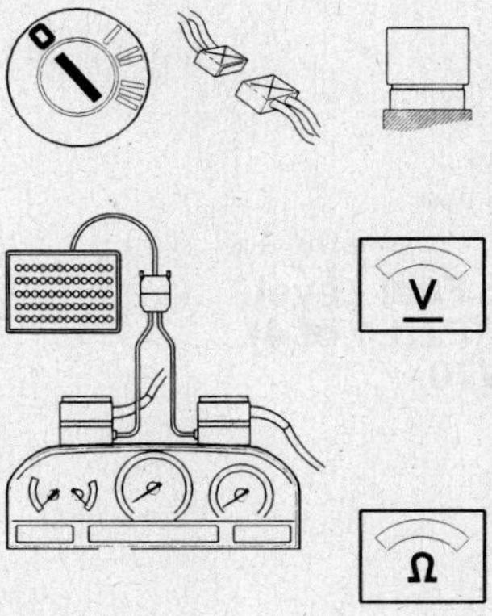

- Ignition off.
- Fuel level sensor disconnected.
- Connect the breakout box and check ground terminals

- Connect combined instrument panel.
- Ignition on.

Connect a voltmeter between #4 (#A4) and #5 (#A5) on the breakout box.

The voltmeter should read 6-8 V.

If reading is OK:
- BB14

If reading is incorrect:
- BB15

BB14

Checking for an open-circuit

Check cable between combined instrument panel #A5 and fuel level sensor for an open-circuit

Then continue with:
- BB18

BB15

Data read-out

Read off all data from the combined instrument panel control module and note values.

Then continue with:
- BB16

BB16

Replacing component

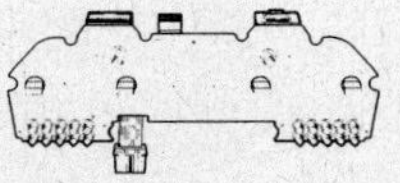

Try a new connection plate

Then continue with:
- BB17

VV9099800006060X

Fig. 10 Code CI-113: Fuel Level Sensor, Signal Too High (Part 6 of 8) C70, S70 & V70

BB17

Programming combined instrument panel

Program the control module with the values previously read off the combined instrument panel control module

Then continue with:
- BB18

BB18

Verification

Hint: After carrying out the repair check that the fault has been remedied.

- Ignition off.
- Reconnect connectors, reinstall components.
- Connect combined instrument panel.
- Test drive the car at speeds above 20 km/h (12 mph), or lift up the front suspension and remove both front wheels.

> **Warning!** Test drive cars with AWD at a speed above 20 km/h (12 mph), or lift up the front and rear suspension and remove all wheels.

> **Note!** When the rear wheels are stationary and the front wheels rotate, diagnostic trouble codes (DTCs) may be stored in the ABS system. Erase any diagnostic trouble codes (DTCs) stored in the ABS system after fault-tracing.

> **Note!** Ensure that the front wheels are not rotating when the gear selector is moved.

- Ignition off.
- Disconnect the Volvo Scan Tool (ST) from the VADIS station. Use it as a stand alone tool and connect it to the data link connector (DLC) in the car.
- Ignition on.

Read off the diagnostic trouble code (DTC) counters.

Is counter value greater than 0?

Yes:
- Fault corrected

No:
- Fault not found

VV9099800006070X

Fig. 10 Code CI-113: Fuel Level Sensor, Signal Too High (Part 7 of 8) C70, S70 & V70

C A. Diagnostic trouble code (DTC) information

Condition

- No change from fuel level sensor for 150 km (94 miles), signal does not change.

Possible source

- Fuel level sensor sticking.

Fault symptom(s)

- The fuel level needle does not move.
- Start fault-tracing with CB. *Faulty signal*

VV9099800007010X

Fig. 11 Code CI-114: Fuel Level Sensor, Faulty Signal (Part 1 of 4). C70, S70 & V70

BB19

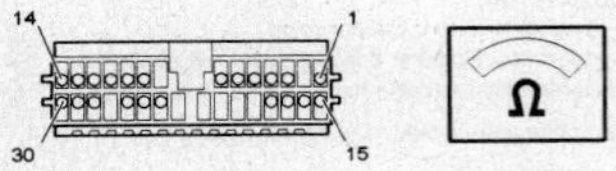

Faulty signal. Intermittent fault

Check fuel level sensor for an intermittent open-circuit and an intermittent short-circuit to supply voltage.

Check combined instrument panel connector A and fuel level sensor connector for loose connections

Check cables between combined instrument panel: #A4 and #A5 and fuel level sensor for an intermittent open-circuit and an intermittent short-circuit to supply voltage

Then continue with:
- Operation done

VV9099800006080X

Fig. 10 Code CI-113: Fuel Level Sensor, Signal Too High (Part 8 of 8) C70, S70 & V70

C B. Faulty signal

CB1

Status check

- Ignition off.
- Disconnect the Volvo Scan Tool (ST) from the VADIS station. Use it as a stand alone tool and connect it to the data link connector (DLC) in the car.
- Ignition on.

Read off diagnostic trouble code (DTC) counter and make a note of the value.

Is counter value greater than 0?

Yes:
- **CB8**

No:
- **CB5**

CB2

Checking other diagnostic trouble codes (DTCs)

> **Note!** The Volvo All-wheel drive (AWD) has a different fuel tank with two fuel level sensors connected in series.

- Ignition on.
- Read off other diagnostic trouble codes (DTCs) in the combined instrument panel.

Only CI-114	1
CI-114 and CI-112	2
CI-114 and CI-113	3

Select one of the above options to continue.

Alternative 1:
- **CB1**

Alternative 2:
- **CB3**

Alternative 3:
- **CB4**

VV9099800007020X

Fig. 11 Code CI-114: Fuel Level Sensor, Faulty Signal (Part 2 of 4). C70, S70 & V70

CB3

Diagnostic trouble codes (DTCs) CI-114 and CI-112 stored

Fault-trace according to A. *CI-112 Fuel level sensor*

Then continue with:
- CB1

CB4

Diagnostic trouble codes (DTCs) CI-114 and CI-113 stored

Fault-trace according to B. *CI-113 Fuel level sensor*

Then continue with:
- CB1

CB5

Replacing component

Try a new fuel level sensor

Then continue with:
- CB6

CB6

Verification

Hint: After carrying out the repair check that the fault has been remedied.

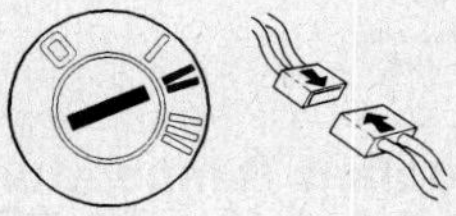

- Ignition off.
- Connect fuel level sensor connector.
- Ignition on.
- Go into scrolling values and read off unattenuated fuel level.
- Tip fuel level sensor to different positions.

Does the unattenuated fuel level value change?

Yes:
- CB7

No:
- Fault not found

CB7

Reinstalling components

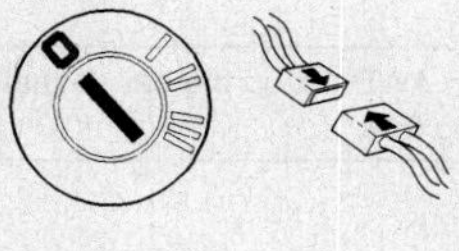

- Ignition off.
- Install fuel level sensor
- Reconnect connectors, reinstall components.

Then continue with:
- Fault corrected

VV9099800007030X

Fig. 11 Code CI-114: Fuel Level Sensor, Faulty Signal (Part 3 of 4). C70, S70 & V70

DA. Diagnostic trouble code (DTC) information

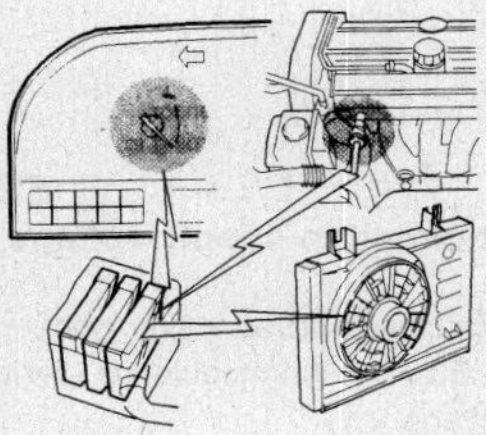

Condition

- Diagnostic trouble code (DTC) CI-121 is stored if the combined instrument panel receives a signal from the engine control module (ECM) corresponding to a temperature below -45 °C (-49 °F) (low frequency) or higher than +150 °C (302 °F) (high frequency).

Possible source

Note! An accessory immobilizer with separate plastic key can cause diagnostic trouble code (DTC) CI-121 if the ignition is switched on before the immobilizer has been deactivated.
This type of diagnostic trouble code (DTC) is not included in fault-tracing.

- Short-circuit to battery voltage in signal cable
- Short-circuit to ground in signal cable
- Open-circuit in signal cable.
- Fault in ignition/fuel injection system.
- Large contact resistance.
- Loose connections.

Fault symptom(s)

- The engine coolant temperature (ECT) gauge constantly displays lowest temperature.
- Start fault-tracing with DB. *Faulty signal*

VV9099800008010X

Fig. 12 Code CI-121: Engine Coolant Temperature Sensor Signal, Faulty Signal (Part 1 of 4). C70, S70 & V70

CB8

Faulty signal. Intermittent fault

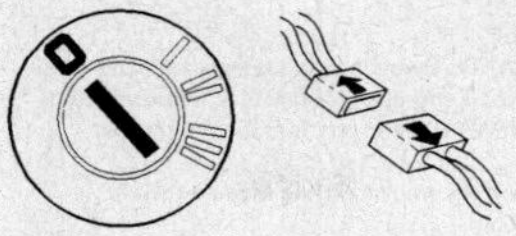

- Ignition off.
- Disconnect fuel level sensor
- Tip it in different directions and check whether the float sticks.
- Replace sticking fuel level sensor.
- Install fuel level sensor

Then continue with:
- Operation done

VV9099800007040X

Fig. 11 Code CI-114: Fuel Level Sensor, Faulty Signal (Part 4 of 4). C70, S70 & V70

DB. Faulty signal

DB1

Checking other diagnostic trouble codes (DTCs)

- Ignition on.
- Read off diagnostic trouble codes (DTCs) in fuel/ignition system.

Is the engine coolant temperature (ECT) sensor diagnostic trouble code (DTC) stored?

Yes:
- DB2

No:
- DB3

DB2

Engine coolant temperature (ECT) sensor diagnostic trouble code (DTC)

Fault-trace according to the Service Manual for the relevant fuel/ignition system.

Then continue with:
- Operation done

DB3

Status check

- Ignition on.
- Go into scrolling values.

Read off engine coolant temperature (ECT).

Does engine coolant temperature (ECT) gauge display -40 °C (-40 °F)?

Yes:
- DB4

No:
- DB9

VV9099800008020X

Fig. 12 Code CI-121: Engine Coolant Temperature Sensor Signal, Faulty Signal (Part 2 of 4). C70, S70 & V70

DB4

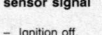

Checking engine coolant temperature (ECT) sensor signal

- Ignition off.
- Connect the breakout box to the engine control module (ECM). (Fenix 5.2, Motronic 4.3, Motronic 4.4 or Diesel MSA 15.7) and check ground terminals

- Disconnect the engine control module (ECM).
- Ignition on.

Connect a voltmeter to the breakout box as follows: #23 (#B23) and #28 (#B28)

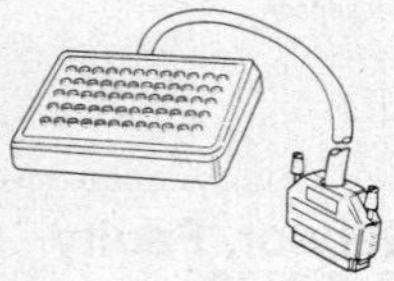
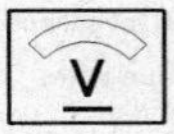

The voltmeter should read approximately 6 V.

If reading is OK:
- **DB7**

If value is lower:
- **DB5**

If value is higher:
- **DB6**

DB5

Checking for an open-circuit and short-circuit to ground

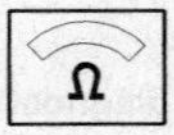

Check cable between combined instrument panel #A26 and engine control module (ECM) #B23.
On cars with ECC: Check cable between combined instrument panel #A26 and ECC control module #C2 for a short-circuit to ground

Then continue with:
- **DB8**

DB6

Checking for a short-circuit to supply voltage

Check cable between combined instrument panel #A26 and engine control module (ECM) #B23.
On cars with ECC: Check cable between combined instrument panel #A26 and ECC control module #C2 for a short-circuit to supply voltage

Then continue with:
- **DB8**

DB7

Checking for contact resistance and oxidation

The cause of the diagnostic trouble code (DTC) has been loose connections in the engine control module (ECM) connector. Check connector for contact resistance and oxidation and remedy

Then continue with:
- **DB8**

VV9099800008030X

Fig. 12 Code CI-121: Engine Coolant Temperature Sensor Signal, Faulty Signal (Part 3 of 4). C70, S70 & V70

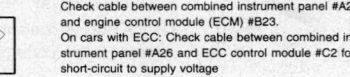

EA. Diagnostic trouble code (DTC) information

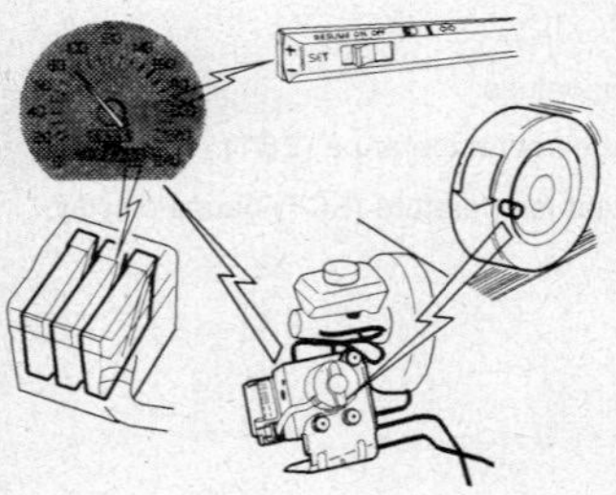

Condition

- The diagnostic trouble code (DTC) is stored within 2 seconds when there is a short-circuit to supply voltage in the signal cable and speed is > 2 km/h (1.2 mph).

Possible source

There is a short-circuit to supply voltage in the speed signal cable between the combined instrument panel and

- ECC.

Fault symptom(s)

> **Note!** The combined instrument panel displays no visible symptoms of this diagnostic trouble code (DTC).

- In cars with ECC, blower fan speed does not drop with increasing speed.
- In cars equipped with a trip computer, incorrect values for average speed, average fuel consumption, actual fuel consumption and trip computer trip odometer are displayed.

- Start fault-tracing with EB. *Signal too high*

VV9099800009010X

Fig. 13 Code CI-123: 48 Pulse vehicle Speed Sensor, Signal Too High (Part 1 of 3). C70, S70 & V70

DB8

Verification

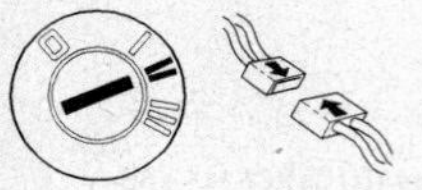

Hint: After carrying out the repair check that the fault has been remedied.

- Ignition off.
- Reconnect connectors, reinstall components.
- Ignition on.
- Go into scrolling values.

Read off engine coolant temperature (ECT).

Does engine coolant temperature (ECT) gauge display -40 °C (-40 °F)?

Yes:
- Fault corrected

No:
- Fault not found

DB9

Faulty signal. Intermittent fault

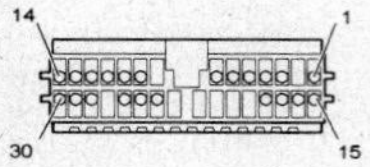

Check combined instrument panel connector A and engine control module (ECM) connector for loose connections and contact resistance and oxidation

Check cable between combined instrument panel #A26 and engine control module (ECM) #C2 for an intermittent open-circuit an intermittent short-circuit to ground and an intermittent short-circuit to supply voltage

On cars with ECC: Check cable between combined instrument panel #A26 and ECC control module #C2 for an intermittent open-circuit an intermittent short-circuit to ground and an intermittent short-circuit to supply voltage according to **ZB4**.

Then continue with:
- Operation done

VV9099800008040X

Fig. 12 Code CI-121: Engine Coolant Temperature Sensor Signal, Faulty Signal (Part 4 of 4). C70, S70 & V70

EB. Signal too high

EB1

Status check

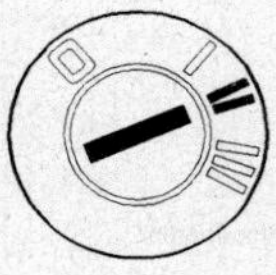

- Gear selector in neutral.
- Lift up the front suspension so that both front wheels are hanging free.

> **Warning!** In cars with AWD, lift up the car so that all wheels are hanging free.

- Ignition on.
- Go into scrolling values.
- Spin the front wheel so that speed exceeds 2 km/h (1.2 mph) for at least 2 seconds while reading off the status of the 48 pulse vehicle speed signal.

Is the status OK displayed?

Yes:
- **EB4**

No:
- **EB2**

EB2

Checking for a short-circuit to supply voltage

On cars with ECC: Check cable between combined instrument panel #A6 and ECC control module #C1 for a short-circuit to supply voltage

Then continue with:
- **EB3**

VV9099800009020X

Fig. 13 Code CI-123: 48 Pulse vehicle Speed Sensor, Signal Too High (Part 2 of 3). C70, S70 & V70

EB3

Verification

Hint: After carrying out the repair check that the fault has been remedied.

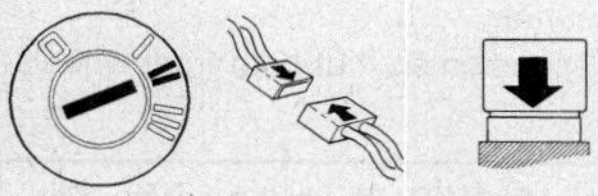

- Ignition off.
- Reconnect connectors, reinstall components.
- Gear selector in neutral.
- Lift up the front suspension so that both front wheels are hanging free.

Warning! In cars with AWD, lift up the car so that all wheels are hanging free.

- Ignition on.
- Go into scrolling values.
- Spin the front wheel so that speed exceeds 2 km/h (1.2 mph) for at least 2 seconds while reading off the status of the 48 pulse vehicle speed signal.

Is the status OK displayed?

Yes:
- Fault corrected

No:
- Fault not found

EB4

Faulty signal. Intermittent fault

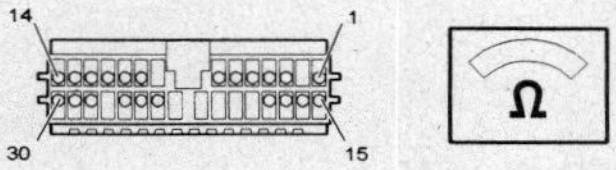

On cars with ECC: Check cable between combined instrument panel #A6 and ECC control module #C1 for an intermittent short-circuit to supply voltage

Then continue with:
- Operation done

VV9099800009030X

Fig. 13 Code CI-123: 48 Pulse vehicle Speed Sensor, Signal Too High (Part 3 of 3). C70, S70 & V70

F B. Faulty signal

F B1

Checking other diagnostic trouble codes (DTCs)

- Ignition on.
- Read off diagnostic trouble codes (DTCs) in combined instrument panel.

Is diagnostic trouble code (DTC) CI-132 stored?

Yes:
- **F B2**

No:
- **F B3**

F B2

Diagnostic trouble code (DTC) CI-132 stored

Fault-trace according to H. *Engine speed (RPM) signal*

Then continue with:
- Operation done

F B3

Status check

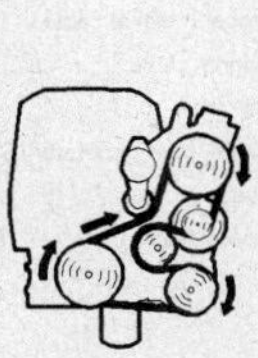

- Start engine.
- Go into scrolling values.

Read off engine speed (RPM).

Is the engine speed (RPM) within its permitted range?

Yes:
- **F B7**

No:
- **F B4**

VV9099800010020X

Fig. 14 Code CI-124: Engine Speed (RPM) Signal, Faulty Signal (Part 2 of 4). C70, S70 & V70

F A. Diagnostic trouble code (DTC) information

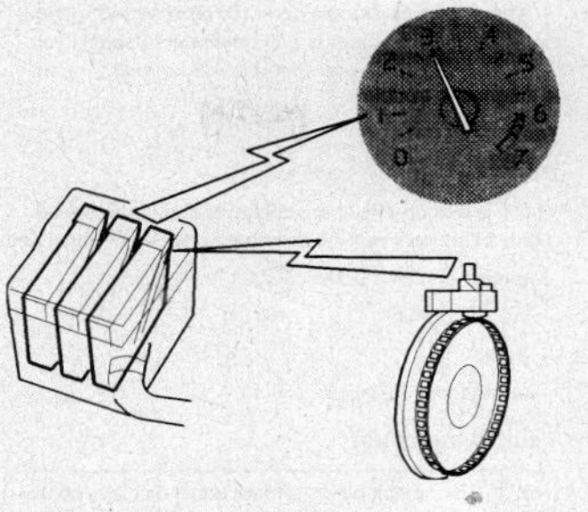

Condition

- The combined instrument panel registers a engine speed (RPM) signal that exceeds 300 Hz (which corresponds to approximately 9,000 rpm).

Possible source

- Loose connections in signal cable/connectors.
- Signal cable insulation damaged.
- The signal cable is too close to a source of interference.
- High contact resistance.

Fault symptom(s)

- Tachometer indicates too high a value.
- Start fault-tracing with FB. *Faulty signal*

VV9099800010010X

Fig. 14 Code CI-124: Engine Speed (RPM) Signal, Faulty Signal (Part 1 of 4). C70, S70 & V70

F B4

Checking cables and terminals

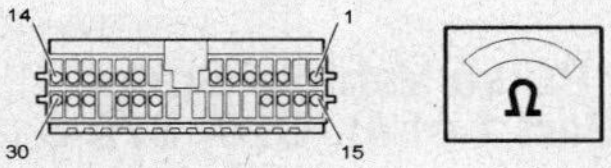

Check combined instrument panel connector A, connector 24/13C and engine control module (ECM) connector for loose connections

Check cable between combined instrument panel #A11 and engine control module (ECM) #B21 for an intermittent open-circuit an intermittent short-circuit to ground and an intermittent short-circuit to supply voltage

Was a fault detected in cables and terminals?

Yes:
- **F B6**

No:
- **F B5**

F B5

Checking for interference

Check that the signal cable is not too close to sources of interference such as electric motors, ignition cables and carphone cables.

Then continue with:
- **F B6**

F B6

Verification

Hint: After carrying out the repair check that the fault has been remedied.

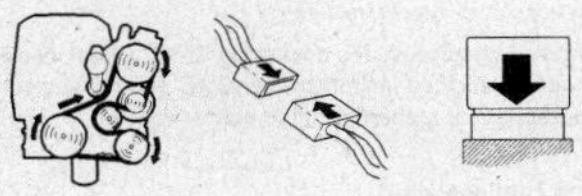

- Ignition off.
- Reconnect connectors, reinstall components.
- Start engine.
- Go into scrolling values.

Read off engine speed (RPM).

Is the engine speed (RPM) within its permitted range?

Yes:
- Fault corrected

No:
- Fault not found

VV9099800010030X

Fig. 14 Code CI-124: Engine Speed (RPM) Signal, Faulty Signal (Part 3 of 4). C70, S70 & V70

F B7

Faulty signal. Intermittent fault

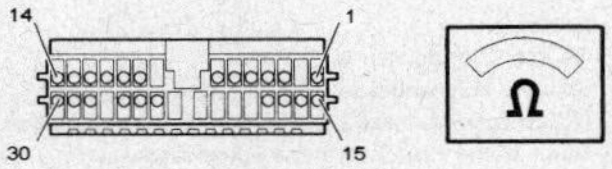

Check combined instrument panel connector A, connector 24/13C and engine control module (ECM) connector for loose connections

Check cable between combined instrument panel #A11 and engine control module (ECM) #B21 for an intermittent open-circuit an intermittent short-circuit to ground and an intermittent short-circuit to supply voltage

Then continue with:
- Operation done

VV9099800010040X

Fig. 14 Code CI-124: Engine Speed (RPM) Signal, Faulty Signal (Part 4 of 4). C70, S70 & V70

G A. Diagnostic trouble code (DTC) information

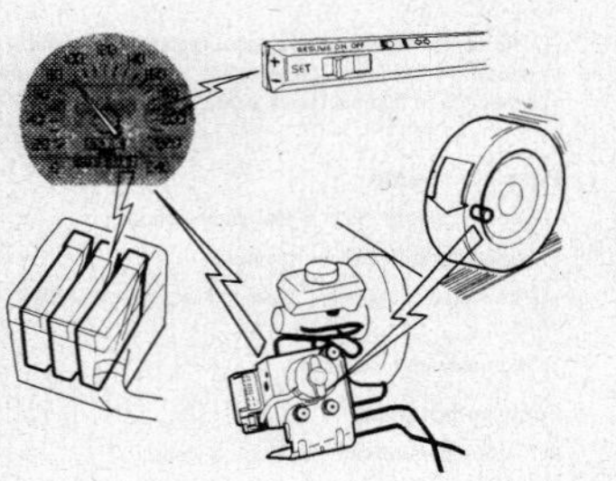

Condition

- The diagnostic trouble code (DTC) is stored within 2 seconds when there is a short-circuit to supply voltage in the signal and speed is > 2 km/h (1.2 mph).

Possible source

There is a short-circuit to supply voltage in the speed signal cable between the combined instrument panel and

- engine control module (ECM)
- cruise control
- Audio
- accessories installed.

Fault symptom(s)

> **Note!** The combined instrument panel displays no visible symptoms of this diagnostic trouble code (DTC).

- A diagnostic trouble code (DTC) is stored in the engine control module (ECM) and malfunction indicator lamp (MIL) lights.
- Cruise control stops working and a diagnostic trouble code (DTC) is stored.
- Audio, automatic volume control not working.
- Start fault-tracing with GB. *Signal too high*

VV9099800011010X

Fig. 15 Code CI-131: 12 Pulse Vehicle Speed Sensor, Signal Too High (Part 1 of 4). C70, S70 & V70

G B2

Checking for a short-circuit to supply voltage

Check cable between the combined instrument panel #A7 and engine control module (ECM) #B18 for a short-circuit to supply voltage

On cars with cruise control: Check cable between combined instrument panel #A7 and cruise control control module #8S for a short-circuit to supply voltage

On cars with radio: Check cable between combined instrument panel #A7 and radio #7B for a short-circuit to supply voltage

On cars with VGLA: Check cable between combined instrument panel #A7 and multiple relay 2/76 #B9 for a short-circuit to supply voltage

On cars with RTI: Check cable between the combined instrument panel #A7 and RTI control module #B3 for a short-circuit to supply voltage

On cars with accessories connected to #C: Check cable between combined instrument panel #C and connected accessories for a short-circuit to supply voltage

Then continue with:
- G B3

G B3

Verification

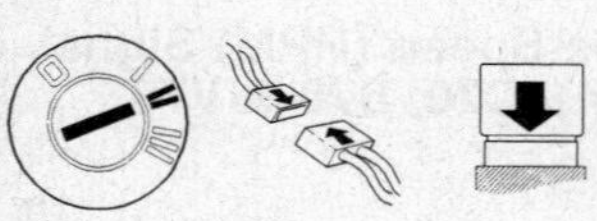

Hint: After carrying out the repair check that the fault has been remedied.

- Ignition off.
- Reconnect connectors, reinstall components.
- Gear selector in neutral.
- Lift up the front suspension so that both front wheels are hanging free.

> **Warning!** In cars with AWD, lift up the car so that all wheels are hanging free.

- Ignition on.
- Go into scrolling values.
- Spin the front wheel so that speed exceeds 2 km/h (1.2 mph) for at least 2 seconds while reading off the status of the 12 pulse vehicle speed signal.

Is the status OK displayed?

Yes:
- Fault corrected

No:
- Fault not found

VV9099800011030X

Fig. 15 Code CI-131: 12 Pulse Vehicle Speed Sensor, Signal Too High (Part 3 of 4). C70, S70 & V70

G B1

Status check

- Gear selector in neutral.
- Lift up the front suspension so that both front wheels are hanging free.

> **Warning!** In cars with AWD, lift up the car so that all wheels are hanging free.

- Ignition on.
- Go into scrolling values.
- Spin the front wheel so that speed exceeds 2 km/h (1.2 mph) for at least 2 seconds while reading off the status of the 12 pulse vehicle speed signal.

Is the status OK displayed?

Yes:
- **G B4**

No:
- **G B2**

VV9099800011020X

Fig. 15 Code CI-131: 12 Pulse Vehicle Speed Sensor, Signal Too High (Part 2 of 4). C70, S70 & V70

G B4

Faulty signal. Intermittent fault

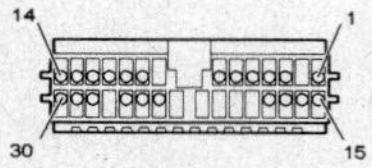

Check cable between combined instrument panel #A7 and engine control module (ECM) #B18 for an intermittent short-circuit to supply voltage

On cars with cruise control: Check cable between combined instrument panel #A7 and cruise control module #8S for an intermittent short-circuit to supply voltage

On cars with radio: Check cable between combined instrument panel #A7 and radio #7B for an intermittent short-circuit to supply voltage

On cars with VGLA: Check cable between combined instrument panel #A7 and multiple relay 2/76 #B9 for a short-circuit to supply voltage

On cars with RTI: Check cable between the combined instrument panel #A7 and RTI control module #B3 for a short-circuit to supply voltage

On cars with accessories connected to #C: Check cable between combined instrument panel #C and connected accessories for an intermittent short-circuit to supply voltage

Then continue with:
- Operation done

VV9099800011040X

Fig. 15 Code CI-131: 12 Pulse Vehicle Speed Sensor, Signal Too High (Part 4 of 4). C70, S70 & V70

H A. Diagnostic trouble code (DTC) information

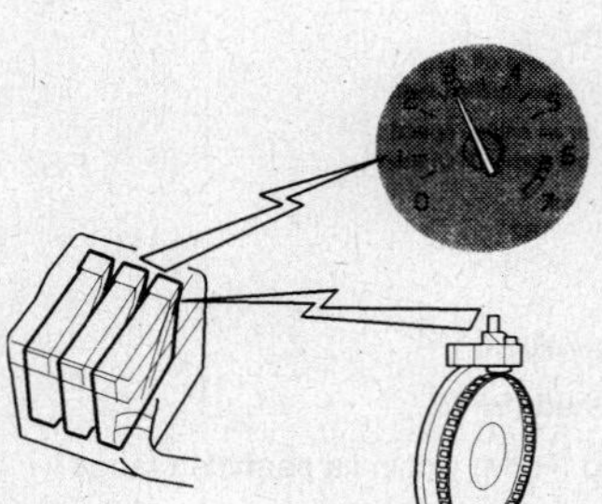

Condition

- Engine speed (RPM) signal missing for at least 10 seconds while the generator (GEN) transmits charging signal (D+).

Possible source

- Short-circuit to battery voltage in signal cable.
- Short-circuit to ground in signal cable.
- Open-circuit in signal cable.
- Open-circuit in signal cable D+ from generator (GEN).
- Contact resistance too large.
- Fault in ignition/fuel injection system.

Fault symptom(s)

- Tachometer not working.
- Start fault-tracing with HB. *Signal missing*

VV9099800012010X

Fig. 16 Code CI-132: Engine Speed (RPM) Signal, Signal Missing (Part 1 of 5). C70, S70 & V70

HB1

Checking other diagnostic trouble codes (DTCs)

- Ignition on.
- Read off diagnostic trouble codes (DTCs) in fuel/ignition system.

Is an engine speed (RPM) sensor signal diagnostic trouble code (DTC) stored?

Yes:
- **HB2**

No:
- **HB3**

HB2

Engine speed (RPM) sensor signal diagnostic trouble code (DTC) stored

Fault-trace according to the Service Manual for the relevant fuel/ignition system.

Then continue with:
- Operation done

HB3

Checking transmission speed signal

- Start engine.
- Go into scrolling values.

Read off engine speed (RPM).

Is the engine speed (RPM) within its permitted range?

Yes:
- **HB11**

No:
- **HB4**

VV9099800012020X

Fig. 16 Code CI-132: Engine Speed (RPM) Signal, Signal Missing (Part 2 of 5). C70, S70 & V70

HB4

Checking warning lamps

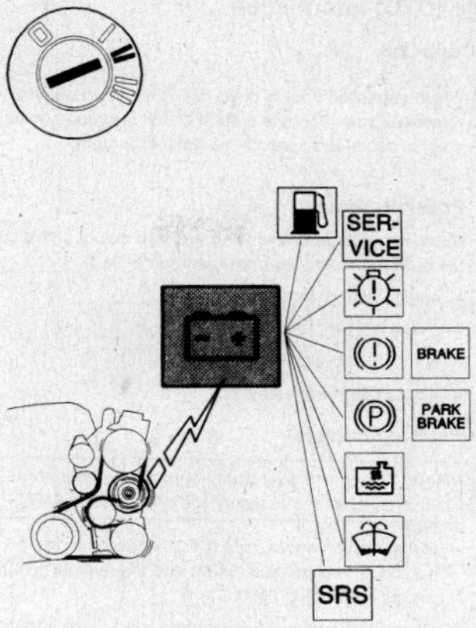

Hint: The combined instrument panel uses charging signal D+ as a reference for the engine speed (RPM) signal.

- Ignition on.
- Check that warning lamps light.

Do the warning lamps light?

Yes:
- **HB6**

No:
- **HB5**

HB5

Checking for an open-circuit

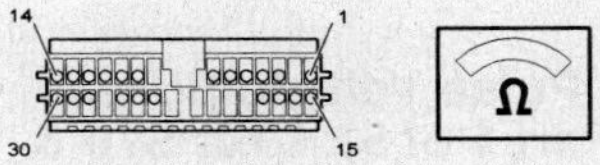

Check cable between combined instrument panel #A13 and generator (GEN) terminal D+ for an open-circuit

Then continue with:
- **HB10**

VV9099800012030X

Fig. 16 Code CI-132: Engine Speed (RPM) Signal, Signal Missing (Part 3 of 5). C70, S70 & V70

HB6

Checking engine speed (RPM) signal voltage

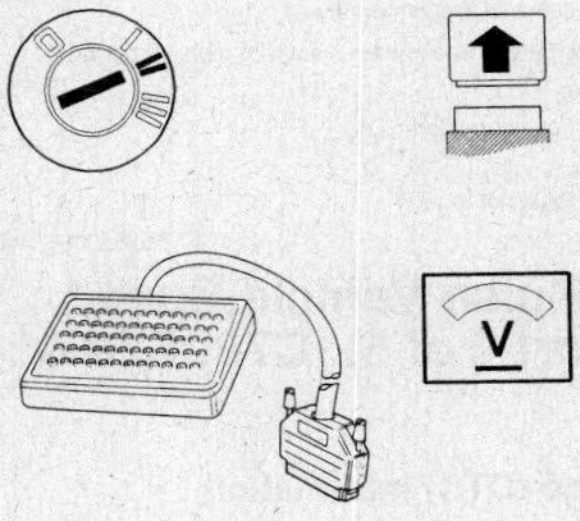

- Ignition off.
- Connect the breakout box to the engine control module (ECM). (Fenix 5.2, Motronic 4.3, Motronic 4.4 or Diesel MSA 15.7) and check ground terminals according to the relevant Service Manual.
- Disconnect the engine control module (ECM).
- Ignition on.

Connect a voltmeter to the breakout box as follows: #21 (#B21) and #28 (#B28)

The voltmeter should read approximately 6 V.

If reading is OK:
- **HB9**

If value is lower:
- **HB7**

If value is higher:
- **HB8**

HB7

Checking for an open-circuit and short-circuit to ground

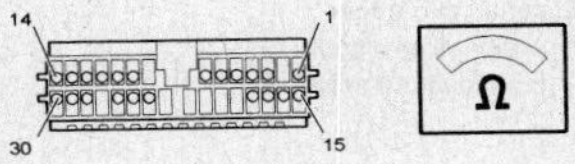

Check cable between combined instrument panel #A11 and engine control module (ECM) #B21 for an open-circuit and a short-circuit to ground

Then continue with:
- **HB10**

HB8

Checking for a short-circuit to supply voltage

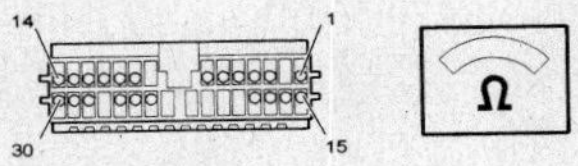

Check cable between combined instrument panel #A11 and engine control module (ECM) #B21 for a short-circuit to supply voltage

Then continue with:
- **HB10**

HB9

Checking for contact resistance and oxidation

The cause of the diagnostic trouble code (DTC) has been loose connections in the engine control module (ECM) connector. Check connector for contact resistance and oxidation and remedy

Then continue with:
- **HB10**

VV9099800012040X

Fig. 16 Code CI-132: Engine Speed (RPM) Signal, Signal Missing (Part 4 of 5). C70, S70 & V70

HB10

Verification

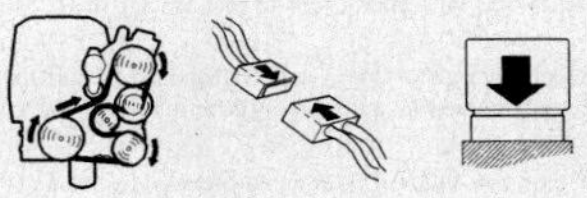

Hint: After carrying out the repair check that the fault has been remedied.

- Ignition off.
- Reconnect connectors, reinstall components.
- Start engine.
- Go into scrolling values.

Read off engine speed (RPM).

Is the engine speed (RPM) within its permitted range?

Yes:
- Fault corrected

No:
- Fault not found

HB11

Faulty signal. Intermittent fault

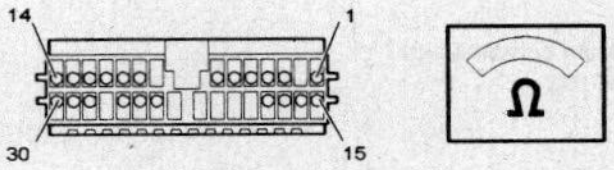

Check combined instrument panel connector A and engine control module (ECM) connector for loose connections and contact resistance and oxidation

Check cable between combined instrument panel #A11 and engine control module (ECM) #B21 for an intermittent open-circuit an intermittent short-circuit to ground and an intermittent short-circuit to supply voltage

Then continue with:
- Operation done

VV9099800012050X

Fig. 16 Code CI-132: Engine Speed (RPM) Signal, Signal Missing (Part 5 of 5). C70, S70 & V70

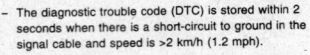

IA. Diagnostic trouble code (DTC) information

Condition

- The diagnostic trouble code (DTC) is stored within 2 seconds when there is a short-circuit to ground in the signal cable and speed is >2 km/h (1.2 mph).

Possible source

Short-circuit to ground in vehicle speed output signal cable between combined instrument panel and

- engine control module (ECM)
- cruise control
- audio, automatic volume control
- any accessories installed.

Fault symptom(s)

Note! The combined instrument panel displays no visible symptoms of this diagnostic trouble code (DTC).

- A diagnostic trouble code (DTC) is stored in the engine control module (ECM) and the malfunction indicator lamp (MIL) lights.
- Cruise control stops working and a diagnostic trouble code (DTC) is stored.
- Audio, automatic volume control not working.
- Start fault-tracing with IB. *Signal too low*

VV9099800013010X

Fig. 17 Code CI-141: 12 Pulse Vehicle Speed Sensor, Signal Too Low (Part 1 of 5). C70, S70 & V70

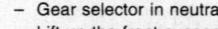

IB. Signal too low

IB1

Status check

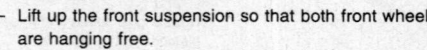

- Gear selector in neutral.
- Lift up the front suspension so that both front wheels are hanging free.

Warning! In cars with AWD, lift up the car so that all wheels are hanging free.

- Ignition on.
- Go into scrolling values under engine management system.
- Spin the front wheel so that speed exceeds 2 km/h (1.2 mph) for at least 2 seconds while reading off the status of the vehicle speed.

Is a greater speed than 0 km/h (0 mph) displayed?

Yes:

- IB4

No:

- IB2

VV9099800013020X

Fig. 17 Code CI-141: 12 Pulse Vehicle Speed Sensor, Signal Too Low (Part 2 of 5). C70, S70 & V70

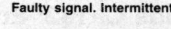

IB2

Checking for a short-circuit to ground

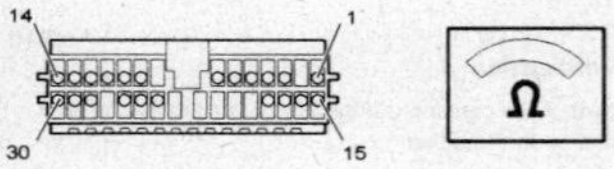

Check cable between the combined instrument panel #A7 and engine control module (ECM) #B18 for a short-circuit to ground

On cars with cruise control: Check cable between combined instrument panel #A7 and cruise control control module #8S for a short-circuit to ground

On cars with radio: Check cable between combined instrument panel #A7 and radio #7B for a short-circuit to ground

On cars with VGLA: Check cable between combined instrument panel #A7 and multiple relay 2/76 #B9 for a short-circuit to supply voltage

On cars with RTI: Check cable between the combined instrument panel #A7 and RTI control module #B3 for a short-circuit to supply voltage

On cars with accessories connected to #C: Check cable between combined instrument panel #C and connected accessory for a short-circuit to ground

Then continue with:

- IB3

VV9099800013030X

Fig. 17 Code CI-141: 12 Pulse Vehicle Speed Sensor, Signal Too Low (Part 3 of 5). C70, S70 & V70

Verification

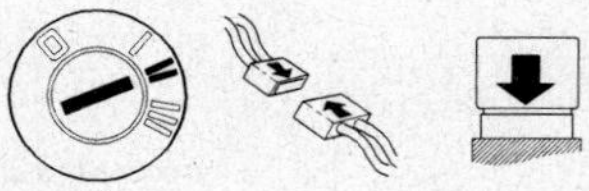

Hint: After carrying out the repair check that the fault has been remedied.

- Ignition off.
- Gear selector in neutral.
- Reconnect connectors, reinstall components.
- Lift up the front suspension so that both front wheels are hanging free.

Warning! In cars with AWD, lift up the car so that all wheels are hanging free.

- Ignition on.
- Go into scrolling values under engine management system.
- Spin the front wheel so that speed exceeds 2 km/h (1.2 mph) for at least 2 seconds while reading off the status of the vehicle speed.

Is a greater speed than 0 km/h (0 mph) displayed?

Yes:

- Fault corrected

No:

- Fault not found

VV9099800013040X

Fig. 17 Code CI-141: 12 Pulse Vehicle Speed Sensor, Signal Too Low (Part 4 of 5). C70, S70 & V70

IB4

Faulty signal. Intermittent fault

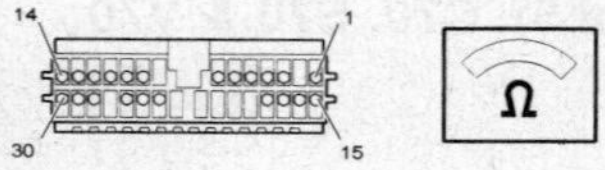

Check cable between combined instrument panel #A7 and engine control module (ECM) #B18 for an intermittent short-circuit to ground

On cars with cruise control: Check cable between combined instrument panel #A7 and cruise control control module #8S for an intermittent short-circuit to ground

On cars with radio: Check cable between combined instrument panel #A7 and radio #7B for an intermittent short-circuit to ground

On cars with VGLA: Check cable between combined instrument panel #A7 and multiple relay 2/76 #B9 for a short-circuit to supply voltage

On cars with RTI: Check cable between the combined instrument panel #A7 and RTI control module #B3 for a short-circuit to supply voltage

On cars with accessories connected to #C: Check cable between combined instrument panel #C and connected accessories for an intermittent short-circuit to ground

Then continue with:

- Operation done

VV9099800013050X

Fig. 17 Code CI-141: 12 Pulse Vehicle Speed Sensor, Signal Too Low (Part 5 of 5). C70, S70 & V70

JA. Diagnostic trouble code (DTC) information

Condition

- Diagnostic trouble code (DTC) CI-142 is stored if the combined instrument panel receives a signal from the outside temperature sensor corresponding to a temperature below -40 °C (-40 °F) (high signal) or higher than +60 °C (140 °F) (low signal) for at least 10 seconds.

Possible source

- Short-circuit to supply voltage in signal cable
- Short-circuit to ground in signal cable
- Open-circuit in signal cable or ground lead
- Contact resistance
- Defective outside temperature sensor

Fault symptom(s)

- The outside temperature gauge display shows - - - - instead of outside temperature.
- Start fault-tracing with JB. *Signal missing*

VV9099800014010X

Fig. 18 Code CI-142: Outside temperature Sensor Signal, Signal Missing (Part 1 of 3). C70, S70 & V70

J B. Signal missing

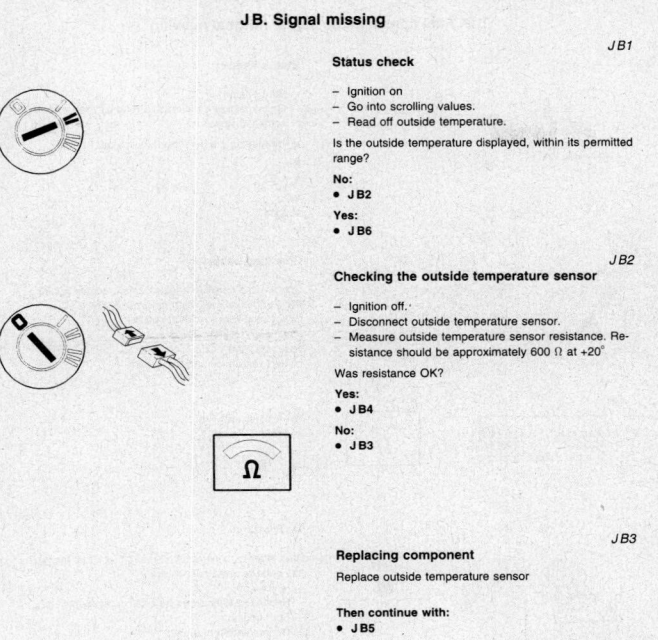

J B1

Status check

- Ignition on
- Go into scrolling values.
- Read off outside temperature.

Is the outside temperature displayed, within its permitted range?

No:
- J B2

Yes:
- J B6

J B2

Checking the outside temperature sensor

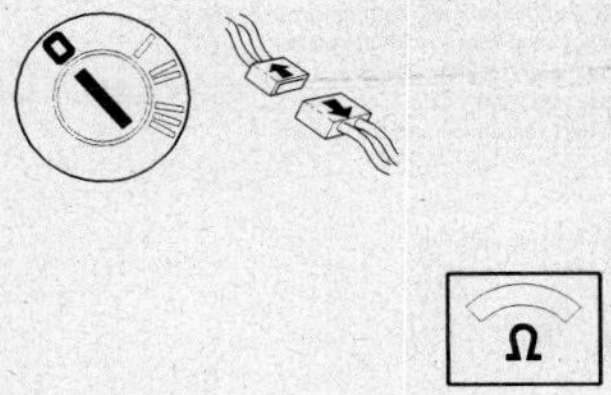

- Ignition off.
- Disconnect outside temperature sensor.
- Measure outside temperature sensor resistance. Resistance should be approximately 600 Ω at +20°

Was resistance OK?

Yes:
- J B4

No:
- J B3

J B3

Replacing component

Replace outside temperature sensor

Then continue with:
- J B5

VV9099800014020X

Fig. 18 Code CI-142: Outside temperature Sensor Signal, Signal Missing (Part 2 of 3). C70, S70 & V70

J B4

Checking cables

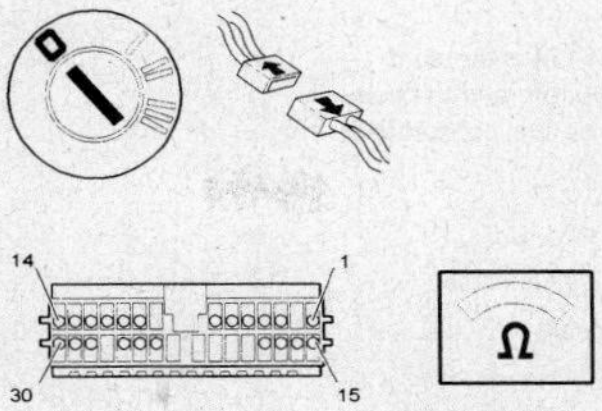

Check cables between outside temperature sensor #1 and combined instrument panel #A24
and outside temperature sensor #2 and combined instrument panel #A25 for an open-circuit
a short-circuit to ground and
a short-circuit to supply voltage
Check cable connectors for contact resistance and oxidation

Then continue with:
- J B5

J B5

Verification

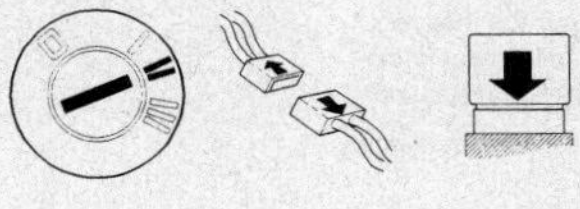

Hint: After carrying out the repair, check that the fault has been remedied as follows:
- Ignition off.
- Reconnect connectors, reinstall components.
- Ignition on
- Go into scrolling values.
- Read off outside temperature.

Is the outside temperature displayed, within its permitted range?

Yes:
- Fault not found

No:
- Fault corrected

J B6

Intermittent fault, Signal faulty

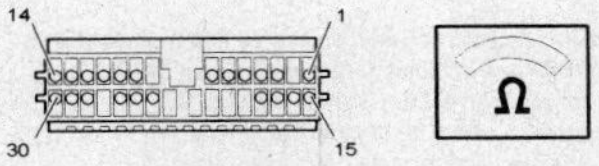

Check cables between outside temperature sensor #1 and combined instrument panel #A24
and outside temperature sensor #2 and combined instrument panel #A25 for an intermittent open-circuit
an intermittent short-circuit to ground
and an intermittent short-circuit to
supply voltage
Check cable connectors for contact resistance and oxidation

Then continue with:
- Operation done

VV9099800014030X

Fig. 18 Code CI-142: Outside temperature Sensor Signal, Signal Missing (Part 3 of 3). C70, S70 & V70

K A. Diagnostic trouble code (DTC) information

Condition

- The diagnostic trouble code (DTC) is stored within 2 seconds when there is a short-circuit to ground in the signal cable and speed is >2 km/h (1.2 mph).

Possible source

Short-circuit to ground in vehicle speed output signal cable between combined instrument panel and
- ECC

Fault symptom(s)

> **Note!** The combined instrument panel displays no visible symptoms of this diagnostic trouble code (DTC).

- In cars with ECC, blower fan speed does not drop with increasing speed.
- In cars equipped with a trip computer, incorrect values for average speed, average fuel consumption, actual fuel consumption and trip computer trip odometer are displayed.
- Start fault-tracing with KB. *Signal too low*

VV9099800015010X

Fig. 19 Code CI-143: 48 Pulse Vehicle Speed Sensor, Signal Too Low (Part 1 of 3). C70, S70 & V70

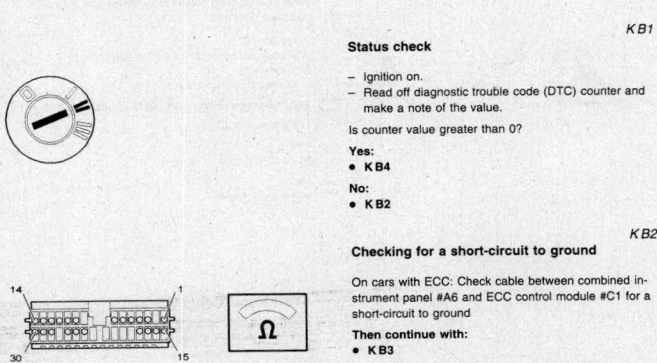

K B1

Status check

- Ignition on.
- Read off diagnostic trouble code (DTC) counter and make a note of the value.

Is counter value greater than 0?

Yes:
- K B4

No:
- K B2

K B2

Checking for a short-circuit to ground

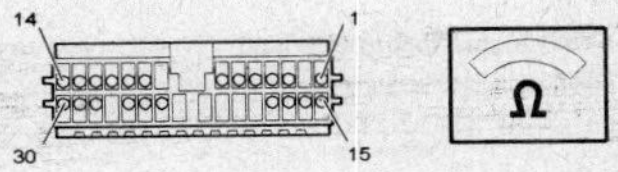

On cars with ECC: Check cable between combined instrument panel #A6 and ECC control module #C1 for a short-circuit to ground

Then continue with:
- K B3

VV9099800015020X

Fig. 19 Code CI-143: 48 Pulse Vehicle Speed Sensor, Signal Too Low (Part 2 of 3). C70, S70 & V70

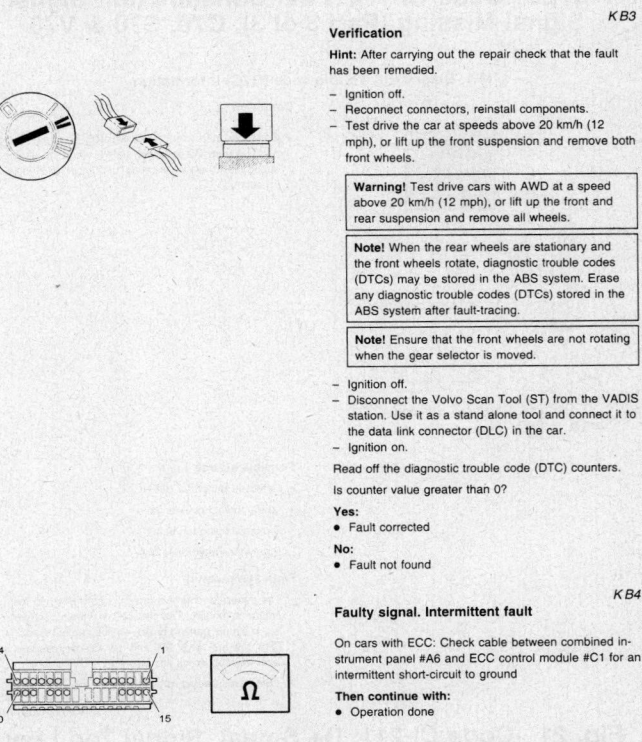

K B3

Verification

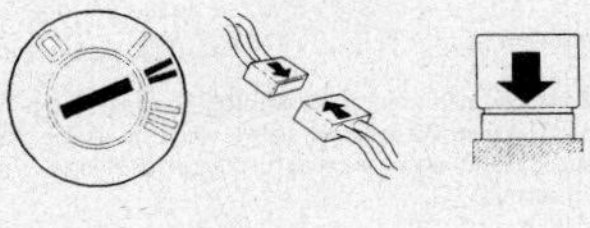

Hint: After carrying out the repair check that the fault has been remedied.

- Ignition off.
- Reconnect connectors, reinstall components.
- Test drive the car at speeds above 20 km/h (12 mph), or lift up the front suspension and remove both front wheels.

> **Warning!** Test drive cars with AWD at a speed above 20 km/h (12 mph), or lift up the front and rear suspension and remove all wheels.

> **Note!** When the rear wheels are stationary and the front wheels rotate, diagnostic trouble codes (DTCs) may be stored in the ABS system. Erase any diagnostic trouble codes (DTCs) stored in the ABS system after fault-tracing.

> **Note!** Ensure that the front wheels are not rotating when the gear selector is moved.

- Ignition off.
- Disconnect the Volvo Scan Tool (ST) from the VADIS station. Use it as a stand alone tool and connect it to the data link connector (DLC) in the car.
- Ignition on.

Read off the diagnostic trouble code (DTC) counters.

Is counter value greater than 0?

Yes:
- Fault corrected

No:
- Fault not found

K B4

Faulty signal. Intermittent fault

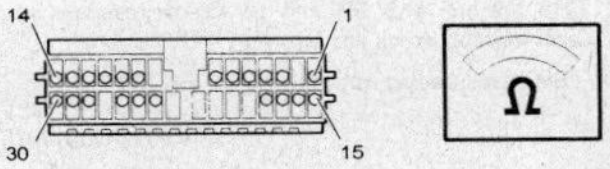

On cars with ECC: Check cable between combined instrument panel #A6 and ECC control module #C1 for an intermittent short-circuit to ground

Then continue with:
- Operation done

VV9099800015030X

Fig. 19 Code CI-143: 48 Pulse Vehicle Speed Sensor, Signal Too Low (Part 3 of 3). C70, S70 & V70

L A. Diagnostic trouble code (DTC) information

Condition

- Diagnostic trouble code (DTC) CI-174 is stored if engine speed (RPM) exceeds 100 rpm and the combined instrument panel registers no fuel consumption signal within 60 seconds.

Possible source

- Short-circuit to supply voltage in signal cable
- Short-circuit to ground in signal cable
- Open-circuit in signal cable.
- One or more diagnostic trouble codes (DTCs) stored in engine control module (ECM).

Fault symptom(s)

- In cars equipped with a trip computer the incorrect average fuel consumption, actual fuel consumption and range to empty fuel tank values are displayed.

- Start fault-tracing with LB. *Fuel consumption signal - Signal missing*

VV9099800016010X

Fig. 20 Code CI-174: Fuel Consumption Signal, Signal Missing (Part 1 of 3). C70, S70 & V70

L B. Fuel consumption signal - Signal missing

L B1

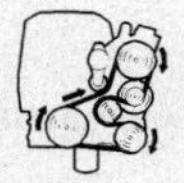

Status check

- Start engine.
- Go into scrolling values and read off the fuel consumption signal.

Is the reading greater than 0 pulses per second?

No:
- L B2

Yes:
- L B4

L B2

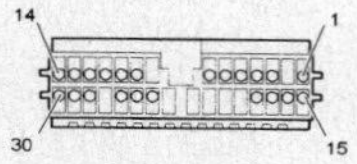

Checking cables

Check cable between engine control module (ECM) #B39 and combined instrument panel #A9 for an open-circuit a short-circuit to ground and a short-circuit to supply voltage Check cable connectors for contact resistance and oxidation

Then continue with:
- L B3

L B3

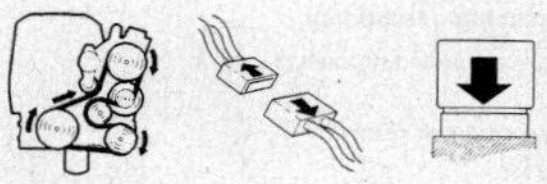

Verification

Hint: After carrying out the repair, check that the fault has been remedied as follows:
- Ignition off.
- Reconnect connectors, reinstall components.
- Start engine.
- Go into scrolling values.
- Read off the fuel consumption signal.

Is the reading greater than 0 pulses per second?

No:
- Fault not found

Yes:
- Fault corrected

VV9099800016020X

Fig. 20 Code CI-174: Fuel Consumption Signal, Signal Missing (Part 2 of 3). C70, S70 & V70

L B4

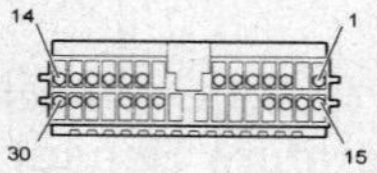

Intermittent fault, Signal faulty

Check cable between engine control module (ECM) #B39 and combined instrument panel #A9 for an open-circuit a short-circuit to ground and a short-circuit to supply voltage Check cable connectors for contact resistance and oxidation

Then continue with:
- Operation done

VV9099800016030X

Fig. 20 Code CI-174: Fuel Consumption Signal, Signal Missing (Part 3 of 3). C70, S70 & V70

M A. Diagnostic trouble code (DTC) information

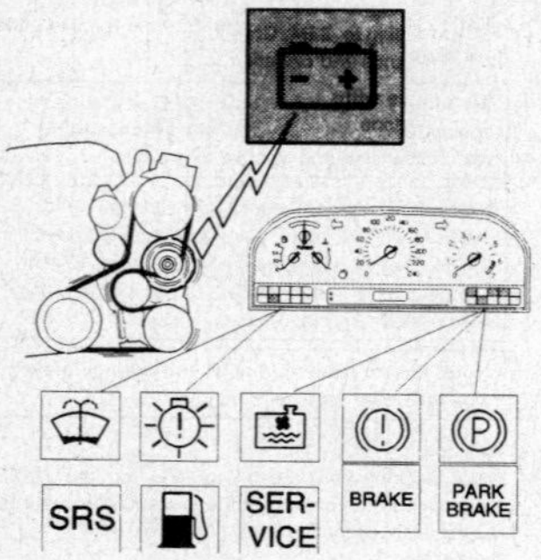

Condition

- Combined instrument panel registers no charging signal (D+) from the generator (GEN) when the engine speed (RPM) signal exceeds 1,000 rpm for at least 10 seconds.

Possible source

- Defective generator (GEN).
- Large contact resistance.
- Broken/slipping fan belt.
- Poorly tensioned drive belt.

Fault symptom(s)

- The generator charge warning lamp is lit when the engine is running. The bulb failure warning sensor, brake circuit, parking brake, engine coolant level, SRS, low fuel level, SRI and low washer reservoir level warning lamps are also lit.

- Start fault-tracing with MB. *Signal too low*

VV9099800017010X

Fig. 21 Code CI-211: D+ Signal, Signal Too Low (Part 1 of 2). C70, S70 & V70

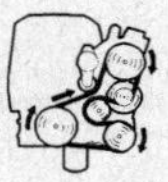

Status check

- Start engine.
- Go into scrolling values.
- Read off status of generator (GEN) charge voltage.

Is the status high?

Yes:
- M B4

No:
- M B2

M B2

Checking the charging system

Check charging system for low charge voltage

Then continue with:
- M B3

M B3

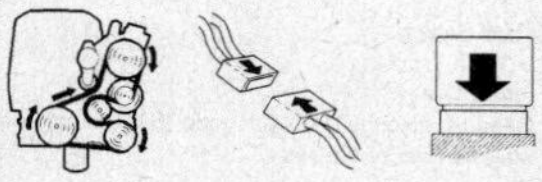

Verification

Hint: After carrying out the repair check that the fault has been remedied.

- Ignition off.
- Reconnect connectors, reinstall components.
- Start engine.
- Go into scrolling values.

Read off status of generator (GEN) charge voltage.

Is the status high?

Yes:
- Fault corrected

No:
- Fault not found

Faulty signal. Intermittent fault

Check charging system for intermittent low charge voltage fault causes and Starter motor 200/700.

Then continue with:
- Operation done

VV9099800017020X

Fig. 21 Code CI-211: D+ Signal, Signal Too Low (Part 2 of 2). C70, S70 & V70

N A. Diagnostic trouble code (DTC) information

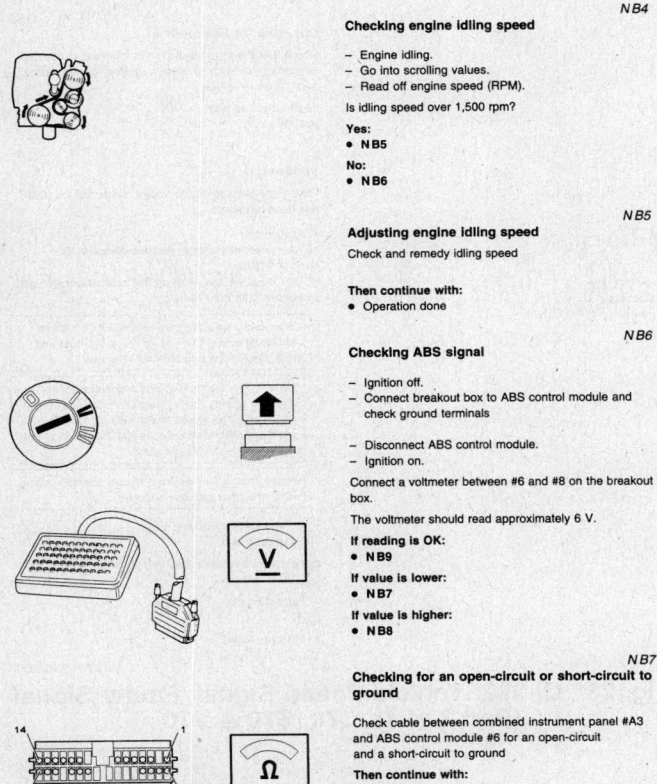

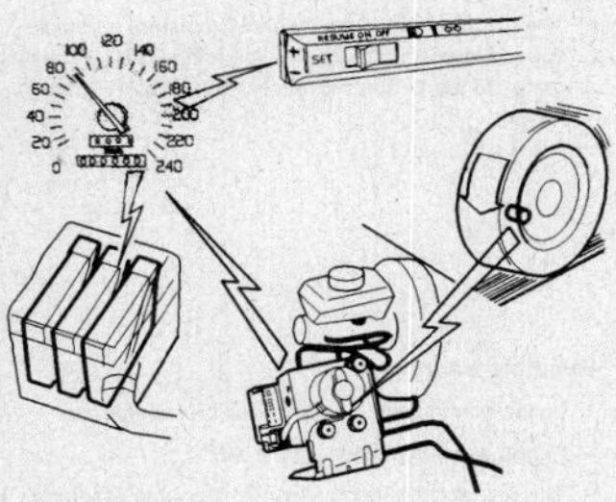

Condition

- The combined instrument panel registers no vehicle speed signal (input signal) when the engine speed (RPM) signal exceeds 1,500 rpm for at least a minute while engine coolant temperature (ECT) is above 50 °C (122 °F).

Possible source

- Open-circuit in signal cable.
- Large contact resistance.
- Fault in ABS system.
- High idling speed, i.e > 1500 rpm.
- Short-circuit to ground in signal cable.
- Short-circuit to supply voltage in the signal cable.

Fault symptom(s)

- Speedometer reading too small or no reading.
- Diagnostic trouble code (DTC) is stored in engine management system.
- In cars with ECC, blower fan speed does not drop with increasing speed.
- In cars equipped with a trip computer, incorrect values for average speed, average fuel consumption, actual fuel consumption and trip computer trip odometer are displayed.
- Cruise control stops working and a diagnostic trouble code (DTC) is stored.

- Start fault-tracing with NB. *Signal missing*

VV9099800018010X

Fig. 22 Code CI-221: Vehicle Speed Sensor Signal, Signal Missing (Part 1 of 5). C70, S70 & V70

N B. Signal missing

N B1

Checking other diagnostic trouble codes (DTCs)

- Ignition on.
- Read diagnostic trouble codes (DTCs) in the ABS system.

Are diagnostic trouble codes (DTCs) ABS-311 and ABS-312 stored?

Yes:
- N B2

No:
- N B3

N B2

Diagnostic trouble codes (DTCs) ABS-311 and ABS-312 stored

Refer to ABS Section.

Then continue with:
- Operation done

N B3

Status check

- Start engine.
- Test drive the car, or lift up the front suspension and remove both front wheels.

> **Warning!** Test drive cars with AWD at a speed above 20 km/h (12 mph), or lift up the front and rear suspension and remove all wheels.

> **Note!** When the rear wheels are stationary and the front wheels rotate, diagnostic trouble codes (DTCs) may be stored in the ABS system. Erase any diagnostic trouble codes (DTCs) stored in the ABS system after fault-tracing.

> **Note!** Ensure that the front wheels are not rotating when the gear selector is moved.

- Go into scrolling values.
- Read off speed.

Is the speed displayed within its permitted range?

Yes:
- N B11

No:
- N B4

VV9099800018020X

Fig. 22 Code CI-221: Vehicle Speed Sensor Signal, Signal Missing (Part 2 of 5). C70, S70 & V70

N B4

Checking engine idling speed

- Engine idling.
- Go into scrolling values.
- Read off engine speed (RPM).

Is idling speed over 1,500 rpm?

Yes:
- N B5

No:
- N B6

N B5

Adjusting engine idling speed

Check and remedy idling speed

Then continue with:
- Operation done

N B6

Checking ABS signal

- Ignition off.
- Connect breakout box to ABS control module and check ground terminals

- Disconnect ABS control module.
- Ignition on.

Connect a voltmeter between #6 and #8 on the breakout box.

The voltmeter should read approximately 6 V.

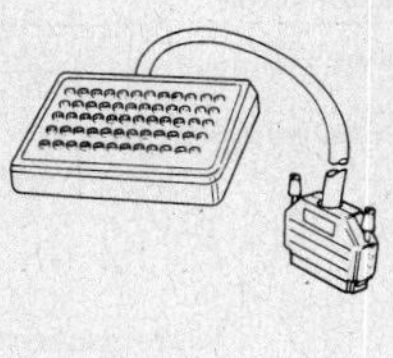

If reading is OK:
- N B9

If value is lower:
- N B7

If value is higher:
- N B8

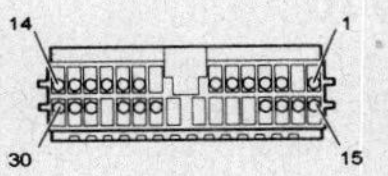

N B7

Checking for an open-circuit or short-circuit to ground

Check cable between combined instrument panel #A3 and ABS control module #6 for an open-circuit and a short-circuit to ground

Then continue with:
- N B10

VV9099800018030X

Fig. 22 Code CI-221: Vehicle Speed Sensor Signal, Signal Missing (Part 3 of 5). C70, S70 & V70

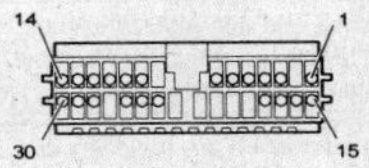

N B8

Checking for a short-circuit to supply voltage

Check cable between combined instrument panel #A3 and ABS control module #6 for a short-circuit to supply voltage

Then continue with:
- N B10

N B9

Fault cause and checking for contact resistance and oxidation

The cause of the diagnostic trouble code (DTC) has been loose connections in the ABS control module connector. Check connector for contact resistance and oxidation

Then continue with:
- N B10

N B10

Verification

Hint: After carrying out the repair check that the fault has been remedied.

- Ignition off.
- Reconnect connectors, reinstall components.
- Start engine.
- Test drive the car, or lift up the front suspension and remove both front wheels.

> **Warning!** Test drive cars with AWD at a speed above 20 km/h (12 mph), or lift up the front and rear suspension and remove all wheels.

> **Note!** When the rear wheels are stationary and the front wheels rotate, diagnostic trouble codes (DTCs) may be stored in the ABS system. Erase any diagnostic trouble codes (DTCs) stored in the ABS system after fault-tracing.

> **Note!** Ensure that the front wheels are not rotating when the gear selector is moved.

- Go into scrolling values.
- Read off speed.

Is the speed displayed within its permitted range?

Yes:
- Fault corrected

No:
- Fault not found

VV9099800018040X

Fig. 22 Code CI-221: Vehicle Speed Sensor Signal, Signal Missing (Part 4 of 5). C70, S70 & V70

NB11

Faulty signal. Intermittent fault

The cause of the diagnostic trouble code (DTC) may have been that the engine speed (RPM) has been over 1,500 rpm for at least a minute with the gear selector in neutral.

Then continue with:

- NB12

NB12

Checking cables and terminals

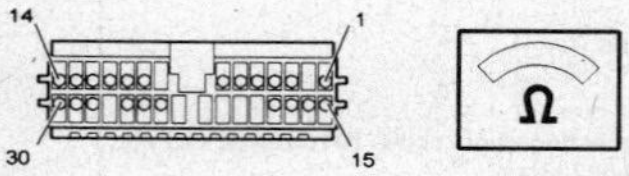

Check combined instrument panel connector A and ABS control module connector for loose connections and contact resistance and oxidation

Check cable between combined instrument panel #A3 and ABS control module #6 for an intermittent open-circuit

Then continue with:

- Operation done

VV9099800018050X

Fig. 22 Code CI-221: Vehicle Speed Sensor Signal, Signal Missing (Part 5 of 5). C70, S70 & V70

OB. Faulty signal

OB1

Checking other diagnostic trouble codes (DTCs)

- Ignition on.
- Read off diagnostic trouble codes (DTCs) in combined instrument panel.

Is diagnostic trouble code (DTC) CI-221 stored?

Yes:

- OB2

No:

- OB3

OB2

Diagnostic trouble code (DTC) CI-221 stored

Fault-trace according to M. *CI-211 D+ signal*

Then continue with:

- Operation done

OB3

Status check

- Start engine.
- Test drive the car, or lift up the front suspension and remove both front wheels.

> **Warning!** Test drive cars with AWD at a speed above 20 km/h (12 mph), or lift up the front and rear suspension and remove all wheels.

> **Note!** When the rear wheels are stationary and the front wheels rotate, diagnostic trouble codes (DTCs) may be stored in the ABS system. Erase any diagnostic trouble codes (DTCs) stored in the ABS system after fault-tracing.

> **Note!** Ensure that the front wheels are not rotating when the gear selector is moved.

- Go into scrolling values.
- Read off speed.

Is the speed displayed within its permitted range?

Yes:

- OB7

No:

- OB4

VV9099800019020X

Fig. 23 CI-222: Vehicle Speed Signal, Faulty Signal (Part 2 of 4). C70, S70 & V70

OA. Diagnostic trouble code (DTC) information

Condition

- The combined instrument panel registers a vehicle speed signal (input signal) exceeding 2,000 Hz (which corresponds to approximately 280 km/h (175 mph)).

Possible source

- Loose connections in signal cable/connectors.
- Signal cable insulation damaged.
- The signal cable is too close to a source of interference.
- High contact resistance.

Fault symptom(s)

- Speedometer reading too small or maximum reading.
- Start fault-tracing with OB. *Faulty signal*

VV9099800019010X

Fig. 23 CI-222: Vehicle Speed Signal, Faulty Signal (Part 1 of 4). C70, S70 & V70

OB4

Checking cables and terminals

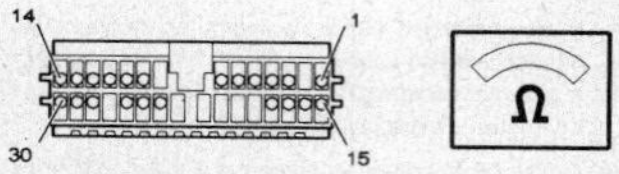

Check combined instrument panel connector A, connector 24/13C and ABS control module connector for loose connections

Check cable between combined instrument panel #A3 and ABS control module #6 for an intermittent open-circuit, an intermittent short-circuit to ground and an intermittent short-circuit to supply voltage

Was a fault detected in cables and terminals?

Yes:

- OB6

No:

- OB5

OB5

Checking for interference

Check that the signal cable is not too close to sources of interference such as electric motors, ignition cables and carphone cables.

Then continue with:

- OB6

OB6

Verification

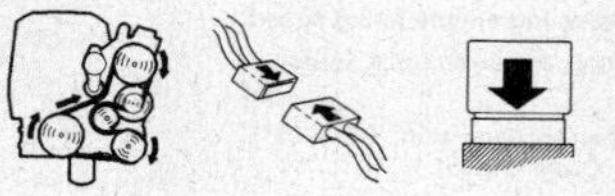

Hint: After carrying out the repair check that the fault has been remedied.

- Ignition off.
- Reconnect connectors, reinstall components.
- Start engine.
- Test drive the car, or lift up the front suspension and remove both front wheels.

> **Warning!** Test drive cars with AWD at a speed above 20 km/h (12 mph), or lift up the front and rear suspension and remove all wheels.

> **Note!** When the rear wheels are stationary and the front wheels rotate, diagnostic trouble codes (DTCs) may be stored in the ABS system. Erase any diagnostic trouble codes (DTCs) stored in the ABS system after fault-tracing.

> **Note!** Ensure that the front wheels are not rotating when the gear selector is moved.

- Go into scrolling values.
- Read off speed.

Is the speed displayed within its permitted range?

Yes:

- Fault corrected

No:

- Fault not found

VV9099800019030X

Fig. 23 CI-222: Vehicle Speed Signal, Faulty Signal (Part 3 of 4). C70, S70 & V70

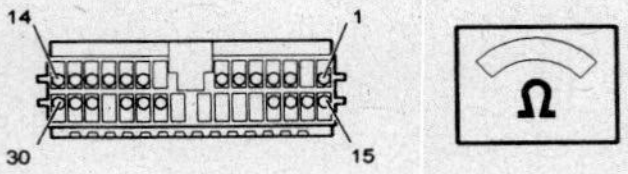

OB7

Faulty signal. Intermittent fault

Check combined instrument panel connector A, connector 24/13C and ABS control module connector for loose connections. Check cable between combined instrument panel #A3 and ABS control module #6 for an intermittent open-circuit an intermittent short-circuit to ground and an intermittent short-circuit to supply voltage

Then continue with:
- Operation done

VV9099800019040X

Fig. 23 CI-222: Vehicle Speed Signal, Faulty Signal (Part 4 of 4). C70, S70 & V70

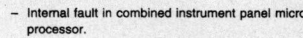

P A. Diagnostic trouble code (DTC) information

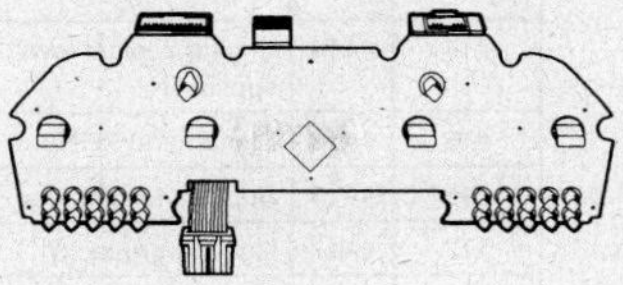

Condition

- Internal fault in combined instrument panel microprocessor.

Possible source

- Internal fault in combined instrument panel microprocessor.

Fault symptom(s)

- The combined instrument panel may display no visible symptoms of this diagnostic trouble code (DTC).

- Start fault-tracing with PB. *Internal fault*

VV9099800020010X

Fig. 24 Code CI-231: Control Module, Internal Fault (Part 1 of 2). C70, S70 & V70

P B. Internal fault

P B1

Status check

- Ignition on.
- Read off diagnostic trouble code (DTC) counter and make a note of the value.

Is counter value greater than 0?

Yes:
- **P B5**

No:
- **P B2**

P B2

Data read-out

Read off all data from the combined instrument panel control module and note values.

Then continue with:
- **P B3**

P B3

Replacing component

Try a new connection plate according to DDJ.

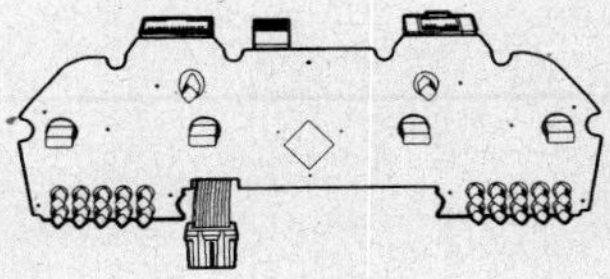

Then continue with:
- **P B4**

P B4

Programming combined instrument panel

Program the control module with the values previously read off the combined instrument panel control module

Then continue with:
- Operation done

P B5

Faulty signal. Intermittent fault

Combined instrument panel control module OK.

Then continue with:
- Operation done

VV9099800020020X

Fig. 24 Code CI-231: Control Module, Internal Fault (Part 2 of 2). C70, S70 & V70

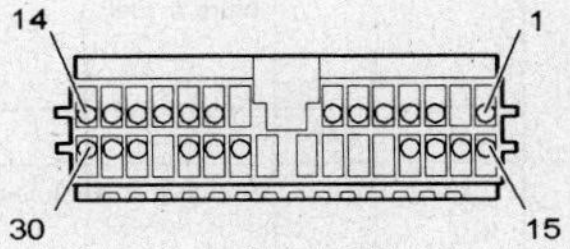

The following values are measured between the relevant terminal in column 1 and terminal # A15 (signal ground) unless otherwise stated.

Note! Check ground terminals before taking readings with the breakout box

U = DC voltage in volts (V)
U_{bat} = battery voltage in volts (V)
U_{low} = voltage approximately 0 V
f = frequency in Hertz (Hz)
t = time in milliseconds (ms)

Break-out box terminal	Ter-mi-nal	Signal type	Ignition on	Idling	Remarks
#1	#A1	Right turn signal lamp	$U \approx U_{low}$ (lamp off) $U \approx U_{bat}$ (lamp on)		
#2	#A2	-	-		-
#3	#A3	Speed input signal	$U \approx U_{low}$ or 6 V (oscillates when the front wheels are rotated slowly)		
#4	#A4	Fuel level sensor (-)	$U \approx U_{low}$		
#5	#A5	Fuel level sensor (+)	$U \approx$ 6-8 V (sensor disconnected) $U \approx$ Full fuel tank (sensor connected) $U \approx$ 5 V Empty fuel tank (sensor connected)		
#6	#A6	Speedometer output signal 48 pulses a revolution	$U \approx$ 0.5 V or U_{bat} -1 V (oscillates when the front wheels are rotated slowly)		
#7	#A7	Speedometer output signal 12 pulses a revolution	$U \approx$ 0.5 V or U_{bat} -1 V (oscillates when the front wheels are rotated slowly)		
#8	#A8	-	-		-
#9	#A9	Fuel consumption	$U \approx U_{bat}$	f ≈ 30 Hz	f increases with engine speed (RPM) and load
#10	#A10	Rheostat	$U \approx$ 0.5 - 1 V (rheostat min) $U \approx U_{bat}$ (rheostat max)		
#11	#A11	Engine speed (RPM) signal	$U \approx U_{bat}$	f ≈ 28 Hz	f increases with engine speed (RPM)
#12	#A12	Gear selector warning lamp	$U \approx U_{low}$ (lamp on) $U \approx U_{bat}$ (lamp off)		
#13	#A13	Generator signal D+	U≈0.5 - 2.5 V	$U \approx U_{bat}$	

VV9099800021010X

Fig. 25 Code CI-232: Control Module, Not Programmed (Part 1 of 2). C70, S70 & V70

Break-out box terminal	Ter-mi-nal	Signal type	Ignition on	Idling	Remarks
#14	#A14	Engine coolant level sensor	$U \approx$ 1.5 - 2.5 V	$U \approx U_{bat}$ (lamp off)	
#15	#A15	Signal ground 31-	$U \approx U_{low}$		
#16	#A16	Supply voltage 30+	$U \approx U_{bat}$		
#17	#A17	Lighting ground 31-	$U \approx U_{low}$		
#18	#A18	Supply voltage 15+	$U \approx U_{bat}$		
#19	#A19	-	-	-	-
#20	#A20	-	-	-	-
#21	#A21	-	-	-	-
#22	#A22	-	-	-	-
#23	#A23	-	-	-	-
#24	#A24	Outside temperature gauge (+)	$U \approx$ 2 V at +20 °C (68 °F)		
#25	#A25	Outside temperature sensor (-)	$U \approx U_{low}$		
#26	#A26	Engine coolant temper-ature signal	Cold engine (+20 °C (68 °F)): f ≈ 40 Hz Engine at operating temperature (+90 °C (194 °F)): f ≈ 22 Hz		
#27	#A27	-	-	-	-
#28	#A28	Brake fluid level sensor	$U \approx$ 1.6 - 2.2 V	$U \approx U_{bat}$ (lamp off)	
#29	#A29	TRACS OFF warning	$U \approx$ 0.5 V (lamp on)	$U \approx U_{bat}$ (lamp off)	
#30	#A30	Oil pressure sensor	$U \approx U_{low}$	$U \approx U_{bat}$	

VV9099800021020X

Fig. 25 Code CI-232: Control Module, Not Programmed (Part 2 of 2). C70, S70 & V70

Starter Motors

INDEX

	Page No.
Diagnosis & Testing	9-69
No Load Test	9-69
Pull In Test	9-69
Starter Specifications	9-70
Troubleshooting	9-69
Control Solenoid Does Not Engage	9-69
Control Solenoid Engages But Starter Motor Does Not	9-69
Drive Does Not Return To Rest When Voltage Is Interrupted	9-69
Drive Returns To Rest Position Before Break In Voltage	9-69
Heavy Sparking, Low RPM	9-69
Long Overrun Time For Starter Motor When Ignition Key Is Released	9-69
Low RPM & High Current Draw	9-69
Low RPM & Low Current Draw	9-69

TROUBLESHOOTING

LOW RPM & LOW CURRENT DRAW

1. Discharged battery.
2. High resistance, caused by dirt in commutator.
3. Worn brushes or spring force.

LOW RPM & HIGH CURRENT DRAW

1. Short circuit in coil.
2. Armature drags against pole shoes due to worn bushing(s) or bent shaft.

HEAVY SPARKING, LOW RPM

1. Weak spring force due to worn brushes or springs.
2. Short circuit or open circuit in armature coil.

DRIVE RETURNS TO REST POSITION BEFORE BREAK IN VOLTAGE

1. Poor connection at terminal 50 or fault in control solenoid.

DRIVE DOES NOT RETURN TO REST WHEN VOLTAGE IS INTERRUPTED

1. The drive is jammed on the armature shaft.
4. Armature seized in bushing.

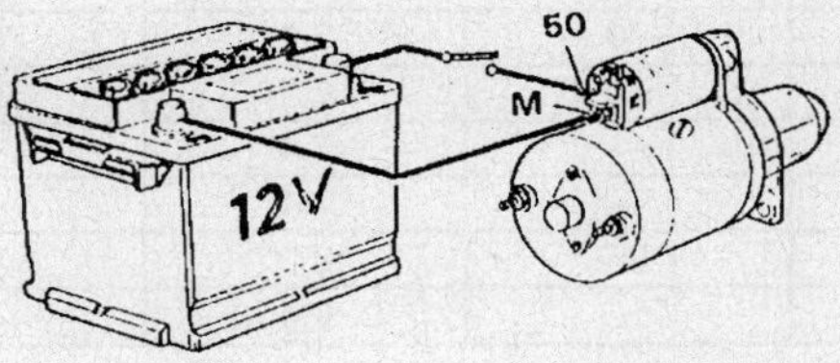

Fig. 1 Control solenoid inspection

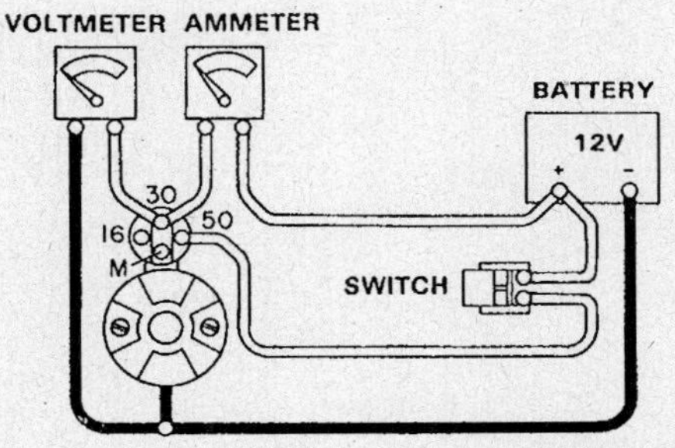

Fig. 2 No load test

CONTROL SOLENOID ENGAGES BUT STARTER MOTOR DOES NOT

1. Defective control solenoid.
2. Poor connection at carbon brushes.
3. Open circuit in field coil.

LONG OVERRUN TIME FOR STARTER MOTOR WHEN IGNITION KEY IS RELEASED

1. Worn brushes.
2. Weak brush spring force.

CONTROL SOLENOID DOES NOT ENGAGE

1. Defective control solenoid.
2. Fault in circuit between terminal 50 on starter motor and ignition switch.
3. Faulty ignition switch.

DIAGNOSIS & TESTING

PULL IN TEST

1. With starter removed from vehicle.
2. Connect battery, **Fig. 1.**
3. When circuit is completed, the drive pinion should extend.
4. If drive pinion does not operate as specified, repair or replace solenoid as necessary.

NO LOAD TEST

1. Connect starter motor, **Fig. 2.**
2. Turn switch On, measure voltmeter and ammeter readings.
3. Compare readings to "Starter Specifications" chart.
4. If reading are not as specified, repair or replace starter motor as necessary.

STARTER SPECIFICATIONS

Year	Manu-facturer/ Type	Part No.	No Load Test			Torque Test①	
			Amperes	Volts	RPM	Amperes	Volts
1998	Bosch DW	0 001 108 088/ 089-090	75	11.5	2900	625-800	4.5
		0 001 110 063-068	95	11.2	2800	650-840	3.8
		0 011 115 002	100	11.6	3140	750-850	4.0
	Bosch EW	0 001 218 017-130	160	10.5	4200	720-950	4.0
	Bosch	0 001 111 142	75	11.5	2900	475-600	3.5
		0 001 108 153	75	11.5	2900	475-600	3.5
1999–2001	Bosch w/ 1.4kW	91 62 171	70	7.4	2900	650-750	4.0
		86 02 085	70	7.4	2900	650-750	4.0
		91 62 617	70	7.4	2900	650-750	4.0
		91 62 618	70	7.4	2900	650-750	4.0
		000 11 08 166	70	7.4	3000	650-750	4.0
	Bosch w/ 1.7kW	91 62 400	—	7.4	—	—	—
		91 68 267	—	7.4	—	—	—
	Bosch w2.0kW	94 59 468	85	8.0	4900	700-1000	4.0
	Bosch w2.2kW	91 62 928	—	7.4	—	—	—

① — Locked starter motor current consumption.

Alternators

INDEX

	Page No.
Alternator Specifications........	9-72
Diagnosis & Testing............ Bosch Alternator w/Integral	9-71
Regulator....................	9-71

DIAGNOSIS & TESTING

When testing an alternator, it is important that a fully charged battery be used.

BOSCH ALTERNATOR w/INTEGRAL REGULATOR

Alternator Output Test

1. With alternator at normal operating temperature, run engine at specified RPM for 3 minutes.
2. Using a suitable shunt or loading alternator with accessories to require 40 amps, check output and compare to **Fig. 1,** for 55 amp alternator or **Fig. 2,** for 70 amp alternator.
3. If alternator does not produce current within specifications, check brushes. If brushes are satisfactory, repeat test using a known good regulator. Indicator on dash must not glow during any part of the testing procedure, if so one or more diodes are defective. Also maximum voltage difference between B+ and D+/61 is ½ volt.

Voltage Regulator Test

1. Run alternator until normal operating temperature is reached.
2. With the engine running at 3000 RPM, measure the voltage between B+ and D– terminals on back of alternator.
3. Correct reading should be 13.4–14.2 volts. If voltage is incorrect, make sure alternator brush length is correct. Minimum brush length is .2 inch (5 mm). If brush length is satisfactory, replace regulator.

Temperature Sensor Test

Some model vehicles use an external temperature sensor located underneath the battery. This sensor, directly connected to the voltage regulator, senses battery temperature and relays this information to the regulator. During cold weather operation, the alternator delivers higher voltage to the battery, thereby charging it at a faster rate. As the battery warms, the charging rate is reduced to prevent excessive gassing. To check sensor operation, proceed as follows:

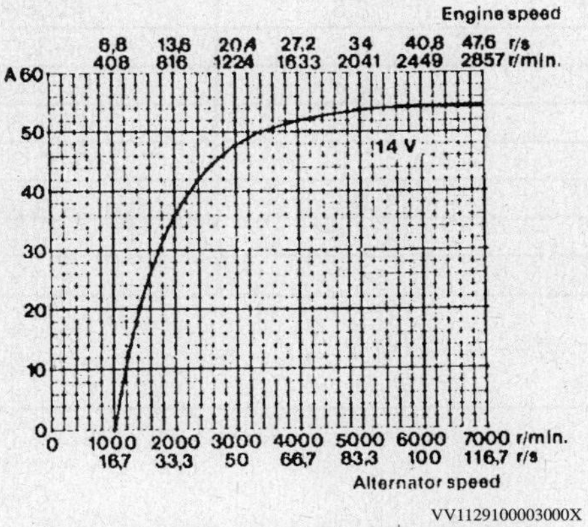

Fig. 1 Alternator output test. Bosch 55 amp alternator w/ integral regulator

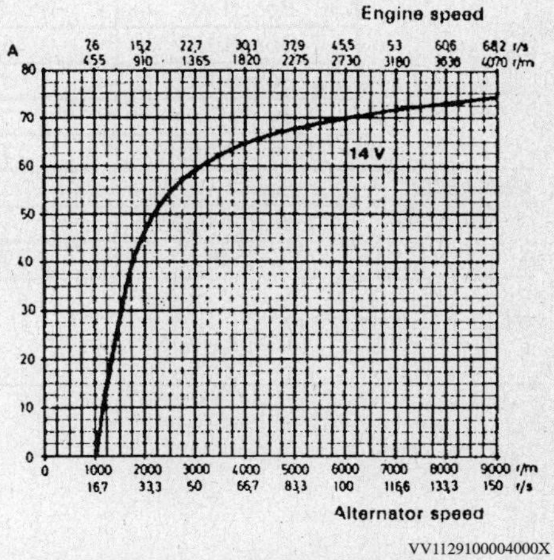

Fig. 2 Alternator output test. Bosch 70 amp alternator w/ integral regulator

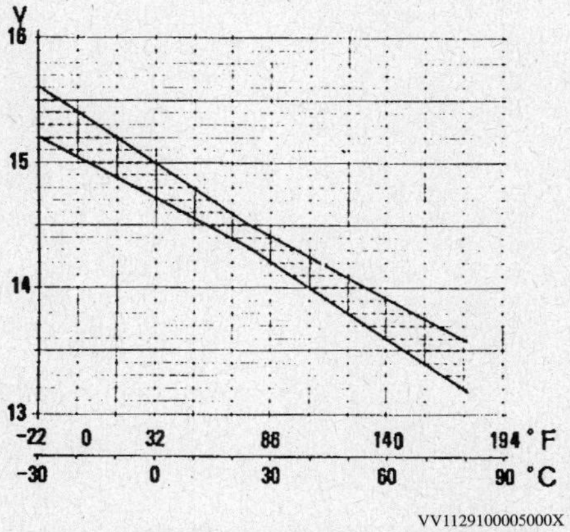

Fig. 3 Charging voltage graph (w/external temperature sensor connected)

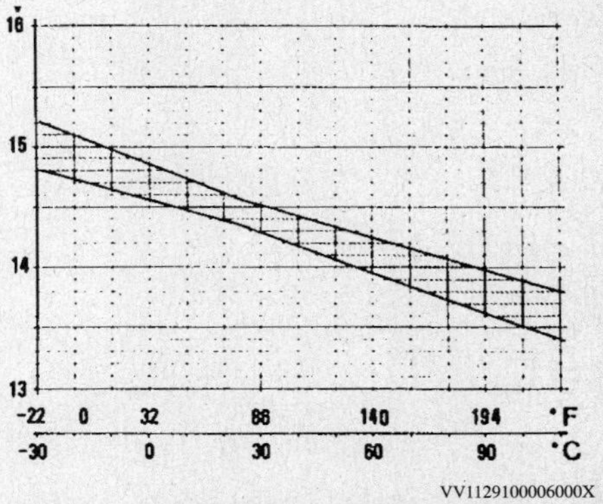

Fig. 4 Charging voltage graph (w/external temperature sensor disconnected)

1. Note and record battery temperature.
2. Connect voltmeter across battery terminals, then with all accessories off, start engine and allow to run at 2000 RPM. Observe charging voltage.
3. With battery temperature as noted in step 1, charging voltage should be within shaded areas of graph, **Fig. 3.** If voltage is as specified, temperature sensor is functioning properly. If not, proceed to next step.
4. Disconnect external temperature sensor from regulator, then repeat steps 1 and 2. With battery temperature as noted, charging voltage should be within shaded areas of graph, **Fig. 4.** If voltage is as specified, replace temperature sensor. If voltage is not as specified, replace voltage regulator.

ALTERNATOR SPECIFICATIONS

Year	Alternator				Regulator	
	Model	Rated Hot Output Amps	Field Winding Resistance Ohms	Output @ 14 Volts Minimum Amps	Type	Voltage @ 125°F
1998	Bosch K1	55	3.5	36/33.3③	Integral	13.8–14.6
	Bosch K1	65	2.8	23/25①	Integral	13.8–14.6
	Bosch N1	80	2.9	31/25①	Integral	13.8–14.6
	Bosch N1	100	2.6	31/25①	Integral	13.8–14.6
	Bosch KC	80	2.6	45/30②	Integral	13.8- 14.6
	Bosch NC	100	2.6	55/30②	Integral	13.8- 14.6
	Bosch NC	120	2.6	60/30②	Integral	13.8-14.6
	Nippondenso	80	2.9	52/33.3③	Integral	13.8–14.6
	Nippondenso	100	2.3	55/33.3③	Integral	13.8-14.6
1999–2001	Bosch KC	120	2.6	—	—	13.5
	Bosch NCB1	120	2.6	—	—	13.5
	DENSO	120	—	—	—	—

① — At 1500 RPM. ② — At 1800 RPM. ③ — At 2000 RPM.

Speed Control Systems

NOTE: On Air Bag Equipped Models, Refer To "Air Bag System Precautions" Located In The Front Of This Manual For System Disarming & Arming Procedures.

NOTE: "Electrical Symbol & Wire Color Code Identification" Located In The Front Of This Manual May Be Used As An Aid When Using Wiring Circuits Found In This Section.

INDEX

	Page No.
Component Diagnosis & Testing	9-74
Speed Control Switch	9-74
Description	9-73
Precautions	9-73
Air Bag Systems	9-73
Battery Ground Cable	9-73
System Diagnosis & Testing	9-73
Less Electronic Tester	9-73
With Electronic Tester	9-73

DESCRIPTION

The speed control system is electrically controlled and vacuum operated. A speed control module stores the exact speed of the vehicle the moment the set button is pressed and released. The system then adjusts the throttle position eight times per second to hold vehicle speed within one mph of the speed set.

A vacuum reservoir is used to maintain the set speed when climbing an incline. The rapid deceleration cutoff is used to deactivate the system if vehicle speed drops by more than 10 mph. This action occurs even if there is no indication that the brakes have been applied. The wheel spin cutoff will deactivate the system if the set, resume, brake or clutch switches do not close and reopen when activated or if a wiring malfunction occurs in these circuits. This prevents the system from operating when system components are malfunctioning.

Test #	Switch Position	Tester Lamps						
		RESUME	SET	BRAKE/CLUTCH	IGNITION	SPEED	VAC	VENT
1	OFF	OFF	OFF	OFF	ON	OFF	OFF	OFF
2	ON	OFF	ON	OFF	ON	OFF	ON	ON
3	RESUME	ON	ON	OFF	ON	OFF	ON	ON
4	SET	ON	OFF	OFF	ON	OFF	ON	ON
5	BRAKE/CLUTCH*	OFF	ON	DIMLY LIT	ON	OFF	ON	ON

* Check each separately.

VV1109100001000X

Fig. 1 Speed control diagnosis chart

PRECAUTIONS

AIR BAG SYSTEMS

Refer to "Air Bag System Precautions" in the front of this manual for system disarming and arming procedures.

BATTERY GROUND CABLE

Prior to service, disconnect battery ground cable and isolate as required.

SYSTEM DIAGNOSIS & TESTING

LESS ELECTRONIC TESTER

1. Check that brake lights work and that the brake switch is properly adjusted. The control unit is grounded through the brake lights. If both brake lights are blown, the control unit will not function.
2. Remove lower dash panel from left side footwell.
3. Check that air valves at brake and clutch pedals are correctly adjusted and do not leak. The valves should be closed when the pedals are up and open when pedals are depressed.
4. Check that vacuum servo hoses and air valve hoses are correctly connected and not kinked.
5. Ensure vacuum hose connected to intake manifold is not blocked or punctured.
6. Disconnect hose from connection marked "VACUUM" on valve housing. Start engine and place thumb on end of hose. Suction should be felt. If no suction is felt, check hose and connection at intake manifold.
7. Reconnect hose, start engine and leave running for about 30 seconds to establish vacuum.
8. Turn engine off and disconnect hose marked "VACUUM" from the valve housing. A hissing sound should be heard. If no sound is heard, there is a vacuum leak in the system. Repair as necessary.

WITH ELECTRONIC TESTER

The most accurate method of fault tracing this speed control system requires the use of test unit, tool No. 9990943-4, or equivalent. This test unit will check the functions of all components including the control unit. Refer to **Figs. 1 through 4,** when testing this system.

1. Connect speed control tester as follows:
   a. Remove lower dash panel from drivers side.
   b. Disconnect speed control harness from control unit.
   c. Connect tester lead to the control unit.
   d. Connect speed control wiring harness to tester unit.
2. Switch tester to position "1." Turn ignition switch on, but do not start engine.
3. Check each switch position of the speed control system and compare, **Fig. 1.**
4. If tester lamps do not light in the correct sequence, proceed as follows:
   a. Check fuse No. 12 and wiring, **Figs. 2 through 4.**
   b. For "Resume and Set" lamps, check yellow and green wires between control unit and switch, **Fig. 5.** If not satisfactory, locate and repair open circuit in wires. If satisfactory, replace switch.
   c. For "Brake/Clutch" lamp, check adjustment of switches on pedals. Check wiring and brake light operation. If not satisfactory, repair as necessary.
   d. For the "Speed" lamp, verify proper operation of the speedometer. Check connection of orange wire at the rear of the instrument cluster. If not satisfactory, repair as necessary.
   e. For "Vac and Vent" light, check three wires going to the servo valve under the hood. If not satisfactory, repair as necessary.
5. **On models less limited-slip differential,** raise left rear wheel off the ground. Rotate wheel slowly while watching "Speed" light on tester. Light

should blink on and off with low light intensity.

6. **On models equipped with limited-slip differential,** raise both rear wheels off the ground and set transmission to "Neutral." Rotate wheels slowly while watching "Speed" light on tester. Light should blink on and off with low light intensity.
7. **On all models,** set speed control to the "OFF" position and start engine. Allow engine to run for approximately 30 seconds to establish vacuum.
8. Turn engine off, then turn ignition switch to "ON" and speed control to "ON." Depress "VAC" and "VENT" buttons on the tester simultaneously. Throttle pedal should be pulled down. If throttle pedal is not pulled down, proceed as follows:
   a. Release the "VAC" button on tester and keep "VENT" button depressed for a minimum of 15 seconds. Throttle pedal should remain steady. If not, the vacuum system has a leak. Repair as necessary.
   b. If vacuum supply is satisfactory, replace control unit.

COMPONENT DIAGNOSIS & TESTING

SPEED CONTROL SWITCH

1. Disconnect electrical connector from speed control switch.
2. Connect a jumper wire from a 12 volt current source to red wire terminal in connector.
3. Connect a test light across ground and the three wires shown in **Fig. 5.**
4. Compare results with those, **Fig. 6.**
5. If indications are not satisfactory, replace switch.

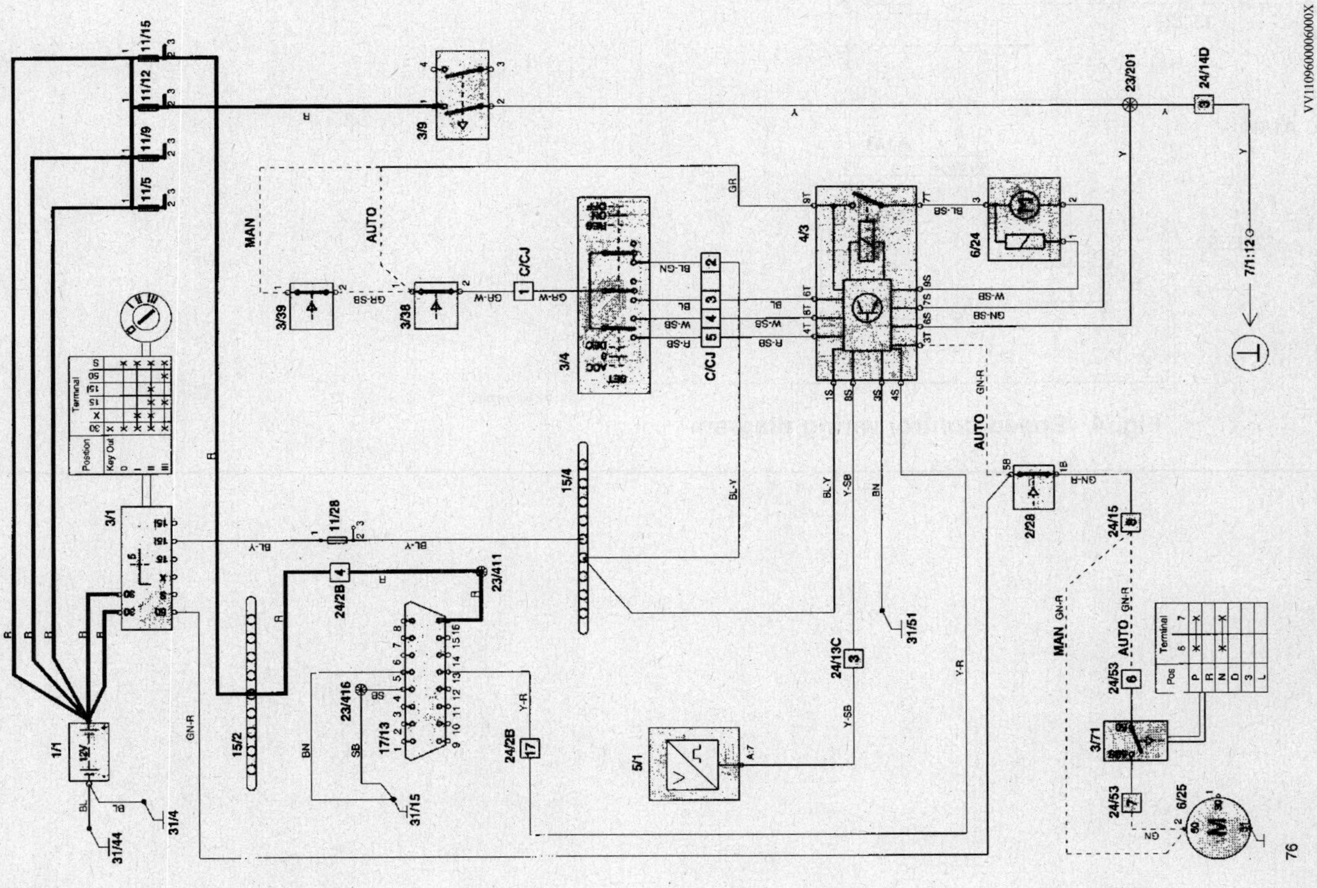

Fig. 2 Speed control wiring diagram

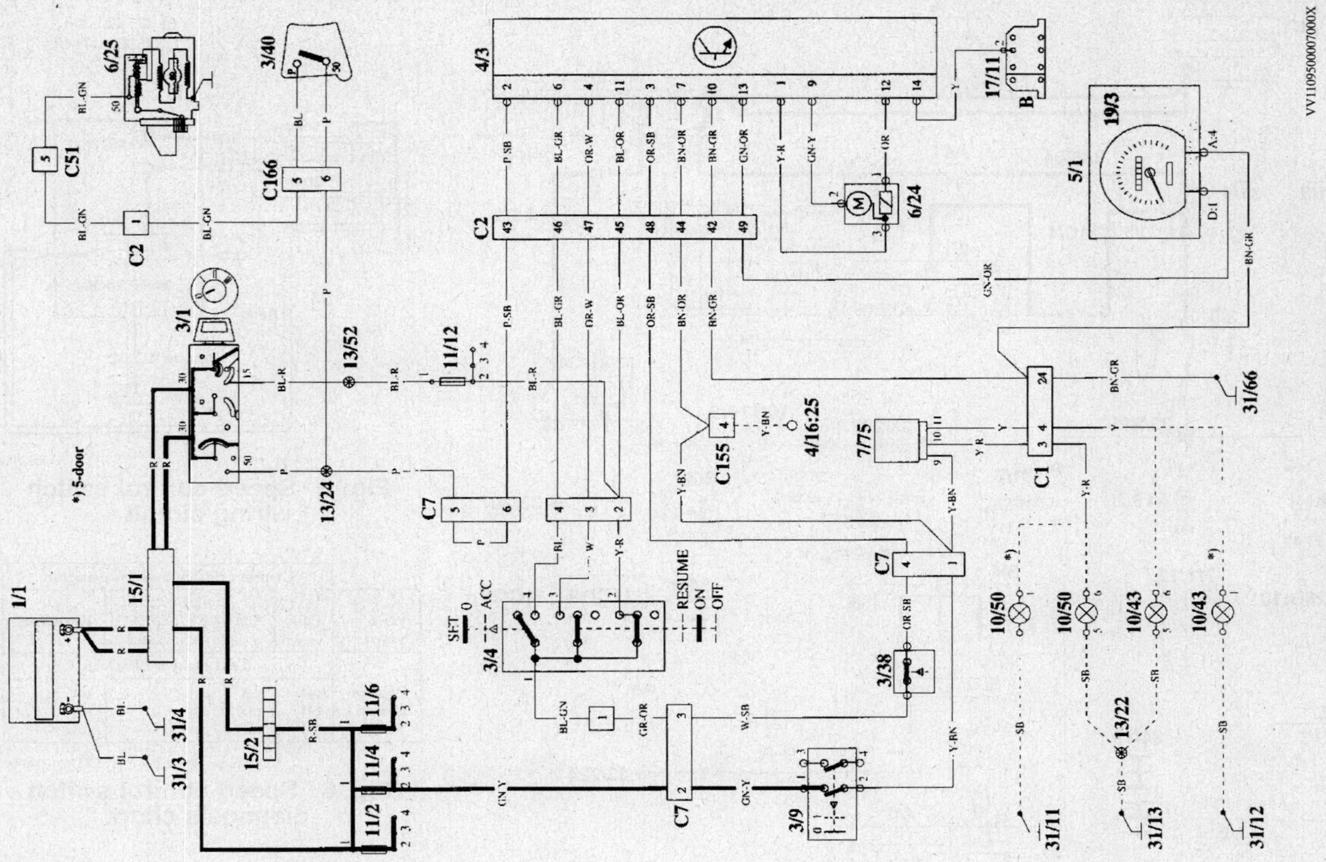

Fig. 3 Speed control wiring diagram

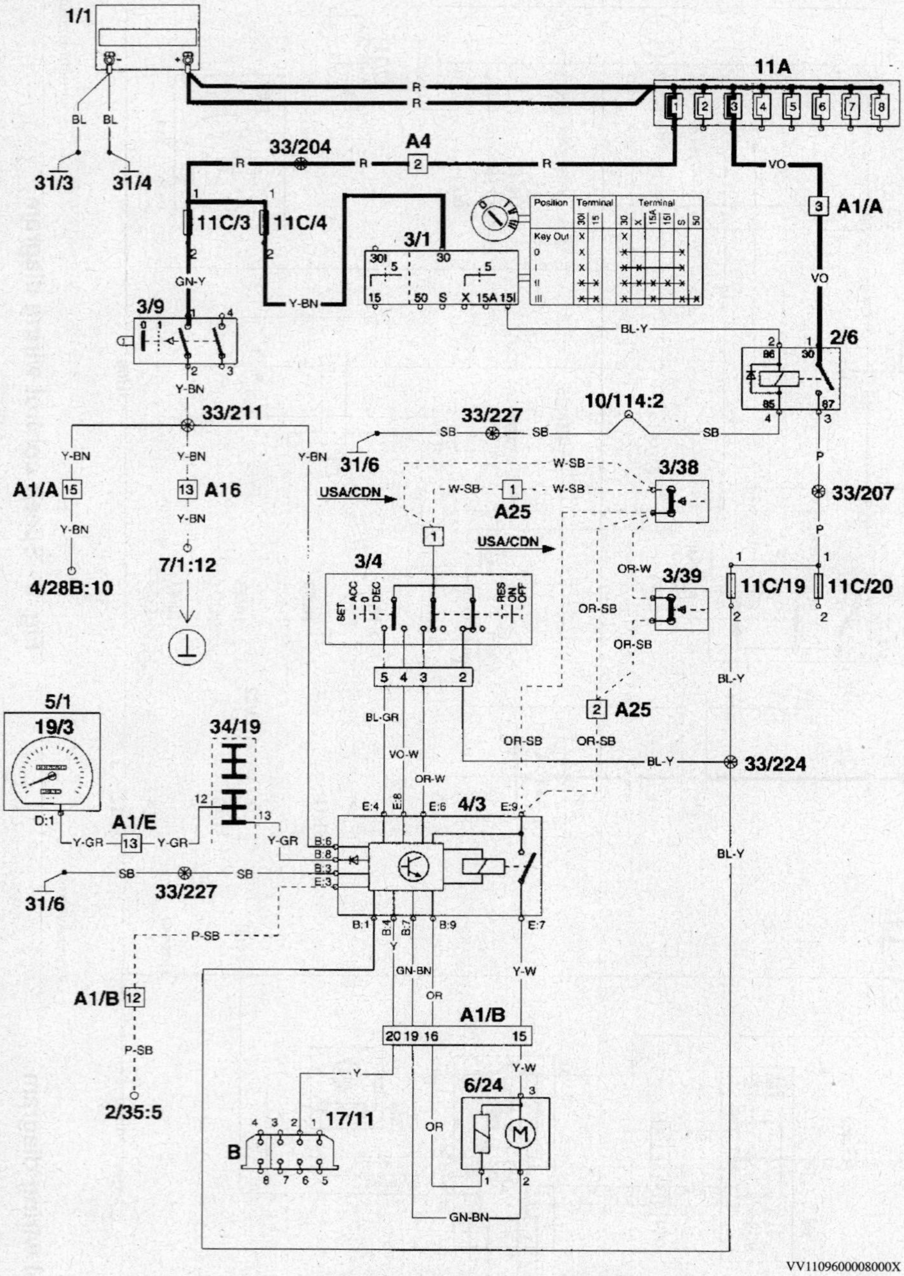

Fig. 4 Speed control wiring diagram

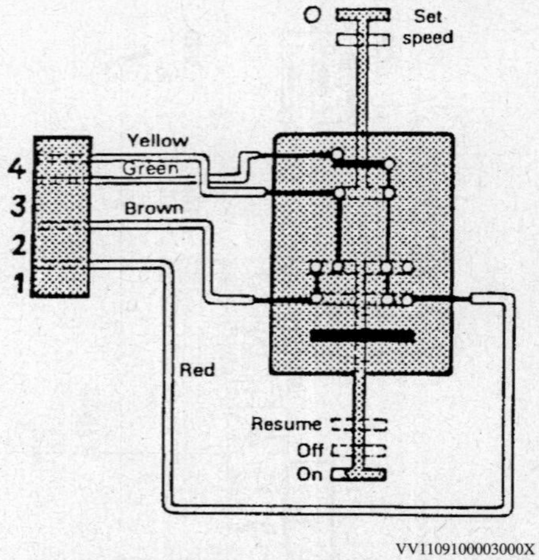

Fig. 5 Speed control switch wiring circuit

Wire color	Cruise control switch position			
	OFF	ON	ON and SET SPEED depressed	RESUME
	Test light indication			
Brown	off	on	on	on
Green	off	on	off	on
Yellow	off	off	on	on

VV1109100004000X

Fig. 6 Speed control switch diagnosis chart

Air Bag System

INDEX

	Page No.
Air Bag System Disarming & Arming	9-77
Air Bag System Arming	9-77
Air Bag System Disarming	9-77
Collision Inspection	9-78
Component Locations	9-78
C70	9-78
S40 & V40	9-78
S60	9-78
S80 & V70	9-78
Component Service	9-78
Air Bag & Seat Belt Tensioner Disposal	9-84
Air Bag Or Seat Belt Tensioner Assembly Disposal	9-83
Contact Reel, Replace	9-79
Drivers Air Bag, Replace	9-78
Passengers Air Bag, Replace	9-78
Roof Panel Air Bag	9-83
Seat Belt Tensioners, Replace	9-81
Sensor Module, Replace	9-80
Side Impact Air Bag System Disposal	9-84
Side Impact Air Bag System, Replace	9-83
Description & Operation	9-77
Diagnosis & Testing	9-78
Precautions	9-77
Roll Over Protection System (ROPS)	9-84
Clearing Diagnostic Trouble Codes	9-93
Component Locations	9-84
Component Service	9-93
ROPS Control Unit, Replace	9-93
Roll Bar Cartridge, Replace	9-93
Diagnosis & Testing	9-84
Accessing Diagnostic Trouble Codes	9-84
Diagnostic Tests	9-84
Diagnostic Trouble Code Interpretation	9-84
ROPS Diagnostic Chart Index.	9-85
Roll Over Protection System Arming & Disarming	9-84
Tightening Specifications	9-95

AIR BAG SYSTEM DISARMING & ARMING

AIR BAG SYSTEM DISARMING

Obtain radio anti-theft code prior to disconnecting the battery ground cable. Always turn microprocessor radios off before disconnecting or connecting the battery ground cable to prevent radio damage.

1. Turn ignition switch to Off position.
2. Disconnect and isolate battery ground cable.
3. Wait at least three minutes after disconnection ground cable prior to performing any service procedures. SRS is designed to retain enough deployment voltage for short time even after battery ground cable has been disconnected. Performing service before minimum three minutes lapse may cause unwanted deployment and possible injury.

AIR BAG SYSTEM ARMING

1. Turn ignition switch to Off position.
2. Connect battery ground cable.
3. Wait at least 10 seconds, then turn ignition switch to On position.
4. SRS warning lamp should light for approximately 10 seconds, then go off. If lamp does not light or remains illuminated after 10 second interval, refer to **MOTORS "Air Bag Manual"** for "Diagnosis & Testing."

DESCRIPTION & OPERATION

The SRS, consists of inflatable air bag assemblies, mounted in the center of the steering wheel and in the righthand portion of the instrument panel. The rear of each assembly incorporates a gas generator which inflates the air bag. A crash sensor records deceleration of the car. A standby power unit supplies the system with power to inflate the bag if the normal power supply is interrupted.

Front seat belt tensioners are also used. The tensioners are activated at the same time the air bags are deployed. Upon activation, the front seat belt tensioners will take up any slack in the belt to restrict the forward movement of the driver and passenger. The system also includes a knee bolster.

The side impact air bags are located on the outside edges of the seat back on the driver's and front passenger's seats. The side impact sensors are located on the B-pillars.

Some models are equipped with roof panel air bag modules at each side of the passenger compartment. The roof panel air bag module is designed to reduce the chance of head injuries to front and rear seat passengers during a side impact. The roof panel air bag module is activated by the same sensor as the side impact air bag. Only the roof panel air bag module on the side of impact will deploy.

Convertible models are equipped with a Roll Over Protection System (ROPS) which includes a deployable roll bar and control unit.

PRECAUTIONS

The SRS must be disarmed prior to disconnecting any SRS electrical connectors or servicing any system components or other components located near an SRS connector. Refer to "Air Bag System Disarming & Arming."

1. **On models equipped with microprocessor radios,** always turn these off before disconnecting or connecting battery ground cable to prevent radio damage.
2. **On all models,** ignition must be turned Off and battery ground cable disconnected when disconnecting or connecting SRS connectors.
3. When making welding repairs, always disconnect drivers and passengers air bags and seat belt tensioner electrical connectors.
4. SRS components must not be opened or repaired. Always install new components.
5. Always replace SRS components which have been damaged.
6. Do not paint air bags to correct cosmetic flaws. They must be replaced.
7. Air bag module(s), seat belt tensioners and sensor modules have an expiration date. This date can be found on sticker located on center console door or lefthand B-pillar.
8. Gold plated connector terminals cannot be repaired. If lead becomes dislodged from connector, wiring harness must be replaced.
9. SRS wiring cannot be repaired or spliced. If damaged, replace wiring harness.
10. Do not use ohmmeter or other current producing device to measure resistance of air bag module or seat belt tensioner. This may lead to unwanted deployment.
11. Disconnect air bag module(s) and seat belt tensioners prior to inspecting resistance of system components or wiring.
12. If air bag module, seat belt tensioner or sensor module have been dropped, do not install component into vehicle.
13. Do not leave undeployed air bag module or seat belt tensioner unattended if work is interrupted. Install into vehicle as soon as unit is removed from packaging.
14. Always place removed air bag module so that horn pad or air bag cover is facing upwards.
15. Air bag modules and seat belt tensioners must not be exposed to grease, or

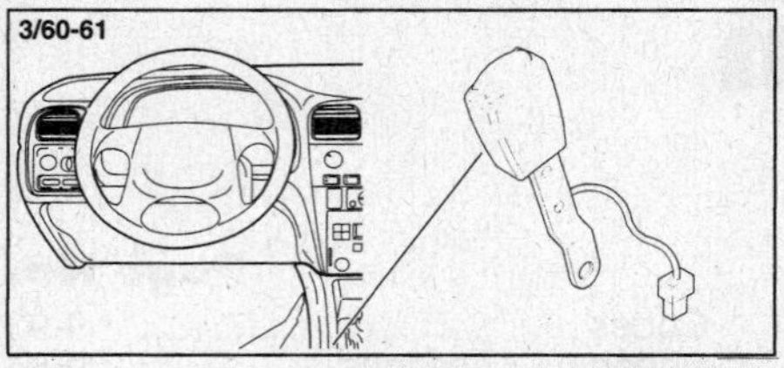

VV8010100328010X

Fig. 1 Seat belt locks. S40 & V40

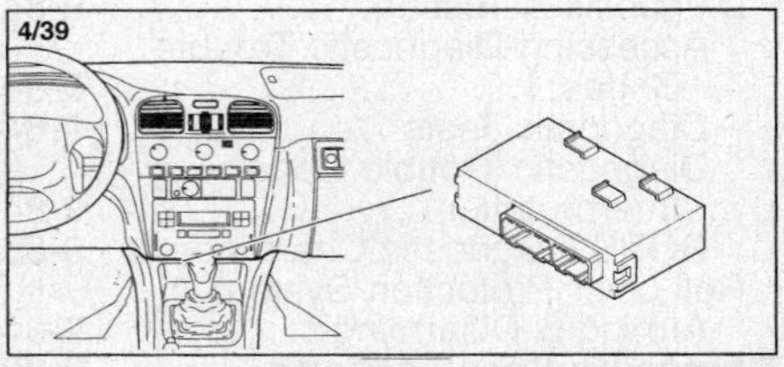

VV8010100328030X

Fig. 4 Control module for locks & alarm. S40 & V40

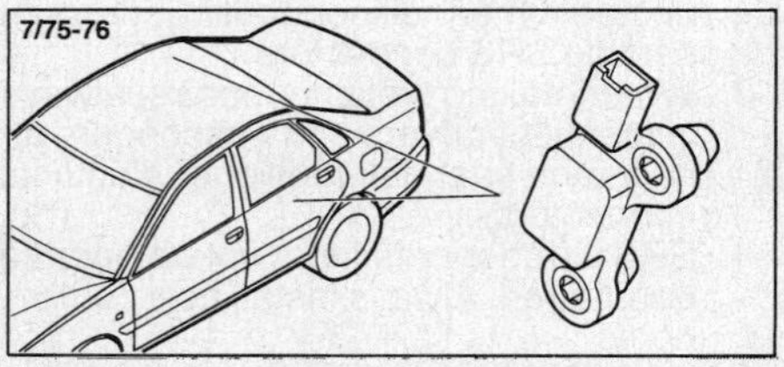

VV8010100328070X

Fig. 7 Rear side impact air bags' sensors. S40 & V40

cleaned with any type of cleaning agent.

16. Do not expose air bag modules or seat belt tensioners to high temperatures even for brief periods. Keep unit clear of all heat sources.
17. Always install safety device to sensor module when servicing side air bag system.

COMPONENT LOCATIONS

S40 & V40

Refer to **Figs. 1 through 15** for SRS component locations.

S60

Refer to **Figs. 16 through 30** for SRS component locations.

C70

Refer to **Fig. 31** for SRS component locations.

S80 & V70

Refer to **Fig. 32** for SRS component locations.

DIAGNOSIS & TESTING

Refer to **MOTOR's "Air Bag Manual"** for system diagnosis and testing.

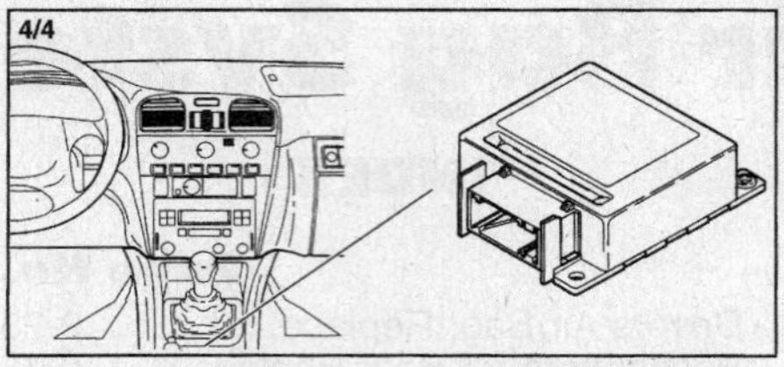

VV8010100328020X

Fig. 2 SRS control module. S40 & V40

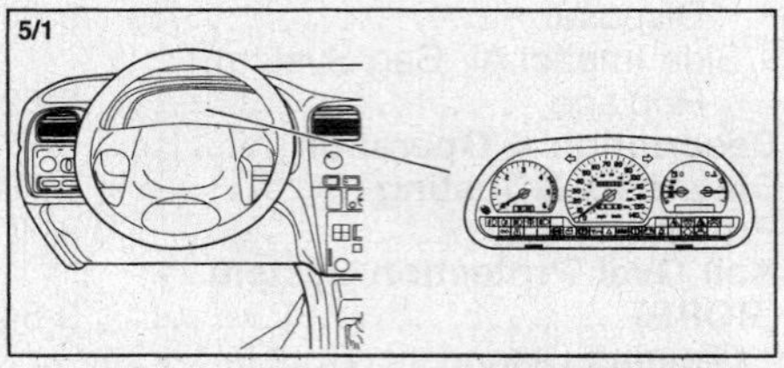

VV8010100328050X

Fig. 5 Combined instrument panel. S40 & V40

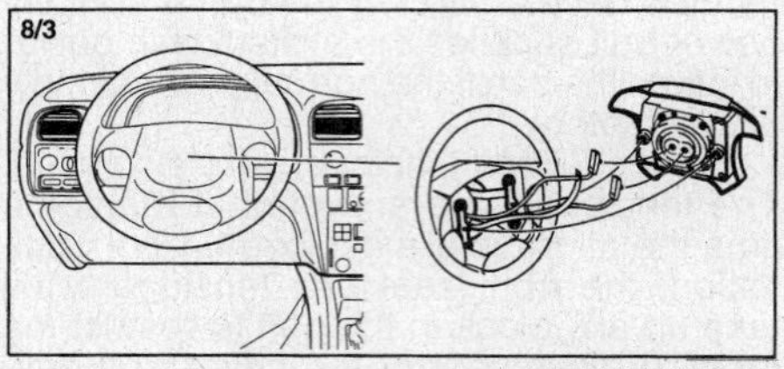

VV8010100328080X

Fig. 8 Driver's air bag module. S40 & V40

COLLISION INSPECTION

On vehicles that have experienced an air bag system deployment, certain SRS components must be replaced. To determine which SRS components require replacement, refer to the MOTORS "Air Bag Manual."

COMPONENT SERVICE

DRIVERS AIR BAG, REPLACE

C70

1. Disarm SRS as outlined under "Air Bag System Disarming & Arming."
2. Loosen Torx T30 screws from countersunk holes in rear of steering wheel. **Do not remove.**
3. Pull module from steering wheel and disconnect connector.
4. Connect test resistor No. 998 8695, or equivalent, to air bag connector.
5. Reverse procedure to install, noting the following:
   a. Tighten air bag module mounting screws specifications.
   b. Arm SRS as outlined under "Air Bag System Disarming & Arming."

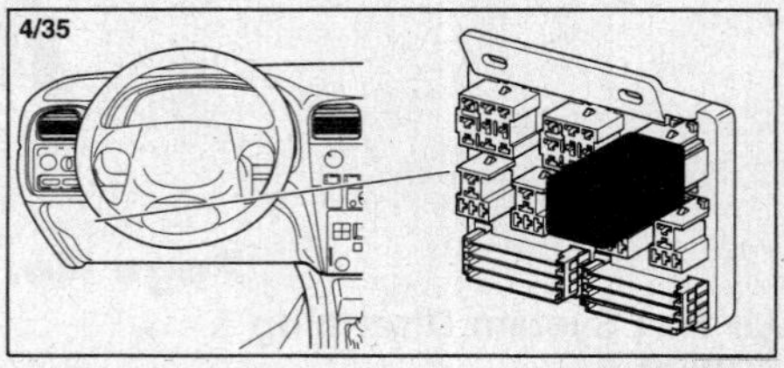

VV8010100328040X

Fig. 3 Control module key-inserted warning/seat belt reminder. S40 & V40

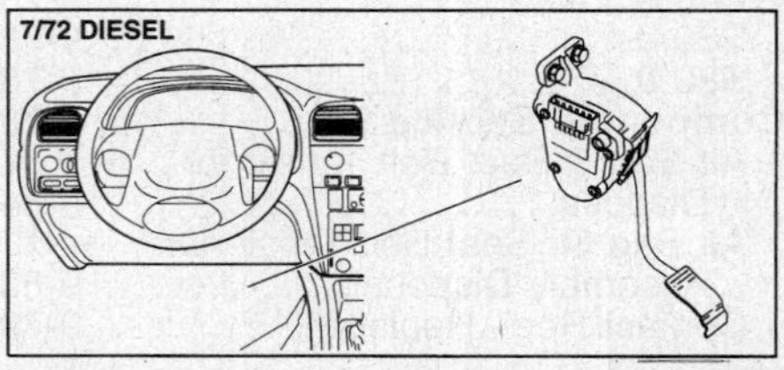

VV8010100328060X

Fig. 6 Front side impact air bags' sensors. S40 & V40

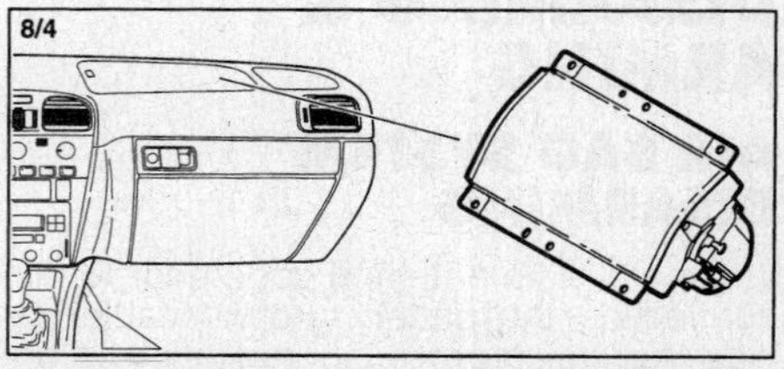

VV8010100328090X

Fig. 9 Passenger's air bag module. S40 & V40

S80

1. Disarm SRS as outlined under "Air Bag System Disarming & Arming."
2. Remove two air bag module mounting screws from rear of steering wheel.
3. Pull module from steering wheel and disconnect connector.
4. Reverse procedure to install. Arm SRS as outlined under "Air Bag System Disarming & Arming."

PASSENGERS AIR BAG, REPLACE

C70

1. Disarm SRS as outlined under "Air Bag System Disarming & Arming."
2. Open glove compartment door.
3. Remove six Torx T20 mounting screws and glove compartment.
4. Remove CD-ROM scanner flap, as required.
5. Disconnect passengers air bag module electrical connector.
6. Remove three passengers air bag module mounting screws.
7. Remove ventilation and radio speaker grilles.
8. Remove 11 mounting screws and instrument panel pad.

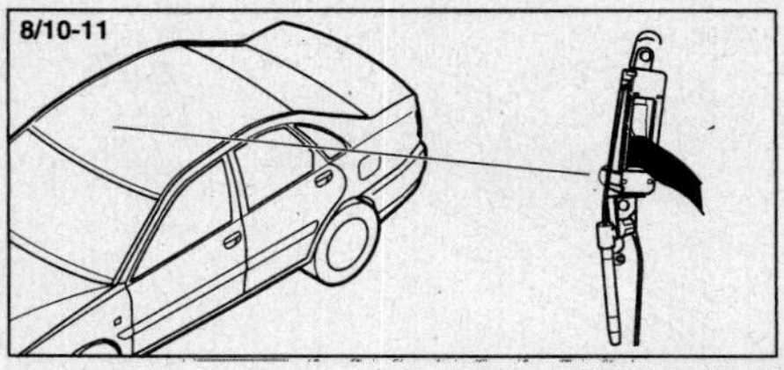

VV8010100330010X

Fig. 10 Seat belt tensioners. S40 & V40

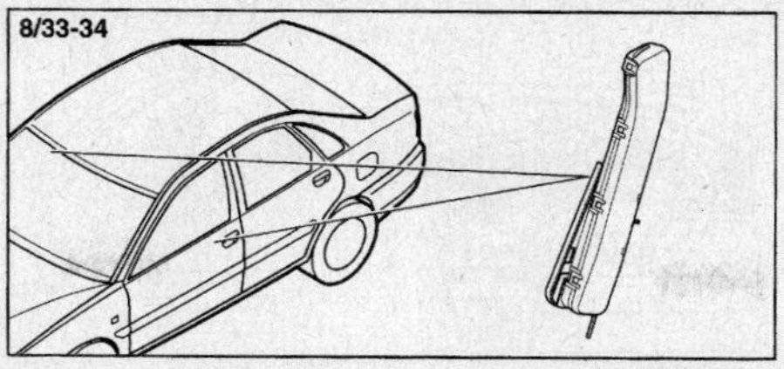

VV8010100330020X

Fig. 11 Front side impact air bag modules. S40 & V40

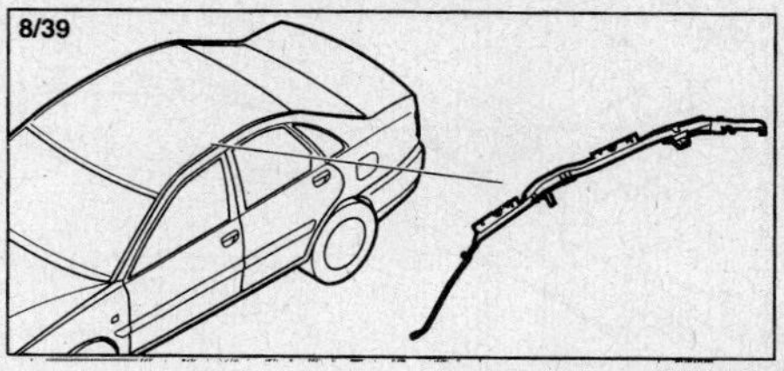

VV8010100330030X

Fig. 12 Lefthand roof panel air bag module. S40 & V40

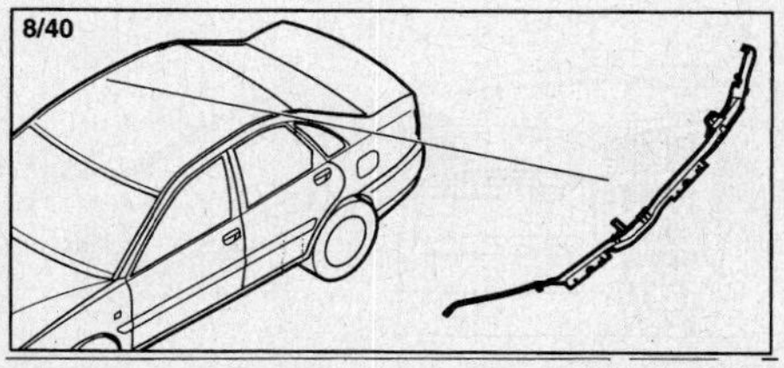

VV8010100330040X

Fig. 13 Righthand roof panel air bag module. S40 & V40

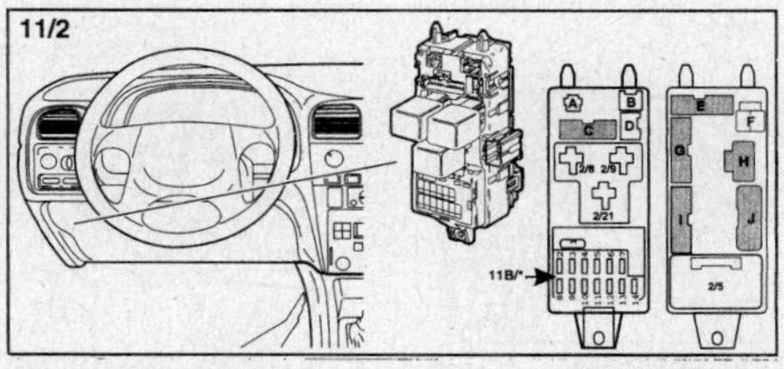

VV8010100330050X

Fig. 14 Passenger compartment fuse box. S40 & V40

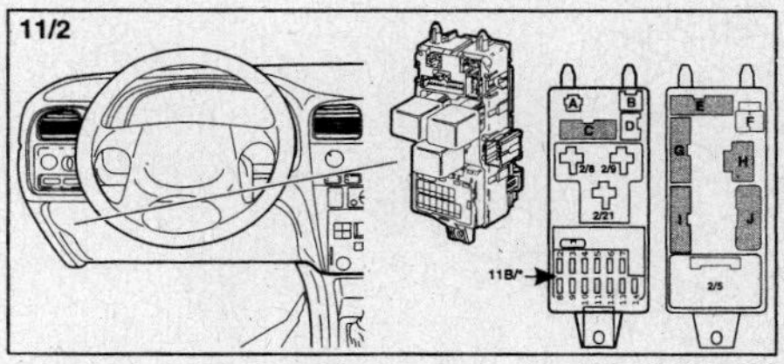

VV8010100330060X

Fig. 15 Distribution rail. S40 & V40

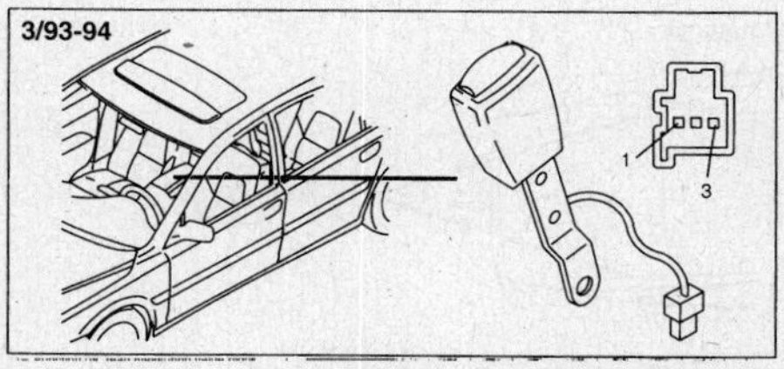

VV8010100332010X

Fig. 16 Seat belt lock switches. S60

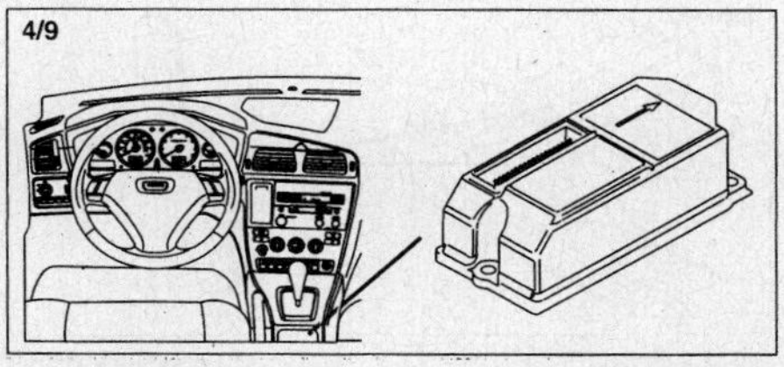

VV8010100332020X

Fig. 17 SRS control module. S60

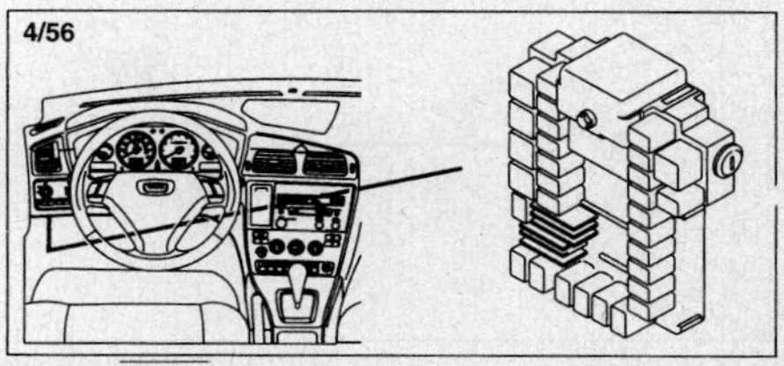

VV8010100332030X

Fig. 18 Central Electronic Module (CEM). S60

9. Remove six mounting nuts and passengers air bag module.
10. Reverse procedure to install, noting the following:
    a. Tighten mounting bolts and nuts to specifications.
    b. Arm SRS as outlined under "Air Bag System Disarming & Arming."

V70

1. Disarm SRS as outlined under "Air Bag System Disarming & Arming."
2. Open glove compartment door.
3. Remove four Torx T20 mounting screws and glove compartment.
4. Disconnect passengers air bag electrical connector.
5. Remove three passengers air bag module mounting screws.
6. Remove ventilation and radio speaker grilles.
7. Remove 11 mounting screws and instrument panel pad.
8. Remove six mounting nuts and passengers air bag module.
9. Reverse procedure to install, noting the following:
    a. Tighten mounting bolts and nuts to specifications.
    b. Arm SRS as outlined under "Air Bag System Disarming & Arming."

S80

1. Disarm SRS as outlined under "Air Bag System Disarming & Arming."
2. Remove A-pillar trim panel.
3. Remove instrument panel as outlined in "Dash Panel Service."
4. Disconnect two connectors from passengers air bag.
5. Remove two mounting screws and air duct.
6. Remove six mounting nuts and air bag module, **Fig. 33.**
7. Reverse procedure to install, noting the following:
    a. Tighten mounting bolts and nuts to specifications.
    b. Arm SRS as outlined under "Air Bag System Disarming & Arming."

CONTACT REEL, REPLACE

Except S80

1. Position front wheels in straight-ahead position.
2. Disarm SRS as outlined under "Air Bag System Disarming & Arming."
3. Remove drivers air bag as outlined under "Driver's Air Bag, Replace."
4. Place alignment marks on steering shaft and steering wheel hub for installation alignment.
5. Remove steering wheel center bolt.
6. Remove screw attached to plastic strip from hole in steering wheel. **Do not remove screw from plastic strip.**
7. Insert screw into hole on contact reel to lock contact reel in position. **Do not turn steering wheel with screw inserted in contact reel hole.**
8. Remove steering column upper and lower covers.
9. Disconnect contact reel connector and horn wire.
10. Remove mounting screws and contact reel.
11. Reverse procedure to install, noting the following:
    a. If contact reel was not locked in position prior to removal it must be centered. Prior to installation, rotate contact reel fully to left, then two full turns to right. Continue turning ¾ turn to screw hole, which should now be at one O'clock position. Install lock screw to hold in position, **Fig. 34.**
    b. When installing steering wheel, align hub and shaft marks made during removal.
    c. Tighten steering wheel center bolt hand tight, then remove centering screw from contact reel and install into parking hole on steering wheel.
    d. **Do not fully tighten center bolt**

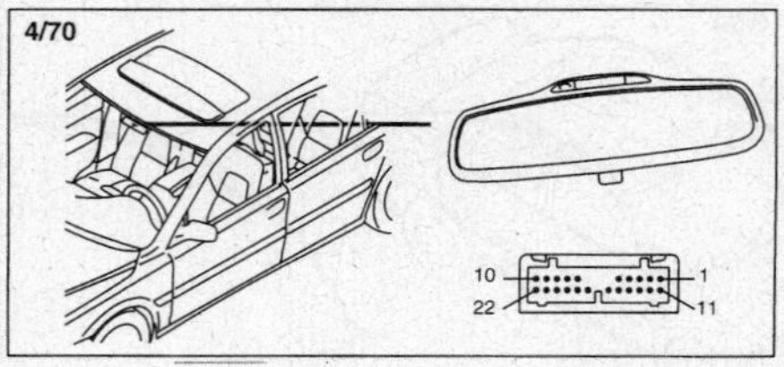

VV8010100332040X

Fig. 19 Upper Electronic Module (UEM). S60

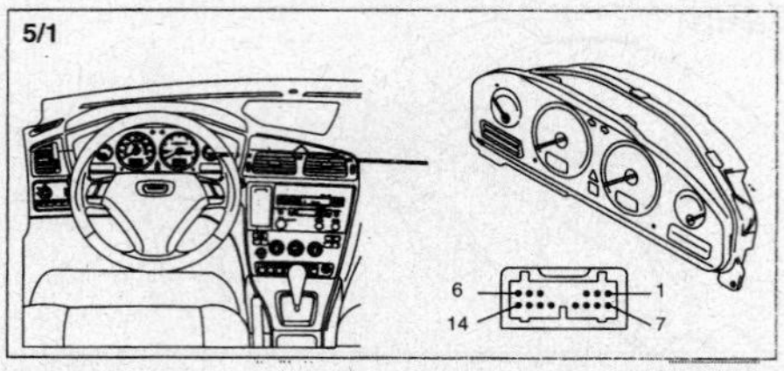

VV8010100332050X

Fig. 20 Combined instrument panel. S60

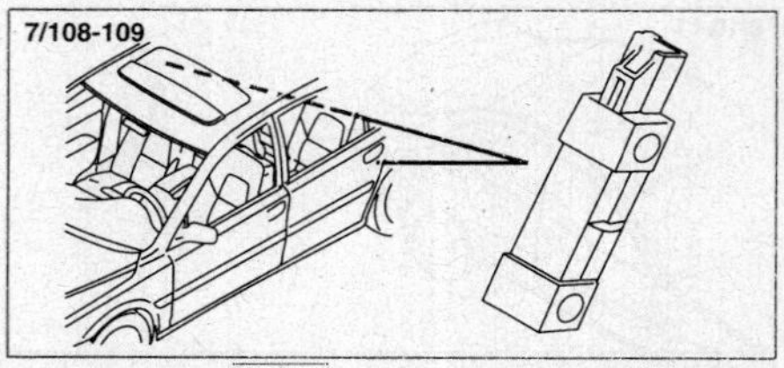

VV8010100332060X

Fig. 21 Rear side impact sensors. S60

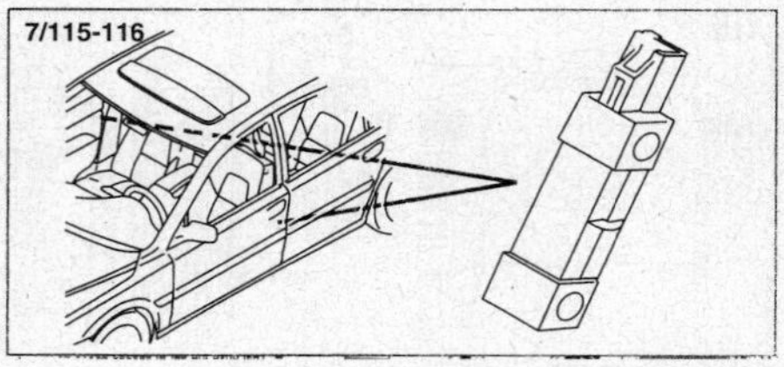

VV8010100332070X

Fig. 22 Front side impact sensors. S60

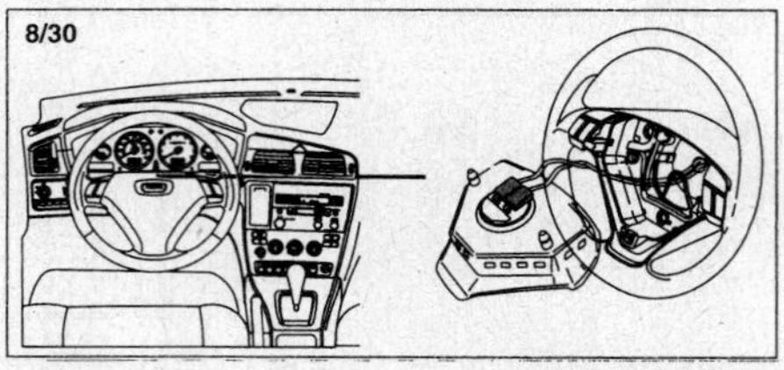

VV8010100332080X

Fig. 23 Driver's air bag module. S60

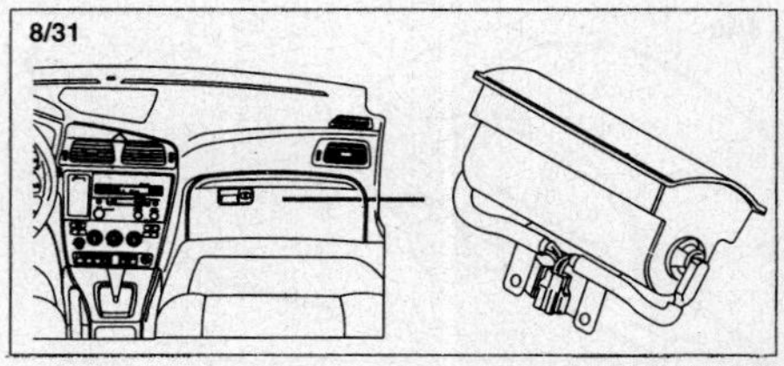

VV8010100332090X

Fig. 24 Passenger's air bag module. S60

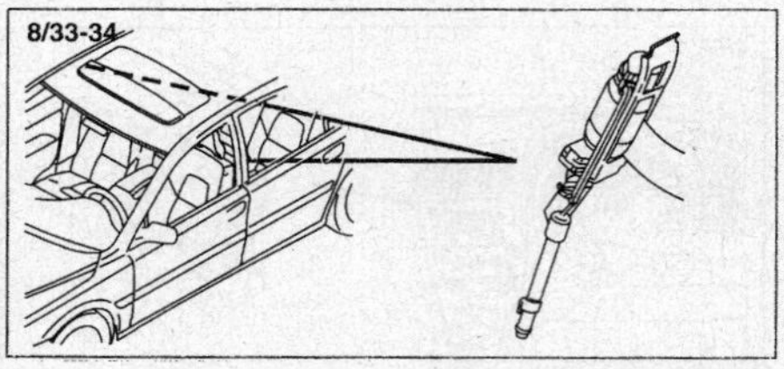

VV8010100333010X

Fig. 25 Front seat belt tensioners. S60

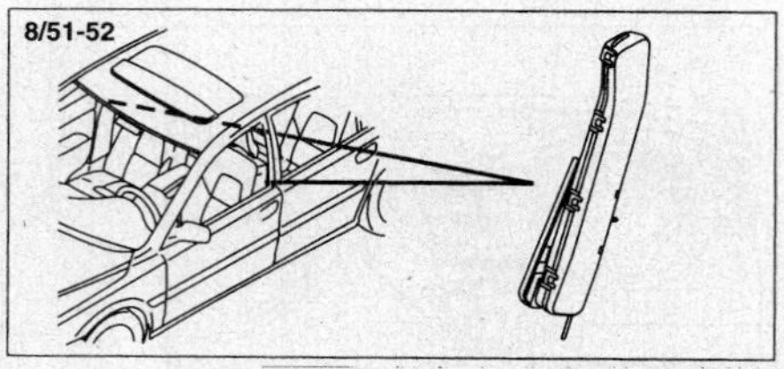

VV8010100333020X

Fig. 26 Front side impact air bag modules. S60

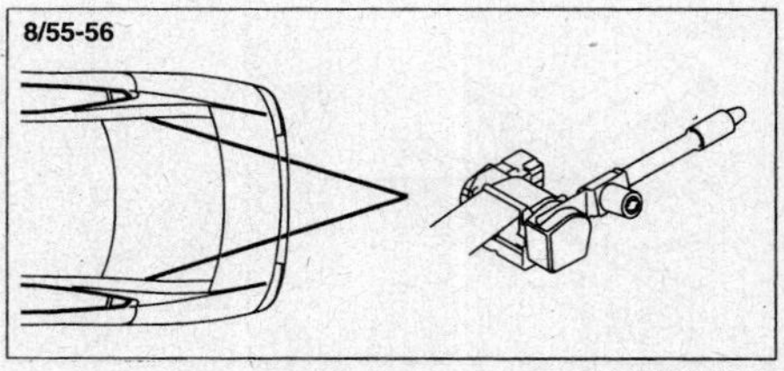

VV8010100333030X

Fig. 27 Rear outside seat belt tensioners. S60

until after steering wheel has been centered.

e. If steering wheel is not centered, remove and install it, again.
f. Tighten contact reel mounting screws and steering wheel nut to specifications.
g. Arm SRS as outlined under "Air Bag System Disarming & Arming."

SENSOR MODULE, REPLACE

C70

1. Disarm SRS as outlined under "Air Bag System Disarming & Arming."
2. Remove rear seat cushion.
3. Remove two screws at rear edge of center console.
4. Remove coin compartment from console.
5. Remove two rear power window switches and disconnect electrical connectors.
6. Remove parking brake panel.
7. Remove cover from console storage compartment.
8. Remove storage compartment with two switches for electrically heated seats from console.
9. Remove two screws below cover in console storage compartment.
10. Disconnect three electrical connectors, then lift console upward at rear edge and pull rearward.
11. Remove control module cover.
12. Remove control module Torx T30 bolts.
13. Push in on control module electrical connector button and move connector lock forward. Disconnect control module electrical connector.
14. Reverse procedure to install, noting the following:
    a. Connect sensor module electrical connector before installing sensor module to mounting bracket.
    b. Connect sensor module electrical connector. Slide sensor module electrical connector clip back until it locks behind button.
    c. Mount module into place with arrow facing front of vehicle.
    d. Tighten mounting screws to specifications.
    e. Arm SRS as outlined under "Air Bag System Disarming & Arming."

V70

1. Disarm SRS as outlined under "Air Bag System Disarming & Arming."
2. Remove cigarette lighter and DLC cover from front center console.
3. Remove two Torx T20 mounting screws from cigarette lighter compartment, then lift cigarette lighter compartment from center console.
4. Disconnect electrical connectors from cigarette lighter compartment. Move DLC to one side and press through cigarette lighter compartment opening.
5. Disconnect electrical connectors at front of center console.
6. Apply hand brake and position gear shift lever in Neutral position.
7. Remove two Torx T15 mounting screws from front of center console.
8. Remove hand brake opening cover from center console.
9. Open center console compartment lid, then remove cover and two Torx T20 mounting screws.
10. Lift center console, while moving slightly rearward. Manual transmission gear shift lever cover must be free of center console before console can be removed.
11. Remove three Torx T30 mounting screws and sensor module.
12. Disconnect sensor module electrical connector by pressing in on electrical connector latch and moving clip forward. **Never touch sensor module pins.**
13. Reverse procedure to install, noting the following:
    a. Connect sensor module electrical connector before installing sensor module to mounting bracket.
    b. Connect sensor module electrical connector. Slide sensor module

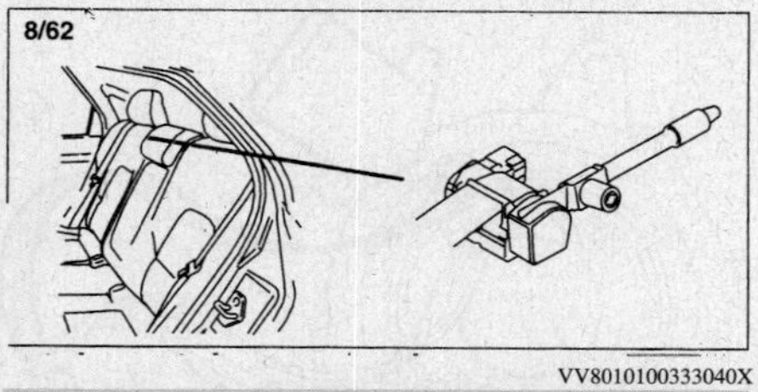

Fig. 28 Rear center seat belt tensioner igniter. S60

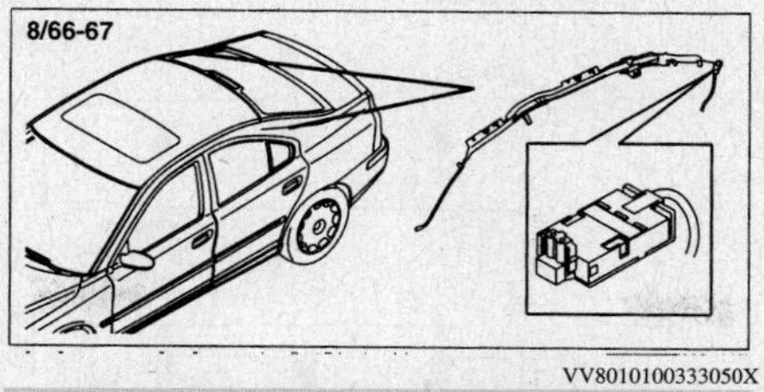

Fig. 29 Roof panel air bag modules. S60

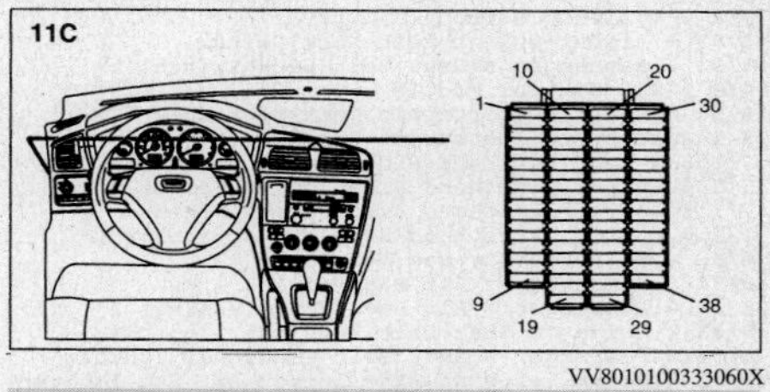

Fig. 30 Passenger compartment fuse box. S60

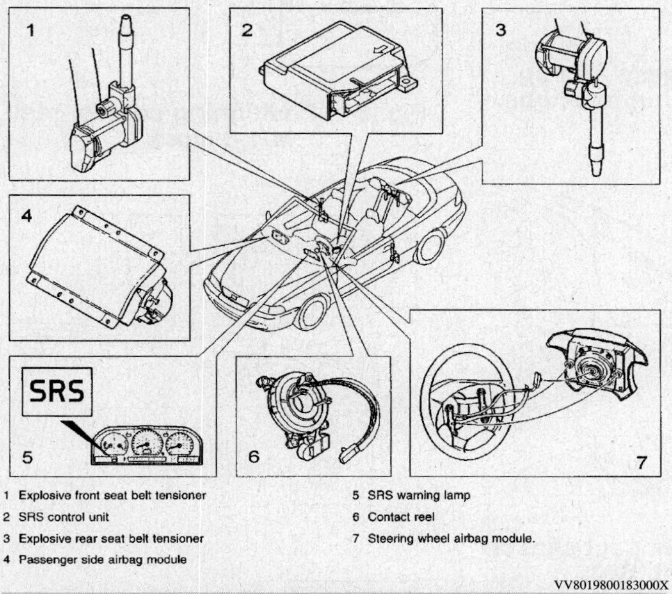

Fig. 31 SRS components. C70

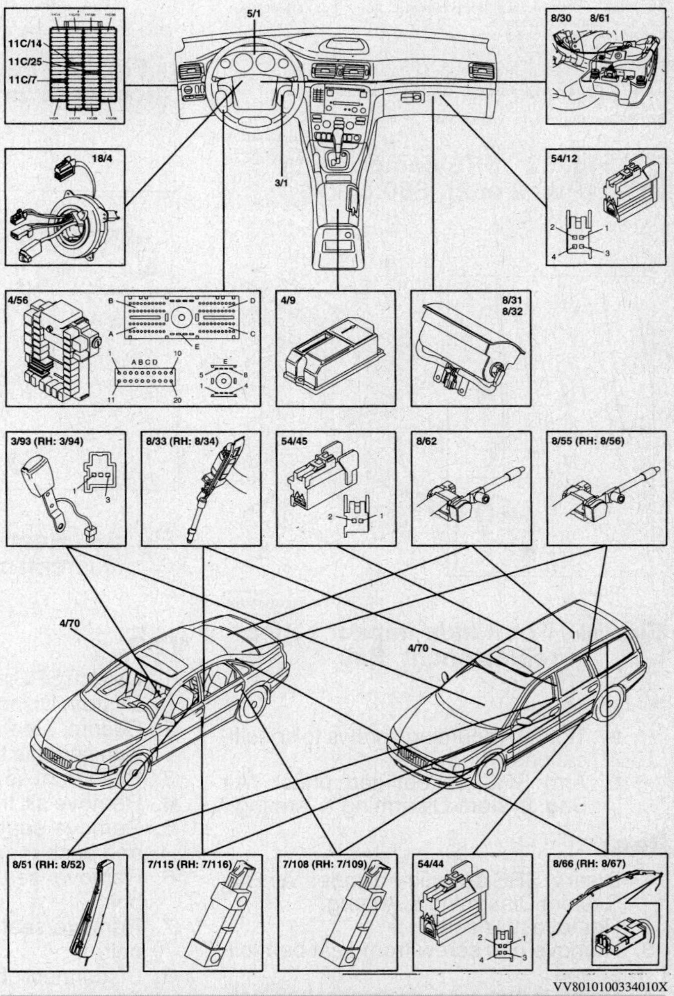

Fig. 32 SRS components (Part 1 of 2). S80 & V70

electrical connector clip back until it engages latch.

c. Ensure arrow on sensor module faces toward front of vehicle.
d. Tighten mounting screws to specifications.
e. Arm SRS as outlined under "Air Bag System Disarming & Arming."

S80

1. Disarm SRS as outlined under "Air Bag System Disarming & Arming."
2. Remove front storage compartment from center console.
3. Disconnect SRS control module electrical connector.
4. Remove three Torx T25 mounting screws and SRS control module.
5. Reverse procedure to install, noting the following:
   a. Mount module into place with arrow facing front of vehicle.
   b. Tighten mounting screws to specifications.
   c. Ensure electrical connector is properly connected.
   d. Arm SRS as outlined under "Air Bag System Disarming & Arming."

SEAT BELT TENSIONERS, REPLACE

C70

Front

1. Disarm SRS as outlined under "Air Bag System Disarming & Arming."
2. Remove panel in front of screw.
3. Remove screw from side rail.
4. Remove seat belt from side rail.
5. Remove rear side panel.
6. Remove two screws attaching spacer and guide.
7. Disconnect seat belt tensioner electrical connector.
8. Loosen screw at bottom edge of seat belt roller and remove tensioner through opening in B-pillar.
9. Reverse procedure to install, noting the following:

3/1 = Ignition Switch
3/93 = Driver's Seat Belt Lock Switch
3/94 = Passenger's Seat Belt Lock Switch
4/9 = SRS Control Module
4/56 = Central Electronic Control Module (CEM)
5/1 = Combined Instrument Panel
7/108 = Rear Lefthand Side Impact Sensor
7/109 = Rear Righthand Side Impact Sensor
7/115 = Front Lefthand Side Impact Sensor
7/116 = Front Righthand Side Impact Sensor
8/30 = Driver's Air Bag Module
8/31 = Passenger's Air Bag Module:
8/32 = Passenger's Air Bag Igniter, Stage 2
8/33 = Driver's Seat Belt Tensioner Igniter
8/34 = Passenger's Seat Belt Tensioner Igniter
8/51 = Front Lefthand Side Impact Air Bag Igniter
8/52 = Front Righthand Side Impact Air Bag Igniter
8/55 = Rear Lefthand Seat Belt Tensioner Igniter
8/56 = Rear Righthand Seat Belt Tensioner Igniter
8/61 = Driver's Air Bag Module Igniter, Stage 2
8/62 = Rear Center Seat Belt Tensioner
8/66 = Lefthand Roof Panel Air Bag Igniter
8/67 = Righthand Roof Panel Air Bag Igniter
11C/No. = Passenger Compartment Fuse Box/Fuse No.
18/4 = Contact Reel
54/No. = Connector No.

4/70 = Upper Electronic Control Module (UEM)
31/No. = Ground No.
53/No. = Junction Point No.

VV8010100334020X

Fig. 32 SRS components (Part 2 of 2). S80 & V70

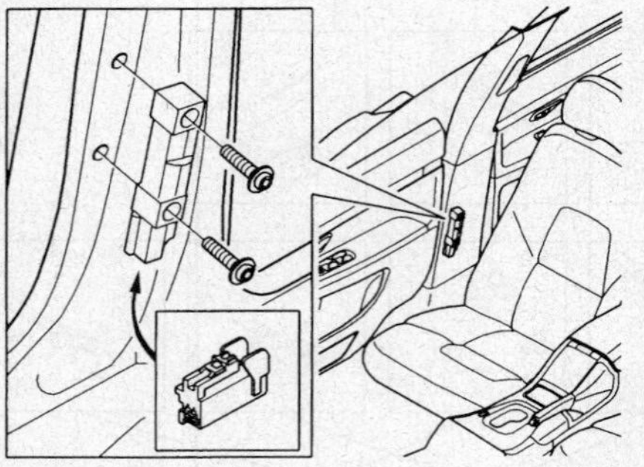

VV8010000193000X

Fig. 35 Front side impact sensor replacement. S80

a. Tighten mounting screws to specifications.
b. Arm SRS as outlined under "Air Bag System Disarming & Arming."

Rear

1. Disarm SRS as outlined under "Air Bag System Disarming & Arming."
2. Remove rear seat.
3. Remove one screw from seat belt roller end.
4. Remove one screw from seat belt lock.
5. Remove rear shelf.
6. Remove two screws from front edge of guide strip, then two mounting screws and guide strip.
7. Disconnect seat belt tensioner electrical connector.
8. Remove mounting screw and seat belt tensioner.
9. Reverse procedure to install, noting the following:
   a. Tighten mounting screws to specifications.
   b. Arm SRS as outlined under "Air Bag System Disarming & Arming."

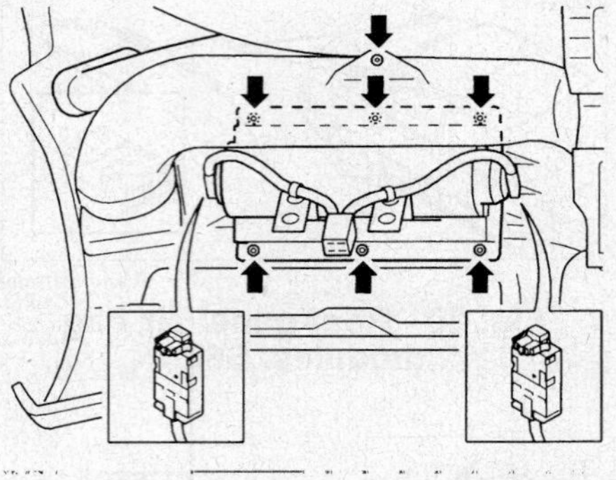

VV8010000192000X

Fig. 33 Passenger's air bag module mounting nut locations. S80

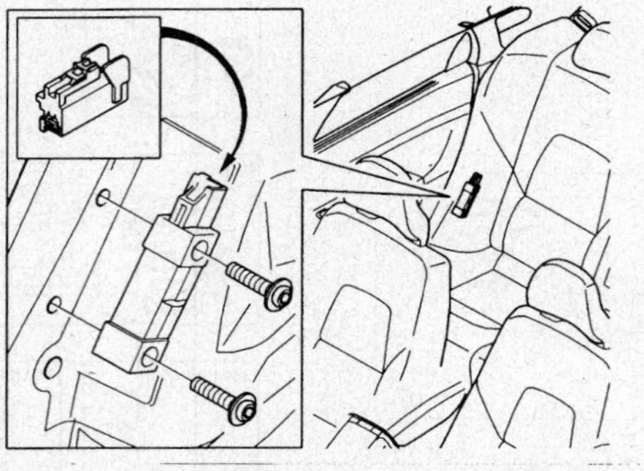

VV8010000194000X

Fig. 36 Rear side impact sensor replacement. S80

V70

1. Disarm SRS as outlined under "Air Bag System Disarming & Arming."
2. Secure side impact air bag module with suitable transport safety device.
3. Push front seat forward.
4. Remove sill trim panel.
5. Remove seat side pocket, lift at front and push rearward.
6. Remove seat belt to seat mounting bolt.
7. Remove seat belt to B-pillar mounting bolt.
8. Disconnect belt tensioner electrical connector.
9. Remove seat belt reel to B-pillar mounting bolts.
10. Remove plunger tube mounting screw.
11. Thread seat belt through slot in B-pillar panel.
12. Reverse procedure to install, noting the following:
    a. Tighten mounting screws to specifications.
    b. Remove safety device from sensor unit.
    c. Arm SRS as outlined under "Air Bag System Disarming & Arming."

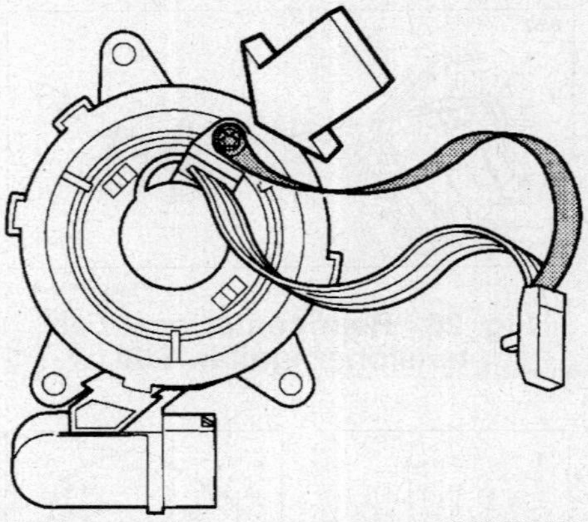

VV8019700152000X

Fig. 34 Positioning contact reel at 1 o'clock

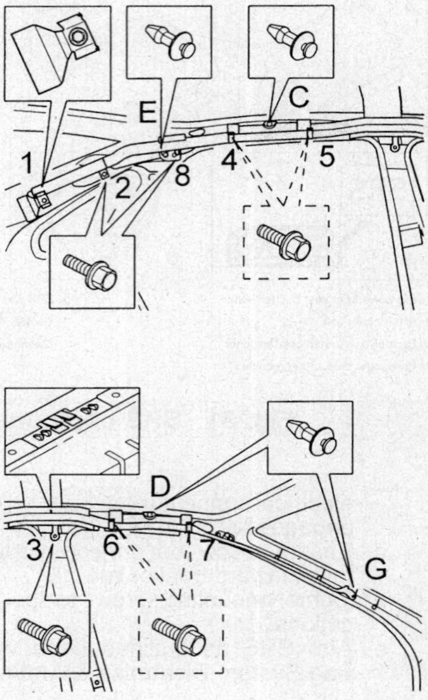

VV8010000195000X

Fig. 37 Roof panel air bag module retaining clip screw locations. S80

S80

Front

1. Disarm SRS as outlined under "Air Bag System Disarming & Arming."
2. Remove B-pillar trim panel.
3. Remove seat belt to B-pillar mounting bolt.
4. Disconnect belt tensioner electrical connector.

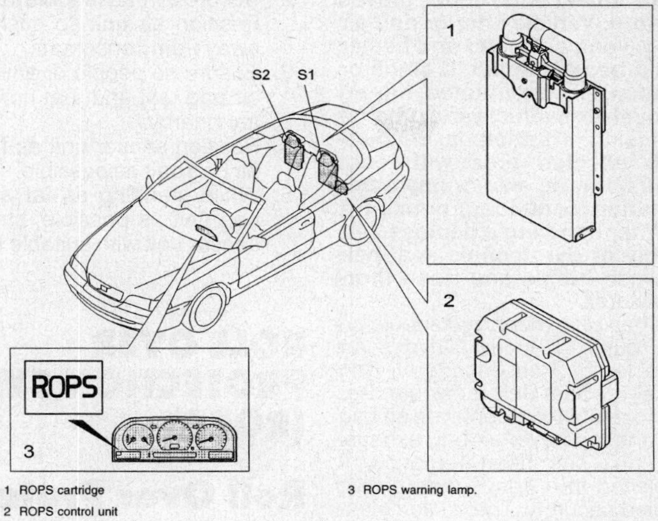

Fig. 38 Roll over protection system components. C70 convertible

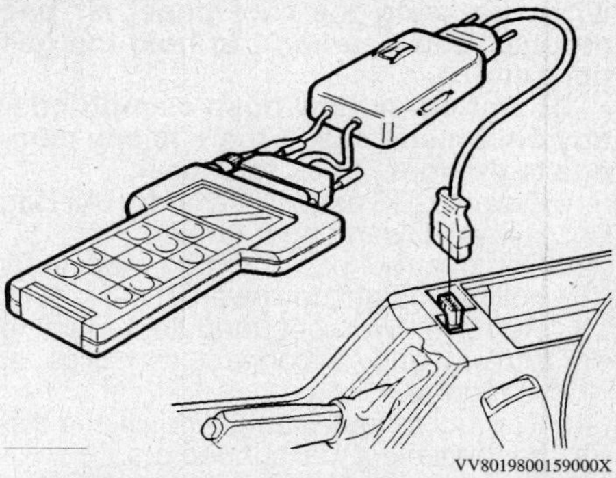

Fig. 39 DLC connector. C70 convertible

Diagnostic trouble code	Comments
ROP-412	Control unit, internal fault
ROP-413	Transport fuse
ROP-427	ROPS warning lamp, faulty signal
ROP-428	ROPS warning lamp, signal too high
ROP-429	Battery voltage, signal too low
ROP-430	Solenoid S1 and S2, faulty signal
ROP-431	Left solenoid S1, signal too low
ROP-432	Left solenoid S1, no signal
ROP-433	Left solenoid S1, signal too high
ROP-441	Right solenoid S2, signal too low
ROP-442	Right solenoid S2, no signal
ROP-443	Right solenoid S2, signal too high
ROP-451	Solenoid S1 and S2, trigger counter
ROP-452	Control unit, incorrect operation

VV8019800160000X

Fig. 40 Roll over protection system diagnostic trouble code interpretation. C70 convertible

5. Replace seat belt reel and tensioner by pulling straight up, leaving clip and fixture in position.
6. Reverse procedure to install, noting the following:
   a. Tighten mounting screws to specifications.
   b. Remove safety device from sensor unit.
   c. Arm SRS as outlined under "Air Bag System Disarming & Arming."

Rear

1. Disarm SRS as outlined under "Air Bag System Disarming & Arming."
2. Remove rear seat and rear shelf.
3. Disconnect seat belt tensioner electrical connector.
4. Remove one nut from seat belt roller end and one screw to end fitting.
5. Reverse procedure to install, noting the following:
   a. Tighten mounting screws to specifications.
   b. Arm SRS as outlined under "Air Bag System Disarming & Arming."

SIDE IMPACT AIR BAG SYSTEM, REPLACE

S80

Front

1. Disarm SRS as outlined under "Air Bag System Disarming & Arming."
2. Remove B-pillar trim panel.
3. Disconnect side impact sensor electrical connector.
4. Remove two mounting screws and side impact sensor, **Fig. 35.**
5. Reverse procedure to install, noting the following:
   a. Tighten mounting screws to specifications.
   b. Arm SRS as outlined under "Air Bag System Disarming & Arming."

Rear

1. Disarm SRS as outlined under "Air Bag System Disarming & Arming."
2. Remove rear seat side bolster.
3. Disconnect side impact sensor electrical connector.
4. Remove two mounting screws and side impact sensor, **Fig. 36.**
5. Reverse procedure to install, noting the following:
   a. Tighten mounting screws to specifications.
   b. Arm SRS as outlined under "Air Bag System Disarming & Arming."

AIR BAG OR SEAT BELT TENSIONER ASSEMBLY DISPOSAL

In the event an air bag assembly or seat belt tensioner must be disposed of, it is recommended that the unit be triggered without removing the system from the vehicle. **Adequate eye and ear protection should be worn at all times when conducting the following procedures.**

Air Bag Deployment

1. Place vehicle outdoors and open all windows and doors.
2. Ensure air bag assembly is firmly mounted to vehicle and there is no loose debris around unit.
3. Connect two 20 ft. long wires to twin terminal ignition connector of air bag module to be deployed.
4. Working from 20 ft. away, connect wires to terminals of a 12 volt power source to trigger the inflator. **Ensure no people, animals or objects are within 20 feet of vehicle when air bag deploys.**
5. If air bag or seat belt tensioner does do not deploy, disconnect wires from power source. Use extreme care when inspecting wiring.
6. In some cases the drivers air bag contact reel is damaged and it may be necessary to splice the wires going directly to air bag assembly. However, unit must remain securely mounted in steering wheel while being deployed.

Seat Belt Tensioner Deployment

1. Place vehicle outdoors and open all windows and doors.
2. Disconnect belt tensioner connector.
3. Ensure seat belt tensioner is firmly mounted to vehicle.
4. Connect two 20 ft. long wires to twin terminal ignition connector of seat belt tensioner to be deployed.
5. Working from 20 ft. away, connect wires to terminals of a 12 volt power source to trigger the inflator. **Ensure no people, animals or objects are within 20 feet of vehicle when unit deploys.**
6. If unit does not deploy, disconnect wires from power source. Use extreme care to inspect wiring and repeat procedure.

ROOF PANEL AIR BAG

S80

Do not fold, bend or twist the roof panel air bag module. Use both hands

when handling the roof panel air bag module. Use one hand to hold the gas generator.

Do not open thew hose clamp under any circumstances. If there is any damage to the roof panel, replace it.

1. Disarm SRS as outlined under "Air Bag System Disarming & Arming."
2. Remove roof panel air bag module by pulling straight downwards.
3. Remove two roof module mounting screws and disconnect two clips at rear edge.
4. Pull roof module straight down and disconnect electrical connectors.
5. Remove rear view mirror panel.
6. Remove sunlid snap fastener.
7. Remove A- and B-pillar trim panels.
8. Remove roof grab handle.
9. Remove C- and D-pillar trim panels.
10. Disconnect sun roof electrical connector.
11. Remove interior sun roof moulding. Turn three moulding retaining clips ¼ turn to release.
12. Fold seat backrest toward rear seat cushion.
13. Place transmission gear selector in rear most position.
14. Remove headliner through front passenger door opening.
15. Disconnect roof panel air bag module igniter electrical connector.
16. Remove mounting screws, retaining clips and roof panel air bag module, **Fig. 37.** Screws Nos. 4, 5, 6 and 7 are removed with grab handles.
17. Reverse procedure to install, noting the following:
    a. Position roof panel air bag module to roof, then install clips C and D.
    b. Install screw No. 1, screws Nos. 2 and 8, then the hook and screw No. 3.
    c. Ensure hook is properly installed.
    d. Screws Nos. 4, 5, 6 and 7 are installed with grab handles.
    e. Tighten mounting screws to specifications.
    f. Arm SRS as outlined under "Air Bag System Disarming & Arming."

AIR BAG & SEAT BELT TENSIONER DISPOSAL

When handling a deployed air bag assembly or pyrotechnical seat belt tensioner, a face shield and rubber gloves should be worn. Vehicle interior and air conditioning, vent, defroster and heater ducts should be vacuumed. If sinus or throat irritation is encountered during air bag removal, exit vehicle and breathe fresh air. If skin irritation is encountered, flush effected area with cool water. If sinus, throat, skin or any other type of irritation continues, consult a physician. After handling a deployed air bag assembly or pyrotechnic seat belt tensioner, wash hands and rinse thoroughly with water.

A unit that has been deployed should be removed as outlined under "Driver's Air Bag Unit, Replace," "Passenger's Air Bag Unit, Replace" or "Seat Belt Tensioner, Replace." Prior to removing a deployed air bag assembly, place tape over air bag exhaust vents. After unit has been removed, it should be placed in a heavy duty plastic bag and sealed securely. The sealed plastic bag should then be placed with automotive scrap. To dispose of a unit that has not been deployed, consult Volvo.

SIDE IMPACT AIR BAG SYSTEM DISPOSAL

Adequate eye and ear protection should be worn at all times when performing the following procedures.

With Side Impact Air Bag System Installed On Vehicle

The following procedure should be performed if vehicle is to be scrapped.

1. Turn ignition Off.
2. Lift front edge of seat pocket and push pocket rearward.
3. Remove safety device from holder inside pocket and attach it to sensor unit.
4. Remove sensor unit from seat.
5. Free firing cables from ties and clips.
6. Close front doors and windows.
7. Position sensor unit on floor behind front seat.
8. Remove safety device from sensor unit.
9. Ensure no people, animals or objects are inside or around vehicle.
10. While standing outside vehicle, strike middle of sensor unit with suitable hammer.

With Side Impact Air Bag System Removed

1. Ensure safety device is attached to sensor unit.
2. Secure air bag module in suitable vise. Position air unit so cushion is facing away from sensor unit.
3. Ensure no people or animals are near air bag unit and that no loose objects are nearby.
4. Position sensor unit as far away from air bag unit as possible.
5. While standing as far away from air bag unit as possible, strike middle of sensor unit with suitable hammer.

ROLL OVER PROTECTION SYSTEM (ROPS)

Roll Over Protection System Arming & Disarming

To avoid accidental activation of the roll bars, a transportation fuse can be activated by using a suitable scan tool to access and activate the transport fuse.

Component Locations

Refer to **Fig. 38,** for roll over protection system (ROPS) component locations.

Diagnosis & Testing

ACCESSING DIAGNOSTIC TROUBLE CODES

With ignition switch in Off position, connect a suitable scan tool to the data link connector (DLC) located under the center console cover, **Fig. 39.**

DIAGNOSTIC TROUBLE CODE INTERPRETATION

Refer to **Fig. 40,** for diagnostic trouble code interpretation.

DIAGNOSTIC TESTS

Refer to **Figs. 41 through 51,** for specific diagnosis and testing.

ROPS DIAGNOSTIC CHART INDEX

Code	Description	Page No.	Fig. No.
C70 CONVERTIBLE			
ROP 412	Control Unit, Internal Fault	9-85	41
ROP 413	Transport Fuse	9-85	42
ROP 427	ROPS Warning Lamp, Faulty Signal	9-85	43
ROP 428	ROPS Warning Lamp, Signal Too High	9-87	44
ROP 429	Battery Voltage, Signal Too Low	9-87	45
ROP 430	Solenoid S1 & S2, Faulty Signal	9-88	46
ROP 431	Left Hand Solenoid S1 & Right Hand Solenoid S2, Signal Too Low	9-89	47
ROP 432	Left Solenoid S1 & Right Solenoid S2, No Signal	9-90	48
ROP 433	Left hand Solenoid S1 & Right Hand Solenoid S2, Signal Too High	9-91	49
ROP 441	Left Hand Solenoid S1 & Right Hand Solenoid S2, Signal Too Low	9-89	47
ROP 442	Left Solenoid S1 & Right Solenoid S2, No Signal	9-90	48
ROP 443	Left hand Solenoid S1 & Right Hand Solenoid S2, Signal Too High	9-91	49
ROP 451	Solenoid S1 & S2 Trigger Counter	9-92	50
ROP 452	Control Unit, Incorrect Operation	9-92	51

AG A. Diagnostic trouble code information

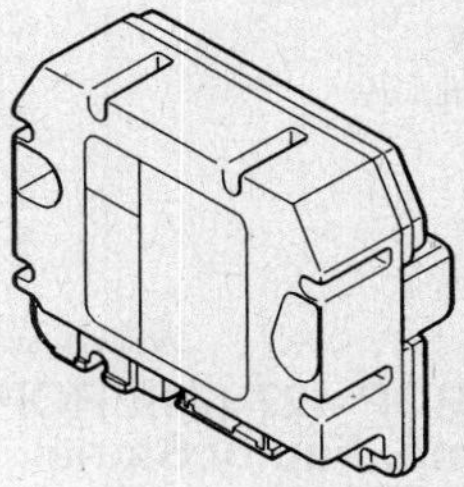

Condition

If self-diagnosis registers a fault in any of the control unit's internal functions, the diagnostic trouble code ROP-412 is displayed.

Possible source

– Internal fault in control unit.

Fault symptom(s)

– ROPS warning lamp on.

Warning! There is a risk that ROPS is not working if this diagnostic trouble code is stored.

Note! The diagnostic trouble code ROP-412 must not be erased if it occurs within the guarantee. Return the control unit to Volvo as applicable.

Note! If diagnostic trouble code ROP-412 is displayed it is not possible to erase the other diagnostic trouble codes.

VV8019800161010X

Fig. 41 Code ROP 412 (AG): Control Unit, Internal Fault (Part 1 of 2). C70 convertible

AG B. Internal fault

AG B1

Replacing the component

– Replace control units that have internal faults; test by replacing the control unit.

Then continue with:

- **AG B2**

AG B2

Verification

– Ignition off.
– Connect the connectors, install the components, etc.
– Ignition on.
– Keep ignition on for **at least** 10 seconds.
Read the diagnostic trouble codes.

Does diagnostic trouble code return?

Yes:

- Fault not found

No:

- Fault corrected

VV8019800161020X

Fig. 41 Code ROP 412 (AG): Control Unit, Internal Fault (Part 2 of 2). C70 convertible

AH A. Diagnostic trouble code information

Condition

The diagnostic trouble code is displayed when the transport fuse is active. The transport fuse can be activated to prevent deployment of the roll bars when the car leans beyond the specified angle of deployment.

Possible source

– The transport fuse is active.

Fault symptom(s)

– ROPS warning lamp on.

VV8019800162010X

Fig. 42 Code ROP 413 (AH): Transport Fuse (Part 1 of 2). C70 convertible

AH B. Transport fuse

AH B1

Transport fuse

The transport fuse can be set to prevent deployment of the roll bars when the car leans beyond the specified angle of deployment. The transport fuse can be de-activated using the Volvo System Tester or equivalent.

De-activate the transport fuse.

Then continue with:

- **AH B2**

AH B2

Verification

Hint: After the repair it is necessary to check that the fault has been rectified.

– Ignition on.
Read the transport fuse condition.

Is the transport fuse de-activated?

Yes:

- Fault corrected

No:

- Fault not found

VV8019800162020X

Fig. 42 Code ROP 413 (AH): Transport Fuse (Part 2 of 2). C70 convertible

AI A. Diagnostic trouble code information

Condition

If the resistance is too high or the voltage too low in the circuit for more than 3 seconds, the diagnostic trouble code ROP-427 is displayed.

Possible source

– Open circuit or short circuit to ground in the wire or in the connector between the combination instrument and the control unit

– The ROPS warning lamp is faulty.

Fault symptom(s)

– ROPS warning lamp, does not light with ignition on (there is an open circuit)

– ROPS warning lamp on (there is a short circuit to ground).

VV8019800163010X

Fig. 43 Code ROP 427 (AI): ROPS Warning Lamp, Faulty Signal (Part 1 of 7). C70 convertible

AI B. Additional diagnostic trouble codes

AI B1

Additional diagnostic trouble codes

Select one of the following options to continue:

Alternative 1:
- *AI C. Faulty signal. Permanent fault*

Alternative 2:
- *AI D. Faulty signal. Intermittent fault*

VV8019800163020X

Fig. 43 Code ROP 427 (AI): ROPS Warning Lamp, Faulty Signal (Part 2 of 7). C70 convertible

AI C. Faulty signal. Permanent fault

AI C1

Function check

Check that the ROPS warning lamp comes on.

Is the lamp on?

Yes:
- **AI C2**

No:
- **AI C4**

AI C2

Checking connector and wire

- Ignition off.
- Disconnect control unit connectors.
- Do a visual check of the control unit contact pins without touching them.
  Check that the plastic strip in pins 24 and 25 is intact. The plastic strip prevents the ROPS warning lamp from short circuiting to ground when the control unit is connected.
  If the plastic strip is broken, replace the control unit.
- Disconnect the ground connection located next to the control unit.
- Ignition on.

If the ROPS warning lamp is not on there is a fault in the connector. Replace the connector.

Additional information:

Is the ROPS warning lamp on?

Yes:
- **AI C3**

No:
- **AI C7**

VV8019800163030X

Fig. 43 Code ROP 427 (AI): ROPS Warning Lamp, Faulty Signal (Part 3 of 7). C70 convertible

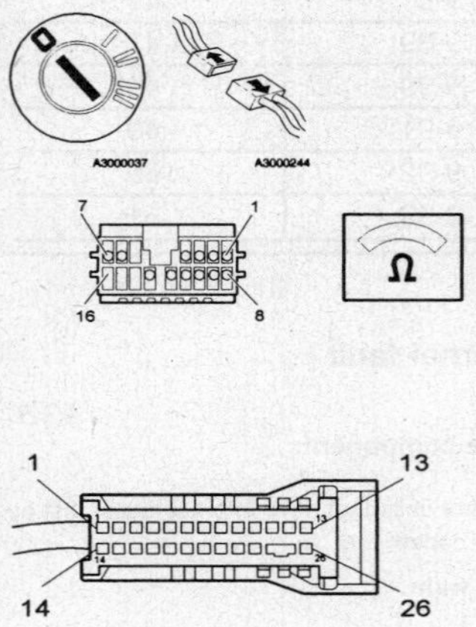

AI C3

Checking the combination instrument

- The fault is in the wires or in the combination instrument.
- Ignition off.
- Disconnect combination instrument connector B.

Check connector B for a short circuit to ground.

Connect an ohmmeter between control unit pin B12 and ground. Check for a short circuit to ground.

If there is a short circuit to ground, replace the wire or repair it, otherwise the fault is in the combination instrument.

Do the necessary corrective action.

Then continue with:
- **AI C7**

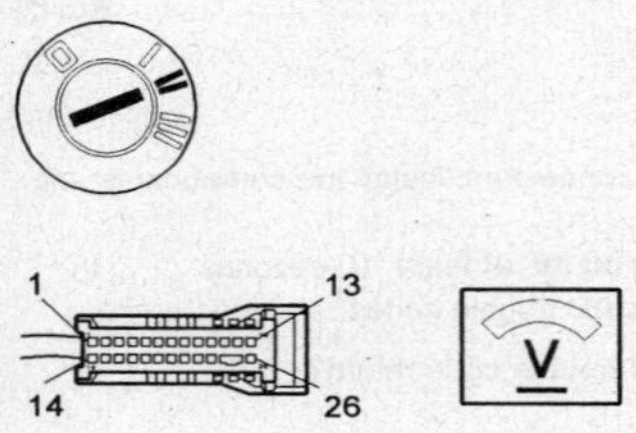

AI C4

Checking the components and wires

- Test with a new lamp.
- Check the connector on the control unit for contact resistance and oxidation.
- Disconnect the ground connection located next to the control unit.
- Ignition on.

Connect a voltmeter between control unit 12 and ground. The voltage should be just less than the battery voltage.

Is the voltage just less than the battery voltage?

Yes:
- **AI C5**

No:
- **AI C6**

VV8019800163040X

Fig. 43 Code ROP 427 (AI): ROPS Warning Lamp, Faulty Signal (Part 4 of 7). C70 convertible

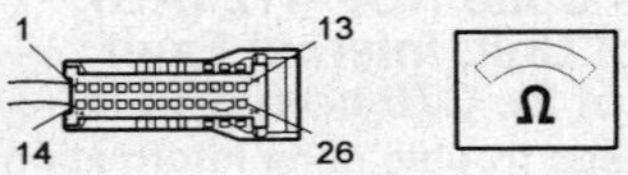

AI C5

Checking ground wire

The results of the check indicate that the wire is intact and that the fault is in the connector or in the ground wire.

Check the ground wire pin 6 on the connector for an open circuit.

Do the necessary corrective action.

Then continue with:
- **AI C7**

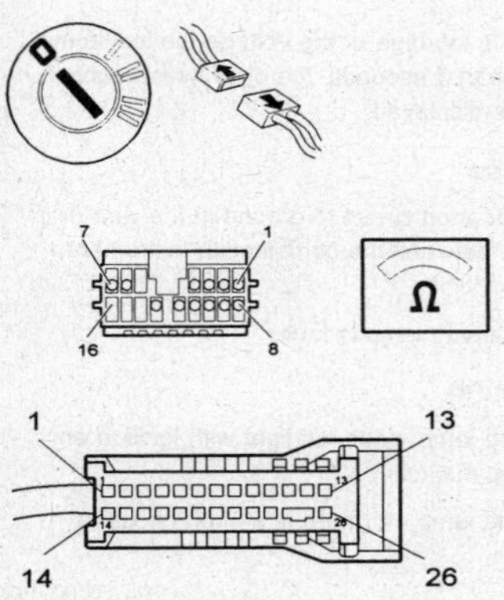

AI C6

Checking signal wire

- The fault is in the wires or in the combination instrument.
- Ignition off.
- Disconnect combination instrument connector B.

Check the wire between the combination instrument connector pin B15 and the control unit connector pin 12 for an open circuit.

If there is an open circuit the wire must be replaced or repaired. If no open circuit is found the fault is in the combination instrument.

Do the necessary corrective action.

Then continue with:
- **AI C7**

VV8019800163050X

Fig. 43 Code ROP 427 (AI): ROPS Warning Lamp, Faulty Signal (Part 5 of 7). C70 convertible

AI C7

Verification

Hint: After the repair it is necessary to check that the fault has been rectified.

- Ignition off.
- Connect the connectors, install the components, etc.
- Ignition on.
- Read the diagnostic trouble codes.

If the diagnostic trouble code status has changed to intermittent then the fault has disappeared.

Has the status changed?

Yes:
- Fault corrected

No:
- Fault not found

VV8019800163060X

Fig. 43 Code ROP 427 (AI): ROPS Warning Lamp, Faulty Signal (Part 6 of 7). C70 convertible

AI D. Faulty signal. Intermittent fault

AI D1

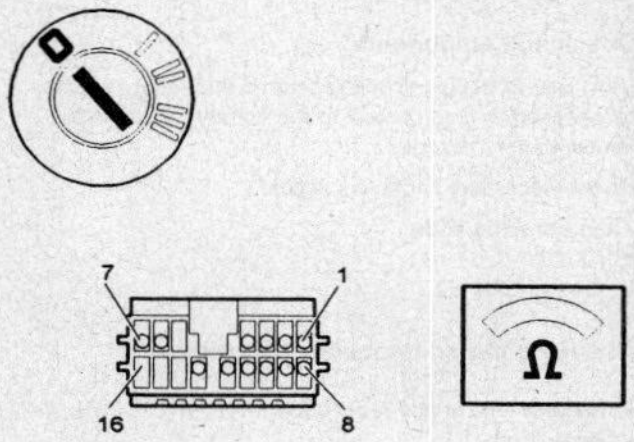

Checking the components and wires

– Ignition off.

Check the B connector on the combination instrument and the control unit connector for contact resistance and oxidation.

Connect an ohmmeter between the control unit pin 12 and the combination instrument pin B15 for an intermittent open circuit.

Connect an ohmmeter between the control unit pin 12 and ground for an intermittent short circuit to ground.

Do the necessary corrective action.

Then continue with:
- Operation done

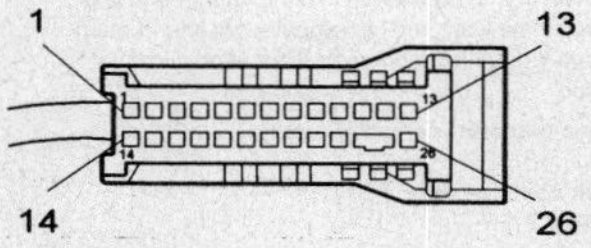

VV8019800163070X

Fig. 43 Code ROP 427 (AI): ROPS Warning Lamp, Faulty Signal (Part 7 of 7). C70 convertible

AJ B. Additional diagnostic trouble codes and status signals

AJ B1

Status signals

Select one of the following options to continue:

Alternative 1:
- *AJ C. Signal too high. Permanent fault*

Alternative 2:
- *AJ D. Signal too high. Intermittent fault*

VV8019800164020X

Fig. 44 Code ROP 428 (AJ): ROPS Warning Lamp, Signal Too High (Part 2 of 4). C70 convertible

AJ D. Signal too high. Intermittent fault

AJ D1

Checking wires

– Make a note of any radio code.
– Ignition off.
– Disconnect the battery negative lead.
– Disconnect control unit.
– Ignition on.

Connect an ohmmeter between control unit pin 12 and the control unit battery voltage 2, and between the control unit generator voltages pins 6 and 12 for an intermittent short circuit to voltage supply.

Do the necessary corrective action.

VV8019800164040X

Fig. 44 Code ROP 428 (AJ): ROPS Warning Lamp, Signal Too High (Part 4 of 4). C70 convertible

AJ A. Diagnostic trouble code information

Condition

If the voltage in the circuit is too high for more than 2 seconds, the diagnostic trouble code ROP-428 is displayed.

Possible source

– There is a short circuit to ground in the wire or in the connectors between the combination instrument and the control unit.

Fault symptom(s)

– ROPS warning lamp, does not light with ignition on.

VV8019800164010X

Fig. 44 Code ROP 428 (AJ): ROPS Warning Lamp, Signal Too High (Part 1 of 4). C70 convertible

AJ C. Signal too high. Permanent fault

AJ C1

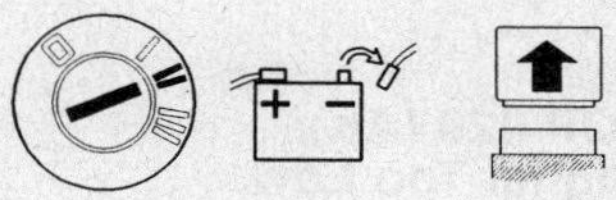

Checking the connector and wires

– Make a note of any radio code.
– Ignition off.
– Disconnect the battery negative lead.
– Disconnect the control unit and the B connector on the combination instrument.
– Ignition on.

Check the wire between the control unit pin 12 and the combination instrument pin B15 for a short circuit to voltage supply.

Do the necessary corrective action.

Then continue with:
- AJ C2

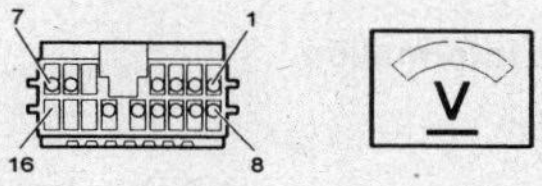

AJ C2

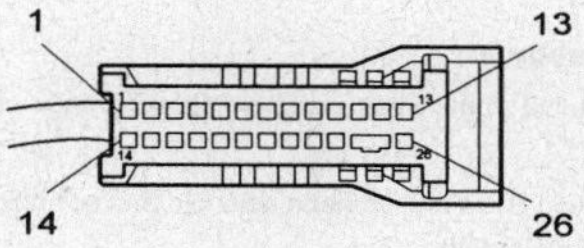

Verification

Hint: After the repair it is necessary to check that the fault has been rectified.

– Ignition off.
– Connect the connectors, install the components, etc.
– Ignition on.
– Read the diagnostic trouble codes.

If the diagnostic trouble code status has changed to intermittent then the fault has disappeared.

Has the status changed?

Yes:
- Fault corrected

No:
- Fault not found

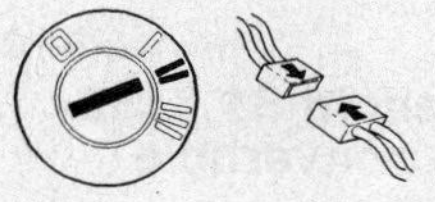

VV8019800164030X

Fig. 44 Code ROP 428 (AJ): ROPS Warning Lamp, Signal Too High (Part 3 of 4). C70 convertible

AK A. Diagnostic trouble code information

Condition

If the battery voltage is less than 9 V for more than 6 seconds (signal too low) after the ignition is switched on, the diagnostic trouble code ROP-429 is displayed.

Possible source

– The charging system is not charging adequately

– Low battery voltage

– There is contact resistance in the connectors.

Fault symptom(s)

– ROPS warning lamp on.

VV8019800165010X

Fig. 45 Code ROP 429 (AK): Battery Voltage, Signal Too Low (Part 1 of 5). C70 convertible

AK B. Additional diagnostic trouble codes and status signals

AK B1

Status signals

Select one of the following options to continue:

Alternative 1:
- *AK C. Signal too low. Permanent fault*

Alternative 2:
- *AK D. Signal too low. Intermittent fault*

VV8019800165020X

Fig. 45 Code ROP 429 (AK): Battery Voltage, Signal Too Low (Part 2 of 5). C70 convertible

AK C. Signal too low. Permanent fault

AK C1

Checking components

Hint: Before trouble-shooting begins, the battery should be checked for bad contact at the battery terminals or for low battery voltage.

Do the necessary corrective action.

Then continue with:
- **AK C2**

AK C2

Checking the components and wires

- Make a note of any radio code.
- Ignition off.
- Check control unit connector for contact resistance and oxidation, and for a short circuit to ground.

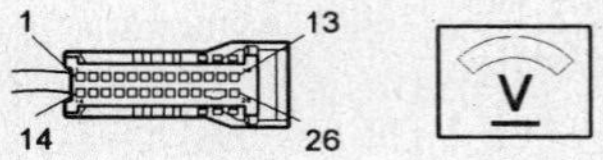

- Ignition on.

Connect a voltmeter between pin 2 and ground and measure the voltage. The voltmeter will show battery voltage if there is no open circuit or short circuit to ground.

Do the necessary corrective action.

Then continue with:
- **AK C3**

AK C3

Checking the alternator

- Start the engine.

Read the voltage.

When the engine is running the voltage should be approximately 13-15 V.

Stop the engine.

When the engine is stopped and the ignition is on, the voltage should be approximately 0.7 V.

If the value deviates from this the alternator must be repaired or replaced.

Do the necessary corrective action.

Then continue with:
- **AK C4**

VV8019800165030X

Fig. 45 Code ROP 429 (AK): Battery Voltage, Signal Too Low (Part 3 of 5). C70 convertible

AK C4

Verification

Hint: After the repair it is necessary to check that the fault has been rectified.

- Ignition off.
- Connect the connectors, install the components, etc.
- Ignition on.
- Read the diagnostic trouble codes.

If the diagnostic trouble code status has changed to intermittent then the fault has disappeared.

Has the status changed?

Yes:
- Fault corrected

No:
- Fault not found

VV8019800165040X

Fig. 45 Code ROP 429 (AK): Battery Voltage, Signal Too Low (Part 4 of 5). C70 convertible

AK D. Signal too low. Intermittent fault

AK D1

Checking components

Hint: Before trouble-shooting begins, the battery should be checked for bad contact at the battery terminals or for low battery voltage.

Do the necessary corrective action.

Then continue with:
- **AK D2**

AK D2

Checking the components and wires

Hint: If the equivalent diagnostic trouble code is displayed and repaired for other systems, e.g. SRS-129 , test by erasing the diagnostic trouble code without trouble-shooting.

- Make a note of any radio code.
- Ignition off.
- Disconnect the battery positive lead.
- Disconnect control unit connectors.
- Check control unit connector for contact resistance and oxidation, and for a short circuit to ground.

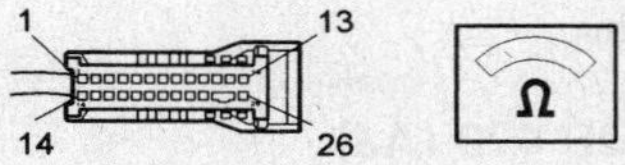

- Ignition on.

Connect a voltmeter between pin 2 and ground and measure the voltage. The voltmeter will show battery voltage if there is no intermittent open circuit or intermittent short circuit to ground.

Do the necessary corrective action.

Then continue with:
- Operation done

VV8019800165050X

Fig. 45 Code ROP 429 (AK): Battery Voltage, Signal Too Low (Part 5 of 5). C70 convertible

AL A. Diagnostic trouble code information

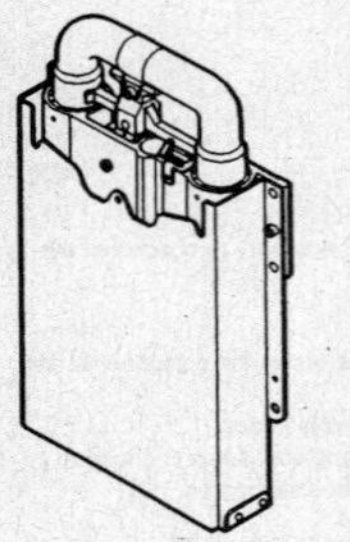

Condition

If the resistance in the circuit is too low for more than 5 seconds, diagnostic trouble code ROP-430 is displayed.

Possible source
- The solenoid signal wires are short circuiting each other.

Hint: Solenoid S1 is the left-hand solenoid and solenoid S2 the right-hand one.

Fault symptom(s)
- ROPS warning lamp on.

VV8019800166010X

Fig. 46 Code ROP 430 (AL): Solenoid S1 & S2, Faulty Signal (Part 1 of 5). C70 convertible

AL B. Additional diagnostic trouble codes and status signals

AL B1

Status signals

Select one of the following options to continue:

Alternative 1:
- *AL C. Faulty signal. Permanent fault*

Alternative 2:
- *AL D. Faulty signal. Intermittent fault*

VV8019800166020X

Fig. 46 Code ROP 430 (AL): Solenoid S1 & S2, Faulty Signal (Part 2 of 5). C70 convertible

AL C. Faulty signal. Permanent fault

AL C1

Checking wires

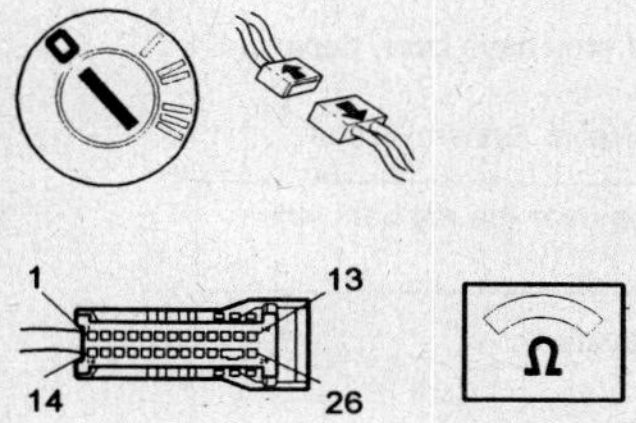

- Ignition off.
- Disconnect control unit connectors.
- Check the connector for a short circuit to voltage supply

Connect an ohmmeter between pins 5 and 21 and check for a short circuit.

The ohmmeter should display infinite resistance.

Does the value deviate from this?

Yes:
- AL C2

No:
- AL C3

AL C2

Replacing the component

Trouble-shooting indicates that there is a short circuit in the wiring between the solenoids. Test by replacing the wire harness.

Then continue with:
- AL C3

AL C3

Verification

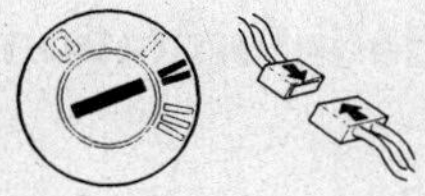

Hint: After the repair it is necessary to check that the fault has been rectified.

- Ignition off.
- Wait 10 seconds to make sure the system is free from voltage.
- Connect the connectors, install the components, etc.
- Ignition on.
- Read the diagnostic trouble codes.

If the status of the diagnostic trouble code has changed to an intermittent fault this indicates that the fault has disappeared.

Has the status changed?

Yes:
- AL C4

No:
- Fault not found

VV8019800166030X

Fig. 46 Code ROP 430 (AL): Solenoid S1 & S2, Faulty Signal (Part 3 of 5). C70 convertible

AL D. Faulty signal. Intermittent fault

AL D1

Checking wires

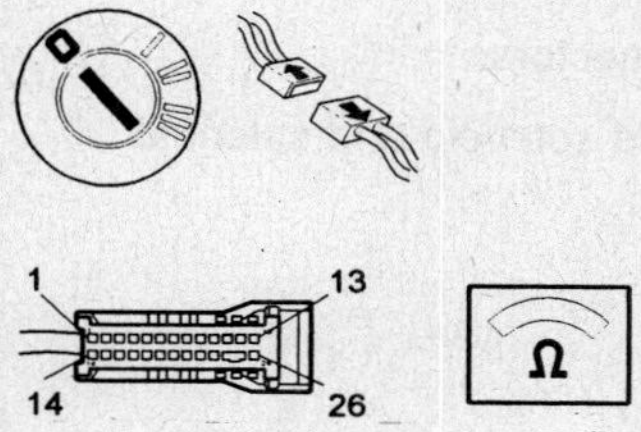

- Ignition off.
- Disconnect control unit connectors.

Connect an ohmmeter between pins 5 and 21 and check for an intermittent short circuit.

Check the connector on the control unit for an intermittent short circuit to voltage supply

The ohmmeter should display infinite resistance.

Do the necessary corrective action.

VV8019800166050X

Fig. 46 Code ROP 430 (AL): Solenoid S1 & S2, Faulty Signal (Part 5 of 5). C70 convertible

AM B. Additional diagnostic trouble codes and status signals

Status signals *AM B1*

Select one of the following options to continue:

Alternative 1:
- *AM C. Signal too low. Permanent fault*

Alternative 2:
- *AM D. Signal too low. Intermittent fault*

VV8019800167020X

Fig. 47 Code ROP 431 & 441 (AM): Lefthand Solenoid S1 & Righthand Solenoid S2, Signal Too Low (Part 2 of 6). C70 convertible

AL C4

Verification continued

- Ignition off.
- Press down the roll bars if they have been deployed.
- Ignition on.

Activate solenoids using the Volvo System Tester.

> **Warning!** Nobody should be over the roll bars when the roll bars are deployed.

Have the solenoids been activated?

Yes:
- Fault corrected

No:
- Fault not found

VV8019800166040X

Fig. 46 Code ROP 430 (AL): Solenoid S1 & S2, Faulty Signal (Part 4 of 5). C70 convertible

AM A. Diagnostic trouble code information

Condition

If the voltage in the circuit is too low for more than 5 seconds, diagnostic trouble code ROP-431 or ROP-441 is displayed.

Possible source

- Signal wire short circuited to ground
- Solenoid defective.

Hint: Solenoid S1 is the left-hand solenoid and solenoid S2 the right-hand solenoid.

Fault symptom(s)

- ROPS warning lamp on.

VV8019800167010X

Fig. 47 Code ROP 431 & 441 (AM): Lefthand Solenoid S1 & Righthand Solenoid S2, Signal Too Low (Part 1 of 6). C70 convertible

AM C. Signal too low. Permanent fault

AM C1

Checking components

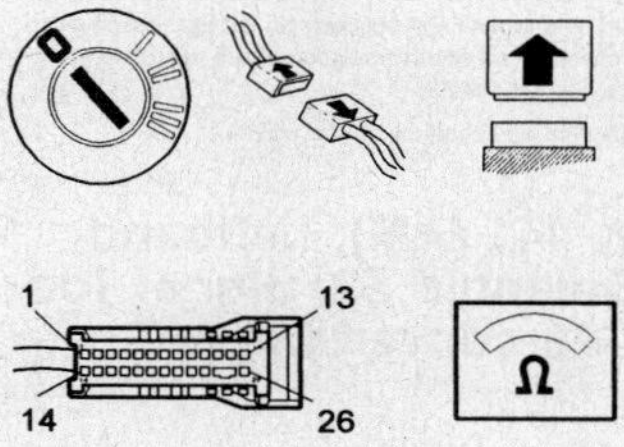

- Ignition off.
- Disconnect solenoid connectors.
- Disconnect control unit.

For S1: Connect an ohmmeter between control unit connector pin 4 and ground and between pin 5 and ground and check for a short circuit to ground

For S2: Connect an ohmmeter between control unit connector pin 17 and ground and between pin 21 and ground and check for a short circuit to ground

The ohmmeter should display infinite resistance.

Does the value deviate from this?

Yes:
- AM C2

No:
- AM C3

AM C2

Replacing the component

Trouble-shooting indicates that there is a short-circuit in the wire harness. Since no repairs may be done on wires that are affected, the wire harness must be replaced.

Then continue with:
- AM C4

VV8019800167030X

Fig. 47 Code ROP 431 & 441 (AM): Lefthand Solenoid S1 & Righthand Solenoid S2, Signal Too Low (Part 3 of 6). C70 convertible

AM C3

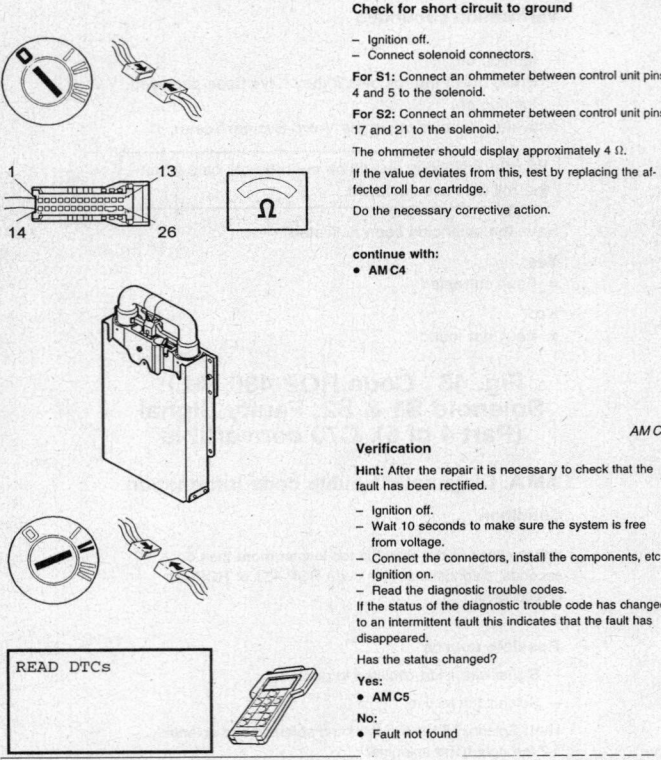

Check for short circuit to ground

- Ignition off.
- Connect solenoid connectors.

For S1: Connect an ohmmeter between control unit pins 4 and 5 to the solenoid.

For S2: Connect an ohmmeter between control unit pins 17 and 21 to the solenoid.

The ohmmeter should display approximately 4 Ω.

If the value deviates from this, test by replacing the affected roll bar cartridge.

Do the necessary corrective action.

continue with:

- **AM C4**

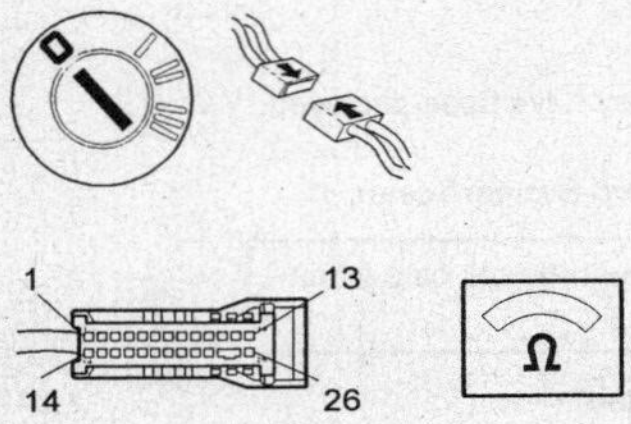

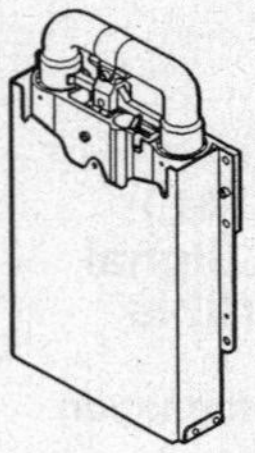

AM C4

Verification

Hint: After the repair it is necessary to check that the fault has been rectified.

- Ignition off.
- Wait 10 seconds to make sure the system is free from voltage.
- Connect the connectors, install the components, etc.
- Ignition on.
- Read the diagnostic trouble codes.

If the status of the diagnostic trouble code has changed to an intermittent fault this indicates that the fault has disappeared.

Has the status changed?

Yes:

- **AM C5**

No:

- Fault not found

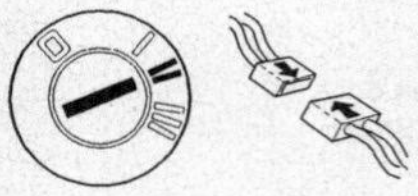

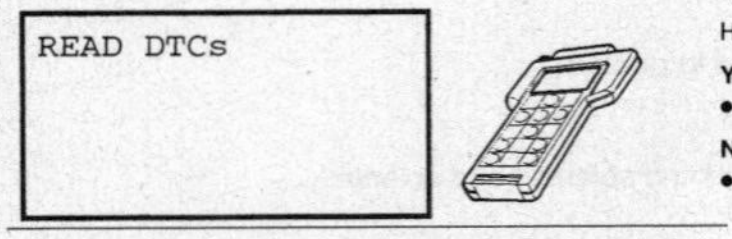

VV8019800167040X

Fig. 47 Code ROP 431 & 441 (AM): Lefthand Solenoid S1 & Righthand Solenoid S2, Signal Too Low (Part 4 of 6). C70 convertible

AM D. Signal too low. Intermittent fault

AM D1

Checking components

- Ignition off.
- Disconnect solenoid connectors.
- Disconnect control unit.

For S1: Connect an ohmmeter between control unit pin 4 and ground and between pin 5 and ground and check for an intermittent short circuit to ground as described in **BW B3**.

For S2: Connect an ohmmeter between control unit pin 17 and ground and between pin 21 and ground and check for an intermittent short circuit to ground as described in **BW B3**.

Do the necessary corrective action.

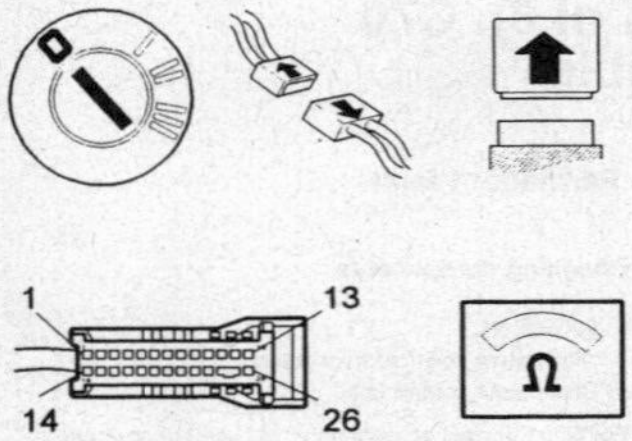

VV8019800167060X

Fig. 47 Code ROP 431 & 441 (AM): Lefthand Solenoid S1 & Righthand Solenoid S2, Signal Too Low (Part 6 of 6). C70 convertible

AN B. Additional diagnostic trouble codes and status signals

AN B1

Status signals

Select one of the following options to continue.

Alternative 1:

- *AN C. No signal. Permanent fault*

Alternative 2:

- *AN D. No signal. Intermittent fault*

VV8019800168020X

Fig. 48 Code ROP 432 & 442 (AN): Left Solenoid S1 & Right Solenoid S2, No Signal (Part 2 of 6). C70 convertible

AM C5

Verification continued

- Ignition off.
- Press down the roll bars if they have been deployed.
- Ignition on.

Activate solenoids using the Volvo System Tester.

> **Warning!** Nobody should be over the roll bars when the roll bars are deployed.

Have the solenoids been activated?

Yes:

- Fault corrected

No:

- Fault not found

VV8019800167050X

Fig. 47 Code ROP 431 & 441 (AM): Lefthand Solenoid S1 & Righthand Solenoid S2, Signal Too Low (Part 5 of 6). C70 convertible

AN A. Diagnostical trouble code information

Condition

If the resistance in the circuit is too high for more than 5 seconds, diagnostic trouble code ROP-432 or ROP-442 is displayed.

Possible source

- Open circuit in ground wire
- Open circuit in signal wire
- Solenoid defective
- Contact resistance in the connectors.

Hint: Solenoid S1 is the left-hand solenoid and solenoid S2 the right-hand solenoid.

Fault symptom(s)

- ROPS warning lamp on.

VV8019800168010X

Fig. 48 Code ROP 432 & 442 (AN): Left Solenoid S1 & Right Solenoid S2, No Signal (Part 1 of 6). C70 convertible

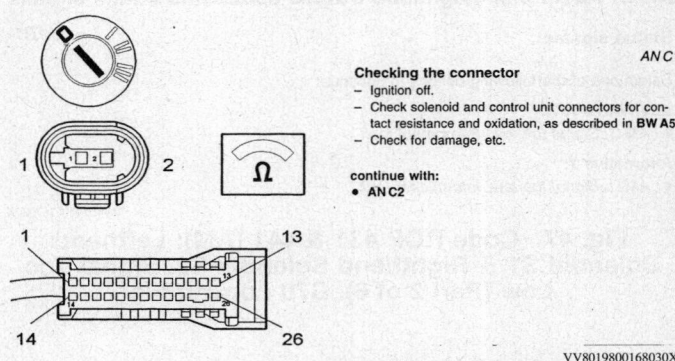

AN C1

Checking the connector

- Ignition off.
- Check solenoid and control unit connectors for contact resistance and oxidation, as described in **BW A5**.
- Check for damage, etc.

continue with:

- **AN C2**

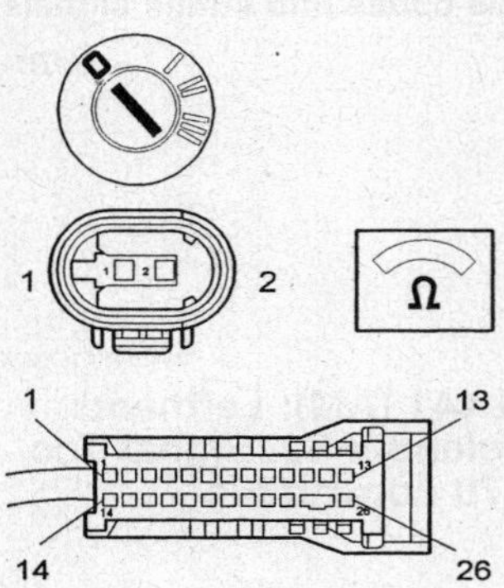

VV8019800168030X

Fig. 48 Code ROP 432 & 442 (AN): Left Solenoid S1 & Right Solenoid S2, No Signal (Part 3 of 6). C70 convertible

AN C2

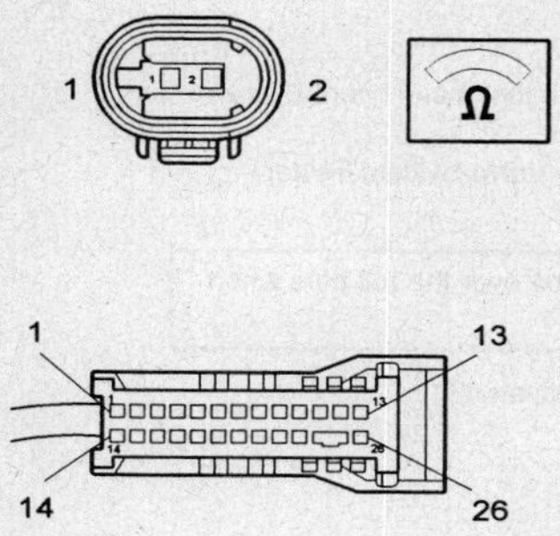

Checking the components and wires

For S1: Check the ground wire between control unit pin 4 and solenoid 2 and the signal wire between control unit pin 5 and solenoid 1; test for open circuits

For S2: Check the ground wire between control unit pin 17 and solenoid 2 and the signal wire between control unit pin 21 and solenoid 1; test for open circuits

Connect solenoid connectors.

For S1: Connect an ohmmeter between control unit pins 4 and 5 (to the solenoid).

For S2: Connect an ohmmeter between control unit pins 17 and 21 (to the solenoid).

The ohmmeter should display approximately 4 Ω.

If the value deviates from this, test by replacing the affected roll bar cartridge.

Do the necessary corrective action.

> **Note!** Be careful not to damage the connectors when testing them.

Then continue with:

- AN C3

AN C3

Verification

Hint: After the repair it is necessary to check that the fault has been rectified.

- Ignition off.
- Wait 10 seconds to make sure the system is free from voltage.
- Connect the connectors, install the components, etc.
- Ignition on.
- Read the diagnostic trouble codes.

If the status of the diagnostic trouble code has changed to an intermittent fault this indicates that the fault has disappeared.

Has the status changed?

Yes:

- AN C4

No:

- Fault not found

VV8019800168040X

Fig. 48 Code ROP 432 & 442 (AN): Left Solenoid S1 & Right Solenoid S2, No Signal (Part 4 of 6). C70 convertible

AN D. No signal. Intermittent fault

AN D1

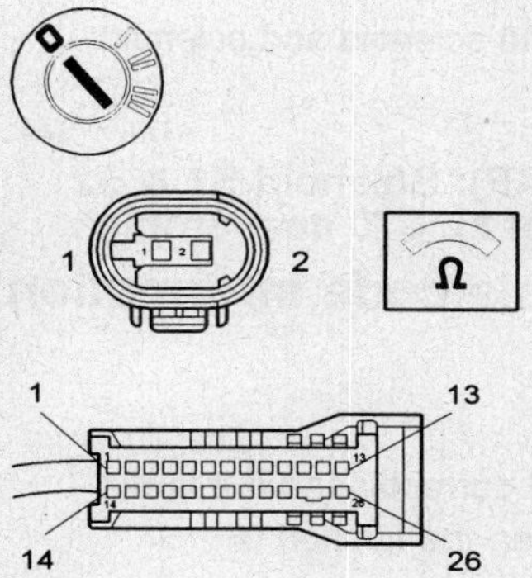

Checking the connector

- Ignition off.

For S1: Check the ground wire between control unit pin 4 and solenoid 2 and the signal wire between control unit pin 5 and solenoid 1; test for intermittent open circuits

For S2: Check the ground wire between control unit pin 17 and solenoid 2 and the signal wire between control unit pin 21 and solenoid 1; test for intermittent open circuits

Check solenoid and control unit connectors for contact resistance and oxidation.

Check for damage, etc.

Replace solenoid connectors.

For S1: Connect an ohmmeter between control unit pins 4 and 5 to the solenoid.

For S2: Connect an ohmmeter between control unit pins 17 and 21 to the solenoid.

The ohmmeter should display approximately 4 Ω.

If the value deviates from this, test by replacing the affected roll bar cartridge.

Do the necessary corrective action.

VV8019800168060X

Fig. 48 Code ROP 432 & 442 (AN): Left Solenoid S1 & Right Solenoid S2, No Signal (Part 6 of 6). C70 convertible

AN C4

Verification continued

- Ignition off.
- Press down the roll bars if they have been deployed.
- Ignition on.

Activate solenoids using the Volvo System Tester or eqivalent.

> **Warning!** Nobody should be over the roll bars when the roll bars are deployed.

Have the solenoids been activated?

Yes:

- Fault corrected

No:

- Fault not found

VV8019800168050X

Fig. 48 Code ROP 432 & 442 (AN): Left Solenoid S1 & Right Solenoid S2, No Signal (Part 5 of 6). C70 convertible

AO A. Diagnostic trouble code information

Condition

If the voltage in the circuit is too high for more than 5 seconds, diagnostic trouble code ROP-433 or ROP-443 is displayed.

Possible source

- Signal wire short circuited to voltage supply
- Short circuit to voltage supply in connector.

Hint: Solenoid S1 is the left-hand solenoid and solenoid S2 the right-hand solenoid.

Fault symptom(s)

- ROPS warning lamp on
- Roll bar deployed.

VV8019800169010X

Fig. 49 Code ROP 433 & 443 (AO): Lefthand Solenoid S1 & Righthand Solenoid S2, Signal Too High (Part 1 of 5). C70 convertible

AO B. Additional diagnostic trouble codes and status signals

AO B1

Status signals

Select one of the following options to continue.

Alternative 1:

- *AO C. Signal too high. Permanent fault*

Alternative 2:

- *AO D. Signal too high. Intermittent fault*

VV8019800169020X

Fig. 49 Code ROP 433 & 443 (AO): Lefthand Solenoid S1 & Righthand Solenoid S2, Signal Too High (Part 2 of 5). C70 convertible

AO C. Signal too high. Permanent fault

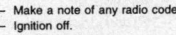

AO C1

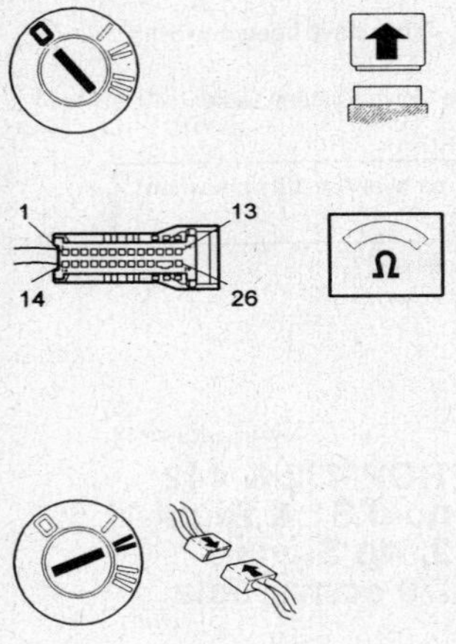

Checking the connector and wires

- Make a note of any radio code.
- Ignition off.
- Disconnect control unit.

For S1: Test between control unit pins 6 and 5 or between pins 2 and 5 for a short circuit to the voltage supply

For S2: Test between control unit pins 6 and 21 or between pins 2 and 21 for a short circuit to the voltage supply

If the wire harness is faulty it must be replaced since no repairs should be done on it.

Do the necessary corrective action.

Then continue with:

- **AO C2**

AO C2

Verification

Hint: After the repair it is necessary to check that the fault has been rectified.

- Ignition off.
- Wait 10 seconds to make sure the system is free from voltage.
- Connect the connectors, install the components, etc.
- Ignition on.
- Read the diagnostic trouble codes.

If the status of the diagnostic trouble code has changed to an intermittent fault this indicates that the fault has disappeared.

Has the status changed?

Yes:

- **AO C3**

No:

- Fault not found

VV8019800169030X

Fig. 49 Code ROP 433 & 443 (AO): Lefthand Solenoid S1 & Righthand Soleness S2, Signal Too High (Part 3 of 5). C70 convertible

AO D. Signal too high. Intermittent fault

AO D1

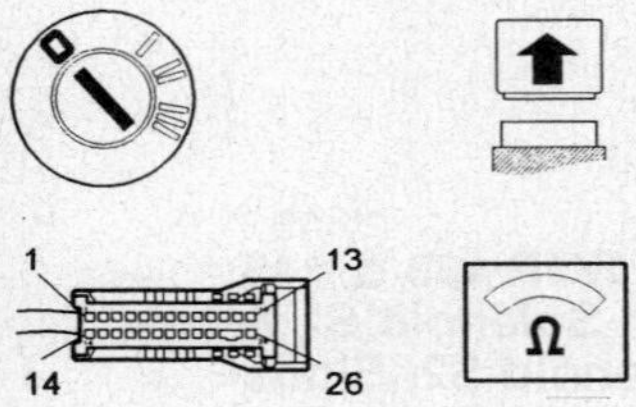

Checking the connector and wires

- Ignition off.
- Disconnect trigger unit.

For S1: Test between trigger unit pins 6 and 5 or between pins 2 and 5 for an intermittent short circuit to the voltage supply

For S2: Test between trigger unit pins 6 and 21 or between pins 2 and 21 for an intermittent short circuit to the voltage supply

VV8019800169050X

Fig. 49 Code ROP 433 & 443 (AO): Lefthand Solenoid S1 & Righthand Soleness S2, Signal Too High (Part 5 of 5). C70 convertible

AP B1

Replacing the component

The solenoids have a trigger counter which records each time a solenoid is activated. When the trigger counter reaches the decimal figure 200, diagnostic trouble code ROP-451 is displayed.
The trigger counter should only be reset when the roll bar cartridge is replaced.

continue with:

- **AP B2**

AP B2

Verification

Hint: After the repair it is necessary to check if the fault has been rectified.

- Ignition off.
- Connect the connectors, install the components, etc.
- Ignition on.

Reset trigger counter.

Can the trigger counter be reset?

Yes:

- Fault corrected

No:

- Fault not found

VV8019800170020X

Fig. 50 Code ROP 451 (AP): Solenoid S1 & S2 trigger Counter (Part 2 of 2). C70 convertible

AO C3

Verification continued

- Ignition off.
- Press down the roll bars if they have been deployed.
- Ignition on.

Activate solenoids using the Volvo System Tester or equivalent.

Warning! Nobody should be over the roll bars when the roll bars are deployed.

Have the solenoids been activated?

Yes:

- Fault corrected

No:

- Fault not found

VV8019800169040X

Fig. 49 Code ROP 433 & 443 (AO): Lefthand Solenoid S1 & Righthand Soleness S2, Signal Too High (Part 4 of 5). C70 convertible

AP A. Diagnostic trouble code information

Condition

The solenoids have a trigger counter which records each time the roll bars are deployed. When the trigger counter reaches the decimal figure 200, diagnostic trouble code ROP-451 is displayed.

Possible source

- The solenoids have been activated 200 times.

Fault symptom(s)

- No diagnostic trouble symptoms unless the ROPS warning lamp comes on.

Hint: Solenoid S1 is the left-hand solenoid and solenoid S2 the right-hand solenoid.

VV8019800170010X

Fig. 50 Code ROP 451 (AP): Solenoid S1 & S2 trigger Counter (Part 1 of 2). C70 convertible

AQ A. Diagnostic trouble code information

Condition

If the control unit is not handled correctly and if it is disconnected from the console when the ignition is switched on with the connector connected, diagnostic trouble code ROP-452 is displayed.

Possible source

- The control unit was handled when the voltage was on

Fault symptom(s)

- ROPS warning lamp on.

VV8019800171010X

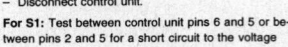

Fig. 51 Code ROP 452 (AQ): Control Unit, Incorrect Operation (Part 1 of 3). C70 convertible

AQ B1

Erase diagnostic trouble codes

The trigger unit is very sensitive to handling faults. The connector must be disconnected from the trigger unit before the trigger unit is disconnected from the console.

When the trigger unit is disconnected no voltage should be supplied. If the diagnostic trouble code has been made, any possible cause of error must be investigated and prevented from occurring again.

The first time the diagnostic trouble code is made it can be erased.

Note! All other diagnostic trouble codes must be intermittent before they can be erased.

– Erase diagnostic trouble code.

Can the diagnostic trouble code be erased?

Yes:
- AQ B3

No:
- AQ B2

AQ B2

Replacing the component

Test by replacing the trigger unit

continue with:
- AQ B3

VV8019800171020X

Fig. 51 Code ROP 452 (AQ): Control Unit, Incorrect Operation (Part 2 of 3). C70 convertible

Component Service

ROLL BAR CARTRIDGE, REPLACE

1. Move rear hood to upright position.
2. Disconnect negative battery lead.
3. Remove rear seat, roll bar panel and rear speaker.
4. **Roll bars are extended by a powerful spring. Extended height is approximately 20 inches. Stay clear of roll bar area when extending.**
5. Do not attempt to repair the cartridge. If there is a fault with the roll bar, replace the whole cartridge.
6. Insert a thin screwdriver into catch, **Fig. 52.** Push top of catch with screwdriver to release spring and extend roll bar.
7. Push out clip on speaker connector.
8. Remove three screws from dividing filter, **Fig. 53,** then the dividing filter and wires through speaker opening.
9. Remove four rubber stoppers from front edge of storage space for rear hood, then remove four screws from roll bar cartridge.
10. Reconnect battery negative cable, turn ignition switch to On position.
11. Move rear hood to lowered position.
12. Disconnect battery negative cable.
13. Push out clip on roll bar cartridge electrical connector, pull wires out through speaker opening and disconnect connector.
14. Loosen two bottom attaching screws of roll bar cartridge, **Fig. 54,** then remove cartridge from vehicle.
15. Reverse procedure to install, noting the following:
    a. After installation, insert a thin screwdriver into catch and release catch to extend roll bar.
    b. A minimum of three ridges on locking pin (1), **Fig. 55,** must be visible on cartridge.
    c. Push safety catch to side once more, then attempt to pull roll bar up until it stops. Roll bar should already be at top position.
    d. Roll bar should not move when you pull it.
    e. If roll bar does move upward, it has not reached it's top position. Perform procedure again by pushing roll bar fully down and releasing.
    f. If roll bar still does not fully extend, replace the roll bar cartridge.
    g. As a final check, push the safety catch to one side and hold in that position.
    h. Push roll bar down until it reaches it's bottom position then release safety catch. Ensure roll bar is locked in it's bottom position.
    i. With ignition switch in position two, reconnect battery ground cable. Ensure ROPS warning light comes on for approximately five seconds and then goes off.

ROPS CONTROL UNIT, REPLACE

1. Move rear hood to full upright position.
2. Turn ignition switch to Off position, then disconnect battery negative cable.
3. Remove rear seat and speaker.
4. Push button (1) in and move lock mounting (2) forward, **Fig. 56.**
5. Pull connector in direction of arrow, **Fig. 56.**

AQ B3

Verification

Hint: After the repair it is necessary to check that the fault has been rectified.

- Ignition off.
- Connect the connectors, install the components, etc.
- Ignition on.
- Wait for **at least** 10 seconds so that the trigger unit can complete the diagnostics.

Read the diagnostic trouble codes.

Is diagnostic trouble code ROP-452 displayed again?

Yes:
- Fault not found

No:
- Fault corrected

VV8019800171030X

Fig. 51 Code ROP 452 (AQ): Control Unit, Incorrect Operation (Part 3 of 3). C70 convertible

6. Avoid touching contacts of ROPS control unit. Electrostatic discharge may cause damage to the control unit.
7. Remove roll bar cartridge as outlined previously, then disconnect control unit electrical connector.
8. Remove three mounting screws, then the control unit.
9. Reverse procedure to install, noting the following:
    a. Ensure battery is disconnected before installation.
    b. Push connector into control unit and secure connector by moving lock mounting back until it locks in behind button. Do this before installing control unit.
    c. Install three mounting screws and **torque** to 90 inch lbs.
    d. Electrical grounding path is through one attaching screw, ensure mounting screws have sufficient contact with body.

Clearing Diagnostic Trouble Codes

Use a suitable diagnostic scan tool to access diagnostic trouble codes. Codes can be erased when all stored codes have been read at least once during the same ignition On session and the code status is intermittent for all codes. Internal diagnostic trouble codes can not be erased.

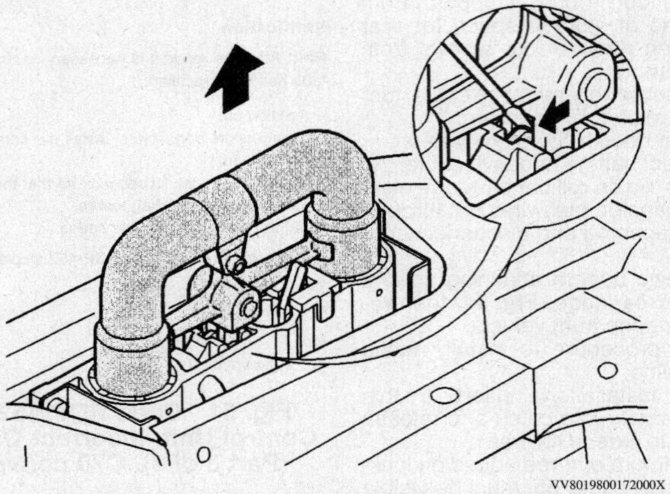

Fig. 52 Extending the roll bar. C70 convertible

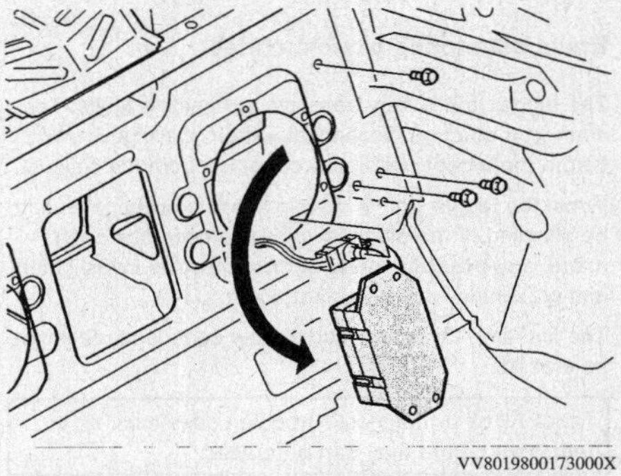

Fig. 53 Dividing filter removal. C70 convertible

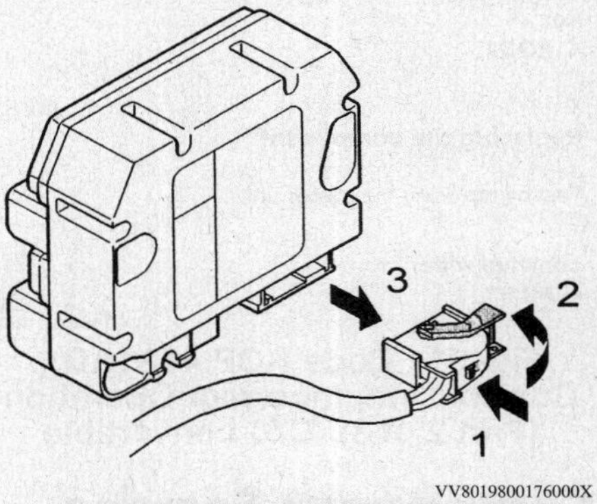

Fig. 56 ROPS control unit connector. C70 convertible

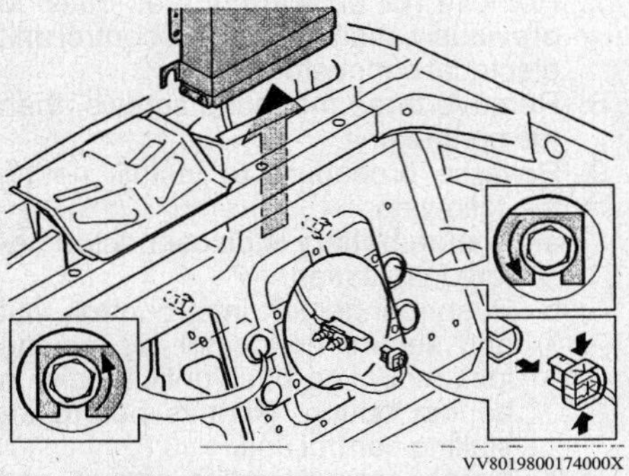

Fig. 54 Roll bar cartridge lower mounting screws. C70 convertible

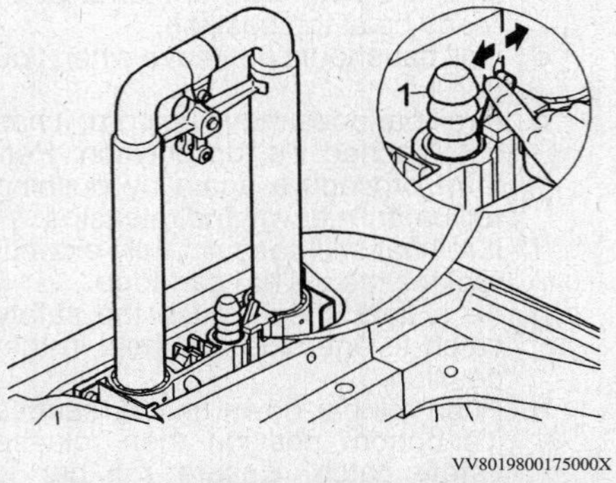

Fig. 55 Roll bar cartridge locking pin. C70 convertible

TIGHTENING SPECIFICATIONS

Year/ Model	Component	Torque/ Ft. Lbs.
1998–2001		
S40 & V40	Air Bag Module, Driver's	88①
	Air Bag Module, Passenger's	80①
	Air Bag Module, Side Impact	27①
	Seat Belt Pretensioner	35
	Side Impact Sensor	44①
C70	Air Bag Module, Driver's	89①
	Air Bag Module, Passenger's	89①
	Contact Reel	22①
	Control Module	89①
	Roll Over Protection System (ROPS) Control Module	88①
	Seat Belt Tensioner	35
	Steering Wheel	30
V70	Air Bag Module, Driver's	89①
	Air Bag Module, Passenger's	89①
	Air Bag Module, Side Impact	26②
	Contact Reel	22①
	Control Module	89①
	Front Seat Track	30
	Knee Bolster	15
	Seat Belt Inertia Reel	30
	Seat Belt Tensioner	54①
	Seat Belt To Sea	30
	Seat Rail	30②
	Sensor	89①
	Steering Wheel	30
S80	Air Bag Module, Passenger's	89①
	Air Bag Module, Roof Panel	89①
	Air Bag Module, Side Impact	53①
	Control Module	89①
	Front Seat Belt	35
	Front Seat Track	35
	Rear Seat Belt Tensioner	35
	Side Impact Sensor	53①

① — Inch lbs.
② — To aid in seat alignment, tighten outer rear mounting bolt last.

Dash Panel Service

NOTE: On Air Bag Equipped Models, Refer To "Air Bag System Precautions" Located In The Front Of This Manual For System Disarming & Arming Procedures.

NOTE: Refer To The "Dash Gauges" Section For Dash Gauge Troubleshooting Procedures.

INDEX

	Page No.
Dash Panel, Replace	9-96
C70, S70 & V70	9-96
S80	9-96
S90 & V90	9-97
Precautions	9-96
Air Bag Systems	9-96
Battery Ground Cable	9-96
Microprocessor Radios	9-96

PRECAUTIONS

AIR BAG SYSTEMS

Refer to "Air Bag System Precautions" in the front of this manual for system disarming and arming procedures.

MICROPROCESSOR RADIOS

On models equipped with microprocessor radios, always switch radio off before disconnecting or connecting battery ground cable to prevent damage to the radio.

BATTERY GROUND CABLE

Prior to service, disconnect battery ground cable and isolate as required.

DASH PANEL

REPLACE

C70, S70 & V70

1. Open glove compartment door.
2. Remove glove compartment attaching screws, then the glove compartment.
3. **On models equipped with CD-ROM scanner,** remove flap.
4. **On all models,** disconnect passenger's air bag module electrical connector.
5. Remove three M6 10 mm passenger's air bag module retaining screws.
6. Remove ventilation and radio speaker grilles by pulling mounting bracket behind grilles with a suitable hook tool.
7. Remove 11 instrument panel pad attaching screws, then the pad assembly, **Fig. 1.**
8. If passenger's air bag module is being replaced, remove six module retaining nuts, then the module.
9. Remove windshield wiper arm mounting nuts, then the arms, **Fig. 2.**
10. Remove five cowl screen mounting screws, then the screen, **Fig. 3.**
11. Remove wiper motor and instrument panel mounting fasteners in engine compartment, **Fig. 4.**
12. Remove instrument panel lefthand and righthand insulator panels, **Figs. 5 and 6.**
13. Disconnect electrical connectors as required, then remove instrument panel mounting fasteners in passenger compartment, **Fig. 7.**
14. Carefully lift instrument panel out of vehicle.
15. Reverse procedure to install, noting the following:
    a. Ensure all electrical connectors and wiring are properly routed to avoid pinching.
    b. Tighten fasteners to specifications.

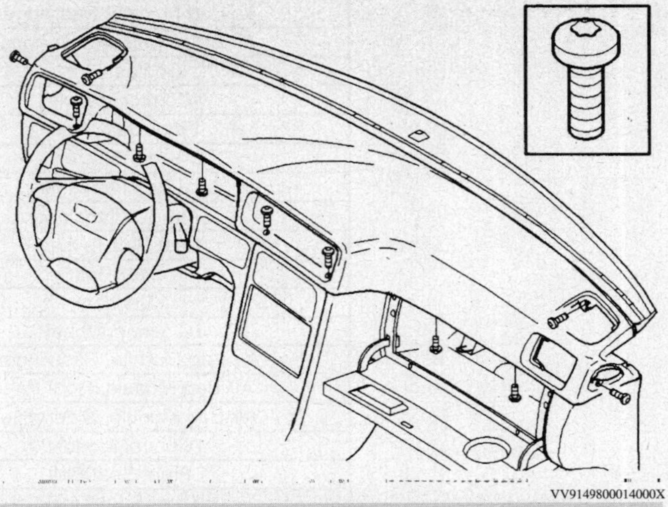

Fig. 1 Instrument panel pad screws. C70, S70 & V70

S80

1. Remove A-pillar trim panel.
2. Remove left and right sound insulation panels.
3. Remove center console coin/CD compartment.
4. Remove center console parking brake trim panel.
5. Remove center console transmission lever trim panel.
6. Remove four center console retaining screws.
7. Remove center console side panel.
8. Remove center console rear ashtray, then the center console.
9. Reverse procedure to install.
10. Remove driver's air bag module retaining bolts, then the module. Disconnect electrical connectors.
11. Remove steering wheel using a suitable puller tool.
12. Remove steering column upper and lower covers.
13. Remove instrument cluster finish panel.
14. Remove four instrument cluster attaching screws.
15. Remove instrument cluster attaching screws, then the instrument cluster.
16. Remove two instrument panel attaching screws through instrument cluster opening.
17. Remove screw cover from lefthand

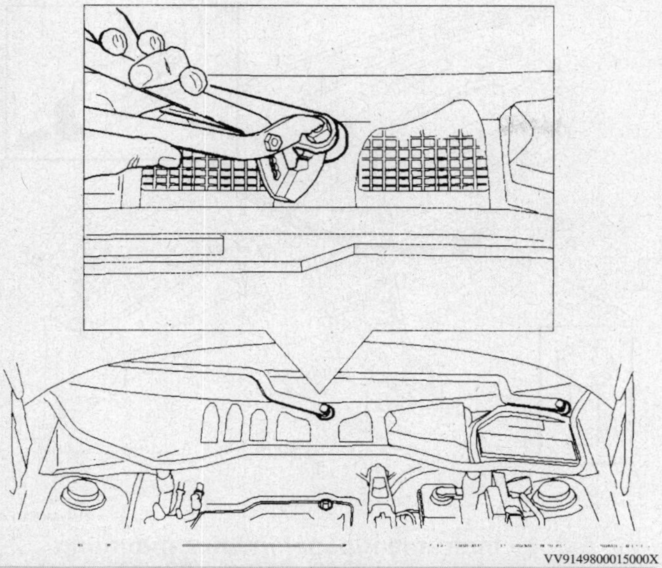

Fig. 2 Windshield wiper arm removal. C70, S70 & V70

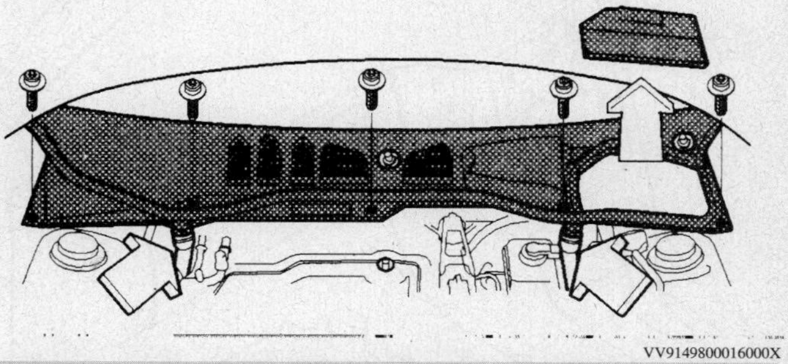

Fig. 3 Cowl screen removal. C70, S70 & V70

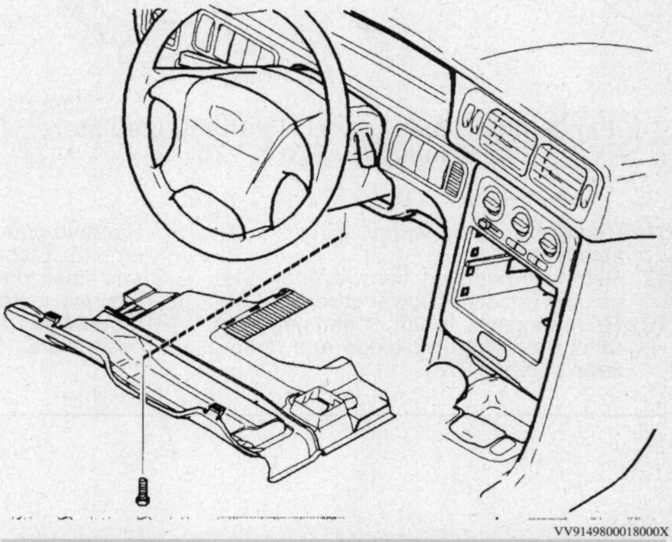

Fig. 5 Instrument panel lefthand insulator panel.C70, S70 & V70

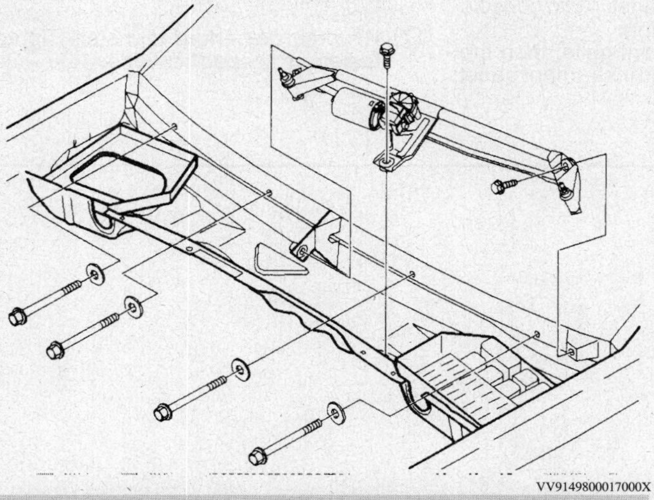

Fig. 4 Wiper motor & instrument panel underhood mounting fasteners. C70, S70 & V70

end of instrument panel.
18. Reach through cover opening and remove two instrument panel attaching screws.
19. Remove RTI (traffic information) component from top of instrument panel, if equipped.
20. Remove center speaker from top of instrument panel.
21. Remove one instrument panel attaching screw from speaker opening.
22. Remove hazard warning switch from instrument panel.
23. Remove sun sensor from instrument panel.
24. Remove two screws from lower portion of climate control panel, then the panel.
25. Remove radio/car phone from instrument panel.
26. Remove two instrument panel attaching screws from under climate control panel opening.
27. Remove screw covers from right end of instrument panel.
28. Remove two screws through screw cover opening.
29. Remove SRS bracket screws.
30. Disconnect all electrical connectors, then carefully remove instrument panel from vehicle.
31. Reverse procedure to install. Tighten fasteners to specifications.

S90 & V90

1. Remove panel below glove compartment, then the glove compartment.
2. Remove righthand side footwell panel, then the A-pillar panel.
3. Disconnect solar sensor connect and cut cable ties.
4. Remove soundproofing panel below steering wheel, knee bolster, footwell panel and A-pillar panel.
5. Remove defroster grille, then screws securing fuse box.
6. Remove ashtray, then console retaining screws and slide console rearward.
7. Remove mounting screws, disconnect electrical connector and remove air bag module
8. Remove steering wheel mounting bolt.
9. Loosen screw at end of plastic strap from Park position in steering wheel.
10. Place screw in pin on contact reel. Screw will now lock contact reel in zero position. **Be careful not to turn steering wheel. Otherwise it will shear head off lockpin.**

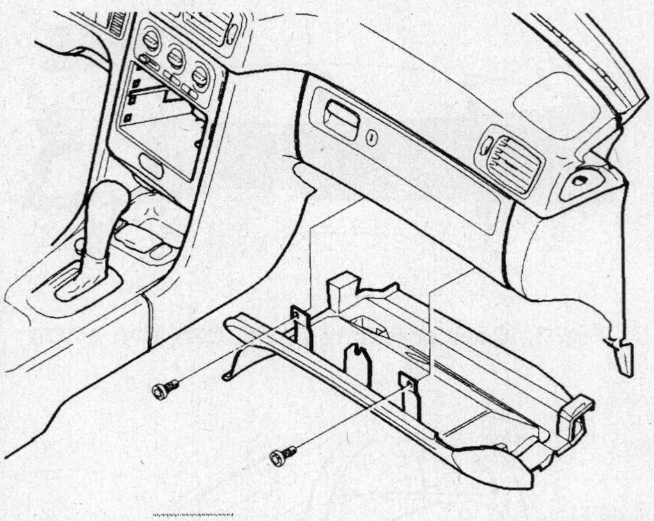

Fig. 6 Instrument panel righthand insulator panel.C70, S70 & V70

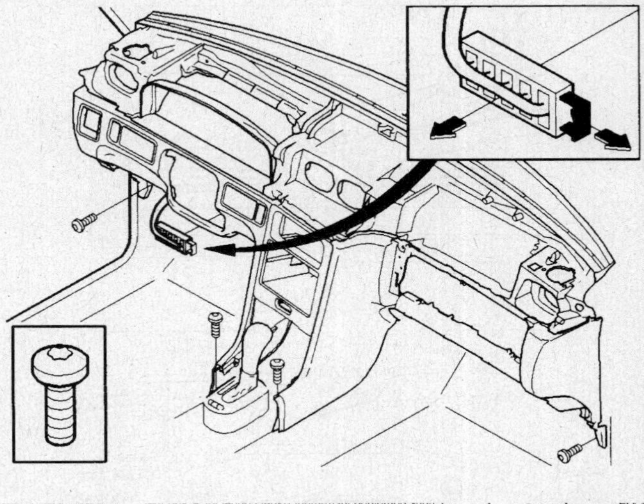

Fig. 7 Instrument panel interior mounting fasteners.C70, S70 & V70

11. Remove steering wheel using a suitable puller tool.
12. Remove mounting screws, then the column upper and lower covers.
13. Remove panel to left of steering column, small trim moldings and headlamp switch.
14. Remove panel to right of steering column, ECC control panel, radio console and small trim molding.
15. Remove outer air vent grille, then the mounting screws and instrument panel cover.
16. Disconnect electrical connectors, then carefully lift instrument panel out of vehicle.
17. Reverse procedure to install. Tighten fasteners to specifications.

Disc Brakes

INDEX

	Page No.
Brake Pad Service	9-99
remove from parse	9-99
Caliper Service	9-99
Rear	9-99
Disc Brake Specifications	9-100
Parking Brake Service	9-99
Parking Brake Shoes, Replace	9-99
Parking Brake, Adjust	9-99
Rotor, Replace	9-99
Front	9-99
Rear	9-99
Tightening Specifications	9-100

BRAKE PAD SERVICE

remove from parse

CALIPER SERVICE

REAR

REMOVAL & OVERHAUL

1. Raise and support rear of vehicle, then remove rear tires.
2. Disconnect brake lines, then remove two caliper attaching bolts and caliper.
3. Remove piston dust cover, then place a piece of wood or suitable material between both pistons. Force pistons out of bore using low pressure compressed air.
4. Using a suitable screwdriver, remove sealing rings, then bleeder screw. **Do not separate brake caliper into two separate halves.**
5. Clean caliper assembly thoroughly using brake fluid or denatured alcohol.
6. Remove any surface rust on cylinder using fine sandpaper.
7. Before assembly, coat all parts with power steering fluid, then install new seal rings and pistons.
8. **On ATE calipers,** check to be sure caliper pistons are in proper position to avoid squeals. Piston recess should incline 20° in relation to lower guide area of caliper. Inspect using template tool No. 2919, or equivalent, **Fig. 1.** If necessary, rotate piston with adjustment tool No. 2918, or equivalent.
9. **On all models,** install new dust cover and bleeder screw.

ROTOR

REPLACE

FRONT

1. Remove retaining spring from caliper.
2. Remove mounting bolts, then the caliper. Hang caliper from a steel wire as not to damage brake hose.
3. Remove caliper mounting bracket.
4. Remove rotor locating pins, then the rotor.
5. Reverse procedure to install. Tighten locating pin and caliper mounting bracket bolts to specifications.

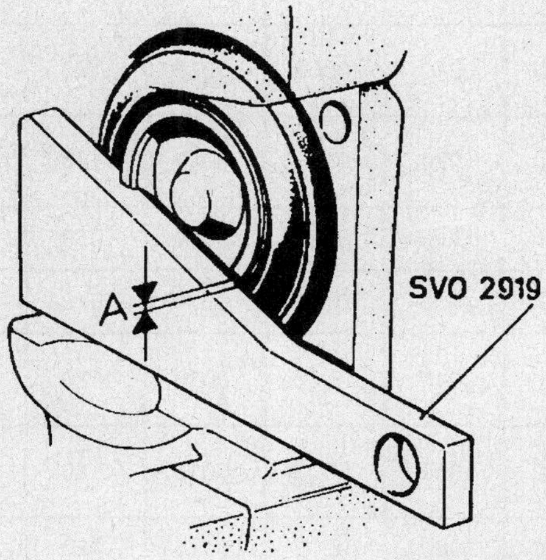

Fig. 1 Caliper piston position inspection. ATE rear caliper

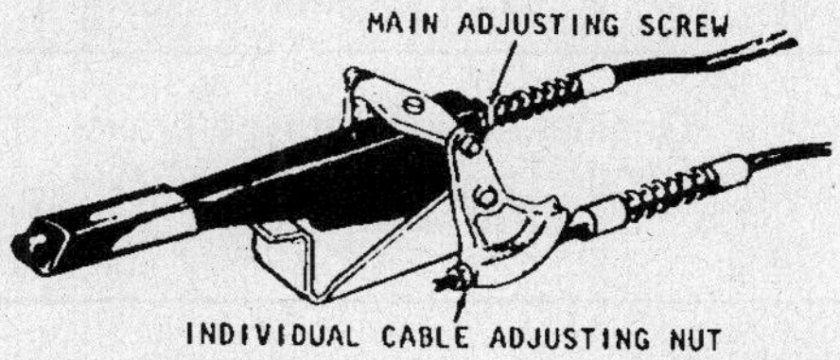

Fig. 2 Parking brake adjustment

REAR

1. Press out split pins with a .12 (3mm) mandrel, the remove retaining spring.
2. Remove brake pads and shims using puller tool No. 999 2917, or equivalent.
3. Remove caliper mounting bolts, then the caliper.
4. Back off parking brake adjusting screw. Access the adjusting screw by turning rotor until adjustment hole lines up with adjusting screw on parking brake shoes.
5. Remove rotor locating pins, then the rotor.
6. Reverse procedure to install. Tighten locating pins and caliper bolts to specifications.

PARKING BRAKE SERVICE

PARKING BRAKE SHOES, REPLACE

1. Loosen parking brake cable adjusting screw. Refer to "Parking Brake Adjustment."
2. Raise and support vehicle, then remove rear wheels.
3. Remove caliper.
4. Remove brake disc, then remove brake shoe springs, brake shoes and adjuster, if applicable. On some models, it may be necessary to work through holes in axle shaft flange to gain access to springs.
5. Before assembly, apply a thin layer of heat resistant graphite grease, or equivalent, on brake shoe sliding surface.
6. Install brake shoes, springs and adjuster, if applicable.
7. Install brake disc and caliper.
8. Adjust parking brake as outlined under "Parking Brake Adjustment."

PARKING BRAKE, ADJUST

1. Remove rear ashtray.
2. Working through ashtray hole, tighten adjusting nut at rear of parking lever so that brake is fully applied after 2–5 notches, **Fig. 2.**

DISC BRAKE SPECIFICATIONS

Model	Year	Front Disc Brake						Rear Disc Brake					
		Brake Lining Wear Limit, Inch②	Rotor					Brake Lining Wear Limit, Inch②	Rotor				
			Thickness, Inch			Thickness Variation Parallelism Inch	Lateral Run Out (T.I.R.) Inch		Thickness, Inch			Thickness Variation Parallelism Inch	Lateral Run-Out (T.I.R.) Inch
			Nom-in- al	Min. Re-finish	Dis-card Limit①				Nom-inal	Min. Re-finish	Dis-card Limit①		
S40/V40	2000–01	.079	.940	.870	.846	—	.0016	.079	.394	.350	.330	—	.0016
S60 w/15" Wheels	2001	.120	1.020	.940	.910	.0003	.0016	.120	.470	.420	.390	.0003	.002
S60 w/16" Wheels	2001	.120	1.100	1.020	.980	.0003	.0016	.120	.470	.420	.390	.0003	.002
C70	1998–2001	.120	1.024	.937	.9055	.0003	.0014	.079	.377	.350	.330	.0003	.002
S70/V70	1998–2000	.110	1.000	.930	.900	.0003	.0014	.079	.400	.350	.330	.0003	.002
V70 w/15" Wheels	2001	.120	1.020	.940	.910	.0003	.0016	.120	.470	.420	.390	.0003.	.002
V70 w/16" Wheels	2001	.120	1.100	1.020	.980	.0003	.0016	.120	.470	.420	.390	.0003.	.002
S80	1999–2001	.120	1.100	1.020	.980	.0003	.0016	.120	.470	.420	.390	.0003	.002
S90 & V90③	1998–99	.118	.866	—	.787	.0003	.0014	.079	.378	—	.330	.0005	.002
S90 & V90④	1998–99	.118	1.024	—	.906	.0003	.0014	.079	.394	—	.315	.0003	.0016

① — Discard thickness is stamped on rotor.
② — Above rivet head or backing plate.
Original equipment type brake lining.
③ — Type I.
④ — Type II.

TIGHTENING SPECIFICATIONS

Year	Component	Torque, Ft. Lbs.
1998–2001	Brake Hoses To Nipple	12
	Brake Pipe Unions	10
	Caliper Locating Pins	72①
	Caliper Mounting Bracket	75
	Caliper Slide Pin	25
	Front Brake Calipers Bolts	74
	Front Dust Shield	18
	Lower Caliper Bolts	25
	Master Cylinder	22
	Nipple To Caliper	12
	Rear Brake Caliper Bolts	43
	Rear Dust Shield	29
	Wheel Lug Nuts	81

① — Inch lbs.

Hydraulic Brake Systems

INDEX

	Page No.
Brake System Bleed	9-101
Bleeding Unit	9-101
Non-Bleeding Unit	9-101
Component Replacement	9-101
Master Cylinder	9-101
Pressure Differential Warning Valve	9-101
Regulating Valve	9-101
Component Service	9-101
Master Cylinder Overhaul	9-101
Description	9-101

DESCRIPTION

The function of hydraulic brake system is to transmit pressure from the master cylinder to caliper pistons. The system will operate properly if fluid is tight and brake fluid cannot be compressed. Normally, brake fluid cannot be compressed. If however the fluid overheats sufficiently it can partially change to a vapor form. Vapor can be compressed and since the master cylinder has a specific volume with which to build up pressure, the compression of vapor can result in excess brake pedal travel before the system has time to develop adequate braking pressure.

Brake fluid is hygroscopic in nature (absorbs water vapor from the air). For this reason it is important to keep brake fluid in a tightly sealed container. If only a small amount of fluid is required, it should be purchased in small cans. Avoid storing small quantities of fluid in bulk containers.

Only brake fluid which meets standard DOT 4 should be used. The boiling point for brake fluid depends on several factors including the ages of the fluid and climatic conditions. Any brake fluid efficiency will deteriorate as it ages. It should be changed at least every three years for cars in normal service.

COMPONENT REPLACEMENT

MASTER CYLINDER

1. Place a cover over the fender to protect paint from brake fluid.
2. Disconnect brake lines and cap openings.
3. Remove retaining nuts, then the master cylinder.
4. Reverse procedure to install. Bleed master cylinder prior to installation.

REGULATING VALVE

The regulating valve must be replaced as an assembly.

1. Disconnect brake pipe from valve, replace unions if necessary.
2. Remove valve from bracket, then disconnect brake hose from valve.
3. Install new valve and bleed system.
4. Ensure there are no leaks.

PRESSURE DIFFERENTIAL WARNING VALVE

1. Remove attaching screw, then disconnect electrical lead.
2. Place a suitable container beneath valve, then disconnect brake lines.
3. Install new valve and connect brake lines and electrical lead.
4. Bleed system and ensure there are no leaks.

COMPONENT SERVICE

MASTER CYLINDER OVERHAUL

Disassemble

1. Remove reservoir from master cylinder.
2. Drain fluid from reservoir, then remove seals.
3. Remove circlip and withdraw pistons and return spring.

Cleaning & Inspection

1. Polish inner surface of the master cylinder with a honing tool (cylinder grinding tool).
2. Clean all pistons parts and cylinder with methylated spirits.
3. Using compressed air, blow air into the equalizer and overflow holes.
4. Check master cylinder bore for scoring, replace as necessary. Replace both pistons, with connecting sleeve and seals as an assembly.
5. Apply brake fluid to master cylinder and lubricate piston seals with suitable grease.

Assemble

1. Assemble pistons, spring seat and spring.
2. Position master cylinder over pistons and spring, then install circlip.
3. Install seals into master cylinder, replace seals if necessary.
4. Connect brake pipes, then install brake fluid reservoir.
5. Fill reservoir with brake fluid, then bleed system.

BRAKE SYSTEM BLEED

BLEEDING UNIT

1. Ensure ignition switch is turned Off.
2. Raise and support vehicle.
3. Clean filer cap on brake fluid reservoir and surrounding area.
4. Remove filler cap.
5. Set bleeding unit to 29–43 psi.
6. Connect bleeding unit to brake fluid reservoir.
7. Depress brake pedal several times to expel any air bubbles from master cylinder. **Repeat this step between bleeding each brake caliper.**
8. Start at front lefthand wheel, remove protective cap from bleed nipple and connect hose from drain bottle.
9. Open bleed nipple and close it again once no further air bubbles can be seen in fluid.
10. Tighten bleed nipple.
11. Remove hose bleed nipple and install protective cap, then proceed to righthand front, lefthand rear and righthand rear wheel.
12. Remove bleeding unit connector from brake fluid reservoir.
13. Ensure if there is any air left in system by depressing brake pedal as if braking sharply. With engine off and brake pedal depressed 3–4 times, pedal travel should not exceed 1.6 inch.
14. If pedal travel exceeds 1.6 inch, bleed again and then check pedal travel, verifying that brake fluid is not over MAX mark.

NON-BLEEDING UNIT

1. Raise and support vehicle.
2. Clean brake fluid reservoir filler cap and surrounding area.
3. Remove filler cap, fill brake fluid reservoir completely.
4. Bleed lefthand front wheel, depress brake pedal several times to remove any air bubbles in master cylinder. **This step must be performed between bleeding each brake caliper.**
5. Remove protective cap from bleed nipple and connect hose from collecting bottle.
6. Open bleed nipple.
7. Push brake pedal right down and hold for 2 seconds, then releasing it. Repeat this 20–30 times until there are no visible air bubbles in drained fluid.
8. Close bleed nipple.
9. Depress brake pedal several times.
10. Open bleed nipple, close it when brake pedal is at bottom, repeat this procedure 3–5 times.
11. Remove hose and install protective cap.
12. Continue bleeding procedures from righthand front wheel, lefthand rear wheel and righthand rear wheel in order.
13. Verify if there is any air left in system by depressing brake pedal sharply. With engine off and brake pedal depressed

3–4 times, pedal travel should not exceed 1.6 inch. If pedal travel is longer than 1.6 inch, bleed system again, then check pedal travel.

14. Verifying that brake fluid is not over MAX mark.

Power Brake Units

INDEX

Page No.			Page No.			Page No.
Power Brake Unit Service	9-102		Check Valve, Replace	9-102	Power Brake Booster, Replace	9-102

POWER BRAKE UNIT SERVICE

POWER BRAKE BOOSTER, REPLACE

1. Remove master cylinder, then disconnect vacuum hose from power brake unit.
2. Disconnect link arm from brake pedal, then remove bracket with clutch pedal stop.
3. Remove nuts attaching power brake unit to dash panel.
4. Pull power brake unit forward, then disconnect fork from link arm and remove brake unit.

CHECK VALVE, REPLACE

1. Disconnect vacuum hose from check valve.
2. Pry out check valve using two screwdrivers, then remove seal.
3. Install new seal, ensuring flange is properly aligned in cylinder.
4. Lubricate seal with grease, then press valve carefully into place.
5. Ensure seal does not move out of its position.
6. Connect vacuum hose, ensure highest point is at attachment to valve.

Anti-lock Brakes

NOTE: On Air Bag Equipped Models, Refer To "Air Bag System Precautions" Located In The Front Of This Manual For System Disarming & Arming Procedures.

NOTE: Electrical Symbol & Wire Color Code Identification Located In The Front Of This Manual May Be Used As An Aid When Using Wiring Circuits Found In This Section.

INDEX

	Page No.
Description	9-103
Diagnosis & Testing	9-105
Accessing Diagnostic Trouble Codes	9-105
Less Volvo Diagnostic Key	9-105
With Volvo Diagnostic Key	9-105
Clearing Diagnostic Trouble Codes	9-114
Diagnostic Tests	9-105
F. Intermittent Faults	9-105
G. Diagnostic Trouble Code (DTC) Table	9-105
H. Test Drive	9-105
J. Diagnostic Trouble Code (DTC)/Diagnosis Table	9-106
K. Symptoms/Diagnosis Table	9-106
L. Mechanical Components, Fault Tracing	9-106
MA. Diagnostic Trouble Codes (DTC), Wheel Sensors	9-106
MB-Diagnostic Trouble Code (DTC) 1-4-1	9-107
MC-Diagnostic Trouble Code (DTC) 1-4-2	9-107
MD-Diagnostic Trouble Code (DTC) 1-4-4	9-107
ME-Diagnostic Trouble Codes (DTC), Valves	9-108
MF-Diagnostic Trouble Code (DTC) 4-2-4	9-108
MG-Diagnostic Trouble Code (DTC) 4-4-1	9-108
MH-Diagnostic Trouble Code (DTC) 4-4-3	9-108
MJ-Diagnostic Trouble Code (DTC) 4-4-4	9-109
NA-ABS-Warning Indicator Does Not Light	9-110
NB-ABS-Warning Indicator Lit, No Diagnostic Trouble Codes (DTC) Displayed	9-111
NC-TRACS Warning Indicator Does Not Light	9-111
ND-TRACS Warning Indicator Lit, No Diagnostic Trouble Codes (DTC) Displayed	9-111
NE-Brake Warning Indicator Does Not Light	9-111
NF-Brake Warning Indicator Does Not Go Out	9-112
NG-Diagnostic Trouble Codes (DTC) Cannot Be Read	9-112
NH-Poor Braking	9-112
NJ-Both Front Wheels Are Wholly Or Partially Locked	9-113
NK-No TRACS Function	9-113
P-Signal Description, Control Module	9-113
Diagnostic Trouble Code Interpretation	9-105
Diagnostic Trouble Code Table	9-105
Reading Diagnostic Trouble Codes	9-105
Intermittent Faults	9-113
Wiring Diagrams	9-105
Precautions	9-103
Air Bag Systems	9-103
Battery Ground Cable	9-103
Microprocessor Radios	9-103
System Service	9-114
Brake System Bleed	9-114
Component Replacement	9-114
Control Module	9-114
Hydraulic Modulator	9-114
Rear Sensor	9-115
Troubleshooting	9-103
Component Fault Tracing	9-103

PRECAUTIONS

AIR BAG SYSTEMS

Refer to "Air Bag System Precautions" in the front of this manual for system disarming and arming procedures.

MICROPROCESSOR RADIOS

On models equipped with microprocessor radios, always switch radio off before disconnecting or connecting battery ground cable to prevent damage to the radio.

BATTERY GROUND CABLE

Prior to service, disconnect battery ground cable and isolate as required.

DESCRIPTION

The Anti-Lock Brake System (ABS) uses a control unit, hydraulic modulator, transient surge protector, front speed sensors and a speedometer sensor to control wheel lock-up. The control unit receives vehicle speed, wheel speed and wheel acceleration information from the sensors, then sends the information to the hydraulic modulator. The hydraulic modulator uses this information to ensure correct hydraulic pressure is maintained at each wheel.

If a lock-up condition should occur, the hydraulic modulator reduces pressure to that particular wheel cylinder by pumping brake fluid from the wheel cylinder back to the master cylinder. If an (ABS) malfunction occurs, the system will shutdown completely and a warning light will come on. The Vehicle can still be driven safely as the normal operation of the brake system will continue.

TROUBLESHOOTING

COMPONENT FAULT TRACING

All procedures must be completed to avoid damaging the control unit.

Refer to wiring diagram and component locations in **Figs. 1 and 2,** during fault tracing procedures.

1. Check fuse in transient surge protector
2. Check all connectors, wires and ground connections for ABS System.
3. Switch ignition off.
4. Disconnect connector from control unit by depressing lock spring and swinging connector out.
5. Remove cover from hydraulic modulator.
6. Remove cover from control unit connector.
7. Remove white protective moldings from sides of connector.
8. Check ground connections in connector.
   a. Always check connectors through holes in side of connector.
   b. Connection numbers are stamped into side of connector
9. Connect ohmmeter between ground and terminals 10, 20, 32 and 34.
   a. Resistance should be zero for all terminals.
   b. If values are not zero, check that wires are undamaged and correctly connected.
10. If a fault is found at terminal 32, test a new solenoid relay (mounted on hydraulic modulator).
11. Switch ignition on.
12. Check transient surge protector as follows:
    a. Connect voltmeter between ground and terminal 1 on control unit connector.

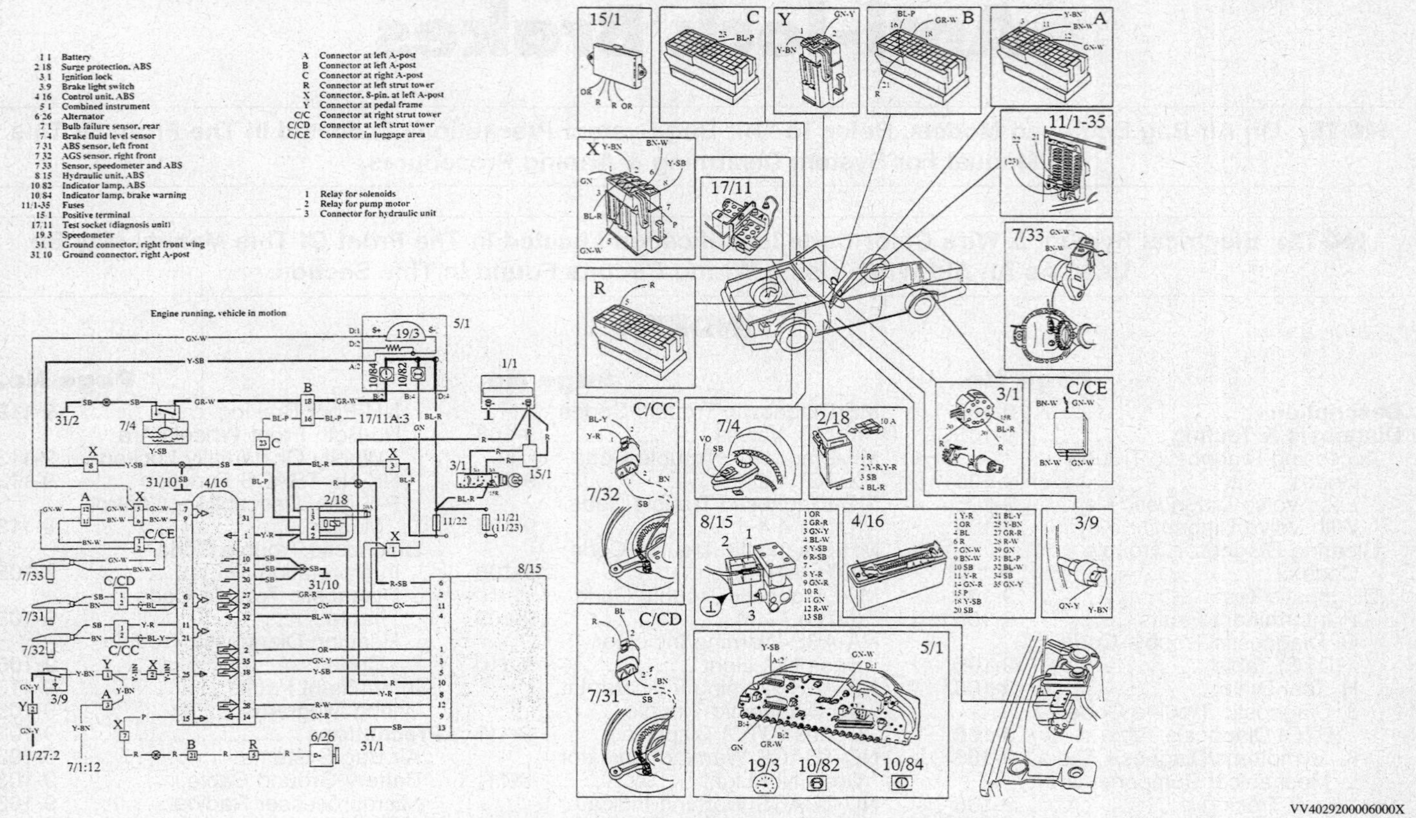

Fig. 1 ABS wiring circuit & electrical components

b. Voltage should be 12 V.
c. If no voltage is registered, take measurement directly on transient surge protector connector.
d. Terminals 1, 2 and 4 should be energized and terminal 3 grounded.
e. If only terminals 1 and 4 are energized when terminal 3 is grounded, transient surge protector is defective and should be replaced.

13. Check power supply to control unit connector by connecting voltmeter between ground and following terminal:
    a. Terminal 25, depress brake pedal at same time.
    b. Terminal 27.
    c. Terminal 28.
    d. Terminal 29.
14. Voltmeter reading obtained should be 12 volts at all terminals except terminal 29. Voltage reading at terminal 29 should be .5–1.0 V.
15. Start engine, voltmeter reading obtained should be 12 volts at terminal 25.
16. If no reading was obtained at:
    a. Terminal 25, check brake light switch, replace if necessary.
    b. Terminal 27, solenoid relay is defective, replace.
    c. Terminal 28, pump relay defective, replace.
    d. Terminal 29, if reading at terminal 27 is correct, reading at terminal 29 should be .5–1.0 V. If not, replace solenoid relay.
17. Switch ignition off.
18. Check voltage to hydraulic modulator connector.
19. Disconnect connector from modulator.
20. Switch ignition on.
21. Connect voltmeter between ground and terminals 6, 7, 10 and 12. Voltmeter should indicate 12 V.
22. If there is no voltage to terminals, perform following checks and make sure wires are undamaged.
    a. Terminal 6. Check wires.
    b. Terminal 7. Connect connector, ABS light should come on. If not, replace bulb.
    c. Terminal 10. Transient surge protector defective, replace.
    d. Terminal 12. Check wires.
23. Switch ignition off.
24. Connect electrical connector and check front sensors as follows:
    a. Connect ohmmeter to control unit electrical connector.
    b. Connect instrument between terminals 4 and 6 for left front sensor, and between terminals 11 and 21 for right front sensor.
    c. Reading obtained should be between .9–2.2 K-ohms.
    d. If reading is not as specified, measure resistance between corresponding terminals of connectors at wheel housings in the engine compartment.
    e. If readings still differ, check that the wiring is intact. If incorrect readings persist, replace sensor.
25. Check pulse wheels for defects. Maximum radial runout is .006 inch.
26. Check rear sensor as follows:
    a. Connect ohmmeter between terminals 7 and 9.
    b. Resistance should be 0.6–1.6 K-ohms. If other readings are obtained, take reading at sensor connector on filler pipe on boot.
    c. If readings are still incorrect, replace sensor.
27. **On rear suspension less Multi-Link,** check wiring to sensors.
28. **On all models,** check hydraulic modulator solenoid valves as follows:
    a. Connect one of ohmmeter test leads to terminal 32 on control unit connector. Move other test lead from terminal 2 to 18 and then to 35.
    b. Readings should be 0.7–1.7 ohms. If not, take reading directly at hydraulic modulator. If reading is still incorrect, replace modulator.
29. Switch ignition on.
30. Check pump relay in hydraulic modulator as follows:
    a. Connect a lead between terminal 28 and ground. **Do not connect for more than 2 seconds.** Modulator should then start.
    b. If modulator does not start, check that the wiring in intact. If fault persists, try connecting by installing a new pump relay.
31. Check valve relay in hydraulic modulator as follows:
    a. Connect voltmeter between pin 32 and ground. Connect a wire between ground and pin 27.
    b. Valve relay should switch on and

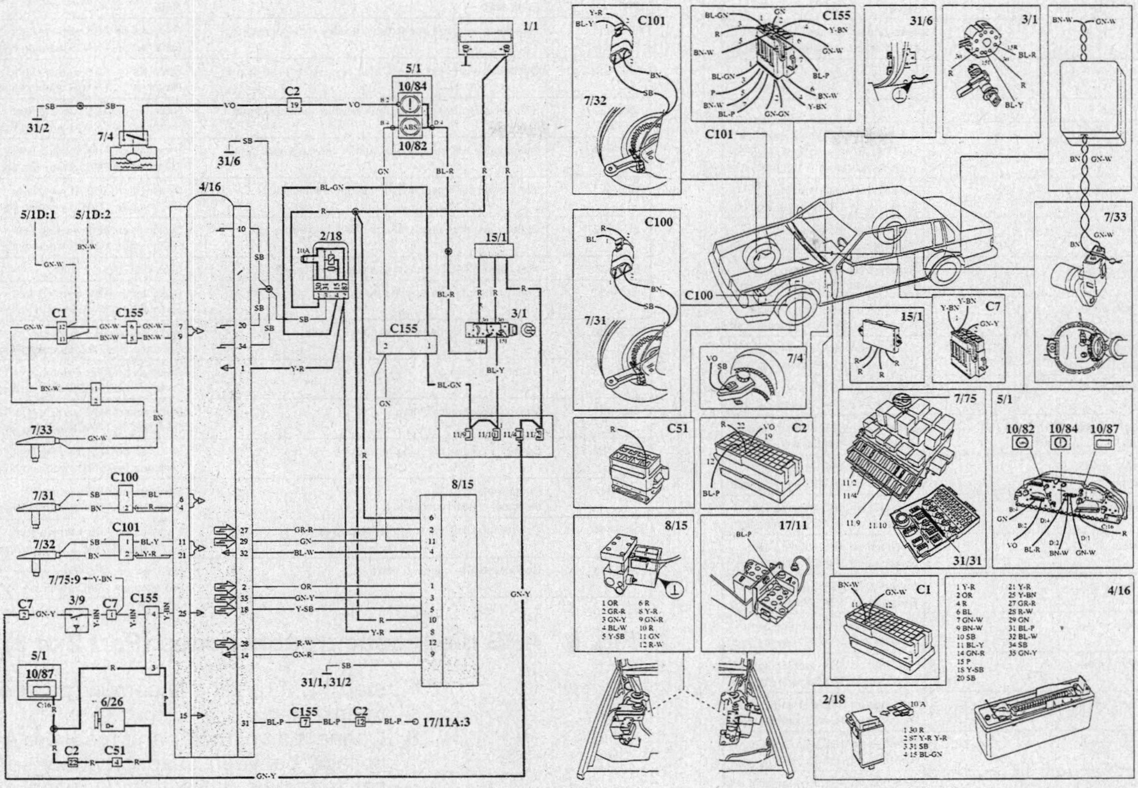

VV4029300007000X

Fig. 2 ABS wiring circuit & electrical components

voltmeter should indicate 12 V.

c. If volts are not as indicated, test with new relay.

32. Switch ignition off.
33. Disconnect test equipment.
34. If no faults were detected during fault tracing, test with new control unit.

DIAGNOSIS & TESTING

The control unit contains a monitoring circuit to detect any internal faults in the control unit and any electrical faults in the sensors, hydraulic modulator or signaling system.

If a fault occurs, the control unit disengages the ABS and illuminates a warning light. When the warning light comes on, a complete fault tracing procedure should be followed. The fault tracing procedure assumes that the standard braking system is fully operational.

Accessing Diagnostic Trouble Codes

LESS VOLVO DIAGNOSTIC KEY

1. Connect diagnostic lead to position 3 on diagnostic output A, then turn ignition switch to On position.
2. Press button once, briefly but firmly. System is now in test mode 1 "On-Board Diagnostic (OBD)" and will display trouble codes.

WITH VOLVO DIAGNOSTIC KEY

1. Turn ignition switch to Off position, then insert memory cassette for car model into Diagnostic Key.
2. Connect connector lead to diagnostic output, turn ignition switch to Off position, then use the ☆ and arrow keys to find "ABS-800" in the display window.
3. Follow instructions in window to get to test mode 1 "On-Board Diagnostic (OBD)" and obtain trouble codes.

Diagnostic Trouble Code Interpretation

READING DIAGNOSTIC TROUBLE CODES

1. Count number of times LED flashes and write down code.
2. Pressing button once more will indicate if there are any further codes stored.
3. When code which was displayed first is displayed again, there are no further codes stored.
4. Correct any faults, then delete diagnostic trouble codes.

DIAGNOSTIC TROUBLE CODE TABLE

Refer to **Fig. 3,** for diagnostic trouble codes (DTC).

Wiring Diagrams

Figs. 4 through 6, for ABS circuit wiring diagram.

Diagnostic Tests

F. INTERMITTENT FAULTS

1. Read and delete any diagnostic trouble codes stored in ABS/TRACS system control module.
2. Test drive vehicle and duplicate driving conditions in which fault appears, refer to procedure "H. Test Drive."
3. Stop vehicle and read any diagnostic trouble codes stored in ABS/TRACS system control module. Refer to "G. Diagnostic Trouble Code (DTC) Table" for trouble code interpretation. If no diagnostic trouble codes have been stored, then Refer to "K. Symptoms/ Diagnosis Table."

G. DIAGNOSTIC TROUBLE CODE (DTC) TABLE

Refer to **Fig. 3,** for diagnostic trouble codes (DTC).

H. TEST DRIVE

Brake problems can make vehicle difficult to operate. Test drive must be performed under safe and controlled conditions.

1. Read any codes stored in control module and delete then turn ignition switch to On position.

DTC	Fault text	Note
ABS-141	EBD-pressure sensor signal, circuit fault	Switches on warning light ABS Switches on warning light TRACS
ABS-142	Brake light switch signal	
ABS-143	Road speed signal, circuit fault	
ABS-144	Brake discs on front wheels overheating	Cars with TRACS only Switches on TRACS warning light Only while temperature is still high
ABS-211	Wheel sensor signal LH front wheel wheel speed incorrect	Switches on ABS warning light Switches on TRACS warning light
ABS-212	Wheel sensor signal RH front wheel wheel speed incorrect	Switches on ABS warning light Switches on TRACS warning light
ABS-213	Wheel sensor signal LH rear wheel wheel speed incorrect	Switches on ABS warning light Switches on TRACS warning light
ABS-214	Wheel sensor signal RH rear wheel wheel speed incorrect	Switches on ABS warning light Switches on TRACS warning light
ABS-221	Wheel sensor signal LH front wheel ABS control phase too long	Switches on ABS warning light Switches on TRACS warning light
ABS-222	Wheel sensor signal RH front wheel ABS control phase too long	Switches on ABS warning light Switches on TRACS warning light
ABS-223	Wheel sensor signal LH rear wheel ABS control phase too long	Switches on ABS warning light Switches on TRACS warning light
ABS-224	Wheel sensor signal RH rear wheel ABS control phase too long	Switches on ABS warning light Switches on TRACS warning light
ABS-311	Wheel sensor signal LH front wheel circuit fault	Switches on ABS warning light Switches on TRACS warning light
ABS-312	Wheel sensor signal RH front wheel circuit fault	Switches on ABS warning light Switches on TRACS warning light
ABS-313	Wheel sensor signal LH rear wheel circuit fault	Switches on ABS warning light Switches on TRACS warning light
ABS-314	Wheel sensor signal RH rear wheel circuit fault	Switches on ABS warning light Switches on TRACS warning light
ABS-321	Wheel sensor signal LH front wheel extrapolation counter	Switches on ABS warning light Switches on TRACS warning light
ABS-322	Wheel sensor signal RH front wheel extrapolation counter	Switches on ABS warning light Switches on TRACS warning light
ABS-323	Wheel sensor signal LH rear wheel extrapolation counter	Switches on ABS warning light Switches on TRACS warning light
ABS-324	Wheel sensor signal RH rear wheel extrapolation counter	Switches on ABS warning light Switches on TRACS warning light

VV4029600015010X

Fig. 3 ABS diagnostic trouble codes (Part 1 of 2)

DTC	Fault text	Note
ABS-411	Inlet valve LH front wheel, fault in valve terminal circuit	Switches on ABS warning light Switches on TRACS warning light
ABS-412	Outlet valve LH front wheel, fault in valve terminal circuit	Switches on ABS warning light Switches on TRACS warning light
ABS-413	Inlet valve RH front wheel, fault in valve terminal circuit	Switches on ABS warning light Switches on TRACS warning light
ABS-414	Outlet valve HR front wheel, fault in valve terminal circuit	Switches on ABS warning light Switches on TRACS warning light
ABS-421	Inlet valve rear wheel,fault in valve terminal circuit	Switches on ABS warning light Switches on TRACS warning light
ABS-422	Outlet valve rear wheel, fault in valve terminal circuit	Switches on ABS warning light Switches on TRACS warning light
ABS-423	Inlet valve TRACS, fault in valve terminal circuit	Cars with TRACS only
ABS-431	Control module - general hardware fault	Switches on ABS warning light Switches on TRACS warning light
ABS-432	Control module - general interference fault	Switches on ABS warning light Switches on TRACS warning light
ABS-433	Battery voltage too high	Switches on ABS warning light Switches on TRACS warning light
ABS-441	Main control module relay	Switches on ABS warning light Switches on TRACS warning light
ABS-442	Control module - creeping powers	Switches on ABS warning light Switches on TRACS warning light
ABS-443	Pump motor electrical or mechanical fault	Switches on ABS warning light Switches on TRACS warning light
ABS-444	Control module - valve reference power	Switches on ABS warning light Switches on TRACS warning light
ABS-445	Control module - general valve fault	Switches on ABS warning light Switches on TRACS warning light

VV4029600015020X

Fig. 3 ABS diagnostic trouble codes (Part 2 of 2)

2. Start engine and observe brake warning indicator. If indicator is lit, car should not be driven. Perform diagnosis procedure "NF. Brake Warning Indicator Does Not Go Out."
3. Drive at least 25 mph to exit diagnostic mode. ABS warning indicator should go out. If not, stop vehicle and read and record codes registered. Refer to "J. Diagnostic Trouble Code (DTC)/ Diagnosis Table."
4. Brake to a stop several times from a reasonable speed on a smooth, dry road. Listen for unusual noises or note if vehicle handles unusually. Pay close attention to clicking or popping noises, observe if vehicle pulls to one side or if brake pedal feels strange. If ABS warning indicator lights, stop vehicle read and record any codes. Note condition under which indicator lights.
5. Read codes and ensure code 1-1-1 is displayed.

J. DIAGNOSTIC TROUBLE CODE (DTC)/DIAGNOSIS TABLE

Refer to **Fig. 7,** for Diagnosis Table.

K. SYMPTOMS/DIAGNOSIS TABLE

Refer to **Fig. 8,** for Symptoms/Diagnosis Table.

L. MECHANICAL COMPONENTS, FAULT TRACING

Refer to **Fig. 9,** for fault tracing on mechanical components.

MA. DIAGNOSTIC TROUBLE CODES (DTC), WHEEL SENSORS

1. Ensure ignition switch is in Off position.
2. Disconnect control module electrical connector, then connect adapter 981 3196 to control module connector.
3. Connect test box 981 3190 to adapter, then the battery ground cable.
4. Connect an ohmmeter between suspect wheel sensor terminals. Left front sensor, terminals 30 and 48. Right front sensor, terminals 29 and 47. Left rear sensor, terminals 28 and 46. Right rear sensor, terminals 27 and 45.
5. Ohmmeter should read between 1040 and 1160 ohms. If reading is incorrect, proceed to step 10. If reading is correct, proceed to next step.
6. Connect ohmmeter between suspect wheel sensor input terminal and ground. Left front sensor, terminal 48. Right front sensor, terminal 47. Left rear sensor, terminal 46. Right rear sensor, terminal 45.
7. Ohmmeter should indicate an open circuit. If reading is incorrect, proceed to step 11. If reading is correct, proceed to next step.
8. Connect a voltmeter and measure AC voltage between suspect wheel sensor terminals while turning wheel by hand. Left front sensor, terminals 30 and 48. Right front sensor, terminals 29 and 47. Left rear sensor, terminals 28 and 46. Right rear sensor, terminals 27 and 45.
9. Voltmeter should read ca. 0.05 to 0.9 V AC. If reading is incorrect, check pulse wheel and sensor for excess dirt or damage. If pulse wheel is satisfactory, wheel sensor should be replaced. If reading is correct, proceed to step 12.
10. Raise and support vehicle, then remove wheel so that suspect sensor is easily accessible. Carefully clean area around sensor connector and brush off any dirt on sensor and pulse wheel with a soft bristle brush. Connect an ohmmeter between terminals 1 and 2 on sensor. Ohmmeter should read between 1040 and 1160 ohms. If reading is incorrect, replace wheel sensor. If reading is correct, check wiring for an open circuit.
11. Raise and support vehicle, then remove wheel so that suspect sensor is easily accessible. Carefully clean area around sensor connector and brush off any dirt on sensor and pulse wheel with a soft bristle brush. Connect ohmmeter between connector terminal 1 and ground. Ohmmeter should indicate an open circuit. If reading is incorrect, replace wheel sensor. If reading is correct, check wiring for short circuits.
12. Check for interference as follows:
    a. Connect ohmmeter between control module housing and ground. Ohmmeter should indicate a closed circuit.

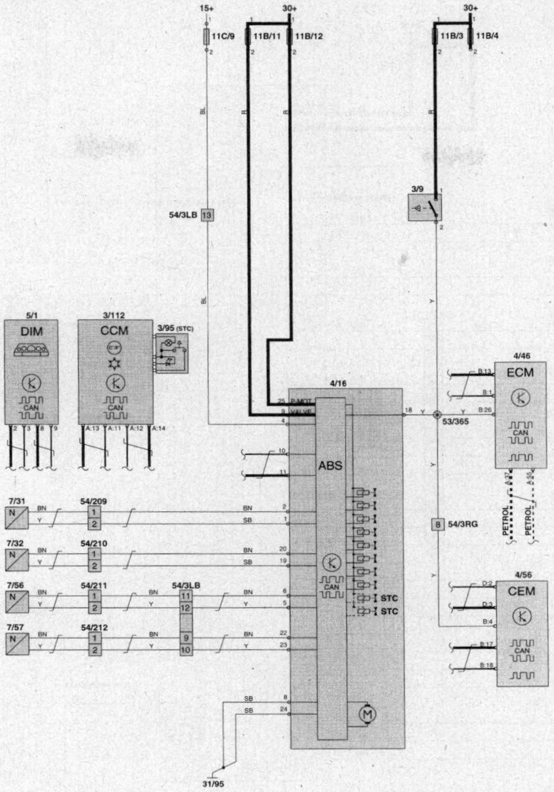

VV4029900017000X

Fig. 4 ABS brake system wiring diagram. S80 w/STC

b. Connect ohmmeter between terminal 1 on test box and ground. Ohmmeter should indicate a closed circuit.
c. Check that sensor wiring is not too close to sources of interference (electric motors, ignition leads, etc.).
d. Check that wiring of suspect sensor is not loose.
e. Check that pulse wheel is not damaged.
f. If tests or components tested in steps a through e are satisfactory, replace control module.

MB-DIAGNOSTIC TROUBLE CODE (DTC) 1-4-1

1. Ensure ignition switch is in Off position.
2. Disconnect control module electrical connector, then connect adapter 981 3196 to control module connector.
3. Connect test box 981 3190 to adapter, then the battery ground cable.
4. Connect jumpers between terminals 1, 2, 21, 34 and 36, then an ohmmeter between terminals 16 and 41. Ohmmeter should read between 224.1 and 273.9 ohms.
5. Turn ignition switch to On position, depress brake pedal as far as it will go and hold, then turn ignition switch to Off position. **So valves do not overheat, ignition must not be switched On for more than 20 seconds. Wait at least 30 seconds before next test.**
6. Release brake pedal slowly while at the same time taking readings from ohmmeter. It should be possible to observe seven distinct resistance readings. **In position 1 brake pedal is fully released. In position 7 brake pedal is fully depressed.**
7. In position 7 resistance should be infinite. In position 6 resistance should be between 928.8 and 1135.2 ohms. In position 5 resistance should be between 735.3 and 898.7 ohms. In position 4 resistance should be between 621 and 759 ohms. In position 3 resistance should be between 507.7 and 619.3 ohms. In position 2 resistance should be between 392.4 and 479.6 ohms. In position 1 resistance should be between 224.1 and 273.9 ohms.
8. If one of the resistance readings is incorrect, check wiring for short circuits. If wiring is satisfactory, pedal sensor must be replaced. Compare color of pedal sensor spacer sleeve with power brake booster color code. If all resistance readings are correct, replace control module.

MC-DIAGNOSTIC TROUBLE CODE (DTC) 1-4-2

1. Check that brake lights work. If brake lights do not work, ensure bulbs are not defective. If bulbs are satisfactory, proceed to step 6. If brake lights work, proceed to next step.
2. Ensure ignition switch is in Off position.
3. Disconnect control module electrical connector, then connect adapter 981 3196 to control module connector.
4. Connect test box 981 3190 to adapter, then the battery ground cable.
5. Connect a voltmeter between terminal 32 and terminal 1, then depress brake pedal. Voltmeter should read battery voltage. If reading is incorrect, check for open or shorted circuit. If reading is correct, delete code and test drive vehicle. If fault occurs again, replace control module.
6. Remove contact pins from brake light contact, then connect voltmeter between contact pin 1 and ground. Voltmeter should read battery voltage. If reading is incorrect, check for break in fuse or wiring. If reading is correct, proceed to next step.
7. Bridge contact pin 1 and contact pin 2 with a wire. Brake light should light. If brake light functions correctly, check that brake light contact is properly adjusted. If contact is properly adjusted, replace brake light contact. If brake light does not function correctly, check that wiring to brake light bulbs is intact.

MD-DIAGNOSTIC TROUBLE CODE (DTC) 1-4-4

Code 1-4-4 is posted when the control module detects that the TRACS system has been used to such an extent that there is a risk of the brakes overheating. In this case, the TRACS system is automatically disengaged and the TRACS warning indicator is lit. When the control module calculates that brake temperature is normal again, the TRACS function is engaged and the TRACS warning indicator goes out.

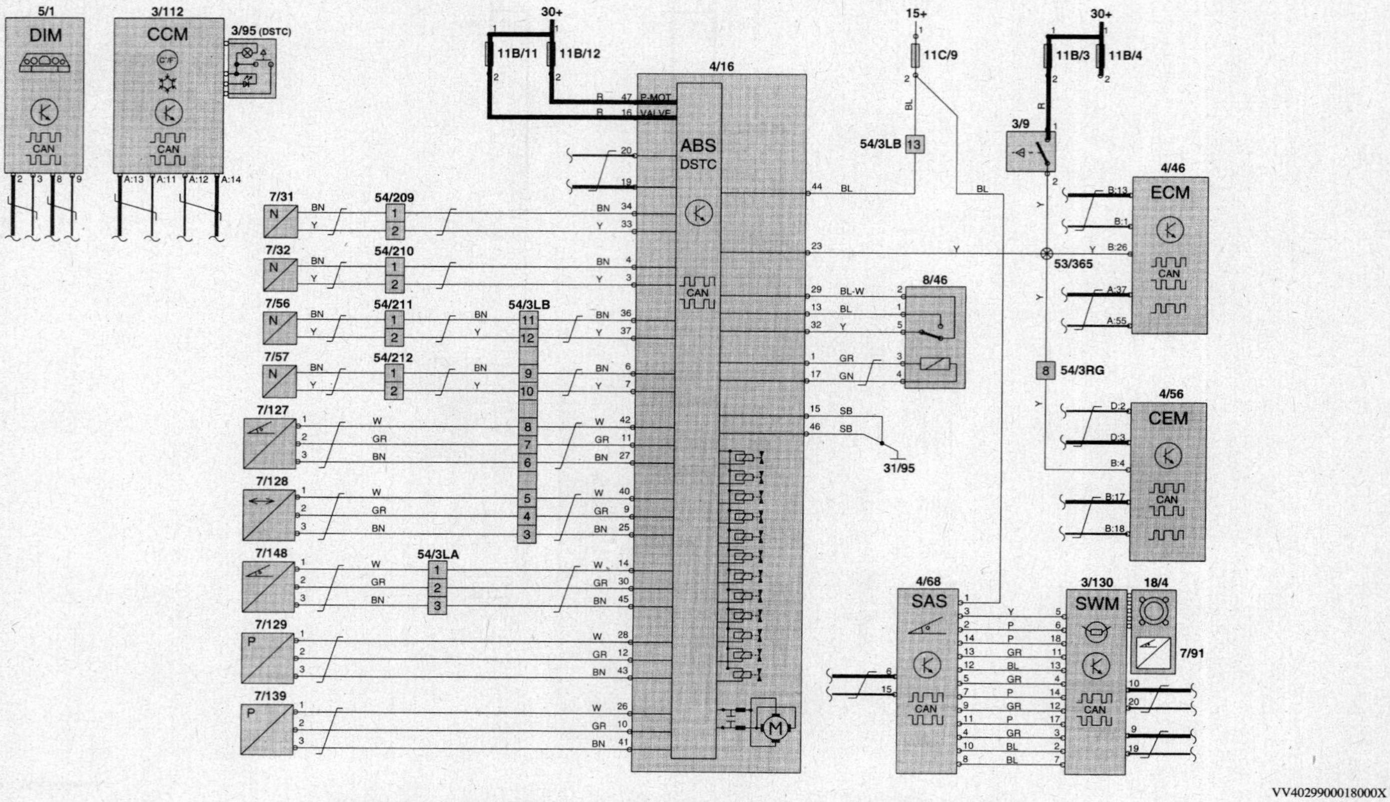

Fig. 5 ABS brake system wiring diagram. S80 w/DSTC

Visually inspect front brakes for signs of overheating damage. Delete code.

ME-DIAGNOSTIC TROUBLE CODES (DTC), VALVES

1. Ensure ignition switch is in Off position.
2. Disconnect control module electrical connector, then connect adapter 981 3196 to control module connector.
3. Connect test box 981 3190 to adapter, then the battery ground cable.
4. Connect an ohmmeter between terminal 3 and left front inlet valve terminal 20, right front inlet valve terminal 38, rear inlet valve terminal 54 and TRACS valve terminal 37. Resistance should be 6–8 ohms for all measurements. Connect ohmmeter between terminal 3 and left front return valve terminal 2, right front return valve terminal 21 and rear return valve terminal 36. Resistance should be 3–5 ohms for all measurements.
5. If readings are incorrect, check for open circuit in wiring. If wiring is satisfactory, replace hydraulic modulator. If readings are correct, proceed to next step.
6. Remove 15-pole connector from combination relay. Connect ohmmeter between terminal 1 and left front inlet valve terminal 20, right front inlet valve terminal 38, rear inlet valve terminal 54 and TRACS valve terminal 37. Connect ohmmeter between terminal 1 and left front return valve terminal 2, right front return valve terminal 21 and rear return valve terminal 36. Ohmmeter should indicate an open circuit for all measurements.
7. If readings are incorrect, check for short circuit in wiring. If wiring is satisfactory, replace hydraulic modulator. If reading are correct, replace control module.

MF-DIAGNOSTIC TROUBLE CODE (DTC) 4-2-4

1. Ensure ignition switch is in Off position.
2. Disconnect control module electrical connector, then connect adapter 981 3196 to control module connector.
3. Connect test box 981 3190 to adapter, then the battery ground cable.
4. Connect an ohmmeter between terminal 13 and terminal 26. Ohmmeter should read ca. 0 ohms. Connect ohmmeter between terminal 26 and ground. Ohmmeter should indicate an open circuit.
5. If one of the readings is incorrect, check for open or short circuit in wiring. If wiring is satisfactory, replace hydraulic modulator. If reading are correct, proceed to next step.
6. Connect an ohmmeter between terminal 13 and terminal 26, then depress brake pedal. Ohmmeter should indicate an open in the circuit.
7. If reading is incorrect, check for short circuit. If circuit is satisfactory, replace hydraulic modulator. If readings are correct, check for properly operating brake light contact. If brake light contact is operating properly, delete code and test drive vehicle. If code appears again, replace control module.

MG-DIAGNOSTIC TROUBLE CODE (DTC) 4-4-1

1. Ensure ignition switch is in Off position.
2. Disconnect control module electrical connector, then connect adapter 981 3196 to control module connector.
3. Connect test box 981 3190 to adapter, then the battery ground cable.
4. Connect an ohmmeter between control module housing and ground. Ohmmeter should indicate a closed circuit. Connect ohmmeter between terminal 1 and ground. Ohmmeter should indicate a closed circuit.
5. If reading is correct, check that wheel sensor is not too close to sources of interference, (electric motors, telephone lines, etc.). Delete code and test drive vehicle. If fault occurs again, replace control module.

MH-DIAGNOSTIC TROUBLE CODE (DTC) 4-4-3

1. Disconnect 15-pole connector from combination relay, then connect a voltmeter between terminal 15 and ground. Voltmeter should indicate battery voltage.
2. If reading is incorrect, check for break in fuse or wiring. If reading is correct, proceed to next step.
3. Connect voltmeter between terminal 15 and terminal 2. Voltmeter should indicate battery voltage.
4. If reading is incorrect, check that wiring

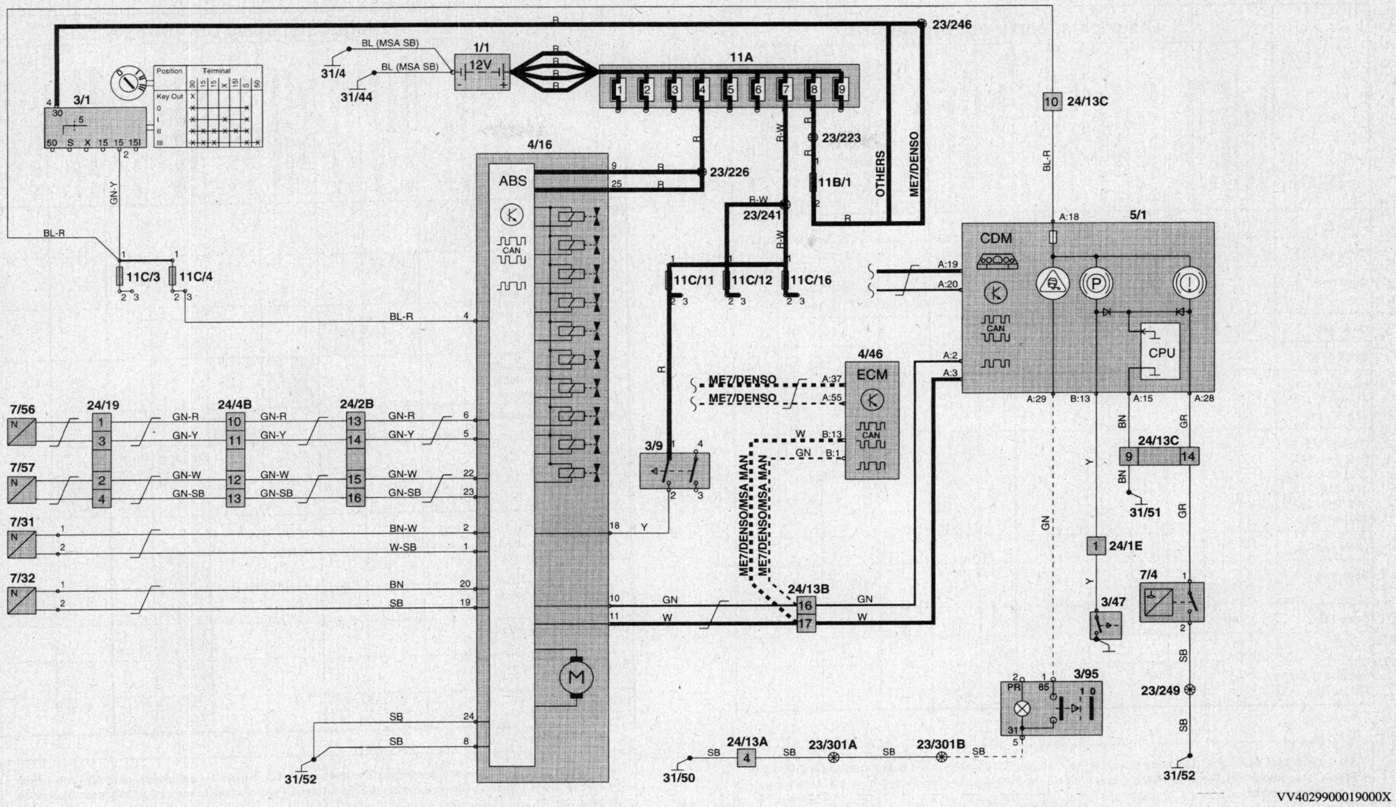

Fig. 6 ABS brake system wiring diagram. C70, S70 & V70

to ground is not shorted or broken. If reading is correct, proceed to next step.

5. Disconnect 4-pole connector from combination relay, then connect an ohmmeter between terminal 2 and terminal 4. Ohmmeter should read between 10 and 40 ohms. Connect ohmmeter between terminal 2 and ground. Ohmmeter should indicate a broken circuit.
6. If one of the readings is incorrect, replace hydraulic modulator. If both readings are correct, proceed to next step.
7. Using two wire bridges, bridge terminal 2 on 15-pole connector and terminal 3 on 4-pole connector, then terminal 15 on 15-pole connector and terminal 1 on 4-pole connector. Pump motor should operate.
8. If pump motor does not operate, replace hydraulic modulator. If pump motor operates, leave bridges in place and proceed to next step.
9. Connect voltmeter between terminal 4 and terminal 2 on 4-pole connector. Voltmeter should read over 0.5 V AC while pump motor is running. Remove bridges.
10. If reading is incorrect, replace hydraulic modulator. If reading is correct, proceed to next step.
11. Connect ohmmeter between terminal 1 on 4-pole connector and terminal 15 on 15-pole connector. Ohmmeter should indicate an open circuit. Connect ohmmeter between terminal 3 on 4-pole connector and terminal 2 on 15-pole connector. Ohmmeter should read 0 ohms. Connect ohmmeter between terminal 2 on 4-pole connector and terminal 8 on 15-pole connector. Ohmmeter should read 0 ohms. Connect ohmmeter between terminal 4 on 4-pole connector and terminal 7 on 15-pole connector. Ohmmeter should read 0 ohms. Connect ohmmeter between terminal 10 and terminal 13 on 15-pole connector. Ohmmeter should read between 45 and 90 ohms.
12. If one of the readings is incorrect, replace combination relay. If all readings are correct, replace connectors, then proceed to next step.
13. Ensure ignition switch is in Off position.
14. Disconnect control module electrical connector, then connect adapter 981 3196 to control module connector.
15. Connect test box 981 3190 to adapter, then the battery ground cable.
16. Connect a wire between terminal 15 on test box and battery positive terminal. Pump motor should operate.
17. If pump motor does not operate, check combination relay for shorted or an open in wiring. If wiring is satisfactory, replace combination relay. If pump motor operates, proceed to next step.
18. Connect ohmmeter between terminal 49 and terminal 31. Ohmmeter should read between 10 and 40 ohms.
19. If reading is incorrect, check for a an open in wiring. If reading is correct, proceed to next step.
20. Connect ohmmeter between terminal 49 and terminal 1, then terminal 31 and terminal 1. Ohmmeter should indicate an open in circuit in both cases.
21. If readings are incorrect, check for grounding. If circuit is not grounded, replace combination relay. If readings are correct, replace control module.

MJ-DIAGNOSTIC TROUBLE CODE (DTC) 4-4-4

1. Ensure ignition switch is in Off position.
2. Disconnect control module electrical connector, then connect adapter 981 3196 to control module connector.
3. Connect test box 981 3190 to adapter, then the battery ground cable.
4. Disconnect 15-pole connector from combination relay, then connect an ohmmeter between ground and terminal 3 on test box, terminal 33 on test box and terminal 34 on test box. Ohmmeter should indicate an open circuit for each check.
5. If one of the readings is incorrect, check for short circuit in wiring. If readings are correct, proceed to next step.
6. Connect ohmmeter between terminal 3 on test box and terminal 9 on 15-pole connector. Ohmmeter should read ca. 0 ohms.
7. If readings are incorrect, proceed to step 16. If readings are correct, proceed to next step.
8. Connect ohmmeter between terminal 34 on test box and terminal 12 on 15-pole connector. Ohmmeter should read ca. 0 ohms.

DTC	Diagnosis, carry out procedure:												
	MJ. Diagnostic trouble code (DTC) 4-4-4	MH. Diagnostic trouble code (DTC) 4-4-3	MG. Diagnostic trouble code (DTC) 4-4-1	MF. Diagnostic trouble code (DTC) 4-2-4	ME. Diagnostic trouble codes (DTC), valves.	MD. Diagnostic trouble codes (DTC) 1-4-4	MC. Diagnostic trouble codes (DTC) 1-4-2	MB. Diagnostic trouble codes 1-4-1	MA. Diagn. trouble codes (DTC), wheel sensors.	RK. Bleeding brakes.	Delete diagn. trouble codes (DTC) and test drive, see proc. H. Test drive.	TD. Hydraulic modulator, replacement.	TC. Control module, replacement.
Code 444	■												
Code 443		■											
Code 442										Do no.1	Do no. 2	Do no. 3	
Code 441			■										
Code 424				■									
Code 411, 412, 413, 414, 421, 422 or 423					■								
Code211, 212, 213, 214, 221, 222, 223, 224, 311, 312, 313, 314, 321, 322, 323, or 324									■				
Code 144						■							
Code 143											Do no. 1		Do no. 2
Code 142							■						
Code 141								■					
Code 121, 122, 123, or 124									■				

After repairs have been completed delete diagnostic trouble codes (DTC) so that 1-1-1 is displayed and test drive the vehicle (see procedure H. Test drive). Carry out procedure E. ABS/TRACS Function check to ensure that the function is operating properly.

VV4029100009000X

Fig. 7 ABS Diagnostic Trouble Code (DTC)/ Diagnosis Table

Symptom	Diagnosis, carry out procedure:								
	NA. ABS warning indocator does not light.	NB. ABS warning indicator lit, no diagnostic trouble codes (DTC) displayed.	NC. TRACS warning indicator does not light.	ND. TRACS warning indicator lit, no trouble codes (DTC) displayed.	NG. Diagnostic trouble codes (DTC cannot be read.	L. Mechanical components, fault tracing.	NH. Poor braking.	NJ. Both the fornt wheels wholly or partially locked.	NK. No TRACS function.
ABS warning indicator does not light.	■								
ABS warning indicator lit, no diagnostic trouble codes (DTC) displayed.		■							
TRACS warning indicator does not light.			■						
TRACS warning indicator lit, no diagnostic trouble codes (DTC) displayed.				■					
Diagnostic trouble codes cannot be read.					■				
Poor braking.						Do no. 1	Do no. 2		
Brakes binding.								■	
No TRACS function.									■
Excessive pedal travel.						■			
Brake pedal bottoms.						■			
Brakes pull to one side.						■			
Brakes grab.						■			
Brakes squeal						■			

After repairs have been completed delete diagnostic trouble codes (DTC) so that 1-1-1 is displayed and test drive the vehicle (see procedure H. Test drive). Carry out procedure E. ABS/TRACS Function check to ensure that the function is operating properly.

VV4029100010000X

Fig. 8 ABS Symptoms/Diagnosis Table

9. If readings are incorrect, check for break in wiring. If readings are correct, proceed to next step.
10. Turn ignition switch to On position. Connect a voltmeter between terminal 3 on 15-pole connector and ground. Connect voltmeter between terminal 4 on 15-pole connector and ground. Turn ignition switch to Off position. Both readings should battery voltage.
11. If readings are incorrect, ensure wiring is intact. If readings are correct, proceed to next step.
12. Connect ohmmeter between terminal 9 and terminal 10 on 15-pole connector. Ohmmeter should read 0 ohms. Connect ohmmeter between terminal 3 and terminal 12 on 15-pole connector. Ohmmeter should read between 45 and 90 ohms.
13. If one of the readings is incorrect, replace combination relay. If both readings are correct, proceed to next step.
14. Connect 15-pole connector, turn ignition switch to On position, connect a jumper between test box terminals 34 and 1, then connect voltmeter between terminal 3 and terminal 1. Voltmeter should indicate battery voltage. Turn ignition switch to Off position.
15. If readings are incorrect, replace combination relay. If readings are correct, replace control module.
16. Disconnect 15-pole connector from hydraulic modulator, then connect ohmmeter between terminal 15 and terminal 1. Ohmmeter should read ca. 0 ohms.
17. If readings are incorrect, replace hydraulic modulator. If readings are correct, proceed to next step.
18. Connect ohmmeter between terminal 1 on hydraulic modulator connector and terminal 3 on test box. Ohmmeter should read ca. 0 ohms.
19. If readings are incorrect, ensure there are no breaks in wiring. If readings are correct, ensure wiring is intact between terminal 15 on hydraulic modulator connector and terminal 9 on 15-pole relay connector.

NA-ABS-WARNING INDICATOR DOES NOT LIGHT

1. Ensure ignition switch is in Off position.
2. Disconnect control module electrical connector, then connect adapter 981 3196 to control module connector.
3. Connect test box 981 3190 to adapter, then the battery ground cable.
4. Disconnect 15-pole connector from combination relay, connect a voltmeter between terminals 52 and 1, then turn ignition switch to On position. Voltmeter should indicate battery voltage. Turn ignition switch to Off position.
5. If reading is incorrect, ensure wiring to bulb and bulb are intact. If bulb and wiring to bulb are satisfactory, replace combination instrument. If readings are correct, proceed to next step.
6. Turn ignition switch to On position, then connect a jumper between terminal 6 on 15-pole connector and ground. ABS warning indicator should light. Turn ignition switch to Off position. **If fuse blows, check wiring for short circuit.**
7. If indicator does not light, check for breaks in wiring. If indicator lights, a double fault may have occurred, proceed to next step.
8. Connect positive lead of a diode tester to relay terminal 6 and negative lead to relay terminal 2 on 15-pole combination relay connector. Diode tester should indicate continuity. Change polarity on diode tester. Diode tester should indicate a break.
9. If readings are incorrect, replace combination relay and continue to next step. If readings are correct, leave relay connector disconnected and proceed to next step.
10. Connect a jumper between terminal 52 and terminal 1, then turn ignition switch to On position. ABS warning indicator should light. Turn ignition switch to Off position.
11. If indicator does not light, check for breaks in wiring. If indicator lights, reconnect system and ensure ABS warning indicator is operating properly. If indicator still does not light, replace control module.

Cause	Remedy
Excessive pedal travel, "spongy" brakes	
Pedal travel excessive due to lateral brake disc run-out.	Check the disc and replace if necessary.
Air in the braking system.	Bleed the braking system.
Brake fluid level low.	Check for leaks, fill and bleed the system.
Brake pedal bottoms	
Brake fluid level.	Check for leaks, fill and bleed the system.
Air in the braking system.	Bleed the braking system.
Leak in the braking system.	Check the braking system, repair the leak and bleed the system.
Faulty clutch master cylinder.	Replace clutch master cylinder.
Leaking hose.	Replace hose.
Worn seal.	Overhaul the brake caliper.
Poor braking	
Moisture on the pads and discs.	Brake several times to dry the pads.
Grease or oil on the pads.	Replace brake pads and check adjacent seals.
Faulty power brake booster non-return valve.	Replace non-return valve.
Faulty power brake booster.	Check the vacuum and the condition of the power brake booster.
	Replace the power brake booster or hoses if necessary.

VV4029100011010X

Fig. 9 ABS Mechanical Components, Fault Tracing (Part 1 of 2)

Cause	Remedy
Brakes pull to one side	
Grease or oil on brake pads.	Replace brake pads and check adjacent seal.
Faulty brake caliper.	Overhaul the brake caliper.
Wrong tire pressure.	Adjust tire pressure.
Uneven tire wear.	Check/adjust wheel alignment.
Wrongly aligned front suspension.	Align front suspension.
Tires not mounted with DOT marking facing out.	Mount tires on rims with DOT marking facing out in order to counter conicity forces.
Brakes grab	
Moisture on pads and discs.	Brake several times to dry the pads.
Wheel hub play.	Replace the wheel hub.
Brake pads worn out.	Replace brake pads.
Vibrations in the brake pedal (caused by variations in the thickness of the brake disc).	Machine* or replace brake disc.(*check warranty conditions)
Brake caliper loose.	Tighten brake caliper.
Brakes squeal	
Affected by weather conditions.	Brake several times to dry.
Brake pads worn out.	Replace brake pads.
Rear brake caliper brake pads vibrate.	Check the brake disc. Replace if necessary.
Brakes binding	
Handbrake cable sticking.	Replace cable.
Wrongly adjusted handbrake.	Adjust the handbrake.
Faulty clutch master cylinder.	Replace clutch master cylinder.
Deformed brake pipes.	Replace brake pipes.

VV4029100011020X

Fig. 9 ABS Mechanical Components, Fault Tracing (Part 2 of 2)

NB-ABS-WARNING INDICATOR LIT, NO DIAGNOSTIC TROUBLE CODES (DTC) DISPLAYED

1. Drive vehicle at a speed of at least 25 mph. If ABS warning indicator does not go out, proceed to next step.
2. Ensure ignition switch is in Off position.
3. Disconnect control module electrical connector, then connect adapter 981 3196 to control module connector.
4. Connect test box 981 3190 to adapter, then the battery ground cable.
5. Connect a jumper between terminal 34 and terminal 1, a voltmeter between terminal 33 and terminal 1, then turn ignition switch to On position. Voltmeter should indicate battery voltage.
6. In reading is incorrect, check for an open in wiring. If wiring is satisfactory, replace combination relay. If reading is correct, leave jumper in place and proceed to next step.
7. With ignition switch in On position, connect an ohmmeter between terminal 52 and terminal 1. Ohmmeter should indicate an open circuit.
8. If reading is incorrect, proceed to next step. If reading is correct, replace control module.
9. Turn ignition switch to Off position, disconnect 15-pole connector from combination relay, then connect ohmmeter between terminal 52 and terminal 1. Ohmmeter should indicate an open circuit.
10. If reading is incorrect, check for short circuit in combination instrument wiring. If reading is correct, replace combination relay.

NC-TRACS WARNING INDICATOR DOES NOT LIGHT

1. Check that control module is intended for TRACS (blue label).
2. Ensure ignition switch is in Off position.
3. Disconnect control module electrical connector, then connect adapter 981 3196 to control module connector.
4. Connect test box 981 3190 to adapter, then the battery ground cable.
5. Connect a jumper between terminal 44 and terminal 1, then turn ignition switch to On position. TRACS warning indicator should light. Turn ignition switch to Off position.
6. If indicator did not light, ensure wiring to bulb and bulb are intact. If bulb and wiring to bulb are satisfactory, replace combination instrument. If readings are correct, replace control module.

ND-TRACS WARNING INDICATOR LIT, NO DIAGNOSTIC TROUBLE CODES (DTC) DISPLAYED

1. Check that control module is intended for TRACS (blue label).
2. Ensure ignition switch is in Off position.
3. Disconnect control module electrical connector, then connect adapter 981 3196 to control module connector.
4. Connect test box 981 3190 to adapter, then the battery ground cable.
5. Turn ignition switch to On position, then connect an ohmmeter between terminal 44 and terminal 1. Ohmmeter should indicate a broken circuit. Turn Ignition switch to Off position.
6. If reading is incorrect, check for a short circuit in combination instrument wiring. If reading is correct, replace control module.

NE-BRAKE WARNING INDICATOR DOES NOT LIGHT

1. **If brake warning indicator does not light when ignition is switched On,** proceed as follows:
   a. Disconnect connector from brake fluid level switch, connect a jumper between terminals 1 and 2, start engine or remove D+ connector from alternator, then ensure charge indicator goes out. Brake warning indicator should light. Turn engine Off or connect D+ connector.
   b. If indicator does not light, ensure bulb is intact and there are no

Note! All readings shown are between the terminal in column 1 and terminal 1 (Signal ground (GND)). Ensure, therefore, that this ground (GND) point is properly connected to the battery negative terminal before readings are taken.

Connection	Signal type Function	Ignition Off		On	
		U (V)	R (Ω)	U (V)	R (Ω)
1	Signal ground (GND)	U_{low}	0	U_{low}	0
2	Output to the return valve (left front wheel), in the hydraulic modulator.	U_{low}	3-5	U_{bat}	∞
3	Power supply to all valves in the hydraulic modulator.	U_{low}	0	U_{bat}	∞
4-12	Not used.		-	-	-
13	Input from the pressure switch (TRACS) in the hydraulic modulator. Normally closed, opens on activation.	U_{low}	-	6-10	∞
14	Not used.	-	-	-	-
15	Output for activation of pump motor relay.	U_{low}	45-90	U_{bat}	∞
16	Terminal for the pedal position sensor in the power brake booster.	U_{low}	249 ± 10 %	0-2	∞
17-19	Not used.	-	-	-	-
20	Output to inlet valve (left front wheel), in the hydraulic modulator.	U_{low}	6-8	U_{bat}	∞
21	Output to return valve (right front wheel), in the hydraulic modulator.	U_{low}	3-5	U_{bat}	∞
22	Not used.	-	-	-	-
23	Input and output for diagnostic output.	U_{low}	-	8-11	∞
24	Not used.	-	-	-	-
25	Input from TRACS switch	U_{low}	∞	U_{bat}	∞
26	Output to (TRACS) pressure switch in the hydraulic modulator. Normally closed, opens on activation.	U_{low}	-	6-10	∞
27	Negative reference for right rear wheel sensor.	U_{low}	0	U_{low}	6-8
28	Negative reference for left rear wheel sensor.	U_{low}	0	U_{low}	6-8
29	Negative reference for right front wheel sensor.	U_{low}	0	U_{low}	6-8
30	Negative reference for left front wheel sensor.	U_{low}	0	U_{low}	6-8
31	Negative reference for pump motor sensor in the hydraulic modulator.	U_{low}	12000	0-2	∞

VV4029100012010X

Fig. 10 ABS control module signal description (Part 1 of 2)

U = Voltage (V)
U_{bat} = Battery voltage
U_{low} = voltage almost 0 V
R = Resistance in ohm (Ω)
∞ = Infinite resistance

Connection	Signal type Function	Ignition Off		On	
		U (V)	R (Ω)	U (V)	R (Ω)
32	Input from brake light contact. High signal indicates braking.	U_{low}	0-2	U_{low}	
33	Input for main relay function check.	U_{low}	0	U_{bat}	∞
34	Output main relay activation. Low signal operates the relay.	U_{low}	45-90	0-2	-
35	30-supply. The power supply from the battery to the control module, for calculating brake temperature.	U_{bat}	∞	U_{bat}	∞
36	Output to return valve in the hydraulic modulator.	U_{low}	3-5	U_{bat}	∞
37	Output to the TRACS valve. A low signal activates the valve.	U_{low}	6-9	U_{bat}	∞
38	Output to inlet valve (right front wheel), in the hydraulic modulator.	U_{low}	6-8	U_{bat}	∞
39-40	Not used.	-	-	-	-
41	Terminal for pedal position sensor in the power brake booster.	U_{low}	0	U_{low}	6-9
42-43	Not used.	-	-	-	-
44	Output to TRACS warning indicator. A low signal lights the lamp.	U_{low}	-	U_{bat}	∞
45	Positive reference for right rear wheel sensor.	U_{low}	1100	U_{bat}	∞
46	Positive reference for left rear wheel sensor.	U_{low}	1100	U_{bat}	∞
47	Positive reference for right front wheel sensor.	U_{low}	1100	U_{bat}	∞
48	Positive reference for left front wheel sensor.	U_{low}	1100	U_{bat}	∞
49	Positive reference for pump motor sensor in the hydraulic modulator.	U_{low}	12000	0-2	∞
50-51	Not used.	-	-	-	-
52	Output to ABS warning indicator. A low signal lights the lamp.	U_{low}	-	U_{bat}	∞
53	15I-supply. The power supply from the ignition switch to the control module.	U_{low}	1-3	U_{bat}	∞
54	Output to the inlet valve (rear wheels), in the hydraulic modulator.	U_{low}	6-8	U_{bat}	∞
55	Not used.	-	-	-	-

VV4029100012020X

Fig. 10 ABS control module signal description (Part 2 of 2)

opens in wiring to fluid level switch. If bulb and wiring to bulb are satisfactory, replace combination instrument. If indicator lights, replace combination instrument.

2. **If brake warning indicator does not light when brake fluid level is too low,** proceed as follows:
   a. Disconnect connector from brake fluid level switch, connect a jumper between terminals 1 and 2, start engine or remove D+ connector from alternator. ensure charge indicator goes out. Brake warning indicator should light. Turn engine Off or connect D+ connector.
   b. If indicator does not light, check for an open in brake fluid warning level switch wiring. If indicator lights, replace brake fluid level switch.

NF-BRAKE WARNING INDICATOR DOES NOT GO OUT

1. Check brake fluid level. Reservoir should be full.
2. Disconnect connector from brake fluid level switch, start engine or remove D+ connector from alternator. Brake warning indicator should go out. Turn engine Off or connect D+ connector.
3. If indicator stayed On, ensure wiring to switch is not grounded. If circuit is not shorted, replace combination instrument. If indicator went out, replace brake fluid level switch.

NG-DIAGNOSTIC TROUBLE CODES (DTC) CANNOT BE READ

1. Ensure ignition switch is in Off position.
2. Disconnect control module electrical connector, then connect adapter 981 3196 to control module connector.
3. Connect test box 981 3190 to adapter, then the battery ground cable.
4. Remove diagnostic output from its connector, turn ignition switch to On position, then connect a voltmeter between terminal 53 and terminal 1. Voltmeter should indicate battery voltage.
5. If reading is incorrect, ensure fuse 11/29 and wiring are intact. If reading is correct, proceed to next step.
6. Connect an ohmmeter between terminal 23 and terminal 1, remove diagnostic key or disconnect selector lead from diagnostic output. Ohmmeter should indicate an open circuit.
7. If reading is incorrect, check wiring for a short circuit. If reading is correct, proceed to next step.
8. Connect ohmmeter between terminal 23 on test box and terminal A3 on diagnostic output connector. Ohmmeter should read ca. 0 ohms.
9. If reading is incorrect, check for an open in wiring. If reading is correct, proceed to next step.
10. Turn ignition switch to On position, then connect voltmeter between terminal A4 on diagnostic output connector and ground. Voltmeter should indicate battery voltage.
11. If reading is incorrect, ensure fuse 11/33 and wiring are intact. If reading is correct, proceed to next step.
12. Connect voltmeter between terminals A8 and A4 on diagnostic output connector. Voltmeter should indicate battery voltage. Turn ignition switch to Off position.
13. If reading is incorrect, ensure wiring is intact. If reading is correct, check diagnostic key or diagnostic output on another system. If diagnostic key or diagnostic output are not faulty, replace control module.

NH-POOR BRAKING

1. Raise and support vehicle enough to allow its wheels to turn freely, release parking brake and place shift lever in Neutral, depress brake pedal and release it again, then turn wheel with suspect valve by hand. Wheel should turn.
2. If wheel did not turn, check that brake caliper is not frozen, parking brake cable is released and brake pads, springs and other components are not sticking or frozen. If wheel turned, proceed to next step.
3. Ensure ignition switch is in Off position.
4. Disconnect control module electrical connector, then connect adapter 981

Carry out a system check as a guideline for normal function. See the fault tracing procedure if other results are obtained.

Do	Normal function	Fault tracing in case of fault
Start mode Ignition: off		
Ignition: On Engine off.	ABS warning indicator (and TRACS warning indicator) lit for 1 to 2 seconds, then go out.	Carry out procedure E. ABS/TRACS - Function check.
	Brake warning indicator lit.	Carry out procedure NE. Brake warning indicator does not light.
Start the engine.	ABS warning indicator (and TRACS warning indicator) lit for 1 to 2 seconds, then go out.	Carry out procedure E. ABS/TRACS - Function check
	Brake warning indicator goes out.	Carry out procedure NF. Brake warning indicator does not go out.

Note! If the car is not fitted with TRACS, only the ABS warning indicator should light.

VV4029100013000X

Fig. 11 ABS system check, normal function

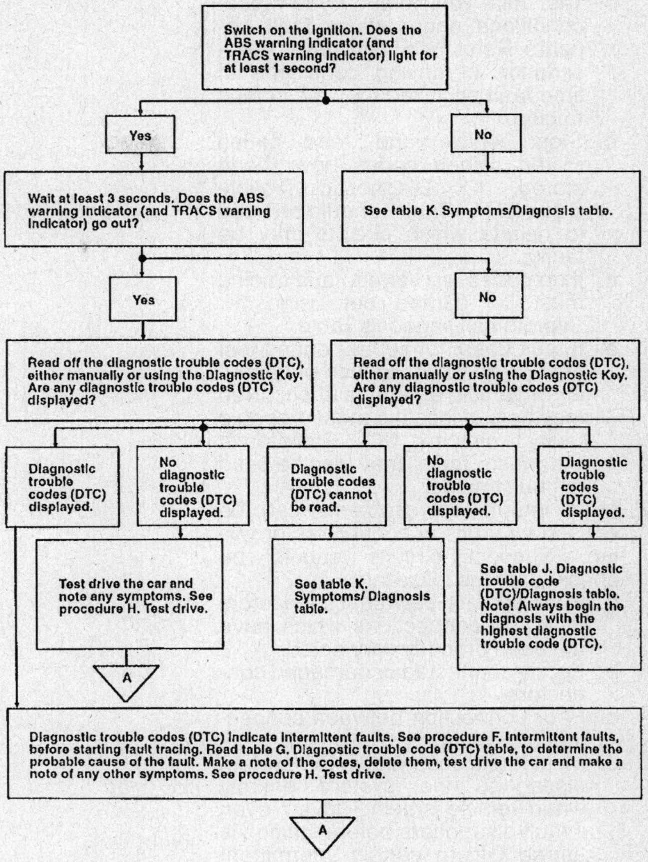

VV4029100014010X

Fig. 12 ABS/TRACS function check (Part 1 of 2)

3196 to control module connector.
5. Connect test box 981 3190 to adapter, then the battery ground cable.
6. Connect a jumper between terminals 34 and 1 of test box and between left front return valve terminal 2, right front return valve terminal 21 or rear return valve terminal 36 and terminal 1. Depress brake pedal and keep it down, turn ignition switch to On position, then turn wheel with suspect valve by hand. Wheel should turn. Turn ignition switch to Off position. **So valves do not overheat, ignition must not be switched On for more than 20 seconds. Wait at least 30 seconds before next test.**
7. If wheel did not turn, replace hydraulic modulator. If wheel turned, proceed to next step.
8. Connect jumper between left front inlet valve terminal 20, right front inlet valve terminal 38 or rear inlet valve terminal 54 and terminal 1. Turn ignition switch to On position, depress brake pedal and keep it down, then turn wheel with suspect valve by hand. Wheel should turn. Turn ignition switch to Off position. **So valves do not overheat, ignition must not be switched On for more than 20 seconds. Wait at least 30 seconds before next test.**
9. If wheel did not turn, replace hydraulic modulator. If wheel turned, the suspect hydraulic modulator valve operates properly. Problem may be intermittent, refer to "F. Intermittent Faults."

NJ-BOTH FRONT WHEELS ARE WHOLLY OR PARTIALLY LOCKED

1. Check that both front wheels are locked or binding equally.
2. If wheels are not locked or binding, proceed to next step. If wheels are locked or binding, refer to "L. Mechanical Components, Fault Tracing."
3. Ensure ignition switch is in Off position.
4. Disconnect control module electrical connector, then connect adapter 981 3196 to control module connector.
5. Connect test box 981 3190 to adapter, then the battery ground cable.
6. Connect jumpers between terminals 34 and 1, terminals 21 and 1 and terminals 2 and 1, then turn ignition switch to On position. Wheels should turn. Turn ignition switch to Off position. Visually inspect brakes. **So valves do not overheat, ignition must not be switched On for more than 20 seconds. Wait at least 30 seconds before next test.**
7. If wheels turn, replace hydraulic modulator. If wheels do not turn, fault is mechanical. Refer to "L. Mechanical Components, Fault Tracing."

NK-NO TRACS FUNCTION

1. TRACS switch must be On for TRACS to operate. Turn ignition switch to On position, set TRACS switch To On position. Indicator lamp should light. Turn ignition switch to Off position.
2. If indicator does not light, check wiring to switch for breaks. If wiring is satisfactory, replace switch. If indicator does light, proceed to next step.
3. Ensure ignition switch is in Off position.
4. Disconnect control module electrical connector, then connect adapter 981 3196 to control module connector.
5. Connect test box 981 3190 to adapter, then the battery ground cable.
6. Turn ignition switch to On position, connect a jumper between terminal 25 and terminal 1. Indicator lamp should light. Turn ignition switch to Off position.
7. If indicator does not light, check wiring to switch for breaks. If wiring is satisfactory, replace switch. If indicator does light, check that fault is not intermittent. Refer to "F. Intermittent Faults." If fault remains, replace control module.

P-SIGNAL DESCRIPTION, CONTROL MODULE

1. Ensure ignition switch is in Off position.
2. Disconnect control module electrical connector, then connect adapter 981 3196 to control module connector.
3. Connect test box 981 3190 to adapter, then the battery ground cable.
4. Perform checks, **Fig. 10.**

Intermittent Faults

1. In case of intermittent faults, the On-Board Diagnostic (OBD) can be used in the following manner to help to ascertain which circuit is faulty:
   a. Read, note and delete any codes stored in control module.

b. Test drive vehicle and try to repeat conditions under which fault appears. Refer to "H. Test Drive." A description of driving conditions at time fault occurred may aid in fault tracing.

c. Stop vehicle and read codes stored. When codes have been stored, "G. Diagnostic Trouble Code (DTC) Table" should be used to decide which circuits may be faulty.

d. If no codes are stored, fault tracing must be carried out using "K. Symptoms/Diagnosis Table."

e. If fault does not appear during test drive, a good description of behavior of vehicle at time fault occurred may help in locating most probable faulty circuit. "K. Symptoms/ Diagnosis Table" may also be used for fault tracing.

2. Most intermittent problems can be caused by faults in connectors or wiring. Suspect circuits should be checked for the following:
   a. Poor contact between connectors or wiring connections which have not been properly connected.
   b. Poorly connected or damaged connectors.
   c. Poor connection between connectors and wiring.
   d. Most faults occurring in the system disengage the system entirely when vehicle is being driven, even if fault disappears before ignition is turned Off. In certain intermittent fault cases, ABS function may return if fault disappears before ignition is turned Off.
3. If ABS warning indicator lights temporarily, the following circuits for input signals to control module should be examined:
   a. Low system voltage. If system voltage is low, control module will light ABS warning indicator. Indicator will remain lit until system voltage returns to normal. When system voltage to control module is correct, system returns to normal function.
   b. Power Cut. If there is a power cut to control module or hydraulic modulator, ABS warning indicator lights temporarily. Affected circuits are main relay, pump motor relay, fuses and related wiring.

Clearing Diagnostic Trouble Codes

1. Check that all codes stored have been read. Codes cannot be deleted until all codes have been displayed at least once and the first code has reappeared.
2. Hold button down for at least 5 seconds and release it. Three seconds after button is released, LED will light up.

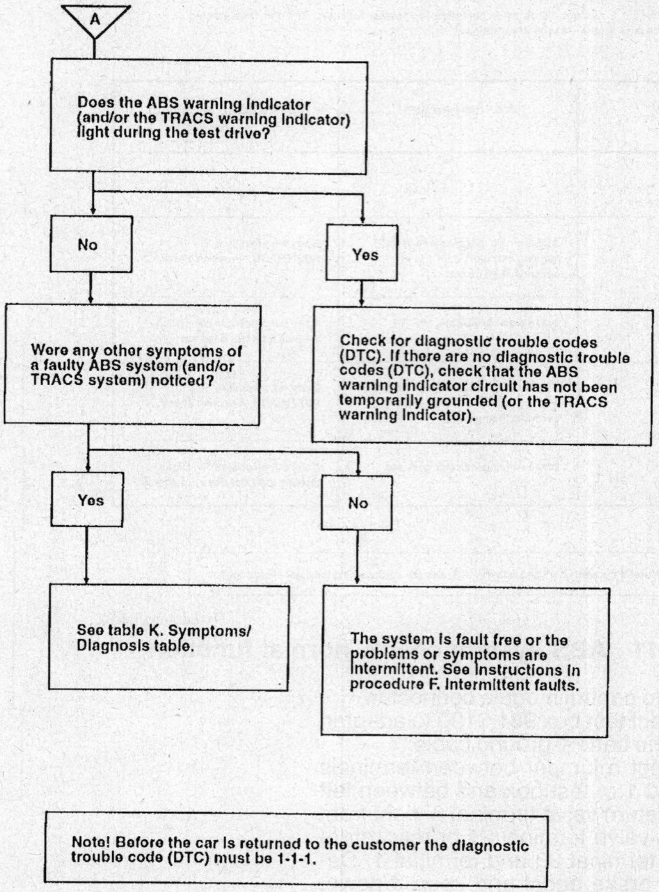

VV4029100014020X

Fig. 12 ABS/TRACS function check (Part 2 of 2)

3. While LED is lit press button again. Hold button down for at least 5 seconds, then release it. LED will go out.
4. Turn ignition switch to Off position.
5. Turn ignition switch to On position and check that all codes have been deleted by pressing button briefly but firmly.
6. If code 1-1-1 is displayed, codes have been deleted.
7. If codes have not been deleted, repeat "Accessing Diagnostic Trouble Codes," and steps 1 through 6 in this section.
8. When codes are deleted and code 1-1-1 has been displayed, drive vehicle at least 25 mph. ABS warning indicator should go out.
9. If ABS warning indicator does not go out check that no new codes have been posted.
10. Carry out a system check as a guideline for normal function. Refer to **Fig. 11**, for procedures.
11. Check ABS/TRACS, refer to **Fig. 12**, for procedures.

SYSTEM SERVICE

Brake System Bleed

Refer to "Brake System Bleed" section under "Hydraulic Brake Systems."

Component Replacement

CONTROL MODULE

1. Ensure ignition is off.
2. Remove sound proofing under instrument panel.
3. Loosen band holding control module and lift module out.
4. Remove control module connector.
5. Reverse procedure to install.

HYDRAULIC MODULATOR

1. Remove cover over hydraulic modulator.
2. Remove both relays and connector.

3. Disconnect ground lead from modulator
4. Remove hydraulic lines to modulator noting position for installation.
5. Remove screw from support and push support to right. Remove hydraulic modulator
6. Reverse procedure to install, transferring three rubber pads to new modulator.

REAR SENSOR

Less Multi-Link Rear Suspension

1. Disconnect electrical connector for rear sensor (located in trunk).
2. Before removing speed sensor from rear axle, check clearance between sensor tip and pulse wheel as follows:
   a. Remove oil plug from axle assembly inspection cover.
   b. Use a feeler gauge to check clearance.
   c. Clearance should be .023–.024 inch.
   d. If clearance is not as specified, it can be adjusted by replacing the shim. Shims are available in thicknesses .0394–.0709 inches, in increments of .008 inch.
3. Remove speed sensor form axle assembly.
4. Reverse procedure to install. Apply a small amount of lubricant No. 11610375-5, or equivalent, to the sensor before installation.

Multi-Link Suspension

1. Lift out spare wheel and fold back carpet to expose filler pipe.
2. Remove covers over filler pipe and break seal on sensor cable connector.
3. Disconnect connector and press out cable and rubber grommet.
4. Raise rear section of vehicle and place jack with fixture 5972, or equivalent, under rear axle.
5. Remove four bolts which hold member to body.
6. Lower rear axle slightly. **Driveshaft must not press against fuel tank.**
7. Disconnect Righthand brake wire from attachment.
8. Remove sensor cable from clamps, noting placement for installation.
9. Clean area around sensor and remove sensor assembly.
10. Reverse procedure to install, using new O-ring on sensor.

Automatic Transmissions

NOTE: On Air Bag Equipped Models, Refer To "Air Bag System Precautions" Located In The Front Of This Manual For System Disarming & Arming Procedures.

NOTE: For Service Procedures Not Listed Here For The THM 4T65–E Transmission, Refer To MOTOR's "Domestic Transmission Manual."

INDEX

	Page No.
Adjustments	9-119
AW 30-40 & 30-43 Transmissions	9-119
AW 50-42 Transmission	9-120
Description	9-116
AW30-40 & AW30-43	9-117
AW50-42	9-117
THM 4T65-E	9-116
Identification	9-116
AW30-40 & AW30-43	9-116
AW50-42	9-116
In-Vehicle Repairs	9-120
AW 30-40 & 30-43 Transmissions	9-120
AW 50-42 Transmission	9-123
Maintenance	9-118
AW 30-40 & 30-43 Transmissions	9-118
AW 50-42 Transmission	9-119
Precautions	9-116
Air Bag Systems	9-116
Battery Ground Cable	9-116
Tightening Specifications	9-126
Transmission, Replace	9-124
AW 30-40 & 30-43	9-124
AW 50-42	9-124
Troubleshooting	9-117
AW 30-40 & 30-43 Transmissions	9-118
AW 50–42 Transmission	9-117

PRECAUTIONS

AIR BAG SYSTEMS

Refer to "Air Bag System Precautions" in the front of this manual for system disarming and arming procedures.

BATTERY GROUND CABLE

Prior to service, disconnect battery ground cable and isolate as required.

IDENTIFICATION

AW30-40 & AW30-43

Refer to **Fig. 1** for transmission identification.

AW50-42

Refer to **Fig. 2** for transmission identification.

DESCRIPTION

THM 4T65-E

The 4T65-E transaxle, **Fig. 3,** is a fully automatic unit which provides four forward speeds including an overdrive top gear. The transmission unit includes a three element hydraulic torque converter and lock-up clutching element, four multiple disc clutch, two bands and a compound reaction planetary gear set. Power transmitted to the drive wheels from the planetary gear through a final drive gear set and differential assembly.

The converter is designed to provide torque multiplication during acceleration and at slow vehicle speed, and lock-up during normal operation for increased operating economy. Operation of the converter lock-up is controlled automatically by the engine fuel system electronic control module. In addition, the converter drives the vane type oil pump by means of a shaft splined to the converter cover.

The torque converter hydraulically couples the engine to the planetary gears through a turbine and shaft assembly which drives the transmission output shaft by means of a drive link chain and sprockets.

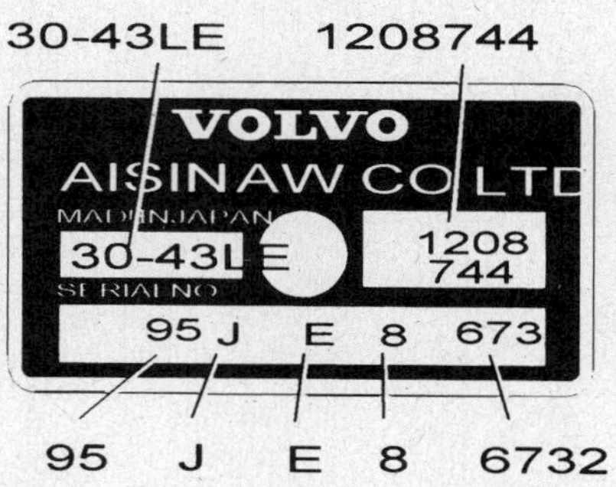

Example:

30–43LE, =, Transmission designation

1208744, =, Volvo P/N

95, =, year of manufacture

J, =, manufactured in September (A=January and so on. **Note!** The letter I is not used.)

E, =, 30–43LE *

8, =, Transmission manufactured for Volvo

6732, =, manufacturing number, starting with 0001 each month.

*) LE indicates that the transmission has a lock-up function and is electronically controlled.

(This transmission is an AW30–43, manufactured in September 1995. Used with the B6304S engine.)

VV5029600146000X

Fig. 1 Transmission identification

Example:

50–42LE = Transmission designation

1208818 = Volvo P/N

95 = year of manufacture

F = manufactured in June (A=January and so on. **NOTE!** The letter I is not used.)

W = Transmission 50–42LE *

8 = Transmission manufactured for Volvo

1243 = manufacturing number, starting with 0001 each month.

*) LE indicates that the transmission has the lock-up function and is electronically controlled.

This transmission is an AW50–42, manufactured in June 1995. (Used with engines B5254S, B5252S.)

VV5029600147000X

Fig. 2 Transmission identification

AW30-40 & AW30-43

The AW30-40/43 transmissions are electronically controlled, four gear automatic transmissions. Economy, sport and winter modes are the three modes of operation that can be selected. The control module receives information about the selected driving mode. Together with signals from a number of sensors describing the running conditions of the vehicle, this information is processed by the Transmission Control Module (TCM), which calculates shifting and lock-up engagement points, depending on driving mode selected.

AW50-42

The AW 50-42 automatic transaxle is an electronically controlled four speed automatic transmission with torque converter lock-up of the three highest gears. A control module receives information about the selected gear and driving mode setting required. Together with signals from a number of sensors describing the running conditions of the car, this information is processed by the control module, which calculates shifting and lock-up engagement points, depending on driving mode selected.

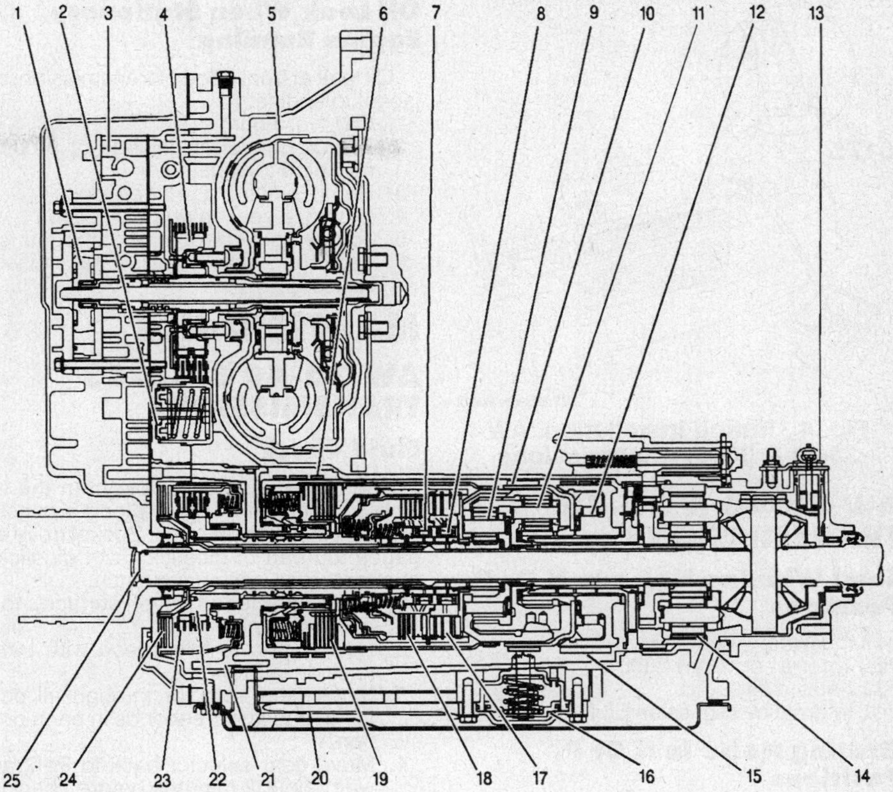

(1) Oil Pump Assembly
(2) Case Cover Assembly
(3) Control Valve Body Assembly
(4) Drive Sprocket
(5) Torque Converter Clutch Assembly
(6) Reverse Band Assembly
(7) Third Clutch Sprag Assembly
(8) Input Clutch Sprag Assembly
(9) Input Carrier Assembly
(10) 2–1 Manual Band Assembly
(11) Reaction Carrier Assembly
(12) 1–2 Roller Clutch Assembly
(13) Vehicle Speed Sensor Assembly
(14) Final Drive/Differential Carrier Assembly
(15) Forward Band Assembly
(16) 2–1 Manual Band Servo Assembly
(17) Input Clutch Assembly
(18) Third Clutch Assembly
(19) Second Clutch Assembly
(20) Oil Filter Assembly
(21) Driven Sprocket Support Assembly
(22) Driven Sprocket
(23) Drive Link Assembly
(24) Fourth Clutch Assembly
(25) Output Shaft

TH5029200003000X

Fig. 3 Turbo Hydra-Matic 4T65-E automatic transaxle

TROUBLESHOOTING

AW 50-42 TRANSMISSION

Loud Whining Noise In Gear Position N Or P

1. Incorrect oil level.
2. Torque converter malfunction.
3. Oil pump malfunction.
4. Internal transaxle malfunction.

Grating Noise In Gear Position N Or P

1. Loose carrier plate screws.
2. Torque converter casing improperly mounted on engine.
3. Broken carrier plate.
4. Torque converter scraping against casing.
5. Internal malfunction.

Squeaking Noise While In Gear

1. Worn bushing in oil pump.
2. Internal transaxle malfunction.

Prominent Knock Or Metallic Noise In Any Gear Other Than 4th

1. Internal transaxle malfunction.

Oil Leak When Stationary

1. Leaky seals or seal seams.
2. Leakage from transmission housing joint.

Oil Leak When Stationary w/Engine Running

1. Oil leak at front edge of transaxle, adjacent to engine:
   a. High oil level.
   b. Torque converter casing improperly mounted to engine.
   c. Pump bushing damaged/loose.
   d. O-ring in oil pump damaged.
   e. Torque converter throat damaged.

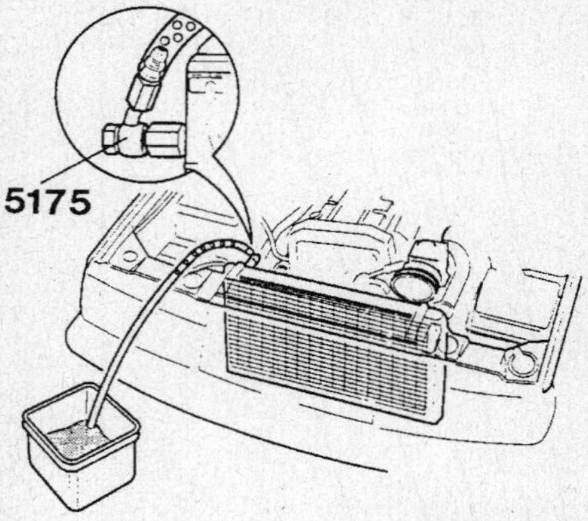

Fig. 4 Fitting installation. AW 30-40 & 30-43 transmissions

AW 30-40 & 30-43 TRANSMISSIONS

Loud Whining Noise In N Or P Positions

1. Incorrect oil level.
2. Torque converter fault.
3. Fault in oil pump.
4. Internal transmission fault.

Grating Noise In N Or P Positions

1. Torque converter casing not properly mounted to engine.
2. Broken carrier plate.
3. Torque converter scraping on casing.
4. Internal fault.

Squeaking Noise While In Gear

1. Worn bushing in oil pump.
2. Internal transmission fault.

Knock Or Metallic Noise In Any Gear Other Than 4th

Internal transmission fault.

Clicking Or Grating Noise On Starting

Park/neutral position interlock partly engaged.

Oil Leak When Stationary, Engine Running

Oil leak at front edge of transmission, adjacent to engine:

1. Oil level high.
2. Torque converter casing not properly mounted to engine.
3. Pump bushing damaged/loose.
4. Oil pump sealing ring damaged.
5. Torque converter throat damaged.
6. Leakage by rear transmission housing.

MAINTENANCE

AW 30-40 & 30-43 TRANSMISSIONS

Fluid Check

The dipstick is accessible from the engine compartment using a long extension with a ½ inch socket drive. Socket drive engages top part of dipstick. Turn dipstick a quarter turn to free spring catch.

1. Park vehicle on level surface, then apply parking brake.
2. Run engine at idle speed with transmission in Park.
3. Move gear selector through all positions, pausing 5 seconds in each position.
4. Move gear selector back to Park and wait about 2 minutes before checking fluid level.
5. With engine at operating temperature, fluid level should be between Hot marks.

Fluid Change

1. Remove drain plug from transmission pan, then allow fluid to drain into suitable container.
2. Install drain plug and **torque** to 15 ft. lbs.
3. Remove upper fluid cooler pipe from cooler. Always use a spanner wrench to prevent movement of hexagonal coupling.
4. Install fitting part No. 5175, or equivalent, as shown in **Fig. 4.** Use nipple and seals from special tool part No. 5320, or equivalent.
5. Install transparent plastic hose to fitting, then place container under hose to catch fluid.

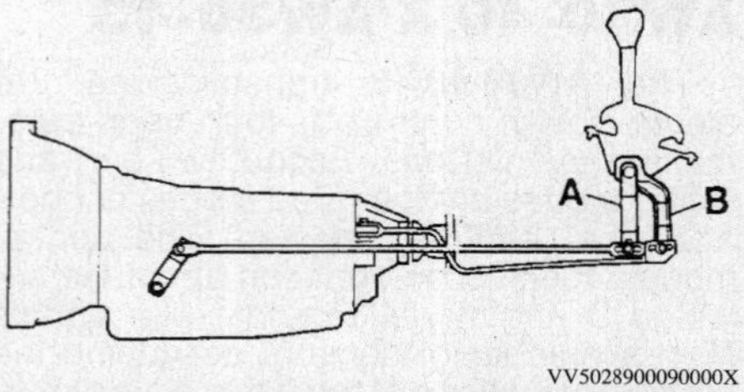

Fig. 5 Gear selector adjustment. AW 30-40 & 30-43 transmissions

6. Apply parking brake and put gear selector in Park.
7. Add 4 quarts of fluid as follows:
   a. Add 2 quarts of fluid to transmission, then start and idle engine.
   b. Stop engine when bubbles appear in tubing.
   c. Add another 2 quarts of fluid to transmission, then start and idle engine again.
   d. Stop engine when bubbles appear in tubing.
   e. Remove nipple and fitting from cooler, then reconnect pipe to cooler.
8. Add another 2.3 quarts of fluid to transmission.
9. Apply parking brake, then start and idle engine.
10. Move gear selector through all positions, pausing 5 seconds in each position.
11. Move gear selector back to Park and wait about 2 minutes before checking fluid level.
12. Top off fluid, if necessary.

AW 50-42 TRANSMISSION

Fluid Check

1. Park vehicle on flat surface with parking brake set.
2. Idle engine with gear selector in Park position.
3. Move gear selector through all positions, stopping in each position for 3 seconds.
4. Return gear position selector to Park and wait 2 minutes before checking oil level.
5. Check oil level with dipstick. The cold range on the dipstick (104°F) is reached after approximately 5 minutes of idling. The hot range on the dipstick (176°F) is reached after about 30 minutes of highway driving.
6. Transaxle oil temperature can be checked using Volvo diagnostic key, test function 5.
7. Ensure oil level is between the MAX and MIN lines of the appropriate temperature range. Difference between MAX and MIN is ½ quart.

Fluid Change

1. Remove splash guard beneath engine.
2. Remove transaxle drain plug and drain oil into suitable container.
3. Replace drain plug seal washer and install drain plug. **Torque** to 30 ft. lbs.
4. Disconnect return hose from control system cover.
5. Install transparent hose on oil return hose connection.
6. Apply parking brake and move gear selector lever to Park.
7. Add approximately 2.1 quarts of oil to transaxle.
8. Start engine and run at idle.
9. Turn off engine when air bubbles become visible in transparent hose.
10. Add additional 2.1 quarts to transaxle.
11. Start engine and run at idle.
12. Turn off engine when air bubbles become visible in transparent hose.
13. Remove transparent hose from connection and connect oil return hose.
14. Add additional 2.1 quarts to transaxle, then start engine and move gear selector through all positions, stopping at each position for 4–5 seconds.
15. Place gear selector in Park and wait 2 minutes with engine idling.
16. Check oil level and fill if necessary. Transaxle oil capacity is 8 quarts.

ADJUSTMENTS

AW 30-40 & 30-43 TRANSMISSIONS

Gear Selector

1. Move gear selector lever to Park position.
2. Loosen control rod and reaction strut nuts.
3. Ensure selector link arm on transmission is in Park position (rearmost position). **Gear selector lever will interfere with instrument panel if arm is adjusted too far back.**
4. Ensure gear lever arm, (A) is vertical or slightly forward, **Fig. 5.** Install locknut on gear lever arm.
5. Press reaction arm (B) gently backwards until slight resistance is felt, **Fig. 5. Torque** nut to 48 inch lbs.

Gear Position Sensor

1. Release oxygen sensor wire from transmission support member routing clip and transmission fluid pan. Disconnect oxygen sensor electrical connectors.
2. Remove front exhaust pipe and front heat shield.
3. With gear selector in Neutral position, loosen gear position fixing/adjusting bolt slightly so sensor can be turned relative to shaft.
4. Position template tool No. 5475, or equivalent, outside nut on gear selector shaft.
5. Turn gear position sensor until groove on template is pointing directly towards lug on gear position sensor as shown in **Fig. 6.**
6. **Torque** fixing/adjusting bolt to 10 ft. lbs.
7. Install heat shield and front exhaust pipe.
8. Connect oxygen sensor connectors and secure to transmission support member and fluid pan.
9. Connect Volvo Diagnostic Key to diagnostic output and delete any stored trouble codes. The code 1-1-1 should

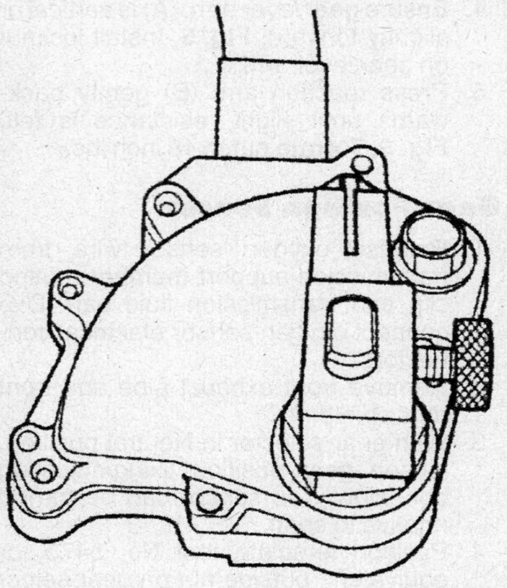

VV5028900094000X

Fig. 6 Gear position sensor adjustment. AW 30-40 & 30-43 transmissions

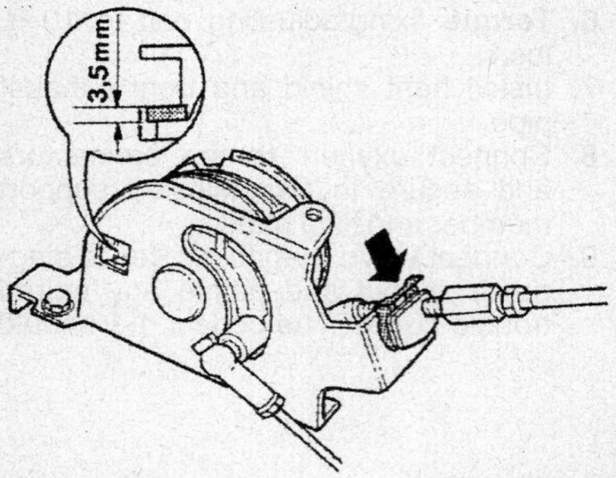

VV5028900092000X

Fig. 9 Throttle control pulley spacer. AW 30-40 & 30-43 transmissions

be displayed when all trouble codes have been deleted.

AW 50-42 TRANSMISSION

Gear Position Sensor

1. Remove battery, tray and air intake manifold.
2. Disconnect transaxle cable from rod arm.
3. Remove rod arm.
4. Insert tool No. 9995475, or equivalent, into control shaft.
5. Check that shaft is set to N position.
6. Disconnect dipstick pipe bracket.
7. Remove gear position sensor screws.
8. Rotate gear position sensor so that mark on switch aligns with identification on tool.
9. **Torque** switch screws to 18 ft. lbs.
10. Install dipstick pipe bracket. **Torque** to 17.5 ft. lbs.
11. Install rod arm on control shaft. **Torque** to 18 ft. lbs.
12. Attach transaxle cable to rod arm, using washer and locking clip.

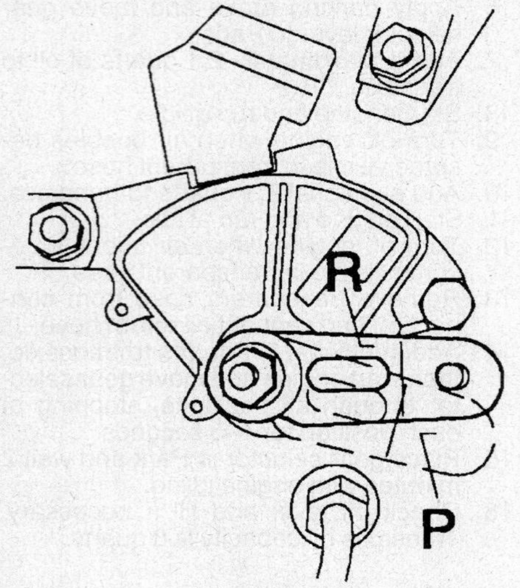

VV5029500117000X

Fig. 7 Transaxle cable adjustment. AW 50-42 transmission

Transaxle Cable

1. Set gear lever to R position.
2. Push rod arm on transaxle forward to P position, **Fig. 7.**
3. Turn rod arm to next position (R).
4. Apply grease to rod arm pin and install cable on studs and rod arm pin. **Torque** nuts to 18 ft. lbs.
5. Install washers and locking clip on rod arm.

IN-VEHICLE REPAIRS

AW 30-40 & 30-43 TRANSMISSIONS

REAR EXTENSION HOUSING SEAL, REPLACE

Removal

1. Using socket tool No. 5244, or equivalent, remove four propeller shaft drive flange bolts.
2. Lift propeller shaft to side and secure with suitable wire or rope.
3. Separate drive flange from output shaft as follows:
   a. Using a punch, remove clamping from output shaft nut.
   b. Remove output shaft nut. To prevent output shaft rotation, secure with counterhold tool No. 5149, or equivalent.
   c. Separate drive flange from output shaft, using remove tool No. 5304, or equivalent, if necessary.
   d. Remove drive flange O-ring.
   e. Ensure drive flange sealing surfaces are free of defects.
4. Remove rear extension housing seal using seal removal tool No. 5069, or equivalent.

Installation

1. Apply small amount of grease to lip of new seal.

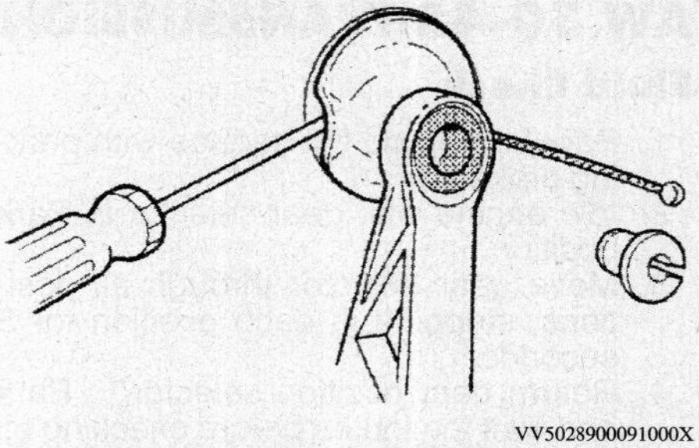

VV5028900091000X

Fig. 8 Kickdown switch installation. AW 30-40 & 30-43 transmissions

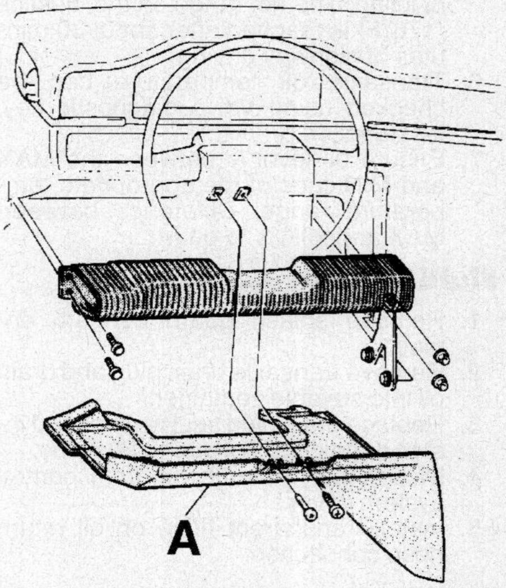

VV5028900093000X

Fig. 10 Driver side panel A removal. AW 30-40 & 30-43 transmissions

2. Install seal using drift tool No. 5492, or equivalent. Tap into position until drift bottoms on rear extension housing.
3. Install drive flange as follows:
   a. Apply a small amount of grease to new drive flange O-ring.
   b. Install drive flange a new nut coated with locking fluid part No. 116103-2, or equivalent. Prevent drive flange from rotating using counterhold tool No. 5149, or equivalent.
   c. **Torque** drive flange nut to 91 ft. lbs.
   d. Secure nut with a punch.
4. Connect propeller shaft to drive flange using new nuts and bolts. **Torque** alternately to 37 ft. lbs.

REAR EXTENSION HOUSING BEARING, REPLACE

1. Drain transmission fluid.
2. Support transmission with suitable transmission jack, then release oxygen sensor cable from transmission support member.
3. Remove transmission support member.
4. Disconnect propeller shaft from drive flange using socket tool No. 5244, or equivalent. Suspend propeller shaft to one side with wire or rope.

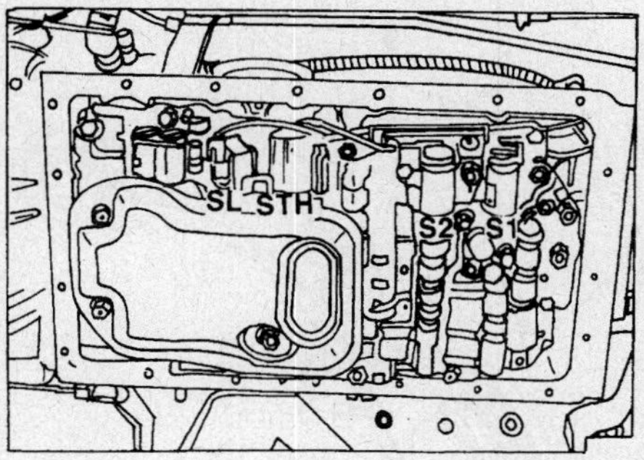

VV5028900095000X

Fig. 11 Solenoid valve replacement. AW 30-40 & 30-43 transmissions

5. Remove four bolts from support bracket, then the support bracket.
6. Remove torque strut circlips and washer.
7. Separate drive flange from output shaft as described under "Rear Extension Housing Seal, Replace."
8. Remove rear extension housing as follows:
   a. Remove six mounting bolts.
   b. Free housing by prying with two screwdrivers under two cast lugs.
   c. Remove rear extension housing.
9. Pry out seal and remove bearing circlip.
10. Press bearing out of housing using a suitable press and drift tool No. 5088, or equivalent.
11. Reverse procedure to install, noting the following:
    a. Press new bearing into rear housing using suitable press and drift tool No. 5496, or equivalent.
    b. Ensure bearing is installed in correct direction. The end with sheet metal seal must face inward. Outer end has two grooves on the inner ring.
    c. Apply a small amount of grease to lip of seal. Install seal using drift tool No 5492, or equivalent.
    d. Apply liquid sealant to rear extension housing contact surfaces.
    e. **Torque** six rear extension housing mounting bolts to 25 ft. lbs. and drive flange bolts to 91 ft. lbs.
    f. **Torque** propeller shaft to drive flange bolts to 37 ft. lbs.
    g. **Torque** transmission support bracket bolts to 35 ft. lbs.

GEAR SELECTOR SHAFT, REPLACE

1. Release oxygen sensor cable from transmission support member and fluid pan. Disconnect oxygen sensor electrical connectors.
2. Remove front exhaust pipe.
3. Remove front heat shield.
4. Disconnect and plug rear transmission fluid line.
5. Remove gear position sensor as follows:
   a. Remove nut, locking washer and rubber washer from gear selector shaft.

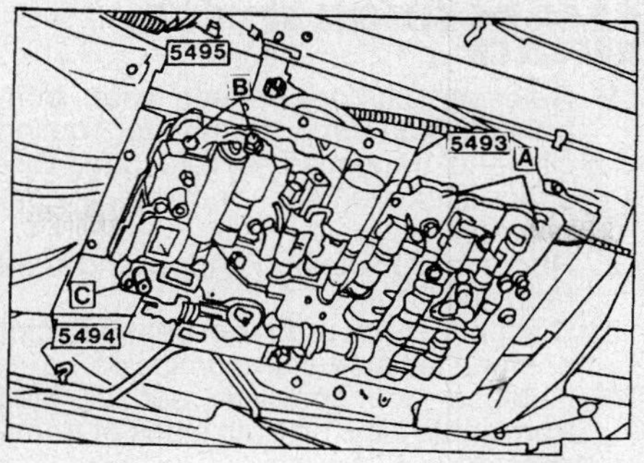

VV5028900096000X

Fig. 12 Valve body removal. AW 30-40 & 30-43 transmissions

   b. Disconnect sensor lead to prevent damage.
   c. Remove gear position sensor securing bolt.
   d. Remove sensor from gear selector shaft and move to one side.
6. Use a screwdriver to pry right side seal out of position.
7. To remove left side seal, remove nut and selector link arm, then remove seal by using a screwdriver to pry out of position.
8. Reverse procedure to install, noting the following:
   a. Apply a small amount of grease to new seals.
   b. Install left side seal using drift tool No. 5476, or equivalent.
   c. **Torque** link arm to 13 ft. lbs.

GEAR SELECTOR SOLENOID, REPLACE

1. Remove gear selector housing and gear lever.
2. Move gear selector lever to Park position and disconnect P-shift lock solenoid latch.
3. Remove P-shift lock solenoid from gear selector housing.
4. Using suitable pliers, release clip securing P-shift lock solenoid.
5. Reverse procedure to install, noting the following:
   a. Move gear selector to Park position, then place bottom edge of P-shift lock solenoid into slot position.
   b. Press solenoid rearward until upper edge snaps into position.
   c. Check gear selector lever movement. Adjust as described under "Adjustments."

PROGRAM SELECTOR, REPLACE

1. Release latch at each end of program selector using a small screwdriver.
2. Disconnect program selector electrical connector.
3. Reverse procedure to install.

KICKDOWN SWITCH & THROTTLE CABLE, REPLACE

Removal

1. Remove throttle control cover as follows:

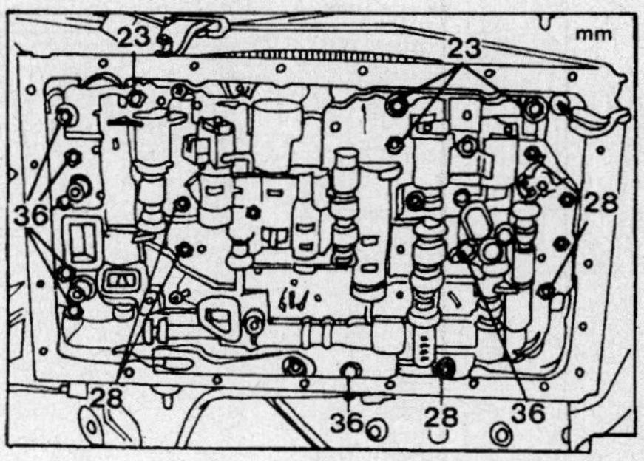

VV5028900097000X

Fig. 13 Valve body bolt length & location. AW 30-40 & 30-43 transmissions

   a. Remove cable tensioner locking clip.
   b. Disconnect cable from throttle control pulley and remove from bracket.
   c. Disconnect kickdown switch electrical connector.
2. Remove control unit as described under "Control Unit, Replace."
3. Disconnect accelerator cable from pedal, then remove kickdown switch from cable.

Installation

1. Squeeze rubber seal together and secure with electrical tape. Leave approximately four inches of tape hanging free, **Fig. 8.**
2. Insert kickdown switch with connector facing upwards.
3. Ensure latch lugs on kickdown switch engage bulkhead correctly.
4. Remove tape and ensure rubber seal seats on bulkhead sound insulation.
5. Hook cable with holder on accelerator pedal, ensuring end bead ends firmly at bottom of holder.
6. Replace cable tensioner locking clip, then connect cable onto throttle control pulley.
7. Insert a 0.14 inch (3.5 mm) spacer on idling stop on throttle control pulley, **Fig. 9.**
8. Ensure locking clip is firmly against bracket. Adjust cable until it is pulled slightly tight.
9. Remove spacer, then attach throttle control pulley to bracket with locking clip.
10. Install control unit and soundproofing panel A.
11. Connect Volvo Diagnostic Key to diagnostic output and delete any stored trouble codes. The code 1-1-1 should be displayed when all trouble codes have been deleted.

CONTROL UNIT, REPLACE

1. Remove fuse No. 24.
2. Remove soundproofing material from driver side panel A, **Fig. 10.**
3. **On models with air bag,** remove knee bolster.
4. **On all models,** remove control unit

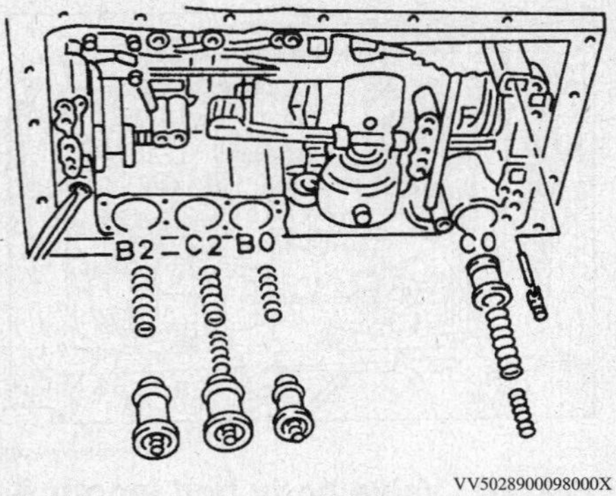

Fig. 14 Accumulator pistons replacement. AW 30-40 & 30-43 transmissions

from mounting bracket using a screwdriver to gently pry bracket free of securing clip.
5. Disconnect control unit electrical connectors.
6. Reverse procedure to install, noting the following:
   a. Connect Volvo Diagnostic Key to diagnostic output and delete any stored trouble codes. The code 1-1-1 should be displayed when all trouble codes have been deleted.
   b. Reset control unit adaptive function to normal values using test functions 5 and 6 following Volvo Diagnostic Key instructions.

SPEED SENSOR, REPLACE

1. Disconnect speed sensor electrical connector and cable.
2. Remove speed sensor.
3. Reverse procedure to install, noting the following:
   a. **Torque** speed sensor to 4 ft. lbs.
   b. Connect Volvo Diagnostic Key to diagnostic output and delete any stored trouble codes. The code 1-1-1 should be displayed when all trouble codes have been deleted.

FLUID TEMPERATURE SENSOR, REPLACE

1. Release oxygen sensor wire from transmission support member routing clip. Disconnect oxygen sensor electrical connectors.
2. Remove front exhaust pipe.
3. Disconnect fluid temperature sensor connector and disconnect wire from front fluid pipe.
4. Disconnect fluid temperature sensor from front fluid pipe.
5. Reverse procedure to install, noting the following:
   a. Apply a small amount of transmission fluid to new temperature sensor O-ring.
   b. **Torque** temperature sensor to 84 inch lbs.
   c. Connect Volvo Diagnostic Key to diagnostic output and delete any stored trouble codes. The code 1-1-1 should be displayed when all trouble codes have been deleted.

GEAR POSITION SENSOR, REPLACE

1. Release oxygen sensor wire from transmission support member routing clip and transmission fluid pan. Disconnect oxygen sensor electrical connectors.
2. Remove front exhaust pipe and front heat shield.
3. Disconnect link arm from gear selector shaft on left side of transmission.
4. Release gear position sensor lead from cable clips on both sides of transmission.
5. Disconnect gear position sensor electrical connector.
6. Disconnect and plug transmission fluid lines.
7. Remove gear position sensor as follows:
   a. Remove gear position sensor nut with locking washer and rubber washer.
   b. Remove gear position sensor fixing/adjusting bolt.
   c. Pull sensor and wire off gear selector shaft.
8. Reverse procedure to install, noting the following:
   a. **Torque** gear position sensor locking washer and nut to 60 inch lbs.
   b. **Torque** link arm on gear selector to 13 ft. lbs.

SOLENOID VALVES, REPLACE

1. Drain transmission fluid and disconnect oxygen sensor lead from fluid pan.
2. Remove fluid pan and dipstick tube.
3. Release cable holder from valve body. Disconnect solenoid valve connectors.
4. Disconnect external solenoid connector from transmission.
5. Remove solenoid valves S1 and S2, **Fig. 11,** as follows:
   a. Remove solenoid valve holder.
   b. Pull out solenoid valves S1 and S2 and remove from valve body.
6. Remove solenoid valves SL and STH, **Fig. 11,** as follows:
   a. Remove fluid filter.
   b. Remove solenoid holder.
   c. Pull out solenoid valves SL and STH and remove from valve body.
7. Reverse procedure to install, noting the following:
   a. Apply a small amount of grease to new solenoid valve O-rings.
   b. **Torque** solenoid valves and fluid filter retaining bolts to 84 inch lbs.
   c. Apply liquid sealant to fluid pan contact surfaces. **Torque** pan attaching bolts to 60 inch lbs.
   d. Connect Volvo Diagnostic Key to diagnostic output and delete any stored trouble codes. The code 1-1-1 should be displayed when all trouble codes have been deleted.

VALVE BODY, REPLACE

Removal

1. Drain transmission fluid.
2. Disconnect oxygen sensor wire from transmission fluid pan.
3. Remove fluid pan and filter, then disconnect solenoid valve connectors.

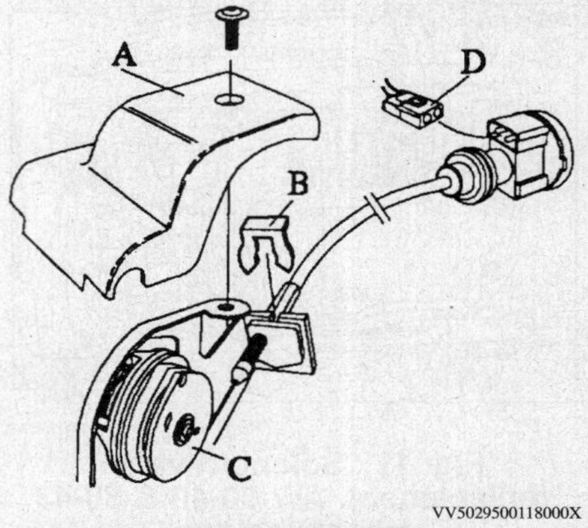

Fig. 15 Throttle cable replacement. AW 50-42 transmission

4. Loosen remaining valve body bolts to valve body is lowered approximately 0.20–0.24 inch (5–6 mm).
5. Remove two bolts at “A” shown in **Fig. 12.** Remove two bolts at “B” and one bolt at “C.”
6. At position “A” **Fig. 12,** insert retainer tool No. 5493, or equivalent, between valve body and transmission housing to keep accumulator pistons No. B2, C2 and B0 in correct position. Secure retainer tool to transmission with a fluid pan bolt.
7. At position “B,” insert retainer tool No. 5495, or equivalent, to keep accumulator piston No. C0 in correct position. Secure retainer tool to transmission with a fluid pan bolt.
8. At position “C,” secure retainer tool No. 5494, or equivalent, to keep non-return valve in correct position.
9. Remove remaining valve body mounting bolts, then remove valve body.

Installation

1. Align pin on gear selector cam with slot in gear selector valve.
2. Install valve body bolts as follows:
   a. First mount valve body and secure in position with two mounting bolts. Only tighten bolts enough to hold valve body in position.
   b. Remove retainer tools securing accumulator pistons and non-return valve in position.
   c. Install valve body bolts, ensuring different length bolts are installed in correct position, **Fig. 13.**
   d. Starting from center, **torque** bolts alternately to 84 inch lbs.
3. Install solenoid valve connectors and wiring harness cable holder. **Torque** cable holder bolts to 84 inch lbs.
4. Install new fluid filter. **Torque** bolts to 84 inch lbs.
5. Place particle magnet in fluid pan depression. Apply liquid gasket material to fluid pan sealing surfaces.
6. Install fluid pan. **Torque** bolts to 84 inch lbs.
7. **Torque** drain plug to 15 ft. lbs.

8. Connect Volvo Diagnostic Key to diagnostic output and delete any stored trouble codes. The code 1-1-1 should be displayed when all trouble codes have been deleted.

ACCUMULATOR PISTONS, REPLACE

1. Remove valve body as described under "Valve Body, Replace."
2. Remove non-return valve housing with spring.
3. Remove accumulator pistons B2, C2 and B0 with springs as follows:
   a. Carefully remove retainer tool, securing accumulator pistons in position.
   b. Remove accumulator pistons B2, C2 and B0 with springs, **Fig. 14.**
   c. If accumulator pistons are difficult to remove, apply compressed air to fluid passage to force pistons out.
4. Remove accumulator piston C0 with springs as follows:
   a. Carefully remove retainer tool, securing accumulator piston C0 in position.
   b. Remove accumulator piston C0 with springs, **Fig. 14.**
   c. If accumulator piston is difficult to remove, apply compressed air to fluid passage to force piston out.
5. Clean and inspect accumulator pistons, non-return valve and all springs. Replace any stiff or worn pistons.
6. Reverse procedure to install, noting the following:
   a. Use new O-rings coated with a small amount of new transmission fluid.
   b. Connect Volvo Diagnostic Key to diagnostic output and delete any stored trouble codes. The code 1-1-1 should be displayed when all trouble codes have been deleted.

PARKING LOCK PAWL, REPLACE

1. Remove valve body as described under "Valve Body, Replace."
2. Remove three bolts securing parking lock pawl retaining plate to transmission.
3. Remove parking lock pawl spring and shaft.
4. Reverse procedure to install. **Torque** parking lock pawl retaining plate bolts to 60 inch lbs.

BRAKE B2 SEAL SLEEVE, REPLACE

1. Remove valve body as described under "Valve Body, Replace."
2. Remove tube with seal for brake B2.
3. Remove sleeve using suitable circlip pliers.
4. Reverse procedure to install. Apply a small amount of transmission fluid to new sleeve seal and insert sleeve with seal pointing up towards brake B2.

BRAKE CYLINDER B1, REPLACE

1. Remove valve body as described under "Valve Body, Replace."
2. Remove piston cover circlip, then pull cover out, using pliers to grip flange.
3. Remove piston by carefully blower compressed air into hole while retaining cover with fingers.
4. Piston rods are available in four different lengths. If replacing piston rod, ensure new rod is same length as original rod.
5. Reverse procedure to install, noting the following:
   a. Replace seal and two O-rings on cover. Apply a small amount of transmission fluid to seal and O-rings.
   b. **Install piston so piston rod seats correctly on brake band attachment.**
   c. Connect Volvo Diagnostic Key to diagnostic output and delete any stored trouble codes. The code 1-1-1 should be displayed when all trouble codes have been deleted.

AW 50-42 TRANSMISSION

OIL PUMP SEAL RING, REPLACE

1. Using seal ring extractor tool No. 9995069, or equivalent, remove seal ring from transaxle.
2. Install new oil seal ring using tool No. 9995117, or equivalent.

DRIVESHAFT SEAL, REPLACE

1. Remove brake hose and ABS cable bracket and let bracket hang loose.
2. Disconnect linkage from anti-roll bar.
3. Disconnect ball joint from link.
4. Using disconnecting tool No. 9995462, or equivalent, between transaxle and inside of left side driveshaft, remove driveshaft. Let driveshaft end rest on subframe.
5. Remove splash guard from beneath engine.
6. Remove bearing cap for right side driveshaft support bearings.
7. Press out inner portion of right side driveshaft and fold out spring strut.
8. Allow right side drive shaft to rest on steering gear hose.
9. Use crowbar or suitable pry too to remove seal ring from transaxle housing.
10. Apply small amount of grease to sealing lip and, using suitable drift and handle, carefully tap in new seal ring.
11. Install right driveshaft. Install bearing cap and **torque** to 18 ft. lbs.
12. Install left side driveshaft. Press driveshaft firmly in firmly so it locks onto differential gear.
13. Ensure driveshaft lock ring fits in its groove.
14. Install link in ball joint on both sides. Apply suitable rust-proofing compound to area between ball joint, link and nuts.
15. Install link to anti-roll bar on both sides. **Torque** to 37 ft. lbs.
16. Install engine splash guard.
17. Install brake hose/ABS cable bracket.

ENGINE SPEED SENSOR, REPLACE

1. Remove battery cables and battery.
2. Remove air cleaner with intake manifold.
3. Remove battery tray.
4. Remove air cleaner bracket.
5. Disassemble transaxle connector.
6. Remove connector from transaxle.
7. Remove cable clamps around cable harness and rubber grommet.
8. Remove sockets from connector casing.
9. Remove socket for RPM sensor cables from connector.
10. Remove engine speed sensor.
11. Apply petroleum jelly to new sensor O-ring and install new sensor.
12. Assemble transaxle connector and install into connector casing.
13. Install connector in vehicle.
14. Install air cleaner bracket, battery tray and air cleaner with intake manifold and connections.
15. Install battery.

OIL TEMPERATURE SENSOR, REPLACE

1. Remove battery cables and battery.
2. Remove air cleaner with intake manifold.
3. Remove battery tray.
4. Remove air cleaner bracket.
5. Disassemble transaxle connector.
6. Detach oil sensor wiring pins from connector socket.
7. Remove under-engine protective cover.
8. Drain oil from transaxle and insert oil plug with new seal. **Torque** plug to 30 ft. lbs.
9. Remove sensor.
10. Apply petroleum jelly to O-ring of new sensor and install new sensor.
11. Push wiring pins into socket.
12. Install protective cover under engine.
13. Assemble connector wiring sockets in connector casing.
14. Install connector in vehicle.
15. Install air cleaner bracket, battery tray and air cleaner with intake manifold and connections.
16. Install battery.

TRANSAXLE CABLE, REPLACE

1. Park vehicle on level surface. Do not apply parking brake.
2. Remove air cleaner, battery and battery tray.
3. Remove locking clip and washers from transaxle control rod arm.
4. Disconnect transaxle cable from rod arm.
5. Remove cigar lighter panel.
6. Remove cover plate below parking brake lever.
7. Remove glove compartment cover.
8. Disconnect center console connectors and remove center console (4 screws).
9. Remove transaxle cable from gear lever mechanism.
10. Fold down carpeting and fold aside side panel around tunnel.
11. Remove screws from cable grommet through cowl panel and.
12. Remove transaxle cable.
13. Reverse procedure to install. **Torque** cable grommet in cowl panel screws to 54 inch lbs.

KICKDOWN SWITCH/THROTTLE CABLE, REPLACE

1. Remove throttle control lever (A), **Fig. 15.**
2. Remove locking clip (B), **Fig. 15,** on cable tensioner.
3. Unhook cable from throttle control pulley (C), **Fig. 15,** and remove it from bracket.
4. Remove kickdown switch (D), **Fig. 15.**
5. Remove sound insulation pad and knee bolster on drivers side.
6. Detach throttle cable from accelerator pedal. Free latch lugs holding kickdown switch in place at cowl panel, then push out switch with throttle cable.
7. Reverse procedure to install.

GEAR POSITION SENSOR, REPLACE

1. Remove battery.
2. Remove air cleaner and air intake manifold assembly.
3. Remove battery shelf, then the air cleaner bracket.
4. Disconnect transmission cable from rod arm.
5. Remove rod arm.
6. Remove nut, lock washer and rubber seal from position sensor.
7. Loosen dipstick pipe bracket.
8. Remove two gear position sensor retaining screws, then the sensor.
9. Reverse procedure to install.

VEHICLE SPEED SENSOR (VSS), REPLACE

1. **On models less turbocharger,** proceed as follows:
   a. Place ignition in Off position.
   b. Remove preheating hose between manifold and air cleaner.
2. **On models with turbocharger,** proceed as follows:
   a. Place ignition in Off position.
   b. Disconnect Mass Air Flow (MAF) sensor connector.
   c. Remove hose between air cleaner and turbocharger unit.
3. **On all models,** remove sensor retaining screw, then the sensor.
4. Reverse procedure to install. Install a new sensor O-ring and tighten sensor to specification.

GEAR SHIFT ASSEMBLY, REPLACE

1. Remove center console, then the gear shift knob.
2. Disconnect transmission cable from gear lever mechanism using a flat nosed pliers, or suitable equivalent, to remove cable pin.
3. Remove retaining clip securing cable sleeve to selector housing.
4. Remove lamp holder from light molding.
5. **On models with shift interlock,** open solenoid connector.
6. **On models with key lock,** proceed as follows:
   a. Place selector lever in P position.
   b. Place ignition in On or Run position.
   c. Disconnect key lock cable from adjustment point and locking plate in gear selector housing.
7. **On all models,** remove gearshift assembly crosspiece.
8. Remove two retaining bolts at front of selector housing, then the gear shift assembly.
9. Reverse procedure to install, noting the following:
   a. Transfer rubber bushings, guide sleeves, gear selector knob, gaiter, light molding and shutter and indicator panel to new assembly.
   b. Tighten fasteners to specification.

TRANSMISSION

REPLACE

AW 30-40 & 30-43

1. Disconnect negative battery ground cable.
2. Attach lifting lug tool No. 5429, or equivalent and lifting yoke tool No. 5428, or equivalent, to engine.
3. Place support rails tool No. 5053, or equivalent, on wing edges of fenders and attach lifting beam tool No. 5115, or equivalent, to relieve weight from transmission bracket.
4. Remove splash guard from under engine, air preheater pipe, then lateral strut.
5. Disconnect electrical connectors from oxygen sensor, starter motor, then open clips on transmission and remove two clips on transmission support member.
6. Remove three connectors from bracket on torque converter housing.
7. Remove front exhaust pipe, disconnect propeller shaft from transmission using socket tool No. 5244, or equivalent. Disconnect control rod and reaction arm from gear selector mechanism by removing circlips and washers.
8. Remove heat shield, then disconnect fluid lines from transmission. Plug pipe end to prevent contamination of fluid.
9. Remove transmission support member, then lower rear of engine as far as possible. Ensure no electrical wires or hoses are trapped between engine and bulkhead.
10. Remove torque converter bolts, then place suitable lift under transmission.
11. Remove transmission to engine mounting bolts, push transmission backwards while holding torque converter in place, then lower unit from vehicle.
12. Reverse procedure to install noting the following:
    a. Ensure carrier plate is not cracked or warped.
    b. Ensure torque converter is properly positioned by placing a straightedge across converter housing and measure distance between converter mounting lug. Distance should be approximately 0.55 inch.
    c. **Torque** converter housing bolts to 35 ft. lbs., and the two starter mounting bolts to 30 ft. lbs.
    d. When tightening converter bolts, tighten until head of bolts are against carrier plate, then **torque** to 22 ft. lbs.
    e. **Torque** propeller shaft attaching bolts to 37 ft. lbs.
    f. Clear diagnostic codes as outlined under "Clearing Diagnostic Trouble Codes."

AW 50-42

1. Undo steering wheel adjustment lever and push wheel as far in and as far up as possible. Lock steering wheel with lever.
2. Place gear selector into N position.
3. Remove battery.
4. Remove air cleaner assembly with intake.
5. Remove battery tray.
6. **On models with turbocharged engine,** proceed as follows:
   a. Disconnect control valve from air cleaner.
   b. Disconnect charge air manifold clamp and hose from manifold.
   c. Remove air cleaner intake to turbocharger.
7. **On all models,** Disconnect transaxle cable from transaxle.
8. Disconnect transaxle connector.
9. Remove wire harness/ground lead clamp on control system cover.
10. Disconnect transaxle ventilation hose from clamp, if equipped.
11. Unhook wiring conduit from transaxle.
12. Disconnect oxygen sensor connector from bracket on transaxle.
13. Disconnect inlet hose at upper cooler quick connector and return hose at transaxle.
14. Drain transaxle oil.
15. Remove dipstick pipe.
16. Disconnect hoses from EGR valve, if equipped.
17. **On models with turbocharged engine,** remove control pulley cover.
18. **On all models,** remove intake to throttle body and pull intake to one side.
19. Disconnect upper oil cooler hose from engine oil cooler and plug oil cooler and hose ports.
20. Remove rear engine mounting nut and transaxle to engine screws.
21. Remove transaxle to starter screws.
22. Disconnect ground lead from transaxle.
23. Lift radiator overflow tank from mounting and allow to hang free.
24. Disconnect ground strap from firewall.
25. Install supports (tool No. 999-5033, or equivalent) on fenders.
26. Install lifting beam tool No. 999-5006, or equivalent, on supports. Place beam directly over eyelet on lifting yoke.
27. Install lifting hook tool No. 999-5460, or equivalent.
28. Pull hook enough to unload engine mountings.
29. Remove front wheels.
30. Remove ABS sensor from left side of axle shaft. **Do not disconnect electrical connector.**
31. Remove brake line brackets and allow to hang.

32. Remove front plastic fender wheelwell liners.
33. Remove left driveshaft nut.
34. Install counterhold tool No. 999-5461, or equivalent, for 4 wheel nuts or tool No. 999-5540, or equivalent, for 5 wheel nuts.
35. Pull end of driveshaft from hub.
36. Remove front splash guard.
37. Remove nuts from control arms and ball joints, then separate control arms from ball joints.
38. Remove carbon filter container and hoses from subframe. Cut bundle tie holding hoses and hand holder on body.
39. Disconnect exhaust pipe clamp behind catalytic converter.
40. Remove oil pipe bracket.
41. Remove two torque rod holder mounting screws on transaxle.
42. Remove righthand driveshaft bearing cap.
43. Pull off righthand driveshaft inner section and fold out spring strut.
44. Install seal plug No. 999-5488, or equivalent, in transaxle.
45. Let driveshaft rest on subframe and oil pipes.
46. Loosen engine mounting/steering gear screw one turn.
47. Remove steering gear mounting nuts in subframe.
48. Position suitable jack under lefthand side of subframe.
49. Remove subframe support bracket screws on body.
50. Lower subframe and remove jack, allowing frame to hang free.
51. Hang steering gear with hook No. 9995045, or equivalent, in hole on the flange of frame member.
52. Remove oxygen sensor wiring clamps from cover.
53. Disconnect vehicle speed sensor connector.
54. Remove cover at rear engine mounting.
55. Remove rear engine mounting from transaxle.
56. Twist and fold out left spring strut.
57. Knock out end of left driveshaft with plastic or copper mallet and pull left driveshaft out of hub.
58. Remove left driveshaft from transaxle.
59. Install seal plug tool No. 999-5462, or equivalent, into transaxle.
60. Lower engine and transaxle until distance between lifting beam and spark plug cover is 12.6 inches. If engine is lowered too far, exhaust pipe may press onto steering gear.
61. Install universal tool No. 999-5972, or equivalent and transaxle fixture tool No. 9995463, or equivalent, on jack.
62. Raise jack so it is lightly in contact with transaxle.
63. Remove six torque converter bolts using Torx TX50 socket.
64. Remove lower plastic nut and fold out righthand fender liner.
65. Remove transaxle to engine mounting bolts while turning crankshaft with socket wrench.
66. Remove transaxle. Ensure torque converter comes out with transaxle and does not slip off stator shaft.
67. Reverse procedure to install, noting the following.
    a. **Torque** transaxle to engine mounting bolts to 37 ft. lbs.
    b. **Torque** torque converter bolts to 22 ft. lbs.
    c. **Torque** subframe mounting bolts to 78 ft. lbs.
    d. **Torque** rear engine mounting bolts to 37 ft. lbs.
    e. Install torque rod mounting to transaxle. On late models **torque** new screws to 26 ft. lbs., then tighten an additional 40°. On early models **torque** new screws to 13 ft. lbs., then an additional 90.
    f. **Torque** ABS sensor to 89 inch lbs.

TIGHTENING SPECIFICATIONS

Year	Component	Torque, Ft. Lbs.
AW 30–40 & 30–43		
1998–99	Cable Holder	84①
	Converter	22
	Converter Housing	35
	Drain Plug	15
	Drive Flange	91
	Fluid Filter	84①
	Fluid Temperature Sensor	84①
	Gear Position Sensor	60①
	Link Arm	13
	Oil Pan	60①
	Parking Lock Pawl	60①
	Propeller Shaft To Drive Flange	37
	Rear Extension Housing	25
	Solenoid Valves	84①
	Speed Sensor	48①
	Starter Motor	30
	Transmission Support Bracket	35
	Valve Body Bolts	84①
AW 50–42		
1998–99	Anti-Roll Bar Bearing Cap (Left Side)	37
	Axle Shaft Nuts	89②
	Bearing Cap (Right side)	19
	Bevel Gear To Transmission	37
	Engine Mount To Subframe	37
	Engine Speed Sensor	48①
	Front Engine Pad Screw	37
	Gearshift Assembly Crosspiece	18
	Links To Anti-Roll Bar	37
	Oil Pipe Bracket	19
	Oil Temperature Sensor	19
	Propeller Shaft Bolts	22
	Rear Engine Mount Cushion	37
	Rear Engine Mount To Transmission	37
	Selector Housing Bolts	18
	Starter Motor Bolts	30
	Steering Gear Nuts	37
	Steering Limiter To Subframe	37
	Steering Shaft Joint	16
	Subframe Bracket Bolts	37
	Subframe To Body Bolts	78
	Tie Rod Locknut	52
	Torque Converter To Driveplate	26
	Torque Rod To Transmission	26
	Transmission To Engine Bolts	37
	Vehicle Speed Sensor	49①
	Vibration Damper	19

① — Inch Lbs.
② — Plus an additional 60° turn.

Drive Axles

INDEX

	Page No.
Assemble	9-127
Disassemble	9-127

DISASSEMBLE

1. Remove rear axle assembly from vehicle, **Fig. 1,** and install in a suitable holding fixture with pinion flange facing downward.
2. Remove axle shafts.
3. Remove differential cover. If the unit is being reconditioned because of noise, the contact pattern should be checked before disassembly.
4. Before disassembly, check markings on carrier and caps. If marks are difficult to read, mark caps with a punch to ensure proper assembly. Remove caps.
5. Install expander tool No. 2394, or equivalent, in holes in carrier housing. Hold tool in place with retainers 2601, or equivalent, **Fig. 2,** Tighten tool tension bolt until all freeplay is eliminated. Turn tension bolt 3–3½ additional turns. **Do not turn tension bolt more than 3½ turns.**
6. Using prying tool No. 2337, or equivalent, remove differential assembly from housing. Loosen tension bolt of expander tool No. 2394, or equivalent, and remove tool.
7. Invert axle case and drain oil.
8. Using a suitable wrench and socket, remove flange nut.
9. Using puller tool No. 2261, or equivalent, remove flange.
10. Using a plastic mallet, drive out pinion from differential housing. Hold pinion with one hand to prevent damage while pinion is driven out.
11. Using handle and drift tool Nos. 1801 and 2599, or equivalents, remove front pinion bearing, washer and oil seal from axle case.
12. Remove rear pinion bearing outer race. On type 1030 axle, use tool Nos. 1801 and 2598, or equivalents, to remove rear pinion bearing outer race. On type 1031 axle, use tool Nos. 1801 and 2843, or equivalents, to remove outer race.
13. **On type 1030 axle,** use puller tool No. 5215, or equivalent, to remove rear pinion bearing. On type 1031 axle, use ring tool No. 5214 and puller tool No. 5216, or equivalents, to remove rear pinion bearing.
14. **On all models,** using puller tool No. 2483, or equivalent, remove differential carrier bearings. Record position of shims and bearings for reassembly.
15. **On models without limited slip differential,** remove lock plate from ring gear bolts, loosen ring gear bolts about halfway and tap on bolt heads to loosen ring gear, then remove bolts and ring gear. Drive out lockpin, **Fig. 3,** and push out shaft for differential gears. Lift out block, differential gears and thrust washers.
16. **On models with limited slip differential,** place marks on differential gear shafts and differential carrier to ensure parts are installed in the same manner as when removed. Remove differential carrier bolts. **Limited slip differential model type 1030, has bolts with left-hand threads.**
17. **On all models,** remove differential carrier and gear plates.
18. Remove ring gear bolts and ring gear. Discard old bolts.

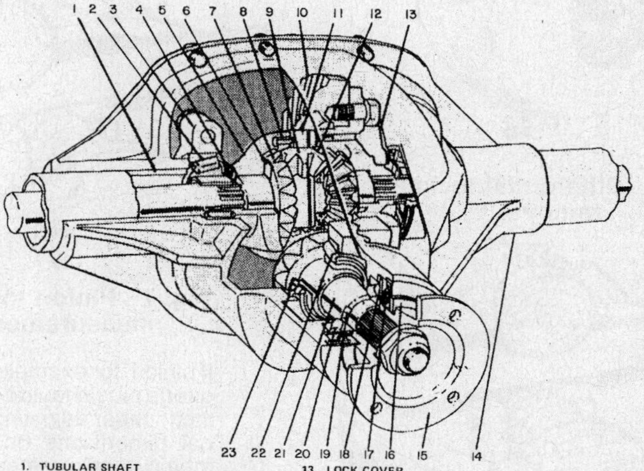

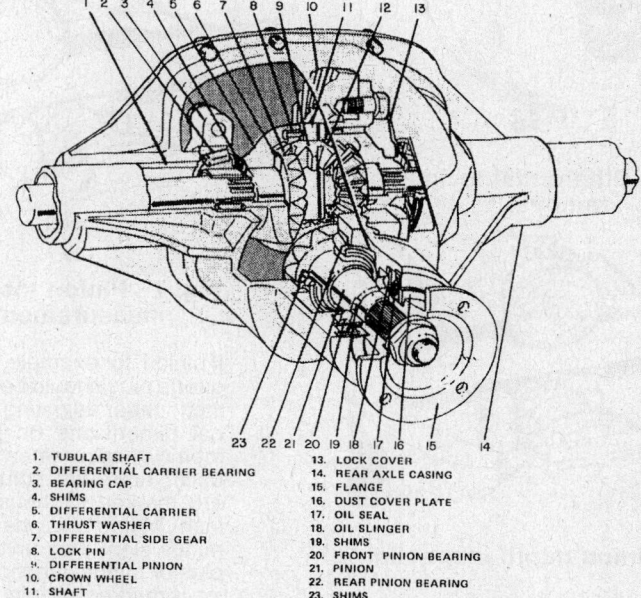

Fig. 1 Exploded view of rear axle assembly

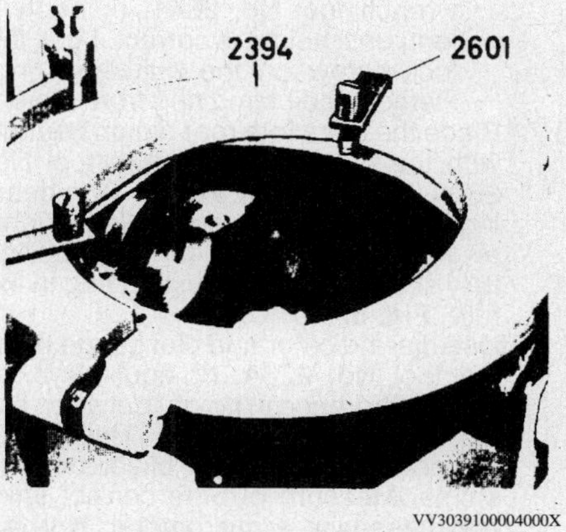

Fig. 2 Expanding rear axle housing

ASSEMBLE

1. **On models less limited slip differential,** install thrust washers and large differential gears into case using suitable nut, bolt and washers to retain them. Tighten nuts to compress thrust washers. Install small differential gears and thrust washers into housing as an assembly and remove nut, bolt and washers. Install differential gear shaft and lockpin.
2. **On models without limited slip differential,** install ring gear onto carrier assembly. Using new bolts, **torque** standard head bolts to 50–58 ft. lbs., **torque** flanged head bolts to 65–80 ft. lbs.
3. **On models with limited slip differential,** install ring gear onto carrier assembly. Coat new bolt threads with a suitable sealing compound and install bolts. **Torque** standard head bolts to

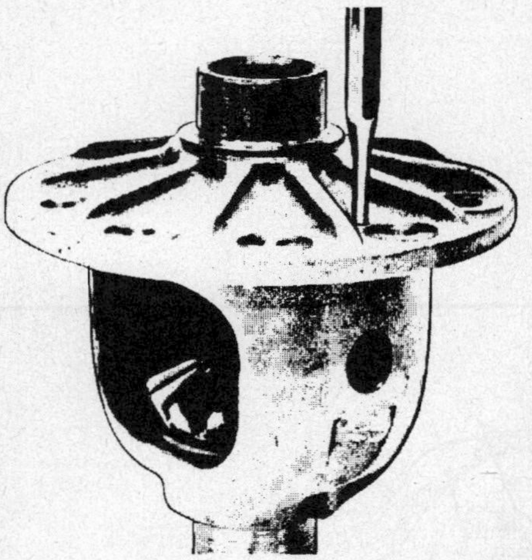

VV3039100005000X

Fig. 3 Differential lockpin removal

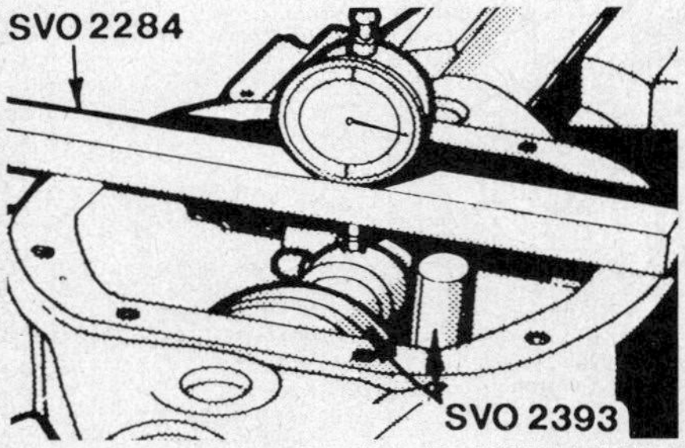

VV3039100008000X

Fig. 6 Pinion depth inspection

50–58 ft. lbs., **torque** flanged head bolts to 65–80 ft. lbs. Install shafts, gears and discs into differential housing. **Torque** bolts to 44–55 ft. lbs.

4. **On type 1030 axle,** install adjusting ring 2685 and wrench 2841 or 5157 onto pinion, **Fig. 4.** On type 1031 axle, install adjusting ring 2840 and wrench 2841 or 5157 onto pinion.
5. **On all models,** install pinion into housing. **Ensure screw head on adjusting ring faces the larger part of the differential carrier. Ensure adjusting ring pin is in the differential carrier recess.**
6. Check pinion depth with dial gauge holder tool No. 2284, or equivalent, and measuring tool No. 2393, or equivalent and a dial indicator as follows:
   a. Place gauge plug on machined surface of pinion, install tool No. 2393, or equivalent, in housing in place of carrier and place dial indicator in tool No. 2284, or equivalent, then place tool across machined surface of housing, **Fig. 5.**
   b. Place dial indicator on tool, **Fig. 6,** and zero indicator. Move indicator retainer so that indicator comes in contact with gauge plug. The machined surface of the pinion is marked with a nominal dimension. The reading taken in **Fig. 7,** should equal the nominal dimension as marked on pinion.

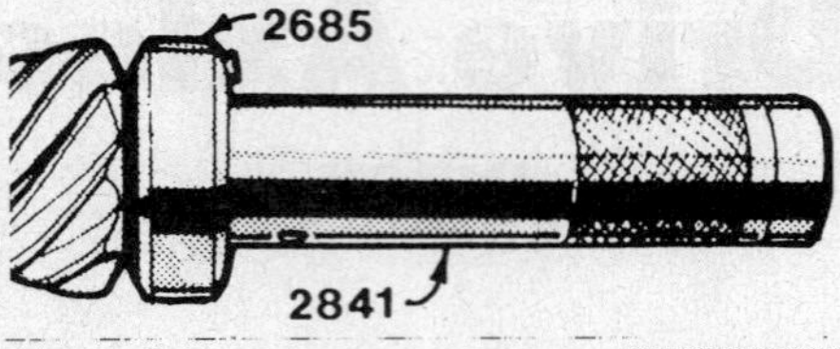

VV3039100006000X

Fig. 4 Adjusting ring & tool for pinion location

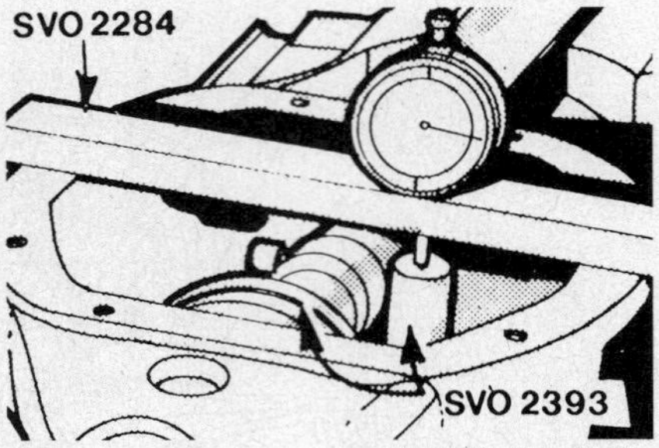

VV3039100009000X

Fig. 7 Pinion location measurement

   c. If pinion, for example, is marked 33, gauge plug should be .33 mm (.013 inch) under adjusting fixture. Nominal dimensions on pinion are in metric measurements on all late units, however, some early units are marked in thousandths of an inch. Metric units have no plus or minus sign. Inch units are marked plus or minus. On inch units, if pinion is marked (–) minus, gauge plug should be higher than adjusting fixture. If marked (+) plus, gauge plug should be lower. Pinion height is adjusted to proper value by turning wrench tool No. 2841, or equivalent, until height is correct. Lock the lock screw on the adjusting ring. Remove adjusting ring from pinion.
7. Place the complete rear pinion bearing with the outer ring in fixture tool No. 2600, or equivalent, **Fig. 8.** Turn bearing back and forth to seat rollers. Tighten knurled nut down to hold bearing fully seated. Place adjusting ring in fixture, **Fig. 8.**
8. Use dial indicator and dial gauge holding tool No. 2284, or equivalent, to check difference in height between adjusting ring and bearing. This is the correct thickness for the pinion bearing shims. Measure out the correct shim thickness with a micrometer. **It is almost impossible to obtain a shim with exactly the correct thickness. Shims must not be more than .02 mm (.0082 inch) thicker than the measured value, but can be up to .05 mm (.002 inch) thinner.**
9. Press rear pinion bearing onto pinion.
10. The measured shims obtained are installed in the housing under the bearing race for the rear pinion bearing. Do not install washer that was under bearing cup originally. The measured shims

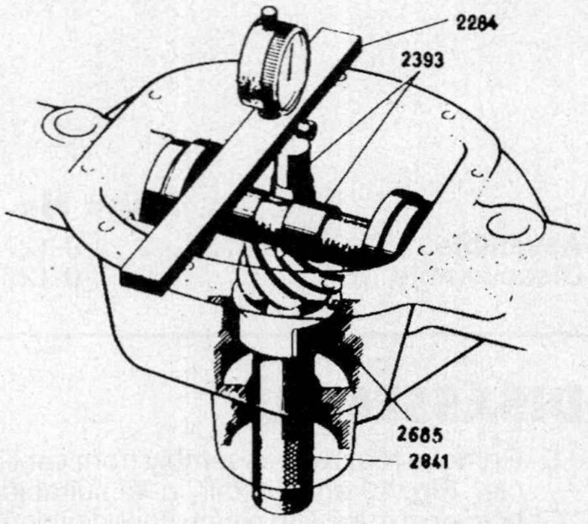

VV3039100007000X

Fig. 5 Rear axle measuring tools

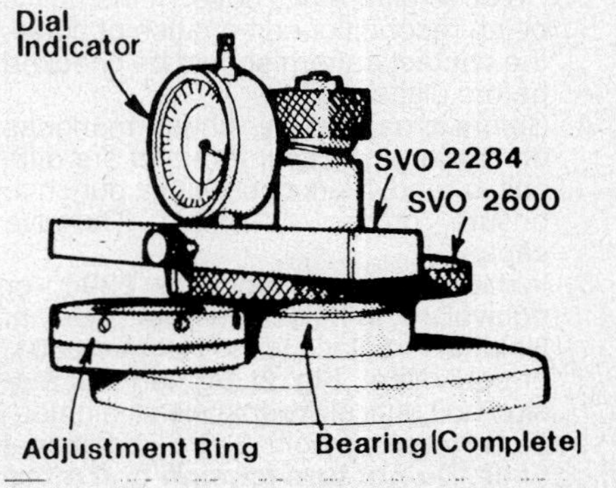

VV3039100010000X

Fig. 8 Ring & bearing measurement

will provide proper pinion depth.

11. Install both bearing races with press tool No. 2686, or equivalent, on type 1030 axles or 2842, or equivalent, on type 1031 axles, **Fig. 9.**
12. Insert pinion into housing, then install three .75 mm (.030 inch) shims and front pinion bearing. Using press tool No. 1845, or equivalent and wrench tool No. 2404, or equivalent, pull in pinion.
13. Replace press tool No. 1845, or equivalent, with washer and nut. **Torque** nut to 185 ft. lbs.
14. Using the dial indicator and dial gauge holder tool No. 2284, or equivalent, check pinion endplay.
15. Remove pinion. Reduce thickness of front shim pack according to dial indicator reading plus .0035 inch (.09 mm) for new bearings. On used bearings, reduce thickness of front shim pack according to dial indicator reading plus .0028 inch (.07 mm).
16. Using the above shim pack, install pinion as outlined in Step 13. Check the torque necessary to rotate the pinion. For used bearings, 13–22 inch lbs. should rotate the pinion. For new bearings, 22–31 inch lbs. Higher torque on new units may occur. Higher torque is not a cause for concern, but if torque

does not meet minimum values, reduce the front bearing shim pack to obtain the correct torque.

17. Lubricate the inside of adjusting rings 2595 and install them on the differential carrier in place of the carrier bearings. The ring with the black oxidized ring should be placed on the ring gear side. Install the differential assembly in the housing.
18. Turn the adjusting rings to adjust the ring gear position to obtain a gear backlash of .15 mm (.006 inch). Tighten the lock screws to specifications. **Previously, the gear contact pattern could be used to determine correct installation of the gears. This is no longer possible because of altered manufacturing and test procedures. The pinion should always be installed according to its number marking regardless of the contact pattern.**
19. Install each carrier bearing assembly in measurement tool No. 2600, or equivalent. Follow procedure outlined to determine the proper shim thickness for each carrier bearing. Place the right bearing in the tool and measure the adjusting ring that was on the right side of the carrier. When each shim pack has been determined, add .07 mm (.003 inch) to each side for preload. Install shims on carrier and press on the carrier bearings.
20. Install expander tool No. 2394, or equivalent, on the housing. Expand the tool until the tool pins are tight in the holes in the housing, then turn the tensioning screw an additional 3–3½ turns. Install the differential and bearing rings.
21. Remove tool No. 2394, or equivalent.
22. Install the caps according to their markings and **torque** to 36–50 ft. lbs.
23. Remove tool No. 2404, or equivalent, from pinion. Install oil seal.
24. Press on the flange with press tool Nos. 1845 or 5156, or equivalents.
25. Install washer and nut. **Torque** nut to 185 ft. lbs.
26. Install differential cover with a new gasket.
27. Install axle shafts.

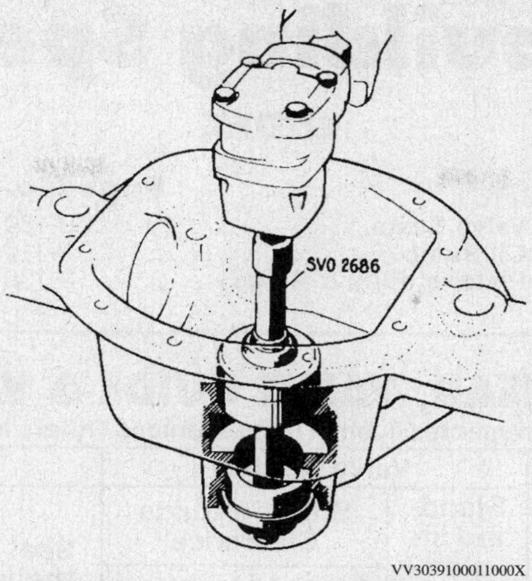

Fig. 9 Bearing race installation

Engine Rebuilding Specifications

INDEX

	Page No.		Page No.		Page No.
Crankshaft, Bearings & Rods	9-133	Valve Seats	9-130	Valve Springs	9-131
Cylinder Block	9-134	Oil Pump	9-110	Valves	9-132
Cylinder Head, Valve Guide &		Pistons, Pins & Rings	9-133		

CYLINDER HEAD, VALVE GUIDE & VALVE SEATS

All Measurements Given In Inches Unless Otherwise Specified.

Engine Model	Engine Liter	Cylinder Head		Valve Guides			Valve Seats			Valve Clearance	
		Warpage Limit	Minimum Height	Standard Inside Diameter	Stem To Guide Clearance		Seat Angle	Seat Width		Intake	Exhaust
					Intake	Exhaust		Intake	Exhaust		
1998											
B5234T	2.3L	②	5.066	.4720	.0012-.0024	.0012-.0024	45	.055-.071	.055-.071	①	①
B5254S/T	2.4L	②	5.066	.4720	.0012-.0024	.0012-.0024	45	.055-.071	.055-.071	①	①
B6304S	2.9L	②	5.066	.4720	.0012-.0024	.0012-.0028	45	.055-.071	.071-.087	①	①
1999–2001											
B5202/4/4T	1.9L	②	5.079	.5000	.0008-.0016	.0008-.0016	—	—	—	①	①
B5234T	2.3L	②	5.079	.5000	.0008-.0016	.0008-.0016	—	—	—	①	①
B5234T3	2.3L	②	5.079	.5000	.0008-.0016	.0008-.0016	—	—	—	①	①
B5234T	2.3L Low Pressure turbo	②	5.079	.5000	.0008-.0016	.0008-.0016	—	—	—	①	①
B5234T	2.3L High Pressure Turbo	②	5.079	.5000	.0008-.0016	.0008-.0016	—	—	—	①	①
B5254S/T	2.4L	②	5.201	.5000	.0008-.0016	.0008-.0016	—	—	—	①	①
B6304S	2.9L		—	—	—	—	—	—	—	—	—
B6284T	2.7L Twin Turbo		—	—	—	—	—	—	—	—	—

① — Equipped w/hydraulic valve lash adjusters, no adjustment required.

② — .020 inch lengthwise or .008 inch crosswise.

VALVE SPRINGS

All Measurements Given In Inches Unless Otherwise Specified.

Engine Model	Engine Liter	Valve Springs	
		Free Length	Compressed Pressure Pounds @ Inches
1998			
B5234T	2.3L	1.67	143-158 @ .964
B5254S/T	2.4L	1.67	143-158 @ .964
B6304S	2.9L	1.69	143-158 @ .964
1999			
B5234T	2.3L	—	—
B5234 T3	2.3L Low Pressure Turbo	—	—
B5234 T3	2.3L High Pressure Turbo	—	—
B5234T	2.3L	—	—
B6304S	2.9L	—	—
2000–01			
B4204T2/3	1.9L	—	—
B5234T	2.3L	—	—
B5234 T3	2.3L Low Pressure Turbo	—	—
B5234 T3	2.3L High Pressure Turbo	—	—
B5234T	2.3L	—	—
B6304S	2.9L	—	—
B6284	2.7L twin Turbo	—	—
B6284	2.7L twin Turbo	—	—

VALVES

All Measurements Given In Inches Unless Otherwise Specified.

Engine Model	Engine Liter	Valves		
		Stem Diameter		Face Angle, Degrees
		Intake	Exhaust	
1998				
B5234T	2.3L	.2744	.2744	44.5
B5254S/T	2.4L	.2744	.2744	44.5
B6304S	2.9L	.2744	.2744	44.5
1999				
B5234T	2.3L	—	—	—
B5234T3	2.3L	—	—	—
B5234T3	2.3L Low Pressure Turbo	—	—	—
B5234T3	2.3L High Pressure Turbo	—	—	—
B5254S/T	2.4L	—	—	—
B6284T	2.7L Twin Turbo	—	—	—
2000–01				
B4204T2/3	1.9L	—	—	—
B5234T	2.3L	—	—	—
B5234T3	2.3L	—	—	—
B5234T3	2.3L Low Pressure Turbo	—	—	—
B5234T3	2.3L High Pressure Turbo	—	—	—
B5254S/T	2.4L	—	—	—
B6284T	2.7L Twin Turbo	—	—	—
B6304S	2.9L	—	—	—
B6304S	2.9L	—	—	—

CRANKSHAFT, BEARINGS & RODS

All Measurements Given In Inches Unless Otherwise Specified.

Engine Model	Engine Liter	Crankshaft			Bearing Clearance		Connecting Rod Side Clearance
		Standard Journal Dia.		Endplay	Main Bear-ing	Connecting Rod Bearing	
		Main Bear-ing	Connecting Rod				
1998							
B5234T	2.3L	2.559	2.086	.0075	—	—	—
B5254S/T	2.4L	2.559	2.086	.0075	—	—	—
B6304S	2.9L	2.559	2.086	.0031-.0075	—	—	—
1999							
B5234T/T3	2.3L	—	—	—	—	—	—
B5234T3	2.3L Low Pres-sure Turbo	—	—	—	—	—	—
B5234T3	2.3L High Pres-sure Turbo	—	—	—	—	—	—
B5254S/T	2.4L	—	—	—	—	—	—
B6284T	2.7L Twin Turbo	—	—	—	—	—	—
2000–01							
B4204T2/3	1.9L	—	—	—	—	—	—
B5234T/T3	2.3L	—	—	—	—	—	—
B5234T3	2.3L Low Pres-sure Turbo	—	—	—	—	—	—
B5234T3	2.3L High Pres-sure Turbo	—	—	—	—	—	—
B5254S/T	2.4L	—	—	—	—	—	—
B6284T	2.7L Twin Turbo	—	—	—	—	—	—
B6304S	2.9L	—	—	—	—	—	—
B6304S	2.9L	—	—	—	—	—	—

PISTONS, PINS & RINGS

All Measurements Given In Inches Unless Otherwise Specified.

Engine Model	Engine Liter	Piston Std. Dia.	Pis-ton Pin Dia.	Piston Pin To Piston Clear-ance	Piston Ring End Gap,①			Piston Ring Side Clearance		
					Top	Second	Oil	Top	Second	Oil
1998										
B5234T	2.3L	⑤	.905	②	.008-.016	.008-.016	.010-.020	.0020-.0033	.0012-.0026	.0008-.0022
B5254S/T	2.4L	③	.905	②	.008-.016	.008-.016	.010-.020	.0020-.0033	.0012-.0026	.0008-.0022
B6304S	2.9L	④	.905	②	.008-.016	.008-.016	.010-.020	.0020-.0033	.0012-.0026	.0008-.022
1999										
B5234T/T3	2.3L	—	—	—	—	—	—	—	—	—
B5234T3	2.3L Low Pressure Turbo	—	—	—	—	—	—	—	—	—
B5234T3	High Pressure Turbo	—	—	—	—	—	—	—	—	—
B5254S/T	2.4L	—	—	—	—	—	—	—	—	—
B6284T	2.7L Twin Turbo	—	—	—	—	—	—	—	—	—
2000–01										
B4204T2/3	1.9L	—	—	—	—	—	—	—	—	—
B5234T/T3	2.3L	—	—	—	—	—	—	—	—	—
B5234T3	2.3L Low Pressure Turbo	—	—	—	—	—	—	—	—	—

Continued

PISTONS, PINS & RINGS—Continued

All Measurements Given In Inches Unless Otherwise Specified.

Engine Model	Engine Liter	Piston Std. Dia.	Piston Pin Dia.	Piston Pin To Piston Clearance	Piston Ring End Gap,①			Piston Ring Side Clearance		
					Top	Second	Oil	Top	Second	Oil
2000–01										
B5234T3	High Pressure Turbo	—	—	—	—	—	—	—	—	—
B5254S/T	2.4L	—	—	—	—	—	—	—	—	—
B6284T	2.7L Twin Turbo	—	—	—	—	—	—	—	—	—
B6304S	2.9L	—	—	—	—	—	—	—	—	—
B6304S	2.9L	—	—	—	—	—	—	—	—	—

① — Pistons marked "C," 3.7816–3.7820 inch; pistons marked "D," 3.7820–3.7824 inch; pistons marked "E," 3.7824–3.7828 inch; pistons marked "G," 3.7832–3.7836 inch.

② — Piston pin should fit in connecting rod & piston using light thumb pressure.

③ — Pistons marked "C", 3.2669–3.2673 inch, pistons marked "D", 3.2673–3.2677 inch; pistons marked "E", 3.2677–3.2681 inch; pistons marked "G", 3.2683–3.2689 inch.

④ — Pistons marked "C", 3.2669–3.2673 inch; pistons marked "D", 3.2673–3.2677 inch; pistons marked "E", 3.2677–3.2681 inch; pistons marked "G", 3.2684–3.2688 inch.

⑤ — Pistons marked "C", 3.1881–3.1885 inch; pistons marked "D", 3.1885–3.1889 inch; pistons marked "E", 3.1889–3.1893 inch; pistons marked "G", 3.1896–3.1902 inch.

CYLINDER BLOCK

All Measurements Given In Inches Unless Otherwise Specified.

Engine, Model	Engine, Liter	Cylinder Bore Std. Dia. Marked			
		C	D	E	G
1998					
B5234T	2.3L	3.1890-3.1894	3.1894-3.1898	3.1898-3.1902	3.1905-3.1909
B5254S/T	2.4L	3.2677-3.2681	3.2681-3.2685	3.2685-3.2689	3.2693-3.2697
B6304S	2.9L	3.2678-3.2681	3.2681-3.2685	3.2685-3.2689	3.2693-3.2697
1999					
B5234T/T3	2.3L	—	—	—	—
B5234T3	2.3L Low Pressure Turbo	—	—	—	—
B5234T3	High Pressure Turbo	—	—	—	—
B5254S/T	2.4L	—	—	—	—
B6284T	2.7L Twin Turbo	—	—	—	—
2000–01					
B4204T2/3	1.9L	—	—	—	—
B5234T/T3	2.3L	—	—	—	—
B5234T3	2.3L Low Pressure Turbo	—	—	—	—
B5234T3	High Pressure Turbo	—	—	—	—
B5254S/T	2.4L	—	—	—	—
B6284T	2.7L Twin Turbo	—	—	—	—
B6304S	2.9L	—	—	—	—
B6304S	2.9L	—	—	—	—

AUDI

TABLE OF CONTENTS

	Page No.
COMPUTERIZED ENGINE CONTROLS	10-28
EMISSIONS:	
Abbreviations & Acronyms	10-142
Application Charts	10-128
Emission Controls	10-136
Emission Control System Application Chart	10-128
Engine Compartment Reference Diagrams	10-132
Technical Service Bulletins	10-139
Vacuum Hose Routings	10-129
ENGINE SYSTEMS IDENTIFICATION	10-3
FUEL SYSTEMS:	
Abbreviations & Acronyms	10-142
Electric Fuel Pumps	10-19
Engine Compartment Reference Diagrams	10-132
Fuel Injection	10-16
Technical Service Bulletins	10-139
ENGINE TUNE UP & PERFORMANCE:	
Abbreviations & Acronyms	10-142
Specifications	10-4
Technical Service Bulletins	10-139
V6 Gasoline Engine	10-7
V8 Gasoline Engine	10-7
4 Cylinder Gasoline Engine	10-5
GENERAL INFORMATION:	
Abbreviations & Acronyms	10-142
Air Bag System Precautions	0-12
Air Quality Standards	0-23
Computer Relearn Procedures	0-10
Electrical Symbol & Wire Color Code Identification	0-33
Engine Systems Identification	10-3
How To Use This Manual	0-1
Quick Reference	10-2
Service Reminder & Warning Lamp Reset Procedure	0-14
Technical Service Bulletins	10-139
Vehicle Identification	0-3
Vehicle Lift Points	0-24
Vehicle Maintenance Schedules	0-45
IGNITION SYSTEMS:	
Abbreviations & Acronyms	10-142
Engine Compartment Reference Diagrams	10-132
Ignition Systems	10-8
Technical Service Bulletins	10-139
INDUCTION SYSTEM:	
Abbreviations & Acronyms	10-142
Engine Compartment Reference Diagrams	10-132
Technical Service Bulletins	10-139
Turbochargers	10-23

Quick Reference

Application	Page No.
ACCESSING DIAGNOSTIC TROUBLE CODES	
1.8L Engine	10-29
2.7L Engine	10-64
2.8L Engine	10-89
3.7L & 4.2L Engines	10-115
CLEARING DIAGNOSTIC TROUBLE CODES	
1.8L Engine	10-46
2.8L Engine	10-104
3.7L & 4.2L Engines	10-120
COMPRESSION PRESSURE SPECIFICATIONS	
4 Cylinder Gasoline Engine	10-5
V6 Gasoline Engine	10-7
V8 Gasoline Engine	10-7
DIAGNOSTIC CHART INDEX	
1.8L Engine	10-47
2.7L Engine	10-73
2.8L Engine	10-104
3.7L & 4.2L Engines	10-122
DIAGNOSTIC TROUBLE CODE INTERPRETATION	
1.8L Engine	10-29
2.7L Engine	10-64
2.8L Engine	10-89
3.7L & 4.2L Engines	10-115
FUEL INJECTOR SPECIFICATIONS	
1.8L Engine	10-29
2.7L Engine	10-64
2.8L Engine	10-88
3.7L & 4.2L Engines	10-114
FUEL PRESSURE SPECIFICATIONS	
1.8L Engine	10-31
2.7L Engine	10-65
2.8L Engine	10-91
3.7L & 4.2L Engines	10-11
IGNITION COIL SPECIFICATIONS	
All	10-8
SENSOR & FUEL INJECTOR SPECIFICATIONS	
1.8L Engine	10-29
2.7L Engine	10-64
2.8L Engine	10-88
3.7L & 4.2L Engines	10-114

Engine Systems Identification

On 4 Cylinder Engines, Engine Code Is Located On Cylinder Head Front Lefthand Lifting Eye And On Engine Block Above Oil Filter. On V6 Engines, Engine Code Is Located On Righthand Side Of Engine Block Between Cylinder Head And Power Steering Pump Or On Flat Surface Of Cylinder Block In Front Of Righthand Cylinder Head. On V8 Engines, Engine Code Is Located On Lefthand Side Of Engine Above Power Steering Pump.

Engine Code	Engine	Fuel System	Page No.	Ignition System	Page No.	Computer System	Page No.
1998–99							
AEB	1.8L	MFI	10-16	Bosch Motronic	10-8	Bosch Motronic	10-28
AFC & AHA	2.8L	MFI	10-16	Bosch Motronic	10-8	Bosch Motronic	10-88
AEW	3.7L	MFI	10-16	Bosch Motronic	10-8	Bosch Motronic	10-114
ABZ	4.2L	MFI	10-16	Bosch Motronic	10-8	Bosch Motronic	10-114
2000–01							
AEB & ATC	1.8L	MFI	10-16	Bosch Motronic	10-8	Bosch Motronic	10-28
AMU & ATW	1.8L	MFI	10-16	Bosch Motronic	10-8	Bosch Motronic	10-28
APB	2.7L	MFI	10-16	Bosch Motronic	10-8	Bosch Motronic	10-64
ACK & AHA	2.8L	MFI	10-16	Bosch Motronic	10-8	Bosch Motronic	10-88
AEW	3.7L	MFI	10-16	Bosch Motronic	10-8	Bosch Motronic	10-114
ABZ	4.2L	MFI	10-16	Bosch Motronic	10-8	Bosch Motronic	10-114

Tune Up Specifications

Engine/ Code	Spark Plug Gap Inch	Ignition Timing		Curb Idle Speed		Fast Idle Speed		Valve Lash, Inch		Fuel Press-ure, psi
		Firing Order Fig.①	Timing ° BTDC②	Man. Trans.	Auto. Trans.	Man. Trans.	Auto. Trans.	Intake	Ex-haust	
1998–99										
1.8L/AEB	.032	⑨	④	④	④	④	④	⑤	⑤	58⑩
2.8L/AFC	.039	⑥	12④	650–750④	650–750④	④	④	⑤	⑤	55–70⑧
3.7L/AEW	.032	⑦	—	—	④	—	④	⑤	⑤	—
4.2L/ABH	.032	⑦	—	—	④	—	④	⑤	⑤	—
2000										
1.8L/ATC⑪	.032	⑨	④	800–920④	640–760④	④	④	⑤	⑤	58⑩
1.8L/ATC⑫	.032	⑨	④	720–840④	—	④	④	⑤	⑤	58⑩
1.8L/ATW	.032	⑨	④	750–850④	750–850④	④	④	⑤	⑤	50
2.7L/APB	—	⑬	④	750–850④	750–850④	④	④	⑤	⑤	58⑧
2.8L/AHA⑪	.064	⑨	④	740–860④	740–860④	④	④	⑤	⑤	55–61⑩
2.8L/AHA⑫	.064	⑨	④	620–740④	620–740④	④	④	⑤	⑤	55–61⑩
2.8L/ATQ	.038	⑥	TDC	—	650–750N④	④	④	⑤	⑤	55–61⑩
4.2L/AKB	.028–.035	③	④	—	—	—	④	⑤	⑤	—
4.2L/ART	.028–.035	③	④	—	—	—	④	⑤	⑤	—
2001										
1.8L/AMU	.032	⑨	④	④	④	④	④	⑤	⑤	—
1.8L/ATC⑪	.032	⑨	④	800–920④	640–760④	④	④	⑤	⑤	58⑩
1.8L/ATC⑫	.032	⑨	④	720–840④	—	④	④	⑤	⑤	58⑩
1.8L/ATW	.032	⑨	④	750–850④	750–850④	④	④	⑤	⑤	50
2.7L/APB	—	⑬	④	750–850④	750–850④	④	④	⑤	⑤	58⑧
2.8L/AHA⑪	.064	⑨	④	740–860④	740–860④	④	④	⑤	⑤	55–61⑩
2.8L/AHA⑫	.064	⑨	④	620–740④	620–740④	④	④	⑤	⑤	55–61⑩
2.8L/ATQ	.038	⑥	TDC	—	650–750N④	④	④	⑤	⑤	55–61⑩
4.2L/AKB	.028–.035	③	④	—	—	—	④	⑤	⑤	—
4.2L/ART	.028–.035	③	④	—	—	—	④	⑤	⑤	—

① — Determine location of number 1 wire before disconnecting spark plug wires.

② — BTDC: Before Top Dead Center.

③ — Firing order 1–5–4–8–6–3–7–2.

④ — Not adjustable. Controlled by electronic control unit.

⑤ — Equipped with hydraulic valve lash adjusters.

⑥ — Firing order 1–4–3–6–2–5. Refer to **Fig. A** for spark plug wire connections.

⑦ — Firing order 1–5–4–8–6–3–7–2. Refer to **Fig. B** for spark plug wire connections.

⑧ — With pressure regulator vacuum hose disconnected & plugged.

⑨ — Firing order 1–3–4–2.

⑩ — Connect suitable fuel pressure gauge between fuel supply & fuel return lines. Disconnect & plug vacuum line from fuel pressure regulator to intake manifold, then use suitable scan tool to trigger fuel pump relay.

⑪ — Front wheel drive.

⑫ — Quattro.

⑬ — Firing order 1–4–3–6–2–5.

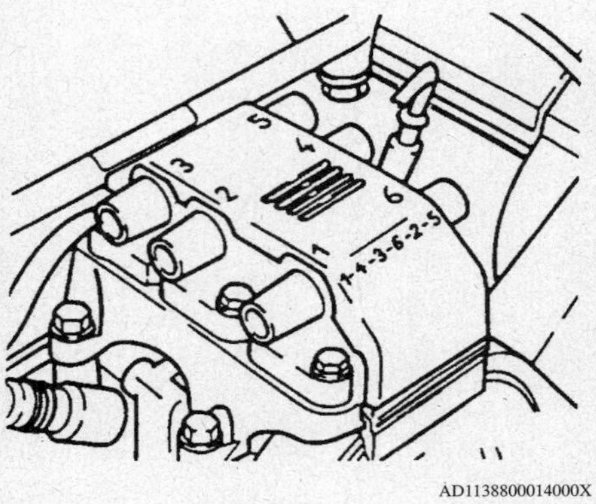

Fig. A

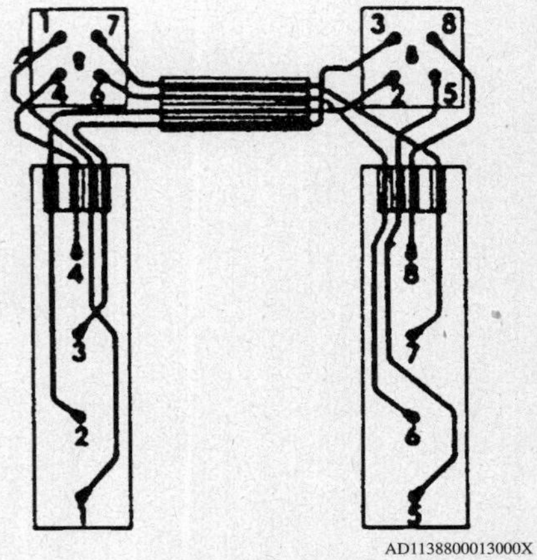

Fig. B

Engine Tune Up & Performance

TABLE OF CONTENTS

	Page No.		Page No.
4 CYLINDER GASOLINE ENGINE	10-5	**V6 GASOLINE ENGINES**	10-7
		V8 GASOLINE ENGINES	10-7

4 Cylinder Gasoline Engine

NOTE: Prior To Performing Any Service Operations Listed In This Section Consult "Technical Service Bulletins" Section For Related Information.

INDEX

	Page No.		Page No.		Page No.
Compression Pressures	10-5	**Ignition Timing**	10-5	**Valves**	10-6
Idle Speed Adjustment	10-5	**Spark Plugs**	10-5	Valve Adjustment	10-6

SPARK PLUGS

Refer to "Tune Up Specifications" charts for spark plug gap.

COMPRESSION PRESSURES

1. Perform compression test with engine at operating temperature, spark plugs removed, oil temperature above 86°F and throttle plate completely open.
2. Disconnect coil high tension wire from distributor cap and connect to suitable ground.
3. Connect compression tester per manufacturers instructions, then crank engine until compression tester shows no further increase in pressure.
4. Compression should be 131–189 psi with a maximum difference of 44 psi. Minimum compression should be 102 psi.

IGNITION TIMING

Ignition timing is controlled by Engine Control Module (ECM) and cannot be adjusted.

IDLE SPEED ADJUSTMENT

Refer to "Tune Up Specifications" chart for proper idle speed.

Idle speed is controlled by Engine Control Module (ECM) and cannot be adjusted. To inspect idle speed, proceed as follows:

1. Turn off all accessories and ensure engine cooling fan is not running.

Display	RPM	Deg. F	Percentages	Conditions
Indicates	Idle Speed	ECT	Oxygen Sensor Control	Adjustment
Range	0–6800 RPM (In 40 RPM Steps)	—	–25% to 25%	
Specified Value	760–960 RPM	176–221	–10% to 10%	111111②

① — Must change at least 2.
② — A/C compressor off, CTP switch closed, oxygen sensor control active, throttle valve closed, engine speed less than 2000 RPM and ECT above 176°F. If 0 is displayed, adjustment conditions not fulfilled.

Fig. 1 Idle data Display Group 1. A4 & S4 w/1.8L engine

2. Ensure exhaust system is free from leaks.
3. Connect scan tool No. VAG 1551/1553A, or equivalent, then press buttons "0" and "4" to select "Basic Setting" function 04, and press "Q" to confirm input.
4. **On A4 and S4 models,** press "0, 0 and 1" to input Display Group 1 and press "Q" to confirm input.
5. **On TT models,** press "0, 5 and 6" to input Display Group 1 and press "Q" to confirm input.
6. **On all models,** ensure the following conditions are met:
   a. ECT is above 185°F.
   b. Cooling fan does not turn on during inspection.
   c. Engine speed is less than 2000 RPM.
   d. EVAP canister purge regulator valve is closed.
   e. Throttle valve is closed.
   f. Oxygen sensor control is active.
   g. Closed throttle position switch is closed.
   h. A/C compressor is off.
   i. Transmission is in Park or Neutral.
7. Perform brief WOT and let engine idle for two additional minutes.
8. Ensure scan tool displayed values are as specified, **Fig. 1.**
9. If idle speed or oxygen sensor control is not as specified, inspect throttle valve control module as outlined under "Computerized Engine Controls."
10. If displayed values are as specified, press "C," then press 0, 5 and 6 to input Display Group number 56, then press "Q" to confirm input.
11. Ensure scan tool displayed values meet specifications, **Figs. 2 and 3.**
12. If RPM or mass air flow are not as specified, inspect throttle valve control module as outlined under "Computerized Engine Controls."
13. Press the arrow button to advance program sequence.
14. Press buttons 0 and 6 to select "End Output" function 06, then press "Q" to confirm input.

15. Road test vehicle, then repeat test. Inspect readiness code. If DTC memory has been erased, generate new readiness code.

VALVES

Valve Adjustment

These engines use hydraulic lash adjusters and do not require adjustment.

Display	RPM	RPM	G/S	Conditions
Indicates	Engine Speed (Actual)	Engine Speed (Specified)	Mass Air Flow	Operating
Range	0–6800 RPM (In 10 RPM Steps)	—	–2.80 to 4.17	—
Specified Value	820–900	860	–1.11 to 1.11 G/S	0000①

① — First & second 0 is always displayed, transmission selector lever in P or N position, A/C compressor off.

Fig. 2 Idle data Display Group 56. A4 & S4 w/1.8L engine

Display	RPM	RPM	X.X%	Conditions
Indicates	Engine Speed (Actual)	Engine Speed (Specified)	Idle Control Torque Change	Operating
Specified Value	①	②	X.X%	00000

① — FWD models, 800–920 RPM; AWD models, 720–840 RPM.
② — FWD models, 860 RPM; AWD models, 780 RPM.

Fig. 3 Idle data Display Group 56. TT w/1.8L engine

V6 Gasoline Engines

NOTE: Prior To Performing Any Service Operations Listed In This Section Consult "Technical Service Bulletins" Section For Related Information.

INDEX

	Page No.		Page No.		Page No.
Compression Pressures	10-7	**Ignition Timing**	10-7	**Valves**	10-7
Idle Speed Adjustment	10-7	**Spark Plugs**	10-7	Valve Adjustment	10-7

SPARK PLUGS

Refer to "Tune Up Specifications" charts for spark plug gap.

COMPRESSION PRESSURES

1. Perform compression test with engine at operating temperature, spark plugs removed, oil temperature above 86°F and throttle wide open. **Disconnect both wires from final power stage and all electrical connectors from injectors.**
2. Install compression tester tool No. VAG 1381 and adapter tool No. 1381/A, or equivalents.
3. Crank starter motor until tester shows no further pressure increase.
4. Compression should be 131–203 psi, with a maximum difference between cylinders of 44 psi.
5. **On 2.7L engines,** minimum compression should be 102 psi.
6. **On 2.8L engines,** minimum compression should be 109 psi.

IGNITION TIMING

Ignition timing is controlled by Engine Control Module (ECM) and cannot be adjusted.

IDLE SPEED ADJUSTMENT

Idle speed is controlled by the Engine Control Module (ECM) and cannot be adjusted. Refer to appropriate fuel injection system if idle speed is not within specifications.

VALVES

Valve Adjustment

These engines use hydraulic lash adjusters and do not require adjustment.

V8 Gasoline Engines

NOTE: Prior To Performing Any Service Operations Listed In This Section Consult "Technical Service Bulletins" Section For Related Information.

INDEX

	Page No.		Page No.		Page No.
Compression Pressures	10-7	**Ignition Timing**	10-7	**Valves**	10-7
Idle Speed Adjustment	10-7	**Spark Plugs**	10-7	Valve Adjustment	10-7
Idle Speed	10-7				

SPARK PLUGS

Refer to "Tune Up Specifications" charts for spark plug gap.

COMPRESSION PRESSURES

1. Ensure engine oil temperature is at least 86°F.
2. Prop throttle wide open, then remove Fuse 1 from righthand A-pillar fuse panel.
3. Install compression recorder tool Nos. VAG1381 and VAG1381/5, or equivalents.
4. Crank engine until no further pressure increase is indicated on tester. Compression should be 145–220 psi with no more than 44 psi difference between cylinders. Minimum compression should not be lower than 110 psi.

IGNITION TIMING

Ignition timing is controlled by the Engine Control Module (ECM) and cannot be adjusted.

IDLE SPEED ADJUSTMENT

Idle Speed

Idle speed is controlled by the Engine Control Module (ECM) and cannot be adjusted.

VALVES

Valve Adjustment

These engines use hydraulic lash adjusters and do not require adjustment.

Ignition Systems

NOTE: If Unsure Of System Used On Vehicle Being Serviced, Refer To "Engine Systems Identification" Chart Located At Beginning Of This Chapter.

NOTE: Prior To Performing Any Service Operations Listed In This Section Consult "Technical Service Bulletins" Section For Related Information.

NOTE: Refer To "Fuel Injection" Section For System Wiring Diagrams, Refer To "Fuel Injection" And "Computerized Engine Controls" For Component And System Testing Not Covered In This Section.

INDEX

	Page No.
Description	10-8
Diagnosis & Testing	10-8
Component Testing	10-8
1.8L Engine	10-8
2.7L Engine	10-11
2.8L Engine	10-13
3.7L & 4.2L Engines	10-14
System Diagnosis	10-8
Precautions	10-8
Air Bag Systems	10-8
Audio Coded Anti-Theft System	10-8
Battery Ground Cable	10-8
Test Conditions	10-8

PRECAUTIONS

Air Bag Systems

Refer to "Air Bag System Precautions" in the front of this manual for system disarming and arming procedures.

Audio Coded Anti-Theft System

Do not use computer memory saver tool. Using the tool will keep the air bag system charged and may cause accidental activation of the air bag unit.

Obtain the security code from the vehicle operator prior to disconnecting the battery or removing the radio. Refer to the owner's manual for security code disarming and arming procedures.

Battery Ground Cable

Prior to service, disconnect battery ground cable and isolate as required.

Test Conditions

1. Ignition switch must be Off when disconnecting or connecting system components and test equipment.
2. Do not disconnect secondary ignition leads with engine running or while cranking engine, except as instructed during test procedures.
3. Procedures must be followed as outlined and components found faulty must be replaced before proceeding with further tests.
4. Before testing system, inspect wiring harness for breaks, frayed insulation and proper routing, and ensure connectors are seated and free from corrosion.

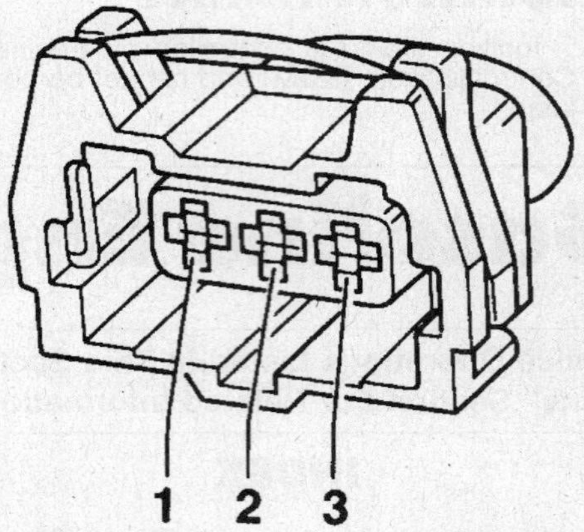

Fig. 1 Camshaft position sensor electrical connector

DESCRIPTION

These ignition systems include power output stages, ignition coils and an Engine Control Module (ECM). These low maintenance systems have few wearing components. There are no routine adjustments to be made.

In the distributorless type ignition systems, the ECM controls spark by using Camshaft Position Sensor (CMP) and Crankshaft Position Sensor (CKP) signals combined with information from other vehicle sensors to control individual coils of a multiple coil pack, producing a properly timed spark for each cylinder as required.

DIAGNOSIS & TESTING

System Diagnosis

Refer to "Fuel Injection" and "Computerized Engine Controls" for system testing not covered in this section.

No adjustments are required on this system. If vehicle performance is unsatisfactory and general diagnosis indicates ignition system fault conditions, system components must be tested as outlined and replaced as required.

Component Testing

Refer to "Fuel Injection" and "Computerized Engine Controls" for component testing not covered in this section.

1.8L ENGINE

CAMSHAFT POSITION SENSOR

A4 & S4

1. Disconnect camshaft position sensor electrical connector.
2. Turn ignition On.
3. Measure voltage between terminals 1 and 3 using a suitable voltmeter, **Fig. 1.** Use adapter cable test kit tool No. VW 1594, or equivalent to measure voltage.
4. Voltage should be approximately 4.5 volts.
5. After completing voltage inspection, proceed as follows:
   a. Connect test box VAG 1598/22, or equivalent to ECM harness connector.
   b. Inspect for an open circuit using a

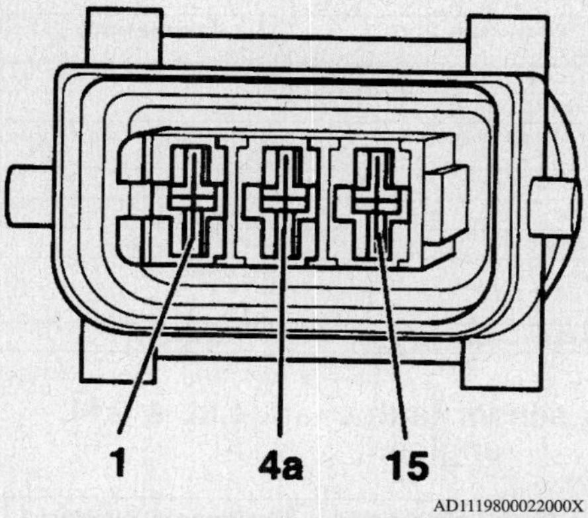

Fig. 2 Coil connector terminal identification. A4 & S4

suitable ohmmeter between the following pins: CMP connector terminal 1 to test box pin 11; CMP connector terminal 2 to test box pin 76; CMP connector terminal 3 to test box pin 67.
   c. Resistance reading should be no greater than 1.5 ohms.
   d. Inspect wiring for short circuit using a suitable ohmmeter between following pins: CMP connector terminal 2 to test box pin 11; CMP connector terminal 3 to test box pin 11; CMP terminal 3 to ECM test box pin 76.
   e. Ohmmeter should show infinite reading.
6. If no shorts or opens exist in wiring and voltage across terminals 1 and 3 of CMP connector is approximately 4.5 volts, replace CMP sensor.
7. If wiring is satisfactory but no voltage exists at CMP connector terminals 1 and 3, proceed as follows:
   a. Replace Motronic ECM.
   b. Perform throttle valve control module relearn procedure as outlined under "Computer Relearn Procedures" in front of this manual.
   c. Generate readiness code if DTC memory has been erased.

TT

1. Disconnect camshaft position sensor electrical connector.
2. Turn ignition On.
3. Measure voltage between terminal 1 and engine ground using adapter cable test kit tool No. VW 1594, or equivalent and a suitable voltmeter, **Fig. 1.** There should be approximately five volts.
4. Measure voltage between terminal 2 and engine ground, which should be battery voltage.
5. Inspect for continuity or a short to battery voltage between terminal 3 and ground. Repair as required.
6. After completing previous inspections, proceed as follows:
   a. Connect test box tool No. VAG 1598/31, or equivalent, to ECM harness electrical connector. **Do not connect to ECM itself.**
   b. Inspect for an open circuit using a

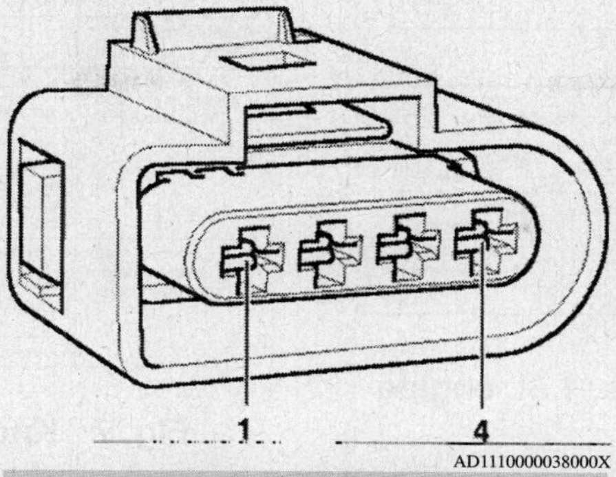

Fig. 3 Coil electrical connector terminal identification. TT

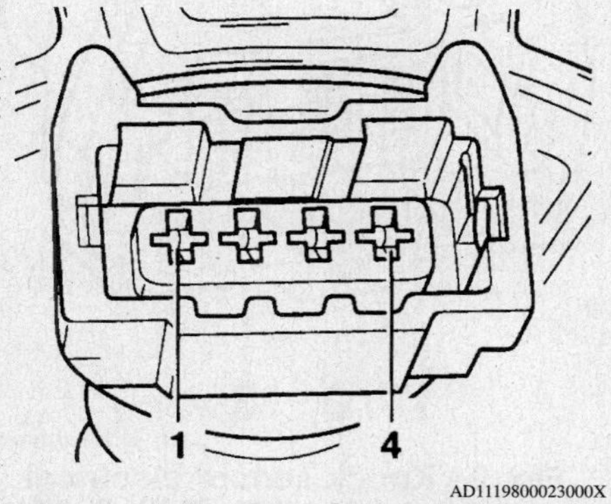

Fig. 5 Power output stage 4 terminal connector identification. 1.8L engine

suitable ohmmeter between the following pins: CMP connector terminal 1 to test box pin 98; CMP connector terminal 2 to test box pin 86; CMP connector terminal 3 to test box pin 108. Repair as required.
7. If no shorts or opens exist in wiring and voltage across terminals 1 and 3 of CMP connector is approximately five volts, replace CMP sensor.
8. If wiring and CMP sensor are satisfactory but measurements do not meet specifications, replace ECM.

IGNITION COIL

A4 & S4

The secondary circuit of the ignition coil incorporates a high tension isolation diode. Ensure proper measuring equipment is used when testing this circuit.

When diagnosing a misfire or rough running concern, the "problem" cylinder can be identified by briefly disconnecting its fuel injector and noting RPM change.

1. Ensure no faults are present in DTC memory. If DTCs are present, repair as required.
2. Measure spark plug connector resistance, which should be approximately 2000 ohms. If resistance is not as specified, proceed as follows:
   a. Connect spark plug connector.
   b. Interchange spark plug with one from normally operating cylinder.

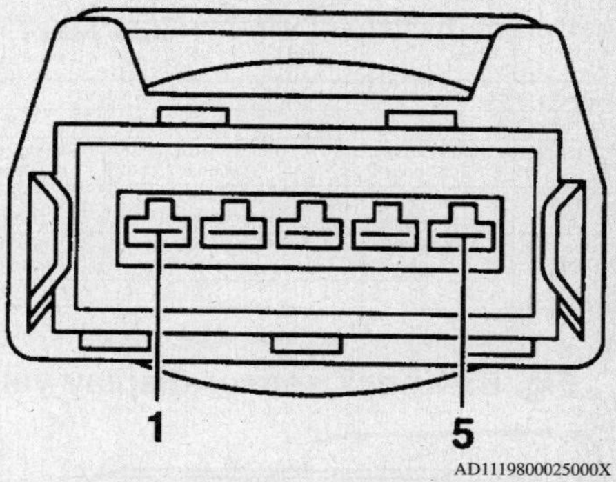

Fig. 4 Power output stage 5 terminal connector identification. A4 & S4

   c. If other cylinder now misfires, replace faulty spark plug.
   d. If same cylinder still misfires, interchange ignition coil with one from normally operating cylinder.
   e. If other cylinder now misfires, replace faulty coil.
   f. If original cylinder still misfires, inspect secondary circuit ground connection for open circuit between coil connector pin 4_a and engine ground, **Fig. 2.**
   g. If ground is satisfactory, refer to "Power Supply & Primary Coil Wiring Inspection" and "Ignition Coil Power Output Stage Inspection."

TT

When diagnosing a misfire or rough running concern, the "problem" cylinder can be identified by briefly disconnecting its fuel injector and noting RPM change.

1. Ensure no faults are present in DTC memory. If DTCs are present, repair as required.
2. Interchange spark plug from misfiring cylinder with one from normally operating cylinder.
3. If misfire follows the spark plug, replace faulty spark plug.
4. If original cylinder still misfires, interchange ignition coil with one from normally operating cylinder.
5. If misfire follows the coil, replace faulty coil.
6. If original cylinder still misfires, proceed as follows:
   a. Disconnect 4-pin electrical connector from ignition coil, **Fig. 3.**
   b. Turn ignition On.
   c. Measure voltage between connector terminal No. 1 and engine ground, which should be battery voltage.
   d. If voltage meets specifications, perform "Ignition Coil Power Output Stage Inspection."
   e. If voltage does not meet specifications, inspect for poor wiring connections and repair as required.

IGNITION COIL POWER OUTPUT STAGE

Power Output Stage Signal

1. Disconnect all fuel injector electrical

	Display groups			
	1	2	3	4
Display group 20: Knock sensor system				
Display	xx.x °	xx.x °	xx.x °	xx.x °
Indicates	Timing correction, cylinder 1	Timing correction, cylinder 2	Timing correction cylinder 3	Timing correction, cylinder 4
Range	0.0°–15.0° (crankshaft)	0.0°–15.0° (crankshaft)	0.0°–15.0° (crankshaft)	0.0°–15.0° (crankshaft)
Specified value	0.0°–10.0° (crankshaft)	0.0°–10.0° (crankshaft)	0.0°–10.0° (crankshaft)	0.0°–10.0° (crankshaft)

AD1119800018000X

Fig. 6 Knock sensor display values. 1.8L engine

Display group: 20 Display fields: 1–4	Possible cause	Correcting action
All cylinders retarded more than 10° (crankshaft)	♦ Knock sensor faulty	– Inspect knock sensor and wiring.
	♦ Connector corroded	
	♦ Knock sensor incorrectly torqued	– Loosen knock sensor and re-tighten to 20 Nm (15 ft lb)
	♦ Components loose on engine	– Tighten components
	♦ Poor fuel quality	– Change fuel
One cylinder reading is very different from the others	♦ Connector corroded	Inspect wiring.
	♦ Engine damage	– Check compression
	♦ Components loose on engine	– Tighten components

AD1119800019000X

Fig. 7 Knock sensor fault chart. 1.8L & 2.8L engines

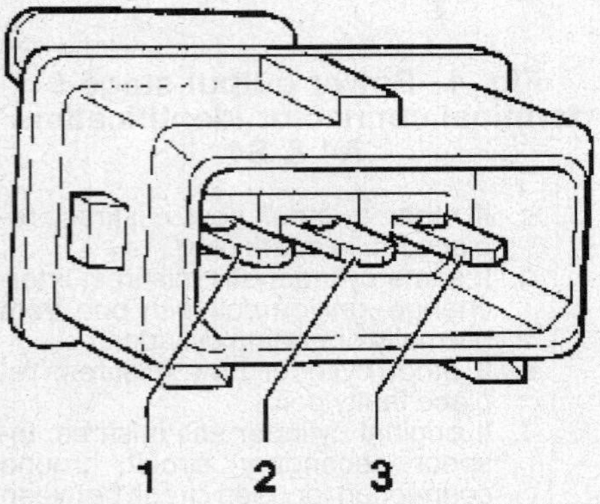

AD1119800020000X

Fig. 8 Knock sensor terminal inspection. 1.8L & 2.8L engines

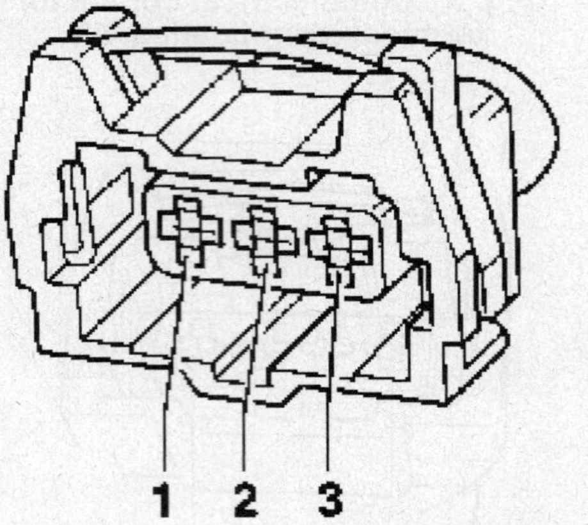

AD1119800021000X

Fig. 9 Knock sensor electrical connector. 1.8L, 2.8L, 3.7L & 4.2L engines

Black 4-pin connector terminal number (power output stage)	Ignition coil terminal 1 at connector for cylinder number:
1	1
2	2
3	3
4	4

AD1119800024000X

Fig. 10 Power output stage to cylinder identification. 1.8L engine

connectors, then clear DTC memory.

2. **On A4 and S4 models,** proceed as follows:
   a. Disconnect 5-pin electrical connector from power output stage, **Fig. 4.**
   b. Connect LED voltage tester tool No. VAG 1527B, or equivalent, between terminals 1, 2, 4, 5 and engine ground.
   c. Crank engine three seconds for each pin. Ensure LED blinks for each pin.
   d. If LED does not blink, connect test box tool No. VAG 1598/22 to ECM harness connector.
   e. Inspect for open circuit between test box and 5 pin electrical connector using a suitable ohmmeter in following sequence: connector terminal 1 to test box pin 70; connector terminal 2 to test box pin 78; connector terminal 4 to test box pin 77; connector terminal 5 to test box pin 71. Ensure resistance is no greater than 1.5 ohms.
   f. If wiring is as specified, inspect for open circuit between 5-pin connector terminal 5 and engine ground using a suitable ohmmeter. Ensure resistance is no greater than 1.5 ohms.
   g. If wiring is as specified and tester LED did not blink, replace ECM. Perform throttle valve control module relearn procedure as outlined under "Computer Relearn Procedures" in front of this manual.
   h. Generate new readiness code.
3. **On TT models,** proceed as follows:
   a. Disconnect 4-pin electrical connector from ignition coil, **Fig. 3.**
   b. Connect voltage tester tool No. VAG 1527B, or equivalent to connector terminals 2 and 3.
   c. Crank engine briefly for each pin. Ensure LED blinks for each pin.
   d. If LED does not blink, connect test box tool No. VAG 1598/31, or equivalent to ECM harness electrical connector. **Do not connect to ECM itself.**
   e. Inspect following wire connections for short circuit between ground and battery voltage: connector terminal 3 and test box pin 102; connector terminal 3 and test box pin 95; connector terminal 3 and test box pin 103; connector terminal 3 and test box pin 94.

Power Output Stage

1. Ensure power output stage signals are as specified under "Power Output Stage Signal."
2. Disconnect 4-pin electrical connector from power output stage, **Fig. 5.**
3. Connect LED voltage tester tool No. VAG 1527B, or equivalent between battery positive and each terminal of power output stage 4 pin connector.
4. Crank engine 3 seconds for each pin. Ensure LED blinks for all pins.
5. If LED does not blink, replace power output stage.

KNOCK SENSOR

1. Connect scan tool No. VAG 1551/1552, or equivalent.
2. Press buttons 0 and 1 to insert "Engine Electronics" address word 01.
3. Ensure engine is running and at idle.
4. Press buttons 0 and 8 to select "Read Measuring Value Block" function 08, then press "Q" to confirm input.
5. Press buttons 0, 2 and 0 to input Display Group number 20, then press "Q" to confirm input.
6. Road test vehicle and compare scan tool display with display readings in **Fig. 6. Have a second technician operate scan tool while on road test.**
7. If knock sensor display values are not as specified in **Fig. 6,** refer to **Fig. 7** for possible causes for knock sensor system fault.
8. If knock sensor values are within specification, proceed as follows:
   a. If DTC memory has been erased, generate new readiness code.
   b. Press right arrow button to advance program sequence.
   c. Press buttons 0 and 6 to select "End Output" function 06, then press "Q" to confirm input.
9. Disconnect knock sensor electrical connector.
10. Measure resistance of the following knock sensor terminals using a suitable ohmmeter and connector test kit tool No. VW 1594, or equivalent, **Fig. 8,** as follows:
    a. Terminal 1 to 2.
    b. Terminals 1 and 2 to 3.
11. Ohmmeter should indicated an infinite reading.
12. If resistance is as specified, proceed as follows:
    a. Connect test box tool No. VAG 1598/22 to Motronic ECM harness connector.
    b. Inspect wiring harness for open circuit between test box and knock sensor electrical connector, **Fig. 9,** using a suitable ohmmeter. Inspect

	Display fields			
	1	2	3	4
Display Group 093: Phase positions of Hall sensors (Bank 1 and Bank 2) with engine idling				
Display	xxx RPM	xx %	0 ± 6 ° crankshaft	0 ± 6 ° crankshaft
Indicates	Engine speed (RPM)	Engine load	Phase position Bank 1	Phase position Bank 2
Work range	min.: 750 RPM max.: 6800 RPM	min.: 15 % max.: 175 %	-20.3 to 14.8 ° KW	-20.3 to 14.8 ° KW
Specified value	750 - 850 RPM		0 ± 6 ° crankshaft	0 ± 6 ° crankshaft
Note			If readouts do not match specifications, unbolt Hall sensor and check whether rotor ring is properly mounted on camshaft. If it is incorrectly mounted, the locating lug will be flattened when the securing bolt is tightened. Also check valve timing.	

AD1110000039000X

Fig. 11 CMP sensor display values. 2.7L engine

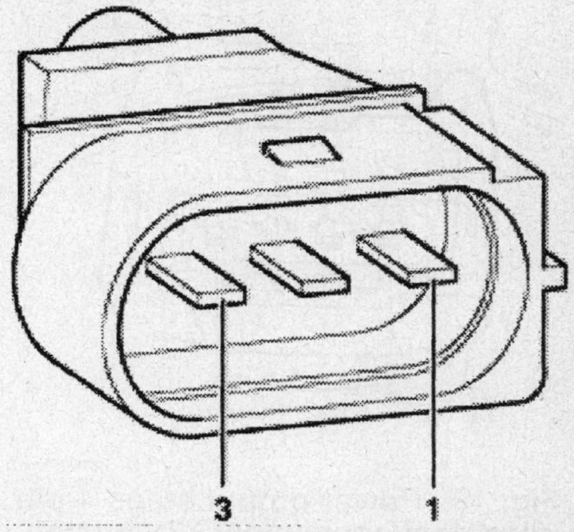

AD1110000040000X

Fig. 12 RPM sensor electrical connector terminal identification. 2.7L engine

the following pins: connector terminal 1 to test box pins 60 and 68; terminal 2 to pin 67; terminal 3 to pin 2. Maximum resistance is 1.5 ohms.

c. Inspect knock sensor wiring for short circuit using a suitable ohmmeter. Inspect the following pins: connector terminals 2 and 3 to test box pin 60 and 68; connector terminal 3 to test box pin 67. Ohmmeter should give infinite reading.

13. If wiring inspection is satisfactory, proceed as follows:
    a. Loosen knock sensor, then **torque** to 15 ft. lbs.
    b. If fault condition still exists, replace knock sensor.
    c. If DTC memory has been erased, generate new readiness code.

POWER SUPPLY & PRIMARY COIL WIRING

1. Ensure ignition coil fuse is satisfactory.
2. Disconnect 4-pin electrical connector from power output stage.
3. Turn ignition On.
4. Connect LED voltage tester tool No. VAG 1527B, or equivalent between 4-pin connector terminals and engine ground. Ensure LED for all four terminals are lit. Power supply for primary circuit is measured via fuse and primary coil of ignition coil.
5. If LED in tester does not light, inspect wiring for open circuit between power output stage and terminal 1 at each coil connector. Refer to **Fig. 2** for coil connector terminal identification. Refer **Figs. 5 and 10** for output stage connector identification and power output stage pin to cylinder identification chart.
6. If wiring is satisfactory, inspect for open circuit between each coil terminal 15 and fuse and power supply. Ensure resistance is not more than 1.5 ohms.

2.7L ENGINE

CAMSHAFT POSITION SENSOR

1. Push back rubber grommet on CMP sensor electrical connector.
2. Connect diode test lamp tool No. VAG 1527, or equivalent, to terminals 1 and 2 of connector from behind without disconnecting connector from sensor, **Fig. 1.**
3. Operate starter for few seconds. Diode test lamp should blink briefly once every two engine revolutions.
4. If diode test lamp does not blink every second revolution, turn ignition Off, then disconnect CMP sensor electrical connector.
5. Turn ignition On.
6. Connect Fluke multimeter tool No. 83, or equivalent, to CMP sensor electrical connector terminal 1, **Fig. 1,** and engine ground.
7. Measure voltage, which should be approximately 5 volts.
8. If voltage is not as indicated, proceed as follows:
    a. Measure voltage between CMP sensor terminal 2 and engine ground, which should be battery voltage.
    b. Connect test box tool No. VAG 1598/31, or equivalent to ECM wiring harness. **Do not connect to ECM itself.**
    c. Connect multimeter between connector terminal 3 and engine ground, then inspect for continuity. Maximum resistance should be 1.5 Ohms.
9. If voltage is as indicated but diode test lamp does not flash, replace CMP sensor.
10. If measurements do not meet specifications, proceed as follows:
    a. Connect test box tool No. VAG 1598/31, or equivalent to ECM wiring harness. **Do not connect to ECM itself.**
    b. Inspect wiring connection from CMP sensor to ECM for open and/ or short circuits to voltage or ground.
    c. Inspect wiring for open circuit between test box and Bank 1 CMP sensor connector using a suitable ohmmeter. Inspect the following pins: CMP connector terminal 1 to test box pin 98; CMP connector terminal 2 to test box pin 87; CMP connector terminal 3 to test box pin 108. Ensure resistance is no greater than 1.5 ohms.
    d. Inspect wiring for open circuit between test box and Bank 2 CMP sensor connector using a suitable ohmmeter. Inspect the following pins: CMP connector terminal 1 to test box pin 98; CMP connector terminal 2 to test box pin 86; CMP connector terminal 3 to test box pin 108. Ensure resistance is no greater than 1.5 ohms.
    e. Correct all opens or shorts as required.
11. If all inspection results so far have met specifications but a CMP fault condition is displayed again after erasing the DTC memory as a test measure, proceed as follows:
    a. Connect vehicle diagnostic testing and information system tool No. VAS 5051 or scan tool No. VAG 1551, or equivalent.
    b. Start and idle engine.
    c. Select engine electronics control module by entering address word "01."
    d. Press buttons 0 and 8 to select function "Read Measuring Value Block," then confirm input with Q button.
    e. Press buttons 0, 9 and 3 to select "Display Group 093," then confirm input with Q button.
    f. Ensure scan tool readings meet specifications, **Fig. 11.**

ENGINE SPEED (RPM) SENSOR

1. Ensure sensor is properly installed and firmly seated.
2. Disconnect RPM sensor electrical connector.
3. Measure resistance between RPM sensor electrical connector terminals 2 and 3, **Fig. 12,** using Fluke multimeter tool No. 83, or equivalent and test lead from VAG 1594 connector test kit.
4. Resistance should be 730–1000 ohms at 68°F.
5. If resistance does not meet specifications, replace RPM sensor.
6. If resistance meets specifications, measure resistance between terminals 1 and 2, then at 1 and 3, which should be infinite.

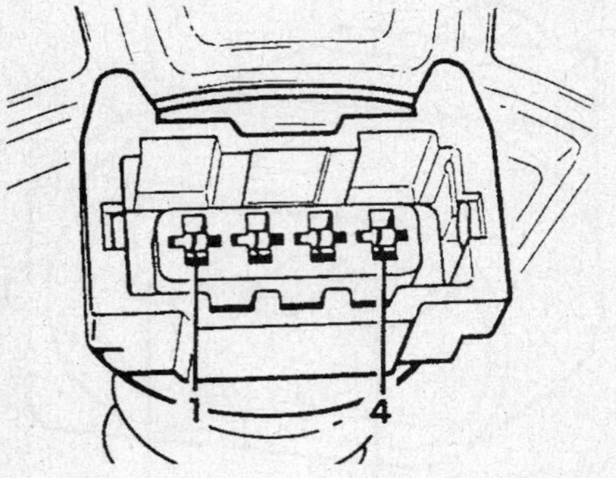

AD1119200009000X

Fig. 13 Power output stage 4-pin electrical connector. 2.7L engine

7. If resistance does not meet specifications, replace RPM sensor.
8. If resistance meets specifications, inspect wiring between RPM sensor connector and ECM as follows:
   a. Connect test box tool No. VAG 1598/31, or equivalent to ECM wiring harness. **Do not connect to ECM itself.**
   b. Inspect continuity of shielded wire between RPM sensor connector terminal 1 and test box socket 108, which should not exceed 1 ohm.
   c. Inspect continuity of negative wire between sensor connector terminal 2 and socket 90, which should not exceed 1 ohm.
   d. Inspect continuity of signal wire between sensor connector terminal 3 and socket 82, which should not exceed 1 ohm.
9. If resistance does not meet specifications, replace RPM sensor.
10. If no open circuits or short circuits are discovered, replace Engine Control Module.

IGNITION COILS

When diagnosing a misfire or rough running concern, the "problem" cylinder can be identified by briefly disconnecting fuel injector of suspect cylinder and noting RPM change.

Compare spark plugs of all cylinders with each other and inspect for soot on the electrodes.

When the offending cylinder has been pinpointed, proceed as follows:

1. Disconnect spark plug connector from ignition coil.
2. Measure connector resistance using a suitable ohmmeter, which should be 2000 ohms. Replace connector if resistance does not meet specifications.
3. If resistance meets specifications, interchange spark plug from misfiring cylinder with one from normally operating cylinder.
4. If misfire follows the spark plug, replace faulty spark plug.
5. If original cylinder still misfires, interchange ignition coil with one from normally operating cylinder.
6. If misfire follows the coil, replace faulty coil.

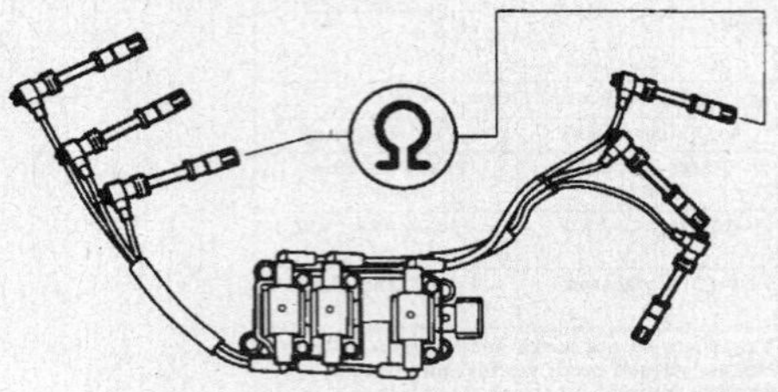

AD1119800027000X

Fig. 14 Ignition wire & coil resistance inspection. 2.8L engine

7. If misfire remains at original cylinder, disconnect ignition coil electrical connector.
8. Inspect connection between coil connector terminal 4_a and engine ground, **Fig. 2.** Repair opens or shorts to voltage as required.
9. If connection is satisfactory, connect multimeter to terminal 15 and ground.
10. Disconnect harness connector from fuel injector of cylinder to be tested.
11. Set multimeter to voltage range.
12. Operate starter and measure voltage, which should be battery voltage.
13. If voltage does not meet specifications, repair wiring fault conditions as required.
14. If voltage is as specified, disconnect ignition coil power output stage electrical connectors.
15. Connect diode test lamp tool No. VAG 1527, or equivalent to both 3-pin output stage electrical connectors.
16. Connect diode test lamp to terminal 1 and ground, **Fig. 9,** next to terminal 2 and ground and then terminal 3 and ground. The diode test lamp should light each time.
17. If diode lamp does not light as specified, turn ignition Off.
18. Inspect for opens or shorts at following connections:
    a. Black 3-pin power output stage terminal 1 and ignition coil connector terminal 1.
    b. Black power output stage terminal 2 and coil connector terminal 2.
    c. Black power output stage terminal 3 and coil connector terminal 3.
    d. Brown 3-pin power output stage terminal 1 and ignition coil connector terminal 4.
    e. Brown power output stage terminal 1 and ignition coil connector terminal 5.
    f. Brown power output stage terminal 1 and ignition coil connector terminal 6.
    g. Repair wiring fault conditions as required.

KNOCK SENSOR

1. Disconnect knock sensor electrical connector.
2. Inspect for short circuits between connector terminals 1 and 2, 1 and 3 and 2 and 3 using a suitable ohmmeter, which should read infinite ohms.
3. If there is any continuity between terminals, replace knock sensor.
4. If no short circuit is discovered, connect test box tool No. VAG 1598/31, or

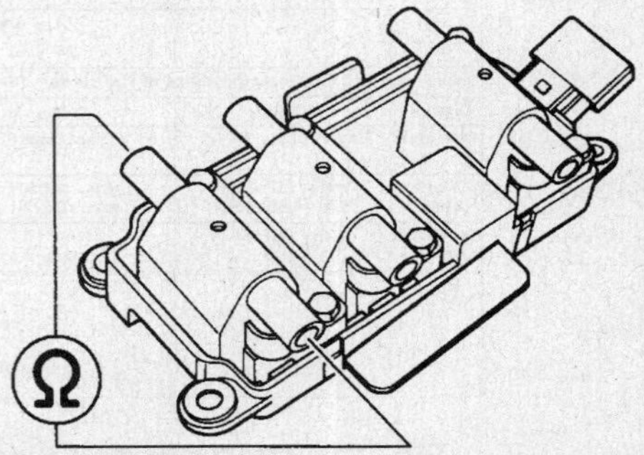

AD1119800028000X

Fig. 15 Ignition coil resistance measurement. 2.8L engine

equivalent to ECM wiring harness. **Do not connect to ECM itself.**

5. Inspect wiring connection from knock sensor to ECM for open or short circuit as follows:
   a. Bank 1 sensor connector terminal 1 to test box pin 99.
   b. Bank 1 sensor connector terminal 2 to test box pin 106.
   c. Bank 1 sensor connector terminal 3 to test box pin 108.
   d. Bank 2 sensor connector terminal 1 to test box pin 99.
   e. Bank 2 sensor connector terminal 2 to test box pin 107.
   f. Bank 2 sensor connector terminal 3 to test box pin 108.
   g. Resistance should not exceed 1.5 ohms.
6. Repair any wiring fault conditions as required.

POWER OUTPUT STAGE SIGNAL

1. Disconnect fuel injector electrical connectors.
2. Turn ignition On.
3. Disconnect power stage 4-pin electrical connector, **Fig. 13.**
4. Connect diode test lamp tool No. VAG 1527, or equivalent in turn to following contacts on two 4-pin power output stage electrical connectors:
   a. Terminal 1 and ground.
   b. Terminal 2 and ground.
   c. Terminal 3 and ground.
5. Diode test lamp should flash briefly.
6. If test lamp does not operate as outlined, turn ignition Off.
7. Connect test box tool No. VAG 1598/31, or equivalent, to ECM wiring harness. **Do not connect to ECM itself.**
8. Inspect following circuits for opens or shorts:
   a. Black 4-pin wiring harness connector terminal 1 to test box socket 94.
   b. Black 4-pin terminal 3 to socket 110.
   c. Black 4-pin terminal 4 to socket 102.
   d. Brown 4-pin wiring harness connector terminal 1 to test box socket 95.
   e. Brown 4-pin terminal 3 to socket 111.
   f. Brown 4-pin terminal 4 to socket 103.
9. Repair any opens or shorts as required.

	Display fields			
	1	2	3	4
Display group 22 [1]: Knock control				
Display	xxx RPM	xx.xx ms	xx.x °	xx.x °
Display	Engine speed (in 40 RPM steps)	Engine load	Ignition angle correction 1	Ignition angle correction 2
Work range	0 – 6800 RPM	0.00 – 12.75 ms	0.0 – 12.0° (crankshaft)	0.0 – 12.0° (crankshaft)
Specified Value	... RPM (test drive)	... ms (test drive)	0.0 – 10.0° (crankshaft)	0.0 – 10.0° (crankshaft)
	---	---		

[1] Display also valid for display groups 23 (cyls. 3 and 4) and 24 (cyls. 5 and 6).

AD1119800026000X

Fig. 16 Knock sensor display values. 2.8L engine

10. If no wiring malfunctions are discovered, proceed as follows:
    a. Connect 4-pin electrical connectors to power output stages.
    b. Disconnect 3-pin electrical connectors from power output stages.
    c. Connect diode test lamp to voltage and to one of three power output stage terminals.
    d. Operate starter for few seconds.
    e. Diode test lamp should flash.
    f. Repeat test with all three terminals on each power output stage 3-pin connector. Diode test lamp should flash each time.
11. If diode test lamp does not flash when testing one or more contacts, proceed as follows:
    a. Disconnect 4-pin electrical connectors from power stages.
    b. Connect diode test lamp to battery positive terminal and to terminal 2 of each 4-pin connector in turn.
12. If diode test lamp lights, replace power output stage.
13. If diode test lamp does not light, inspect for and correct open circuit.

2.8L ENGINE

CAMSHAFT POSITION SENSOR

1. Disconnect camshaft position sensor electrical connector.
2. Turn ignition On.
3. Measure voltage between terminals 1 and 3, **Fig. 1,** using a suitable voltmeter. Voltage should be 9–14.5 volts.
4. Turn ignition Off.
5. If voltage is as specified, proceed as follows:
    a. Connect test box tool No. VAG 1598/22 to ECM harness connector.
    b. Inspect wiring for open circuit between test box and CMP sensor connector using a suitable ohmmeter. Inspect the following pins: CMP connector terminal 1 to test box pin 11; CMP connector terminal 2 to test box pin 44; CMP connector terminal 3 to test box pin 14.
    c. Ensure resistance is no greater than 1.5 ohms.
    d. Inspect wiring for short circuit between test box and CMP sensor connector using a suitable ohmmeter. Inspect the following pins: CMP connector terminal 3 to test box pins 11 and 44; CMP connector terminal 2 to test box pin 11.
    e. Ensure ohmmeter gives an infinite reading.
6. If wiring and voltage are as specified, replace CMP sensor.
7. If wiring is as specified and no voltage is present at terminals 1 and 3, proceed as follows:
    a. Replace ECM.
    b. Perform throttle valve control module relearn procedure as outlined under “Computer Relearn Procedures” in front of this manual.
    c. Generate new readiness code.

IGNITION COILS

When diagnosing a misfire or rough running concern, the “problem” cylinder can be identified by briefly disconnecting fuel injector of suspect cylinder and noting RPM change.

1. Ensure no DTCs are stored in ECM memory. If DTCs are present, service as required.
2. Interchange spark plug with one from normally operating cylinder.
3. If other cylinder now misfires, replace faulty spark plug.
4. If original cylinder still misfires, inspect ignition coil as follows:
    a. Disconnect ignition coil 5-pin connector.
    b. Remove ignition wires from spark plugs.
    c. Measure resistance between spark plug connectors of respective ignition coil, **Fig. 14,** using connector test kit tool No. VAG 1594, or equivalent, and a suitable ohmmeter. Resistance should be 18,000–25,000 ohms.
    d. If resistance is as specified, remove ignition wires from coils.
    e. Measure resistance of ignition wires, which should be 4000–6000 ohms.
    f. Measure resistance between ends of respective ignition coils, **Fig. 15,** which should be 8000–14,000 ohms.
    g. If resistances are satisfactory, refer to “Power Output Stage Signal.”

KNOCK SENSOR

1. Connect scan tool No. VAG 1551/1552, then press buttons 0 and 1 to insert “Engine Electronics” address 01 with engine running at idle.
2. Press buttons 0 and 8 to select “Read Measuring Value Block” function 08, then press “Q” to confirm input.
3. Press buttons according to following Display Group numbers:

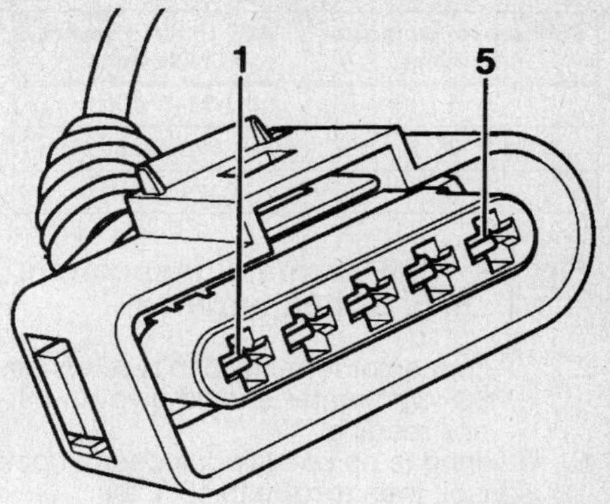

AD1119800029000X

Fig. 17 Ignition coil terminal identification. 2.8L engine

    a. 022: Display Group 22, cylinders 1 and 2.
    b. 023: Display Group 23, cylinders 3 and 4.
    c. 024: Display Group 24, cylinders 5 and 6.
    d. Press “Q” to confirm input.
4. Road test vehicle. Test must be carried out with engine speed greater than 2600 RPM and engine load greater than 3 ms. Compare scan tool display with **Fig. 16. Have a second technician operate scan tool while on road test.**
5. If display values are not as specified, refer to **Fig. 7.**
6. If display values are satisfactory, press right arrow button.
7. Press buttons 0 and 6 to select “End Output” function 06, then press “Q” to confirm input.
8. Inspect readiness code. If DTC memory has been erased, generate new readiness code.
9. If a poor connection is suspected, proceed as follows:
    a. Disconnect knock sensor electrical connector.
    b. Measure resistance of knock sensor terminals using connector test kit VW 1594, or equivalent, and a suitable ohmmeter, as follows: terminals 1 and 2, 1 and 3, 2 and 3. Ohmmeter should give an infinite reading. Refer to **Fig. 8** for knock sensor terminal identification.
    c. If resistance is as specified, connect test box VAG 1598/22 to ECM harness connector.
    d. Inspect wiring for open circuit between test box and knock sensor harness connector using a suitable ohmmeter. Inspect connector terminal 1 to test box pin 60, terminal 1 to test box pin 68, then connector terminals 2 and 3 to test box pin 67. Resistance should read no greater than 1.5 ohms. Refer to **Fig. 9** for harness connector pin identification.
    e. Inspect wiring for short circuits in the following connector terminals and test box pins: connector terminal 2 and 3 to test box pin 60; connector terminal 2 to test box pin 68;

CMP sensor connector terminal	VAG 1598/19 socket (ECM terminal)
1	A3 (+5 volts)
2	B2 (signal)
3	D12 (Ground)

AD1119800030000X

Fig. 18 CMP terminal inspection. 3.7L & 4.2L engines

connector terminal 3 to test box pin 68. Ohmmeter should give an infinite reading.
10. If wiring is as specified, loosen knock sensor, then **torque** to 15 ft. lbs.
11. If knock sensor fault condition is still present, replace knock sensor.
12. Inspect readiness code. If DTC memory has been cleared, generate new readiness code.

POWER OUTPUT STAGE SIGNAL

1. Remove fuel injector electrical connectors.
2. Turn ignition On.
3. Inspect fuse for ignition coils and service as required.
4. Connect LED tester tool No. VAG 1527 between engine ground and ignition coil connector terminal 3, **Fig. 17.**
5. Crank engine for several seconds. Ensure LED in tester flashes.
6. Repeat test for terminals 4 and 5.
7. If LED flashes, replace ignition coils with power output stage.
8. If LED does not flash, proceed as follows:
   a. Connect test box tool No. VAG 1598/22, or equivalent to ECM harness connector.
   b. Inspect wiring between test box and 5 pin connector for continuity and short circuit as follows: connector terminal 3 to test box pin 71; connector terminal 4 to test box pin 78; connector terminal 5 to test box pin 70.
   c. Connect LED voltage tester tool No. VAG 1527, or equivalent to terminal 2 of ignition coil connector and battery positive. If LED does not light, service open circuit as required.
   d. Turn ignition On, then connect LED voltage tester tool No. VAG 1527, or equivalent to coil connector terminal 1 and engine ground. If tester does not light, serve open circuit as required.
   e. If wiring is satisfactory and fault is still present, replace ECM.
   f. Perform throttle valve control module relearn procedure as outlined under "Computer Relearn Procedures" in front of this manual.
   g. Generate new readiness code.

3.7L & 4.2L ENGINES

CAMSHAFT POSITION SENSOR

1. Inspect CMP sensor signal. Push back rubber boot at back of CMP sensor harness connector, **Fig. 1.** Leave sensor connected.
2. Connect LED voltage tester VAG

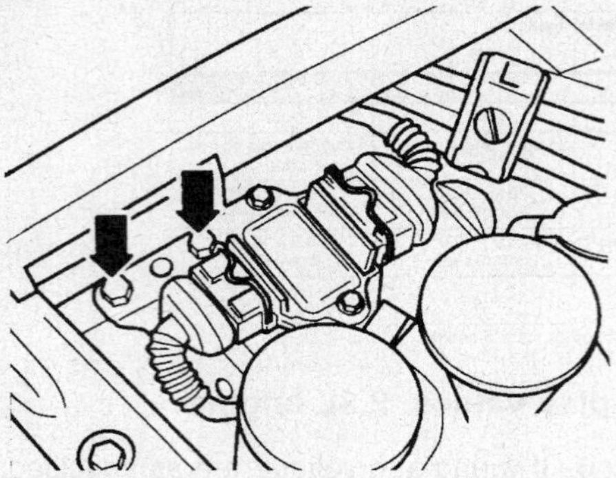

AD1119800031000X

Fig. 19 Power output stage removal. 3.7L & 4.2L engines

Power output stage 5-pin connector terminal	VAG 1598/19 test box socket (ECM terminal)
Black (-N122-)	
1	B8
2	B7
4	B6
5	B5
Brown (-N192-)	
1	B14
2	B13
4	B15
5	B16

AD1119800033000X

Fig. 21 ECM & power output stage test pin identification. 3.7L & 4.2L engines

1527B, or equivalent to terminals 1 and 2 from back of connector.
3. Crank engine and observe voltage tester. If LED does not flash, inspect CMP wiring as follows:
   a. Disconnect CMP sensor.
   b. Turn ignition On.
   c. Measure voltage between CMP connector terminal 1 and engine ground using a suitable voltmeter. Voltage should be 4.5–5.5 volts.
   d. Install a suitable voltmeter between terminal 2 of CMP connector and engine ground.
   e. Turn ignition On.
   f. Voltmeter should read battery voltage.
   g. Turn ignition Off.
   h. Measure resistance between CMP connector terminal 3 and engine ground using a suitable ohmmeter. Continuity should exist.
   i. If continuity does not exist, service open wire as required.
   j. If continuity does exist, replace CMP sensor.
   k. Inspect CMP circuit for open, short to power and short to ground. Connect test box tool No. VAG 1598/19 to ECM harness connector. Refer to "Fuel Injection" for ECM terminal identification and **Fig. 18** for terminal inspection.
   l. If after clearing DTC memory, CMP

Power output stage 4-pin connector terminal	Ignition coil 3-pin connector terminal 1
Black connector	Cylinder
1	1
2	4
3	6
4	7
Brown connector	Cylinder
1	2
2	3
3	5
4	8

AD1119800032000X

Fig. 20 Power output stage to cylinder identification. 3.7L & 4.2L engines

faults are still present and test results to this point have been satisfactory, remove CMP sensor and ensure trigger wheel is properly installed. Service as required.
   m. If CMP trigger wheel is satisfactory, inspect camshaft drive belt adjustment as outlined under "Timing Belt, Replace" in Chassis & Mechanical Systems section.

IGNITION COIL

A high tension isolation diode is integrated into the ignition coil secondary circuit. Ensure proper measuring equipment is used when measuring side of ignition coil.

1. Inspect ignition system fuses. Service as required.
2. Remove bracket with power output stages, **Fig. 19.**
3. Disconnect both 4 pin connectors from output stage.
4. Turn ignition On.
5. Connect one lead of LED voltage tester tool No. VAG 1527B, or equivalent to ground and other lead to each pin of both connectors. LED should light for all pins.
6. If LED does not light, proceed as follows:
   a. Disconnect 3-pin harness connector from each applicable ignition coil.
   b. Inspect wiring for open between power output stage and ignition coil connector terminal 1, **Fig. 2.**
   c. Refer to **Fig. 20** for power output stage to cylinder identification.
7. If wiring is satisfactory, inspect for open or short circuit between ignition coil connector terminal 15 and ignition fuse. Refer to **Fig. 2** for coil connector terminal identification.
8. If terminal 15 wiring inspection is satisfactory, inspect ignition primary and secondary circuit as follows:
   a. Measure resistance of primary side of ignition coil using a suitable ohmmeter. Resistance should be .3–.5 ohms when measured between terminals 1 and 15.
   b. Measure resistance between coil

	Display fields			
	1	2	3	4
Display group 15: Knock control, bank 1, testing at 3300 RPM				
Display	Volts	Volts	Volts	Volts
Indicates	Knock sensor signal Cylinder 1	Knock sensor signal Cylinder 2	Knock sensor signal Cylinder 3	Knock sensor signal Cylinder 4
Range	---	---	---	---
Specified values	1–25 V	1–25 V	1–25 V	1–25 V
Notes	If displayed values are not as specified, check knock sensor ⇒ page 28-26			

Note on display groups 15 and 16:

At higher RPM, knock sensor signal voltage can reach up to approx. 35 volts.

AD1119800034000X

Fig. 22 Bank 1 knock sensor display. 3.7L & 4.2L engines

	Display fields			
	1	2	3	4
Display group 16: Knock control, bank 2, testing at 3300 RPM				
Display	V	V	V	V
Indicates	Knock sensor signal Cylinder 5	Knock sensor signal Cylinder 6	Knock sensor signal Cylinder 7	Knock sensor signal Cylinder 8
Range	---	---	---	---
Specified values	1–25 V	1–25 V	1–25 V	1..25 V
Notes	If displayed values are not as specified, check knock sensor			

Note on display groups 15 and 16:

At higher RPM, knock sensor signal voltage can reach up to approx. 35 volts.

AD1119800035000X

Fig. 23 Bank 2 knock sensor display. 3.7 & 4.2L engines

Knock sensor harness connector terminal	VAG 1598/19 test box socket (ECM terminal)
1	A20
2	A19
3	D11

AD1119800036000X

Fig. 24 Bank 1 knock sensor terminal identification. 3.7L & 4.2L engines

Knock sensor harness connector terminal	VAG 1598/19 test box socket (ECM terminal)
1	A21
2	A19
3	D11

AD1119800037000X

Fig. 25 Bank 2 knock sensor terminal identification. 3.7L & 4.2L engines

connector terminal 4_a and engine ground, which should be no greater than 1.5 ohms.

c. If resistance inspections are satisfactory, replace ignition coils and generate new readiness code.

IGNITION COIL POWER OUTPUT STAGE

Power Output Stage Signal

1. Remove bracket and power output stages, **Fig. 19**.
2. Disconnect all fuel injector electrical connectors and hold-downs.
3. Disconnect 5 pin connectors from both power output stages. Refer to **Fig. 4** for power output stage 5-pin connector view.
4. Connect one lead of LED voltage tester tool No. 1527B, or equivalent to engine ground. Connect other lead in sequence to terminals 1, 2, 4 and 5 and crank engine.
5. LED should flash for each terminal.
6. If LED does not flash, connect test box tool No. VAG 1598/19, or equivalent to ECM harness connector.
7. Inspect wiring between power output stage and ECM for open, short to power or short to ground. Refer to "Fuel Injection" for ECM terminal identification and **Fig. 21** for ECM and power output stage terminal test pin identification.
8. If wiring between ECM and power output stage is satisfactory, proceed as follows:
   a. Measure resistance of terminal 3 of 5 terminal power output stage connector and ground using a suitable ohmmeter. Resistance should be no greater than 1.5 ohms.
   b. If wiring and connections are satisfactory, replace ECM and generate new readiness code.

Power Output Stage

1. Ensure both 5 terminal connectors are connected to power output stage.
2. Disconnect both 4 terminal connectors from power output stages.
3. Connect voltage tester VAG 1527B, or equivalent between battery positive and one terminal of power output stage 4 terminal connector. Crank engine and observe LED of voltage tester. LED should flash.
4. Repeat test for remaining pins of each 4 terminal connector.
5. If LED does not flash at 1 or more terminals, replace power output stage and generate new readiness code.

KNOCK SENSOR

1. Connect scan tool VAG 1551/1552, or equivalent, then press 0 and 0 to insert "Engine Electronics" address word 01. Ensure engine is running and at idle.
2. Press buttons 0 and 8 to select "Read Measuring Value Block" function 08, then press "Q" to confirm input.
3. Press buttons 0, 1 and 5 to input Display Group number 15, then press "Q" to confirm input.
4. Inspect bank 1 knock sensor operation. Engine speed should be 3300 RPM. Refer to **Fig. 22** for bank 1 knock sensor display values.
5. Press 3 to advance to Display Group 16. Inspect bank 2 knock sensor display. Refer to **Fig. 23** for bank 2 knock sensor display values.
6. Press right arrow button to advance program sequence.
7. Press buttons 0 and 6 to select "End Output" function 06, then press "Q" to confirm input.
8. If display values are not as specified, proceed as follows to inspect knock sensor system:
   a. Disconnect knock sensor electrical connector.
   b. Measure resistance between knock sensor terminals using a suitable ohmmeter.
   c. Ensure no continuity exists between any of the terminals. If continuity exists, replace sensor.
   d. If knock sensor is not shorted but signal is improper, inspect readiness code and generate new code if required.
   e. Connect test box tool No. VAG 1598/19, or equivalent to ECM harness connector.
   f. Inspect knock sensor wiring for open, short to power or short to ground. Refer to **Fig. 9** for knock sensor electrical connector and **Figs. 24 and 25** for knock sensor terminal identification.
   g. If there are no open or short circuits, replace knock sensor and generate new readiness code.

Fuel Injection

NOTE: If Unsure Of System Used On Vehicle Being Serviced, Refer To Engine Systems Identification Chart Located At Beginning Of This Chapter.

NOTE: Prior To Performing Any Service Operations Listed In This Section Consult Technical Service Bulletin Section For Related Information.

NOTE: Electrical Symbol & Wire Color Code Identification Located In Front Of This Manual May Be Used As An Aid When Using Wiring Circuits Found In This Section.

NOTE: Refer To "Ignition Systems" And "Computerized Engine Controls" For Component And System Testing Not Covered In This Section.

INDEX

	Page No.
Description	10-16
Diagnosis & Testing	10-16
Accessing Diagnostic Trouble Codes	10-16
Clearing Diagnostic Trouble Codes	10-16
Diagnostic Tests	10-16
Diagnostic Trouble Code Interpretation	10-16
Precautions	10-16
Air Bag Systems	10-16
Audio Coded Anti-Theft System	10-16
Electrical Connection & Terminal Repair	10-16
System Service	10-16
Adjustments	10-18
Engine Speed (RPM) Sensor	10-18
Throttle Position Sensor	10-18
Component Replacement	10-16
Engine Control Module (ECM)	10-16
Intake Air Temperature (IAT) Sensor	10-18
Troubleshooting	10-16
Heated Oxygen Sensor (HO_2S)	10-18

PRECAUTIONS

Always clean fuel lines before loosening and be sure to replace seals and fuel hose clamps. Keep a fully charged fire extinguisher readily available.

Air Bag Systems

Refer to "Air Bag System Precautions" in the front of this manual for system disarming and arming procedures.

Audio Coded Anti-Theft System

Do not use computer memory saver tool. Using the tool will keep the air bag system charged and may cause accidental activation of the air bag unit.

Obtain the security code from the vehicle operator prior to disconnecting the battery or removing the radio. Refer to the owner's manual for security code disarming and arming procedures.

Electrical Connection & Terminal Repair

If connector terminal or pin replacement is required, use only gold plated components.

DESCRIPTION

The Engine Control Module (ECM) controls fuel injector opening times. A separate power output stage is provided for each injector.

TROUBLESHOOTING

Possible and likely engine fuel injection system performance fault conditions are listed in Table 1, **Fig. 1,** with recommended troubleshooting procedures in Table 2, **Fig. 2.**

DIAGNOSIS & TESTING

Accessing Diagnostic Trouble Codes

Refer to "Computerized Engine Controls" to access diagnostic trouble codes.

Diagnostic Trouble Code Interpretation

Refer to "Computerized Engine Controls" for diagnostic trouble code interpretation.

Diagnostic Tests

Refer to "Computerized Engine Controls" for diagnostic tests.

Clearing Diagnostic Trouble Codes

Refer to "Computerized Engine Controls" to clear diagnostic trouble codes.

SYSTEM SERVICE

Component Replacement

ENGINE CONTROL MODULE (ECM)

Refer to "Coding ECM" prior to replacing the ECM.

Always wait at least 30 seconds after battery is disconnected before disconnecting ECM.

CODING ECM

The information contained below is the most current available at the time of writing. It is always possible that manufacturer changes will occur, so it is recommended that the vehicle manufacturer be contacted prior to coding any ECM to obtain the latest information.

On A8 models, vehicle information is hard coded into the ECM. Service coding on the models can be inspected but service coding of the ECM is not possible.

Driveability problems	Possible causes (for explanations see Table 2)																				
	1	2	3	4	5	6	7	8	9	10	11	12	13	14	15	16	17	18	19	20	21
Engine has poor performance			0	–	0	0	0	0	0			0	0					•	0		
Fuel consumption too high	–	•	0	–	0	0	0						–						0		
Sulfur odor from exhaust system			0																♦		
Malfunction Indicator Lamp is on (USA only)	0		0		0								0								
Engine has starting problems	–	0	–	–	–	–	0	0		0		–		0			0				

Explanation of symbols: ♦ frequent • less frequent 0 seldom - not a cause

AD1029200067020X

Fig. 1 Table 1, performance fault conditions (Part 2 of 2)

Driveability problems	Possible causes (for explanations see Table 2)																				
	1	2	3	4	5	6	7	8	9	10	11	12	13	14	15	16	17	18	19	20	21
Engine has poor performance			0	–	0	0	0	0	0			0	0					•	0		
Fuel consumption too high	–	•	0	–	0	0	0						–						0		
Sulfur odor from exhaust system			0																♦		
Malfunction Indicator Lamp is on (USA only)	0		0		0								0								
Engine has starting problems	–	0	–	–	–	–	0	0		0		–		0			0				

Explanation of symbols: ♦ frequent • less frequent 0 seldom - not a cause

AD1029200068010X

Fig. 2 Table 2, troubleshooting (Part 1 of 5)

Index	Possible cause	Recommendations and background information
4	Throttle body faulty	♦ Air leak in second stage leads to false learned values. DTC code 01257 (IAC valve) can be stored. ♦ A faulty MPI control module or Mass Air Flow (MAF) sensor is not likely. ♦ With On Board Diagnostics fault is difficult to recognize, since usually there is no strong air leak value. - basic setting of engine - using VAG 1551, check function 04, display channels 4 and 5, check whether specified values lie at upper or lower limit range. If the values lie outside or even close to the tolerance limit ♦ Throttle body can only be checked visually for sticking after removing throttle body.
5	Throttle Position Sensor and Closed Throttle Switch faulty at the same time	♦ No acceleration enrichment ♦ Throttle position sensor has faulty setting, tolerance problem or faulty resistor. (misfiring, bucking or poor throttle response). ♦ Throttle position sensor sticks in wide open throttle position (fuel consumption too high). - check DTC memory and individual measurement (function 09), channel 11 with VAG 1551 This value must also increase gradually as the gas pedal movement/throttle opening is increased. - check for tight fit of connector and condition of wires.
6	Mass Air Flow (MAF) sensor (G70) total failure, connector fallen off, break in wiring	♦ Temperature compensation is not OK (cannot be checked), try another G70 to check whether that corrects problem. ♦ Ground offset not OK - read DTC memory with VAG 1551 and repair fault. ♦ Dynamic problems can occur with G70 (Part No. without index A) - read channel 5 with VAG 1551 (function 09) individual measurements. There is an intermittent open circuit if the display is greater than 5 or fluctuates. Check control module ground connection and MAF sensor connector. (except for control module 4A0 906 266 - here channel 5 gives average injection time, cylinders 4-6).
7	Injectors leaking or poor spray pattern caused by contamination or tolerance problems	♦ Fuel gets into combustion chamber (burst of fuel). Injectors that are leaking even slightly can lead to spontaneous cold starts because of fuel seeping into the intake port. This can lead to knocking during start ups and to poor initial throttle response (lack of fuel pressure). - Checking: Let engine warm up for at least 10 minutes and shut engine off. Remove fuel rails including injectors without separating supply and return lines. If you can see bubbles or droplets on any of the injector tips, replace the affected injector. Avoid replacing all injectors. - check injection quantity - install O-rings very carefully (before installing lubricate O-rings with engine oil).

AD1029200068020X

Fig. 2 Table 2, troubleshooting (Part 2 of 5)

Driveability problems	Possible causes (for explanations see Table 2)																				
	1	2	3	4	5	6	7	8	9	10	11	12	13	14	15	16	17	18	19	20	21
Engine stalls intermittently	0	0		0		0							0								
Engine stalls immediately after starting	0	0																			
Engine stalls when shifting into Drive (Auto.Trans.)	0																				
Idle speed irregular , RPM fluctuates	0	0	0			–	0	0	–	0	0										
Idle speed irregular (hunting)	0	0		0		0				0											
Idle speed too high	0			0	0					0											
Idle speed vibrations noticeable inside car	–		–										–							0	0
Vibrations at 1800 RPM	–		–										–							0	0
Engine shakes/misfires during warm-up			0		0			0	0			0				0					
Engine always misfires, shakes		0	0					0	0		0						0				
Engine accelerates poorly		•	♦		0	0	0						–			0					
Engine misfires intermittently			0		0	0							0								
Engine shakes/misfires in idle range		0	•																		
Engine shakes/misfires when cold					0					0											
Engine stalls, does not restart			–				0			0	•	–	0	•	0						

Explanation of symbols: ♦ frequent • less frequent 0 seldom - not a cause

AD1029200067010X

Fig. 1 Table 1, performance fault conditions (Part 1 of 2)

Index	Possible cause	Recommendations and background information
8	Spark plugs faulty, wet, fouled caused by frequent cold starts, high oil consumption, oil level too high	♦ Spark plugs damaged during installation ♦ Spark plug connector lose or broken - check spark plugs - avoid preventive repairs
9	Ignition coil faulty	♦ Power output stage harness connector loose or terminals not contacting properly ♦ Ignition cable oxidized, faulty or incorrectly connected - check power output stage for ignition system and ignition coils
10	Engine Coolant Temperature (ECT) sensor (G62) out of tolerance	♦ Mixture is either too rich or too lean. - check resistance Check basic engine setting with VAG 1551 (function 4), display channel 1 and check whether these values are realistic
11	Engine Speed (RPM) sensor (G28) or wiring faulty	- to check - check RPM sensor and starter ring gear for damage. To visually inspect starter ring gear, remove starter motor and turn engine by hand.
12	Knock sensors G61 and G66 faulty	♦ Ignition angle retarded by knock control system - With VAG 1551 perform individual measurement (function 09) channels 12 and 13 to check actual ignition angle. - If the value for channel 12 is greater or equal to 128, injection is being controlled by ignition map II which is designed for fuels with octane number less than ROZ 95. Another cause may be noise from nearby components that are misinterpreted as knock signals. ♦ Values in channel 13 multiplied by 1.33 give the current average ignition angle of all cylinders in units of crank shaft degrees.
13	Engine Control module faulty o ground connection not OK	♦ Electrical contact problems on connector ♦ No ignition spark, no injection signal, no DTC read out possible with VAG 1551 Scan Tool. - DTC memory displays Engine Control Module as faulty. Check ground connections and connector engagement for elec contact problems. - check Engine Control Module version - before replacing control module, pull off connector and reconnect again, then repeat test.

AD1029200068030X

Fig. 2 Table 2, troubleshooting (Part 3 of 5)

On TT models, control modules with part Nos. 8N0 906 018 C and 8N0 906 018 K were equipped with "06500" as a permanent code and cannot be coded again.

Reading ECM Code

1. Connect vehicle diagnostic, testing and information system tool No. VAS 5051 or VAG1551 scan tool, or equivalent, to Data Link Connector (DLC).
2. Follow scan tool manufacturer's instructions to access control module information and record ECM code.
3. Refer to coding tables, **Figs. 3 through 6** to ensure proper code has been entered.

Coding ECM

1. **On models equipped with Motronic system,** proceed as follows:
   a. Connect a suitable scan tool to Data Link Connector (DLC), then follow tool manufacturer's instruction to access ECM coding functions.
   b. Refer to ECM coding tables, **Figs. 3 through 6,** to locate proper code for vehicle.
   c. Enter code following scan tool manufacturer's instructions.
2. **On all models,** it may be required to allow ECM to relearn idle, timing and other functions by allowing vehicle to idle for a short period then driving vehicle for a short distance.

REPLACING ECM

A4 & S4 w/1.8L Engine & A8

For replacement of ECM, refer to "Engine Compartment Reference Diagrams."

A4 & S4 w/2.7L & 2.8L Engines

1. Connect a suitable scan tool to Data Link Connector (DLC).
2. Access control module information and record ECM code. Refer to "Coding ECM."
3. Remove cover of electrical box found in lefthand side of air inlet plenum.
4. Remove ECM from mounting, then disconnect electrical connectors.
5. Reverse procedure to install.

Cabriolet

The ECM may be placed into a service position for testing purposes without complete removal by following steps outlined below.

1. Connect a suitable scan tool to the Data Link Connector (DLC).
2. Access control module information and record ECM code. Refer to "Coding ECM."
3. Disconnect battery ground cable.
4. Remove under dash cover below glove box.
5. Locate marked area of carpet, then using a sharp knife cut along marks.
6. Pull carpeting aside to expose ECM carrier plate, then remove mounting screws and carrier plate.
7. Remove lefthand carrier plate bracket from base plate.
8. Insert a suitable screwdriver between ECM carrier plate and plastic shaft, then twist screwdriver to release latch tabs.
9. Pull ECM down slightly, then remove screwdriver and pull ECM down into service position.
10. To completely remove ECM, pull out past service stop tabs.
11. Disconnect ECM from harness connector, then remove from carrier plate.
12. Reverse procedure to install.

A6 & S6

1. Remove plenum cover.
2. Remove cover of electronic box.
3. Remove mounting bracket using a suitable screwdriver.
4. Remove ECM harness connector, then the ECM.
5. Reverse procedure to install.

Index	Possible cause	Recommendations and background information
14	Hall sensor (G40) faulty	♦ Hall sensor damaged by creeping (moving) camshaft seal. - install seal without using lubricants ♦ Hall sensor connector terminals are pushed in too far and not making contact. - check Hall sensor and connector fit
15	Crankshaft Position (CKP) sensor (G4) faulty	♦ Engine does not start ♦ Fault during driving cannot be detected since engine continues to run on RPM signal. - check CKP sensor ♦ Carbon blast if necessary
16	Intake valve carbon deposits because of insufficient additives in fuel	♦ Use fuel additive ♦ Use high quality fuel with sufficient additives
17	Fuel pressure regulator faulty	♦ With VAG 1551 Scan Tool (function 08) measuring value block, check oxygen sensor control, value 8. ♦ Fuel pump supply too low. - check fuel supply quantity - check system pressure and residual pressure - check fuel pressure under actual operating condition (test drive) - the system pressure must not drop too low even under actual operating conditions (test drive).
18	Multi-path intake manifold not OK , especially over 4000 RPM	-check for vacuum hose leaks and correct routing according to vacuum hose diagram

AD1029200068040X

Fig. 2 Table 2, troubleshooting (Part 4 of 5)

Index	Possible cause	Recommendations and background information
19	a.) Catalytic converter melted. b.) Sulfur odor after shutting off engine.	a.) Measure exhaust back pressure at CO tap tube at 2000 RPM, using VAG 1397A . Specified value must not be higher than 0.3 bar (1.3 bar absolute pressure). Ask customer whether car was towed or whether any starting aids such as ether, etc.,were used. Read DTC memory and check ignition and injection system. b.) Explanation: Sulfur odor develops from sulfur dioxide that is stored as sulfate in the catalytic converter during slightly lean operation (deceleration). With rich engine operation (idle or fast acceleration), sulfate is reduced to hydrogen sulfide which causes the odor. Odor formation depends on the kind of fuel used. The odor decreases as the car accumulates approx. 6300 miles or 10000 km. Replacing the catalytic converter would make odor worse.
20	Exhaust system	♦ Tolerance and resonance problems - align exhaust system
21	Torque arm	- re-adjusting the torque arm can help in some cases.

AD1029200068050X

Fig. 2 Table 2, troubleshooting (Part 5 of 5)

Country/Emissions	Drivetrain/Options	Transmission	Vehicle type
00 = ———	0 = Front-wheel drive without traction control (ASR)	0 = 5-speed manual	0 = ———
01 = ———	1 = Front-wheel drive with traction control (ASR)	1 = ———	1 = ———
02 = ———	2 = All-wheel drive without traction control (ASR)	2 = ———	2 = A6
03 = ———	3 = All-wheel drive with traction control (ASR)	3 = ———	3 = ———
04 = ———	4 = ———	4 = ———	4 = ———
05 = ———	5 = ———	5 = Automatic trans. 01V	5 = ———
06 = USA, equipped with EVAP system Leak Detection Pump (LDP)	6 = ———	6 = ———	6 = ———

AD1029800140000X

Fig. 3 ECM coding table. A4 & S4 w/1.8L engine & A6 & S6

Country/ Emission standard	Power train / Additional systems	Transmission	Type of vehicle
00 = ———	0 = ———	0 = ———	0 = ———
01 = ———	1 = ———	1 = 6-speed manual transmission	1 = A4
02 = ———	2 = ———	2 = ———	2 = ———
03 = ———	3 = ———	3 = ———	3 = ———
04 = ———	4 = ———	4 = ———	4 = ———
05 = ———	5 = ———	5 = 5-speed automatic transmission (ZF) (5HP24)	5 = ———
06 = USA; TLEV (Exhaust emission standard) NOTE: Vehicles with Leak Detection Pump (LDP)	6 = All-wheel drive without Anti Slip Regulation (ASR)/Electronic Stability Program (ESP) (with CAN-Bus system)	6 = ———	6 = ———
07 = ———	7 = All-wheel drive with Anti Slip Regulation (ASR)/Electronic Stability Program (ESP) (with CAN-Bus system)	7 = ———	7 = ———

AD1020000164000X

Fig. 4 ECM coding table. A4 & S4 w/2.7L engine

Coding	Model
01273	A8 4.2 liter, engine code ABZ
01153	A8 3.7 liter, engine code AEW

AD1029800141000X

Fig. 5 ECM coding table. A8

Country/Exhaust	06	USA; TLEV (exhaust norm); identification: vehicle with LDP
Drivetrain/additional (optional) functions	5	Front Wheel Drive with Anti-Slip Regulation (ASR)/ Electronic Stability Program (ESP), CAN-bus system
	6	All Wheel Drive (AWD) with Anti-Slip Regulation (ASR)/Electronic Stability Program (ESP), CAN-bus system
Transmission	0	5 speed manual transmission
	1	6 speed manual transmission
	5	5 speed automatic transmission
Vehicle type	0	Audi TT

AD1020000163000X

Fig. 6 ECM coding table. TT

TT

1. Connect a suitable scan tool to Data Link Connector (DLC).
2. Access control module information and record ECM code. Refer to "Coding ECM." Control modules with part Nos. 8N0 906 018 C and 8N0 906 018 K are equipped with "06500" as a permanent code and cannot be coded again.
3. Turn ignition Off.
4. Remove windshield wiper arms.
5. Disconnect plenum chamber cover and place it on windshield side.
6. Press bracket locking lugs to side with a suitable screwdriver, then remove ECM toward front.
7. Disengage locking lugs and remove ECM electrical connector.
8. Reverse procedure to install.

HEATED OXYGEN SENSOR (HO_2S)

1. Disconnect harness connectors, then cut and remove tie wraps.
2. Remove HO_2S using socket tool No. 3337/9, or equivalent.
3. Reverse procedure to install, noting the following:
   a. Coat sensor threads with anti-seize compound. **Do not allow compound to enter probe slits.**
   b. Position tie wraps carefully to avoid contact between sensor wiring and exhaust pipe.

INTAKE AIR TEMPERATURE (IAT) SENSOR

1. Disconnect IAT sensor electrical connector.
2. Remove sensor mounting bolt, then the sensor.
3. Reverse procedure to install.

Adjustments

ENGINE SPEED (RPM) SENSOR

A6 & S6

1. Turn crankshaft to TDC position mark on pulley.
2. Remove Crankshaft Position (CKP) sensor.
3. Hole in crankshaft for TDC can be seen or felt through CKP sensor hole.
4. Inset crankshaft fixture tool No. 3242, or equivalent, into CKP sensor hole and tighten slightly.
5. Remove heat shield and engine speed (RPM) sensor.
6. Loosen RPM sensor bracket.
7. Insert adjust tool No. 3308, or equivalent, into RPM sensor hole and engage ring gear.
8. Tighten sensor bracket.
9. Install RPM sensor.

THROTTLE POSITION SENSOR

Adjusting closed throttle position switch automatically adjusts throttle position sensor.

Electric Fuel Pumps

NOTE: Prior To Performing Any Service Operations Listed In This Section Consult Technical Service Bulletin Section For Related Information.

NOTE: Refer To "Fuel Injection" Section For System Wiring Diagrams, Refer To "Fuel Injection" And "Computerized Engine Controls" For Component And System Testing Not Covered In This Section.

INDEX

	Page No.
Fuel Pressure Relief	10-19
1.8L, 2.8L, 3.7L & 4.2L Engines	10-19
2.7L Engine	10-19
Fuel Pump Replacement	10-19
A4 & S4	10-19
A6 & S6	10-19
AWD Models	10-19
FWD Models	10-20
A8	10-20
Cabriolet	10-21
Installation	10-21
Removal	10-21
TT	10-21

FUEL PRESSURE RELIEF

1.8L, 2.8L, 3.7L & 4.2L Engines

Wrap a suitable cloth around hose connections before disconnecting lines, then release pressure by carefully pulling hoses off ports.

2.7L Engine

1. Remove engine cover panels.
2. Remove air ducts.
3. Remove coolant expansion tank bolts, then position tank aside with all hoses intact.
4. Disconnect coolant level monitor electrical connector.
5. Remove hose clamp at arrow, **Fig. 1.**
6. Remove intake pipe, then disconnect hose and water pipe. **Plug lower section of intake pipe.**
7. Disconnect fuel pressure regulator vacuum hose.
8. At this point fuel system is still under pressure. Place a suitable cloth around fuel supply line connection, **Fig. 2.**
9. Relieve pressure by loosening fuel supply line connection.

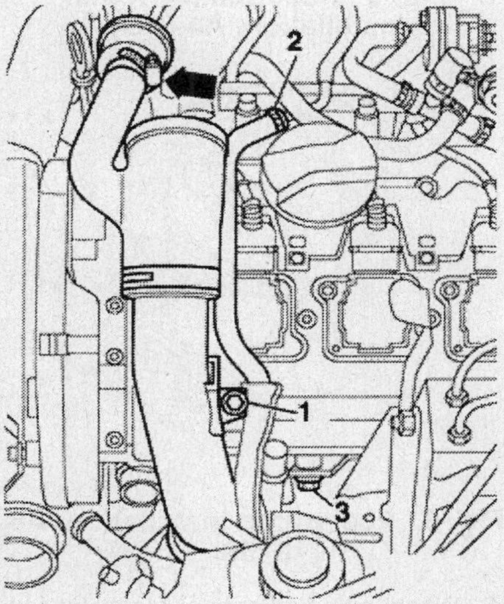

1- Intake Pipe
2- Hose
3- Water Pipe Bolt

AD1060000094000X

Fig. 1 Intake pipe removal. 2.7L engine

FUEL PUMP REPLACEMENT

A4 & S4

Fuel tank should be no more than ⅔ full when replacing pump.

1. Obtain radio anti-theft protection code as outlined under "Precautions."
2. Remove cover for fuel pump module flange located under luggage compartment trim.
3. Disconnect fuel pump.
4. Disconnect blue fuel supply and return lines, then loosen sealing ring using tool No. 3217, or equivalent.
5. Pull flange out and remove from tank.
6. Disconnect and remove fuel level sensor.
7. Install fuel pump wrench tool No. 3307, or equivalent, through fuel tank opening and position at inner fuel reservoir housing, **Fig. 3.**
8. Turn inner part of reservoir housing counterclockwise 15°, then remove fuel pump with inner part of reservoir housing.
9. Reverse procedure to install, noting the following:
   a. Install fuel pump hose and wiring into position, **Fig. 4.**
   b. When installing flange turn in direction illustrated in **Fig. 4.**
   c. **On AWD models,** turn flange until arrows marked "QUATTRO" are aligned, **Fig. 5.**
   d. **On FWD models,** turn flange until arrows marked "FRONT" are aligned, **Fig. 5.**
   e. **On AWD models,** wiring for fuel level sensor must be routed between fuel transfer pump line and fuel tank housing.
   f. **On FWD models,** wiring for fuel level sensor must be routed between fuel return line and fuel tank housing.

A6 & S6

AWD MODELS

When working on fuel system, ensure fuel tank is not more than ⅓ full. If it is required to drain fuel tank, use fuel cart tool No. VAG 1433A, or equivalent.

1. Remove trunk compartment lining, then remove closing flange cover.
2. Mark fuel pressure and return lines, then remove from closing flange.
3. Disconnect fuel pump electrical connector.
4. Remove closing ring using closing ring wrench tool No. 3087, or equivalent.
5. Remove closing flange and seal from fuel tank opening.
6. On inside of closing flange, remove both harness connectors to fuel gauge.
7. Disengage distributor connector at lower part of accumulator by pressing distributor connector to lefthand side of vehicle and lift upward.
8. Release fuel return line from distributor connector, then disconnect line.
9. Turn inner part of accumulator approximately 15° toward lefthand to stop using fuel pump wrench 3307, or equivalent, then remove fuel pump together with inner part of accumulator.
10. Reverse procedure to install noting the following:
    a. Use new replacement hose clamps.

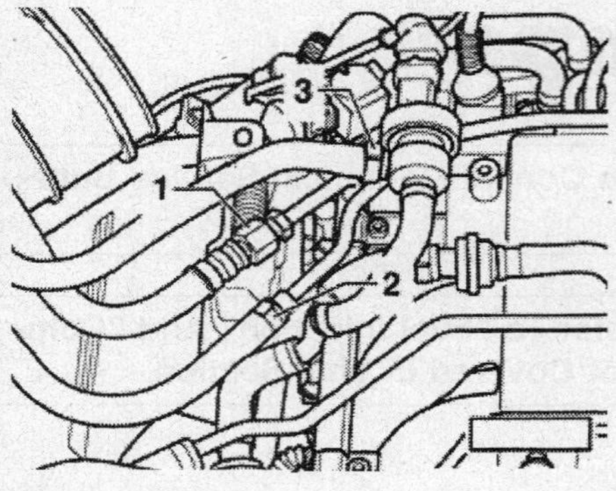

1- Intake Supply Line
2- Fuel Return Line
3- EVAP Valve

AD1060000095000X

Fig. 2 Fuel supply & return lines. 2.7L engine

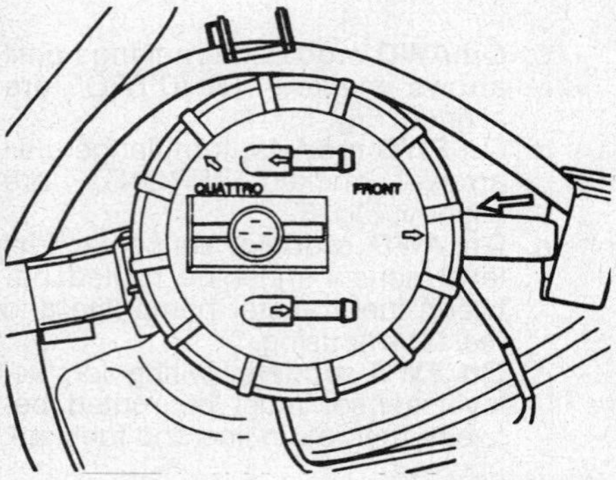

AD1029600071000X

Fig. 5 Flange installation. A4 & S4

b. Install fuel pump into tank with notch (1) on fuel pump module lining up with marking (2) on outside of accumulator, **Fig. 6.**
c. Turn fuel pump module approximately 15° to righthand stop using fuel pump wrench 3307, or equivalent. Notch (1) must align with marking (3), **Fig. 6.**
d. When installing, turn closing flange in direction of arrow.
e. Moisten O-rings with fuel before installing closing flange. Ensure closing flange is positioned as illustrated, **Fig. 7.**

FWD MODELS

When working on fuel system, ensure fuel tank is not more than ⅓ full. If it is required to drain fuel tank, use fuel cart tool No. VAG 1433A, or equivalent.

1. Remove trunk compartment lining, then remove closing flange cover.
2. Mark fuel pressure and return lines, then remove from closing flange.
3. Disconnect fuel pump electrical connector.
4. Remove union nut using ring nut spanner tool No. 3217, or equivalent.
5. Lift closing flange and seal from tank opening.

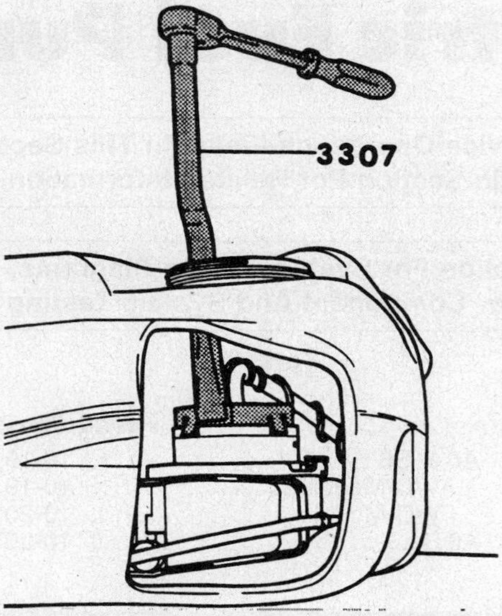

AD1029600069000X

Fig. 3 Fuel pump wrench installation. A4 & S4

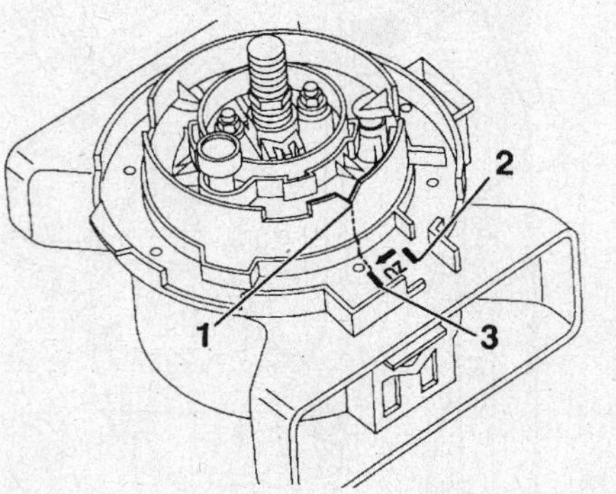

AD1029800151000X

Fig. 6 Fuel pump installation. A6 & S6

6. Disconnect fuel sender electrical connector.
7. Remove fuel return line at inside of closing flange.
8. Turn fuel pump module to lefthand approximately 15° to stop using fuel pump wrench tool No. 3307, or equivalent, then lift out.
9. Reverse procedure to install noting the following:
   a. Install new replacement hose clamps.
   b. Install fuel pump into tank with notch (1) on fuel pump module lining up with marking (2) on outside of accumulator, **Fig. 6.**
   c. Turn fuel pump module approximately 15° to righthand stop using fuel pump wrench 3307, or equivalent. Notch (1) must align with marking (3), **Fig. 6.**
   d. When installing, turn closing flange in direction of arrow.
   e. Moisten O-rings with fuel before installing closing flange. Ensure closing flange is positioned as illustrated, **Fig. 7.**
   f. **Torque** union nut to 59 ft. lbs.

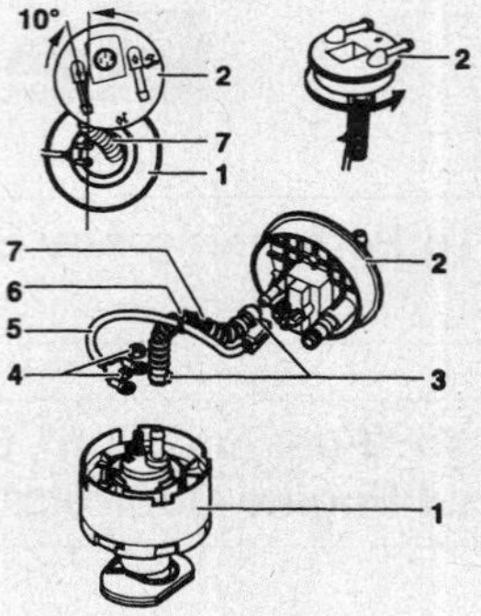

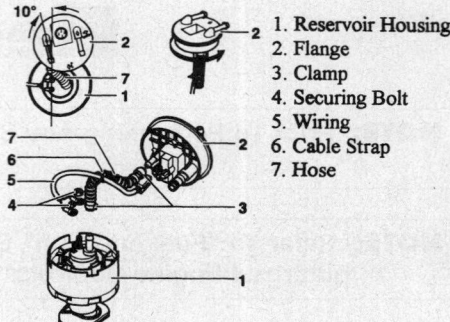

1. Reservoir Housing
2. Flange
3. Clamp
4. Securing Bolt
5. Wiring
6. Cable Strap
7. Hose

AD1029600070000X

Fig. 4 Exploded view of fuel pump assembly. A4 & S4

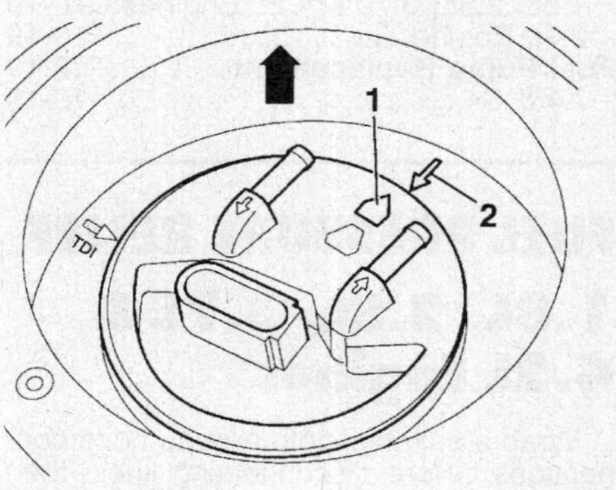

AD1029800152000X

Fig. 7 Closing flange position. A6

A8

1. Remove fuel pump cover, then the trunk compartment trim.
2. Disconnect fuel pump electrical connectors.
3. Relieve fuel system pressure by slowly opening fuel supply line.
4. Mark and disconnect fuel lines from pump.
5. Remove fuel level sensor and compression spring using fuel level sensor wrench tool No. 2012A, or equivalent.
6. Remove fuel level sensor using a suitable pair of pliers.
7. Open fuel pump lock ring using fuel pump locking tool No. 3342, or equivalent.
8. Loosen mounting tube and leave installed, **Fig. 8.**
9. Press firmly on mounting tube to separate fuel pump with reservoir from intake housing in fuel reservoir.
10. Remove mounting tube, then the fuel pump with reservoir.
11. Pull and turn clockwise at same time to remove fuel pump from tank.
12. Reverse procedure to install noting the following:
    a. Remove fuel from righthand cavity of fuel tank.
    b. Inspect connection between filler tube and integrated reservoir.
    c. Visually inspect integrated reservoir and connectors to transfer pump lines.
    d. After installation, add approximately ¾ gallon of fuel and let engine run

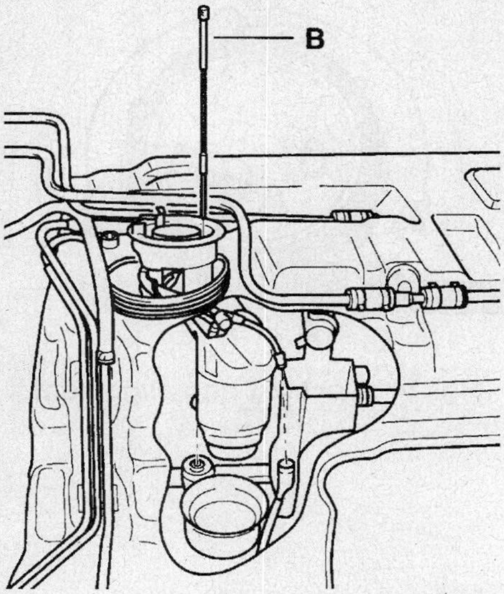

AD1029800153000X

Fig. 8 Fuel pump mounting tube location. A8

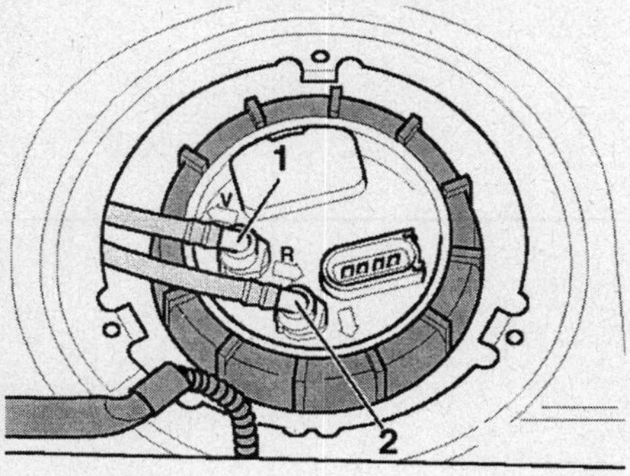

1. Fuel supply line
2. Fuel return line

AD1020000165000X

Fig. 11 Fuel line identification. TT

for 10 minutes. Stop engine and let vehicle stand for approximately 6 hours.

e. If engine starts normally after 6 hours and runs for 10 minutes without trouble, integrated reservoir is leak tight.

Cabriolet

REMOVAL

1. Obtain radio anti-theft protection code as outlined under "Precautions."
2. Remove screws and fuel gauge sender cover located under luggage compartment trim, then disconnect fuel gauge and pump electrical connector from outer side of flange assembly.
3. Wrap fuel lines in a suitable shop towel, then slowly open fuel lines to bleed off residual pressure. Disconnect fuel lines.
4. Unscrew nut from flange assembly and fuel tank using collar nut tool No. 3217, or equivalent. Note position of

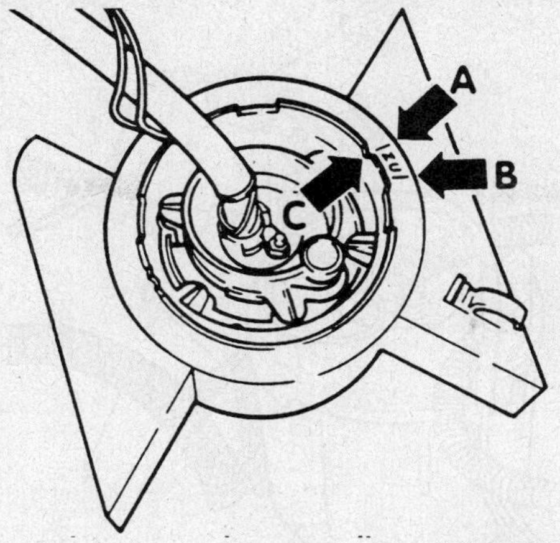

AD1029100001000X

Fig. 9 Fuel pump alignment. Cabriolet

alignment marks on tank and flange for later assembly.

5. Disconnect fuel lines and electrical connector from inner side of flange assembly.
6. Remove fuel level sender by pressing release catch on side of sender unit, then lifting sender from tank.
7. Insert fuel pump wrench tool No. 3307, or equivalent, through tank opening and place on inner part of surge housing.
8. Rotate inner part of surge housing approximately 15° and lift out fuel pump.

INSTALLATION

1. Install fuel pump with upper section of surge housing so that notch "C" aligns with mark "A" on upper part of housing, **Fig. 9.**
2. Apply fuel pump wrench tool No. 3307, or equivalent, and rotate upper section of housing to righthand stop. Align marks "C" and "B."
3. Push fuel return line, **Fig. 10,** onto flange assembly until clamp latches to flange pin.
4. **On FWD models,** connect fuel sending unit harness connector to inner side of flange assembly so that wiring lies over fuel supply line and does not interfere with level sensor operation, **Fig. 10.**
5. **On AWD models,** connect fuel sending unit harness connector to flange assembly so that wiring lies over fuel return line and does not interfere with level sensor operation.
6. **On all models,** install flange assembly to tank, note alignment marks, then install collar nut and tighten using collar nut wrench tool No. 3217, or equivalent.
7. Install fuel lines and electrical connector to outer side of flange assembly.
8. Install fuel gauge sender cover located under luggage compartment trim.

TT

1. Pump fuel from fuel tank into storage unit tool No. VAG 1433A, or equivalent

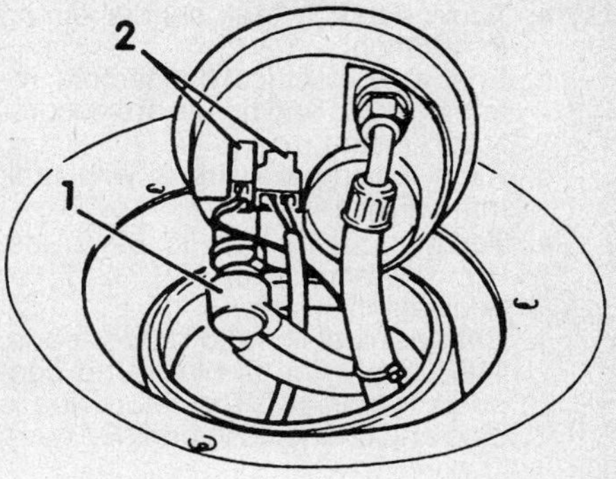

AD1029100002000X

Fig. 10 Fuel pump flange assembly. Cabriolet

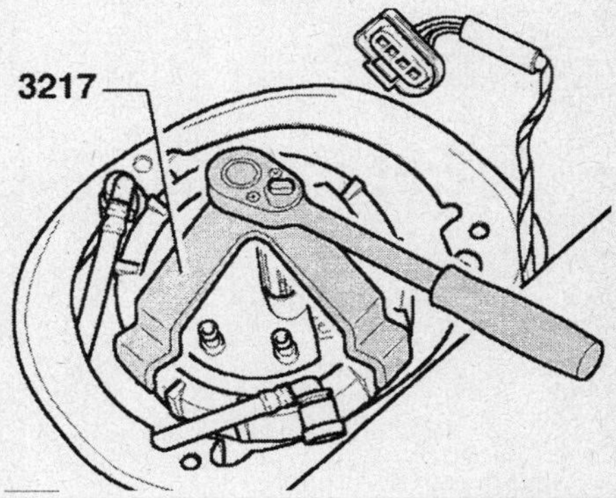

AD1020000166000X

Fig. 12 Fuel tank unit removal. TT

until tank is less than ⅓ full.

2. Remove rear seat cushion.
3. Remove fuel tank unit access cover in floor pan.
4. Disconnect fuel tank unit electrical connector.
5. Note fuel line orientation at tank unit. The supply line is black and connects to port "V." The return line is blue and connects to port "R."
6. **Fuel lines are under pressure.** Wrap a suitable cloth around hose connections before disconnecting lines, then release pressure by carefully pulling hoses off ports, **Fig. 11.**
7. Remove lock ring using wrench tool No. 3217, or equivalent, **Fig. 12.**
8. Pull fuel pump and sealing ring out of tank opening and set aside with lines attached.
9. Reach into tank and disconnect electrical connector, **Fig. 13.**
10. Press hose coupling release button and disconnect wire.
11. Pull retaining strap upward, then disengage strap and wire to fuel pump.
12. Pull fuel pump and sealing ring out of tank opening. Discard flange seal.
13. Drain any fuel remaining in pump into a suitable container.
14. Reverse procedure to install, noting the following:
    a. Insert new flange seal into tank opening.

b. Avoid bending tank sender during installation.
c. Ensure all electrical connectors, retaining strap and hoses are securely connected.
d. Align locking ring mark with tank mark, **Fig. 14.**
e. **Torque** locking ring to 59 ft. lbs. using wrench tool No. 3217, or equivalent.
f. Connect fuel lines to proper ports. The supply line is black and connects to port "V." The return line is blue and connects to port "R."

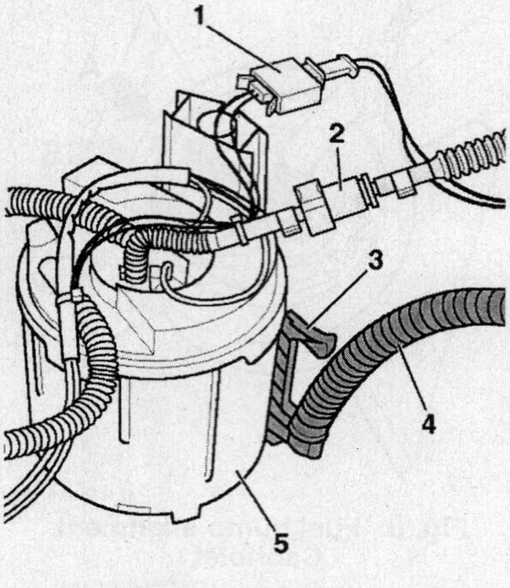

1. Electrical connector
2. Hose coupling
3. Retaining strap
4. Wiring harness
5. Fuel pump unit

AD1020000167000X

Fig. 13 Fuel pump & sender unit details. TT

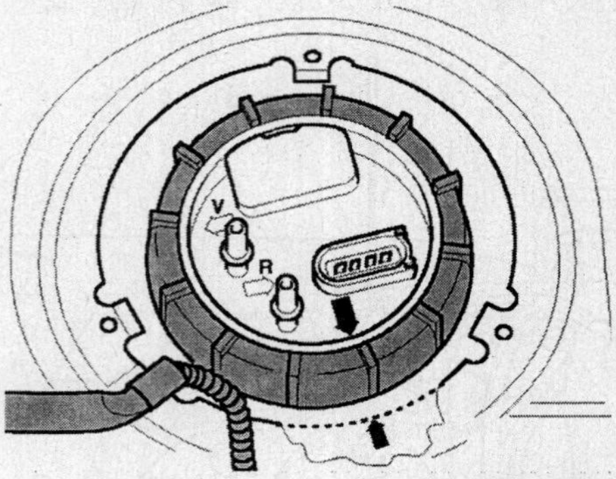

AD1020000168000X

Fig. 14 Locking ring alignment. TT

Turbochargers

NOTE: Prior To Performing Any Service Operations Listed In This Section Consult Technical Service Bulletin Section For Related Information.

INDEX

	Page No.
Description	10-23
Diagnosis & Testing	10-23
Air Recirculation Valve	10-23
Actuation Inspection	10-23
Electrical Inspection	10-23
Bypass Valve	10-23
Actuation Inspection	10-23
Electrical Inspection	10-23
Vacuum Inspection	10-24
Charge Pressure Sender	10-24
Turbocharger & Wastegate	10-24
Boost Pressure Inspection	10-24
Precautions	10-23
System Service	10-24
Intercooler, Replace	10-24
TT	10-24
Turbocharger, Replace	10-24
A4 & S4	10-24
TT	10-26

PRECAUTIONS

Thoroughly clean all unions and surrounding areas before disconnecting.

Place removed components on clean surface and cover with film or paper. **Do not use fluffy cloth.**

Carefully cover or seal opened components if repairs cannot be carried out immediately.

Only install clean components. Only unpack replacement components immediately prior to installation. **Do not use components that have been stored loose.**

DESCRIPTION

The turbocharger is an exhaust-driven device which compresses air/fuel mixture that is used to increase engine power on a demand basis, allowing a smaller, more economical engine to be used.

A turbine in exhaust gas flow is connected through a shaft to impeller compressor. During normal, steady operation, turbine does not rotate with sufficient speed to boost pressure to compress air/fuel mixture. As speed increases, mixture is compressed, allowing denser mixture to enter combustion chambers and develop more engine power during combustion cycle.

Intake manifold pressure boost is controlled by a wastegate valve which is used to bypass a portion of exhaust gases around turbine at a predetermined point in cycle, limiting boost pressure.

DIAGNOSIS & TESTING

Air Recirculation Valve

ACTUATION INSPECTION

1. Connect VAG 1551 scan tool, or equivalent, to DLC.
2. Start and idle engine.
3. Select "Engine Electronics" control unit by entering "Address Word 01."
4. If display indicates a malfunction relating to turbocharger air recirculation valve, disconnect hoses from valve.
5. Install an auxiliary hose to one of the connections on valve.
6. Start output diagnostic test mode and activate air recirculation valve.
7. Valve should click and open and close. Confirm by blowing into auxiliary hose.
8. If valve does not click, inspect resistance of valve as outlined under "Electrical Inspection."
9. If valve does not open and close properly, replace valve.

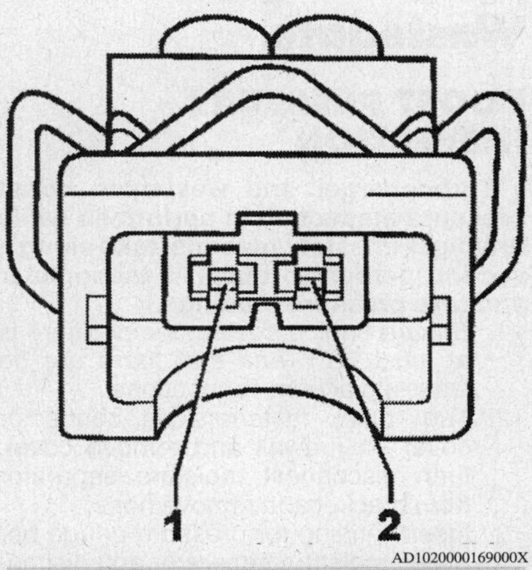

Fig. 1 Air recirculation valve electrical connector

ELECTRICAL INSPECTION

1. Disconnect air recirculation valve electrical connector.
2. Measure valve resistance using a suitable ohmmeter, which should be 27–30 ohms.
3. Replace air recirculation valve if resistance does not meet specifications.
4. If resistance is as specified, inspect related fuse and replace if blown.
5. Connect voltage tester tool No. VAG 1527B, or equivalent to valve electrical connector terminal 1, **Fig. 1,** and ground.
6. Crank engine and observe tester. LED should light.
7. If LED does not light, inspect for and repair open circuit in wiring from terminal 1 to fuel pump relay via fuse.
8. If wiring is satisfactory, inspect and replace fuel pump relay as required.
9. If LED lights, connect voltage tester to air recirculation valve electrical connector terminals 1 and 2.
10. Start output diagnostic test mode and activate air recirculation valve. LED should flash.
11. Connect test box tool No. VAG 1598/31, or equivalent, to ECM wiring harness. **Do not connect to ECM itself.**
12. Inspect for open circuit or short between air recirculation valve electrical connector terminal 2 and test box socket 104, then at socket 105. Repair as required.
13. If wiring is satisfactory, replace ECM.

Bypass Valve

ACTUATION INSPECTION

With bypass valve power off, long vacuum connector is closed. Both short vacuum connections are interconnected. When power is applied to valve, connection between long and both short vacuum connections is opened.

1. Remove wastegate bypass regulator valve.
2. Ensure bypass valve electrical connector is connected.
3. Enter DTM using a suitable scan tool.
4. Select wastegate bypass regulator valve.
5. Blow into long connector during DTM to determine whether valve opens properly.
6. If valve does not operate as specified, inspect wiring and ECM signal. If voltage and signal are satisfactory, replace valve.

ELECTRICAL INSPECTION

1. Disconnect bypass valve electrical connector.
2. Measure resistance using a suitable

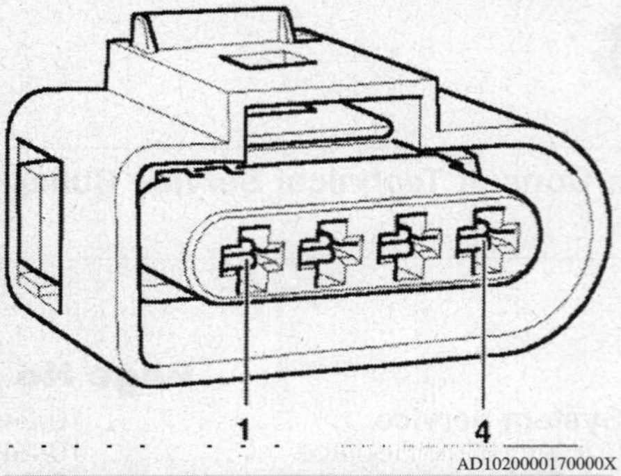

Fig. 2 Charge pressure sender electrical connector terminal identification

Altitude, Ft.	Outside Temperature, °F				
	12–32	32–50	50–68	68–86	Above 86
MANUAL TRANSAXLE					
0–5905	26.22	28.12	28.93	29.24	29.79
5905–7546	24.76	26.45	27.22	27.51	28.02
7546–9843	22.99	24.66	25.37	25.64	26.12
AUTOMATIC TRANSAXLE					
0–7546	23.71	24.37	25.89	27.18	27.86
7546–9843	22.19	22.80	24.22	25.44	26.08

Fig. 3 Boost pressure values, psi

ohmmeter, which should be 25–35 ohms.
3. Replace bypass valve if resistance does not meet specifications.

VACUUM INSPECTION

1. Attach suitable hand vacuum pump to bypass valve.
2. Operate vacuum pump to apply vacuum. Bypass valve must open.
3. After 30 seconds, operate venting valve. Bypass valve must close.
4. If bypass valve does not open or close, or if valve leaks, replace bypass valve and ensure all hose connections are tight and free of leaks.

Charge Pressure Sender

1. Connect VAG 1551 scan tool, or equivalent, to DLC.
2. Start and idle engine.
3. Select "Engine Electronics" control unit by entering "Address Word 01."
4. If display indicates a malfunction relating to charge pressure sender, disconnect electrical connector from sender.
5. Turn ignition On.
6. Measure voltage at connector terminals 1 and 3, **Fig. 2,** using a suitable voltmeter. There should be approximately five volts.
7. If voltage does not meet specifications, connect test box tool No. VAG 1598/31, or equivalent, to ECM wiring harness and to the ECM.
8. Inspect for open circuit or short between charge pressure sender electrical connector terminal 1 and test box socket 108, then at terminal 3 and socket 98. Repair as required.
9. If voltage meets specifications, connect electrical connector to charge pressure sender.
10. Connect voltmeter between test box sockets 101 and 108.
11. Start and idle engine, then note voltage, which should be approximately 1.9 volts.
12. Open and quickly release throttle. Voltage should briefly jump to 2–3 volts.
13. If voltage does not meet specifications, inspect for open circuit or short between charge pressure sender electrical connector terminal 4 and test box socket 101. Repair as required.
14. If wiring is satisfactory, replace charge pressure sender.

Turbocharger & Wastegate

BOOST PRESSURE INSPECTION

Turbocharger and wastegate boost pressure inspection is performed while driving. For safety reasons, take along a second person to observe tachometer and take pressure readings.

1. Ensure engine coolant temperature is at least 86°F and that there are no leaks at vacuum connections.
2. Turn quick fasteners on connector cover on firewall and remove cover, then disconnect moisture separator from bracket and remove hose.
3. Insert T-fitting for pressure gauge between moisture separator and disconnected hose, then route measuring hose from T-fitting over rear edge of hood and through passenger's side window.
4. Connect turbocharger tester (pressure gauge) tool No. VW 1397/A, or equivalent, to measuring hose. Ensure last measurements have been cleared from turbocharger tester.
5. Prior to measuring boost pressure, drive vehicle for approximately two miles on uninterrupted road at a speed of 40 mph.
6. Fully depress accelerator pedal in 4th gear starting at approximately 37 mph and have assistant observe tachometer.
7. When engine speed reaches 3000 RPM, read gauge pressure.
8. Proper pressure values are based on altitude. Refer to chart, **Fig. 3.** Boost pressure may vary slightly through temperature range.
9. If boost pressure reading is satisfactory but performance is poor below 2300 RPM, inspect bypass valve.
10. If boost pressure reading is not satisfactory, temporarily replace wastegate and inspect boost pressure again.
11. If boost pressure reading is still not satisfactory, replace turbocharger.

SYSTEM SERVICE

Intercooler, Replace

TT

1. Remove front noise insulator retainers, then the insulator.
2. Remove front bumper.
3. Remove righthand headlamp assembly.
4. Remove EVAP canister.
5. Disconnect air hose from top of charge air cooler.
6. Remove two charge air cooler upper mounting bolts.
7. Remove charge air cooler cowl clips, then the cowl.
8. Disconnect air hose from bottom of charge air cooler.
9. Remove charge air cooler lower mounting bolt, then lower the cooler out of vehicle.
10. Reverse procedure to install. Inspect and adjust headlamp alignment as required.

Turbocharger, Replace

A4 & S4

1.8L ENGINE

1. Remove front noise insulator retainers, then the insulator.
2. Mark running direction with felt pen or chalk, then remove serpentine belt.
3. Remove A/C compressor mounting bolts, then position compressor aside with lines intact.
4. Remove turbocharger bracket bolts, **Fig. 4.**
5. Disconnect oil return line at turbocharger and position aside.
6. Remove air guide ducts at turbocharger.
7. Remove oil supply line banjo fitting.
8. Disconnect coolant supply hose from boost pressure regulator valve actuator support.
9. Pinch off coolant supply hose using clamp tool No. 3094, or equivalent.
10. Remove intake air duct between cowl and air cleaner housing.
11. Remove air cleaner housing cover.
12. Disconnect electrical connectors, hoses and lines at following components:
    a. Wastegate bypass regulator valve.
    b. EVAP purge regulator valve.

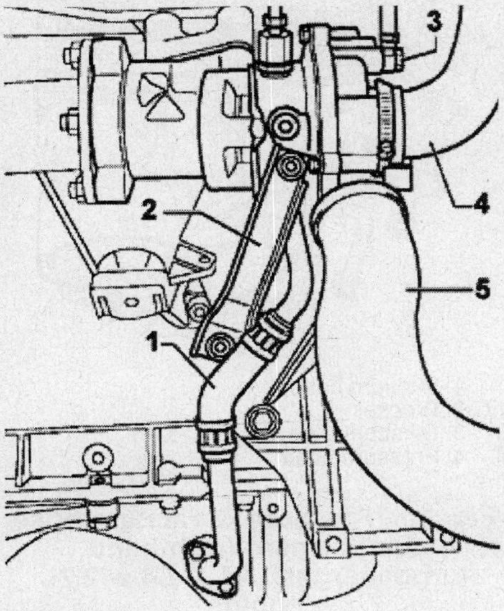

1. Oil return line
2. Turbocharger bracket
3. Oil supply line
4. Air guide duct
5. Air guide duct

AD1029800180000X

Fig. 4 Turbocharger bracket & oil line replacement. A4 & S4 w/1.8L engine

c. Power output stage.
d. MAF sensor.

13. Disconnect hose connections, then remove air cleaner housing.
14. Remove engine appearance covers.
15. Unbolt crankcase ventilation hose at cylinder head cover and heat shield, **Fig. 5.**
16. Unbolt both oil supply line bolts.
17. Remove heat shield.
18. Pinch off coolant return hose using clamp tool No. 3094, or equivalent.
19. Remove coolant return hose sleeve.
20. Remove coolant return hose at line to turbocharger. Line will remain bolted to turbocharger.
21. Disconnect oil supply line at turbocharger.
22. Remove catalytic converter to turbocharger bolts. **Do not bend flexible coupling more than 10° or it may be damaged.**
23. Remove turbocharger to exhaust manifold bolts.
24. Position turbocharger aside and disconnect coolant supply line.
25. Remove turbocharger from vehicle.
26. Reverse procedure to install, noting the following:
    a. Loosely bolt coolant supply line to boost pressure regulator valve actuator support before tightening turbocharger mounting bolts.
    b. Tighten banjo fitting, then the bracket mounting bolts before tightening turbocharger mounting bolts.
    c. Add proper engine oil to turbocharger through oil supply line connection flange.

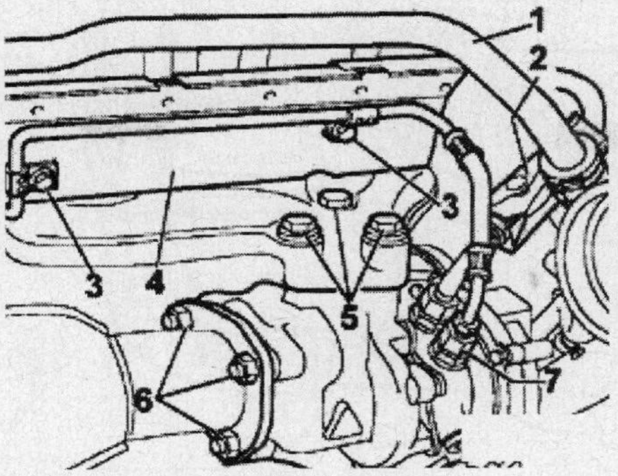

1. Crankcase ventilation hose
2. Coolant return hose sleeve
3. Oil supply line bolts
4. Heat shield
5. Turbocharger to exhaust manifold bolts
6. Turbocharger to catalytic converter bolts
7. Oil supply line

AD1029800181000X

Fig. 5 Turbocharger replacement. A4 & S4 w/1.8L engine

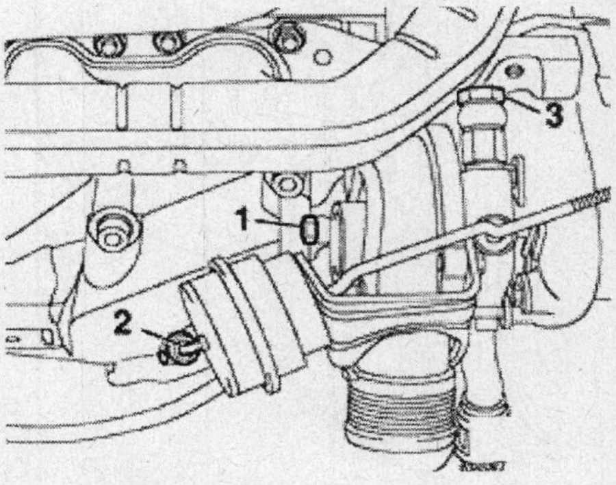

1. Vacum pipe
2. Vacuum hose
3. Line banjo bolt

AD1020000177000X

Fig. 7 Vacuum hose & line replacement (lefthand turbocharger). A4 & S4 w/2.7L engine

    d. Tighten all bolts, fittings and nuts to specifications under "1.8L Engine" in "Chassis" section.
    e. Start and idle engine for approximately one minute. **Do not increase engine speed just yet.** This ensures turbocharger is properly lubricated.

2.7L ENGINE

Lefthand

1. Drain coolant into a suitable container.
2. Move heat insulation aside in direction of arrow, **Fig. 6.**
3. Disconnect vacuum hose.
4. Remove lower section of pressure pipe.

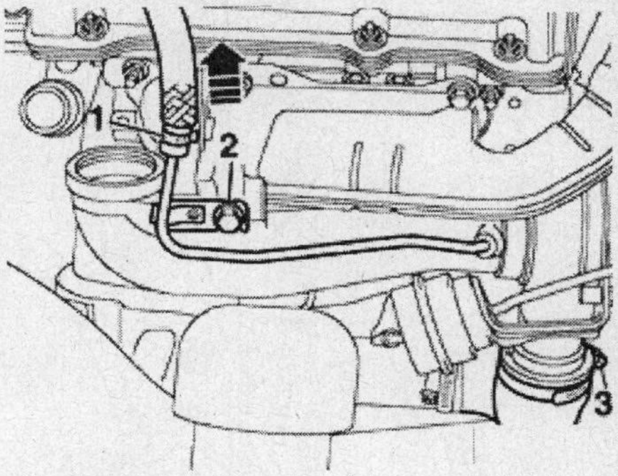

1. Vacuum hose
2. Pressure pipe bolt
3. Pressure hose

AD1020000176000X

Fig. 6 Pressure & vacuum hose replacement (lefthand turbocharger). A4 & S4 w/2.7L engine

5. Disconnect pressure hose from turbocharger.
6. Disconnect vacuum line, **Fig. 7.**
7. Disconnect vacuum hose.
8. Disconnect oil supply line.
9. Disconnect oil return line, **Fig. 8.**
10. Disconnect coolant line.
11. Remove turbocharger mounting bolts, then the turbocharger.
12. Reverse procedure to install, noting the following:
    a. Discard gaskets, O-rings, seals and self-locking nuts. **Do not install old ones.**
    b. Ensure "Abgasturbocharger" lettering on pressure hose is visible as illustrated, **Fig. 9,** and clamp heads are aligned with X marks on the hose.
    c. Tighten all bolts, fittings and nuts to specifications under "2.7L Engine" in "Chassis" section.

Righthand

1. Drain coolant into a suitable container.
2. Remove righthand cylinder head appearance cover.
3. Disconnect all upper air intake pipe hoses.
4. Plug lower section of intake pipe.
5. Remove lower section of intake pipe.
6. Move heat insulation aside in direction of arrow, **Fig. 10.**
7. Disconnect vacuum hose.
8. Remove transaxle cooler line bracket bolt.
9. Disconnect oil supply line.
10. Disconnect pressure hose from turbocharger.
11. Disconnect oil return line, **Fig. 11,** then the coolant line.
12. Remove hose bracket bolt at cylinder head.
13. Remove turbocharger mounting bolts, then the turbocharger.
14. Reverse procedure to install, noting the following:

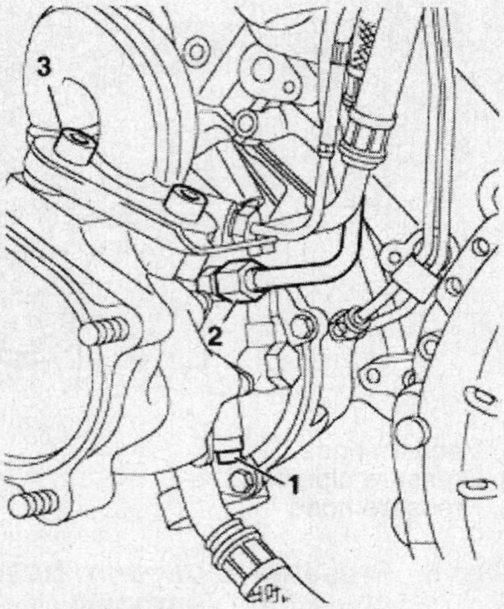

1. Oil return line
2. Coolant line
3. Turbocharger mounting bolts

AD1020000178000X

Fig. 8 Oil return & coolant line replacement (lefthand turbocharger). A4 & S4 w/2.7L engine

a. Discard gaskets, O-rings, seals and self-locking nuts. **Do not install old ones.**
b. Ensure "Abgasturbocharger" lettering on pressure hose is visible as illustrated, **Fig. 9,** and clamp heads are aligned with X marks on the hose.
c. Tighten all bolts, fittings and nuts to specifications under "2.7L Engine" in "Chassis" section.

TT

1. Drain coolant into a suitable container.
2. Drain engine oil.
3. Remove engine appearance covers.
4. Remove front noise insulator retainers, then the insulator.
5. Remove righthand drive axle heat shield.
6. Remove front exhaust pipe. **Do not bend flexible coupling more than 10° or it may be damaged.**
7. Remove upper air to lower air hose, **Fig. 12.**
8. Remove upper air pipe bracket bolt.
9. Remove oil return pipe.
10. Loosen turbocharger bracket bolt a few turns, **Fig. 13.**
11. Remove turbocharger bracket from block bolts.
12. Remove coolant return pipe bracket bolt.
13. Remove coolant supply pipe to block bolt.
14. Disconnect crankcase breather pressure control valve from hose, **Fig. 14.**
15. Disconnect charge pressure control valve electrical connector.
16. Disconnect hose from upper air pipe.
17. Disconnect hose from charge pressure control valve.
18. Disconnect hose from air pipe.

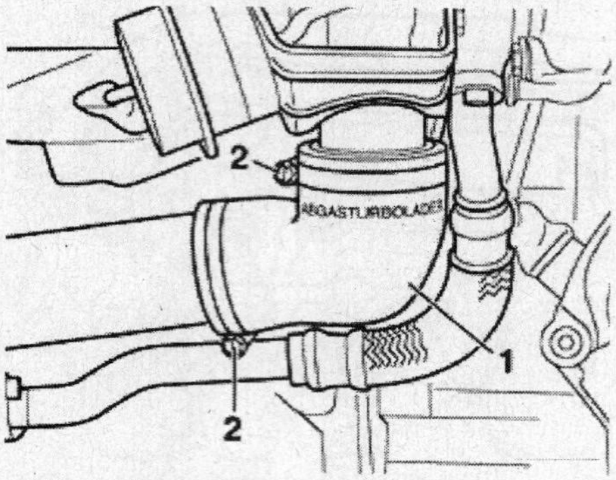

1. Turbocharger hose
2. Clamp heads

AD1020000179000X

Fig. 9 Pressure hose & clamp orientation. A4 & S4 w/2.7L engine

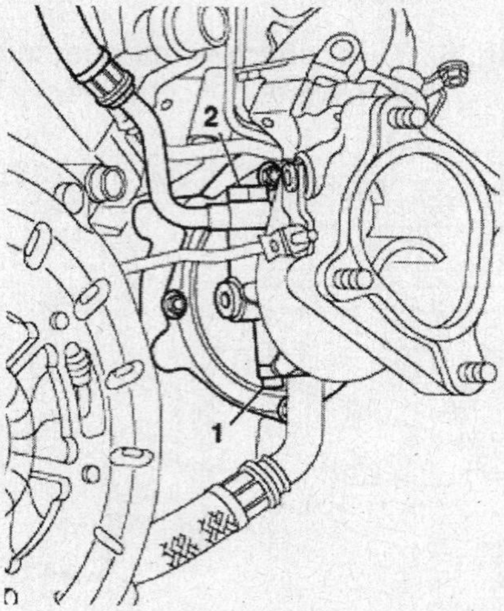

1. Oil return line
2. Coolant line

AD1020000175000X

Fig. 11 Oil return & coolant lines (righthand turbocharger). A4 & S4 w/2.7L engine

19. Disconnect vacuum pipe from air recirculation valve.
20. Disconnect air intake hose from air cleaner.
21. Remove air intake hose locking clip at turbocharger, then the hose.
22. Disconnect hose from non-return valve.
23. Disconnect coolant return hose from Y-connection on right next to cylinder head.
24. Disconnect hose from upper air pipe.
25. Remove heat shield bolts from rear of cylinder head.
26. Remove upper air pipe clamp bolts.
27. Remove upper air pipe and heat shield.
28. Remove turbocharger to exhaust manifold mounting bolts.
29. Remove gasket. Turbocharger will drop slightly.
30. Remove all exhaust manifold mounting bolts and washers, then the manifold.

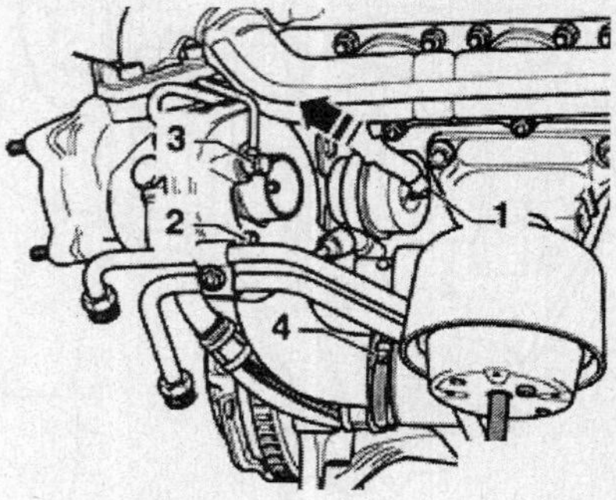

1. Vacuum hose
2. Bracket
3. Oil supply line
4. Pressure hose

AD1020000174000X

Fig. 10 Pressure & vacuum hose replacement (righthand turbocharger). A4 & S4 w/2.7L engine

31. Unbolt oil supply pipe retainer from turbocharger.
32. Bolt turbocharger bracket back onto block.
33. Remove oil supply pipe and coolant return pipe bolts from turbocharger.
34. Remove spacer sleeve from coolant return pipe.
35. Disconnect coolant return pipe.
36. Unbolt turbocharger bracket from cylinder block and remove turbocharger.
37. Reverse procedure to install, noting the following:
    a. Discard all gaskets, O-rings, seals and self-locking nuts. **Do not install old ones.**
    b. Fill new turbocharger with proper engine oil through oil supply port.
    c. Bolt turbocharger bracket onto turbocharger but do not tighten bolts just yet.
    d. Position turbocharger against engine from below, then tighten bolts by hand to secure bracket to block.
    e. **Torque** oil supply pipe banjo bolt to 22 ft. lbs.
    f. **Torque** oil supply pipe retainer bolt to 89 inch lbs.
    g. Install coolant return pipe with spacer sleeve and bolt it to turbocharger. **Torque** to 26 ft. lbs.
    h. Unbolt turbocharger bracket from engine block again.
    i. Install exhaust manifold. **Torque** nuts to 18 ft. lbs.
    j. Mount turbocharger to exhaust manifold.
    k. Continue installation by reversing installation sequence, then start and idle engine for approximately one minute. **Do not increase engine speed just yet.** This ensures turbocharger is properly lubricated.
    l. Inspect fluid levels and correct as required.

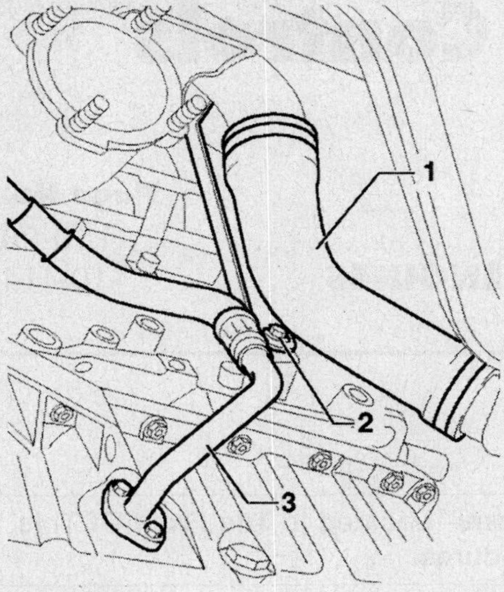

1. Air hose
2. Upper air pipe
3. Oil return pipe

AD1020000171000X

Fig. 12 Turbocharger air hose & oil return pipe replacement. TT

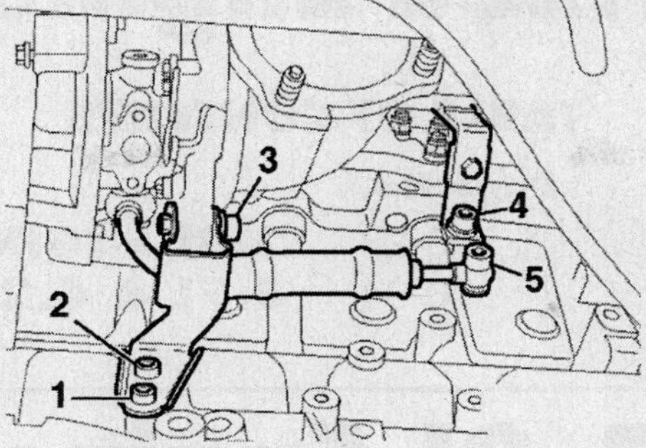

1. Bracket bolt
2. Bracket bolt
3. Turbocharger bolt
4. Coolant return pipe bolt
5. Coolant supply pipe bolt

AD1020000172000X

Fig. 13 Turbocharger bracket mount & coolant pipe replacement. TT

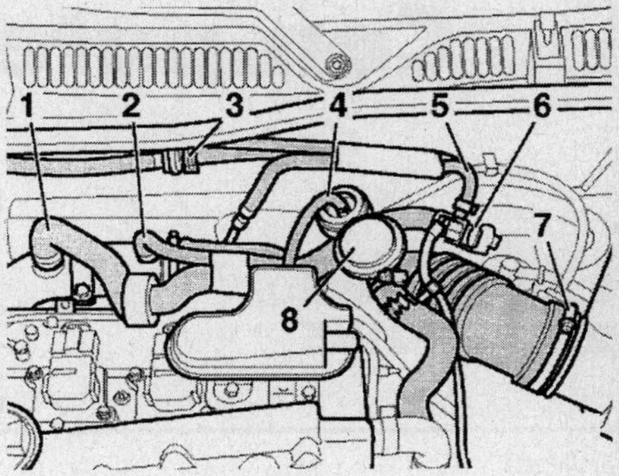

1. Air pipe hose
2. Upper air pipe hose
3. Non-return valve hose
4. Recirculation valve hose
5. Charge pressure control valve hose
6. Charge pressure control valve hose
7. Air intake hose
8. Pressure control valve

AD1020000173000X

Fig. 14 Turbocharger vacuum & control hose replacement. TT

Computerized Engine Controls

TABLE OF CONTENTS

	Page No.		Page No.
1.8L ENGINE	10-28	**2.8L ENGINE**	10-88
2.7L ENGINE	10-64	**3.7L & 4.2L ENGINES**	10-114

1.8L Engine

NOTE: On Air Bag Equipped Models, Refer To "Air Bag System Precautions" Located In The Front Of This Manual For System Disarming & Arming Procedures.

NOTE: If Unsure Of System Used On Vehicle Being Serviced, Refer To Engine Systems Identification Chart Located At Beginning Of This Chapter.

NOTE: Prior To Performing Any Service Operations Listed In This Section Consult Technical Service Bulletin Section For Related Information.

NOTE: "Electrical Symbol & Wire Color Code Identification" Located In The Front Of This Manual May Be Used As An Aid When Using Wiring Circuits Found In This Section.

INDEX

	Page No.
Description	10-29
Diagnosis & Testing	10-29
Accessing Diagnostic Trouble Codes	10-29
Clearing Diagnostic Trouble Codes	10-46
Component & System Tests	10-29
Accelerator Pedal Position Sensor	10-45
Closed Throttle Position (CTP) Switch	10-42
Crankshaft Position (CKP) Sensor	10-35
ECM Signal	10-36
Engine Coolant Temperature (ECT) Sensor	10-34
Front Heated Oxygen Sensor	10-36
Fuel Injector	10-36
Fuel Pressure	10-31
Fuel Pump Relay	10-29
Mass Air Flow (MAF) Sensor	10-33
RPM Sensor	10-43
Rear Heated Oxygen Sensor	10-40
Throttle Position (TP) Sensor	10-43
Diagnostic Tests	10-29
A4 & S4	10-29
TT	10-29
Diagnostic Trouble Code Interpretation	10-29
Wiring Diagrams	10-29
A4 & S4	10-29
TT	10-29
Diagnostic Chart Index	10-47
Precautions	10-29
Air Bag Systems	10-29
Audio Coded Anti-Theft System	10-29
Battery Ground Cable	10-29
Electrical Connection & Terminal Repair	10-29
Fuel System	10-29
Sensor & Fuel Injector Specifications	10-29
System Service	10-46

SENSOR & FUEL INJECTOR SPECIFICATIONS

Component	Temperature, °F	Resistance, Ohms
ECT Sensor	86	1500–2000
	176	275–375
Fuel Injector①	68	12–15
Fuel Injector②	68	12–13
HO2S Heater	—	4.9–19.9
IAT Sensor	86	1500–2000
	176	275–375
Oxygen Sensor③	68	1–5

① — A4 & S4.
② — TT.
③ — Terminals 1 and 2.

PRECAUTIONS

Fuel System

Always clean fuel lines before loosening and be sure to replace seals and fuel hose clamps. Keep a fully charged fire extinguisher readily available.

Air Bag Systems

Refer to "Air Bag System Precautions" in the front of this manual for system disarming and arming procedures.

Battery Ground Cable

Prior to service, disconnect battery ground cable and isolate as required.

Audio Coded Anti-Theft System

Do not use computer memory saver tool. Using the tool will keep the air bag system charged and may cause accidental activation of the air bag unit.

Obtain the security code from the vehicle operator prior to disconnecting the battery or removing the radio. Refer to the owner's manual for security code disarming and arming procedures.

Electrical Connection & Terminal Repair

If connector terminal or pin replacement is required, use only gold-plated components.

DESCRIPTION

The Motronic Engine Control Module (ECM) features On-Board Diagnostic (OBD) capability. If a fault condition occurs at monitored sensors or components they are stored in Diagnostic Trouble Code (DTC) memory. The Motronic ECM, after evaluating information, differentiates between faults and stores them until DTC memory is erased. Motronic ECM is equipped with Output Diagnosis Test Mode (DTM) inspections. Output DTM inspections can only be performed while engine is not running. DTC memory should only be activated while engine is running, if possible. If a fault condition is present for a sufficient length of time, it is stored as a static DTC. If a fault condition appears momentarily or for insufficient time to be classified as static, it will be stored as sporadic or intermittent DTC. If sporadic or intermittent fault condition does not occur during next 50 engine starts, it will be automatically erased from DTC memory.

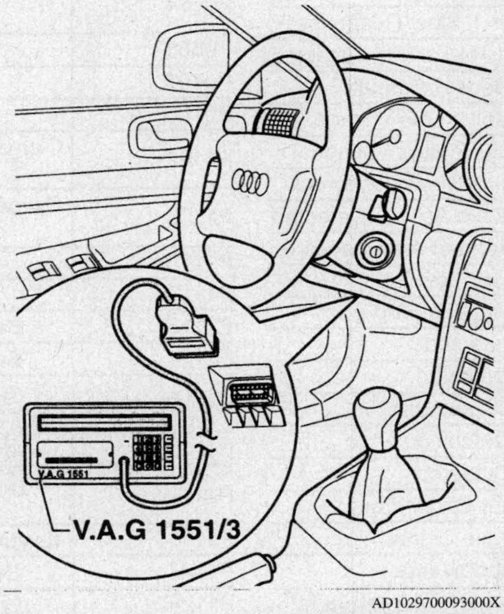

Fig. 1 Data Link Connector (DLC)

DIAGNOSIS & TESTING

Accessing Diagnostic Trouble Codes

1. Connect diagnostic scan tool No. VAG 1551, or equivalent, to Data Link Connector (DLC), **Fig. 1,** using connector harness tool No. VAG 1551/3.
2. Follow scan tool manufacturer's instructions to access DTCs.

Diagnostic Trouble Code Interpretation

Refer to **Fig. 2** for Diagnostic Trouble Code (DTC) identification and description.

Wiring Diagrams

A4 & S4

Refer to **Figs. 3 and 4** for system wiring diagram.

TT

Refer to **Figs. 5 and 6** for system wiring diagram.

Diagnostic Tests

A4 & S4

Refer to **Figs. 7 through 27** for diagnostic tests.

TT

Refer to **Figs. 28 through 59** for diagnostic tests.

Component & System Tests

For component locations, refer to "Engine Compartment Reference Diagrams" to aid in location during diagnosis and testing procedures.

FUEL PUMP RELAY

A4 & S4

The fuel pump relay is located in the central electric and control module panel.

1. Remove side under dash panels required to access fuse relay panel.
2. Remove fuses from fuse panel position Nos. 28, 29 and 34, **Fig. 60.**
3. Connect a suitable LED voltage tester to either terminal of fuse No. 28 and ground.

Code	Description
P0101	MAF Or VAF Circuit Range/Performance
P0102	MAF Or VAF Circuit Low Input
P0103	MAF Circuit High Input
P0106	MAP Or BARO Pressure Range/Performance
P0107	MAP Or BARO Pressure Sensor Low Input
P0108	MAP Or BARO Pressure Sensor High Input
P0112	IAT Circuit Low Input
P0113	IAT Circuit High Input
P0116	ECT Circuit Fault
P0117	ECT Circuit Low Input
P0118	ECT Circuit High Input
P0121	Throttle/Pedal Position Sensor Circuit Fault
P0122	Throttle/Pedal Position Sensor Circuit Low Input
P0123	Throttle/Pedal Position Sensor Circuit High Input
P0130	Oxygen Sensor Bank 1 Sensor 1 Fault
P0131	Oxygen Sensor Bank 1 Sensor 1 Low Voltage
P0132	Oxygen Sensor Bank 1 Sensor 1 High Voltage
P0133	Oxygen Sensor Bank 1 Sensor 1 Slow Response
P0134	Oxygen Sensor Bank 1 Sensor 1 No Activity Detected
P0136	Oxygen Sensor Bank 1 Sensor 2 Fault
P0137	Oxygen Sensor Bank 1 Sensor 2 Low Voltage
P0138	Oxygen Sensor Bank 1 Sensor 2 High Voltage
P0139	Oxygen Sensor Bank 1 Sensor 2 Slow Response
P0140	Oxygen Sensor Bank 1 Sensor 2 No Activity Detected
P0236	Turbocharger Boost Sensor Range/Performance
P0237	Turbocharger Boost Sensor Low Input
P0238	Turbocharger Boost Sensor High Input
P0300	Random Misfire Detected
P0301	Cylinder 1 Misfire Detected
P0302	Cylinder 2 Misfire Detected
P0303	Cylinder 3 Misfire Detected
P0304	Cylinder 4 Misfire Detected
P0321	Engine Speed Sensor Input Circuit Fault
P0322	Engine Speed Sensor No Signal
P0327	Knock Sensor 1 Circuit Low Input

Fig. 2 Diagnostic trouble code interpretation (Part 1 of 6)

Code	Description
P0328	Knock Sensor 1 Circuit High Input
P0332	Knock Sensor 2 Circuit Low Input
P0333	Knock Sensor 2 Circuit High Input
P0411	Secondary AIR System Improper Flow
P0422	Main Catalyst Bank 1 Efficiency Below Threshold
P0441	EVAP System Improper Purge Flow Fault
P0442	EVAP System Small Leak Detected
P0455	EVAP System Large Leak Detected
P0501	Vehicle Speed Sensor Fault
P0506	Idle Control System RPM Lower Than Expected
P0507	Idle Control System RPM Higher Than Expected
P0560	System Voltage Fault
P0562	System Voltage Low
P0563	System Voltage High
P0571	Cruise/Brake Switch Improper Signal
P0601	Internal Control Module Memory Inspection Sum Error
P0604	Internal Control Module Random Access Memory Error
P0605	Internal Control Module ROM Test Error
P0707	Transmission Range Sensor Low Input
P0708	Transmission Range Sensor High Input
P1102	Oxygen Sensor Heating Circuit Bank 1 Sensor 1 Short To Voltage
P1105	Oxygen Sensor Heating Circuit Bank 1 Sensor 2 Short To Voltage
P1111	Oxygen Control Bank 1 System Too Lean
P1112	Oxygen Control Bank 1 System Too Rich
P1113	Bank 1, Sensor 1 Internal Resistance Too High
P1114	Bank 1, Sensor 2 Internal Resistance Too High
P1115	Oxygen Sensor Heater Circuit Bank 1 Sensor 1 Short To Ground
P1116	Oxygen Sensor Heater Circuit Bank 1 Sensor 1 Open
P1117	Oxygen Sensor Heater Circuit Bank 1 Sensor 2 Short To Ground
P1118	Oxygen Sensor Heater Circuit Bank 1 Sensor 2 Open
P1127	Long Term Fuel Trim Bank 1 System Too Rich
P1128	Long Term Fuel Trim Bank 1 System Too Lean
P1136	Long Term Fuel Trim Bank 1 System Too Lean
P1137	Long Term Fuel Trim Bank 1 System Too Rich
P1149	Oxygen Sensor Control Bank 1 Out Of Range

Fig. 2 Diagnostic trouble code interpretation (Part 2 of 6)

4. Operate starter. Fuel pump relay must operate, and voltage tester must light.
5. If fuel pump does not operate, proceed as follows:
   a. Remove fuel pump relay.
   b. Turn ignition On.
   c. Inspect for voltage using a suitable voltmeter between relay connector terminals 28 and 34, then 32 and 34. There should be battery voltage.
   d. If voltage reading is not as specified, repair wiring as required.
6. If test lamp does not light, repeat test after connecting LED tester to opposite fuse terminal.
7. If test lamp still does not light, correct wiring between fuse No. 28 and fuel pump relay pin 30.
8. Connect a suitable LED voltage tester to either terminal of fuse No. 29 and ground.
9. Connect a suitable scan tool to Diagnostic Link Connector (DLC), access "Output Diagnostic Test Mode," then trigger fuel pump relay.
10. Fuel pump relay must operate, and voltage tester must light.
11. If test lamp does not light, repeat test after connecting LED tester to opposite fuse terminal.
12. If test lamp still does not light, correct wiring between fuse No. 29 and fuel pump relay pin 30.
13. Perform preceding steps on fuse No. 34.
14. If wiring or connector repairs are required, refer to "Precautions."
15. Inspect fuel pump relay signal as follows:
    a. Remove fuel pump relay.
    b. Remove fuses 28, 29 and 34 from fuse panel.
    c. Connect LED voltage tester VAG 1527BB, or equivalent to relay connector terminals 28 and 29. LED should light dimly.
    d. Crank engine and ensure LED continues to light dimly.
    e. If LED does not light when engine is cranked, connect test box tool No. VAG 1598/22, or equivalent to ECM harness connector.
    f. Inspect for open circuit between relay connector terminal 29 and test box pin 4 using a suitable ohmmeter. Resistance should read 1 ohm or less.
    g. If resistance is not as specified, repair open wire.
    h. If wiring is satisfactory and LED does not light, replace ECM.

Code	Description
P1171	Throttle Actuation Potentiometer Sign. 2 Range/ Performance
P1172	Throttle Actuation Potentiometer Sign. 2 Signal Too Low
P1173	Throttle Actuation Potentiometer Sign. 2 Signal Too High
P1176	Oxygen Sensor Correction Behind Catalyst B1 Limit Attained
P1196	Oxygen Sensor Heater Circuit Bank 1 Sensor 1 Electrical Fault
P1198	Oxygen Sensor Heater Circuit Bank 1 Sensor 2 Electrical Fault
P1203	Cylinder 3 Fuel Injection Circuit Electrical Fault
P1213	Cylinder 1 Fuel Injector Short To Voltage
P1214	Cylinder 2 Fuel Injector Short To Voltage
P1215	Cylinder 3 Fuel Injector Short To Voltage
P1216	Cylinder 4 Fuel Injector Short To Voltage
P1225	Cylinder 1 Fuel Injector Short To Ground
P1226	Cylinder 2 Fuel Injector Short To Ground
P1227	Cylinder 3 Fuel Injector Short To Ground
P1228	Cylinder 4 Fuel Injector Short To Ground
P1237	Cylinder 1 Fuel Injector Open Circuit
P1238	Cylinder 2 Fuel Injector Open Circuit
P1239	Cylinder 3 Fuel Injector Open Circuit
P1240	Cylinder 4 Fuel Injector Open Circuit
P1250	Fuel Level Too Low
P1287	Turbocharger Bypass Valve Open
P1288	Turbocharger Bypass Valve Short To Voltage
P1289	Turbocharger Bypass Valve Short To Ground
P1325	Cylinder 1 Knock Control Limit Attained
P1326	Cylinder 2 Knock Control Limit Attained
P1327	Cylinder 3 Knock Control Limit Attained
P1328	Cylinder 4 Knock Control Limit Attained
P1335	Engine Torque Monitoring 2 Control Limit Exceeded
P1336	Engine Torque Monitoring Adaptation At Limit
P1337	Camshaft Position Sensor Bank 1 Short To Ground
P1338	Camshaft Position Sensor Bank 1 Open Circuit Or Short To Voltage
P1340	CKP/CMP Signals Out Of Sequence

Fig. 2 Diagnostic trouble code interpretation (Part 3 of 6)

Code	Description
P1355	Cylinder 1 Ignition Circuit Open Circuit
P1356	Cylinder 1 Ignition Circuit Short To Voltage
P1357	Cylinder 1 Ignition Circuit Short To Ground
P1358	Cylinder 2 Ignition Circuit Open Circuit
P1359	Cylinder 2 Ignition Circuit Short To Voltage
P1360	Cylinder 2 Ignition Circuit Short To Ground
P1361	Cylinder 3 Ignition Circuit Open Circuit
P1362	Cylinder 3 Ignition Circuit Short To Voltage
P1363	Cylinder 3 Ignition Circuit Short To Ground
P1364	Cylinder 4 Ignition Circuit Open Circuit
P1365	Cylinder 4 Ignition Circuit Short To Voltage
P1366	Cylinder 4 Ignition Circuit Short To Ground
P1386	Internal Control Module Knock Control Error
P1387	Internal Control Module Fault
P1388	Internal Control Module Fault
P1410	Tank Ventilation Valve Short To Voltage
P1421	Secondary AIR Circuit Short To Ground
P1422	Secondary AIR Circuit Control Circuit Short To Voltage
P1424	Secondary AIR Bank 1 Leak
P1425	Tank Vent Valve Short To Ground
P1426	Tank Vent Valve Open

Fig. 2 Diagnostic trouble code interpretation (Part 4 of 6)

i. If wiring and signal to relay is satisfactory, replace fuel pump relay.

TT

The fuel pump relay is located at Position 4 of micro-central electrics in driver's left-hand footwell.

1. Ensure battery is fully charged.
2. Remove driver's side storage compartment.
3. Connect scan tool No. VAG 1551, or equivalent, to DLC.
4. Turn ignition On.
5. Select control module for engine electronics using "address word" 01.
6. Initiate Output Diagnostic Test Mode and activate EVAP canister purge regulator valve.
7. Ensure fuel pump relay triggers and fuel pump operates.
8. If relay does not trigger, proceed as follows:
   a. Turn ignition Off.
   b. Connect test box tool No. VAG 1598/31, or equivalent, to ECM wiring harness. **Do not connect to ECM itself.**
   c. Inspect relay activation.
   d. Connect test box sockets 2 and 65 to each other using wire from connector test tool kit No. VAG 1594, or equivalent.
   e. Turn ignition On.
   f. If relay triggers, replace ECM.
   g. If relay does not trigger, turn ignition Off.
   h. Connect a suitable voltmeter to relay socket terminal 19 and ground.
   i. Turn ignition On and measure voltage, which should be battery voltage.
   j. If voltage does not meet specifications, inspect for and repair wiring fault conditions.
   k. If voltage is as specified, turn ignition Off.
   l. Inspect for open circuit or short between fuel pump relay connector terminal 16 and test box socket 65. Repair as required.
   m. If wiring connections are satisfactory, replace fuel pump relay.
9. If fuel pump does not operate, diagnose voltage supply for fuel pump and components through relay as follows:
   a. Remove fuses S28, S32, S34 and S43 from fuse holder, **Fig. 60.**
   b. Initiate Output Diagnostic Test Mode and activate EVAP canister purge regulator valve.
   c. Connect voltmeter to ground and probe one terminal of following fuses: S28, S32, S34 and S43. There should be battery voltage at each location.
   d. If voltages do not meet specifications, repeat test at another fuse socket terminal. There should be battery voltage at each location.
   e. If voltages do not meet specifications, inspect for and repair wiring fault conditions.
   f. If voltages are as specified and wiring connections are satisfactory, replace fuel pump relay.

FUEL PRESSURE

1. Ensure fuel pump relay operation is satisfactory, fuel filter is in perfect condition and battery is fully charged.
2. **On A4 and S4 models,** proceed as follows:
   a. Connect fuel pressure tester tool

Code	Description
P1432	Secondary AIR Valve Open
P1433	Secondary AIR Relay Open
P1434	Secondary AIR Pump Relay Circuit Short To Voltage
P1435	Secondary AIR Pump Relay Circuit Short To Ground
P1467	EVAP Canister Purge Solenoid Valve Short To Voltage
P1468	EVAP Canister Purge Solenoid Valve Short To Ground
P1469	EVAP Canister Purge Solenoid Valve Open Circuit
P1471	EVAP Emission Control LDP Circuit Short To Voltage
P1472	EVAP Emission Control LDP Circuit Short To Ground
P1473	EVAP Emission Control LDP Circuit Open
P1475	EVAP Emission Control LDP Circuit Fault/Signal Circuit Open
P1476	EVAP Emission Control LDP Circuit Fault/Insufficient Vacuum
P1477	EVAP Emission Control LDP Circuit Fault
P1478	EVAP Emission Control LDP Circuit Clamped Tube
P1500	Fuel Pump Relay Electrical Fault
P1501	Fuel Pump Relay Short To Ground
P1502	Fuel Pump Relay Short To Voltage
P1505	Closed Throttle Position Switch Does Not Close/Open Circuit
P1506	Closed Throttle Position Switch Does Not Open/Short To Ground
P1523	Crash Signal Implausible
P1539	Clutch Vacuum Vent Valve Switch Improper Signal
P1542	Throttle Actuation Potentiometer Range/Performance
P1543	Throttle Actuation Potentiometer Signal Too Low
P1544	Throttle Actuation Potentiometer Signal Too High
P1545	Throttle Position Control Fault
P1546	Boost Pressure Control Valve Short To Voltage
P1547	Boost Pressure Control Valve Short To Ground
P1548	Boost Pressure Control Valve Open
P1555	Charge Pressure upper Limit Exceeded
P1556	Charge Pressure Negative Deviation
P1557	Charge Pressure Positive Deviation
P1558	Throttle Actuator Electrical Fault
P1559	Idle Speed Control Throttle Position Adaptation Fault

Fig. 2 Diagnostic trouble code interpretation (Part 5 of 6)

Code	Description
P1560	Maximum Engine Speed Exceeded
P1564	Idle Speed Control Throttle Position Low Voltage During Adaptation
P1564	Idle Speed Control Throttle Position Lower Impact Not Attained
P1565	Idle Speed Control Throttle Position Lower Limit Not Attained
P1568	Idle Speed Control Throttle Position Mechanical Malfunction
P1569	Cruise Control Switch Improper Signal
P1570	Control Module Locked
P1579	Idle Speed Control Throttle Position Adaptation Not Started
P1602	Power Supply Terminal 30 Low Voltage
P1603	Internal Control Module Malfunction
P1604	Internal Control Module Driver Error
P1606	Rough Road Spec Engine Torque ABS-ECU Electrical Fault
P1609	Crash Shutdown Activated
P1611	MIL Call-Up/Transmission Control Module Short To Ground
P1612	ECM Improper Coding
P1613	MIL Call-Up Circuit/Transmission Control Module Short To Ground
P1624	MIL Request Sign Active
P1630	APP Sensor 1 Signal Too Low
P1631	APP Sensor 1 Signal Too High
P1633	APP Sensor 2 Signal Too Low
P1634	APP Sensor 2 Signal Too High
P1639	APP Sensor 1 & 2 Range/Performance
P1640	Internal Control Module EEPROM Error
P1645	Data Bus Powertrain Missing Message From AWD Control
P1648	Data Bus Powertrain Malfunction
P1649	Data Bus Powertrain Missing Message From ABS Control Module
P1676	Drive By Wire MIL Circuit Electrical Malfunction
P1677	Drive By Wire MIL Circuit Short To Voltage
P1681	Control Unit Programming Not Finished
P1690	MIL Malfunction
P1693	MIL Short To Voltage
P1853	CAN-Bus Implausible Message From Brake Control

Fig. 2 Diagnostic trouble code interpretation (Part 6 of 6)

No. VAG 1318, or equivalent, between fuel supply line and fuel manifold.

b. Ensure tester tool lever is in open position.
c. Start engine and let run at idle.
d. Observe fuel pressure, which should be 50 psi.
e. Disconnect vacuum hose from fuel pressure regulator.
f. Fuel pressure should increase to 58 psi.
g. Connect vacuum hose and turn engine off.

3. **On TT models,** proceed as follows:
   a. Disconnect fuel supply hose with white marking from supply line.
   b. Connect fuel pressure tester tool No. VAG 1318 with adapter Nos. VAG 1318/7 and VAG 1318/17, or equivalent, at supply line, **Fig. 61.**
   c. Ensure tester tool lever is in open position.
   d. Start engine and let run at idle.
   e. Observe fuel pressure, which should be 36 psi.
   f. Disconnect vacuum hose from fuel pressure regulator.
   g. Fuel pressure should increase to 44 psi.
   h. Connect vacuum hose and turn engine off.
4. **On all models,** close tester tool lever and inspect for residual pressure by monitoring decrease in pressure over the next 10 minutes.
5. **On A4 and S4 models,** pressure should read at least 36 psi after 10 minutes.
6. **On TT models,** pressure should read at least 22 psi after 10 minutes.
7. **On all models,** if residual pressure drops below specifications, proceed as follows:
   a. Start engine and allow pressure to build.
   b. After pressure has risen, turn engine off.
   c. Close fuel pressure tester valve and monitor pressure as outlined.
   d. If pressure still drops below specifications, inspect fuel pump check valve and system for leaks.
   e. If pressure no longer drops below specifications, inspect fuel pressure tester after shutoff valve, fuel pressure regulator and fuel injectors.

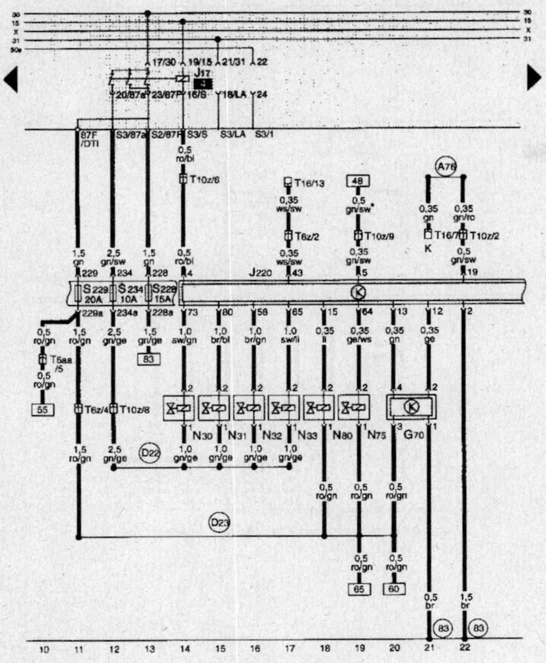

G70 – Mass Air Flow (MAF) Sensor
J17 – Fuel Pump (FP) Relay
J220 – Motronic Engine Control Module (ECM)
N30 – Injector, Cyl. 1
N31 – Injector, Cyl. 2
N32 – Injector, Cyl. 3
N33 – Injector, Cyl. 4
N75 – Wastegate Bypass Regulator Valve
N80 – Evaporative Emission (EVAP) Canister Purge Regulator Valve
T6z – Wire Connector, 6 Point, red, connector station, electronics box in plenum chamber
T6aa – Wire Connector, 6 Point, brown, connector station right, A–pillar
T10z – Wire Connector, 10 Point, yellow, connector station, electronics box in plenum chamber
T16 – Wire Connector, 16 Point, center console, rear (diagnostic connection)
(83) – Ground connection –1–, in right front wiring harness
(A76) – Connector (K–diagnosis wire), in instrument planel wiring harness
(D22) – Connector (over fuse 234), in wiring harness front, right
(D23) – Connector (over fuse 229), in wiring harness front, right
* – Automatic Transmission Only

AD1029800094010X

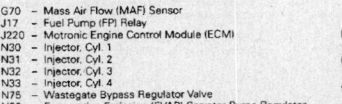

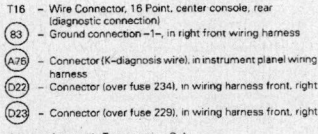

Fig. 3 MFI system wiring diagram (Part 1 of 6). 1998–99 A4 & S4

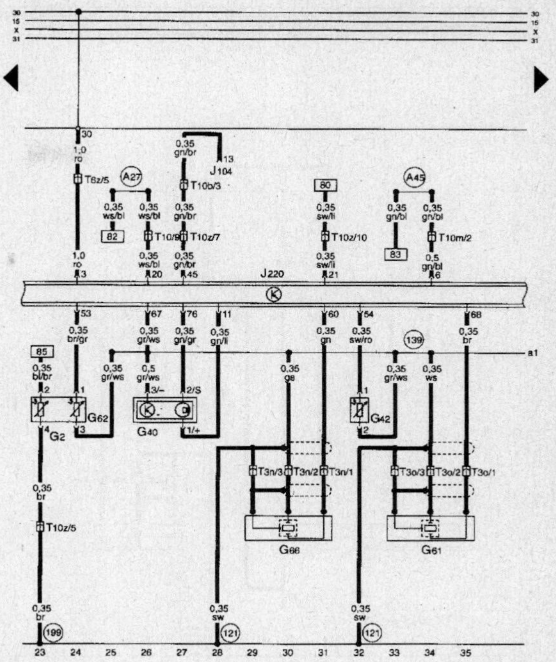

G2 – Engine Coolant Temperature (ECT) Sensor
G40 – Camshaft Position (CMP) Sensor
G42 – Intake Air Temperature (IAT) Sensor
G61 – Knock Sensor (KS) 1
G62 – Engine Coolant Temperature (ECT) Sensor
G66 – Knock Sensor (KS) 2
J104 – ABS Control Module (w/EDL)
J220 – Motronic Engine Control Module (ECM)
T3n – Wire Connector, 3 Point, blue, in engine compartment, left
T3o – Wire Connector, 3 Point,blue, in engine compartment, right
T6z – Wire Connector, 6 Point, red, connector station, electronics box in plenum chamber
T10 – Wire Connector, 10 Point brown, connector station, electronics box in plenum chamber
T10b – Wire Connector, 10 Point, orange, connector station left, A–pillar
T10m – Wire Connector, 10 Point, black, connector station, electronics box in plenum chamber
T10z – Wire Connector, 10 Point, yellow, connector station, electronics box in plenum chamber
(121) – Ground connection –2–, in right front wiring harness
(139) – Ground connection (sensor ground), in Motronic Multi-port Fuel Injection (MFI) wiring harness
(199) – Ground connection –3–, in right front wiring harness
(A27) – Wire connection (vihicle speed signal), in instrument panel wiring harness
(A45) – Wire connection (RPM–signal), in instrument panel wiring harness

AD1029800094020X

Fig. 3 MFI system wiring diagram (Part 2 of 6). 1998–99 A4 & S4

MASS AIR FLOW (MAF) SENSOR

A4 & S4

Functional Inspection

Before performing MAF sensor inspection, ensure all electrical accessories are off and fuse for MAF circuit is satisfactory. Ensure cooling fan does not turn on during inspection.

1. Connect scan tool No. VAG 1551/1552, or equivalent, and press buttons 0 and 1 to insert "Engine Electronics" address word 01. Ensure engine is running at idle.
2. Press buttons 0 and 8 to select "Read Measuring Value Block" function 08, then press "Q" to confirm input.
3. Press buttons 0, 0 and 2 to input Display Group number 2, then press "Q" to confirm input.
4. Compare scan tool display with **Fig. 62.**
5. If display data is satisfactory, proceed as follows:
   a. Press right arrow button to advance program sequence.
   b. Press buttons 0 and 6 to select "End Output" function 06, then press "Q" to confirm input.
   c. Turn ignition Off.
6. If display data is not as specified in **Fig. 62,** refer to **Fig. 63** for possible fault causes.

Voltage Inspection

1. Disconnect MAF sensor.
2. Turn ignition On.
3. Measure voltage between pins 1 and 3 of MAF connector using a suitable voltmeter, **Fig. 64.**
4. Voltage should read 9–14.5 volts.
5. If no voltage is present service wiring as required.
6. If voltage is present, inspect wiring as outlined under "Wiring Inspection."

Wiring Inspection

1. Ensure ignition is turned Off.
2. Connect test box tool No. VAG 1598/22, or equivalent to ECM harness connector.
3. Inspect wiring for open using a suitable ohmmeter between MAF connector terminal 2 and test box pin 12, then MAF terminal 4 and test box pin 13. Resistance should be no more than 1.5 ohms.
4. If resistance is greater than 1.5 ohms, service open circuit as required.
5. If resistance is 1.5 ohms or lower inspect MAF connector terminal 4 and test box pin 12 for short circuit. Ohmmeter should read open.
6. Inspect connector terminal 2 and 4 to vehicle ground using a suitable voltmeter, which should read 0 volts.
7. If wiring is satisfactory, replace MAF sensor.

TT

Functional Inspection

1. Ensure all electrical accessories are off and fuse for MAF circuit is satisfactory.
2. Ensure cooling fan does not turn on during inspection.
3. Connect scan tool No. VAG 1551, or equivalent, to DLC.
4. Start and idle engine, then select control module for engine electronics using "Address Word 01."
5. Press buttons 0 and 4 to select Basic Setting, then press Q button to confirm input.
6. Press buttons 0, 0 and 2 to select "Display Group Number 002," then press Q button to confirm input.
7. Compare scan tool display with **Fig. 65.**
8. If display data is satisfactory, proceed as follows:
   a. Press right arrow button to advance

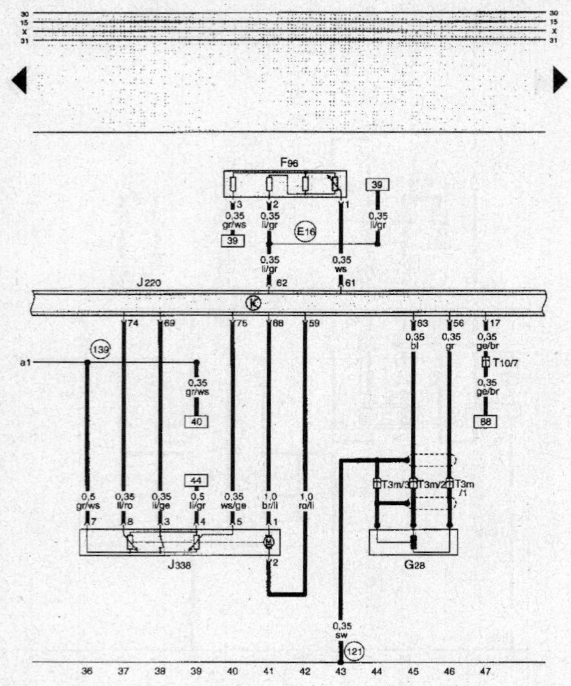

F96 – Barometric Pressure (BARO) Sensor
G28 – Engine Speed (RPM) Sensor
J220 – Motronic Engine Control Module (ECM)
J338 – Throttle Valve Control Module
T3m – Wire Connector, 3 Point, grey, in engine compartment, left
T10 – Wire Connector, 10 Point brown, connector station, electronics box in plenum chamber
(121) – Ground connection –2–, in right front wiring harness
(139) – Ground connection (sensor ground), in Motronic Multiport Fuel Injection (MFI) wiring harness
(E16) – Plus connection (5 Volts), in Motronic Multiport Fuel Injection (MFI) wiring harness

AD1029800094030X

Fig. 3 MFI system wiring diagram (Part 3 of 6). 1998–99 A4 & S4

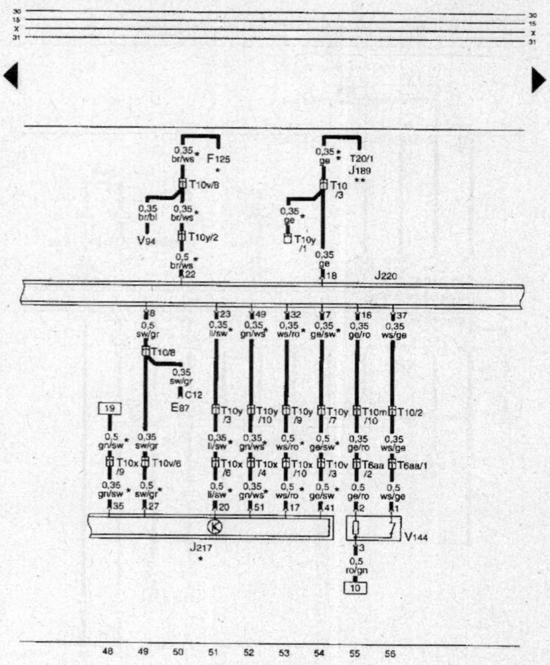

E87 – A/C Control Head
F125 – Multi–Function Transmission Range (TR) Switch
J189 – Auto Check System
J217 – Transmission Control Module (TCM)
J220 – Motronic Engine Control Module (ECM)
T6aa – Wire Connector, 6 Point, brown, connector station right, A–pillar
T10 – Wire Connector, 10 Point, brown, connector station, electronics box in plenum chamber
T10m – Wire Connector, 10 Point, black, connector station, electronics box in plenum chamber
T10v – Wire Connector, 10 Point, brown, connector station right, A–pillar
T10x – Wire Connector, 10 Point, blue, connector station right, A–pillar
T10y – Wire Connector, 10 Point, blue, connector station, electronics box in plenum chamber
T20 – Wire Connector, 20 Point, black, on instrument cluster
V144 – Diagnosis pump for fuel system

* – Automatic Transmission Only
** – ACS and Trip Computer Only

AD1029800094040X

Fig. 3 MFI system wiring diagram (Part 4 of 6). 1998–99 A4 & S4

program sequence.

b. Press buttons 0 and 6 to select "End Output" function 06, then press "Q" to confirm input.
c. Turn ignition Off.

9. If display is not as specified in **Fig. 65,** refer to **Fig. 66** for possible fault causes.

Voltage Inspection

1. Disconnect MAF sensor electrical connector.
2. Connect a suitable voltmeter between connector terminal 2, **Fig. 67,** and ground.
3. Crank engine and observe voltage, which should be battery voltage.
4. If voltage does not meet specifications, inspect wiring connection from terminal 2 to fuel pump relay via fuse for open circuit and short circuit to ground. Repair as required.
5. If voltage is as specified, connect voltmeter to terminals 2 and 3, then crank engine observe voltage, which should be battery voltage.
6. If voltage is as specified, connect voltmeter to terminals 3 and 4, then turn ignition On and observe voltage, which should be approximately five volts.
7. If voltages do not meet specifications, proceed to "Wiring Inspection."

Wiring Inspection

1. Turn ignition Off.
2. Connect test box tool No. VAG 1598/31, or equivalent, to ECM wiring harness. **Do not connect to ECM itself.**
3. Inspect for opens or shorts as follows:
   a. Between MAF sensor electrical connector terminal 3 and test box socket 27.
   b. Terminal 4 and socket 53.
   c. Terminal 5 and socket 29.
   d. Repair any fault conditions as required.
4. If wiring connections are satisfactory, replace MAF sensor.

ENGINE COOLANT TEMPERATURE (ECT) SENSOR

A4 & S4

Functional Inspection

1. Ensure engine is cold.
2. Connect scan tool No. VAG 1551/1552, or equivalent, then press buttons 0 and 1 to insert "Engine Electronics" address word 01. Engine should be running and at idle.
3. Press buttons 0 and 8 to select "Read Measuring Value Block" function 08, then press "Q" to confirm input.
4. Press buttons 0, 0 and 1 to input Display Group 1, then press "Q" to confirm input.
5. Compare scan tool display with ECT display data in **Fig. 68.**
6. If temperature does not increase evenly, replace ECT sensor.
7. If temperature increases evenly and fault is still present, perform ECT wiring inspection.
8. Press right arrow button to advance program sequence.
9. Press buttons 0 and 6 to select "End Output" function 06, the press "Q" to confirm input.
10. Turn ignition Off.

Wiring Inspection

1. Connect test box tool No. 1598/22, or equivalent to ECM harness connector.
2. Disconnect ECT sensor. Refer to **Fig. 69** for ECT connector pin identification.
3. Inspect the following pins for open circuit using a suitable ohmmeter: connector terminal 1 to test box pin 53; connector terminal 3 to test box pin 67. Resistance should read 1.5 ohms or less. Service wiring as required.
4. Inspect the following pins for short using a suitable ohmmeter:

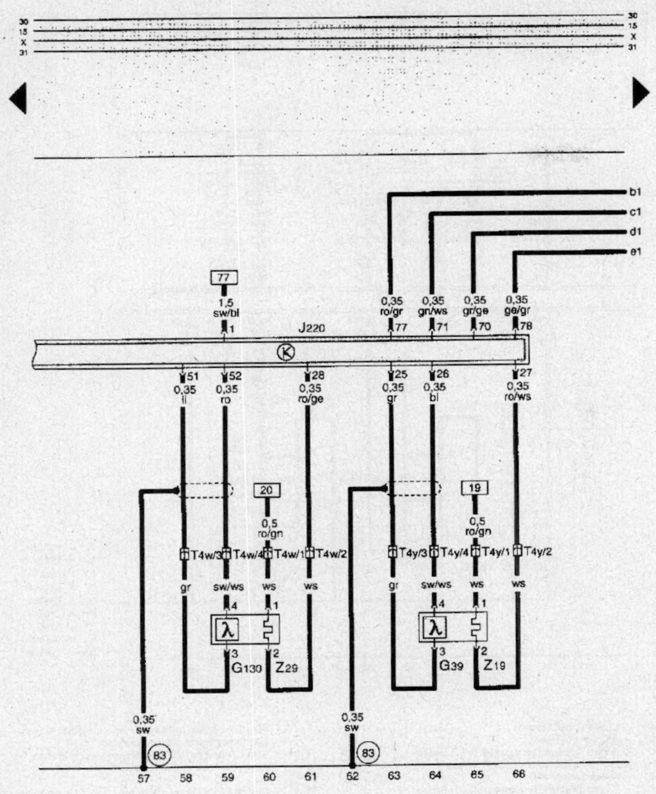

G39 – Heated Oxygen (HO2S) Sensor
G130 – Oxygen Sensor (OS2) Behind Three Way Catalytic Converter (TWC)
J220 – Motronic Engine Control Module (ECM)
T4w – Wire Connector, 4 Point, green, in engine compartment, right
T4y – Wire Connector, 4 Point, black, in engine compartment, right
Z19 – Oxygen Sensor (O2S) I Heater
Z29 – Heater for Lambda-probe 1
(83) – Ground connection -1-, in right front wiring harness

AD1029800094050X

Fig. 3 MFI system wiring diagram (Part 5 of 6). 1998–99 A4 & S4

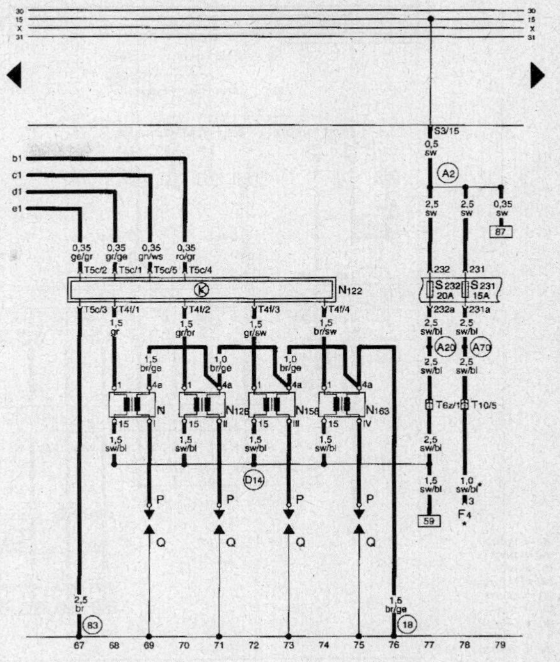

F4 – Back-Up Light Swtich
N – Ignition Coil
N122 – Power Output Stage
N128 – Ignition Coil 2
N158 – Ignition Coil 3
N163 – Ignition Coil 4
P – Spark Plug Connector
Q – Spark Plugs
T4f – Wire Connector, 4 Point, black, on Power Output Stage
T5c – Wire Connector, 5 Point, black, on Power Output Stage
T6z – Wire Connector, 6 Point, red, connector station, electronics box in plenum chamber
T10 – Wire Connector, 10 Point, brown, connector station, electronics box in plenum chamber
(18) – Ground connection, on engine block
(83) – Ground connection -1-, in right front wiring harness

(A2) – Plus connection (15), in instrument panel wiring harness
(A20) – Wire connection (15a), in instrument panel wiring harness
(A70) – Connector (15a, fuse 231), in instrument panel wiring harness
(D14) – Wire connection (ignition coil – control module), in right front wiring harness
* – Manual Transmission Only

AD1029800094060X

Fig. 3 MFI system wiring diagram (Part 6 of 6). 1998–99 A4 & S4

a. Connector terminal 1 to ground.
b. Connector terminal 1 to test box pin 67.
c. Connector terminal 1 to terminal 3.
d. Connector terminal 3 to ground.

5. If ohmmeter does not give open circuit reading, service wiring as required.
6. If wiring is satisfactory, measure resistance of ECT and replace as required.

TT

Functional Inspection

1. Ensure engine is cold.
2. Connect scan tool No. VAG 1551, or equivalent, to DLC.
3. Select control module for engine electronics using "Address Word 01."
4. Press buttons 0 and 8 for "Read Measuring Value Block," then press Q button to confirm input.
5. Press buttons 0, 0 and 4 for "Display Group Number 04," then confirm with Q button.
6. Start and idle engine.
7. Observe display in Display Field 3, **Fig. 70. Do not confuse coolant temperature sensor which transmits its signal to the ECM with coolant temperature sensor that sends its signal to the A/C.**
8. If temperature does not increase evenly, disconnect coolant temperature sensor electrical connector.
9. **On models equipped with square headed sensor,** connect a suitable ohmmeter between sensor terminals 1 and 3, **Fig. 71.**
10. **On models equipped with oval headed sensor,** connect a suitable ohmmeter between sensor terminals 3 and 4, **Fig. 72.**
11. **On all models,** observe resistance, which should meet specifications listed in "Sensor & Fuel Injector Specifications."
12. Replace coolant temperature sensor if resistances do not meet specifications.

Wiring Inspection

1. Turn ignition Off.
2. Connect test box tool No. VAG 1598/31, or equivalent, to ECM wiring harness. **Do not connect to ECM itself.**
3. **On models equipped with square headed sensor,** inspect for shorts or grounds between coolant temperature sensor terminal 1 and test box socket 108, then at terminal 3 and socket 93. Repair as required.
4. **On models equipped with oval headed sensor,** inspect for shorts or grounds between coolant temperature sensor terminal 3 and test box socket 108, then at terminal 4 and socket 93. Repair as required.
5. **On all models,** inspect wiring for shorts to each other and repair as required.
6. If wiring is satisfactory, replace ECM.

CRANKSHAFT POSITION (CKP) SENSOR

A4 & S4

Before performing the following diagnostic procedures, ensure sensor attaching bolts are tight and that no metal shavings are present on sensor or sensor wheel.

1. Disconnect CKP sensor. Refer to **Fig. 73** for CKP harness terminal identification.
2. Connect test box tool No. VAG 1598/22, or equivalent to ECM harness connector.

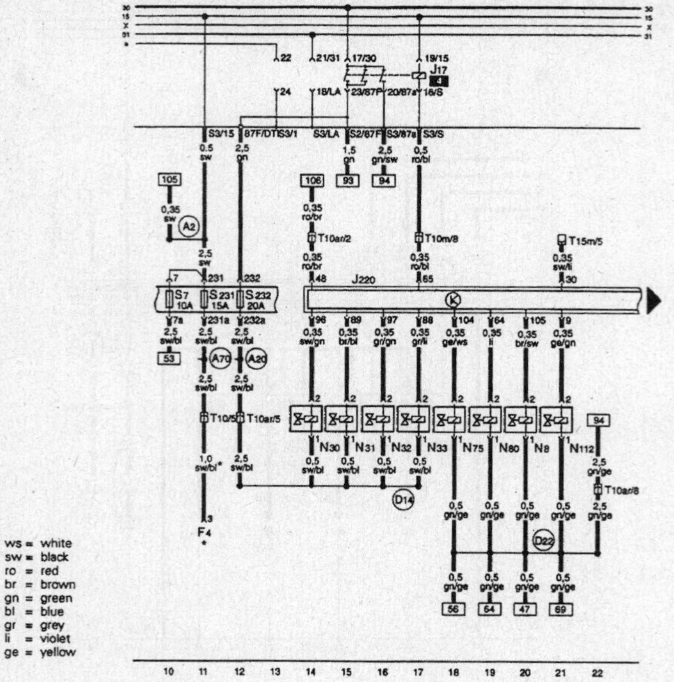

F4 – Back-Up Light Switch
J17 – Fuel Pump (FP) Relay
J220 – Motronic Engine Control Module (ECM)
N8 – Central Idle, Idle Air Control (IAC) Cut-Off Valve
N30 – Injector, Cyl. 1
N31 – Injector, Cyl. 2
N32 – Injector, Cyl. 3
N33 – Injector, Cyl. 4
N80 – Evaporative Emission (EVAP) Canister Purge Regulator Valve
N112 – Secondary Air Injection (AIR) Solenoid Valve
S7 – Fuse in fuse holder
S231 – Fuse in fuse holder
S232 – Fuse in fuse holder
T10 – Wire Connector, 10 Point brown, connector station, electronics box in plenum chamber
T10m – Wire Connector, 10 Point, black, connector station, electronics box in plenum chamber
T10ar – Wire Connector, 10 Point, orange, connector station, electronics box in plenum chamber
T15m – Wire Connector, 15 Point, red, connector station, electronics box in plenum chamber
(A2) – Plus connection (15), in instrument panel wiring harness
(A20) – Wire connection (15a), in instrument panel wiring harness
(A70) – Connector (15a, fuse 231), in instrument panel wiring harness
(D14) – Wire connection (ignition coil – control module), in right front wiring harness
(D22) – Connector (over fuse 234), in wiring harness front, right
* – Manual Transmission Only

AD1020000184010X

Fig. 4 MFI system wiring diagram (Part 1 of 7). 2000 A4 & S4

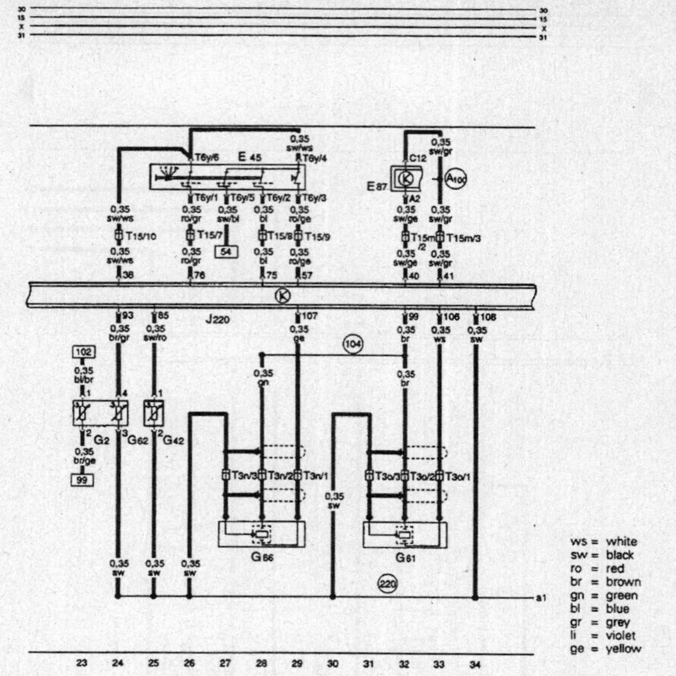

E45 – Cruise Control Switch
E87 – A/C Control Head
G2 – Engine Coolant Temperature (ECT) Sensor
G42 – Intake Air Temperature (IAT) Sensor
G61 – Knock Sensor (KS) 1
G62 – Engine Coolant Temperature (ECT) Sensor
G66 – Knock Sensor (KS) 2
J220 – Motronic Engine Control Module (ECM)
T3n – Wire Connector, 3 Point, blue, in engine compartment, left
T3o – Wire Connector, 3 Point, green, in engine compartment, left
T6y – Wire Connector, 6 Point, black, near steering column
T15 – Wire Connector, 15 Point, white, connector station, electronics box in plenum chamber
T15m – Wire Connector, 15 Point, red, connector station, electronics box in plenum chamber
(104) – Ground connection, in right front wiring harness (sensor grounds)
(220) – Ground connection (sensor ground), in engine compartment wiring harness
(A100) – Connector –2– (87), in instrument planel wiring harness

AD1020000184020X

Fig. 4 MFI system wiring diagram (Part 2 of 7). 2000 A4 & S4

3. Inspect the following pin for open circuit using a suitable ohmmeter:
   a. Connector terminal 1 to test box pin 56.
   b. Connector terminal 2 to test box pin 63.
   c. Connector terminal 3 to test box pin 2.
4. If resistance is greater than 1.5 ohms, service open circuit as required.
5. If resistance is as specified, inspect the following pins for short circuit using a suitable ohmmeter:
   a. Connector terminal 1 to test box pin 2.
   b. Connector terminal 1 to test box pin 63.
   c. Connector terminal 2 to test box pin 56.
6. If ohmmeter does not give open reading, service short circuit as required.
7. If ohmmeter does give open reading, replace crankshaft position sensor.

TT

On these models the CKP sensor is known as the Engine Speed (RPM) sensor. Refer to "RPM Sensor" for diagnosis and testing.

FUEL INJECTOR

1. Disconnect injector harness connector.
2. Measure fuel injector resistance.
3. Compare resistance with specifications listed in "Fuel Injector & Sensor Specifications."
4. If resistance is not within specifications, replace injector.
5. If wiring or connector repairs are required, refer to "Precautions."

ECM SIGNAL

1. Disconnect fuel injector electrical connectors.
2. Connect LED voltage tester tool No. VAG 1527BB, or equivalent between connector terminals using adapter cable tool No. VW 1594, or equivalent.
3. Crank engine and inspect for LED operation.
4. Repeat test for remaining cylinders.
5. If LED does not light, inspect wiring between fuel injector and ECM for open or short using a suitable volt/ohmmeter. Repair as required.

FRONT HEATED OXYGEN SENSOR

A4 & S4

Functional Inspection

1. Ensure engine temperature is at least 185°F.
2. Connect scan tool No. VAG 1552, or equivalent and press buttons 0 and 1 to insert "Engine Electronics" address word 01 with engine running at idle.
3. Press buttons 0 and 8 to select "Read Measuring Value Block" function 08, then press "Q" to confirm input.
4. Press buttons 0, 3 and 2 to input Display Group number 32, then press "Q" to confirm input.
5. Compare scan tool data with **Fig. 74.**
6. If display values in **Fig. 74** are as specified, refer to Display Group 33, **Fig. 75.** Press "C" button, then press 0, 3 and 3 to input Display Group 33. Press "Q" to confirm input.
7. If display values in **Fig. 74** are not as specified, refer to evaluation of Display Group 32, **Fig. 76.**
8. If display values in **Fig. 75,** Field 1 are not as specified, proceed as follows:

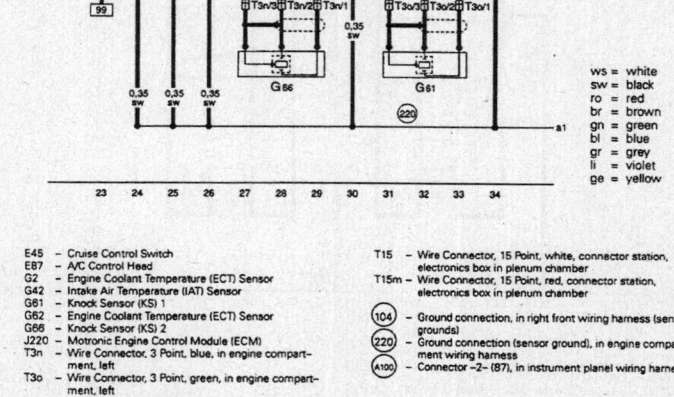

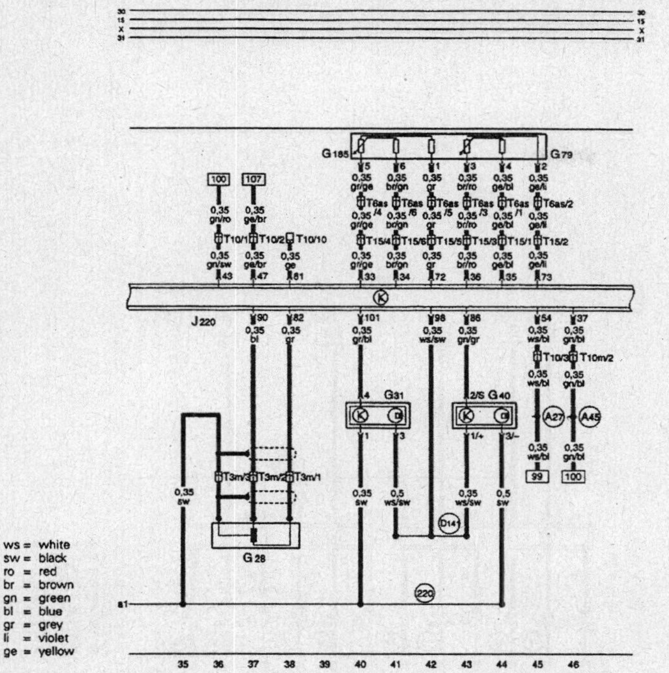

G28 – Engine Speed (RPM) Sensor
G31 – Charge Air Pressure Sensor
G40 – Camshaft Position (CMP) Sensor
G79 – Throttle Position (TP) Sensor
G185 – Sender –2– for accelerator pedal position
J220 – Motronic Engine Control Module (ECM)
T3m – Wire Connector, 3 Point, grey, in engine compartment, left
T6as – Wire Connector, 6 Point, black, in engine compartment, rear
T10 – Wire Connector, 10 Point brown, connector station, electronics box in plenum chamber
T10m – Wire Connector, 10 Point, black, connector station, electronics box in plenum chamber
T15 – Wire Connector, 15 Point, white, connector station, electronics box in plenum chamber

(220) – Ground connection (sensor ground), in engine compartment wiring harness
(A27) – Wire connection (vihicle speed signal), in instrument panel wiring harness
(A45) – Wire connection (RPM–signal), in instrument panel wiring harness
(D141) – Connector (5V), in wiring harness, engine pre–wiring

AD1020000184030X

Fig. 4 MFI system wiring diagram (Part 3 of 7). 2000 A4 & S4

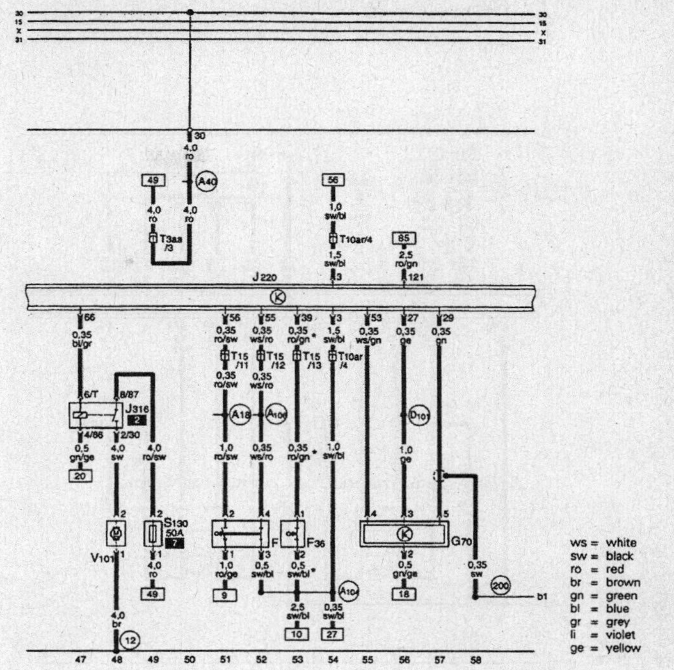

F – Brake Light Switch
F36 – Clutch Vacuum Vent Valve Switch
G70 – Mass Air Flow (MAF) Sensor
J220 – Motronic Engine Control Module (ECM)
J316 – Secondary Air Injection (AIR) Relay
S130 – Fuse for secondary air pump
T3aa – Wire Connector, 3 Point, white, connector station, electronics box in plenum chamber
T15 – Wire Connector, 15 Point, white, connector station, electronics box in plenum chamber
V101 – Secondary Air Injection (AIR) Pump Motor

(12) – Ground connection, in engine compartment, left
(200) – Ground connection (shielding), in engine compartment wiring harness
(A18) – Wire connection (54), in instrument panel wiring harness
(A40) – Wire connection (vihicle speed signal), in instrument panel wiring harness
(A104) – Plus connection –2– (15), in instrument penel wiring harness
(A106) – Connector –2– (86s), in instrument panel wiring harness
(D101) – Wire connection –1–, in engine compartment wiring harness
* – Manual transmission Only

AD1020000184040X

Fig. 4 MFI system wiring diagram (Part 4 of 7). 2000 A4 & S4

a. Road test vehicle to condition oxygen sensor and repeat test.
b. If display value in Field 1 of **Fig. 75** is still not within specifications, refer to “Front Heated Oxygen Sensor Heater Inspection.”
c. If display value in Field 1 of **Fig. 75** is within specifications, view oxygen sensor voltage in Field 2.
d. Press right arrow button to advance program.
e. Press “Q” to confirm input, then turn ignition Off.

9. If Display Group values in Field 2 of **Fig. 75** are not as specified, refer to evaluation of Display Group 33, **Fig. 77.**

Heater Inspection

1. Inspect oxygen sensor fuse and repair as required.
2. Ensure engine temperature is at least 185°F.
3. Connect scan tool No. VAG 1551/1552, or equivalent.
4. Press buttons 0 and 1 to insert “Engine Electronics” address word 01 with engine running at idle.
5. Press buttons 0 and 8 to select “Read Measuring Value Block” function 08, then press “Q” to confirm input.
6. Press buttons 0, 4 and 1 to input Display Group 41, then press “Q” to confirm input.
7. Compare scan tool display with oxygen sensor heater Display Group, **Fig. 78.**
8. If values are as specified, oxygen heater system is operating normally at this time. Proceed as follows to end test:
   a. Press right arrow button to advance program, then buttons 0 and 6 to select “End Output” function 06.
   b. Press “Q” to confirm input.
   c. Turn ignition Off.
9. If values in **Fig. 78** are not as specified, proceed as follows:
   a. Disconnect heated oxygen sensor.
   b. Connect a suitable ohmmeter between terminals 1 and 2 of oxygen sensor using connector test kit VW 1594, or equivalent.
10. If resistance is not with specifications, replace heated oxygen sensor.
11. If resistance is within specifications, proceed as follows:
    a. Connect a suitable voltmeter to oxygen sensor connector terminals 1 and 2 using connector test kit tool No. 1594, or equivalent.
    b. Measure voltage while monitoring scan tool Display Group 41, Field 2. If Field 2 display is “Htg.bC.ON” voltage should read 11–14.5 volts. If display switches between “Htg.bC.ON” and “Htg.bC.OFF,” voltage should vary between 0–12 volts.
    c. If no voltage is present, connect a suitable voltmeter between oxygen sensor connector terminal 1 and ground using connector test kit tool No. 1594, or equivalent. Voltage should be 11–14.5 volts.
    d. If voltage is still not present, inspect and repair wiring between terminal 1 and relay panel, then repair as required.
    e. If voltage is present, connect a suitable voltmeter between oxygen sensor connector terminal 2 and battery positive using connector test kit tool No. 1594, or equivalent.
    f. Measure voltage while monitoring scan tool Display Group 41, Field 2. If Field 2 display is “Htg.bC.ON,” voltage should read 11–14.5 volts. If display switches between “Htg.bC.ON” and “Htg.bC.OFF,” voltage should vary between 0–12 volts.
    g. Turn ignition Off.
    h. If no voltage was present, connect

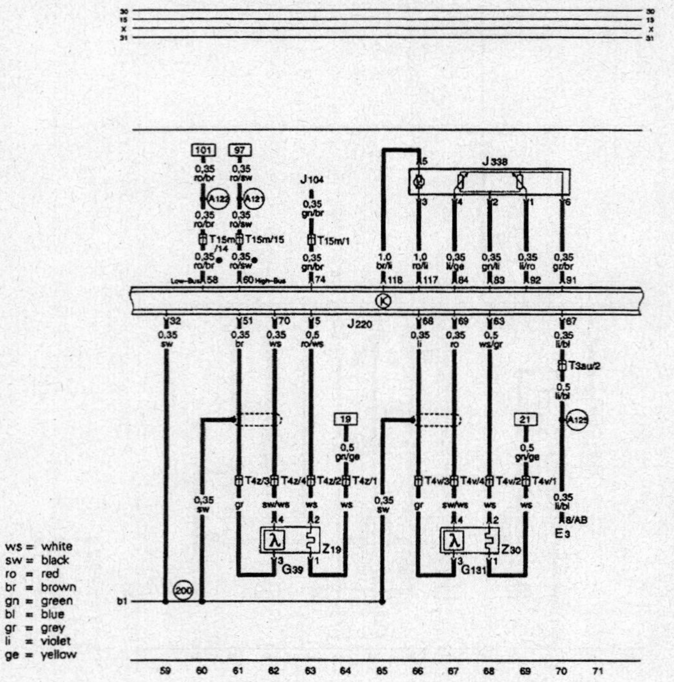

E3 – Emergency Flasher Switch
G39 – Heated Oxygen Sensor (HO2S)
G131 – Oxygen Sensor (O2S) 2 Behind Three Way Catalytic Converter
J104 – ABS Control Module (w/EDL)
J220 – Motronic Engine Control Module (ECM)
J338 – Throttle Valve Control Module
T3au – Wire Connector, 3 Point, red, connector station, electronics box in plenum chamber
T4v – Wire Connector, 4 Point, brown, in engine compartment, left
T4z – Wire Connector, 4 Point, black, in engine compartment, left
T15m – Wire Connector, 15 Point, red, connector station, electronics box in plenum chamber
Z19 – Oxygen Sensor (O2S) 1 Heater
Z30 – Heater for Lambda–probe 2

(200) – Ground connection (shielding), in engine compartment wiring harness
(A121) – Connection (high bus), in instrument planel wiring harness
(A122) – Connection (low bus), in instrument planel wiring harness
(A125) – Connection (crash signal), in instrument panel wiring harness
● – CAN–Bus

AD1020000184050X

Fig. 4 MFI system wiring diagram (Part 5 of 7). 2000 A4 & S4

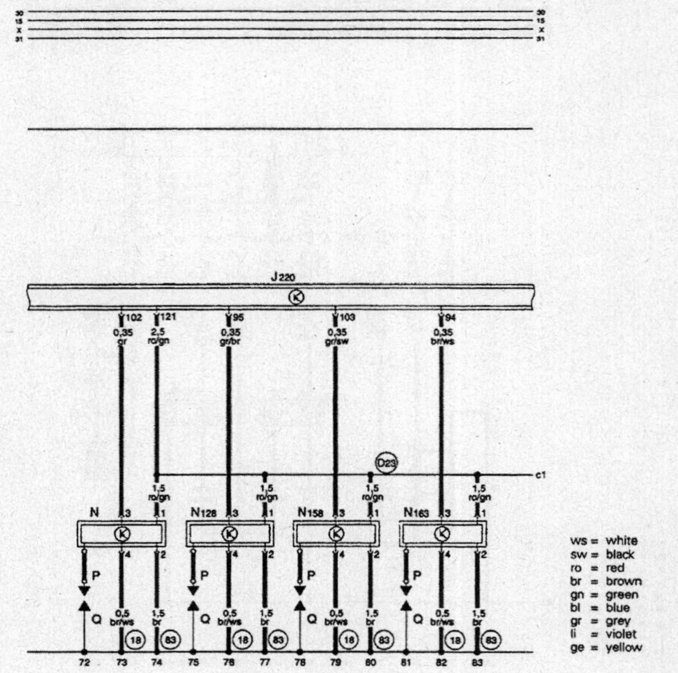

J220 – Motronic Engine Control Module (ECM)
N – Ignition Coil
N128 – Ignition Coil 2
N158 – Ignition Coil 3
N163 – Ignition Coil 4
P – Spark Plug Connector
Q – Spark Plugs

(18) – Ground connection, on engine block
(83) – Ground connection –1–, in right front wiring harness
(D23) – Connector (over fuse 229), in wiring harness front, right

AD1020000184060X

Fig. 4 MFI system wiring diagram (Part 6 of 7). 2000 A4 & S4

test box tool No. VAG 1598/22, or equivalent to ECM harness connector.

i. Measure resistance between oxygen sensor connector terminal 2 and test box pin 27 using a suitable ohmmeter. If resistance is 1.5 ohms or greater, repair open circuit as required.
j. If wiring inspection is satisfactory, replace ECM and generate new readiness code.

Reference Voltage Inspection

1. Disconnect oxygen sensor.
2. Connect a suitable voltmeter between harness connector terminals 3 and 4 using connector test kit tool No. 1594, or equivalent.
3. Start engine and monitor voltage.
4. Voltmeter should read .40–.50 volts.
5. Turn ignition Off.
6. If voltage is not as specified, refer to "Front Heated Oxygen Sensor Wiring Inspection."
7. If voltage is as specified, replace heated oxygen sensor.

Wiring Inspection

1. Connect test box tool No. VAG 1598/22, or equivalent to ECM harness connector.
2. Disconnect oxygen sensor connector.
3. Measure resistance between connector terminal 3 and test box pin 25 using a suitable ohmmeter, then connector terminal 4 and test box pin 26. If resistance is greater than 1.5 ohms, service open circuit as required.
4. If resistance is 1.5 ohms or less, inspect the following for short circuits:
   a. Connector terminal 4 to test box pin 25.
   b. Connector terminal 3 to test box pin 2.
   c. Connector terminal 4 to test box pin 2.
   d. If ohmmeter does not give open reading, service short circuit as required.
   e. If wiring inspection is satisfactory, replace ECM and generate new readiness code.

TT

Functional Inspection

1. Road test vehicle and bring to operating temperature.
2. Connect scan tool No. VAG 1551, or equivalent, to DLC.
3. Start and idle engine, then select control module for engine electronics using "Address Word 01."
4. Press buttons 0 and 4 to select Basic Setting, then press Q button to confirm input.
5. Press buttons 0, 3 and 0 to select "Display Group Number 030," then press Q button to confirm input.
6. Display oxygen sensor status in Display Field 1, **Fig. 79.**
7. Press buttons 0, 3 and 2 to select "Display Group Number 032," then press Q button to confirm input.
8. Display oxygen sensor status in Display Fields 1 and 2, **Fig. 80.**
9. Press buttons 0, 3 and 3 to select "Display Field Number 033," then press Q button to confirm input.
10. Inspect oxygen sensor control in Display Fields 1 and 2, **Fig. 81.**
11. If specified value in Display Field 1 is not obtained or if value does not fluctuate at least 2%, road test vehicle to clear possible residue from oxygen sensor and repeat test.

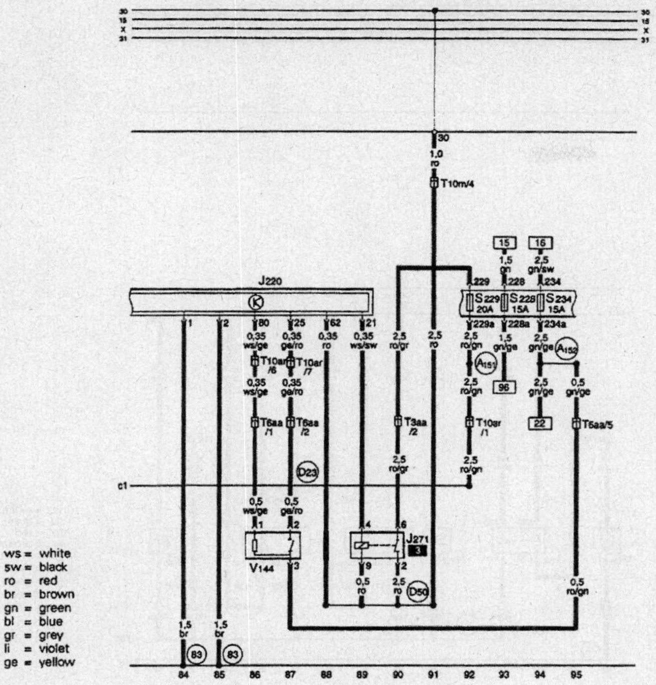

J220 – Motronic Engine Control Module (ECM)
J271 – Motronic Engine Control Module (ECM) Power Supply Relay
S228 – Fuse in fuse holder
S229 – Fuse in fuse holder
S234 – Fuse in fuse holder
T3aa – Wire Connector, 3 Point, white, connector station, electronics box in plenum chamber
T6aa – Wire Connector, 6 Point, brown, connector station right, A-pillar
T10m – Wire Connector, 10 Point, black, connector station, electronics box in plenum chamber
T10ar – Wire Connector, 10 Point, orange, connector station, electronics box in plenum chamber
V144 – Leak Detection Pump (LDP)

(83) – Ground connection -1-, in right front wiring harness
(A151) – Connector -4- (87), in instrument planel wiring harness
(A152) – Connector -5- (87), in instrument planel wiring harness
(D23) – Connector (over fuse 229), in wiring harness front, right
(D50) – Plus connection (30), in engine compartment wiring harness

AD1020000184070X

Fig. 4 MFI system wiring diagram (Part 7 of 7). 2000 A4 & S4

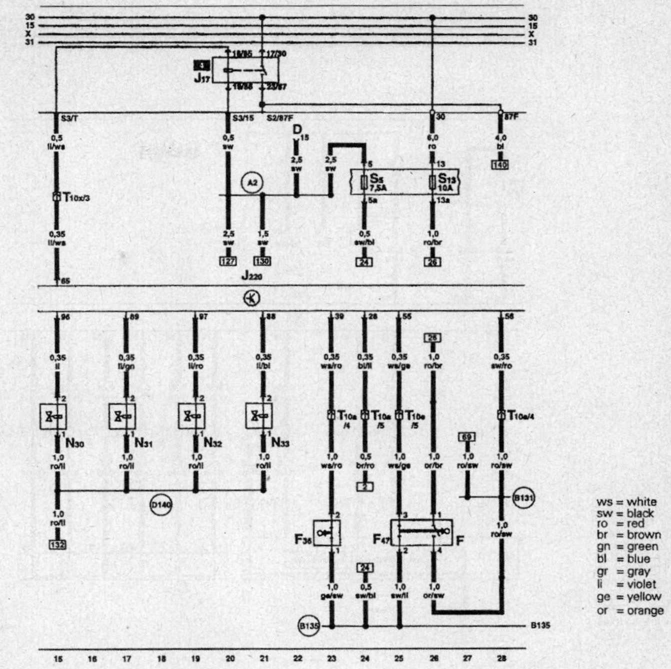

D – Ignition/Starter Switch
F – Brake Light Switch
F36 – Clutch Vacuum Vent Valve Switch
F47 – Vacuum Vent Valve, Brake
J17 – Fuel Pump (FP) Relay
J220 – Motronic Engine Control Module (ECM)
N30 – Cylinder 1 Fuel Injector
N31 – Cylinder 2 Fuel Injector
N32 – Cylinder 3 Fuel Injector
N33 – Cylinder 4 Fuel Injector
S5 – Fuse
S13 – Fuse
T10a – Connector 10 pin, green, in E-box plenum chamber
T10e – Connector 10 pin, black, in E-box plenum chamber
T10x – Connector 10 pin, orange, in E-box plenum chamber

(A2) – Plus connection (15), in instrument panel wiring harness
(B131) – Connector (54), in wiring harness interior
(B135) – Connector (15a), in wiring harness interior
(D140) – Connector (injectors), in wiring harness, engine pre-wiring

AD1020000183010X

Fig. 5 MFI system wiring diagram (Part 1 of 8). TT w/AMU engine

12. If specified value in Display Field 1 is still not obtained or if value still does not fluctuate at least 2%, proceed to "Primary Voltage Inspection."

Primary Voltage Inspection

1. Disconnect front oxygen sensor 4-pin electrical connector.
2. Connect a suitable voltmeter between connector terminals 3 and 4, **Fig. 82.**
3. Turn ignition On, then measure voltage, which should be 0.400–0.500 volts.
4. If voltage meets specifications, replace front oxygen sensor.
5. If voltage does not meet specifications, proceed as follows:
   a. Turn ignition Off.
   b. Connect a suitable ohmmeter between front oxygen sensor electrical connector terminals 1 and 2, **Fig. 82.**
   c. Measure resistance, which should be as specified under "Sensor & Fuel Injector Specifications."
6. If resistance does not meet specifications, replace front oxygen sensor.
7. If resistance meets specifications, connect a suitable voltmeter between connector terminals 1 and 2, **Fig. 82.**
8. Start engine and observe voltage, which should be battery voltage, possibly fluctuating.
9. If there is no voltage, connect voltmeter between terminal 1 and ground, then crank engine and observe voltage, which should be battery voltage.
10. If voltage does not meet specifications, inspect wiring connection for open circuit from connector terminal 1 to fuel pump relay via fuse.
11. If voltage meets specifications, connect voltmeter between terminal 2 and battery positive terminal.
12. Start engine and observe voltage, which should be battery voltage, possibly fluctuating.
13. If there is no voltage, connect test box tool No. VAG 1598/31, or equivalent, to ECM wiring harness. **Do not connect to ECM itself.**
14. Inspect for an open circuit between connector terminal 2 and test box socket 5. Repair as required.
15. If wiring connection is satisfactory, replace ECM.

Aging Inspection

1. Road test vehicle and bring to operating temperature.
2. Connect scan tool No. VAG 1551, or equivalent, to DLC.
3. Start and idle engine, then select control module for engine electronics using "Address Word 01."
4. Press buttons 0 and 4 to select Basic Setting, then press Q button to confirm input.
5. Press buttons 0, 3 and 4 to select "Display Field Number 034," then press Q button to confirm input.
6. Set engine speed to 1800–2200 RPM using idle speed adjuster tool No. VAG 1788/10, or equivalent.
7. Continue test as soon as Display 4 indicates "Test ON." This might require a few minutes.
8. Display status in Display Fields 3 and 4, **Fig. 83.** Period duration is the time between two oxygen sensor rich–lean–rich voltage jumps and is a measurement of sensor aging condition. If specified time is exceeded, Display Field 4 will indicate "=B1 - S1 not OK."
9. If specified value in Display Fields 3 and 4 is not obtained, road test vehicle to clear possible residue from oxygen sensor and repeat test.
10. If specified value in Display Fields 3 and 4 is still not obtained, replace front oxygen sensor.

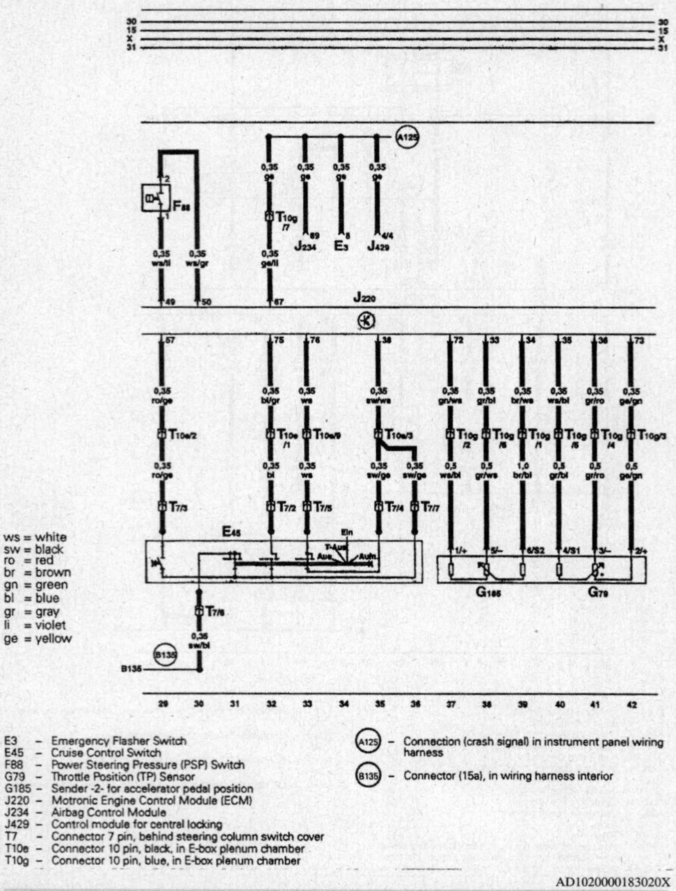

Fig. 5 MFI system wiring diagram (Part 2 of 8). TT w/AMU engine

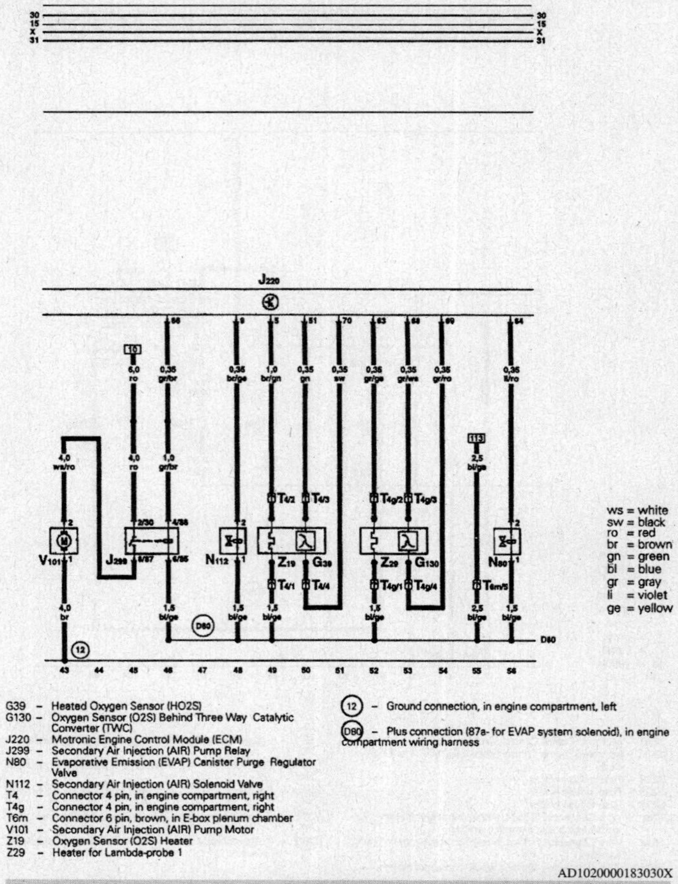

Fig. 5 MFI system wiring diagram (Part 3 of 8). TT w/AMU engine

REAR HEATED OXYGEN SENSOR

A4 & S4

Functional Inspection

1. Ensure engine temperature is at least 185°F.
2. Connect scan tool No. VAG 1551/ 1552, or equivalent, then press buttons 0 and 1 to insert engine electronics address word 01 with engine running at idle.
3. Press buttons 0 and 8 to select "Read Measuring Value Block" function 08, then press "Q" to confirm input.
4. Press buttons 0, 3 and 6 to input Display Group 36, then press "Q" to confirm input.
5. Compare scan tool display to display values in **Fig. 84.**
6. If displayed values are not as specified, proceed as follows:
   a. Road test vehicle to condition oxygen sensor and test again.
   b. If Display Group values are still not as specified, refer to "Rear Heated Oxygen Sensor Heater Inspection."
   c. Briefly accelerate engine over 3000 RPM.
7. If displayed values are as specified, refer to **Fig. 85** for Display Group 36 evaluation.

Heater Inspection

1. Inspect oxygen sensor heater fuse and repair as required.
2. Ensure engine temperature is at least 185°F.
3. Connect scan tool No. VAG 1552, or equivalent, then press buttons 0 and 1 to insert "Engine Electronics" address word 01 with engine running at idle.
4. Press buttons 0 and 8 to select "Read Measuring Value Block" function 08 and press "Q" to confirm input.
5. Press buttons 0, 4 and 1 to input Display Group 41, then press "Q" to confirm input.
6. Compare scan tool display with rear oxygen sensor heater display in **Fig. 86.**
7. If scan tool display is as specified, proceed as follows:
   a. Press right arrow button to advance program.
   b. Press buttons 0 and 6 to select "End Output" function 06, then press "Q" to confirm input.
   c. Turn ignition Off.
8. If scan tool display is not as specified, proceed as follows:
   a. Disconnect oxygen sensor.
   b. Measure resistance between oxygen sensor terminals 1 and 2 using connector test kit tool No. VW 1594, or equivalent and a suitable ohmmeter.
9. If resistance is not within specifications, replace oxygen sensor.
10. If resistance is within specifications, proceed as follows:
    a. Measure voltage between oxygen sensor harness connector terminals 1 and 2 using a suitable voltmeter and connector test kit tool No. VW 1594, or equivalent.
    b. Monitor voltage and scan tool Display Group 41, Field 4.
    c. If scan tool display is "Htg.aC.ON," voltage should read 11–14.5 volts.
    d. If scan tool display switches between "Htg.aC.On" and "Htg.aC.OFF," voltage should vary between 0–12 volts.
11. If no voltage is present, proceed as follows:
    a. Connect a suitable voltmeter between oxygen sensor harness connector terminal 1 and ground using connector test kit tool No. VW 1594, or equivalent.
    b. Voltage should read 11–14.5 volts.
    c. If no voltage is present, inspect and repair wiring as required between terminal 1 and relay panel.

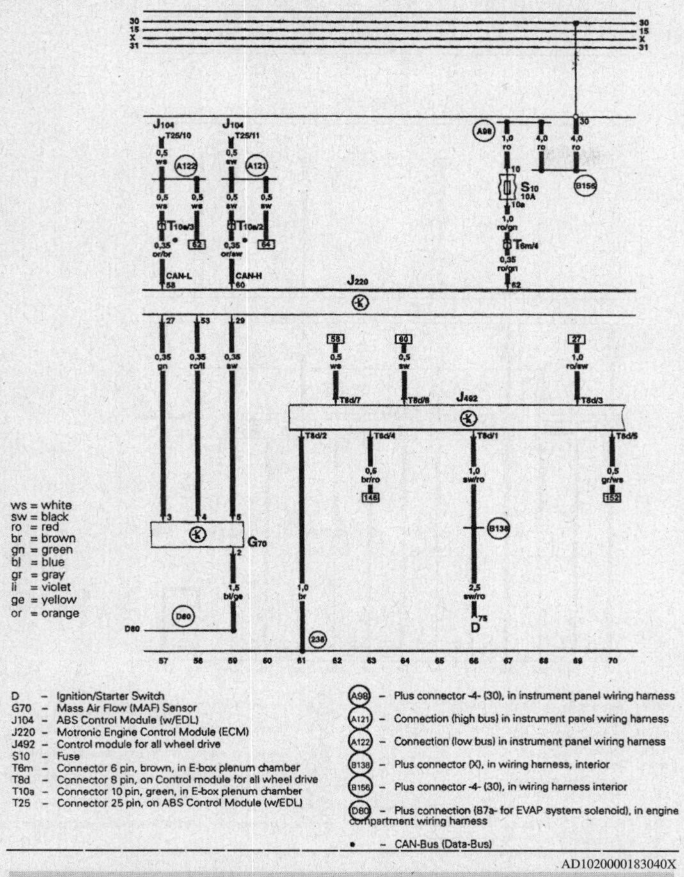

ws = white
sw = black
ro = red
br = brown
gn = green
bl = blue
gr = gray
li = violet
ge = yellow
or = orange
D – Ignition/Starter Switch
G70 – Mass Air Flow (MAF) Sensor
J104 – ABS Control Module (w/EDL)
J220 – Motronic Engine Control Module (ECM)
J492 – Control module for all wheel drive
S10 – Fuse
T6m – Connector 6 pin, brown, in E-box plenum chamber
T8d – Connector 8 pin, on Control module for all wheel drive
T10a – Connector 10 pin, green, in E-box plenum chamber
T25 – Connector 25 pin, on ABS Control Module (w/EDL)
A98 – Plus connector -4- (30), in instrument panel wiring harness
A121 – Connection (high bus) in instrument panel wiring harness
A122 – Connection (low bus) in instrument panel wiring harness
B138 – Plus connector (X), in wiring harness, interior
B156 – Plus connector -4- (30), in wiring harness interior
D80 – Plus connection (87a- for EVAP system solenoid), in engine compartment wiring harness
• – CAN-Bus (Data-Bus)
AD1020000183040X

Fig. 5 MFI system wiring diagram (Part 4 of 8). TT w/AMU engine

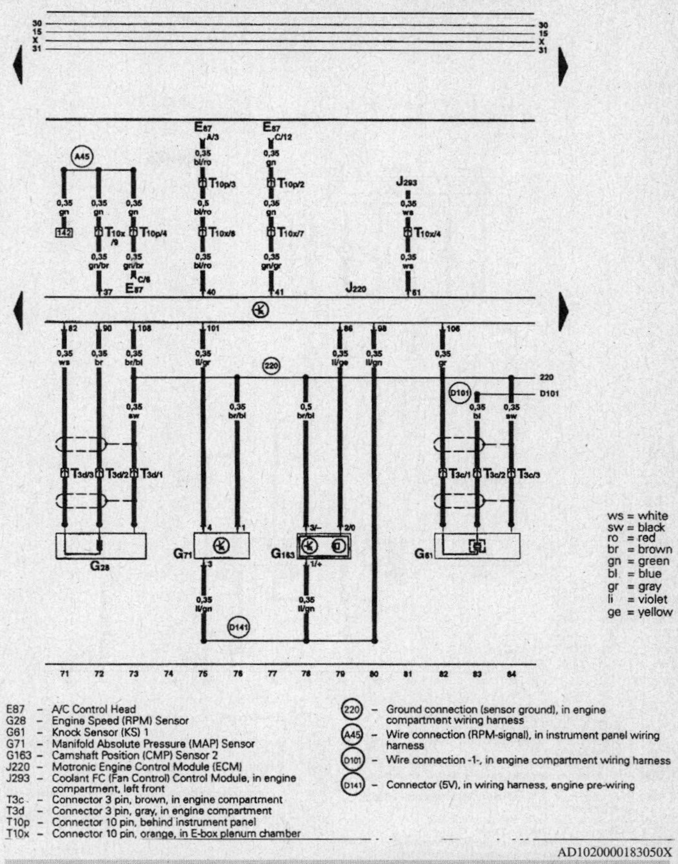

Fig. 5 MFI system wiring diagram (Part 5 of 8). TT w/AMU engine

12. If voltage is present, proceed as follows:
    a. Connect a suitable voltmeter between oxygen sensor harness connector terminal 2 and battery positive using connector test kit tool No. VW 1594, or equivalent.
    b. Monitor voltage and scan tool Display Group 41, Field 4.
    c. If scan tool display is "Htg.aC.On," voltage should be 11–14.5 volts.
    d. If scan tool display switches between "Htg.aC.ON" and "Htg.a-C.OFF" voltage should vary between 0–12 volts.
    e. Turn ignition Off.
13. If no voltage is present, proceed as follows:
    a. Connect test box tool No. VAG 1598/22, or equivalent to ECM harness connector.
    b. Measure resistance between oxygen sensor connector terminal 2 and test box pin 28 using a suitable ohmmeter.
14. If resistance is greater than 1.5 ohms, service open circuit as required.
15. If wiring inspection is satisfactory, replace ECM and generate new readiness code.

Voltage Inspection

1. Disconnect oxygen sensor.
2. Connect a suitable voltmeter between oxygen sensor harness connector terminals 3 and 4 using connector test kit tool No. VW 1594, or equivalent.
3. Start engine and measure voltage.
4. Voltage should read .4–.5 volts.
5. Turn ignition Off.
6. If voltage is not as specified, refer to "Rear Heated Oxygen Sensor Wiring Inspection."
7. If voltage is as specified, replace oxygen sensor.

Wiring Inspection

1. Connect test box tool No. VAG 1598/22, or equivalent, to ECM harness connector.
2. Disconnect oxygen sensor connector.
3. Inspect for open or short circuit between the following connector terminals and test box pins using a suitable ohmmeter:
    a. Connector terminal 3 to test box pin 51, then connector terminal 4 to test box pin 52. Resistance should read 1.5 ohms or less.
    b. Connector terminal 4 to test box pin 51, connector terminal 3 to test box pin 2 and connector terminal 4 to test box pin 2. Ohmmeter should read open circuit.
4. If resistance readings are not as specified, service wiring as required.
5. If resistance readings are as specified, replace ECM and generate new readiness code.

TT

Functional Inspection

1. Road test vehicle and bring to operating temperature.
2. Connect scan tool No. VAG 1551, or equivalent, to DLC.
3. Start and idle engine, then select control module for engine electronics using "Address Word 01."
4. Press buttons 0 and 4 to select Basic Setting, then press Q button to confirm input.
5. Press buttons 0, 3 and 4 to select "Display Group Number 034," then press Q button to confirm input.
6. Set engine speed to 2800–3200 RPM using idle speed adjuster tool No. VAG 1788/10, or equivalent.
7. Continue test as soon as Display Field 2 indicates an exhaust temperature of more than 662°F (350°C). This might require a few minutes.
8. Press C button.
9. Set engine speed to 1800–2200 RPM.
10. Press buttons 0, 3 and 0 to select "Display Group Number 030," then press Q button to confirm input.

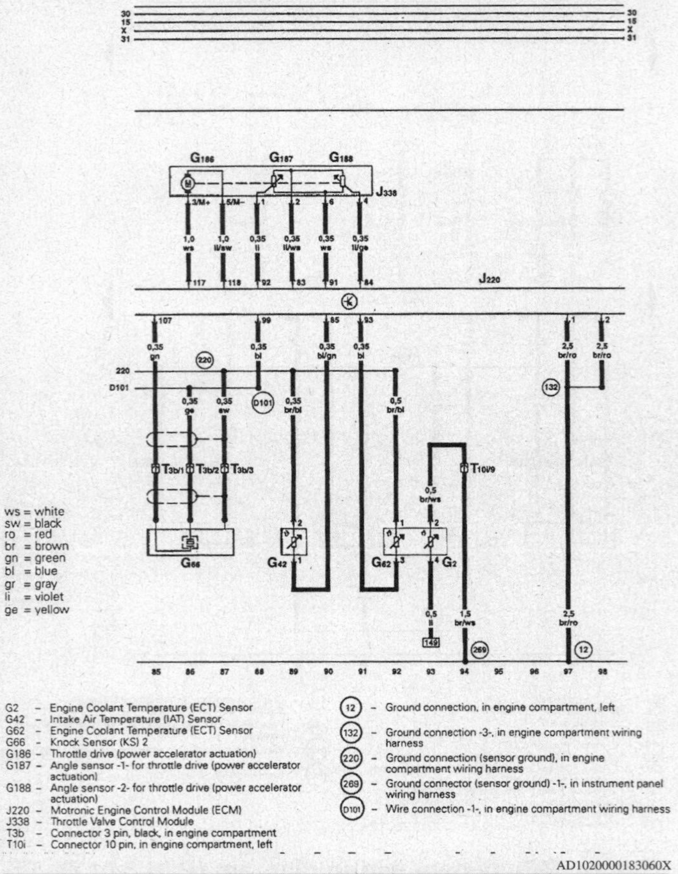

Fig. 5 MFI system wiring diagram (Part 6 of 8). TT w/AMU engine

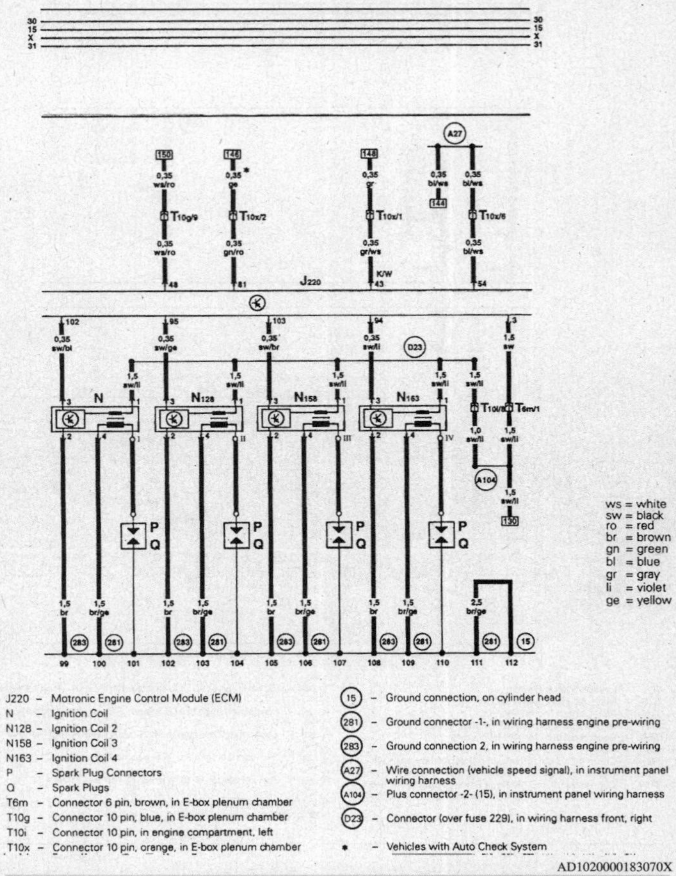

Fig. 5 MFI system wiring diagram (Part 7 of 8). TT w/AMU engine

11. Observe oxygen sensor status for oxygen rear heated oxygen sensor in Display Field 2, **Fig. 87.**
12. Press buttons 0, 3 and 7 to select "Display Group Number 037," then press Q button to confirm input.
13. Observe oxygen sensor voltage in Display Field 2.
14. Observe duration of oxygen sensor control in Display Field 3 and diagnostic result in Display Field 4, **Fig. 88.**
15. If displayed values are as specified, refer to **Fig. 89** for Display Group 37 evaluation.
16. If specified value in Display Fields 3 and 4 is not obtained, road test vehicle to clear possible residue from oxygen sensor and repeat test.
17. If specified value in Display Fields 3 and 4 is still not obtained, replace rear heated oxygen sensor.

Voltage Inspection

1. Disconnect rear oxygen sensor 4-pin electrical connector.
2. Connect a suitable voltmeter between connector terminals 3 and 4, **Fig. 82.**
3. Turn ignition On and measure voltage, which should be 0.4–0.5 volts.
4. If voltage meets specifications, replace rear oxygen sensor.
5. If voltage does not meet specifications, turn ignition Off.
6. Connect test box tool No. VAG 1598/31, or equivalent, to ECM wiring harness. **Do not connect to ECM itself.**
7. Inspect for an open circuit between connector terminal 2 and test box socket 68, then at terminal 4 and socket 69. Repair as required.
8. If voltage does not meet specifications, proceed as follows:
   a. Turn ignition Off.
   b. Connect a suitable ohmmeter between rear oxygen sensor electrical connector terminals 1 and 2, **Fig. 82.**
   c. Measure resistance, which should be as specified under "Sensor & Fuel Injector Specifications."
9. If wiring connection is satisfactory, replace ECM.

Heater Inspection

1. Connect a suitable voltmeter between rear oxygen sensor connector terminals 1 and 2, **Fig. 82.**
2. Start engine and observe voltage, which should be battery voltage, possibly fluctuating.
3. If there is no voltage, connect voltmeter between terminal 1 and ground, then crank engine and observe voltage, which should be battery voltage.
4. If voltage does not meet specifications, inspect wire connection from connector terminal 1 to fuel pump relay via fuse for open circuit.
5. If voltage meets specifications, connect voltmeter between terminal 2 and battery positive terminal.
6. Start engine and observe voltage, which should be battery voltage, possibly fluctuating.
7. If there is no voltage, connect test box tool No. VAG 1598/31, or equivalent, to ECM wiring harness. **Do not connect to ECM itself.**
8. Inspect for an open circuit between connector terminal 2 and test box socket 63. Repair as required.
9. If wiring connection is satisfactory, replace ECM.

CLOSED THROTTLE POSITION (CTP) SWITCH

1. Ensure following test conditions are met:
   a. Throttle valve is in closed position.
   b. Cruise control system is properly adjusted.
   c. Inspect and service power supply to throttle valve control module as required.
2. Connect scan tool No. VAG 1551/1552, or equivalent, then press buttons 0 and 1 to insert "Engine Electronics" address word 01 with engine running at idle.

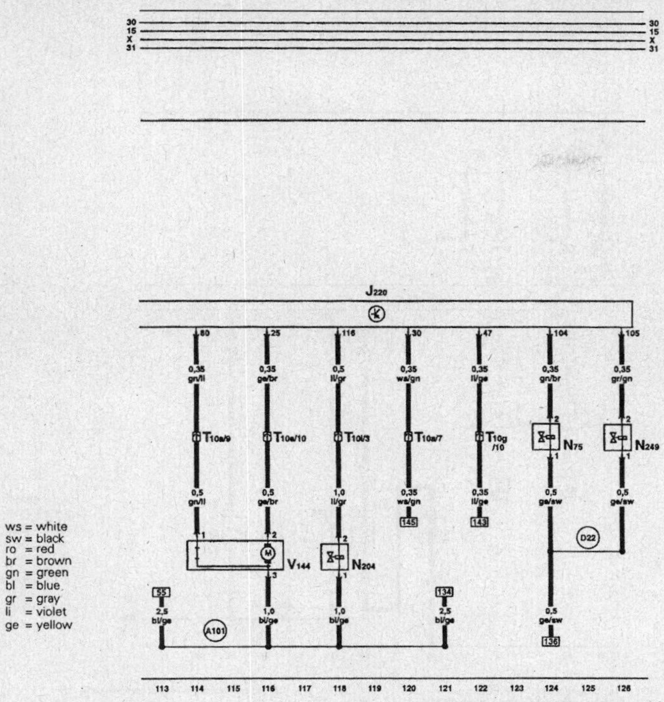

J220 – Motronic Engine Control Module (ECM)
N75 – Wastegate Bypass Regulator Valve
N204 – Valve for tank ventilation
N249 – Recirculating valve for turbocharger
T10a – Connector 10 pin, green, in E-box plenum chamber
T10i – Connector 10 pin, in engine compartment, left
V144 – Leak Detection Pump (LDP)

A101 – Connector -3- (87), in instrument panel wiring harness
D22 – Connector (over fuse 234), in wiring harness front, right

AD1020000183080X

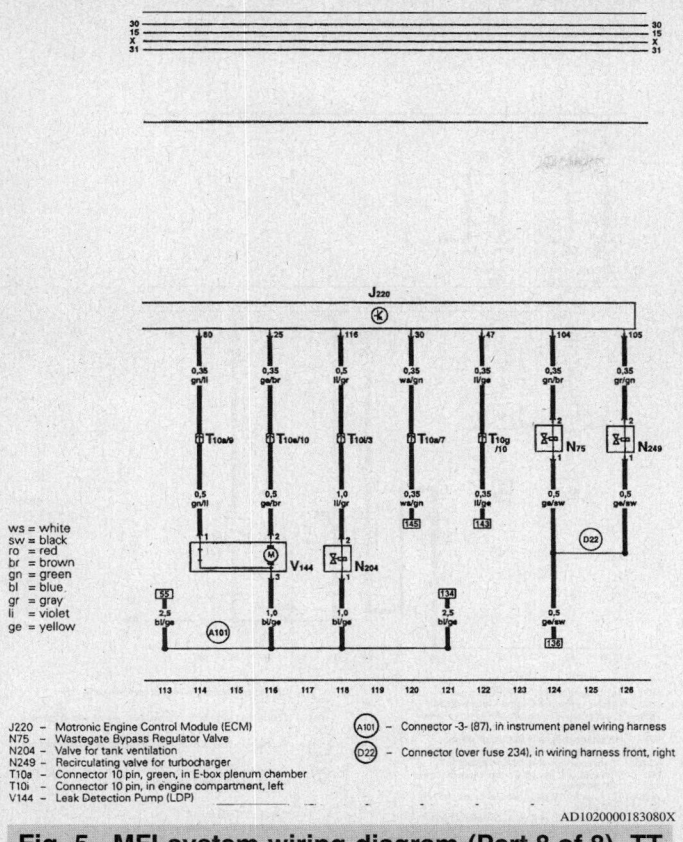

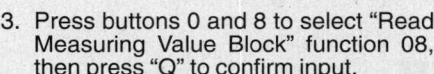

Fig. 5 MFI system wiring diagram (Part 8 of 8). TT w/AMU engine

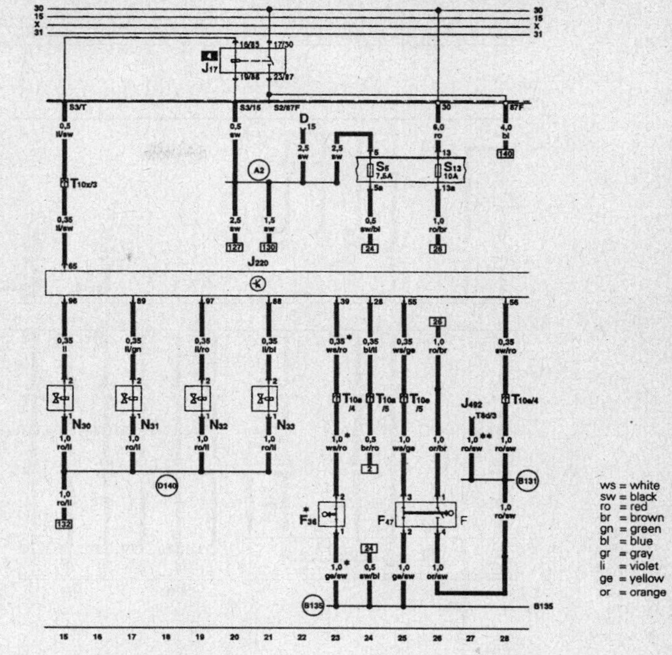

D – Ignition/Starter Switch
F – Brake Light Switch
F36 – Clutch Vacuum Vent Valve Switch
F47 – Vacuum Vent Valve, Brake
J17 – Fuel Pump (FP) Relay
J220 – Motronic Engine Control Module (ECM)
J492 – Control module for all wheel drive
N30 – Cylinder 1 Fuel Injector
N31 – Cylinder 2 Fuel Injector
N32 – Cylinder 3 Fuel Injector
N33 – Cylinder 4 Fuel Injector
S5 – Fuse
S13 – Fuse
T8d – Connector 8 pin, on Control module for all wheel drive
T10a – Connector 10 pin, green, in E-box plenum chamber
T10e – Connector 10 pin, black, in E-box plenum chamber
T10x – Connector 10 pin, orange, in E-box plenum chamber

A2 – Plus connection (15), in instrument panel wiring harness
B131 – Connector (54), in wiring harness interior
B135 – Connector (15a), in wiring harness interior
D140 – Connector (injectors), in wiring harness, engine pre-wiring

* – Vehicles with manually shifted transmission
** – Vehicles with all wheel drive

AD1020000182010X

Fig. 6 MFI system wiring diagram (Part 1 of 8). TT w/ATC engine

3. Press buttons 0 and 8 to select "Read Measuring Value Block" function 08, then press "Q" to confirm input.
4. Press buttons 0, 0 and 5 to input Display Group 5, then press "Q" to confirm input.
5. Compare scan tool data with engine electronics data, **Fig. 90.**
6. If scan tool data display does not agree with **Fig. 90,** proceed as follows:
   a. Turn ignition Off.
   b. Connect test box tool No. VAG 1598/22, or equivalent, to ECM harness connector.
   c. Measure resistance between test box pins 67 and 69 using a suitable ohmmeter.
   d. Resistance should be 5 ohms.
   e. As throttle is opened slowly, ohmmeter should read open circuit.
7. If resistance is not as specified, proceed as follows:
   a. Disconnect 8-pin connector from throttle valve control module. Refer to **Fig. 91** for pin identification.
   b. Measure resistance between harness connector terminal 3 and test box pin 69.
   c. Measure resistance between harness connector terminal 7 and test box pin 67.
   d. Resistance should be 1.5 ohms or less.
8. If resistance is greater than 1.5 ohms, service open circuit as required.
9. If resistance is 1.5 ohms or less, measure resistance between 8 pin connector terminal 7 and test box pin 69. Ohmmeter should read open circuit. If open circuit is not indicated, service short as required.
10. Reconnect throttle valve control module.
11. If wiring inspection is satisfactory, replace throttle valve control module.

RPM SENSOR

TT

1. Disconnect RPM sensor electrical connector.
2. Connect a suitable ohmmeter to sensor terminals 2 and 3, **Fig. 92,** then measure resistance, which should be 730–1000 ohms at 68°F.
3. Measure resistance between terminals 1 and 2, then between terminals 1 and 3, which should all be infinite.
4. If resistances do not meet specifications, replace sensor.
5. If resistances meet specifications, ensure ignition is turned Off, then connect test box tool No. VAG 1598/31, or equivalent, to ECM wiring harness. **Do not connect to ECM itself.**
6. Inspect for opens or shorts as follows: between RPM sensor electrical connector terminal 1 and test box socket 108; between terminal 2 and socket 90; between terminal 3 and socket 82. Repair as required.
7. If wiring is satisfactory, replace ECM.

THROTTLE POSITION (TP) SENSOR

A4 & S4

Functional Inspection

1. Ensure throttle valve is closed and throttle cable is properly adjusted.
2. Ensure cruise control is adjusted properly.
3. Inspect power supply to throttle valve control module and repair as required.
4. Connect scan tool VAG 1551/1552, or equivalent, then press buttons 0 and 1 to insert "Engine Electronics" address word 01 with ignition On.
5. Press buttons 0 and 8 to select "Read Measuring Value Block" function 08, then press "Q" to confirm input.
6. Press buttons 0, 0 and 3 to input Display Group 3, then press "Q" to confirm input.
7. Compare scan tool display with load measurement values in **Fig. 93.**
8. Open throttle valve while monitoring degree value in Display Field 3 of **Fig. 93.**

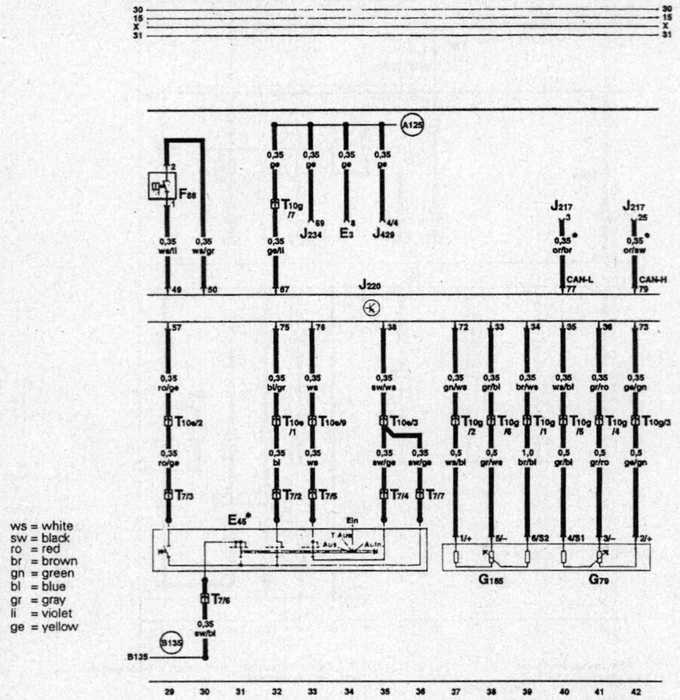

E3 – Emergency Flasher Switch
E45 – Cruise Control Switch
F88 – Power Steering Pressure (PSP) Switch
G79 – Throttle Position (TP) Sensor
G185 – Sender -2- for accelerator pedal position
J217 – Transmission Control Module (TCM)
J220 – Motronic Engine Control Module (ECM)
J234 – Airbag Control Module
J429 – Control module for central locking
T7 – Connector 7 pin, behind steering column switch cover
T10e – Connector 10 pin, black, in E-box plenum chamber
T10g – Connector 10 pin, blue, in E-box plenum chamber

(85) – Ground connection -1-, in engine compartment wiring harness
(A125) – Connection (crash signal) in instrument panel wiring harness
(B135) – Connector (15a), in wiring harness interior

• – CAN-Bus (Data-Bus)
* – Vehicles with Cruise Control

AD1020000182020X

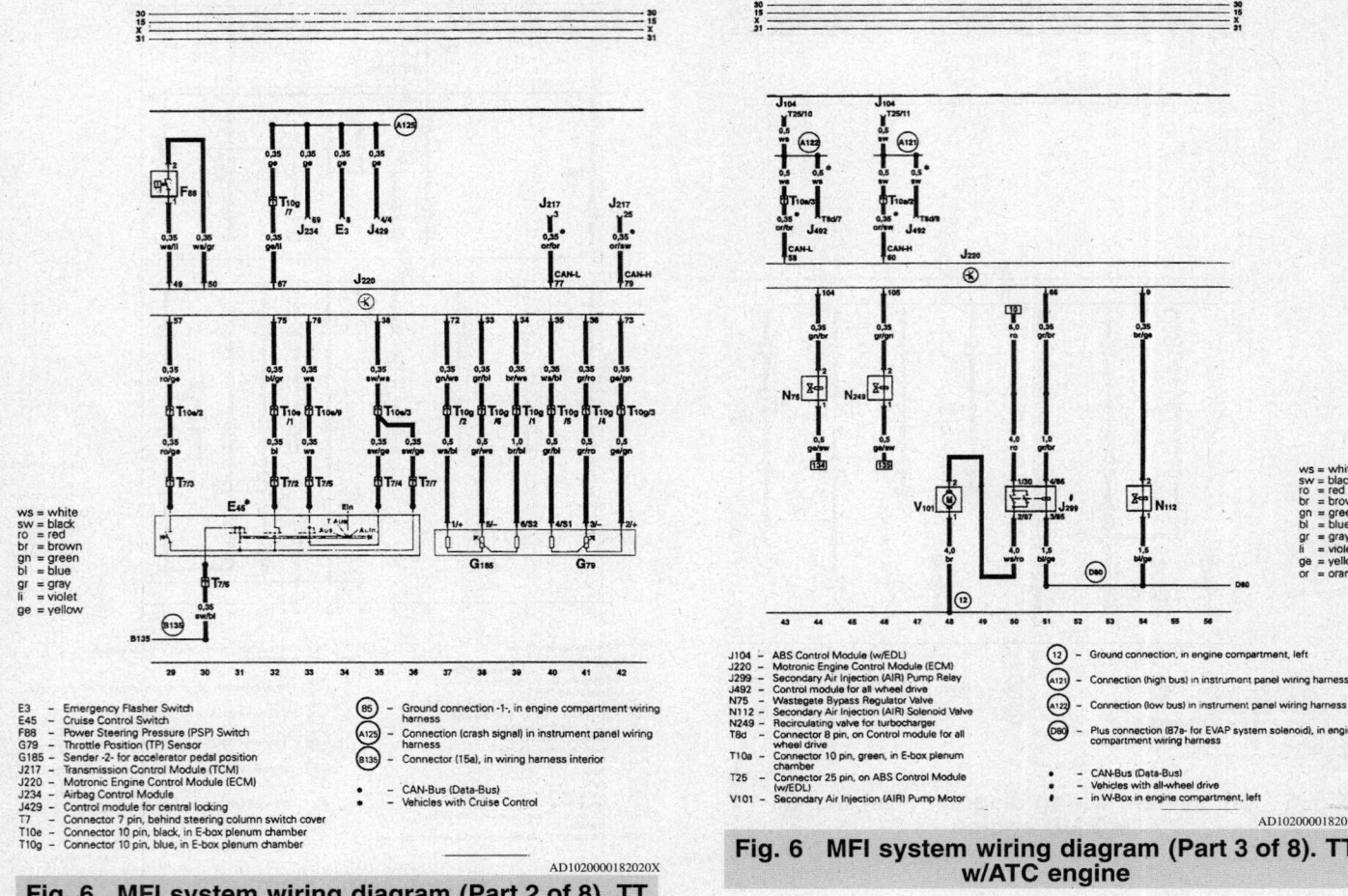

Fig. 6 MFI system wiring diagram (Part 2 of 8). TT w/ATC engine

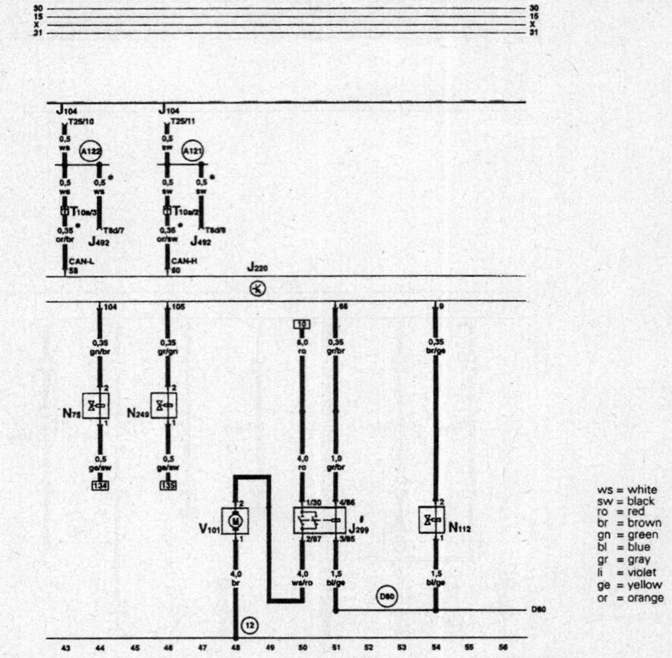

J104 – ABS Control Module (w/EDL)
J220 – Motronic Engine Control Module (ECM)
J299 – Secondary Air Injection (AIR) Pump Relay
J492 – Control module for all wheel drive
N75 – Wastegate Bypass Regulator Valve
N112 – Secondary Air Injection (AIR) Solenoid Valve
N249 – Recirculating valve for turbocharger
T8d – Connector 8 pin, on Control module for all wheel drive
T10a – Connector 10 pin, green, in E-box plenum chamber
T25 – Connector 25 pin, on ABS Control Module (w/EDL)
V101 – Secondary Air Injection (AIR) Pump Motor

(12) – Ground connection, in engine compartment, left
(A121) – Connection (high bus) in instrument panel wiring harness
(A122) – Connection (low bus) in instrument panel wiring harness
(D80) – Plus connection (87a- for EVAP system solenoid), in engine compartment wiring harness

• – CAN-Bus (Data-Bus)
* – Vehicles with all-wheel drive
# – in W-Box in engine compartment, left

AD1020000182030X

Fig. 6 MFI system wiring diagram (Part 3 of 8). TT w/ATC engine

9. If value does not evenly increase over range of throttle movement, refer to "Wiring Inspection."
10. Press right arrow button to advance program.
11. Press buttons 0 and 6 to select "End Output" function 06, then press "Q" to confirm input.
12. If wiring inspection is satisfactory, replace throttle valve control module and perform throttle valve control module relearn procedure as outlined under "Computer Relearn Procedures" in front of this manual.

Wiring Inspection

1. Connect test box tool No. VAG 1598/22, or equivalent, to ECM harness connector.
2. Measure resistance between test box pins 2 and 75 using a suitable ohmmeter and connector test kit tool No. VW 1594, or equivalent. Ohmmeter should read open circuit.
3. Remove ohmmeter from circuit.
4. Turn ignition On, then measure voltage of test box pins 2 and 75 using a suitable voltmeter.
5. Record voltage reading and turn ignition Off.
6. If voltmeter read 0 volts, proceed as follows:
   a. Disconnect 8-pin connector from throttle valve control module. Refer to **Fig. 91** for connector pin identification.
   b. Measure resistance between throttle valve control module harness connector terminal 5 to test box pin 75 using a suitable ohmmeter.
   c. If resistance is more than 1.5 ohms, service open wire as required.
   d. If resistance is 1.5 ohms or less, replace throttle valve control module and generate new readiness code.
7. If voltmeter reads approximately five volts, proceed as follows:
   a. Disconnect 8-pin connector from throttle valve control module.
   b. Measure resistance between test box pins 62 and 75 using a suitable ohmmeter and connector test kit tool No. VW 1594, or equivalent.
   c. If ohmmeter does not read open circuit, service short as required.
8. If voltmeter reads battery voltage, inspect 8 pin connector terminal 5 for short to power and service as required.

TT

Functional Inspection

1. Start and idle engine, then select control module for engine electronics using "Address Word 01."
2. Press buttons 0 and 8 to select "Read Measuring Value Block," then press Q button to confirm input.
3. Press buttons 0, 6 and 2 to select "Display Group Number 062," then press Q button to confirm input.
4. Observe specified value for E-Gas potentiometer voltages, **Fig. 94.**
5. Observe Display Fields 1 and 2 while slowly depressing accelerator pedal completely to floor, which should appear as follows:
   a. Percentage indication in Display Field 1 must climb uniformly. Tolerance range 3–93 % is not used completely.
   b. Percentage indication in Display Field 2 must decrease uniformly. Tolerance range 97–3 % is not used completely.
6. If percentage indications do not meet specifications, proceed to "Wiring Inspection" as outlined under "Accelerator Pedal Position Sensor," then inspect Accelerator Pedal Position

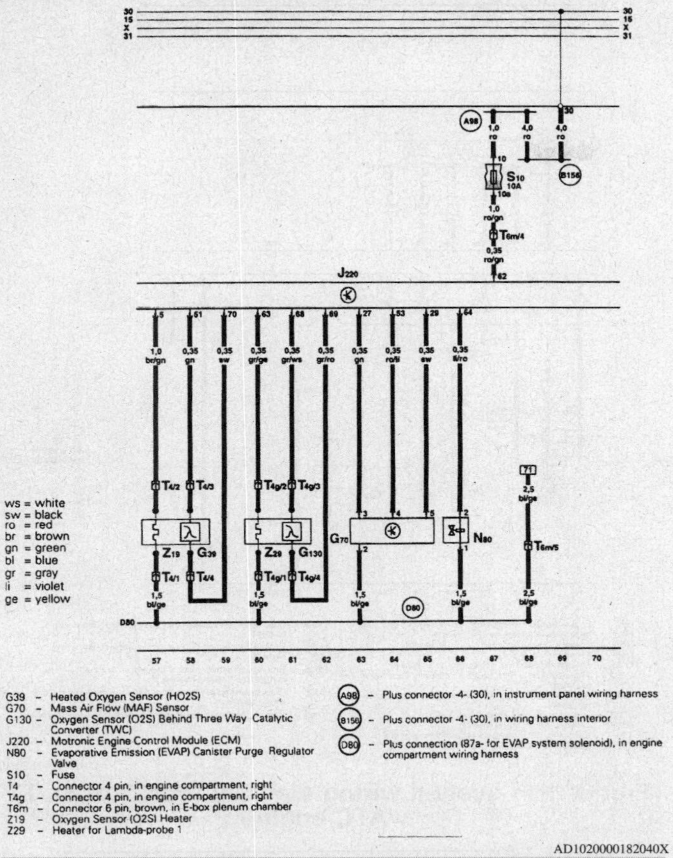

Fig. 6 MFI system wiring diagram (Part 4 of 8). TT w/ATC engine

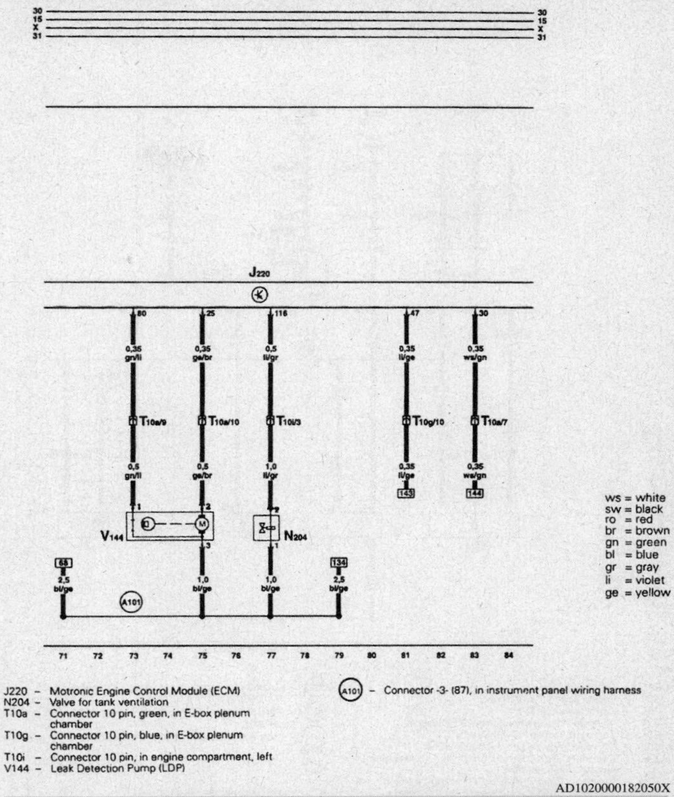

Fig. 6 MFI system wiring diagram (Part 5 of 8). TT w/ATC engine

(APP) sensor.

Wiring Inspection

1. Disconnect throttle valve control module electrical connector.
2. Turn ignition On.
3. Connect a suitable voltmeter between terminal 2 and ground, **Fig. 95,** then between terminals 2 and 6. There should be approximately five volts.
4. If voltages meet specifications, ensure ignition is turned Off, then connect test box tool No. VAG 1598/31, or equivalent, to ECM wiring harness. **Do not connect to ECM itself.**
5. Inspect for open circuits and shorts as follows:
   a. Between throttle valve control module electrical connector terminal 1 and test box socket 92.
   b. Connector terminal 2 and socket 83.
   c. Connector terminal 3 and socket 117.
   d. Connector terminal 4 and socket 84.
   e. Connector terminal 5 and socket 118.
   f. Connector terminal 6 and socket 91.
6. Repair wiring fault conditions as required.
7. If wiring and connections are satisfactory, replace throttle valve control module.

ACCELERATOR PEDAL POSITION SENSOR

TT

The Throttle Position (TP) sensor and the Accelerator Pedal Position (APP) sender are located at the accelerator pedal and transmit the driver's intentions to the ECM completely independently of each other. Both sensors are incorporated into one housing.

1. Connect scan tool No. VAG 1551, or equivalent, to DLC.
2. Turn ignition On, then select control module for engine electronics using "Address Word 01."
3. Press buttons 0 and 8 to select "Read Measuring Value Block," then press Q button to confirm input.
4. Press buttons 0, 6 and 2 to select "Display Group Number 062," then press Q button to confirm input.
5. Observe specified value for E-Gas potentiometer voltages, **Fig. 94.**
6. Observe Display Fields 1 and 2 while slowly depressing accelerator pedal completely to floor, which should appear as follows:
   a. Percentage indication in Display Field 1 must climb uniformly. Tolerance range 12–97% is not used completely.
   b. Percentage indication in Display Field 2 must decrease uniformly. Tolerance range 4–49% is not used completely.
7. If percentage indications do not meet specifications, proceed as follows:
   a. Remove driver's side storage compartment.
   b. Disconnect APP sensor electrical connector, **Fig. 96.**
   c. Connect a suitable voltmeter to connector terminals as follows: 1 and ground; 1 and 5; 2 and ground; 2 and 3. There should be approximately five volts.
8. If voltages meet specifications, inspect signal wires.
9. If voltages do not meet specifications, ensure ignition is turned Off, then connect test box tool No. VAG 1598/31, or equivalent, to ECM wiring harness. **Do not connect to ECM itself.**
10. Inspect for open circuits and shorts as follows:
    a. Between APP sensor electrical connector terminal 1 and test box socket 72.
    b. Terminal 2 and socket 73.
    c. Terminal 3 and socket 36.
    d. Terminal 4 and socket 35.
    e. Terminal 5 and socket 33.
    f. Terminal 6 and socket 34.
11. Repair wiring fault conditions as required.

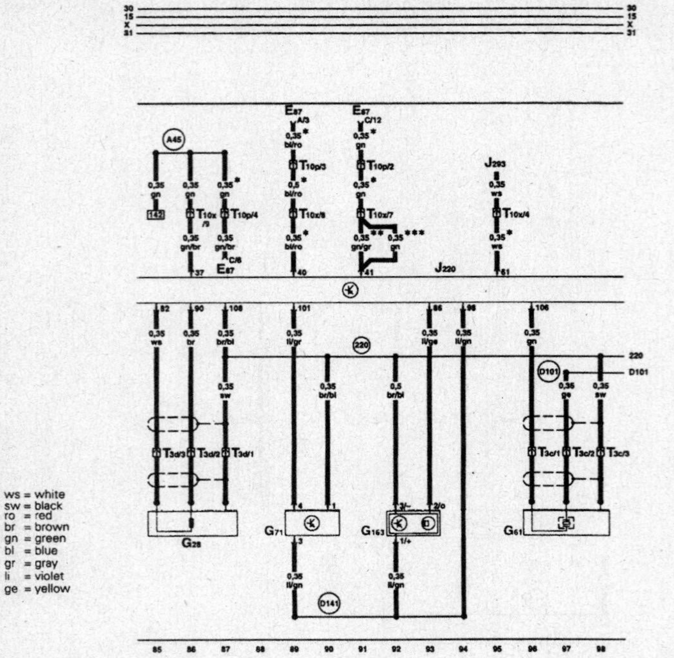

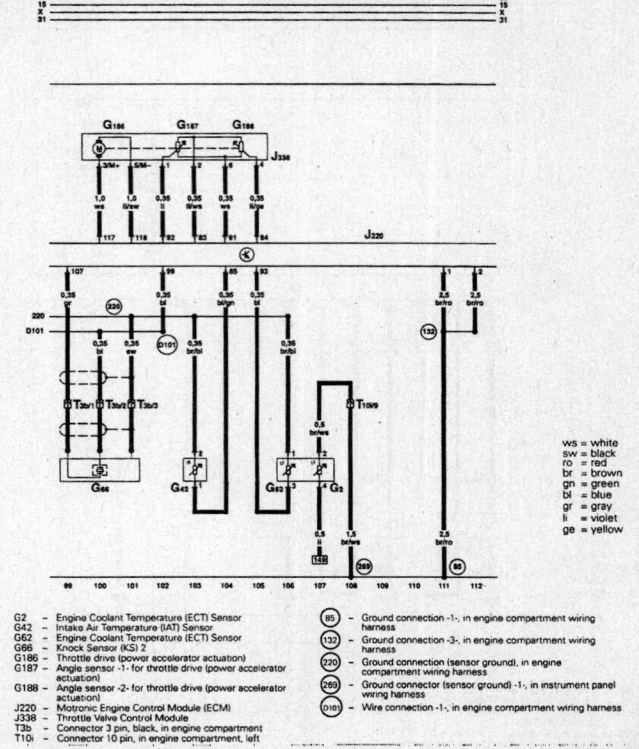

E87 – A/C Control Head
G28 – Engine Speed (RPM) Sensor
G61 – Knock Sensor (KS) 1
G71 – Manifold Absolute Pressure (MAP) Sensor
G163 – Camshaft Position (CMP) Sensor 2
J220 – Motronic Engine Control Module (ECM)
J293 – Coolant FC (Fan Control) Control Module, in engine compartment, left front
T3c – Connector 3 pin, brown, in engine compartment
T3d – Connector 3 pin, gray, in engine compartment
T10p – Connector 10 pin, behind instrument panel
T10x – Connector 10 pin, orange, in E-box plenum chamber

(220) – Ground connection (sensor ground), in engine compartment wiring harness
(A45) – Wire connection (RPM-signal), in instrument panel wiring harness
(D101) – Wire connection -1-, in engine compartment wiring harness
(D141) – Connector (5V), in wiring harness, engine pre-wiring
* – Vehicles with Air conditioner
** – Vehicles with manually shifted transmission
*** – Vehicles with automatic transmission

AD1020000182060X

Fig. 6 MFI system wiring diagram (Part 6 of 8). TT w/ATC engine

12. If wiring and connections are satisfactory, replace APP sensor.

Clearing Diagnostic Trouble Codes

Fault memory cannot be erased until it has first been inspected.

Follow tool manufacturer's instructions to clear DTCs.

SYSTEM SERVICE

Refer to "Fuel Injection" section for adjustment and replacement procedures.

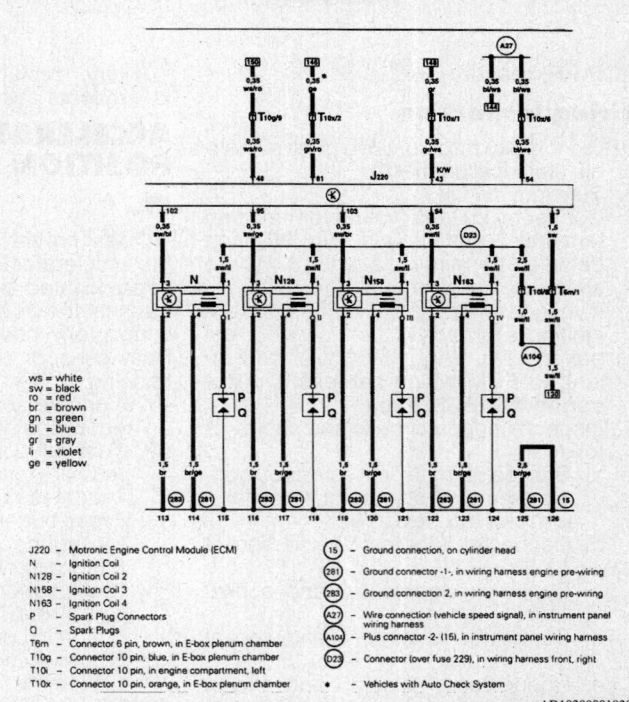

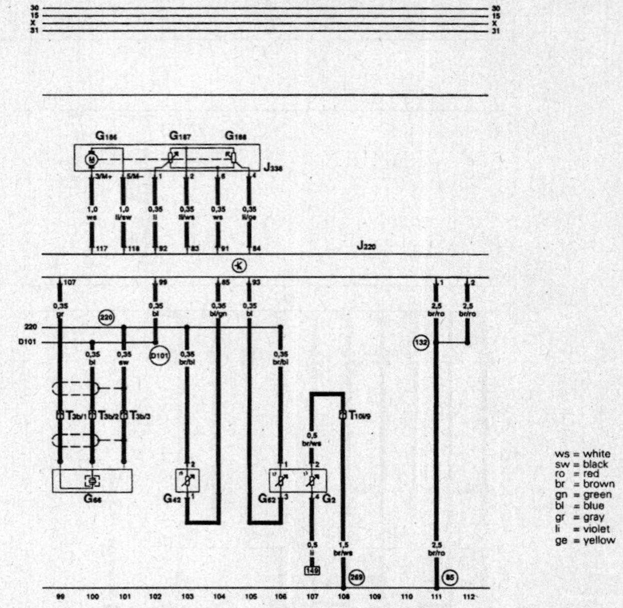

G2 – Engine Coolant Temperature (ECT) Sensor
G42 – Intake Air Temperature (IAT) Sensor
G62 – Engine Coolant Temperature (ECT) Sensor
G66 – Knock Sensor (KS) 2
G186 – Throttle drive (power accelerator actuation)
G187 – Angle sensor -1- for throttle drive (power accelerator actuation)
G188 – Angle sensor -2- for throttle drive (power accelerator actuation)
J220 – Motronic Engine Control Module (ECM)
J338 – Throttle Valve Control Module
T3b – Connector 3 pin, black, in engine compartment
T10i – Connector 10 pin, in engine compartment, left

(85) – Ground connection -1-, in engine compartment wiring harness
(132) – Ground connection -3-, in engine compartment wiring harness
(220) – Ground connection (sensor ground), in engine compartment wiring harness
(269) – Ground connector (sensor ground) -1-, in instrument panel wiring harness
(D101) – Wire connection -1-, in engine compartment wiring harness

AD1020000182070X

Fig. 6 MFI system wiring diagram (Part 7 of 8). TT w/ATC engine

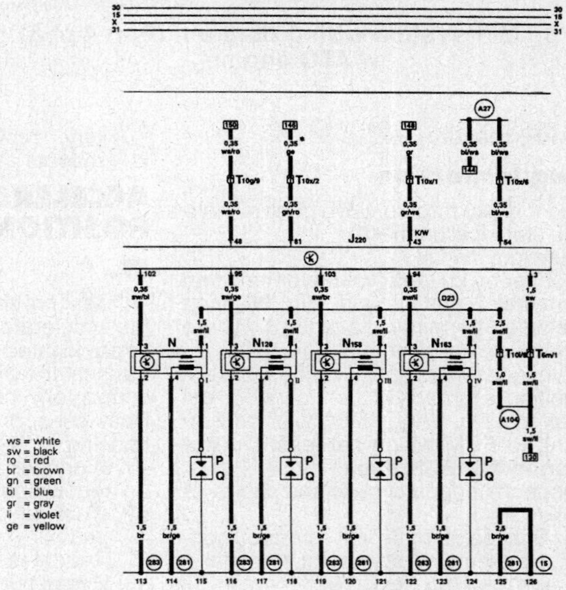

J220 – Motronic Engine Control Module (ECM)
N – Ignition Coil
N128 – Ignition Coil 2
N158 – Ignition Coil 3
N163 – Ignition Coil 4
P – Spark Plug Connectors
Q – Spark Plugs
T6m – Connector 6 pin, brown, in E-box plenum chamber
T10g – Connector 10 pin, blue, in E-box plenum chamber
T10i – Connector 10 pin, in engine compartment, left
T10x – Connector 10 pin, orange, in E-box plenum chamber

(15) – Ground connection, on cylinder head
(281) – Ground connector -1-, in wiring harness engine pre-wiring
(283) – Ground connection 2, in wiring harness engine pre-wiring
(A27) – Wire connection (vehicle speed signal), in instrument panel wiring harness
(A104) – Plus connector -2- (15), in instrument panel wiring harness
(D23) – Connector (over fuse 229), in wiring harness front, right
* – Vehicles with Auto Check System

AD1020000182080X

Fig. 6 MFI system wiring diagram (Part 8 of 8). TT w/ATC engine

DIAGNOSTIC CHART INDEX

Code	Description	Page No.	Fig. No.
A4 & S4			
P0102	Mass Or Volume Air Flow Circuit Low Input	10-52	7
P0103	MAF Circuit High Input	10-52	7
P0107	MAP Or BARO Pressure Sensor Low Input	10-52	7
P0108	MAP Or BARO Pressure Sensor High Input	10-52	7
P0112	IAT Circuit Low Input	10-52	7
P0113	IAT Circuit High Input	10-52	7
P0116	ECT Circuit Fault	10-52	7
P0117	ECT Circuit Low Input	10-52	7
P0118	ECT Circuit High Input	10-52	7
P0121	Throttle/Pedal Position Sensor Circuit Fault	10-52	8
P0122	Throttle/Pedal Position Sensor Circuit Low Input	10-52	8
P0123	Throttle/Pedal Position Sensor Circuit High Input	10-52	8
P0130	O2 Sensor Bank 1 Sensor 1 Fault	10-52	8
P0131	O2 Sensor Bank 1 Sensor 1 Low Voltage	10-52	8
P0132	O2 Sensor Bank 1 Sensor 1 High Voltage	10-52	8
P0133	O2 Sensor Bank 1 Sensor 1 Slow Response	10-52	8
P0134	O2 Sensor Bank 1 Sensor 1 No Activity Detected	10-52	8
P0136	O2 Sensor Bank 1 Sensor 2 Fault	10-52	9
P0137	O2 Sensor Bank 1 Sensor 2 Low Voltage	10-52	9
P0138	O2 Sensor Bank 1 Sensor 2 High Voltage	10-52	9
P0140	O2 Sensor Bank 1 Sensor 2 No Activity Detected	10-52	9
P0300	Random Misfire Detected	10-52	10
P0301	Cylinder 1 Misfire Detected	10-52	10
P0302	Cylinder 2 Misfire Detected	10-52	10
P0303	Cylinder 3 Misfire Detected	10-52	10
P0304	Cylinder 4 Misfire Detected	10-52	10
P0321	Engine Speed Sensor Input Circuit Fault	10-52	10
P0322	Engine Speed Sensor No Signal	10-52	10
P0327	Knock Sensor 1 Circuit Low Input	10-52	11
P0332	Knock Sensor 2 Circuit Low Input	10-52	11
P0422	Main Catalyst Bank 1 Efficiency Below Threshold	10-52	11
P0441	EVAP System Improper Purge Flow Fault	10-52	11
P0442	EVAP System Small Leak Detected	10-52	11
P0455	EVAP System Large Leak Detected	10-52	11
P0501	Vehicle Speed Sensor Fault	10-52	12
P0506	Idle Control System RPM Lower Than Expected	10-52	12
P0507	Idle Control System RPM Higher Than Expected	10-52	12
P0560	System Voltage Fault	10-52	12
P0562	System Voltage Low	10-52	12
P0563	System Voltage High	10-52	12
P0601	Internal Control Module Memory Check Sum Error	10-53	13
P0604	Internal Control Module Random Access Memory Error	10-53	13
P0707	Transmission Range Sensor Low Input	10-53	13
P0708	Transmission Range Sensor High Input	10-53	13
P1102	O2 Sensor Heating Circuit Bank 1 Sensor 1 Short To Voltage	10-53	13
P1105	O2 Sensor Heating Circuit Bank 1 Sensor 2 Short To Voltage	10-53	13
P1127	Long Term Fuel Trim Bank 1 System Too Rich	10-53	14
P1128	Long Term Fuel Trim Bank 1 System Too Lean	10-53	15
P1136	Long Term Fuel Trim Bank 1 System Too Rich	10-53	16
P1137	Long Term Fuel Trim Bank 1 System Too Lean	10-53	17
P1176	O2 Sensor Correction Behind Catalyst B1 Limit Attained	10-53	18
P1196	O2 Sensor Heater Circuit Bank 1 Sensor 1 Electrical Fault	10-53	18
P1198	O2 Sensor Heater Circuit Bank 1 Sensor 2 Electrical Fault	10-53	18
P1213	Cylinder 1 Fuel Injector Short To Voltage	10-53	18
P1214	Cylinder 2 Fuel Injector Short To Voltage	10-53	18
P1215	Cylinder 3 Fuel Injector Short To Voltage	10-54	19

Continued

DIAGNOSTIC CHART INDEX—Continued

Code	Description	Page No.	Fig. No.
A4 & S4			
P1216	Cylinder 4 Fuel Injector Short To Voltage	10-54	19
P1225	Cylinder 1 Fuel Injector Short To Ground	10-54	19
P1226	Cylinder 2 Fuel Injector Short To Ground	10-54	19
P1227	Cylinder 3 Fuel Injector Short To Ground	10-54	19
P1228	Cylinder 4 Fuel Injector Short To Ground	10-54	19
P1237	Cylinder 1 Fuel Injector Open Circuit	10-54	19
P1238	Cylinder 2 Fuel Injector Open Circuit	10-54	19
P1239	Cylinder 3 Fuel Injector Open Circuit	10-54	19
P1240	Cylinder 4 Fuel Injector Open Circuit	10-54	19
P1250	Fuel Level Too Low	10-54	20
P1325	Cylinder 1 Knock Control Limit Attained	10-54	21
P1326	Cylinder 2 Knock Control Limit Attained	10-54	21
P1327	Cylinder 3 Knock Control Limit Attained	10-54	21
P1328	Cylinder 4 Knock Control Limit Attained	10-54	21
P1337	Camshaft Position Sensor Bank 1 Short To Ground	10-54	21
P1338	Camshaft Position Sensor Bank 1 Open Circuit Or Short To Voltage	10-54	21
P1386	Internal Control Module Knock Control Error	10-54	21
P1410	Tank Ventilation Valve Short To Voltage	10-54	22
P1425	Tank Ventilation Valve Short To Ground	10-54	22
P1426	Tank Ventilation Valve Open	10-54	22
P1471	EVAP Emission Control LDP Circuit Short To Voltage	10-54	22
P1472	EVAP Emission Control LDP Circuit Short To Ground	10-54	22
P1473	EVAP Emission Control LDP Circuit Open	10-54	22
P1475	EVAP Emission Control LDP Circuit Fault/Signal Circuit Open	10-54	22
P1476	EVAP Emission Control LDP Circuit Fault/Insufficient Vacuum	10-54	22
P1477	EVAP Emission Control LDP Circuit Fault	10-54	22
P1500	Fuel Pump Relay Electrical Fault	10-54	23
P1501	Fuel Pump Relay Short To Ground	10-54	23
P1502	Fuel Pump Relay Short To Voltage	10-54	23
P1505	Closed Throttle Position Switch Does Not Close/Open Circuit	10-54	23
P1506	Closed Throttle Position Switch Does Not Open/Short To Ground	10-54	23
P1543	Throttle Actuation Potentiometer Signal Too Low	10-54	23
P1544	Throttle Actuation Potentiometer Signal Too High	10-54	23
P1545	Throttle Position Control Fault	10-54	23
P1546	Boost Pressure Control Valve Short To Voltage	10-54	24
P1547	Boost Pressure Control Valve Short To Ground	10-54	24
P1548	Boost Pressure Control Valve Open	10-54	24
P1555	Charge Pressure Upper Limit Exceeded	10-54	24
P1556	Charge Pressure Negative Deviation	10-54	24
P1557	Charge Pressure Positive Deviation	10-54	24
P1558	Throttle Actuator Electrical Fault	10-54	24
P1559	Idle Speed Control Throttle Position Adaptation Fault	10-54	24
P1560	Maximum Engine Speed Exceeded	10-55	25
P1564	Idle Speed Control Throttle Position Low Voltage During Adaptation	10-55	25
P1602	Power Supply Terminal 30 Low Voltage	10-55	25
P1606	Rough Road Spec Engine Torque ABS-ECU Electrical Fault	10-55	25
P1611	MIL Call-Up/Transaxle Control Module Short To Ground	10-55	26
P1612	ECM Improper Coding	10-55	26
P1613	MIL Call-Up Circuit/Transaxle Control Module Short To Ground	10-55	26
P1624	MIL Request Sign Active	10-55	27
P1640	Internal Control Module EEPROM Error	10-55	27
P1681	Control Unit Programming Not Finished	10-55	27
TT			
P0101	Mass Or Volume Air Flow Circuit Range/Performance	10-55	28
P0102	Mass Or Volume Air Flow Circuit Low Input	10-55	28
P0103	Mass Or Volume Air Flow Circuit High Input	10-55	28

Continued

DIAGNOSTIC CHART INDEX—Continued

Code	Description	Page No.	Fig. No.
TT			
P0106	MAP Or BARO Pressure Sensor Range/Performance	10-55	28
P0112	IAT Circuit Low Input	10-55	29
P0113	IAT Circuit High Input	10-55	29
P0116	ECT Circuit Range/Performance	10-55	29
P0117	ECT Circuit Low Input	10-55	29
P0118	ECT Circuit High Input	10-55	29
P0130	O2 Sensor Circuit Bank 1 Sensor 1 Malfunction	10-55	30
P0131	O2 Sensor Circuit Bank 1 Sensor 1 Low Voltage	10-55	30
P0132	O2 Sensor Circuit Bank 1 Sensor 1 High Voltage	10-55	30
P0133	O2 Sensor Circuit Bank 1 Sensor 1 Slow Response	10-55	30
P0134	O2 Sensor Circuit Bank 1 Sensor 1 No Activity Detected	10-55	30
P0136	O2 Sensor Circuit Bank 1 Sensor 2 Malfunction	10-55	31
P0137	O2 Sensor Circuit Bank 1 Sensor 2 Low Voltage	10-55	31
P0138	O2 Sensor Circuit Bank 1 Sensor 2 High Voltage	10-55	31
P0139	O2 Sensor Circuit Bank 1 Sensor 2 Slow Response	10-55	31
P0140	O2 Sensor Circuit Bank 1 Sensor 2 No Activity Detected	10-55	31
P0236	Turbocharger Boost Sensor (A) Range/Performance	10-55	32
P0237	Turbocharger Boost Sensor (A) Low Input	10-55	32
P0238	Turbocharger Boost Sensor (A) High Input	10-55	32
P0300	Random/Multiple Cylinder Misfire Detected	10-56	33
P0301	Cylinder 1 Misfire Detected	10-56	33
P0302	Cylinder 2 Misfire Detected	10-56	33
P0303	Cylinder 3 Misfire Detected	10-56	33
P0304	Cylinder 4 Misfire Detected	10-56	33
P0321	Ignition/Distributor Engine Speed Input Circuit Range/Performance	10-56	33
P0322	Ignition/Distributor Engine Speed Input Circuit No Signal	10-56	33
P0327	Knock Sensor 1 Circuit Low Input	10-56	34
P0328	Knock Sensor 1 Circuit High Input	10-56	34
P0332	Knock Sensor 2 Circuit Low Input	10-56	34
P0333	Knock Sensor 2 Circuit High Input	10-56	34
P0411	Secondary AIR Injection System Improper Flow Detected	10-56	34
P0422	Main Catalyst Bank 1 Efficiency Below Threshold	10-56	34
P0441	EVAP Emission Control System Improper Purge Flow	10-56	35
P0442	EVAP Emission Control System Small Leak Detected	10-56	35
P0455	EVAP Emission Control System Large Leak Detected	10-56	35
P0501	Vehicle Speed Sensor Range/Performance	10-56	35
P0506	Idle Control System RPM Lower Than Expected	10-56	35
P0507	Idle Control System RPM Higher Than Expected	10-56	35
P0560	System Voltage Malfunction	10-56	35
P0562	System Voltage Low	10-56	35
P0563	System Voltage High	10-56	35
P0571	Cruise/Brake Switch (A) Improper Signal	10-56	36
P0601	Internal Control Module Memory	10-56	36
P0604	Internal Control Module Random Access	10-56	36
P0605	Internal Control Module ROM Test Error	10-56	36
P1102	O2 Sensor Heating Circuit Bank 1 Sensor 1 Short To Voltage	10-56	36
P1105	O2 Sensor Heating Circuit Bank 1 Sensor 2 Short To Voltage	10-56	36
P1111	O2 Control Bank 1 System Too Lean	10-56	36
P1112	O2 Control Bank 1 System Too Rich	10-56	36
P1113	Bank 1 Sensor 1 Internal Resistance Too High	10-56	37
P1114	Bank 1 Sensor 2 Internal Resistance Too High	10-56	37
P1115	O2 Sensor Heater Circuit Bank 1 Sensor 1 Short To Ground	10-56	37
P1116	O2 Sensor Heater Circuit Bank 1 Sensor 1 Open	10-56	37
P1117	O2 Sensor Heater Circuit Bank 1 Sensor 2 Short To Ground	10-56	37
P1118	O2 Sensor Heater Circuit Bank 1 Sensor 2 Open	10-56	37
P1127	Long Term Fuel Trim Mult. Bank 1 System Too Rich	10-56	38

Continued

DIAGNOSTIC CHART INDEX—Continued

Code	Description	Page No.	Fig. No.
TT			
P1128	Long Term Fuel Trim Mult. Bank 1 System Too Lean	10-56	38
P1136	Long Term Fuel Trim Add. Fuel Bank 1 System Too Lean	10-56	39
P1137	Long Term Fuel Trim Add. Fuel Bank 1 System Too Rich	10-56	39
P1149	O2 Control Bank 1 Out Of Range	10-56	39
P1171	Throttle Actuation Potentiometer Sign. 2 Range/Performance	10-57	40
P1172	Throttle Actuation Potentiometer Sign. 2 Signal Too Low	10-57	40
P1173	Throttle Actuation Potentiometer Sign. 2 Signal Too High	10-57	40
P1176	O2 Correction Behind Catalyst B1 Limit Attained	10-57	40
P1203	Cylinder 3 Fuel Injector Circuit Electrical Malfunction	10-57	41
P1213	Cylinder 1 Fuel Injector Circuit Short To Voltage	10-57	41
P1214	Cylinder 2 Fuel Injector Circuit Short To Voltage	10-57	41
P1215	Cylinder 3 Fuel Injector Circuit Short To Voltage	10-57	41
P1216	Cylinder 4 Fuel Injector Circuit Short To Voltage	10-57	41
P1225	Cylinder 1 Fuel Injector Circuit Short To Ground	10-57	41
P1226	Cylinder 2 Fuel Injector Circuit Short To Ground	10-57	41
P1227	Cylinder 3 Fuel Injector Circuit Short To Ground	10-57	41
P1228	Cylinder 4 Fuel Injector Circuit Short To Ground	10-57	41
P1237	Cylinder 1 Fuel Injector Circuit Open	10-57	42
P1238	Cylinder 2 Fuel Injector Circuit Open	10-57	42
P1239	Cylinder 3 Fuel Injector Circuit Open	10-57	42
P1240	Cylinder 4 Fuel Injector Circuit Open	10-57	42
P1250	Fuel Level Too Low	10-57	43
P1287	Turbocharger Bypass Valve Open	10-57	44
P1288	Turbocharger Bypass Valve Short To Voltage	10-57	44
P1289	Turbocharger Bypass Valve Short To Ground	10-57	44
P1325	Cylinder 1 Knock Control Limit Attained	10-57	45
P1326	Cylinder 2 Knock Control Limit Attained	10-57	45
P1327	Cylinder 3 Knock Control Limit Attained	10-57	45
P1328	Cylinder 4 Knock Control Limit Attained	10-57	45
P1335	Engine Torque Monitoring 2 Control Limit Exceeded	10-57	45
P1336	Engine Torque Monitoring Adaptation At Limit	10-57	45
P1337	CMP Sensor Bank 1 Short To Ground	10-57	46
P1338	CMP Sensor Bank 1 Open Circuit Or Short To Voltage	10-57	46
P1340	CKP/CMP Signals Out Of Sequence	10-57	46
P1355	Cylinder 1 Ignition Circuit Open Circuit	10-57	47
P1356	Cylinder 1 Ignition Circuit Short To Voltage	10-57	47
P1357	Cylinder 1 Ignition Circuit Short To Ground	10-57	47
P1358	Cylinder 2 Ignition Circuit Open Circuit	10-57	47
P1359	Cylinder 2 Ignition Circuit Short To Voltage	10-57	47
P1360	Cylinder 2 Ignition Circuit Short To Ground	10-58	48
P1361	Cylinder 3 Ignition Circuit Open Circuit	10-58	48
P1362	Cylinder 3 Ignition Circuit Short To Voltage	10-58	48
P1363	Cylinder 3 Ignition Circuit Short To Ground	10-58	48
P1364	Cylinder 4 Ignition Circuit Open Circuit	10-58	48
P1365	Cylinder 4 Ignition Circuit Short To Voltage	10-58	48
P1366	Cylinder 4 Ignition Circuit Short To Ground	10-58	48
P1386	Internal Control Module	10-58	49
P1387	Internal Control Module	10-58	49
P1388	Internal Control Module	10-58	49
P1410	Tank Ventilation Valve Circuit Short To Voltage	10-58	49
P1421	Secondary AIR Valve Circuit Short To Ground	10-58	49
P1422	Secondary AIR Valve Circuit Short To Voltage	10-58	49
P1424	Secondary AIR System Bank 1 Leak Detected	10-58	49
P1425	Tank Ventilation Valve Short To Ground	10-58	49
P1426	Tank Ventilation Valve Open	10-58	49
P1432	Secondary AIR Injection Valve Open	10-58	50

Continued

DIAGNOSTIC CHART INDEX—Continued

Code	Description	Page No.	Fig. No.
TT			
P1433	Secondary AIR Pump Relay	10-58	50
P1434	Secondary AIR Pump Relay Circuit Short To Voltage	10-58	50
P1435	Secondary AIR Pump Relay Circuit Short To Ground	10-58	50
P1467	EVAP Canister Purge Solenoid Valve Short Circuit To Voltage	10-58	50
P1468	EVAP Canister Purge Solenoid Valve Short Circuit To Ground	10-58	50
P1469	EVAP Canister Purge Solenoid Valve Open Circuit	10-58	50
P1471	EVAP Emission Control LDP Circuit Short To Voltage	10-58	51
P1472	EVAP Emission Control LDP Circuit Short To Ground	10-58	51
P1473	EVAP Emission Control LDP Open Circuit	10-58	51
P1475	EVAP Emission Control LDP Circuit Malfunction/Signal Circuit Open	10-58	51
P1476	EVAP Emission Control LDP Circuit Malfunction/Insufficient Vacuum	10-58	51
P1477	EVAP Emission Control LDP Circuit Malfunction	10-58	52
P1478	EVAP Emission Control LDP Circuit Clamped Tube Detected	10-58	52
P1500	Fuel Pump Relay Circuit Electrical Malfunction	10-58	52
P1502	Fuel Pump Relay Circuit Short To Voltage	10-58	52
P1523	Crash Signal Implausible	10-58	52
P1539	Clutch Vacuum Vent Valve Switch Improper Signal	10-58	53
P1542	Throttle Actuation Potentiometer Range/Performance	10-58	53
P1543	Throttle Actuation Potentiometer Signal Too Low	10-58	53
P1544	Throttle Actuation Potentiometer Signal Too High	10-58	53
P1545	Throttle Position Control Malfunction	10-58	53
P1546	Boost Pressure Control Valve Short To Voltage	10-59	54
P1547	Boost Pressure Control Valve Short To Ground	10-59	54
P1548	Boost Pressure Control Valve Open	10-59	54
P1555	Charge Pressure Upper Limit Exceeded	10-59	54
P1556	Charge Pressure Control Negative Deviation	10-59	54
P1557	Charge Pressure Control Positive Deviation	10-59	54
P1558	Throttle Actuator Electrical Malfunction	10-59	54
P1559	Idle Speed Control Throttle Position Adaptation Malfunction	10-59	54
P1560	Maximum Engine Speed Exceeded	10-59	54
P1565	Idle Speed Control Throttle Position Lower Limit Not Attained	10-59	55
P1568	Idle Speed Control Throttle Position Mechanical Malfunction	10-59	55
P1569	Cruise Control Switch Improper Signal	10-59	55
P1570	Control Module Locked	10-59	55
P1579	Idle Speed Control Throttle Position Adaptation Not Started	10-59	55
P1602	Power Supply Terminal 30 Low Voltage	10-59	55
P1603	Internal Control Module Malfunction	10-59	56
P1604	Internal Control Module Driver Error	10-59	56
P1606	Rough Road Spec Engine Torque ABS-ECU Electrical Malfunction	10-59	56
P1609	Crash Shutdown Activated	10-59	56
P1612	ECM Improper Coding	10-59	56
P1630	Accelerator Pedal Position Sensor 1 Signal Too Low	10-59	57
P1631	Accelerator Pedal Position Sensor 1 Signal Too High	10-59	57
P1633	Accelerator Pedal Position Sensor 2 Signal Too Low	10-59	57
P1634	Accelerator Pedal Position Sensor 2 Signal Too High	10-59	57
P1639	Accelerator Pedal Position Sensor 1 & 2 Range/Performance	10-59	57
P1640	Internal Control Module EEPROM Error	10-59	58
P1645	Data Bus Powertrain Missing Message From AWD Control	10-59	58
P1648	Data Bus Powertrain Malfunction	10-59	58
P1649	Data Bus Powertrain Missing Message From ABS Control Module	10-59	58
P1676	Drive By Wire MIL Circuit Electrical Malfunction	10-59	59
P1677	Drive By Wire MIL Circuit Short To Voltage	10-59	59
P1690	MIL Malfunction	10-59	59
P1693	MIL Short Circuit To Voltage	10-59	59
P1853	CAN-Bus Implausible Message From Brake Control	10-59	59

Diagnostic Trouble Code (DTC) SAE	VAG	Malfunction text	MIL	Corrective action
P0102	16486	Mass or Volume Air Flow Circ. Low Input	2 Dcy	– Check Mass Air Flow (MAF) sensor -G70-
P0103	16487	Mass or Volume Air Flow Circ. High Input		
P0107	16491	Manifold Abs. Pressure or Bar. Pressure Low Input	2 Dcy	– Check Manifold Absolute Pressure (MAP) sensor -G71-
P0108	16492	Manifold Abs. Pressure or Bar. Pressure High Input		
P0112	16496	Intake Air Temp. Circ. Low Input	2 Dcy	– Check Intake Air Temperature (IAT) sensor -G42-
P0113	16497	Intake Air Temp. Circ. High Input		
P0116	16500	Engine Coolant Temp. Circ. Range/Performance	2 Dcy	– Check Engine Coolant Temperature (ECT) sensor -G62-
P0117	16501	Engine Coolant Temp. Circ. Low Input		
P0118	16502	Engine Coolant Temp. Circ. High Input		

AD0159800204000X

Fig. 7 Codes P0102, P0103, P0107, P0108, P0112, P0113, P0116, P0117 & P0118. A4 & S4

Diagnostic Trouble Code (DTC) SAE	VAG	Malfunction text	MIL	Corrective action
P0136	16520	O2 Sensor Circ., Bank1–Sensor2 Malfunction	2 Dcy	– Check Oxygen Sensor (O2S) behind Three Way Catalytic Converter (TWC) -G130-
P0137	16521	O2 Sensor Circ., Bank1–Sensor2 Low Voltage		
P0138	16522	O2 Sensor Circ., Bank1–Sensor2 High Voltage		
P0140	16524	O2 Sensor Circ., Bank1–Sensor2 No Activity Detected		

AD0159800206000X

Fig. 9 Codes P0136, P0137, P0138 & P0140. A4 & S4

Diagnostic Trouble Code (DTC) SAE	VAG	Malfunction text	MIL	Corrective action
P0327	16711	Knock Sensor 1 Circ. Low Input	Immed.	– Check knock sensors and knock sensor control
P0332	16716	Knock Sensor 2 Circ. Low Input		
P0422	16806	Main Catalyst, Bank1 Efficiency Below Threshold	2 Dcy	– Replace Three Way Catalytic Converter (TWC)
P0441	16825	EVAP Emission Contr. Sys. Incorrect Purge Flow	2 Dcy	– Check Evaporative Emissions (EVAP) canister purge regulator valve Diagnostic Test Mode (DTM)
P0442	16826	EVAP Emission Contr. Sys. (Small Leak) Leak Detected	➤ m.y. 1997: **Off**	– Check EVAP system
P0455	16839	EVAP Emission Contr. Sys. (Gross Leak) Leak Detected	m.y. 1998 ➤: **2 Dcy**	

AD0159800208000X

Fig. 11 Codes P0327, P0332, P0422, P0441, P0442 & P0455. A4 & S4

Diagnostic Trouble Code (DTC) SAE	VAG	Malfunction text	MIL	Corrective action
P0121	16505	Throttle/Pedal Pos. Sensor A Circ. Range/Performance	2 Dcy	– Check Throttle Position (TP) sensor -G69-
P0122	16506	Throttle/Pedal Pos. Sensor A Circ. Low Input		
P0123	16507	Throttle/Pedal Pos. Sensor A Circ. High Input		
P0130	16514	O2 Sensor Circ., Bank1–Sensor1 Malfunction	2 Dcy	– Check Heated Oxygen Sensor (HO2S) -G39- and O2S control ⇒
P0131	16515	O2 Sensor Circ., Bank1–Sensor1 Low Voltage		
P0132	16516	O2 Sensor Circ., Bank1–Sensor1 High Voltage		
P0133	16517	O2 Sensor Circ., Bank1–Sensor1 Slow Response	2 Dcy	– Check Heated Oxygen Sensor (HO2S) aging ⇒
P0134	16518	O2 Sensor Circ., Bank1–Sensor1 No Activity Detected	2 Dcy	– Check HO2S -G39- and O2S control ⇒

AD0159800205000X

Fig. 8 Codes P0121, P0122, P0123, P0130, P0131, P0132, P0133 & P0134. A4 & S4

Diagnostic Trouble Code (DTC) SAE	VAG	Malfunction text	MIL	Corrective action
P0300	16684	Random/Multiple Cylinder Misfire Detected	2 Dcy / blink	– Fuel level too low, check fuel level and add if necessary – Check misfire detection – Check fuel injectors – Output Diagnostic Test Mode (DTM) – Check engine speed (RPM) sensor -G28-
P0301	16685	Cyl. 1 Misfire Detected		
P0302	16686	Cyl. 2 Misfire Detected		
P0303	16687	Cyl. 3 Misfire Detected		
P0304	16688	Cyl. 4 Misfire Detected		
P0321	16705	Ign./Distributor Eng. Speed Inp. Circ. Range/Performance	2 Dcy	– Check engine speed (RPM) sensor -G28-
P0322	16706	Ign./Distributor Eng. Speed Inp. Circ. No Signal	Immed.	

Note on misfire malfunctions:

For malfunctions that may be caused by low fuel volume (i.e. combustion misfire) a low-fuel malfunction (DTC "P1250") is also stored when there is less than 2 gallons of fuel remaining in the tank.

AD0159800207000X

Fig. 10 Codes P0300, P0301, P0302, P0303, P0304, P0321 & P0322. A4 & S4

Diagnostic Trouble Code (DTC) SAE	VAG	Malfunction text	MIL	Corrective action
P0501	16885	Vehicle Speed Sensor Range/Performance	2 Dcy	– Check vehicle speed signal
P0506	16890	Idle Control System RPM Lower Than Expected	2 Dcy	– Check throttle body and throttle valve control module
P0507	16891	Idle Control System RPM Higher Than Expected		
P0560	16944	System Voltage Malfunction	2 Dcy	– Check Engine Control Module (ECM) power supply
P0562	16946	System Voltage Low Voltage		
P0563	16947	System Voltage High Voltage		

AD0159800209000X

Fig. 12 Codes P0501, P0506, P0507, P0560, P0562 & P0563. A4 & S4

Diagnostic Trouble Code (DTC) SAE	VAG	Malfunction text	MIL	Corrective action
P0601	16985	Internal Contr. Module Memory Check Sum Error	2 Dcy	Replace ECM
P0604	16988	Internal Contr. Module Random Access Memory (RAM) Error		
P0707	17091	Transm. Range Sensor Circ. Low Input	Off	– Check transmission driving range signal -F125-
P0708	17092	Transm. Range Sensor Circ. High Input		
P1102	17510	O2 Sensor Heating Circ., Bank1–Sensor1 Short to B+	2 Dcy	– Check Oxygen Sensor (O2S) heater -Z19-
P1105	17513	O2 Sensor Heating Circ., Bank1–Sensor2 Short to B+		– Check Oxygen Sensor (O2S) heater -Z29-

AD0159800210000X

Fig. 13 Codes P0601, P0604, P0707, P0708, P1102 & P1105. A4 & S4

Diagnostic Trouble Code (DTC) SAE	VAG	Malfunction text	MIL	Corrective action
P1127	17535	Long Term Fuel Trim mult., Bank1 System too Rich [1]	2 Dcy	– Check Mass Air Flow (MAF) sensor -G70-
				– Check HO2S -G39- and O2S control
				– Check Oxygen Sensor (O2S) behind Three Way Catalytic Converter (TWC) -G130-
				– Check fuel pressure regulator and residual fuel pressure
				– Check fuel injectors
				– Output Diagnostic Test Mode (DTM)

[1] The term "mult." = multiplicative; applies to entire engine speed (RPM) and load range.

AD0159800211000X

Fig. 14 Code P1127. A4 & S4

Diagnostic Trouble Code (DTC) SAE	VAG	Malfunction text	MIL	Corrective action
P1128	17536	Long Term Fuel Trim mult., Bank1 System too Lean [1]	2 Dcy	– Check HO2S -G39- and O2S control
				– Check Oxygen Sensor (O2S) behind Three Way Catalytic Converter (TWC) -G130-
				– Check fuel pressure regulator and residual fuel pressure
				– Check fuel injectors
				– Output Diagnostic Test Mode (DTM)
				– Check EVAP canister purge regulator valve

[1] The term "mult." = multiplicative; applies to entire engine speed (RPM) and load range.

AD0159800212000X

Fig. 15 Code P1128. A4 & S4

Diagnostic Trouble Code (DTC) SAE	VAG	Malfunction text	MIL	Corrective action
P1136	17544	Long Term Fuel Trim Add. Fuel, Bank1 System too Lean [2]	2 Dcy	– Check intake air system for leaks ("false air") ⇒ page 24-97
				– Check HO2S -G39- and O2S control ⇒ page 24-17
				– Check Mass Air Flow (MAF) sensor -G70- ⇒ page 24-57
				– Check fuel pressure regulator and residual fuel pressure ⇒ page 24-93
				– Check fuel injectors ⇒ page 24-87 – Output Diagnostic Test Mode (DTM) ⇒ page 01-41

[2] The term "Add." = additive; applies only with engine running at idle speed.

AD0159800213000X

Fig. 16 Code P1136. A4 & S4

Diagnostic Trouble Code (DTC) SAE	VAG	Malfunction text	MIL	Corrective action
P1137	17545	Long Term Fuel Trim Add. Fuel, Bank1 System too Rich [2]	2 Dcy	– Check HO2S -G39- and O2S control
				– Check fuel pressure regulator and residual pressure
				– Check exhaust system for leakage

[2] The term "Add." = additive; applies only with engine running at idle speed.

AD0159800214000X

Fig. 17 Code P1137. A4 & S4

Diagnostic Trouble Code (DTC) SAE	VAG	Malfunction text	MIL	Corrective action
P1176	17584	O2 Correction Behind Catalyst, B1 Limit Attained	2 Dcy	– Check intake air system for leaks ("false air")
				– Check Heated Oxygen Sensor (HO2S) aging
				– Check Oxygen Sensor (O2S) heater -Z29-
				– Check O2S behind TWC
P1196	17604	O2 Sensor Heater Circ., Bank1–Sensor1 Electrical Malfunction	2 Dcy	– Check Oxygen Sensor (O2S) heater -Z19-
P1198	17606	O2 Sensor Heater Circ., Bank1–Sensor2 Electrical Malfunction		– Check Oxygen Sensor (O2S) heater -Z29-
P1213	17621	Cyl.1–Fuel Inj. Circ. Short to B+	Immed.	– Check fuel injectors – Output Diagnostic Test Mode (DTM)
P1214	17622	Cyl.2–Fuel Inj. Circ. Short to B+		

AD0159800215000X

Fig. 18 Codes P1176, P1196, P1198, P1213 & P1214. A4 & S4

Diagnostic Trouble Code (DTC) SAE	VAG	Malfunction text	MIL	Corrective action
P1215	17623	Cyl.3–Fuel Inj. Circ. Short to B+	Immed.	– Check fuel injectors – Output Diagnostic Test Mode (DTM)
P1216	17624	Cyl.4–Fuel Inj. Circ. Short to B+		
P1225	17633	Cyl.1–Fuel Inj. Circ. Short to Ground		
P1226	17634	Cyl.2–Fuel Inj. Circ. Short to Ground		
P1227	17635	Cyl.3–Fuel Inj. Circ. Short to Ground		
P1228	17636	Cyl.4–Fuel Inj. Circ. Short to Ground		
P1237	17645	Cyl.1–Fuel Inj. Circ. Open Circuit		
P1238	17646	Cyl.2–Fuel Inj. Circ. Open Circuit		
P1239	17647	Cyl.3–Fuel Inj. Circ. Open Circuit		
P1240	17648	Cyl.4–Fuel Inj. Circ. Open Circuit		

AD0159800216000X

Fig. 19 Codes P1215, P1216, P1225, P1226, P1227, P1228, P1237, P1238, P1239 & P1240. A4 & S4

Diagnostic Trouble Code (DTC) SAE	VAG	Malfunction text	MIL	Corrective action
P1325	17733	Cyl.1–Knock Contr. Limit Attained	Off	– Check knock sensors and knock sensor control
P1326	17734	Cyl.2–Knock Contr. Limit Attained		
P1327	17735	Cyl.3–Knock Contr. Limit Attained		
P1328	17736	Cyl.4–Knock Contr. Limit Attained		
P1337	17745	Camshaft Pos. Sensor, Bank1 Short to Ground	2 Dcy	– Check Camshaft Position (CMP) sensor -G40
P1338	17746	Camshaft Pos. Sensor, Bank1 Open Circ./Short to B+		
P1386	17794	Internal Control Module Knock Control Circ. Error	Off	– Replace ECM

AD0159800218000X

Fig. 21 Codes P1325, P1326, P1327, P1328, P1337, P1338 & P1386: Motronic 3.2. A4 & S4

Diagnostic Trouble Code (DTC) SAE	VAG	Malfunction text	MIL	Corrective action
P1500	17908	Fuel Pump Relay Circ. Electrical Malfunction	Immed.	– Check fuel pump relay and relay actuation
P1501	17909	Fuel Pump Relay Circ. Short to Ground		
P1502	17910	Fuel Pump Relay Circ. Short to B+		
P1505	17913	Closed Throttle Pos. Switch Does Not Close/Open Circ.	2 Dcy	– Check throttle body and throttle valve control module
P1506	17914	Closed Throttle Pos. Switch Does Not Open/Short to Ground		
P1543	17951	Throttle Actuation Potentiometer Signal too Low	Immed.	
P1544	17952	Throttle Actuation Potentiometer Signal too High		
P1545	17953	Throttle Pos. Contr. Malfunction	2 Dcy	

AD0159800220000X

Fig. 23 Codes P1500, P1501, P1502, P1505, P1506, P1543, P1544 & P1545. A4 & S4

Diagnostic Trouble Code (DTC) SAE	VAG	Malfunction text	MIL	Corrective action
P1250	17658	Fuel Level Too Low	Off	– Fuel volume less than 2 gallons, add fuel. – Check wiring between ECM and instrument cluster – Check signal from fuel gauge, and fuel gauge

Note on misfire malfunctions:

For malfunctions that may be caused by low fuel volume (i.e. combustion misfire) a low-fuel malfunction (DTC "P1250") is also stored when there is less than 2 gallons of fuel remaining in the tank.

AD0159800217000X

Fig. 20 Code P1250. A4 & S4

Diagnostic Trouble Code (DTC) SAE	VAG	Malfunction text	MIL	Corrective action
P1410	17818	Tank Ventilation Valve Circ. Short to B+	2 Dcy	– Check Evaporative Emissions (EVAP) canister purge regulator valve Diagnostic Test Mode (DTM)
P1425	17833	Tank Vent Valve Short to Ground		
P1426	17834	Tank Vent Valve Open		
P1471	17879	EVAP Emission Contr. LDP Circ. Short to B+	➤ m.y. 1997: **Off** m.y. 1998 ➤: **2 Dcy**	– Check EVAP system
P1472	17880	EVAP Emission Contr. LDP Circ. Short to Ground		
P1473	17881	EVAP Emission Contr. LDP Circ. Open Circ.		
P1475	17883	EVAP Emission Contr. LDP Circ. Malfunction/Signal Circ. Open		
P1476	17884	EVAP Emission Contr. LDP Circ. Malfunction/Insufficient Vacuum		
P1477	17885	EVAP Emission Contr. LDP Circ. Malfunction		

AD0159800219000X

Fig. 22 Codes P1410, P1425, P1426, P1471, P1472, P1473, P1475, P1476 & P1477. A4 & S4

Diagnostic Trouble Code (DTC) SAE	VAG	Malfunction text	MIL	Corrective action
P1546	17954	Boost Pressure Contr. Valve Short to B+	Off	– Check intake air boost (charge pressure) regulation
P1547	17955	Boost Pressure Contr. Valve Short to Ground		
P1548	17956	Boost Pressure Contr. Valve Open		
P1555	17963	Charge Pressure Upper Limit Exceeded	Off	– Check intake air boost (charge pressure)
P1556	17964	Charge Pressure Negative Deviation		– Check intake air boost (charge pressure) regulation
P1557	17965	Charge Pressure Positive Deviation		
P1558	17966	Throttle Actuator Electrical Malfunction	2 Dcy	– Check throttle body and throttle valve control module
P1559	17967	Idle Speed Contr. Throttle Pos. Adaptation Malfunction **(Adaptation of throttle valve control module -J338- to Motronic ECM has been interrupted, e.g. the accelerator pedal was depressed or the engine was started during throttle valve control module adjustment)**	Off	

AD0159800221000X

Fig. 24 Codes P1546, P1547, P1548, P1555, P1556, P1557, P1558 & P1559. A4 & S4

Diagnostic Trouble Code (DTC) SAE	VAG	Malfunction text	MIL	Corrective action
P1560	17968	Maximum Engine Speed Exceeded	Off	– Carry out engine mechanical repairs as necessary
P1564	**17972**	**Idle Speed Contr. Throttle Pos. Low Voltage During Adaptation (Voltage less than 10 volts during adaptation of throttle valve control module -J338-)**	**Off**	**– Check voltage supply to Engine Control Module (ECM)**
P1565	**17973**	**Throttle Valve Control Module–J338 lower stop not attained (Lower stop of the throttle potentiometer can not be attained during adaptation of throttle valve control module -J338- e.g. accelerator pedal cable adjusted incorrectly, throttle dirty)**	**2 Dcy**	**– Adjust accelerator pedal cable – Clean throttle**
P1602	18010	Power Supply (B+) Terminal 30 Low Voltage	Off	– Check Engine Control Module (ECM) power supply
P1606	18014	Rough Road Spec Engine Torque ABS-ECU Electrical Malfunction	Off	– Check ABS control module signal for rough road recognition

AD0159800222000X

Fig. 25 Codes P1560, P1564, P1602 & P1606. A4 & S4

Diagnostic Trouble Code (DTC) SAE	VAG	Malfunction text	MIL	Corrective action
P1624	18032	MIL Request Sign. active	Immed.	– Check DTC memory for Transmission Control Module (TCM) and correct malfunctions
P1640	18048	Internal Contr. Module (EEPROM) Error	2 Dcy	– Replace ECM
P1681	**18089**	**Contr. Unit Programming Programming not Finished**	**Immed.**	**– Replace ECM**

Note for DTC P1624/18032:

If this malfunction is detected by the Transmission Control Module (TCM), the MIL is switched on by the ECM. In this case, the ECM stores the malfunction "MIL Request Sign. active" (DTC P1624/18032). After repairing the malfunction, erase DTC memory (ECM).

AD0159800224000X

Fig. 27 Codes P1624, P1640 & P1681. A4 & S4

DTC SAE	VAG	DTC text	Corrective action
P0112	16496	Intake Air Temp.Circ. Low Input [4]	– Check Intake Air Temperature (IAT) sensor -G42
P0113	16497	Intake Air Temp.Circ. High Input [4]	
P0116	16500	Engine Coolant Temp. Circ. Range/Performance [4]	– Check Engine Coolant Temperature (ECT) sensor -G62
P0117	16501	Engine Coolant Temp. Circ. Low Input [4]	
P0118	16502	Engine Coolant Temp. Circ. High Input [4]	

4) For these malfunctions, ECM does not switch on the Malfunction Indicator Lamp (MIL) unless malfunction is recognized again after another engine start.

AD0150000296000X

Fig. 29 Codes P0112, P0113, P0116, P0117 & P0118. TT

DTC SAE	VAG	DTC text	Corrective action
P0136	16520	O2 Sensor Circ.,Bank1-Sensor2 Malfunction [4]	– Check oxygen sensor regulation
P0137	16521	O2 Sensor Circ.,Bank1-Sensor2 Low Voltage [4]	
P0138	16522	O2 Sensor Circ.,Bank1-Sensor2 High Voltage [4]	
P0139	16523	O2 Sensor Circ.,Bank1-Sensor2 Slow Response [4]	
P0140	16524	O2 Sensor Circ.,Bank1-Sensor2 No Activity Detected [4]	

4) For these malfunctions, ECM does not switch on the Malfunction Indicator Lamp (MIL) unless malfunction is recognized again after another engine start.

AD0150000298000X

Fig. 31 Codes P0136, P0137, P0138, P0139 & P0140. TT

Diagnostic Trouble Code (DTC) SAE	VAG	Malfunction text	MIL	Corrective action
P1611	18019	MIL Call-up Circ./Transm. Contr. Module Short to Ground	2 Dcy	– Check wiring between TCM and ECM
P1612	18020	Electronic Control Module Incorrect Coding	Off	– Code Motronic ECM
P1613	18021	MIL Call-up Circ. Open/Short to B+	2 Dcy	– Check DTC memory for Transmission Control Module (TCM) and correct malfunctions – Check wiring between TCM and ECM

AD0159800223000X

Fig. 26 Codes P1611, P1612 & P1613. A4 & S4

DTC SAE	VAG	DTC text	Corrective action
P0101	16485	Mass or Volume Air Flow Circ Range/Performance [4]	
P0102	16486	Mass or Volume Air Flow Circ Low Input [4]	– Check Mass Air Flow (MAF) sensor -G70
P0103	16487	Mass or Volume Air Flow Circ High Input [4]	
P0106	16490	Manifold Abs.Pressure or Bar.Pressure ⇒ -G71/-F96 [1] Range/Performance [4]	– Check charge air pressure sensor -G31

AD0150000295000X

Fig. 28 Codes P0101, P0102, P0103 & P0106. TT

DTC SAE	VAG	DTC text	Corrective action
P0130	16514	O2 Sensor Circ.,Bank1-Sensor1 Malfunction [4]	– Check oxygen sensor regulation
P0131	16515	O2 Sensor Circ.,Bank1-Sensor1 Low Voltage [4]	
P0132	16516	O2 Sensor Circ.,Bank1-Sensor1 High Voltage [4]	
P0133	16517	O2 Sensor Circ.,Bank1-Sensor1 Slow Response [4]	
P0134	16518	O2 Sensor Circ.,Bank1-Sensor1 No Activity Detected [4]	

4) For these malfunctions, ECM does not switch on the Malfunction Indicator Lamp (MIL) unless malfunction is recognized again after another engine start.

AD0150000297000X

Fig. 30 Codes P0130, P0131, P0132, P0133 & P0134. TT

DTC SAE	VAG	DTC text	Corrective action
P0236	16620	Turbocharger Boost Sensor (A) Range/Performance [4]	– Check charge air pressure sensor -G31
P0237	16621	Turbocharger Boost Sensor (A) Low Input [4]	
P0238	16622	Turbocharger Boost Sensor (A) High Input [4]	

4) For these malfunctions, ECM does not switch on the Malfunction Indicator Lamp (MIL) unless malfunction is recognized again after another engine start.

AD0150000299000X

Fig. 32 Codes P0236, P0237 & P0238. TT

DTC		DTC text	Corrective action
SAE	VAG		
P0300	16684	Random/Multiple Cylinder Misfire Detected	- Check fuel injectors
P0301	16685	Cyl.1 Misfire Detected	- Check spark plugs and spark plug wires with connector
P0302	16686	Cyl. 2 Misfire Detected	- Check ignition coils with power output stage
P0303	16687	Cyl. 3 Misfire Detected	- Check misfire recognition
P0304	16688	Cyl. 4 Misfire Detected	- Fill fuel tank with gas
P0321	16705	Ign./Distributor Eng.Speed Inp.Circ. Range/Performance [4]	- Check engine speed (RPM) sensor
P0322	16706	Ign./Distributor Eng.Speed Inp.Circ No Signal [4]	

[4] For these malfunctions, ECM does not switch on the Malfunction Indicator Lamp (MIL) unless malfunction is recognized again after another engine start.

Notes:

For malfunctions potentially caused by fuel shortage (e.g. combustion misfires) the DTC "P1250, Fuel Level Too Low" is also indicated. This means that combustion misfires could not be recognized on account of a technical malfunction, but rather because there is/was too little fuel in fuel tank.

AD0150000300000X

Fig. 33 Codes P0300, P0301, P0302, P0303, P0304, P0321 & P0322. TT

DTC		DTC text	Corrective action
SAE	VAG		
P0441	16825	EVAP Emission Contr.Sys.Incorrect Purge Flow [4]	- Check EVAP canister purge regulator valve, Output Diagnostic Test Mode
P0442	16826	EVAP Emission Contr.Sys.(Small Leak) Leak Detected [4]	- Check tank system and tank ventilation system for leaks.
P0455	16839	EVAP Emission Contr.Sys.(Gross Leak) Leak Detected [4]	
P0501	16885	Vehicle Speed Sensor Range/Performance [4]	- Check Vehicle Speed Sensor
P0506	16890	Idle Control System RPM Lower than Expected [4]	- Check throttle valve control module
P0507	16891	Idle Control System RPM Higher than Expected [4]	- Adapt throttle valve control module
P0560	16944	System Voltage Malfunction	- Check voltage supply
P0562	16946	System Voltage Low Voltage	
P0563	16947	System Voltage High Voltage	

[4] For these malfunctions, ECM does not switch on the Malfunction Indicator Lamp (MIL) unless malfunction is recognized again after another engine start.

AD0150000302000X

Fig. 35 Codes P0441, P0442, P0455, P0501, P0506, P0507, P0560, P0562 & P0563. TT

DTC		DTC text	Corrective action
SAE	VAG		
P1113	17521	Bank1, Sensor1 Internal Resistance too High [4]	- Check oxygen sensor heating
P1114	17522	Bank1, Sensor2 Internal Resistance too High [4]	
P1115	17523	O2 Sensor Heater Circ.,Bank1-Sensor1 Short to Ground [4]	
P1116	17524	O2 Sensor Heater Circ.,Bank1-Sensor1 Open [4]	
P1117	17525	O2 Sensor Heater Circ.,Bank1-Sensor2 Short to Ground [4]	
P1118	17526	O2 Sensor Heater Circ.,Bank1-Sensor2 Open [4]	

[4] For these malfunctions, ECM does not switch on the Malfunction Indicator Lamp (MIL) unless malfunction is recognized again after another engine start.

AD0150000304000X

Fig. 37 Codes P1113, P1114, P1115, P1116, P1117 & P1118. TT

DTC		DTC text	Corrective action
SAE	VAG		
P0327	16711	Knock Sensor 1 Circ. Low Input	- Check Knock Sensors
P0328	16712	Knock Sensor 1 Circ. High Input	
P0332	16716	Knock Sensor 2 Circ. Low Input	
P0333	16717	Knock Sensor 2 Circ. High Input	
P0411	16795	Sec.Air Inj. Sys. Incorrect Flow Detected	- Check secondary air injection system
P0422	16806	Main Catalyst,Bank1 Efficiency Below Threshold [4]	- Perform work steps 1 - 12

[4] For these malfunctions, ECM does not switch on the Malfunction Indicator Lamp (MIL) unless malfunction is recognized again after another engine start.

AD0150000301000X

Fig. 34 Codes P0327, P0328, P0332, P0333, P0411 & P0422. TT

DTC		DTC text	Corrective action
SAE	VAG		
P0571	16955	Cruise/Brake Switch (A) Circ. [1] Incorrect signal	- Check Brake light switch -F- and brake pedal switch
P0601	16985	Internal Contr.Module Memory [4]	- Replace Engine Control Module (ECM)
P0604	16988	Internal Contr.Module Random Access [4]	
P0605	16989	Internal Contr.Module ROM Test Error [4]	
P1102	17510	O2 Sensor Heating Circ.,Bank1-Sensor1 Short to B+ [4]	- Check heated oxygen sensor
P1105	17513	O2 Sensor Heating Circ.,Bank1-Sensor2, Short to B+ [4]	
P1111	17519	O2 Control (Bank1) System too lean	- Check oxygen sensor regulation
P1112	17520	O2 Control (Bank1) System too rich	

[1] Brake pedal switch - F47 - is monitored in addition to brake light switch - F - .

[4] For these malfunctions, ECM does not switch on the Malfunction Indicator Lamp (MIL) unless malfunction is recognized again after another engine start.

AD0150000303000X

Fig. 36 Codes P0571, P0601, P0604, P0605, P1102, P1105, P1111 & P1112. TT

DTC		DTC text	Corrective action
SAE	VAG		
P1127	17535	Long Term Fuel Trim mult.,Bank1 System too Rich [4]	- Road test vehicle (fuel in oil). - Check fuel system pressure - Check fuel injectors
P1128	17536	Long Term Fuel Trim mult.,Bank1 System too Lean [4]	- Check mass air flow sensor - Check oxygen sensor control - Check fuel injectors

Notes:

mult. = multiple, means that malfunction is valid across entire range of engine speed and engine load.

[4] For these malfunctions, ECM does not switch on the Malfunction Indicator Lamp (MIL) unless malfunction is recognized again after another engine start.

AD0150000305000X

Fig. 38 Codes P1127 & P1128. TT

DTC		DTC text	Corrective action
SAE	VAG		
P1136	17544	Long Term Fuel Trim Add.Fuel,Bank1, System too Lean [4]	- Perform road test (fuel in oil)
P1137	17545	Long Term Fuel Trim Add.Fuel,Bank1, System too Rich [4]	- Check fuel system pressure - Check oxygen sensor control - Check Evaporative Emission (EVAP) Canister Purge Regulator Valve - Check mass air flow sensor
P1149	17557	O2 Control (Bank1) Out of range	- Check oxygen sensor regulation

Notes:

add. = additive, means that malfunction is only valid at closed throttle (idle).

[4] For these malfunctions, ECM does not switch on the Malfunction Indicator Lamp (MIL) unless malfunction is recognized again after another engine start.

AD0150000306000X

Fig. 39 Codes P1136, P1137 & P1149. TT

DTC		DTC text	Corrective action
SAE	VAG		
P1171	17579	Throttle Actuation Potentiometer Sign.2. Range/Performance [1] [3]	- Check angle sensor -2- for throttle drive (power accelerator actuation) -G188
P1172	17580	Throttle Actuation Potentiometer Sign.2. Signal too Low [1] [3]	
P1173	17581	Throttle Actuation Potentiometer Sign.2. Signal too High [1] [3]	
P1176	17584	O2 correction Behind Catalyst,B1 Limit Attained [4]	- Check oxygen sensor aging, oxygen sensor before catalytic converter - Check oxygen sensor and oxygen sensor control

[1] For these malfunctions, ECM switches on the EPC warning lamp in instrument cluster.

[3] For these malfunctions, ECM switches on the Malfunction Indicator Lamp (MIL) in instrument cluster immediately after recognizing the malfunction.

[4] For these malfunctions, ECM does not switch on the Malfunction Indicator Lamp (MIL) unless malfunction is recognized again after another engine start.

AD0150000307000X

Fig. 40 Codes P1171, P1172, P1173 & P1176. TT

DTC		DTC text	Corrective action
SAE	VAG		
P1237	17645	Cyl.1-Fuel Inj.Circ. Open Circ. [4]	- Check fuel injectors
P1238	17646	Cyl.2-Fuel Inj.Circ. Open Circ. [4]	
P1239	17647	Cyl.3-Fuel Inj.Circ. Open Circ. [4]	
P1240	17648	Cyl.4-Fuel Inj.Circ. Open Circ. [4]	

[4] For these malfunctions, ECM does not switch on the Malfunction Indicator Lamp (MIL) unless malfunction is recognized again after another engine start.

AD0150000309000X

Fig. 42 Codes P1237, P1238, P1239 & P1240. TT

DTC		DTC text	Corrective action
SAE	VAG		
P1287	17695	Turbocharger bypass valve Open [4]	- Check recirculating valve for turbocharger -N249
P1288	17696	Turbocharger bypass valve Short to B+ [4]	
P1289	17697	Turbocharger bypass valve Short to Ground [4]	

[4] For these malfunctions, ECM does not switch on the Malfunction Indicator Lamp (MIL) unless malfunction is recognized again after another engine start.

AD0150000311000X

Fig. 44 Codes P1287, P1288 & P1289. TT

DTC		DTC text	Corrective action
SAE	VAG		
P1337	17745	Camshaft Pos.Sensor,Bank1 Short to Ground [4]	- Check Camshaft Position (CMP) sensor
P1338	17746	Camshaft Pos.Sensor,Bank1 Open Circ./Short to B+ [4]	
P1340	17748	Crankshaft-/Camshaft Pos.Sens.Signals Out of Sequence [4]	- Unscrew Camshaft Position (CMP) sensor and check whether rotor trim is mounted properly at camshaft. (If mounted improperly, locking lug will get squished when mounting bolt is tightened). - Also check engine timing

[4] For these malfunctions, ECM does not switch on the Malfunction Indicator Lamp (MIL) unless malfunction is recognized again after another engine start.

AD0150000313000X

Fig. 46 Codes P1337, P1338 & P1340. TT

DTC		DTC text	Corrective action
SAE	VAG		
P1203	17611	Cyl.3-Fuel Inj.Circ. Electrical Malfunction [4]	- Check fuel injectors
P1213	17621	Cyl.1-Fuel Inj.Circ. Short to B+ [4]	
P1214	17622	Cyl.2-Fuel Inj.Circ. Short to B+ [4]	
P1215	17623	Cyl.3-Fuel Inj.Circ. Short to B+ [4]	
P1216	17624	Cyl.4-Fuel Inj.Circ. Short to B+ [4]	
P1225	17633	Cyl.1-Fuel Inj.Circ. Short to Ground [4]	
P1226	17634	Cyl.2-Fuel Inj.Circ. Short to Ground [4]	
P1227	17635	Cyl.3-Fuel Inj.Circ. Short to Ground [4]	
P1228	17636	Cyl.4-Fuel Inj.Circ. Short to Ground [4]	

[4] For these malfunctions, ECM does not switch on the Malfunction Indicator Lamp (MIL) unless malfunction is recognized again after another engine start.

AD0150000308000X

Fig. 41 Codes P1203, P1213, P1214, P1215, P1216, P1225, P1226, P1227 & P1228. TT

DTC		DTC text	Corrective action
SAE	VAG		
P1250	17658	Fuel Level too Low [1]	- Fill fuel tank with fuel - Check wire connection between ECM and instrument cluster - Check signal from sender for fuel gauge and fuel gauge

[1] *The DTC "Fuel Level Too Low" is stored when there is/was too little fuel in fuel tank. The DTC is stored as a static malfunction and is not switched to sporadic even if fuel tank has been filled with fuel (e.g. by the customer) in the meantime. In this way, it can be determined that subsequent malfunctions were caused by lack of fuel, e.g. combustion misfires or oxygen control related malfunctions.*

AD0150000310000X

Fig. 43 Code P1250. TT

DTC		DTC text	Corrective action
SAE	VAG		
P1325	17733	Cyl.1-Knock Contr. Limit Attained	- Check knock sensors
P1326	17734	Cyl.2-Knock Contr. Limit Attained	
P1327	17735	Cyl.3-Knock Contr. Limit Attained	
P1328	17736	Cyl.4-Knock Contr. Limit Attained	
P1335	17743	Engine Torque Monitoring 2 Control Limit Exceeded [1] [3]	- Large leak; check hose setup - Check intake air temperature sensor
P1336	17744	Engine Torque Monitoring Adaption at Limit	- Check Mass Air Flow (MAF) sensor - Check engine coolant temperature sensor

[1] For these malfunctions, ECM switches on the EPC warning lamp in instrument cluster.

[3] For these malfunctions, ECM switches on the Malfunction Indicator Lamp (MIL) in instrument cluster immediately after recognizing the malfunction.

AD0150000312000X

Fig. 45 Codes P1325, P1326, P1327, P1328, P1335 & P1336. TT

DTC		DTC text	Corrective action
SAE	VAG		
P1355	17763	Cyl. 1, ignition circuit Open Circuit	- Check activation of power output stages
P1356	17764	Cyl. 1, ignition circuit Short to B+	
P1357	17765	Cyl. 1, ignition circuit Short to ground	
P1358	17766	Cyl. 2, ignition circuit Open Circuit	
P1359	17767	Cyl. 2, ignition circuit Short Circuit to B+	

AD0150000314000X

Fig. 47 Codes P1355, P1356, P1357, P1358 & P1359. TT

DTC SAE	DTC VAG	DTC text	Corrective action
P1360	17768	Cyl. 2, ignition circuit Short circuit to Ground	- Check activation of power output stage
P1361	17769	Cyl. 3, ignition circuit Open Circuit	
P1362	17770	Cyl. 3, ignition circuit Short Circuit to B+	
P1363	17771	Cyl. 3, ignition circuit Short Circuit to ground	
P1364	17772	Cyl. 4, ignition circuit Open Circuit	
P1365	17773	Cyl. 4, ignition circuit Short circuit to B+	
P1366	17774	Cyl. 4, ignition circuit Short circuit to ground	

AD0150000315000X

Fig. 48 Codes P1360, P1361, P1362, P1363, P1364, P1365 & P1366. TT

DTC SAE	DTC VAG	DTC text	Corrective action
P1432	17840	Sec.Air Inj.Valve Open 4)	- Check Secondary Air Injection (AIR) pump relay -J299-
P1433	17841	Secondary air pump relay -J299 Open 4)	
P1434	17842	Sec.Air Inj.Sys.Pump Relay Circ. Short to B+ 4)	
P1435	17843	Secondary air pump relay -J299 Short to Ground 4)	
P1467	17875	EVAP Canister Purge Solenoid Valve Short Circuit to B+ 4)	- Check Evaporative Emission (EVAP) canister purge regulator valve -N115-
P1468	17876	EVAP Canister Purge Solenoid Valve Short Circuit to Ground 4)	
P1469	17877	EVAP Canister Purge Solenoid Valve Open Circuit 4)	

1) For these malfunctions, ECM switches on the EPC warning lamp in instrument cluster.

4) For these malfunctions, ECM does not switch on the Malfunction Indicator Lamp (MIL) unless malfunction is recognized again after another engine start.

AD0150000317000X

Fig. 50 Codes P1432, P1433, P1434, P1435, P1467, P1468 & P1469. TT

DTC SAE	DTC VAG	DTC text	Corrective action
P1477	17885	EVAP Emission Contr.LDP Circ. Malfunction 4)	- Check leak detection pump for fuel system
P1478	17886	EVAP Emission Contr.LDP Circ. Clamped Tube Detected 4)	- Check the lines (pressure/vacuum) to leak detection pump
P1500	17908	Fuel Pump Relay Circ. Electrical Malfunction 4)	- Check Fuel Pump (FP) relay
P1502	17910	Fuel Pump Relay Circ. Short to B+ 4)	
P1523	17931	Crash-Signal unplausible 2)	- Diagnose air bag system

2) DTC is stored upon appropriate signal from airbag control module.

4) For these malfunctions, ECM does not switch on the Malfunction Indicator Lamp (MIL) unless malfunction is recognized again after another engine start.

AD0150000319000X

Fig. 52 Codes P1477, P1478, P1500, P1502 & P1503. TT

DTC SAE	DTC VAG	DTC text	Corrective action
P1386	17794	Internal Control module	- Replace ECM ⇒ Page 24-25
P1387	17795	Internal Contr. module 4)	
P1388	17796	Internal Contr. module 1) 3)	
P1410	17818	Tank Ventilation Valve Circ. Short to B+ 4)	- Check Evaporative Emission (EVAP) canister purge regulator valve
P1421	17829	Sec.Air Inj.Valve Circ. Short to Ground 4)	- Check secondary air system
P1422	17830	Sec.Air Inj.Sys.Contr.Valve Circ. Short to B+ 4)	
P1424	17832	Sec.Air Inj.Sys.,Bank1 Leak Detected	- Check hose lines and components of secondary air system
P1425	17833	Tank Vent Valve Short to Ground 4)	- Check Evaporative Emission (EVAP) canister purge regulator valve -N80
P1426	17834	Tank Vent Valve Open 4)	

1) ECM switches on the EPC warning lamp in instrument cluster.

3) ECM switches on the MIL in instrument cluster immediately after recognizing the malfunction.

4) ECM does not switch MIL on unless malfunction is recognized again after another engine start.

AD0150000316000X

Fig. 49 Codes P1386, P1387, P1388, P1410, P1421, P1422, P1424, P1425 & P1426. TT

DTC SAE	DTC VAG	DTC text	Corrective action
P1471	17879	EVAP Emission Contr.LDP Circ. Short to B+ 4)	- Check Leak Detection Pump (LDP)
P1472	17880	EVAP Emission Contr.LDP Circ. Short to Ground 4)	
P1473	17881	EVAP Emission Contr.LDP Circ. Open Circ. 4)	
P1475	17883	EVAP Emission Contr.LDP Circ. Malfunction/Signal Circ. Open 4)	- Check Leak Detection Pump (LDP)
P1476	17884	EVAP Emission Contr.LDP Circ. Malfunction/Insufficient Vacuum 4)	- Check lines (pressurized/vacuum) to Leak Detection Pump (LDP)

4) For these malfunctions, ECM does not switch on the Malfunction Indicator Lamp (MIL) unless malfunction is recognized again after another engine start.

AD0150000318000X

Fig. 51 Codes P1471, P1472, P1473, P1475 & P1476. TT

DTC SAE	DTC VAG	DTC text	Corrective action
P1539	17947	Clutch Vacuum Vent Valve Switch Incorrect signal 4)	- Check clutch pedal switch
P1542	17950	Throttle Actuation Potentiometer Range/Performance 1) 3)	- Check Angle sensor -1- for throttle drive (power accelerator actuation) -G187-
P1543	17951	Throttle Actuation Potentiometer Signal too Low 1) 3)	
P1544	17952	Throttle Actuation Potentiometer Signal too High 1) 3)	
P1545	17953	Throttle Pos.Contr. Malfunction 1) 3)	- Check throttle valve control module

1) For these malfunctions, ECM switches on the EPC warning lamp in instrument cluster.

3) For these malfunctions, ECM switches on the Malfunction Indicator Lamp (MIL) in instrument cluster immediately after recognizing the malfunction.

4) For these malfunctions, ECM does not switch on the Malfunction Indicator Lamp (MIL) unless malfunction is recognized again after another engine start.

AD0150000320000X

Fig. 53 Codes P1539, P1542, P1543, P1544 & P1545. TT

DTC		DTC text	Corrective action
SAE	VAG		
P1546	17954	Boost Pressure Contr.Valve Short to B+	- Check wastegate bypass regulator valve -N75-
P1547	17955	Boost Pressure Contr.Valve Short to Ground	
P1548	17956	Boost Pressure Contr.Valve Open	
P1555	17963	Charge Pressure Upper Limit exceeded	
P1556	17964	Charge Pressure Contr. Negative Deviation	
P1557	17965	Charge Pressure Contr. Positive Deviation	
P1558	17966	Throttle Actuator Electrical Malfunction 1) 3)	- Check throttle valve control module
P1559	17967	Idle Speed Contr.Throttle Pos. Adaptation Malfunction 1) 4)	- Perform adaptation
P1560	17968	Maximum Engine Speed Exceeded	- Repair mechanical damage

1) ECM switches on EPC warning lamp in instrument cluster.

3) ECM switches on the MIL in instrument cluster immediately after recognizing the malfunction.

4) ECM does not switch on the MIL unless malfunction is recognized again after another engine start.

AD0150000321000X

Fig. 54 Codes P1546, P1547, P1548, P1555, P1556, P1557, P1558, P1559 & P1560. TT

DTC		DTC text	Corrective action
SAE	VAG		
P1603	18011	Internal Control Module Malfunction 4)	- Replace Engine Control Module (ECM)
P1604	18012	Internal Control Module Driver Error 1) 3)	
P1606	18014	Rough Road Spec Engine Torque ABS-ECU Electrical Malfunction	- Check wire connection between ECM and ABS control module (CAN-bus drive):
P1609	18017	Crash shut-down activated	- Check airbag system OBD
P1612	18020	Electronic Control Module Incorrect Coding 2)	- Code ECM

1) For these malfunctions, ECM switches on the EPC warning lamp in instrument cluster.

3) For these malfunctions, ECM switches on the Malfunction Indicator Lamp (MIL) in instrument cluster immediately after recognizing the malfunction.

4) For these malfunctions, ECM does not switch on the Malfunction Indicator Lamp (MIL) unless malfunction is recognized again after another engine start.

AD0150000323000X

Fig. 56 Codes P1603, P1604, P1606, P1609 & P1612. TT

DTC		DTC text	Corrective action
SAE	VAG		
P1640	18048	Internal Contr.Module (EEPROM) Error 4)	- Replace ECM
P1645	18053	Data Bus Powertrain Missing message f.all wheel drive contr.	- Check CAN-bus
P1648	18056	Data Bus Powertrain Malfunction	
P1649	18057	Data Bus Powertrain Missing message from ABS Control Module	

4) For these malfunctions, ECM does not switch on the Malfunction Indicator Lamp (MIL) unless malfunction is recognized again after another engine start.

AD0150000325000X

Fig. 58 Codes P1640, P1645, P1648 & P1649. TT

DTC		DTC text	Corrective action
SAE	VAG		
P1565	17973	Idle Speed Control Throttle Position lower limit not attained 1) 3)	- Check throttle valve control module
P1568	17976	Idle Speed Contr. Throttle Pos. mechanical Malfunction 1) 3)	
P1569	17977	Cruise control switch Incorrect signal	- Diagnostic of cruise control switch
P1570	17978	Control Module Locked	- Perform adaptation for immobilizer to ECM
P1579	17987	Idle Speed Contr.Throttle Pos. Adaptation not started	- Perform adaptation of throttle valve control module while maintaining test requirements
P1602	18010	Power Supply (B+) Terminal 30 Low Voltage	- Check control module voltage supply

1) For these malfunctions, ECM switches on the EPC warning lamp in instrument cluster.

3) For these malfunctions, ECM switches on the Malfunction Indicator Lamp (MIL) in instrument cluster immediately after recognizing the malfunction.

AD0150000322000X

Fig. 55 Codes P1565, P1568, P1569, P1570, P1579 & P1602. TT

DTC		DTC text	Corrective action
SAE	VAG		
P1630	18038	Accelera.Pedal Pos.Sensor 1 Signal too Low 1) 3)	- Check accelerator pedal position sensor
P1631	18039	Accelera.Pedal Pos.Sensor 1 Signal too High 1) 3)	
P1633	18041	Accelera.Pedal Pos.Sensor 2 Signal too Low 1) 3)	
P1634	18042	Accelera.Pedal Pos.Sensor 2 Signal too High 1) 3)	
P1639	18047	Accelera.Pedal Pos.Sensor 1+2 Range/Performance 1) 3)	

1) For these malfunctions, ECM switches on the EPC warning lamp in instrument cluster.

3) For these malfunctions, ECM switches on the Malfunction Indicator Lamp (MIL) in instrument cluster immediately after recognizing the malfunction.

AD0150000324000X

Fig. 57 Codes P1630, P1631, P1633, P1634 & P1639. TT

DTC		DTC text	Corrective action
SAE	VAG		
P1676	18084	Drive by Wire-MIL Circ. Electrical Malfunction 1)	- Check E-Gas MIL
P1677	18085	Drive by Wire-MIL Circ. Short to B+ 1)	
P1690	18098	Malfunction Indication Light Malfunction	
P1693	18101	Malfunction Indication Light Short circuit to B+	- Check exhaust warning light -K83-
P1853	18261	CAN-Bus Unplausible Message from Brake Contr.	- Check CAN-Bus

1) For these malfunctions, ECM switches on the EPC warning lamp in instrument cluster.

Notes:

The malfunction light for power acceleration - K132 - (in wiring diagram: malfunction light for power accelerator activation - K132) is also called the EPC warning lamp.

AD0150000326000X

Fig. 59 Codes P1676, P1677, P1690, P1693 & P1853. TT

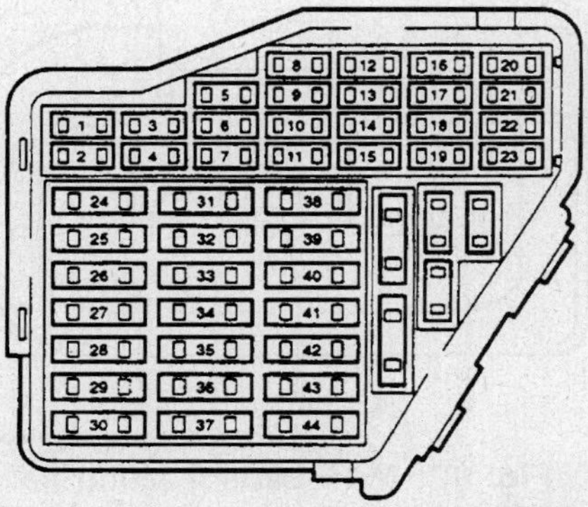

AD1029500073000X

Fig. 60 Fuse/relay panel

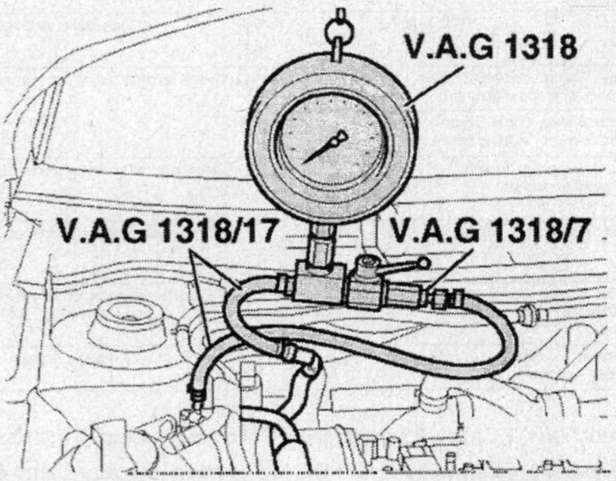

AD1020000185000X

Fig. 61 Fuel pressure inspection. TT

Display group: 2 Display field: 2	Possible cause	Corrective action
less than 0.50 ms	• Smaller values can only occur while driving during deceleration	
more than 1.50 ms	• Shift into drive range (auto. transmission) • Engine is affected by additional consumers	– Move shift lever to P or N – Illuminate load (A/C, power steering, generator)
	• Poor idle (does not run on all cylinders)	– Check spark plugs – Check fuel injectors
	• Throttle valve control module -J338 faulty	– Check throttle valve control module
Display field: 4	**Possible cause**	**Corrective action**
less than 1.8 g/s	• Large amount of false air between intake air duct and Mass Air Flow (MAF) sensor	– Check intake air system for leaks (false air)
larger than 4.0 g/s	• Shift lever in drive range (auto. transmission) • Engine affected by additional consumers	– Move shift lever to P or N – Eliminate load (A/C, power steering, generator)
	• Open circuits in wiring 3 or 4 between MAF sensor and ECM	– Check voltage supply
	• Open circuit in wiring 1 or 2 between MAF sensor and ECM	– Check wiring

AD1029800103000X

Fig. 63 MAF sensor troubleshooting chart. A4 & S4

	Display fields 1	2	3	4
Display group 2: Air mass taken in with engine at idle and operating temperature				
Display	xxx /min	xx.x %	x.x ms	xxx.x g/s
Indicated	Engine speed (RPM) (in increments of 40)	Load	mean injection time	Air mass
Work area	min.: 800 RPM max.: 6800 RPM	min.: 15 % max.: 175 %	min.: 2.0 ms max.: 19.0 ms	min.: 2.0 g/s max.: 170.0 g/s
Specified value:	800 – 920 RPM	15.0 – 25.0 %	2.0 – 4.0 ms	2.0 – 4.5 g/s
Note:	---	---	If specified value is not obtained: Evaluation display field 3	If specified value is not obtained: Evaluation display field 4

AD1020000186000X

Fig. 65 MAF sensor display data. TT

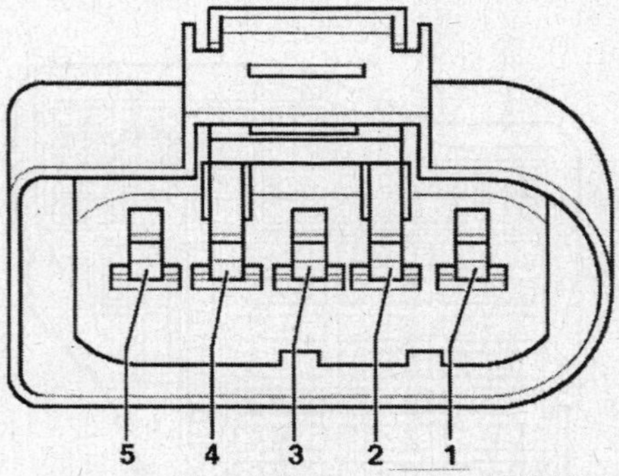

AD1020000188000X

Fig. 67 MAF sensor electrical connector terminal identification. TT

	Display fields 1	2	3	4
Display group 2: Load measurement				
Display	xxx RPM	xx.xx ms	xx.xx ms	xx.x g/s
Indicates	Engine speed (in 40 RPM steps)	Engine load	Injection time	Mass air flow
Range	0–6800 RPM	0.00–8.50 ms	0.00–25.00 ms	
Specified value	760–960 RPM	0.50–1.50 ms	**1.00–3.00 ms**	1.8–4.0 g/s
	2520 RPM	0.80–2.00 ms	**1.50–4.00 ms**	**7.5–12.0 g/s**

AD1029800102000X

Fig. 62 MAF sensor display data. A4 & S4

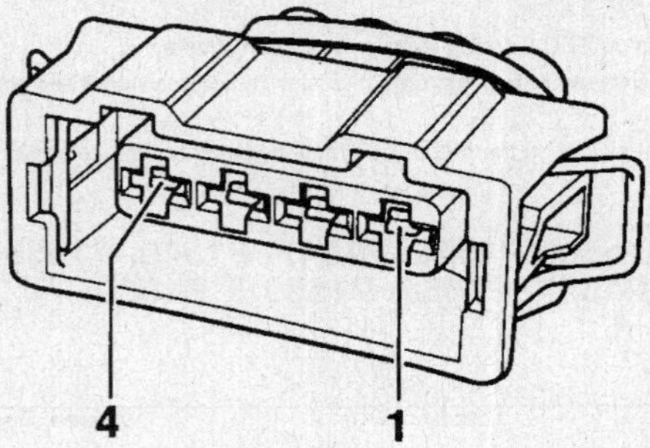

AD1029800104000X

Fig. 64 MAF sensor electrical connector terminal identification. A4 & S4

Display field: 3	Possible cause	Corrective action
less than 2.0 ms	◆ Smaller values can only occur when driving in deceleration mode	
larger than 4.0 ms	◆ Engine under load due to power accessories	– Reduce load (A/C system/power steering/generator)
	◆ Poor idle (does not run on all cylinders)	– Check spark plugs – Check fuel injectors
	◆ Throttle valve control module -J338-malfunctioning	– Check throttle valve control module
Smaller than 2.0 g/s	◆ Large un-metered air mass between intake manifold and Mass Air Flow (MAF) sensor ◆ Voltage supply of Mass Air Flow (MAF) sensor and wire connections to engine	– Check intake system for leaks (un-metered air) – Check voltage supply and wire connections
Larger than 4.5 g/s	◆ Engine under load due to power accessories.	– Reduce load (A/C system/power steering/generator)
	◆ Voltage supply of Mass Air Flow (MAF) sensor and wire connections to engine	– Check voltage supply and wire connections

AD1020000187000X

Fig. 66 MAF sensor troubleshooting chart. TT

	Display fields 1	2	3	4
Display group 1: Basic function, engine idle speed				
Display	xxxx RPM	xxx.x °C	xx.x%	XXXXXX
Indicates	Engine speed (in 40 RPM steps)	Engine coolant temperature	Oxygen sensor control	Adjustment conditions
Range	0–6800 RPM	-46.5° to 141.0°C	–25.0 to 25.0 %	---
Specified value	0 RPM	approx. ambient temperature[1]	In the range from –10.0 to 10.0% the displayed value must fluctuate by at least 2 %	---
	---		---	---

[1] If indicated temperature deviates significantly from the ambient temperature, check ECT sensor wiring for resistance or open circuits.

AD1029800109000X

Fig. 68 ECT display data. A4 & S4

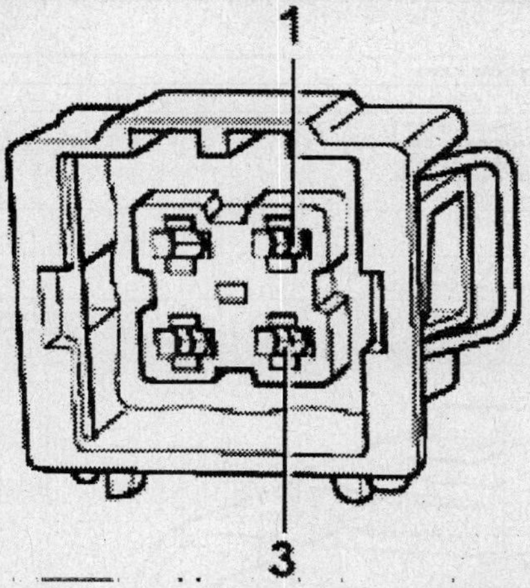

AD1020000192000X

Fig. 69 Temperature sensor. A4 & S4

	Display fields			
	1	2	3	4
Display group 4: Coolant temperature engine in idle				
Display	xxxx RPM	xx.x V	xxx.x °C	xxx.x °C
Display	Engine speed	battery voltage	coolant temperature	intake air temperature
Working range	0 - 6800 RPM	10.0 - 15.0 V	-48.0 to 143.0 °C	-48.0 to 143.0 °C
Specified value	xxxx RPM	12.0 - 15.0 V	Temperature value must increase evenly	from outside temperature to 20 °C

AD1020000189000X

Fig. 70 ECT display data. TT

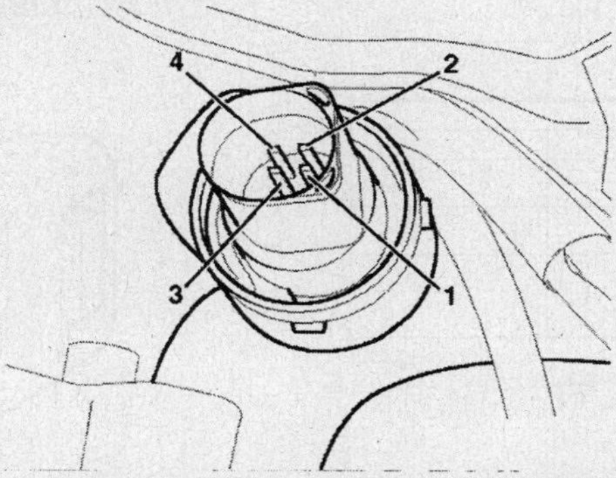

AD1020000191000X

Fig. 72 ECT sensor terminal identification. TT w/oval headed sensor

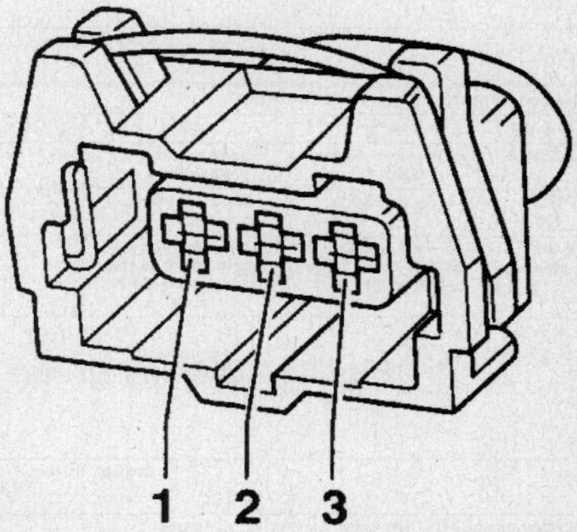

AD1029800112000X

Fig. 73 CKP sensor harness terminal identification. A4 & S4

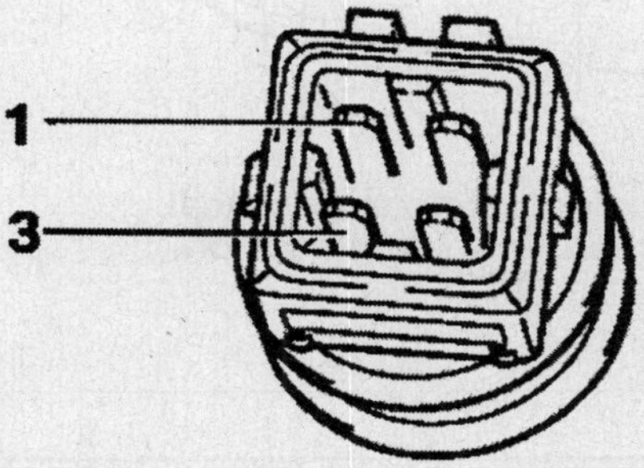

AD1020000190000X

Fig. 71 ECT sensor terminal identification. TT w/square headed sensor

	Display fields			
	1	2	3	4
Display group 32: Oxygen sensor control learning values				
Display	xx.x %	xx.x %		
Indicates	Oxygen sensor control learning value at idle (additive) (before TWC)	Oxygen sensor control learning value at partial load (multiplicative) (before TWC)		
Range	-26.0 to 26.0 %	-25.0 to 25.0 %		
Specified value	-8.0 to 8.0 % (can vary slightly)	-8.0 to 8.0 % (can vary slightly)		

AD1029800114000X

Fig. 74 Front oxygen sensor display data. A4 & S4

Display group: 32 Display fields: 1 + 2	Possible cause	Corrective action
O2S control learning value: -26.0 to -8.0 %	♦ Engine oil dilution (when partial load learning value is normal, ⇒ display field 2)	– Change engine oil, or carry out extensive road test and check again.
	♦ Fuel pressure too high	– Check fuel pressure regulator
	♦ Fuel injector leaking	– Check fuel injectors
	♦ Oxygen Sensor (O2S) heater malfunction	– Check O2S heater
O2S control learning value: 8.0-26.0 %	♦ Intake air leaks ("false air") or exhaust manifold leaks (when partial load learning value is normal, ⇒ display field 2)	– Check intake air system for leaks – Check exhaust system for leaks
	♦ Fuel pressure too low	– Check fuel pressure regulator
	♦ Oxygen Sensor (O2S) heater malfunction	– Check O2S heater
	♦ Fuel injector does not open, or partially opens	– Check fuel injectors
O2S control learning value: constant 0.0 %	♦ Oxygen sensor control learning not active	– Check Mass Air Flow (MAF) sensor -G70-

AD1029800116000X

Fig. 76 Evaluation of display group 32. A4 & S4

	Display fields			
	1	2	3	4
Display group 33: Oxygen sensor control				
Display	xx.x %	x.xxx V		
Indicates	Oxygen sensor control (before TWC)	Oxygen sensor voltage (before TWC)		
Range	-25.0 to 25.0 %	0.000-1.000 V		
Specified value	Within the range from -10.0 to 10.0 % the value must change by at least 2 %	Within the range from 0.000 to 1.000 V the value must fluctuate at least 30 times per minute, and change by at least 0.3 volts		

AD1029800115000X

Fig. 75 Display group 33. A4 & S4

Display group: 33 Display field: 2	Possible cause	Corrective action
approx. 0.435 V	♦ Open circuit in wiring between HO2S connector terminal 4 and ECM	– Check reference voltage
approx. 0.435 V	♦ Open circuit in wiring between HO2S connector terminal 3 and ECM	
approx. 1.085 V	♦ Short circuit to positive (B+) between HO2S connector terminal 4 and ECM	– Check HO2S wiring
approx. 0.000 V	♦ Short circuit to Ground between HO2S connector terminal 4 and ECM	

AD1029800117000X

Fig. 77 Evaluation of display group 33. A4 & S4

	Display fields			
	1	2	3	4
Display group 41: Oxygen Sensor (O2S) heating				
Display	xx.x Ω	Htg.bC.ON/Htg.bC.OFF	xx.x Ω	Htg.aC.ON/Htg.aC.OFF
Indicates	Resistance of oxygen sensor heater (before TWC)	O2S heater on or O2S heater off (before TWC)	Resistance of oxygen sensor heater (after TWC)	O2S heater on or O2S heater off (after TWC)
Range	0.0-65.0 Ω	---	---	---
Specified value	4.9-19.9 Ω	Htg.bC.ON	---	---
			---	---

AD1029800118000X

Fig. 78 Front oxygen sensor heater display group. A4 & s4

	Display fields			
	1	2	3	4
Display group 30: Oxygen sensor status				
Display	X X X	X X X		
Indicated	Oxygen sensor status, bank 1, sensor 1	Oxygen sensor status, bank 2, sensor 1		
Work area	0 = off 1 = on	0 = off 1 = on		
Specified value:	1 1 1	1 1 0		

AD1020000194000X

Fig. 79 Display group 30. TT

	Display fields			
	1	2	3	4
Display group 32: Oxygen sensor adaptation values				
Display	xx.x %	xx.x %		
Indicated	Oxygen sensor adaptation value bank 1, sensor 1 at idle (additive)	Oxygen sensor adaptation value bank 1, sensor 1 at partial throttle (multiple)		
Work area	-25.0 to 25.0 %	-25.0 to 25.0 %		
Specified value:	-10.0 to 10.0 % can fluctuate slightly	-10.0 to 10.0 % can fluctuate slightly		

AD1020000195000X

Fig. 80 Display group 32. TT

	Display fields			
	1	2	3	4
Display group 33: Oxygen sensor control				
Display	xx.x %	x.xxx V		
Indicated	Oxygen sensor control Bank 1	Oxygen sensor voltage bank 1		
Work area	-25.0 to 25.0 %	0.000 - 1.000 V		
Specified value:	Value must fluctuate at least 2 % in the range -10.0 to 10.0 %	Value must fluctuate approx. 0.3 V in the range 0.000 - 1.000 volts		

AD1020000196000X

Fig. 81 Display group 33. TT

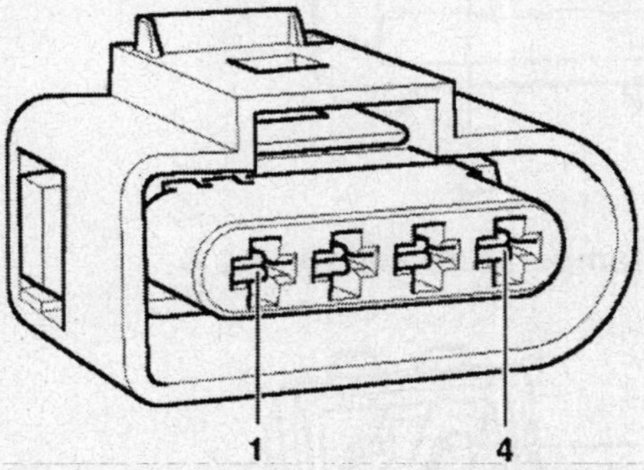

AD1020000197000X

Fig. 82 Oxygen sensor electrical connector terminal identification. TT

	Display fields			
	1	2	3	4
Display group 34: Diagnostic oxygen sensor aging				
Display	xxxx RPM	xxx °C	x.x s	---
Indicated	Engine speed (RPM)	Exhaust temperature	Period duration Oxygen sensor before catalytic converter	Diagnostic condition
Work area	0 - 6800	70 - 850 °C	0 - 3.0 s	Test OFF Test ON B1-S2 OK B1-S2 not OK
Specified value:	1800 - 2200 RPM	more than 350 °C	0.0 - 2.7 s	B1-S2 OK

AD1020000198000X

Fig. 83 Display Group 34. TT

	Display fields			
	1	2	3	4
Display group 36: Heated Oxygen Sensor (HO2S) behind Three Way Catalytic Converter (TWC)				
Display	x.xxx V	B1-S2 ON B1-S2 OFF		
Indicates	Voltage supply to HO2S behind TWC	HO2S behind TWC ON/OFF		
Range	0.000–1.000 V	---		
Specified value	0.000–1.000 V (can oscillate slightly)	B1-S2 ON		

AD1029800119000X

Fig. 84 Rear heated oxygen sensor display data. A4 & S4

Display group: 36 Display field: 1	Possible causes	Corrective action
approx. 0.435 V	♦ Open circuit in wiring -4- between oxygen sensor and ECM	– Check basic voltage
approx. 0.440 V	♦ Open circuit in wiring -4- between oxygen sensor and ECM	
approx. 1.085 V	♦ Short circuit to B+ in wiring -4- between oxygen sensor and ECM	– Check wiring for oxygen sensor
approx. 0.000 V	♦ Short circuit to Ground in wiring -4- between oxygen sensor and ECM	

AD1029800120000X

Fig. 85 Evaluation of display group 36. A4 & S4

	Display fields			
	1	2	3	4
Display group 41: Oxygen Sensor (O2S) heater, before and after Three Way Catalytic Converter (TWC)				
Display	xx.x Ω	Htg.bC.ON/Htg.bC.OFF	xx.x Ω	Htg.aC.ON/Htg.aC.OFF
Indicates	Resistance of Oxygen Sensor (O2S) heater before TWC	O2S heater on or O2S heater off (before TWC)	Resistance of oxygen sensor (O2S) heater (after TWC)	O2S heater on or O2S heater off (after TWC)
Range	---	---	0.0–65.0 Ω	---
Specified value	---	---	4.9–19.9 Ω	Htg.aC.ON
	---	---		---

AD1029800121000X

Fig. 86 Rear oxygen sensor heater display values. A4 & S4

	Display fields			
	1	2	3	4
Display group 30: Oxygen sensor status with engine at idle				
Display	X X X	X X X		
Indicated	Oxygen sensor status, bank 1, sensor 1	Oxygen sensor status bank 2, sensor 1		
Work area	0 = off 1 = on	0 = off 1 = on		
Specified value:	1 1 1	1 1 0		

AD1020000199000X

Fig. 87 Rear oxygen sensor display group 30. TT

	Display fields			
	1	2	3	4
Display group 37: Diagnostic oxygen sensor control system				
Display	xxx %	x.xxx volts	xxx ms	---
Indicated	Engine load	Oxygen sensor voltage bank 2, sensor 1	Duration of oxygen sensor control before catalytic converter, bank 1	Diagnostic condition
Work area	15 - 150 %	0.000 - 1.000 V	-1200 to 1200 ms	Test OFF Test ON System OK System not OK
Specified value:	12 - 30 %	0.100 - 0.900 V	-150 to 150 ms	SYST. i.O.

AD1020000200000X

Fig. 88 Rear oxygen sensor Display Group 37. TT

Display field: 2	Possible cause	Corrective action
Constant approx. 0.450 V	◆ Open circuit in wire 4 between oxygen sensor and control module	– Check primary voltage
	◆ Open circuit in wire 3 between oxygen sensor and control module	
Larger than 1.100 V	◆ Short circuit to B+ in wire 4 between oxygen sensor and control module	– Check oxygen sensor wiring and oxygen sensor behind catalytic converter
Smaller than 0.150 V	◆ Short circuit to Ground in wire 4 between oxygen sensor and control module	

AD1020000201000X

Fig. 89 Evaluation of display group 37. TT

	Display fields 1	2	3	4
Display group 5: Engine electronics				
Display	xxx RPM	xx.xx ms	xxx km/h	Idle Part throt Full throt Decel Enrich
Indicates	Engine speed (in 40 RPM steps)	Engine Load	Vehicle speed	Operational condition
Range	0–6800 RPM	0.00–8.50 ms	---	---
Specified value	760–960 RPM	0.50–1.50 ms	0 km/h	Throttle closed: "Idle" Throttle slightly open: "Part throt"
	---	---	---	

AD1029800137000X

Fig. 90 Engine electronics data

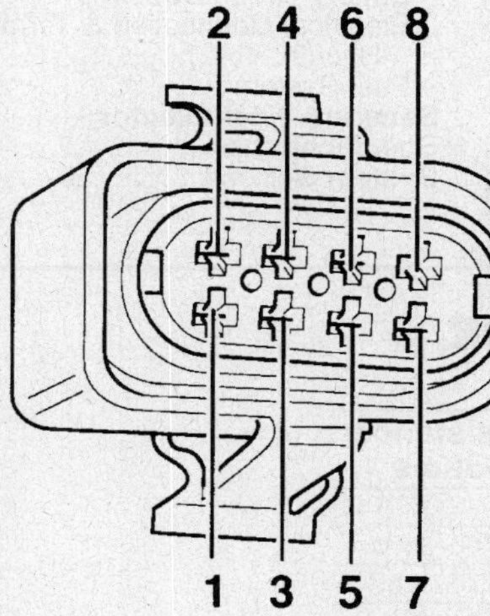

AD1029800135000X

Fig. 91 Throttle valve control module connector pin identification

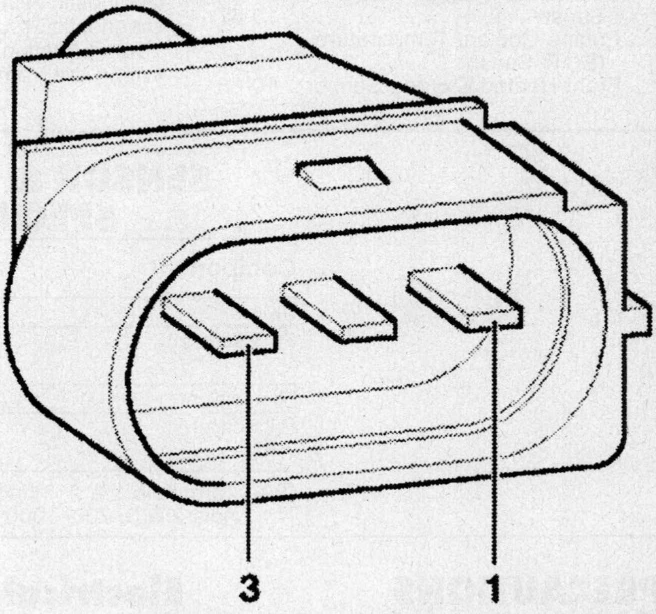

AD1020000193000X

Fig. 92 RPM sensor terminal identification. TT

	Display fields 1	2	3	4
Display group 3: Load measurement				
Display	xxx RPM	xx.x g/s	xxx ∠°	xx.x ° BTDC
Indicates	Engine speed (in 40 RPM steps)	Mass air flow	Throttle angle	Ignition timing
Range	0–6800 RPM	---	0–90 ∠°	0.0°–50.0° BTDC
Specified value	0 RPM	---	0–5 ∠°	0.0°
	---	---		---

AD1029800134000X

Fig. 93 Load measurement values. A4 & S4

	Display fields 1	2	3	4
Display group 62: E-Gas potentiometer voltages				
Display	xx %	xx %	xx %	xx %
Indicated	Throttle valve angle (angle sensor 1)	Throttle valve angle (angle sensor 2)	Sensor for pedal position	Sensor 2 for pedal position
Work area	min.: 0 % max.: 100 %	min.: 0 % max.: 100 %	min.: 0 % max.: 100 %	min.: 0 % max.: 100 %
Specified value:	3 – 93 %	97 – 3 %	12 – 97 %	4 – 49 %

AD1020000202000X

Fig. 94 Display group 62. TT

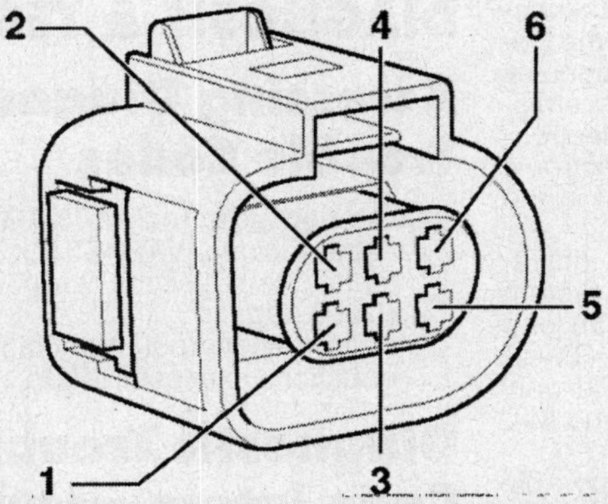

AD1020000203000X

Fig. 95 Throttle valve control module connector terminal identification. TT

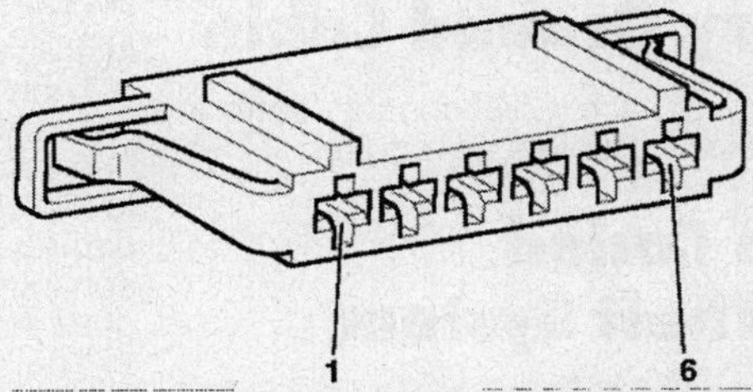

AD1020000204000X

Fig. 96 APP sensor electrical connector terminal identification. TT

2.7L Engine

INDEX

	Page No.
Description	10-64
Diagnosis & Testing	10-64
Accessing Diagnostic Trouble Codes	10-64
Component & System Tests	10-65
Accelerator Pedal Position (APP) Sensor	10-71
Crankshaft Position (CKP) Sensor	10-67
Engine Coolant Temperature (ECT) Sensor	10-67
Front Heated Oxygen Sensor	10-68
Fuel Injector	10-67
Fuel Pressure	10-65
Fuel Pump Relay	10-65
Mass Air Flow (MAF) Sensor	10-66
RPM Sensor	10-70
Rear Heated Oxygen Sensor	10-68
Throttle Position (TP) Sensor	10-70
Diagnostic Tests	10-65
Diagnostic Trouble Code Interpretation	10-64
Wiring Diagrams	10-64
Diagnostic Chart Index	10-73
Precautions	10-64
Air Bag Systems	10-64
Audio Coded Anti-Theft System	10-64
Battery Ground Cable	10-64
Electrical Connection & Terminal Repair	10-64
Fuel System	10-64
Sensor & Fuel Injector Specifications	10-64
System Service	10-71

SENSOR & FUEL INJECTOR SPECIFICATIONS

Component	Temperature, °F	Resistance, Ohms
CKP	68	①
ECT Sensor	86	1500–2000
	176	275–375
Fuel Injector	68	14–16
IAT Sensor	68	2400
	140	600

① — Terminals 1 & 2, infinity; terminals 1 & 3, infinity, terminals 2 & 3, 730–1000 ohms.

PRECAUTIONS

Fuel System

Always clean fuel lines before loosening and be sure to replace seals and fuel hose clamps. Keep a fully charged fire extinguisher readily available.

Air Bag Systems

Refer to "Air Bag System Precautions" in the front of this manual for system disarming and arming procedures.

Battery Ground Cable

Prior to service, disconnect battery ground cable and isolate as required.

Audio Coded Anti-Theft System

Do not use computer memory saver tool. Using the tool will keep the air bag system charged and may cause accidental activation of the air bag unit.

Obtain the security code from the vehicle operator prior to disconnecting the battery or removing the radio. Refer to the owner's manual for security code disarming and arming procedures.

Electrical Connection & Terminal Repair

If connector terminal or pin replacement is required, use only gold-plated components.

DESCRIPTION

The instrument cluster Exhaust Malfunction Indicator Lamp (MIL) will light if the Engine Control Module (ECM) recognizes malfunctions which effect exhaust emissions. Malfunctions relating to the electronic throttle are also indicated by a Electronic Power Control (EPC) warning lamp in the instrument cluster.

If the "Check Engine" Malfunction Indicator Lamp (MIL) starts to blink, the system has detected a fault condition that can lead to Three Way Catalytic Converter (TWC) damage. In this case driving should only continue with reduced power until the MIL goes out or lights continuously.

The system also recognizes sporadic (intermittent) faults. If a fault is present for a sufficient time it is stored as a static fault. If a condition appears momentarily or of insufficient time to be classified as static, it will be stored in a portion of fault memory where it will receive different attention than a static fault. If within next 50 engine starts the fault no longer appears it will be automatically erased.

The DTC memory is a permanent memory and does not depend on the power supply. Diagnostic Trouble Codes (DTCs) are stored in the memory until intentionally erased.

DTCs can only be accessed with a scan tool No. VAG 1551, or equivalent, in Operating Mode 1 "Rapid Data Transfer."

DIAGNOSIS & TESTING

Accessing Diagnostic Trouble Codes

1. Connect scan tool No. VAG 1551 and cable tool No. VAG1551/3, or equivalents, to the Data Link Connector (DLC), **Fig. 1.**
2. Follow scan tool manufacturer's instructions to access DTCs.

Diagnostic Trouble Code Interpretation

Refer to **Fig. 1** for Diagnostic Trouble Code (DTC) interpretation.

Wiring Diagrams

Refer to **Fig. 2** for MFI system wiring diagrams.

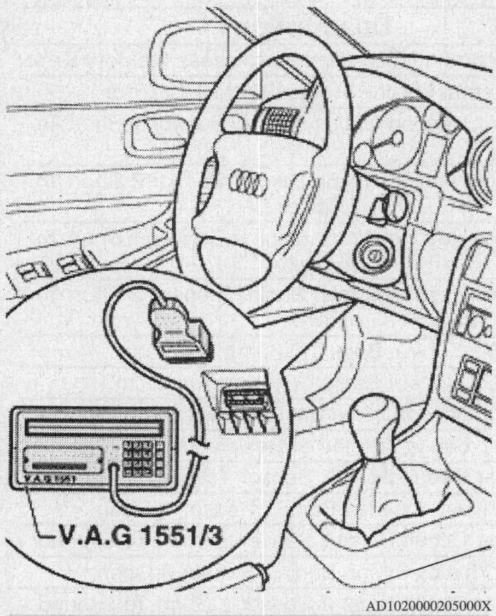

Fig. 1 Data Link Connector (DLC). A4 & S4

Code	Description
P0102	MAF Circuit Low Input
P0103	MAF Circuit High Input
P0106	MAP Or BARO Sensor Range/Performance
P0112	IAT Circuit Low Input
P0113	IAT Circuit High Input
P0116	ECT Circuit Fault
P0117	ECT Circuit Low Input
P0118	ECT Circuit High Input
P0130	O2 Sensor Bank 1 Sensor 1 Fault
P0131	O2 Sensor Bank 1 Sensor 1 Low Voltage
P0132	O2 Sensor Bank 1 Sensor 1 High Voltage
P0133	O2 Sensor Bank 1 Sensor 1 Slow Response
P0134	O2 Sensor Bank 1 Sensor 1 No Activity Detected
P0136	O2 Sensor Bank 1 Sensor 2 Fault
P0137	O2 Sensor Bank 1 Sensor 2 Low Voltage
P0138	O2 Sensor Bank 1 Sensor 2 High Voltage
P0139	O2 Sensor Bank 1 Sensor 2 Slow Response
P0140	O2 Sensor Bank 1 Sensor 2 No Activity Detected
P0150	O2 Sensor Bank 2 Sensor 1 Fault
P0151	O2 Sensor Bank 2 Sensor 1 Low Voltage
P0152	O2 Sensor Bank 2 Sensor 1 High Voltage
P0153	O2 Sensor Bank 2 Sensor 1 Slow Response
P0154	O2 Sensor Bank 2 Sensor 1 No Activity Detected
P0156	O2 Sensor Bank 2 Sensor 2 Fault
P0157	O2 Sensor Bank 2 Sensor 2 Low Voltage
P0157	Turbocharger Boost Sensor (A) Circuit High Input
P0158	O2 Sensor Bank 2 Sensor 2 High Voltage
P0160	O2 Sensor Bank 2 Sensor 2 No Activity Detected
P0237	Turbocharger Boost Sensor (A) Circuit Low Input

Fig. 1 Diagnostic Trouble Code (DTC) interpretation (Part 1 of 8)

Diagnostic Tests

Refer to **Figs. 3 through 59** for diagnostic trouble code interpretation. Refer to "Diagnostic Chart Index" for code definitions and specific diagnostic test for diagnosis procedures.

Component & System Tests

For component locations, refer to "Engine Compartment Reference Diagrams" to aid in location during diagnosis and testing procedures.

FUEL PUMP RELAY

The fuel pump relay is located in the central electrics in the lefthand footwell relay position 4.

1. Ensure battery is fully charged.
2. Remove lefthand front footwell storage bin.
3. Remove fuel pump fuse from fuse holder.
4. Connect diode test lamp tool No. VAG 1527B, or equivalent, between ground and one of the two fuel pump fuse contacts.
5. Crank engine and observe test lamp, which should light. Relay should also click.
6. If relay does not click, proceed as follows:
   a. Turn ignition On.
   b. Measure voltage between ground and relay panel contact 19, **Fig. 60,** which should be battery voltage.
   c. Measure voltage between ground and relay panel contact 17, which should be battery voltage.
   d. If voltages do not meet specifications, repair circuits as required.
7. If relay clicks but test lamp does not light, repeat test on other terminal.
8. If test lamp still does not light, repair open circuit in wiring between fuel pump fuse and terminal 23 in relay position 4.
9. If voltage supply, activation and wiring for fuel pump relay are satisfactory, replace fuel pump relay.

FUEL PRESSURE

1. Ensure fuel pump relay operation is satisfactory, fuel filter is unrestricted and battery is fully charged.
2. Connect fuel pressure gauge tool No. VAG 1318 to supply pipe using adapter tool No. 1318/7, pressure hose tools No. 1318/8 and 1318/15, or equivalent, between fuel supply line and fuel manifold.
3. Disconnect vacuum hose between fuel pressure regulator and intake manifold at fuel pressure regulator end. Plug end of hose.
4. Ensure pressure gauge lever is in Open position.
5. Start and idle engine.
6. If fuel flows out fuel pressure regulator vacuum connection, replace regulator.
7. Observe fuel pressure gauge, which should be 55–61 psi.
8. If pressure does not meet specifications, install a new fuel pressure regulator and repeat pressure test.
9. If pressure is lower than specifications, inspect fuel pump and supply lines for damage and replace as required.
10. If pressure is higher than specifications, inspect return line for damage such as pinching and replace as required.
11. Start and idle engine.
12. Turn off all electrical accessories.
13. Connect vacuum hose to fuel pressure regulator and observe drop in pressure on gauge, which should be approximately 7 psi.
14. If pressure drop does not meet specifications, inspect vacuum hose for cracks and splits and for blockages at intake manifold.
15. If vacuum hoses are satisfactory, replace fuel pressure regulator.
16. To inspect residual pressure, proceed as follows:
    a. Start engine and allow pressure to build.
    b. After pressure has risen, turn ignition Off.
    c. Close fuel pressure tester valve and record pressure.
    d. Observe pressure after 10 minutes, which should be a minimum 44 psi with engine at operating temperature or a minimum of 32 psi with engine cold.
    e. If pressure does not meet specifications, inspect fuel system and lines

Code	Description
P0300	Random Misfire Detected
P0301	Cylinder 1 Misfire Detected
P0302	Cylinder 2 Misfire Detected
P0303	Cylinder 3 Misfire Detected
P0304	Cylinder 4 Misfire Detected
P0305	Cylinder 5 Misfire Detected
P0306	Cylinder 6 Misfire Detected
P0321	Engine Speed Sensor Input Circuit Fault
P0322	Engine Speed Sensor No Signal
P0327	Knock Sensor 1 Circuit Low Input
P0328	Knock Sensor 1 Circuit High Input
P0332	Knock Sensor 2 Circuit Low Input
P0333	Knock Sensor 2 Circuit High Input
P0341	CMP Sensor Circuit Range/Performance
P0346	CMP Sensor Circuit 2 Range/Performance
P0411	Secondary Air Injection System Improper Flow Detected
P0421	Warm Up Catalyst Bank 1 Efficiency Below Threshold
P0422	Main Catalyst Bank 1 Efficiency Below Threshold
P0431	Warm Up Catalyst Bank 2 Efficiency Below Threshold
P0432	Main Catalyst Bank 2 Efficiency Below Threshold
P0441	EVAP System Improper Purge Flow Fault
P0442	EVAP System Small Leak Detected
P0455	EVAP System Large Leak Detected
P0501	Vehicle Speed Sensor Fault
P0506	Idle Control System RPM Lower Than Expected
P0507	Idle Control System RPM Higher Than Expected
P0560	System Voltage Malfunction
P0562	System Voltage Low Voltage
P0563	System Voltage High Voltage
P0571	Cruise Brake Switch (A) Improper Signal
P0601	Internal Control Module Memory Inspection Sum Error

Fig. 1 Diagnostic Trouble Code (DTC) interpretation (Part 2 of 8)

Code	Description
P0604	Internal Control Module Random Access Memory Error
P0605	Internal Control Module ROM Test Error
P1102	O2 Sensor Heating Circuit Bank 1 Sensor 1 Short To Power
P1105	O2 Sensor Heating Circuit Bank 1 Sensor 2 Short To Power
P1107	O2 Sensor Heating Circuit Bank 2 Sensor 1 Short To Power
P1110	O2 Sensor Heating Circuit Bank 2 Sensor 2 Short To Power
P1111	O2 Control Bank 1 System Too Lean
P1112	O2 Control Bank 1 System Too Rich
P1113	Bank 1 Sensor 1 Internal Resistance Too High
P1114	Bank 1 Sensor 2 Internal Resistance Too High
P1115	O2 Heater Circuit Bank 1 Sensor 1 Short To Ground
P1116	O2 Heater Circuit Bank 1 Sensor 1 Open
P1117	O2 Heater Circuit Bank 1 Sensor 2 Short To Ground
P1118	O2 Heater Circuit Bank 1 Sensor 2 Open
P1119	O2 Heater Circuit Bank 2 Sensor 1 Short To Ground
P1120	O2 Heater Circuit Bank 2 Sensor 1 Open
P1121	O2 Heater Circuit Bank 2 Sensor 2 Short To Ground
P1122	O2 Heater Circuit Bank 2 Sensor 2 Open
P1127	Long Term Fuel Trim Bank 1 System Too Rich
P1128	Long Term Fuel Trim Bank 1 System Too Lean
P1129	Long Term Fuel Trim Bank 2 System Too Rich
P1130	Long Term Fuel Trim Bank 2 Too Lean
P1131	Bank 2 Sensor 1 Internal Resistance Too High
P1136	Long Term Fuel Trim Bank 1 System Too Lean
P1137	Long Term Fuel Trim Bank 1 System Too Rich
P1138	Long Term Fuel Trim Bank 2 System Too Lean
P1139	Long Term Fuel Trim Bank 2 System Too Rich
P1140	Bank 2 Sensor 1 Internal Resistance Too High
P1141	Load Calculation Cross Inspection Range Fault
P1147	O2 Control Bank 2 System Too Lean

Fig. 1 Diagnostic Trouble Code (DTC) interpretation (Part 3 of 8)

for leaks, fuel pump check valve integrity and injector seal condition. Repair or replace as required.

MASS AIR FLOW (MAF) SENSOR

Functional Inspection

1. Connect scan tool No. VAG 1551 and cable tool No. VAG1551/3, or equivalents, to Data Link Connector (DLC), **Fig. 1.**
2. Bring engine to operating temperature.
3. Turn off all electrical accessories.
4. Ensure MAF sensor fuse is satisfactory.
5. Ensure cooling fan does not turn on during inspection.
6. Select engine electronics control module by entering "Address Word 01."
7. Press buttons 0 and 4 to select Basic Setting, then press Q button to confirm input.
8. Press buttons 0, 0 and 2 to select "Display Group Number 002," then press Q button to confirm input.
9. Compare scan tool display with **Fig. 61.**
10. If display data is satisfactory, proceed as follows:
    a. Press right arrow button to advance program sequence.
    b. Press buttons 0 and 6 to select "End Output" function 06, then press "Q" to confirm input.
    c. Turn ignition Off.
11. If display is not as specified in **Fig. 61,** refer to **Fig. 62** for possible fault causes.

Voltage Inspection

1. Disconnect MAF sensor electrical connector.
2. Connect a suitable voltmeter between connector terminal 2, **Fig. 63,** and ground.
3. Crank engine and observe voltage, which should be battery voltage.
4. If voltage does not meet specifications, inspect wiring connection from terminal 2 to fuel pump relay via fuse for open circuit and short circuit to ground. Repair as required.
5. If voltage is as specified, connect voltmeter to terminals 2 and 3, then crank engine observe voltage, which should be battery voltage.
6. If voltage is as specified, connect voltmeter to terminals 3 and 4, then turn ignition On and observe voltage, which should be approximately five volts.
7. If voltages do not meet specifications, proceed to "Wiring Inspection."

Wiring Inspection

1. Turn ignition Off.
2. Connect test box tool No. VAG 1598/31, or equivalent, to ECM wiring harness. **Do not connect to ECM itself.**
3. Inspect for opens or shorts as follows:
    a. Between MAF sensor electrical connector terminal 3 and test box socket 27.
    b. Terminal 4 and socket 53.
    c. Terminal 5 and socket 29.
    d. Maximum resistance is 1.5 ohms.
    e. Repair any fault conditions as required.
4. If wiring connections are satisfactory, replace MAF sensor.

Code	Description
P1148	O2 Control Bank 2 System Too Rich
P1149	O2 Control Bank 1 Out Of Range
P1150	O2 Control Bank 2 Out Of Range
P1171	Throttle Actuation Potentiometer Signal 2 Range/ Performance
P1172	Throttle Actuation Potentiometer Signal 2 Signal Too Low
P1173	Throttle Actuation Potentiometer Signal 2 Signal Too High
P1176	O2 Sensor Correction Behind Catalyst B1 Limit Attained
P1177	O2 Sensor Correction Behind Catalyst B2 Limit Attained
P1213	Cylinder 1 Fuel Injector Short To Power
P1214	Cylinder 2 Fuel Injector Short To Power
P1215	Cylinder 3 Fuel Injector Short To Power
P1216	Cylinder 4 Fuel Injector Short To Power
P1217	Cylinder 5 Fuel Injector Short To Power
P1218	Cylinder 6 Fuel Injector Short To Power
P1225	Cylinder 1 Fuel Injector Short To Ground
P1226	Cylinder 2 Fuel Injector Short To Ground
P1227	Cylinder 3 Fuel Injector Short To Ground
P1228	Cylinder 4 Fuel Injector Short To Ground
P1229	Cylinder 5 Fuel Injector Short To Ground
P1230	Cylinder 6 Fuel Injector Short To Ground
P1237	Cylinder 1 Fuel Injector Open Circuit
P1238	Cylinder 2 Fuel Injector Open Circuit
P1239	Cylinder 3 Fuel Injector Open Circuit
P1240	Cylinder 4 Fuel Injector Open Circuit
P1241	Cylinder 5 Fuel Injector Open Circuit
P1242	Cylinder 6 Fuel Injector Open Circuit
P1250	Fuel Level Too Low
P1287	Turbocharger Bypass Valve Open
P1288	Turbocharger Bypass Valve Short To Voltage
P1289	Turbocharger Bypass Valve Short To Ground
P1296	Cooling System Malfunction

Fig. 1 Diagnostic Trouble Code (DTC) interpretation (Part 4 of 8)

Code	Description
P1325	Cylinder 1 Knock Control Limit Attained
P1326	Cylinder 2 Knock Control Limit Attained
P1327	Cylinder 3 Knock Control Limit Attained
P1328	Cylinder 4 Knock Control Limit Attained
P1329	Cylinder 5 Knock Control Limit Attained
P1330	Cylinder 6 Knock Control Limit Attained
P1335	Engine Torque Monitoring 2 Control Limit Exceeded
P1336	Engine Torque Monitoring Adaptation At Limit
P1337	Camshaft Position Sensor Bank 1 Short To Ground
P1338	Camshaft Position Sensor Bank 1 Open Circuit Or Short To Power
P1340	CKP & CMP Sensors Out Of Sequence
P1347	Bank 2 CKP & CMP Sensor Signals Out Of Sequence
P1355	Cylinder 1 Ignition Circuit Open
P1356	Cylinder 1 Ignition Circuit Short To Voltage
P1357	Cylinder 1 Ignition Circuit Short To Ground
P1358	Cylinder 2 Ignition Circuit Open
P1359	Cylinder 2 Ignition Circuit Short To Voltage
P1360	Cylinder 2 Ignition Circuit Short To Ground
P1361	Cylinder 3 Ignition Circuit Open
P1362	Cylinder 3 Ignition Circuit Short To Voltage
P1363	Cylinder 3 Ignition Circuit Short To Ground
P1364	Cylinder 4 Ignition Circuit Open
P1365	Cylinder 4 Ignition Circuit Short To Voltage
P1366	Cylinder 4 Ignition Circuit Short To Ground
P1367	Cylinder 5 Ignition Circuit Open
P1368	Cylinder 5 Ignition Circuit Short To Voltage
P1369	Cylinder 5 Ignition Circuit Short To Ground
P1370	Cylinder 6 Ignition Circuit Open
P1371	Cylinder 6 Ignition Circuit Short To Voltage
P1372	Cylinder 6 Ignition Circuit Short To Ground
P1386	Internal Control Module Knock Control Error

Fig. 1 Diagnostic Trouble Code (DTC) interpretation (Part 5 of 8)

ENGINE COOLANT TEMPERATURE (ECT) SENSOR

Functional Inspection

1. Ensure engine is cold.
2. Connect scan tool No. VAG 1551, or equivalent, to DLC.
3. Start and idle engine.
4. Select control module for engine electronics using "Address Word 01."
5. Press buttons 0 and 8 for "Read Measuring Value Block," then press Q button to confirm input.
6. Press buttons 0, 0 and 4 for "Display Group Number 04," then confirm with Q button.
7. Observe display in Display Field 3, **Fig. 64.**
8. If temperature does not increase evenly, disconnect coolant temperature sensor electrical connector.
9. **On models equipped with square headed sensor,** connect a suitable ohmmeter between sensor terminals 1 and 3, **Fig. 65.**
10. **On models equipped with oval headed sensor,** connect a suitable ohmmeter between sensor terminals 3 and 4, **Fig. 66.**
11. **On all models,** observe resistance, which should meet specifications listed in "Sensor & Fuel Injector Specifications."
12. Replace coolant temperature sensor if resistances do not meet specifications.

Wiring Inspection

1. Turn ignition Off.
2. Connect test box tool No. VAG 1598/31, or equivalent, to ECM wiring harness. **Do not connect to ECM itself.**
3. **On models equipped with square headed sensor,** inspect for shorts or grounds between coolant temperature sensor terminal 1 and test box socket 93, then at terminal 3 and socket 108. Repair as required.
4. **On models equipped with oval headed sensor,** inspect for shorts or grounds between coolant temperature sensor terminal 3 and test box socket 108, then at terminal 4 and socket 93. Repair as required.
5. **On all models,** inspect wiring for shorts to each other and repair as required.
6. If wiring is satisfactory, replace ECM.

CRANKSHAFT POSITION (CKP) SENSOR

On these models the CKP sensor is known as the Engine Speed (RPM) sensor. Refer to "RPM Sensor" for diagnosis and testing.

FUEL INJECTOR

1. Disconnect injector harness connector.
2. Measure fuel injector resistance.
3. Compare resistance with specifications listed previously.
4. If resistance is not within specifications, replace injector.
5. If wiring or connector repairs are required, refer to "Precautions."

Code	Description
P1387	Internal Control Module Knock Control Circuit Error
P1388	Internal Control Module Drive By Wire Error
P1391	Camshaft Position Sensor Bank 2 Short To Ground
P1392	Camshaft Position Sensor Bank 2 Open Circuit Or Short To Power
P1410	Tank Ventilation Valve Short To Power
P1411	Secondary AIR System Bank 2 Flow Too Low
P1414	Secondary AIR System Bank 2 Leak Detected
P1420	Secondary AIR Valve Circuit Short To Voltage
P1421	Secondary AIR Valve Circuit Short To Ground
P1422	Secondary AIR Control Valve Circuit Short To Power
P1423	Secondary AIR Bank 1 Flow Too Low
P1424	Secondary AIR Bank 1 Leak Detected
P1425	Tank Vent Valve Short To Ground
P1426	Tank Vent Valve Open
P1432	Secondary Air Injection Valve Open
P1433	Secondary Air Injection Pump Relay Circuit Open
P1434	Secondary Air Injection Pump Relay Circuit Short To Power
P1435	Secondary Air Injection Pump Relay Short To Ground
P1453	Exhaust Gas Temperature Sensor 1 Open Or Short To Voltage
P1454	Exhaust Gas Temperature Sensor 1 Short To Ground
P1455	Exhaust Gas Temperature Sensor 1 Range/ Performance
P1456	Exhaust Gas Temperature Control Bank 1 Limit Attained
P1457	Exhaust Gas Temperature Sensor 2 Open Or Short To Voltage
P1458	Exhaust Gas Temperature Sensor 2 Short To Ground
P1459	Exhaust Gas Temperature Sensor 2 Range/ Performance
P1460	Exhaust Gas Temperature Control Bank 2 Limit Attained
P1461	Exhaust Gas Temperature Control Bank 1 Range/ Performance
P1462	Exhaust Gas Temperature Control Bank 2 Range/ Performance
P1470	EVAP Emission Control LDP Circuit Electrical Malfunction
P1471	EVAP Emission Control LDP Circuit Short To Power

Fig. 1 Diagnostic Trouble Code (DTC) interpretation (Part 6 of 8)

Code	Description
P1472	EVAP Emission Control LDP Circuit Short To Ground
P1473	EVAP Emission Control LDP Circuit Open
P1475	EVAP Emission Control LDP Circuit Malfunction/Signal Circuit Open
P1476	EVAP Emission Control LDP Circuit Fault/Insufficient Vacuum
P1477	EVAP Emission Control LDP Circuit Fault
P1478	EVAP Emission Control LDP Circuit Clamped Tube Detected
P1500	Fuel Pump Relay Electrical Fault
P1501	Fuel Pump Relay Short To Ground
P1502	Fuel Pump Relay Short To Voltage
P1519	Intake Camshaft Control Bank 1 Fault
P1522	Intake Camshaft Control Bank 2 Fault
P1523	Crash Signal From Air Bag Control Unit Range/ Performance
P1529	Camshaft Control Circuit Short To Voltage
P1530	Camshaft Control Circuit Short To Ground
P1531	Camshaft Control Circuit Open
P1539	Clutch Pedal Switch Range/Performance
P1542	Throttle Actuation Potentiometer Range/Performance
P1543	Throttle Actuation Potentiometer Signal Too Low
P1544	Throttle Actuation Potentiometer Signal Too High
P1545	Throttle Position Control Fault
P1546	Boost Pressure Control Valve Short To Voltage
P1547	Boost Pressure Control Valve Short To Ground
P1548	Boost Pressure Control Valve Open
P1555	Charge Pressure Upper Limit Exceeded
P1556	Charge Pressure Control Negative Deviation
P1557	Charge Pressure Positive Deviation
P1558	Throttle Actuator Electrical Fault
P1559	Idle Speed Control Throttle Position Adaptation Fault
P1560	Maximum Engine Speed Exceeded
P1564	Idle Speed Control Throttle Position Low Voltage During Adaptation

Fig. 1 Diagnostic Trouble Code (DTC) interpretation (Part 7 of 8)

FRONT HEATED OXYGEN SENSOR

FUNCTIONAL INSPECTION

Bank 1

1. Road test vehicle and bring to operating temperature.
2. Connect scan tool No. VAG 1551, or equivalent, to DLC.
3. Start and idle engine, then select control module for engine electronics using "Address Word 01."
4. Press buttons 0 and 4 to select Basic Setting, then press Q button to confirm input.
5. Press buttons 0, 3 and 4 to select "Display Group Number 034," then press Q button to confirm input.
6. Operate engine at 1900–2200 RPM, then continue test as soon as Display Field 4 indicates "Test ON."
7. Observe oxygen sensor status, **Fig. 67.**
8. If specified value in Display Fields 3 and 4 is not obtained, replace HO_2S Bank 1.

Bank 2

1. Road test vehicle and bring to operating temperature.
2. Connect scan tool No. VAG 1551, or equivalent, to DLC.
3. Start and idle engine, then select control module for engine electronics using "Address Word 01."
4. Press buttons 0 and 4 to select Basic Setting, then press Q button to confirm input.
5. Press buttons 0, 3 and 5 to select "Display Group Number 035," then press Q button to confirm input.
6. Operate engine at 1900–2200 RPM, then continue test as soon as Display Field 4 indicates "Test ON."
7. Observe oxygen sensor status, **Fig. 68.**
8. If specified value in Display Fields 3 and 4 is not obtained, replace HO_2S Bank 2.

REAR HEATED OXYGEN SENSOR

Functional Inspection

1. Road test vehicle and bring to operating temperature. **Do not erase DTC memory.**
2. Connect scan tool No. VAG 1551, or equivalent, to DLC.
3. Start and idle engine, then select control module for engine electronics using "Address Word 01."
4. Press buttons 0 and 4 to select Basic Setting, then press Q button to confirm input.
5. Press buttons 0, 3 and 4 to select "Display Group Number 034," then press Q

Code	Description
P1565	Idle Speed Control Throttle Position Lower Impact Not Attained
P1568	Idle Speed Control Throttle Position Mechanical Malfunction
P1569	Cruise Control Switch Improper Signal
P1570	Control Module Locked
P1579	Idle Speed Control Throttle Position Adaptation Not Started
P1600	Power Supply Terminal 15 Low Voltage
P1602	Power Supply Terminal 30 Low Voltage
P1603	Internal Control Module Malfunction
P1604	Internal Control Module Malfunction
P1606	Rough Road Spec Engine Torque ABS-ECU Electrical Fault
P1609	Crash Shutdown Activated
P1612	ECM Improper Coding
P1620	ECT Signal Open Or Short To Voltage
P1621	ECT Signal Short To Ground
P1622	ECT Signal Range/Performance
P1624	MIL Request Sign Active
P1626	CAN Bus Missing Message From Transmission Control
P1630	APP Sensor 1 Signal Too Low
P1631	APP Sensor 1 Signal Too High
P1633	APP Sensor 2 Signal Too Low
P1634	APP Sensor 2 Signal Too High
P1639	APP Sensor 1 & 2 Range/Performance
P1640	Internal Control Module EEPROM Error
P1648	Data Bus Powertrain Malfunction
P1649	Data Bus Powertrain Missing Message From ABS Control Module
P1676	Drive By Wire MIL Circuit Electrical Malfunction
P1677	Drive By Wire MIL Circuit Short To Voltage
P1690	MIL Lamp Fault
P1693	MIL Short To Voltage
P1851	Data Bus Powertrain Missing Message From Brake Control
P1853	Data Bus Powertrain Implausible Message From Brake Control
P1854	Data Bus Powertrain Hardware Faulty

Fig. 1 Diagnostic Trouble Code (DTC) interpretation (Part 8 of 8)

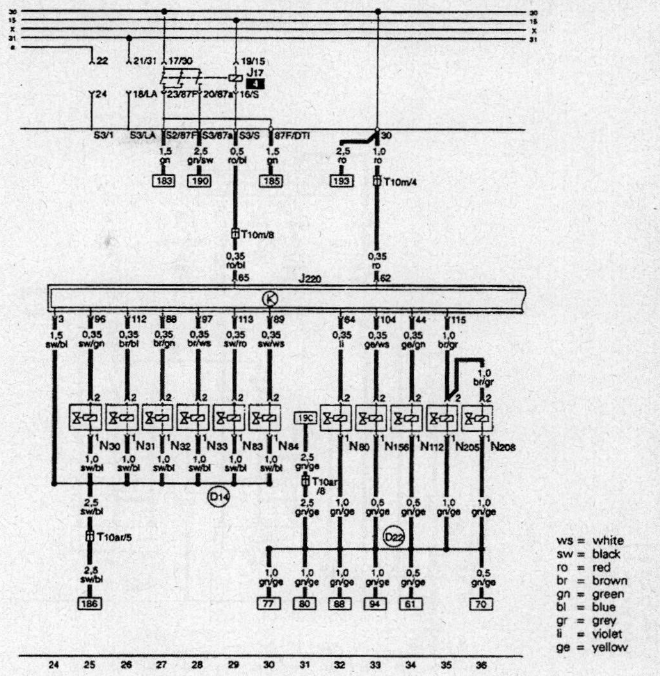

J17 – Fuel Pump (FP) Relay
J220 – Motronic Engine Control Module (ECM)
N30 – Injector, Cyl. 1
N31 – Injector, Cyl. 2
N32 – Injector, Cyl. 3
N33 – Injector, Cyl. 4
N80 – Evaporative (EVAP) Canister Purge Regulator Valve
N83 – Injector, Cyl. 5
N84 – Injector, Cyl. 6
N112 – Secondary Air Injection (AIR) Solenoid Valve
N156 – Intake Manifold Change-Over Valve
N205 – Valve -1- for camshaft adjustment
N208 – Valve -2- for camshaft adjustment
T10m – Wire Connector, 10 Point, black, connector station, electronics box in plenum chamber
T10ar – Wire Connector, 10 Point, orange, connector station, electronics box in plenum chamber
D14 – Wire connection (ignition coil – control module), in right front wiring harness
D22 – Connector (over fuse 234), in wiring harness front, right

AD1020000206010X

Fig. 2 MFI system wiring diagram (Part 1 of 7)

button to confirm input.
6. Set engine speed to 2800–3200 RPM using idle speed adjuster tool No. VAG 1788/10, or equivalent.
7. Continue test as soon as Display Field 2 indicates an exhaust temperature of more than 608°F (320°C). This might require a few minutes.
8. Press C button.
9. Set engine speed to 1900–2200 RPM.
10. Press buttons 0, 3 and 0 to select "Display Group Number 030," then press Q button to confirm input.
11. Observe oxygen sensor status for oxygen rear heated oxygen sensor in Display Field 2, **Fig. 69.**
12. Press C button.
13. Press buttons 0, 4 and 3 to select "Display Group Number 043," **Fig. 70,** then press Q button to confirm input.
14. Set engine speed to 1900–2200 RPM.
15. Observe specified value in Display Field 4.
16. Press buttons 0, 4 and 4 to select "Display Group Number 044," **Fig. 71,** then press Q button to confirm input.
17. If specified value of "B2-S2 OK" is reached , press C button.
18. Road test vehicle for approximately 10 minutes.
19. Press buttons 0, 3 and 7 to select "Display Group Number 037," **Fig. 72,** then press Q button to confirm input.
20. Observe oxygen sensor voltage in Display Field 2.
21. Observe dwell time between front and rear oxygen sensors in Display Field 3 and diagnostic result in Display Field 4.
22. Press C button.
23. Press buttons 0, 3 and 8 to select "Display Group Number 038," **Fig. 73,** then press Q button to confirm input.
24. If displayed values are as specified, refer to **Fig. 74** for Display Groups 37 and 38 evaluation.
25. If specified value in Display Groups 37 and 38 Fields 3 or 4 is not obtained, inspect exhaust system and catalytic converter for leakage and damage.
26. If difference of measuring block values in Display Fields 3 (Oxygen Sensor Correction Value) is too large (+500 ms, –500 ms), ensure oxygen sensors are installed in their proper locations.
27. If no cause can be pinpointed, replace front oxygen sensor.

Heater Inspection

1. Connect scan tool No. VAG 1551, or equivalent, to DLC.
2. Start and idle engine, then select control module for engine electronics using "Address Word 01."
3. Press buttons 0 and 8 to select "Read Measuring Value Block," then press Q button to confirm input.
4. Press buttons 0, 4 and 1 to select "Display Group Number 041," **Fig. 75,** then

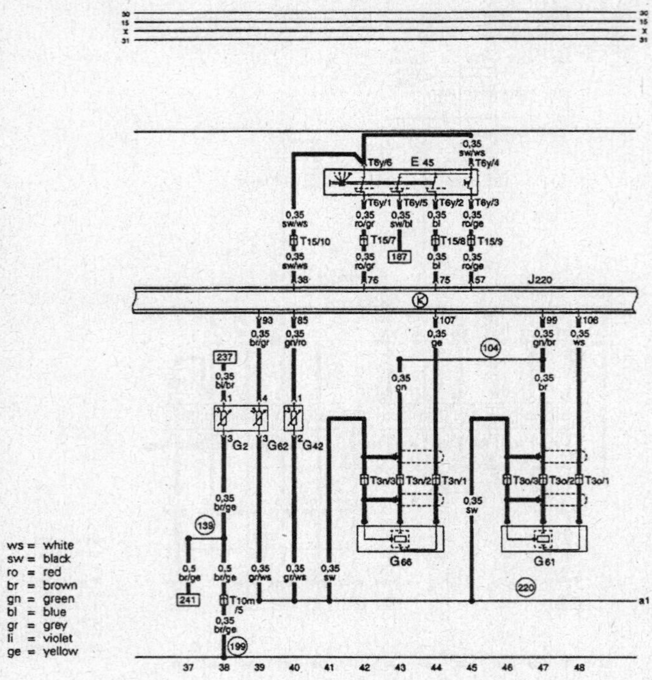

E45 – Cruise Control Switch
G2 – Engine Coolant Temperature (ECT) Sensor
G42 – Inteke Air Temperature (IAT) Sensor
G61 – Knock Sensor (KS) 1
G62 – Engine Coolant Temperature (ECT) Sensor
G66 – Knock Sensor (KS) 2
J220 – Motronic Engine Control Module (ECM)
T3n – Wire Connector, 3 Point, blue, in engine compartment, left
T3o – Wire Connector, 3 Point, blue, in engine compartment, right
T6y – Wire Connector, 6 Point, black, near steering column
T10m – Wire Connector, 10 Point, black, connector station, electronics box in plenum chamber
T15 – Wire Connector, 15 Point, white, connector station, electronics box in plenum chamber

(104) – Ground connection, in right front wiring harness (sensor grounds)
(139) – Ground connection (sensor grounds), in Motronic Multiport Fuel Injection (MFI) wiring harness
(199) – Ground connection –3–, in instrument panel wiring harness
(220) – Ground connection (sensor ground), in engine compartment wiring harness

AD1020000206020X

Fig. 2 MFI system wiring diagram (Part 2 of 7)

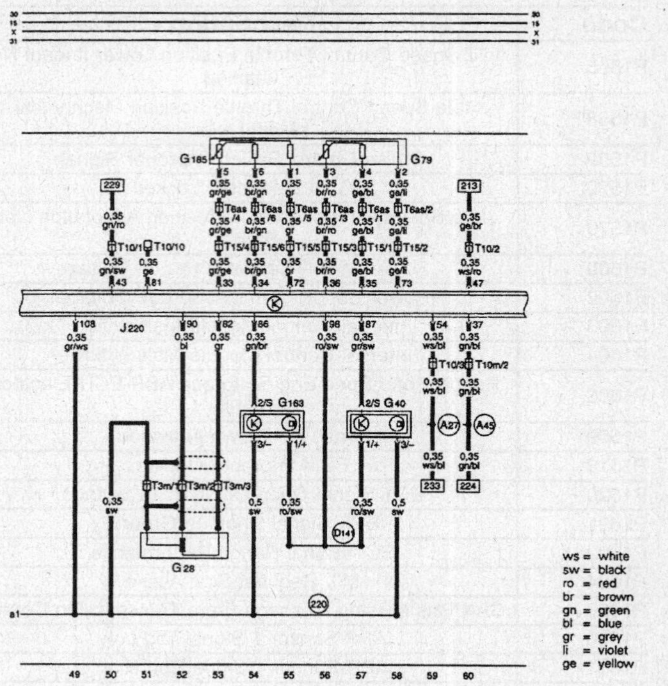

G28 – Engine Speed (RPM) Sensor
G40 – Camshaft Position (CMP) Sensor
G79 – Throttle Position (TPP) Sensor
G185 – Sender –2– for accelerator pedal position
J220 – Motronic Engine Control Module (ECM)
T3m – Wire Connector, 3 Point, grey, in engine compartment, left
T6as – Wire Connector, 6 Point, black, in engine compartment, rear
T10 – Wire Connector, 10 Point brown, connector station, electronics box in plenum chamber
T10m – Wire Connector, 10 Point black, connector station, electronics box in plenum chamber
T15 – Wire Connector, 15 Point, white, connector station, electronics box in plenum chamber

(220) – Ground connection (sensor ground), in engine compartment wiring harness
(A27) – Wire Connection (vehicle speed signal), in instrument panel wiring harness
(A45) – Wire Connection (RPM–signal), in instrument panel wiring harness
(D141) – Connector (5V), in wiring harness, engine pre–wiring

AD1020000206030X

Fig. 2 MFI system wiring diagram (Part 3 of 7)

confirm entry with Q button.

5. Adjust engine speed to approximately 3000 RPM and observe oxygen sensor heater resistance, **Fig. 75.**
6. Press C button.
7. Press buttons 0, 4 and 2 to select "Display Group Number 042," **Fig. 76,** then confirm entry with Q button.
8. Observe oxygen sensor heater resistance, **Fig. 75.**
9. If resistances do not meet specifications, proceed to "Voltage Inspection."

Voltage Inspection

1. Disconnect rear oxygen sensor 4-pin electrical connector.
2. Connect a suitable voltmeter between connector terminals 1 and 2, **Fig. 77.**
3. Crank engine and observe voltage, which should be battery voltage.
4. If there is no voltage reading, connect voltmeter between terminal 1 and ground.
5. Crank engine and observe voltage, which should be battery voltage.
6. If voltage does not meet specifications, inspect wiring connection for open circuit from connector terminal 1 to fuel pump relay via fuse.
7. If voltage meets specifications, connect voltmeter between terminal 2 and battery positive terminal.
8. Start engine and observe voltage, which should be battery voltage with possible fluctuations.
9. If voltage does not meet specifications, turn ignition Off, then connect test box tool No. VAG 1598/31, or equivalent, to ECM wiring harness. **Do not connect to ECM itself.**
10. Inspect for open circuits as follows:
    a. Connector terminal 2 and test box socket 5.
    b. Terminal 2 and socket 4.
    c. Terminal 2 and socket 63.
    d. Terminal 2 and socket 6.
    e. Maximum resistance is 1.5 ohms.
    f. Repair wiring as required.
11. If wiring is satisfactory but oxygen sensor heater still has no ground, replace rear oxygen sensor.

RPM SENSOR

1. Disconnect RPM sensor electrical connector.
2. Connect a suitable ohmmeter to sensor terminals 2 and 3, **Fig. 78,** then measure resistance, which should be 730–1000 ohms at 68°F.
3. Measure resistance between terminals 1 and 2, then between terminals 1 and 3, which should all be infinite.
4. If resistances do not meet specifications, replace sensor.
5. If resistances meet specifications, ensure ignition is turned Off, then connect test box tool No. VAG 1598/31, or equivalent, to ECM wiring harness. **Do not connect to ECM itself.**
6. Inspect for opens or shorts as follows: between RPM sensor electrical connector terminal 1 and test box socket 108; between terminal 2 and socket 90; between terminal 3 and socket 82. Repair as required.
7. If wiring is satisfactory, replace ECM.

THROTTLE POSITION (TP) SENSOR

Functional Inspection

1. Start and idle engine, then select control module for engine electronics using "Address Word 01."
2. Press buttons 0 and 8 to select "Read Measuring Value Block," then press Q button to confirm input.
3. Press buttons 0, 6 and 2 to select "Display Group Number 062," then press Q button to confirm input.
4. Observe specified value for E-Gas potentiometer voltages, **Fig. 79.**
5. Observe Display Fields 3 and 4 while

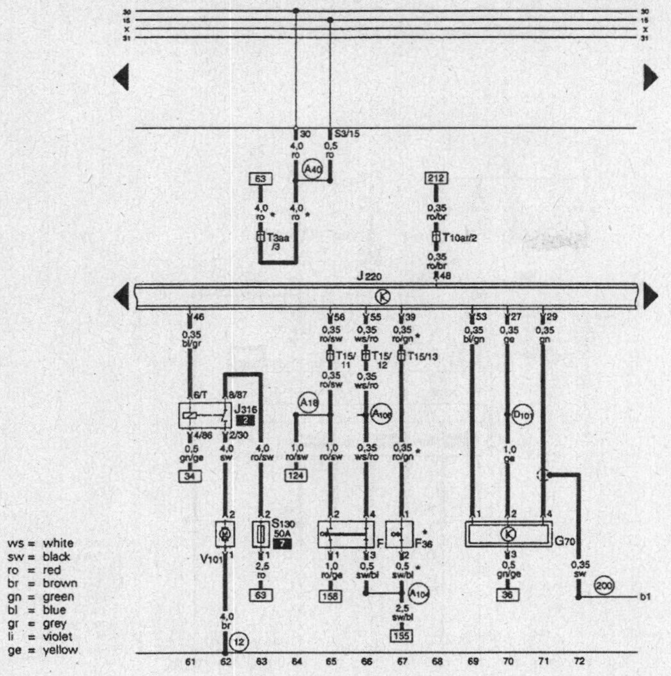

F – Brake Light Switch
F36 – Clutch Vacuum Vent Valve Switch
G70 – Mass Air Flow (MAF) Sensor
J220 – Motronic Engine Control Module (ECM)
J318 – Secondary Air Injection (AIR) Relay
S130 – Fuse for secondary air pump
T3aa – Wire Connector, 3 Point, white, connector station, electronics box in plenum chamber
T10ar – Wire Connector, 10 Point, orange, connector station, electronics box in plenum chamber
V101 – Secondary Air Injection (AIR) Pump Motor

(12) – Ground connection, in engine compartment, left
(200) – Ground connection (shielding), in engine compartment wiring harness
(A18) – Wire connection (54), in instrument panel wiring harness
(A40) – Plus connection –1– (30), in instrument panel wiring harness
(A104) – Plus connector –2– (15), in instrument panel wiring harness
(A106) – Connector –2– (86s), in instrument panel wiring harness
(D101) – Wire connection –1–, in engine compartment wiring harness
* – Manual Transmission Only

AD1020000206040X

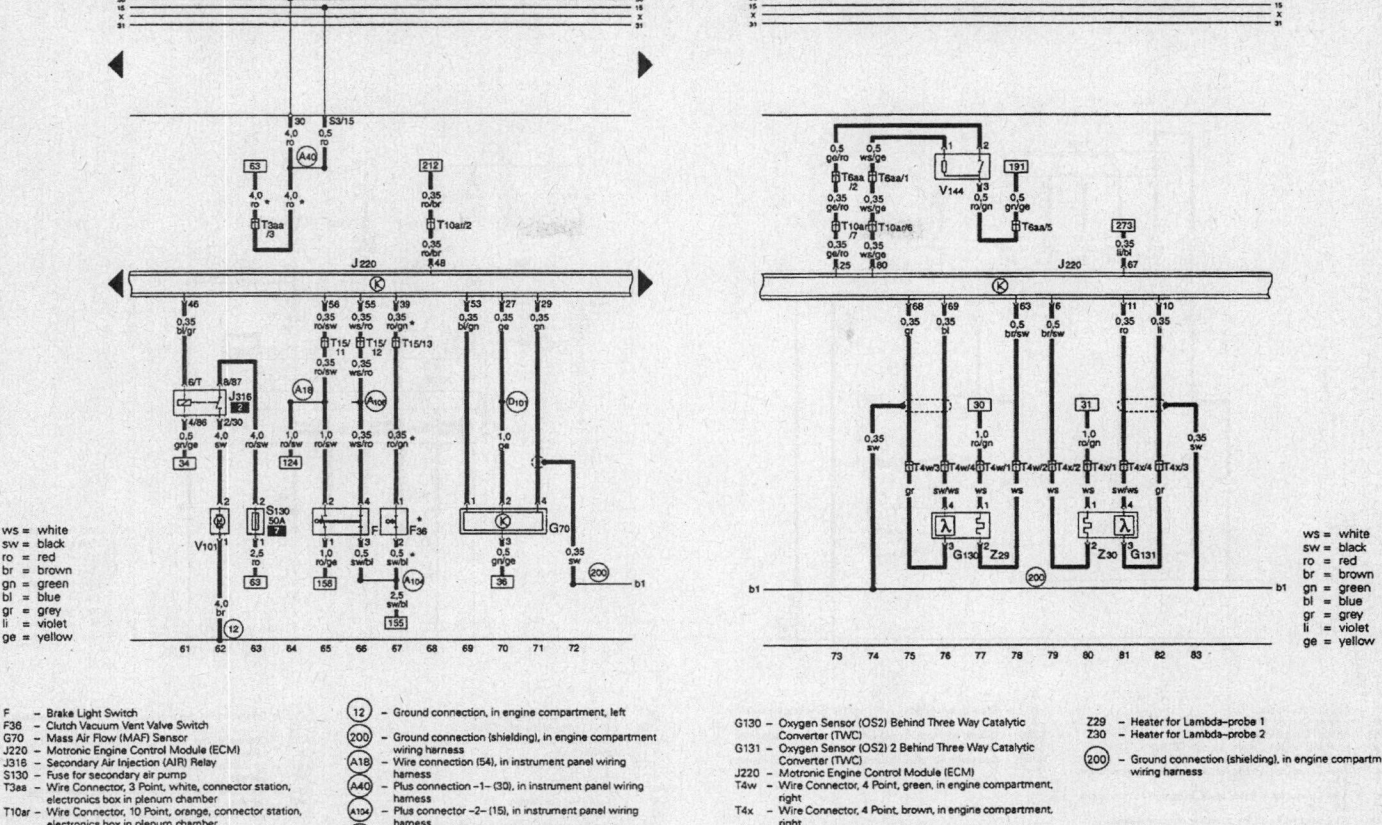

Fig. 2 MFI system wiring diagram (Part 4 of 7)

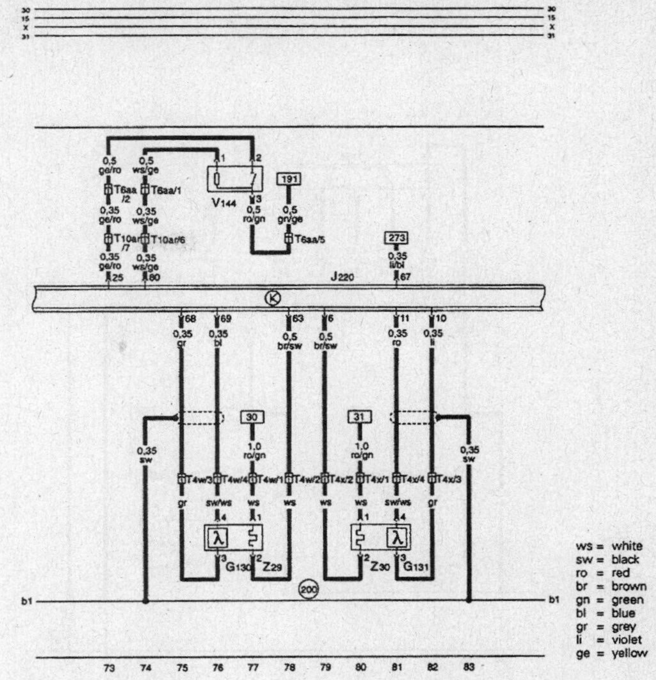

G130 – Oxygen Sensor (OS2) Behind Three Way Catalytic Converter (TWC)
G131 – Oxygen Sensor (OS2) 2 Behind Three Way Catalytic Converter (TWC)
J220 – Motronic Engine Control Module (ECM)
T4w – Wire Connector, 4 Point, green, in engine compartment, right
T4x – Wire Connector, 4 Point, brown, in engine compartment, right
T6aa – Wire Connector, 6 Point, brown, connector station right, A-pillar
T10ar – Wire Connector, 10 Point, orange, connector station, electronics box in plenum chamber
V144 – Leak Detection Pump (LDP)
Z29 – Heater for Lambda-probe 1
Z30 – Heater for Lambda-probe 2
(200) – Ground connection (shielding), in engine compartment wiring harness

AD1020000206050X

Fig. 2 MFI system wiring diagram (Part 5 of 7)

slowly depressing accelerator pedal completely to floor, which should appear as follows:

a. Percentage indication in Display Field 3 must climb uniformly. Tolerance range 3–93 % is not used completely.
b. Percentage indication in Display Field 4 must climb uniformly. Tolerance range 4–49% is not used completely.

6. If percentage indications do not meet specifications, proceed to "Wiring Inspection," then inspect Accelerator Pedal Position (APP) Sensor.

Wiring Inspection

1. Disconnect throttle valve control module electrical connector.
2. Turn ignition On.
3. Connect a suitable voltmeter between terminal 2 and ground, **Fig. 80,** then between terminals 1 and 3. There should be approximately five volts.
4. Measure voltages between terminal 5 and ground, then between terminals 5 and 4. There should be approximately five volts.
5. If voltages meet specifications, ensure ignition is turned Off, then connect test box tool No. VAG 1598/31, or equivalent, to ECM wiring harness. **Do not connect to ECM itself.**
6. Inspect for open circuits and shorts as follows:
   a. Between throttle valve control module electrical connector terminal 1 and test box socket 72.
   b. Terminal 2 and socket 73.
   c. Terminal 3 and socket 36.
   d. Terminal 4 and socket 35.
   e. Terminal 5 and socket 33.
   f. Terminal 6 and socket 34.
7. Repair wiring fault conditions as required.
8. If wiring and connections are satisfactory, replace throttle valve control module.

ACCELERATOR PEDAL POSITION (APP) SENSOR

The Throttle Position (TP) sensor and the Accelerator Pedal Position (APP) sender are located at the accelerator pedal and transmit the driver's intentions to the ECM completely independently of each other. Both sensors are incorporated into one housing.

1. Connect scan tool No. VAG 1551, or equivalent, to DLC.
2. Turn ignition On, then select control module for engine electronics using "Address Word 01."
3. Press buttons 0 and 8 to select "Read Measuring Value Block," then press Q button to confirm input.
4. Press buttons 0, 6 and 2 to select "Display Group Number 062," **Fig. 79,** then press Q button to confirm input.
5. Observe specified value for E-Gas potentiometer voltages, **Fig. 79.**
6. Observe Display Fields 3 and 4 while slowly depressing accelerator pedal completely to floor, which should appear as follows:
   a. Percentage indication in Display Field 3 must climb uniformly. Tolerance range 3–93 % is not used completely.
   b. Percentage indication in Display Field 4 must climb uniformly. Tolerance range 4–49 % is not used completely.
7. If percentage indications do not meet specifications, replace accelerator position sensors.

SYSTEM SERVICE

Refer to "Fuel Injection" section for adjustment and replacement procedures.

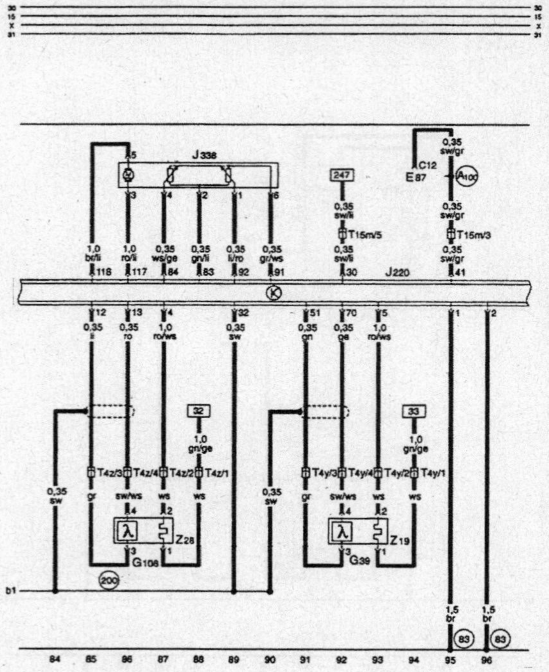

ws = white
sw = black
ro = red
br = brown
gn = green
bl = blue
gr = grey
li = violet
ge = yellow

- E87 – A/C Control Head
- G39 – Heated Oxygen Sensor (HO2S) 1
- G108 – Heated Oxygen Sensor (HO2S) 2
- J220 – Motronic Engine Control Module (ECM)
- J338 – Throttle Valve Control Module
- T4y – Wire Connector, 4 Point, black, in engine compartment, right
- T4z – Wire Connector, 4 Point, black, in engine compartment, left
- T15m – Wire Connector, 15 Point, red, connector station, electronics box in plenum chamber
- Z19 – Oxygen Sensor (O2S) I Heater
- Z28 – Oxygen Sensor (O2S) II Heater

- (83) – Ground connection –1–, in right front wiring harness
- (200) – Ground connection (shielding), in engine compartment wiring harness
- (A100) – Connector –2– (87), in instrument panel wiring harness

AD1020000206060X

Fig. 2 MFI system wiring diagram (Part 6 of 7)

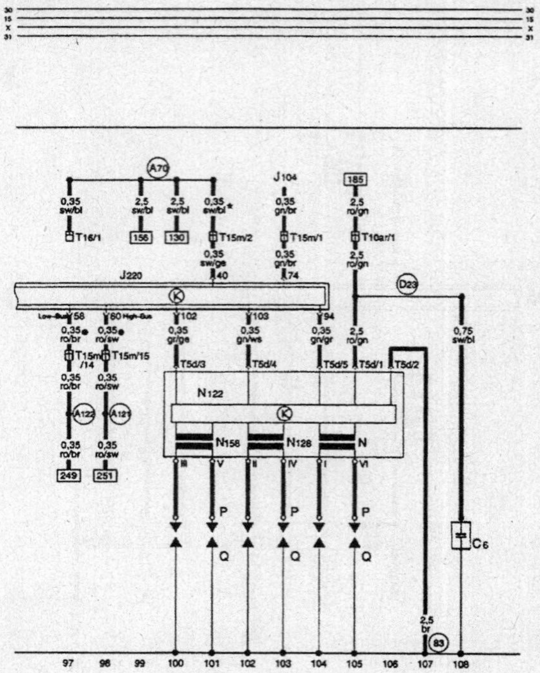

ws = white
sw = black
ro = red
br = brown
gn = green
bl = blue
gr = grey
li = violet
ge = yellow

- C6 – Distributor Ignition (DI) Capacitor
- J104 – ABS Control Module (w/EDL)
- J220 – Motronic Engine Control Module (ECM)
- N – Ignition Coil
- N122 – Power Output Stage
- N128 – Ignition Coil 2
- N158 – Ignition Coil 3
- P – Spark Plug Connector
- Q – Spark Plugs
- T5d – Wire Connector, 5 Point, near ignition coil
- T10ar – Wire Connector, 10 Point, orange, connector station, electronics box in plenum chamber
- T15m – Wire Connector, 15 Point, red, connector station, electronics box in plenum chamber
- T16 – Wire Connector, 16 Point, Data Link Connector (DLC), behind instrument panel, left

- (83) – Ground connection –1–, in right front wiring harness
- (A70) – Connector (15a, fuse 231), in instrument panel wiring harness
- (A121) – Connector (High–Bus), in instrument panel wiring harness
- (A122) – Connector (Low–Bus), in instrument panel wiring harness
- (D23) – Connector (over fuse 229), in wiring harness front, right
- * – Front wheel drive Only
- ● – CAN–Bus

AD1020000206070X

Fig. 2 MFI system wiring diagram (Part 7 of 7)

DIAGNOSTIC CHART INDEX

Code	Description	Page No.	Fig. No.
P0102	MAF Circuit Low Input	10-78	3
P0103	MAF Circuit High Input	10-78	3
P0106	MAP Or BARO Sensor Range/Performance	10-78	3
P0112	IAT Circuit Low Input	10-78	4
P0113	IAT Circuit High Input	10-78	4
P0116	ECT Circuit Fault	10-78	4
P0117	ECT Circuit Low Input	10-78	4
P0118	ECT Circuit High Input	10-78	4
P0130	O2 Sensor Bank 1 Sensor 1 Fault	10-78	5
P0131	O2 Sensor Bank 1 Sensor 1 Low Voltage	10-78	5
P0132	O2 Sensor Bank 1 Sensor 1 High Voltage	10-78	5
P0133	O2 Sensor Bank 1 Sensor 1 Slow Response	10-78	5
P0134	O2 Sensor Bank 1 Sensor 1 No Activity Detected	10-78	5
P0136	O2 Sensor Bank 1 Sensor 2 Fault	10-78	6
P0137	O2 Sensor Bank 1 Sensor 2 Low Voltage	10-78	6
P0138	O2 Sensor Bank 1 Sensor 2 High Voltage	10-78	6
P0139	O2 Sensor Bank 1 Sensor 2 Slow Response	10-78	6
P0140	O2 Sensor Bank 1 Sensor 2 No Activity Detected	10-78	6
P0150	O2 Sensor Bank 2 Sensor 1 Fault	10-78	7
P0151	O2 Sensor Bank 2 Sensor 1 Low Voltage	10-78	7
P0152	O2 Sensor Bank 2 Sensor 1 High Voltage	10-78	7
P0153	O2 Sensor Bank 2 Sensor 1 Slow Response	10-78	7
P0154	O2 Sensor Bank 2 Sensor 1 No Activity Detected	10-78	7
P0156	O2 Sensor Bank 2 Sensor 2 Fault	10-78	8
P0157 (VAG 16541)	O2 Sensor Bank 2 Sensor 2 Low Voltage	10-78	8
P0157 (VAG 16622)	Turbocharger Boost Sensor (A) Circuit High Input	10-78	9
P0158	O2 Sensor Bank 2 Sensor 2 High Voltage	10-78	8
P0159	O2 Sensor Bank 2 Sensor 2 Slow Response	10-78	8
P0160	O2 Sensor Bank 2 Sensor 2 No Activity Detected	10-78	8
P0237	Turbocharger Boost Sensor (A) Circuit Low Input	10-78	9
P0300	Random Misfire Detected	10-78	10
P0301	Cylinder 1 Misfire Detected	10-78	10
P0302	Cylinder 2 Misfire Detected	10-78	10
P0303	Cylinder 3 Misfire Detected	10-78	10
P0304	Cylinder 4 Misfire Detected	10-78	10
P0305	Cylinder 5 Misfire Detected	10-78	10
P0306	Cylinder 6 Misfire Detected	10-78	10
P0321	Engine Speed Sensor Input Circuit Fault	10-79	11
P0322	Engine Speed Sensor No Signal	10-79	11
P0327	Knock Sensor 1 Circuit Low Input	10-79	11
P0328	Knock Sensor 1 Circuit High Input	10-79	11
P0332	Knock Sensor 2 Circuit Low Input	10-79	11
P0333	Knock Sensor 2 Circuit High Input	10-79	11
P0341	CMP Sensor Circuit Range/Performance	10-79	11
P0346	CMP Sensor Circuit 2 Range/Performance	10-79	11
P0421	Warm Up Catalyst Bank 1 Efficiency Below Threshold	10-79	12
P0431	Warm Up Catalyst Bank 2 Efficiency Below Threshold	10-79	12
P0441	EVAP System Improper Purge Flow Fault	10-79	13
P0442	EVAP System Small Leak Detected	10-79	13
P0455	EVAP System Large Leak Detected	10-79	13
P0501	Vehicle Speed Sensor Fault	10-79	14
P0506	Idle Control System RPM Lower Than Expected	10-79	14
P0507	Idle Control System RPM Higher Than Expected	10-79	14
P0560	System Voltage Malfunction	10-79	14
P0562	System Voltage Low Voltage	10-79	14

Continued

DIAGNOSTIC CHART INDEX—Continued

Code	Description	Page No.	Fig. No.
P0563	System Voltage High Voltage	10-79	14
P0571	Cruise Brake Switch (A) Improper Signal	10-79	14
P0601	Internal Control Module Memory Inspection Sum Error	10-79	15
P0604	Internal Control Module Random Access Memory Error	10-79	15
P0605	Internal Control Module ROM Test Error	10-79	15
P1102	O2 Sensor Heating Circuit Bank 1 Sensor 1 Short To Power	10-79	16
P1105	O2 Sensor Heating Circuit Bank 1 Sensor 2 Short To Power	10-79	16
P1107	O2 Sensor Heating Circuit Bank 2 Sensor 1 Short To Power	10-79	16
P1110	O2 Sensor Heating Circuit Bank 2 Sensor 2 Short To Power	10-79	16
P1111	O2 Control Bank 1 System Too Lean	10-79	16
P1112	O2 Control Bank 1 System Too Rich	10-79	16
P1113	Bank 1 Sensor 1 Internal Resistance Too High	10-79	17
P1114	Bank 1 Sensor 2 Internal Resistance Too High	10-79	17
P1115	O2 Heater Circuit Bank 1 Sensor 1 Short To Ground	10-79	17
P1116	O2 Heater Circuit Bank 1 Sensor 1 Open	10-79	17
P1117	O2 Heater Circuit Bank 1 Sensor 2 Short To Ground	10-79	17
P1118	O2 Heater Circuit Bank 1 Sensor 2 Open	10-79	17
P1119	O2 Heater Circuit Bank 2 Sensor 1 Short To Ground	10-79	18
P1120	O2 Heater Circuit Bank 2 Sensor 1 Open	10-79	18
P1121	O2 Heater Circuit Bank 2 Sensor 2 Short To Ground	10-79	18
P1122	O2 Heater Circuit Bank 2 Sensor 2 Open	10-79	18
P1127	Long Term Fuel Trim Bank 1 System Too Rich	10-79	19
P1128	Long Term Fuel Trim Bank 1 System Too Lean	10-79	19
P1129	Long Term Fuel Trim Bank 2 System Too Rich	10-79	19
P1130	Long Term Fuel Trim Bank 2 System Too Lean	10-79	19
P1131	Bank 2 Sensor 1 Internal Resistance Too High	10-79	19
P1136	Long Term Fuel Trim Bank 1 System Too Lean	10-80	20
P1137	Long Term Fuel Trim Bank 1 System Too Rich	10-80	20
P1138	Long Term Fuel Trim Bank 2 System Too Lean	10-80	20
P1139	Long Term Fuel Trim Bank 2 System Too Rich	10-80	20
P1140	Bank 2 Sensor 1 Internal Resistance Too High	10-80	20
P1147	O2 Control Bank 2 System Too Lean	10-80	21
P1148	O2 Control Bank 2 System Too Rich	10-80	21
P1149	O2 Control Bank 1 Out Of Range	10-80	21
P1150	O2 Control Bank 2 Out Of Range	10-80	21
P1171	Throttle Actuation Potentiometer Signal 2 Range/Performance	10-80	22
P1172	Throttle Actuation Potentiometer Signal 2 Signal Too Low	10-80	22
P1173	Throttle Actuation Potentiometer Signal 2 Signal Too High	10-80	22
P1176	O2 Sensor Correction Behind Catalyst B1 Limit Attained	10-80	22
P1177	O2 Sensor Correction Behind Catalyst B2 Limit Attained	10-80	22
P1213	Cylinder 1 Fuel Injector Short To Power	10-80	23
P1214	Cylinder 2 Fuel Injector Short To Power	10-80	23
P1215	Cylinder 3 Fuel Injector Short To Power	10-80	23
P1216	Cylinder 4 Fuel Injector Short To Power	10-80	23
P1217	Cylinder 5 Fuel Injector Short To Power	10-80	23
P1218	Cylinder 6 Fuel Injector Short To Power	10-80	23
P1225	Cylinder 1 Fuel Injector Short To Ground	10-80	24
P1226	Cylinder 2 Fuel Injector Short To Ground	10-80	24
P1227	Cylinder 3 Fuel Injector Short To Ground	10-80	24
P1228	Cylinder 4 Fuel Injector Short To Ground	10-80	24
P1229	Cylinder 5 Fuel Injector Short To Ground	10-80	24
P1230	Cylinder 6 Fuel Injector Short To Ground	10-80	24
P1237	Cylinder 1 Fuel Injector Open Circuit	10-80	25
P1238	Cylinder 2 Fuel Injector Open Circuit	10-80	25
P1239	Cylinder 3 Fuel Injector Open Circuit	10-80	25
P1240	Cylinder 4 Fuel Injector Open Circuit	10-80	25
P1241	Cylinder 5 Fuel Injector Open Circuit	10-80	25

Continued

DIAGNOSTIC CHART INDEX—Continued

Code	Description	Page No.	Fig. No.
P1242	Cylinder 6 Fuel Injector Open Circuit	10-80	25
P1250	Fuel Level Too Low	10-80	26
P1287	Turbocharger Bypass Valve Open	10-80	27
P1288	Turbocharger Bypass Valve Short To Voltage	10-80	27
P1289	Turbocharger Bypass Valve Short To Ground	10-80	27
P1296	Cooling System Malfunction	10-80	27
P1325	Cylinder 1 Knock Control Limit Attained	10-81	28
P1326	Cylinder 2 Knock Control Limit Attained	10-81	28
P1327	Cylinder 3 Knock Control Limit Attained	10-81	28
P1328	Cylinder 4 Knock Control Limit Attained	10-81	28
P1329	Cylinder 5 Knock Control Limit Attained	10-81	28
P1330	Cylinder 6 Knock Control Limit Attained	10-81	28
P1335	Engine Torque Monitoring 2 Control Limit Exceeded	10-81	29
P1336	Engine Torque Monitoring Adaptation At Limit	10-81	29
P1337	Camshaft Position Sensor Bank 1 Short To Ground	10-81	30
P1338	Camshaft Position Sensor Bank 1 Open Circuit Or Short To Power	10-81	30
P1340	CKP & CMP Sensors Out Of Sequence	10-81	30
P1347	Bank 2 CKP & CMP Sensor Signals Out Of Sequence	10-81	30
P1355	Cylinder 1 Ignition Circuit Open	10-81	31
P1356	Cylinder 1 Ignition Circuit Short To Voltage	10-81	31
P1357	Cylinder 1 Ignition Circuit Short To Ground	10-81	31
P1358	Cylinder 2 Ignition Circuit Open	10-81	31
P1359	Cylinder 2 Ignition Circuit Short To Voltage	10-81	31
P1360	Cylinder 2 Ignition Circuit Short To Ground	10-81	31
P1361	Cylinder 3 Ignition Circuit Open	10-81	32
P1362	Cylinder 3 Ignition Circuit Short To Voltage	10-81	32
P1363	Cylinder 3 Ignition Circuit Short To Ground	10-81	32
P1364	Cylinder 4 Ignition Circuit Open	10-81	32
P1365	Cylinder 4 Ignition Circuit Short To Voltage	10-81	32
P1366	Cylinder 4 Ignition Circuit Short To Ground	10-81	32
P1367	Cylinder 5 Ignition Circuit Open	10-81	33
P1368	Cylinder 5 Ignition Circuit Short To Voltage	10-81	33
P1369	Cylinder 5 Ignition Circuit Short To Ground	10-81	33
P1370	Cylinder 6 Ignition Circuit Open	10-81	33
P1371	Cylinder 6 Ignition Circuit Short To Voltage	10-81	33
P1372	Cylinder 6 Ignition Circuit Short To Ground	10-81	33
P1386	Internal Control Module Knock Control Error	10-81	34
P1387	Internal Control Module Knock Control Circuit Error	10-81	34
P1388	Internal Control Module Drive By Wire Error	10-81	34
P1391	Camshaft Position Sensor Bank 2 Short To Ground	10-81	35
P1392	Camshaft Position Sensor Bank 2 Open Circuit Or Short To Power	10-81	35
P1410	Tank Ventilation Valve Short To Power	10-81	35
P1411	Secondary AIR System Bank 2 Flow Too Low	10-81	36
P1414	Secondary AIR System Bank 2 Leak Detected	10-81	36
P1420	Secondary AIR Valve Circuit Short To Voltage	10-82	37
P1421	Secondary AIR Valve Circuit Short To Ground	10-82	37
P1422	Secondary AIR Control Valve Circuit Short To Power	10-82	37
P1423	Secondary AIR Bank 1 Flow Too Low	10-82	38
P1424	Secondary AIR Bank 1 Leak Detected	10-82	38
P1425	Tank Vent Valve Short To Ground	10-82	38
P1426	Tank Vent Valve Open	10-82	38
P1432	Secondary Air Injection Valve Open	10-82	39
P1433	Secondary Air Injection Pump Relay Circuit Open	10-82	39
P1434	Secondary Air Injection Pump Relay Circuit Short To Power	10-82	39
P1435	Secondary Air Injection Pump Relay Short To Ground	10-82	39
P1453	Exhaust Gas Temperature Sensor 1 Open Or Short To Voltage	10-82	40
P1454	Exhaust Gas Temperature Sensor 1 Short To Ground	10-82	40

Continued

DIAGNOSTIC CHART INDEX—Continued

Code	Description	Page No.	Fig. No.
P1455	Exhaust Gas Temperature Sensor 1 Range/Performance	10-82	40
P1456	Exhaust Gas Temperature Control Bank 1 Limit Attained	10-82	40
P1457	Exhaust Gas Temperature Sensor 2 Open Or Short To Voltage	10-82	40
P1458	Exhaust Gas Temperature Sensor 2 Short To Ground	10-82	40
P1459	Exhaust Gas Temperature Sensor 2 Range/Performance	10-82	41
P1460	Exhaust Gas Temperature Control Bank 2 Limit Attained	10-82	41
P1461	Exhaust Gas Temperature Control Bank 1 Range/Performance	10-82	42
P1462	Exhaust Gas Temperature Control Bank 2 Range/Performance	10-82	42
P1470	EVAP Emission Control LDP Circuit Electrical Malfunction	10-82	43
P1471	EVAP Emission Control LDP Circuit Short To Power	10-82	43
P1472	EVAP Emission Control LDP Circuit Short To Ground	10-82	43
P1473	EVAP Emission Control LDP Circuit Open	10-82	43
P1475	EVAP Emission Control LDP Circuit Malfunction/Signal Circuit Open	10-82	44
P1476	EVAP Emission Control LDP Circuit Fault/Insufficient Vacuum	10-82	44
P1477	EVAP Emission Control LDP Circuit Fault	10-82	45
P1478	EVAP Emission Control LDP Circuit Clamped Tube Detected	10-82	45
P1500	Fuel Pump Relay Electrical Fault	10-82	46
P1501	Fuel Pump Relay Short To Ground	10-82	46
P1502	Fuel Pump Relay Short To Voltage	10-82	46
P1519	Intake Camshaft Control Bank 1 Fault	10-83	47
P1522	Intake Camshaft Control Bank 2 Fault	10-83	47
P1523	Crash Signal From Air Bag Control Unit Range/Performance	10-83	47
P1529	Camshaft Control Circuit Short To Voltage	10-83	48
P1530	Camshaft Control Circuit Short To Ground	10-83	48
P1531	Camshaft Control Circuit Open	10-83	48
P1539	Clutch Pedal Switch Range/Performance	10-83	48
P1542	Throttle Actuation Potentiometer Range/Performance	10-83	49
P1543	Throttle Actuation Potentiometer Signal Too Low	10-83	49
P1544	Throttle Actuation Potentiometer Signal Too High	10-83	49
P1545	Throttle Position Control Fault	10-83	49
P1546	Boost Pressure Control Valve Short To Voltage	10-83	49
P1547	Boost Pressure Control Valve Short To Ground	10-83	49
P1548	Boost Pressure Control Valve Open	10-83	49
P1555	Charge Pressure Upper Limit Exceeded	10-83	50
P1556	Charge Pressure Control Negative Deviation	10-83	50
P1557	Charge Pressure Positive Deviation	10-83	50
P1558	Throttle Actuator Electrical Fault	10-83	51
P1559	Idle Speed Control Throttle Position Adaptation Fault	10-83	51
P1560	Maximum Engine Speed Exceeded	10-83	51
P1564	Idle Speed Control Throttle Position Low Voltage During Adaptation	10-83	51
P1565	Idle Speed Control Throttle Position Lower Impact Not Attained	10-83	51
P1568	Idle Speed Control Throttle Position Mechanical Malfunction	10-83	51
P1569	Cruise Control Switch Improper Signal	10-83	52
P1570	Control Module Locked	10-83	52
P1579	Idle Speed Control Throttle Position Adaptation Not Started	10-83	52
P1600	Power Supply Terminal 15 Low Voltage	10-83	52
P1602	Power Supply Terminal 30 Low Voltage	10-83	52
P1603	Internal Control Module Malfunction	10-83	53
P1604	Internal Control Module Malfunction	10-83	53
P1606	Rough Road Spec Engine Torque ABS-ECU Electrical Fault	10-83	53
P1609	Crash Shutdown Activated	10-83	53
P1612	ECM Improper Coding	10-83	53
P1620	ECT Signal Open Or Short To Voltage	10-84	54
P1621	ECT Signal Short To Ground	10-84	54
P1622	ECT Signal Range/Performance	10-84	54
P1624	MIL Request Sign Active	10-84	55
P1626	CAN Bus Missing Message From Transmission Control	10-84	55

Continued

DIAGNOSTIC CHART INDEX—Continued

Code	Description	Page No.	Fig. No.
P1630	APP Sensor 1 Signal Too Low	10-84	56
P1631	APP Sensor 1 Signal Too High	10-84	56
P1633	APP Sensor 2 Signal Too Low	10-84	56
P1634	APP Sensor 2 Signal Too High	10-84	56
P1639	APP Sensor 1 & 2 Range/Performance	10-84	57
P1640	Internal Control Module EEPROM Error	10-84	57
P1648	Data Bus Powertrain Malfunction	10-84	57
P1649	Data Bus Powertrain Missing Message From ABS Control Module	10-84	57
P1676	Drive By Wire MIL Circuit Electrical Malfunction	10-84	58
P1677	Drive By Wire MIL Circuit Short To Voltage	10-84	58
P1690	MIL Lamp Fault	10-84	58
P1693	MIL Short To Voltage	10-84	58
P1851	Data Bus Powertrain Missing Message From Brake Control	10-84	59
P1853	Data Bus Powertrain Implausible Message From Brake Control	10-84	59
P1854	Data Bus Powertrain Hardware Faulty	10-84	59

DTC SAE	DTC VAG	Description of malfunction	Corrective action
P0102	16486	Mass or Volume Air Flow Circuit Low input [2]	- Check Mass Air Flow (MAF) sensor
P0103	16487	Mass or Volume Air Flow Circuit High input [2]	
P0106	16490	Manifold Abs.Pressure or Bar. Pressure Range/Performance [2] [4]	Check Charge Air Pressure Sensor

[2] With this malfunction the exhaust Malfunction Indicator Light (MIL) is only switched on by the ECM, if the malfunction is recognized after the engine has been restarted.

[4] Absolute manifold pressure will be determined by the Charge Air Pressure Sensor the air pressure is determined by the Barometric Pressure (BARO) Sensor (in Engine Control Module (ECM)

AD0150000327000X

Fig. 3 Codes P0102, P0103 & P0106

DTC SAE	DTC VAG	Description of malfunction	Corrective action
P0130	16514	02 Sensor Circ., Bank1-Sensor1 Malfunction [2]	- Check oxygen sensor control or oxygen sensor heater and wiring
P0131	16515	02 Sensor Circ., Bank1-Sensor1 Low Voltage [2]	
P0132	16516	02 Sensor Circ., Bank1-Sensor1 High Voltage [2]	
P0133	16517	02 Sensor Circ., Bank1-Sensor1 Slow Response [2]	
P0134	16518	02 Sensor Circ., Bank1-Sensor1 No Activity Detected [2]	

AD0150000329000X

Fig. 5 Codes P0130, P0131, P0132, P0133 & P0134

DTC SAE	DTC VAG	Description of malfunction	Corrective action
P0150	16534	02 Sensor Circ., Bank2-Sensor1 Malfunction [2]	- Check oxygen sensor control or oxygen sensor heater and wiring
P0151	16535	02 Sensor Circ., Bank2-Sensor1 Low voltage [2]	
P0152	16536	02 Sensor Circ., Bank2-Sensor1 High Voltage [2]	
P0153	16537	02 Sensor Circ., Bank2-Sensor1 Slow Response [2]	
P0154	16538	02 Sensor Circ., Bank2-Sensor1 No Activity Detected [2]	

AD0150000331000X

Fig. 7 Codes P0150, P0151, P0152, P0153 & P0154

DTC SAE	DTC VAG	Description of malfunction	Corrective action
P0237	16621	Turbocharger Boost Sensor (A) Circ Low Input [2]	Check Charge Air Pressure Sensor -G31
P0157	16622	Turbocharger Boost Sensor (A) Circ High Input [2]	

AD0150000333000X

Fig. 9 Codes P0157 & P0237

DTC SAE	DTC VAG	Description of malfunction	Corrective action
P0112	16496	Intake Air Temp. Circ. Low Input [2]	- Check Intake Air Temperature (IAT) sensor
P0113	16497	Intake Air Temp. High Input [2]	
P0116	16500	Engine Coolant Temp. Circ. Range/Performance	- Check Engine Coolant Temperature (ECT) sensor
P0117	16501	Engine Coolant Temp. Circ. Low Input [2]	
P0118	16502	Engine Coolant Temp. Circ. High Input [2]	

AD0150000328000X

Fig. 4 Codes P0112, P0113, P0116, P0117 & P0118

DTC SAE	DTC VAG	Description of malfunction	Corrective action
P0136	16520	02 Sensor Circ., Bank1-Sensor2 Malfunction [2]	- Check oxygen sensor heater
P0137	16521	02 Sensor Circ., Bank1-Sensor2 Low Voltage [2]	- Check oxygen sensor signal wire and activation
P0138	16522	02 Sensor Circ., Bank1-Sensor2 High Voltage [2]	
P0139	16523	02 Sensor Circ., Bank1-Sensor2 Slow Response [2]	- Check oxygen sensor and oxygen sensor control behind catalytic converter
P0140	16524	02 Sensor Circ., Bank1-Sensor2 No Activity Detected [2]	

AD0150000330000X

Fig. 6 Codes P0136, P0137, P0138, P0139 & P0140

DTC SAE	DTC VAG	Description of malfunction	Corrective action
P0156	16540	02 Sensor Circ., Bank2-Sensor2 Malfunction [2]	- Check oxygen sensor heater
P0157	16541	02 Sensor Circ., Bank2-Sensor2 Low Voltage [2]	- Check oxygen sensor signal wire and activation
P0158	16542	02 Sensor Circ., Bank2-Sensor2 High Voltage [2]	
P0159	16543	02 Sensor Circ., Bank2-Sensor2 Slow Response [2]	- Check oxygen sensor and oxygen sensor control behind catalytic converter
P0160	16544	02 Sensor Circ., Bank2-Sensor2 No Activity Detected [2]	- Check oxygen sensor heater

AD0150000332000X

Fig. 8 Codes P0156, P0157, P0158, P0159 & P0160

DTC SAE	DTC VAG	Description of malfunction	Corrective action
P0300	16684	Random/Multiple Cylinder Misfire Detected [2]	- Check cause for misfire ⇒ Page 28-52
P0301	16685	Cyl.1 Misfire Detected [2]	- Check fuel tank level
P0302	16686	Cyl.2 Misfire Detected [2]	
P0303	16687	Cyl.3 Misfire Detected [2]	
P0304	16688	Cyl.4 Misfire Detected [2]	
P0305	16689	Cyl.5 Misfire Detected [2]	
P0306	16690	Cyl.6 Misfire Detected [2]	

[2] With this malfunction the exhaust Malfunction Indicator Light (MIL) is only switched on by the ECM, if the malfunction is recognized after the engine has been restarted.

The Malfunction Indicator Light (MIL) will blink if the Engine Control Module (ECM) recognizes misfire that could damage the catalytic converters.

Notes:

- *On malfunction which could be caused by lack of fuel (e.g.: misfire) the malfunction P1250 "Fuel level too low" will be displayed in addition. That means, the misfiring was detected due to lack of fuel in the tank and not due to a technical malfunction.*
- *Depending on malfunction recognition, the MIL comes on immediately or after it has been confirmed.*

AD0150000334000X

Fig. 10 Codes P0300, P0301, P0302, P0303, P0304, P0305 & P0306

DTC		Description of malfunction	Corrective action
SAE	VAG		
P0321	16705	Ign./Distributor Eng. Speed Inp. Circ. Range/Performance [2]	- Check Engine Speed Sensor
P0322	16706	Ign./Distributor Eng. Speed Inp. Circ. No Signal [2]	
P0327	16711	Knock Sensor 1 Circ. Low Input	- Check Knock Sensor
P0328	16712	Knock Sensor 1 Circ. High Input	
P0332	16716	Knock Sensor 2 Circ. Low Input	
P0333	16717	Knock Sensor 2 Circ. High Input	
P0341	16725	Camshaft Pos. Sensor Circ. Range/Performance [2]	- Check Camshaft Position Sensor
P0346	16730	Camshaft Pos. Sensor Circ. 2 Range/Performance [2]	

AD0150000335000X

Fig. 11 Codes P0321, P0322, P0327, P0328, P0332, P0333, P0341 & P0346

DTC		Description of malfunction	Corrective action
P0441	16825	EVAP Emission Contr. Sys. Incorrect Purge Flow [2]	- Check EVAP canister purge regulator valve, perform output Diagnostic Test Mode (DTM) ⇒
P0442	16826	EVAP Emission Contr. Sys. (Small Leak) Leak Detected [2]	- Check EVAP system and tank system for leaks
P0455	16839	EVAP Emission Contr. Sys. (Gross Leak) Leak Detected	

AD0150000337000X

Fig. 13 Codes P0441, P0442 & P0455

DTC		Description of malfunction	Corrective action
SAE	VAG		
P0601	16985	Internal Contr. Module Memory Check Sum Error [2]	- Replace Engine Control Module (ECM)
P0604	16988	Internal Contr. Module Random Access Memory (RAM) Error [2]	
P0605	16989	Internal Contr. Module ROM Test Error [2]	

AD0150000339000X

Fig. 15 Codes P0601, P0604 & P0605

DTC		Description of malfunction	Corrective action
SAE	VAG		
P1113	17521	Bank1-Sensor1 Internal Resistance too High [2]	- Check oxygen sensor heater
P1114	17522	Bank1-Sensor2 Internal Resistance too High [2]	- Check oxygen sensor signal wire and activation
P1115	17523	O2 Sensor Heater Circ., Bank1-Sensor1 Short to Ground [2]	- Check oxygen sensor heater
P1116	17524	O2 Sensor Heater Circ., Bank1-Sensor1 Open [2]	
P1117	17525	O2 Sensor Heater Circ., Bank1-Sensor2 Short to Ground [2]	
P1118	17526	O2 Sensor Heater Circ., Bank1-Sensor2 Open [2]	

AD0150000341000X

Fig. 17 Codes P1113, P1114, P1115, P1116, P1117 & P1118

DTC		Description of malfunction	Corrective action
SAE	VAG		
P1119	17527	O2 Sensor Heater Circ., Bank2-Sensor1 Short to Ground [2]	- Check oxygen sensor heater
P1120	17528	O2 Sensor Heater Circ., Bank2-Sensor1 Open [2]	
P1121	17529	O2 Sensor Heater Circ., Bank2-Sensor2 Short to Ground [2]	
P1122	17530	O2 Sensor Heater Circ., Bank2-Sensor2 Open [2]	

AD0150000342000X

Fig. 18 Codes P1119, P1120, P1121 & P1122

DTC		Description of malfunction	Corrective action
SAE	VAG		
P0421	16805	Warm Up Catalyst, Bank 1 Efficiency Below Threshold [2]	- Generate readiness code if same DTC is displayed again, replace warm up catalytic converter bank 1
P0431	16815	Warm Up Catalyst, Bank 2 Efficiency Below Threshold [2]	- Generate readiness code if same DTC is displayed again, replace warm up catalytic converter bank 1

AD0150000336000X

Fig. 12 Codes P0421 & P0431

DTC		Description of malfunction	Corrective action
SAE	VAG		
P0501	16885	Vehicle Speed Sensor Range/Performance [2]	- Check Vehicle Speed Signal (VSS)
P0506	16890	Idle Control System RPM Lower than Expected [2]	- Carry out adaptation of Throttle Valve Control Module
P0507	16891	Idle Control System RPM Higher than Expected [2]	- Check for unmetered (false) air
P0560	16944	System Voltage Malfunction	- Check control module voltage supply
P0562	16946	System Voltage Low Voltage	
P0563	16947	System Voltage High Voltage	
P0571	16955	Cruise/Brake Switch (A) Circ. Incorrect Signal	- Check brake light switch and/or brake pedal switch

AD0150000338000X

Fig. 14 Codes P0501, P0506, P0507, P0560, P0562, P0563 & P0571

DTC		Description of malfunction	Corrective action
SAE	VAG		
P1102	17510	O2 Sensor Heating Circ., Bank1-Sensor1 Short to B+ [2]	- Check oxygen sensor heater
P1105	17513	O2 Sensor Heating Circ., Bank1-Sensor2 Short to B+ [2]	
P1107	17515	O2 Sensor Heating Circ., Bank2-Sensor1 Short to B+ [2]	
P1110	17518	O2 Sensor Heating Circ., Bank2-Sensor2 Short to B+ [2]	
P1111	17519	O2 Control (Bank 1) System too lean	- Check oxygen sensor adaptation values and oxygen sensor control
P1112	17520	O2 Bank 1 System too rich	

AD0150000340000X

Fig. 16 Codes P1102, P1105, P1107, P1110, P1111 & P1112

DTC		Description of malfunction	Corrective action
SAE	VAG		
P1127	17535	Long Term Fuel Trim mult., Bank1 System too rich [2]	- Carry out road test (Fuel in engine oil) - Check fuel pressure
P1128	17536	Long Term Fuel Trim mult., Bank1 System too lean [2]	- Check Mass Air Flow (MAF) Sensor ⇒ Page 24-59 - Check for unmetered (false) air
P1129	17537	Long Term Fuel Trim mult., Bank2 System too rich [2]	- Check oxygen sensor before catalytic converter - Check oxygen sensor behind catalytic converter
P1130	17538	Long Term Fuel Trim mult., Bank2 System too rich [2]	- Check fuel injectors
P1131	17539	Bank2-Sensor1 Internal Resistance too High [2]	- Check oxygen sensor heater - Check oxygen sensor signal wire and activation

[2] With this malfunction the exhaust Malfunction Indicator Light (MIL) is only switched on by the ECM, if the malfunction is recognized after the engine has been restarted.

Notes:

mult. = multiplikative means that the malfunction affects the entire RPM and load range.

AD0150000343000X

Fig. 19 Codes P1127, P1128, P1129, P1130 & P1131

DTC		Description of malfunction	Corrective action
SAE	VAG		
P1136	17544	Long Term Fuel Trim Add. Fuel, Bank1 System too Lean [2]	- Carry out road test (fuel in engine oil)
P1137	17545	Long Term Fuel Trim Add. Fuel, Bank1 System too Rich [2]	- Check fuel pressure
P1138	17546	Long Term Fuel Trim Add. Fuel, Bank2 System too Lean [2]	- Check Mass Air Flow (MAF) Sensor
P1139	17547	Long Term Fuel Trim Add. Fuel, Bank2 System too Rich [2]	- Check oxygen sensor before catalytic converter - Check oxygen sensor behind catalytic converter - Check EVAP canister valve 1
P1140	17548	Bank2-Sensor2 Internal Resistance too High [2]	- Check oxygen sensor heater - Check oxygen sensor signal wire and activation

Notes:

add. = additive means that the malfunction in only at idle.

AD0150000344000X

Fig. 20 Codes P1136, P1137, P1138, P1139 & P1140

DTC		Description of malfunction	Corrective action
SAE	VAG		
P1171	17579	Throttle Actuation Potentiometer Signal 2 Range/Performance [1] [3]	- Check throttle actuation potentiometer
P1172	17580	Throttle Actuation Potentiometer Signal 2 Signal too Low [1] [3]	
P1173	17581	Throttle Actuation Potentiometer Signal 2 Signal too High [1] [3]	
P1176	17584	O2 Correction Behind Catalyst, B1 Limit Attained [2]	- Check oxygen sensor aging of oxygen sensors before catalytic converters
P1177	17585	O2 Correction Behind Catalyst, B2 Limit Attained [2]	- Check oxygen sensors and oxygen sensor control behind catalytic converters

1) With this malfunction the EPC (Electronic Power Control) Malfunction Indicator Light (MIL) in the instrument cluster is switched on by the ECM immediately after the malfunction has been recognized.

2) With this malfunction the exhaust Malfunction Indicator Light (MIL) is only switched on by the ECM, if the malfunction is recognized after the engine has been restarted.
MIL

3) With this malfunction the exhaust Malfunction Indicator Light (MIL) is switched on by the ECM, immediately after the malfunction has been recognized.

AD0150000346000X

Fig. 22 Codes P1171, P1172, P1173, P1176 & P1177

DTC		Description of malfunction	Corrective action
SAE	VAG		
P1225	17633	Cyl. 1-Fuel Inj. Circ. Short to Ground [2]	- Check fuel injectors
P1226	17634	Cyl. 2-Fuel Inj. Circ. Short to Ground [2]	
P1227	17635	Cyl. 3-Fuel Inj. Circ. Short to Ground [2]	
P1228	17636	Cyl. 4-Fuel Inj. Circ. Short to Ground [2]	
P1229	17637	Cyl. 5-Fuel Inj. Circ. Short to Ground [2]	
P1230	17638	Cyl. 6-Fuel Inj. Circ. Short to Ground [2]	

AD0150000348000X

Fig. 24 Codes P1225, P1226, P1227, P1228, P1229 & P1230

DTC		Description of malfunction	Corrective action
SAE	VAG		
P1250	17658	Fuel Level Too Low [4]	- Fill fuel tank and erase DTC memory - Check DTC memory from instrument cluster.

4) The malfunction "Fuel Level too Low" will be stored if the fuel level in the tank is or was too low. The malfunction remains as a static malfunction and will not be set a sporadic malfunction even if the customer fills the tank with fuel in the meantime. Therefore it is possible to recognize malfunctions which have been stored due to lack of fuel e.g.: misfiring or malfunction regarding oxygen sensor control.

AD0150000350000X

Fig. 26 Code P1250

DTC		Description of malfunction	Corrective action
SAE	VAG		
P1147	17555	O2 Control (Bank2) System too Lean	- Check oxygen sensor adaptation values and oxygen sensor control
P1148	17556	O2 Control (Bank2) System too Rich	
P1149	17557	O2 Control (Bank1) Out of Range	- Check oxygen sensor adaptation values and oxygen sensor control
P1150	17558	O2 Control (Bank2) Out of Range	- Check fuel pressure - Check for unmetered (false) air

AD0150000345000X

Fig. 21 Codes P1147, P1148, P1149 & P1150

DTC		Description of malfunction	Corrective action
SAE	VAG		
P1213	17621	Cyl. 1-Fuel Inj. Circ. Short to B+ [2]	- Check fuel injectors
P1214	17622	Cyl. 2-Fuel Inj. Circ. Short to B+ [2]	
P1215	17623	Cyl. 3-Fuel Inj. Circ. Short to B+ [2]	
P1216	17624	Cyl. 4-Fuel Inj. Circ. Short to B+ [2]	
P1217	17625	Cyl. 5-Fuel Inj. Circ. Short to B+ [2]	
P1218	17626	Cyl. 6-Fuel Inj. Circ. Short to B+ [2]	

AD0150000347000X

Fig. 23 Codes P1213, P1214, P1215, P1216, P1217 & P1218

DTC		Description of malfunction	Corrective action
SAE	VAG		
P1237	17645	Cyl. 1-Fuel Inj. Circ. Open Circ. [2]	- Check fuel injectors
P1238	17646	Cyl. 2-Fuel Inj. Circ. Open Circ. [2]	
P1239	17647	Cyl. 3-Fuel Inj. Circ. Open Circ. [2]	
P1240	17648	Cyl. 4-Fuel Inj. Circ. Open Circ. [2]	
P1241	17649	Cyl. 5-Fuel Inj. Circ. Open Circ. [2]	
P1242	17650	Cyl. 6-Fuel Inj. Circ. Open Circ. [2]	

AD0150000349000X

Fig. 25 Codes P1237, P1238, P1239, P1240, P1241 & P1242

DTC		Description of malfunction	Corrective action
SAE	VAG		
P1287	17695	Turbocharger bypass valve Open	- Check recirculating valve for turbocharger -N249
P1288	17696	Turbocharger bypass valve Short to B+	
P1289	17697	Turbocharger bypass valve Short to Ground	
P1296	17704	Cooling System Malfunction [2]	- Check Engine Coolant Temperature (ECT) sensor

AD0150000351000X

Fig. 27 Codes P1287, P1288, P1289 & P1296

DTC SAE	DTC VAG	Description of malfunction	Corrective action
P1325	17733	Cyl.1-Knock Contr. Limit Attained	- Check Knock Control
P1326	17734	Cyl.2-Knock Contr. Limit Attained	
P1327	17735	Cyl.3-Knock Contr. Limit Attained	
P1328	17736	Cyl.4-Knock Contr. Limit Attained	
P1329	17737	Cyl.5-Knock Contr. Limit Attained	
P1330	17738	Cyl.6-Knock Contr. Limit Attained	

AD0150000352000X

Fig. 28 Codes P1325, P1326, P1327, P1328, P1329 & P1330

DTC SAE	DTC VAG	Description of malfunction	Corrective action
P1337	17745	Camshaft Pos. Sensor, Bank1 Short to Ground [2]	- Check Camshaft Position (CMP) sensor
P1338	17746	Camshaft Pos. Sensor, Bank1 Open Circ./Short to B+ [2]	
P1340	17748	Crankshaft Pos./Engine Speed Sensor Out of Sequence [2]	- Check phase position of Camshaft Position (CMP) sensor
P1347	17755	Bank2, Crankshaft-/Camshaft os.Sens.Sign. Out of Sequence [2]	

AD0150000354000X

Fig. 30 Codes P1337, P1338, P1340 & P1347

DTC SAE	DTC VAG	Description of malfunction	Corrective action
P1361	17769	Cyl. 3, ignition circuit Open Circuit [2]	- Check activation of power output stages
P1362	17770	Cyl. 3, ignition circuit Short to B+ [2]	
P1363	17771	Cyl. 3, ignition circuit Short to ground [2]	
P1364	17772	Cyl. 4, ignition circuit Open Circuit [2]	
P1365	17773	Cyl. 4, ignition circuit Short Circuit to B+ [2]	
P1366	17774	Cyl. 4, ignition circuit Short Circuit to ground [2]	

AD0150000356000X

Fig. 32 Codes P1361, P1362, P1363, P1364, P1365 & P1366

DTC SAE	DTC VAG	Description of malfunction	Corrective action
P1386	17794	Internal Control Module Knock Control Circ.Error	- Replace Engine Control Module (ECM)
P1387	17795	Internal Control Module Altitude Sensor Error [2]	
P1388	17796	Internal Control Module Drive by wire error [1] [3]	

[1] With this malfunction the EPC (Electronic Power Control) Malfunction Indicator Light (MIL) in the instrument cluster is switched on by the ECM.

[2] With this malfunction the exhaust Malfunction Indicator Light (MIL) is only switched on by the ECM, if the malfunction is recognized after the engine has been restarted.

[3] With this malfunction the exhaust Malfunction Indicator Light (MIL) is switched on by the ECM, immediately after the malfunction has been recognized.

AD0150000358000X

Fig. 34 Codes P1386, P1387 & P1388

DTC SAE	DTC VAG	Description of malfunction	Corrective action
P1391	17799	Camshaft Pos. Sensor, Bank2 Short to Ground [2]	- Check Camshaft Position (CMP) sensor
P1392	17800	Camshaft Pos. Sensor, Bank2 Open Circ./Short to B+ [2]	
P1410	17818	Tank Ventilation Valve Circ. Short to B+	- Check EVAP canister purge regulator valve

AD0150000359000X

Fig. 35 Codes P1391, P1392 & P1410

DTC SAE	DTC VAG	Description of malfunction	Corrective action
P1335	17743	Engine Torque Monitoring 2 Control Limit Exceeded [1] [3]	- Check hoses - Check Intake Air Temperature (IAT) sensor - Check Mass Air Flow (MAF) sensor - Check Engine Coolant Temperature (ECT) sensor
P1336	17744	Engine Torque Monitoring Adaptation at limit	- Check hoses - Check Intake Air Temperature (IAT) sensor - Check Mass Air Flow (MAF) sensor - Check Engine Coolant Temperature (ECT) sensor

[1] With this malfunction the EPC (Electronic Power Control) Malfunction Indicator Light (MIL) in the instrument cluster is switched on by the ECM.

[3] With this malfunction the exhaust Malfunction Indicator Light (MIL) is switched on by the ECM, immidiately after the malfunction has been recognized.

AD0150000353000X

Fig. 29 Codes P1335 & P1336

DTC SAE	DTC VAG	Description of malfunction	Corrective action
P1355	17763	Cyl. 1, ignition circuit Open Circuit [2]	- Check activation of power output stages
P1356	17764	Cyl. 1, ignition circuit Short to B+ [2]	
P1357	17765	Cyl. 1, ignition circuit Short to ground [2]	
P1358	17766	Cyl. 2, ignition circuit Open Circuit [2]	
P1359	17767	Cyl. 2, ignition circuit Short Circuit to B+ [2]	
P1360	17768	Cyl. 2, ignition circuit Short Circuit to ground [2]	

AD0150000355000X

Fig. 31 Codes P1355, P1356, P1357, P1358, P1359 & P1360

DTC SAE	DTC VAG	Description of malfunction	Corrective action
P1367	17775	Cyl. 5, ignition circuit Open Circuit [2]	- Check activation of power output stages ⇒
P1368	17776	Cyl. 5, ignition circuit Short to B+ [2]	
P1369	17777	Cyl. 5, ignition circuit Short to ground [2]	
P1370	17778	Cyl. 6, ignition circuit Open Circuit [2]	
P1371	17779	Cyl. 6, ignition circuit Short Circuit to B+ [2]	
P1372	17780	Cyl. 6, ignition circuit Short Circuit to ground [2]	

AD0150000357000X

Fig. 33 Codes P1367, P1368, P1369, P1370, P1371 & P1372

DTC		Description of malfunction	Corrective action
P1411	17819	Sec. Air Inj.Sys.,Bank2 Flow too low [2]	- Check fuse for secondary air injection pump. - Check vacuum hoses - Check piping from pump to secondary air injection valve (Combi valve)
P1414	17822	Sec. Air Inj.Sys.,Bank2 Leak Detected [2]	- Check piping from pump to secondary air injection valve (combi valve) bank 2

AD0150000360000X

Fig. 36 Codes P1411 & P1414

DTC SAE	DTC VAG	Description of malfunction	Corrective action
P1420	17828	Sec. Air Inj. Valve Circ. Electrical Malfunction [2]	- Check Secondary Air Injection (AIR) Solenoid Valve -N112
P1421	17829	Sec. Air Inj. Valve Circ. Short to Ground [2]	
P1422	17830	Sec. Air Inj. Valve Circ. Short to B+ [2]	

AD0150000361000X

Fig. 37 Codes P1420, P1421 & P1422

DTC SAE	DTC VAG	Description of malfunction	Corrective action
P1432	17840	Sec. Air Inj.Valve Open [2]	- Check Secondary Air Injection (AIR) Solenoid Valve
P1433	17841	Sec. Air Inj. Sys. Pump Relay Circ. Open [2]	Check Secondary Air Injection (AIR) Pump Relay
P1434	17842	Sec. Air Inj. Sys. Pump Relay Circ. Short to B+ [2]	
P1435	17843	Sec. Air Inj. Sys. Pump Relay Circ. Short to Ground [2]	

AD0150000363000X

Fig. 39 Codes P1432, P1433, P1434 & P1435

DTC SAE	DTC VAG	Description of malfunction	Corrective action
P1459	17867	Exhaust gas temperature sensor 2 Range/performance	
P1460	17868	Exhaust gas temperature control bank 2 Limit attained	Check haust gas temperature control

AD0150000365000X

Fig. 41 Codes P1459 & P1460

DTC SAE	DTC VAG	Description of malfunction	Corrective action
P1470	17878	EVAP Emission Contr. LDP Circ Electrical Malfunction [2]	- Check Leak Detection Pump (LDP)
P1471	17879	EVAP Emission Contr. LDP Circ Short to B+ [2]	
P1472	17880	EVAP Emission Contr. LDP Circ Short to Ground [2]	
P1473	17881	EVAP Emission Contr. LDP Circ Open Circuit [2]	

AD0150000367000X

Fig. 43 Codes P1470, P1471, P1472 & P1473

DTC SAE	DTC VAG	Description of malfunction	Corrective action
P1477	17885	EVAP Emission Contr. LDP Circ Malfunction [2]	- Check Leak Detection Pump (LDP)
P1478	17886	EVAP Emission Contr. LDP Circ Clamped Tube Detected [2]	- Check hoses (pressure/vacuum) to LDP.

AD0150000369000X

Fig. 45 Codes P1477 & P1478

DTC SAE	DTC VAG	Description of malfunction	Corrective action
P1423	17831	Sec. Air Inj.Sys.,Bank1 Flow too low [2]	- Check fuse for secondary air injection pump - Check vacuum hoses - Check piping from pump to secondary air injection valve (Combi valve)
P1424	17832	Sec. Air Inj. Sys., Bank1 Leak Detected [2]	- Check piping from pump to secondary air injection valve (Combi valve) bank 1
P1425	17833	Tank Vent. Valve Short to Ground [2]	- Check EVAP canister valve 1
P1426	17834	Tank Vent. Valve Open [2]	

AD0150000362000X

Fig. 38 Codes P1423, P1424, P1425 & P1426

DTC SAE	DTC VAG	Description of malfunction	Corrective action
P1453	17861	Exhaust gas temperature sensor 1 Open/short to B+	Check Sensor -1- for exhaust temperature
P1454	17862	Exhaust gas temperature sensor 1 Short to ground	
P1455	17863	Exhaust gas temperature sensor 1 Range/performance	
P1456	17864	Exhaust gas temperature control bank 1 Limit attained	Check exhaust gas temperature control
P1457	17865	Exhaust gas temperature sensor 2 Open/short to B+	Check Sensor -2- for exhaust temperature
P1458	17866	Exhaust gas temperature sensor 2 Short to ground	

AD0150000364000X

Fig. 40 Codes P1453, P1454, P1455, P1456, P1457 & P1458

DTC SAE	DTC VAG	Description of malfunction	Corrective action
P1461	17869	Exhaust gas temperature control bank 1 Range/Performance	Check ex haust gas temperature control
P1462	17870	Exhaust gas temperature control bank 2 Range/Performance	

AD0150000366000X

Fig. 42 Codes P1461 & P1462

DTC SAE	DTC VAG	Description of malfunction	Corrective
P1475	17883	EVAP Emission Contr. LDP Circ Malfunction/Signal Circ. Open [2]	- Check hoses (pressure/vacuum) to leak detection pump - Check wiring to pump according to wiring diagram
P1476	17884	EVAP Emission Contr. LDP Circ Malfunction/Insufficient Vacuum [2]	

AD0150000368000X

Fig. 44 Codes P1475 & P1476

DTC SAE	DTC VAG	Description of malfunction	Corrective action
P1500	17908	Fuel Pump Relay Circ. Electrical Malfunction [2]	- Check Fuel Pump (FP) relay
P1501	17909	Fuel Pump Relay Circ. Short to ground [2]	
P1502	17910	Fuel Pump Relay Circ. Short to B+ [2]	

AD0150000370000X

Fig. 46 Codes P1500, P1501 & P1502

DTC SAE	DTC VAG	Description of malfunction	Corrective action
P1519	17927	Intake Camshaft Contr., Bank1 Malfunction [2]	- Check camshaft adjustment, Checking function of camshaft adjustment
P1522	17930	Intake Camshaft Contr., Bank2 Malfunction [2]	
P1523	17931	Crash Signal from Airbag Control Unit Range/Performance	- Check Crash-Signal

AD0150000371000X

Fig. 47 Codes P1519, P1522 & P1523

DTC SAE	DTC VAG	Description of malfunction	Corrective action
P1529	17937	Camshaft Control Circuit Short to B+ [2]	Check camshaft adjustment, Checking solenoid valves for camshaft adjustment
P1530	17938	Camshaft Control Circuit Short to Ground [2]	
P1531	17939	Camshaft Control Circuit Open [2]	
P1539	17947	Clutch pedal switch Range/Performance [2]	- Check Clutch Vacuum Vent Valve Switch

AD0150000372000X

Fig. 48 Codes P1529, P1530, P1531 & P1539

DTC SAE	DTC VAG	Description of malfunction	Corrective action
P1542	17950	Throttle Actuation Potentiometer Range/Performance [1] [3]	- Check angle sensor for throttle drive
P1543	17951	Throttle Actuation Potentiometer Signal too Low [1] [3]	
P1544	17952	Throttle Actuation Potentiometer Signal too High [1] [3]	- Check angle sensor for throttle drive
P1545	17953	Throttle Pos. Contr. Malfunction [1] [3]	- Check throttle valve control module
P1546	17954	Boost Pressure Contr.Valve Short to B+	Repair Turbocharger system
P1547	17955	Boost Pressure Contr.Valve Short to Ground	
P1548	17956	Boost Pressure Contr.Valve Open	

[1] With this malfunction the EPC (Electronic Power Control) Malfunction Indicator Light (MIL) in the instrument cluster is switched on by the ECM immediately after the malfunction has been recognized.

[3] With this malfunction the exhaust Malfunction Indicator Light (MIL) is switched on by the ECM, immidiately after the malfunction has been recognized.

AD0150000373000X

Fig. 49 Codes P1542, P1543, P1544, P1545, P1546, P1547 & P1548

DTC SAE	DTC VAG	Description of malfunction	Corrective action
P1555	17963	Charge Pressure Upper Limit exceeded	Repair Manual Turbocharger system
P1556	17964	Charge Pressure Contr. Negative Deviation	Repair Turbocharger system
P1557	17965	Charge Pressure Contr. Positive Deviation	

AD0150000374000X

Fig. 50 Codes P1555, P1556 & P1557

DTC SAE	DTC VAG	Description of malfunction	Corrective action
P1558	17966	Throttle Actuator Electrical Malfunction [1] [3]	- Check throttle valve control module
P1559	17967	Idle Speed Contr. Throttle Pos. Adaptation Malfunction [2]	- Perform adaptation
P1560	17968	Maximum Engine Speed Exceeded	- Repair mechanical damage
P1564	17972	Idle Speed Control Throttle Position Low Voltage During Adaptation	- Charge battery or repeat adaptation
P1565	17973	Idle Speed Control Throttle Position Lower Limit not Attained [1] [3]	- Check throttle valve control module
P1568	17976	Idle Speed Control Throttle Position Mechanical Malfunction [1] [3]	

[1] With this malfunction the EPC (Electronic Power Control) Malfunction Indicator Light (MIL) in the instrument cluster is switched on by the ECM.

[2] With this malfunction the exhaust Malfunction Indicator Light (MIL) is only switched on by the ECM, if the malfunction is recognized after the engine has been restarted.

[3] With this malfunction the exhaust Malfunction Indicator Light (MIL) is switched on by the ECM, immediately after the malfunction has been recognized.

AD0150000375000X

Fig. 51 Codes P1558, P1559, P1560, P1564, P1565 & P1568

DTC SAE	DTC VAG	Description of malfunction	Corrective action
P1569	17977	Cruise control switch Incorrect signal	- Check switch for Cruise Control System (CCS)
P1570	17978	Control Module Locked	- Perform adaptation for immobilizer to ECM
P1579	17987	Idle Speed Contr.Throttle Pos. Adaptation not started	- Perform adaptation of throttle valve control module while maintaining test requirements
P1600	18008	Power Supply (B+) Terminal 15 Low Voltage	- Check voltage supply for Engine Control Module (ECM)
P1602	18010	Power Supply (B+) Terminal 30 Low Voltage	

AD0150000376000X

Fig. 52 Codes P1569, P1570, P1579, P1600 & P1602

DTC SAE	DTC VAG	Description of malfunction	Corrective action
P1603	18011	Internal Control Module Malfunction [2]	- Replace Engine Control Module (ECM)
P1604	18012	Internal Control Module Malfunction [1] [3]	
P1606	18014	Rough Road Spec Engine Torque ABS-ECU Electrical Malfunction	- Check wire connection between ECM and ABS control module
P1609	18017	Crash shut-down activated	Accident with airbag triggered or a output Test Diagnostic Mode (TDM) has been carried out, therefore erase DTC Memory in ECM; Notes crash signal
P1612	18020	Electronic Control Module [2] Incorrect Coding	- Check or code Engine Control Module (ECM)

[1] With this malfunction the EPC (Electronic Power Control) Malfunction Indicator Light (MIL) in the instrument cluster is switched on by the ECM.

[2] With this malfunction the exhaust Malfunction Indicator Light (MIL) is only switched on by the ECM, if the malfunction is recognized after the engine has been restarted.

[3] With this malfunction the exhaust Malfunction Indicator Light (MIL) is switched on by the ECM, immediately after the malfunction has been recognized.

AD0150000377000X

Fig. 53 Codes P1603, P1604, P1606, P1609 & P1612

DTC		Description of malfunction	Corrective action
SAE	VAG		
P1620	18028	Engine coolant temperature signal Open/short to B+	- Check coolant temperature signal
P1621	18029	Engine coolant temperature signal Short to ground	
P1622	18030	Engine coolant temperature signal Range/Performance	

Notes:

The Engine Control Module (ECM) receives the "Coolant temperature signal" from the instrument cluster. When the ECM receives this signal the boost pressure will be decreased.

AD0150000378000X

Fig. 54 Codes P1620, P1621 & P1622

DTC		Description of malfunction	Corrective action
SAE	VAG		
P1630	18038	Accelera. Pedal Pos. Sensor 1 Signal too Low 1) 3)	- Check acceleration pedal position sensor
P1631	18039	Accelera. Pedal Pos. Sensor 1 Signal too High 1) 3)	
P1633	18041	Accelera. Pedal Pos. Sensor 2 Signal too Low 1) 3)	
P1634	18042	Accelera. Pedal Pos. Sensor 2 Signal too High 1) 3)	

1) With this malfunction the EPC (Electronic Power Control) Malfunction Indicator Light (MIL) in the instrument cluster is switched on by the ECM.

3) With this malfunction the exhaust Malfunction Indicator Light (MIL) is switched on by the ECM, immediately after the malfunction has been recognized.

AD0150000380000X

Fig. 56 Codes P1630, P1631, P1633 & P1634

DTC		Description of malfunction	Corrective action
SAE	VAG		
P1676	18084	Drive by Wire-MIL Circ. Electrical Malfunction 1)	- Significance of Electronic Power Control (EPC) warning light
P1677	18085	Drive by Wire-MIL Circ. Short to B+ 1)	
P1690	18098	Malfunction Indication Light Malfunction 2)	- Check wiring for exhaust Malfunction Indicator Light (MIL)
P1693	18101	Malfunction Indication Light Short circuit to B+ 2)	

1) With this malfunction the EPC (Electronic Power Control) Malfunction Indicator Light (MIL) in the instrument cluster is switched on by the ECM.

2) With this malfunction the exhaust Malfunction Indicator Light (MIL) is only switched on by the ECM, if the malfunction is recognized after the engine has been restarted.

Notes:

The malfunction light for power acceleration -K132- is also called the EPC warning lamp.

AD0150000382000X

Fig. 58 Codes P1676, P1677, P1690 & P1693

DTC		Description of malfunction	Corrective action
SAE	VAG		
P1851	18259	Data Bus Powertrain Missing Message from Brake Contr	- Check DTC memory of ABS control module - Check data exchange between Engine-/ABS-/Transmission control module
P1853	18261	Data Bus Powertrain Unplausible Message from Brake Contr.	
P1854	18262	Data Bus Powertrain Hardware Defective	

1) With this malfunction the EPC (Electronic Power Control) Malfunction Indicator Light (MIL) in the instrument cluster is switched on by the ECM.

2) With this malfunction the exhaust Malfunction Indicator Light (MIL) is only switched on by the ECM, if the malfunction is recognized after the engine has been restarted.

AD0150000383000X

Fig. 59 Codes P1851, P1853 & P1854

DTC		Description of malfunction	Corrective action
SAE	VAG		
P1624	18032	MIL Request Sign. active	Exhaust relevant malfunction from Transmission Control Module (TCM), MIL is switched on by TCM - Check DTC Memory of TCM
P1626	18034	Data-Bus Powertrain 2) Missing message from fuel injection pump	- Check CAN-Bus

2) With this malfunction the exhaust Malfunction Indicator Light (MIL) is only switched on by the ECM, if the malfunction is recognized after the engine has been restarted.

Notes:

- *MIL stands for Malfunction Indicator Light. Once the Engine Control Module (ECM) recognizes a malfunction that decreases the exhaust emissions it switches the MIL on.*
- *The MIL is switched on only by the Engine Control Module (ECM), since the ECM has the only connection to the MIL..*
- *Malfunction that decrease the exhaust emissions can also be recognized by the Transmission Control Module (TCM), These malfunction are also indicated by the MIL.*
- *Once the TCM recognizes a malfunction that decreases the exhaust emissions it sends a message to the ECM, the ECM then switches the MIL on. Parallel to this is the malfunction P1624 stored in thè ECM noting that the MIL is switched on due to a transmission problem and not because of a engine problem.*

AD0150000379000X

Fig. 55 Codes P1624 & P1626

DTC		Description of malfunction	Corrective action
SAE	VAG		
P1639	18047	Accelera. Pedal Pos. Sensor1+2 Range/Performance 1) 3)	- Check acceleration pedal position sensor
P1640	18048	Internal Control Module (EEPROM) Error 2)	- Replace Engine Control Module (ECM)
P1648	18056	Data Bus Powertrain Malfunction	- Check data exchange between Engine-/ABS-/Transmission control module
P1649	18057	Data Bus Powertrain Missing message from ABS Control Module	- Check DTC memory of ABS control module - Check data exchange between Engine-/ABS-/Transmission control module

1) With this malfunction the EPC (Electronic Power Control) Malfunction Indicator Light (MIL) in the instrument cluster is switched on by the ECM.

2) With this malfunction the exhaust Malfunction Indicator Light (MIL) is only switched on by the ECM, if the malfunction is recognized after the engine has been restarted.

3) With this malfunction the exhaust Malfunction Indicator Light (MIL) is switched on by the ECM, immediately after the malfunction has been recognized.

AD0150000381000X

Fig. 57 Codes P1639, P1640, P1648 & P1649

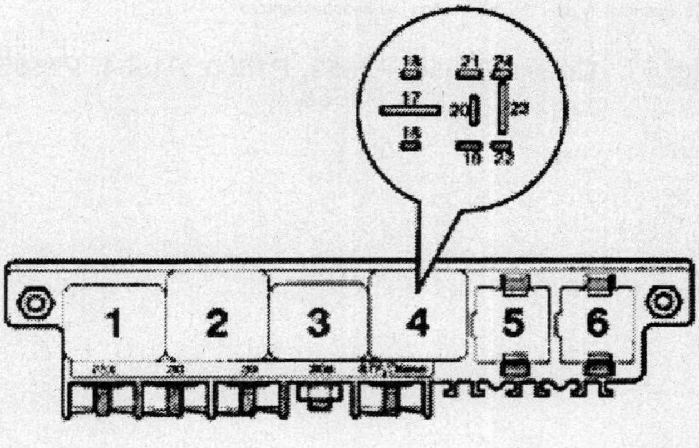

AD1020000207000X

Fig. 60 Fuel pump relay location & terminal identification

	Display fields			
	1	2	3	4
Display Group 002: Intake air mass at idling speed with engine at operating temperature				
Display	xxx RPM	xx.x %	x.x ms	xxx.x g/s
Indicates	Engine speed (in steps of 40 RPM)	Load	Average injection period	Air mass
Work range	min.: 750 rpm max.: 6800 rpm	min.: 15 % max.: 175 %	min.: 2.0 ms max.: 19.0 ms	min.: 3.0 g/s max.: approx: 225g/s
Specification	750 - 850 rpm	15.0 - 25.0 %	2.0 - 4.0 ms1.	3.0 - 4.5 g/s
Note	---	---	If readout does not match specification, see table for display field 3	If readout does not match specification, see table for display field 4

AD1020000208000X

Fig. 61 MAF sensor display group 002

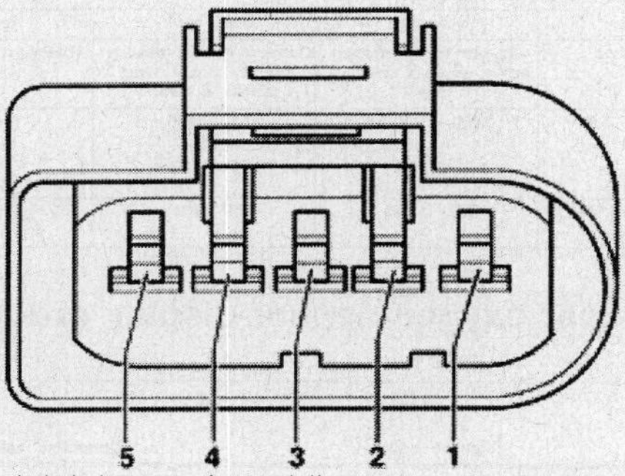

AD1020000210000X

Fig. 63 MAF sensor electrical connector terminal identification

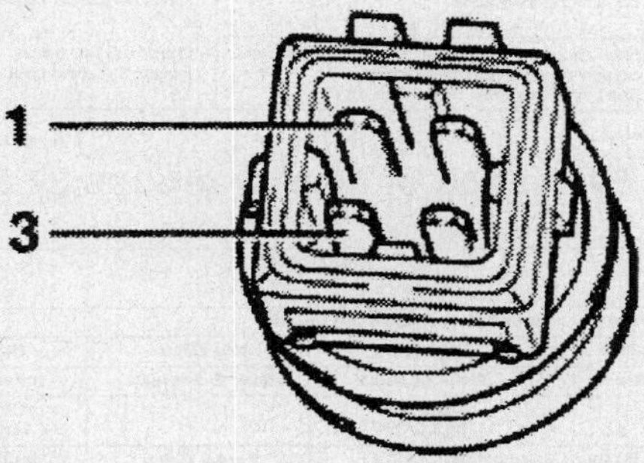

AD1020000212000X

Fig. 65 ECT sensor terminal identification. Square headed sensor

	Display fields			
	1	2	3	4
Display field 034: Diagnostic oxygen sensor aging (Bank 1)				
Display	xxxx/RPM	xxx °C	x.x s	Test ON
Indicated	Engine speed (RPM)	Exhaust temperature	Period duration oxygen sensor before catalytic converter	Diagnostic condition
Working range	0 - 6800	70 - 850 °C	0 - 3.0 Seconds	Test OFF Test ON B1-S1 OK B1-S1 not OK
Specification	1900 - 2200/RPM	greater than 260 °C	0.1 - 1.0 s	B1-S1 OK

AD1020000214000X

Fig. 67 Front oxygen sensor display group 34

Display field 3	Possible cause of malfunction	Corrective action
Less than 2.0 ms	◆ Lower values can only occur when vehicle is on fuel-shut off (overrun)	
More than 4.0 ms	◆ Load on engine due to ancillaries	- Eliminate load (air conditioner, power steering, alternator)
	◆ Rough idle (engine not running on all cylinders)	- Check spark plugs - Check fuel injectors
	◆ Throttle Valve Control Module -J338 faulty	- Check Throttle Valve Control Module
Less than 3.0 g/s	◆ Large quantity of un-metered air between intake manifold and Mass Air Flow (MAF) sensor ◆ Voltage supply to Mass Air Flow (MAF) sensor or wiring to Engine Control Module (ECM)	- Check intake system for leaks (un-metered air) - Check voltage supply and wiring ⇒
More than 4.5 g/s	◆ Load on engine due to accessories	- Eliminate load (A/C, power steering, generator)
	◆ Voltage supply to Mass Air Flow (MAF) sensor or wiring to Engine Control Module (ECM)	- Check voltage supply and wiring ⇒

AD1020000209000X

Fig. 62 MAF sensor troubleshooting chart

	Display fields			
	1	2	3	4
Display Group 004: Coolant temperature with engine idle				
Display	xxxx RPM	xx.xxx V	xxx.x °C	xxx.x °C
Indicates	Engine speed RPM	Battery voltage	Coolant temperature	Intake air temperature
Specified value	XXXX RPM	12.000...14.500 V	Temperature must increase evenly	Ambient temperature until 120°C

AD1020000211000X

Fig. 64 ECT display group 84

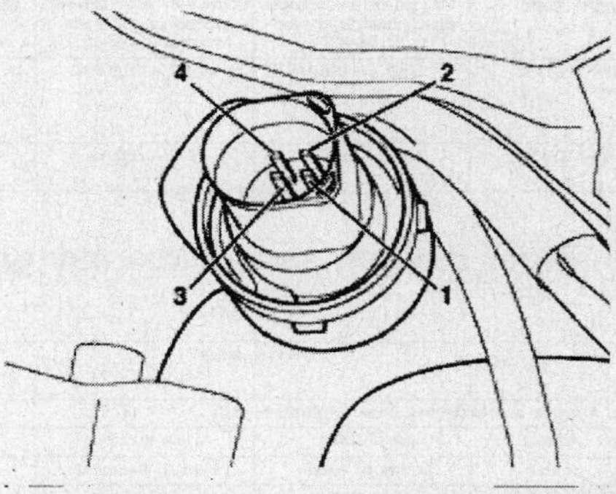

AD1020000213000X

Fig. 66 ECT sensor terminal identification. Oval headed sensor

	Display fields			
	1	2	3	4
Display field 035: Diagnostic oxygen sensor aging (Bank 2)				
Display	xxxx/RPM	xxx °C	x.x s	Test ON
Indicated	Engine speed (RPM)	Exhaust temperature	Period duration oxygen sensor before catalytic converter	Diagnostic condition
Working range	0 - 6800	70 - 850 °C	0 - 3.0 Seconds	Test OFF Test ON B1-S1 OK B1-S1 not OK
Specification	1900 - 2200/RPM	greater than 260 °C	0.1 - 1.0 s	B1-S1 OK

AD1020000215000X

Fig. 68 Front oxygen sensor display group 35

	Display fields			
	1	2	3	4
Display group 030: Oxygen sensor status with engine at idle				
Display	X X X	X X X	X X X	X X X
Indicated	Oxygen sensor status, bank 1, sensor 1	Oxygen sensor status bank 1, sensor 2	Oxygen sensor status, bank 2, sensor 1	Oxygen sensor status bank 2, sensor 2
Working area	0 = off 1 = on	0 = off 1 = on	0 = off 1 = on	0 = off 1 = on
Specified value:	1 1 1	1 1 1	1 1 1	1 1 1

AD1020000216000X

Fig. 69 Rear oxygen sensor display group 30

	Display fields			
	1	2	3	4
Display group 043: Oxygen sensor aging oxygen sensor behind catalytic converter (Bank 1)				
Display	xxxx/RPM	xxx °C	x.xxx V	Test ON
Indicated	Engine speed (RPM)	Exhaust temperature	Voltage of oxygen sensor behind CAT, Bank 1	Diagnostic condition
Work range	0 - 6800/RPM	70 - 850 °C	0.000 - 1.000 Volt	Test OFF Test ON B1-S2 OK B1-S2 not OK
Specified value	1900 - 2200/RPM	greater than 320 °C	0.000 - 1.000 Volt	B1-S2 OK

AD1020000217000X

Fig. 70 Rear oxygen sensor display group 43

	Display fields			
	1	2	3	4
Display group 044: Oxygen sensor aging oxygen sensor behind catalytic converter (Bank 2)				
Display	xxxx/RPM	xxx °C	x.xxx V	Test ON
Indicated	Engine speed (RPM)	Exhaust temperature	Voltage of oxygen sensor behind CAT, Bank 1	Diagnostic condition
Work range	0 - 6800/RPM	70 - 850 °C	0.000 - 1.000 Volt	Test OFF Test ON B2-S2 OK B2-S2 not OK
Specified value	1900 - 2200/RPM	greater than 320 °C	0.000 - 1.000 Volt	B1-S2 OK

AD1020000218000X

Fig. 71 Rear oxygen sensor display group 44

	Display fields			
	1	2	3	4
Display group 037: Diagnostic oxygen sensor control (Bank 1)				
Display	xxx %	x.xxx Volt	xxx ms	Test ON
Indicated	Engine load	Oxygen sensor voltage behind catalytic converter, Bank 1	Correction value between oxygen sensor 1 and sensor 2, bank 1	Diagnostic condition
Work range	15.0 - 175.0 %	0.000 - 1.000 V	-1200 - 1200 ms	Test OFF Test ON SYST. OK SYST. not OK
Specified value	15.0 - 25.0 %	0.000 - 1.000 V	-500 - 500 ms	SYST. OK

AD1020000219000X

Fig. 72 Rear oxygen sensor display group 37

	Display fields			
	1	2	3	4
Display group 038: Diagnostic oxygen sensor control (Bank 2)				
Display	xxx %	x.xxx Volt	xxx ms	Test ON
Indicated	Engine load	Oxygen sensor voltage behind catalytic converter, Bank 2	Correction value between oxygen sensor 1 and sensor 2, bank 2	Diagnostic condition
Work range	15.0 - 175.0 %	0.000 - 1.000 V	-1200 - 1200 ms	Test OFF Test ON SYST. OK SYST. not OK
Specified value	15.0 - 25.0 %	0.000 - 1.000 V	-500 - 500 ms	SYST. OK

AD1020000220000X

Fig. 73 Rear oxygen sensor display group 38

Display Group: 037/038 Display field: 2	Possible cause	Corrective action
approx.: 0.450 V	◆ Open circuit in wire 4 between oxygen sensor and control module	- Check signal wire and activation
	◆ Open circuit in wire 3 between oxygen sensor and control module	
	◆ Oxygen sensor heater faulty	- Check oxygen sensor heater
	◆ Oxygen sensor faulty	- Replace oxygen sensor
greater than 1.100 V	◆ Short circuit to B+ in wire 4 between oxygen sensor and control module	- Check oxygen sensor wiring bank 1 sensor 2 (behind converter)
smaller than 0.100 V	◆ Short circuit to Ground (GND) in wire 4 between oxygen sensor and control module ◆ Short circuit between wire 3 and 4	- Check oxygen sensor wiring bank 2 sensor 2 (behind converter)

AD1020000221000X

Fig. 74 Evaluation of display groups 37 & 38

	Display fields			
	1	2	3	4
Display Group 041: Oxygen sensor heater, Bank 1 (at idle speed)				
Display	xxx kOhm	Htg.bC.ON	xxx kOhm	Htg.aC.ON
Indicates	Bank 1, Sensor 1	Status of heater	Bank 1, Sensor 2	Status of heater
Range		Htg.bC.ON Htg.bC.OFF		Htg.aC.ON Htg.aC.OFF
Specified value	0 - 0.5 kOhm	Htg.bC.ON/OFF	0 - 0.5 kOhm	Htg.aC.ON/OFF
Note	It can take a few minutes until specification are obtained		It can take a few minutes until specified values are obtained	

AD1020000222000X

Fig. 75 Oxygen sensor heater display group 41

	Display fields			
	1	2	3	4
Display Group 042: Oxygen sensor heater, Bank 2 (at idle speed)				
Display	xxx kOhm	Htg.bC.ON	xxx kOhm	Htg.aC.ON
Indicates	Bank 2, Sensor 1	Status of heater	Bank 2, Sensor 2	Status of heater
Range		Htg.bC.ON Htg.bC.OFF		Htg.aC.ON Htg.aC.OFF
Specified value	0 - 0.5 kOhm	Htg.bC.ON/OFF	0 - 0.5 kOhm	Htg.aC.ON/OFF
Note	It can take a few minutes until specifications are obtained		It can take a few minutes until specifications are obtained	

AD1020000223000X

Fig. 76 Oxygen sensor heater display group 42

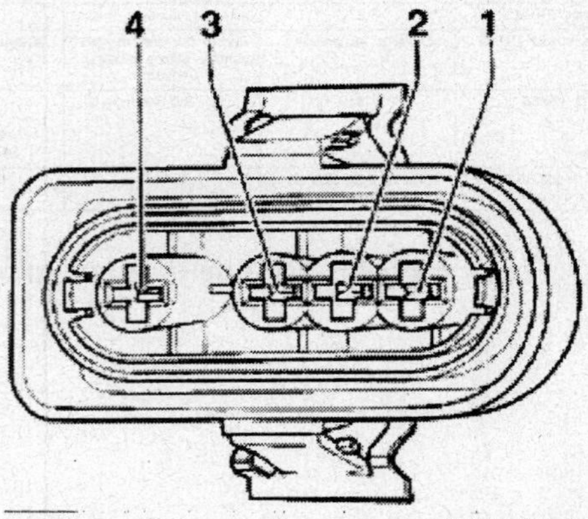

AD1020000224000X

Fig. 77 Rear oxygen sensor electrical connector terminal identification

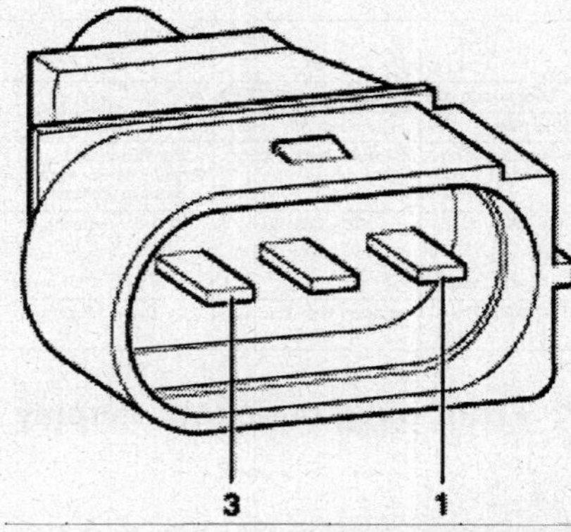

AD1020000225000X

Fig. 78 RPM sensor connector terminal identification

	Display fields			
	1	2	3	4
Display Group 062: Electronic throttle potentiometer voltages				
Display	xx %	xx %	xx %	xx %
Indicates	Throttle valve angle (angle sensor 1)	Throttle valve angle (angle sensor 2)	Accelerator position sensor 1	Accelerator position sensor 2
Work Range	min.: 0 % max.: 100 %	min.: 0 % max.: 100 %	min.: 0 % max.: 100 %	min.: 0 % max.: 100 %
Specified value	3 - 93 %	97 - 3 %	12 - 97 % (Idle value: 12 - 18%)	4 - 49 % (Idle value: 4 - 13%)

AD1020000226000X

Fig. 79 Electronic throttle potentiometer display group 62

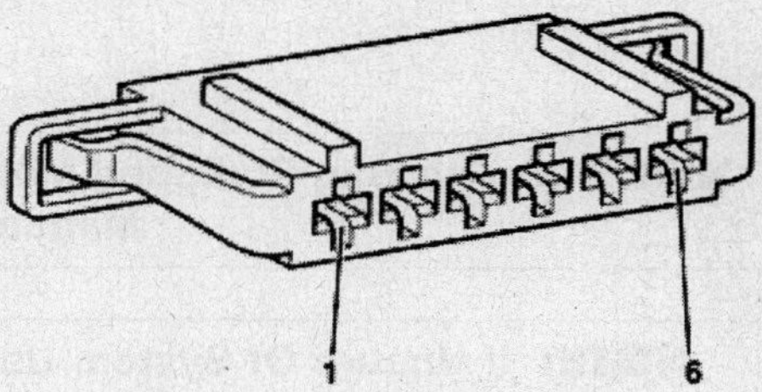

AD1020000227000X

Fig. 80 Throttle valve control module connector terminal identification

2.8L Engine

NOTE: On Air Bag Equipped Models, Refer To "Air Bag System Precautions" Located In The Front Of This Manual For System Disarming & Arming Procedures.

NOTE: If Unsure Of System Used On Vehicle Being Serviced, Refer To "Engine Systems Identification" Chart Located At Beginning Of This Chapter.

NOTE: Prior To Performing Any Service Operations Listed In This Section Consult "Technical Service Bulletins" Section For Related Information.

NOTE: "Electrical Symbol & Wire Color Code Identification" Located In The Front Of This Manual May Be Used As An Aid When Using Wiring Circuits Found In This Section.

INDEX

	Page No.
Description	10-89
Diagnosis & Testing	10-89
Accessing Diagnostic Trouble Codes	10-89
Clearing Diagnostic Trouble Codes	10-104
Component & System Tests	10-89
Closed Throttle Position (CTP) Switch	10-102
Crankshaft Position (CKP) Sensor	10-95
Engine Control Module (ECM)	10-103
Engine Coolant Temperature (ECT) Sensor	10-94
Fuel Injector	10-96
Fuel Pressure	10-91
Fuel Pump Relay	10-89
Heated Oxygen Sensor (HO2S)	10-98
Idle Air Control (IAC) Valve	10-97
Mass Air Flow (MAF) Sensor	10-93
Throttle Position (TP) Sensor	10-103
Diagnostic Tests	10-89
Diagnostic Trouble Code Interpretation	10-89
Wiring Diagrams	10-89
Diagnostic Chart Index	10-104
Precautions	10-89
Air Bag Systems	10-89
Audio Coded Anti-Theft System	10-89
Battery Ground Cable	10-89
Electrical Connection & Terminal Repair	10-89
Fuel System	10-89
Sensor & Fuel Injector Specifications	10-88
System Service	10-104

SENSOR & FUEL INJECTOR SPECIFICATIONS

Engine & Sensor	Temperature, °F	Nominal Value
2.8L 2V		
CKP	—	1000 Ohms
ECT	68	2500 Ohms
	176	330 Ohms
Fuel Injector (Bosch)	—	15–17 Ohms
Fuel Injector (Siemens)	—	13.5–14.5 Ohms
MAF	—	1.50 Volts @ Idle
		3.40 Volts @ 4000 RPM
O2S①	—	10 Ohms
TP	—	Terminals 1–2, 1500–2600 Ohms
		Terminals 2–3, 750–1300 Ohms
2.8L 5V		
ECT	68	1500–2000 Ohms
	176	275–375 Ohms
Fuel Injector	—	13.5–15.5 Ohms
HO2S Heater	—	2.4–9.2 Ohms
IAT	86	1500–2000 Ohms
	176	275–375 Ohms

① — Terminals 1 & 2.

PRECAUTIONS

Fuel System

Always clean fuel lines before loosening and be sure to replace seals and fuel hose clamps. Keep a fully charged fire extinguisher readily available.

Air Bag Systems

Refer to "Air Bag System Precautions" in the front of this manual for system disarming and arming procedures.

Battery Ground Cable

Prior to service, disconnect battery ground cable and isolate as required.

Audio Coded Anti-Theft System

Do not use computer memory saver tool. Using the tool will keep the air bag system charged and may cause accidental activation of the air bag unit.

After two improper attempts at entering security code, radio will lock up electronically. The display shows SAFE and will not change. To unlock, leave radio On for approximately 1 hour up to 48 hours, then enter code as it would be after a power disconnection.

1. Obtain radio code from vehicle operator.
2. Switch radio On. Radio should display SAFE.
3. Push and hold AM/FM and SCAN buttons until 1000 remains on display. **If AM/FM and SCAN buttons are held down too long or pushed again, the radio will misinterpret the 1000 as an attempt at coding and one improper coding attempt will be logged.**
4. Enter radio code using first four program station buttons. Security code will appear on display.
5. Starting with lefthand button, tap button until first digit is displayed. Move to next button and repeat procedure.
6. Push and hold AM/FM and SCAN buttons once again until display changes to SAFE.
7. Release AM/FM and SCAN buttons. Radio display will change to a radio station frequency and will now play.

Electrical Connection & Terminal Repair

If connector terminal or pin replacement is required, use only gold-plated components.

DESCRIPTION

Diagnostic Trouble Codes (DTCs) are stored in a permanent fault memory until intentionally erased.

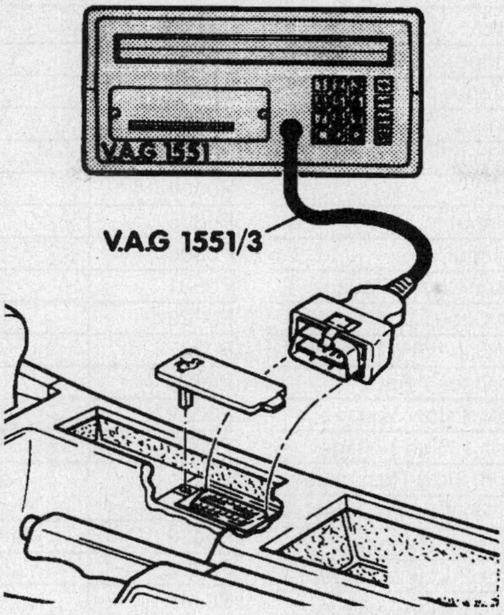

Fig. 1 Diagnostic Link Connector (DLC). A6

This system also recognizes sporadic (intermittent) faults. If a fault is present for a sufficient time it is stored as a static fault. If a condition appears momentarily or of insufficient time to be classified as static, it will be stored in a portion of fault memory where it will receive different attention than a static fault. If within next 50 engine starts fault no longer appears, then fault will be automatically erased.

Faults which affect exhaust or emission requirements will be displayed by engine warning lamp (On Board Diagnostics, OBD) on instrument panel.

DIAGNOSIS & TESTING

Accessing Diagnostic Trouble Codes

1. Connect diagnostic tester tool No. VAG 1551, or equivalent, to diagnostic connectors, **Fig. 1 through 3,** using connector harness tool No. VAG 1551/3.
2. **On A4 models,** remove DLC cover found next to rear ashtray in center console.
3. **On A6 models,** remove DLC cover found in front tray of center console.
4. **On Cabriolet models,** remove rear ashtray from center console to access DLC.
5. **On all models,** follow scan tool manufacturer's instructions to access DTCs.

Diagnostic Trouble Code Interpretation

Refer to **Fig. 4** for Diagnostic Trouble Code (DTC) interpretation.

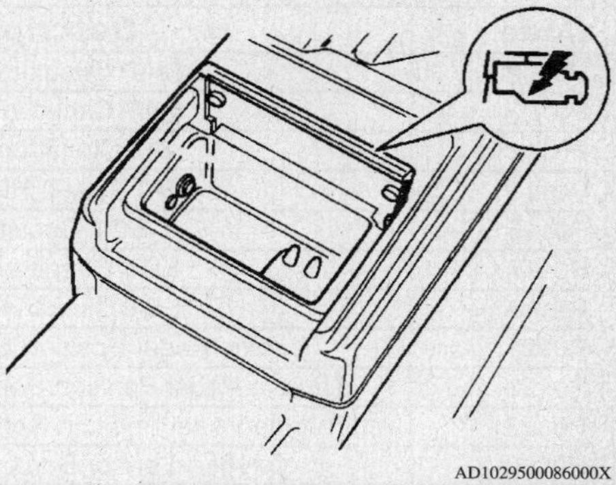

Fig. 2 Diagnostic Link Connector (DLC). Cabriolet

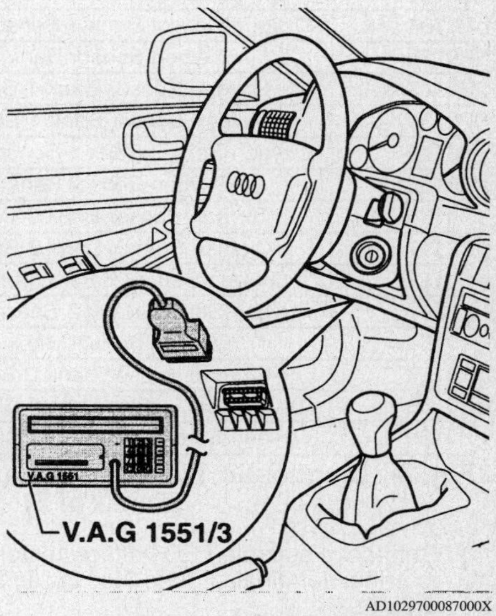

Fig. 3 Data Link Connector (DLC). A4

Wiring Diagrams

Refer to **Figs. 5 through 7** for system wiring diagrams.

Diagnostic Tests

Refer to **Figs. 8 through 35** for diagnostic trouble code interpretation. Refer to "Diagnostic Chart Index" for code definitions and specific diagnostic test for diagnosis procedures.

Component & System Tests

FUEL PUMP RELAY

FUNCTIONAL INSPECTION

A4 & S4

The fuel pump relay is located in the central electric panel under the instrument cluster.

1. Remove side under-dash panels required to access fuse relay panel.
2. Remove fuses from fuse panel position Nos. 28, 29 and 34.

Code	Description
P0102	MAF Circuit Low Input
P0103	MAF Circuit High Input
P0112	IAT Circuit Low Input
P0113	IAT Circuit High Input
P0116	ECT Circuit Fault
P0117	ECT Circuit Low Input
P0118	ECT Circuit High Input
P0121	Throttle/Pedal Position Sensor Circuit Fault
P0122	Throttle/Pedal Position Sensor Circuit Low Input
P0123	Throttle/Pedal Position Sensor Circuit High Input
P0130	Oxygen Sensor Bank 1 Sensor 1 Fault
P0131	Oxygen Sensor Bank 1 Sensor 1 Low Voltage
P0132	Oxygen Sensor Bank 1 Sensor 1 High Voltage
P0133	Oxygen Sensor Bank 1 Sensor 1 Slow Response
P0134	Oxygen Sensor Bank 1 Sensor 1 No Activity Detected
P0136	Oxygen Sensor Bank 1 Sensor 2 Fault
P0137	Oxygen Sensor Bank 1 Sensor 2 Low Voltage
P0138	Oxygen Sensor Bank 1 Sensor 2 High Voltage
P0140	Oxygen Sensor Bank 1 Sensor 2 No Activity Detected
P0150	Oxygen Sensor Bank 2 Sensor 1 Fault
P0151	Oxygen Sensor Bank 2 Sensor 1 Low Voltage
P0152	Oxygen Sensor Bank 2 Sensor 1 High Voltage
P0153	Oxygen Sensor Bank 2 Sensor 1 Slow Response
P0154	Oxygen Sensor Bank 2 Sensor 1 No Activity Detected
P0156	Oxygen Sensor Bank 2 Sensor 2 Fault
P0157	Oxygen Sensor Bank 2 Sensor 2 Low Voltage
P0158	Oxygen Sensor Bank 2 Sensor 2 High Voltage
P0160	Oxygen Sensor Bank 2 Sensor 2 No Activity Detected

Fig. 4 Diagnostic Trouble Code (DTC) interpretation (Part 1 of 5)

Code	Description
P0300	Random Misfire Detected
P0301	Cylinder 1 Misfire Detected
P0302	Cylinder 2 Misfire Detected
P0303	Cylinder 3 Misfire Detected
P0304	Cylinder 4 Misfire Detected
P0305	Cylinder 5 Misfire Detected
P0306	Cylinder 6 Misfire Detected
P0321	Engine Speed Sensor Input Circuit Fault
P0322	Engine Speed Sensor No Signal
P0327	Knock Sensor 1 Circuit Low Input
P0328	Knock Sensor 1 Circuit High Input
P0332	Knock Sensor 2 Circuit Low Input
P0333	Knock Sensor 2 Circuit High Input
P0411	Secondary Air Injection System Improper Flow Detected
P0422	Main Catalyst Bank 1 Efficiency Below Threshold
P0432	Main Catalyst Bank 2 Efficiency Below Threshold
P0441	EVAP System Improper Purge Flow Fault
P0442	EVAP System Small Leak Detected
P0455	EVAP System Large Leak Detected
P0501	Vehicle Speed Sensor Fault
P0506	Idle Control System RPM Lower Than Expected
P0507	Idle Control System RPM Higher Than Expected
P0601	Internal Control Module Memory Inspection Sum Error
P0604	Internal Control Module Random Access Memory Error
P1102	Oxygen Sensor Heating Circuit Bank 1 Sensor 1 Short To Power
P1105	Oxygen Sensor Heating Circuit Bank 1 Sensor 2 Short To Power
P1107	Oxygen Sensor Heating Circuit Bank 2 Sensor 1 Short To Power
P1110	Oxygen Sensor Heating Circuit Bank 2 Sensor 2 Short To Power

Fig. 4 Diagnostic Trouble Code (DTC) interpretation (Part 2 of 5)

3. Connect a suitable LED voltage tester to either terminal of fuse No. 28 and ground.
4. Operate starter. Fuel pump relay must operate and voltage tester must light.
5. If fuel pump does not operate, proceed as follows:
   a. Remove fuel pump relay.
   b. Turn ignition On.
   c. Inspect for voltage between relay connector terminals 28 and 34 using a suitable voltmeter, then between 32 and 34.
   d. Voltage should be battery voltage.
   e. If voltage reading is not as specified, repair wiring as required.
6. If test lamp does not light, repeat test after connecting LED tester to opposite fuse terminal.
7. If test lamp still does not light, correct wiring between fuse No. 28 and fuel pump relay pin 30, **Fig. 36.**
8. Connect a suitable LED voltage tester to either terminal of fuse No. 29 and ground.
9. Connect a suitable scan tool to Diagnostic Link Connector (DLC), access "Output Diagnostic Test Mode," then trigger fuel pump relay.
10. Fuel pump relay must operate and voltage tester must light.
11. If test lamp does not light, repeat test after connecting LED tester to opposite fuse terminal.
12. If test lamp still does not light, correct wiring between fuse No. 29 and fuel pump relay pin 30, **Fig. 36.**
13. Perform preceding steps on fuse No. 34.
14. If wiring or connector repairs are required, refer to "Precautions."
15. Inspect fuel pump relay signal as follows:
   a. Remove fuel pump relay.
   b. Remove fuses 28, 29 and 34 from fuse panel.
   c. Connect LED voltage tester VAG 1527BB, or equivalent to relay connector terminals 28 and 29. LED should light dimly.
   d. Crank engine and ensure LED continues to light dimly.
   e. If LED does not light when engine is cranked, connect test box tool No. VAG 1598/22, or equivalent to ECM harness connector.
   f. Inspect for open circuit between relay connector terminal 29 and test box pin 4 using a suitable ohmmeter. Resistance should read 1 ohm or less.
   g. If resistance is not as specified, repair open wire.
   h. If wiring is satisfactory and LED does not light, replace ECM.
   i. If wiring and signal to relay is satisfactory, replace fuel pump relay.

A6 & S6

The fuel pump relay is located in the micro central relay panel, relay position number 4.

1. Initiate output diagnostic test mode and advance to test of cylinder 1 fuel injector using a suitable scan tool.
2. While in output diagnostic test mode, inspect for fuel pump relay operation.
3. If relay does not operate, proceed as follows:
   a. Remove fuses 28, 29 and 34 from fuse panel. Refer to **Fig. 38** for fuse location.
   b. Initiate output diagnostic test mode and advance to test of cylinder 1 fuel injector.
   c. Measure voltage between both terminals of fuses 28, 29 and 34 and ground using a suitable voltmeter. Voltage should be battery voltage. If no voltage is present, repair wiring as required. If wiring is satisfactory, replace fuel pump relay.
4. If fuel pump does not run, proceed as follows:
   a. Ensure ignition is turned Off.
   b. Connect test box tool No. VAG 1598/22, or equivalent to ECM harness connector.

Code	Description
P1127	Long Term Fuel Trim Bank 1 System Too Rich
P1128	Long Term Fuel Trim Bank 1 System Too Lean
P1129	Long Term Fuel Trim Bank 2 System Too Rich
P1130	Long Term Fuel Trim Bank 2 Too Lean
P1136	Long Term Fuel Trim Bank 1 System Too Lean
P1137	Long Term Fuel Trim Bank 1 System Too Rich
P1138	Long Term Fuel Trim Bank 2 System Too Lean
P1139	Long Term Fuel Trim Bank 2 System Too Rich
P1141	Load Calculation Cross Inspection Range Fault
P1176	Oxygen Sensor Correction Behind Catalyst B1 Limit Attained
P1177	Oxygen Sensor Correction Behind Catalyst B2 Limit Attained
P1196	Oxygen Sensor Heater Circuit Bank 1 Sensor 1 Electrical Fault
P1197	Oxygen Sensor Heater Circuit Bank 2 Sensor 1 Electrical Fault
P1198	Oxygen Sensor Heater Circuit Bank 1 Sensor 2 Electrical Fault
P1199	Oxygen Sensor Heater Circuit Bank 2 Sensor 2 Electrical Fault
P1213	Cylinder 1 Fuel Injector Short To Power
P1214	Cylinder 2 Fuel Injector Short To Power
P1215	Cylinder 3 Fuel Injector Short To Power
P1216	Cylinder 4 Fuel Injector Short To Power
P1217	Cylinder 5 Fuel Injector Short To Power
P1218	Cylinder 6 Fuel Injector Short To Power

Fig. 4 Diagnostic Trouble Code (DTC) interpretation (Part 3 of 5)

Code	Description
P1225	Cylinder 1 Fuel Injector Short To Ground
P1226	Cylinder 2 Fuel Injector Short To Ground
P1227	Cylinder 3 Fuel Injector Short To Ground
P1228	Cylinder 4 Fuel Injector Short To Ground
P1229	Cylinder 5 Fuel Injector Short To Ground
P1230	Cylinder 6 Fuel Injector Short To Ground
P1237	Cylinder 1 Fuel Injector Open Circuit
P1238	Cylinder 2 Fuel Injector Open Circuit
P1239	Cylinder 3 Fuel Injector Open Circuit
P1240	Cylinder 4 Fuel Injector Open Circuit
P1241	Cylinder 5 Fuel Injector Open Circuit
P1242	Cylinder 6 Fuel Injector Open Circuit
P1250	Fuel Level Too Low
P1325	Cylinder 1 Knock Control Limit Attained
P1326	Cylinder 2 Knock Control Limit Attained
P1327	Cylinder 3 Knock Control Limit Attained
P1328	Cylinder 4 Knock Control Limit Attained
P1329	Cylinder 5 Knock Control Limit Attained
P1330	Cylinder 6 Knock Control Limit Attained
P1337	Camshaft Position Sensor Bank 1 Short To Ground
P1338	Camshaft Position Sensor Bank 1 Open Circuit Or Short To Power
P1386	Internal Control Module Knock Control Error
P1391	Camshaft Position Sensor Bank 2 Short To Ground
P1392	Camshaft Position Sensor Bank 2 Open Circuit Or Short To Power
P1410	Tank Ventilation Valve Short To Power
P1421	Secondary Air Injection Valve Circuit Short To Ground

Fig. 4 Diagnostic Trouble Code (DTC) interpretation (Part 4 of 5)

c. Connect test box pins 2 and 4 using test lead tool No. VAG 1594, or equivalent.
d. Turn ignition On. Fuel pump relay should operate.

5. If relay operates now but did not during output diagnostic test mode, replace ECM and perform throttle valve control module relearn procedure as outlined under "Computer Relearn Procedures" in front of this manual.
6. Generate new readiness code.
7. If relay does not operate, proceed as follows:
   a. Turn ignition Off.
   b. Remove fuel pump relay.
   c. Turn ignition On.
   d. Measure voltage between relay socket pin 19 and ground using a suitable voltmeter. Refer to **Fig. 37** for relay socket terminal identification.
   e. Voltmeter should read battery voltage.
8. If battery voltage is not present at pin 19, repair wiring as required.
9. If battery voltage is present at pin 19, proceed as follows:
   a. Turn ignition Off.
   b. Inspect wiring for open or short to power or ground between relay socket pin 16 and test box pin 4 using a suitable volt/ohmmeter.
   c. If wiring is satisfactory, replace fuel pump relay.

Cabriolet

The fuel pump relay is located in relay position No. 10 of the central electric panel located in the lefthand side of the air inlet plenum under the vehicle hood.

1. Remove central panel cover to access fuse relay panel.
2. Remove fuses from fuse panel position No. 13.
3. Connect a suitable LED voltage tester tool No. VAG 1527B, or equivalent, to either terminal of fuse No. 13 and ground.
4. Connect a suitable scan tool to Diagnostic Link Connector (DLC), access "Output Diagnostic Test Mode," then trigger fuel pump relay.
5. Fuel pump relay must operate and voltage tester must light.
6. If relay does not operate, proceed to "Relay Activation Inspection."
7. If test lamp does not light, repeat test after connecting LED tester to opposite fuse terminal.
8. If test lamp still does not light, correct wiring between fuse No. 13 and fuel pump relay terminal No. 52, **Fig. 39.**
9. Remove fuse No. 28, then connect a suitable LED voltage tester to either terminal of fuse No. 28 and ground.
10. Connect a suitable scan tool to Diagnostic Link Connector (DLC), access "Output Diagnostic Test Mode," then trigger fuel pump relay.
11. Fuel pump relay must operate and voltage tester must light.
12. If test lamp does not light, repeat test after connecting LED tester to opposite fuse terminal.
13. If test lamp still does not light, correct wiring between fuse No. 28 and fuel pump terminal pin 59.
14. If wiring or connector repairs are required, refer to "Precautions."

FUEL PRESSURE

A4 & S4

1. Ensure fuel pump relay operation is satisfactory, fuel filter is unrestricted and battery is fully charged.
2. Connect fuel pressure tester tool No. VAG 1318, or equivalent between fuel supply line and fuel manifold with lever in Open position.
3. Start engine and let run at idle.
4. Fuel pressure should be 50 psi.
5. Disconnect vacuum hose from fuel pressure regulator.
6. Fuel pressure should increase to 58 psi.
7. Connect vacuum hose and turn ignition Off.
8. Inspect for residual pressure by monitoring decrease in pressure. After 10 minutes, pressure should read at least 36 psi.
9. If pressure drops below 36 psi, proceed as follows:
   a. Start engine and allow pressure to build.
   b. After pressure has risen, turn engine off.
   c. Close valve of fuel pressure tester and monitor pressure as outlined.

Code	Description
P1422	Secondary Air Injection Control Valve Circuit Short To Power
P1425	Tank Vent Valve Short To Ground
P1426	Tank Vent Valve Open
P1432	Secondary Air Injection Valve Open
P1433	Secondary Air Injection Pump Relay Circuit Open
P1434	Secondary Air Injection Pump Relay Circuit Short To Power
P1435	Secondary Air Injection Pump Relay Short To Ground
P1436	Secondary Air Injection Pump Relay Circuit Electrical Fault
P1471	EVAP Emission Control LDP Circuit Short To Power
P1472	EVAP Emission Control LDP Circuit Short To Ground
P1473	EVAP Emission Control LDP Circuit Open
P1476	EVAP Emission Control LDP Circuit Fault/Insufficient Vacuum
P1477	EVAP Emission Control LDP Circuit Fault
P1500	Fuel Pump Relay Electrical Fault
P1501	Fuel Pump Relay Short To Ground
P1502	Fuel Pump Relay Short To Power
P1505	Closed Throttle Position Switch Does Not Close/Open Circuit
P1512	Intake Manifold Changeover Valve Short To Power
P1515	Intake Manifold Changeover Valve Short To Ground
P1516	Intake Manifold Changeover Valve Short To Circuit Open
P1519	Intake Camshaft Control Bank 1 Fault
P1522	Intake Camshaft Control Bank 2 Fault
P1543	Throttle Actuation Potentiometer Signal Too Low
P1544	Throttle Actuation Potentiometer Signal Too High
P1545	Throttle Position Control Fault
P1558	Throttle Actuator Electrical Fault
P1559	Idle Speed Control Throttle Position Adaptation Fault
P1560	Maximum Engine Speed Exceeded
P1564	Idle Speed Control Throttle Position Low Voltage During Adaptation
P1565	Idle Speed Control Throttle Position Lower Impact Not Attained
P1600	Power Supply Terminal 15 Low Voltage
P1602	Power Supply Terminal 30 Low Voltage
P1606	Rough Road Spec Engine Torque ABS-ECU Electrical Fault
P1612	ECM Improper Coding
P1624	MIL Request Sign Active
P1626	CAN Bus Missing Message From Transmission Control
P1640	Internal Control Module EEPROM Error
P1681	Control Unit Programming Not Finished
P1690	MIL Lamp Fault

Fig. 4 Diagnostic Trouble Code (DTC) interpretation (Part 5 of 5)

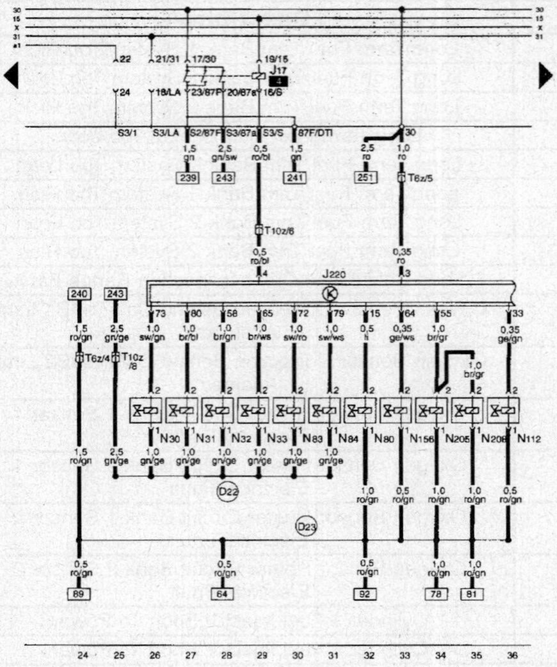

J17 – Fuel Pump (FP) Relay
J220 – Motronic Engine Control Module (ECM)
N30 – Injector, Cyl. 1
N31 – Injector, Cyl. 2
N32 – Injector, Cyl. 3
N33 – Injector, Cyl. 4
N80 – Evaporative (EVAP) Canister Purge Regulator Valve
N83 – Injector, Cyl. 5
N84 – Injector, Cyl. 6
N112 – Secondary Air Injection (AIR) Solenoid Valve
N156 – Intake Manifold Change-Over Valve
N205 – Valve -1- for camshaft adjustment
N208 – Valve -2- for camshaft adjustment
T6z – Wire Connector, 6 Point, red, connector station, electronics box in plenum chamber
T10z – Wire Connector, 10 Point, yellow, connector station, electronics box in plenum chamber
D22 – Connector (over fuse 234), in wiring harness front, right
D23 – Connector (over fuse 229), in wiring harness front, right

AD1029800096010X

Fig. 5 MFI system wiring diagram (Part 1 of 7). A4 & S4

d. If pressure still drops below 36 psi, inspect system for leaks and inspect fuel pump check valve.
e. If pressure no longer drops below 36 psi, inspect fuel pressure tester after shut off valve, fuel pressure regulator and fuel injectors.

A6 & S6

1. Ensure fuel pump relay operation is satisfactory, fuel filter is in perfect condition and battery is fully charged.
2. Connect fuel pressure tester tool No. VAG 1318, or equivalent between fuel supply line and fuel manifold with lever in Open position.
3. Disconnect fuel pressure regulator to intake manifold vacuum hose at regulator and plug.
4. Ensure all electrical accessories are off.
5. Start engine and allow to idle.
6. Fuel pressure should be 55–60 psi.
7. If pressure is not as specified, replace fuel pressure regulator and retest.
8. If after replacement of pressure regulator pressure is not as specified, inspect fuel pump or supply line for damage and repair as required.
9. If pressure is higher than specified, inspect return line for damage and repair as required.
10. If pressure is as specified, install vacuum line to pressure regulator. Pressure should drop approximately 7 psi.
11. If pressure does not change, inspect vacuum line and repair if required.
12. If no leaks are present and vacuum line is satisfactory, replace fuel pressure regulator.
13. Inspect system residual pressure as follows:
    a. Turn engine off and monitor pressure after 10 minutes.
    b. Pressure should read approximately 31.9 psi on cold engine and 43.5 psi on hot engine.
    c. If pressure is not as specified, start engine, allow fuel pressure to increase then turn engine off.
    d. Close shutoff valve of pressure tester.
    e. If pressure does not drop, inspect pressure gauge and lines and fuel pump check valve.
    f. If pressure does drop, the following items may be at fault: fuel pressure

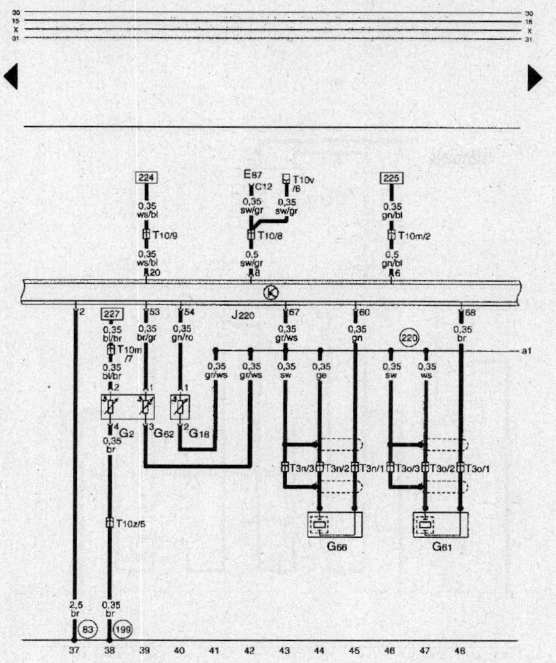

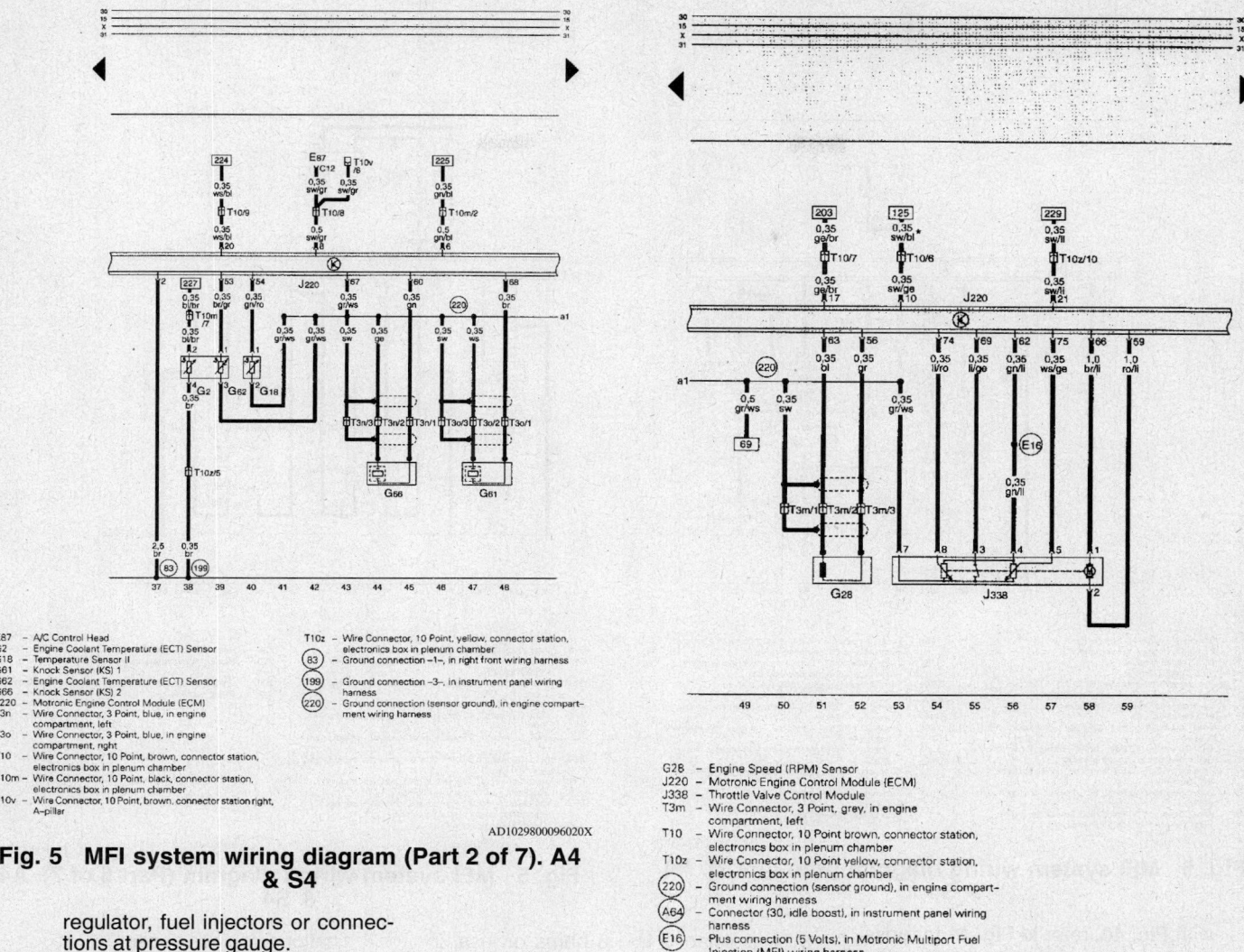

E87 – A/C Control Head
G2 – Engine Coolant Temperature (ECT) Sensor
G18 – Temperature Sensor II
G61 – Knock Sensor (KS) 1
G62 – Engine Coolant Temperature (ECT) Sensor
G66 – Knock Sensor (KS) 2
J220 – Motronic Engine Control Module (ECM)
T3n – Wire Connector, 3 Point, blue, in engine compartment, left
T3o – Wire Connector, 3 Point, blue, in engine compartment, right
T10 – Wire Connector, 10 Point, brown, connector station, electronics box in plenum chamber
T10m – Wire Connector, 10 Point, black, connector station, electronics box in plenum chamber
T10v – Wire Connector, 10 Point, brown, connector station right, A-pillar
T10z – Wire Connector, 10 Point, yellow, connector station, electronics box in plenum chamber
(83) – Ground connection –1–, in right front wiring harness
(199) – Ground connection –3–, in instrument panel wiring harness
(220) – Ground connection (sensor ground), in engine compartment wiring harness

Fig. 5 MFI system wiring diagram (Part 2 of 7). A4 & S4

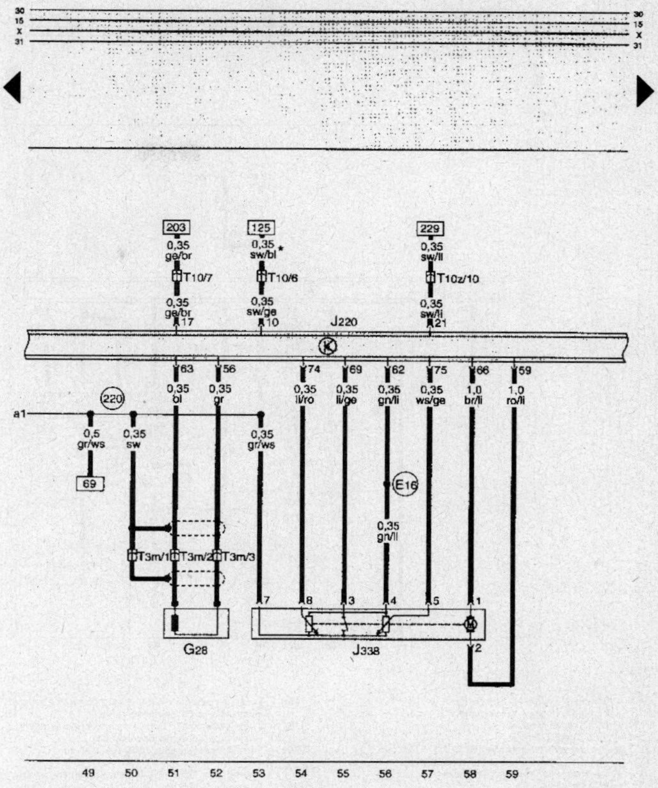

G28 – Engine Speed (RPM) Sensor
J220 – Motronic Engine Control Module (ECM)
J338 – Throttle Valve Control Module
T3m – Wire Connector, 3 Point, grey, in engine compartment, left
T10 – Wire Connector, 10 Point brown, connector station, electronics box in plenum chamber
T10z – Wire Connector, 10 Point yellow, connector station, electronics box in plenum chamber
(220) – Ground connection (sensor ground), in engine compartment wiring harness
(A64) – Connector (30, idle boost), in instrument panel wiring harness
(E16) – Plus connection (5 Volts), in Motronic Multiport Fuel Injection (MFI) wiring harness
* – Quattro Only

Fig. 5 MFI system wiring diagram (Part 3 of 7). A4 & S4

regulator, fuel injectors or connections at pressure gauge.

MASS AIR FLOW (MAF) SENSOR

A4 & S4

Supply Voltage Inspection

Ensure fuse No. 32 is in satisfactory condition.

1. Disconnect MAF sensor electrical connector, then connect suitable multimeter between terminal Nos. 2 and 3. Turn ignition On.
2. If reading is not battery voltage, inspect fuse No. 34, then measure continuity from terminal No. 3 to fuse and from terminal No. 2 to engine ground.
3. Resistance must be .5 ohms maximum.

Signal Wire Inspection

1. Connect test box tool No. VAG 1598/19, or equivalent, to ECM wiring harness. ECM is not connected.
2. Measure resistance between MAF sensor connector terminal No. 1 and test box socket No. A12 using a suitable ohmmeter. Maximum resistance is 1 ohm.
3. If resistance does not meet specifications, repair wiring as required.

Functional Inspection

1. Push back MAF sensor connector protective cover, but leave cover connected to sensor.
2. Connect suitable multimeter with auxiliary harness tool No. VAG 1594, or equivalent, to contact Nos. 2 and 1, then turn ignition On.
3. Meter should read .3–1.1 volts.
4. Start engine and allow to idle.
5. Turn all electrical consumers off. **Do not allow cooling fans to run during test.**
6. Vary engine speed from idle to 4000 RPM.
7. If readings do not vary from 1.5–3.4 volts, replace MAF sensor.

A6

Functional Inspection

Before performing MAF sensor inspection, ensure all electrical accessories are off and fuse for MAF circuit is satisfactory.

1. Connect scan tool No. VAG 1551/1552, or equivalent, then press buttons 0 and 1 to insert "Engine Electronics" address word 01. Engine should be running and at idle.
2. Press buttons 0 and 8 to select "Read Measuring Value Block" function 08, then press "Q" to confirm input.
3. Press buttons 0, 0 and 2 to input Display Group 02, then press "Q" to confirm input.
4. Compare scan tool data with Display Group data, **Fig. 40.**
5. If Display Group values are satisfactory, proceed as follows:
   a. Press right arrow button to advance program sequence.
   b. Press buttons 0 and 6 to select "End Output" function 06, then press "Q" to confirm input.
   c. Turn ignition Off.
6. If Display Group values do not agree

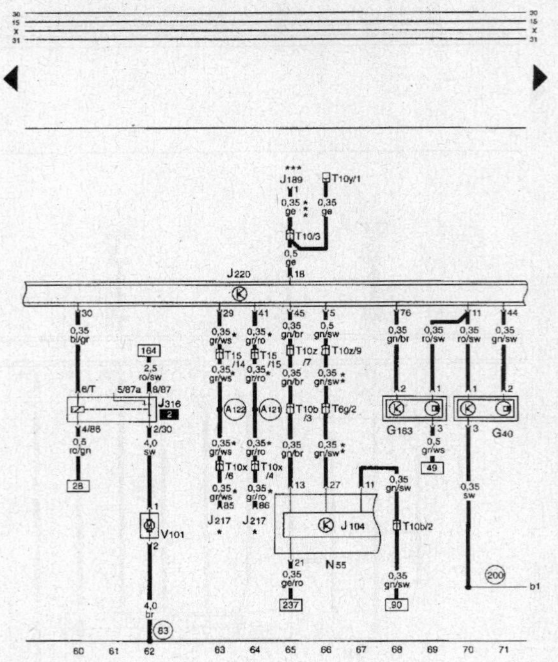

G40 – Camshaft Position (CMP) Sensor
G163 – Camshaft Position (CMP) Sensor 2
J104 – ABS Control Module
J189 – Auto Check System
J217 – Transmission Control Module (TCM)
J220 – Motronic Engine Control Module (ECM)
J316 – Secondary Air Injection (AIR) Relay
N55 – ABS Hydraulic Unit
T6g – Wire Connector, 6 Point, grey, connector station right, A–pillar
T10 – Wire Connector, 10 Point, brown, connector station, electronics box in plenum chamber
T10b – Wire Connector, 10 Point, orange, connector station left, A–pillar
T10x – Wire Connector, 10 Point, blue, connector station right, A–pillar
T10y – Wire Connector, 10 Point, blue, connector station, electronics box in plenum chamber
T10z – Wire Connector, 10 Point, yellow, connector station, electronics box in plenum chamber
T15 – Wire Connector, 15 Point, white, connector station, electronics box in plenum chamber
V101 – Secondary Air Injection (AIR) Pump Motor
(83) – Ground connection –1–, in front wiring harness
(200) – Ground connection (shielding), in engine compartment wiring harness
(A121) – Connector (High–Bus), in instrument panel wiring harness
(A122) – Connector (Low–Bus), in instrument panel wiring harness
* – Automatic Transmission Only
** – ASC Only
*** – Auto Check System Only

AD1029800096040X

Fig. 5 MFI system wiring diagram (Part 4 of 7). A4 & S4

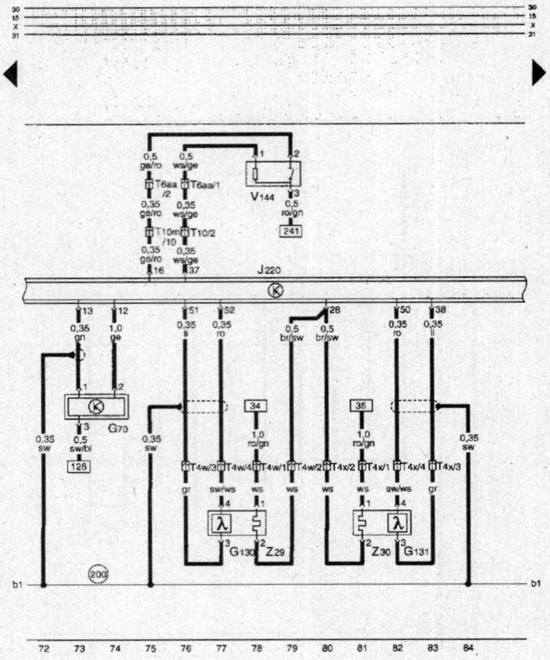

G70 – Mass Air Flow (MAF) Sensor
G130 – Oxygen Sensor (OS2) Behind Three Way Catalytic Converter (TWC)
G131 – Oxygen Sensor (OS2) 2 Behind Three Way Catalytic Converter (TWC)
J220 – Motronic Engine Control Module (ECM)
T4w – Wire Connector, 4 Point, green, in engine compartment, right
T4x – Wire Connector, 4 Point, brown, in engine compartment, right
T6aa – Wire Connector, 6 Point, brown, connector station right, A–pillar
T10 – Wire Connector, 10 Point, brown, connector station, electronics box in plenum chamber
T10m – Wire Connector, 10 Point, black, connector station, electronics box in plenum chamber
V144 – Diagnosis pump for fuel system
Z29 – Heater for Lambda–probe 1
Z30 – Heater for Lambda–probe 2
(200) – Ground connection (shielding), in engine compartment wiring harness

AD1029800096050X

Fig. 5 MFI system wiring diagram (Part 5 of 7). A4 & S4

with **Fig. 40,** refer to **Fig. 41** for possible causes of MAF circuit fault condition.

Voltage Inspection

1. Disconnect MAF sensor.
2. Turn ignition On.
3. Measure voltage between MAF sensor terminals 2 and 3, **Fig. 42,** using a suitable voltmeter.
4. Voltage should read 9–14.5 volts.
5. If no voltage is present, repair wiring as required.
6. If voltage is as specified, proceed to "Wiring Inspection."

Wiring Inspection

1. Ensure ignition is turned Off.
2. Connect test box tool No. VAG 1598/22, or equivalent to ECM harness connector.
3. Measure resistance between terminal 1 of MAF connector, **Fig. 42,** and test box pin 13 using a suitable ohmmeter. Measure resistance between MAF connector terminal 2 and test box pin 12.
4. Resistance should read 1.5 ohms or less.
5. If resistance is greater than 1.5 ohms, service open circuit as required.
6. If resistance is 1.5 ohms or less, inspect wiring for short circuit as follows:
   a. Measure resistance between MAF connector terminal 1 and test box pin 12. Ohmmeter should give an open reading.
   b. Measure voltage between MAF connector terminals 1 and 2 to ground using a suitable voltmeter, which should read 0 volts.
   c. If volt/ohmmeter values are not as specified, service short circuit as required.
7. If wiring inspection is satisfactory, replace MAF sensor, then generate new readiness code.

ENGINE COOLANT TEMPERATURE (ECT) SENSOR

A4, CABRIOLET & S4

1. Disconnect Engine Coolant Temperature (ECT) sensor electrical connector.
2. Connect suitable ohmmeter between ECT sensor electrical connector terminal Nos. 1 and 3.
3. At 68°F, resistance should be approximately 2500 ohms. At 176°F, resistance should be approximately 330 ohms. If resistance is not within specifications, replace sensor.
4. If resistance is within specifications, inspect wiring from sensor to Engine Control Module (ECM) as follows:
   a. Connect test box tool No. VAG 1598/19, or equivalent, to ECM harness. ECM is not connected.
   b. Inspect for maximum 1 ohm resistance between ECT sensor connector terminal No. 3 and engine ground.
   c. Inspect for maximum 1 ohm resistance between ECT sensor connector terminal No. 1 and test box contact No. 16A.
   d. Inspect both wires for short to each other.
   e. If specified values are not obtained, refer to wiring diagrams to trace and repair short and/or break in wiring between ECT sensor and ECM connector.
5. If wiring and ECT sensor are satisfactory, replace ECM.
6. If wiring or connector repairs are required, refer to "Precautions."

A6

Functional Test

1. Ensure engine is cold.

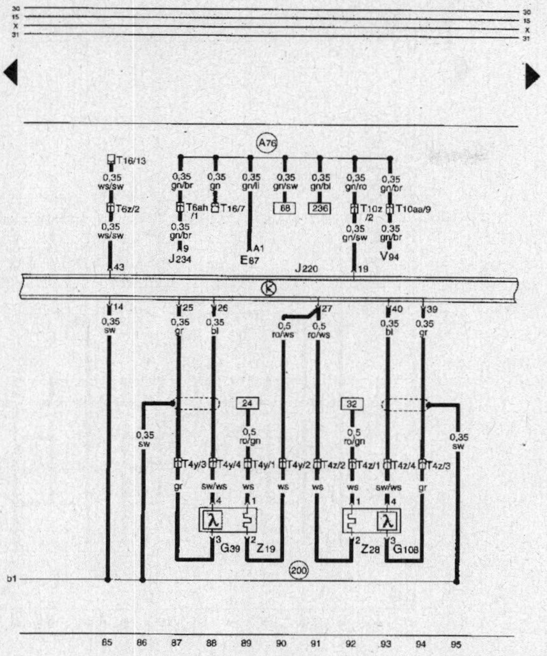

E87 – A/C Control Head
G39 – Heated Oxygen Sensor (HO2S) 1
G108 – Heated Oxygen Sensor (HO2S) 2
J220 – Motronic Engine Control Module (ECM)
J234 – Airbag Control Module
T4y – Wire Connector, 4 Point, black, in engine compartment, right
T4z – Wire Connector, 4 Point, black, in engine compartment, left
T6z – Wire Connector, 6 Point, red, connector station, electronics box in plenum chamber
T6ah – Wire Connector, 6 Point, green, connector station right, A–pillar
T10z – Wire Connector, 10 Point, yellow, connector station, electronics box in plenum chamber
T10aa – Wire Connector, 10 Point, orange, connector station right, A–pillar
T16 – Wire Connector, 16 Point, center console, rear (diagnostic connection)
V94 – Central Locking / Alarm System / Interior Light Delay Control Module
Z19 – Oxygen Sensor (O2S) I Heater
Z28 – Oxygen Sensor (O2S) II Heater
(200) – Ground connection (shielding), in engine compartment wiring harness
(A76) – Connector (K–diagnosis wire), in instrument planel wiring harness

AD1029800096060X

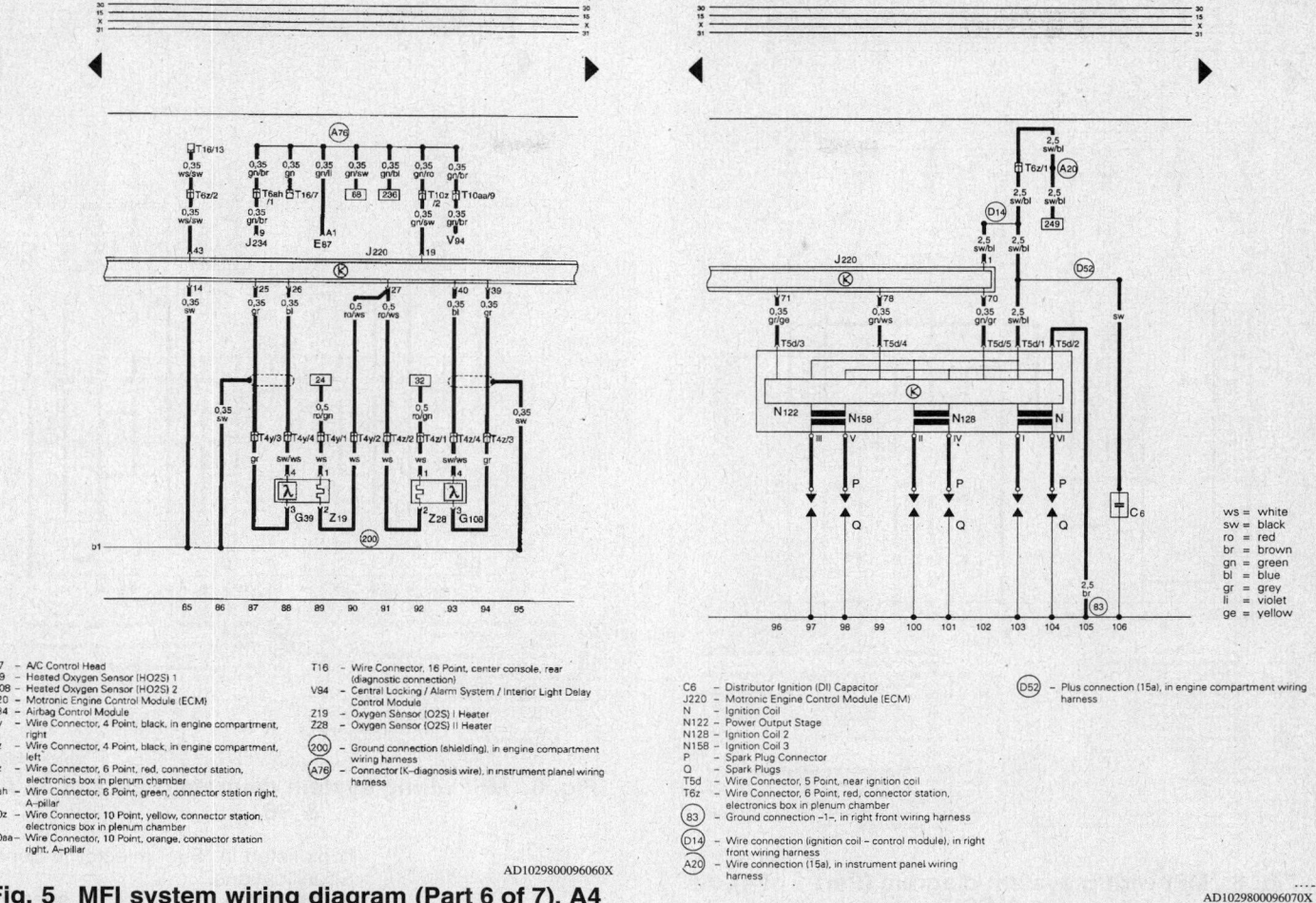

Fig. 5 MFI system wiring diagram (Part 6 of 7). A4 & S4

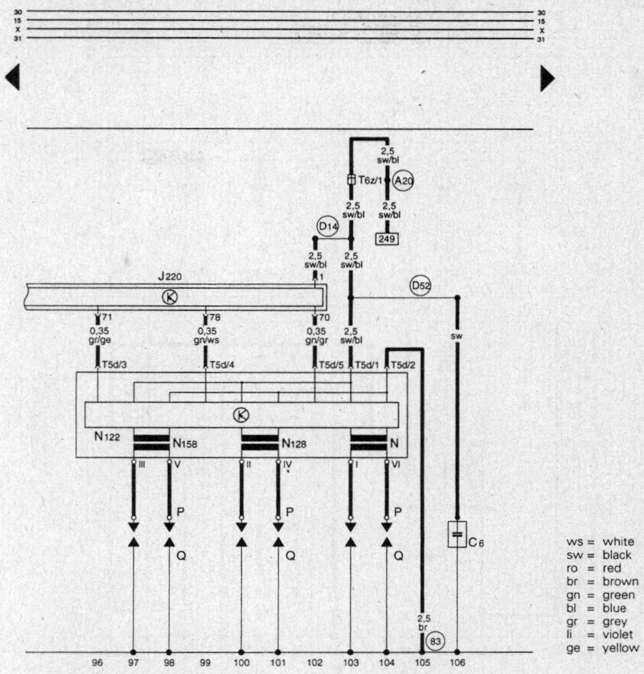

C6 – Distributor Ignition (DI) Capacitor
J220 – Motronic Engine Control Module (ECM)
N – Ignition Coil
N122 – Power Output Stage
N128 – Ignition Coil 2
N158 – Ignition Coil 3
P – Spark Plug Connector
Q – Spark Plugs
T5d – Wire Connector, 5 Point, near ignition coil
T6z – Wire Connector, 6 Point, red, connector station, electronics box in plenum chamber
(83) – Ground connection –1–, in right front wiring harness
(D14) – Wire connection (ignition coil – control module), in right front wiring harness
(A20) – Wire connection (15a), in instrument panel wiring harness
(D52) – Plus connection (15a), in engine compartment wiring harness

AD1029800096070X

Fig. 5 MFI system wiring diagram (Part 7 of 7). A4 & S4

2. Connect scan tool No. VAG 1551/1552, or equivalent and press buttons 0 and 1 to insert "Engine Electronics" address word 01. Turn ignition On.
3. Press buttons 0 and 8 to select "Read Measuring Value Block" function 08, then press "Q" to confirm input.
4. Press buttons 0 and 4 to input Display Group 4, then press "Q" to confirm input.
5. Compare scan tool data with ECT sensor data in **Fig. 43.**
6. Start engine and allow to idle.
7. If temperature increase is erratic, proceed as follows:
   a. Press right arrow button to advance sequence.
   b. Press buttons 0 and 6 to "End Output" function 06, then press "Q" to confirm input.
   c. Turn ignition Off.
   d. Replace ECT sensor and retest system.
8. If temperature increases evenly and fault is still present, perform ECT wiring inspection.

Wiring Inspection

1. Refer to **Fig. 44** for ECT connector pin identification.
2. Connect test box tool No. VAG 1598/22, or equivalent to ECM harness connector.
3. Disconnect ECT sensor.
4. Inspect the following pins for open circuit using a suitable ohmmeter: connector terminal 1 to test box pin 53; connector terminal 3 to test box pin 67.
5. If resistance is greater than 1.5 ohms, service wiring as required.
6. If resistance is 1.5 ohms or less, inspect the following pins for short circuit:
   a. Connector terminal 1 to ground.
   b. Connector terminal 1 to test box pin 67.
   c. Connector terminal 1 to connector terminal 3.
   d. Connector terminal 3 to ground.
7. If ohmmeter does not read open circuit, service wiring as required.
8. If ohmmeter does read open circuit, inspect voltage reading of connector pins 1 and 3 to ground. Voltage should be 0 volts.
9. If wiring is satisfactory, measure resistance of ECT sensor pins 1 and 3 and replace as required.

CRANKSHAFT POSITION (CKP) SENSOR

Before performing the following diagnostic procedures, ensure sensor attaching bolts are tight and that no metal shavings are present on sensor or sensor wheel.

A4, CABRIOLET & S4

1. Disconnect gray engine speed (RPM) sensor electrical connector.
2. Connect suitable multimeter between terminal Nos. 1 and 2 of sensor half of connector.
3. If resistance is not approximately 1000 ohms, replace RPM sensor.
4. If resistance is approximately 1000 ohms, connect suitable multimeter between terminal Nos. 1 and 3, then Nos. 2 and 3.
5. If resistance is not infinity, replace RPM sensor.
6. If resistance is infinity, inspect wiring between sensor and Engine Control Module (ECM) as follows:
   a. Connect test box tool No. VAG 1598/19, or equivalent, to ECM

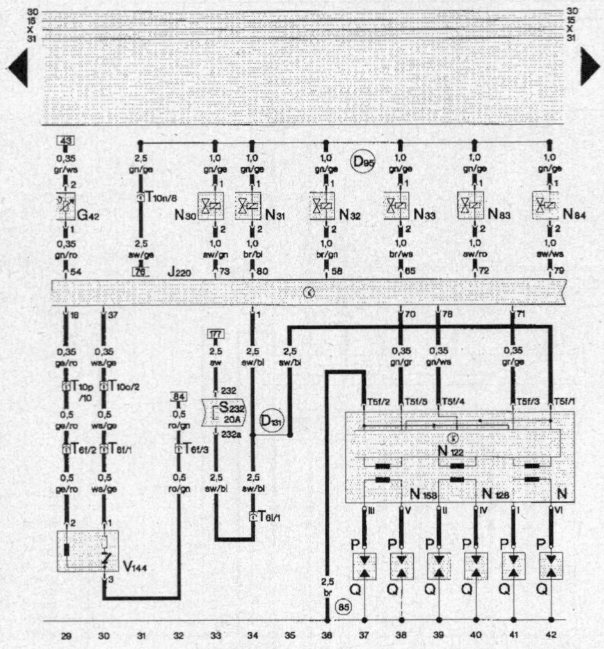

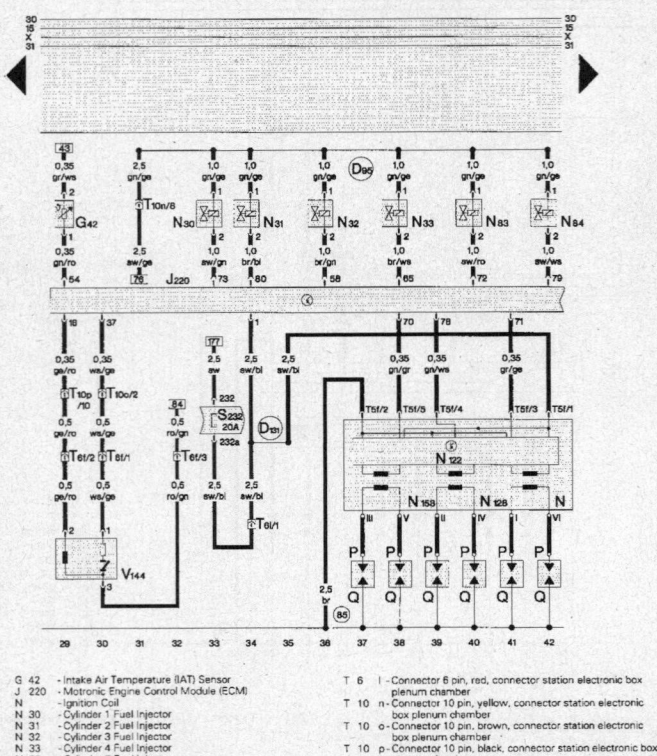

G 42 - Intake Air Temperature (IAT) Sensor
J 220 - Motronic Engine Control Module (ECM)
N - Ignition Coil
N 30 - Cylinder 1 Fuel Injector
N 31 - Cylinder 2 Fuel Injector
N 32 - Cylinder 3 Fuel Injector
N 33 - Cylinder 4 Fuel Injector
N 83 - Cylinder 5 Fuel Injector
N 84 - Cylinder 6 Fuel Injector
N 122 - Power Output Stage
N 128 - Ignition Coil 2
N 158 - Ignition Coil 3
P - Spark Plug Connectors
Q - Spark Plugs
S 232 - Fuse
T 5 f - Connector 5 pin, ignition coil unit
T 6 f - Connector 6 pin; darkbrown, connector station A pillar, right
T 6 l - Connector 6 pin, red, connector station electronic box plenum chamber
T 10 n - Connector 10 pin, yellow, connector station electronic box plenum chamber
T 10 o - Connector 10 pin, brown, connector station electronic box plenum chamber
T 10 p - Connector 10 pin, black, connector station electronic box plenum chamber
V 144 - Leak Detection Pump (LDP)

(85) - Ground connection -1-, in engine compartment wiring harness
(D95) - Wire connection (injectors), in engine compartment wiring harness
(D131) - Wire connection (15), above circuit Breaker, in engine compartment wiring harness

AD1029800098010X

Fig. 6 MFI wiring system diagram (Part 1 of 4). A6 & S6

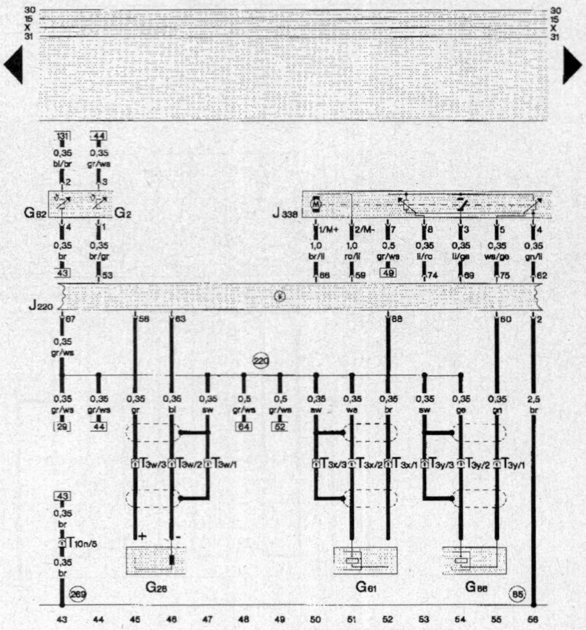

G 2 - Engine Coolant Temperature (ECT) Sensor
G 28 - Engine Speed (RPM) Sensor
G 61 - Knock Sensor (KS) 1
G 62 - Engine Coolant Temperature (ECT) Sensor
G 66 - Knock Sensor (KS) 2
J 220 - Motronic Engine Control Module (ECM)
J 338 - Throttle Valve Control Module
T 3 w - Connector 3 pin, grey, on engine speed sensor
T 3 x - Connector 3 pin, blue, on knock sensor 1
T 3 y - Connector 3 pin, blue, on knock sensor 2
T 10 n - Connector 10 pin, yellow, connector station electronic box plenum chamber

(85) - Ground connection -1-, in engine compartment wiring harness
(220) - Ground connection (sensor ground), in engine compartment wiring harness
(269) - Ground connector (sensor ground) -1-, in instrument panel wiring harness

AD1029800098020X

Fig. 6 MFI wiring system diagram (Part 2 of 4). A6 & S6

electrical connector. ECM is not connected.
   b. Measure resistance between sensor harness connector terminal No. 3 and engine ground, **Fig. 45.**
   c. Measure resistance between sensor connector ground terminal No. 1 and test box contact No. A11.
   d. Measure resistance between sensor connector terminal No. 2 and test box contact No. A9.
   e. Resistance should not exceed 1 ohm.
   f. If resistance is more than 1 ohm, refer to wiring diagrams to trace and repair short or break in wiring.
7. If wiring is satisfactory, remove starter and inspect teeth on starter ring gear for damage.
8. Turn engine slowly in normal direction of rotation using a suitable wrench and inspect flywheel for runout or damaged teeth.
9. If ring gear is satisfactory, replace ECM.
10. If wiring or connector repairs are required, refer to "Precautions."

A6

1. Disconnect CKP sensor. Refer to **Fig. 46** for CKP sensor terminal identification.
2. Connect test box tool No. VAG 1598/22, or equivalent to ECM harness connector.
3. Inspect the following pins for open circuit using a suitable ohmmeter.
   a. Connector terminal 1 to test box pin 67.
   b. Connector terminal 2 to test box pin 63.
   c. Connector terminal 3 to test box pin 56.
4. If resistance is greater than 1.5 ohms, service wiring as required.
5. If resistance is 1.5 ohms or less, inspect the following pins for short circuit using a suitable ohmmeter:
   a. Connector terminal 2 to test box pin 67.
   b. Connector terminal 1 to test box pin 63.
   c. Connector terminal 1 to test box pin 56.
6. If ohmmeter does not give open reading, service short in wiring as required.
7. If wiring inspection is satisfactory, replace CKP sensor.

FUEL INJECTOR

RESISTANCE INSPECTION

1. Disconnect injector harness connector.
2. Measure fuel injector resistance.
3. Compare resistance with specifications listed in "Fuel Injector & Sensor Specifications."
4. If resistance is not within specifications, replace injector.
5. If wiring or connector repairs are required, refer to "Precautions."

VOLTAGE SUPPLY INSPECTION

A4, Cabriolet & S4

1. Ensure fuel pump relay and fuel pump relay activation are satisfactory.
2. **On A4 and S4 models,** ensure fuse No. 34 is satisfactory.
3. **On Cabriolet models,** ensure fuse No. 21 is satisfactory.
4. **On all models,** disconnect injector harness and connect suitable LED tester between connector terminal No. 1 and engine ground.
5. Initiate "Output Diagnostic Test Mode" as outlined in "Computerized Engine Controls" and activate fuel pump relay.
6. If tester does not light, inspect continuity between terminal No. 1 and fuse No. 34.
7. If tester lights, inspect fuel injector activation.
8. If wiring or connector repairs are required, refer to "Precautions."

ECM SIGNAL

A6

1. Disconnect fuel injector electrical connectors.
2. Connect LED voltage tester tool No. VAG 1527BB, or equivalent between

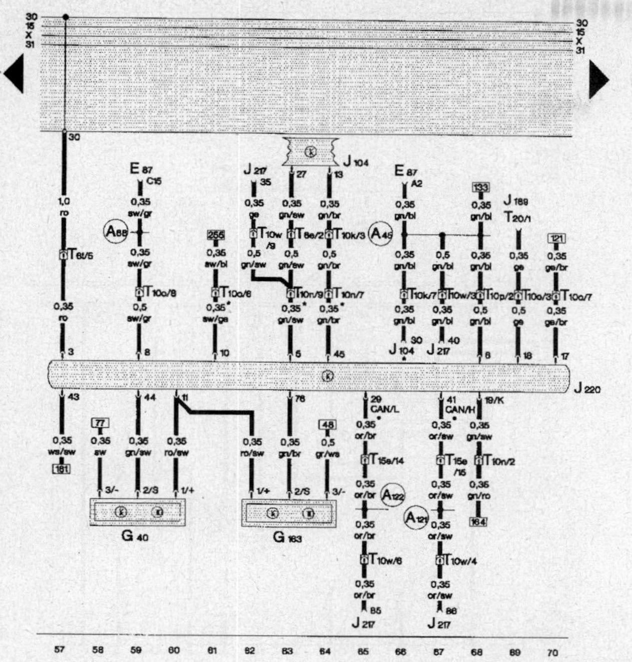

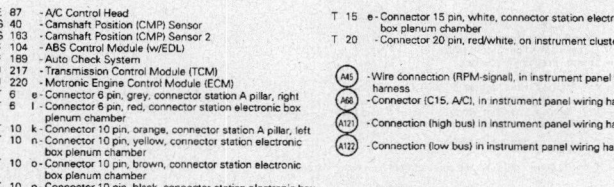

E 87 - A/C Control Head
G 40 - Camshaft Position (CMP) Sensor
G 163 - Camshaft Position (CMP) Sensor 2
J 104 - ABS Control Module (w/EDL)
J 189 - Auto Check System
J 217 - Transmission Control Module (TCM)
J 220 - Motronic Engine Control Module (ECM)
T 6 e - Connector 6 pin, grey, connector station A pillar, right
T 6 l - Connector 6 pin, red, connector station electronic box plenum chamber
T 10 k - Connector 10 pin, orange, connector station A pillar, left
T 10 n - Connector 10 pin, yellow, connector station electronic box plenum chamber
T 10 o - Connector 10 pin, brown, connector station electronic box plenum chamber
T 10 p - Connector 10 pin, black, connector station electronic box plenum chamber
T 10 w - Connector 10 pin, blue, connector station A pillar, right
T 15 e - Connector 15 pin, white, connector station electronic box plenum chamber
T 20 - Connector 20 pin, red/white, on instrument cluster
A45 - Wire connection (RPM-signal), in instrument panel wiring harness
A68 - Connector (C15, A/C), in instrument panel wiring harness
A121 - Connection (high bus) in instrument panel wiring harness
A122 - Connection (low bus) in instrument panel wiring harness
* - CAN-Bus
• - Vehicles with front wheel drive

AD1029800098030X

Fig. 6 MFI wiring system diagram (Part 3 of 4). A6 & S6

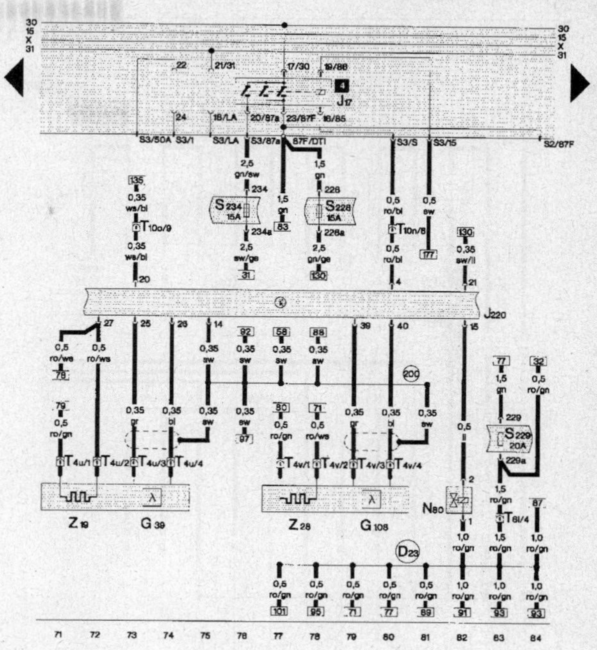

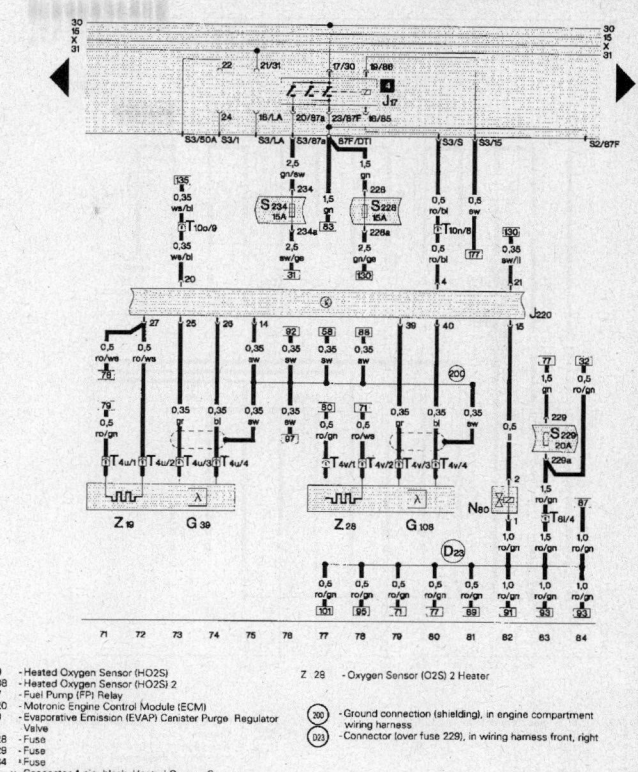

G 39 - Heated Oxygen Sensor (HO2S)
G 108 - Heated Oxygen Sensor (HO2S) 2
J 17 - Fuel Pump (FP) Relay
J 220 - Motronic Engine Control Module (ECM)
N 80 - Evaporative Emission (EVAP) Canister Purge Regulator Valve
S 228 - Fuse
S 229 - Fuse
S 234 - Fuse
T 4 u - Connector 4 pin, black, Heated Oxygen Sensor
T 4 v - Connector 4 pin, black, Heated Oxygen Sensor 2
T 6 l - Connector 6 pin, red, connector station electronic box plenum chamber
T 10 n - Connector 10 pin, yellow, connector station electronic box plenum chamber
T 10 o - Connector 10 pin, brown, connector station electronic box plenum chamber
Z 19 - Oxygen Sensor (O2S) Heater
Z 28 - Oxygen Sensor (O2S) 2 Heater
200 - Ground connection (shielding), in engine compartment wiring harness
D23 - Connector (over fuse 229), in wiring harness front, right

AD1029800098040X

Fig. 6 MFI wiring system diagram (Part 4 of 4). A6 & S6

connector terminals using adapter cable tool No. VW1594, or equivalent.

3. Crank engine and inspect for LED operation.
4. Repeat test for remaining cylinders.
5. If LED does not light, inspect wiring between fuel injector and ECM for open or short using a suitable volt/ohmmeter.

ACTIVATION INSPECTION

A4, Cabriolet & S4

1. Disconnect harness connector of injector to be tested.
2. Connect suitable LED tester between terminal No. 2, **Fig. 47,** and battery positive terminal.
3. Crank engine briefly.
4. If tester does not blink, connect test box tool No. VAG 1598/19, or equivalent, to ECM wiring harness. ECM is not connected.
5. Measure resistance between individual fuel injector connector terminal No. 1 and test box socket, as follows:
   a. Between fuel injector No. 1 and test box socket D1.
   b. Between fuel injector No. 2 and test box socket D2.
   c. Between fuel injector No. 3 and test box socket D3.
   d. Between fuel injector No. 4 and test box socket D4.
   e. Between fuel injector No. 5 and test box socket D5.
   f. Between fuel injector No. 6 and test box socket D6.
6. If resistance is more than 1 ohm, refer to wiring diagrams to repair breaks or short circuits as required.
7. If tester does not flash for any fuel injector, inspect ECM voltage supply.
8. If voltage supply is satisfactory, replace ECM.
9. If wiring or connector repairs are required, refer to "Precautions."

IDLE AIR CONTROL (IAC) VALVE

ELECTRICAL INSPECTION

A4, Cabriolet & S4

1. Disconnect Idle Air Control (IAC) valve harness connector.
2. Measure IAC valve resistance. At room temperature, resistance is lower, while at operating temperature it is higher.
3. If resistance is not 7–11 ohms, replace IAC valve.
4. If wiring or connector repairs are required, refer to "Precautions."

MECHANICAL INSPECTION

A4, Cabriolet & S4

1. Remove IAC valve from engine, leaving electrical connector attached.
2. Visually inspect rotary slide valve for scoring, binding or rubbing. **When inspecting valve travel, do not move rotary slide valve with screwdriver or other tool.**
3. Connect a suitable scan tool to the Diagnostic Link Connector.
4. Select Output Diagnosis Test Mode (DTM), as outlined under "Computerized Engine Controls," then activate IAC.
5. During output inspection step when valve is being triggered, ensure valve is operating properly from stop to stop.
6. If scoring impairs free movement, rotary slide valve binds, runs slowly or will not travel to both stops, replace IAC valve.
7. If wiring or connector repairs are required, refer to "Precautions."

ACTIVATION INSPECTION

A4, Cabriolet & S4

1. Push cap back from IAC connected valve harness.
2. Initiate "Output Diagnostic Test Mode" as outlined in "Computerized Engine Controls," then activate IAC valve.

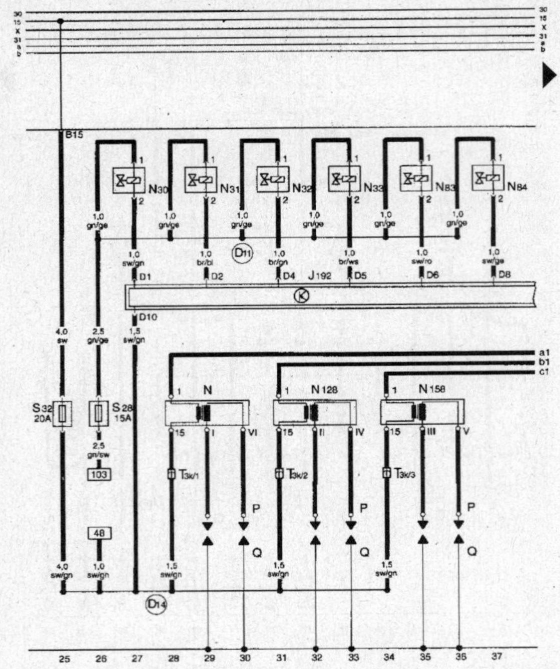

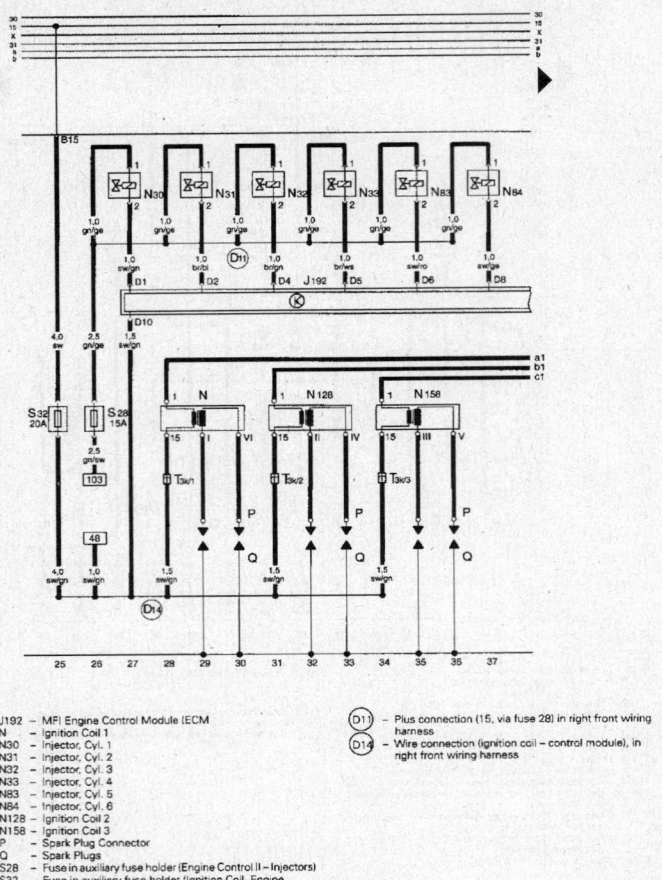

J192 – MFI Engine Control Module (ECM
N – Ignition Coil 1
N30 – Injector, Cyl. 1
N31 – Injector, Cyl. 2
N32 – Injector, Cyl. 3
N33 – Injector, Cyl. 4
N83 – Injector, Cyl. 5
N84 – Injector, Cyl. 6
N128 – Ignition Coil 2
N158 – Ignition Coil 3
P – Spark Plug Connector
Q – Spark Plugs
S28 – Fuse in auxiliary fuse holder (Engine Control II – Injectors)
S32 – Fuse in auxiliary fuse holder (Ignition Coil, Engine Control II)
T3k – Wire Connector, 3 Point, white, on Ignition Coils, connector 15

(D11) – Plus connection (15, via fuse 28) in right front wiring harness
(D14) – Wire connection (ignition coil – control module), in right front wiring harness

AD1029800097010X

Fig. 7 MFI wiring system diagram (Part 1 of 7). Cabriolet

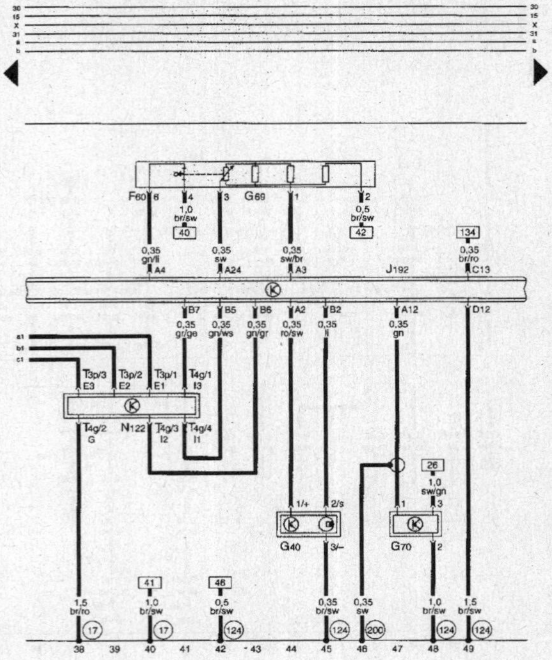

F60 – Closed Throttle Position (CTP) Switch
G40 – Camshaft Position (CMP) Sensor
G69 – Throttle Position (TP) Sensor
G70 – Mass Air Flow (MAF) Sensor
J192 – MFI Engine Control Module (ECM)
N122 – Power Output Stage
T3p – Wire Connector, 3 Point, white, on Power Output Stage
T4g – Wire Connector, 4 Point, brown, on Power Output Stage
(17) – Ground connection, on intake manifold
(124) – Ground connection, in engine compartment right wiring harness
(200) – Ground connection (shielding), in engine compartment wiring harness

AD1029800097020X

Fig. 7 MFI wiring system diagram (Part 2 of 7). Cabriolet

3. Connect suitable LED voltage tester between terminal No. 1 and engine ground, then between terminal No. 2 and battery positive post.
4. If tester does not blink on terminal No. 1 and light on terminal No. 2 connection, inspect for an open or short circuit between the following terminals:
   a. IAC terminal No. 2 and Engine Control Module (ECM) connector D terminal No. 9.
   b. IAC terminal No. 1 and Engine Control Module (ECM) connector D terminal No. 11.
5. If wiring is satisfactory and activation fails, replace ECM.
6. If activation and wiring are satisfactory, but valve does not react, replace valve.
7. If wiring or connector repairs are required, refer to "Precautions."

HEATED OXYGEN SENSOR (HO2S)

If an oxygen sensor fault is present (sensor voltage does not fluctuate, sensor does not respond or responds too slowly), the following causes are possible: oxygen sensor tip plugged, sensor not reaching operating temperature, thermally overloaded sensor, open circuit, sensor damage due to cleaners or exposure to silicone.

A4, CABRIOLET & S4

A4 and S4 models use a 4-pin connector containing both heater and signal leads for HO2S sensors used both before and after Three-Way Catalytic Converters (TWC).

Cabriolet models use a 2-pin connector, **Fig. 47,** for the heater circuit and a separate shielded lead for the signal lead for HO2S sensor before TWC and a 4-pin connector, **Fig. 48,** containing both heater and signal leads after TWC.

Oxygen Sensor Heater Inspection

The following procedure has been updated by a Technical Service Bulletin.

1. Disconnect heated oxygen sensor harness connection for heater.
2. Connect suitable ohmmeter between ground terminal No. 2 and positive terminal No. 1, **Figs. 47 and 48.**
3. Start and run engine.
4. If reading is not 12–14 volts, refer to wiring diagrams and measure circuit resistance. There should be a maximum of 1 ohm resistance between terminal No. 1 and fuse, and between terminal No. 2 and engine ground.
5. If resistance is not within specifications, refer to wiring diagrams to trace and repair circuit.
6. If wiring circuits are satisfactory, inspect fuel pump relay as outlined under "Fuel Pump Relay."
7. **On Cabriolet models,** if fuel pump relay is satisfactory, proceed as follows:
   a. Connect test harness tool No. VAG 1315 A/1, or equivalent, into 2-pin connector.
   b. Connect suitable amp meter and run engine.
   c. Specification for oxygen sensor heater draw is greater than three amps on cold start, then .7–1 amp after approximately 40 seconds.
   d. Amperage draw should decrease from initial reading as sensor heats up.
8. **On A4 and S4 models,** if fuel pump relay is satisfactory, proceed as follows:
   a. Measure resistance of oxygen sensor heater using a suitable ohmmeter connected to terminal Nos. 1 and 2.
   b. Specification is two to five ohms. Resistance will vary sharply with small temperature changes in heater.
9. **On all models,** if resistances do not meet specifications, replace oxygen sensor.

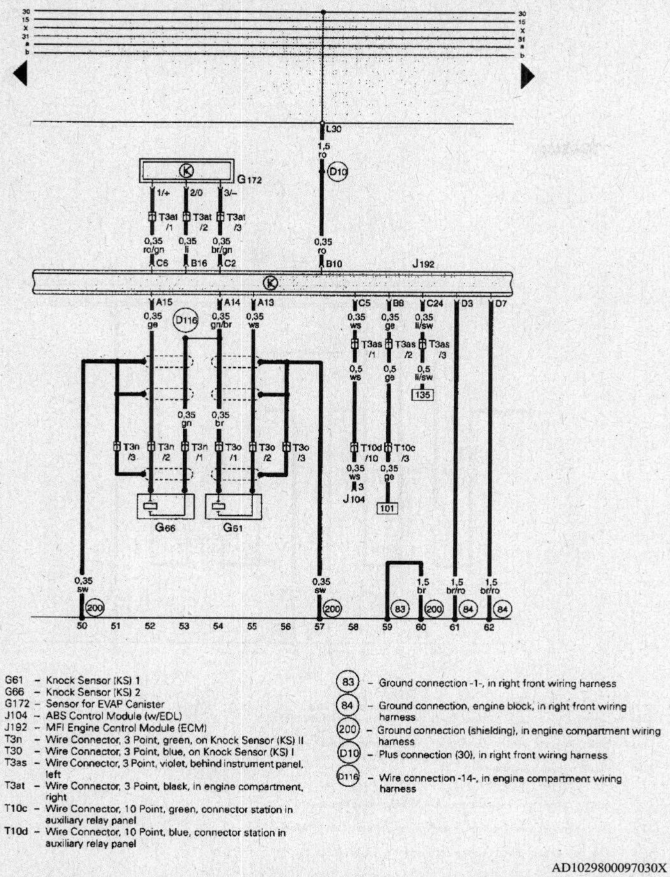

Fig. 7 MFI wiring system diagram (Part 3 of 7). Cabriolet

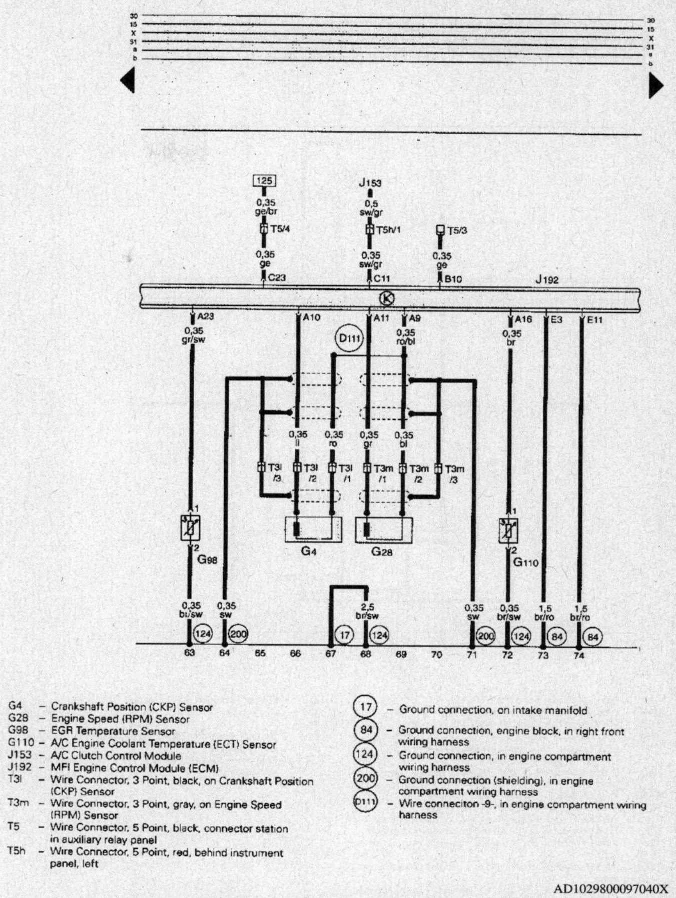

Fig. 7 MFI wiring system diagram (Part 4 of 7). Cabriolet

10. If wiring or connector repairs are required, refer to "Precautions."

Control Inspection

The following procedure has been updated by a Technical Service Bulletin.

1. **On Cabriolet models,** disconnect the separate oxygen sensor signal wire harness connector and connect a suitable ohmmeter between signal wire for sensor and ground.
2. **On A4 and S4 models,** connect a suitable ohmmeter between pin 4 (signal) and pin 3 (ground) of connector leading to sensor, **Fig. 48.**
3. **On all models,** if resistance is infinite, replace HO2S.
4. If above specification is satisfactory, connect suitable voltmeter between signal wire to Engine Control Module (ECM) wiring harness and engine ground, then turn ignition On.
5. **On A4 and S4 models,** if measurement is not 350–450 mVolts, inspect wiring as follows:
   a. Turn ignition Off.
   b. Connect test box tool No. 1598/19, or equivalent, to ECM wiring harness. ECM is not connected.
   c. **HO2S bank Nos. 1 and 2 before TWC,** using a suitable ohmmeter inspect for 1 ohm maximum resistance between harness connector pin four on for HO2S bank No. 1 and test box socket pin A20, then harness connector pin four for HO2S bank No. 2 and test box socket A21.
   d. **HO2S bank Nos. 1 and 2 after TWC,** using a suitable ohmmeter inspect for 1 ohm maximum resistance between harness connector for H02S bank No. 1, pin four and test box socket C20, then pin three and test box socket C17. Inspect for 1 ohm maximum resistance between harness connector for H02S bank No. 2, pin four and test box socket C20, then pin three and test box socket C17.
   e. If not to specifications, refer to wiring diagrams to trace and repair breaks or shorts.
   f. If wiring is satisfactory, replace ECM.
6. **On Cabriolet models,** if measurement is not 350–450 mVolts, inspect wiring as follows:
   a. Turn ignition Off.
   b. Connect test box tool No. 1598/19, or equivalent, to ECM wiring harness. ECM is not connected.
   c. **HO2S bank Nos. 1 and 2 before TWC,** using a suitable ohmmeter inspect for 1 ohm maximum resistance between harness connector signal wire on for HO2S bank No. 1 and test box socket pin A20, then harness connector for signal wire for HO2S bank No. 2 and test box socket A21.
   d. **HO2S bank Nos. 1 and 2 after TWC,** using a suitable ohmmeter inspect for 1 ohm maximum resistance between harness connector for H02S No. 1, pin four and test box socket C20, then pin three and test box socket C17. Inspect for 1 ohm maximum resistance between harness connector for H02S bank No. 2, pin four and test box socket C20, then pin three and test box socket C17.
   e. If not to specifications, refer to wiring diagrams to trace and repair breaks or shorts.
   f. If wiring is satisfactory, replace ECM.
7. **On all models,** if wiring or connector repairs are required, refer to "Precautions."

A6

This procedure has been revised by a Technical Service Bulletin.

Front Heated Oxygen Sensor Functional Inspection

1. Ensure engine temperature is at least 176°F.
2. Connect scan tool No. VAG 1551/

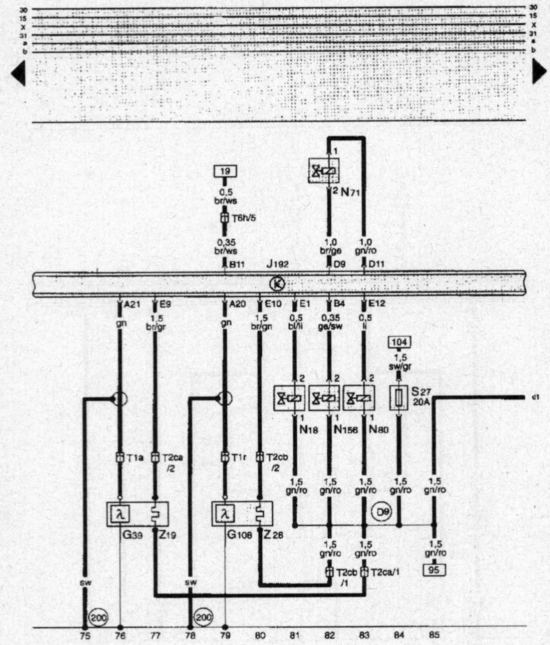

G39 – Heated Oxygen Sensor (HO2S) 1
G108 – Heated Oxygen Sensor (HO2S) 2
J192 – MFI Engine Control Module (ECM)
J221 – Shift Lock Control Module
N18 – EGR Vacuum Regulator Solenoid Valve
N71 – Idle Air Control (IAC) Valve
N80 – Evaporative Emiision (EVAP) Canister Purge Regulator Valve
N156 – Intake Manifold Change – Over Valve
S27 – Fuse in auxiliary fuse holder (Engine Control II)
T1a – Wire Connector, single, in engine compartment, right
T1r – Wire Connector, single, in engine compartment, right
T2ac – Wire Connector, double, black, in engine compartment, right
T2cb – Wire Connector, double, black, in engine compartment, right
T6h – Wire Connector, 6 Point, black, behind instrument panel, left
Z19 – Oxygen Sensor (O2S) 1 Heater
Z28 – Oxygen Sensor (O2S) 2 Heater
(200) – Ground connection (shielding), in engine compartment wiring harness
(D9) – Plus connection (15, via fuse 27), in right front wiring harness

AD1029800097050X

Fig. 7 MFI wiring system diagram (Part 5 of 7). Cabriolet

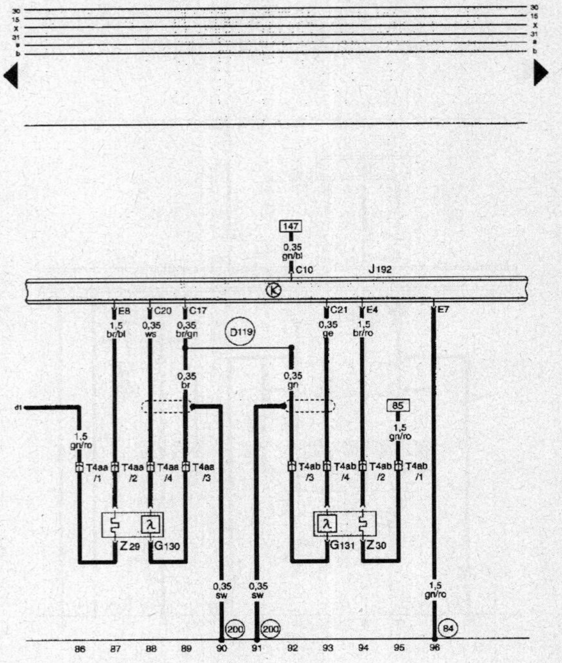

G130 – Oxygen Sensor (O2S) Behind Three Catalytic Converter (TWC)
G131 – Oxygen Sensor (O2S) 2 Behind Three Catalytic Converter (TWC)
J192 – MFI Engine Control Module (ECM)
T4aa – Wire Connector, 4 Point, green, in engine compartment, left
T4ab – Wire Connector, 4 Point, brown, in engine compartment, left
Z29 – Heater for Lambda–probe 1
Z30 – Heater for Lambda–probe 2
(84) – Ground connection, engine block, in right front wiring harness
(200) – Ground connection (shielding), in engine compartment wiring harness
(D119) – Wire connection –17–, in engine copartment wiring harness

AD1029800097060X

Fig. 7 MFI wiring system diagram (Part 6 of 7). Cabriolet

1552, or equivalent, then press buttons 0 and 1 to insert “Engine Electronics” address word 01 with engine running at idle.
3. Press buttons 0 and 8 to select “Read Measuring Value Block” function 08, then press “Q” to confirm input.
4. Compare scan tool data with oxygen sensor data in **Fig. 49.**
5. If display values are not as specified in **Fig. 49,** refer to evaluation of Display Group 32, **Fig. 50.**
6. If display values are as specified in **Fig. 49,** proceed as follows:
   a. Press “C” button on scan tool.
   b. Press buttons 0, 3 and 3 to input Display Group 33, then press “Q” to confirm input.
   c. Compare scan tool data with oxygen sensor control values, **Fig. 51.**
7. If display values are not as specified in **Fig. 51,** Fields 1 and 3, proceed as follows:
   a. Road test vehicle to condition oxygen sensor and repeat test.
   b. If display values in Fields 1 and 3 are not as specified, refer to “Front Heated Oxygen Sensor Heater Inspection.”
   c. If display values in Fields 1 and 3 are as specified, monitor oxygen sensor voltages in Fields 2 and 4 of Display Group 33. Press right arrow button to advance program. Press buttons 0 and 6 to select “End Output,” then press “Q” to confirm input.
   d. Turn ignition Off.
8. If display values are not as specified in **Fig. 51,** Fields 2 and 4, refer to evaluation of Display Group 33, **Fig. 52.**

Front Heated Oxygen Sensor Heater Inspection

1. Inspect and service oxygen sensor fuse as required.
2. Ensure engine temperature is at least 176°F.
3. Connect scan tool No. VAG 1552, or equivalent, then press buttons 0 and 1 to insert “Engine Electronics” address word 01 with engine running at idle.
4. Press buttons 0 and 8 to select “Read Measuring Value Block” function 08, then press “Q” to confirm input.
5. Press buttons 0, 4 and 0 to input Display Group 40, then press “Q” to confirm input.
6. Compare scan tool data with oxygen sensor heater data in **Fig. 53.**
7. If display values are as specified, proceed as follows:
   a. Press right arrow button of scan tool.
   b. Press buttons 0 and 6 to select “End Output,” then press “Q” to confirm input.
   c. Turn ignition Off.
8. If display values are not as specified, proceed as follows:
   a. Disconnect oxygen sensor.
   b. Measure resistance between terminals 1 and 2 of oxygen sensor using a suitable ohmmeter and connector test kit tool No. VW 1594, or equivalent. Refer to **Fig. 48** for terminal identification.
9. If resistance is not within specifications, replace oxygen sensor.
10. If resistance is within specifications, proceed as follows:
    a. Measure voltage between oxygen sensor connector terminals 1 and 2 using a suitable voltmeter and connector test kit tool No. VW 1594, or equivalent.
    b. Monitor voltmeter and scan tool Display Group 40, Field 2. If Field 2 display is “Htg.bC.ON,” voltage should be 11–14.5 volts. If Field 2 display is “Htg.bC.ON” or “Htg.bC.OFF,” voltage should vary between 0–12 volts.
11. If no voltage is present, proceed as follows:
    a. Measure voltage between terminal 1 of oxygen sensor connector and ground using connector test kit tool

No. VW 1594, or equivalent and a suitable voltmeter.

b. Voltage should read 11–14.5 volts.

c. If no voltage is present, inspect wiring between terminal 1 and relay panel and service as required.

12. If voltage is present, proceed as follows:

a. Measure voltage between terminal 2 of oxygen sensor connector and battery positive using a suitable voltmeter and connector test kit tool No. VW 1594.

b. Monitor voltmeter and scan tool Display Group 40, Field 2. If Field 2 display reads "Htg.bC.ON," voltage should read 11–14.5 volts. If Field 2 display reads "Htg.bC.ON" or "Htg-.bC.OFF," voltage should vary between 0–12 volts.

c. Turn ignition Off.

13. If no voltage is present, proceed as follows:

a. Connect test box tool No. VAG 1598/22, or equivalent to ECM harness connector.

b. Measure resistance between oxygen sensor connector terminal 2 and test box pin 27 using a suitable ohmmeter.

14. If resistance is greater than 1.5 ohms, service open circuit as required.

15. If wiring inspection is satisfactory, replace ECM and generate new readiness code.

Front Heated Oxygen Sensor Voltage Inspection

1. Disconnect oxygen sensor.
2. Measure voltage between terminals 3 and 4 of oxygen sensor connector using a suitable ohmmeter and connector test kit tool No. VW 1594, or equivalent. Refer to **Fig. 48** for terminal identification.
3. Start engine and monitor voltage.
4. Voltmeter should read .4–.5 volts.
5. Turn ignition Off.
6. If voltage is as specified, replace oxygen sensor.
7. If voltage is not as specified, refer to "Front Heated Oxygen Sensor Wiring Inspection."

Front Heated Oxygen Sensor Wiring Inspection (Bank 1, Sensor 1)

1. Disconnect oxygen sensor. Refer to **Fig. 48** for connector terminal identification.
2. Connect test box tool No. VAG 1598/22, or equivalent to ECM harness connector.
3. Measure resistance between connector terminal 3 and test box pin 25 and connector terminal 4 and test box pin 26 using a suitable ohmmeter.
4. If resistance is greater than 1.5 ohms, service open circuit as required.
5. If resistance is less than 1.5 ohms, proceed as follows:

a. Measure resistance between connector terminal 4 and test box pins 14 and 25.

b. Measure resistance between connector terminal 3 and test box pin 14.

c. Ohmmeter should give open reading.

6. If wiring is satisfactory, replace ECM and generate new readiness code.

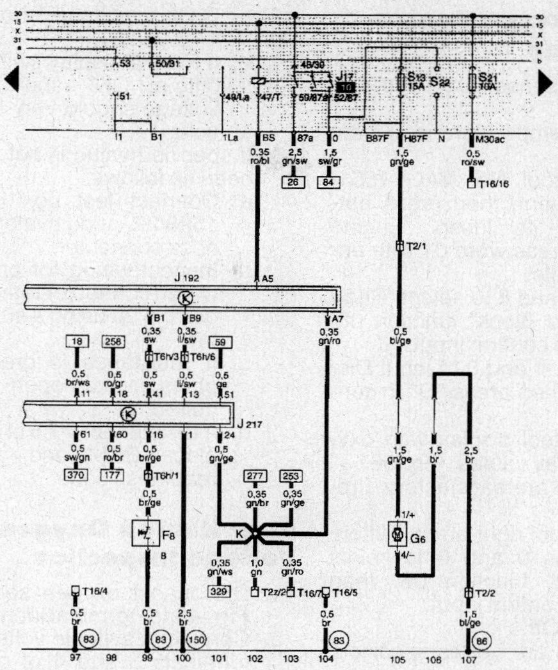

F8 – Kick Down Switch
G6 – Fuel Pump (FP)
J17 – Fuel Pump (RP) Relay
J192 – MFI Engine Control Module (ECM)
J217 – Transmission Control Module (TCM)
T2 – Wire Connector, double, white, below rear seat, left
T2z – Wire Connector, double, white, in Plenum, near Relay Panel (Data Link Connector)
T6h – Wire Connector, 6 Point, black, behind instrument panel, left
T16 – Wire Connector, 16 Point, black, near Rear Ashtray Light
(83) – Ground connection -1-, in right front wiring harness
(86) – Ground connection -1-, in rear wiring harness
(150) – Ground connection, in automatic tranmission wiring harness
K – Wire Distributor For Data Link Connector (DLC); Terminal K

AD1029800097070X

Fig. 7 MFI wiring system diagram (Part 7 of 7). Cabriolet

Front Heated Oxygen Sensor Wiring Inspection (Bank 2, Sensor 1)

1. Disconnect oxygen sensor. Refer to **Fig. 48** for connector terminal identification.
2. Connect test box tool No. VAG 1598/22, or equivalent to ECM harness connector.
3. Measure resistance between connector terminal 3 and test box pin 39 using a suitable ohmmeter, then between connector terminal 4 and test box pin 40.
4. If resistance is greater than 1.5 ohms, repair open circuit as required.
5. If resistance is less than 1.5 ohms, proceed as follows:

a. Measure resistance between connector terminal 4 and test box pins 14 and 39.

b. Measure resistance between connector terminal 3 and test box pin 14.

c. Ohmmeter should give open reading.

6. If wiring is satisfactory, replace ECM and generate new readiness code.

Rear Heated Oxygen Sensor Functional Inspection

1. Ensure engine temperature is at least 176°F.
2. Connect scan tool VAG 1551/1552, or equivalent, then press buttons 0 and 1 to insert "Engine Electronics" address word 01 with engine running at idle.
3. Press buttons 0 and 8 to select "Read Measuring Value Block" function 08, then press "Q" to confirm input.
4. Press buttons 0, 3 and 6 to input Display Group 36, then press "Q" to confirm input.
5. Compare scan tool display with oxygen sensor display data in **Fig. 54.**
6. If display values in **Fig. 54** are as specified, refer to **Fig. 55** for evaluation of Display Group 36.
7. If display values in **Fig. 54** are not as specified, proceed as follows:

a. Road test vehicle to condition oxygen sensor and repeat test.

b. Inspect oxygen sensor heater circuit as outlined under "Rear Heated Oxygen Sensor Heater Inspection."

c. Briefly accelerate engine to 3000 RPM.

Rear Heated Oxygen Sensor Heater Inspection

1. Inspect oxygen sensor fuse and service as required.
2. Ensure engine temperature is at least 176°F.
3. Connect scan tool No. VAG 1551/1552, or equivalent, then press buttons 0 and 1 to insert "Engine Electronics" address word 01 with engine running at idle.
4. Press buttons 0 and 8 to select "Read Measuring Value Block" function 08, then press "Q" to confirm input.
5. Press buttons 0, 4 and 0 to input Display Group 40, then press "Q" to confirm input.
6. Compare scan tool display with oxygen sensor display values, **Fig. 56.**
7. If display values are satisfactory, proceed as follows:
   a. Press scan tool right arrow button.
   b. Press buttons 0 and 6 to select "End Output" function 06, then press "Q" to confirm input.
   c. Turn ignition Off.
8. If display values are not as specified, proceed as follows:
   a. Disconnect oxygen sensor. Refer to **Fig. 48** for connector terminal identification.
   b. Measure resistance between oxygen sensor terminals 1 and 2 using a suitable ohmmeter and connector test kit tool No. VW 1594, or equivalent.
9. If resistance is not within specifications, replace oxygen sensor.
10. If resistance is within specifications, proceed as follows:
    a. Connect a suitable voltmeter between oxygen sensor connector terminals 1 and 2 using connector test kit tool No. VW 1594, or equivalent.
    b. Measure voltage while monitoring scan tool Display Group 40, Field 4.
    c. If Field 4 display is "Htg.aC.ON," voltage should read 11–14.5 volts.
    d. If Field 4 display is switching between "Htg.aC.ON" and "Htg.aC.OFF," voltage should vary between 0–12 volts.
11. If no voltage is present, proceed as follows:
    a. Measure voltage between oxygen sensor harness connector terminal 1 and ground using a suitable voltmeter and connector test kit tool No. VW 1594 or equivalent.
    b. Voltmeter should read 11–14.5 volts.
    c. If no voltage is present, service open wire as required.
12. If voltage is present, proceed as follows:
    a. Connect a suitable voltmeter between oxygen sensor harness connector terminal 2 and battery positive using connector test kit tool No. VW 1594 or equivalent.
    b. Measure voltage while monitoring scan tool Display Group 40, Field 4.
    c. If Field 4 display reads "Htg.aC.ON," voltage should read 11–14.5 volts.
    d. If Field 4 display switches between "Htg.aC.ON" and "Htg.aC.OFF," voltage should vary between 0–12 volts.
13. If specified value is not obtained, proceed as follows:
    a. Connect test box tool No. VAG 1598/22, or equivalent to ECM harness connector.
    b. Inspect wiring for open circuit between connector terminal 2 and test box pin 28 using a suitable ohmmeter.
    c. If resistance is greater than 1.5 ohms, repair open circuit as required.
    d. If resistance is 1.5 ohms or less, replace ECM and generate new readiness code.

Rear Heated Oxygen Sensor Voltage Inspection

1. Disconnect oxygen sensor. Refer to **Fig. 48** for terminal identification.
2. Connect a suitable voltmeter between terminals 3 and 4 of oxygen sensor connector.
3. Start engine and monitor voltage. Voltmeter should read .4–.5 volts.
4. Turn ignition Off.
5. If voltage is not as specified, refer to "Rear Heated Oxygen Sensor Wiring Inspection."
6. If voltage is as specified, replace oxygen sensor.

Rear Heated Oxygen Sensor Wiring Inspection (Bank 1, Sensor 2)

1. Disconnect oxygen sensor. Refer to **Fig. 48** for terminal identification.
2. Connect test box tool No. VAG 1598/22, or equivalent to ECM harness connector.
3. Inspect the following circuits for open using a suitable ohmmeter:
   a. Connector terminal 3 to test box pin 51.
   b. Connector terminal 4 to test box pin 52.
4. If resistance is greater than 1.5 ohms, service open circuit as required.
5. If resistance is 1.5 ohms or less, inspect the following circuits for shorts using a suitable ohmmeter:
   a. Connector terminal 4 to test box pins 51 and 14.
   b. Connector terminal 3 to test box pin 14.
6. If ohmmeter reads open circuit, replace ECM and generate new readiness code.
7. If ohmmeter does not read open circuit, service short as required.

Rear Heated Oxygen Sensor Wiring Inspection (Bank 2, Sensor 2)

1. Disconnect oxygen sensor. Refer to **Fig. 48** for terminal identification.
2. Connect test box tool No. VAG 1598/22, or equivalent to ECM harness connector.
3. Inspect the following circuits for open using a suitable ohmmeter:
   a. Connector terminal 3 to test box pin 38.
   b. Connector terminal 4 to test box pin 50.
4. If resistance is greater than 1.5 ohms, service open circuit as required.
5. If resistance is 1.5 ohms or less, inspect the following circuits for shorts using a suitable ohmmeter:
   a. Connector terminal 4 to test box pins 38 and 14.
   b. Connector terminal 3 to test box pin 14.
6. If ohmmeter reads open circuit, replace ECM and generate new readiness code.
7. If ohmmeter does not read open circuit, service short as required.

CLOSED THROTTLE POSITION (CTP) SWITCH

A4 & S4

Electrical Inspection

Ensure throttle cable is properly adjusted and Mass Air Flow (MAF) sensor has proper output voltage.

1. Remove intake air hose and disconnect throttle body harness connector.
2. Connect suitable ohmmeter to contact 4 and 6, then open throttle slightly and measure resistance.
3. Resistance should be 0 ohms at closed throttle and infinite ohms with throttle slightly open.
4. If not within specifications, adjust CTP switch as outlined under "System Service."
5. Ensure air intake hose fits tightly when installing on throttle body.
6. If wiring or connector repairs are required, refer to "Precautions."

Wiring Inspection

1. Connect test box tool No. VAG 1598 with adapter harness tool No. VAG 1598/11, or test box tool No. 1598/19, or equivalent, to ECM wiring harness.
2. Disconnect connector from throttle body.
3. Measure resistance of circuit, connector contact 4 to engine compartment wiring harness ground using a suitable ohmmeter.
4. Specification is maximum 1 ohm.
5. Measure resistance of circuit, connector contact 6 to tester box terminal No. 49. maximum resistance is one ohm.
6. If maximum 1 ohm resistance is exceeded, find and repair wiring damage between engine compartment 6-pin connector and ECM connector.
7. If wiring or connector repairs are required, refer to "Precautions."

A6

1. Ensure the following test conditions are met:
   a. Throttle valve in closed position.
   b. Cruise control system is properly adjusted.

c. Inspect and service power supply to throttle valve control module as required.
2. Connect scan tool No. VAG 1551/1552, or equivalent, then press buttons 0 and 1 to insert "Engine Electronics" address word 01 with engine running at idle.
3. Press buttons 0 and 8 to select "Read Measuring Value Block" function 08, then press "Q" to confirm input.
4. Press buttons 0, 0 and 5 to input Display Group 5, then press "Q" to confirm input.
5. Compare scan tool data with engine electronics data, **Fig. 57.**
6. If scan tool data display does not agree with **Fig. 57,** proceed as follows:
   a. Turn ignition Off.
   b. Connect test box tool No. VAG 1598/22, or equivalent to ECM harness connector.
   c. Measure resistance between test box pins 67 and 69 using a suitable ohmmeter.
   d. Resistance should be five ohms.
   e. As throttle is slowly opened, ohmmeter should read open circuit.
7. If resistance is not as specified, proceed as follows:
   a. Disconnect 8-pin connector from throttle valve control module. Refer to **Fig. 58** for pin identification.
   b. Measure resistance between harness connector terminal 3 and test box pin 69.
   c. Measure resistance between harness connector terminal 7 and test box pin 67.
   d. Resistance should be 1.5 ohms or less.
8. If resistance is greater than 1.5 ohms, service open circuit as required.
9. If resistance is 1.5 ohms or less, measure resistance between 8 pin connector terminal 7 and test box pin 69. Ohmmeter should read open circuit. If open circuit is not indicated, service short as required.
10. Reconnect throttle valve control module.
11. If wiring inspection is satisfactory, replace throttle valve control module.

THROTTLE POSITION (TP) SENSOR

FUNCTIONAL INSPECTION

A6

1. Ensure throttle valve is closed and throttle cable is properly adjusted.
2. Ensure cruise control is adjusted properly.
3. Inspect power supply to throttle valve control module and repair as required.
4. Connect scan tool VAG 1551/1552, or equivalent, then press buttons 0 and 1 to insert "Engine Electronics" address word 01 with ignition On.
5. Press buttons 0 and 8 to select "Read Measuring Value Block" function 08, then press "Q" to confirm input.
6. Press buttons 0, 0 and 3 to input Display Group 3, then press "Q" to confirm input.
7. Compare scan tool display with load measurement values.
8. Open throttle valve while monitoring degree value in Display Field 3 of **Fig. 59.**
9. If value does not evenly increase over range of throttle movement, refer to "Wiring Inspection."
10. Press right arrow button to advance program.
11. Press buttons 0 and 6 to select "End Output" function 06, then press "Q" to confirm input.
12. If wiring inspection is satisfactory, replace throttle valve control module and perform relearn procedure as outlined under "Computer Relearn Procedures" in front of this manual.

VOLTAGE INSPECTION

A4, Cabriolet & S4

1. Disconnect TP sensor harness connector, **Fig. 60,** then turn ignition On.
2. Connect a suitable voltmeter to connector terminal Nos. 1 and 2, then to terminal Nos. 1 and 3 and measure voltage.
3. Specification is 4.5–5.5 volts. If specification is not reached on both circuits, refer to "Resistance Inspection."
4. If specification is not reached on one circuit, connect a suitable circuit test (breakout) box to the ECM connector, then measure resistances as follows:
   a. Between TP harness connector terminal No. 2 and test box terminal No. D12.
   b. Between TP harness connector terminal No. 1 and test box terminal No. A3.
   c. Between TP harness connector terminal No. 3 and test box terminal No. A24.
5. If resistance is more than 1 ohm on any circuit, refer to wiring diagrams, then trace and repair damaged circuit.
6. If resistance is less than 1 ohm on all circuits, replace ECM.
7. If wiring or connector repairs are required, refer to "Precautions."

WIRING INSPECTION

A6

1. Connect test box tool No. VAG 1598/22, or equivalent to ECM harness connector.
2. Measure resistance between test box pins 2 and 75 using a suitable ohmmeter and connector test kit tool No. VW 1594, or equivalent. Ohmmeter should read open circuit.
3. Remove ohmmeter from circuit.
4. Turn ignition On, then measure voltage of test box pins 2 and 75 using a suitable voltmeter.
5. Record voltage reading and turn ignition Off.
6. If voltmeter read 0 volts, proceed as follows:
   a. Disconnect 8 pin connector from throttle valve control module.
   b. Measure resistance between throttle valve control module harness connector terminal 5 to test box pin 75 using a suitable ohmmeter.
   c. If resistance is more than 1.5 ohms, service open wire as required.
   d. If resistance is 1.5 ohms or less, replace throttle valve control module and generate new readiness code.
7. If voltmeter reads approximately five volts, proceed as follows:
   a. Disconnect 8 pin connector from throttle valve control module.
   b. Measure resistance between test box pins 62 and 75 using a suitable ohmmeter and connector test kit tool No. VW 1594, or equivalent.
   c. If ohmmeter does not read open circuit, service short as required.
8. If voltmeter reads battery voltage, inspect 8 pin connector terminal 5 for short to power and service as required.

RESISTANCE INSPECTION

A4, Cabriolet & S4

1. Disconnect connector from TP sensor.
2. Connect a suitable ohmmeter to terminal Nos. 1 and 2 of sensor, **Fig. 61,** then measure resistance, which should be 1500–2600 ohms.
3. Connect ohmmeter to terminal Nos. 2 and 3 of sensor and measure resistance, which should be 750–1300 ohms.
4. With ohmmeter connected to terminal Nos. 2 and 3 of sensor, slowly move throttle to full open while observing ohmmeter. Resistance should gradually increase to a maximum of 3600 ohms.
5. If one of the above tests do not meet specifications, replace throttle sensor as outlined under "System Service."
6. If wiring or connector repairs are required, refer to "Precautions."

ENGINE CONTROL MODULE (ECM)

If ECM replacement is required refer to "Coding ECM."

A4, CABRIOLET & S4

1. Ensure fuses 28, 29, 32 and 34 are in satisfactory condition.
2. Connect test box tool No. VAG 1598/19, or equivalent, to Engine Control Module (ECM) wiring.
3. Turn ignition On.
4. Connect suitable LED type voltage tester between test box terminal No. D10 and in sequence as follows:
   a. Ground.
   b. A19.
   c. D3.
   d. D7.
   e. D12.
   f. E3.
   g. E7.
   h. E11.
5. Led should light. If LED does not light, refer to wiring diagrams, then trace and repair damaged wiring circuit.
6. If wiring or connector repairs are required, refer to "Precautions."

Clearing Diagnostic Trouble Codes

Fault memory cannot be erased until it has first been inspected.

Follow tool manufacturer's instructions to clear DTCs.

SYSTEM SERVICE

Refer to "Fuel Injection" section for adjustment and replacement procedures.

DIAGNOSTIC CHART INDEX

Code	Description	Page No.	Fig. No.
P0102	MAF Circuit Low Input	10-106	8
P0103	MAF Circuit High Input	10-106	8
P0112	IAT Circuit Low Input	10-106	8
P0113	IAT Circuit High Input	10-106	8
P0116	ECT Circuit Fault	10-106	8
P0117	ECT Circuit Low Input	10-106	8
P0118	ECT Circuit High Input	10-106	8
P0121	Throttle/Pedal Position Sensor Circuit Fault	10-106	8
P0122	Throttle/Pedal Position Sensor Low Input	10-106	8
P0123	Throttle/Pedal Position Sensor High Input	10-106	8
P0130	Oxygen Sensor Bank 1 Sensor 1 Fault	10-106	9
P0131	Oxygen Sensor Bank 1 Sensor 1 Low Voltage	10-106	9
P0132	Oxygen Sensor Bank 1 Sensor 1 High Voltage	10-106	9
P0133	Oxygen Sensor Bank 1 Sensor 1 Slow Response	10-106	9
P0134	Oxygen Sensor Bank 1 Sensor 1 No Activity Detected	10-106	9
P0136	Oxygen Sensor Bank 1 Sensor 2 Fault	10-106	9
P0137	Oxygen Sensor Bank 1 Sensor 2 Low Voltage	10-106	9
P0138	Oxygen Sensor Bank 1 Sensor 2 High Voltage	10-106	9
P0140	Oxygen Sensor Bank 1 Sensor 2 No Activity Detected	10-106	9
P0150	Oxygen Sensor Bank 2 Sensor 1 Fault	10-107	10
P0151	Oxygen Sensor Bank 2 Sensor 1 Low Voltage	10-107	10
P0152	Oxygen Sensor Bank 2 Sensor 1 High Voltage	10-107	10
P0153	Oxygen Sensor Bank 2 Sensor 1 Slow Response	10-107	10
P0154	Oxygen Sensor Bank 2 Sensor 1 No Activity Detected	10-107	10
P0156	Oxygen Sensor Bank 2 Sensor 2 Fault	10-107	10
P0157	Oxygen Sensor Bank 2 Sensor 2 Low Voltage	10-107	10
P0158	Oxygen Sensor Bank 2 Sensor 2 High Voltage	10-107	10
P0160	Oxygen Sensor Bank 2 Sensor 2 No Activity Detected	10-107	10
P0300	Random Misfire Detected	10-107	11
P0301	Cylinder 1 Misfire Detected	10-107	11
P0302	Cylinder 2 Misfire Detected	10-107	11
P0303	Cylinder 3 Misfire Detected	10-107	11
P0304	Cylinder 4 Misfire Detected	10-107	11
P0305	Cylinder 5 Misfire Detected	10-107	11
P0306	Cylinder 6 Misfire Detected	10-107	11
P0321	Engine Speed Sensor Input Circuit Fault	10-107	11
P0322	Engine Speed Sensor No Signal	10-107	11
P0327	Knock Sensor 1 Circuit Low Input	10-107	12
P0328	Knock Sensor 1 Circuit High Input	10-107	12
P0332	Knock Sensor 2 Circuit Low Input	10-107	12
P0333	Knock Sensor 2 Circuit High Input	10-107	12
P0411	Secondary Air Injection System Improper Flow Detected	10-107	12
P0422	Main Catalyst Bank 1 Efficiency Below Threshold	10-107	12
P0432	Main Catalyst Bank 2 Efficiency Below Threshold	10-107	12
P0441	EVAP System Improper Purge Flow Fault	10-107	13
P0442	EVAP System Small Leak Detected	10-107	13
P0455	EVAP System Large Leak Detected	10-107	13
P0501	Vehicle Speed Sensor Fault	10-107	13
P0506	Idle Control System RPM Lower Than Expected	10-107	13
P0507	Idle Control System RPM Higher Than Expected	10-107	13
P0601	Internal Control Module Memory Inspection Sum Error	10-107	14

Continued

DIAGNOSTIC CHART INDEX—Continued

Code	Description	Page No.	Fig. No.
P0604	Internal Control Module Random Access Memory Error	10-107	14
P1102	Oxygen Sensor Heating Circuit Bank 1 Sensor 1 Short To Power	10-107	14
P1105	Oxygen Sensor Heating Circuit Bank 1 Sensor 2 Short To Power	10-107	14
P1107	Oxygen Sensor Heating Circuit Bank 2 Sensor 1 Short To Power	10-107	14
P1110	Oxygen Sensor Heating Circuit Bank 2 Sensor 2 Short To Power	10-107	14
P1127	Long Term Fuel Trim Bank 1 System Too Rich	10-107	15
P1128	Long Term Fuel Trim Bank 1 System Too Lean	10-108	16
P1129	Long Term Fuel Trim Bank 2 System Too Rich	10-108	17
P1130	Long Term Fuel Trim Bank 2 System Too Lean	10-108	18
P1136	Long Term Fuel Trim Bank 1 System Too Lean	10-108	19
P1137	Long Term Fuel Trim Bank 1 System Too Rich	10-108	20
P1138	Long Term Fuel Trim Bank 2 System Too Lean	10-108	21
P1139	Long Term Fuel Trim Bank 2 System Too Rich	10-108	22
P1141	Load Calculation Cross Inspection Range Fault	10-108	22
P1176	Oxygen Sensor Correction Behind Catalyst B1 Limit Attained	10-108	23
P1177	Oxygen Sensor Correction Behind Catalyst B2 Limit Attained	10-108	23
P1196	Oxygen Sensor Heater Circuit Bank 1 Sensor 1 Electrical Fault	10-109	24
P1197	Oxygen Sensor Heater Circuit Bank 2 Sensor 1 Electrical Fault	10-109	24
P1198	Oxygen Sensor Heater Circuit Bank 1 Sensor 2 Electrical Fault	10-109	24
P1199	Oxygen Sensor Heater Circuit Bank 2 Sensor 2 Electrical Fault	10-109	24
P1213	Cylinder 1 Fuel Injector Short To Power	10-109	24
P1214	Cylinder 2 Fuel Injector Short To Power	10-109	24
P1215	Cylinder 3 Fuel Injector Short To Power	10-109	24
P1216	Cylinder 4 Fuel Injector Short To Power	10-109	24
P1217	Cylinder 5 Fuel Injector Short To Power	10-109	24
P1218	Cylinder 6 Fuel Injector Short To Power	10-109	25
P1225	Cylinder 1 Fuel Injector Short To Ground	10-109	25
P1226	Cylinder 2 Fuel Injector Short To Ground	10-109	25
P1227	Cylinder 3 Fuel Injector Short To Ground	10-109	25
P1228	Cylinder 4 Fuel Injector Short To Ground	10-109	25
P1229	Cylinder 5 Fuel Injector Short To Ground	10-109	25
P1230	Cylinder 6 Fuel Injector Short To Ground	10-109	25
P1237	Cylinder 1 Fuel Injector Open Circuit	10-109	26
P1238	Cylinder 2 Fuel Injector Open Circuit	10-109	26
P1239	Cylinder 3 Fuel Injector Open Circuit	10-109	26
P1240	Cylinder 4 Fuel Injector Open Circuit	10-109	26
P1241	Cylinder 5 Fuel Injector Open Circuit	10-109	26
P1242	Cylinder 6 Fuel Injector Open Circuit	10-109	26
P1250	Fuel Level Too Low	10-109	27
P1325	Cylinder 1 Knock Control Limit Attained	10-109	28
P1326	Cylinder 2 Knock Control Limit Attained	10-109	28
P1327	Cylinder 3 Knock Control Limit Attained	10-109	28
P1328	Cylinder 4 Knock Control Limit Attained	10-109	28
P1329	Cylinder 5 Knock Control Limit Attained	10-109	28
P1330	Cylinder 6 Knock Control Limit Attained	10-109	28
P1337	Camshaft Position Sensor Bank 1 Short To Ground	10-109	28
P1338	Camshaft Position Sensor Bank 1 Open Circuit Or Short To Power	10-109	28
P1386	Internal Control Module Knock Control Error	10-109	28
P1391	Camshaft Position Sensor Bank 2 Short To Ground	10-109	29
P1392	Camshaft Position Sensor Bank 2 Open Circuit Or Short To Power	10-109	29
P1410	Tank Ventilation Valve Short To Power	10-109	29
P1421	Secondary Air Injection Valve Circuit Short To Ground	10-109	29
P1422	Secondary Air Injection Control Valve Circuit Short To Power	10-109	29
P1425	Tank Vent Valve Short To Ground	10-109	29
P1426	Tank Vent Valve Open	10-109	29
P1432	Secondary Air Injection Valve Open	10-109	30
P1433	Secondary Air Injection Pump Relay Circuit Open	10-109	30

Continued

DIAGNOSTIC CHART INDEX—Continued

Code	Description	Page No.	Fig. No.
P1434	Secondary Air Injection Pump Relay Circuit Short To Power	10-109	30
P1435	Secondary Air Injection Pump Relay Circuit Short To Ground	10-109	30
P1436	Secondary Air Injection Pump Relay Circuit Electrical Fault	10-109	30
P1471	EVAP Emission Control LDP Circuit Short To Power	10-109	30
P1472	EVAP Emission Control LDP Circuit Short To Ground	10-109	30
P1473	EVAP Emission Control LDP Circuit Short To Power	10-109	30
P1476	EVAP Emission Control LDP Circuit Fault/Insufficient Vacuum	10-109	30
P1477	EVAP Emission Control LDP Circuit Fault	10-109	30
P1500	Fuel Pump Relay Electrical Fault	10-110	31
P1501	Fuel Pump Relay Short To Ground	10-110	31
P1502	Fuel Pump Relay Short To Power	10-110	31
P1505	Fuel Pump Relay Electrical Fault	10-110	31
P1512	Intake Manifold Changeover Valve Short To Power	10-110	31
P1515	Intake Manifold Changeover Valve Short To Ground	10-110	31
P1516	Intake Manifold Changeover Valve Circuit Open	10-110	31
P1519	Intake Camshaft Control Bank 1 Fault	10-110	31
P1543	Intake Camshaft Control Bank 2 Fault	10-110	32
P1544	Throttle Actuation Potentiometer Signal Too High	10-110	32
P1545	Throttle Position Control Fault	10-110	32
P1558	Throttle Actuator Electrical Fault	10-110	32
P1559	Idle Speed Control Throttle Position Adaptation Fault	10-110	32
P1560	Maximum Engine Speed Exceeded	10-110	32
P1564	Idle Speed Control Throttle Position Low Voltage During Adaptation	10-110	32
P1565	Idle Speed Control Throttle Position Lower Impact Not Attained	10-110	33
P1600	Power Supply Terminal 15 Low Voltage	10-110	33
P1602	Power Supply Terminal 30 Low Voltage	10-110	33
P1606	Rough Road Spec Engine Torque ABS-ECU Electrical Fault	10-110	33
P1612	ECM Improper Coding	10-110	34
P1624	MIL Request Sign Active	10-110	35
P1626	CAN Bus Missing Message From Transmission Control	10-110	35
P1640	Internal Control Module EEPROM Error	10-110	35
P1681	Control Unit Programming Not Finished	10-110	35
P1690	MIL Lamp Fault	10-110	35

Diagnostic Trouble Code (DTC) SAE	VAG	Malfunction text	MIL	Corrective action
P0102	16486	Mass or Volume Air Flow Circ. Low Input	2 Dcy	– Check Mass Air Flow (MAF) sensor -G70
P0103	16487	Mass or Volume Air Flow Circ. High Input		
P0112	16496	Intake Air Temp. Circ. Low Input	2 Dcy	– Check Intake Air Temperature (IAT) sensor -G42
P0113	16497	Intake Air Temp. Circ. High Input		
P0116	16500	Engine Coolant Temp. Circ. Range/Performance	2 Dcy	– Check Engine Coolant Temperature (ECT) sensor -G62
P0117	16501	Engine Coolant Temp. Circ. Low Input		
P0118	16502	Engine Coolant Temp. Circ. High Input		
P0121	16505	Throttle/Pedal Pos. Sensor A Circ. Range/Performance	2 Dcy	– Check Throttle Position (TP) sensor -G69
P0122	16506	Throttle/Pedal Pos. Sensor A Circ. Low Input		
P0123	16507	Throttle/Pedal Pos. Sensor A Circ. High Input		

AD0159800225000X

Fig. 8 Codes P0102, P0103, P0112, P0113, P0116, P0117, P0118, P0121, P0122 & P0123

Diagnostic Trouble Code (DTC) SAE	VAG	Malfunction text	MIL	Corrective action
P0130	16514	O2 Sensor Circ., Bank1–Sensor1 Malfunction	2 Dcy	– Check Heated Oxygen Sensor (HO2S) -G39- and O2S control (bank 1, sensor 1)
P0131	16515	O2 Sensor Circ., Bank1–Sensor1 Low Voltage		
P0132	16516	O2 Sensor Circ., Bank1–Sensor1 High Voltage		
P0133	16517	O2 Sensor Circ., Bank1–Sensor1 Slow Response	2 Dcy	– Check HO2S -G39- aging (bank 1, sensor 1)
P0134	16518	O2 Sensor Circ., Bank1–Sensor1 No Activity Detected	2 Dcy	– Check HO2S -G39- and O2S control (bank 1, sensor 1)
P0136	16520	O2 Sensor Circ., Bank1–Sensor2 Malfunction	2 Dcy	– Check Oxygen Sensor (O2S) behind Three Way Catalytic Converter (TWC) -G130- (bank 1, sensor 2)
P0137	16521	O2 Sensor Circ., Bank1–Sensor2 Low Voltage		
P0138	16522	O2 Sensor Circ., Bank1–Sensor2 High Voltage		
P0140	16524	O2 Sensor Circ., Bank1–Sensor2 No Activity Detected		

AD0159800226000X

Fig. 9 Codes P0130, P0131, P0132, P0133, P0134, P0136, P0137, P0138 & P0140

Diagnostic Trouble Code (DTC) SAE	VAG	Malfunction text	MIL	Corrective action
P0150	16534	O2 Sensor Circ., Bank2–Sensor1 Malfunction	2 Dcy	– Check Heated Oxygen Sensor (HO2S) -G108- and Oxygen Sensor (O2S) control (bank 2, sensor 1)
P0151	16535	O2 Sensor Circ., Bank2–Sensor1 Low Voltage		
P0152	16536	O2 Sensor Circ., Bank2–Sensor1 High Voltage		
P0153	16537	O2 Sensor Circ., Bank2–Sensor1 Slow Response	2 Dcy	– Check HO2S -G108- aging (bank 2, sensor 1)
P0154	16538	O2 Sensor Circ., Bank2–Sensor1 No Activity Detected	2 Dcy	– Check HO2S -G108- and O2S control (bank 2, sensor 1)
P0156	16540	O2 Sensor Circ., Bank2–Sensor2 Malfunction	2 Dcy	– Check O2S 2 behind Three Way Catalytic Converter (TWC) -G131- (bank 2, sensor 2)
P0157	16541	O2 Sensor Circ., Bank2–Sensor2 Low Voltage		
P0158	16542	O2 Sensor Circ., Bank2–Sensor2 High Voltage		
P0160	16544	O2 Sensor Circ., Bank2–Sensor2 No Activity Detected		

AD0159800227000X

Fig. 10 Codes P0150, P0151, P0152, P0153, P0154, P0156, P0157, P0158 & P0160

Diagnostic Trouble Code (DTC) SAE	VAG	Malfunction text	MIL	Corrective action
P0327	16711	Knock Sensor1 Circ. Low Input	Immed.	– Check knock sensors and knock sensor control
P0328	16712	Knock Sensor1 Circ. High Input		
P0332	16716	Knock Sensor2 Circ. Low Input		
P0333	16717	Knock Sensor2 Circ. High Input		
P0411	16795	Sec. Air Inj. Sys. Incorrect Flow Detected	2 Dcy	– Check secondary Air Injection (AIR) system
P0422	16806	Main Catalyst, Bank1 Efficiency Below Threshold	2 Dcy	– Check Heated Oxygen Sensor (HO2S) -G39- and O2S control (bank 1, sensor 1)
P0432	16816	Main Catalyst, Bank2 Efficiency Below Threshold	2 Dcy	– Check HO2S -G108- and O2S control (bank 2, sensor 1)

AD0159800229000X

Fig. 12 Codes P0327, P0328, P0332, P0333, P0411, P0422 & P0432

Diagnostic Trouble Code (DTC) SAE	VAG	Malfunction text	MIL	Corrective action
P0601	16985	Internal Contr. Module Memory Check Sum Error	2 Dcy	Replace ECM
P0604	16988	Internal Contr. Module Random Access Memory (RAM) Error		
P1102	17510	O2 Sensor Heating Circ., Bank1–Sensor1 Short to B+	2 Dcy	– Check Oxygen Sensor (O2S) heater -Z19- (bank 1, sensor 1, before TWC)
P1105	17513	O2 Sensor Heating Circ., Bank1–Sensor2 Short to B+	2 Dcy	– Check O2S heater -Z29- (bank 1, sensor 2, behind TWC)
P1107	17515	O2 Sensor Heating Circ., Bank2–Sensor1 Short to B+	2 Dcy	– Check O2S heater -Z28- (bank 2, sensor 1, before TWC)
P1110	17518	O2 Sensor Heating Circ., Bank2–Sensor2 Short to B+	2 Dcy	– Check O2S heater -Z30- (bank 2, sensor 2, behind TWC)

AD0159800231000X

Fig. 14 Codes P0601, P0604, P1102, P1105, P1107 & P1110

Diagnostic Trouble Code (DTC) SAE	VAG	Malfunction text	MIL	Corrective action
P0300	16684	Random/Multiple Cylinder Misfire Detected	2 Dcy / blink	– Fuel level too low, check fuel level and add if necessary – Check misfire detection – Check fuel injectors – Carry out output Diagnostic Test Mode (DTM) – Check engine speed (RPM) sensor -G28
P0301	16685	Cyl. 1 Misfire Detected		
P0302	16686	Cyl. 2 Misfire Detected		
P0303	16687	Cyl. 3 Misfire Detected		
P0304	16688	Cyl. 4 Misfire Detected		
P0305	16689	Cyl. 5 Misfire Detected		
P0306	16690	Cyl. 6 Misfire Detected		
P0321	16705	Ign./Distributor Eng. Speed Inp. Circ. Range/Performance	2 Dcy	– Check engine speed (RPM) sensor -G28
P0322	16706	Ign./Distributor Eng. Speed Inp. Circ. No Signal	Immed.	

Note on misfire malfunctions:

For malfunctions that may be caused by low fuel volume (i.e. combustion misfire) a low-fuel malfunction (DTC P1250) is also stored when there is less than 2 gallons of fuel remaining in the tank.

AD0159800228000X

Fig. 11 Codes P0300, P0301, P0302, P0303, P0304, P0305, P0306, P0321 & P0322

Diagnostic Trouble Code (DTC) SAE	VAG	Malfunction text	MIL	Corrective action
P0441	16825	EVAP Emission Contr. Sys. Incorrect Purge Flow	2 Dcy	– Check Evaporative Emissions (EVAP) canister purge regulator valve -N80 Diagnostic Test Mode (DTM)
P0442	16826	EVAP Emission Contr. Sys. (Small Leak) Leak Detected	2 Dcy	– Check Evaporative Emission (EVAP) system
P0455	16839	EVAP Emission Contr. Sys. (Gross Leak) Leak Detected		
P0501	16885	Vehicle Speed Sensor Range/Performance	Immed.	– Check vehicle speed signal
P0506	16890	Idle Control System RPM Lower Than Expected	2 Dcy	– Check idle speed – Check throttle valve control module
P0507	16891	Idle Control System RPM Higher Than Expected		– Check fuel pressure, fuel pressure regulator, and residual fuel pressure

AD0159800230000X

Fig. 13 Codes P0441, P0442, P0455, P0501, P0506 & P0507

Diagnostic Trouble Code (DTC) SAE	VAG	Malfunction text	MIL	Corrective action
P1127	17535	Long Term Fuel Trim mult., Bank1 System too Rich [1]	2 Dcy	– Check Mass Air Flow (MAF) sensor -G70- – Check Heated Oxygen Sensor (HO2S) -G39 (bank 1, sensor 1) and O2S control – Check Oxygen Sensor (O2S) behind Three Way Catalytic Converter (TWC) -G130- (bank 1, sensor 2) and O2S control – Check fuel pressure, fuel pressure regulator and residual fuel pressure – Check fuel injectors Diagnostic Test Mode (DTM)

[1] The term "mult." = multiplicative; applies to entire engine speed (RPM) and load range.

AD0159800232000X

Fig. 15 Code P1127

Diagnostic Trouble Code (DTC) SAE	VAG	Malfunction text	MIL	Corrective action
P1128	17536	Long Term Fuel Trim mult., Bank1 System too Lean [1]	2 Dcy	– Check Heated Oxygen Sensor (HO2S) -G39- (bank 1, sensor 1) and O2S control – Check Oxygen Sensor (O2S) behind Three Way Catalytic Converter (TWC) -G130- (bank 1, sensor 2) and O2S control Check fuel pressure, fuel pressure regulator and residual fuel pressure – Check fuel injectors and Diagnostic Test Mode (DTM), page 01-48 – Check EVAP canister purge regulator valve ⇒ output Diagnostic Test Mode (DTM)

[1] The term "mult." = multiplicative; applies to entire engine speed (RPM) and load range.

AD0159800233000X

Fig. 16 Code P1128

Diagnostic Trouble Code (DTC) SAE	VAG	Malfunction text	MIL	Corrective action
P1129	17537	Long Term Fuel Trim mult., Bank2 System too Rich [1]	2 Dcy	– Check Mass Air Flow (MAF) sensor -G70 – Check Heated Oxygen Sensor (HO2S) 2 -G108- (bank 2, sensor 1) and O2S control – Check Oxygen Sensor (O2S) 2 behind Three Way Catalytic Converter (TWC) -G131- (bank 2, sensor 2) and O2S control – Check fuel pressure, fuel pressure regulator and residual fuel pressure – Check fuel injectors Diagnostic Test Mode (DTM)

[1] The term "mult." = multiplicative; applies to entire engine speed (RPM) and load range.

AD0159800234000X

Fig. 17 Code P1129

Diagnostic Trouble Code (DTC) SAE	VAG	Malfunction text	MIL	Corrective action
P1130	17538	Long Term Fuel Trim mult., Bank2 System too Lean [1]	2 Dcy	– Check Heated Oxygen Sensor (HO2S) 2 -G108- (bank 2, sensor 1) and O2S control – Check Oxygen Sensor (O2S) 2 behind Three Way Catalytic Converter (TWC) -G131- (bank 2, sensor 2) and O2S control – Check fuel pressure, fuel pressure regulator and residual fuel pressure – Check fuel injectors Diagnostic Test Mode (DTM), page 01-48 – Check EVAP canister purge regulator valve output Diagnostic Test Mode (DTM)

[1] The term "mult." = multiplicative; applies to entire engine speed (RPM) and load range.

AD0159800235000X

Fig. 18 Code P1130

Diagnostic Trouble Code (DTC) SAE	VAG	Malfunction text	MIL	Corrective action
P1136	17544	Long Term Fuel Trim Add. Fuel, Bank1 System too Lean [2]	2 Dcy	– Check intake air system for leaks ("false air") – Check Heated Oxygen Sensor (HO2S) -G39- (bank 1, sensor 1) and O2S control – Check Mass Air Flow (MAF) sensor -G70- – Check fuel pressure, fuel pressure regulator and residual fuel pressure – Check fuel injectors and Diagnostic Test Mode (DTM)

[2] The term "Add." = additive; applies only with engine running at idle speed.

AD0159800236000X

Fig. 19 Code P1136

Diagnostic Trouble Code (DTC) SAE	VAG	Malfunction text	MIL	Corrective action
P1137	17545	Long Term Fuel Trim Add. Fuel, Bank1 System too Rich [2]	2 Dcy	– Check Heated Oxygen Sensor (HO2S) -G39- (bank 1, sensor 1) and O2S control – Check fuel pressure, fuel pressure regulator and residual pressure – Check exhaust system for leakage

[2] The term "Add." = additive; applies only with engine running at idle speed.

AD0159800237000X

Fig. 20 Code P1137

Diagnostic Trouble Code (DTC) SAE	VAG	Malfunction text	MIL	Corrective action
P1138	17546	Long Term Fuel Trim Add. Fuel, Bank2 System too Lean [2]	2 Dcy	– Check intake air system for leaks ("false air") – Check Heated Oxygen Sensor (HO2S) 2 -G108- (bank 2, sensor 1) and O2S control – Check Mass Air Flow (MAF) sensor -G70 – Check fuel pressure, fuel pressure regulator and residual fuel pressure – Check fuel injectors Diagnostic Test Mode (DTM)

[2] The term "Add." = additive; applies only with engine running at idle speed.

AD0159800238000X

Fig. 21 Code P1138

Diagnostic Trouble Code (DTC) SAE	VAG	Malfunction text	MIL	Corrective action
P1139	17547	Long Term Fuel Trim Add. Fuel, Bank2 System too Rich [2]	2 Dcy	– Check Heated Oxygen Sensor (HO2S) 2 -G108- (bank 2, sensor 1) and O2S control – Check fuel pressure, fuel pressure regulator and residual pressure – Check exhaust system for leakage
P1141	17549	Load Calculation Cross Check Range/Performance	2 Dcy	– Check Mass Air Flow (MAF) sensor -G70 – Check throttle valve control module

[2] The term "Add." = additive; applies only with engine running at idle speed.

AD0159800239000X

Fig. 22 Codes P1139 & P1141

Diagnostic Trouble Code (DTC) SAE	VAG	Malfunction text	MIL	Corrective action
P1176	17584	O2 Correction Behind Catalyst, B1 Limit Attained	Off	– Check intake air system for leaks ("false air") – Check Heated Oxygen Sensor (HO2S) aging (bank 1, sensor 1) – Check Oxygen Sensor (O2S) heater -Z29- (bank 1, sensor 2) – Check O2S behind TWC (bank 1, sensor 2)
P1177	17585	O2 Correction Behind Catalyst, B2 Limit Attained	Off	– Check intake air system for leaks ("false air") Check Heated Oxygen Sensor (HO2S) 2 aging (bank 2, sensor 1) – Check Oxygen Sensor (O2S) 2 heater -Z29- (bank 2, sensor 2) – Check O2S 2 behind TWC (bank 2, sensor 2)

AD0159800240000X

Fig. 23 Codes P1176 & P1177

Diagnostic Trouble Code (DTC)		Malfunction text	MIL	Corrective action
SAE	VAG			
P1196	17604	O2 Sensor Heater Circ., Bank1–Sensor1 Electrical Malfunction	2 Dcy	– Check Oxygen Sensor (O2S) heater -Z19- (bank 1, sensor 1)
P1197	17605	O2 Sensor Heater Circ., Bank2–Sensor1 Electrical Malfunction	2 Dcy	– Check Oxygen Sensor (O2S) heater -Z28- (bank 2, sensor 1)
P1198	17606	O2 Sensor Heater Circ., Bank1–Sensor2 Electrical Malfunction	2 Dcy	– Check Oxygen Sensor (O2S) heater -Z29- (bank 1, sensor 2)
P1199	17607	O2 Sensor Heater Circ., Bank2–Sensor2 Electrical Malfunction	2 Dcy	– Check Oxygen Sensor (O2S) heater -Z30- (bank 2, sensor 2)
P1213	17621	Cyl.1–Fuel Inj. Circ. Short to B+	Immed.	– Check fuel injectors Diagnostic Test Mode (DTM)
P1214	17622	Cyl.2–Fuel Inj. Circ. Short to B+		
P1215	17623	Cyl.3–Fuel Inj. Circ. Short to B+		
P1216	17624	Cyl.4–Fuel Inj. Circ. Short to B+		
P1217	17625	Cyl.5–Fuel Inj. Circ. Short to B+		

AD0159800241000X

Fig. 24 Codes P1196, P1197, P1198, P1199, P1213, P12114, P1215, P1216 & P1217

Diagnostic Trouble Code (DTC)		Malfunction text	MIL	Corrective action
SAE	VAG			
P1237	17645	Cyl.1–Fuel Inj. Circ. Open Circuit	Immed.	– Check fuel injectors Diagnostic Test Mode (DTM)
P1238	17646	Cyl.2–Fuel Inj. Circ. Open Circuit		
P1239	17647	Cyl.3–Fuel Inj. Circ. Open Circuit		
P1240	17648	Cyl.4–Fuel Inj. Circ. Open Circuit		
P1241	17649	Cyl.5–Fuel Inj. Circ. Open Circuit		
P1242	17650	Cyl.6–Fuel Inj. Circ. Open Circuit		

AD0159800243000X

Fig. 26 Codes P1237, P1238, P1239, P1240, P1241 & P1242

Diagnostic Trouble Code (DTC)		Malfunction text	MIL	Corrective action
SAE	VAG			
P1325	17733	Cyl.1–Knock Contr. Limit Attained	Off	– Check knock sensors and knock sensor control
P1326	17734	Cyl.2–Knock Contr. Limit Attained		
P1327	17735	Cyl.3–Knock Contr. Limit Attained		
P1328	17736	Cyl.4–Knock Contr. Limit Attained		
P1329	17737	Cyl.5–Knock Contr. Limit Attained		
P1330	17738	Cyl.6–Knock Contr. Limit Attained		
P1337	17745	Camshaft Pos. Sensor, Bank1 Short to Ground	2 Dcy	– Check Camshaft Position (CMP) sensor -G40-
P1338	17746	Camshaft Pos. Sensor, Bank1 Open Circ./Short to B+		
P1386	17794	Internal Control Module Knock Control Circ. Error	2 Dcy	– Replace ECM

AD0159800245000X

Fig. 28 Codes P1325, P1326, P1327, P1328, P1329, P1330, P1337, P1338 & P1386

Diagnostic Trouble Code (DTC)		Malfunction text	MIL	Corrective action
SAE	VAG			
P1218	17626	Cyl.6–Fuel Inj. Circ. Short to B+	Immed.	– Check fuel injectors Diagnostic Test Mode (DTM)
P1225	17633	Cyl.1–Fuel Inj. Circ. Short to Ground		
P1226	17634	Cyl.2–Fuel Inj. Circ. Short to Ground		
P1227	17635	Cyl.3–Fuel Inj. Circ. Short to Ground		
P1228	17636	Cyl.4–Fuel Inj. Circ. Short to Ground		
P1229	17637	Cyl.5–Fuel Inj. Circ. Short to Ground		
P1230	17638	Cyl.6–Fuel Inj. Circ. Short to Ground		

AD0159800242000X

Fig. 25 Codes P1218, P1225, P1226, P1227, P1228, P1229 & P1230

Diagnostic Trouble Code (DTC)		Malfunction text	MIL	Corrective action
SAE	VAG			
P1250	17658	Fuel Level Too Low	Off	– Fuel volume less than 2 gallons; add fuel – Check fuel level signal – Check fuel level sensor signal and fuel gauge

Note on misfire malfunctions:

For malfunctions that may be caused by low fuel volume (i.e. combustion misfire) a low-fuel malfunction (DTC P1250) is also stored when there is less than 2 gallons of fuel remaining in the tank.

AD0159800244000X

Fig. 27 Code P1250

Diagnostic Trouble Code (DTC)		Malfunction text	MIL	Corrective action
SAE	VAG			
P1391	17799	Camshaft Pos. Sensor, Bank2 Short to Ground	2 Dcy	– Check Camshaft Position (CMP) sensor 2 -G163-
P1392	17800	Camshaft Pos. Sensor, Bank2 Open Circ./Short to B+		
P1410	17818	Tank Ventilation Valve Circ. Short to B+	2 Dcy	– Check Evaporative Emissions (EVAP) canister purge regulator valve Diagnostic Test Mode (DTM)
P1421	17829	Sec. Air Inj. Valve Circ. Short to Ground	Immed.	– Check Secondary Air Injection (AIR) system output Diagnostic Test Mode (DTM)
P1422	17830	Sec. Air Inj. Sys. Contr. Valve Circ. Short to B+		
P1425	17833	Tank Vent Valve Short to Ground	2 Dcy	– Check Evaporative Emissions (EVAP) canister purge regulator valve Diagnostic Test Mode (DTM)
P1426	17834	Tank Vent Valve Open		

AD0159800246000X

Fig. 29 Codes P1391, P1392, P1410, P1421, P1422, P1425 & P1426

Diagnostic Trouble Code (DTC)		Malfunction text	MIL	Corrective action
SAE	VAG			
P1432	17840	Sec. Air Inj. Valve Open	2 Dcy	– Check Secondary Air Injection (AIR) system output Diagnostic Test Mode (DTM)
P1433	17841	Sec. Air Inj. Sys. Pump Relay Circ. Open		
P1434	17842	Sec. Air Inj. Sys. Pump Relay Circ. Short to B+		
P1435	17843	Sec. Air Inj. Sys. Pump Relay Circ. Short to Ground		
P1436	17844	Sec. Air Inj. Sys. Pump Relay Circ. Electrical Malfunction		
P1471	17879	EVAP Emission Contr. LDP Circ. Short to B+	2 Dcy	– Check Leak Detection Pump (LDP)
P1472	17880	EVAP Emission Contr. LDP Circ. Short to Ground		
P1473	17881	EVAP Emission Contr. LDP Circ. Open Circ.		
P1476	17884	EVAP Emission Contr. LDP Circ. Malfunction/Insufficient Vacuum	2 Dcy	– Check Evaporative Emission (EVAP) system
P1477	17885	EVAP Emission Contr. LDP Circ. Malfunction		

AD0159800247000X

Fig. 30 Codes P1432, P1433, P1434, P1435, P1436, P1471, P1472, P1473, P1476 & P1477

Diagnostic Trouble Code (DTC) SAE	VAG	Malfunction text	MIL	Corrective action
P1500	17908	Fuel Pump Relay Circ. Electrical Malfunction	Immed.	– Check fuel pump relay and relay actuation
P1501	17909	Fuel Pump Relay Circ. Short to Ground		
P1502	17910	Fuel Pump Relay Circ. Short to B+		
P1505	17913	Closed Throttle Pos. Switch Does Not Close/Open Circ.	2 Dcy	– Check throttle body and throttle valve control module
P1512	17920	Intake Manifold Changeover Valve Circ. Short to B+	Immed.	– Check Intake Manifold Tuning (IMT) valve (change-over valve)
P1515	17923	Intake Manifold Changeover Valve Circ. Short to Ground		
P1516	17924	Intake Manifold Changeover Valve Circ. Open		
P1519	17927	Intake Camshaft Contr., Bank1 Malfunction	2 Dcy	– Check camshaft adjustment
P1522	17930	Intake Camshaft Contr., Bank2 Malfunction		

AD0159800248000X

Fig. 31 Codes P1500, P1501, P1502, P1505, P1512, P1515, P1516, P1519 & P1522

Diagnostic Trouble Code (DTC) SAE	VAG	Malfunction text	MIL	Corrective action
P1543	17951	Throttle Actuation Potentiometer Signal too Low	2 Dcy	– Check throttle drive and angle sensor for throttle drive
P1544	17952	Throttle Actuation Potentiometer Signal too High		
P1545	17953	Throttle Pos. Contr. Malfunction		
P1558	17966	Throttle Actuator Electrical Malfunction		
P1559	17967	Idle Speed Contr. Throttle Pos. Adaptation Malfunction (Adaptation of throttle valve control module to engine control module interrupted by application of accelerator pedal or by starting engine.)	Off	– Check adaptation of throttle valve control module to Engine Control Module (ECM)
P1560	17968	Maximum Engine Speed Exceeded	Off	– Carry out engine mechanical repairs as necessary
P1564	17972	Idle Speed Contr. Throttle Pos. Low Voltage During Adaptation (Supply voltage under 10 V during adaptation of throttle valve control module to engine control module.)	Off	Check voltage supply to ECM

AD0159800249000X

Fig. 32 Codes P1543, P1544, P1545, P1558, P1559, P1560 & P1564

Diagnostic Trouble Code (DTC) SAE	VAG	Malfunction text	MIL	Corrective action
P1565	17973	Idle Speed Contr. Throttle Pos. Lower Impact Not Attained (Lower specification not attained during adaptation of throttle valve control module to engine control module, e.g., accelerator pedal cable incorrectly adjusted, throttle body dirty, etc.)	2 Dcy	– Clean throttle body – Check accelerator pedal cable adjustment
P1600	18008	Power Supply (B+) Terminal 15 Low Voltage	Immed.	– Check voltage supply to Engine Control Module (ECM)
P1602	18010	Power Supply (B+) Terminal 30 Low Voltage	Off	– Check voltage supply to ECM
P1606	18014	Rough Road Spec Engine Torque ABS-ECU Electrical Malfunction	Off	– Check ABS/EDL control module signal for rough road recognition Check ABS/ASR control module signal for rough road recognition

AD0159800250000X

Fig. 33 Codes P1565, P1600, P1602 & P1606

Diagnostic Trouble Code (DTC) SAE	VAG	Malfunction text	MIL	Corrective action
P1612	18020	Electronic Control Module Incorrect Coding (Vehicle with automatic transmission is coded for manual transmission.)	Immed.	– Code ECM
		Electronic Control Module Incorrect Coding (Vehicle with ASR is not coded for ASR)	Off	

AD0159800251000X

Fig. 34 Code P1612

Diagnostic Trouble Code (DTC) SAE	VAG	Malfunction text	MIL	Corrective action
P1624	18032	MIL Request Sign. active	Immed.	– Check DTC memory for Transmission Control Module (TCM) and correct malfunctions
P1626	18034	CAN-Bus Missing Message from Transm. Contr.	2 Dcy	– Check CAN-Bus
P1640	18048	Internal Contr. Module (EEPROM) Error	2 Dcy	– Replace ECM
P1681	18089	Contr. Unit Programming Programming not Finished	Immed.	– Replace ECM
P1690	18098	Malfunction Indicator Light Malfunction	Off	Check wire from ECM to Malfunction Indicator Lamp (MIL)

Note for DTC P1624/18032:

If this malfunction is detected by the Transmission Control Module (TCM), the MIL is switched on by the ECM. In this case, the ECM stores the malfunction "MIL Request Sign. active" (DTC P1624/18032). After repairing the malfunction, erase DTC memory of the ECM.

AD0159800252000X

Fig. 35 Codes P1624, P1626, P1640, P1681 & P1690

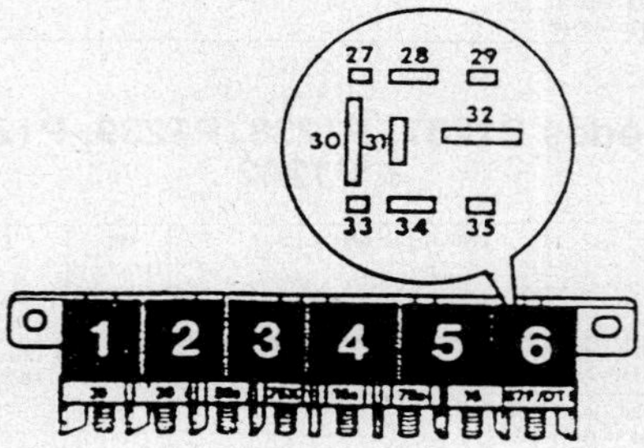

AD1029200048000X

Fig. 36 Relay position No. 6 terminal identification

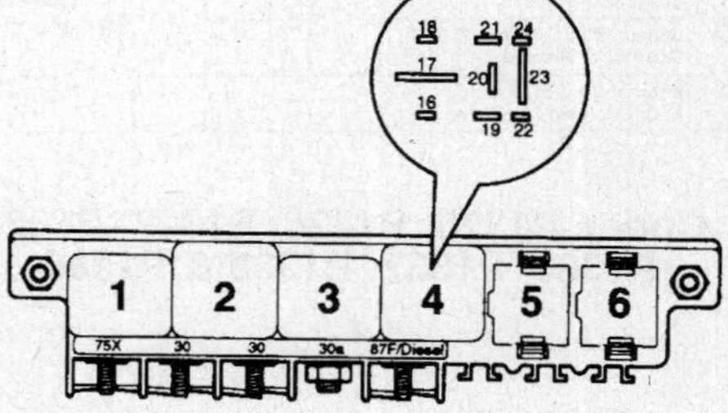

AD1029800100000X

Fig. 37 Fuel pump relay location. A6

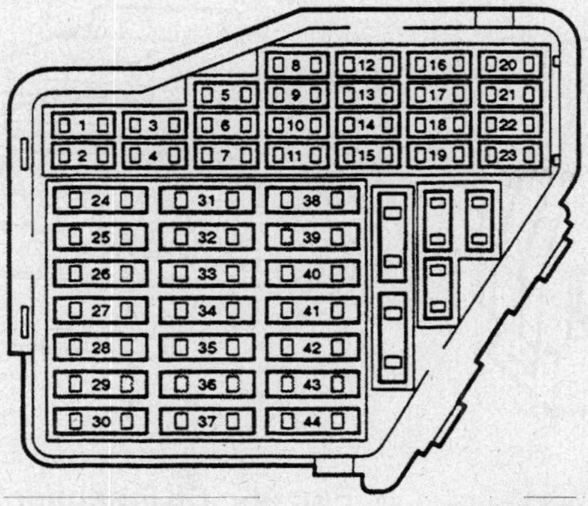

AD1020100230000X

Fig. 38 Fuse/relay panel

	Display fields			
	1	2	3	4
Display group 2: Load measurement				
Display	xxx RPM	xx.xx ms	xx.xx ms	xx.x g/s
Indicates	Engine speed (in 40 RPM steps)	Engine load	Injection time	Mass air flow
Range	0 – 6800 RPM	0.00 – 12.75 ms	0.00 – 20.00 ms	0.0 – 140 g/s
Specified value	600 – 760 RPM (all-wheel drive) *or* 680 – 840 RPM (front-wheel drive)	1.00 – 2.50 ms	2.00 – 5.00 ms	2.8 – 5.6 g/s
	2520 RPM	0.80 – 2.50 ms	1.60 – 5.00 ms	10.0 – 15.0 g/s
	---		---	

AD1029800105000X

Fig. 40 MAF sensor Display Group data. A6

Display group: 2 / **Display field: 4**	**Possible malfunction cause**	**Corrective action**
less than 2.8 g/s	♦ Large amount of false air between intake air duct and Mass Air Flow (MAF) sensor	– Check intake air system for leaks (false air)
larger than 5.6 g/s	♦ Shift lever in drive range (auto. transmission) ♦ Engine affected by additional consumers	– Move shift lever into P or N – Eliminate load (A/C, power steering, generator)
	♦ Open circuits in wire **1** or **2** between MAF sensor and ECM	– Check voltage supply
	♦ Open circuit in wire **3** between MAF sensor and **relay panel**	– Check wiring

AD1029800106020X

Fig. 41 MAF circuit troubleshooting chart (Part 2 of 2). A6

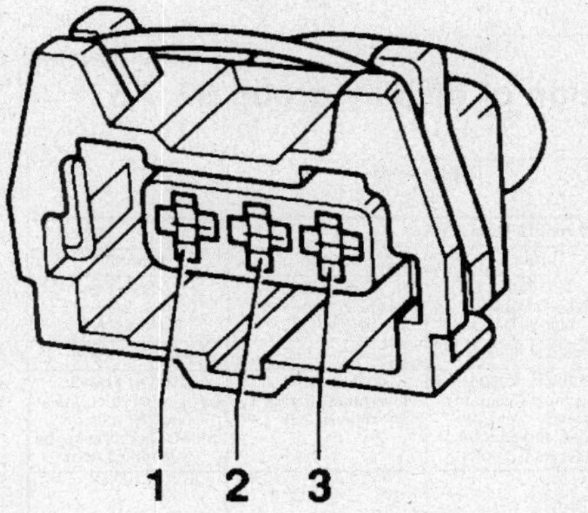

AD1029500074000X

Fig. 42 MAF sensor electrical connector terminal identification

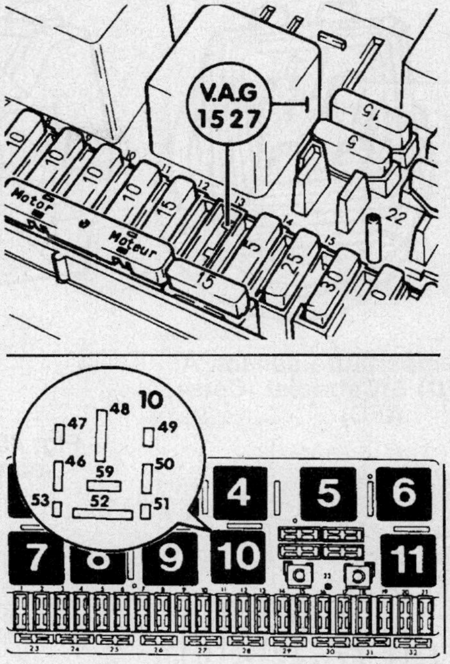

AD1029500079000X

Fig. 39 Fuse/relay panel. A6 & Cabriolet (Code AFC)

Display group: 2 / **Display field: 2**	**Possible malfunction cause**	**Corrective Action**
less than 1.00 ms	♦ Smaller values can only occur while driving during deceleration	
more than 2.50 ms	♦ Shift lever in drive range (auto. transmission) ♦ Engine is affected by additional consumers	– Move shift lever into P or N – Eliminate load (A/C, power steering, generator)
	♦ Poor idle (does not run on all cylinders)	– Check spark plugs (checking ignition coils) – Check fuel injectors
	♦ Throttle valve control module -J338- faulty	– Check throttle valve control module

AD1029800106010X

Fig. 41 MAF circuit troubleshooting chart (Part 1 of 2). A6

	Display fields			
	1	2	3	4
Display group 4: General engine data				
Display	xxx RPM	xx.xxx V	xxx.x °C	xxx.x °C
Indicates	Engine speed (in 40 RPM steps)	Battery Positive Voltage (B+)	Engine coolant temperature	Intake air temperature
Range	0 – 6800 RPM	0.000 – 16.500 V	-46.5 to 141.0	-46.5 to 141.0
Specified value	0 RPM	10.000 – 14.500 V	approx. ambient temperature [1), 2)]	---
	---	---		---

[1)] After a long standing period (approx. 12 hours).

[2)] If indicated temperature deviates significantly from the ambient temperature, check ECT sensor wiring for resistance or open circuits.

AD1029800110000X

Fig. 43 ECT sensor display data. A6

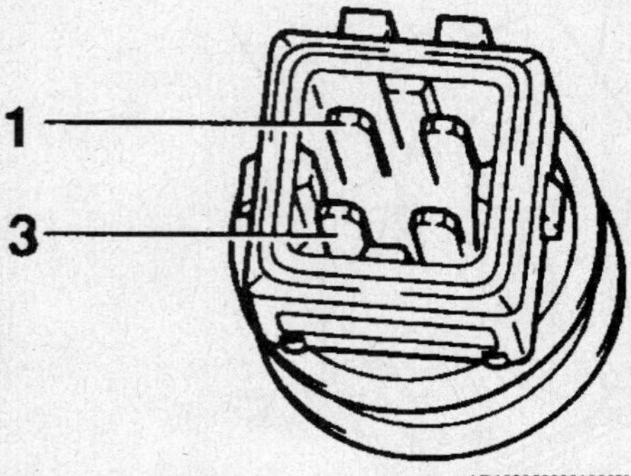

AD1029500081000X

Fig. 44 Temperature sensor. A6 (Code AFC) & Cabriolet (Code AFC)

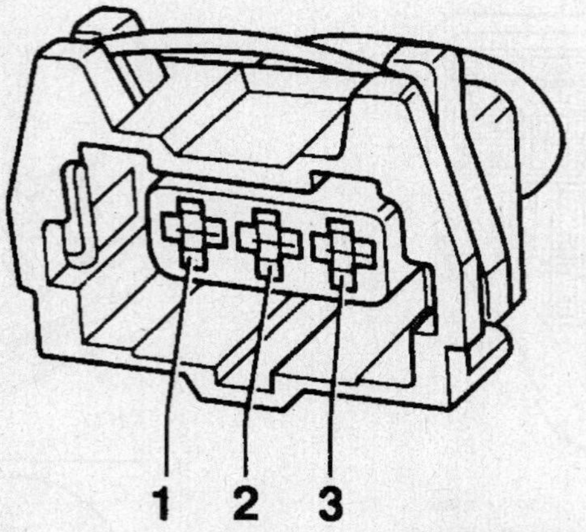

AD1029500083000X

Fig. 45 RPM sensor harness connector pin locations

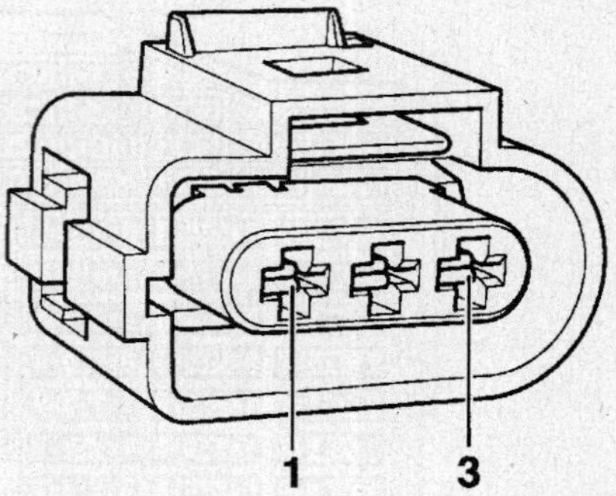

AD1029800113000X

Fig. 46 CKP sensor connector terminal identification. A6

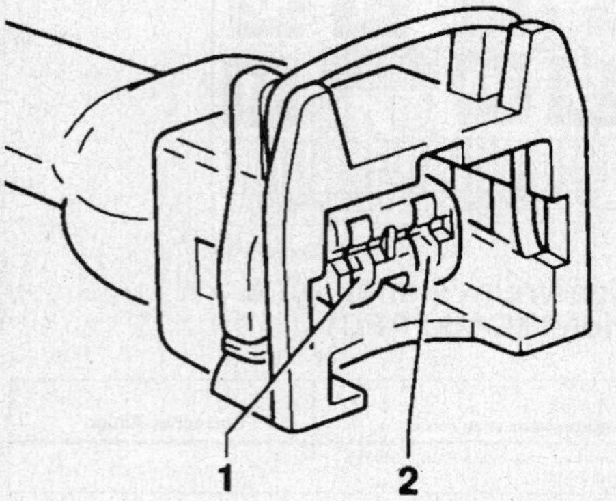

AD1029500075000X

Fig. 47 2-pin harness connector location. A4, Cabriolet & S4

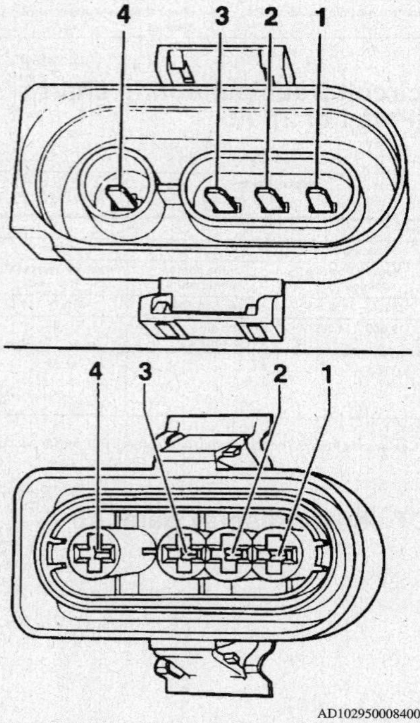

AD1029500084000X

Fig. 48 Oxygen sensor 4-pin connector

	Display fields			
	1	2	3	4
Display group 32: Oxygen Sensor (O2S) control learning values (before TWC)				
Display	xx.x %	xx.x %	xx.x %	xx.x %
Indicates	O2S control learning value at idle (additive) (before TWC) Bank 1, Sensor 1	O2S control learning value at **part load** (multiplicative) (before TWC) Bank 1, Sensor 1	O2S control learning value at idle (additive) (before TWC) Bank 2, Sensor 1	O2S control learning value at **part load** (multiplicative) (before TWC) Bank 2, Sensor 1
Range	−25.0 to +25.0 %	−25.0 to +25.0 %	−25.0 to +25.0 %	−25.0 to +25.0 %
Specified value	−10.0 to +10.0 % (can vary slightly)	−10.0 to +10.0 % (can vary slightly)	−10.0 to +10.0 % (can vary slightly)	−10.0 to +10.0 % (can vary slightly)

AD1029800122000X

Fig. 49 Front oxygen sensor display values. A6

Display group: 32 / **Display fields: 1–4**	**Possible malfunction cause**	**Corrective action**
O2S control learning value: −25.0 to −10.0 %	• Engine oil dilution (when partial load learning value is normal ⇒ **display fields 2 and 4**)	– Change engine oil, or carry out extensive road test and check again
	• Fuel pressure too high	– Check fuel pressure regulator
	• Fuel injector leaking	– Check fuel injectors
	• Oxygen Sensor (O2S) heater malfunction	– Check O2S heater
O2S control learning value: 10.0 to 25.0 %	• Intake air leaks ("false air") or exhaust manifold leaks (when partial load learning value is normal ⇒ **display fields 2 and 4**)	– Check intake air system for leaks – Check exhaust system for leaks
	• Fuel pressure too low	– Check fuel pressure regulator
	• Oxygen Sensor (O2S) heater malfunction	– Check O2S heater
	• Fuel injector does not open, or partially opens	– Check fuel injectors
O2S control learning value: constant 0.0 %	• Oxygen sensor control learning not active	– Check Mass Air Flow (MAF) sensor -G70-

AD1029800124000X

Fig. 50 Evaluation of display group 32. A6

	Display fields			
	1	2	3	4
Display group 33: Oxygen Sensor (O2S) control (before TWC)				
Display	xx.x %	x.xxx V	xx.x %	x.xxx V
Indicates	O2S control Bank 1, Sensor 1 (before TWC)	O2S voltage Bank 1, Sensor 1 (before TWC)	O2S control Bank 2, Sensor 1 (before TWC)	O2S voltage Bank 2, Sensor 1 (before TWC)
Range	−25.0 to +25.0 %	0.000 to 1.000 V	−25.0 to +25.0 %	0.000 to 1.000 V
Specified value	−10.0 to +10.0 % value must change by at least 2 %	0.000 to 1.000 V value must fluctuate at least 30 times per minute, and change by at least 0.3 volts	−10.0 to +10.0 % value must change by at least 2 %	0.000 to 1.000 V value must fluctuate at least 30 times per minute, and change by at least 0.3 volts

AD1029800123000X

Fig. 51 Front oxygen sensor control values. A6

Display group: 33 Display fields: 2, 4	Possible malfunction cause	Corrective action
approx. 0.435 V	• Open circuit in wiring between HO2S connector terminal 4 and ECM	– Check reference voltage
approx. 0.435 V	• Open circuit in wiring between HO2S connector terminal 3 and ECM	
approx. 1.086 V	• Short circuit to positive (B+) between HO2S connector terminal 4 and ECM	– Check HO2S wiring, bank 1, sensor 1 – Check HO2S wiring, bank 2, sensor 1
approx. 0.000 V	• Short circuit to Ground between HO2S connector terminal 4 and ECM	

AD1029800125000X

Fig. 52 Evaluation of display group 33. A6

	Display fields 1	2	3	4
Display group 40: Oxygen Sensor (O2S) heating (before and after TWC)				
Display	xx.x Ω	Htg.bC.ON/Htg.bC.OFF	xx.x Ω	Htg.aC.ON/Htg.aC.OFF
Indicates	Resistance of O2S heater (before TWC) (B1-S1 and B2-S1)	O2S heater ON *or* O2S heater OFF (before TWC) (B1-S1 and B2-S1)	Resistance of O2S heater (after TWC) (B1-S2 and B2-S2)	O2S heater ON *or* O2S heater OFF (after TWC) (B1-S2 and B2-S2)
Range	0.0 – 65.0 Ω	---	---	---
Specified value	2.4 – 9.2 Ω	Htg.bC.ON	---	---
			---	---

AD1029800126000X

Fig. 53 Oxygen sensor heater display data. A6

	Display fields 1	2	3	4
Display group 36: Heated Oxygen Sensor (HO2S) behind Three Way Catalytic Converter (TWC), Banks 1, 2				
Display	x.xxx V	Test OFF/Test ON B1-S2 ok B1-S2 n.ok	x.xxx V	Test OFF/Test ON B2-S2 ok B2-S2 n.ok
Indicates	Voltage supply to HO2S behind TWC (Bank 1, Sensor 2)	Diagnostic status Diagnostic result	Voltage supply to HO2S 2 behind TWC (Bank 2, Sensor 2)	Diagnostic status Diagnostic result
Range	0.000 – 1.000 V	---	0.000 – 1.000 V	---
Specified value	0.000 – 1.000 V (can oscillate slightly)	B1-S2 OK	0.000 – 1.000 V (can oscillate slightly)	B2-S2 OK

AD1029800127000X

Fig. 54 Rear oxygen sensor display data. A6

Display group: 36 Display fields: 1, 3	Possible malfunction cause	Corrective action
approx. 0.435 V	• Open circuit in wire 4 between oxygen sensor and ECM	– Check reference voltage
approx. 0.440 V	• Open circuit in wire 3 between oxygen sensor and ECM	
approx. 1.085 V	• Short circuit to B+ in wire 4 between oxygen sensor and ECM	– Check **O2S** wiring, bank 1, sensor 2 – Check **O2S** wiring, bank 2, sensor 2
approx. 0.000 V	• Short circuit to Ground in wire 4 between oxygen sensor and ECM	

AD1029800128000X

Fig. 55 Evaluation of display group 36. A6

	Display fields 1	2	3	4
Display group 40: Oxygen Sensor (O2S) heating (before and after TWC)				
Display	xx.x Ω	Htg.bC.ON/Htg.bC.OFF	xx.x Ω	Htg.aC.ON/Htg.aC.OFF
Indicates	Resistance of O2S heater (before TWC) (B1-S1 and B2-S1)	O2S heater ON *or* O2S heater OFF (before TWC) (B1-S1 and B2-S1)	Resistance of O2S heater (after TWC) (B1-S2 and B2-S2)	O2S heater ON *or* O2S heater OFF (after TWC) (B1-S2 and B2-S2)
Range	---	---	0.0 – 65.0 Ω	---
Specified value	---	---	2.4 – 9.2 Ω	Htg.aC.ON
	---	---	If not as specified	

AD1029800129000X

Fig. 56 Rear oxygen sensor display values. A6

	Display fields 1	2	3	4
Display group 5: Engine electronics				
Display	xxx RPM	xx.xx ms	xxx km/h	Idle Part throt Full throt Decel Enrich
Indicates	Engine speed (in 40 RPM steps)	Engine load	Vehicle speed	Operational condition
Range	0 – 6800 RPM	0.00 – 12.75 ms	---	---
Specified value	600 – 760 RPM (all-wheel drive) 680 – 840 RPM (front-wheel drive)	1.00 – 2.50 ms	0 km/h	Throttle closed: "Idle" Throttle slightly open: "Part throt"
	---	---	---	

AD1029800138000X

Fig. 57 Engine electronics data. A6

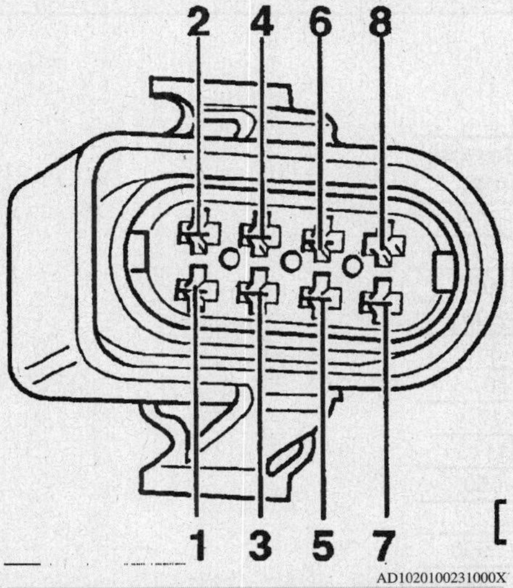

AD1020100231000X

Fig. 58 Throttle valve control module connector pin identification

	Display fields 1	2	3	4
Display group 3: Load measurement				
Display	xxx RPM	xx.x g/s	xxx ∠°	xx.x ° BTDC
Indicates	Engine speed (in 40 RPM steps)	Mass air flow	Throttle angle	Ignition timing
Range	0-6800 RPM	---	0-90 ∠°	0.0°-50.0° BTDC
Specified value	0 RPM	---	0-5 ∠°	0.0°
	---	---	---	---

AD1020100232000X

Fig. 59 Load measurement values. A6

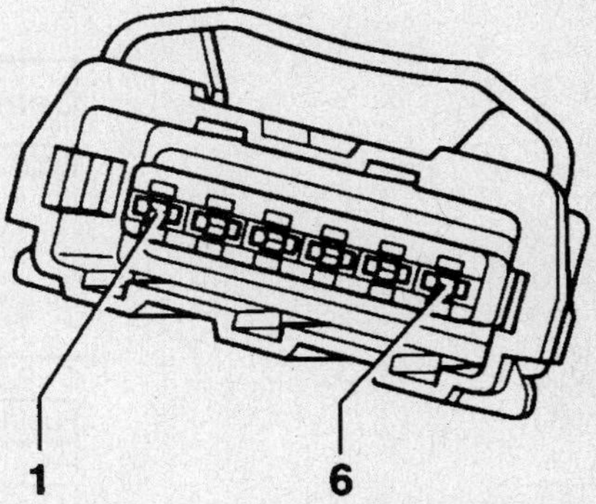

AD1029500077000X

Fig. 60 CTP switch harness connector pin locations. A4, Cabriolet & S4

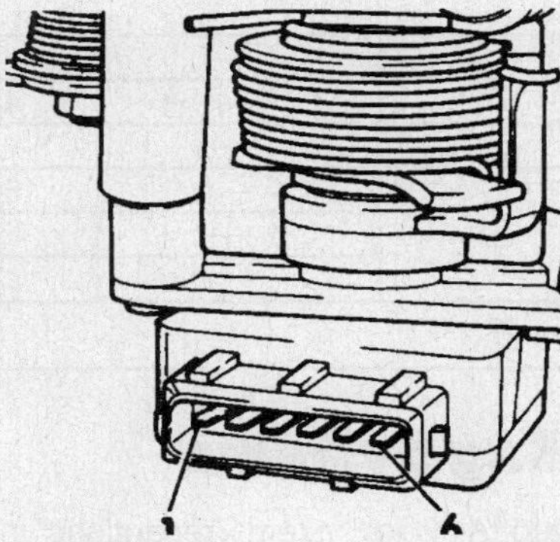

AD1029500076000X

Fig. 61 CTP switch connector pin locations. A4, Cabriolet & S4

3.7L & 4.2L Engines

NOTE: On Air Bag Equipped Models, Refer To "Air Bag System Precautions" Located In The Front Of This Manual For System Disarming & Arming Procedures.

NOTE: If Unsure Of System Used On Vehicle Being Serviced, Refer To Engine Systems Identification Chart Located At Beginning Of This Chapter.

NOTE: Prior To Performing Any Service Operations Listed In This Section Consult "Technical Service Bulletins Section" For Related Information.

NOTE: "Electrical Symbol & Wire Color Code Identification" Located In The Front Of This Manual May Be Used As An Aid When Using Wiring Circuits Found In This Section.

INDEX

	Page No.
Description	10-115
Diagnosis & Testing	10-115
Accessing Diagnostic Trouble Codes	10-115
Clearing Diagnostic Trouble Codes	10-120
Component & System Tests	10-115
Closed Throttle Position (CTP) Switch	10-119
Crankshaft Position (CKP) Sensor	10-117
Engine Coolant Temperature (ECT) Sensor	10-117
Front Heated Oxygen Sensor	10-118
Fuel Injector	10-117
Fuel Pressure	10-116
Fuel Pump Relay	10-115
Idle Air Control (IAC) Valve	10-118
Mass Air Flow (MAF) Sensor	10-116
Rear Heated Oxygen Sensor	10-119
Throttle Position (TP) Sensor	10-120
Diagnostic Tests	10-115
Diagnostic Trouble Code Interpretation	10-115
Wiring Diagrams	10-115
Diagnostic Chart Index	10-122
Precautions	10-114
Air Bag Systems	10-114
Audio Coded Anti-Theft System	10-115
Battery Ground Cable	10-115
Electrical Connection & Terminal Repair	10-115
Fuel System	10-114
Sensor & Fuel Injector Specifications	10-114
System Service	10-127

SENSOR & FUEL INJECTOR SPECIFICATIONS

Component	Temperature, °F	Resistance, Ohms
ECT	68	2000–3000
	86	1500–2000
	132	900–1000
	158	400–500
	194	200–300
CKP Sensor	—	1000
Fuel Injector	—	15–17
IAC	—	7–11
IAT Sensor	—	450–650
Oxygen Sensor①	—	10
Throttle Position	—	1500–2500
	—	750–1300
	—	3600

① — Terminals 1 and 2.

PRECAUTIONS

Fuel System

Always clean fuel lines before loosening and be sure to replace seals and fuel hose clamps. Keep a fully charged fire extinguisher readily available.

Air Bag Systems

Refer to "Air Bag System Precautions" in the front of this manual for system disarming and arming procedures.

Battery Ground Cable

Prior to service, disconnect battery ground cable and isolate as required.

Audio Coded Anti-Theft System

Do not use computer memory saver tool. Using the tool will keep the air bag system charged and may cause accidental activation of the air bag unit.

After two improper attempts at entering security code, radio will lock up electronically. The display shows SAFE and will not change. To unlock, leave radio On for approximately 1 hour up to 48 hours, then enter code as it would be after a power disconnection.

1. Obtain radio code from vehicle operator.
2. Switch radio On. Radio should display SAFE.
3. Push and hold AM/FM and SCAN buttons until 1000 remains on display. **If AM/FM and SCAN buttons are held down too long or pushed again, the radio will misinterpret the 1000 as an attempt at coding and one improper coding attempt will be logged.**
4. Enter radio code using first four program station buttons. Security code will appear on display.
5. Starting with lefthand button, tap button until first digit is displayed. Move to next button and repeat procedure.
6. Push and hold AM/FM and SCAN buttons once again until display changes to SAFE.
7. Release AM/FM and SCAN buttons. Radio display will change to a radio station frequency and will now play.

Electrical Connection & Terminal Repair

If connector terminal or pin replacement is required, use only gold-plated components.

DESCRIPTION

Diagnostic Trouble Codes (DTCs) are stored in a permanent fault memory until intentionally erased.

This system also recognizes sporadic (intermittent) faults. If a fault is present for a sufficient time it is stored as a static fault. If a condition appears momentarily or of insufficient time to be classified as static, it will be stored in a portion of fault memory where it will receive different attention than a static fault. If within next 50 engine starts fault no longer appears, then fault will be automatically erased.

Faults which affect exhaust or emission requirements will be displayed by engine warning lamp (On Board Diagnostics, OBD) on instrument panel.

Code	Description
P0102	MAF Or Volume Air Flow Circuit Low Input
P0103	MAF Circuit High Input
P0112	IAT Circuit Low Input
P0113	IAT Circuit High Input
P0116	ECT Circuit Fault
P0117	ECT Circuit Low Input
P0118	ECT Circuit High Input
P0121	Throttle/Pedal Position Sensor Circuit Fault
P0122	Throttle/Pedal Position Sensor Circuit Low Input
P0123	Throttle/Pedal Position Sensor Circuit High Input
P0130	Oxygen Sensor Bank 1 Sensor 1 Fault
P0131	Oxygen Sensor Bank 1 Sensor 1 Low Voltage
P0132	Oxygen Sensor Bank 1 Sensor 1 High Voltage
P0133	Oxygen Sensor Bank 1 Sensor 1 Slow Response
P0134	Oxygen Sensor Bank 1 Sensor 1 No Activity Detected
P0136	Oxygen Sensor Bank 1 Sensor 2 Fault
P0137	Oxygen Sensor Bank 1 Sensor 2 Low Voltage
P0138	Oxygen Sensor Bank 1 Sensor 2 High Voltage
P0140	Oxygen Sensor Bank 1 Sensor 2 No Activity Detected
P0150	Oxygen Sensor Bank 2 Sensor 1 Fault
P0151	Oxygen Sensor Bank 2 Sensor 1 Low Voltage
P0152	Oxygen Sensor Bank 2 Sensor 1 High Voltage
P0153	Oxygen Sensor Bank 2 Sensor 1 Slow Response
P0154	Oxygen Sensor Bank 2 Sensor 1 No Activity Detected
P0156	Oxygen Sensor Bank 2 Sensor 2 Fault
P0157	Oxygen Sensor Bank 2 Sensor 2 Low Voltage
P0158	Oxygen Sensor Bank 2 Sensor 2 High Voltage
P0160	Oxygen Sensor Bank 2 Sensor 2 No Activity Detected
P0300	Random Misfire Detected
P0301	Cylinder 1 Misfire Detected

Fig. 1 Diagnostic Trouble Code (DTC) Interpretation (Part 1 of 4)

DIAGNOSIS & TESTING

Accessing Diagnostic Trouble Codes

Connect a suitable scan tool to the Data Link Connector (DLC) located under the lefthand side of the instrument panel.

Diagnostic Trouble Code Interpretation

Refer to **Fig. 1** for Diagnostic Trouble Code (DTC) interpretation.

Wiring Diagrams

Refer to **Fig. 2** for system wiring diagram.

Diagnostic Tests

Refer to **Figs. 3 through 18** for diagnostic trouble code interpretation. Refer to "Diagnostic Chart Index" for code definitions and specific diagnostic test for diagnosis procedures.

Component & System Tests

For component locations, refer to "Engine Compartment Reference Diagrams" to aid in location during diagnosis and testing procedures.

FUEL PUMP RELAY

The fuel pump relay is located on the central electrical panel in the righthand side footwell in relay position 6.

1. Remove fuel pump relay.
2. Turn ignition On.
3. Measure voltage with a suitable voltmeter between terminals 28 and 34, then 32 and 34. Voltmeter should read battery voltage.
4. If voltage is not as specified, repair wiring as required.
5. If voltage is satisfactory, proceed as follows to inspect fuel pump relay:
   a. Measure voltage between relay socket terminals 28 and 29 using LED voltage tester tool No. VAG 1527B, or equivalent.
   b. Turn ignition On. LED should light for one second, then go out. LED may dimly light after one second.
   c. Crank engine and observe LED.
   d. LED should light continuously while engine is cranked.

6. If LED does not light, connect test box tool No. VAG 1598/19 or equivalent to ECM harness connector.
7. Inspect for continuity between relay socket pin 29 and test box pin A4 using a suitable ohmmeter. If no continuity is present, repair wiring as required.
8. If wiring is satisfactory and LED does not light, replace ECM and generate new readiness code.
9. If wiring is satisfactory, proceed as follows:
   a. Remove cover for fuse panel at righthand A-pillar, **Fig. 19.**
   b. Connect LED voltage tester tool No. VAG 1527B, or equivalent between both terminals of fuse 1 and ground, then fuse 3 and ground.
   c. Crank engine for 3 seconds.
   d. Fuel pump relay should be actuated and LED should light up.
10. If LED does not light, proceed as follows:
   a. Remove fuel pump relay.
   b. Measure resistance between relay socket pin 30 and fuse 1 using a suitable ohmmeter, then between fuse 3 and relay socket pin 31.
   c. If no open circuit exists, replace fuel pump relay.

FUEL PRESSURE

1. Ensure fuel pump relay operation is satisfactory, fuel filter is in perfect condition and battery is fully charged.
2. Connect fuel pressure tester tool No. VAG 1318, or equivalent between fuel supply line and fuel manifold with lever in Open position.
3. Disconnect fuel pressure regulator to intake manifold vacuum hose at regulator and plug.
4. Start engine and allow to idle.
5. Fuel pressure should be 61 psi.
6. Turn ignition Off.
7. Inspect for residual pressure by monitoring decrease in pressure. After 10 minutes, pressure should read at least 44 psi.
8. If residual pressure is not as specified, proceed as follows:
   a. Start engine and allow pressure to rise.
   b. Stop engine and close valve on fuel pressure gauge.
   c. If pressure holds, inspect fuel pressure regulator, fuel injectors and connection between pressure gauge and regulator.
   d. If pressure drops, inspect pressure gauge connection, fuel supply line and fuel pump check valve.

MASS AIR FLOW (MAF) SENSOR

Functional Inspection

1. Connect scan tool No. VAG 1552, then press buttons 0 and 1 to insert "Engine Electronics" address word 01. Engine should be running at idle.
2. Press buttons 0 and 8 to select "Read Measuring Value Block" function 08, then press "Q" to confirm input.
3. Press buttons 0, 0 and 7 to input Display Group 7, then press "Q" to confirm input.
4. Compare scan tool display with **Fig. 20.**
5. If displayed values are satisfactory, proceed to "Supply Voltage Inspection" and "Signal Wiring Inspection."
6. If displayed values are not satisfactory, inspect air intake system for leaks. If no leaks are present, proceed as follows:
   a. Proceed to "Supply Voltage Inspection."
   b. Press right arrow button to advance program sequence.
   c. Press buttons 0 and 6 to select "End Output" function 06, then press "Q" to confirm input.

Code	Description
P0302	Cylinder 2 Misfire Detected
P0303	Cylinder 3 Misfire Detected
P0304	Cylinder 4 Misfire Detected
P0305	Cylinder 5 Misfire Detected
P0306	Cylinder 6 Misfire Detected
P0307	Cylinder 7 Misfire Detected
P0308	Cylinder 8 Misfire Detected
P0321	Engine Speed Sensor Input Circuit Fault
P0322	Engine Speed Sensor No Signal
P0327	Knock Sensor 1 Circuit Low Input
P0328	Knock Sensor 1 Circuit High Input
P0332	Knock Sensor 2 Circuit Low Input
P0333	Knock Sensor 2 Circuit High Input
P0422	Main Catalyst Bank 1 Efficiency Below Threshold
P0432	Main Catalyst Bank 2 Efficiency Below Threshold
P0441	EVAP System Improper Purge Flow Fault
P0501	Vehicle Speed Sensor Fault
P0560	System Voltage Fault
P0562	System Voltage Low
P0563	System Voltage High
P0601	Internal Control Module Memory Check Sum Error
P0604	Internal Control Module Random Access Memory Error
P1102	Oxygen Sensor Heating Circuit Bank 1 Sensor 1 Short To Power
P1105	Oxygen Sensor Heating Circuit Bank 1 Sensor 2 Short To Power
P1107	Oxygen Sensor Heating Circuit Bank 2 Sensor 1 Short To Power
P1110	Oxygen Sensor Heating Circuit Bank 2 Sensor 2 Short To Power
P1127	Long Term Fuel Trim Bank 1 System Too Rich
P1128	Long Term Fuel Trim Bank 1 System Too Lean
P1129	Long Term Fuel Trim Bank 2 System Too Rich

Fig. 1 Diagnostic Trouble Code (DTC) Interpretation (Part 2 of 4)

Supply Voltage Inspection

1. Inspect MAF sensor fuse. Service as required.
2. Remove upper air cleaner housing.
3. Disconnect MAF sensor.
4. Connect LED voltage tester tool No. VAG 1527B, or equivalent between harness connector terminal 3 and engine ground.
5. Crank engine and ensure LED lights.
6. If LED does not light up, inspect wiring for open or short to ground between connector terminal 3 and fuse.
7. If fuses and wiring are satisfactory but LED does not light, refer to "Fuel Pump Relay."
8. If voltage supply is satisfactory, connect test box tool No. VAG 1598/19 or equivalent to ECM harness connector.
9. Inspect MAF connector terminal 1 and test box terminal E7 for open or short using a suitable volt/ohmmeter. Repair as required.
10. If supply voltage inspection is satisfactory, perform "Signal Wiring Inspection."

Signal Wiring Inspection

1. Connect test box tool No. VAG 1598/19, or equivalent to ECM harness connector.
2. Inspect the following terminals for open or short using a suitable volt/ohmmeter: MAF connector terminal 2 to test box pin B18; MAF terminal 4 to test box pin B19. Repair as required.
3. If wiring and connections are satisfactory, inspect intake system for leaks. If no leaks present, replace MAF sensor and generate new readiness code.

ENGINE COOLANT TEMPERATURE (ECT) SENSOR

Functional Test

1. Connect scan tool No. VAG 1551/1552, or equivalent, then press buttons 0 and 1 to insert "Engine Electronics" address word 01. Engine should be running at idle.
2. Press buttons 0 and 8 to select "Read Measuring Value Block" function 08, then press "Q" to confirm input.
3. Press buttons 0, 0 and 3 to input Display Group 3, then press "Q" to confirm input.
4. Compare scan tool data with ECT sensor data in **Fig. 21.**
5. Press right arrow button to advance program.
6. Press buttons 0 and 6 to select "End Output" function 06, then press "Q" to confirm input.
7. If scan tool display does not agree with **Fig. 21,** perform ECT wiring inspection.

Wiring Inspection

1. Disconnect ECT sensor.
2. Measure resistance of ECT sensor using a suitable ohmmeter. If resistance is not within specifications, replace ECT sensor and retest system.
3. If ECT sensor resistance is satisfactory, connect test box tool No. VAG 1598/19, or equivalent to ECM harness connector.
4. Inspect the following pins for open, short to power or short to ground using a suitable volt/ohmmeter: ECT connector terminal 1 to test box terminal A23; connector terminal 2 to test box pin A19. Service wiring as required.
5. If wiring and sensor tests are satisfactory, replace ECM and generate new readiness code.

CRANKSHAFT POSITION (CKP) SENSOR

Before performing the following diagnostic procedures, ensure sensor attaching bolts are tight and that no metal shavings are present on sensor or sensor wheel.

1. Disconnect CKP sensor.
2. Measure resistance between CKP sensor terminals 1 and 2 using a suitable ohmmeter. Resistance should be 500–2000 ohms.
3. If resistance is not as specified, replace sensor and retest system.
4. If sensor resistance is as specified, inspect sensor for short as follows:
   a. Measure resistance of CKP sensor terminals 1 and 3 using a suitable ohmmeter, then terminals 2 and 3.
   b. Ohmmeter should read open circuit.
   c. If ohmmeter does not read open circuit, replace CKP sensor.
5. If sensor inspection is satisfactory, proceed as follows to inspect sensor harness.
   a. Connect test box tool No. VAG 1598/19, or equivalent to ECM harness connector.
   b. Inspect the following connector terminals and test box pins for open or short circuits using a suitable volt/ohmmeter: connector terminal 1 to test box pin A18; connector terminal 2 to test box pin A17; connector terminal 3 to test box pin D11.
   c. If no open or short circuit exists, replace ECM and generate new readiness code.

Code	Description
P1130	Long Term Fuel Trim Bank 1 System Too Lean
P1136	Long Term Fuel Trim Bank 1 System Too Lean
P1137	Long Term Fuel Trim Bank 1 System Too Rich
P1138	Long Term Fuel Trim Bank 2 System Too Lean
P1139	Long Term Fuel Trim Bank 2 System Too Rich
P1141	Load Calculation Cross Check Range/Performance Fault
P1176	Oxygen Sensor Correction Behind Catalyst B1 Limit Attained
P1177	Oxygen Sensor Correction Behind Catalyst B2 Limit Attained
P1196	Oxygen Sensor Heater Circuit Bank 1 Sensor 1 Electrical Fault
P1197	Oxygen Sensor Heater Circuit Bank 2 Sensor 1 Electrical Fault
P1198	Oxygen Sensor Heater Circuit Bank 1 Sensor 2 Electrical Fault
P1199	Oxygen Sensor Heater Circuit Bank 2 Sensor 2 Electrical Fault
P1201	Cylinder 1 Fuel Injector Circuit Fault
P1202	Cylinder 2 Fuel Injector Circuit Fault
P1203	Cylinder 3 Fuel Injector Circuit Fault
P1204	Cylinder 4 Fuel Injector Circuit Fault
P1205	Cylinder 5 Fuel Injector Circuit Fault
P1206	Cylinder 6 Fuel Injector Circuit Fault
P1207	Cylinder 7 Fuel Injector Circuit Fault
P1208	Cylinder 8 Fuel Injector Circuit Fault
P1213	Cylinder 1 Fuel Injector Short To Power
P1214	Cylinder 2 Fuel Injector Short To Power
P1215	Cylinder 3 Fuel Injector Short To Power
P1216	Cylinder 4 Fuel Injector Short To Power
P1217	Cylinder 5 Fuel Injector Short To Power
P1218	Cylinder 6 Fuel Injector Short To Power
P1219	Cylinder 7 Fuel Injector Short To Power
P1220	Cylinder 8 Fuel Injector Short To Power
P1250	Fuel Level Too Low
P1280	Fuel Injector Air Control Valve Flow Too Low
P1283	Fuel Injector Air Control Valve Circuit Electrical Fault
P1286	Fuel Injector Air Control Valve Circuit Short To Power
P1325	Cylinder 1 Knock Control Limit Attained

Fig. 1 Diagnostic Trouble Code (DTC) Interpretation (Part 3 of 4)

FUEL INJECTOR

Resistance Inspection

1. Disconnect injector harness connector.
2. Measure fuel injector resistance.
3. Compare resistance with specifications listed in "Fuel Injector & Sensor Specifications."
4. If resistance is not within specifications, replace injector.
5. If wiring or connector repairs are required, refer to "Precautions."

ECM Signal

1. Disconnect fuel injector electrical connectors.
2. Connect LED voltage tester tool No. VAG 1527BB, or equivalent between connector terminals using adapter cable tool No. VW1594, or equivalent.
3. Crank engine and inspect for LED operation.
4. Repeat test for remaining cylinders.
5. If LED does not light, inspect wiring between fuel injector and ECM for open or short using a suitable volt/ohmmeter.

IDLE AIR CONTROL (IAC) VALVE

Electrical Inspection

1. Disconnect Idle Air Control (IAC) valve harness connector.
2. Measure IAC valve resistance. At room temperature, resistance is lower, while at operating temperature it is higher.
3. If resistance is not 7–11 ohms, replace IAC valve.
4. If wiring or connector repairs are required, refer to "Precautions."

Mechanical Inspection

1. Remove IAC valve from engine, leaving electrical connector attached.
2. Visually inspect rotary slide valve for scoring, binding or rubbing. **When inspecting valve travel, do not move rotary slide valve with screwdriver or other tool.**
3. Connect a suitable scan tool to the Diagnostic Link Connector.
4. Select Output Diagnosis Test Mode (DTM), as outlined under "Computerized Engine Controls," then activate IAC.
5. During output inspect step when valve is being triggered, ensure valve is operating properly from stop to stop.
6. If scoring impairs fee movement, rotary slide valve binds, runs slowly or will not travel to both stops, replace IAC valve.
7. If wiring or connector repairs are required, refer to "Precautions."

Code	Description
P1326	Cylinder 2 Knock Control Limit Attained
P1327	Cylinder 3 Knock Control Limit Attained
P1328	Cylinder 4 Knock Control Limit Attained
P1329	Cylinder 5 Knock Control Limit Attained
P1330	Cylinder 6 Knock Control Limit Attained
P1331	Cylinder 7 Knock Control Limit Attained
P1332	Cylinder 8 Knock Control Limit Attained
P1386	Internal Control Module Knock Control Error
P1391	Camshaft Position Sensor Bank 2 Short To Ground
P1392	Camshaft Position Sensor Bank 2 Short To Power
P1409	Tank Ventilation Valve Circuit Electrical Fault
P1410	Tank Ventilation Valve Short To Power
P1500	Fuel Pump Relay Electrical Fault
P1502	Fuel Pump Relay Short To Power
P1505	Closed Throttle Position Switch Does Not Close/Open Circuit
P1506	Closed Throttle Position Switch Does Not Open/Short To Ground
P1507	Idle System Learned Value Lower Limit Attained
P1508	Idle System Learned Value Upper Limit Attained
P1509	Idle Air Control Circuit Electrical Fault
P1510	Idle Air Control Circuit Short To Power
P1511	Intake Manifold Changeover Valve Circuit Electrical Fault
P1512	Intake Manifold Changeover Valve Circuit Short To Power
P1517	Main Relay Circuit Electrical Circuit Fault
P1518	Main Relay Circuit Short To Power
P1560	Maximum Engine Speed Exceeded
P1602	Power Supply Terminal 30 Low Voltage
P1606	Rough Road Spec Engine Torque ABS-ECU Electrical Fault
P1612	ECM Improper Coding
P1624	MIL Request Sign Active
P1625	CAN-Bus Implausible Message From Transmission Controller
P1640	Internal Control Module EEPROM Error
P1690	MIL Fault
P1693	MIL Short To Power

Fig. 1 Diagnostic Trouble Code (DTC) Interpretation (Part 4 of 4)

FRONT HEATED OXYGEN SENSOR

Functional Inspection

1. Ensure oxygen sensor is installed properly and exhaust system has no leaks.
2. Connect scan tool No. VAG 1552, or equivalent, then press buttons 0 and 1 to insert "Engine Electronics" address word 01 with engine running at idle.
3. Press buttons 0 and 8 to select "Read Measuring Value Block" function 08, then press "Q" to confirm input.
4. Press buttons 0, 0 and 3 to input Display Group 3, then press "Q" to confirm input.
5. Compare scan tool values with engine idle data in **Fig. 22.**
6. Press "C" button of scan tool, then press buttons 0, 2 and 6 to input Display Group 26. Press "Q" to confirm input.
7. Compare scan tool display with oxygen sensor display in **Fig. 23.**
8. If oxygen sensor no voltage condition, heating or wiring fault exist, refer to appropriate test.
9. If voltage is a constant 450 mV, refer to "Front Heated Oxygen Sensor Heater Inspection."

Heater Inspection

1. Connect scan tool No. VAG 1551, or equivalent, then press buttons 0 and 1 to insert "Engine Electronics" address word 01 with engine running at idle.
2. Press buttons 0 and 8 to select "Read Measuring Value Block" function 08, then press "Q" to confirm input.
3. Press buttons 0, 2 and 8 to input Display Group 28, then press "Q" to confirm input.
4. Compare scan tool data with oxygen sensor heater data, **Fig. 24.**
5. Press right arrow button to advance program.
6. Press buttons 0 and 6 to select "End Output" function 06, then press "Q" to confirm input.
7. If fault condition is not indicated, intermittent fault may be present.
8. If fault condition is indicated, disconnect oxygen sensor and measure resistance between sensor terminals 1 and 2 using a suitable ohmmeter.
9. If resistance is not within specifications, replace oxygen sensor.
10. If resistance is within specifications, proceed as follows:
    a. Inspect oxygen sensor fuses and repair as required.
    b. Connect test box tool No. 1598/19, or equivalent to ECM harness connector.
    c. Inspect for open or short circuit from lefthand oxygen sensor harness connector terminal 2 to test box pin E8 using a suitable volt/ohmmeter, then from righthand oxygen sensor harness connector terminal 2 to test box pin E4.
    d. If heater inspection is satisfactory, replace ECM.

Voltage & Wiring Inspection

1. Disconnect oxygen sensor.
2. Connect a suitable voltmeter between oxygen sensor harness connector terminals 3 and 4.
3. Turn ignition On.
4. Voltage should be 400–500 mV.
5. If voltage is not as specified, proceed as follows:
    a. Connect test box tool No. 1598/19, or equivalent to ECM harness connector.
    b. Inspect following circuits for open or short circuits using a suitable

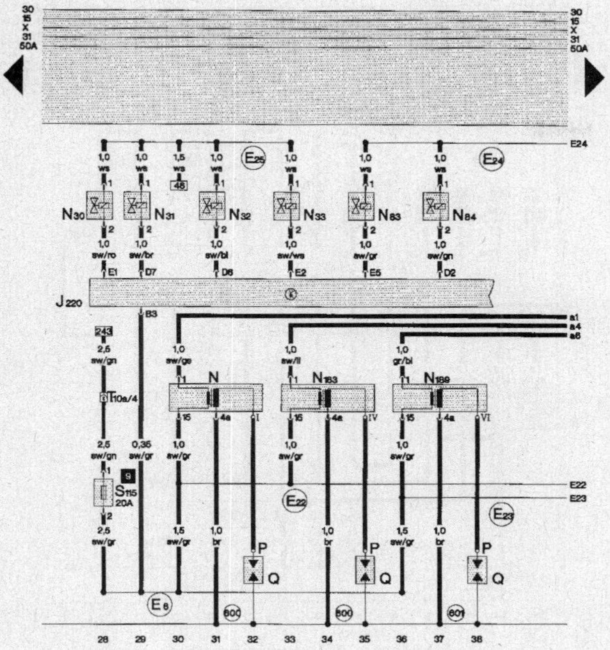

J 220 - Motronic Engine Control Module (ECM)
N - Ignition Coil
N 30 - Cylinder 1 Fuel Injector
N 31 - Cylinder 2 Fuel Injector
N 32 - Cylinder 3 Fuel Injector
N 33 - Cylinder 4 Fuel Injector
N 83 - Cylinder 5 Fuel Injector
N 84 - Cylinder 6 Fuel Injector
N 163 - Ignition Coil 4
N 189 - Ignition Coil 6
P - Spark Plug Connectors
Q - Spark Plugs
S 115 - Fuse for ignition coil terminal 15
T 10 a - 10-Pin Connector, black, connector station electronic box plenum chamber

(800) - Ground Point on cylinder head, right
(801) - Ground Point on cylinder head, left
(E6) - Plus connection -1- (15), in Motronic Multiport Fuel Injection (MFI) wiring harness
(E22) - Connector (15 ignition right), in wiring harness Motronic
(E23) - Connector (15 ignition left), in wiring harness Motronic
(E24) - Connector (87a intervalve left), in wiring harness Motronic
(E25) - Connector (87a intervalve right), in wiring harness Motronic

AD1029800099010X

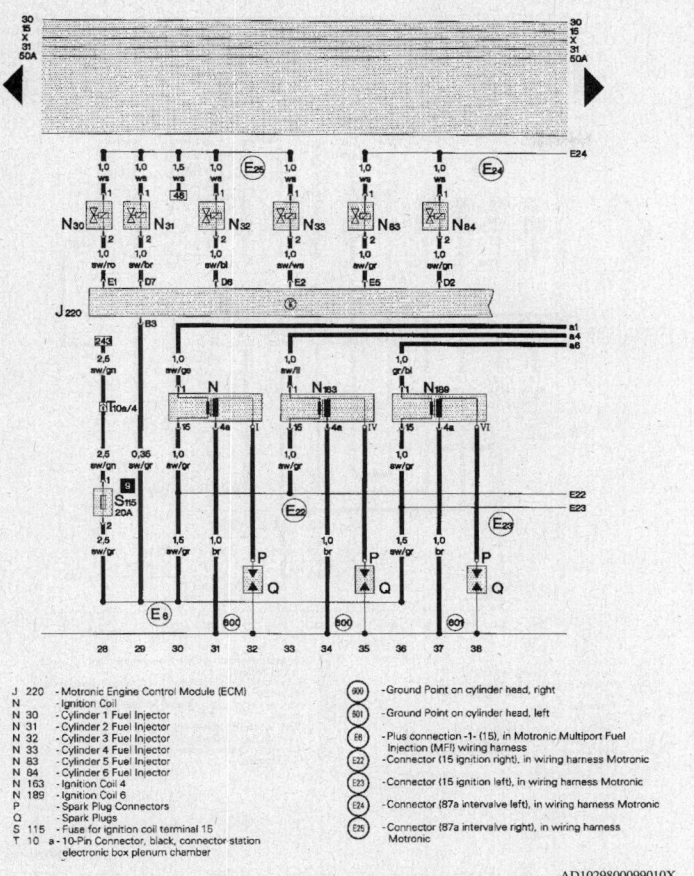

Fig. 2 MFI system diagram (Part 1 of 8)

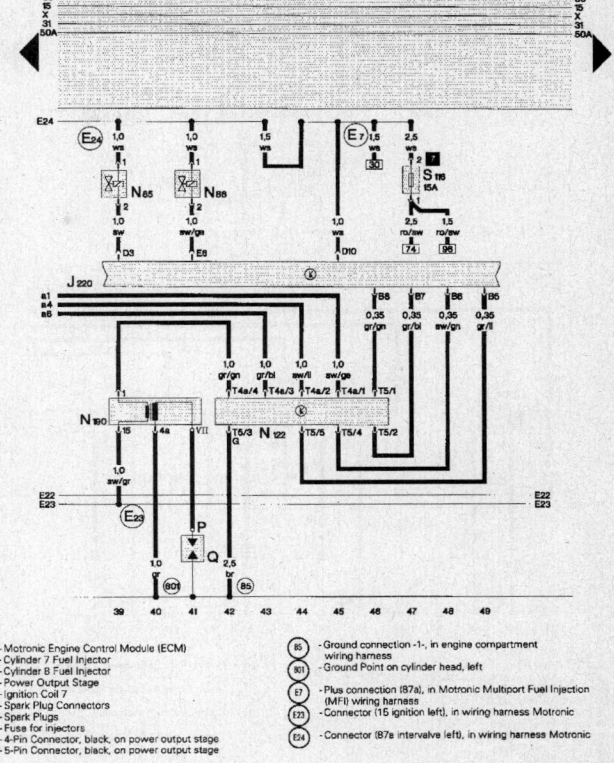

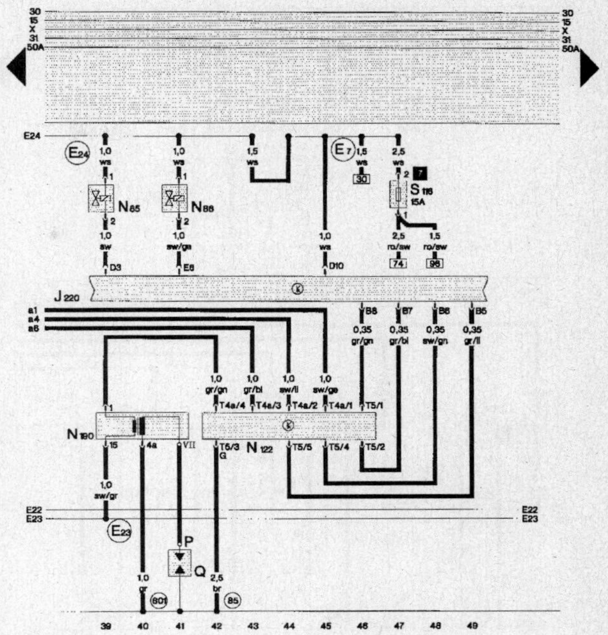

J 220 - Motronic Engine Control Module (ECM)
N 85 - Cylinder 7 Fuel Injector
N 86 - Cylinder 8 Fuel Injector
N 122 - Power Output Stage
N 190 - Ignition Coil 7
P - Spark Plug Connectors
Q - Spark Plugs
S 116 - Fuse for injectors
T 4 a - 4-Pin Connector, black, on power output stage
T 5 - 5-Pin Connector, black, on power output stage

(85) - Ground connection -1-, in engine compartment wiring harness
(801) - Ground Point on cylinder head, left
(E7) - Plus connection (87a), in Motronic Multiport Fuel Injection (MFI) wiring harness
(E23) - Connector (15 ignition left), in wiring harness Motronic
(E24) - Connector (87a intervalve left), in wiring harness Motronic

AD1029800099020X

Fig. 2 MFI system diagram (Part 2 of 8)

volt/ohmmeter: righthand oxygen sensor connector terminal 3 to test box pin B20 and connector terminal 4 to test box pin B24; lefthand oxygen sensor connector terminal 3 to test box pin B21 and connector terminal 4 to test box pin B23.

6. If wiring is satisfactory, replace ECM.

REAR HEATED OXYGEN SENSOR

Functional Inspection

1. Ensure oxygen sensor is installed properly and exhaust system is free from leaks.
2. Connect scan tool No. VAG 1552, or equivalent, then press buttons 0 and 1 to insert "Engine Electronics" address word 01 with engine running at idle.
3. Press buttons 0 and 8 to select "Read Measuring Value Block" function 08, then press "Q" to confirm input.
4. Press buttons 0, 0 and 3 to input Display Group 3, then press "Q" to confirm input.
5. Compare scan tool values with engine idle data in **Fig. 22.**
6. Press "C" button of scan tool, then press buttons 0, 2 and 7 to input Display Group 27. Press "Q" to confirm input.
7. Compare scan tool display with oxygen sensor display in **Fig. 25.**
8. Press right arrow button to advance program sequence.
9. Press buttons 0 and 6 to select "End Output" function 06, then press "Q" to confirm input.
10. If a fault is indicated, refer to appropriate test.

Heater Inspection

Refer to "Front Heated Oxygen Sensor Heater Inspection."

Wiring Inspection

1. Disconnect oxygen sensor.
2. Connect a suitable voltmeter between oxygen sensor harness connector terminals 3 and 4.
3. Turn ignition On.
4. Voltage should be 400–500 mV.
5. If voltage is not as specified, proceed as follows:
   a. Connect test box tool No. 1598/19, or equivalent to ECM harness connector.
   b. Inspect following circuits for open or short circuits using a suitable volt/ohmmeter: righthand oxygen sensor connector terminal 3 to test box pin C17 and connector terminal 4 to test box pin C21; lefthand oxygen sensor connector terminal 3 to test box pin C18 and connector terminal 4 to test box pin C20.
6. If wiring is satisfactory, replace ECM.

CLOSED THROTTLE POSITION (CTP) SWITCH

Functional Inspection

1. Ensure accelerator pedal and cruise control are properly adjusted.
2. Inspect throttle position sensor for contamination.
3. Connect scan tool No. VAG 1551/1552, or equivalent, then press buttons 0 and 1 to insert "Engine Electronics" address word 01 with engine running at idle.
4. Press buttons 0 and 8 to select "Read Measuring Value Block" function 08, then press "Q" to confirm input.
5. Press buttons 0, 0 and 4 to input Display Group 4, then press "Q" to confirm input.
6. Compare scan tool data with engine idle display data in **Fig. 26.**
7. If "Part throt" is displayed in scan tool Display Field 4 after long period of accelerator pedal travel, proceed as follows:
   a. Remove throttle body.
   b. Loosen CTP attaching screws.
   c. Rotate CTP switch in counterclockwise direction until stop is reached.
   d. Tighten CTP switch.
8. Depress accelerator pedal ¼ inch. Display Field 4 should read "Part throt."
9. If fault is still present, refer to "Wiring Inspection" and "Switch Inspection."

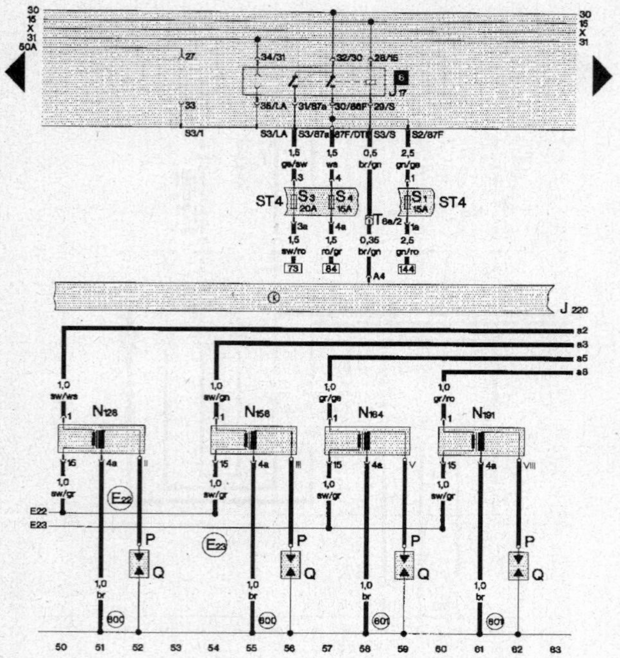

J 17 - Fuel Pump (FP) Relay
J 220 - Motronic Engine Control Module (ECM)
N 128 - Ignition Coil 2
N 158 - Ignition Coil 3
N 164 - Ignition Coil 5
N 191 - Ignition Coil 8
P - Spark Plug Connectors
Q - Spark Plugs
S 1 - Fuse
S 3 - Fuse
S 4 - Fuse
T 6 e - 6-Pin Connector, brown, connector station electronic box plenum chamber

(600) - Ground Point on cylinder head, right
(601) - Ground Point on cylinder head, left
(E22) - Connector (15 ignition right), in wiring harness Motronic
(E23) - Connector (15 ignition left), in wiring harness Motronic

AD1029800099030X

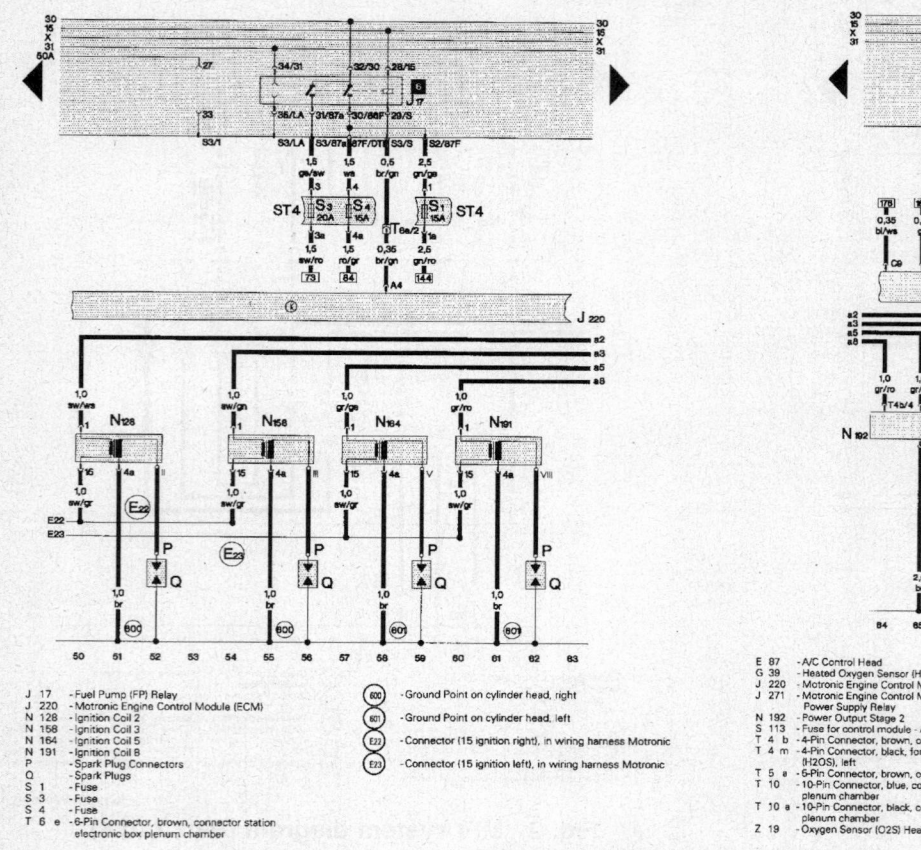

Fig. 2 MFI system diagram (Part 3 of 8)

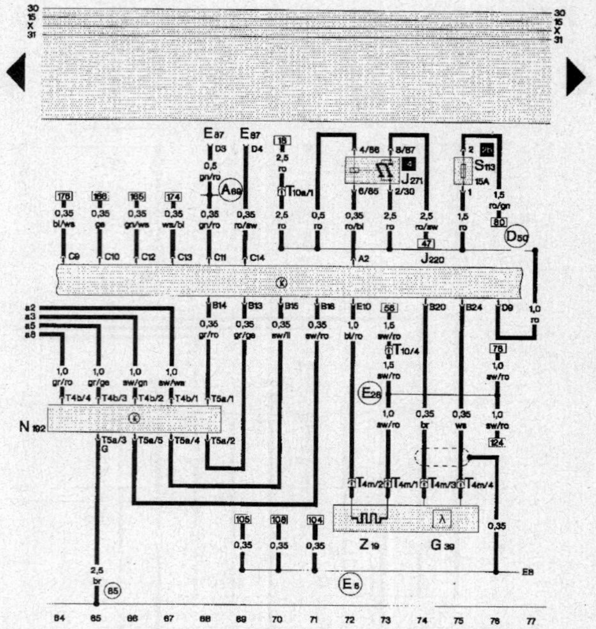

E 87 - A/C Control Head
G 39 - Heated Oxygen Sensor (HO2S)1
J 220 - Motronic Engine Control Module (ECM)
J 271 - Motronic Engine Control Module (ECM) Power Supply Relay
N 192 - Power Output Stage 2
S 113 - Fuse for control module - Auto. Trans.
T 4 b - 4-Pin Connector, brown, on power output stage
T 4 m - 4-Pin Connector, black, for heated oxygen sensor (H2OS), left
T 5 a - 5-Pin Connector, brown, on power output stage
T 10 - 10-Pin Connector, blue, connector station electronic box plenum chamber
T 10 a - 10-Pin Connector, black, connector station electronic box plenum chamber
Z 19 - Oxygen Sensor (O2S) Heater

(85) - Ground connection -1-, in engine compartment wiring harness
(A89) - Connector (A/C compressor), in instrument panel wiring harness
(D50) - Plus connection (30), in engine compartment wiring harness
(E8) - Wire connection (screening), in Motronic Multiport Fuel Injection (MFI) wiring harness
(E28) - Connector, Oxygen Sensor (O2S) Heater, in wiring harness Motronic

AD1029800099040X

Fig. 2 MFI system diagram (Part 4 of 8)

Wiring Inspection

1. Connect test box tool No. 1598/19, or equivalent to ECM harness connector.
2. Disconnect throttle position sensor.
3. Inspect test box pin B4 to TPS connector terminal 6 for open or short circuit using a suitable volt/ohmmeter.
4. Inspect test box pin D11 to TPS connector terminal 4 for open or short circuit.
5. If open or short is present, repair as required.
6. If wiring inspection is satisfactory, refer to "Switch Inspection."

Switch Inspection

1. Ensure TPS is connected.
2. Connect test box tool No. 1598/19, or equivalent to ECM harness connector.
3. Measure resistance between test box pins D11 and B4 using a suitable ohmmeter.
4. Continuity should be present when throttle valve is closed and open circuit should be indicated when throttle valve is open.
5. If ohmmeter readings are not as specified, replace throttle position sensor.

THROTTLE POSITION (TP) SENSOR

Functional Inspection

1. Ensure throttle cable and CTP switch is properly adjusted.
2. Connect scan tool No. VAG 1551/1552, or equivalent, then press buttons 0 and 1 to insert "Engine Electronics" address word 01 with engine running at idle.
3. Press buttons 0 and 8 to select "Read Measuring Value Block" function 08, then press "Q" to confirm input.
4. Press buttons 0, 0 and 4 to input Display Group 4, then press "Q" to confirm input.
5. Compare scan tool data with basic functions display data, **Fig. 27.**
6. Press right arrow button to advance program.
7. Press buttons 0 and 6 to "End Output" function 06, then press "Q" to confirm input.
8. If throttle angle measurement is not as specified, refer to "Voltage Inspection."

Voltage Inspection

1. Disconnect throttle position sensor.
2. Turn ignition On.
3. Measure voltage between TPS terminals 1 and 2 using a suitable voltmeter, then between terminals 2 and 3.
4. Voltage should read 4.5–5.5 volts.
5. If both measurements are not as specified, measure resistance of TPS.
6. If only one measurement is outside the specified range, proceed as follows to inspect ECM wiring:
   a. Turn ignition Off.
   b. Connect test box tool No. VAG 1598/19, or equivalent to ECM harness connector.
   c. Disconnect throttle position sensor.
   d. Inspect for open or shorts in following circuits using a suitable volt/ohmmeter: TPS connector terminal 1 to test box pin A3; TPS connector terminal 2 to test box pin A19; TPS connector terminal 3 to test box pin A24.
   e. If wiring inspection is satisfactory, replace ECM and generate new readiness code.

Resistance Inspection

1. Disconnect throttle position sensor.
2. Measure resistance between following TPS connector terminals using a suitable ohmmeter:
   a. Terminals 1 and 2.
   b. Terminals 2 and 3.
   c. Terminals 2 and 3 at WOT.
3. If resistance is not within specifications, replace TPS.
4. If resistance is within specifications, perform wiring inspection.

Clearing Diagnostic Trouble Codes

Fault memory cannot be erased until it has first been inspected.

Follow tool manufacturer's instructions to clear DTCs.

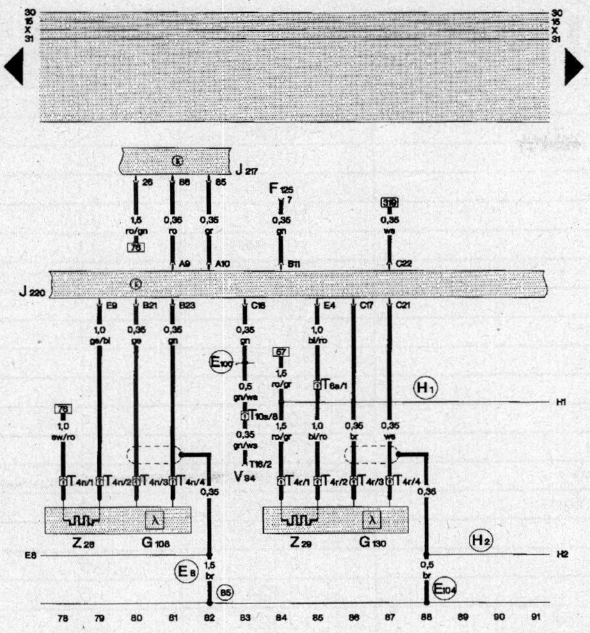

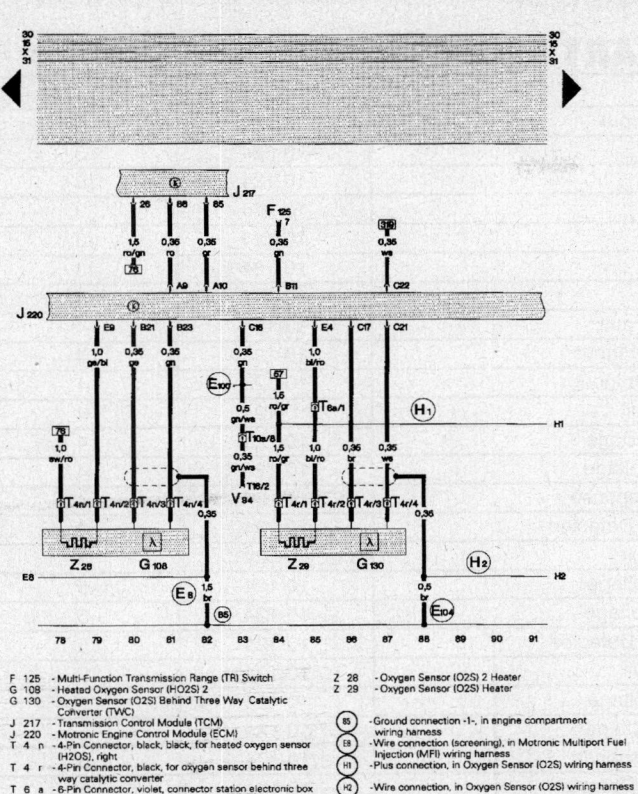

F 125 - Multi-Function Transmission Range (TR) Switch
G 108 - Heated Oxygen Sensor (HO2S) 2
G 130 - Oxygen Sensor (O2S) Behind Three Way Catalytic Converter (TWC)
J 217 - Transmission Control Module (TCM)
J 220 - Motronic Engine Control Module (ECM)
T 4 n - 4-Pin Connector, black, black, for heated oxygen sensor (H2OS), right
T 4 r - 4-Pin Connector, black, for oxygen sensor behind three way catalytic converter
T 6 a - 6-Pin Connector, violet, connector station electronic box plenum chamber
T 10 s - 10-Pin Connector, black, connector station wheel house right
T 16 - 16-Pin Connector, Connector C on V94
V 94 - Central Locking/Alarm System/Interior Light Delay Control Module
Z 28 - Oxygen Sensor (O2S) 2 Heater
Z 29 - Oxygen Sensor (O2S) Heater

(85) - Ground connection -1-, in engine compartment wiring harness
(E8) - Wire connection (screening), in Motronic Multiport Fuel Injection (MFI) wiring harness
(H1) - Plus connection, in Oxygen Sensor (O2S) wiring harness
(H2) - Wire connection, in Oxygen Sensor (O2S) wiring harness
(E100) - Connector (Multi-function Switch), in instrument panel wiring harness
(E104) - Ground connection, in instrument panel wiring harness

AD1029800099050X

Fig. 2 MFI system diagram (Part 5 of 8)

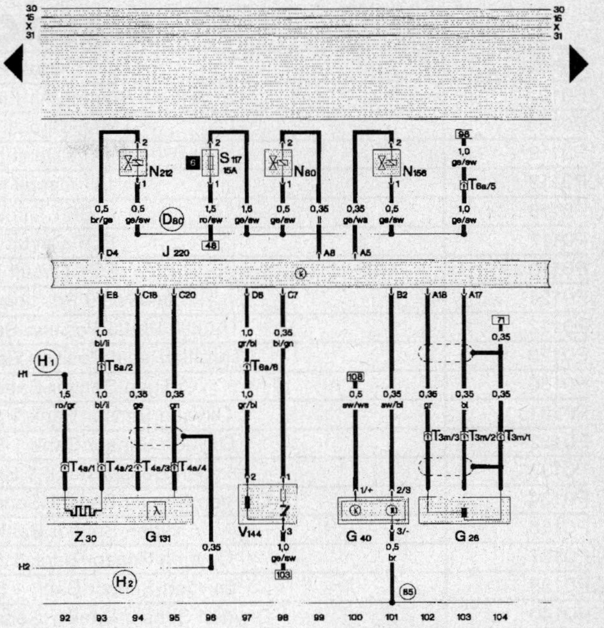

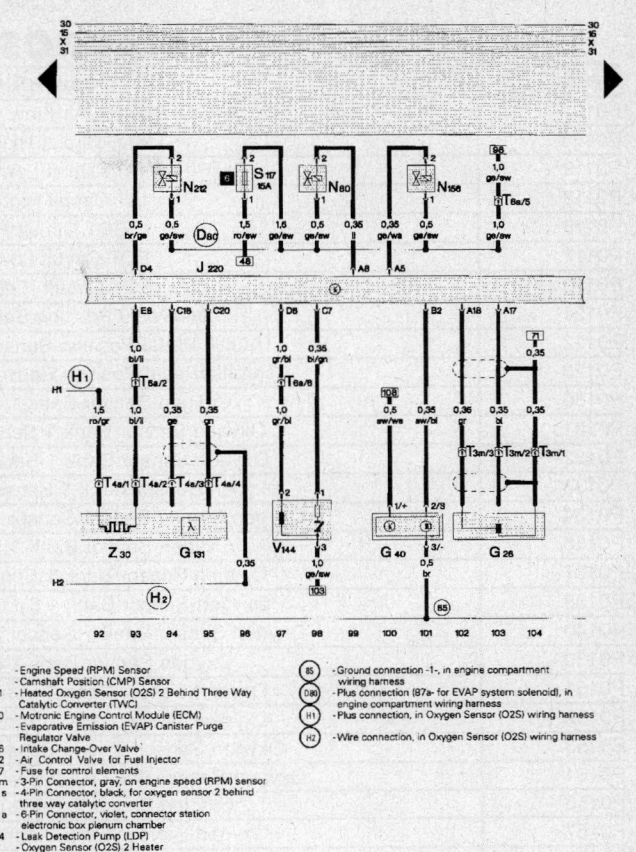

G 28 - Engine Speed (RPM) Sensor
G 40 - Camshaft Position (CMP) Sensor
G 131 - Heated Oxygen Sensor (O2S) 2 Behind Three Way Catalytic Converter (TWC)
J 220 - Motronic Engine Control Module (ECM)
N 80 - Evaporative Emission (EVAP) Canister Purge Regulator Valve
N 156 - Intake Change-Over Valve
N 212 - Air Control Valve for Fuel Injector
S 117 - Fuse for control elements
T 3 m - 3-Pin Connector, gray, on engine speed (RPM) sensor
T 4 s - 4-Pin Connector, black, for oxygen sensor 2 behind three way catalytic converter
T 6 a - 6-Pin Connector, violet, connector station electronic box plenum chamber
V 144 - Leak Detection Pump (LDP)
Z 30 - Oxygen Sensor (O2S) 2 Heater

(85) - Ground connection -1-, in engine compartment wiring harness
(D80) - Plus connection (87a- for EVAP system solenoid), in engine compartment wiring harness
(H1) - Plus connection, in Oxygen Sensor (O2S) wiring harness
(H2) - Wire connection, in Oxygen Sensor (O2S) wiring harness

AD1029800099060X

Fig. 2 MFI system diagram (Part 6 of 8)

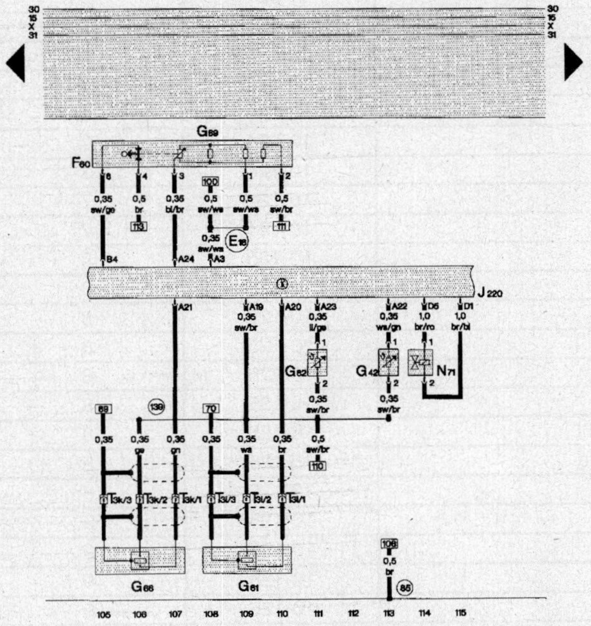

F 60 - Closed Thottle Position (CTP) Switch
G 42 - Intake Air Temperature (IAT) Sensor
G 61 - Knock Sensor (KS) 1
G 62 - Engine Coolant Temperature (ECT) Sensor
G 66 - Knock Sensor (KS) 2
G 69 - Throttle Position (TP) Sensor
J 220 - Motronic Engine Control Module (ECM)
N 71 - Idle Air Control (IAC) Valve
T 3 i - 3-Pin Connector, green, on knock sensor (KS) 1
T 3 k - 3-Pin Connector, brown, on knock sensoe (KS) 2

(85) - Ground connection -1-, in engine compartment wiring harness
(139) - Ground connection (sensor Ground), in Motronic Multiport Fuel Injection (MFI) wiring harness
(E16) - Plus connection (5 Volts), in Motronic Multiport Fuel Injection (MFI) wiring harness

AD1029800099070X

Fig. 2 MFI system diagram (Part 7 of 8)

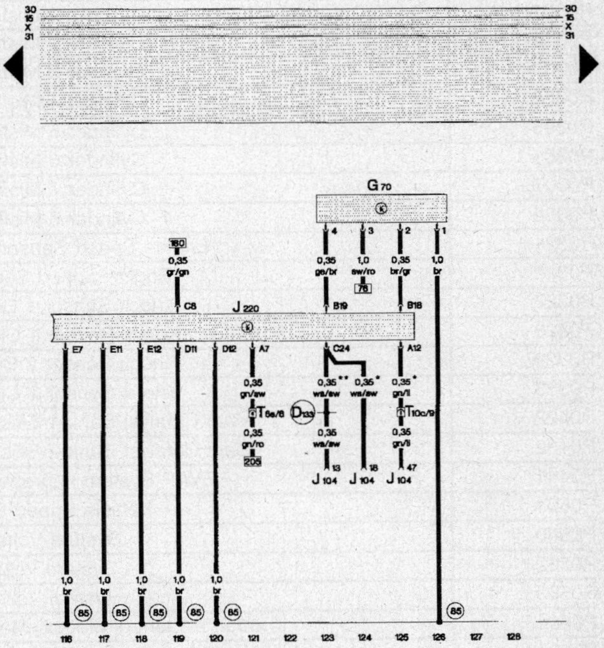

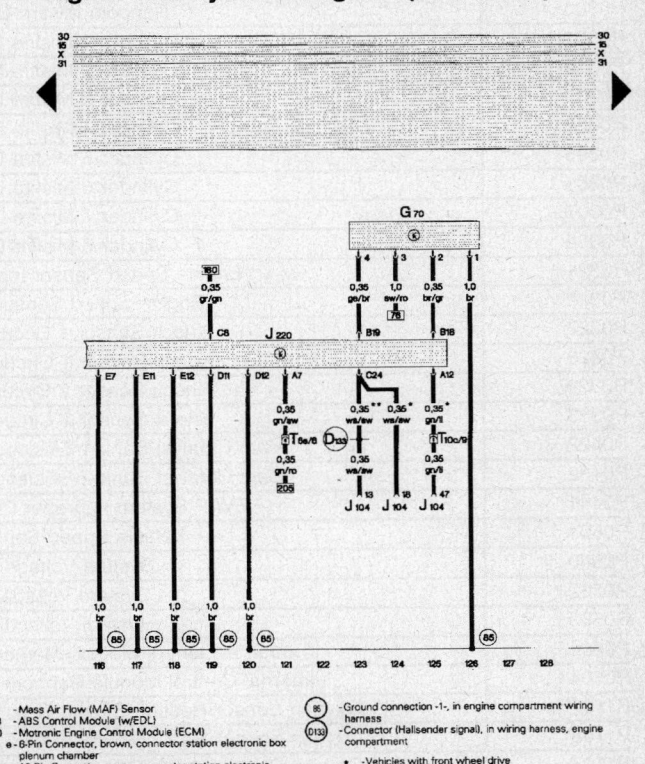

G 70 - Mass Air Flow (MAF) Sensor
J 104 - ABS Control Module (w/EDL)
J 220 - Motronic Engine Control Module (ECM)
T 6 e - 6-Pin Connector, brown, connector station electronic box plenum chamber
T 10 c - 10-Pin Connector, green, connector station electronic box plenum chamber

(85) - Ground connection -1-, in engine compartment wiring harness
(D133) - Connector (Hallsender signal), in wiring harness, engine compartment

* - Vehicles with front wheel drive
** - Vehicles with quattro

AD1029800099080X

Fig. 2 MFI system diagram (Part 8 of 8)

DIAGNOSTIC CHART INDEX

Code	Description	Page No.	Fig. No.
P0102	MAF Or Volume Air Flow Circuit Low Input	10-124	3
P0103	MAF Circuit High Input	10-124	3
P0112	IAT Circuit Low Input	10-124	3
P0113	IAT Circuit High Input	10-124	3
P0116	ECT Circuit Fault	10-124	3
P0117	ECT Circuit Low Input	10-124	3
P0118	ECT Circuit High Input	10-124	3
P0121	Throttle/Pedal Position Sensor Circuit Fault	10-124	4
P0122	Throttle/Pedal Position Sensor Circuit Low Input	10-124	4
P0123	Throttle/Pedal Position Sensor Circuit High Input	10-124	4
P0130	Oxygen Sensor Bank 1 Sensor 1 Fault	10-124	4
P0131	Oxygen Sensor Bank 1 Sensor 1 Low Voltage	10-124	4
P0132	Oxygen Sensor Bank 1 Sensor 1 High Voltage	10-124	4
P0133	Oxygen Sensor Bank 1 Sensor 1 Slow Response	10-124	4
P0134	Oxygen Sensor Bank 1 Sensor 1 No Activity Detected	10-124	4
P0136	Oxygen Sensor Bank 1 Sensor 2 Fault	10-124	5
P0137	Oxygen Sensor Bank 1 Sensor 2 Low Voltage	10-124	5
P0138	Oxygen Sensor Bank 1 Sensor 2 High Voltage	10-124	5
P0140	Oxygen Sensor Bank 1 Sensor 2 No Activity Detected	10-124	5
P0150	Oxygen Sensor Bank 2 Sensor 1 Fault	10-124	5
P0151	Oxygen Sensor Bank 2 Sensor 1 Low Voltage	10-124	5
P0152	Oxygen Sensor Bank 2 Sensor 1 High Voltage	10-124	5
P0153	Oxygen Sensor Bank 2 Sensor 1 Slow Response	10-124	5
P0154	Oxygen Sensor Bank 2 Sensor 1 No Activity Detected	10-124	5
P0156	Oxygen Sensor Bank 2 Sensor 2 Fault	10-124	6
P0157	Oxygen Sensor Bank 2 Sensor 2 Low Voltage	10-124	6
P0158	Oxygen Sensor Bank 2 Sensor 2 High Voltage	10-124	6
P0160	Oxygen Sensor Bank 2 Sensor 2 No Activity Detected	10-124	6
P0300	Random Misfire Detected	10-124	7
P0301	Cylinder 1 Misfire Detected	10-124	7
P0302	Cylinder 2 Misfire Detected	10-124	7
P0303	Cylinder 3 Misfire Detected	10-124	7
P0304	Cylinder 4 Misfire Detected	10-124	7
P0305	Cylinder 5 Misfire Detected	10-124	7
P0306	Cylinder 6 Misfire Detected	10-124	7
P0307	Cylinder 7 Misfire Detected	10-124	7
P0308	Cylinder 8 Misfire Detected	10-124	7
P0321	Engine Speed Sensor Input Circuit Fault	10-125	8
P0322	Engine Speed Sensor No Signal	10-125	8
P0327	Knock Sensor 1 Circuit Low Input	10-125	8
P0328	Knock Sensor 1 Circuit High Input	10-125	8
P0332	Knock Sensor 2 Circuit Low Input	10-125	8
P0333	Knock Sensor 2 Circuit High Input	10-125	8
P0422	Main Catalyst Bank 1 Efficiency Below Threshold	10-125	8
P0432	Main Catalyst Bank 2 Efficiency Below Threshold	10-125	8
P0441	EVAP System Improper Purge Flow Fault	10-125	8
P0501	Vehicle Speed Sensor Fault	10-125	9
P0560	System Voltage Fault	10-125	9
P0562	System Voltage Low	10-125	9
P0563	System Voltage High	10-125	9
P0601	Internal Control Module Memory Check Sum Error	10-125	9
P0604	Internal Control Module Random Access Memory Error	10-125	9
P1102	Oxygen Sensor Heating Circuit Bank 1 Sensor 1 Short To Power	10-125	10
P1105	Oxygen Sensor Heating Circuit Bank 1 Sensor 2 Short To Power	10-125	10
P1107	Oxygen Sensor Heating Circuit Bank 2 Sensor 1 Short To Power	10-125	10
P1110	Oxygen Sensor Heating Circuit Bank 2 Sensor 2 Short To Power	10-125	10
P1127	Long Term Fuel Trim Bank 1 System Too Rich	10-125	10

Continued

DIAGNOSTIC CHART INDEX—Continued

Code	Description	Page No.	Fig. No.
P1128	Long Term Fuel Trim Bank 1 System Too Lean	10-125	10
P1129	Long Term Fuel Trim Bank 2 System Too Rich	10-125	10
P1130	Long Term Fuel Trim Bank 1 System Too Lean	10-125	10
P1136	Long Term Fuel Trim Bank 1 System Too Lean	10-125	11
P1137	Long Term Fuel Trim Bank 1 System Too Rich	10-125	11
P1138	Long Term Fuel Trim Bank 2 System Too Lean	10-125	11
P1139	Long Term Fuel Trim Bank 2 System Too Rich	10-125	11
P1141	Load Calculation Cross Check Range/Performance Fault	10-125	12
P1176	Oxygen Sensor Correction Behind Catalyst B1 Limit Attained	10-125	12
P1177	Oxygen Sensor Correction Behind Catalyst B2 Limit Attained	10-125	12
P1196	Oxygen Sensor Heater Circuit Bank 1 Sensor 1 Electrical Fault	10-125	12
P1197	Oxygen Sensor Heater Circuit Bank 2 Sensor 1 Electrical Fault	10-125	12
P1198	Oxygen Sensor Heater Circuit Bank 1 Sensor 2 Electrical Fault	10-125	12
P1199	Oxygen Sensor Heater Circuit Bank 2 Sensor 2 Electrical Fault	10-125	12
P1201	Cylinder 1 Fuel Injector Circuit Fault	10-125	13
P1202	Cylinder 2 Fuel Injector Circuit Fault	10-125	13
P1203	Cylinder 3 Fuel Injector Circuit Fault	10-125	13
P1204	Cylinder 4 Fuel Injector Circuit Fault	10-125	13
P1205	Cylinder 5 Fuel Injector Circuit Fault	10-125	13
P1206	Cylinder 6 Fuel Injector Circuit Fault	10-125	13
P1207	Cylinder 7 Fuel Injector Circuit Fault	10-125	13
P1208	Cylinder 8 Fuel Injector Circuit Fault	10-125	13
P1213	Cylinder 1 Fuel Injector Short To Power	10-125	14
P1214	Cylinder 2 Fuel Injector Short To Power	10-125	14
P1215	Cylinder 3 Fuel Injector Short To Power	10-125	14
P1216	Cylinder 4 Fuel Injector Short To Power	10-125	14
P1217	Cylinder 5 Fuel Injector Short To Power	10-125	14
P1218	Cylinder 6 Fuel Injector Short To Power	10-125	14
P1219	Cylinder 7 Fuel Injector Short To Power	10-125	14
P1220	Cylinder 8 Fuel Injector Short To Power	10-125	14
P1250	Fuel Level Too Low	10-125	14
P1280	Fuel Injector Air Control Valve Flow Too Low	10-125	14
P1283	Fuel Injector Air Control Valve Circuit Electrical Fault	10-125	14
P1286	Fuel Injector Air Control Valve Circuit Short To Power	10-125	14
P1325	Cylinder 1 Knock Control Limit Attained	10-126	15
P1326	Cylinder 2 Knock Control Limit Attained	10-126	15
P1327	Cylinder 3 Knock Control Limit Attained	10-126	15
P1328	Cylinder 4 Knock Control Limit Attained	10-126	15
P1329	Cylinder 5 Knock Control Limit Attained	10-126	15
P1330	Cylinder 6 Knock Control Limit Attained	10-126	15
P1331	Cylinder 7 Knock Control Limit Attained	10-126	15
P1332	Cylinder 8 Knock Control Limit Attained	10-126	15
P1386	Internal Control Module Knock Control Error	10-126	15
P1391	Camshaft Position Sensor Bank 2 Short To Ground	10-126	16
P1392	Camshaft Position Sensor Bank 2 Short To Power	10-126	16
P1409	Tank Ventilation Valve Circuit Electrical Fault	10-126	16
P1410	Tank Ventilation Valve Short To Power	10-126	16
P1500	Fuel Pump Relay Electrical Fault	10-126	16
P1502	Fuel Pump Relay Short To Power	10-126	16
P1505	Closed Throttle Position Switch Does Not Close/Open Circuit	10-126	16
P1506	Closed Throttle Position Switch Does Not Open/Short To Ground	10-126	16
P1507	Idle System Learned Value Lower Limit Attained	10-126	16
P1508	Idle System Learned Value Upper Limit Attained	10-126	16
P1509	Idle Air Control Circuit Electrical Fault	10-126	17
P1510	Idle Air Control Circuit Short To Power	10-126	17
P1511	Intake Manifold Changeover Valve Circuit Electrical Fault	10-126	17
P1512	Intake Manifold Changeover Valve Circuit Short To Power	10-126	17

Continued

DIAGNOSTIC CHART INDEX—Continued

Code	Description	Page No.	Fig. No.
P1517	Main Relay Circuit Electrical Circuit Fault	10-126	17
P1518	Main Relay Circuit Short To Power	10-126	17
P1560	Maximum Engine Speed Exceeded	10-126	17
P1602	Power Supply Terminal 30 Low Voltage	10-126	17
P1606	Rough Road Spec Engine Torque ABS-ECU Electrical Fault	10-126	17
P1612	ECM Improper Coding	10-126	17
P1624	MIL Request Sign Active	10-126	18
P1625	CAN-Bus Implausible Message From Transmission Controller	10-126	18
P1640	Internal Control Module EEPROM Error	10-126	18
P1690	MIL Fault	10-126	18
P1693	MIL Short To Power	10-126	18

Diagnostic Trouble Code (DTC) SAE	VAG	Description of malfunction	MIL	Corrective action
P0102	16486	Mass or Volume Air Flow Circ. Low Input	2 Dcy	– Check Mass Air Flow (MAF) sensor -G70
P0103	16487	Mass or Volume Air Flow Circ. High Input		
P0112	16496	Intake Air Temp. Circ. Low Input	2 Dcy	– Check Intake Air Temperature (IAT) sensor
P0113	16497	Intake Air Temp. Circ. High Input		
P0116	16500	Engine Coolant Temp. Circ. Range/Performance	2 Dcy	– Check Engine Coolant Temperature (ECT) sensor
P0117	16501	Engine Coolant Temp. Circ. Low Input		
P0118	16502	Engine Coolant Temp. Circ. High Input		

AD0159800253000X

Fig. 3 Codes P0102, P0103, P0112, P0113, P0116, P0117 & P0118

Diagnostic Trouble Code (DTC) SAE	VAG	Description of malfunction	MIL	Corrective action
P0121	16505	Throttle/Pedal Pos. Sensor A Circ. Range/Performance	2 Dcy	– Check Throttle Position (TP) sensor
P0122	16506	Throttle/Pedal Pos. Sensor A Circ. Low Input		
P0123	16507	Throttle/Pedal Pos. Sensor A Circ. High Input		
P0130	16514	O2 Sensor Circ., Bank1–Sensor1 Malfunction	2 Dcy	– Check HO2S -G39
P0131	16515	O2 Sensor Circ., Bank1–Sensor1 Low Voltage		
P0132	16516	O2 Sensor Circ., Bank1–Sensor1 High Voltage		
P0133	16517	O2 Sensor Circ., Bank1–Sensor1 Slow Response		
P0134	16518	O2 Sensor Circ., Bank1–Sensor1 No Activity Detected		

AD0159800254000X

Fig. 4 Codes P0121, P0122, P0123, P0130, P0131, P0132, P0133 & P0134

Diagnostic Trouble Code (DTC) SAE	VAG	Description of malfunction	MIL	Corrective action
P0136	16520	O2 Sensor Circ., Bank1–Sensor2 Malfunction	2 Dcy	– Check O2S behind TWC -G130
P0137	16521	O2 Sensor Circ., Bank1–Sensor2 Low Voltage		
P0138	16522	O2 Sensor Circ., Bank1–Sensor2 High Voltage		
P0140	16524	O2 Sensor Circ., Bank1–Sensor2 No Activity Detected		
P0150	16534	O2 Sensor Circ., Bank2–Sensor1 Malfunction	2 Dcy	– Check HO2S 2 -G108
P0151	16535	O2 Sensor Circ., Bank2–Sensor1 Low Voltage		
P0152	16536	O2 Sensor Circ., Bank2–Sensor1 High Voltage		
P0153	16537	O2 Sensor Circ., Bank2–Sensor1 Slow Response		
P0154	16538	O2 Sensor Circ., Bank2–Sensor1 No Activity Detected		

AD0159800255000X

Fig. 5 Codes P0136, P0137, P0138, P0140, P0150, P0151, P0152, P0153 & P0154

Diagnostic Trouble Code (DTC) SAE	VAG	Description of malfunction	MIL	Corrective action
P0156	16540	O2 Sensor Circ., Bank2–Sensor2 Malfunction	2 Dcy	– Check O2S 2 behind TWC -G131
P0157	16541	O2 Sensor Circ., Bank2–Sensor2 Low Voltage		
P0158	16542	O2 Sensor Circ., Bank2–Sensor2 High Voltage		
P0160	16544	O2 Sensor Circ., Bank2–Sensor2 No Activity Detected		

AD0159800256000X

Fig. 6 Codes P0156, P0157, P0158 & P0160

Diagnostic Trouble Code (DTC) SAE	VAG	Description of Malfuncton	MIL	Corrective Action
P0300	16684	Random/Multiple Cylinder Misfire Detected	2 Dcy / Blinking	– Check for cause of misfire – Check fuel tank level
P0301	16685	Cyl. 1 Misfire Detected		
P0302	16686	Cyl. 2 Misfire Detected		
P0303	16687	Cyl. 3 Misfire Detected		
P0304	16688	Cyl. 4 Misfire Detected		
P0305	16689	Cyl. 5 Misfire Detected		
P0306	16690	Cyl. 6 Misfire Detected		
P0307	16691	Cyl. 7 Misfire Detected		
P0308	16692	Cyl. 8 Misfire Detected		

AD0159800257000X

Fig. 7 Codes P0300, P0301, P0302, P0303, P0304, P0305, P0306, P0307 & P0308

Diagnostic Trouble Code (DTC)		Description of malfunction	MIL	Corrective action
SAE	VAG			
P0321	16705	Ign./Distributor Eng. Speed Inp. Circ. Range/Performance	2 Dcy	– Check Engine Speed (RPM) sensor -G28
P0322	16706	Ign./Distributor Eng. Speed Inp. Circ. No Signal	On	
P0327	16711	Knock Sensor 1 Circ. Low Input	Off	– Check Knock Sensor (KS) 1 -G61- and knock sensor control
P0328	16712	Knock Sensor 1 Circ. High Input		
P0332	16716	Knock Sensor 2 Circ. Low Input		
P0333	16717	Knock Sensor 2 Circ. High Input		
P0422	16806	Main Catalyst, Bank1 Efficiency Below Threshold	2 Dcy	– Check HO2S – Check O2S behind TWC
P0432	16816	Main Catalyst, Bank 2 Efficiency Below Threshold		
P0441	16825	EVAP Emission Contr. Sys. Incorrect Purge Flow	2 Dcy	– Check Evaporative Emissions (EVAP) canister purge regulator valve

AD0159800258000X

Fig. 8 Codes P0321, P0322, P0327, P0328, P0332, P0333, P0422, P0432 & P0441

Diagnostic Trouble Code (DTC)		Description of malfunction	MIL	Corrective action
SAE	VAG			
P1102	17510	O2 Sensor Heating Circ., Bank1–Sensor1 Short to B+	2 Dcy	– Check Oxygen Sensor (O2S) heater
P1105	17513	O2 Sensor Heating Circ., Bank1–Sensor2 Short to B+		
P1107	17515	O2 Sensor Heating Circ., Bank2–Sensor1 Short to B+		
P1110	17518	O2 Sensor Heating Circ., Bank2–Sensor2 Short to B+		
P1127	17535	Long Term Fuel Trim mult., Bank1 [1] System too Rich	2 Dcy	– Check fuel system pressure – Check Mass Air Flow (MAF) sensor -G70 – Check HO2S – Check O2S behind TWC – Check fuel injectors – Check fuel tank level
P1128	17536	Long Term Fuel Trim mult., Bank1 [1] System too Lean		
P1129	17537	Long Term Fuel Trim mult., Bank2 [1] System too Rich		
P1130	17538	Long Term Fuel Trim mult., Bank2 [1] System too Lean		

[1] The term "mult." = multiplicative; applies to entire engine speed (RPM) and load range.

AD0159800260000X

Fig. 10 Codes P1102, P1105, P1107, P1110, P1127, P1128, P1129 & P1130

Diagnostic Trouble Code (DTC)		Description of malfunction	MIL	Corrective action
SAE	VAG			
P1141	17549	Load Calculation Cross Check Range/Performance	2 Dcy	– Check Mass Air Flow (MAF) sensor -G70 – Check Throttle Position (TP) sensor
P1176	17584	O2 Correction Behind Catalyst, B1 Limit Attained	2 Dcy	– Check HO2S – Check O2S after TWC – Check O2S heater
P1177	17585	O2 Correction Behind Catalyst, B2 Limit Attained		
P1196	17604	O2 Sensor Heater Circ., Bank1–Sensor1 Electrical Malfunction	2 Dcy	– Check O2S heater
P1197	17605	O2 Sensor Heater Circ., Bank2–Sensor1 Electrical Malfunction		
P1198	17606	O2 Sensor Heater Circ., Bank1–Sensor2 Electrical Malfunction	2 Dcy	– Check O2S heater
P1199	17607	O2 Sensor Heater Circ., Bank2–Sensor2 Electrical Malfunction		

AD0159800262000X

Fig. 12 Codes P1141, P1176, P1177, P1196, P1197, P1198, & P1199

Diagnostic Trouble Code (DTC)		Description of malfunction	MIL	Corrective action
SAE	VAG			
P0501	16885	Vehicle Speed Sensor Range/Performance	2 Dcy	– Check Vehicle Speed Sensor (VSS) signal
P0560	16944	System Voltage Malfunction	2 Dcy	– Check voltage supply from Engine Control Module (ECM)
P0562	16946	System Voltage Low Voltage		
P0563	16947	System Voltage High Voltage		
P0601	16985	Internal Contr. Module Memory Check Sum Error	2 Dcy	– Replace ECM
P0604	16988	Internal Contr. Module Random Access Memory (RAM) Error		

AD0159800259000X

Fig. 9 Codes P0501, P0560, P0562, P0563, P0601 & P0604

Diagnostic Trouble Code (DTC)		Description of malfunction	MIL	Corrective action
SAE	VAG			
P1136	17544	Long Term Fuel Trim Add. Fuel, Bank1 [2] System too Lean	2 Dcy	– Perform road test (fuel in engine oil) – Check fuel pressure regulator and residual pressure – Check Mass Air Flow (MAF) sensor -G70 – Check HO2S – Check fuel tank level – Check Evaporative Emissions (EVAP) canister purge regulator valve
P1137	17545	Long Term Fuel Trim Add. Fuel, Bank1 [2] System too Rich		
P1138	17546	Long Term Fuel Trim Add. Fuel, Bank2 [2] System too Lean		
P1139	17547	Long Term Fuel Trim Add. Fuel, Bank2 [2] System too Rich		

[2] The term "Add." = additive; applies only with engine running at idle speed.

AD0159800261000X

Fig. 11 Codes P1136, P1137, P1138 & P1139

Diagnostic Trouble Code (DTC)		Description of malfunction	MIL	Corrective action
SAE	VAG			
P1201	17609	Cyl.1–Fuel Inj. Circ. Electrical Malfunction	On	– Check fuel injectors
P1202	17610	Cyl.2–Fuel Inj. Circ. Electrical Malfunction		
P1203	17611	Cyl.3–Fuel Inj. Circ. Electrical Malfunction		
P1204	17612	Cyl.4–Fuel Inj. Circ. Electrical Malfunction		
P1205	17613	Cyl.5–Fuel Inj. Circ. Electrical Malfunction		
P1206	17614	Cyl.6–Fuel Inj. Circ. Electrical Malfunction		
P1207	17615	Cyl.7–Fuel Inj. Circ. Electrical Malfunction		
P1208	17616	Cyl.8–Fuel Inj. Circ. Electrical Malfunction		

AD0159800263000X

Fig. 13 Codes P1201, P1202, P1203, P1204, P1205, P1206, P1207 & P1208

Diagnostic Trouble Code (DTC)		Description of malfunction	MIL	Corrective action
SAE	VAG			
P1213	17621	Cyl.1–Fuel Inj. Circ. Short to B+	On	– Check fuel injectors
P1214	17622	Cyl.2–Fuel Inj. Circ. Short to B+		
P1215	17623	Cyl.3–Fuel Inj. Circ. Short to B+		
P1216	17624	Cyl.4–Fuel Inj. Circ. Short to B+		
P1217	17625	Cyl.5–Fuel Inj. Circ. Short to B+		
P1218	17626	Cyl.6–Fuel Inj. Circ. Short to B+		
P1219	17627	Cyl.7–Fuel Inj. Circ. Short to B+		
P1220	17628	Cyl.8–Fuel Inj. Circ. Short to B+		
P1250	17658	Fuel Level Too Low [1]	Off	– Check fuel tank level
P1280	17688	Fuel Inj. Air Contr. Valve Circ. Flow too Low	2 Dcy	– Check fuel injection air control valve -N212
P1283	17691	Fuel Inj. Air Contr. Valve Circ. Electrical Malfunction	2 Dcy	– Carry out fuel injection air control valve -N212- electrical test
P1286	17694	Fuel Inj. Air Contr. Valve Circ. Short to B+		

[1] This DTC is displayed only in conjunction with misfiring or fuel system malfunctions

AD0159800264000X

Fig. 14 Codes P1213, P1214, P1215, P1216, P1217, P1218, P1219, P1220, P1250, P1280, P1283 & P1286

Diagnostic Trouble Code (DTC) SAE	VAG	Description of malfunction	MIL	Corrective action
P1325	17733	Cyl.1–Knock Contr. Limit Attained	Off	– Check knock sensor control
P1326	17734	Cyl.2–Knock Contr. Limit Attained		
P1327	17735	Cyl.3–Knock Contr. Limit Attained		
P1328	17736	Cyl.4–Knock Contr. Limit Attained		
P1329	17737	Cyl.5–Knock Contr. Limit Attained		
P1330	17738	Cyl.6–Knock Contr. Limit Attained		
P1331	17739	Cyl.7–Knock Contr. Limit Attained		
P1332	17740	Cyl.8–Knock Contr. Limit Attained		
P1386	17794	Internal Control Module Knock Control Circ. Error	Off	– Replace ECM

AD0159800265000X

Fig. 15 Codes P1325, P1326, P1327, P1328, P1329, P1330, P1331, P1332 & P1386

Diagnostic Trouble Code (DTC) SAE	VAG	Description of malfunction	MIL	Corrective action
P1509	17917	Idle Air Control Circ. Electrical Malfunction	2 Dcy	– Check Idle Air Control (IAC) valve
P1510	17918	Idle Air Control Circ. Short to B+		
P1511	17919	Intake Manifold Changeover Valve Circ. Electrical Malfunction	Off	– Check intake manifold change-over valve
P1512	17920	Intake Manifold Changeover Valve Circ. Short to B+		
P1517	17925	Main Relay Circ. Electrical Malfunction	On	– Check Motronic ECM power supply relay
P1518	17926	Main Relay Circ. Short to B+		
P1560	17968	Maximum Engine Speed Exceeded	Off	– Rectify mechanical faults
P1602	18010	Power Supply (B+) Terminal 30 Low Voltage	Off	– Check power supply from ECM
P1606	18014	Rough Road Spec Engine Torque ABS-ECU Electrical Malfunction	Off	– Check signal for traction control (ASR)
P1612	18020	Electronic Control Module Incorrect Coding	Off	– Replace ECM

AD0159800267000X

Fig. 17 Codes P1509, P1510, P1511, P1512, P1517, P1518, P1560, P1602, P1606 & P1612

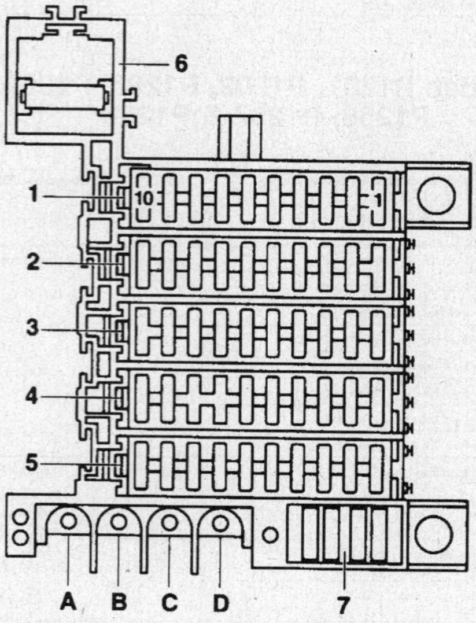

AD1029800101000X

Fig. 19 Fuse panel identification

Diagnostic Trouble Code (DTC) SAE	VAG	Description of malfunction	MIL	Corrective action
P1391	17799	Camshaft Pos. Sensor, Bank2 Short to Ground	2 Dcy	– Check Camshaft Position (CMP) sensor
P1392	17800	Camshaft Pos. Sensor, Bank2 Open Circ./Short to B+		
P1409	17817	Tank Ventilation Valve Circ. Electrical Malfunction	2 Dcy	– Check Evaporative Emissions (EVAP) canister purge regulator valve
P1410	17818	Tank Ventilation Valve Circ. Short to B+		
P1500	17908	Fuel Pump Relay Circ. Electrical Malfunction	Off	– Check fuel pump relay -J17
P1502	17910	Fuel Pump Relay Circ. Short to B+		
P1505	17913	Closed Throttle Pos. Does Not Close/Open Circ.	2 Dcy	– Check Closed Throttle Position (CTP) switch
P1506	17914	Closed Throttle Pos. Does Not Open/Short to Ground		
P1507	17915	Idle Sys. Learned Value Lower Limit Attained	2 Dcy	– Check idle stabilization
P1508	17916	Idle Sys. Learned Value Upper Limit Attained		

AD0159800266000X

Fig. 16 Codes P1391, P1392, P1409, P1410, P1500, P1502, P1505, P1506, P1507 & P1508

Diagnostic Trouble Code (DTC) SAE	VAG	Description of malfunction	MIL	Corrective action
P1624	18032	MIL Request Sign. active	On	– Check DTC memory via "Automatic Test Sequence" by inserting address word "00"
P1625	18033	CAN-Bus Unplausible Message from Transm. Contr.	2 Dcy	– Check CAN-Bus
P1640	18048	Internal Contr. Module (EEPROM) Error	2 Dcy	– Replace ECM
P1690	18098	Malfunction Indicator Light Malfunction	Off	– Check operation of MIL -K83
P1693	18101	Malfunction Indicator Light Short to B+		

AD0159800268000X

Fig. 18 Codes P1624, P1625, P1640, P1690 & P1693

	Display fields 1	2	3	4
Display group 7: Mass Air Flow (MAF) sensor				
Display	g/s	g/s	---	---
Indicates	Mass air flow (specified)	Mass air flow (actual)	Duty cycle for Idle Air Control (IAC) valve	Learned value for idle air control
Range	---	---	---	---
Specified value	ABZ: 3.9–6.5 g/s AEW: 3.4–6.5 g/s	ABZ: 3.9–6.5 g/s AEW: 3.4–6.5 g/s	0.8–1.2	75–100

AD1029800107000X

Fig. 20 MAF sensor display data

	Display fields 1	2	3	4
Display group 3: Basic functions, engine idle speed				
Display	RPM	Volt	°C	°C
Indicates	Engine speed	Battery Positive Voltage (B+)	Engine coolant temperature	Intake air temperature
Range	0–6300 RPM	---	-40° to 125°C	---
Specified value	ABZ: 720–800 RPM AEW: 680–760 RPM	11–14.5 V	85° to 105°C	---
Notes			The temperature value must increase.	

AD1029800111000X

Fig. 21 ECT sensor display data

	Display fields 1	2	3	4
Display group 3: Basic functions, engine idle speed				
Display	RPM	Volts	°C	°C
Indicates	Engine speed	Battery Positive Voltage (B+)	Engine coolant temperature	Intake air temperature
Range	0–6300 RPM	---	-40° to +125°C	---
Specified value	Idle speed	11 to 14.5 V	85°C	---

AD1029800130000X

Fig. 22 Engine idle display data

	Display fields			
	1	2	3	4
Display group 26: Heated Oxygen Sensors (HO2S and HO2S 2)				
Display	V	V	---	---
Indicates	HO2S (bank 1)	HO2S 2 (bank 2)	HO2S (bank 1) readiness	HO2S 2 (bank 2) readiness
Range	0 to 1 V	0 to 1 V	B1-S1 ON B1-S1 OFF	B2-S1 ON B2-S1 OFF
Specified value	0 to +0.9 V	0 to +0.9 V	B1-S1 ON (after 3 min.)	B2-S1 ON (after 3 min.)
Notes	♦ If there is no voltage, check wiring and wiring connections for open circuit		♦ If B1-S1 OFF or B2-S1 OFF is displayed, check O2S heating ♦ Check wiring and wiring connections for oxygen sensor signal	

AD1029800131000X

Fig. 23 Front oxygen sensor display data

	Display fields			
	1	2	3	4
Display group 27: Oxygen Sensors (O2S and O2S 2) behind Three Way Catalytic Converter (TWC)				
Display	V	V	---	---
Indicates	O2S behind TWC (bank 1)	O2S 2 behind TWC (bank 2)	O2S behind TWC (bank 1) readiness	O2S 2 behind TWC (bank 2) readiness
Range	---	---	B1-S2 ON B1-S2 OFF B1-S2 OK B1-S2 n.OK	B2-S2 ON B2-S2 OFF B2-S2 OK B2-S2 n.OK
Specified value	-0.5 to +0.9 V	-0.5 to +0.9 V	B1-S1 OK	B2-S1 OK
Notes			♦ If B1-S2 n.OK or B2-S2 n.OK are displayed, check O2S heating ♦ Check wiring and wiring connections for oxygen sensor signal	

AD1029800133000X

Fig. 25 Rear oxygen sensor display data

SYSTEM SERVICE

Refer to "Fuel Injection" section for adjustment and replacement procedures.

	Display fields			
	1	2	3	4
Display group 28: Oxygen Sensor (O2S) heating				
Display	Ohms	Ohms	---	---
Indicates	O2S heating resistance, HO2S and HO2S 2 (banks 1 + 2)	O2S heating resistance, O2S and O2S 2 behind TWC (banks 1 + 2)	O2S heating, HO2S and HO2S 2 (banks 1 + 2)	O2S heating, O2S and O2S 2 behind TWC (banks 1 + 2)
Range	---	---	---	---
Specified value	2.5–9.2 Ohms	2.5–9.2 Ohms	Htg.bc.ON	Htg.ac.ON
Notes			Check O2S heating	Oxygen sensors behind TWC cycle for the first few minutes (display fluctuates between "ON" and "OFF") Check O2S heating

AD1029800132000X

Fig. 24 Oxygen sensor heater data

	Display fields			
	1	2	3	4
Display group 4: Basic functions, engine idle speed				
Display	∠°	∠°	ms	---
Indicated	Throttle valve angle (actual)	Throttle valve angle (learned)	Engine load	**Operating condition**
Range	---	---	---	**Idle Part throt Full throt Enrich Decel**
Specified value	5–10 ∠°	0 ∠°	2.5–3.5 ms	**Idle**

AD1029800139000X

Fig. 26 Engine idle display data

	Display fields			
	1	2	3	4
Display group 4: Basic functions, ignition on				
Display	∠°	∠°	ms	---
Indicates	**Throttle valve angle (actual)**	Throttle valve angle (learned)	Engine load (Fuel injection time)	Operating condition
Range	---	---	---	Idle Part throt Full throt Enrich Decel
Specified values	**Accelerator pedal not depressed: 5–10 ∠°**	---	---	Idle
	Accelerator pedal fully depressed: 80–90 ∠°			Full load

AD1029800136000X

Fig. 27 Basic functions display data

Emission Control System Application Charts

Engine Liters/ Models	Certification Type		Trans. Type		Computerized Engine Management	Fuel Induction System Type	Ignition Timing, Deg. BTDC @ RPM	TSB	EPA & CARB Emission Recall	Emission Control System SRI	Emission Control Systems								
	CA	FED	A/T	M/T							PCV	ACL	AIS	EGR	EVAP	CAT	SPK	FR	O2S
1998–99																			
1.8L Turbo	X	X	X	X	YES⑩	MFI	②	⑥	—	—	X	—	—	—	X	X①	X⑪	X	X③
2.8L Except A6	X	X	X	X	YES⑩	MFI	②	⑦	—	—	X	—	—	X⑤	X	X④	X⑪	X	X③
2.8L A6	X	X	X	X	YES⑩	MFI	②	⑦⑬	—	—	X	—	—	X⑤	X	X①	X⑪	X	X⑨
3.7L	X	X	X	X	YES⑩	MFI	②	—	—	—	X	—	—	—	X	X①	X⑪	X	X⑨
4.2L	X	X	X	X	YES⑩	MFI	②	—	—	—	X	—	—	—	X	X①	X⑪	X	X⑨
2000–01																			
1.8L Turbo	X	X	X	X	YES⑩	MFI	②	—	—	—	X	—	—	—	X	X①	X⑪	X	X③
2.7L	X	X	X	X	YES⑩	MFI	②	—	—	—	X	—	—	—	X	X①	X⑪	X	X⑫
2.8L	X	X	X	X	YES⑩	MFI	②	—	—	—	X	—	—	—	X	X①	X⑪	X	X⑫
4.2L	X	X	X	X	YES⑩	MFI	②	—	—	—	X	—	—	—	X	X①	X⑪	X	X⑫

X — Equipped
— Not Equipped
① — Type, TWC; number of catalytic converters, 2.
② — Computer controlled. Non-adjustable.
③ — Two O2S.
④ — FWD models, type, TWC; number of catalytic converters, 1. FWD models, type, TWC; number of catalytic converters, 2.
⑤ — Electronically controlled EGR.
⑥ — On these models there may be misfiring w/MIL lighting & DTCs P0300 through P0304 stored in DTC memory. Service modifications can be performed.
⑦ — On 1998–99 models equipped w/5-valve engines there may be misfiring w/MIL lighting & DTCs P0300 through P0306 stored in DTC memory. Service modifications can be performed.
⑧ — On models which experience a service reminder lamp than will not reset, a service modification can be performed.
⑨ — Two HO2S & Two O2S.
⑩ — Motronic Engine Control/OBD II.
⑪ — EI/Solid State Distributorless Ignition.
⑫ — Four HO2S.
⑬ — Some models may experience lack of performance, poor idle or MIL lighting.
ACL — Air Cleaner (Thermostatic Air Cleaner)
AIS — Air Injection System
A/T — Automatic Transmission
BTDC — Before Top Dead Center
CA — California
CAT — Catalytic Converter
EGR — Exhaust Gas Recirculation
EVAP — Evaporative Emission Control System
FED — Federal
FR — Fillpipe Restrictor
MFI — Multi-Port Fuel Injection
M/T — Manual Transmission
OBD II — On Board Diagnostics II
O2S — Oxygen Sensor
PCV — Positive Crankcase Ventilation
RPM — Revolutions Per Minute
SFI — Sequential Fuel Injection
SPK — Spark Control
SRI — Service Reminder Indicator
TSB — Technical Service Bulletin
TWC — Three-Way Catalytic Converter

Vacuum Hose Routings

INDEX

	PAGE NO.	FIG. NO.
A4 & S4:		
1.8L Engine	10-129	1
2.7L Engine	10-129	2
2.8L Engine:		
Automatic Transaxle & MMS 410	10-130	3
Manual Transaxle & MMS 410	10-130	4
A6	10-130	5
A8	10-130	6
CABRIOLET w/MMS 411	10-131	7
S6	10-131	8
TT	10-131	9

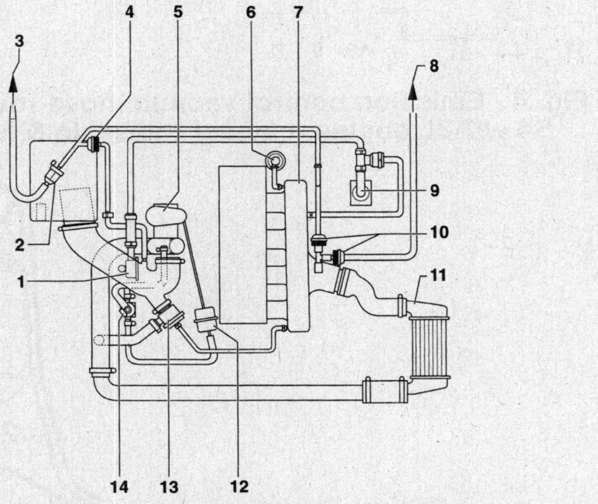

1. PCV Valve
2. EVAP Canister Purge Regulator Valve
3. To EVAP Canister
4. Canister Check Valve
5. Turbocharger
6. Fuel Pressure Regulator
7. Intake Manifold
8. To Leak Detection Pump
9. Crankcase Venitilation
10. Canister Check Valve
11. Charge Air Cooler
12. Vacuum Diaphragm
13. BP Pressure Recirculation Valve
14. Wastegate Bypass Pressure

AD1039800026000X

Fig. 1 Emission control vacuum hose routing. A4 & S4 w/1.8L engine

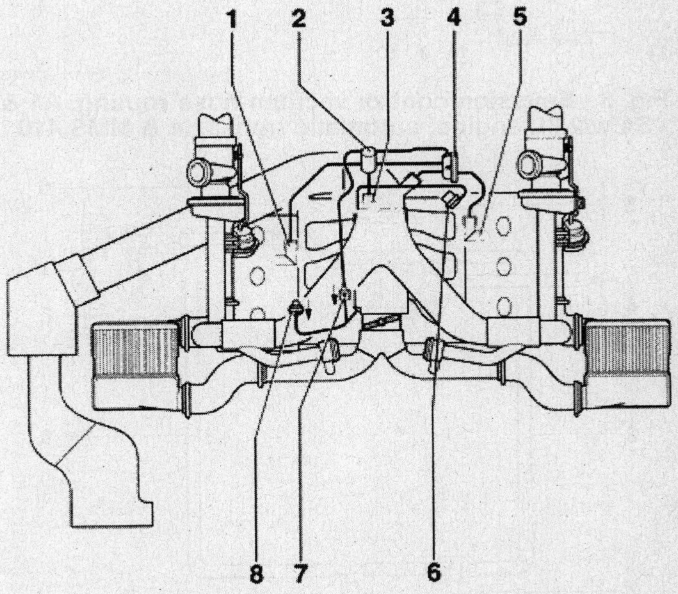

AD1030000058000X

Fig. 2 Emission control vacuum hose routing. A4 & S4 w/2.7L engine

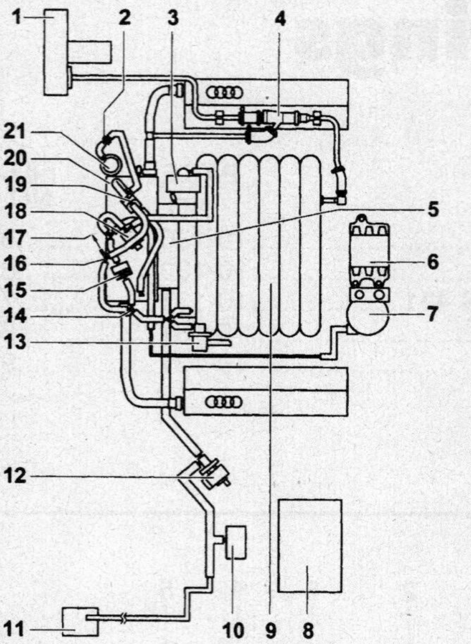

1. Brake Booster
2. Check Valve
3. Vacuum Cannister
4. Vacuum Booster
5. Throttle Body
6. Ignition Coils
7. Vacuum Reservoir
8. Air Cleaner
9. Intake Manifold
10. EVAP Cannister Sensor
11. Evap Cannister
12. Evap Cannister Purge Regulator Valve
13. Fuel Pressure Regulator
14. Tee Connector
15. Check Valve
16. Tee Connector
17. To A/C
18. Intake Manifold Change-over Valve
19. EGR Vacuum Regulator Solenoid Valve
20. Sound Dampener
21. EGR Valve

AD1039500004000X

Fig. 3 Emission control vacuum hose routing. A4 & S4 w/2.8L engine, automatic transaxle & MMS 410

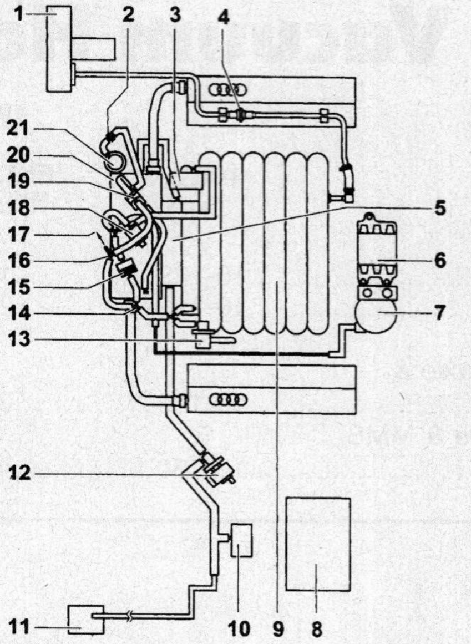

1. Brake Booster
2. Check Valve
3. Vacuum Cannister
4. Check Valve
5. Throttle Body
6. Ignition Coils
7. Vacuum Reservoir
8. Air Cleaner
9. Intake Manifold
10. EVAP Cannister Sensor
11. Evap Cannister
12. Evap Cannister Purge Regulator Valve
13. Fuel Pressure Regulator
14. Tee Connector
15. Check Valve
16. Tee Connector
17. To A/C
18. Intake Manifold Change-over Valve
19. EGR Vacuum Regulator Solenoid Valve
20. Sound Dampener
21. EGR Valve

AD1039500003000X

Fig. 4 Emission control vacuum hose routing. A4 & S4 w/2.8L engine, manual transaxle & MMS 410

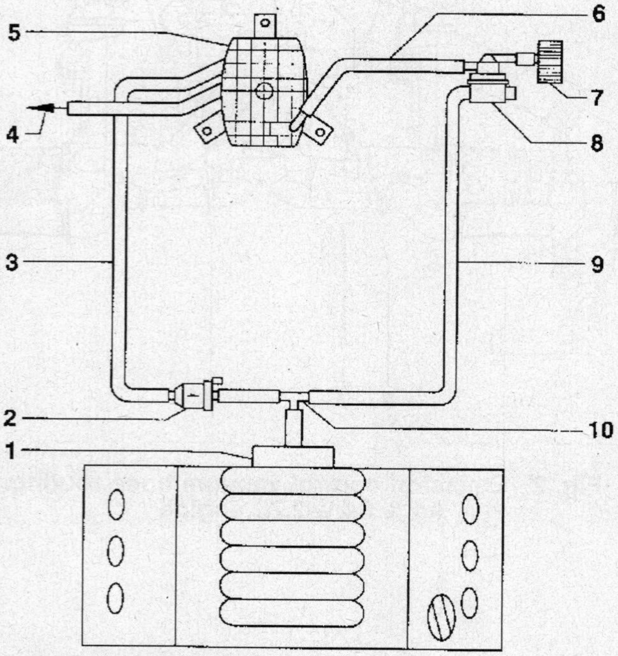

1. Throttle valve control module
2. Evaporative emission canister purge
3. Vent line from evap canister to purge regulator valve
4. Vent line from gravity valve at fuel tank
5. EVAP canister
6. Hose-from leak detection pump to EVAP canister pressure side
7. Air cleaner for LDP
8. Leak detection pump
9. Vacuum line-from LDP to throttle valve control module
10. T-connector

AD1039800021000X

Fig. 5 Emission control vacuum hose routing. A6

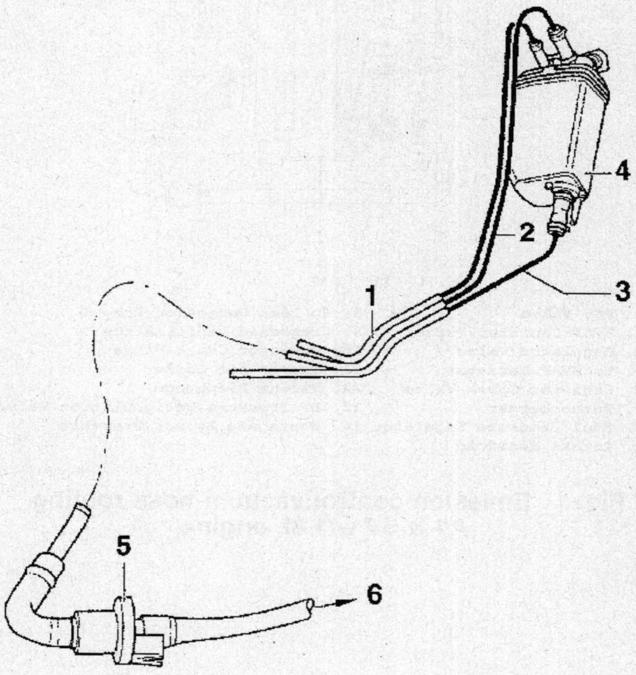

1. Expansion tank line
2. Vacuum line to engine
3. Vent line
4. EVAP canister
5. EVAP canister purge regulator valve
6. Vacuum line to throttle body/intake manifold

AD1039800022000X

Fig. 6 Emission control vacuum hose routing. A8

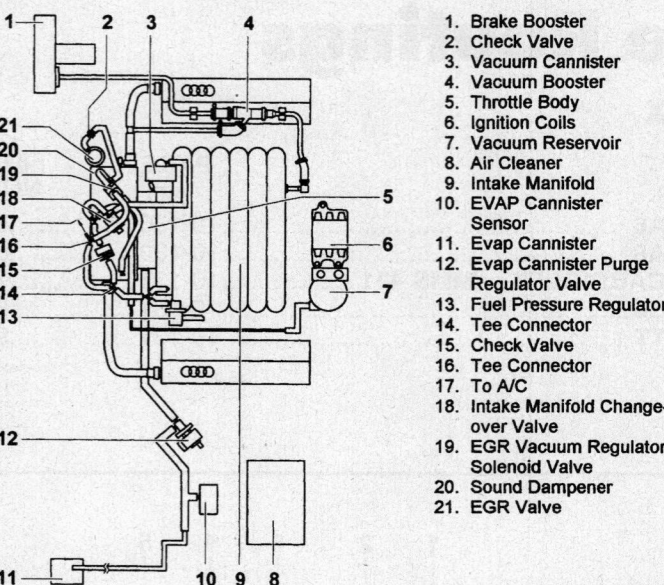

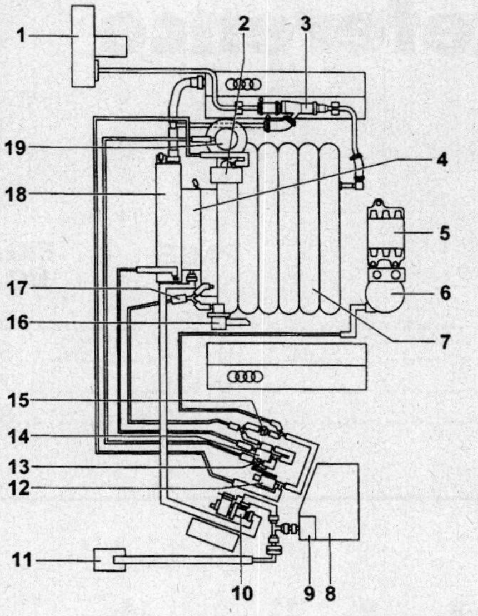

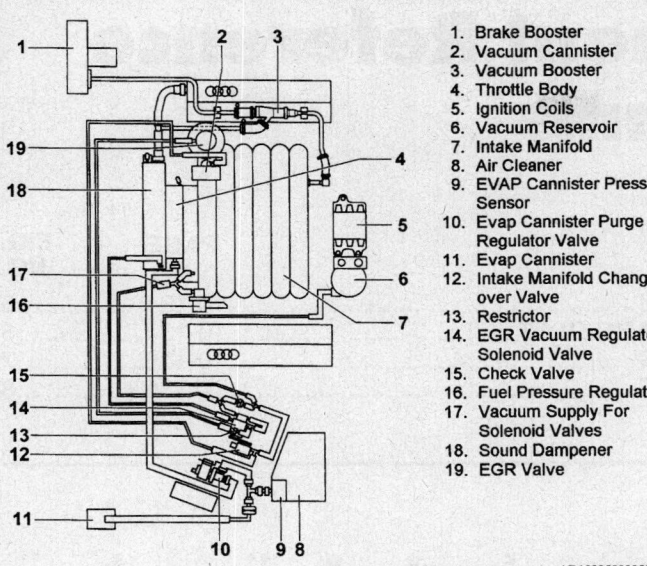

1. Brake Booster
2. Vacuum Cannister
3. Vacuum Booster
4. Throttle Body
5. Ignition Coils
6. Vacuum Reservoir
7. Intake Manifold
8. Air Cleaner
9. EVAP Cannister Pressure Sensor
10. Evap Cannister Purge Regulator Valve
11. Evap Cannister
12. Intake Manifold Change-over Valve
13. Restrictor
14. EGR Vacuum Regulator Solenoid Valve
15. Check Valve
16. Fuel Pressure Regulator
17. Vacuum Supply For Solenoid Valves
18. Sound Dampener
19. EGR Valve

AD1039500005000X

Fig. 7 Emission control vacuum hose routing. Cabriolet w/MMS 411

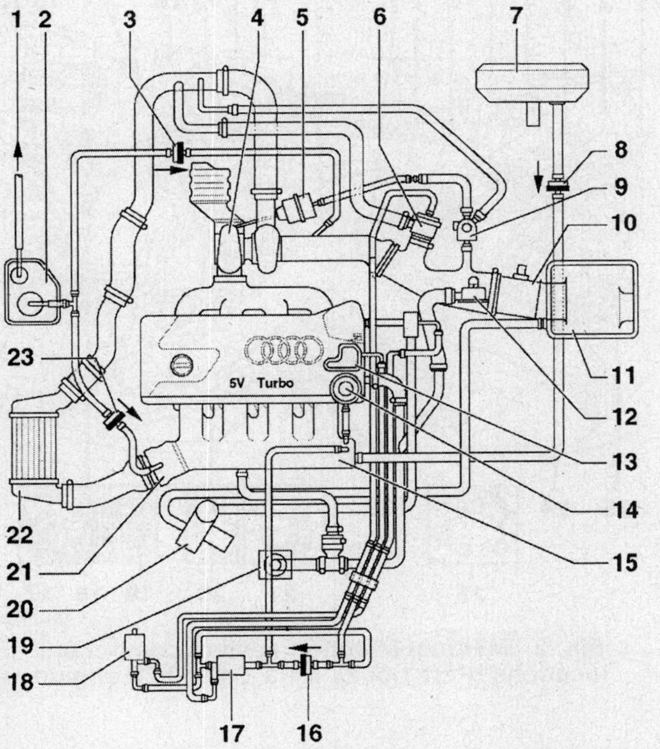

AD1030000059000X

Fig. 9 Emission control vacuum hose routing (Part 1 of 2). TT

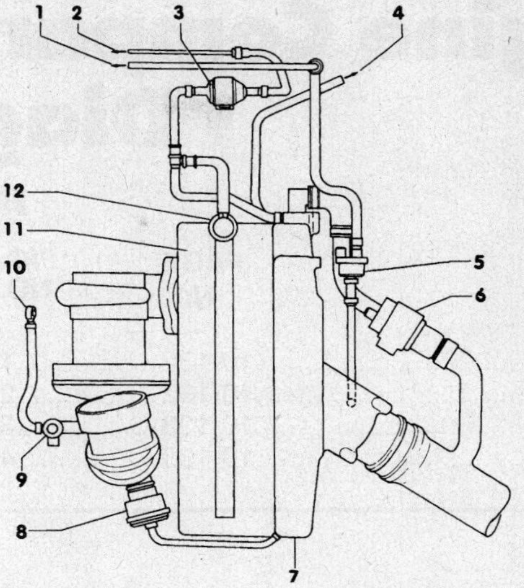

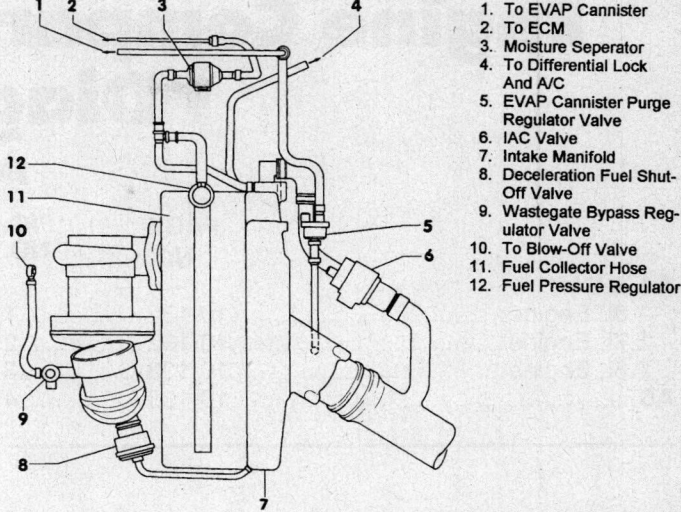

1. To EVAP Cannister
2. To ECM
3. Moisture Seperator
4. To Differential Lock And A/C
5. EVAP Cannister Purge Regulator Valve
6. IAC Valve
7. Intake Manifold
8. Deceleration Fuel Shut-Off Valve
9. Wastegate Bypass Regulator Valve
10. To Blow-Off Valve
11. Fuel Collector Hose
12. Fuel Pressure Regulator

AD1039500006000X

Fig. 8 Emission control vacuum hose routing. S6

1. Secondary air inlet valve
2. Crankcase breather
3. Secondary AIR pump motor
4. Throttle valve control module
5. EVAP canister check valves
6. Charge air cooler
7. Vacuum reservoir check valve
8. LDP vacuum reservoir
9. EVAP canister purge regulator valve
10. Test connector
11. Leak Detection Pump (LDP)
12. To EVAP canister
13. To EVAP canister
14. Turbocharger
15. Charge pressure control vacuum unit
16. Mechanical air recirculation valve
17. Brake servo
18. Brake servo check valve
19. Charge pressure control solenoid valve
20. MAF sensor
21. Air cleaner
22. Crankcase breather pressure regulator valve
23. Secondary AIR combination valve
24. Vacuum reservoir
25. Fuel pressure regulator
26. Intake manifold & IAT sender
27. Check valve
28. Turbocharger air recirculation valve

AD1030100060000X

Fig. 9 Emission control vacuum hose routing (Part 2 of 2). TT

Engine Compartment Reference Diagrams

INDEX

	PAGE NO.	FIG. NO.
A4 & S4:		
1.8L Engine	10-132	1
2.7L Engine	10-132	2
2.8L Engine	10-133	3
A6	10-133	4
A8	10-134	5
CABRIOLET	10-134	6
S6	10-135	7
TT	10-135	8

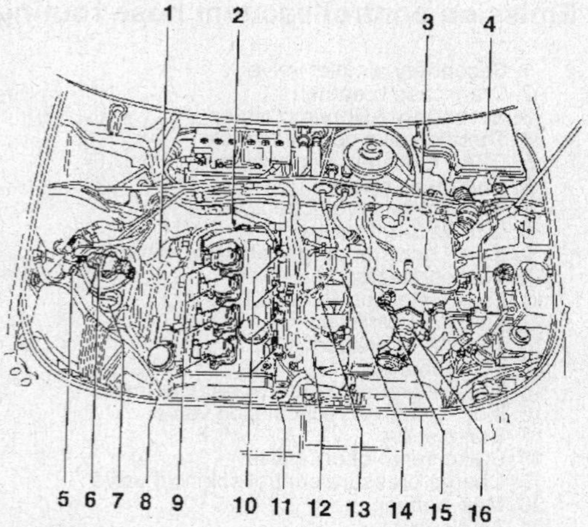

1. Heated oxygen sensor
2. ECT
3. Harness connector for; oxygen sensors, crankshaft position sensor and knock sensors
4. Electronics box with ECM and BARO sensor
5. EVAP purge regulator valve
6. Power output stage
7. MAF sensor
8. Wastegate bypass regulator valve
9. Ignition coils
10. Fuel injectors
11. Camshaft position sensor
12. Knock Sensor (KS)1
13. Knock Sensor (KS)2
14. Crankshaft position sensor (behind oil filter housing on cylinder block)
15. IAT sensor
16. Throttle valve control module

AD1039800023000X

Fig. 1 MFI fuel injection system component locations. A4 & S4 w/1.8L engine

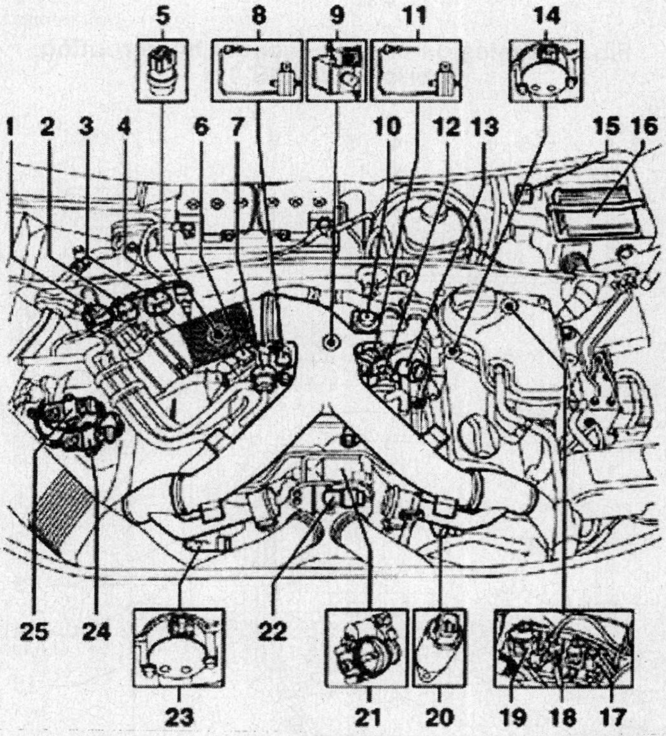

AD1020000228000X

Fig. 2 MFI fuel injection system component locations (Part 1 of 2). A4 & S4 w/2.7L engine

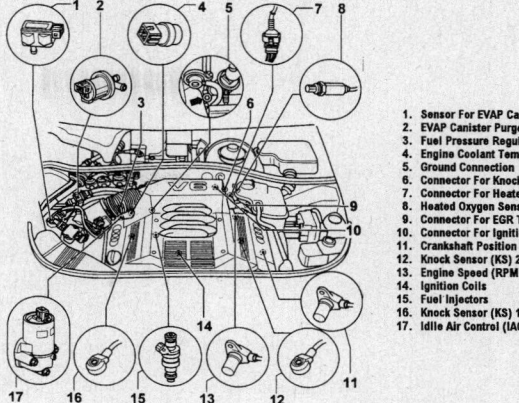

1. Rear O2S connector (4-pin green)
2. Rear O2S lconnector (4-pin brown)
3. O2S electrical connector (4-pin black)
4. Knock sensor 1 connector
5. ECT sensor
6. Wastegate bypass regulator valve
7. EVAP canister purge regulator valve
8. Exhaust temperature sensor 1
9. Secondary AIR injection solenoid valve
10. Secondary AIR pump motor
11. Exhaust temperature sensor 2
12. Turbocharger recirculation valve
13. Fuel pressure regulator valve
14. CMP sensor 2
15. Secondary AIR pump relay
16. ECM
17. Engine Speed (RPM) sensor connector
18. Knock sensor 2 connector
19. HO2S 2 connector
20. Camshaft adjuster valve
21. Throttle valve control module
22. Charge air pressure sensor
23. CMP sensor 1
24. Power output stage Bank 2
25. Power output stage Bank 1

AD1020100233000X

Fig. 2 MFI fuel injection system component locations (Part 2 of 2). A4 & S4 w/2.7L engine

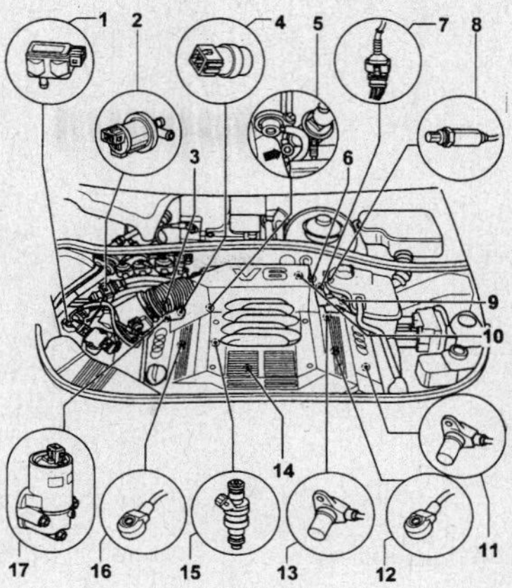

1. Sensor For EVAP Canister
2. EVAP Canister Purge Regulator Valve
3. Fuel Pressure Regulator
4. Engine Coolant Temperature (ECT) Sensor
5. Ground Connection
6. Connector For Knock Sensor (KS) 2
7. Connector For Heated Oxygen Sensor (HO2S)
8. Heated Oxygen Sensor (HO2S)
9. Connector For EGR Temperature Sensor
10. Connector For Ignition Coils
11. Crankshaft Position (CKP) Sensor
12. Knock Sensor (KS) 2
13. Engine Speed (RPM) Sensor
14. Ignition Coils
15. Fuel Injectors
16. Knock Sensor (KS) 1
17. Idlle Air Control (IAC) Valve

AD1039500014010X

Fig. 3 MFI fuel injection system component locations (Part 1 of 2). A4 & S4 w/2.8L engine

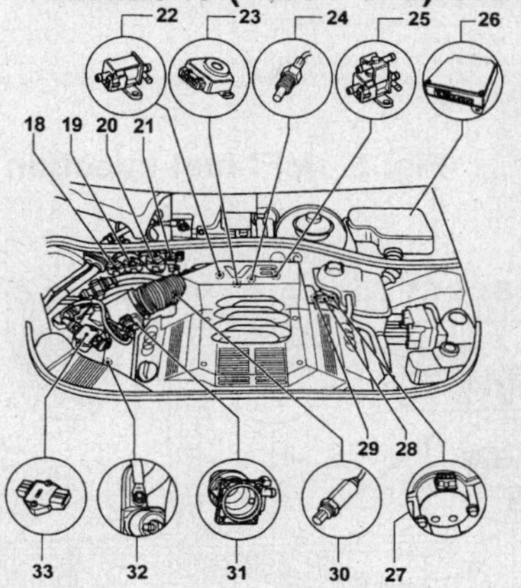

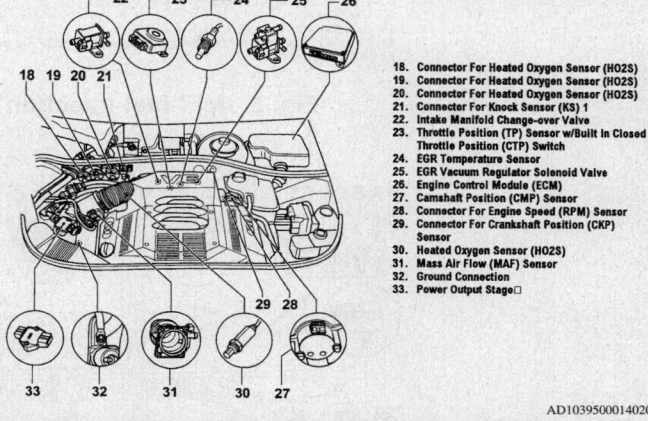

18. Connector For Heated Oxygen Sensor (HO2S)
19. Connector For Heated Oxygen Sensor (HO2S)
20. Connector For Heated Oxygen Sensor (HO2S)
21. Connector For Knock Sensor (KS) 1
22. Intake Manifold Change-over Valve
23. Throttle Position (TP) Sensor w/Built In Closed Throttle Position (CTP) Switch
24. EGR Temperature Sensor
25. EGR Vacuum Regulator Solenoid Valve
26. Engine Control Module (ECM)
27. Camshaft Position (CMP) Sensor
28. Connector For Engine Speed (RPM) Sensor
29. Connector For Crankshaft Position (CKP) Sensor
30. Heated Oxygen Sensor (HO2S)
31. Mass Air Flow (MAF) Sensor
32. Ground Connection
33. Power Output Stage□

AD1039500014020X

Fig. 3 MFI fuel injection system component locations (Part 2 of 2). A4 & S4 w/2.8L engine

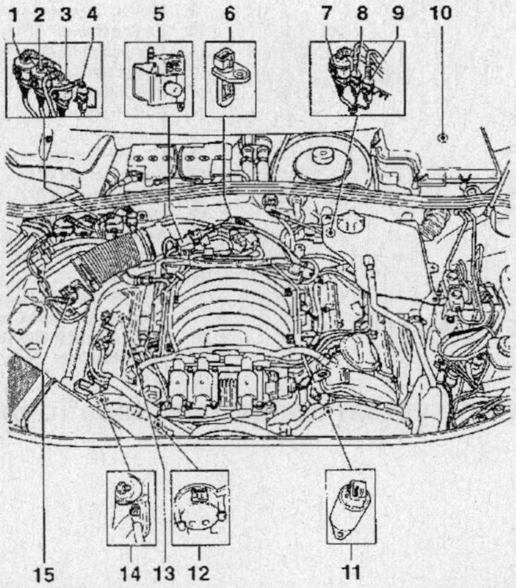

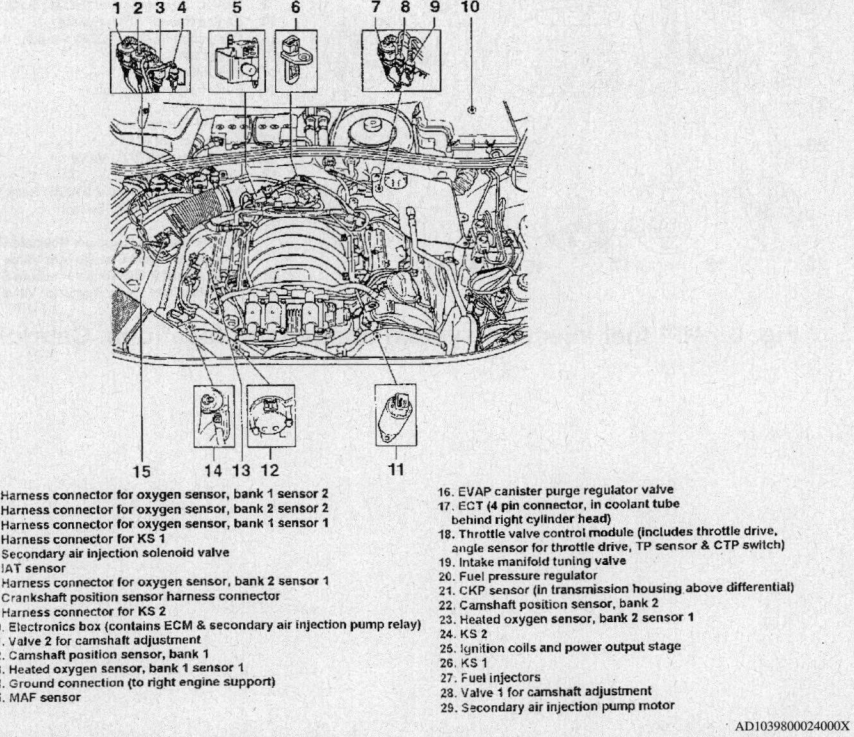

1. Harness connector for oxygen sensor, bank 1 sensor 2
2. Harness connector for oxygen sensor, bank 2 sensor 2
3. Harness connector for oxygen sensor, bank 1 sensor 1
4. Harness connector for KS 1
5. Secondary air injection solenoid valve
6. IAT sensor
7. Harness connector for oxygen sensor, bank 2 sensor 1
8. Crankshaft position sensor harness connector
9. Harness connector for KS 2
10. Electronics box (contains ECM & secondary air injection pump relay)
11. Valve 2 for camshaft adjustment
12. Camshaft position sensor, bank 1
13. Heated oxygen sensor, bank 1 sensor 1
14. Ground connection (to right engine support)
15. MAF sensor
16. EVAP canister purge regulator valve
17. ECT (4 pin connector, in coolant tube behind right cylinder head)
18. Throttle valve control module (includes throttle drive, angle sensor for throttle drive, TP sensor & CTP switch)
19. Intake manifold tuning valve
20. Fuel pressure regulator
21. CKP sensor (in transmission housing above differential)
22. Camshaft position sensor, bank 2
23. Heated oxygen sensor, bank 2 sensor 1
24. KS 2
25. Ignition coils and power output stage
26. KS 1
27. Fuel injectors
28. Valve 1 for camshaft adjustment
29. Secondary air injection pump motor

AD1039800024000X

Fig. 4 MFI fuel injection system component locations. A6

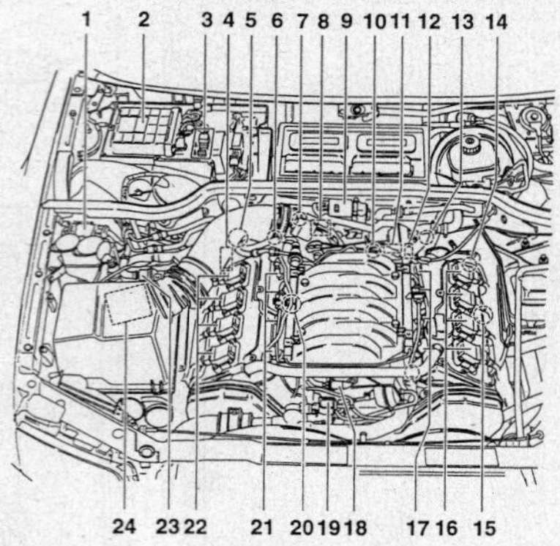

1. Power output stage
2. ECM
3. ECM power relay and fuses
4. Harness connector for oxygen sensor, bank 1 sensor 1
5. Harness connector for oxygen sensor, bank 1 sensor 2 (under right front carpet)
6. ECT sensor (rear cylinder head)
7. IAT sensor
8. Throttle position sensor
9. IAC valve
10. Crankshaft position sensor
11. Harness connector for oxygen sensor, bank 2 sensor 1
12. CKP harness connector
13. Harness connector for oxygen sensor, bank 2 sensor 2 (under right front carpet)
14. Camshaft position sensor
15. KS 2
16. Ignition coils, bank 2
17. Fuel injectors, bank 2
18. Air valve for fuel injectors
19. Intake manifold changeover valve
20. KS 1
21. Fuel injectors, bank 1
22. Ignition coils, bank 1
23. EVAP canister purge regulator valve
24. MAF sensor

AD1039800025000X

Fig. 5 MFI fuel injection system component locations. A8

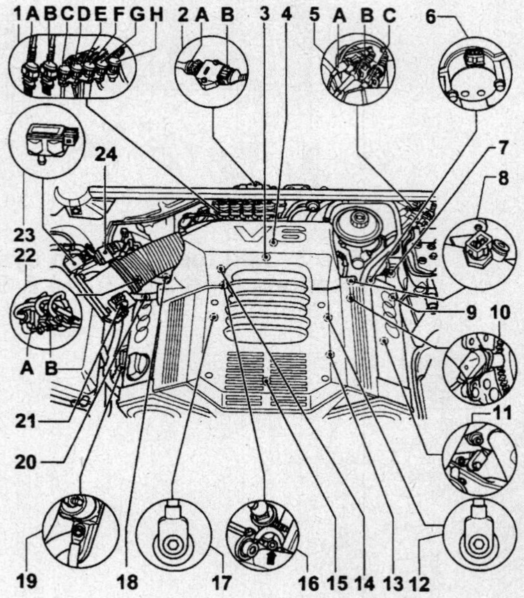

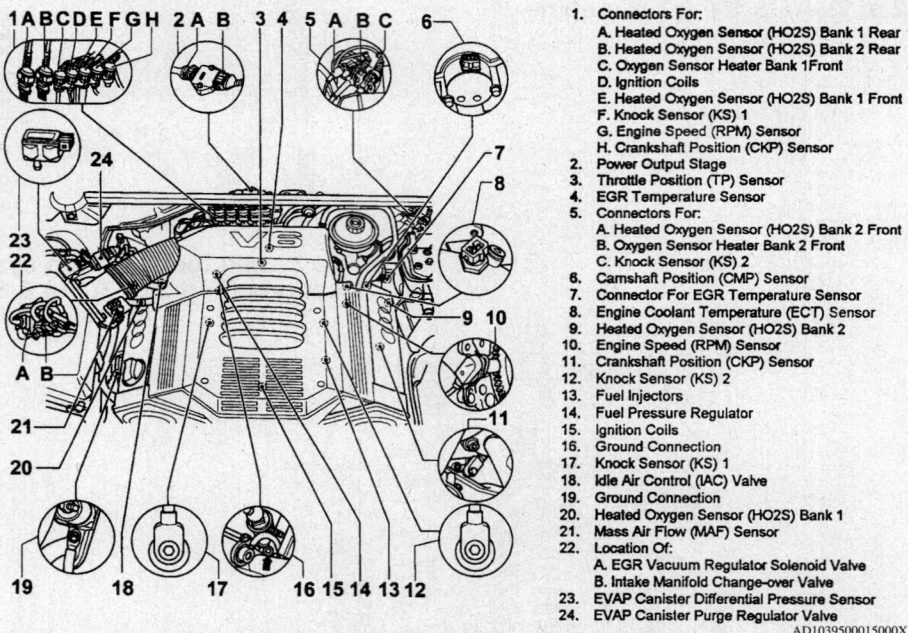

1. Connectors For:
   A. Heated Oxygen Sensor (HO2S) Bank 1 Rear
   B. Heated Oxygen Sensor (HO2S) Bank 2 Rear
   C. Oxygen Sensor Heater Bank 1Front
   D. Ignition Coils
   E. Heated Oxygen Sensor (HO2S) Bank 1 Front
   F. Knock Sensor (KS) 1
   G. Engine Speed (RPM) Sensor
   H. Crankshaft Position (CKP) Sensor
2. Power Output Stage
3. Throttle Position (TP) Sensor
4. EGR Temperature Sensor
5. Connectors For:
   A. Heated Oxygen Sensor (HO2S) Bank 2 Front
   B. Oxygen Sensor Heater Bank 2 Front
   C. Knock Sensor (KS) 2
6. Camshaft Position (CMP) Sensor
7. Connector For EGR Temperature Sensor
8. Engine Coolant Temperature (ECT) Sensor
9. Heated Oxygen Sensor (HO2S) Bank 2
10. Engine Speed (RPM) Sensor
11. Crankshaft Position (CKP) Sensor
12. Knock Sensor (KS) 2
13. Fuel Injectors
14. Fuel Pressure Regulator
15. Ignition Coils
16. Ground Connection
17. Knock Sensor (KS) 1
18. Idle Air Control (IAC) Valve
19. Ground Connection
20. Heated Oxygen Sensor (HO2S) Bank 1
21. Mass Air Flow (MAF) Sensor
22. Location Of:
    A. EGR Vacuum Regulator Solenoid Valve
    B. Intake Manifold Change-over Valve
23. EVAP Canister Differential Pressure Sensor
24. EVAP Canister Purge Regulator Valve

AD1039500015000X

Fig. 6 MFI fuel injection system component locations. Cabriolet

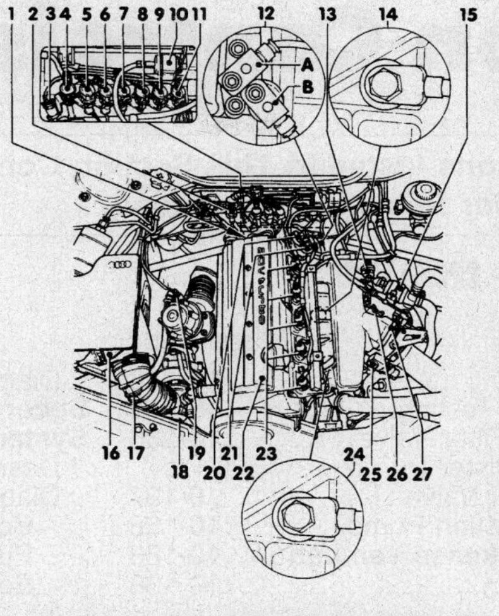

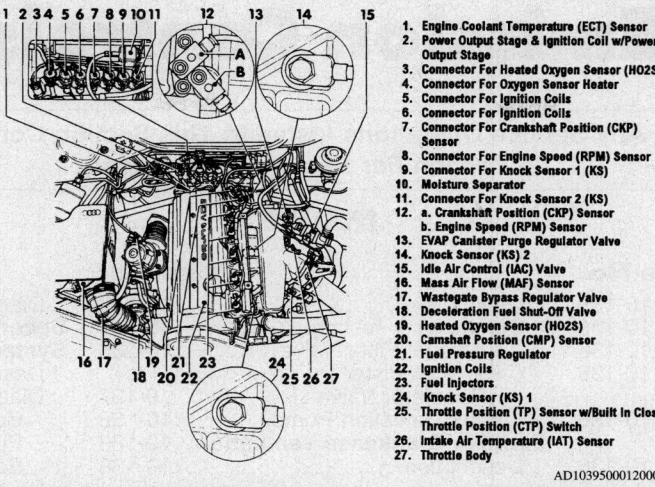

1. Engine Coolant Temperature (ECT) Sensor
2. Power Output Stage & Ignition Coil w/Power Output Stage
3. Connector For Heated Oxygen Sensor (HO2S)
4. Connector For Oxygen Sensor Heater
5. Connector For Ignition Coils
6. Connector For Ignition Coils
7. Connector For Crankshaft Position (CKP) Sensor
8. Connector For Engine Speed (RPM) Sensor
9. Connector For Knock Sensor 1 (KS)
10. Moisture Separator
11. Connector For Knock Sensor 2 (KS)
12. a. Crankshaft Position (CKP) Sensor
    b. Engine Speed (RPM) Sensor
13. EVAP Canister Purge Regulator Valve
14. Knock Sensor (KS) 2
15. Idle Air Control (IAC) Valve
16. Mass Air Flow (MAF) Sensor
17. Wastegate Bypass Regulator Valve
18. Deceleration Fuel Shut-Off Valve
19. Heated Oxygen Sensor (HO2S)
20. Camshaft Position (CMP) Sensor
21. Fuel Pressure Regulator
22. Ignition Coils
23. Fuel Injectors
24. Knock Sensor (KS) 1
25. Throttle Position (TP) Sensor w/Built In Closed Throttle Position (CTP) Switch
26. Intake Air Temperature (IAT) Sensor
27. Throttle Body

AD1039500012000X

Fig. 7 Bosch Motronic fuel injection system component locations. S6

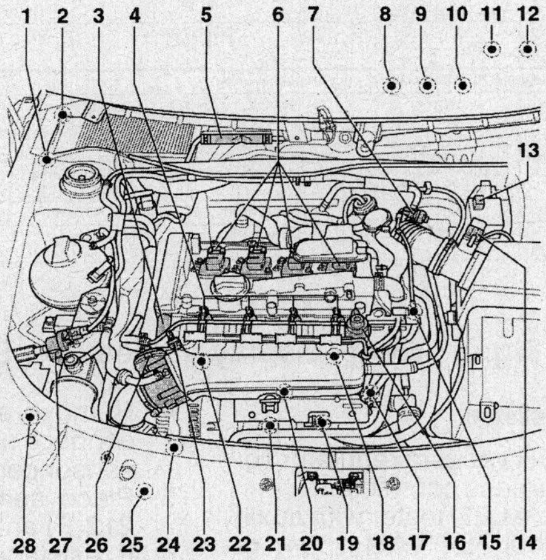

1. Leak Detection Pump (LDP)
2. Bank 1 sensor 1 & Bank 2 sensor 2
3. Camshaft Position (CMP) sensor 2
4. Fuel injectors
5. Engine Control Module (ECM)
6. Ignition coils
7. Wastegate bypass regulator valve
8. Throttle Position (TP) & Accelerator Pedal Position (APP) sensor
9. Brake lamp switch & brake pedal switch
10. Clutch vacuum vent valve switch
11. Exhaust warning lamp
12. Power accelerator activation (EPC) lamp
13. Secondary AIR pump relay
14. Mass Air Flow (MAF) sensor
15. Engine Coolant Temperature (ECT) sensor
16. Fuel pressure regulator
17. Speedometer Vehicle Speed Sensor (VSS)
18. Knock Sensor (KS)
19. Turbocharger boost pressure recirculation valve
20. Electrical connector
21. Secondary AIR solenoid valve
22. Knock Sensor (KS) 1
23. Intake Air Temperature (IAT) sensor
24. Secondary AIR pump motor
25. Power steering pressure switch
26. Throttle valve control module
27. EVAP canister purge regulator valve
28. Charge air pressure sensor

AD1020000229000X

Fig. 8 MFI fuel injection system component locations. TT

Emission Controls

NOTE: Prior To Performing Any Service Operations Listed In This Section Consult Technical Service Bulletin Section For Related Information.

INDEX

	Page No.
Exhaust Gas Recirculation	10-136
Description	10-136
Diagnosis & Testing	10-136
EGR Temperature Sensor	10-136
EGR Vacuum Regulator Solenoid	10-136
Fuel Evaporative Control System	10-136
Description	10-136
Diagnosis & Testing	10-136
Charcoal Filter Valve	10-136
EVAP Canister Purge Regulator Valve	10-137
Leak Detection Pump	10-138
Positive Crankcase Ventilation	10-138
Description	10-138
Diagnosis & Testing	10-138
Secondary Air Injection (AIR) System	10-138
Description	10-138
Diagnosis & Testing	10-138
Combi Valve	10-138
Pump Motor & Circuit	10-138
Solenoid Valve	10-138

EXHAUST GAS RECIRCULATION

Description

The EGR system reduces formation of nitrogen oxides by recirculating small amounts of exhaust gases into the combustion cycle.

Diagnosis & Testing

EGR VACUUM REGULATOR SOLENOID

A6

Activation Inspection

1. Connect suitable LED tester to terminal Nos. 1 and 2.
2. Initiate "Output Diagnostic Test Mode" as outlined in "Computerized Engine Controls."
3. If tester does not blink when EGR vacuum regulator solenoid valve is activated, connect test box tool No. VAG 1598 with adapter harness tool No. VAG 1598/12, or equivalent, to Engine Control Module (ECM) wiring harness.
4. If LED tester lights continuously, inspect wiring between EGR vacuum regulator solenoid connector terminal No. 2 and test box socket 14 for short to ground.
5. If LED tester does not blink, inspect for 1 ohm maximum continuity between terminal No. 2 and socket 14.
6. Repair short or break between terminal No. 2 and ECM connector D terminal No. 14.
7. If wiring is satisfactory, remove ECM.

Electrical Inspection

1. Disconnect EGR vacuum regulator solenoid valve harness connector and measure valve's resistance.
2. If resistance is not 25–30 ohms, replace.

	Display fields 1	2	3	4
Display group 70: EVAP canister purge regulator valve				
Display	xxx %	xx.x %	xx.xx g/s	Test OFF/Test ON EVAP OK EVAP notOK
Indicated	EVAP canister purge regulator valve duty cycle during diagnosis	Oxygen sensor deviation during diagnosis	Idle Air Control (IAC) valve deviation during diagnosis	Diagnosis condition Diagnosis results
Range	0–100 %	–25.0 to 25.0 %	–2.70 to 4.16 g/s	---
Specified value	0–100 %	– 5.4 to 9.4 %	0.00–0.33 g/s	EVAP OK

AD1039800019000X

Fig. 1 EVAP display values. A4, S4 & TT

Voltage Inspection

1. Disconnect EGR vacuum regulator solenoid valve harness connector.
2. Connect suitable LED tester with auxiliary test set tool No. VAG 1594, or equivalent, to positive terminal No. 1 and engine ground.
3. Initiate "Output Diagnostic Test Mode" as outlined in "Computerized Engine Controls" and activate fuel pump relay.
4. If tester does not light, inspect circuit breaker, then wiring continuity for .5 ohm maximum resistance between terminal No. 1 and circuit breaker.
5. Inspect fuel pump replay.

EGR TEMPERATURE SENSOR

A6

1. Disconnect EGR temperature sensor and connect suitable multimeter to contacts, then Turn ignition On.
2. If voltage is not 4.5–5 volts, repair break between connector contact 1 and Engine Control Module (ECM) contact 7B as well as between contact 2 and engine ground. **Use only gold-plated contacts to repair EGR temperature sensor terminal connector.**
3. If voltage is within specifications, disconnect multimeter and turn ignition Off.
4. Remove sensor from EGR valve and connect suitable multimeter between sensor contacts.
5. Place sensor in boiling water (176–212°F) and measure resistance.
6. If resistance does not change, replace sensor.

FUEL EVAPORATIVE CONTROL SYSTEM

Description

This system prevents fuel fumes from entering atmosphere. Fuel fumes are stored in charcoal filter. When engine is started, charcoal filter valve opens, which allows fuel fumes stored in charcoal filter to be drawn into intake manifold to be burned during normal combustion.

Diagnosis & Testing

CHARCOAL FILTER VALVE

1. Remove charcoal filter valve.
2. Connect suitable vacuum pump to smaller hose connection.
3. Blow into large opening. Air passage should be blocked.
4. Draw vacuum on valve.
5. Blow into large opening. Air passage should be opened.
6. Replace valve if required.

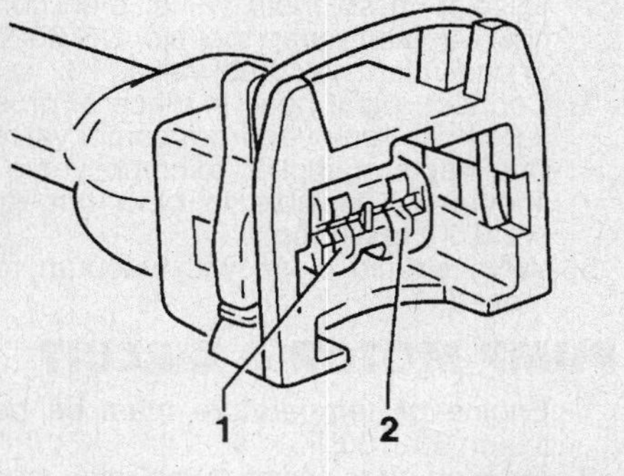

Fig. 2 EVAP canister purge regulator valve electrical connector. A4, S4 & TT

EVAP CANISTER PURGE REGULATOR VALVE

A4, S4 & TT

Functional Inspection

1. Ensure engine temperature is at least 176°F.
2. Connect scan tool No. VAG 1551/1552, or equivalent, then press buttons 0 and 1 to insert "Engine Electronics" Address Word 01 with engine running at idle.
3. Press buttons 0 and 8 to select "Read Measuring Value Block" function 08, then press "Q" to confirm input.
4. Press buttons 0, 7 and 0 to input Display Group 70, then press "Q" to confirm input.
5. Press button 4 to select "Basic Setting" function 04.
6. If diagnosis is initiated by ECM, display changes from "Test Off" to "Test On" in Display Field 4.
7. Compare scan tool display with EVAP display values, **Fig. 1.**
8. Continue to run engine until "EVAP satisfactory" is displayed in Field 4.
9. If display changes from "Test On" to "Test Off" during test, briefly accelerate engine to repeat test.
10. If "EVAP Not OK" is displayed in Field 4, refer to "Blockage & Leak Inspection."
11. If "EVAP OK" is displayed in Field 4, press right arrow button to advance program. Press buttons 0 and 6 to select "End Output" function 06, then press "Q" to confirm input.

Blockage & Leak Inspection

The EVAP canister purge regulator valve is closed when power is off.

1. Remove EVAP canister purge regulator valve. Leave harness connector connected.
2. Start output diagnostic test mode and select N-80.
3. Blow into long connection during output DTM and inspect opening and closing operation of valve. Replace as required.
4. If valve is satisfactory, inspect all hose connections between tank and valve for blockage or leaks and correct as required.

Resistance Inspection

1. Disconnect EVAP canister purge regulator valve.
2. Measure resistance across terminals using a suitable ohmmeter. Resistance should be 22–30 ohms.
3. If resistance is not as specified, replace valve.
4. If resistance is as specified, refer to "Voltage Inspection."

Voltage Inspection

1. Inspect EVAP system fuses and replace as required.
2. Disconnect EVAP canister purge regulator valve.
3. Connect LED voltage tester tool No. VAG 1527B, or equivalent, between harness connector terminal 1 and ground, **Fig. 2.**
4. Crank engine and observe LED.
5. If LED does not light, inspect continuity of wiring from socket 1 to fuel pump relay via fuse. Repair open circuit as required.
6. If wiring is satisfactory, refer to "Fuel Pump Relay" under "Fuel Injection."

Signal Inspection

1. Connect LED voltage tester tool No. VAG 1527B, or equivalent, between harness connector terminal 1 and 2, **Fig. 2.**
2. Start output diagnostic test mode for EVAP canister purge regulator valve. To initiate DTM a second time, the engine must be started and stopped again.
3. If LED lights and stays lit, proceed as follows:
   a. Connect test box tool No. VAG 1598/31, or equivalent, to ECM wiring harness. **Do not connect to ECM itself.**
   b. Inspect for short circuit to ground in wiring between EVAP valve connector terminal 2 and test box socket 64. Repair as required.
4. If LED does not flash, inspect for open circuit or short circuit to voltage in wiring between EVAP valve connector terminal 2 and test box socket 64. Maximum resistance is 1.5 ohms. Repair as required.
5. If wiring is satisfactory, replace ECM.

A6

Electrical Inspection

1. Disconnect EVAP canister purge regulator valve electrical connector, then measure resistance of valve.
2. If resistance is not 20–28 ohms, replace solenoid valve.

Voltage Supply Inspection

1. Disconnect electrical connector, then connect suitable LED between connector terminal No. 1 and engine ground using jumpers from adapter kit tool No. VAG 1594, or equivalent. Operate starter for several seconds.

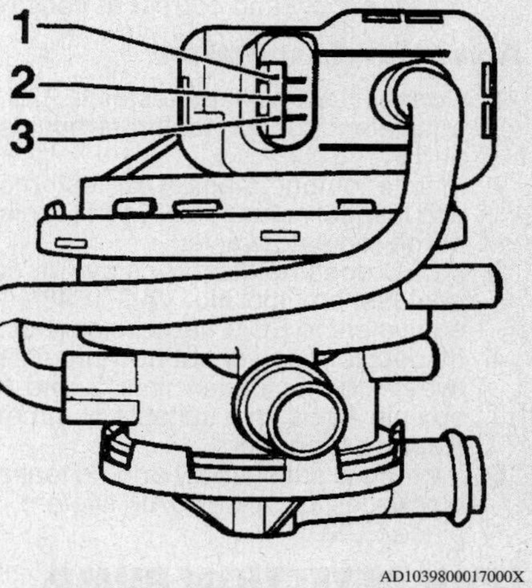

Fig. 3 Leak detection pump terminal identification

2. If tester does not light, inspect system power supply and correct as required.
3. Inspect fuel pump relay and actuation.

Actuation Inspection

1. Connect suitable LED tester using jumpers from adapter kit tool No. VW 1594, or equivalent, between EVAP canister purge regulator valve connector terminal Nos. 1 and 2, then refer to "Computerized Engine Controls" section and perform "Output Diagnostic Test Mode (DTM)."
2. If tester does not flash or lights continuously, connect test box tool No. VAG 1598 using adapter cable tool No. VAG 1598-12, or equivalents, to Engine Control Module (ECM). ECM is not connected.
3. If tester lights continuously, inspect wiring from EVAP canister purge regulator valve electrical connector terminal No. 2 to test box connector 12 for short to ground.
4. If tester does not flash, measure continuity from EVAP canister purge regulator valve electrical connector terminal No. 2 to test box connector 12. Resistance must be 1 ohm maximum.
5. Repair open or short circuits between EVAP canister purge regulator valve electrical connector terminal No. 2 and ECM terminal No. 12.
6. If wiring is satisfactory, replace ECM.

A8

Electrical Inspection

1. Disconnect EVAP canister purge regulator valve electrical connector, then measure resistance of valve.
2. If resistance is not 20–35 ohms, replace solenoid valve.

Voltage Supply Inspection

1. Disconnect electrical connector, then connect suitable LED between connector terminal No. 1 and engine ground using jumpers from adapter kit tool No. VAG 1594, or equivalent. Operate starter for several seconds.
2. If tester does not light, inspect system

power supply and correct as required.

Actuation Inspection

1. Connect LED voltage tester 1527B, or equivalent to connector terminals 1 and 2.
2. Initiate output diagnostic test mode and inspect actuation of EVAP canister purge regulator valve.
3. If LED does not flash or stays lit, connect test box tool No. VAG 1598/19 or equivalent to ECM harness connector.
4. Inspect for open or shorted circuits between connector terminal 2 and test box pin A8 using a suitable ohmmeter. Repair as required.
5. If wiring is satisfactory and no leaks or blockages exist in EVAP system, replace ECM.

LEAK DETECTION PUMP

RESISTANCE INSPECTION

1. Disconnect leak detection pump.
2. Measure resistance of pump electrical terminals 1 and 3, **Fig. 3,** using a suitable ohmmeter. Resistance should be 640–720 ohms.
3. Measure resistance between pump electrical terminals 2 and 3, which should be 18–28 ohms.
4. If resistance is not as specified, replace leak detection pump.

VOLTAGE INSPECTION

1. Disconnect lead detection pump.
2. Connect LED voltage tester tool No. VAG 1527B, or equivalent, between harness connector terminal 3 and ground, **Fig. 4.**
3. Start and idle engine.
4. If LED does not light, inspect fuse and LDP wiring. If fuse and wiring are satisfactory, refer to "Fuel Pump Relay" under "Fuel Injection."

POSITIVE CRANKCASE VENTILATION

Description

This system recirculates emissions from the crankcase into the intake system. Crankcase vapors are then drawn into the combustion chamber and burned.

Diagnosis & Testing

1. Start and idle engine.
2. Disconnect PCV valve and listen for a distinct hissing sound, which indicates system is not plugged. Clean or replace hoses if required.
3. Place finger over end of PCV valve. A strong vacuum should be felt.

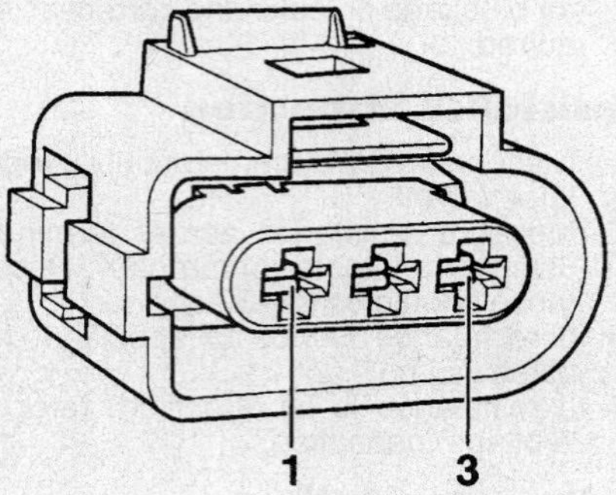

Fig. 4 Leak detection pump harness connector terminal identification

4. Insert suitable rod or stick into end of valve against plunger.
5. Briefly accelerate engine and observe rod or stick, which should follow plunger movement as vacuum stabilizes.
6. Replace PCV valve if plunger does not move.

SECONDARY AIR INJECTION (AIR) SYSTEM

The Following information has been modified by a Technical Service Bulletin.

Description

The Air Injection Reactor (AIR) is used to shorten cold start catalyst light off time by injection of air behind the exhaust valve into the fuel rich exhaust stream for a predetermined time.

The AIR system is controlled by the ECM through the Pump Relay, Combi Valve and Solenoid Valve.

This system will operate for a variable time dependent on temperature after the initial cold start with engine temperatures between 60–95°F and for five seconds (after a 20 second delay) for subsequent starts with engine temperatures between 60–185°F.

Diagnosis & Testing

COMBI VALVE

Do not use compressed air while testing this valve or component damage will occur.

1. Remove pump pressure hose from combi valve.
2. Disconnect vacuum hose to combi valve from solenoid valve, then connect vacuum pump tool No. US 8026, or equivalent, to combi valve.
3. Connect a test hose in place of pressure hose removed from combi valve.
4. With vacuum applied to combi valve it should be possible to blow through pressure test hose.
5. Valve should close with vacuum removed.

PUMP MOTOR & CIRCUIT

1. Engine oil temperature must be between 60–185°F.
2. Fuse on air injection pump relay must be good.
3. Remove pressure hose from pump at combi valve and route upward.
4. Start engine and allow to idle, wait 20 approximately seconds.
5. Pump should run for 5 seconds and air should be felt at pressure hose.
6. If pump motor does not run, proceed as follows:
   a. Turn ignition Off.
   b. Disconnect connector at pump motor.
   c. Connect LED tester tool No. 1527B, or equivalent, to connector terminals.
   d. Start engine and allow to idle, then wait approximately 20 seconds.
   e. LED should light for five seconds.
7. If LED does not light, proceed to "Computerized Engine Controls."
8. If LED lights, test motor using a suitable 12 volt source and connectors.
9. If motor tests good, proceed to "Computerized Engine Controls."

SOLENOID VALVE

1. Engine oil temperature must be between 60–185°F.
2. Inspect fuse on air injection pump relay.
3. Remove vacuum hose from combi valve and route upward, then connect a suitable vacuum gauge to hose.
4. Start engine and allow to idle, then wait approximately 20 seconds.
5. Pump should run for five seconds and vacuum should be noted at hose.
6. If vacuum is not noted, proceed as follows:
   a. Turn ignition Off.
   b. Disconnect connector at solenoid valve.
   c. Connect LED tester tool No. 1527B, or equivalent, to connector terminals.
   d. Start engine and allow to idle, wait approximately 20 seconds.
   e. LED should light for 5 seconds.
7. If LED lights, replace valve. If LED does not light refer to "Computerized Engine Controls."

Technical Service Bulletins

INDEX

Page No.

Code P0411, MIL Lighting 10-140
2001 TT w/Turbocharged Engine 10-140
Code P1557 Stored In Memory .. 10-140
2000 A6 & S4 w/2.7L Engine ... 10-140
Cold Hesitation, Poor Idle 10-139
DTC 00537/2341, 00554/2331 10-139
A6 & Cabriolet 10-139
Engine Cranks, Does Not Start .. 10-140
1998–2000 A4 & A6 w/2.8L 5-Valve Engine 10-140
Engine Misfire, Hard To Start, Poor Mileage 10-139
Groaning & Howling From Engine Compartment 10-141
2000–01 TT w/Turbocharged Engine 10-141
Idle Speed Low, Fluctuating 10-141
All Models w/1.8L Turbocharged Engine & 2.8L 5-Valve Engine 10-141
Lack Of Performance, Poor Idle, MIL Lighting 10-139
Lack Of Power 10-139
A4 & S4 w/1.8L Turbocharged Engine & Automatic Transaxle 10-139
Poor Idle, Lack Of Power 10-139
A4 & S4 w/1.8L Turbocharged Engine 10-139

COLD HESITATION, POOR IDLE

Vehicle may hesitate when cold or idle poorly.

This condition may be caused when heated oxygen sensor operates too slowly or is out of range as result of contact cleaner or other substances being drawn into sensor interior and destroying or altering sensor operation.

To correct this condition, replace oxygen sensor if corrosion is found on terminals.

Do not use contact cleaner or any similar material when repairing or replacing heated oxygen sensors.

DTC 00537/2341, 00554/2331

A6 & Cabriolet

On these models, Malfunction Indicator Lamp (MIL) may light and store Diagnostic Trouble Codes (DTCs) 00537/2341 and 00554/2331, "Oxygen Sensor Below Limit/ Exceeded."

Rubber elbow shaped hose at front of intake manifold may split and cause vacuum leak which can trigger these DTCs.

To correct these fault conditions, inspect hose and replace elbow if required. Clear DTCs, then road test vehicle and inspect for DTCs.

ENGINE MISFIRE, HARD TO START, POOR MILEAGE

Engine may misfire, be hard to start and/ or provide poor fuel mileage.

These conditions may be caused by high voltage leakage through rips and/or tears in ignition cable connector insulation. Improper removal of connectors from spark plugs or distributor cap can cause these rips and/ or tears.

To correct this condition, use special ignition cable pliers tool when removing cables.

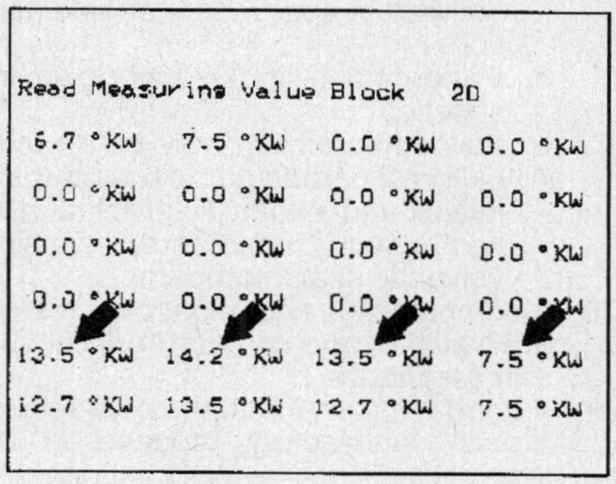

ADA019800002000X

Fig. 1 Display group 20 measuring block. A4 & S4 w/1.8L turbocharged engine & automatic transaxle

LACK OF PERFORMANCE, POOR IDLE, MIL LIGHTING

Some models equipped with 2.8L engines (engine code AAH) may exhibit lack of performance, poor idle or MIL lighting. On models with MMS 311, 410 and 411, VAG codes 17733, 17734, 17735, 17736, 17737 and 17738 may be present. These conditions may be due to carbon build up on top of pistons, in combustion chambers and on intake valves caused by using fuels that do not contain a sufficient blend of detergents. If vehicle has these conditions with any of the DTCs specified, proceed as follows:

1. Ensure knock sensor is properly tightened.
2. Inspect knock sensor system operation.
3. If knock sensor system is operating properly, decarbonize combustion chamber using decarb tool Kit No. US9025 and Wynn's X-Trend VIC combustion chamber cleaner, or equivalents. Follow tool kit instructions for complete procedure.
4. Change oil after carbon removal.

POOR IDLE, LACK OF POWER

A4 & S4 w/1.8L Turbocharged Engine

On some models, a poor idle or lack of power condition may be present. This condition may be caused by a power interruption to the ECM (dead or disconnected battery or ECM replacement). If power is interrupted, the throttle valve control module must be adapted to the ECM as outlined under "Relearn Procedures" in "Computer Relearn Procedures" in the front of this manual.

LACK OF POWER

A4 & S4 w/1.8L Turbocharged Engine & Automatic Transaxle

On some models, a lack of power condition may be present due to a faulty ECM. Use the following procedure to diagnose the ECM.

1. Connect scan tool No. VAG 1551, or equivalent.
2. Start engine, then press 1 to select "Rapid Data Transfer" operating mode 01.
3. Press buttons 0 and 1 to insert "Engine Electronics" address word 01, then press "Q" to confirm input.
4. Press right arrow button.
5. Press buttons 0 and 8 to select "Read Measuring Value Block" function 08, then press "Q" to confirm input.
6. Observe Field 3 which displays ECT.
7. When engine has reached 113–149°F, road test vehicle with second technician to operate scan tool.
8. Press "C" button, then press buttons 0, 2 and 0 to select Display Group 20. Press "Q" to confirm input.
9. Accelerate from a stop at wide open throttle while pushing print button as

many times as possible. Repeat procedure with ECT above 176°F.
10. Add figures from 4 channels (arrows) of Display Group 20, **Fig. 1,** using scan tool printouts.
11. If in any of printed rows, sum of values is greater than 15°, replace ECM with updated unit.
12. If in all rows printed, sum of values is 15° or less, inspect turbocharger and wastegate system.

ENGINE CRANKS, DOES NOT START

1998–2000 A4 & A6 w/2.8L 5-Valve Engine

On these models this condition may occur after the vehicle has sat several hours. An overnight situation is a typical example.

Ensure the battery is fully charged and fuel tank has a sufficient quantity of fuel, then proceed as follows:

1. Connect scan tool No. VAG 1551, or equivalent, to DLC.
2. Select vehicle system "01-Engine Electronics."
3. Select diagnosis function "02-Interrogate Fault Memory" to search for stored DTCs.
4. Select "Print" and "Save Result." **Do not print screens.**
5. Select "Yes" when "Erase Old Log?" appears.
6. Diagnose and correct any DTCs.
7. Reset readiness code.
8. Select Back arrow.
9. Select diagnosis function "08-Read Data Block."
10. Read Data Blocks 04, 06, 32, 55 and 60. Select "Print" and "Save Result" for each Data Block. **Do not print screens.**
11. Turn ignition On.
12. Ensure values in Display Fields 3 and 4 in Data Block 04 approximately equal ambient temperature.
13. Select back arrow on navigation bar.
14. Select "Print," then "Self-Diagnosis Log."
15. Inspect coolant temperature sensor manufacturing date, which must be later than week 19 of 1998. This will appear as 19/98 stamped into side of sensor housing.
16. Inspect and record fuel pressure as outlined under "Fuel Pressure" in "Diagnosis & Testing" in "2.8L Engine" section.
17. Ensure throttle linkage operates properly and travels smoothly from CTP through WOT.
18. Crank engine while observing throttle angle specifications in data block 60. Throttle angle must be greater than 6°.
19. If coolant temperature sensor, fuel pressure and throttle linkage are satisfactory, proceed as follows:
    a. Perform compression inspection as outlined in appropriate engine section.
    b. Perform a cylinder leak-down inspection.
    c. Low compression may be an indication of carbon particle buildup on intake and exhaust valves and in combustion chambers, causing valves to seat improperly.
20. If compression and leak-down results are satisfactory, contact Audi for further assistance.
21. If compression and leak-down results are not satisfactory, proceed as follows:
    a. Install old spark plugs.
    b. Remove thermostat.
    c. Install revised thermostat part No. 078 121 113 G with O-ring part No. N901 368 02. **Ensure jiggle pin port is at 12 o'clock position. Temperature gauge will read slightly higher because new thermostat opens at 198°F compared to 189°F for old one. On A4 models,** revised thermostat was installed in production after VIN 8DXA279411. **On A6 models,** revised thermostat was installed in production after VIN 4BXN116771.
22. Depress accelerator to floor and crank engine until it starts.
23. Road test vehicle for 10 miles with engine RPM between 4000–5000 RPM. Use appropriate lower gear to keep within posted speed limits. An alternate method is to park vehicle in a safe area and keep engine running at constant 4000–5000 RPM for five minutes.
24. Turn ignition Off.
25. Remove carbon deposits using decarb tool kit No. US 9025 and Wynn's X-Tend V.I.C. Combustion Chamber Cleaner part No. 61510.
26. Change engine oil. **Do not use 20W-50 oil.**
27. Remove spark plugs.
28. Disconnect fuel injector wiring and crank engine for a minimum of 30 seconds.
29. Connect injector wiring.
30. Install new NGK spark plugs part No. BKR6EQUPA (Audi part No. 101 000 067 AA).
31. Remove fuel injectors and replace with revised 4-hole red top injectors part No. 078 133 551 BA. **On A4 models,** revised injectors were installed in production after VIN 8DYA013500. **On A6 models,** revised injectors were installed in production after VIN 4BYN096000.
32. Ensure battery is fully charged.
33. Start engine. It may be required to fully depress accelerator to floor while cranking.
34. Bring engine to operating temperature.
35. Road test vehicle for 10 miles with engine RPM between 4000–6000 RPM under load. Use appropriate lower gear to keep within posted speed limits.
36. Advise owner to switch to high detergent fuel to prevent recurrence of carbon buildup.

ADA010100003000X

Fig. 2 Charge pressure valve vacuum hose

CODE P0411, MIL LIGHTING

2001 TT w/Turbocharged Engine

On these models these conditions may be caused by a faulty charge pressure bypass valve which cannot hold sufficient vacuum.

To correct this condition, proceed as follows:

1. Remove engine upper cover.
2. Disconnect vacuum hose at charge pressure bypass valve, **Fig. 2.**
3. Connect hand vacuum pump tool No. VAG 1390, or equivalent, to charge pressure bypass valve.
4. Operate pump and create at least 15 inches of vacuum.
5. If valve holds at least 15 inches of vacuum, continue diagnosis for Code P0411.
6. If valve does not hold at least 15 inches of vacuum, replace charge pressure bypass valve.

CODE P1557 STORED IN MEMORY

2000 A6 & S4 w/2.7L Engine

On these models, A6 through VIN 4B_YN090649 and S4 through VIN 8D_YA139999, this condition may be caused by a loss of pressure to the turbocharger due to tears or cracks in the intake duct under the retaining clamps.

To correct this condition, proceed as follows:

1. Remove engine upper covers.
2. Remove intake air duct.
3. Inspect air duct for cracks and tears.

4. If duct is damaged, install a new duct with clamps, **Fig. 3.**
5. Install engine upper covers.
6. Clear any stored trouble codes, then set readiness code.

GROANING & HOWLING FROM ENGINE COMPARTMENT

2000–01 TT w/Turbocharged Engine

On these models, these noises may be noticed during acceleration under partial load between 2000–3000 RPM and may be caused by pulsations in the charge pressure bypass valve internal diaphragm.

To correct this condition, road test the vehicle and listen for the noises under the specified conditions. If the noises occur, replace the charge pressure bypass valve part No. 06A 145 710N.

IDLE SPEED LOW, FLUCTUATING

All Models w/1.8L Turbocharged Engine & 2.8L 5-Valve Engine

On these models these conditions may be caused by throttle valve control module contamination.

To correct this condition, proceed as follows:

1. Remove intake boot from throttle valve control module housing.
2. Inspect interior surfaces of throttle valve control module housing and throttle plate for a dirt or oil film.
3. If no contamination is discovered, install intake boot and continue with diagnosis.
4. If contamination is discovered, clean interior surfaces using a clean soft cloth.
5. In case of heavy deposits, apply Wynn's X-Tend V.I.C. Combustion Chamber Cleaner part No. 61510 to a clean soft cloth, then clean interior surfaces as required.
6. Install intake boot.
7. Perform throttle valve control module relearn procedure as outlined under "Computer Relearn Procedures" in front of this manual.
8. If throttle valve control module relearn cannot be performed, replace throttle valve control module.

Abbreviations & Acronyms

A/C: Air conditioning
ACL: Air Cleaner
AIR: Air Pump (Secondary Air Injection)
AP: Accelerator Pedal
BARO: Barometric Pressure Sensor
CAC: Charge Air Cooler
CL: Closed Loop
CKP: Crankshaft Position (Sensor)
CMP: Camshaft Position (Sensor)
CO: Carbon Monoxide
CO FT: CO Fuel Trim Adjustment
CTP: Closed Throttle Position
DLC: Data Link Connector
DTC: Diagnostic Trouble Code
DTM: Diagnostic Test Mode
ECT: Engine Coolant Temperature
EGR: Exhaust Gas Recirculation System
EI: Electronic Ignition (System)
EGRT: Exhaust Gas Recirculation Temperature
EOP: Engine Oil Pressure
EVAP: Evaporative Emission Control System
FC: Fan Control
F4WD: Full Time Four Wheel Drive
HO2S: Heated Oxygen Sensor
IAC: Idle Air Control (Thermal Idle Air Control)
IAT: Intake Air Temperature (Sensor)
ICM: Ignition Or Knock Control Module
ISC: Idle Speed Control
KS: Knock Sensor
LDP: Leak Detection Pump
LOAD: Calculated Load Value
MAF: Mass Air Flow
MAP: Manifold Absolute Pressure
MC: Mixture Control
MDP: Manifold Differential Pressure
MIL: Malfunction Indicator Lamp
MPI: Multi-Point Injection
OBD: On Board Diagnostic System
OL: Open Loop
OXS: Oxygen Sensor
PNP: Park Neutral Position (Switch)
SC: Supercharger
SRI: Service Reminder Indicator
SRT: System Readiness Test
TCC: Torque Converter Clutch
TCM: Transmission Control Module
TVV: Thermal Vacuum Valve
TWC: Three Way Catalytic Converter
VAF: Volume Air Flow
VSS: Vehicle Speed Sensor
WOT: Wide Open Throttle
4GR: Fourth Gear

BMW

TABLE OF CONTENTS

Page No.

EMISSIONS:
Abbreviations & Acronyms 11-150
Application Chart 11-134
Emissions Controls 11-144
Emission Control System Application Chart . . . 11-134
Engine Compartment Reference Diagrams 11-135
Technical Service Bulletins 11-146

ENGINE SYSTEMS IDENTIFICATION 11-2

FUEL SYSTEMS:
Abbreviations & Acronyms 11-150
Electric Fuel Pumps 11-17
Engine Compartment Reference Diagrams 11-135
Fuel Injection 11-12
Technical Service Bulletins 11-146

ENGINE TUNE UP & PERFORMANCE:
Abbreviations & Acronyms 11-150
Specifications 11-2

Page No.

V8 Gasoline Engine 11-7
V12 Gasoline Engine. 11-8
4 Cylinder Gasoline Engine 11-5
6 Cylinder Gasoline Engine 11-6

GENERAL INFORMATION:
Abbreviations & Acronyms 11-150
Air Bag System Precautions 0-12
Air Quality Standards 0-23
Computer Relearn Procedures 0-10
Electrical Symbol & Wire Color Code Identification 0-33
Engine System Identification 11-2
How To Use This Manual. 0-1
Quick Reference. 11-1
Service Reminder & Warning Lamp Reset Procedure 0-14
Technical Service Bulletins 11-146
Vehicle Identification. 0-3
Vehicle Maintenance Schedules 0-45

IGNITION SYSTEMS:
Abbreviations & Acronyms 11-150
Engine Compartment Reference Diagrams 11-135
Ignition Systems. 11-9

Quick Reference

Application	Page No.
ACCESSING DIAGNOSTIC TROUBLE CODES	
All	11-23
CLEARING DIAGNOSTIC TROUBLE CODES	
All	11-24
COMPRESSION PRESSURE SPECIFICATIONS	
Four-Cylinder Engine	11-5
Six-Cylinder Engine	11-6
V8 Gasoline Engine	11-7
V12 Engine	11-8
FUEL PRESSURE SPECIFICATIONS	
All	11-19
IGNITION COIL SPECIFICATIONS	
All	11-10
SENSOR & FUEL INJECTOR SPECIFICATIONS	
All	11-22

Engine Systems Identification

Various codes may be stamped into the engine block in various places. An engine number will have eight digits such as 0 001 0 000. The first digit represents the assembly line and the next three digits the engine serial number. The fifth digit is the factory code (N for new and A for exchange) , while last three digits represent the production day (12 7 being December 1997). The engine code is a series of numbers and letters without hyphens or dashes. The first two digits represent the engine size in liters (18 = 1.8 liters). The next digit or two is the number of cylinders (i.e. 4, 6, 8 or 12). The next letter will be E for fuel injected, V for corroborated or T for turbocharged. The next letter is an BMW change index. The next letter is a country code and a final K is for catalytic converter.

The fourth through seventh digits of the Vehicle Identification Number (VIN) denotes the vehicle description which includes engine size and number of cylinders. The VIN number is stamped on a plate which is attached to the top lefthand side of the instrument panel.

Model	Engine Series	Displacement, Liters	Fuel Injection System	Page No.	Ignition System	Page No.	Computer System	Page No.
1998								
M3	S52	3.2L	Multi-Point Fuel Injection	11-12	Direct Ignition	11-9	DME MS41 (Siemens)	11-20
Z3 M Coupe & Roadster	S52	3.2L	Multi-Point Fuel Injection	11-12	Direct Ignition	11-9	DME MS41 (Siemens)	11-20
Z3 1.9	M44	1.9L	Multi-Point Fuel Injection	11-12	Direct Ignition	11-9	DME M5.2 (Bosch HFM-Motronic)	11-20
Z3 2.8	M52	2.8L	Multi-Point Fuel Injection	11-12	Direct Ignition	11-9	DME MS41 (Siemens)	11-20
318i/ti	M44	1.9L	Multi-Point Fuel Injection	11-12	Direct Ignition	11-9	DME M5.2 (Bosch HFM-Motronic)	11-20
323i/is	M52	2.5L	Multi-Point Fuel Injection	11-12	Direct Ignition	11-9	DME MS41 (Siemens)	11-20
328i/is	M52	2.8L	Multi-Point Fuel Injection	11-12	Direct Ignition	11-9	DME MS41 (Siemens)	11-20
528i	M52	2.8L	Multi-Point Fuel Injection	11-12	Direct Ignition	11-9	DME MS41 (Siemens)	11-20
540i	M62	4.4L	Multi-Point Fuel Injection	11-12	Direct Ignition	11-9	DME M5.2 (Bosch HFM-Motronic)	11-20
740i/iL	M62	4.4L	Multi-Point Fuel Injection	11-12	Direct Ignition	11-9	DME M5.2 (Bosch HFM-Motronic)	11-20
750iL	M73	5.4L	Multi-Point Fuel Injection	11-12	Electronic Ignition	11-9	DME M5.2 (Bosch HFM-Motronic)	11-20
1999								
M3	S52	3.2L	Multi-Point Fuel Injection	11-12	Direct Ignition	11-9	DME MS41 (Siemens)	11-20
318ti	M44	1.9L	Multi-Point Fuel Injection	11-12	Direct Ignition	11-9	DME M5.2 (Bosch HFM-Motronic)	11-20
Z3 M Coupe & Roadster	S52	3.2L	Multi-Point Fuel Injection	11-12	Direct Ignition	11-9	DME MS41 (Siemens)	11-20
Z3 2.3	M52 TU	2.5L	Multi-Point Fuel Injection	11-12	Direct Ignition	11-9	DME MS42 (Siemens)	11-20
Z3 2.8	M52 TU	2.8L	Multi-Point Fuel Injection	11-12	Direct Ignition	11-9	DME MS42 (Siemens)	11-20
323i/is Coupe & Convertible	M52	2.5L	Multi-Point Fuel Injection	11-12	Direct Ignition	11-9	DME MS41 (Siemens)	11-20
323i Sedan	M52 TU	2.5L	Multi-Point Fuel Injection	11-12	Direct Ignition	11-9	DME MS42 (Siemens)	11-20
328i/is Coupe & Convertible	M52	2.8L	Multi-Point Fuel Injection	11-12	Direct Ignition	11-9	DME MS41 (Siemens)	11-20
328i/is	M52 TU	2.8L	Multi-Point Fuel Injection	11-12	Direct Ignition	11-9	DME MS42 (Siemens)	11-20
528i	M52 TU	2.8L	Multi-Point Fuel Injection	11-12	Direct Ignition	11-9	DME MS42 (Siemens)	11-20
540i	M62	4.4L	Multi-Point Fuel Injection	11-12	Direct Ignition	11-9	DME M5.2 (Bosch HFM-Motronic)	11-20
740i/iL	M62	4.4L	Multi-Point Fuel Injection	11-12	Direct Ignition	11-9	DME M5.2 (Bosch HFM-Motronic)	11-20
750iL	M73	5.4L	Multi-Point Fuel Injection	11-12	Electronic Ignition	11-9	DME M5.2 (Bosch HFM-Motronic)	11-20

Continued

Model	Engine Series	Displacement, Liters	Fuel Injection System	Page No.	Ignition System	Page No.	Computer System	Page No.
2000								
M5	S62	5.0L	Multi-Point Fuel Injection	11-12	Electronic Ignition	11-9	DME MSS52 (Siemens)	11-20
X5	M62	4.4L	Multi-Point Fuel Injection	11-12	Direct Ignition	11-9	DME M5.2.1 (Bosch HFM-Motronic)	11-20
Z3 M Coupe & Roadster	S52	3.2L	Multi-Point Fuel Injection	11-12	Electronic Ignition	11-9	DME MS41 (Siemens)	11-20
Z3 2.3	M52 TU	2.5L	Multi-Point Fuel Injection	11-12	Direct Ignition	11-9	DME MS42 (Siemens)	11-20
Z3 2.8	M52 TU	2.8L	Multi-Point Fuel Injection	11-12	Direct Ignition	11-9	DME MS42 (Siemens)	11-20
323Ci/i	M52 TU	2.5L	Multi-Point Fuel Injection	11-12	Electronic Ignition	11-9	DME MS42 (Siemens)	11-20
328Ci/i	M52 TU	2.8L	Multi-Point Fuel Injection	11-12	Electronic Ignition	11-9	DME MS42 (Siemens)	11-20
540i	M62	4.4L	Multi-Point Fuel Injection	11-12	Direct Ignition	11-9	DME M5.2.1 (Bosch HFM-Motronic)	11-20
740i/iL	M62	4.4L	Multi-Point Fuel Injection	11-12	Direct Ignition	11-9	DME M5.2.1 (Bosch HFM-Motronic)	11-20
750iL	M73	5.4L	Multi-Point Fuel Injection	11-12	Direct Ignition	11-9	DME M5.2.1 (Bosch HFM-Motronic)	11-20
2001								
M3	S54	3.2L	Multi-Point Fuel Injection	11-12	Multi-Point Fuel Injection	11-9	Siemens MS S54	11-20
M5	S62	5.0L	Multi-Point Fuel Injection	11-12	Electronic Ignition	11-9	DME MSS52 (Siemens)	11-20
X5 3.0i	M54	3.0L	Multi-Point Fuel Injection	11-12	Direct Ignition	11-9	DME MS43 (Siemens)	11-20
X5 4.4i	M62	4.4L	Multi-Point Fuel Injection	11-12	Direct Ignition	11-9	DME M7.2 (Bosch HFM-Motronic)	11-20
Z3 M Coupe & Roadster	S54	3.2L	Multi-Point Fuel Injection	11-12	Multi-Point Fuel Injection	11-9	Siemens MS S54	11-20
Z3 2.5i	M54	2.5L	Multi-Point Fuel Injection	11-12	Multi-Point Fuel Injection	11-9	DME MS43 (Siemens)	11-20
Z3 3.0i	M54	3.0L	Multi-Point Fuel Injection	11-12	Direct Ignition	11-9	DME MS43 (Siemens)	11-20
325Ci/i/ix	M54	2.5L	Multi-Point Fuel Injection	11-12	Multi-Point Fuel Injection	11-9	DME MS43 (Siemens)	11-20
325Ci/i/ix	M54	2.8L	Multi-Point Fuel Injection	11-12	Multi-Point Fuel Injection	11-9	DME MS43 (Siemens)	11-20
525i	M54	2.5L	Multi-Point Fuel Injection	11-12	Direct Ignition	11-9	DME MS43 (Siemens)	11-20
530i	M54	3.0L	Multi-Point Fuel Injection	11-12	Direct Ignition	11-9	DME MS43 (Siemens)	11-20
540i	M62	4.4L	Multi-Point Fuel Injection	11-12	Direct Ignition	11-9	DME M7.2 (Bosch HFM-Motronic)	11-20
740i/iL	M62	4.4L	Multi-Point Fuel Injection	11-12	Direct Ignition	11-9	DME M7.2 (Bosch HFM-Motronic)	11-20
750iL	M73	5.4L	Multi-Point Fuel Injection	11-12	Direct Ignition	11-9	DME M5.2.1 (Bosch HFM-Motronic)	11-20

Tune Up Specifications

Year & Engine	Spark Plug Gap Inch	Ignition Timing		Curb Idle Speed (A/C Off)②		Curb Idle Speed (A/C On ②)		Fuel Pump Pressure, psi.①	Valve Lash, Inch	
		Firing Order	Timing BTDC	Man. Trans.	Auto. Trans.	Man. Trans.	Auto. Trans.		Intake	Exhaust
1998–99										
1.9L	.028	⑦	③	800③	800③	800③	800③	51–58	⑨	⑨
2.5L	.028	⑧	⑨	⑨	⑨	⑨	⑨	51–58	⑨	⑨
2.8L	.028	⑧	⑨	700⑨	680D⑨	740⑨	720D⑨	51–58	⑨	⑨
3.2L	.024	⑧	⑨	780⑨	—	780⑨	—	51–58	⑨	⑨
4.4L	.028	⑤	③	—	550D	—	650D	51	⑨	⑨
5.4L	.028	⑥	③	—	600D	—	700D	51	⑨	⑨
2000–01										
2.5L	④	⑧	—	—	—	—	—	—	⑨	⑨
2.8L	④	⑧	—	—	—	—	—	—	⑨	⑨
3.0L	④	⑧	—	—	—	—	—	—	⑨	⑨
3.2L	④	⑧	—	—	—	—	—	—	⑨	⑨
4.4L	④	⑤	—	—	—	—	—	—	⑨	⑨
5.0L	④	⑤	—	—	—	—	—	—	⑨	⑨
5.4L	④	⑥	—	—	—	—	—	—	⑨	⑨

BTDC — Before Top Dead Center
C — Cold
① — With engine idling.
② — When adjusting idle speed, set parking brake & chock drive wheels.
③ — Equipped w/Motronic Control System.
④ — Equipped with platinum plugs, no adjustment needed.
⑤ — Firing order, 1-5-4-8-6-3-7-2.
⑥ — Cylinder numbering front to rear, right bank, 1-2-3-4-5-6; left bank 7-8-9-10-11-12. Firing order, 1-7-5-11-3-9-6-12-2-8-4-10.
⑦ — Firing order, 1-3-4-2.
⑧ — Equipped w/Siemens MS.
⑨ — Equipped w/hydraulic valve lash adjusters.

Engine Tune Up & Performance

TABLE OF CONTENTS

	Page No.
FOUR-CYLINDER GASOLINE ENGINE	11-5
SIX-CYLINDER GASOLINE ENGINE	11-6
V12 GASOLINE ENGINE	11-8
V8 GASOLINE ENGINE	11-7

Four-Cylinder Gasoline Engine

NOTE: If Unsure Of The System Used On The Vehicle Being Serviced, Refer To "Engine Systems Identification" Chart. Further Assistance For The Proper Use Of Information Contained In This Section Can Also Be Found In The Front Of This Tabbed Section Under "How To Use This Manual."

NOTE: On Air Bag Equipped Models, Refer To "Air Bag System Precautions" Located In The Front Of This Manual For System Disarming & Arming Procedures.

NOTE: Refer To "Computer Relearn Procedures" Located In The Front Of This Manual When Battery Power To The Computer Has Been Interrupted.

NOTE: Prior To Performing Any Service Operations Listed In This Section, Consult The "Technical Service Bulletins" Section For Related Information.

INDEX

	Page No.
Compression Pressures	11-5
Idle Speed & Mixture Adjustments	11-5
Ignition Timing	11-5
Spark Plugs	11-5
Valves	11-5
Valve Adjustment	11-5

SPARK PLUGS

On 1998 models, spark plugs should be replaced every 30,000 miles. On 1999–2001 models, spark plugs should be replaced every 100,000 miles. **Torque** to 23 ft. lbs.

COMPRESSION PRESSURES

1. Relieve fuel pressure as outlined under "Precautions."
2. **On models equipped with automatic transmission,** place gear selector in P position.
3. **On models equipped with manual transmission,** place gearshift lever in neutral position.
4. **On all models,** set hand brake.
5. Turn ignition switch to Off position.
6. Disconnect Digital Motor Electronics (DME) master relay.
7. Remove spark plugs.
8. Install compression tester adapter tool No. 11 0 226, or equivalent, into spark plug bore by hand.
9. Connect compression gauge tool No. 11 0 224, or equivalent, onto adapter.
10. Fully depress accelerator pedal and operate starter motor until compression pressure reading is at maximum.
11. Normal compression pressure should measure 145–160 psi.
12. Maximum permissible difference between individual cylinders is 6 psi.

IGNITION TIMING

Ignition timing is controlled by the Digital Motor Electronic (DME) system and an Electronic Control Module (ECM) and is not adjustable. Refer to "Ignition Systems" and "Computerized Engine Controls" sections for diagnosis and testing procedures. **Ignition timing intervals may vary according to driving conditions and/or vehicle usage.**

IDLE SPEED & MIXTURE ADJUSTMENTS

The idle mixture and idle speed can not be adjusted, but should be checked at regular intervals to ensure engine control systems are performing properly.

VALVES

Valve Adjustment

These engines are equipped with hydraulic valve clearance compensating elements. No adjustment is necessary.

Six-Cylinder Gasoline Engine

NOTE: If Unsure Of The System Used On The Vehicle Being Serviced, Refer To "Engine Systems Identification" Chart. Further Assistance For The Proper Use Of Information Contained In This Section Can Also Be Found In The Front Of This Tabbed Section Under "How To Use This Manual."

NOTE: On Air Bag Equipped Models, Refer To "Air Bag System Precautions" Located In The Front Of This Manual For System Disarming & Arming Procedures.

NOTE: Refer To "Computer Relearn Procedures" Located In The Front Of This Manual When Battery Power To The Computer Has Been Interrupted.

NOTE: Prior To Performing Any Service Operations Listed In This Section, Consult The "Technical Service Bulletins" Section For Related Information.

INDEX

	Page No.
Compression Pressures	11-6
Idle Speed & Mixture Adjustments	11-6
Ignition Timing	11-6
Spark Plugs	11-6
Valves	11-6
Valve Adjustment	11-6

SPARK PLUGS

On 1998 models, spark plugs should be replaced every 30,000 miles. On 1999–2001 models, spark plugs should be replaced every 100,000 miles. **Torque** to 23 ft. lbs.

COMPRESSION PRESSURES

1. Relieve fuel pressure as outlined under "Precautions."
2. **On models equipped with automatic transmission,** place gear selector in P position.
3. **On models equipped with manual transmission,** place gearshift lever in neutral position.
4. **On all models,** set hand brake.
5. Turn ignition switch to Off position.
6. Disconnect Digital Motor Electronics (DME) master relay.
7. Remove spark plugs.
8. Install compression tester adapter tool No. 11 0 226, or equivalent, into spark plug bore by hand.
9. Connect compression gauge tool No. 11 0 224, or equivalent, onto adapter.
10. Fully depress accelerator pedal and operate starter motor until compression pressure reading is at maximum.
11. **On all models except 2001 M3, Z3 M Coupe and Z3 M Roadster,** normal compression pressure should measure 145–160 psi.
12. **On 2001 M3, Z3 M Coupe and Z3 M Roadster models,** normal compression pressure should measure 160–174 psi.
13. **On all models,** maximum permissible difference between individual cylinders is 6 psi.

IGNITION TIMING

Ignition timing is controlled by the Digital Motor Electronic (DME) system and an Electronic Control Module (ECM) and is not adjustable. Refer to "Ignition Systems" and "Computerized Engine Controls" sections for diagnosis and testing procedures. **Ignition timing intervals may vary according to driving conditions and/or vehicle usage.**

IDLE SPEED & MIXTURE ADJUSTMENTS

The idle mixture and idle speed can not be adjusted, but should be checked at regular intervals to ensure engine control systems are performing properly.

VALVES

Valve Adjustment

These engines are equipped with hydraulic valve clearance compensating elements. No adjustment is necessary.

V8 Gasoline Engine

NOTE: If Unsure Of The System Used On The Vehicle Being Serviced, Refer To "Engine Systems Identification" Chart. Further Assistance For The Proper Use Of Information Contained In This Section Can Also Be Found In The Front Of This Tabbed Section Under "How To Use This Manual."

NOTE: On Air Bag Equipped Models, Refer To "Air Bag System Precautions" Located In The Front Of This Manual For System Disarming & Arming Procedures.

NOTE: Refer To "Computer Relearn Procedures" Located In The Front Of This Manual When Battery Power To The Computer Has Been Interrupted.

NOTE: Prior To Performing Any Service Operations Listed In This Section, Consult The "Technical Service Bulletins" Section For Related Information.

INDEX

	Page No.
Compression Pressures	11-7
Idle Speed & Mixture Adjustments	11-7
Ignition Timing	11-7
Spark Plugs	11-7
Valves	11-7
Valve Adjustment	11-7

SPARK PLUGS

On 1998 models, spark plugs should be replaced every 30,000 miles. On 1999–2001 models, spark plugs should be replaced every 100,000 miles. **Torque** to 23 ft. lbs.

COMPRESSION PRESSURES

1. Relieve fuel pressure as outlined under "Precautions."
2. **On models equipped with automatic transmission,** place gear selector in P position.
3. **On models equipped with manual transmission,** place gearshift lever in neutral position.
4. **On all models,** set hand brake.
5. Turn ignition switch to Off position.
6. Disconnect Digital Motor Electronics (DME) master relay.
7. Remove spark plugs.
8. Install compression tester adapter tool No. 11 0 226, or equivalent, into spark plug bore by hand.
9. Connect compression gauge tool No. 11 0 224, or equivalent, onto adapter.
10. Fully depress accelerator pedal and operate starter motor until compression pressure reading is at maximum.
11. Normal compression pressure should measure 174–203 psi.
12. Maximum permissible difference between individual cylinders is 6 psi.

IGNITION TIMING

Ignition timing is controlled by the Digital Motor Electronic (DME) system Electronic Control Module (ECM). Refer to "Ignition Systems" and "Computerized Engine Controls" sections for diagnosis and testing procedures. **Ignition timing intervals may vary according to driving conditions and/or vehicle usage.**

IDLE SPEED & MIXTURE ADJUSTMENTS

The idle mixture and idle speed can not be adjusted, but should be checked at regular intervals to ensure engine control systems are performing properly.

VALVES

Valve Adjustment

These engines are equipped with hydraulic valve clearance compensating elements. No adjustment is necessary.

V12 Gasoline Engine

NOTE: If Unsure Of The System Used On The Vehicle Being Serviced, Refer To "Engine Systems Identification" Chart. Further Assistance For The Proper Use Of Information Contained In This Section Can Also Be Found In The Front Of This Tabbed Section Under "How To Use This Manual."

NOTE: On Air Bag Equipped Models, Refer To "Air Bag System Precautions" Located In The Front Of This Manual For System Disarming & Arming Procedures.

NOTE: Refer To "Computer Relearn Procedures" Located In The Front Of This Manual When Battery Power To The Computer Has Been Interrupted.

NOTE: Prior To Performing Any Service Operations Listed In This Section, Consult The "Technical Service Bulletins" Section For Related Information.

INDEX

	Page No.
Compression Pressures	11-8
Idle Speed & Mixture Adjustments	11-8
Ignition Timing	11-8
Spark Plugs	11-8
Valves	11-8
Valve Adjustment	11-8

SPARK PLUGS

On 1998 models, spark plugs should be replaced every 30,000 miles. On 1999–2001 models, spark plugs should be replaced every 100,000 miles. **Torque** to 23 ft. lbs.

COMPRESSION PRESSURES

1. Relieve fuel pressure as outlined under "Precautions."
2. Place gear selector in P position.
3. Set hand brake.
4. Turn ignition switch to Off position.
5. Disconnect Digital Motor Electronics (DME) master relay.
6. Remove spark plugs.
7. Install compression tester adapter tool No. 11 0 226, or equivalent, into spark plug bore by hand.
8. Connect compression gauge tool No. 11 0 224, or equivalent, onto adapter.
9. Fully depress accelerator pedal and operate starter motor until compression pressure reading is at maximum.
10. Normal compression pressure should measure 145–174 psi.
11. Maximum permissible difference between individual cylinders is 6 psi.

IGNITION TIMING

Ignition timing is controlled by the Digital Motor Electronic (DME) system Electronic Control Module (ECM). Refer to "Ignition Systems" and "Computerized Engine Controls" sections for diagnosis and testing procedures. **Ignition timing intervals may vary according to driving conditions and/or vehicle usage.**

IDLE SPEED & MIXTURE ADJUSTMENTS

The idle mixture and idle speed can not be adjusted, but should be checked at regular intervals to ensure engine control systems are performing properly.

VALVES

Valve Adjustment

These engines are equipped with hydraulic valve clearance compensating elements. No adjustment is necessary.

Ignition Systems

NOTE: Refer To "Computerized Engine Controls" Section For Additional Diagnosis & Testing Of The Digital Motor Electronic (DME) Systems.

NOTE: If Unsure Of The System Used On The Vehicle Being Serviced, Refer To "Engine Systems Identification" Chart. Further Assistance For The Proper Use Of Information Contained In This Section Can Also Be Found In The Front Of This Tabbed Section Under "How To Use This Manual."

NOTE: On Air Bag Equipped Models, Refer To "Air Bag System Precautions" Located In The Front Of This Manual For System Disarming & Arming Procedures.

NOTE: Prior To Performing Any Service Operations Listed In This Section, Consult The "Technical Service Bulletins" Section For Related Information.

INDEX

	Page No.
Description	11-9
DME M5.2 & M7.2 Systems	11-9
DME MS41, MS42, MS43, MS54 & MSS52	11-9
Diagnosis & Testing	11-10
Component Testing	11-10
Coil	11-10
Spark Plug Connector	11-10
Precautions	11-9
Adaptive System	11-9
Air Bag Systems	11-9
Battery Ground Cable	11-9
Digital Motor Electronics (DME)	11-9
System Service	11-10
Component Replacement	11-10
Ignition Coil	11-10

PRECAUTIONS

Air Bag Systems

Refer to "Air Bag System Precautions" in the front of this manual for system disarming and arming procedures.

Battery Ground Cable

Prior to service, disconnect battery ground cable and isolate as required.

Digital Motor Electronics (DME)

1. Always switch ignition to Off position before working on ignition system.
2. Never touch component under current with engine running.
3. Always remove DME master relay for the compression test to avoid activation of ignition coils by ignition final stages of the DME control unit.
4. Always switch ignition to Off position before connecting or disconnecting testers and adapters or replacing components.
5. The secondary side (high voltage side) of ignition systems must always be under a load of at least 4,000 ohms.
6. Never start engine after removing distributor cap of disconnecting ignition coil terminal No. 4 wire.
7. Never connect a shielded capacitor or test lamp to ignition coil terminal No. 1.
8. Never connect ignition coil terminal No. 1 to ground or battery positive.
9. Do not use terminal No. 1 to interlock starting when servicing or installing an alarm system.
10. Never start engine without its secondary circuit connected (spark plug connector removed and ground connection to terminal No. 4a.

Adaptive System

All control units store basic values. The adaptive system compares the input valves with stored map values. If a new or decommissioned control unit is install or has been without power for more than one hour, input valves of the engine must be read in and stored for the adaptive system. This procedure could cause erratic idling and disturbed overrunning of the engine after starting. Depending on the engine, it could require some time before all values are adapted.

If possible, run engine to operating temperature before exchanging control unit. When new unit is installed, operate engine at different engine speeds to help adaptation.

DESCRIPTION

DME M5.2 & M7.2 Systems

A separate output stage-controlled ignition coil is used for each cylinder which supplies the high tension signal through the spark plug connector to the spark plug. Adjustments to ignition timing can be controlled quickly and independently.

Since there are no rotating components, the effective range for ignition timing control is increased to approximately 59° crankshaft angle per cylinder. A camshaft sensor is used to maintain the correct firing sequence.

The spark plugs are equipped with sealed ground electrodes which reduce burn-off wear and extend change intervals.

The DME control module determines the ignition timing (ignition angle) on the basis of engine speed and load signals which are output through the ignition output stages. It also takes into consideration other input signals such as the engine temperature, intake temperature, throttle valve position and the electronic transmission control module.

DME MS41, MS42, MS43, MS54 & MSS52

Ignition system control and monitoring is similar to the Bosch DME M5.2 system. This includes monitoring of each ignition coil primary and secondary functions.

The RPM/reference and camshaft position sensors are used to determine precise ignition coil triggering. If the camshaft sensor is defective, the system can trigger the coils in double ignition to provide emergency, fail-safe running.

The ignition coils primary side is monitored at the final stage. If a fault occurs with one coil, the respective fuel injector will be shut down to prevent raw fuel entering the catalyst. A diagnostic trouble code will be stored in memory and depending on diagnostic (OBD) requirements, the MIL lamp will illuminate.

The secondary side is monitored using ignition feedback resistor and the mechanical misfire detection feature of the M5.2 system. The control module monitors the voltage drop across the ground side of the secondary coil circuit if a ground pulse is missing and the respective fuel injector is shut down.

The control module monitors the engine speed via the crankshaft position sensor. It notes lack of crankshaft speed increase when a cylinder was supposed to fire as a misfire, shuts down the respective fuel injector and logs a diagnostic trouble code in memory.

DIAGNOSIS & TESTING

Refer to "Computerized Engine Controls" section for diagnosis and testing.

Component Testing

COIL

M44

Primary winding resistance should be approximately .82 ohms. Secondary resistance should be approximately 8250 ohms.

M52 & M62

Primary winding resistance should be approximately .5 ohms (code No. 2051118335) or .37 ohms (code No. 20510171101). Secondary resistance should be approximately 6000 ohms (code No. 2051118335) or 9000 ohms (code No. 20510171101).

M73

Primary winding resistance should be approximately 72–88 ohms.

SPARK PLUG CONNECTOR

M44, M52, M54, M62, S52, S54 & S62

Bosch

Resistance should be 800–1200 ohms.

Bremi

Resistance should be 1440–2160 ohms.

M73

Resistance should be 4500–5500 ohms.

SYSTEM SERVICE

Component Replacement

IGNITION COIL

M44

1. Disconnect ignition coil primary connector.
2. Remove mounting nuts and ignition coil.
3. Disconnect corresponding ignition coil and spark plug lead.
4. Reverse procedure to install.

M52

1. Disconnect clips cover remove mounting screws.
2. Remove oil filler neck cap and ignition coil cover.
3. Disconnect ignition coil electrical connectors.
4. Remove mounting screws and ignition coils.
5. Reverse procedure to install, noting the following:
   a. Screw down grounding strap to mounting and cylinders No. 1 and 6 ignition coils.
   b. **On models equipped with metal cover,** screw down cable duct grounding strap to mounting between cylinders No. 2 and 3.
   c. **On models equipped with plastic cover,** screw down ignition coils' connecting plate grounding strap to cylinder No. 1 coil retaining pin.
   d. **On models equipped with plastic cover,** screw down cable duct grounding strap to ignition coils connecting plate between cylinders Nos. 2 and 3.

M52TU

1. **On 323Ci, 325, 328Ci and 330 and 2000 323i and 328i and 1999 323i & 328i Sedan models,** remove microfilter housings.
2. **On all models,** disconnect clips cover remove mounting screws.
3. Remove oil filler neck cap and ignition coil cover.
4. Disconnect ignition coil electrical connectors.
5. Remove mounting screws and ignition coils.
6. Reverse procedure to install, noting the following:
   a. Screw down grounding strap to mounting and cylinders No. 1 and 6 ignition coils.
   b. **On models equipped with metal cover,** screw down cable duct grounding strap to mounting between cylinders Nos. 2 and 3.
   c. **On models equipped with plastic cover,** screw down ignition coils' connecting plate grounding strap to cylinder No. 1 coil retaining pin.
   d. **On models equipped with plastic cover,** screw down cable duct grounding strap to ignition coils connecting plate between cylinders No. 2 and 3.

M54

1. Remove engine vent and valve cover mounting screws, then the oil filler cap and valve cover.
2. Disconnect and remove ignition coil.
3. Reverse procedure to install.

M62

X5

1. Turn fasteners 90° counterclockwise and remove acoustic cover.
2. Remove sealing caps, nuts and ignition coil covers.
3. Disconnect coil electrical connectors.
4. Remove mounting screws and coil. Mark coil ground strap position.
5. Reverse procedure to install, noting the following:
   a. Screw thin grounding strap to ignition coil for cylinders No. 2 or 7.
   b. Screw thick grounding strap to ignition coil for cylinders No. 3 or 7.

540 & 740

1. Remove sealing caps, mounting nuts and acoustic cover, or pressure stud fasteners and remove acoustic cover.
2. Remove sealing caps, nuts and ignition coil covers.
3. Disconnect coil electrical connectors.
4. Remove mounting screws and coil. Mark coil ground strap position.
5. Reverse procedure to install. Screw grounding straps to ignition coil for cylinders No. 3 and 6.

M73

1. Disconnect coil electrical connector.
2. Remove sealing cap.
3. Remove mounting nuts and ignition coils.
4. Reverse procedure to install.

S52

1. Disconnect clips cover remove mounting screws.
2. Remove oil filler neck cap and ignition coil cover.
3. Disconnect ignition coil electrical connectors.
4. Remove mounting screws and ignition coils.
5. Reverse procedure to install, noting the following:
   a. Screw down grounding strap to mounting and cylinders Nos. 1 and 6 ignition coils.
   b. **On models equipped with metal cover,** screw down cable duct grounding strap to mounting between cylinders Nos. 2 and 3.

S54

1. Disconnect clips and thread heater cable out of duct.
2. Turn toggle approximately 90° and remove interior ventilation microfilter to front.
3. Remove mounting screws and heater bulkhead to top.
4. Remove engine vent and valve cover mounting screws, then the oil filler cap and valve cover.
5. Disconnect and remove ignition coil.
6. Reverse procedure to install.

S62

1. Remove nuts and ignition coils' covers.
2. Remove cable holder mounting nuts.
3. Remove ignition coil's mounting screws and disconnect electrical connectors.
4. Remove ignition coils.
5. Reverse procedure to install.

Fuel Injection

NOTE: If Unsure Of The System Used On The Vehicle Being Serviced, Refer To "Engine Systems Identification" Chart. Further Assistance For The Proper Use Of Information Contained In This Section Can Also Be Found In The Front Of This Tabbed Section Under "How To Use This Manual."

NOTE: On Air Bag Equipped Models, Refer To "Air Bag System Precautions" Located In The Front Of This Manual For System Disarming & Arming Procedures.

NOTE: Refer To "Computer Relearn Procedures" Located In The Front Of This Manual When Battery Power To The Computer Has Been Interrupted.

NOTE: Prior To Performing Any Service Operations Listed In This Section, Consult The "Technical Service Bulletins" Section For Related Information.

NOTE: "Electrical Symbol & Wire Color Code Identification" Located In The Front Of This Manual May Be Used As An Aid When Using Wiring Circuits Found In This Section.

INDEX

Page No.

Description 11-13
DME 5.2 & 7.2 Systems 11-13
DME MS41, MS42, MS43, MS54 & MSS52 11-13
Diagnosis & Testing 11-14
Component Testing 11-14
Fuel Injector 11-14
Fuel Pump/Pressure Regulator 11-14
System Testing 11-14
Precautions 11-12
Adaptive System 11-13
Air Bag Systems 11-12
Battery Ground Cable 11-12
Digital Motor Electronics (DME) . 11-12
Fuel System Pressure Relief 11-12
Sensor & Fuel Injector Specifications 11-12
System Service 11-14
Component Replacement 11-14
Fuel Injector 11-15
Fuel Pressure Regulator 11-15
Fuel Rail 11-14
Troubleshooting 11-13
Engine Fails To Start-Cold 11-13
Engine Fails To Start-Hot 11-13
Engine Starts & Stalls 11-13
Erratic Idle During Warm-Up 11-13
Excessive Fuel Consumption ... 11-14
Excessive HC/CO Emissions 11-14
Hard Starting-Cold 11-13
Hard Starting-Hot 11-13
Hesitation On Acceleration 11-13
Incorrect Idle Speed 11-13
Poor Acceleration-Low Power Output 11-13
Spark Knock On Acceleration ... 11-13

SENSOR & FUEL INJECTOR SPECIFICATIONS

Component/Sensor	Temperature, °F	Resistance, Ohms
Fuel Evaporation Valve	—	25–65
Fuel Injector	—	15–17

PRECAUTIONS

Air Bag Systems

Refer to "Air Bag System Precautions" in the front of this manual for system disarming and arming procedures.

Battery Ground Cable

Prior to service, disconnect battery ground cable and isolate as required.

Fuel System Pressure Relief

Relieve fuel system pressure before disconnecting any fuel line or fuel system component.

1. Remove fuel pump relay(s).
2. Connect battery ground cable and crank engine for 10 seconds.
3. When fuel system repairs are complete, install fuel pump relays and crank engine to restore fuel pump pressure.

Digital Motor Electronics (DME)

1. Always switch ignition to Off position before working on ignition system.
2. Never touch component under current with engine running.
3. Always remove DME master relay for the compression test to avoid activation of ignition coils by ignition final stages of the DME control unit.
4. Always switch ignition to Off position before connecting or disconnecting

testers and adapters or replacing components.
5. The secondary side (high voltage side) of ignition systems must always be under a load of at least 4,000 ohms.
6. Never start engine after removing distributor cap of disconnecting ignition coil terminal No. 4 wire.
7. Never connect a shielded capacitor or test lamp to ignition coil terminal No. 1.
8. Never connect ignition coil terminal No. 1 to ground or battery positive.
9. Do not use terminal No. 1 to interlock starting when servicing or installing an alarm system.
10. Never start engine without its secondary circuit connected (spark plug connector removed and ground connection to terminal No. 4a.

Adaptive System

All control units store basic values. The adaptive system compares the input valves with stored map values. If a new or decommissioned control unit is installed or has been without power for more than one hour, input valves of the engine must be read in and stored for the adaptive system. This procedure could cause erratic idling and disturbed overrunning of the engine after starting. Depending on the engine, it could require some time before all values are adapted.

If possible, run engine to operating temperature before exchanging control unit. When new unit is installed, operate engine at different engine speeds to help adaptation.

DESCRIPTION

DME 5.2 & 7.2 Systems

The fuel injection system is an electronically controlled pulse time system which uses measurements of intake air flow to regulate the amount of fuel injected into the engine. The system is controlled by a Digital Motor Electronics (DME) control module which monitors intake air flow, exhaust gas oxygen content and other engine and vehicle operating conditions through a group of sensors. The DME unit computes the amount of fuel necessary to maintain ideal air/fuel mixture ratios based on these sensor signals and its internal memory, and controls operation of the fuel injectors and electric fuel pump to maintain ideal air/fuel mixtures. Separate injectors for each cylinder consist of solenoid operated valves which spray fuel into the intake manifold near each intake valve. The injectors are activated by voltage pulses from the DME unit, and injectors are energized once each crankshaft revolution, delivering ½ the amount of the fuel necessary for proper combustion each time they are energized. The DME unit controls the amount of fuel delivered during each crankshaft revolution, and thereby the air/fuel mixtures, by varying the amount of time the injectors are energized during each pulse.

Curb idle speed is controlled by the basic throttle position adjustment and by air flow through the idle air bypass channel. The idle bypass channel allows sufficient air to bypass the closed throttle plate to maintain a stable curb idle speed and compensate for accessory loading. Air flow through the idle bypass channel is controlled by an electronically operated Idle Air Control (IAC) valve. The IAC valve is controlled by a separate control module, and is considered part of the Digital Motor Electronics (DME) control system. The DME system provides central microprocessor control of the fuel injection system, ignition timing and engine idle speed.

DME MS41, MS42, MS43, MS54 & MSS52

These are fully sequential fuel injection systems operating the same as the DME M5.2 system with basic injector opening timing determined from the primary signals of the crankshaft position sensor and air mass sensors. These values are modified based on input from the engine coolant and intake air temperature sensors, exhaust oxygen content and throttle position.

The camshaft position sensor input is used to initiate the correct injector firing order. If the camshaft positions sensor fails, the control module can maintain full-sequential injection until the engine is turned off. On the next restart, the control module will trigger the injectors in parallel. Fuel injector final stages are monitored and diagnostic trouble codes stored in memory.

TROUBLESHOOTING

Engine Fails To Start-Cold

1. Improper fuel injection pressure.
2. Defective fuel injectors or injector control circuit.
3. Defective DME control module or poor contact at DME connectors.
4. Defective air flow sensor, or poor contact at sensor connector.
5. Defective fuel pump control or master relay.
6. Open in fuel pump control circuit or defective pump.

Engine Starts & Stalls

1. Defective fuel injectors or injector control circuit.
2. Defective DME control module or poor contact at DME connectors.

Hard Starting-Cold

1. Incorrect fuel pump pressure.
2. Defective pressure regulator.
3. Inoperative cold start valve.
4. Defective thermo-time switch.
5. Inoperative throttle positioner.

Engine Fails To Start-Hot

1. Incorrect fuel injection pressure.
2. Defective fuel injectors or injector control circuit.
3. Defective DME control module or poor contact at DME connectors.
4. Defective air flow sensor or poor contact at sensor connector.
5. Defective fuel pump control or master relay.

Hard Starting-Hot

1. Incorrect fuel injection or fuel pump pressure.
2. Defective pressure regulator.
3. Defective fuel injectors or injector control circuit.

Erratic Idle During Warm-Up

1. Defective coolant temperature sensor.
2. Defective throttle housing.

Incorrect Idle Speed

1. Defective throttle housing.
2. Defective idle control temperature switch.
3. Defective Idle Air Control (IAC) valve.
4. Defective IAC control module.

Hesitation On Acceleration

1. Incorrect fuel injection or fuel pump pressure.
2. Defective fuel injectors or injector control circuit.
3. Open in oxygen sensor circuit or defective oxygen sensor.

Spark Knock On Acceleration

1. Defective DME unit or poor contact at DME connectors.

Poor Acceleration-Low Power Output

1. Incorrect fuel injection or fuel pump pressure.
2. Defective pressure regulator.
3. Defective coolant temperature sensor.
4. Defective fuel injectors or injector control circuit.
5. Defective DME unit or poor contact at DME connectors.
6. Defective air flow sensor or poor contact at sensor connector.
7. Open in oxygen sensor circuit or defective oxygen sensor.

Excessive Fuel Consumption

1. Incorrect fuel injection pressure.
2. Leaking fuel injector(s) or cold start valve.
3. Defective thermo-time switch.
4. Defective coolant temperature sensor.
5. Defective DME or poor contact at DME connectors.
6. Defective air flow sensor or poor contact at sensor connector.

Excessive HC/CO Emissions

1. Incorrect fuel injection pressure.
2. Defective pressure regulator.
3. Leaking injector(s) or cold start valve.
4. Open in oxygen sensor circuit or defective oxygen sensor.

DIAGNOSIS & TESTING

System Testing

Refer to "Computerized Engine Controls" section for system diagnostic procedures.

Component Testing

FUEL INJECTOR

1. Relieve fuel system pressure as outlined under "Precautions."
2. Remove, then assemble injectors into suitable injector tester station.
3. **On M44 and M73 models,** pressurize each injector to 42.6–44.4 psi.
4. **On M52 and M62 models,** pressurize each injector to 49.9–51.7 psi.
5. Inspect injectors. Leakage must not exceed one drop of fluid per minute at recommended pressure.
6. Connect tester activating harness to each injector using suitable adapters.
7. Place graduated cylinder under injector to be tested, energize injector for one minute by connecting tester harness wires to battery and observe spray pattern and discharge rate.
8. Injectors should spray fluid in an even, conical 30° pattern. Each injector should deliver 5.75 ounces per minute.
9. Disconnect test harness from injectors.
10. Measure injector solenoid coils resistance. Resistance should be 15–17.5 ohms at 68°F.
11. Replace faulty injectors.

FUEL PUMP/PRESSURE REGULATOR

1. Relieve fuel system pressure as outlined under "Precautions."
2. Connect suitable pressure gauge into fuel feed hose in front of fuel pressure regulator using suitable T-fitting.
3. Remove fuel pump relay(s) and bridge terminals 87 and 30 with suitable electrical push button tool.
4. Hold down push button to activate fuel pump and observe delivery pressure.
5. Refer to "Gasoline Engine Tune Up Specifications" for fuel pressure.
6. If test pressure is not reached, release push button and place suitable fuel line clamp between gauge and regulator.
7. Activate fuel pump and read pressure. If pressure is not 14.5–29 psi above specified value, check for defective fuel pressure regulator. If specification is not reached, check for defect in fuel pump, filter or lines.

SYSTEM SERVICE

Component Replacement

FUEL RAIL

M44

1. Relieve fuel system pressure as outlined under "Precautions."
2. Remove upper intake manifold as outlined in appropriate engine section.
3. Remove intake hose fuel injectors' air lines inlet hose.
4. Disconnect fuel injector inlet hoses.
5. Disconnect clamp and fuel return line.
6. Remove mounting bolt and fuel feed line.
7. Remove clip and fuel return hose.
8. Remove mounting bolts and fuel rail
9. Reverse procedure to install, noting following:
   a. Install new O-rings and coat with suitable antiseize agent.
   b. Install new fuel lines and hose clips.
   c. **Torque** mounting bolts to 15 ft. lbs.

M52 & S52

1. Relieve fuel system pressure as outlined under "Precautions."
2. Remove fuel injector cover.
3. Disconnect VANOS solenoid valve and oxygen sensors' connectors.
4. Move connector strip aside.
5. Remove intake and return fuel lines.
6. Remove pressure regulator vacuum hose as required.
7. Remove mounting bolts and fuel injection rail with injectors.
8. Reverse procedure to install, noting the following:
   a. Install new O-rings as required.
   b. Coat O-rings with suitable antiseize agent.

M52TU

1. Relieve fuel system pressure as outlined under "Precautions."
2. Remove fuel injector cover.
3. Disconnect lower pressure hose and Intake Air Temperature (IAT) sensor.
4. Disconnect fuel injectors' terminal strip.
5. Mark oxygen sensor connectors for install alignment.
6. Disconnect oxygen sensor connectors.
7. Mark fuel lines for installation alignment.
8. Remove fuel lines.
9. Remove mounting bolts and fuel injection rail with injectors.
10. Reverse procedure to install, noting the following:
    a. Install new O-rings as required.
    b. Coat O-rings with suitable antiseize agent.

M54

1. Relieve fuel system pressure as outlined under "Precautions."
2. Remove fuel injector's cover.
3. Mark oxygen sensor connectors for installation reference.
4. Disconnect oxygen sensor connectors.
5. Disconnect Intake Air Temperature (IAT) sensor and VANOS adjustment solenoid valve.
6. Disconnect fuel injector connector strip.
7. **On X5, 325 and 330 models,** remove heater bulkhead.
8. **On Z3 models,** remove battery positive lead cable and engine wiring harness from bulkhead.
9. **On all models,** disconnect from hold and remove fuel line from cylinder head rear.
10. Remove mounting bolts and fuel injection rail with injectors.
11. Reverse procedure to install, noting the following:
    a. Install new O-rings as required.
    b. Coat O-rings with suitable antiseize agent.

S54

1. Relieve fuel system pressure as outlined under "Precautions."
2. Remove heater bulkhead.
3. Remove mounting bolt and cable bracket.
4. Disconnect fuel injector rail wiring harness from bracket.
5. Disconnect connector strip using disconnect tool No. 12 1 120, or equivalent, alternating from front to back injectors working toward middle. Place connector aside.
6. Disconnect retainer and fuel line
7. Remove fuel rail and air pipe mounting bolts.
8. Remove fuel rail.
9. Reverse procedure to install, noting the following:
   a. Install new O-rings as required.
   b. Coat O-rings with suitable SAE 90 lubricant.

M62

1. Relieve fuel system pressure as outlined under "Precautions."
2. Remove acoustic cover.
3. Remove retaining bands and disconnect accelerator cable from throttle valve lever.
4. From ignition coil covers.
5. Disconnect ignition coil connectors.
6. Remove cable ducts and place aside.
7. Clamp, then remove fuel delivery and return lines.
8. Disconnect fuel pressure regulator vacuum hose.
9. Disconnect fuel rail connector.
10. Remove fuel rail with injectors.

11. Reverse procedure to install, noting the following:
    a. Install new O-rings as required.
    b. Coat O-rings with suitable antiseize agent.

S62

1. Relieve fuel system pressure as outlined under "Precautions."
2. Remove intake manifold as outlined in appropriate engine section.
3. Disconnect connectors and cable from guides.
4. Disconnect throttle actuator, idle speed control valve and electrical changeover valve connectors.
5. Disconnect lefthand knock sensor pair.
6. Disconnect from mounts and raise cable ducts' approximately 0.078 inch.
7. Disconnect cable strips, tilt up and tie back to hood.
8. Disconnect clamp and vacuum hose.
9. Remove mounting bolts and fuel rail with injectors.
10. Remove mounting bolts under lefthand cable duct and remove fuel line bracket.
11. Disconnect fuel lines.
12. Reverse procedure to install, noting the following:
    a. Install new O-rings as required.
    b. Coast O-rings with suitable petroleum jelly.
13. Remove acoustic cover.
14. Remove retaining bands and disconnect accelerator cable from throttle valve lever.
15. From ignition coil covers.
16. Disconnect ignition coil connectors.
17. Remove cable ducts and place aside.
18. Clamp, then remove fuel delivery and return lines.
19. Disconnect fuel pressure regulator vacuum hose.
20. Disconnect fuel rail connector.
21. Remove fuel rail with injectors.
22. Reverse procedure to install, noting the following:
    a. Install new O-rings as required.
    b. Coat O-rings with suitable antiseize agent.

M73

1. Relieve fuel system pressure as outlined under "Precautions."
2. Disconnect engine wiring harness, lift up and secure to hood.
3. Disconnect clips and remove hoses.
4. Disconnect clips and fuel injector strips.
5. Disconnect clips and remove fuel hoses.
6. Loosen hose clips and pull off fuel injector strips.
7. Remove mounting bolts and fuel rail with fuel injectors.
8. Reverse procedure to install.

FUEL INJECTOR

M44, M52, S52 & S54

1. Remove fuel rail as outlined under "Fuel Rail."
2. Lift retainer out and pull fuel injector off fuel rail.
3. Note production data code, plastic washer position and color of receptacle housing or spray nozzle protector for assembly.
4. Reverse procedure to install, using new O-rings lubricated with petroleum jelly or SAE 90 transmission oil.

M54

1. Remove fuel rail as outlined under "Fuel Rail."
2. Disconnect fuses and pull injectors out of fuel rail.
3. Reverse procedure to install, using new injectors lubricated with petroleum jelly

M62 & S62

1. Remove fuel rail as outlined under "Fuel Rail."
2. Disconnect and remove circlips.
3. Remove fuel injector.
4. Reverse procedure to install, using new O-rings lubricated with petroleum jelly

M73

1. Remove fuel rail as outlined under "Fuel Rail."
2. Remove clips and injectors.
3. Reverse procedure to install, noting the following:
    a. Replace seals as required.
    b. Coat seals with suitable acid-free grease.

FUEL PRESSURE REGULATOR

M44

1. Relieve fuel system pressure as outlined under "Precautions."
2. Mark vacuum supply line position on injection pipe for installation reference.
3. Disconnect vacuum hoses.
4. **On models mounted with nut,** remove mounting bolts and bracket, then the mounting nut and clamping bracket.
5. **On models mounted with bracket,** remove bracket.
6. **On models mounted with circlip,** remove vacuum hose and circlip.
7. Turn and remove fuel pressure regulator.
8. Reverse procedure to install, noting the following:
    a. Note nominal pressure stamped on regulator. Only regulators with same nominal pressure may be installed.
    b. Install new seal rings.
    c. Pressure regulator must be seated firmly.
    d. Ensure clamp recess aligns with vacuum connection to prevent hose damage.

M52 & S52

1. Relieve fuel system pressure as outlined under "Precautions" and remove engine cover.
2. **On models with regulator on engine,** remove injection rail with fuel injectors as outlined under "Fuel Rail."
3. **On models with regulator mounting on frame,** remove mounting bolts and cover.
4. **On all models,** remove vacuum hose and circlip or locking bracket.
5. Note vacuum connection position for installation reference.
6. Turn regulator and remove.
7. Reverse procedure to install, using new O-rings. Ensure clip lug engages injector tube recesses.

M52TU

1. Relieve fuel system pressure as outlined under "Precautions" and remove engine cover.
2. Remove microfilter and cable duct as required.
3. Remove fuel injector cover.
4. Record vacuum line routing for installation reference.
5. Turn and remove pressure regulator.
6. Reverse procedure to install, noting the following:
    a. Install new sealing ring.
    b. Ensure circlip lugs engage injector tube recesses.

M54

Fuel pressure regulator is an integrated part of the fuel filter. Refer to appropriate engine section.

S54

1. Relieve fuel system pressure as outlined under "Precautions."
2. Remove mounting bolts and underbody cover.
3. Disconnect vacuum hose and remove snap ring.
4. Remove fuel pressure regulator.
5. Reverse procedure to install. Ensure lugs snap into place and apply thin coat of suitable petroleum jelly to O-rings.

M62

1998 540 & 740

1. Relieve fuel system pressure as outlined under "Precautions" and remove engine cover.
2. Remove caps, mounting nuts and acoustic cover.
3. Disconnect vacuum hose.
4. Remove circlip.
5. Note vacuum connection location for installation, turn and remove regulator.
6. Reverse procedure to install, using new O-rings. Ensure clip lug engages injector tube recesses.

1999–2001 540 & 740

1. Relieve fuel system pressure as outlined under "Precautions" and remove engine cover.
2. Remove mounting bolts and underbody cover.
3. Disconnect vacuum hose and locking bracket.
4. Remove fuel pressure regulator.
5. Reverse procedure to install using new

O-rings. Apply thin coat of suitable petroleum jelly to O-rings.

2000-01 X5

Fuel pressure regulator is an integrated part of the fuel filter. Refer to appropriate engine section.

S62

1. Relieve fuel system pressure as outlined under "Precautions."
2. Remove mounting bolts and lower floor plate lefthand cover.
3. Remove mounting bolts and lower fuel filter with lines connected.
4. Disconnect vacuum hose and remove snap ring.
5. Remove fuel pressure regulator.
6. Reverse procedure to install, noting the following:
   a. Ensure lugs snap into place.
   b. Apply thin coat of suitable petroleum jelly to O-rings.

M73

1998

1. Relieve fuel system pressure as outlined under "Precautions" and remove engine cover.
2. Turn mounting screws 90° and remove cylinder head cover.
3. Disconnect vacuum hose and remove circlip.
4. Note vacuum connection location for assembly reference.
5. Turn and remove regulator.
6. Reverse procedure to install using new O-rings. Ensure clip lug engages injector tube recesses.

1999-2001

1. Relieve fuel system pressure as outlined under "Precautions" and remove engine cover.
2. Remove mounting bolts and passenger's side floor plate cover.
3. Disconnect vacuum hose and locking bracket.
4. Remove fuel pressure regulator.
5. Reverse procedure to install using new O-rings. Apply thin coat of suitable petroleum jelly to O-rings.

Electric Fuel Pumps

NOTE: If Unsure Of The System Used On The Vehicle Being Serviced, Refer To "Engine Systems Identification" Chart. Further Assistance For The Proper Use Of Information Contained In This Section Can Also Be Found In The Front Of This Tabbed Section Under "How To Use This Manual."

NOTE: On Air Bag Equipped Models, Refer To "Air Bag System Precautions" Located In The Front Of This Manual For System Disarming & Arming Procedures.

NOTE: Refer To "Computer Relearn Procedures" Located In The Front Of This Manual When Battery Power To The Computer Has Been Interrupted.

INDEX

	Page No.
Diagnosis & Testing	11-18
System Pressure Test	11-18
Fuel Pressure Relief	11-18
Fuel Pump Relay Location	11-17
M3	11-17
Z3, 525, 528, 530, 540 & 740	11-17
318	11-17
323, 325, 328 & 330	11-17
323Ci, 325, 328Ci & 330 & 2000 323i & 328i & 1999 323i & 328i Sedans	11-17
750	11-17
Fuel Pump Replacement	11-18
M44	11-18
M52, M54, S52 & S54	11-18
323, 325, 328 & 330	11-18
525, 528 & 530	11-18
M3	11-18
Z3	11-18
M62 & S62	11-18
M73	11-18
Fuel Pump Specifications	11-19
Precautions	11-17
Adaptive System	11-17
Air Bag Systems	11-17
Battery Ground Cable	11-17
Digital Motor Electronics (DME)	11-17

PRECAUTIONS

Air Bag Systems

Refer to "Air Bag System Precautions" in the front of this manual for system disarming and arming procedures.

Battery Ground Cable

Prior to service, disconnect battery ground cable and isolate as required.

Digital Motor Electronics (DME)

1. Always switch ignition to Off position before working on ignition system.
2. Never touch component under current with engine running.
3. Always remove DME master relay for the compression test to avoid activation of ignition coils by ignition final stages of the DME control unit.
4. Always switch ignition to Off position before connecting or disconnecting testers and adapters or replacing components.
5. The secondary side (high voltage side) of ignition systems must always be under a load of at least 4000 ohms.
6. Never start engine after removing distributor cap of disconnecting ignition coil terminal No. 4 wire.
7. Never connect a shielded capacitor or test lamp to ignition coil terminal No. 1.
8. Never connect ignition coil terminal No. 1 to ground or battery positive.
9. Do not use terminal No. 1 to interlock starting when servicing or installing an alarm system.
10. Never start engine without its secondary circuit connected (spark plug connector removed and ground connection to terminal No. 4a.

Adaptive System

All control units store basic values. The adaptive system compares the input valves with stored map values. If a new or decommissioned control unit is install or has been without power for more than one hour, input valves of the engine must be read in and stored for the adaptive system. This procedure could cause erratic idling and disturbed overrunning of the engine after starting. Depending on the engine, it could require some time before all values are adapted.

If possible, run engine to operating temperature before exchanging control unit. When new unit is installed, operate engine at different engine speeds to help adaptation.

FUEL PUMP RELAY LOCATION

M3

1998-99

The fuel pump relay is in the fuse panel, on the rear lefthand side of the engine compartment.

2001

The fuel pump relay is in the fuse panel, behind the glove compartment on the rear lefthand side of the engine compartment.

Z3, 525, 528, 530, 540 & 740

The fuel pump relay is located in the E box, located on the righthand rear of the engine compartment.

318

The fuel pump relay is in the fuse panel, on the rear lefthand side of the engine compartment.

323, 325, 328 & 330

323is & 328is & 1998-99 328i & 1998 323i & 1999 323i & 328i Convertibles

The fuel pump relay is in the fuse panel, on the rear lefthand side of the engine compartment.

323CI, 325, 328CI & 330 & 2000 323I & 328I & 1999 323I & 328I SEDANS

The fuel pump relay is in the fuse panel, behind the glove compartment on the rear lefthand side of the engine compartment.

750

Fuel pump relay Number One for cylinders 1 through 6 and Number Two for cylinders 7 through 12 are located in auxiliary relay box No. 2, located in front of righthand front shock tower.

FUEL PRESSURE RELIEF

Relieve fuel system pressure before disconnecting any fuel line or fuel system component.

1. Remove fuel pump relay(s).
2. Connect battery ground cable and crank engine for 10 seconds.
3. When fuel system repairs are complete, install fuel pump relays and crank engine to restore fuel pump pressure.

DIAGNOSIS & TESTING

System Pressure Test

1. Relieve fuel system pressure as outlined under "Precautions."
2. Connect suitable pressure gauge into fuel feed hose in front of fuel pressure regulator using suitable T-fitting.
3. Remove fuel pump relay(s) and bridge terminals 87 and 30 with suitable electrical push button tool.
4. Hold down push button to activate fuel pump and observe delivery pressure.
5. Refer to "Tune Up Specifications" for fuel pressure.
6. If test pressure is not reached, release push button and place a suitable fuel line clamp between gauge and regulator.
7. Activate fuel pump and read pressure. If pressure is not 14.5–29 psi above specified value, check for defective fuel pressure regulator. If specification is not reached, check for defect in fuel pump, filter or lines.

FUEL PUMP REPLACEMENT

Prior to disconnecting fuel lines, disconnect master relay and carefully depressurize fuel system as outlined under "Precautions."

M44

1. Relieve fuel system pressure as outlined under "Precautions."
2. Drain enough fuel from tank to ensure pump unit can be removed without spillage.
3. **On Z3 models,** procede as follows:
   a. Remove passenger seat.
   b. Cut and fold carpet.
   c. Remove mounting screws and cover.
4. **On all models,** disconnect fuel pump and fuel level sensor electrical connectors.
5. Disconnect fuel inlet hose.
6. Remove ring nut using ring nut wrench tool No. 16 1 020, or equivalent.
7. Mark position of unit in fuel tank for installation reference.
8. Lift and rotate unit from fuel tank.**Do not deform fuel level sensor arm or altitude sensor tube.**
9. Reverse procedure to install, noting the following.
   a. Ensure altitude sensor tube is properly positioned into fuel tank baffle.
   b. Ensure match marks of unit and tank are aligned.
   c. Replace ring nut and seal.

M52, M54, S52 & S54

M3

1998-99

1. Relieve fuel system pressure as outlined under "Precautions."
2. Remove enough fuel from tank to ensure pump unit can be removed without spillage.
3. Remove rear seat cushion, then the righthand access cover.
4. Disconnect electrical connectors and fuel lines.
5. Remove ring nut using ring nut wrench tool No. 16 1 020, or equivalent.
6. Mark position of unit in fuel tank for installation reference.
7. Lift and rotate unit from fuel tank. **Do not deform fuel level sensor arm or altitude sensor tube.**
8. Reverse procedure to install. Install new ring nut and seal.

2001

1. Relieve fuel system pressure as outlined under "Precautions."
2. Remove enough fuel from tank to ensure pump unit can be removed without spillage.
3. Remove rear seat cushion.
4. Fold floor trim panel forward, cut and fold insulating mat.
5. Disconnect rubber grommet.
6. Remove mounting nuts and cover.
7. Disconnect electrical connectors, clips and fuel hose.
8. Remove ring nut using ring nut wrench tool No. 16 1 020, or equivalent.
9. Mark position of unit in fuel tank for installation reference.
10. Lift and rotate unit from fuel tank. **Do not deform fuel level sensor arm or altitude sensor tube.**
11. Reverse procedure to install. Install new ring nut and seal.

Z3

1. Relieve fuel system pressure as outlined under "Precautions."
2. Remove enough fuel from tank to ensure pump unit can be removed without spillage.
3. Remove passenger's seat.
4. Cut and fold carpet, then remove mounting screws and cover.
5. Disconnect hose clip using pliers tool No. 32 3 020, or equivalent, then the fuel lines and electrical connector.
6. Remove ring nut using ring nut wrench tool No. 16 1 020, or equivalent.
7. Mark position of unit in fuel tank for installation reference.
8. Lift and rotate unit from fuel tank. **Do not deform fuel level sensor arm or altitude sensor tube.**
9. Reverse procedure to install. Install new ring nut and seal.

323, 325, 328 & 330

323is & 328is & 1998-99 328i & 1998 323i & 1999 323i & 328i Convertibles

Refer to "1998–99" under "M3."

323Ci, 325, 328Ci & 330 & 2000 323i & 328i & 1999 323i & 328i Sedans

Refer to "2001" under "M3."

525, 528 & 530

1. Relieve fuel system pressure as outlined under "Precautions."
2. Remove enough fuel from tank to ensure pump unit can be removed without spillage.
3. Remove rear seat cushion and rubber grommet.
4. Cut and fold insulating mat.
5. Remove mounting screws and cover.
6. Disconnect electrical connectors and fuel lines.
7. Remove ring nut using ring nut wrench tool No. 16 1 020, or equivalent.
8. Mark position of unit in fuel tank for installation reference.
9. Lift and rotate unit from fuel tank. **Do not deform fuel level sensor arm or altitude sensor tube.**
10. Reverse procedure to install. Install new ring nut and seal.

M62 & S62

1. Relieve fuel system pressure as outlined under "Precautions."
2. Remove enough fuel from tank to ensure pump unit can be removed without spillage.
3. Remove rear seat cushion and rubber grommet.
4. Cut and fold insulating mat.
5. Remove mounting screws and cover.
6. Disconnect electrical connectors and fuel lines.
7. Remove ring nut using ring nut wrench tool No. 16 1 020, or equivalent.
8. Mark position of unit in fuel tank for installation reference.
9. Lift and rotate unit from fuel tank. **Do not deform fuel level sensor arm or altitude sensor tube.**
10. Reverse procedure to install. Install new ring nut and seal.

M73

1. Relieve fuel system pressure as outlined under "Precautions."
2. Remove enough fuel from tank to ensure pump unit can be removed without spillage.
3. Remove rear seat cushion and rubber grommet.
4. Cut and fold insulating mat.
5. Remove mounting screws and cover.
6. Disconnect electrical connectors and fuel lines.

7. Remove ring nut using ring nut wrench tool No. 16 1 020, or equivalent.
8. Mark position of unit in fuel tank for installation reference.
9. Lift and rotate unit from fuel tank. **Do not deform fuel level sensor arm or altitude sensor tube.**
10. Reverse procedure to install. Install new ring nut and seal.

FUEL PUMP SPECIFICATIONS

Model	Year	Fuel Pressure, psi
M3	1998–99	52–58
	2001	72
M5	2000–01	72
X5	2000–01	58
Z3	1998–99	52–58
	2001	58
318	1998–99	52–58
323is & 328is	1998–99	52–58
323i & 328i Convertibles	1998–99	52–58
323i & 328i Sedans	1999–2000	58
323Ci/i & 328Ci/i	2000	58
325 & 330	2001	58
528	1998–2000	58
525 & 530	2001	58
540	1998–2000	58
740 & 750	1998–2001	58

Computerized Engine Controls

NOTE: If Unsure Of The System Used On The Vehicle Being Serviced, Refer To "Engine Systems Identification" Chart. Further Assistance For The Proper Use Of Information Contained In This Section Can Also Be Found In The Front Of This Tabbed Section Under "How To Use This Manual."

NOTE: On Air Bag Equipped Models, Refer To "Air Bag System Precautions" Located In The Front Of This Manual For System Disarming & Arming Procedures.

NOTE: Refer To "Computer Relearn Procedures" Located In The Front Of This Manual When Battery Power To The Computer Has Been Interrupted.

NOTE: Prior To Performing Any Service Operations Listed In This Section, Consult The "Technical Service Bulletins" Section For Related Information.

NOTE: "Electrical Symbol & Wire Color Code Identification" Located In The Front Of This Manual May Be Used As An Aid When Using Wiring Circuits Found In This Section.

TABLE OF CONTENTS

Page No.

APPLICATION CHART 11-20

DIGITAL MOTOR ELECTRONICS (DME) 11-22

Application Chart

Model	Engine Series	Displacement, Liters	Computer System
1998			
M3	S52	3.2L	DME MS41 (Siemens)
Z3 M Coupe & Roadster	S52	3.2L	DME MS41 (Siemens)
Z3 1.9	M44	1.9L	DME M5.2 (Bosch HFM-Motronic)
Z3 2.8	M52	2.8L	DME MS41 (Siemens)
318i/ti	M44	1.9L	DME M5.2 (Bosch HFM-Motronic)
323i/is	M52	2.5L	DME MS41 (Siemens)
328i/is	M52	2.8L	DME MS41 (Siemens)
528i	M52	2.8L	DME MS41 (Siemens)
540i	M62	4.4L	DME M5.2 (Bosch HFM-Motronic)
740i/iL	M62	4.4L	DME M5.2 (Bosch HFM-Motronic)
750iL	M73	5.4L	DME M5.2 (Bosch HFM-Motronic)
1999			
M3	S52	3.2L	DME MS41 (Siemens)
318ti	M44	1.9L	DME M5.2 (Bosch HFM-Motronic)
Z3 M Coupe & Roadster	S52	3.2L	DME MS41 (Siemens)
Z3 2.3	M52 TU	2.5L	DME MS42 (Siemens)
Z3 2.8	M52 TU	2.8L	DME MS42 (Siemens)
323i/is Coupe & Convertible	M52	2.5L	DME MS41 (Siemens)
323i Sedan	M52 TU	2.5L	DME MS42 (Siemens)

Continued

Model	Engine Series	Displacement, Liters	Computer System
1999			
328i/is Coupe & Convertible	M52	2.8L	DME MS41 (Siemens)
328i/is	M52 TU	2.8L	DME MS42 (Siemens)
528i	M52 TU	2.8L	DME MS42 (Siemens)
540i	M62	4.4L	DME M5.2 (Bosch HFM-Motronic)
740i/iL	M62	4.4L	DME M5.2 (Bosch HFM-Motronic)
750iL	M73	5.4L	DME M5.2 (Bosch HFM-Motronic)
2000			
M5	S62	5.0L	DME MSS52 (Siemens)
X5	M62	4.4L	DME M5.2.1 (Bosch HFM-Motronic)
Z3 M Coupe & Roadster	S52	3.2L	DME MS41 Siemens)
Z3 2.3	M52 TU	2.5L	DME MS42 (Siemens)
Z3 2.8	M52 TU	2.8L	DME MS42 (Siemens)
323Ci/i	M52 TU	2.5L	DME MS42 (Siemens)
328Ci/i	M52 TU	2.8L	DME MS42 (Siemens)
528i	M52 TU	2.8L	DME MS42 (Siemens)
540i	M62	4.4L	DME M5.2.1 (Bosch HFM-Motronic)
740i/iL	M62	4.4L	DME M5.2.1 (Bosch HFM-Motronic)
750iL	M73	5.4L	DME M5.2.1 (Bosch HFM-Motronic)
2001			
M3	S54	3.2L	DME MS54 (Siemens)
M5	S62	5.0L	DME MSS52 (Siemens)
X5 3.0i	M54	3.0L	DME MS43 (Siemens)
X5 4.4i	M62	4.4L	DME M7.2 (Bosch HFM-Motronic)
Z3 M Coupe & Roadster	S54	3.2L	DME MS54 (Siemens)
Z3 2.5i	M54	2.5L	DME MS43 (Siemens)
Z3 3.0i	M54	3.0L	DME MS43 (Siemens)
325Ci/i/ix	M54	2.5L	DME MS43 (Siemens)
330Ci/i/ix	M54	3.0L	DME MS43 (Siemens)
525i	M54	2.5L	DME MS43 (Siemens)
530i	M54	3.0L	DME MS43 (Siemens)
540i	M62	4.4L	DME M7.2 (Bosch HFM-Motronic)
740i/iL	M62	4.4L	DME M7.2 (Bosch HFM-Motronic)
750iL	M73	5.4L	DME M5.2.1 (Bosch HFM-Motronic)

Digital Motor Electronics (DME)

INDEX

	Page No.
Description	11-22
M41, M42, MS43, MSS52 & MS S54	11-23
Fuel Injection Control	11-23
Idle Speed Control	11-23
Ignition System Control	11-23
Oxygen Sensor Heating	11-23
M5.2 & M7.2	11-23
Fuel Injection Control	11-23
Ignition System Control	11-23
Ignition Timing Control	11-23
Diagnosis & Testing	11-23
Accessing Diagnostic Trouble Codes	11-23
Clearing Diagnostic Trouble Codes	11-24
Connector Terminal Identification	11-24
DME M5.2	11-24
DME MS41	11-24
DME MS42	11-24
Diagnostic Tests	11-24
Diagnostic Trouble Code Interpretation	11-23
Symptom Related Diagnosis	11-24
Wiring Diagrams	11-24
DME 5.2	11-24
DME M5.2	11-24
DME MS41	11-24
DME MS42	11-24
Diagnostic Chart Index	11-109
Precautions	11-22
Adaptive System	11-22
Air Bag Systems	11-22
Battery Ground Cable	11-22
Digital Motor Electronics (DME)	11-22
Sensor & Fuel Injector Specifications	11-22
System Service	11-130
Adjustments	11-130
Throttle Body	11-130
Component Replacement	11-130
Digital Motor Electronics (DME) Control Module	11-130
Engine Coolant Temperature (ECT) Sensor	11-132
Intake Air Temperature (IAT) Sensor	11-132
Mass Air Flow (MAF) Sensor	11-132
Throttle Body	11-130
Throttle Position Sensor (TPS)	11-133

SENSOR & FUEL INJECTOR SPECIFICATIONS

Component	Temperature, °F	Resistance, Ohms
Engine Coolant & Engine Oil Temperature Sensors	50–104	500–8000
	104–158	200–3000
	158–212	55–800
Fuel Injector	—	10–18
Intake Air Temperature Sensor	50–104	2000–11,000
	104–158	500–3000
	158–212	300–1000

PRECAUTIONS

Air Bag Systems

Refer to "Air Bag System Precautions" in the front of this manual for system disarming and arming procedures.

Battery Ground Cable

Prior to service, disconnect battery ground cable and isolate as required.

Digital Motor Electronics (DME)

1. Always switch ignition to Off position before working on ignition system.
2. Never touch component under current with engine running.
3. Always remove DME master relay for the compression test to avoid activation of ignition coils by ignition final stages of the DME control unit.
4. Always switch ignition to Off position before connecting or disconnecting testers and adapters or replacing components.
5. The secondary side (high voltage side) of ignition systems must always be under a load of at least 4,000 ohms.
6. Never start engine after removing distributor cap of disconnecting ignition coil terminal No. 4 wire.
7. Never connect a shielded capacitor or test lamp to ignition coil terminal No. 1.
8. Never connect ignition coil terminal No. 1 to ground or battery positive.
9. Do not use terminal No. 1 to interlock starting when servicing or installing an alarm system.
10. Never start engine without its secondary circuit connected (spark plug connector removed and ground connection to terminal No. 4a.

Adaptive System

All control units store basic values. The adaptive system compares the input valves with stored map values. If a new or decommissioned control unit is install or has been without power for more than one hour, input valves of the engine must be read in and stored for the adaptive system. This procedure could cause erratic idling and disturbed overrunning of the engine after starting. Depending on the engine, it could require some time before all values are adapted.

If possible, run engine to operating temperature before exchanging control unit. When new unit is installed, operate engine at different engine speeds to help adaptation.

DESCRIPTION

The DME system operates in conjunction with the electronic throttle control, electronic transmission control, automatic stability control, engine drag torque control, anti-theft system, electronics vehicle module and on-board computer systems.

In addition to fuel injection and ignition, the DME controls the cold start, engine speed, acceleration enrichment, dynamic torque cutout, catalytic converter protection function, adaptive emission, adaptive fuel evaporation, characteristics map switch over for electronic transmission, relay control, A/C compressor cutout and self-diagnosis.

The following components supply the DME system with input signals:

Pulse generator for engine speed/ position and cylinder references.
Intake air temperature sensor.
Engine temperature sensor.
Air mass meters.
Oxygen sensors.

Battery.
Electronic throttle control system control unit.
Electronic transmission control unit.
ABS/ASC/MSR control unit (anti-lock brakes, automatic stability control and engine torque drag control).

The DME system outputs the necessary signals to the following components:

Fuel injectors.
Ignition coils.
Fuel evaporation control valves.
Fuel pump relays.
Main relays (control unit supply).
MIL Lamp.
Oxygen sensors.
Oxygen sensor heater relay.
Air mass meters.
Electronic throttle control unit.
Electronic transmission control unit.
ABS/ASC/MSR control unit.

M5.2 & M7.2

The Bosch Motronic systems control fuel injection and digital ignition under variable operating conditions.

The DME also operates in conjunction with the electronic transmission control, instrument cluster, anti-theft and on-board computer systems.

FUEL INJECTION CONTROL

The DME control module calculates the correct injection timing on the basis of engine speed, air mass, throttle position, oxygen sensor voltage, engine temperature and intake air temperature.

The change in the fuel/air mixture is achieved by the opening duration of the injectors. The battery voltage or electrical system voltage is also taken into consideration in calculating the injection timing.

IGNITION SYSTEM CONTROL

A separate output stage-controlled ignition coil is used for each cylinder which feeds the high tension through the spark plug connector to the spark plug. In this manner, changes in ignition timing can be controlled quickly and independently.

IGNITION TIMING CONTROL

The DME control module determines the ignition timing (ignition angle) on the basis of engine speed and load signals which are output through the ignition output stages. Also taken into consideration are input signals such as the engine temperature, intake air temperature, engine knock, position of throttle valve and signals from the electronic transmission control.

M41, M42, MS43, MSS52 & MS S54

The Siemens MS41 management system operates similar to the Bosch Motronic system. The MS41 system outputs controls include: ignition control, fuel injection control, idle speed control, oxygen sensor heating, purge control, main relay/fuel pump relay control, VANOS control, exhaust flap control, ASC control (ignition/injection), A/C compressor control, EWS II drive away protection and OBD II fault monitoring.

The Siemens MS42 management systems operates similar to Siemens MS41 system. The MS42 system includes knock control with two sensor, variable valve timing, electromechanical throttle system, dual resonance intake system, engine cooling and other functions included in control strategy. Also included is double VANOS (Variable NOckenwellen Steuerung) This variable camshaft control is a steplessly variable valve timing system.

IGNITION SYSTEM CONTROL

Refer to "Ignition Systems."

FUEL INJECTION CONTROL

Refer to "Fuel Injection."

IDLE SPEED CONTROL

A dual winding idle speed control valve is used to maintain idle speed. The valve is mounted under the throttle housing intake manifold area. The valve air inlet is connect to the air intake boot upstream of the throttle plate with a hose. The outlet is ported directly into the intake manifold underside. The control parameters are the same as the Bosch system.

OXYGEN SENSOR HEATING

The MS41 uses internal final stage control for the O2 sensor heating similar to the Bosch system.

DIAGNOSIS & TESTING

Accessing Diagnostic Trouble Codes

Stored Diagnostic Trouble Codes (DTCs) can be accessed by connecting a suitably programmed scan tool to the Diagnostic Link Connector (DLC).

Diagnostic Trouble Code Interpretation

Refer to **Fig. 1** for Diagnostic Trouble Code (DTC) interpretation.

Code	Interpretation
P0101	Air Mass Flow Sensor Signal
P0111	Intake Air Temperature Sensor Signal
P0116	Engine Coolant Temperature Sensor Signal
P0120	Throttle Position Sensor Signal
P0125	Coolant Temperature Plausibility
P0130	Oxygen Sensor Before Catalytic Converter Signal, Bank 1
P0133	Oxygen Sensor Control Frequency Faulty
P0134	Voltage Excursion Before Catalytic Converter Sensor, Bank 1
P0135	Oxygen Sensor Heater Before Catalytic Converter, Bank 1
P0136	Oxygen Sensor After Catalytic Converter, Bank 1
P0141	Oxygen Sensor Heater After Catalytic Converter, Bank 2
P0150	Oxygen Sensor Heater Before Catalytic Converter Signal, Bank 2
P0153	Oxygen Sensor Bank 1 Frequency Faulty
P0154	Voltage Excursion Before Catalytic Converter, Bank 2
P0155	Oxygen Sensor Heater Before Catalytic Converter, Bank 2
P0156	Oxygen Sensor Heater After Catalytic Converter, Bank 2 Signal
P0161	Oxygen Sensor Heating After Catalytic Converter, Bank 1
P0170	Oxygen Sensor Control Bank 1
P0173	Oxygen Sensor Control Bank 1
P0188	Oxygen Sensor Control Too Large, Bank 1
P0189	Oxygen Sensor Control Too Large, Bank 2
P0201	Fuel Injector, Cyl. No. 1
P0202	Fuel Injector, Cyl. No. 2
P0203	Fuel Injector, Cyl. No. 3
P0204	Fuel Injector, Cyl. No. 4

Fig. 1 DTC interpretation (Part 1 of 3). DME MS42

Code	Interpretation
P0205	Fuel Injector, Cyl. No. 5
P0206	Fuel Injector, Cyl. No. 6
P0301	Misfire Cylinder No. 1
P0302	Misfire Cylinder No. 2
P0303	Misfire Cylinder No. 3
P0304	Misfire Cylinder No. 4
P0305	Misfire Cylinder No. 5
P0306	Misfire Cylinder No. 6
P0325	Knock Sensor 1 Signal
P0330	Knock Sensor 2 Signal
P0335	Crankshaft Sensor Signal
P0340	Intake Camshaft Sensor Signal
P0412	Secondary Air Solenoid Valve
P0420	Catalytic Converter Efficiency, Bank 1
P0430	Catalytic Converter Efficiency, Bank 2
P0440	Tank Ventilation
P0441	Fuel System Major Leak Detected
P0442	Fuel System Minor Leak Detected
P0443	Tank Venting Solenoid Valve
P0500	Vehicle Speed Signal
P0505	Idle Speed Plausibility
P0600	CAN EGS Signal
P0601	Control Unit Internal Fault
P1115	Maximum Coolant Temperature Plausibility
P1132	Oxygen Sensor Before Catalytic Converter Bank 1 Heat Output
P1133	Oxygen Sensor Before Catalytic Converter Bank 2 Heat Output
P1140	Plausibility Error: Air Mass/Pedal Position
P1145	Fuel Circuit Changeover Solenoid Valve
P1161	Engine Oil Temperature Sensor Signal
P1178	Oxygen Sensor Switching Line, Bank 1
P1179	Oxygen Sensor Switching Line, Bank 2
P1180	Oxygen Sensor Post Catalytic Converter Leak Test, Bank 1
P1181	Oxygen Sensor Post Catalytic Converter Leak Test, Bank 2
P1184	Oxygen Sensor No. 1 Post Catalytic Converter Sensor Too Slow
	Oxygen Sensor No. 2 Post Catalytic Converter Sensor Too Slow

Fig. 1 DTC interpretation (Part 2 of 3). DME MS42

Code	Interpretation
P1186	Oxygen Sensor After Catalytic Converter Heater Output, Bank 1
P1187	Oxygen Sensor After Catalytic Converter Heater Output, Bank 2
P1190	Oxygen Sensor Control Precatalytic Converter, Bank 1
P1191	Oxygen Sensor Control Precatalytic Converter, Bank 2
P1192	Oxygen Sensor Post Catalytic Converter, Bank 1
P1193	Oxygen Sensor Post Catalytic Converter, Bank 2
P1397	Exhaust Camshaft Sensor Signal
P1421	Secondary Air System Flow Rate Too Low, Bank 2
P1423	Secondary Air System Flow Rate Too Low, Bank 1
P1432	Secondary Air Valve Stuck Open
P1453	Secondary Air Pump Relay
P1470	Tank Leak Diagnosis Pump Solenoid Valve
P1475	Tank Leak Diagnosis Pump (Reed Switch Not Closed)
P1476	Tank Ventilation Blocked Line
P1477	Tank Leak Diagnosis Pump (Reed Switch Does Not Open)
P1478	Small Leak
P1509	Idle Speed Control Valve/Opening Coil
P1510	Idle Speed Control Valve
P1519	Intake Camshaft Control VANOS End Position Fault
P1520	Exhaust Camshaft Control VANOS End Position Fault
P1522	Intake Camshaft Control VANOS Position
P1523	Exhaust Camshaft Control VANOS Position
P1524	Accelerator Pedal Position Sensor Signal
P1525	Intake VANOS Solenoid Valve
P1529	Exhaust VANOS Solenoid Valve
P1542	Accelerator Pedal Position Sensor Signal
P1550	Idle Speed Control Valve/Closing Coil
P1580	Throttle Activation Duty Factor Plausibility
P1593	Intake Manifold Solenoid Valve
P1622	Map Cooling
P1623	Voltage Regulator Reference Voltage
P1624	Thermostat Map Cooling Fault

Fig. 1 DTC interpretation (Part 3 of 3). DME MS42

Wiring Diagrams

DME M5.2

Refer to **Figs. 2 through 4** for DME system wiring diagrams.

DME 5.2

Refer to **Figs. 5 through 7** for DME system wiring diagrams.

DME MS41

Refer to **Figs. 8 through 10** for DME system wiring diagrams.

DME MS42

Refer to **Figs. 11 through 13** for DME system wiring diagrams.

Connector Terminal Identification

DME M5.2

Refer to **Figs. 14 and 15** for connector terminal identification.

DME MS41

Refer to **Figs. 16 through 18** for connector terminal identification.

DME MS42

Refer to **Figs. 19 through 23** for connector terminal identification.

Symptom Related Diagnosis

Refer to **Figs. 24 through 34** for symptom related diagnosis.

Diagnostic Tests

Conduct fault symptoms test first, **Fig. 35**, then the Global Tests, **Figs. 36 and 37.**

Refer to **Figs. 38 through 79** for diagnostic tests.

Clearing Diagnostic Trouble Codes

Clear Diagnostic Trouble Codes (DTCs) only when all causes of detection have been repaired.

Clear DTCs by disconnecting battery or the DME control unit connector. All DTCs will be cleared except for current DTCs.

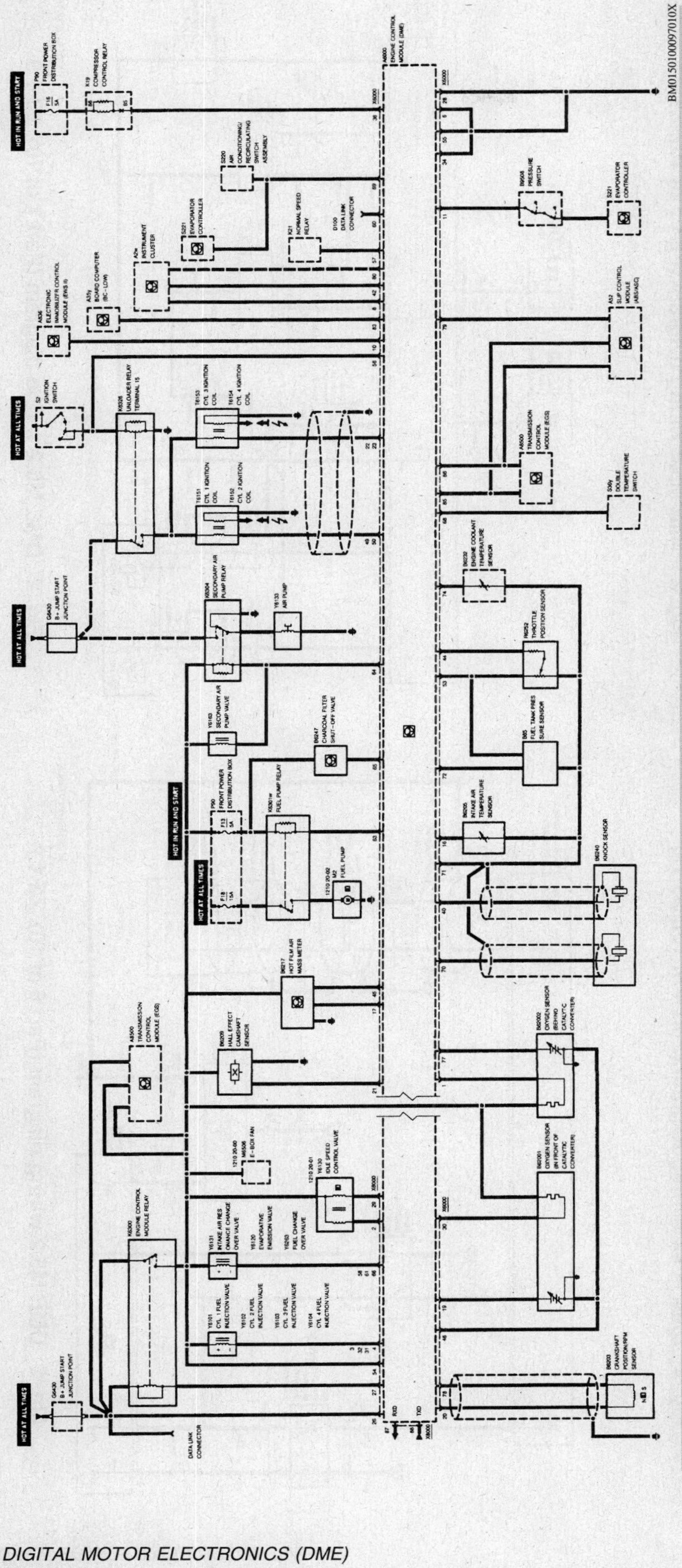

BM0150100097010X

Fig. 2 DME M5.2 wiring diagram (Part 1 of 10). Z3 1.9

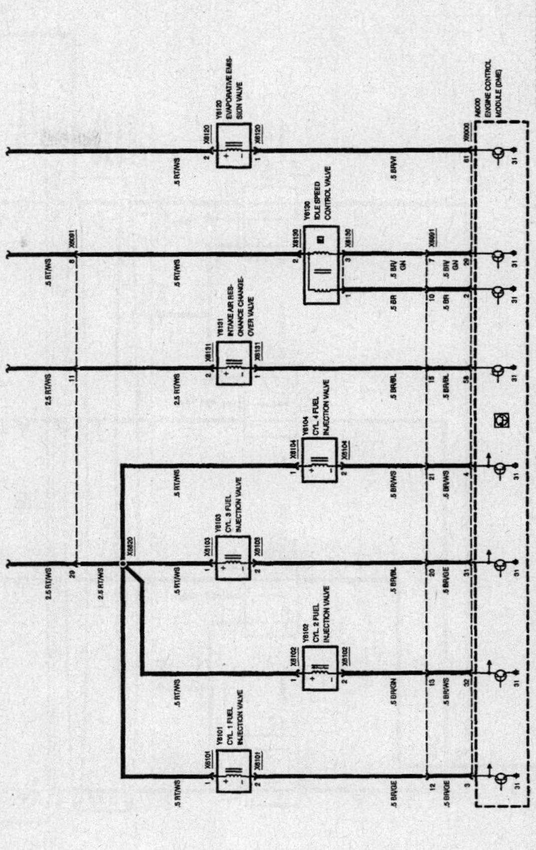

BM0150100097030X

Fig. 2 DME M5.2 wiring diagram (Part 3 of 10). Z3 1.9

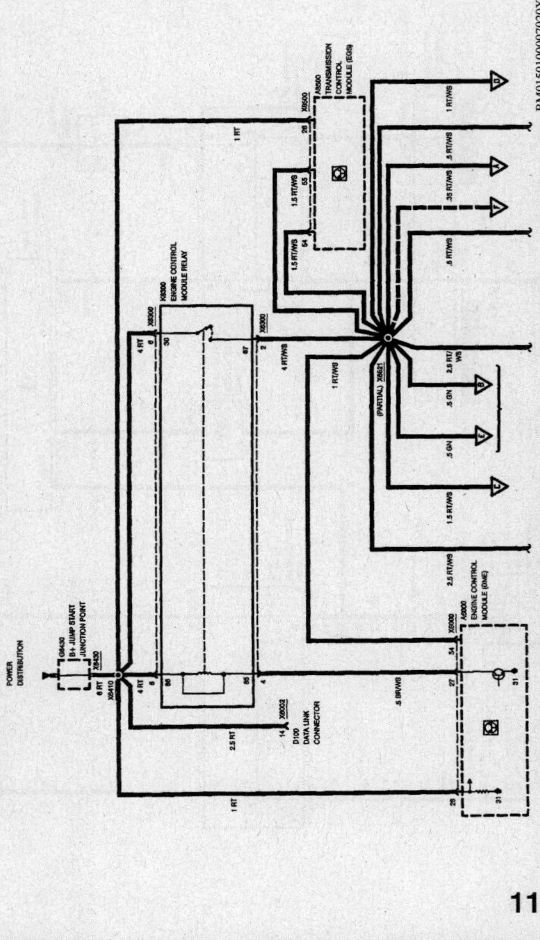

BM0150100097020X

Fig. 2 DME M5.2 wiring diagram (Part 2 of 10). Z3 1.9

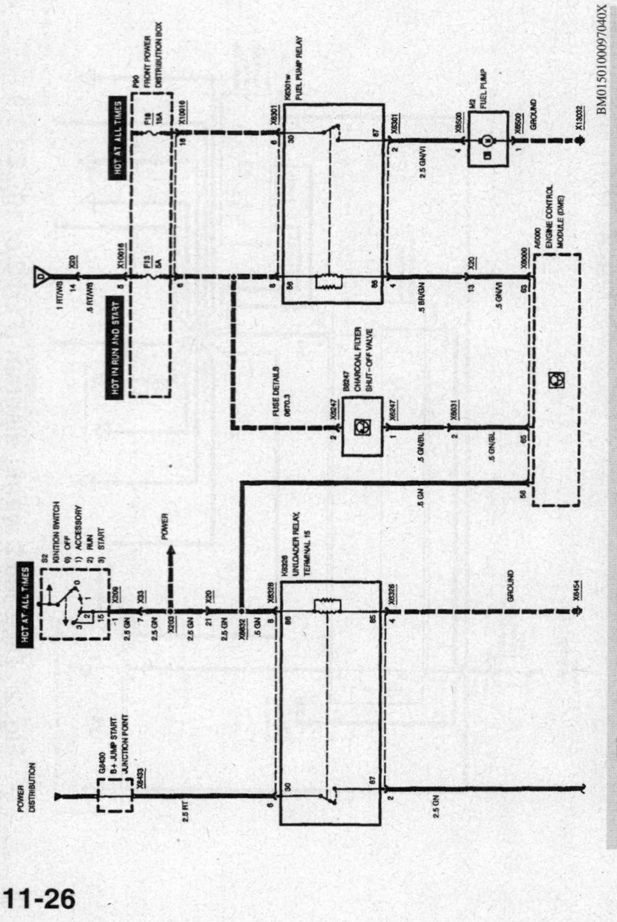

Fig. 2 DME M5.2 wiring diagram (Part 4 of 10). Z3 1.9

BM0150100097040X

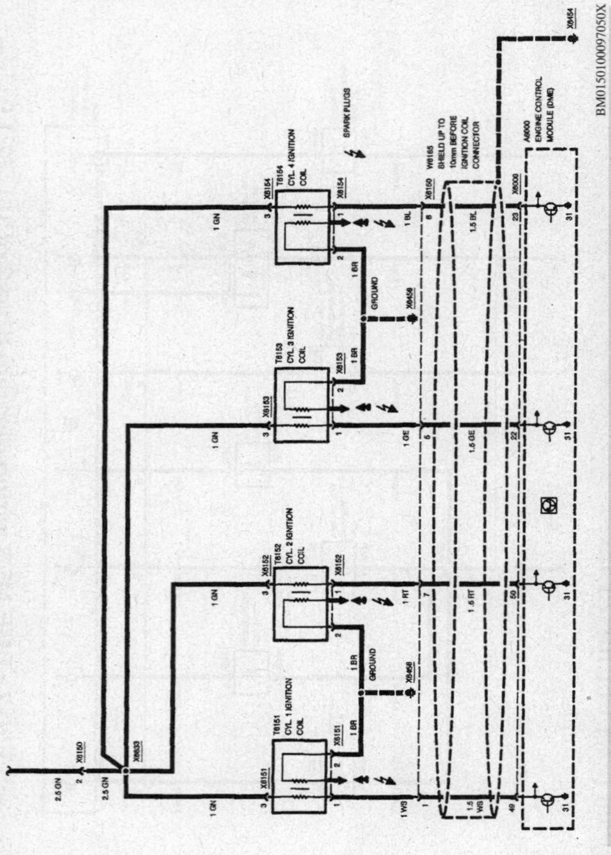

Fig. 2 DME M5.2 wiring diagram (Part 5 of 10). Z3 1.9

BM01501000097050X

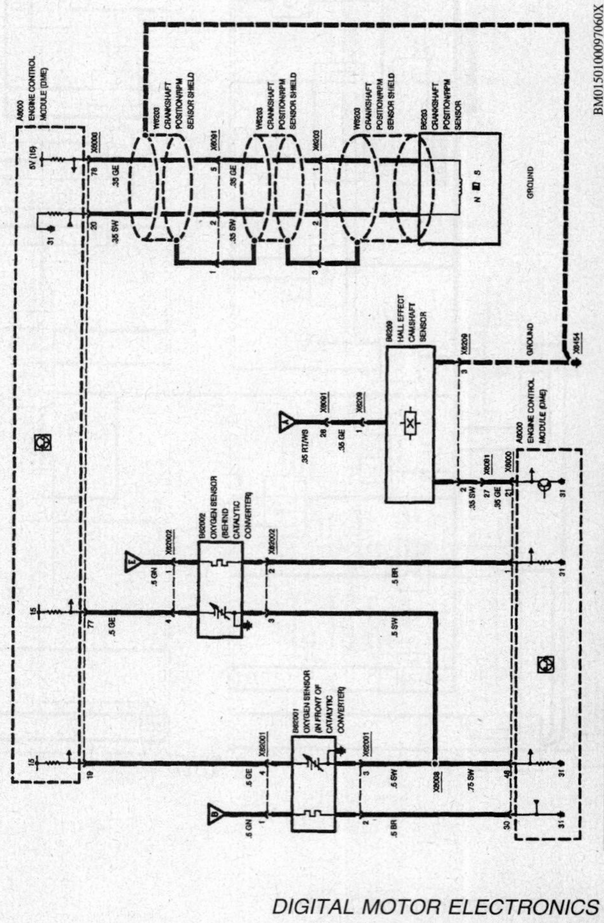

Fig. 2 DME M5.2 wiring diagram (Part 6 of 10). Z3 1.9

BM01501000097060X

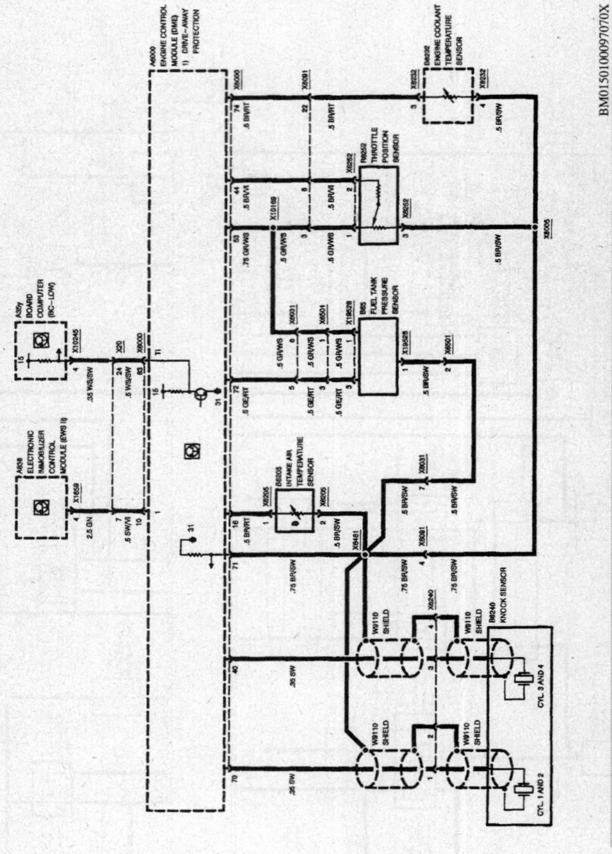

Fig. 2 DME M5.2 wiring diagram (Part 7 of 10). Z3 1.9

BM01501000097070X

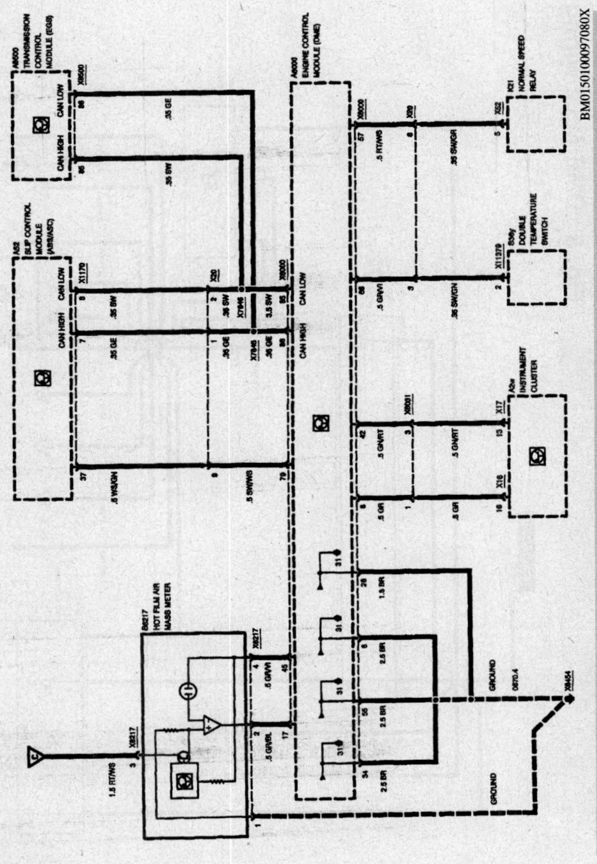

BM01510000097080X

Fig. 2 DME M5.2 wiring diagram (Part 8 of 10). Z3 1.9

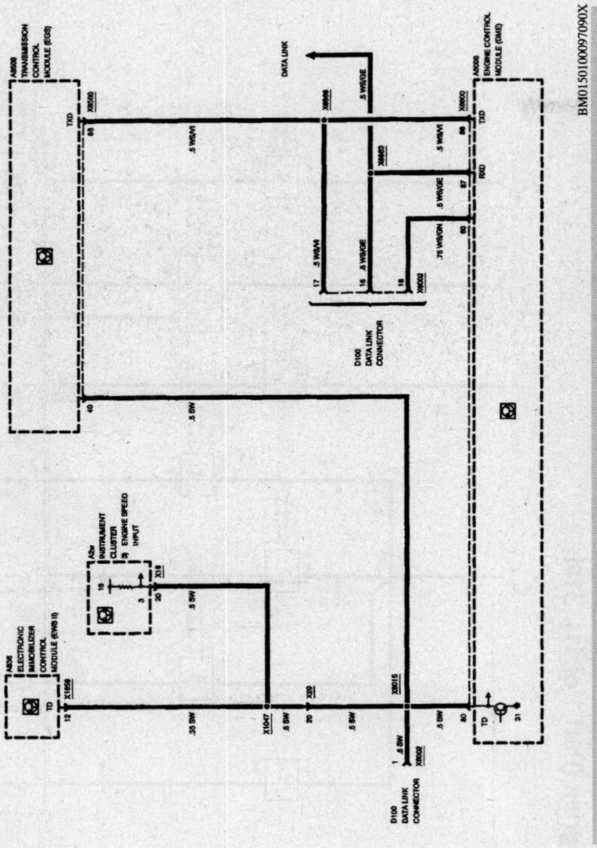

BM01510000097090X

Fig. 2 DME M5.2 wiring diagram (Part 9 of 10). Z3 1.9

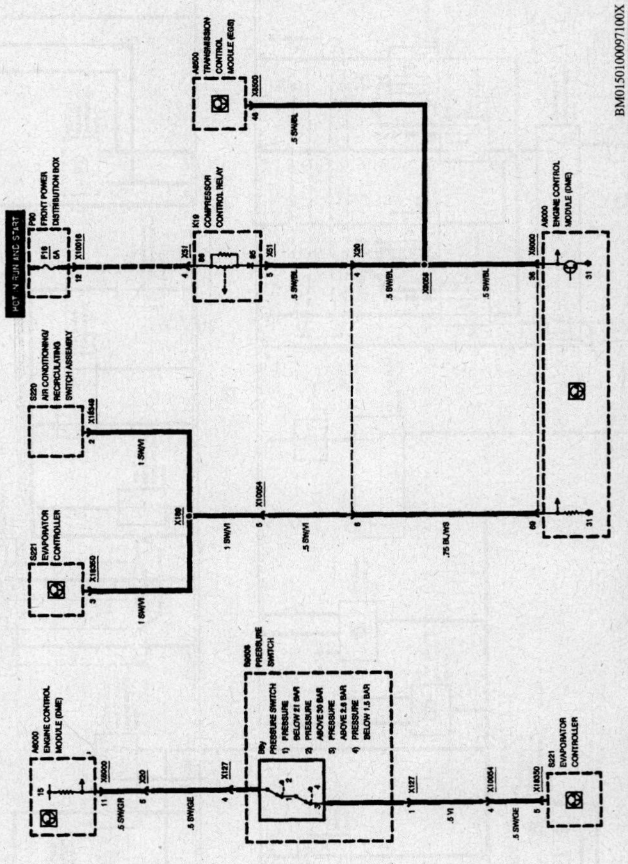

BM01510000097100X

Fig. 2 DME M5.2 wiring diagram (Part 10 of 10). Z3 1.9

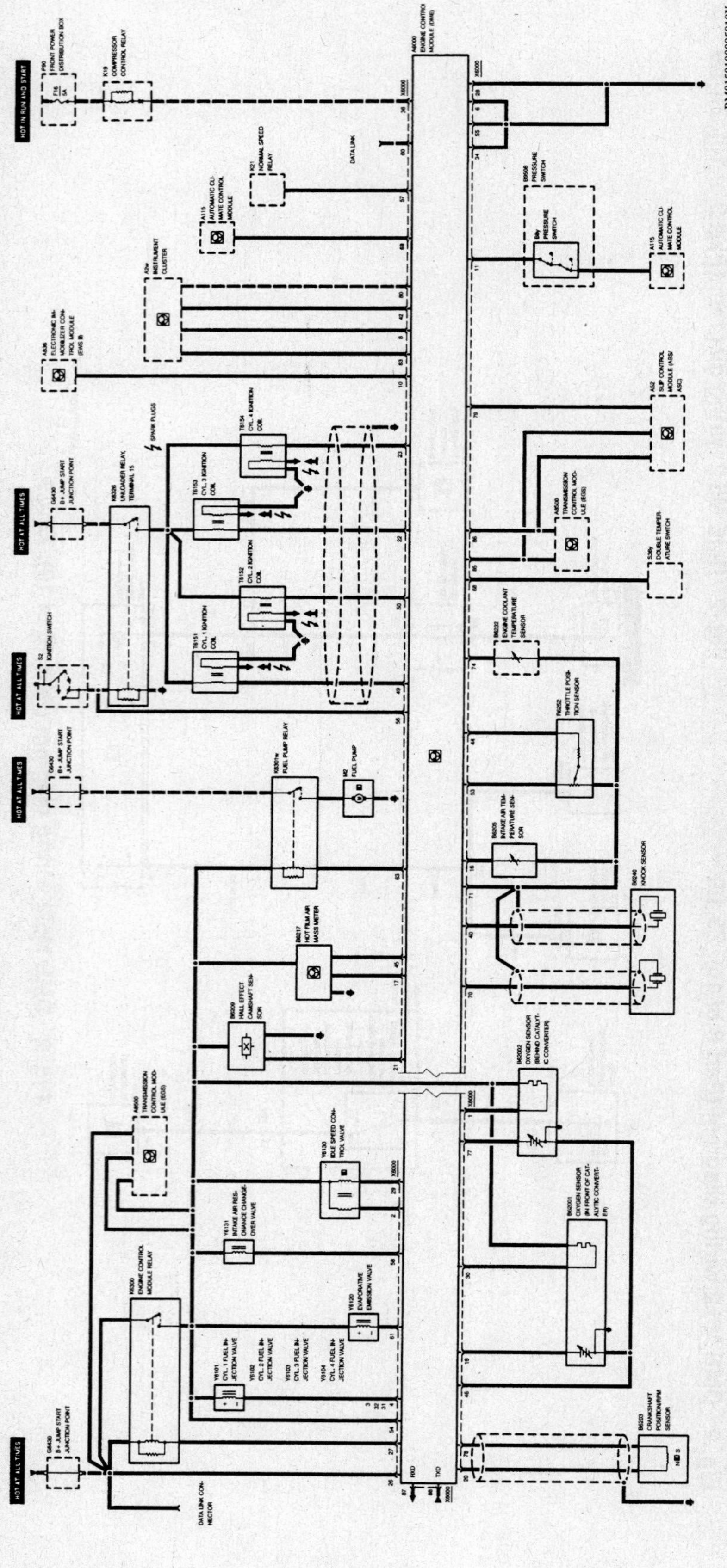

BM0150100095010X

Fig. 3 DME M5.2 wiring diagram (Part 1 of 11). 318i

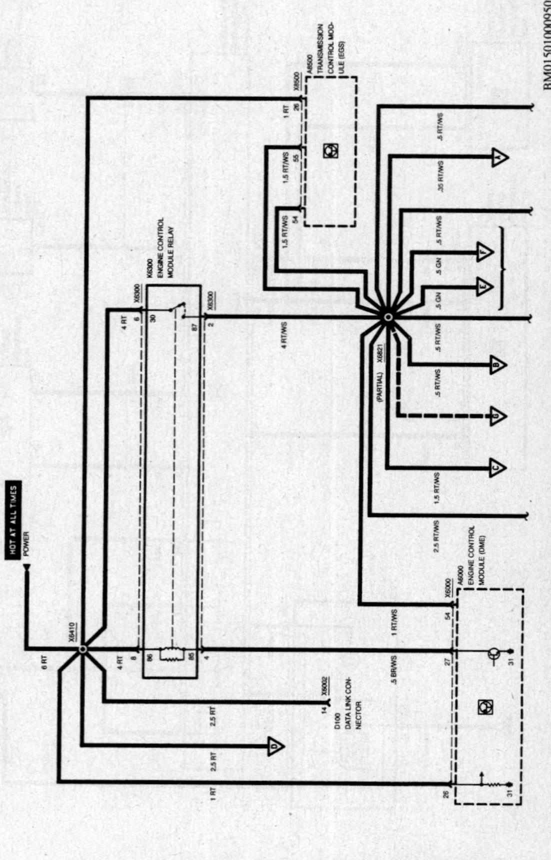

BM0150100095020X

Fig. 3 DME M5.2 wiring diagram (Part 2 of 11). 318i

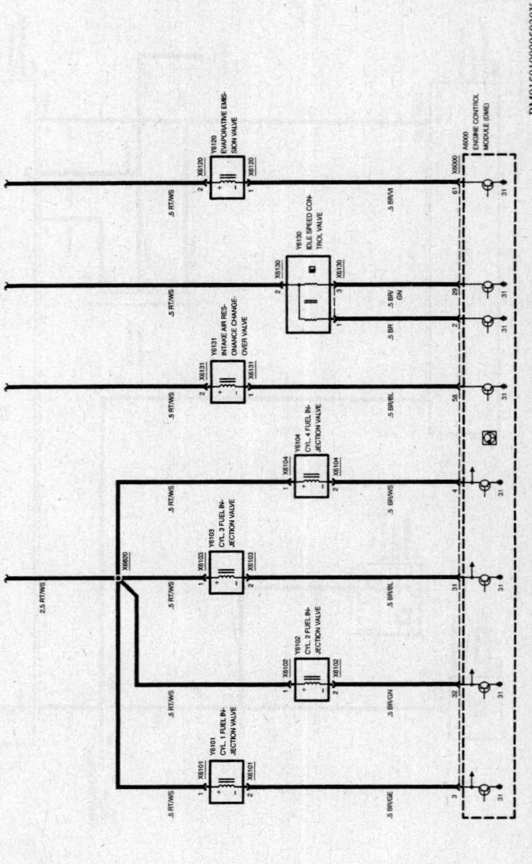

BM0150100095030X

Fig. 3 DME M5.2 wiring diagram (Part 3 of 11). 318i

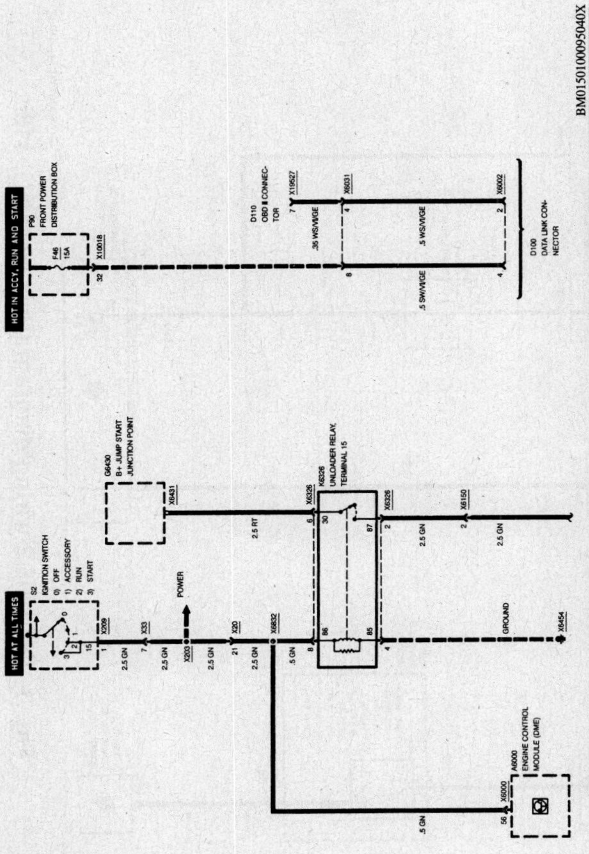

BM0150100095040X

Fig. 3 DME M5.2 wiring diagram (Part 4 of 11). 318i

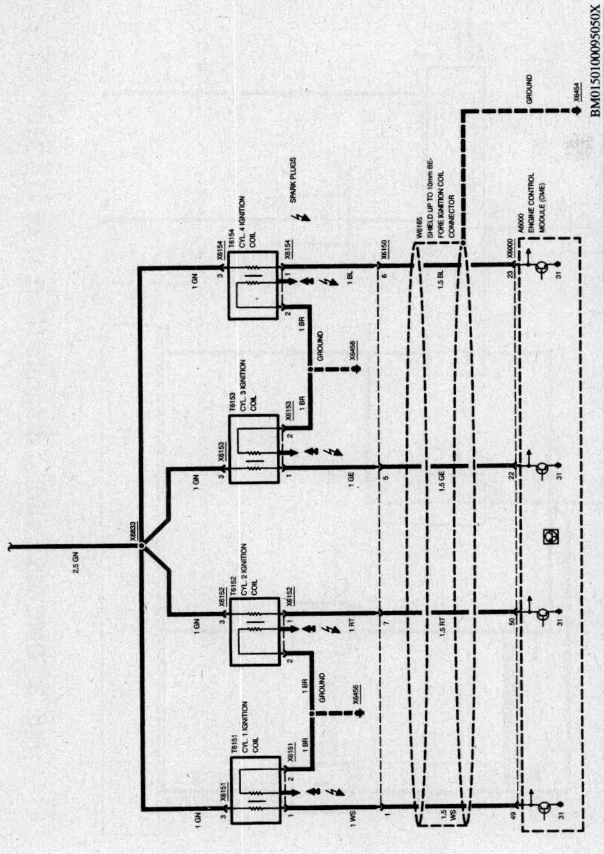

BM0150100095050X

Fig. 3 DME M5.2 wiring diagram (Part 5 of 11). 318i

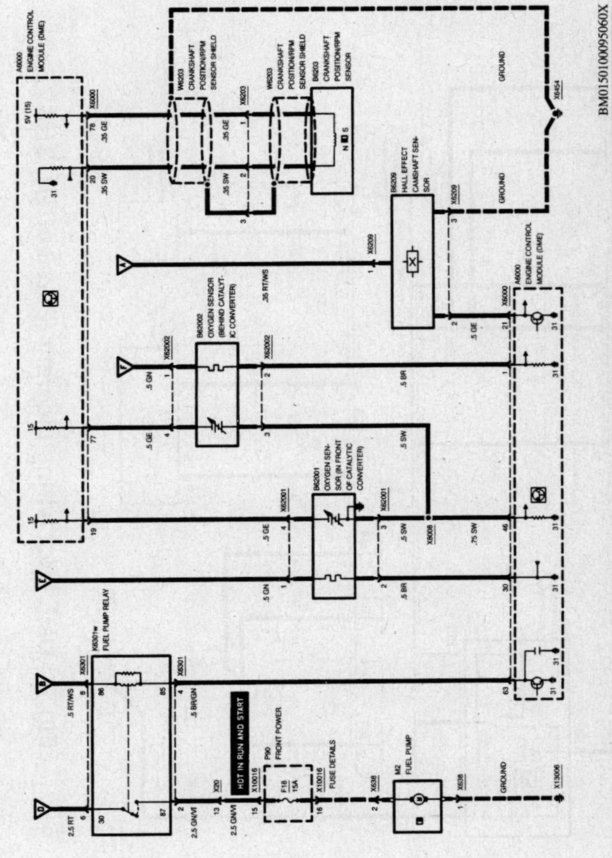

BM0150100095060X

Fig. 3 DME M5.2 wiring diagram (Part 6 of 11). 318i

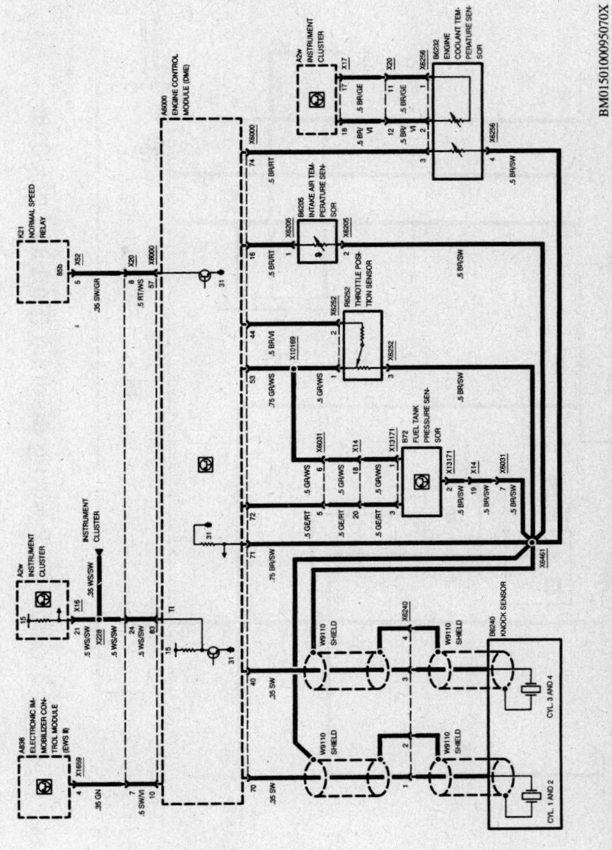

BM0150100095070X

Fig. 3 DME M5.2 wiring diagram (Part 7 of 11). 318i

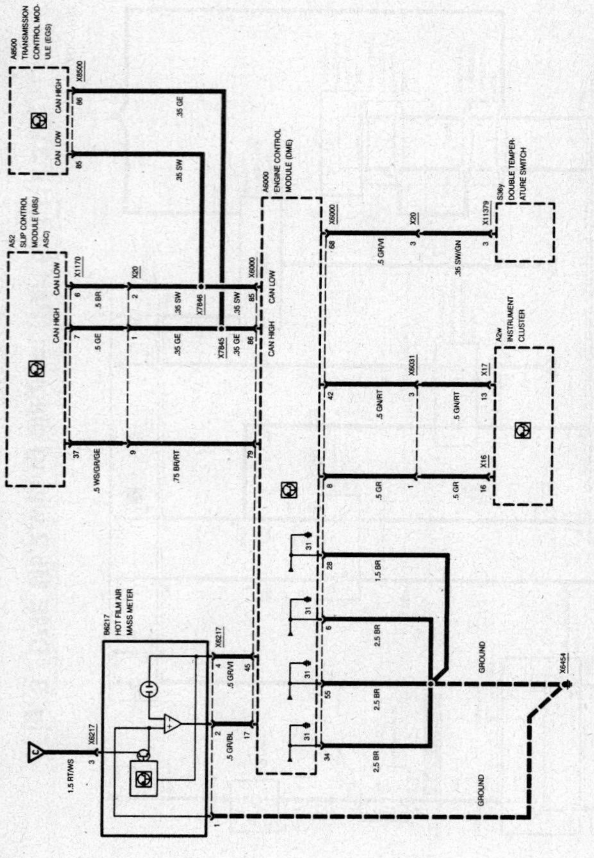

BM0150100095080X

Fig. 3 DME M5.2 wiring diagram (Part 8 of 11). 318i

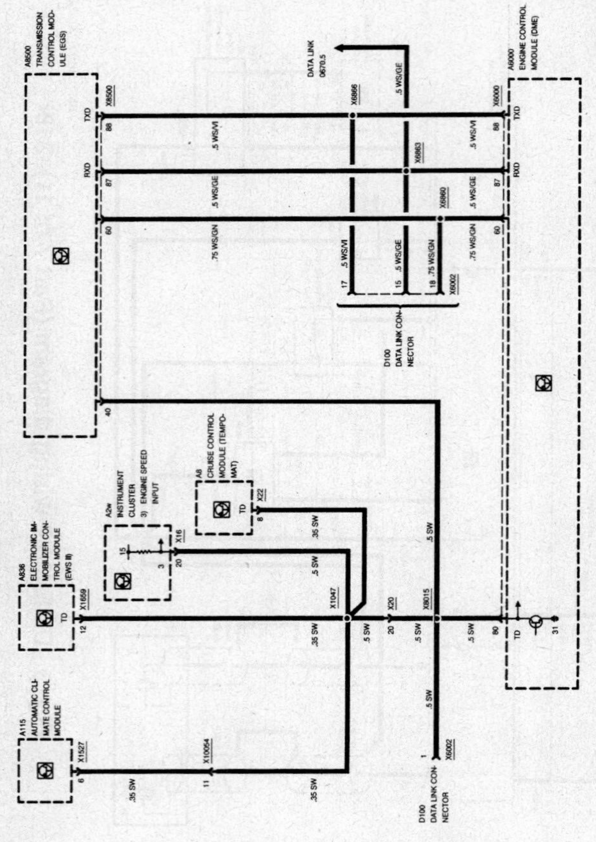

BM0150100095090X

Fig. 3 DME M5.2 wiring diagram (Part 9 of 11). 318i

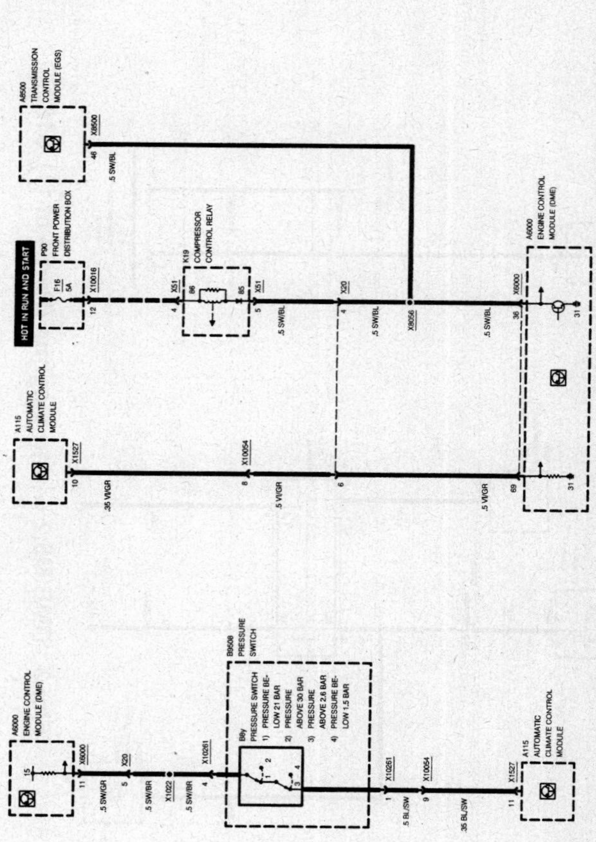

BM0150100095100X

Fig. 3 DME M5.2 wiring diagram (Part 10 of 11). 318i

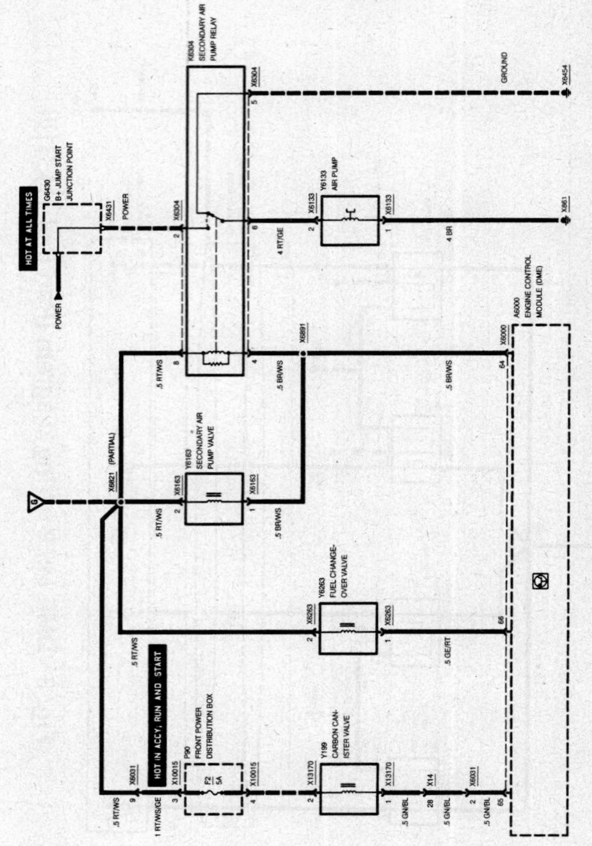

BM0150100095110X

Fig. 3 DME M5.2 wiring diagram (Part 11 of 11). 318i

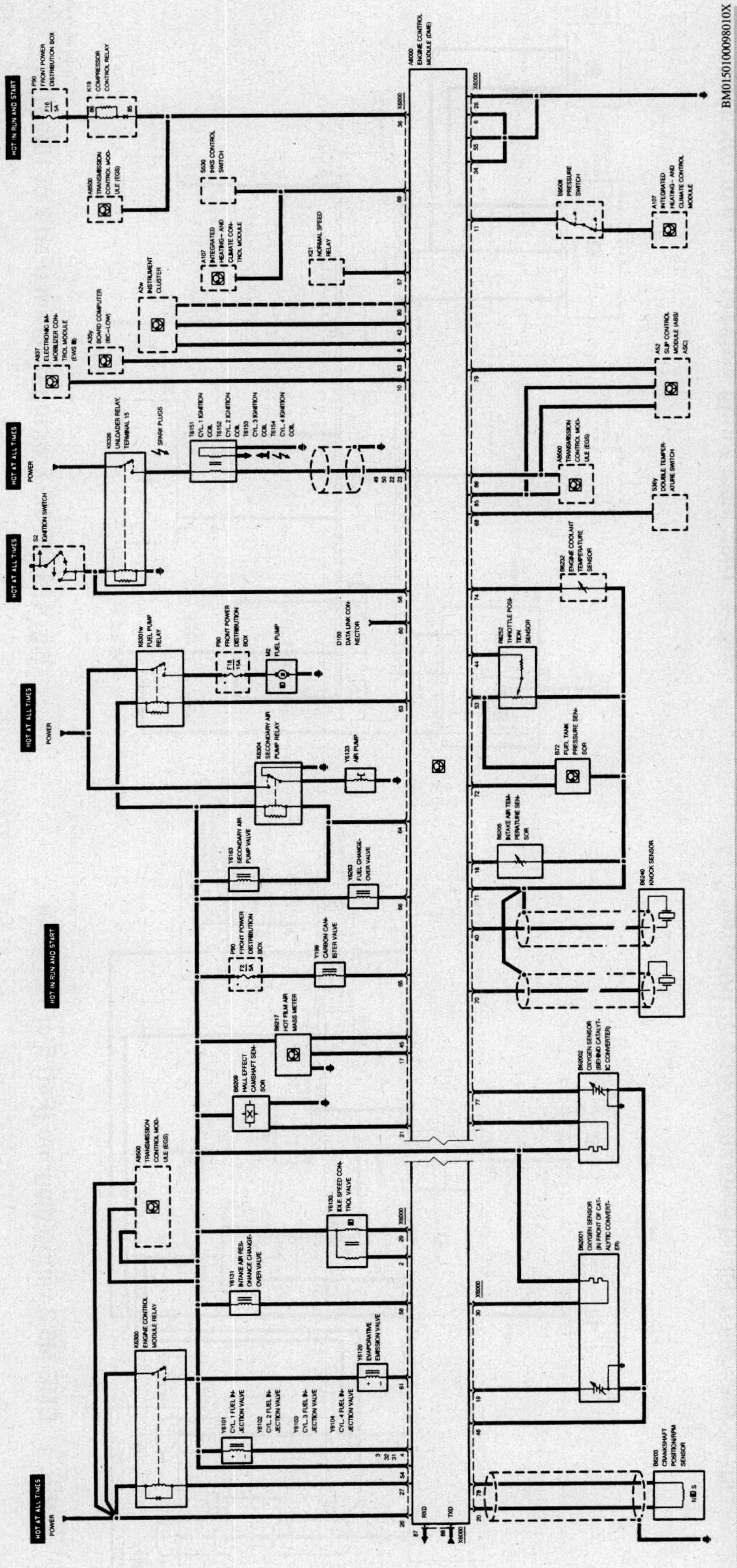

Fig. 4 DME M5.2 wiring diagram (Part 1 of 10). 318ti

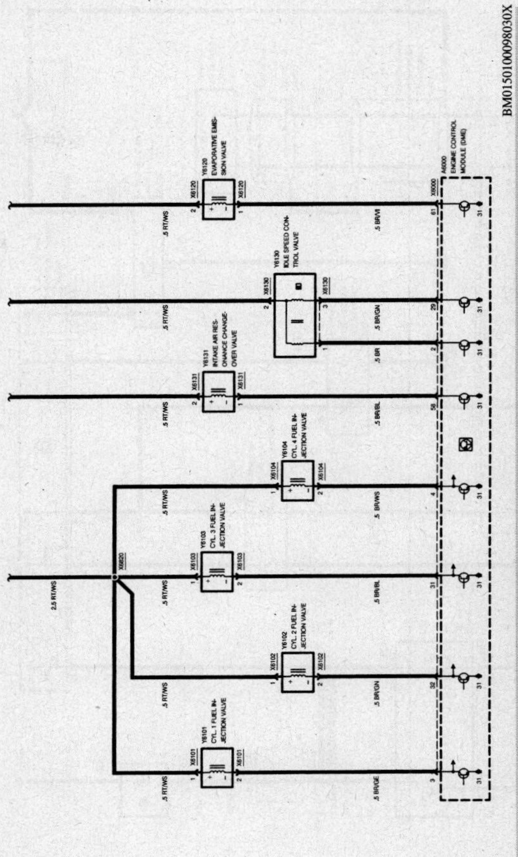

Fig. 4 DME M5.2 wiring diagram (Part 3 of 10). 318ti

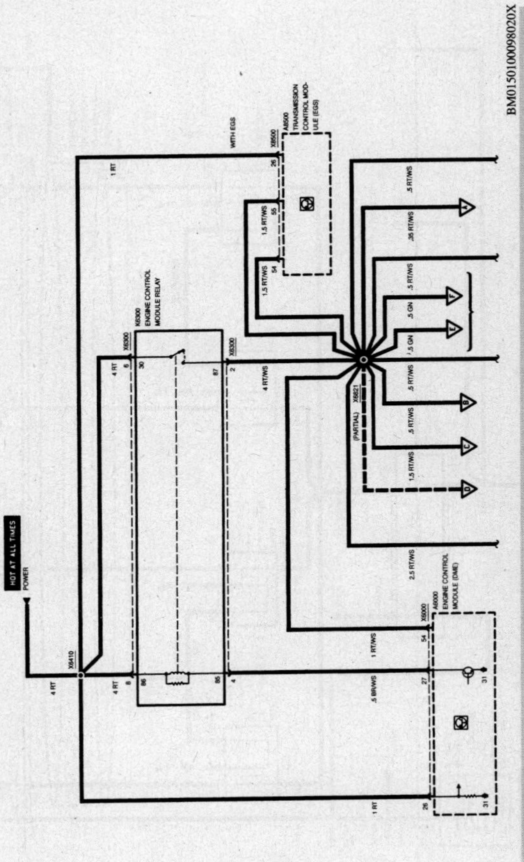

Fig. 4 DME M5.2 wiring diagram (Part 2 of 10). 318ti

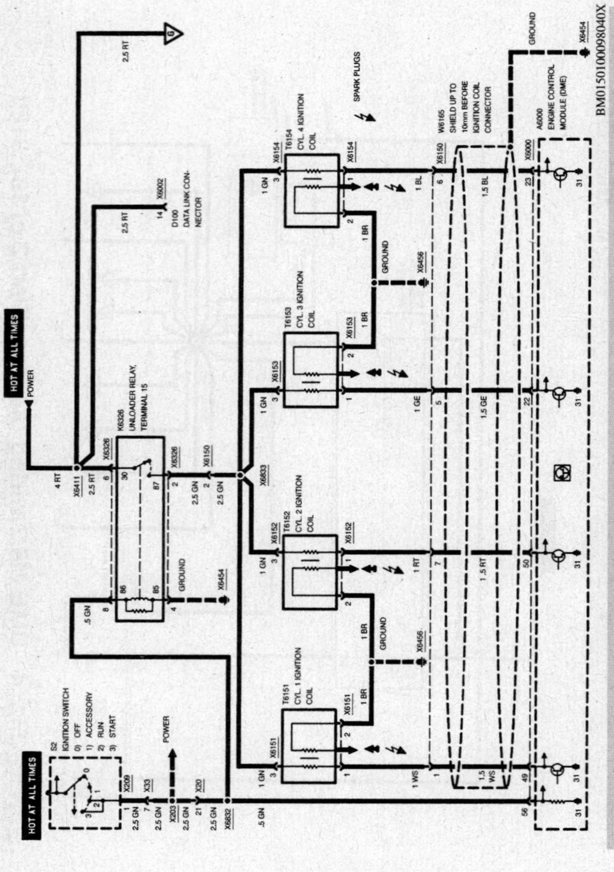

BM0150100098040X

Fig. 4 DME M5.2 wiring diagram (Part 4 of 10). 318ti

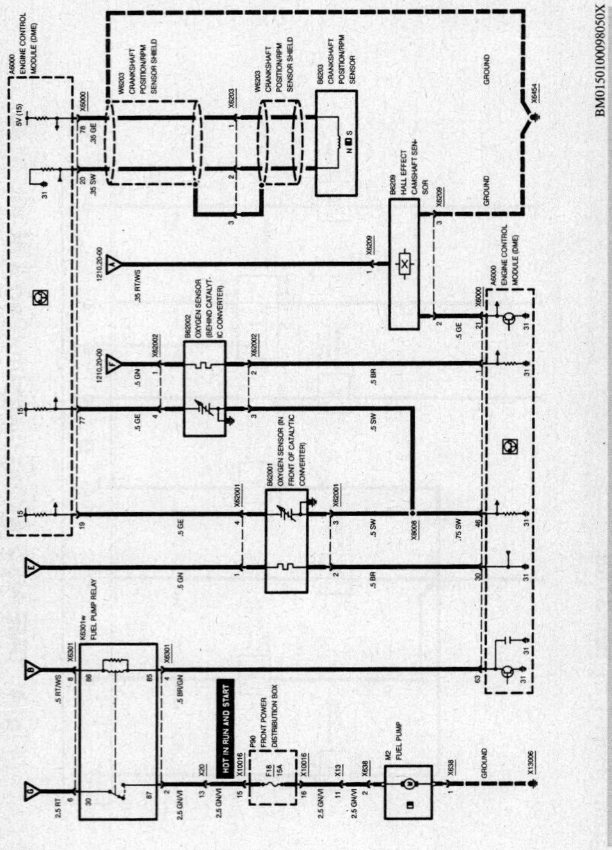

BM0150100098050X

Fig. 4 DME M5.2 wiring diagram (Part 5 of 10). 318ti

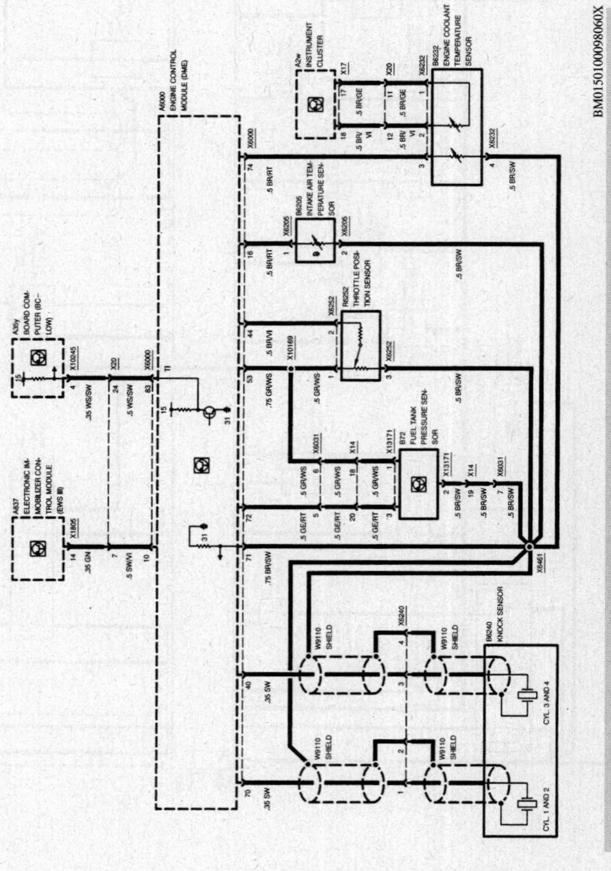

BM0150100098060X

Fig. 4 DME M5.2 wiring diagram (Part 6 of 10). 318ti

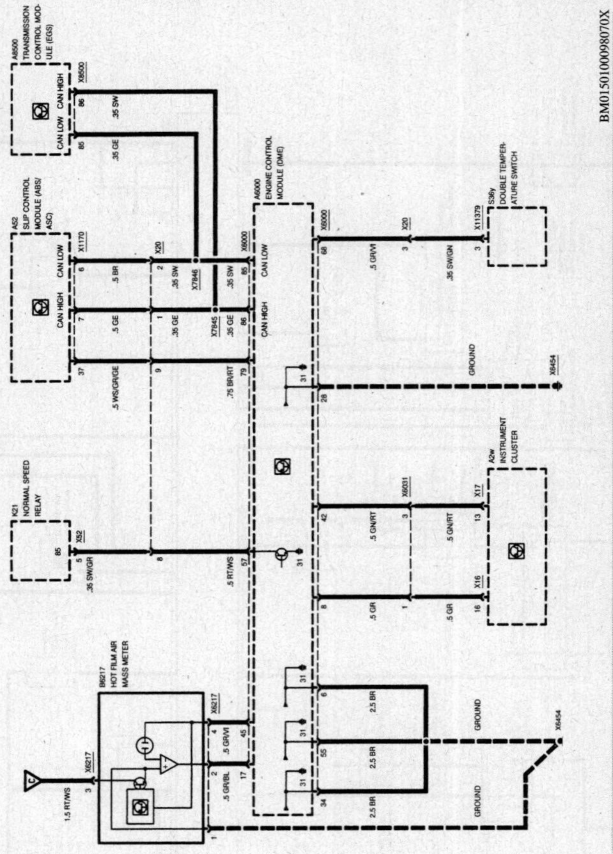

BM0150100098070X

Fig. 4 DME M5.2 wiring diagram (Part 7 of 10). 318ti

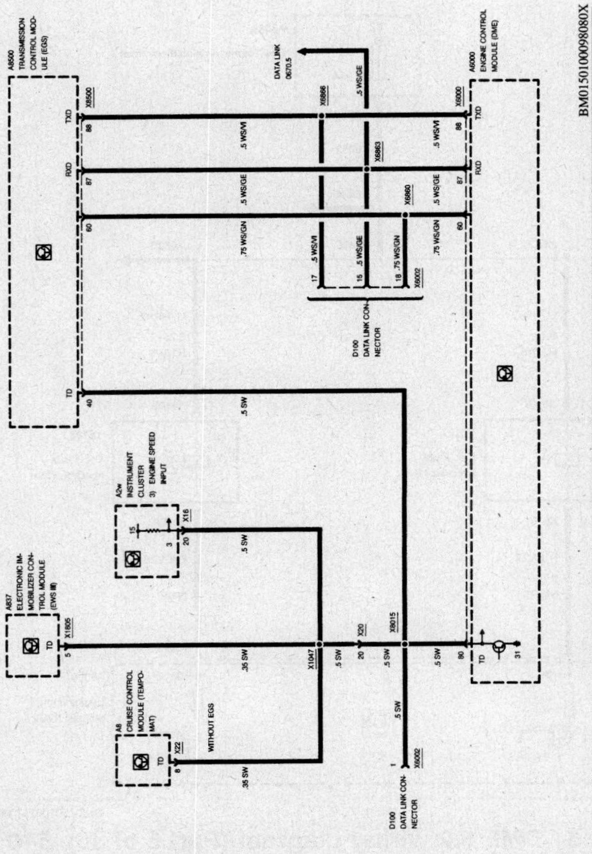

Fig. 4 DME M5.2 wiring diagram (Part 8 of 10). 318ti

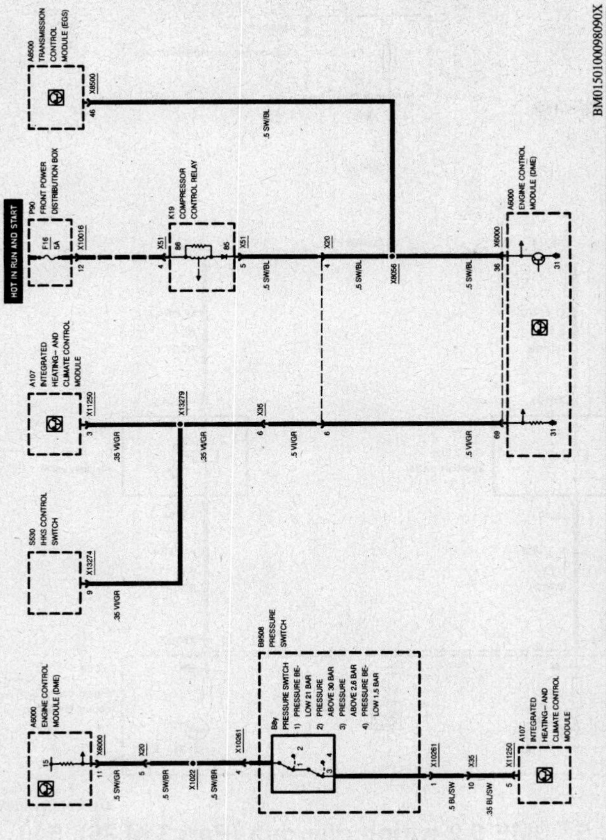

Fig. 4 DME M5.2 wiring diagram (Part 9 of 10). 318ti

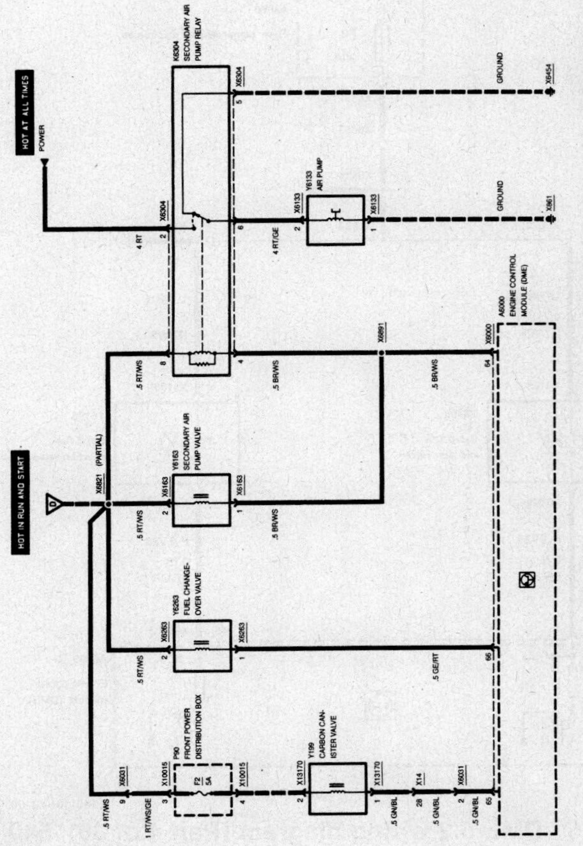

Fig. 4 DME M5.2 wiring diagram (Part 10 of 10). 318ti

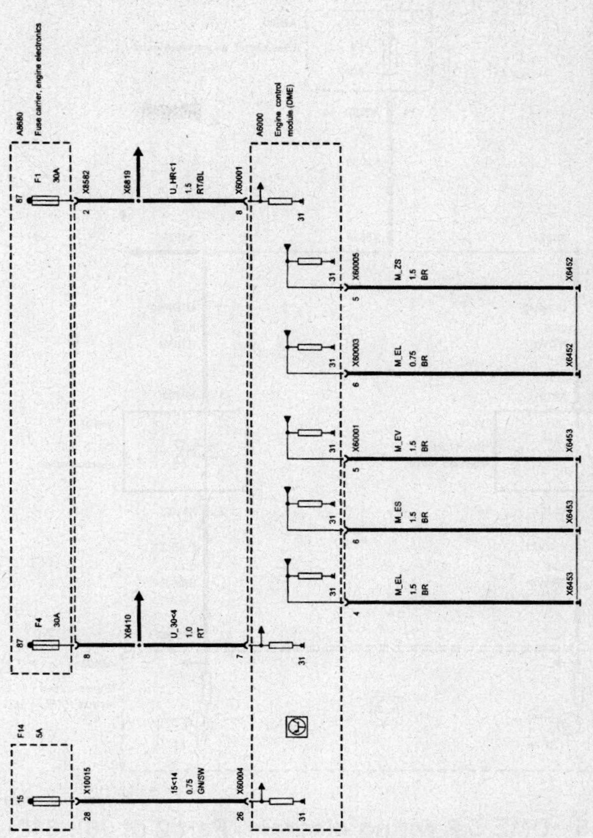

Fig. 5 DME 5.2 wiring diagram (Part 1 of 36). 540

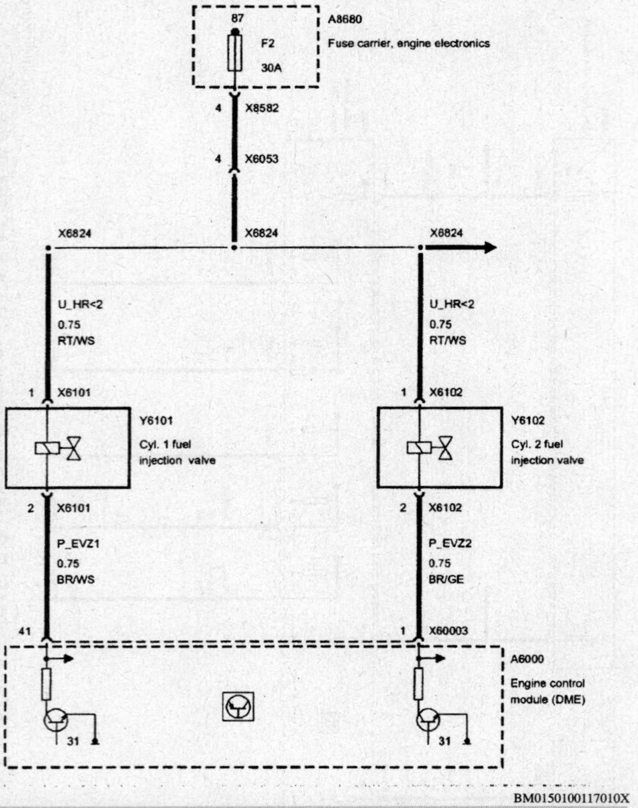

Fig. 5 DME 5.2 wiring diagram (Part 2 of 36). 540

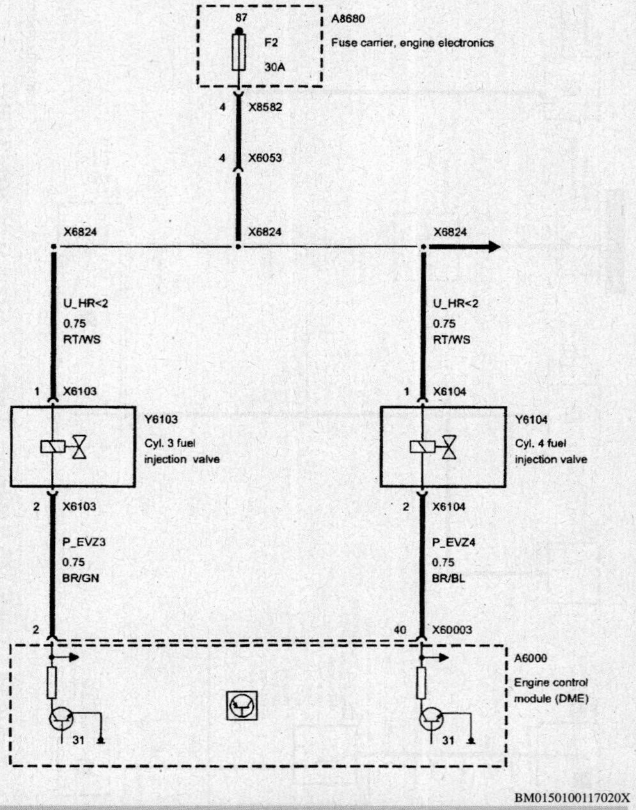

Fig. 5 DME 5.2 wiring diagram (Part 3 of 36). 540

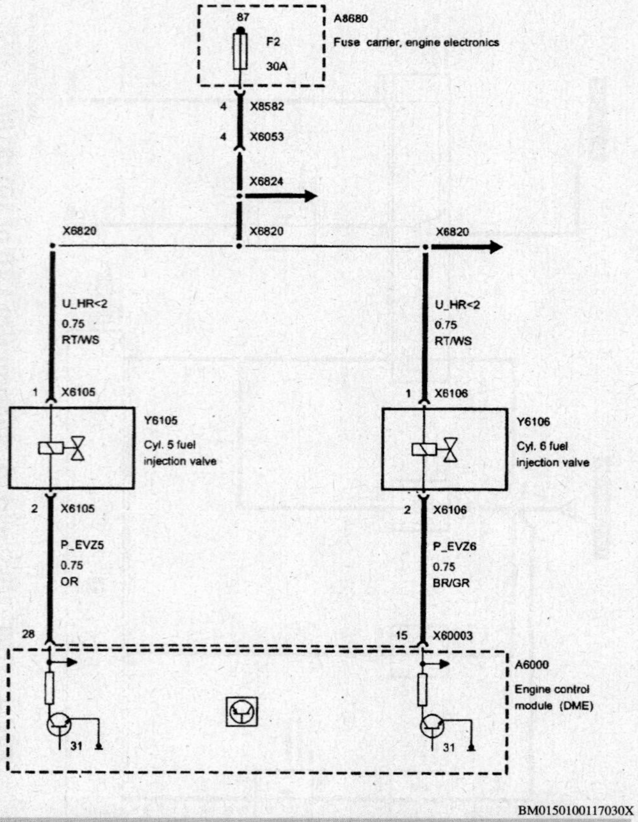

Fig. 5 DME 5.2 wiring diagram (Part 4 of 36). 540

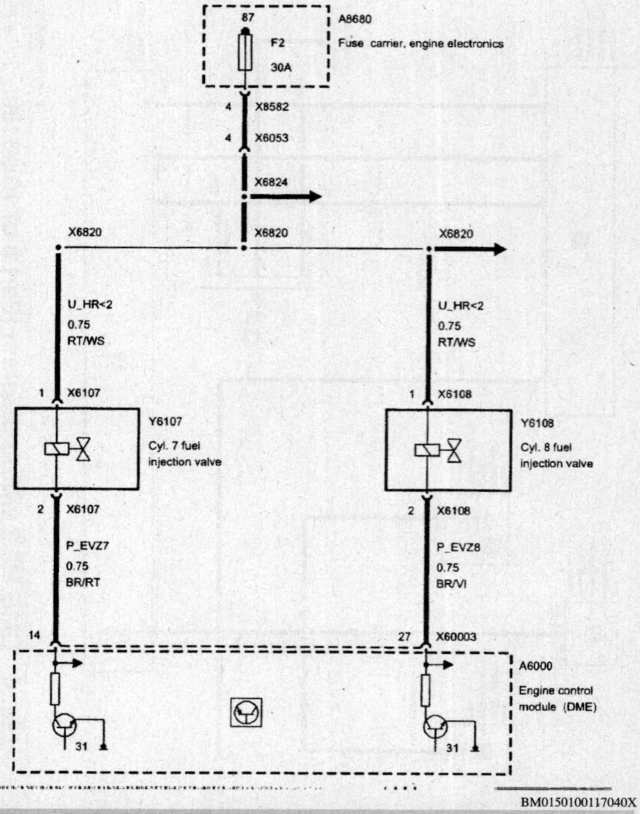

Fig. 5 DME 5.2 wiring diagram (Part 5 of 36). 540

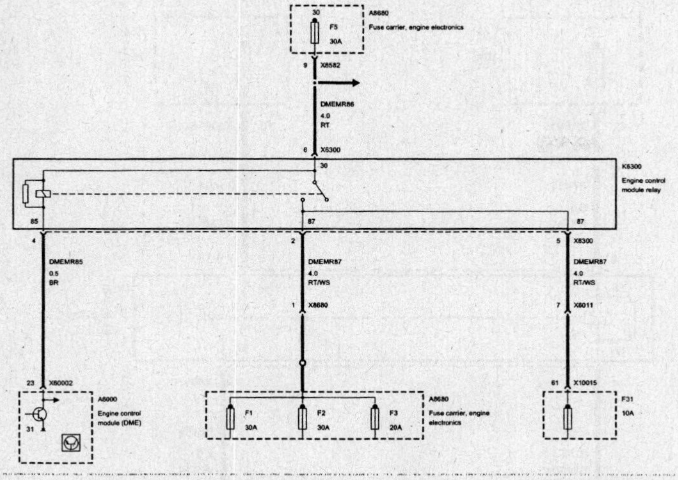

BM0150100117050X

Fig. 5 DME 5.2 wiring diagram (Part 6 of 36). 540

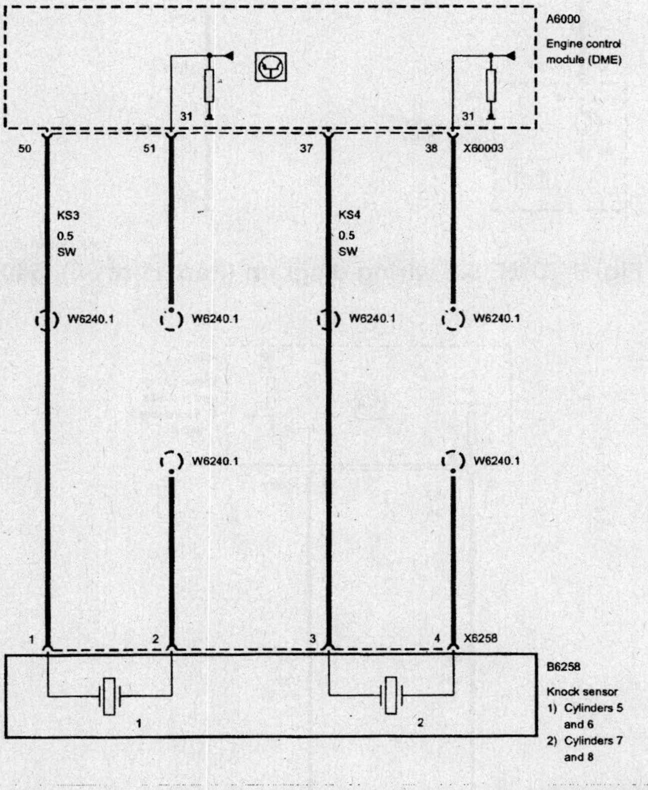

BM0150100117070X

Fig. 5 DME 5.2 wiring diagram (Part 8 of 36). 540

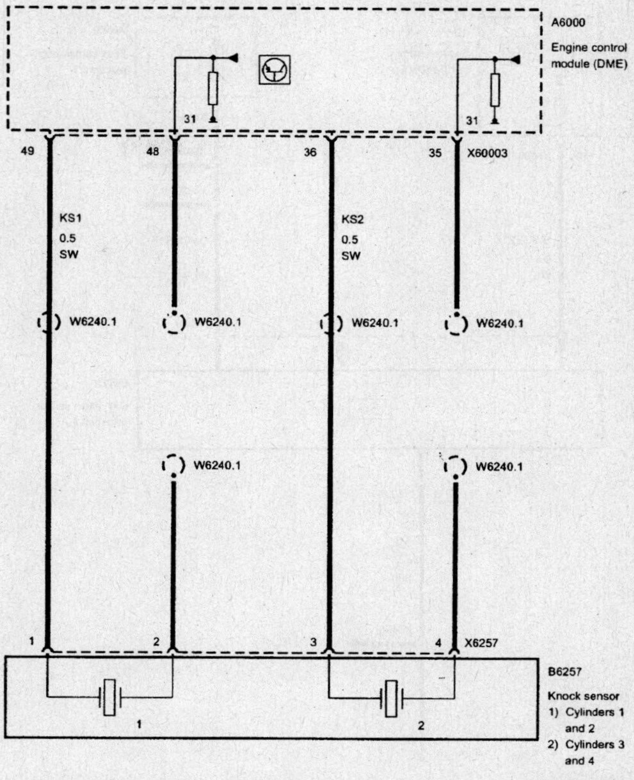

BM0150100117060X

Fig. 5 DME 5.2 wiring diagram (Part 7 of 36). 540

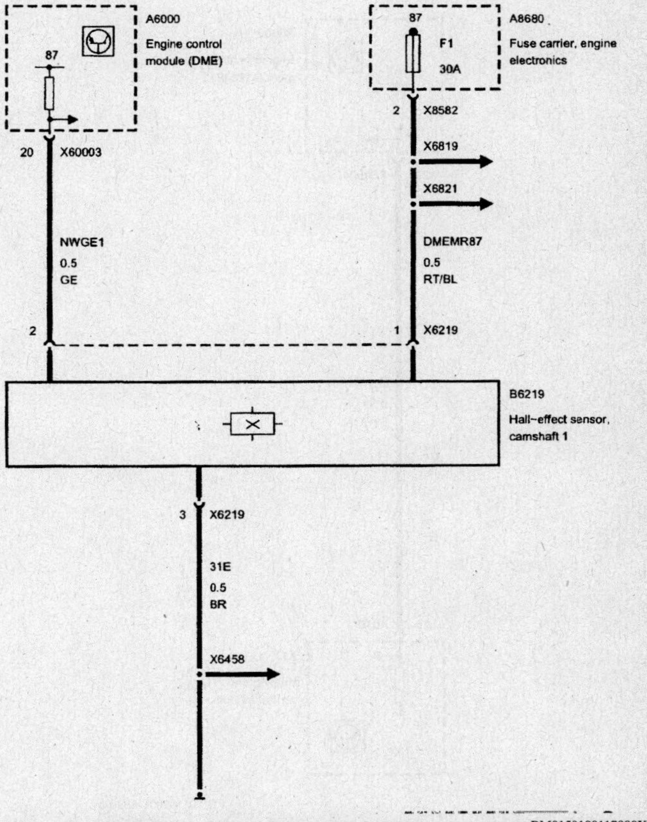

BM0150100117080X

Fig. 5 DME 5.2 wiring diagram (Part 9 of 36). 540

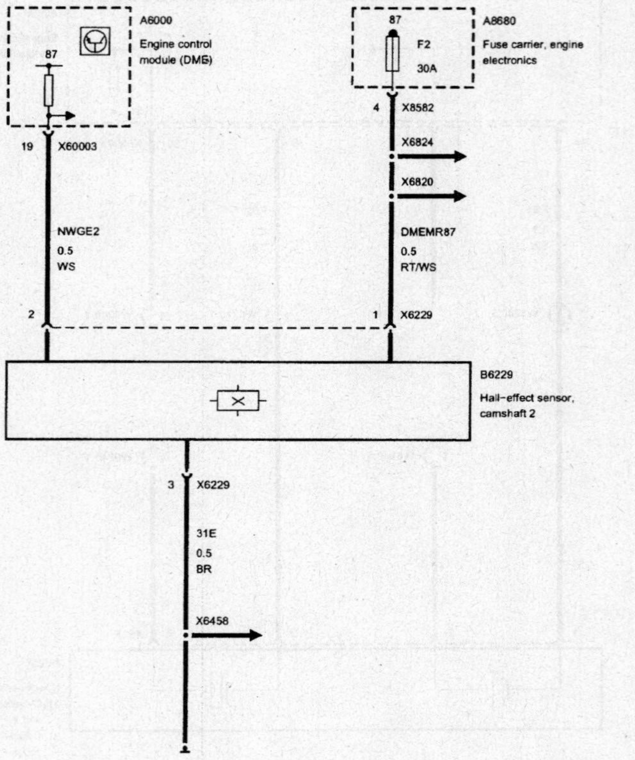

BM0150100117090X

Fig. 5 DME 5.2 wiring diagram (Part 10 of 36). 540

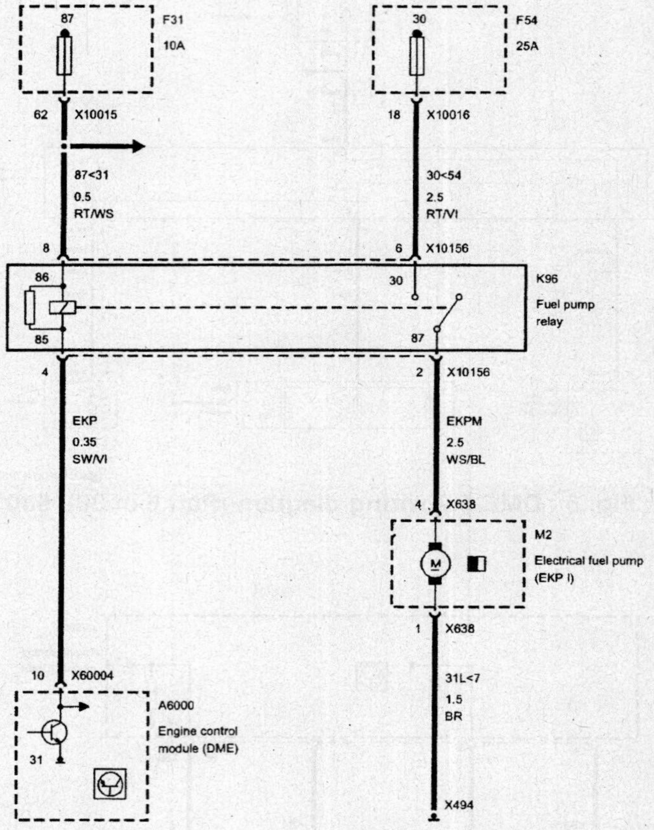

BM0150100118010X

Fig. 5 DME 5.2 wiring diagram (Part 11 of 36). 540

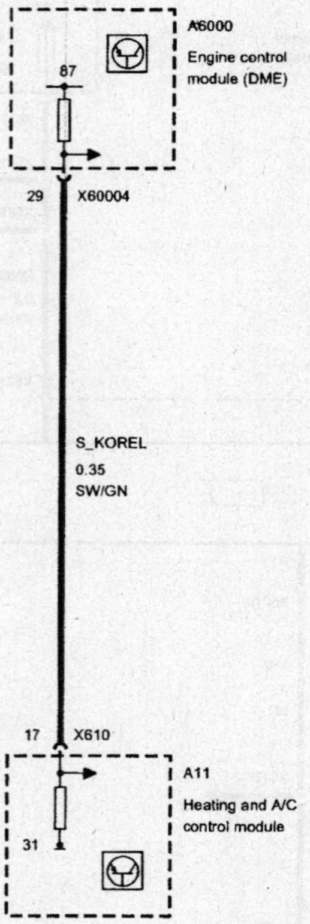

BM0150100118020X

Fig. 5 DME 5.2 wiring diagram (Part 12 of 36). 540

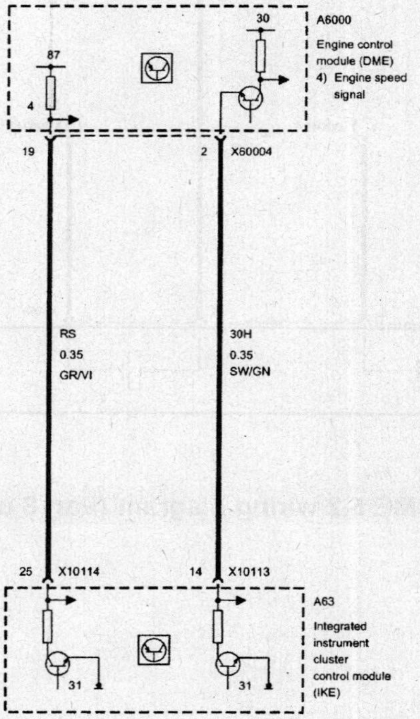

BM0150100118030X

Fig. 5 DME 5.2 wiring diagram (Part 13 of 36). 540

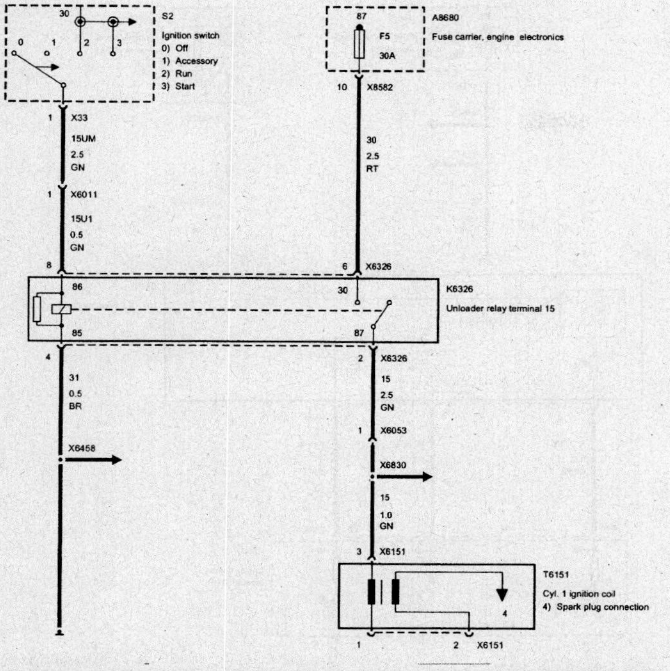

BM0150100118040X

Fig. 5 DME 5.2 wiring diagram (Part 14 of 36). 540

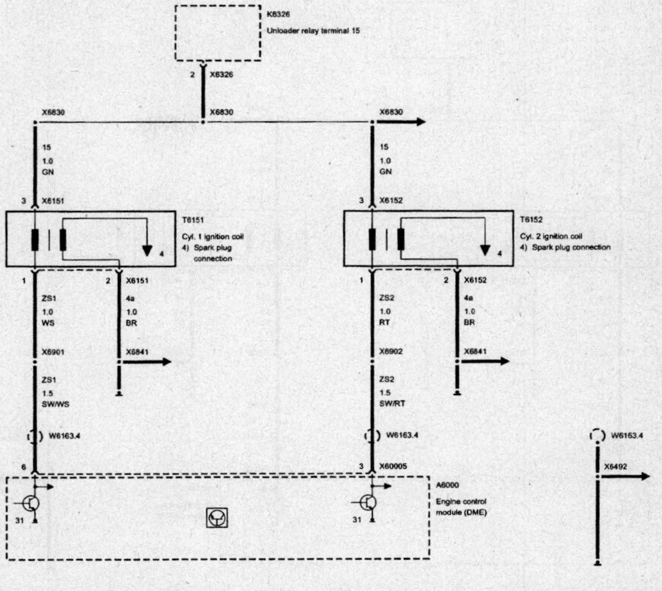

BM0150100118050X

Fig. 5 DME 5.2 wiring diagram (Part 15 of 36). 540

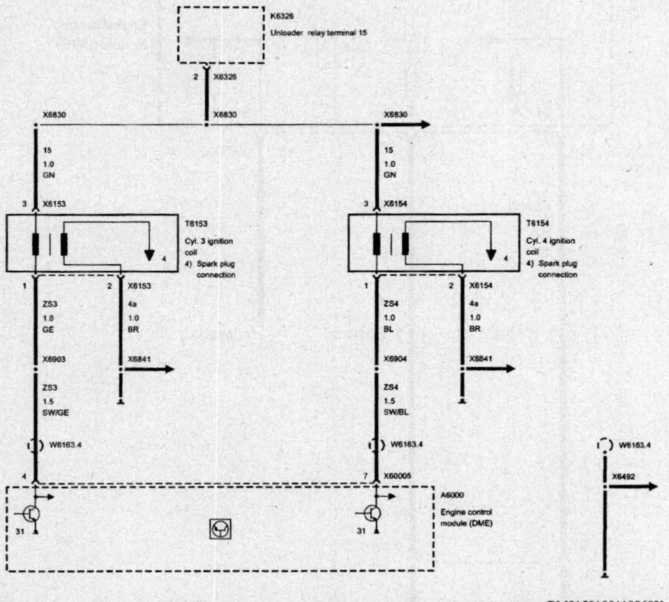

BM0150100118060X

Fig. 5 DME 5.2 wiring diagram (Part 16 of 36). 540

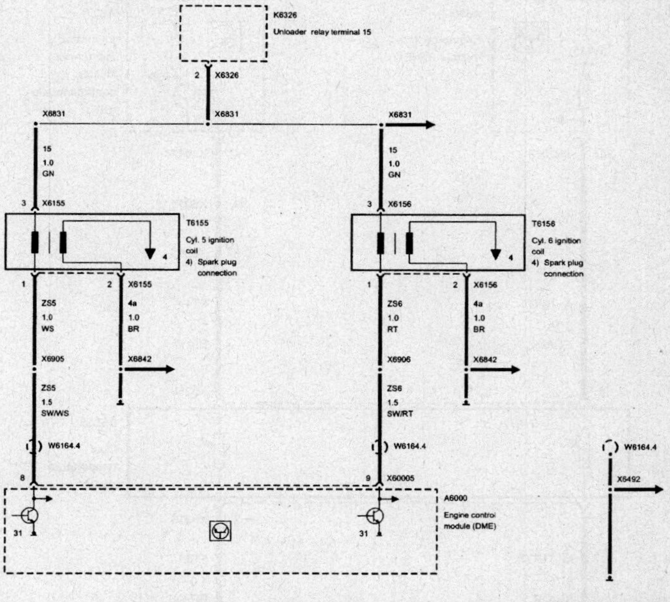

BM0150100118070X

Fig. 5 DME 5.2 wiring diagram (Part 17 of 36). 540

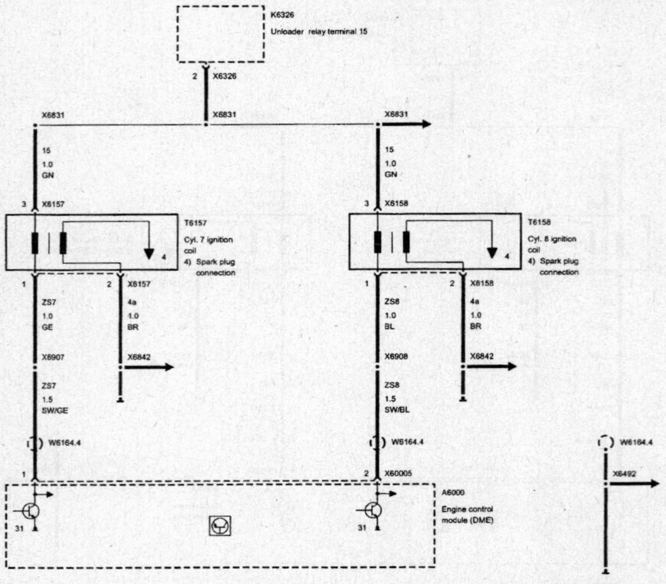

BM0150100118080X

Fig. 5 DME 5.2 wiring diagram (Part 18 of 36). 540

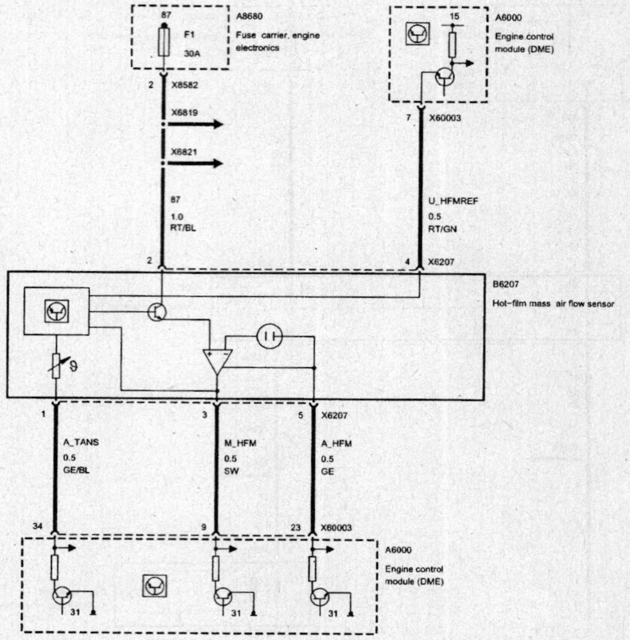

BM0150100118090X

Fig. 5 DME 5.2 wiring diagram (Part 19 of 36). 540

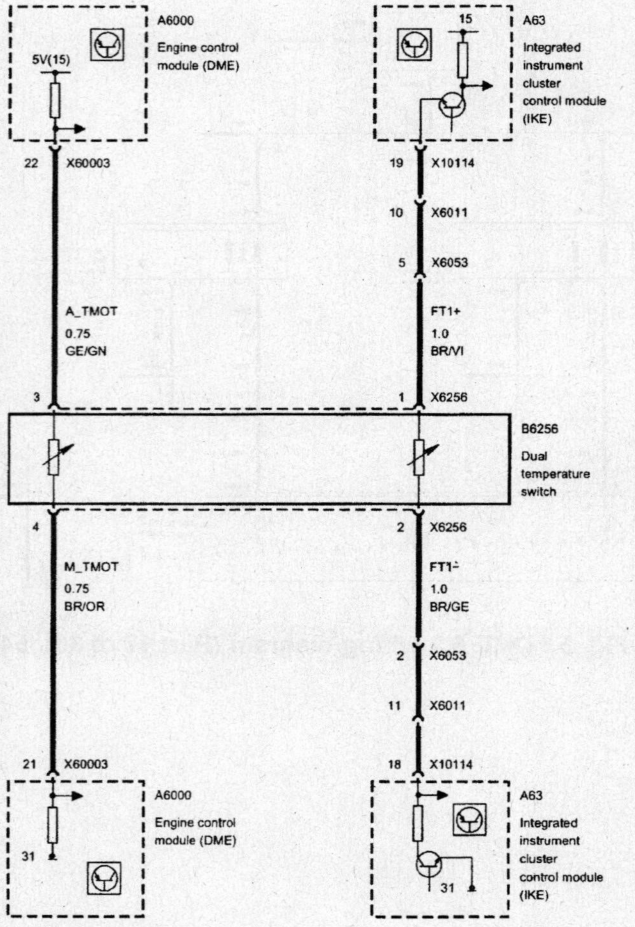

BM0150100118000X

Fig. 5 DME 5.2 wiring diagram (Part 20 of 36). 540

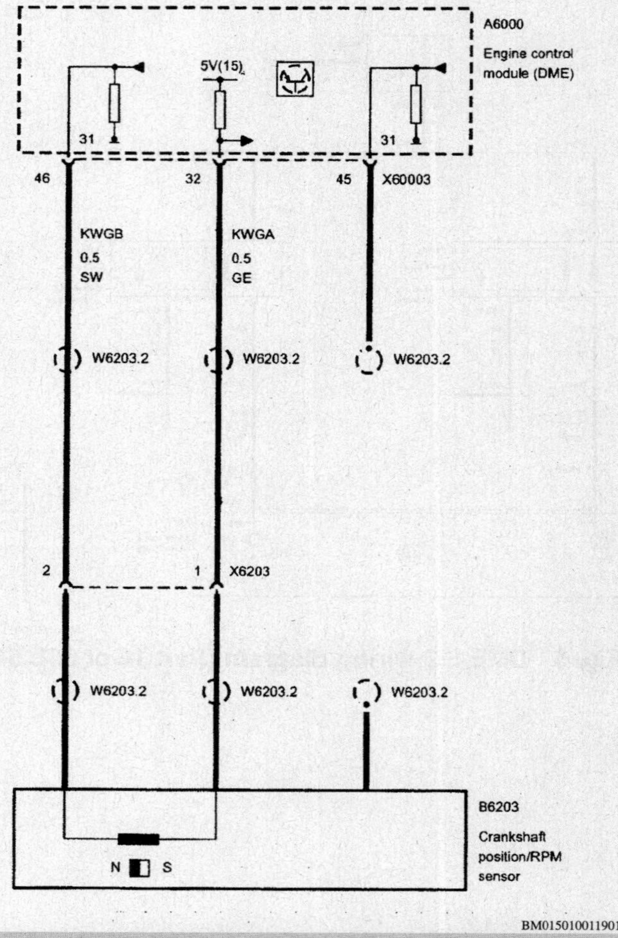

BM0150100119010X

Fig. 5 DME 5.2 wiring diagram (Part 21 of 36). 540

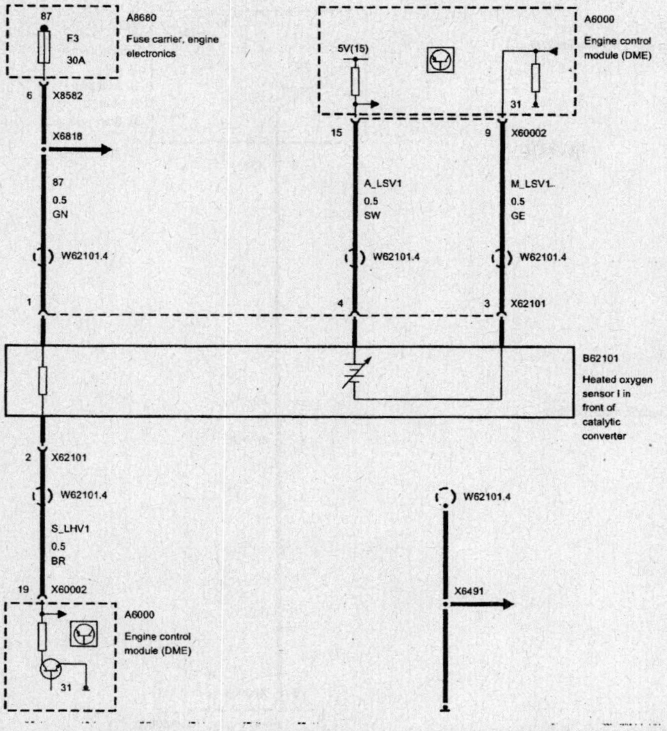

BM0150100119020X

Fig. 5 DME 5.2 wiring diagram (Part 22 of 36). 540

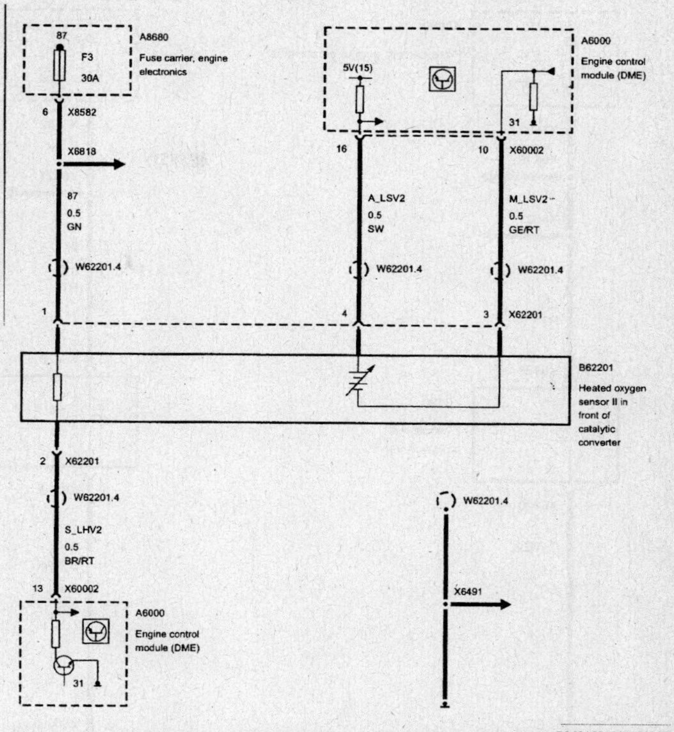

BM0150100119030X

Fig. 5 DME 5.2 wiring diagram (Part 23 of 36). 540

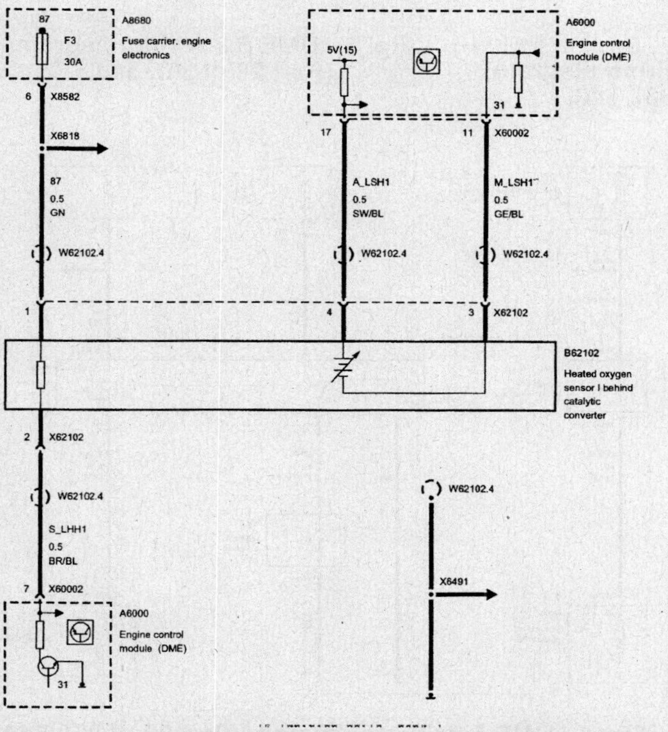

BM0150100119040X

Fig. 5 DME 5.2 wiring diagram (Part 24 of 36). 540

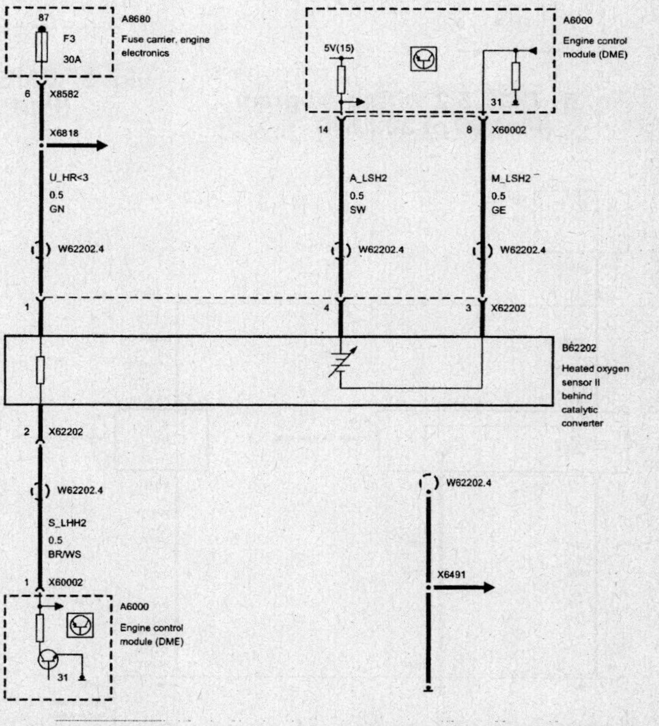

BM0150100119050X

Fig. 5 DME 5.2 wiring diagram (Part 25 of 36). 540

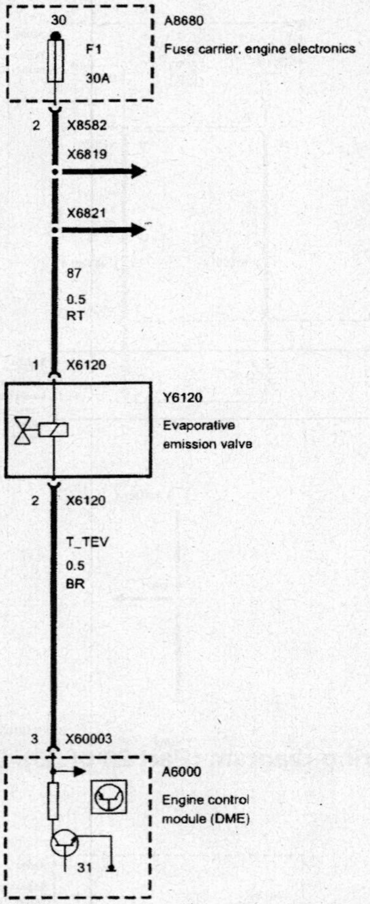

BM0150100119060X

Fig. 5 DME 5.2 wiring diagram (Part 26 of 36). 540

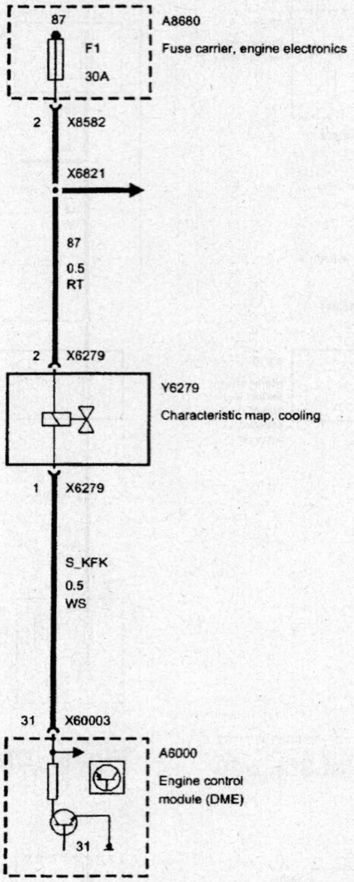

BM0150100119070X

Fig. 5 DME 5.2 wiring diagram (Part 27 of 36). 540

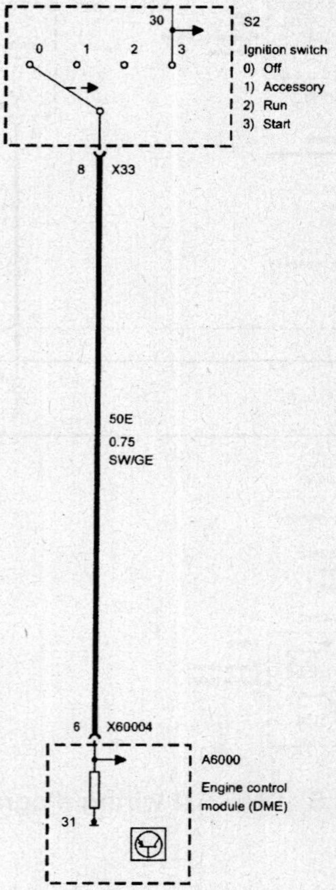

BM0150100119080X

Fig. 5 DME 5.2 wiring diagram (Part 28 of 36). 540

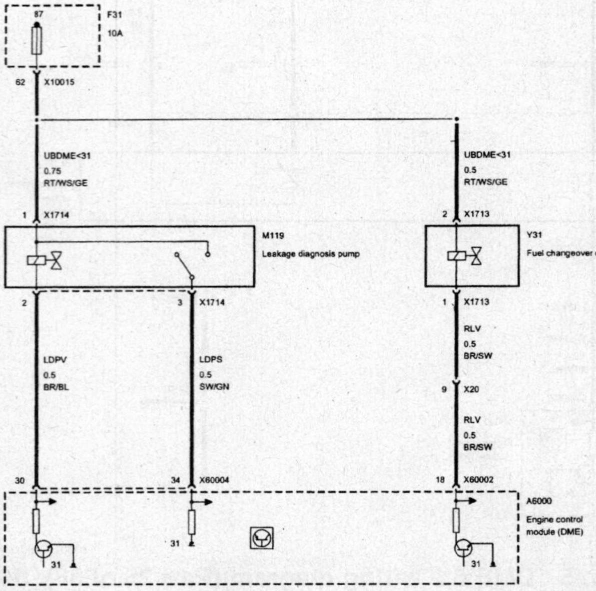

BM0150100119090X

Fig. 5 DME 5.2 wiring diagram (Part 29 of 36). 540

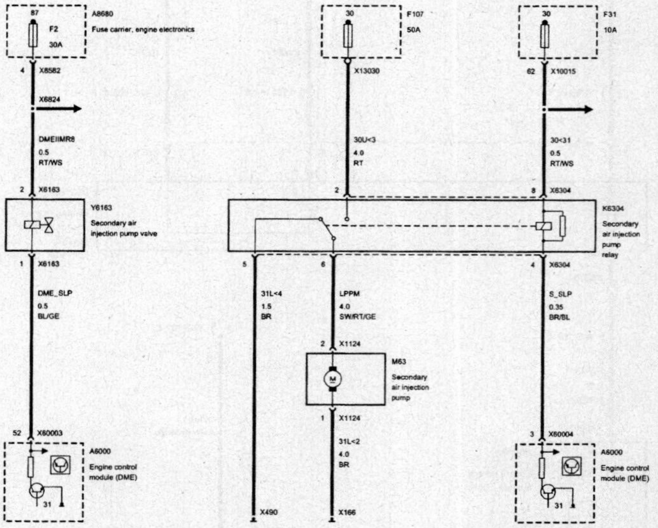

BM0150100119000X

Fig. 5 DME 5.2 wiring diagram (Part 30 of 36). 540

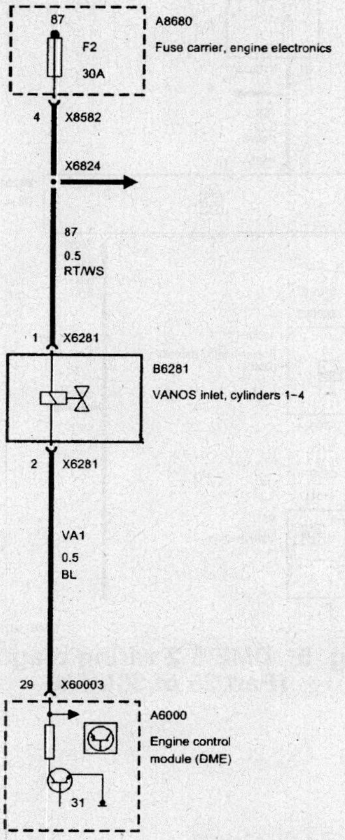

BM0150100120010X

Fig. 5 DME 5.2 wiring diagram (Part 31 of 36). 540

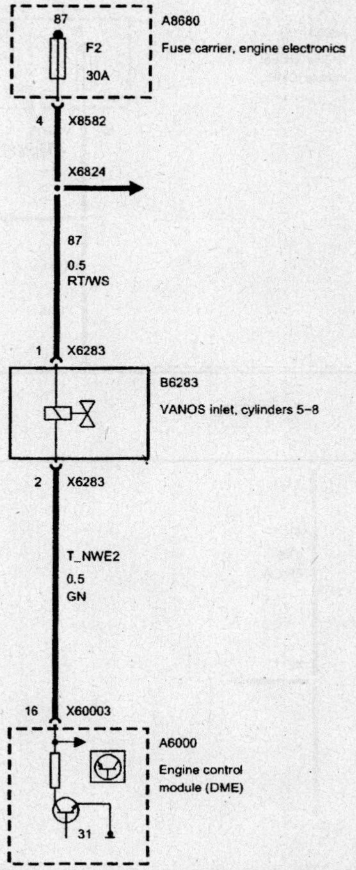

BM0150100120020X

Fig. 5 DME 5.2 wiring diagram (Part 32 of 36). 540

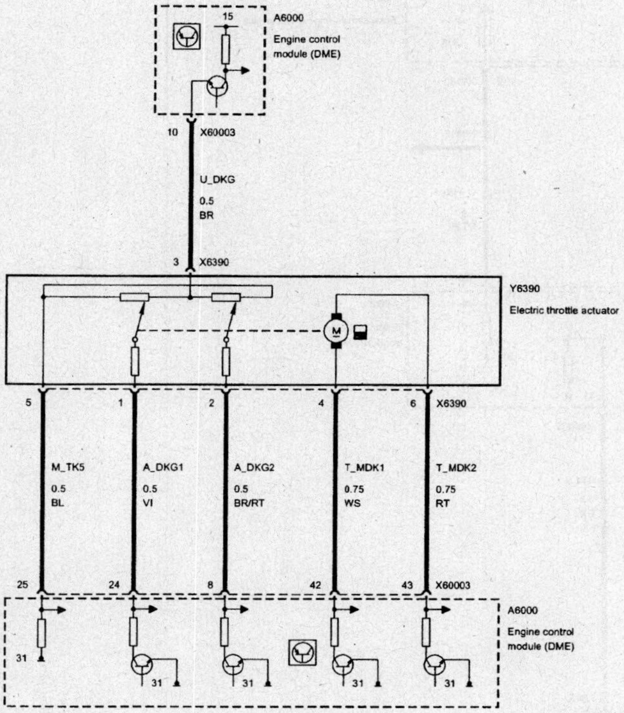

BM0150100120030X

Fig. 5 DME 5.2 wiring diagram (Part 33 of 36). 540

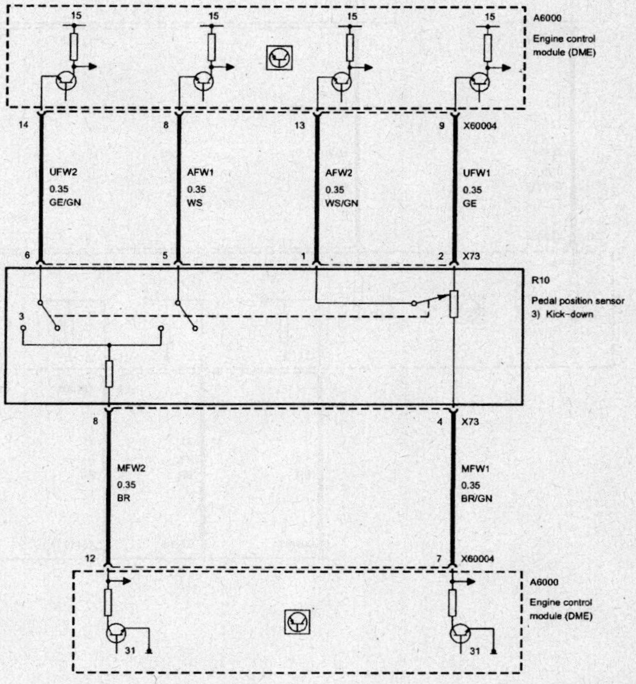

BM0150100120040X

Fig. 5 DME 5.2 wiring diagram (Part 34 of 36). 540

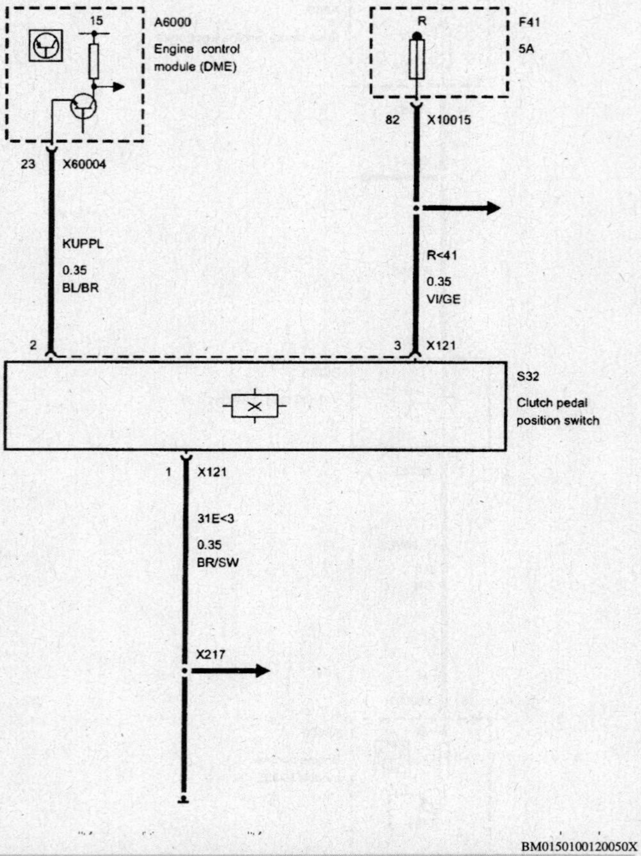

Fig. 5 DME 5.2 wiring diagram (Part 35 of 36). 540

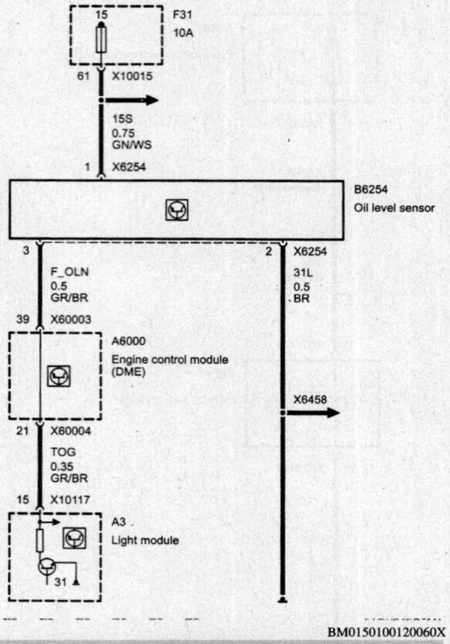

Fig. 5 DME 5.2 wiring diagram (Part 36 of 36). 540

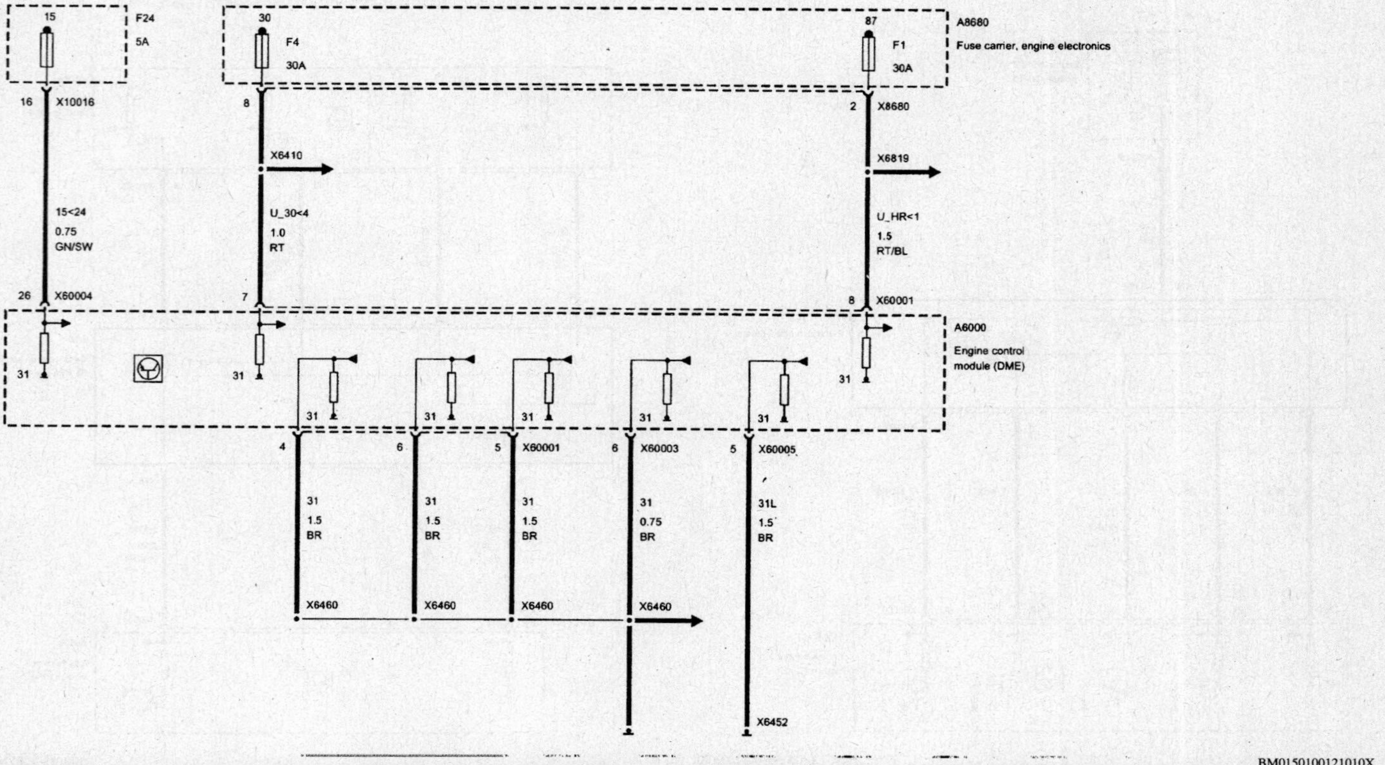

Fig. 6 DME 5.2 wiring diagram (Part 1 of 41). 740

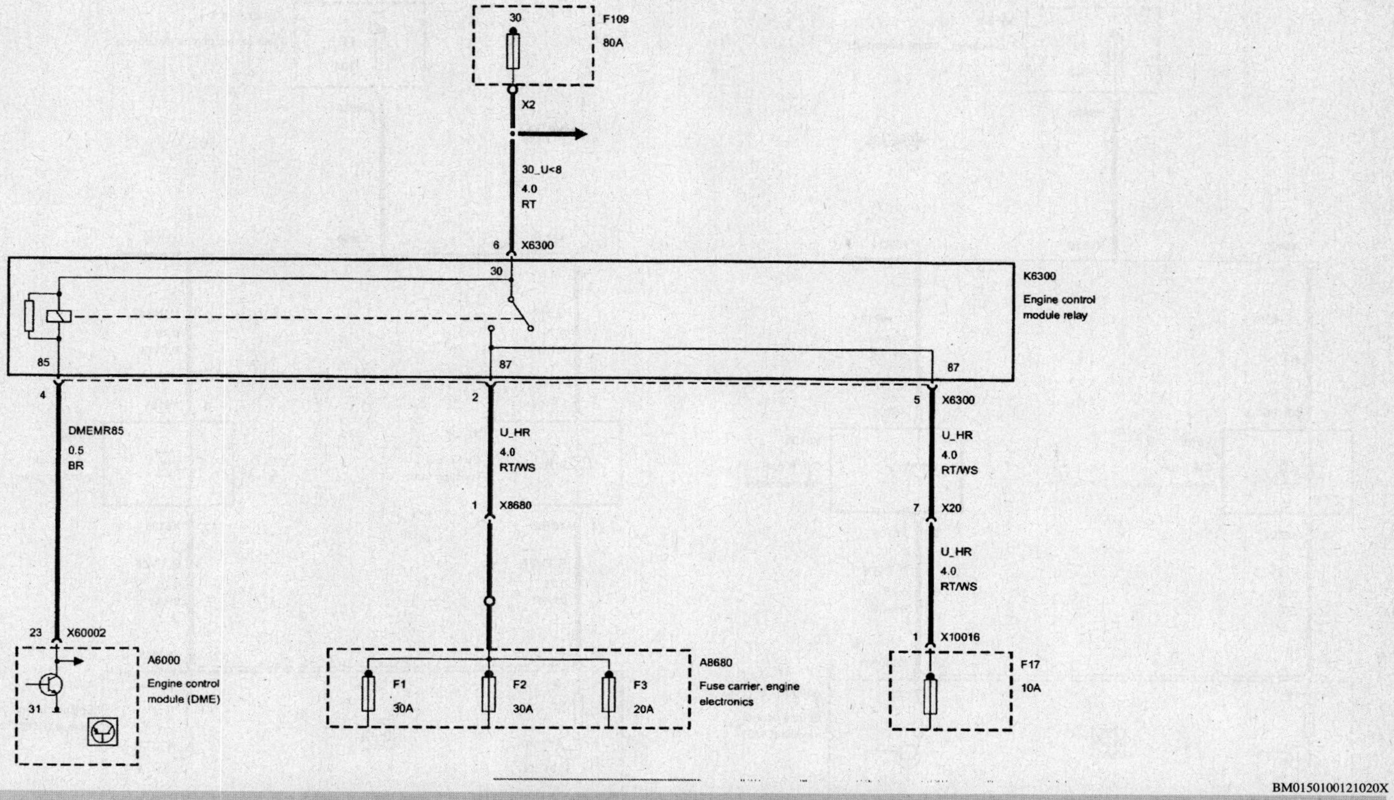

Fig. 6 DME 5.2 wiring diagram (Part 2 of 41). 740

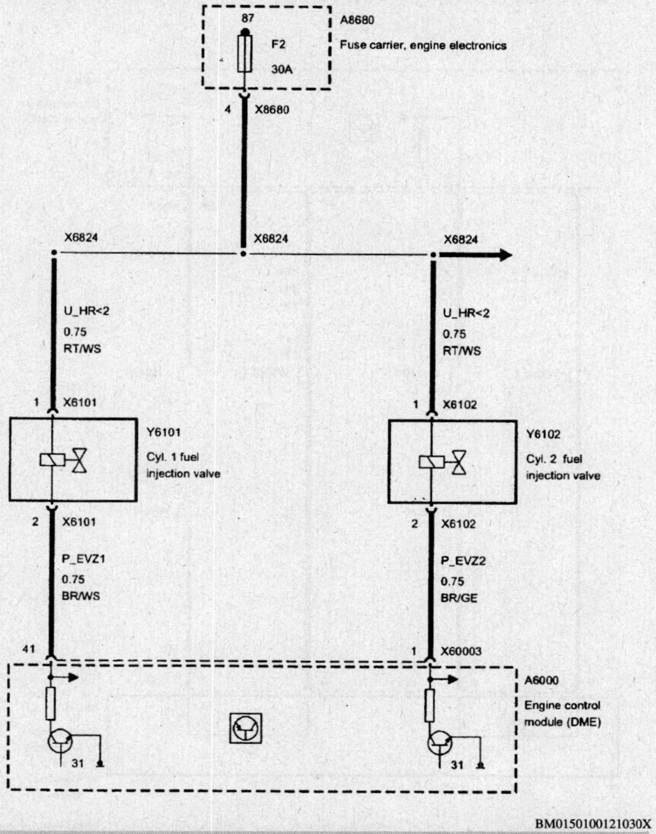

Fig. 6 DME 5.2 wiring diagram (Part 3 of 41). 740

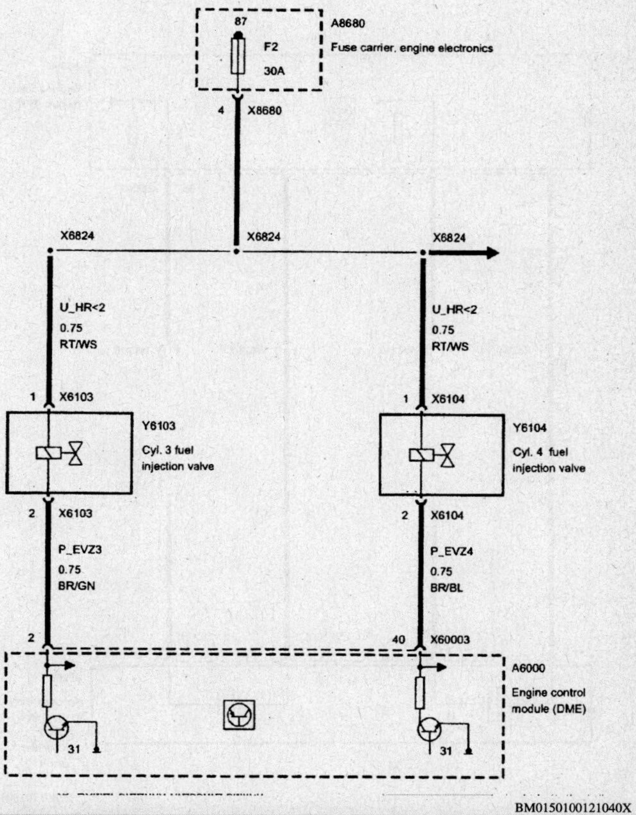

Fig. 6 DME 5.2 wiring diagram (Part 4 of 41). 740

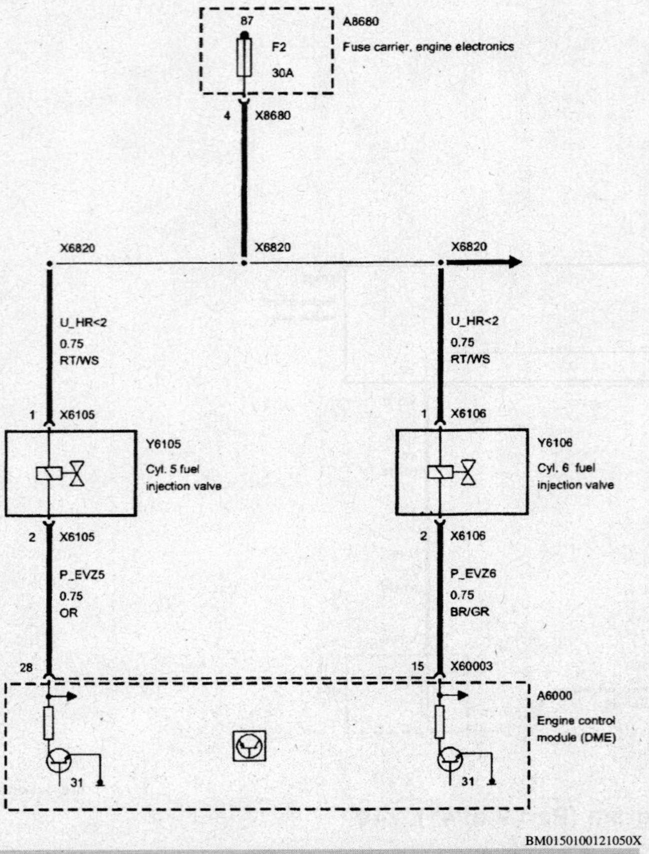

Fig. 6 DME 5.2 wiring diagram (Part 5 of 41). 740

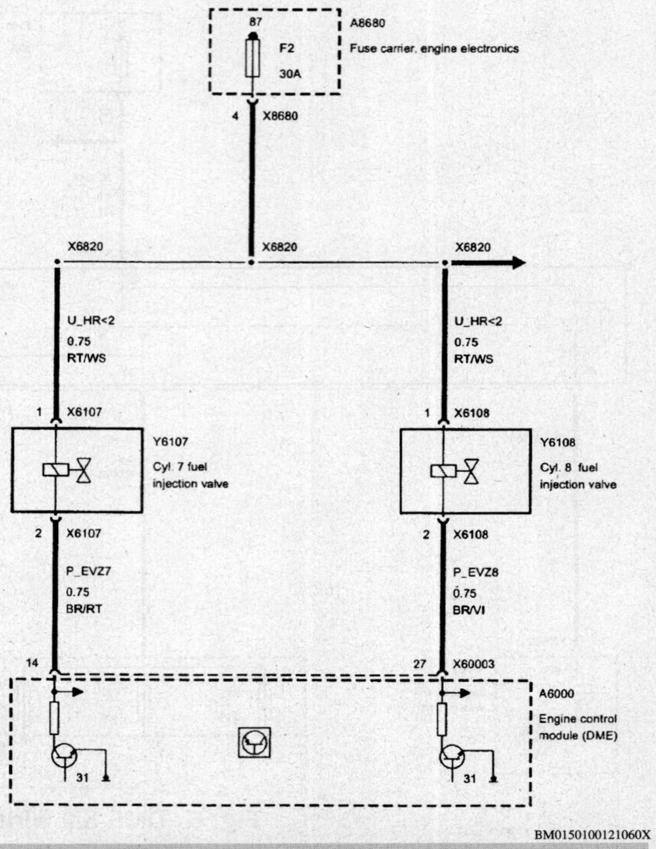

Fig. 6 DME 5.2 wiring diagram (Part 6 of 41). 740

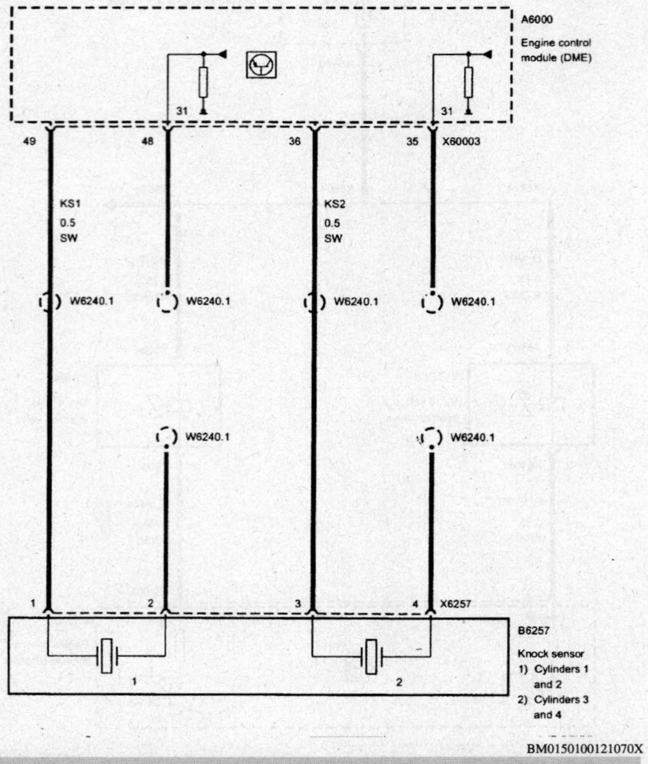

Fig. 6 DME 5.2 wiring diagram (Part 7 of 41). 740

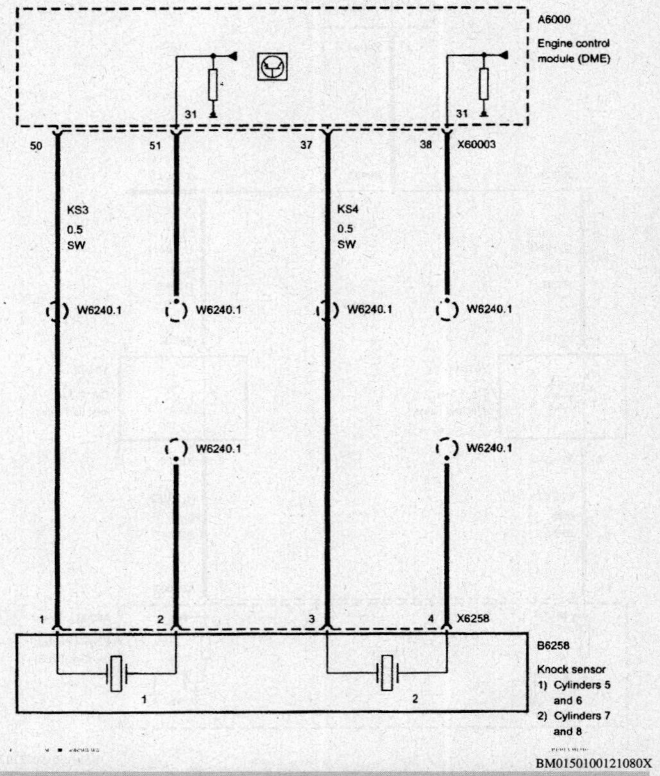

Fig. 6 DME 5.2 wiring diagram (Part 8 of 41). 740

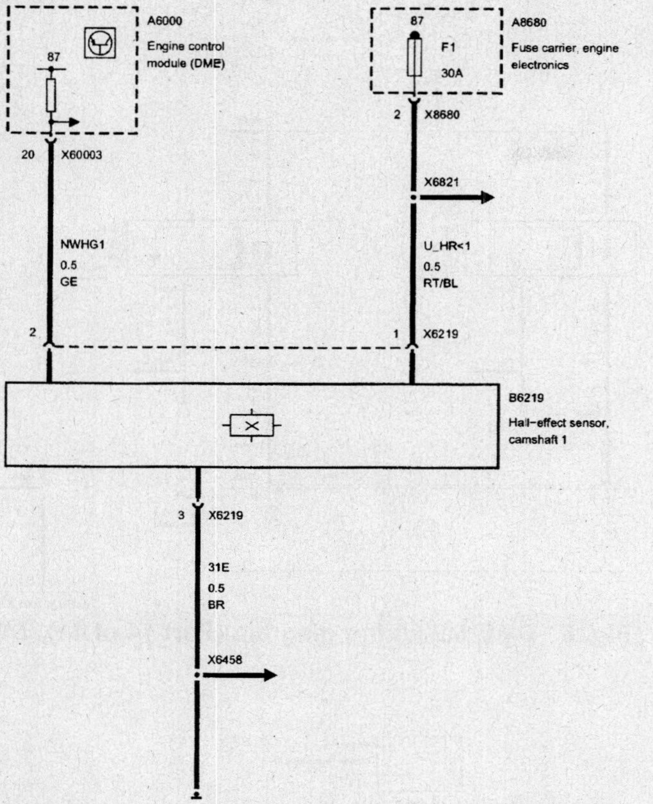

BM0150100121090X

Fig. 6 DME 5.2 wiring diagram (Part 9 of 41). 740

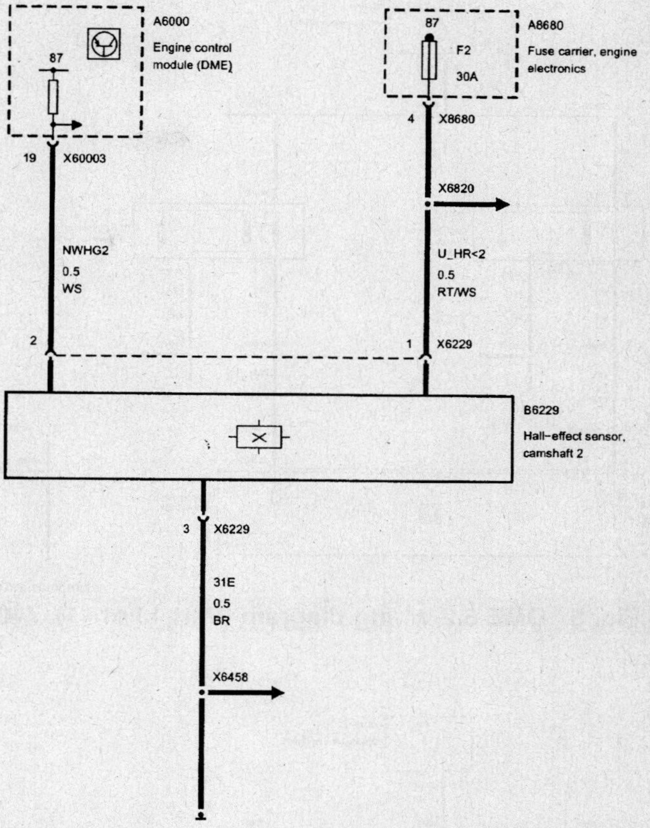

BM0150100121000X

Fig. 6 DME 5.2 wiring diagram (Part 10 of 41). 740

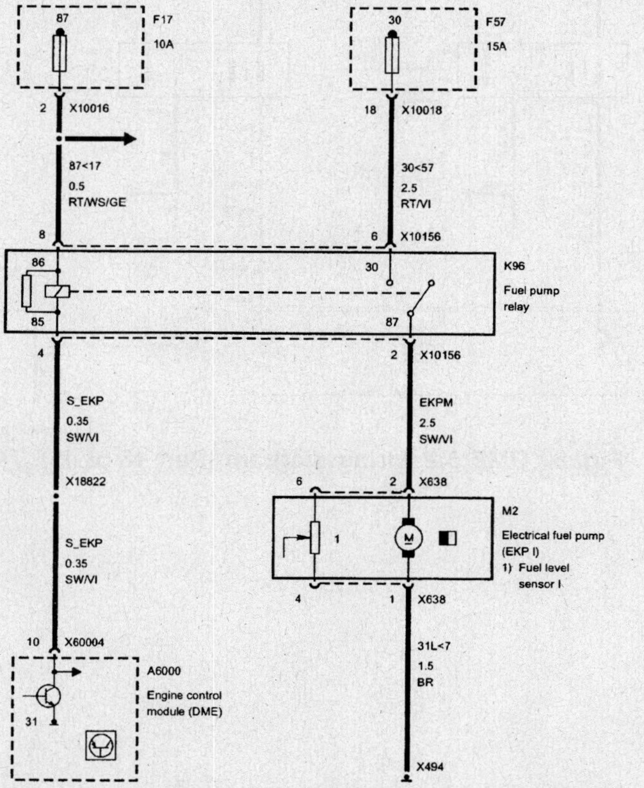

BM0150100122010X

Fig. 6 DME 5.2 wiring diagram (Part 11 of 41). 740

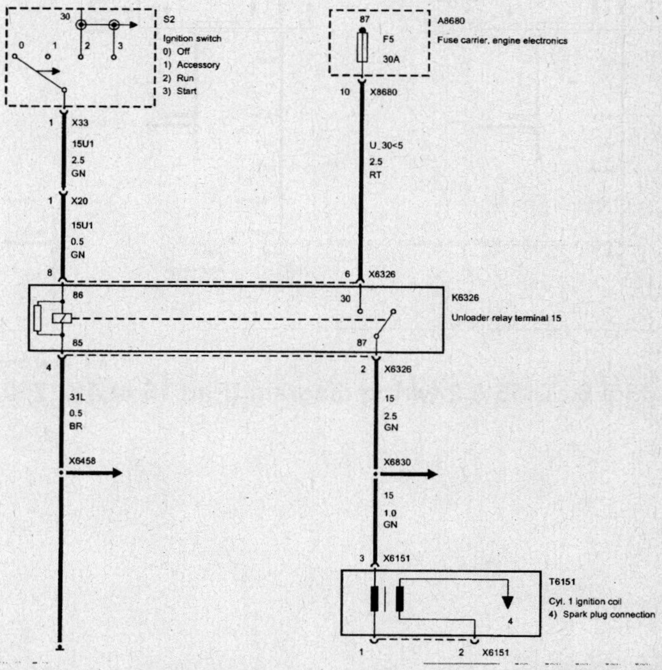

BM0150100122020X

Fig. 6 DME 5.2 wiring diagram (Part 12 of 41). 740

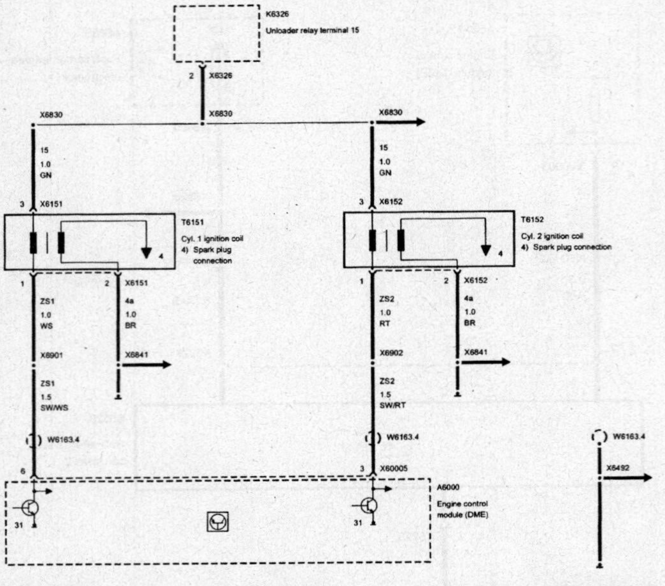

BM0150100122030X

Fig. 6 DME 5.2 wiring diagram (Part 13 of 41). 740

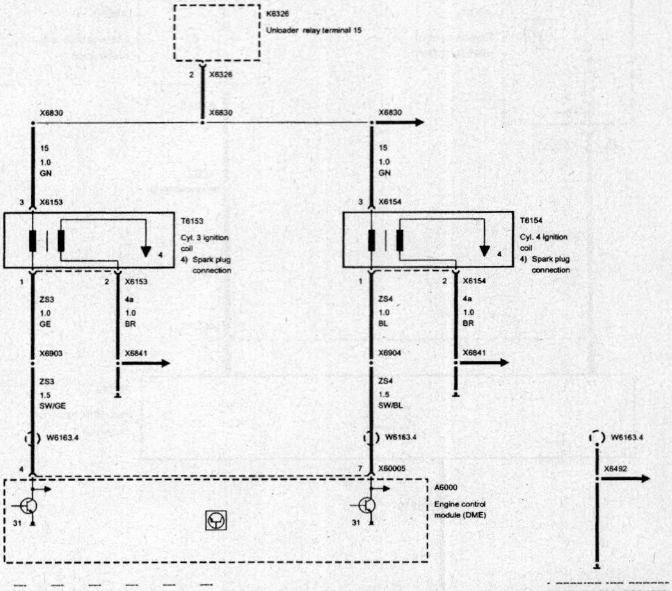

BM0150100122040X

Fig. 6 DME 5.2 wiring diagram (Part 14 of 41). 740

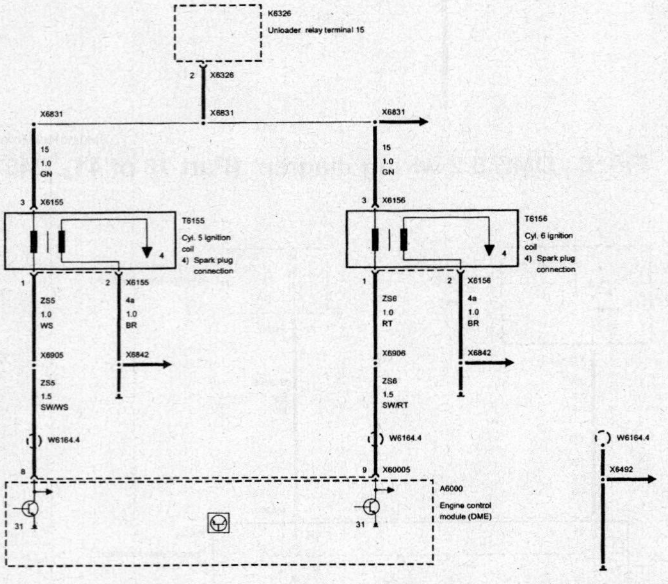

BM0150100122050X

Fig. 6 DME 5.2 wiring diagram (Part 15 of 41). 740

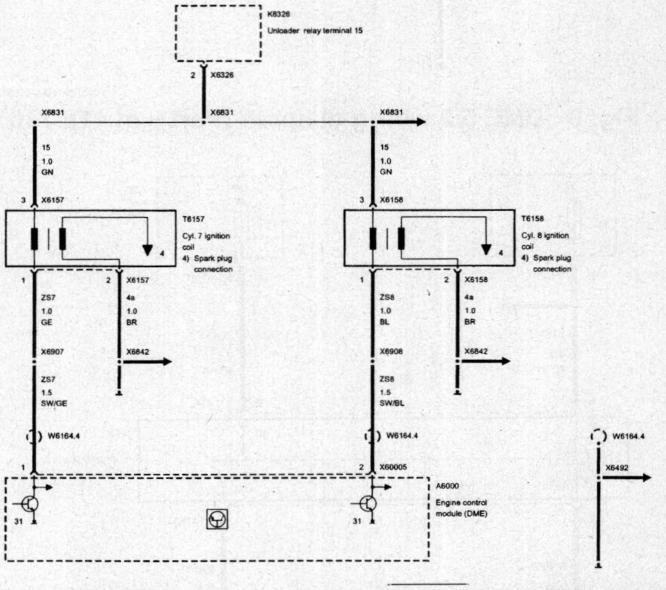

BM0150100122060X

Fig. 6 DME 5.2 wiring diagram (Part 16 of 41). 740

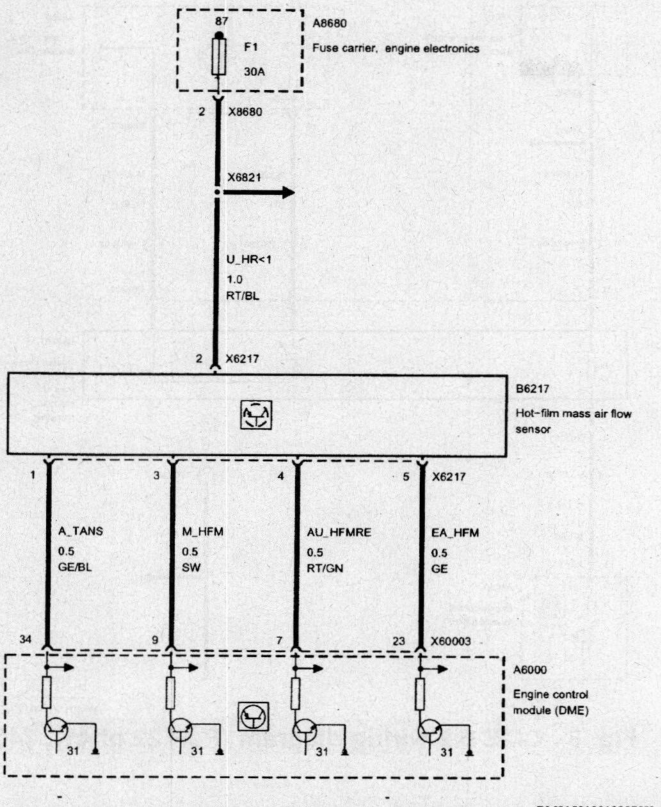

BM0150100122070X

Fig. 6 DME 5.2 wiring diagram (Part 17 of 41). 740

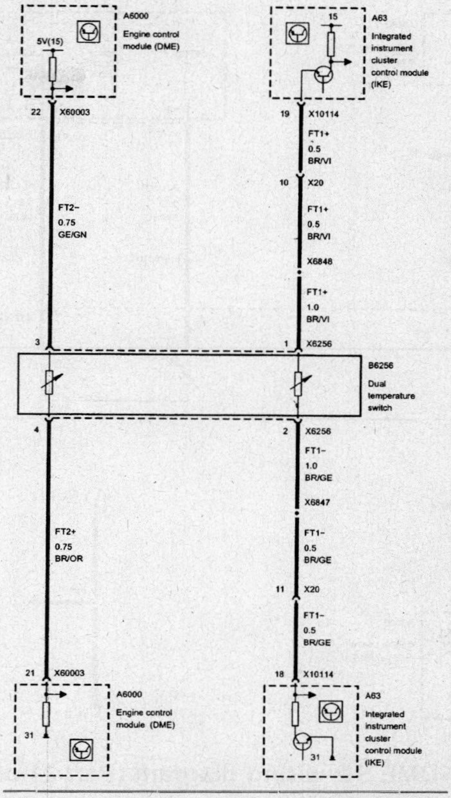

BM0150100122080X

Fig. 6 DME 5.2 wiring diagram (Part 18 of 41). 740

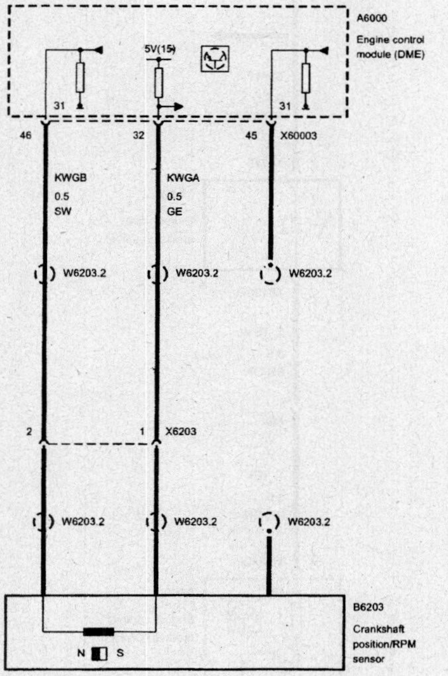

BM0150100122090X

Fig. 6 DME 5.2 wiring diagram (Part 19 of 41). 740

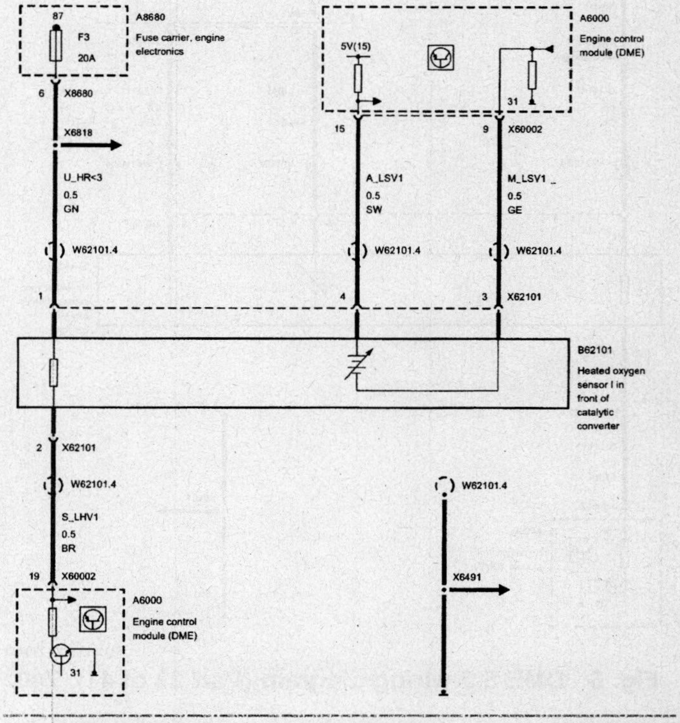

BM0150100123010X

Fig. 6 DME 5.2 wiring diagram (Part 20 of 41). 740

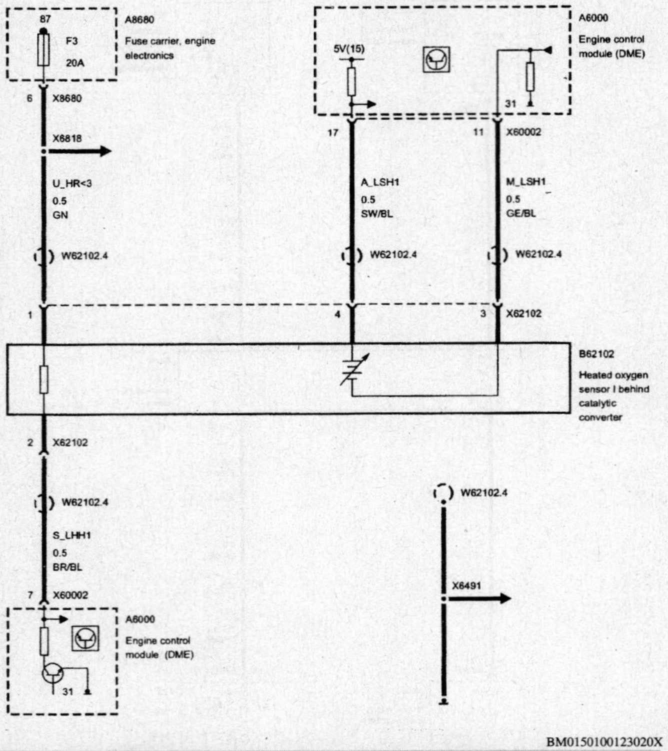

Fig. 6 DME 5.2 wiring diagram (Part 21 of 41). 740

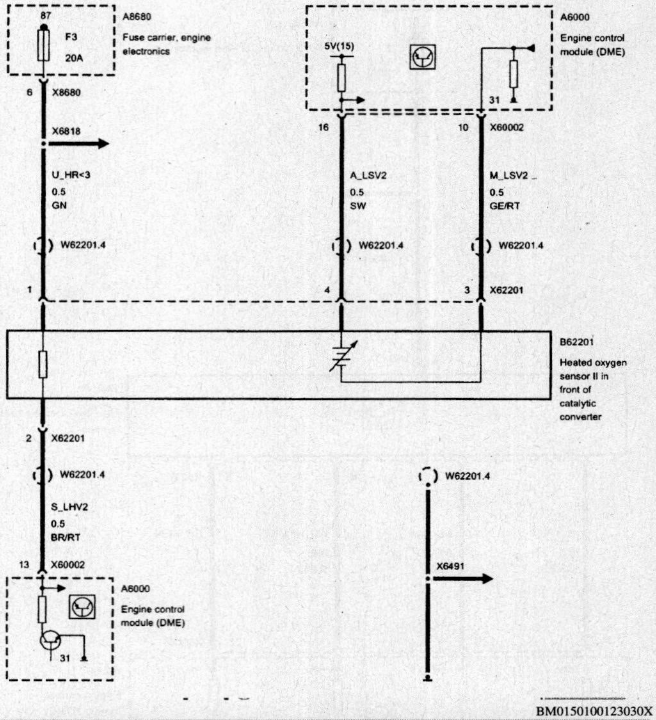

Fig. 6 DME 5.2 wiring diagram (Part 22 of 41). 740

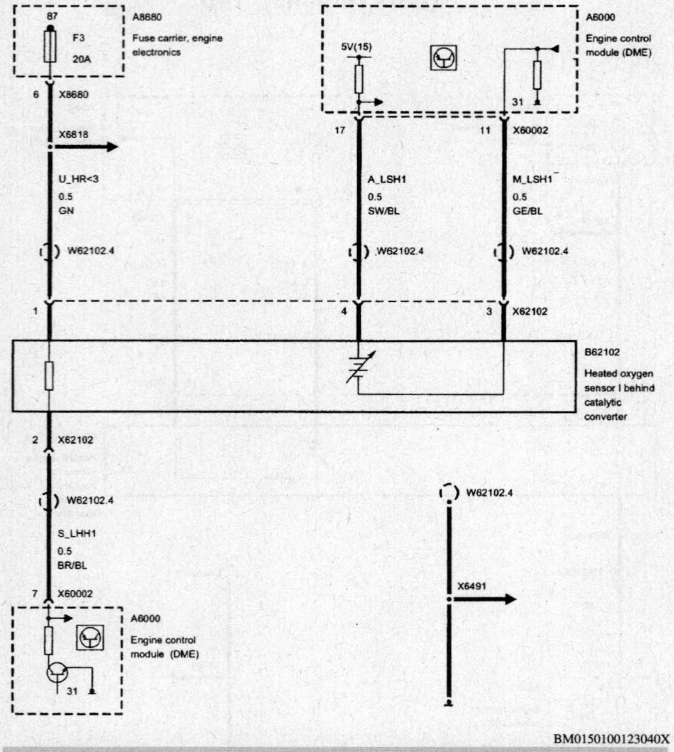

Fig. 6 DME 5.2 wiring diagram (Part 23 of 41). 740

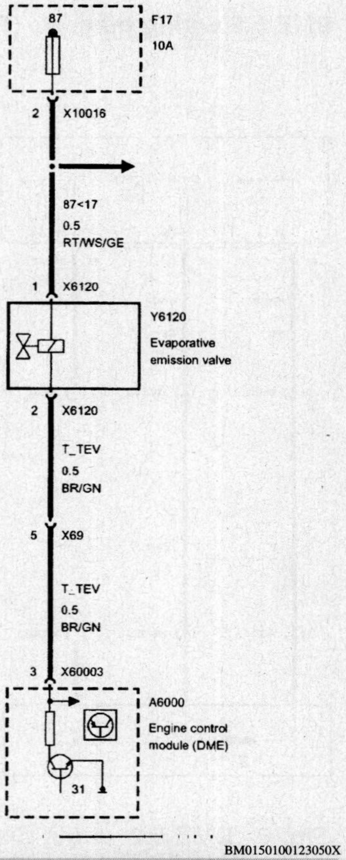

Fig. 6 DME 5.2 wiring diagram (Part 24 of 41). 740

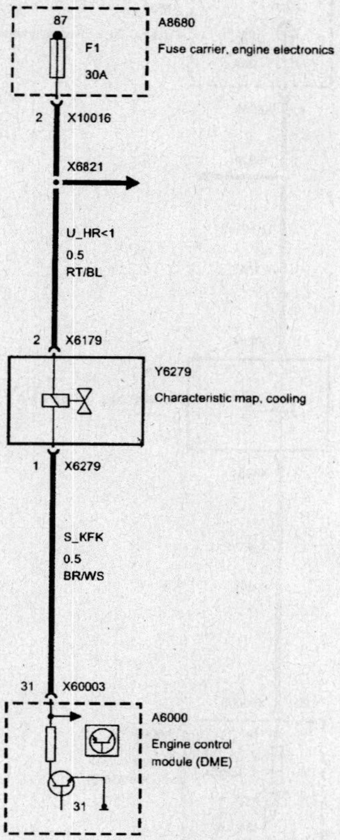

BM0150100123060X

Fig. 6 DME 5.2 wiring diagram (Part 25 of 41). 740

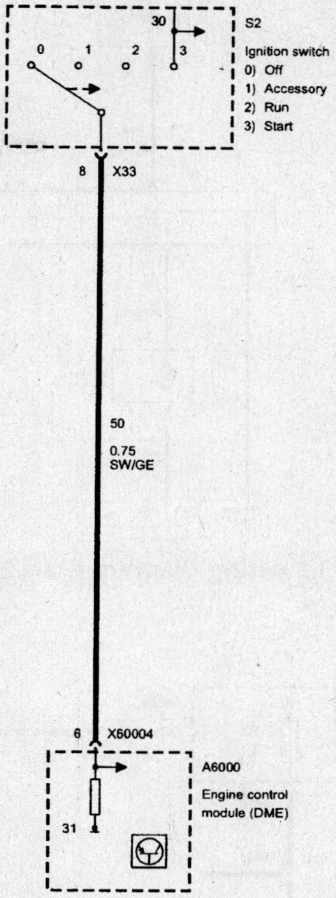

BM0150100123070X

Fig. 6 DME 5.2 wiring diagram (Part 26 of 41). 740

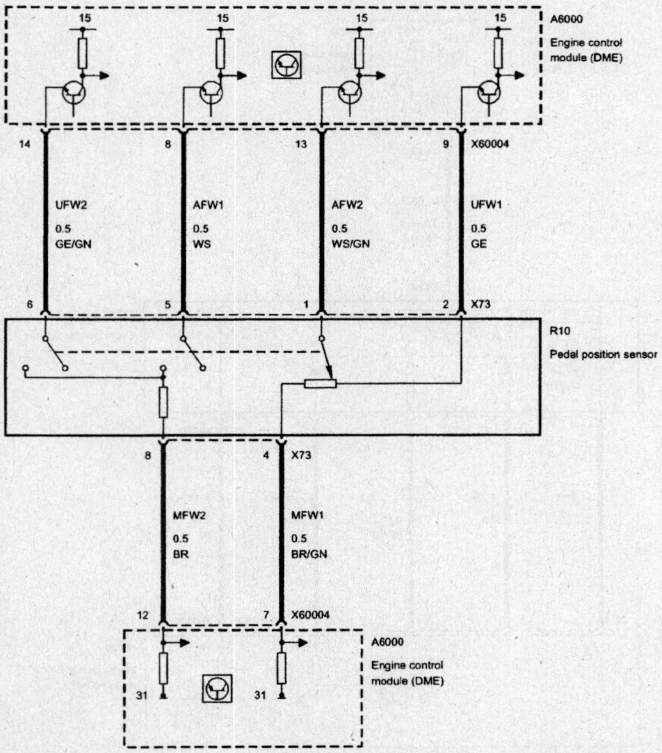

BM0150100123080X

Fig. 6 DME 5.2 wiring diagram (Part 27 of 41). 740

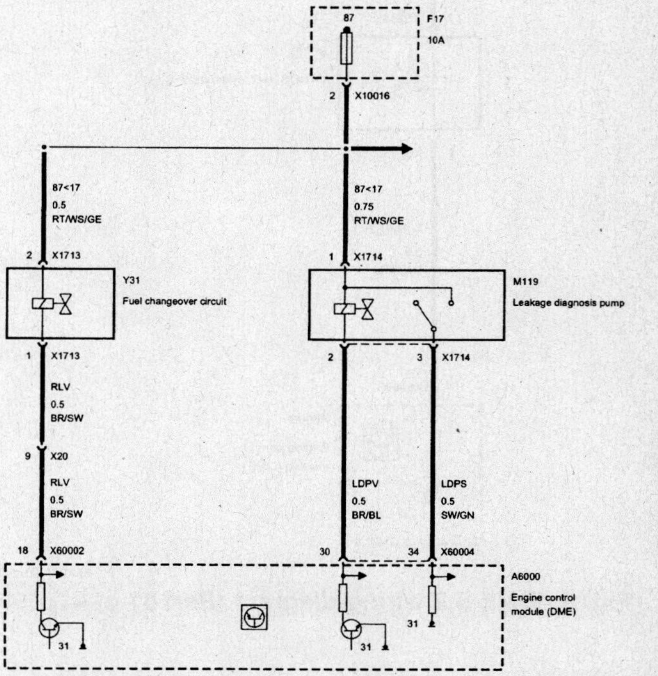

BM0150100123090X

Fig. 6 DME 5.2 wiring diagram (Part 28 of 41). 740

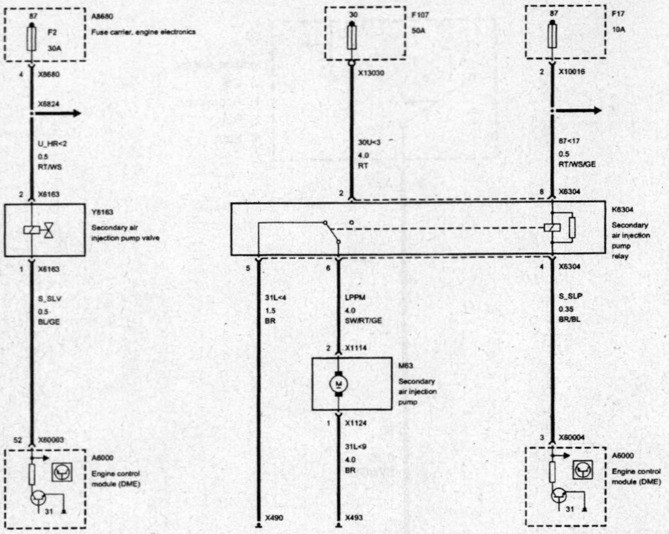

BM0150100123000X

Fig. 6 DME 5.2 wiring diagram (Part 29 of 41). 740

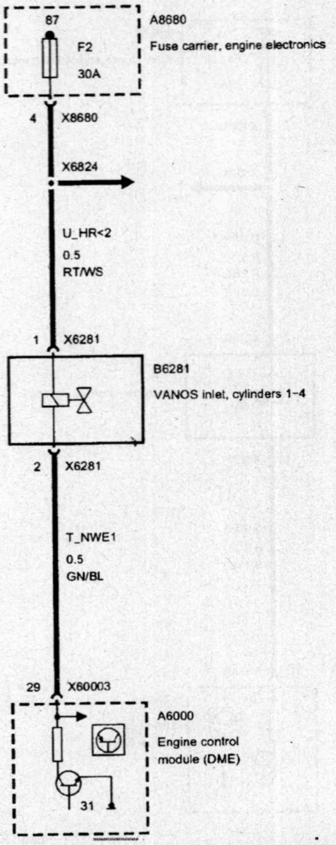

BM0150100124010X

Fig. 6 DME 5.2 wiring diagram (Part 30 of 41). 740

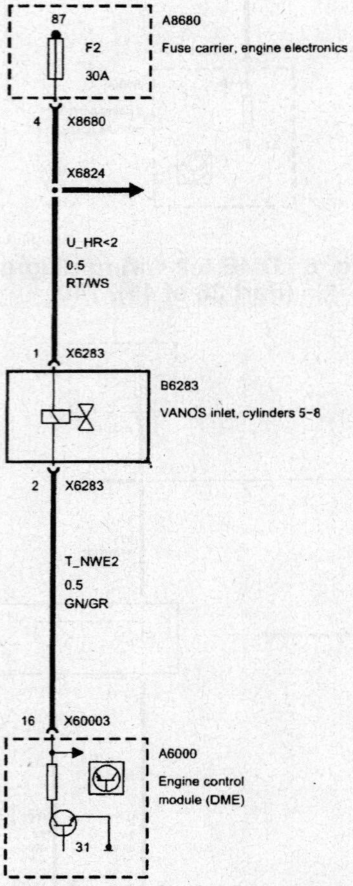

BM0150100124020X

Fig. 6 DME 5.2 wiring diagram (Part 31 of 41). 740

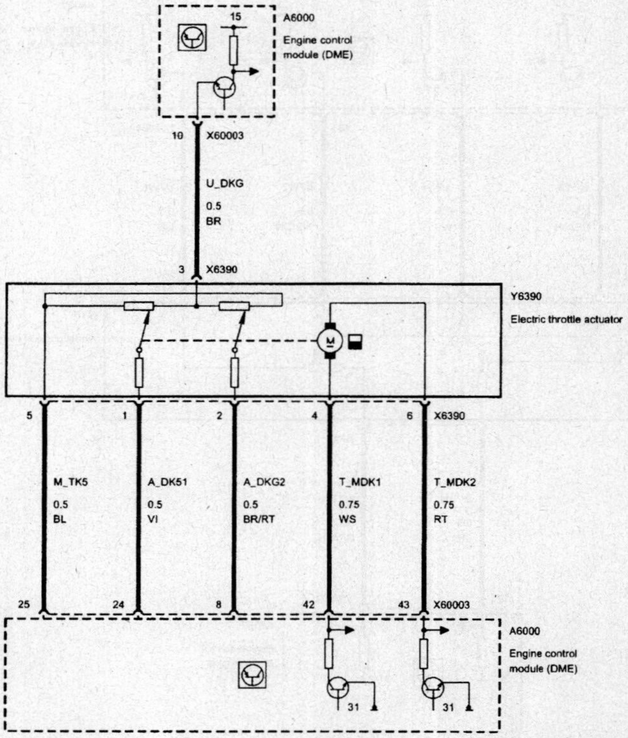

BM0150100124030X

Fig. 6 DME 5.2 wiring diagram (Part 32 of 41). 740

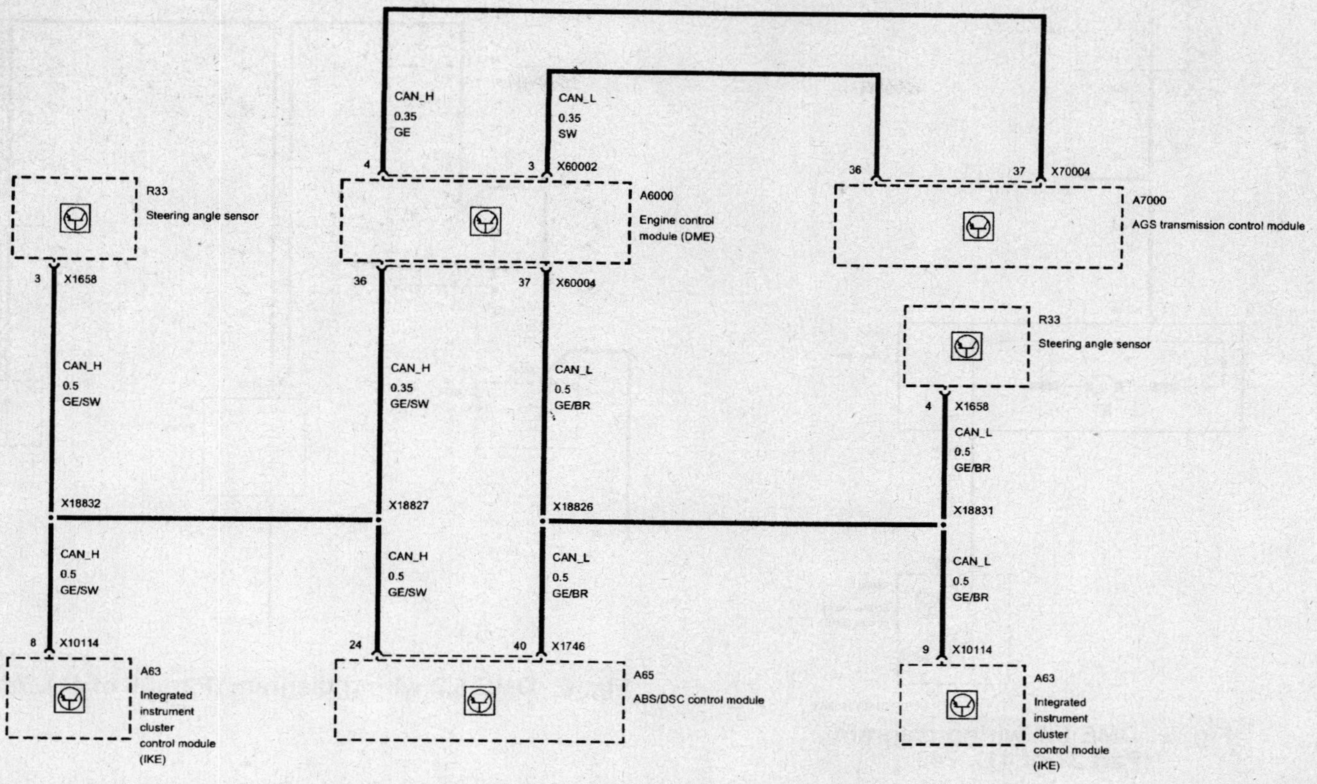

BM0150100124040X

Fig. 6 DME 5.2 wiring diagram (Part 33 of 41). 740

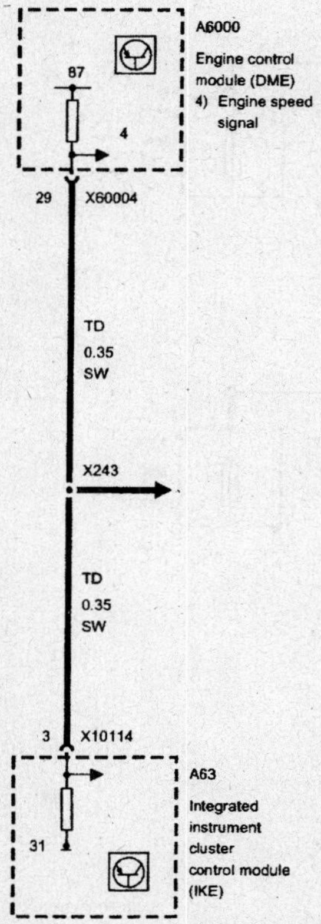

BM0150100124050X

Fig. 6 DME 5.2 wiring diagram (Part 34 of 41). 740

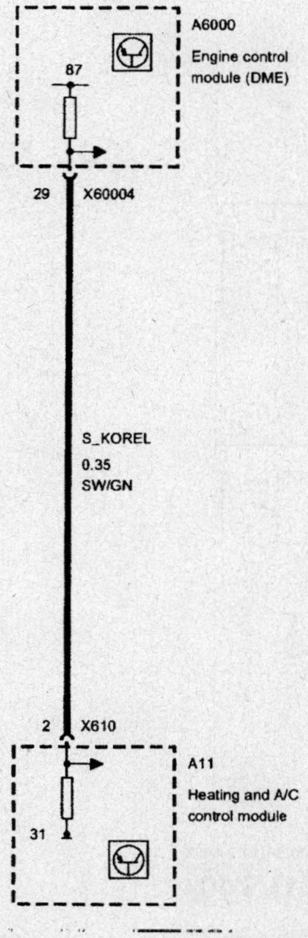

BM0150100124060X

Fig. 6 DME 5.2 wiring diagram (Part 35 of 41). 740

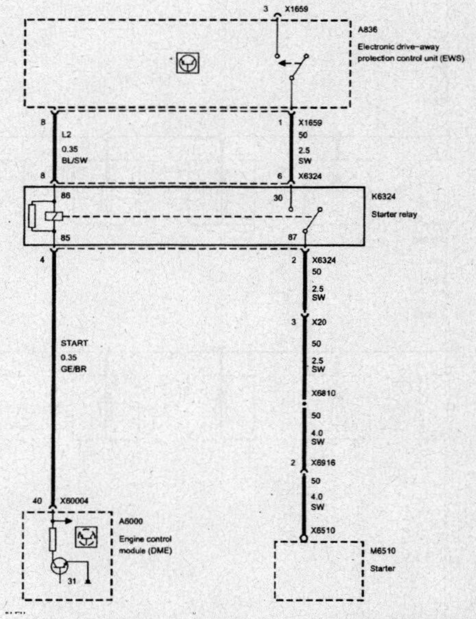

BM0150100124070X

Fig. 6 DME 5.2 wiring diagram (Part 36 of 41). 740

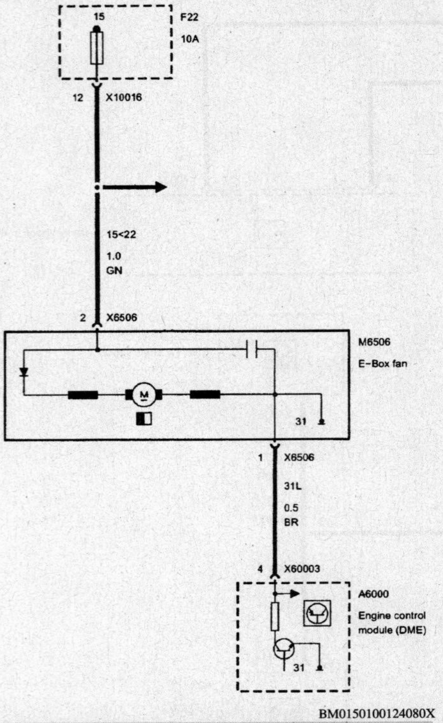

Fig. 6 DME 5.2 wiring diagram (Part 37 of 41). 740

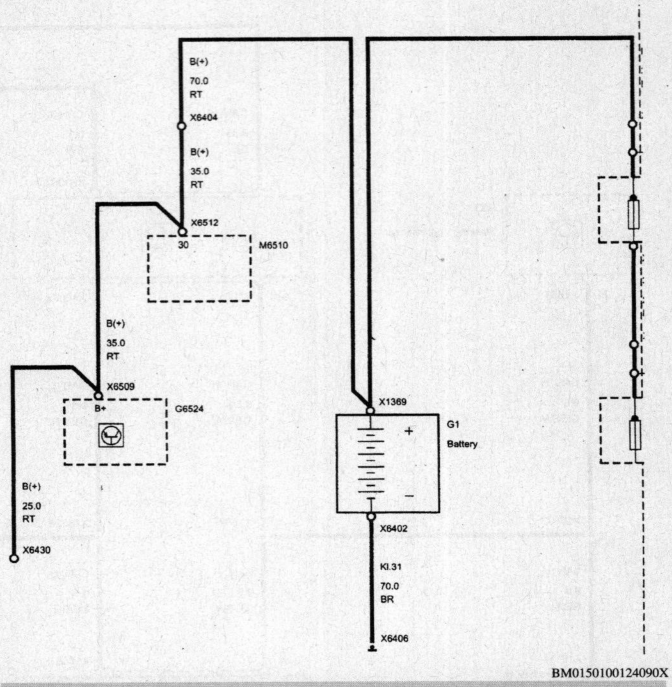

Fig. 6 DME 5.2 wiring diagram (Part 38 of 41). 740

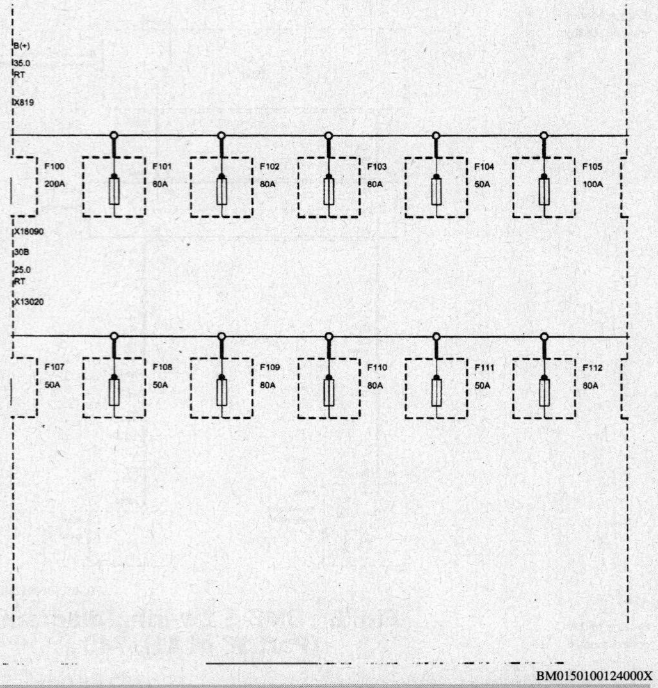

Fig. 6 DME 5.2 wiring diagram (Part 39 of 41). 740

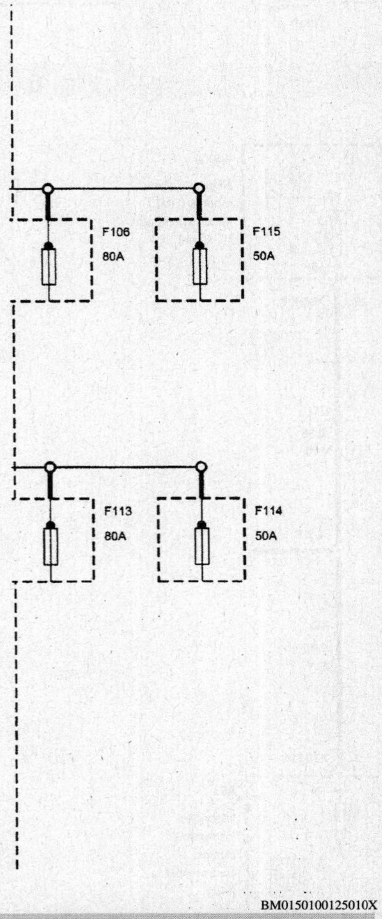

Fig. 6 DME 5.2 wiring diagram (Part 40 of 41). 740

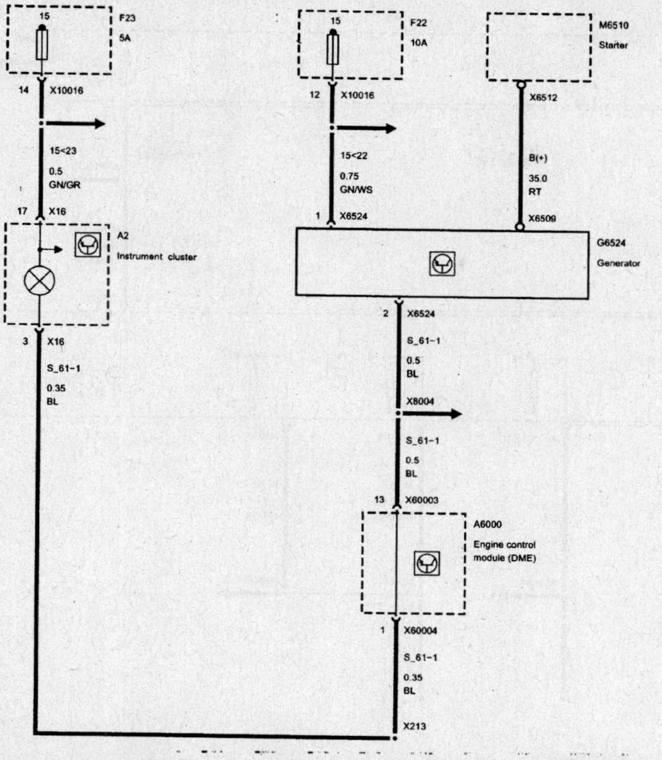

BM0150100125020X

Fig. 6 DME 5.2 wiring diagram (Part 41 of 41). 740

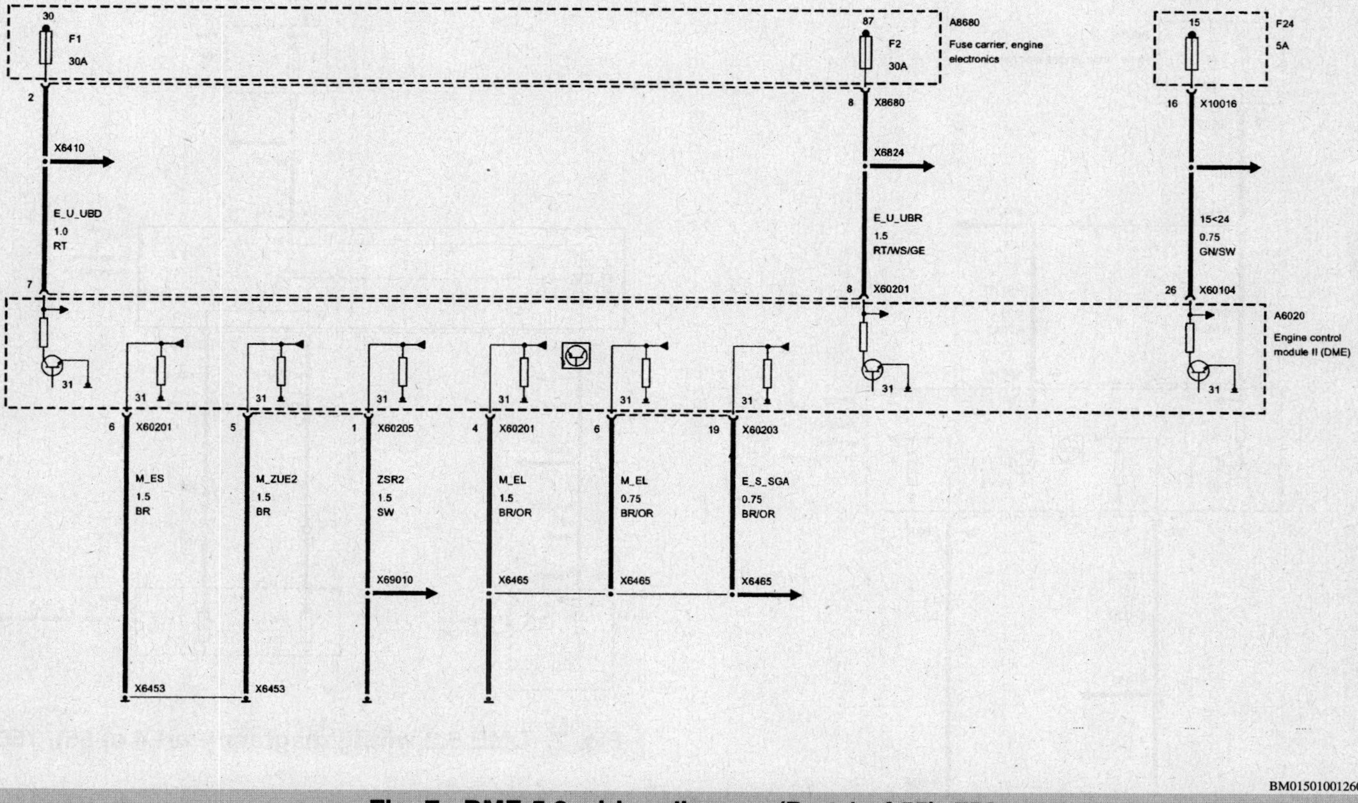

BM0150100126010X

Fig. 7 DME 5.2 wiring diagram (Part 1 of 55). 750

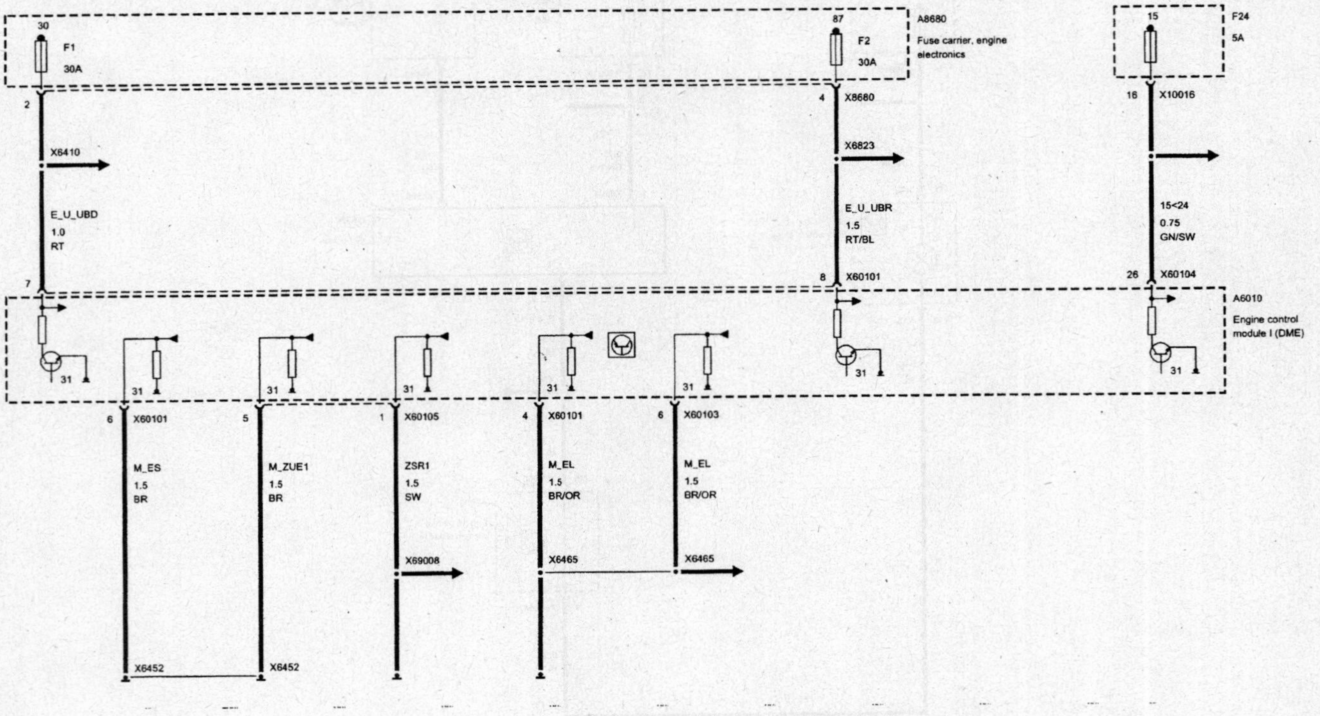

BM0150100126020X

Fig. 7 DME 5.2 wiring diagram (Part 2 of 55). 750

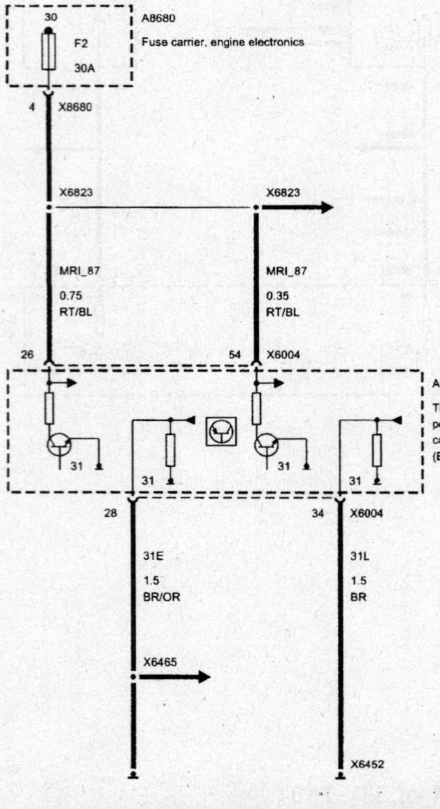

BM0150100126030X

Fig. 7 DME 5.2 wiring diagram (Part 3 of 55). 750

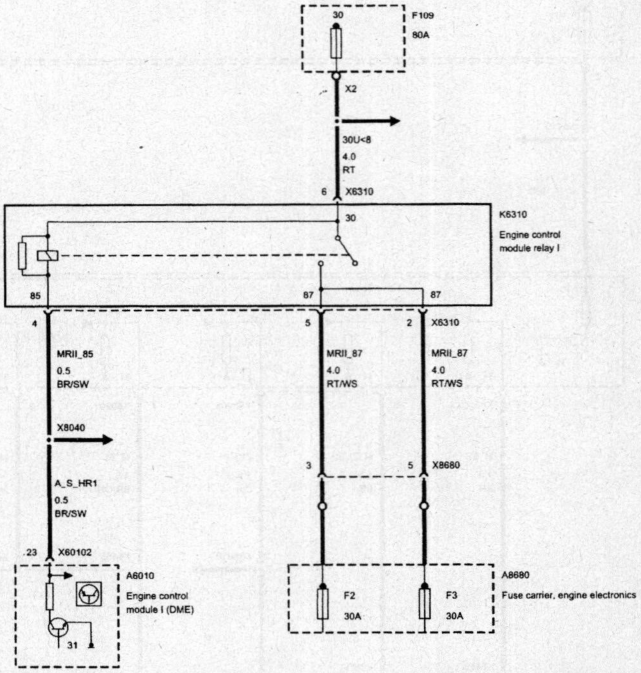

BM0150100126040X

Fig. 7 DME 5.2 wiring diagram (Part 4 of 55). 750

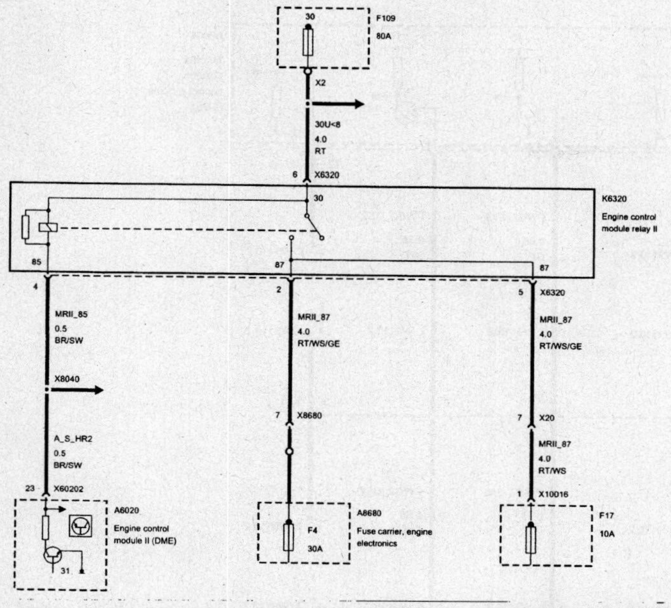

BM0150100126050X

Fig. 7 DME 5.2 wiring diagram (Part 5 of 55). 750

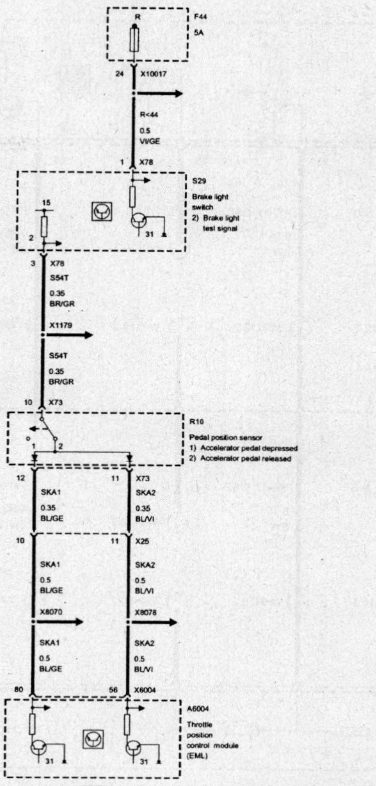

BM0150100126060X

Fig. 7 DME 5.2 wiring diagram (Part 6 of 55). 750

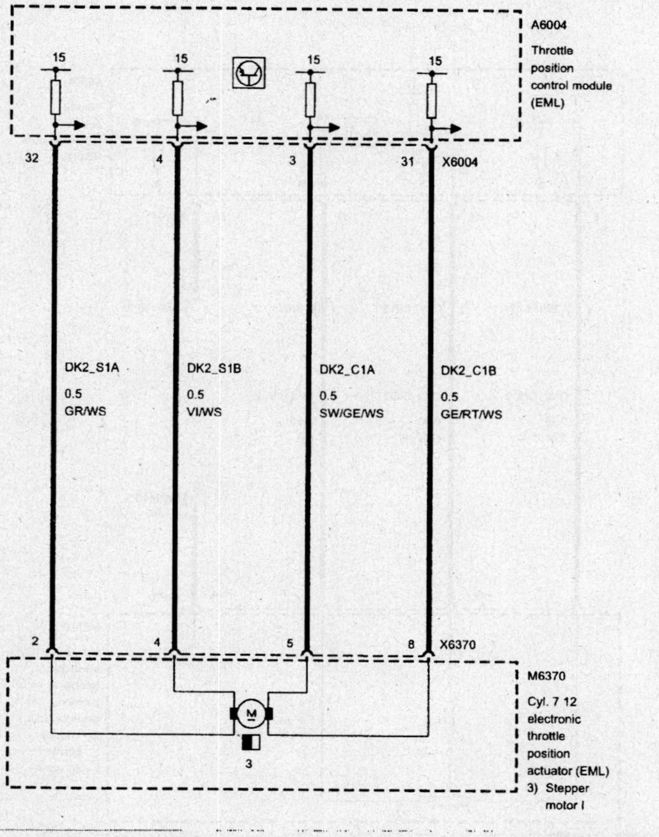

BM0150100126070X

Fig. 7 DME 5.2 wiring diagram (Part 7 of 55). 750

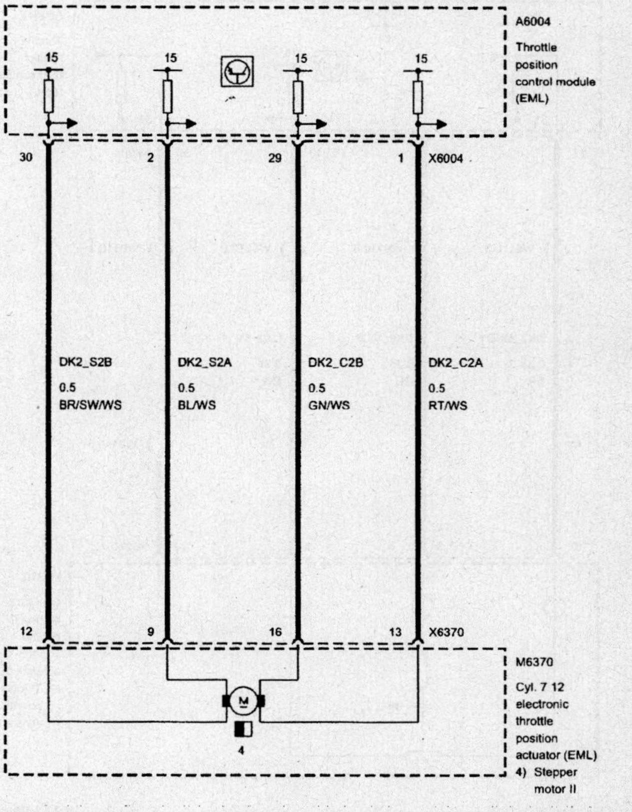

BM0150100126080X

Fig. 7 DME 5.2 wiring diagram (Part 8 of 55). 750

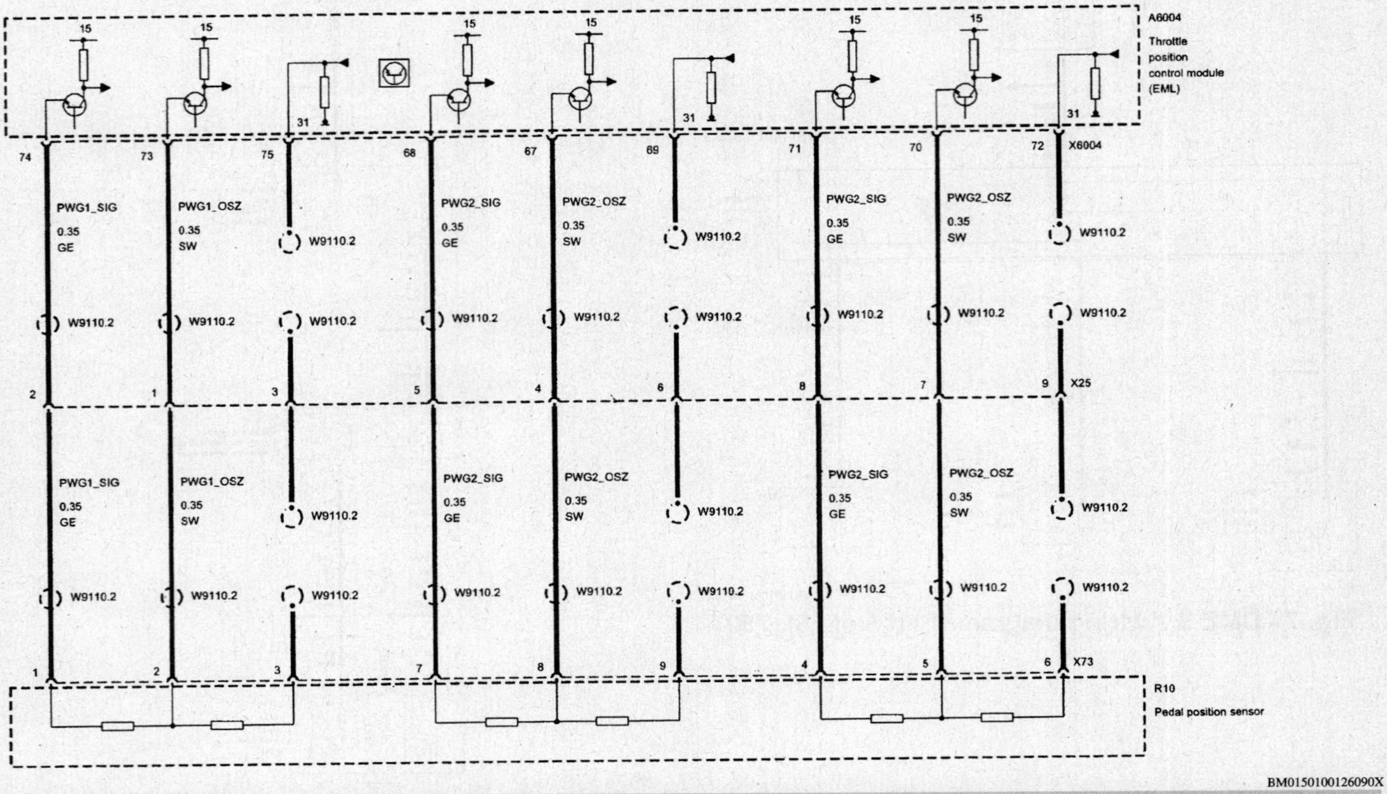

Fig. 7 DME 5.2 wiring diagram (Part 9 of 55). 750

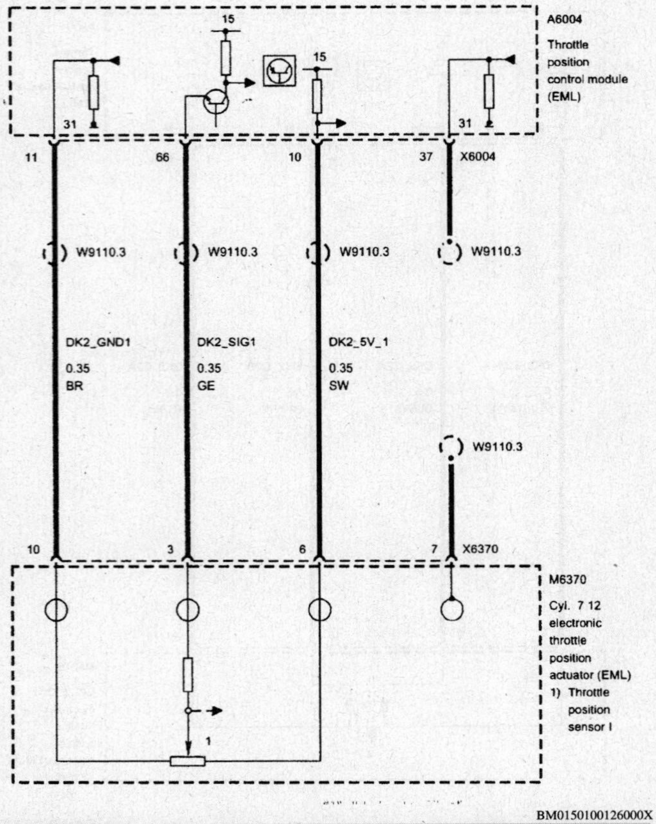

Fig. 7 DME 5.2 wiring diagram (Part 10 of 55). 750

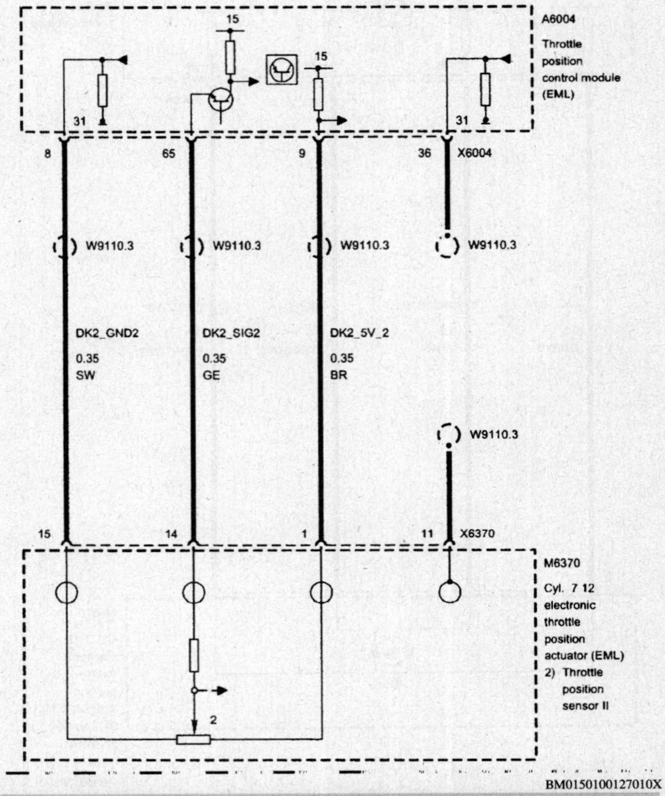

Fig. 7 DME 5.2 wiring diagram (Part 11 of 55). 750

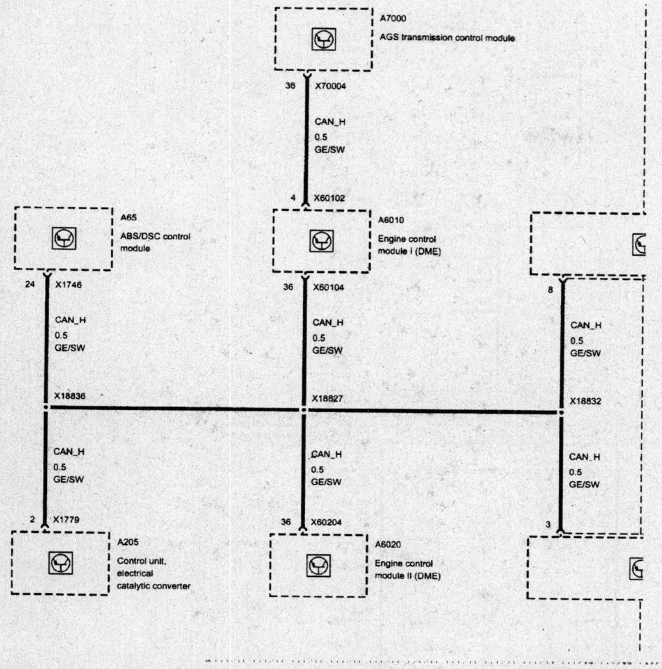

BM0150100127020X

Fig. 7 DME 5.2 wiring diagram (Part 12 of 55). 750

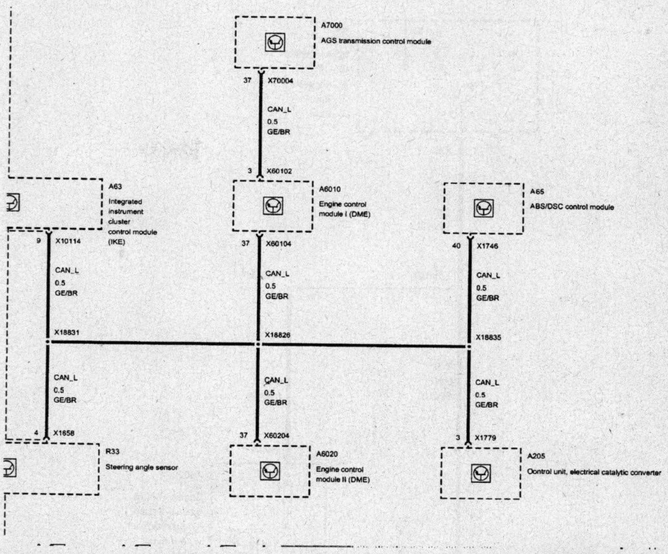

BM0150100127030X

Fig. 7 DME 5.2 wiring diagram (Part 13 of 55). 750

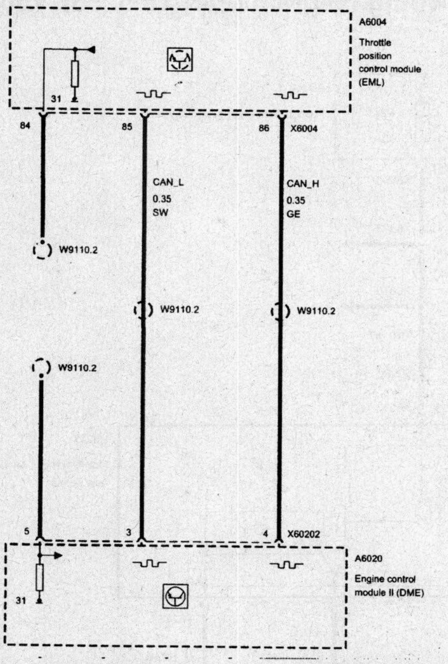

BM0150100127040X

Fig. 7 DME 5.2 wiring diagram (Part 14 of 55). 750

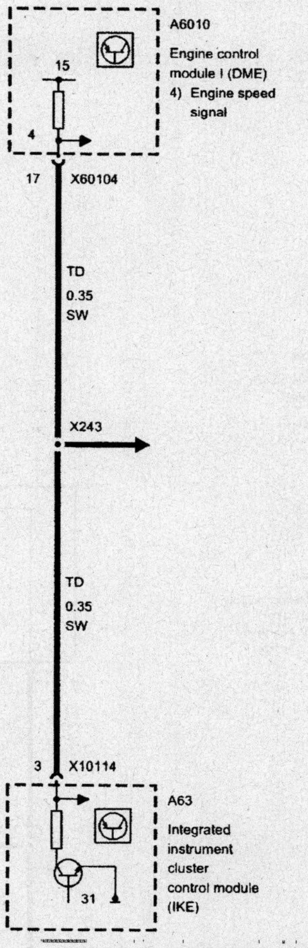

BM0150100127050X

Fig. 7 DME 5.2 wiring diagram (Part 15 of 55). 750

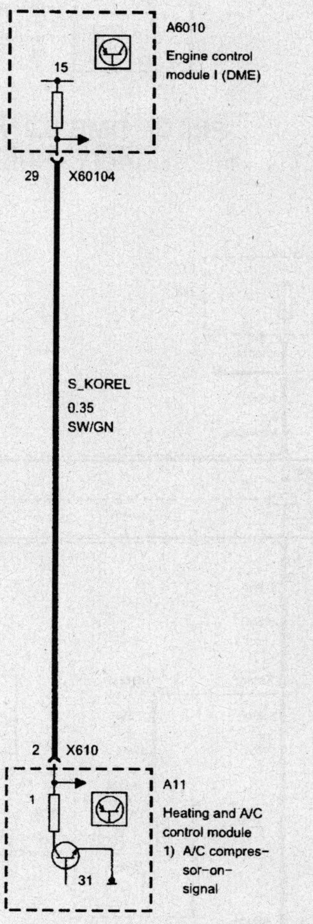

BM0150100127060X

Fig. 7 DME 5.2 wiring diagram (Part 16 of 55). 750

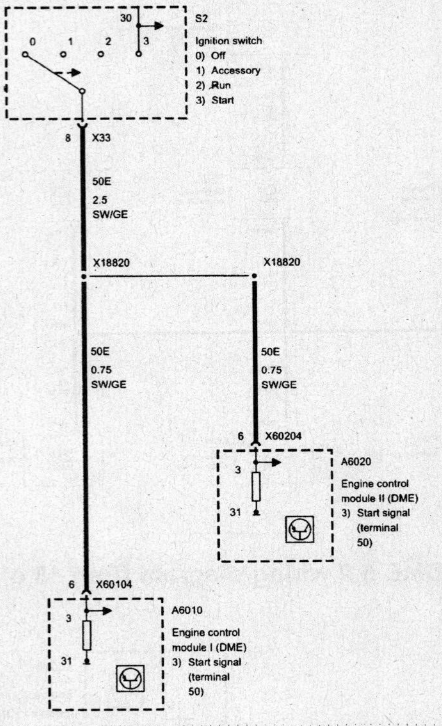

BM0150100127070X

Fig. 7 DME 5.2 wiring diagram (Part 17 of 55). 750

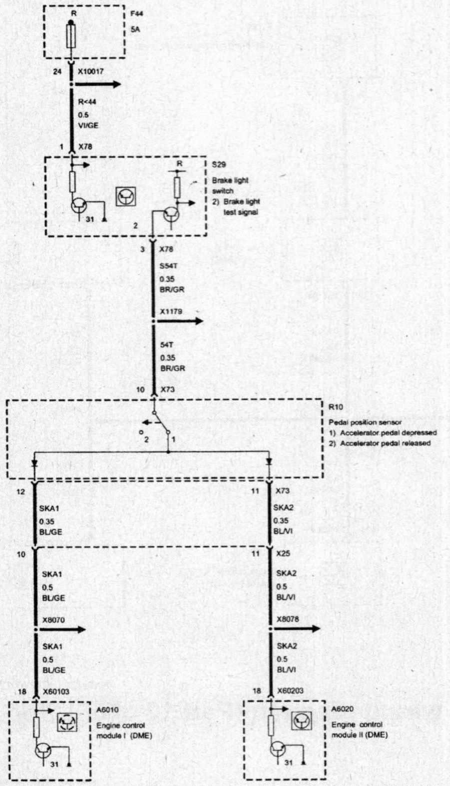

BM0150100127080X

Fig. 7 DME 5.2 wiring diagram (Part 18 of 55). 750

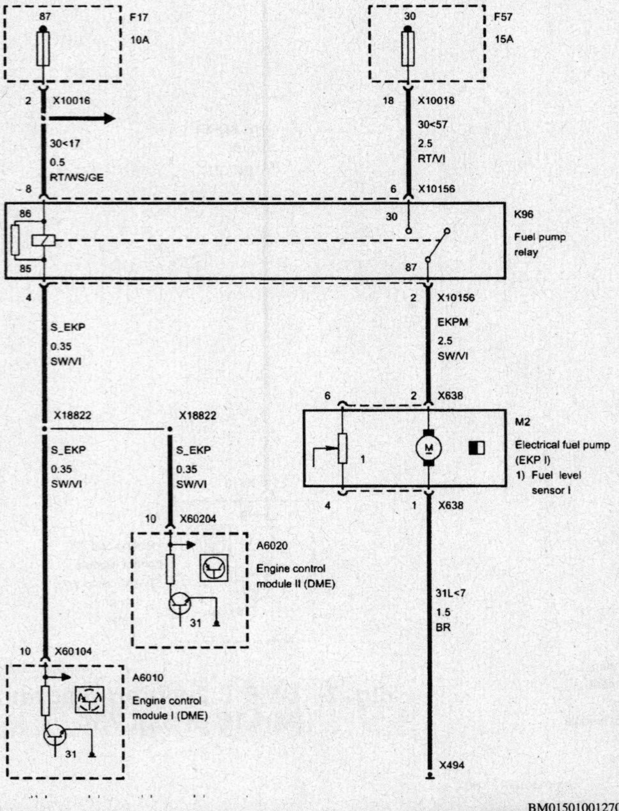

BM0150100127090X

Fig. 7 DME 5.2 wiring diagram (Part 19 of 55). 750

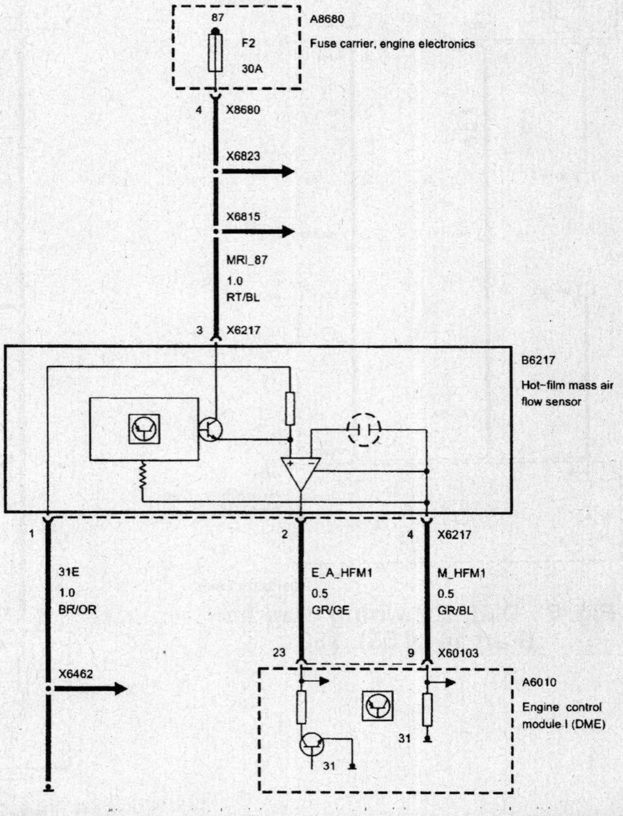

BM0150100127000X

Fig. 7 DME 5.2 wiring diagram (Part 20 of 55). 750

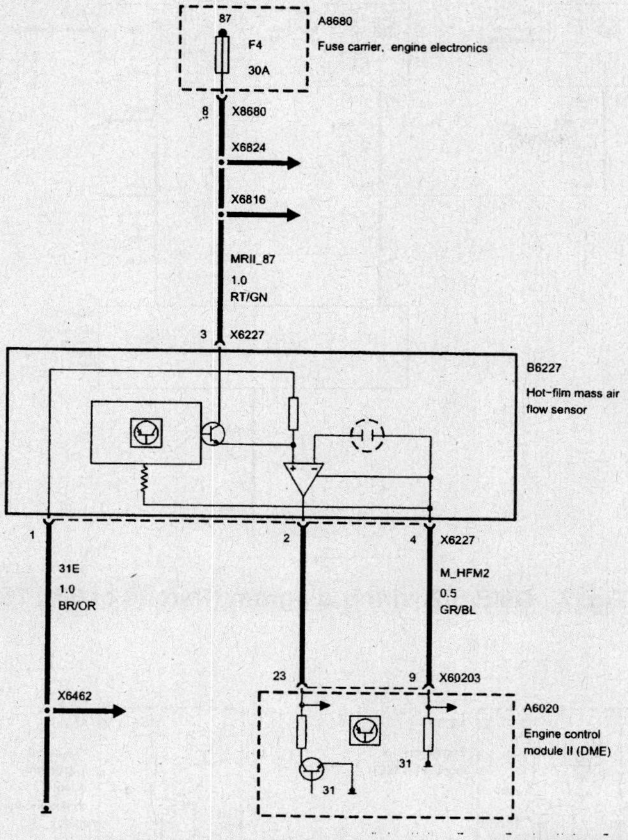

BM0150100128010X

Fig. 7 DME 5.2 wiring diagram (Part 21 of 55). 750

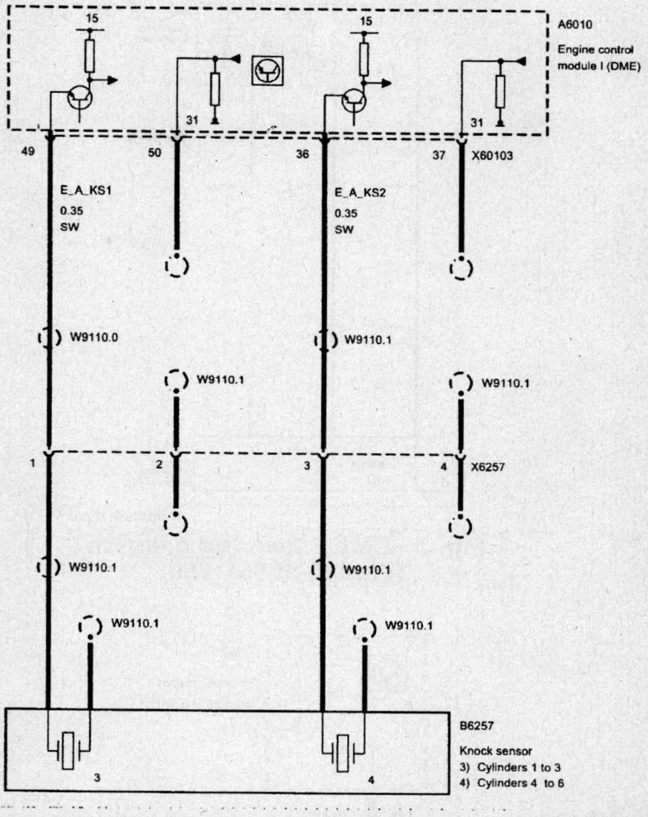

BM0150100128020X

Fig. 7 DME 5.2 wiring diagram (Part 22 of 55). 750

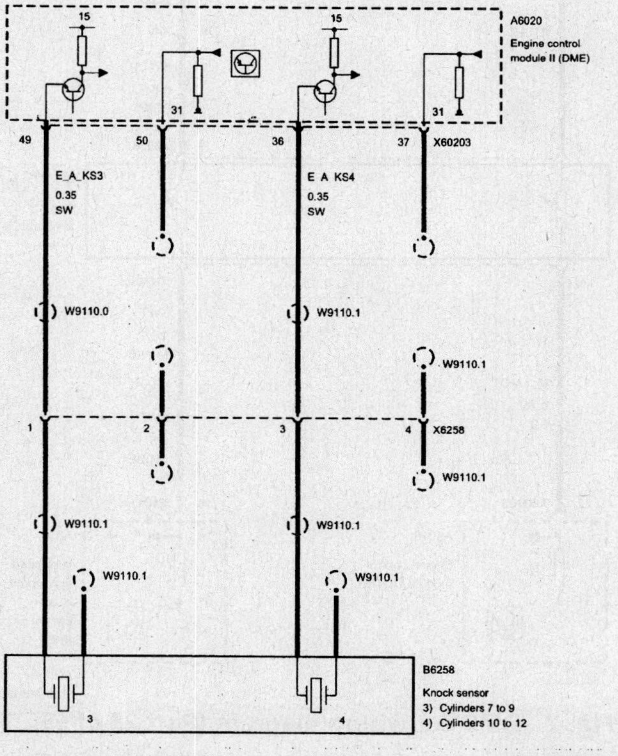

BM0150100128030X

Fig. 7 DME 5.2 wiring diagram (Part 23 of 55). 750

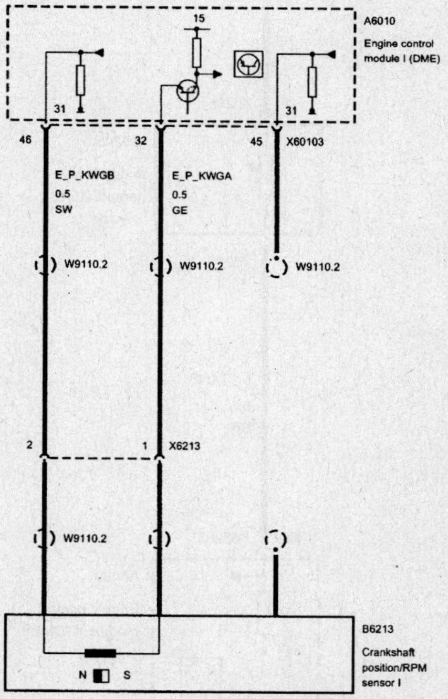

BM0150100128040X

Fig. 7 DME 5.2 wiring diagram (Part 24 of 55). 750

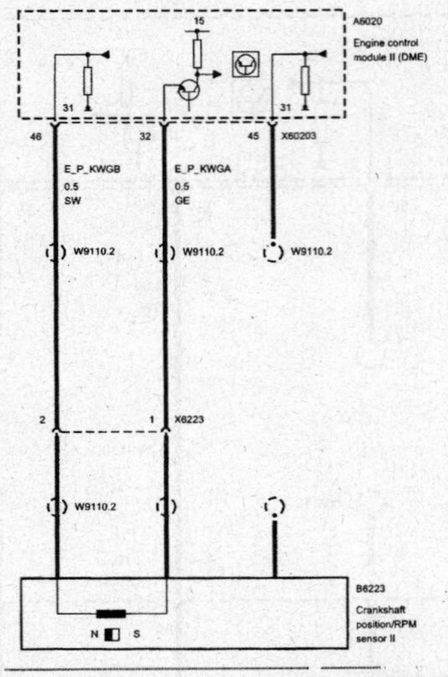

Fig. 7 DME 5.2 wiring diagram (Part 25 of 55). 750

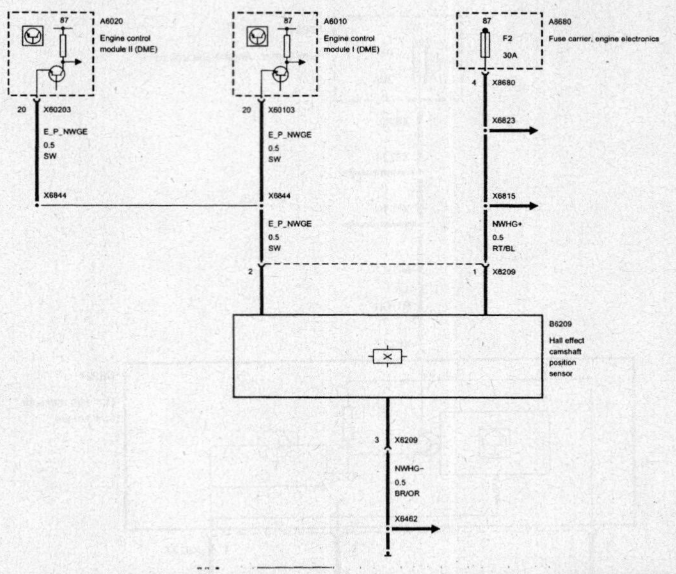

Fig. 7 DME 5.2 wiring diagram (Part 26 of 55). 750

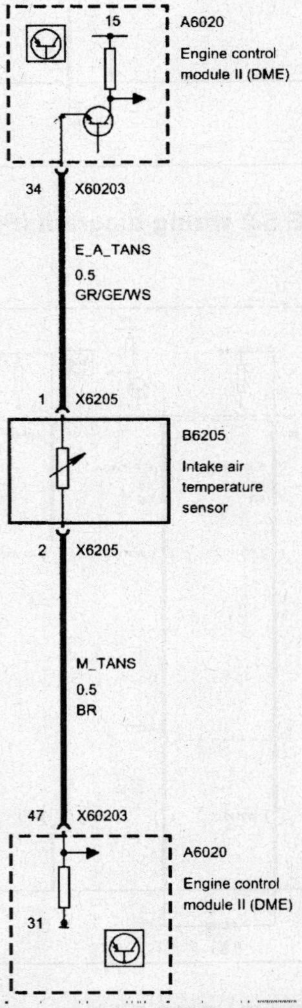

Fig. 7 DME 5.2 wiring diagram (Part 27 of 55). 750

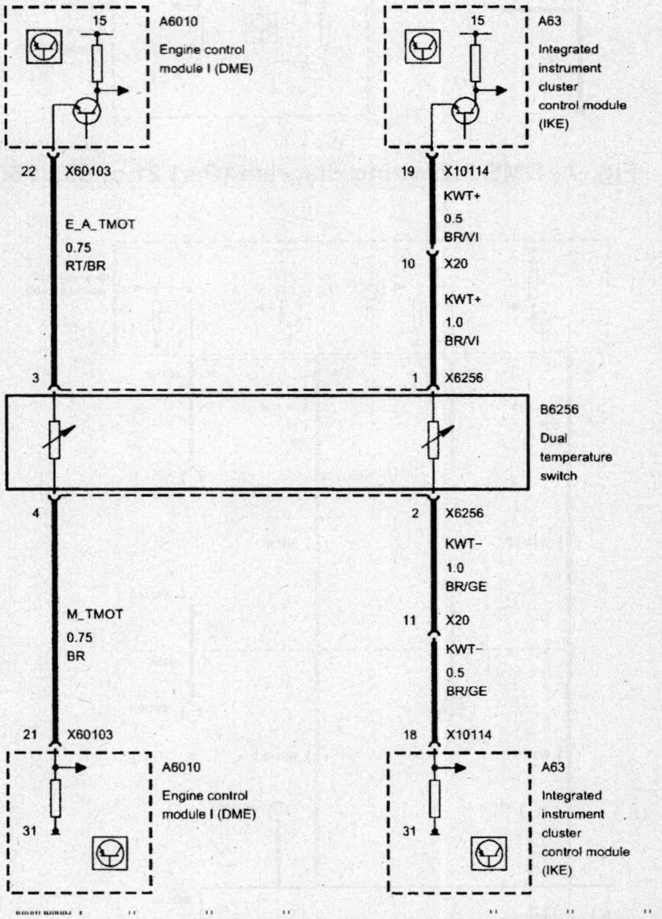

Fig. 7 DME 5.2 wiring diagram (Part 28 of 55). 750

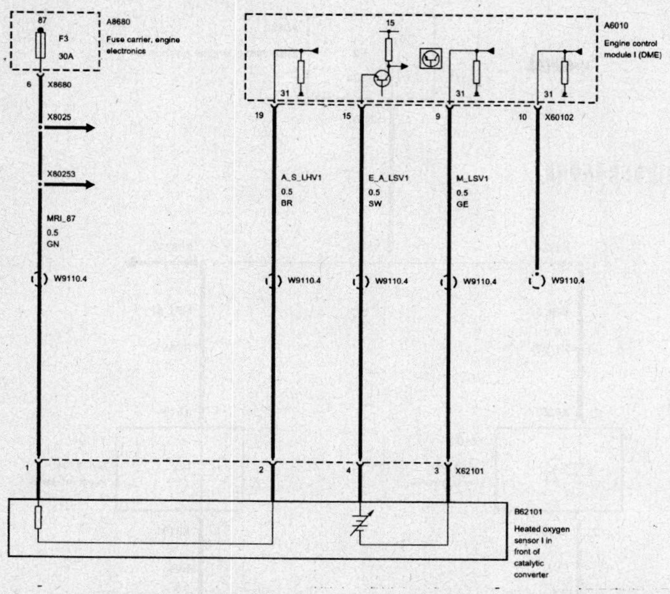

BM0150100128090X

Fig. 7 DME 5.2 wiring diagram (Part 29 of 55). 750

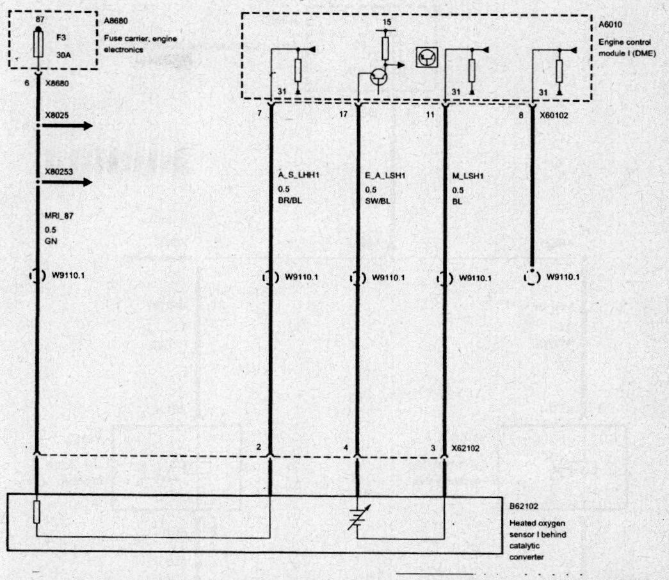

BM0150100129010X

Fig. 7 DME 5.2 wiring diagram (Part 30 of 55). 750

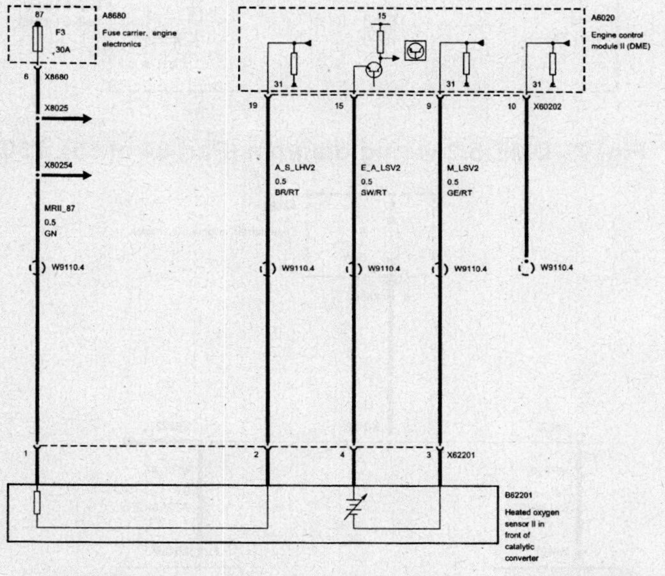

BM0150100129020X

Fig. 7 DME 5.2 wiring diagram (Part 31 of 55). 750

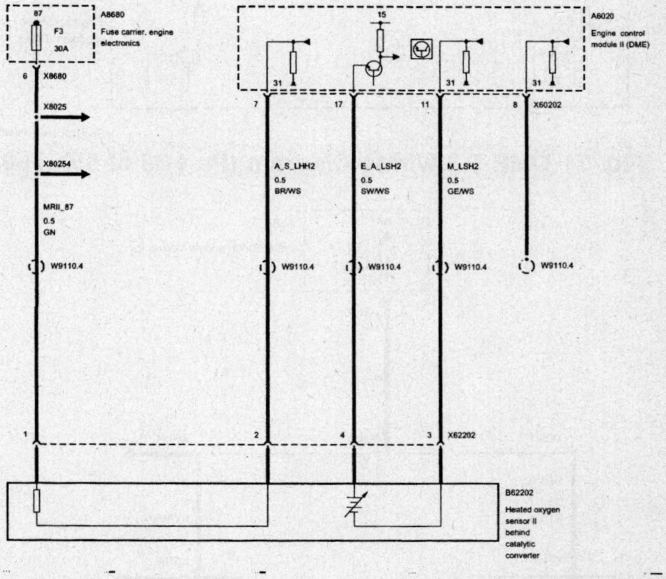

BM0150100129030X

Fig. 7 DME 5.2 wiring diagram (Part 32 of 55). 750

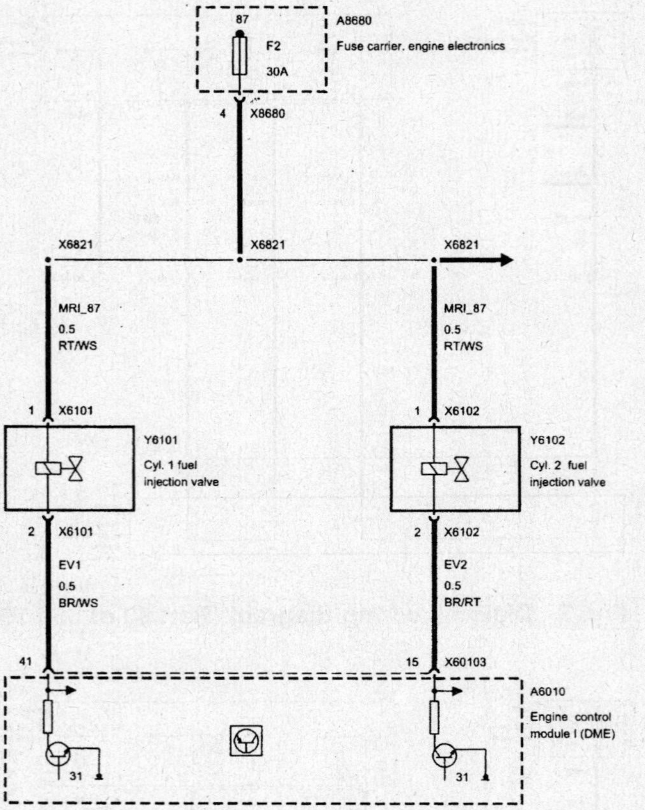

BM0150100129040X

Fig. 7 DME 5.2 wiring diagram (Part 33 of 55). 750

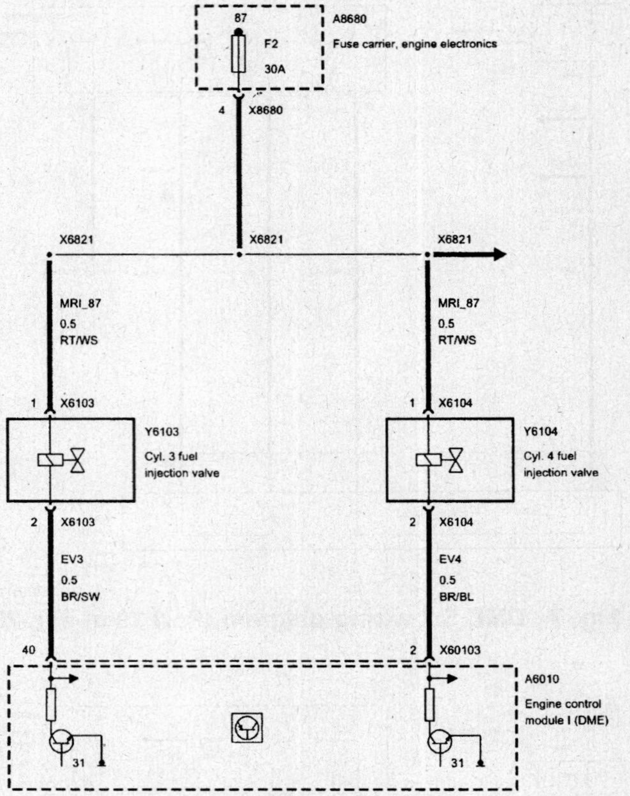

BM0150100129050X

Fig. 7 DME 5.2 wiring diagram (Part 34 of 55). 750

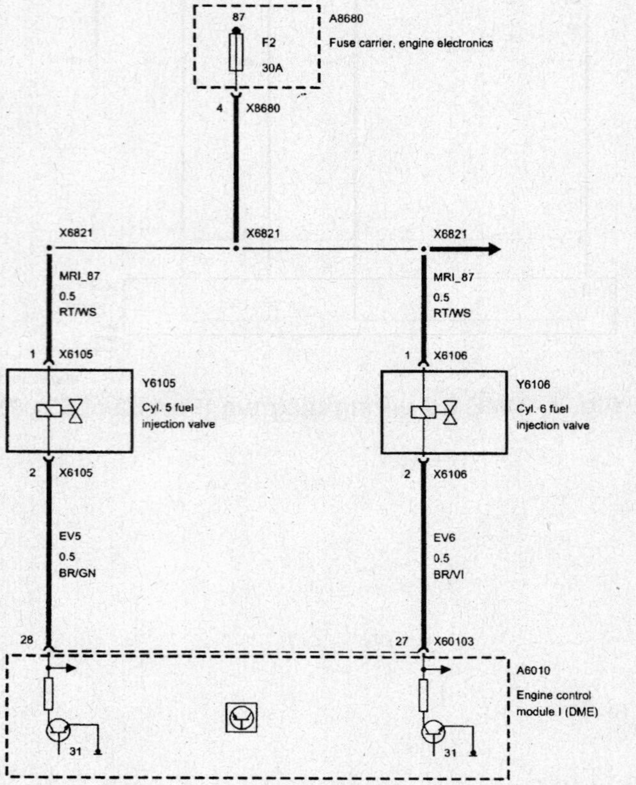

BM0150100129060X

Fig. 7 DME 5.2 wiring diagram (Part 35 of 55). 750

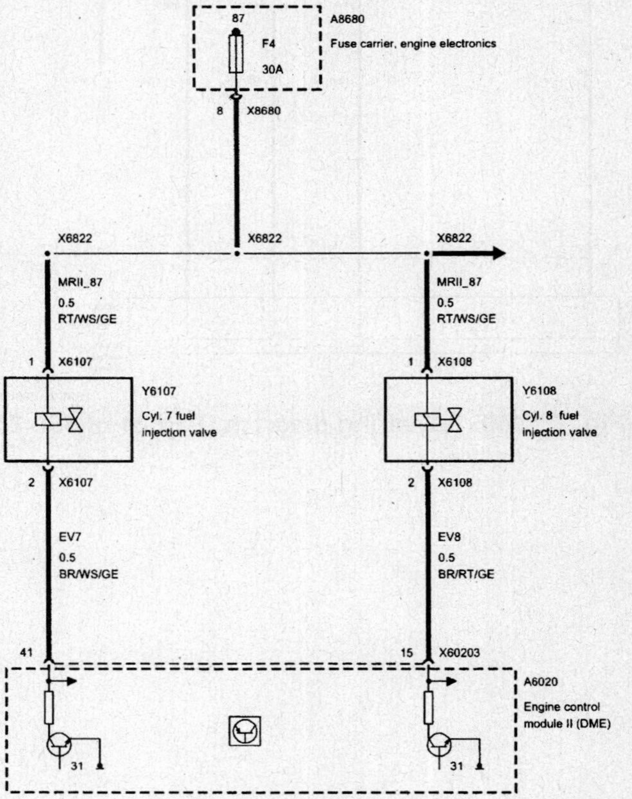

BM0150100129070X

Fig. 7 DME 5.2 wiring diagram (Part 36 of 55). 750

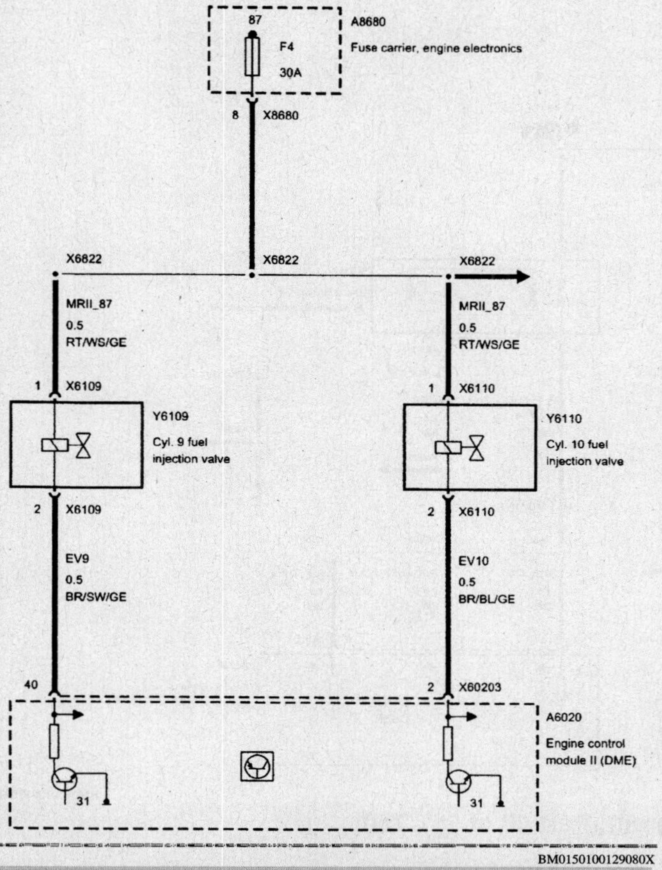

Fig. 7 DME 5.2 wiring diagram (Part 37 of 55). 750

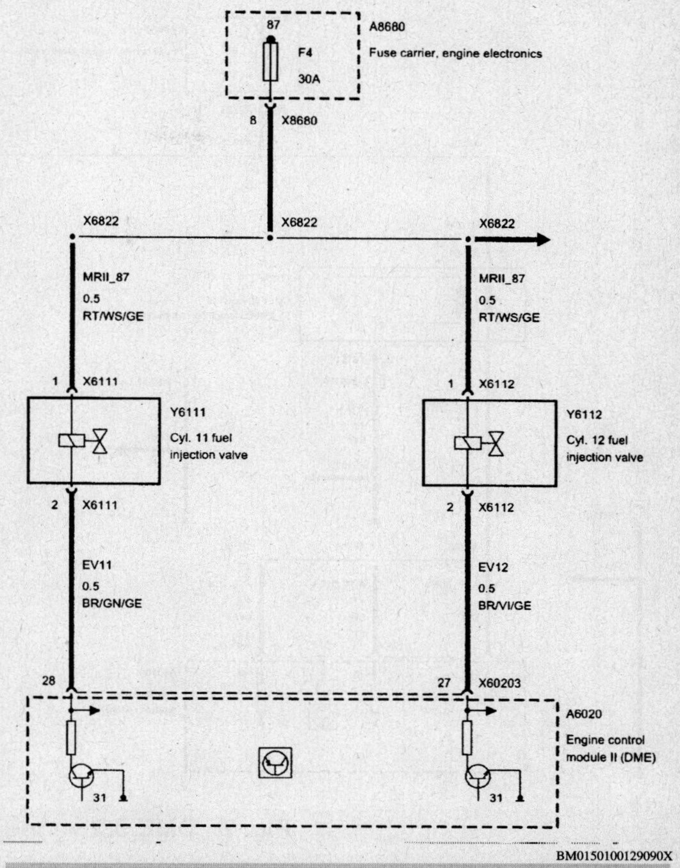

Fig. 7 DME 5.2 wiring diagram (Part 38 of 55). 750

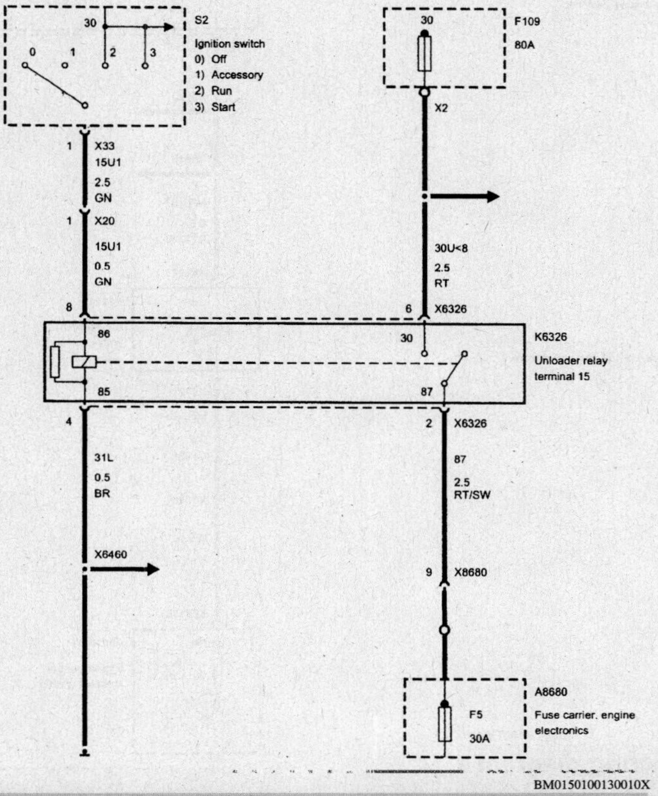

Fig. 7 DME 5.2 wiring diagram (Part 39 of 55). 750

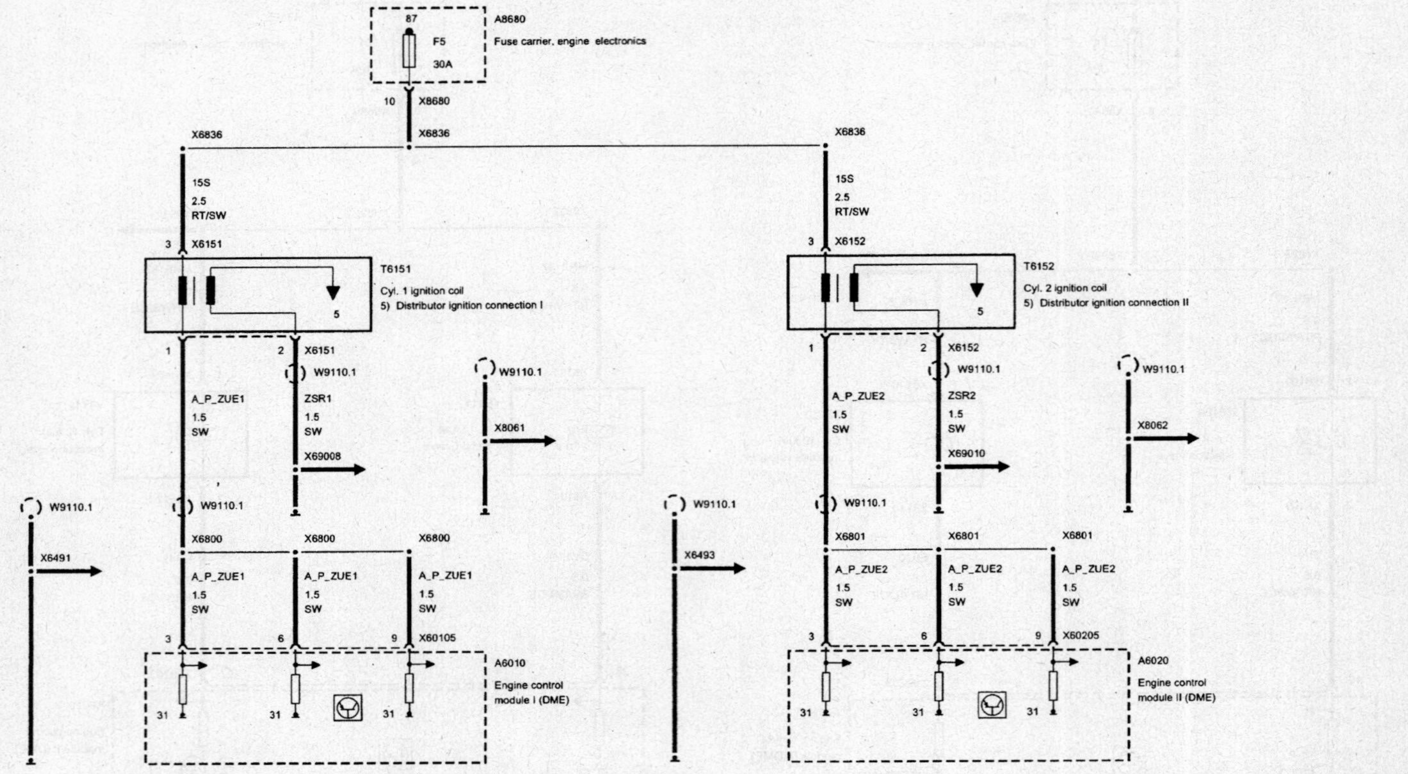

BM0150100130020X

Fig. 7 DME 5.2 wiring diagram (Part 40 of 55). 750

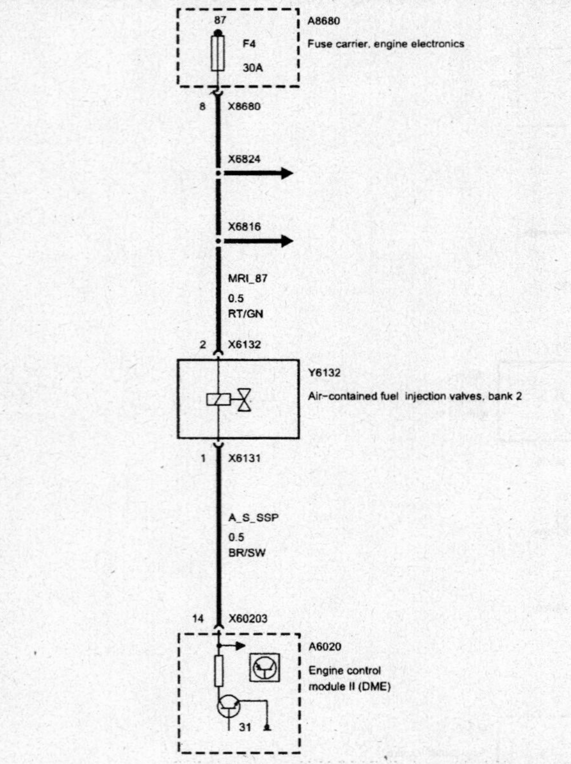

BM0150100130030X

Fig. 7 DME 5.2 wiring diagram (Part 41 of 55). 750

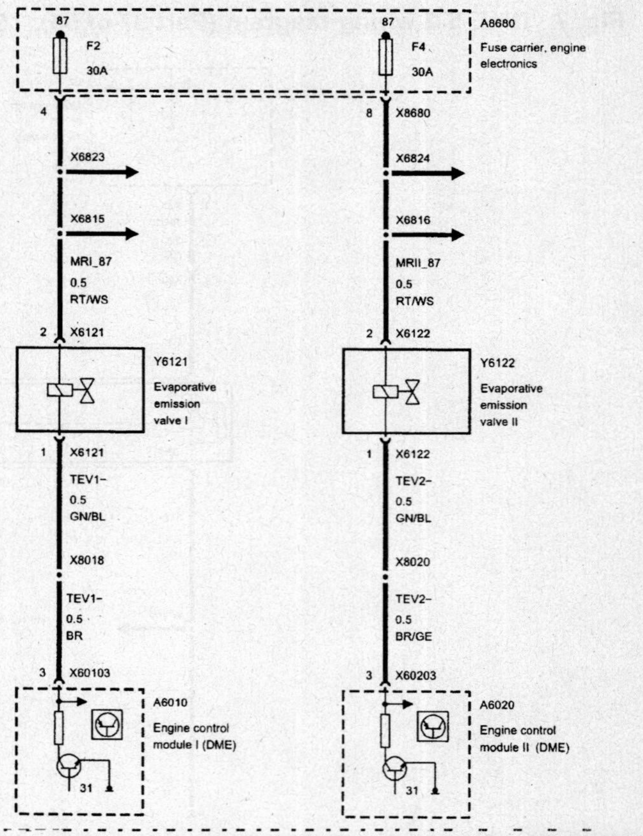

BM0150100130040X

Fig. 7 DME 5.2 wiring diagram (Part 42 of 55). 750

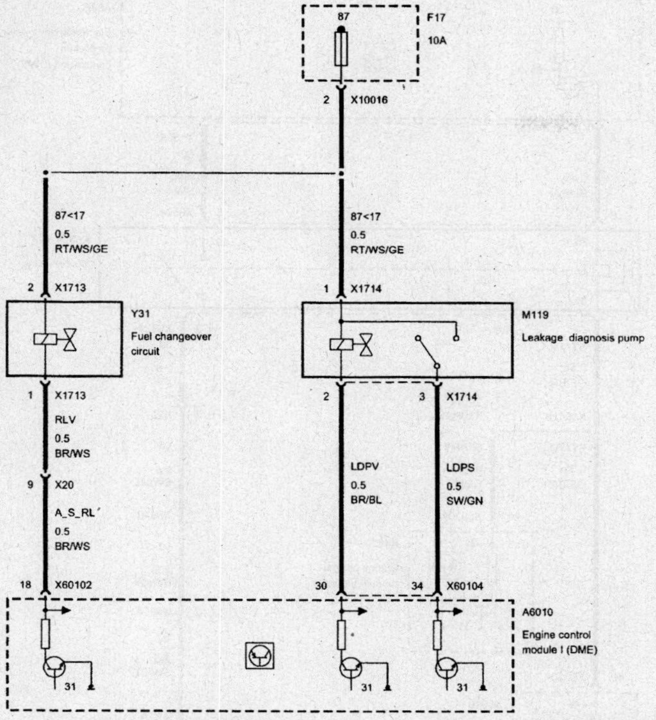

BM0150100130050X

Fig. 7 DME 5.2 wiring diagram (Part 43 of 55). 750

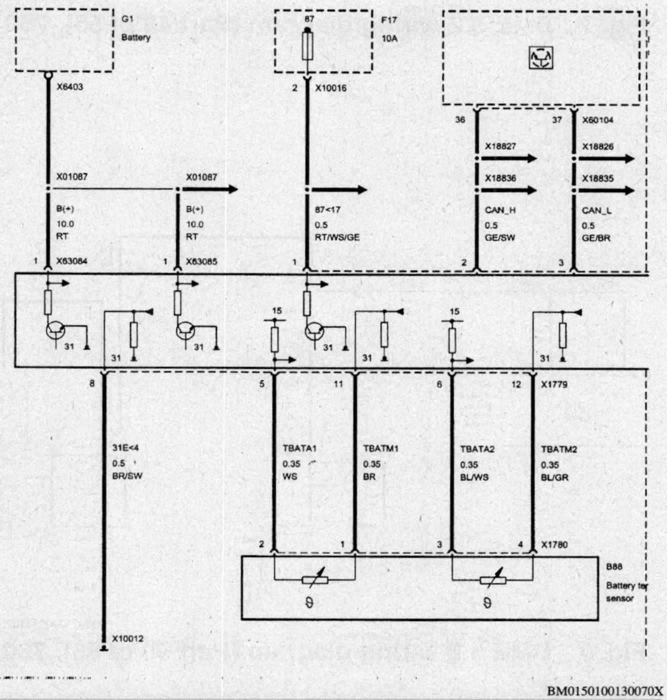

BM0150100130070X

Fig. 7 DME 5.2 wiring diagram (Part 45 of 55). 750

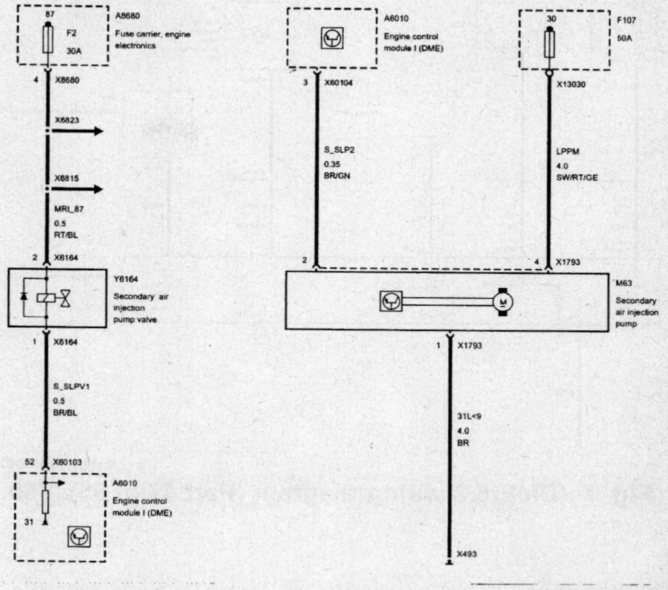

BM0150100130060X

Fig. 7 DME 5.2 wiring diagram (Part 44 of 55). 750

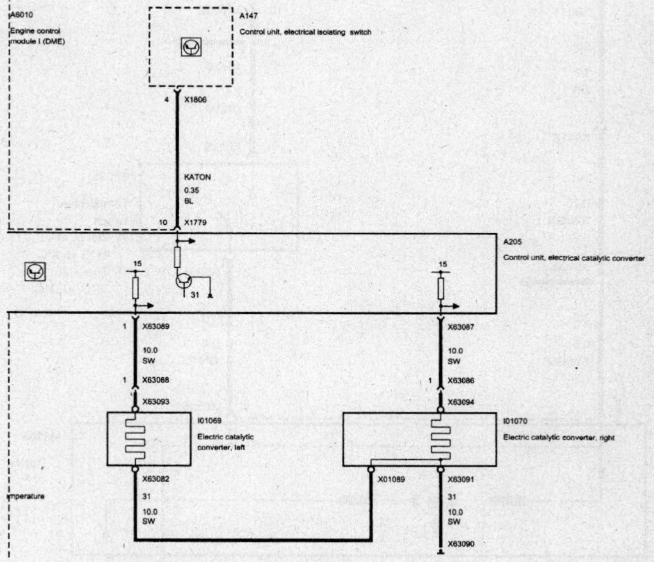

BM0150100130080X

Fig. 7 DME 5.2 wiring diagram (Part 46 of 55). 750

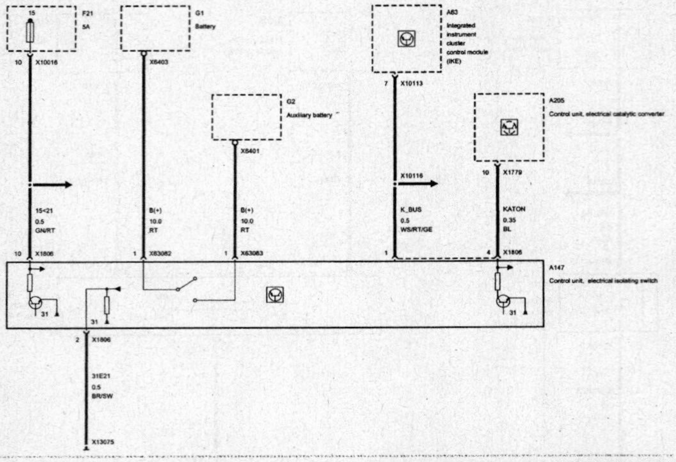

BM015010013009OX

Fig. 7 DME 5.2 wiring diagram (Part 47 of 55). 750

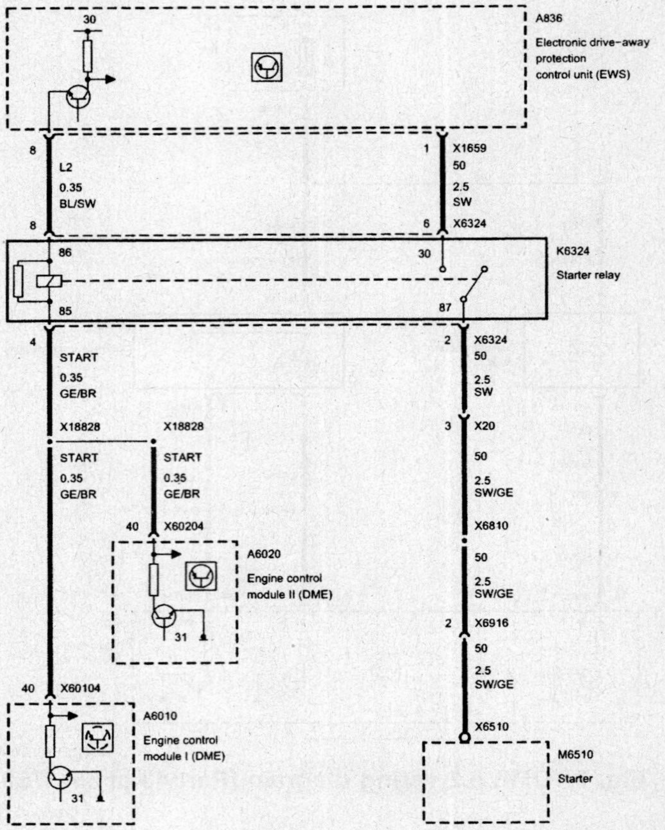

BM015010013000OX

Fig. 7 DME 5.2 wiring diagram (Part 48 of 55). 750

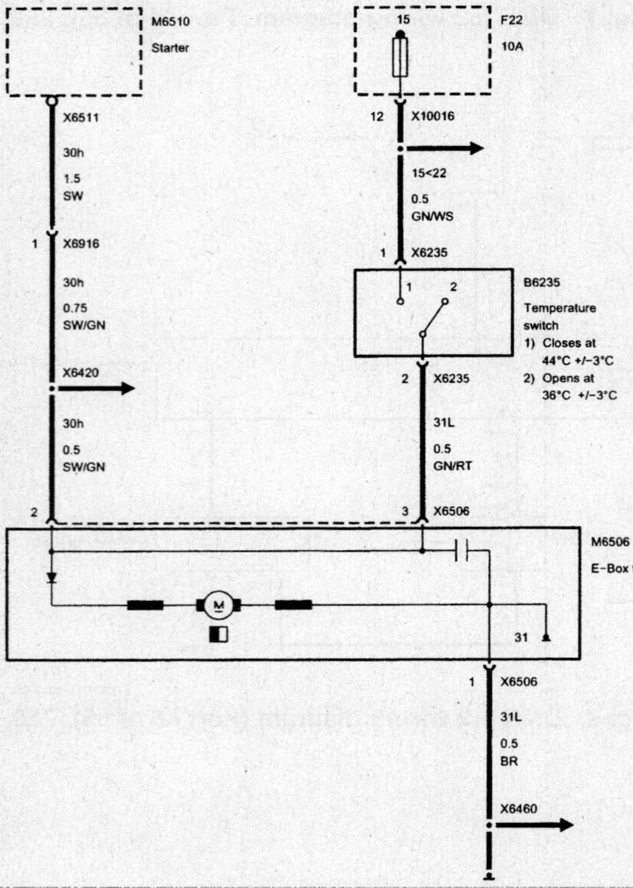

BM0150100131010X

Fig. 7 DME 5.2 wiring diagram (Part 49 of 55). 750

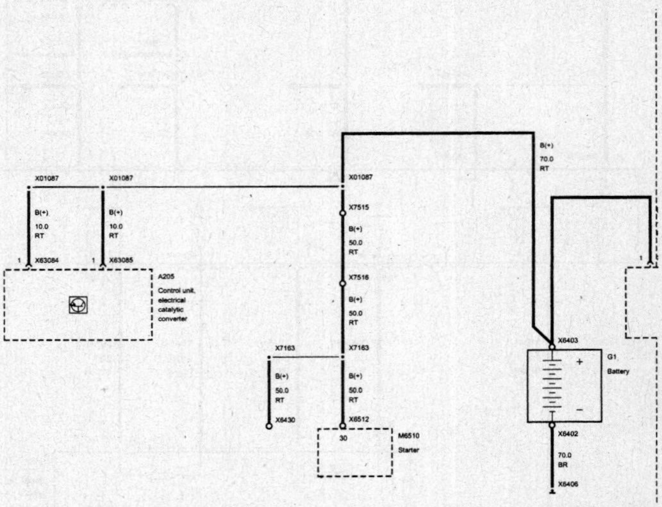

BM0150100131020X

Fig. 7 DME 5.2 wiring diagram (Part 50 of 55). 750

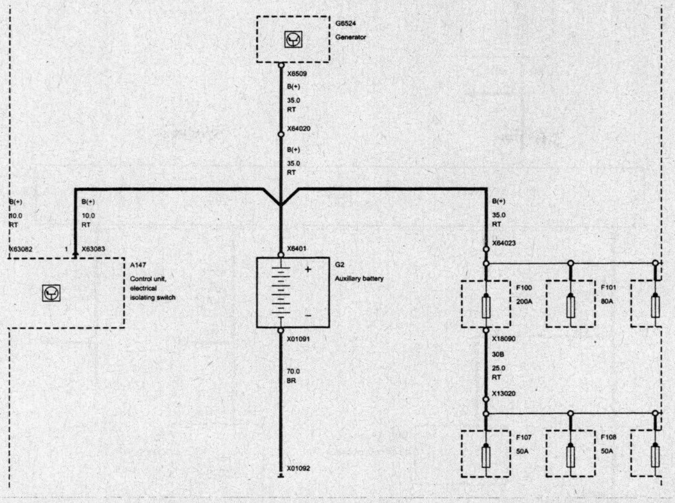

BM0150100131030X

Fig. 7 DME 5.2 wiring diagram (Part 51 of 55). 750

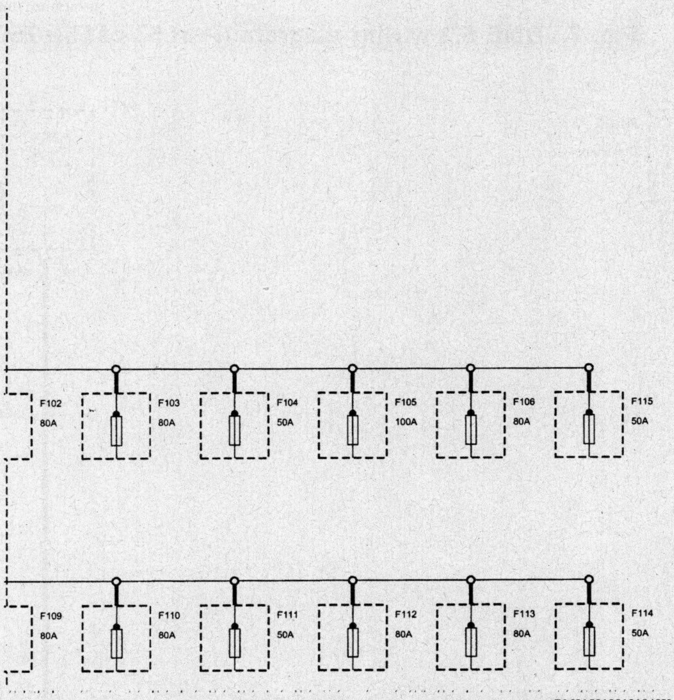

BM0150100131040X

Fig. 7 DME 5.2 wiring diagram (Part 52 of 55). 750

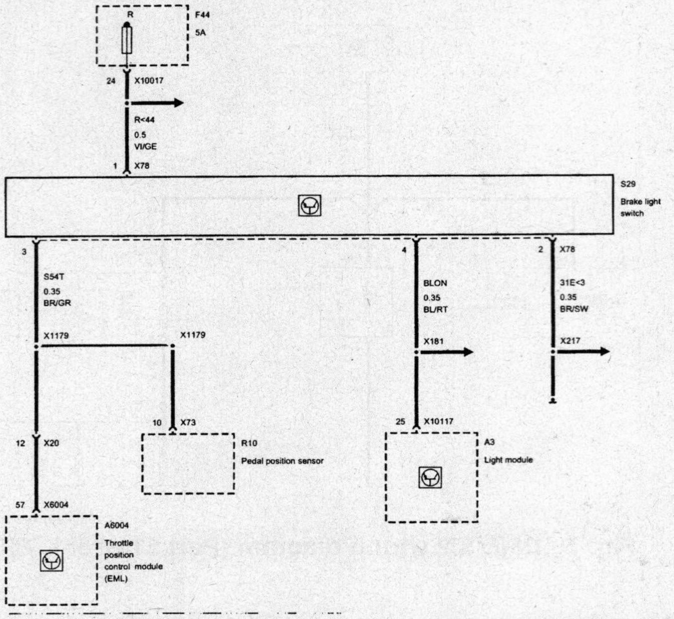

BM0150100131050X

Fig. 7 DME 5.2 wiring diagram (Part 53 of 55). 750

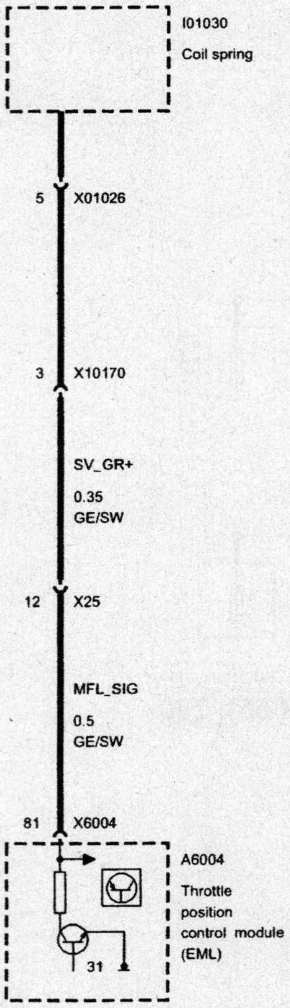

BM0150100131060X

Fig. 7 DME 5.2 wiring diagram (Part 54 of 55). 750

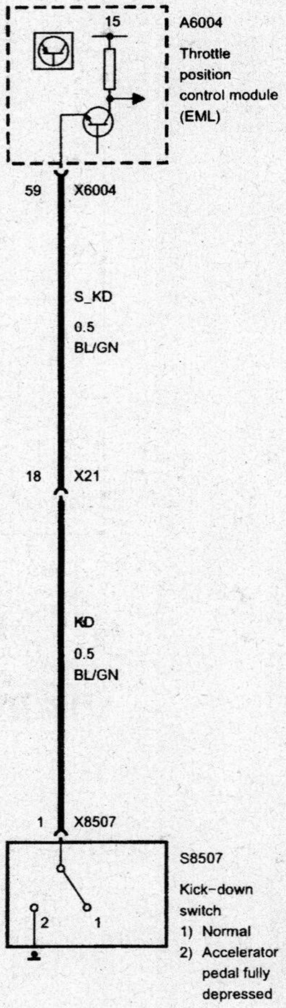

BM0150100131070X

Fig. 7 DME 5.2 wiring diagram (Part 55 of 55). 750

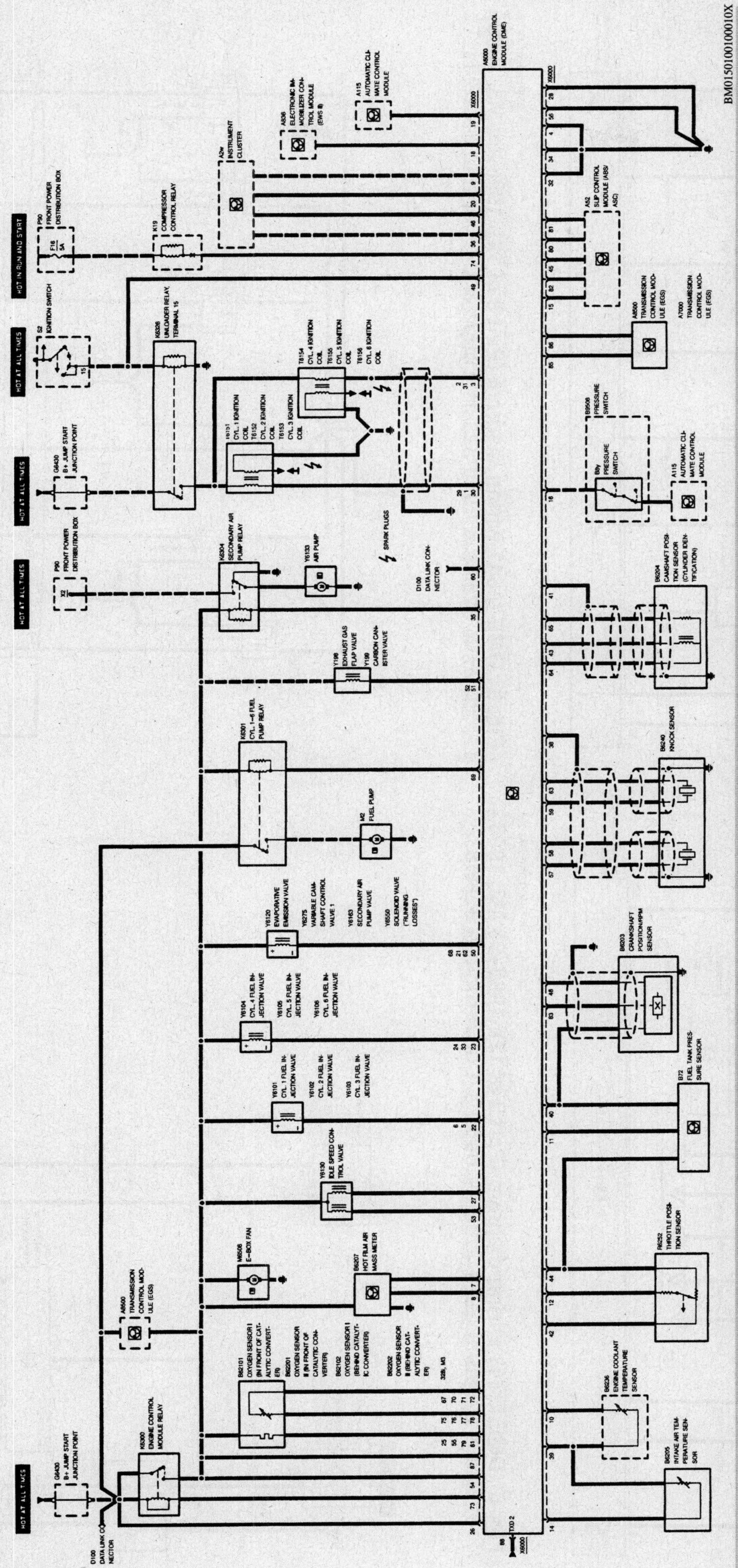

BM0150100100010X

Fig. 8 DME MS41 wiring diagram (Part 1 of 12). 1998–99 M3, 1998 323i/is & 328i/is & 1999 323i/is Coupe & Convertible & 328i/is Coupe & Convertible

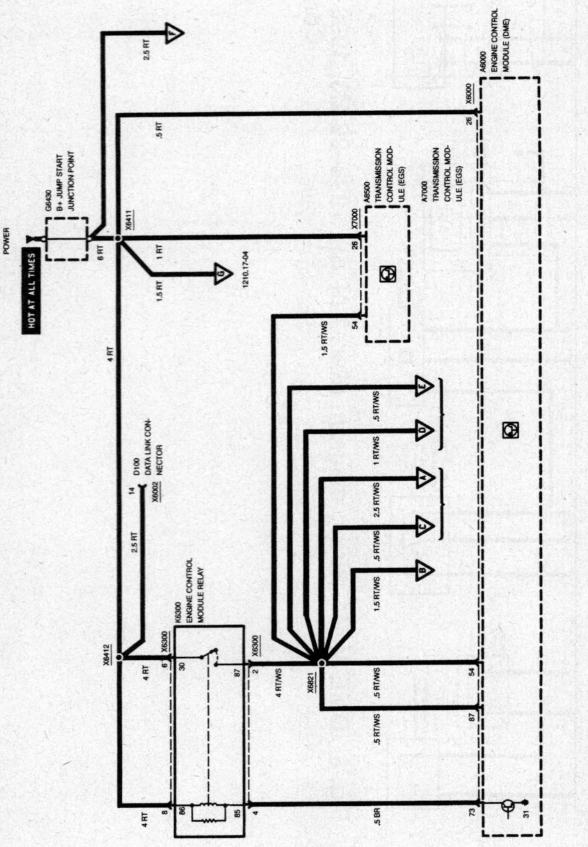

BM01501001000020X

Fig. 8 DME MS41 wiring diagram (Part 2 of 12). 1998–99 M3, 1998 323i/is & 328i/is & 1999 323i/is Coupe & Convertible & 328i/is

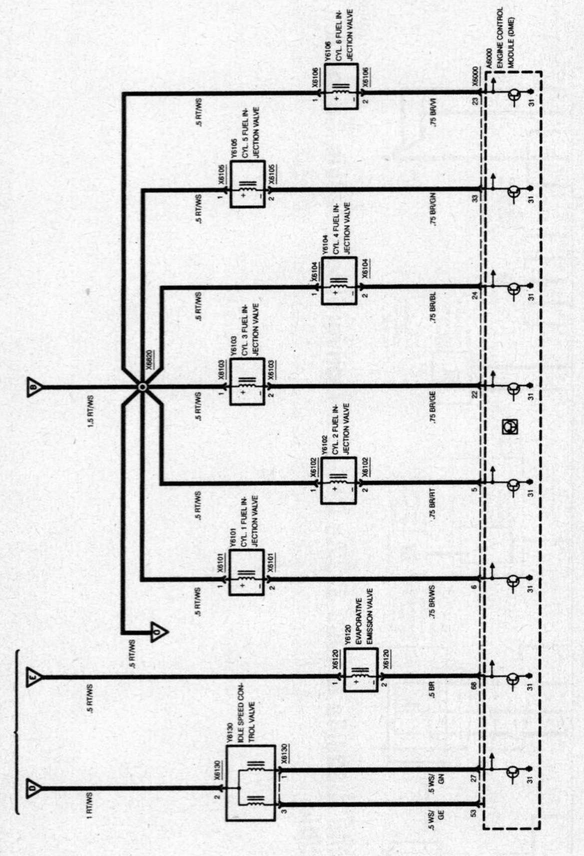

BM01501001000030X

Fig. 8 DME MS41 wiring diagram (Part 3 of 12). 1998–99 M3, 1998 323i/is & 328i/is & 1999 323i/is Coupe & Convertible & 328i/is

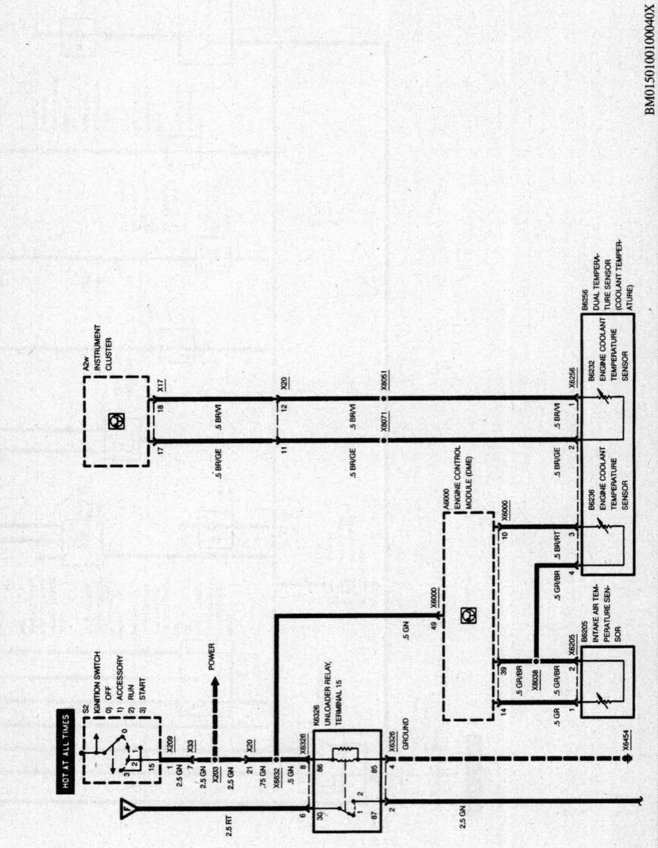

BM01501001000040X

Fig. 8 DME MS41 wiring diagram (Part 4 of 12). 1998–99 M3, 1998 323i/is & 328i/is & 1999 323i/is Coupe & Convertible & 328i/is

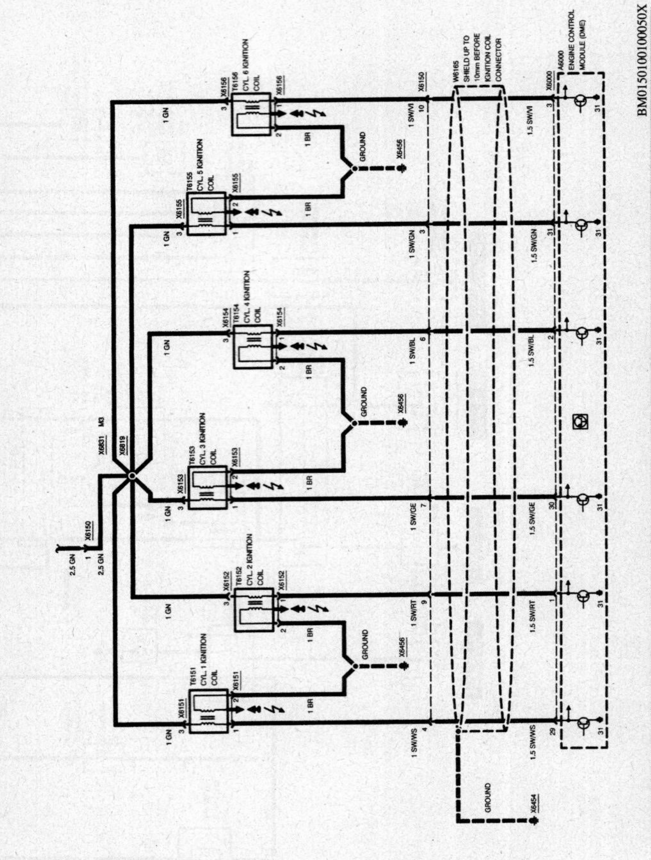

BM01501001000050X

Fig. 8 DME MS41 wiring diagram (Part 5 of 12). 1998–99 M3, 1998 323i/is & 328i/is & 1999 323i/is Coupe & Convertible & 328i/is

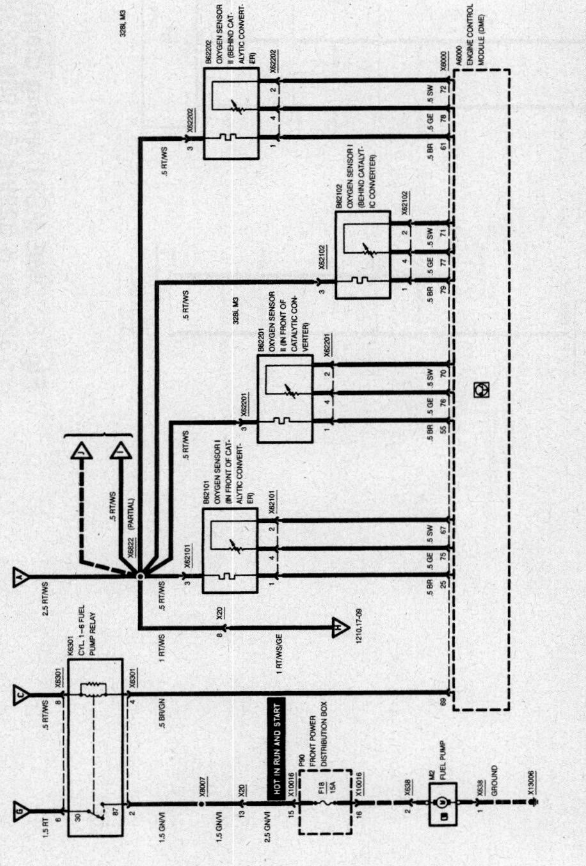

BM01501010006 0X

Fig. 8 DME MS41 wiring diagram (Part 6 of 12). 1998–99 M3, 1998 323i/is & 328i/is & 1999 323i/is Coupe & Convertible & 328i/is

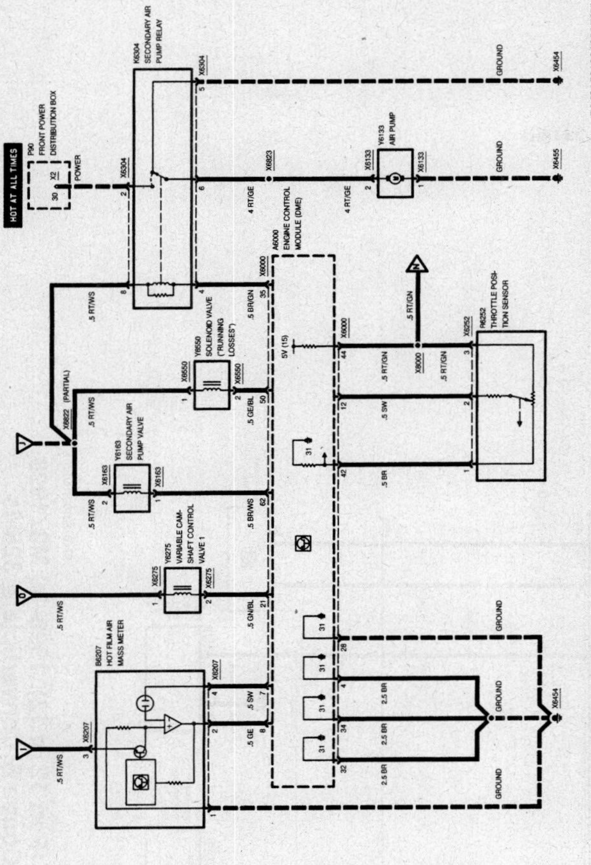

BM01501010007 0X

Fig. 8 DME MS41 wiring diagram (Part 7 of 12). 1998–99 M3, 1998 323i/is & 328i/is & 1999 323i/is Coupe & Convertible & 328i/is

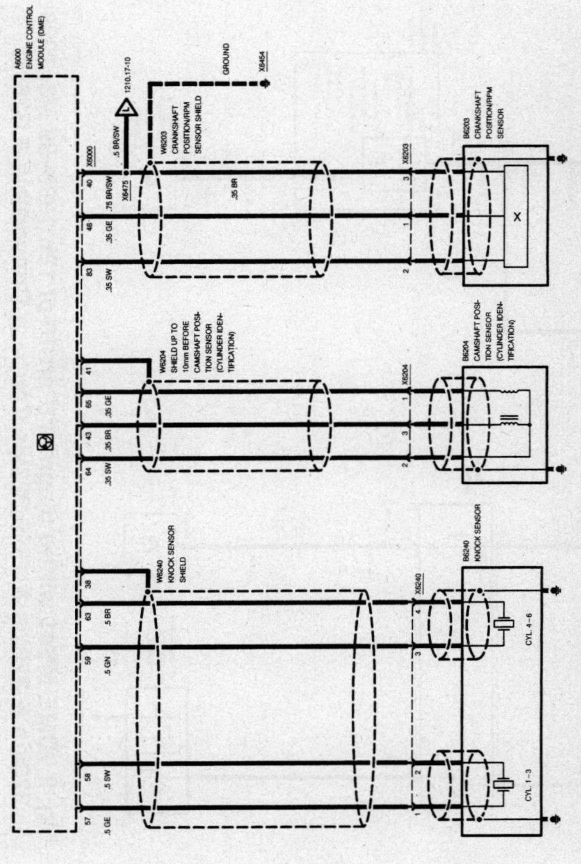

BM01501010008 0X

Fig. 8 DME MS41 wiring diagram (Part 8 of 12). 1998–99 M3, 1998 323i/is & 328i/is & 1999 323i/is Coupe & Convertible & 328i/is

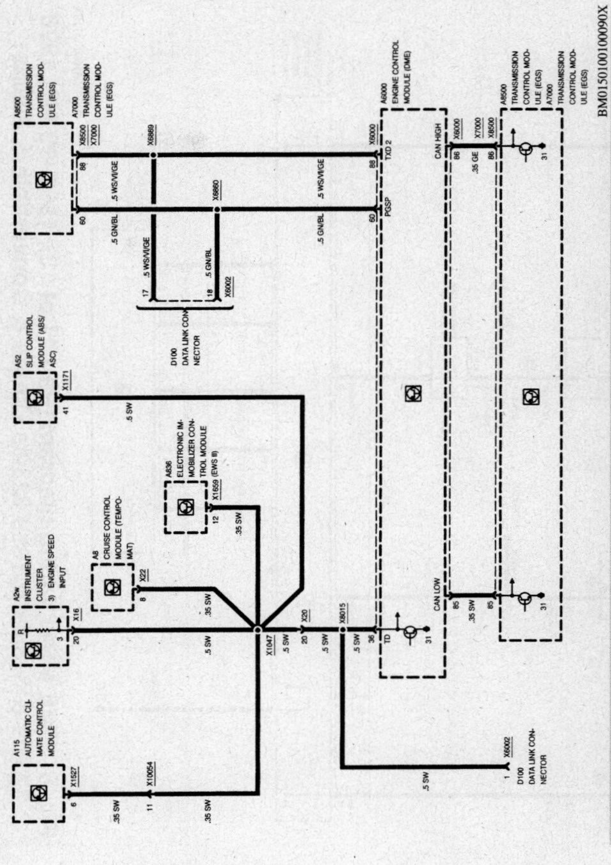

BM01501010009 0X

Fig. 8 DME MS41 wiring diagram (Part 9 of 12). 1998–99 M3, 1998 323i/is & 328i/is & 1999 323i/is Coupe & Convertible & 328i/is

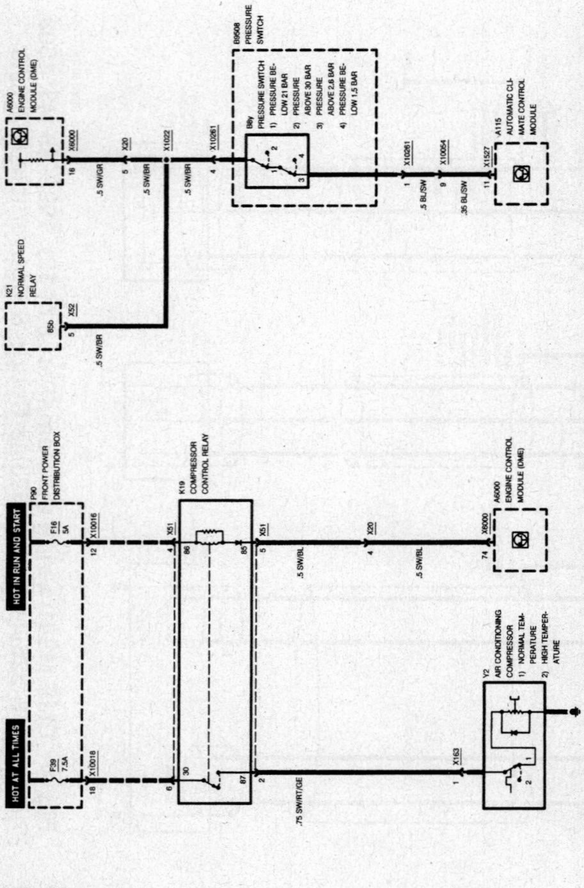

BM015010010100X

Fig. 8 DME MS41 wiring diagram (Part 10 of 12). 1998–99 M3, 1998 323i/is & 328i/is & 1999 323i/is Coupe & Convertible & 328i/is

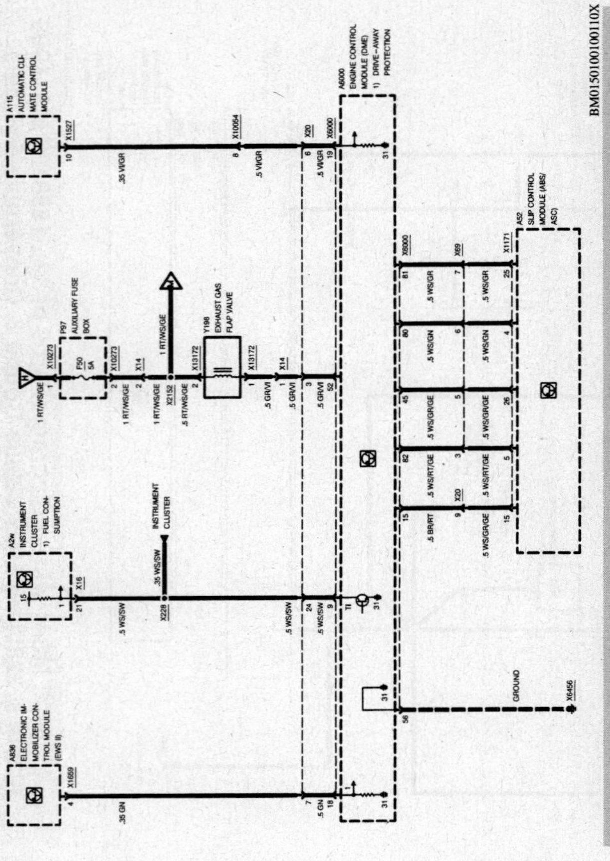

BM015010010110X

Fig. 8 DME MS41 wiring diagram (Part 11 of 12). 1998–99 M3, 1998 323i/is & 328i/is & 1999 323i/is Coupe & Convertible & 328i/is

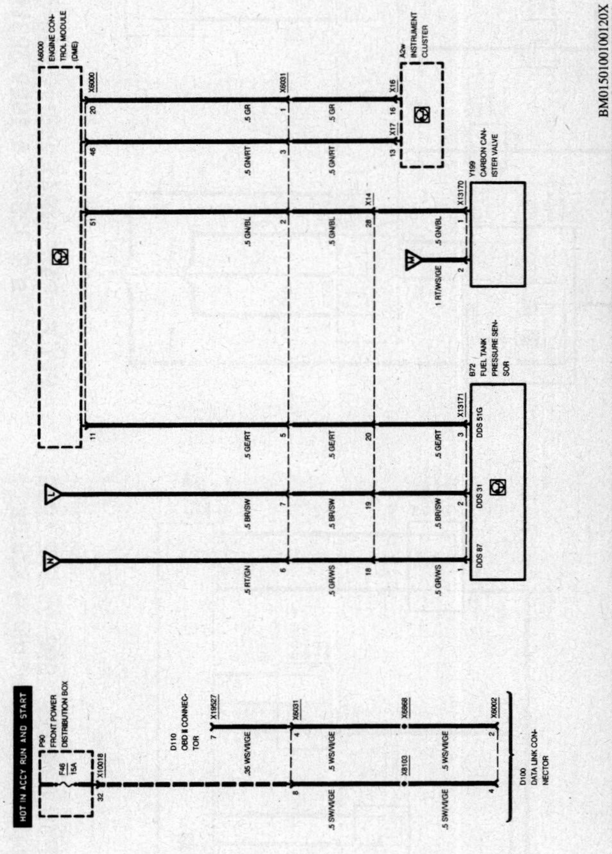

BM015010010120X

Fig. 8 DME MS41 wiring diagram (Part 12 of 12). 1998–99 M3, 1998 323i/is & 328i/is & 1999 323i/is Coupe & Convertible & 328i/is

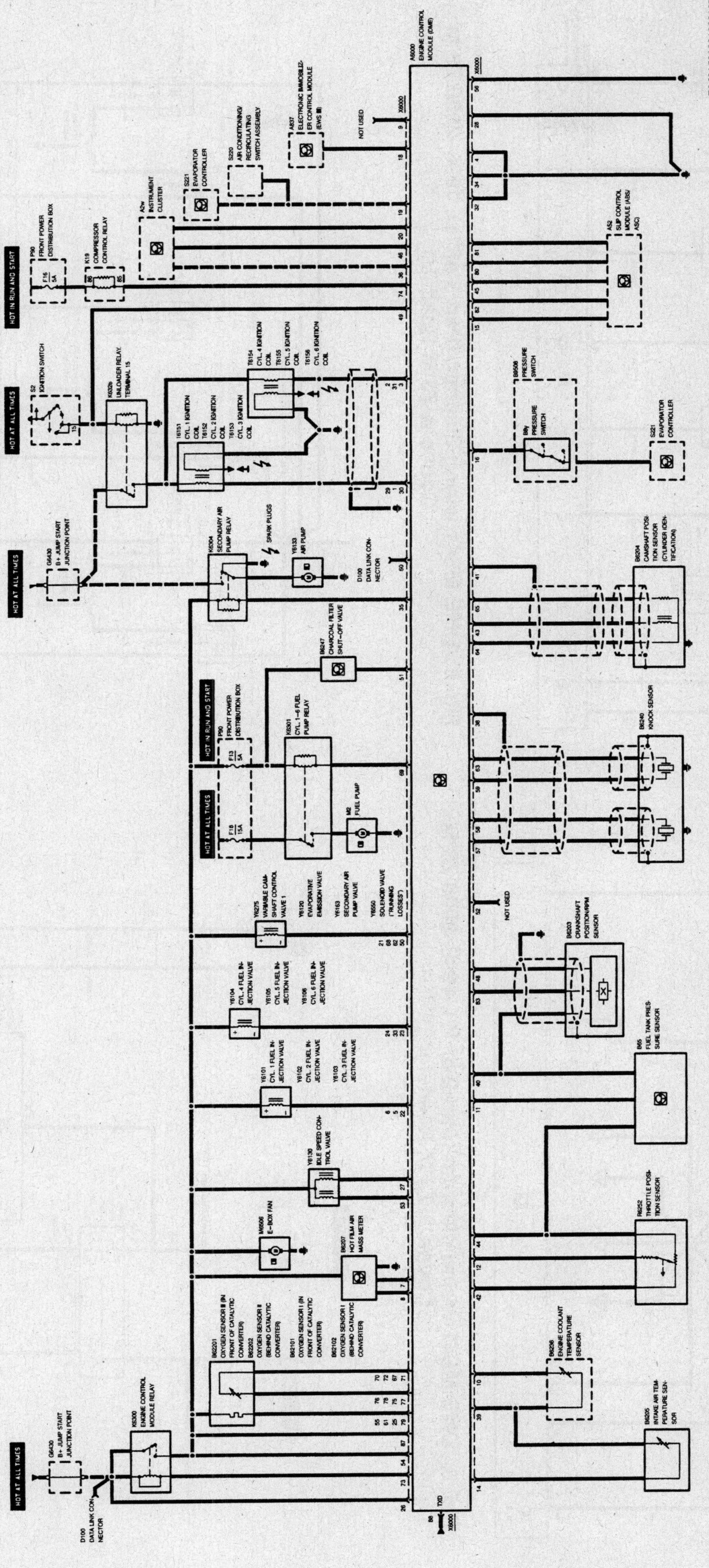

BM01501001003010X

Fig. 9 DME MS41 wiring diagram (Part 1 of 11). 1998–2000 Z3 M Coupe & Z3 M Roadster

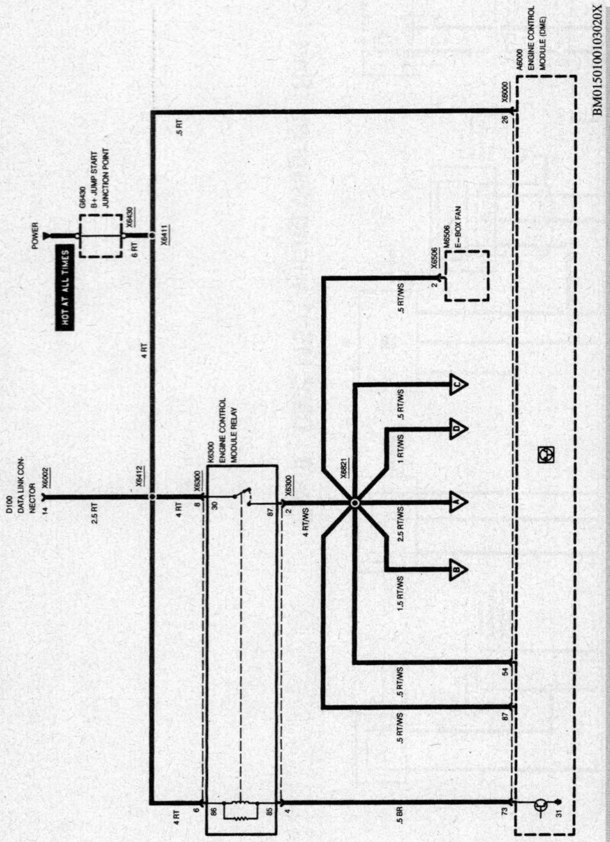

Fig. 9 DME MS41 wiring diagram (Part 2 of 11). 1998–2000 Z3 M Coupe & Z3 M Roadster

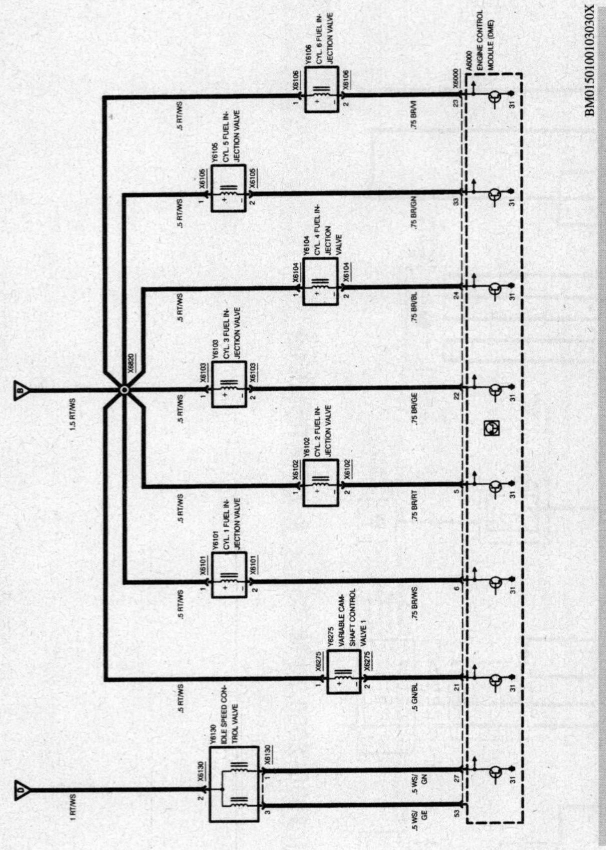

Fig. 9 DME MS41 wiring diagram (Part 3 of 11). 1998–2000 Z3 M Coupe & Z3 M Roadster

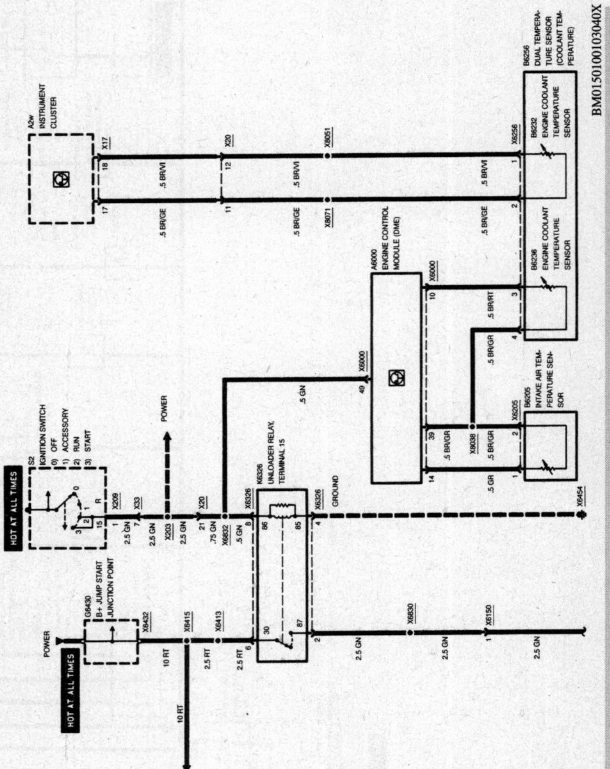

Fig. 9 DME MS41 wiring diagram (Part 4 of 11). 1998–2000 Z3 M Coupe & Z3 M Roadster

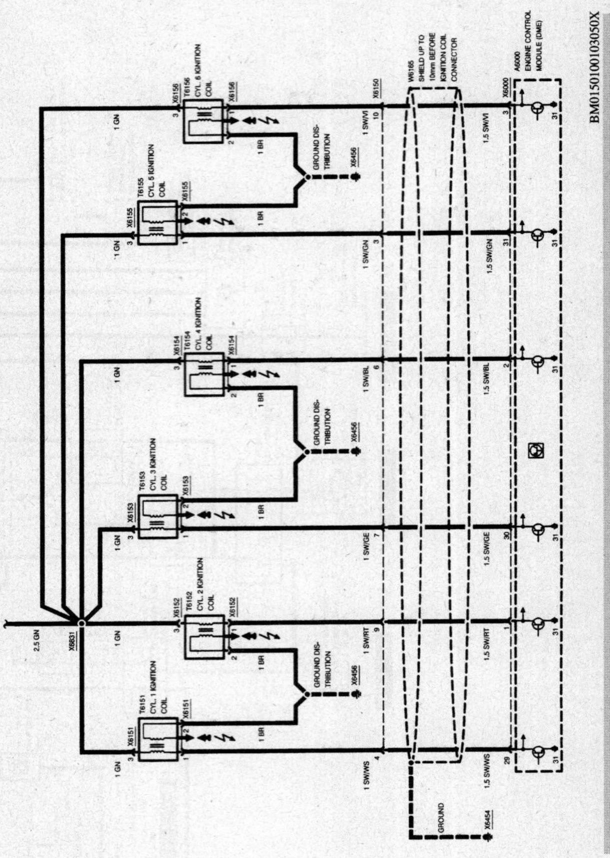

Fig. 9 DME MS41 wiring diagram (Part 5 of 11). 1998–2000 Z3 M Coupe & Z3 M Roadster

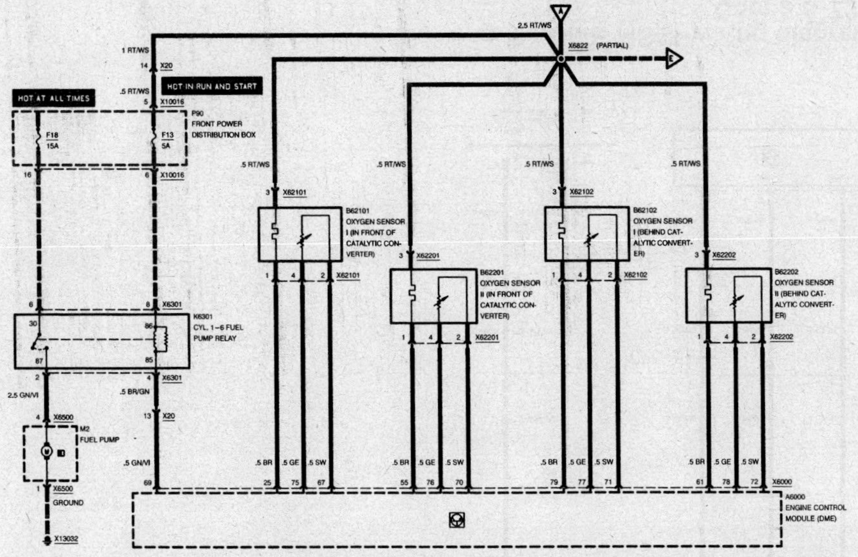

BM0150100103060X

Fig. 9 DME MS41 wiring diagram (Part 6 of 11). 1998–2000 Z3 M Coupe & Z3 M Roadster

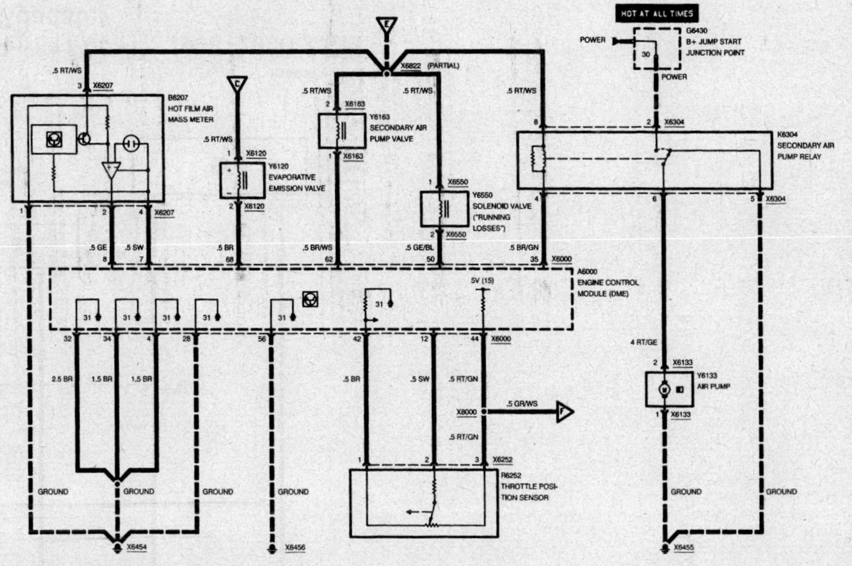

BM0150100103070X

Fig. 9 DME MS41 wiring diagram (Part 7 of 11). 1998–2000 Z3 M Coupe & Z3 M Roadster

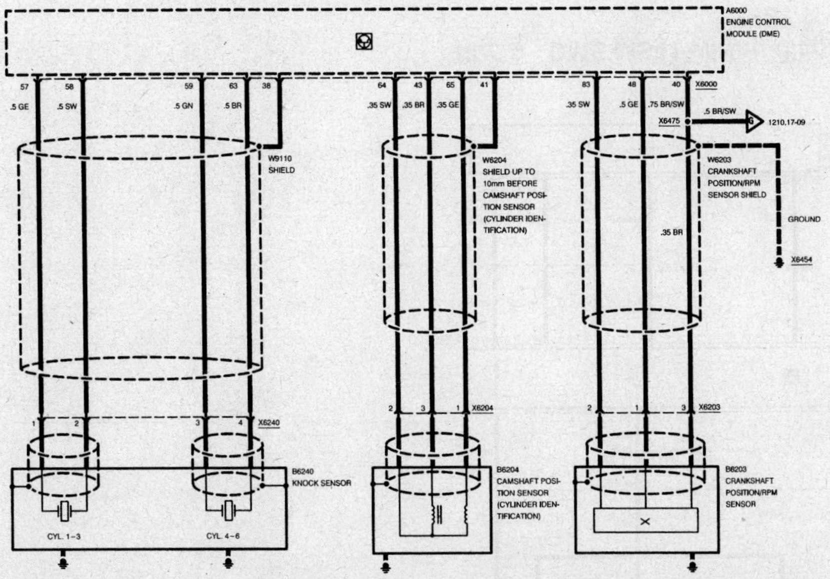

BM0150100103080X

Fig. 9 DME MS41 wiring diagram (Part 8 of 11). 1998–2000 Z3 M Coupe & Z3 M Roadster

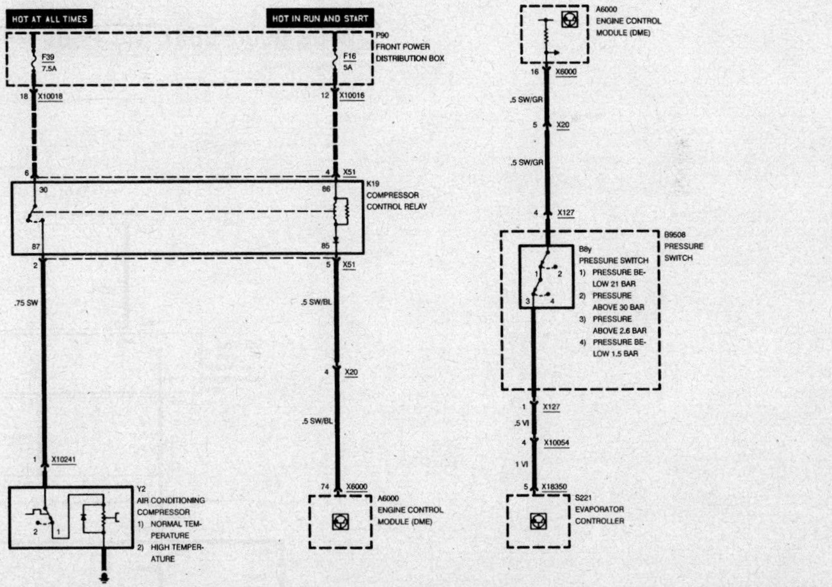

BM0150100103090X

Fig. 9 DME MS41 wiring diagram (Part 9 of 11). 1998–2000 Z3 M Coupe & Z3 M Roadster

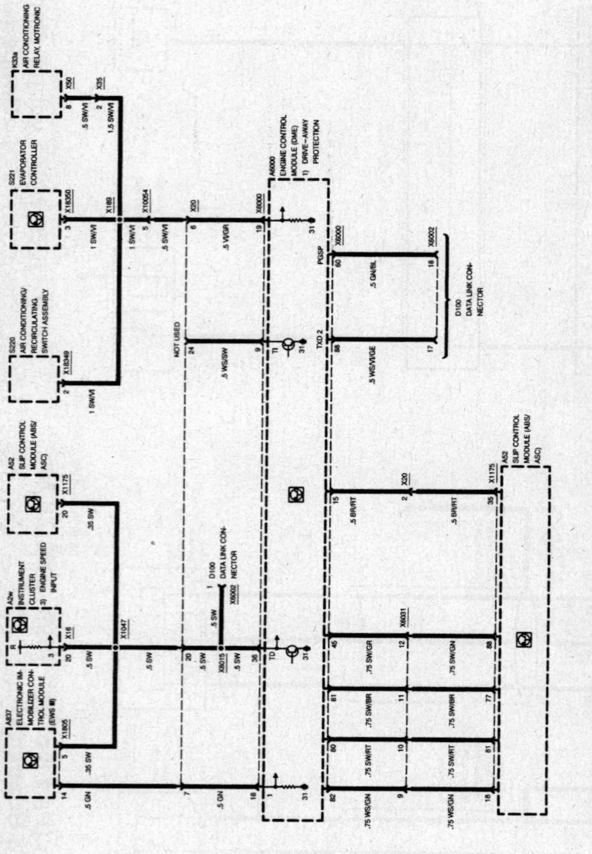

BM01501001031OOX

Fig. 9 DME MS41 wiring diagram (Part 10 of 11). 1998–2000 Z3 M Coupe & Z3 M Roadster

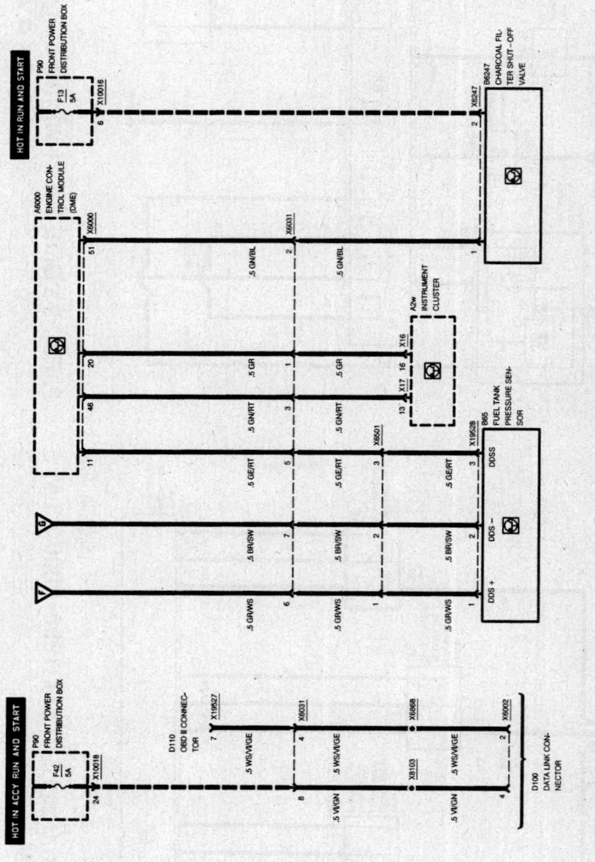

BM01501001031IOX

Fig. 9 DME MS41 wiring diagram (Part 11 of 11). 1998–2000 Z3 M Coupe & Z3 M Roadster

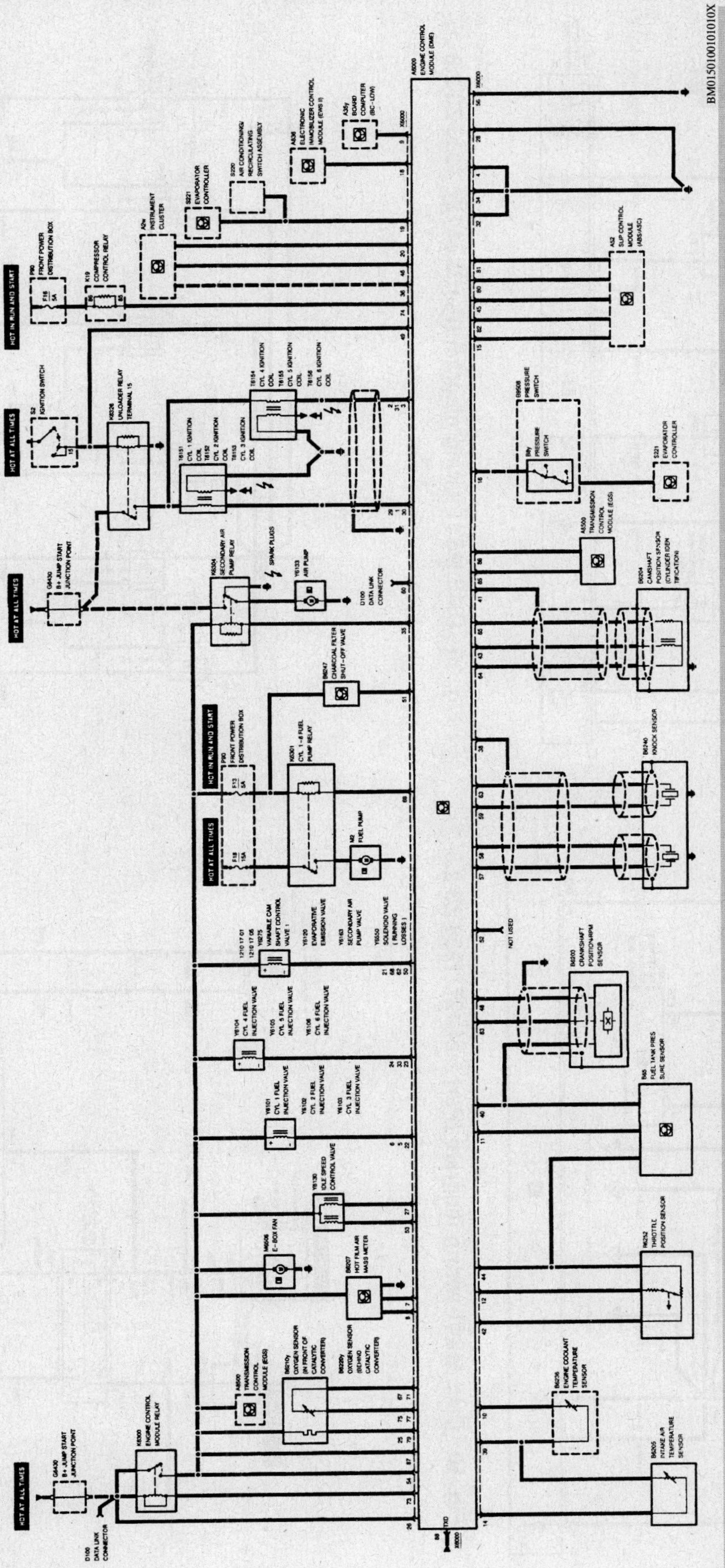

Fig. 10 DME MS41 wiring diagram (Part 1 of 12). 1998 Z3 2.8

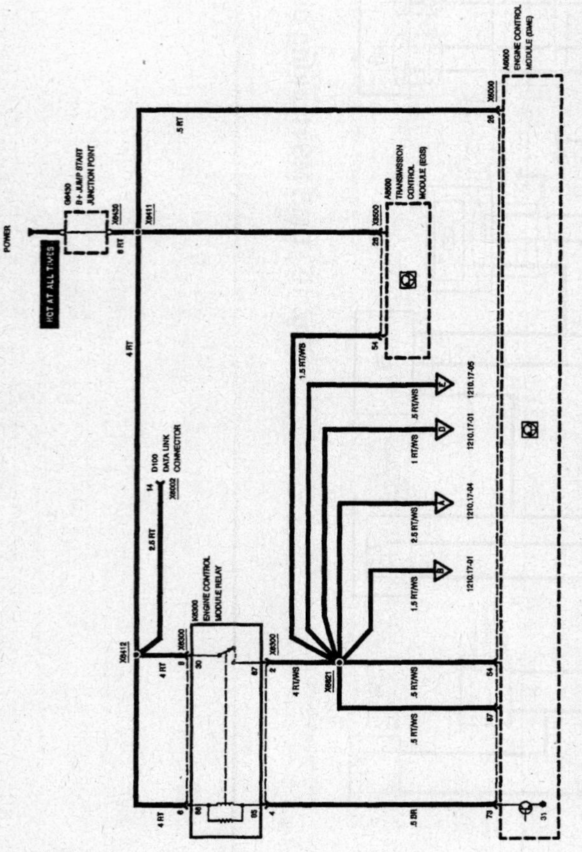

BM01501001020X

Fig. 10 DME MS41 wiring diagram (Part 2 of 12). 1998 Z3 2.8

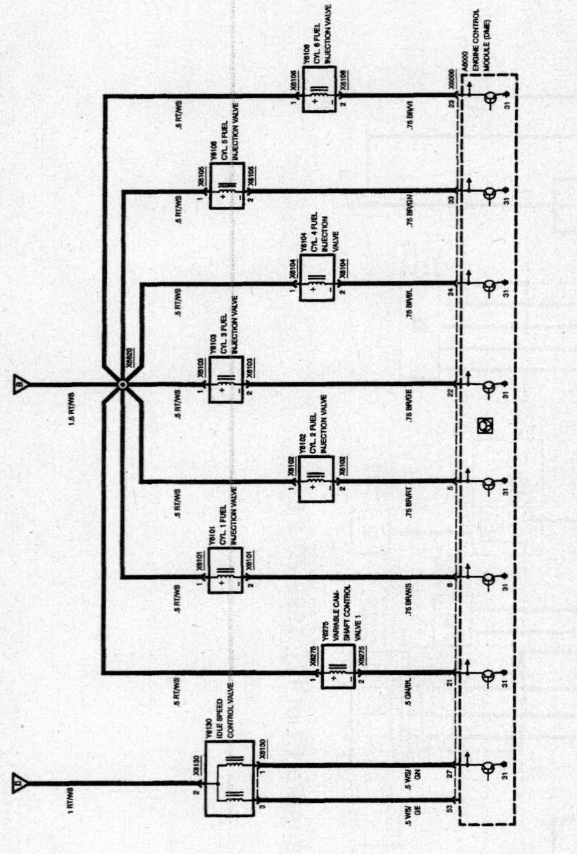

BM01501001030X

Fig. 10 DME MS41 wiring diagram (Part 3 of 12). 1998 Z3 2.8

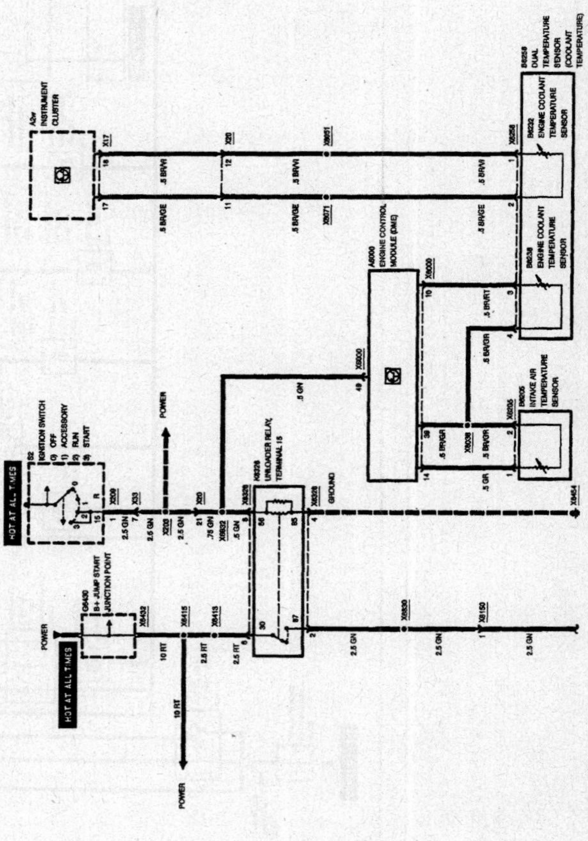

BM01501001040X

Fig. 10 DME MS41 wiring diagram (Part 4 of 12). 1998 Z3 2.8

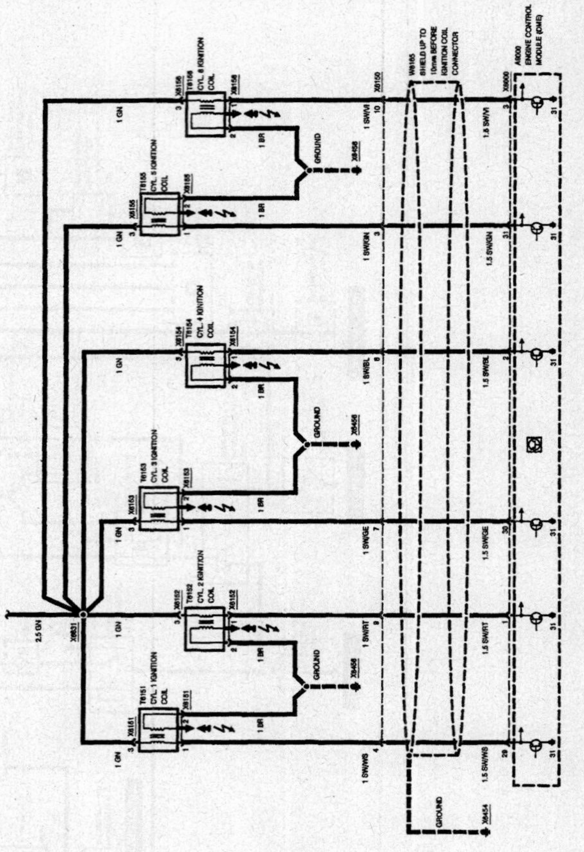

BM01501001050X

Fig. 10 DME MS41 wiring diagram (Part 5 of 12). 1998 Z3 2.8

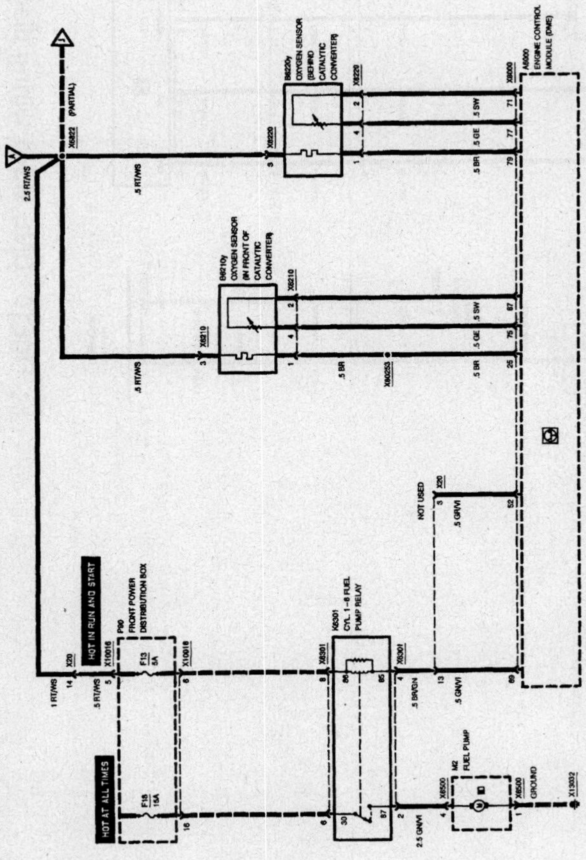

BM01501001010060X

Fig. 10 DME MS41 wiring diagram (Part 6 of 12). 1998 Z3 2.8

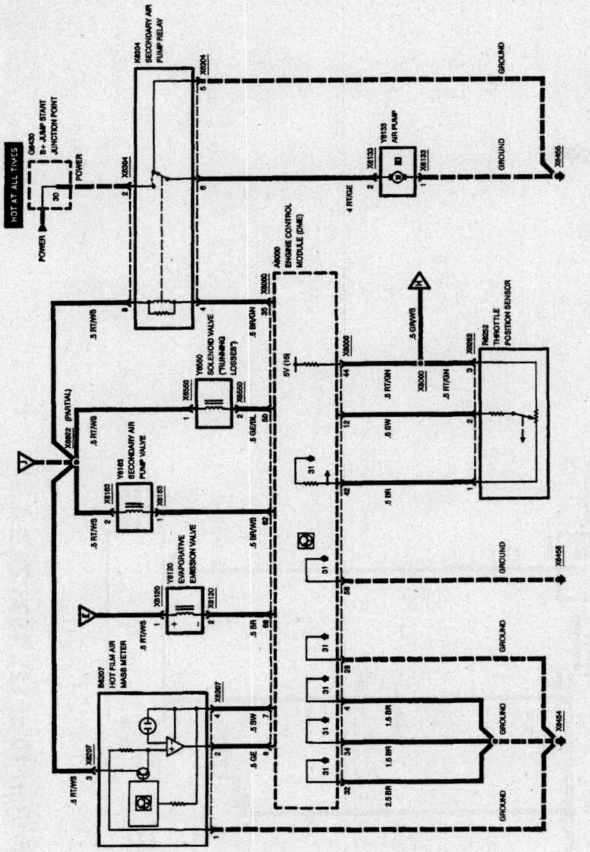

BM01501001010070X

Fig. 10 DME MS41 wiring diagram (Part 7 of 12). 1998 Z3 2.8

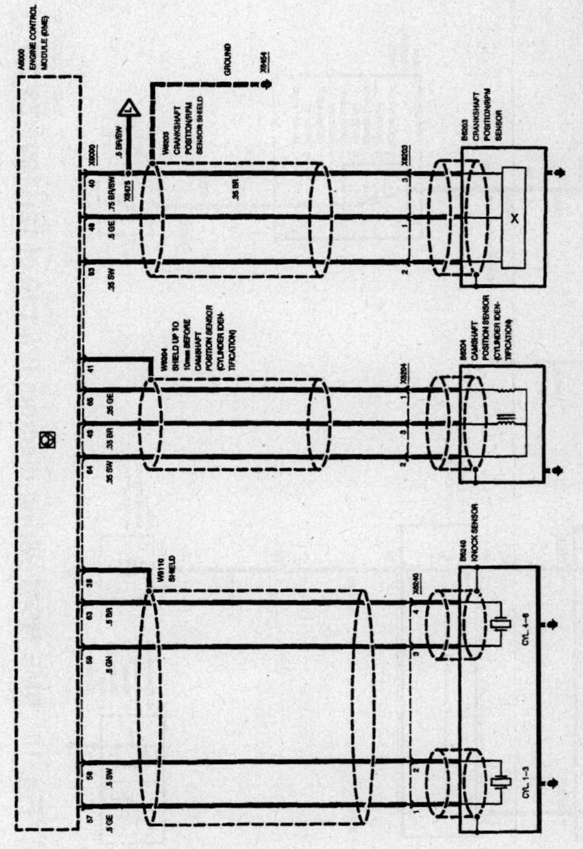

BM01501001010080X

Fig. 10 DME MS41 wiring diagram (Part 8 of 12). 1998 Z3 2.8

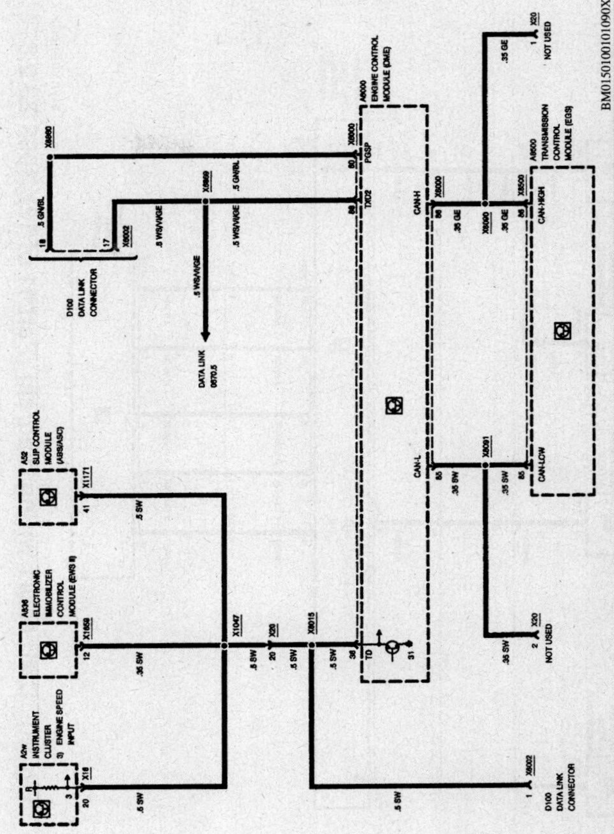

BM01501001010090X

Fig. 10 DME MS41 wiring diagram (Part 9 of 12). 1998 Z3 2.8

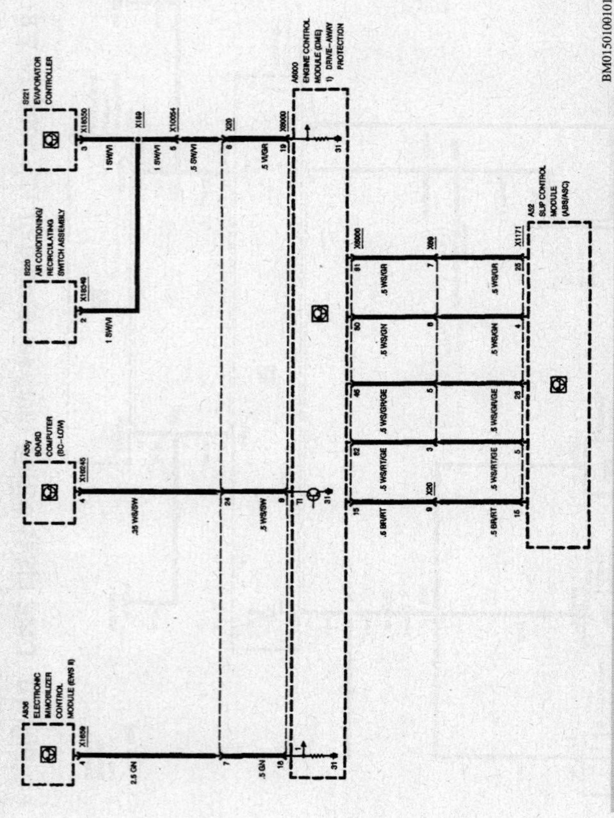

BM0150100101110X

Fig. 10 DME MS41 wiring diagram (Part 11 of 12). 1998 Z3 2.8

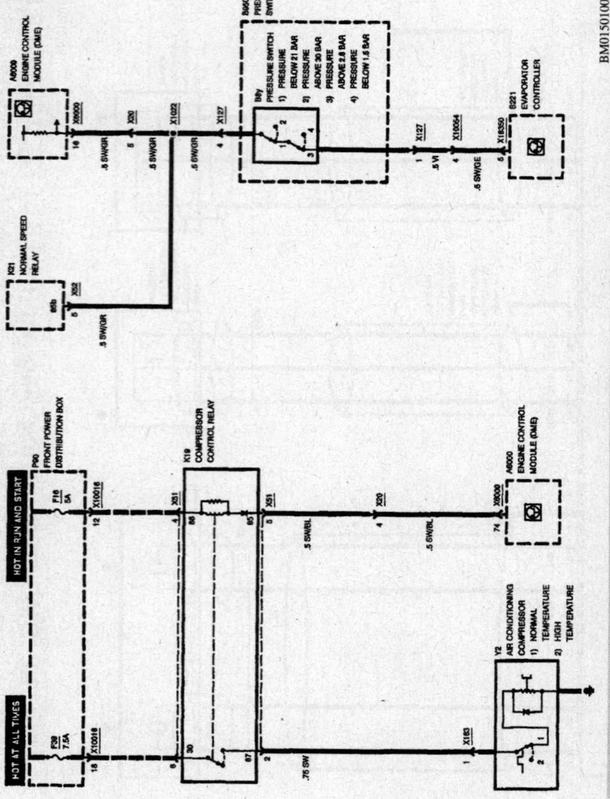

BM0150100101100X

Fig. 10 DME MS41 wiring diagram (Part 10 of 12). 1998 Z3 2.8

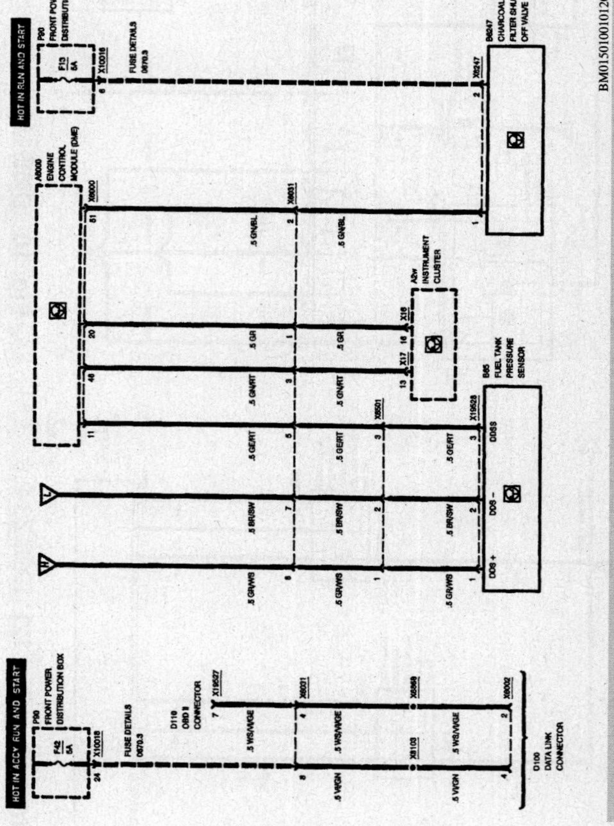

BM0150100101200X

Fig. 10 DME MS41 wiring diagram (Part 12 of 12). 1998 Z3 2.8

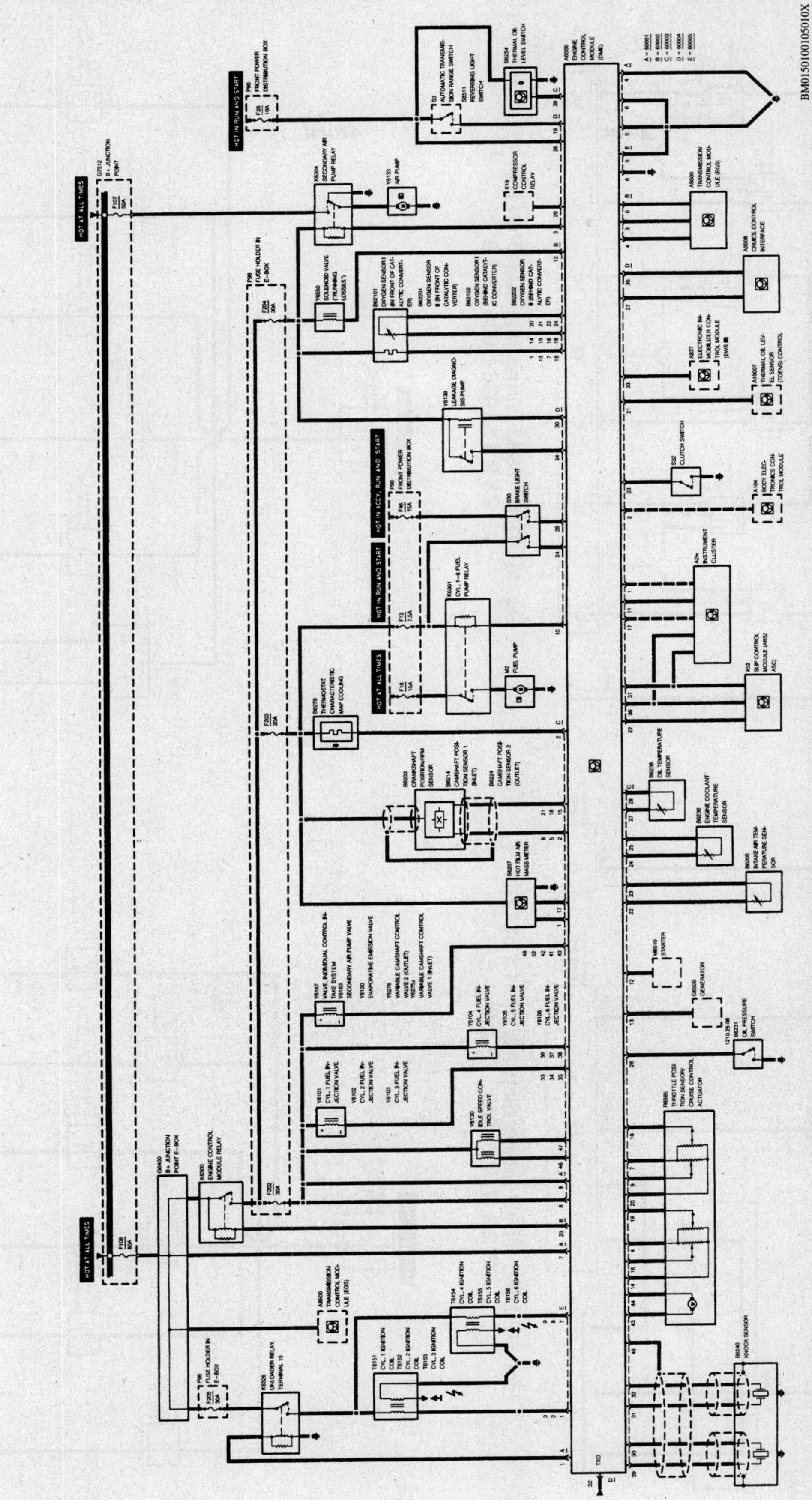

Fig. 11 DME MS42 wiring diagram (Part 1 of 12). Z3 2.3 & 1998–2000 Z3 2.8

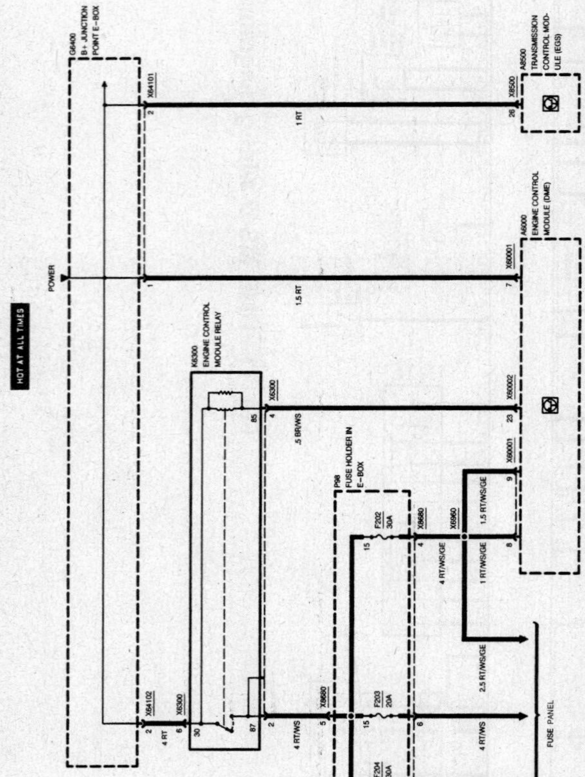

BM0150100105020X

Fig. 11 DME MS42 wiring diagram (Part 2 of 12). Z3 2.3 &1998–2000 Z3 2.8

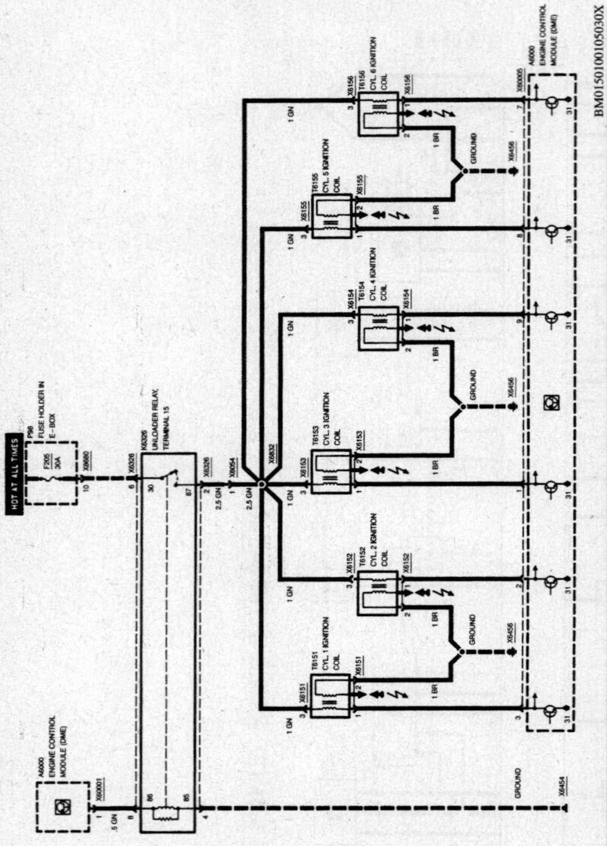

BM0150100105030X

Fig. 11 DME MS42 wiring diagram (Part 3 of 12). Z3 2.3 &1998–2000 Z3 2.8

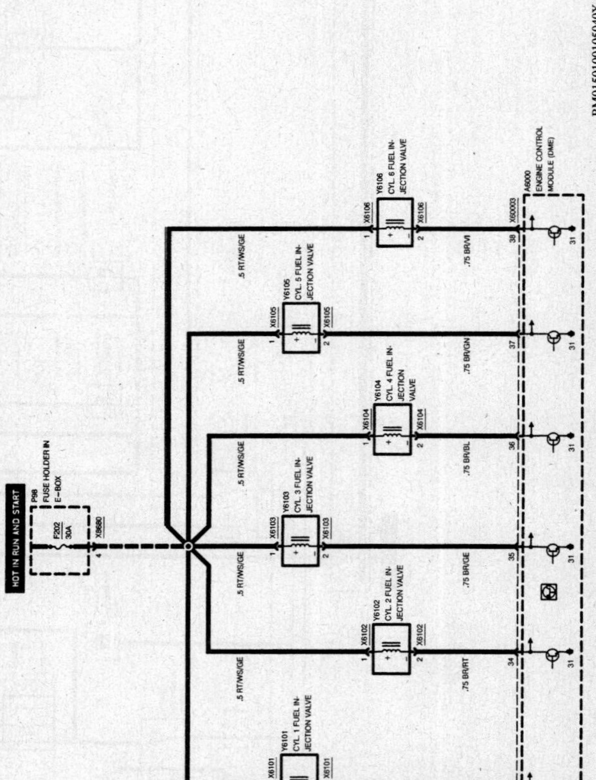

BM0150100105040X

Fig. 11 DME MS42 wiring diagram (Part 4 of 12). Z3 2.3 &1998–2000 Z3 2.8

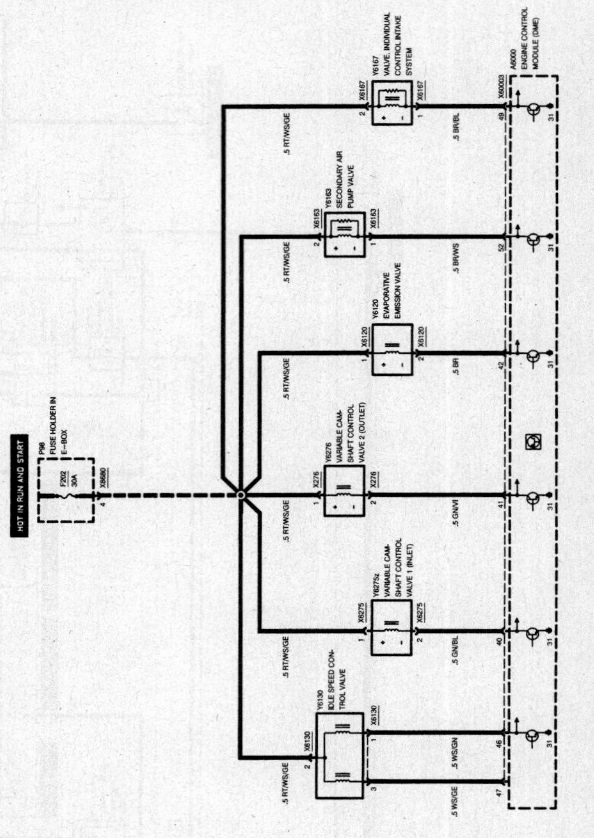

BM0150100105050X

Fig. 11 DME MS42 wiring diagram (Part 5 of 12). Z3 2.3 &1998–2000 Z3 2.8

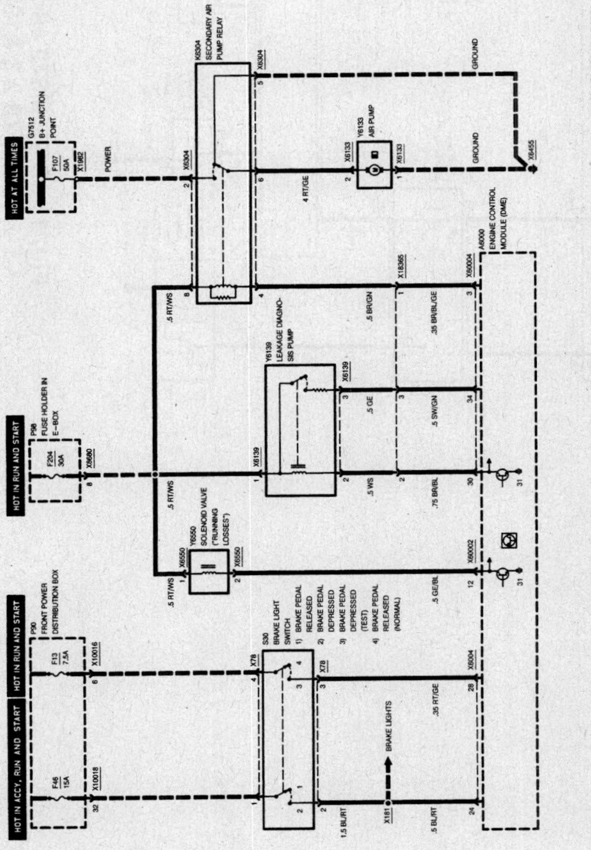

BM0150100105060X

Fig. 11 DME MS42 wiring diagram (Part 6 of 12). Z3 2.3 &1998–2000 Z3 2.8

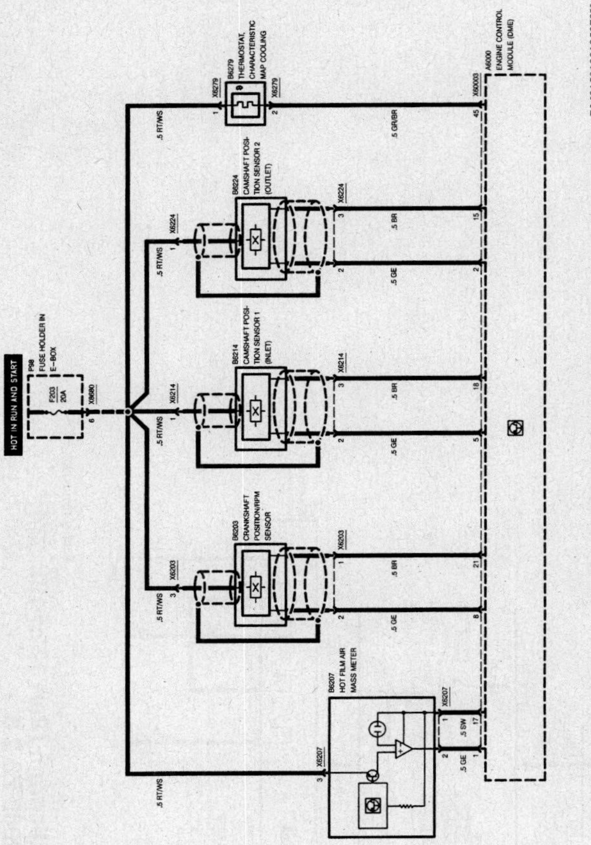

BM0150100105070X

Fig. 11 DME MS42 wiring diagram (Part 7 of 12). Z3 2.3 &1998–2000 Z3 2.8

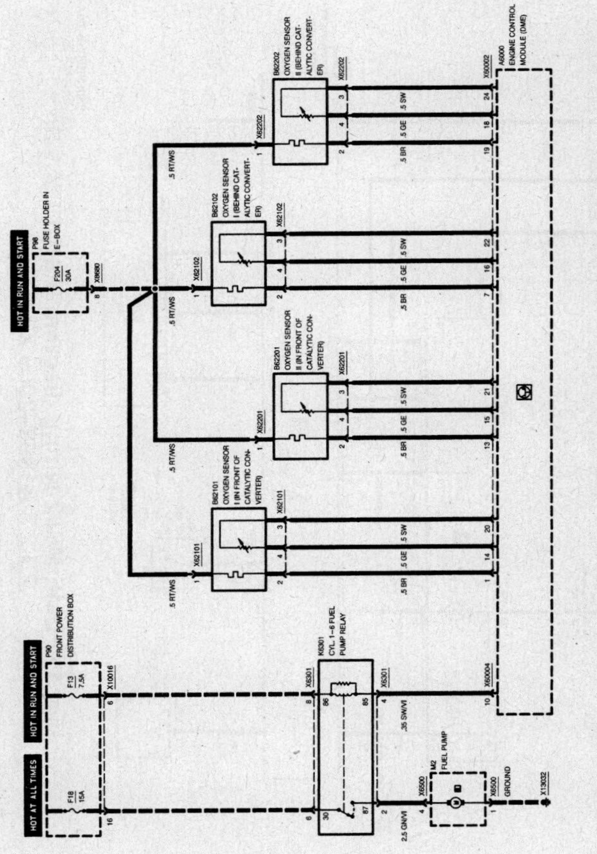

BM0150100105080X

Fig. 11 DME MS42 wiring diagram (Part 8 of 12). Z3 2.3 &1998–2000 Z3 2.8

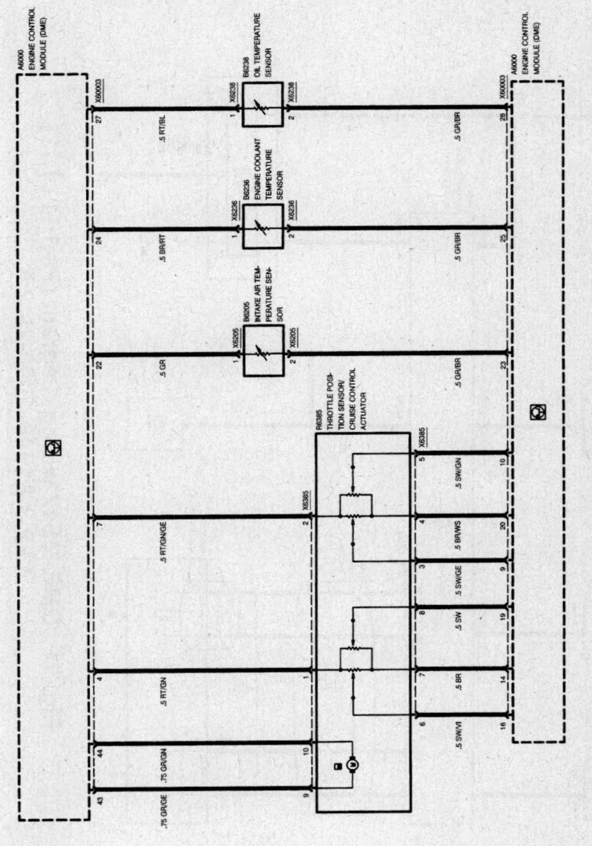

BM0150100105090X

Fig. 11 DME MS42 wiring diagram (Part 9 of 12). Z3 2.3 &1998–2000 Z3 2.8

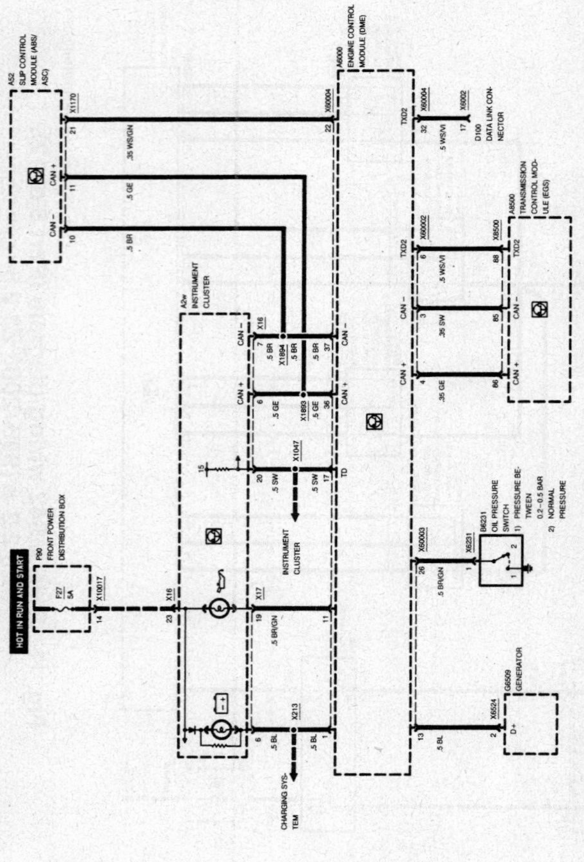

BM01501001051 00X

Fig. 11 DME MS42 wiring diagram (Part 10 of 12). Z3 2.3 &1998–2000 Z3 2.8

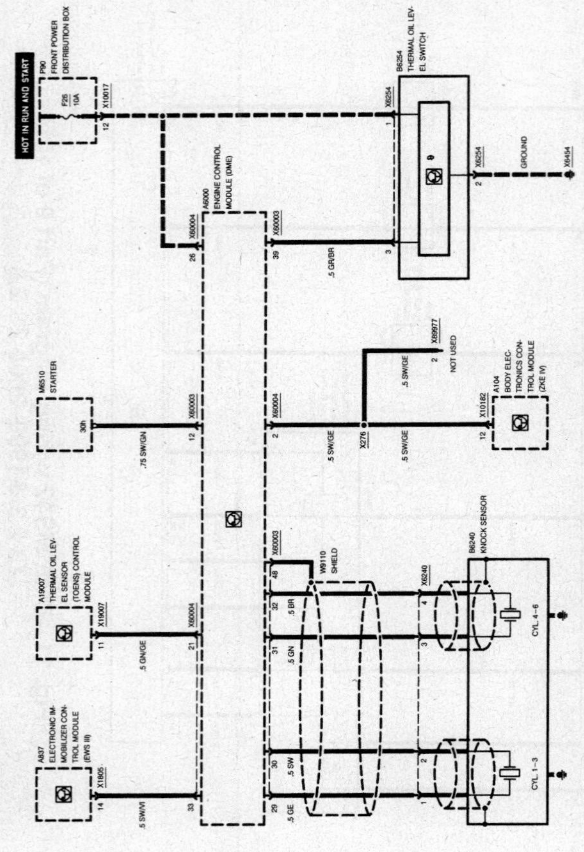

BM01501001051 10X

Fig. 11 DME MS42 wiring diagram (Part 11 of 12). Z3 2.3 &1998–2000 Z3 2.8

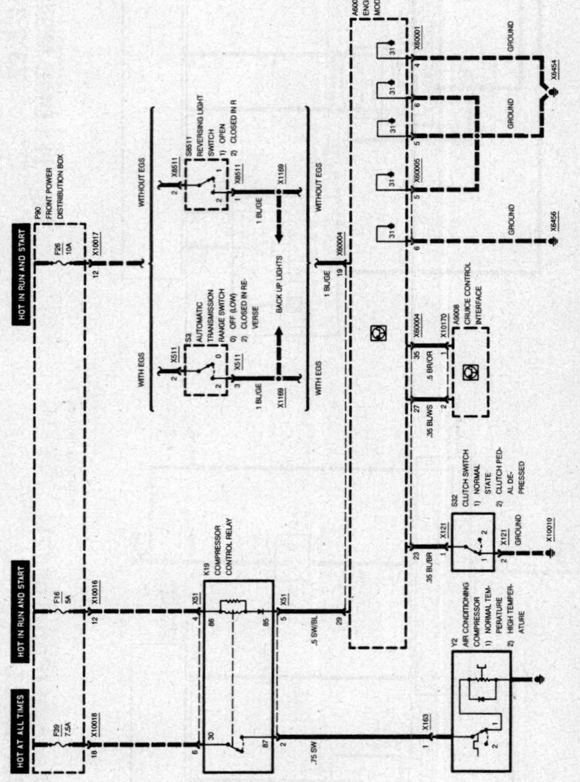

BM01501001051 20X

Fig. 11 DME MS42 wiring diagram (Part 12 of 12). Z3 2.3 &1998–2000 Z3 2.8

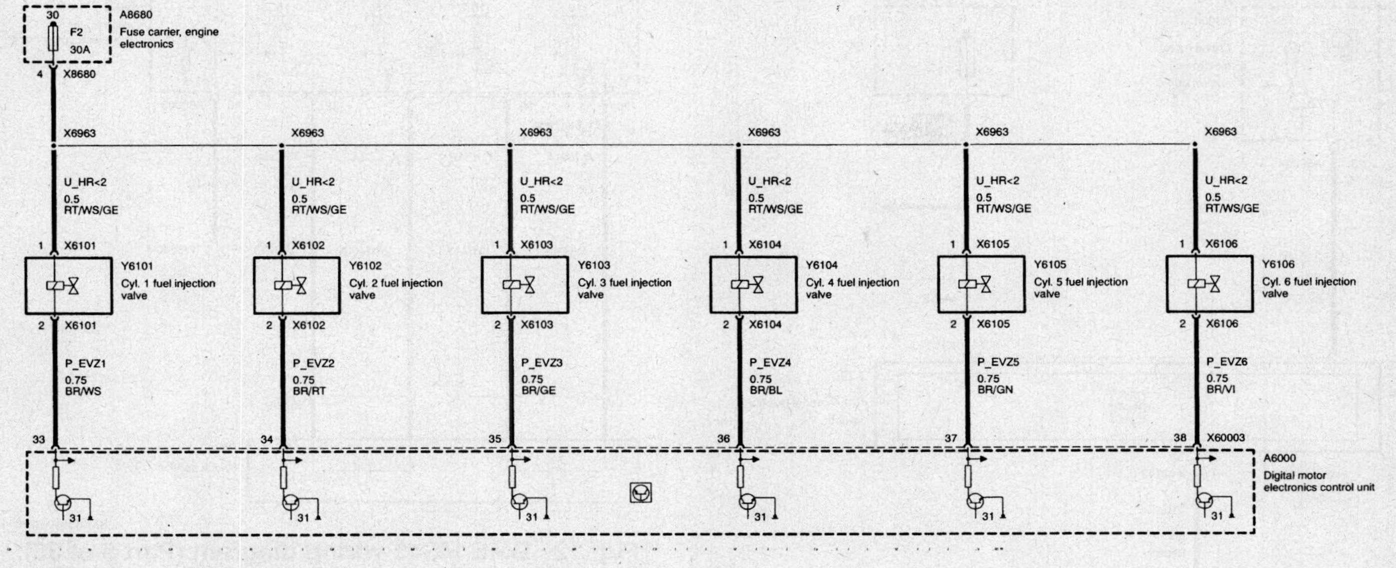

BM0150100111010X

Fig. 12 DME MS42 wiring diagram (Part 1 of 35). 1999 323i Sedan & 328i Sedan & 2000 323Ci/i & 328Ci/i

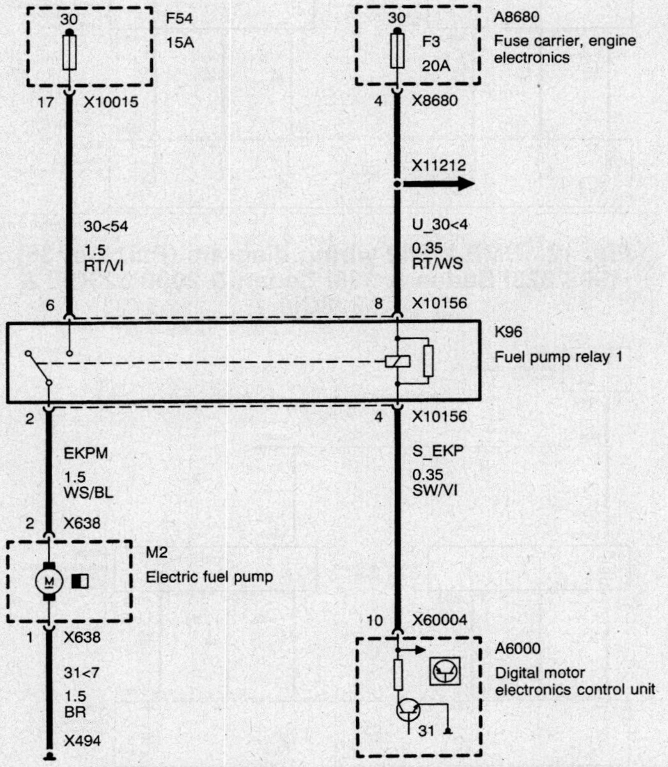

BM0150100111020X

Fig. 12 DME MS42 wiring diagram (Part 2 of 35). 1999 323i Sedan & 328i Sedan & 2000 323Ci/i & 328Ci/i

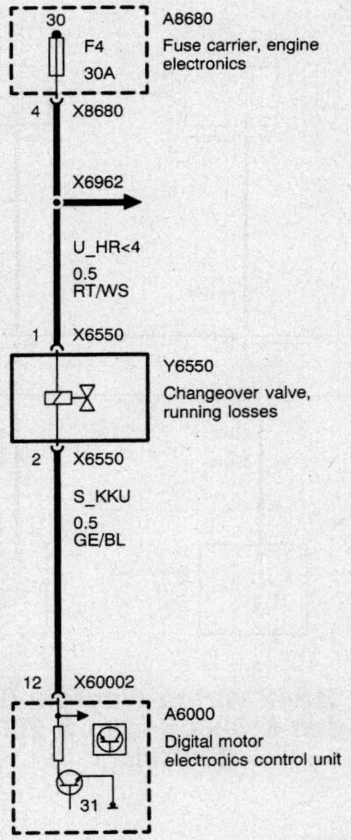

BM0150100111030X

Fig. 12 DME MS42 wiring diagram (Part 3 of 35). 1999 323i Sedan & 328i Sedan & 2000 323Ci/i & 328Ci/i

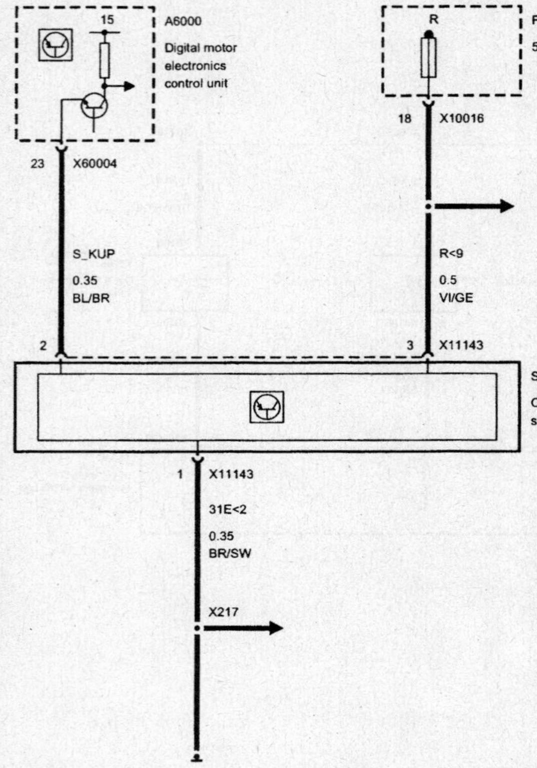

BM0150100111040X

Fig. 12 DME MS42 wiring diagram (Part 4 of 35). 1999 323i Sedan & 328i Sedan & 2000 323Ci/i & 328Ci/i

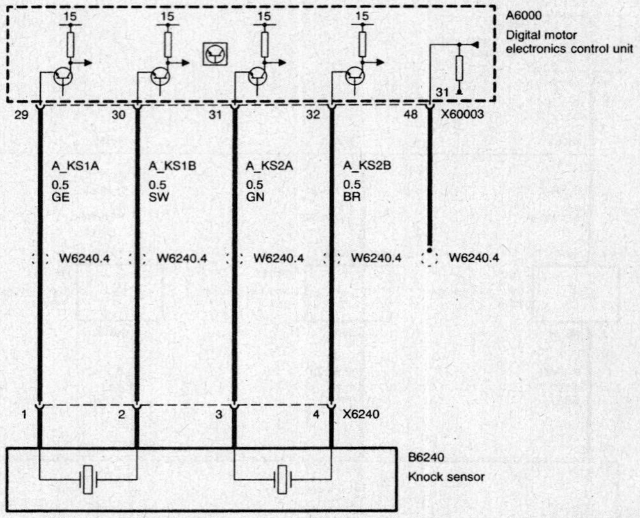

BM0150100111050X

Fig. 12 DME MS42 wiring diagram (Part 5 of 35). 1999 323i Sedan & 328i Sedan & 2000 323Ci/i & 328Ci/i

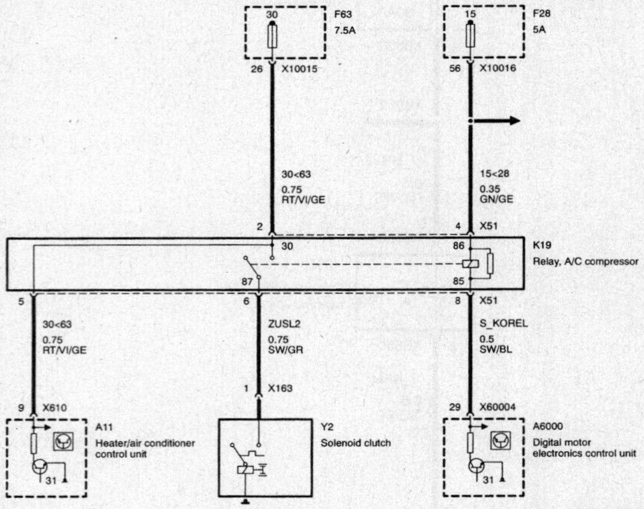

BM0150100111060X

Fig. 12 DME MS42 wiring diagram (Part 6 of 35). 1999 323i Sedan & 328i Sedan & 2000 323Ci/i & 328Ci/i

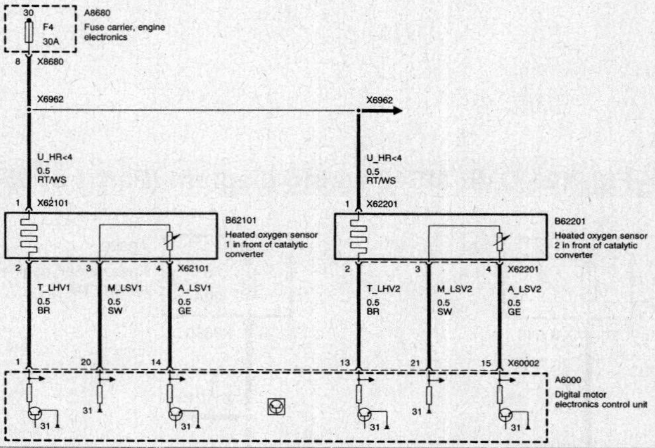

BM0150100111070X

Fig. 12 DME MS42 wiring diagram (Part 7 of 35). 1999 323i Sedan & 328i Sedan & 2000 323Ci/i & 328Ci/i

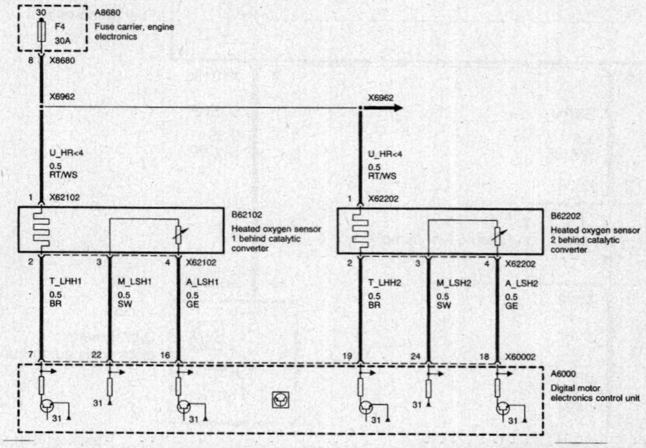

BM0150100111080X

Fig. 12 DME MS42 wiring diagram (Part 8 of 35). 1999 323i Sedan & 328i Sedan & 2000 323Ci/i & 328Ci/i

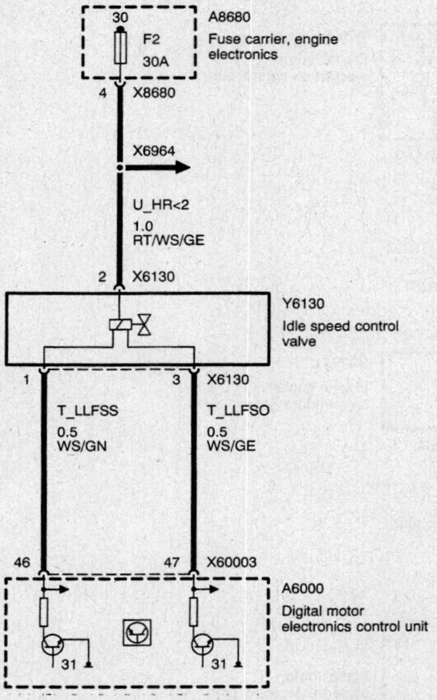

BM0150100111090X

Fig. 12 DME MS42 wiring diagram (Part 9 of 35). 1999 323i Sedan & 328i Sedan & 2000 323Ci/i & 328Ci/i

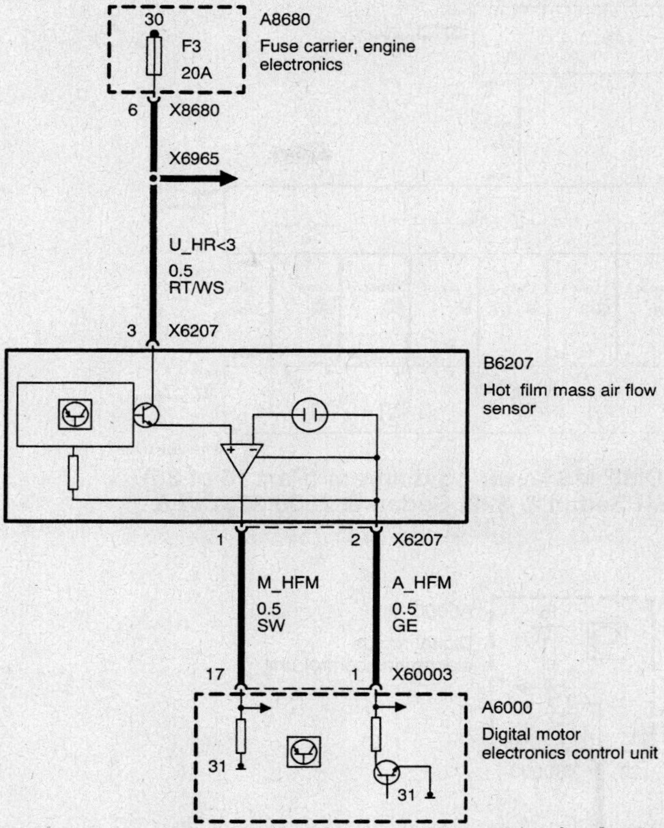

BM0150100111100X

Fig. 12 DME MS42 wiring diagram (Part 10 of 35). 1999 323i Sedan & 328i Sedan & 2000 323Ci/i & 328Ci/i

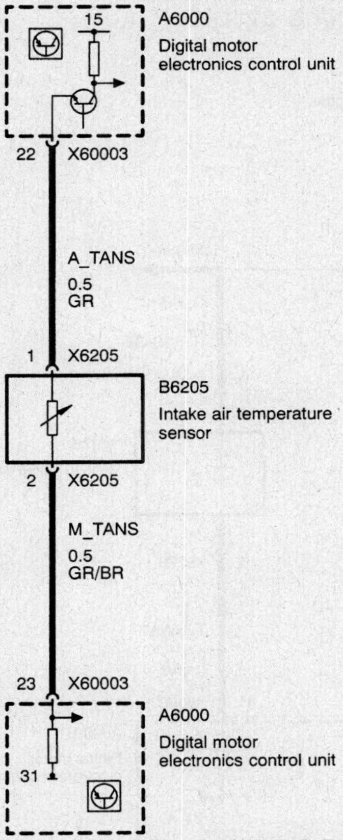

BM0150100111110X

Fig. 12 DME MS42 wiring diagram (Part 11 of 35). 1999 323i Sedan & 328i Sedan & 2000 323Ci/i & 328Ci/i

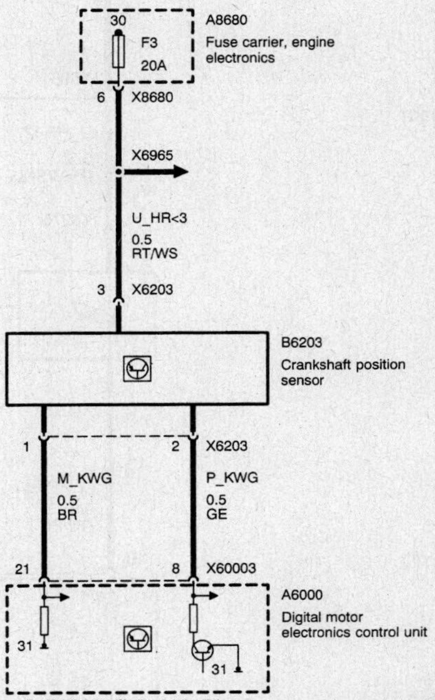

BM0150100111120X

Fig. 12 DME MS42 wiring diagram (Part 12 of 35). 1999 323i Sedan & 328i Sedan & 2000 323Ci/i & 328Ci/i

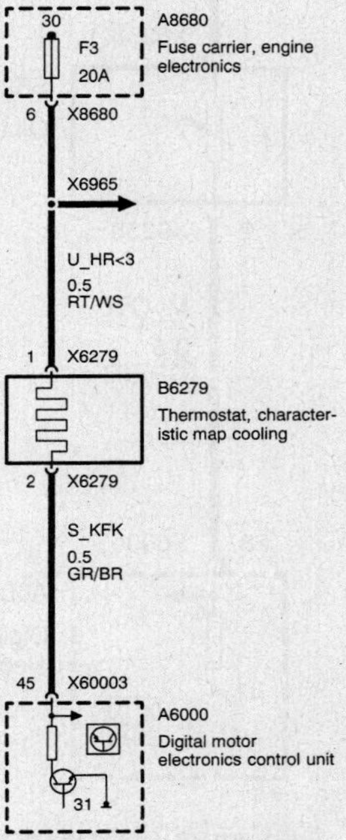

BM0150100111130X

Fig. 12 DME MS42 wiring diagram (Part 13 of 35). 1999 323i Sedan & 328i Sedan & 2000 323Ci/i & 328Ci/i

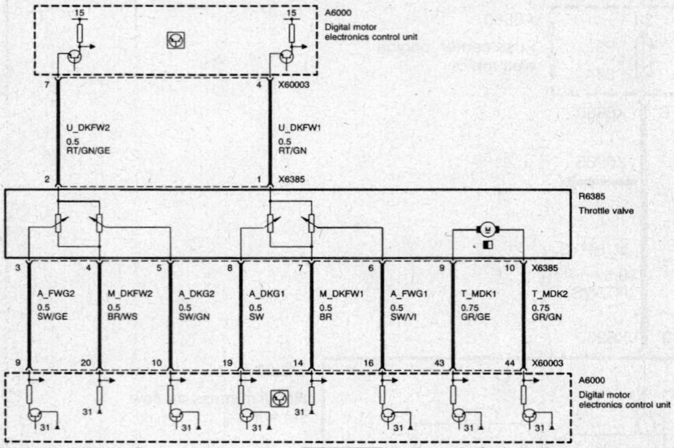

BM0150100111140X

Fig. 12 DME MS42 wiring diagram (Part 14 of 35). 1999 323i Sedan & 328i Sedan & 2000 323Ci/i & 328Ci/i

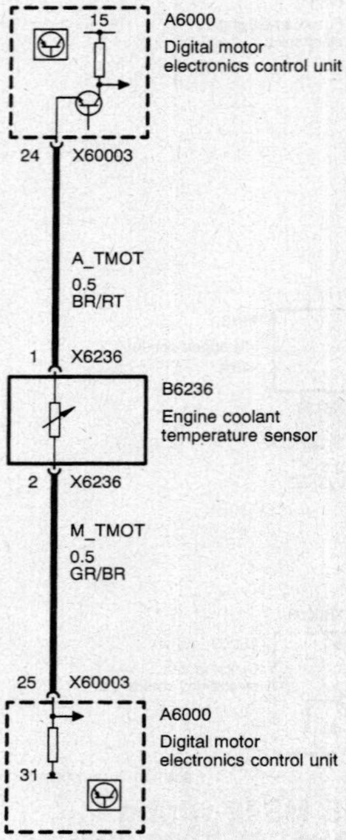

BM0150100111150X

Fig. 12 DME MS42 wiring diagram (Part 15 of 35). 1999 323i Sedan & 328i Sedan & 2000 323Ci/i & 328Ci/i

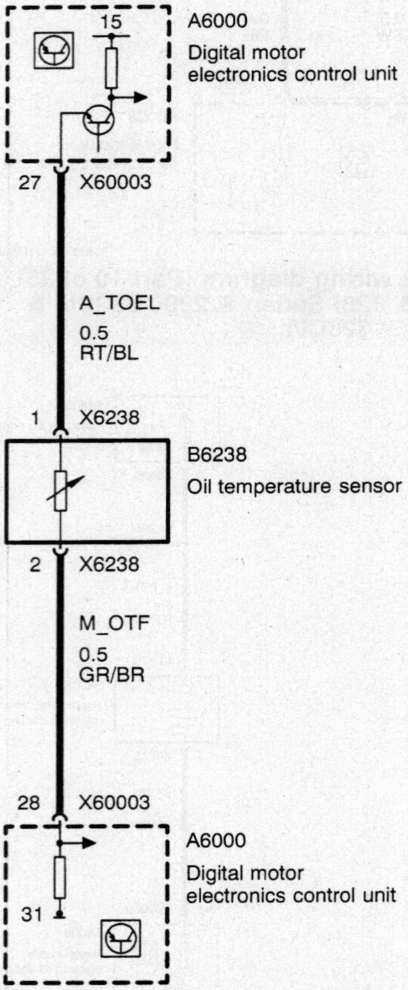

BM0150100111160X

Fig. 12 DME MS42 wiring diagram (Part 16 of 35). 1999 323i Sedan & 328i Sedan & 2000 323Ci/i & 328Ci/i

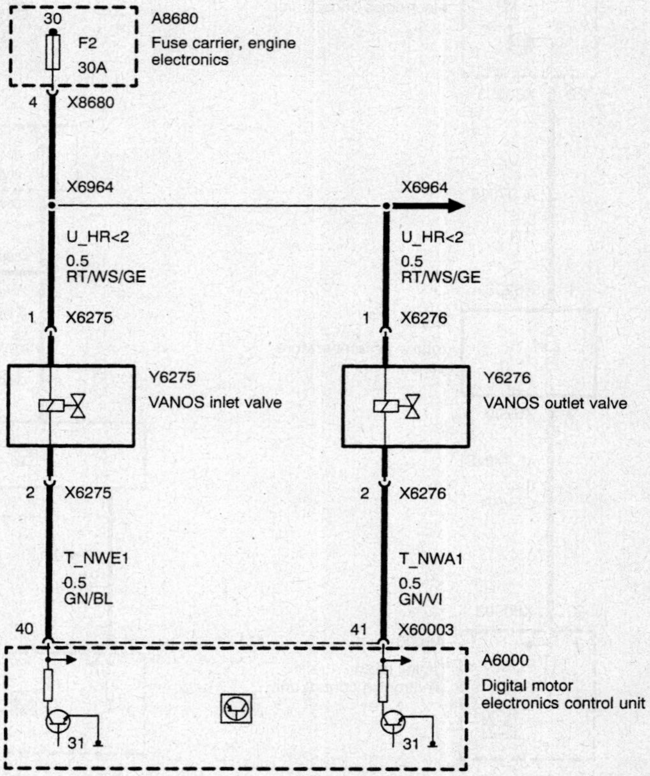

BM0150100111170X

Fig. 12 DME MS42 wiring diagram (Part 17 of 35). 1999 323i Sedan & 328i Sedan & 2000 323Ci/i & 328Ci/i

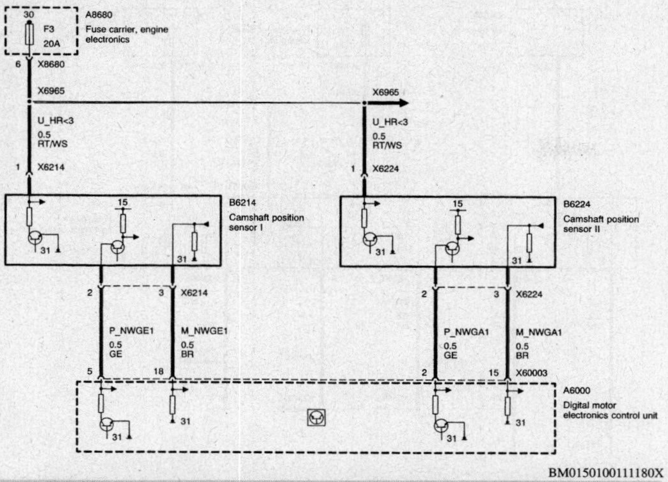

Fig. 12 DME MS42 wiring diagram (Part 18 of 35). 1999 323i Sedan & 328i Sedan & 2000 323Ci/i & 328Ci/i

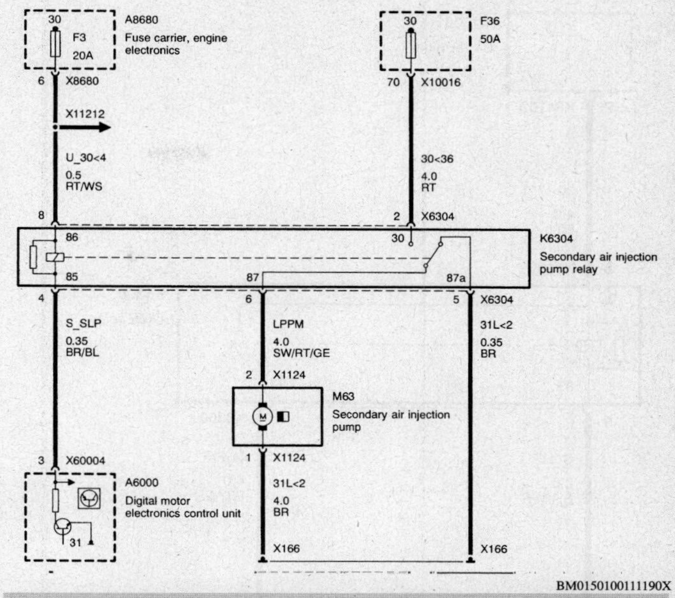

Fig. 12 DME MS42 wiring diagram (Part 19 of 35). 1999 323i Sedan & 328i Sedan & 2000 323Ci/i & 328Ci/i

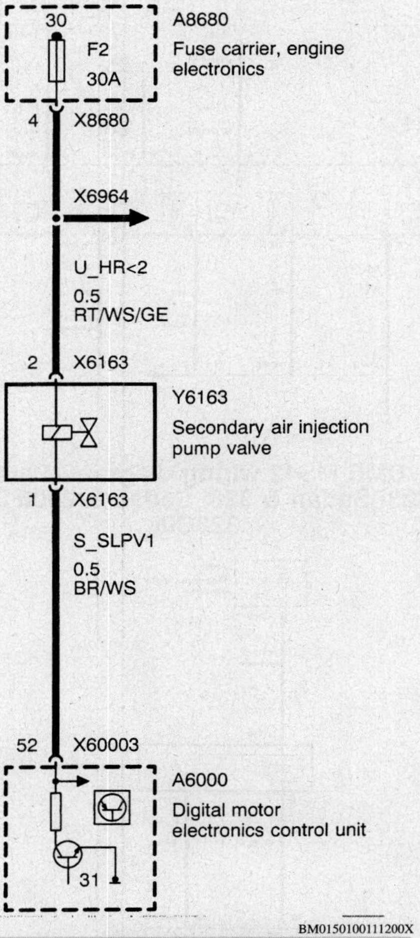

Fig. 12 DME MS42 wiring diagram (Part 20 of 35). 1999 323i Sedan & 328i Sedan & 2000 323Ci/i & 328Ci/i

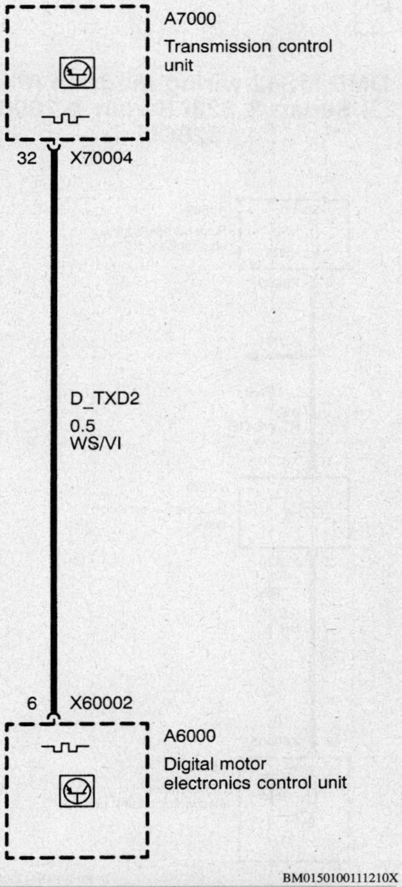

Fig. 12 DME MS42 wiring diagram (Part 21 of 35). 1999 323i Sedan & 328i Sedan & 2000 323Ci/i & 328Ci/i

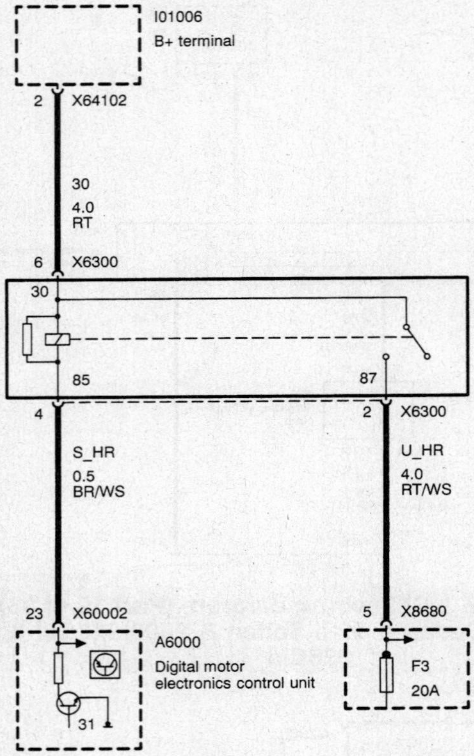

BM0150100111220X

Fig. 12 DME MS42 wiring diagram (Part 22 of 35). 1999 323i Sedan & 328i Sedan & 2000 323Ci/i & 328Ci/i

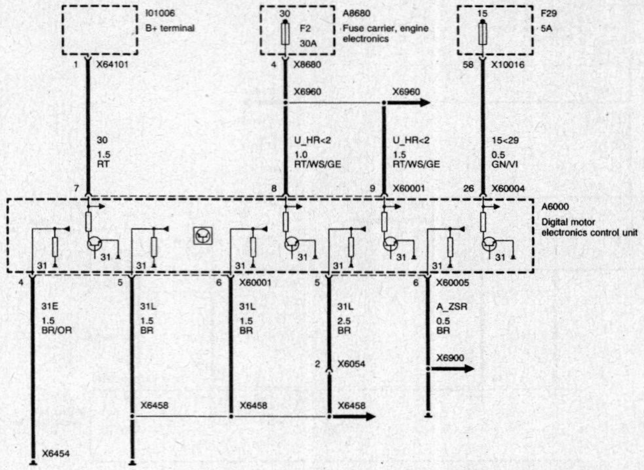

BM0150100111230X

Fig. 12 DME MS42 wiring diagram (Part 23 of 35). 1999 323i Sedan & 328i Sedan & 2000 323Ci/i & 328Ci/i

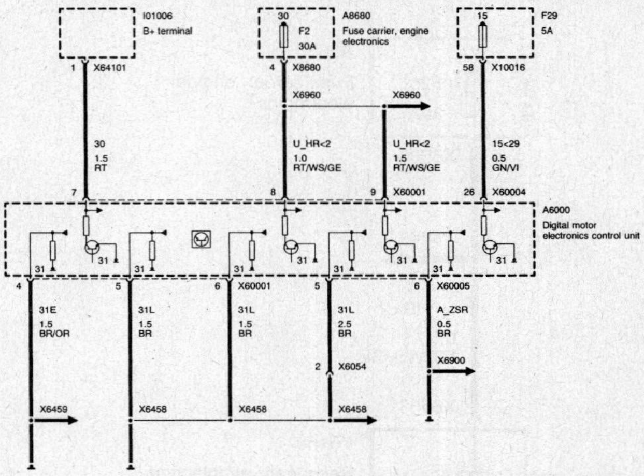

BM0150100111240X

Fig. 12 DME MS42 wiring diagram (Part 24 of 35). 1999 323i Sedan & 328i Sedan & 2000 323Ci/i & 328Ci/i

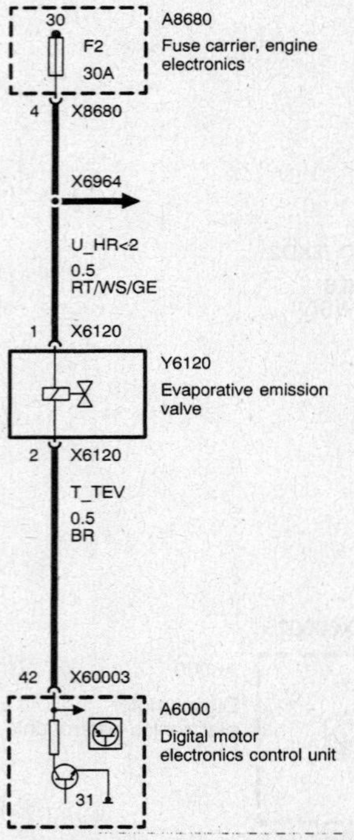

BM0150100111250X

Fig. 12 DME MS42 wiring diagram (Part 25 of 35). 1999 323i Sedan & 328i Sedan & 2000 323Ci/i & 328Ci/i

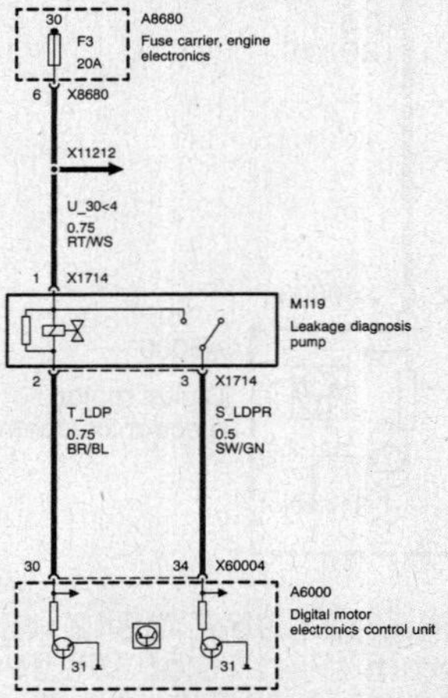

BM0150100111260X

Fig. 12 DME MS42 wiring diagram (Part 26 of 35). 1999 323i Sedan & 328i Sedan & 2000 323Ci/i & 328Ci/i

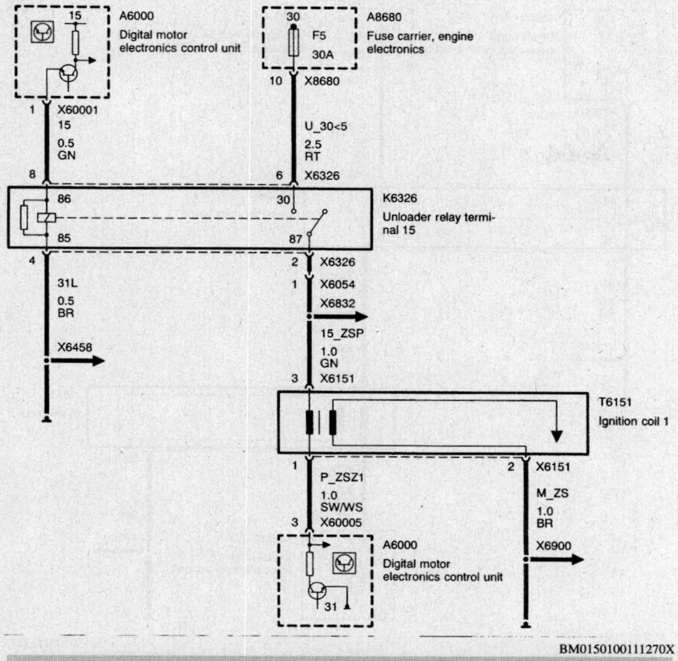

Fig. 12 DME MS42 wiring diagram (Part 27 of 35). 1999 323i Sedan & 328i Sedan & 2000 323Ci/i & 328Ci/i

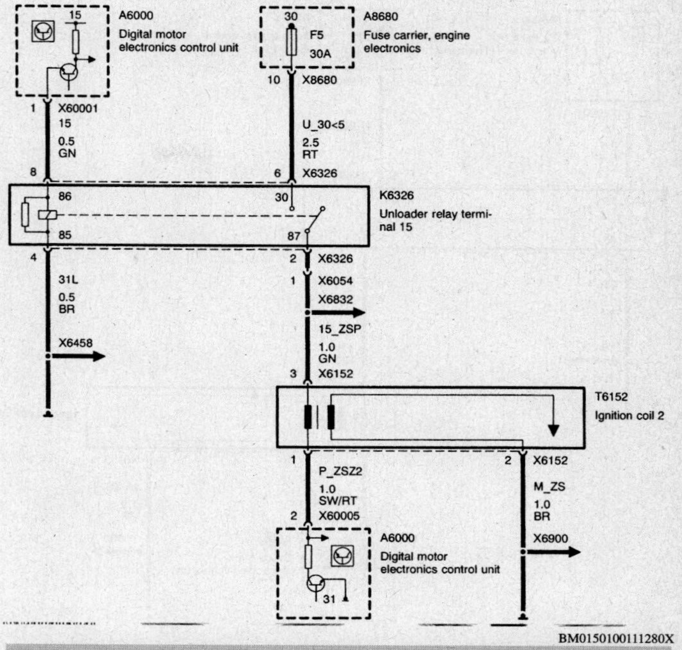

Fig. 12 DME MS42 wiring diagram (Part 28 of 35). 1999 323i Sedan & 328i Sedan & 2000 323Ci/i & 328Ci/i

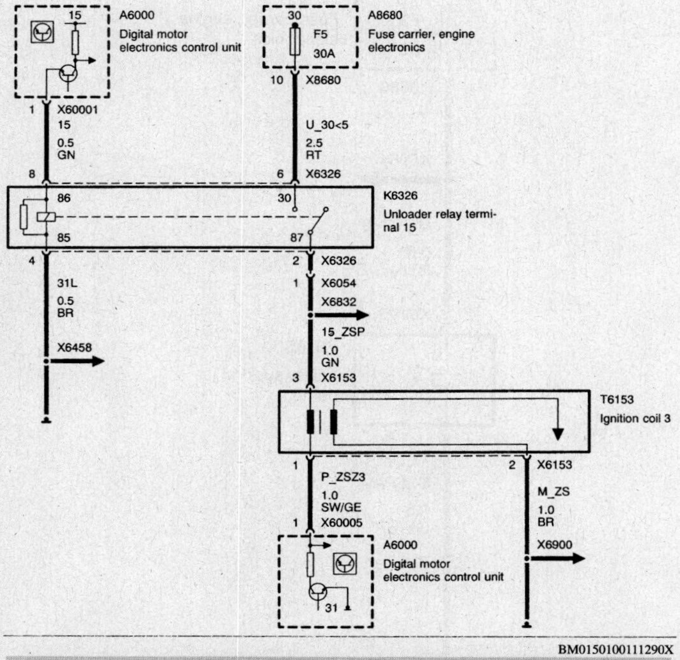

Fig. 12 DME MS42 wiring diagram (Part 29 of 35). 1999 323i Sedan & 328i Sedan & 2000 323Ci/i & 328Ci/i

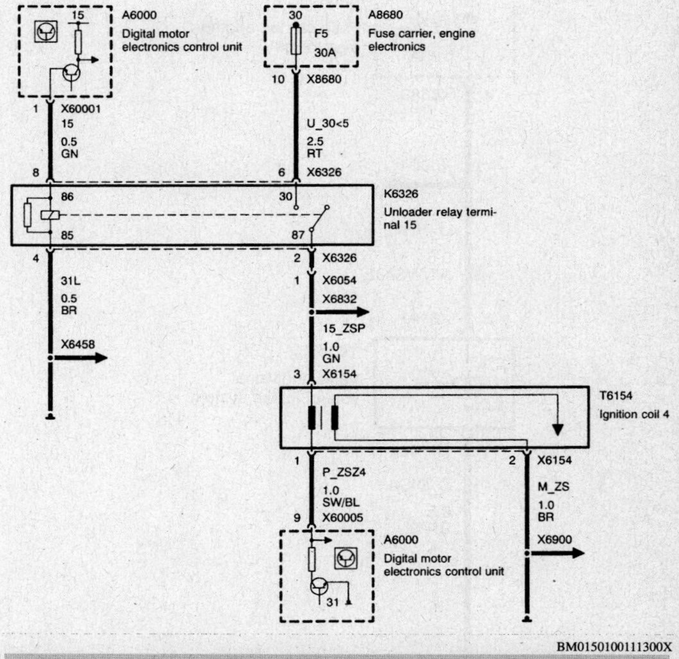

Fig. 12 DME MS42 wiring diagram (Part 30 of 35). 1999 323i Sedan & 328i Sedan & 2000 323Ci/i & 328Ci/i

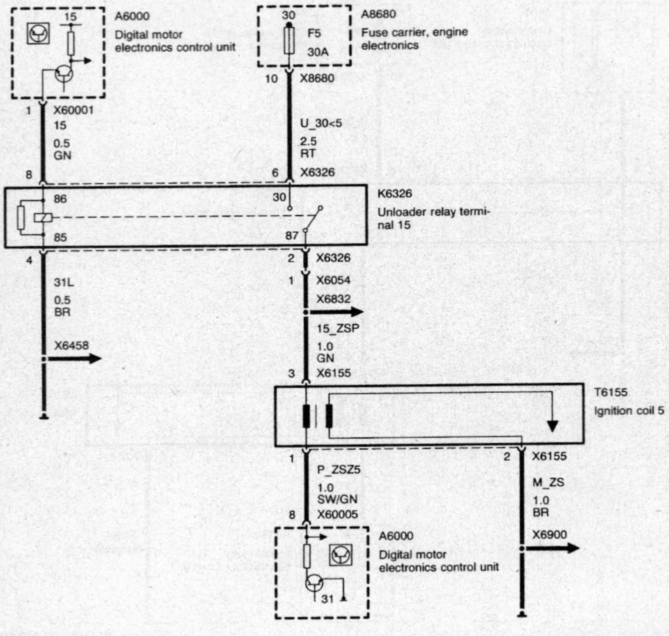

BM0150100111310X

Fig. 12 DME MS42 wiring diagram (Part 31 of 35). 1999 323i Sedan & 328i Sedan & 2000 323Ci/i & 328Ci/i

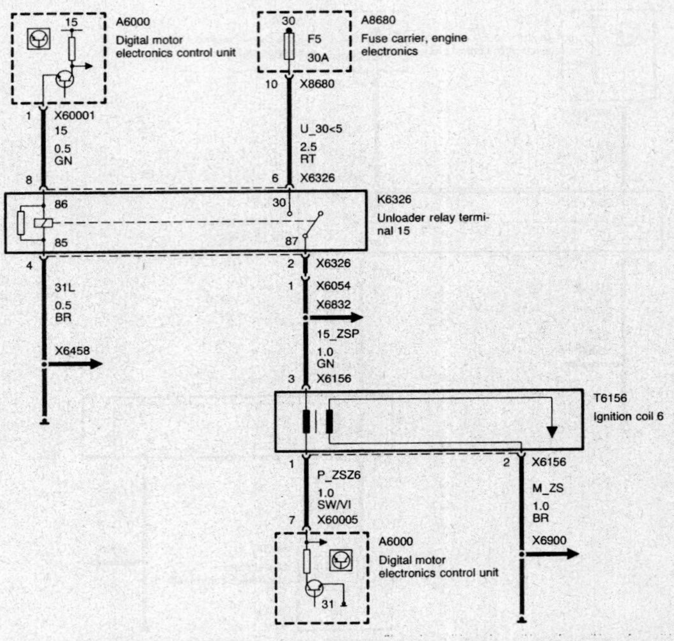

BM0150100111320X

Fig. 12 DME MS42 wiring diagram (Part 32 of 35). 1999 323i Sedan & 328i Sedan & 2000 323Ci/i & 328Ci/i

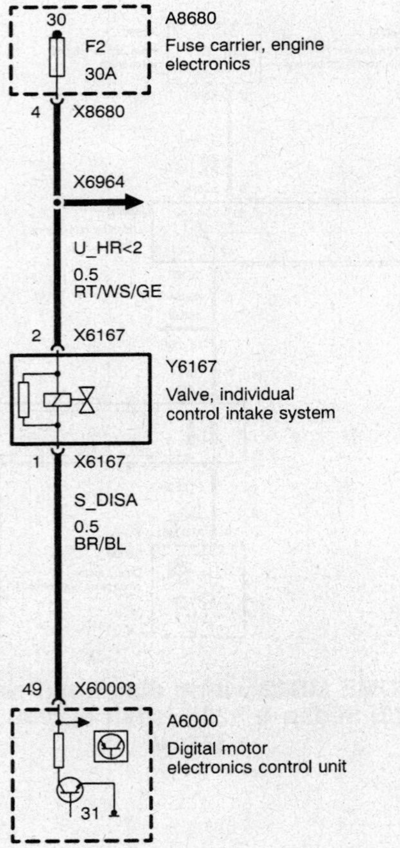

BM0150100111330X

Fig. 12 DME MS42 wiring diagram (Part 33 of 35). 1999 323i Sedan & 328i Sedan & 2000 323Ci/i & 328Ci/i

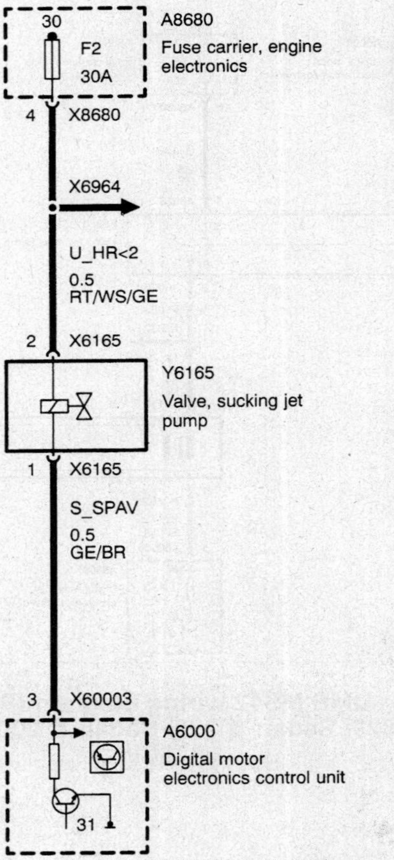

BM0150100111340X

Fig. 12 DME MS42 wiring diagram (Part 34 of 35). 1999 323i Sedan & 328i Sedan & 2000 323Ci/i & 328Ci/i

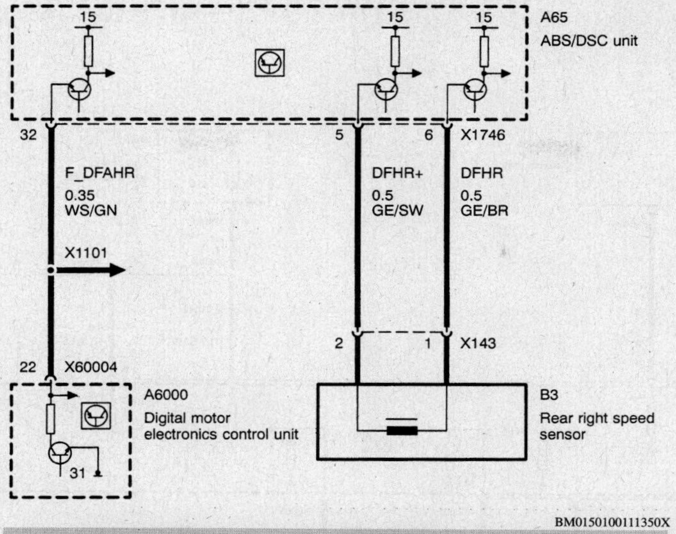

Fig. 12 DME MS42 wiring diagram (Part 35 of 35). 1999 323i Sedan & 328i Sedan & 2000 323Ci/i & 328Ci/i

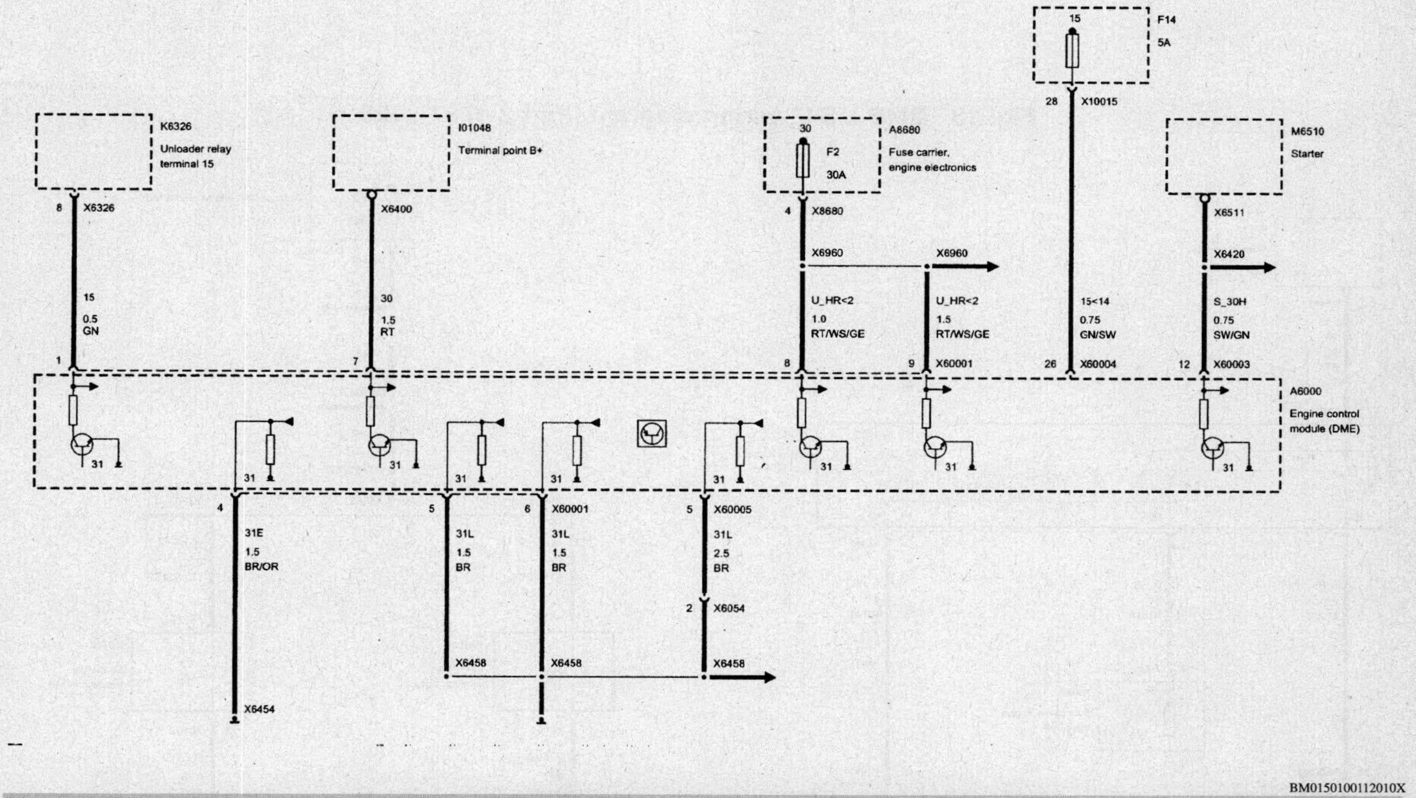

Fig. 13 DME MS42 wiring diagram (Part 1 of 37). 528

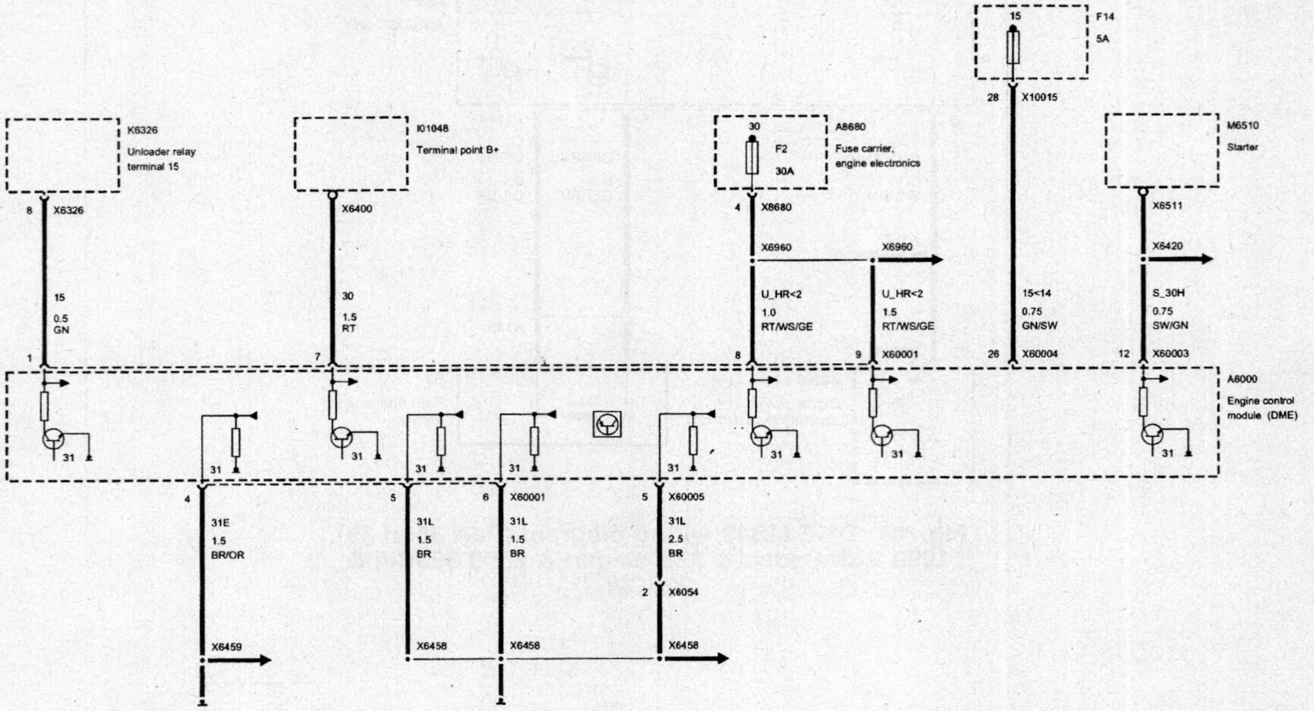

BM0150100112020X

Fig. 13 DME MS42 wiring diagram (Part 2 of 37). 528

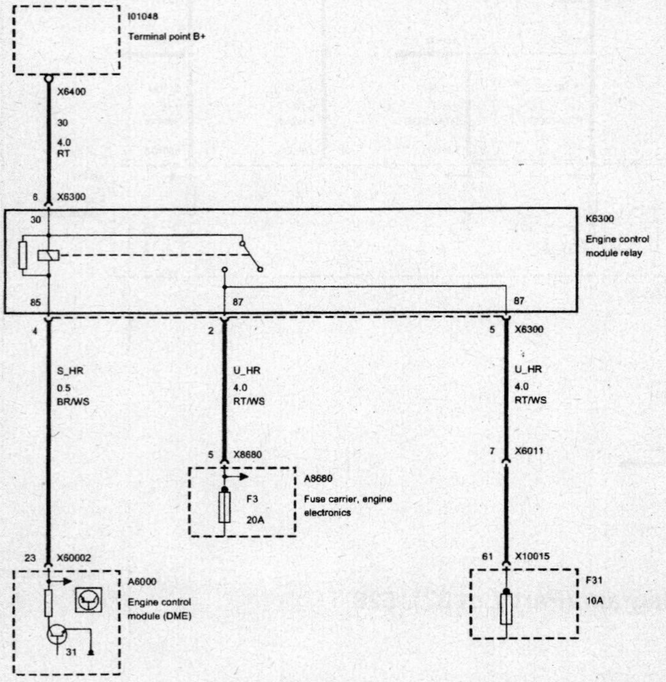

BM0150100112030X

Fig. 13 DME MS42 wiring diagram (Part 3 of 37). 528

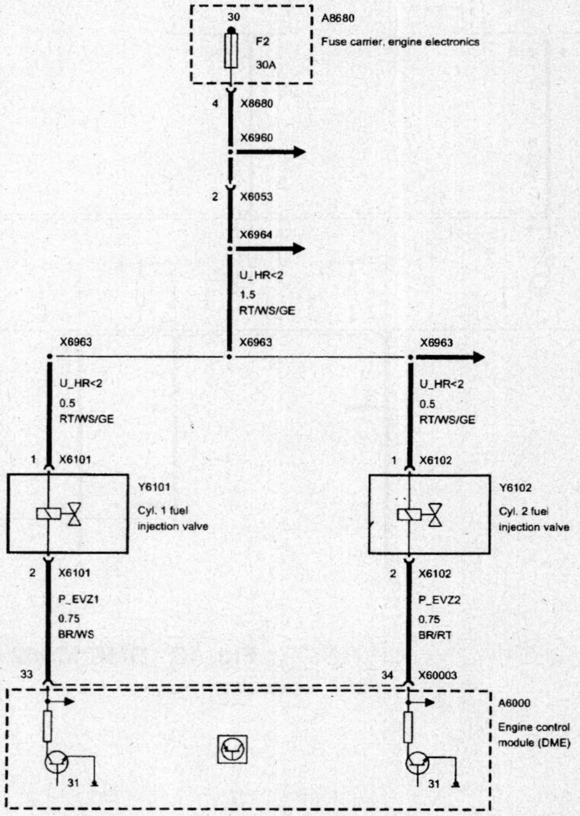

BM0150100112040X

Fig. 13 DME MS42 wiring diagram (Part 4 of 37). 528

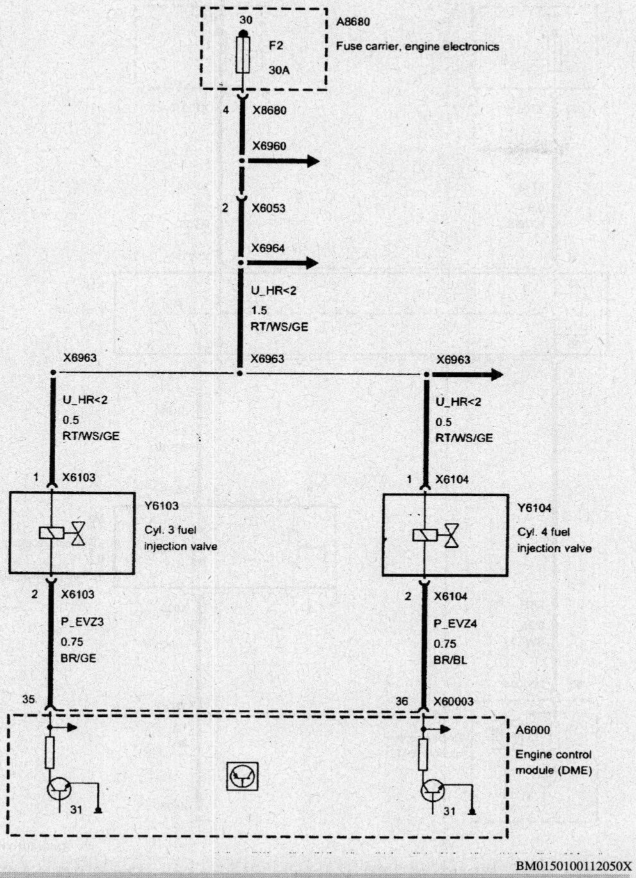

Fig. 13 DME MS42 wiring diagram (Part 5 of 37).
528

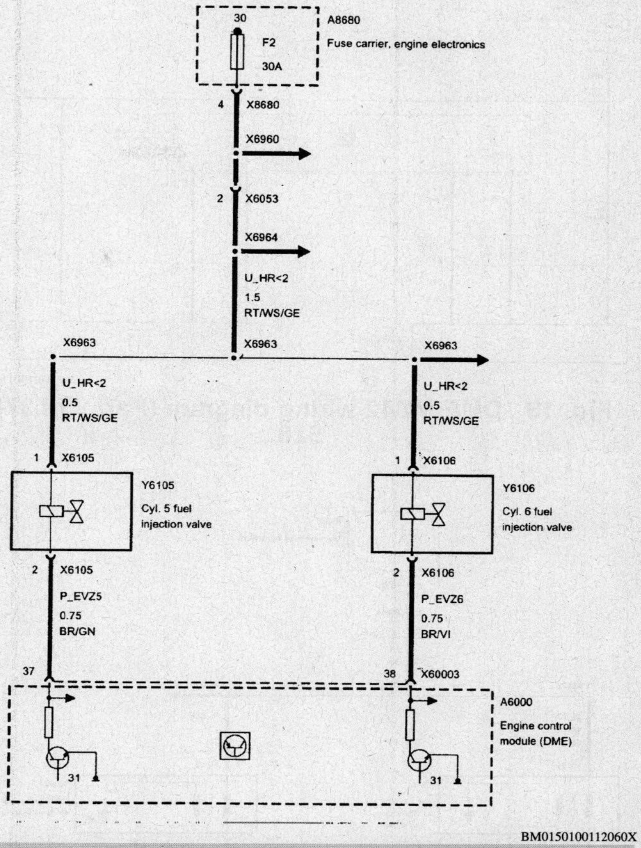

Fig. 13 DME MS42 wiring diagram (Part 6 of 37).
528

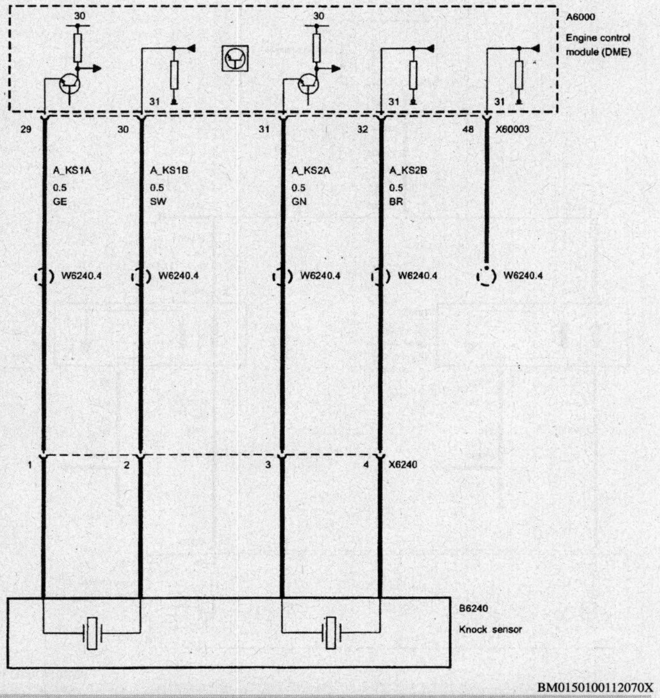

Fig. 13 DME MS42 wiring diagram (Part 7 of 37).
528

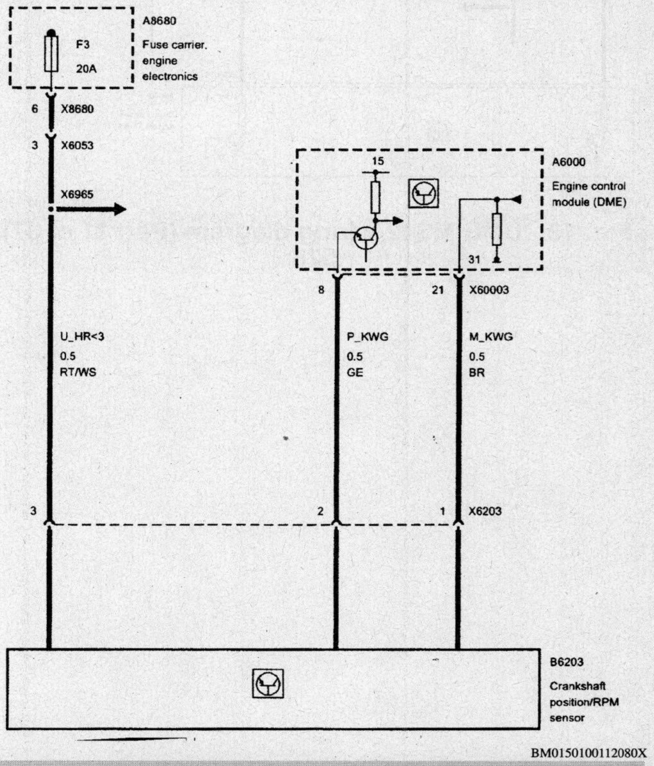

Fig. 13 DME MS42 wiring diagram (Part 8 of 37).
528

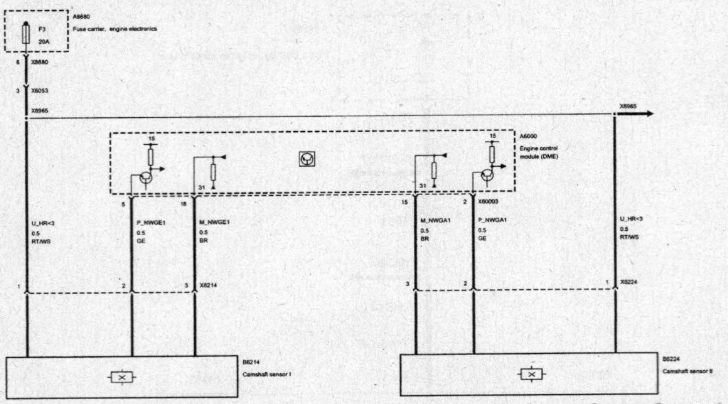

BM0150100112090X

Fig. 13 DME MS42 wiring diagram (Part 9 of 37). 528

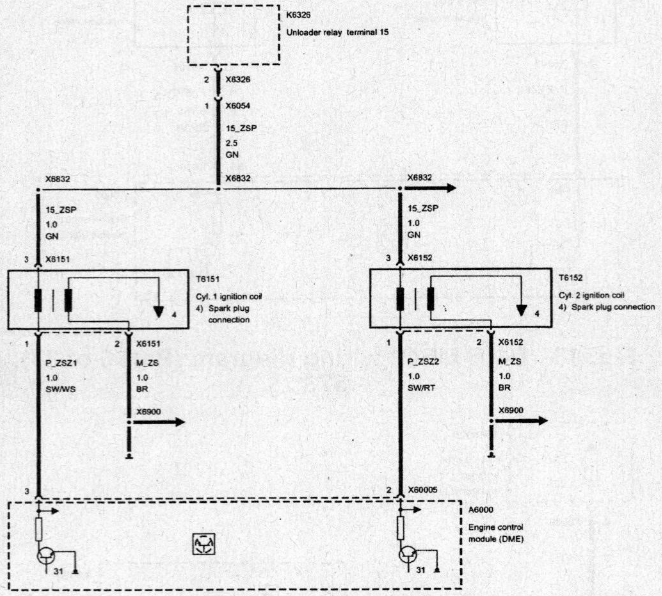

BM0150100113020X

Fig. 13 DME MS42 wiring diagram (Part 11 of 37). 528

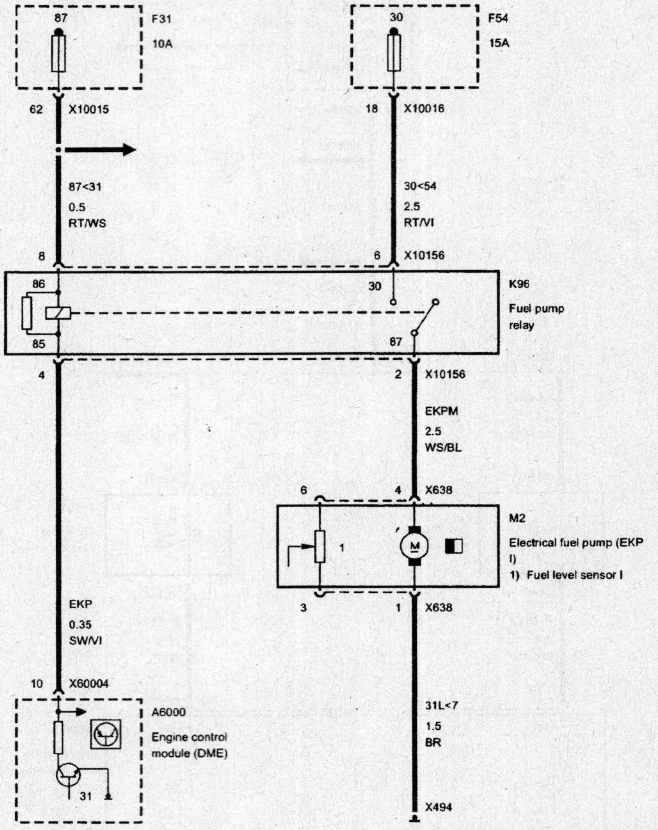

BM0150100113010X

Fig. 13 DME MS42 wiring diagram (Part 10 of 37). 528

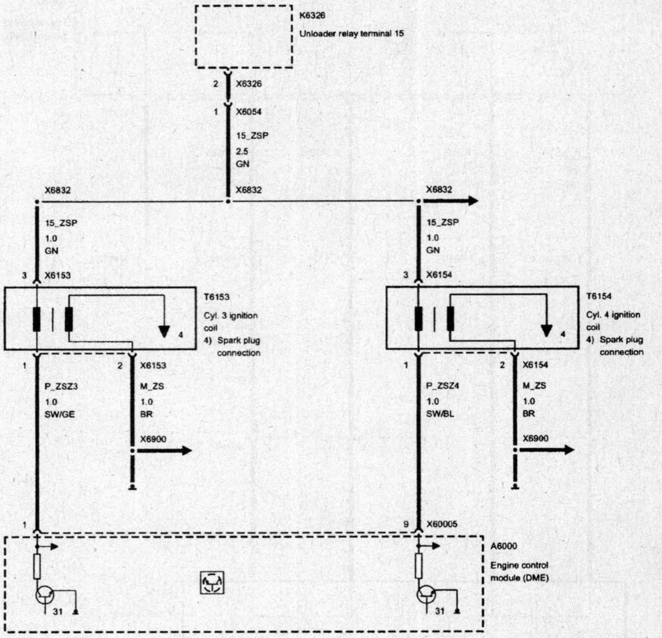

BM0150100113030X

Fig. 13 DME MS42 wiring diagram (Part 12 of 37). 528

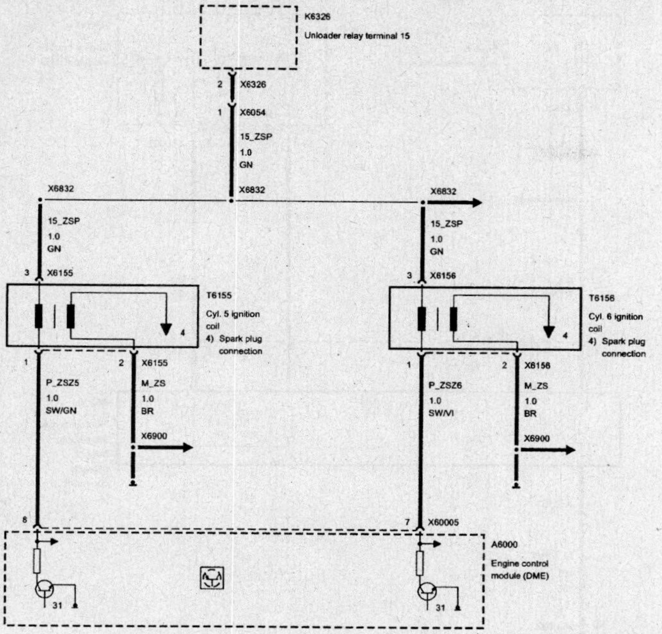

BM0150100113040X

Fig. 13 DME MS42 wiring diagram (Part 13 of 37). 528

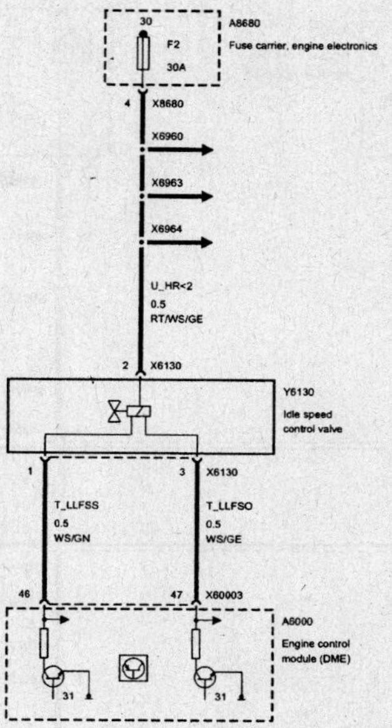

BM0150100113050X

Fig. 13 DME MS42 wiring diagram (Part 14 of 37). 528

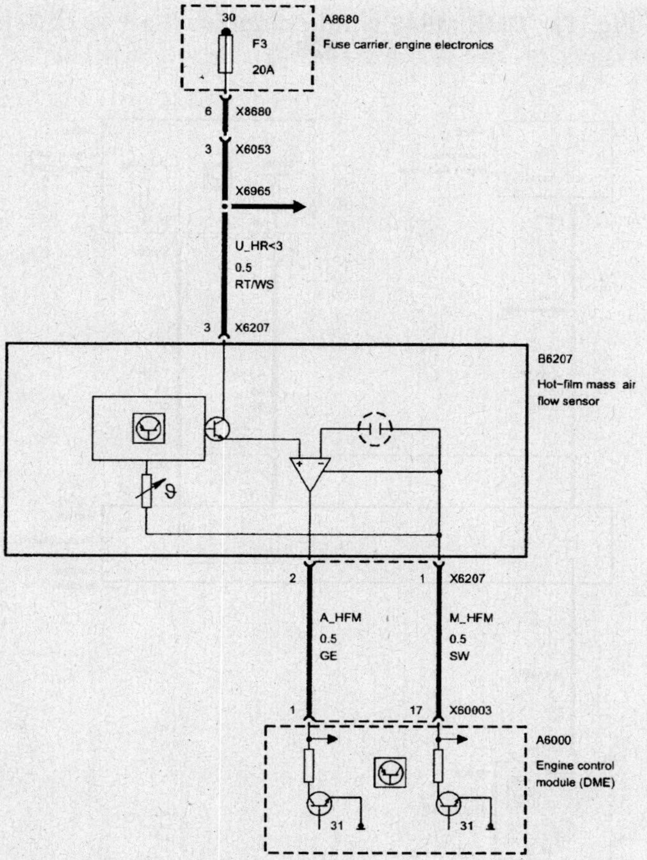

BM0150100113060X

Fig. 13 DME MS42 wiring diagram (Part 15 of 37). 528

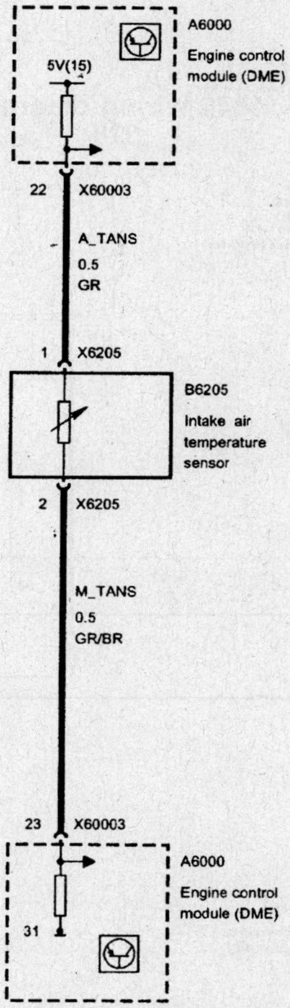

BM0150100113070X

Fig. 13 DME MS42 wiring diagram (Part 16 of 37). 528

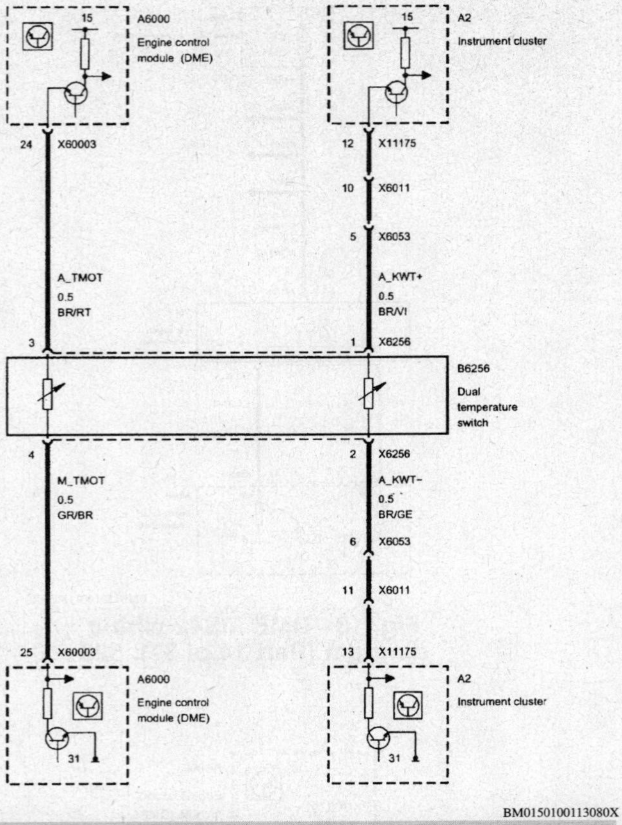

Fig. 13 DME MS42 wiring diagram (Part 17 of 37). 528

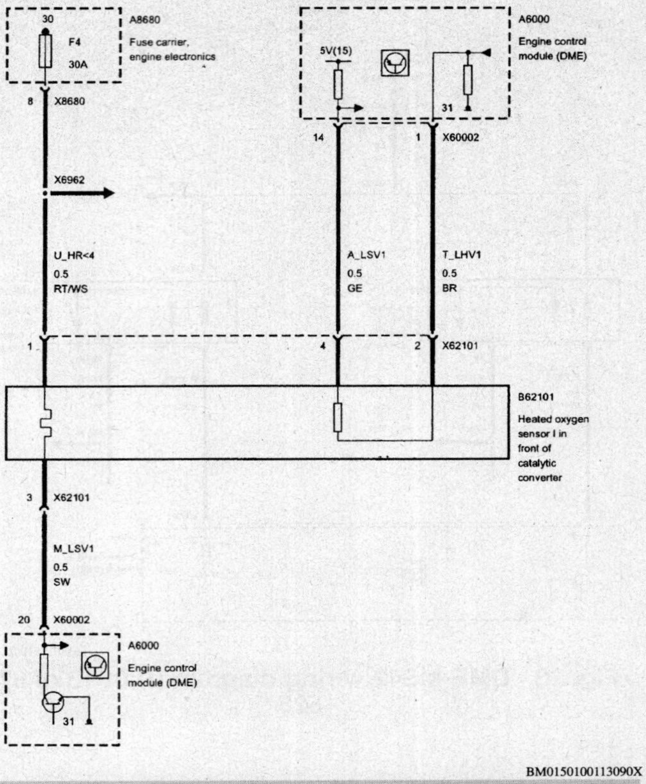

Fig. 13 DME MS42 wiring diagram (Part 18 of 37). 528

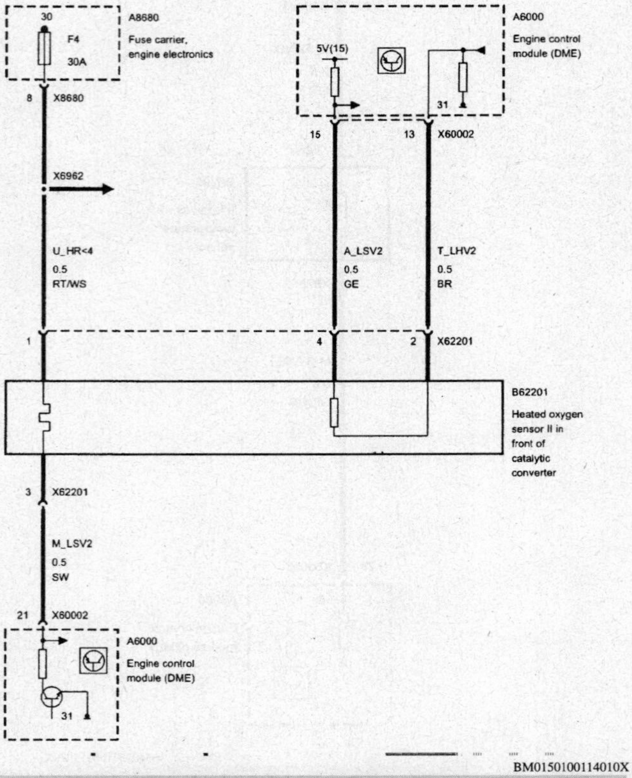

Fig. 13 DME MS42 wiring diagram (Part 19 of 37). 528

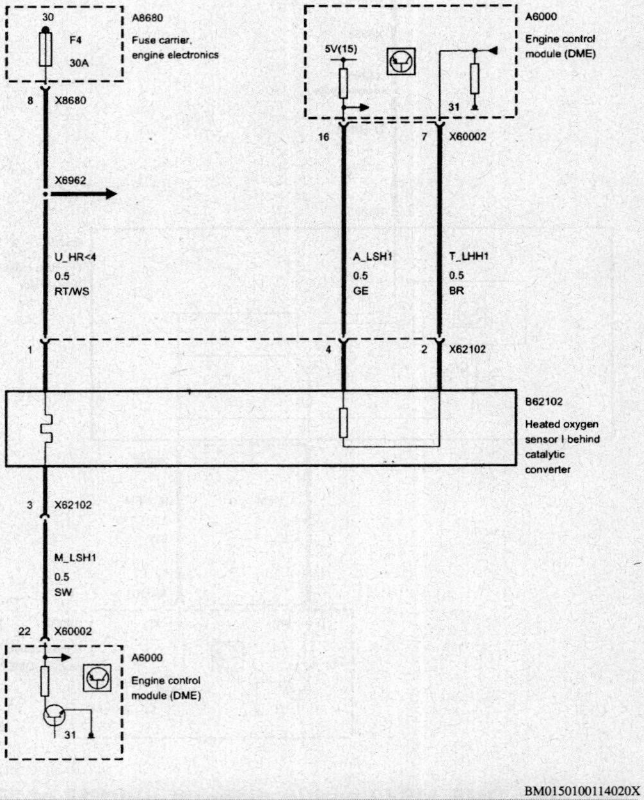

Fig. 13 DME MS42 wiring diagram (Part 20 of 37). 528

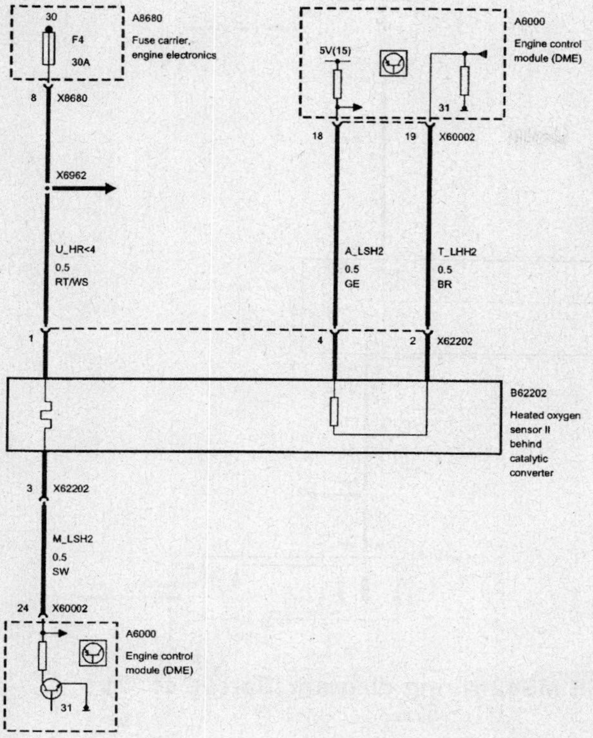

BM0150100114030X

Fig. 13 DME MS42 wiring diagram (Part 21 of 37). 528

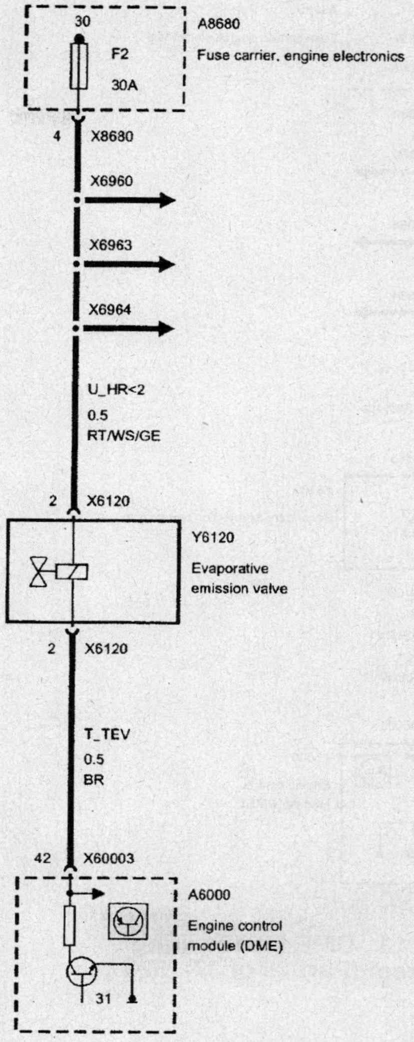

BM0150100114040X

Fig. 13 DME MS42 wiring diagram (Part 22 of 37). 528

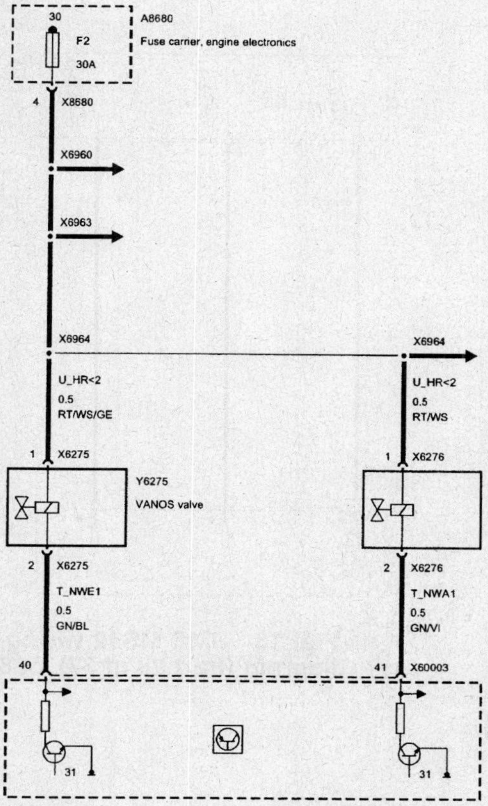

BM0150100114050X

Fig. 13 DME MS42 wiring diagram (Part 23 of 37). 528

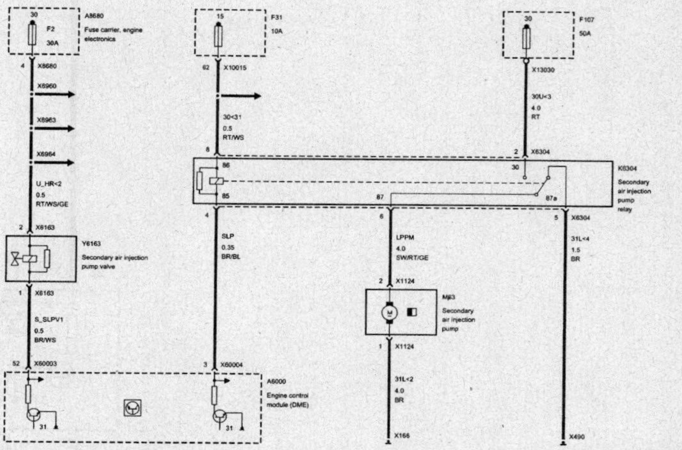

BM0150100114060X

Fig. 13 DME MS42 wiring diagram (Part 24 of 37). 528

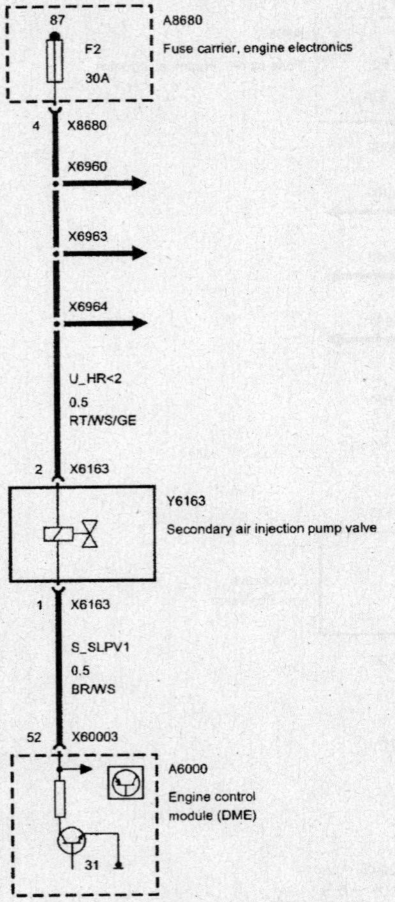

BM0150100114070X

Fig. 13 DME MS42 wiring diagram (Part 25 of 37). 528

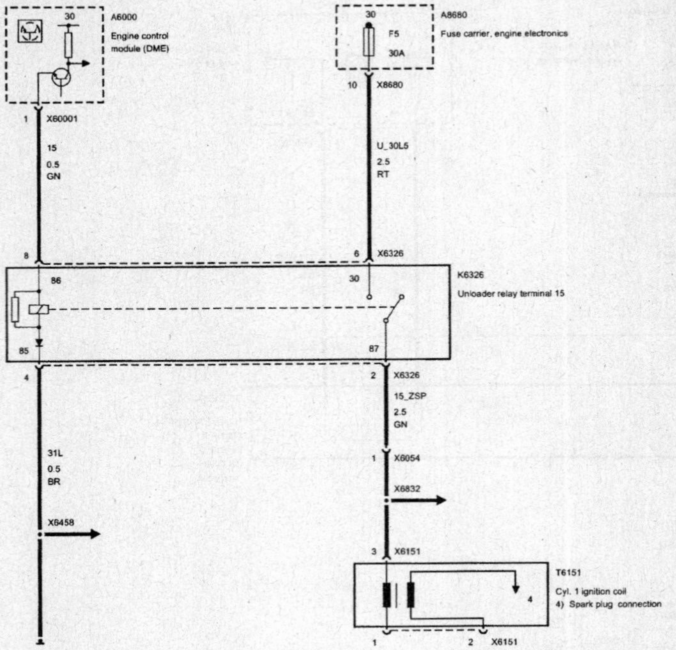

BM0150100114080X

Fig. 13 DME MS42 wiring diagram (Part 26 of 37). 528

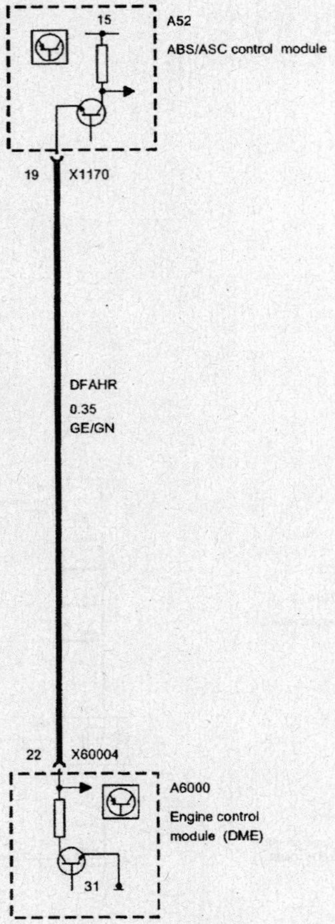

BM0150100114090X

Fig. 13 DME MS42 wiring diagram (Part 27 of 37). 528

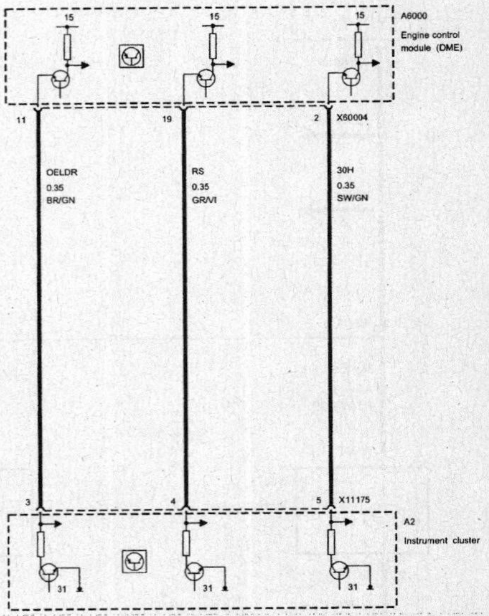

BM0150100115010X

Fig. 13 DME MS42 wiring diagram (Part 28 of 37). 528

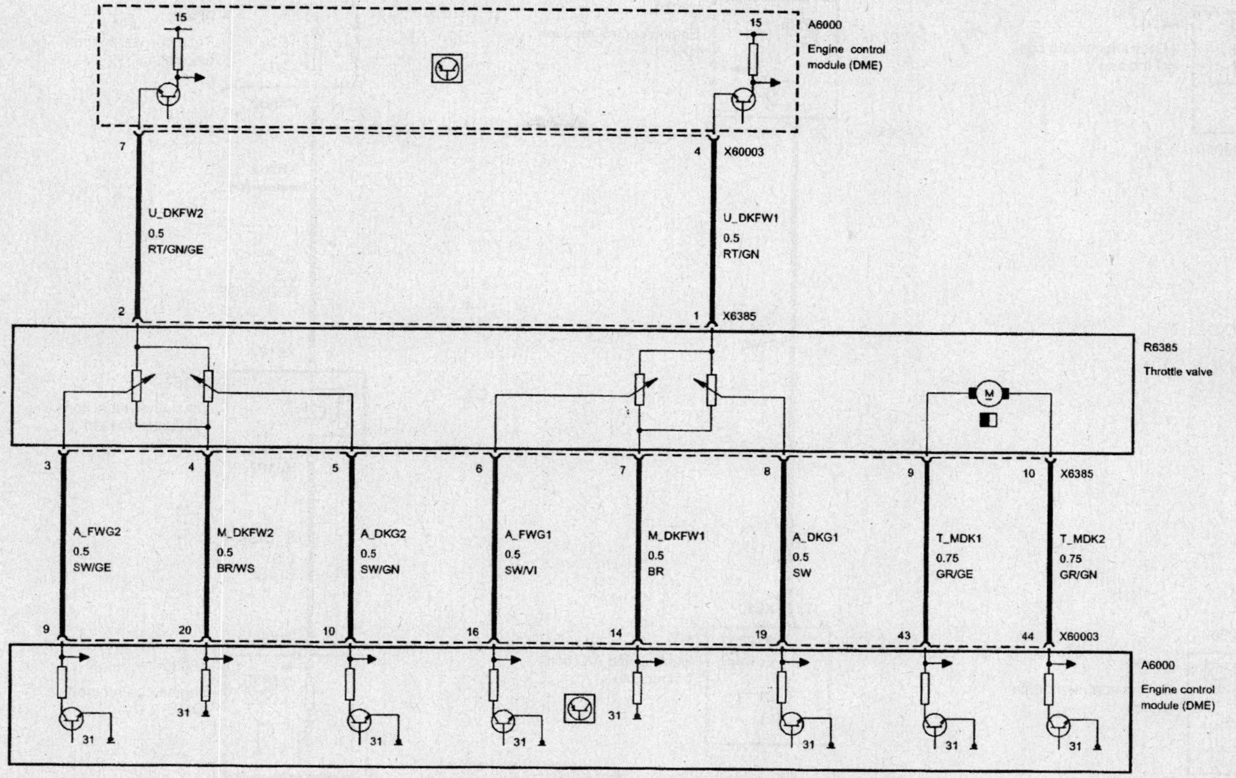

BM0150100115020X

Fig. 13 DME MS42 wiring diagram (Part 29 of 37). 528

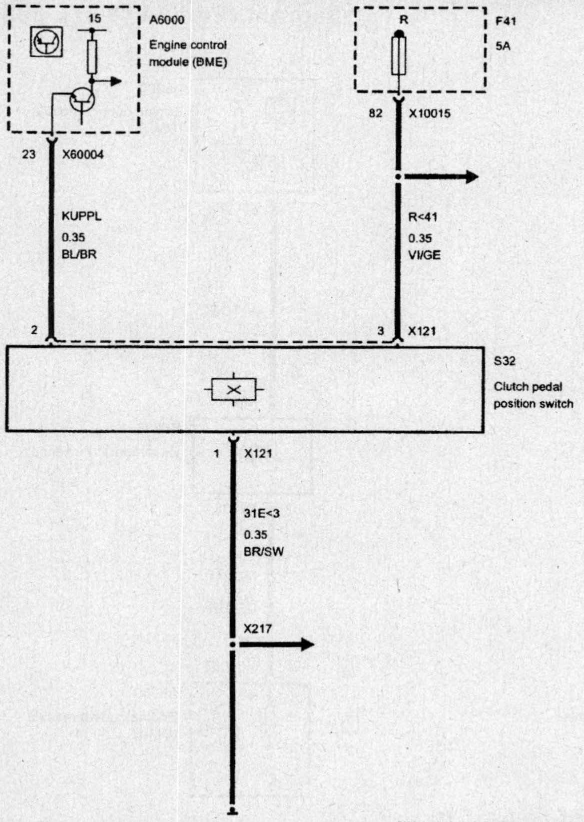

BM0150100115030X

Fig. 13 DME MS42 wiring diagram (Part 30 of 37). 528

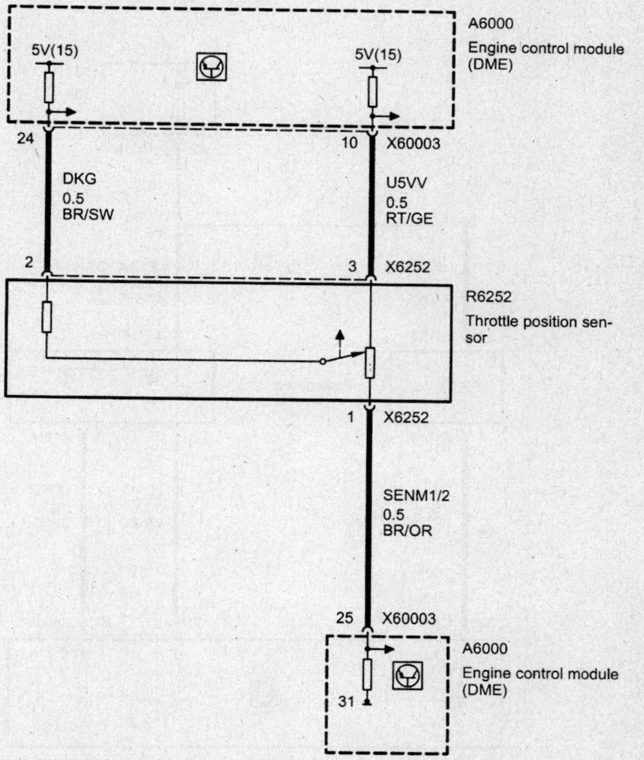

BM0150100115040X

Fig. 13 DME MS42 wiring diagram (Part 31 of 37). 528

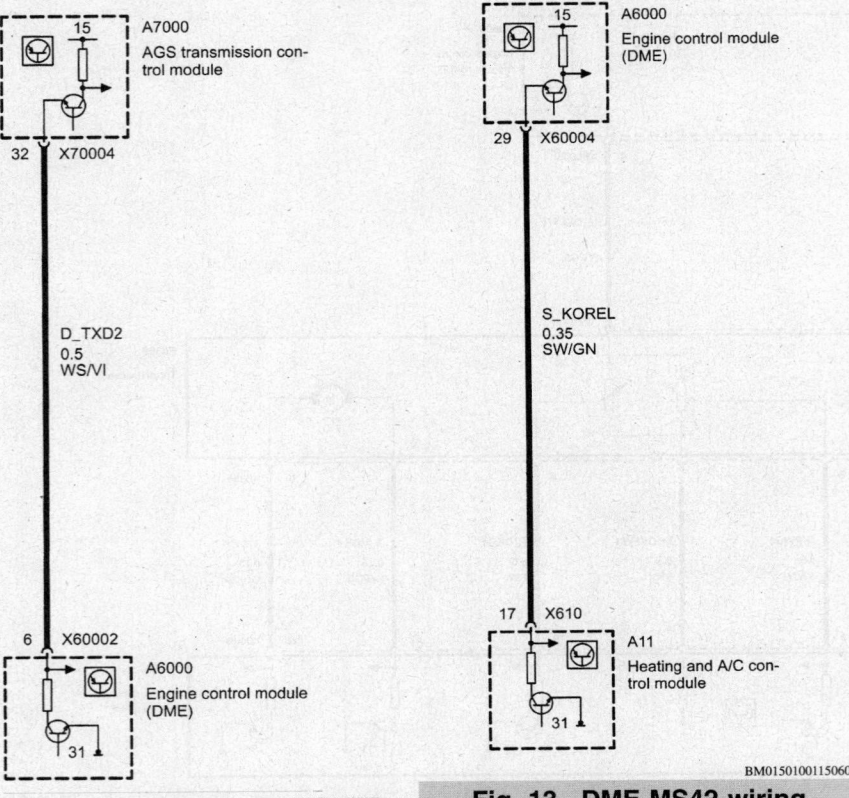

Fig. 13 DME MS42 wiring diagram (Part 32 of 37). 528

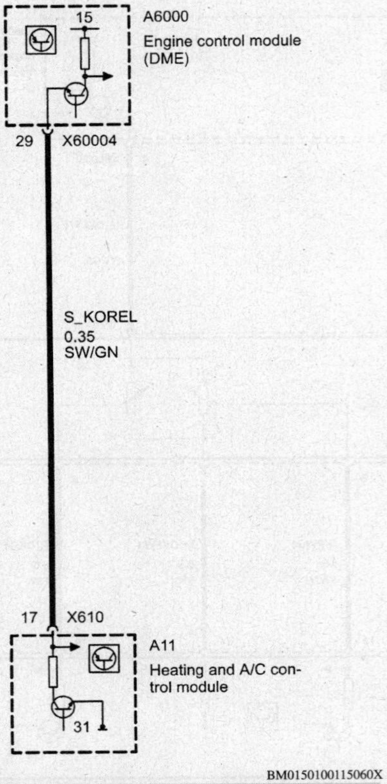

Fig. 13 DME MS42 wiring diagram (Part 33 of 37). 528

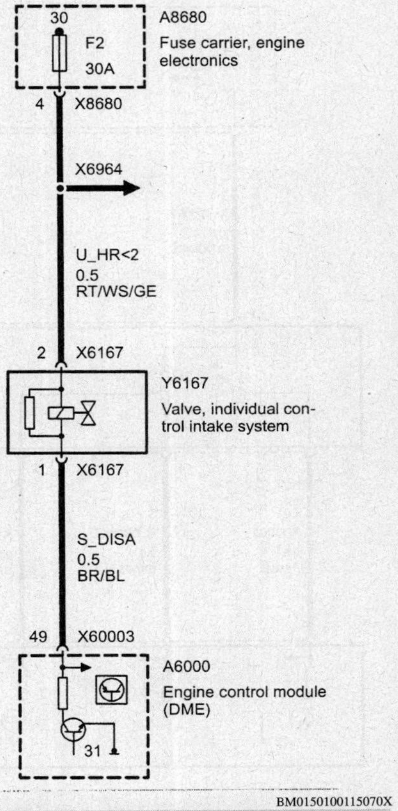

Fig. 13 DME MS42 wiring diagram (Part 34 of 37). 528

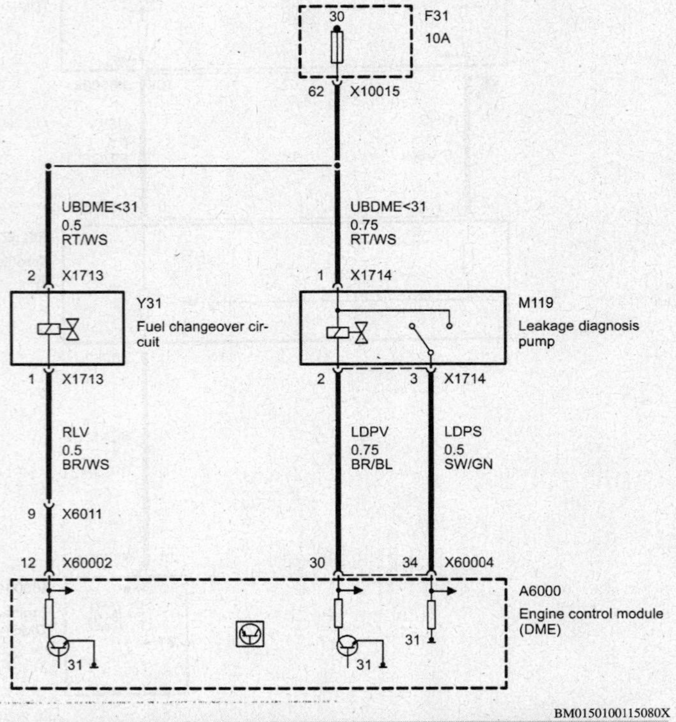

Fig. 13 DME MS42 wiring diagram (Part 35 of 37). 528

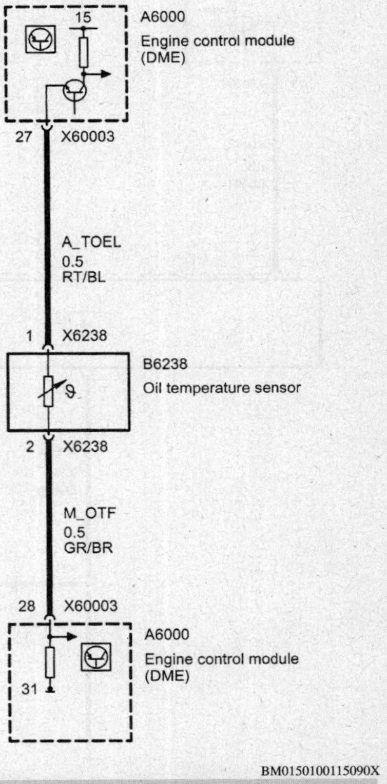

Fig. 13 DME MS42 wiring diagram (Part 36 of 37). 528

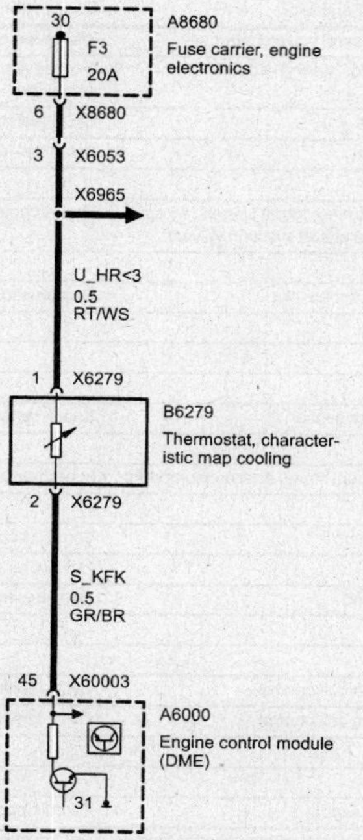

BM0150100116010X

Fig. 13 DME MS42 wiring diagram (Part 37 of 37). 528

Pin	Type	Description/Function	Connection
29	A	Idle speed control valve control	Idle speed control valve
30	A	Oxygen sensor heating (–)	Oxygen sensor (in front of catalytic converter)
31	A	Activate valve	Cyl. 3 fuel injection valve
32	A	Activate valve	Cyl. 2 fuel injection valve
33		Not used	
34	M	Ground, remaning output stages (except for ignition and fuel injection valves)	Ground point
35		Not used	
36	A	A/C compressor cut-out	Compressor control relay
37		Not used	
38		Not used	
39		Not used	
40	E	Cyl. 3-4 knock sensor	Knock sensor
41		Not used	
42	E	TI-measurement signal (fuel consumption)	Instrument cluster
43		Not used	
44	E	Throttle position	Throttle position sensor
45	M	Ground	Hot film air mass meter
46	M	Sensor ground	Oxygen sensors
47		Not used	
48		Not used	
49	A	Cyl. 1 ignition coil control	Cyl. 1 ignition coil
50	A	Cyl. 2 ignition coil control	Cyl. 2 ignition coil
51		Not used	
52		Not used	
53	A	Component supply (+)	Throttle position sensor/Fuel tank pressure sensor
54	E	Battery voltage from engine control module relay	Engine control module relay, terminal 87
55	M	Ground, ignition	Ground point
56	E	Ignition switch, terminal 15	Ignition switch, terminal 15
57	A	Activate auxiliary fan	Normal speed relay

E = Input, A = Output, M = Ground

BM0150100094020X

Fig. 14 DME M5.2 88-pin connector X6000 pin identification (Part 2 of 3). Z3 1.9 & 318ti

Pin	Type	Description/Function	Connection
1	A	Oxygen sensor heating (–)	Oxygen sensor (behind catalytic converter)
2	A	Activate valve	Idle speed control valve
3	A	Activate valve	Cyl. 1 fuel injection valve
4	A	Activate valve	Cyl. 4 fuel injection valve
5		Not used	
6	M	Ground, fuel injection valve output stages	Ground point
7		Not used	
8	A	"Check engine" indicator control	Instrument cluster
9		Not used	
10	E	Drive away protection signal	Electronic immobilizer control module (EWS III)
11	E	Activate A/C	Pressure switch
12		Not used	
13		Not used	
14		Not used	
15		Not used	
16	E	Intake air temperature	Intake air temperature sensor
17	E	Signal input	Hot film air mass meter
18		Not used	
19	E	Oxygen sensor signal	Oxygen sensor (in front of catalytic converter)
20	E	Crankshaft position/RPM	Crankshaft position/RPM sensor
21	E	Camshaft position	Hall effect camshaft sensor
22	A	Cyl. 3 ignition coil control	Cyl. 3 ignition coil
23	A	Cyl. 4 ignition coil control	Cyl. 4 ignition coil
24		Not used	
25		Not used	
26	E	Battery voltage	B+ junction point
27	A	Engine control module relay control	Engine control module relay, terminal 85
28	M	Ground for electronics and shielding of sensors	Ground point

E = Input, A = Output, M = Ground

BM0150100094010X

Fig. 14 DME M5.2 88-pin connector X6000 pin identification (Part 1 of 3). Z3 1.9 & 318ti

Pin	Type	Description/Function	Connection
58	A	Activate valve	Intake air resonance changeover valve
59		Not used	
60	E	Programming voltage	Data link connector
61	A	Activate valve	Evaporation emission valve
62		Not used	
63	A	Activate relay	Fuel pump relay
64	A	Activate relay/valve	Secondary air pump relay/Secondary air pump valve
65	A	Activate valve	Carbon canister valve
66	A	Activate valve	Fuel changeover valve
67		Not used	
68	E	Signal above 80°C	Double temperature switch
69	E	A/C-ON-signal	Air conditioning operating unit
70	E	Cyl 1-2 knock sensor	Knock sensor
71	M	Ground for sensors	Temperature-/ knock-/ throttle position-sensors
72	E	Fuel tank pressure signal	Fuel tank pressure sensor
73		Not used	
74	E	Temperature signal	Engine coolant temperature sensor
75		Not used	
76		Not used	
77	E	Oxygen sensor signal	Oxygen sensor (behind catalytic converter)
78	E	Crankshaft position/RPM	Crankshaft position/RPM sensor
79	E	Speed signal right rear	ABS/ASC control module
80	E	Crankshaft RPM speed signal TD	Instrument cluster
81		Not used	
82		Not used	
83	E	Vehicle speed signal	On-board computer
84		Not used	
85	E/A	CAN-LOW	EGS/ASC control module
86	E/A	CAN-HIGH	EGS/ASC control module
87	A	RxD diagnosis data line	Data link connector
88	E/A	TxD diagnosis data line	Data link connector

E = Input, A = Output, M = Ground

BM0150100094030X

Fig. 14 DME M5.2 88-pin connector X6000 pin identification (Part 3 of 3). Z3 1.9 & 318ti

Pin	Type	Description/Function	Connection
89	M	Oxygen sensor heating ground	Oxygen sensor (behind catalytic converter)
90	A	Activate valve	Idle speed control valve
91	A	Activate valve	Cyl. 1 fuel injection valve
92	A	Activate valve	Cyl. 4 fuel injection valve
93		Not used	
94	M	Ground, fuel injection valve output stages	Ground point
95		Not used	
96	A	"Check engine" indicator control	Instrument cluster
97		Not used	
98	E	Drive away protection signal	Electronic immobilizer control module (EWS II)
99	E	Activate A/C	Pressure switch
100		Not used	
101		Not used	
102		Not used	
103		Not used	
104	E	Intake air temperature	Intake air temperature sensor
105	M	Ground	Hot film air mass meter
106		Not used	
107	E	Oxygen sensor signal	Oxygen sensor (in front of catalytic converter)
108	E	Crankshaft position/RPM	Crankshaft position/RPM sensor
109	E	Camshaft position	Hall effect camshaft sensor
110	A	Cyl. 3 ignition coil control	Cyl. 3 ignition coil
111	A	Cyl. 4 ignition coil control	Cyl. 4 ignition coil
112		Not used	
113		Not used	
114	E	Battery voltage	B+ jump start junction point
115	A	Engine control module relay control	Engine control module relay, terminal 85
116	M	Ground for electronics and shielding of sensors	Ground point

E = Input, A = Output, M = Ground

BM0150100096010X

Fig. 15 DME M5.2 88-pin connector X6000 pin identification (Part 1 of 3). 318i

Pin	Type	Description/Function	Connection
117	A	Idle speed control valve control	Idle speed control valve
118	M	Oxygen sensor heating ground	Oxygen sensor (in front of catalytic converter)
119	A	Activate valve	Cyl. 3 fuel injection valve
120	A	Activate valve	Cyl. 2 fuel injection valve
121		Not used	
122	M	Ground, remaning output stages (except for ingnition and fuel injection valves)	Ground point
123		Not used	
124	A	A/C compressor cut-out	Compressor control relay
125		Not used	
126		Not used	
127		Not used	
128	E	Cyl. 3-4 knock sensor	Knock sensor
129		Not used	
130	E	TI-measurement signal (fuel consumption)	Instrument cluster
131		Not used	
132	E	Throttle position	Throttle position sensor
133	E	Signal input	Hot film air mass meter
134	M	Sensor ground	Oxygen sensors
135		Not used	
136		Not used	
137	A	Cyl. 1 ignition coil control	Cyl. 1 ignition coil
138	A	Cyl. 2 ignition coil control	Cyl. 2 ignition coil
139		Not used	
140		Not used	
141	A	Component supply +	Throttle position sensor
142	E	Battery voltage from engine control module relay	Engine control module relay, terminal 87
143	M	Ground, ignition	Ground point
144	E	Ignition switch, terminal 15	Ignition switch, terminal 15
145	A	Activate auxiliary fan	Normal speed relay
146	A	Activate valve	Intake air resonance change over valve

E = Input, A = Output, M = Ground

BM0150100096020X

Fig. 15 DME M5.2 88-pin connector X6000 pin identification (Part 2 of 3). 318i

Pin	Type	Description/Function	Connection
147		Not used	
148	E	Programming voltage	Data link connector
149	A	Activate valve	Evaporation emission valve
150		Not used	
151	A	Activate relay	Fuel pump relay
152	A	Secondary air pump valve control	Secondary air pump valve
153	A	Carbon canister valve control	Carbon canister valve
154	A	Fuel changeover valve	Fuel changeover valve
155		Not used	
156	E	Signal above 80°C	Double temperature switch
157	E	Signal A/C on	Air conditioning operating unit
158	E	Cyl 1-2 knock sensor	Knock sensor
159	M	Ground for sensors	Temperature-/knock-/throttle position-sensors
160	E	Fuel tank pressure	Fuel tank pressure sensor
161		Not used	
162	E	Temperature signal	Engine coolant temperature sensor
163		Not used	
164		Not used	
165	E	Oxygen sensor signal	Oxygen sensor (behind catalytic converter)
166	E	Crankshaft position/RPM	Crankshaft position/RPM sensor
167	E	Speed signal right rear	ABS/ASC control module
168	A	Crankshaft RPM speed signal TD	Instrument cluster
169		Not used	
170		Not used	
171	E	Vehicle speed signal	Instrument cluster
172		Not used	
173	E/A	CAN-LOW	EGS/ASC control module
174	E/A	CAN-HIGH	EGS/ASC control module
175	A	RxD diagnosis data line	Data link connector
176	E/A	TxD diagnosis data line	Data link connector

E = Input, A = Output, M = Ground

BM0150100096030X

Fig. 15 DME M5.2 88-pin connector X6000 pin identification (Part 3 of 3). 318i

Pin	Type	Description/Function	Connection
1	A	Cyl. 2 ignition coil control	Cyl. 2 ignition coil
2	A	Cyl. 4 ignition coil control	Cyl. 4 ignition coil
3	A	Cyl. 6 ignition coil control	Cyl. 6 ignition coil
4	M	Ground	Ground point
5	A	Cyl. 2 fuel injection valve control	Cyl. 2 fuel injection valve
6	A	Cyl. 1 fuel injection valve control	Cyl. 1 fuel injection valve
7	M	Ground	Hot wire air mass meter
8	E	Hot wire air mass meter	Hot wire air mass meter
9	E	TI-measurement signal (fuel consumption)	Not used
10	E	Engine coolant temperature	Engine coolant temperature sensor
11	E	Fuel tank pressure	Fuel tank pressure sensor
12	E	Throttle position signal	Throttle position sensor
13		Not used	
14	E	Intake air temperature	Intake air temperature sensor
15	E	Speed signal right rear	ABS/ASC control module
16	E	Activate A/C	Pressure switch
17		Not used	
18	E	Drive away protection signal (code)	Electronic immobilizer control module (EWS III)
19	E	A/C-ON-signal	Air conditioning operating unit
20	A	"Check engine" indicator control	Instrument cluster
21	A	Camshaft control	Variable camshaft control valve
22	A	Cyl. 3 fuel injection valve control	Cyl. 3 fuel injection valve
23	A	Cyl. 6 fuel injection valve control	Cyl. 6 fuel injection valve
24	A	Cyl. 4 fuel injection valve control	Cyl. 4 fuel injection valve
25	M	Oxygen sensor heating ground	Oxygen sensor I (in front of catalytic converter)
26	E	Battery voltage	B+ jump start junction point
27	A	Activate valve	Idle speed control valve
28	M	Ground	Ground point
29	A	Cyl. 1 ignition coil control	Cyl. 1 ignition coil

E = Input, A = Output, M = Ground

BM0150100104010X

Fig. 16 DME MS41 88-pin connector X6000 pin identification (Part 1 of 4). 1999–2000 Z3 M Coupe & Z3 M Roadster

Pin	Type	Description/Function	Connection
30	A	Cyl. 3 ignition coil control	Cyl. 3 ignition coil
31	A	Cyl. 5 ignition coil control	Cyl. 5 ignition coil
32	M	Ground	Ground point
33	A	Cyl. 5 fuel injection valve control	Cyl. 5 fuel injection valve
34	M	Ground	Ground point
35	A	Activate relay	Secondary air pump relay
36	A	Crankshaft RPM speed signal TD	Instrument cluster
37		Not used	
38	M	Ground	Shield knock sensor
39	M	Ground	Temperature sensors
40	M	Ground	Crankshaft position/RPM sensor Fuel tank pressure sensor
41	M	Ground	Shield camshaft position sensor
42	M	Ground	Throttle position sensor
43	M	Ground	Camshaft position sensor
44	A	Voltage supply	Throttle position sensor Fuel tank pressure sensor
45	A	Throttle position signal	ABS/ASC control module
46	E	TI-measurement signal (fuel consumption)	Instrument cluster
47		Not used	
48	A	Voltage supply	Crankshaft position/RPM sensor
49	E	Terminal 15	Ignition switch
50	A	Running losses	Solenoid valve
51	A	Activate valve	Charcoal filter shut off valve
52		Not used	
53	A	Activate valve	Idle speed control valve
54	E	Battery voltage, terminal 87	Engine control module relay
55	M	Oxygen sensor heating ground	Oxygen sensor II (in front of catalytic converter)
56	M	Ground	Ground point
57	E	Cyl. 1-3 knock sensor	Knock sensor
58	E	Cyl. 1-3 knock sensor	Knock sensor
59	E	Cyl. 4-6 knock sensor	Knock sensor

E = Input, A = Output, M = Ground

BM0150100104020X

Fig. 16 DME MS41 88-pin connector X6000 pin identification (Part 2 of 4). 1999–2000 Z3 M Coupe & Z3 M Roadster

Pin	Type	Description/Function	Connection
85		Not used	
86		Not used	
87	E	Battery voltage, terminal 87	Engine control module relay
88	E/A	TxD diagnosis data link	Data link connector

E = Input, A = Output, M = Ground

BM0150100104040X

Fig. 16 DME MS41 88-pin connector X6000 pin identification (Part 4 of 4). 1999–2000 Z3 M Coupe & Z3 M Roadster

Pin	Type	Description/Function	Connection
60	E	Programming voltage	Data link connector
61	M	Oxygen sensor heating ground	Oxygen sensor II (behind catalytic converter)
62	E	Activate valve	Secondary air pump value
63	E	Cyl. 4-6 knock sensor	Knock sensor
64	E	Camshaft position	Camshaft position sensor
65	E	Camshaft position	Camshaft position sensor
66		Not used	
67	M	Oxygen sensor signal ground	Oxygen sensor I (in front of catalytic converter)
68	E	Activate valve	Evaporative emission valve
69	E	Activate relay	Fuel pump relay
70	M	Oxygen sensor signal ground	Oxygen sensor II (in front of catalytic converter)
71	M	Oxygen sensor signal ground	Oxygen sensor I (behind catalytic converter)
72	M	Oxygen sensor signal ground	Oxygen sensor II (in front of catalytic converter)
73	E	Activate relay	Engine control module relay
74	A	Activate A/C compressor	Compressor control relay
75	E	Sensor signal	Oxygen sensor I (in front of catalytic converter)
76	E	Sensor signal	Oxygen sensor II (in front of catalytic converter)
77	E	Sensor signal	Oxygen sensor I (behind catalytic converter)
78	E	Sensor signal	Oxygen sensor II (behind catalytic converter)
79	M	Oxygen sensor heating ground	Oxygen sensor I (behind catalytic converter)
80	A	ASC signal ZA	Slip control module ABS/ASC
81	A	ASC signal ZWV	Slip control module ABS/ASC
82	A	ASC signal MSR	Slip control module ABS/ASC
83	E	Sensor signal	Crankshaft position/RPM sensor
84		Not used	

E = Input, A = Output, M = Ground

BM0150100104030X

Fig. 16 DME MS41 88-pin connector X6000 pin identification (Part 3 of 4). 1999–2000 Z3 M Coupe & Z3 M Roadster

Pin	Type	Description/Function	Connection
1	A	Cyl. 2 ignition coil control	Cyl. 2 ignition coil
2	A	Cyl. 4 ignition coil control	Cyl. 4 ignition coil
3	A	Cyl. 6 ignition coil control	Cyl. 6 ignition coil
4	M	Ground	Ground point
5	A	Cyl. 2 fuel injection valve control	Cyl. 2 fuel injection valve
6	A	Cyl. 1 fuel injection valve control	Cyl. 1 fuel injection valve
7	M	Ground	Hot wire air mass meter
8	E	Hot wire air mass meter	Hot wire air mass meter
9	E	Ti-measurement signal (fuel consumption)	Board computer
10	E	Engine coolant temperature	Engine coolant temperature sensor
11	E	Fuel tank pressure	Fuel tank pressure sensor
12	E	Throttle position signal	Throttle position sensor
13		Not used	
14	E	Intake air temperature	Intake air temperature sensor
15	E	Speed signal right rear	ABS/ASC control module
16	E	Activate A/C	Pressure switch
17		Not used	
18	E	Drive away protection signal (code)	Electronic immobilizer control module (EWS II)
19	E	A/C on signal	Air conditioning operating unit
20	A	"Check engine" indicator control	Instrument cluster
21	A	Camshaft control	Variable camshaft control valve
22	A	Cyl. 3 fuel injection valve control	Cyl. 3 fuel injection valve
23	A	Cyl. 6 fuel injection valve control	Cyl. 6 fuel injection valve
24	A	Cyl. 4 fuel injection valve control	Cyl. 4 fuel injection valve
25	M	Oxygen sensor heating ground	Oxygen sensor (in front of catalytic converter)
26	E	Battery voltage	B+ jump start junction point
27	A	Activate valve	Idle speed control valve
28	M	Ground	Ground point
29	A	Cyl. 1 ignition coil control	Cyl. 1 ignition coil

E = Input, A = Output, M = Ground

BM0150100102010X

Fig. 17 DME MS41 88-pin connector X6000 pin identification (Part 1 of 3). 1998 Z3 2.8

Pin	Type	Description/Function	Connection
30	A	Cyl. 3 ignition coil control	Cyl. 3 ignition coil
31	A	Cyl. 5 ignition coil control	Cyl. 5 ignition coil
32	M	Ground	Ground point
33	A	Cyl. 5 fuel injection valve control	Cyl. 5 fuel injection valve
34	M	Ground	Ground point
35	A	Activate relay	Secondary air pump relay
36	A	Crankshaft RPM speed signal TD	Instrument cluster
37		Not used	
38	M	Ground	Shield knock sensor
39	M	Ground	Temperature sensors
40	M	Ground	Crankshaft position/RPM sensor Fuel tank pressure sensor
41	M	Ground	Shield camshaft position sensor
42	M	Ground	Throttle position sensor
43	M	Ground	Camshaft position sensor
44	A	Voltage supply	Throttle position sensor Fuel tank pressure sensor
45	A	Throttle position signal	ABS/ASC control module
46	E	Ti-measurement signal (fuel consumption)	Instrument cluster
47		Not used	
48	A	Voltage supply	Crankshaft position/RPM sensor
49	E	Terminal 15	Ignition switch
50	A	Running losses	Solenoid valve
51	A	Activate valve	Charcoal filter shut off valve
52	A	Signal exhaust flap	Not used
53	A	Activate valve	Idle speed control valve
54	E	Battery voltage, terminal 87	Engine control module relay
55		Not used	
56	M	Ground	Ground point
57	E	Cyl. 1-3 knock sensor	Knock sensor
58	E	Cyl. 1-3 knock sensor	Knock sensor
59	E	Cyl. 4-6 knock sensor	Knock sensor
60	E	Programming voltage	Data link connector

E = Input, A = Output, M = Ground

BM0150100102020X

Fig. 17 DME MS41 88-pin connector X6000 pin identification (Part 2 of 3). 1998 Z3 2.8

Pin	Type	Description/Function	Connection
1	A	Cyl. 2 ignition coil control	Cyl. 2 ignition coil
2	A	Cyl. 4 ignition coil control	Cyl. 4 ignition coil
3	A	Cyl. 6 ignition coil control	Cyl. 6 ignition coil
4	M	Ground	Ground point
5	A	Cyl. 2 fuel injection valve control	Cyl. 2 fuel injection valve
6	A	Cyl. 1 fuel injection valve control	Cyl. 1 fuel injection valve
7	M	Ground	Hot wire air mass meter
8	E	Hot wire air mass meter	Hot wire air mass meter
9	E	TI-measurement signal (fuel consumption)	Instrument cluster
10	E	Engine coolant temperature	Engine coolant temperature sensor
11	E	Fuel tank pressure	Fuel tank pressure sensor
12	E	Throttle position signal	Throttle position sensor
13		Not used	
14	E	Intake air temperature	Intake air temperature sensor
15	E	Speed signal right rear	ABS/ASC control module
16	E	Activate A/C	Pressure switch
17		Not used	
18	E	Drive-away protection signal (code)	Electronic immobilizer control module (EWS II)
19	E	A/C-ON-signal	Air conditioning operating unit
20	A	"Check engine" indicator control	Instrument cluster
21	A	Camshaft control	Variable camshaft control valve
22	A	Cyl. 3 fuel injection valve control	Cyl. 3 fuel injection valve
23	A	Cyl. 6 fuel injection valve control	Cyl. 6 fuel injection valve
24	A	Cyl. 4 fuel injection valve control	Cyl. 4 fuel injection valve
25	M	Oxygen sensor heating ground	Oxygen sensor (in front of catalytic converter)
26	E	Battery voltage	B+ jump start junction point
27	A	Activate valve	Idle speed control valve
28	M	Ground	Ground point
29	A	Cyl. 1 ignition coil control	Cyl. 1 ignition coil

E = Input, A = Output, M = Ground

BM0150100099010X

Fig. 18 DME MS41 88-pin connector X6000 pin identification (Part 1 of 3). 1998 323i/is & 328i/is & 1999 323i/is Coupe & Convertible & 328i/is Coupe & Convertible

Pin	Type	Description/Function	Connection
61		Not used	
62	E	Activate valve	Secondary air pump value
63	E	Cyl. 4-6 knock sensor	Knock sensor
64	E	Camshaft position	Camshaft position sensor
65	E	Camshaft position	Camshaft position sensor
66		Not used	
67	M	Oxygen sensor signal ground	Oxygen sensor (in front of catalytic converter)
68	E	Activate valve	Evaporative emission valve
69	E	Activate relay	Fuel pump relay
70		Not used	
71	M	Oxygen sensor signal ground	Oxygen sensor (behind catalytic converter)
72		Not used	
73	E	Activate relay	Engine control module relay
74	A	Activate A/C compressor	Compressor control relay
75	E	Sensor signal	Oxygen sensor (in front of catalytic converter)
76		Not used	
77	E	Sensor signal	Oxygen sensor (behind catalytic converter)
78		Not used	
79	M	Oxygen sensor heating ground	Oxygen sensor (behind catalytic converter)
80	A	ASC signal ZA	Slip control module ABS/ASC
81	A	ASC signal ZWV	Slip control module ABS/ASC
82	A	ASC signal MSR	Slip control module ABS/ASC
83	E	Sensor signal	Crankshaft position/RPM sensor
84		Not used	
85	E/A	CAN-LOW	Transmission control module EGS
86	E/A	CAN-HIGH	Transmission control module EGS
87	E	Battery voltage, terminal 87	Engine control module relay
88	E/A	TxD diagnosis data link	Data link connector

E = Input, A = Output, M = Ground

BM0150100102030X

Fig. 17 DME MS41 88-pin connector X6000 pin identification (Part 3 of 3). 1998 Z3 2.8

Pin	Type	Description/Function	Connection
30	A	Cyl. 3 ignition coil control	Cyl. 3 ignition coil
31	A	Cyl. 5 ignition coil control	Cyl. 5 ignition coil
32	M	Ground	Ground point
33	A	Cyl. 5 fuel injection valve control	Cyl. 5 fuel injection valve
34	M	Ground	Ground point
35	A	Activate relay	Secondary air pump relay
36	A	Crankshaft RPM speed signal TD	Instrument cluster
37		Not used	
38	M	Ground	Shield knock sensor
39	M	Ground	Temperature sensors
40	M	Ground	Crankshaft position/RPM sensor Fuel tank pressure sensor
41	M	Ground	Shield camshaft position sensor
42	M	Ground	Throttle position sensor
43	E	Camshaft position	Camshaft position sensor
44	A	Voltage supply	Throttle position sensor Fuel tank pressure sensor
45	A	Throttle position signal	ABS/ASC control module
46	E	TI-measurement signal (fuel consumption)	Instrument cluster
47		Not used	
48	A	Voltage supply	Crankshaft position/RPM sensor
49	E	Terminal 15	Ignition switch
50	A	Running losses	Solenoid valve
51	A	Activate valve	Carbon canister valve
52	A	Signal exhaust flap	Exhaust gas flap valve
53	A	Activate valve	Idle speed controle valve
54	E	Battery voltage, terminal 87	Engine control module relay
55	M	Oxygen sensor heating ground	Oxygen sensor (in front of catalytic converter)
56	M	Ground	Ground point
57	E	Cyl. 1-3 knock sensor	Knock sensor
58	E	Cyl. 1-3 knock sensor	Knock sensor
59	E	Cyl. 4-6 knock sensor	Knock sensor

E = Input, A = Output, M = Ground

BM0150100099020X

Fig. 18 DME MS41 88-pin connector X6000 pin identification (Part 2 of 3). 1998 323i/is & 328i/is & 1999 323i/is Coupe & Convertible & 328i/is Coupe & Convertible

Pin	Type	Description/Function	Connection
60	E	Programming voltage	Data link connector
61	M	Oxygen sensor heating ground	Oxygen sensor (behind catalytic converter)
62	A	Activate valve	Secondary air pump value
63	E	Cyl. 4-6 knock sensor	Knock sensor
64	M	Ground	Camshaft position sensor
65	E	Camshaft position	Camshaft position sensor
66		Not used	
67	M	Oxygen sensor signal ground	Oxygen sensor (in front of catalytic converter)
68	A	Activate valve	Evaporative emission valve
69	A	Activate relay	Fuel pump relay
70	M	Oxygen sensor signal ground	Oxygen sensor (in front of catalytic converter)
71	M	Oxygen sensor signal ground	Oxygen sensor (behind catalytic converter)
72	M	Oxygen sensor signal ground	Oxygen sensor (behind catalytic converter)
73	E	Activate relay	Engine control module relay
74	A	Activate A/C compressor	Compressor control relay
75	E	Sensor signal	Oxygen sensor (in front of catalytic converter)
76	E	Sensor signal	Oxygen sensor (in front of catalytic converter)
77	E	Sensor signal	Oxygen sensor (behind catalytic converter)
78	E	Sensor signal	Oxygen sensor (behind catalytic converter)
79	M	Oxygen sensor heating ground	Oxygen sensor (behind catalytic converter)
80	A	ASC signal ZA	Slip control module ABS/ASC
81	A	ASC signal ZWV	Slip control module ABS/ASC
82	A	ASC signal MSR	Slip control module ABS/ASC
83	E	Sensor signal	Crankshaft position/RPM sensor
84		Not used	
85	E/A	CAN LOW	Transmission control module EGS
86	E/A	CAN HIGH	Transmission control module EGS
87	E	Battery voltage, terminal 87	Engine control module relay
88	E/A	TxD diagnosis data link	Data link connector

E = Input, A = Output, M = Ground

BM0150100099030X

Fig. 18 DME MS41 88-pin connector X6000 pin identification (Part 3 of 3). 1998 323i/is & 328i/is & 1999 323i/is Coupe & Convertible & 328i/is Coupe & Convertible

Pin	Type	Signal	Description/Function	Connection
1	M	T_LHV1	Oxygen sensor heating ground	Oxygen sensor 1 (in front of catalytic converter)
2			Not used	
3	E/A	D_CAN-L	CAN bus low	Transmission control module (EGS)
4	E/A	D_CAN-H	CAN bus high	Transmission control module (EGS)
5			Not used	
6	E/A	D_TXD2	Diagnosis	Transmission control module (EGS)
7	M	T_LHH1	Oxygen sensor heating ground	Oxygen sensor 1 (behind catalytic converter)
8			Not used	

E = Input, A = Output, M = Ground

BM0150100107010X

Fig. 20 DME MS42 24-pin connector X60002 pin identification (Part 1 of 2). Z3 2.3 & 1999–2000 Z3 2.8

Pin	Type	Signal	Description/Function	Connection
1	E	A_HFM	Signal air mass meter	Hot film air mass meter
2	E	P_NWGA1	Signal camshaft position	Camshaft position sensor 2 (outlet)
3			Not used	
4	A	U_DKFW1	Voltage supply	Throttle position sensor 1

E = Input, A = Output, M = Ground

BM0150100108010X

Fig. 21 DME MS42 52-pin connector X60003 pin identification (Part 1 of 3). Z3 2.3 & 1999–2000 Z3 2.8

Pin	Type	Signal	Description/Function	Connection
1	A	15	Activate relay	Unloader relay terminal 15
2			Not used	
3			Not used	
4	M	31E	Ground	Ground point
5	M	31L	Ground	Ground point
6	M	31L	Ground	Ground point
7	E	30	Voltage supply	B+ junction point E-box
8	E	U_HR<2	Voltage supply	Fuse holder in E-box
9	E	U_HR<2	Voltage supply	Fuse holder in E-box

BM0150100106000X

Fig. 19 DME MS42 nine-pin connector X60001 pin identification. Z3 2.3 & 1999–2000 Z3 2.8

Pin	Type	Signal	Description/Function	Connection
9			Not used	
10			Not used	
11			Not used	
12	A	S_KKU	Activate valve	Solenoid valve (Running Losses)
13	M	T_LHV2	Oxygen sensor heating ground	Oxygen sensor 2 (in front of catalytic converter)
14	E	A_LSV1	Sensor signal	Oxygen sensor 1 (in front of catalytic converter)
15	E	A_LSV2	Sensor signal	Oxygen sensor 2 (in front of catalytic converter)
16	E	A_LSH1	Sensor signal	Oxygen sensor 1 (behind catalytic converter)
17			Not used	
18	E	A_LSH2	Sensor signal	Oxygen sensor 2 (behind catalytic converter)
19	M	T_LHH2	Oxygen sensor heating ground	Oxygen sensor 2 (behind catalytic converter)
20	M	M_LSV1	Signal ground	Oxygen sensor 1 (in front of catalytic converter)
21	M	M_LSV2	Signal ground	Oxygen sensor 2 (in front of catalytic converter)
22	M	M_LSH1	Signal ground	Oxygen sensor 1 (behind catalytic converter)
23	A	S_HR	Activate relay	Engine control module relay
24	M	M_LSH2	Signal ground	Oxygen sensor 2 (behind catalytic converter)

BM0150100107020X

Fig. 20 DME MS42 24-pin connector X60002 pin identification (Part 2 of 2). Z3 2.3 & 1999–2000 Z3 2.8

Pin	Type	Signal	Description/Function	Connection
5	E	P_NWGE1	Signal camshaft position	Camshaft position sensor 1 (inlet)
6			Not used	
7	A	U_DKFW2	Voltage supply	Throttle position sensor 2
8	E	P_KWG	Signal crankshaft position	Crankshaft position sensor
9	E	A_FWG2	Throttle position signal	Throttle position sensor 2 (cruise control)
10	E	A_DKG2	Throttle position signal	Throttle position sensor 2 (DME)
11			Not used	
12	E	S_30H	Start signal	Starter
13	E	S_61-1	Charging signal	Generator
14	M	M_DKFW1	Ground	Throttle position sensor 1
15	M	M_NWGA1	Ground	Camshaft position sensor 2 (outlet)
16	E	A_FWG1	Throttle position signal	Throttle position sensor 1 (cruise control)
17	M	M_HFM	Ground	Hot film air massmeter
18	M	M_NWGE1	Ground	Crankshaft position sensor 1 (inlet)
19	E	A_DKG1	Throttle position signal	Throttle position sensor 1 (DME)
20	M	M_DKFW2	Ground	Throttle position sensor 2
21	M	M_KWG	Ground	Crankshaft position sensor
22	E	A_TANS	Temperature signal	Intake air temperature sensor
23	M	M_TANS	Ground	Intake air temperature sensor
24	E	A_TMOT	Temperature signal	Engine coolant temperature sensor
25	M	M_TMOT	Ground	Engine coolant temperature sensor
26	E	A_OLD	Pressure signal	Oil pressure switch
27	E	A_TOEL	Temperature signal	Oil temperature sensor
28	M	M_OTF	Ground	Oil temperature sensor
29	E	A_KS1A	Cyl. 1-3 knock sensor	Knock sensor
30	E	A_KS1B	Cyl. 1-3 knock sensor	Knock sensor
31	E	A_KS2A	Cyl. 4-6 knock sensor	Knock sensor
32	E	A_KS2B	Cyl. 4-6 knock sensor	Knock sensor
33	A	P_EVZ1	Activate valve	Cyl. 1 fuel injection valve
34	A	P_EVZ2	Activate valve	Cyl. 2 fuel injection valve
35	A	P_EVZ3	Activate valve	Cyl. 3 fuel injection valve

E = Input, A = Output, M = Ground

BM0150100108020X

Fig. 21 DME MS42 52-pin connector X60003 pin identification (Part 2 of 3). Z3 2.3 & 1999–2000 Z3 2.8

Pin	Type	Signal	Description/Function	Connection
36	A	P_EVZ4	Activate valve	Cyl. 4 fuel injection valve
37	A	P_EVZ5	Activate valve	Cyl. 5 fuel injection valve
38	A	P_EVZ6	Activate valve	Cyl. 6 fuel injection valve
39	E	F_OLN	Level signal	Oil level sensor
40	A	T_NWE1	Activate valve	Variable camshaft control valve 1 (inlet)
41	A	T_NWA1	Activate valve	Variable camshaft control valve 2 (outlet)
42	A	T_TEV	Activate valve	Evaporative emission valve
43	A	T_MDK1	Activate motor	Cruise control actuator
44	A	T_MDK2	Activate motor	Cruise control actuator
45	A	S_KFK	Cooling signal	Thermostat, characteristic map cooling
46	A	T_LLFSS	CLOSE signal	Idle speed control valve
47	A	T_LLFSO	OPEN signal	Idle speed control valve
48	M	W_KS	Ground	Shield knock sensor
49	A	S_DISA	Activate valve	Valve, individual control intake system
50			Not used	
51			Not used	
52	A	S_SLPV1	Activate valve	Secondary air pump valve

BM0150100108030X

Fig. 21 DME MS42 52-pin connector X60003 pin identification (Part 3 of 3). Z3 2.3 & 1999–2000 Z3 2.8

Pin	Type	Signal	Description/Function	Connection
37	E/A	CAN–	CAN bus low	Instrument cluster, ABS/ASC control module
38			Not used	
39			Not used	
40			Not used	

BM0150100109030X

Fig. 22 DME MS42 40-pin connector X60004 pin identification (Part 3 of 3). Z3 2.3 & 1999–2000 Z3 2.8

Pin	Type	Signal	Description/Function	Connection
1	A	61	Charging signal	Instrument cluster
2	A	30H	Start signal	Body electronics control module (ZKE IV)
3	A	SLP	Activate relay	Secondary air pump relay
4			Not used	
5			Not used	
6			Not used	
7			Not used	

E = Input, A = Output, M = Ground

BM0150100109010X

Fig. 22 DME MS42 40-pin connector X60004 pin identification (Part 1 of 3). Z3 2.3 & 1999–2000 Z3 2.8

Pin	Type	Signal	Description/Function	Connection
8			Not used	
9			Not used	
10	A	EKP	Activate relay	Fuel pump relay
11	A	OELD	Oil pressure signal	Instrument cluster
12			Not used	
13			Not used	
14			Not used	
15			Not used	
16			Not used	
17	A	TD	Crankshaft RPM speed signal TD	Instrument cluster
18			Not used	
19	E	RFL	Reverse signal	Reversing light switch/ Automatic transmission range switch
20			Not used	
21	A	A-OELN	Oil level signal	Thermal oil level sensor (TOENS) control module
22	E	DFAHR	Speed signal right rear	ABS/ASC control module
23	E	KUPP	Clutch signal	Clutch switch
24	E	KL 54 ON	Brake signal	Brake light switch
25			Not used	
26	E	15A26	Terminal 15	Fuse 26
27	E	MFL	Cruise control signal	Cruise control interface
28	E	S_BLTS	Brake signal	Brake light switch
29	A	S_KOREL	Activate relay	Compressor control relay
30	A	LDPV	Activate valve	Leakage diagnosis pump
31			Not used	
32	E/A	TXDII	TXD diagnosis data link	Data link connector
33	E	EWSDME	Drive-away protection signal (code)	Electronic immobilizer control module (EWS III)
34	E	LDPS	Leakage signal	Leakage diagnosis pump
35	M	31	Ground	Cruise control interface
36	E/A	CAN+	CAN bus high	Instrument cluster, ABS/ASC control module

E = Input, A = Output, M = Ground

BM0150100109020X

Fig. 22 DME MS42 40-pin connector X60004 pin identification (Part 2 of 3). Z3 2.3 & 1999–2000 Z3 2.8

Pin	Type	Signal	Description/Function	Connection
1	A	P_ZSZ3	Ignition coil signal	Cyl. 3 ignition coil
2	A	P_ZSZ2	Ignition coil signal	Cyl. 2 ignition coil
3	A	P_ZSZ1	Ignition coil signal	Cyl. 1 ignition coil
4			Not used	
5	M	31L	Ground	Ground point
6	M	A_ZSR	Ground	Ground point
7	A	P_ZSZ6	Ignition coil signal	Cyl. 6 ignition coil
8	A	P_ZSZ5	Ignition coil signal	Cyl. 5 ignition coil
9	A	P_ZSZ4	Ignition coil signal	Cyl. 4 ignition coil

BM0150100110000X

Fig. 23 DME MS42 nine-pin connector X60005 pin identification. Z3 2.3 & 1999–2000 Z3 2.8

DIAGNOSTIC CHART INDEX

Description	Page No.	Fig. No.
DIAGNOSTIC TESTS		
Air Conditioning Compressor Relay Test	11-113	38
Brake Lamp Switch Test	11-113	39
CAN-Bus Test	11-113	40
Characteristic Map Cooling Test	11-114	41
Clutch Switch Test	11-114	42
Coolant Outlet Temperature Test	11-114	43
CO Matching Test	11-115	44
Crankshaft Position Sensor Test	11-115	45
DME Control Unit Test	11-115	46
Double Knock Sensor Test	11-116	47
Electric Fan Test	11-116	48
Engine Coolant Temperature Sensor Test	11-117	49
Engine Oil Temperature Sensor Test	11-117	50
Exhaust Camshaft Sensor Test	11-117	51
Exhaust Flap Test	11-117	52
Fuel Circuit Changeover Test	11-118	53
Fuel Injector Test	11-118	54
Fuel Pump Relay Test	11-118	55
Fuel Tank Leak Diagnosis Pump Test	11-118	56
Fuel Tank Vent Valve Test	11-119	57
Idle Actuator Test	11-119	58
Idle Speed Matching Test	11-120	59
Ignition Coil Test	11-120	60
Intake Air Temperature Sensor Test	11-121	61
Intake Camshaft Sensor Test	11-121	62
Intake Pipe Changeover Test	11-121	63
Main Voltage Relay Test	11-122	64
Mass Air Flow Sensor Test	11-122	65
Misfire Detection Test	11-122	66
Mixture Preparation Test	11-123	67
Motor Driven Throttle Test	11-123	68
Oxygen Sensor After Catalytic Converter Test	11-126	69
Oxygen Sensor Before Catalytic Converter Test	11-126	70
Power & Ground Supply Test	11-126	71
Road Speed Signal Test	11-127	72
Secondary Air Pump Test	11-127	73
Secondary Air Valve Test	11-127	74
Steering Wheel Multifunction Test	11-128	75
Suction Jet Pump Test	11-128	76
VANOS Test	11-129	77
Vehicle Immobilization Test	11-129	78
Vehicle Immobilization Matching Test	11-129	79
GLOBAL TEST		
Fault Symptoms Test	11-112	35
Idle Setpoint/Actual Value Comparison Global Test	11-112	37
Mixture Adaptation Values Global Test	11-112	36
SYMPTOM RELATED DIAGNOSIS		
Cruise Control	11-111	33
Engine Shuts Down Again After Start	11-110	26
Engine Shuts Down While Driving	11-111	31
Engine Temperature Too High/Too Low	11-112	34
Engine Will Not Start: How Does The Starter Turn Engine Over?	11-110	24
Engine Will Not Start: When Does The Long Starting Time Occur?	11-110	25
Idle Speed Irregular, Hunting, Too High, Too Low	11-110	27
Fuel Consumption Too High	11-111	29
MIL Lamp Comes On During Engine Operation	11-111	32
Poor Traction & Power Loss	11-111	30
Problems While Driving	11-111	28

- 1: Not at all although indicator lamps are OKAY? — Check → - Starter according to circuit diagram. - EWS: **Test module suspected**
- 2: Normally but no ignition sparks — Check → - EWS: **Test module suspected**
- 3: Only weakly — Check → - Power supply (battery, positive - ground supply). **Test module suspected** - Starter - Oil viscosity
- 4: Lightly compression strokes not discernible — Check → Compression too low
- 5: Normally — Check → - Plausibility temperature sensor, display temperature measured values: - No fuel supply, fuel tank empty - Changeover valve running losses (US models only) - Ignition in general. The engine will not start, however, the starter turns so check following component first: - K6326 power-saving relay terminal 15 - Check fuse according to circuit diagram.
- 6: Back to fault symptom selection

BM0150100176010X

Fig. 24 Engine Will Not Start: How Does The Starter Turn Engine Over?

- Engine speed status is checked. — Check → Check bowden cable setting: Too tight?
- Engine temperature status is checked — Check → Is the indicated cooling temperature plausible? **Test module suspected**
- 1: Engine shuts down when accelerator pedal pressed lightly — Check → Check for inadequate fuel delivers **Test module suspected**
- 2: Engine continues to run when accelerator pressed lightly — Check → - Idle actuator stuck, stiff - Secondary air in intake system - Ignition
- Back to fault symptom selection

BM0150100176030X

Fig. 26 Engine Shuts Down Again After Start

- 1: Only when the engine is hot? — Check → - Fuel supply (pressure retaining system). **Test module suspected.** - Changeover valve running losses (US models only)
- 2: Only at outside temperatures > 0°C? — Check → - Leak in fuel injector
- 3: Only at outside temperatures < -20°C? — Check → - Incorrect oil viscosity - Plausibility of temperature sensor
- 4: Always? — Check → - Fuel supply. **Test module suspected** - Leak in fuel injector
- 5: Back to fault symptom selection

BM0150100176020X

Fig. 25 Engine Will Not Start: When Does The Long Starting Time Occur?

- Read off smooth running values in the case of irregular idle speed caused by poor running cylinder — Check → Read smooth running values
- Setpoint/actual value comparison, idle speed status ... — Check → Check bowden cable setting: Too tight?
- Check P/N switch status ... — Check → Check CAN; Check EGS
- Check A/C compressor status ... — Check → Check air conditioning system
- Setpoint/actual value comparison, idle speed — Check → - Note idle speed adjustment in service - Idle actuator stuck, stiff - Secondary air in intake system
- Setpoint/actual value comparison, camshaft position, intake/exhaust — Check → - Valve timing set incorrectly - VANOS. **Test module suspected**
- Are the indicated temperatures (engine, coolant outlet, intake air, oil temperature) plausible? — Check → **Test module suspected**

Remaining troubleshooting procedures:

1: Ignition
2: Idle actuator
3: Fuel tank vent valve — **Test module suspected**
4: Suction jet pump — **Test module suspected**
5: Changeover valve running losses (US models only) — **Test module suspected**
6: Back to fault symptom selection

BM0150100176040X

Fig. 27 Idle Speed Irregular, Hunting, Too High, Too Low

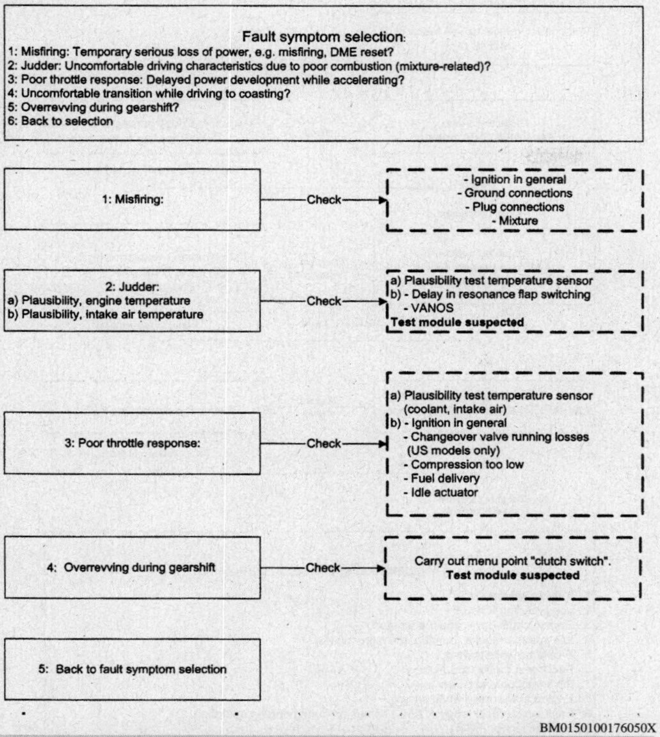

1: Misfiring: Temporary serious loss of power, e.g. misfiring, DME reset?
2: Judder: Uncomfortable driving characteristics due to poor combustion (mixture-related)?
3: Poor throttle response: Delayed power development while accelerating?
4: Uncomfortable transition while driving to coasting?
5: Overrevving during gearshift?
6: Back to selection

b) - Delay in resonance flap switching

4: Overrevving during gearshift

Carry out menu point "clutch switch".

Fig. 28 Problems While Driving

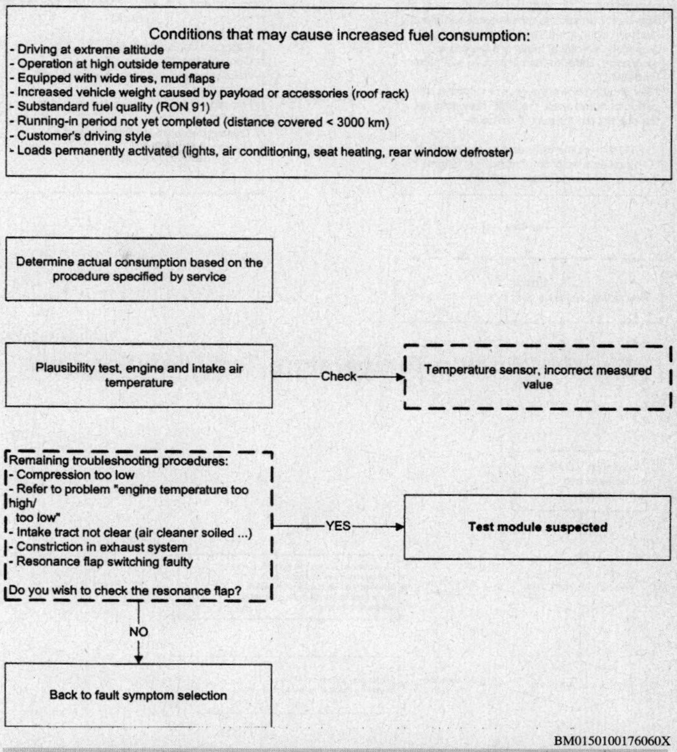

- Driving at extreme altitude

- Equipped with wide tires, mud flaps
- Increased vehicle weight caused by payload or accessories (roof rack)
- Substandard fuel quality (RON 91)
- Running-in period not yet completed (distance covered < 3000 km)
- Customer's driving style
- Loads permanently activated (lights, air conditioning, seat heating, rear window defroster)
Determine actual consumption based on the procedure specified by service

- Intake tract not clear (air cleaner soiled ...)
- Constriction in exhaust system
- Resonance flap switching faulty
Do you wish to check the resonance flap?

Fig. 29 Fuel Consumption Too High

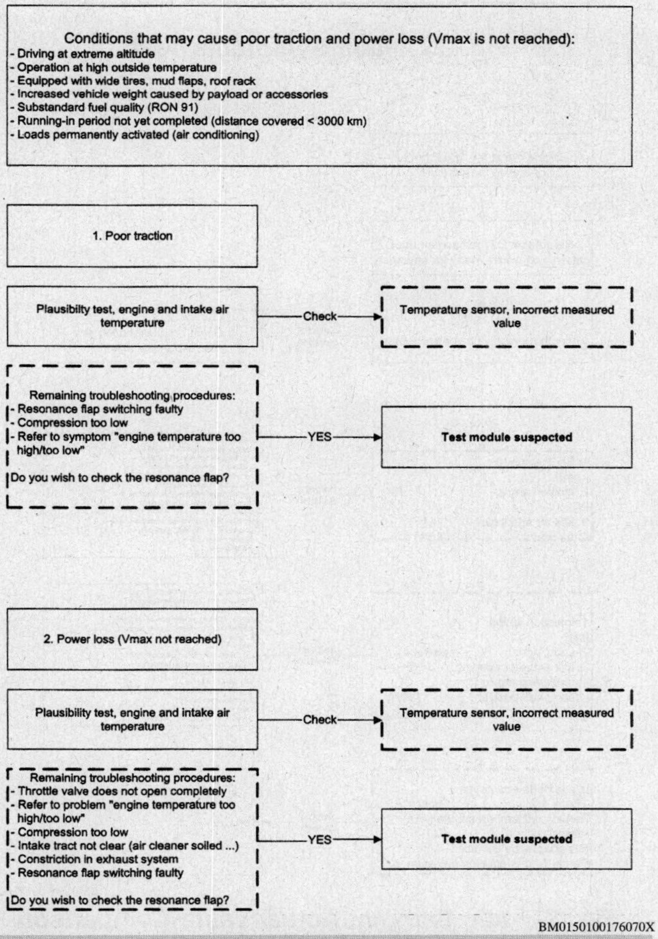

Conditions that may cause poor traction and power loss (Vmax is not reached):
- Driving at extreme altitude

- Equipped with wide tires, mud flaps, roof rack
- Increased vehicle weight caused by payload or accessories
- Substandard fuel quality (RON 91)
- Running-in period not yet completed (distance covered < 3000 km)

- Resonance flap switching faulty

Do you wish to check the resonance flap?

2. Power loss (Vmax not reached)

- Throttle valve does not open completely

- Intake tract not clear (air cleaner soiled ...)
- Constriction in exhaust system
- Resonance flap switching faulty
Do you wish to check the resonance flap?

Fig. 30 Poor Traction & Power Loss

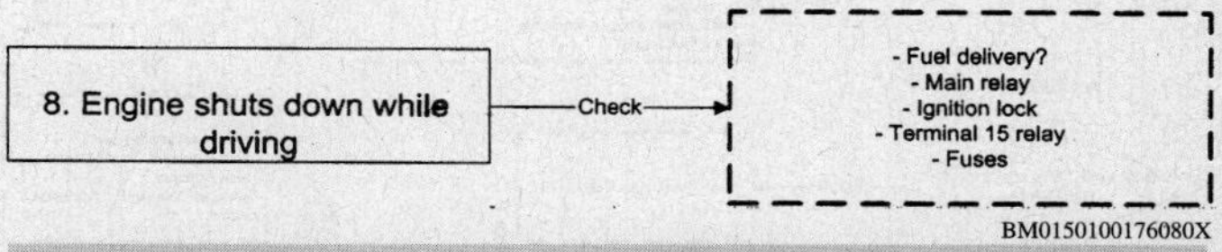

Fig. 31 Engine Shuts Down While Driving

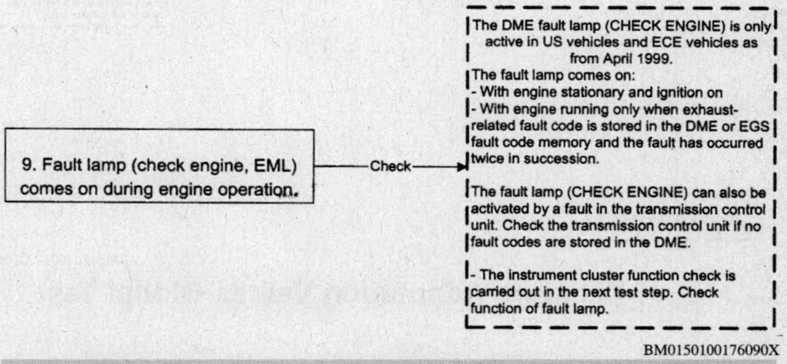

9. Fault lamp (check engine, EML) comes on during engine operation.
Check
The DME fault lamp (CHECK ENGINE) is only active in US vehicles and ECE vehicles as from April 1999.
The fault lamp comes on:
- With engine stationary and ignition on
- With engine running only when exhaust-related fault code is stored in the DME or EGS fault code memory and the fault has occurred twice in succession.
The fault lamp (CHECK ENGINE) can also be activated by a fault in the transmission control unit. Check the transmission control unit if no fault codes are stored in the DME.
- The instrument cluster function check is carried out in the next test step. Check function of fault lamp.
BM0150100176090X

Fig. 32 MIL Lamp Comes On During Engine Operation

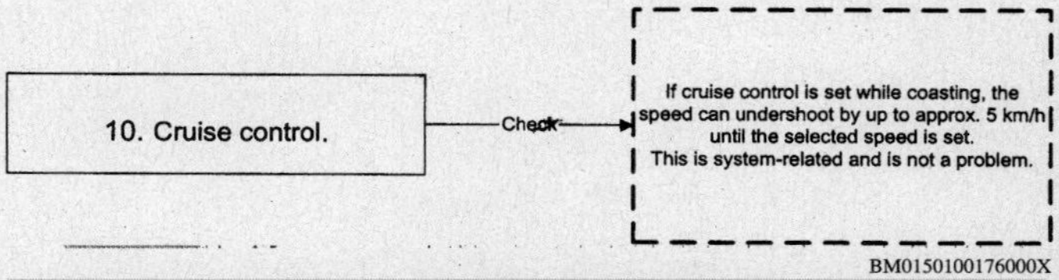

10. Cruise control.
Check
If cruise control is set while coasting, the speed can undershoot by up to approx. 5 km/h until the selected speed is set.
This is system-related and is not a problem.
BM0150100176000X

Fig. 33 Cruise Control

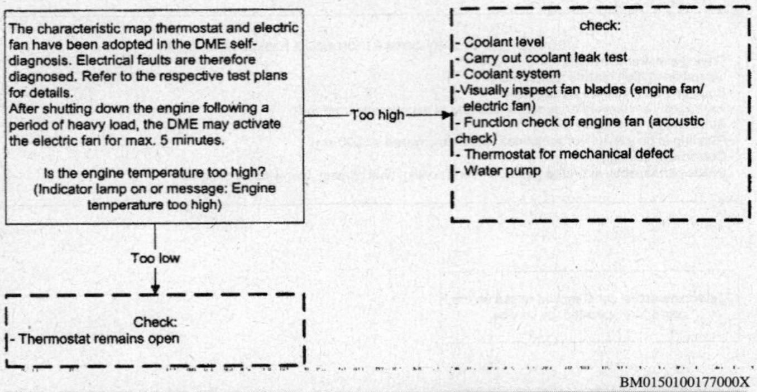

Fig. 34 Engine Temperature Too High/Too Low

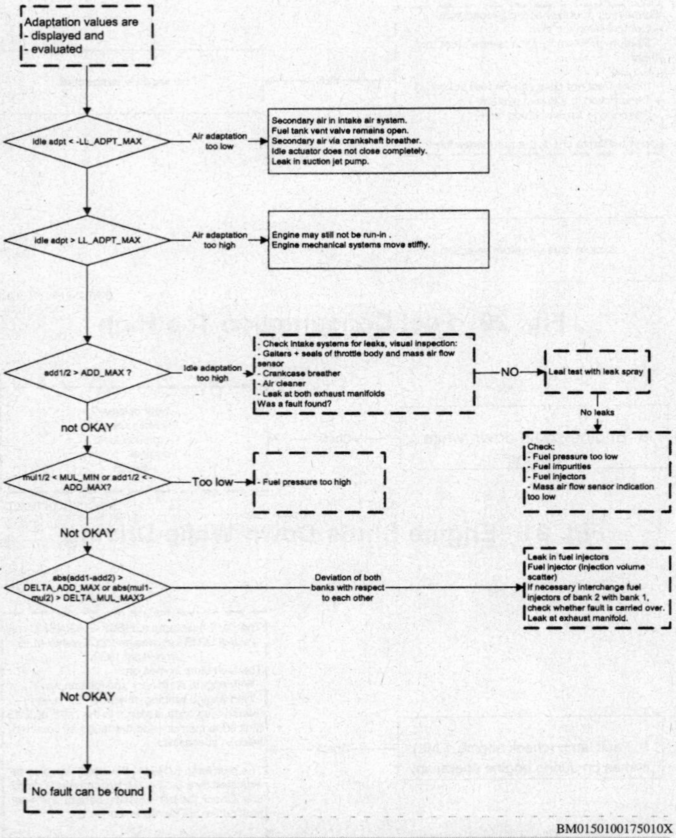

Fig. 36 Mixture Adaptation Values Global Test

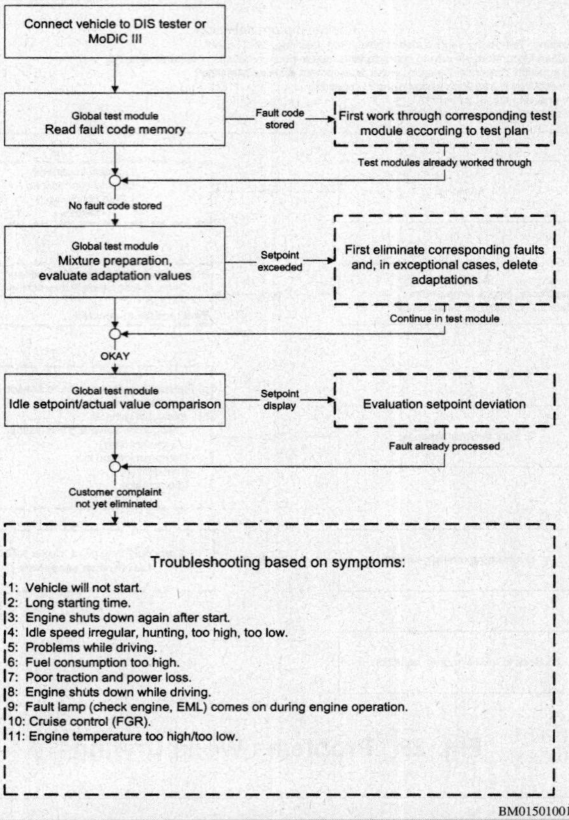

Fig. 35 Fault Symptoms Test

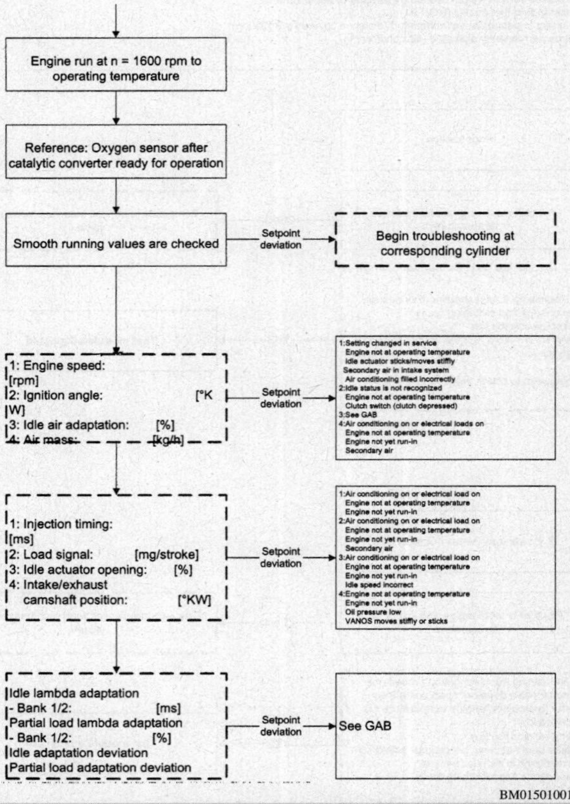

Fig. 37 Idle Setpoint/Actual Value Comparison Global Test

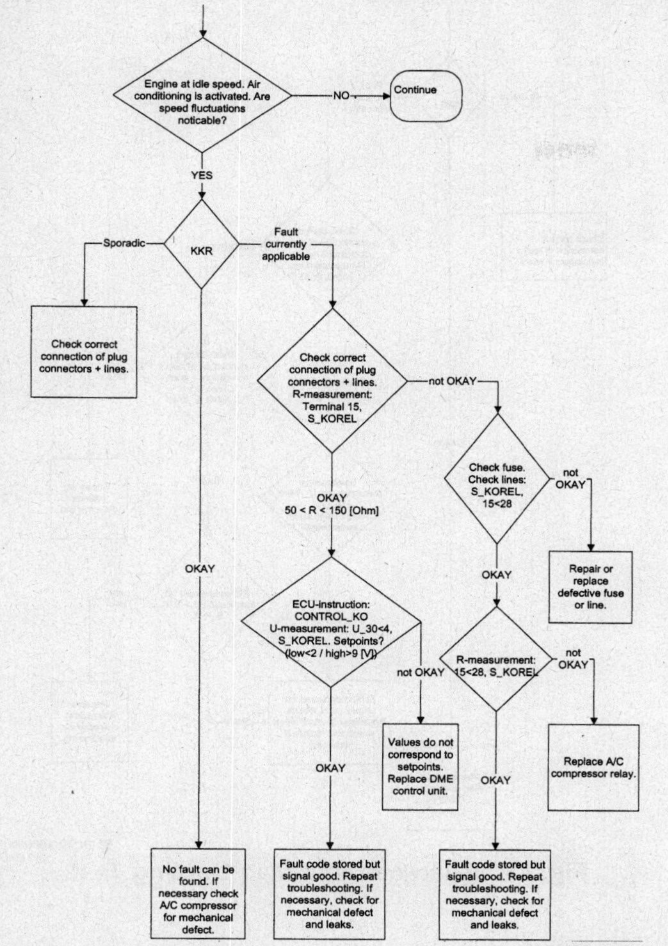

BM0150100161010X

Fig. 38 Air Conditioning Compressor Relay Test (Part 1 of 2)

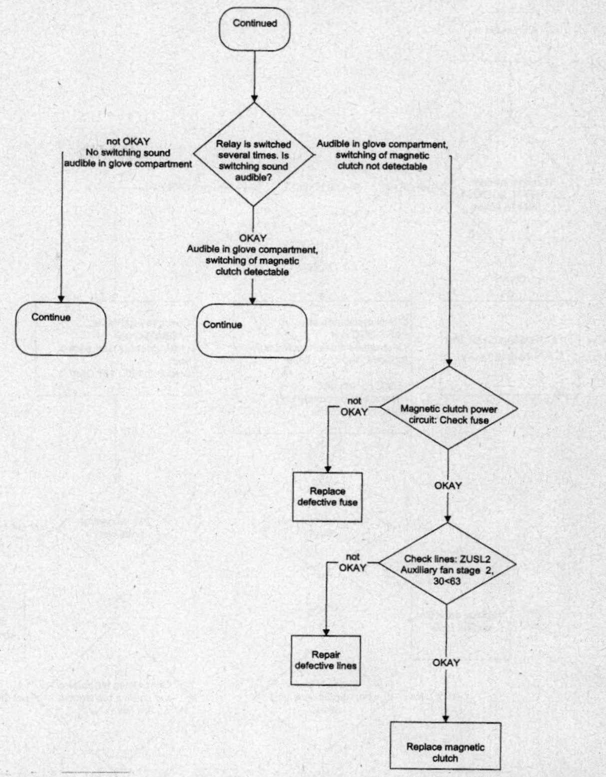

BM0150100161020X

Fig. 38 Air Conditioning Compressor Relay Test (Part 2 of 2)

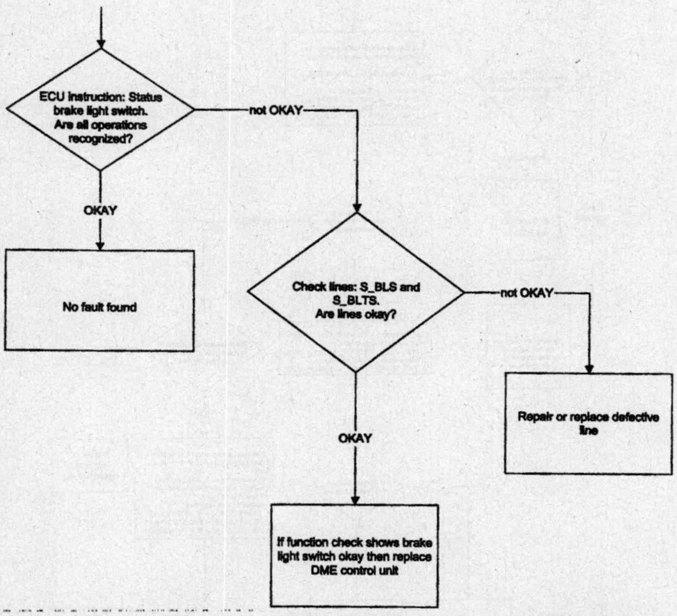

BM0150100132000X

Fig. 39 Brake Lamp Switch Test

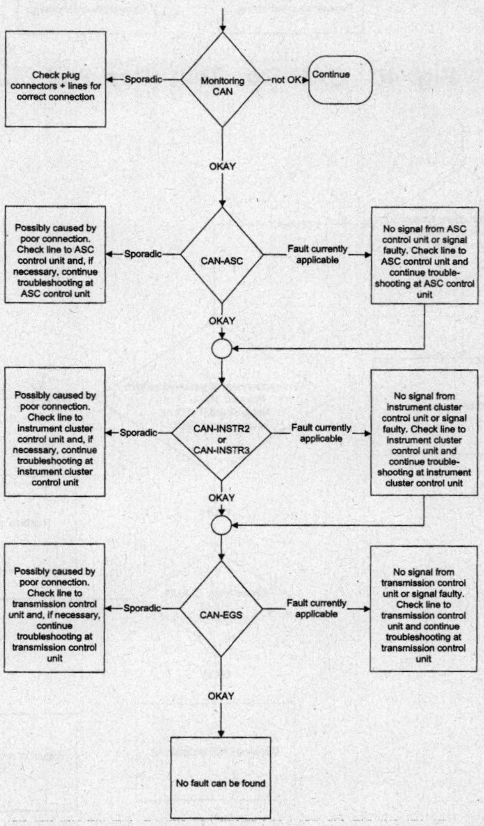

BM0150100166010X

Fig. 40 CAN-Bus Test (Part 1 of 2)

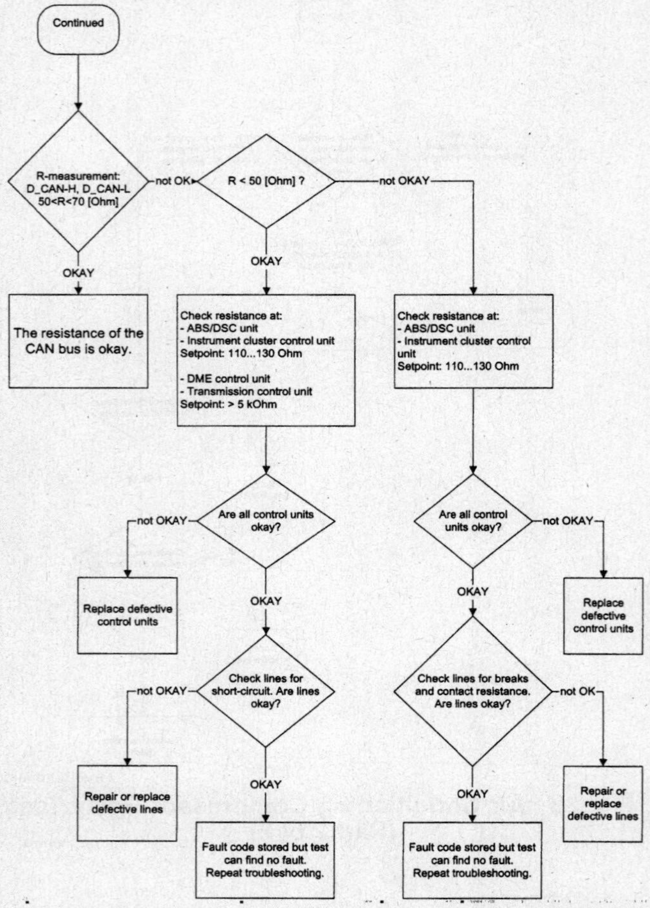

BM0150100166020X

Fig. 40 CAN-Bus Test (Part 2 of 2)

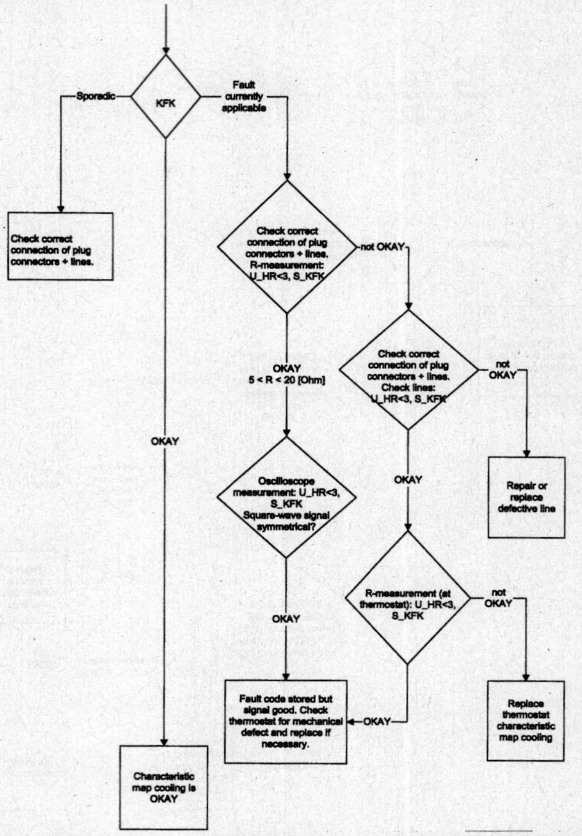

BM0150100139000X

Fig. 41 Characteristic Map Cooling Test

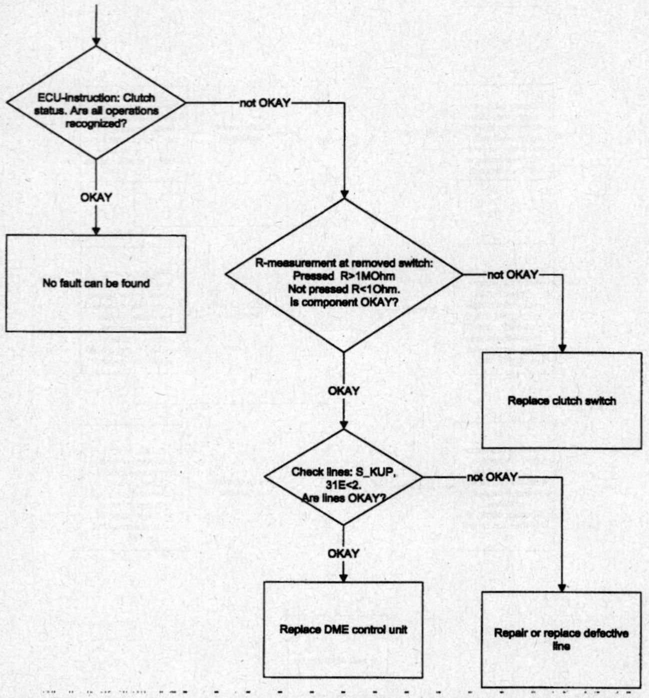

BM0150100135000X

Fig. 42 Clutch Switch Test

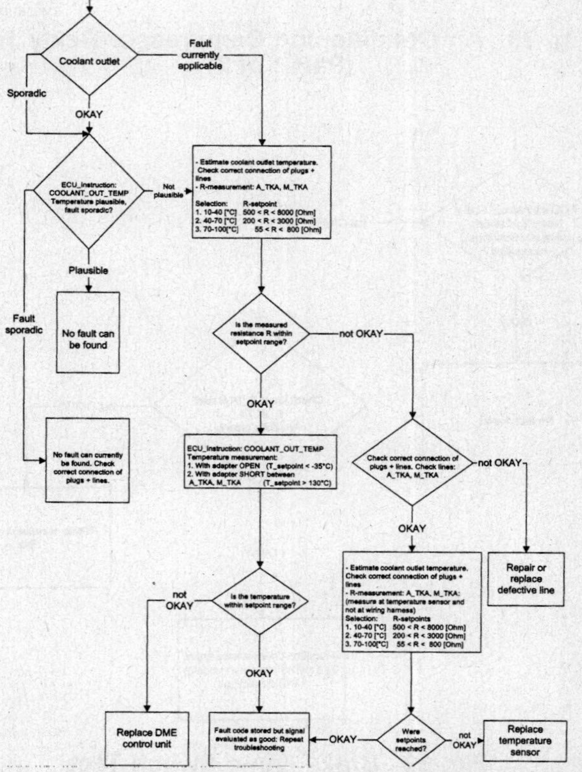

BM0150100150000X

Fig. 43 Coolant Outlet Temperature Test

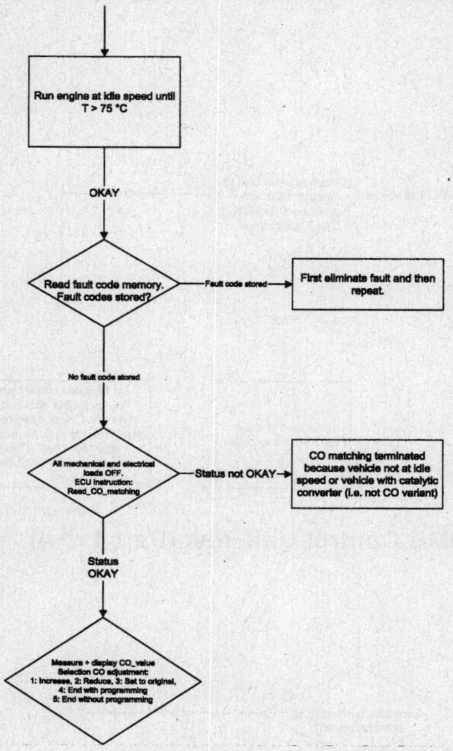

BM0150100133000X

Fig. 44 CO Matching Test

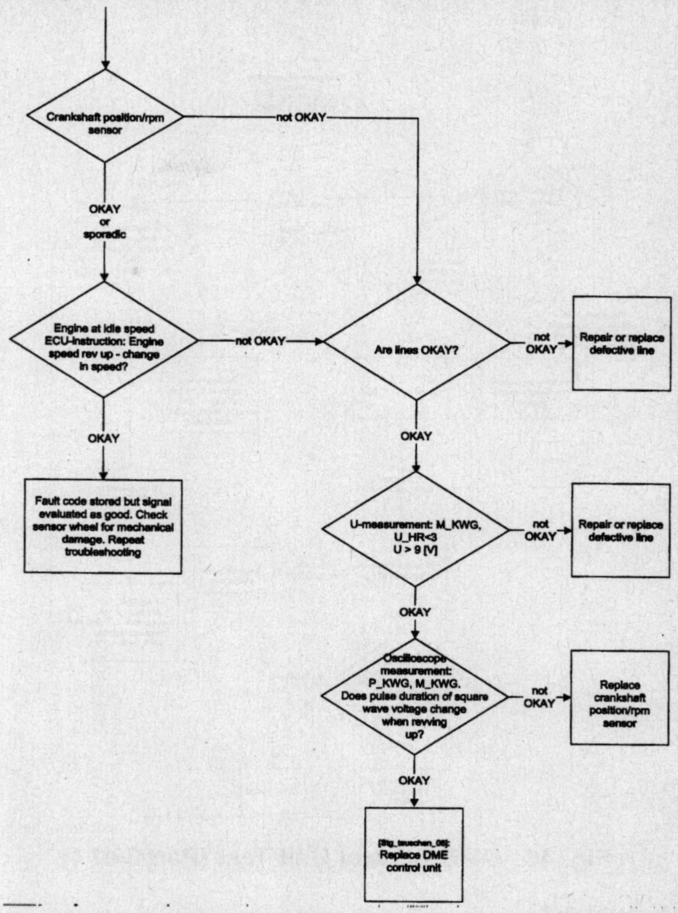

BM0150100138000X

Fig. 45 Crankshaft Position Sensor Test

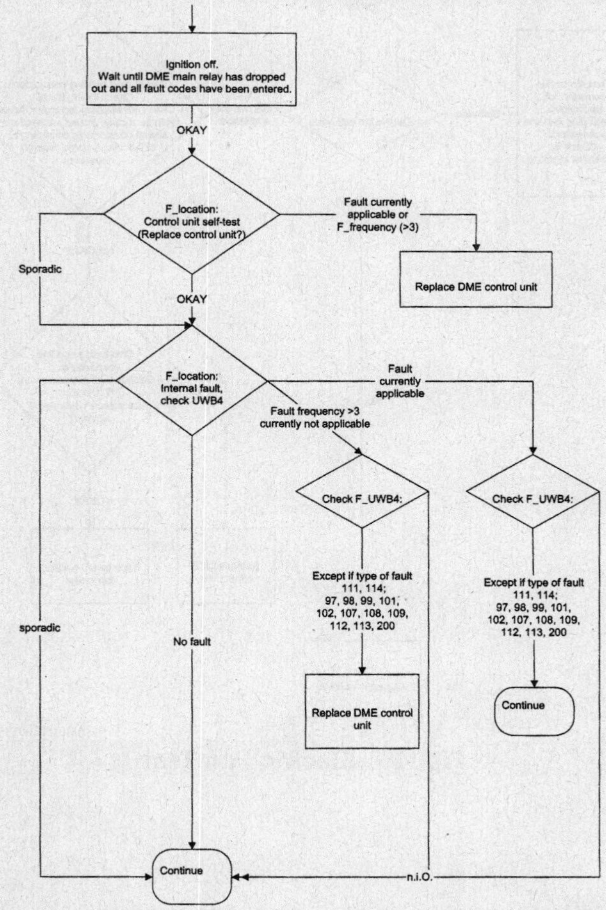

BM0150100171010X

Fig. 46 DME Control Unit Test (Part 1 of 4)

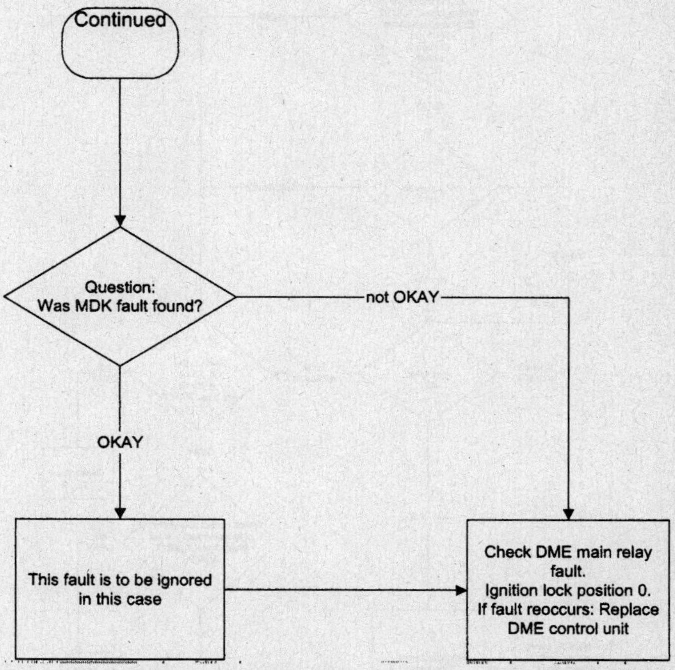

BM0150100171020X

Fig. 46 DME Control Unit Test (Part 2 of 4)

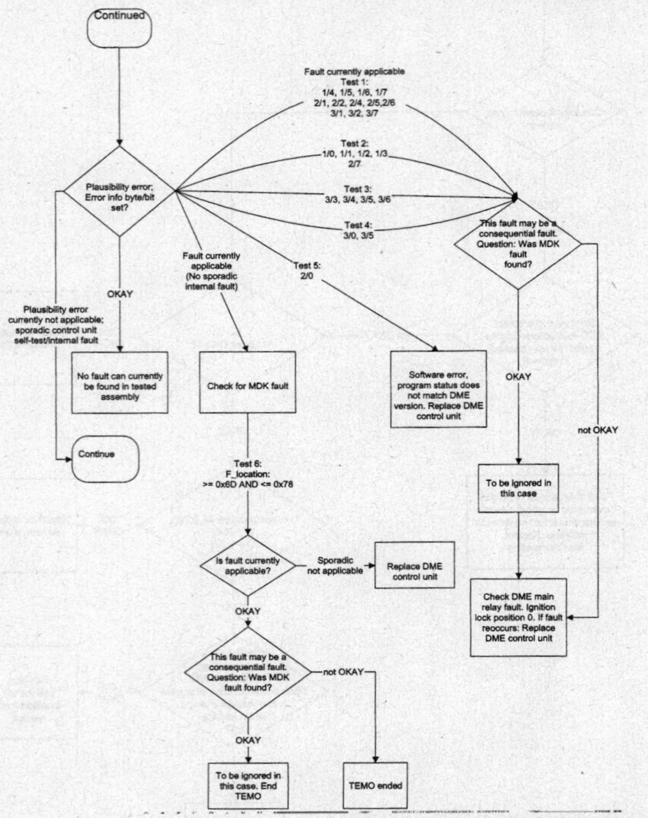

BM0150100171030X

Fig. 46 DME Control Unit Test (Part 3 of 4)

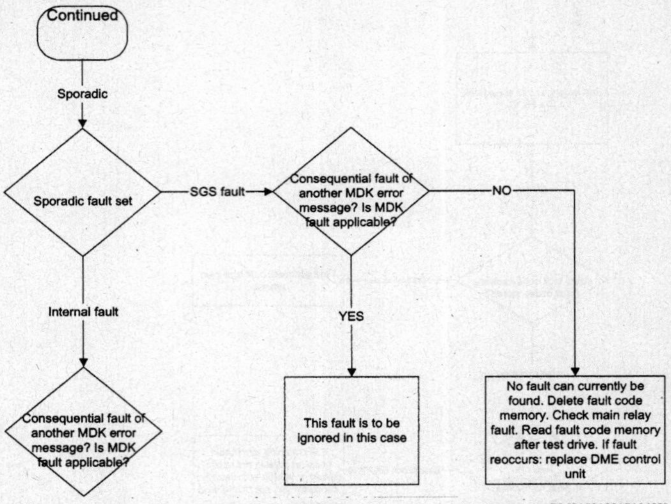

BM0150100171040X

Fig. 46 DME Control Unit Test (Part 4 of 4)

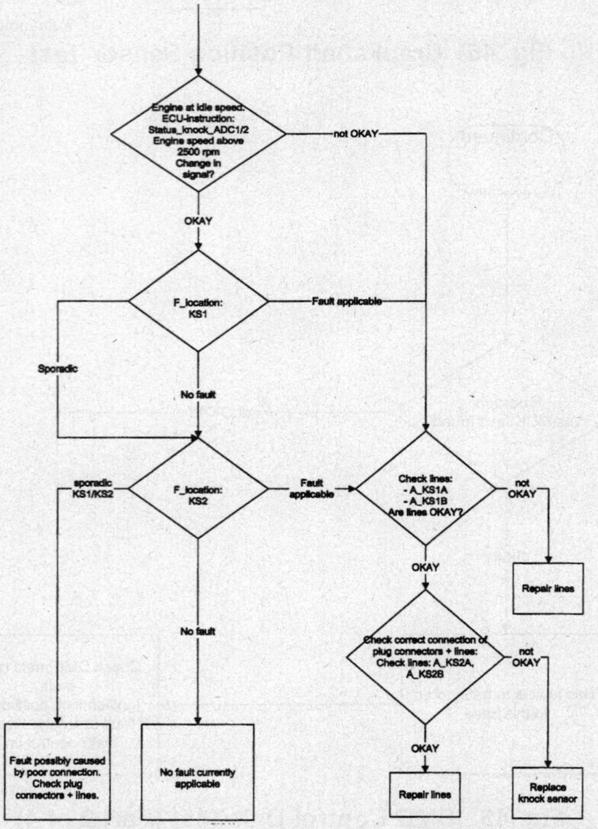

BM0150100141000X

Fig. 47 Double Knock Sensor Test

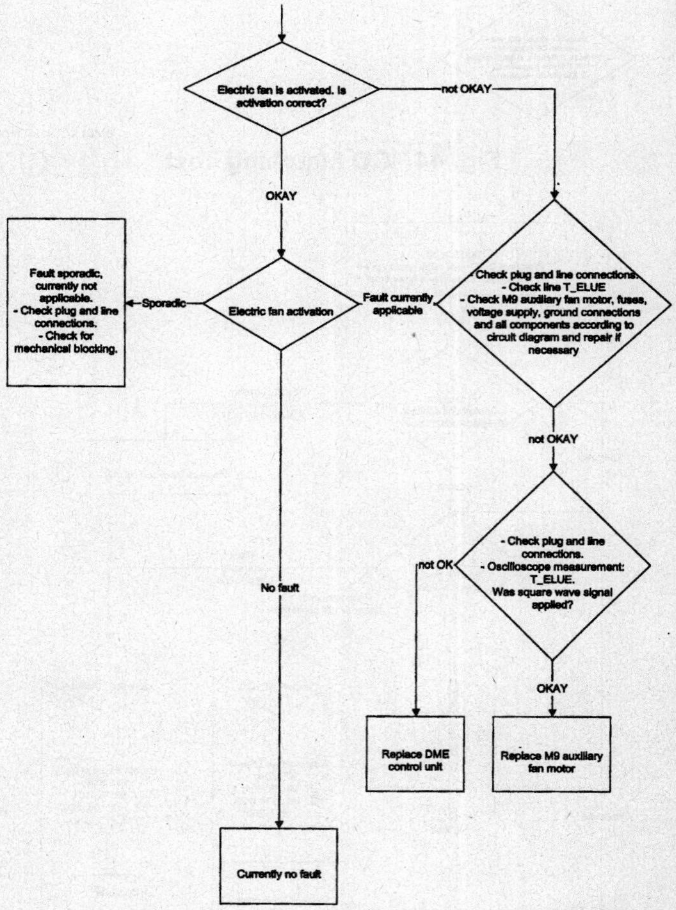

BM0150100136000X

Fig. 48 Electric Fan Test

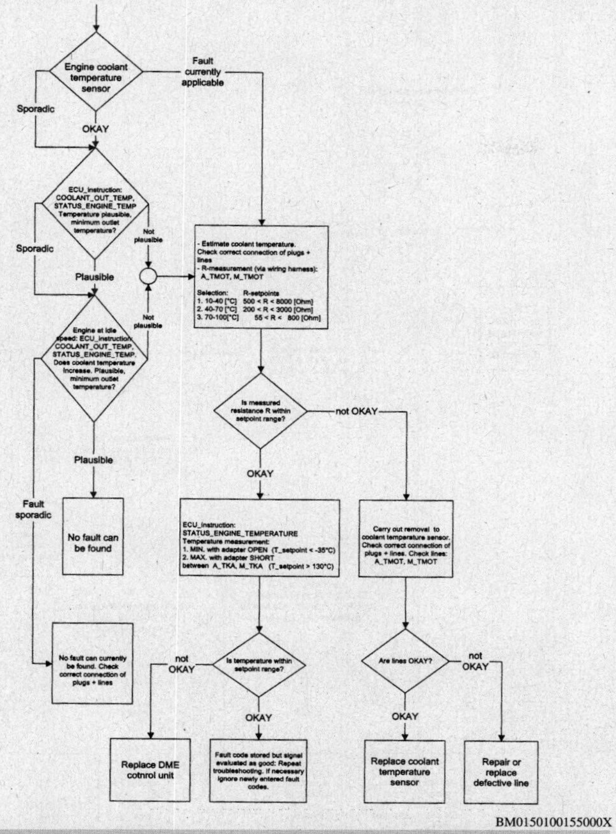

Fig. 49 Engine Coolant Temperature Sensor Test

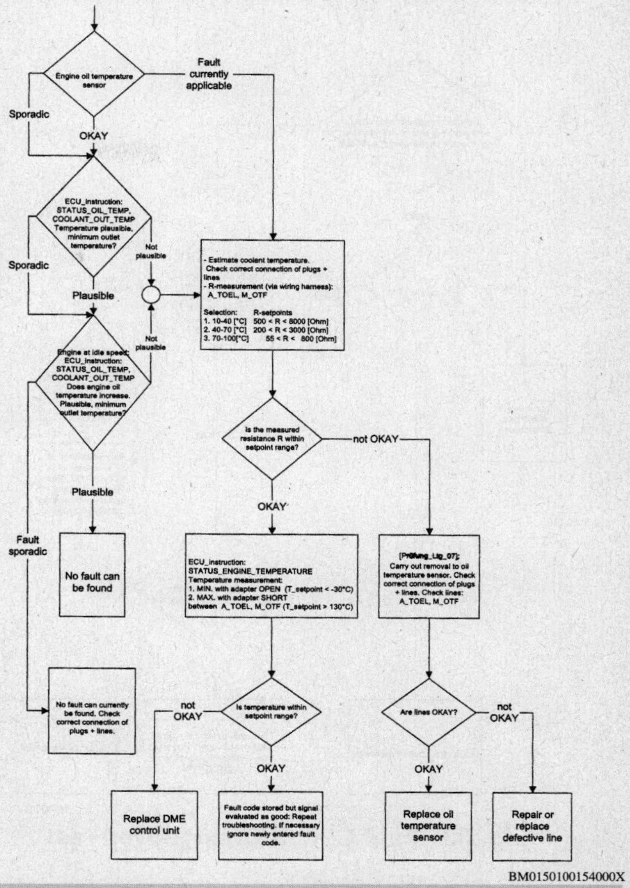

Fig. 50 Engine Oil Temperature Sensor Test

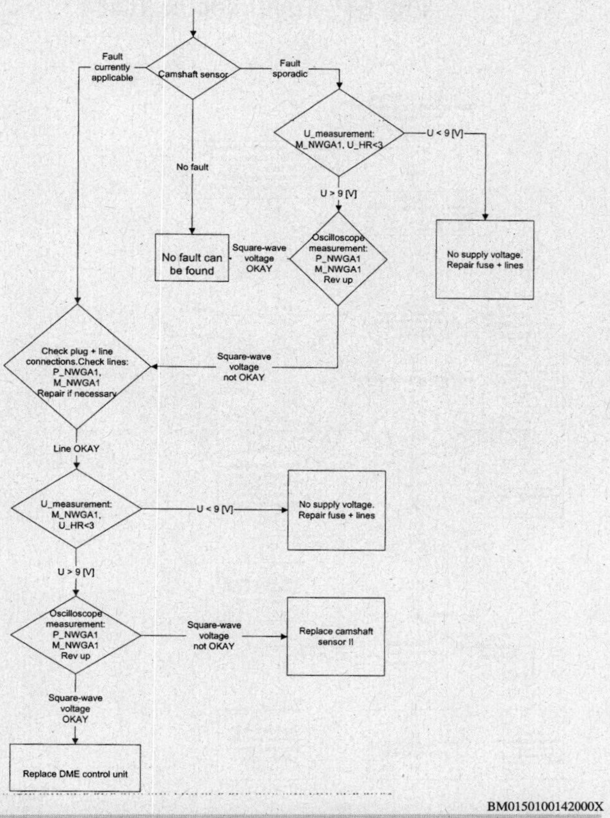

Fig. 51 Exhaust Camshaft Sensor Test

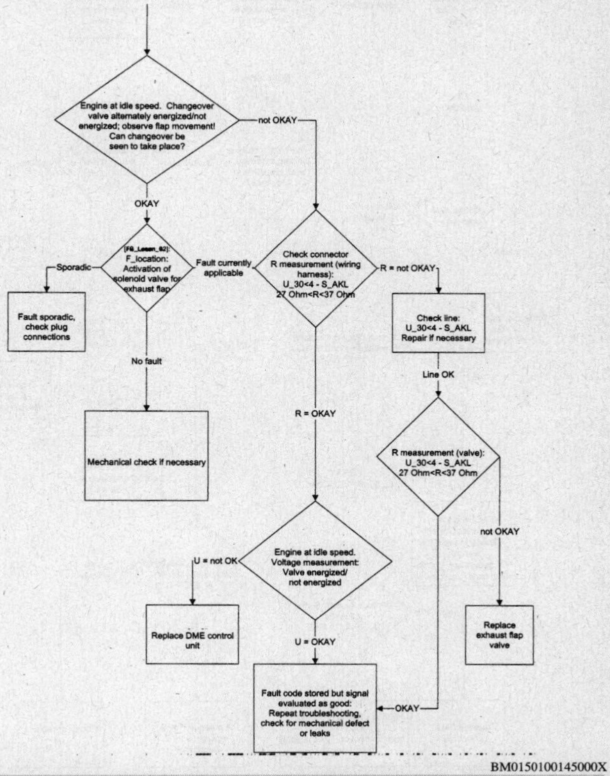

Fig. 52 Exhaust Flap Test

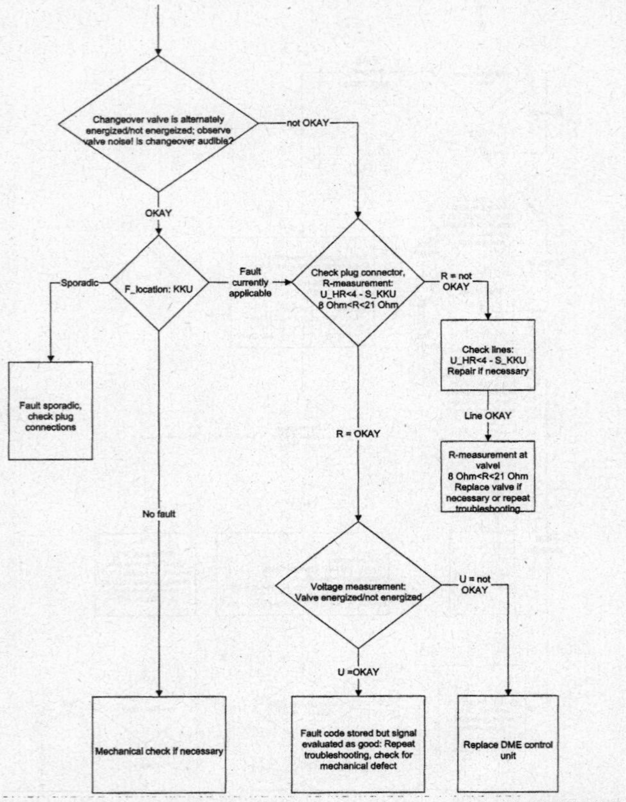

BM0150100172000X

Fig. 53 Fuel Circuit Changeover Test

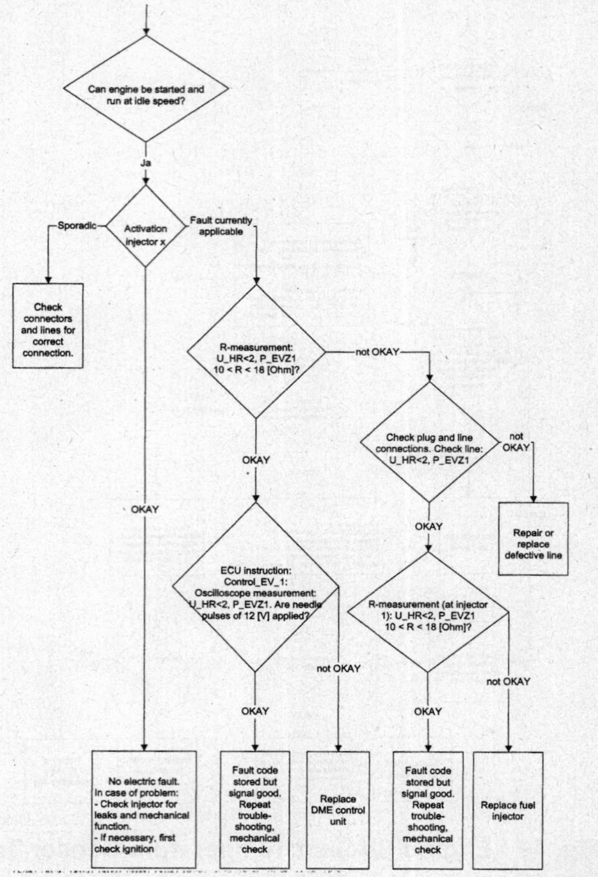

BM0150100147000X

Fig. 54 Fuel Injector Test

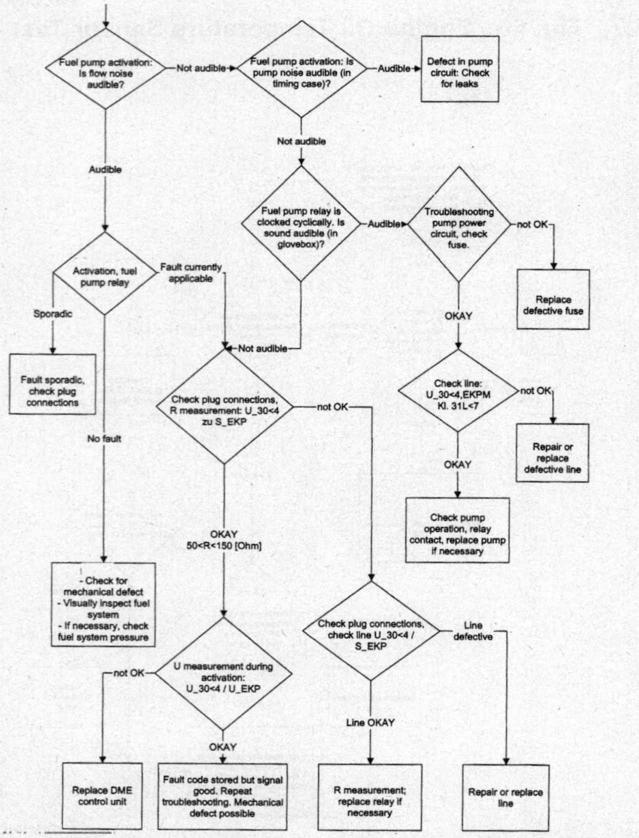

BM0150100152000X

Fig. 55 Fuel Pump Relay Test

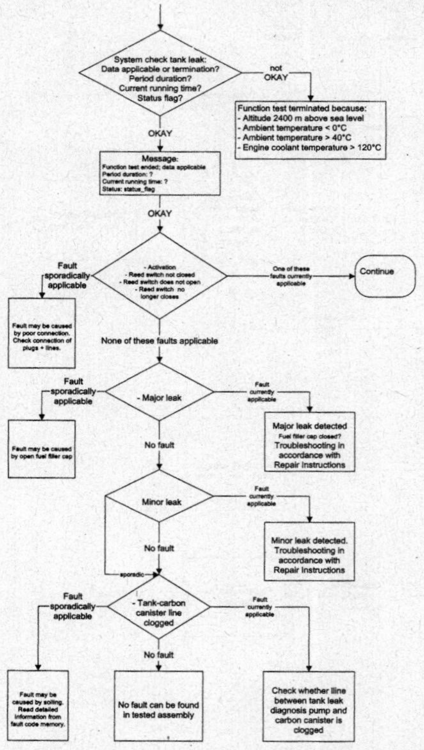

BM0150100169010X

Fig. 56 Fuel Tank Leak Diagnosis Pump Test (Part 1 of 2)

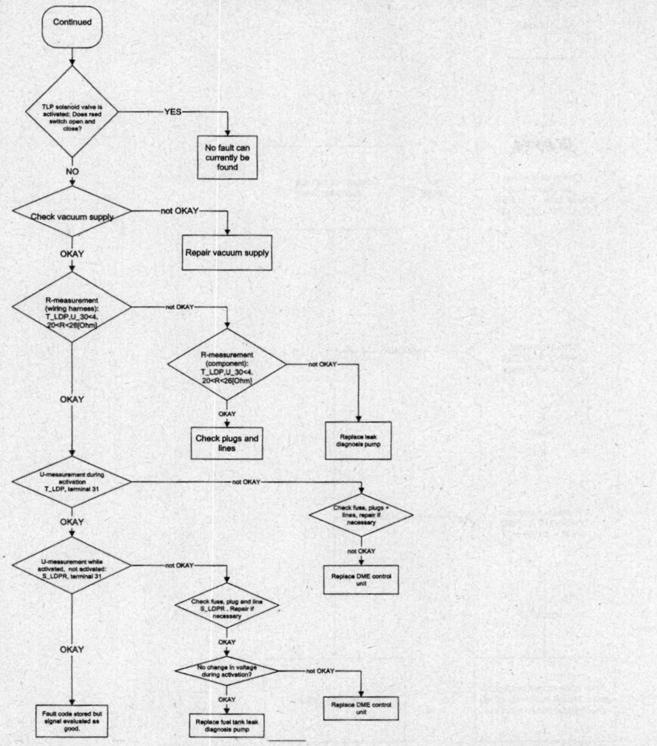

BM0150100169020X

Fig. 56 Fuel Tank Leak Diagnosis Pump Test (Part 2 of 2)

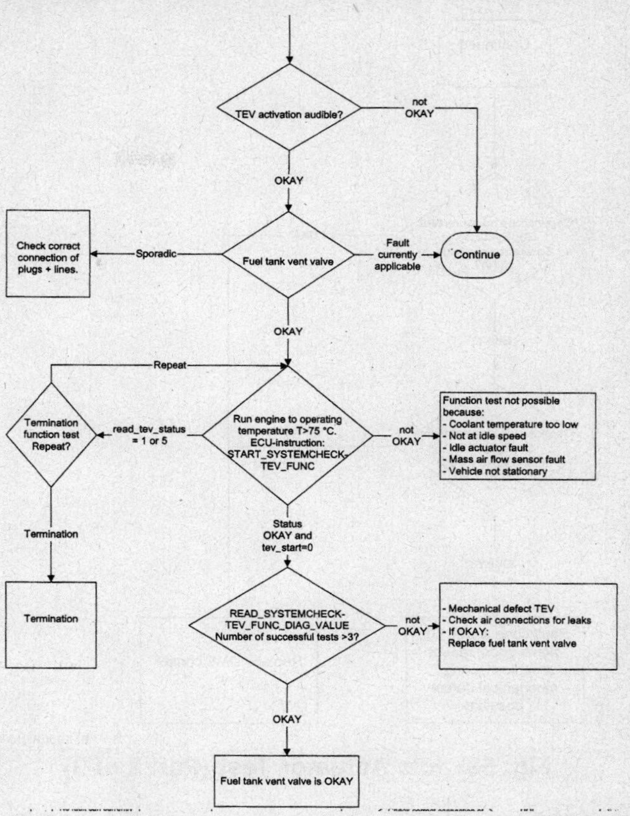

BM0150100158010X

Fig. 57 Fuel Tank Vent Valve Test (Part 1 of 2)

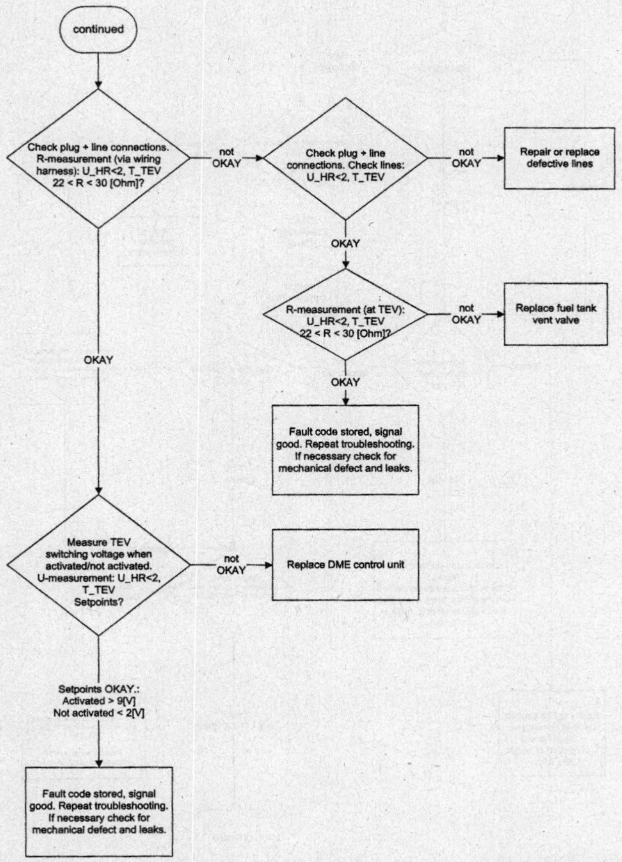

BM0150100158020X

Fig. 57 Fuel Tank Vent Valve Test (Part 2 of 2)

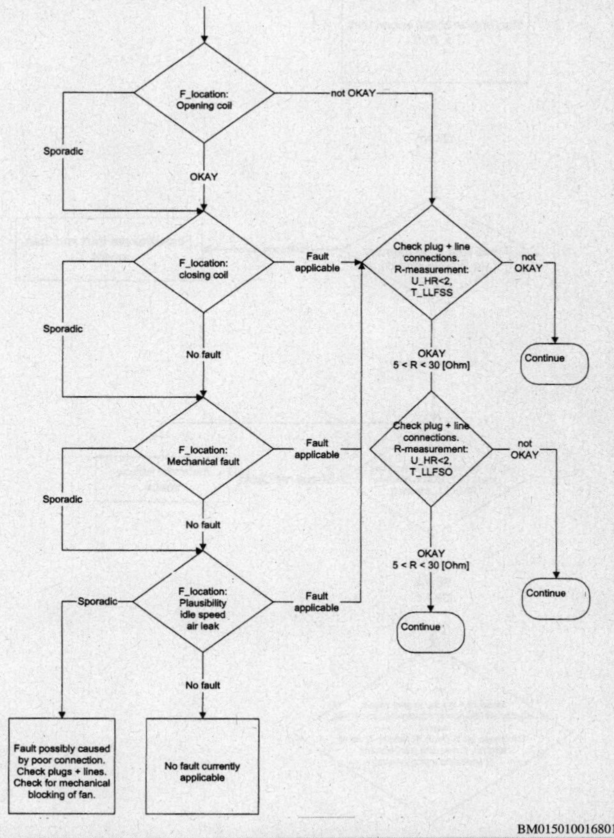

BM0150100168010X

Fig. 58 Idle Actuator Test (Part 1 of 3)

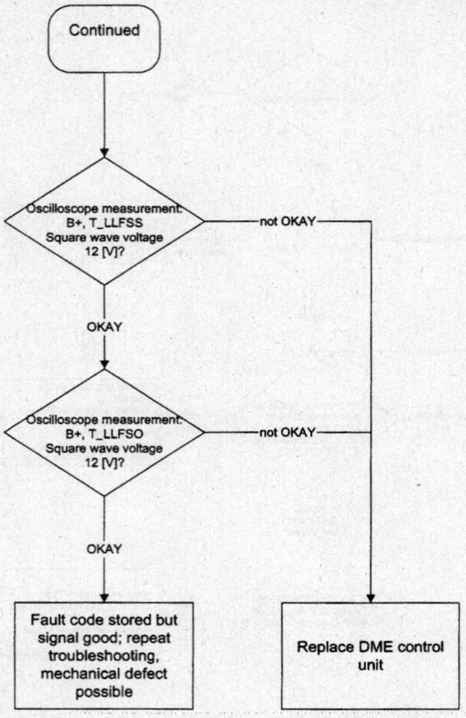

BM0150100168020X

Fig. 58 Idle Actuator Test (Part 2 of 3)

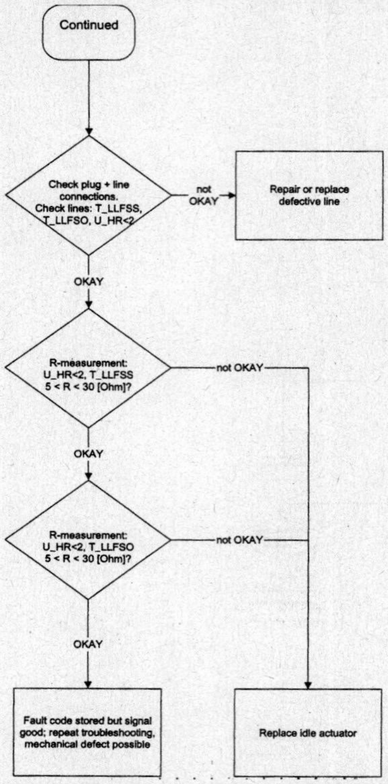

BM0150100168030X

Fig. 58 Idle Actuator Test (Part 3 of 3)

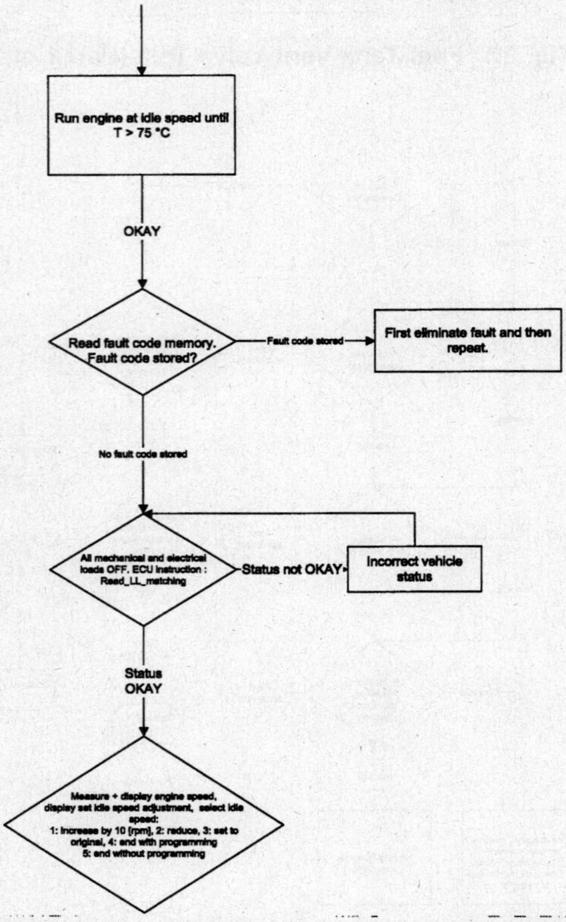

BM0150100134000X

Fig. 59 Idle Speed Matching Test

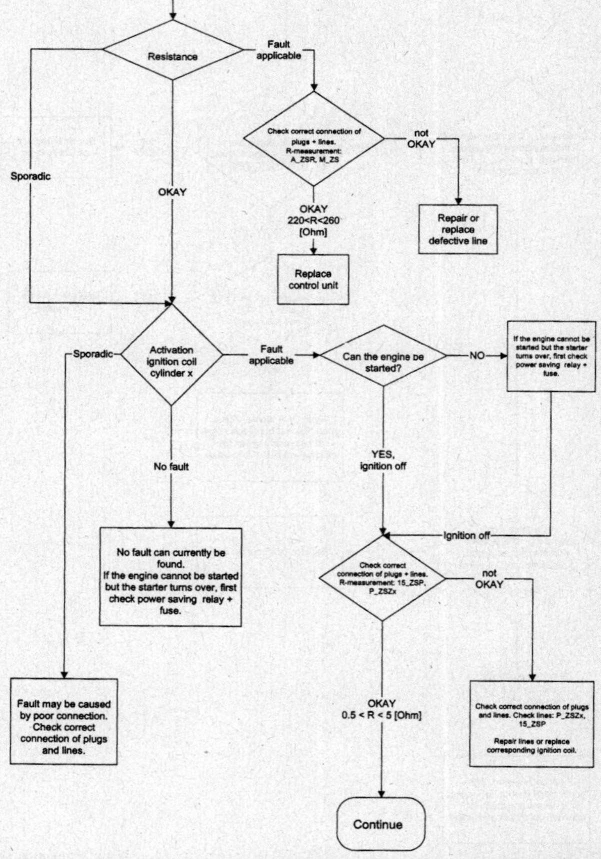

BM0150100165010X

Fig. 60 Ignition Coil Test (Part 1 of 2)

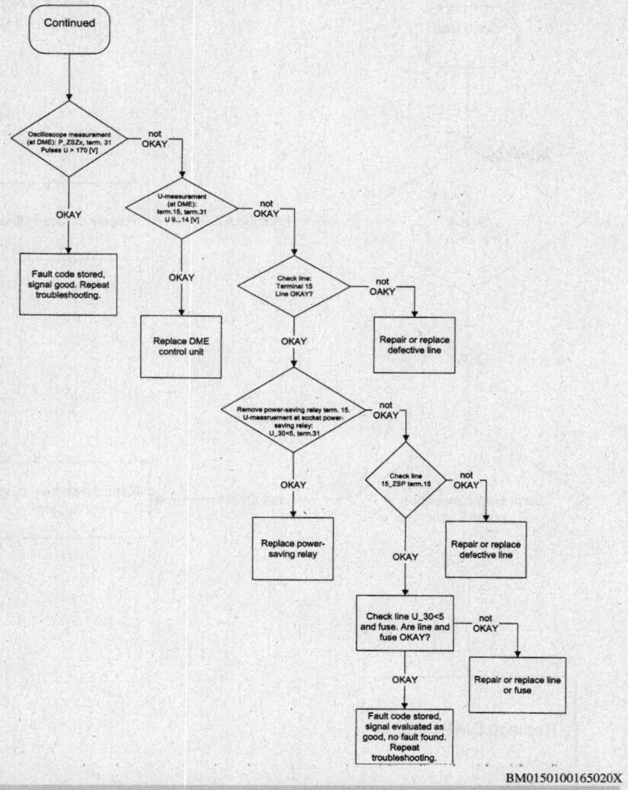

Fig. 60 Ignition Coil Test (Part 2 of 2)

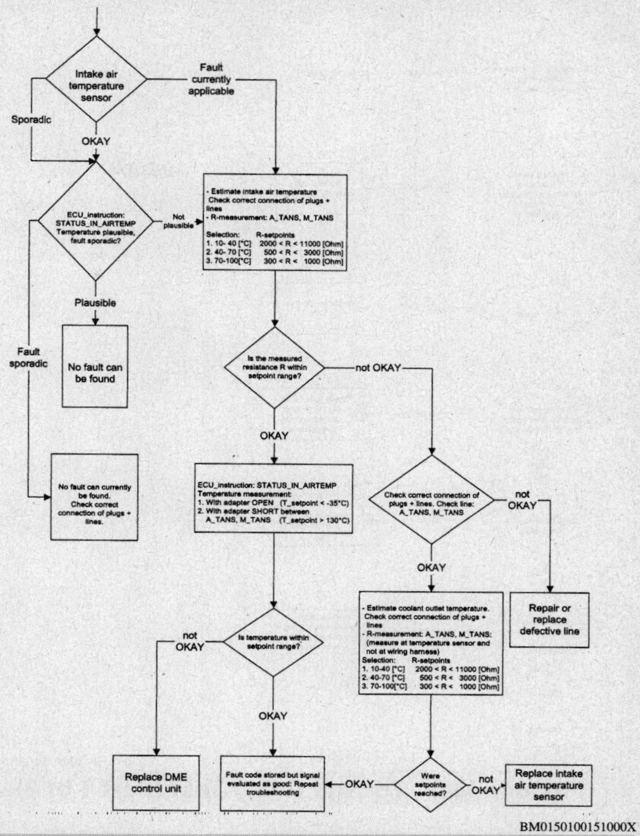

Fig. 61 Intake Air Temperature Sensor Test

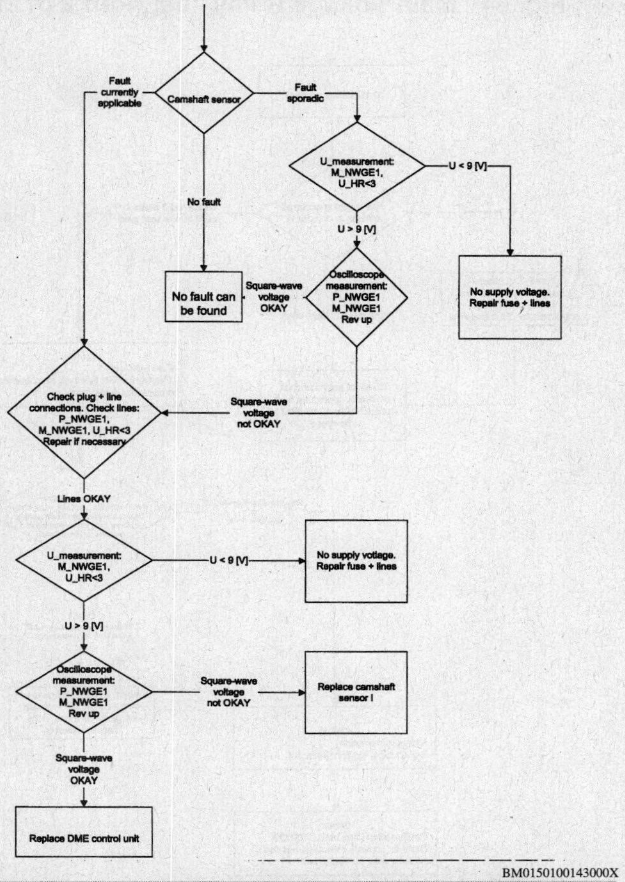

Fig. 62 Intake Camshaft Sensor Test

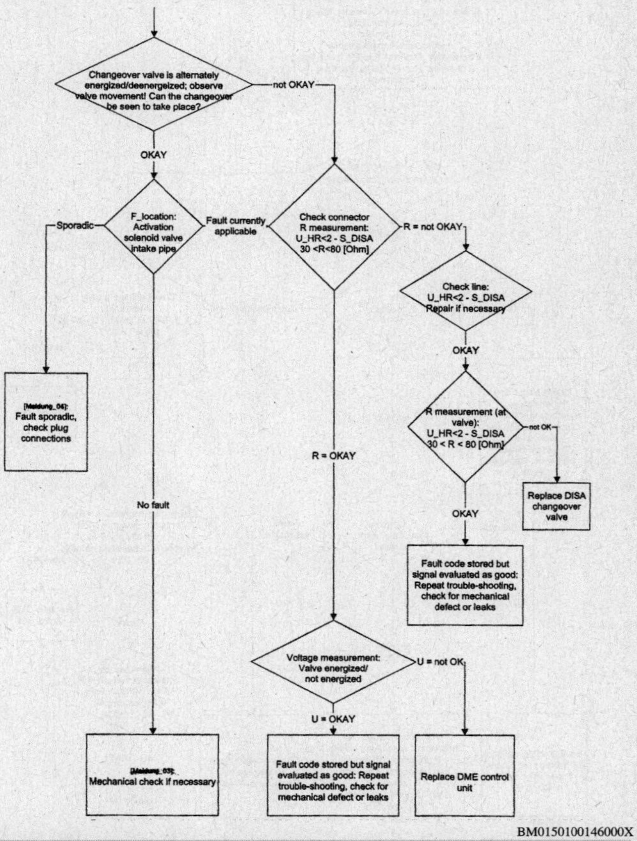

Fig. 63 Intake Pipe Changeover Test

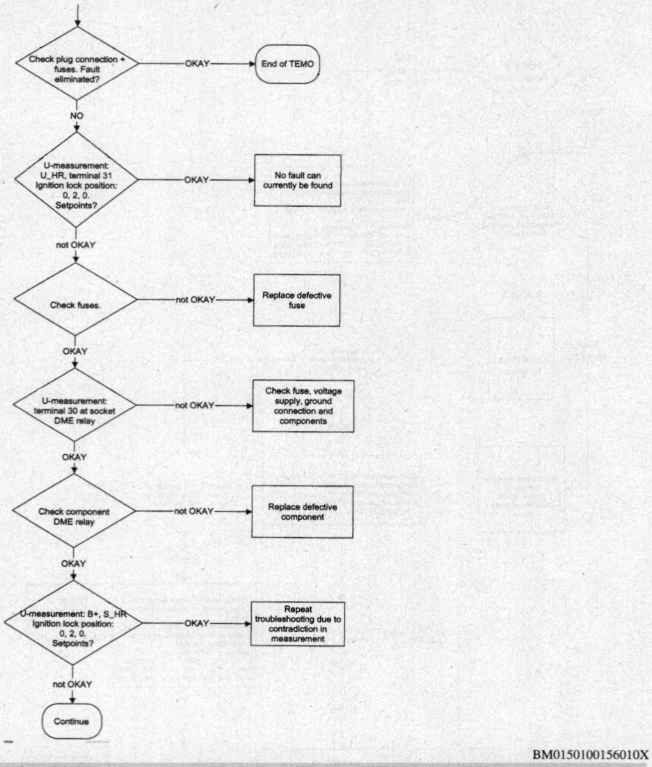

Fig. 64 Main Voltage Relay Test (Part 1 of 2)

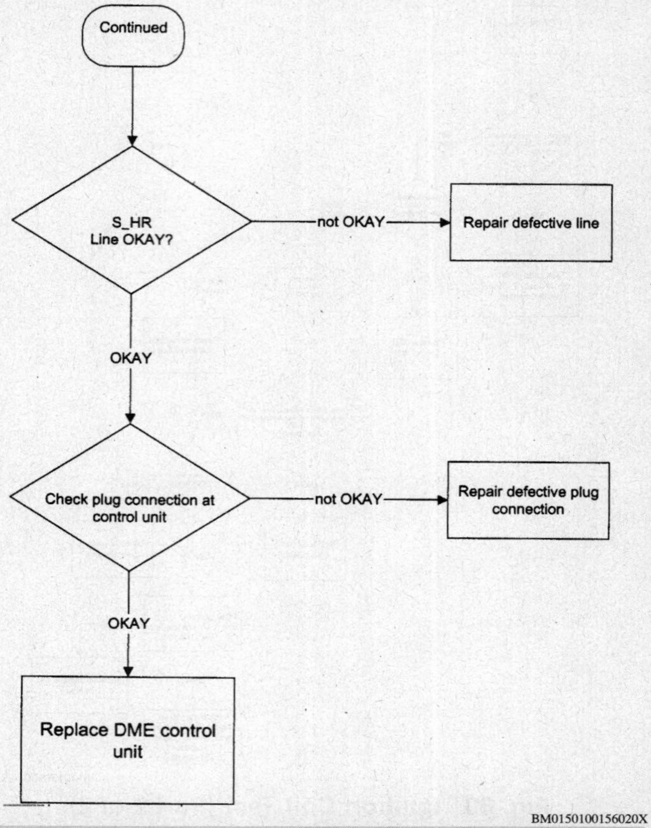

Fig. 64 Main Voltage Relay Test (Part 2 of 2)

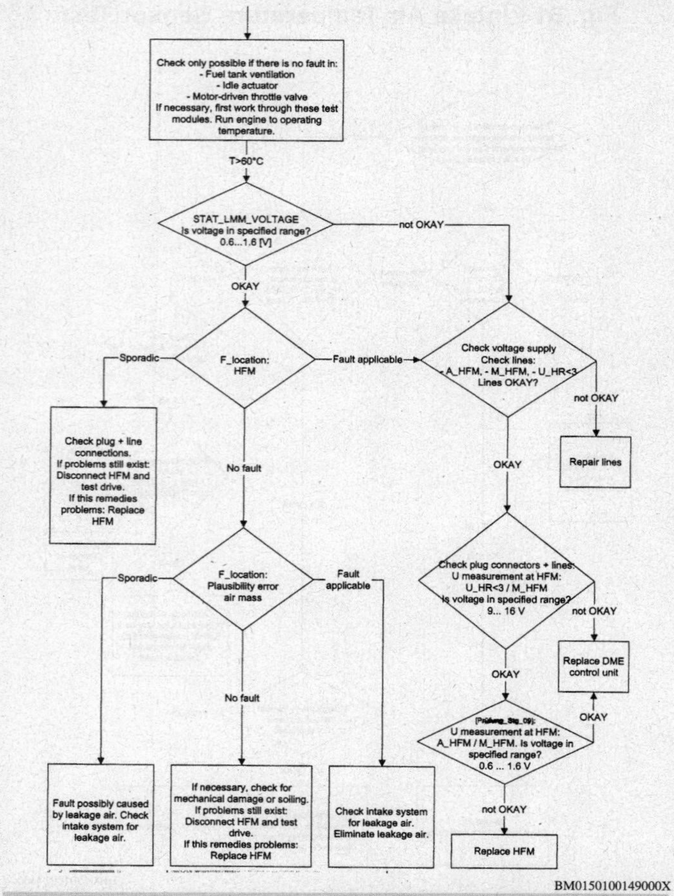

Fig. 65 Mass Air Flow Sensor Test

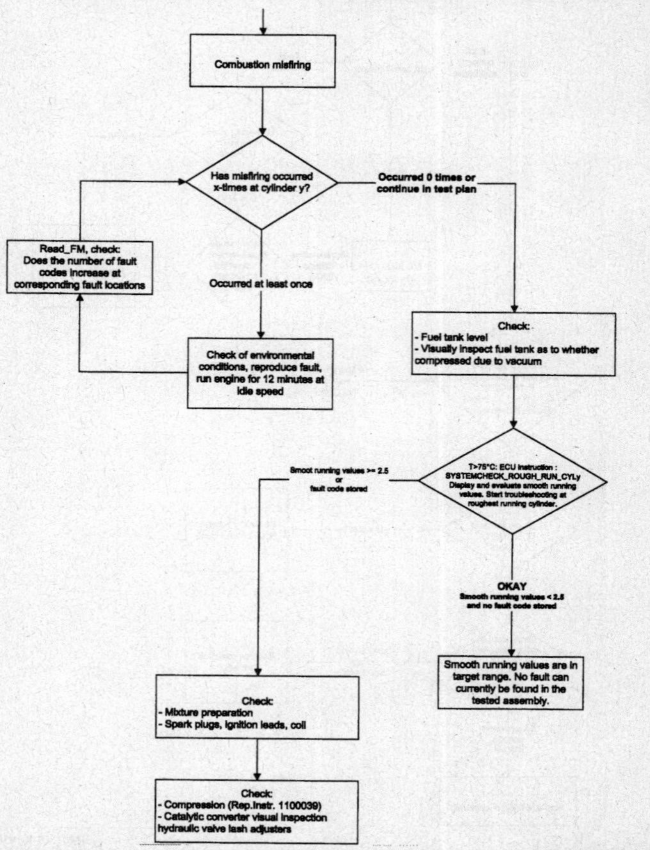

Fig. 66 Misfire Detection Test

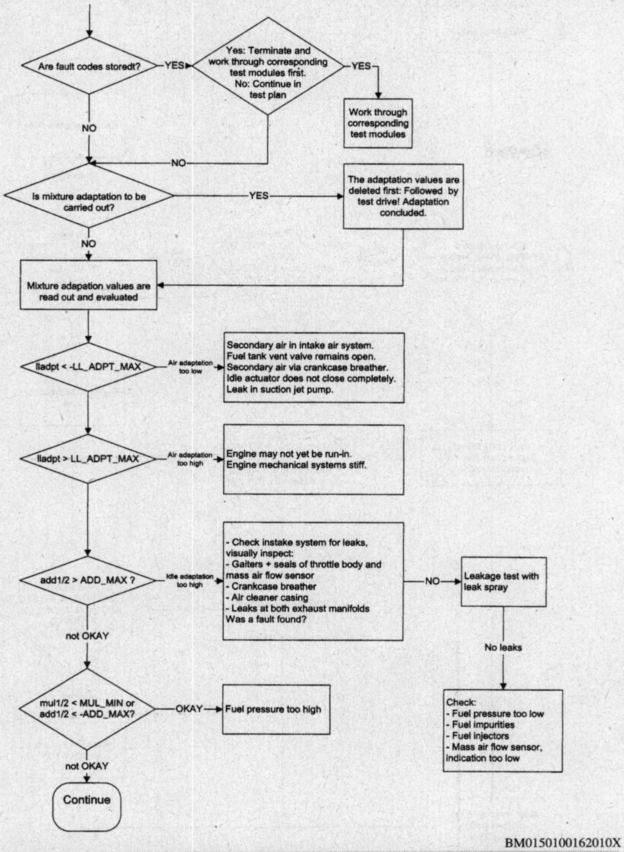

Fig. 67 Mixture Preparation Test (Part 1 of 2)

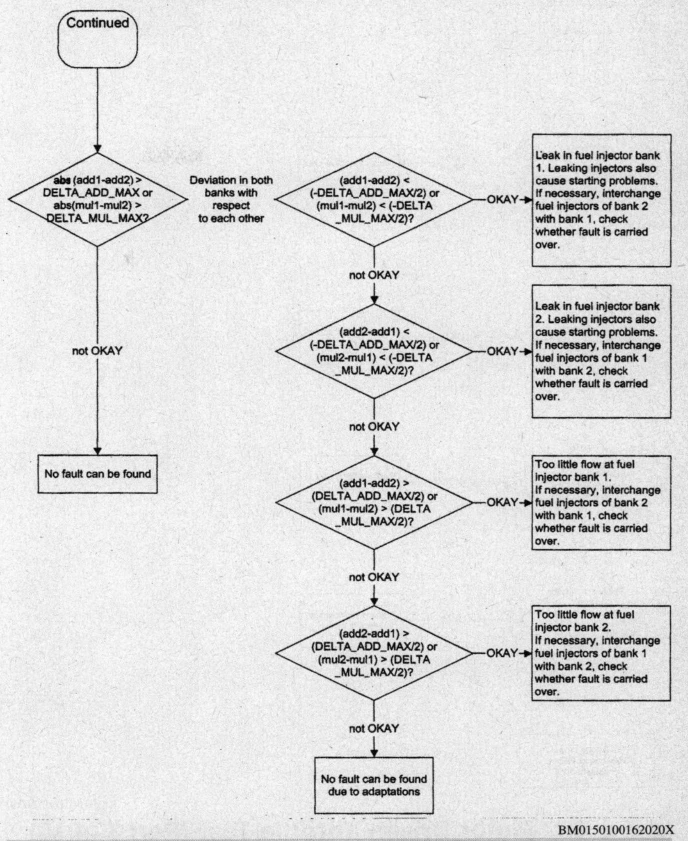

Fig. 67 Mixture Preparation Test (Part 2 of 2)

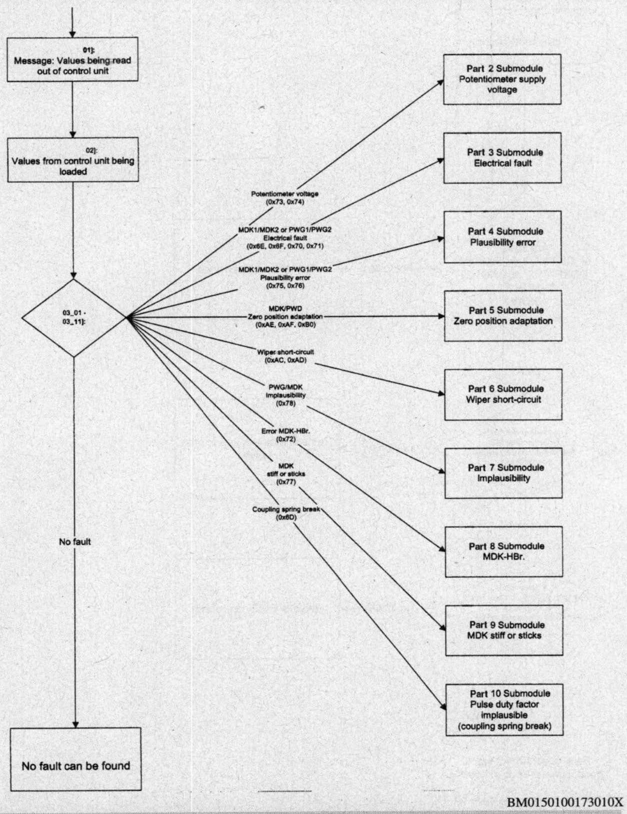

Fig. 68 Motor Driven Throttle Test (Part 1 of 10)

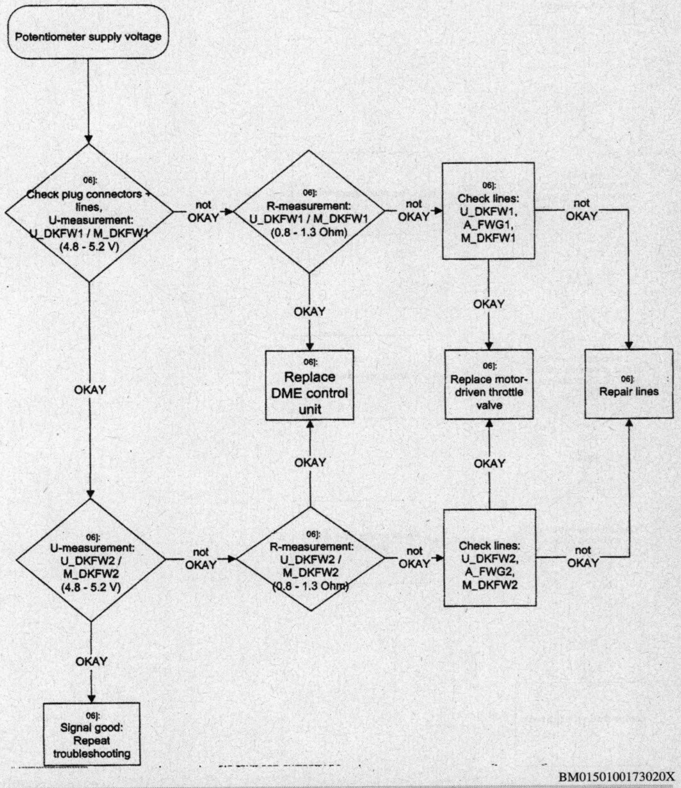

Fig. 68 Motor Driven Throttle Test (Part 2 of 10)

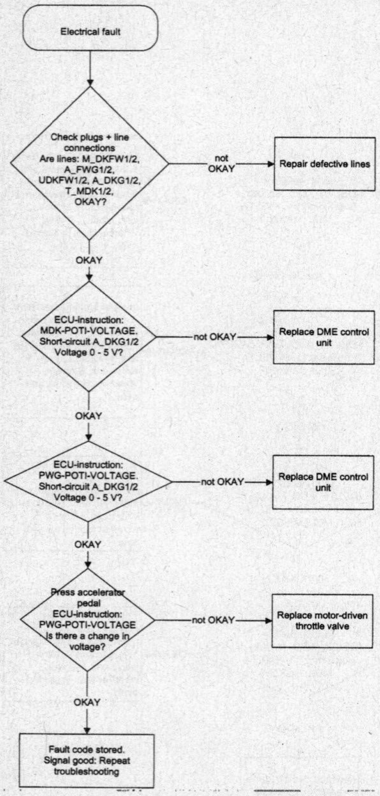

BM0150100173030X

Fig. 68 Motor Driven Throttle Test (Part 3 of 10)

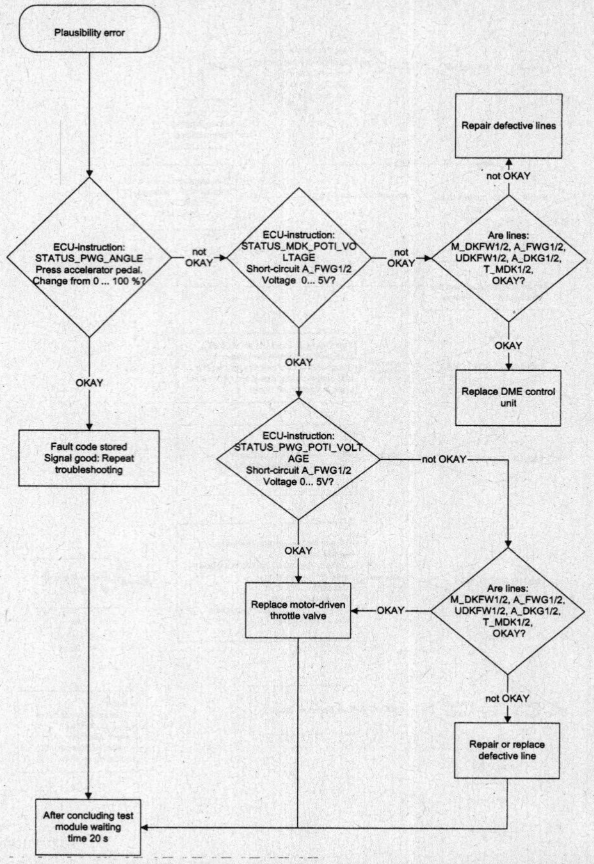

BM0150100173040X

Fig. 68 Motor Driven Throttle Test (Part 4 of 10)

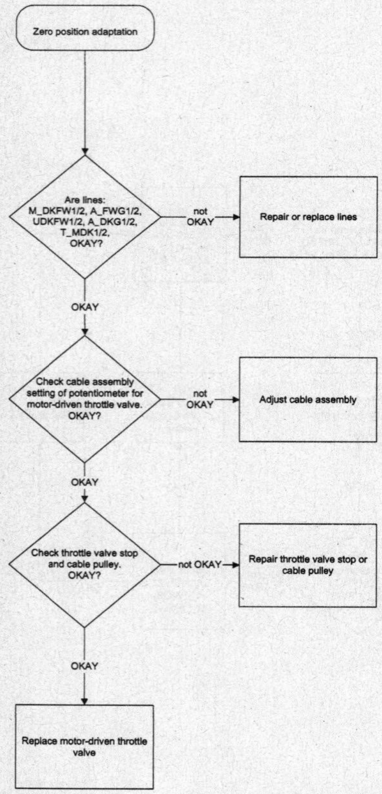

BM0150100173050X

Fig. 68 Motor Driven Throttle Test (Part 5 of 10)

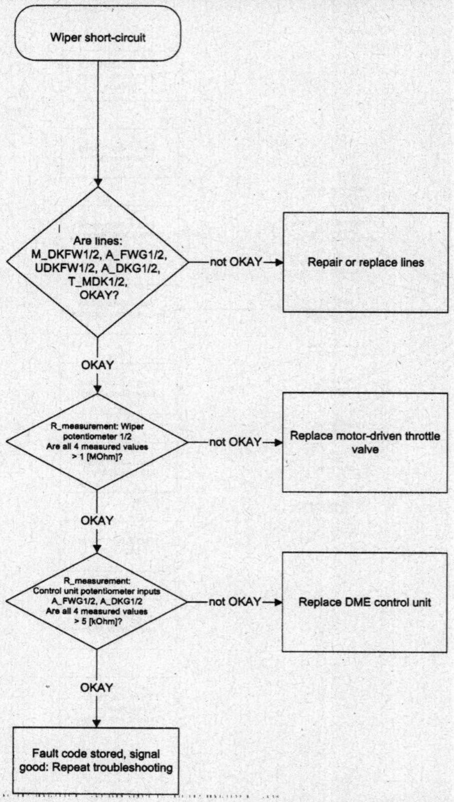

BM0150100173060X

Fig. 68 Motor Driven Throttle Test (Part 6 of 10)

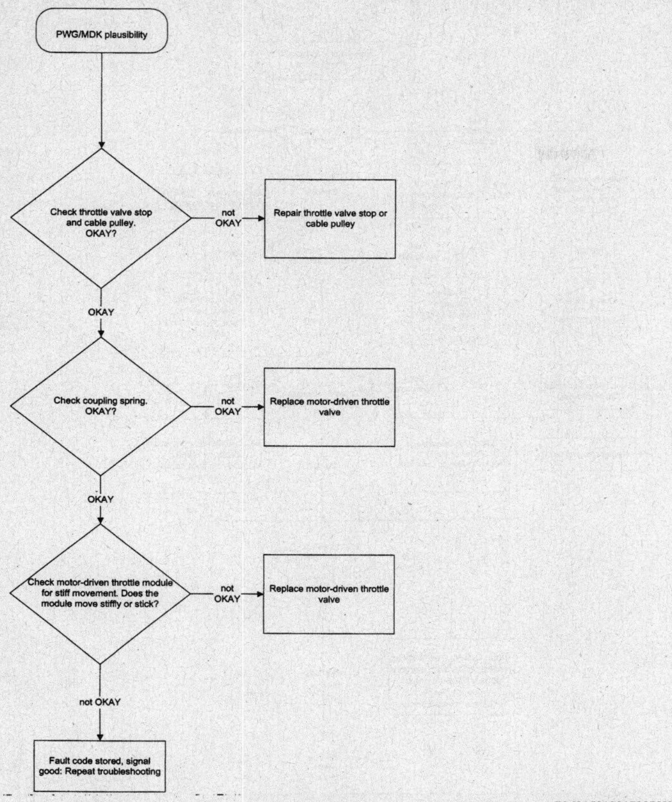

BM0150100173070X

Fig. 68 Motor Driven Throttle Test (Part 7 of 10)

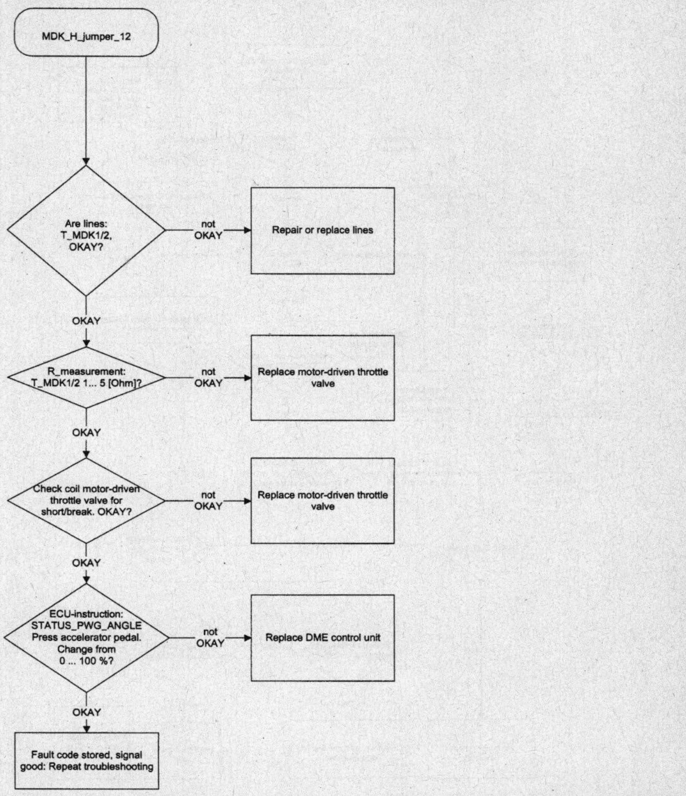

BM0150100173080X

Fig. 68 Motor Driven Throttle Test (Part 8 of 10)

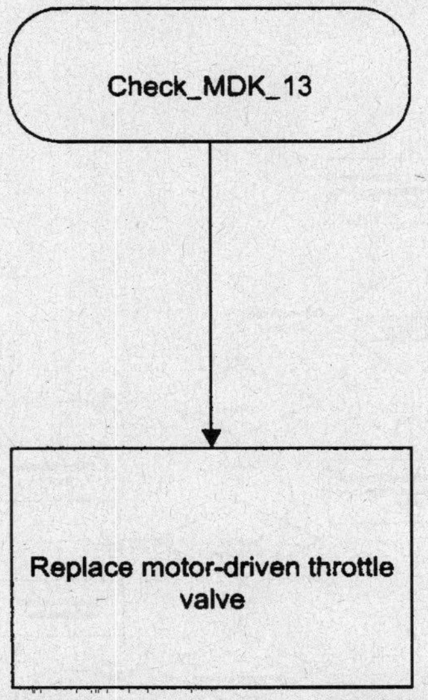

BM0150100173090X

Fig. 68 Motor Driven Throttle Test (Part 9 of 10)

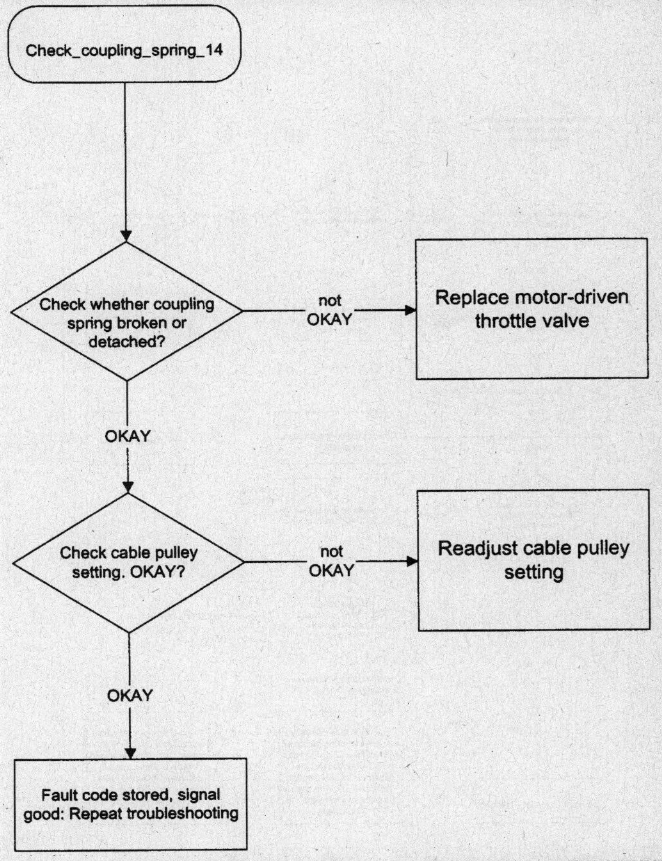

BM0150100173000X

Fig. 68 Motor Driven Throttle Test (Part 10 of 10)

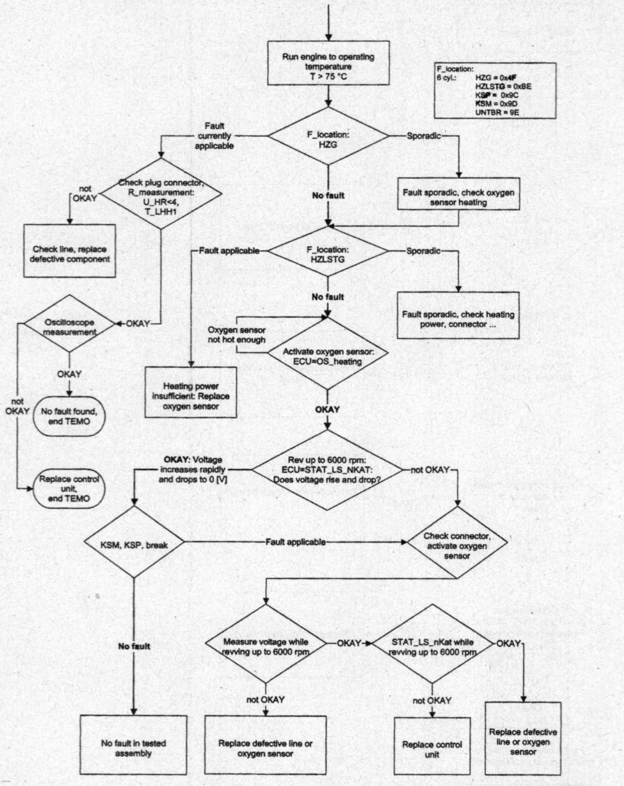

BM0150100153000X

Fig. 69 Oxygen Sensor After Catalytic Converter Test

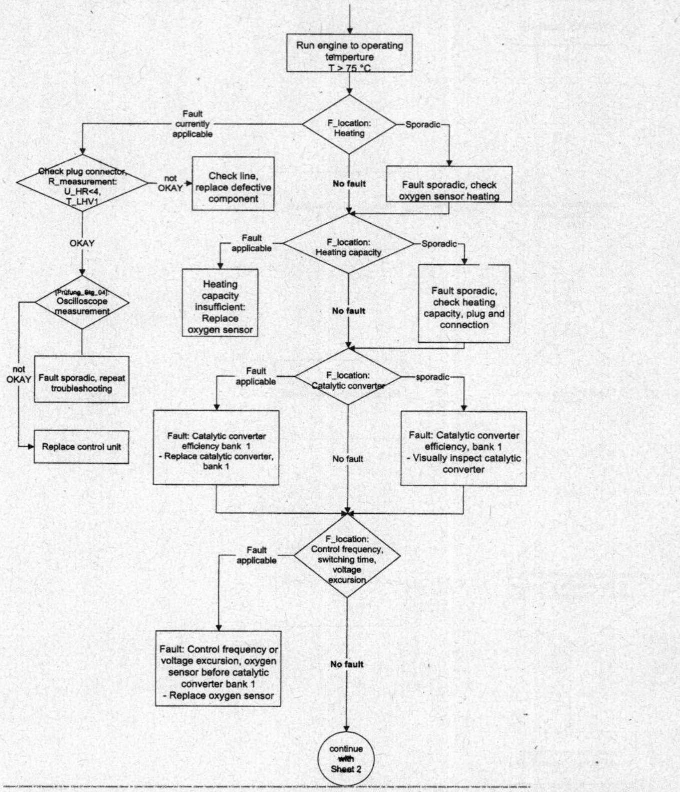

BM0150100170010X

Fig. 70 Oxygen Sensor Before Catalytic Converter Test (Part 1 of 2)

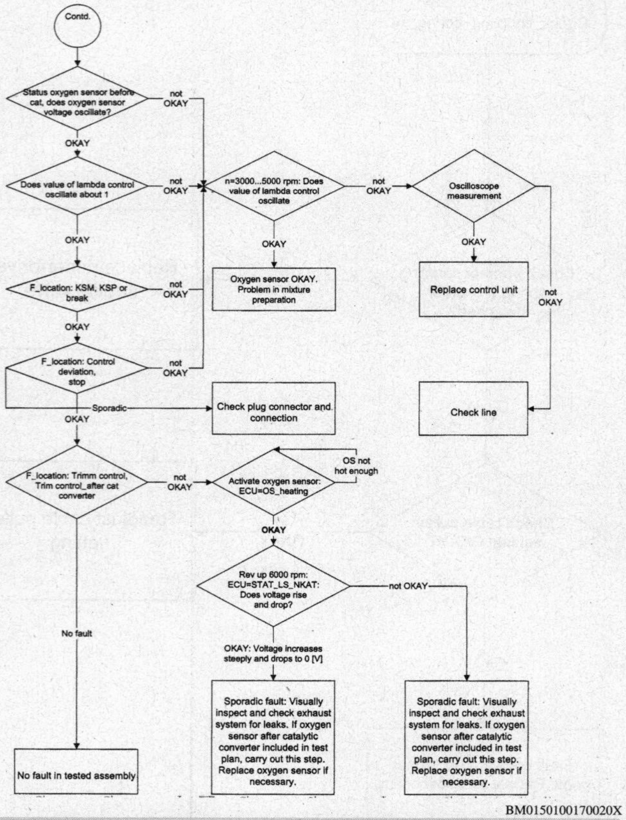

BM0150100170020X

Fig. 70 Oxygen Sensor Before Catalytic Converter Test (Part 2 of 2)

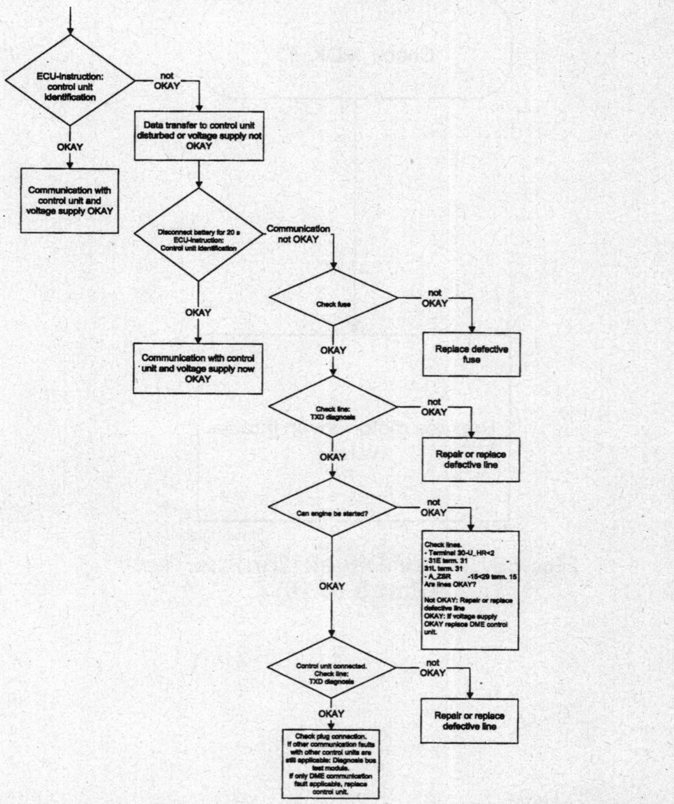

BM0150100137000X

Fig. 71 Power & Ground Supply Test

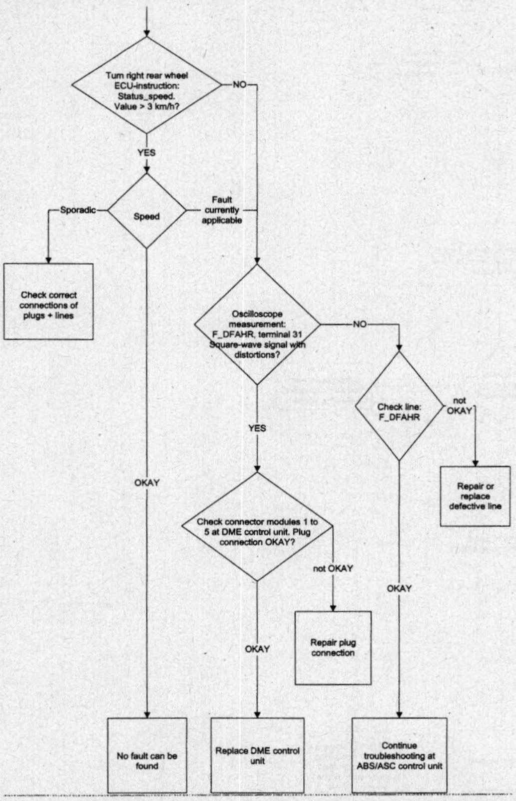

Fig. 72 Road Speed Signal Test

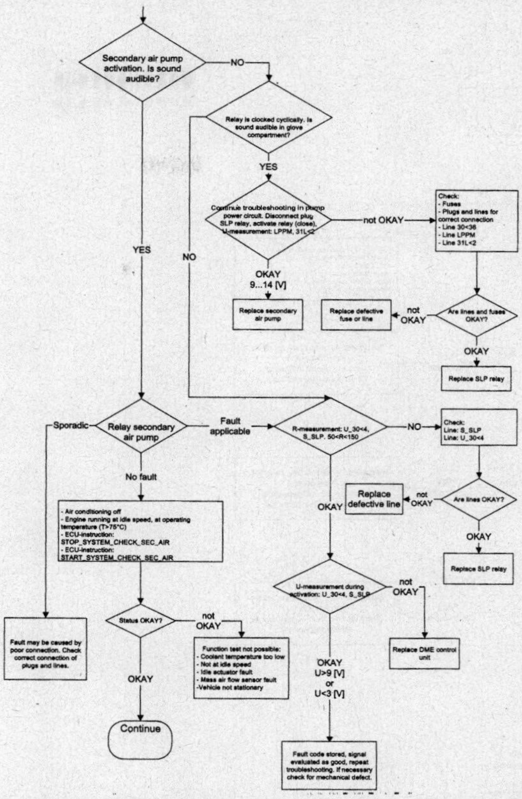

Fig. 73 Secondary Air Pump Test (Part 1 of 2)

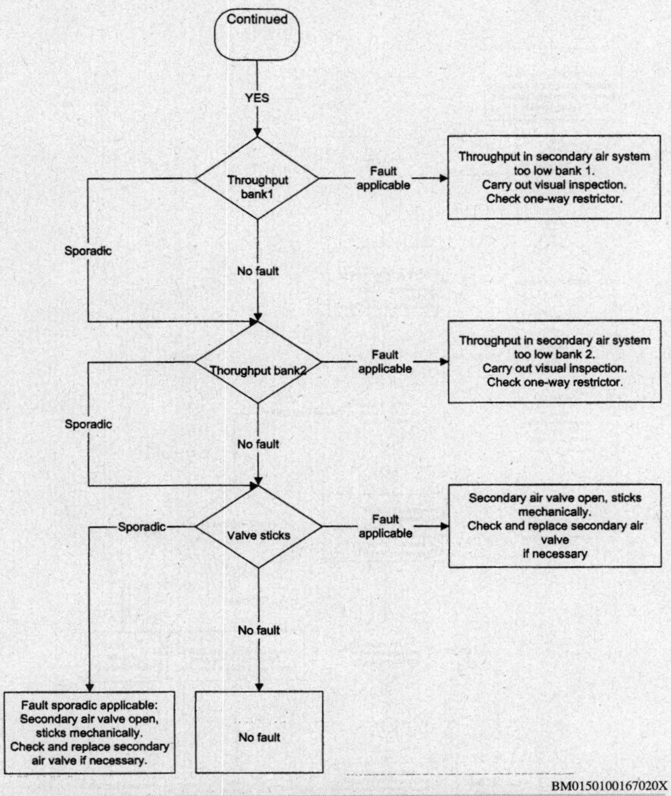

Fig. 73 Secondary Air Pump Test (Part 2 of 2)

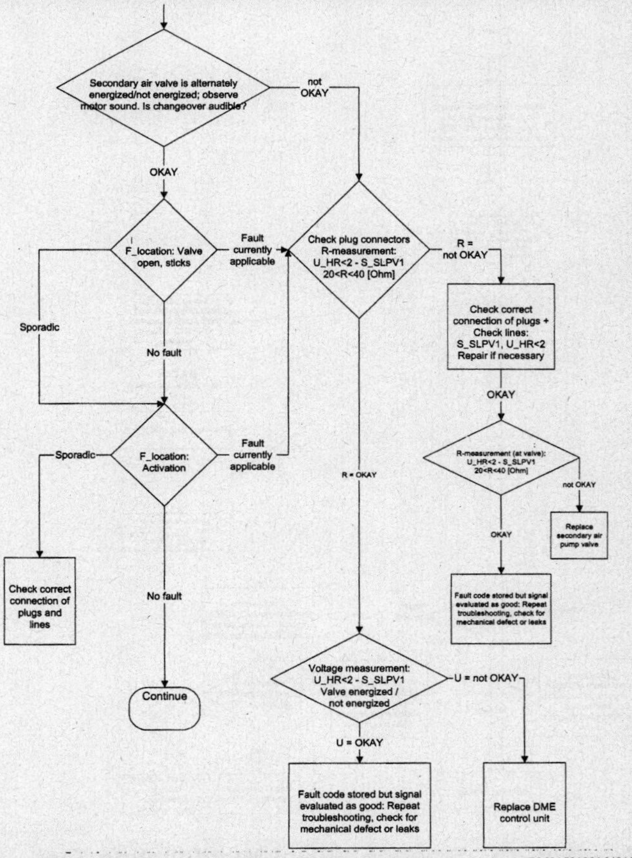

Fig. 74 Secondary Air Valve Test (Part 1 of 2)

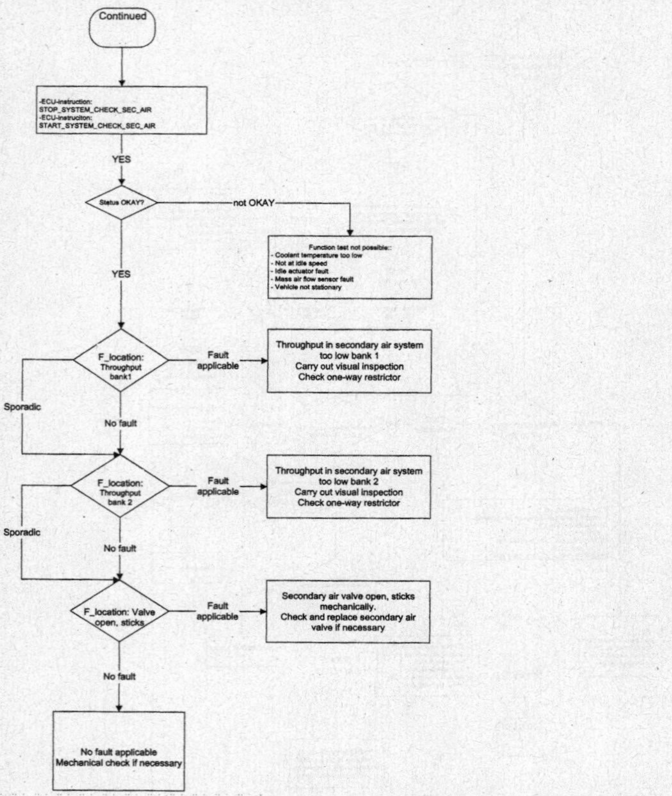

BM0150100164020X

Fig. 74 Secondary Air Valve Test (Part 2 of 2)

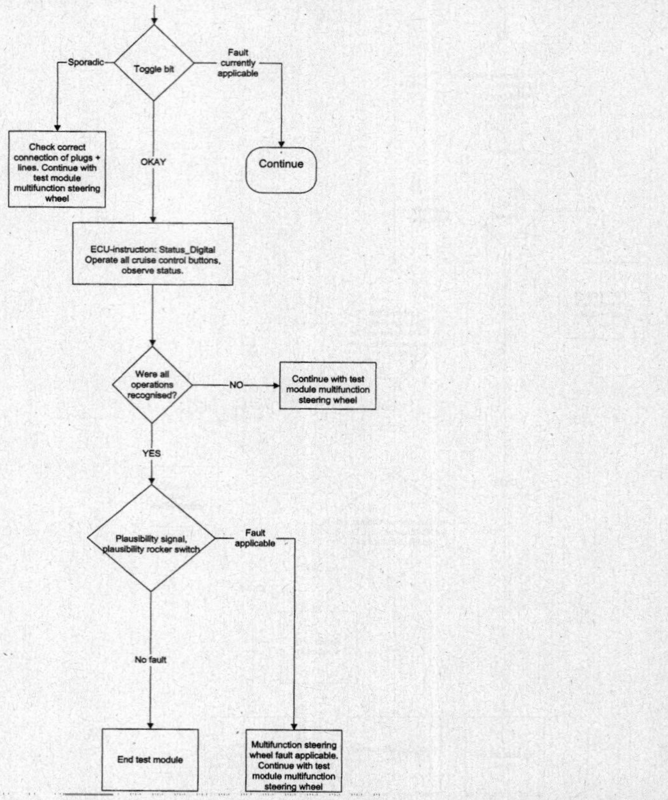

BM0150100160010X

Fig. 75 Steering Wheel Multifunction Test (Part 1 of 2)

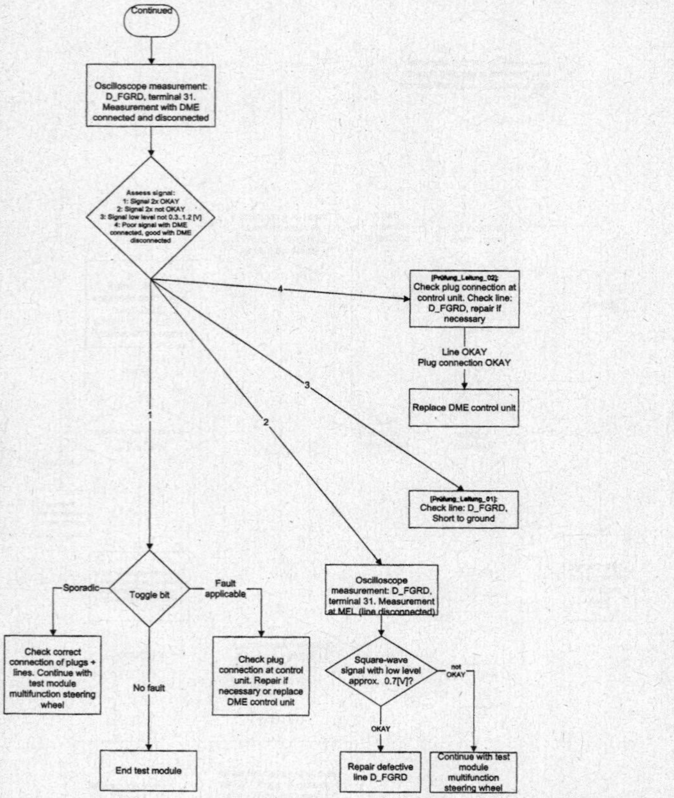

BM0150100160020X

Fig. 75 Steering Wheel Multifunction Test (Part 2 of 2)

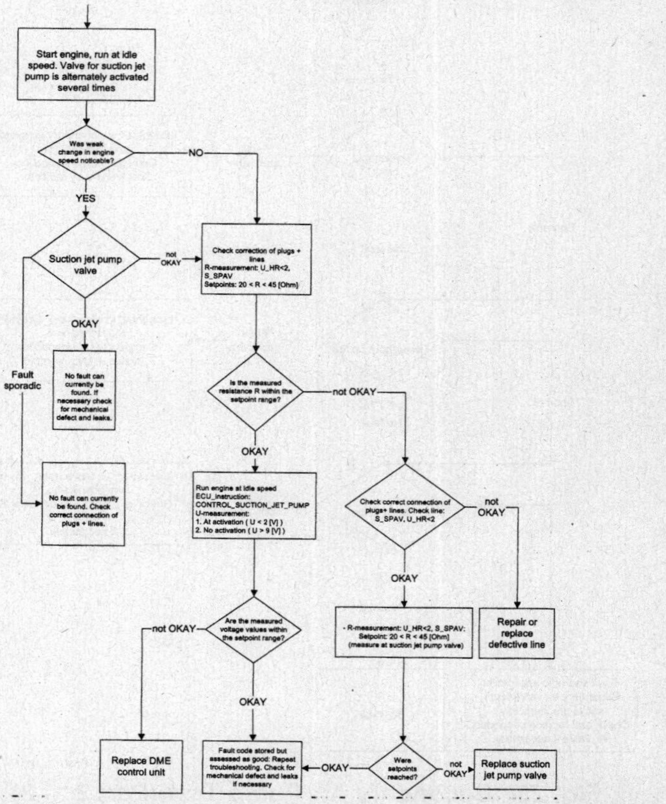

BM0150100148000X

Fig. 76 Suction Jet Pump Test

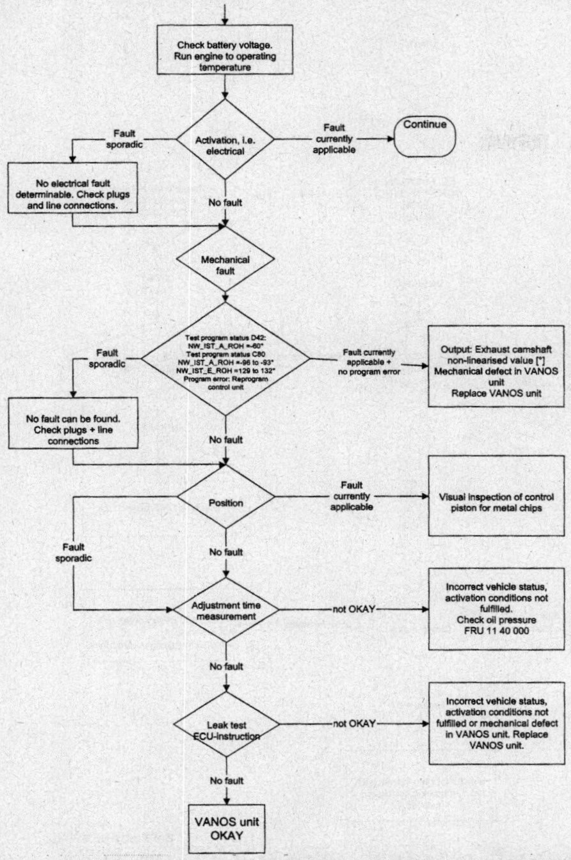

BM0150100163010X

Fig. 77 VANOS Test (Part 1 of 2)

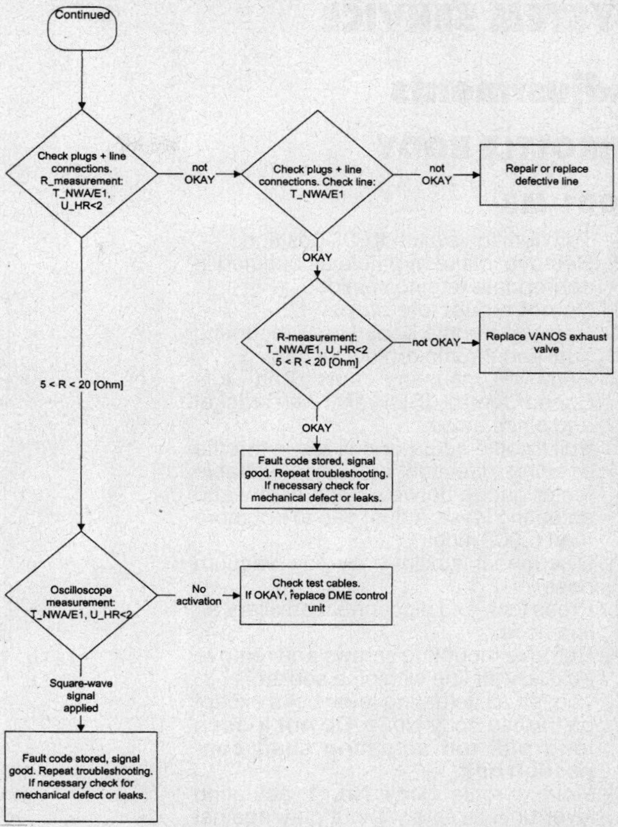

BM0150100163020X

Fig. 77 VANOS Test (Part 2 of 2)

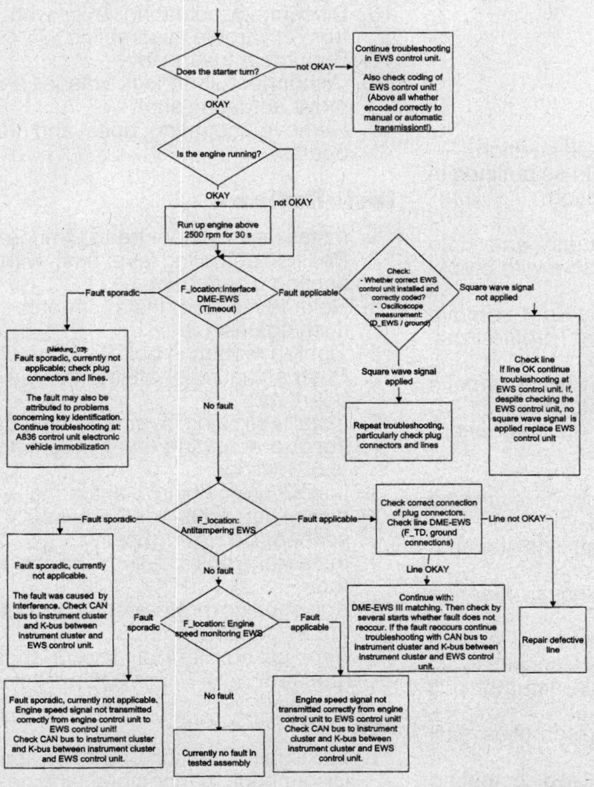

BM0150100157000X

Fig. 78 Vehicle Immobilization Test

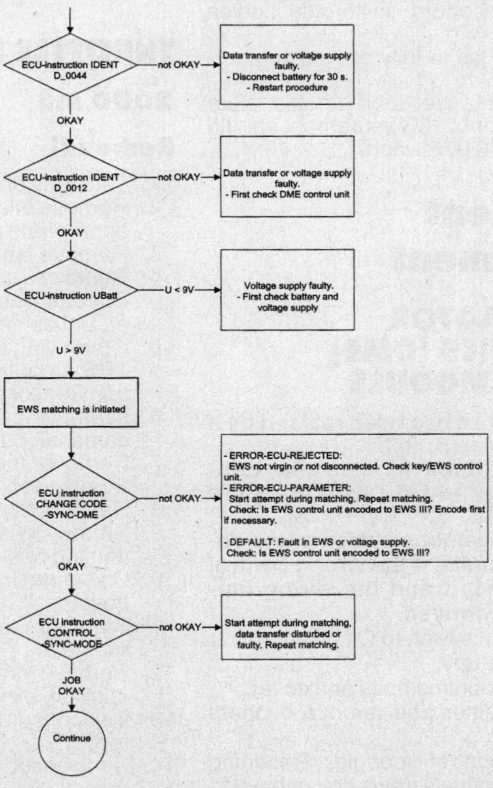

BM0150100159010X

Fig. 79 Vehicle Immobilization Matching Test (Part 1 of 2)

SYSTEM SERVICE

Adjustments

THROTTLE BODY

2001 M3

1. Turn ignition switch to Off position.
2. Remove intake manifold as outlined in appropriate engine section.
3. **Do not adjust idle stops.**
4. Remove throttle body No. 6 mounting nuts and throttle protective cap.
5. Remove mounting nuts and Idle Speed Control (ISC) valve with bracket and place aside.
6. Pull throttle actuator pull rod in throttle opening direction and slide suitable feeler gauge between stop screw and actuating lever. Adjust gap to not more than 0.002 inch.
7. Disconnect auxiliary air line vacuum hose.
8. Press lock and disconnect auxiliary air line hose.
9. Remove mounting screws and remove auxiliary air line with pipe socket.
10. Loosen all actuating lever bolts except on throttle body No. 1. **Do not loosen long pull rod actuating shaft connection bolt.**
11. Move throttle body No. 1 actuating lever until it rests without play against stop screw. **Do not exert any pressure.**
12. **Torque** mounting bolt to 62 inch lbs.
13. Repeat procedure on throttle bodies No. 3–6.
14. Move throttles to fully open using servomotor.
15. Measure gap between throttle plate and top of open. Measurement should be 0.9631–0.9788 inch.

Component Replacement

DIGITAL MOTOR ELECTRONICS (DME) CONTROL MODULE

This procedure has been revised by a Technical Service Bulletin.

Wait at least three minutes after turning ignition key to Off position before disconnect DME.

Bosch and Siemens systems use different control units. If the wrong control unit is installed, it and the wiring harness will be destroyed.

1. Turn ignition switch to Off position.
2. Remove battery.
3. Remove mounting bolts and cover.
4. Unlock retainer and remove connector.
5. Remove control module. Retaining spring mounting screws do not have to be removed.
6. Reverse procedure to install.

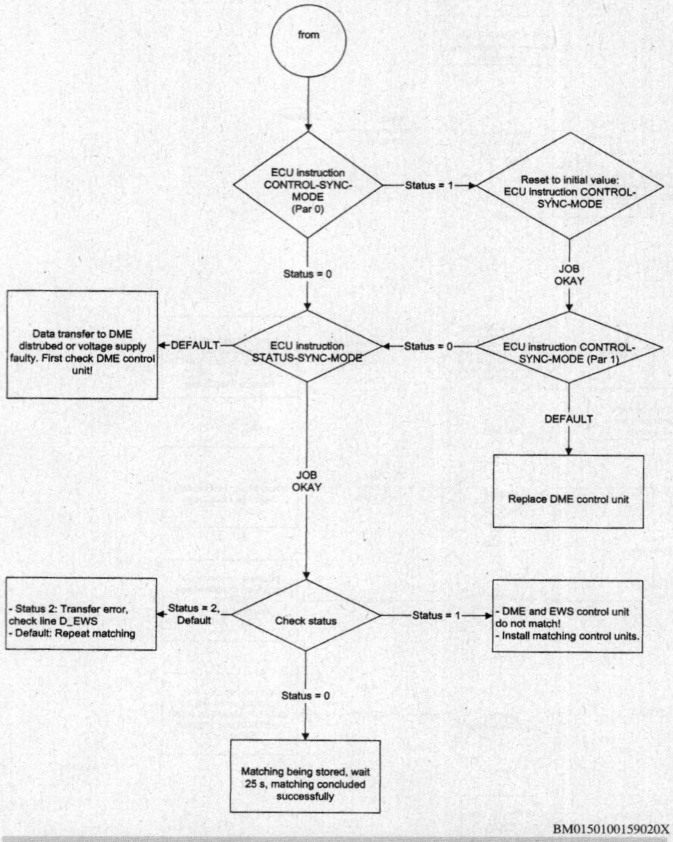

Fig. 79 Vehicle Immobilization Matching Test (Part 2 of 2)

THROTTLE BODY

2000 M3

Removal

1. Turn ignition switch to Off position.
2. Remove intake manifold as outlined in appropriate engine section.
3. Remove fan cowl.
4. Remove mounting nuts and Idle Speed Control (ISC) valve with bracket. Set aside.
5. If removing throttle body No. 1, remove TPS as outlined under "Throttle Position Sensor (TPS)."
6. If removing throttle body No. 6, remove camshaft pulse generator inlet.
7. Remove fuel rail as outlined under "Fuel Injection."
8. Remove microfilter.
9. Press locks and disconnect engine venting hose.
10. Disconnect auxiliary air line vacuum hose.
11. Press lock and disconnect auxiliary air line hose.
12. Remove mounting screws and remove auxiliary air line with pipe socket.
13. Disconnect long throttle actuator pull rod.
14. Disconnect throttle assemblies pull rods.
15. Disconnect long pull rod actuating lever bolts.
16. Disconnect actuating lever with shaft from all throttle assemblies.
17. Support actuating lever.
18. Disconnect shaft lock washer and remove actuating shaft
19. Remove mounting bolts and throttle bodies.

Installation

1. Install new cylinder head O-rings.
2. Position actuating lever flush with connecting pipe mount.
3. Hold lever and install throttle body flush against block.
4. Tighten mounting bolts.
5. Push actuating shaft into throttle body bearings.
6. Install actuating lever mounting bolt.
7. **Torque** actuating lever mounting bolt to 62 inch lbs.
8. Install remaining actuating lever mounting bolts as previously described. **Do not tighten.**
9. Install long pull rod clip, then clip all pull rods.
10. Adjust basic throttle setting as outlined under "Adjustments."
11. Replace auxiliary air line O-rings, as required.

M5

1. Turn ignition switch to Off position.
2. Disconnect connectors and cables from guides.

3. Disconnect lefthand knock sensor pair.
4. Disconnect throttle body actuator and cable duct. Raise duct approximately 0.079 inch.
5. Disconnect fuel injector cable strip, push upward and tie back to engine hood.
6. Disconnect Throttle Position Sensor (TPS) connector.
7. Disconnect clip and vacuum hose.
8. Disconnect pull rods at servomotor ball heads.
9. Remove injection pipe with injectors.
10. Disconnect hose clamps and remove intake manifold sealing flange.
11. Disconnect clip and hose from T-piece.
12. Remove mounting nuts. It may be necessary to pull rod to gain access.
13. Remove flange bottom nuts and throttle body.
14. Reverse procedure to install, noting the following:
    a. Install new O-rings coated with suitable petroleum jelly.
    b. Coat sealing flange sealing surfaces with suitable petroleum jelly.
    c. Replace fuel injector O-rings as required.
    d. Coat O-rings with suitable petroleum jelly.

X5 3.0, Z3 2.5, Z3 3.0, 325, 330, 525 & 530

1. Turn ignition switch to Off position.
2. Disconnect air intake filter housing mounting bolt.
3. Disconnect connector and MAF sensor.
4. Disconnect hose and clips, then remove air intake filter housing.
5. Disconnect vacuum line and clamp, then remove intake hose.
6. Disconnect resonance flap and ISC valve connectors.
7. Disconnect oil pressure and temperature switches.
8. Disconnect tank venting valve.
9. Remove cable duct mounting bolts.
10. **On 325 and 330 models,** proceed as follows:
    a. Disconnect fuel lines and cable from oil level sensor holder on oil dipstick guide tube.
    b. Disconnect oil return line from oil dipstick guide tube.
    c. Remove mounting bolt and oil dipstick guide tube.
11. **On all models,** remove mounting bolts and throttle body.
12. Reverse procedure to install. Install new throttle body seal ring.

X5 4.4

1. Turn ignition switch to Off position.
2. Remove acoustic cover.
3. Disconnect clamp and remove hose from MAF sensor.
4. Disconnect clamp and vacuum hose from intake hose.
5. Remove air intake hose.
6. Disconnect connector.
7. Remove mounting bolts and throttle body.
8. Reverse procedure to install, noting the following
    a. Replace gasket, as required.
    b. Coat gasket with suitable acid-free grease.

Z3 COUPE & Z3 2.3 & 1999-2000 Z3 2.8

1. Remove MAF sensor as outlined under "Mass Air Flow (MAF) Sensor."
2. Disconnect throttle cable.
3. Disconnect hose clamps, then the intake hose from the throttle body and Idle Speed Control (ISC) valve.
4. Disconnect resonance flap and ISC valve connectors.
5. Disconnect oil pressure and temperature switches.
6. Remove cable duct mounting bolts.
7. Disconnect fuel lines and cable from oil level sensor holder on oil dipstick guide tube.
8. Disconnect oil return line from oil dipstick guide tube.
9. Remove mounting bolt and oil dipstick guide tube.
10. Press cable duct aside and disconnect throttle body connector.
11. Remove mounting bolts and throttle body.
12. Reverse procedure to install. Install new throttle body seal ring.

Z3 1.9 & 318

1. Remove mounting bolt and cover.
2. Disconnect accelerator and cruise control cables, as required.
3. Disconnect hose connector and remove gaiter.
4. Remove upper air intake filter housing with Mass Air Flow (MAF) sensor.
5. Disconnect throttle valve switch connector and vacuum hose.
6. Disconnect preheating element hoses. Cap hoses.
7. Remove mounting nuts and throttle body.
8. Reverse procedure to install, noting the following:
    a. Install new seals.
    b. Ensure seals seat properly.
    c. Adjust cables.

1998 Z3 2.8, 323, 328 & 528 & 1999 323 & 328 COUPES & CONVERTIBLES

1. Remove MAF sensor as outlined under "Mass Air Flow (MAF) Sensor."
2. Disconnect cable.
3. Remove mounting bolts and disconnect front bracket.
4. Remove throttle body.
5. Reverse procedure to install, noting the following
    a. Replace gasket, as required.
    b. Coat gasket with suitable acid-free grease.
    c. Adjust cable clearance to 0.020–0.039 inch.
    d. Ensure crankcase venting hose is installed.

2000 323CI/I & 328CI/I & 1999 323I SEDAN & 328I SEDAN

1. Disconnect engine wiring harness holder and air intake filter housing retainers.
2. Remove mounting bolts and intake filter housing.
3. Remove MAF sensor as outlined under "Mass Air Flow (MAF) Sensor."
4. Disconnect throttle cable.
5. Disconnect hose clamps, then the intake hose from the throttle body and Idle Speed Control (ISC) valve.
6. Disconnect resonance flap and ISC valve connectors.
7. Disconnect oil pressure and temperature switches.
8. Remove cable duct mounting bolts.
9. Disconnect fuel lines and cable from oil level sensor holder on oil dipstick guide tube.
10. Disconnect oil return line from oil dipstick guide tube.
11. Remove mounting bolt and oil dipstick guide tube.
12. Press cable duct aside and disconnect throttle body connector.
13. Remove mounting bolts and throttle body.
14. Reverse procedure to install, noting the following:
    a. Install new throttle body seal ring.
    b. Replace MAF sensor to air cleaner seal, as required.
    c. Coat seal with suitable acid-free grease.
    d. Insert intake filter housing guide pin into rubber mount bore hole.

1999-2000 528

1. Disconnect air intake filter housing retainers.
2. Remove mounting bolts and intake filter housing.
3. Remove MAF sensor as outlined under "Mass Air Flow (MAF) Sensor."
4. Disconnect throttle cable.
5. Disconnect hose clamps, then the intake hose from the throttle body and Idle Speed Control (ISC) valve.
6. Disconnect resonance flap and ISC valve connectors.
7. Disconnect oil pressure and temperature switches.
8. Remove cable duct mounting bolts.
9. Disconnect fuel lines and cable from oil level sensor holder on oil dipstick guide tube.
10. Disconnect oil return line from oil dipstick guide tube.
11. Remove mounting bolt and oil dipstick guide tube.
12. Press cable duct aside and disconnect throttle body connector.
13. Remove mounting bolts and throttle body.
14. Reverse procedure to install, noting the following:
    a. Install new throttle body seal ring.
    b. Replace MAF sensor to air cleaner seal, as required.
    c. Coat seal with suitable acid-free grease.
    d. Insert intake filter housing guide pin into rubber mount bore hole.

540 & 740

1. Remove acoustic cover.
2. Disconnect clamps and intake hose.
3. Disconnect Intake Air Temperature (IAT) sensor.

4. Disconnect clips and remove air filter intake housing hose.
5. Disconnect accelerator and cruise cables.
6. Remove throttle body vacuum hose.
7. Remove mounting bolts and throttle body neck.
8. Disconnect connector and vacuum lines.
9. Remove intake pipe with air cleaner housing upper section.
10. Disconnect connect, then remove mounting bolts and throttle body.
11. Reverse procedure to install, noting the following:
    a. Replace O-ring, as required.
    b. Install new seal.
    c. Adjust cruise control cable freeplay to 0.039–0.79 inch.

750

Lefthand Bank

1. Remove manifold silencer cover.
2. Disconnect vacuum hose from throttle body.
3. Disconnect connector.
4. Remove mounting bolts, bracket with positive battery terminal and throttle body.
5. Disconnect clamp and hoses.
6. Reverse procedure to install, noting the following:
    a. Install new fuel hose to tank vent valve and clips.
    b. Install new gasket.

Righthand Bank

1. Remove manifold silencer cover.
2. Disconnect vacuum hose from throttle body.
3. Disconnect connector.
4. Remove mounting bolts and throttle body.
5. Disconnect clamp and hoses.
6. Reverse procedure to install, noting the following:
    a. Install new fuel hose to tank vent valve and clips.
    b. Install new gasket.

MASS AIR FLOW (MAF) SENSOR

2001 M3

1. Turn ignition switch to Off position.
2. Disconnect MAF sensor connector.
3. Remove mounting bolts and MAF sensor.
4. Reverse procedure to install. Replace gasket, as required.

X5 3.0, Z3 2.5, Z3 2.5, 325, 330, 525 & 530

1. Turn ignition switch to Off position.
2. Disconnect air intake filter housing retainers.
3. Disconnect plug and MAF sensor.
4. Disconnect hose clip and intake hose, then remove sensor.
5. Reverse procedure to install, noting the following:
    a. Replace gasket, as required.
    b. Coat gasket with suitable acid-free grease.

X5 4.4, 540 & 740

1. Turn ignition switch to Off position.
2. Disconnect MAF sensor connector.
3. Disconnect clip and air intake hose.
4. Disconnect clips and MAF sensor from air cleaner upper section.
5. Reverse procedure to install.
6. Reverse procedure to install, noting the following:
    a. Replace gasket, as required.
    b. Coat gasket with suitable acid-free grease.

Z3 COUPE & Z3 2.3 & 1999-2000 Z3 2.8

1. Turn ignition switch to Off position.
2. Disconnect air intake filter housing.
3. Disconnect MAF sensor connector.
4. Disconnect intake hose vacuum line.
5. Disconnect hose clip.
6. Disconnect clamps and remove intake hose with MAF sensor.
7. Reverse procedure to install, noting the following:
    a. Replace gasket, as required.
    b. Coat gasket with suitable acid-free grease.

Z3 1.9L & 318

1. Disconnect intake side hose clips.
2. Turn and disconnect connector.
3. Disconnect hose clip.
4. Remove MAF sensor.
5. Reverse procedure to install.

1998-99 M3, 1998-2000 Z3 M COUPE & Z3 M ROADSTER & 1998 Z3 2.8, 323, 328 & 528 & 1999 323 & 328 COUPES & CONVERTIBLES

1. Twist and disconnect connector.
2. Disconnect hose clip and remover throttle body rubber gaiter.
3. Remove clamps and MAF sensor with bellows.
4. Remove rubber gaiter.
5. Reverse procedure to install.

1999-2000 528 & 2000 323CI/I & 328CI/I & 1999 323I SEDAN & 328I SEDAN

1. Turn ignition switch to Off position.
2. Disconnect MAF sensor connector.
3. Disconnect intake hose vacuum line.
4. Disconnect hose clip and intake filter housing clamps.
5. Remove intake hose with MAF sensor.
6. Reverse procedure to install, noting the following:
    a. Replace gasket, as required.
    b. Coat gasket with suitable acid-free grease.

325 & 330

1. Turn ignition switch to Off position.
2. Disconnect MAF sensor connector.
3. Disconnect intake hose vacuum line.
4. Remove intake hose with MAF sensor.
5. Reverse procedure to install, noting the following:
    a. Replace gasket, as required.
    b. Coat gasket with suitable acid-free grease.

ENGINE COOLANT TEMPERATURE (ECT) SENSOR

2001 M3

1. Remove intake manifold as outlined in appropriate engine section.
2. Disconnect connector and Idle Speed Control (ISC) valve.
3. Disconnect connector and remove ECT sensor.
4. Reverse procedure to install. **Torque** sensor to 115 inch lbs.

X5 3.0, Z3 COUPE & Z3 2.3, Z3 2.5 & Z3 3.0, 325, 330, 525 & 538 & 1999-2000 Z3 2.8 & 528 & 2000 323CI/I & 328CI/I & 1999 323I SEDAN & 328I SEDAN

1. Remove intake manifold as outlined in appropriate engine section.
2. Disconnect connector and remove ECT sensor.
3. Reverse procedure to install. **Torque** sensor to 115 inch lbs.

X5 4.4, 540 & 740

1. Disconnect vacuum lines.
2. Disconnect connect and remove ECT sensor.
3. Reverse procedure to install. **Torque** sensor to 16 ft. lbs.

Z3 1.9 & 318

1. Disconnect connector.
2. Remove ECT sensor.
3. Reverse procedure to install, noting the following:
    a. Install new sealing ring.
    b. **Torque** sensor to 115 inch lbs.

1998-99 M3, 1998-2000 Z3 M COUPE & Z3 M ROADSTER & 1998 Z3 2.8, 323, 328 & 528 & 1999 323 & 328 COUPES & CONVERTIBLES

1. Remove fuel injectors' cover.
2. Disconnect crankcase venting.
3. Disconnect connector and remove double DME and ECT sensor.
4. Reverse procedure to install. **Torque** sensor to 115 inch lbs.

750

1. Turn ignition switch to Off position.
2. Remove righthand bank non-return valve.
3. Disconnect connector and remove ECT sensor.
4. Reverse procedure to install using new seal. **Torque** sensor to 115 inch lbs.

INTAKE AIR TEMPERATURE (IAT) SENSOR

X5 3.0, Z3 COUPE & Z3 2.3, Z3 2.5 & Z3 3.0, 325, 330, 525 & 530 & 1999-2000 Z3 2.8 & 528 & 2000 323CI/I & 328CI/I & 1999 323I SEDAN & 328I SEDAN

1. Turn ignition switch to Off position.
2. Remove fuel injectors's cover.
3. Disconnect IAT sensor connector.

4. Press catch and remove sensor.
5. Reverse procedure to install, noting the following:
   a. Replace sealing ring, as required.
   b. Coat sealing ring with suitable anti-seize agent.

X5 4.4, 540 & 740

1. Remove acoustic cover.
2. Disconnect connect.
3. Press locking unit and remove IAT sensor.
4. Reverse procedure to install.

Z3 1.9 & 318

1. Disconnect connector.
2. Press interlock, disconnect clip and remove IAT sensor.
3. Reverse procedure to install.

1998 Z3 2.8, 323 & 328 & 1999 323 & 328 COUPES & CONVERTIBLES

1. Remove MAF sensor as outlined under "Mass Air Flow (MAF) Sensor."
2. Remove mounting bolts, throttle valve neck and gasket. Cable and preheating hoses remain connected.
3. Disconnect connector.
4. Press interlock, disconnect clip and remove IAT sensor.
5. Reverse procedure to install. Install new throttle valve neck gasket.

1998 528

1. Remove throttle body as outlined under "Throttle Body." Cables and preheating until remain connected.
2. Disconnect connector, interlock and clip, then remove sensor.
3. Reverse procedure to install.

750

1. Turn ignition switch to Off position.
2. Press retaining spring down and disconnect connector.
3. Disconnect clip and remove IAT sensor.
4. Reverse procedure to install.

THROTTLE POSITION SENSOR (TPS)

1. **On M5 models,** proceed as follows:
   a. Remove intake manifold as outlined in appropriate engine section.
   b. Disconnect connectors and cables from guide.
   c. Disconnect lefthand knock sensor pair.
2. **On all models,** disconnect connector.
3. Remove mounting screws and TPS.
4. Reverse procedure to install, noting the following:
   a. Ensure sealing ring is correctly positioned.
   b. TPS is self-adjusting.

Emission Control System Application Charts

Engine Liter	Certification Type		Trans. Type		Computerized Engine Management	Fuel Induction System Type	Ignition Timing, Deg. BTDC @ RPM	TSB	EPA & CARB Emission Recall	Emission Control System SRI	Emission Control Systems								
	CA	FED	A/T	M/T							PCV	ACL	AIS	EGR	EVAP	CAT	SPK	FR	O2S
1998																			
1.9L Z3	X	X	X	X	YES⑨	SFI	②	—	—	—	X	—	—	—	X	X①	X⑥	X	X⑩
1.9L Except Z3	X	X	X	X	YES⑧	SFI	②	—	—	—	X	—	—	—	X	X①	X⑥	X	X⑩
2.5L	X	X	X	X	YES⑪	SFI	②	—	—	—	X	—	X⑦	—	X	X①	X⑥	X	X⑩
2.8L	X	X	X	X	YES⑪	SFI	②	—	—	—	X	—	X⑦	—	X	X③	X⑥	X	X⑫
3.2L	X	X	X	X	YES⑪	SFI	②	—	—	—	X	—	—	—	X	X①	X⑥	X	X⑩
4.4L	X	X	X	X	YES⑨	MFI	②	—	—	—	X	—	—	—	X	X③	X⑤	X	X⑫
5.4L	X	X	X	X	YES⑨	MFI	②	—	—	—	X	—	—	—	X	X③	X⑤	X	X⑫
1999																			
1.9L/116/L4	X	X	X	X	YES⑬	SFI	②	—	—	—	X	—	—	—	X	X①	X⑥	X	X⑩
2.5L/152/L6	X	X	X	X	YES⑪	SFI	②	—	—	—	X	—	X⑦	—	X	X①	X⑥	X	X⑩
2.8L/170/L6	X	X	X	X	YES⑪	SFI	②	—	—	—	X	—	X⑦	—	X	X①	X⑥	X	X⑩
3.2L/192/L6	X	X	X	X	YES⑪	SFI	②	—	—	—	X	—	—	—	X	X①	X⑥	X	X⑩
4.4L/268/V8	X	X	X	X	YES⑭	SFI	②	—	—	—	X	—	—	—	X	X③	X⑤	X	X⑫
5.4L/328/V12	X	X	X	X	YES⑮	SFI	②	—	—	—	X	—	—	—	X	X⑯	X⑤	X	X⑫
2000																			
5.0L/303/V8	X	X	X	X	YES⑭	SFI	②	—	—	—	X	—	—	—	X	X	X⑤	X	X
2001																			
2.5L/152/L6	X	X	X	X	YES④	SFI	②	—	—	—	X	—	X⑦	—	X	X①	X⑥	X	X⑩
3.0L/182/L6 DOHC	X	X	X	X	YES④	SFI	②	—	—	—	X	—	—	—	X	X①	X⑥	X	X⑩
3.2L/192/L6	X	X	X	X	YES④	SFI	②	—	—	—	X	—	—	—	X	X①	X⑥	X	X⑩
4.4L/268/V8	X	X	X	X	YES⑭	SFI	②	—	—	—	X	—	—	—	X	X③	X⑤	X	X⑫
5.0L/303/V8	X	X	X	X	YES⑭	SFI	②	—	—	—	X	—	—	—	X	X	X⑤	X	X
5.4L/328/V12	X	X	X	X	YES⑮	SFI	②	—	—	—	X	—	—	—	X	X⑯	X⑤	X	X⑫

X — Equipped
— Not Equipped
① — Type, TWC; number of catalytic converters, 1.
② — Electronically controlled, no adjustment.
③ — Type, TWC; number of catalytic converters, 2.
④ — Siemans MS42
⑤ — DI/Electronic Breakerless.
⑥ — EI/Direct Ignition System.
⑦ — Pump type.
⑧ — ML-Motronic.
⑨ — HFM-Motronic.
⑩ — Two HO2S.
⑪ — Siemans MS41.
⑫ — Four HO2S.
⑬ — Bosch Motronic M5.2.
⑭ — 5 Series, Bosch Motronic M7.2; 7 Series, Bosch Motronic 5.2.1.
⑮ — Bosch Motronic M5.2.1.
⑯ — Three catalytic converters, with HC absorber catalyst, electrically heated catalyst & conventional three-way catalyst.
ACL — Air Cleaner (Thermostatic Air Cleaner)
AIS — Air Injection System
A/T — Automatic Transmission
BTDC — Before Top Dead Center
CA — California
CAT — Catalytic Converter
CID — Cubic Inch Displacement
DME — Digital Motor Electronic (Motronic) Control System
DI — Distributor Ignition
EGR — Exhaust Gas Recirculation
EI — Electronic Ignition
EVAP — Evaporative Emission Control System
FED — Federal
FI — Fuel Injection
FR — Fillpipe Restrictor
MFI — Multi-Port Fuel Injection
M/T — Manual Transmission
O2S — Oxygen Sensor
PCV — Positive Crankcase Ventilation
RPM — Revolutions Per Minute
SFI — Sequential Fuel Injection
SPK — Spark Control
SRI — Service Reminder Indicator
TSB — Technical Service Bulletin
TWC — Three-Way Catalytic Converter
VP-20 — Bosch VP-20 Diesel Engine Control System
1 BBL — One Barrel Carburetor
2 BBL — Two Barrel Carburetor
2X2 BBL — Two Two Barrel Carburetors

Engine Compartment Reference Diagrams

INDEX

	PAGE NO.	FIG. NO.
Engine Compartment:		
318ti	11-135	1
M3, 318i, 318is, 323is & 328is & 1998–99 328i & 1998 323i & 1999 323i & 328i Convertibles	11-138	2
Z3	11-142	3

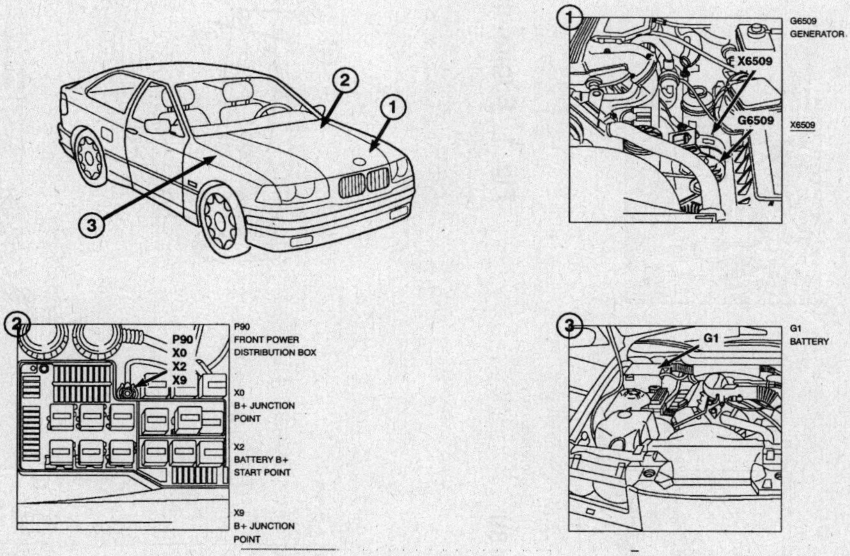

BM1010000004000X

Fig. 1 Engine compartment (Part 1 of 10). 318ti

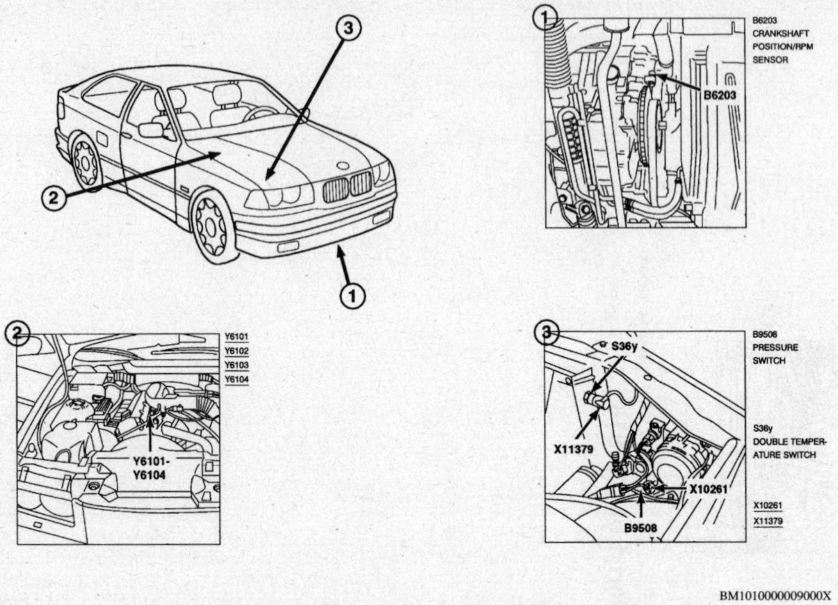

Fig. 1 Engine compartment (Part 2 of 10). 318ti

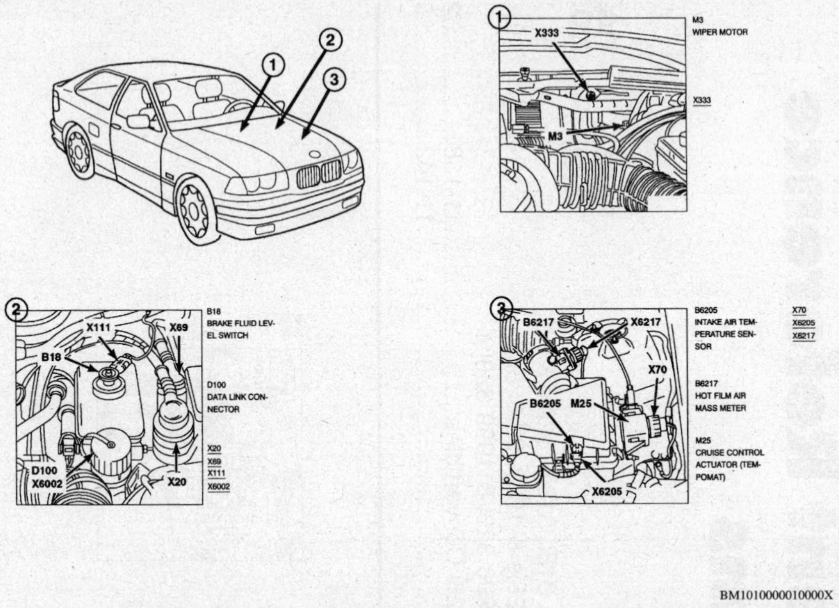

Fig. 1 Engine compartment (Part 3 of 10). 318ti

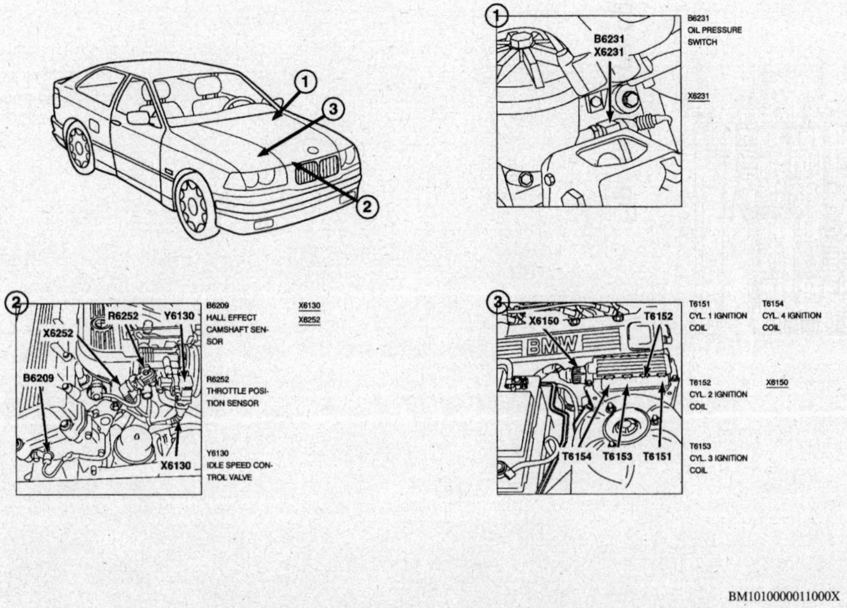

Fig. 1 Engine compartment (Part 4 of 10). 318ti

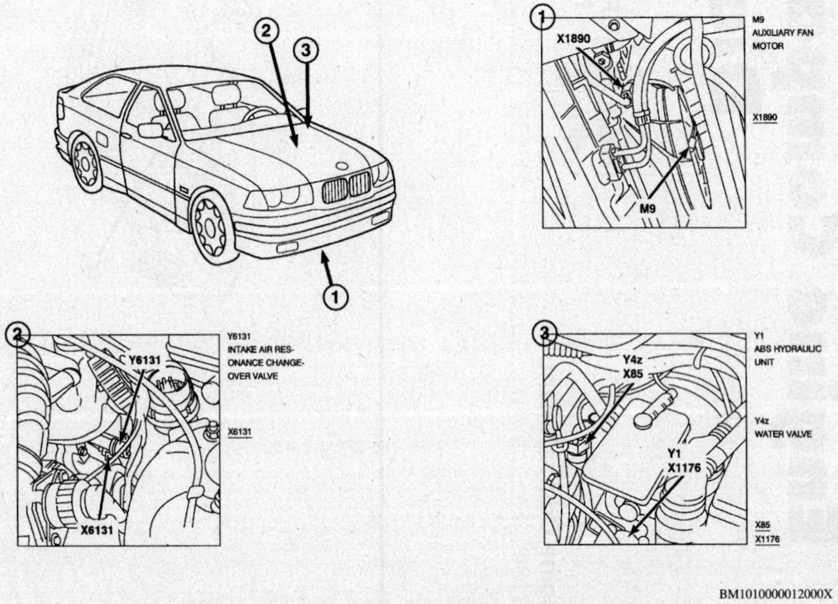

Fig. 1 Engine compartment (Part 5 of 10). 318ti

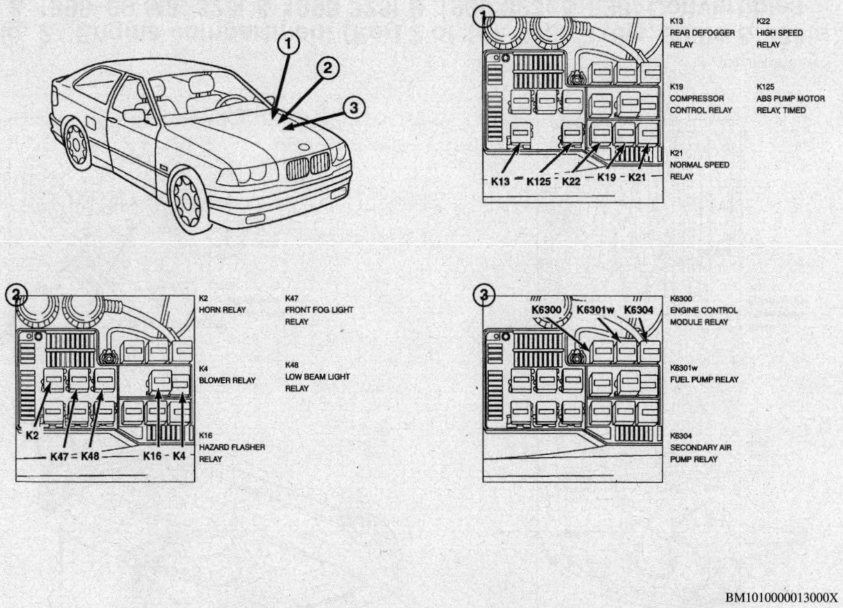

Fig. 1 Engine compartment (Part 6 of 10). 318ti

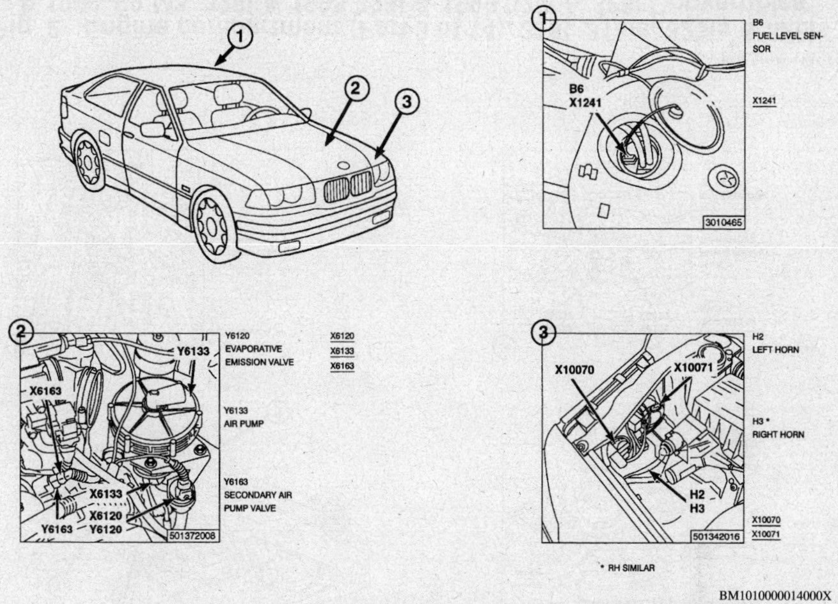

Fig. 1 Engine compartment (Part 7 of 10). 318ti

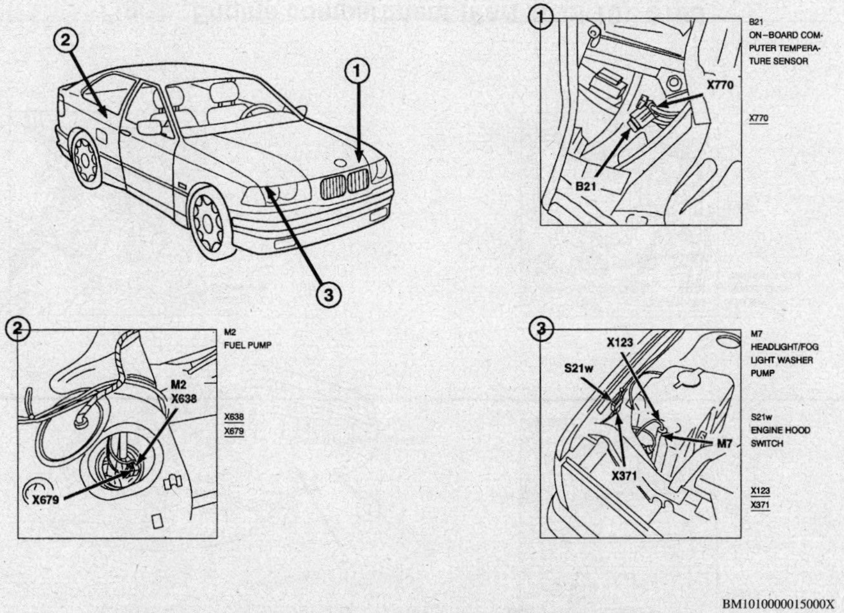

Fig. 1 Engine compartment (Part 8 of 10). 318ti

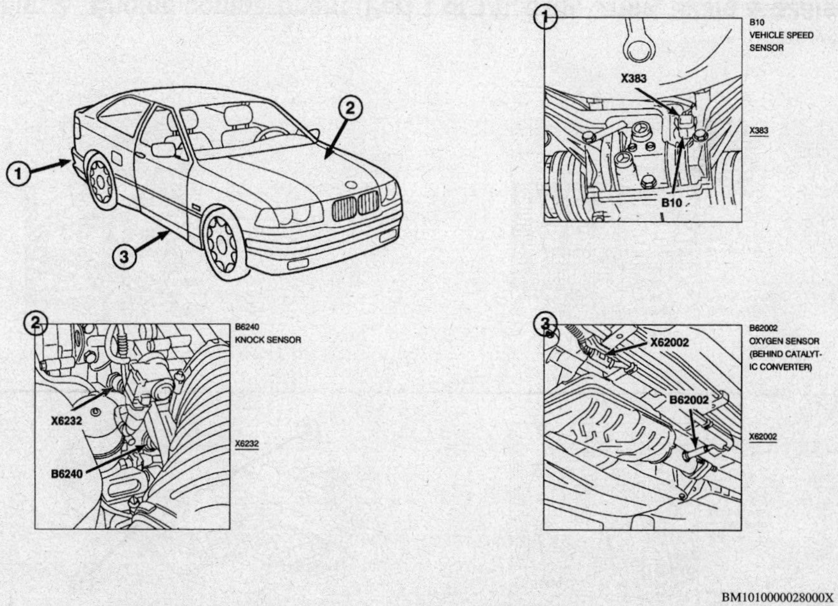

Fig. 1 Engine compartment (Part 9 of 10). 318ti

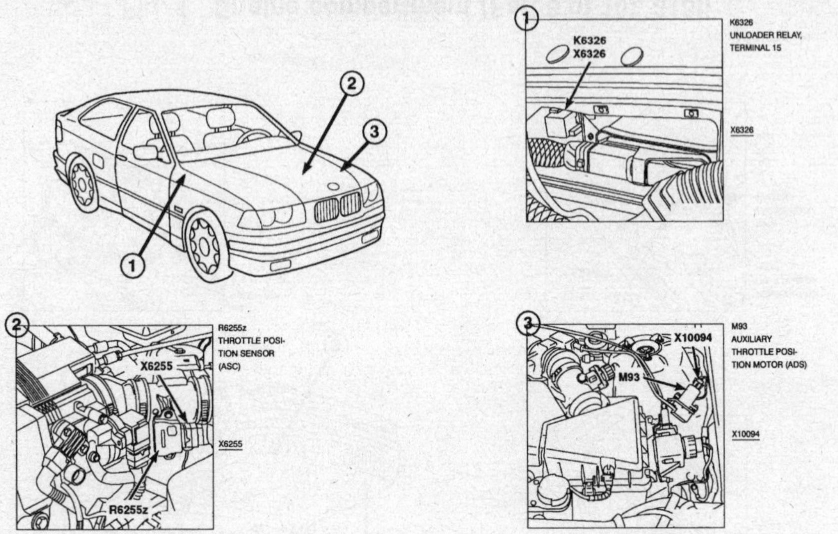

BM1010000029000X

Fig. 1 Engine compartment (Part 10 of 10). 318ti

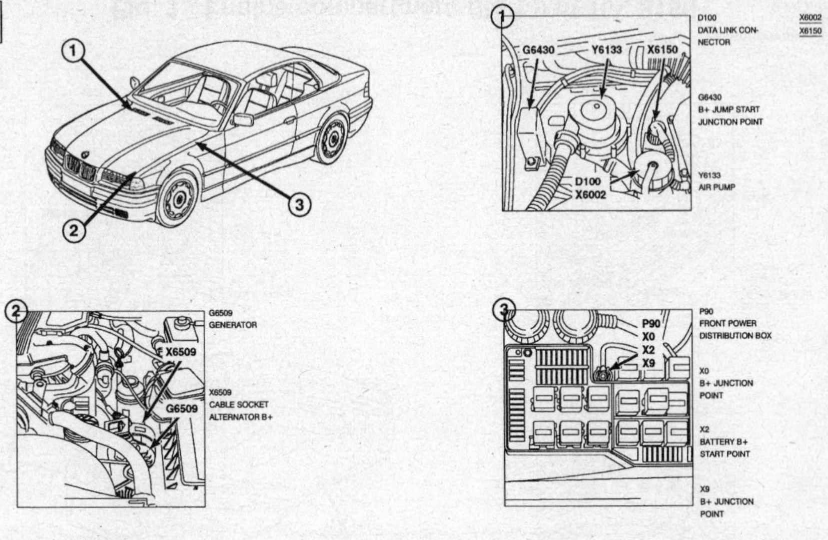

BM1010000038000X

Fig. 2 Engine compartment (Part 1 of 14). 318i, 318is, 323is & 328is & 1998–99 M3, 328i & 1998 323i & 1999 323i & 328i Convertibles

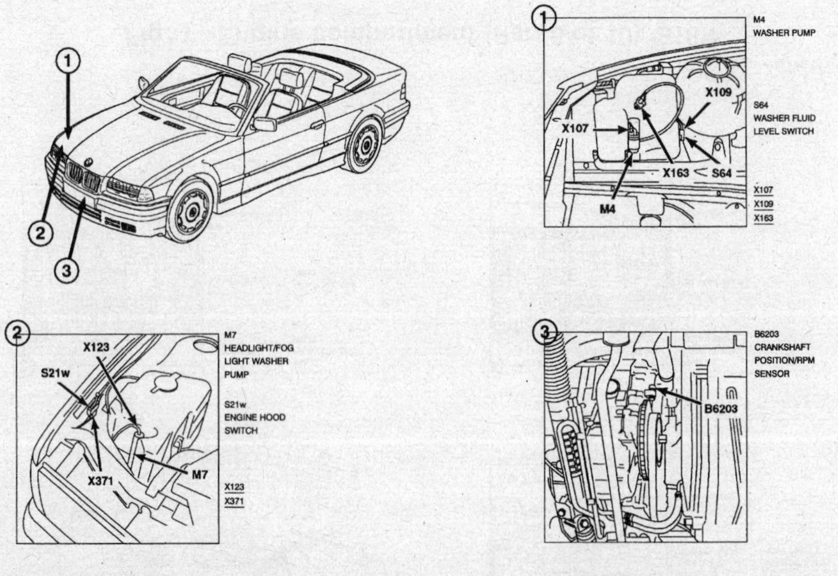

BM1010000043000X

Fig. 2 Engine compartment (Part 2 of 14). 318i, 318is, 323is & 328is & 1998–99 M3, 328i & 1998 323i & 1999 323i & 328i Convertibles

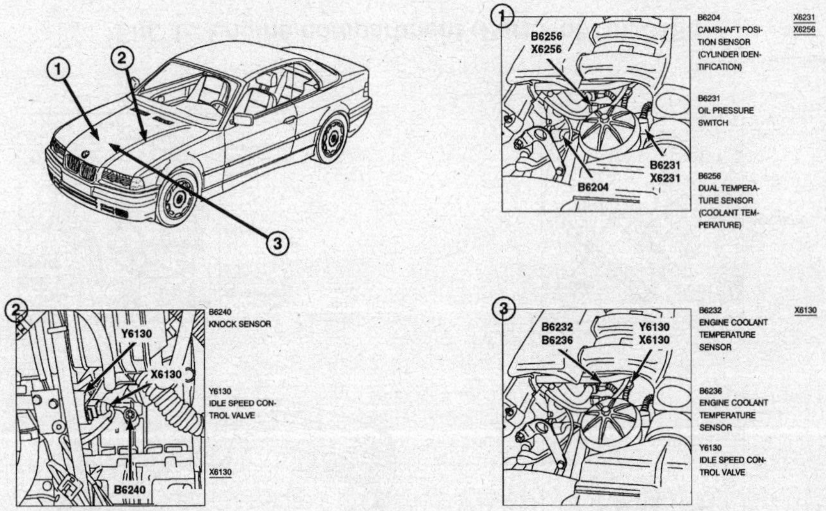

BM1010000044000X

Fig. 2 Engine compartment (Part 3 of 14). 318i, 318is, 323is & 328is & 1998–99 M3, 328i & 1998 323i & 1999 323i & 328i Convertibles

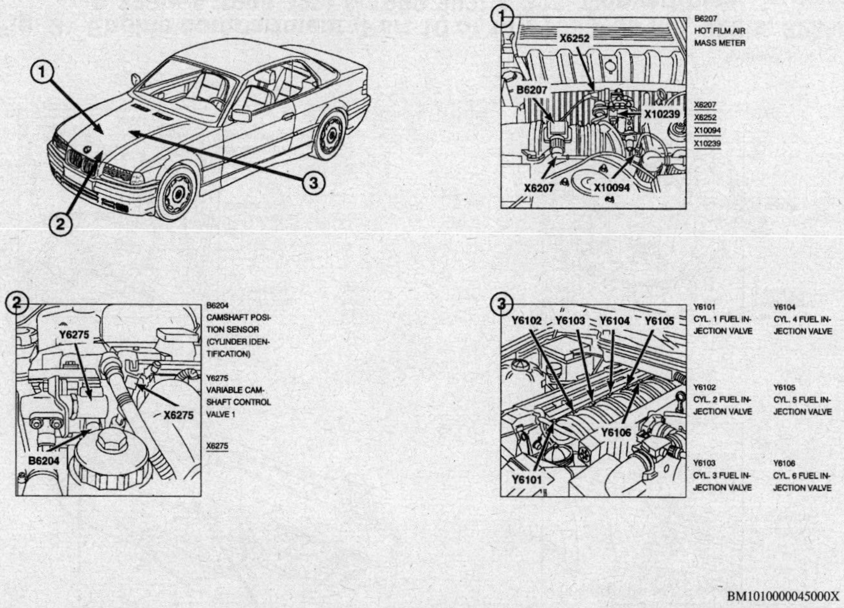

Fig. 2 Engine compartment (Part 4 of 14). 318i, 318is, 323is & 328is & 1998–99 M3, 328i & 1998 323i & 1999 323i & 328i Convertibles

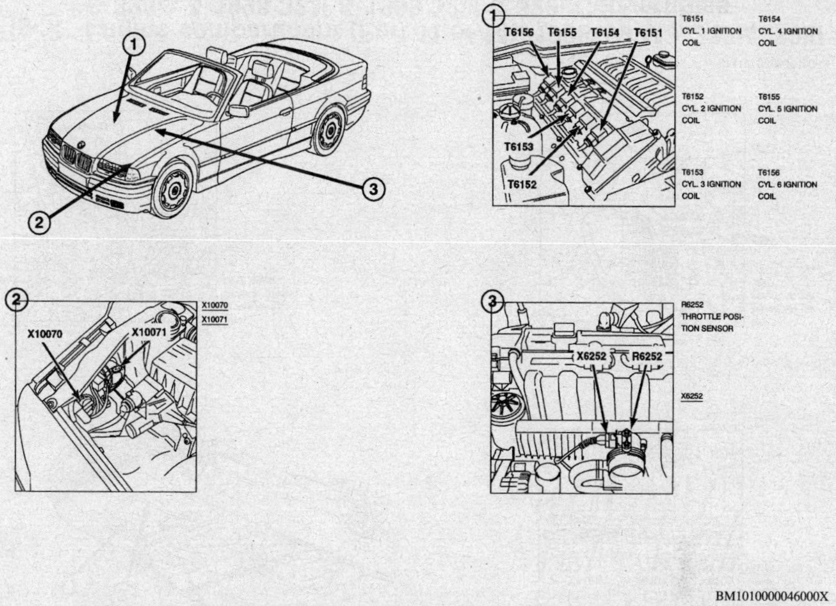

Fig. 2 Engine compartment (Part 5 of 14). 318i, 318is, 323is & 328is & 1998–99 M3, 328i & 1998 323i & 1999 323i & 328i Convertibles

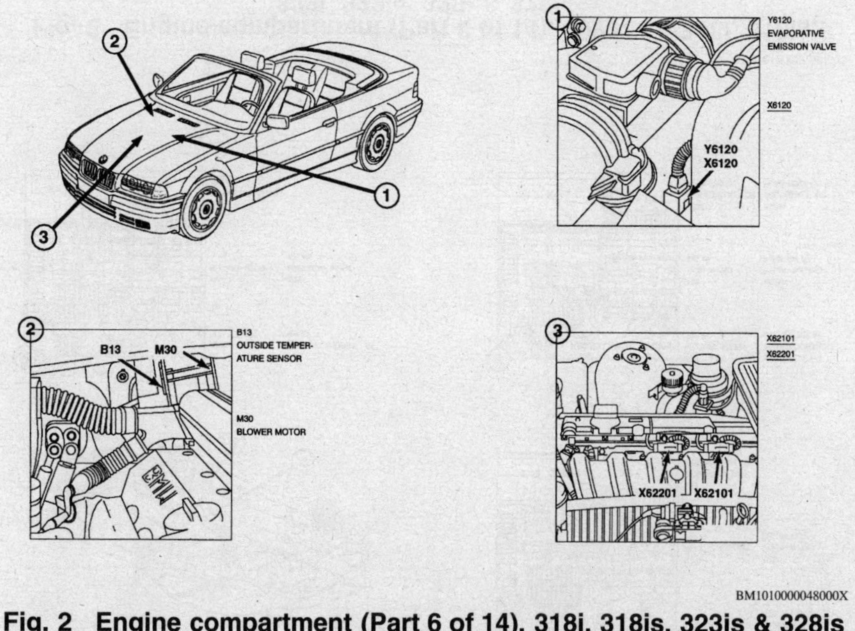

Fig. 2 Engine compartment (Part 6 of 14). 318i, 318is, 323is & 328is & 1998–99 M3, 328i & 1998 323i & 1999 323i & 328i Convertibles

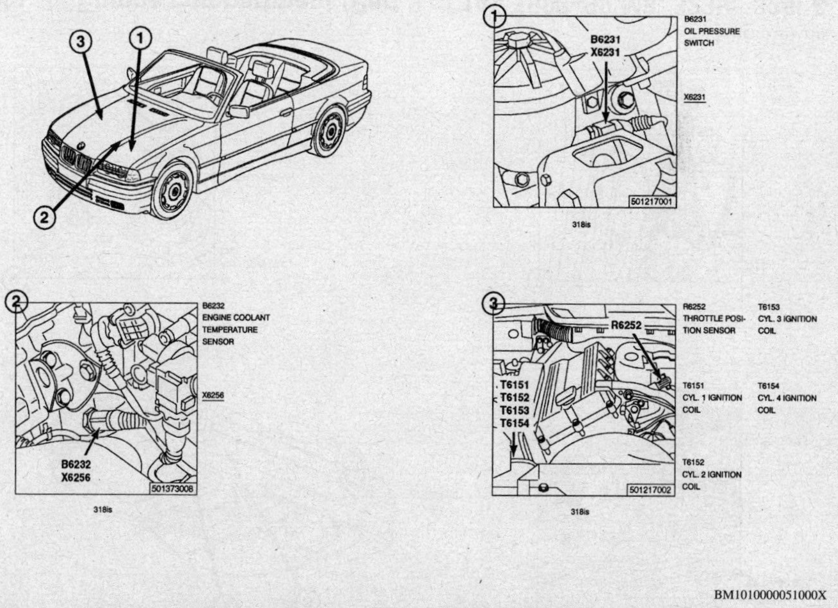

Fig. 2 Engine compartment (Part 7 of 14). 1998 318is

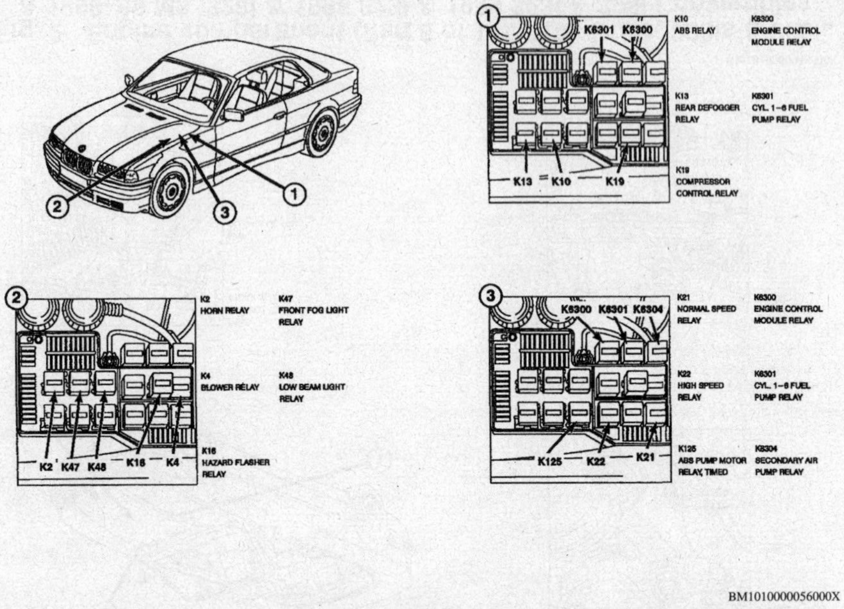

Fig. 2 Engine compartment (Part 8 of 14). 1998 M3, 318i, 318is, 323i, 323is, 328i & 328is

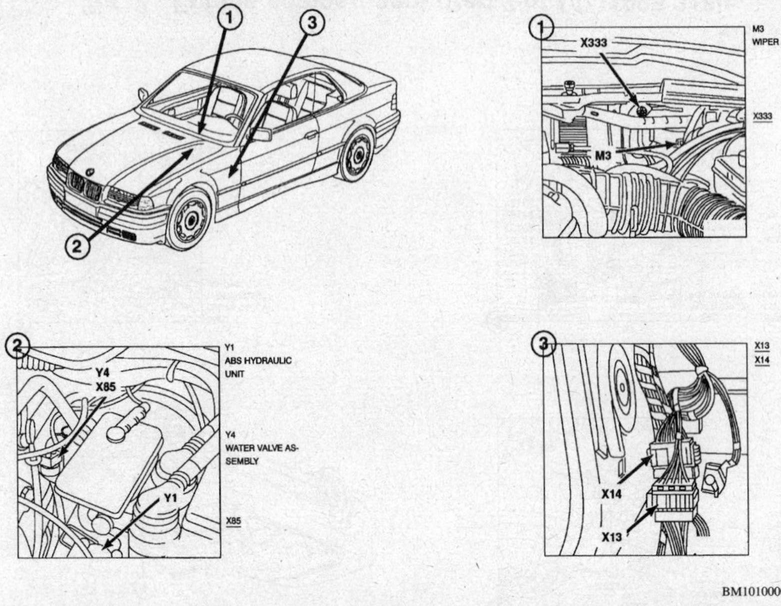

Fig. 2 Engine compartment (Part 9 of 14). 1998–99 M3, 323is, 328i & 328is & 1998 323i & 1999 323i & 328i Convertibles

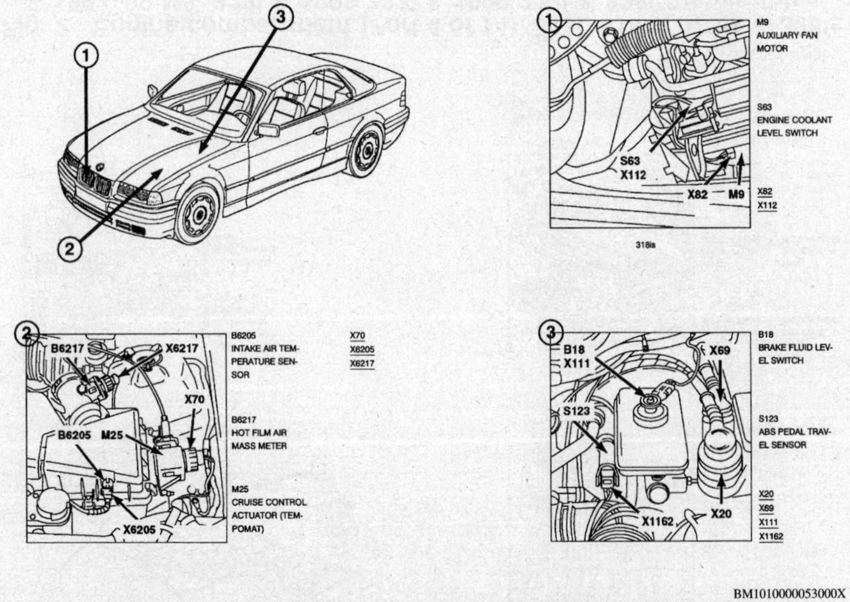

Fig. 2 Engine compartment (Part 10 of 14). 1998–99 M3, 323is, 328i & 328is & 1998 323i & 1999 323i & 328i Convertibles

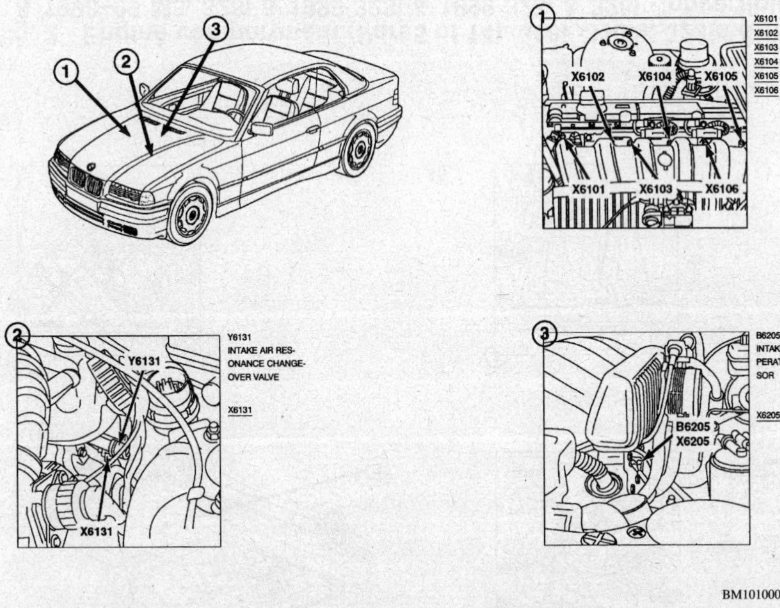

Fig. 2 Engine compartment (Part 11 of 14). 1998–99 M3, 323is, 328i & 328is & 1998 323i & 1999 323i & 328i Convertibles

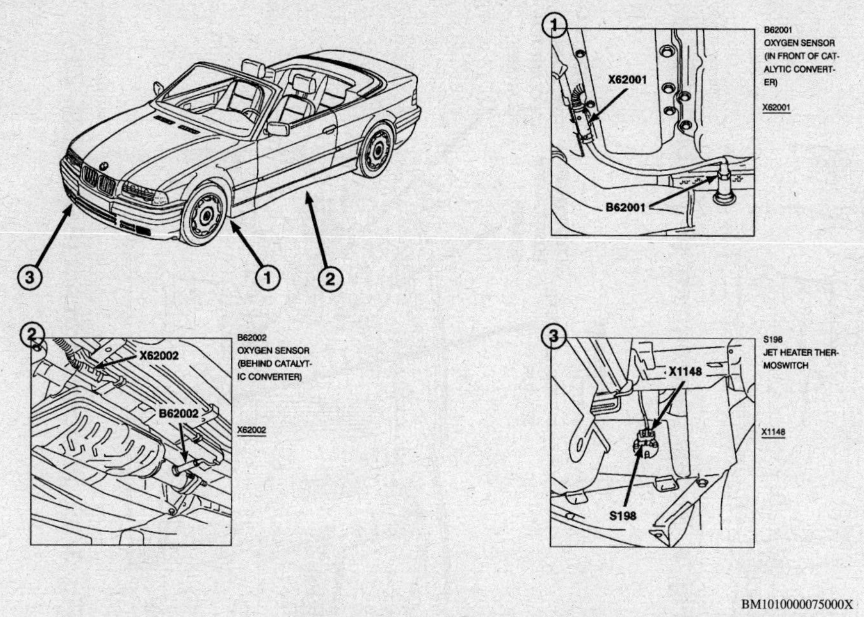

Fig. 2 Engine compartment (Part 12 of 14). 1998–99 M3, 323is, 328i & 328is & 1998 323i & 1999 323i & 328i Convertibles

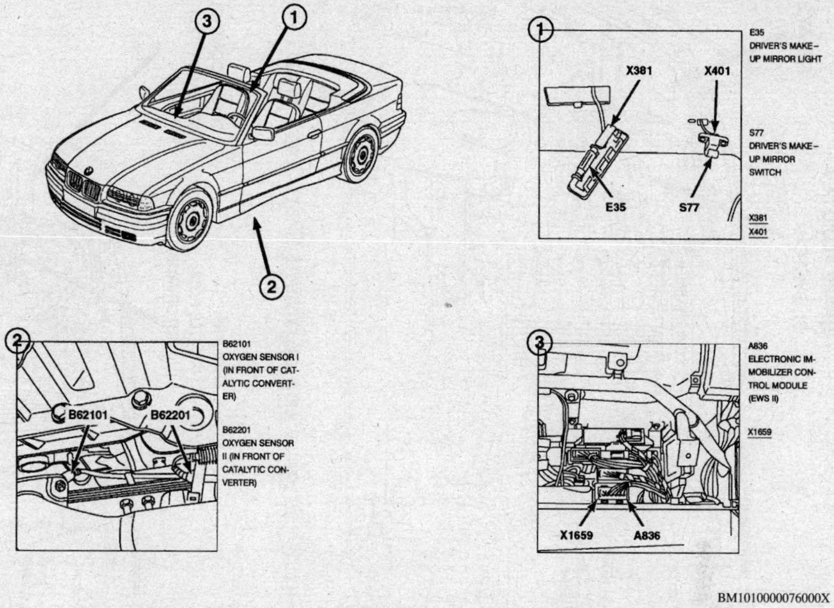

Fig. 2 Engine compartment (Part 13 of 14). 1998–99 M3, 323is, 328i & 328is & 1998 323i & 1999 323i & 328i Convertibles

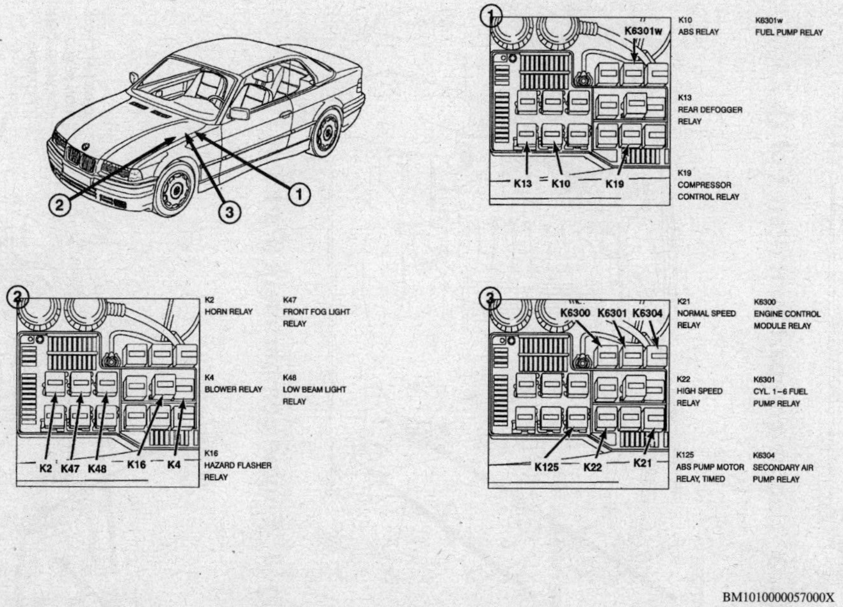

Fig. 2 Engine compartment (Part 14 of 14). 1999 M3, 323i & 328i Coupes & Convertibles

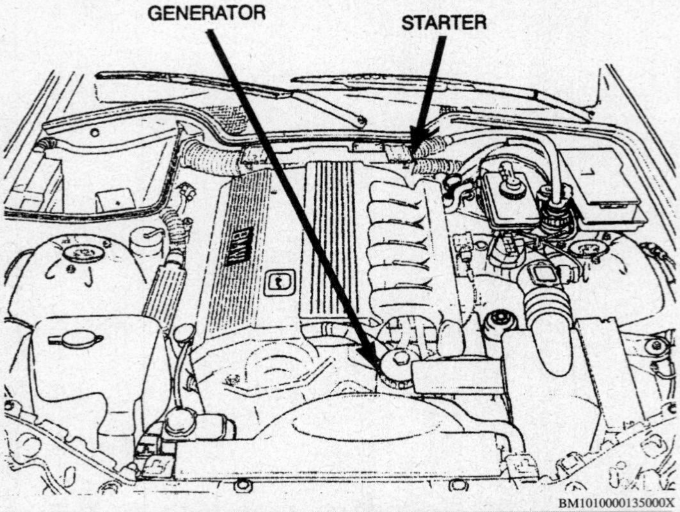

Fig. 3 Engine compartment (Part 1 of 7). Z3

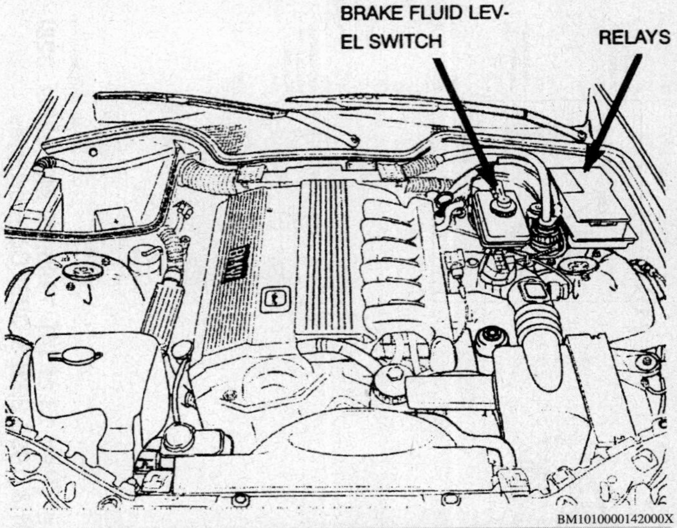

Fig. 3 Engine compartment (Part 2 of 7). Z3

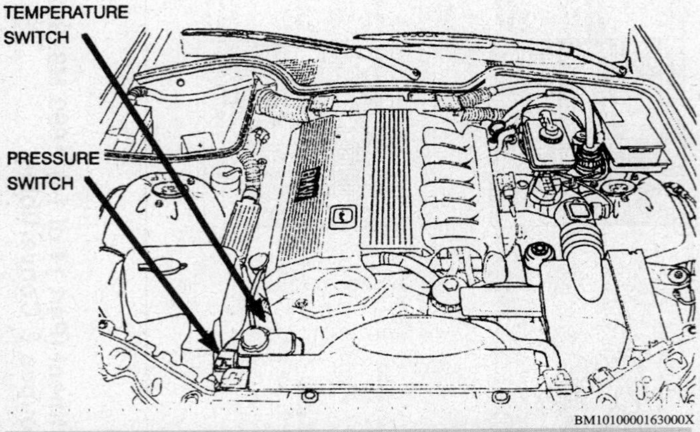

Fig. 3 Engine compartment (Part 3 of 7). Z3

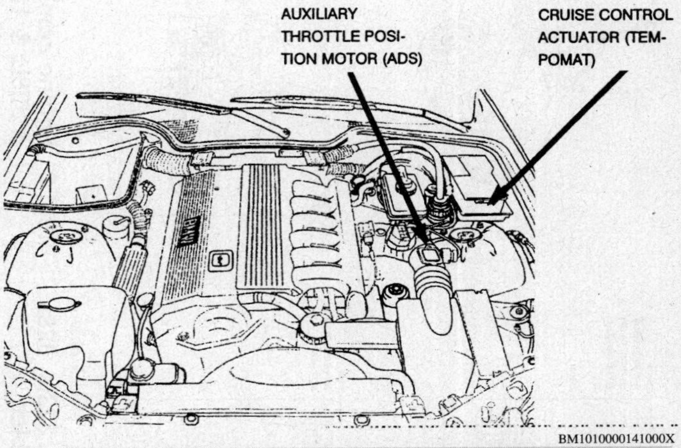

Fig. 3 Engine compartment (Part 4 of 7). Z3

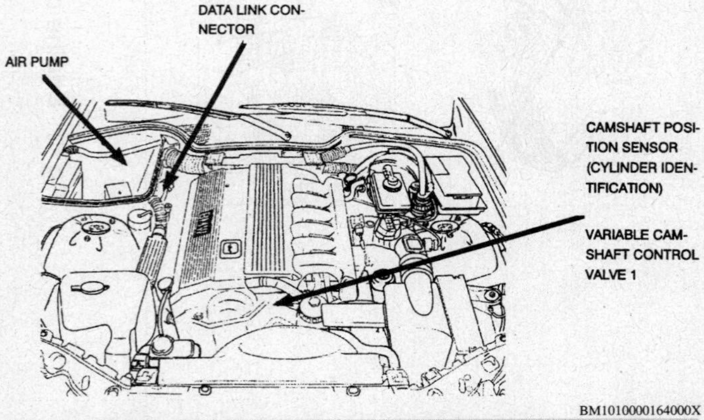

Fig. 3 Engine compartment (Part 5 of 7). Z3

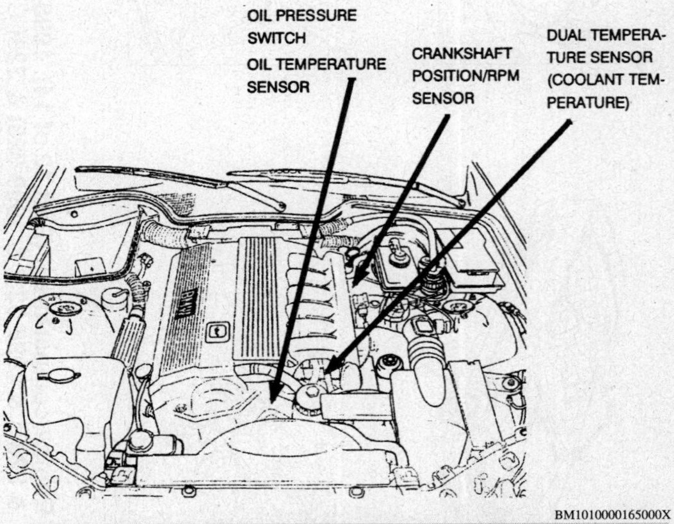

Fig. 3 Engine compartment (Part 6 of 7). Z3

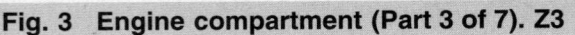

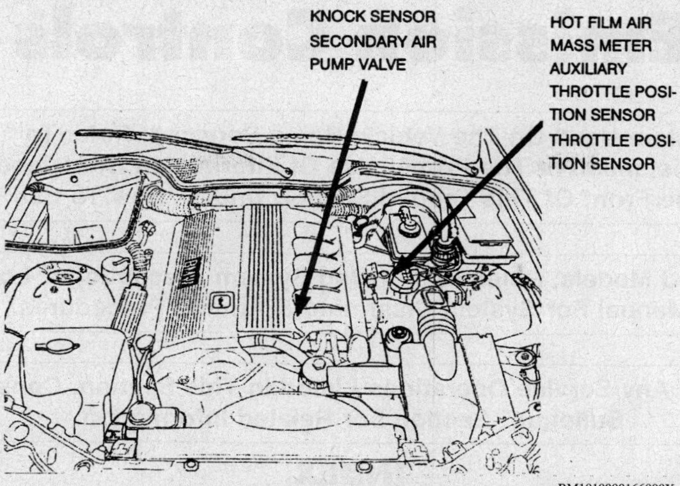

Fig. 3 Engine compartment (Part 7 of 7). Z3

Emission Controls

NOTE: If Unsure Of The System Used On The Vehicle Being Serviced, Refer To "The Engine Systems Identification" Chart. Further Assistance For The Proper Use Of Information Contained In This Section Can Also Be Found In The Front Of This Tabbed Section Under "How To Use This Manual."

NOTE: On Air Bag Equipped Models, Refer To "Air Bag System Precautions" Located In The Front Of This Manual For System Disarming & Arming Procedures.

NOTE: Prior To Performing Any Service Operations Listed In This Section, Consult The "Technical Service Bulletins" Section For Related Information.

INDEX

	Page No.
Catalytic Converter	11-144
Description	11-144
System Service	11-144
Closed Crankcase Ventilation System	11-144
Description	11-144
System Service	11-144
Exhaust Gas Recirculation (EGR)	11-144
Description	11-144
Diagnosis & Testing	11-144
Black Switching Valve	11-145
Coolant Temperature Switch & Relay	11-145
Coolant Temperature Switch, Relay & RPM Switch	11-145
EGR Valve	11-144
Pressure Converter	11-145
RPM Switch	11-145
Red Switching Valve	11-145
Fuel Evaporative Emission Controls	11-145
Description	11-145
System Service	11-145

CATALYTIC CONVERTER

Description

The catalytic converter continues the process of consuming unburned hydrocarbons in the exhaust system, lowering engine emissions.

Vehicles equipped with a catalytic converter should not be operated with leaded fuel. Damage to the converter and oxygen sensor will result.

System Service

BMW catalytic converters are maintenance free, requiring only periodic inspection for cracks, damage, or rattling.

CLOSED CRANKCASE VENTILATION SYSTEM

Description

All models use a closed crankcase ventilation system to prevent crankcase vapors from escaping to the atmosphere. A hose links the valve cover to the intake manifold. The crankcase is subjected to constant vacuum, allowing blow-by and other crankcase vapors to be drawn into the engine and burned. Baffles on the valve cover prevent lubricating oil from being drawn into the system.

Some vehicles employ an additional vacuum line which links the vent tube to the intake manifold, as well as the air cleaner housing. This vacuum line aids in increasing the efficiency with which vapors are extracted from the engine.

System Service

Service of the system is limited to periodic inspection of hoses and clamps. Any cracked or leaking hoses must be replaced. The check valve cover to ensure accumulated sludge is not blocking the system. If this condition is present, the valve cover must be removed, cleaned in a suitable parts solvent and installed with a new gasket.

EXHAUST GAS RECIRCULATION (EGR)

Description

This system is used to reduce the level of oxides of nitrogen (NOx) emitted. By venting a regulated amount of exhaust gas to the intake manifold, the formation of NOx is inhibited during the combustion cycle. The EGR system uses a vacuum operated valve to control exhaust gas flow.

Exhaust gas is drawn from the exhaust manifold, filtered, and admitted to the intake manifold through the EGR valve. The EGR valve vacuum control system uses electro vacuum controls to coordinate EGR system function with engine speed, coolant temperature and ignition timing, in order to provide EGR during acceleration and steady part throttle engine operation. These control elements include a coolant temperature sensor, revolution counter/switch (RPM switch), a control relay, a pressure converter, and a vacuum control valve.

Diagnosis & Testing

EGR VALVE

Single Vacuum Port Type

1. With engine at idle, disconnect vacuum line from valve, and apply light vacuum to vacuum port.
2. Observe engine idle characteristics. If speeds drop and idle becomes uneven, EGR valve is good. If engine speed does not drop, or test results are indefinite, proceed with next step.
3. With engine off, remove EGR valve and inspect for clogging. If valve appears to be serviceable, reconnect vacuum line, but do not install valve in manifold.
4. Plug EGR valve intake manifold port. Connect tachometer and start engine. **Ensure EGR valve outlet port is away from any heat sensitive materials.**
5. Bring engine speed to just over 2500 RPM. Observe outlet of EGR valve for pressure. If no pressure is felt, check for vacuum leaks on EGR vacuum circuit. If vacuum is correct, valve diaphragm is defective (leaking) or valve is seized. Replace if not functioning properly.

Dual Vacuum Port Type

1. With engine at idle, and at normal operating temperature, disconnect blue hose from valve, but do not plug hose.

2. Observe engine idle. If engine idle remains same, proceed to next step. If idle drops, check throttle idle setting, and vacuum from thermo valve. Correct if needed. Retest. If idle speed still drops, EGR valve is defective.
3. Disconnect blue and red hoses from EGR valve. Disconnect black hose from vacuum control valve. Connect black hose to red hose vacuum port of EGR valve.
4. Observe engine idle. If idle speed remains same, EGR valve is defective. If idle drops sharply, proceed to next step.
5. Connect blue hose to proper EGR valve port. With black vacuum control valve hose connected to red hose EGR valve port (as in previous step), observe engine idle speed. If idle remains same, system is good. If idle speed drops sharply, check for defective hoses, defective EGR valve, or defective pressure converter.
6. Connect all lines to proper location.

PRESSURE CONVERTER

1. With engine at idle, and at normal operating temperature, check exhaust backpressure/control pressure by removing red hose from pressure converter. Check hose end for pressure feed. If no pressure is felt, backpressure line or hose is blocked or leaking. Correct if needed.
2. Remove white hose and check for intake vacuum at hose end. If no vacuum is present, check hose for leaks/ blockage. Replace hose if defective.
3. Remove red hose and blue hose from pressure converter. Check for control vacuum at blue hose end. If no vacuum is present, pressure converter is defective.

RED SWITCHING VALVE

The red switching valve controls EGR operation by monitoring coolant temperature at the coolant temperature switch. This valve also receives engine speed input from the RPM switch. The function of the switching valve is to close the EGR valve at temperatures below 113°F, and at engine speeds above 3750 RPM.

1. With engine off and coolant temperature below 113°F, remove red hose from EGR valve.
2. With ignition switch in off position, blow air orally through red hose. There should be no air flow through switching valve. If present, valve is defective.
3. With engine off, and ignition switch in on position, blow air orally through red hose. Air should flow through switching valve. If not, valve is defective.

BLACK SWITCHING VALVE

To test systems with a black switching valve in the EGR circuit, proceed as follows:

1. With engine off, place ignition switch in on position. Remove harness connector from black switching valve.
2. Connect test lamp to both harness contacts.
3. Place transmission in 4th gear. Test lamp should light. If not, check transmission switch harness connector to see if contact is being made. If connection is good, check switch continuity. Switch should show continuity if transmission is in 4th gear. If not, replace switch.

COOLANT TEMPERATURE SWITCH & RELAY

1. With engine off and coolant temperature below 113°F, remove harness connector from red switching valve. Place ignition switch in on position.
2. Connect test lamp leads to both harness contacts. Test lamp should light when connected. If not, check continuity of coolant temperature switch. Switch should show continuity. Replace switch if defective.
3. If test lamp fails to light, and temperature switch is good, check for a short or open in circuit ground. If ground is good, switching relay is defective.

COOLANT TEMPERATURE SWITCH, RELAY & RPM SWITCH

1. With engine off and coolant temperature above 113°F, remove harness connector from red switching valve. Place ignition switch in on position.
2. Connect test lamp leads to both harness contacts. Test lamp should not light when connected. If test lamp lights, check continuity of coolant temperature switch. Switch should not show continuity. Replace if defective.
3. If test lamp lights, and temperature switch is good, check RPM switch as outlined under "RPM Switch." If RPM switch is good, switching relay is defective.

RPM SWITCH

1. With engine running at idle, remove harness connector from blue switching valve.
2. Connect test lamp leads to both harness contacts. Test lamp should not light. If test lamp lights, RPM switch (marked "Drehzahlschalter") is defective.
3. If RPM switch is good in previous step, with test lamp connected in same way, raise engine speed to just over 3750 RPM. Test lamp should light as engine reaches 3750 RPM. If lamp does not light, check for short or open in circuit ground. If none is present, RPM switch is defective.

FUEL EVAPORATIVE EMISSION CONTROLS

Description

These systems use a non-vented fuel tank linked to a vapor storage (expansion) tank. The vapor storage tank is connected to a charcoal canister, which absorbs fuel vapors and holds them until they are drawn into the engine to be burned. The charcoal canister is connected to the intake system, so engine vacuum can draw vapors out of the canister.

System Service

The fuel evaporative emissions system is maintenance free, requiring only periodic inspection for leaks, cracked components, and defective filler cap gaskets.

Technical Service Bulletins

INDEX

	Page No.
DTC 79	11-149
750	11-149
DTC 80	11-146
M44	11-146
M73	11-146
DTC 93	11-147
M44	11-147
DTC 183	11-147
M62 & M73	11-147
DTC 227/228	11-147
328 & 528	11-147
DTC 245	11-148
323i & 328i	11-148
DTC 253	11-148
Z3 M Coupe & Z3 M Roadster	11-148
DTCs 10, 12, 18 & 20	11-148
540 & 740	11-148
DTCs 10, 12, 18, 20, 139 & 140	11-148
540 & 740	11-148
DTCs 80 & 81	11-146
M62	11-146
DTCs 83 & 244	11-147
M3, Z3 M Coupe, Z3 M Roadster, Z3 2.3, Z3 2.8, 323i, 328i & 528i	11-147
DTCs 109–120 & 169–176	11-147
Z3 2.3, Z3 2.8, 323, 328 & 528	11-147
DTCs 180/181	11-147
S62	11-147
DTCs 183/188	11-147
M62TU	11-147
DTCs 191 & 194	11-147
528	11-147
DTCs 229, 230, 235 & 236	11-148
M3, 328 & 528	11-148
DTCs 245 & 246	11-146
M52	11-146
S52	11-146
DTCs 251 & 254	11-147
M52 & S52	11-147
Engine Cranks But Does Not Start	11-148
M3, 328 & 539	11-148
Z3	11-148
Engine Hesitates & Stumbles At Idle	11-148
X5 3.0i, Z3 3.0 & 330xi	11-148
Engine Runs Rough On Cold Start	11-147
M3, Z3 M Coupe & Z3 M Roadster	11-147
Engine Speed Hangs During Shifts	11-148
Z3 2.3, Z3 2.8, 323i, 328i & 528i	11-148
Low Idle Speed & Stumble	11-148
540 & 740	11-148
No Start	11-147
528	11-147

DTC 80

M44

On some of these models the MIL lamp may be lit with Diagnostic Trouble Code (DTC) 80 may be set.

This condition may be caused by the secondary air injection system.

To correct this condition, proceed as follows:

1. Inspect secondary air injection system operation.
2. If pump is not operating correctly, inspect air pump relay. Replace as required.
3. If relay is operating correctly, inspect pump wiring and electrical connectors. Repair as required.
4. Inspect pump. Replace as required.
5. If pump seized because of moisture, inspect non-return valve for sticking. Replace valve with revised unit (part date code of 99T075, or later) as required.
6. Inspect non-return valve vacuum lines. Replace line with revised unit (part No. 11 73 7 501 180) as required.

M73

On some of these models the MIL lamp may be lit with Diagnostic Trouble Code (DTC) 80 set.

This condition may be caused by the secondary air injection system.

To correct this condition, proceed as follows:

1. Inspect secondary air injection system operation.
2. If pump is not operating correctly, inspect air pump relay. Replace as required.
3. If relay is operating correctly, inspect pump wiring and electrical connectors. Repair as required.
4. Inspect pump. Replace as required.
5. If pump seized because of moisture, inspect non-return valve for sticking. Replace as required.
6. Inspect non-return valve vacuum lines. Replace line as required.

DTCS 245 & 246

M52

On some of these models the MIL lamp may be lit with Diagnostic Trouble Codes (DTCs) 245 and/or 246 set.

This condition may be caused by the secondary air injection system.

To correct this condition, proceed as follows:

1. Inspect secondary air injection system operation.
2. If pump is not operating correctly, inspect air pump relay. Replace relay with revised unit (part No. 12 63 1 741 690) as required.
3. If relay is operating correctly, inspect pump wiring and electrical connectors. Repair as required.
4. Inspect pump. Replace as required.
5. If pump seized because of moisture, inspect non-return valve for sticking. Replace as required.
6. Inspect non-return valve vacuum lines. Replace as required.

S52

On some of these models the MIL lamp may be lit with Diagnostic Trouble Codes (DTCs) 245 and/or 246 set.

This condition may be caused by the secondary air injection system.

To correct this condition, proceed as follows:

1. Inspect secondary air injection system operation.
2. If pump is not operating correctly, inspect air pump relay. Replace as required.
3. If relay is operating correctly, inspect pump wiring and electrical connectors. Repair as required.
4. Inspect pump. Replace as required.
5. If pump seized because of moisture, inspect non-return valve for sticking. Replace as required.
6. Inspect non-return valve vacuum lines. Replace as required.

DTCS 80 & 81

M62

On some of these models the MIL lamp may be lit with Diagnostic Trouble Codes (DTCs) 80 and/or 81 set.

This condition may be caused by the secondary air injection system.

To correct this condition, proceed as follows:

1. Inspect secondary air injection system operation.
2. If pump is not operating correct, inspect air pump relay. Replace as required.
3. If relay is operating correctly, inspect pump wiring and electrical connectors. Repair as required.
4. Inspect pump. Replace as required.
5. If pump seized because of moisture, inspect non-return valve for sticking. Replace as required.

6. Inspect non-return valve vacuum lines. Replace as required.

DTC 93

M44

On some of these models the MIL lamp my be lit with Diagnostic Trouble Code (DTC) 93 stored.

This condition may be caused by insufficient sealing pressure. The fuel filler cap may not be turned to full stop or the retaining strap may be caught between the filler pipe and cap.

To correct this condition, remove the retaining strap.

DTCS 251 & 254

M52 & S52

On some of these models the MIL lamp my be lit with Diagnostic Trouble Codes (DTCs) 251 and/or 254 stored.

This condition may be caused by insufficient sealing pressure. The fuel filler cap may not be turned to full stop or the retaining strap may be caught between the filler pipe and cap.

To correct this condition, remove the retaining strap.

DTC 183

M62 & M73

On some of these models the MIL lamp my be lit with Diagnostic Trouble Codes (DTC) 183 stored.

This condition may be caused by insufficient sealing pressure. The fuel filler cap may not be turned to full stop or the retaining strap may be caught between the filler pipe and cap.

To correct this condition, remove the retaining strap.

DTCS 183/188

M62TU

On some of these models the MIL lamp my be lit with Diagnostic Trouble Codes (DTCs) 183 and/or 188 stored.

This condition may be caused by insufficient sealing pressure. The fuel filler cap may not be turned to full stop or the retaining strap may be caught between the filler pipe and cap.

To correct this condition, remove the retaining strap.

DTCS 180/181

S62

On some of these models the MIL lamp my be lit with Diagnostic Trouble Codes (DTCs) 180 and/or 181 stored.

This condition may be caused by insufficient sealing pressure. The fuel filler cap may not be turned to full stop or the retaining strap may be caught between the filler pipe and cap.

To correct this condition, remove the retaining strap.

DTCS 191 & 194

528

On some of these models built between September 1997 and August 1998, the MIL lamp may be lit with Diagnostic Trouble Codes (DTCs) 191 and/or 194 set.

This condition may be caused by the T-connector below the intake manifold being crushed and a leak in the Evaporative (EVAP) emission control system.

To correct this condition, proceed as follows:

1. Replace pinched or restricted T-fitting with revised unit (part No. 11 72 1 439 973).
2. Inspect system for leaks.

ENGINE RUNS ROUGH ON COLD START

M3, Z3 M Coupe & Z3 M Roadster

On some of these M3 models built before August 1999, Z3 M Coupe models built after June 1998 and Z3 M Roadster models built after February 1998, the engine may run rough during the first few minutes of engine operations following initial cold start. The engine may also hesitate and/or have poor throttle response during the first few minutes of engine operating following initial cold start.

This condition may be caused by DME programing.

To correct this condition, reprogram the DME using the latest software.

DTC 83 & 244

M3, Z3 M Coupe, Z3 M Roadster, Z3 2.3, Z3 2.8, 323i, 328i & 528i

On some of these M3, 323i and 328i models built before January 1999, 528i models built before September 1998, Z3 2.3 and Z3 2.8 models built before October 1998, and Z3 M Coupe and Z3 M Roadster models built before February 1999, the MIL lamp may be lit with Diagnostic Trouble Codes (DTCs) 83 and/or 244 stored.

This condition may be caused by an internal Crankshaft Position (CKP) sensor failure.

To correct this condition, install revised CKP sensor (part No. 12 14 1 709 616) and adapter harness (part No. 12 51 4 592 703) to supply sensor with 12-volt operating voltage instead of five-volt DME supplied power, as follows:

1. Remove CKP sensor below starter motor. If sensor connector can be disconnected, new style sensor is already installed and no further repairs are required.
2. Remove oil filter housing cover and cover housing with suitable shop rag.
3. Disconnect CKP sensor electrical connector from engine harness below intake manifold.
4. Remove fuel rail cover and disconnect VANOS solenoid valve connector.
5. Install revised CKP sensor and new O-ring.
6. Connect new adapter harness to CKP sensor, engine wiring harness and VANOS solenoid valve.
7. Secure harness going to VANOS valve to VANOS oil line using suitable cable ties. **Do not tension harness lead to VANOS solenoid.**

NO START

528

On some of these models built before November 1998 there may be a no crank, no start condition. In addition, the instrument cluster transmission range display may be off, the charge indicator lamp may flash or be permanently on, Diagnostic Trouble Codes (DTC) 11 may be set, and fuse 15 may be blown.

This condition may be caused by a faulty oil level switch.

To correct this condition, install revised oil level switch (part No. 12 61 1 433 509)..

DTC 227/228

328 & 528

On some of these 1998 models the MIL lamp may be lit and Diagnostic Trouble Codes (DTCs) 227 and/or 228 may be set.

This condition may be caused by the incorrect Mass Air Flow (MAF) sensor being installed.

To correct this condition, install correct MAF sensor (part No. 13 62 1 703 275).

DTCS 109-120 & 169-176

Z3 2.3, Z3 2.8, 323, 328 & 528

On some of these 1999–2000 models the MIL lamp may be set and Diagnostic Trouble Codes (DTCs) 109–120 and/or 169–176 may be set.

This condition may be caused by the motor driven throttle valve.

To correct this condition, proceed as follows:

1. Inspect motor drive throttle valve wiring for an open or short to ground. Repair as required.

2. Replace motor drive throttle valve.
3. Turn ignition switch to Off position for 30 seconds.
4. Turn ignition switch to On position and clear DTCs.
5. Press accelerator pedal to wide open throttle four times.

ENGINE SPEED HANGS DURING SHIFTS

Z3 2.3, Z3 2.8, 323i, 328i & 528i

On some of these 323i and 328i models built between April 1998 and March 1999, 528 models built between September 1998 and March 1999, and Z3 2.3 and Z3 2.8 models built between August 1998 and March 1999, and equipped with manual transmission, the engine RPM may momentarily hang up during shifts, and/or gears may not engage smoothly during 1-2 and 2-3 shifts.

This condition may be caused by the clutch pedal switch or Engine Control Module.

To correct this condition, proceed as follows:

1. Ensure clutch depressed signal is being received by the DME.
2. Inspect clutch (cruise control interrupt) switch. If three-wire switch is installed, reprogram DME with latest software. If two-wire switch is install, proceed to next step.
3. Install new three-wire switch (part No. 61 31 8 381 612).
4. Connect new adapter wire harness (part No. 61 11 0 004 349) to three-wire switch using three-pin female connector (housing part No. 61 13 1 383 738 and blue cover part No. 61 13 1 383 826), noting the following:
   a. Pin No. 1 (brown/blue) goes to ground pin No. 2 of old two-pin connector.
   b. Pin No. 2 (blue/brown) goes to DME pin No. 23 via pin No. 1 of old two-pin connector.
   c. Pin No. 3 (violet/yellow) is to be connected to 12-volt power supply at brake switch.
5. Connect harness two-pin male connector to original two-pin female clutch switch connector.
6. Connect violet/yellow wire to violet/yellow 12-volt power supply wire from brake light switch connector using quick connector (part No. 61 13 8 364 566).

ENGINE CRANKS BUT DOES NOT START

Z3

On some of these models built after August 1998 the engine may crank but does not start. Diagnostic Trouble Code (DTC) 209 may be set.

This condition may be caused by the Electronic Driveaway Protection (EWS) module.

To correct this condition install EWS module located on the lefthand side of the vehicle below the instrument cluster.

M3, 328 & 539

On some of these models the engine may crank but does not start.

This condition may be caused by the Electronic Driveaway Protection (EWS) module communication with the DME.

Reprogram DME with latest software.

DTC 245

323i & 328i

On some of these models built between April and July 1998 Diagnostic Trouble Code (DTC) 245 may be set.

This condition may be caused by the secondary air non-return valve vacuum hose routing.

To correct this condition, proceed as follows:

1. Inspect non-return valve vacuum line running below the oxygen sensor wiring.
2. If the line is too long it may be damaged by the oxygen sensor or exhaust manifold.
3. If there is damage to plastic tube in front of the oxygen sensor, proceed as follows:
   a. Cut damaged portion.
   b. Install plastic tube into appropriate length of rubber hose.
4. If there is damage to rubber hose, install appropriate length rubber hose.
5. Ensure rubber hose runs through first holding clip.
6. Route hose through second clip used to secure oxygen sensor connector and wiring underneath oxygen sensor wiring harness.

ENGINE HESITATES & STUMBLES AT IDLE

X5 3.0i, Z3 3.0 & 330xi

On some of these models the engine may hesitate and stumble at idle especially when turning the steering wheel. No Diagnostic Trouble Codes (DTCs) are set.

This condition may be caused by DME programming.

To correct this condition reprogram DME with latest software.

DTC 253

Z3 M Coupe & Z3 M Roadster

On some of these models built between February and September 1998 may set Diagnostic Trouble Code (DTC) 253.

This condition may be caused by the tank the pressure sensor.

To correct this condition, proceed as follows:

1. Inspect vent line from charcoal canister for blockage or restrictions. Repair as required.
2. Reprogram DME with latest software.

DTC 229, 230, 235 & 236

M3, 328 & 528

On some of these models built before December 1997 the MIL lamp may be lit and Diagnostic Trouble Codes (DTCs) 229, 230, 235 and/or 236 set.

This condition may be caused by DME programming

To correct this condition, reprogram DME with latest software.

DTC 10, 12, 18, 20, 139 & 140

540 & 740

On some of these models built between April 1997 and August 1999 the MIL lamp may be lit and Diagnostic Trouble Codes (DTCs) 10, 12, 18, 20, 139 and/or 140 set.

This condition may be caused by DME software.

To correct this condition, proceed as follows:

1. If DTCs 139 or 140 are set, inspect thermostat and wiring. Repair as required.
2. Reprogram DME with latest software.

DTC 10, 12, 18 & 20

540 & 740

On some of these models built between April 1997 and August 1998 may have MIL lamp lit and Diagnostic Trouble Codes (DTCs) 10, 12, 18 and/or 20 set.

This condition may be caused by DME programming

To correct this condition, reprogram DME with latest software.

LOW IDLE SPEED & STUMBLE

540 & 740

On some of these models the engine may stumble and engine idle speed appears too low when the air conditioning is off, the steering wheel is turned fully right or left and the automatic transmission is in reverse gear.

This condition may be caused by steering and transmission load requirements.

To correct this condition increase the idle speed 100 RPM by reprogramming the DME.

DTC 79
750

On some of these models built between August and October 1998 the MIL lamp may be lit and Diagnostic Trouble Code (DTC) 79 set.

This condition may be caused by secondary air pump circuit wiring.

To correct this condition, proceed as follows:

1. Remove E-box cover, then DME No. 1 module connectors No. 4 and 5.
2. Disconnect locking tap and remove gray connector with pin No. 3.
3. Remove pin No. 3 and brown/green wire using suitable tool.
4. Remove wiring harness electrical tape.
5. Remove DME No. 2 module connectors No. 4 and 5.
6. Disconnect locking tap and remove black connector with pin No. 31.
7. Remove pin No. 31 and brown/blue wire using suitable tool.
8. Remove wiring harness electrical tape.
9. Install brown/green wire into pin location No. 31 and brown/blue wire in pin location No. 3.
10. Install connectors and wrap wiring harnesses with suitable electrical tape.
11. Install E-box cover.

Abbreviations & Acronyms

ADM: ADV Module
AEGS: Automatic Transmission Control
ASC: Automatic Stability Control
CCM: Check Control Module
DDE: Digital Diesel Electronics
DK: Throttle Valve
DME: Digital Engine Electronics
DWA: Anti-Theft
EDC: Electronic Damper Control
EH: Electronic-Hydraulic
EKP: Electronic Fuel Pump
EML: Electronic Throttle Control
EV: Injector Valve
HG: Manual Transmission
KD: Kickdown
KW: Crankshaft
LL: Idle
LLS: Idle Speed Actuator
LMM: Air Flow Meter
MF: Microfilm
MSR: Engine Drag Torque Control
MV: Solenoid Valve
RxD: Diagnosis Initiation Line
SG: Control Module
TD: Engine Speed Signal
TE: Fuel Evaporation Control
ti: Injection Timing
TL: Partial Load
tL: Load Signal
TR: Crankshaft Reference
TxD: Diagnostic Data Line
U-Batt: Battery Voltage
U-Vers: Voltage Supply
VANOS: Variable Camshaft Control Module
VL: Full Load

JAGUAR

TABLE OF CONTENTS

Page No.

EMISSIONS:
Abbreviations & Acronyms 12-76
Application Charts 12-71
Emissions Controls 12-73
Emission Control System Application Chart . . . 12-71
Technical Service Bulletins 12-75
Vacuum Hose Routings 12-72

ENGINE SYSTEMS IDENTIFICATION 12-2

FUEL SYSTEMS:
Abbreviations & Acronyms 12-76
Electric Fuel Pumps 12-69
Fuel Injection 12-8
Technical Service Bulletins 12-75
Tune Up Specifications 12-2

ENGINE TUNE UP & PERFORMANCE:
Abbreviations & Acronyms 12-76
Technical Service Bulletins 12-75

Page No.
Tune Up Specifications 12-2
V6 Gasoline Engine 12-3
V8 Gasoline Engine 12-4

GENERAL INFORMATION:
Abbreviations & Acronyms 12-76
Air Bag System Precautions 0-12
Air Quality Standards 0-23
Computer Relearn Procedures 0-10
Electrical Symbol & Wire Color Code Identification 0-33
Engine System Identification 12-2
How To Use This Manual 0-1
Quick Reference 12-1
Service Reminder & Warning Lamp Reset Procedure 0-14
Technical Service Bulletins 12-75
Vehicle Identification 0-3
Vehicle Maintenance Schedules 0-45

IGNITION SYSTEMS:
Abbreviations & Acronyms 12-76
Ignition Systems 12-5
Technical Service Bulletins 12-75

Quick Reference

Application	Page No.
ACCESSING DIAGNOSTIC TROUBLE CODES	
4.0L	12-30
3.0L	12-10
CLEARING DIAGNOSTIC TROUBLE CODES	
4.0L	12-67
3.0L	12-11
DIAGNOSTIC CHART INDEX	
3.0L	12-14
SENSOR SPECIFICATIONS	
4.0L	12-29
3.0L	12-9

Engine Systems Identification

On eight cylinder engines, the engine code is stamped on a raised pad on the front of the engine block near the thermostat housing.

Engine, Liter	Year	Ignition System	Page No.	Fuel & Computer System	Page No.
3.0L	2000–01	Coil On-Plug Ignition System	12-6	Electronic Sequential Port	12-8
4.0L	1998–2001	Coil On-Plug Ignition System	12-7	Electronic Sequential Port	12-28

Tune Up Specifications

Year & Engine	Spark Plug Gap Inch	Ignition Timing			Curb Idle Speed②		Fast Idle Speed②		Fuel Pressure, psi	Valve Lash, Inch	
		Firing Order	Timing BTDC	Timing Mark	Man. Trans.	Auto. Trans.	Man. Trans.	Auto. Trans.		Intake	Exhaust
1998–99											
4.0L	.052	④	①	③	—	①	—	①	—	—	—
2000–01											
3.0L	.054	⑤	①	③	—	①	—	①	—	.007–.009C	.009–.011C
4.0L	.043	④	①	③	—	①	—	①	—	.007–.009C	.009–.011C

BTDC — Before Top Dead Center
C — Cold
N — Neutral
① — Controlled by engine management system.
② — When adjusting idle speed, set parking brake & block drive wheels.
③ — Equipped w/crankshaft position sensor.
④ — Firing order 1-5-4-2-6-3-7-8.
⑤ — Firing order 1-4-2-5-3-6.

Engine Tune Up & Performance

TABLE OF CONTENTS

	Page No.		Page No.
V6 GASOLINE ENGINE	12-3	V8 GASOLINE ENGINE	12-4

V6 Gasoline Engine

NOTE: If Unsure Of The System Used On The Vehicle Being Serviced, Refer To "The Engine Systems Identification Chart."Further Assistance For The Proper Use Of Information Contained In This Section Can Also Be Found In The Front Of This Tabbed Section Under "How To Use This Manual"

NOTE: On Air Bag Equipped Models, Refer To "Air Bag System Precautions" Located In The Front Of This Manual For System Disarming & Arming Procedures.

NOTE: Refer To "Computer Relearn Procedures" Located In The Front Of This Manual When Battery Power To The Computer Has Been Interrupted.

NOTE: Prior To Performing Any Service Operations Listed In This Section, Consult The "Technical Service Bulletins" Section For Related Information.

INDEX

	Page No.		Page No.		Page No.
Idle Speed Adjustment	12-3	Spark Plugs	12-3	Valve Arrangement	12-3
Ignition Timing	12-3	Valves	12-3		

SPARK PLUGS

On models equipped with normally aspirated engines, spark plugs should be replaced at 100,000 mile intervals.

On models equipped with supercharged engines, spark plugs should be replaced at 60,000 mile intervals.

On all models, refer to "Tune Up Specifications" for spark plug gap.

IGNITION TIMING

The ignition timing is controlled by the Engine Control Module (ECM) and is not adjustable. Refer to "Fuel Injection" for fault conditions related to this system.

IDLE SPEED ADJUSTMENT

The idle speed is controlled by the Engine Control Module (ECM) and is not adjustable. Refer to "Fuel Injection" for fault conditions related to this system.

VALVES

Valve Arrangement

Each cylinder head incorporates dual overhead camshafts operating four valves per cylinder via solid aluminium-alloy valve lifters. Steel shims in the tops of the lifters allow valve clearance adjustments.

V8 Gasoline Engine

NOTE: If Unsure Of The System Used On The Vehicle Being Serviced, Refer To "The Engine Systems Identification Chart."Further Assistance For The Proper Use Of Information Contained In This Section Can Also Be Found In The Front Of This Tabbed Section Under "How To Use This Manual"

NOTE: On Air Bag Equipped Models, Refer To "Air Bag System Precautions" Located In The Front Of This Manual For System Disarming & Arming Procedures.

NOTE: Refer To "Computer Relearn Procedures" Located In The Front Of This Manual When Battery Power To The Computer Has Been Interrupted.

NOTE: Prior To Performing Any Service Operations Listed In This Section, Consult The "Technical Service Bulletins" Section For Related Information.

INDEX

	Page No.
Idle Speed Adjustment	12-4
Ignition Timing	12-4
Spark Plugs	12-4
Valves	12-4
Valve Arrangement	12-4

SPARK PLUGS

This procedure has been revised by a Technical Service Bulletin.

On models equipped with normally aspirated engines, spark plugs should be replaced at 100,000 mile intervals.

On models equipped with supercharged engines, spark plugs should be replaced at 60,000 mile intervals.

On all models, refer to "Tune Up Specifications" for spark plug gap.

IGNITION TIMING

The ignition timing is controlled by the Engine Control Module (ECM) and is not adjustable. Refer to "Fuel Injection" for fault conditions related to this system.

IDLE SPEED ADJUSTMENT

The idle speed is controlled by the Engine Control Module (ECM) and is not adjustable. Refer to "Fuel Injection" for fault conditions related to this system.

VALVES

Valve Arrangement

Each cylinder head incorporates dual overhead camshafts operating four valves per cylinder via solid aluminium-alloy valve lifters. Steel shims in the tops of the lifters allow valve clearance adjustments.

Ignition Systems

NOTE: If Unsure Of The System Used On The Vehicle Being Serviced, Refer To "The Engine Systems Identification Chart."Further Assistance For The Proper Use Of Information Contained In This Section Can Also Be Found In The Front Of This Tabbed Section Under "How To Use This Manual"

NOTE: On Air Bag Equipped Models, Refer To "Air Bag System Precautions" Located In The Front Of This Manual For System Disarming & Arming Procedures.

NOTE: Refer To "Computer Relearn Procedures" Located In The Front Of This Manual When Battery Power To The Computer Has Been Interrupted.

NOTE: Prior To Performing Any Service Operations Listed In This Section, Consult The "Technical Service Bulletins" Section For Related Information.

TABLE OF CONTENTS

	Page No.
COIL ON-PLUG IGNITION SYSTEM 3.0L ENGINE	12-6
COIL ON-PLUG IGNITION SYSTEM 4.0L ENGINE	12-7

Coil On–Plug Ignition System 3.0L Engine

INDEX

	Page No.
Description	12-6
Camshaft Position Sensor	12-6
Crankshaft Position Sensor	12-6
Ignition System	12-6
Diagnosis & Testing	12-6
Precautions	12-6
Air Bag Systems	12-6
Battery Ground Cable	12-6
System Service	12-6
Component Replacement	12-6
Camshaft Position Sensor	12-6
Crankshaft Position Sensor	12-6
Ignition Coil	12-6

PRECAUTIONS

Air Bag Systems

Refer to "Air Bag System Precautions" in the front of this manual for system disarming and arming procedures.

Battery Ground Cable

Prior to service, disconnect battery ground cable and isolate as required.

DESCRIPTION

IGNITION SYSTEM

The ignition system consists of an ignition coil located on each individual cylinder and each individual spark plug. The ignition timing can be adjusted more rapidly and independently.

This ignition system enables the driver to drive the vehicle home if a coil or coil wiring failure occurs.

CRANKSHAFT POSITION SENSOR

The crankshaft position sensor signal is the basis for ignition timing calculations. The alternating voltage signal from the sensor is converted by (PCM).

CAMSHAFT POSITION SENSOR

The camshaft position sensor sends an alternating voltage signal to the (PCM) from which the position of number one cylinder is calculated. The signal from this sensor is only required during starting. When the engine is running, the profile ignition pick-up (PIP) signal is used to sequentially control the fuel injectors.

DIAGNOSIS & TESTING

Refer to the "Fuel Injection" section for diagnosis & testing procedures.

SYSTEM SERVICE

Component Replacement

IGNITION COIL

1. **On righthand bank,** remove intake manifold as outlined under "Intake Manifold Replace."
2. **On lefthand bank,** remove engine cover
3. **On all banks,** disconnect electrical Connectors.
4. Remove attaching bolt, then the ignition coil.
5. Reverse procedure to install. **Torque** coil to 48 inch lbs.

CRANKSHAFT POSITION SENSOR

1. Raise and support vehicle.
2. Disconnect electrical connector from sensor.
3. Remove crankshaft position sensor.
4. Reverse procedure to install. **Torque** to 84 inch lbs.

CAMSHAFT POSITION SENSOR

1. Raise and support vehicle.
2. Disconnect electrical connector from sensor.
3. Remove camshaft position sensor.
4. Reverse procedure to install. **Torque** to 84 inch lbs.

Coil On–Plug Ignition System 4.0L Engine

INDEX

	Page No.
Description	12-7
Camshaft Position Sensor	12-7
Crankshaft Position Sensor	12-7
Ignition Coil Module (ICM)	12-7
Knock Sensor	12-7
Diagnosis & Testing	12-7
Precautions	12-7
Air Bag Systems	12-7
Battery Ground Cable	12-7
System Service	12-7
Component Replacement	12-7
Camshaft Position (CMP) Sensor	12-8
Crankshaft Position Sensor	12-7
Ignition Coil	12-7
Ignition Control Module (ICM)	12-7
Knock Sensor	12-7

PRECAUTIONS

Air Bag Systems

Refer to "Air Bag System Precautions" in the front of this manual for system disarming and arming procedures.

Battery Ground Cable

Prior to service, disconnect battery ground cable and isolate as required.

DESCRIPTION

Ignition Coil Module (ICM)

The ICM provides an interface between the Engine Control Module (ECM) and the on-plug coils.

Ignition amplifier module No. 1 drives coils 1A, 2B, 3B and 4A; No. 2 drives 1B, 2A, 3A & 4B, A being the righthand bank and B the lefthand.

1. When the following criteria are met:
   a. Engine not in starting position.
   b. Misfire detection not operative.
   c. Engine speed less than 2500 RPM.
   d. Battery output more than 10 volts.
2. A hardware inspection is made on the coils when they are to energize according to ignition timing.
3. If the coils are not energized properly a counter is started.
4. Once the counter exceeds a set number, a failure judgment is made and relevant DTC P0351–P0358 are set.
5. Coils are also inspection relevant to each amplifier. Non operational result set DTCs P1367 and P1368.
6. If engine speed fluxion is more than misfire detection level, a misfire counter is set.
7. When a preset criteria is exceeded, a fault is set.

Knock Sensor

Between 700–6800 RPM, the Engine Control Module (ECM) will retard individual cylinder timing when detonation occurs. During acceleration, at critical load and speed conditions, the ECM retards ignition timing to prevent detonation.

If sensor output is less than .6 volts, a low input DTC is set. If output is more than 4.5 volts, a high DTC is set.

Crankshaft Position Sensor

The crankshaft position sensor is mounted on the sump body. Signals are generated by the drive plate passing the sensor magnet.

1. The diagnostic inspects for a crank sensor pulse during engine cranking and normal running.
2. If there is not output during cranking a counter is set.
3. Battery voltage is inspected and starter is deemed operating at a set threshold.
4. When counter exceeds set value and battery voltage increased as starter has stop operating, a failure judgment is made.
5. At engines speeds of more than 1000 RPM, the 30° crank angle time counter is inspected.
6. If the counter is above a set threshold, a failure judgment is made.
7. Rational inspections are made against camshaft position sensor.

Camshaft Position Sensor

The camshaft position sensor is mounted on the lefthand bank with the sensor ring installed to the inlet camshaft. Signals are generated by the sensor ring passing the sensor magnet.

1. Diagnostic inspects for cam sensor pulse during engine cranking and normal running.
2. If there is not output during cranking a counter is set.
3. Battery voltage is inspected and starter is deemed operating at a set threshold.
4. When counter exceeds set value and battery voltage increased as starter has stop operating, a failure judgment is made.
5. A time counter will start if no pulses are detected with engine speeds more than 500 RPM.
6. If the counter exceeds threshold, a failure judgment is made.
7. If the camshaft sensor pulse does not registered against the relevant crankshaft position, a failure judgment is made.

DIAGNOSIS & TESTING

Refer to the "Fuel Injection" section for diagnosis & testing procedures.

SYSTEM SERVICE

Component Replacement

IGNITION CONTROL MODULE (ICM)

1. Disconnect ICM multi-plug.
2. Remove mounting bolts and ICM.
3. Reverse procedure to install.

IGNITION COIL

1. **On righthand cylinder head,** remove air intake tube/meter/air cleaner cover.
2. **On all cylinder heads,** remove mounting bolts and cover.
3. Pull wiring harness fro retaining clips, then disconnect coil connector.
4. Disconnect fixing and remove coil.
5. Reverse procedure to install. **Torque** coil and cover mounting bolts to 35–53 inch lbs.

KNOCK SENSOR

1. Remove engine cover.
2. Disconnect knock sensor multi-plug.
3. Remove knock sensor using suitable crowfoot and extension.
4. Reverse procedure to install. **Torque** knock sensor to 23–30 ft. lbs.

CRANKSHAFT POSITION SENSOR

1. Remove ABS controller cover.
2. Disconnect crankshaft position sensor harness multi-plug.
3. Disconnect harness to engine clips.

4. Remove mounting bolt and crankshaft position sensor.
5. Reverse procedure to install. **Torque** crankshaft position sensor mounting bolt to 71–106 inch lbs.

CAMSHAFT POSITION (CMP) SENSOR

1. Remove engine covers.
2. Relieve fuel system pressure as outlined under "Precautions."
3. Remove mounting bolts and position coolant expansion tank aside.
4. Remove mounting bolts and disconnect intake manifold fuel feed line.
5. Remove O-ring, then plug line and manifold.
6. Disconnect camshaft position sensor harness multi-plug.
7. Remove mounting bolt and sensor. Remove O-ring and plug sensor head location.
8. Reverse procedure to install. **Torque** sensor mounting bolt to 80–97 inch lbs.

Fuel Injection

TABLE OF CONTENTS

	Page No.
3.0L ENGINE FUEL INJECTION	12-8
4.0L ENGINE FUEL INJECTION	12-28

3.0L Engine Fuel Injection

NOTE: If Unsure Of The System Used On The Vehicle Being Serviced, Refer To "The Engine Systems Identification Chart."Further Assistance For The Proper Use Of Information Contained In This Section Can Also Be Found In The Front Of This Tabbed Section Under "How To Use This Manual"

NOTE: On Air Bag Equipped Models, Refer To "Air Bag System Precautions" Located In The Front Of This Manual For System Disarming & Arming Procedures.

NOTE: Refer To "Computer Relearn Procedures" Located In The Front Of This Manual When Battery Power To The Computer Has Been Interrupted.

NOTE: Prior To Performing Any Service Operations Listed In This Section, Consult The "Technical Service Bulletins" Section For Related Information.

NOTE: Electrical Symbol & Wire Color Code Identification Located In The Front Of This Manual May Be Used As An Aid When Using Wiring Circuits Found In This Section.

INDEX

	Page No.
Description	12-9
Camshaft Position Sensor (CMP)	12-10
Crankshaft Position Sensor (CKP)	12-10
Cylinder Head Temperature	12-9
Heated Oxygen Sensor (HO2S)	12-10
Intake Air Temperature (IAT)	12-10
Knock Sensor Control	12-10
Mass Air Flow Sensor (MAF)	12-9
PCM	12-9
Throttle Position Sensor (TP)	12-10
Variable Camshaft Timing (VCT)	12-10
Diagnosis & Testing	12-10
Accessing Diagnostic Trouble Codes	12-10
Clearing Diagnostic Trouble Codes	12-11
Connector Terminal Identification	12-11
Diagnostic Tests	12-11
Diagnostic Trouble Code Interpretation	12-10
Wiring Diagrams	12-11
Diagnostic Chart Index	12-14
Precautions	12-9
Air Bag Systems	12-9
Battery Ground Cable	12-9
Sensor & Fuel Injector Specifications	12-9
System Service	12-27
Component Replacement	12-27
Camshaft Position Sensor	12-27
Crankshaft Position Sensor	12-27
Fuel Injector	12-27
Heated Oxygen Sensor	12-27
Intake Air Temperature (IAT) Sensor	12-27
Mass Air Flow (MAF) Sensor	12-27
Powertrain Control Module (PCM)	12-27
Supply Manifold	12-27
Throttle Body	12-27
Throttle Position Sensor	12-27
Fuel System Pressure Relief	12-27

SENSOR & FUEL INJECTOR SPECIFICATIONS

Component	Temperature °F	Resistance, K ohms	Voltage
Engine Fuel Tem. Sensor (EFT)	68	37.30	3.07
Engine Oil Tem. Sensor	104	16.5	2.13
Engine Coolant Tem. Sensor	140	7.70	1.33
Intake Air Tem. Sensor	176	3.84	0.78

PRECAUTIONS

Air Bag Systems

Refer to "Air Bag System Precautions" in the front of this manual for system disarming and arming procedures.

Battery Ground Cable

Prior to service, disconnect battery ground cable and isolate as required.

DESCRIPTION

The engine management system consists of a powertrain control module and a number of sensors and actuators. Sensors supply the PCM with input signals that relate to engine operating conditions and the actuators respond to output signals from the PCM.

PCM

The powertrain control module controls coil on plug system, electronic returnless fuel system, digital transmission range control, cruise control and the electronic throttle control system.

Cylinder Head Temperature

Cylinder head temperature is broadcast every second by the PCM. This message allows for temperature readings from –40 – 214°C. Also the cylinder head temperature sensor replaces the traditional engine coolant temperature sensor.

Mass Air Flow Sensor (MAF)

The mass air flow sensor measures the mass of air entering the intake system, the measurement being based on the constant temperature hot wire principle. The change in heating current is measured as a voltage drop across a precision resistor and is assigned to a corresponding mass air flow calculation by the powertrain control module.

Code	Description
P0102	Mass Air Flow Circuit Malfunction
P0103	Mass Air Flow Circuit Malfunction
P0112	Intake Air Temperature Circuit Malfunction
P0113	Intake Air Temperature Circuit Malfunction
P1112	Intake Air Temperature Circuit Malfunction
P1289	Cylinder Head Temperature Circuit Malfunction
P1290	Cylinder Head Temperature Circuit Malfunction
P1121	Throttle Position Sensor Circuit Malfunction
P0122	Throttle Position Sensor Circuit Malfunction
P0123	Throttle Position Sensor Circuit Malfunction
P0124	Throttle Position Sensor Circuit Malfunction
P0131	Heated Oxygen Sensor Circuit Malfunction. Bank 1 Upstream
P0132	Heated Oxygen Sensor Circuit Malfunction. Bank 1 Upstream
P0135	Heated Oxygen Sensor Circuit Malfunction. Bank 1 Upstream
P0136	Heated Oxygen Sensor Circuit Malfunction. Bank 1 Downstream
P0138	Heated Oxygen Sensor Circuit Malfunction. Bank 1 Downstream
P0141	Heated Oxygen Sensor Circuit Malfunction. Bank 1 Downstream
P0151	Heated Oxygen Sensor Circuit Malfunction. Bank 2 Upstream
P0152	Heated Oxygen Sensor Circuit Malfunction. Bank 2 Upstream
P0155	Heated Oxygen Sensor Circuit Malfunction. Bank 2 Upstream
P0156	Heated Oxygen Sensor Circuit Malfunction. Bank 2 Downstream
P0158	Heated Oxygen Sensor Circuit Malfunction. Bank 2 Downstream
P0161	Heated Oxygen Sensor Circuit Malfunction. Bank 2 Downstream
P0180	Fuel Temperature Sensor Circuit A Malfunction
P1183	Engine Oil Temperature Circuit Malfunction
P1184	Engine Oil Temperature Circuit Malfunction
P0325	Knock Sensor Circuit 1 Malfunction
P0330	Knock Sensor Circuit 2 Malfunction
P0340	Camshaft Position Sensor Circuit Malfunction
P0341	Camshaft Position Sensor Circuit B Malfunction
P1380	Variable Cam Timing Solenoid A Malfunction
P1385	Variable Cam Timing Solenoid B Malfunction
P1633	KAM Voltage Too Low

Fig. 1 Diagnostic Trouble Code Interpretation

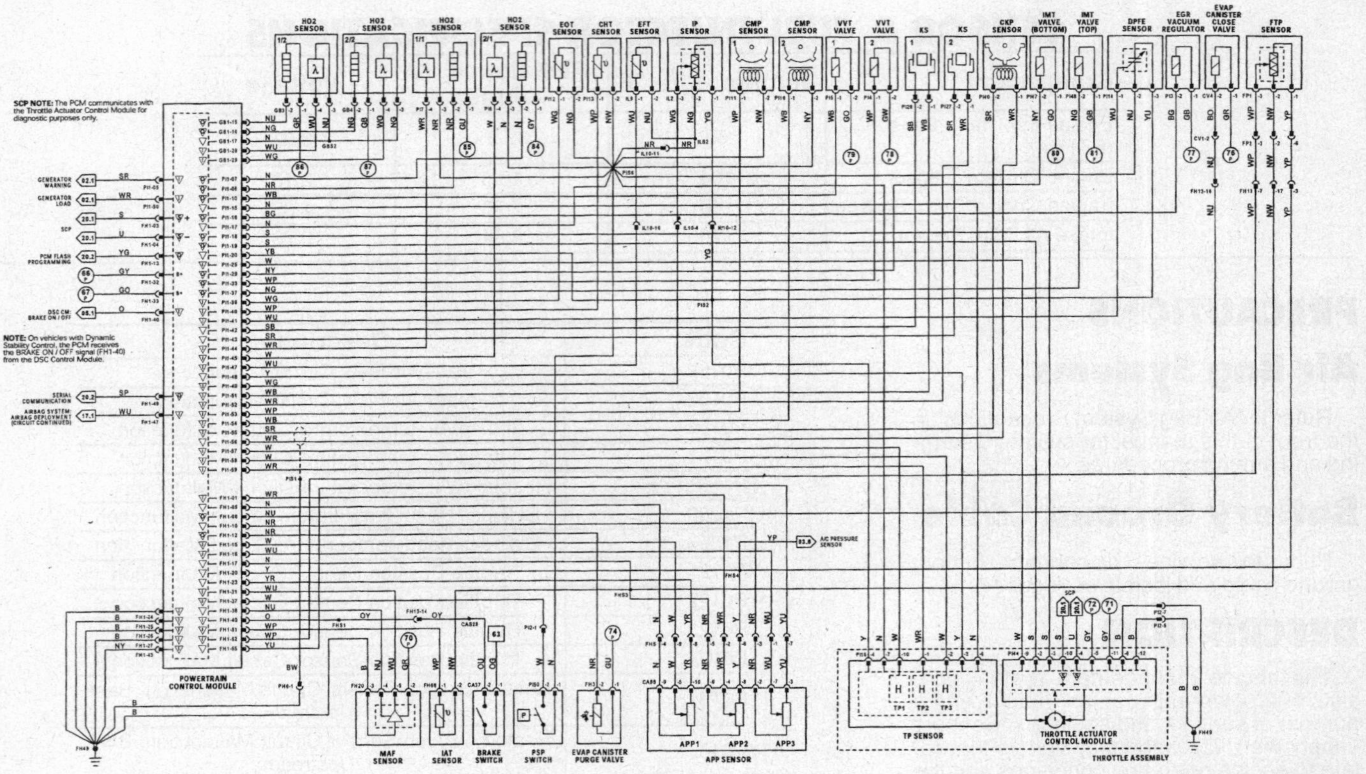

JC1020100076010X

Fig. 2 Engine management system wiring diagram (Part 1 of 2)

Intake Air Temperature (IAT)

The intake air temperature sensor is atemperature dependent resistor. It's temperature changes inversely with respect to ambient temperature. When the intake air changes temperature, the resistance of the sensor changes thus changing the output voltage. The output voltage is assigned to a corresponding intake air temperature by the PCM.

Crankshaft Position Sensor (CKP)

The crankshaft position sensor is an inductive pulse generator which scans 36–1 cast protrusions on the ignition pulse ring and is located on the engine timing cover. The crankshaft position sensor sends an alternating voltage signal to the PCM where it is converted and becomes the digital, profile ignition pick-up (PIP) signal.

Camshaft Position Sensor (CMP)

The camshaft position sensor sends an alternating voltage signal to the PCM from which the position of number one cylinder is calculated. The signal is required only during starting, when the engine is running the PIP signal is used to sequentially control the fuel injectors.

Variable Camshaft Timing (VCT)

The solenoid affects the inlet camshaft timing only, it is engine oil driven and provides 50° of rotation for camshaft adjustment under different types of engine torque and load conditions.

Knock Sensor Control

The knock sensor control utilizes two sensors mounted directly onto the engine block. the objective is to limit the timing adjustment to cylinders where knock is actually occurring, while allowing others to continue operating normally.

Throttle Position Sensor (TP)

The sensor is a triple hall effect hall sensor which is secured to the throttle body and operated by the throttle plate shaft. When the throttle plate is opened, a magnet moves past a PN junction changing the output voltage. The output voltages are assigned by the PCM

Heated Oxygen Sensor (HO2S)

The heated oxygen sensor is installed ahead of the catalyst in the exhaust flow. It is controlled by the PCM to control the air/fuel mixture. To ensure the sensor quickly reaches it's operating temperature, it is equipped with a heating element which operates when the ignition is switched on.

DIAGNOSIS & TESTING

Accessing Diagnostic Trouble Codes

Connect a suitable programmed scan tool to the Data Link Connector (DLC) located on the instrument panel adjacent to the driver's side A pillar.

Follow tool manufacturer's instructions to read codes.

Diagnostic Trouble Code Interpretation

Refer to **Fig. 1** for diagnostic trouble code interpretation.

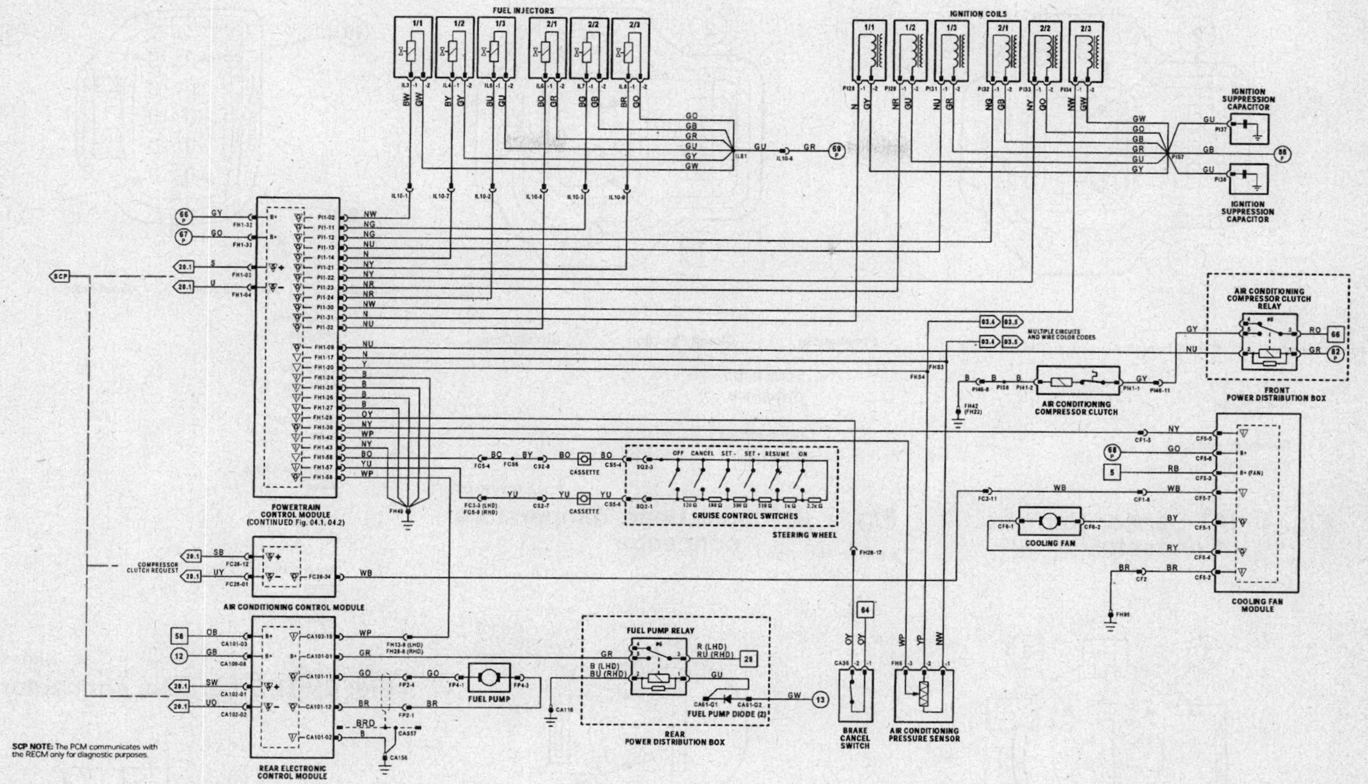

JC1020100076020X

Fig. 2 Engine management system wiring diagram (Part 2 of 2)

Wiring Diagrams

Refer to **Fig. 2** for wiring diagrams.

Connector Terminal Identification

Refer to **Figs. 3 through 21** for connector terminal identification.

Diagnostic Tests

Refer to **Figs. 22 through 38,** for diagnostic tests.

Clearing Diagnostic Trouble Codes

To clear diagnostic trouble codes, install a suitable scan tool and follow tool manufacturer's instructions.

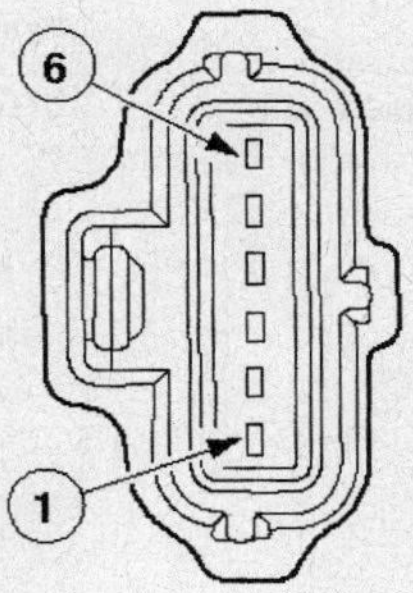

Pin Number	Circuit Function	Circuit Color
2	Voltage supply	Green/red
3	Ground supply	Brown
4	Signal ground	Brown/blue
5	Signal supply	White/blue

JC1020100077000X

Fig. 3 MAF sensor harness connector

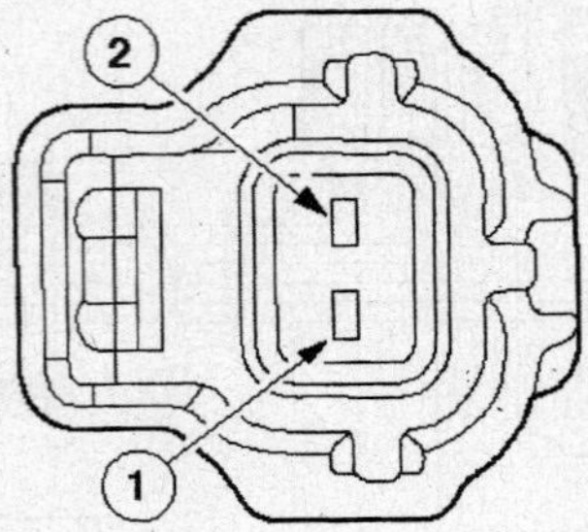

Pin Number	Circuit Function	Circuit Color
1	Signal supply	White/purple
2	Reference voltage	Brown/white

JC1020100078000X

Fig. 4 IAT Sensor Harness Connector

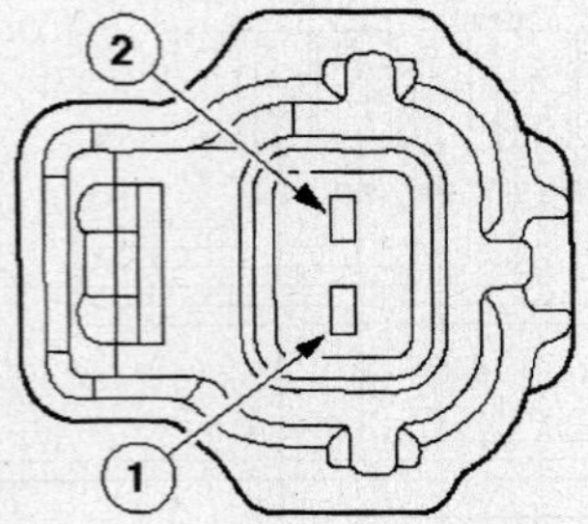

Pin Number	Circuit Function	Circuit Color
1	Signal supply	White/purple
2	Signal ground	Brown/white

JC1020100079000X

Fig. 5 Cylinder Head Temperature connector

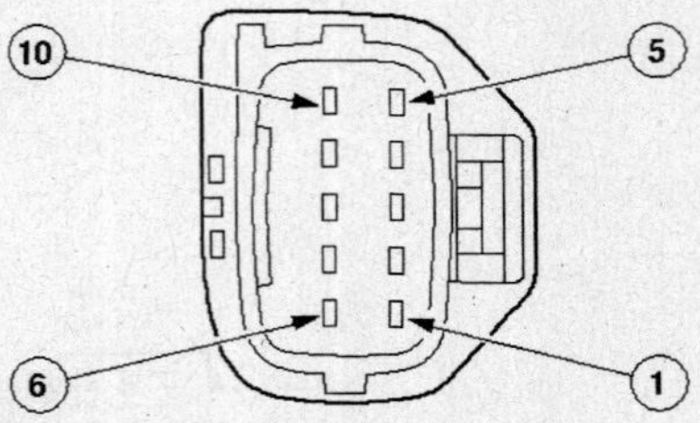

Pin Number	Circuit Function	Circuit Color
1	Signal return	White/red
2	Signal return	White
3	Signal supply	Yellow
4	Reference voltage	Yellow
6	Signal ground	Brown
7	Signal ground	Brown
10	Signal return	White

JC1020100080000X

Fig. 6 TPS harness connector

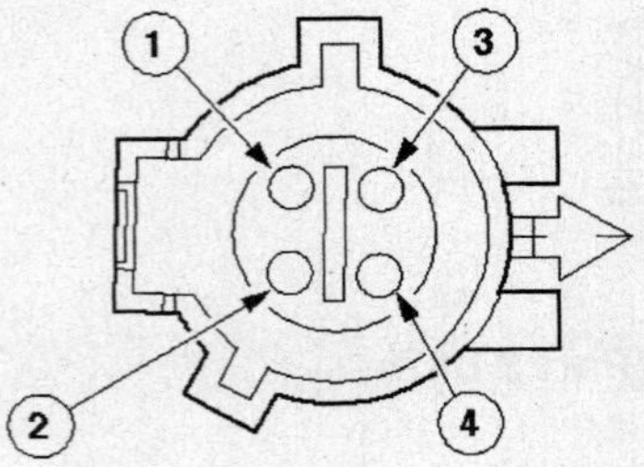

Pin Number	Circuit Function	Circuit Color
1	Voltage supply	Green/yellow
2	Ground supply	Brown
3	Lambda signal ground	Brown
4	Lambda signal voltage	White

JC1020100081000X

Fig. 7 HO2S 2/1 harness connector

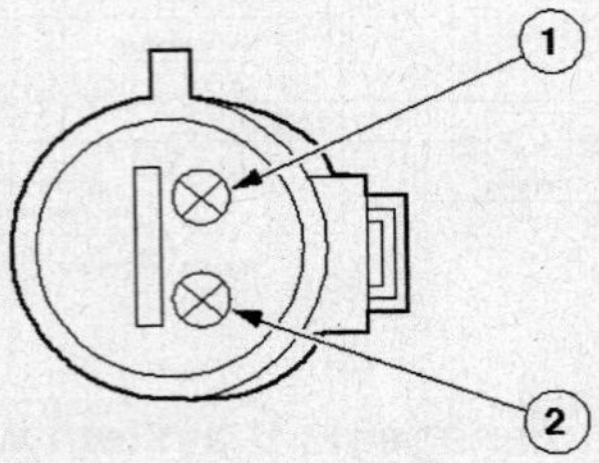

Pin Number	Circuit Function	Circuit Color
1	Voltage supply	Green/red
2	Ground supply	Brown/orange
3	Lambda signal ground	Brown/blue
4	Lambda signal voltage	White/blue

JC1020100082000X

Fig. 8 HO2S 1/2 harness connector

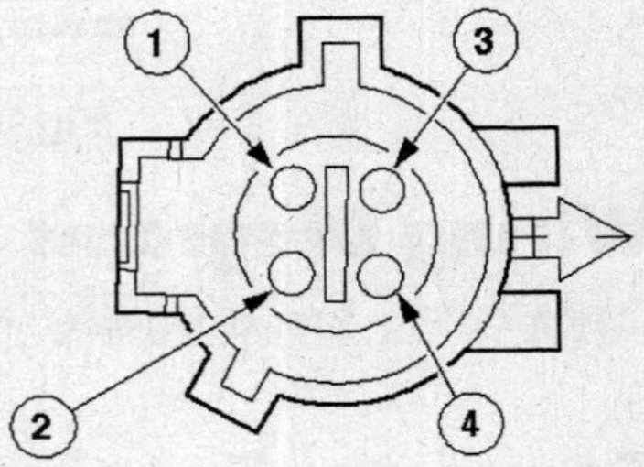

Pin Number	Circuit Function	Circuit Color
1	Voltage supply	Green/blue
2	Ground supply	Brown/red
3	Lambda signal ground	Brown/red
4	Lambda signal voltage	White/red

JC1020100083000X

Fig. 9 HO2S 1/1 harness connector

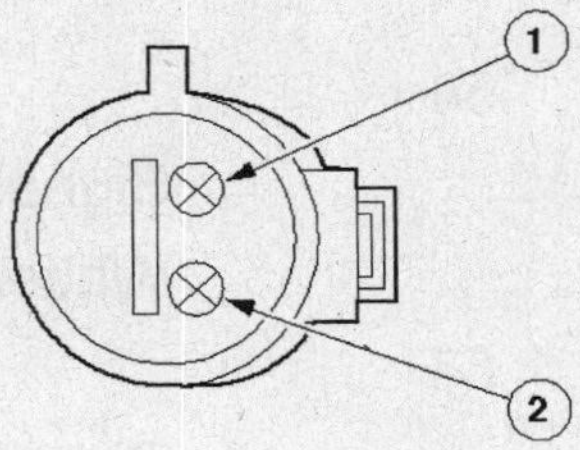

Pin Number	Circuit Function	Circuit Color
1	Voltage supply	Green/black
2	Ground supply	Black/green
3	Lambda signal ground	Brown/green
4	Lambda signal voltage	White/green

JC1020100084000X

Fig. 10 HO2S 2/2 harness connector

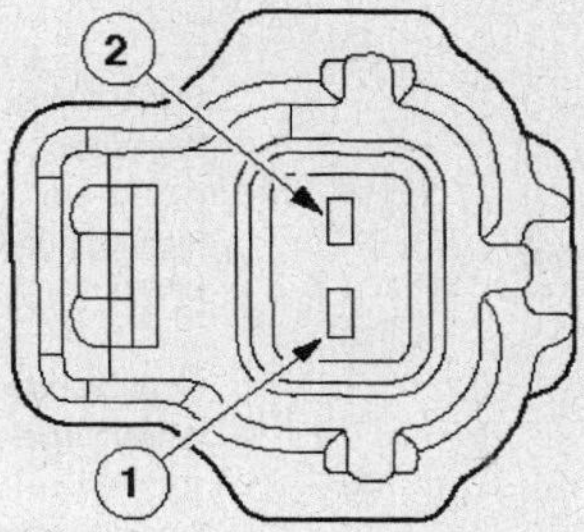

Pin Number	Circuit Function	Circuit Color
1	Signal voltage	White/blue
2	Signal ground	Brown/blue

JC1020100085000X

Fig. 11 Engine Fuel Temperature harness connector

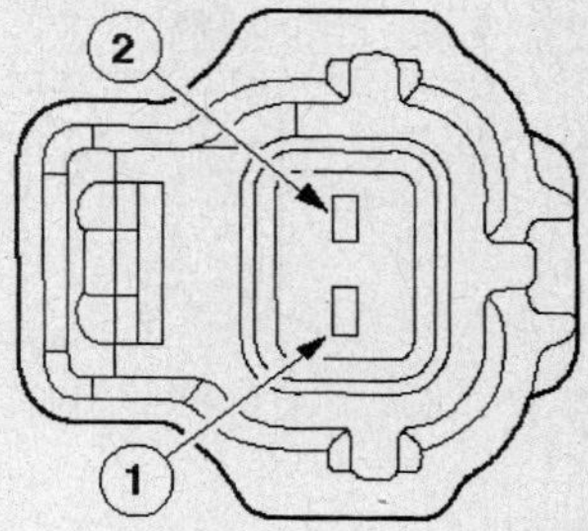

Pin Number	Circuit Function	Circuit Color
1	Signal supply	White/green
2	Signal ground	Brown/green

JC1020100086000X

Fig. 12 Engine oil temperature harness connector

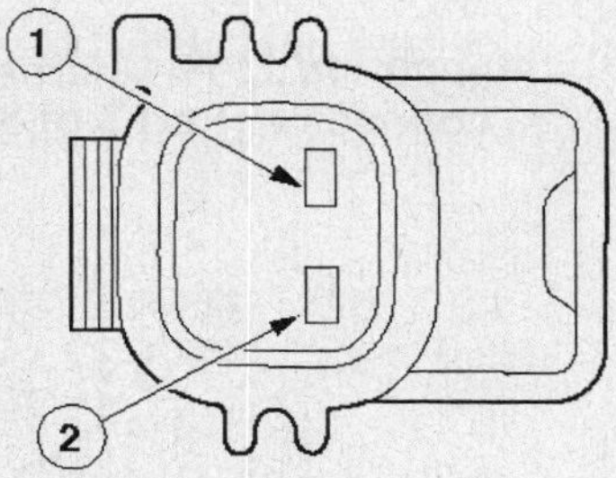

Pin Number	Circuit Function	Circuit Color
1	Signal supply	White/black
2	Signal ground	Slate/black

JC1020100087000X

Fig. 13 Knock sensor 1 harness connector

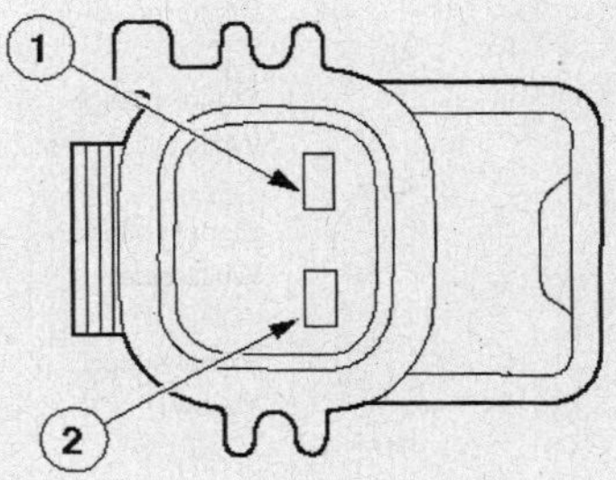

Pin Number	Circuit Function	Circuit Color
1	Signal supply	White/red
2	Signal ground	Slate/red

JC1020100088000X

Fig. 14 Knock sensor 2 harness connector

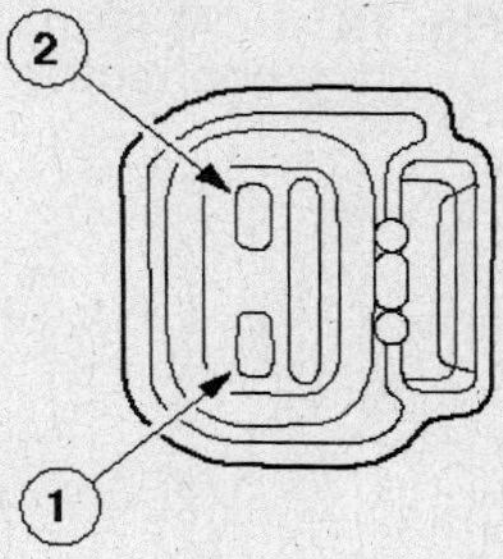

Pin Number	Circuit Function	Circuit Color
1	Signal supply	White/black
2	Signal ground	Brown/yellow

JC1020100089000X

Fig. 15 Camshaft position sensor 1 harness connector

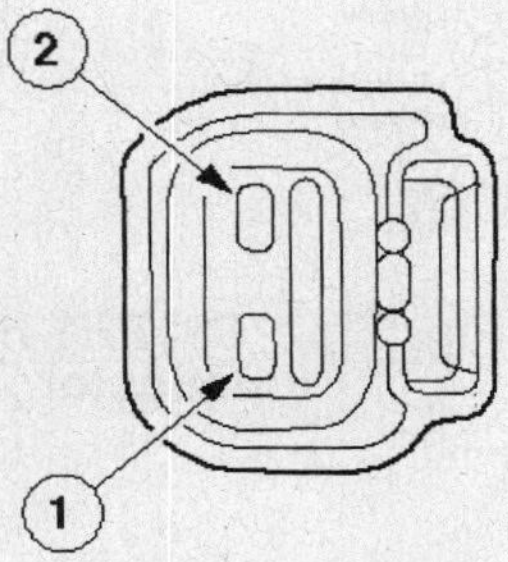

Pin Number	Circuit Function	Circuit Color
1	Signal supply	White/purple
2	Signal ground	Brown/white

JC1020100090000X

Fig. 16 Camshaft position sensor 2 harness connector

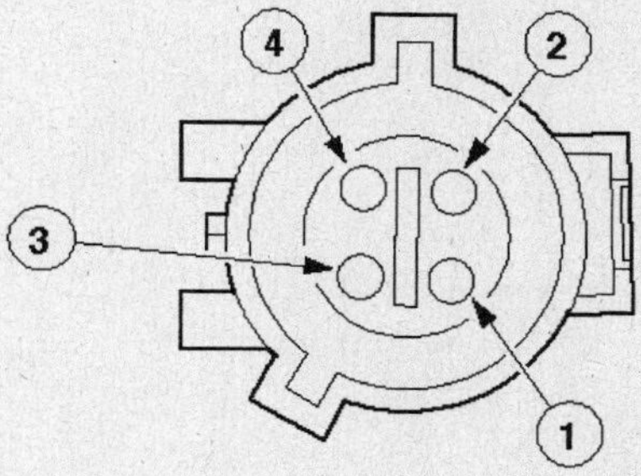

Pin Number	Circuit Function	Circuit Color
1	Voltage supply	Green/orange
2	Signal ground	White/black

JC1020100091000X

Fig. 17 Variable camshaft timing solenoid 1 harness connector

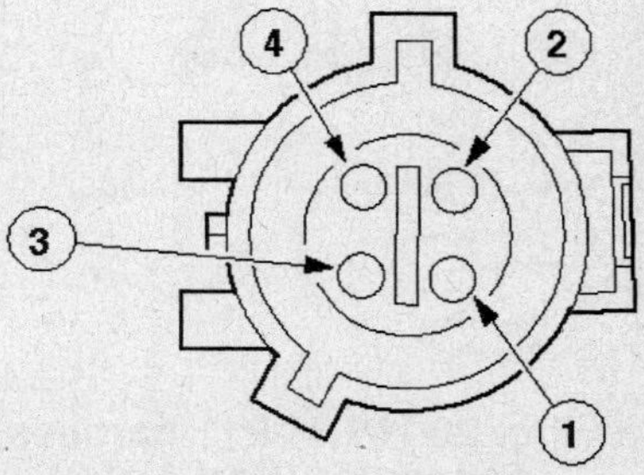

Pin Number	Circuit Function	Circuit Color
1	Voltage supply	Green/white
2	Signal ground	White/purple

JC1020100092000X

Fig. 18 Variable camshaft timing solenoid 2 harness connector

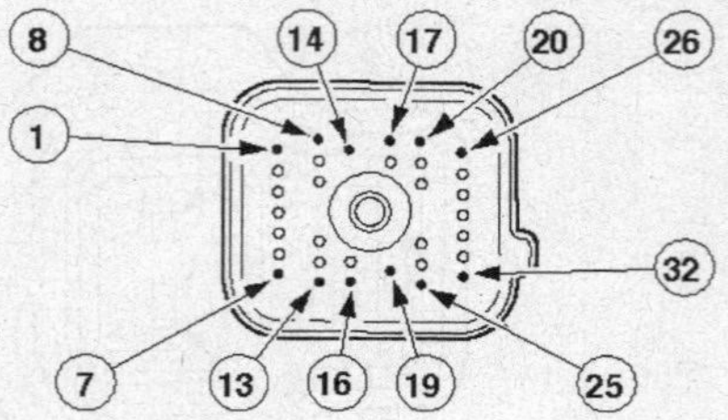

Pin Number	Circuit Function	Circuit Color
15	Signal supply	Black/orange
16	Signal supply	Black/green
17	Signal ground	Brown
28	Signal voltage	White/blue
29	Signal voltage	White/green

JC1020100093000X

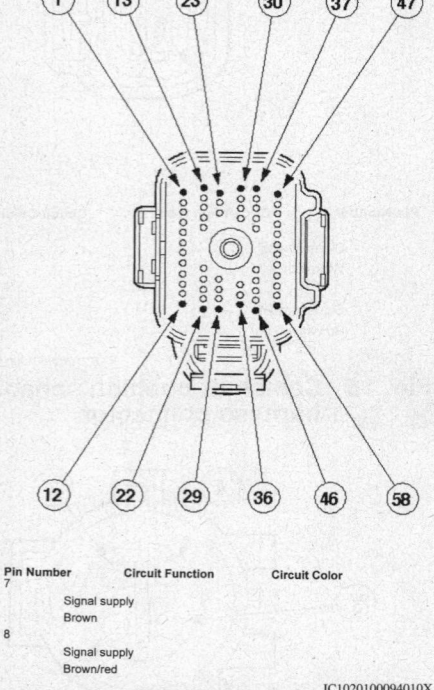

Fig. 19 PCM (GBI) harness connector

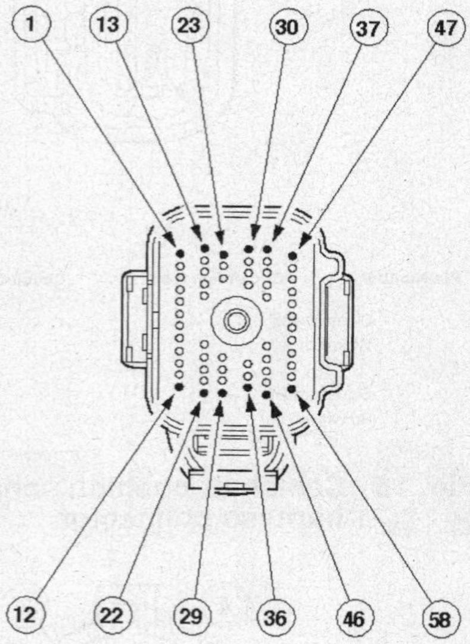

Pin Number	Circuit Function	Circuit Color
7	Signal supply	Brown
8	Signal supply	Brown/red

JC1020100094010X

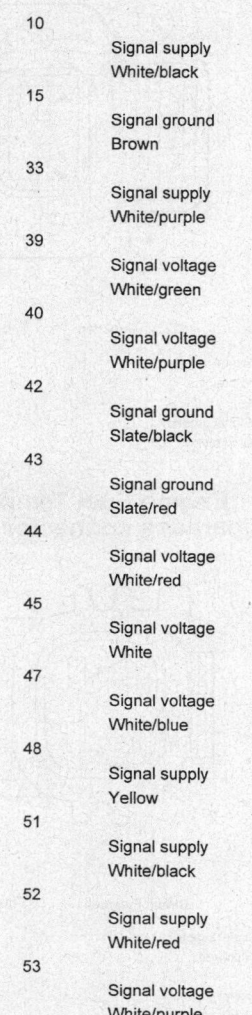

Fig. 20 PCM P11 harness connector (Part 1 of 3)

10	Signal supply	White/black
15	Signal ground	Brown
33	Signal supply	White/purple
39	Signal voltage	White/green
40	Signal voltage	White/purple
42	Signal ground	Slate/black
43	Signal ground	Slate/red
44	Signal voltage	White/red
45	Signal voltage	White
47	Signal voltage	White/blue
48	Signal supply	Yellow
51	Signal supply	White/black
52	Signal supply	White/red
53	Signal voltage	White/purple

JC1020100094020X

Fig. 20 PCM P11 harness connector (Part 2 of 3)

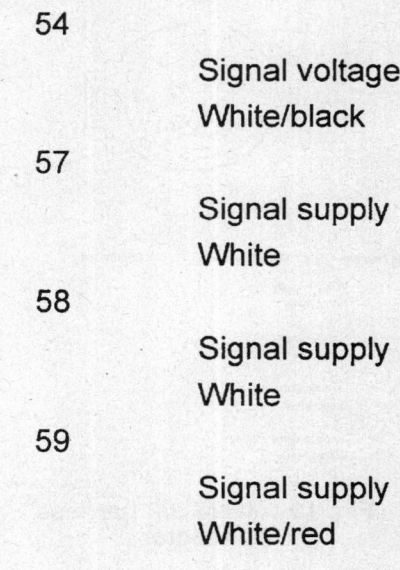

54	Signal voltage	White/black
57	Signal supply	White
58	Signal supply	White
59	Signal supply	White/red

JC1020100094030X

Fig. 20 PCM P11 harness connector (Part 3 of 3)

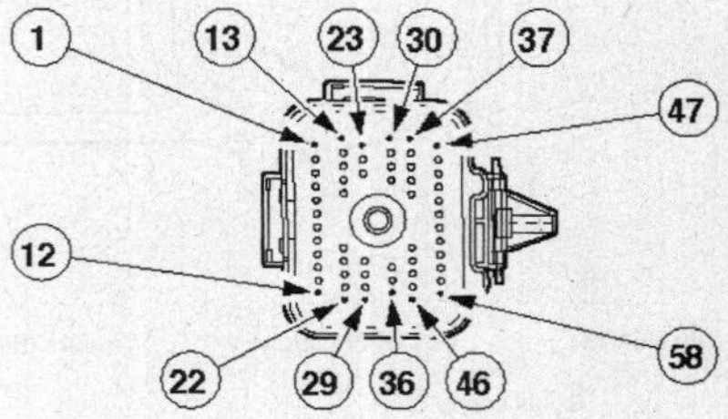

Pin Number	Circuit Function	Circuit Color
13	Voltage supply	Yellow/green
31	Signal return	White/blue
38	Signal ground	Brown/blue
49	Serial communication	Slate/purple
51	Signal supply	White/purple

JC1020100095000X

Fig. 21 PCM FH1 harness connector

DIAGNOSTIC CHART INDEX

Code	Description	Page No.	Fig. No.
P0102	Mass Air Flow Circuit Malfunction	12-15	22
P0103	Mass Air Flow Circuit Malfunction	12-15	22
P0112	Intake Air Temperature Circuit Malfunction	12-16	23

Continued

DIAGNOSTIC CHART INDEX—Continued

Code	Description	Page No.	Fig. No.
P0113	Intake Air Temperature Circuit Malfunction	12-16	23
P0122	Throttle Position Sensor Circuit Malfunction	12-17	25
P0123	Throttle Position Sensor Circuit Malfunction	12-17	25
P0124	Throttle Position Sensor Circuit Malfunction	12-17	25
P0131	Heated Oxygen Sensor Circuit Malfunction. Bank 1 Upstream	12-18	26
P0132	Heated Oxygen Sensor Circuit Malfunction. Bank 1 Upstream	12-18	26
P0135	Heated Oxygen Sensor Circuit Malfunction. Bank 1 Upstream	12-18	26
P0136	Heated Oxygen Sensor Circuit Malfunction. Bank 1 Downstream	12-19	27
P0138	Heated Oxygen Sensor Circuit Malfunction. Bank 1 Downstream	12-19	27
P0141	Heated Oxygen Sensor Circuit Malfunction. Bank 1 Downstream	12-19	27
P0151	Heated Oxygen Sensor Circuit Malfunction. Bank 2 Upstream	12-21	28
P0152	Heated Oxygen Sensor Circuit Malfunction. Bank 2 Upstream	12-21	28
P0155	Heated Oxygen Sensor Circuit Malfunction. Bank 2 Upstream	12-21	28
P0156	Heated Oxygen Sensor Circuit Malfunction. Bank 2 Downstream	12-22	29
P0158	Heated Oxygen Sensor Circuit Malfunction. Bank 2 Downstream	12-22	29
P0161	Heated Oxygen Sensor Circuit Malfunction. Bank 2 Downstream	12-22	29
P0180	Fuel Temperature Sensor Circuit A Malfunction	12-23	30
P0325	Knock Sensor Circuit 1 Malfunction	12-24	32
P0330	Knock Sensor Circuit 2 Malfunction	12-24	33
P0340	Camshaft Position Sensor Circuit Malfunction	12-25	34
P0341	Camshaft Position Sensor Circuit B Malfunction	12-25	35
P1112	Intake Air Temperature Circuit Malfunction	12-16	23
P1121	Throttle Position Sensor Circuit Malfunction	12-17	25
P1183	Engine Oil Temperature Circuit Malfunction	12-23	31
P1184	Engine Oil Temperature Circuit Malfunction	12-23	31
P1289	Cylinder Head Temperature Circuit Malfunction	12-16	24
P1290	Cylinder Head Temperature Circuit Malfunction	12-16	24
P1380	Variable Cam Timing Solenoid A Malfunction	12-26	36
P1385	Variable Cam Timing Solenoid B Malfunction	12-26	37
P1633	KAM Voltage Too Low	12-27	38

A1 : CHECK THE VOLTAGE SUPPLY TO THE MASS AIR FLOW (MAF) SENSOR

1. Switch the ignition to the OFF position.
2. Disconnect the Mass Air Flow (MAF) sensor electrical connector FH20.
3. Switch the ignition to the RUN position.
4. Measure the voltage between the mass air flow sensor electrical connector FH20 pin 2, (GR) and ground.

•Is the voltage greater than 10 volts?

-> Yes
Goto **<<A2>>**

-> No
REPAIR the circuit between the mass air flow sensor electrical connector FH20 pin 2, (GR) and the spliced joint FHS5. CLEAR DTC. TEST the system for normal operation.

A2 : CHECK THE MASS AIR FLOW (MAF) SENSOR GROUND CIRCUIT FOR OPEN

1. Switch the ignition to the OFF position.
2. Measure the resistance between the mass air flow sensor electrical connector FH20 pin 3, (B) and ground.

•Is the resistance greater than 10,000 ohms?

-> Yes
REPAIR the circuit between the mass air flow sensor electrical connector FH20 pin 3, (B) and the ground point FH49. CLEAR DTC. TEST the system for normal operation.

-> No
Goto **<<A3>>**

A3 : CHECK THE MASS AIR FLOW (MAF) SENSOR SIGNAL GROUND CIRCUIT FOR OPEN

1. Remove the powertrain control module (PCM)

2. Measure the resistance between the mass air flow sensor FH20 pin 4, (NU) and the powertrain control module FH1 pin 38, (NU).

•Is the resistance greater than 10,000 ohms?

-> Yes
REPAIR the circuit between the mass air flow sensor FH20 pin 4, (NU) and the powertrain control module FH1 pin 38, (NU). CLEAR DTC. TEST the system for normal operation.

-> No
Goto **<<A4>>**

JC1020100096010X

Fig. 22 Codes P0102 & P0103: Mass Air Flow Circuit Malfunction (Part 1 of 2)

A4 : CHECK THE MASS AIR FLOW (MAF) SENSOR SIGNAL GROUND CIRCUIT FOR SHORT TO GROUND

1. Measure the resistance between the mass air flow sensor FH20 pin 4, (NU) and ground.

•Is the resistance less than 10,000 ohms?

-> Yes
REPAIR the circuit between the mass air flow sensor FH20 pin 4, (NU) and the powertrain control module FH1 pin 38, (NU). INSTALL the powertrain control module (PCM). CLEAR DTC. TEST the system for normal operation.

-> No
Goto **<<A5>>**

A5 : CHECK THE MASS AIR FLOW (MAF) SENSOR SIGNAL CIRCUIT FOR OPEN

1. Measure the resistance between the mass air flow sensor FH20 pin 5, (WU) and the powertrain control module FH1 pin 31, (WU).

•Is the resistance greater than 0.5 ohms?

-> Yes
REPAIR the circuit between the mass air flow sensor FH20 pin 5, (WU) and the powertrain control module FH1 pin 31, (WU). INSTALL the powertrain control module (PCM). CLEAR DTC. TEST the system for normal operation.

-> No
Goto **<<A6>>**

A6 : CHECK THE MASS AIR FLOW (MAF) SENSOR SIGNAL CIRCUIT FOR SHORT TO GROUND

1. Measure the resistance between the mass air flow sensor FH20 pin 5, (WU) and ground.

•Is the resistance greater than 0.5 ohms?

-> Yes
INSTALL a new mass air fow (MAF) sensor. CLEAR DTC. TEST the system for normal operation.

-> No
REPAIR the circuit between the mass air flow sensor FH20 pin 5, (WU) and the powertrain control module FH1 pin 31, (WU). INSTALL the powertrain control module (PCM). CLEAR DTC. TEST the system for normal operation.

JC1020100096020X

Fig. 22 Codes P0102 & P0103: Mass Air Flow Circuit Malfunction (Part 2 of 2)

B1 : CARRY OUT AN AIR INTAKE SYSTEM CHECK

1. Switch the ignition to the OFF position.
2. Inspect the air intake system for obvious signs of obstructions or air leaks.

•Is there any obvious signs of obstructions or air leaks?

-> Yes
RECTIFY the obstruction or air leak. CLEAR DTC. TEST the system for normal operation.

-> No
Goto **<<B2>>**

B2 : CHECK THE RESISTANCE OF THE INTAKE AIR TEMPERATURE (IAT) SENSOR

1. Disconnect the intake air temperature (IAT) sensor electrical connector FH68.
2. Measure the resistance of the intake air temperature (IAT) sensor across pins 1 and 2.

•Does the resistance of the sensor decrease as the temperature increases?

-> Yes
Goto **<<B3>>**

-> No
INSTALL a new intake air temperature (IAT) sensor. CLEAR DTC. TEST the system for normal operation.

B3 : CHECK THE INTAKE AIR TEMPERATURE (IAT) SUPPLY VOLTAGE

1. Switch the ignition to the RUN position.
2. Measure the voltage between the intake air temperature (IAT) sensor electrical connector FH68 pin 1, (WP) and ground.

•Is the voltage between 4 and 6 volts?

-> Yes
Goto **<<B6>>**

-> No
Goto **<<B4>>**

JC1020100097010X

Fig. 23 Codes P0112, P0113 & P1112: Intake Air Temperature Circuit Malfunction (Part 1 of 3)

B7 : CHECK THE INTAKE AIR TEMPERATURE (IAT) SIGNAL GROUND CIRCUIT FOR SHORT TO GROUND

1. Measure the resistance between the intake air temperature (IAT) sensor electrical connector FH68 pin 2, (NW) and ground.

•Is the resistance less than 10,000 ohms?

-> Yes
REPAIR the circuit between the intake air temperature (IAT) sensor electrical connector FH68 pin 2, (NW) and the spliced joint FHS3 circuit (NW). CLEAR DTC. TEST the system for normal operation.

-> No
INSTALL a new powertrain control module.
CLEAR DTC. TEST the system for normal operation.

JC1020100097030X

Fig. 23 Codes P0112, P0113 & P1112: Intake Air Temperature Circuit Malfunction (Part 3 of 3)

C1 : CHECK THE VOLTAGE SUPPLY TO THE CYLINDER HEAD TEMPERATURE (CHT) SENSOR

1. Switch the ignition to the OFF position.
2. Disconnect the cylinder head temperature (CHT) sensor electrical connector PI13.
3. Switch the ignition to the RUN position.
4. Measure the voltage between the cylinder head temperature (CHT) sensor electrical connector PI13 pin 1, (WP) and ground.

•Is the voltage between 4 and 6 volts?

-> Yes
Goto **<<C4>>**

-> No
Goto **<<C2>>**

C2 : CHECK THE CYLINDER HEAD TEMPERATURE (CHT) SUPPLY CIRCUIT FOR OPEN

1. Switch the ignition to the OFF position.
2. Measure the resistance between the cylinder head temperature (CHT) sensor electrical connector PI13 pin 1, (WP) and ground.

•Is the resistance greater than 10,000 ohms?

-> Yes
REPAIR the circuit between the cylinder head temperature (CHT) sensor electrical connector PI13, pin 1, (WP) and the powertrain control module electrical connector PI1 pin 40, (WP). CLEAR DTC. TEST the system for normal operation.

-> No
Goto **<<C3>>**

C3 : CHECK THE CYLINDER HEAD TEMPERATURE (CHT) SUPPLY CIRCUIT FOR SHORT TO GROUND

1. Remove the powertrain control module (PCM).
2. Measure the resistance between the cylinder head temperature (CHT) sensor electrical connector PI13 pin 1, (WP) and ground.

•Is the resistance less than 10,000 ohms?

-> Yes
REPAIR the circuit between the cylinder head temperature (CHT) sensor electrical connector PI13 pin 1, (WP) and the powertrain control module electrical connector PI1 pin 40, (WP). CLEAR DTC. TEST the system for normal operation.

-> No
INSTALL a new powertrain control module.
CLEAR DTC. TEST the system for normal operation.

JC1020100098010X

Fig. 24 Codes P1289 & P1290: Cylinder Head Temperature Circuit Malfunction (Part 1 of 2)

B4 : CHECK THE INTAKE AIR TEMPERATURE (IAT) SUPPLY CIRCUIT FOR OPEN

1. Switch the ignition to the OFF position.
2. Measure the resistance between the intake air temperature (IAT) sensor electrical connector FH68 pin 1, (WP) and ground.

•Is the resistance greater than 10,000 ohms?

-> Yes
REPAIR the circuit between the intake air temperature (IAT) sensor electrical connector FH68 pin 1, (WP) and the powertrain control module electrical connector FH1 pin 51, (WP). CLEAR DTC. TEST the system for normal operation.

-> No
Goto **<<B5>>**

B5 : CHECK THE INTAKE AIR TEMPERATURE (IAT) SUPPLY CIRCUIT FOR SHORT TO GROUND

1. Remove the powertrain control module (PCM).
2. Measure the resistance between the intake air temperature (IAT) sensor electrical connector FH68 pin 1, (WP) and ground.

•Is the resistance less than 10,000 ohms?

-> Yes
REPAIR the circuit between the intake air temperature (IAT) sensor electrical connector FH68 pin 1, (WP) and the powertrain control module electrical connector FH1 pin 51, (WP). CLEAR DTC. TEST the system for normal operation.

-> No
INSTALL a new powertrain control module.
CLEAR DTC. TEST the system for normal operation.

B6 : CHECK THE INTAKE AIR TEMPERATURE (IAT) SIGNAL GROUND CIRCUIT FOR OPEN

1. Remove the powertrain control module (PCM).
2. Raise and support the vehicle.
3. Disconnect the fuel tank wiring harness electrical connector FP2 attached to the fuel tank heat shield.
4. Disconnect the a/c pressure sensor electrical connector.
5. Disconnect the accelerator pedal electrical connector CA88.
6. Switch the ignition to the OFF position.
7. Measure the resistance between the intake air temperature (IAT) sensor electrical connector FH68 pin 2, (NW) and the powertrain control module electrical connector FH1 pin 17, (N).

•Is the resistance greater than 10,000 ohms?

-> Yes
REPAIR the circuit between the intake air temperature (IAT) sensor electrical connector FH68 pin 2, (NW) and the spliced joint FHS3 circuit (NW). CLEAR DTC. TEST the system for normal operation.

-> No
Goto **<<B7>>**

JC1020100097020X

Fig. 23 Codes P0112, P0113 & P1112: Intake Air Temperature Circuit Malfunction (Part 2 of 3)

C4 : CHECK THE CYLINDER HEAD TEMPERATURE (CHT) SIGNAL GROUND CIRCUIT FOR OPEN

1. Switch the ignition to the OFF position.
2. Measure the resistance between the cylinder head temperature (CHT) sensor electrical connector PI13 pin 2, (NW) and ground.

•Is the resistance greater than 10,000 ohms?

-> Yes
REPAIR the circuit between the cylinder head temperature (CHT) sensor electrical connector PI13 pin 2, (NW) and the spliced joint P1S6 circuit (NW). CLEAR DTC. TEST the system for normal operation.

-> No
Goto **<<C5>>**

C5 : CHECK THE CYLINDER HEAD TEMPERATURE (CHT) SIGNAL GROUND CIRCUIT FOR SHORT TO GROUND

1. Remove the powertrain control module (PCM).
2. Raise and support the vehicle.
3. Disconnect both heated exhaust gas oxygen (HEGO) sensor electrical connectors PI6, PI7.
4. Disconnect the engine oil temperature sensor electrical connector PI12.
5. Disconnect the engine fuel temperature sensor electrical connector IL9.
6. Disconnect both camshaft position sensor electrical connectors PI10, PI11.
7. Disconnect the injection pressure sensor electrical connector IL2.
8. Disconnect the throttle position sensor electrical connector PI16.
9. Measure the resistance between the cylinder head temperature (CHT) sensor electrical connector PI13 pin 2, (NW) and ground.

•Is the resistance less than 10,000 ohms?

-> Yes
REPAIR the circuit between the cylinder head temperature (CHT) sensor electrical connector PI13 pin 2, (NW) and the spliced joint P1S6 circuit (NW). CLEAR DTC. TEST the system for normal operation.

-> No
INSTALL a new cylinder head temperature (CHT) sensor.

JC1020100098020X

Fig. 24 Codes P1289 & P1290: Cylinder Head Temperature Circuit Malfunction (Part 2 of 2)

D1 : CHECK THE VOLTAGE SUPPLY TO THE THROTTLE POSITION (TP) SENSOR AT PIN 4

1. Switch the ignition to the OFF position.
2. Disconnect the throttle position (TP) sensor electrical connector PI16.
3. Switch the ignition to the RUN position.
4. Measure the voltage between the throttle position (TP) sensor electrical connector PI16 pin 4, (Y) and ground.

•Is the voltage between 4 and 6 volts?

-> Yes
Goto <<**D2**>>

-> No
REPAIR the circuit between the throttle position sensor electrical connector PI16 pin 4, (Y) and the spliced joint PIS5. CLEAR DTC. TEST the system for normal operation.

D2 : CHECK THE VOLTAGE SUPPLY TO THE THROTTLE POSITION (TP) SENSOR AT PIN 3

1. Measure the voltage between the throttle position (TP) sensor electrical connector PI16 pin 3, (Y) and ground.

•Is the voltage between 4 and 6 volts?

-> Yes
Goto <<**D5**>>

-> No
Goto <<**D3**>>

D3 : CHECK THE VOLTAGE SUPPLY TO THE THROTTLE POSITION (TP) SENSOR FOR OPEN

1. Switch the ignition to the OFF position.
2. Measure the resistance between the throttle position (TP) sensor electrical connector PI16 pin 3, (Y) and ground.

•Is the resistance greater than 10,000 ohms?

-> Yes
REPAIR the circuit between the throttle position (TP) sensor PI16 pin 3, (Y) and the powertrain control module (PCM) electrical connector PI1 pin 48, (Y). CLEAR DTC. TEST the system for normal operation.

-> No
Goto <<**D4**>>

JC1020100099010X

Fig. 25 Code P1121, P0122, P0123 & P0124: Throttle Position Sensor Circuit Malfunction (Part 1 of 5)

D4 : CHECK THE VOLTAGE SUPPLY TO THE THROTTLE POSITION (TP) SENSOR FOR SHORT TO GROUND

1. Remove the powertrain control module (PCM).

2. Measure the resistance between the throttle position (TP) sensor electrical connector PI16 pin 3, (Y) and ground.

•Is the resistance less than 10,000 ohms?

-> Yes
REPAIR the circuit between the throttle position (TP) sensor PI16 pin 3, (Y) and the powertrain control module (PCM) electrical connector PI1 pin 48, (Y). INSTALL the powertrain control module (PCM). CLEAR DTC. TEST the system for normal operation.

-> No
INSTALL a new powertrain control module (PCM).
CLEAR DTC. TEST the system for normal operation.

D5 : CHECK THE THROTTLE POSITION SENSOR SIGNAL GROUND PIN 7 WIRE FOR OPEN

1. Switch the ignition to the OFF position.
2. Measure the resistance between the throttle position sensor electrical connector PI16 pin 7, (N) and ground.

•Is the resistance greater than 10,000 ohms?

-> Yes
REPAIR the circuit between the throttle position (TP) sensor PI16 pin 7, (N) and the spliced joint PIS6. CLEAR DTC. TEST the system for normal operation.

-> No
Goto <<**D6**>>

D6 : CHECK THE THROTTLE POSITION SENSOR FOR OPEN AT PIN 10

1. Remove the powertrain control module (PCM).

2. Measure the resistance between the throttle position sensor electrical connector PI16 pin 10, (W) and the powertrain control module electrical connector PI1 pin 57 (W).

•Is the resistance greater than 10,000 ohms?

-> Yes
REPAIR the circuit between the throttle position (TP) sensor PI16 pin 10, (W) and the powertrain control module electrical connector PI1 pin 57, (W). CLEAR DTC. TEST the system for normal operation.

-> No
Goto <<**D7**>>

JC1020100099020X

Fig. 25 Code P1121, P0122, P0123 & P0124: Throttle Position Sensor Circuit Malfunction (Part 2 of 5)

D7 : CHECK THE THROTTLE POSITION SENSOR FOR OPEN AT PIN 1

1. Measure the resistance between the throttle position sensor electrical connector PI16 pin 1, (WR) and powertrain control module electrical connector PI1 pin 59, (WR).

•Is the resistance greater than 10,000 ohms?

-> Yes
REPAIR the circuit between the throttle position (TP) sensor PI16 pin 1, (WR) and the powertrain control module electrical connector PI1 pin 59, (WR). CLEAR DTC. TEST the system for normal operation.

-> No
Goto <<**D8**>>

D8 : CHECK THE THROTTLE POSITION SENSOR FOR OPEN AT PIN 2

1. Measure the resistance between the throttle position sensor electrical connector PI16 pin 2, (W) and the powertrain control module electrical connector PI1 pin 58, (W).

•Is the resistance greater than 10,000 ohms?

-> Yes
REPAIR the circuit between the throttle position (TP) sensor PI16 pin 2, (W) and the powertrain control module electrical connector PI1 pin 58, (W). CLEAR DTC. TEST the system for normal operation.

-> No
Goto <<**D9**>>

D9 : CHECK THE THROTTLE POSITION SENSOR FOR OPEN AT PIN 6

1. Measure the resistance between the throttle position sensor electrical connector PI16 pin 6, (N) and ground.

•Is the resistance greater than 10,000 ohms?

-> Yes
REPAIR the circuit between the throttle position (TP) sensor PI16 pin 6, (N) and the powertrain control module electrical connector PI1 pin 15, (N). CLEAR DTC. TEST the system for normal operation.

-> No
Goto <<**D10**>>

JC1020100099030X

Fig. 25 Code P1121, P0122, P0123 & P0124: Throttle Position Sensor Circuit Malfunction (Part 3 of 5)

D10 : CHECK THE THROTTLE POSITION SENSOR FOR SHORT TO GROUND AT PIN 6

1. Remove the powertrain control module (PCM).

2. Measure the resistance between the throttle position sensor electrical connector PI16 pin 6, (N) and ground.

•**Is the resistance less than 10,000 ohms?**

-> **Yes**
REPAIR the circuit between the throttle position (TP) sensor PI16 pin 6, (N) and the powertrain control module electrical connector PI1 pin 15, (N). INSTALL the powertrain control module (PCM). CLEAR DTC. TEST the system for normal operation.

-> **No**
Goto <<D11>>

D11 : CHECK THE THROTTLE POSITION SENSOR FOR SHORT TO GROUND AT PIN 2

1. Measure the resistance between the throttle position sensor electrical connector PI16 pin 2, (W) and ground.

•**Is the resistance less than 10,000 ohms?**

-> **Yes**
REPAIR the circuit between the throttle position (TP) sensor PI16 pin 2, (W) and the powertrain control module electrical connector PI1 pin 58, (W). INSTALL the powertrain control module (PCM). CLEAR DTC. TEST the system for normal operation.

-> **No**
Goto <<D12>>

D12 : CHECK THE THROTTLE POSITION SENSOR FOR SHORT TO GROUND AT PIN 1

1. Measure the resistance between the throttle position sensor electrical connector PI16 pin 1, (WR) and ground.

•**Is the resistance less than 10,000 ohms?**

-> **Yes**
REPAIR the circuit between the throttle position (TP) sensor PI16 pin 1, (WR) and the powertrain control module electrical connector PI1 pin 59, (WR). INSTALL the powertrain control module (PCM). CLEAR DTC. TEST the system for normal operation.

JC1020100099050X

Fig. 25 Code P1121, P0122, P0123 & P0124: Throttle Position Sensor Circuit Malfunction (Part 4 of 5)

E1 : CHECK THE VOLTAGE AND SIGNAL GROUND SUPPLY TO THE OXYGEN SENSOR

1. Switch the ignition switch to the OFF position.
2. Raise and support the vehicle.
3. Disconnect the right hand oxygen sensor electrical connector PI6.
4. Switch the ignition switch to the RUN position.
5. Measure the voltage between the right hand oxygen sensor electrical connector PI6 pin 1, and pin 3.

•**Is the voltage greater than 10.5 volts?**

-> **Yes**
Goto <<E3>>

-> **No**
Goto <<E2>>

E2 : CHECK THE OXYGEN SENSOR VOLTAGE SUPPLY CIRCUIT

1. Measure the voltage between the right hand oxygen sensor electrical connector PI6 pin 1, (GY) and ground.

•**Is the voltage greater than 10.5 volts?**

-> **Yes**
REPAIR the circuit between the right hand oxygen sensor electrical connector PI6 pin 2, (N) and the powertrain electrical connector PI1 pin 7, (N). CLEAR DTC. TEST the system for normal operation.

-> **No**
REPAIR the circuit between the right hand oxygen sensor electrical connector PI6 pin 1, (GY) and the spliced joint PIS7. CLEAR DTC. TEST the system for normal operation.

E3 : CHECK THE OXYGEN SENSOR HEATER CONTINUITY

1. Switch the ignition switch to the OFF position.
2. Measure the resistance between the oxygen sensor electrical connector PI6 pin 1, and pin 2.

•**Is the resistance between 3 and 10 ohms?**

-> **Yes**
Goto <<E4>>

-> **No**
INSTALL a new oxygen sensor.
CLEAR DTC. TEST the system for normal operation.

JC1020100100010X

Fig. 26 Codes P0131, P0132 & P0135: Heated Oxygen Sensor Circuit Malfunction (Part 1 of 5). Bank 1 Upstream

D13 : CHECK THE THROTTLE POSITION SENSOR FOR SHORT TO GROUND AT PIN 10

1. Measure the resistance between the throttle position sensor electrical connector PI16 pin 10, (W) and ground.

•**Is the resistance less than 10,000 ohms?**

-> **Yes**
REPAIR the circuit between the throttle position (TP) sensor PI16 pin 10, (W) and the powertrain control module electrical connector PI1 pin 57, (W). INSTALL the powertrain control module (PCM). CLEAR DTC. TEST the system for normal operation.

-> **No**
Goto <<D14>>

D14 : CHECK THE THROTTLE POSITION SENSOR SIGNAL GROUND PIN 7 WIRE FOR SHORT TO GROUND

1. Raise and support the vehicle.
2. Disconnect both heated exhaust gas oxygen (HEGO) sensor electrical connectors PI6, PI7.
3. Disconnect the engine oil temperature sensor electrical connector PI12.
4. Disconnect the engine fuel temperature sensor electrical connector IL9.
5. Disconnect the cylinder head temperature sensor electrical connector PI13.
6. Disconnect both camshaft position sensor electrical connectors PI10, PI11.
7. Disconnect the injection pressure sensor electrical connector IL2.
8. Measure the resistance between the throttle position sensor electrical connector PI16 pin 7, (N) and ground.

•**Is the resistance less than 10,000 ohms?**

-> **Yes**
REPAIR the circuit between the throttle position (TP) sensor PI16 pin 7, (N) and the spliced joint PIS5. INSTALL the powertrain control module (PCM). CLEAR DTC. TEST the system for normal operation.

-> **No**
INSTALL a new powertrain control module (PCM). CLEAR DTC. TEST the system for normal operation.

JC1020100099060X

Fig. 25 Code P1121, P0122, P0123 & P0124: Throttle Position Sensor Circuit Malfunction (Part 5 of 5)

E4 : CHECK THE OXYGEN SENSOR FOR FAILURE

1. Connect the oxygen sensor electrical connector PI6.
2. RUN the engine until the oxygen sensor has warmed up and maintain a speed of approximately 2500 rpm.
3. Disconnect the oxygen sensor electrical connector.
4. Measure the voltage between the oxygen sensor electrical connector P16 pin 3, and pin 4.

•**Is the voltage between 100mV and 1.0 Volt?**

-> **Yes**
Goto <<E5>>

-> **No**
INSTALL a new oxygen sensor. CLEAR DTC. TEST the system for normal operation.

E5 : CHECK THE OXYGEN SENSOR FOR FAILURE

1. Connect the oxygen sensor electrical connector P16.
2. REDUCE the engine speed to idle.
3. Disconnect the oxygen sensor electrical connector P16.
4. Measure the voltage between the oxygen sensor electrical connector P16 pin 3, and pin 4.

•**Has the voltage dropped to less than 400mV?**

-> **Yes**
Goto <<E6>>

-> **No**
INSTALL a new oxygen sensor. CLEAR DTC. TEST the system for normal operation.

E6 : CHECK THE OXYGEN SENSOR FOR FAILURE

1. Connect the oxygen sensor electrical connector PI6.
2. INCREASE the engine speed to approximately 2500 rpm.
3. Disconnect the oxygen sensor electrical connector PI6.

•**Has the voltage increased to between 100 mV to 1.0 Volt?**

-> **Yes**
Goto <<E7>>

-> **No**
INSTALL a new oxygen sensor. CLEAR DTC. TEST the system for normal operation.

JC1020100100020X

Fig. 26 Codes P0131, P0132 & P0135: Heated Oxygen Sensor Circuit Malfunction (Part 2 of 5). Bank 1 Upstream

E7 : CHECK THE HEATED OXYGEN SENSOR FOR SHORT TO GROUND

1. Switch the ignition switch to the OFF position.
2. Disconnect the oxygen sensor electrical connector PI6.
3. Measure the resistance between the oxygen sensor electrical connector PI6 pin 1, (GY) and the oxygen sensor body, and between the oxygen sensor electrical connector PI6 pin 3, (N) and the oxygen sensor body.

•Is the resistance greater than 10 M ohms?

-> Yes
Goto <<E8>>

-> No
INSTALL a new oxygen sensor. CLEAR DTC. TEST the system for normal operation.

E8 : CHECK THE OXYGEN SENSOR SIGNAL GROUND CIRCUIT FOR OPEN

1. Measure the resistance between the oxygen sensor electrical connector PI6 pin 3, (N) and ground.

•Is the resistance greater than 10,000 ohms?

-> Yes
REPAIR the circuit between the oxygen sensor electrical connector PI6 pin 3, (N) and the spliced joint PIS6. CLEAR DTC. TEST the system for normal operation.

-> No
Goto <<E9>>

E9 : CHECK THE OXYGEN SENSOR INPUT CIRCUIT FOR OPEN

1. Remove the powertrain control module (PCM).
2. Measure the resistance between the oxygen sensor electrical connector PI6 pin 4, (W) and the powertrain control module electrical connector PI1 pin 45, (W).

•Is the resistance greater than 10,000 ohms?

-> Yes
REPAIR the circuit between the oxygen sensor electrical connector PI6 pin 4, (W) and the powertrain control module electrical connector PI1 pin 45, (W). INSTALL the powertrain control module (PCM). CLEAR DTC. TEST the system for normal operation.

JC1020100100030X

Fig. 26 Codes P0131, P0132 & P0135: Heated Oxygen Sensor Circuit Malfunction (Part 3 of 5). Bank 1 Upstream

E13 : CHECK THE OXYGEN SENSOR SIGNAL GROUND CIRCUIT FOR SHORT TO GROUND

1. Disconnect both heated exhaust gas oxygen (HEGO) sensor electrical connectors PI6, PI7.
2. Disconnect the engine oil temperature sensor electrical connector PI12.
3. Disconnect the engine fuel temperature sensor electrical connector IL9.
4. Disconnect the cylinder head temperature sensor electrical connector PI13.
5. Disconnect both camshaft position sensor electrical connectors PI10, PI11.
6. Disconnect the injection pressure sensor electrical connector IL2.
7. Disconnect the throttle position sensor electrical connector PI16.
8. Measure the resistance between the oxygen sensor electrical connector PI6 pin 3, (N) and ground.

•Is the resistance less than 10,000 ohms?

-> Yes
REPAIR the signal ground circuit between the oxygen sensor electrical connector PI6 pin 3, (N) and the spliced joint PIS6. INSTALL the powertrain control module (PCM).
CLEAR DTC. TEST the system for normal operation.

-> No
INSTALL a new powertrain control module (PCM).
CLEAR DTC. TEST the system for normal operation.

JC1020100100050X

Fig. 26 Codes P0131, P0132 & P0135: Heated Oxygen Sensor Circuit Malfunction (Part 5 of 5). Bank 1 Upstream

E10 : CHECK THE OXYGEN SENSOR CIRCUIT FOR SHORT TO GROUND

1. Measure the resistance between the oxygen sensor electrical connector PI6 pin 4, (W) and ground.

•Is the resistance less than 10,000 ohms?

-> Yes
REPAIR the signal ground circuit between the oxygen sensor electrical connector PI6 pin 4, (W) and the powertrain control module electrical connector PI1 pin 45, (W). INSTALL the powertrain control module (PCM).
CLEAR DTC. TEST the system for normal operation.

-> No
Goto <<E11>>

E11 : CHECK THE OXYGEN SENSOR HEATER CIRCUIT FOR OPEN

1. Measure the resistance between the oxygen sensor electrical connector PI6 pin 2, (N)and the powertrain control module electrical connector PI1 pin 7, (N).

•Is the resistance greater than 10,000 ohms?

-> Yes
REPAIR the circuit between the oxygen sensor electrical connector PI6 pin 2, (N) and the powertrain control module electrical connector PI1 pin 7, (N). INSTALL the powertrain control module (PCM).
CLEAR DTC. TEST the system for normal operation.

-> No
Goto <<E12>>

E12 : CHECK THE OXYGEN SENSOR HEATER CIRCUIT FOR SHORT TO GROUND

1. Measure the resistance between the oxygen sensor electrical connector PI6 pin 2, (N) and ground.

•Is the resistance less than 10,000 ohms?

-> Yes
REPAIR the output circuit between the oxygen sensor electrical connector PI6 pin 2, (N) and the powertrain control module electrical connector PI1 pin 7, (N). INSTALL the powertrain control module (PCM). CLEAR DTC. TEST the system for normal operation.

-> No
Goto <<E13>>

JC1020100100040X

Fig. 26 Codes P0131, P0132 & P0135: Heated Oxygen Sensor Circuit Malfunction (Part 4 of 5). Bank 1 Upstream

F1 : CHECK THE VOLTAGE AND SIGNAL GROUND SUPPLY TO THE CATALYST MONITOR SENSOR

1. Switch the ignition switch to the OFF position.
2. Raise and support the vehicle.
3. Disconnect the right hand catalyst monitor sensor electrical connector GB3.
4. Switch the ignition switch to the RUN position.
5. Measure the voltage between the right hand catalyst monitor sensor electrical connector GB3 pin 1, and pin 3.

•Is the voltage greater than 10.5 volts?

-> Yes
Goto <<F3>>

-> No
Goto <<F2>>

F2 : CHECK THE CATALYST MONITOR SENSOR VOLTAGE SUPPLY CIRCUIT

1. Measure the voltage between the right hand catalyst monitor sensor electrical connector GB3 pin 1, (GR) and ground.

•Is the voltage greater than 10.5 volts?

-> Yes
REPAIR the circuit between the right hand catalyst monitor sensor electrical connector GB3 pin 2, (BO) and the powertrain electrical connector GB1 pin 15, (BO). CLEAR DTC. TEST the system for normal operation.

-> No
REPAIR the circuit between the right hand catalyst monitor sensor electrical connector GB3 pin 1, (GR) and the spliced joint GBS1. CLEAR DTC. TEST the system for normal operation.

F3 : CHECK THE CATALYST MONITOR SENSOR HEATER CONTINUITY

1. Switch the ignition switch to the OFF position.
2. Measure the resistance between the right hand catalyst monitor sensor electrical connector GB3 pin 1, and pin 2.

•Is the resistance between 3 and 10 ohms?

-> Yes
Goto <<F4>>

-> No
INSTALL a new right hand catalyst monitor sensor.
CLEAR DTC. TEST the system for normal operation.

JC1020100101010X

Fig. 27 Codes P0136, P0138 & P0141: Heated Oxygen Sensor Circuit Malfunction (Part 1 of 5). Bank 1 Downstream

F4 : CHECK THE CATALYST MONITOR SENSOR FOR FAILURE

1. Connect the right hand catalyst monitor sensor electrical connector GB3.
2. RUN the engine until the catalyst monitor sensor has warmed up and maintain a speed of approximately 2500 rpm.
3. Disconnect the right hand catalyst monitor sensor electrical connector GB3.
4. Measure the voltage between the right hand catalyst monitor sensor electrical connector GB3 pin 3, and pin 4.

•Is the voltage between 600mV and 1.0 Volt?

-> Yes
Goto <<F5>>

-> No
INSTALL a new right hand catalyst monitor sensor.
CLEAR DTC. TEST the system for normal operation.

F5 : CHECK THE CATALYST MONITOR SENSOR FOR FAILURE

1. Connect the right hand catalyst monitor sensor electrical connector GB3.
2. REDUCE the engine speed to idle.
3. Disconnect the right hand catalyst monitor sensor electrical connector GB3.
4. Measure the voltage between the right hand catalyst monitor sensor electrical connector GB3 pin 3, and pin 4.

•Has the voltage dropped to less than 400mV?

-> Yes
Goto <<F6>>

-> No
INSTALL a new right hand catalyst monitor sensor.
CLEAR DTC. TEST the system for normal operation.

F6 : CHECK THE CATALYST MONITOR SENSOR FOR FAILURE

1. Connect the catalyst monitor sensor electrical connector GB3.
2. INCREASE the engine speed to approximately 2500 rpm.
3. Disconnect the catalyst monitor sensor electrical connector GB3.

•Has the voltage increased to between 600 mV to 1.0 Volt?

-> Yes
Goto <<F7>>

-> No
INSTALL a new catalyst monitor sensor.
CLEAR DTC. TEST the system for normal operation.

JC1020100101020X

Fig. 27 Codes P0136, P0138 & P0141: Heated Oxygen Sensor Circuit Malfunction (Part 2 of 5). Bank 1 Downstream

F10 : CHECK THE CATALYST MONITOR SENSOR CIRCUIT FOR SHORT TO GROUND

1. Measure the resistance between the catalyst monitor sensor electrical connector GB3 pin 4, (WU) and ground.

•Is the resistance less than 10,000 ohms?

-> Yes
REPAIR the input circuit between the catalyst monitor sensor electrical connector GB3 pin 4, (WU) and the powertrain control module electrical connector GB1 pin 28, (WU). INSTALL the powertrain control module (PCM). CLEAR DTC. TEST the system for normal operation.

-> No
Goto <<F11>>

F11 : CHECK THE CATALYST MONITOR SENSOR HEATER CIRCUIT FOR OPEN

1. Measure the resistance between the catalyst monitor sensor electrical connector GB3 pin 2, (BO) and the powertrain control module electrical connector GB1 pin 15, (BO).

•Is the resistance greater than 10,000 ohms?

-> Yes
REPAIR the output circuit between the catalyst monitor sensor electrical connector GB3 pin 2, (BO) and the powertrain control module electrical connector GB1 pin 15, (BO). INSTALL the powertrain control module (PCM). CLEAR DTC. TEST the system for normal operation.

-> No
Goto <<F12>>

F12 : CHECK THE OXYGEN SENSOR HEATER CIRCUIT FOR SHORT TO GROUND

1. Measure the resistance between the catalyst monitor sensor electrical connector GB3 pin 2, (BO) and ground.

•Is the resistance less than 10,000 ohms?

-> Yes
REPAIR the output circuit between the catalyst monitor sensor electrical connector GB3 pin 2, (BO) and the powertrain control module electrical connector GB1 pin 15, (BO). INSTALL the powertrain control module (PCM). CLEAR DTC. TEST the system for normal operation.

-> No
Goto <<F13>>

JC1020100101040X

Fig. 27 Codes P0136, P0138 & P0141: Heated Oxygen Sensor Circuit Malfunction (Part 4 of 5). Bank 1 Downstream

F7 : CHECK THE CATALYST MONITOR SENSOR FOR SHORT TO GROUND

1. Switch the ignition switch to the OFF position.
2. Disconnect the oxygen sensor electrical connector GB3.
3. Measure the resistance between the catalyst monitor sensor electrical connector GB3 pin 1, (GR) and the monitor sensor body, and between the catalyst monitor sensor electrical connector GB3 pin 3, (NU) and the monitor sensor body.

•Is the resistance greater than 10 M ohms?

-> Yes
Goto <<F8>>

-> No
INSTALL a new catalyst monitor sensor. CLEAR DTC. TEST the system for normal operation.

F8 : CHECK THE CATALYST MONITOR SENSOR SIGNAL GROUND CIRCUIT FOR OPEN

1. Measure the resistance between the catalyst monitor sensor electrical connector GB3 pin 3, (NU) and ground.

•Is the resistance greater than 10,000 ohms?

-> Yes
REPAIR the circuit between the catalyst monitor sensor electrical connector GB3 pin 3, (NU) and the spliced joint GB53. CLEAR DTC. TEST the system for normal operation.

-> No
Goto <<F9>>

F9 : CHECK THE CATALYST MONITOR SENSOR INPUT CIRCUIT FOR OPEN

1. Remove the powertrain control module (PCM).
2. Measure the resistance between the catalyst monitor sensor electrical connector GB3 pin 4, (WU) and the powertrain control module electrical connector GB1 pin 28, (WU).

•Is the resistance greater than 10,000 ohms?

-> Yes
REPAIR the circuit between the catalyst monitor sensor electrical connector GB3 pin 4, (WU) and the powertrain control module electrical connector GB1 pin 28, (WU). INSTALL the powertrain control module (PCM). CLEAR DTC. TEST the system for normal operation.

-> No
Goto <<F10>>

JC1020100101030X

Fig. 27 Codes P0136, P0138 & P0141: Heated Oxygen Sensor Circuit Malfunction (Part 3 of 5). Bank 1 Downstream

F13 : CHECK THE CATALYST MONITOR SENSOR SIGNAL GROUND CIRCUIT FOR SHORT TO GROUND

1. Disconnect both catalyst monitor sensor electrical connectors GB3, GB4.
2. Measure the resistance between the catalyst monitor sensor electrical connector GB3 pin 3, (NU) and ground.

•Is the resistance less than 10,000 ohms?

-> Yes
REPAIR the signal ground circuit between the catalyst monitor sensor electrical connector GB3 pin 3, (NU) and the spliced joint GBS3. INSTALL the powertrain control module (PCM).
CLEAR DTC. TEST the system for normal operation.

-> No
INSTALL a new powertrain control module (PCM).
CLEAR DTC. TEST the system for normal operation.

JC1020100101050X

Fig. 27 Codes P0136, P0138 & P0141: Heated Oxygen Sensor Circuit Malfunction (Part 5 of 5). Bank 1 Downstream

G1 : CHECK THE VOLTAGE AND SIGNAL GROUND SUPPLY TO THE OXYGEN SENSOR

1. Switch the ignition switch to the OFF position.
2. Raise and support the vehicle.
3. Disconnect the left hand oxygen sensor electrical connector PI7.
4. Switch the ignition switch to the RUN position.
5. Measure the voltage between the left hand oxygen sensor electrical connector PI7 pin 1, and pin 3.

•Is the voltage greater than 10.5 volts?

-> Yes
Goto <<G3>>

-> No
Goto <<G2>>

G2 : CHECK THE OXYGEN SENSOR VOLTAGE SUPPLY CIRCUIT

1. Measure the voltage between the left hand oxygen sensor electrical connector PI7 pin 1, (GU) and ground.

•Is the voltage greater than 10.5 volts?

-> Yes
REPAIR the circuit between the left hand oxygen sensor electrical connector PI7 pin 2, (NR) and the powertrain electrical connector PI1 pin 8, (N). CLEAR DTC. TEST the system for normal operation.

-> No
REPAIR the circuit between the left hand oxygen sensor electrical connector PI7 pin 1, (GU) and the spliced joint PIS7. CLEAR DTC. TEST the system for normal operation.

G3 : CHECK THE OXYGEN SENSOR HEATER CONTINUITY

1. Switch the ignition switch to the OFF position.
2. Measure the resistance between the oxygen sensor electrical connector PI7 pin 1, (GU) and pin 2 (NR).

•Is the resistance between 3 and 10 ohms?

-> Yes
Goto <<G4>>

-> No
INSTALL a new oxygen sensor. CLEAR DTC. TEST the system for normal operation.

JC1020100102010X

Fig. 28 Codes P0151, P0152 & P0155: Heated Oxygen Sensor Circuit Malfunction (Part 1 of 5). Bank 2 Upstream

G4 : CHECK THE OXYGEN SENSOR FOR FAILURE

1. Connect the oxygen sensor electrical connector PI7.
2. RUN the engine until the oxygen sensor has warmed up and maintain a speed of approximately 2500 rpm.
3. Disconnect the oxygen sensor electrical connector PI7.
4. Measure the voltage between the oxygen sensor electrical connector PI7 pin 3, (NR) and pin 4 (WR).

•Is the voltage between 600mV and 1.0 Volt?

-> Yes
Goto <<G5>>

-> No
INSTALL a new oxygen sensor. CLEAR DTC. TEST the system for normal operation.

G5 : CHECK THE OXYGEN SENSOR FOR FAILURE

1. Connect the oxygen sensor electrical connector PI7.
2. REDUCE the engine speed to idle.
3. Disconnect the oxygen sensor electrical connector PI7.
4. Measure the voltage between the oxygen sensor electrical connector PI7 pin 3, (NR) and pin 4 (WR).

•Has the voltage dropped to less than 400mV?

-> Yes
Goto <<G6>>

-> No
INSTALL a new oxygen sensor. CLEAR DTC. TEST the system for normal operation.

G6 : CHECK THE OXYGEN SENSOR FOR FAILURE

1. Connect the oxygen sensor electrical connector PI7.
2. INCREASE the engine speed to approximately 2500 rpm.
3. Disconnect the oxygen sensor electrical connector PI7.

•Has the voltage increased to between 600 mV to 1.0 Volt?

-> Yes
Goto <<G7>>

-> No
INSTALL a new oxygen sensor. CLEAR DTC. TEST the system for normal operation.

JC1020100102020X

Fig. 28 Codes P0151, P0152 & P0155: Heated Oxygen Sensor Circuit Malfunction (Part 2 of 5). Bank 2 Upstream

G7 : CHECK THE HEATED OXYGEN SENSOR FOR SHORT TO GROUND

1. Switch the ignition switch to the OFF position.
2. Disconnect the oxygen sensor electrical connector PI7.
3. Measure the resistance between the oxygen sensor electrical connector PI7 pin 1, (GU) and the oxygen sensor body, and between the oxygen sensor electrical connector PI7 pin 3, (NR) and the oxygen sensor body.

•Is the resistance greater than 10 M ohms?

-> Yes
Goto <<G8>>

-> No
INSTALL a new oxygen sensor. CLEAR DTC. TEST the system for normal operation.

G8 : CHECK THE OXYGEN SENSOR SIGNAL GROUND CIRCUIT FOR OPEN

1. Measure the resistance between the oxygen sensor electrical connector PI7 pin 3, (NR) and ground.

•Is the resistance greater than 10,000 ohms?

-> Yes
REPAIR the circuit between the oxygen sensor electrical connector PI7 pin 3, (NR) and the spliced joint P1S6. CLEAR DTC. TEST the system for normal operation.

-> No
Goto <<G9>>

G9 : CHECK THE OXYGEN SENSOR INPUT CIRCUIT FOR OPEN

1. Remove the powertrain control module (PCM).
2. Measure the resistance between the oxygen sensor electrical connector PI7 pin 4, (WR) and the powertrain control module electrical connector PI1 pin 44, (WR).

•Is the resistance greater than 10,000 ohms?

-> Yes
REPAIR the circuit between the oxygen sensor electrical connector PI7 pin 4, (WR) and the powertrain control module electrical connector PI1 pin 44, (WR) . CLEAR DTC. TEST the system for normal operation.

-> No
Goto <<G10>>

JC1020100102030X

Fig. 28 Codes P0151, P0152 & P0155: Heated Oxygen Sensor Circuit Malfunction (Part 3 of 5). Bank 2 Upstream

G10 : CHECK THE OXYGEN SENSOR CIRCUIT FOR SHORT TO GROUND

1. Measure the resistance between the oxygen sensor electrical connector PI7 pin 4, (WR) and ground.

•Is the resistance less than 10,000 ohms?

-> Yes
REPAIR the signal ground circuit between the oxygen sensor electrical connector PI7 pin 4, (WR) and the powertrain control module electrical connector PI1 pin 44, (WR). INSTALL the powertrain control module (PCM). CLEAR DTC. TEST the system for normal operation.

-> No
Goto <<G11>>

G11 : CHECK THE OXYGEN SENSOR HEATER CIRCUIT FOR OPEN

1. Measure the resistance between the oxygen sensor electrical connector PI7 pin 2, (NR) and the powertrain control module electrical connector PI1 pin 8, (NR).

•Is the resistance greater than 10,000 ohms?

-> Yes
REPAIR the circuit between the oxygen sensor electrical connector PI7 pin 2, (NR) and the powertrain control module electrical connector PI1 pin 8, (NR). INSTALL the powertrain control module (PCM). CLEAR DTC. TEST the system for normal operation.

-> No
Goto <<G12>>

G12 : CHECK THE OXYGEN SENSOR HEATER CIRCUIT FOR SHORT TO GROUND

1. Measure the resistance between the oxygen sensor electrical connector PI7 pin 2, (BU) and ground.

•Is the resistance less than 10,000 ohms?

-> Yes
REPAIR the output circuit between the oxygen sensor electrical connector PI7 pin 2, (NR) and the powertrain control module electrical connector PI1 pin 8, (NR). INSTALL the powertrain control module (PCM). CLEAR DTC. TEST the system for normal operation.

-> No
Goto <<G13>>

JC1020100102040X

Fig. 28 Codes P0151, P0152 & P0155: Heated Oxygen Sensor Circuit Malfunction (Part 4 of 5). Bank 2 Upstream

G13 : CHECK THE OXYGEN SENSOR SIGNAL GROUND CIRCUIT FOR SHORT TO GROUND

1. Disconnect both heated exhaust gas oxygen (HEGO) sensor electrical connectors PI6, PI7.
2. Disconnect the engine oil temperature sensor electrical connector PI12.
3. Disconnect the engine fuel temperature sensor electrical connector IL9.
4. Disconnect the cylinder head temperature sensor electrical connector PI13.
5. Disconnect both camshaft position sensor electrical connectors PI10, PI11.
6. Disconnect the injection pressure sensor electrical connector IL2.
7. Disconnect the throttle position sensor electrical connector PI16.
8. Measure the resistance between the oxygen sensor electrical connector PI7 pin 3, (NR) and ground.

•Is the resistance less than 10,000 ohms?

-> Yes
REPAIR the signal ground circuit between the oxygen sensor electrical connector PI7 pin 3, (NR) and the spliced joint PIS6. INSTALL the powertrain control module (PCM).
CLEAR DTC. TEST the system for normal operation.

-> No
INSTALL a new powertrain control module (PCM).
CLEAR DTC. TEST the system for normal operation.

JC1020100102050X

Fig. 28 Codes P0151, P0152 & P0155: Heated Oxygen Sensor Circuit Malfunction (Part 5 of 5). Bank 2 Upstream

H4 : CHECK THE CATALYST MONITOR SENSOR FOR FAILURE

1. Connect the left hand catalyst monitor sensor electrical connector GB4.
2. RUN the engine until the catalyst monitor sensor has warmed up and maintain a speed of approximately 2500 rpm.
3. Disconnect the left hand catalyst monitor sensor electrical connector GB4.
4. Measure the voltage between the left hand catalyst monitor sensor electrical connector GB4 pin 3, (NG) and pin 4 (WG).

•Is the voltage between 600mV and 1.0 Volt?

-> Yes
Goto <<H5>>

-> No
INSTALL a new left hand catalyst monitor sensor.
CLEAR DTC. TEST the system for normal operation.

H5 : CHECK THE CATALYST MONITOR SENSOR FOR FAILURE

1. Connect the left hand catalyst monitor sensor electrical connector GB4.
2. REDUCE the engine speed to idle.
3. Disconnect the left hand catalyst monitor sensor electrical connector GB4.
4. Measure the voltage between the left hand catalyst monitor sensor electrical connector GB4 pin 3, (NG) and pin 4 (WG).

•Has the voltage dropped to less than 400mV?

-> Yes
Goto <<H6>>

-> No
INSTALL a new left hand catalyst monitor sensor.
CLEAR DTC. TEST the system for normal operation.

H6 : CHECK THE CATALYST MONITOR SENSOR FOR FAILURE

1. Connect the catalyst monitor sensor electrical connector GB4.
2. INCREASE the engine speed to approximately 2500 rpm.
3. Disconnect the catalyst monitor sensor electrical connector GB4.

•Has the voltage increased to between 600 mV to 1.0 Volt?

-> Yes
Goto <<H7>>

-> No
INSTALL a new catalyst monitor sensor. CLEAR DTC. TEST the system for normal operation.

JC1020100103020X

Fig. 29 Codes P0156, P0158 & P0161: Heated Oxygen Sensor Circuit Malfunction (Part 2 of 5). Bank 2 Downstream

H1 : CHECK THE VOLTAGE AND SIGNAL GROUND SUPPLY TO THE CATALYST MONITOR SENSOR

1. Switch the ignition switch to the OFF position.
2. Raise and support the vehicle.
3. Disconnect the left hand catalyst monitor sensor electrical connector GB4.
4. Switch the ignition switch to the RUN position.
5. Measure the voltage between the left hand catalyst monitor sensor electrical connector GB4 pin 1, (GB)and pin 3 (NG).

•Is the voltage greater than 10.5 volts?

-> Yes
Goto <<H3>>

-> No
Goto <<H2>>

H2 : CHECK THE CATALYST MONITOR SENSOR VOLTAGE SUPPLY CIRCUIT

1. Measure the voltage between the left hand catalyst monitor sensor electrical connector GB4 pin 1, (GB) and ground.

•Is the voltage greater than 10.5 volts?

-> Yes
REPAIR the circuit between the left hand catalyst monitor sensor electrical connector GB4 pin 2, (BG) and the spliced joint GB53. CLEAR DTC. TEST the system for normal operation.

-> No
REPAIR the circuit between the left hand catalyst monitor sensor electrical connector GB4 pin 1, (GB) and the spliced joint GBS1. CLEAR DTC. TEST the system for normal operation.

H3 : CHECK THE CATALYST MONITOR SENSOR HEATER CONTINUITY

1. Switch the ignition switch to the OFF position.
2. Measure the resistance between the left hand catalyst monitor sensor electrical connector GB4 pin 1, (GB) and pin 2 (BG).

•Is the resistance between 3 and 10 ohms?

-> Yes
Goto <<H4>>

-> No
INSTALL a new left hand catalyst monitor sensor.
CLEAR DTC. TEST the system for normal operation.

JC1020100103010X

Fig. 29 Codes P0156, P0158 & P0161: Heated Oxygen Sensor Circuit Malfunction (Part 1 of 5). Bank 2 Downstream

H7 : CHECK THE CATALYST MONITOR SENSOR FOR SHORT TO GROUND

1. Switch the ignition switch to the OFF position.
2. Measure the resistance between the catalyst monitor sensor electrical connector GB4 pin 1, (GB) and the monitor sensor body, and between the catalyst monitor sensor electrical connector GB4 pin 3, (NG) and the monitor sensor body.

•Is the resistance greater than 10 M ohms?

-> Yes
Goto <<H8>>

-> No
INSTALL a new catalyst monitor sensor.
CLEAR DTC. TEST the system for normal operation.

H8 : CHECK THE CATALYST MONITOR SENSOR SIGNAL GROUND CIRCUIT FOR OPEN

1. Measure the resistance between the catalyst monitor sensor electrical connector GB4 pin 3, (NG) and ground.

•Is the resistance greater than 10,000 ohms?

-> Yes
REPAIR the circuit between the catalyst monitor sensor electrical connector GB4 pin 3, (NG) and the spliced joint GB53. CLEAR DTC. TEST the system for normal operation.

-> No
Goto <<H9>>

H9 : CHECK THE CATALYST MONITOR SENSOR CIRCUIT FOR OPEN

1. Remove the powertrain control module (PCM).
2. Measure the resistance between the catalyst monitor sensor electrical connector GB4 pin 4, (WG) and the powertrain control module electrical connector GB1 pin 29, (WG).

•Is the resistance greater than 10,000 ohms?

-> Yes
REPAIR the circuit between the catalyst monitor sensor electrical connector GB4 pin 4, (WG) and the powertrain control module electrical connector GB1 pin 29, (WG). INSTALL the powertrain control module (PCM). CLEAR DTC. TEST the system for normal operation.

-> No
Goto <<H10>>

JC1020100103030X

Fig. 29 Codes P0156, P0158 & P0161: Heated Oxygen Sensor Circuit Malfunction (Part 3 of 5). Bank 2 Downstream

H10 : CHECK THE CATALYST MONITOR SENSOR CIRCUIT FOR SHORT TO GROUND

1. Measure the resistance between the catalyst monitor sensor electrical connector GB4 pin 4, (WG) and ground.

•Is the resistance less than 10,000 ohms?

-> Yes
REPAIR the input circuit between the catalyst monitor sensor electrical connector GB4 pin 4, (WG) and the powertrain control module electrical connector GB1 pin 29, (WG). INSTALL the powertrain control module (PCM). CLEAR DTC. TEST the system for normal operation.

-> No
Goto <<H11>>

H11 : CHECK THE CATALYST MONITOR SENSOR HEATER CIRCUIT FOR OPEN

1. Measure the resistance between the catalyst monitor sensor electrical connector GB4 pin 2, (BG) and the powertrain control module electrical connector GB1 pin 16, (BG).

•Is the resistance greater than 10,000 ohms?

-> Yes
REPAIR the output circuit between the catalyst monitor sensor electrical connector GB4 pin 2, (BG) and the powertrain control module electrical connector GB1 pin 16, (BG). INSTALL the powertrain control module (PCM). CLEAR DTC. TEST the system for normal operation.

-> No
Goto <<H12>>

H12 : CHECK THE OXYGEN SENSOR HEATER CIRCUIT FOR SHORT TO GROUND

1. Measure the resistance between the catalyst monitor sensor electrical connector GB4 pin 2, (BG) and ground.

•Is the resistance less than 10,000 ohms?

-> Yes
REPAIR the output circuit between the catalyst monitor sensor electrical connector GB4 pin 2, (BG) and the powertrain control module electrical connector GB1 pin 16, (BG). INSTALL the powertrain control module (PCM). CLEAR DTC. TEST the system for normal operation.

-> No
Goto <<H13>>

JC1020100103040X

Fig. 29 Codes P0156, P0158 & P0161: Heated Oxygen Sensor Circuit Malfunction (Part 4 of 5). Bank 2 Downstream

I1 : CHECK THE ELECTRONIC FUEL TEMPERATURE SENSOR RESISTANCE

1. Switch the ignition switch to the OFF position.
2. REMOVE the plastic engine cover.
3. Disconnect the electronic fuel temperature sensor electrical connector IL9.
4. Carry out the Fuel Temperature Sensor Component Test.

•Is the fuel temperature sensor ok?

-> Yes
Goto <<I2>>

-> No
INSTALL a new fuel temperature sensor. CLEAR DTC. TEST the system for normal operation.

I2 : CHECK THE SIGNAL GROUND CIRCUIT FOR OPEN

1. Measure the resistance between the fuel temperature sensor electrical connector IL9 pin 2, (NU) and ground.

•Is the resistance less than 10,000 ohms?

-> Yes
Goto <<I3>>

-> No
REPAIR the circuit between the fuel temperature sensor electrical connector IL9 pin 2, (NU) and the spliced joint PIS6. CLEAR DTC. TEST the system for normal operation.

I3 : CHECK THE INPUT CIRCUIT FOR OPEN

1. Remove the powertrain control module (PCM).

2. Measure the resistance between the fuel temperature sensor electrical connector IL9 pin 1, (WU) and the powertrain control module electrical connector PI1 pin 47, (WU).

•Is the resistance less than 10,000 ohms?

-> Yes
Goto <<I4>>

-> No
REPAIR the circuit between the fuel temperature sensor electrical connector IL9 pin 1, (WU) and the powertrain control module electrical connector PI1 pin 47, (WU). CLEAR DTC. TEST the system for normal operation.

JC1020100104010X

Fig. 30 Code P0180: Fuel Temperature Sensor Circuit A Malfunction (Part 1 of 2)

H13 : CHECK THE CATALYST MONITOR SENSOR SIGNAL GROUND CIRCUIT FOR SHORT TO GROUND

1. Disconnect both catalyst monitor sensor electrical connectors GB3, GB4.
2. Measure the resistance between the catalyst monitor sensor electrical connector GB4 pin 3, (NG) and ground.

•Is the resistance less than 10,000 ohms?

-> Yes
REPAIR the signal ground circuit between the catalyst monitor sensor electrical connector GB4 pin 3, (NG) and the spliced joint GBS3. INSTALL the powertrain control module (PCM).
CLEAR DTC. TEST the system for normal operation.

-> No
INSTALL a new powertrain control module (PCM).
CLEAR DTC. TEST the system for normal operation.

JC1020100103050X

Fig. 29 Codes P0156, P0158 & P0161: Heated Oxygen Sensor Circuit Malfunction (Part 5 of 5). Bank 2 Downstream

I4 : CHECK THE INPUT CIRCUIT FOR SHORT TO GROUND

1. Measure the resistance between the fuel temperature sensor electrical connector IL9 pin 1, (WU) and ground.

•Is the resistance greater than 10,000 ohms?

-> Yes
Goto <<I5>>

-> No
REPAIR the circuit between the fuel temperature sensor electrical connector IL9 pin 1, (WU) and the powertrain control module electrical connector PI1 pin 47, (WU). CLEAR DTC. TEST the system for normal operation.

I5 : CHECK THE SIGNAL GROUND CIRCUIT FOR SHORT TO GROUND

1. Raise and support the vehicle.
2. Disconnect both heated exhaust gas oxygen (HEGO) sensor electrical connectors PI6, PI7.
3. Disconnect the engine oil temperature sensor electrical connector PI12.
4. Disconnect the cylinder head temperature sensor electrical connector PI13.
5. Disconnect both camshaft position sensor electrical connectors PI10, PI11.
6. Disconnect the injection pressure sensor electrical connector IL2.
7. Disconnect the throttle position sensor electrical connector PI16.
8. Measure the resistance between the fuel temperature sensor electrical connector IL9 pin 2, (NU) and ground.

•Is the resistance less than 10,000 ohms?

-> Yes
REPAIR the circuit between the fuel temperature sensor electrical connector IL9 pin 2, (NU) and the spliced joint P1S6. INSTALL the powertrain control module (PCM).
CLEAR DTC. TEST the system for normal operation.

-> No
INSTALL a new powertrain control module (PCM).
CLEAR DTC. TEST the system for normal operation.

JC1020100104020X

Fig. 30 Code P0180: Fuel Temperature Sensor Circuit A Malfunction (Part 2 of 2)

J1 : CHECK THE ENGINE OIL TEMPERATURE SENSOR RESISTANCE

1. Switch the ignition switch to the OFF position.
2. Raise and support the vehicle.
3. Disconnect the engine oil temperature sensor electrical connector PI12.
4. Carry out the Engine Oil Temperature Sensor Component Test.

•Is the engine oil temperature sensor ok?

-> Yes
Goto <<J2>>

-> No
INSTALL a new engine oil temperature sensor. CLEAR DTC. TEST the system for normal operation.

J2 : CHECK THE SIGNAL GROUND CIRCUIT FOR OPEN

1. Measure the resistance between the engine oil temperature sensor electrical connector PI12 pin 2, (NG) and ground.

•Is the resistance less than 10,000 ohms?

-> Yes
Goto <<J3>>

-> No
REPAIR the circuit between the engine oil temperature sensor electrical connector PI12 pin 2, (NG) and the spliced joint P1S6. CLEAR DTC. TEST the system for normal operation.

J3 : CHECK THE INPUT CIRCUIT FOR OPEN

1. Remove the powertrain control module (PCM).

2. Measure the resistance between the engine oil temperature sensor electrical connector PI12 pin 1, (WG) and the powertrain control module electrical connector PI1 pin 39, (WG).

•Is the resistance less than 10,000 ohms?

-> Yes
Goto <<J4>>

-> No
REPAIR the circuit between the engine oil temperature sensor electrical connector PI12 pin 1, (WG) and the powertrain control module electrical connector PI1 pin 39, (WG). CLEAR DTC. TEST the system for normal operation.

JC1020100105010X

Fig. 31 Codes P1183 & P1184: Engine Oil Temperature Circuit Malfunction (Part 1 of 2)

J4 : CHECK THE INPUT CIRCUIT FOR SHORT TO GROUND

1. Measure the resistance between the engine oil temperature sensor electrical connector PI12 pin 1, (WG) and ground.

•Is the resistance greater than 10,000 ohms?

-> Yes
Goto <<J5>>

-> No
REPAIR the circuit between the engine oil temperature sensor electrical connector PI12 pin 1, (WG) and the powertrain control module electrical connector PI1 pin 39, (WG). CLEAR DTC. TEST the system for normal operation.

J5 : CHECK THE SIGNAL GROUND CIRCUIT FOR SHORT TO GROUND

1. Raise and support the vehicle.
2. Disconnect both heated exhaust gas oxygen (HEGO) sensor electrical connectors PI6, PI7.
3. Disconnect the engine fuel temperature sensor electrical connector IL9.
4. Disconnect the cylinder head temperature sensor electrical connector PI13.
5. Disconnect both camshaft position sensor electrical connectors PI10, PI11.
6. Disconnect the injection pressure sensor electrical connector IL2.
7. Disconnect the throttle position sensor electrical connector PI16.
8. Measure the resistance between the engine oil temperature sensor electrical connector PI12 pin 2, (NG) and ground.

•Is the resistance less than 10,000 ohms?

-> Yes
REPAIR the circuit between the engine oil temperature sensor electrical connector PI12 pin 2, (NG) and the spliced joint PIS6. INSTALL the powertrain control module (PCM).
CLEAR DTC. TEST the system for normal operation.

-> No
INSTALL a new powertrain control module (PCM).
CLEAR DTC. TEST the system for normal operation.

JC1020100105020X

Fig. 31 Codes P1183 & P1184: Engine Oil Temperature Circuit Malfunction (Part 2 of 2)

K4 : CHECK THE KNOCK SENSOR INPUT CIRCUIT FOR SHORT TO GROUND

1. Measure the resistance between the knock sensor electrical connector PI26 pin 1, (WB) and ground.

•Is the resistance less than 10,000 ohms?

-> Yes
REPAIR the circuit between the knock sensor electrical connector PI26 pin 1, (WB) and the powertrain control module electrical connector PI1 pin 51, (WB). INSTALL the powertrain control module (PCM). CLEAR DTC. TEST the system for normal operation.

-> No
Goto <<K5>>

K5 : CHECK THE KNOCK SENSOR SIGNAL GROUND CIRCUIT FOR OPEN

1. Measure the resistance between the knock sensor electrical connector PI26 pin 2, (SB) and the powertrain control module electrical connector PI1 pin 42, (SB).

•Is the resistance greater than 10,000 ohms?

-> Yes
REPAIR the circuit between the knock sensor electrical connector PI26 pin 2, (SB) and the powertrain control module electrical connector PI1 pin 42, (SB). INSTALL the powertrain control module (PCM). CLEAR DTC. TEST the system for normal operation.

-> No
Goto <<K6>>

K6 : CHECK THE KNOCK SENSOR SIGNAL GROUND CIRCUIT FOR SHORT TO GROUND

1. Measure the resistance between the knock sensor electrical connector PI26 pin 2, (SB) and ground.

•Is the resistance less than 10,000 ohms?

-> Yes
REPAIR the circuit between the knock sensor electrical connector PI26 pin 2, (SB) and the powertrain control module electrical connector PI1 pin 42, (SB). INSTALL the powertrain control module (PCM). CLEAR DTC. TEST the system for normal operation.

-> No
INSTALL a new powertrain control module (PCM).
CLEAR DTC. TEST the system for normal operation.

JC1020100106020X

Fig. 32 Code P0325: Knock Sensor Circuit 1 Malfunction (Part 2 of 2)

K1 : CHECK THE KNOCK SENSOR FOR CORRECT INSTALLATION

1. Switch the ignition switch to the OFF position.
2. Raise and support the vehicle.
3. Check the knock sensor for correct intallation.

•Is the knock sensor correctly installed?

-> Yes
Goto <<K2>>

-> No
INSTALL the knock sensor correctly. CLEAR DTC. TEST the system for normal operation.

K2 : CHECK THE RESISTANCE OF THE KNOCK SENSOR

1. Lower the vehicle.
2. Remove the plastic engine cover.
3. Disconnect the knock sensor electrical connector PI26.
4. Measure the resistance between the knock sensor electrical connector PI26 pin 1, (WB) and pin 2, (SB).

•Is the resistance between 4.5 and 5.5 M ohms?

-> Yes
Goto <<K3>>

-> No
INSTALL a new knock sensor. CLEAR DTC. TEST the system for normal operation.

K3 : CHECK THE KNOCK SENSOR INPUT CIRCUIT FOR OPEN

1. Remove the powertrain control module (PCM).

2. Measure the resistance between the knock sensor electrical connector PI26 pin 1, (WB) and the powertrain control module electrical connector PI1 pin 51, (WB).

•Is the resistance greater than 10,000 ohms?

-> Yes
REPAIR the circuit between the knock sensor electrical connector PI26 pin 1, (WB) and the powertrain control module electrical connector PI1 pin 51, (WB). INSTALL the powertrain control module (PCM).

-> No
Goto <<K4>>

JC1020100106010X

Fig. 32 Code P0325: Knock Sensor Circuit 1 Malfunction (Part 1 of 2)

L1 : CHECK THE KNOCK SENSOR FOR CORRECT INSTALLATION

1. Switch the ignition switch to the OFF position.
2. Raise and support the vehicle.
3. Check the knock sensor for correct intallation

•Is the knock sensor correctly installed?

-> Yes
Goto <<L2>>

-> No
INSTALL the knock sensor correctly. CLEAR DTC. TEST the system for normal operation.

L2 : CHECK THE RESISTANCE OF THE KNOCK SENSOR

1. Lower the vehicle.
2. Remove the plastic engine cover.
3. Disconnect the knock sensor electrical connector PI27.
4. Measure the resistance between the knock sensor electrical connector PI27 pin 1, (WR) and pin 2, (SR).

•Is the resistance between 4.5 and 5.5 M ohms?

-> Yes
Goto <<L3>>

-> No
INSTALL a new knock sensor. CLEAR DTC. TEST the system for normal operation.

L3 : CHECK THE KNOCK SENSOR INPUT CIRCUIT FOR OPEN

1. Remove the powertrain control module (PCM).

2. Measure the resistance between the knock sensor electrical connector PI27 pin 1, (WR) and the powertrain control module electrical connector PI1 pin 52, (WR).

•Is the resistance greater than 10,000 ohms?

-> Yes
REPAIR the circuit between the knock sensor electrical connector PI27 pin 1, (WR) and the powertrain control module electrical connector PI1 pin 52, (WR). INSTALL the powertrain control module (PCM). CLEAR DTC. TEST the system for normal operation.

-> No
Goto <<L4>>

JC1020100107010X

Fig. 33 Code P0330: Knock Sensor Circuit 2 Malfunction (Part 1 of 2)

L4 : CHECK THE KNOCK SENSOR INPUT CIRCUIT FOR SHORT TO GROUND

1. Measure the resistance between the knock sensor electrical connector PI27 pin 1, (WR) and ground.

•Is the resistance less than 10,000 ohms?

-> Yes
REPAIR the circuit between the knock sensor electrical connector PI27 pin 1, (WR) and the powertrain control module electrical connector PI1 pin 52, (WR). INSTALL the powertrain control module (PCM). CLEAR DTC. TEST the system for normal operation.

-> No
Goto **<<L5>>**

L5 : CHECK THE KNOCK SENSOR SIGNAL GROUND CIRCUIT FOR OPEN

1. Measure the resistance between the knock sensor electrical connector PI27 pin 2, (SR) and the powertrain control module electrical connector PI1 pin 43, (SR).

•Is the resistance greater than 10,000 ohms?

-> Yes
REPAIR the circuit between the knock sensor electrical connector PI27 pin 2, (SR) and the powertrain control module electrical connector PI1 pin 43, (SR). INSTALL the powertrain control module (PCM). CLEAR DTC. TEST the system for normal operation.

-> No
Goto **<<L6>>**

L6 : CHECK THE KNOCK SENSOR SIGNAL GROUND CIRCUIT FOR SHORT TO GROUND

1. Measure the resistance between the knock sensor electrical connector PI27 pin 2, (SR) and ground.

•Is the resistance less than 10,000 ohms?

-> Yes
REPAIR the circuit between the knock sensor electrical connector PI27 pin 2, (SR) and the powertrain control module electrical connector PI1 pin 43, (SR). INSTALL the powertrain control module (PCM). CLEAR DTC. TEST the system for normal operation.

-> No
INSTALL a new powertrain control module (PCM).
CLEAR DTC. TEST the system for normal operation.

JC1020100107020X

Fig. 33 Code P0330: Knock Sensor Circuit 2 Malfunction (Part 2 of 2)

M1 : CHECK THE CAMSHAFT POSITION SENSOR FOR CORRECT INSTALLATION

1. Switch the ignition switch to the OFF position.
2. Check the camshaft position sensor for correct intallation

•Is the camshaft position sensor correctly installed?

-> Yes
Goto **<<M2>>**

-> No
INSTALL the camshaft position sensor correctly. CLEAR DTC. TEST the system for normal operation.

M2 : CHECK THE RESISTANCE OF THE CAMSHAFT POSITION SENSOR

1. Remove the plastic engine cover.
2. Disconnect the camshaft position sensor electrical connector PI11.
3. Measure the resistance between the camshaft position sensor electrical connector PI11 pin 1, (WB) and pin 2, (NY).

•Is the resistance between 200 and 400 ohms?

-> Yes
Goto **<<M3>>**

-> No
INSTALL a new camshaft position sensor. CLEAR DTC. TEST the system for normal operation.

M3 : CHECK THE CAMSHAFT POSITION SENSOR SIGNAL GROUND CIRCUIT FOR OPEN

1. Measure the resistance between the camshaft position sensor electrical connector PI11 pin 2, (NY) and ground.

•Is the resistance greater than 10,000 ohms?

-> Yes
REPAIR the circuit between the camshaft position sensor electrical connector PI11 pin 2, (NY) and the spliced joint PIS6. INSTALL the powertrain control module (PCM).
CLEAR DTC. TEST the system for normal operation.

-> No
Goto **<<M4>>**

JC1020100108010X

Fig. 34 Code P0340: Camshaft Position Sensor Circuit Malfunction (Part 1 of 2)

M4 : CHECK THE CAMSHAFT POSITION SENSOR INPUT CIRCUIT FOR OPEN

1. Remove the powertrain control module (PCM).

2. Measure the resistance between the camshaft position sensor electrical connector PI11 pin 1, (WB) and the powertrain control module electrical connector PI1 pin 53, (WB).

•Is the resistance greater than 10,000 ohms?

-> Yes
REPAIR the circuit between the camshaft position sensor electrical connector PI11 pin 1, (WB) and the powertrain control module electrical connector PI1 pin 53, (WB). INSTALL the powertrain control module (PCM). CLEAR DTC. TEST the system for normal operation.

-> No
Goto **<<M5>>**

M5 : CHECK THE CAMSHAFT POSITION SENSOR INPUT CIRCUIT FOR SHORT TO GROUND

1. Measure the resistance between the camshaft position sensor electrical connector PI11 pin 1, (WB) and ground.

•Is the resistance less than 10,000 ohms?

-> Yes
REPAIR the circuit between the camshaft position sensor electrical connector PI11 pin 1, (WB) and the powertrain control module electrical connector PI1 pin 53, (WB). INSTALL the powertrain control module (PCM). CLEAR DTC. TEST the system for normal operation.

-> No
Goto **<<M6>>**

M6 : CHECK THE CAMSHAFT POSITION SENSOR SIGNAL GROUND CIRCUIT FOR SHORT TO GROUND

1. Raise and support the vehicle.
2. Disconnect the left-hand camshaft position sensor electrical connector PI10.
3. Disconnect both heated exhaust gas oxygen (HEGO) sensor electrical connectors PI6, PI7.
4. Disconnect the engine oil temperature sensor electrical connector PI12.
5. Disconnect the engine fuel temperature sensor electrical connector IL9.
6. Disconnect the cylinder head temperature sensor electrical connector PI13.
7. Disconnect the injection pressure sensor electrical connector IL2.
8. Disconnect the throttle position sensor electrical connector PI16.
9. Measure the resistance between the camshaft position sensor electrical connector PI11 pin 2, (NY) and ground.

•Is the resistance less than 10,000 ohms?

-> Yes
REPAIR the circuit between the camshaft position sensor electrical connector PI11 pin 2, (NY) and the spliced joint P1S6. INSTALL the powertrain control module (PCM).
CLEAR DTC. TEST the system for normal operation.

-> No
INSTALL a new powertrain control module (PCM).
CLEAR DTC. TEST the system for normal operation.

JC1020100108020X

Fig. 34 Code P0340: Camshaft Position Sensor Circuit Malfunction (Part 2 of 2)

N1 : CHECK THE CAMSHAFT POSITION SENSOR FOR CORRECT INSTALLATION

1. Switch the ignition switch to the OFF position.
2. Check the camshaft position sensor for correct installation

•Is the camshaft position sensor correctly installed?

-> Yes
Goto **<<N2>>**

-> No
INSTALL the camshaft position sensor correctly. CLEAR DTC. TEST the system for normal operation.7

N2 : CHECK THE RESISTANCE OF THE CAMSHAFT POSITION SENSOR

1. Remove the plastic engine cover.
2. Disconnect the camshaft position sensor electrical connector PI10.
3. Measure the resistance between the camshaft position sensor electrical connector PI10 pin 2, (WP) and pin 1, (NW).

•Is the resistance between 200 and 400 ohms?

-> Yes
Goto **<<N3>>**

-> No
INSTALL a new camshaft position sensor. CLEAR DTC. TEST the system for normal operation.

N3 : CHECK THE CAMSHAFT POSITION SENSOR SIGNAL GROUND CIRCUIT FOR OPEN

1. Measure the resistance between the camshaft position sensor electrical connector PI10 pin 1, (NW) and ground.

•Is the resistance greater than 10,000 ohms?

-> Yes
REPAIR the circuit between the camshaft position sensor electrical connector PI10 pin 1, (NW) and the spliced joint P1S6. INSTALL the powertrain control module (PCM).
CLEAR DTC. TEST the system for normal operation.

-> No
Goto **<<N4>>**

JC1020100109010X

Fig. 35 Code P0341: Camshaft Position Sensor Circuit B Malfunction (Part 1 of 2)

N4 : CHECK THE CAMSHAFT POSITION SENSOR INPUT CIRCUIT FOR OPEN

1. Remove the powertrain control module (PCM).

2. Measure the resistance between the camshaft position sensor electrical connector PI10 pin 2, (WP) and the powertrain control module electrical connector PI1 pin 54, (WP).

•Is the resistance greater than 10,000 ohms?

-> Yes
REPAIR the circuit between the camshaft position sensor electrical connector PI10 pin 2, (WP) and the powertrain control module electrical connector PI1 pin 54, (WP). INSTALL the powertrain control module (PCM). CLEAR DTC. TEST the system for normal operation.

-> No
Goto **<<N5>>**

N5 : CHECK THE CAMSHAFT POSITION SENSOR INPUT CIRCUIT FOR SHORT TO GROUND

1. Measure the resistance between the camshaft position sensor electrical connector PI10 pin 2, (WP) and ground.

•Is the resistance less than 10,000 ohms?

-> Yes
REPAIR the circuit between the camshaft position sensor electrical connector PI10 pin 2, (WP) and the powertrain control module electrical connector PI1 pin 54, (WP). INSTALL the powertrain control module (PCM). CLEAR DTC. TEST the system for normal operation.

-> No
Goto **<<N6>>**

N6 : CHECK THE CAMSHAFT POSITION SENSOR SIGNAL GROUND CIRCUIT FOR SHORT TO GROUND

1. Disconnect the right-hand camshaft position sensor electrical connector PI11.
2. Disconnect both heated exhaust gas oxygen (HEGO) sensor electrical connectors PI6, PI7.
3. Disconnect the engine oil temperature sensor electrical connector PI12.
4. Disconnect the engine fuel temperature sensor electrical connector IL9.
5. Disconnect the cylinder head temperature sensor electrical connector PI13.
6. Disconnect the injection pressure sensor electrical connector IL2.
7. Disconnect the throttle position sensor electrical connector PI16.
8. Measure the resistance between the camshaft position sensor electrical connector PI10 pin 1, (NW) and ground.

•Is the resistance less than 10,000 ohms?

-> Yes
REPAIR the circuit between the camshaft position sensor electrical connector PI10 pin 1, (NW) and the spliced joint P1S6. INSTALL the powertrain control module (PCM).
CLEAR DTC. TEST the system for normal operation.

-> No
INSTALL a new powertrain control module (PCM).
CLEAR DTC. TEST the system for normal operation.

JC1020100109020X

Fig. 35 Code P0341: Camshaft Position Sensor Circuit B Malfunction (Part 2 of 2)

P1 : CHECK THE RESISTANCE OF THE VARIABLE CAMSHAFT TIMING OIL CONTROL SOLENOID

1. Switch the ignition switch to the OFF position.
2. Disconnect the left-hand variable camshaft timing oil control solenoid PI4.
3. Measure the resistance between the variable camshaft timing oil control solenoid electrical connector PI4 pin 1, (GW) and pin 2, (WP).

•Is the resistance between 5 and 20 ohms?

-> Yes
Goto **<<P2>>**

-> No
INSTALL a new left-hand variable camshaft timing oil control solenoid. For additional information, refer to **<<Variable Camshaft Timing Oil Control Solenoid>>**CLEAR DTC. TEST the system for normal operation.

P2 : CHECK THE VOLTAGE SUPPLY TO THE VARIABLE CAMSHAFT TIMING OIL CONTROL SOLENOID AT PIN 1

1. Switch the ignition switch to the RUN position.
2. Measure the resistance between the variable camshaft timing oil control solenoid electrical connector PI4 pin 1, (GW) and ground.

•Is the voltage greater than 10.5 volts?

-> Yes
Goto **<<P3>>**

-> No
REPAIR the circuit between the variable camshaft timing oil control solenoid electrical connector PI4 pin 1, (GW) and the spliced joint FHS 10. CLEAR DTC. TEST the system for normal operation.

P3 : CHECK THE VARIABLE CAMSHAFT TIMING OIL CONTROL SOLENOID OUTPUT CIRCUIT FOR OPEN

1. Remove the powertrain control module (PCM). For additional information, refer to**<<Powertrain Control Module (PCM)>>**
2. Measure the resistance between the variable camshaft timing oil control solenoid electrical connector PI4 pin 2, (WP) and the powertrain control module electrical connector PI1 pin 33, (WP).

•Is the resistance greater than 10,000 ohms?

-> Yes
REPAIR the circuit between the variable camshaft timing oil control solenoid electrical connector PI4 pin 2, (WP) and the powertrain control module electrical connector PI1 pin 33, (WP). INSTALL the powertrain control module (PCM). For additional information, refer to**<<Powertrain Control Module (PCM)>>**CLEAR DTC. TEST the system for normal operation.

-> No
Goto **<<P4>>**

JC1020100111010X

Fig. 37 Code P1385: Variable Cam Timing Solenoid B Malfunction (Part 1 of 2)

O1 : CHECK THE RESISTANCE OF THE VARIABLE CAMSHAFT TIMING OIL CONTROL SOLENOID

1. Switch the ignition switch to the OFF position.
2. Disconnect the right-hand variable camshaft timing oil control solonoid PI5.
3. Measure the resistance between the variable camshaft timing oil control solenoid electrical connector PI5 pin 1, (GO) and pin 2, (WB).

•Is the resistance between 5 and 20 ohms?

-> Yes
Goto **<<O2>>**

-> No
INSTALL a new right-hand variable camshaft timing oil control solenoid.
CLEAR DTC. TEST the system for normal operation.

O2 : CHECK THE VOLTAGE SUPPLY TO THE VARIABLE CAMSHAFT TIMING OIL CONTROL SOLENOID AT PIN 1

1. Switch the ignition switch to the RUN position.
2. Measure the resistance between the variable camshaft timing oil control solenoid electrical connector PI5 pin 1, (GO) and ground.

•Is the voltage greater than 10 volts?

-> Yes
Goto **<<O3>>**

-> No
REPAIR the circuit between the variable camshaft timing oil control solenoid electrical connector PI5 pin 1, (GO) and the spliced joint FHS 10. CLEAR DTC. TEST the system for normal operation.

O3 : CHECK THE VARIABLE CAMSHAFT TIMING OIL CONTROL SOLENOID OUTPUT CIRCUIT FOR OPEN

1. Remove the powertrain control module (PCM).

2. Measure the resistance between the variable camshaft timing oil control solenoid electrical connector PI5 pin 2, (WB) and the powertrain control module electrical connector PI1, pin 10 (WP).

•Is the resistance greater than 10,000 ohms?

-> Yes
REPAIR the circuit between the variable camshaft timing oil control solenoid electrical connector PI5 pin 2, (WB) and the powertrain control module electrical connector PI1 pin 10, (WP). INSTALL the powertrain control module (PCM). CLEAR DTC. TEST the system for normal operation.

-> No
Goto **<<O4>>**

JC1020100110010X

Fig. 36 Code P1380: Variable Cam Timing Solenoid A Malfunction (Part 1 of 2)

O4 : CHECK THE VARIABLE CAMSHAFT TIMING OIL CONTROL SOLENOID OUTPUT CIRCUIT FOR SHORT TO GROUND

1. Measure the resistance between the variable camshaft timing oil control solenoid electrical connector PI5 pin 2, (WB) and ground.

•Is the resistance less than 10,000 ohms?

-> Yes
REPAIR the circuit between the variable camshaft timing oil control solenoid electrical connector PI5 pin 2, (WB) and the powertrain control module electrical connector PI1 pin 10, (WP). INSTALL the powertrain control module (PCM). CLEAR DTC. TEST the system for normal operation.

-> No
INSTALL a new powertrain control module (PCM).
CLEAR DTC. TEST the system for normal operation.

JC1020100110020X

Fig. 36 Code P1380: Variable Cam Timing Solenoid A Malfunction (Part 2 of 2)

P4 : CHECK THE VARIABLE CAMSHAFT TIMING OIL CONTROL SOLENOID OUTPUT CIRCUIT FOR SHORT TO GROUND

1. Measure the resistance between the variable camshaft timing oil control solenoid electrical connector P14 pin 2, (WP) and ground.

•Is the resistance less than 10,000 ohms?

-> Yes
REPAIR the circuit between the variable camshaft timing oil control solenoid electrical connector P14 pin 2, (WP) and the powertrain control module electrical connector PI1 pin 33, (WP). INSTALL the powertrain control module (PCM). For additional information, refer to**<<Powertrain Control Module (PCM)>>**CLEAR DTC. TEST the system for normal operation.

-> No
INSTALL a new powertrain control module (PCM). For additional information, refer to**<<Powertrain Control Module (PCM)>>**CLEAR DTC. TEST the system for normal operation.

JC1020100111020X

Fig. 37 Code P1385: Variable Cam Timing Solenoid B Malfunction (Part 2 of 2)

SYSTEM SERVICE

Fuel System Pressure Relief

1. Ensure ignition switch is Off.
2. Remove schrader valve cap.
3. Connect fuel pressure gauge to schrader valve.
4. Catch any displaced fuel in a suitable container.
5. Depressurize system according to tool manufacturer's instructions.
6. Close fuel container lid securely, remove tool and install valve cap.

Component Replacement

FUEL INJECTOR

1. Relieve fuel system pressure as outlined under "Fuel System Pressure Relief."
2. Disconnect fuel pulse damper electrical connector, then the vacuum hose.
3. Remove fuel supply manifold retaining bolt, then detach fuel supply manifold and lower intake manifold.
4. Remove retaining bolts from lefthand lower intake manifold, then the manifold.
5. Remove retaining bolts from righthand lower intake manifold, then the manifold.
6. Remove fuel injectors from engine.
7. Reverse procedure to install. **Install new fuel injector O-rings and coat O-ring seals with clean engine oil.**

SUPPLY MANIFOLD

Refer to "Fuel Injector" in this section for replacement procedure.

CAMSHAFT POSITION SENSOR

1. Raise and support vehicle.
2. Disconnect electrical connector from camshaft position sensor.
3. Remove camshaft position sensor from vehicle.
4. Reverse procedure to install.

Q1 : CHECK THE VOLTAGE SUPPLY TO THE POWERTRAIN CONTROL MODULE

1. Switch the ignition switch to the OFF position.
2. Remove the powertrain control module (PCM). For additional information, refer to**<<Powertrain Control Module (PCM)>>**
3. Switch the ignition switch to the RUN position.
4. Measure the voltage between the powertrain control module electrical connector FH1 pin 49, (SP) and ground.

•Is the voltage greater than 10.5 volts?

-> Yes
INSTALL a new powertrain control module (PCM). For additional information, refer to**<<Powertrain Control Module (PCM)>>**CLEAR DTC. TEST the system for normal operation.

-> No
Repair the circuit between the powertrain control module electrical connector FH1 pin 49, (SP) and the spliced joint FHS-10. CLEAR DTC. TEST the system for normal operation.

JC1020100112000X

Fig. 38 Code P1633: KAM Voltage Too Low

CRANKSHAFT POSITION SENSOR

1. Raise and support vehicle.
2. Disconnect electrical connector from crankshaft position sensor.
3. Remove crankshaft position sensor from vehicle.
4. Reverse procedure to install.

THROTTLE POSITION SENSOR

1. Disconnect throttle position sensor electrical connector.
2. Remove retaining screws, then the sensor.
3. Reverse procedure to install.

THROTTLE BODY

1. Turn Expansion cap counterclockwise a quarter turn to relieve cooling system pressure, then tighten expansion tank cap.
2. Disconnect intake air temperature sensor electrical connector, then the engine breather hoses.
3. Remove air cleaner outlet tube, then disconnect throttle position sensor and electronic throttle body electrical connectors.
4. Detach throttle body, then discard gasket.
5. Disconnect coolant hoses and remove throttle body.
6. Reverse procedure to install.

MASS AIR FLOW (MAF) SENSOR

1. Disconnect electrical connector from MAF.
2. Loosen hose clamp, then remove air cleaner cover.
3. Remove mass air flow sensor from vehicle.
4. Reverse procedure to install.

HEATED OXYGEN SENSOR

1. Raise and support vehicle. **Ensure not to damage sensor casting or twist cable.**
2. Disconnect electrical connector from oxygen sensor.
3. Remove sensor from vehicle.
4. Reverse procedure to install.

INTAKE AIR TEMPERATURE (IAT) SENSOR

1. Disconnect electrical connector from IAT sensor.
2. Remove sensor from vehicle.
3. Reverse procedure to install.

POWERTRAIN CONTROL MODULE (PCM)

1. Raise and support vehicle, then detach front lefthand splash shield.
2. Disconnect electrical connectors from PCM.
3. Lower vehicle, then remove retaining screw and lower trim panel.
4. Remove weather strip from door, then the scuff panel trim and cowl side trim panel.
5. Remove PCM bracket retaining nut, then the bracket and power control module.
6. Reverse procedure to install.

4.0L Engine Fuel Injection

NOTE: If Unsure Of The System Used On The Vehicle Being Serviced, Refer To "The Engine Systems Identification Chart."Further Assistance For The Proper Use Of Information Contained In This Section Can Also Be Found In The Front Of This Tabbed Section Under "How To Use This Manual"

NOTE: On Air Bag Equipped Models, Refer To "Air Bag System Precautions" Located In The Front Of This Manual For System Disarming & Arming Procedures.

NOTE: Refer To "Computer Relearn Procedures" Located In The Front Of This Manual When Battery Power To The Computer Has Been Interrupted.

NOTE: Prior To Performing Any Service Operations Listed In This Section, Consult The "Technical Service Bulletins" Section For Related Information.

NOTE: Electrical Symbol & Wire Color Code Identification Located In The Front Of This Manual May Be Used As An Aid When Using Wiring Circuits Found In This Section.

INDEX

	Page No.
Description	12-29
Camshaft Position	12-30
Climate Control Compressor	12-29
Cranking Signal	12-29
ECM	12-29
Electronic Throttle Body	12-29
Engine Coolant Temperature (ECT) Sensor	12-29
Engine Speed & Crankshaft Position	12-30
Exhaust Gas Recirculation (EGR)	12-30
Heated Oxygen Sensor (HO_2S)	12-30
Intake Air Temperature (IAT)	12-29
Knock Sensor	12-30
Mass Air Flow Meter (MAF)	12-29
Oxygen Sensor (O_2)	12-30
Variable Valve Timing (VVT)	12-30
Diagnosis & Testing	12-30
Accessing Diagnostic Trouble Codes	12-30
Clearing Diagnostic Trouble Codes	12-67
Connector Terminal Identification	12-31
Diagnostic Tests	12-31
Code P0101: Mass Air Flow Circuit Malfunction	12-31
Code P0111 & P0112: Intake Air Temperature Sensor Malfunction	12-32
Code P0113: Intake Air Temperature Sensor Circuit High Input	12-39
Code P0117: ECT Sensor Circuit Low Input	12-39
Code P0118: ECT Circuit High Input	12-39
Code P0121: Throttle Position Sensor Malfunction	12-40
Code P0133: O_2 Sensor Circuit Slow Response (Bank 1 Sensor 1)	12-42
Code P0140: O_2 Sensor No Activity Detected (Bank 1 Sensor 2)	12-44
Code P0153: O_2 Sensor Circuit Slow Response (Bank 2 Sensor 1)	12-47
Code P0160: O_2 Sensor No Activity Detected (Bank 2 Sensor 2)	12-49
Codes P0131 P0132 & P0135: O_2 Sensor Circuit Malfunction	12-41
Codes P0137 & P0138: O_2 Sensor Circuit Malfunction (Bank 1 Sensor 2)	12-43
Codes P0151, P0152 & P0155: O_2 Sensor Circuit Malfunction (Bank 2 Sensor 1)	12-46
Codes P0157 & P0158: O_2 Sensor Circuit Malfunction (Bank 2 Sensor 2)	12-48
Code P0335: Crankshaft Position Sensor Circuit Malfunction	12-53
Code P0400: EGR Flow Malfunction	12-55
Code P0405: EGR Sensor "A" Circuit Low Input	12-56
Code P0406: EGR Sensor "B" Circuit Low Input	12-56
Code P0441: EVAP System Improper Purge Flow	12-57
Code P0442: Evaporative Emissions Control System Leak Detected	12-57
Code P0460: Fuel Level Sensor Circuit Malfunction	12-59
Code P0560: System Voltage Malfunction	12-59
Code P0603: Internal Control Module Keep Alive Memory Error	12-59
Code P1224: Electronic Throttle Control Position Error	12-60
Code P1226: Mechanical Guard Circuit Range Performance	12-61
Code P1227 & P1228 Mechanical Guard Circuit Malfunction	12-61
Code P1229: Throttle Position Error	12-61
Code P1230: Fuel Pump Relay Malfunction	12-61
Code P1240: Sensor Power Supply Malfunction	12-62
Code P1243: Sensor Power Supply Analogue Ground Malfunction	12-64
Code P1367: Ignition System Failure	12-65
Code P1368: Ignition System Failure	12-65
Code P1392 & P1397: VVT Solenoid Circuit Low Input	12-65
Code P1396: VVT Solenoid Malfunction	12-66
Code P1474: Intercooler Coolant Pump Relay	12-66
Code P1516: Park/Neutral Switch	12-67
Code P1609: Internal Control Module Keep Alive Memory Error	12-67
Codes P0102, P0103 & P1104: Mass Air Flow Circuit Malfunction	12-32
Codes P0116 & P0125: ECT Sensor Performance Fault Condition	12-39
Codes P0121, P0122, P0123, P0222 & P0223: Throttle Position Sensor Malfunction	12-40

Page No.

Codes P0122 & P0222: Throttle Position Sensor 12-40
Codes P0123 & P0223: Throttle Position Sensor 12-40
Codes P0201, P0202, P0203, P0204, P0205, P0206, P0207 & P0208: Injector Circuit Malfunction Normally Aspired Engine 12-51
Codes P0201, P0202, P0203, P0204, P0205, P0206, P0207 & P0208: Injector Circuit Malfunction Supercharged Engine 12-51
Codes P0327, P0328, P0332 & P0333: Knock Sensor Circuit 12-52
Codes P0340 & P1336: Camshaft Position Sensor Malfunction 12-53
Codes P0351, P0352, P0353, P0354, P0355, P0356, P0357 & P0358: Ignition Coil Primary Circuit Malfunction 12-54
Codes P0400, P0405 & P0406: EGR Malfunction 12-56
Codes P0444 & P0445: EVAP System Purge Control Valve Circuit Malfunction........... 12-57
Codes P0447 & P0448: Evaporative Emission Control System Canister Close Valve (CCV) Circuit Open/Short Circuit........... 12-58
Codes P0452 & P0453: Evaporative Emission Control System Pressure Sensor Low/High Input 12-58
Codes P0506 & P0507: Idle Speed Control System Malfunction 12-59
Codes P1241 & P1242: Sensor Power Supply 12-64
Codes P1245 & P1246: Crank Signal Low Circuit........... 12-64
Codes P1393 & P1398: VVT Solenoid Circuit High Input .. 12-65
Diagnostic Trouble Code Interpretation 12-30
Wiring Diagrams................ 12-33
Precautions...................... 12-29
Air Bag Systems................ 12-29
Battery Ground Cable........... 12-29
Sensor & Fuel Injector Specifications 12-29
System Service 12-67
Component Replacement 12-67
Engine Control Module (ECM)...................... 12-68
Fuel Injector 12-67
Fuel Rail..................... 12-68
Intake Air Temperature (IAT) Sensor 12-68
Mass Air Flow (MAF) Meter... 12-68
Throttle Body 12-68
Throttle Cable 12-68
Fuel System Pressure Relief.... 12-67

SENSOR & FUEL INJECTOR SPECIFICATIONS

Sensor	Year	Nominal Value
Crankshaft Position (CKP)	1998–2001	950–1250 Ohms
Fuel Injector	1998–2001	12–18 Ohms
Knock Sensor (KS)	1998–2001	500–620 kOhms
Oxygen Sensor (O_2S)	1998–2001	.5 Ohms

PRECAUTIONS

Air Bag Systems

Refer to "Air Bag System Precautions" in the front of this manual for system disarming and arming procedures.

Battery Ground Cable

Prior to service, disconnect battery ground cable and isolate as required.

DESCRIPTION

ECM

The ECM controls all engine functions and exhaust emissions. A microprocessor within the ECM receives signals from various sensors. The ECM uses this information to control the following: fuel injection, idle speed, ignition, evaporative loss system, engine cooling fans and climate control compressor clutch demand. Adaptive functions are incorporated in the ECM to cater for continuous adjustments to its computations to suit prevailing conditions. Because the system also controls emissions to suit all modes, neither CO levels or idle speed require service attention or adjustment, except of course should an error occur.

Electronic Throttle Body

The electronic throttle body assembly, in response to signals from both the driver and the ECM, adjusts idle speed, cruise control, traction control, power limitation and catalyst warm-up.

Mass Air Flow Meter (MAF)

This sensor measures air flow through the engine inlet system and is calibrated to measure kg/hour. The sensor is located in the air flow meter assembly and outputs an analogue voltage signal to the ECM.

Intake Air Temperature (IAT)

The IAT sensor measures inlet air temperature. The sensor is located in the air flow meter assembly and outputs an analogue voltage signal to the ECM. Should the sensor fail, the ECM will substitute a default value equal to 122°F.

Engine Coolant Temperature (ECT) Sensor

The sensor outputs a voltage signal to the ECM which decreases as temperature increases.

Climate Control Compressor

The ECM will allow the compressor clutch to be engaged if the engine temperature and load demand are normal. Should the driver require maximum power or the coolant temperature be high, the request will be denied.

Cranking Signal

The ECM reacts to a signal from the

Body Processor Module (BPM) when the starter motor relay is energized. This signal is used to trigger starting, fuel and ignition strategies.

Engine Speed & Crankshaft Position

Engine speed and crank position are monitored by a sensor which is mounted on the cylinder block behind the crankshaft drive plate. It indicates rotational speed to the ECM in the form of 12 pulses per crank revolution. Engine speed is used for both fuel and ignition synchronization, as well as other functions.

Camshaft Position

The camshaft position sensor provides one signal every 720 degrees of crankshaft rotation indicating a cylinder at TDC prior to the firing stroke.

Variable Valve Timing (VVT)

By energizing a solenoid to allow the passage of pressurized oil on each of the inlet camshaft drives, the ECM can vary by a single stepped amount, the relative timing of the intake valves.

Knock Sensor

This sensor uses a piezo-electric sensing element to detect knock which may occur under acceleration at critical conditions. Should detonation be present the ECM will retard ignition timing of individual cylinders.

Exhaust Gas Recirculation (EGR)

The EGR valve (where installed) reduces NOx emissions by recirculating a portion of the exhaust gases back into the inlet manifold

Oxygen Sensor (O_2)

These sensors, one per bank, are situated downstream of the catalyst. The comparison of upstream and downstream signals allows determination of catalyst conversion efficiency.

Heated Oxygen Sensor (HO_2S)

The HO_2S, one per bank, are situated upstream of the catalysts. Integral to the sensors are heaters (under ECM control) which allow the sensors to reach their operating temperature as soon as possible after engine start. A comparison between the level of oxygen in the exhaust gas to that in the atmosphere produces an output signal. This signal is used by the engine closed loop fuel strategy to make fueling corrections and so control overall emission levels.

DIAGNOSIS & TESTING

Accessing Diagnostic Trouble Codes

Connect a suitable programmed scan tool to the Data Link Connector (DLC) located on the instrument panel adjacent to the driver's side A pillar.

Follow tool manufacturer's instructions to read codes.

Diagnostic Trouble Code Interpretation

Refer to **Fig. 1** for diagnostic trouble code interpretation.

Code	Description
P0101	Mass Air Flow Circuit Malfunction
P0102	Mass Air Flow Circuit Low Input
P0103	Mass Air Flow Circuit High Input
P0111	IAT Circuit Malfunction
P0112	IAT Circuit Low Input
P0113	IAT Circuit High Input
P0116	ECT Circuit Malfunction
P0117	ECT Circuit Low Input
P0118	ECT Circuit High Input
P0121	TPS Circuit Malfunction (Sensor A)
P0122	TPS Circuit Low Input (Sensor A)
P0123	TPS Circuit High Input (Sensor A)
P0125	Insufficient Coolant Temperature For Closed Loop Fuel Control
P0131	O_2 Sensor Circuit Low Voltage (Bank 1 Sensor 1)
P0132	O_2 Sensor Circuit High Voltage (Bank 1 Sensor 1)
P0133	O_2 Sensor Circuit Slow Response (Bank 1 Sensor 1)
P0135	O_2 Heater Circuit Malfunction (Bank 1 Sensor 1)
P0137	O_2 Sensor Low Voltage (Bank 1 Sensor 2)
P0138	O_2 Sensor Circuit High Voltage (Bank 1 Sensor 2)
P0140	O_2 Sensor No Activity Detected (Bank 1 Sensor 2)
P0151	O_2 Sensor Low Voltage (Bank 2 Sensor 1)
P0152	O_2 Sensor Circuit High Voltage (Bank 2 Sensor 1)
P0153	O_2 Sensor Circuit Slow Response (Bank 2 Sensor 1)
P0155	O_2 Heater Circuit Malfunction (Bank 2 Sensor 1)
P0157	O_2 Sensor Low Voltage (Bank 2 Sensor 2)
P0158	O_2 Sensor Circuit High Voltage (Bank 2 Sensor 2)
P0160	O_2 Sensor No Activity Detected (Bank 2 Sensor 2)
P0201	Injector Circuit Malfunction (Cylinder 1)
P0202	Injector Circuit Malfunction (Cylinder 2)
P0203	Injector Circuit Malfunction (Cylinder 3)
P0204	Injector Circuit Malfunction (Cylinder 4)
P0205	Injector Circuit Malfunction (Cylinder 5)
P0206	Injector Circuit Malfunction (Cylinder 6)
P0207	Injector Circuit Malfunction (Cylinder 7)
P0208	Injector Circuit Malfunction (Cylinder 8)
P0222	TPS Circuit Low Input (Sensor B)
P0223	TPS Circuit High Voltage (Sensor B)
P0327	Knock Sensor Circuit Low Input (Sensor 1)
P0328	Knock Sensor Circuit High Input (Sensor 1)
P0332	Knock Sensor Circuit Low Input (Sensor 2)
P0333	Knock Sensor Circuit High Input (Sensor 2)
P0335	Crankshaft Position Sensor Circuit Malfunction
P0340	Camshaft Position Sensor Circuit Malfunction
P0351	Ignition Coil Circuit Malfunction (Coil 1A)
P0352	Ignition Coil Circuit Malfunction (Coil 2A)
P0353	Ignition Coil Circuit Malfunction (Coil 3A)

Fig. 1 Diagnostic Trouble Code Interpretation (Part 1 of 2)

Wiring Diagrams

Refer to **Figs. 2 through 4** for wiring diagrams.

Connector Terminal Identification

Refer to **Fig. 5** for connector terminal identification.

Diagnostic Tests

CODE P0101: MASS AIR FLOW CIRCUIT MALFUNCTION

Tachometer Inspection

1. Ensure tachometer is working properly.
2. If tachometer is working properly, proceed to "Throttle Function."
3. If tachometer is not working properly, rectify possible crank position sensor faults (DTC P0335) and test system for normal operation.

Throttle Function

1. Ensure throttle is operating properly.
2. If throttle operation is satisfactory, proceed to "Air Intake System Inspection."
3. If throttle operation is not satisfactory, correct possible throttle blade or position sensor fault(s) (DTCs P0121, 0122, 0123, 0222, 0223) and test system for normal operation.

Air Intake System Inspection

1. Ensure air cleaner is free from obstruction
2. Inspect air meter to throttle body seal.
3. Inspect engine breather to inlet duct.
4. If air intake system is operating properly, proceed to "Inspect Continuity Harness."
5. If air intake system is not operating properly, correct fault and test system for normal operation.

Inspect Continuity Harness

1. Disconnect EM12 and PI35 connectors.
2. Measure resistance between EM12 terminal No. 13 and PI35 terminal No. 2.
3. If resistance is less than .5 ohms, proceed to "Inspect Continuity MAF Grounds."
4. If resistance is more than .5 ohms, repair harness/connector PI1/52 and test system for normal operation.

Inspect Continuity MAF Grounds

1. Measure resistance between EM12 terminal No. 18 and connector PI35 terminal No. 5. If resistance is less than .5 ohms, proceed to step next step. If resistance is more than .5 ohms, proceed to last step.
2. Measure resistance between EM12 terminal No. 19 and connector PI35 terminal No. 5. If resistance is less than .5 ohms, proceed to "Inspect Harness Short To Ground." If resistance is more than .5 ohms, proceed to next step.
3. Inspect EM12, PI35 and PI1 for corrosion, bent/pushed back pins or locate and repair harness/splice PIS10 fault. Test system for normal operation.

Code	Description
P0354	Ignition Coil Circuit Malfunction (Coil 4A)
P0355	Ignition Coil Circuit Malfunction (Coil 1B)
P0356	Ignition Coil Circuit Malfunction (Coil 2B)
P0357	Ignition Coil Circuit Malfunction (Coil 3B)
P0358	Ignition Coil Circuit Malfunction (Coil 4B)
P0400	EGR Flow Malfunction
P0405	EGR Sensor Circuit Low Input (Sensor A)
P0406	EGR Sensor Circuit Low Input (Sensor B)
P0441	EVAP System Improper Purge Flow
P0442	Evaporate Emissions Control System Leak Detected
P0444	EVAP System Purge Control Valve Circuit Open
P0445	EVAP System Purge Control Valve Circuit Shorted
P0447	Evaporative Emission Control System Canister Close Valve (CCV) Circuit Open Circuit
P0448	Evaporative Emission Control System Canister Close Valve (CCV) Circuit Short Circuit
P0452	Evaporative Emission Control System Pressure Sensor Low Input
P0453	Evaporative Emission Control System Pressure Sensor High Input
P0460	Fuel Level Sensor Circuit Malfunction
P0506	Idle Control System RPM Lower Than Expected
P0507	Idle Control System RPM Higher Than Expected
P0560	System Voltage Malfunction
P0603	Internal Keep Alive Memory Error
P0603	Internal Keep Alive Memory Error
P1104	Mass Air Flow Ground Malfunction
P1224	Electronic Throttle Control Position Error
P1226	Mechanical Guard Circuit Malfunction
P1227	Mechanical Guard Circuit Low Input
P1228	Mechanical Guard Circuit High Input
P1229	Throttle Control Circuit Malfunction
P1230	Fuel Pump Relay Malfunction
P1240	Sensor Power Supply Malfunction
P1241	Sensor Power Supply Low Input
P1242	Sensor Power Supply High Input
P1243	Sensor Power Supply Analogue Ground Malfunction
P1245	Crank Signal Low Input
P1246	Crank Signal High Input
P1336	Crank/Camshaft Sensor Malfunction
P1367	Ignition System Failure
P1368	Ignition System Failure
P1392	VVT Solenoid Circuit A Low Input
P1393	VVT Solenoid Circuit A High Input
P1396	VVT Solenoid B Malfunction
P1397	VVT Solenoid B Low Input
P1398	VVT Solenoid Circuit B High Input
P1474	Intercooler Pump Relay
P1516	Park/Neutral Switch
P1609	ECM Internal Control Module CPU To CPU Communication Failure

Fig. 1 Diagnostic Trouble Code Interpretation (Part 2 of 2)

Inspect Harness Short To Ground

1. Measure insulation resistance between EM12 terminal No. 13 and EM12 terminal No. 18. If resistance is more than 10 Mohms, proceed to next step. If resistance is less than 10 Mohms, proceed to last step.
2. Measure insulation resistance between EM12 terminal No. 13 and EM12 terminal No. 19. If resistance is more than 10 Mohms, proceed to "Inspect For Short To B+." If resistance is less than 10 Mohms, proceed to next step.
3. Inspect EM12, PI35 and PI1 for corrosion, bent/pushed back pins or locate and repair harness fault. Test system for normal operation.

Inspect For Short To B+

1. Measure voltage between EM12 terminal No. 13 and EM12 terminal No. 18. If voltage is zero, proceed to next step. If voltage is more than zero, proceed to last step.
2. Measure voltage between EM12 terminal No. 13 and EM12 terminal No. 19. If voltage is zero, proceed to "Measure Sensor Output." If voltage is more than zero, proceed to next step.
3. Inspect EM12, PI35 and PI1 for corrosion, bent/pushed back pins or locate and repair harness fault. Test system for normal operation.

Measure Sensor Output

1. Using appropriate leads, link PI35/1 and PI35/5 to MAF corresponding pins.
2. Measure output voltage at MAF pin 2 and pin 5 (ground) with engine at idle speed and normal operating temperature.
3. If output voltage is between .7–1.7 volts, proceed to "End." If output voltage is not .7–1.7 volts, replace air flow meter and proceed to "End."

End

1. Perform appropriate service drive cycle and inspect for presence of DTC.
2. If fault code has cleared, fault condition has been corrected and no further diagnosis is required.
3. If fault code has not cleared, further diagnosis is required.

CODES P0102, P0103 & P1104: MASS AIR FLOW CIRCUIT MALFUNCTION

Measure Supply Voltage

1. Measure voltage at PI35/1.
2. If battery voltage is present, proceed to "Inspect Continuity Harness."
3. If battery voltage is not present, locate and repair fuse F12 (10 amp) harness, splices EMS16 and PIS6, connectors PI1/28 and EM20/10 and test system for normal operation.

Inspect Continuity Harness

1. Disconnect EM12 and PI35, then measure resistance between EM12/13 and PI35/2.
2. If resistance is less than .5 ohms, proceed to "Inspect Continuity MAF Grounds."
3. If resistance is more than. 5 ohms, repair harness/connector PI1/52 and test system for normal operation.

Inspect Continuity MAF Grounds

1. Measure resistance between PI35/5 and EM12/18. If resistance is .5 ohms or less, proceed to next step. If resistance is more than .5 ohms, proceed to last step.
2. Measure resistance between PI35/5 and EM12/19. If resistance is .5 ohms or less, proceed to "Inspect Harness Short To Ground." If resistance is more than .5 ohms, proceed to next step.
3. Inspect EM12, PI35 and PI1 for corrosion, bent/pushed back pins or locate and repair harness/splice PIS10 fault. Test system for normal operation.

Inspect Harness Short To Ground

1. Measure insulation resistance between EM12/13 and EM12/18. If resistance is more than 10 Mohms, proceed to next step. If resistance is less than 10 Mohms, proceed to last step.
2. Measure insulation resistance between EM12/13 and EM12/19. If resistance is more than 10 Mohms, proceed to "Inspect For Short To B+." If resistance is less than 10 Mohms, proceed to next step.
3. Inspect EM12, PI35 and PI1 for corrosion, bent/pushed back pins or locate and repair harness fault. Test system for normal operation.

Inspect For Short To B+

1. Measure voltage between EM12/13 and EM12/18. If voltage is zero, proceed to next step. If voltage is more than zero, proceed to last step.
2. Measure voltage between EM12/13 and EM12/19. If voltage is zero, proceed to "Measure Sensor Output." If voltage is more than zero, proceed to next step.
3. Inspect EM12, PI35 and PI1 for corrosion, bent/pushed back pins or locate and repair harness fault. Test system for normal operation.

Measure Sensor Output

1. Using appropriate leads, link PI35/1 and PI35/5 to MAF corresponding pins.
2. With engine at idle speed and normal operating temperature, measure output voltage at MAF pin 2 and pin 5 (ground).
3. If output voltage is between .7–1.7 volts, proceed to "End." If voltage is not between .7–1.7 volts, replace air flow meter assembly and proceed to "End."

End

1. Perform appropriate service drive cycle and inspect for presence of DTC.
2. If fault code has cleared, fault condition has been corrected and no further diagnosis is required.
3. If fault code has not cleared, further diagnosis is required.

CODE P0111 & P0112: INTAKE AIR TEMPERATURE SENSOR MALFUNCTION

Air Intake System Inspection

1. Inspect air intake system as follows:
   a. Ensure air cleaner is free from obstruction
   b. Inspect air meter to throttle body seal.
   c. Inspect engine breather to inlet duct.
2. If air intake system satisfactory, proceed to "Inspect IAT Sensor Range."
3. If air intake system is not satisfactory, repair as required and test system for normal operation.

Inspect IAT Sensor Range

1. With MAF meter plug PI35 disconnected, measure resistance between IAT pins PI35/3 and PI35/4.
2. If temperature/resistance relationship is satisfactory, proceed to "Inspect Continuity Harness."
3. If temperature/resistance relationship is not satisfactory, remove sensor and test over at least three different temperatures (including ambient). If required, replace sensor and test system for normal operation.

Inspect Continuity Harness

1. With EM12 and PI35 disconnected, measure resistance between EM12/12 and PI35/3.
2. If resistance is less than .5 ohms, proceed to "Inspect Continuity Harness."
3. Repair harness/connector (PI1/57) and test system for normal operation.

Inspect Continuity Harness

To avoid an improper result, disconnect connectors; EM11 (ECM), and PI42 and PI6 (electronic throttle body).

1. Measure resistance between EM10/20 and MAF meter connector PI35/4.
2. If resistance is less than .5 ohms, proceed to "End."
3. If resistance is more than .5 ohms, repair harness/connector (PI1/31). Connect PI42 and PI6 (electronic throttle body), EM10, EM11 (ECM) and PI35 (MAF meter) and test system for normal operation.

End

1. Perform appropriate service drive cycle and inspect for presence of DTC.
2. If fault code has cleared, fault condition has been corrected and no further diagnosis is required.
3. If fault code has not cleared, further diagnosis is required.

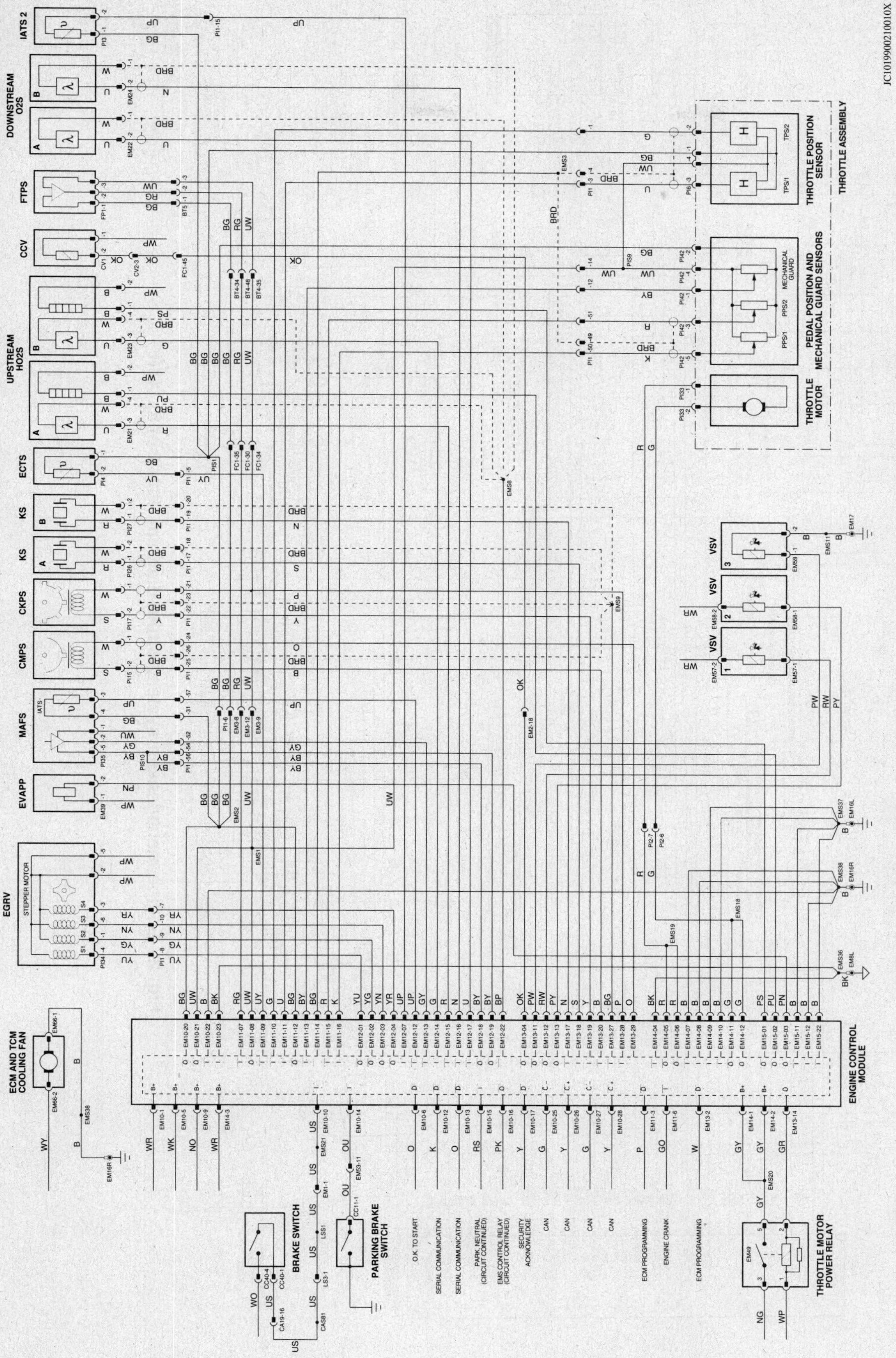

Fig. 2 Engine management system wiring diagram (Part 1 of 2). XJR

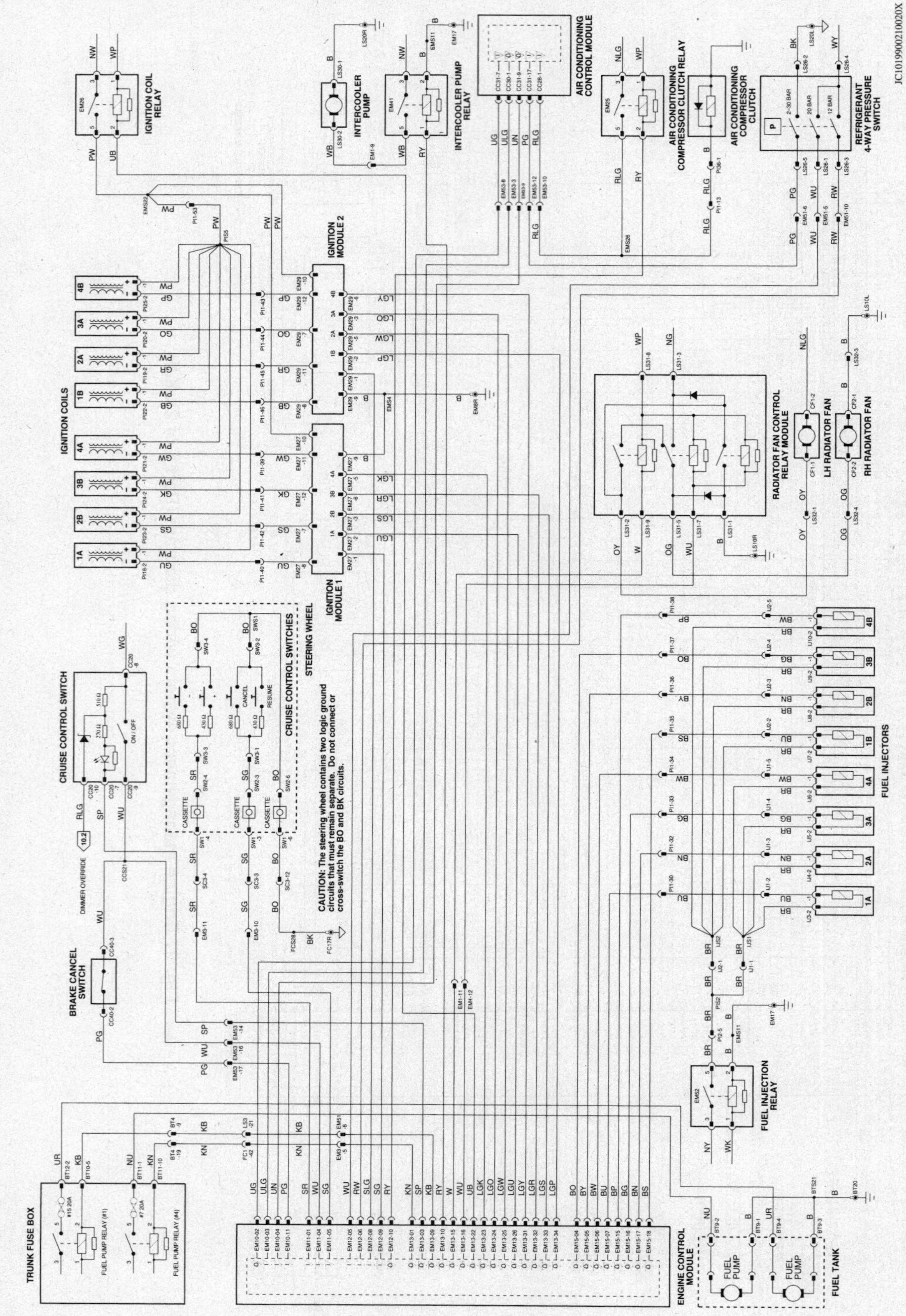

Fig. 2 Engine management system wiring diagram (Part 2 of 2). XJR

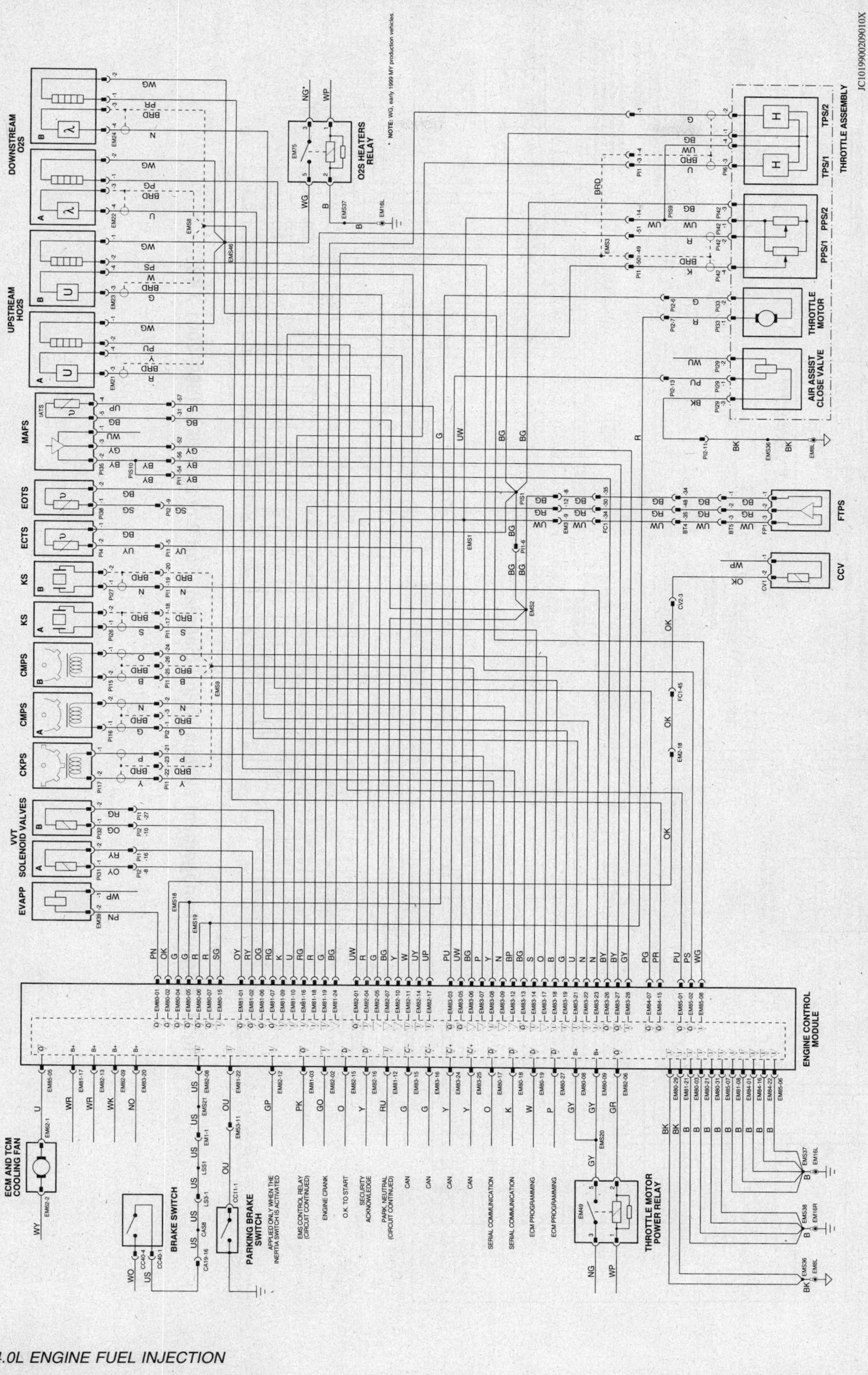

Fig. 3 Engine management system wiring diagram (Part 1 of 2). XJ8 & 1999–2001 XK8

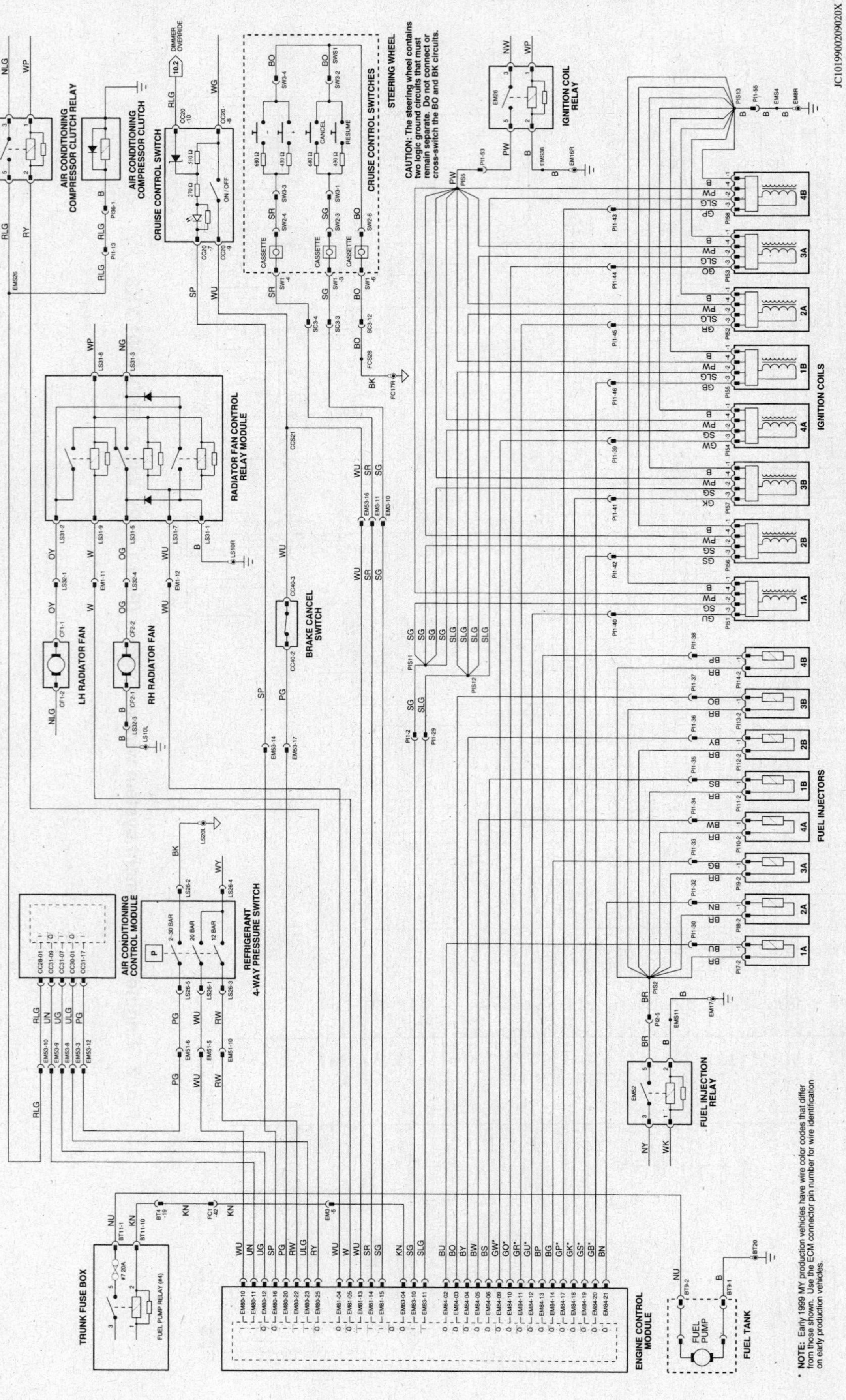

Fig. 3 Engine management system wiring diagram (Part 2 of 2). XJ8 & 1999–2001 XK8

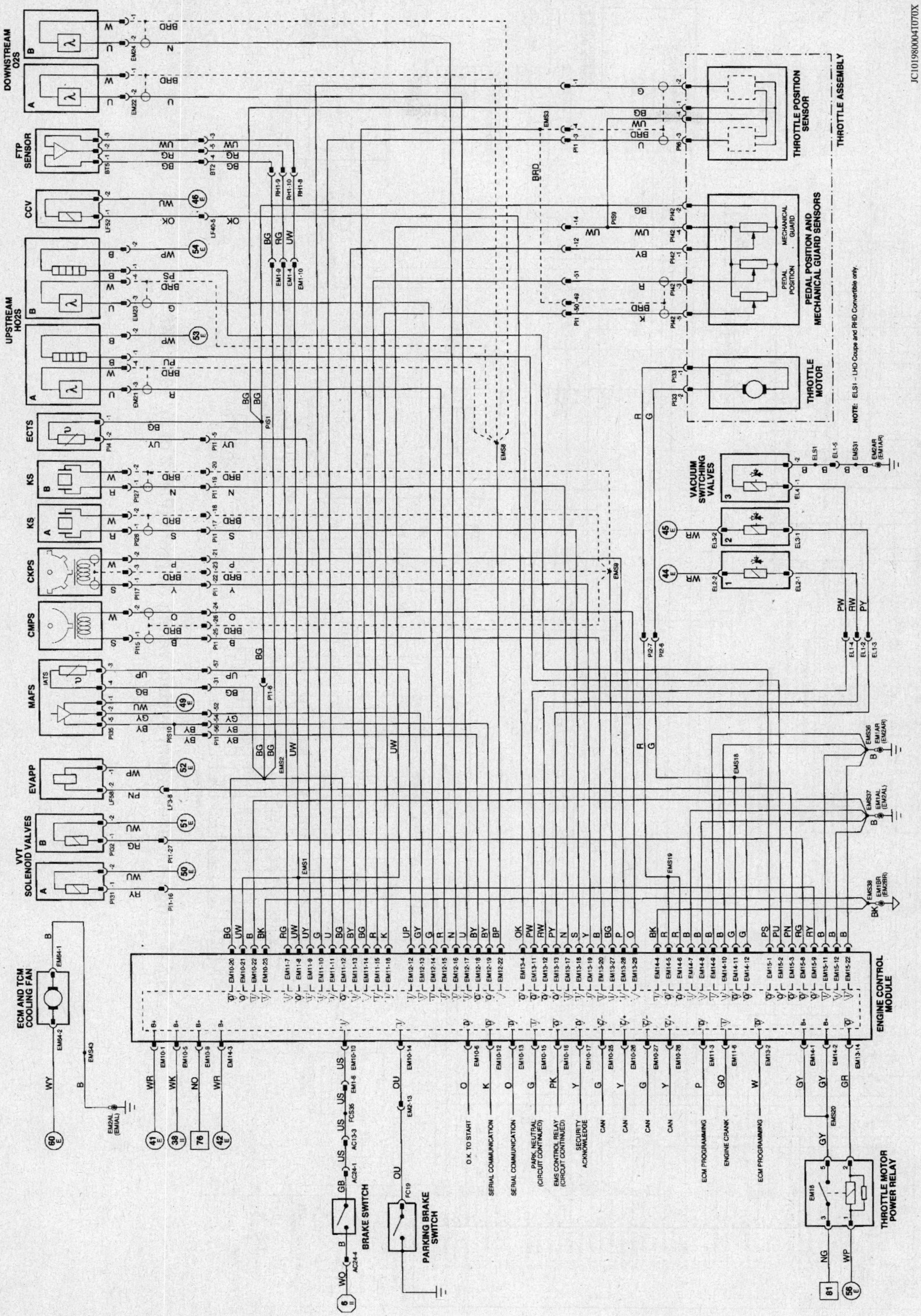

Fig. 4 Engine management system wiring diagram (Part 1 of 2). 1998 XK8

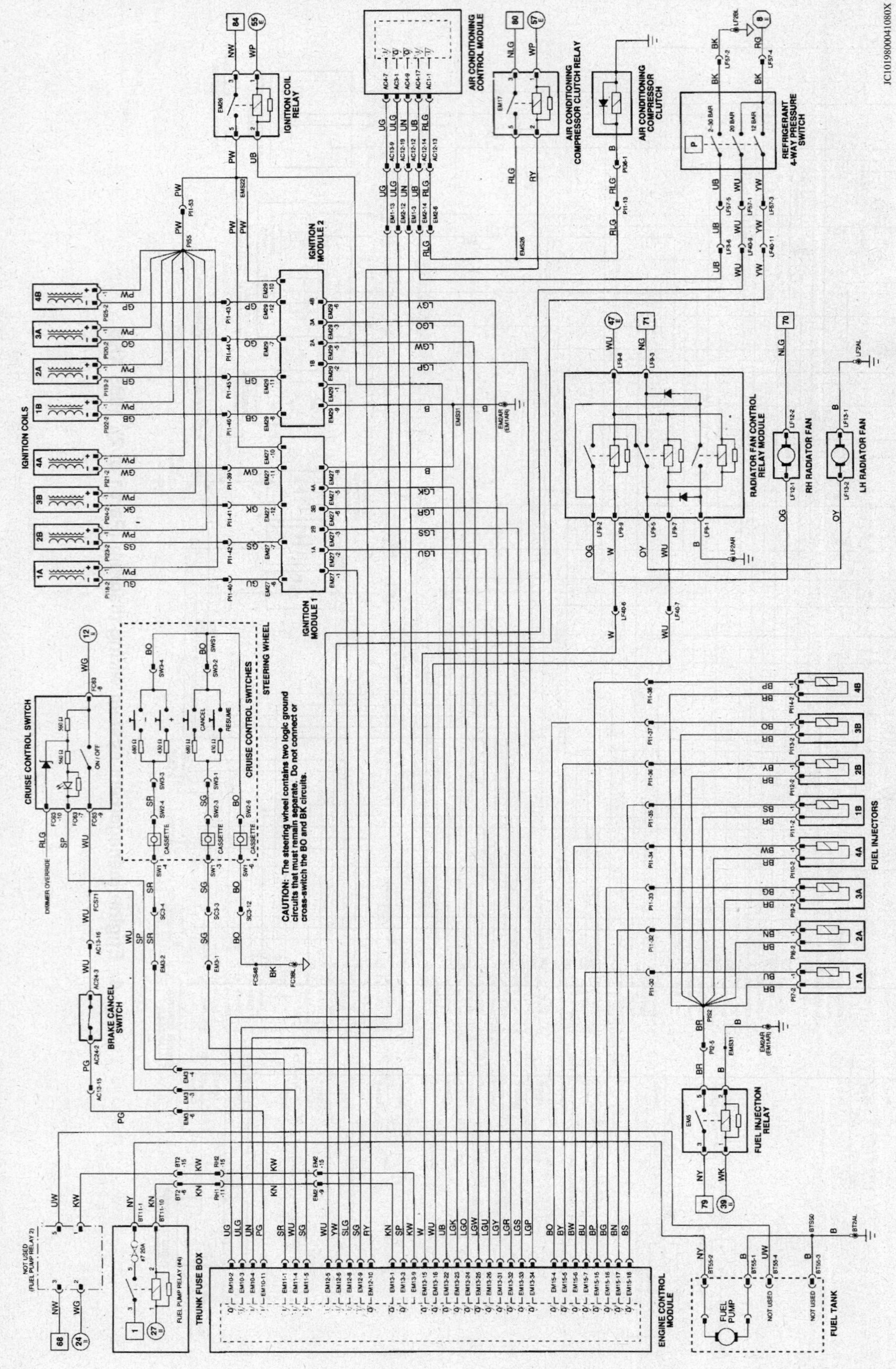

Fig. 4 Engine management system wiring diagram (Part 2 of 2). 1998 XK8

CODE P0113: INTAKE AIR TEMPERATURE SENSOR CIRCUIT HIGH INPUT

Inspect IAT Sensor Range

1. With MAF meter plug disconnected, inspect for an IAT sensor short at pins PI35/3 and PI35/4.
2. If resistance is more than 100 ohms, proceed to "Inspect For Short To B+."
3. If resistance is less than 100 ohms, replace sensor (MAF meter assembly) and proceed to "Inspect For Short To B+."

Inspect For Short To B+

1. Measure voltage at connector PI35/3.
2. If battery voltage is not present, proceed to "Measure Supply Voltage."
3. If battery voltage is present, locate and repair harness/connector (PI1/57) short to B+ and test system for normal operation.

Measure Supply Voltage

1. Measure voltage at connector between pins PI35/3 and PI35/4.
2. If voltage is less than 50.5 volts, connect MAF meter connector and proceed to "End."
3. If voltage is more than 50.5 volts, replace ECM and test system for normal operation.

End

1. Perform appropriate service drive cycle and inspect for presence of DTC.
2. If fault code has cleared, fault condition has been corrected and no further diagnosis is required.
3. If fault code has not cleared, further diagnosis is required.

CODES P0116 & P0125: ECT SENSOR PERFORMANCE FAULT CONDITION

Engine Coolant System Inspection

1. Measure engine temperature rise using a thermocouple or equivalent measuring device.
2. If engine temperature increases, proceed to "Inspect ECT Sensor Range."
3. If engine temperature does not increase, inspect the following:
   a. Coolant level.
   b. Coolant for contamination.
   c. Thermostat operation.

Inspect ECT Sensor Range

1. With engine at any temperature within specified range, disconnect connector PI4 and measure resistance between sensor pins 1 and 2.
2. If temperature/resistance relationship is satisfactory, proceed to "Inspect Continuity Harness."
3. If temperature/resistance relationship is not satisfactory, remove sensor and test over at least 3 temperature ranges. Replace sensor if required and test system for normal operation.

Inspect Continuity Harness

1. Disconnect EM11 and measure resistance between EM11/9 and PI4/2.
2. If resistance is more than .5 ohms, proceed to "Inspect Continuity Harness."
3. If resistance is less than .05 ohms, repair harness/connector (PI1/5) and test system for normal operation.

Inspect Continuity Harness

To avoid an improper result, disconnect connectors PI42 and PI6 (electronic throttle body) and PI35 (MAF meter).

1. Disconnect EM10 and measure resistance between EM11/12 and PI4/1.
2. If resistance is less than .5 ohms, proceed to "Inspect Continuity Harness."
3. If resistance is more than .5 ohms, repair harness/connector (PI1/6) or splice EMS2 and test system for normal operation.

Inspect Continuity Harness

1. With electronic throttle body connectors PI42 and PI6 disconnected, measure resistance between ECM connector EM10/20 and ECT connector PI4/1.
2. If resistance is less than .5 ohms, proceed to "End."
3. If resistance is more than .5 ohms, repair harness/connector (PI1/6) or splice EMS2. Connect PI42 and PI6 (electronic throttle body), PI35 (MAF meter), EM10, EM11 and ETC connector and test system for normal operation.

End

1. Perform appropriate service drive cycle and inspect for presence of DTC.
2. If fault code has cleared, fault condition has been corrected and no further diagnosis is required.
3. If fault code has not cleared, further diagnosis is required.

CODE P0117: ECT SENSOR CIRCUIT LOW INPUT

Inspect ECT Sensor Open Circuit

1. Disconnect connector PI4 and measure resistance between ECT sensor pins 1 and 2.
2. If resistance is less than 30K ohms, proceed to "Inspect Continuity Harness."
3. Is resistance more than 30K ohms, replace sensor and proceed to "End."

Inspect Continuity Harness

1. Measure resistance between ECM connector EM11/9 and ECT connector PI4/2.
2. If resistance is less than .5 ohms, proceed to "Inspect Continuity Harness."
3. If resistance is more than .5 ohms, repair harness/connector (PI1/5) and test system for normal operation.

Inspect Continuity Harness

To avoid an improper result, disconnect connectors PI42 and PI6 (electronic throttle body) and PI35 (MAF meter).

1. Disconnect ECM connector EM10 and measure resistance between ECM connector EM11/12 and ECT connector PI4/1.
2. If resistance is less than .5 ohms, proceed to "Inspect Continuity Harness."
3. If resistance is more than .5 ohms, repair harness/connector (PI1/6) and test system for normal operation.

Inspect Continuity Harness

1. With electronic throttle body connectors PI42 and PI6 disconnected, measure resistance between ECM connector EM10/20 and ECT connector PI4/1.
2. If resistance is less than .5 ohms, proceed to "End."
3. If resistance is more than .5 ohms, repair harness/connector (PI1/6). Connect PI42 and PI6 (electronic throttle body), PI35 (MAF meter), EM10, EM11 (ECM), ETC and test system for normal operation.

End

1. Perform appropriate service drive cycle and inspect for presence of DTC.
2. If fault code has cleared, fault condition has been corrected and no further diagnosis is required.
3. If fault code has not cleared, further diagnosis is required.

CODE P0118: ECT CIRCUIT HIGH INPUT

Inspect ECT Sensor Short

1. Disconnect PI4 and measure resistance between sensor pins 1 and 2.
2. If resistance is less than 100 ohms, replace sensor and proceed to "End."
3. If resistance is more than 100 ohms, proceed to "Inspect For Short To B+."

Inspect For Short To B+

1. Measure voltage at ECT connector PI4/2.
2. If battery voltage is present, locate and repair harness/connector (PI1/5) short to B+ and test system for normal operation.
3. If battery voltage is not present, proceed to "Inspect Continuity Harness."

Inspect Continuity Harness

1. Measure voltage between PI4/1 and PI4/2.
2. If voltage is more than 5.2 volts, replace ECM.
3. If voltage is less than 5.2 volts, proceed to "End."

End

1. Perform appropriate service drive cycle and inspect for presence of DTC.
2. If fault code has cleared, fault condition has been corrected and no further diagnosis is required.

3. If fault code has not cleared, further diagnosis is required.

CODE P0121: THROTTLE POSITION SENSOR MALFUNCTION

Measure Sensor Supply Voltage

1. Disconnect PI6 and PI42, then measure voltage between PI6/4 and PI6/1.
2. If voltage is 4.75–5.25 volts, proceed to "Codes P0121, P0122, P0123, P0222 and P0223: Throttle Position Sensor Malfunction"
3. If voltage is not 4.75–5.25 volts, proceed to "Inspect Harness Ground Continuity."

Inspect Harness Ground Continuity

1. With EM10, EM11, PI6 PI4 and PI42 disconnected, measure resistance between EM10/20 and PI6/1, then between EM11/12 and PI6/1.
2. If resistance is less than. 5 ohms, proceed to "Inspect Harness Supply Continuity."
3. If resistance is more than. 5 ohms, inspect EM10, EM11, PI1 and PI6 for bent/pushed back pins or locate and repair harness/splices EMS2 and PIS1.

Inspect Harness Supply Continuity

1. With EM10, EM11, PI6 PI4 and PI42 disconnected, measure resistance between EM10/21 and PI6/4, then between EM11/8 and PI6/4.
2. If resistance is less than .5 ohms, proceed to "Inspect Sensor Supply Voltage."
3. If resistance is more than .5 ohms, inspect EM10, EM11, PI1 and PI6 for bent/pushed back pins or locate and repair harness/splices EMS1 and PIS9.

Measure Sensor Supply Voltage

1. Disconnect EM11, then measure voltage between EM11/12 and EM11/8.
2. If voltage is 4.75–5.25 volts, connect EM11 and go to "Codes P0121, P0122, P0123, P0222 & P0223: Throttle Position Sensor Malfunction."
3. If voltage is not 4.75–5.25 volts, inspect EM10, for bent/pushed back pins or locate and repair harness/splice EMS1 and EMS2, then proceed to "End."

End

1. Perform appropriate service drive cycle and inspect for presence of DTC.
2. If fault code has cleared, fault condition has been corrected and no further diagnosis is required.
3. If fault code has not cleared, further diagnosis is required.

CODES P0122 & P0222: THROTTLE POSITION SENSOR

Harness Short To Screen

1. With EM10, EM11, PI6 and PI42 disconnected, measure insulation resistance between EM11/14 and the following terminals:
   a. EM10/20.
   b. EM10/21.
   c. EM11/8.
   d. EM11/12.
2. If all measurements are more than 10 Mohms, proceed to "Inspect Harness Core To Core Insulation."
3. If any of the measurements are less than 10 Mohms, inspect EM10, and EM11 for corrosion, bent/pushed back pins or locate and repair harness/connector PI1. Test system for normal operation.

Inspect Harness Core To Core Insulation

1. With EM10, EM11, PI6 and PI42 disconnected, measure insulation resistance between the following terminals:
   a. EM10/21 and EM10/20.
   b. EM11/12 and EM11/8.
   c. EM11/11 and EM11/10.
2. If all resistances are more than 10 Mohms, proceed to "Codes P0123 & P0223: Throttle Position Sensor."
3. If any resistance measurement is less than 10 Mohms, inspect EM10, and EM11 for corrosion, bent/pushed back pins or locate and repair harness/connector PI1 then proceed to "End."

End

1. Perform appropriate service drive cycle and inspect for presence of DTC.
2. If fault code has cleared, fault condition has been corrected and no further diagnosis is required.
3. If fault code has not cleared, further diagnosis is required.

CODES P0123 & P0223: THROTTLE POSITION SENSOR

Inspect Ground Continuity

1. With EM10, EM11, PI6 PI4 and PI42 disconnected, measure resistance between EM10/20 and PI6/1.
2. If resistance is less than .5 ohms, proceed to "Inspect ECM Ground."
3. If resistance is more than .5 ohms, inspect EM10 and PI6 for bent/pushed back pins or locate and repair harness/splice PIS1.

Inspect ECM Ground

1. With EM10, EM11, PI6 PI4 and PI42 disconnected, measure resistance between EM11/12 and PI6/1.
2. If resistance is less than .5 ohms, proceed to "Inspect Harness Supply Continuity."
3. If resistance is more than .5 ohms, inspect EM11 and PI6 for bent/pushed back pins or locate and repair harness/splice PIS1.

Inspect Harness Supply Continuity

1. With EM10, EM11, PI6 PI4 and PI42 disconnected, measure resistance between EM10/21 and PI6/4.
2. If resistance is less than .5 ohms, proceed to "Inspect Harness Supply Continuity."
3. If resistance is more than .5 ohms, inspect EM10 and PI6 for bent/pushed back pins or locate and repair harness/splice PIS1.

Inspect Harness Supply Continuity

1. With EM10, EM11, PI6 PI4 and PI42 disconnected, measure resistance between EM11/8 and PI6/4.
2. If resistance is less than .5 ohms, proceed to "Inspect Harness Signal Continuity (Sensor A)."
3. If resistance is more than .5 ohms, inspect EM11 and PI6 for bent/pushed back pins or locate and repair harness/splice PIS1.

Inspect Harness Signal Continuity (Sensor A)

1. With EM11 and PI6 disconnected, measure resistance between EM11/11 and PI6/3.
2. If resistance is less than .5 ohms, proceed to "Inspect Harness Signal Continuity (Sensor B)."
3. If resistance is more than .5 ohms, inspect EM11 and PI6 for bent/pushed back pins or locate and repair harness/connector PI1.

Inspect Harness Signal Continuity (Sensor B)

1. With, EM11, and PI6 disconnected, measure resistance between EM11/10 and PI6/2.
2. If resistance is less than .5 ohms, proceed to "Codes P0121, P0122, P0123, P0222 & P0223: Throttle Position Sensor Malfunction."
3. If resistance is more than .5 ohms, inspect EM11 and PI6 for bent/pushed back pins or locate and repair harness/connector PI1 and proceed to "End."

End

1. Perform appropriate service drive cycle and inspect for presence of DTC.
2. If fault code has cleared, fault condition has been corrected and no further diagnosis is required.
3. If fault code has not cleared, further diagnosis is required.

CODES P0121, P0122, P0123, P0222 & P0223: THROTTLE POSITION SENSOR MALFUNCTION

Further Diagnosis Required

1. Perform appropriate service drive cycle and inspect for presence of DTC.

2. If fault code has cleared, fault condition has been corrected and no further diagnosis is required.
3. If fault code has not cleared, further diagnosis is required.

CODES P0131 P0132 & P0135: O_2 SENSOR CIRCUIT MALFUNCTION

Inspect O_2 Sensor Heater Continuity

1. With EM21 disconnected, measure resistance between EM21/1 and EM21/2.
2. If resistance is between 4–10 ohms, proceed to "Inspect For O_2 Sensor Failure."
3. If resistance is not between 4–10 ohms, replace O_2 sensor, connect plug(s) and proceed to "Stop."

Inspect For O_2 Sensor Failure

1. Run engine for a period to warm sensor and then maintain a steady speed of approximately 2500 RPM.
2. With EM21 disconnected, measure voltage between EM21/3 and EM21/4.
3. If voltage is between .6–1 volt, proceed to "Inspect For O_2 Sensor Failure."
4. If voltage is between .6–1 volt, replace O_2 sensor; connect plug(s) and proceed to "Stop."

Inspect For O_2 Sensor Failure

1. Maintain engine speed of 2500 RPM, then suddenly decelerate to idle.
2. If voltage dropped to 400 mVolts or less, proceed to "Inspect For O_2 Sensor Failure."
3. If voltage did not drop to 400 mVolts or less, replace O_2 sensor; connect plug(s) and proceed to "Stop."

Inspect For O_2 Sensor Failure

1. With engine at idle speed, suddenly accelerate to approximately 2500 RPM.
2. If voltage rises to between .6–1 volt, proceed to "Heated O_2 Sensor Short Circuit To Ground."
3. If voltage does not rise to between .6–1 volt, replace O_2 sensor; connect plug(s) and proceed to "Stop."

Stop

1. Perform appropriate service drive cycle and inspect for presence of DTC.
2. If fault code has cleared, fault condition has been corrected and no further diagnosis is required.
3. If fault code has not cleared, further diagnosis is required.

Heated O_2 Sensor Short Circuit To Ground

1. With EM21 disconnected measure insulation resistance between sensor pin 001 and sensor body, then between pin 003 and sensor body.
2. If resistance is more than 10 Mohms, proceed to "Signal Ground 1 Continuity."
3. If resistance is less than 10 Mohms, replace O_2 sensor and connect plug(s) and proceed to "Stop."

Stop

1. Perform appropriate service drive cycle and inspect for presence of DTC.
2. If fault code has cleared, fault condition has been corrected and no further diagnosis is required.
3. If fault code has not cleared, further diagnosis is required.

Signal Ground 1 Continuity

1. With EM10 and EM14 disconnected, measure resistance between EM10/23 and chassis ground EM1BR (EM2BR).
2. If resistance is less than .5 ohms, proceed to "Signal Ground 2 Continuity."
3. If resistance is more than .5 ohms, inspect connector EM10 for corrosion, damage, or pushed back pin. Inspect ground stud EM1BR (EM2BR) for corrosion. Repair harness, splice EMS38, connector or ground as required, then connect plug(s) and proceed to "Stop."

Signal Ground 2 Continuity

1. With EM10 and EM14 disconnected, measure resistance between EM14/4 and chassis ground EM1BR (EM2BR).
2. If resistance is less than .5 ohms, proceed to "Inspect For Heated O_2 Sensor Continuity."
3. If resistance is more than .5 ohms, inspect connector EM14 for corrosion, damage, or pushed back pin. Inspect ground stud EM1BR (EM2BR) for corrosion. Repair harness, splice EMS38, connector or ground as required, then connect plug(s) and proceed to "Stop."

Stop

1. Perform appropriate service drive cycle and inspect for presence of DTC.
2. If fault code has cleared, fault condition has been corrected and no further diagnosis is required.
3. If fault code has not cleared, further diagnosis is required.

Inspect For Heated O_2 Sensor Continuity

1. With EM12 and EM21 disconnected, measure resistance between EM12/15 and EM21/3.
2. If resistance is less than .5 ohms, proceed to "Heated O_2 Sensor Screen Ground Continuity."
3. If resistance is more than .5 ohms, inspect connectors EM12, and EM21 for corrosion or damaged/pushed back pins. Repair connector(s) or harness as required, then connect plug(s) and proceed to "End."

Heated O_2 Sensor Screen Ground Continuity

1. With EM12 and EM21 disconnected, measure resistance between EM12/22 and EM21/4.
2. If resistance is less than .5 ohms, proceed to "Inspect For Short To B+."
3. If resistance is less than .5 ohms, inspect connectors EM12, and EM21 for corrosion or damaged/pushed back pins. Repair connectors or harness as required, then connect plug(s) and proceed to "End."

Inspect For Short To B+

1. With EM10 and EM12 disconnected, measure voltage between EM10/23 and EM12/15.
2. If voltage is zero, proceed to "Inspect For Short To B+."
3. If voltage is more than zero, inspect connectors EM10, EM12, and EM21 for corrosion or damaged/pushed back pins. Repair connectors or harness as required, then connect plug(s) and proceed to "End."

Inspect For Short To B+

1. With EM10 and EM12 disconnected, measure voltage between EM10/23 and EM12/22.
2. If voltage is zero, proceed to "Inspect For Short To B+ At O_2 Sensor Heater."
3. If voltage is more than zero, inspect connectors EM10, EM12, and EM21 for corrosion or damaged/pushed back pins. Repair connectors or harness as required, then connect plug(s) and proceed to "End."

Inspect For Short To B+ At O_2 Sensor Heater

1. Remove EMS fuse F14, then disconnect EM10 and EM15.
2. Using a suitable link, connect EM10/16 and EM10/22.
3. Measure voltage between EM10/23 and EM15/2.
4. If voltage is zero, replace EMS fuse F14 but retain link lead and proceed to "Inspect B+ At O_2 Sensor Heater Circuit."
5. If voltage is more than zero, inspect connectors EM10, EM15, and EM21 for corrosion or damaged/pushed back pins. Repair connectors or harness as required, then connect plug(s) and proceed to "End."

Inspect B+ At O_2 Sensor Heater Circuit

1. With EM10 and EM15 disconnected, measure voltage between EM10/23 and EM15/2.
2. If battery voltage is present, remove link lead and connect all connectors and proceed to "End."
3. If battery voltage is not present, inspect EMS fuse F14, then ensure EMS control relay (relay 1) is energized, proceed to "End."

End

1. Perform appropriate service drive cycle and inspect for presence of DTC.
2. If fault code has cleared, fault condition has been corrected and no further diagnosis is required.
3. If fault code has not cleared, further diagnosis is required.

CODE P0133: O_2 SENSOR CIRCUIT SLOW RESPONSE (BANK 1 SENSOR 1)

Inspect For Low Exhaust Temperature

1. Start and run engine until engine and exhaust system are at normal operating temperature.
2. If normal operating temperature can be reached, proceed to "Inspect For O_2 Sensor Heater Continuity."
3. If normal operating temperature cannot be reached, Repair possible leaking exhaust manifold/catalyst and other general causes of an over rich mixture and engine cooling system operation. Test system for proper operation and proceed to "Stop."

Inspect For O_2 Sensor Heater Continuity

1. With EM21 disconnected, measure resistance between EM21/1 and EM21/2.
2. If resistance is between 4–10 ohms, proceed to "Inspect For O_2 Sensor Failure."
3. If resistance is not between 4–10 ohms, replace O_2 sensor, connect plug(s) and proceed to "Stop."

Inspect For O_2 Sensor Failure

1. Run engine for a period to warm sensor and then maintain a steady speed of approximately 2500 RPM.
2. Measure voltage between EM21/3 and EM21/4.
3. If voltage is between .6–1 volt, proceed to "Inspect For O_2 Sensor Failure."
4. If voltage is not between .6–1 volt, replace O_2 sensor, connect plug(s) and proceed to "Stop."

Inspect For O_2 Sensor Failure

1. Maintain engine speed of 2500 RPM, then suddenly decelerate to idle.
2. If voltage drops to 400 mVolts or less, proceed to "Inspect For O_2 Sensor Failure."
3. If voltage does not drop to 400 mVolts or less, replace O_2 sensor, connect plug(s) and proceed to "Stop."

Inspect For O_2 Sensor Failure

1. With engine at idle speed, suddenly accelerate to approximately 2500 RPM.
2. If voltage rises to .6–1 volt, proceed to "Inspect For O_2 Sensor Failure."
3. If voltage does not rise to .6–1 volt, replace O_2 sensor, connect plug(s) and proceed to "Stop."

Inspect For O_2 Sensor Failure

1. Run engine at 1500 RPM for approximately 2 minutes.
2. If displayed voltage drops below 400 mVolts and then rises above 500 mVolts cycling approximately every four seconds, proceed to "Heated O_2 Sensor Short Circuit To Ground."
3. If displayed voltage does not cycle as outlined in previous step, replace O_2 sensor, connect plug(s) and proceed to "Stop."

Stop

1. Perform appropriate service drive cycle and inspect for presence of DTC.
2. If fault code has cleared, fault condition has been corrected and no further diagnosis is required.
3. If fault code has not cleared, further diagnosis is required.

Heated O_2 Sensor Short Circuit To Ground

1. With EM21 disconnected, measure insulation resistance between sensor pin 001 and sensor body, then between pin 003 and sensor body.
2. If resistance is more than 10 Mohms, proceed to "Signal Ground 1 Continuity."
3. If resistance is less than 10M, replace O_2 sensor, connect plug(s) and proceed to "Stop."

Stop

1. Perform appropriate service drive cycle and inspect for presence of DTC.
2. If fault code has cleared, fault condition has been corrected and no further diagnosis is required.
3. If fault code has not cleared, further diagnosis is required.

Signal Ground 1 Continuity

1. With EM10 and EM14 disconnected, measure resistance between EM10/23 and chassis ground EM1BR (EM2BR).
2. If resistance is less than .5 ohms, proceed to "Signal Ground 2 Continuity."
3. If resistance is more than .5 ohms, inspect connector EM10 for corrosion, damage, or pushed back pin. Inspect ground stud EM1BR (EM2BR) for corrosion. Repair harness, splice EMS38, connector or ground as required. Connect plug(s) and proceed to "Inspect For Heated O_2 Sensor Continuity."

Signal Ground 2 Continuity

1. With EM10 and EM14 disconnected, measure resistance between EM14/4 and chassis ground EM1BR (EM2BR).
2. If resistance is less than .5 ohms, proceed to "Heated O_2 Sensor Screen Ground Continuity."
3. If resistance is more than .5 ohms, inspect the following:
   a. Connector EM14 for corrosion, damage, or pushed back pin.
   b. Ground stud EM1BR (EM2BR) for corrosion.
   c. Splice EMS38 for corrosion.
4. Repair harness, connector or ground as required.
5. Connect plug(s) and proceed to "Inspect For Heated O_2 Sensor Continuity."

Inspect For Heated O_2 Sensor Continuity

1. With EM12 and EM21 disconnected, measure resistance between EM12/15 and EM21/3.
2. If resistance is less than .5 ohms, proceed to "Heated O_2 Sensor Screen Ground Continuity."
3. If resistance is more than .5 ohms, inspect connectors EM12, and EM21 for corrosion, damaged/pushed back pins. Repair connectors or harness as required, then connect plug(s) and proceed to "End."

Heated O_2 Sensor Screen Ground Continuity

1. With EM12 and EM21 disconnected, measure resistance between EM12/22 and EM21/4.
2. If resistance is less than .5 ohms, proceed to "Inspect For Short To B+."
3. If resistance is more than .5 ohms, inspect connectors EM12, and EM21 for corrosion or damaged/pushed back pins. Repair connectors or harness as required. Connect plug(s) and proceed to "End."

Inspect For Short To B+

1. With EM10 and EM12 disconnected, measure voltage between EM10/23 and EM12/15.
2. If voltage is zero, proceed to "Inspect For Short To B+."
3. If voltage is more than zero, inspect connectors EM10, EM12 and EM21 for corrosion or damaged/pushed back pins. Repair connectors or harness as required. Connect plug(s) and proceed to "End."

Inspect For Short To B+

1. With EM10 and EM12 disconnected, measure voltage between EM10/23 and EM12/22.
2. If voltage is zero, proceed to "Inspect For Short To B+ At O_2 Sensor Heater."
3. If voltage is more than zero, inspect connectors EM10, EM12 and EM21 for corrosion or damaged/pushed back pins. Repair connectors or harness as required. Connect plug(s) and proceed to "End."

Inspect For Short To B+ At O_2 Sensor Heater

1. Remove EMS fuse F14.
2. Disconnect EM10 and EM15.
3. Using a link lead, bridge EM10/16 and EM10/22.
4. Measure voltage between EM10/23 and EM15/2.
5. If voltage is zero, replace EMS fuse F14 and proceed to "Measure B+ At O_2 Sensor Heater Circuit."
6. If voltage is more than zero, inspect connectors EM10, EM15 and EM21 for corrosion or damaged/pushed back pins. Repair connectors or harness as required. Connect plug(s) and proceed to "End."

Measure B+ At O_2 Sensor Heater Circuit

1. With EM10 and EM15 disconnected

and link lead connected, measure voltage between EM10/23 and EM15/2.
2. If battery voltage is present, remove link lead and connect all connectors and proceed to "End."
3. If battery voltage is not present, inspect EMS fuse F14, EMS control relay (relay 1) and all connectors, then proceed to "End."

End

1. Perform appropriate service drive cycle and inspect for presence of DTC.
2. If fault code has cleared, fault condition has been corrected and no further diagnosis is required.
3. If fault code has not cleared, further diagnosis is required.

CODES P0137 & P0138: O_2 SENSOR CIRCUIT MALFUNCTION (BANK 1 SENSOR 2)

Inspect For O_2 Sensor Failure

1. Run engine for a period to warm sensor and then maintain a steady speed of approximately 2500 RPM.
2. Measure voltage between EM22/1 and EM22/2.
3. If voltage is between .6–1.0 volt, proceed to "Inspect For O_2 Sensor Failure."
4. If voltage is not between .6–1.0 volt, replace O_2 sensor, connect plug and proceed to "Stop."

Inspect For O_2 Sensor Failure

1. With engine speed at 2500 RPM, suddenly decelerate to idle.
2. Measure voltage between EM22/1 and EM22/2.
3. If voltage drops to 400 mVolts or less, proceed to "Inspect For O_2 Sensor Failure."
4. If voltage does not drop to 400 mVolts or less, replace O_2 sensor, connect plug and proceed to "Stop."

Inspect For O_2 Sensor Failure

1. With engine at idle speed, suddenly accelerate to approximately 2500 RPM.
2. Measure voltage between EM22/1 and EM22/2.
3. If voltage rises to between .6–1.0 volt, proceed to "Inspect For O_2 Sensor Failure."
4. If voltage does not rise to between .6–1.0 volt, replace O_2 sensor, connect plug and proceed to "Stop."

Inspect For O_2 Sensor Failure

1. Run engine at 1500 RPM for approximately 3 minutes.
2. Measure voltage between EM22/1 and EM22/2.
3. If displayed voltage drops below 400 mVolts and then rises above 500 mVolts, cycling approximately every 180 seconds, proceed to "Inspect For O_2 Sensor Continuity."
4. If displayed voltage does not cycle as outlined in previous step, replace O_2 sensor, connect plug(s) and proceed to "Stop."

Stop

1. Perform appropriate service drive cycle and inspect for presence of DTC.
2. If fault code has cleared, fault condition has been corrected and no further diagnosis is required.
3. If fault code has not cleared, further diagnosis is required.

Inspect For O_2 Sensor Continuity

1. With EM12 and EM22 disconnected, measure resistance between EM12/17 and EM22/2.
2. If resistance is less than .5 ohms, proceed to "O_2 Sensor Screen Ground Continuity."
3. If resistance is more than .5 ohms, inspect connectors EM12, and EM22 for corrosion, damaged/pushed back pins. Repair connectors or harness as required. Connect plug(s) and proceed to "Stop."

O_2 Sensor Screen Ground Continuity

1. With EM12 and EM22 disconnected, measure resistance between EM12/22 and EM22/1.
2. If resistance is less than .5 ohms, proceed to "O_2 Sensor Short Circuit To Ground."
3. If resistance is more than .5 ohms, inspect connectors EM12, and EM22 for corrosion, damaged/pushed back pins. Repair connectors or harness as required. Connect plug(s) and proceed to "Stop."

O_2 Sensor Short Circuit To Ground

1. With EM22 disconnected measure insulation resistance between sensor pin 001 and sensor body, then between pin 002 and sensor body.
2. If resistance is more than 10 Mohms, proceed to "Signal Ground 1 Continuity."
3. If resistance is less than 10 Mohms, replace O_2 sensor, connect all plugs and proceed to "Stop."

Stop

1. Perform appropriate service drive cycle and inspect for presence of DTC.
2. If fault code has cleared, fault condition has been corrected and no further diagnosis is required.
3. If fault code has not cleared, further diagnosis is required.

Signal Ground 1 Continuity

1. With EM10 and EM14 disconnected, measure resistance between EM10/23 and chassis ground EM1BR (EM2BR).
2. If resistance is less than .5 ohms, proceed to "Signal Ground 2 Continuity."
3. If resistance is less than .5 ohms, proceed as follows:
   a. Inspect connector EM10 for corrosion, damage, or pushed back pin.
   b. Inspect ground stud EM1BR (EM2BR) for corrosion.
   c. Splice EMS38 for corrosion.
   d. Repair connectors, harness or grounds as required.
   e. Connect plug(s) and proceed to "Stop."

Signal Ground 2 Continuity

1. With EM10 and EM14 disconnected, measure resistance between EM14/4 and chassis ground EM1BR (EM2BR).
2. If resistance is less than .5 ohms, proceed as follows:
   a. Inspect connector EM14 for corrosion, damage, or pushed back pin.
   b. Inspect ground stud EM1BR (EM2BR) for corrosion.
   c. Splice EMS38 for corrosion.
   d. Repair connectors, harness or grounds as required.
   e. Connect plug(s) and proceed to "Stop."

Stop

1. Perform appropriate service drive cycle and inspect for presence of DTC.
2. If fault code has cleared, fault condition has been corrected and no further diagnosis is required.
3. If fault code has not cleared, further diagnosis is required.

Inspect For O_2 Sensor Continuity

1. With EM12 and EM22 disconnected, measure resistance between EM12/17 and EM22/2
2. Is resistance less than .5 ohms?
   a. Yes, go to "O_2 Sensor Screen Ground Continuity."
   b. No, Inspect connectors EM12, and EM22 for corrosion, damaged/pushed back pins or repair harness; connect plug(s) and go to"End."

O_2 Sensor Screen Ground Continuity

1. With EM12 and EM22 disconnected, measure resistance between EM12/22 and EM22/1.
2. If resistance is less than .5 ohms, proceed to "Inspect For Short To B+."
3. If resistance is more than .5 ohms, inspect connectors EM12 and EM22 for corrosion, damaged/pushed back pins. Repair connectors or harness as required. Connect plug(s) and proceed to "End."

Inspect For Short To B+

1. With EM10 and EM12 disconnected, measure voltage between EM10/23 and EM12/17.
2. If voltage is zero, proceed to "Inspect For Short To B+."
3. If voltage is more than zero, inspect connectors EM10, EM12 and EM22 for corrosion, damaged/pushed back pins. Repair connectors or harness as required. Connect plug(s) and proceed to "End."

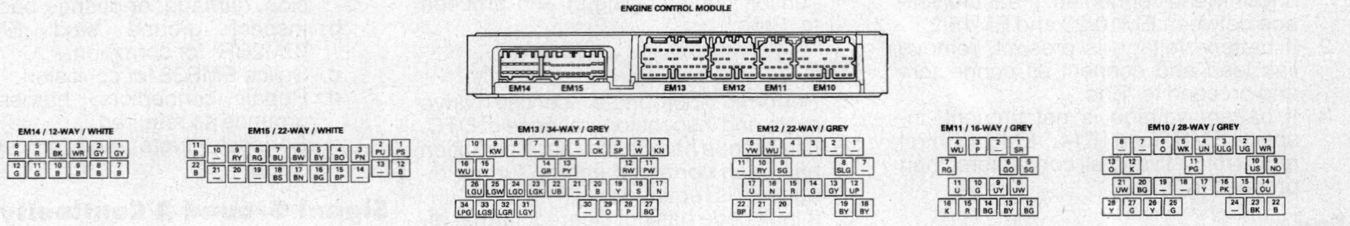

JC1019800040010X

Fig. 5 ECM connector terminal identification (Part 1 of 2)

Inspect For Short To B+

1. With EM10 and EM12 disconnected, measure voltage between EM10/23 and EM12/22.
2. If voltage is zero, proceed to "Inspect Harness Short To Ground."
3. If voltage is more than zero, inspect connectors EM10, EM12 and EM22 for corrosion, damaged/pushed back pins. Repair connectors or harness as required. Connect plug(s) and proceed to "End."

Inspect Harness Short To Ground

1. Measure insulation resistance between EM12/17 and ground EM10/23.
2. If resistance is more than 10 Mohms, proceed to "Inspect Harness Short Core To Core."
3. If resistance is less than 10 Mohms, inspect connectors EM12 and EM22 for corrosion, damaged/pushed back pins. Repair connectors or harness as required. Connect plug(s) and proceed to "End."

Inspect Harness Short Core To Core

1. Measure insulation resistance between EM12/17 and EM15/2.
2. If resistance is more than 10 Mohms, connect all plugs and proceed to "End."
3. If resistance is less than 10 Mohms, inspect connectors EM12, EM15 and EM22 for corrosion, bent/pushed back pins, or locate and repair harness/ connector fault and proceed to "End."

End

1. Perform appropriate service drive cycle and inspect for presence of DTC.
2. If fault code has cleared, fault condition has been corrected and no further diagnosis is required.
3. If fault code has not cleared, further diagnosis is required.

CODE P0140: O_2 SENSOR NO ACTIVITY DETECTED (BANK 1 SENSOR 2)

Inspect For Low Exhaust Temperature

1. Ensure engine and exhaust system are operating properly and at normal operating temperature.
2. If engine and exhaust system are operating properly, proceed to "Inspect For O_2 Sensor Failure."
3. If engine and exhaust system are not operating properly. Repair leaking exhaust manifold/catalyst or other general causes of an over rich mixture.

Inspect For O_2 Sensor Failure

1. Run engine for a period to warm sensor, then maintain a steady speed of approximately 2500 RPM.
2. Measure voltage between EM22/1 and EM22/2.
3. If voltage is between .6–1.0 volt, proceed to "Inspect For O_2 Sensor Failure."
4. If voltage is not between .6–1.0 volt, replace O_2 sensor, connect plug and "Stop."

Inspect For O_2 Sensor Failure

1. With engine at 2500 RPM, suddenly decelerate to idle speed.
2. Measure voltage between EM22/1 and EM22/2.
3. If voltage is 400 mVolts or less, stop engine and proceed to "Stop."
4. If voltage is more than 400 mVolts replace O_2 sensor, connect plug and proceed to "Stop."

Inspect For O_2 Sensor Failure

1. With engine at idle speed, suddenly accelerate to approximately 2500 RPM.
2. Measure voltage between EM22/1 and EM22/2.
3. If voltage rises to between .6–1 volt, proceed to "Inspect For O_2 Sensor Failure."
4. If voltage does not rise to between .6–1 volt, replace O_2 sensor, connect plug and proceed to "Stop."

Inspect For O_2 Sensor Failure

1. Run engine at 1500 RPM for approximately 3 minutes.
2. Measure voltage between EM22/1 and EM22/2.
3. If displayed voltage drops below 400 mVolts and then rises above 500 mVolts cycling approximately every 180 seconds, proceed to "Inspect For O_2 Sensor Continuity."
4. If displayed voltage does not cycle as outlined in previous step, replace O_2 sensor, connect plug(s) and proceed to "Stop."

Pin	Description	Active	Inactive
EM10-1	IGNITION SWITCHED POWER SUPPLY	B+	0 V
EM10-5	IGNITION SWITCHED POWER SUPPLY	B+	B+
EM10-6	OK TO START – ENCODED COMMUNICATIONS		
EM10-7	BRAKE SWITCH – NOT USED		
EM10-9	BATTERY POWER SUPPLY	B+	B+
EM10-10	BRAKE SWITCH	GROUND	B+
EM10-12	SERIAL COMMUNICATIONS		
EM10-13	SERIAL COMMUNICATIONS		
EM10-14	PARKING BRAKE SWITCH	GROUND (APPLIED)	B+
EM10-15	PARK / NEUTRAL CONFIRMATION	B+ (P, N)	GROUND (R,D,4,3,2)
EM10-16	EMS CONTROLLED RELAY ACTIVATE	GROUND	B+
EM10-17	SECURITY ACKNOWLEDGE	ENCODED COMMUNICATIONS	
EM10-20	IATS / ECTS / TPS / MECHANICAL GUARD POSITION / PEDAL POSITION COMMON REFERENCE GROUND	GROUND	GROUND
EM10-21	MECHANICAL GUARD POSITION / PEDAL POSITION / TPS COMMON REFERENCE VOLTAGE	5 V	5 V
EM10-22	GROUND	GROUND	GROUND
EM10-23	GROUND	GROUND	GROUND
EM10-25	CAN NETWORK	15 – 1500 Hz	
EM10-26	CAN NETWORK	15 – 1500 Hz	
EM10-27	CAN NETWORK	15 – 1500 Hz	
EM10-28	CAN NETWORK	15 – 1500 Hz	
EM11-3	ECM PROGRAMMING	B+	B+
EM11-6	ENGINE CRANK	GROUND (CRANKING)	B+
EM11-7	NOT USED		
EM11-8	MECHANICAL GUARD POSITION / PEDAL POSITION / TPS COMMON REFERENCE VOLTAGE	5 V	5 V
EM11-9	ECT FEEDBACK	0.41 V @ 195°F (DECREASING WITH TEMPERATURE)	
EM11-10	TPS FEEDBACK	0.5 V – IDLE; 4.75 V – WOT	
EM11-11	TPS FEEDBACK	0.5 V – IDLE; 4.75 V – WOT	
EM11-12	IATS / ECTS / TPS / MECHANICAL GUARD POSITION / PEDAL POSITION COMMON REFERENCE GROUND	GROUND	GROUND
EM11-13	MECHANICAL GUARD POSITION FEEDBACK	0.5 V – IDLE; 4.75 V – WOT	
EM11-14	MECHANICAL GUARD POSITION / PEDAL POSITION / TPS SHIELD	GROUND	GROUND
EM11-15	PEDAL POSITION FEEDBACK	0.5 V – IDLE; 4.75 V – WOT	
EM11-16	PEDAL POSITION FEEDBACK	0.5 V – IDLE; 4.75 V – WOT	
EM12-12	IATS FEEDBACK	0.98 V @ 10°C, DECREASING WITH TEMPERATURE	
EM12-13	MAFS FEEDBACK	1.2 V @ IDLE, INCREASING WITH RPM INCREASE	
EM12-14	'B' BANK HO2S	0.1 – 0.9 V @ IDLE (SWING)	
EM12-15	'A' BANK HO2S	0.1 – 0.9 V @ IDLE (SWING)	
EM12-16	NOT USED		
EM12-17	NOT USED		
EM12-18	MAFS REFERENCE GROUND	GROUND	GROUND
EM12-19	MAFS REFERENCE GROUND	GROUND	GROUND
EM12-22	H02S COMMON SHIELD	GROUND	GROUND
EM13-2	ECM PROGRAMMING		
EM13-4	NOT USED		
EM13-11	VACUUM SWITCHING VALVE #3 ACTIVATE	GROUND	B+
EM13-12	VACUUM SWITCHING VALVE #1 ACTIVATE	GROUND	B+
EM13-13	VACUUM SWITCHING VALVE #2 ACTIVATE	GROUND	B+
EM13-14	THROTTLE MOTOR POWER RELAY ACTIVATE	GROUND	B+
EM13-17	'B' BANK KNOCK SENSOR FEEDBACK	0 KHz – NO KNOCK, 2 – 20 KHz – KNOCK	
EM13-18	'A' BANK KNOCK SENSOR FEEDBACK	0 KHz – NO KNOCK, 2 – 20 KHz – KNOCK	
EM13-19	CKPS SIGNAL	5 V @ 1000 RPM – 566 Hz; 2000 RPM – 1132 Hz	
EM13-20	CMPS SIGNAL	5 Hz @ IDLE	
EM13-27	CMPS / CKPS / KNOCK SENSORS COMMON SHIELD	GROUND	GROUND
EM13-28	CKPS SIGNAL	5 V @ 1000 RPM – 566 Hz; 2000 RPM – 1132 Hz	
EM13-29	CMPS SIGNAL GROUND	GROUND	GROUND
EM14-1	THROTTLE MOTOR POWER SUPPLY	B+	GROUND
EM14-2	THROTTLE MOTOR POWER SUPPLY	B+	GROUND
EM14-3	IGNITION SWITCHED POWER SUPPLY	B+	GROUND
EM14-4	GROUND	GROUND	GROUND
EM14-5	THROTTLE MOTOR POWER SUPPLY	B+	GROUND
EM14-6	THROTTLE MOTOR POWER SUPPLY	B+	GROUND
EM14-7	GROUND	GROUND	GROUND
EM14-8	GROUND	GROUND	GROUND
EM14-9	GROUND	GROUND	GROUND
EM14-10	GROUND	GROUND	GROUND
EM14-11	THROTTLE MOTOR POWER SUPPLY	GROUND	GROUND
EM14-12	THROTTLE MOTOR POWER SUPPLY	B+	GROUND
EM15-1	UPSTREAM 'B' BANK HO2S HEATER GROUND	GROUND	GROUND
EM15-2	UPSTREAM 'A' BANK HO2S HEATER GROUND	GROUND	GROUND
EM15-3	EVAP VALVE ACTIVATE	GROUND (VALVE OPEN)	B+
EM15-8	VARIABLE VALVE TIMING SOLENOID 'B' BANK	GROUND	B+
EM15-9	VARIABLE VALVE TIMING SOLENOID 'A' BANK	GROUND	B+
EM15-11	GROUND	GROUND	GROUND
EM15-12	GROUND	GROUND	GROUND
EM15-22	GROUND	GROUND	GROUND

JC1019800040020X

Fig. 5 ECM connector terminal identification (Part 2 of 2)

Stop

1. Perform appropriate service drive cycle and inspect for presence of DTC.
2. If fault code has cleared, fault condition has been corrected and no further diagnosis is required.
3. If fault code has not cleared, further diagnosis is required.

Inspect For O_2 Sensor Continuity

1. With EM12 and EM22 disconnected, measure resistance between EM12/17 and EM22/2.
2. If resistance is less than .5 ohms, proceed to "O_2 Sensor Screen Ground Continuity."
3. If resistance is more than .5 ohms, inspect connectors EM12 and EM22 for corrosion, damaged/pushed back pins. Repair connectors or harness as required. Connect plug(s) and proceed to "Stop."

O_2 Sensor Screen Ground Continuity

1. With EM12 and EM22 disconnected, measure resistance between EM12/22 and EM22/1.
2. If resistance is less than .5 ohms, proceed to "O_2 Sensor Short Circuit To Ground."
3. If resistance is more than .5 ohms, inspect connectors EM12 and EM22 for corrosion, damaged/pushed back pins. Repair connectors or harness as required. Connect plug(s) and proceed to "Stop."

O_2 Sensor Short Circuit To Ground

1. With EM22 disconnected measure insulation resistance between sensor pin 001 and sensor body, then between pin 002 and sensor body.
2. If resistance is more than 10 Mohms, proceed to "Signal Ground 1 Continuity."
3. If resistance is less than 10 Mohms, replace O_2 sensor, connect all plugs and proceed to "Stop."

Stop

1. Perform appropriate service drive cycle and inspect for presence of DTC.
2. If fault code has cleared, fault condition has been corrected and no further diagnosis is required.
3. If fault code has not cleared, further diagnosis is required.

Signal Ground 1 Continuity

1. With EM10 and EM14 disconnected, measure resistance between EM10/23 and chassis ground EM1BR (EM2BR).
2. If resistance is less than .5 ohms, proceed to "Signal Ground 2 Continuity."
3. If resistance is more than .5 ohms, proceed as follows:
   a. Inspect connector EM10 for corrosion, damage, or pushed back pin.
   b. Inspect ground stud EM1BR (EM2BR) for corrosion.
   c. Inspect splice EMS38 for corrosion.
   d. Repair connector, ground stud or harness as required.
   e. Connect plug(s) and proceed to "Stop."

Signal Ground 2 Continuity

1. With EM10 and EM14 disconnected, measure resistance between EM14/4 and chassis ground EM1BR (EM2BR).
2. If resistance is less than .5 ohms, proceed to "Inspect For O_2 Sensor Continuity."
3. If resistance is more than .5 ohms, proceed as follows:
   a. Inspect connector EM14 for corrosion, damage, or pushed back pin.
   b. Inspect ground stud EM1BR (EM2BR) for corrosion.
   c. Inspect splice EMS38 for corrosion.
   d. Repair connector, ground stud or harness as required.
   e. Connect plug(s) and proceed to "Stop."

Stop

1. Perform appropriate service drive

cycle and inspect for presence of DTC.
2. If fault code has cleared, fault condition has been corrected and no further diagnosis is required.
3. If fault code has not cleared, further diagnosis is required.

Inspect For O_2 Sensor Continuity

1. With EM12 and EM22 disconnected, measure resistance between EM12/17 and EM22/2.
2. If resistance is less than .5 ohms, proceed to "O_2 Sensor Screen Ground Continuity."
3. If resistance is more than .5 ohms, inspect connectors EM12 and EM22 for corrosion or damaged/pushed back pins. Repair connectors or harness as required. Connect plug(s) and proceed to "End."

O_2 Sensor Screen Ground Continuity

1. With EM12 and EM22 disconnected, measure resistance between EM12/22 and EM22/1.
2. If resistance is less than .5 ohms, proceed to "Inspect For Short To B+."
3. If resistance is more than .5 ohms, inspect connectors EM12 and EM22 for corrosion or damaged/pushed back pins. Repair connectors or harness as required. Connect plug(s) and proceed to "End."

Inspect For Short To B+

1. With EM10 and EM12 disconnected, measure voltage between EM10/23 and EM12/15.
2. If voltage is zero, proceed to "Inspect For Short To B+."
3. If voltage is more than zero, inspect connectors EM10, EM12 and EM22 for corrosion or damaged/pushed back pins. Repair connectors or harness as required. Connect plug(s) and proceed to "End."

Inspect For Short To B+

1. With EM10 and EM12 disconnected, measure voltage between EM10/23 and EM12/22.
2. If voltage is zero, proceed to "Inspect Harness Short To Ground."
3. If voltage is more than zero, inspect connectors EM10, EM12 and EM22 for corrosion or damaged/pushed back pins. Repair connectors or harness as required. Connect plug(s) and proceed to "End."

Inspect Harness Short To Ground

1. With EM10 and EM12 and EM22 disconnected, measure insulation resistance between EM12/17 and ground EM10/23.
2. If resistance is more than 10 Mohms, proceed to "Inspect Harness Short Core To Core."
3. If resistance is less than 10 Mohms, inspect EM12 and EM22 for corrosion or bent/pushed back pins. Locate and repair harness/connector fault, then connect plug(s) and proceed to "End."

Inspect Harness Short Core To Core

1. Measure insulation resistance between EM12/17 and EM12/22.
2. If resistance is more than 10 Mohms, connect all plugs and proceed to "End."
3. If resistance is less than 10 Mohms, inspect EM12, EM15 and EM22 for corrosion or bent/pushed back pins. Locate and repair harness/connector fault, then connect plug(s) and proceed to "End."

End

1. Perform appropriate service drive cycle and inspect for presence of DTC.
2. If fault code has cleared, fault condition has been corrected and no further diagnosis is required.
3. If fault code has not cleared, further diagnosis is required.

CODES P0151, P0152 & P0155: O_2 SENSOR CIRCUIT MALFUNCTION (BANK 2 SENSOR 1)

Inspect O_2 Sensor Heater Continuity

1. With EM23 disconnected, measure resistance between EM23/1 and EM23/2.
2. If resistance is between 4–10 ohms, proceed to "Inspect For O_2 Sensor Failure."
3. If resistance is not between 4–10 ohms, replace O_2 sensor, connect plug and proceed to "Stop."

Inspect For O_2 Sensor Failure

1. Run engine for a period to warm sensor and then maintain a steady speed of approximately 2500 RPM.
2. With EM23 disconnected, measure voltage between EM23/3 and EM23/4.
3. If voltage is between .6–1.0 volt, proceed to "Inspect For O_2 Sensor Failure."
4. If voltage is between .6–1.0 volt, connect plug and proceed to "Stop."

Inspect For O_2 Sensor Failure

1. Maintain engine speed of 2500 RPM, then suddenly decelerate to idle.
2. With EM23 disconnected, measure voltage between EM23/3 and EM23/4.
3. If voltage dropped to 400 mVolts or less, proceed to "Inspect For O_2 Sensor Failure."
4. If voltage did not drop to 400 mVolts or less, replace O_2 sensor, connect plug and proceed to "Stop."

Inspect For O_2 Sensor Failure

1. With engine at idle speed, suddenly accelerate to approximately 2500 RPM.
2. With EM23 disconnected, measure voltage between EM23/3 and EM23/4.
3. If voltage rises to between .6–1 volt, proceed to "Heated O_2 Sensor Short Circuit To Ground."
4. If voltage does not rise to between .6–1 volt, replace O_2 sensor, connect plug and proceed to "Stop."

Heated O_2 Sensor Short Circuit To Ground

1. With EM23 disconnected measure insulation resistance between sensor pin 001 and sensor body, then between pin 003 and sensor body.
2. If resistance is more than 10 Mohms, proceed to "Signal Ground 1 Continuity."
3. If resistance is less than 10 Mohms, replace O_2 sensor, connect plug and proceed to "Stop."

Stop

1. Perform appropriate service drive cycle and inspect for presence of DTC.
2. If fault code has cleared, fault condition has been corrected and no further diagnosis is required.
3. If fault code has not cleared, further diagnosis is required.

Signal Ground 1 Continuity

1. With EM10 and EM14 disconnected, measure resistance between EM10/23 and chassis ground EM1BR (EM2BR).
2. If resistance is less than .5 ohms, proceed to "Signal Ground 2 Continuity."
3. If resistance is more than .5 ohms, proceed as follows:
   a. Inspect connector EM10 for corrosion, damage, or pushed back pin.
   b. Inspect ground stud EM1BR (EM2BR) for corrosion.
   c. Splice EMS38 for damage or corrosion.
   d. Repair harness, connector or ground as required.
   e. Connect plug(s) and proceed to "Stop."

Signal Ground 2 Continuity

1. With EM10 and EM14 disconnected, measure resistance between EM14/4 and chassis ground EM1BR (EM2BR).
2. If resistance is less than .5 ohms, proceed to "Inspect For Heated O_2 Sensor Continuity."
3. If resistance is less than .5 ohms, proceed as follows:
   a. Inspect connector EM14 for corrosion, damage, or pushed back pin.
   b. Inspect ground stud EM1BR (EM2BR) for corrosion.
   c. Splice EMS38 for damage or corrosion.
   d. Repair harness, connector or ground as required.
   e. Connect plug(s) and proceed to "Stop."

Stop

1. Perform appropriate service drive cycle and inspect for presence of DTC.
2. If fault code has cleared, fault condition has been corrected and no further diagnosis is required.

3. If fault code has not cleared, further diagnosis is required.

Inspect For Heated O_2 Sensor Continuity

1. With EM12 and EM23 disconnected, measure resistance between EM12/14 and EM23/3.
2. If resistance is less than .5 ohms, proceed to "Heated O_2 Sensor Screen Ground Continuity."
3. If resistance is less than .5 ohms, inspect connectors EM12 and EM23 for corrosion or damaged/pushed back pins. Repair connectors or harness as required. Connect plug(s) and proceed to "End."

Heated O_2 Sensor Screen Ground Continuity

1. With EM12 and EM23 disconnected, measure resistance between EM12/22 and EM23/4.
2. If resistance is less than .5 ohms, proceed to "Inspect For Short To B+."
3. If resistance is more than .5 ohms, inspect connectors EM12 and EM23 for corrosion or damaged/pushed back pins. Repair connectors or harness as required. Connect plug(s) and proceed to "End."

Inspect For Short To B+

1. With EM10 and EM12 disconnected, measure voltage between EM10/23 and EM12/14.
2. If voltage is zero, proceed to "Inspect For Short To B+."
3. If voltage is more than zero, inspect connectors EM10, EM12 and EM23 for corrosion or damaged/pushed back pins. Repair connectors or harness as required. Connect plug(s) and proceed to "End."

Inspect For Short To B+

1. With EM10 and EM12 disconnected, measure voltage between EM10/23 and EM12/22.
2. If voltage is zero, proceed to "Inspect For Short To B+ At O_2 Sensor Heater."
3. If voltage is more than zero, inspect connectors EM10, EM12 and EM23 for corrosion or damaged/pushed back pins. Repair connectors or harness as required. Connect plug(s) and proceed to "End."

Inspect For Short To B+ At O_2 Sensor Heater

1. Remove EMS fuse F14.
2. Disconnect EM10 and EM15.
3. Using a link lead, bridge EM10/16 and EM10/22.
4. Measure voltage between EM10/23 and EM15/1.
5. If voltage is zero, replace EMS fuse F14 and proceed to "Measure B+ At O_2 Sensor Heater Circuit."
6. If voltage is more than zero, inspect connectors EM10, EM15 and EM23 for corrosion or damaged/pushed back pins. Repair connectors or harness as required. Connect plug(s) and proceed to "End."

Measure B+ At O_2 Sensor Heater Circuit

1. With EM10 and EM15 disconnected, measure voltage between EM10/23 and EM15/1.
2. Using a link lead, bridge EM10/16 and EM10/22.
3. If battery voltage is present, remove link lead and connect all connectors, then proceed to "End."
4. If battery voltage is not present, inspect EMS fuse F14, ensure EMS control relay (relay 1) is energized, then proceed to "End."

End

1. Perform appropriate service drive cycle and inspect for presence of DTC.
2. If fault code has cleared, fault condition has been corrected and no further diagnosis is required.
3. If fault code has not cleared, further diagnosis is required.

CODE P0153: O_2 SENSOR CIRCUIT SLOW RESPONSE (BANK 2 SENSOR 1)

Inspect For Low Exhaust Temperature

1. Ensure engine and exhaust system are operating properly and at normal operating temperature.
2. If engine and exhaust system are operating properly, proceed to "Inspect For O_2 Sensor Heater Continuity."
3. If engine and exhaust system are not operating properly. Repair leaking exhaust manifold/catalyst or other general causes of an over rich mixture.

Inspect For O_2 Sensor Heater Continuity

1. With EM23 disconnected, measure resistance between EM23/1 and EM23/2.
2. If resistance is between 4–10 ohms, proceed to "Inspect For O_2 Sensor Failure."
3. If resistance is not between 4–10 ohms, replace O_2 sensor, connect plug and proceed to "Stop."

Inspect For O_2 Sensor Failure

1. Run engine for a period to warm sensor and then maintain a steady speed of approximately 2500 RPM
2. Measure voltage between EM23/3 and EM23/4.
3. If voltage is between .6–1 volt, proceed to "Inspect For O_2 Sensor Failure."
4. If voltage is not between .6–1 volt, replace O_2 sensor, connect plug and proceed to "Stop."

Inspect For O_2 Sensor Failure

1. With engine running at 2500 RPM, suddenly decelerate to idle.
2. Measure voltage between EM23/3 and EM23/4.
3. If voltage drops to 400 mVolts or less, proceed to "Inspect For O_2 Sensor Failure."
4. If voltage does not drop to 400 mVolts or less, replace O_2 sensor, connect plug and proceed to "Stop."

Inspect For O_2 Sensor Failure

1. With engine at idle speed, suddenly accelerate to approximately 2500 RPM.
2. Measure voltage between EM23/3 and EM23/4.
3. If voltage rises to between .6–1 volt, proceed to "Inspect For O_2 Sensor Failure."
4. If voltage does not rise to between .6–1 volt, replace O_2 sensor, connect plug and proceed to "Stop."

Inspect For O_2 Sensor Failure

1. Run engine at 1500 RPM for approximately two minutes.
2. Measure voltage between EM23/3 and EM23/4.
3. If displayed voltage drops below 400 mVolts and then rises above 500 mVolts cycling approximately every four seconds, proceed to "Heated O_2 Sensor Short Circuit To Ground."
4. If displayed voltage does not cycle as outlined in previous step, replace O_2 sensor, connect plug(s) and proceed to "Stop."

Stop

1. Perform appropriate service drive cycle and inspect for presence of DTC.
2. If fault code has cleared, fault condition has been corrected and no further diagnosis is required.
3. If fault code has not cleared, further diagnosis is required.

Heated O_2 Sensor Short Circuit To Ground

1. With EM23 disconnected measure insulation resistance between sensor pin 001 and sensor body, then between pin 003 and sensor body.
2. If resistance is more than 10 Mohms, proceed to "Signal Ground 1 Continuity."
3. If resistance is less than 10 Mohms, replace O_2 sensor, connect plug(s) and proceed to "Stop."

Stop

1. Perform appropriate service drive cycle and inspect for presence of DTC.
2. If fault code has cleared, fault condition has been corrected and no further diagnosis is required.
3. If fault code has not cleared, further diagnosis is required.

Signal Ground 1 Continuity

1. With EM10 and EM14 disconnected, measure resistance between EM10/23 and chassis ground EM1BR (EM2BR).
2. If resistance is less than .5 ohms, proceed to "Signal Ground 2 Continuity."
3. If resistance is more than .5 ohms, proceed as follows:

a. Inspect connector EM10 for corrosion, damage, or pushed back pin.
b. Inspect ground stud EM1BR (EM2BR) for corrosion.
c. Inspect splice EMS38 for damage or corrosion.
d. Repair connector, ground stud or splice as required.
e. Connect plug(s) and proceed to "Inspect For Heated O_2 Sensor Continuity."

Signal Ground 2 Continuity

1. With EM10 and EM14 disconnected, measure resistance between EM14/4 and chassis ground EM1BR (EM2BR).
2. If resistance is less than .5 ohms, proceed to "Heated O_2 Sensor Screen Ground Continuity."
3. If resistance is more than .5 ohms, proceed as follows:
   a. Inspect connector EM14 for corrosion, damage, or pushed back pin.
   b. Inspect ground stud EM1BR (EM2BR) for corrosion.
   c. Inspect splice EMS38 for damage or corrosion.
   d. Repair connector, ground stud or splice as required.
   e. Connect plug(s) and proceed to "Inspect For Heated O_2 Sensor Continuity."

Inspect For Heated O_2 Sensor Continuity

1. With EM12 and EM23 disconnected, measure resistance between EM12/14 and EM23/3.
2. If resistance is less than .5 ohms, proceed to "Heated O_2 Sensor Screen Ground Continuity."
3. If resistance is more than .5 ohms, inspect connectors EM12 and EM23 for corrosion, damaged/pushed back pins. Repair connectors or harness as required, then connect plug(s) and proceed to "End."

Heated O_2 Sensor Screen Ground Continuity

1. With EM12 and EM23 disconnected, measure resistance between EM12/22 and EM23/4.
2. If resistance is less than .5 ohms, proceed to "Inspect For Short To B+."
3. If resistance is more than .5 ohms, inspect connectors EM12 and EM23 for corrosion, damaged/pushed back pins. Repair connectors or harness as required, then connect plug(s) and proceed to "End."

Inspect For Short To B+

1. With EM10 and EM12 disconnected, measure voltage between EM10/23 and EM12/14.
2. If voltage is zero, proceed to "Inspect For Short To B+."
3. If voltage is more than zero, inspect connectors EM10, EM12 and EM23 for corrosion, damaged/pushed back pins. Repair connectors or harness as required, then connect plug(s) and proceed to "End."

Inspect For Short To B+

1. With EM10 and EM12 disconnected, measure voltage between EM10/23 and EM12/22.
2. If voltage is zero, proceed to "Inspect For Short To B+ At O_2 Sensor Heater."
3. If voltage is more than zero, inspect connectors EM10, EM12 and EM23 for corrosion, damaged/pushed back pins. Repair connectors or harness as required, then connect plug(s) and proceed to "End."

Inspect For Short To B+ At O_2 Sensor Heater

1. Remove EMS fuse F14.
2. Disconnect EM10 and EM15.
3. Using a link lead, bridge EM10/16 and EM10/22.
4. Measure voltage between EM10/23 and EM15/1.
5. If voltage is zero, replace EMS fuse F14 but retain link lead and proceed to "Measure B+ At O_2 Sensor Heater Circuit."
6. If voltage is not zero, inspect connectors EM10, EM15 and EM23 for corrosion, damaged/pushed back pins. Repair connectors or harness as required, then connect plug(s) and proceed to "End."

Measure B+ At O_2 Sensor Heater Circuit

1. With EM10 and EM15 disconnected, measure voltage between EM10/23 and EM15/2.
2. If battery voltage is present, remove link lead, connect all connectors and proceed to "End."
3. If battery voltage is not present, inspect EMS fuse F14, ensure EMS control relay (relay 1) is energized, then proceed to "End."

End

1. Perform appropriate service drive cycle and inspect for presence of DTC.
2. If fault code has cleared, fault condition has been corrected and no further diagnosis is required.
3. If fault code has not cleared, further diagnosis is required.

CODES P0157 & P0158: O_2 SENSOR CIRCUIT MALFUNCTION (BANK 2 SENSOR 2)

Inspect For O_2 Sensor Failure

1. Run engine for a period to warm sensor and then maintain a steady speed of approximately 2500 RPM.
2. Measure voltage between EM24/1 and EM24/2.
3. If voltage is between .6–1 volt, proceed to "Inspect For O_2 Sensor Failure."
4. If voltage is not between .6–1 volt, replace O_2 sensor, connect plug and proceed to "Stop."

Inspect For O_2 Sensor Failure

1. With engine running at 2500 RPM, suddenly decelerate to idle.
2. Measure voltage between EM24/1 and EM24/2.
3. If voltage drops 400 mVolts or less, proceed to "Inspect For O_2 Sensor Failure."
4. If voltage does not drop to 400 mVolts or less, replace O_2 sensor, connect plug and proceed to "Stop."

Inspect For O_2 Sensor Failure

1. With engine at idle speed, suddenly accelerate to approximately 2500 RPM.
2. Measure voltage between EM24/1 and EM24/2.
3. If voltage rises to between .6–1 volt, proceed to "Inspect For O_2 Sensor Failure."
4. If voltage does not rise to between .6–1 volt, replace O_2 sensor, connect plug and proceed to "Stop."

Inspect For O_2 Sensor Failure

1. Run engine at 1500 RPM for approximately three minutes.
2. Measure voltage between EM24/1 and EM24/2.
3. If displayed voltage drops below 400 mVolts and then rises above 500 mVolts, cycling approximately every 180 seconds, proceed to "Inspect For O_2 Sensor Continuity."
4. If displayed voltage does not cycle as outlined in previous step, replace O_2 sensor, connect plug(s) and proceed to "Stop."

Stop

1. Perform appropriate service drive cycle and inspect for presence of DTC.
2. If fault code has cleared, fault condition has been corrected and no further diagnosis is required.
3. If fault code has not cleared, further diagnosis is required.

Inspect For O_2 Sensor Continuity

1. With EM12 and EM24 disconnected, measure resistance between EM12/16 and EM24/2.
2. If resistance is less than .5 ohms, proceed to "O_2 Sensor Screen Ground Continuity."
3. If resistance is more than .5 ohms, inspect connectors EM12 and EM24 for corrosion, damaged/pushed back pins. Repair connectors or harness as required, connect plug(s) and proceed to "Stop."

O_2 Sensor Screen Ground Continuity

1. With EM12 and EM24 disconnected, measure resistance between EM12/22 and EM24/1.
2. If resistance is less than .5 ohms, proceed to "O_2 Sensor Short Circuit To Ground."
3. If resistance is more than .5 ohms, inspect connectors EM12 and EM24 for corrosion, damaged/pushed back pins. Repair connectors or harness as

required, connect plug(s) and proceed to "Stop."

O_2 Sensor Short Circuit To Ground

1. With EM24 disconnected measure insulation resistance between sensor pin 001 and sensor body, then between pin 002 and sensor body.
2. If resistance is more than 10 Mohms, proceed to "Signal Ground 1 Continuity."
3. If resistance is less than 10 Mohms, replace O_2 sensor, connect all plugs and proceed to "Stop."

Stop

1. Perform appropriate service drive cycle and inspect for presence of DTC.
2. If fault code has cleared, fault condition has been corrected and no further diagnosis is required.
3. If fault code has not cleared, further diagnosis is required.

Signal Ground 1 Continuity

1. With EM10 and EM14 disconnected, measure resistance between EM10/23 and chassis ground EM1BR (EM2BR).
2. If resistance is less than .5 ohms, proceed to "Signal Ground 2 Continuity."
3. If resistance is more than .5 ohms, proceed as follows:
   a. Inspect connector EM10 for corrosion, damage, or pushed back pin.
   b. Inspect ground stud EM1BR (EM2BR) for corrosion.
   c. Inspect splice EMS38 for corrosion or damage.
   d. Repair connector, ground or harness as required.
   e. Connect plug(s) and proceed to "Stop."

Signal Ground 2 Continuity

1. With EM10 and EM14 disconnected, measure resistance between EM14/4 and chassis ground EM1BR (EM2BR).
2. If resistance is less than .5 ohms, proceed to "Inspect For O_2 Sensor Continuity."
3. If resistance is more than .5 ohms, proceed as follows:
   a. Inspect connector EM10 for corrosion, damage, or pushed back pin.
   b. Inspect ground stud EM1BR (EM2BR) for corrosion.
   c. Inspect splice EMS38 for corrosion or damage.
   d. Repair connector, ground or harness as required.
   e. Connect plug(s) and proceed to "Stop."

Stop

1. Perform appropriate service drive cycle and inspect for presence of DTC.
2. If fault code has cleared, fault condition has been corrected and no further diagnosis is required.
3. If fault code has not cleared, further diagnosis is required.

Inspect For O_2 Sensor Continuity

1. With EM12 and EM24 disconnected, measure resistance between EM12/16 and EM24/2.
2. If resistance is less than .5 ohms, proceed to "O_2 Sensor Screen Ground Continuity."
3. If resistance is more than .5 ohms, inspect connectors EM12 and EM24 for corrosion, damaged/pushed back pins. Repair connectors or harness as required, connect plug(s) and proceed to "End."

O_2 Sensor Screen Ground Continuity

1. With EM12 and EM24 disconnected, measure resistance between EM12/22 and EM24/1.
2. If resistance is less than .5 ohms, proceed to "Inspect For Short To B+."
3. If resistance is more than .5 ohms, inspect connectors EM12 and EM24 for corrosion, damaged/pushed back pins. Repair connectors or harness as required, connect plug(s) and proceed to "End."

Inspect For Short To B+

1. With EM10 and EM12 disconnected, measure voltage between EM10/23 and EM12/16.
2. If voltage is zero, proceed to "Inspect For Short To B+."
3. If voltage is not zero, inspect connectors EM10, EM12 and EM24 for corrosion, damaged/pushed back pins. Repair connectors or harness as required, connect plug(s) and proceed to "End."

Inspect For Short To B+

1. With EM10 and EM12 disconnected, measure voltage between EM10/23 and EM12/22.
2. If voltage is zero, proceed to "Inspect Harness Short To Ground."
3. If voltage is not zero, inspect connectors EM10, EM12 and EM24 for corrosion, damaged/pushed back pins. Repair connectors or harness as required, connect plug(s) and proceed to "End."

Inspect Harness Short To Ground

1. Measure insulation resistance between EM12/16 and ground EM10/23.
2. If resistance is more than 10 Mohms, proceed to "Inspect Harness Short Core To Core."
3. If resistance is less than 10 Mohms, inspect connectors EM12 and EM24 for corrosion, damaged/pushed back pins. Repair connectors or harness as required, connect plug(s) and proceed to "End."

Inspect Harness Short Core To Core

1. Measure insulation resistance between EM12/16 and EM15/1.
2. If resistance is more than 10 Mohms, connect all plugs and proceed to "End."
3. If resistance is less than 10 Mohms, inspect connectors EM12, EM15 and EM24 for corrosion, damaged/pushed back pins. Repair connectors or harness as required, connect plug(s) and proceed to "End."

End

1. Perform appropriate service drive cycle and inspect for presence of DTC.
2. If fault code has cleared, fault condition has been corrected and no further diagnosis is required.
3. If fault code has not cleared, further diagnosis is required.

CODE P0160: O_2 SENSOR NO ACTIVITY DETECTED (BANK 2 SENSOR 2)

Inspect For Low Exhaust Temperature

1. Ensure engine and exhaust system are operating properly and at normal operating temperature.
2. If engine and exhaust system are operating properly, proceed to "Inspect For O_2 Sensor Failure."
3. If engine and exhaust system are not operating properly. Repair leaking exhaust manifold/catalyst or other general causes of an over rich mixture.

Inspect For O_2 Sensor Failure

1. Run engine for a period to warm sensor and then maintain a steady speed of approximately 2500 RPM.
2. With EM24 disconnected, measure voltage between EM24/1 and EM24/2.
3. If voltage is between .6–1 volt, proceed to "Inspect For O_2 Sensor Failure."
4. If voltage is not between .6–1 volt, replace O_2 sensor, connect plugs and proceed to "Stop."

Inspect For O_2 Sensor Failure

1. With engine running at 2500 RPM, suddenly decelerate to idle.
2. With EM24 disconnected, measure voltage between EM24/1 and EM24/2.
3. If voltage drops to 400 mVolts or less, proceed to "Inspect For O_2 Sensor Failure."
4. If voltage does not drop to 400 mVolts or less, replace O_2 sensor, connect plugs and proceed to "Stop."

Inspect For O_2 Sensor Failure

1. With engine at idle speed, suddenly accelerate to approximately 2500 RPM.
2. With EM24 disconnected, measure voltage between EM24/1 and EM24/2.
3. If voltage rises to between .6–1 volt, proceed to "Inspect For O_2 Sensor Failure."
4. If voltage does not rise to between .6–1 volt, replace O_2 sensor, connect plugs and proceed to "Stop."

Inspect For O_2 Sensor Failure

1. Run engine at 1500 RPM for approximately three minutes.
2. Measure voltage between EM24/1 and EM24/2.
3. If displayed voltage drops below 400 mVolts and then rises above 500 mVolts cycling approximately every 180 seconds, proceed to "Inspect For O_2 Sensor Continuity."
4. If displayed voltage does not cycle as outlined in previous step, replace O_2 sensor, connect plug(s) and proceed to "Stop."

Stop

1. Perform appropriate service drive cycle and inspect for presence of DTC.
2. If fault code has cleared, fault condition has been corrected and no further diagnosis is required.
3. If fault code has not cleared, further diagnosis is required.

Inspect For O_2 Sensor Continuity

1. With EM12 and EM24 disconnected, measure resistance between EM12/16 and EM24/2.
2. If resistance is less than .5 ohms, proceed to "O_2 Sensor Screen Ground Continuity."
3. If resistance is more than .5 ohms, inspect connectors EM12 and EM24 for corrosion, damaged/pushed back pins. Repair connector or harness as required, connect plug(s) and proceed to "Stop."

O_2 Sensor Screen Ground Continuity

1. With EM12 and EM24 disconnected, measure resistance between EM12/22 and EM24/1.
2. If resistance is less than .5 ohms, proceed to "O_2 Sensor Short Circuit To Ground."
3. If resistance is more than .5 ohms, inspect connectors EM12 and EM24 for corrosion, damaged/pushed back pins. Repair connector or harness as required, connect plug(s) and proceed to "Stop."

O_2 Sensor Short Circuit To Ground

1. With EM24 disconnected measure insulation resistance between sensor pin 001 and sensor body, then between pin 002 and sensor body.
2. If resistance is more than 10 Mohms, proceed to "Signal Ground 1 Continuity."
3. If resistance is less than 10 Mohms, replace O_2 sensor, connect all plugs and proceed to "Stop."

Stop

1. Perform appropriate service drive cycle and inspect for presence of DTC.
2. If fault code has cleared, fault condition has been corrected and no further diagnosis is required.
3. If fault code has not cleared, further diagnosis is required.

Signal Ground 1 Continuity

1. With EM10 and EM14 disconnected, measure resistance between EM10/23 and chassis ground EM1BR (EM2BR).
2. If resistance is less than .5 ohms, proceed to "Signal Ground 2 Continuity."
3. If resistance is more than .5 ohms, proceed as follows:
   a. Inspect connector EM10 for corrosion, damage, or pushed back pin.
   b. Inspect ground stud EM1BR (EM2BR) for corrosion.
   c. Inspect splice EMS38 for corrosion or damage.
   d. Repair connector, ground or harness as required.
   e. Connect plug(s) and proceed to "Stop."

Signal Ground 2 Continuity

1. With EM10 and EM14 disconnected, measure resistance between EM14/4 and chassis ground EM1BR (EM2BR).
2. If resistance is less than .5 ohms, proceed to "Inspect For O_2 Sensor Continuity."
3. If resistance is more than .5 ohms, proceed as follows:
   a. Inspect connector EM14 for corrosion, damage, or pushed back pin.
   b. Inspect ground stud EM1BR (EM2BR) for corrosion.
   c. Inspect splice EMS38 for corrosion or damage.
   d. Repair connector, ground or harness as required.
   e. Connect plug(s) and proceed to "Stop."

Stop

1. Perform appropriate service drive cycle and inspect for presence of DTC.
2. If fault code has cleared, fault condition has been corrected and no further diagnosis is required.
3. If fault code has not cleared, further diagnosis is required.

Inspect For O_2 Sensor Continuity

1. With EM12 and EM24 disconnected, measure resistance between EM12/16 and EM24/2.
2. If resistance is less than .5 ohms, proceed to "O_2 Sensor Screen Ground Continuity."
3. If resistance is more than .5 ohms, inspect connectors EM12 and EM24 for corrosion or damaged/pushed back pins. Repair connectors or harness as required, then connect plug(s) and proceed to "End."

O_2 Sensor Screen Ground Continuity

1. With EM12 and EM24 disconnected, measure resistance between EM12/22 and EM24/1.
2. If resistance is less than .5 ohms, proceed to "Inspect For Short To B+."
3. If resistance is more than .5 ohms, inspect connectors EM12 and EM24 for corrosion or damaged/pushed back pins. Repair connectors or harness as required, then connect plug(s) and proceed to "End."

Inspect For Short To B+

1. With EM10 and EM12 disconnected, measure voltage between EM10/23 and EM12/16.
2. If voltage is zero, proceed to "Inspect For Short To B+."
3. If voltage is more than zero, inspect connectors EM10, EM12 and EM24 for corrosion or damaged/pushed back pins. Repair connectors or harness as required, then connect plug(s) and proceed to "End."

Inspect For Short To B+

1. With EM10 and EM12 disconnected, measure voltage between EM10/23 and EM12/22.
2. If voltage is zero, proceed to "Inspect Harness Short To Ground."
3. If voltage is more than zero, inspect connectors EM10, EM12 and EM24 for corrosion or damaged/pushed back pins. Repair connectors or harness as required, then connect plug(s) and proceed to "End."

Inspect Harness Short To Ground

1. With EM10 and EM12 and EM24 disconnected, measure insulation resistance between EM12/16 and ground EM10/23.
2. If resistance is more than 10 Mohms, proceed to "Inspect Harness Short Core To Core."
3. If resistance is less than 10 Mohms, inspect connectors EM12 and EM24 for corrosion or damaged/pushed back pins. Repair connectors or harness as required, then connect plug(s) and proceed to "End."

Inspect Harness Short Core To Core

1. Measure insulation resistance between EM12/16 and EM12/22.
2. If resistance is more than 10 Mohms, connect all plugs and proceed to "End."
3. If resistance is less than 10 Mohms, inspect connectors EM12, EM15 and EM24 for corrosion or damaged/pushed back pins. Repair connectors or harness as required, then connect plug(s) and proceed to "End."

End

1. Perform appropriate service drive cycle and inspect for presence of DTC.
2. If fault code has cleared, fault condition has been corrected and no further diagnosis is required.
3. If fault code has not cleared, further diagnosis is required.

CODES P0201, P0202, P0203, P0204, P0205, P0206, P0207 & P0208: INJECTOR CIRCUIT MALFUNCTION NORMALLY ASPIRED ENGINE

Measure Injector Coil Resistance

Prior to this, or any other test, ensure all injector connectors are properly located. The recorded DTC will indicate which injector(s) is at fault.

1. With injector connector(s) PI7, PI8, PI9, PI10, PI11, PI12, PI13, PI14 disconnected, measure resistance between injector pins.
2. If resistance is 12–18 ohms, proceed to "Inspect Injector Coil Insulation."
3. If resistance is not 12–18 ohms, replace injector.

Inspect Injector Coil Insulation

1. Measure resistance between pin 1 (injector) and injector body.
2. If resistance is more than 10 Mohms, proceed to "Inspect Injector Supply."
3. If resistance is less than 10 Mohms, replace injector.

Measure Injector Supply

If B+ is not present at all connectors inspect EMS fuse F5 and PI main relay.

1. **On righthand bank,** measure voltage between ground EM1AR and appropriate connector:
   a. PI7/2.
   b. PI8/2.
   c. PI9/2.
   d. PI10/2.
2. **On lefthand bank,** measure voltage between ground EM1AR and appropriate connector:
   a. PI11/2.
   b. PI12/2.
   c. PI13/2.
   d. PI14/2.
3. **On both banks,** if battery voltage is present, proceed to "Inspect Injector Ground."
4. If battery voltage is not present, proceed to "Inspect Injector Feed Continuity."

Inspect Injector Feed Continuity

1. Remove PI main relay.
2. Measure resistance between pin 5 PI Main relay socket and injector connectors PI7/2, PI8/2, PI9/2, PI10/2, PI11/2, PI12/2, PI13/2 and PI14/2.
3. If resistance is less than .5 ohms, proceed to "Inspect Fuse To Relay Continuity."
4. If resistance is more than .5 ohms, repair harness between appropriate connector, splice PIS2 and pin 5 PI Main relay socket. Test system for normal operation.

Inspect Fuse To Relay Continuity

1. Remove Engine Management fuse F5.
2. Measure resistance between load side of fuse F5 and pin 3 of the PI Main relay socket.
3. If resistance is less than .5 ohms, replace fuse F5 and PI main relay, then proceed to "Inspect Injector Circuit Continuity."
4. If resistance is more than .5 ohms, repair connector EM19/9, EM5/3, PI main relay or harness.

Inspect Injector Circuit Continuity

1. With EM15 disconnected, measure resistance between the following connector terminals:
   a. EM15/7 and PI7/1.
   b. EM15/17 and PI8/1.
   c. EM15/16 and PI9/1.
   d. EM15/6 and PI10/1.
   e. EM15/18 and PI11/1.
   f. EM15/5 and PI12/1.
   g. EM15/4 and PI13/1.
   h. EM15/15 and PI14/1.
2. If resistance is less than .5 ohms, proceed to "Inspect Injector Ground."
3. If resistance is more than .5 ohms, repair harness/connector EM15, PI1/30 to PI1/38, or PI7 to PI14 and test system for normal operation.

Inspect Injector Ground

This test is appropriate for a ground fault on 1B, 2A, 3A, 4B, therefore codes P0205, P0202, P0203 and P0208 will be present.

1. Measure resistance between EM15/22 and ground EM1AR.
2. If resistance is less than .5 ohms, proceed to "Inspect Injector Ground."
3. If resistance is more than .5 ohms, inspect connector EM15/22 for bent/damaged pin, harness or ground EM1AR and test system for normal operation.

Inspect Injector Ground

This test is appropriate for a ground fault on 1A, 2B, 3B, 4A, therefore codes P0201, P0206, P0207 and P0204 will be present.

1. Measure resistance between EM15/11 and ground EM1AR.
2. If resistance is less than .5 ohms, proceed to "Inspect For Short To 1B, 2A, 3A, 4B Ground."
3. If resistance is more than .5 ohms, inspect connector EM15/11 for bent/damaged pin. Repair connector, harness or ground as required, then test system for normal operation.

Inspect For Short To 1B, 2A, 3A, 4B Ground

1. Disconnect connectors EM15 and PI7 to PI14.
2. Measure insulation resistance between EM15/11 and the following connector terminals:
   a. EM15/15.
   b. EM15/16.
   c. EM15/17.
   d. EM15/18.
3. If resistance is more than 10 Mohms, proceed to "Inspect For Short To 1A, 2B, 3B, 4A Ground."
4. If resistance is less than 10 Mohms, repair harness or connector (PI001/38, 033, 032, 035) and test system for normal operation.

Inspect For Short To 1A, 2B, 3B, 4A Ground

1. Disconnect connectors EM015 and IJ003–IJ0010.
2. Measure insulation resistance between EM015/011 and the following connector terminals:
   a. EM015/4.
   b. EM015/5.
   c. EM015/6.
   d. EM015/7.
3. If resistance is more than 10 Mohms, proceed to "Inspect Harness Short Core To Core."
4. If resistance is less than 10 Mohms, repair harness connector (PI1/37, 036, 034, 030) and test system for normal operation.

Inspect Harness Short Core To Core

1. Remove PI main relay.
2. Disconnect connectors EM015 and IJ003–IJ0010.
3. Measure insulation resistance, between the following terminals:
   a. EM15/4 and EM15/15.
   b. EM15/5 and EM15/16.
   c. EM15/6 and EM15/17.
   d. EM15/7 and EM15/18.
4. If resistance is more than 10 Mohms, proceed to "End."
5. If resistance is less than 10 Mohms, repair harness connector (PI1/37, 036, 034, 030) and test system for normal operation.

End

1. Perform appropriate service drive cycle and inspect for presence of DTC.
2. If fault code has cleared, fault condition has been corrected and no further diagnosis is required.
3. If fault code has not cleared, further diagnosis is required.

CODES P0201, P0202, P0203, P0204, P0205, P0206, P0207 & P0208: INJECTOR CIRCUIT MALFUNCTION SUPERCHARGED ENGINE

Measure Injector Coil Resistance

Prior to this, or any other test, ensure all injector connectors are properly located. The recorded DTC will indicate which injector(s) is at fault.

1. With injector connector(s) IJ003, IJ004, IJ005, IJ006, IJ007, IJ008, IJ009 and IJ0010 disconnected, measure resistance between injector pins.
2. If resistance is 12–18 ohms, proceed

to "Inspect Injector Coil Insulation."
3. If resistance is not 12–18 ohms, replace injector.

Inspect Injector Coil Insulation

1. Measure resistance between injector pin 1 and injector body.
2. Measure resistance between injector pin 2 and injector body.
3. If resistance is more than 10 Mohms, proceed to "Inspect Injector Supply."
4. If resistance is less than 10 Mohms, replace injector.

Inspect Injector Supply

If B+ is not present at all connectors inspect EMS fuse F5 and PI main relay.

1. **On righthand bank,** measure voltage between ground EM017 and appropriate connector:
   a. IJ003/002.
   b. IJ004/002.
   c. IJ005/002.
   d. IJ006/002.
2. **On lefthand bank,** measure voltage between ground EM017 and appropriate connector:
   a. IJ007/002.
   b. IJ008/002.
   c. IJ009/002.
   d. IJ0010/002.
3. **On both banks,** if battery voltage is present, proceed to "Inspect Injector Ground."
4. If battery voltage is not present, proceed to "Inspect Injector Feed Continuity."

Inspect Injector Feed Continuity

1. Remove PI main relay.
2. Measure resistance between pin 5 PI main relay socket and injector connectors IJ003/002, IJ004/002, IJ005/002, IJ006/002, IJ007/002, IJ008/002, IJ009/002 and IJ0010/002.
3. If resistance is less than .5 ohms, proceed to "Inspect Fuse To Relay Continuity."
4. If resistance is more than .5 ohms, repair harness between appropriate connector, splice PIS02, IJS01 or IJS02, PI002/055 and pin 5 PI main relay socket. Test system for normal operation.

Inspect Fuse To Relay Continuity

1. Remove Engine Management fuse F5.
2. Measure resistance between load side of fuse F5 and pin 3 of the PI main relay socket.
3. If resistance is less than .5 ohms, replace fuse F5 and PI main relay, then proceed to "Inspect Injector Circuit Continuity."
4. If resistance is more than .5 ohms, repair connector EM19/009, EM5/003, PI main relay pin 3 or harness.

Inspect Injector Circuit Continuity

1. With EM15 disconnected, measure resistance between the following connector terminals:
   a. EM015/007 and IJ003/001.
   b. EM015/017 and IJ004/001.
   c. EM015/016 and IJ005/001.
   d. EM015/006 and IJ006/001.
   e. EM015/018 and IJ007/001.
   f. EM015/005 and IJ008/001.
   g. EM015/004 and IJ009/001.
   h. EM015/015 and IJ0010/001.
2. If resistance is less than .5 ohms, proceed to "Inspect Injector Ground."
3. If resistance is more than .5 ohms, repair harness/connector EM015, PI001/030 to PI001/036, IJ001/002 to IJ001/005, IJ002/002 to IJ002/005 or IJ003 to IJ010. Test system for normal operation.

Inspect Injector Ground

This test is appropriate for a ground fault on 1B, 2A, 3A, 4B, therefore codes P0205, P0202, P0203 and P0208 will be present.

1. Measure resistance between EM015/022 and ground EM016L.
2. If resistance is less than .5 ohms, proceed to "Inspect Injector Ground."
3. If resistance is more than .5 ohms, inspect connector EM015/022 for bent/damaged pin, harness or ground EM016L and test system for normal operation.

Inspect Injector Ground

This test is appropriate for a ground fault on 1A, 2B, 3B, 4A, therefore codes P0201, P0206, P0207 and P0204 will be present.

1. Measure resistance between EM015/011 and ground EM016L.
2. If resistance is less than .5 ohms, proceed to "Inspect For Short To 1B, 2A, 3A, 4B Ground."
3. If resistance is more than .5 ohms, inspect connector EM015/011 for bent/damaged pin. Repair connector, harness or ground as required, then test system for normal operation.

Inspect For Short To 1B, 2A, 3A, 4B Ground

1. Disconnect connectors EM015 and IJ003– IJ010.
2. Measure insulation resistance between EM015/011 and the following connector terminals:
   a. EM015/015.
   b. EM015/016.
   c. EM015/017.
   d. EM015/018.
3. If resistance is more than 10 Mohms, proceed to "Inspect For Short To 1A, 2B, 3B, 4A Ground."
4. If resistance is less than 10 Mohms, repair harness or connector PI001/038, 033, 032, 035, IJ001/003 and IJ001/004, IJ002/002 and IJ002/005, then test system for normal operation.

Inspect For Short To 1A, 2B, 3B, 4A Ground

1. Disconnect connectors EM015 and IJ003–IJ010.
2. Measure insulation resistance between EM15/022 and the following connector terminals:
   a. EM015/004.
   b. EM015/005.
   c. EM015/006.
   d. EM015/007.
3. If resistance is more than 10 Mohms, proceed to "Inspect Harness Short Core To Core."
4. If resistance is less than 10 Mohms, repair harness connector PI001/037, 036, 034, 030, IJ001/002 and IJ001/005, IJ002/003 and IJ002/004, then test system for normal operation.

Inspect Harness Short Core To Core

1. Remove PI main relay.
2. Disconnect connectors EM015 and IJ001–IJ010.
3. Measure insulation resistance, between the following terminals:
   a. EM015/004 and EM015/015.
   b. EM015/005 and EM015/016.
   c. EM015/006 and EM015/017.
   d. EM015/007 and EM015/018.
4. If resistance is more than 10 Mohms, proceed to "End."
5. If resistance is less than 10 Mohms, repair harness connector PI001/0037, 036, 034. 030, IJ001/002 and IJ001/005, IJ002/003 and IJ002/004, then test system for normal operation.

End

1. If fault code is cleared, system is working properly
2. If fault code has not cleared, contact Jaguar Service.

CODES P0327, P0328, P0332 & P0333: KNOCK SENSOR CIRCUIT

Inspect Harness Short To Ground

1. With PI26, PI27 and EM13 disconnected, measure insulation resistance between connector terminal EM13/27 and the following connector terminals:
   a. EM13/17.
   b. EM13/18.
   c. EM13/19.
   d. EM13/20.
   e. EM13/28.
   f. EM13/29.
2. If all resistances are more than 10 Mohms, proceed to "Inspect Harness Core To Core Insulation."
3. If resistance is less than 10 Mohms, inspect connectors EM13, PI26 and PI27 for corrosion, damaged or pushed back pins. Repair harness connector PI1/17, PI1/18, PI1/19, PI1/20 and test system for normal operation

Inspect Harness Core To Core Insulation

1. Measure insulation resistance between EM13/18 and EM13/17.
2. If resistance is more than 10 Mohms, proceed to "Inspect Harness Ground Continuity."
3. If resistance is less than 10 Mohms, inspect connectors EM13, PI26 and

PI27 for corrosion, damaged or pushed back pins. Repair harness connector PI1/17, PI1/18, PI1/19, PI1/20 and test system for normal operation.

Inspect Harness Ground Continuity

1. Measure resistance between EM13/27 and PI26/2, then between EM13/27 and PI27/2.
2. If resistance is less than .5 ohms, proceed to "Inspect Harness Circuit Continuity."
3. If resistance is more than .5 ohms, inspect connectors EM13 and PI26 for corrosion, damaged or pushed back pins. Repair as required. Repair harness connector PI1/18 and test system for normal operation.

Inspect Harness Circuit Continuity

1. Measure resistance between EM13/18 and PI26/1, then between EM13/17 and PI27/1.
2. If resistance is less than .5 ohms, proceed to "Inspect For Short To B+."
3. If resistance is more than .5 ohms, inspect connectors EM13, PI26 and PI27 for corrosion, damaged or pushed back pins. Repair as required. If connectors are satisfactory, repair harness connector PI1/17 or PI1/18, then test system for normal operation.

Inspect For Short To B+

1. Measure voltage between EM13/17 and EM13/2, then between EM13/18 and EM13/27.
2. If voltage is more than zero, proceed to "Inspect Sensor Installed Condition."
3. If voltage is zero, inspect connectors EM13 and PI26 for corrosion, damaged or pushed back pins. Repair as required. If connectors are satisfactory, repair harness connector PI1/17, then test system for normal operation.

Inspect Sensor Installed Condition

1. If sensor is located properly, proceed to "Measure Sensor Resistance."
2. If sensor is not located properly, properly fit sensor and test system for normal operation.

Measure Sensor Resistance

1. Connect PI26 and PI27.
2. Measure righthand bank sensor coil resistance between EM13/18 and EM13/27.
3. Measure lefthand bank sensor coil resistance between EM13/17 and EM13/27.
4. If resistance is 500K–620K ohms, proceed to "End."
5. If resistance is not 500K–620K ohms, replace sensor(s) and test system for normal operation.

End

1. Perform appropriate service drive cycle and inspect for presence of DTC.
2. If fault code has cleared, fault condition has been corrected and no further diagnosis is required.
3. If fault code has not cleared, further diagnosis is required.

CODE P0335: CRANKSHAFT POSITION SENSOR CIRCUIT MALFUNCTION

Inspect Harness Short To Ground

1. Remove engine covers for access to PI26 and PI27.
2. Remove ABS modulator cover to access to PI17.
3. With EM13, PI17, PI26 and PI27 disconnected, measure insulation resistance between EM13/27 and EM13/19, then between EM13/27 and EM13/28.
4. If resistance is more than 10 Mohms, connect PI26 and PI27 only and proceed to "Inspect Harness Short Core To Core."
5. If resistance is less than 10 Mohms, inspect EM13, PI17 and PI1 for corrosion, bent/pushed back pins, or locate and repair harness/splice EMS9. Test system for normal operation.

Inspect Harness Short Core To Core

1. Measure insulation resistance between EM13/19 and EM13/28.
2. If resistance is more than 10 Mohms, proceed to "Inspect Harness Ground Continuity."
3. If resistance is less than 10 Mohms, inspect EM13 and PI17 for corrosion, bent/pushed back pins, or locate and repair harness/connector PI1. Test system for normal operation.

Inspect Harness Ground Continuity

1. Measure resistance between EM13/28 and PI17/2.
2. If resistance is less than .5 ohms, proceed to "Inspect Harness Signal Continuity."
3. If resistance is less than .5 ohms, inspect EM13 and PI17 for corrosion, bent/pushed back pins, or locate and repair harness/connector PI1/21. Test system for normal operation.

Inspect Harness Signal Continuity

1. Measure resistance between EM13/19 and PI17/1.
2. If resistance is less than .5 ohms, proceed to "Inspect For Short To B+."
3. If resistance is more than .5 ohms, inspect EM13 and PI17 for corrosion, bent/pushed back pins, or locate and repair harness/connector PI1/22. Test system for normal operation.

Inspect For Short To B+

1. Measure voltage between EM13/19 and EM13/27.
2. If voltage is zero, proceed to "Inspect Sensor Continuity."
3. If voltage is not zero, inspect EM13 and PI17 for corrosion, bent/pushed back pins, or locate and repair harness/connector PI1. Test system for normal operation.

Inspect Sensor Continuity

1. Measure resistance between PI17/2 and PI17/1.
2. If resistance is between 950–1250 ohms, proceed to "Inspect Sensor Installed Condition."
3. If resistance is not between 950–1250 ohms, replace crankshaft position sensor and proceed to "End."

Inspect Sensor Installed Condition

1. Ensure sensor is mounted properly, inspect for the presence of any debris on sensor pick-up face.
2. If sensor is mounted properly and clean, proceed to "End."
3. If sensor is not mounted properly or dirty, repair as required and test system for normal operation.

End

1. Perform appropriate service drive cycle and inspect for presence of DTC.
2. If fault code has cleared, fault condition has been corrected and no further diagnosis is required.
3. If fault code has not cleared, further diagnosis is required.

CODES P0340 & P1336: CAMSHAFT POSITION SENSOR MALFUNCTION

Inspect Sensor Continuity

1. With EM13 disconnected measure resistance between EM13/20 and EM13/29.
2. If resistance is 1850–2500 ohms, proceed to "Inspect Mechanical Condition."
3. If resistance is not 1850–2500 ohms, proceed to "Inspect Harness Ground Continuity."

Inspect Harness Ground Continuity

1. Remove engine covers and displace coolant expansion tank, see removal instructions.
2. Disconnect PI15 and measure resistance between EM13/29 and PI15/2.
3. If resistance is less than .5 ohms, proceed to "Inspect Harness Signal Continuity."
4. If resistance is more than .5 ohms, inspect EM13 and PI15 for corrosion and bent/pushed back pins, or locate and repair harness/connector PI1/24. Test system for normal operation.

Inspect Harness Signal Continuity

1. Measure resistance between EM13/20 and PI15/1.

2. If resistance is less than .5 ohms, proceed to "Inspect Harness Short To Ground."
3. If resistance is more than .5 ohms, inspect EM13 and PI15 for corrosion, bent/pushed back pins, or locate and repair harness/connector PI1/25. Test system for normal operation.

Inspect Harness Short To Ground

1. With EM13, PI15, PI26 and PI27 disconnected, measure insulation resistance between EM13/27 and the following terminals:
   a. EM13/2.
   b. EM13/29.
2. If resistance is more than 10 Mohms, connect P126 and P127, then proceed to "Inspect Harness Short Core To Core."
3. If resistance is less than 10 Mohms, inspect EM13, PI15 and PI1 for corrosion, bent/pushed back pins, or locate and repair harness/splice EMS9. Test system for normal operation.

Inspect Harness Short Core To Core

1. Measure insulation resistance between EM13/29 and EM13/20.
2. If resistance is more than 10 Mohms, proceed to "Inspect For Short To B+."
3. If resistance is less than 10 Mohms, inspect EM13 and PI15 for corrosion, bent/pushed back pins, or locate and repair harness/connector PI1. Test system for normal operation.

Inspect For Short To B+

1. Measure voltage between EM13/20 and EM13/27.
2. If voltage is zero, proceed to "Inspect Mechanical Condition."
3. If voltage is not zero, inspect EM13 and PI15 for corrosion, bent/pushed back pins, or locate and repair harness/connector PI1.

Inspect Mechanical Condition

1. Ensure cam sensor is mounted properly and securely.
2. Ensure cam sensor ring tooth is present.
3. If cam sensor is satisfactory, proceed to "End."
4. If cam sensor is not satisfactory, repair or replace as required.

End

1. Perform appropriate service drive cycle and inspect for presence of DTC.
2. If fault code has cleared, fault condition has been corrected and no further diagnosis is required.
3. If fault code has not cleared, further diagnosis is required.

CODES P0351, P0352, P0353, P0354, P0355, P0356, P0357 & P0358: IGNITION COIL PRIMARY CIRCUIT MALFUNCTION

Inspect Coil Supply

Prior to this, or any other test, ensure all connectors are properly located. If B+ is not present at all connectors inspect fuse F18 and ignition relay (2).

1. With appropriate righthand bank connector disconnected, measure voltage between ground the following connector terminals:
   a. EM2AR (EM1AR).
   b. PI18/1.
   c. PI19/1.
   d. PI20/1.
   e. PI21/1.
2. With appropriate lefthand bank connector disconnected, measure voltage between ground ant the following connector terminals:
   a. EM2AR (EM1AR).
   b. PI22/1.
   c. PI23/1.
   d. PI24/1.
   e. PI25/1.
3. If battery voltage is present at each terminal, proceed to "Measure Coil Resistance."
4. If battery voltage is not present at each terminal, proceed to "Inspect Fuse To Relay Continuity."

Measure Coil Resistance

Recorded DTC will indicate which cylinder.

1. With coil connector(s) PI18, PI19, PI20, PI21, PI22, PI23, PI24, PI25 disconnected, measure resistance between coil pins.
2. If resistance is .54–1.04 ohms, proceed to "Inspect Relay To Coil Continuity."
3. If resistance is not .54–1.04 ohms, replace coil(s) and test system for normal operation.

Inspect Relay To Coil Continuity

1. Remove Ignition relay (2).
2. Measure resistance between pin 5 Ignition coil relay socket and in turn pin 1 coil connector(s) PI18, PI19, PI20, PI21, PI22, PI23, PI24, PI25.
3. If resistance is less than .5 ohms, proceed to "Inspect Fuse To Relay Continuity."
4. If resistance is more than .5 ohms, proceed as follows:
   a. Inspect EM26, PI1/53, PI18 to PI25 and pin 5 of the ignition coil relay socket for corrosion or bent/pushed back pins.
   b. Locate and repair harness connector PI1.
   c. Inspect splices PIS5 and EMS22 for corrosion or damage.
   d. Test system for normal operation.

Inspect Fuse To Relay Continuity

1. Remove ignition fuse F18.
2. Measure resistance between load side of F18 and pin 3 Ignition relay (2) socket.
3. If resistance is less than .5 ohms, proceed to "Measure B+ At Relay Coil."
4. If resistance is more than .5 ohms, inspect EM19/6, EM26/3 and pin 3 ignition coil relay socket for corrosion and bent/pushed back pins or locate and repair harness. Test system for normal operation.

Measure B+ At Relay Coil

1. Measure voltage between relay socket pin 2 and ground EM1AR.
2. If battery voltage is present, proceed to "Measure B+ At ECM."
3. If battery voltage is not present, inspect connectors EM26, EM19 for bent/pushed back pins or locate and repair harness/splice EMS30. Test system for normal operation.

Measure B+ At ECM

1. With EM13 disconnected, measure voltage between EM13/22 and ground EM1AR.
2. If battery voltage is present, proceed to "End."
3. If battery voltage is not present, proceed to "Inspect Continuity Relay To ECM."

Inspect Continuity Relay To ECM

1. With ignition relay (2) removed, measure resistance between relay pin 1 and EM13/22.
2. If resistance is less than .5 ohms, proceed to "Inspect Harness Continuity Coil To Control Module."
3. If resistance is more than .5 ohms, proceed as follows:
   a. Inspect connectors EM26, EM13 and relay socket 1 for bent/pushed back pins.
   b. Inspect harness for open circuit. Repair as required.
   c. Test system for normal operation.

Inspect Harness Continuity Coil To Control Module

The recorded DTC will indicate which cylinder(s).

1. With coil connectors PI18, PI19, PI20, PI21, PI22, PI23, PI24, PI25, EM27 and EM29 disconnected, measure resistance between the following connector terminals:
   a. PI18/2 and EM27/8.
   b. PI21/2 and EM27/11.
   c. PI23/2 and EM27/7.
   d. PI24/2 and EM27/12.
   e. PI19/2 and EM29/11.
   f. PI20/2 and EM29/7.
   g. PI22/2 and EM29/8.
   h. PI25/2 and EM29/12.
2. If resistance is less than .5 ohms, proceed to "Inspect Harness Continuity

ECM To Control Module."
3. If resistance is more than .5 ohms, proceed as follows:
   a. Inspect connectors PI18, PI19, PI20, PI21, PI22, PI23, PI24, PI25, PI1 and EM27 for bent/pushed back pins.
   b. Inspect harness for open or short circuit. Repair as required.
   c. Test system for normal operation.

Inspect Harness Continuity ECM To Control Module

The recorded DTC will indicate which cylinder(s).

1. With connectors EM27, EM29 and EM13 disconnected, measure resistance between the following connector terminals:
   a. EM27/2 and EM13/26.
   b. EM27/3 and EM13/33.
   c. EM27/6 and EM13/32.
   d. EM27/5 and EM13/23.
   e. EM29/2 and EM13/34.
   f. EM29/5 and EM13/25.
   g. EM29/3 and EM13/24.
   h. EM29/6 and EM13/31.
2. If resistance is less than .5 ohms, proceed to "Inspect Ground Continuity Control Module."
3. If resistance is more than .5 ohms, proceed as follows:
   a. Inspect connectors EM27 and EM13 for bent/pushed back pins.
   b. Inspect harness for open or short circuit. Repair as required.
   c. Test system for normal operation.

Inspect Ground Continuity Control Module

1. Measure resistance between EM27/9 (1 control module) and ground EM2AR (EM1AR), then between EM29/9 (2 control module) and ground EM2AR (EM1AR).
2. If resistance is less than .5 ohms, proceed to "Inspect For Short To B+ - (1 Control Module)."
3. If resistance is less than .5 ohms, proceed as follows:
   a. Inspect connector EM27 for bent/pushed back pins.
   b. Inspect harness for open or short circuit. Repair as required.
   c. Test system for normal operation.

Inspect For Short To B+ - (1 Control Module)

1. Remove fuse F18.
2. With EM12, EM13 and EM27 disconnected, measure voltage between ground EM27/9 and the following connector terminals:
   a. EM13/26.
   b. EM13/33.
   c. EM13/32.
   d. EM13/23.
3. If voltage is zero at every measurement, proceed to "Inspect For Short To B+ - (2 Control Module)."
4. If voltage is not zero at every measurement, proceed as follows:
   a. Inspect connectors EM13 and EM27 for bent/pushed back pins.
   b. Inspect harness for open or short circuit. Repair as required.
   c. Test system for normal operation.

Inspect For Short To B+ - (2 Control Module)

1. With EM12, EM13 and EM29 disconnected, measure voltage between ground EM29/9 and the following connector terminals:
   a. EM13/34.
   b. EM13/25.
   c. EM13/24.
   d. EM13/31.
2. If voltage is not present at any terminal, proceed to "Inspect For Short To B+."
3. If voltage is present at any terminal, proceed as follows:
   a. Inspect connectors EM13 and EM29 for bent/pushed back pins.
   b. Inspect harness for open or short circuit. Repair as required.
   c. Test system for normal operation.

Inspect For Short To B+

1. With EM27 and EM29 disconnected, measure voltage between EM27/10 and ground EM27/9, then between EM29/10 and ground EM29/9.
2. If voltage is not present, replace fuse F18 and proceed to "End."
3. If voltage is present, proceed as follows:
   a. Inspect connectors EM27, EM29 and PI1 for bent/pushed back pins.
   b. Inspect harness and splice EMS22 for an open or short circuit.
   c. Test system for normal operation.

Inspect Harness Short Core To Core

1. Disconnect connectors EM27, EM29 and PI18 to PI24.
2. Remove Ignition relay (2).
3. Measure insulation resistance, between the following connector terminals:
   a. EM27/7 and EM29/7.
   b. EM27/8 and EM29/8.
   c. EM27/11 and EM29/11.
   d. EM27/12 and EM29/12.
4. If resistance is more than 10 Mohms, proceed to "Inspect For Short 1 Module To Ground."
5. If resistance is less than 10 Mohms, proceed as follows:
   a. Inspect connectors EM29, PI1 and PI18 to PI24 for bent/pushed back pins.
   b. Inspect harness for open or short circuit. Repair as required.
   c. Test system for normal operation.

Inspect For Short 1 Module To Ground

1. With connectors EM12, EM13, EM27, EM29, PI18, PI21, PI23 and PI24 disconnected and fuse F18 removed, measure resistance between EM27/8 and EM27/9.
2. If resistance is more than 10 Mohms, proceed to "Inspect For Short 2 Module To Ground."
3. If resistance is less than 10 Mohms, proceed as follows:
   a. Inspect connectors EM27, PI1 and PI18, PI21, PI23 and PI24 for bent/pushed back pins.
   b. Inspect harness for open or short circuit. Repair as required.
   c. Test system for normal operation.

Inspect For Short 2 Module To Ground

1. With connectors EM12, EM13, EM27, EM29, PI19, PI20, PI22 and PI25 disconnected, measure resistance between EM29/8 and EM29/9.
2. If resistance is more than 10 Mohms, replace fuse F18 and proceed to "End."
3. If resistance is less than 10 Mohms, proceed as follows:
   a. Inspect connectors EM29, PI1, PI19, PI20, PI22 and PI25 for bent/pushed back pins.
   b. Inspect harness for open or short circuit. Repair as required.
   c. Test system for normal operation.

End

1. Perform appropriate service drive cycle and inspect for presence of DTC.
2. If fault code has cleared, fault condition has been corrected and no further diagnosis is required.
3. If fault code has not cleared, further diagnosis is required.

CODE P0400: EGR FLOW MALFUNCTION

Inspect Transfer Pipe

1. Inspect EGR to exhaust manifold pipe for damage and leaks.
2. If EGR and exhaust pipe are satisfactory, proceed to "Inspect Stepper Coil Open Circuit."
3. If EGR and exhaust pipe are not satisfactory, repair as required and test system for normal operation.

Inspect Stepper Coil Open Circuit

1. With EM12 disconnected, measure resistance between EM12/1 and EM12/3, then between EM12/2 and EM12/4.
2. If coil resistance is more than 80 ohms, proceed to "Inspect Harness Continuity."
3. If coil resistance is less than 80 ohms, proceed to "Measure Current Draw."

Measure Current Draw

If fuse F14 has blown, other failures will be present.

1. Disconnect EM12 and EM10 connectors.
2. Connect a suitable link lead between EM10/16 and EM10/22 (to energize EMS control relay).
3. Measure current between ground EM10/22 and the following connector terminals:
   a. EM12/1.
   b. EM12/2.
   c. EM12/3.
   d. EM12/4.

4. If current is .3–1 amps, proceed to "Inspect Stepper Motor Insulation."
5. If current is not .3–1 amps, proceed to "Inspect Harness Continuity."

Inspect Harness Continuity

1. Disconnect PI34 and measure resistance between the following connector terminals:
   a. EM12/1 and PI34/4.
   b. EM12/2 and PI34/1.
   c. EM12/3 and PI34/6.
   d. EM12/4 and PI34/3.
2. If resistance is less than .5 ohms, proceed to "Inspect Stepper Motor Insulation."
3. If resistance is more than .5 ohms, proceed as follows:
   a. Inspect EM12 and PI34 for bent/pushed back pins.
   b. Repair harness or connectors PI1/8, PI1/9, PI1/10 or PI1/7.

Inspect Stepper Motor Insulation

1. With PI34 disconnected, connect test meter probe between each EGR socket pin and EGR body.
2. If resistance is more than 10 Mohms, proceed to "Inspect EGR Mechanical Condition."
3. If resistance is less than 10 Mohms, replace EGR valve and test system for normal operation.

Inspect EGR Mechanical Condition

1. Remove and inspect EGR.
2. If valve is gummed or jammed, replace EGR, connect P134, EM10 and EM12, then proceed to "End."
3. If valve is not gummed or jammed, proceed to "Codes P0400, P0405 & P0406: EGR Malfunction."

End

1. Perform appropriate service drive cycle and inspect for presence of DTC.
2. If fault code has cleared, fault condition has been corrected and no further diagnosis is required.
3. If fault code has not cleared, further diagnosis is required.

CODE P0405: EGR SENSOR "A" CIRCUIT LOW INPUT

Inspect Stepper Coil Open Circuit

1. With EM12 disconnected measure resistance between EM12/1 and EM12/3, then between EM12/2 and EM12/4.
2. If coil resistance is more than 80 ohms, replace EGR valve and test system for normal operation.
3. If coil resistance is less than 80 ohms, proceed to "Measure Current Draw."

Measure Current Draw

If fuse F14 is blown, other failures will be present.

1. Disconnect EM12 and EM10.
2. Use a suitable link lead, bridge terminals EM10/16 and EM10/22 (to energize EMS control relay).
3. Measure current between ground EM10/22 and the following connector terminals:
   a. EM12/1.
   b. EM12/2.
   c. EM12/3.
   d. EM12/4.
4. If current is .3–1 amp, proceed to "End."
5. If current is not .3–1 amp, proceed to "Codes P0400, P0405 & P0406: EGR Malfunction."

End

1. Perform appropriate service drive cycle and inspect for presence of DTC.
2. If fault code has cleared, fault condition has been corrected and no further diagnosis is required.
3. If fault code has not cleared, further diagnosis is required.

CODE P0406: EGR SENSOR "B" CIRCUIT LOW INPUT

Inspect Stepper Coil Short Circuit

1. With EM12 disconnected measure resistance between EM12/1 and EM12/3, then between EM12/2 and EM12/4.
2. If coil resistance is more than 40 ohms, replace EGR valve, connect EM12 and proceed to "End."
3. If coil resistance is less than 40 ohms, proceed to "Codes P0400, P0405 and P0406."

End

1. Perform appropriate service drive cycle and inspect for presence of DTC.
2. If fault code has cleared, fault condition has been corrected and no further diagnosis is required.
3. If fault code has not cleared, further diagnosis is required.

CODES P0400, P0405 & P0406: EGR MALFUNCTION

Do not use this test unless directed to do so.

Inspect For Short To B+

1. With connectors EM10, EM12 and PI34 disconnected measure voltage between EM12/1 and ground EM10/22.
2. If voltage is zero, proceed to "Measure B+ At Stepper Motor."
3. If voltage is not zero, inspect EM10, EM12 and PI34 for bent/pushed back pins. Repair harness or connector PI1/8 as required.

Measure B+ At Stepper Motor

If fuse F14 or relay 1 are faulty, the engine will not start.

1. Using a suitable link lead, bridge terminals EM10/16 and EM10/22 (to energize EMS control relay).
2. Measure voltage between ground EM10/22 and PI34/2.
3. If battery voltage is present, proceed to "Measure B+ At Stepper Motor."
4. If battery voltage is not present, ensure fuse F14 and EMS control Relay 1 are energized, then proceed to "Inspect EGR Ground Continuity."

Measure B+ At Stepper Motor

1. Measure voltage between ground EM10/22 and PI34/5.
2. If battery voltage is present, proceed to "Inspect Harness Short To Chassis."
3. If battery voltage is not present, ensure fuse F14 and EMS control Relay 1 are energized, then proceed to "Inspect EGR Ground Continuity."

Inspect Harness Short To Chassis

1. Measure insulation resistance between EM12/1 and ground EM10/22.
2. If resistance is more than 10 Mohms, proceed to "Inspect Harness Short Core To Core."
3. If resistance is less than 10 Mohms, inspect EM10, EM12 and PI34 for corrosion or bent/pushed back pins. Repair harness or connector PI1 as required, then proceed to "End."

Inspect Harness Short Core To Core

1. Measure insulation resistance between the following terminals:
   a. EM12/1 and EM12/2.
   b. EM12/2 and EM12/3.
   c. EM12/3 and EM12/4.
   d. EM12/4 and EM12/1.
2. If resistance is more than 10 Mohms, proceed to "Inspect Harness Continuity."
3. If resistance is less than 10 Mohms, inspect EM12 and PI34 for corrosion or bent/pushed back pins. Repair harness or connector PI1 as required, then proceed to "End."

Inspect Harness Continuity

1. Measure resistance between the following terminals:
   a. EM12/1 and PI34/4.
   b. EM12/2 and PI34/1.
   c. EM12/3 and PI34/6.
   d. EM12/4 and PI34/3.
2. If resistance is less than .5 ohms, proceed to "Inspect EGR Ground Continuity."
3. If resistance is more than .5 ohms, inspect EM12 and PI34 for corrosion or bent/pushed back pins. Repair harness or connector PI1 as required, then proceed to "End."

Inspect EGR Ground Continuity

1. Measure resistance between EM10/22 and ground EM1AL (EM2AL).
2. If resistance is less than .5 ohms, proceed to "Inspect B+ Continuity."
3. If resistance is more than .5 ohms, inspect EM10 for corrosion, bent/pushed back pin, then inspect condition of ground EM1AL (EM2AL). Repair as required and proceed to "End."

Inspect B+ Continuity

1. Measure resistance between PI34/2 and EM19/8.
2. If resistance is less than .5 ohms, proceed to "End."
3. If resistance is more than .5 ohms, inspect EM19, splice EMS30, connectors PI1/47 and PI34 for corrosion, bent/pushed back pins. Repair as required. Proceed to "End."

End

1. Perform appropriate service drive cycle and inspect for presence of DTC.
2. If fault code has cleared, fault condition has been corrected and no further diagnosis is required.
3. If fault code has not cleared, further diagnosis is required.

CODE P0441: EVAP SYSTEM IMPROPER PURGE FLOW

Mechanical System Inspection

1. Inspect the following:
   a. Canister for blockage or saturation.
   b. Purge line for blockage, damage or leaks.
   c. Vacuum system.
2. If system is satisfactory, proceed to "Inspect Purge Valve Continuity."
3. If system is not satisfactory, repair as required and test system for normal operation.

Inspect Purge Valve Continuity

1. With EM58 disconnected, measure resistance of EVAP valve coil at pins 1 and 2.
2. If resistance is 25–40 ohms, connect EM58 and proceed to "Measure Electrical Feed."
3. If resistance is not 25–40 ohms, replace EVAP valve.

Measure Electrical Feed

1. Disconnect EM15 and EM10.
2. Using a suitable link lead, bridge EM10/16 and EM10/23 (to energize EMS control relay).
3. Measure voltage between EM15/3 and EM10/22.
4. If battery voltage is present, proceed to "Measure Current Draw."
5. If battery voltage is not present, proceed to "Codes P0444 and P0445: EVAP System Purge Control Valve Circuit Malfunction."

Measure Current Draw

1. With EM15 and EM10 disconnected, measure current between EM15/3 and EM10/22.
2. If current is .25–.64 amps, proceed to "End."
3. If current is not .25–.64 amps, proceed to "Codes P0444 & P0445: EVAP System Purge Control Valve Circuit Malfunction."

End

1. Perform appropriate service drive cycle and inspect for presence of DTC.
2. If fault code has cleared, fault condition has been corrected and no further diagnosis is required.
3. If fault code has not cleared, further diagnosis is required.

CODE P0442: EVAPORATIVE EMISSIONS CONTROL SYSTEM LEAK DETECTED

Mechanical System Inspection

1. Turn ignition switch to O position.
2. Inspect the following:
   a. Is fuel cap missing or improperly installed?
   b. Is fuel cap seal faulty?
   c. Is there a leak or damage on carbon canisters or EVAP hoses and plumbing?
   d. Is CCV improperly installed?
   e. Is purge valve vacuum line leaking or blocked?
   f. If purge line blocked?
   g. If purge line damaged or leaking?
3. If Yes, repair program and proceed to "End."
4. If No, proceed to "Measure Purge Valve Resistance."

Measure Purge Valve Resistance

1. Turn ignition switch to O position.
2. Disconnect EM039 purge valve connector.
3. Measure EVAP valve coil resistance between pins 1 and 2.
4. If resistance is 25–40 ohms, proceed to "Inspect Electrical Feed."
5. If resistance is not 25–40 ohms, replace EVAP valve.

Inspect Electrical Feed

1. Turn ignition switch to II position.
2. Disconnect EM015, EM039 and EM010.
3. Energize EMS control relay by bridging EM010/016 and EM010/023 using suitable link.
4. Measure voltage between EM039/001 and EM010/022.
5. If measurement is battery positive voltage, proceed to "Measure Current Draw."
6. If measurement is not battery positive voltage, inspect harness/connectors EM010, EM039 and splice EMS30 for bent/pushed back pins, damage or corrosion.
7. Repair as required and test system for normal operation.

Measure Current Draw

1. Turn ignition switch to O position.
2. Disconnect EM039.
3. Measure resistance between EM015/003 and EM039/002.
4. If resistance is less than .5 ohms, proceed to "End."
5. If resistance is not less than .5 ohms, proceed to "Codes P0444 & P0445: EVAP System Purge Control Valve Circuit Malfunction" "Inspect For Short To B+."

End

1. If code has been cleared, system is operating properly.
2. If code has not been cleared, contact Jaguar Service.

CODES P0444 & P0445: EVAP SYSTEM PURGE CONTROL VALVE CIRCUIT MALFUNCTION

Inspect Purge Valve Continuity

1. With EM58 disconnected, measure resistance of EVAP valve coil at pins 1 and 2.
2. If resistance is 25–40 ohms, connect EM58 and proceed to "Inspect Electrical Feed."
3. If resistance is not 25–40 ohms, replace EVAP valve.

Inspect Electrical Feed

1. With EM15 and EM10 disconnected, measure voltage between EM15/3 and EM10/22.
2. If battery voltage is present, proceed to "Measure Current Draw."
3. If battery voltage is not present, proceed to "Inspect For Short To B+."

Measure Current Draw

1. With EM15 and EM10 disconnected, measure current between EM15/3 and EM10/22.
2. If current is .25–.64 amps, proceed to "Inspect For Short To B+."
3. If current is not .25–.64 amps, proceed to "Inspect For Short To B+."

Inspect For Short To B+

1. With EM15, EM10 and EM58 disconnected, measure voltage between EM15/3 and EM10/22.
2. If voltage is zero, proceed to "Inspect For B+ At EVAP Valve."
3. If voltage is not zero, proceed as follows:
   a. Inspect EM10 and EM58 for bent/pushed back pins.
   b. Inspect harness and connector EM19/8 for an open or short circuit.
   c. Inspect splice EMS30 for corrosion or damage.
   d. Test system for normal operation.

Inspect For B+ At EVAP Valve

Should F14 or relay 1 be at fault engine will not start.

1. Measure voltage between ground EM10/22 and EM58/2.
2. If battery voltage is present, proceed to "Inspect For Short To Ground."
3. If battery voltage is not present, replace fuse F14 or EMS control relay 1.

Inspect For Short To Ground

1. With EM15, EM10 and EM58 disconnected, measure insulation resistance between EM15/3 and ground EM10/22.
2. If resistance is more than 10 Mohms, connect EM10 and proceed to "Inspect Harness Continuity."

3. If resistance is less than 10 Mohms, proceed as follows:
   a. Inspect EM15 and EM58 for corrosion or bent/pushed back pins.
   b. Repair harness or connector as required.
   c. Test system for normal operation.

Inspect Harness Continuity

1. Measure resistance between EM15/3 and EM58/1.
2. If resistance is less than .5 ohms, proceed to "End."
3. If resistance is less than .5 ohms, proceed as follows:
   a. Inspect EM15 and EM58 for corrosion or bent/pushed back pins.
   b. Repair harness or connector as required.
   c. Test system for normal operation.

End

1. Perform appropriate service drive cycle and inspect for presence of DTC.
2. If fault code has cleared, fault condition has been corrected and no further diagnosis is required.
3. If fault code has not cleared, further diagnosis is required.

CODES P0447 & P0448: EVAPORATIVE EMISSION CONTROL SYSTEM CANISTER CLOSE VALVE (CCV) CIRCUIT OPEN/ SHORT CIRCUIT

Measure CCV Resistance

1. Turn ignition switch to O position.
2. Disconnect CV001.
3. Measure resistance between CCV coil at pins 1 and 2.
4. If resistance is 25–40 ohms, connect CCV and proceed to "Inspect Electrical Feed."
5. If resistance is not 25–40 ohms, replace CCV.

Inspect Electrical Feed

The engine will not start if F14 or relay 1 are at fault.

1. Disconnect CV001.
2. Measure voltage at harness pin 2 to ground (EM010/022).
3. If measurement is battery positive voltage, proceed to "Inspect For Short To B+."
4. If measurement is not battery positive voltage, inspect fuse F14 and ensure EMS relay 1 is energized.
5. Repair as required and test for normal system operation.

Inspect For Short To B+

1. Disconnect EM013 and CV001.
2. Measure voltage between EM013/044 and ground EM010/022.
3. If measurement is less than one volt, proceed to "Inspect Harness Continuity."
4. If measurement is not less than one volt, inspect harness/connectors EM013 and CV001 for bent/pushed back pins, damage or corrosion.
5. Repair as required and test system for normal operation.

Inspect Harness Continuity

1. Turn ignition switch to II position.
2. Disconnect CV001 and EM013.
3. Measure resistance between EM013/ 004 and CV001/002.
4. If resistance is less than .5 ohms, proceed to "Inspect For Short To Ground."
5. If resistance is not less than .5 ohms, inspect harness/connects EM013, EM002, FC001 and CV001 for damage, corrosion and bent/pushed back pins.
6. Repair as required and test system for normal operation.

Inspect For Short To Ground

1. Disconnect EM013 and CV001.
2. Measure insulation resistance between EM013/004 and ground EM010/ 022.
3. If resistance is more than 10 Mohms, connect EM010 and proceed to "End."
4. If resistance is less than 10 Mohms, inspect harness/connect EM013, EM002, FC001 and CV001 for damage, corrosion and bent/pushed back pins.
5. Repair as required and test system for normal operation.

End

1. If code as been cleared, system is operating properly.
2. If code is still present, contact Jaguar Service

CODES P0452 & P0453: EVAPORATIVE EMISSION CONTROL SYSTEM PRESSURE SENSOR LOW/ HIGH INPUT

Inspect Sensor Input Harness Continuity

1. Disconnect EM011 and EM010.
2. Remove Fuel Tank Pressure (FTP) sensor connector FP001.
3. Measure resistance between EM011/ 007 and FP001/002.
4. If resistance is less than .5 ohms, proceed to "Inspect Sensor Supply Ground Harness Continuity."
5. If resistance is not less than .5 ohms, inspect harness/connectors EM011, FP001, EM003, FC001, BT004 and BT005 for damage, corrosion and bent/pushed back pins.
6. Repair as required and test system for normal operation.

Inspect Sensor Supply Ground Harness Continuity

1. Ensure EM011, FP001 and EM010 are disconnected.
2. Measure resistance between EM010/ 020 and FP001/001, then EM011/02 and FP001/001.
3. If resistance is less than .5 ohms, proceed to "Inspect Sensor Supply Five Volts Harness Continuity."
4. If resistance is not less than .5 ohms, inspect harness/connectors EM011, FP001, EM003, FC001, BT004 and BT005, and splices EMS1 and EMS2 for damage, corrosion and bent/ pushed back pins.
5. Repair as required and test system for normal operation.

Inspect Sensor Supply Five Volts Harness Continuity

1. Ensure EM011, FP001 and EM010 are disconnected.
2. Measure resistance between EM011/ 018 and FP001/003.
3. If resistance is less than .5 ohms, proceed to "Inspect Harness Isolation."
4. If resistance is not less than .5 ohms, inspect harness/connectors EM011, FP001, EM003, BT004 and BT005 for damage, corrosion and bent/pushed back pins.
5. Repair as required and test system for normal operation.

Inspect Harness Isolation

1. Ensure EM011, FP001 and EM010 are disconnected.
2. Measure resistance between FP001/ 002 and FP001/001, then FP002 and FP001/003.
3. If resistance is more than 10 Mohms, proceed to "Inspect Sensor Power Supply Voltage."
4. If resistance is less than 10 Mohms, inspect harness/connectors EM011, FP001, EM003, BT004 and BT005 for damage, corrosion and bent/pushed back pins.
5. Repair as required and test system for normal operation.

Measure Sensor Power Supply Voltage

1. Connect EM011 and EM010.
2. Disconnect FP001.
3. Measure voltage between sensor connector pins 1 and 3.
4. If measurement is more than four volts, connect FP001 and proceed to "Inspect For Sensor Input Short To B+."
5. If measurement is less than four volts, inspect harness/connector integrity.
6. Repair as required and test system for normal operation.

Inspect For Sensor Input Short To B+

1. Disconnect EM001. EM010 and FP001.
2. Measure voltage between sensor connector pins 1 and 2.
3. If measurement is battery positive voltage, proceed to "Replace Fuel Tank Pressure Sensor."
4. If measurement is not battery positive voltage, inspect harness/connectors EM011, FP001, EM003, FC001, BT004 and BT005 for damage, corrosion and bent/pushed back pins.

Replace Fuel Tank Pressure Sensor

1. Replace fuel tank pressure sensor.
2. Test system for normal operation.
3. Proceed to "End."

End

1. If code as been cleared, system is operating properly.
2. If code is still present, contact Jaguar Service

CODE P0460: FUEL LEVEL SENSOR CIRCUIT MALFUNCTION

Inspect Continuity Fuel Sensor

1. With connectors BT7 and BT8 disconnected, measure resistance between fuel level sensor pins.
2. If resistance is 70–1000 ohms, proceed to "Inspect For Short To Ground."
3. If resistance is not 70–1000 ohms, replace level sensor and test system for normal operation.

Inspect For Short To Ground

1. With connectors FC25, FC26, BT7 and BT8 disconnected, measure insulation resistance between FC26/13 and FC25/26, then between FC26/14 and FC25/26.
2. If resistance is more than 10 Mohms, proceed to "Inspect Core To Core Insulation."
3. If resistance is less than 10 Mohms, proceed as follows:
   a. Inspect connectors FC25, FC26, RH001, BT2, BT7 and BT8 for corrosion, damage, bent or pushed back pins.
   b. Repair as required, then test system for normal operation.

Inspect Core To Core Insulation

1. With connectors FC25, FC26, BT7 and BT8 disconnected, measure insulation resistance between FC26/13 and FC26/14.
2. If resistance is more than 10 Mohms, proceed to "Inspect Ground Continuity."
3. If resistance is less than 10 Mohms, proceed as follows:
   a. Inspect connectors FC25, FC26, RH001, BT2, BT7 and BT8 for corrosion, damage, bent or pushed back pins.
   b. Repair as required, then test system for normal operation.

Inspect Ground Continuity

1. With connectors FC25, FC26, and BT7 disconnected, measure resistance between FC26/14 and BT7.
2. If resistance is less than .5 ohms, proceed to "Inspect Signal Continuity."
3. If resistance is more than .5 ohms, proceed as follows:
   a. Inspect connectors/pins FC26, RH001/14, BT2/18 and BT7 for corrosion, damage, bent or pushed back pins.
   b. Repair as required, then test system for normal operation.

Inspect Signal Continuity

1. With connectors FC25, FC26, and BT8 disconnected, measure resistance between FC26/13 and BT8.
2. If resistance is less than .5 ohms, proceed to "End."
3. If resistance is less than .5 ohms, proceed as follows:
   a. Inspect connectors/pins FC26, RH001/13, BT2/17 and BT8 for corrosion, damage, bent or pushed back pins.
   b. Repair as required, then test system for normal operation.

End

1. Perform appropriate service drive cycle and inspect for presence of DTC.
2. If fault code has cleared, fault condition has been corrected and no further diagnosis is required.
3. If fault code has not cleared, further diagnosis is required.

CODES P0506 & P0507: IDLE SPEED CONTROL SYSTEM MALFUNCTION

Throttle Function

1. If throttle operation is satisfactory, proceed to "Air Intake System Inspection."
2. If throttle operation is not satisfactory, repair possible throttle blade or position sensor fault(s) (DTCs P0121, 0122, 0123, 0222, 0223) and test system for normal operation.

Air Intake System Inspection

1. Inspect the following air intake system components:
   a. Air cleaner is free of obstructions.
   b. Air meter to throttle body seal.
   c. Engine breather to inlet duct.
   d. Throttle body to engine free of air leaks.
   e. Vacuum system.
2. If air intake system is satisfactory, proceed to "End."
3. If air intake system is not satisfactory, repair fault(s) and test system for normal operation.

End

1. Perform appropriate service drive cycle and inspect for presence of DTC.
2. If fault code has cleared, fault condition has been corrected and no further diagnosis is required.
3. If fault code has not cleared, further diagnosis is required.

CODE P0560: SYSTEM VOLTAGE MALFUNCTION

Inspect Fuse

1. Inspect underhood fuse F4.
2. If fuse F4 is satisfactory, proceed to "Measure Battery Supply."
3. If fuse F4 is blown, replace fuse (5A) and test system for normal operation.

Measure Battery Supply

1. With EM10 disconnected, measure voltage between EM10/9 and ground EM1AL (EM2AL).
2. If battery voltage is present, proceed to "End."
3. If battery voltage is not present, proceed to "Inspect Harness Continuity - Battery Supply."

Inspect Harness Continuity - Battery Supply

1. With EM10, EM20 and EM7 disconnected, measure resistance between EM10/9 and EM20/8.
2. If resistance is less than .5 ohms, proceed to "Inspect Harness Short To Ground."
3. If resistance is more than .5 ohms, proceed as follows:
   a. Inspect EM10 and EM20 for corrosion, bent or pushed back pins.
   b. Inspect splice EMS41 for corrosion or damage.
   c. Repair as required, then test system for normal operation.

Inspect Harness Short To Ground

1. With EM10, EM20 and EM7 disconnected, measure resistance between EM10/9 and ground EM1AL (EM2AL), then between EM20/8 and ground EM1AL (EM2AL).
2. If resistance is more than 10 Mohms, proceed to "End."
3. If resistance is less than 10 Mohms, proceed as follows:
   a. Inspect EM10 and EM20 for corrosion or bent/pushed back pins.
   b. Inspect harness and splice EMS41 for corrosion or damage.
   c. Repair as required, then test system for normal operation.

End

1. Perform appropriate service drive cycle and inspect for presence of DTC.
2. If fault code has cleared, fault condition has been corrected and no further diagnosis is required.
3. If fault code has not cleared, further diagnosis is required.

CODE P0603: INTERNAL CONTROL MODULE KEEP ALIVE MEMORY ERROR

Replace ECM

1. Replace ECM and proceed to "End."

End

1. Drive vehicle for a period from cold to normal engine operating temperature. Operate engine at idle speed, brisk acceleration and a steady cruising speed.
2. Inspect for presence of DTC.
3. If fault code has cleared, fault condition has been corrected and no further diagnosis is required.
4. If fault code has not cleared, further diagnosis is required.

CODE P1224: ELECTRONIC THROTTLE CONTROL POSITION ERROR

Inspect Fuse

1. Inspect fuse F9 and fuse F14.
2. If fuses are satisfactory, proceed to "Inspect Relay Supply."
3. If fuse(s) are not satisfactory, replace fuse(s) and test system for normal operation.

Inspect Relay Supply

1. With throttle motor power relay 2 removed, measure voltage between relay socket pin 3 and ground EM1AL (EM2AL).
2. If battery voltage is present, proceed to "Inspect Throttle Motor Coil Continuity."
3. If battery voltage is not present, proceed to "Inspect Harness Continuity - Relay Contact."

Inspect Throttle Motor Coil Continuity

1. With PI33 disconnected, measure resistance across connectors 1 and 2.
2. If resistance is .54–1.04 ohms, proceed to "Inspect Throttle Motor Coil Insulation."
3. If resistance is not .54–1.04 ohms, replace electronic throttle assembly and test system for normal operation.

Inspect Throttle Motor Coil Insulation

1. With PI33 disconnected, measure insulation resistance between pin 1 and throttle body.
2. If resistance is more than 10 Mohms, proceed to "Measure Relay Coil Supply."
3. If resistance is less than 10 Mohms, replace electronic throttle assembly and test system for normal operation.

Measure Relay Coil Supply

1. With EM13 and EM14 disconnected measure voltage between EM13/14 and EM14/8.
2. If battery voltage is present, replace relay and proceed to "End."
3. If battery voltage is not present, proceed to "Inspect Harness Continuity."

Inspect Harness Continuity

1. With EM13 and EM16 disconnected measure resistance between and EM13/14 and relay socket pin 1.
2. If resistance is less than .5 ohms, proceed to "Measure B+ At Relay Coil."
3. If resistance is more than .5 ohms, inspect connectors EM13 and EM16 for corrosion, damage, bent or pushed back pins. Repair as required and test system for normal operation.

Measure B+ At Relay Coil

1. With EM14 disconnected measure voltage between and EM14/8 and relay socket pin 2.
2. If battery voltage is present, proceed to "Inspect Harness Continuity - Relay Coil."
3. If battery voltage is not present, proceed as follows:
   a. Inspect connectors EM16 and EM19 for bent/pushed back pins.
   b. Inspect harness and splice EMS30 for an open or short.
   c. Repair as required.
   d. Test system for normal operation.

Inspect Harness Continuity - Relay Coil

1. With EM14 disconnected, measure resistance between and EM14/1 and relay socket pin 5, then between EM14/2 and relay socket pin 5.
2. If resistance is less than .5 ohms, proceed to "Inspect Harness Continuity - Relay Contact."
3. If resistance is more than .5 ohms, proceed as follows:
   a. Inspect connectors EM16 and EM14 for bent or pushed back pins.
   b. Inspect harness and splice EMS20 for an open or short.
   c. Repair as required.
   d. Test system for normal operation.

Inspect Harness Continuity - Relay Contact

1. With EM19 disconnected measure resistance between and EM19/2 and relay socket pin 3.
2. If resistance is less than .5 ohms, proceed to "Inspect Harness Continuity - Throttle +Ve."
3. If resistance is more than .5 ohms, proceed as follows:
   a. Inspect connectors EM16 and EM19 for bent or pushed back pins.
   b. Inspect harness for an open or short.
   c. Repair as required.
   d. Test system for normal operation.

Inspect Harness Continuity - Throttle +Ve

1. With EM14 disconnected, measure resistance between EM14/6 and PI33/1, then between EM14/5 and PI33/1.
2. If resistance is less than .5 ohms, proceed to "Inspect Harness Continuity - Throttle -Ve."
3. If resistance is more than .5 ohms, proceed as follows:
   a. Inspect connectors EM14, PI2 and PI33 for bent or pushed back pins.
   b. Inspect harness and splice EMS19 for an open or short.
   c. Repair as required.
   d. Test system for normal operation.

Inspect Harness Continuity - Throttle -Ve

1. With EM14 disconnected, measure resistance between EM14/12 and PI33/2, then between EM14/11 and PI33/2.
2. If resistance is less than .5 ohms, proceed to "Inspect Harness Continuity - Throttle Ground."
3. If resistance is more than .5 ohms, proceed as follows:
   a. Inspect connectors EM14, PI2 and PI33 for bent or pushed back pins.
   b. Inspect harness and splice EMS18 for an open or short.
   c. Repair as required.
   d. Test system for normal operation.

Inspect Harness Continuity - Throttle Ground

1. With EM10, EM14 and EM15 disconnected, measure resistance between EM14/8 and EM1AL (EM2AL), then between EM14/7 and EM1AL (EM2AL).
2. If resistance is less than .5 ohms, proceed to "Inspect For Short To B+."
3. If resistance is more than .5 ohms, proceed as follows:
   a. Inspect connectors EM10, EM14 and EM15 for bent/pushed back pins.
   b. Inspect harness splice EMS37 and ground stud for an open or short.
   c. Repair as required.
   d. Test system for normal operation.

Inspect For Short To B+

1. Remove fuse F14.
2. With EM12, EM13, EM14 and EM15 disconnected, measure voltage between EM13/14 and EM14/8.
3. If voltage is zero, proceed to "Inspect For Short To B+."
4. If voltage is more than zero, inspect connector EM13 for bent/pushed back pins. Repair as required and test system for normal operation.

Inspect For Short To B+

1. Remove fuse F9.
2. Measure voltage between EM14/8 and relay socket pin 3.
3. If voltage is zero, proceed to "Inspect For Short To B+."
4. If voltage is more than zero, inspect connectors EM14, EM16 and relay base for bent/pushed back pins. Repair as required and test system for normal operation.

Inspect For Short To B+

1. Measure voltage between EM14/8 and relay socket pin 5.
2. If voltage is zero, connect EM12, EM13, and EM15 and proceed to "Inspect For Short To B+."
3. If voltage is more than zero, inspect connectors EM14, EM16, EM19 and relay base for bent/pushed back pins. Repair as required and test system for normal operation.

Inspect For Short To B+

1. With PI33 connected, measure voltage between EM14/8 and EM14/5, then between EM14/8 and EM14/6.
2. If voltage is zero, proceed to "Inspect Harness Core To Core Insulation."
3. If voltage is more than zero, inspect connectors EM14, PI33 and PI2 for bent/pushed back pins. Repair as required and test system for normal operation.

Inspect Harness Core To Core Insulation

1. With EM13 disconnected, measure insulation resistance between EM13/14 and EM14/1, then between EM13/14 and EM14/2.
2. If resistance is more than 10 Mohms, proceed to "Inspect Harness Core To Core Insulation."
3. If resistance is less than 10 Mohms, proceed as follows:
   a. Inspect connectors EM14, EM13 and EM16 for bent/pushed back pins.
   b. Inspect harness for open or short circuit.
   c. Repair as required.
   d. Test system for normal operation.

Inspect Harness Core To Core Insulation

1. With EM13 disconnected, measure insulation resistance between the following connector terminals:
   a. EM14/5 and EM14/11.
   b. EM14/5 and EM14/12.
   c. EM14/6 and EM14/11.
   d. EM14/6 and EM14/12.
2. If resistance is more than 10 M ohms, proceed to "End."
3. If resistance is less than 10 M ohms, proceed as follows:
   a. Inspect connectors EM14, EM13 and EM16 for bent/pushed back pins.
   b. Inspect harness for open or short circuit.
   c. Repair as required.
   d. Test system for normal operation.

End

1. Perform appropriate service drive cycle and inspect for presence of DTC.
2. If fault code has cleared, fault condition has been corrected and no further diagnosis is required.
3. If fault code has not cleared, further diagnosis is required.

CODE P1226: MECHANICAL GUARD CIRCUIT RANGE PERFORMANCE

Mechanical Inspection

1. Using a known good assembly as reference, inspect throttle input shaft for smooth operation and 'normal' spring return.
2. If throttle is working properly, proceed to "Measure Sensor Supply Voltage."
3. If throttle is not working properly, replace electronic throttle assembly and test system for normal operation.

Measure Sensor Supply Voltage

1. Disconnect PI42 connector.
2. Measure voltage between PI42/4 and PI42/2.
3. If voltage is 4.75–5.25 volts, proceed to "End."
4. If voltage is 4.75–5.25 volts, proceed to "Inspect Harness Signal Continuity."

Inspect Harness Signal Continuity

1. With EM11 and PI42 disconnected, measure resistance between EM11/13 and PI42/1.
2. If resistance is less than .5 ohms, proceed to "End."
3. If resistance is less than .5 ohms, inspect EM11 and PI42 for bent/pushed back pins. Repair harness or connector PI1/12.
   a. Yes, go to "End."
   b. No,

End

1. Perform appropriate service drive cycle and inspect for presence of DTC.
2. If fault code has cleared, fault condition has been corrected and no further diagnosis is required.
3. If fault code has not cleared, further diagnosis is required.

CODE P1227 & P1228 MECHANICAL GUARD CIRCUIT MALFUNCTION

Measure Sensor Supply Voltage

1. Disconnect PI42 connector.
2. Measure voltage between PI42/4 and PI42/2.
3. If voltage is 4.75–5.25 volts, proceed to "Inspect Harness Signal Continuity."
4. If voltage is not 4.75–5.25 volts, proceed to "Harness Short To Screen."

Harness Short To Screen

1. With EM10, EM11, PI6 and PI42 disconnected, measure insulation resistance between the following terminals:
   a. EM11/14 and EM10/20.
   b. EM11/14 and EM10/21.
   c. EM11/14 and EM11/8.
   d. EM11/14 and EM11/12.
   e. EM11/14 and EM11/13.
   f. EM11/14 and EM11/15.
   g. EM11/14 and EM11/16.
2. If all resistances are more than 10 Mohms, proceed to "Inspect Harness Core To Core Insulation."
3. If all resistances are not more than 10 Mohms, inspect EM10 and EM11 for corrosion or bent/pushed back pins. Repair harness or connector PI1 as required. Test system for normal operation.

Inspect Harness Core To Core Insulation

1. With EM10, EM11, PI6 and PI42 disconnected, measure insulation resistance between:
   a. EM10/21 and EM10/20.
   b. EM11/12 and EM11/8.
   c. EM11/12 and EM11/13.
   d. EM11/12 and EM11/15.
   e. EM11/12 and EM11/16.
   f. EM11/13 and EM11/15.
   g. EM11/13 and EM11/16.
2. If all resistances are more than 10 Mohms, proceed to "Inspect Harness Signal Continuity."
3. If all resistances are not more than 10 Mohms, inspect EM10 and EM11 for corrosion or bent/pushed back pins. Repair harness or connector PI1 as required. Test system for normal operation.

Inspect Harness Signal Continuity

1. With, EM11, and PI42 disconnected, measure resistance between EM11/13 and PI42/1.
2. If resistance is less than .5 ohms, proceed to "End."
3. If resistance is more than .5 ohms, inspect EM11 and PI42 for bent or pushed back pins. Repair harness or connector as required. Test system for normal operation.

End

1. Perform appropriate service drive cycle and inspect for presence of DTC.
2. If fault code has cleared, fault condition has been corrected and no further diagnosis is required.
3. If fault code has not cleared, further diagnosis is required.

CODE P1229: THROTTLE POSITION ERROR

Replace ECM

1. Replace ECM.
2. Proceed to "End."

End

1. Drive vehicle for a period from cold to normal engine operating temperature. Operate engine at idle speed, brisk acceleration and a steady cruising speed.
2. Inspect for presence of DTC.
3. If fault code has cleared, fault condition has been corrected and no further diagnosis is required.
4. If fault code has not cleared, further diagnosis is required.

CODE P1230: FUEL PUMP RELAY MALFUNCTION

Inspect Fuse

1. Inspect fuse F7 (located in trunk).
2. If fuse is satisfactory, proceed to "Inspect Short To Supply."
3. If fuse is not satisfactory, replace fuse and test system for normal operation.

Inspect Short To Supply

1. With EM13 disconnected, inspect for battery voltage between EM13/1 and ground BT2AL.
2. If battery voltage is present, proceed to "Inspect Harness Short To Ground."
3. If battery voltage is not present, proceed to "Measure Supply Voltage."

Measure Supply Voltage

1. With relay 4 removed, inspect for battery voltage at relay socket between pins 3 and 5.
2. If battery voltage is present, proceed to

"Inspect Circuit Continuity."
3. If battery voltage is not present, proceed to "Inspect Fuel Pump Ground Continuity."

Inspect Circuit Continuity

1. Measure resistance between relay socket pin 5 and ground BT2AL.
2. If resistance is less than 10 ohms, proceed to "Measure Fuel Pump Drawn Current."
3. If resistance is more than 10 ohms, proceed to "Inspect Fuel Pump Continuity."

Measure Fuel Pump Drawn Current

With EM13 disconnected, this test will cause the fuel pump to operate continuously. **Do not exceed more than 10 seconds running time.**

1. With ignition energized, measure current drawn between relay socket pins 3 and 5.
2. If current is between 2.5–9 amps, proceed to "Measure B+ At Relay Coil."
3. If current is between 2.5–9 amps, proceed to "Inspect Fuel Pump Continuity."

Measure B+ At Relay Coil

1. Using a link lead, connect EM13/1 to ground BT2AL
2. With ignition on, inspect for battery voltage at relay socket between pins 1 and 2.
3. If battery voltage is present, proceed to "Inspect Fuel Pump Continuity."
4. If battery voltage is not present, proceed to "Inspect Relay Coil Circuit Continuity."

Inspect Relay Coil Circuit Continuity

1. With EM13 disconnected, measure resistance between EM13/1 and relay socket pin 1.
2. If resistance is less than .5 ohms, proceed to "Inspect ECM Ground Continuity."
3. If resistance is more than .5 ohms, proceed as follows:
   a. Inspect connectors EM13, EM2/9, RH001/11, BT2/6 and BT11/10 for corrosion, damaged, bent or pushed back pins.
   b. Repair as required.
   c. Test system for normal operation.

Inspect ECM Ground Continuity

1. With EM14 disconnected, measure resistance between EM14/10 and ground EM1AR.
2. If resistance is less than .5 ohms, replace relay and test system for normal operation.
3. If resistance is more than .5 ohms, proceed as follows:
   a. Inspect connector EM14, splice EMS36 and ground EM1AR for corrosion, damage, bent or pushed back pins.
   b. Repair as required.
   c. Test system for normal operation.

Inspect Fuel Pump Continuity

1. With BT55 disconnected, measure resistance across fuel pump connectors reference BT55/1 and BT55/2.
2. If resistance is less than 5 ohms, proceed to "Inspect Fuel Pump Ground Continuity."
3. If resistance is more than 5 ohms, replace fuel pump and test system for normal operation.

Inspect Fuel Pump Ground Continuity

1. With BT55 disconnected, measure resistance between BT55/1 and ground BT2AL.
2. If resistance is less than .5 ohms, proceed to "Inspect Circuit Continuity."
3. If resistance is more than .5 ohms, inspect connector BT55 and ground BT55 for corrosion, damage, bent or pushed back pins, Repair as required, then test system for normal operation.

Inspect Circuit Continuity

1. With BT55 disconnected and relay 4 removed, measure resistance between BT55/2 and relay socket pin 5.
2. If resistance is less than .5 ohms, proceed to "Inspect Harness Short To Ground."
3. If resistance is more than .5 ohms, inspect connector BT55, fuse holder F7 and BT11/11 for corrosion, damage, bent or pushed back pins. Repair as required, then test system for normal operation.

Inspect Harness Short To Ground

1. With EM13 and BT55 disconnected, measure insulation resistance between EM13/1 and ground BT2AL.
2. If resistance is more than 10 Mohms, proceed to "Inspect Core To Core Insulation."
3. If resistance is less than 10 Mohms, inspect connector BT55, fuse holder F7 and BT11/11 for corrosion, damage, bent or pushed back pins. Repair as required, then test system for normal operation.

Inspect Core To Core Insulation

1. With conditions as A13, measure insulation resistance between EM13/1 and relay socket pin 5.
2. If resistance is more than 10 Mohms, proceed to "End."
3. If resistance is less than 10 Mohms, inspect connectors EM13, EM2/9, RH001/11, BT2/6, BT11/1, BT55/2 and BT11/10 for corrosion, damage, bent or pushed back pins. Repair as required, then test system for normal operation.

End

1. Perform appropriate service drive cycle and inspect for presence of DTC.
2. If fault code has cleared, fault condition has been corrected and no further diagnosis is required.
3. If fault code has not cleared, further diagnosis is required.

CODE P1240: SENSOR POWER SUPPLY MALFUNCTION

Measure Sensor Supply Voltage

1. Disconnect PI42 and PI6, then measure voltage between PI42/4 and PI42/2.
2. If voltage is 4.8–5.2 volts, proceed to "Inspect Harness Continuity - Signal (Pedal Demand)."
3. If voltage is not 4.8–5.2 volts, proceed to "Inspect Harness Continuity - Power (Mechanical Guard)."
4. Measure voltage between PI6/4 and PI6/1.
5. If voltage is 4.8–5.2 volts, proceed to "Inspect Harness Continuity - Signal (Throttle Position)."
6. If voltage is not 4.8–5.2 volts, proceed to "Inspect Harness Continuity - Power (Throttle Position)."

Inspect Harness Continuity - Power (Mechanical Guard)

1. With EM10 and EM11 disconnected, measure resistance between PI42/4 and EM11/8, then between PI42/4 and EM10/21.
2. If resistance is less than .5 ohms, proceed to "Inspect Harness Continuity-Ground (Mechanical Guard)."
3. If resistance is more than .5 ohms, proceed as follows:
   a. Inspect PI42, EM11, EM10 and PI1 for bent/pushed back pins.
   b. Inspect splice EMS1 for corrosion or damage.
   c. Repair as required, then proceed to "Measure Sensor Supply Voltage."

Inspect Harness Continuity - Ground (Mechanical Guard)

1. With EM10 and EM11 disconnected, measure resistance between PI42/2 and EM11/12, then between PI42/2 and EM10/20.
2. If resistance is less than .5 ohms, proceed to "Inspect Harness Continuity - Power (Throttle Position)."
3. If resistance is more than .5 ohms, proceed as follows:
   a. Inspect PI42, EM11, EM10 and PI1 for bent/pushed back pins.
   b. Inspect splice EMS2 for corrosion or damage.
   c. Repair as required, then proceed to "Measure Sensor Supply Voltage."

Inspect Harness Continuity - Power (Throttle Position)

1. With EM10 and EM11 disconnected, measure resistance between PI6/4 and EM11/8, then between PI6/4 and EM10/21.
2. If resistance is less than .5 ohms, proceed to "Inspect Harness Continuity - Ground (Throttle Position)."
3. If resistance is more than .5 ohms, proceed as follows:
   a. Inspect PI42, EM11, EM10 and PI1

for bent/pushed back pins.
b. Inspect splice EMS1 for corrosion or damage.
c. Repair as required, then proceed to "Measure Sensor Supply Voltage."

Inspect Harness Continuity - Ground (Throttle Position)

1. With EM10 and EM11 disconnected, measure resistance between PI6/1 and EM11/12, then between PI6/1 and EM10/20.
2. If resistance is less than .5 ohms, proceed to "Inspect Harness Continuity - Signal (Throttle Position)."
3. If resistance is more than .5 ohms, proceed as follows:
   a. Inspect PI42, EM11, EM10 and PI1 for bent/pushed back pins.
   b. Inspect splice EMS2 for corrosion or damage.
   c. Repair as required, then proceed to "Measure Sensor Supply Voltage."

Inspect Harness Continuity - Signal (Throttle Position)

1. With EM11 and PI6 disconnected, measure resistance between PI6/3 and EM11/11, then between PI6/2 and EM10/10.
2. If resistance is less than .5 ohms, proceed to "Inspect Harness Continuity - Signal (Pedal Demand)."
3. If resistance is more than .5 ohms, inspect PI6, EM10 and PI1 for bent/pushed back pins. Repair as required, then test system for normal operation.

Inspect Harness Continuity - Signal (Pedal Demand)

1. With EM11 and PI42 disconnected, measure resistance between PI42/3 and EM11/15, then between PI42/5 and EM11/16.
2. If resistance is less than .5 ohms, proceed to "Inspect Harness Continuity - Signal (Mechanical Guard)."
3. If resistance is more than .5 ohms, inspect PI42, EM11, and PI1 for bent/pushed back pins. Repair as required, then test system for normal operation.

Inspect Harness Continuity - Signal (Mechanical Guard)

1. With EM11 and PI42 disconnected, measure resistance between PI42/1 and EM11/13.
2. If resistance is less than .5 ohms, proceed to "Harness Short To Screen."
3. If resistance is more than .5 ohms, inspect PI42, EM11 and PI1 for bent/pushed back pins. Repair as required, then test system for normal operation.

Harness Short To Screen

1. With EM10, EM11, PI6 and PI42 disconnected, measure insulation resistance between EM11/14 and the following connector terminals:
   a. EM10/20.
   b. EM10/21.
   c. EM11/8.
   d. EM11/10.
   e. EM11/11.
   f. EM11/12.
   g. EM11/13.
   h. EM11/15.
   i. EM11/16.
2. If all resistances are more than 10 Mohms, proceed to "Inspect Harness Core To Core Insulation."
3. If all resistances are not more than 10 Mohms, inspect EM10, EM11, PI6 and PI42 for corrosion, bent/pushed back pins. Repair as required, then test system for normal operation.

Inspect Harness Core To Core Insulation

1. With EM10, EM11, PI6 and PI42 disconnected, measure insulation resistance between the following connector terminals:
   a. EM10/21 and EM10/20.
   b. EM11/12 and EM11/8.
   c. EM11/12 and EM11/10.
   d. EM11/12 and EM11/11.
   e. EM11/12 and EM11/13.
   f. EM11/12 and EM11/15.
   g. EM11/12 and EM11/16.
2. If all resistances are more than 10 Mohms, proceed to "Measure Output Voltage - Pedal Demand 1 & 2 (Closed Position)."
3. If any resistance reading is less than 10 Mohms, inspect EM10, EM11, PI6 and PI42 for corrosion or bent/pushed back pins. Repair harness or connector as required and test system for normal operation.

Measure Output Voltage - Pedal Demand 1 & 2 (Closed Position)

1. Disconnect EM11 connector.
2. Position throttle to CLOSED and measure voltage between EM11/12 and EM11/15, then between EM11/12 and EM11/16.
3. If voltage is .28–1.08 volts, proceed to "Measure Output Voltage - Pedal Demand 1 & 2 (Full Position)."
4. If voltage is not .28–1.08 volts, replace electronic throttle assembly.

Measure Output Voltage - Pedal Demand 1 & 2 (Full Position)

1. Disconnect EM11 connector.
2. Position throttle to FULL and measure voltage between EM11/12 and EM11/15, then between EM11/12 and EM11/16.
3. If voltage is 3.5–4.5 volts, proceed to "Measure Output Voltage - Mechanical Guard (Closed Position)."
4. If voltage is not 3.5–4.5 volts, replace electronic throttle assembly.

Measure Output Voltage - Mechanical Guard (Closed Position)

1. Disconnect EM11 connector.
2. Position throttle to CLOSED, then measure voltage between EM11/12 and EM11/13.
3. If voltage is 1.08–2.80 volts, proceed to "Measure Output Voltage - Mechanical Guard (Full Position)."
4. If voltage is not 1.08–2.80 volts, replace electronic throttle assembly.

Measure Output Voltage - Mechanical Guard (Full Position)

1. Disconnect EM11 connector.
2. Position throttle to FULL, then measure voltage between EM11/12 and EM11/13.
3. If voltage is 3.5–4.5 volts, proceed to "Measure Output Voltage - Throttle Position 1 & 2 (Closed Position)."
4. If voltage is not 3.5–4.5 volts, replace electronic throttle assembly.

Measure Output Voltage - Throttle Position 1 & 2 (Closed Position)

1. Disconnect EM11 connector.
2. Position throttle to CLOSED, measure voltage between EM11/12 and EM11/11, then between EM11/12 and EM11/10.
3. If voltage is. 2 volts, proceed to "Measure Output Voltage - Throttle Position 1 & 2 (Full Position)."
4. If voltage is not. 2 volts, replace electronic throttle assembly.

Measure Output Voltage - Throttle Position 1 & 2 (Full Position)

1. Disconnect EM11 connector.
2. Position throttle to FULL, measure voltage between EM11/12 and EM11/11, then between EM11/12 and EM11/10.
3. If voltage is 4.8 volts, proceed to "Measure Sensor Supply Voltage."
4. If voltage is not 4.8 volts, replace electronic throttle assembly.

Measure Sensor Supply Voltage

1. Disconnect EM10 connector.
2. Using a suitable jumper wire, connect EM10/16 and EM10/23 (to energize EMS control relay).
3. Measure voltage between EM10/21 and EM10/20.
4. If voltage is 4.8–5.2 volts, remove jumper, then connect EM10 proceed to "Measure Sensor Supply Voltage."
5. If voltage is not 4.8–5.2 volts, proceed as follows:
   a. Inspect EM11 for bent or pushed back pins.
   b. Inspect harness and splices EMS1 and EMS2.
   c. Repair harness or connector as required.
   d. Test system for normal operation.
   e. If connector, harness and splices are satisfactory, replace ECM.

Measure Sensor Supply Voltage

1. Disconnect EM11 connector, then measure voltage between EM11/12 and EM11/8.

2. If voltage is 4.8–5.2 volts, proceed to "End."
3. If voltage is not 4.8–5.2 volts, proceed as follows:
   a. Inspect EM10 for bent or pushed back pins.
   b. Inspect harness and splices EMS1 and EMS2.
   c. Repair harness or connector as required.
   d. Test system for normal operation.
   e. If connector, harness and splices are satisfactory, replace ECM.

End

1. Perform appropriate service drive cycle and inspect for presence of DTC.
2. If fault code has cleared, fault condition has been corrected and no further diagnosis is required.
3. If fault code has not cleared, further diagnosis is required.

CODES P1241 & P1242: SENSOR POWER SUPPLY

Measure Sensor Supply Voltage

1. Disconnect EM10 connector.
2. Using a suitable jumper, connect terminals M10/16 and EM10/23 (to energize EMS control relay).
3. Measure voltage between EM10/21 and EM10/20.
4. If voltage is 4.8–5.2 volts, remove jumper, connect EM10 and proceed to "Measure Sensor Supply Voltage."
5. If voltage is not 4.8–5.2 volts, proceed as follows:
   a. Inspect EM10 and EM11 for bent or pushed back pins.
   b. Inspect harness and splices EMS1 and EMS2.
   c. Repair harness or connector as required.
   d. Test system for normal operation.

Measure Sensor Supply Voltage

1. Disconnect EM11 connector.
2. Measure voltage between EM11/12 and EM11/8.
3. If voltage is 4.8–5.2 volts, connect EM11 and proceed to "End."
4. If voltage is not 4.8–5.2 volts, proceed as follows:
   a. Inspect EM10 and EM11 for bent or pushed back pins.
   b. Inspect harness and splices EMS1 and EMS2.
   c. Repair harness or connector as required.
   d. Test system for normal operation.

End

1. Perform appropriate service drive cycle and inspect for presence of DTC.
2. If fault code has cleared, fault condition has been corrected and no further diagnosis is required.
3. If fault code has not cleared, further diagnosis is required.

CODE P1243: SENSOR POWER SUPPLY ANALOGUE GROUND MALFUNCTION

Inspect ECM Ground

1. With EM14 disconnected measure resistance between EM14/4 and ground EM1BR (EM2BR).
2. If resistance is less than .5 ohms, proceed to "Inspect ECM Ground."
3. If resistance is more than .5 ohms, inspect EM14 for bent or pushed back pins. Inspect harness and splice EMS38 for open or short circuit. Repair as required, then test system for normal operation.

Inspect ECM Ground

1. With EM10 disconnected measure resistance between EM10/23 and ground EM1BR (EM2BR).
2. If resistance is less than .5 ohms, proceed to "End."
3. If resistance is more than .5 ohms, inspect EM10 for bent or pushed back pins. Inspect harness and splice EMS38 for open or short circuit. Repair as required, then test system for normal operation.

End

1. Perform appropriate service drive cycle and inspect for presence of DTC.
2. If fault code has cleared, fault condition has been corrected and no further diagnosis is required.
3. If fault code has not cleared, further diagnosis is required.

CODES P1245 & P1246: CRANK SIGNAL LOW CIRCUIT

Inspect Harness Short To Ground

1. With EM10, EM11 and FC14 (BPM) disconnected, measure insulation resistance between EM11/6 and EM10/23.
2. If resistance is more than 10 Mohms, proceed to "Inspect Harness Ground Continuity."
3. If resistance is less than 10 Mohms, proceed as follows:
   a. Inspect EM11 and FC14 for corrosion, bent or pushed back pins.
   b. Inspect harness, connector EM1 and splice EMS38 for open or short circuit.
   c. Repair as required, then test system for normal operation.

Inspect Harness Ground Continuity

1. With EM10 and EM14 disconnected.
2. Measure resistance between EM10/23 and EM1BR (EM2BR), then between EM14/4 and EM1BR (EM2BR).
3. If resistance is less than .5 ohms, proceed to "Inspect Harness Signal Continuity."
4. If resistance is more than .5 ohms, proceed as follows:
   a. Inspect EM10 and EM14 for corrosion, bent or pushed back pins.
   b. Inspect harness splice EMS38 for open or short circuit.
   c. Repair as required, then test system for normal operation.

Inspect Harness Signal Continuity

1. Disconnect FC14 and measure resistance between EM11/6 and FC14/73.
2. If resistance is less than .5 ohms, proceed to "Inspect For Short To B+."
3. If resistance is more than .5 ohms, proceed as follows:
   a. Inspect EM11 and FC14 for corrosion, bent or pushed back pins.
   b. Inspect harness, connector EM1 and splice EMS38 for open or short circuit.
   c. Repair as required, then test system for normal operation.

Inspect For Short To B+

1. With EM10, EM11 and FC14 (BPM) disconnected, measure voltage between EM11/6 and EM10/23.
2. If voltage is zero, connect FC14 and proceed to "Inspect Crank Static Input Signal - (From BPM)."
3. If voltage is not zero, proceed as follows:
   a. Inspect EM11 and FC14 for corrosion, bent or pushed back pins.
   b. Inspect harness, connector EM1 and splice EMS38 for open or short circuit.
   c. Repair as required, then test system for normal operation.

Inspect Crank Static Input Signal - (From BPM)

1. With, EM11 and EM10 disconnected, measure voltage between EM11/6 and EM10/23.
2. If battery voltage is present, proceed to "Inspect Crank Dynamic Input Signal - (From BPM)."
3. If battery voltage is present, proceed as follows:
   a. Inspect EM11 and FC14 for corrosion, bent or pushed back pins.
   b. Inspect harness, connector EM1 and splice EMS38 for open or short circuit.
   c. Repair as required, then test system for normal operation.

Inspect Crank Dynamic Input Signal - (From BPM)

1. With, EM11 and EM10 disconnected, operate starter and measure voltage between EM11/6 and EM10/23.
2. If voltage drops to between .7–1 volt, proceed to "End."
3. If voltage does not drop to between .7–1 volt, replace ECM or BPM and proceed to "End."

End

1. Perform appropriate service drive cycle and inspect for presence of DTC.
2. If fault code has cleared, fault condition

has been corrected and no further diagnosis is required.
3. If fault code has not cleared, further diagnosis is required.

CODE P1367: IGNITION SYSTEM FAILURE

Measure Amplifier Supply

1. With EM27 disconnected, measure voltage between EM27/9 and EM27/10.
2. If battery voltage is present, proceed to "Inspect Amplifier Ground Continuity."
3. If battery voltage is not present, proceed to "Codes P0351, P0352, P0353, P0354, P0355, P0356, P0357 and P0358: Ignition Coil Primary Circuit Malfunction."

Inspect Amplifier Ground Continuity

Disconnection of all connectors between amplifier and ECM or amplifier and coils, for any bank, will cause either P1367 or P1368 to be set. Ensure all connectors are, or have been, properly located before condemning an amplifier module.

1. With EM27 disconnected, measure resistance between EM27/9 and ground EM2AR.
2. If resistance is less than .5 ohms, replace amplifier module and proceed to "End."
3. If resistance is more than .5 ohms, proceed to "Codes P0351, P0352, P0353, P0354, P0355, P0356, P0357 and P0358: Ignition Coil Primary Circuit Malfunction."

End

1. Perform appropriate service drive cycle and inspect for presence of DTC.
2. If fault code has cleared, fault condition has been corrected and no further diagnosis is required.
3. If fault code has not cleared, further diagnosis is required.

CODE P1368: IGNITION SYSTEM FAILURE

Measure Amplifier Supply

1. With EM29 disconnected, measure voltage between EM29/9 and EM29/10.
2. If battery voltage is present, proceed to "Inspect Amplifier Ground Continuity."
3. If battery voltage is not present, proceed to "Codes P0351, P0352, P0353, P0354, P0355, P0356, P0357 and P0358: Ignition Coil Primary Circuit Malfunction."

Inspect Amplifier Ground Continuity

Disconnection of all connectors between the amplifier and the ECM or amplifier and the coils, for any bank, will cause either P1367 or P1368 to be set. Ensure all connectors are, or have been, properly located before condemning an amplifier module.

1. Measure resistance between EM29/9 and ground EM2AR.
2. If resistance is less than .5 ohms, replace amplifier module and proceed to "End."
3. If resistance is more than .5 ohms, proceed to "Codes P0351, P0352, P0353, P0354, P0355, P0356, P0357 and P0358: Ignition Coil Primary Circuit Malfunction."

End

1. Perform appropriate service drive cycle and inspect for presence of DTC.
2. If fault code has cleared, fault condition has been corrected and no further diagnosis is required.
3. If fault code has not cleared, further diagnosis is required.

CODE P1392 & P1397: VVT SOLENOID CIRCUIT LOW INPUT

Inspect Fuse/Relay

1. Inspect fuse F12 is good and that EMS control relay is energized.
2. If fuse is good and control relay is energized, proceed to "Inspect VVT Coil Continuity."
3. If fuse is not good or control relay is not energized, replace as required and test system for normal operation.

Inspect VVT Coil Continuity

1. With VVT connector (PI31 - A bank or PI32 - B bank) disconnected, measure resistance between pins 1 and 2 at VVT actuator.
2. If resistance is less than 20 ohms, proceed to "Inspect Harness Continuity."
3. If resistance is more than 20 ohms, replace VVT solenoid and test system for normal operation.

Inspect Harness Continuity

1. With EM15 and PI31 (PI32) disconnected, measure resistance between EM15/9 (EM15/8) and PI31/1 (PI32/1).
2. If resistance is less than .5 ohms, proceed to "Inspect Harness (Ground) Continuity."
3. If resistance is more than .5 ohms, proceed as follows:
   a. Inspect harness connectors EM15, PI31, and PI32 for corrosion, damage, bent or pushed back pins.
   b. Inspect connectors terminals PI1/16 and PI1/27 for corrosion, damage, bent or pushed back pins.
   c. Repair as required.
   d. Test system for normal operation.

Inspect Harness (Ground) Continuity

1. With EM14 disconnected, measure resistance between EM14/9 and ground EM1AR (EM2AR).
2. If resistance is less than .5 ohms, connect EM14, EM15, PI31 and PI32 and proceed to "End."
3. If resistance is more than .5 ohms, inspect harness/connector EM14, ground stud and splice EMS36 for corrosion, damage, bent or pushed back pins. Repair as required and test system for normal operation.

End

1. Perform appropriate service drive cycle and inspect for presence of DTC.
2. If fault code has cleared, fault condition has been corrected and no further diagnosis is required.
3. If fault code has not cleared, further diagnosis is required.

CODES P1393 & P1398: VVT SOLENOID CIRCUIT HIGH INPUT

Inspect VVT Coil Continuity

1. With VVT connector (PI31 - A bank) or (PI32 - B bank) disconnected, measure resistance between pins 1 and 2 at VVT actuator.
2. If resistance is less than 20 ohms, proceed to "Inspect Short To B+."
3. If resistance is more than 20 ohms, replace VVT solenoid and test system for normal operation.

Inspect Short To B+

1. Remove fuse F12.
2. With EM15, EM14, PI31 or PI32 disconnected, measure voltage between EM15/9 and EM14/9.
3. If voltage is zero, connect EM15 and EM14, replace fuse F12, then proceed to "Measure B+ At VVT Solenoid."
4. If voltage is not zero, proceed as follows:
   a. Inspect EM15, EM14, PI31 or PI32 for bent or pushed back pins.
   b. Inspect harness and connectors PI1/16 or PI1/27.
   c. Repair as required and test system for normal operation.

Measure B+ At VVT Solenoid

1. Measure voltage between PI31/2 (PI32/2) and ground EM1AR (EM2AR).
2. If battery voltage is present, proceed to "Inspect Harness Short To Ground."
3. If battery voltage is not present, proceed as follows:
   a. Inspect EM20/10 and PI31 (PI32) for bent or pushed back pins.
   b. Inspect harness, splice EMS16 or connector PIS6 for open or short circuit.
   c. Repair as required and test system for normal operation.

Inspect Harness Short To Ground

1. With EM15 and EM14 disconnected, measure insulation resistance between EM15/9 (EM15/8) and ground EM14/9.
2. If resistance is more than 10 Mohms, do not connect EM14 and EM15, then proceed to "Inspect Harness Short Core To Core."
3. If resistance is more than 10 Mohms, proceed as follows:
   a. Inspect EM15 and EM14 for corrosion, bent or pushed back pins.

b. Repair harness or connector as required.
c. Test system for normal operation.

Inspect Harness Short Core To Core

1. With EM15, EM14, PI31 and PI32 disconnected, measure insulation resistance between EM15/9 and EM15/8.
2. If resistance is more than 10 Mohms, connect all connectors and proceed to "End."
3. If resistance is less than 10 Mohms, proceed as follows:
   a. Inspect EM15 and PI31 (PI32) for corrosion, bent or pushed back pins.
   b. Inspect harness, then connectors PI1/16 and PI1/27 for an open or short circuit.
   c. Repair as required, then test system for normal operation.

End

1. Perform appropriate service drive cycle and inspect for presence of DTC.
2. If fault code has cleared, fault condition has been corrected and no further diagnosis is required.
3. If fault code has not cleared, further diagnosis is required.

CODE P1396: VVT SOLENOID MALFUNCTION

Inspect VVT Coil Continuity

1. With VVT connector PI32 disconnected, measure resistance between pins 1 and 2 at VVT actuator.
2. If resistance is less than 20 ohms, proceed to "Inspect Short To B+."
3. If resistance is more than 20 ohms, replace VVT solenoid and test system for normal operation.

Inspect Short To B+

1. Remove fuse F12.
2. With EM15, EM14, PI31 and PI32 disconnected, measure voltage between EM15/8 and EM14/9.
3. If voltage is zero, connect EM15 and EM14, then replace fuse F12 and proceed to "Measure B+ At VVT Solenoid."
4. If voltage is not zero, proceed as follows:
   a. Inspect EM15, PI1 or PI32 for bent or pushed back pins.
   b. Inspect harness for an open or short circuit.
   c. Repair as required and test system for normal operation.

Measure B+ At VVT Solenoid

1. Measure voltage between PI32/2 and ground EM1AR (EM2AR).
2. If battery voltage is present, proceed to "Inspect Harness Short To Ground."
3. If battery voltage is not present, proceed as follows:
   a. Inspect EM20/10 and PI31 (PI32) for bent or pushed back pins.
   b. Inspect harness and splice EMS16 for an open or short circuit.
   c. Inspect fuse F12 and EMS control Relay 1.
   d. Repair or replace as required, then test system for normal operation

Inspect Harness Short To Ground

1. With EM15 and EM14 disconnected, measure insulation resistance between EM15/8 and ground EM14/9.
2. If resistance is more than 10 Mohms, do not connect EM15 and EM14, then proceed to "Inspect Harness Short Core To Core."
3. If resistance is less than 10 Mohms, proceed as follows:
   a. Inspect EM15 and EM14 for corrosion, bent or pushed back pins.
   b. Inspect harness for open or short circuit.
   c. Repair as required, then test system for normal operation.

Inspect Harness Short Core To Core

1. With EM15, EM14, PI31 and PI32 disconnected, measure insulation resistance between EM15/9 and EM15/8.
2. If resistance is more than 10 Mohms, connect all connectors and proceed to "Inspect Harness Continuity."
3. If resistance is less than 10 Mohms, proceed as follows:
   a. Inspect EM15, PI31 and PI32 for corrosion, bent or pushed back pins.
   b. Inspect harness, then connectors PI1/16 and PI1/27 for an open or short circuit.
   c. Repair as required, then test system for normal operation.

Inspect Harness Continuity

1. With EM15 and PI32 disconnected, measure resistance between EM15/8 and PI32/1.
2. If resistance is less than .5 ohms, proceed to "Inspect Harness (Ground) Continuity."
3. If resistance is more than .5 ohms, proceed as follows:
   a. Inspect harness connectors EM15, PI32 and PI1/27 for corrosion, damage, bent or pushed back pins.
   b. Repair as required, then test system for normal operation.

Inspect Harness (Ground) Continuity

1. With EM14 disconnected, measure resistance between EM14/9 and ground EM1AR (EM2AR).
2. If resistance is less than .5 ohms, connect EM14, EM15, PI31 or (PI32) and proceed to "Inspect Mechanical Condition."
3. If resistance is more than .5 ohms, proceed as follows:
   a. Inspect harness and connector EM14 for corrosion, damage, bent or pushed back pins.
   b. Inspect ground stud and splice EMS36 for corrosion, damage, bent or pushed back pins.
   c. Repair as required, then test system for normal operation.

Inspect Mechanical Condition

1. Remove VVT(s) and ensure there is no foreign matter blocking oil passageway.
2. If mechanical condition is satisfactory, proceed to "End."
3. If mechanical condition is not satisfactory, repair or replace as required.

End

1. Perform appropriate service drive cycle and inspect for presence of DTC.
2. If fault code has cleared, fault condition has been corrected and no further diagnosis is required.
3. If fault code has not cleared, further diagnosis is required.

CODE P1474: INTERCOOLER COOLANT PUMP RELAY

Inspect Fuse

1. Turn ignition switch to O position.
2. Inspect fuse F2 in engine management fuse box.
3. If fuse is good, proceed to "Measure Relay Socket Supply Voltage."
4. If fuse is not good, replace and test system for normal operation.

Measure Relay Socket Supply Voltage

1. Turn ignition switch is in O position.
2. Remove intercooler coolant pump replay from inside ECM housing.
3. Turn ignitions switch to II position.
4. Measure battery voltage at relay socket between pins 3 and 2.
5. If measurement is battery voltage, proceed to "Measure Relay Coil Supply Voltage."
6. If measurement is not battery voltage, proceed to "Inspect Relay Socket Supply Continuity."

Inspect Relay Socket Supply Continuity

1. Turn ignition switch is in O position.
2. Remove engine management fuse F2.
3. Measure resistance between relay socket pin 3 and load side of fuse F2.
4. If resistance is less than .5 ohms, proceed to "Inspect Relay Socket Ground Continuity."
5. If resistance is not less than .5 ohms, inspect harness/connectors EM020 and EM041 (relay socket) for corrosion, damage, bent or pushed back pins.
6. Repair as required and test system for normal operation.

Inspect Relay Socket Ground Continuity

1. Turn ignition switch to O position.
2. Measure resistance between relay socket pin 1 and ground EM017.
3. If resistance is less than .5 ohms, proceed to "Measure Relay Coil Supply Voltage."

4. If resistance is not less than .5 ohms, inspect harness/connectors EM020 and EM041 (relay socket), and splice EMS11 for corrosion, damage, bent or pushed back pins.
5. Repair as required and test system for normal operation.

Measure Relay Coil Supply Voltage

1. Turn ignition switch to II position.
2. Measure voltage between relay socket pin 2 and ground EM017.
3. If measurement is battery positive voltage, proceed to "End."
4. If measurement is not battery positive voltage, proceed to "Inspect ECM Supply To Relay Continuity."

Inspect ECM Supply To Relay Continuity

1. Turn ignition switch to O position.
2. Disconnect EM013 inside ECM housing.
3. Measure resistance between EM013/010 and relay socket pin 2.
4. If resistance is less than .5 ohms, replace relay and test system for normal operation.
5. If resistance is not less than .5 ohms, inspect harness/connector EM013 and relay socket for corrosion, damage, bent or pushed back pins.
6. Repair as required and test system for normal operation.

End

1. If fault code has been cleared, system is operating properly.
2. If fault code is still present, contact Jaguar Service.

CODE P1516: PARK/ NEUTRAL SWITCH

Status Inspection

1. Turn ignition switch to II position.
2. Slow move selector lever from P to 1 and back.
3. If with lever at D when moving from 2 to P, 3 or 4 illuminate proceed to "Inspect Selector Cable Adjustment."
4. If with lever at D when moving from 2 to P, 3 or 4 did not illuminate proceed to "Inspect Switch P/N."

Inspect Selector Cable Adjustment

1. Inspect selector cable adjustment.
2. If adjustment is proper, proceed to "Inspect Switch P/N."
3. If adjustment is not proper, correct as required.
4. Test system for normal operation.

Inspect Switch P/N

1. Turn ignition switch to O position.
2. Disconnect EM047.
3. Measure resistance between EM047/00K and EM047/00J.
4. If with selector lever at P and N resistance is less than .5 ohms, and with selector lever at R, D, 4, 3 and 2, resistance is more than 50 KOhms, proceed to "Inspect Harness Signal Continuity."
5. If resistance is not a previously specified, replace transmission rotary position switch and test system for normal operation.

Inspect Harness Signal Continuity

1. Turn ignition switch to O position.
2. Disconnect EM047 and EM010.
3. Measure resistance between EM010/015 and EM047/00K.
4. If resistance is not less than .5 ohms, inspect EM047 and EM010 for corrosion, bent/pushed back pins or harness location. Repair as required and test system for normal operation.
5. If resistance is less than .5 ohms, ensure fuse EMS control F10 has not failed.
6. Disconnect EM047 and EM020.
7. Measure resistance between EM020/070 and EM007/00J.
8. If resistance is less than .5 ohms, proceed to "End."
9. If resistance is not less than .5 ohms, inspect EM047 and EM020 for corrosion, bent/pushed back pins or harness location. Repair as required and test system for normal operation.

End

1. If fault code has been cleared, system is operating properly.
2. If fault code is still present, contact Jaguar Service.

CODE P1609: INTERNAL CONTROL MODULE KEEP ALIVE MEMORY ERROR

This procedure has been revised by a Technical Service Bulletin.

Replace ECM

1. Inspect for possible short circuit on flash programming pin on harness to ECM.
2. Inspect for possible short circuit on fuel pump relay line.
3. If short circuit is found, trace and repair as required.
4. Clear DTC and inspect or reoccurrence.
5. If fault code reoccurs, replace ECM and proceed to "End."

End

1. Drive vehicle for a period from cold to normal engine operating temperature. Operate engine at idle speed, brisk acceleration and a steady cruising speed.
2. Inspect for presence of DTC.
3. If fault code has cleared, fault condition has been corrected and no further diagnosis is required.
4. If fault code has not cleared, further diagnosis is required.

Clearing Diagnostic Trouble Codes

To clear diagnostic trouble codes, install a suitable scan tool and follow tool manufacturer's instructions.

SYSTEM SERVICE

Fuel System Pressure Relief

1. Ensure ignition switch is Off.
2. Remove fuel crossover pipe valve cap.
3. Place suitable cloth under valve to collect any spilled fuel.
4. Place container suitable for collecting fuel next to vehicle.
5. Connect fuel injection pressure test equipment tool JD 209, or equivalent, to valve.
6. Place tool's drain/bleed tube into fuel container.
7. Depressurize system according to tool manufacturer's instructions.
8. Close fuel container lid securely, remove tool, discard cloth and install valve cap.

Component Replacement

FUEL INJECTOR

XJ8 & XK8

1. Relieve fuel system pressure as outlined in this section.
2. Remove engine cover.
3. Disconnect injector connectors and place harness conduit aside.
4. Remove mounting bolts and fuel injector clamp plate.
5. Remove fuel injector using injector removal tool No. JD-231, or equivalent.
6. Reverse procedure to install, noting the following:
   a. Install new seals lubricated with suitable petroleum jelly.
   b. **Torque** mounting bolts to 35–53 inch lbs.

XJR

No. 1

1. Relieve fuel system pressure as outlined in this section.
2. Disconnect connector and position aside.
3. Loosen, but do not remove, support bracket mounting nut and position injector harness aside.
4. Mark orientation and carefully pry injector retaining clip out. **Do not allow clip to be ejected and lost.**
5. Carefully lever injector from fuel rail using suitable tool.
6. Reverse procedure to install, noting the following:
   a. Install new O-ring lubricated with petroleum jelly.
   b. Press injector in firmly until it clicks into place.

c. Hold injector down firmly to fit clip.
d. **Torque** mounting bolts to 35–53 inch lbs.

No. 2, 3 & 4

1. Relieve fuel system pressure as outlined in this section.
2. Drain radiator coolant into suitable container.
3. Remove air cleaner assembly and throttle body.
4. Remove EGR valve.
5. Remove throttle induction elbow, supercharger outlet duct and gasket.
6. Remove coolant outlet line and supercharger drive belt.
7. Remove supercharger.
8. Remove lefthand or righthand intercooler as required.
9. Disconnect injector connectors, then remove mounting nuts and position harness aside.
10. Disconnect connector and position aside.
11. Loosen, but do not remove, support bracket mounting nut. Position injector harness aside.
12. Mark orientation and carefully pry injector retaining clip out. **Do not allow clip to be ejected and lost.**
13. Carefully lever injector from fuel rail using suitable tool.
14. Reverse procedure to install, noting the following:
    a. Install new O-ring lubricated with petroleum jelly.
    b. Press injector in firmly until it clicks into place.
    c. Hold injector down firmly to fit clip.
    d. **Torque** harness mounting bolts to 35–53 inch lbs.

FUEL RAIL

XJR

1. Relieve fuel system pressure as outlined in this section.
2. Drain radiator coolant into suitable container.
3. Remove air cleaner assembly and throttle body.
4. Remove EGR valve.
5. Remove throttle induction elbow, supercharger outlet duct and gasket.
6. Remove coolant outlet line and supercharger drive belt.
7. Remove supercharger.
8. Remove lefthand or righthand intercooler as required.
9. **When removing lefthand fuel rail,** remove mounting bolts and position fuel pressure regulator aside.
10. **When removing righthand fuel rail,** remove mounting bolts and position fuel feed line aside.
11. **On all models,** remove mounting bolts and position fuel aside.
12. Remove crossover pipe mounting bolt, then the fuel rail and seals from intercooler adapter
13. Reverse procedure to install, noting the following:
    a. Install new seals and O-rings.
    b. **Torque** pressure regulator and fuel feed line to 71–106 inch lbs.
    c. **Torque** fuel rail mounting bolts to 13–18 ft. lbs.

THROTTLE BODY

1. Remove air cleaner assembly.
2. Disconnect electrical connectors and vacuum hose.
3. Disconnect inner cable by rotating throttle quadrant.
4. Release throttle cable locking nut and disconnect out cable from abutment bracket. **Do not disturb adjusting nut.**
5. Remove coolant hoses. Mop up spilled coolant.
6. Disconnect connector from bracket under lefthand side.
7. Remove mounting bolts and throttle body. Block inlet opening.
8. Remove throttle cable and intake duct brackets.
9. Reverse procedure to install, noting the following:
    a. **Torque** throttle cable and intake duct brackets to 36–53 inch lbs.
    b. **Torque** throttle body mounting bolts to 13–18 ft. lbs.
    c. Ensure there is neither tension or slack in throttle cable.
    d. Ensure pedal to kickdown switch contact does not move switch.
    e. Measure kickdown switch voltage.
    f. If measurement is not 3.66–3.76 voltage, rotate switch to obtain specification.

MASS AIR FLOW (MAF) METER

1. Disconnect electrical connector.
2. Remove MAF meter to air cleaner mounting bolts.
3. Remove air cleaner lid, then release band clip and remove MAF meter.
4. Reverse procedure to install, using new seal.

INTAKE AIR TEMPERATURE (IAT) SENSOR

The IAT sensor is part of the MAF meter and is not serviceable.

ENGINE CONTROL MODULE (ECM)

1. Remove housing cover, mounting screws and security bracket.
2. Disconnect electrical connectors and remove ECM.
3. Remove mounting bolts and bracket.
4. Reverse procedure to install.

THROTTLE CABLE

1. Remove windshield wiper and arm assembly.
2. Remove plenum chamber finisher.
3. Disconnect throttle cable from electronic throttle assembly by rotating throttle quadrant to release cable nipple.
4. Disconnect outer cable from abutment bracket by disconnect locking nut.
5. Disconnect plenum chamber closing plate grommet and route cable/grommet though aperture.
6. Remove throttle cable from bulkhead clip.
7. route cable through water deflector bracket.
8. Ensure driver's seat is fully rearward, then remove A-post lower trim pad.
9. Remove throttle cable to pedal split pin and cable retaining sleeve, then disconnect cable from pedal.
10. Remove cable from engine compartment side.
11. Reverse procedure to install, noting the following:
    a. Ensure quadrant to abutment gap is .0472 inch.
    b. Tighten lock nut without altering gap or introducing twist to outer cable.
    c. Ensure there is neither tension or slack in throttle cable.
    d. Ensure pedal to kickdown switch contact does not move switch.
    e. Measure kickdown switch voltage.
    f. If measurement is not 3.66–3.76 voltage, rotate switch to obtain specifications.

Electric Fuel Pumps

NOTE: If Unsure Of The System Used On The Vehicle Being Serviced, Refer To "The Engine Systems Identification Chart."Further Assistance For The Proper Use Of Information Contained In This Section Can Also Be Found In The Front Of This Tabbed Section Under "How To Use This Manual"

NOTE: On Air Bag Equipped Models, Refer To "Air Bag System Precautions" Located In The Front Of This Manual When Battery Power To The Computer Has Been Intterupted.

NOTE: Refer To "Computer Relearn Procedures" Located In The Front Of This Manual When Battery Power To The Computer Has Been Interrupted.

NOTE: Prior To Performing Any Service Operations Listed In This Section, Consult The "Technical Service Bulletins" Section For Related Information.

INDEX

	Page No.
Description	12-69
Fuel Pressure Relief	12-69
S-Type	12-69
XJR, XJ8 & XK8	12-69
Fuel Pump Relay Location	12-69
XJ8 & XK8	12-69
XJR	12-69
Fuel Pump Replacement	12-69
Except S-Type	12-69
S-Type	12-70
Module, Fuel Delivery (Rightside)	12-70
Module, Transfer (Leftside)	12-70
Fuel Pump Specifications	12-70
Fuel Tank, Replace	12-70
Except S-Type	12-70
S-Type	12-70
Precautions	12-69
Air Bag Systems	12-69
Battery Ground Cable	12-69

PRECAUTIONS

Air Bag Systems

Refer to "Air Bag System Precautions" in the front of this manual for system disarming and arming procedures.

Battery Ground Cable

Prior to service, disconnect battery ground cable and isolate as required.

DESCRIPTION

Fuel is drawn from the fuel tank into the in-tank fuel module by the fuel pump, with the fuel passing through a venturi on the fuel pump pressure side. Fuel is pumped from the base of the fuel tank through a flexible hose to an in-line filter. From the filter, fuel flows through under vehicle lines to the front of the vehicle, where flexible hose connects the fuel line to the fuel rail.

A fuel pressure regulator, referenced to manifold vacuum, controls fuel line pressure and maintains a constant pressure across the fuel injector nozzles. Pressure is kept constant within 35–45 psi.

FUEL PUMP RELAY LOCATION

XJR

The fuel pump relay is located on the righthand rear side of the luggage compartment, above the bulb failure module.

XJ8 & XK8

The fuel pump relay is located in the engine compartment relay center.

FUEL PRESSURE RELIEF

XJR, XJ8 & XK8

1. Ensure ignition switch is Off.
2. Remove fuel crossover pipe valve cap.
3. Place suitable cloth under valve to collect any spilled fuel.
4. Place container suitable for collecting fuel next to vehicle.
5. Connect fuel injection pressure test equipment tool JD 209, or equivalent, to valve.
6. Place tool's drain/bleed tube into fuel container.
7. Depressurize system according to tool manufacturer's instructions.
8. Close fuel container lid securely, remove tool, discard cloth and install valve cap.

S-Type

1. Ensure ignition switch is Off.
2. Remove schrader valve cap.
3. Connect fuel pressure gauge to schrader valve.
4. Catch any displaced fuel in a suitable container.
5. Depressurize system according to tool manufacturer's instructions.
6. Close fuel container lid securely, remove tool and install valve cap.

FUEL PUMP REPLACEMENT

Except S-Type

The fuel pump assembly is mounted at the top of the fuel tank. Fuel pump replacement requires removing the fuel tank from the vehicle. **Only remove fuel tank in a well ventilated area, equipped with fire extinguishers and absorbing sand.**

1. Relieve fuel system pressure as outlined under "Precautions."
2. Remove fuel tank from vehicle as outlined under "Fuel Tank, Replace."
3. Release clip and disconnect breather hose from evaporative loss flange.
4. Using retaining ring removal tool No. JD174, or equivalent, remove evaporative loss flange retaining ring.
5. Reposition flange for access and disconnect fuel pump harness multi-plug.
6. Release internal hose securing clamps with removal tool No. JD175, or equivalent.
7. Disconnect hoses from fuel pump.
8. Release tie wrap connector from rubber mounting, then remove fuel pump assembly using a twisting motion.
9. Reverse procedure to install. **Torque** fuel sender unit locking ring to 48–108 inch lbs.

S-Type

MODULE, TRANSFER (LEFTSIDE)

1. Open fuel filler flap, then remove filler cap.
2. Remove rear seat, then the blanking grommets.
3. Disconnect jet pump/sender unit electrical connector, then the fuel tubes.
4. Remove jet pump module locking ring. **Ensure damage to fuel level float does not occur.**
5. Remove jet pump.
6. Reverse procedure to install. Install a new O-ring.

MODULE, FUEL DELIVERY (RIGHTSIDE)

1. Open fuel filler flap, then remove filler cap.
2. Remove rear seat, then the blanking grommets.
3. Disconnect fuel pump/sender unit electrical connector.
4. Disconnect fuel delivery tubes, then remove pump module locking ring.
5. Place fuel pump/sender unit cover aside.
6. Using fuel pump access holes to gain access to fuel, drain fuel tank.
7. Detach fuel pump from fuel tank, **ensure damage to fuel level float does not occur.**
8. Remove fuel pump from tank.
9. Reverse procedure to install. Install a new O-ring.

FUEL TANK

REPLACE

Except S-Type

1. Remove trunk floor carpet, front liner, rear lamp assembly interior trim finisher, trunk seal and side liner.
2. Relieve fuel system pressure as outlined under "Precautions."
3. Raise and support vehicle, then drain fuel into suitable container.
4. Disconnect fuel tank fuel lines using connector tool No. JD-203, or equivalent. Plug lines and tank.
5. Disconnect fuel filler latch box drain line clip.
6. Disconnect and position trunk wiring harness aside.
7. Disconnect tank wiring harness connections.
8. Remove fuel filler latch box drain pipe.
9. Disconnect vapor outlet line.
10. Open fuel filler flap and remove filler cap.
11. Remove filler neck spring ring and pull filler latch box free.
12. Loosen mounting strap clamp nuts and bolts, the remove lower bracket mounting bolts.
13. Disconnect lefthand trunk lid strut rear pivot and secure strut under lid.
14. Disconnect ground cable and remove tank.
15. Reverse procedure to install, noting the following:
    a. **Torque** ground strap mounting bolt to 97–115 inch lbs.
    b. **On 2000–01 models through VIN F21165, torque** strap mounting bolt to 16–21 ft. lbs., then **torque** strap nut to 44–53 inch lbs.
    c. **On 2000–01 models from VIN F21166,** proceed as follows: tighten retaining strap snail cam bolts finger tight.
    d. **On 2000-01 models from VIN F21166,** place socket tool No. 310-094, or equivalent, over lefthand strap snail cam bolt so the drive peg engages with cam hole, **Fig. 1.**
    e. **On 2000-01 models from VIN F21166,** rotate cam clockwise with a 10 MM drive socket and **torque** to 53 inch lbs.
    f. **On 2000-01 models from VIN F21166,** hold socket tool with an open end wrench, tehn remove torque wrench and socket.
    g. **On 2000-01 models from VIN F21166,** insert a ⅜ inch drive deep-well 10 MM socket through tool bore and engage with snail cam retaining bolt.
    h. **On 2000-01 models from VIN F21166, torque** snail cam retaining bolt to 18 ft. lbs.
    i. **On 2000-01 models from VIN F21166,** remove tool setup, then repeat procedure on righthand side snail cam bolt.

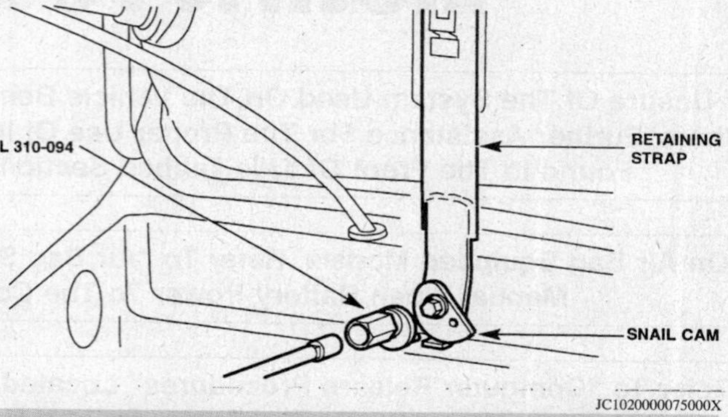

Fig. 1 Fuel tank strap snail cam installation. 2000–01 models from VIN F21166

S-Type

1. Drain fuel tank as outlined in "Fuel Tank Replace."
2. Remove driveshaft.
3. Disconnect fuel tank electrical connector, then remove fuel filler pipe to fuel tank hose.
4. Disconnect evaporative emission pipe, then detach fuel tank support straps and remove fuel tank.
5. Reverse procedure to install.

FUEL PUMP SPECIFICATIONS

Fuel pump system pressure is 35–45 psi.

Emission Control System Application Charts

Engine Liters/Type	Certification Type		Trans. Type		Computerized Engine Management	Fuel Induction System Type	Ignition Timing, Deg. BTDC @ RPM	TSB	EPA & CARB Emission Recall	Emission Control System SRI	Emission Control Systems								
	CA	FED	AT	MT							PCV	ACL	AIS	EGR	EVAP	CAT	SPK	FR	O2S
1998–2001																			
4.0L	X	X	X	—	YES①	SFI	②	—	—	—	X	—	—	—	X	X③	X④	X	X⑥
4.0L Supercharged	X	X	X	X	YES①	SFI	②	—	—	—	X	—	—	—	X	X③	X④	X	X⑥
1999–2001																			
3.0L/181/V6	X	X	X	—	YES	SFI	②	—	—	—	X	—	—	X⑦	X	X③	X⑤	X	X⑥
4.0L/244/V8 S-Type	X	X	X	—	YES	SFI	②	—	—	—	X	—	—	—	X	X③	X⑤	X	X⑥

X — Equipped
— Not Equipped
① — V8 Engine Management System/OBD II.
② — Electronically controlled. No adjustment.
③ — Type, TWC; number of catalytic converters, 2.
④ — EI.
⑤ — EI/COP.
⑥ — Two HO2S & two O2S.
⑦ — Differential pressure type EGR.
ACL — Air Cleaner (Thermostatic Air Cleaner)
AIS — Air Injection System
AT — Automatic Transmission
BTDC — Before Top Dead Center
CA — California
CAT — Catalytic Converter
CID — Cubic Inch Displacement
DI — Distributor Ignition
DLC — Data Link Connector
EGR — Exhaust Gas Recirculation
EVAP — Evaporative Emission Control System
FED — Federal
FR — Fillpipe Restrictor
MFI — Multiport Fuel Injection
MT — Manual Transmission
OC — Oxidation Catalytic Converter
O_2S — Oxygen Sensor
PCV — Positive Crankcase Ventilation
RPM — Revolutions Per Minute
SPK — Spark Control
SRI — Service Reminder Indicator
TSB — Technical Service Bulletin
TWC — Three-Way Catalytic Converter

Vacuum Hose Routings

INDEX

	PAGE NO.	FIG. NO.
S-TYPE:		
3.0L Engine	12-72	1
4.0L Engine	12-72	2
XJ SERIES:		
V8 Engine	12-72	3

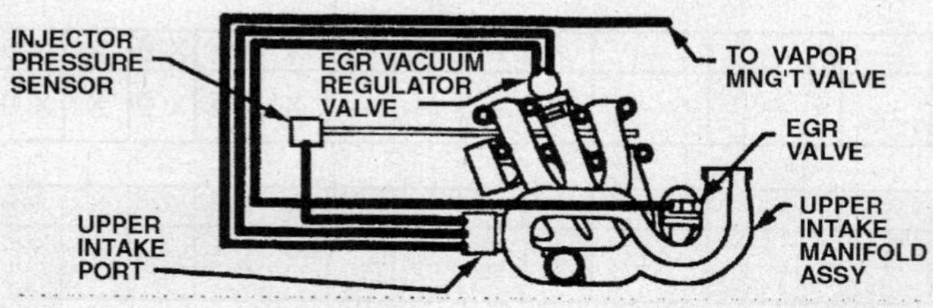

Fig. 1 Vacuum hose routing. S-Type w/3.0L engine

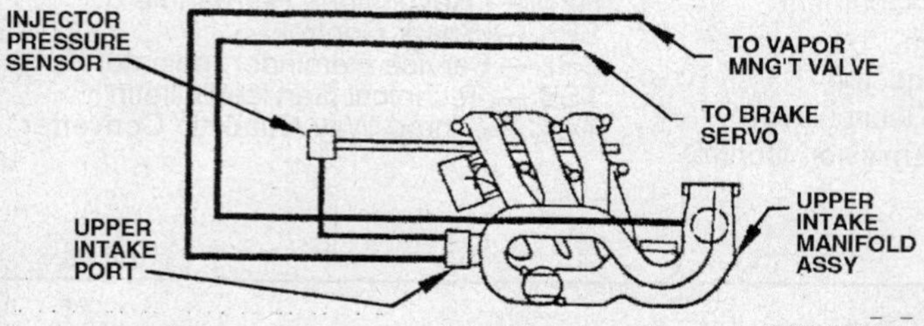

Fig. 2 Vacuum hose routing. S-Type w/4.0L engine

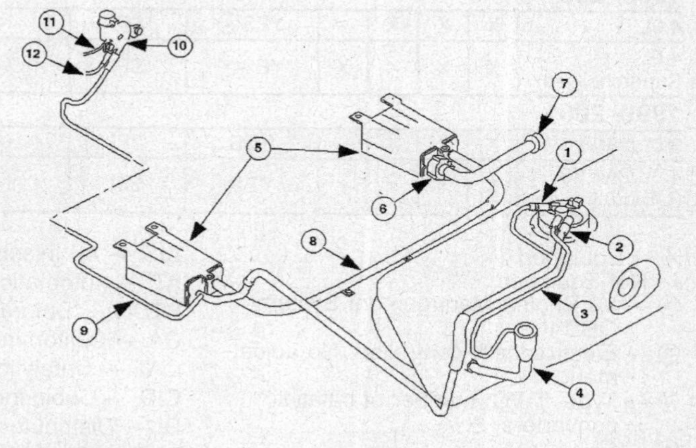

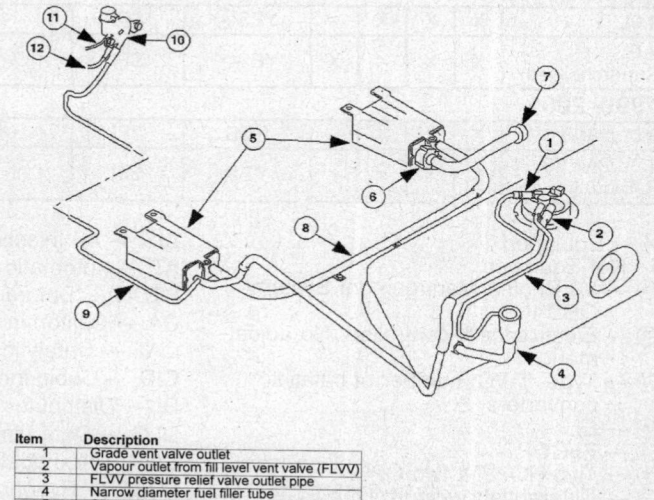

Item	Description
1	Grade vent valve outlet
2	Vapour outlet from fill level vent valve (FLVV)
3	FLVV pressure relief valve outlet pipe
4	Narrow diameter fuel filler tube
5	Charcoal canisters
6	Canister close valve
7	Vent pipe air filter
8	Vapour pipe connecting canisters
9	Canister purge outlet pipe
10	EVAP canister purge valve (engine bay)
11	Vacuum control signal from induction elbow
12	EVAP purge valve outlet to induction elbow

JC1030100048000X

Fig. 3 Vacuum hose diagram. XJ Series w/V8 engine

Emission Controls

NOTE: If Unsure Of The System Used On The Vehicle Being Serviced, Refer To "The Engine Systems Identification Chart."Further Assistance For The Proper Use Of Information Contained In This Section Can Also Be Found In The Front Of This Tabbed Section Under "How To Use This Manual"

NOTE: On Air Bag Equipped Models, Refer To "Air Bag System Precautions" Located In The Front Of This Manual For System Disarming & Arming Procedures.

NOTE: Refer To "Computer Relearn Procedures" Located In The Front Of This Manual When Battery Power To The Computer Has Been Interrupted.

NOTE: Prior To Performing Any Service Operations Listed In This Section, Consult The "Technical Service Bulletins" Section For Related Information.

INDEX

	Page No.
Catalytic Converter	12-73
Description	12-73
System Service	12-73
Catalytic Converter, Replace	12-73
Crankcase Ventilation System	12-73
Description	12-73
Evaporative Emission Control System	12-74
Description	12-74
Evaporative Emission Control Valve	12-74
System Service	12-74
Charcoal Canister, Replace	12-74
Engine Breather Filter, Replace	12-74
Engine Breather Heater Element, Replace	12-74
Purge Valve, Replace	12-74
Exhaust Gas Recirculation (EGR)	12-73
System Service	12-73
EGR Valve, Replace	12-73

CRANKCASE VENTILATION SYSTEM

Description

To ensure piston blow-by gases do not escape from the engine crankcase to the atmosphere, a depression is maintained in the crankcase under all operating temperatures.

The emissions are fed into the engine intake manifolds at part throttle through restrictors located in the outlet pipes of the oil separator, and into the air cleaner outlet tube from the lifter block housing at full throttle.

Blow-by gases are removed from the crankcase through the part load oil separator which is mounted below the jack shaft cover, this separator contains two knit mesh screens. Each of the part load oil separator tubes has a restrictor installed to ensure the blow-by gases are consumed equally by each bank of the engine in proportion to manifold vacuum.

Under full throttle conditions, crankcase gases are drawn into the intake manifold through the full throttle breather hose, air cleaner outlet tube and the throttle.

CATALYTIC CONVERTER

Description

The catalytic converter used on these vehicles reduces the emission of carbon monoxide, hydrocarbons and oxides of nitrogen.

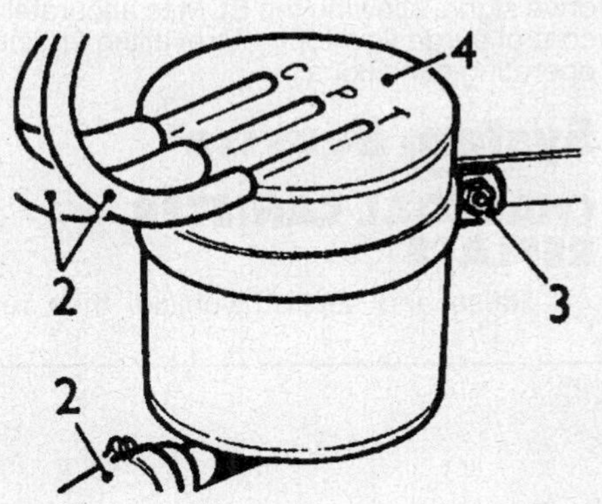

Fig. 1 Charcoal canister removal

System Service

CATALYTIC CONVERTER, REPLACE

1. Remove oxygen sensor, then raise and support vehicle.
2. Remove strap to catalyst retaining nut and bolt.
3. Loosen strap to bellhousing retaining bolt and position aside.
4. Remove catalytic converter to intermediate pipe nut and bolt.
5. Loosen clamp and slide rearward.
6. Disconnect exhaust system from catalytic converter.
7. Remove catalytic converter to manifold retaining nuts, then the catalytic converter assembly.
8. Remove and discard seal rings, then the seal from the intermediate pipe.
9. Clean all sealing surfaces.
10. Reverse procedure to install.

EXHAUST GAS RECIRCULATION (EGR)

System Service

EGR VALVE, REPLACE

XJ8, XK8 & XJR

1. Remove air cleaner assembly.
2. Disconnect EGR valve electrical connector.
3. Place suitable drain container under vehicle.
4. Clamp EGR coolant hose and disconnect from throttle body.
5. Remove EGR transfer pipe mounting bolts.
6. Remove mounting bolts and position EGR valve aside.
7. Remove hoses and EGR valve.
8. Reverse procedure to install, noting the following:
   a. Install new seals.

b. **Torque** EGR and transfer pipe mounting bolts to 13–18 ft. lbs.

EVAPORATIVE EMISSION CONTROL SYSTEM

Description

The evaporative emission control system collects vapors from both the fuel system, and the engine crankcase. These are stored in a charcoal canister until they are drawn into the engine intake system to be burned in the engine. An engine breather filter prevents crankcase by-products from being drawn into the vapor control system. A vapor separator prevents liquid fuel from entering the vapor system.

When the engine is running, manifold vacuum acts on the pressure control valve, which opens the vent line from the fuel tank to the charcoal canister. Air enters the charcoal canister and flows to the tank to replace the fuel delivered to the engine and maintain atmospheric pressure in the tank.

If the pressure control valve fails, the fuel tank cap will vent the fuel tank pressure at 2.0–2.5 psi.

When canister purge is enabled, the ECM meters purge flow to the intake manifold through the normally closed evaporative emission control (purge) valve. Canister purge is enabled by the ECM based on engine coolant temperature only when closed loop fuel metering control is operational.

The ECM detects purge flow in two ways. If closed loop fuel metering correction indicates a large movement toward lean when purging is enabled, or if the idle air control valve corrects for increased air flow when purging is enabled, the ECM has confirmation that purging is taking place.

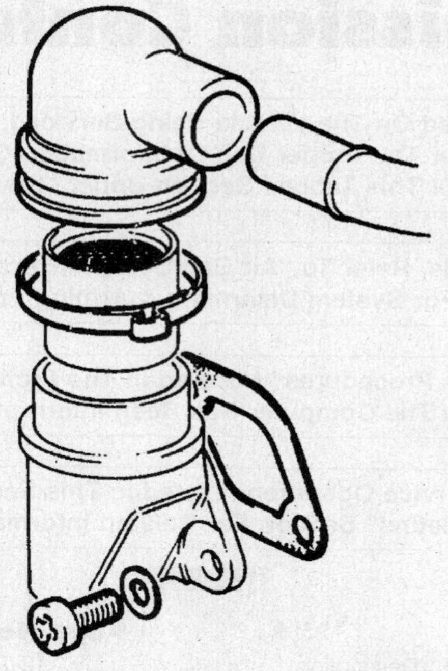

Fig. 2 Breather filter removal

EVAPORATIVE EMISSION CONTROL VALVE

The evaporative emission control valve is a normally closed pulse width modulated valve. The amount of valve opening and canister flow is determined by the ECM drive signal allowing the ECM to accurately control purge flow for the prevailing engine operating conditions.

System Service

CHARCOAL CANISTER, REPLACE

1. Raise and support vehicle, then remove front righthand wheel.
2. Disconnect hoses (2) from canister (4). Note location of hose to container mounting, **Fig. 1.**
3. Remove mounting strap nut (3), and lift canister from vehicle.
4. Reverse procedure to install. Align canister in mount.

ENGINE BREATHER FILTER, REPLACE

1. Remove hose clip securing the rubber cover to breather housing, **Fig. 2.**
2. Disconnect breather pipe.
3. Remove rubber cover and lift out filter.

ENGINE BREATHER HEATER ELEMENT, REPLACE

1. Disconnect heater element cable harness block connector.
2. Loosen breather hose to element securing clip, then disconnect hose from element.
3. Loosen intake elbow to heater element securing clip.
4. Disconnect hose and remove heater element.
5. Reverse procedure to install.

PURGE VALVE, REPLACE

XJ8, XK8 & XJR

1. Disconnect electrical connector.
2. Remove mounting screws and purge valve.
3. Remove vacuum line, the disconnect clip and upper vapor hose.
4. Disconnect clip and lower vapor hose.
5. Reverse procedure to install.

Technical Service Bulletins

INDEX

	Page No.
Difficult Cold Start	12-75
XJ8 & XK8	12-75

DIFFICULT COLD START

XJ8 & XK8

On these models, there may be a no-start condition. This may include prolonged cranking accompanied by black exhaust smoke.

This condition may be caused by Engine Control Module (ECM) software. To correct this condition, update ECM to most current specifications.

Abbreviations & Acronyms

AIR: Secondary Air Injection
AIRC: Secondary Air Injection Check Valve
AIRD: Secondary Air Injection Delay Valve
AIRP: Secondary Air Injection Pump
AIRPC: Secondary Air Injection Magnetic Clutch
AIRR: Secondary Air Injection Relay
AIRS: Secondary Air Injection Switching Valve
AIRV: Secondary Air Injection Solenoid Vacuum Valve
ALDL: Assembly Line Data Link
BARO: Barometric Absolute Pressure Sensor
CCM: Central Control Module
CKFS: Flywheel Sensor
CMPS: Camshaft Position Sensor
CKPS: Crankshaft Position Sensor
CLS: Closed Loop System
CO: Carbon Monoxide
CTP: Closed Throttle Position
CV: Crankcase Ventilation System
DI: Distributor Ignition
DIC: Distributor Ignition Cap
DLC: Data Link Connector
DSM: Diagnostic Status Manager
DTC: Diagnostic Trouble Code
DTM: Diagnostic Test Mode
ECL: Engine Coolant Level
ECM: Engine Control Module
ECTS: Engine Coolant Temperature Sensor
ECU: Electronic Control Unit
EEPROM: Electronically Erasable Programmable Read Only Memory
EFE: Early Fuel Evaporation
EGR: Exhaust Gas Recirculation System
EGRS: Exhaust Gas Recirculation Solenoid Vacuum Valve
EGRT: Exhaust Gas Recirculation Temperature Sensor
EGRV: Exhaust Gas Recirculation Valve
EI: Electronic Ignition
EMS: Engine Management System
EPROM: Electronically Programmable Read Only Memory
EVAP: Evaporative Emission Control System
EVAPP: Evaporative Emission Purge Valve
FI: Fuel Injector
FPM: Fuel Pump Module
FPR: Fuel Pump Relay
HC: Hydrocarbon
HO_2S: Heated Oxygen Sensor
HT: High Tension
IAT: Intake Air Temperature
IATS: Intake Air Temperature Sensor
IATSF: Intake Air Temperature Sensor Injection
IATSI: Intake Air Temperature Sensor Ignition
IAVC: Idle Air Control Valve
IC: Ignition Control System
ICM: Ignition Control Module
IFSS: Inertia Fuel Shut-Off Switch
ISC: Idle Speed Control
JDS: Jaguar Diagnostic System
KS: Knock Sensor
LT: Low Tension
MAF: Mass Air Flow
MAFS: Mass Air Flow Sensor
MAP: Manifold Absolute Pressure
MAPS: Manifold Absolute Pressure Sensor
MFI: Multi-Port Fuel Injection
MIL: Malfunction Indicator Lamp
O_2S: Oxygen Sensor
OBD: On Board Diagnostic System
OBD II: On Board Diagnostic System Two
PAIR: Pulsed Secondary Air Injection
PCMF: Powertrain Control Module Fuel
PCMI: Powertrain Control Module Ignition
PDU: Portable Diagnostic Unit
PNPS: Park/Neutral Position Switch
PTIS: Powertrain Input Signals
PWM: Pulse Width Modulation
RAM: Random Access Memory
RFI: Radio Frequency Interference
ROM: Read Only Memory
RPM: Revolutions Per Minute
SAE: Society Of Automotive Engineers
SFI: Sequential Multi-Port Electronic Fuel Injection
ST: Scan Tool
TCC: Torque Converter Clutch
TCM: Transmission Control Module
TDC: Top Dead Center
TPS: Throttle Position Sensor
TVS: Thermal Vacuum Switch
TVV: Thermal Vacuum Valve
TWC: Three Way Catalytic Converter
VCM: Vehicle Condition Monitor
VIN: Vehicle Identification Number
VSS: Vehicle Speed Sensor
WOT: Wide Open Throttle
WOTS: Wide Open Throttle Switch

LAND ROVER

TABLE OF CONTENTS

Page No.

EMISSIONS:
Abbreviations & Acronyms 13-32
Application Charts 13-26
Emissions Controls 13-29
Emission Control System Application Chart . . . 13-26
Engine Compartment Reference Diagrams 13-27
Technical Service Bulletins 13-31

ENGINE SYSTEMS IDENTIFICATION 13-2

FUEL SYSTEMS:
Abbreviations & Acronyms 13-32
Electric Fuel Pumps 13-25
Engine Compartment Reference Diagrams 13-27
Fuel Injection 13-6
Technical Service Bulletins 13-31

ENGINE TUNE UP & PERFORMANCE:
Abbreviations & Acronyms 13-32
Specifications 13-2
V8 Gasoline Engine 13-3

GENERAL INFORMATION:
Abbreviations & Acronyms 13-32
Air Bag System Precautions 0-12
Air Quality Standards 0-23
Computer Relearn Procedure 0-10
Electrical Symbol & Wire Color Code Identification 0-33
Engine Systems Identification 13-2
How To Use This Manual 0-1
Quick Reference 13-1
Service Reminder & Warning Lamp Reset Procedure 0-14
Technical Service Bulletins 13-31
Vehicle Identification 0-3
Vehicle Lift Points 0-24
Vehicle Maintenance Schedules 0-45

IGNITION SYSTEMS:
Abbreviations & Acronyms 13-32
Engine Compartment Reference Diagrams 13-27
Ignition Systems 13-4
Technical Service Bulletins 13-31

Quick Reference

Application	Page No.
ACCESSING DIAGNOSTIC TROUBLE CODES	
All	13-8
CLEARING DIAGNOSTIC TROUBLE CODES	
All	13-9
COMPRESSION PRESSURE SPECIFICATIONS	
All	13-3
DIAGNOSTIC TROUBLE CODE INTERPRETATION	
All	13-8

Engine Systems Identification

Model	Engine	Fuel System	Page No.	Ignition System	Page No.	Computer System	Page No.
1998–2001							
Discovery	4.0L	Electronic Fuel Injection (SFI)	13-6	GEMS Direct Ignition System	13-4	Engine Control Module (ECM)	13-6
Range Rover HSE	4.0L & 4.6L	Electronic Fuel Injection (SFI)	13-6	GEMS Direct Ignition System	13-4	Engine Control Module (ECM)	13-6
Range Rover SE	4.0L & 4.6L	Electronic Fuel Injection (SFI)	13-6	GEMS Direct Ignition System	13-4	Engine Control Module (ECM)	13-6

Tune Up Specifications

Year & Engine	Spark Plug Gap, Inch	Ignition Timing			Curb Idle Speed, RPM②		Valve Lash
		Firing Order	Timing, °BTDC①	Timing Mark Location	Man. Trans.	Auto. Trans.	
1998–2001							
4.0L	.035	③	—	—	680–720	680–720	④
4.6L	.035	③	—	—	680–720	680–720	④

BTDC — Before Top Dead Center
N — Neutral
① — At specified curb idle speed.
② — When adjusting idle speed, set parking brake & chock drive wheels.
③ — Cylinder, numbering front to rear, left bank, 1, 3, 5, 7; right bank, 2, 4, 6, 8. Firing order, 1–8–4–3–6–5–7–2.
④ — Equipped w/hydraulic lash adjusters.

Engine Tune Up & Performance

NOTE: On Air Bag Equipped Models, Refer To "Air Bag System Precautions" Located In The Front Of This Manual For System Disarming & Arming Procedures.

NOTE: If Unsure Of The System Used On The Vehicle Being Serviced, Refer To The "Engine Systems Identification Chart." Further Assistance For The Proper Use Of Information Contained In This Section Can Also Be Found In The Front Of This Tabbed Section Under "How To Use This Manual."

NOTE: Prior to Performing Any Service Operations Listed In This Section, Consult The "Technical Service Bulletins" Section For Related Information.

V8 Gasoline Engine

INDEX

	Page No.
Compression Pressures	13-3
Engine Identification	13-3
Idle Speed & Mixture	
Adjustments	13-3
Ignition Timing	13-3
Spark Plugs	13-3
Valves	13-3
Valve Adjustment	13-3

ENGINE IDENTIFICATION

The engine serial number is stamped on a cast pad on the lefthand side of the engine block between cylinder Nos. 3 and 5, **Fig. 1.**

The compression ratio is stamped above the serial number.

SPARK PLUGS

Torque spark plugs to 15 ft. lbs. Refer to "Gasoline Engine Tune Up Specifications" for spark plug gap.

COMPRESSION PRESSURES

1. Start and run vehicle until normal operating temperatures are reached.
2. Remove spark plugs.
3. Disconnect coil leads.
4. Insert compression gauge into spark plug hole and turn engine over until compression stabilizes.
5. Pressure should read 167–180 psi.
6. If pressure is less than 150 psi, inspect valves and/or rings for damage, wear, or improper adjustment.

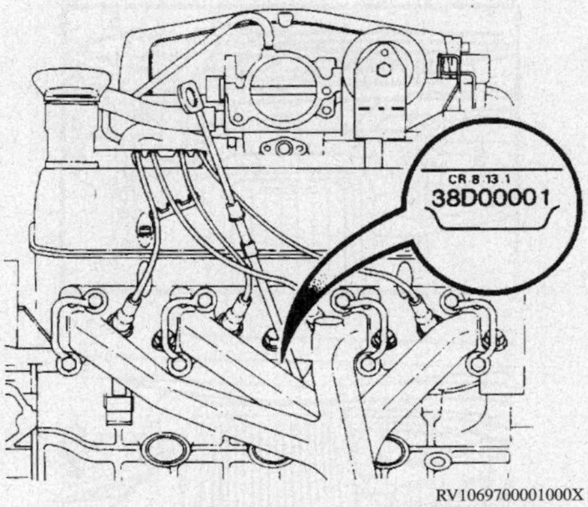

Fig. 1 Engine identification location

7. Low pressure in adjoining cylinders may indicate a faulty head gasket.

IGNITION TIMING

1. Connect suitable timing light and tachometer to engine according to manufacturer's instructions.
2. Disconnect vacuum hose from distributor.
3. Start and run engine until operating temperature is reached.
4. Ensure engine idle speed does not exceed 800 RPM.
5. Run engine at idle speed and read timing setting at timing marks located on crankshaft vibration damper. Refer to "Gasoline Engine Tune Up Specifications" for ignition timing.
6. If timing setting is not within specification, turn off engine and loosen distributor clamp.
7. Turn distributor to advance or retard ignition as necessary, then tighten distributor clamp.
8. Recheck timing until within specification, then install vacuum hose.

IDLE SPEED & MIXTURE ADJUSTMENTS

Base idle speed is set at factory and should not require further adjustment.

VALVES

Valve Adjustment

These engines use hydraulic lash adjusters. No adjustment is required.

Ignition Systems

NOTE: On Air Bag Equipped Models, Refer To “Air Bag System Precautions” Located In The Front Of This Manual For System Disarming & Arming Procedures.

NOTE: Refer To “Computer Relearn Procedures” Located In The Front Of This Manual When Battery Power To The Computer Has Been Interupted.

NOTE: If Unsure Of The System Used On The Vehicle Being Serviced, Refer To The “Engine Systems Identification Chart.” Further Assistance For The Proper Use Of Information Contained In This Section Can Also Be Found In The Front Of This Tabbed Section Under “How To Use This Manual.”

NOTE: Prior to Performing Any Service Operations Listed In This Section, Consult The “Technical Service Bulletins” Section For Related Information.

INDEX

	Page No.
Description	13-4
Diagnosis & Testing	13-4
System Service	13-4
Component Replacement	13-4
Ignition Coils	13-4

DESCRIPTION

The GEMS direct electronic ignition system uses four Lucas 2DIS2 double ended coils (part No. 4430019). They are mounted on a bracket attached to the rear of the engine. The ignition circuits are controlled by the ECM, producing sparks in two cylinders simultaneously; one on the compression stroke, the other on the exhaust stroke. Ignition coil No. 1 feeds cylinder Nos. 1 and 6. Coil No. 2 feeds cylinder Nos. 5 and 8. Coil No. 3 feeds cylinder Nos. 4 and 7, and coil No. 4 feeds cylinder Nos. 2 and 3.

DIAGNOSIS & TESTING

The electronic ignition system is controlled by GEMS ECM. Refer to “Fuel Injection” for diagnostic procedures.

SYSTEM SERVICE

Component Replacement

IGNITION COILS

1998

1. Disconnect high tension leads from ignition coils, **Fig. 1.**
2. Note or label positions of leads and place them aside.

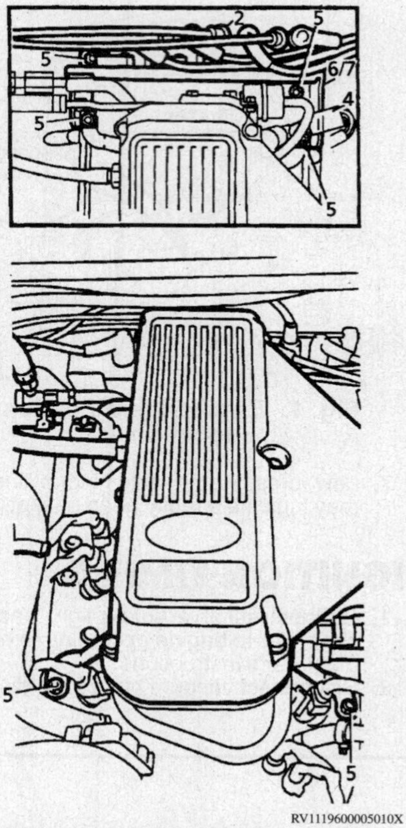

Fig. 1 Ignition coil replacement (Part 1 of 2). 1998

3. Disconnect ignition coil connector.
4. Remove six nuts securing fuel rail and ignition coil bracket to inlet manifold.
5. Lift fuel rail slightly to gain access, then remove ignition coil bracket from inlet manifold studs. **Do not completely withdraw injectors from fitted locations.**
6. Remove ignition coil assembly.
7. Remove terminal cover.
8. Remove two nuts securing wires to coil terminals.
9. Remove wires from terminals, noting wire positions, **Fig. 2.**
10. Remove attaching screws from ignition coil to bracket, then pull coil from bracket.
11. Reverse procedure to install. **Torque** fuel rail and ignition coil bracket screws to 72 inch lbs.

1999-2001

1. Remove upper inlet manifold gasket.
2. Remove two lower coil attaching bolts, **Fig. 3.**
3. Disconnect ignition coil electrical harness connectors.
4. Disconnect spark plug cables from rocker covers, then from spark plugs.
5. Remove coil assembly from between engine and firewall.
6. Reverse procedure to install.

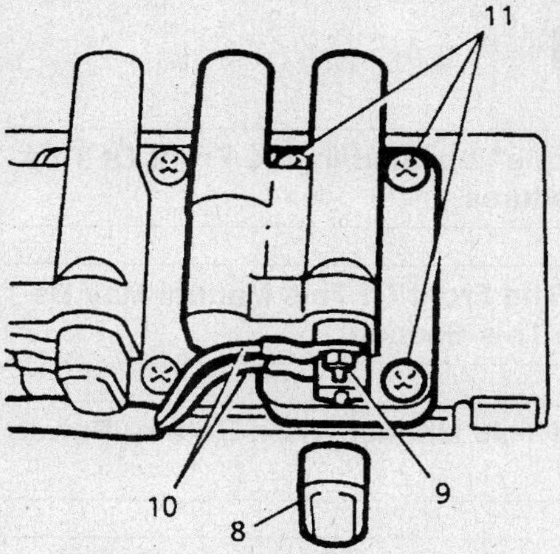

1. Battery Negative Lead
2. High Tension Leads
4. Ignition Coil Multi-Plug
5. Fuel Rail Retaining Nuts
6. Ignition Coil Bracket
7. Ignition Coil Assembly
8. Terminal Cover
9. Terminal Wire Retaining Nuts
10. Terminal Wires
11. Ignition Coil Retaining Nuts

RV1119600005020X

Fig. 1 Ignition coil replacement (Part 2 of 2). 1998

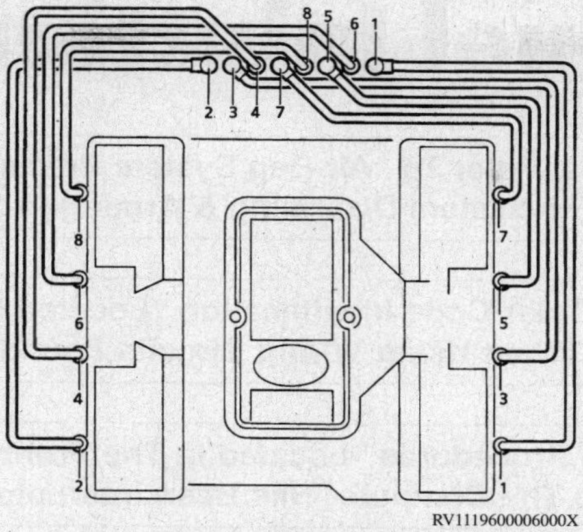

Fig. 2 Spark plug wire routing. 1998

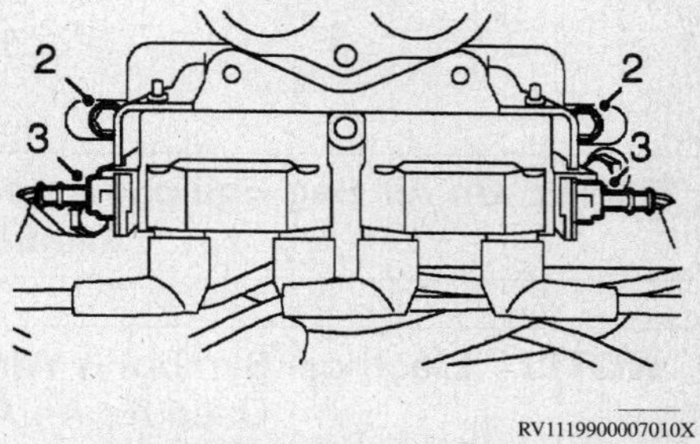

Fig. 3 Ignition coil replacement (Part 1 of 2). 1999–2001

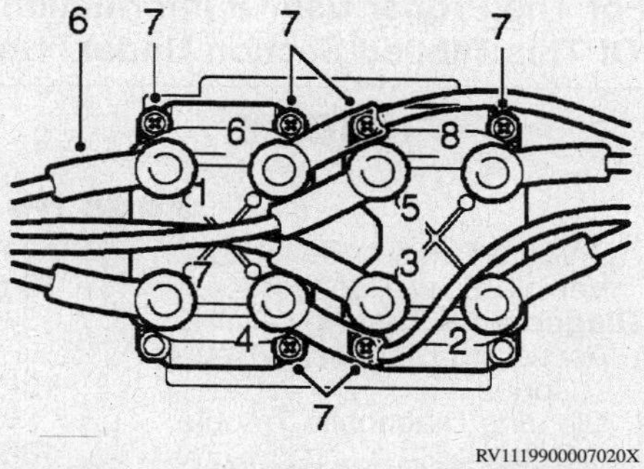

Fig. 3 Ignition coil replacement (Part 2 of 2). 1999–2001

Fuel Injection

NOTE: On Air Bag Equipped Models, Refer To "Air Bag System Precautions" Located In The Front Of This Manual For System Disarming & Arming Procedures.

NOTE: "Electrical Symbol & Wire Color Code Identification" Located In The Front Of This Manual May Be Used As An Aid When Using Wiring Circuits Found In This Section.

NOTE: Refer To "Computer Relearn Procedures" Located In The Front Of This Manual When Battery Power To The Computer Has Been Interupted.

NOTE: If Unsure Of The System Used On The Vehicle Being Serviced, Refer To The "Engine Systems Identification Chart." Further Assistance For The Proper Use Of Information Contained In This Section Can Also Be Found In The Front Of This Tabbed Section Under "How To Use This Manual."

INDEX

	Page No.
Description	13-6
Air Flow Sensor	13-8
Camshaft Position Sensor	13-7
Crankshaft Position Sensor	13-7
Engine Control Module	13-6
Engine Coolant Temperature Sensor	13-7
Fuel Injectors	13-7
Fuel Pressure Regulator	13-8
Fuel Pump Relay	13-7
Fuel Pump	13-8
Fuel Temperature Sensor	13-7
Heated Oxygen Sensors	13-8
Idle Air Control Valve	13-7
Inertia Fuel Shutoff Switch	13-8
Intake Air Temperature Sensor	13-7
Knock Sensor	13-7
Main Relay	13-7
Mass Air Flow Sensor	13-7
Relay Module	13-8
Throttle Position Sensor	13-8
Vehicle Speed Sensor	13-8
Diagnosis & Testing	13-8
Accessing Diagnostic Trouble Codes	13-8
Clearing Diagnostic Trouble Codes	13-9
Diagnostic Trouble Code Interpretation	13-8
Wiring Diagrams	13-8
Discovery	13-8
Range Rover	13-8
Precautions	13-6
Air Bag Systems	13-6
Battery Ground Cable	13-6
Fuel System Pressure Relief	13-6
Discovery	13-6
Range Rover	13-6
Radio Coded Theft Protection System	13-6
System Service	13-9
Component Replacement	13-9
Air Flow Sensor	13-9
Camshaft Position Sensor	13-9
Crankshaft Position Sensor	13-9
Engine Control Module	13-9
Engine Coolant Temperature Sensor	13-10
Fuel Injection Relays	13-9
Fuel Pressure Regulator	13-9
Fuel Temperature Sensor	13-10
Heated Oxygen Sensor	13-10
Idle Air Control Valve	13-9
Inertia Fuel Shutoff Switch	13-9
Knock Sensor	13-10
Mass Air Flow Sensor	13-10
Relay Module	13-10
Throttle Position Sensor	13-9
Vehicle Speed Sensor	13-9

PRECAUTIONS

Air Bag Systems

Refer to "Air Bag System Precautions" in the front of this manual for system disarming and arming procedures.

Battery Ground Cable

Prior to service, disconnect battery ground cable and isolate as required.

Radio Coded Theft Protection System

Anti-theft radios have a coded theft protection circuit. **The code number must be obtained before disconnecting battery, removing radio fuse or removing radio.** After service procedures have been performed, reconnect radio power supply and enter code.

Fuel System Pressure Relief

DISCOVERY

1. Remove fuel pump relay from relay panel located in righthand footwell area, behind "A" pillar trim panel. The fuel pump relay has a blue base.
2. Start engine.
3. Run engine until it stalls.
4. After engine stalls, crank engine two or three times to ensure fuel pressure is released.
5. Turn ignition switch off and install fuel pump relay.

RANGE ROVER

Fuel pressure may be relieved at the fuel rail feed union or fuel filter unions.

1. Position shop towel around union to protect against fuel spray.
2. Carefully loosen union and allow fuel pressure to release.
3. Tighten union when fuel pressure has been relieved.

DESCRIPTION

Engine Control Module

The ECM is located in the righthand footwell, behind the "A" pillar trim panel. The ECM microprocessor is connected to the main harness by a 40 pin connector.

Code	Description
P0101	MAFS Circuit Performance Out Of Range
P0102	MAFS Circuit Low Input
P0103	MAFS Circuit High Input
P0111	Sensor Fails To Detect Valid Rising/Falling Temperature
P0112	Air Temperature Sensor Circuit Low Range Fault
P0113	Air Temperature Sensor Circuit High Range Fault
P0116	Water Temperature Falling Temperature Fault
P0117	ECT Sensor Circuit Low Range Fault
P0118	ECT Sensor Circuit High Range Fault
P0121	Throttle Output Signal Error Fault
P0122	TPS Circuit Low Input
P0123	TPS Circuit High Input
P0125	Water Temperature Warm Up Fault
P0130	HO2S Cycle Fault, Bank "A" Upstream
P0131	HO2S Circuit Low Voltage, Upstream Sensor, Bank "A"
P0132	HO2S Circuit High Voltage, Upstream Sensor, Bank "A"
P0133	HO2S Circuit Slow Response, Upstream Sensor, Bank "A"
P0136	HO2S Cycle Fault, Bank "A" Downstream
P0137	HO2S Circuit Low Voltage, Downstream Sensor, Bank "A"
P0138	HO2S Circuit High Voltage, Downstream Sensor, Bank "A"
P0139	HO2S Circuit Slow Response, Downstream Sensor, Bank "A"
P0150	HO2S Cycle Fault, Bank "B" Upstream

Fig. 1 Diagnostic trouble code identification (Part 1 of 5)

Code	Description
P0151	HO2S Circuit Low Voltage, Upstream Sensor, Bank "B"
P0152	HO2S Circuit High Voltage, Upstream Sensor, Bank "B"
P0153	HO2S Circuit Slow Response, Upstream, Bank "B"
P0156	HO2S Cycle Fault, Bank "B" Downstream
P0157	HO2S Circuit Low Voltage, Downstream Sensor, Bank "B"
P0158	HO2S Circuit High Voltage, Downstream Sensor, Bank "B"
P0159	HO2S Circuit Slow Response, Downstream, Bank "B"
P0171	System Too Lean, Bank "A"
P0172	System Too Rich, Bank "A"
P0174	System Too Lean, Bank "B"
P0175	System Too Rich, Bank "B"
P0181	Fuel Temperature Validity Fault
P0182	EFTS Circuit Low Range Fault
P0183	EFTS Circuit High Range Fault
P0201	Injector Circuit Fault, Cylinder No. 1
P0202	Injector Circuit Fault, Cylinder No. 2
P0203	Injector Circuit Fault, Cylinder No. 3
P0204	Injector Circuit Fault, Cylinder No. 4
P0205	Injector Circuit Fault, Cylinder No. 5
P0206	Injector Circuit Fault, Cylinder No. 6
P0207	Injector Circuit Fault, Cylinder No. 7
P0208	Injector Circuit Fault, Cylinder No. 8

Fig. 1 Diagnostic trouble code identification (Part 2 of 5)

Main Relay

The main relay supplies power feed to the ECM, fuel injectors (8 amps), and air flow sensor (4 amps). Failure of the main relay will result in the engine not starting due to the absence of fuel and ignition.

Fuel Pump Relay

The fuel pump relay is fed from the ignition relay and controlled by the ECM. The relay is activated in the ignition key position two to prime the fuel system. Failure of the relay will result in no fuel pressure.

Crankshaft Position Sensor

The crankshaft position sensor is located on the lefthand side of converter housing. The signal produced informs the ECM of the engine turning, how fast the engine is turning, and which stage the engine is in its cycle. Failure of the CKP sensor will result in a no start condition

Camshaft Position Sensor

The camshaft position sensor is located in the engine front cover and produces four pulses for every two revolutions. The signals are used in two areas, injector timing corrections for fully sequential and active knock control. If the sensor fails the injection will be correct or one revolution out of synchronization.

Fuel Injectors

The eight fuel injectors are fitted between the pressurized fuel rail and inlet manifold. Each injector has a solenoid operated needle valve with a movable plunger attached to the nozzle valve. When the solenoid is energized, the plunger is pulled off its seat and allows pressurized fuel into the intake manifold.

Engine Coolant Temperature Sensor

The engine coolant temperature sensor is located in the front of the thermostat housing. The sensor provides information to the ECM to increase injector opening time during start-up and warm-up.

Mass Air Flow Sensor

The hot wire type mass airflow sensor is mounted to the air filter and connected by flexible hose to the plenum chamber inlet. Failure will result in the engine starting and then dying at 550 RPM when the ECM detects no MAF Sensor signal.

Intake Air Temperature Sensor

The intake air temperature sensor is located in the body of the air cleaner. The signal from the sensor is used to retard ignition timing if the air temperature rises above 131° F.

Knock Sensor

A sensor is located in each cylinder bank between the 2/4 and the 3/5 cylinders. If a knock is detected the sensor sends voltage to the ECM to retard the ignition in one or more cylinders until the knock quits.

Fuel Temperature Sensor

The fuel temperature sensor is located in the fuel rail, on the righthand side of the ram housing. The sensor provides information to the ECM to adjust injector operation in high ambient temperatures.

Idle Air Control Valve

The idle air control valve is screwed into a housing attached to the rear of the plenum chamber. The ECM will open the valve to allow extra air into the plenum chamber under increased loads. It also controls idle speed when the vehicle is stationary.

Code	Description
P0300	Misfire On Multiple Cylinders
P0301	Misfire On Cylinder No. 1
P0302	Misfire On Cylinder No. 2
P0303	Misfire On Cylinder No. 3
P0304	Misfire On Cylinder No. 4
P0305	Misfire On Cylinder No. 5
P0306	Misfire On Cylinder No. 6
P0307	Misfire On Cylinder No. 7
P0308	Misfire On Cylinder No. 8
P0326	Continuous Knock On Bank "A"
P0327	Knock Background Noise Low, Bank "A"
P0328	Knock Background Noise High, Bank "A"
P0331	Continuous Knock On Bank "B"
P0332	Knock Background Noise Low, Bank "B"
P0333	Knock Background Noise High, Bank "B"
P0335	CKP Sensor Circuit Fault
P0336	Crankshaft Signal Out Of Range
P0340	CMP Sensor Circuit Fault
P0420	Catalyst Efficiency Low, Bank A
P0430	Catalyst Efficiency Low, Bank B
P0441	EVAP Purge Valve Incorrect Flow Fault
P0442	EVAP Loss Control System, Small Leak
P0443	EVAP Purge Valve Circuit Open Or Short Circuit
P0446	Purge Canister Closure Valve Information
P0448	EVAP Loss Control System, Major Leak

Fig. 1 Diagnostic trouble code identification (Part 3 of 5)

Code	Description
P0451	EVAP System Pressure Sensor Range/Performance Fault
P0452	EVAP Pressure Transducer Out Of Range Low
P0453	EVAP Pressure Transducer Out Of Range High
P0461	Fuel Level Measurement Is Not Valid
P0496	EVAP Loss Control System, Major Leak
P0500	VSS Signal Out Of Range
P0506	Low Idle Speed
P0507	High Idle Speed
P0560	Battery Voltage Below Minimum Limit
P0562	Measuring Circuit OK, But Battery Voltage Too Low
P0563	Battery Voltage Above Maximum Limit
P0605	ECM Self Check Fault
P1137	HO2S Failed To Switch To Rich, Bank "A"
P1138	HO2S Problem With Switching Lean, Sensor(s), Bank "A"
P1139	HO2S Circuit Switching Period Too Long, Bank "A"
P1157	HO2S Failed To Switch To Rich, Bank "B"
P1158	HO2S Failed To Switch To Lean, Bank "B"
P1159	HO2S Circuit Switching Period Too Long Bank B
P1171	System Too Lean, Bank A & Bank B
P1172	System Too Rich, Bank A & Bank B
P1176	FMFR Correction At Maximum Positive Value
P1177	FMFR Correction At Maximum Negative Value
P1178	AMFR Correction At Maximum Positive Value
P1179	AMFR Correction At Maximum Negative Value
P1185	HO2S Heater Circuit Open, Upstream Sensors

Fig. 1 Diagnostic trouble code identification (Part 4 of 5)

Heated Oxygen Sensors

The two heated oxygen sensors are located in the exhaust downpipes. The sensors monitor the oxygen content of the exhaust gases and feed information to the ECM to adjust air/fuel mixture.

Fuel Pressure Regulator

The fuel pressure regulator is mounted in the fuel rail, at the rear of plenum chamber. It is controlled by plenum chamber vacuum, ensuring fuel rail pressure is maintained at a constant 36 psi above that of the manifold. When pressure exceeds the setting, excess fuel is returned to the tank.

Fuel Pump

The fuel pump is located in the fuel tank, and is self-priming.

Air Flow Sensor

The air flow sensor is located on a bracket attached to the lefthand side of the air cleaner. The sensor consists of a cast alloy body through which air flows. A portion of this air flows through the bypass in which two wire elements measure the mass of air and send information to the ECM to adjust fuel flow.

Throttle Position Sensor

The throttle position sensor is mounted on the side of the plenum chamber inlet neck and is directly coupled to the throttle butterfly shaft. It senses movement of the accelerator pedal and sends information to the ECM to open or close the fuel injectors.

Vehicle Speed Sensor

The vehicle speed sensor is located on the side of the transfer case. It provides information to the ECM for fuel flow rate and idle air control valve operation.

Inertia Fuel Shutoff Switch

The inertia fuel shutoff switch is located on the bulkhead, next to the washer reservoir. In the event of a sudden impact, the switch shuts off fuel flow to the injectors.

Relay Module

The fuel injection system relays are located in the righthand footwell, behind the "A" pillar trim panel. The main relay supplies power for the fuel injection system and the fuel pump relay provides power for the fuel pump to pressurize the system.

DIAGNOSIS & TESTING

Accessing Diagnostic Trouble Codes

When a fault occurs in the engine management system (GEMS), the Malfunction Indicator Lamp (MIL) is illuminated. GEMS diagnostic trouble codes are stored in the ECM and may be retrieved by connecting the Test Book Electronic Tester or a suitable OBD II scan tool to the Data Link Connector (DLC). The DLC is located at the passenger side footwell.

Diagnostic Trouble Code Interpretation

Refer to **Fig. 1** for diagnostic trouble code interpretation.

Wiring Diagrams

DISCOVERY

Refer to **Fig. 2 through 13** for wiring diagrams.

RANGE ROVER

Refer to **Figs. 14 through 28** for wiring circuits.

Clearing Diagnostic Trouble Codes

To clear diagnostic trouble codes, follow scan tool manufacture instructions.

SYSTEM SERVICE

Component Replacement

AIR FLOW SENSOR

1. Remove intake hose clamp and disconnect sensor electrical connector.
2. Remove clips securing air cleaner to air flow sensor, then sensor.
3. Reverse procedure to install.

CRANKSHAFT POSITION SENSOR

1. Raise and support vehicle.
2. Remove two bolts securing sensor shield to engine backplate.
3. Remove sensor shield.
4. Disconnect electrical connector and remove sensor.
5. Remove spacer from sensor.
6. Reverse procedure to install, then **torque** bolts to 48 inch lbs. **Ensure spacer is correctly installed.**

CAMSHAFT POSITION SENSOR

1. Disconnect sensor electrical connector from clip, then disconnect.
2. Remove sensor to front cover attaching bolts.
3. Remove sensor and discard old O-ring.
4. Reverse procedures to install, then **torque** bolts to 72 inch lbs.

THROTTLE POSITION SENSOR

1. Disconnect sensor electrical connector.
2. Remove screws securing sensor to plenum chamber, then pull sensor off throttle shaft.
3. Remove old gasket.
4. Reverse procedure to install.

IDLE AIR CONTROL VALVE

1. Disconnect sensor electrical connector.
2. Unscrew valve from rear of plenum chamber and remove old washer.
3. Reverse procedure to install, noting the following:
   a. Install new washer.
   b. Apply Loctite 241, or equivalent, to threads.
   c. **Torque** valve to 14 ft. lbs.

VEHICLE SPEED SENSOR

1. Disconnect sensor electrical connector.
2. Remove screw securing sensor to transfer case, then sensor.
3. Reverse procedure to install.

Code	Description
P1186	HO2S Heater Short Circuit, Upstream Sensors
P1187	HO2S Heater Short Circuit, Upstream Sensors
P1188	HO2S Heater Circuit High Resistance, Upstream Sensors
P1189	HO2S Heater Circuit Type 1 Low Resistance, Upstream
P1190	HO2S Heater Circuit Type 2 Low Resistance, Upstream
P1191	HO2S Heater Circuit Open, Downstream Sensors
P1192	HO2S Heater Short Circuit, Downstream Sensors
P1193	HO2S Heater Circuit Inferred Open Circuit, Downstream Sensors
P1194	HO2S Heater Circuit High Resistance, Downstream Sensors
P1195	HO2S Heater Circuit Type 1 Low Resistance, Downstream
P1196	HO2S Heater Circuit Type 2 Low Resistance, Downstream
P1199	Fuel Level Sensor Circuit Fault
P1201	Injector Open Circuit Or Ground Short, Cylinder No. 1
P1202	Injector Open Circuit Or Ground Short, Cylinder No. 2
P1203	Injector Open Circuit Or Ground Short, Cylinder No. 3
P1204	Injector Open Circuit Or Ground Short, Cylinder No. 4
P1205	Injector Open Circuit Or Ground Short, Cylinder No. 5
P1206	Injector Open Circuit Or Ground Short, Cylinder No. 6
P1207	Injector Open Circuit Or Ground Short, Cylinder No. 7
P1208	Injector Open Circuit Or Ground Short, Cylinder No. 8
P1440	Purge Valve Stuck Open
P1447	Purge Canister Closure Valve, Poor Performance
P1508	IACV Stepper Motor Open Circuit
P1509	IACV Stepper Motor Short Circuit
P1622	More Than One Wrong Security Code Received By ECM
P1701	Transfer Box Line Fault
P1703	Transfer Box Line Open Circuit Short Fault
P1708	Transfer Box Line Short Circuit Fault
P1775	Gearbox Fault
P1776	Gearbox Ignition Retard Request Duration Fault
P1777	Gearbox Ignition Retard Request Line Fault

Fig. 1 Diagnostic trouble code identification (Part 5 of 5)

ENGINE CONTROL MODULE

1. Remove footwell side trim panel covering ECM.
2. Disconnect sensor electrical connector.
3. Remove ECM attaching bolts.
4. Remove upper retaining clip and remove ECM.
5. Reverse procedure to install.

FUEL INJECTION RELAYS

1. Remove front door seal from "A" pillar.
2. Remove lower trim panel.
3. Pull relay from base. Fuel pump relay has a blue base and main relay has a black base.
4. Reverse procedure to install.

FUEL PRESSURE REGULATOR

1. Depressurize fuel system as outlined under "Fuel System Pressure Relief."
2. Disconnect vacuum hose from regulator.
3. Remove coil bracket nuts and lay coil to side.
4. Remove regulator connecting pipe from clip.
5. Remove regulator from fuel rail.
6. Remove and discard O-ring.
7. Reverse procedures to install noting the following:
   a. **Torque** regulator to fuel rail bolts to 84 inch lbs.
   b. **Torque** coil mounting bracket nuts to 72 inch lbs.

INERTIA FUEL SHUTOFF SWITCH

1. Disconnect switch electrical connector, located on bulkhead, next to washer reservoir.
2. Remove switch from mounting bracket.
3. Reverse procedure to install.

FUEL TEMPERATURE SENSOR

Fuel leakage will not occur when sensor is removed, therefore it is not necessary to release fuel system pressure.

1. Remove sensor from fuel rail.
2. Reverse procedure to install.

ENGINE COOLANT TEMPERATURE SENSOR

1. Position drain pan to collect coolant spillage under sensor.
2. Disconnect sensor electrical connector.
3. Remove sensor from thermostat housing.
4. Remove and discard copper washer.
5. Reverse procedure to install, ensuring to install new copper washer.

KNOCK SENSOR

Lefthand

1. Raise and support vehicle.
2. Depress spring clip and disconnect electrical connector from LH sensor.
3. Remove sensor. **Do not apply tape or sealant to sensor threads.**
4. Reverse procedures to install, **torque** bolts to 22 ft. lbs. **Failure to tighten to correct torque will result in malfunction or damage to sensor.**

Righthand

1. Raise and support vehicle.
2. Remove bolt securing starter motor heat shield.
3. Remove heat shield clip.
4. Depress spring clip and disconnect sensor.
5. Reverse procedures to install, **torque** bolts to 22 ft. lbs.

RELAY MODULE

1. Remove ECM cover.
2. Remove ECM and move aside to access relay module position.
3. Disconnect plugs, then remove module from bracket.
4. Reverse procedures to install.

HEATED OXYGEN SENSOR

1. Raise and support vehicle.
2. Remove front sensor clip securing oxygen sensor lead to harness.
3. Remove rear sensor electrical connector from bracket and disconnect.
4. On both sensors disconnect sensor electrical connector from bracket behind cylinder head.
5. Using oxygen sensor wrench tool No. LRT-12–047, or equivalent, remove sensor.
6. Clean sensor mating face on exhaust pipe. **The new sensor thread is pretreated with anti-seize compound. Do not allow compound to contact sensor nose or enter exhaust.**
7. Reverse procedures to install, then **torque** sensor to 15 ft. lbs.

MASS AIR FLOW SENSOR

1. Loosen air intake hose to MAF sensor clip.
2. Disconnect sensor multi-plug.
3. Remove sensor to air cleaner clips.
4. Remove sensor and discard O-ring.
5. Reverse procedures to install.

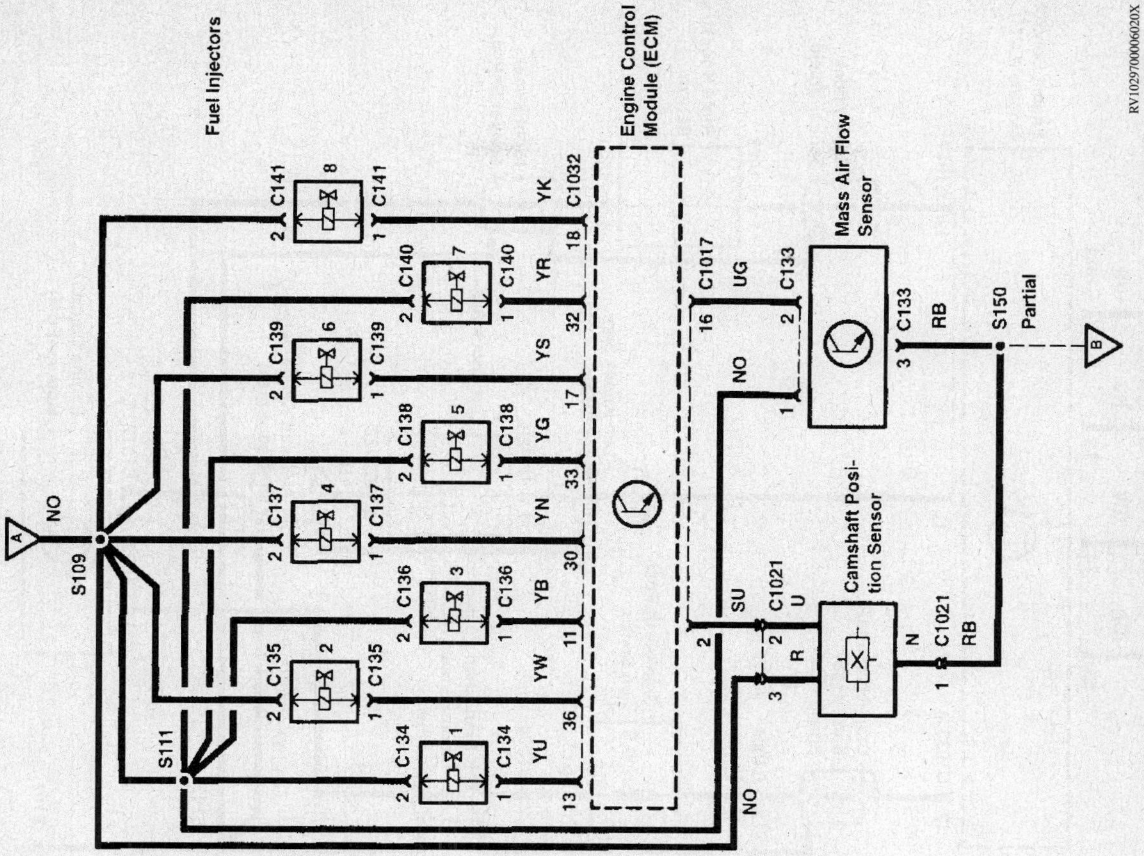

Fig. 3 Engine control wiring circuit (CMP, fuel injectors & MAF). Discovery

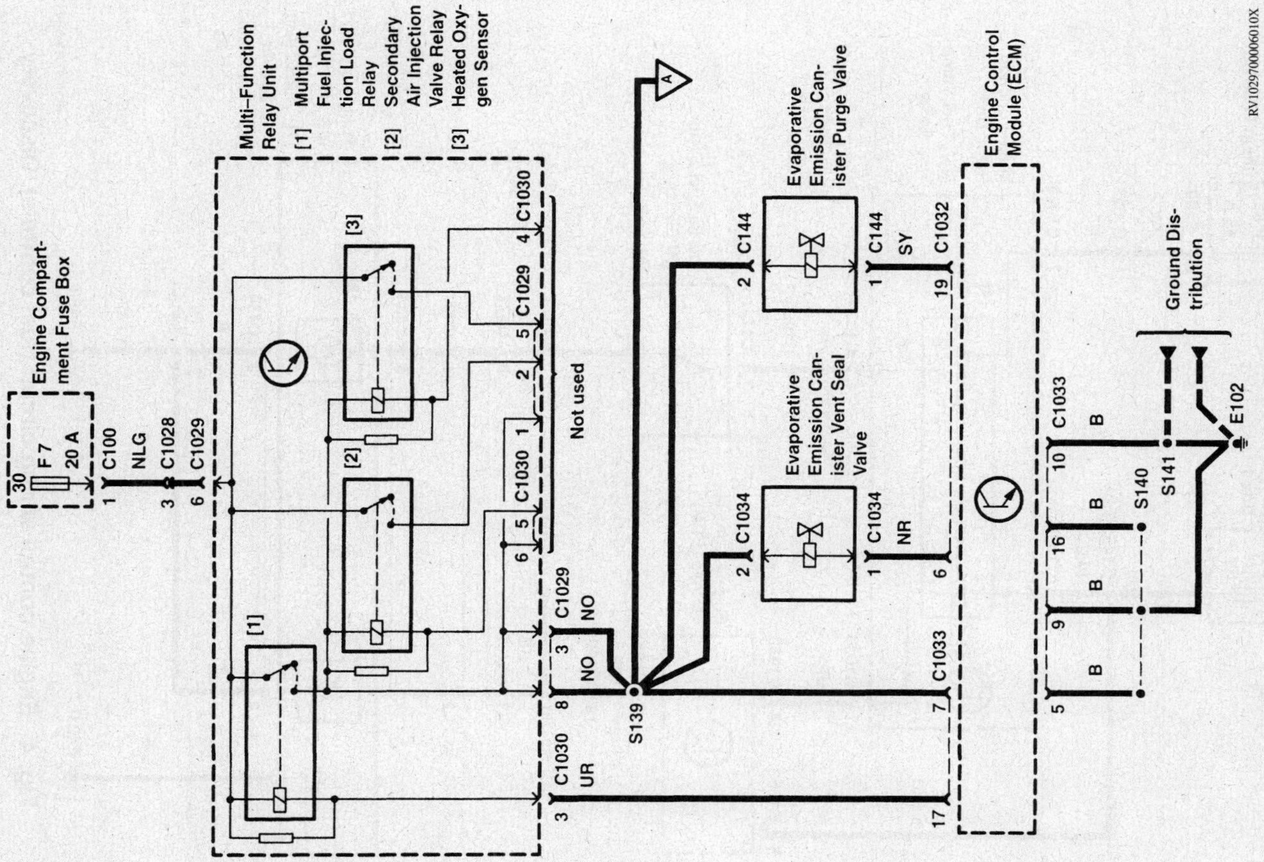

Fig. 2 Engine control wiring circuit (EVAP & Multi-Function relay unit). Discovery

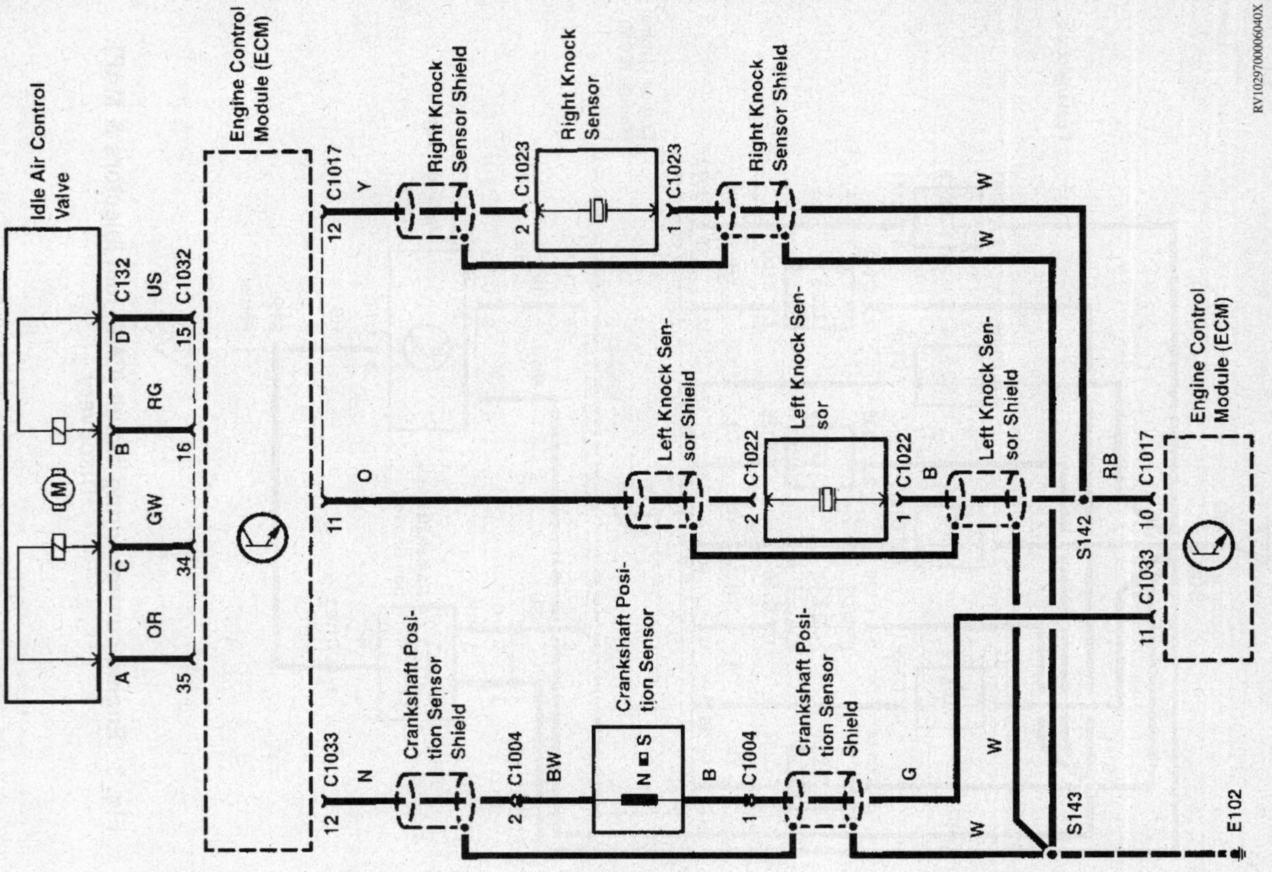

Fig. 5 Engine control wiring circuit (CKP, IAC & Knock Sensor). Discovery

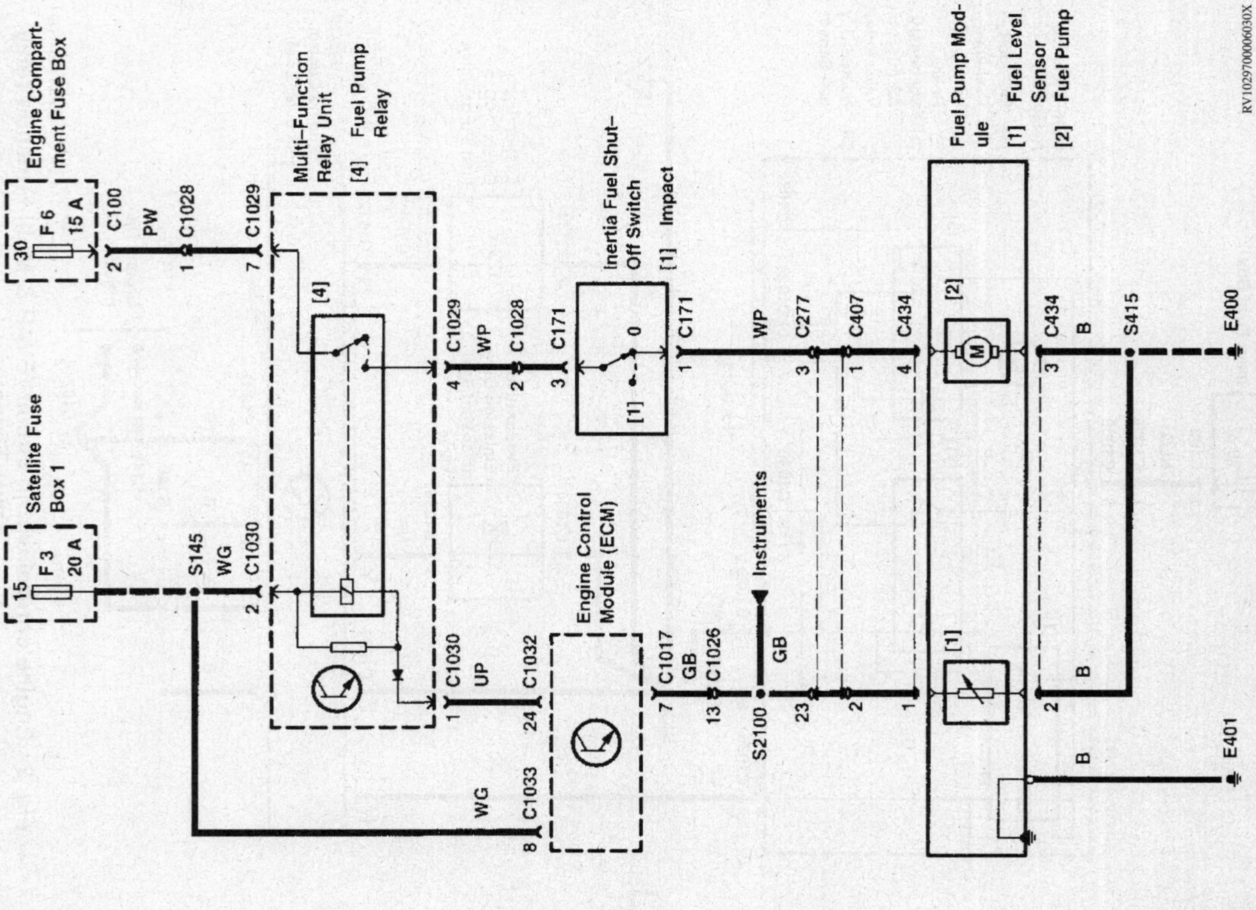

Fig. 4 Engine control wiring circuit (fuel controls). Discovery

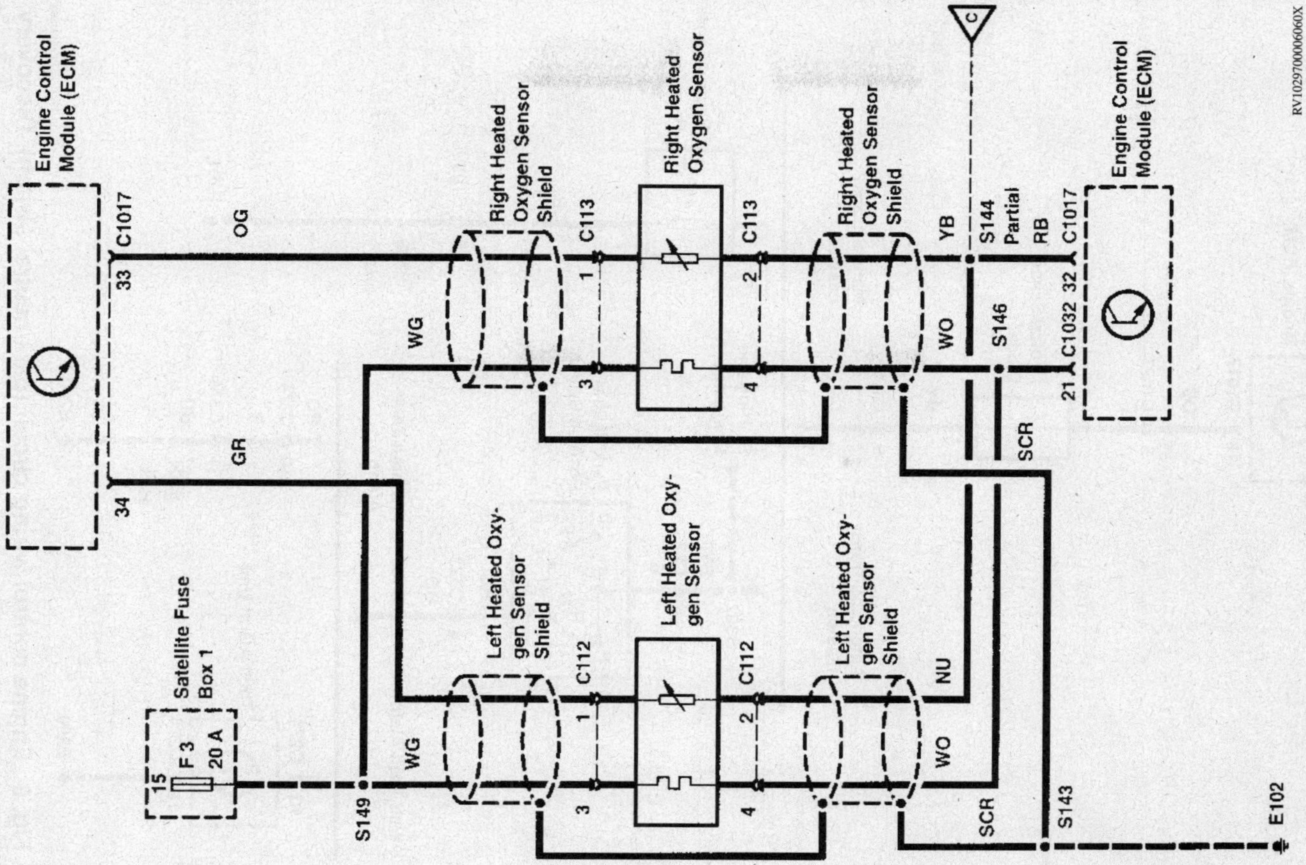

Fig. 7 Engine control wiring circuit (pre-catalyst heated oxygen sensors). Discovery

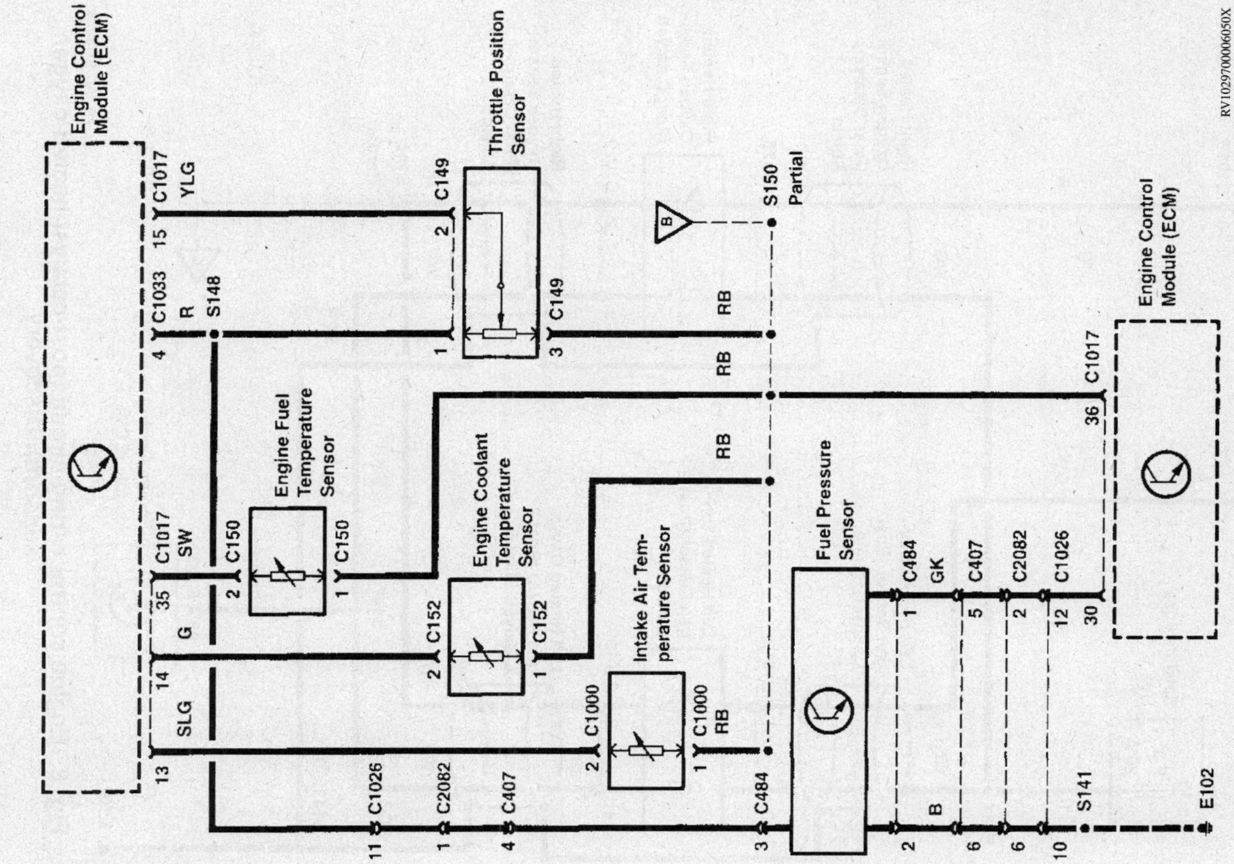

Fig. 6 Engine control wiring circuit (ECT, EFP, FP & TP sensors). Discovery

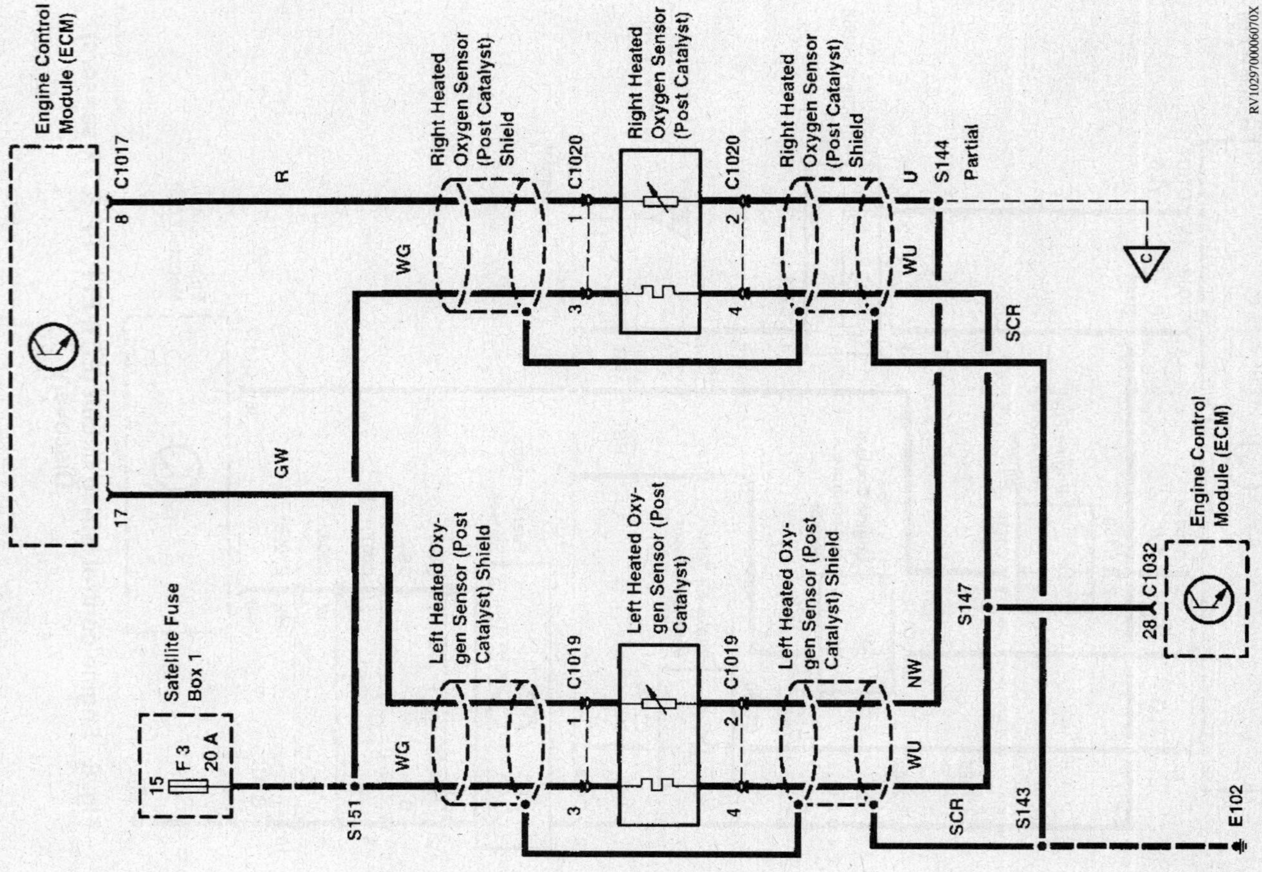

Fig. 8 Engine control wiring circuit (post-catalyst heated oxygen sensors). Discovery

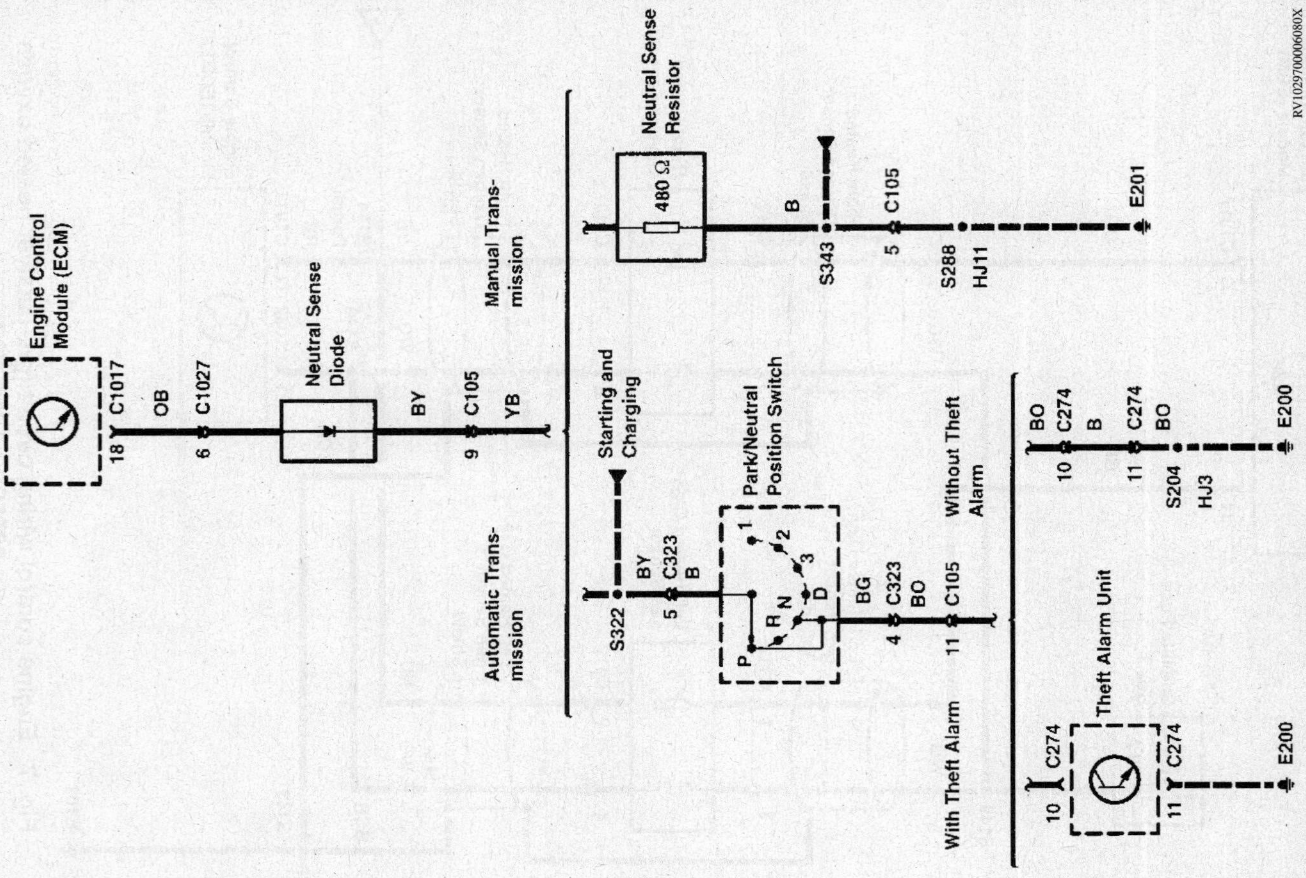

Fig. 9 Engine control wiring circuit (park/neutral switch). Discovery

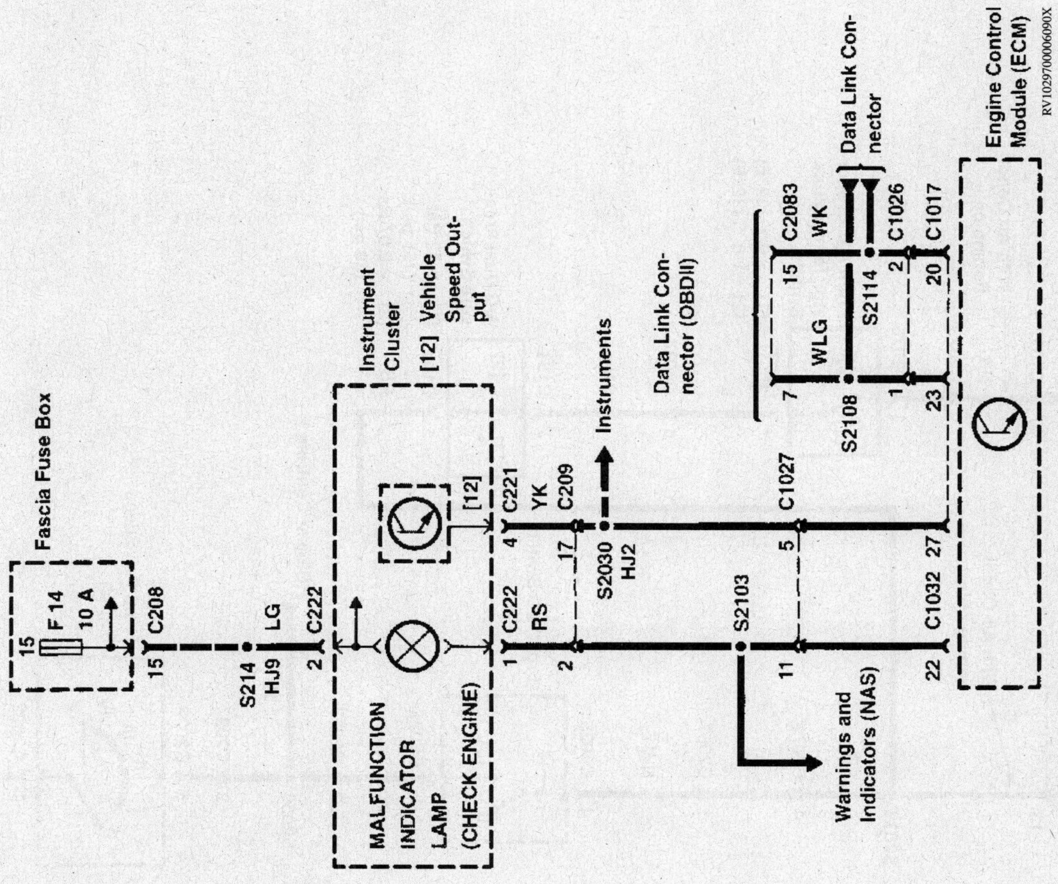

Fig. 10 Engine control wiring circuit (DLC & MIL). Discovery

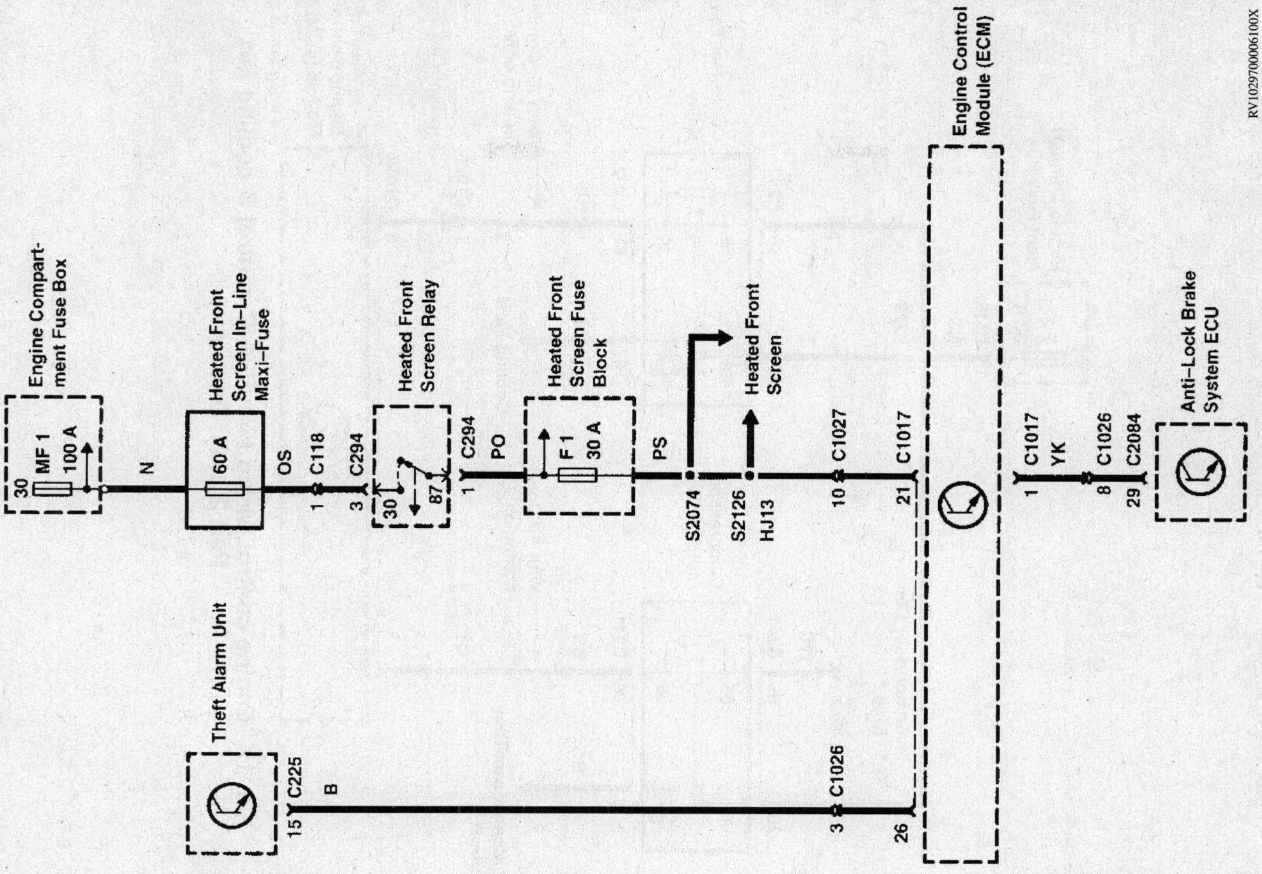

Fig. 11 Engine control wiring circuit (theft alarm). Discovery

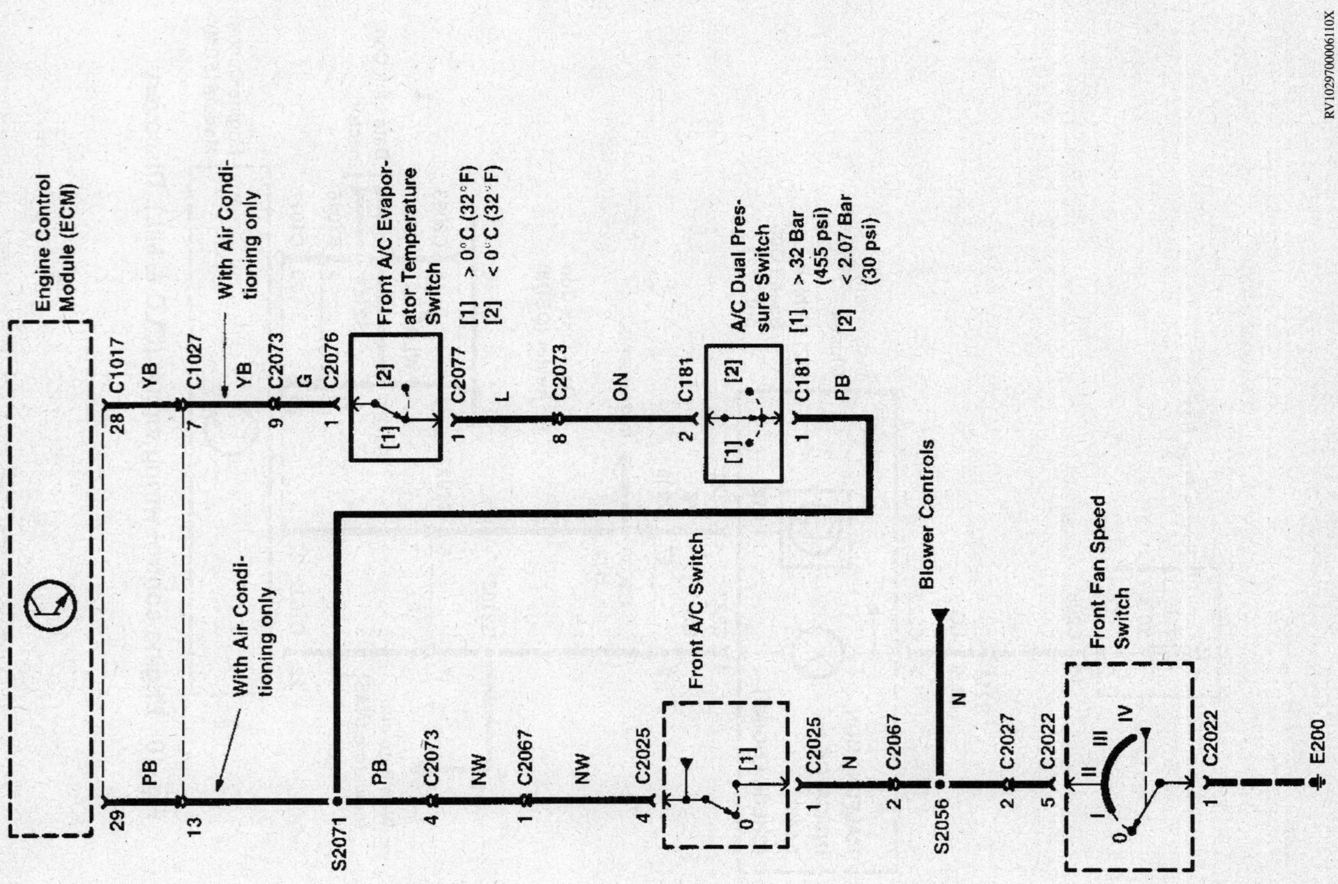

Fig. 12 Engine control wiring circuit (A/C control & cooling fan, Part 1 of 2). Discovery

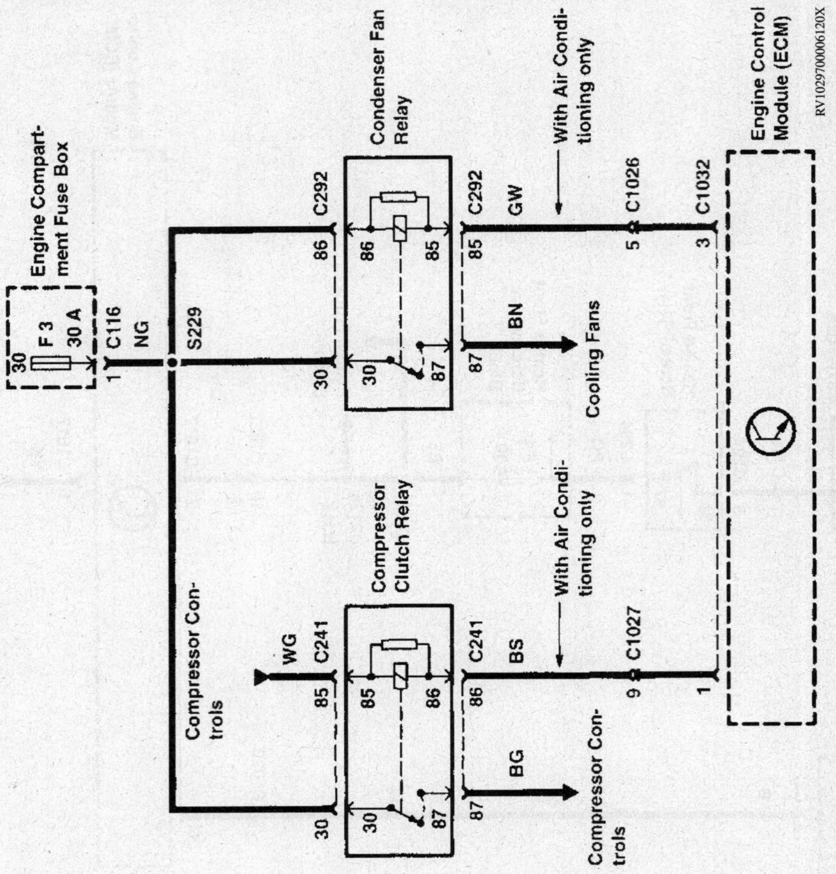

Fig. 12 Engine control wiring circuit (A/C control & cooling fan, Part 2 of 2). Discovery

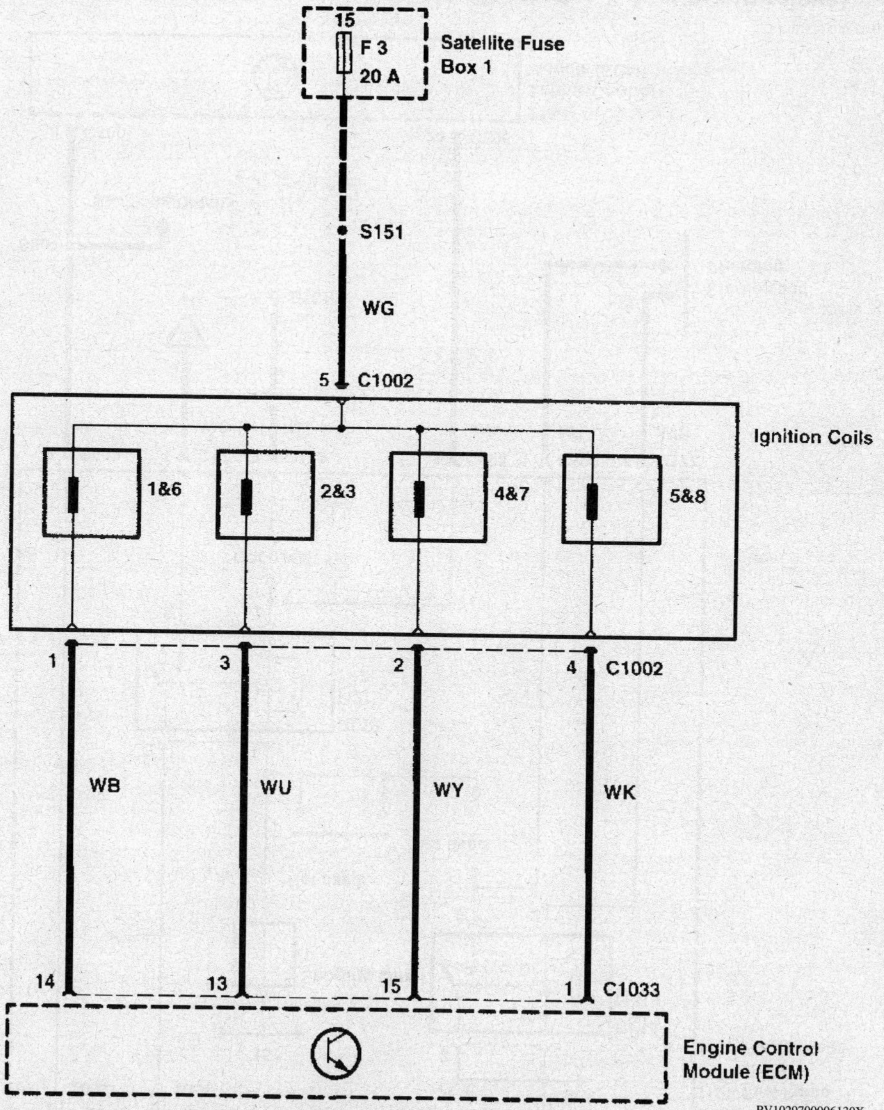

Fig. 13 Engine control wiring circuit (ignition coils). Discovery

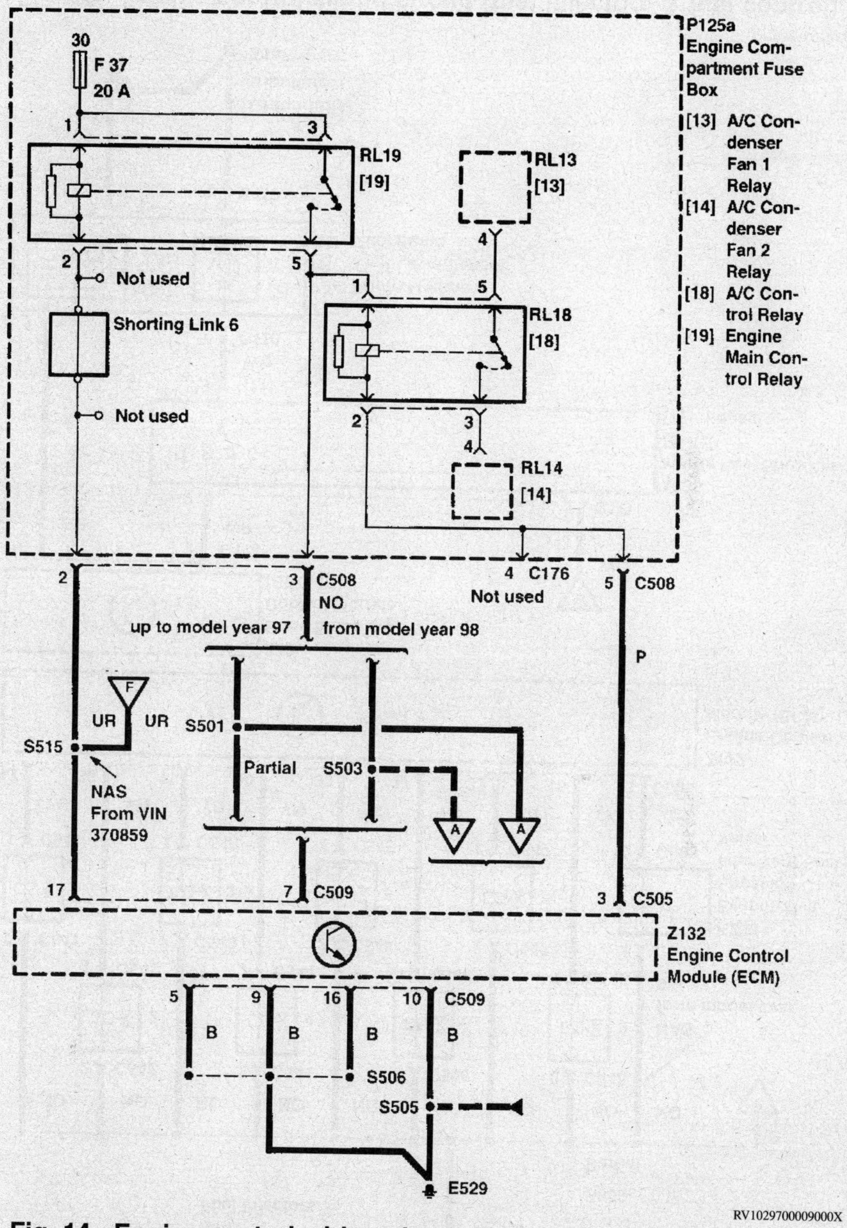

Fig. 14 Engine control wiring circuit (A/C controls). Range Rover

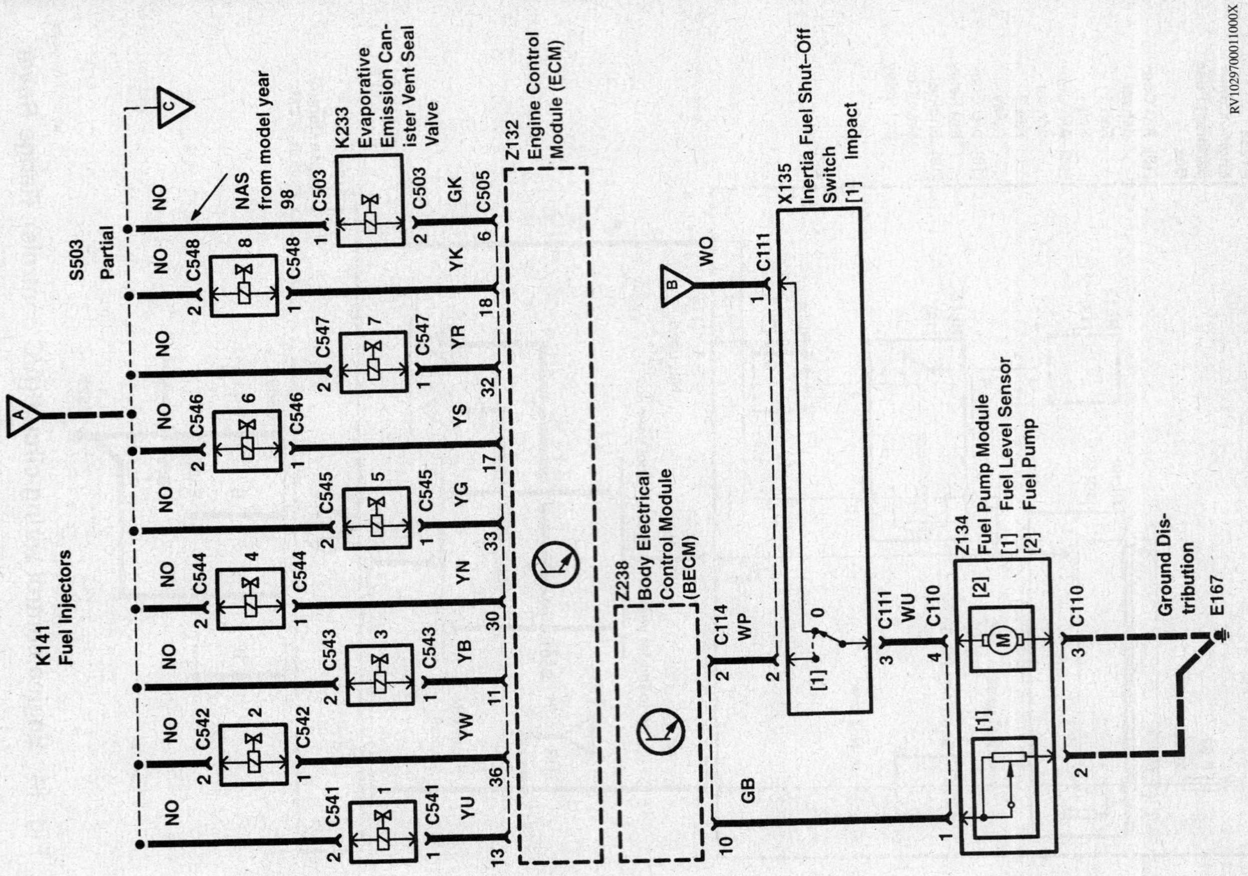

Fig. 16 Engine control wiring circuit (fuel injectors & fuel control). Range Rover

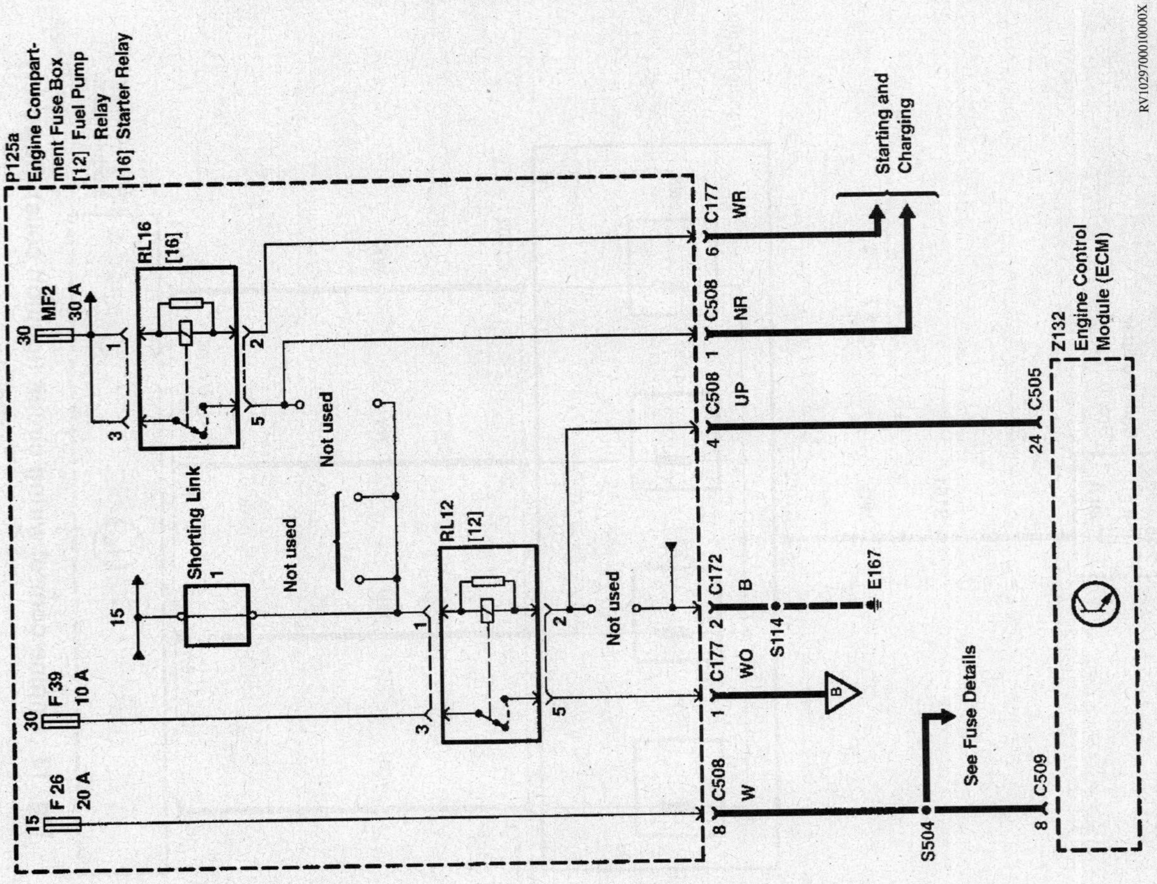

Fig. 15 Engine control wiring circuit (starter & fuel pump relays). Range Rover

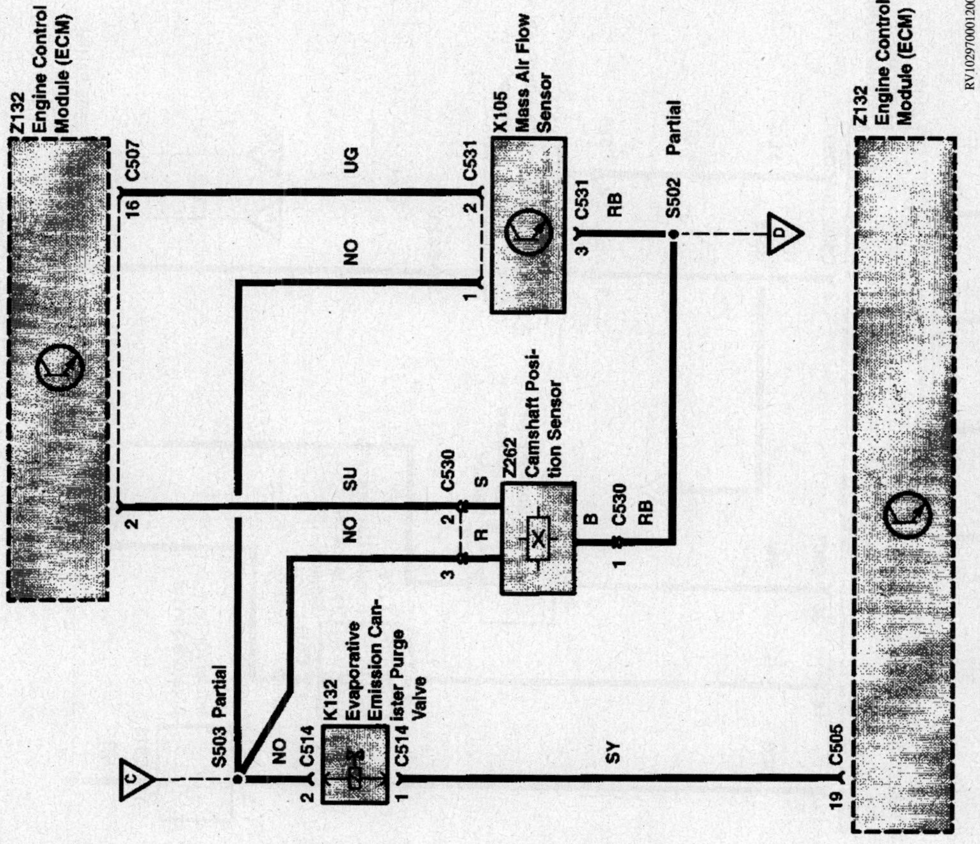

Fig. 17 Engine control wiring circuit (CMP, MAF & EVAP). Range Rover

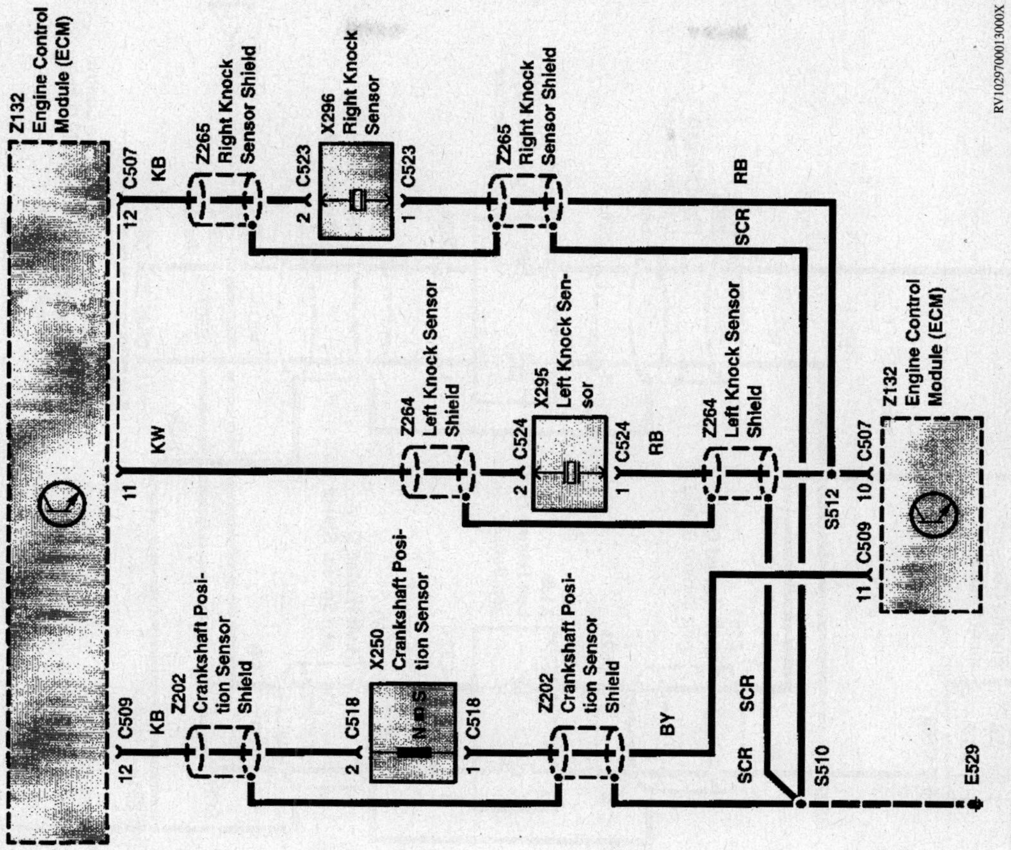

Fig. 18 Engine control wiring circuit (CKP & Knock sensors). Range Rover

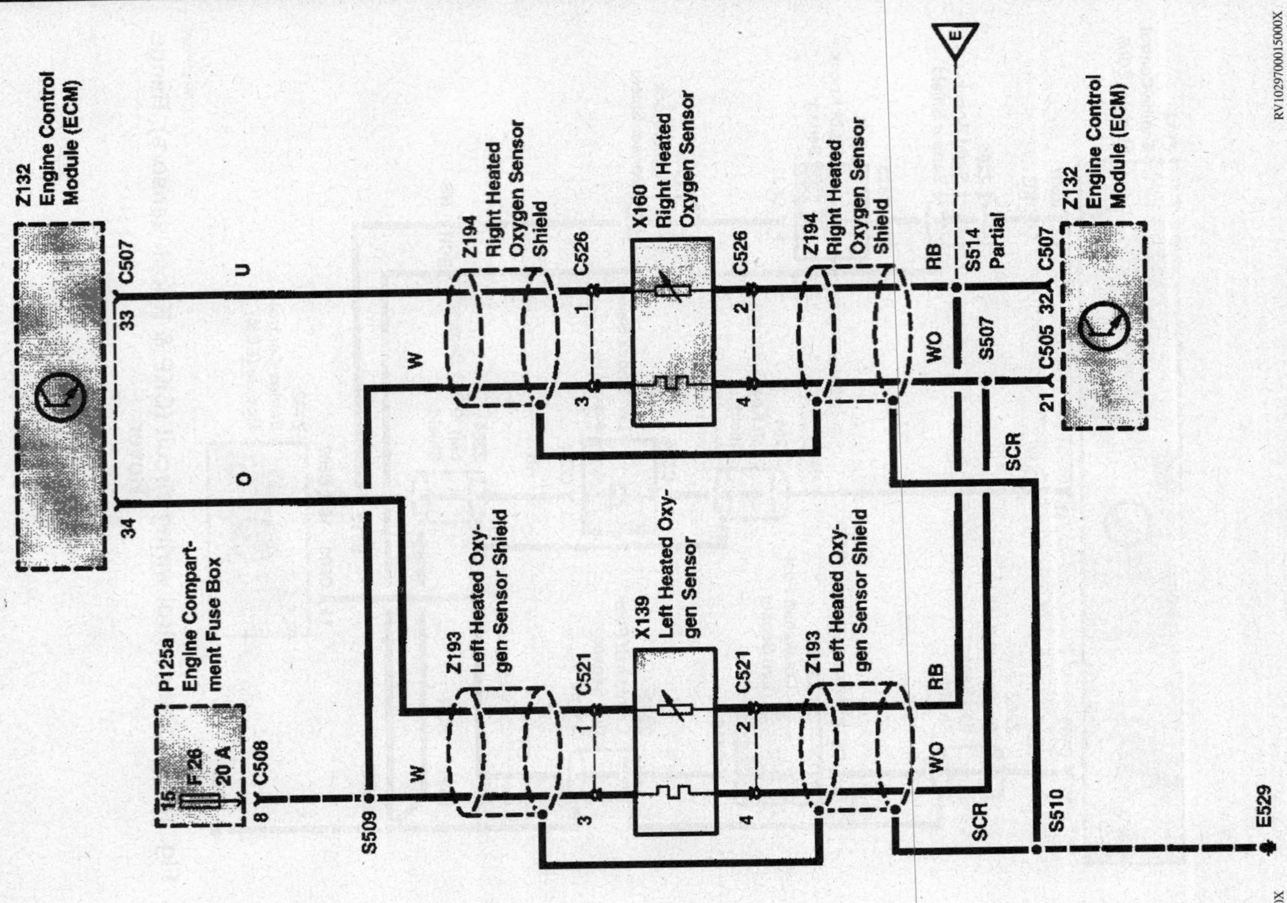

Fig. 20 Engine control wiring circuit (pre-catalyst heated oxygen sensors). Range Rover

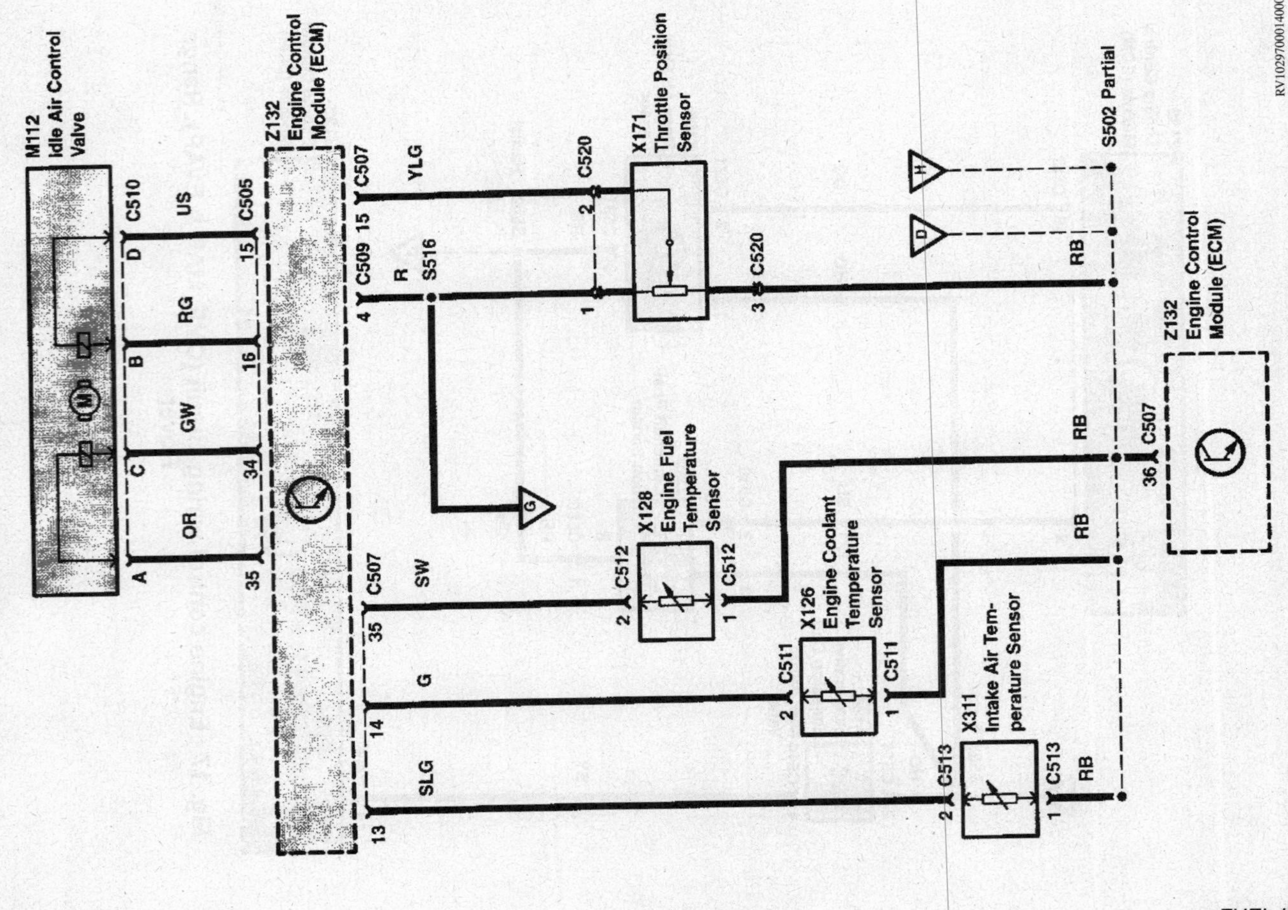

Fig. 19 Engine control wiring circuit (ECT, IAC, IAT & TP). Range Rover

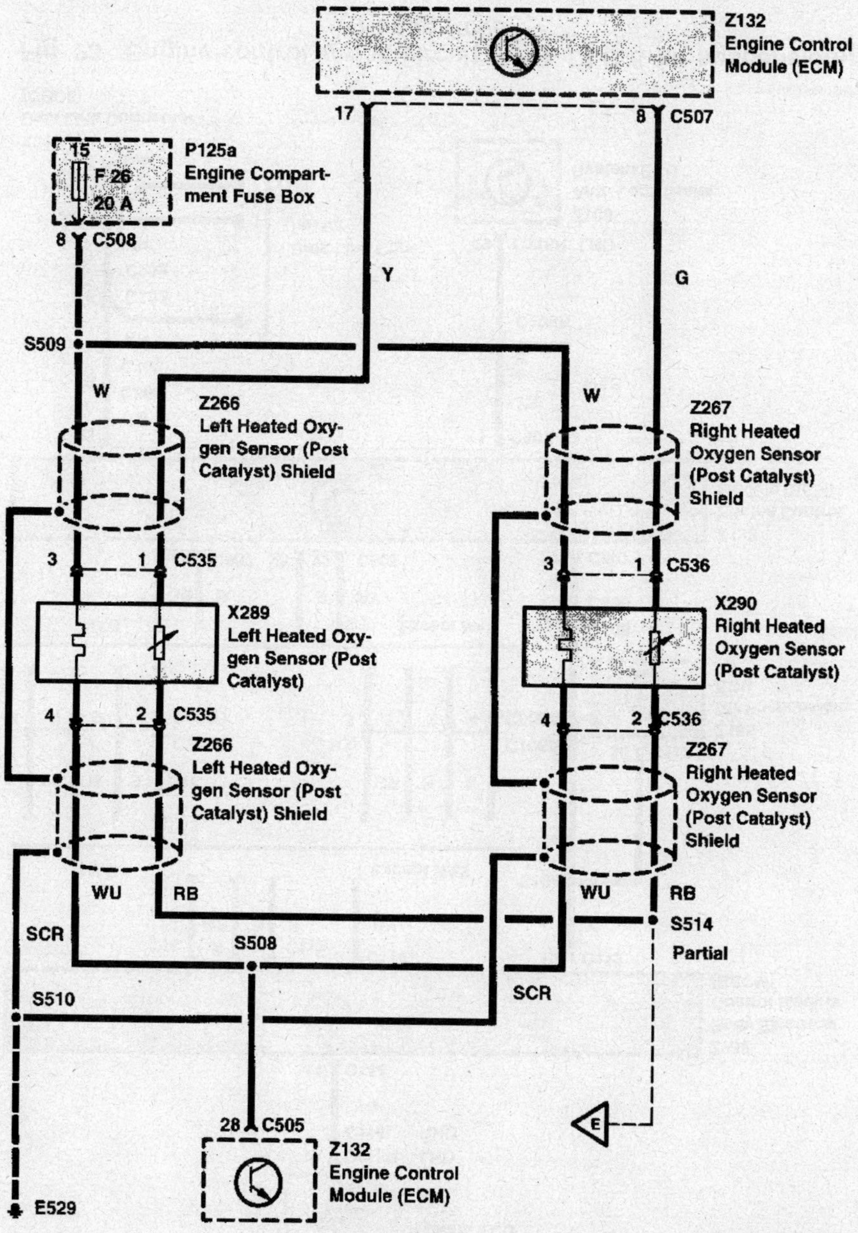

Fig. 21 Engine control wiring circuit (post-catalyst heated oxygen sensors). Range Rover

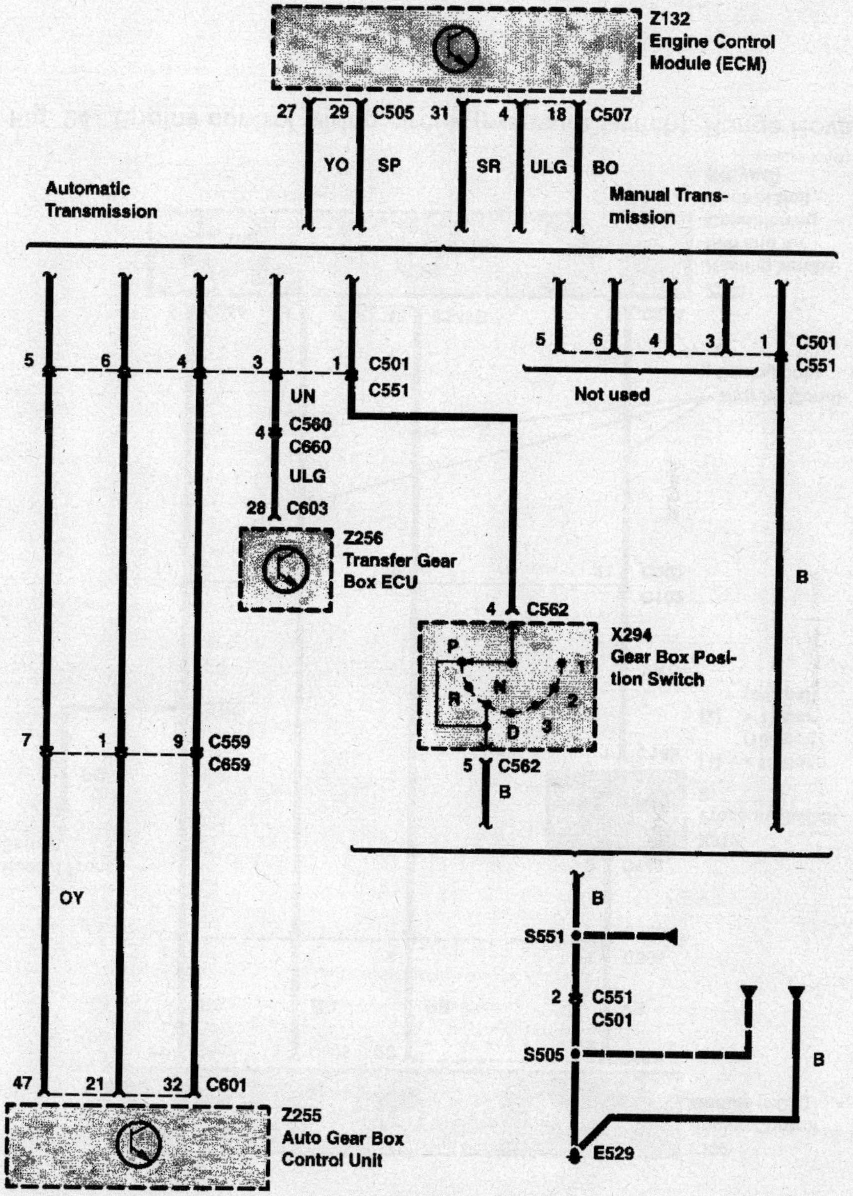

Fig. 22 Engine control wiring circuit (transmission controls). Range Rover

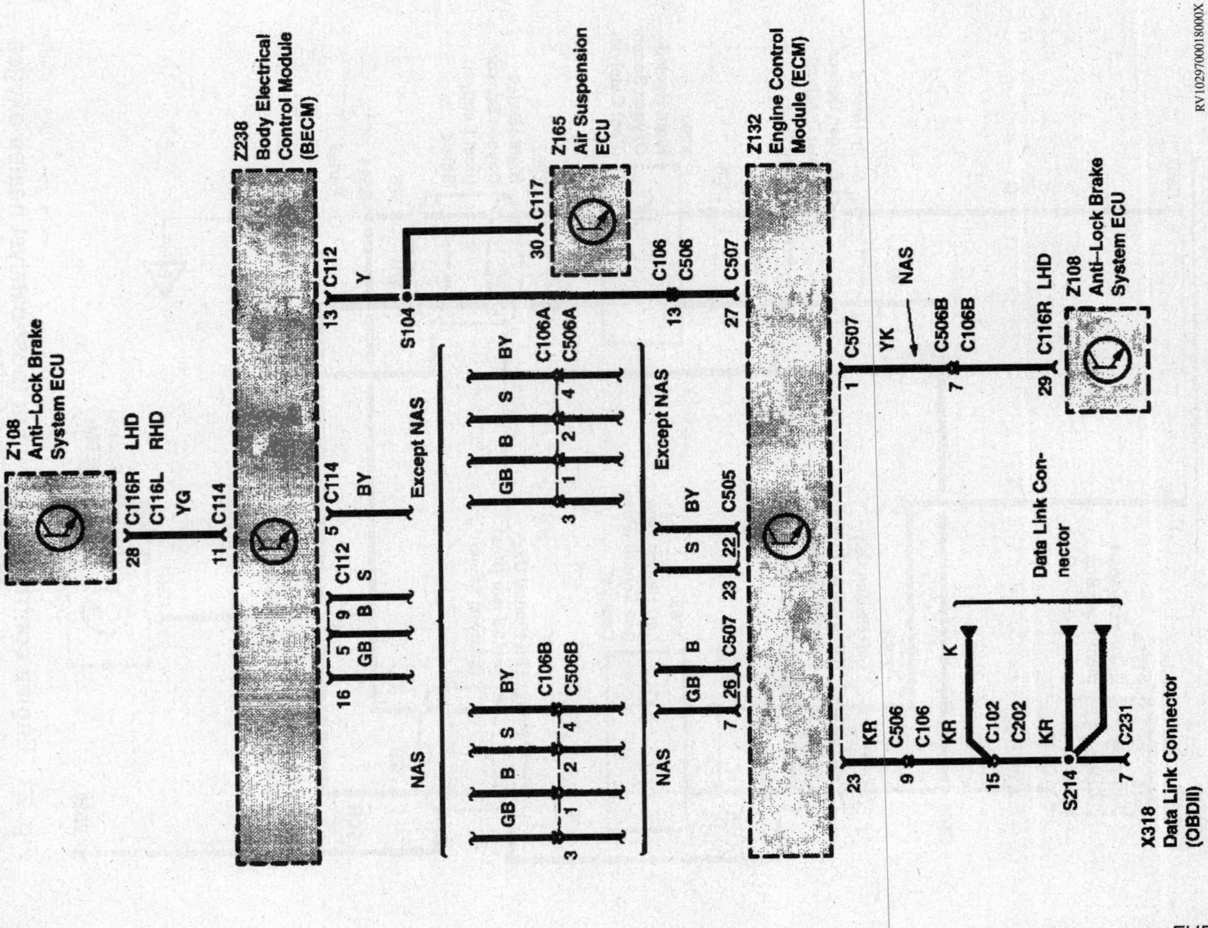

Fig. 23 Engine control wiring circuit (ABS, DLC & air suspension). Range Rover

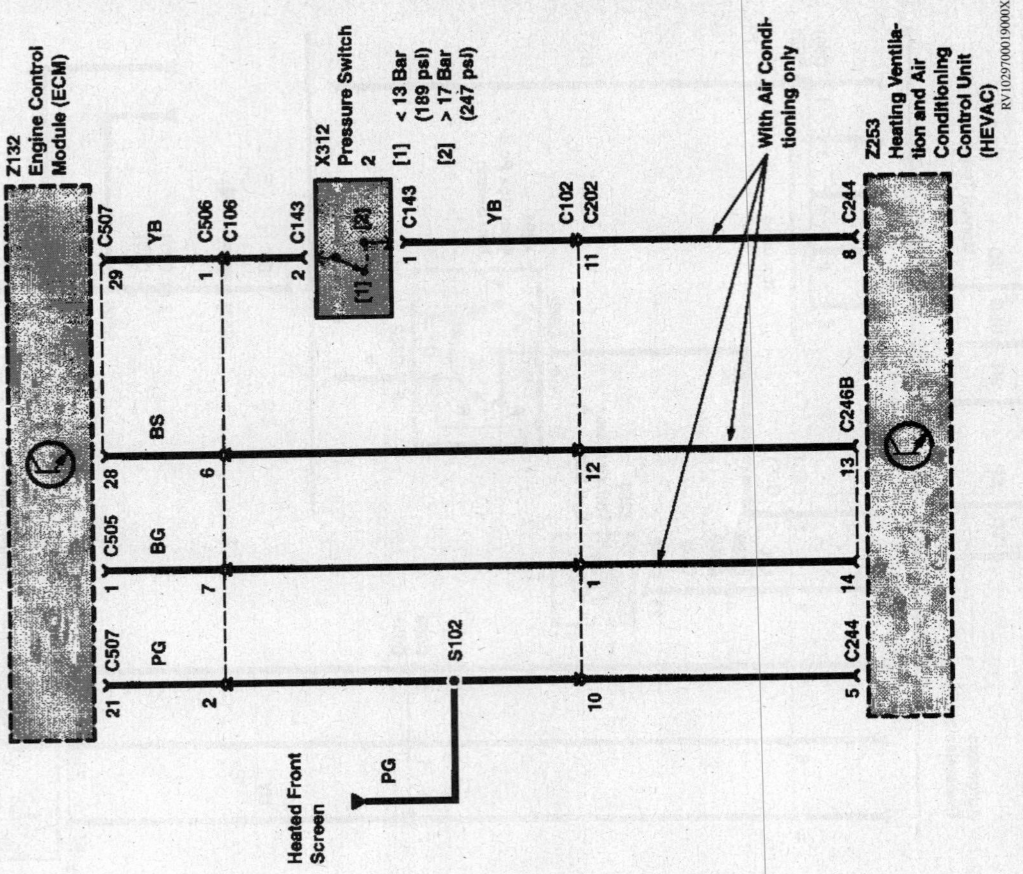

Fig. 24 Engine control wiring circuit (pressure switch). Range Rover

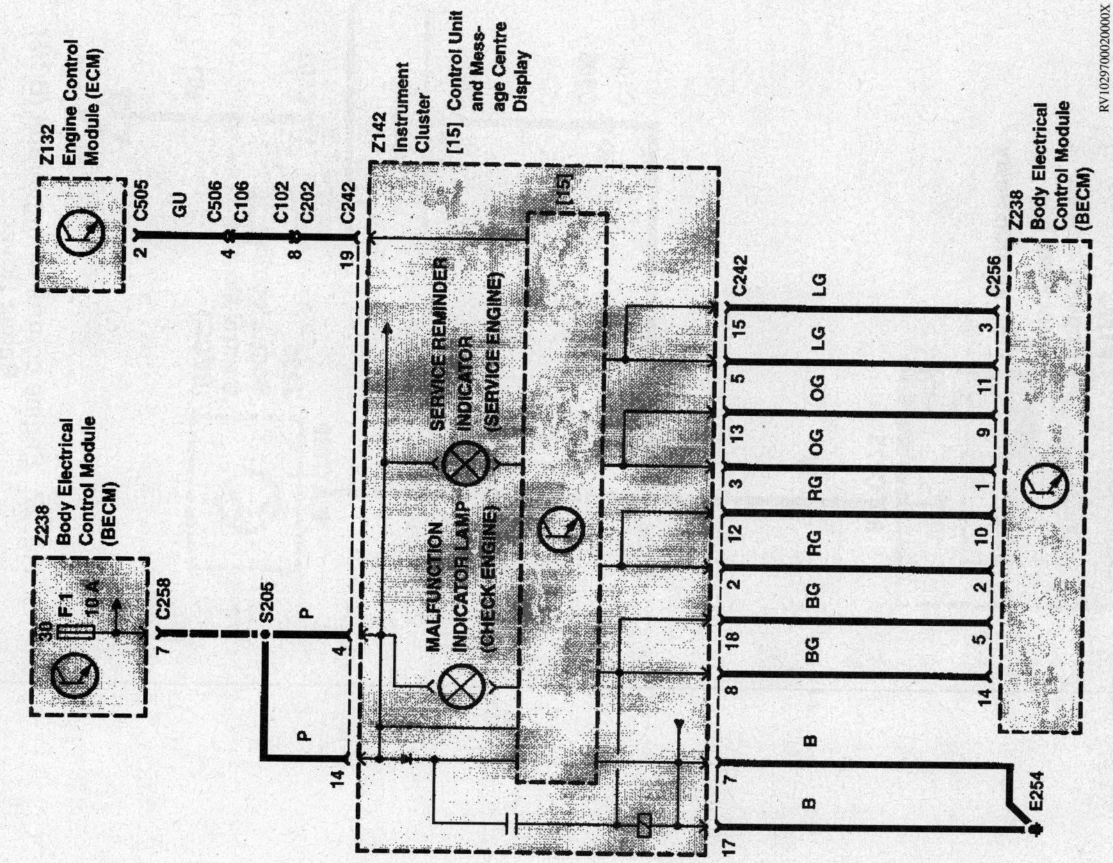

Fig. 25 Engine control wiring circuit (MIL & service reminder indicator). Range Rover

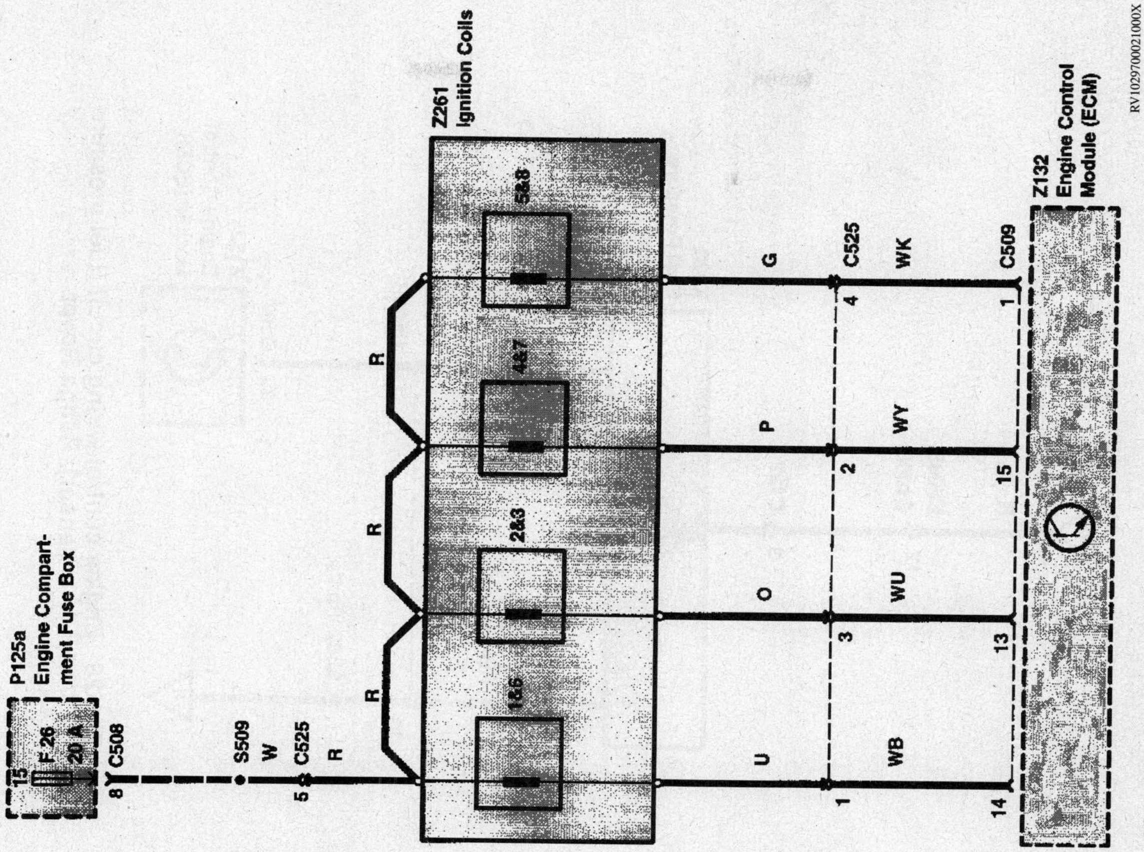

Fig. 26 Engine control wiring circuit (ignition coils). Range Rover

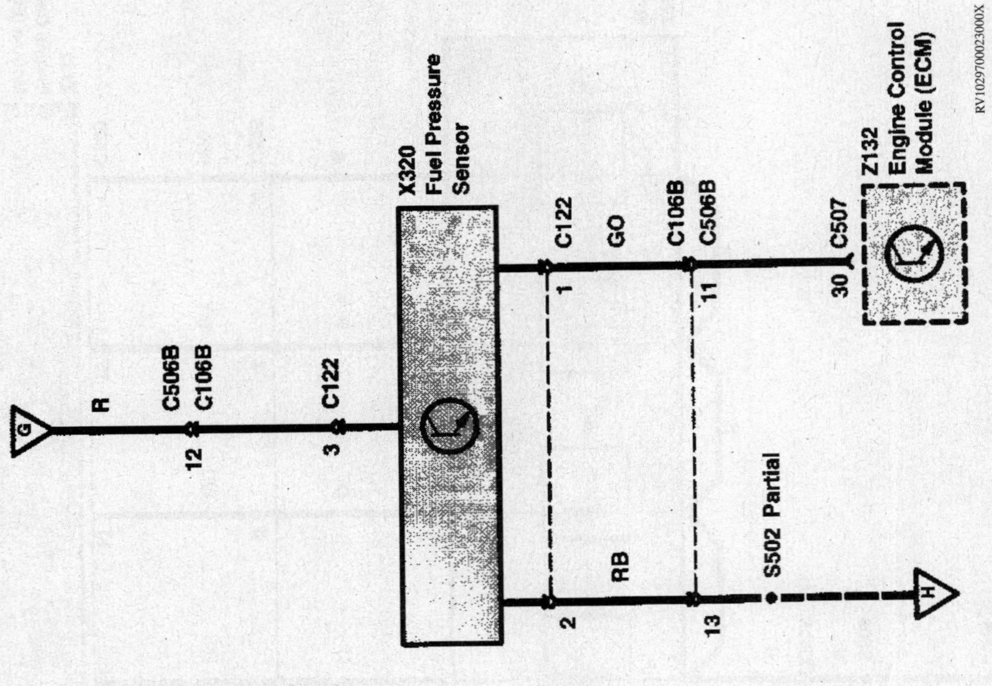

Fig. 28 Engine control wiring circuit (fuel pressure sensor). Range Rover

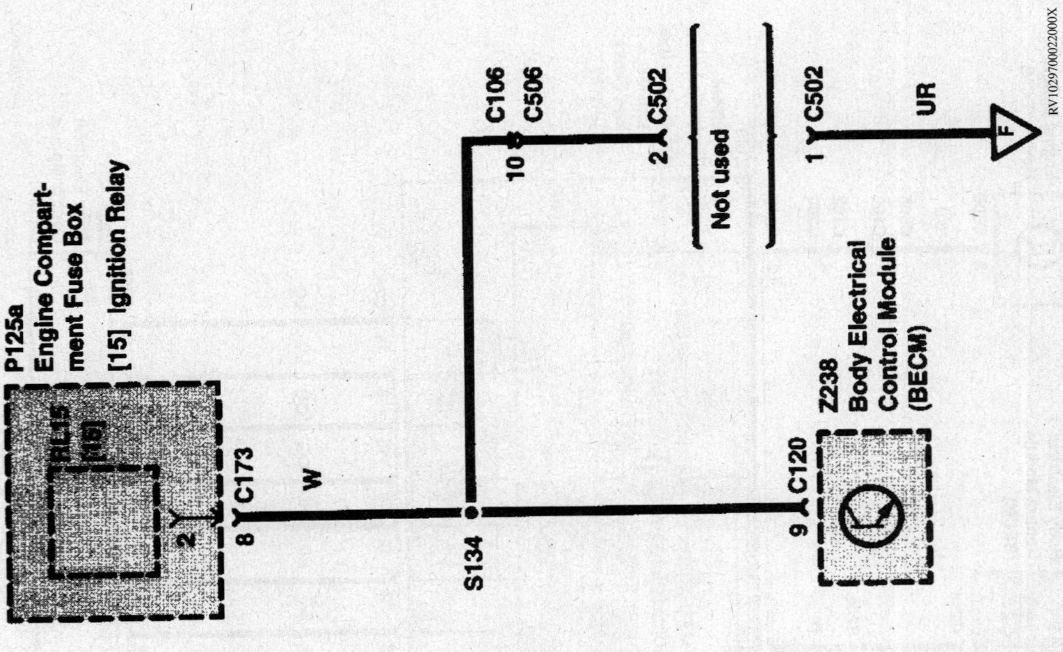

Fig. 27 Engine control wiring circuit (BCM). Range Rover

Electric Fuel Pumps

INDEX

	Page No.
Fuel Pressure Relief	13-25
Fuel Pump Relay Location	13-25
Fuel Pump Replacement	13-25
Discovery	13-25
Range Rover	13-25
Precautions	13-25
Battery Ground Cable	13-25

PRECAUTIONS

The fuel injection system retains residual pressure when the vehicle is not operating. The fuel system pressure must be released before performing any engine repair procedure. Refer to "Fuel Pressure Relief Procedure."

BATTERY GROUND CABLE

Prior to service, disconnect battery ground cable and isolate as required.

FUEL PUMP RELAY LOCATION

The fuel pump relay is located in the righthand side engine compartment fuse/relay box.

FUEL PRESSURE RELIEF

1. Position cloth around relevant union to protect against fuel spray.
2. Carefully slacken union.
3. **Torque** union to 16 ft. lbs. once pressure has relieved.

FUEL PUMP REPLACEMENT

Discovery

1. Release fuel system pressure as outlined under "Fuel Pressure Relief Procedure."
2. Remove carpet from load space floor and fold back floor insulation to reveal access panel.
3. Remove floor access panel and disconnect fuel pump connector.
4. Disconnect fuel lines.
5. Using fuel pump wrench tool No. LST-131, or equivalent, remove pump unit retaining ring.
6. Carefully remove fuel pump unit from tank, **Fig. 1.**
7. Reverse procedure to install. **Torque** fuel pump unit retaining ring to 34 ft. lbs.

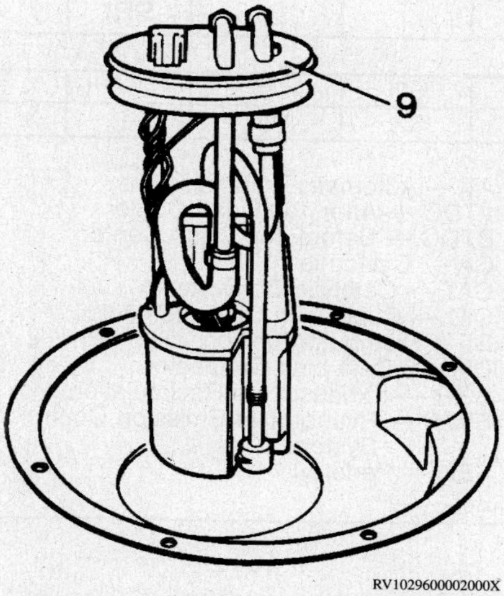

Fig. 1 Fuel pump replacement. Discovery

Range Rover

1. Release fuel system pressure as outlined under "Fuel Pressure Relief Procedure."
2. Drain fuel from tank into suitable container.
3. Remove fuel filler neck.
4. Raise and support vehicle.
5. Position suitable container under fuel filter to catch spillage, then disconnect feed pipe from fuel filter.
6. Disconnect fuel return pipe forward of tank.
7. Plug fuel pipes and connections.
8. Support fuel tank with jack.
9. Remove three nuts and two bolts securing tank cradle to floor pan.
10. Lower tank slightly and disconnect electrical connector from fuel tank unit.
11. Lower tank assembly, then disconnect feed and return pipes from top of tank unit.
12. Disconnect fill breather pipe from tank unit.
13. Disconnect feed and return pipes from tank unit.
14. Remove tank unit retaining ring (18) using tool No. LRT-19-001, or equivalent, **Fig. 2.**
15. Remove tank unit rubber seal (19) and discard.
16. Reverse procedure to install.

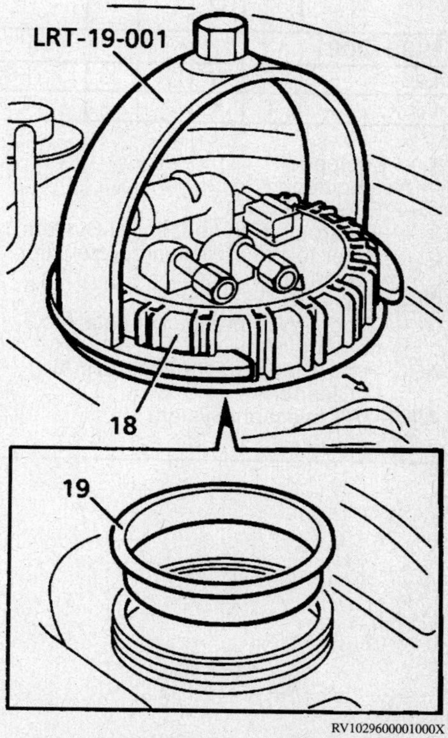

Fig. 2 Fuel pump replacement. Range Rover

Emission Control System Application Charts

Engine/ Year	Certification Type		Trans. Type		Computerized Engine Management	Fuel Induction System Type	Ignition Timing, Deg. BTDC @ RPM	Emission Control System SRI	Emission Control Systems								
	CA	FED	AT	MT					PCV	ACL	AIS	EGR	EVAP	CAT	SPK	FR	O2S
1998–2001																	
4.0L	X	X	X	X	YES②	SFI	③	—	X	—	—	—	X	X⑤	X①	X	X④
4.6L	X	X	X	—	YES②	SFI	③	—	X	—	—	—	X	X⑤	X①	X	X④

X — Equipped
— Not Equipped
① — EI/GEMS.
② — Electronic Engine Control System.
③ — Refer to the emission control information label.
④ — Two O2S.
⑤ — Type, TWC; number of catalytic converters, 2.
ACL — Air Cleaner (Thermostatic Air Cleaner)
AIS — Air Injection System
AT — Automatic Transmission
ATDC — After Top Dead Center
BTDC — Before Top Dead Center
CA — California
CAT — Catalytic Converter
CID — Cubic Inch Displacement
DI — Distributor Ignition
DLC — Data Link Connector
EGR — Exhaust Gas Recirculation
EVAP — Evaporative Emission Control System
FED — Federal
FR — Fillpipe Restrictor
MFI — Multi-Port Fuel Injection
MT — Manual Transmission
O2S — Oxygen Sensor
PCV — Positive Crankcase Ventilation
RPM — Revolutions Per Minute
SFI — Sequential Fuel Injection
SPK — Spark Control
SRI — Service Reminder Indicator
TSB — Technical Service Bulletin
TWC — Three-Way Catalytic Converter

Engine Compartment Reference Diagrams

INDEX

	PAGE NO.	FIG. NO.
DISCOVERY:		
Body	13-27	2
Engine	13-27	1
RANGE ROVER	13-28	3

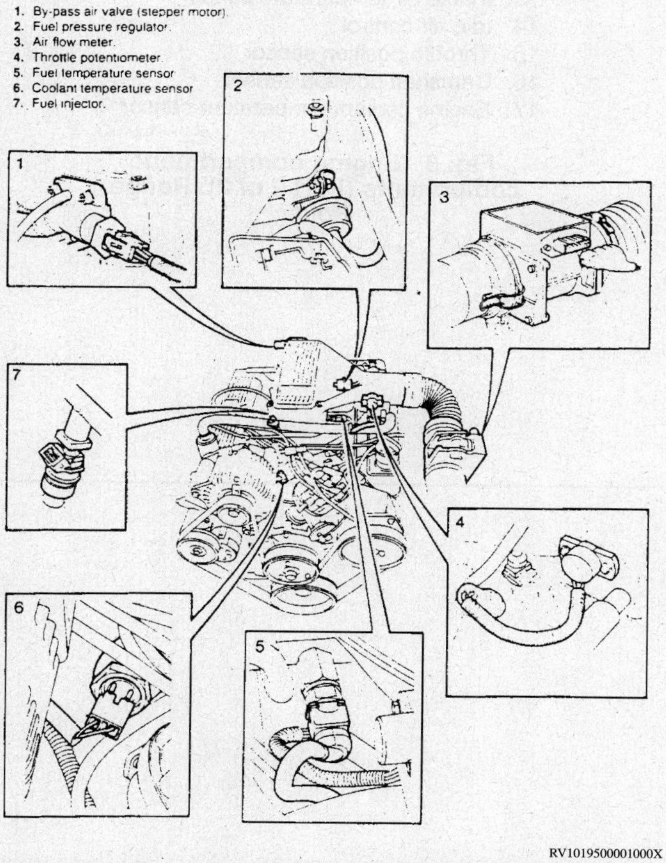

Fig. 1 Engine mounted components. Discovery

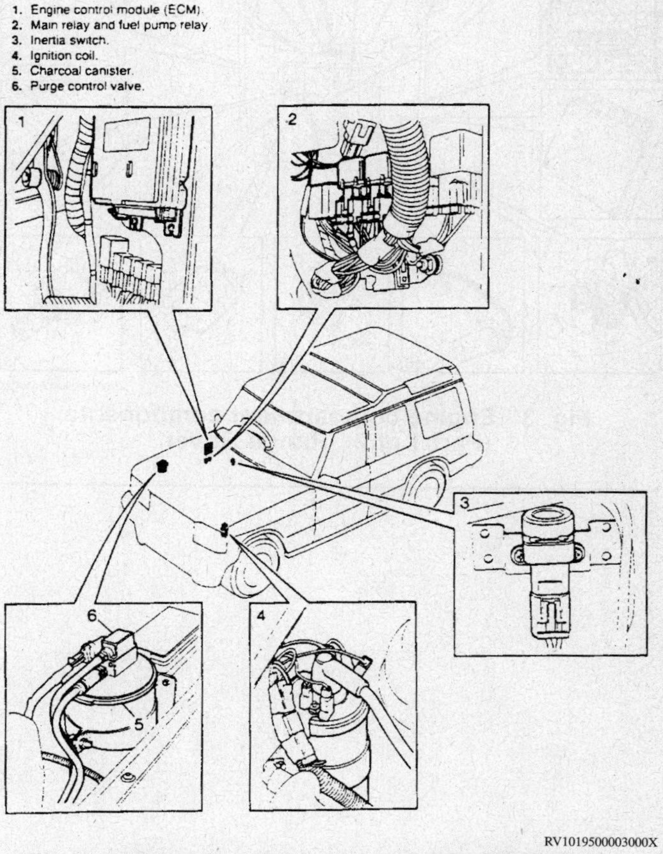

Fig. 2 Body mounted components. Discovery

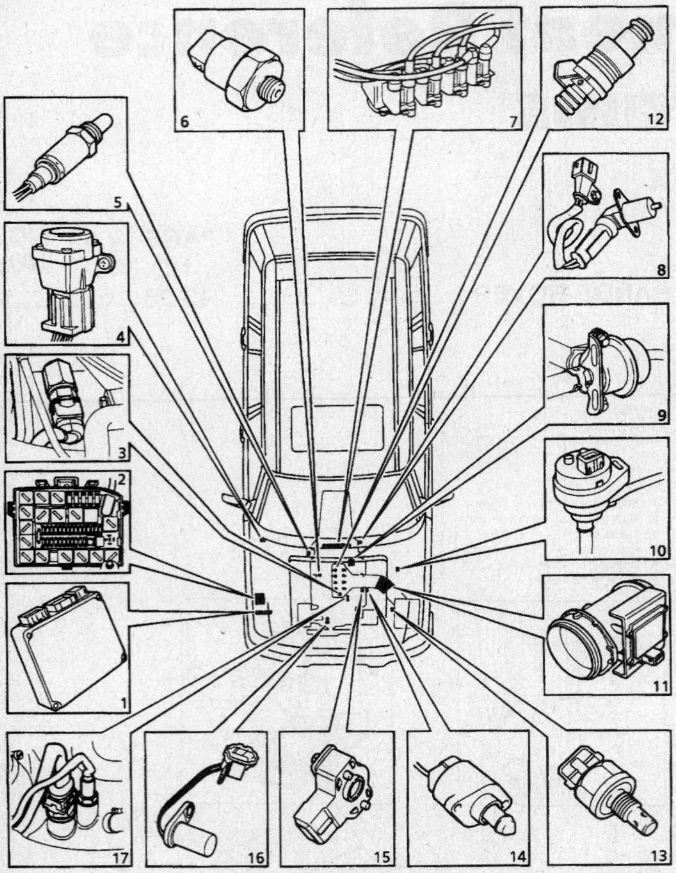

Fig. 3 Engine compartment components (Part 1 of 2). Range Rover

1. Engine control module
2. Relays in underbonnet fuse/relay box
   - Main relay
   - Ignition relay
   - Starter motor relay
   - Fuel pump relay
3. Engine fuel temperature sensor
4. Inertia switch
5. Oxygen sensor
6. Knock sensors (2 off)
7. Ignition coils
8. Crankshaft position sensor
9. Fuel pressure regulator
10. Purge valve/canister
11. Mass air flow sensor
12. Injectors
13. Intake air temperature sensor
14. Idle air control
15. Throttle position sensor
16. Camshaft position sensor
17. Engine coolant temperature sensor

RV101960000500BX

Fig. 3 Engine compartment components (Part 2 of 2). Range Rover

Emission Controls

INDEX

	Page No.
Evaporative Emission Control (EVAP) System	13-29
Description	13-29
Maintenance	13-29
System Service	13-29
Charcoal Canister	13-29
Purge Control Valve	13-29
Oxygen Sensor System	13-29
Description	13-29
System Service	13-29
Component Replacement	13-29
Positive Crankcase Ventilation (PCV) System	13-29
Description	13-29
System Service	13-29
Component Replacement	13-29

POSITIVE CRANKCASE VENTILATION (PCV) SYSTEM

Description

The purpose of the PCV system is to ensure any noxious gas generated in the engine crankcase is rendered harmless by burning in the combustion chambers.

Oil laden noxious gas in the crankcase is drawn through an oil separator located on the righthand rocker cover, **Fig. 1**, where the oil is separated and returned to the oil pan. The gas flows through a restrictor in the three-way connector and into the inlet plenum chamber, where it is drawn into the combustion chambers and burned.

System Service

COMPONENT REPLACEMENT

PCV Air Intake Filter

The PVC air intake filter is located at the rear of the lefthand rocker cover, beneath the throttle linkage bracket.

1. Pry filter cover upward to remove.
2. Remove sponge filter from cover and discard.
3. Insert new filter into cover.
4. Press filter onto mounting until it clips into place.

PCV Breather Filter

1. Remove hose clamp and pull hose off canister.
2. Screw canister off rocker cover.
3. Remove O-ring and inspect for damage.
4. Inspect condition of wire screen within canister. If in poor condition, replace whole assembly. If in acceptable condition, clean with mineral spirits.
5. Reverse procedure to install.

OXYGEN SENSOR SYSTEM

Description

The oxygen sensor consists of a titanium metal sensor surrounded by a gas perme-

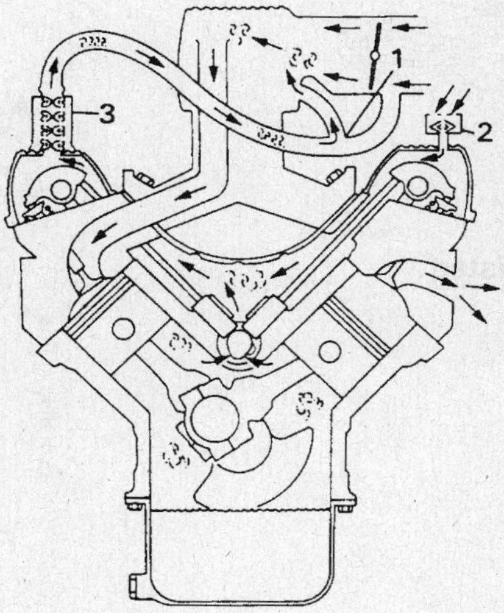

1. Three way connector
2. Air filter
3. Oil separator

RV1039500001000X

Fig. 1 PCV system

able ceramic coating. Oxygen in the exhaust reacts with the titanium wire altering the wires resistance. The ECM reads this change and adjusts the injected fuel quantity to achieve correct air/fuel ratio, thus reducing emissions.

System Service

COMPONENT REPLACEMENT

Oxygen Sensor

Removal of oxygen sensors must only be performed when engine is cold.

1. Disconnect sensor connector.
2. Unscrew sensor from downpipe.
3. Reverse procedure to install. Ensure to coat threads with anti-seize compound.

EVAPORATIVE EMISSION CONTROL (EVAP) SYSTEM

Description

The system consists of a vapor separator tank, connected to the fuel tank and located between the body inner and outer panels on the righthand side of the vehicle, near the rear wheel arch, **Fig. 2.** A charcoal canister is in the engine compartment near the righthand wheel arch. These two components are connected by a pipe running the length of the chassis.

A pressure relief valve is fitted in the hose to the charcoal canister and releases vapor to the canister when the pressure reaches. 7 – 1.0. A pressure relief valve is also fitted to relieve pressure buildup in the system, and vent it to the atmosphere. A shutoff valve is fitted to the top of the separator to prevent liquid fuel being transmitted to the canister in the event of vehicle roll over, **Fig. 3.**

A purge valve is attached to the canister and is controlled by the ECM to allow stored vapor in the canister to be released.

System Service

PURGE CONTROL VALVE

1. Disconnect purge control valve connector.
2. Remove hose from valve.
3. Remove valve from charcoal canister.
4. Reverse procedure to install using new O-ring.

CHARCOAL CANISTER

1. Remove purge control valve from charcoal canister.
2. Remove hose from valve.
3. Loosen mounting bolt and remove canister.
4. Reverse procedure to install.

Maintenance

The EVAP system should be checked periodically for leaks.

1. Adsorption canister and purge valve.
2. Location of vapor separator and pipes.
3. Fuel tank.

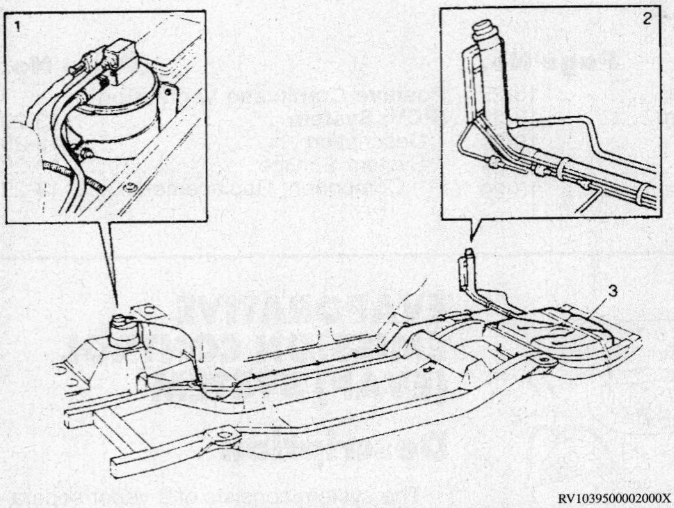

Fig. 2 Vapor separator & canister

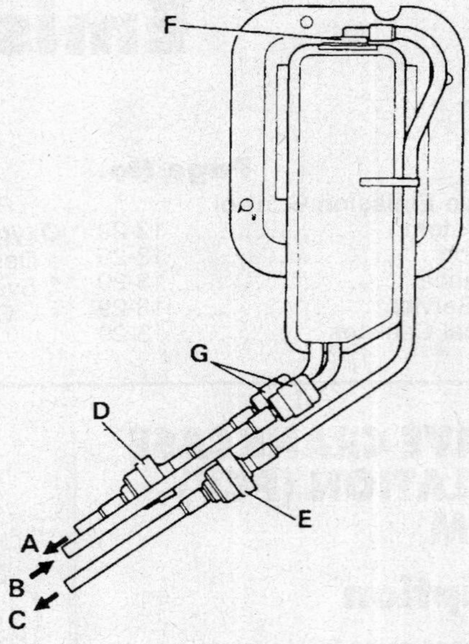

A	Pressure relief to atmosphere.
B	From fuel tank to separator.
C	To adsorption canister.
D	Pressure relief valve.
E	Pressure relief valve.
F	Shut-off valve.
G	"Speed Fit" connectors.

RV1039500003000X

Fig. 3 Evaporative emission control system

Technical Service Bulletins

INDEX

	Page No.
Erratic Fuel Gauge Readings, Hard Starting	13-31
Range Rover 4.0 SE	13-31
High Speed Misfire	13-31
Discovery	13-31
No Start Or Hard Start	13-31

ERRATIC FUEL GAUGE READINGS, HARD STARTING

Range Rover 4.0 SE

On these models, fuel gauge readings may be erratic and the vehicle may be hard to start.

This condition may be caused by loose or poor ground connections. To correct this, ensure two black ground cables from right-hand side of engine block to righthand suspension tower (top of inner fender and ending at negative battery terminal) are clean and secure, then **torque** all fasteners to 10 ft. lbs.

HIGH SPEED MISFIRE

Discovery

On these models built between Discovery VINs 092968–097888 and Range Rover Country VINs 651066–652331, there may be high speed misfire while accelerating.

This condition may be caused by incorrect position of the low tension wires at the ignition module three-pin connector and distributor. To correct this condition, proceed as follows:

1. Check ignition module 3-pin connector between coil and power steering reservoir, and ensure outer blue wire is at "A" and outer red wire is at "B," **Fig. 1.**
2. Ensure distributor connector is blue lead at pin No. 1, black lead at pin No. 2 and red lead at pin No. 3.
3. Adjust ignition timing to specification.

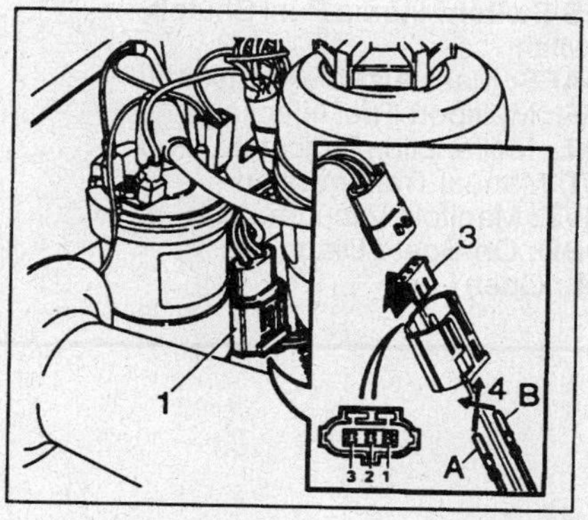

RVA019500001000X

Fig. 1 Ignition module connector inspection. Discovery

NO START OR HARD START

On these models built after Defender VIN 917122, between Discovery VINs 081991–094035 and Range Rover Country VINs 464554–651319, the engine may be hard to start or may not start.

This may be caused by an ignition module and/or coil failure. To correct this condition, install remote module mounting kit (part No. STC 1856), and/or replacement coil (part No. PRC 6574) as follows:

1. Remove distributor from front cover. Refer to "Ignition Systems" for procedure.
2. Remove module from distributor.
3. Install red dummy module and **torque** screws to 12 inch lbs.
4. Install distributor and set to TDC.
5. Place heat sink bracket on fender near coil and connect pickup lead to bracket.
6. Route 3-pin mini timing connector end of lead under front of air cleaner housing and connect to dummy module.
7. Secure original engine harness connector on harness with tie strap.
8. **On Range Rover models,** proceed as follows:
   a. Disconnect capacitor lead and positive feed wire from twin-blade connector on coil positive terminal.
   b. Remove twin blade connector from coil.
   c. Install triple blade connector from kit at coil positive terminal.
   d. **Torque** to 26 inch lbs.
   e. Install feed wire and capacitor to new connector.
9. **On all models,** install heat sink bracket under coil and locate to inner fender, then, if necessary, install replacement coil.
10. Connect two lead connectors to coil and secure wiring to engine harness with tie strap.
11. Ensure all wiring is clear of moving parts.
12. Reset ignition timing.

Abbreviations & Acronyms

ATDC: After Top Dead Center
AT: Automatic Transmission
B+: Battery Positive Voltage
BBDC: Before Bottom Dead Center
BDC: Bottom Dead Center
BTDC: Before Top Dead Center
CANPV: Canister Purge Valve
CL: Closed Loop
CTP: Closed Throttle Position
DI: Distributor Ignition
DLC: Data Link Connector
DTC: Diagnostic Trouble Code
ECL: Engine Coolant Level
ECM: Engine Control Module
ECT: Engine Coolant Temperature
ECTS: Engine Coolant Temperature Sensor
ECU: Electronic Control Unit
EFTS: Engine Fuel Temperature Sensor
EVAP: Evaporative Emission System
FCM: Fan Control Module
FP: Fuel Pump
HO2S: Heated Oxygen Sensor
IAC: Idle Air Control
IACV: Idle Air Control Valve
IAT: Intake Air Temperature
ICM: Ignition Control Module
IFS: Inertia Fuel Shutoff
IFS Switch: Inertia Fuel Shutoff Switch
MAFS: Mass Air Flow Sensor
MFI: Multiport Fuel Injection
MIL: Malfunction Indicator Lamp
MT: Manual Transmission
MVZ: Manifold Vacuum Zone
OBD: On-Board Diagnosis
OL: Open Loop
PNP: Park/Neutral Position
PNPS: Park/Neutral Position Switch
PROM: Programmable Read Only Memory
RM: Relay Module
RPM: Engine Speed
SRI: Service Reminder Indicator
SSRM: Solid State Relay Module
TB: Throttle Body
TDC: Top Dead Center
TPS: Throttle Position Sensor
TR: Transmission Range
TRS: Transmission Range Selector
TWC: Three-Way Catalytic Converter
VSS: Vehicle Speed Sensor
WOT: Wide Open Throttle

MERCEDES-BENZ

TABLE OF CONTENTS

	Page No.
COMPUTERIZED ENGINE CONTROLS	14-28
EMISSIONS:	
Abbreviations & Acronyms	14-232
Application Charts	14-222
Emissions Controls	14-227
Emission Control System Application Chart	14-222
Technical Service Bulletins	14-230
Vacuum Hose Routings	14-224
ENGINE SYSTEMS IDENTIFICATION	14-3
FUEL SYSTEMS:	
Abbreviations & Acronyms	14-232
Electric Fuel Pumps	14-21
Technical Service Bulletins	14-230
ENGINE TUNE UP & PERFORMANCE:	
Abbreviations & Acronyms	14-232
Specifications	14-7
Technical Service Bulletins	14-230
104 6 Cylinder Gasoline Engine	14-12
111 4 Cylinder Gasoline Engine	14-11
112 V6 Gasoline Engine	14-13
113 V8 Gasoline Engine	14-14
119 V8 Gasoline Engine	14-15
120 V12 Gasoline Engine	14-16
606 6 Cylinder Diesel Engines	14-17
GENERAL INFORMATION:	
Abbreviations & Acronyms	14-232
Air Bag System Precautions	0-12
Air Quality Standards	0-23
Computer Relearn Procedure	0-10
Electrical Symbol & Wire Color Code	0-33
Engine Systems Identification	14-3
How To Use This Manual	0-1
Quick Reference	14-2
Service Reminder & Warning Lamp Reset Procedure	0-14
Vehicle Identification	0-3
Vehicle Maintenance Schedules	0-45
IGNITION SYSTEMS:	
Abbreviations & Acronyms	14-232
Ignition Systems	14-19
Technical Service Bulletins	14-230
INDUCTION SYSTEM:	
Abbreviations & Acronyms	14-232
Superchargers	14-26
Turbochargers	14-24

Quick Reference

Application	Page No.
ACCESSING DIAGNOSTIC TROUBLE CODES	
104 Engine (ME 2.1 Engine Management)	14-31
111 Engine (ME 2.1 Engine Management)	14-51
112 Engine (ME 2.0 Engine Management)	14-82
113 Engine (ME 2.0 Engine Management)	14-113
119 Engine (ME 1.0 Engine Management)	14-140
120 Engine (ME 1.0 Engine Management)	14-166
606 Diesel Engine	14-199
CLEARING DIAGNOSTIC TROUBLE CODES	
104 Engine (ME 2.1 Engine Management)	14-32
111 Engine (ME 2.1 Engine Management)	14-52
112 Engine (ME 2.0 Engine Management)	14-83
113 Engine (ME 2.0 Engine Management)	14-114
119 Engine (ME 1.0 Engine Management)	14-141
120 Engine (ME 1.0 Engine Management)	14-167
606 Diesel Engine	14-210
COMPRESSION PRESSURE SPECIFICATIONS	
104 Six-Cylinder Gasoline Engine	14-12
111 Four-Cylinder Gasoline Engine	14-11
112 V6 Gasoline Engine	14-13
113 V8 Gasoline Engine	14-14
119 V8 Gasoline Engine	14-15
120 V12 Gasoline Engine	14-16
606 Six Cylinder Diesel Engine	14-17
DIAGNOSTIC CHART INDEX	
104 Engine (ME 2.1 Engine Management)	14-40
111 Engine (ME 2.1 Engine Management)	14-71
112 Engine (ME 2.0 Engine Management)	14-102
113 Engine (ME 2.0 Engine Management)	14-129
119 Engine (ME 1.0 Engine Management)	14-154
120 Engine (ME 1.0 Engine Management)	14-186
606 Diesel Engine	14-214
FUEL PRESSURE SPECIFICATIONS	
104 Engine (ME 2.1 Engine Management)	14-32
111 Engine (ME 2.1 Engine Management)	14-52
112 Engine (ME 2.0 Engine Management)	14-83
113 Engine (ME 2.0 Engine Management)	14-114
119 Engine (ME 1.0 Engine Management)	14-141
120 Engine (ME 1.0 Engine Management)	14-167
606 Diesel Engine	14-221
SENSOR & FUEL INJECTOR SPECIFICATIONS	
104 Engine (ME 2.1 Engine Management)	14-30
111 Engine (ME 2.1 Engine Management)	14-50
112 Engine (ME 2.0 Engine Management)	14-81
113 Engine (ME 2.0 Engine Management)	14-112
119 Engine (ME 1.0 Engine Management)	14-139
120 Engine (ME 1.0 Engine Management)	14-165
606 Diesel Engine	14-208

Engine Systems Identification

The Emission Control System Information Label Is Located On The Radiator Crossmember. There Are Two Labeling Systems Figs. 1 and 2.

Model (Series)	Engine		Fuel System	Page No.	Ignition System	Page No.	Computer System	Page No.
	Liter	Series						
1998								
C43 (202.033)	4.3L	113.944	Multi-Point Fuel Injection	14-111	ME 2.0 Engine Management System	14-19	ME 2.0 Engine Management System	14-111
C230 (202.023)	2.3L	111.974	Multi-Point Fuel Injection	14-49	ME 2.1 Engine Management System	14-19	ME 2.1 Engine Management System	14-49
C280 (202.029)	2.8L	112.920	Multi-Point Fuel Injection	14-80	ME 2.0 Engine Management System	14-19	ME 2.0 Engine Management System	14-80
CL500 (140.070)	5.0L	119.980	Multi-Point Fuel Injection	14-138	ME 1.0 Engine Management System	14-19	ME 1.0 Engine Management System	14-138
CL600 (140.076)	6.0L	120.982	Multi-Point Fuel Injection	14-164	ME 1.0 Engine Management System	14-19	ME 1.0 Engine Management System	14-164
CLK320 (208.365)	3.2L	112.940	Multi-Point Fuel Injection	14-80	ME 2.0 Engine Management System	14-19	ME 2.0 Engine Management System	14-80
E300 (210.025)	3.0L③	606.962	Electronic In-Line Fuel Injection (IFI)	14-207	Diesel Ignition	14-19	Electronic In-Line Fuel Injection (IFI)	14-207
E320 (210.065, 210.082⑥, 210.265⑦ & 210.282⑧)	3.2L	112.941	Multi-Point Fuel Injection	14-80	ME 2.0 Engine Management	14-19	ME 2.0 Engine Management	14-80
E430 (210.070)	4.3L	113.940	Multi-Point Fuel Injection	14-111	ME 2.0 Engine Management	14-19	ME 2.0 Engine Management	14-111
ML320 (163.154)	3.2L	112.942	Multi-Point Fuel Injection	14-80	ME 2.0 Engine Management System	14-19	ME 2.0 Engine Management System	14-80
S320 (140.032④ & 140.033⑤)	3.2L	104.994	Multi-Point Fuel Injection	14-29	ME 2.1 Engine Management System	14-19	ME 2.1 Engine Management System	14-29
S420 (140.043)	4.2L	119.981	Multi-Point Fuel Injection	14-138	ME 1.0 Engine Management System	14-19	ME 1.0 Engine Management System	14-138
S500 (140.051)	5.0L	119.980	Multi-Point Fuel Injection	14-138	ME 1.0 Engine Management System	14-19	ME 1.0 Engine Management System	14-138
S600 (140.057)	6.0L	120.982	Multi-Point Fuel Injection	14-164	ME 1.0 Engine Management System	14-19	ME 1.0 Engine Management System	14-164
SL500 (129.067)	5.0L	119.982	Multi-Point Fuel Injection	14-138	ME 1.0 Engine Management System	14-19	ME 1.0 Engine Management System	14-138
SL600 (129.076)	6.0L	120.983	Multi-Point Fuel Injection	14-164	ME 1.0 Engine Management System	14-19	ME 1.0 Engine Management System	14-164
SLK230 (170.447)	2.3L①	111.973	Multi-Point Fuel Injection	14-49	ME 2.1 Engine Management System	14-19	ME 2.1 Engine Management System	14-49
1999								
C43 (202.033)	4.3L	113.944	Multi-Point Fuel Injection	14-111	ME 2.0 Engine Management System	14-19	ME 2.0 Engine Management System	14-111
C230 (202.024)	2.3L①	111.975	Multi-Point Fuel Injection	14-49	ME 2.1 Engine Management System	14-19	ME 2.1 Engine Management System	14-49
C280 (202.029)	2.8L	112.920	Multi-Point Fuel Injection	14-80	ME 2.0 Engine Management System	14-19	ME 2.0 Engine Management System	14-80
CL500 (140.070)	5.0L	119.980	Multi-Point Fuel Injection	14-138	ME 1.0 Engine Management System	14-19	ME 1.0 Engine Management System	14-138
CL600 (140.076)	6.0L	120.982	Multi-Point Fuel Injection	14-164	ME 1.0 Engine Management System	14-19	ME 1.0 Engine Management System	14-164
CLK320 (208.365 & 208.465②)	3.2L	112.940	Multi-Point Fuel Injection	14-80	ME 2.0 Engine Management System	14-19	ME 2.0 Engine Management System	14-80
CLK430 (208.370)	4.3L	113.943	Multi-Point Fuel Injection	14-111	ME 2.0 Engine Management System	14-19	ME 2.0 Engine Management System	14-111
E55 (210.074)	5.5L	113.980	Multi-Point Fuel Injection	14-111	ME 2.0 Engine Management System	14-19	ME 2.0 Engine Management System	14-111
E300 (210.025)	3.0L③	606.962	Electronic In-Line Fuel Injection (IFI)	14-207	Diesel Ignition	14-19	Electronic In-Line Fuel Injection (IFI)	14-207

Continued

Model (Series)	Engine		Fuel System	Page No.	Ignition System	Page No.	Computer System	Page No.
	Liter	Series						
1999								
E320 (210.065, 210.082⑥, 210.265⑦ & 210.282⑧)	3.2L	112.941	Multi-Point Fuel Injection	14-80	ME 2.0 Engine Management	14-19	ME 2.0 Engine Management	14-80
E430 (210.070)	4.3L	113.940	Multi-Point Fuel Injection	14-111	ME 2.0 Engine Management System	14-19	ME 2.0 Engine Management System	14-111
ML320 (163.154)	3.2L	112.942	Multi-Point Fuel Injection	14-80	ME 2.0 Engine Management System	14-19	ME 2.0 Engine Management System	14-80
ML430 (163.172)	4.3L	113.942	Multi-Point Fuel Injection	14-111	ME 2.0 Engine Management System	14-19	ME 2.0 Engine Management System	14-111
S320 (140.032④ & 140.033⑤)	3.2L	104.994	Multi-Point Fuel Injection	14-29	ME 2.1 Engine Management System	14-19	ME 2.1 Engine Management System	14-29
S420 (140.043)	4.2L	119.981	Multi-Point Fuel Injection	14-138	ME 1.0 Engine Management System	14-19	ME 1.0 Engine Management System	14-138
S500 (140.051)	5.0L	119.980	Multi-Point Fuel Injection	14-138	ME 1.0 Engine Management System	14-19	ME 1.0 Engine Management System	14-138
S600 (140.057)	6.0L	120.982	Multi-Point Fuel Injection	14-164	ME 1.0 Engine Management System	14-19	ME 1.0 Engine Management System	14-164
SL500 (129.068)	5.0L	113.961	Multi-Point Fuel Injection	14-111	ME 2.0 Engine Management System	14-19	ME 2.0 Engine Management System	14-111
SL600 (120.983)	6.0L	130.982	Multi-Point Fuel Injection	14-164	ME 1.0 Engine Management System	14-19	ME 1.0 Engine Management System	14-164
SLK230 (170.447)	2.3L①	111.973	Multi-Point Fuel Injection	14-49	ME 2.1 Engine Management System	14-19	ME 2.1 Engine Management System	14-49
2000								
C43 (202.033)	4.3L	113.944	Multi-Point Fuel Injection	14-111	ME 2.0 Engine Management System	14-19	ME 2.0 Engine Management System	14-111
C230 (202.024)	2.3L①	111.975	Multi-Point Fuel Injection	14-49	ME 2.1 Engine Management System	14-19	ME 2.1 Engine Management System	14-49
C280 (202.029)	2.8L	112.920	Multi-Point Fuel Injection	14-80	ME 2.0 Engine Management System	14-19	ME 2.0 Engine Management System	14-80
CL500 (215.375)	5.0L	113.960	Multi-Point Fuel Injection	14-111	ME 2.0 Engine Management System	14-19	ME 2.0 Engine Management System	14-111
CLK320 (208.365 & 208.465②)	3.2L	112.940	Multi-Point Fuel Injection	14-80	ME 2.0 Engine Management System	14-19	ME 2.0 Engine Management System	14-80
CLK430 (208.370 & 208.470②)	4.3L	113.943	Multi-Point Fuel Injection	14-111	ME 2.0 Engine Management System	14-19	ME 2.0 Engine Management System	14-111
E55 (210.074)		113.980	Multi-Point Fuel Injection	14-111	ME 2.0 Engine Management System	14-19	ME 2.0 Engine Management System	14-111
E320 (210.065, 210.082⑥, 210.265⑦ & 210.282⑧)	3.2L	112.941	Multi-Point Fuel Injection	14-80	ME 2.0 Engine Management System	14-19	ME 2.0 Engine Management System	14-80
E430 (210.070 & 210.083⑥ -	4.3L	113.940	Multi-Point Fuel Injection	14-111	ME 2.0 Engine Management System	14-19	ME 2.0 Engine Management System	14-111
ML55 (163.174)	5.5L	113.981	Multi-Point Fuel Injection	14-111	ME 2.0 Engine Management System	14-19	ME 2.0 Engine Management System	14-111
ML320 (163.154)	3.2L	112.942	Multi-Point Fuel Injection	14-80	ME 2.0 Engine Management System	14-19	ME 2.0 Engine Management System	14-80
ML430 (163.172)	4.3L	113.942	Multi-Point Fuel Injection	14-111	ME 2.0 Engine Management System	14-19	ME 2.0 Engine Management System	14-111
S430 (220.170)	4.3L	113.941	Multi-Point Fuel Injection	14-111	ME 2.0 Engine Management System	14-19	ME 2.0 Engine Management System	14-111
S500 (220.175)	5.0L	113.960	Multi-Point Fuel Injection	14-111	ME 2.0 Engine Management System	14-19	ME 2.0 Engine Management System	14-111
SL500 (129.068)	5.0L	113.961	Multi-Point Fuel Injection	14-111	ME 2.0 Engine Management System	14-19	ME 2.0 Engine Management System	14-111

Continued

Model (Series)	Engine		Fuel System	Page No.	Ignition System	Page No.	Computer System	Page No.
	Liter	Series						
2000								
SL600 (129.076)	6.0L	120.983	Multi-Point Fuel Injection	14-164	ME 2.0 Engine Management System	14-19	ME 2.0 Engine Management System	14-164
SLK230 (170.447)	2.3L①	111.973	Multi-Point Fuel Injection	14-49	ME 2.1 Engine Management System	14-19	ME 2.1 Engine Management System	14-49
2001								
C240 (203.061)	2.4L	112.912	Multi-Point Fuel Injection	14-80	ME 2.8 Engine Management System	14-19	ME 2.8 Engine Management System	14-80
C320 (203.064	3.2L	112.946	Multi-Point Fuel Injection	14-80	ME 2.8 Engine Management System	14-19	ME 2.8 Engine Management System	14-80
CL55 (215.373)	5.5L	113.982	Multi-Point Fuel Injection	14-111	ME 2.8 Engine Management System	14-19	ME 2.8 Engine Management System	14-111
CL500 (215.375)	5.0L	113.960	Multi-Point Fuel Injection	14-111	ME 2.8 Engine Management System	14-19	ME 2.8 Engine Management System	14-111
CL600 (215.378)	6.0L	137.970	Multi-Point Fuel Injection	—	ME 2.7 Engine Management System	14-19	ME 2.7 Engine Management System	—
CLK55 (208.374)	5.5L	113.984	Multi-Point Fuel Injection	14-111	ME 2.8 Engine Management System	14-19	ME 2.8 Engine Management System	14-111
CLK320 (208.365 & 208.465 ②)	3.2L	112.940	Multi-Point Fuel Injection	14-80	ME 2.8 Engine Management System	14-19	ME 2.8 Engine Management System	14-80
CLK430 (208.370 & 208.470 ②)	4.3L	113.943	Multi-Point Fuel Injection	14-111	ME 2.8 Engine Management System	14-19	ME 2.8 Engine Management System	14-111
E55 (210.074)	5.5L	113.980	Multi-Point Fuel Injection	14-111	ME 2.8 Engine Management System	14-19	ME 2.8 Engine Management System	14-111
E320 (210.065, 210.082⑥, 210.265⑦ & 210.282⑧)	3.2L	112.941	Multi-Point Fuel Injection	14-80	ME 2.8 Engine Management System	14-19	ME 2.8 Engine Management System	14-80
E430 (210.070 & 210.083⑥)	4.3L	113.940	Multi-Point Fuel Injection	14-111	ME 2.8 Engine Management System	14-19	ME 2.8 Engine Management System	14-111
ML55 (163.174)	5.5L	113.981	Multi-Point Fuel Injection	14-111	ME 2.8 Engine Management System	14-19	ME 2.8 Engine Management System	14-111
ML320 (163.154)	3.2L	112.942	Multi-Point Fuel Injection	14-80	ME 2.8 Engine Management System	14-19	ME 2.8 Engine Management System	14-80
ML430 (163.172)	4.3L	113.942	Multi-Point Fuel Injection	14-111	ME 2.8 Engine Management System	14-19	ME 2.8 Engine Management System	14-111
S55 (220.173)	5.5L	113.982	Multi-Point Fuel Injection	14-111	ME 2.8 Engine Management System	14-19	ME 2.8 Engine Management System	14-111
S430 (220.170)	4.3L	113.941	Multi-Point Fuel Injection	14-111	ME 2.8 Engine Management System	14-19	ME 2.8 Engine Management System	14-111
S500 (220.175)	5.0L	113.960	Multi-Point Fuel Injection	14-111	ME 2.8 Engine Management System	14-19	ME 2.8 Engine Management System	14-111
S600 (220.178)	6.0L	137.970	Multi-Point Fuel Injection	—	ME 2.7 Engine Management System	14-19	ME 2.7 Engine Management System	—
SL500 (129.068)	5.0L	113.961	Multi-Point Fuel Injection	14-111	ME 2.0 Engine Management System	14-19	ME 2.0 Engine Management System	14-111
SL600 (129.076)	6.0L	120.983	Multi-Point Fuel Injection	14-164	ME 2.0 Engine Management System	14-19	ME 2.0 Engine Management System	14-164
SLK230 (170.449)	2.3L①	111.983	Multi-Point Fuel Injection	14-49	ME 2.1 Engine Management System	14-19	ME 2.1 Engine Management System	14-49
SLK320 (170.465)	3.2L	112.947	Multi-Point Fuel Injection	14-80	ME 2.8 Engine Management System	14-19	ME 2.8 Engine Management System	14-80

① — Supercharged engine.
② — Cabriolet.
③ — Turbo diesel engine.
④ — Short Wheel Base.
⑤ — Long Wheel Base.
⑥ — 4-MATIC.
⑦ — Station Wagon.
⑧ — Station Wagon & 4-MATIC.

Digit	Description
W	Year: W=1998
M	Manufacturer's Identification
B	
X	
V	Family Type: T=Light Duty Truck & V=Light Duty Vehicle
0	Displacement (i.e. 2.3 Liters)
2	
3	
G	Fuel: D=Diesel & G=Gasoline
S	Aspiration: N=Natural, S=Supercharged & T=Turbocharged
U	Catalyst: B=Both Underhood & Underfloor, & U=Underfloor

Fig. 1 Emission control label. Second, third & fourth digits: "MBX"

Digit	Description
W	Year: W=1998
M	Manufacturer's Identification
B	
3	Displacement (i.e. 3.2 Liters)
2	
V	Vehicle Class : D=Diesel & V=Gasoline
J	Fuel Delivery & Valves Per Cylinder: J=Electronic Fuel Injection w/3 Or More Valves, G=Mechanical Fuel Injection w/3 & 6=Mechanical Fuel Injection w/3 valves
G	Combustion: D=Diesel & G=Gasoline
F	Emission Limiting Values: A=50,000 miles, C=100,000 miles & F=100,000 miles & cold CO-value
E	Catalyst Type: E, F=Three-way catalyst, A=Oxidation catalyst & R=No catalyst
K	On-Board Diagnostic (OBD) System: A=No OBD & OBD I, & K=OBD II

Fig. 2 Emission control label. Second, third & fourth digits: "MBNo."

Tune Up Specifications

TABLE OF CONTENTS

Page No.

DIESEL ENGINE PERFORMANCE SPECIFICATIONS 14-9

GASOLINE ENGINE TUNE UP SPECIFICATIONS 14-7

Gasoline Engine Tune Up Specifications

Model	Spark Plug Gap, Inch	Ignition			Curb Idle Speed, RPM①	Fuel Pressure, psi③	Valve Lash, Inch	
		Firing Order	Timing Deg. BTDC.	Timing Mark			Intake	Exhaust
1998								
C230	.032	A	5–20⑤	⑦	680–850N	54–61	⑨	⑨
C280, CLK320, E320 & ML320	.032	B	5–25⑩	⑦	650–800N	54–61	⑨	⑨
CL500, S420, S500 & SL500	.032	⑧	5–20④	⑦	600–750N	54–61	⑨	⑨
CL600, S600 & SL600	.032	②	5–20④	⑦	600–750N	54–61	⑨	⑨
C43 & E430	.032	C	⑩	⑦	—	54–61	⑨	⑨
S320	.032	⑥	5–20⑤	⑦	600–800N	54–61	⑨	⑨
SLK230	.032	A	5–20⑤	⑦	680–850N	54–61	⑨	⑨
1999								
C43, CLK430, E430, ML430 & SL500	.032	C	⑩	⑦	—	54–61	⑨	⑨
C230 & SLK230	.032	A	5–20⑤	⑦	680–850N	54–61	⑨	⑨
C280, CLK320, E320 & ML320	.032	B	5–25⑩	⑦	650–800N	54–61	⑨	⑨
CL500, S420 & S500	.032	⑧	5–20④	⑦	600–750N	54–61	⑨	⑨
CL600, S600 & SL600	.032	②	5–20④	⑦	600–750N	54–61	⑨	⑨
S320	.032	⑥	5–20⑤	⑦	650–800N	54–61	⑨	⑨
2000								
C43, CL500, CLK430, E55, E430, ML55, ML430, S430, S500 & SL500	.032	C	⑩	⑦	—	54–61	⑨	⑨
C230 & SLK230	.032	A	5–20⑤	⑦	680–850N	54–61	⑨	⑨
C280, CLK320, E320 & ML320	.032	B	5–25⑩	⑦	650–800N	54–61	⑨	⑨
SL600	.032	②	5–20⑩	⑦	600–750N	54–61	⑨	⑨
2001								
CL55, CL500, CLK430, CLK55, E55, E430, ML55, ML430, S430 & S500	.032	C	⑪	⑦	—	54–61	⑨	⑨
SLK230	.032	A	5–20⑤	⑦	680–850N	54–61	⑨	⑨
C240, C320, CLK320, E320 & ML320	.032	B	5–25⑪	⑦	650–800N	54–61	⑨	⑨
CL600 & S600	—	D	⑫	—	—	—	⑨	⑨
SL500	.032	C	⑩	⑦	—	54–61	⑨	⑨
SL600	—	②	5–20⑩	⑦	600–750N	54–61	⑨	⑨

BTDC — Before Top Dead Center N — Neutral

(1) — When adjusting idle speed, set parking brake & chock driver wheels.

(2) — Cylinder numbering front to rear, righthand bank, 1, 2, 3, 4, 5, 6; lefthand hand bank, 7, 8, 9, 10, 11, 12. Firing order 1-12-5-8-3-10-6-7-2-11-4-9.

(3) — Less vacuum.

(4) — Equipped w/ME-1.0 engine management system, non-adjustable.

(5) — Equipped w/ME-2.1 engine management system, non-adjustable.

(6) — Firing order 1-5-3-6-2-4.

(7) — Equipped w/crankshaft position sensor.

(8) — Cylinder numbering front to rear, righthand bank, 1, 2, 3, 4; lefthand hand bank, 5, 6, 7, 8. Firing order 1-5-4-8-6-3-7-2.

(9) — Equipped w/hydraulic valve lash adjusters.

(10) — Equipped w/ME-2.0 engine management system, non-adjustable.

(11) — Equipped w/ME-2.8 engine management system, non-adjustable.

(12) — Equipped w/ME-2.7 engine management system, non-adjustable.

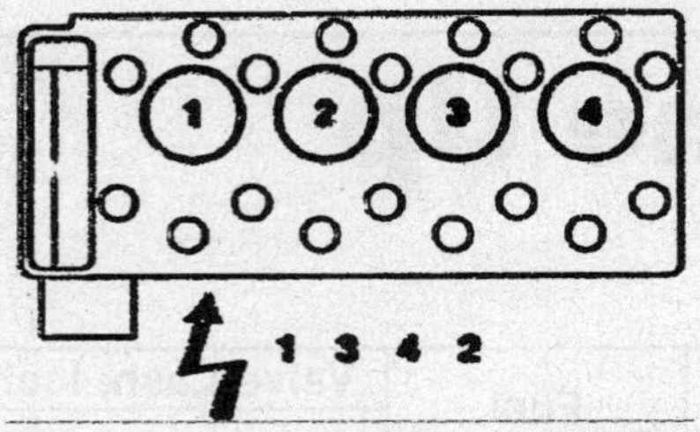

MB1130100080000X

Fig. A 111 engine firing order

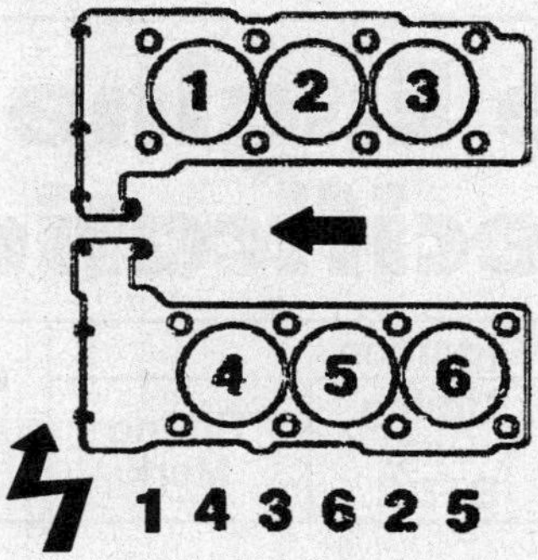

MB1130100081000X

Fig. B 112 engine firing order

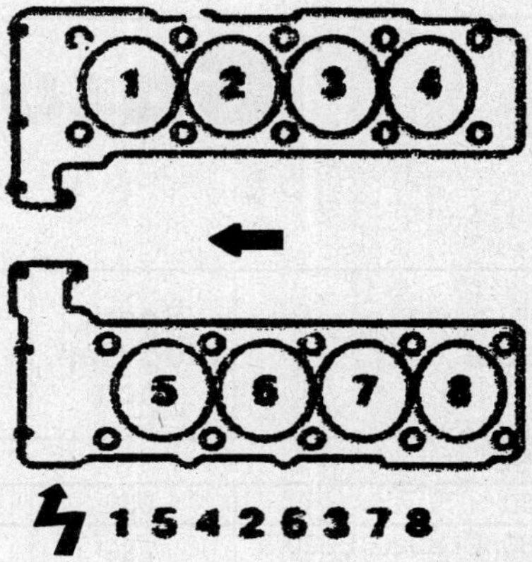

MB1130100082000X

Fig. C 113 engine firing order

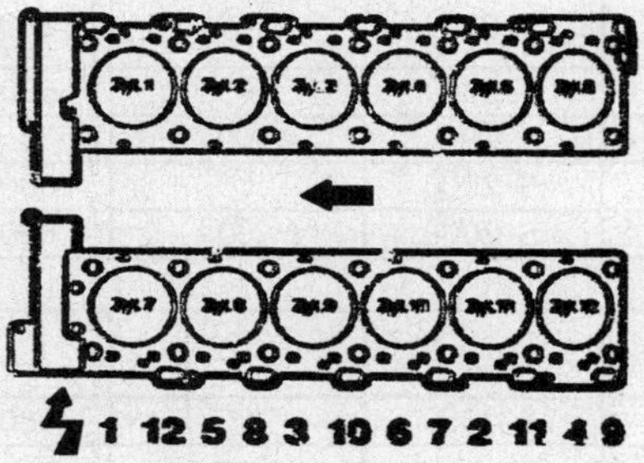

MB1130100083000X

Fig. D 137 engine firing order

Diesel Engine Performance Specifications

Engine, Series	Injection Pump Timing, ATDC	Idle Speed		Injector Nozzle Opening Pressure, psi		Boost Pressure @ 4000 RPM
		w/Electronic Control	Less Electronic Control	New Injection Nozzle	Used Injection Nozzle	
606.962	13.5-14.5	560-660	—	1668-1813	1595	—

ATDC — After Top Dead Center

Engine Tune Up & Performance

NOTE: If Unsure Of The System Used On The Vehicle Being Serviced, Refer To The "Engine Systems Identification Chart." Further Assistance For The Proper Use Of Information Contained In This Section Can Also Be Found In The Front Of This Tabbed Section Under "How To Use This Manual."

NOTE: On Air Bag Equipped Models, Refer To "Air Bag System Precautions" Located In The Front Of This Manual For System Disarming & Arming Procedures.

TABLE OF CONTENTS

	Page No.
104 6 CYLINDER GASOLINE ENGINE	14-12
111 4 CYLINDER GASOLINE ENGINE	14-11
112 V6 GASOLINE ENGINE	14-13
113 V8 GASOLINE ENGINE	14-14
119 V8 GASOLINE ENGINE	14-15
120 V12 GASOLINE ENGINE	14-16
606 6 CYLINDER DIESEL ENGINE	14-17

111 4 Cylinder Gasoline Engine

INDEX

	Page No.
Compression Pressures	14-11
Engine Identification	14-11
Idle Speed Adjustment	14-11
Ignition Timing	14-11
Spark Plugs	14-11
Valves	14-11
Valve Adjustment	14-11

ENGINE IDENTIFICATION

The emission control system information label is located on the radiator crossmember. The Vehicle Identification Number (VIN) is located on the instrument panel on the driver's side and can be viewed through the windshield.

SPARK PLUGS

Spark plugs should replaced be every 30,000 miles

On California models, spark plugs should be checked and adjusted or replaced as recommended maintenance as defined by California Air Resources Board Regulations only.

Refer to "Tune Up Specifications" for spark plug gap. **Torque** spark plugs 15–22 ft. lbs.

COMPRESSION PRESSURES

1. Warm engine to normal operating temperature of 176°F.
2. Remove spark plug.
3. Crank engine with starter several times to eliminate cylinder combustion residues. **Do not crank engine with ignition switch or with compression tester contact switch.**
4. Install suitable compression tester into spark plug bore.
5. Open throttle valves wide open.
6. Crank engine with starter eight revolutions. **Do not crank engine with ignition switch or with compression tester contact switch.**
7. Record compression readings.
8. **On models equipped less supercharger,** normal compression pressure should measure 160–218 psi.
9. **On models equipped with supercharger,** normal compression pressure should measure 109–152 psi.
10. **On all models,** maximum permissible difference between individual cylinders is 22 psi.

IGNITION TIMING

Ignition timing is controlled by the engine management system. Ignition timing is not adjustable.

Refer to "Tune Up Specifications" for firing order.

IDLE SPEED ADJUSTMENT

Idle speed is electronically controlled.

Refer to "Tune Up Specifications" for idle speed.

VALVES

Valve Adjustment

Hydraulic valve lifters are used on these engines and require no periodic service adjustments.

104 6 Cylinder Gasoline Engine

INDEX

	Page No.
Compression Pressures	14-12
Engine Identification	14-12
Idle Speed & Mixture Adjustments	14-12
Ignition Timing	14-12
Spark Plugs	14-12
Valves	14-12
Valve Adjustment	14-12

ENGINE IDENTIFICATION

The engine identification code is located at the front left of the engine crankcase. The first six digits identify the engine type. The emission control system information label is located on the radiator crossmember. The Vehicle Identification Number (VIN) is located directly above the instrument panel (on instrument panel or windshield post) at the driver's side and can be viewed through the windshield.

SPARK PLUGS

Spark plugs should be replaced spark plugs every 45,000 miles.

On California models, spark plugs should be checked and adjusted or replaced as recommended maintenance as defined by California Air Resources Board Regulations only.

Refer to "Tune Up Specifications" for spark plug gap. **Torque** spark plugs to 15–22 ft. lbs.

COMPRESSION PRESSURES

1. Warm engine to normal operating temperature.
2. Remove spark plug.
3. Crank engine several times to eliminate cylinder combustion residues. **Do not crank engine with ignition switch.**
4. Install suitable compression tester into spark plug bore.
5. Open throttle valves wide open.
6. Crank engine with starter eight revolutions. **Do not crank engine with ignition switch or with compression tester contact switch.**
7. Record compression readings.
8. Normal compression pressure should measure 145–203 psi.
9. Maximum permissible difference between individual cylinders is 22 psi.

IGNITION TIMING

Ignition timing is controlled by the engine management system. Ignition timing is not adjustable.

Refer to "Tune Up Specifications" for firing order.

IDLE SPEED & MIXTURE ADJUSTMENTS

Idle speed is electronically controlled.

Refer to "Tune Up Specifications" for idle speed.

VALVES

Valve Adjustment

Hydraulic valve lifters are used on these engines and require no periodic service adjustments.

112 V6 Gasoline Engine

INDEX

	Page No.
Compression Pressures	14-13
Engine Identification	14-13
Idle Speed & Mixture	
Adjustments	14-13
Ignition Timing	14-13
Spark Plugs	14-13
Valves	14-13
Valve Adjustment	14-13

ENGINE IDENTIFICATION

The emission control system information label is located on the radiator crossmember. The Vehicle Identification Number (VIN) is located on the instrument panel on the driver's side and can be viewed through the windshield.

SPARK PLUGS

Spark plugs should be replaced every 100,000 miles

On California models, spark plugs should be checked and adjusted or replaced as recommended maintenance as defined by California Air Resources Board Regulations only.

Refer to "Tune Up Specifications" for spark plug gap. **Torque** spark plugs 15–22 ft. lbs.

COMPRESSION PRESSURES

1. Warm engine to normal operating temperature, 176°F.
2. Remove engine trim panel, air cleaner and resonance pipe.
3. **On ML320 model,** remove fuse and relay module heat shield.
4. **On all models,** remove one spark plug from each cylinder.
5. Remove ignition coils.
6. Crank engine several times to eliminate cylinder combustion residues using starter motor. **Do not crank engine with ignition switch; use compression tester contact switch.**
7. Install suitable compression tester into spark plug bore.
8. Open throttle valves wide open.
9. Crank engine with starter at least eight revolutions. **Do not crank engine with ignition switch; use compression tester contact switch.**
10. Record compression readings.
11. **On C280, C320, CLK320, E320, ML320 and SLK320 models,** compression readings should be as follows:
    a. Normal compression pressure should measure 174–203 psi.
    b. Compression wear limit is 131 psi.
12. **On C240 models,** compression readings should be as follows:
    a. Normal compression pressure should measure 159–189 psi.
    b. Compression wear limit is 145 psi.
13. **On all models,** maximum permissible difference between individual cylinders is 22 psi.

IGNITION TIMING

Ignition timing is controlled by the engine management system. Ignition timing is not adjustable.

Refer to "Tune Up Specifications" for firing order.

IDLE SPEED & MIXTURE ADJUSTMENTS

Idle speed is electronically controlled.

Refer to "Tune Up Specifications" for idle speed.

VALVES

Valve Adjustment

Hydraulic valve lifters are used on these engines and require no periodic service adjustments.

113 V8 Gasoline Engine

INDEX

	Page No.
Compression Pressures	14-14
Engine Identification	14-14
Idle Speed & Mixture	
Adjustments	14-14
Ignition Timing	14-14
Spark Plugs	14-14
Valves	14-14
Valve Adjustment	14-14

ENGINE IDENTIFICATION

The emission control system information label is located on the radiator crossmember. The Vehicle Identification Number (VIN) is located on the instrument panel on the driver's side and can be viewed through the windshield.

SPARK PLUGS

Spark plugs should be replaced every 100,000 miles

On California models, spark plugs should be checked and adjusted or replaced as recommended maintenance as defined by California Air Resources Board Regulations only.

Refer to "Tune Up Specifications" for spark plug gap. **Torque** spark plugs 15–22 ft. lbs.

COMPRESSION PRESSURES

1. Warm engine to normal operating temperature, 176°F.
2. Remove engine trim panel, air cleaner and resonance pipe.
3. **On ML430 models,** remove fuse and relay module heat shield.
4. **On all models,** remove one spark plug from each cylinder.
5. Remove ignition coils.
6. Crank engine several times to eliminate cylinder combustion residues using starter motor. **Do not crank engine with ignition switch; use compression tester contact switch.**
7. Install suitable compression tester into spark plug bore.
8. Open throttle valves wide open.
9. Crank engine with starter at least eight revolutions. **Do not crank engine with ignition switch; use compression tester contact switch.**
10. Record compression readings.
11. **On C43, CLK430, E430, ML430 and S430 and 1999–2001 SL500 and 2000–01 CL500 and S500 models,** compression readings should be as follows:
    a. Normal compression pressure should measure 174–203 psi.
    b. Compression wear limit is 131 psi.
12. **On CL55, CLK55, E55, ML55 and S55 models,** compression readings should be as follows:
    a. Normal compression pressure should measure 159–189 psi.
    b. Compression wear limit is 145 psi.
13. **On all models,** maximum permissible difference between individual cylinders is 22 psi.

IGNITION TIMING

Ignition timing is controlled by the engine management system. Ignition timing is not adjustable.

Refer to "Tune Up Specifications" for firing order.

IDLE SPEED & MIXTURE ADJUSTMENTS

Idle speed is electronically controlled.

Refer to "Tune Up Specifications" for idle speed.

VALVES

Valve Adjustment

Hydraulic valve lifters are used on these engines and require no periodic service adjustments.

119 V8 Gasoline Engine

INDEX

	Page No.
Compression Pressures	14-15
Engine Identification	14-15
Idle Speed & Mixture	
Adjustments	14-15
Ignition Timing	14-15
Spark Plugs	14-15
Valves	14-15
Valve Adjustment	14-15

ENGINE IDENTIFICATION

The engine identification code is located at the rear left of the engine crankcase. The emission control system information label is located on the radiator crossmember. The Vehicle Identification Number (VIN) is located directly above the instrument panel (on instrument panel or windshield post) at the driver's side and can be viewed through the windshield.

SPARK PLUGS

Spark plugs should be replaced every 60,000 miles

On California models, spark plugs should be checked and adjusted or replaced as recommended maintenance as defined by California Air Resources Board Regulations only.

Refer to "Tune Up Specifications" for spark plug gap. **Torque** spark plugs to 15–22 ft. lbs.

COMPRESSION PRESSURES

1. Warm engine to normal operating temperature.
2. Remove spark plug.
3. Crank engine with starter several times to eliminate cylinder combustion residues.
4. Install suitable compression tester into spark plug bore.
5. Open throttle valves wide open.
6. Crank engine with starter eight revolutions.
7. Record compression readings.
8. Normal compression pressure should measure 145–203 psi.
9. Maximum permissible difference between individual cylinders is 22 psi.

IGNITION TIMING

Ignition timing is controlled by the engine management system. Ignition timing is not adjustable.

Refer to "Tune Up Specifications" for firing order.

IDLE SPEED & MIXTURE ADJUSTMENTS

Idle speed is electronically controlled.

Refer to "Tune Up Specifications" for idle speed.

VALVES

Valve Adjustment

Hydraulic valve lifters are used on these engines and require no periodic service adjustments.

120 V12 Gasoline Engine

INDEX

	Page No.
Compression Pressures	14-16
Engine Identification	14-16
Idle Speed & Mixture	
Adjustments	14-16
Ignition Timing	14-16
Spark Plugs	14-16
Valves	14-16
Valve Adjustment	14-16

ENGINE IDENTIFICATION

The engine identification code is located at the left rear of the engine crankcase. The emission control system information label is located on the radiator crossmember. The Vehicle Identification Number (VIN) is located directly above the instrument panel (on instrument panel or windshield post) at the driver's side and can be viewed through the windshield.

SPARK PLUGS

Spark plugs should be replaced every 60,000 miles

On California models, spark plugs should be checked and adjusted or replaced as recommended maintenance as defined by California Air Resources Board Regulations only.

Refer to "Tune Up Specifications" for spark plug gap. **Torque** spark plugs to 15–22 ft. lbs.

COMPRESSION PRESSURES

1. Warm engine to normal operating temperature of 176°F.
2. Remove spark plug.
3. Crank engine with compression tester contact switch several times with throttle closed and parking brake applied to eliminate cylinder combustion residues.
4. Install suitable compression tester into spark plug bore.
5. Open throttle valves wide open.
6. Crank engine with starter eight revolutions.
7. Record compression readings.
8. Normal compression pressure should measure 145–203 psi.
9. Maximum permissible difference between individual cylinders is 22 psi.

IGNITION TIMING

Ignition timing is controlled by the engine management system. Ignition timing is not adjustable.

On all models, refer to "Tune Up Specifications" for firing order.

IDLE SPEED & MIXTURE ADJUSTMENTS

Idle speed is electronically controlled.

Refer to "Tune Up Specifications" for idle speed.

VALVES

Valve Adjustment

Hydraulic valve lifters are used on these engines and require no periodic service adjustments.

606 6 Cylinder Diesel Engine

INDEX

	Page No.
Compression Pressures	14-17
Engine Identification	14-17
Glow Plugs	14-17
Idle Speed & Mixture	
Adjustments	14-18
Idle Speed Adjustment	14-17
Injection Pump Timing	14-17
Injector Nozzle Pressure	14-17
Valves	14-18
Valve Adjustment	14-18

ENGINE IDENTIFICATION

The engine identification code is located at the left rear of the engine crankcase. The emission control system information label is located on the radiator crossmember. The Vehicle Identification Number (VIN) is located directly above the instrument panel (on instrument panel or windshield post) at the driver's side and can be viewed through the windshield.

GLOW PLUGS

Torque glow plugs to 15 ft. lbs.

COMPRESSION PRESSURES

1. Warm engine to operating temperature, 176°F.
2. Remove nozzle holder.
3. Disconnect starter harness connector.
4. Ensure transmission is in neutral.
5. Crank engine over several times to clean out residue using compression tester contact switch. **Do not use starter to crank engine.**
6. Install suitable compression checker into precombustion chamber.
7. Crank engine at least nine revolutions using compression tester contact switch. **Do not use starter to crank engine.**
8. Record compression readings.
9. Normal compression pressure should be 421–508 psi.
10. Maximum permissible difference between individual cylinders should not be more than 44 psi.

INJECTION PUMP TIMING

1. Remove fuel injection pump plug from governor housing.
2. **When using adapter tool No. 617 589 00 21 00, or equivalent,** proceed as follows:
   a. Connect RI transmitter cable tool No. 617 589 10 21 00, or equivalent, between governor housing and adapter, **Fig. 1.**
   b. Connect suitable digital tester (SUN MES 1500, Bear DEACE, or equivalent) through adapter.
   c. Connect TDC transmitter tool No. 603 589 00 21 00, or equivalent, to adapter, battery and TDC impulse transmitter.
3. **If adapter tool is not available,** proceed as follows:
   a. Connect RI transmitter cable tool No. 617 589 10 21 00, or equivalent, between governor housing and suitable digital tester (SUN MES 1500, Bear DEACE, or equivalent), **Fig. 2.**
   b. Connect TDC transmitter tool No. 603 589 00 21 00, or equivalent, to battery and TDC impulse transmitter.
4. **On all models,** run engine at idle and inspect fuel injection pump timing.
5. Timing should be 14–16° ATDC.
6. If timing is not as specified, adjust timing by turning adjusting screw clockwise to retard fuel injection pump timing or counterclockwise to advance fuel injection pump timing.
7. If adjustment range is insufficient, injection pump must be removed, reset and installed.
8. Remove tools and install plug.

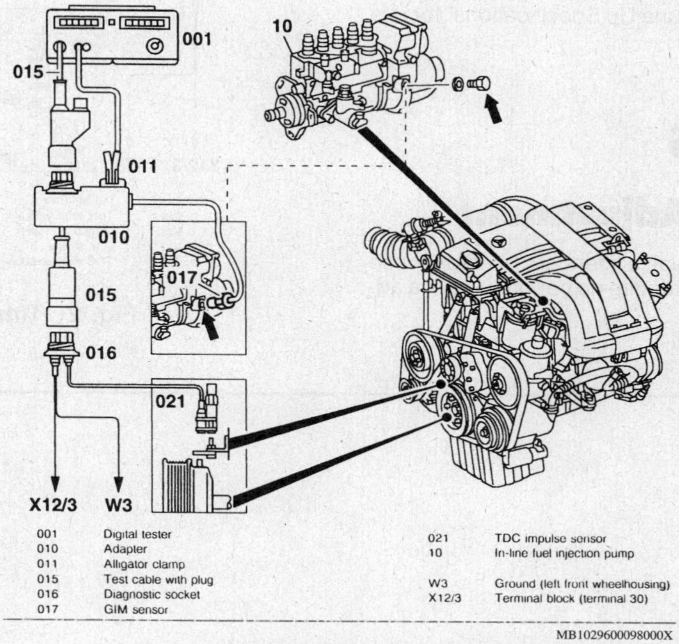

Fig. 1 Timing adjustment w/adapter

INJECTOR NOZZLE PRESSURE

1. Remove injection nozzle, then connect a tester and gauge following manufacturer's instructions.
2. Refer to "Tune Up Specifications" opening pressure.
3. Difference in ejection pressures between nozzles should not exceed 72.5 psi.
4. Spray patterns should be uniform and injected at correct angle of nozzle being tested.

IDLE SPEED ADJUSTMENT

1. Connect suitable digital tester with TDC impulse sensor tool No. 603 589 00 21 00, or equivalent, and suitable hand held tester.
2. Ensure throttle linkage has free movement and is in good condition.
3. With transmission in D position and

parking braking applied, run engine until coolant temperature is more than 140°F.

4. Adjust idle speed with Closed Throttle Position (CTP) stop.

IDLE SPEED & MIXTURE ADJUSTMENTS

Idle speed is electronically controlled. Refer to "Tune Up Specifications" for idle speed.

VALVES

Valve Adjustment

Hydraulic valve lifters are used on these engines and require no periodic service adjustments.

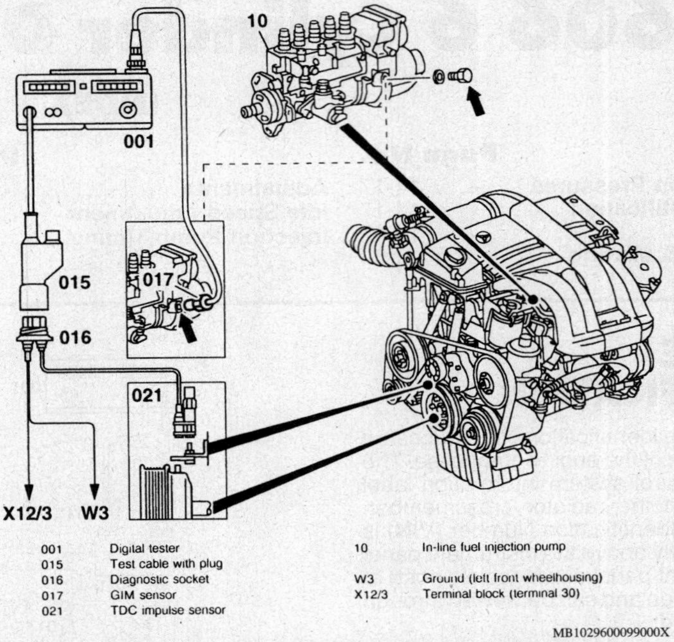

Fig. 2 Timing adjustment less adapter

Ignition Systems

NOTE: If Unsure Of The System Used On The Vehicle Being Serviced, Refer To The "Engine Systems Identification Chart." Further Assistance For The Proper Use Of Information Contained In This Section Can Also Be Found In The Front Of This Tabbed Section Under "How To Use This Manual."

NOTE: On Air Bag Equipped Models, Refer To "Air Bag System Precautions" Located In The Front Of This Manual For System Disarming & Arming Procedures.

INDEX

	Page No.
Description	14-20
Diagnosis & Testing	14-20
Precautions	14-19
Air Bag Systems	14-19
Battery Ground Cable	14-19
Drive Authorization System (DAS)	14-19
ECM Recognition	14-19
ECM Self-Adaptation	14-19
ESP/ASR/ETS/ABS Control Modules	14-19
ME 1.0 Engine Management System	14-19
Throttle Valve Position	14-19
System Service	14-20
Component Replacement	14-20
Ignition Coil	14-20
Troubleshooting	14-20

PRECAUTIONS

Air Bag Systems

Refer to "Air Bag System Precautions" in the front of this manual for system disarming and arming procedures.

Battery Ground Cable

Prior to service, disconnect battery ground cable and isolate as required.

ME 1.0 Engine Management System

1. Both control module coupling must be disconnected or connect with ignition switch in Off position.
2. Do not short circuit ignition coils terminal No. 1.
3. Do not operate the ignition system at starting speed unless the ignition cables are fully connected.
4. Do not conduct are test at starting speed or when engine is running. This includes: holding ignition cable No. 4 at a distance to ground, disconnecting a plug connector or pulling cable No. 4 out of the ignition coils.
5. High output side of ignition system must always carry at least two ohms resistance (spark plug connected).
6. Do not load ignition coil with more than 28,000 volts.
7. Ignition coil iron cores must always be connected to ground. **Use caution, coil cores can be charged with up to 400 volts.**
8. **Do not work on this system if you have a pacemaker.**
9. Ensure engine and ignition switch are in Off position when connecting and disconnecting ignition coil.
10. When working at start speeds during test such as compression check, switch ignition to off position and disconnect control module connector No. 2.

ECM Self-Adaptation

After repair work, the Engine Control Module (ECM) will automatically adapt itself after the vehicle has made approximately 10 trips. A trip includes engine running for more than 20 minutes, engine oil temperature of more than 19°F, engine speed of more than 700 RPM and emission related logic chain functions.

However, after fixing a malfunction or installation of a test ECM, the self-adaptation function must be reset as outlined under "Computer Relearn" in "Service Reminder & Warning Lamp Reset Procedures" at the front of this manual.

ECM Recognition

The ECM must be coded for vehicle model, catalytic converter and country version with the Hand-Held Tester.

Before replacing the ECM, read existing stored code numbers with the Hand-Held Tester. When the new ECM is installed, enter the stored code numbers from the Hand-Held Tester. If code numbers cannot be read, the corresponding codes number must be obtained from Mercedes-Benz spare parts microfiche, then manually entered with a Hand-Held Tester.

Drive Authorization System (DAS)

The Drive Authorization System (DAS) is activated by the Remote Central Locking (RCL) infrared remote control transmitter or master key. The ECM and RCL control module are permanently locked together by an identification code. This code cannot be erased. Trial installation of an ECM or RCL control module from another vehicle is not possible. After 40 start, a new ECM cannot be used in any other vehicle. The code number and VIN must be entered into the ECM with a Hand-Held Tester.

Throttle Valve Position

After replacing the Engine Control Module (ECM) or actuator, the throttle valve mechanical end stop and wide open position must be determined and recorded, allowing learned data to be erased with a Hand-Held Tester or new data learned.

1. Disconnect and connect battery power supply.
2. With vehicle parked, transmission in P or N position, no pressure on accelerator pedal and ignition switch in Off position, ensure engine coolant temperature is 41–212°F.
3. Turn ignition switch to On position for more than 50 seconds.
4. Turn ignition switch to Off position for more than 10 seconds.
5. If engine runs rough after battery power interruption, proceed as follows:
   a. Ensure engine coolant temperature is more than 176°F.
   b. Drive vehicle on dynamometer with transmission in 4 position or on road in 3 position.
   c. Increase engine speed to more than 3500 RPM and coast until speed is less than 1200 RPM.

ESP/ASR/ETS/ABS Control Modules

The Electronic Stability Program (ESP), Acceleration Slip Regulation (ASR), Electronic Traction System (ETS) and/or Antilock Brake System (ABS) control modules must not be disconnected. The Engine Control Module (ECM) and Transmission Control Module (TCM) rely on those control modules for Vehicle Speed Sensor (VSS) information. To disable brake and engine regulation of those modules, proceed as follows:

1. Turn ignition switch to Off position.
2. Connect Hand-Held Tester to Data Link Connector (DLC).
3. Jump sockets No. 1 and 6.
4. Start engine. MIL must light.
5. If Hand-Held Tester is not available, disconnect VSS front axle connector.
6. When testing is complete, connect VSS and erase Diagnostic Trouble Codes with Hand-Held Tester.

DESCRIPTION

Refer to specific engine under "Computerized Engine Controls."

TROUBLESHOOTING

Refer to specific engine under "Computerized Engine Controls."

DIAGNOSIS & TESTING

Refer to specific engine under "Computerized Engine Controls."

SYSTEM SERVICE

Component Replacement

IGNITION COIL

104 & 111 Engines

1. Remove mounting bolt and cable duct cover.
2. Disconnect cables and remove ignition coils.
3. Reverse procedure to install.

112 & 113 Engines

1. **On S430 and 2000–01 CL500 and S500 models,** unclip engine face engine cover.
2. **On all models,** remove engine trim panel or air cleaner from cylinder head covers.
3. Remove mounting bolts.
4. Disconnect spark plug connectors.
5. Remove ignition coils.
6. Reverse procedure to install. **Torque** mounting bolt to 71 inch lbs.

119 Engine

1. Remove mounting bolts and cover.
2. Remove coil. Mark cable routing for installation.
3. Reverse procedure to install.

Electric Fuel Pumps

NOTE: If Unsure Of The System Used On The Vehicle Being Serviced, Refer To The "Engine Systems Identification Chart." Further Assistance For The Proper Use Of Information Contained In This Section Can Also Be Found In The Front Of This Tabbed Section Under "How To Use This Manual."

NOTE: On Air Bag Equipped Models, Refer To "Air Bag System Precautions" Located In The Front Of This Manual For System Disarming & Arming Procedures.

NOTE: "Electrical Symbol & Wire Color Code Identification" Located In The Front Of This Manual May Be Used As An Aid When Using Wiring Circuits Found In This Section.

INDEX

	Page No.
Description	14-21
Diagnosis & Testing	14-21
Fuel Pressure Relief	14-21
Fuel Pump Relay Location	14-21
C43, C230, C240, C280, C320, CLK55, CLK320, CLK430, SLK230 & SLK320	14-21
CL500, CL600, S320, S420, S500, S600, SL500 & SL600	14-21
E320 & E430	14-21
ML320 & ML430	14-21
Fuel Pump Replacement	14-21
C230	14-21
E300	14-22
E55, E320 & E430	14-22
ML55, ML320 & ML430	14-22
S320	14-22
S420 & 1998–99 CL500, CL600, S500 & S600 & 1998 SL500	14-23
S430 & 1999–2001 SL500 & 2000–01 S500	14-23
SLK230	14-23
1998–2000	14-23
2001	14-23

DESCRIPTION

The fuel pump is an electrically operated roller cell pump. The eccentrically arranged rotor disc in the pump housing feature metal rollers around the circumference, which are mounted in slot-shaped recesses and are pressed against the pump housing by centrifugal force. The rollers act as a continuous seat and fuel is moved in the cavities between the rollers.

FUEL PUMP RELAY LOCATION

C43, C230, C240, C280, C320, CLK55, CLK320, CLK430, SLK230 & SLK320

The fuel pump relay is located in the righthand front corner of the luggage compartment.

CL500, CL600, S320, S420, S500, S600, SL500 & SL600

The fuel pump relay is located in the righthand side of the luggage compartment.

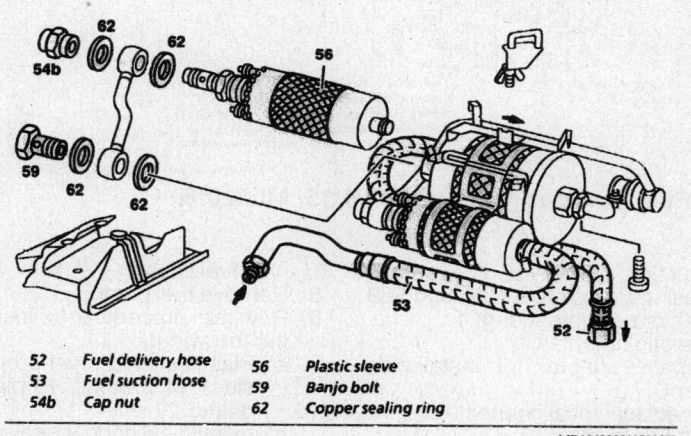

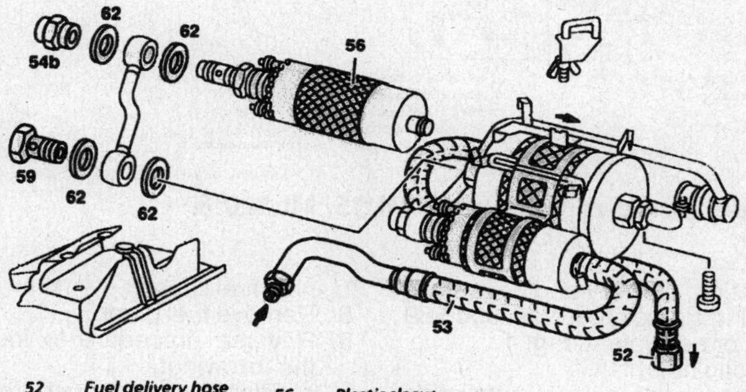

Fig. 1 Fuel pump replacement. C230

E320 & E430

The fuel relay pump is located next to the battery below the rear seat cushion, in the rear fuse box.

ML320 & ML430

The fuel pump relay is located in the electrical box on the lefthand side of the engine compartment.

FUEL PRESSURE RELIEF

1. Ensure ignition switch is in Off position.
2. Remove fuel pump protective box.
3. Disconnect fuel pump negative terminal.
4. Start engine and allow to run until it stalls from fuel starvation.
5. Crank engine to ensure pressure is released.

DIAGNOSIS & TESTING

Refer to specific engine under "Computerized Engine Controls."

FUEL PUMP REPLACEMENT

C230

1. Relieve fuel pressure as described under "Precautions."

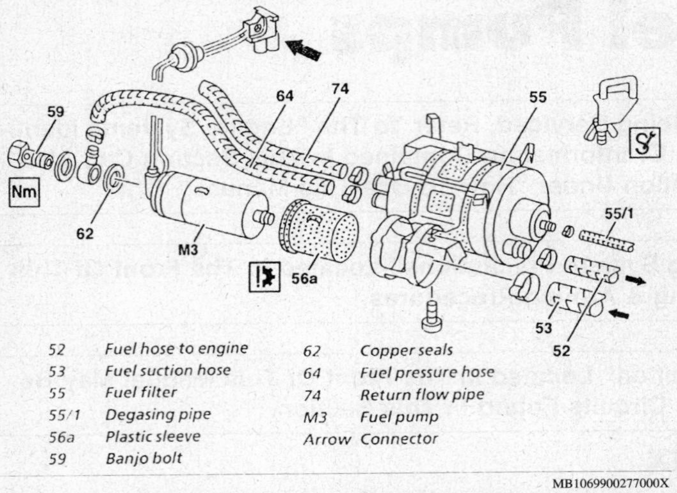

Fig. 2 Fuel pump replacement. E55, E320 & E430

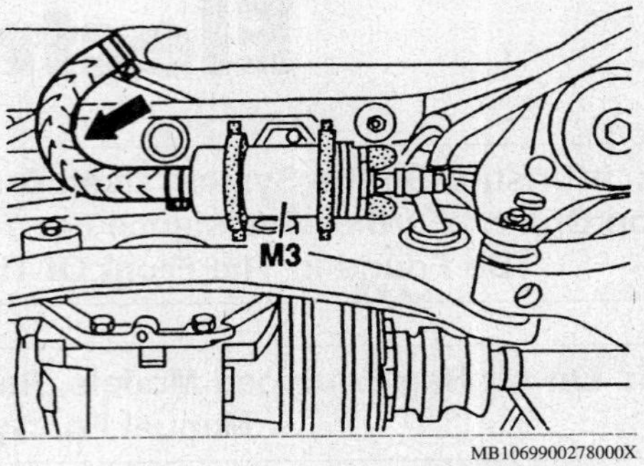

Fig. 3 Fuel pump replacement. E320 station wagon

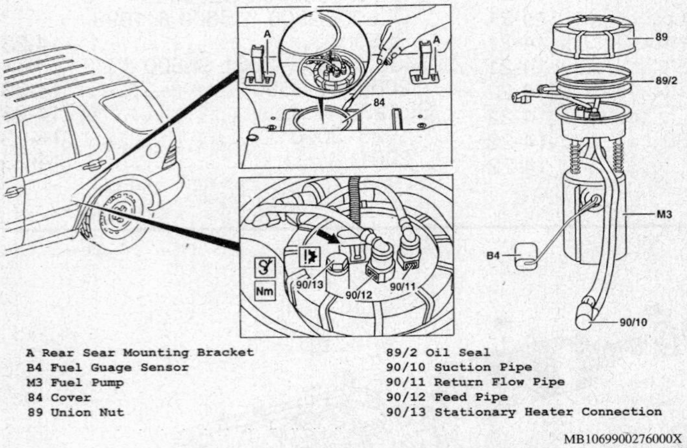

Fig. 4 Fuel pump replacement. ML55, ML320 & ML430

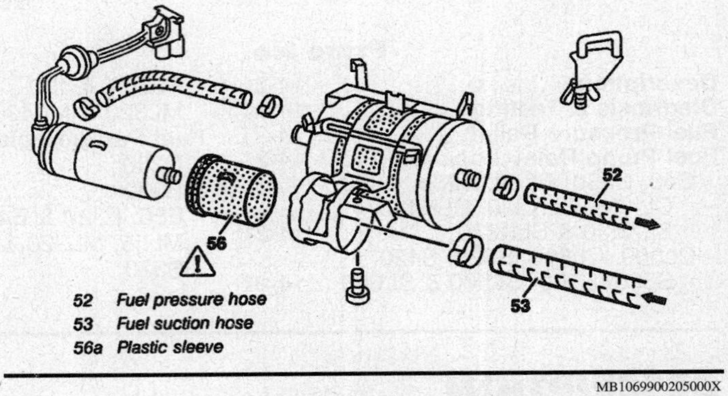

Fig. 5 Fuel pump replacement

2. Pinch suction, delivery and degassing hoses using clamps tool Nos. 000 589 40 37 00, or equivalent, **Fig. 1.**
3. Remove cap nuts.
4. Mark spacer/adapter for installation alignment.
5. Disconnect electrical connectors.
6. Remove fuel pump.
7. Reverse procedure to install. **Torque** banjo bolt and cap nuts to 18 ft. lbs.

E300

1. Remove air cleaner.
2. Disconnect fuel suction and pressure lines.
3. Remove mounting nuts and fuel pump from fuel injection pump.
4. Reverse procedure to install with new gasket.

E55, E320 & E430

1. Relieve fuel pressure as described under "Precautions."
2. Remove banjo bolt, **Figs. 2 and 3.**
3. **On E320 station wagon models,** do not pinch fuel hose at elbow.
4. **On all models,** pinch off and disconnect fuel lines.
5. Remove fuel pump.
6. Reverse procedure to install, noting the following:
   a. Plastic sleeve must project at both sides of bracket. Replace as required.
   b. Install new copper seals.

ML55, ML320 & ML430

1. Relieve fuel pressure as described under "Precautions."
2. Remove lefthand rear seat mounting bracket, raise seat and support with suitable 20-inch long wooden block, **Fig. 4.**
3. Turn carpeting up to expose fuel pump body. **Do not bend carpeting.**
4. Remove body cover by heating cover with hot air fan to loosen sealant.
5. Disconnect electrical connector.
6. Disconnect fuel lines using pliers No. 163 589 00 37 00, or equivalent. **Do not kink fuel lines.**
7. **If fuel pump is working,** proceed as follows:
   a. Disconnect fuel feed line from fuel rail. Collect spilled fuel in suitable container.
   b. Connect suitable 10 mm fuel hose to fuel feed line and insert other end into suitable container.
   c. Remove fuel pump relay.
   d. Bridge relay, turn ignition switch to On position and drain fuel tank into suitable container. If tank is full, this procedure may take approximately 15 minutes.
8. **If fuel pump is not working,** proceed as follows:
   a. Connect adapter hose No. 168 589 00 91 00 and extractor hose No. 168 589 00 90 00, or equivalents, to fuel feed line and drain fuel tank into suitable container using suitable suction pump.
9. **On all models,** remove union nut using pronged wrench tool No. 163 589 01 07 00, or equivalent.
10. Remove fuel pump.
11. Reverse procedure to install, noting the following:
    a. Install new seal
    b. **Torque** union nuts to 18 ft. lbs.

S320

1. Relieve fuel pressure as described under "Precautions."
2. Pinch suction, delivery and degassing hoses using clamps tool Nos. 000 589 40 37 00, or equivalent.
3. Remove cap nuts.

4. Mark spacer/adapter for installation alignment.
5. Disconnect electrical connectors.
6. Remove fuel pump.
7. Reverse procedure to install. **Torque** banjo bolt and cap nuts to 18 ft. lbs.

S420 & 1998-99 CL500, CL600, S500 & S600 & 1998 SL500

1. Pinch off fuel suction and delivery hoses using clamp tool No. 000 589 40 37 00, or equivalent, **Fig. 5.**
2. Remove cap nut or banjo bolt.
3. Remove fuel pump.
4. Reverse procedure to install, noting the following:
   a. Replace copper sealing rings.
   b. **Torque** banjo bolt and cap nuts to 18 ft. lbs.
   c. Plastic sleeve must project at both sides of bracket.

S430 & 1999-2001 SL500 & 2000-01 S500

1. Relieve fuel pressure as described under "Precautions."
2. Remove fuel pump cover.
3. Pinch of fuel suction and pressure hoses.
4. Disconnect electrical connections.
5. Remove fuel pump.
6. Reverse procedure to install. Install new fuel hose clamps.

SLK230

1998-2000

1. Relieve fuel pressure as described under "Precautions."
2. Pinch suction and delivery hoses using clamps tool Nos. 000 589 40 37 00, or equivalent.
3. Remove cap nuts.
4. Remove fuel pump.
5. Reverse procedure to install. **Torque** banjo bolt and cap nuts to 18 ft. lbs.

2001

1. Relieve fuel pressure as described under "Precautions."
2. Remove fuel pump cover.
3. Pinch suction and delivery hoses using clamps tool Nos. 000 589 40 37 00, or equivalent.
4. Remove clamps and disconnect electrical connectors.
5. Remove fuel pump.
6. Reverse procedure to install.

Turbochargers

NOTE: If Unsure Of The System Used On The Vehicle Being Serviced, Refer To The "Engine Systems Identification Chart." Further Assistance For The Proper Use Of Information Contained In This Section Can Also Be Found In The Front Of This Tabbed Section Under "How To Use This Manual."

NOTE: On Air Bag Equipped Models, Refer To "Air Bag System Precautions" Located In The Front Of This Manual For System Disarming & Arming Procedures.

INDEX

	Page No.
Description	14-24
Precautions	14-24
Air Bag Systems	14-24
Battery Ground Cable	14-24
System Service	14-24
Component Replacement	14-24
Charge Air Distribution Pipe	14-24
Charge Air Pipe	14-25
Intercooler	14-25
Turbocharger	14-24
Troubleshooting	14-24
Boost Pressure	14-24
Overload Protection	14-24

PRECAUTIONS

Air Bag Systems

Refer to "Air Bag System Precautions" in the front of this manual for system disarming and arming procedures.

Battery Ground Cable

Prior to service, disconnect battery ground cable and isolate as required.

DESCRIPTION

The exhaust gas turbocharger is installed between the exhaust manifold and pipe. It is connected to the engine oil circuit for lubrication and cooling.

Exhaust gases pass thought the exhaust manifold into the turbine housing and flow onto the turbine wheel. This energy rotates the turbine wheel, and via a shaft, the compressor wheel at the same speed. The maximum speed is approximately 135,000 RPM. Fresh air drawn into the compressor wheel is sent to the engine.

A boost pressure control valve limits boost pressure to 13.78 psi. An engine overload protection system is used to prevent engine failure.

TROUBLESHOOTING

Boost Pressure

1. Connect suitable pressure gauge with suitable Y fitting into boost pressure line between switchover valve and fuel injection pump aneroid compensator.
2. **If using dynamometer,** drive vehicle with shift lever in 3 position at full load and 4000 RPM.
3. **If road testing,** drive vehicle with shift lever in 2 or 3 position. Accelerate at full throttle and hold engine speed at 4000 RPM with parking brake. **Make test as short as possible.**
4. **In all tests,** if gauge reading is not 10.87–13.78 psi, proceed to next step.
5. Inspect overload protection system as outlined under "Overload Protection."
6. Inspect turbocharger for leaks at the following points:
   a. Between exhaust manifold and turbocharger.
   b. Between turbocharger fresh air discharge and intake manifold.
   c. Between intake and exhaust manifolds, and cylinder head.
7. Inspect boost pressure line between intake manifold and aneroid compensator for leaks.
8. Inspect hose between boost pressure control valve and turbocharger compressor housing for leaks, kinks and restrictions.
9. Inspect wastegate.

Overload Protection

1. Inspect boost pressure lines for leaks.
2. Remove switchover valve boost pressure line and connect suitable pressure tester to boost pressure line.
3. Turn preglow/starter switch to Off position and apply 11.60–13.05 psi. If pressure does not drop more than .725 psi in one minute, proceed to next step. If pressure drops more than .725 psi in one minute, inspect individual boost pressure lines, switchover valves and vacuum amplifier for leaks.
4. Turn preglow/starter switch to 2 position, remove overload protection switch connect and connect to ground. If there is an audible actuation, proceed to step 7. If there is no audible actuation, proceed to next step.
5. Remove switchover valve and measure voltage between plug terminal No. 2 and ground. If battery voltage is not present, inspect for open circuit. If measurement is battery voltage, proceed to next step.
6. Inspect wire from switchover valve terminal No. 1 to engine overload protection switch for continuity. If resistance is more than one ohm, repair open circuit in wiring. If resistance is less than one ohm, replace switchover valve.
7. Connect pressure switch connector. If valve switches, replace overload protection switch. If valve does not switch, system is functioning properly.

SYSTEM SERVICE

Component Replacement

TURBOCHARGER

1. Disconnect air intake and charged air hoses.
2. Remove exhaust pipe clamp.
3. Disconnect oil line from turbocharger and loosen at engine block, then turn pipe away.
4. Remove oil drain line.
5. Remove mounting nuts and turbocharger.
6. Reverse procedure install, noting the following:
   a. Install new oil drain line O-ring as required.
   b. **Torque** mounting nuts to 15–18 ft. lbs.

CHARGE AIR DISTRIBUTION PIPE

1. Remove charge air distribution pipe and cover intake ports.
2. Remove mounting bolts and cylinder head cover trim panel.
3. Remove EGR valve and O-ring.
4. Remove engine compartment panel, mounting bolt and EGR pipe.
5. Reverse procedure to install, noting following:
   a. Inspect and replace, O-ring as required.
   b. When installing cylinder No. 1 leak

fuel hose insure it is routed correct to return flow hose.

c. **Torque** mounting bolts to 15 ft. lbs.

CHARGE AIR PIPE

1. Remove charge air pipes and hoses.
2. Remove O-rings and hose clips.
3. Unplug, compress retaining clips and remove intake air temperature sensor.
4. Reverse procedure to install, use new O-ring and **torque** hose clips to 27 inch lbs.

INTERCOOLER

1. Remove front bumper.
2. Remove mounting bolts and intercooler, then the air scoop.
3. Reverse procedure to install thoroughly cleaning hose clip points. **Torque** hose clips to 27 inch lbs.

Superchargers

NOTE: If Unsure Of The System Used On The Vehicle Being Serviced, Refer To The "Engine Systems Identification Chart." Further Assistance For The Proper Use Of Information Contained In This Section Can Also Be Found In The Front Of This Tabbed Section Under "How To Use This Manual."

NOTE: On Air Bag Equipped Models, Refer To "Air Bag System Precautions" Located In The Front Of This Manual For System Disarming & Arming Procedures.

INDEX

	Page No.
Description	14-26
Precautions	14-26
Air Bag Systems	14-26
Battery Ground Cable	14-26
System Service	14-26
Adjustments	14-27
Electromagnetic Clutch	14-27
Oil Level	14-27
Component Replacement	14-26
Air Intake	14-27
Downstream Charge Air Duct	14-27
Electromagnetic Clutch	14-26
Intercooler	14-27
Pressure Connection	14-27
Supercharger	14-26

PRECAUTIONS

Air Bag Systems

Refer to "Air Bag System Precautions" in the front of this manual for system disarming and arming procedures.

Battery Ground Cable

Prior to service, disconnect battery ground cable and isolate as required.

DESCRIPTION

The supercharger increases engine output in the lower engine speed ranges. It compresses intake air. The air mass is determined downstream of the intercooler and corresponding quantity of fuel is metered to match the increased air mass.

Components of the supercharger system are the Hot Film Mass (HFM) air flow sensor, recirculated air flap actuator, electromagnetic clutch, supercharger, intake connection, pressure connection/compressor outlet, suction pipe, balancing pipe, intercooler and suction/charge pipe, **Fig. 1.**

The supercharger is a Rootes blower with two three-vane rotors offset 60.° Crankshaft-driven by an additional V-belt that is engaged by an electromagnetic clutch at the belt pulley of the supercharger. The two contra-rotating rotors are linked by two oil-lubricated gears. The rotors are coated with an epoxy rosin to resist oil and fuel from the crankcase breather.

Inflowing air is inducted at the suction side axially, the rotors compress the air by changing the volume of the working chambers and transport it to the radially delivery side. Suction pipe boost pressure is approximately 7.25 psi. The working chambers are by a 0.008 inch gap. The rotors rotate without making contact with each other of the housing.

B2/5 Hot film mass (HMF) air flow sensor
M16/7 Recirculated air flap actuator
Y2/1 Electromagnetic clutch
50 Supercharger
50/1 Intake connection
50/2 Pressure connection/compressor outlet
75 Suction pipe
76 Balancing pipe
110/2 Intercooler
110/6 Suction/charge pipe

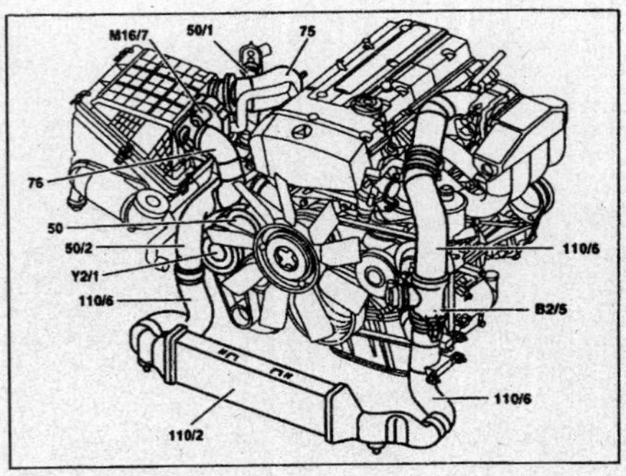

MB1059800011000X

Fig. 1 Supercharging function. SLK230

SYSTEM SERVICE

Component Replacement

SUPERCHARGER

1998-2000

1. Drain cooling system into suitable container.
2. Remove air cleaner.
3. Disconnect suction and pressure lines at supercharger. Seal supercharger openings.
4. **On C230 models,** pinch off secondary air injection valve suction connection and disconnect vacuum hose.
5. **On all models,** remove sensor block cover at front of cylinder head.
6. Disconnect electromagnetic clutch connector, **Fig. 2.**
7. Remove water pump to radiator hose.
8. Remove shroud and fan.
9. Remove supercharger drive belt.
10. **On SLK230 models,** remove pressure connection at compressor.
11. **On all models,** remove mounting bolts and supercharger compressor.
12. Reverse procedure to install, noting the following:
    a. Install bottom mounting bolt before install supercharger.
    b. **Torque** mounting bolts to 15 ft. lbs.

2001

1. Remove inlet and pressure connections.
2. Remove drive belt.
3. Remove mounting bolts and supercharger.
4. Reverse procedure to install.

ELECTROMAGNETIC CLUTCH

1. Remove supercharger as outlined under "Supercharger."
2. Clamp supercharger in vice by front, bottom attachment eye using suitable protective jaw.
3. Apply 12 volts to magnetic clutch connector, loop drive belt around pulley, hold tight and remove center mounting bolt.
4. Disconnect voltage and remove clutch hub. If hub is tight, press it off with M8 bolt.
5. Inspect drive shaft and supercharger

housing for dropped shims and foreign objects.
6. Make up shims to approximately 0.0354 inch, insert suitable Phillips screwdriver and guide shims into clutch hub.
7. Fit hub onto drive shaft with old center bolt and apply 12 volts to magnetic clutch connector.
8. Check gap at three rivets with suitable feeler gauge and note average. If gap is not 0.0098–0.0157 inch, adjust by adding or remove shims.
9. Remove tapered locking ring and bearing body with belt pulley, then the cable guide securing plate.
10. Remove coil body.
11. Reverse procedure to install, noting the following:
    a. **Torque** coil body mounting bolts to 35 inch lbs.
    b. Ensure cables are not pinched.
    c. Install tapered locking ring with chamfer up.
    d. Use new center bolt and **torque** to 13 ft. lbs.
    e. Run clutch in by briefly blipping throttle from idle to approximately 3000 RPM at least 20 times.
    f. Final inspection is possible, only after 100–120 engagements.

INTERCOOLER

1998–2000

1. Remove front bumper and radiator.
2. Remove mounting bolts and place air conditioning condenser aside. **Do not kink pipes.**
3. Remove air cleaner.
4. Remove charge air duct as outlined under "Downstream Charge Air Duct."
5. Remove intercooler.
6. Reverse procedure to install, noting the following:
    a. Thoroughly clean hose clip connection points.
    b. **Torque** hose clips to 27 inch lbs.
    c. Ensure air scoop properly engages charge air cooler.

2001

1. Remove radiator grille and front bumper.
2. Remove air scoop.
3. Remove intercooler.
4. Reverse procedure to install.

DOWNSTREAM CHARGE AIR DUCT

1. Disconnect hot film mass air flow sensor.
2. Remove charge air duct.

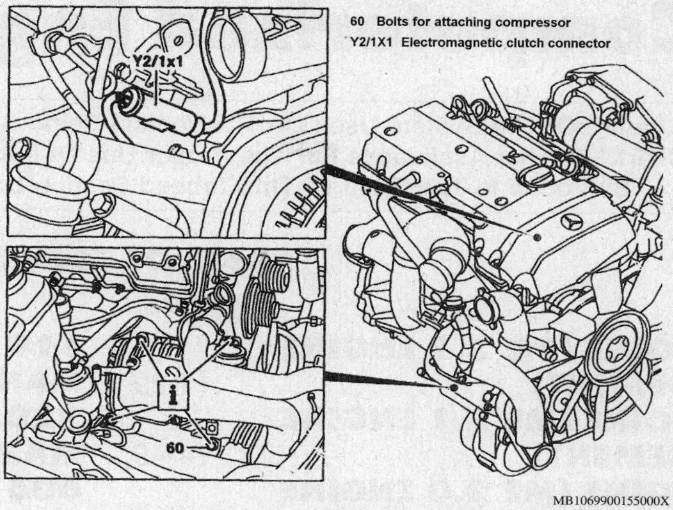

Fig. 2 Supercharger replacement. 1998–2000

3. Reverse procedure to install.

AIR INTAKE

1. Disconnect suction and pressure pipes at supercharger and seal openings.
2. Remove air cleaner.
3. Remove air intake and seal.
4. Reverse procedure to install. **Torque** air intake mounting bolts to 18 ft. lbs. and air intake/pressure connection to 11 ft. lbs.

PRESSURE CONNECTION

1. Disconnect suction and pressure pipes at supercharger and seal openings.
2. Remove air cleaner.
3. Disconnect charge air cooler hose at pressure connection and seal hose.
4. Remove pressure connection.
5. Reverse procedure to install with new gasket. **Torque** pressure connection mounting bolts to 18 ft. lbs. and air intake/pressure connection to 11 ft. lbs.

Adjustments

ELECTROMAGNETIC CLUTCH

1. Remove fan and fan shroud, then the sensor block cover.
2. Disconnect electromagnetic clutch connector.
3. Mark clutch hub relative to supercharger housing for assembly.
4. Clamp hinged support tight at sensor block on cylinder head front and mount dial gauge with preload on clutch hub rivet.
5. Apply 12 volts from terminal block X12/3 to magnetic clutch connector using suitable cable. Read and record measurement.
6. Rotate engine at crankshaft and repeat previous step at other two rivets. Add three readings, divide by three and record this average.
7. Remove center mounting bolt by applying voltage to magnetic clutch and tensioning drive bolt by hand.
8. Insert Allen key or drill bit through hub hole to prevent shims from dropping out and remove clutch hub. If hub is tight, press it off with M8 bolt.
9. Inspect drive shaft and supercharger housing for dropped shims and foreign objects.
10. Measure shims with caliper gauge and calculate total thickness. If gap is not 0.0098–0.0157 inch, adjust by adding or removing shims.
11. Reverse procedure to install. **Torque** clutch hub center bolt to 13 ft. lbs. and fan clutch mounting to 30 ft. lbs.

OIL LEVEL

1. Disconnect suction and compressor pipe, then seal openings.
2. Remove air cleaner, then the oil filter and inspection plug.
3. Oil level must not be below bottom edge of threaded hole.
4. Adjust oil level using compressor oil No. 000-989-62-01, or equivalent.
5. Reverse procedure to install. **Torque** plug to 89 inch lbs.

Computerized Engine Controls

NOTE: If Unsure Of The System Used On The Vehicle Being Serviced, Refer To The "Engine Systems Identification Chart." Further Assistance For The Proper Use Of Information Contained In This Section Can Also Be Found In The Front Of This Tabbed Section Under "How To Use This Manual."

TABLE OF CONTENTS

	Page No.
104 ENGINE (ME 2.1 ENGINE MANAGEMENT)	14-29
111 ENGINE (ME 2.1 ENGINE MANAGEMENT)	14-49
112 ENGINE (ME 2.0 ENGINE MANAGEMENT)	14-80
113 ENGINE (ME 2.0 ENGINE MANAGEMENT)	14-111
119 ENGINE (ME 1.0 ENGINE MANAGEMENT)	14-138
120 ENGINE (ME 1.0 ENGINE MANAGEMENT)	14-164
606 DIESEL ENGINE	14-207

104 Engine (ME 2.1 Engine Management)

NOTE: On Air Bag Equipped Models, Refer To "Air Bag System Precautions" Located In The Front Of This Manual For System Disarming & Arming Procedures.

NOTE: Refer To "Computer Relearn Procedures" Located In The Front Of This Manual When Battery Power To The Computer Has Been Interrupted.

NOTE: "Electrical Symbol Identification" Located In Front Of This Manual May Be Used As An Aid When Using Wiring Diagrams Found In This Section.

NOTE: Prior To Performing Any Service Listed In This Section Consult Technical Service Bulletin Section For Related Information.

INDEX

	Page No.
Description	14-31
Diagnosis & Testing	14-31
Accessing Diagnostic Trouble Codes	14-31
Generic Scan Tool	14-31
Hand-Held Tester	14-31
Clearing Diagnostic Trouble Codes	14-32
Component Tests	14-32
Fuel Injector	14-32
Fuel Pump	14-32
Components Locations	14-31
Connector Terminal Identification	14-31
Diagnostic Tests	14-31
Diagnostic Trouble Code Interpretation	14-31
Symbol Explanation	14-31
Symptom Related Diagnosis	14-31
Wiring Diagrams	14-31
Diagnostic Chart Index	14-40
Precautions	14-30
Air Bag Systems	14-30
Battery Ground Cable	14-30
Drive Authorization System (DAS)	14-30
ECM Recognition	14-30
ECM Self-Adaptation	14-30
ESP/ASR/ETS/ABS Control Modules	14-31
Ignition System	14-30
Sensor & Fuel Injector Specifications	14-30
System Service	14-47
Adjustments	14-48
Camshaft Position (CMP) Sensor	14-48
Throttle Control Cable	14-48
Component Replacement	14-47
Camshaft Position (CMP) Sensor	14-48
Crankshaft Position (CKP) Sensor	14-47
Diaphragm Pressure Regulator	14-47
Fuel Injectors	14-47
Fuel Rail	14-47
Hot Film Air Mass (HFM) Sensor	14-47
Idle Speed Control (ISC) Actuator	14-48
Knock Sensor	14-48
Oxygen Sensor	14-47
Throttle Control Cable	14-48

SENSOR & FUEL INJECTOR SPECIFICATIONS

Temperature, °F	Resistance, Ohms①	Voltage①
ADJUSTABLE CAMSHAFT TIMING SOLENOID		
158	7–12	—
CAMSHAFT POSITION SENSOR		
—	900–1600	—
CRANKSHAFT POSITION (CKP) SENSOR		
—	700–1400	—
ENGINE COOLANT TEMPERATURE (ECT) SENSOR		
68	3090	3.4
86	2000	2.9
104	1330	2.4
122	900	1.9
140	630	1.5
158	440	1.2
176	320	.9
194	230	.7
212	170	.5
FUEL INJECTOR		
—	14–17	—
INTAKE AIR TEMPERATURE (IAT) SENSOR		
50	3600	3.1
68	2420	2.7
104	1660	2.2
122	1170	1.8
140	850	1.4
158	600	1.1
MASS AIR FLOW (MAF) SENSOR		
158	—	0.9–1.1

① — Tolerance ± 5%.

PRECAUTIONS

Air Bag Systems

Refer to "Air Bag System Precautions" in the front of this manual for system disarming and arming procedures.

Battery Ground Cable

Prior to service, disconnect battery ground cable and isolate as required.

Ignition System

1. Both control module coupling must be disconnected or connected with ignition switch in the Off position.
2. Do not short circuit ignition coils terminal No. 1.
3. Do not operate the ignition system at starting speed unless the ignition cables are fully connected.
4. Do not conduct test at starting speed or when engine is running.
5. High output side of ignition system must always carry at least two ohms resistance (spark plug connected).
6. Do not load ignition coil with more than 28,000 volts.
7. Ignition coil iron cores must always be connected to ground. **Use caution, coil cores can be charged with up to 400 volts. Do not work on this system if you have a pacemaker.**
8. Ensure engine and ignition switch are in Off position when connecting and disconnecting ignition coil.
9. When working at start speeds during test such as compression check, switch ignition to off position and disconnect control module connector No. 2.

ECM Self-Adaptation

After repair work, the Engine Control Module (ECM) will automatically adapt itself after the vehicle has made approximately 10 trips. A trip includes a vehicle speed of more than 2.5 mph, engine speed of more than 700 RPM and engine shutoff of more than 30 seconds.

However, after fixing a malfunction or installation of a test ECM, the self-adaptation function must be reset as outlined under "Computer Relearn" at the front of this manual.

ECM Recognition

The ECM must be coded for vehicle model, catalytic converter, transmission, cruise control, acceleration slip regulation (ASR), electronic traction system (ETS) and country version with the Hand-Held Tester.

Before replacing the ECM, read and store existing code numbers with the Hand-Held Tester. When the new ECM is installed, enter the stored code numbers from the Hand-Held Tester. If code numbers cannot be read, the corresponding codes number must be obtained from Mercedes-Benz spare parts microfiche and manually entered with a Hand-Held Tester.

Drive Authorization System (DAS)

The Drive Authorization System (DAS) is activated by the electronic key. The ECM and RCL control module are permanently locked together by an identification code. This code cannot be erased. Trial installation of an ECM or RCL control module from another vehicle is not possible. After 40 starts, a new ECM cannot be used in any other vehicle. The code number and VIN must be entered into the ECM with a Hand-Held Tester.

ESP/ASR/ETS/ABS Control Modules

The Electronic Stability Program (ESP), Acceleration Slip Regulation (ASR), Electronic Traction System (ETS) and/or Anti-lock Brake System (ABS) control modules must not be disconnected. The Engine Control Module (ECM) and Transmission Control Module (TCM) rely on those control modules for Vehicle Speed Sensor (VSS) information. To disable brake and engine regulation of those modules, proceed as follows:

1. Turn ignition switch to Off position.
2. Connect Hand-Held Tester adapter to Data Link Connector (DLC).
3. Jump sockets No. 1 and 6.
4. Start engine. MIL must light.
5. If Hand-Held Tester is available, disconnect VSS front axle connector.
6. When testing is complete, connect VSS and erase Diagnostic Trouble Codes with Hand-Held Tester.

DESCRIPTION

The Motor Electronics (ME) sequential multi-port fuel injection/ignition system is a further development of the LH-Sequential multi-port Fuel Injection System (LH-SFI) and Distributor Ignition System (DI), and of the HFM-SFI systems respectively.

The fuel is injected by electromagnetic fuel injection valves activated sequentially by the ME-SFI control module. The principal measured variable for determining the fuel metering is the engine air mass detected by the hot film mass air flow sensor. Idle speed control is carried out by the EA/CC/ISC actuator operated by the ME-SFI control module.

The high voltage is distributed without any moving parts directly by the ignition coils to the spark plugs. The knock sensor system function is integrated in the ME-SFI control module.

The intake camshaft is adjusted map-controlled by the HFM-SFI control module in order to boost torque and output in the mid/upper engine speed/load range.

The shift points of the automatic transmission are retarded in line with temperature, vehicle speed and time in order to more rapidly heat up the catalytic converter to operating temperature.

Depending on year, equipment and model, RCL, ME-SFI, ETC, ETS/SPS, ESP/SPS, ASR/SPS control modules, instrument cluster and electronic ignition switch are interlinked by the CAN.

DIAGNOSIS & TESTING

Symbol Explanation

Refer to **Figs. 1 through 3** for explanations of symbols, connections and steps included in the charts.

Description	Symbol
ABS adaptor	
Socket box tester 35-pole	
Socket box tester 126-pole	
Signal generator	
Hand-held tester (HHT)	
Impulse counter scan tool	
On-off ratio tester	
Pressure gauge	
Digital multimeter	
Resistance substitution unit	
Bridge	
DANGER! High Voltage	ϟ
Brake pad wear indicator	(◯)

Description	Symbol
Pin	—
Socket	>—
Battery	
DC generator	(G)
DC motor	(M)
Capacitor	
Coil	
Resistance	
Ground	
Systems check O.K.	√
Fault	F
Resistance too high	> Ω
Resistance too low	< Ω
Short circuit to ground	⊓ −

Description	Symbol
Short circuit to positive	⊓ +
Open circuit	−//−
Short circuit	⊓
Direct current measured with multimeter	(A)
Alternating current measured w/multimeter	(A)
Direct voltage measured w/multimeter	(V)
Alternating voltage measured w/multimeter	(V)
Resistance measured with multimeter	(Ω)
Signal generator Square wave form	
Signal generator Sine form	
Oscilloscope	
Adaptor wire with LED	

MB8019600011000X

Fig. 1 Test equipment & component symbols explanation

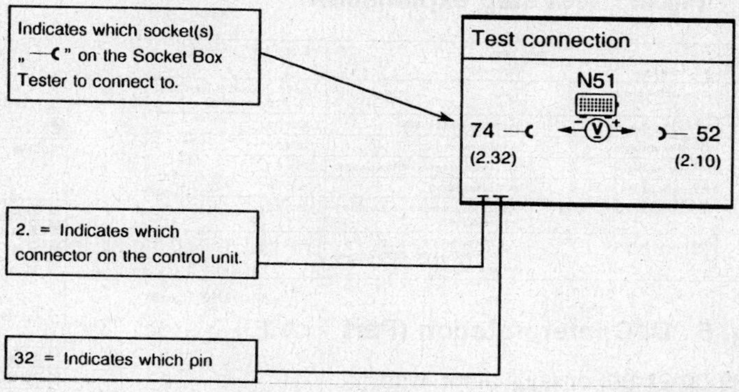

MB8019600006000X

Fig. 2 Test connections explanation

Accessing Diagnostic Trouble Codes

GENERIC SCAN TOOL

Follow tool manufacturers instructions and connect suitably programmed scan tool to generic scan tool connection X11/22.

HAND-HELD TESTER

1. Turn ignition switch to Off position.
2. Attach test cable tool No. 965 589 00 40 00, or equivalent, to Hand-Held Tester tool No. 965 589 00 01 00, or equivalent.
3. Connect cable to Data Link Connector (DLC), **Fig. 4**.
4. Turn multiplexer cable locking ring completely to left detent stop.
5. Attach multiplexer cable to data link connector via locking pins.
6. To lock multiplexer cable to connector, turn locking ring to the right.
7. Follow tool manufacturer's instructions.

Diagnostic Trouble Code Interpretation

Refer to **Fig. 5** for DTC interpretation.

Black square items are emission related and may activate MIL during test cycle.

Symptom Related Diagnosis

Refer to **Fig. 6** for symptom related diagnosis.

Components Locations

Refer to **Figs. 7 and 8** for component locations.

Wiring Diagrams

Refer to **Fig. 9** for wiring diagrams.

Connector Terminal Identification

Refer to **Fig. 10** for engine control module connector terminal identification.

Diagnostic Tests

1. Turn ignition switch to Off position.
2. Connect 126-pole socket box tool No.

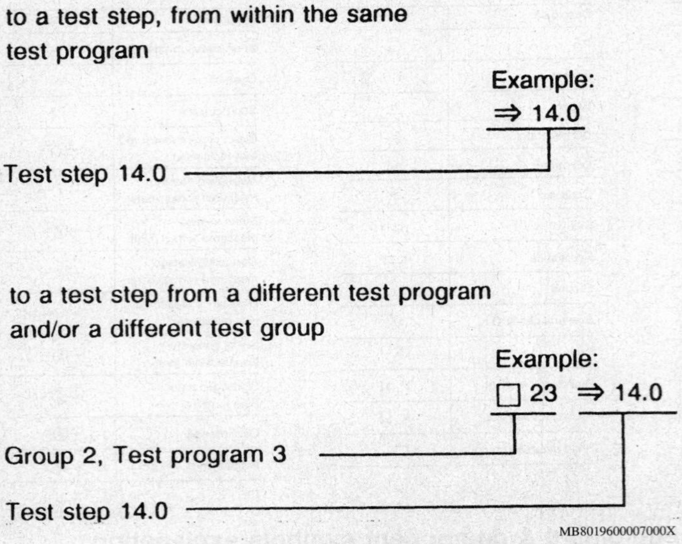

Fig. 3 Test step explanation

DTC	Possible cause		Test step/Remedy
	SAE nomenclature	Explanation	
-	No malfunction in system		In case of complaint, perform □ 23, 24, 25 or 26 in its entirety
P0 100 ■	MAF circuit malfunction	Hot film MAF sensor (B2/5)	□ 23⇒ 5.0
P0 105 ■	MAP circuit malfunction	Pressure sensor (B28)	□ 23⇒ 7.0
P0 110 ■	IAT circuit malfunction	IAT sensor (in Hot film MAF sensor B2/5)	□ 23⇒ 6.0
P0 115 ■	ECT circuit malfunction	ECT sensor (B11/4)	□ 23⇒ 9.0
P0 120	Throttle position circuit malfunction	Actual value potentiometer in EA/CC/ISC actuator (M16/1)	□ 25⇒ 3.0
P0 130 ■	O2S 1 circuit malfunction	A. O2S 1 (before TWC) (G3/2) B. O2S 1 (before TWC) (G3/2) voltage increase insufficient	□ 23⇒ 11.0

MB1029800512010X

Fig. 5 DTC interpretation (Part 1 of 10)

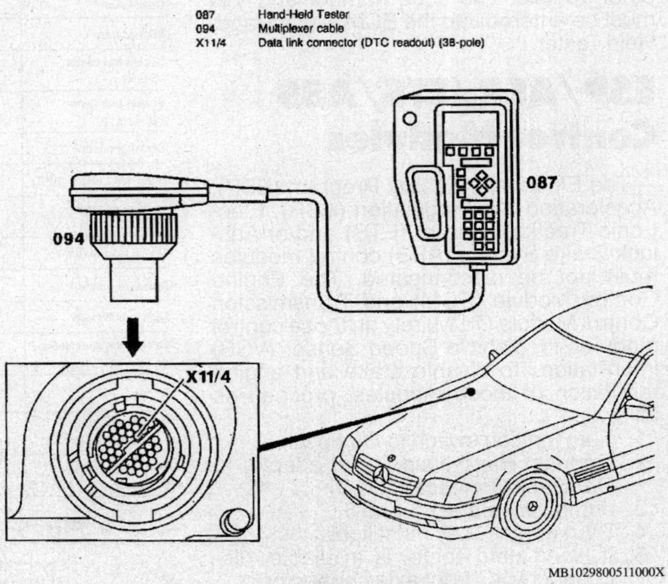

Fig. 4 DLC tool connection

DTC	Possible cause		Test step/Remedy 1)
	SAE nomenclature	Explanation	
P0 133 ■	O2S 1 circuit slow response	A O2S 1 (before TWC) (G3/2), ageing correction value exceeded B O2S 1 (before TWC) (G3/2), ageing time period too long	□ 23⇒ 11.0
P0 135 ■	O2S 1 heater circuit malfunction	O2S 1 heater (before TWC) (G3/2)	□ 23 ⇒ 12.0
P0 136 ■	O2S 2 circuit malfunction	O2S 2 (after TWC) (G3/1)	□ 23 ⇒ 13.0
P0 141 ■	O2S 2 heater circuit malfunction	Right O2S 2 heater (after TWC) (G3/1)	□ 23⇒ 14.0
P0 170 ■	Fuel trim malfunction	A Self adaptation of fuel mixture "partial load" at limit from engine control module (N3/10). B Self adaptation of fuel mixture "CTP" at limit from engine control module (N3/10).	Intake air leak, injectors, diaphragm pressure regulator, engine wear.
P0 201 ■	Injector circuit malfunction - cyl. 1	Injector (Y62y1) – cylinder 1	□ 23⇒ 15.0
P0 202 ■	Injector circuit malfunction - cyl. 2	Injector (Y62y2) – cylinder 2	□ 23⇒ 16.0
P0 203 ■	Injector circuit malfunction - cyl. 3	Injector (Y62y3) – cylinder 3	□ 23 ⇒ 17.0
P0 204 ■	Injector circuit malfunction - cyl. 4	Injector (Y62y4) – cylinder 4	□ 23 ⇒ 18.0
P0 205 ■	Injector circuit malfunction - cyl. 5	Injector (Y62y5) – cylinder 5	□ 23 ⇒ 19.0
P0 206 ■	Injector circuit malfunction - cyl. 6	Injector (Y62y6) – cylinder 6	□ 23 ⇒ 20.0

MB1029800512020X

Fig. 5 DTC interpretation (Part 2 of 10)

129 589 00 21 00, or equivalent, with contact module tool No. 140 589 46 63 00, or equivalent, to engine control module, **Fig. 11.**

3. Connect interior harness connector to test cable connection No. 1 and engine harness connector to test cable connection No. 2.
4. Conduct tests as directed using suitable multimeter.
5. Conduct test as directed in **Figs. 12 through 51** using suitable digital multimeter.

Clearing Diagnostic Trouble Codes

The Diagnostic Trouble Code (DTC) memory is cleared when the vehicle battery is disconnected.

When an component has been repaired or replaced, the related DTC will be cleared. After three trips the CHECK ENGINE Malfunction Indicator Lamp (MIL) will go out and after 40 warm-up periods the DTC is automatically erased. A trip includes engine running for more than 20 minutes, engine oil temperature of more than 19°F, engine speed of more than 700 RPM and emission related logic chain functions. A warm-up period includes an engine coolant temperature at start-up of less than 95°F and increasing to more than 176°F.

To erase DTCs with a Hand-Held Tester, follow the tool manufacturer's instructions.

Component Tests

FUEL PUMP

1. Connect suitable pressure gauge to test connection, **Fig. 52.**
2. Conduct tests as directed in **Fig. 53.**
3. Connect 126-pole socket box tool No. 129 589 00 21 00, or equivalent, to Engine Control Module (ECM) with test cable tool No. 210 589 08 63 00, or equivalent, **Fig. 54.**
4. Conduct tests as directed, **Fig. 55.**
5. Release fuel pressure and allow fuel to drain into suitable measuring cup.

FUEL INJECTOR

1. Connect 126-pole socket box tool No. 129 589 00 21 00, or equivalent, to Engine Control Module (ECM) with test cable tool No. 140 589 46 63 00, or equivalent, **Fig. 56.**
2. Disconnect injector connectors, then remove fuel rail with injectors. **Do not disconnect fuel feed and return lines.**
3. Connect self-made harness to one injector after another, hold over suitable measuring glass and test as directed, **Fig. 57.**

DTC	Possible cause		Test step/Remedy
	SAE nomenclature	Explanation	
P0 300 ■	Random misfire detected	A Random misfire B Random misfire, TWC damaging	☐ 24 ⇒ 8.0 – 10.0 ☐ 24 ⇒ 11.0 ☐ 36 ⇒ 1.0 – 2.0 Compression pressure
P0 301 ■	Cylinder 1 misfire detected	A Cylinder 1 misfire B Cylinder 1 misfire, TWC damaging	☐ 24 ⇒ 10.0 ☐ 24 ⇒ 11.0 ☐ 36 ⇒ 1.0 – 2.0 Compression pressure
P0 302 ■	Cylinder 2 misfire detected	A Cylinder 2 misfire B Cylinder 2 misfire, TWC damaging	☐ 24 ⇒ 8.0 ☐ 24 ⇒ 11.0 ☐ 36 ⇒ 1.0 – 2.0 Compression pressure
P0 303 ■	Cylinder 3 misfire detected	A Cylinder 3 misfire B Cylinder 3 misfire, TWC damaging	☐ 24 ⇒ 9.0 ☐ 24 ⇒ 11.0 ☐ 36 ⇒ 1.0 – 2.0 Compression pressure
P0 304 ■	Cylinder 4 misfire detected	A Cylinder 4 misfire B Cylinder 4 misfire, TWC damaging	☐ 24 ⇒ 9.0 ☐ 24 ⇒ 11.0 ☐ 36 ⇒ 1.0 – 2.0 Compression pressure

MB102980051203OX

Fig. 5 DTC interpretation (Part 3 of 10)

DTC	Possible cause		Test step/Remedy
	SAE nomenclature	Explanation	
P0 305 ■	Cylinder 5 misfire detected	A Cylinder 5 misfire B Cylinder 5 misfire, TWC damaging	☐ 24 ⇒ 8.0 ☐ 24 ⇒ 11.0 ☐ 36 ⇒ 1.0 – 2.0 Compression pressure
P0 306 ■	Cylinder 6 misfire detected	A Cylinder 6 misfire B Cylinder 6 misfire, TWC damaging	☐ 24 ⇒ 10.0 ☐ 24 ⇒ 11.0 ☐ 36 ⇒ 1.0 – 2.0 Compression pressure
P0 325 ■	KS 1 circuit malfunction	Front KS 1 (A16)	Wiring, connector, A16
P0 330 ■	KS 2 circuit malfunction	Rear KS 2 (A16)	Wiring, connector, A16
P0 335 ■	CKP sensor circuit malfunction	CKP sensor (L5)	☐ 24 ⇒ 6.0
P0 341 ■	CMP sensor circuit range/performance	Camshaft Hall-effect sensor (B6/1)	☐ 24 ⇒ 7.0
P0 410 ■ Only (USA)	Air injection system malfunction	AIR system malfunction (logic chain)	☐ 23 ⇒ 23.0
P0 422 ■	TWC efficiency below threshold	TWC efficiency below threshold	Replace TWC
P0 440 ■ Only (USA) **Models 140/210 Model 129 as of 09/97**	EVAP system malfunction	EVAP malfunction (logic chain)	☐ 23 ⇒ 27.0 – 29.0

MB102980051204OX

Fig. 5 DTC interpretation (Part 4 of 10)

DTC	Possible cause		Test step/Remedy
	SAE nomenclature	Explanation	
P0 441 ■	EVAP system incorrect purge flow	EVAP not functioning	☐ 23 ⇒ 27.0 – 28.0
P0 442 ■ Only (USA) **Mod. 140/210 Mod. 129 as of 09/97**	EVAP system leak detected (small leak)	EVAP system, small leak	☐ 23 ⇒ 29.0
P0 443 ■	EVAP system purge control valve circuit malfunction	Purge control valve (Y58/1)	☐ 23 ⇒ 27.0
P0 446 ■ Only (USA) **Mod. 140/210 Mod. 129 as of 09/97**	EVAP system vent control malfunction	A. Activated charcoal canister shut-off valve (Y58/4) B. End stage activated charcoal canister shut-off valve (Y58/4)	☐ 23 ⇒ 30.0
P0 450 ■ Only (USA) **Mod. 140/210 Mod. 129 as of 09/97**	EVAP system pressure sensor malfunction	A. Fuel tank pressure sensor (B4/3) electrical fault B. Fuel tank pressure sensor (B4/3) electrical fluctuations	☐ 23 ⇒ 31.0 Charcoal canister plugged.
Mod. 129 up to 08/97 Mod. 202		Purge monitoring pressure sensor (B4/4)	☐ 23 ⇒ 32.0

MB102980051205OX

Fig. 5 DTC interpretation (Part 5 of 10)

DTC	Possible cause		Test step/Remedy [1]
	SAE nomenclature	Explanation	
P0 455 ■ Only (USA) **Mod. 140/210 Mod. 129 as of 09/97**	EVAP system leak detected (large leak)	EVAP system, large leak Fuel tank pressure sensor (B4/3)	☐ 23 ⇒ 29.0 ☐ 23 ⇒ 31.0
P0 460	Fuel level sensor circuit low input	Fuel tank level too low	Fill fuel tank
P0 500	VSS sensor malfunction	A VSS left front B VSS left rear	Test ASR, ETS
P0 507	ISC rpm higher than expected	Idle control system	☐ 25 ⇒ 1.0 – 3.0
P0 560	System voltage malfunction	Voltage supply to engine control module (N3/10)	☐ 23 ⇒ 1.0 – 2.0
P0 565	Cruise control switch	CC switch (S40)	☐ 26 ⇒ 1.0
P0 600	Serial communication link malfunction	CAN bus from ESP/SPS control module (N47-5)	Test ESP
P0 604	Internal control module random Access memory (RAM) error	Engine control module (N3/10)	(N3/10)
P0 605	Internal control module read only memory (ROM) error	Engine control module (N3/10)	(N3/10)
P0 606	PCM processor fault	Engine control module (N3/10)	(N3/10)

MB102980051206OX

Fig. 5 DTC interpretation (Part 6 of 10)

DTC	Possible cause		Test step/Remedy [1]
	SAE nomenclature	Explanation	
P0 700 ■	Transmission control system malfunction	Read DTC memory of transmission control module	Test ETC,
P0 702 ■	Transmission control system electrical	Read DTC memory of transmission control module	Test ETC,
P0 715 ■	Input/turbine speed sensor circuit malfunction	Read DTC memory of transmission control module	Test ETC,
P0 720 ■	Output speed sensor circuit malfunction	Read DTC memory of transmission control module	Test ETC,
P0 730 ■	Incorrect gear ratio	Read DTC memory of transmission control module	Test ETC,
P0 740 ■	Torque converter clutch circuit malfunction	Read DTC memory of transmission control module	Test ETC,
P0 743 ■	Torque converter clutch circuit electrical	Read DTC memory of transmission control module	Test ETC,
P0 748 ■	Pressure control solenoid electrical	Read DTC memory of transmission control module	Test ETC,
P0 753 ■	Shift solenoid A electrical	Read DTC memory of transmission control module	Test ETC,
P0 758 ■	Shift solenoid B electrical	Read DTC memory of transmission control module	Test ETC,

MB102980051207OX

Fig. 5 DTC interpretation (Part 7 of 10)

DTC	Possible cause		Test step/Remedy [1]
	SAE nomenclature	Explanation	
P0 763 ■	Shift solenoid C electrical	Read DTC memory of transmission control module	Test ETC,
P0 802	Resonance intake manifold switchover valve	Resonance intake manifold switchover valve (Y22/6)	☐ 23 ⇒ 24.0
P0 809	Angle deviation between camshaft and crankshaft	Angle deviation between camshaft and crankshaft	Check basic adjustment of camshaft
P0 811	CAN from electronic ignition lock	CAN from electronic ignition lock	☐ 23 ⇒ 33.0
P1 163	Oil level switch	Oil level switch (S43)	☐ 23 ⇒ 35.0
P1 182 **Model 202 only**	Starter relay	Starter relay module in passenger-side fuse and relay module box (K40/4)	☐ 23 ⇒ 4.0
P1 186	Fuel safety shut-off recognized	EA/CC/ISC actuator (M16/1)	☐ 25 ⇒ 3.0 – 4.0, EA/CC/ISC actuator (M16/1) sticks or jammed, Check intake system for residue.
P1 386 ■	Knock sensor control from ECM (N3/10) at end stop	Knock sensor regulation from engine control module (N3/10) at end stop	1. Increased knock tendency due to bad fuel, carbon in combustion chamber or mechanical damage. 2. Engine control module (N3/10)

MB102980051208OX

Fig. 5 DTC interpretation (Part 8 of 10)

DTC	Possible cause		Test step/Remedy [1]
	SAE nomenclature	Explanation	
P1 420 ■ Only (USA)	AIR pump switchover valve	AIR pump switchover valve (Y32)	☐ 23 ⇒ 22.0
P1 453 ■ Only (USA)	AIR relay module	AIR relay module (K17), relay module (K40) or passenger-side fuse and relay module box (K40/4)	☐ 23 ⇒ 21.0
P1 491		Refrigerant pressure in A/C system too high	Check automatic A/C system
P1 519 ■	Adjustable camshaft timing solenoid	Adjustable camshaft timing solenoid (Y49) (logic chain)	☐ 23 ⇒ 26.0
P1 525 ■	Adjustable camshaft timing solenoid	Adjustable camshaft timing solenoid (Y49)	☐ 23 ⇒ 25.0
P1 542	Pedal value sensor	Pedal value sensor (B37)	☐ 26 ⇒ 1.0 – 2.0
P1 570	CAN signal from DAS control module to engine control module	A. Start attempted with "locked" DAS B. CAN signal from DAS control module (N54/1) to engine control module (N3/10) interrupted. C. Engine control module (ME-SFI) and DAS control module are not compatible.	User error Check correct operation of DAS ☐ 23 ⇒ 33.0, Check control modules and part no.

MB102980051209OX

Fig. 5 DTC interpretation (Part 9 of 10)

DTC	Possible cause		Test step/Remedy [1]
	SAE nomenclature	Explanation	
P1 580 ■	EA/CC/ISC actuator	EA/CC/ISC actuator (M16/1)	☐ 25 ⇒ 3.0 – 4.0
P1 584	Stop lamp switch	Stop lamp switch (S9/1)	Test ETS, ASR
P1 605		Poor road/traction condition recognition signal (via comparison of VSS rpm signals)	Test ASR/ESP
P1 642		Engine control module incorrectly coded (coded for MT, vehicle has AT)	Check version coding and correct.
P1 643		Engine control module incorrectly coded (coded for MT, vehicle has AT) or No CAN transmission from transmission control module (N15/3)	Check version coding and correct.
P1 644		Transmission version can not be checked due to low voltage at transmission control module (N15/3)	Test ETC,
P1 747 ■	CAN signal from ETC	A. CAN failure: Transmission protection malfunction from transmission control module (N15/3) B. CAN failure: Instrument cluster	Test ETC, Test instrument cluster (A1),

MB102980051210OX

Fig. 5 DTC interpretation (Part 10 of 10)

Complaint/Problem	Possible cause	Test step/Remedy 1)	Actual value Engine test Menu item
Engine starts and accelerates poorly when cold	Injector (Y62) activation and injection duration. Hot film MAF sensor (B2/5). ECT sensor (B11/4). Ignition voltage too low. Intake air leak.	□ 23 ⇒ 15.0 – 20.0 □ 23 ⇒ 5.0 □ 23 ⇒ 9.0 □ 24 ⇒ 11.0 Remedy leak.	2/7 1/7 3/7 – –
Engine does not start	Voltage supply is missing. Malfunction of drive authorization system (DAS) . Fuel pumps defective. No compression, oil pressure too high. Ignition voltage too low.	□ 23 ⇒ 1.0 – 2.0 □ 23 ⇒ 33.0 □ 34 ⇒ 2.0 check compression and oil pressure. □ 24 ⇒ 11.0	– DAS 1/1 – – –
Engine has uneven idle	Camshaft timing. Injector (Y62) activation and injection duration. Intake air leak.	□ 23 ⇒ 25.0 – 26.0 □ 23 ⇒ 15.0 – 20.0 Remedy leak.	2/7 2/7 –
Engine has insufficient output	TWC flow restricted. O2S 1 (G3/2) (before TWC). ECT sensor (B11/4). Hot film MAF sensor (B2/5). Camshaft timing.	Check exhaust back pressure, □ 23 ⇒ 11.0 – 12.0 □ 23 ⇒ 9.0 □ 23 ⇒ 5.0 □ 23 ⇒ 25.0 – 26.0	– 5/7 3/7 1/7 2/7

MB1029800513010X

Fig. 6 Symptom related diagnosis (Part 1 of 2)

Complaint/Problem	Possible cause	Test step/Remedy	Actual value Engine test Menu item
Engine runs unevenly (shakes)	Injector (Y62) activation and injection duration. Injector leaking, spray pattern. O2S 1 (G3/2) (before TWC). Ignition voltage too low. Compression on one or more cylinders too low. Intake air leak.	□ 23 ⇒ 15.0 – 20.0 □ 36 ⇒ 1.0 □ 23 ⇒ 11.0 – 12.0 □ 24 ⇒ 11.0 Check compression. Remedy leak.	2/7 – 5/7 – – –
Engine runs unevenly (misfiring)	Ignition voltage too low. Hot film MAF sensor (B2/5).	□ 24 ⇒ 11.0 □ 23 ⇒ 5.0	– 1/7
Engine surges after cold start	Intake air leak.	Remedy leak.	–
Transition failure during warm-up	ECT sensor (B11/4). Hot film MAF sensor (B2/5). Intake air leak.	□ 23 ⇒ 9.0 □ 23 ⇒ 5.0 Remedy leak.	3/7 1/7 –
Transition failure when warm or increased fuel consumption	O2S 1 (G3/2) (before TWC). Purge control valve (Y58/1) stuck in open position.	□ 23 ⇒ 11.0 – 12.0 □ 23 ⇒ 27.0 – 28.0	5/7 3/7
Engine vibrates	Hot film MAF sensor (B2/5). Ignition voltage too low. O2S 1 (G3/2) (before TWC).	□ 23 ⇒ 5.0 □ 24 ⇒ 11.0 □ 23 ⇒ 11.0 – 12.0	1/7 – 5/7
EA is in "limp-home" mode	Nominal value potentiometer in pedal value sensor (B37). EA/CC/ISC actuator actual value potentiometer.	□ 25 ⇒ 1.0 – 2.0 □ 25 ⇒ 3.0	4/7 4/7

MB1029800513020X

Fig. 6 Symptom related diagnosis (Part 2 of 2)

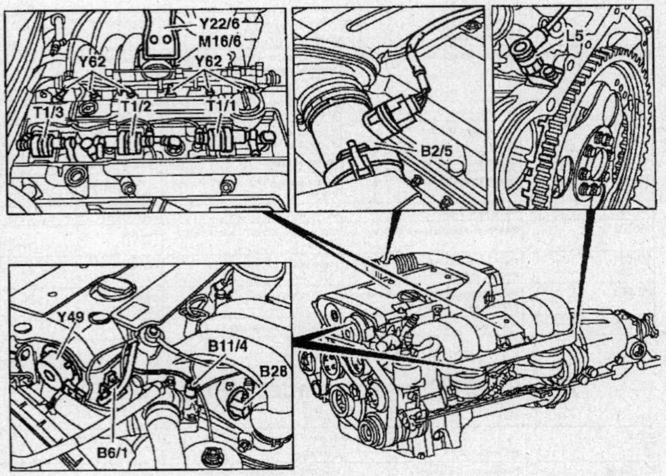

B2/5 Hot film MAF sensor
B6/1 Camshaft Hall-effect sensor
B11/4 ECT sensor
B28 Pressure sensor (only USA)
L5 CKP sensor
M16/1 EA/CC/ISC actuator
T1/1 Ignition coil cylinders 2 and 5
T1/2 Ignition coil cylinders 3 and 4
T1/3 Ignition coil cylinders 1 and 6
Y22/6 Resonance intake manifold switchover valve
Y49 Adjustable camshaft timing solenoid
Y62 Injectors

MB1029800514010X

Fig. 7 ME engine management component locations (Part 1 of 2). 104 engine

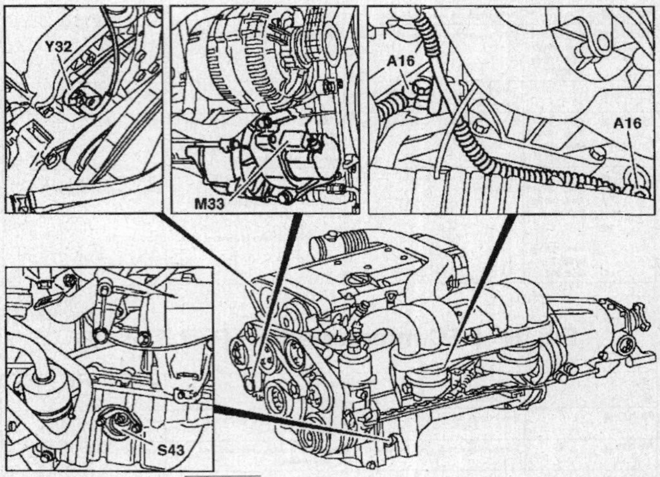

M33 AIR pump (only USA J TAW ROK)
S43 Oil level switch
Y32 AIR pump switchover valve (only USA J TAW ROK)

MB1029800514020X

Fig. 7 ME engine management component locations (Part 2 of 2). 104 engine

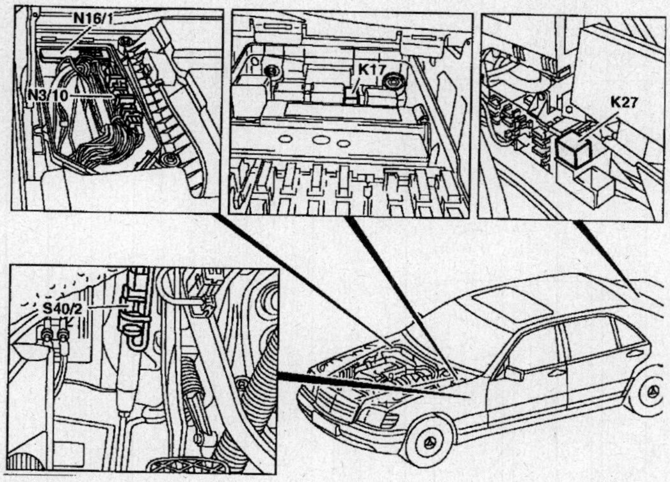

K17 AIR relay module (only USA)
K27 FP relay module
N3/10 Engine control module (ME-SFI)
N16/1 Base module (BM)
S40/2 Clutch pedal switch (not USA)

MB1029800516010X

Fig. 8 ME engine management component locations (Part 1 of 3). S320

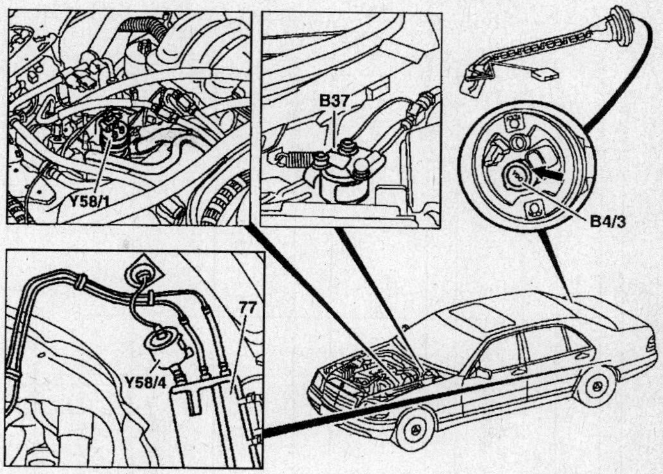

B4/3 Fuel tank pressure sensor (only USA)
B37 Pedal value sensor
Y58/1 Purge control valve
Y58/4 Activated charcoal canister shut-off valve (only USA)
77 Active charcoal canister

MB1029800516020X

Fig. 8 ME engine management component locations (Part 2 of 3) S320

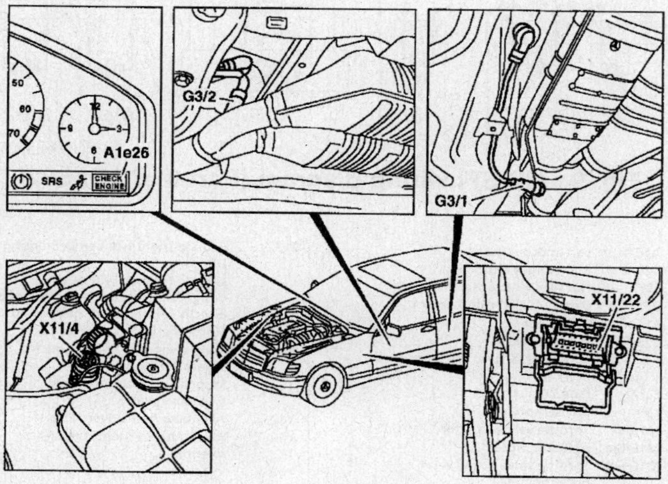

A1e26 CHECK ENGINE MIL (only USA)
G3/1 O2S 2 (after TWC) (only USA)
G3/2 O2S 1 (before TWC)
X11/4 Data link connector (DTC readout)
X11/22 Diagnostic module (OBD II) generic scan tool connector (only USA)

MB1029800516030X

Fig. 8 ME engine management component locations (Part 3 of 3). S320

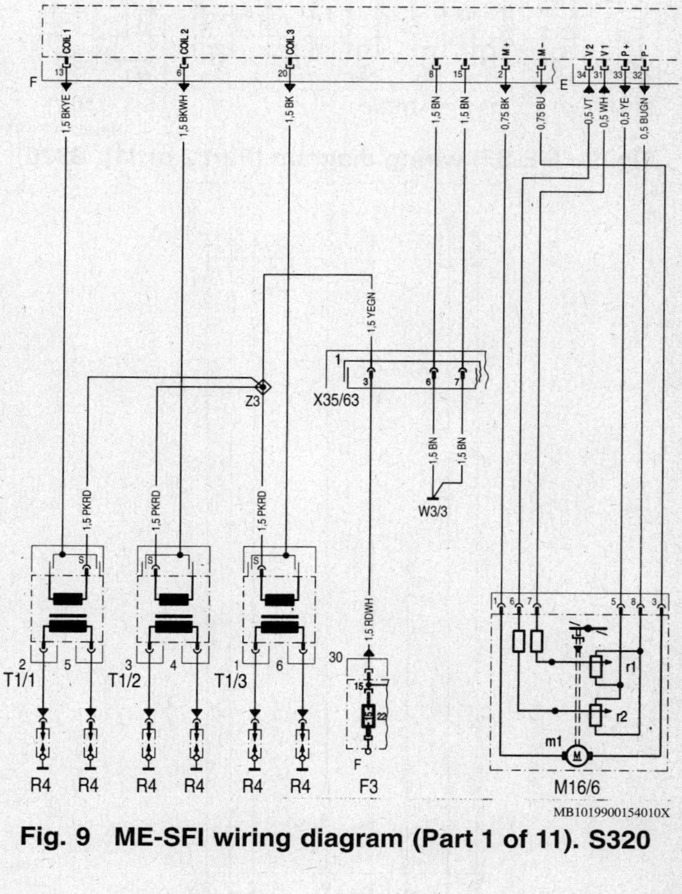

Fig. 9 ME-SFI wiring diagram (Part 1 of 11). S320

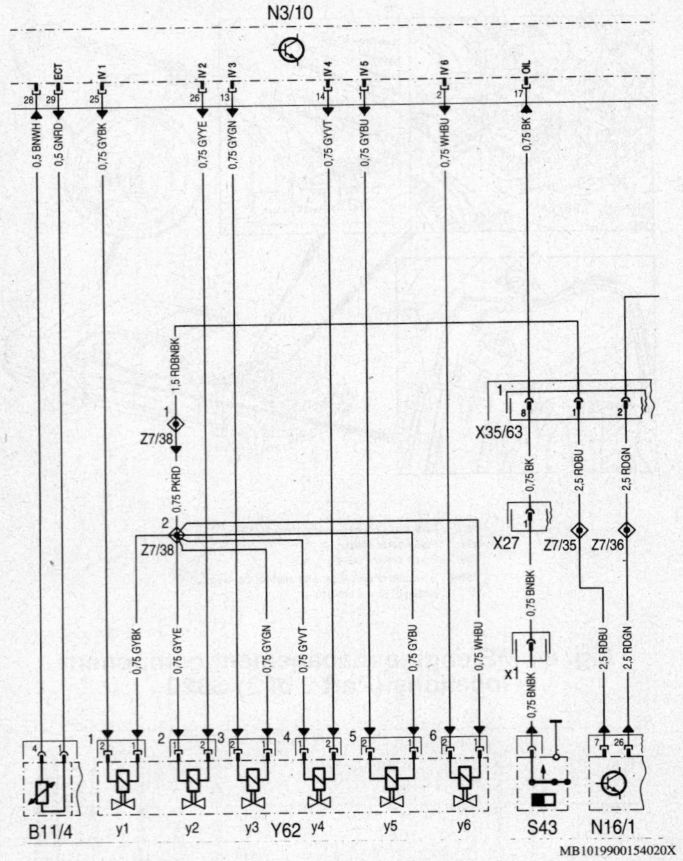

Fig. 9 ME-SFI wiring diagram (Part 2 of 11). S320

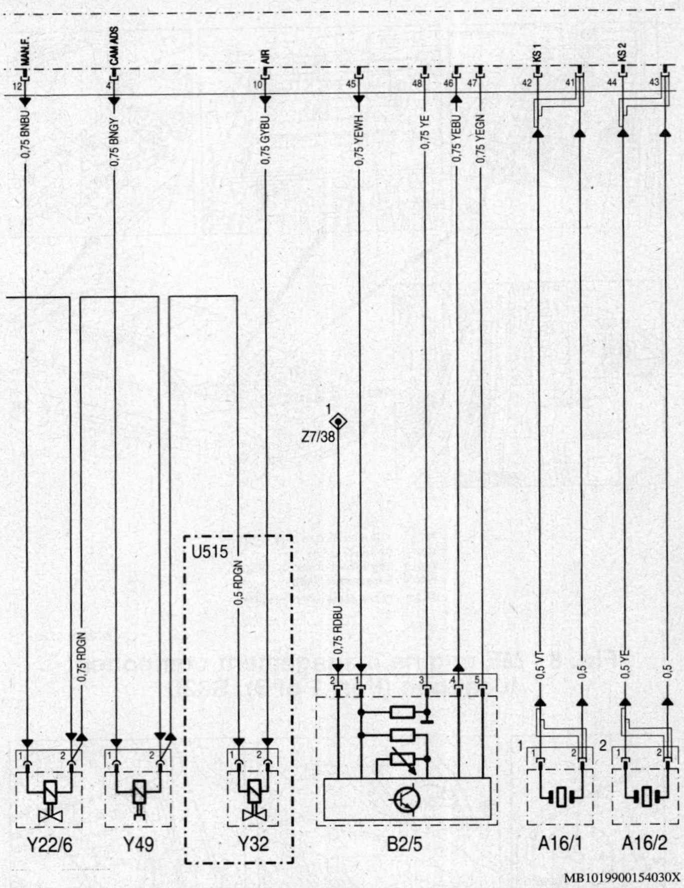

Fig. 9 ME-SFI wiring diagram (Part 3 of 11). S320

Fig. 9 ME-SFI wiring diagram (Part 4 of 11). S320

A16/1	Left knock sensor 1
A16/2	Right knock sensor 2
B2/5	Hot film MAF sensor
B6/1	Camshaft Hall-effect sensor
B11/4	ECT sensor
B28	Pressure sensor
F3	Fuse box (35-fuse, in fuse and relay box F1)
F3f22	Fuse 22
L5	CKP sensor
M16/6	Throttle valve actuator
M16/6m1	Actuator motor
M16/6r1	Throttle valve actual value potentiometer
M16/6r2	Drive actual value potentiometer
N3/10	Engine control module (ME-SFI)
N16/1	Base module (BM)
R4	Spark plugs
S43	Oil level switch
S43x1	Oil level switch connector
T1/1	Ignition coil 1
T1/2	Ignition coil 2
T1/3	Ignition coil 3
U515	Valid for secondary air injection (AIR)
W3/3	Ground (right front wheelhousing - DI)
	Ground location without designation, component grounded directly on engine, chassis or body.
X27	Starter harness connector
X35/63	Control module box/engine separation point
Y22/6	Resonance intake manifold switchover valve
Y32	AIR pump switchover valve
Y49	Adjustable camshaft timing solenoid
Y62	Injectors
Y62y1	Injector (cylinder 1)
Y62y2	Injector (cylinder 2)
Y62y3	Injector (cylinder 3)
Y62y4	Injector (cylinder 4)
Y62y5	Injector (cylinder 5)
Y62y6	Injector (cylinder 6)
Z3	Circuit 15 connector sleeve
Z7/35	Connector sleeve, circuit 87M, feed from BM (N16/1)
Z7/36	Circuit 87 M2e connector sleeve
Z7/38	Circuit 87 M1i connector sleeve

MB1019900154050X

Fig. 9 ME-SFI wiring diagram (Part 5 of 11). S320

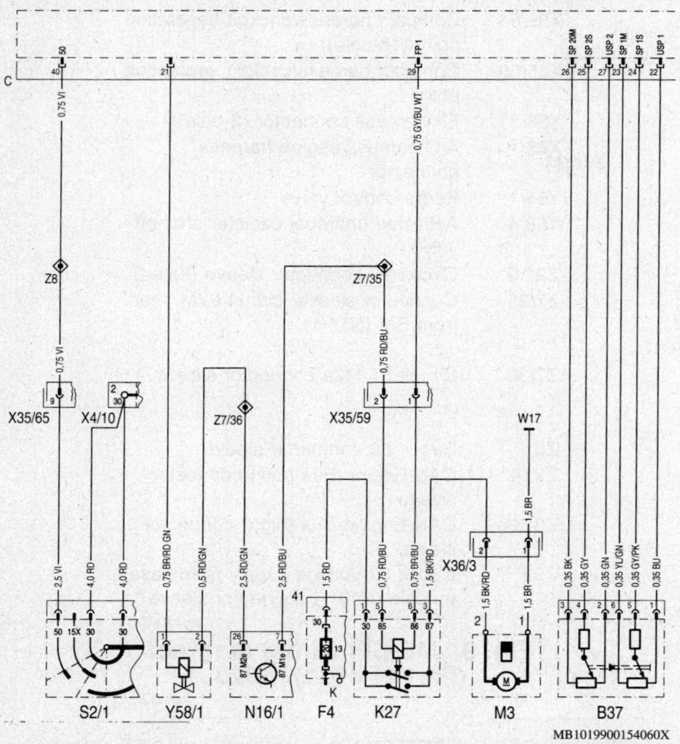

Fig. 9 ME-SFI wiring diagram (Part 6 of 11). S320

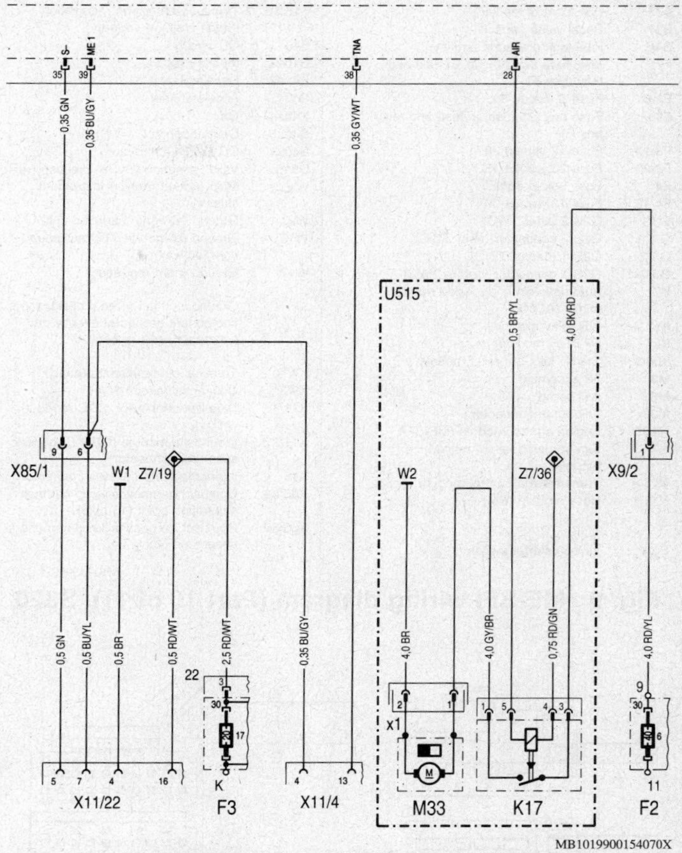

Fig. 9 ME-SFI wiring diagram (Part 7 of 11). S320

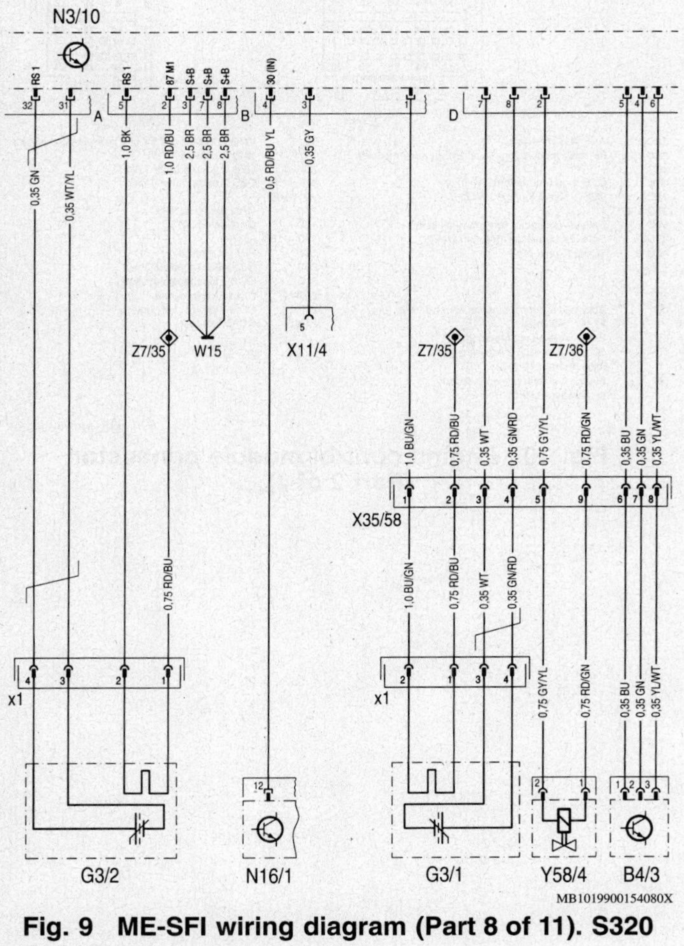

Fig. 9 ME-SFI wiring diagram (Part 8 of 11). S320

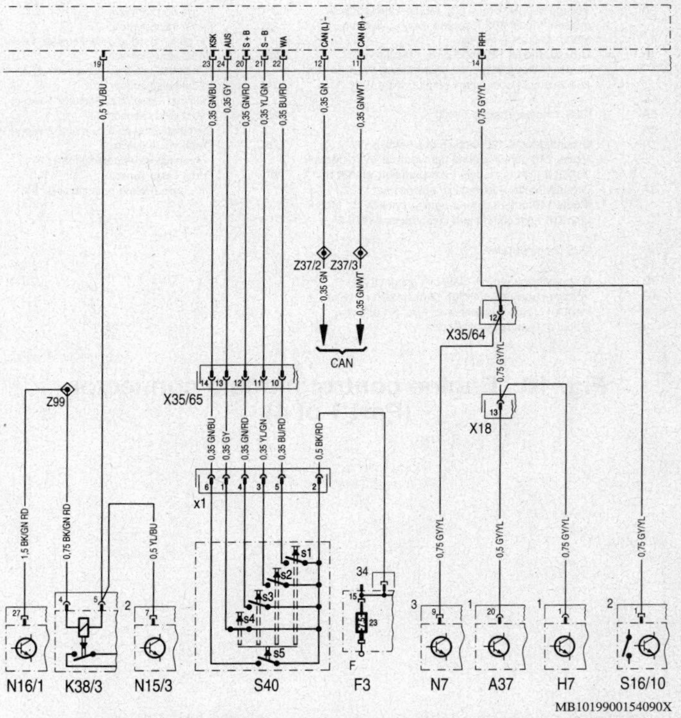

Fig. 9 ME-SFI wiring diagram (Part 9 of 11). S320

A37	PSE control module
B37	Pedal value sensor
B4/3	Fuel tank pressure sensor
F2	Maxi-fuse box (6-fuse, in fuse and relay box F1)
F2-6	Fuse 6, circuit 30
F3	Fuse box (35-fuse, in fuse and relay box F1)
F3-17	Fuse 17, circuit 30
F3-23	Fuse 23, circuit 15
F4	Fuse box in trunk
F4-13	Fuse 13, circuit 30
G3/1	O2S 2 (after TWC)
G3/1x1	O2S 2 connector (after TWC)
G3/2	O2S 1 (before TWC)
G3/2x1	O2S 1 connector (before TWC)
H7	Automatic dimming inside rearview mirror (ADM)
K17	AIR relay module
K27	FP relay module
K38/3	Starter lock-out relay module
M3	FP assembly
M33	AIR pump
M33x1	AIR pump connector
N3/10	Engine control module (ME-SFI)
N7	Exterior lamp failure monitoring module
N15/3	Transmission control module
N16/1	Base module (BM)
S2/1	Ignition/starter switch
S16/10	Transmission range recognition switch (voltage coded)
S40	CC switch
S40s1	Memory recall
S40s2	Decelerate/set
S40s3	Accelerate/set
S40s4	Off
S40s5	Control contact
S40x1	CC switch connector
U515	Valid for secondary air injection (AIR)
W1	Main ground (behind instrument cluster)
W2	Ground (at right headlamp unit)
W15	Ground (electronics output ground - right footwell)
W17	Ground (right rear seat)
	Ground location without designation, component grounded directly on engine, chassis or body.
X4/10	Terminal block (circuit 30/30Ü)
X9/2	Connector (circuit 30/15)
X11/4	Data link connector (DTC readout)
X11/22	Diagnostic module (OBD II) generic scan tool connector
X18	Interior/taillamp harness connector
X35/58	Compact harness/taillamp harness separation point (10-pole)
X35/59	Compact harness/taillamp harness separation point

MB1019900154100X

Fig. 9 ME-SFI wiring diagram (Part 10 of 11). S320

X35/64	Compact harness/cockpit separation point (18-pole)
X35/65	Compact harness/cockpit separation point
X36/3	FP harness connector (2-pole)
X85/1	A/C harness/engine harness connector
Y58/1	Purge control valve
Y58/4	Activated charcoal canister shut-off valve
Z7/19	Circuit 30 connector sleeve (fused)
Z7/35	Connector sleeve, circuit 87M, feed from BM (N16/1)
Z7/36	Circuit 87 M2e connector sleeve
Z8	Circuit 50 connector sleeve
Z37/2	CAN-Engine-Bus (low) connector sleeve
Z37/3	CAN-Engine-Bus (high) connector sleeve
Z99	Circuit 87 voltage supply from base module (N16/1) connector sleeve

MB1019900154110X

Fig. 9 ME-SFI wiring diagram (Part 11 of 11). S320

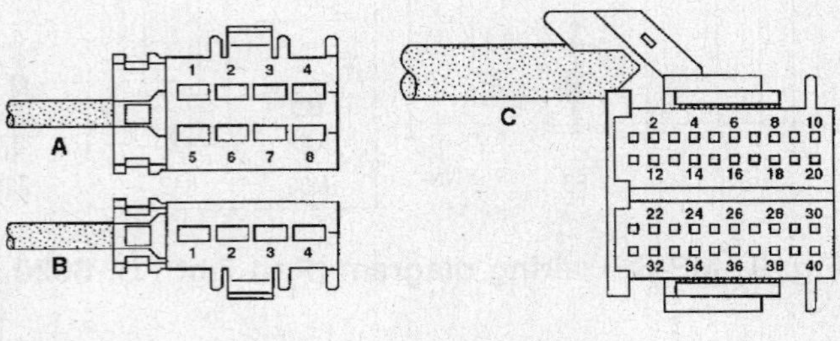

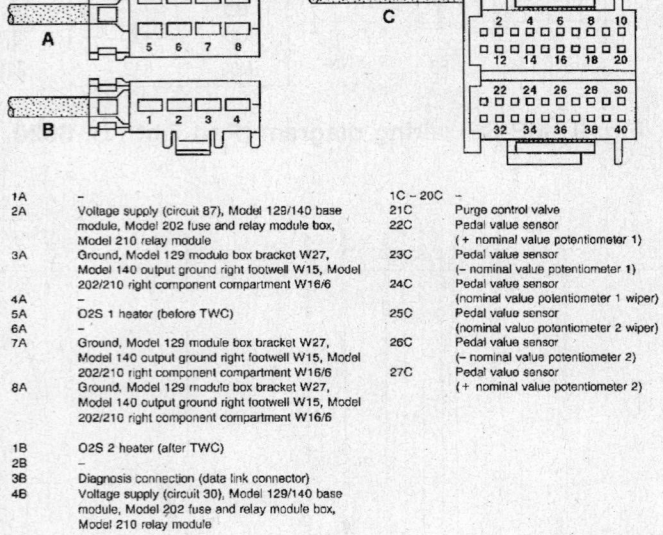

1A	–
2A	Voltage supply (circuit 87), Model 129/140 base module, Model 202 fuse and relay module box, Model 210 relay module
3A	Ground, Model 129 module box bracket W27, Model 140 output ground right footwell W15, Model 202/210 right component compartment W16/6
4A	–
5A	O2S 1 heater (before TWC)
6A	–
7A	Ground, Model 129 module box bracket W27, Model 140 output ground right footwell W15, Model 202/210 right component compartment W16/6
8A	Ground, Model 129 module box bracket W27, Model 140 output ground right footwell W15, Model 202/210 right component compartment W16/6
1B	O2S 2 heater (after TWC)
2B	–
3B	Diagnosis connection (data link connector)
4B	Voltage supply (circuit 30), Model 129/140 base module, Model 202 fuse and relay module box, Model 210 relay module
1C – 20C	–
21C	Purge control valve
22C	Pedal value sensor (+ nominal value potentiometer 1)
23C	Pedal value sensor (– nominal value potentiometer 1)
24C	Pedal value sensor (nominal value potentiometer 1 wiper)
25C	Pedal value sensor (nominal value potentiometer 2 wiper)
26C	Pedal value sensor (– nominal value potentiometer 2)
27C	Pedal value sensor (+ nominal value potentiometer 2)

MB1029800520010X

Fig. 10 Engine control module connector (Part 1 of 4)

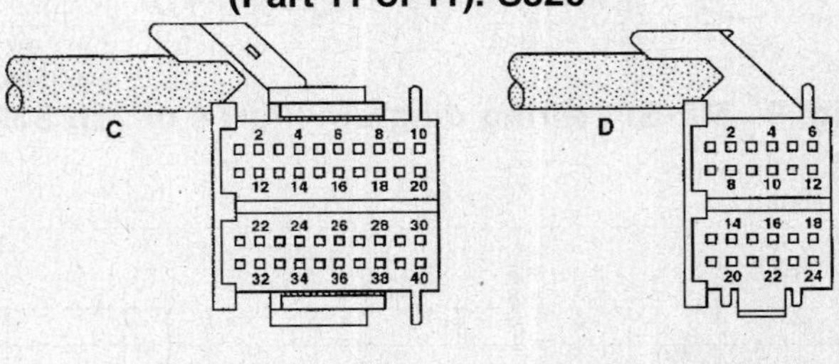

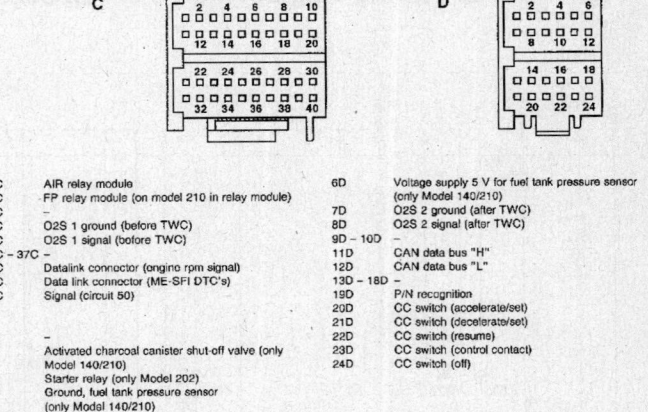

28C	AIR relay module
29C	FP relay module (on model 210 in relay module)
30C	–
31C	O2S 1 ground (before TWC)
32C	O2S 1 signal (before TWC)
33C – 37C	–
38C	Datalink connector (engine rpm signal)
39C	Data link connector (ME-SFI DTC's)
40C	Signal (circuit 50)
1D	–
2D	Activated charcoal canister shut-off valve (only Model 140/210)
3D	Starter relay (only Model 202)
4D	Ground, fuel tank pressure sensor (only Model 140/210)
5D	Signal, fuel tank pressure sensor (only Model 140/210)
6D	Voltage supply 5 V for fuel tank pressure sensor (only Model 140/210)
7D	O2S 2 ground (after TWC)
8D	O2S 2 signal (after TWC)
9D – 10D	–
11D	CAN data bus "H"
12D	CAN data bus "L"
13D – 18D	–
19D	P/N recognition
20D	CC switch (accelerate/set)
21D	CC switch (decelerate/set)
22D	CC switch (resume)
23D	CC switch (control contact)
24D	CC switch (off)

MB1029800520020X

Fig. 10 Engine control module connector (Part 2 of 4)

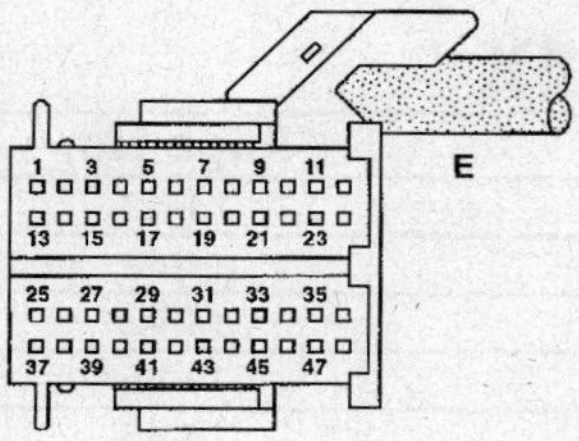

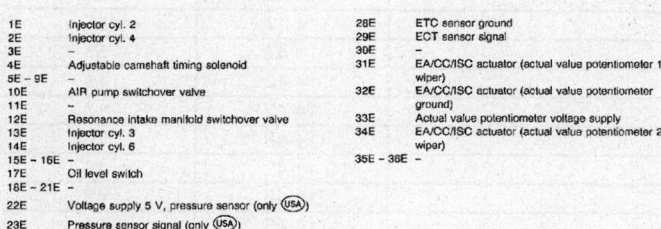

1E	Injector cyl. 2
2E	Injector cyl. 4
3E	–
4E	Adjustable camshaft timing solenoid
5E – 9E	–
10E	AIR pump switchover valve
11E	–
12E	Resonance intake manifold switchover valve
13E	Injector cyl. 3
14E	Injector cyl. 6
15E – 16E	–
17E	Oil level switch
18E – 21E	–
22E	Voltage supply 5 V, pressure sensor (only USA)
23E	Pressure sensor signal (only USA)
24E	Pressure sensor ground (only USA)
25E	Injector cyl. 1
26E	Injector cyl. 5
27E	AIR pump relay in relay module (only Model 210)
28E	ETC sensor ground
29E	ECT sensor signal
30E	–
31E	EA/CC/ISC actuator (actual value potentiometer 1 wiper)
32E	EA/CC/ISC actuator (actual value potentiometer ground)
33E	Actual value potentiometer voltage supply
34E	EA/CC/ISC actuator (actual value potentiometer 2 wiper)
35E – 36E	–

MB1029800520030X

Fig. 10 Engine control module connector (Part 3 of 4)

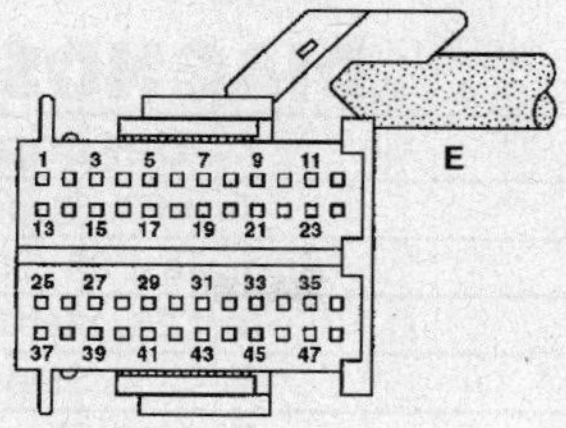

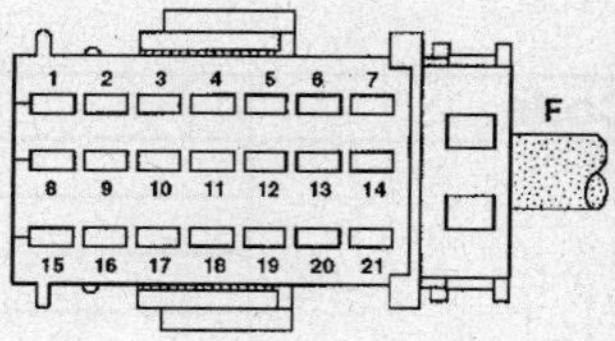

37E	CKP sensor ground
38E	CKP sensor signal
39E	Camshaft Hall-effect sensor ground
40E	Camshaft Hall-effect sensor signal
41E	KS 1 ground
42E	KS 1 signal
43E	KS 2 ground
44E	KS 2 signal
45E	IAT sensor (in hot film MAF sensor)
46E	Hot film MAF sensor voltage supply 5 V
47E	Hot film MAF sensor signal
48E	Hot film MAF sensor ground

1F	EA/CC/ISC actuator (–)
2F	EA/CC/ISC actuator (+)
3F – 5F	–
6F	Ignition coil T1/2, cyl. 3 and 4
7F	–
8F	Output ground, Model 129 module box bracket W27, Model 140 output ground right footwell W15, Model 202/210 right component compartment W16/6
9F – 12F	–
13F	Ignition coil T1/1, cyl. 2 and 5
14F	–
15F	Output ground, Model 129 module box bracket W27, Model 140 output ground right footwoll W15, Model 202/210 right component compartment W16/6
16F – 19F	–
20F	Ignition coil T1/3, cyl. 1 and 6
21F	–

MB1029800520040X

Fig. 10 Engine control module connector (Part 4 of 4)

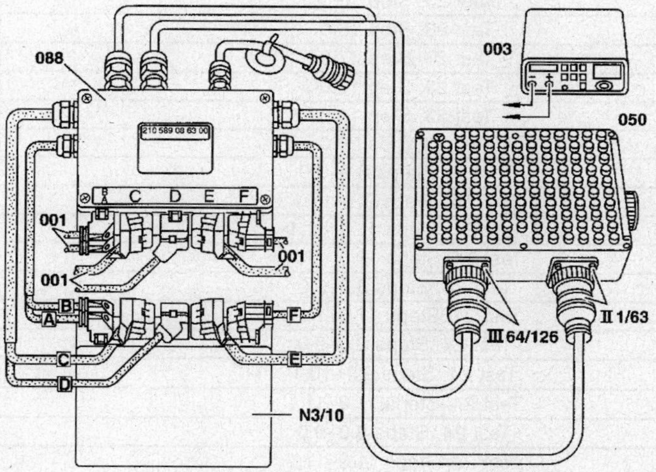

001	Engine control module connectors
003	Digital multimeter
050	Socket box (126-pole)
088	Test cable
N3/10	Engine control module (ME-SFI)

MB1029800519000A

Fig. 11 Test connections

DIAGNOSTIC CHART INDEX

Code	Description	Page No.	Fig. No.
—	Test 23, Steps 2.2–4.0	14-42	14
	Test 23, Step 8.0	14-42	18
	Test 23, Steps 9.2–10.0	14-42	20
	Test 24, Steps 2.1–2.2	14-45	41
	Test 24, Steps 3.0–5.0	14-45	42
	Test 32, Fuel System Pressure & Internal Leakage Test	14-46	53
	Test 34, Fuel Pump Test	14-47	55
	Test 36: Injector Test	14-47	57
P0100	Test 23, Steps 4.1–5.2	14-42	15
P0105	Test 23, Steps 6.1–7.1	14-42	17
P0110	Test 23, Steps 5.3–6.0	14-42	16
P0115	Test 23, Steps 9.0–9.1	14-42	19
P0120	Test 25, Steps 3.0–3.1	14-46	49
P0130	Test 23, Steps 11.0–12.0	14-43	21
P0133	Test 23, Steps 11.0–12.0	14-43	21
P0135	Test 23, Steps 11.0–12.0	14-43	21
P0136	Test 23, Steps 13.0–14.0	14-43	22
P0140	Test 23, Steps 13.0–14.0	14-43	22
P0186	Test 25, Steps 3.0–3.1	14-46	49
P0201	Test 23, Step 15.0	14-43	23
P0202	Test 23, Step 16.0	14-43	24
P0203	Test 23, Step 17.0	14-43	25
P0204	Test 23, Step 18.0	14-43	26
P0205	Test 23, Step 19.0	14-43	27
P0206	Test 23, Step 20.0	14-43	28
P0300	Test 24, Steps 8.0–9.0	14-45	45
	Test 24, Steps 9.1–10.1	14-45	46
	Test 24, Steps 11.0–11.1	14-45	47
P0301	Test 24, Steps 11.0–11.1	14-45	47
P0302	Test 24, Steps 8.0–9.0	14-45	45
	Test 24, Steps 11.0–11.1	14-45	47
P0303	Test 24, Steps 8.0–9.0	14-45	45
	Test 24, Steps 9.1–10.1	14-45	46
	Test 24, Steps 11.0–11.1	14-45	47
P0304	Test 24, Steps 8.0–9.0	14-45	45
	Test 24, Steps 11.0–11.1	14-45	47
P0305	Test 24, Steps 8.0–9.0	14-45	45
	Test 24, Steps 11.0–11.1	14-45	47
P0306	Test 24, Steps 9.1–10.1	14-45	46
	Test 24, Steps 11.0–11.1	14-45	47
P0335	Test 24, Steps 6.0–6.1	14-45	43
P0341	Test 24, Steps 7.0–7.1	14-45	44
P0410	Test 23, Steps 22.0–23.0	14-43	30
P0440	Test 23, Steps 27.0–28.0	14-44	33
	Test 23, Steps 29.0–30.0	14-44	34
P0441	Test 23, Steps 27.0–28.0	14-44	33
P0442	Test 23, Steps 29.0–30.0	14-44	34
P0443	Test 23, Steps 27.0–28.0	14-44	33
P0445	Test 23, Steps 29.0–30.0	14-44	34
P0450	Test 23, Steps 31.0–31.1	14-44	35
	Test 23, Steps 32.0–32.1	14-44	36
P0455	Test 23, Steps 29.0–30.0	14-44	34
	Test 23, Steps 31.0–31.1	14-44	35
P0507	Test 25, Steps 1.0–2.1	14-46	48
	Test 25, Steps 3.0–3.1	14-46	49

Continued

DIAGNOSTIC CHART INDEX—Continued

Code	Description	Page No.	Fig. No.
P0560	Test 23, Steps 1.0–1.1	14-42	12
	Test 23, Steps 1.2–2.1	14-42	13
	Test 24, Steps 1.0–1.1	14-44	39
	Test 24, Steps 1.2–2.0	14-45	40
P0565	Test 26, Step 1.0	14-46	51
P0600	Test 23, Steps 33.0–33.2	14-44	37
P0802	Test 23, Step 24.0	14-44	31
P1163	Test 23, Steps 34.0–35.0	14-44	38
P1185	Test 25, Steps 4.0–5.0	14-46	50
P1420	Test 23, Steps 21.0–22.0	14-43	29
P1453	Test 23, Steps 21.0–22.0	14-43	29
P1519	Test 23, Steps 25.0–26.0	14-44	32
P1525	Test 23, Steps 25.0–26.0	14-44	32
P1542	Test 25, Steps 1.0–2.1	14-46	48
P1570	Test 23, Steps 33.0–33.2	14-44	37
P1580	Test 25, Steps 3.0–3.1	14-46	49
	Test 25, Steps 4.0–5.0	14-46	50
P1747	Test 23, Steps 33.0–33.2	14-44	37

⇒		Test scope	Test connection	Test condition	Nominal value	Possible cause/remedy
1.0	P0 560	**Engine control module (ME-SFI) (N3/10)** Voltage supply Circuit 30	N3/10 3 (3A) —(Ⓥ)— 12 (4B)	Ignition: **ON**	11 – 14 V	⇒ 1.1 – 1.2
1.1		Ground wire	N3/10 → X11/4 3 (3A) —(Ⓥ)— 2 7 (7A) —(Ⓥ)— 2 112 (8F) —(Ⓥ)— 2 119 (15F) —(Ⓥ)— 2	Ignition: **ON**	11 – 14 V	Wiring, **Model 129:** Ground, module box bracket (W27). **Model 140:** Output ground (W15), right footwell. **Model 202, 210:** Output ground (W16/6), right component compartment, ⇒ 1.2

MB1029800521000X

Fig. 12 Code P0560: Test 23, Steps 1.0–1.1

⇒		Test scope	Test connection	Test condition	Nominal value	Possible cause/remedy
1.2		Voltage supply Circuit 30	X11/4 → N3/10 1 —(Ⓥ)— 12 (4B)	Ignition: **ON**	11 – 14 V	Wiring, **Model 129, 140:** Base moduel (N16/1) or fuse on base module. **Model 202:** Passenger-side fuse and relay module box (K40/4). **Model 210:** Relay module (K40).
2.0	P0 560	**Engine control module (ME-SFI) (N3/10)** Voltage supply Circuit 87	N3/10 8 (8A) —(Ⓥ)— 2 (2A)	Ignition: **ON**	11 – 14 V	⇒ 2.1 – 2.2
2.1		Electronics ground	N3/10 → X11/4 8 (8A) —(Ⓥ)— 2	Ignition: **ON**	11 – 14 V	Wiring, **Model 129:** Control module box bracket (W27). **Model 140:** Output ground (W15), right footwell. **Model 202 and 210:** Output ground (W16/6), right component compartment, ⇒ 2.2

MB1029800522000X

Fig. 13 Code P0560: Test 23, Steps 1.2–2.1

⇒		Test scope	Test connection	Test condition	Nominal value	Possible cause/remedy
2.2		Voltage supply Circuit 87	X11/4 → N3/10 1 —(Ⓥ)— 2 (2A)	Ignition: **ON** Ignition: **OFF**	11 – 14 V < 1 V	Wiring, **Model 129, 140:** Base module (N16/1) or fuse on base module. **Model 202:** Passenger-side fuse and relay module box (K40/4). **Model 210:** Relay module (K40).
3.0		**Starter signal circuit 50**	N3/10 8 (8A) —(Ⓥ)— 32 (40C)	Engine: Crank	11 – 14 V while cranking	Wiring, Ignition/starter switch (S2/1).
4.0		**Model 202 only** **Starter relay in fuse and relay module box (K40/4)** Activation	N3/10 35 (3D) —(Ⓥ)— 2 (2A)	Selector lever position: P/N → Engine: **Start** Selector lever position: R, D, 3, 2 → Engine: **Start**	 11 – 14 V < 1 V	⇒ 4.1 Engine control module (N3/10).

MB1029800523000X

Fig. 14 Code —: Test 23, Steps 2.2–4.0

⇒		Test scope	Test connection	Test condition	Nominal value	Possible cause/remedy
4.1		P/N recognition	N3/10 51 (19D) —(Ⓥ)— 2 (2A)	Ignition: **ON** Selector lever position: P/N → R, D, 4, 3, 2, 1, →	 11 – 14 V < 2 V	Wiring, Test ETC
5.0	P0 100	**Hot film MAF sensor (B2/5)** Hot film signal	N3/10 104 (48E) —(Ⓥ)— 103 (47E)	Ignition: **ON** Engine: **at Idle** Engine coolant temperature > 70°C	0.9 – 1.1 V 1.3 – 1.7 V [2]	Wiring, ⇒ 5.1 – 5.3 Air intake system leak, B2/5
5.1		**Hot film MAF sensor (B2/5)** Voltage supply 5 V	N3/10 → B2/5 104 (48E) —(Ⓥ)— 4	Disconnect MAF sensor (B2/5) connector and measure directly on socket 4 (br/yl). Ignition: **ON**	4.7 – 5.2 V	Wiring, N3/10
5.2		**Ground wire for hot film MAF sensor (B2/5)**	B2/5 → N3/10 3 —(Ⓥ)— 102 (46E)	Disconnect MAF sensor (B2/5) connector and measure directly on socket 3 (br). Ignition: **ON**	4.7 – 5.2 V	Wiring.

2) Increasing rpm, increasing voltage.

MB1029800524000X

Fig. 15 Code P0100: Test 23, Steps 4.1–5.2

⇒		Test scope	Test connection	Test condition	Nominal value	Possible cause/remedy
5.3		**Hot film MAF sensor (B2/5)** Voltage supply 12 V	N3/10 → B2/5 104 (48E) —(Ⓥ)— 2	Disconnect MAF sensor (B2/5) connector and connect plus of voltmeter to socket 2 (rd/bu). Ignition: **ON**	11 – 14 V	Wiring, **Model 129, 140:** Base module (N16/1) or fuse on base module. **Model 202:** Passenger-side fuse and relay module box (K40/4). **Model 210:** Relay module (K40).
6.0	P0 110	**IAT sensor in hot film MAF sensor (B2/5)** Voltage	N3/10 104 (48E) —(Ⓥ)— 101 (45E)	Ignition: **ON**	°C V 10 3.1 20 2.7 30 2.2 40 1.8 50 1.4 60 1.1 ± 5%	⇒ 6.1 N3/10

MB1029800525000X

Fig. 16 Code P0110: Test 23, Steps 5.3–6.0

⇒		Test scope	Test connection	Test condition	Nominal value	Possible cause/remedy
6.1		IAT sensor Resistance	N3/10 104 (48E) —(Ω)— 101 (45E)	Ignition: **OFF** Disconnect connector **E** on engine control module (N3/10).	oC Ω 10 3600 20 2420 30 1660 40 1170 50 850 60 600 ± 5%	Wiring, B2/5
7.0	P0 105	**Pressure sensor (B28)** Sensor signal	N3/10 80 (24E) —(Ⓥ)— 79 (23E)	Connect vacuum tester to pressure sensor (B28) using Y-fitting Ignition: **ON** Engine: **at Idle**	 > 3.5 V < 2 V and pressure climbs to > 500 mbar.	⇒ 7.1, Vacuum line, Wiring, B28
7.1		Pressure sensor (B28) Voltage supply	N3/10 80 (24E) —(Ⓥ)— 78 (22E)	Ignition: **ON**	4.7 – 5.3 V	N3/10

MB1029800526000X

Fig. 17 Code P0105: Test 23, Steps 6.1–7.1

⇒		Test scope	Test connection	Test condition	Nominal value	Possible cause/remedy
8.0		**Model 129, 140, 202** **FP relay module (K27)** **Model 210** **Relay module (K40)** Activation	N3/10 21 (29C) —(Ⓥ)— 2 (2A)	Ignition: **ON** Engine: **Start**	11 – 14 V for approx. 1 sec. [3] 11 – 14 V during cranking and while engine runs.	Wiring, K27 or K40, N3/10 **Note:** On Model 202 the activation of the fuel pump takes place via the passenger-side fuse and relay module box (K40/4).
		Current draw K27 or K40	N3/10 8 (8A) —(Ⓐ)— 21 (29C)	Ignition: **ON**	0.1 – 0.3 A	

3) The activation of the FP occurs only once after ignition "ON". For the next activation, the engine must have run briefly.

MB1029800527000X

Fig. 18 Code —: Test 23, Step 8.0

⇒		Test scope	Test connection	Test condition	Nominal value	Possible cause/remedy
9.0	P0 115	**ECT sensor (B11/4)** Voltage	N3/10 84 (28E) —(Ⓥ)— 85 (29E)	Ignition: **ON**	°C V 20 3.4 30 2.9 40 2.4 50 1.9 60 1.5 70 1.2 80 0.9 90 0.7 100 0.5 ±5 %	⇒ 9.1, N3/10
9.1		Resistance (B11/4)	N3/10 84 (28E) —(Ω)— 85 (29E)	Ignition: **OFF** Disconnect connector **E** on engine control module (N3/10).	°C Ω 20 3090 30 2000 40 1330 50 900 60 630 70 440 80 320 90 230 100 170 ±5 %	Wiring, ⇒ 9.2

MB1029800528000X

Fig. 19 Code P0115: Test 23, Steps 9.0–9.1

⇒		Test scope	Test connection	Test condition	Nominal value	Possible cause/remedy
9.2		ECT sensor (B11/4) Resistance	B11/4 1 —(Ω)— 2	Disconnect connector on ECT sensor (B11/4).	Nominal value, see ⇒ 9.1	B11/4
10.0		**Engine control module (N3/10)** TN-signal output	N3/10 [3] 8 (8A) —(oscilloscope)— 30 (38C) N3/10 [4] 8 (8A) —(Ⓥ)— 30 (38C)	Engine: **Start** or Engine: **at Idle**	Signal 7.5 – 9.0 V	Wiring, N3/10

3) Test with oscilloscope.
4) Test with multimeter only if oscilloscope is not available.

MB1029800529000X

Fig. 20 Code —: Test 23, Steps 9.2–10.0

⇒		Test scope	Test connection	Test condition	Nominal value	Possible cause/remedy
11.0	P0 130 P0 133	**O2S 1** **(before TWC) (G3/1)** O2S signal	N3/10 23 (31C) — V — 24 (32C)	ECT > 80 ° C, run engine at idle for at least two minutes.	fluctuates from – 0.2 V to + 1.0 V, by more than 0.3 V	Wiring, ⇒ 12.0 G3/1
12.0	P0 135	**O2S 1** **(before TWC) (G3/1)** O2S heater activation	N3/10 5 (5A) — V — 2 (2A)	ECT > 80 ° C, run engine at idle for at least two minutes.	11 – 14 V	Wiring, G3/1 N3/10
		O2S 1 (G3/1) Current draw	N3/10 3 (3A) — A — 5 (5A)	Ignition: **ON**	0.6 – 3.4 A	

MB1029800530000X

Fig. 21 Codes P0130, P0133 & P0135: Test 23, Steps 11.0–12.0

⇒		Test scope	Test connection	Test condition	Nominal value	Possible cause/remedy
15.0	P0 201	**Injector (Y62y1)** Activation and injection time	N3/10 81 (25E) — — 2 (2A)	**ECT approx. 20° C** at start **ECT approx. 80° C** at idle accelerate briefly	Injection time: approx. 8 ms approx. 3 – 5 ms approx. 14 ms	Wiring, Y62y1, N3/10 **Further possibilities:** ECT sensor (B11/4), IAT sensor in hot film MAF sensor (B2/5), O2S 1 (G3/2).
		Resistance (Y62y1)	N3/10 81 (25E) — Ω — 2 (2A)	Ignition: **OFF**	14 – 17 Ω	

MB1029800532000X

Fig. 23 Code P0201: Test 23, Step 15.0

⇒		Test scope	Test connection	Test condition	Nominal value	Possible cause/remedy
17.0	P0 203	**Injector (Y62y3)** Activation and injection time	N3/10 69 (13E) — — 2 (2A)	**ECT approx. 20° C** at start **ECT approx. 80° C** at idle accelerate briefly	Injection time: approx. 8 ms approx. 3 – 5 ms approx. 14 ms signal	Wiring, Y62y3, N3/10 **Further possibilities:** ECT sensor (B11/4), IAT sensor in hot film MAF sensor (B2/5), O2S 1 (G3/2).
		Resistance (Y62y3)	N3/10 69 (13E) — Ω — 2 (2A)	Ignition: **OFF**	14 – 17 Ω	

MB1029800534000X

Fig. 25 Code P0203: Test 23, Step 17.0

⇒		Test scope	Test connection	Test condition	Nominal value	Possible cause/remedy
19.0	P0 205	**Injector (Y62y5)** Activation and injection time	N3/10 82 (25E) — — 2 (2A)	**ECT approx. 20° C** at start **ECT approx. 80° C** at idle accelerate briefly	Injection time: approx. 8 ms approx. 3 – 5 ms approx. 14 ms signal	Wiring, Y62y5, N3/10 **Further possibilities:** ECT sensor (B11/4), IAT sensor in hot film MAF sensor (B2/5), O2S 1 (G3/2).
		Resistance (Y62y5)	N3/10 82 (25E) — Ω — 2 (2A)	Ignition: **OFF**	14 – 17 Ω	

MB1029800536000X

Fig. 27 Code P0205: Test 23, Step 19.0

⇒		Test scope	Test connection	Test condition	Nominal value	Possible cause/remedy
21.0	P1 453	**Model 129, 140** **AIR relay module (K17),** **Model 202, Passenger-side fuse and relay module box (K40/4),** **Model 210** **Relay module (K40)** Activation	N3/10 20 (28C) — V — 2 (2A)	Disconnect ECT sensor (B11/4) connector. Simulate 2.5 kΩ resistance at sockets 1 and 2 with resistance substitution unit. Engine: **at Idle**	11 – 14 V for approx. two minutes and AIR pump runs.	Wiring, AIR pump fuse, K17, K40 or K40/4, N3/10
		(K17), (K40) or (K40/4) Current draw	N3/10 3 (3A) — A — 20 (28C)	Ignition: **ON**	0.1 – 0.3 A	
22.0	P1 420	**AIR pump switchover valve (Y32)** Activation	N3/10 66 (10E) — V — 2 (2A)	Disconnect ECT sensor (B11/4) connector. Simulate 2.5 kΩ resistance at sockets 1 and 2 with resistance substitution unit. Engine: **at Idle**	11 – 14 V for approx. two minutes and AIR pump runs.	Wiring, Y32, N3/10

MB1029800538000X

Fig. 29 Codes P1420 & P1453: Test 23, Steps 21.0–22.0

⇒		Test scope	Test connection	Test condition	Nominal value	Possible cause/remedy
13.0	P0 136	**O2S 2** **(after TWC) (G3/2)** O2S signal	N3/10 39 (7D) — V — 40 (8D)	ECT > 80° C, Engine: **Start** Raise and hold engine speed at 2000 – 3000 rpm for approx. 2 minutes.		Wiring, ⇒ 14.0, G3/2, N3/10
			N3/10 3 (3A) ←→ 20 (28C) 3 (3A) ←→ 66 (10E)	Engine: **at Idle** Bridge sockets on socket box	> 550 mV AIR pump runs. Voltage changes to < 40 mV within 60 seconds.	
14.0	P0 141	**O2S 2** **(after TWC) (G3/2)** O2S heater activation	N3/10 9 (1B) — V — 2 (2A)	Engine: **at Idle** ECT > 80° C, run engine at idle for at least 2 minutes.	11 – 14 V or voltage fluctuates between 1 – 14 V	Wiring, G3/2, N3/10
		O2S 2 (G3/2) Current draw	N3/10 3 (3A) — A — 9 (1B)	Ignition: **ON**	0.6 – 3.4 A	

MB1029800531000X

Fig. 22 Codes P0136 & P0140: Test 23, Steps 13.0–14.0

⇒		Test scope	Test connection	Test condition	Nominal value	Possible cause/remedy
16.0	P0 202	**Injector (Y62y2)** Activation and injection time	N3/10 57 (1E) — — 2 (2A)	**ECT approx. 20° C** at start **ECT approx. 80° C** at idle accelerate briefly	Injection time: approx. 8 ms approx. 3 – 5 ms approx. 14 ms signal	Wiring, Y62y2, N3/10 **Further possibilities:** ECT sensor (B11/4), IAT sensor in hot film MAF sensor (B2/5), O2S 1 (G3/2).
		Resistance (Y62y2)	N3/10 57 (1E) — Ω — 2 (2A)	Ignition: **OFF**	14 – 17 Ω	

MB1029800533000X

Fig. 24 Code P0202: Test 23, Step 16.0

⇒		Test scope	Test connection	Test condition	Nominal value	Possible cause/remedy
18.0	P0 204	**Injector (Y62y4)** Activation and injection time	N3/10 58 (2E) — — 2 (2A)	**ECT approx. 20° C** at start **ECT approx. 80° C** at idle accelerate briefly	Injection time: approx. 8 ms approx. 3 – 5 ms approx. 14 ms signal	Wiring, Y62y4, N3/10 **Further possibilities:** ECT sensor (B11/4), IAT sensor in hot film MAF sensor (B2/5), O2S 1 (G3/2).
		Resistance (Y62y4)	N3/10 58 (2E) — Ω — 2 (2A)	Ignition: **OFF**	14 – 17 Ω	

MB1029800535000X

Fig. 26 Code P0204: Test 23, Step 18.0

⇒		Test scope	Test connection	Test condition	Nominal value	Possible cause/remedy
20.0	P0 206	**Injector (Y62y6)** Activation and injection time	N3/10 70 (14E) — — 2 (2A)	**ECT approx. 20° C** at start **ECT approx. 80° C** at idle accelerate briefly	Injection time: approx. 8 ms approx. 3 – 5 ms approx. 14 ms signal	Wiring, Y62y6, N3/10 **Further possibilities:** ECT sensor (B11/4), IAT sensor in hot film MAF sensor (B2/5), O2S 1 (G3/2).
		Resistance (Y62y6)	N3/10 70 (14E) — Ω — 2 (2A)	Ignition: **OFF**	14 – 17 Ω	

MB1029800537000X

Fig. 28 Code P0206: Test 23, Step 20.0

⇒		Test scope	Test connection	Test condition	Nominal value	Possible cause/remedy
[22.0]		Current draw (Y32)	N3/10 3 (3A) — A — 66 (10E)	Ignition: **ON**	0.4 – 0.6 A	
23.0	P0 410	**AIR system** (logic chain)	N3/10 23 (31C) — V — 24 (32C)	**Note:** The O2S 1 signal before TWC is measured. With ETC > 80°C run engine at idle for at least 2 minutes.	The O2S voltage oscillates in the area of –0.2 V and +1.0 V	Y32 binding, AIR combi valve, AIR pump no output.
			N3/10 3 (3A) ←→ 20 (28C) 3 (3A) ←→ 66 (10E)	Bridge sockets on socket box	AIR pump runs. Voltage changes to < 100 mV within 20 seconds	

6) The resistance of one solenoid is 7 – 12 Ω.

MB1029800539000X

Fig. 30 Code P0410: Test 23, Steps 22.0–23.0

⇒		Test scope	Test connection	Test condition	Nominal value	Possible cause/remedy
24.0	P0 802	**Resonance intake manifold switchover valve (Y22/6)** Activation	N3/10 68 (12E) –V– 2 (2A)	Engine: **Start** Engine speed: < approx. 3500 rpm Engine speed: > approx. 3500 rpm	< 1 V 11 – 14 V	Wiring, Y22/6, N3/10
		Y22/6 Current draw	N3/10 3 (3A) –A– 68 (12E)	Ignition: **ON**	0.4 – 0.6 A	

MB1029800540000X

Fig. 31 Code P0802: Test 23, Step 24.0

⇒		Test scope	Test connection	Test condition	Nominal value	Possible cause/remedy
27.0	P0 441 P0 443	**Purge control valve (Y58/1)** Activation	N3/10 13 (21C) –⊕– 2 (2A)	Engine: **at idle** and at operating temperature.	After approx. 1 minute, purge control valve (Y58/1) must noticeably cycle Signal see	Wiring, Y58/1, ⇒ 28.0, N3/10
		Current draw (Y58/1)	N3/10 3 (3A) –A– 13 (21C)	Ignition: **ON**	0.2 – 0.4 A	
28.0	P0 440 P0 441	**Purge control valve (Y58/1)** Vacuum control		Connect vacuum tester to purge control valve (Y58/1) between purge line to charcoal canister Engine at operating temperature and at idle.	After approx. 1 minute, > 50 mbar and needle oscillates, Y58/1 must cycle.	Vacuum line, Y58/1

MB1029800542000X

Fig. 33 Codes P0440, P0441 & P0443: Test 23, Steps 27.0–28.0

⇒		Test scope	Test connection	Test condition	Nominal value	Possible cause/remedy
31.0	P0 450 P0 455	Only (USA) **Model 140, 210** **Model 129 as of 09/97** **Fuel tank pressure sensor (B4/3)** Sender signal Activated charcoal canister shut-off valve (Y58/4) activated	N3/10 36 (4D) –V– 37 (5D) N3/10 3 (3A) ←→ 34 (2D)	Disconnect purge line (A) to charcoal canister on purge control valve (Y58/1). Connect vacuum tester to purge line Ignition: **ON** Apply approx. 25 mbar of vacuum.	 > 2.9 V < 2.3 V	⇒ 31.1, Wiring, Vacuum line, Charcoal canister plugged, B4/3
31.1		Only (USA) Fuel tank pressure sensor (B4/3) Voltage supply	N3/10 36 (4D) –V– 38 (6D)	Ignition: **ON**	4.7 – 5.3 V	N3/10

MB1029800544000X

Fig. 35 Codes P0450 & P0455: Test 23, Steps 31.0–31.1

⇒		Test scope	Test connection	Test condition	Nominal value	Possible cause/remedy
33.0	P0 600 P1 570 P1 747	**CAN data bus**	N3/10 43 (11D) –Ω– 44 (12D)	Ignition: **OFF**	55 – 65 Ω	⇒ 33.1 – 33.2 Data line.
33.1		**CAN element in DAS control module (N54/1)** Resistance	N3/10 43 (11D) –Ω– 44 (12D)	Ignition: **OFF** Disconnect connector **D** from engine control module N3/10.	115 – 125 Ω	Wiring, N54 or N54/1
33.2		**CAN element in engine control module (N3/10)** Resistance	N3/10 43 (11D) –Ω– 44 (12D)	Ignition: **OFF** Disconnect connector **D** from test cable.	115 – 125 Ω	N3/10

MB1029800546000X

Fig. 37 Codes P0600, P1570 & P1747: Test 23, Steps 33.0–33.2

⇒		Test scope	Test connection	Test condition	Nominal value	Possible cause/remedy
34.0	P1 163	**Oil level switch (S43)**	N3/10 73 (17E) –V– 2 (2A)	Ignition: **ON** Oil level okay. Oil level low.	 11 – 14 V < 1 V	Wiring, S43
35.0		**Diagnosis line** Activation	N3/10 3 (3A) –V– 31 (39C)	Ignition: **ON**	11 – 14 V	Wiring, N3/10

MB1029800547000X

Fig. 38 Code P1163: Test 23, Steps 34.0–35.0

⇒		Test scope	Test connection	Test condition	Nominal value	Possible cause/remedy
25.0	P1 525	**Adjustable camshaft timing solenoid (Y49)** Current draw	Y49 1 –A– 2	**Note to test connection:** Connect test cable (102 589 04 63 00) to solenoid. Engine: **at idle** ECT > 70°C Increase engine speed to approx. 2000 rpm.	 1 – 1.5 A	⇒ 25.1, ⇒ 26.0, N3/10
25.1		Resistance (Y49)	N3/10 60 (4E) –Ω– 2 (2A)	Ignition: **OFF**	7 – 12 Ω	Wiring, Y49
26.0	P1 519	**Adjustable camshaft timing solenoid (Y49)** Mechanical function	N3/10 60 (4E) ←→ 3 (3A)	Engine: **at idle** Bridge sockets on socket box for a maximum of 10 seconds.	Engine runs rough or stalls	Check function of camshaft adjuster.

MB1029800541000X

Fig. 32 Codes P1519 & P1525: Test 23, Steps 25.0–26.0

⇒		Test scope	Test connection	Test condition	Nominal value	Possible cause/remedy
29.0	P0 440 P0 442 P0 455	Only (USA) **Model 140, 210 only,** **Model 129 as of 09/97** **Purge system** Leaks Activated charcoal canister shut-off valve (Y58/4) Activate	N3/10 3 (3A) ←→ 34 (2D)	Disconnect purge line (A) to charcoal canister on purge control valve (Y58/1). Connect vacuum tester to purge line Ignition: **ON** Apply approx. 25 mbar of vacuum.	 After approx. 1 minute, < 5 mbar vacuum loss.	Fuel tank cap, Purge line to charcoal canister, Purge line from charcoal canister to Y58/4, Charcoal canister, Y58/4
30.0	P0 446	Only (USA) **Model 140, 210 only,** **Model 129 as of 09/97** **Activated charcoal canister shut-off valve (Y58/4)** Current draw	N3/10 3 (3A) –A– 34 (2D)	Ignition: **ON**	0.5 – 0.9 A	Wiring, Y58/4

MB1029800543000X

Fig. 34 Codes P0440, P0442, P0445 & P0455: Test 23, Steps 29.0–30.0

⇒		Test scope	Test connection	Test condition	Nominal value	Possible cause/remedy
32.0	P0 450	Only (USA) **Model 129, 202 up to 08/97** **Purge monitoring pressure sensor (B4/4)** Sender signal	N3/10 36 (4D) –V– 37 (5D)	Disconnect purge line (A) to charcoal canister on purge monitoring pressure sensor (B4/4). Connect vacuum tester to purge monitoring pressure sensor Ignition: **ON** Apply approx. 300 mbar of vacuum.	 > 3.5 V < 3 V	Wiring, ⇒ 32.1, B4/4
32.1		Purge monitoring pressure sensor (B4/4) Voltage supply	N3/10 36 (4D) –V– 38 (6D)	Ignition: **ON**	4.7 – 5.3 V	N3/10

MB1029800545000X

Fig. 36 Code P0450: Test 23, Steps 32.0–32.1

⇒		Test scope	Test connection	Test condition	Nominal value	Possible cause/Remedy
1.0	P0 560	**Engine control module (N3/10)** Voltage supply circuit 30	N3/10 3 (3A) –V– 12 (4B)	Ignition: **ON**	11 – 14 V	⇒ 1.1 – 1.2
1.1		Ground wire	N3/10 / X11/4 3 (3A) –V– 2 7 (7A) –V– 2 112 (8F) –V– 2 119 (15F) –V– 2	Ignition: **ON**	11 – 14 V	Wiring, **Model 129** Ground (W27), module box bracket. **Model 140** Output ground (W15), right footwell. **Model 202, 210** Output ground (W16/6), right component compartment,

MB1029800548000X

Fig. 39 Code P0560: Test 24, Steps 1.0–1.1

⇒		Test scope	Test connection	Test condition	Nominal value	Possible cause/Remedy
1.2		Voltage supply circuit 30	X11/4 1 —(V)— 12 N3/10 (4B)	Ignition: **ON**	11 – 14 V	Wiring, **Model 129, 140** Base module (N16/1) or fuse on base module, **Model 202** Passenger-side fuse and relay module box (K40/4), **Model 210** Relay module (K40).
2.0	P0 560	**Engine control module (N3/10)** Voltage supply circuit 87	N3/10 8 (8A) —(V)— 2 (2A)	Ignition: **ON**	11 – 14 V	⇒ 2.1 – 2.2

MB1029800549000X

Fig. 40 Code P0560: Test 24, Steps 1.2–2.0

⇒		Test scope	Test connection	Test condition	Nominal value	Possible cause/Remedy
2.1		Electronics ground	N3/10 8 (8A) —(V)— 2 X11/4	Ignition: **ON**	11 – 14 V	Wiring, **Model 129** Ground (W27), module box bracket. **Model 140** Output ground (W15), right footwell, **Model 202, 210** Output ground (W16/6), right component compartment,
2.2		Voltage supply circuit 87	X11/4 1 —(V)— 2 N3/10 (2A)	Ignition: **ON** Ignition: **OFF**	11 – 14 V < 1 V	Wiring, **Model 129, 140** Base module (N16/1) or fuse on base module, **Model 202** Passenger-side fuse and relay module box (K40/4), **Model 210** Relay module (K40).

MB1029800550000X

Fig. 41 Code —: Test 24, Steps 2.1–2.2

⇒		Test scope	Test connection	Test condition	Nominal value	Possible cause/Remedy
3.0		**Ignition coil (T1/1)** Cylinder 2 and 5 Voltage supply	N3/10 3 (3A) —(V)— 117 (13F)	Ignition: **ON** Starter: **Crank**	11 – 14 V > 10 V	Wiring, Fuses: Model 129, fuse 34 Model 140, fuse 22 Model 202, fuse and relay module box fuse 6 Model 210, fuse 19 Ignition coil (T1/1)
4.0		**Ignition coil (T1/2)** Cylinder 3 and 4 Voltage supply	N3/10 3 (3A) —(V)— 110 (6F)	Ignition: **ON** Starter: **Crank**	11 – 14 V > 10 V	Wiring, Fuses: Model 129, fuse 34 Model 140, fuse 22 Model 202, fuse and relay module box fuse 6 Model 210, fuse 19 Ignition coil (T1/2)
5.0		**Ignition coil (T1/3)** Cylinder 1 and 6 Voltage supply	N3/10 3 (3A) —(V)— 124 (20F)	Ignition: **ON** Starter: **Crank**	11 – 14 V > 10 V	Wiring, Fuses: Model 129, fuse 34 Model 140, fuse 22 Model 202, fuse and relay module box fuse 6 Model 210, fuse 19 Ignition coil (T1/3)

MB1029800551000X

Fig. 42 Code —: Test 24, Steps 3.0–5.0

⇒		Test scope	Test connection	Test condition	Nominal value	Possible cause/Remedy
6.0	P0 335	**CKP sensor (L5)** Signal Voltage	N3/10 2) 93 (37E) —(oscilloscope)— 94 (38E) N3/10 3) 93 (37E) —(V)— 94 (38E)	Starter: **Crank** Engine: **at Idle** Starter: **Crank** Engine: **at Idle**	Signal, > 2.5 V~ > 5 V~ 4)	⇒ 6.1, Teeth on starter ring gear.
6.1		Resistance of CKP sensor (L5)	N3/10 93 (37E) —(Ω)— 94 (38E)	Ignition: **OFF** Unplug connector **E** on engine control module (N3/10).	700 – 1400 Ω	Wiring, L5.

2) Test with oscilloscope.
3) Test with multimeter only if oscilloscope is unavailable.
4) Voltage increases with increasing rpm.

MB1029800552000X

Fig. 43 Code P0335: Test 24, Steps 6.0–6.1

⇒		Test scope	Test connection	Test condition	Nominal value	Possible cause/Remedy
7.0	P0 341	**Camshaft Hall-effect sensor (B6/1)** Hall-effect signal	N3/10 2) 95 (39E) —(oscilloscope)— 96 (40E) N3/10 3) 96 (40E) —(V)— 2 (2A)	Engine: **at Idle** Engine: **at Idle**	Signal, 1.2 – 1.7 V Value changes	⇒ 7.1, Wiring B6/1.
7.1		Voltage supply to camshaft Hall-effect sensor (B6/1)	B6/1 1 —(V)— 3	Ignition: **ON** Disconnect connector from Hall-effect sensor (B6/1) and test directly on sockets 1 and 3 of connector.	11 – 14 V	Wiring.

2) Test with oscilloscope.
3) Test with multimeter only if oscilloscope is unavailable.

MB1029800553000X

Fig. 44 Code P0341: Test 24, Steps 7.0–7.1

⇒		Test scope	Test connection	Test condition	Nominal value	Possible cause/Remedy
8.0	P0 300 P0 302 P0 305	**Primary voltage** Ignition coil (T1/1), Cylinders 2 and 5	N3/10 117 (13F) —(oscilloscope)— 2 (2A)	**Test connection Note:** Individual primary pattern Range 400 V Duration 100% Starter: **Crank**	200 – 350 V	⇒ 8.1,
8.1		Primary winding of T1/1 and T1/2	N3/10 117 (13F) —(Ω)— 110 (6F)	Ignition: **OFF**	0.9 – 1.6 Ω 6)	Wiring T1/1 or T1/2 .
9.0	P0 300 P0 303 P0 304	**Primary voltage** Ignition coil (T1/2) Cylinders 3 and 4	N3/10 110 (6F) —(oscilloscope)— 2 (2A)	**Test connection Note:** Individual primary pattern Range 400 V Duration 100% Starter: **Crank**	200 – 350 V	⇒ 9.1,

6) The resistance of a single coil at 20°C is approx. 0.6 Ω.

MB1029800554000X

Fig. 45 Codes P0300, P0302, P0303, P0304 & P0305: Test 24, Steps 8.0–9.0

⇒		Test scope	Test connection	Test condition	Nominal value	Possible cause/Remedy
9.1		Primary winding of T1/2 and T1/1	N3/10 110 (6F) —(Ω)— 117 (13F)	Ignition: **OFF**	0.9 – 1.6 Ω 6)	Wiring T1/2 or T1/1.
10.0	P0 300 P0 301 P0 306	**Primary voltage** Ignition coil (T1/3) Cylinders 1 and 6	N3/10 124 (20F) —(oscilloscope)— 2 (2A)	**Test connection Note:** Individual primary pattern Range 400 V Duration 100% Starter: **Crank**	200 – 350 V	⇒ 10.1,
10.1		Primary winding of T1/3 and T1/2	N3/10 124 (20F) —(Ω)— 110 (6F)	Ignition: **OFF**	0.9 – 1.6 Ω 6)	Wiring T1/3 or T1/2.

6) The resistance of a single coil at 20°C is approx. 0.6 Ω.

MB1029800555000X

Fig. 46 Codes P0300, P0303 & P0306: Test 24, Steps 9.1–10.1

⇒		Test scope	Test connection	Test condition	Nominal value	Possible cause/Remedy
11.0	P0 300 P0 301 P0 302 P0 303 P0 304 P0 305 P0 306	**Firing voltage** Ignition coil (T1/1) to (T1/3)	Engine analyzer —(oscilloscope)—	**Test connection Note:** Individual secondary pattern Range 20 kV Duration 100% Connect kV pick-ups successively to T1/1 through T1/3. Starter: **Crank**	8 – 20 kV	⇒ 11.1, Spark plugs, N3/10.
11.1		Secondary winding of T1/1, T1/2 and T1/3	T1/1 T1/2 T1/3 cir. 4a —(Ω)— cir. 4b	Disconnect both ignition cables on T1/1, T1/2 or T1/3	6 – 8.5 kΩ	T1/1, T1/2 or T1/3

MB1029800556000X

Fig. 47 Codes P0300, P0301, P0302, P0303, P0304, P0305 & P0306: Test 24, Steps 11.0–11.1

⇒		Test scope	Test connection	Test condition	Nominal value	Possible cause/remedy
1.0	P1 542 P0 507	**Pedal value sensor (B37)** Signal Nominal value potentiometer 1	N3/10 15 (23C) — 16 (24C)	Ignition: **ON** Accelerator pedal position: CTP WOT with kick-down	 0.2 – 0.5 V 4.3 – 4.8 V	⇒ 1.1, Wiring, B37
1.1		**Pedal value sensor (B37)** Voltage supply	N3/10 15 (23C) — 14 (22C)	Ignition: **ON**	4.75 – 5.25 V	Wiring, N3/10
2.0	P1 542 P0 507	**Pedal value sensor (B37)** Signal Nominal value potentiometer 2	N3/10 18 (26C) — 17 (25C)	Ignition: **ON** Accelerator pedal position: CTP WOT with kick-down	 0.1 – 0.4 V 2.1 – 2.6 V	⇒ 2.1, Wiring, B37
2.1		Voltage supply [1] Nominal value potentiometer 2	N3/10 18 (26C) — 19 (27C)	Ignition: **ON**	2.25 – 2.75 V	Wiring N3/10

1) This test step not valid for Pedal value sensor using a hall-type sensor.

MB1029800557000X

Fig. 48 Codes P0507 & P1542: Test 25, Steps 1.0–2.1

⇒		Test scope	Test connection	Test condition	Nominal value	Possible cause/remedy
4.0	P1 186 P1 580	**EA/CC/ISC actuator (M16/6)** Activation of actuator motor	N3/10 105 (1F) — 106 (2F)	Ignition: **ON** Engine: **at idle** ECT > 70 °C	0.8 – 2.3 V 1.0 – 2.5 V Value oscillates.	Wiring, M16/6 N3/10
4.1		Resistance	N3/10 105 (1F) — 106 (2F)	Ignition: **OFF**	< 10 Ω	
5.0		**Model 202 only** **P/N recognition**	N3/10 51 (19D) — 2 (2A)	Ignition: **ON** Selector lever position: P/N → R, D, 4, 3, 2, 1 →	 11 – 14 V < 2.0 V	Wiring, Test ETC,

MB1029800559000X

Fig. 50 Codes P1185 & P1580: Test 25, Steps 4.0–5.0

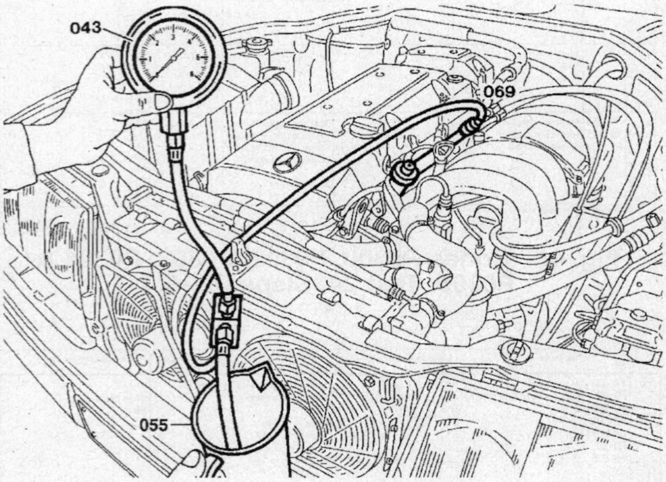

043 Pressure gauge, part no. 103 589 00 21 00
055 Measuring glass
069 Pressure hose, part no. 119 589 04 63 00

MB1029800561000X

Fig. 52 Fuel pressure connection

⇒		Test scope	Test connection	Test condition	Nominal value	Possible cause/remedy
3.0	P0 507 P0 120 P0 186 P1 580	**EA/CC/ISC actuator (M16/6)** Signal Actual value potentiometer 1	N3/10 88 (32E) — 87 (31E)	Ignition: **ON** Accelerator pedal position: CTP WOT or kick-down	 4.0 – 4.6 V < CTP value	⇒ 3.1, Wiring, M16/6
		Actual value potentiometer 2	N3/10 88 (32E) — 90 (34E)	Accelerator pedal position: CTP WOT or kick-down	 0.3 – 0.9 V > CTP value	
3.1		Voltage supply Actual value potentiometers 1 and 2	N3/10 88 (32E) — 89 (33E)	Ignition: **ON**	4.75 – 5.25 V	Wiring N3/10

MB1029800558000X

Fig. 49 Codes P0120, P0186, P0507 & P1580: Test 25, Steps 3.0–3.1

⇒		Test scope	Test connection	Test condition	Nominal value	Possible cause/Remedy
1.0	P0 565	**CC switch (S40)**		Ignition: **ON** CC switch not activated.	 < 1 V	Wiring, S40.
		V Decelerate/set	N3/10 3 (3A) — 53 (21D)	Decelerate activated.	11 – 14 V	
		SP Memory recall	N3/10 3 (3A) — 54 (22D)	Memory activated.	11 – 14 V	
		B Accelerate/set	N3/10 3 (3A) — 52 (20D)	Accelerate activated	11 – 14 V	
		A Off	N3/10 3 (3A) — 56 (24D)	CC switch not activated. Off activated.	11 – 14 V < 1 V	
		Control contact	N3/10 3 (3A) — 55 (23D)	CC switch not activated. CC switch in position: **Activate decelerate/ accelerate/off/memory**	< 1 V 11 – 14 V	

MB1029800560000X

Fig. 51 Code P0565: Test 26, Step 1.0

⇒		Test scope	Test connection	Test condition	Nominal value	Possible cause/Remedy
1.0		**Fuel pressure at idle (with vacuum)**	Pressure gauge connected to test connection.	Engine: **at idle** Valve on pressure gauge closed.	3.2 – 3.6 bar	Check fuel pumps □ 33, Diaphragm pressure regulator.
2.0		**Fuel pressure at idle (without vacuum)**	Pressure gauge connected to test connection.	Engine: **at idle** Disconnect vacuum hose from diaphragm pressure regulator.	3.7 – 4.2 bar	Diaphragm pressure regulator.
3.0		**Fuel system leakage**	Pressure gauge connected to test connection.	Engine: **OFF** After 30 minutes	> 3.0 bar > 2.5 bar	If the pressure drops quickly, replace check valve in fuel pumps. If the pressure drops slowly, check injectors □ 36, Replace diaphragm pressure regulator or O-rings on diaphragm pressure regulator.

MB1029800562000X

Fig. 53 Code —: Test 32, Fuel System Pressure & Internal Leakage Test

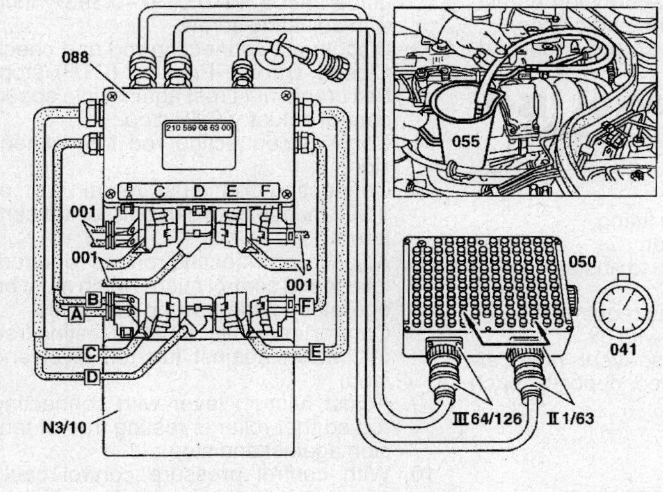

001 Engine control module connectors A–F
041 Stop watch
050 Socket box tester, 126 pole
055 Measuring glass
088 Test cable
N3/10 Engine control module (ME-SFI)

MB1029800563000X

Fig. 54 Fuel pump test connections

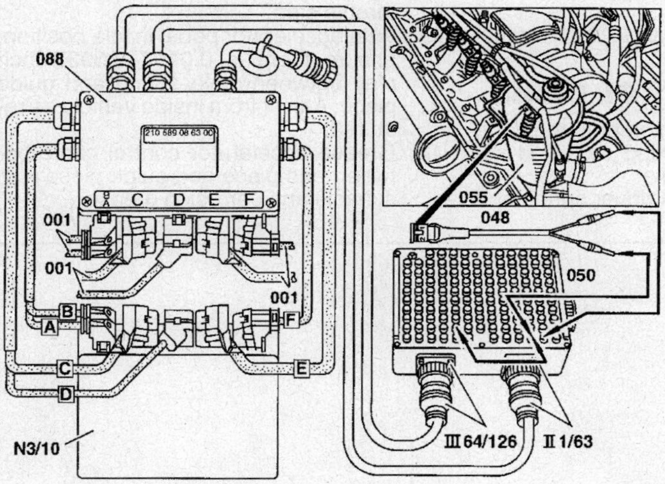

001 Engine control module connectors A–F
048 Self made harness
050 Socket box tester, 126 pole
055 Measuring glass
088 Test cable
N3/10 Engine control module (ME-SFI)

MB1029800565000X

Fig. 56 Injector test connection

⇒		Test scope	Test connection	Test condition	Nominal value	Possible cause/Remedy
1.0		**Fuel pump** Delivery capacity	N3/10 3 (3A) ←→ 21 (29C)	Disconnect fuel return hose from fuel line and place end in measuring glass. Ignition: **ON**	1 liter of fuel within 35 seconds.	Check fuel lines for restrictions (kinks and dents), Replace fuel filter, ⇒ 2.0
2.0		**Fuel pumps** Current draw		On Models 129, 140 and 202 disconnect fuel pump relay module and connect multimeter to sockets 1 and 3 On Model 210 disconnect connector B of relay module and connect multimeter to sockets 1 and 3. Ignition: **ON**	5 – 9 A	Fuel pump

1) Observe Preparation for Test, see ☐ 33.

MB1029800564000X

Fig. 55 Code —: Test 34, Fuel Pump Test

⇒		Test scope	Test connection	Test condition	Nominal value	Possible cause/Remedy
1.0		**Injectors** Leakage test	N3/10 3 (3A) ←→ 21 (29C)	Fuel rail and fuel injectors removed. Ignition: **ON**	Injectors must not drip.	Replace dripping injectors, ⇒ 2.0.
2.0		**Injectors** Operation and spray pattern test	N3/10 3 (3A) ←→ 21 (29C)	Ignition: **ON** Hold each injector (one after another) into a container and, using the self-made test harness, manually activate the injector by connecting harness banana plugs to socket box sockets 3 (–) and 2 (+).	Injectors must spray evenly	Replace defective injectors.

MB1029800566000X

Fig. 57 Code —: Test 36: Injector Test

SYSTEM SERVICE

Component Replacement

FUEL RAIL

1. Relieve fuel system pressure through fuel rail service valve.
2. Remove oil filter.
3. Remove mounting bolts, nuts and fuel rail.
4. Disconnect fuel feed and return flow lines.
5. Reverse procedure to install with new O-rings. **Torque** mounting bolts and nuts to 18 ft. lbs.

FUEL INJECTORS

1. Remove fuel rail as outlined under "Fuel Rail."
2. Remove anti-twist lock and fuel injector.
3. Reverse procedure to install, noting the following:
   a. Install new O-rings lightly moistened with oil.
   b. New anti-twist lock must engage four-point lug on injector valve.

DIAPHRAGM PRESSURE REGULATOR

1. Relieve fuel system pressure through fuel rail service valve.
2. Disconnect diaphragm pressure diaphragm vacuum hose.
3. Remove circlip and pressure damper.
4. Reverse procedure to install with new O-ring. Apply suitable engine oil to O-ring.

HOT FILM AIR MASS (HFM) SENSOR

1. Disconnect HFM sensor electrical connector.
2. Remove air mass sensor from air intake duct.
3. Reverse procedure to install. Inspect sensor O-ring as required.

OXYGEN SENSOR

1. Disconnect oxygen sensor electrical connector.
2. Remove oxygen sensor with oxygen sensor socket tool Nos. 111 589 03 09 00 and 000 589 71 03 00, or equivalents.
3. Coat oxygen sensor threads with hot lubricating paste part No. 000 989 76 51, or equivalent.
4. **Torque** oxygen sensor to 41 ft. lbs.

CRANKSHAFT POSITION (CKP) SENSOR

1. Remove starter motor as outlined in "Electrical" section.
2. Remove cruise control actuator.
3. Disconnect connector or coupling.
4. Remove mounting bolt and CKP sensor.
5. Reverse procedure to install.

CAMSHAFT POSITION (CMP) SENSOR

1. Remove valve cover.
2. Disconnect camshaft position sensor electrical connector.
3. Remove mounting bolts and CMP sensor.
4. Reverse procedure to install with new seal. Adjust sensor as outlined under "Adjustments."

KNOCK SENSOR

1. Remove starter motor as outlined in "Electrical" section
2. Knock sensor.
3. Disconnect, compress retaining clip and remove connector.
4. Remove knock sensor.
5. Reverse procedure to install.

THROTTLE CONTROL CABLE

1. Pull plastic nipple out and remove guide piece.
2. Compress plastic clip and pull bracket off accelerator control lever with accelerator control cable.
3. Remove bracket with expanding pin and disconnect accelerator control cable mount.
4. Press accelerator control cable out from inside vehicle. **Do not press rubber grommet out.**
5. Remover accelerator control cable from engine compartment.
6. Reverse procedure to install, noting the following:
   a. Grease accelerator control cable with suitable anti-corrosion grease between guide and end pieces.
   b. Adjust cable as outlined under "Adjustments."

IDLE SPEED CONTROL (ISC) ACTUATOR

1. Remove air cleaner cross pipe and resonance flap.
2. Remove connection fitting.
3. Remove ISC actuator.
4. Reverse procedure to install, noting the following:
   a. Replace O-ring as required.
   b. Lubricate O-ring with oil.
   c. Ensure crankcase vent hose arrows at positioned opposite each other.

Adjustments

CAMSHAFT POSITION (CMP) SENSOR

1. Rotate crankshaft until camshaft gear segment and camshaft position sensor are opposite each other.
2. Measure gap between camshaft gear segment and camshaft position sensor.
3. If clearance is not 0.0197 inch, adjust with shims.

THROTTLE CONTROL CABLE

1. Check ease of movement, then the condition of connecting rods and accelerator control cable.
2. Adjust play between driver spring and guide piece to 0.0197–0.3937 inch with adjusting screw.
3. Disconnect connecting rod and check Closed Throttle Position (CTP) stop. Bell crank must rest against idle speed control actuator CTP stop.
4. Connect connecting rod free of tension.
5. Connecting rod must remain set at 3.307 inches between ball socket centers.
6. Adjusting connecting rod, as required.
7. Idle speed control microswitch must be operated (closed) when doing this.
8. Control lever roller must be resting free of tension against fulcrum level end stop.
9. Adjust fulcrum lever with connecting rod so that roller is resting free of tension against end stop.
10. With control pressure control cable connected, turn adjust screw until drag lever tip is at same level as fulcrum lever tip.
11. With engine off, depress accelerator pedal to full throttle stop at kickdown switch without operating switch.
12. Adjust bell crank until it is resting against idle speed control actuator full throttle stop.
13. With accelerator pedal in idle position, ensure there is 0.0197–0.3937 inch play between drive spring and guide piece. Adjust from inside vehicle as required.
14. Grease accelerator control cable between end piece and guide piece with suitable anti-corrosion grease.

111 Engine (ME 2.1 Engine Management)

NOTE: On Air Bag Equipped Models, Refer To "Air Bag System Precautions" Located In The Front Of This Manual For System Disarming & Arming Procedures.

NOTE: Refer To "Computer Relearn Procedures" Located In The Front Of This Manual When Battery Power To The Computer Has Been Interrupted.

NOTE: "Electrical Symbol Identification" Located In Front Of This Manual May Be Used As An Aid When Using Wiring Diagrams Found In This Section.

NOTE: Prior To Performing Any Service Listed In This Section Consult "Technical Service Bulletin" Section For Related Information.

INDEX

	Page No.
Description	14-51
Diagnosis & Testing	14-51
Accessing Diagnostic Trouble Codes	14-51
Generic Scan Tool	14-51
Hand-Held Tester	14-51
Clearing Diagnostic Trouble Codes	14-52
Component Tests	14-52
Fuel Injector	14-52
Fuel Pump	14-52
Components Locations	14-51
Connector Terminal Identification	14-52
Diagnostic Tests	14-52
Diagnostic Trouble Code Interpretation	14-51
Symbol Explanation	14-51
Symptom Related Diagnosis	14-51
Wiring Diagrams	14-52
Diagnostic Chart Index	14-71
Precautions	14-50
Air Bag Systems	14-50
Battery Ground Cable	14-50
Drive Authorization System (DAS)	14-50
ECM Recognition	14-50
ECM Self-Adaptation	14-50
ESP/ASR/ETS/ABS Control Modules	14-51
Ignition System	14-50
Sensor & Fuel Injector Specifications	14-50
System Service	14-78
Adjustments	14-79
Camshaft Position (CMP) Sensor	14-79
Throttle Control Cable	14-79
Component Replacement	14-78
Camshaft Position (CMP) Sensor	14-79
Crankshaft Position (CKP) Sensor	14-78
Diaphragm Pressure Regulator	14-78
Electronic Accelerator Actuator	14-79
Fuel Injectors	14-78
Fuel Rail	14-78
Hot Film Air Mass (HFM) Sensor	14-78
Idle Speed Control (ISC) Actuator	14-79
Knock Sensor	14-79
Oxygen Sensor	14-78
Throttle Control Cable	14-79

SENSOR & FUEL INJECTOR SPECIFICATIONS

Temperature, °F	Resistance, Ohms①	Voltage①
ADJUSTABLE CAMSHAFT TIMING SOLENOID		
158	7–12	—
CAMSHAFT POSITION SENSOR		
—	900–1600	—
CRANKSHAFT POSITION (CKP) SENSOR		
—	700–1400	—
ENGINE COOLANT TEMPERATURE (ECT) SENSOR		
68	3090	3.4
86	2000	2.9
104	1330	2.4
122	900	1.9
140	630	1.5
158	440	1.2
176	320	.9
194	230	.7
212	170	.5
FUEL INJECTOR		
—	14–17	—
INTAKE AIR TEMPERATURE (IAT) SENSOR		
50	3600	3.1
68	2420	2.7
104	1660	2.2
122	1170	1.8
140	850	1.4
158	600	1.1
MASS AIR FLOW (MAF) SENSOR		
158	—	0.9–1.1

① — Tolerance ± 5%.

PRECAUTIONS

Air Bag Systems

Refer to "Air Bag System Precautions" in the front of this manual for system disarming and arming procedures.

Battery Ground Cable

Prior to service, disconnect battery ground cable and isolate as required.

Ignition System

1. Both control module coupling must be disconnected or connect with ignition switch in Off position.
2. Do not short circuit ignition coils terminal No. 1.
3. Do not operate the ignition system at starting speed unless the ignition cables are fully connected.
4. Do not conduct are test at starting speed or when engine is running. This includes: holding ignition cable No. 4 at a distance to ground, disconnecting a plug connector or pulling cable No. 4 out of the ignition coils.
5. High output side of ignition system must always carry at least two ohms resistance (spark plug connected).
6. Do not load ignition coil with more than 28,000 volts.
7. Ignition coil iron cores must always be connected to ground. **Use caution, coil cores can be charged with up to 400 volts.**
8. **Do not work on this system if you have a pacemaker.**
9. Ensure engine and ignition switch are in Off position when connecting and disconnecting ignition coil.
10. When working at start speeds during test such as compression check, switch ignition to off position and disconnect control module connector No. 2.

ECM Self-Adaptation

After repair work, the Engine Control Module (ECM) will automatically adapt itself after the vehicle has made approximately 10 trips. A trip includes a vehicle speed of more than 2.5 mph, engine speed of more than 700 RPM and engine shutoff of more than 30 seconds.

However, after fixing a malfunction or installation of a test ECM, the self-adaptation function must be reset as outlined under "Computer Relearn" at the front of this manual.

ECM Recognition

The ECM must be coded for vehicle model, catalytic converter, transmission, cruise control, acceleration slip regulation (ASR), electronic traction system (ETS) and country version with the Hand-Held Tester.

Before replacing the ECM, read and store existing code numbers with the Hand-Held Tester. When the new ECM is installed, enter the stored code numbers from the Hand-Held Tester. If code numbers cannot be read, the corresponding codes number must be obtained from Mercedes-Benz spare parts microfiche and manually entered with a Hand-Held Tester.

Drive Authorization System (DAS)

The DAS can only be activated or deactivated by the electronic ignition key. The ECM, RCL and DAS control module are

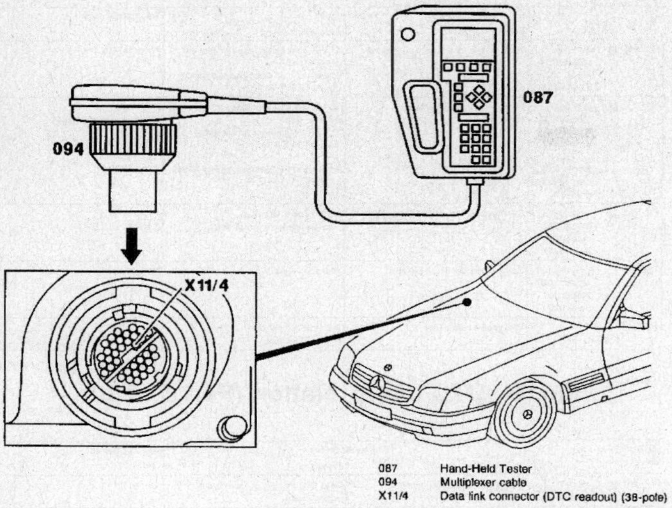

MB1029800567000X

Fig. 1 DLC tool connection

DTC	Possible cause		Test step/Remedy
	SAE nomenclature	Explanation	
–	No malfunction in system		In case of complaint, perform □ 23, 24, 25 or 26 in its entirety.
P0 100 ■	MAF circuit malfunction	Hot film MAF sensor (B2/5)	□ 23⇒ 4.0
P0 105 ■	MAP circuit malfunction	Pressure sensor (B28)	□ 23⇒ 6.0
P0 110 ■	IAT circuit malfunction	IAT sensor (in Hot film MAF sensor B2/5)	□ 23⇒ 5.0
P0 115 ■	ECT circuit malfunction	ECT sensor (B11/4)	□ 23⇒ 8.0
P0 120	Throttle position circuit malfunction	Actual value potentiometer in CC/ISC actuator (M16/2)	□ 25⇒ 3.0
P0 130 ■	O2S 1 circuit malfunction	A. O2S 1 (before TWC) (G3/2) B. O2S 1 (before TWC) (G3/2) voltage increase insufficient	□ 23⇒ 10.0

MB1029800568010X

Fig. 2 DTC interpretation (Part 1 of 10)

DTC	Possible cause		Test step/Remedy [1]
	SAE nomenclature	Explanation	
P0 133 ■	O2S 1 circuit slow response	A O2S 1 (before TWC) (G3/2), ageing correction value exceeded B O2S 1 (before TWC) (G3/2), ageing time period too long	□ 23⇒ 10.0
P0 135 ■	O2S 1 heater circuit malfunction	O2S 1 heater (before TWC) (G3/2)	□ 23 ⇒ 11.0
P0 136 ■	O2S 2 circuit malfunction	O2S 2 (after TWC) (G3/1)	□ 23 ⇒ 12.0
P0 141 ■	O2S 2 heater circuit malfunction	Right O2S 2 heater (after TWC) (G3/1)	□ 23⇒ 13.0
P0 170 ■	Fuel trim malfunction	A Self adaptation of fuel mixture "partial load" at limit from engine control module (N3/10). B Self adaptation of fuel mixture "CTP" at limit from engine control module (N3/10).	Intake air leak, injectors, diaphragm pressure regulator, engine wear.
P0 201 ■	Injector circuit malfunction - cyl. 1	Injector (Y62y1) – cylinder 1	□ 23⇒ 14.0
P0 202 ■	Injector circuit malfunction - cyl. 2	Injector (Y62y2) – cylinder 2	□ 23⇒ 15.0
P0 203 ■	Injector circuit malfunction - cyl. 3	Injector (Y62y3) – cylinder 3	□ 23 ⇒ 16.0
P0 204 ■	Injector circuit malfunction - cyl. 4	Injector (Y62y4) – cylinder 4	□ 23 ⇒ 17.0

MB1029800568020X

Fig. 2 DTC interpretation (Part 2 of 10)

DTC	Possible cause		Test step/Remedy [1]
	SAE nomenclature	Explanation	
P0 300 ■	Random misfire detected	A Random misfire B Random misfire, TWC damaging	□ 24 ⇒ 7.0 – 8.0 □ 24 ⇒ 9.0 □ 36 ⇒ 1.0 – 2.0 Compression pressure
P0 301 ■	Cylinder 1 misfire detected	A Cylinder 1 misfire B Cylinder 1 misfire, TWC damaging	□ 24 ⇒ 7.0 □ 24 ⇒ 9.0 □ 36 ⇒ 1.0 – 2.0 Compression pressure
P0 302 ■	Cylinder 2 misfire detected	A Cylinder 2 misfire B Cylinder 2 misfire, TWC damaging	□ 24 ⇒ 8.0 □ 24 ⇒ 9.0 □ 36 ⇒ 1.0 – 2.0 Compression pressure
P0 303 ■	Cylinder 3 misfire detected	A Cylinder 3 misfire B Cylinder 3 misfire, TWC damaging	□ 24 ⇒ 8.0 □ 24 ⇒ 9.0 □ 36 ⇒ 1.0 – 2.0 Compression pressure
P0 304 ■	Cylinder 4 misfire detected	A Cylinder 4 misfire B Cylinder 4 misfire, TWC damaging	□ 24 ⇒ 7.0 □ 24 ⇒ 9.0 □ 36 ⇒ 1.0 – 2.0 Compression pressure

MB1029800568030X

Fig. 2 DTC interpretation (Part 3 of 10)

permanently locked together by an identification code. This code cannot be erased. Trial installation of an ECM or RCL control module from another vehicle is not possible. After 40 starts, a new ECM cannot be used in any other vehicle. The code number and VIN must be entered into the ECM with a Hand-Held Tester.

ESP/ASR/ETS/ABS Control Modules

The Electronic Stability Program (ESP), Acceleration Slip Regulation (ASR), Electronic Traction System (ETS) and/or Anti-lock Brake System (ABS) control modules must not be disconnected. The Engine Control Module (ECM) and Transmission Control Module (TCM) rely on those control modules for Vehicle Speed Sensor (VSS) information. To disable brake and engine regulation of those modules, proceed as follows:

1. Turn ignition switch to Off position.
2. Connect Hand-Held Tester adapter to Data Link Connector (DLC).
3. Jump sockets No. 1 and 6.
4. Start engine. MIL must light.
5. If Hand-Held Tester is available, disconnect VSS front axle connector.
6. When testing is complete, connect VSS and erase Diagnostic Trouble Codes with Hand-Held Tester.

DESCRIPTION

Refer to "104 Engine (ME 2.1 Engine Management)" section.

DIAGNOSIS & TESTING

Symbol Explanation

Refer to "104 Engine (ME 2.1 Engine Management)" section for explanations of symbols, connections and steps included in the charts.

Accessing Diagnostic Trouble Codes

GENERIC SCAN TOOL

Follow tool manufacturers instructions and connect suitably programmed scan tool to generic scan tool connection X11/22.

HAND-HELD TESTER

1. Turn ignition switch to Off position.
2. Attach test cable tool No. 965 589 00 40 00, or equivalent, to Hand-Held Tester tool No. 965 589 00 01 00, or equivalent.
3. Connect cable to Data Link Connector (DLC), **Fig. 1**.
4. Turn multiplexer cable locking ring completely to left detent stop.
5. Attach multiplexer cable to data link connector via locking pins.
6. To lock multiplexer cable to connector, turn locking ring to the right.
7. Follow tool manufacturer's instructions.

Diagnostic Trouble Code Interpretation

Refer to **Fig. 2** for DTC interpretation. **Black square items are emission related and may activate MIL during test cycle.**

Symptom Related Diagnosis

Refer to **Fig. 3** for symptom related diagnosis.

Components Locations

Refer to **Figs. 4 through 6** for component locations.

DTC		Possible cause		Test step/Remedy
		SAE nomenclature	Explanation	
P0 325 ■		KS 1 circuit malfunction	Front KS 1 (A16)	Wiring, connector, A16
P0 335		CKP sensor circuit malfunction	CKP sensor (L5)	□ 24 ⇒ 5.0
P0 341 ■		CMP sensor circuit range/performance	Camshaft Hall-effect sensor (B6/1)	□ 24 ⇒ 6.0
P0 400	Only (USA) Model 202	Exhaust gas recirculation flow malfunction	Exhaust gas recirculation malfunction (logic chain)	□ 23 ⇒ 22.0 – 23.0
P0 410 ■	Only (USA) Models 170, 202	Air injection system malfunction	AIR system malfunction (logic chain)	□ 23 ⇒ 20.0
P0 422 ■		TWC efficiency below threshold	TWC efficiency below threshold	Replace TWC
P0 440 ■	Only (USA) Model 170 Model 202 as of 09/97	EVAP system malfunction	EVAP system leak (logic chain)	□ 23 ⇒ 26.0 – 28.0
P0 441 ■		EVAP system incorrect purge flow	EVAP not functioning	□ 23 ⇒ 26.0 – 27.0
P0 442 ■	Only (USA) Model 170 Model 202 as of 09/97	EVAP system leak detected (small leak)	EVAP system, small leak	□ 23 ⇒ 28.0
P0 443 ■		EVAP system purge control valve circuit malfunction	Purge control valve (Y58/1)	□ 23 ⇒ 26.0

MB1029800568040X

Fig. 2 DTC interpretation (Part 4 of 10)

DTC		Possible cause		Test step/Remedy
		SAE nomenclature	Explanation	
P0 446 ■	Only (USA) Model 170 Model 202 as of 09/97	EVAP system vent control malfunction	A. Activated charcoal canister shut-off valve (Y58/4) B. End stage activated charcoal canister shut-off valve (Y58/4)	□ 23 ⇒ 29.0
P0 450 ■	Only (USA) Model 170 Model 202 as of 09/97	EVAP system pressure sensor malfunction	A. Fuel tank pressure sensor (B4/3) electrical fault B. Fuel tank pressure sensor (B4/3) electrical fluctuations	□ 23 ⇒ 30.0 Charcoal canister plugged.
	Model 202 only (USA), up ot 08/97		Purge monitoring pressure sensor (B4/4)	□ 23 ⇒ 31.0
P0 455 ■	Only (USA) Model 170 Model 202 as of 09/97	EVAP system leak detected (large leak)	EVAP system, large leak Fuel tank pressure sensor (B4/3)	□ 23 ⇒ 28.0 □ 23 ⇒ 30.0
P0 460	Only (USA) Model 170 Model 202 as of 09/97	Fuel level sensor circuit low input	Fuel tank level too low	Fill fuel tank.
P0 500		VSS sensor malfunction	A VSS left front B VSS left rear	Test ASR/ETS

MB1029800568050X

Fig. 2 DTC interpretation (Part 5 of 10)

DTC	Possible cause		Test step/Remedy
	SAE nomenclature	Explanation	
P0 507	ISC rpm higher than expected	Idle control system	□ 25 ⇒ 1.0 – 3.0
P0 560	System voltage malfunction	Voltage supply at engine control module (N3/10)	□ 23 ⇒ 1.0 – 2.0
P0 565	Cruise control switch	CC switch (S40)	□ 26 ⇒ 1.0
P0 600	Serial communication link malfunction	CAN bus from ESP/SPS control module (N47-5)	□ 23 ⇒ 32.0
P0 604	Internal control module random Access memory (RAM) error	A. Engine control module (N3/10) B. Engine control module (N3/10)	(N3/10)
P0 605	Internal control module read only memory (ROM) error	Engine control module (N3/10)	(N3/10)
P0 700 ■	Transmission control system malfunction	Read DTC memory of transmission control module	Test ETC
P0 702 ■	Transmission control system electrical	Read DTC memory of transmission control module	Test ETC
P0 715 ■	Input/turbine speed sensor circuit malfunction	Read DTC memory of transmission control module	Test ETC
P0 720 ■	Output speed sensor circuit malfunction	Read DTC memory of transmission control module	Test ETC
P0 730 ■	Incorrect gear ratio	Read DTC memory of transmission control module	Test ETC

MB1029800568060X

Fig. 2 DTC interpretation (Part 6 of 10)

DTC		Possible cause		Test step/Remedy
		SAE nomenclature	Explanation	
P0 740 ■		Torque converter clutch circuit malfunction	Read DTC memory of transmission control module	Test ETC
P0 743 ■		Torque converter clutch circuit electrical	Read DTC memory of transmission control module	Test ETC
P0 748 ■		Pressure control solenoid electrical	Read DTC memory of transmission control module	Test ETC
P0 753 ■		Shift solenoid A electrical	Read DTC memory of transmission control module	Test ETC
P0 758 ■		Shift solenoid B electrical	Read DTC memory of transmission control module	Test ETC
P0 763 ■		Shift solenoid C electrical	Read DTC memory of transmission control module	Test ETC
P0 801		Engine/climate control electric cooling fan malfunction	Engine/climate control electric cooling fan (M4/3)	□ 23 ⇒ 38.0
P0 803	Model 170 only	Air flap/air filter actuator malfunction	Air flap/air filter actuator (M16/7)	□ 23 ⇒ 37.0
P0 805	Model 170 only	Supercharger function	Supercharger function	□ 23 ⇒ 35.0
P0 806	Model 170 only	Magnetic supercharger clutch	Magnetic supercharger clutch (Y2/1)	□ 23 ⇒ 36.0

MB1029800568070X

Fig. 2 DTC interpretation (Part 7 of 10)

Wiring Diagrams

Refer to **Figs. 7 through 12** for wiring diagrams.

Connector Terminal Identification

Refer to **Fig. 13** for engine control module connector terminal identification.

Diagnostic Tests

1. Turn ignition switch to Off position.
2. Connect 126-pole socket box tool No. 129 589 00 21 00, or equivalent, with contact module tool No. 201 589 00 99 00, or equivalent, to Engine Control Module, **Fig. 14.**
3. Connect interior harness connector to test cable connection No. 1 and engine harness connector to test cable connection No. 2.
4. Conduct tests as directed in **Figs. 15 through 52** using suitable multimeter.

Clearing Diagnostic Trouble Codes

The Diagnostic Trouble Code (DTC) memory is cleared when the vehicle battery is disconnected.

When an component has been repaired or replaced, the related DTC will be cleared. After three trips the CHECK ENGINE Malfunction Indicator Lamp (MIL) will go out and after 40 warm-up periods the DTC is automatically erased. A trip includes engine running for more than 20 minutes, engine oil temperature of more than 19°F, engine speed of more than 700 RPM and emission related logic chain functions. A warm-up period includes an engine coolant temperature at start-up of less than 95°F and increasing to more than 176°F.

To erase DTCs with a Hand-Held Tester, follow the tool manufacturer's instructions.

Component Tests

FUEL PUMP

1. Connect suitable pressure gauge to test connection, **Fig. 53.**
2. Conduct tests as directed, **Fig. 54.**
3. Connect 126-pole socket box tool No. 129 589 00 21 00, or equivalent, to Engine Control Module (ECM) with test cable tool No. 201 589 00 99 00, or equivalent, **Fig. 55.**
4. Conduct tests as directed, **Fig. 56.**
5. Release fuel pressure and allow fuel to drain into suitable measuring cup.

FUEL INJECTOR

1. Connect 126-pole socket box tool No. 129 589 00 21 00, or equivalent, to Engine Control Module (ECM) with test cable tool No. 210 589 08 63 00, or equivalent, **Fig. 57.**
2. Disconnect injector connectors, then remove fuel rail with injectors. **Do not disconnect fuel feed and return lines.**
3. Connect self-made harness to one injector after another, hold over suitable measuring glass and test as directed, **Fig. 58.**

DTC		Possible cause		Test step/Remedy
		SAE nomenclature	Explanation	
P0 809		Angle deviation between camshaft and crankshaft	Angle deviation between camshaft and crankshaft	Check basic adjustment of camshaft.
P0 811		CAN from electronic ignition lock	CAN from electronic ignition lock	□ 23 ⇒ 32.0
P1 163		Oil level switch	Oil level switch (S43)	□ 23 ⇒ 34.0
P1 181		Engine/climate control electric cooling fan malfunction	Engine/climate control electric cooling fan (M4/3) functional fault	□ 23 ⇒ 38.0
P1 182	**Model 170 only** **Model 202 as of 06/97**	Starter lock-out relay module (N65k2) Starter relay (K40/4k2)	Starter relay in passenger-side fuse and relay module box (K40/4)	□ 23 ⇒ 3.0
P1 186		Fuel safety shut-off recognized	EA/CC/ISC actuator (M16/1)	□ 23 ⇒ 3.0, EA/CC/ISC actuator (M16/1) sticks or jammed, Check intake system for residue.
P1 386 ■		Knock sensor control from ECM (N3/10) at end stop	Knock sensor regulation from engine control module (N3/10) at end stop	1. Increased knock tendency due to bad fuel, carbon in combustion chamber or mechanical damage, 2. Engine control module (N3/10).

MB1029800568080X

Fig. 2 DTC interpretation (Part 8 of 10)

DTC	Possible cause		Test step/Remedy
	SAE nomenclature	Explanation	
P1 580 ■	EA/CC/ISC actuator	EA/CC/ISC actuator (M16/6)	□ 25 ⇒ 3.0 – 4.0
P1 584	Stop lamp switch	Stop lamp switch (S9/1)	Test ETS, ASR
P1 642	Engine control module incorrectly coded	Engine control module incorrectly coded (coded for MT, vehicle has AT)	Check version coding and correct.
P1 643	Engine control module incorrectly coded or No CAN transmission from transmission control module	Engine control module incorrectly coded (coded for MT, vehicle has AT) or No CAN transmission from transmission control module (N15/3)	Check version coding and correct. Test ETC
P1 644	Transmission version can not be checked due to low voltage at transmission control module	Transmission version can not be checked due to low voltage at transmission control module (N15/3)	Test ETC
P1 747 ■	CAN signal from ETC	A. CAN failure: Transmission protection malfunction from transmission control module (N15/3) B. CAN failure: Instrument cluster	Test ETC Test instrument cluster

MB1029800568100X

Fig. 2 DTC interpretation (Part 10 of 10)

Complaint/Problem	Possible cause	Test step/Remedy [1]	Actual value Engine test Menu item
Engine runs unevenly (shakes)	Injector (Y62) activation and injection duration. Injector leaking, spray pattern. O2S 1 (G3/2) (before TWC). Ignition voltage too low. Compression on one or more cylinders too low. Intake air leak.	□ 23 ⇒ 14.0 – 17.0 □ 36 ⇒ 1.0 □ 23 ⇒ 10.0 – 11.0 □ 24 ⇒ 9.0 Check compression. Remedy air leak.	2/7 – 5/7 – – –
Engine runs unevenly (misfiring)	Ignition voltage too low. Hot film MAF sensor (B2/5).	□ 24 ⇒ 9.0 □ 23 ⇒ 4.0	– 1/7
Engine surges after cold start	Intake air leak.	Remedy air leak.	–
Transition failure during warm-up	ECT sensor (B11/4). Hot film MAF sensor (B2/5). Intake air leak.	□ 23 ⇒ 8.0 □ 23 ⇒ 4.0 Remedy leak.	3/7 1/7 –
Transition failure when warm or increased fuel consumption	O2S 1 (G3/2) (before TWC). Purge control valve (Y58/1) stuck in open position.	□ 23 ⇒ 10.0 – 11.0 □ 23 ⇒ 26.0 – 27.0	5/7 3/7
Engine vibrates	Hot film MAF sensor (B2/5). Ignition voltage too low. O2S 1 (G3/2) (before TWC).	□ 23 ⇒ 4.0 □ 24 ⇒ 9.0 □ 23 ⇒ 10.0 – 11.0	1/7 – 5/7
EA is in "limp-home" mode	Nominal value potentiometer in pedal value sensor (B37). EA/CC/ISC actuator actual value potentiometer.	□ 25 ⇒ 1.0 – 2.0 □ 25 ⇒ 3.0	4/7 4/7

1) Observe Preparation for Test, see □ 22.

MB1029800569020X

Fig. 3 Symptom related diagnosis (Part 2 of 2)

DTC		Possible cause		Test step/Remedy
		SAE nomenclature	Explanation	
P1 400 ■	Only (USA) **Model 202**	EGR switchover valve malfunction	EGR switchover valve (Y27)	□ 23 ⇒ 21.0
P1 420 ■	Only (USA) **Models 170, 202**	AIR pump switchover valve	AIR pump switchover valve (Y32)	□ 23 ⇒ 19.0
P1 453 ■	Only (USA) **Model 202**	AIR relay module	AIR relay module in passenger-side fuse and relay module box (K40/4)	□ 23 ⇒ 18.0
P1 491		Refrigerant pressure in A/C system too high	Refrigerant pressure in A/C system too high	Check automatic A/C system.
P1 519 ■		Adjustable camshaft timing solenoid	Adjustable camshaft timing solenoid (Y49) (logic chain)	□ 23 ⇒ 25.0
P1 525 ■		Adjustable camshaft timing solenoid	Adjustable camshaft timing solenoid (Y49)	□ 23 ⇒ 24.0
P1 542		Pedal value sensor	Pedal value sensor (B37)	□ 25 ⇒ 1.0 – 2.0
P1 570		CAN signal from DAS control module to engine control module	A. Start attempted with "locked" DAS B. CAN signal from DAS control module (N54/1) to engine control module (N3/10) interrupted. C. Engine control module (ME-SFI) and DAS control module are not compatible.	User error, Check correct operation of DAS. □ 23 ⇒ 31.0 Check control modules and part no.

MB1029800568090X

Fig. 2 DTC interpretation (Part 9 of 10)

Complaint/Problem	Possible cause	Test step/Remedy	Actual value Engine test Menu item
Engine starts and accelerates poorly when cold	Injector (Y62) activation and injection duration. Hot film MAF sensor (B2/5). ECT sensor (B11/4). Ignition voltage too low. Intake air leak.	□ 23 ⇒ 14.0 – 17.0 □ 23 ⇒ 4.0 □ 23 ⇒ 8.0 □ 24 ⇒ 9.0 Remedy air leak.	2/7 1/7 3/7 – –
Engine does not start	Voltage supply is missing. Malfunction of drive authorization system (DAS) . Fuel pumps defective. No compression, oil pressure too high. Ignition voltage too low.	□ 23 ⇒ 1.0 – 2.0 □ 23 ⇒ 32.0 □ 34 ⇒ 2.0 Check compression and oil pressure. □ 24 ⇒ 9.0	– DAS 1/1 – – –
Engine has uneven idle	Camshaft timing. Injector (Y62) activation and injection duration. Intake air leak.	□ 23 ⇒ 24.0 – 25.0 □ 23 ⇒ 14.0 – 17.0 Remedy air leak.	2/7 2/7 –
Engine has insufficient output	TWC flow restricted. O2S 1 (G3/2) (before TWC). ECT sensor (B11/4). Hot film MAF sensor (B2/5). Camshaft timing.	Check exhaust back pressure □ 23 ⇒ 10.0 – 11.0 □ 23 ⇒ 8.0 □ 23 ⇒ 4.0 □ 23 ⇒ 24.0 – 25.0	– 5/7 3/7 1/7 2/7

MB1029800569010X

Fig. 3 Symptom related diagnosis (Part 1 of 2)

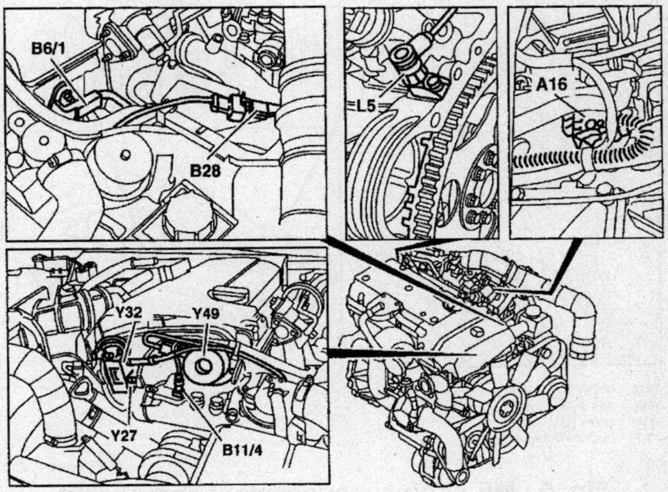

A16 Knock sensor
B6/1 Camshaft Hall-effect sensor
B11/4 ECT sensor
B28 Pressure sensor
L5 CKP sensor
Y27 EGR switchover valve (Model 202 only)
Y32 AIR pump switchover valve
Y49 Adjustable camshaft timing solenoid

MB1029800570010X

Fig. 4 ME engine management component locations (Part 1 of 2). 111 engine

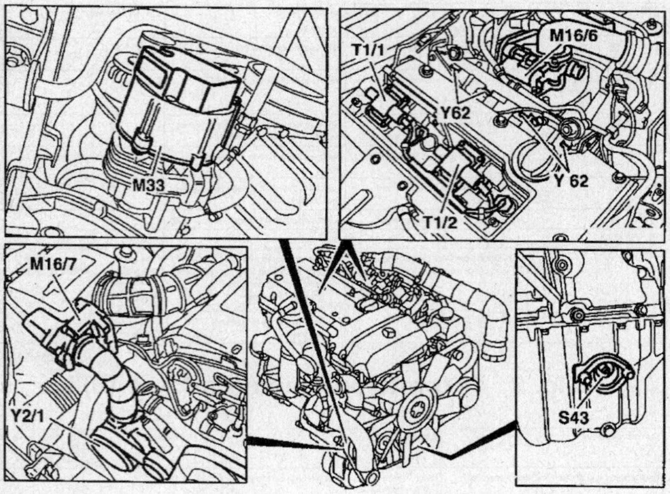

M16/6 ISC actuator
M16/7 Air flap/air filter actuator
M33 AIR pump (Model 202 only (USA))
S43 Oil level switch
T1/1 Ignition coil, cylinder 1 and 4
T1/2 Ignition coil, cylinder 2 and 3
Y2/1 Magnetic super charger clutch (Model 170 only)
Y62 Injectors

MB1029800570020X

Fig. 4 ME engine management component locations (Part 2 of 2). 111 engine

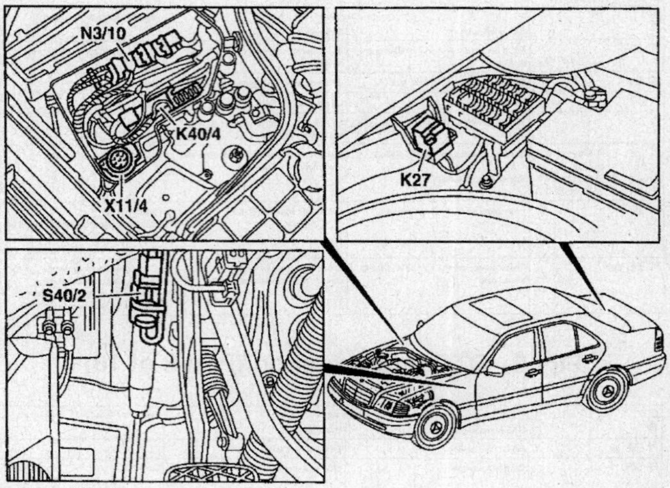

K27 FP relay module
K40/4 Passenger-side fuse and relay module box with:
Starter relay
Relay module, AIR pump (only (USA))
N3/10 Engine control module (ME-SFI)
S40/2 Clutch pedal switch (not (USA))
X11/4 Data link connector (DTC readout)

MB1029800572010X

Fig. 5 ME engine management component locations (Part 1 of 4). C230

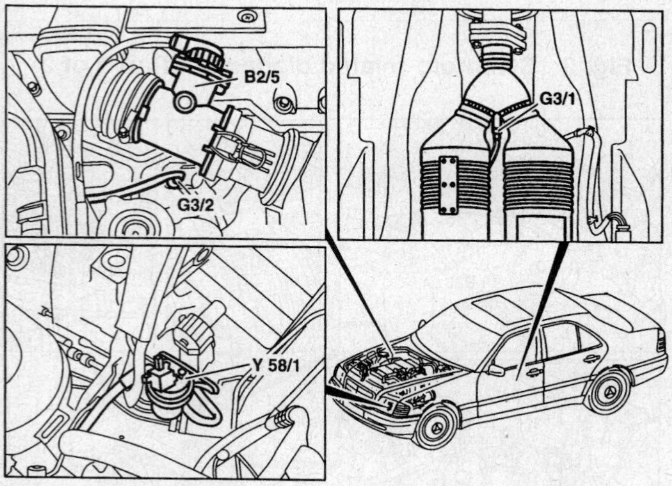

B2/5 Hot film MAF sensor
G3/1 O2S 2 (after TWC) (only (USA))
G3/2 O2S 1 (before TWC)
Y58/1 Purge control valve

MB1029800572020X

Fig. 5 ME engine management component locations (Part 2 of 4). C230

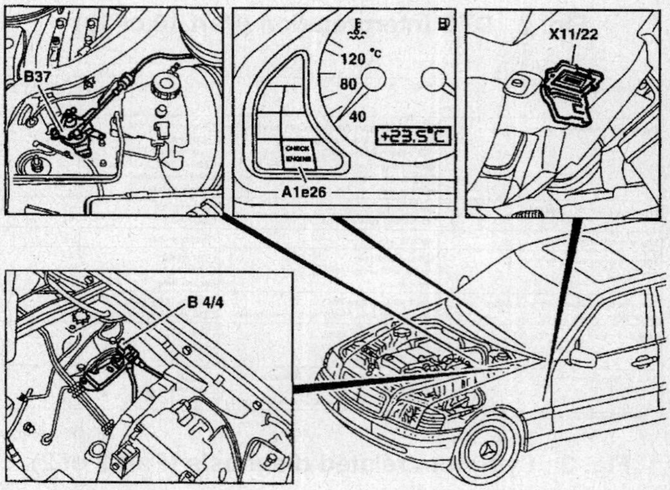

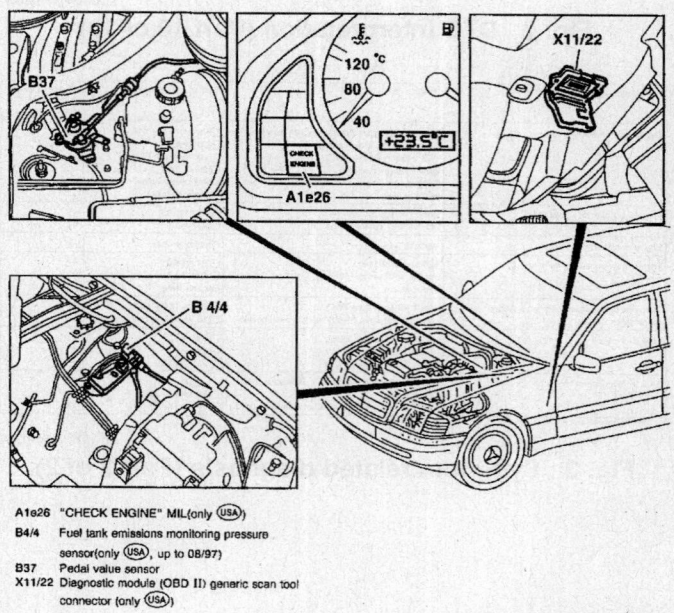

A1e26 "CHECK ENGINE" MIL(only (USA))
B4/4 Fuel tank emissions monitoring pressure sensor(only (USA), up to 08/97)
B37 Pedal value sensor
X11/22 Diagnostic module (OBD II) generic scan tool connector (only (USA))

MB1029800572030X

Fig. 5 ME engine management component locations (Part 3 of 4). C230

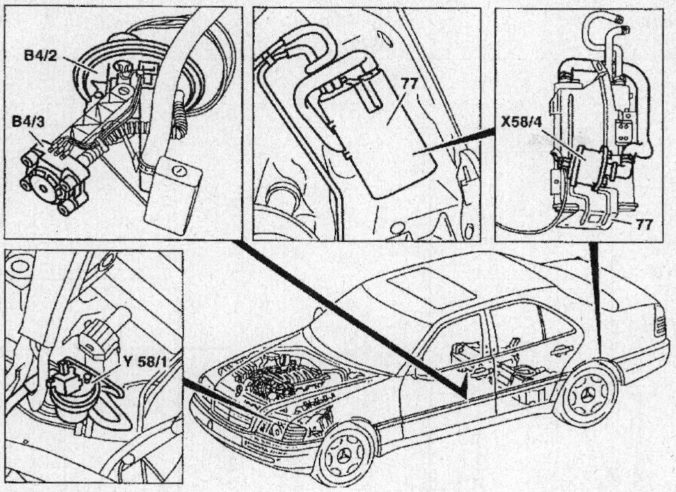

B4/2 Right fuel level sensor
B4/3 Fuel tank pressure sensor (USA) as of 09/97)
Y58/4 Activated charcoal canister shut-off valve (USA) as of 09/97)
Y58/1 Purge control valve
77 Activated charcoal canister

MB1029800572040X

Fig. 5 ME engine management component locations (Part 4 of 4). C230

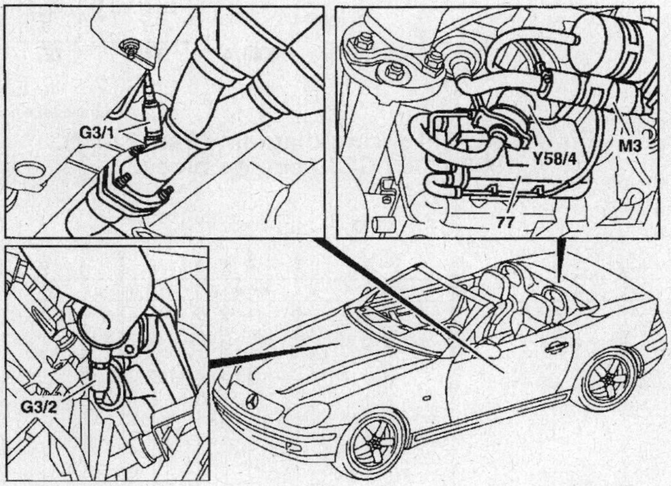

G3/1 O2S 2 (after TWC) (only USA)
G3/2 O2S 1 (before TWC)
M3 Fuel pump
Y58/4 Activated charcoal canister shut-off valve (only USA)
77 Activated charcoal canister

MB1029800571020X

Fig. 6 ME engine management component locations (Part 2 of 3). SLK230

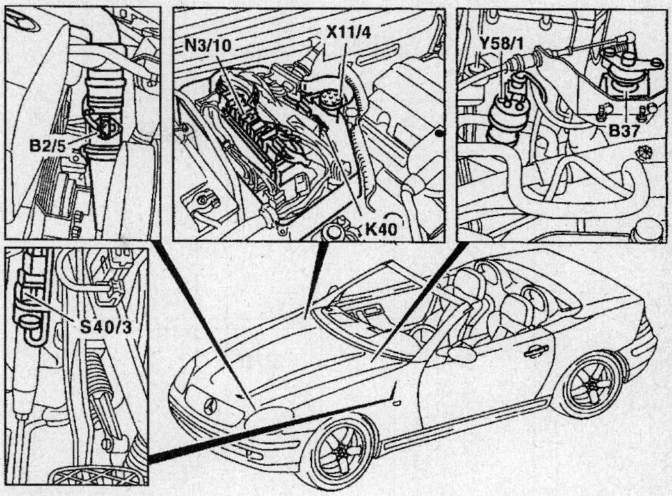

B2/5 Hot film MAF sensor
B37 Pedal value sensor
K40 Relay module with:
FP relay
AIR pump relay (only USA)
N3/10 Engine control module (ME-SFI)
S40/2 Clutch pedal switch (not USA)
X11/4 Data link connector (DTC readout) (38-pole)
Y58/1 Purge control valve

MB1029800571010X

Fig. 6 ME engine management component locations (Part 1 of 3). SLK230

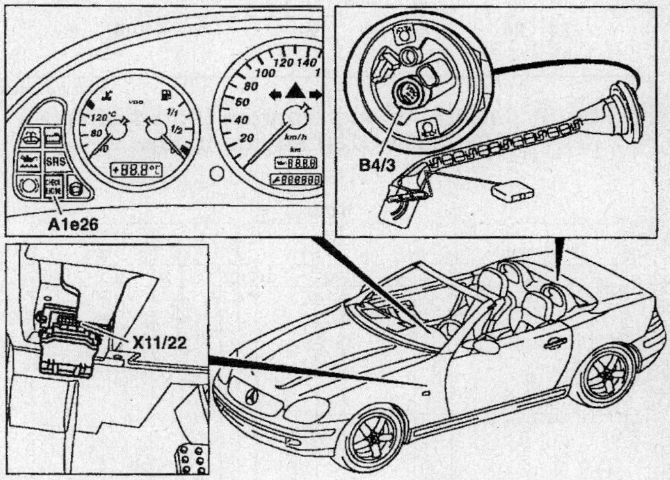

A1e26 "CHECK ENGINE" MIL (only USA)
B4/3 Fuel tank pressure sensor (only USA)
X11/22 Diagnostic module (OBD II) generic scan tool connector (only USA)

MB1029800571030X

Fig. 6 ME engine management component locations (Part 3 of 3). SLK230

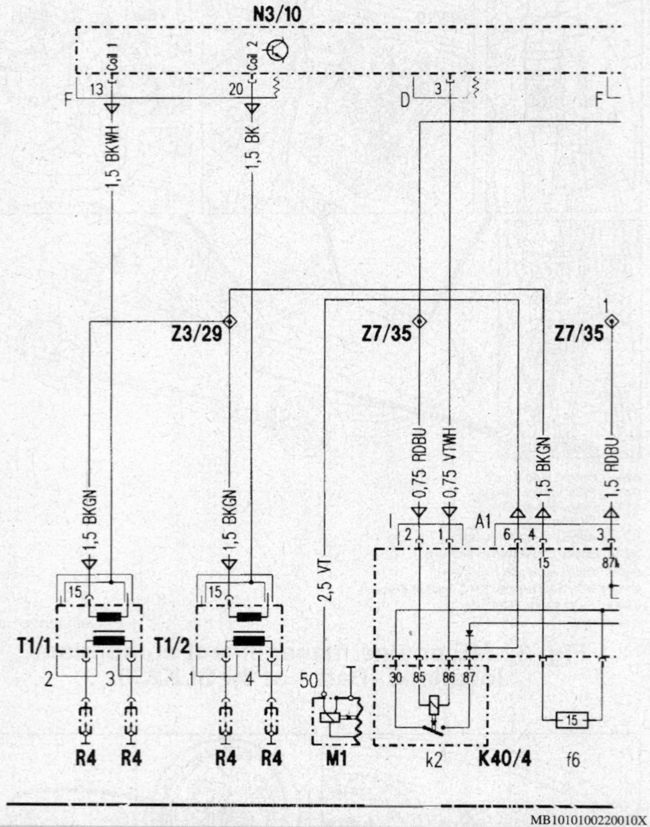

Fig. 7 ME-SFI wiring diagram (Part 1 of 7). 1998–2000 C230 engine block

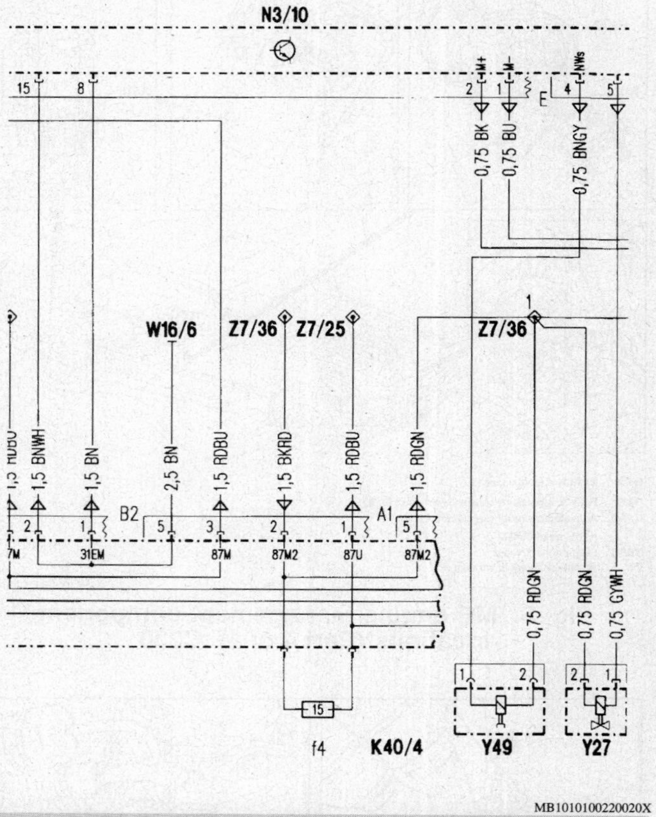

Fig. 7 ME-SFI wiring diagram (Part 2 of 7). 1998–2000 C230 engine block

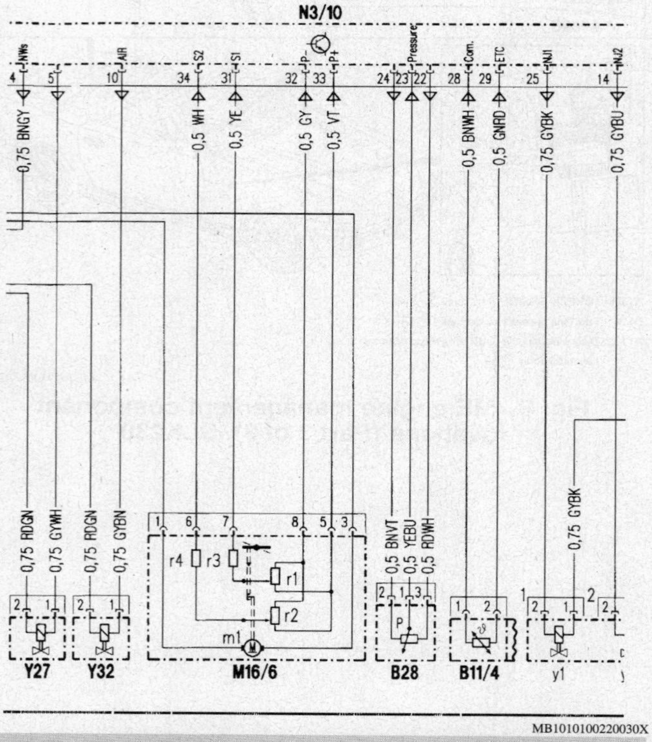

Fig. 7 ME-SFI wiring diagram (Part 3 of 7). 1998–2000 C230 engine block

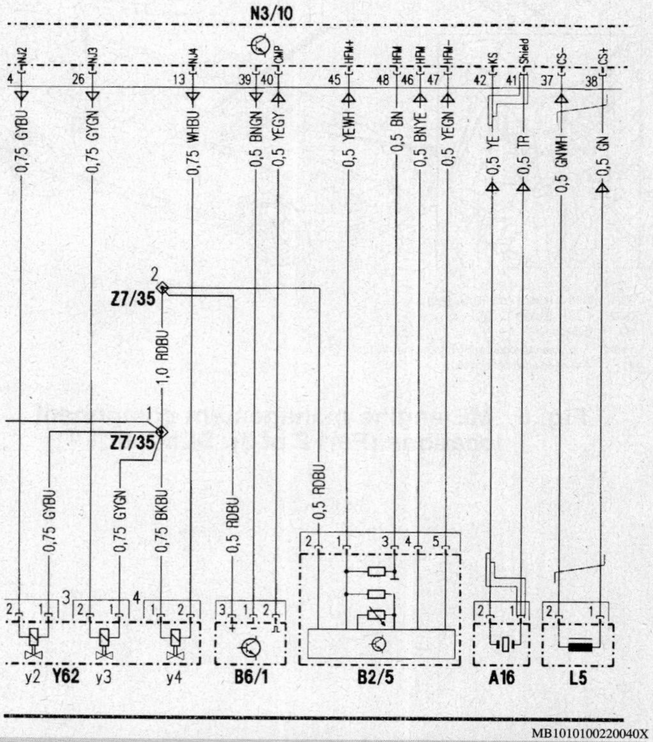

Fig. 7 ME-SFI wiring diagram (Part 4 of 7). 1998–2000 C230 engine block

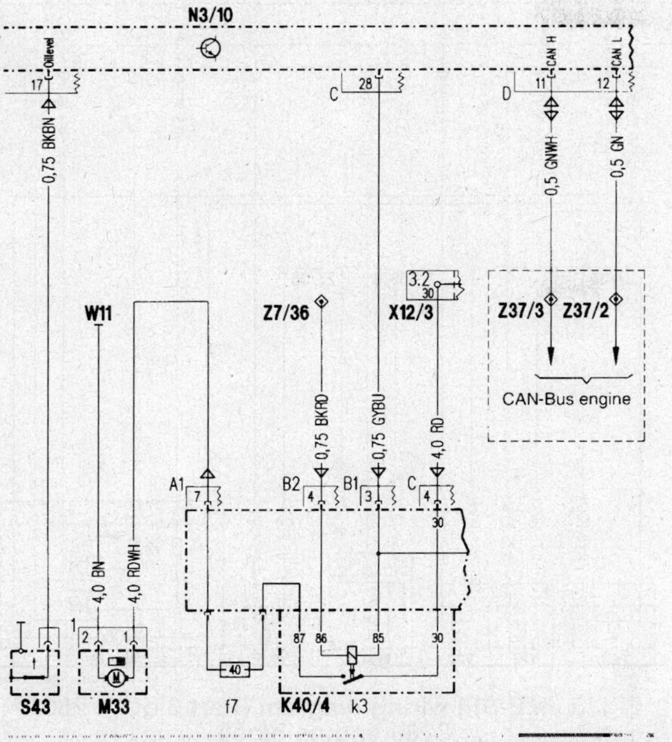

MB1010100220050X

Fig. 7 ME-SFI wiring diagram (Part 5 of 7). 1998–2000 C230 engine block

A16	Knock sensors	M16/6r4	Actual value potentiometer (wiper 2)
B2/5	Hot film MAF sensor	M33	AIR pump
B6/1	Camshaft Hall-effect sensor	N3/10	Engine control module (ME-SFI)
B11/4	ECT sensor		
B28	Pressure sensor		
K40/4	Passenger-side fuse and relay module box	R4	Spark plugs
K40/4f4	Fuse 2, Motronic		
K40/4f6	Fuse, ignition coils	S43	Oil level switch
K40/4f7	Maxi-fuse, AIR pump	T1/1	Ignition coil 1
K40/4k2	Starter relay	T1/2	Ignition coil 2
K40/4k3	Relay module, AIR pump	W11	Ground (engine - connection point for ground wires)
L5	CKP sensor		
M1	Starter	W16/6	Ground (electronics ground - component compartment - right)
M16/6	Throttle valve actuator		
M16/6m1	Actuator motor	X12/3	Terminal block (circuit 30)
M16/6r1	Throttle valve actual value potentiometer	Y27	EGR switchover valve
M16/6r2	Drive actual value potentiometer	Y32	AIR pump switchover valve
M16/6r3	Actual value potentiometer (wiper 1)	Y49	Adjustable camshaft timing solenoid

MB1010100220060X

Fig. 7 ME-SFI wiring diagram (Part 6 of 7). 1998–2000 C230 engine block

Y62	Injectors
Y62y1	Injector (cylinder 1)
Y62y2	Injector (cylinder 2)
Y62y3	Injector (cylinder 3)
Y62y4	Injector (cylinder 4)
Z3/29	Circuit 15 connector sleeve (fused)
Z7/25	Circuit 87 (unfused) connector sleeve (HFM-SFI/base module)
Z7/35	Connector sleeve, circuit 87M, feed from BM (N16/1)
Z7/36	Circuit 87 M2e connector sleeve
Z37/2	Engine CAN-Bus (low) connector sleeve
Z37/3	Engine CAN-Bus (high) connector sleeve

MB1010100220070X

Fig. 7 ME-SFI wiring diagram (Part 7 of 7). 1998–2000 C230 engine block

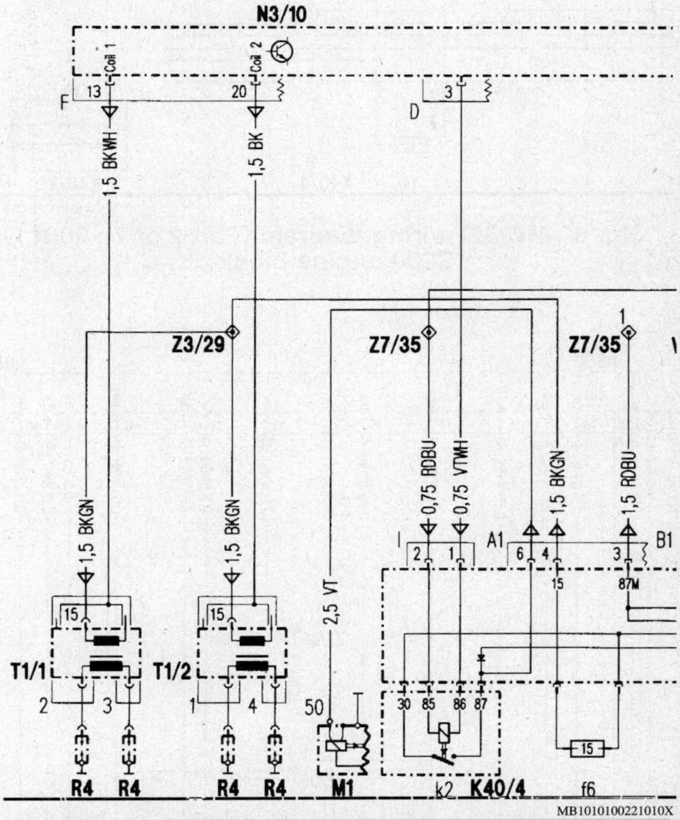

MB1010100221010X

Fig. 8 ME-SFI wiring diagram (Part 1 of 7). 2001 C230 engine block

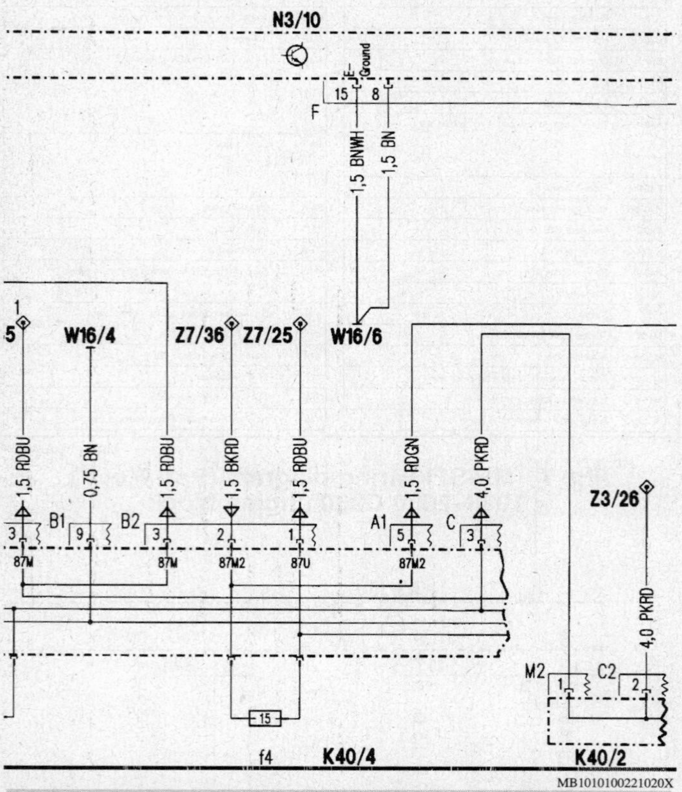

Fig. 8 ME-SFI wiring diagram (Part 2 of 7). 2001 C230 engine block

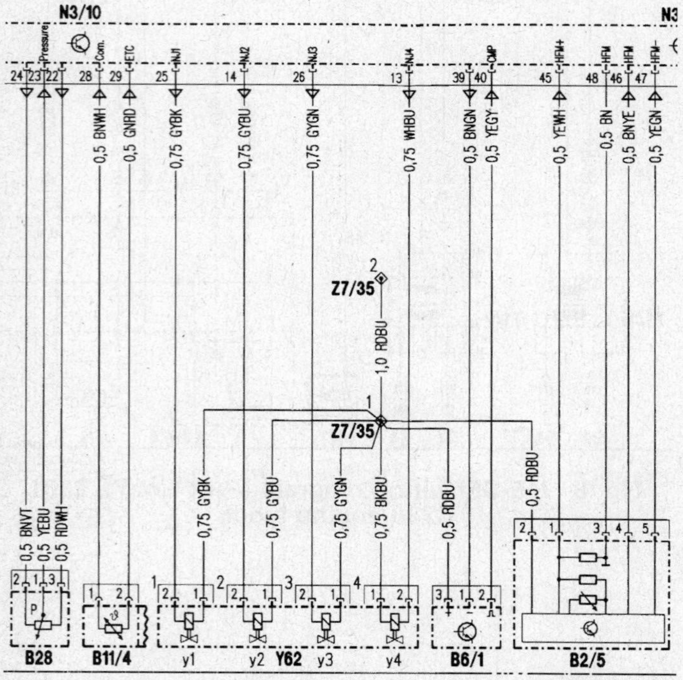

Fig. 8 ME-SFI wiring diagram (Part 4 of 7). 2001 C230 engine block

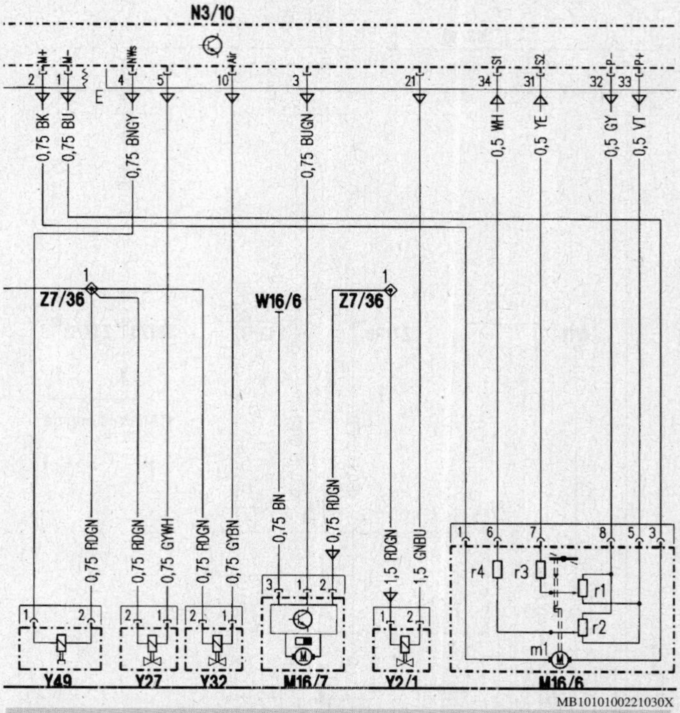

Fig. 8 ME-SFI wiring diagram (Part 3 of 7). 2001 C230 engine block

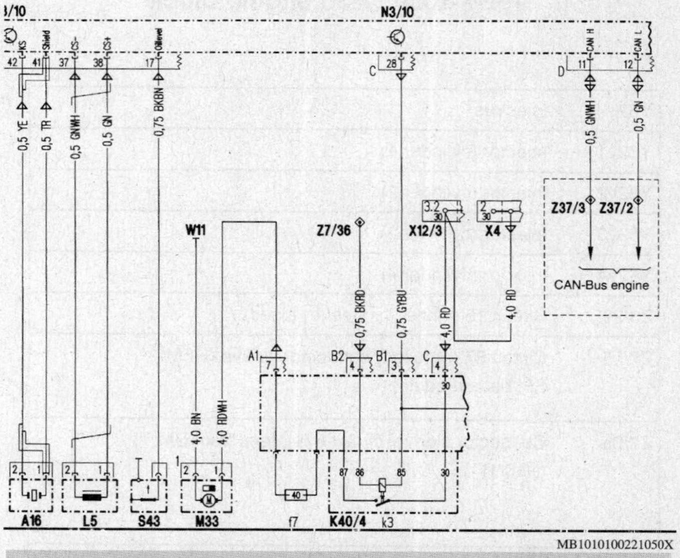

Fig. 8 ME-SFI wiring diagram (Part 5 of 7). 2001 C230 engine block

A16	Knock sensors
B2/5	Hot film MAF sensor
B6/1	Camshaft Hall-effect sensor
B11/4	ECT sensor
B28	Pressure sensor
K40/2	Driver-side fuse and relay module box
K40/4	Passenger-side fuse and relay module box
K40/4f4	Fuse 2, Motronic
K40/4f6	Fuse, ignition coils
K40/4f7	Maxi-fuse, AIR pump
K40/4k2	Starter relay
K40/4k3	Relay module, AIR pump
L5	CKP sensor
M1	Starter
M16/6	Throttle valve actuator
M16/6m1	Actuator motor
M16/6r1	Throttle valve actual value potentiometer
M16/6r2	Drive actual value potentiometer

M16/6r3	Actual value potentiometer (wiper 1)
M16/6r4	Actual value potentiometer (wiper 2)
M16/7	Recirculated air flap actuator
M33	AIR pump
N3/10	Engine control module (ME-SFI)
R4	Spark plugs
S43	Oil level switch
T1/1	Ignition coil 1
T1/2	Ignition coil 2
W11	Ground (engine - connection point for ground wires)
W16/4	Ground (output ground - component compartment - right)

MB1010100221060X

Fig. 8 ME-SFI wiring diagram (Part 6 of 7). 2001 C230 engine block

W16/6	Ground (electronics ground - component compartment - right)
X4	Terminal block (circuit 30, left footwell)
X12/3	Terminal block (circuit 30)
Y2/1	Magnetic supercharger clutch
Y27	EGR switchover valve
Y32	AIR pump switchover valve
Y49	Adjustable camshaft timing solenoid
Y62	Injectors
Y62y1	Injector (cylinder 1)
Y62y2	Injector (cylinder 2)
Y62y3	Injector (cylinder 3)
Y62y4	Injector (cylinder 4)
Z3/26	Circuit 15 (unfused) connector sleeve
Z3/29	Circuit 15 connector sleeve (fused)
Z7/25	Circuit 87 (unfused) connector sleeve (HFM-SFI/base module)
Z7/35	Connector sleeve, circuit 87M, feed from BM (N16/1)

Z7/36	Circuit 87 M2e connector sleeve
Z37/2	Engine CAN-Bus (low) connector sleeve
Z37/3	Engine CAN-Bus (high) connector sleeve

MB1010100221070X

Fig. 8 ME-SFI wiring diagram (Part 7 of 7). 2001 C230 engine block

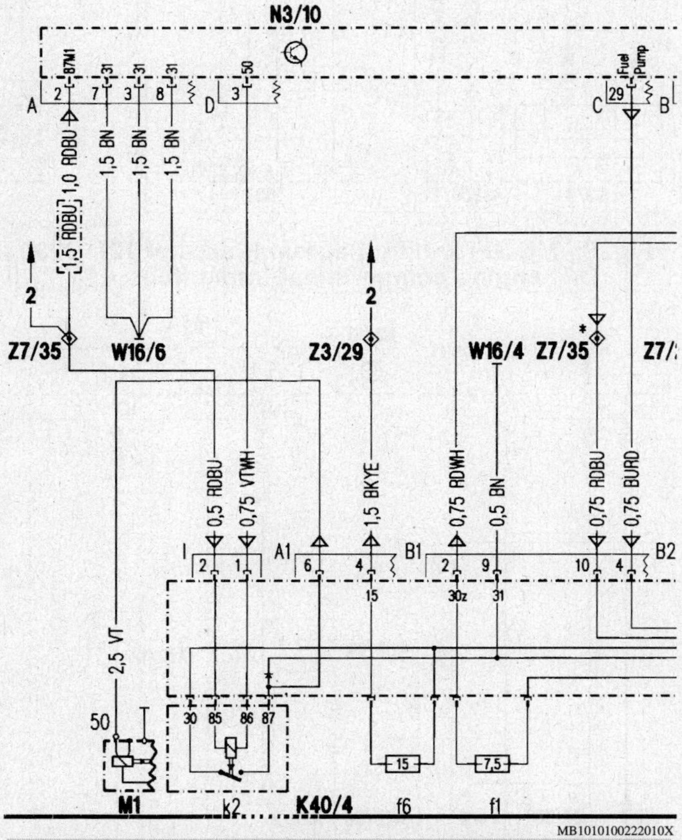

MB1010100222010X

Fig. 9 ME-SFI wiring diagram (Part 1 of 12). C230 engine compartment/frame floor

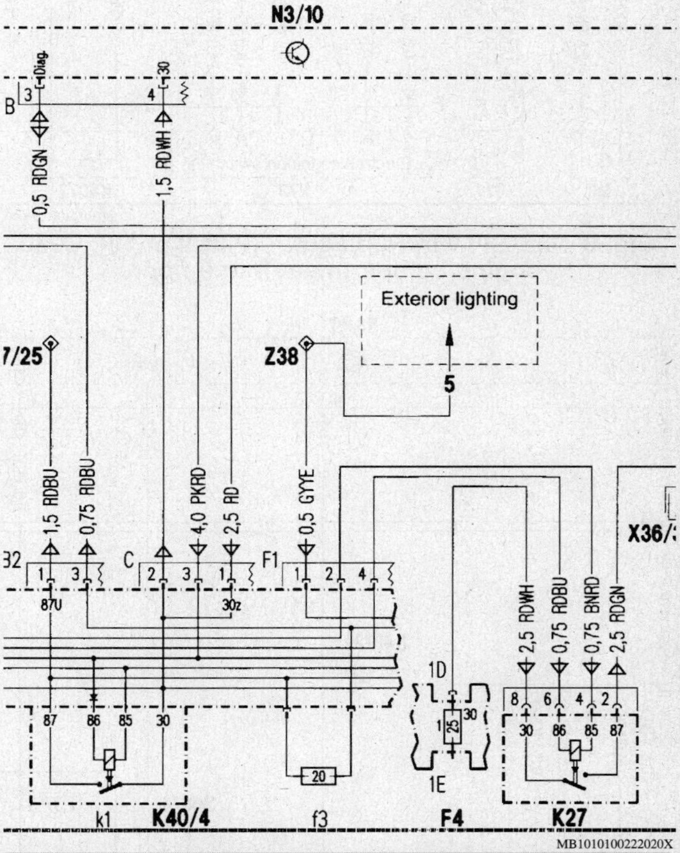

MB1010100222020X

Fig. 9 ME-SFI wiring diagram (Part 2 of 12). C230 engine compartment/frame floor

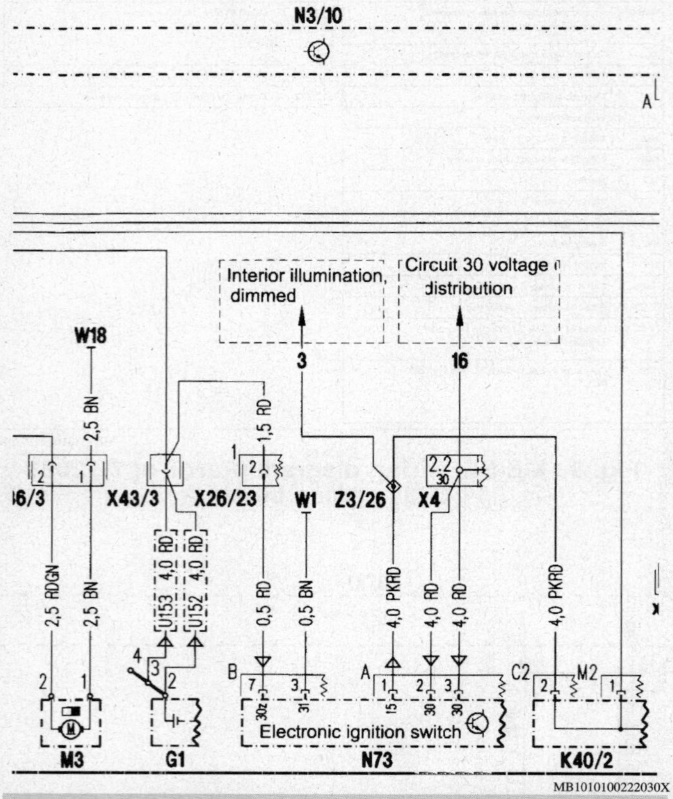

Fig. 9 ME-SFI wiring diagram (Part 3 of 12). C230 engine compartment/frame floor

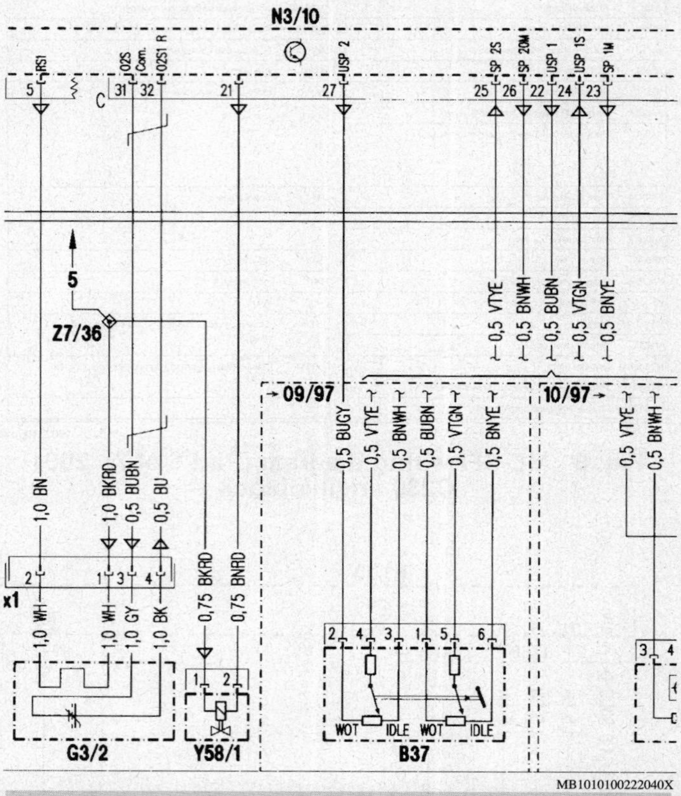

Fig. 9 ME-SFI wiring diagram (Part 4 of 12). C230 engine compartment/frame floor

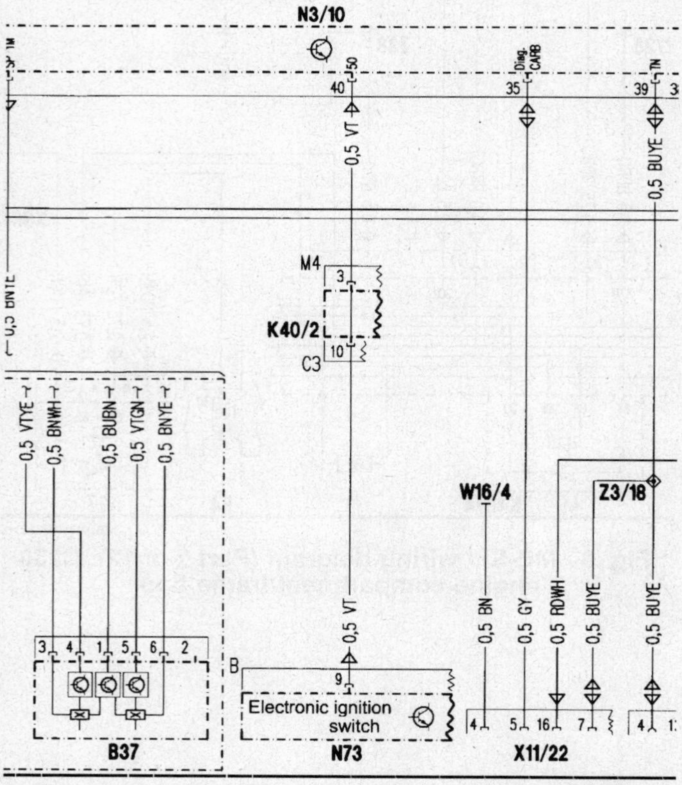

Fig. 9 ME-SFI wiring diagram (Part 5 of 12). C230 engine compartment/frame floor

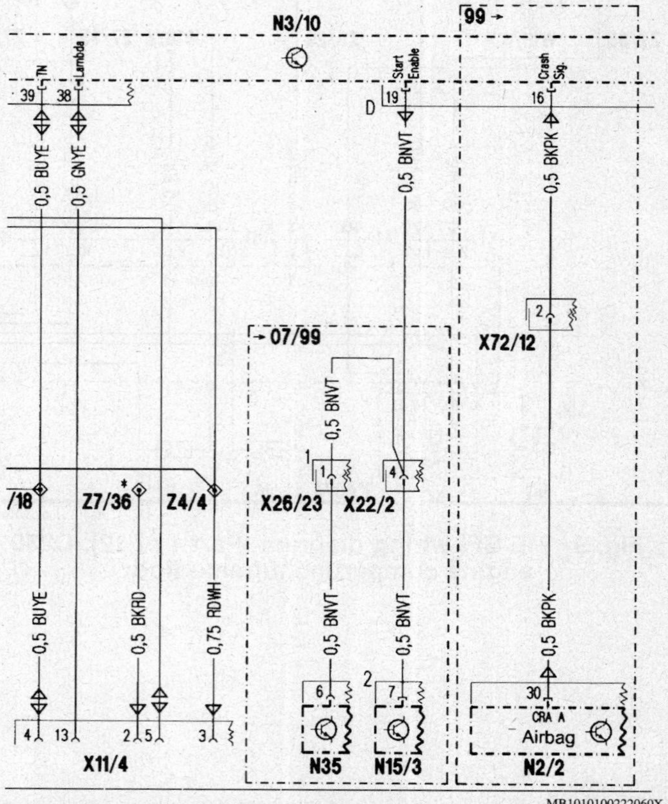

Fig. 9 ME-SFI wiring diagram (Part 6 of 12). C230 engine compartment/frame floor

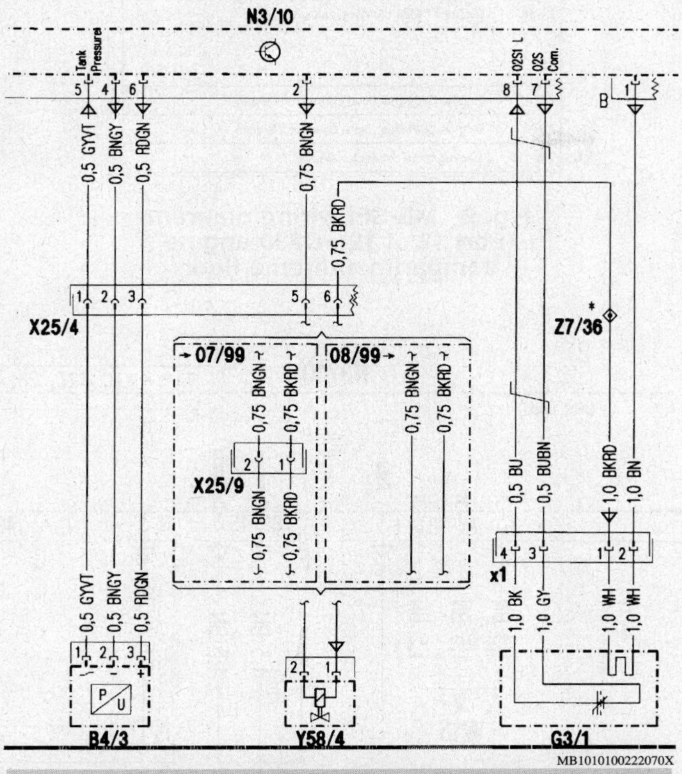

Fig. 9 ME-SFI wiring diagram (Part 7 of 12). C230 engine compartment/frame floor

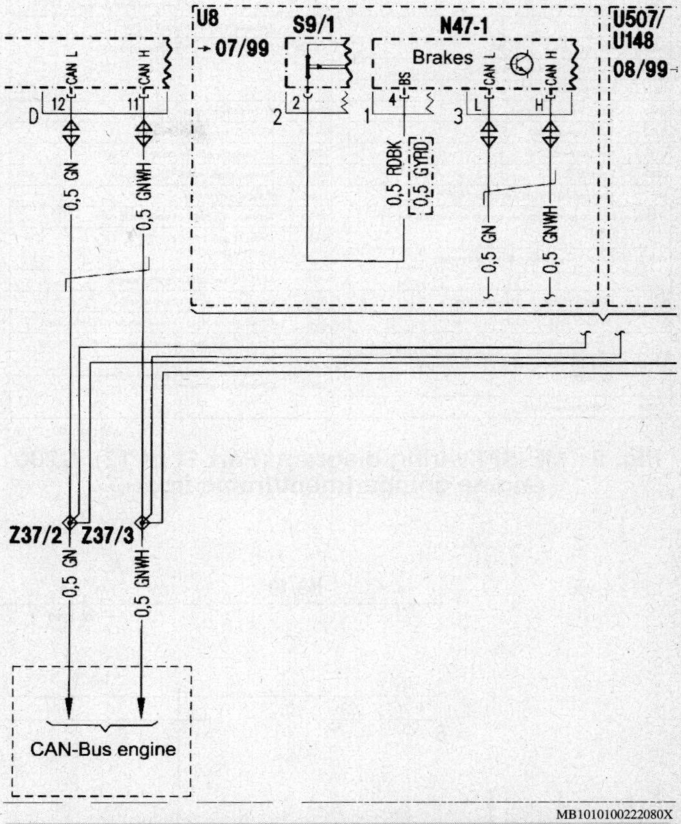

Fig. 9 ME-SFI wiring diagram (Part 8 of 12). C230 engine compartment/frame floor

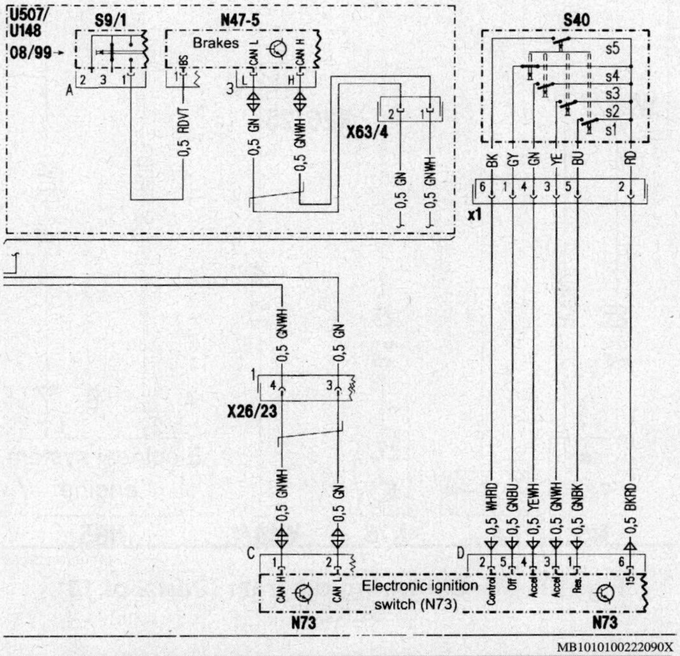

Fig. 9 ME-SFI wiring diagram (Part 9 of 12). C230 engine compartment/frame floor

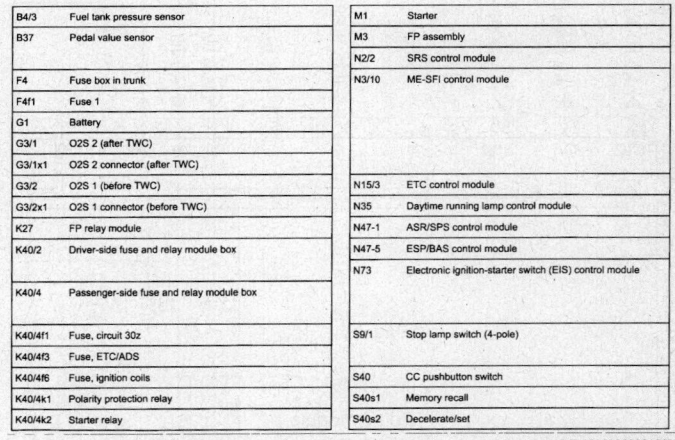

B4/3	Fuel tank pressure sensor
B37	Pedal value sensor
F4	Fuse box in trunk
F4f1	Fuse 1
G1	Battery
G3/1	O2S 2 (after TWC)
G3/1x1	O2S 2 connector (after TWC)
G3/2	O2S 1 (before TWC)
G3/2x1	O2S 1 connector (before TWC)
K27	FP relay module
K40/2	Driver-side fuse and relay module box
K40/4	Passenger-side fuse and relay module box
K40/4f1	Fuse, circuit 30z
K40/4f3	Fuse, ETC/ADS
K40/4f6	Fuse, ignition coils
K40/4k1	Polarity protection relay
K40/4k2	Starter relay

M1	Starter
M3	FP assembly
N2/2	SRS control module
N3/10	ME-SFI control module
N15/3	ETC control module
N35	Daytime running lamp control module
N47-1	ASR/SPS control module
N47-5	ESP/BAS control module
N73	Electronic ignition-starter switch (EIS) control module
S9/1	Stop lamp switch (4-pole)
S40	CC pushbutton switch
S40s1	Memory recall
S40s2	Decelerate/set

MB1010100222100X

Fig. 9 ME-SFI wiring diagram (Part 10 of 12). C230 engine compartment/frame floor

S40s3	Accelerate/set
S40s4	Off
S40s5	Control contact
S40x1	CC pushbutton switch connector
U8	Valid for ASR
U148	Valid for Teves system
U152	Valid for model 202
U153	Valid for model 208
U507	Valid for ESP
W1	Main ground (behind instrument cluster)
W16/4	Ground (output ground - component compartment - right)
W16/6	Ground (electronics ground - component compartment - right)
W18	Ground (left front seat crossmember)
X4	Terminal block (circuit 30, left footwell)
X11/4	Diagnostic test clutch
X11/22	Diagnostic module (OBD II) generic scan tool connector
X22/2	AT/engine connector
X25/4	Fuel tank connector (pressure, charcoal filter)
X25/9	Activated charcoal filter connector
X26/23	Engine compartment/cockpit connector
X36/3	FP harness connector (2-pole)
X43/3	REST/CL connector, circuit 30Z
X63/4	CAN databus adaptor connector (2-pole)
X72/12	Auxiliary heater/crash signal connector
Y58/1	Purge control valve
Y58/4	Activated charcoal canister shutoff valve
Z3/18	Circuit 15 connector sleeve (HFM-SFI, interior/engine)
Z3/26	Circuit 15 (unfused) connector sleeve
Z3/29	Circuit 15 connector sleeve (fused)
Z4/4	Circuit 30Z connector sleeve (solder joint in harness)
Z7/25	Circuit 87 (unfused) connector sleeve (HFM-SFI/base module)
Z7/35	Circuit 87 M1e connector sleeve

MB1010100222110X

Fig. 9 ME-SFI wiring diagram (Part 11 of 12). C230 engine compartment/frame floor

Z7/36	Circuit 87 M2e connector sleeve
Z37/2	Engine CAN-Bus (low) connector sleeve
Z37/3	Engine CAN-Bus (high) connector sleeve
Z38	Backup lamp connector sleeve

MB1010100222120X

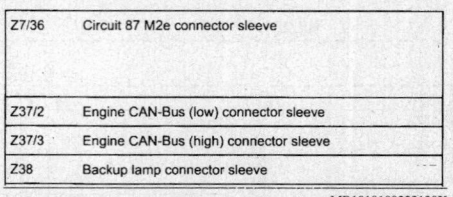

Fig. 9 ME-SFI wiring diagram (Part 12 of 12). C230 engine compartment/frame floor

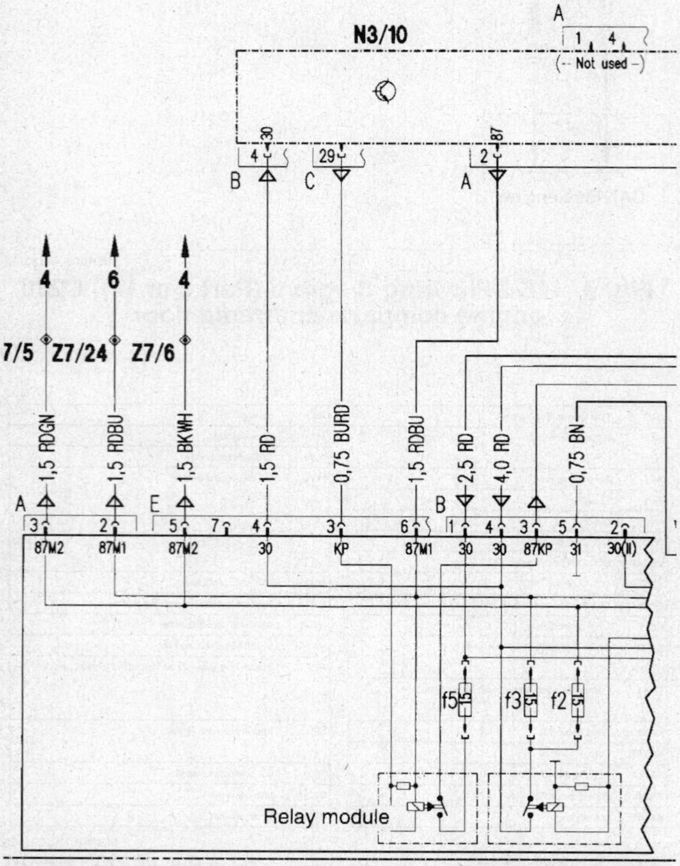

MB1010100225010X

Fig. 10 ME-SFI wiring diagram (Part 1 of 13). SLK230

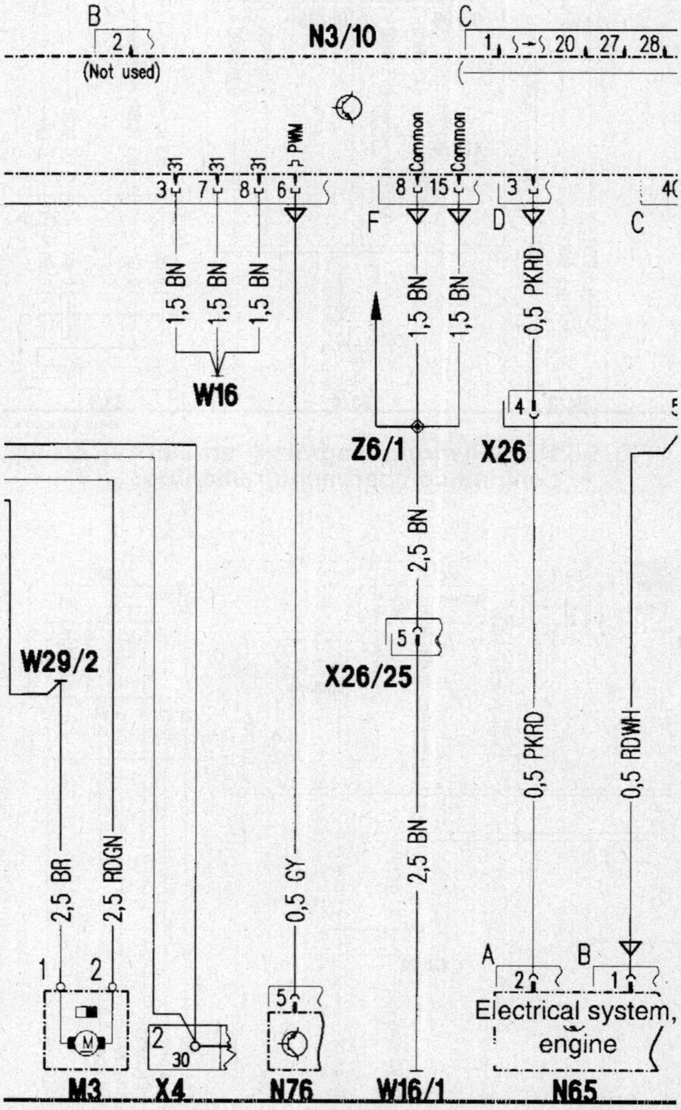

MB1010100225020X

Fig. 10 ME-SFI wiring diagram (Part 2 of 13). SLK230

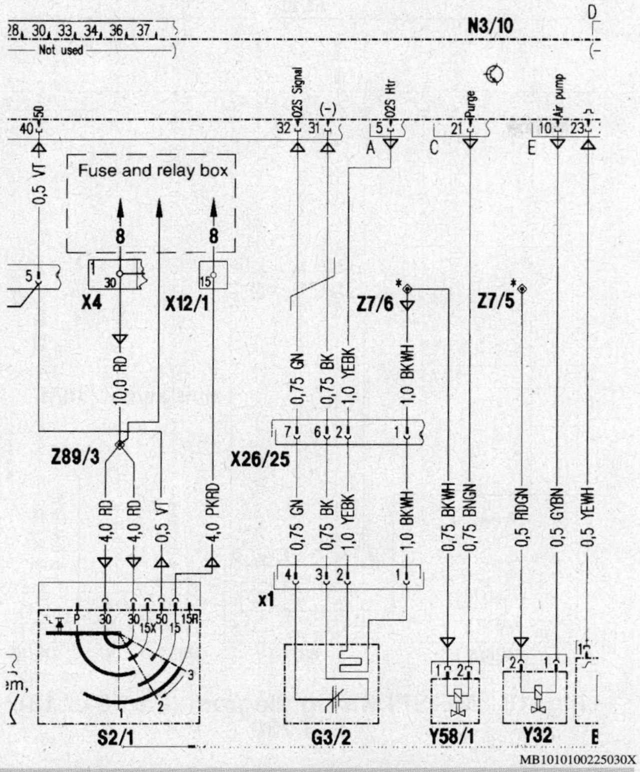

Fig. 10 ME-SFI wiring diagram (Part 3 of 13). SLK230

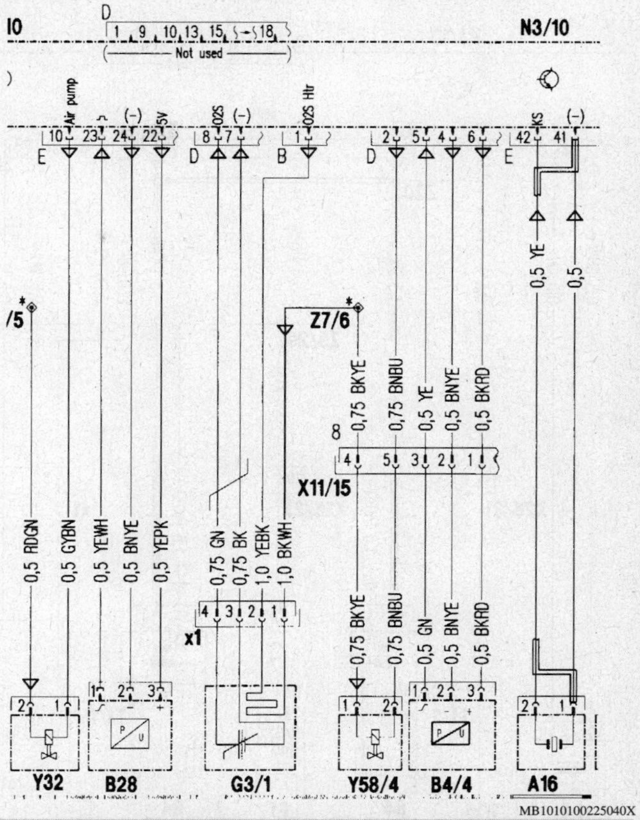

Fig. 10 ME-SFI wiring diagram (Part 4 of 13). SLK230

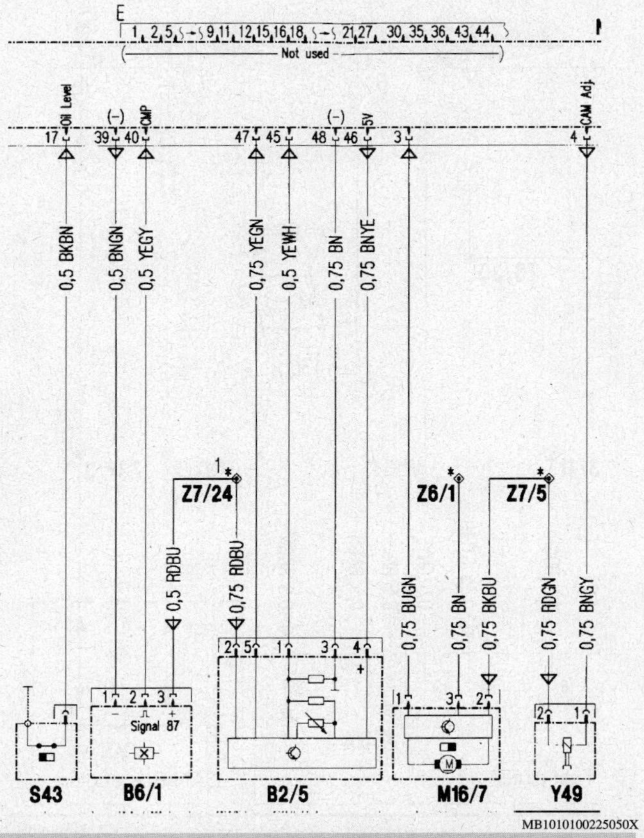

Fig. 10 ME-SFI wiring diagram (Part 5 of 13). SLK230

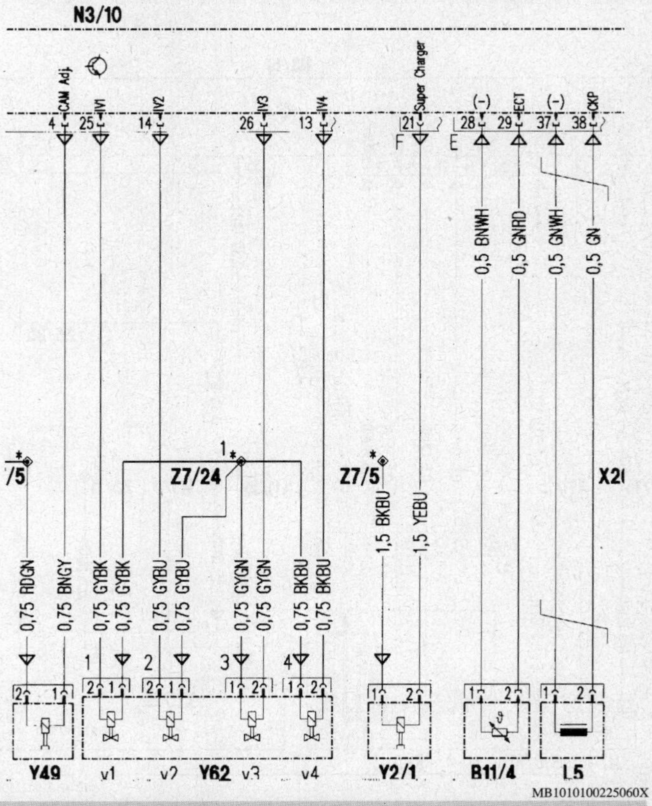

Fig. 10 ME-SFI wiring diagram (Part 6 of 13). SLK230

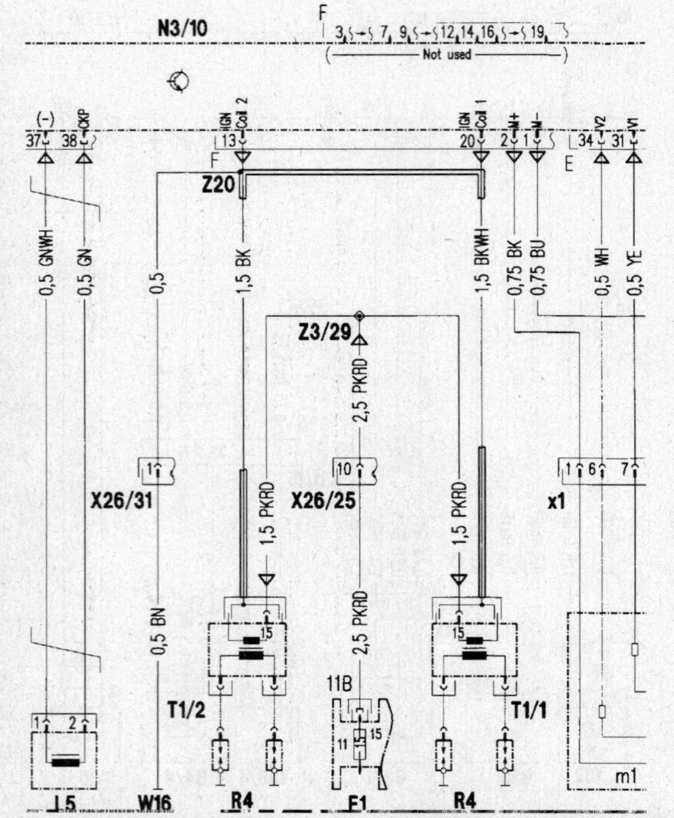

Fig. 10 ME-SFI wiring diagram (Part 7 of 13). SLK230

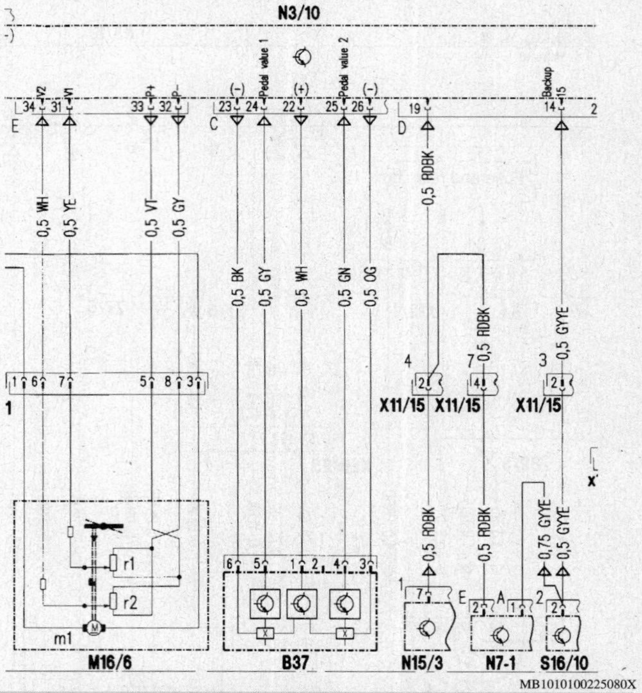

Fig. 10 ME-SFI wiring diagram (Part 8 of 13). SLK230

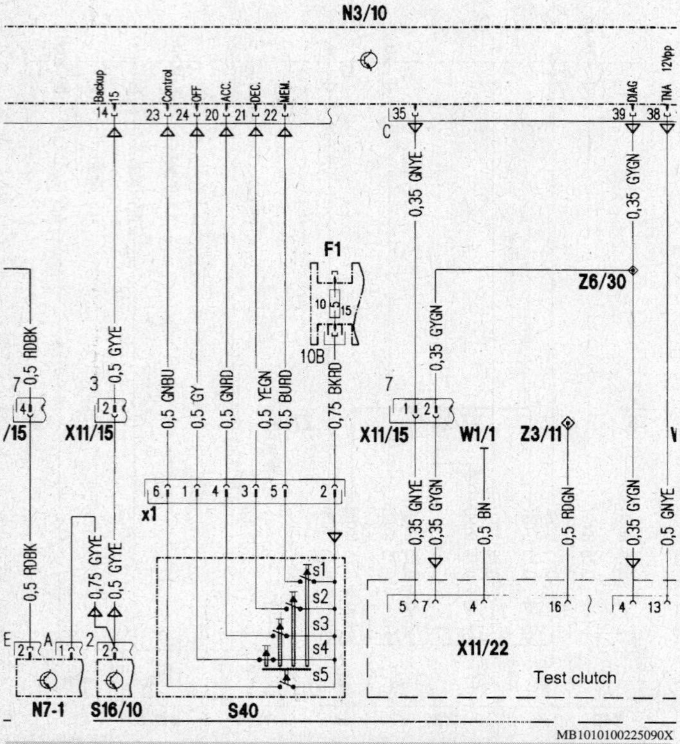

Fig. 10 ME-SFI wiring diagram (Part 9 of 13). SLK230

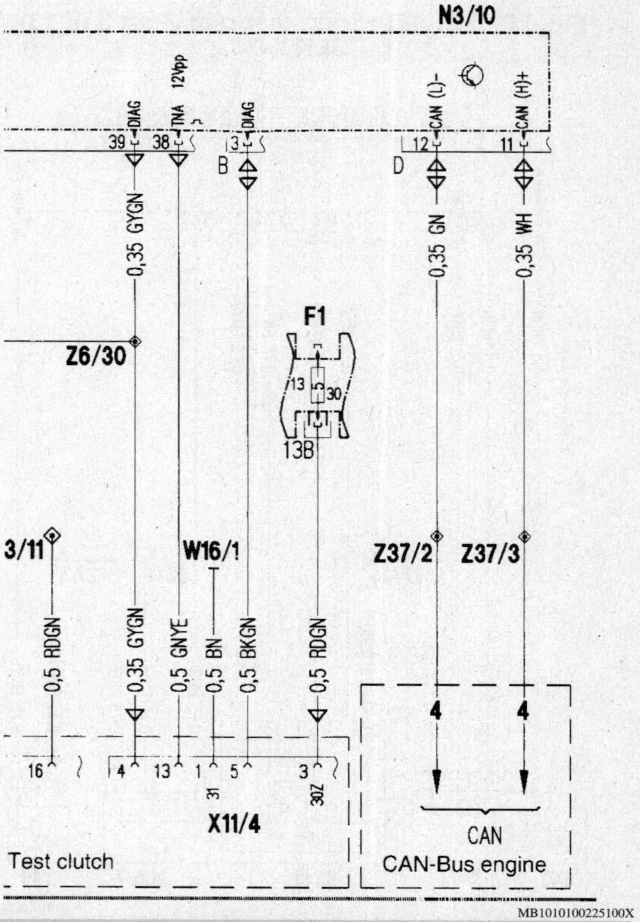

Fig. 10 ME-SFI wiring diagram (Part 10 of 13). SLK230

A16	Knock sensors
B2/5	Hot film MAF sensor
B4/4	Fuel tank emissions monitoring pressure sensor
B6/1	Camshaft Hall-effect sensor
B11/4	ECT sensor
B28	Pressure sensor
B37	#PEdal value sensor
F1	Fuse and relay box
F1f10	Fuse 10
F1F11	Fuse 11
F1f13	Fuse 13
G3/1	O2S 2 (after TWC)
G3/1x1	O2S 2 connector (after TWC)
G3/2	O2S 1 (before TWC)
G3/2x1	O2S 1 connector (before TWC)
K40	Relay module
K40f2	EDC, 87 M2 fuse

K40f3	87 M1 fuse
K40f5	FP fuse
K40k1	FP relay
K40k9	Motor 87 M1/M2 relay
L5	CKP sensor
M3	FP assembly
M16/6	Throttle valve setting element
M16/6m1	Actuator motor
M16/6r1	Throttle valve actual value potentiometer
M16/6r2	Drive actual value potentiometer
M16/6x1	ISC actuator connector
M16/7	Recirculated air flap actuator
N3/10	Engine control module (ME-SFI)

MB1010100225110X

Fig. 10 ME-SFI wiring diagram (Part 11 of 13). SLK230

N7-1	Illumination control module
N15/3	ETC control module
N65	Pulse module (traction systems, HCS, ATA, AAC)
N76	Engine/climate control electric cooling fan control module
R4	Spark plugs
S2/1	Ignition/starter switch
S16/10	Transmission range recognition switch (voltage coded)
S40	CC switch
S40s1	Memory recall
S40s2	Decelerate/set
S40s3	Accelerate/set
S40s4	Off
S40s5	Control contact
S40x1	CC switch connector
S43	Oil level switch
T1/1	Ignition coil 1

T1/2	Ignition coil 2
W1/1	Ground (cockpit frame)
W16	Ground (component compartment)
W16/1	Ground (right front spring tower)
W29/2	Ground (right A-pillar)
X4	Terminal block (circuit 30, fuse and relay box) (2-pole)
X11/4	Data link connector (DTC readout)
X11/15	Diagnostic intermediate connector (taillamp harness) (16-pole)
X11/22	Diagnostic module (OBD II) generic scan tool connector
X12/1	Terminal block (circuit 15 unfused)
X26	Interior/engine wiring harness connector

MB1010100225120X

Fig. 10 ME-SFI wiring diagram (Part 12 of 13). SLK230

X26/25	Engine/chassis connector (24-pole)
X26/31	Engine/engine compartment connector
Y2/1	Magnetic su#PErcharger clutch
Y32	AIR pump switchover valve
Y49	Adjustable camshaft timing solenoid
Y58/1	Purge control valve
Y58/4	Activated charcoal canister shut-off valve
Y62	Injectors
Y62y1	Injector (cylinder 1)
Y62y2	Injector (cylinder 2)
Y62y3	Injector (cylinder 3)
Y62y4	Injector (cylinder 4)
Z3/11	Circuit 15 (fused) connector sleeve
Z3/29	Circuit 15 connector sleeve (fused)

Z6/1	Ground connector sleeve
Z6/30	Diagnostic (ME-SFI) connector sleeve
Z7/5	Circuit 87 connector sleeve
Z7/6	Circuit 87 connector sleeve (chassis)
Z7/24	Circuit 87 connector sleeve
Z20	Shielding placed inside insulated tubing
Z37/2	Engine CAN-Bus (low) connector sleeve
Z37/3	Engine CAN-Bus (high) connector sleeve
Z89/3	Circuit 30 connector sleeve

MB1010100225130X

Fig. 10 ME-SFI wiring diagram (Part 13 of 13). SLK230

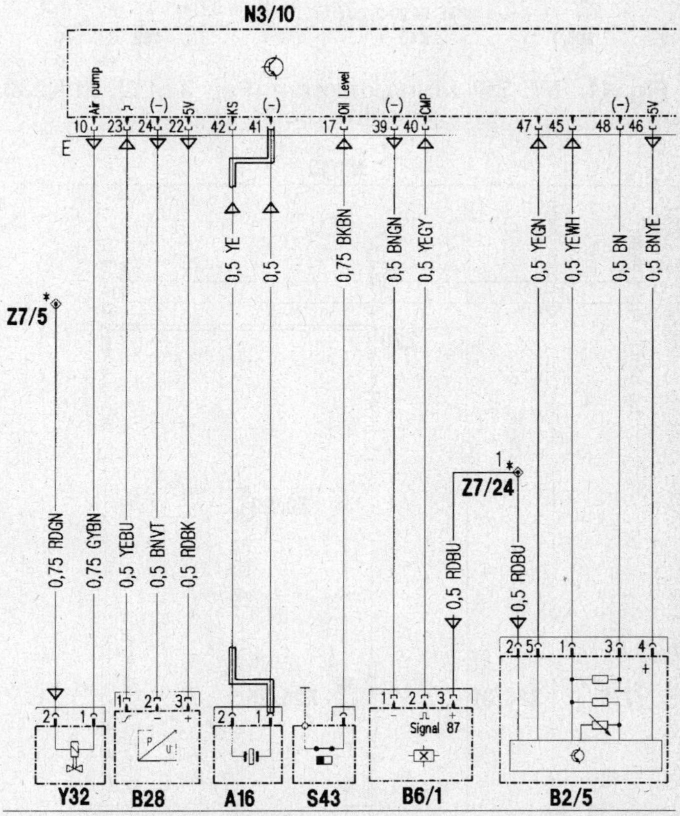

MB1010100227010X

Fig. 11 ME-SFI wiring diagram (Part 1 of 6). SLK230 engine block

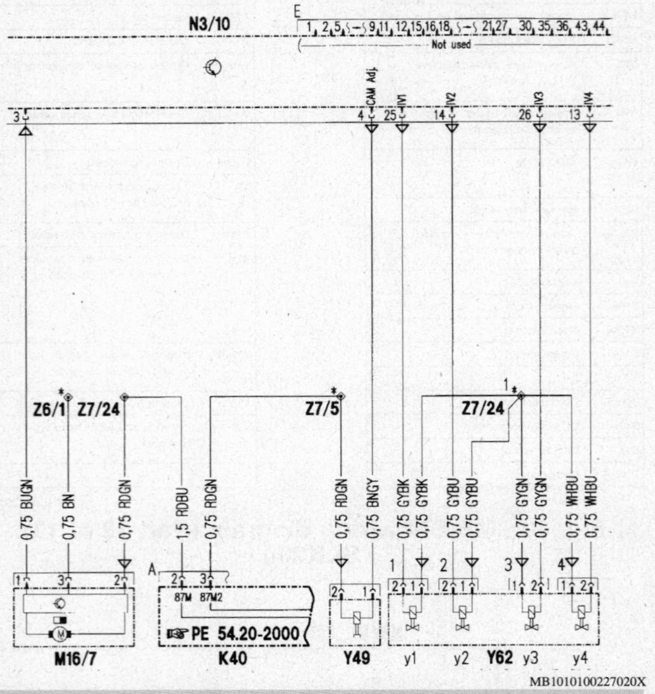

Fig. 11 ME-SFI wiring diagram (Part 2 of 6). SLK230 engine block

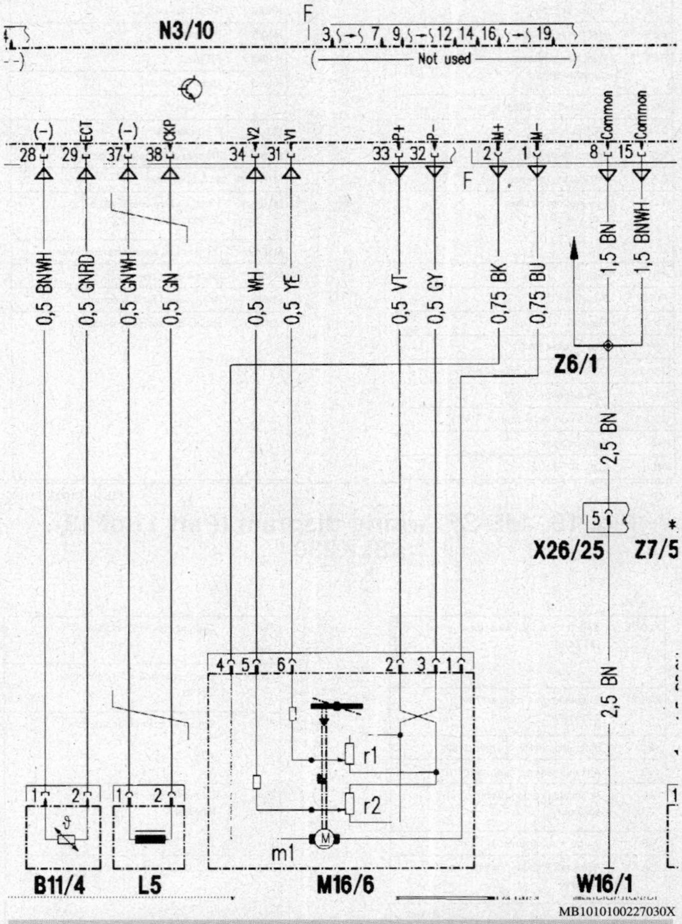

Fig. 11 ME-SFI wiring diagram (Part 3 of 6). SLK230 engine block

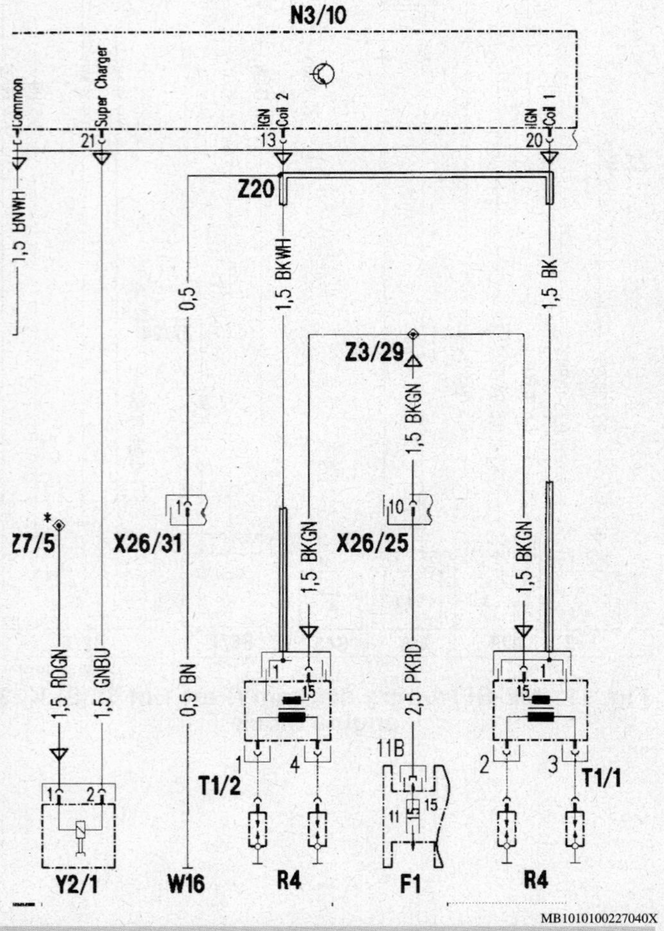

Fig. 11 ME-SFI wiring diagram (Part 4 of 6). SLK230 engine block

A16	Knock sensors	S43	Oil level switch
B2/5	Hot film MAF sensor	T1/1	Ignition coil 1
B6/1	Camshaft Hall-effect sensor	T1/2	Ignition coil 2
B11/4	ECT sensor	W16	Ground (component compartment)
B28	Pressure sensor	W16/1	Ground (right front spring tower)
F1	Fuse and relay box	X26/25	Engine/chassis connector (24-pole)
F1f11	Fuse 11		
K40	Relay module	X26/31	Engine/engine compartment connector
L5	CKP sensor		
M16/6	Throttle valve setting element	Y2/1	Magnetic supercharger clutch
M16/6m1	Actuator motor	Y32	AIR pump switchover valve
M16/6r1	Throttle valve actual value potentiometer	Y49	Adjustable camshaft timing solenoid
M16/6r2	Drive actual value potentiometer	Y62	Injectors
M16/7	Recirculated air flap actuator	Y62y1	Injector (cylinder 1)
N3/10	Engine control module (ME-SFI)	Y62y2	Injector (cylinder 2)
		Y62y3	Injector (cylinder 3)
		Y62y4	Injector (cylinder 4)
R4	Spark plugs	Z3/29	Circuit 15 connector sleeve (fused)

MB1010100227050X

Fig. 11 ME-SFI wiring diagram (Part 5 of 6). SLK230 engine block

Z6/1	Ground connector sleeve
Z7/5	Circuit 87 connector sleeve
Z7/24	Circuit 87 connector sleeve
Z20	Shielding placed inside insulated tubing

MB1010100227060X

Fig. 11 ME-SFI wiring diagram (Part 6 of 6). SLK230 engine block

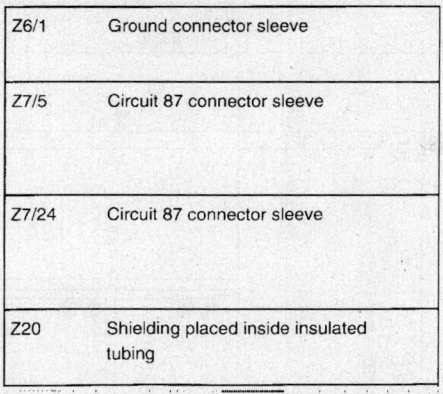

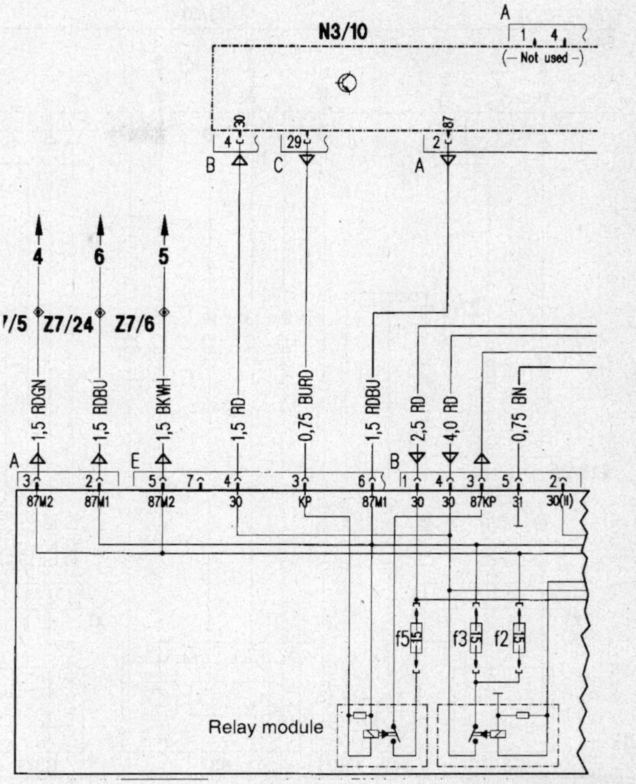

MB1010100226010X

Fig. 12 ME-SFI wiring diagram (Part 1 of 11). SLK230 engine compartment/frame floor

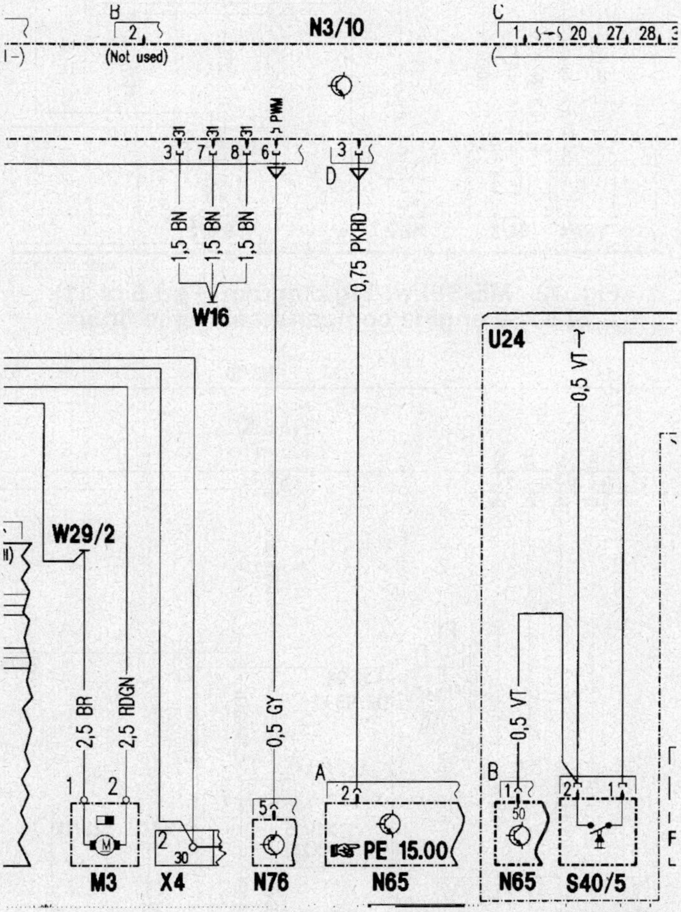

MB1010100226020X

Fig. 12 ME-SFI wiring diagram (Part 2 of 11). SLK230 engine compartment/frame floor

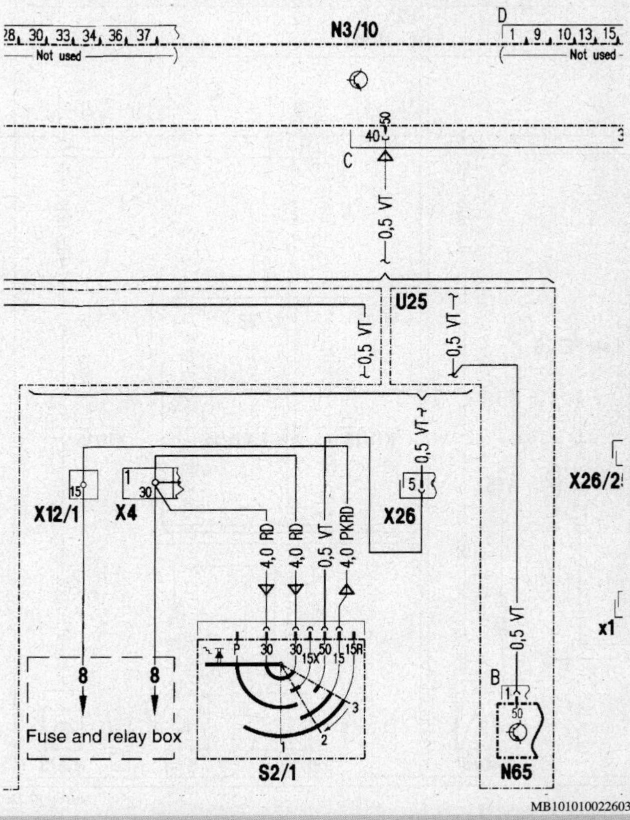

MB1010100226030X

Fig. 12 ME-SFI wiring diagram (Part 3 of 11). SLK230 engine compartment/frame floor

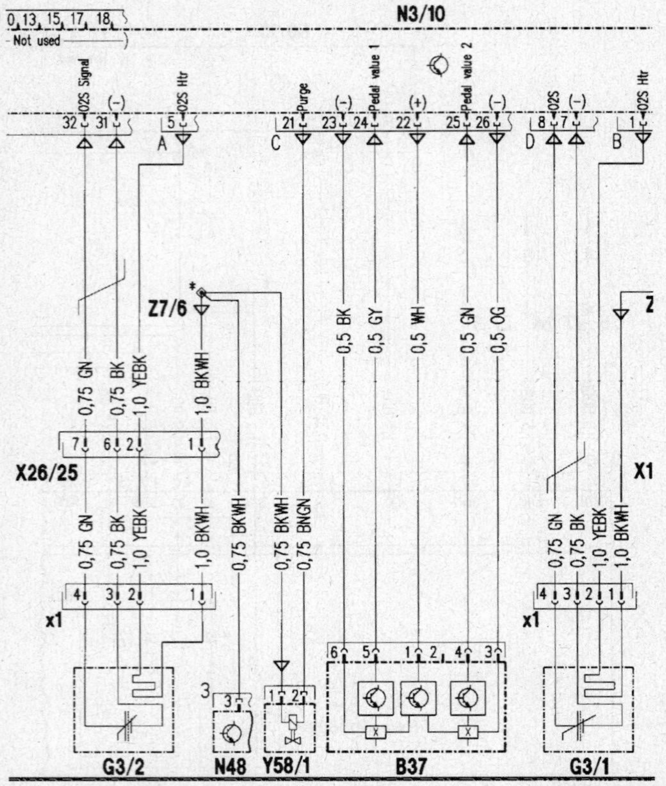

Fig. 12 ME-SFI wiring diagram (Part 4 of 11). SLK230 engine compartment/frame floor

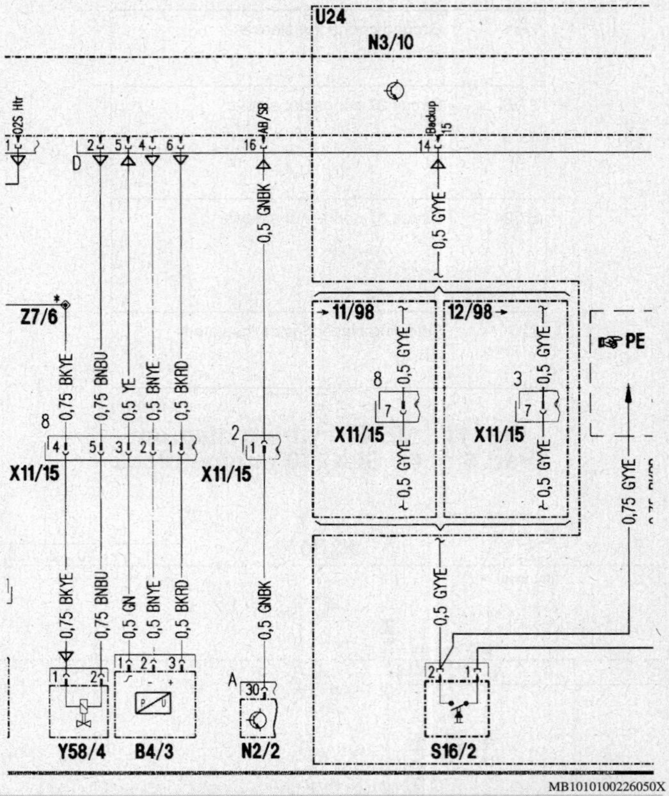

Fig. 12 ME-SFI wiring diagram (Part 5 of 11). SLK230 engine compartment/frame floor

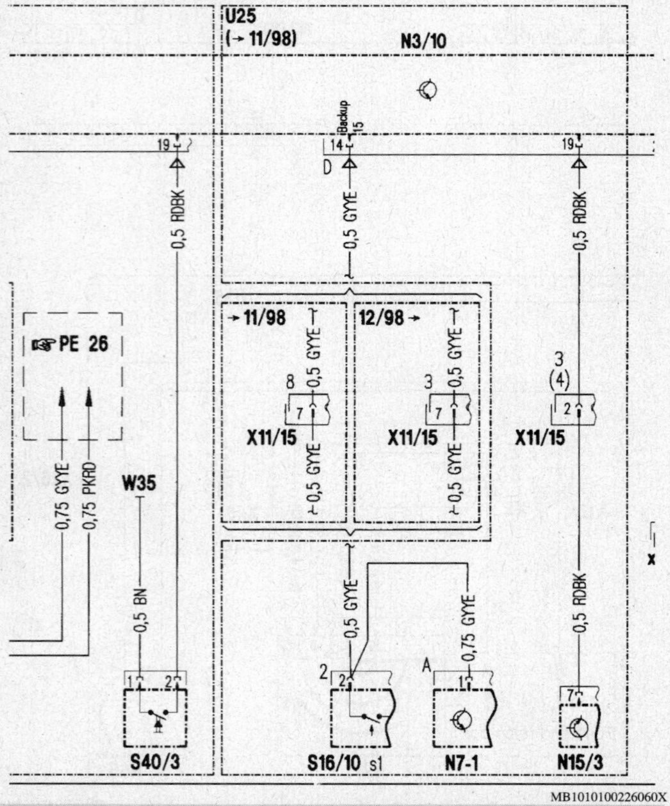

Fig. 12 ME-SFI wiring diagram (Part 6 of 11). SLK230 engine compartment/frame floor

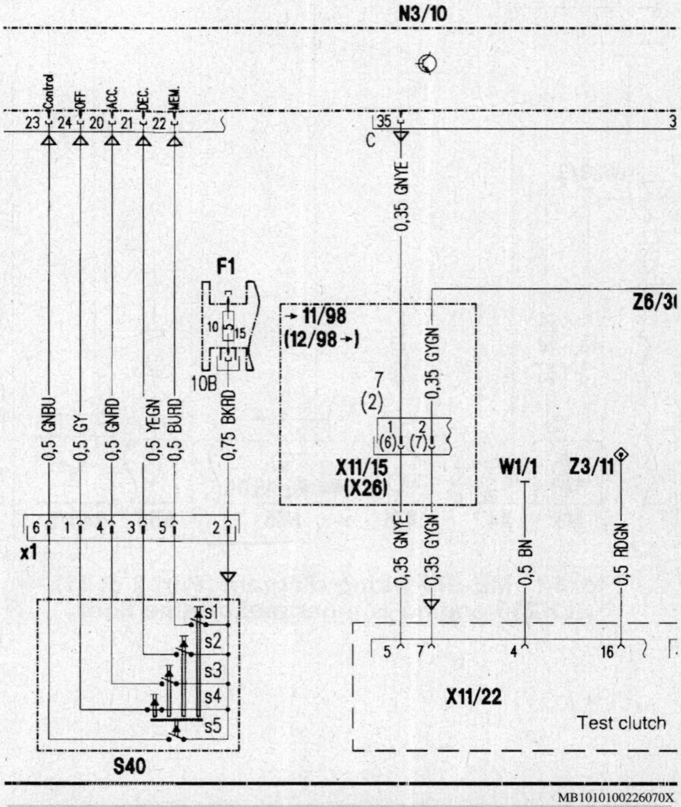

Fig. 12 ME-SFI wiring diagram (Part 7 of 11). SLK230 engine compartment/frame floor

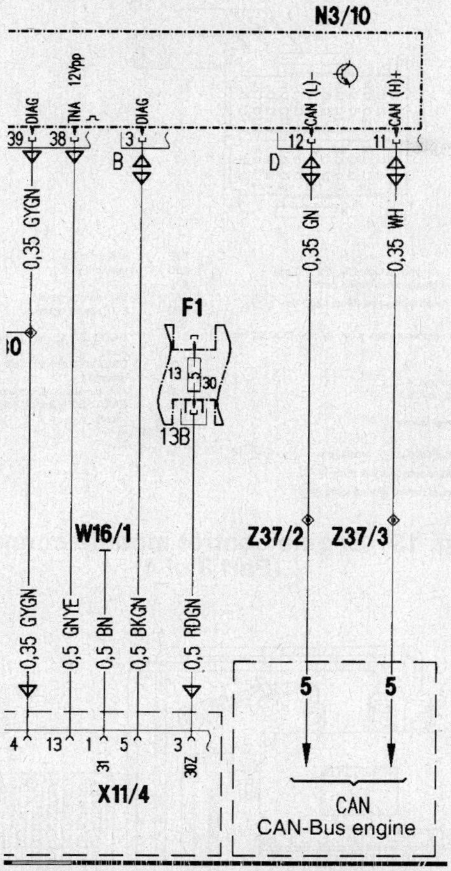

MB1010100226080X

Fig. 12 ME-SFI wiring diagram (Part 8 of 11). SLK230 engine compartment/frame floor

B4/3	Fuel tank pressure sensor
B37	Pedal value sensor
F1	Fuse and relay box
F1f10	Fuse 10
F1f13	Fuse 13
G3/1	O2S 2 (after TWC)
G3/1x1	O2S 2 connector (after TWC)
G3/2	O2S 1 (before TWC)
G3/2x1	O2S 1 connector (before TWC)
K40	Relay module
K40f2	EDC, 87 M2 fuse
K40f3	87 M1 fuse
K40f5	FP fuse
K40k1	FP relay
K40k9	Motor 87 M1/M2 relay
M3	FP assembly
N2/2	SRS control module

N3/10	Engine control module (ME-SFI)
N7-1	Illumination control module
N15/3	ETC control module
N48	BAS control module
N65	Pulse module (traction systems, HCS, ATA, AAC)
N76	Engine/climate control electric cooling fan control module
S2/1	Ignition/starter switch
S16/2	Backup lamp switch
S16/10	Transmission range recognition switch (voltage coded)
S16/10s1	Backup lamp switch
S40	CC switch

MB1010100226090X

Fig. 12 ME-SFI wiring diagram (Part 9 of 11). SLK230 engine compartment/frame floor

Z7/6	Circuit 87 connector sleeve (chassis)
Z7/24	Circuit 87 connector sleeve
Z37/2	Engine CAN-Bus (low) connector sleeve

MB1010100226110X

Fig. 12 ME-SFI wiring diagram (Part 11 of 11). SLK230 engine compartment/frame floor

S40/3	Clutch pedal switch
S40/5	Clutch pedal engage/release switch
S40s1	Memory recall
S40s2	Decelerate/set
S40s3	Accelerate/set
S40s4	Off
S40s5	Control contact
S40x1	CC switch connector
U24	Valid for MT
U25	Valid for AT
W1/1	Ground (cockpit frame)
W16	Ground (component compartment)
W16/1	Ground (right front spring tower)
W29/2	Ground (right A-pillar)
W35	Ground (left front spring tower)
X4	Terminal block (circuit 30, fuse and relay box) (2-pole)
X11/4	Data link connector (DTC readout)

X11/15	Diagnostic intermediate connector (taillamp harness) (16-pole)
X11/22	Diagnostic module (OBD II) generic scan tool connector
X12/1	Terminal block (circuit 15 unfused)
X26	Interior/engine wiring harness connector
X26/25	Engine/chassis connector (24-pole)
Y58/1	Purge control valve
Y58/4	Activated charcoal canister shut-off valve
Z3/11	Circuit 15 (fused) connector sleeve
Z6/30	Diagnostic (ME-SFI) connector sleeve
Z7/5	Circuit 87 connector sleeve

MB1010100226100X

Fig. 12 ME-SFI wiring diagram (Part 10 of 11). SLK230 engine compartment/frame floor

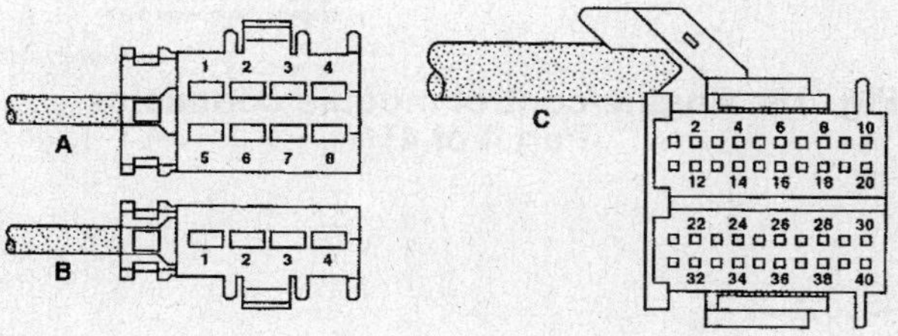

1A	–
2A	Voltage supply (circuit 87), Model 170 relay module, Model 202/208 fuse and relay module box
3A	Ground, Model 170 component compartment W16, Model 202/208 right component compartment W16/6
4A	–
5A	O2S 1 heater (before TWC)
6A	Control of engine/climate control electric cooling fan
7A	Ground, Model 170 component compartment W16, Model 202/208 right component compartment W16/6
8A	Ground, Model 170 component compartment W16, Model 202/208 right component compartment W16/6
1B	O2S 2 heater (after TWC) (only USA)
2B	–
3B	Diagnosis connection (data link connector)
4B	Voltage supply (circuit 30), Model 170 relay module, Model 202/208 fuse and relay module box
1C – 20C	–
21C	Purge control valve
22C	Pedal value sensor (+ nominal value potentiometer 1)
23C	Pedal value sensor (– nominal value potentiometer 1)
24C	Pedal value sensor (nominal value potentiometer 1 wiper)
25C	Pedal value sensor (nominal value potentiometer 2 wiper)
26C	Pedal value sensor (– nominal value potentiometer 2)
27C	Pedal value sensor (+ nominal value potentiometer 2)
28C	AIR relay module in fuse and relay module box (Model 202.023 only USA)
29C	FP relay module (on model 170 in relay module)

MB1029800574010X

Fig. 13 Engine control module connector (Part 1 of 4)

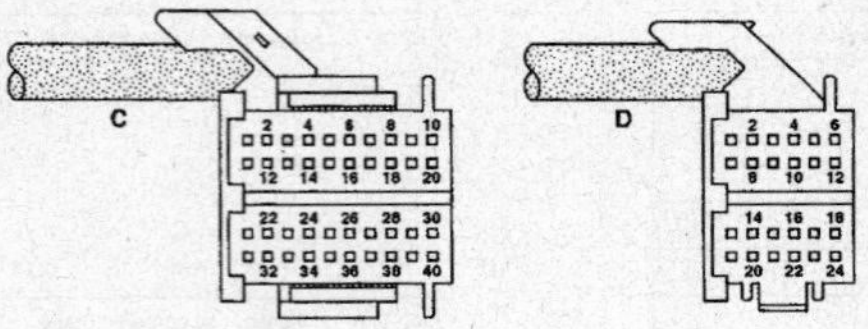

Figure 3

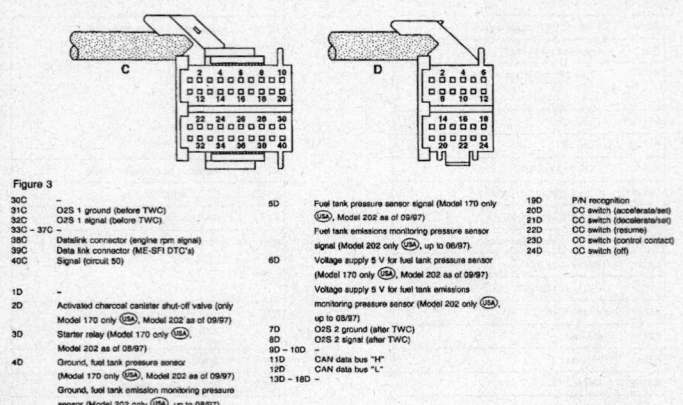

30C	–
31C	O2S 1 ground (before TWC)
32C	O2S 1 signal (before TWC)
33C – 37C	–
38C	Datalink connector (engine rpm signal)
39C	Data link connector (ME-SFI DTC's)
40C	Signal (circuit 50)
1D	–
2D	Activated charcoal canister shut-off valve (only Model 170 only (USA), Model 202 as of 09/97)
3D	Starter relay (Model 170 only (USA), Model 202 as of 08/97)
4D	Ground, fuel tank pressure sensor (Model 170 only (USA), Model 202 as of 09/97) Ground, fuel tank emission monitoring pressure sensor (Model 202 only (USA), up to 08/97)
5D	Fuel tank pressure sensor signal (Model 170 only (USA), Model 202 as of 09/97) Fuel tank emissions monitoring pressure sensor signal (Model 202 only (USA), up to 08/97).
6D	Voltage supply 5 V for fuel tank pressure sensor (Model 170 only (USA), Model 202 as of 09/97) Voltage supply 5 V for fuel tank emissions monitoring pressure sensor (Model 202 only (USA), up to 08/97)
7D	O2S 2 ground (after TWC)
8D	O2S 2 signal (after TWC)
9D – 10D	–
11D	CAN data bus "H"
12D	CAN data bus "L"
13D – 18D	–
19D	P/N recognition
20D	CC switch (accelerate/set)
21D	CC switch (decelerate/set)
22D	CC switch (resume)
23D	CC switch (control contact)
24D	CC switch (off)

MB1029800574020X

Fig. 13 Engine control module connector (Part 2 of 4)

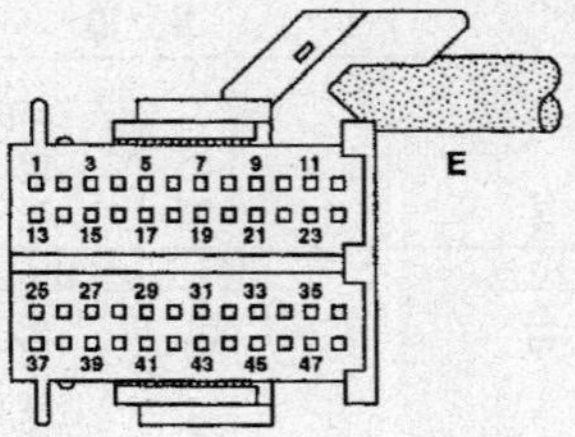

Figure 4

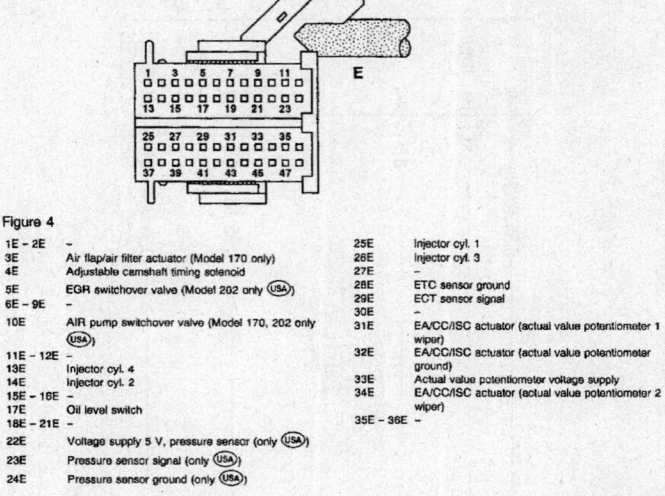

1E – 2E	–
3E	Air flap/air filter actuator (Model 170 only)
4E	Adjustable camshaft timing solenoid
5E	EGR switchover valve (Model 202 only (USA))
6E – 9E	–
10E	AIR pump switchover valve (Model 170, 202 only (USA))
11E – 12E	–
13E	Injector cyl. 4
14E	Injector cyl. 2
15E – 16E	–
17E	Oil level switch
18E – 21E	–
22E	Voltage supply 5 V, pressure sensor (only (USA))
23E	Pressure sensor signal (only (USA))
24E	Pressure sensor ground (only (USA))
25E	Injector cyl. 1
26E	Injector cyl. 3
27E	–
28E	ETC sensor ground
29E	ECT sensor signal
30E	–
31E	EA/CC/ISC actuator (actual value potentiometer 1 wiper)
32E	EA/CC/ISC actuator (actual value potentiometer ground)
33E	Actual value potentiometer voltage supply
34E	EA/CC/ISC actuator (actual value potentiometer 2 wiper)
35E – 36E	–

MB1029800574030X

Fig. 13 Engine control module connector (Part 3 of 4)

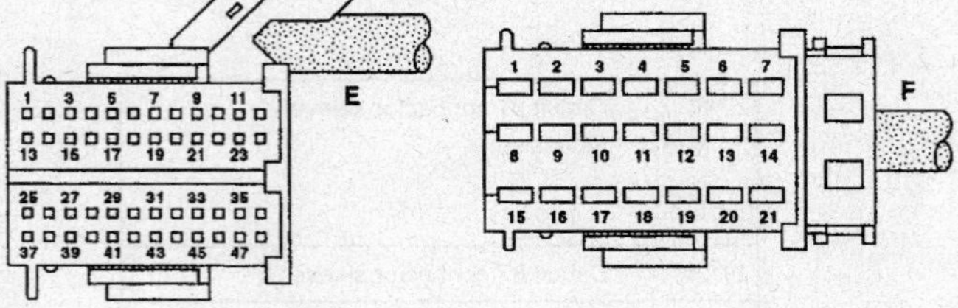

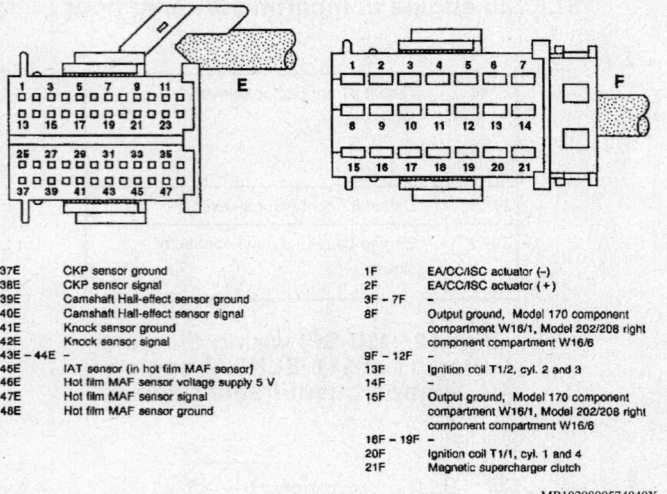

37E	CKP sensor ground
38E	CKP sensor signal
39E	Camshaft Hall-effect sensor ground
40E	Camshaft Hall-effect sensor signal
41E	Knock sensor ground
42E	Knock sensor signal
43E – 44E	–
45E	IAT sensor (in hot film MAF sensor)
46E	Hot film MAF sensor voltage supply 5 V
47E	Hot film MAF sensor signal
48E	Hot film MAF sensor ground
1F	EA/CC/ISC actuator (–)
2F	EA/CC/ISC actuator (+)
3F – 7F	–
8F	Output ground, Model 170 component compartment W16/1, Model 202/208 right component compartment W16/6
9F – 12F	–
13F	Ignition coil T1/2, cyl. 2 and 3
14F	–
15F	Output ground, Model 170 component compartment W16/1, Model 202/208 right component compartment W16/6
16F – 19F	–
20F	Ignition coil T1/1, cyl. 1 and 4
21F	Magnetic supercharger clutch

MB1029800574040X

Fig. 13 Engine control module connector (Part 4 of 4)

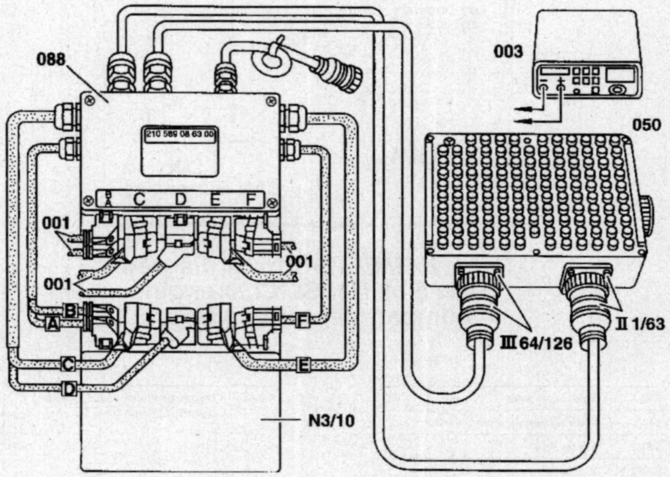

001	Engine control module connectors
003	Digital multimeter
050	Socket box (126-pole)
088	Test cable
N3/10	Engine control module (ME-SFI)

MB1029800573000X

Fig. 14 Test connections

DIAGNOSTIC CHART INDEX

Code	Description	Page No.	Fig. No.
—	Test 23, Step 7.0	14-73	21
	Test 23, Steps 8.2–9.0	14-73	23
	Test 24, Steps 3.0–4.0	14-76	44
	Test 32, Fuel System Pressure & Internal Leakage Test	14-77	54
	Test 34, Fuel Pump Test	14-78	56
	Test 36, Step 1.0	14-78	58
P0100	Test 23, Steps 4.0–4.3	14-73	18
P0105	Test 23, Step 6.0	14-73	20
P0110	Test 23, Steps 5.0–5.1	14-73	19
P0115	Test 23, Steps 8.0–8.1	14-22	22
P0121	Test 25, Steps 3.0–3.1	14-77	50
P0130	Test 23, Steps 10.0–11.0	14-74	24
P0133	Test 23, Steps 10.0–11.0	14-74	24
P0135	Test 23, Steps 10.0–11.0	14-74	24
P0136	Test 23, Steps 12.0–13.0	14-74	25
P0141	Test 23, Steps 12.0–13.0	1474	25
P0201	Test 23, Step 14.0	14-74	26
P0202	Test 23, Step 15.0	14-74	27
P0203	Test 23, Step 16.0	14-74	28
P0204	Test 23, Step 17.0	14-74	29
P0300	Test 24, Steps 7.0–8.1	14-76	47
	Test 24, Steps 9.0–9.1	14-77	48
P0301	Test 24, Steps 7.0–8.1	14-76	47
P0302	Test 24, Steps 7.0–8.1	14-76	47
	Test 24, Steps 9.0–9.1	14-77	48
P0303	Test 24, Steps 7.0–8.1	14-76	47
	Test 24, Steps 9.0–9.1	14-77	48
P0304	Test 24, Steps 7.0–8.1	14-76	47
	Test 24, Steps 9.0–9.1	14-77	48
P0335	Test 24, Steps 5.0–5.1	14-76	45
P0341	Test 24, Steps 6.0–6.1	14-76	46
P0400	Test 23, Steps 22.0–23.0	14-75	33
P0410	Test 23, Steps 18.0–19.0	14-74	30
	Test 23, Steps 19.0–20.0	14-74	31
P0440	Test 23, Steps 26.0–27.0	14-75	35
	Test 23, Steps 28.0–29.0	14-75	36
P0441	Test 23, Steps 26.0–27.0	14-75	35
P0442	Test 23, Steps 26.0–27.0	14-75	35
	Test 23, Steps 28.0–29.0	14-75	36
P0443	Test 23, Steps 26.0–27.0	14-75	35
P0446	Test 23, Steps 28.0–29.0	14-75	36
P0450	Test 23, Steps 30.0–30.1	14-75	37
	Test 23, Steps 31.0–31.1	14-75	38
P0455	Test 23, Steps 28.0–29.0	14-75	36
	Test 23, Steps 30.0–30.1	14-75	37
P0507	Test 25, Steps 1.0–2.1	14-77	49
	Test 25, Steps 3.0–3.1	14-77	50
P0560	Test 23, Steps 1.0–1.1	14-73	15
	Test 23, Steps 1.2–2.2	14-73	16
	Test 24, Steps 1.0–1.1	14-76	42
	Test 24, Steps 1.2–2.2	14-76	43
P0565	Test 26, Step 1.0	14-77	52
P0600	Test 23, Steps 32.0–33.0	14-75	39
P0801	Test 23, Steps 36.0–38.0	14-76	41
P0803	Test 23, Steps 36.0–38.0	14-76	41
P0805	Test 23, Steps 34.0–36.0	14-76	40
P0806	Test 23, Steps 34.0–36.0	14-76	40

Continued

DIAGNOSTIC CHART INDEX—Continued

Code	Description	Page No.	Fig. No.
P1182	Test 23, Steps 3.0–3.1	14-22	17
P1186	Test 25, Steps 3.0–3.1	14-77	50
	Test 25, Steps 4.0–5.0	14-77	51
P1400	Test 23, Step 21.0	14-75	32
P1420	Test 23, Steps 18.0–19.0	14-74	30
P1453	Test 23, Steps 18.0–19.0	14-74	30
P1519	Test 23, Steps 24.0–25.0	14-75	34
P1525	Test 23, Steps 24.0–25.0	14-75	34
P1542	Test 25, Steps 1.0–2.1	14-77	49
P1570	Test 23, Steps 32.0–33.0	14-75	39
P1580	Test 25, Steps 3.0–3.1	14-77	50
	Test 25, Steps 4.0–5.0	14-77	51
P1747	Test 23, Steps 32.0–33.0	14-75	39

⇒		Test scope	Test connection	Test condition	Nominal value	Possible cause/remedy
1.0	P0 560	**Engine control module (ME-SFI) (N3/10)** Voltage supply Circuit 30	N3/10 3 (3A) – V – 12 (4B)	Ignition: **ON**	11 – 14 V	⇒ 1.1 – 1.2
1.1		Ground wire	N3/10 3 (3A) – V – X11/4 2 N3/10 7 (7A) – V – X11/4 2 N3/10 112 (8F) – V – X11/4 2 N3/10 119 (15F) – V – X11/4 2	Ignition: **ON**	11 – 14 V	Wiring, **Model 170 and 202:** Output ground (W16/6), right component compartment. ⇒ 1.2

MB1029800600000X

Fig. 15 Code P0560: Test 23, Steps 1.0–1.1

⇒		Test scope	Test connection	Test condition	Nominal value	Possible cause/remedy
3.0	P1 182	**Model 170/208, Model 202 as of 08/97 only** **Starter lock-out relay module (N65k2) or K40k2** Activation	N3/10 35 (3D) – V – 2 (2A)	Engine coolant temperature >20°C Ignition/starter switch: Turn to starter contact briefly.	11 – 14 V or if engine does not start for approx. 5 seconds	⇒ 3.1 Engine control module (N3/10)
3.1		**Starter signal circuit 50**	N3/10 8 (8A) – V – 32 (40C)	Engine: **Crank**	11 – 14 V while cranking	Wiring, Ignition/starter switch (S2/1)

MB1029800576000X

Fig. 17 Code P1182: Test 23, Steps 3.0–3.1

⇒		Test scope	Test connection	Test condition	Nominal value	Possible cause/remedy
5.0	P0 110	**IAT sensor in hot film MAF sensor (B2/5)** Voltage	N3/10 104 (48E) – V – 101 (45E)	Ignition: **ON**	°C V 10 3.1 20 2.7 30 2.2 40 1.8 50 1.4 60 1.1 ± 5%	⇒ 5.1 N3/10
5.1		IAT sensor Resistance	N3/10 104 (48E) – Ω – 101 (45E)	Ignition: **OFF** Disconnect connector **E** on engine control module (N3/10).	oC Ω 10 3600 20 2420 30 1660 40 1170 50 850 60 600 ± 5%	Wiring, B2/5

MB1029800578000X

Fig. 19 Code P0110: Test 23, Steps 5.0–5.1

⇒		Test scope	Test connection	Test condition	Nominal value	Possible cause/remedy
7.0		**Model 202** **FP relay module (K27)** **Model 170** **In relay module (K40)** Activation	N3/10 21 (29C) – V – 2 (2A)	Ignition: **ON** Engine: **Start**	11 – 14 V for approx. 1 sec. [3] 11 – 14 V during cranking and while engine runs.	Wiring, K27 or K40, N3/10 **Note:** On Model 202 the activation of the fuel pump takes place via the passenger-side fuse and relay module box (K40/4).
		Current draw K27 or K40	N3/10 8 (8A) – A – 21 (29C)	Ignition: **ON**	0.1 – 0.3 A	

3) The activation of the FP occurs only once after ignition "ON". For the next activation, the engine must have run briefly.

MB1029800580000X

Fig. 21 Code —: Test 23, Step 7.0

⇒		Test scope	Test connection	Test condition	Nominal value	Possible cause/remedy
8.0	P0 115	**ECT sensor (B11/4)** Voltage	N3/10 84 (28E) – V – 85 (29E)	Ignition: **ON**	°C V 20 3.4 30 2.9 40 2.4 50 1.9 60 1.5 70 1.2 80 0.9 90 0.7 100 0.5 ±5 %	⇒ 8.1, N3/10
8.1		Resistance (B11/4)	N3/10 84 (28E) – Ω – 85 (29E)	Ignition: **OFF** Disconnect connector **E** on engine control module (N3/10).	°C Ω 20 3090 30 2000 40 1330 50 900 60 630 70 440 80 320 90 230 100 170 ±5 %	Wiring, ⇒ 8.2

MB1029800581000X

Fig. 22 Code P0115: Test 23, Steps 8.0–8.1

⇒		Test scope	Test connection	Test condition	Nominal value	Possible cause/remedy
1.2		Voltage supply Circuit 30	X11/4 1 – V – N3/10 12 (4B)	Ignition: **ON**	11 – 14 V	Wiring, **Model 170:** Relay module (K40). **Model 202:** Passenger-side fuse and relay module box (K40/4).
2.0	P0 560	**Engine control module (ME-SFI) (N3/10)** Voltage supply Circuit 87	N3/10 8 (8A) – V – 2 (2A)	Ignition: **ON**	11 – 14 V	⇒ 2.1 – 2.2
2.1		Electronics ground	N3/10 8 (8A) – V – X11/4 2	Ignition: **ON**	11 – 14 V	Wiring, **Model 170 and 202:** Output ground (W16/6), right component compartment. ⇒ 2.2
2.2		Voltage supply Circuit 87	X11/4 1 – V – N3/10 2 (2A)	Ignition: **ON** Ignition: **OFF**	11 – 14 V < 1 V	Wiring, **Model 170:** Relay module (K40). **Model 202:** Passenger-side fuse and relay module box (K40/4).

MB1029800575000X

Fig. 16 Code P0560: Test 23, Steps 1.2–2.2

⇒		Test scope	Test connection	Test condition	Nominal value	Possible cause/remedy
4.0	P0 100	**Hot film MAF sensor (B2/5)** Hot film signal	N3/10 104 (48E) – V – 103 (47E)	Ignition: ON Engine: **at idle** Engine coolant temperature >70°C	0.9 – 1.1 V 1.3 – 1.7 V [2]	Wiring, ⇒ 4.0 – 4.3 Air intake system leak, B2/5.
4.1		**Hot film MAF sensor (B2/5)** Voltage supply 5 V	N3/10 104 (48E) – V – B2/5 4	Disconnect MAF sensor (B2/5) connector and measure directly on socket 4 (br/yl). Ignition: **ON**	4.7 – 5.2 V	Wiring, N3/10
4.2		**Ground wire for hot film MAF sensor (B2/5)**	B2/5 3 – V – N3/10 102 (46E)	Disconnect MAF sensor (B2/5) connector and measure directly on socket 3 (br). Ignition: **ON**	4.7 – 5.2 V	Wiring.
4.3		**Hot film MAF sensor (B2/5)** Voltage supply 12 V	N3/10 104 (48E) – V – B2/5 2 (2)	Disconnect MAF sensor (B2/5) connector and connect plus of voltmeter to socket 2 (rd/bu). Ignition: **ON**	11 – 14 V	Wiring, **Model 170:** Relay module (K40) **Model 202:** Passenger-side fuse and relay module box (K40/4).

2) Increasing rpm, increasing voltage.

MB1029800577000X

Fig. 18 Code P0100: Test 23, Steps 4.0–4.3

⇒		Test scope	Test connection	Test condition	Nominal value	Possible cause/remedy
6.0	P0 105	**Pressure sensor (B28)** Sensor signal	N3/10 80 (24E) – V – 79 (23E)	Connect vacuum tester to pressure sensor (B28) using Y-fitting Ignition: **ON** Engine: **at idle**	> 3.5 V < 2 V and vacuum climbs to > 500 mbar.	⇒ 6.1, Vacuum line, Wiring, B28
		Pressure sensor (B28) Voltage supply	N3/10 80 (24E) – V – 78 (22E)	Ignition: **ON**	4.7 – 5.3 V	N3/10

MB1029800579000X

Fig. 20 Code P0105: Test 23, Step 6.0

⇒		Test scope	Test connection	Test condition	Nominal value	Possible cause/remedy
8.2		ECT sensor (B11/4) Resistance	B11/4 1 – Ω – 2	Disconnect connector on ECT sensor (B11/4).	Nominal value, see ⇒ 8.1	B11/4
9.0		**Engine control module (N3/10)** TN-signal output	N3/10 [3] 8 (8A) – oscilloscope – 30 (38C) N3/10 [4] 8 (8A) – V – 30 (38C)	Engine: **Start** or Engine: **at idle**	Signal, see Figure 2. 7.5 – 9.0 V	Wiring, N3/10

3) Test with oscilloscope.
4) Test with multimeter only if oscilloscope is not available.

MB1029800582000X

Fig. 23 Code —: Test 23, Steps 8.2–9.0

⇒		Test scope	Test connection	Test condition	Nominal value	Possible cause/remedy
10.0	P0 130 P0 133	**O2S 1** **(before TWC) (G3/2)** O2S signal	N3/10 23 (31C) —V— 24 (32C)	ECT > 80 ° C, run engine at idle for at least two minutes.	fluctuates from – 0.2 V to + 1.0 V, by more than 0.3 V	Wiring, ⇒ 11.0 G3/2
11.0	P0 135	**O2S 1** **(before TWC) (G3/2)** O2S heater activation	N3/10 5 (5A) —V— 2 (2A)	ECT > 80 ° C, run engine at idle for at least two minutes.	11 – 14 V	Wiring, G3/2 N3/10
		O2S 1 (G3/2) Current draw	N3/10 3 (3A) —A— 5 (5A)	Ignition: **ON**	0.6 – 3.4 A	

MB1029800583000X

Fig. 24 Codes P0130, P0133 & P0135: Test 23, Steps 10.0–11.0

⇒		Test scope	Test connection	Test condition	Nominal value	Possible cause/remedy
14.0	P0 201	**Injector (Y62y1)** Activation and injection time	N3/10 81 (25E) —⊕— 2 (2A)	**ECT approx. 20° C** at start **ECT approx. 80° C** at idle accelerate briefly	Injection time: approx. 8 ms approx. 2.7 – 4 ms approx. 14 ms	Wiring, Y62y1, N3/10 **Further possibilities:** ECT sensor (B11/4), IAT sensor in hot film MAF sensor (B2/5), O2S 1 (G3/2).
		Resistance (Y62y1)	N3/10 81 (25E) —Ω— 2 (2A)	Ignition: **OFF**	14 – 17 Ω	

MB1029800585000X

Fig. 26 Code P0201: Test 23, Step 14.0

⇒		Test scope	Test connection	Test condition	Nominal value	Possible cause/remedy
16.0	P0 203	**Injector (Y62y3)** Activation and injection time	N3/10 82 (26E) —⊕— 2 (2A)	**ECT approx. 20° C** at start **ECT approx. 80° C** at idle accelerate briefly	Injection time: approx. 8 ms approx. 2.7 – 4 ms approx. 14 ms	Wiring, Y62y3, N3/10 **Further possibilities:** ECT sensor (B11/4), IAT sensor in hot film MAF sensor (B2/5), O2S 1 (G3/2).
		Resistance (Y62y3)	N3/10 82 (26E) —Ω— 2 (2A)	Ignition: **OFF**	14 – 17 Ω	

MB1029800587000X

Fig. 28 Code P0203: Test 23, Step 16.0

⇒		Test scope	Test connection	Test condition	Nominal value	Possible cause/remedy
18.0	P1 453 P0 410	**Model 202 only** **AIR pump relay in passenger-side fuse and relay module box (K40/4),** Activation	N3/10 20 (28C) —V— 2 (2A)	Disconnect ECT sensor (B11/4) connector. Simulate 2.5 kΩ resistance at sockets 1 and 4 with resistance substitution unit. Engine: **at idle**	11 – 14 V for approx. two minutes **and** AIR pump runs.	Wiring, AIR pump fuse, K40/4, N3/10
		Current draw (K40/4)	N3/10 3 (3A) —A— 20 (28C)	Ignition: **ON**	0.1 – 0.3 A	
19.0	P1 420 P0 410	**AIR pump switchover valve (Y32)** Activation	N3/10 66 (10E) —V— 2 (2A)	Disconnect ECT sensor (B11/4) connector. Simulate 2.5 kΩ resistance at sockets 1 and 4 with resistance substitution unit. Engine: **at idle**	11 – 14 V for approx. two minutes **and** AIR pump runs.	Wiring, Y32, N3/10

MB1029800589000X

Fig. 30 Codes P0410, P1420 & P1453: Test 23, Steps 18.0–19.0

⇒		Test scope	Test connection	Test condition	Nominal value	Possible cause/remedy
12.0	P0 136	**O2S 2** **(after TWC) (G3/1)** O2S signal	N3/10 39 (7D) —V— 40 (8D)	ECT > 80° C, Engine: **Start** Raise and hold engine speed at 2000 – 3000 rpm for approx. 2 minutes.	> 550 mV	Wiring, ⇒ 14.0, G3/1, N3/10
			N3/10 3 (3A) ←→ 20 (28C) 3 (3A) ←→ 66 (10E)	Bridge sockets on socket box	AIR pump runs. Voltage changes to < 40 mV within 60 seconds.	
13.0	P0 141	**O2S 2** **(after TWC) (G3/1)** O2S heater activation	N3/10 9 (1B) —V— 2 (2A)	Engine: **at idle** ECT > 80° C, run engine at idle for at least 2 minutes.	11 – 14 V or voltage fluctuates between 1 – 14 V	Wiring, G3/1, N3/10
		O2S 2 (G3/1) Current draw	N3/10 3 (3A) —A— 9 (1B)	Ignition: **ON**	0.6 – 3.4 A	

MB1029800584000X

Fig. 25 Codes P0136 & P0141: Test 23, Steps 12.0–13.0

⇒		Test scope	Test connection	Test condition	Nominal value	Possible cause/remedy
15.0	P0 202	**Injector (Y62y2)** Activation and injection time	N3/10 70 (14E) —⊕— 2 (2A)	**ECT approx. 20° C** at start **ECT approx. 80° C** at idle accelerate briefly	Injection time: approx. 8 ms approx. 2.7 – 4 ms approx. 14 ms	Wiring, Y62y2, N3/10 **Further possibilities:** ECT sensor (B11/4), IAT sensor in hot film MAF sensor (B2/5), O2S 1 (G3/2).
		Resistance (Y62y2)	N3/10 70 (14E) —Ω— 2 (2A)	Ignition: **OFF**	14 – 17 Ω	

MB1029800586000X

Fig. 27 Code P0202: Test 23, Step 15.0

⇒		Test scope	Test connection	Test condition	Nominal value	Possible cause/remedy
17.0	P0 204	**Injector (Y62y4)** Activation and injection time	N3/10 69 (13E) —⊕— 2 (2A)	**ECT approx. 20° C** at start **ECT approx. 80° C** at idle accelerate briefly	Injection time: approx. 8 ms approx. 2.7 – 4 ms approx. 14 ms	Wiring, Y62y4, N3/10 **Further possibilities:** ECT sensor (B11/4), IAT sensor in hot film MAF sensor (B2/5), O2S 1 (G3/2).
		Resistance (Y62y4)	N3/10 69 (13E) —Ω— 2 (2A)	Ignition: **OFF**	14 – 17 Ω	

MB1029800588000X

Fig. 29 Code P0204: Test 23, Step 17.0

⇒		Test scope	Test connection	Test condition	Nominal value	Possible cause/remedy
[19.0]		Current draw (Y32)	N3/10 3 (3A) —A— 66 (10E)	Ignition: **ON**	0.4 – 0.6 A	
20.0	P0 410	**AIR system** (logic chain)	N3/10 23 (31C) —V— 24 (32C)	**Note:** The O2S 1 signal before TWC is measured. With ETC > 80°C run engine at idle for at least 2 minutes.	The O2S voltage oscillates in the area of –0.2 V and +1.0 V	Y32 binding, AIR combi valve, AIR pump or supercharger no output.
		Model 202 or 170:	N3/10 3 (3A) ←→ 20 (28C) 3 ←→ 125 3 (3A) ←→ 66 (10E)	Bridge sockets on socket box.	AIR pump runs. Voltage changes to < 100 mV within 20 seconds. **Model 170:** < 50 mV within 6 seconds.	

6) The resistance of one solenoid is 7 – 12 Ω.

MB1029800590000X

Fig. 31 Code P0410: Test 23, Steps 19.0–20.0

⇒		Test scope	Test connection	Test condition	Nominal value	Possible cause/remedy
21.0	P1400	**Model 202 only** **EGR switchover valve (Y27)** Activation	N3/10 61 (5E) –(V)– 2 (2A)	Engine: **at Idle** ECT > 60 °C Accelerate briefly	11 – 14 V	Wiring, Y27, N3/10, ⇒ 22.0 – 23.0
		Y27 Current draw	N3/10 3 (3A) –(A)– 61 (5E)	Ignition: **ON**	0.3 – 0.5 A	

MB1029800591000X

Fig. 32 Code P1400: Test 23, Step 21.0

⇒		Test scope	Test connection	Test condition	Nominal value	Possible cause/remedy
24.0	P1525	**Adjustable camshaft timing solenoid (Y49)** Current draw	Y49 1 –(A)– 2	**Test connection note:** Connect test cable (102 589 04 63 00) to solenoid. Engine: **at Idle** ECT > 70°C Increase engine speed to approx. 2000 rpm.	1 – 1.5 A	⇒ 24.1, ⇒ 25.0, N3/10
24.1		Resistance Y49	N3/10 60 (4E) –(Ω)– 2 (2A)	Ignition: **OFF**	7 – 12 Ω	Wiring, Y49
25.0	P1519	**Adjustable camshaft timing solenoid (Y49)** Mechanical function	N3/10 60 (4E) ←→ 3 (3A)	Engine: **at Idle** Bridge sockets on socket box for a maximum of 10 seconds.	Engine runs rough or stalls	Check function of camshaft adjuster

MB1029800593000X

Fig. 34 Codes P1519 & P1525: Test 23, Steps 24.0–25.0

⇒		Test scope	Test connection	Test condition	Nominal value	Possible cause/remedy
28.0	P0440 P0442 P0455	Only (USA) **Model 170** **Model 202 as of 09/97** **Purge system** Leaks Activated charcoal canister shut-off valve (Y58/4) Activate	N3/10 3 (3A) ←→ 34 (2D)	Disconnect purge line to charcoal canister on purge control valve (Y58/1). Connect vacuum tester to purge line (Figure 5 and 6). Ignition: **ON** Apply approx. 25 mbar of vacuum.	After approx. 1 minute, < 5 mbar vacuum loss.	Fuel tank cap, Purge line to charcoal canister, Purge line from charcoal canister to Y58/4, Charcoal canister, Y58/4
29.0	P0446	Only (USA) **Model 170** **Model 202 as of 09/97** **Activated charcoal canister shut-off valve (Y58/4)** Current draw	N3/10 3 (3A) –(A)– 34 (2D)	Ignition: **ON**	0.5 – 0.9 A	Wiring, Y58/4

MB1029800595000X

Fig. 36 Codes P0440, P0442, P0446, & P0455: Test 23, Steps 28.0–29.0

⇒		Test scope	Test connection	Test condition	Nominal value	Possible cause/remedy
31.0	P0450	Only (USA) **Model 202 only, up to 08/97** **Purge monitoring pressure sensor (B4/4)** Sender signal	N3/10 36 (4D) –(V)– 37 (5D)	Disconnect vacuum line at purge monitoring pressure sensor (B4/4). Connect vacuum tester to purge monitoring pressure sensor Ignition: **ON** Apply approx. 300 mbar of vacuum.	> 3.5 V < 3 V	⇒ 31.1, Wiring, B4/4
31.1		Purge monitoring pressure sensor (B4/4) Voltage supply	N3/10 36 (4D) –(V)– 38 (6D)	Ignition: **ON**	4.7 – 5.3 V	N3/10

MB1029800601000X

Fig. 38 Code P0450: Test 23, Steps 31.0–31.1

⇒		Test scope	Test connection	Test condition	Nominal value	Possible cause/remedy
22.0	P0400	**Model 202 only** **EGR switchover valve (Y27)** Vacuum control		**Test connection note:** Connect vacuum tester to EGR valve. Engine: **Start** and run at >3000 rpm	> 400 mbar	Vacuum line, EGR valve, Y27
23.0	P0400	**Model 202 only** **EGR valve** Mechanical test		**Test connection note:** Engine: at Idle Apply 500 mbar vacuum to EGR valve. Engine: **OFF** Apply 500 mbar vacuum to EGR valve and pull off vacuum hose.	Engine runs uneven. EGR valve closes audibly	EGR valve

MB1029800592000X

Fig. 33 Code P0400: Test 23, Steps 22.0–23.0

⇒		Test scope	Test connection	Test condition	Nominal value	Possible cause/remedy
26.0	P0440 P0441 P0443	**Purge control valve (Y58/1)** Activation	N3/10 13 (21C) –(±)– 2 (2A)	Engine: **at Idle** and at operating temperature.	After approx. 1 minute, purge control valve (Y58/1) must noticeably cycle signal	Wiring, Y58/1, ⇒ 27.0, N3/10
		Current draw (Y58/1)	N3/10 3 (3A) –(A)– 13 (21C)	Ignition: **ON**	0.2 – 0.4 A	
27.0	P0440 P0441	**Purge control valve (Y58/1)** Vacuum control		Connect vacuum tester to purge control valve (Y58/1) between purge line to charcoal canister Engine at operating temperature and at idle.	After approx. 1 minute, > 50 mbar and needle oscillates, Y58/1 must cycle.	Vacuum line, Y58/1

MB1029800594000X

Fig. 35 Codes P0440, P0441, P0442 & P0443: Test 23, Steps 26.0–27.0

⇒		Test scope	Test connection	Test condition	Nominal value	Possible cause/remedy
30.0	P0450 P0455	Only (USA) **Model 170** **Model 202 as of 09/97** **Fuel tank pressure sensor (B4/3)** Sender signal Activated charcoal canister shut-off valve (Y58/4) Activate	N3/10 36 (4D) –(V)– 37 (5D) N3/10 3 (3A) ←→ 34 (2D)	Disconnect purge line to charcoal canister on purge control valve (Y58/1). Connect vacuum tester to purge line Ignition: **ON** Apply approx. 25 mbar of vacuum.	> 2.3 V < 2.3 V	⇒ 30.1, Wiring, Vacuum line, Charcoal canister plugged, B4/3
30.1		Only (USA) Fuel tank pressure sensor (B4/3) Voltage supply	N3/10 36 (4D) –(V)– 38 (6D)	Ignition: **ON**	4.7 – 5.3 V	N3/10

MB1029800596000X

Fig. 37 Codes P0450 & P0455: Test 23, Steps 30.0–30.1

⇒		Test scope	Test connection	Test condition	Nominal value	Possible cause/remedy
32.0	P0600 P1570 P1747	**CAN data bus**	N3/10 43 (11D) –(Ω)– 44 (12D)	Ignition: **OFF**	55 – 65 Ω	⇒ 32.1 – 32.2 Data line.
32.1		**CAN element in DAS control module (N54/1)** Resistance	N3/10 43 (11D) –(Ω)– 44 (12D)	Ignition: **OFF** Disconnect connector **D** from engine control module N3/10.	115 – 125 Ω	Wiring, N54/1 or electronic key.
32.2		**CAN element in engine control module (N3/10)** Resistance	N3/10 43 (11D) –(Ω)– 44 (12D)	Ignition: **OFF** Disconnect connector **D** from test cable.	115 – 125 Ω	N3/10
33.0	P1163	**Oil level switch (S43)**	N3/10 73 (17E) –(V)– 2 (2A)	Ignition: **ON** Oil level okay. Oil level low.	11 – 14 V < 1 V	Wiring, S43

MB1029800597000X

Fig. 39 Codes P0600, P1570 & P1747: Test 23, Steps 32.0–33.0

⇒		Test scope	Test connection	Test condition	Nominal value	Possible cause/remedy
34.0		**Diagnosis line** Activation	N3/10 3 — (V) — 31 (3A) (39C)	Ignition: **ON**	11 – 14 V	Wiring, N3/10
35.0	P0 805	**Model 170 only** **Supercharger function**		Connect pressure tester to intake manifold. Drive vehicle on dynamometer or road in transm. range 3 with full load at approx. 3500 rpm. Or with transm. in "P" and parking brake set, briefly accelerate engine to full throttle (1-2 seconds)	> 280 mbar pressure	⇒ 36.0 – 37.0 Air flap/air filter actuator (M16/7) binding, Charge air line plugged, Supercharger defective.
36.0	P0 806	**Model 170 only** **Magnetic supercharger clutch (Y2/1)** Activation	N3/10 125 — (V) — 2 (21F) (2A)	Engine: **At Idle:** **Rapidly depress accelerator pedal (+2,200 rpm) or activate with HHT:**	0 V 11 – 14 V, as long as the supercharger is engaged.	Wiring, Y2/1, N3/10, K40

MB1029800598000X

Fig. 40 Codes P0805 & P0806: Test 23, Steps 34.0–36.0

⇒		Test scope	Test connection	Test condition	Nominal value	Possible cause/Remedy
1.0	P0 560	**Engine control module (N3/10)** Voltage supply circuit 30	N3/10 3 — (V) — 12 (3A) (4B)	Ignition: **ON**	11 – 14 V	⇒ 1.1 – 1.2
1.1		Ground wire	N3/10 X11/4 3 — (V) — 2 (3A) X11/4 7 — (V) — 2 (7A) X11/4 112 — (V) — 2 (8F) X11/4 119 — (V) — 2 (15F)	Ignition: **ON**	11 – 14 V	Wiring, **Model 170 and 202** Output ground (W16/6), right component compartment

MB1029800602000X

Fig. 42 Code P0560: Test 24, Steps 1.0–1.1

⇒		Test scope	Test connection	Test condition	Nominal value	Possible cause/Remedy
3.0		**Ignition coil (T1/1)** Cylinder 1 and 4 Voltage supply	N3/10 3 — (V) — 124 (3A) (20F)	Ignition: **ON** Starter: **Crank**	11 – 14 V > 10 V	Wiring, Fuses: Model 170, fuse 11 Model 202, fuse and relay module box fuse 6 Ignition coil (T1/1)
4.0		**Ignition coil (T1/2)** Cylinder 2 and 3 Voltage supply	N3/10 3 — (V) — 117 (3A) (13F)	Ignition: **ON** Starter: **Crank**	11 – 14 V > 10 V	Wiring, Fuses: Model 170, fuse 11 Model 202, fuse and relay module box fuse 6 Ignition coil (T1/2)

MB1029800604000X

Fig. 44 Code —: Test 24, Steps 3.0–4.0

⇒		Test scope	Test connection	Test condition	Nominal value	Possible cause/Remedy
6.0	P0 341	**Camshaft Hall-effect sensor (B6/1)** Hall-effect signal	N3/10 2) 95 — — 96 (39E) (40E) N3/10 3) 96 — (V) — 2 (40E) (2A)	Engine: **at Idle** Engine: **at Idle**	Signal 1.2 – 1.7 V Value changes	⇒ 6.1, Wiring B6/1
6.1		Voltage supply to camshaft Hall-effect sensor (B6/1)	B6/1 1 — (V) — 3	Ignition: **ON** Disconnect connector from Hall-effect sensor (B6/1) and test directly on sockets 1 and 3 of connector.	11 – 14 V	Wiring.

2) Test with oscilloscope.
3) Test with multimeter only if oscilloscope is unavailable.

MB1029800605000X

Fig. 46 Code P0341: Test 24, Steps 6.0–6.1

⇒		Test scope	Test connection	Test condition	Nominal value	Possible cause/remedy
[36.0]		Y2/1 Current draw	N3/10 3 — (A) — 125 (3A) (21F)	Ignition: **ON**	2.6 – 4.5 A	
37.0	P0 803	**Model 170 only** **Air flap/air filter actuator (M16/7)** Activation	N3/10 59 — (V) — 2 (3E) (2A)	Ignition: **ON** **HHT activation "Open"** **HHT activation "Closed"**	1.0 – 1.4 V 10.5 – 11.5 V ≈ 1.75 V	Wiring, M16/7, N3/10
38.0	P0 801	**Engine/climate control electric cooling fan control module (N76)** Activation	N3/10 6 — (V) — 2 (6A) (2A)	Engine: **at Idle** ECT < 70 °C A/C system: **ON** ECT > 85 °C	1 – 1.9 V and fan is stopped. 2 – 4 V and fan runs. Between 2.5 – 12.5 V and fan runs according to activation.	N3/10

MB1029800599000X

Fig. 41 Codes P0801 & P0803: Test 23, Steps 36.0–38.0

⇒		Test scope	Test connection	Test condition	Nominal value	Possible cause/Remedy
1.2		Voltage supply circuit 30	N3/10 X11/4 1 — (V) — 12 (4B)	Ignition: **ON**	11 – 14 V	Wiring, **Model 170** Relay module (K40), **Model 202** Passenger-side fuse and relay module box (K40/4).
2.0	P0 560	**Engine control module (N3/10)** Voltage supply circuit 87	N3/10 8 — (V) — 2 (8A) (2A)	Ignition: **ON**	11 – 14 V	⇒ 2.1 – 2.2
2.1		Electronics ground	N3/10 X11/4 8 — (V) — 2 (8A)	Ignition: **ON**	11 – 14 V	Wiring, **Model 170 and 202** Output ground (W16/6), right component compartment.
2.2		Voltage supply circuit 87	N3/10 X11/4 1 — (V) — 2 (2A)	Ignition: **ON** Ignition: **OFF**	11 – 14 V < 1 V	Wiring, **Model 170** Relay module (K40). **Model 202** Passenger-side fuse and relay module box (K40/4).

MB1029800603000X

Fig. 43 Code P0560: Test 24, Steps 1.2–2.2

⇒		Test scope	Test connection	Test condition	Nominal value	Possible cause/Remedy
5.0	P0 335	**CKP sensor (L5)** Signal Voltage	N3/10 2) 93 — — 94 (37E) (38E) N3/10 3) 93 — (V) — 94 (37E) (38E)	Starter: **Crank** Engine: **at Idle** Starter: **Crank** Engine: **at Idle**	Signal > 2.5 V~ > 5 V~ 4)	⇒ 5.1, Teeth on starter ring gear.
5.1		Resistance of CKP sensor (L5)	N3/10 93 — (Ω) — 94 (37E) (38E)	Ignition: **OFF** Unplug connector **E** on engine control module (N3/10).	700 – 1400 Ω	Wiring, L5

2) Test with oscilloscope.
3) Test with multimeter only if oscilloscope is unavailable.
4) Voltage increases with increasing rpm.

MB1029800608000X

Fig. 45 Code P0335: Test 24, Steps 5.0–5.1

⇒		Test scope	Test connection	Test condition	Nominal value	Possible cause/Remedy
7.0	P0 300 P0 301 P0 304	**Primary voltage** Ignition coil (T1/1), Cylinders 1 and 4	N3/10 124 — — 2 (20F) (2A)	**Test connection Note:** Individual primary pattern Range 400 V Duration 100% Starter: **Crank**	200 – 350 V	⇒ 7.1
7.1		Primary winding of T1/1 and T1/2	N3/10 124 — (Ω) — 117 (20F) (13F)	Ignition: **OFF**	0.9 – 1.6 Ω 6)	Wiring T1/1 or T1/2
8.0	P0 300 P0 302 P0 303	**Primary voltage** Ignition coil (T1/2) Cylinders 2 and 3	N3/10 117 — — 2 (13F) (2A)	**Test connection Note:** Individual primary pattern Range 400 V Duration 100% Starter: **Crank**	200 – 350 V	⇒ 8.1
8.1		Primary winding of T1/2 and T1/1	N3/10 117 — (Ω) — 124 (13F) (20F)	Ignition: **OFF**	0.9 – 1.6 Ω 6)	Wiring T1/2 or T1/1

6) The resistance of a single coil at 20 °C is approx. 0.6 Ω.

MB1029800606000X

Fig. 47 Codes P0300, P0301, P0302, P0303 & P0304: Test 24, Steps 7.0–8.1

⇒		Test scope	Test connection	Test condition	Nominal value	Possible cause/Remedy
9.0	P0 300 P0 301 P0 302 P0 303 P0 304	**Firing voltage** Ignition coil (T1/1) and (T1/2)	Engine analyzer	**Test connection Note:** Individual secondary pattern Range 20 kV Duration 100% Connect kV pick-ups successively to T1/1 and T1/2. Starter: **Crank**	8 – 20 kV	⇒ 9.1, Spark plugs, N3/10
9.1		Secondary winding of T1/1 or T1/2	T1/1 T1/2 cir. 4a cir. 4b	Disconnect both ignition cables on T1/1 or T1/2	6 – 8.5 kΩ	T1/1 or T1/2

MB1029500607000X

Fig. 48 Codes P0300, P0302, P0303 & P0304: Test 24, Steps 9.0–9.1

⇒		Test scope	Test connection	Test condition	Nominal value	Possible cause/remedy
1.0	P1 542 P0 507	**Pedal value sensor (B37)** Signal Nominal value potentiometer 1	N3/10 15 (23C) — 16 (24C)	Ignition: **ON** Accelerator pedal position: CTP WOT or kick-down	 0.2 – 0.5 V 4.3 – 4.8 V	⇒ 1.1, Wiring, B37
1.1		Voltage supply Nominal value potentiometer 1	N3/10 15 (23C) — 14 (22C)	Ignition: **ON**	4.75 – 5.25 V	Wiring N3/10
2.0	P1 542 P0 507	**Pedal value sensor (B37)** Signal Nominal value potentiometer 2	N3/10 18 (26C) — 17 (25C)	Ignition: **ON** Accelerator pedal position: CTP WOT and kick-down	 0.1 – 0.4 V 2.1 – 2.5 V	⇒ 2.1, Wiring, B37
2.1		Voltage supply [1] Nominal value potentiometer 2	N3/10 18 (26C) — 19 (27C)	Ignition: **ON**	2.25 – 2.75 V	Wiring N3/10

[1] Test step not valid for pedal value sensor with hall effect.

MB1029800609000X

Fig. 49 Codes P0507 & P1542: Test 25, Steps 1.0–2.1

⇒		Test scope	Test connection	Test condition	Nominal value	Possible cause/remedy
3.0	P0 507 P0 120 P1 186 P1 580	**EA/CC/ISC actuator (M16/6)** Signal Actual value potentiometer 1 Actual value potentiometer 2	N3/10 88 (32E) — 87 (31E) N3/10 88 (32E) — 90 (34E)	Ignition: **ON** Accelerator pedal position: CTP WOT or kick-down Accelerator pedal position: CTP WOT or kick-down	 4.0 – 4.6 V < CTP value 0.3 – 0.9 V > CTP value	⇒ 3.1, Wiring, M16/6
3.1		Voltage supply Actual value potentiometers 1 and 2	N3/10 88 (32E) — 89 (33E)	Ignition: **ON**	4.75 – 5.25 V	Wiring N3/10

MB1029800610000X

Fig. 50 Codes P0121, P0507, P1186 & P1580: Test 25, Steps 3.0–3.1

⇒		Test scope	Test connection	Test condition	Nominal value	Possible cause/remedy
4.0	P1 186 P1 580	**EA/CC/ISC actuator (M16/6)** Activation of actuator motor Resistance of actuator motor	N3/10 105 (1F) — 106 (2F) N3/10 105 (1F) — 106 (2F)	Ignition: **ON** Engine: **at Idle** ECT > 70 °C Ignition: **OFF**	0.8 – 2.3 V 1.0 – 2.5 V Value oscillates. < 10 Ω	Wiring, M16/6 N3/10
5.0		**P/N recognition**	N3/10 51 (19D) — 2 (2A)	Ignition: **ON** Selector lever position: P/N → R, D, 4, 3, 2, 1 →	 11 – 14 V < 1.5 V	Wiring, Test ETC

MB1029800611000X

Fig. 51 Codes P1186 & P1580: Test 25, Steps 4.0–5.0

⇒		Test scope	Test connection	Test condition	Nominal value	Possible cause/Remedy
1.0	P0 565	**CC switch (S40)** **V** Decelerate/set	N3/10 3 (3A) — 53 (21D)	Ignition: **ON** CC switch not activated. Decelerate activated.	 < 1 V 11 – 14 V	Wiring, S40
		SP Memory recall	N3/10 3 (3A) — 54 (22D)	Memory activated.	11 – 14 V	
		B Accelerate/set	N3/10 3 (3A) — 52 (20D)	Accelerate activated.	11 – 14 V	
		A Off	N3/10 3 (3A) — 56 (24D)	CC switch not activated. Off activated.	11 – 14 V < 1 V	
		Control contact	N3/10 3 (3A) — 55 (23D)	CC switch not activated. CC switch in position: **Activate decelerate/accelerate/memory/off**	< 1 V 11 – 14 V	

MB1029800612000X

Fig. 52 Code P0565: Test 26, Step 1.0

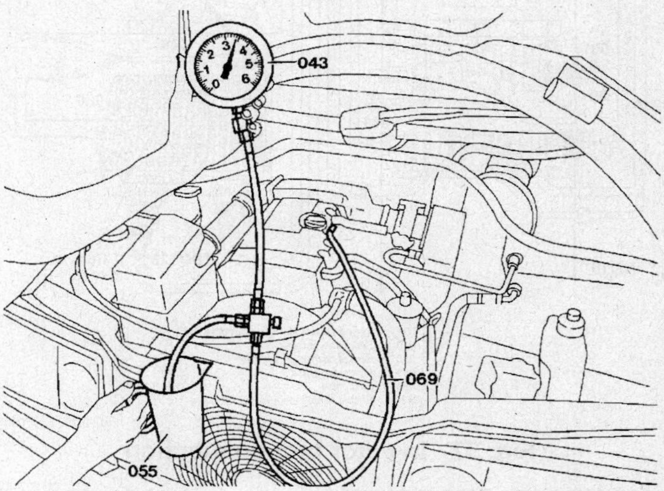

043 Pressure gauge, part no. 103 589 00 21 00
055 Measuring glass
069 Pressure hose, part no. 119 589 04 63 00

MB1029800613000A

Fig. 53 Fuel pressure connection

⇒		Test scope	Test connection	Test condition	Nominal value	Possible cause/Remedy
1.0		**Fuel pressure at idle (with vacuum)**	Pressure gauge connected to test connection.	Engine: **at Idle** Valve on pressure gauge closed.	3.2 – 3.6 bar	Check fuel pumps ☐ 33, Diaphragm pressure regulator.
2.0		**Fuel pressure at idle (without vacuum)**	Pressure gauge connected to test connection.	Engine: **at Idle** Disconnect vacuum hose from diaphragm pressure regulator.	3.7 – 4.2 bar	Diaphragm pressure regulator.
3.0		**Fuel system leakage**	Pressure gauge connected to test connection.	Engine: **OFF** After 30 minutes	> 3.0 bar > 2.5 bar	If the pressure drops quickly, replace check valve in fuel pumps. If the pressure drops slowly, check injectors ☐ 36, Replace diaphragm pressure regulator or O-rings on diaphragm pressure regulator.

MB1029800614000X

Fig. 54 Code —: Test 32, Fuel System Pressure & Internal Leakage Test

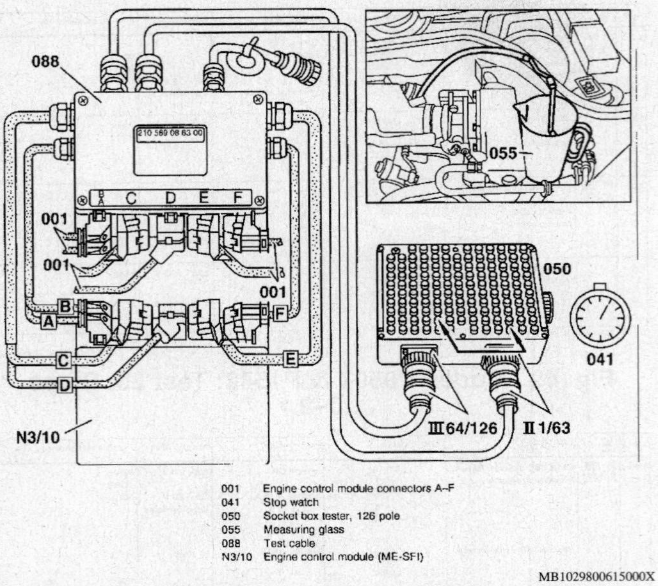

Fig. 55 Fuel pump test connections

⇒		Test scope	Test connection	Test condition	Nominal value	Possible cause/Remedy
1.0		**Fuel pump** Delivery capacity	N3/10 3 (3A) ←→ 21 (29C)	Disconnect fuel return hose from fuel line and place end in measuring glass. Ignition: **ON**	1 liter of fuel within 35 seconds.	Check fuel lines for restrictions (kinks and dents). Replace fuel filter, ⇒ 2.0.
2.0		**Fuel pumps** Current draw		On Model 202 disconnect fuel pump relay module and connect multimeter to sockets 1 and 3. On Model 170 disconnect connector B of relay module and connect multimeter to sockets 1 and 3. Ignition: **ON**	5 – 9 A	Fuel pump

MB1029800616000X

Fig. 56 Code —: Test 34, Fuel Pump Test

Test step DTC	Test scope	Test connection	Test condition	Nominal value	Possible cause/Remedy 1)
⇒ 1.0	**Injectors** Leakage test	N3/4 29 (1.29) ←→ 39 (1.39)	Fuel rail and fuel injectors removed. Ignition: **ON**	Fuel injectors must not drip.	Replace dripping injectors, ⇒ 2.0
⇒ 2.0	**Injectors** Operation and spray pattern test	N3/4 29 (1.29) ←→ 39 (1.39)	Ignition: **ON** Hold each injector, one after another, into a container and, using the self-made test harness, manually activate the injector by connecting harness banana plugs to socket box sockets 32 (–) and 39 (+).	Fuel injectors must spray evenly	Replace defective injectors.

MB1029800618000X

Fig. 58 Code —: Test 36, Step 1.0

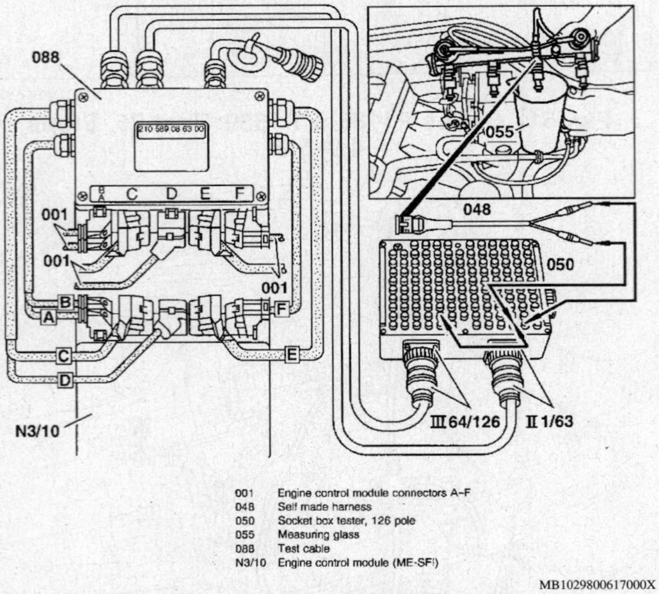

Fig. 57 Injector test connection

SYSTEM SERVICE

Component Replacement

FUEL RAIL

C230 & 1998-2000 SLK230

Refer to "104 Engine (ME 2.1 Engine Management)" section.

2001 SLK230

1. Remove intake manifold/fuel rail trim panel.
2. Relieve fuel system pressure through service valve located on fuel distributor.
3. Disconnect fuel feed line.
4. Disconnect injector connector strip. **Do not remove strip separately.**
5. Disconnect Camshaft Position (CMP) sensor connector.
6. Remove mounting bolts and lift fuel rail with injectors evenly off intake manifold.
7. Disconnect fuel feed and return flow lines.
8. Reverse procedure to install with new O-rings. **Torque** mounting bolts and nuts to 18 ft. lbs.

FUEL INJECTORS

Refer to "104 Engine (ME 2.1 Engine Management)" section.

DIAPHRAGM PRESSURE REGULATOR

C230 & 1998-2000 SLK230

Refer to "104 Engine (ME 2.1 Engine Management)" section.

2001 SLK230

1. Remove intake manifold/fuel rail cover.
2. Relieve fuel system pressure through fuel rail service valve.
3. Pull out locking arm and remove diaphragm pressure regulator.
4. Reverse procedure to install using new O-ring lubricated with oil.

HOT FILM AIR MASS (HFM) SENSOR

Refer to "104 Engine (ME 2.1 Engine Management)" section.

OXYGEN SENSOR

Refer to "104 Engine (ME 2.1 Engine Management)" section.

CRANKSHAFT POSITION (CKP) SENSOR

1. **On C230 models,** remove starter as outlined in "Electrical" section.
2. **On 1998–2000 SLK230 and 1999–2000 C230 models,** remove cruise control actuator.
3. **On all models,** disconnect connector or coupling.
4. Remove mounting bolt and CKP sensor.
5. Reverse procedure to install using new seal. **Torque** mounting bolt to 71 inch lbs.

CAMSHAFT POSITION (CMP) SENSOR

1. **On 1998–2000 SLK230 models,** remove engine compartment panel.
2. **On all models,** disconnect camshaft position sensor electrical connector.
3. Remove mounting bolts and CMP sensor.
4. Reverse procedure to install, noting the following:
   a. Install new seal.
   b. **Torque** mounting bolt to 71 inch lbs.
   c. **On C230 and 1998–2000 SLK230 models,** adjust sensor as outlined under "Adjustments."

KNOCK SENSOR

1. Disconnect, compress retaining clip and remove connector.
2. Remove knock sensor.
3. Reverse procedure to install. **Torque** sensor to 15 ft. lbs.

THROTTLE CONTROL CABLE

1998 C230

Less Plastic Bearing Bracket

1. Disconnect accelerator control cable at ball head.
2. Press plastic clip together and pull out of control lever bracket with accelerator control cable.
3. Disconnect accelerator pedal lever control cable mount by removing bracket with expanding bolt.
4. Press accelerator control cable out from inside vehicle. **Do not press rubber grommet out.**
5. Remover control cable from engine compartment.
6. Reverse procedure to install, noting the following:
   a. Grease accelerator control cable with suitable anti-corrosion grease between guide and end pieces.
   b. Adjust cable as outlined under "Adjustments."

With Plastic Bearing Bracket

1. Remove throttle control cover.
2. Move fulcrum lever by hand into Wide-Open Throttle (WOT) position. Hold in this position.
3. Disconnect guide piece clip and remove from fulcrum lever with cable.
4. Press plastic clip together and pull out of bearing bracket with control cable.
5. Disconnect throttle control cable from accelerator pedal.
6. Press accelerator control cable out from inside vehicle. **Do not press rubber grommet out.**
7. Remover accelerator control cable from engine compartment.
8. Reverse procedure to install, noting the following:
   a. Grease accelerator control cable with suitable anti-corrosion grease between guide and end pieces.
   b. Adjust cable as outlined under "Adjustments."

1998–2000 SLK230 & 1999–2000 C230

1. Disconnect accelerator control cable at ball head.
2. Press plastic clip together and pull out of control lever bracket with accelerator control cable.
3. Disconnect accelerator pedal lever control cable mount by removing bracket.
4. Press accelerator control cable out from inside vehicle. **Do not press rubber grommet out.**
5. Remover control cable from engine compartment.
6. Reverse procedure to install. Adjust cable as outlined under "Adjustments."

ELECTRONIC ACCELERATOR ACTUATOR

2001 SLK230

1. Remove intake manifold trim panel.
2. Disconnect air injection and vacuum lines.
3. Remove mounting bolts and throttle valve body.
4. Disconnect electronic accelerator pedal actuator connector.
5. Disconnect actuator vacuum line.
6. Remove mounting bolts and actuator.
7. Reverse procedure to install. **Torque** actuator mounting bolt to 71 inch lbs.

IDLE SPEED CONTROL (ISC) ACTUATOR

1. **On 1998 C230 models,** remove air cleaner cross pipe.
2. **On SLK230 and 1999–2000 C230 models,** remove charge air pipe.
3. **On 1999–2000 C230 models,** remove crankcase vent hose.
4. **On all models,** remove idle speed control module.
5. Reverse procedure to install, noting the following:
   a. Replace O-ring as required.
   b. Lubricate O-ring with oil.
   c. Ensure crankcase vent hose arrows at positioned opposite each other.

Adjustments

CAMSHAFT POSITION (CMP) SENSOR

Refer to "104 Engine (ME 2.1 Engine Management)" section.

THROTTLE CONTROL CABLE

C230

Less Plastic Bearing Bracket

1. Check ease of movement, then the condition of connecting rods and accelerator control cable.
2. Adjust play between driver spring and guide piece with adjusting screw to 0.0197–0.3937 inch.
3. Disconnect connecting rod and check Closed Throttle Position (CTP) stop.
4. Press bell crank against actuator spring force. Bell crank must rest against idle speed control actuator CTP stop.
5. Position connecting rod at ball pin free of tension.
6. Connect connecting rod and lock.
7. With control pressure control cable connected, turn adjust screw until drag lever and fulcrum lever tips are at same level.
8. With engine off, depress accelerator pedal to full throttle stop at kickdown switch without operating switch.
9. Adjust bell crank until it is resting against idle speed control actuator full throttle stop.
10. With accelerator pedal in idle position, there must be 0.0197–0.3937 inch. play between drive spring and guide piece. Adjust from inside.
11. Grease accelerator control cable between end piece and guide piece with suitable anti-corrosion grease.

With Plastic Bearing Bracket

1. Turn ignition switch to Off position.
2. Disconnect throttle control bearing bracket cover.
3. Check ease of movement, then the condition of connecting rods and accelerator control cable.
4. Disconnect connecting rod at throttle valve lever.
5. Turn throttle valve lever clockwise by hand against spring force and hold at actuator Closed Throttle Position (CTP) stop.
6. Position connecting rod throttle valve lever against ball pin free of stress and adjust ball socket in or out, as required.
7. Press connecting rod onto throttle valve lever ball pin with locknut disconnected.
8. Ensure accelerator pedal is in CTP and collar rest free of stress against fulcrum CTP end stop.
9. Disconnect Wide-Open Throttle (WOT) stop by turning it to left.
10. Depress accelerator pedal until throttle valve lever is resting against WOT stop.
11. Lock WOT stop in position by turning it to right.
12. Ensure CTP and WOT settings are correct.

SLK230 & 1999–2000 C230

1. Check ease of movement, then the condition of relay lever and accelerator control cable.
2. Ensure relay lever rests against Close Throttle Position (CTP) stop.
3. Turn adjusting bolt until no accelerator pedal travel exists as idle, as required.
4. Depress accelerator pedal until it touches kick-down switch.
5. Ensure relay lever rests against Wide Open Throttle (WOT) stop.
6. Turn adjusting bolt until relay lever rests against WOT stop.

112 Engine (ME 2.0 Engine Management)

NOTE: On Air Bag Equipped Models, Refer To "Air Bag System Precautions" Located In The Front Of This Manual For System Disarming & Arming Procedures.

NOTE: Refer To "Computer Relearn Procedures" Located In The Front Of This Manual When Battery Power To The Computer Has Been Interrupted.

NOTE: "Electrical Symbol Identification" Located In Front Of This Manual May Be Used As An Aid When Using Wiring Diagrams Found In This Section.

NOTE: Prior To Performing Any Service Listed In This Section Consult Technical Service Bulletin Section For Related Information.

INDEX

	Page No.
Description	14-82
System	14-82
Diagnosis & Testing	14-82
Accessing Diagnostic Trouble Codes	14-82
Generic Scan Tool	14-82
Hand-Held Tester	14-82
Clearing Diagnostic Trouble Codes	14-83
Component Tests	14-83
Fuel Injector	14-83
Fuel Pump	14-83
Components Locations	14-82
Connector Terminal Identification	14-83
Diagnostic Tests	14-83
Diagnostic Trouble Code Interpretation	14-82
Symbol Explanation	14-82
Symptom Related Diagnosis	14-82
Wiring Diagrams	14-83
Diagnostic Chart Index	14-102
Precautions	14-81
Air Bag Systems	14-81
Battery Ground Cable	14-81
Drive Authorization System (DAS)	14-81
ECM Recognition	14-81
ECM Self-Adaptation	14-81
ESP/ASR/ETS/ABS Control Modules	14-82
Ignition System	14-81
Sensor & Fuel Injector Specifications	14-81
System Service	14-109
Adjustments	14-110
Throttle Control Cable	14-110
Component Replacement	14-109
Camshaft Position Sensor	14-110
Crankshaft Position Sensor	14-110
Electronic Accelerator Actuator	14-110
Fuel Injector	14-109
Fuel Rail	14-109
Hot Film Mass Air Flow (MAF) Sensor	14-109
Knock Sensor	14-110
Oxygen Sensor	14-110
Throttle Control Cable	14-110

SENSOR & FUEL INJECTOR SPECIFICATIONS

Temperature, °F	Resistance, Ohms①	Voltage①
ADJUSTABLE CAMSHAFT TIMING SOLENOID		
158	7–12	—
CAMSHAFT POSITION SENSOR		
—	900–1600	—
CRANKSHAFT POSITION (CKP) SENSOR		
—	700–1400	—
ENGINE COOLANT TEMPERATURE (ECT) SENSOR		
68	3090	3.4
86	2000	2.9
104	1330	2.4
122	900	1.9
140	630	1.5
158	440	1.2
176	320	.9
194	230	.7
212	170	.5
FUEL INJECTOR		
—	14–18	—
INTAKE AIR TEMPERATURE (IAT) SENSOR		
50	3600	3.1
68	2420	2.7
104	1660	2.2
122	1170	1.8
140	850	1.4
158	600	1.1
MASS AIR FLOW (MAF) SENSOR		
158	—	0.9–1.1

① — Tolerance ± 5%

PRECAUTIONS

Air Bag Systems

Refer to "Air Bag System Precautions" in the front of this manual for system disarming and arming procedures.

Battery Ground Cable

Prior to service, disconnect battery ground cable and isolate as required.

Ignition System

1. Both control module coupling must be disconnected or connect with ignition switch in Off position.
2. Do not short circuit ignition coils terminal No. 1.
3. Do not operate the ignition system at starting speed unless the ignition cables are fully connected.
4. Do not conduct are test at starting speed or when engine is running. This includes: holding ignition cable No. 4 at a distance to ground, disconnecting a plug connector or pulling cable No. 4 out of the ignition coils.
5. High output side of ignition system must always carry at least two ohms resistance (spark plug connected).
6. Do not load ignition coil with more than 28,000 volts.
7. Ignition coil iron cores must always be connected to ground. **Use caution, coil cores can be charged with up to 400 volts.**
8. **Do not work on this system if you have a pacemaker.**
9. Ensure engine and ignition switch are in Off position when connecting and disconnecting ignition coil.
10. When working at start speeds during test such as compression check, switch ignition to off position and disconnect control module connector No. 2.

ECM Self-Adaptation

After repair work, the Engine Control Module (ECM) will automatically adapt itself after the vehicle has made approximately 10 trips. A trip includes a vehicle speed of more than 2.5 mph, engine speed of more than 700 RPM and engine shutoff of more than 30 seconds.

However, after fixing a malfunction or installation of a test ECM, the self-adaptation function must be reset as outlined under "Computer Relearn" at the front of this manual.

ECM Recognition

The ECM must be coded for vehicle model, catalytic converter, transmission, cruise control, acceleration slip regulation (ASR), electronic traction system (ETS) and country version with the Hand-Held Tester.

Before replacing the ECM, read and store existing code numbers with the Hand-Held Tester. When the new ECM is installed, enter the stored code numbers from the Hand-Held Tester. If code numbers cannot be read, the corresponding codes number must be obtained from Mercedes-Benz spare parts microfiche and manually entered with a Hand-Held Tester.

Drive Authorization System (DAS)

The DAS can only be activated or deactivated by the electronic ignition key. The ECM, RCL and DAS control module are

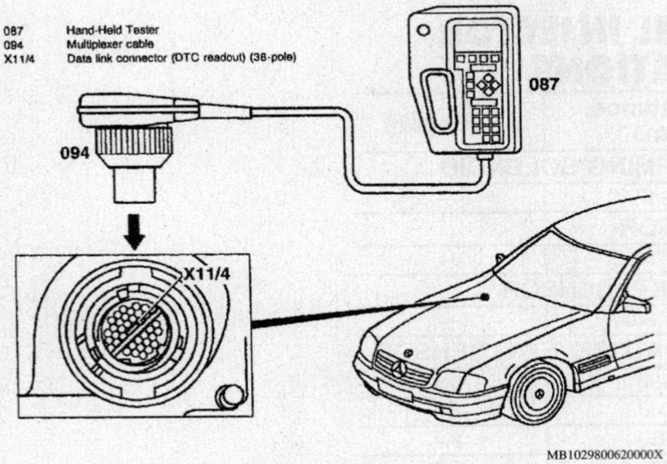

MB1029800620000X

Fig. 1 DLC tool connection

DTC	Possible cause: SAE nomenclature	Possible cause: Explanation	Test step/Remedy
-	No malfunction in system		In case of complaint, perform □ 23, 24, 25 or 26 in its entirety
P0 100 ■	MAF circuit malfunction	Hot film MAF sensor (B2/5)	□ 23⇒ 4.0
P0 105 ■ Only USA	MAP circuit malfunction	Pressure sensor (B28)	□ 23⇒ 6.0
P0 110 ■	IAT circuit malfunction	IAT sensor (in Hot film MAF sensor B2/5)	□ 23⇒ 5.0
P0 115 ■	ECT circuit malfunction	ECT sensor (B11/4)	□ 23⇒ 8.0
P0 120	Throttle position circuit malfunction	Actual value potentiometer in EA/CC/ISC actuator (M16/6)	□ 25⇒ 3.0
P0 130 ■	O2S 1 circuit malfunction	A. O2S 1 (before TWC) (G3/4) B. O2S 1 (before TWC) (G3/4) voltage increase insufficient	□ 23⇒ 11.0

MB1029800621010X

Fig. 2 DTC interpretation (Part 1 of 11)

DTC	Possible cause: SAE nomenclature	Possible cause: Explanation	Test step/Remedy
P0 133 ■	O2S 1 circuit slow response	A O2S 1 (before TWC) (G3/4), ageing correction value exceeded B O2S 1 (before TWC) (G3/4), ageing time period too long C O2S 1 (before TWC) (G3/4), ageing O2S 1 sensor response too slow	□ 23⇒ 11.0
P0 135 ■	O2S 1 heater circuit malfunction	O2S 1 heater (before TWC) (G3/4)	□ 23 ⇒ 13.0
P0 136 ■ Only USA	O2S 2 circuit malfunction	O2S 2 (after TWC) (G3/6)	□ 23 ⇒ 15.0
P0 141 ■ Only USA	O2S 2 heater circuit malfunction	Right O2S 2 heater (after TWC) (G3/6)	□ 23⇒ 17.0
P0 150 ■	O2S 1 circuit malfunction	A O2S 1 heater (before TWC) (G3/3) B O2S 1 heater (before TWC) (G3/3), voltage increase too slow	□ 23⇒ 10.0
P0 153 ■	O2S 1 circuit slow response	A O2S 1 heater (before TWC) (G3/3), ageing correction value exceeded B O2S 1 heater (before TWC) (G3/3), ageing time period too long C O2S 1 heater (before TWC) (G3/3), ageing O2S 1 sensor response too slow	□ 23⇒ 10.0
P0 155 ■	O2S 2 heater circuit malfunction	Left O2S 1 heater (before TWC) (G3/3)	□ 23⇒ 12.0
P0 156 ■ Only USA	O2S 2 circuit malfunction	Left O2S 2 (after TWC) (G3/5)	□ 23⇒ 14.0
P0 161 ■ Only USA	O2S 2 heater circuit malfunction	Right O2S 2 heater (after TWC) (G3/5)	□ 23⇒ 16.0

MB1029800621020X

Fig. 2 DTC interpretation (Part 2 of 11)

DTC	Possible cause: SAE nomenclature	Possible cause: Explanation	Test step/Remedy
P0 170 ■	Fuel trim malfunction	A Self adaptation of fuel mixture "partial load", right cylinder bank, at limit from engine control module (N3/10). B Self adaptation of fuel mixture "CTP", right cylinder bank, at limit from engine control module (N3/10).	Intake air leak, injectors, diaphragm pressure regulator, engine wear.
P0 173 ■	Fuel trim malfunction	A Self adaptation of fuel mixture "partial load", left cylinder bank, at limit from engine control module (N3/10). B Self adaptation of fuel mixture "CTP", left cylinder bank, at limit from engine control module (N3/10).	Intake air leak, injectors, diaphragm pressure regulator, engine wear.
P0 201 ■	Injector circuit malfunction - cyl. 1	Injector (Y62y1) – cylinder 1	□ 23⇒ 18.0
P0 202 ■	Injector circuit malfunction - cyl. 2	Injector (Y62y2) – cylinder 2	□ 23⇒ 19.0
P0 203 ■	Injector circuit malfunction - cyl. 3	Injector (Y62y3) – cylinder 3	□ 23 ⇒ 20.0
P0 204 ■	Injector circuit malfunction - cyl. 4	Injector (Y62y4) – cylinder 4	□ 23 ⇒ 21.0
P0 205 ■	Injector circuit malfunction - cyl. 5	Injector (Y62y5) – cylinder 5	□ 23 ⇒ 22.0
P0 206 ■	Injector circuit malfunction - cyl. 6	Injector (Y62y6) – cylinder 6	□ 23 ⇒ 23.0
P0 300 ■	Random misfire detected	A Random misfire B Random misfire, TWC damaging	□ 24 ⇒ 11.0 – 17.0 □ 36 ⇒ 1.0 – 2.0 Compression pressure

MB1029800621030X

Fig. 2 DTC interpretation (Part 3 of 11)

permanently locked together by an identification code. This code cannot be erased. Trial installation of an ECM or RCL control module from another vehicle is not possible. After 40 starts, a new ECM cannot be used in any other vehicle. The code number and VIN must be entered into the ECM with a Hand-Held Tester.

ESP/ASR/ETS/ABS Control Modules

The Electronic Stability Program (ESP), Acceleration Slip Regulation (ASR), Electronic Traction System (ETS) and/or Antilock Brake System (ABS) control modules must not be disconnected. The Engine Control Module (ECM) and Transmission Control Module (TCM) rely on those control modules for Vehicle Speed Sensor (VSS) information. To disable brake and engine regulation of those modules, proceed as follows:

1. Turn ignition switch to Off position.
2. Connect Hand-Held Tester adapter to Data Link Connector (DLC).
3. Jump sockets No. 1 and 6.
4. Start engine. MIL must light.
5. If Hand-Held Tester is available, disconnect VSS front axle connector.
6. When testing is complete, connect VSS and erase Diagnostic Trouble Codes with Hand-Held Tester.

DESCRIPTION

System

Refer to "104 Engine (ME 2.1 Engine Management)" section.

DIAGNOSIS & TESTING

Symbol Explanation

Refer to "104 Engine (ME 2.1 Engine Management)" section for explanations of symbols, connections and steps included in the charts.

Accessing Diagnostic Trouble Codes

GENERIC SCAN TOOL

Follow tool manufacturers instructions and connect suitably programmed scan tool to generic scan tool connection X11/22.

HAND-HELD TESTER

1. Turn ignition switch to Off position.
2. Attach test cable tool No. 965 589 00 40 00, or equivalent, to Hand-Held Tester tool No. 965 589 00 01 00, or equivalent.
3. Connect cable to Data Link Connector (DLC), **Fig. 1**.
4. Turn multiplexer cable locking ring completely to left detent stop.
5. Attach multiplexer cable to data link connector via locking pins.
6. To lock multiplexer cable to connector, turn locking ring to the right.
7. Follow tool manufacturer's instructions.

Diagnostic Trouble Code Interpretation

Refer to **Fig. 2** for DTC interpretation. **Black square items are emission related and may activate MIL during test cycle.**

Symptom Related Diagnosis

Refer to **Fig. 3** for symptom related diagnosis.

Components Locations

Refer to **Figs. 4 through 7** for component locations.

DTC	Possible cause: SAE nomenclature	Possible cause: Explanation	Test step/Remedy
P0 301 ■	Cylinder 1 misfire detected	A Cylinder 1 misfire B Cylinder 1 misfire, TWC damaging	☐ 24 ⇒ 11.0 ☐ 24 ⇒ 17.0 ☐ 36 ⇒ 1.0 – 2.0 Compression pressure
P0 302 ■	Cylinder 2 misfire detected	A Cylinder 2 misfire B Cylinder 2 misfire, TWC damaging	☐ 24 ⇒ 12.0 ☐ 24 ⇒ 17.0 ☐ 36 ⇒ 1.0 – 2.0 Compression pressure
P0 303 ■	Cylinder 3 misfire detected	A Cylinder 3 misfire B Cylinder 3 misfire, TWC damaging	☐ 24 ⇒ 13.0 ☐ 24 ⇒ 17.0 ☐ 36 ⇒ 1.0 – 2.0 Compression pressure
P0 304 ■	Cylinder 4 misfire detected	A Cylinder 4 misfire B Cylinder 4 misfire, TWC damaging	☐ 24 ⇒ 14.0 ☐ 24 ⇒ 17.0 ☐ 36 ⇒ 1.0 – 2.0 Compression pressure
P0 305 ■	Cylinder 5 misfire detected	A Cylinder 5 misfire B Cylinder 5 misfire, TWC damaging	☐ 24 ⇒ 15.0 ☐ 24 ⇒ 17.0 ☐ 36 ⇒ 1.0 – 2.0 Compression pressure
P0 306 ■	Cylinder 6 misfire detected	A Cylinder 6 misfire B Cylinder 6 misfire, TWC damaging	☐ 24 ⇒ 16.0 ☐ 24 ⇒ 17.0 ☐ 36 ⇒ 1.0 – 2.0 Compression pressure

MB1029800621040X

Fig. 2 DTC interpretation (Part 4 of 11)

DTC	Possible cause: SAE nomenclature	Possible cause: Explanation	Test step/Remedy
P0 325 ■	KS 1 circuit malfunction	Right KS 1 (A16g1)	Wiring, connector, A16g1
P0 330 ■	KS 2 circuit malfunction	Left KS 2 (A16g2)	Wiring, connector, A16g2
P0 335 ■	CKP sensor circuit malfunction	CKP sensor (L5)	☐ 24 ⇒ 9.0
P0 341 ■	CMP sensor circuit range/performance	Camshaft Hall-effect sensor (B6/1)	☐ 24 ⇒ 10.0
P0 400 ■	Exhaust gas recirculation flow malfunction	Exhaust gas recirculation malfunction (logic chain)	☐ 23 ⇒ 27.0
P0 410 ■ Only (USA)	Air injection system malfunction	AIR system malfunction (logic chain)	☐ 23 ⇒ 24.0– 26.0
P0 422 ■	TWC (left) efficiency below threshold	TWC efficiency below threshold	Replace left TWC
P0 432 ■	TWC (right) efficiency below threshold	TWC efficiency below threshold	Replace right TWC
P0 440 ■ Only (USA)	EVAP system malfunction	EVAP malfunction (logic chain)	☐ 23 ⇒ 30.0 – 31.0
P0 441 ■	EVAP system incorrect purge flow	EVAP not functioning	☐ 23 ⇒ 29.0 – 30.0
P0 442 ■ Only (USA)	EVAP system leak detected (small leak)	EVAP system, small leak	☐ 23 ⇒ 31.0
P0 443 ■	EVAP system purge control valve circuit malfunction	Purge control valve (Y58/1)	☐ 23 ⇒ 29.0
P0 446 ■ Only (USA)	EVAP system vent control malfunction	A. Activated charcoal canister shut-off valve (Y58/4) B. End stage activated charcoal canister shut-off valve (Y58/4) within N3/10	☐ 23 ⇒ 32.0, N3/10

MB1029800621050X

Fig. 2 DTC interpretation (Part 5 of 11)

DTC	Possible cause: SAE nomenclature	Possible cause: Explanation	Test step/Remedy
P0 450 ■ Only (USA)	EVAP system pressure sensor malfunction	A. Fuel tank pressure sensor (B4/3) electrical fault B. Fuel tank pressure sensor (B4/3) electrical fluctuations	☐ 23 ⇒ 33.0 Charcoal canister plugged.
P0 455 ■ Only (USA)	EVAP system leak detected (large leak)	EVAP system, large leak Fuel tank pressure sensor (B4/3) (voltage supply)	☐ 23 ⇒ 31.0 ☐ 23 ⇒ 33.0
P0 460	Fuel level sensor circuit low input	Fuel tank level too low	Fill fuel tank
P0 500	VSS sensor malfunction	A VSS left front B VSS left rear	Test ASR, ESP
P0 507	ISC rpm higher than expected	Idle control system, unplausible	☐ 25 ⇒ 1.0 – 3.0
P0 560	System voltage malfunction	Voltage supply to engine control module (N3/10)	☐ 23 ⇒ 1.0 – 2.0
P0 565	Cruise control switch	CC switch (S40)	☐ 26 ⇒ 1.0
P0 600	Serial communication link malfunction	CAN bus from ESP/SPS control module (N47-5)	☐ 23 ⇒ 34.0
P0 604	Internal control module random Access memory (RAM) error	A Engine control module (N3/10) B Engine control module (N3/10)	(N3/10)
P0 605	Internal control module read only memory (ROM) error	Engine control module (N3/10)	(N3/10)
P0 606	PCM prosessor fault	Engine control module (N3/10)	(N3/10)

MB1029800621060X

Fig. 2 DTC interpretation (Part 6 of 11)

DTC	Possible cause: SAE nomenclature	Possible cause: Explanation	Test step/Remedy
P0 700 ■	Transmission control system malfunction	Read DTC memory of transmission control module.	Test ETC
P0 702 ■	Transmission control system electrical	Read DTC memory of transmission control module.	Test ETC
P0 715 ■	Input/turbine speed sensor circuit malfunction	Read DTC memory of transmission control module.	Test ETC
P0 720 ■	Output speed sensor circuit malfunction	Read DTC memory of transmission control module.	Test ETC
P0 730 ■	Incorrect gear ratio	Read DTC memory of transmission control module.	Test ETC
P0 740 ■	Torque converter clutch circuit malfunction	Read DTC memory of transmission control module.	Test ETC
P0 743 ■	Torque converter clutch circuit electrical	Read DTC memory of transmission control module.	Test ETC
P0 748 ■	Pressure control solenoid electrical	Read DTC memory of transmission control module.	Test ETC
P0 753 ■	Shift solenoid A electrical	Read DTC memory of transmission control module.	Test ETC
P0 758 ■	Shift solenoid B electrical	Read DTC memory of transmission control module.	Test ETC

MB1029800621070X

Fig. 2 DTC interpretation (Part 7 of 11)

Wiring Diagrams

Refer to **Figs. 8 through 14** for wiring diagrams.

Connector Terminal Identification

Refer to **Fig. 15** for engine control module connector terminal identification.

Diagnostic Tests

1. Turn ignition switch to Off position.
2. Connect 126-pole socket box tool No. 129 589 00 21 00, or equivalent, with contact module tool No. 210 589 08 63 00, or equivalent, to Engine Control Module, **Fig. 16.**
3. Connect interior harness connector to test cable connection No. 1 and engine harness connector to test cable connection No. 2.
4. Conduct tests as directed in **Figs. 17 through 59** using suitable multimeter.

Clearing Diagnostic Trouble Codes

The Diagnostic Trouble Code (DTC) memory is cleared when the vehicle battery is disconnected.

When an component has been repaired or replaced, the related DTC will be cleared. After three trips the CHECK ENGINE Malfunction Indicator Lamp (MIL) will go out and after 40 warm-up periods the DTC is automatically erased. A trip includes engine running for more than 20 minutes, engine oil temperature of more than 19°F, engine speed of more than 700 RPM and emission related logic chain functions. A warm-up period includes an engine coolant temperature at start-up of less than 95°F and increasing to more than 176°F.

To erase DTCs with a Hand-Held Tester, follow the tool manufacturer's instructions.

Component Tests

FUEL PUMP

1. Connect suitable pressure gauge to test connection, **Fig. 60.**
2. Conduct tests as directed, **Fig. 61.**
3. Connect 126-pole socket box tool No. 129 589 00 21 00, or equivalent, to Engine Control Module (ECM) with test cable tool No. 140 589 46 63 00, or equivalent, **Fig. 62.**
4. Conduct tests as directed, **Fig. 63.**
5. Release fuel pressure and allow fuel to drain into suitable measuring cup.

FUEL INJECTOR

1. Connect 126-pole socket box tool No. 129 589 00 21 00, or equivalent, to Engine Control Module (ECM) with test cable tool No. 140 589 46 63 00, or equivalent, **Fig. 64.**
2. Disconnect injector connectors, then remove fuel rail with injectors. **Do not disconnect fuel feed and return lines.**
3. Connect self-made harness to one injector after another, hold over suitable measuring glass and test as directed, **Fig. 65.**

DTC	Possible cause: SAE nomenclature	Possible cause: Explanation	Test step/Remedy
P0 763 ■	Shift solenoid C electrical	Read DTC memory of transmission control module.	Test ETC
P0 801	Engine/climate control electric cooling fan malfunction	Engine/climate control electric cooling fan (M4/3).	□ 23 ⇒ 36.0
P0 802	Resonance intake mainfold switchover valve malfunction	Resonance intake mainfold switchover valve (Y22/6).	□ 23 ⇒ 28.0
P0 809	Angle deviation between camshaft and crankshaft	Angle deviation between camshaft and crankshaft.	Check basic adjustment of camshaft
P0 811	CAN from electronic ignition lock	CAN from electronic ignition lock.	□ 23 ⇒ 34.0
P1 031	O2 sensors (G3/3, G3/4) reversed	O2 sensors (G3/3, G3/4) reversed.	Check proper connection of O2 sensors in ETM
P1 177	Oil sensor	Oil sensor (level, temperature, quality)(B40), Oil temperature implausible.	□ 23 ⇒ 35.0
P1 178	Oil sensor	Oil sensor (level, temperature, quality)(B40), Oil level implausible.	□ 23 ⇒ 35.0
P1 179	Oil sensor	Oil sensor (level, temperature, quality)(B40), Oil quality implausible.	□ 23 ⇒ 35.0
P1 180	Oil sensor	Oil sensor (level, temperature, quality)(B40), Oil temperature too high.	□ 23 ⇒ 35.0
P1 185	Oil sensor	Oil sensor (level, temperature, quality)(B40), water in oil.	□ 23 ⇒ 35.0

MB1029800621080X

Fig. 2 DTC interpretation (Part 8 of 11)

DTC	Possible cause: SAE nomenclature	Possible cause: Explanation	Test step/Remedy
P1 186	Fuel safety shut-off recognized	EA/CC/ISC actuator (M16/6)	□ 25 ⇒ 3.0 – 4.0, EA/CC/ISC actuator (M16/6) sticks or jammed, Check intake system for residue.
P1 386 ■	Knock sensor control from ECM (N3/10) at end stop	Knock sensor regulation from engine control module (N3/10) at end stop	1. Increased knock tendency due to bad fuel, carbon in combustion chamber or mechanical damage.
P1 400 ■	EGR valve vacuum transducer	EGR valve vacuum transducer (Y31/1) faulty	□ 23 ⇒ 27.0
P1 420 ■ Only (USA)	AIR pump switchover valve	AIR pump switchover valve (Y32)	□ 23 ⇒ 25.0
P1 453 ■ Only (USA)	AIR relay module, AIR pump	Relay module, AIR pump (K40/4k3) in relay module (K40)	□ 23 ⇒ 24.0
P1 491		Refrigerant pressure in A/C system too high	Check automatic A/C system.
P1 542	Pedal value sensor	Pedal value sensor (B37)	□ 25 ⇒ 1.0 – 2.0

MB1029800621090X

Fig. 2 DTC interpretation (Part 9 of 11)

DTC	Possible cause: SAE nomenclature	Possible cause: Explanation	Test step/Remedy
P1 570	CAN signal from DAS control module to engine control module	A. Start attempted with "locked" DAS B. CAN signal from DAS control module (N54/1) to engine control module (N3/10) interrupted. C. Engine control module (ME-SFI) and DAS control module are not compatible.	User error, Check correct operation of DAS □ 23 ⇒ 34.0 Check control modules and part no.
P1 580 ■	EA/CC/ISC actuator	EA/CC/ISC actuator (M16/1)	□ 25 ⇒ 3.0 – 4.0
P1 584	Stop lamp switch	Stop lamp switch (S9/1)	Test ETS, ASR
P1 605		Poor road/traction condition recognition signal (via comparison of VSS rpm signals)	Test ASR/ESP
P1 642		Engine control module incorrectly coded (coded for MT, vehicle has AT)	Check version coding and correct.

MB1029800621100X

Fig. 2 DTC interpretation (Part 10 of 11)

DTC	Possible cause: SAE nomenclature	Possible cause: Explanation	Test step/Remedy
P1 643		Engine control module incorrectly coded (coded for MT, vehicle has AT) or No CAN transmission from transmission control module (N15/3)	Check version coding and correct. Test ETC
P1 644		Transmission version can not be checked due to low voltage at transmission control module (N15/3)	Test ETC
P1 747 ■	CAN signal from ETC	A. CAN failure: Transmission protection malfunction from transmission control module (N15/3) B. CAN failure: Instrument cluster	Test ETC Test instrument cluster (A1)

MB1029800621110X

Fig. 2 DTC interpretation (Part 11 of 11)

Complaint/Problem	Possible cause	Test step/Remedy	Actual value Engine test Menu item
Engine starts and accelerates poorly when cold	Injector (Y62) activation and injection duration. Hot film MAF sensor (B2/5). ECT sensor (B11/4). Ignition voltage too low. Intake air leak.	□ 23 ⇒ 18.0 – 23.0 □ 23 ⇒ 4.0 – 5.0 □ 23 ⇒ 8.0 □ 24 ⇒ 17.0 Remedy air leak.	2/7 1/7 3/7 – –
Engine does not start	Voltage supply from engine control module (N3/10) is missing. Malfunction of drive authorization system (DAS). Fuel pumps defective. No compression due to high oil pressure. Ignition voltage too low.	□ 23 ⇒ 1.0 – 3.0 □ 23 ⇒ 34.0 □ 34 ⇒ 2.0 Check compression and oil pressure. □ 24 ⇒ 17.0	– DAS 1/1 – – –
Engine has uneven idle	Injector (Y62) activation and injection duration. Intake air leak.	□ 23 ⇒ 18.0 – 23.0 Remedy leak.	2/7 –
Engine has insufficient output	TWC flow restricted. O2S 1 (G3/3 or G3/4) (before TWC). ECT sensor (B11/4). Hot film MAF sensor (B2/5).	Check exhaust back pressure □ 23 ⇒ 10.0 – 13.0 □ 23 ⇒ 8.0 □ 23 ⇒ 4.0	– 5/7 3/7 1/7, 2/7

MB1029800622010X

Fig. 3 Symptom related diagnosis (Part 1 of 2)

Complaint/Problem	Possible cause	Test step/Remedy	Actual value Engine test Menu item
Engine runs unevenly (shakes)	Injector (Y62) activation and injection duration. Injector leaking, spray pattern. O2S 1 (G3/3 or G3/4) (before TWC). Ignition voltage too low. Compression on one or more cylinders too low. Intake air leak.	□ 23 ⇒ 18.0 – 23.0 □ 36 ⇒ 1.0– 2.0 □ 23 ⇒ 10.0 – 13.0 □ 24 ⇒ 17.0 Check compression. Remedy air leak.	2/7 – 5/7 – – –
Engine runs unevenly (misfiring)	Ignition voltage too low. Hot film MAF sensor (B2/5).	□ 24 ⇒ 17.0 □ 23 ⇒ 4.0	– 1/7
Engine surges after cold start	Intake air leak.	Remedy air leak.	–
Transition failure during warm-up	ECT sensor (B11/4). Hot film MAF sensor (B2/5). Intake air leak.	□ 23 ⇒ 8.0 □ 23 ⇒ 4.0 Remedy air leak.	3/7 1/7 –
Transition failure when warm or increased fuel consumption	O2S 1 (G3/3 or G3/4) (before TWC). Purge control valve (Y58/1) stuck in open position.	□ 23 ⇒ 10.0 – 13.0 □ 23 ⇒ 29.0 – 30.0	5/7 3/7
Engine bucks, jerks	Hot film MAF sensor (B2/5). Ignition voltage too low. O2S 1 (G3/3 or G3/4) (before TWC).	□ 23 ⇒ 4.0– 5.0 □ 24 ⇒ 17.0 □ 23 ⇒ 10.0 – 13.0	1/7 – 5/7
EA is in "limp-home" mode	Nominal value potentiometer in pedal value sensor (B37). EA/CC/ISC actuator actual value potentiometer.	□ 25 ⇒ 1.0 – 2.0 □ 25 ⇒ 3.0	4/7 4/7

MB1029800622020X

Fig. 3 Symptom related diagnosis (Part 2 of 2)

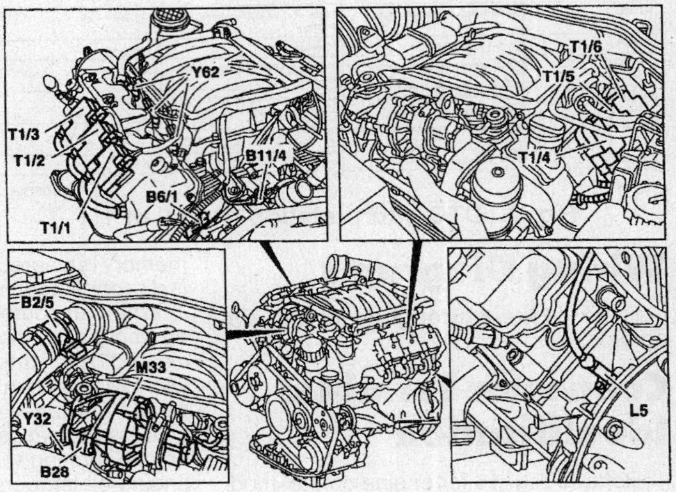

B2/5 Hot film MAF sensor
B6/1 Camshaft Hall-effect sensor
B11/4 ECT sensor
B28 Pressure sensor (only USA)
L5 CKP sensor
M33 AIR pump (only USA)
T1/1 Ignition coil 1
T1/2 Ignition coil 2
T1/3 Ignition coil 3
T1/4 Ignition coil 4
T1/5 Ignition coil 5
T1/6 Ignition coil 6
Y32 Air pump switchover valve (only USA)
Y62 Injectors

MB1029800623010X

Fig. 4 ME engine management component locations (Part 1 of 2). 112 engine

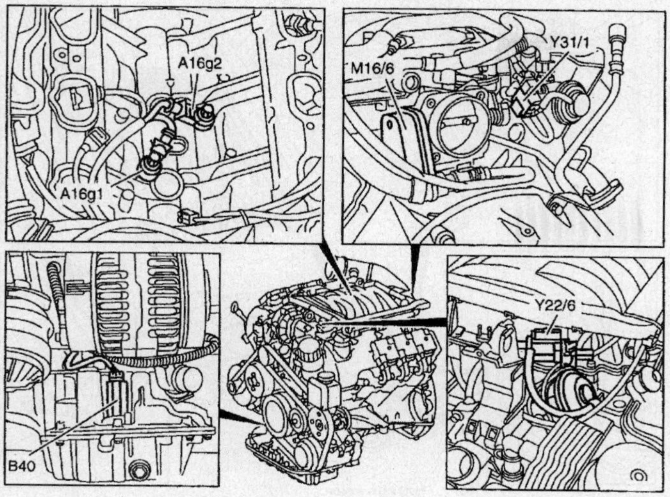

A16g1 KS 1 (right side of engine)
A16g2 KS 2 (left side of engine)
M16/1 EA/CC/ISC actuator
Y22/6 Resonance intake mainfold switchover valve
Y31/1 EGR valve vacuum transducer
B40 Oil sensor (level/temperature/quality)

MB1029800623020X

Fig. 4 ME engine management component locations (Part 2 of 2). 112 engine

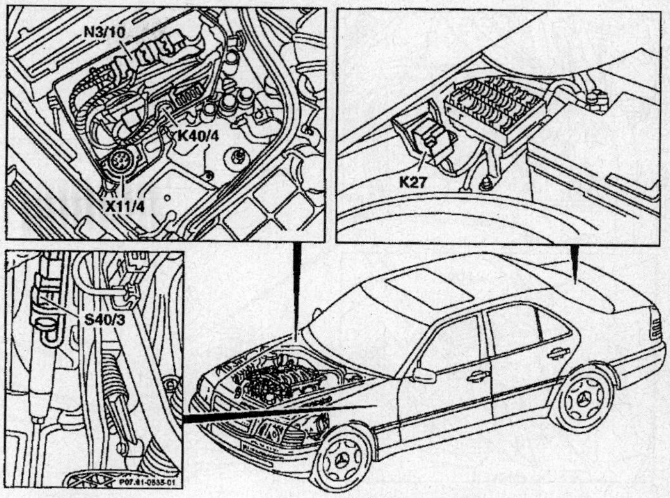

K27 FP relay module
K40/4 Passenger-side fuse and relay module box with:
k2 starter relay
k3 relay module AIR pump (only USA)
N3/10 Engine control module (ME-SFI)
S40/3 Clutch pedal switch (not USA)
X11/4 Data link connector (DTC readout) (38-pole)

MB1029800625010X

Fig. 5 ME engine management component locations (Part 1 of 4). C280 & CLK320

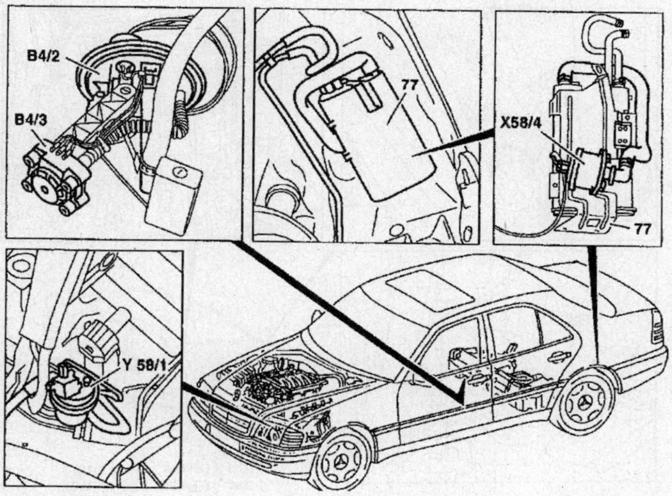

B4/2 Right fuel level sensor
B4/3 fuel tank pressure sensor (only USA)
Y58/1 Purge control valve
Y58/4 Activated charcoal canister shut-off valve (only USA)
77 Activated charcxoal canister

MB1029800625020X

Fig. 5 ME engine management component locations (Part 2 of 4). C280 & CLK320

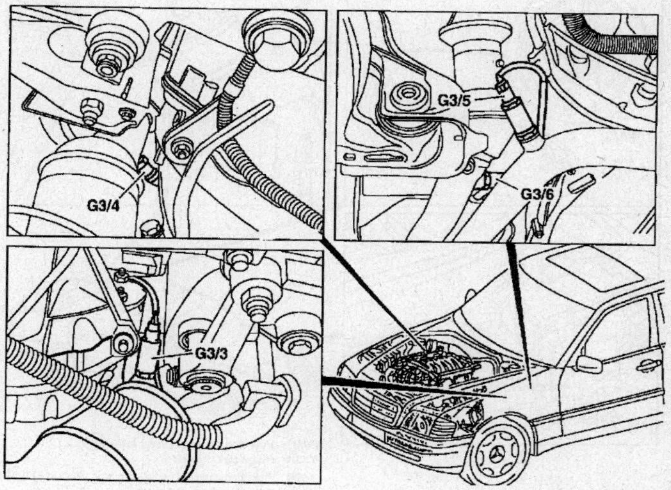

G3/3 Left 02S 1 (before TWC)
G3/4 Right 02S 1 (before TWC)
G3/5 Left 02S 2 (after TWC) (only USA)
G3/6 Right 02s 2 (after TWC) (only USA)

MB1029800625030X

Fig. 5 ME engine management component locations (Part 3 of 4). C280 & CLK320

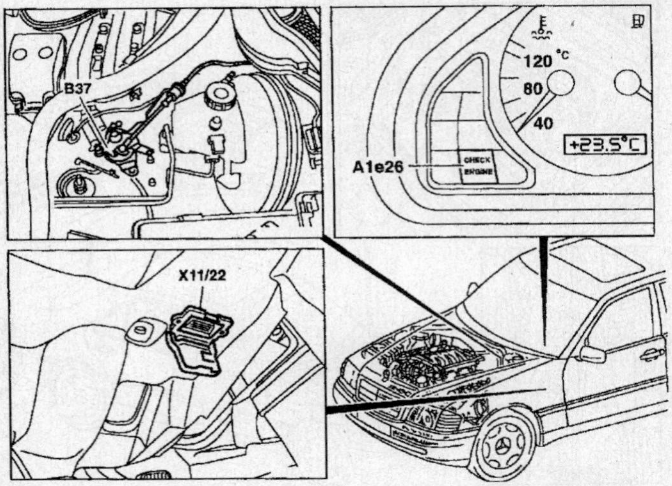

A1e26 "CHECK ENGINE" MIL (only USA)
B37 Pedal value sensor
X11/22 Diagnostic module (OBD II) generic scan tool connector (only USA)

MB1029800625040X

Fig. 5 ME engine management component locations (Part 4 of 4). C280 & CLK320

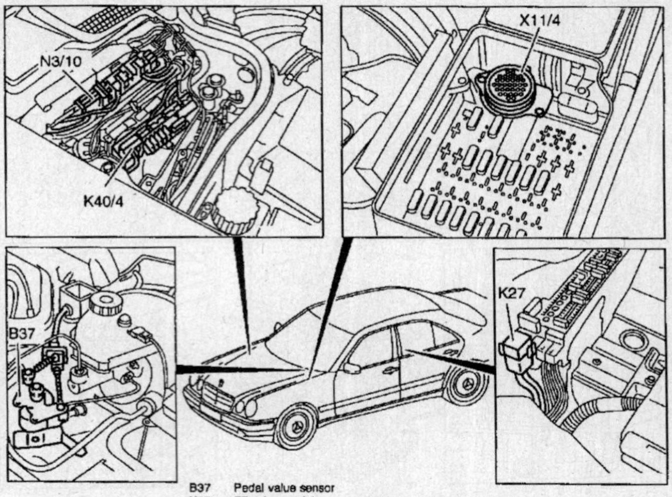

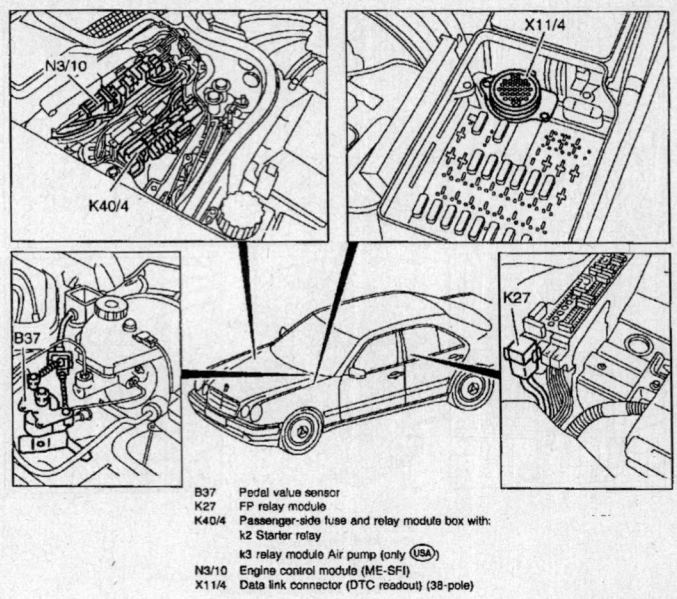

B37 Pedal value sensor
K27 FP relay module
K40/4 Passenger-side fuse and relay module box with:
k2 Starter relay
k3 relay module Air pump (only USA)
N3/10 Engine control module (ME-SFI)
X11/4 Data link connector (DTC readout) (38-pole)

MB1029800626010X

Fig. 6 ME engine management component locations (Part 1 of 4). E320

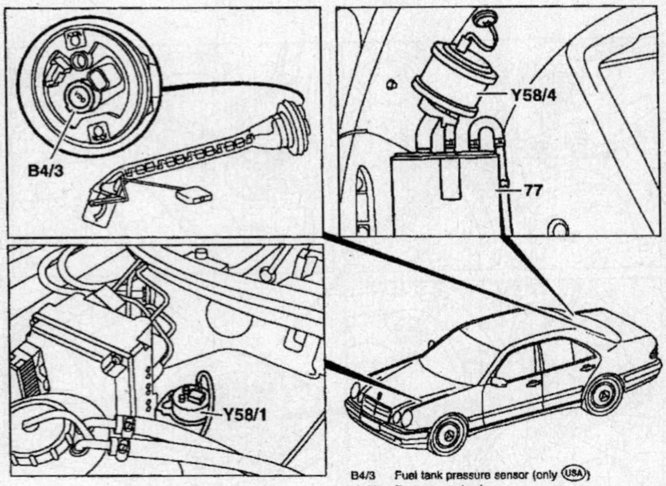

B4/3 Fuel tank pressure sensor (only USA)
Y58/1 Purge control valve
Y58/4 Activated charcoal canister shut-off valve (only USA)
77 Activated charcoal canister

MB1029800626020X

Fig. 6 ME engine management component locations (Part 2 of 4). E320

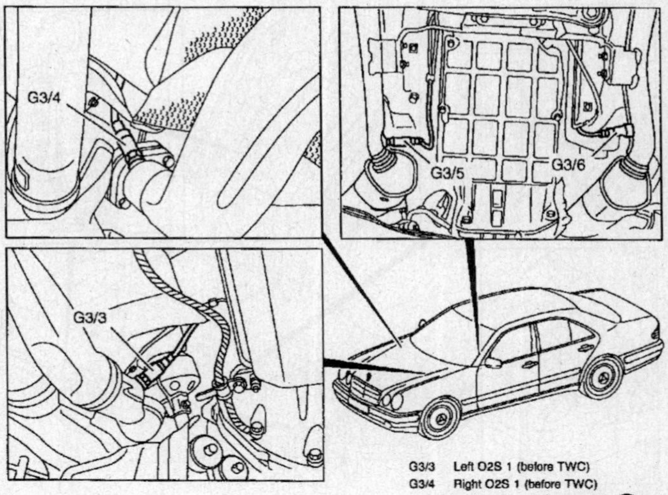

G3/3 Left O2S 1 (before TWC)
G3/4 Right O2S 1 (before TWC)
G3/5 Left O2S 2 (after TWC) (only USA)
G3/6 Right O2S 2 (after TWC) (only USA)

MB1029800626030X

Fig. 6 ME engine management component locations (Part 3 of 4). E320

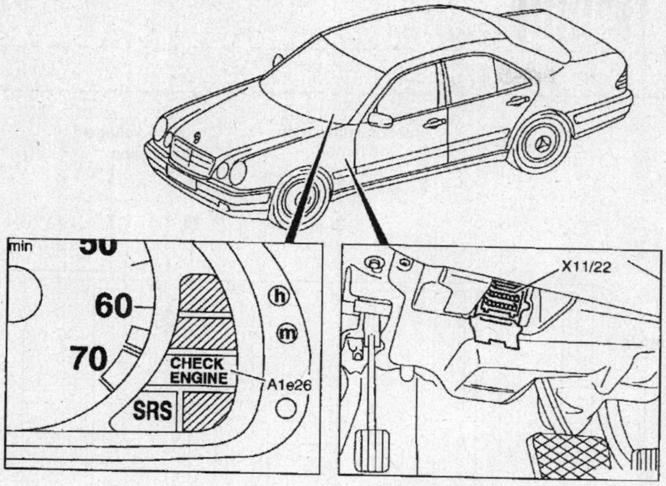

A1e26 "CHECK ENGINE MIL" (only USA)
X11/22 Diagnostic module (OBD II) generic scan tool connector (only USA)

MB1029800626040X

Fig. 6 ME engine management component locations (Part 4 of 4). E320

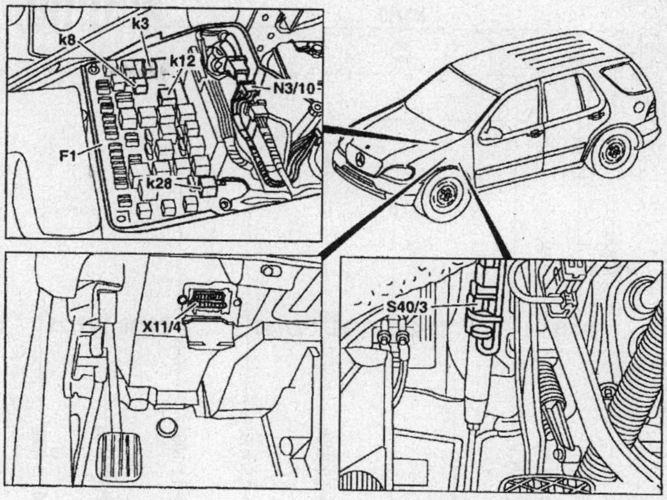

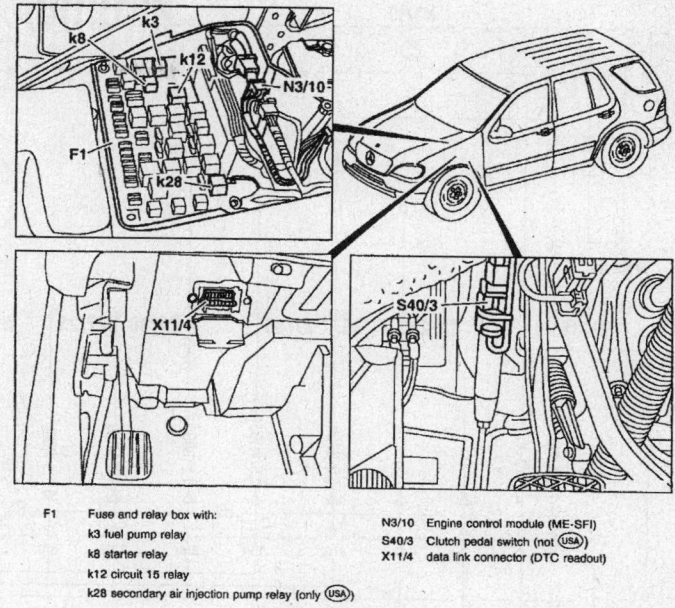

F1 Fuse and relay box with:
k3 fuel pump relay
k8 starter relay
k12 circuit 15 relay
k28 secondary air injection pump relay (only USA)

N3/10 Engine control module (ME-SFI)
S40/3 Clutch pedal switch (not USA)
X11/4 data link connector (DTC readout)

MB1029800624010X

Fig. 7 ME engine management component locations (Part 1 of 3). ML320

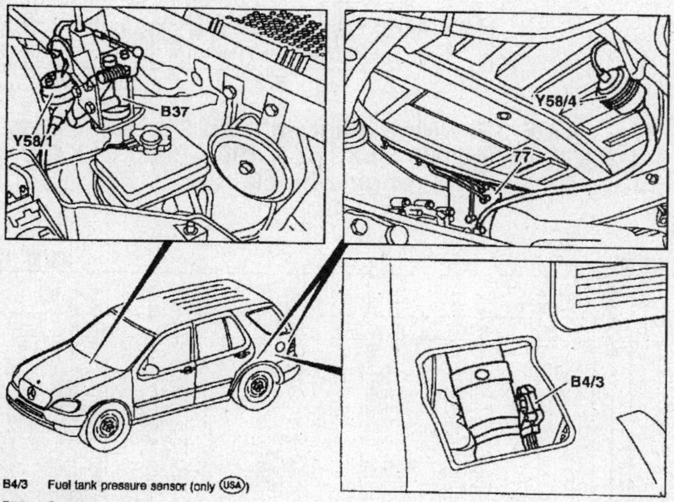

B4/3 Fuel tank pressure sensor (only USA)
B37 Pedal value sensor
Y58/1 Purge control valve
Y58/4 Activated charcoal canister shut-off valve (only USA)
77 Activated charcoal canister

MB1029800624020X

Fig. 7 ME engine management component locations (Part 2 of 3). ML320

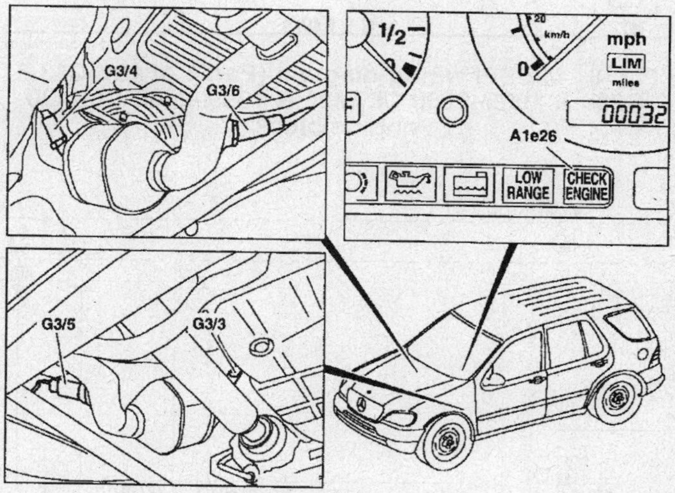

A1e26 "CHECK ENGINE" MIL (only USA)
G3/3 Left 02S 1 (before TWC)
G3/4 Right 02S 1 (before TWC)
G3/5 Left 02S 2 (after TWC) (only USA)
G3/6 Right 02s 2 (after TWC) (only USA)

MB1029800624030X

Fig. 7 ME engine management component locations (Part 3 of 3). ML320

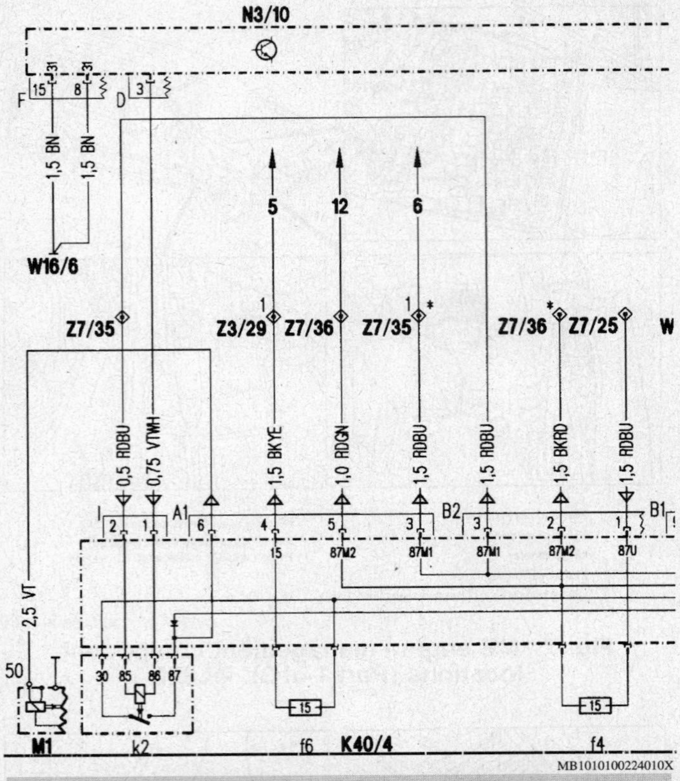

Fig. 8 ME-SFI wiring diagram (Part 1 of 10). C43 & C280 & 1998–2000 CLK320 & 1999–2000 CLK430 engine block

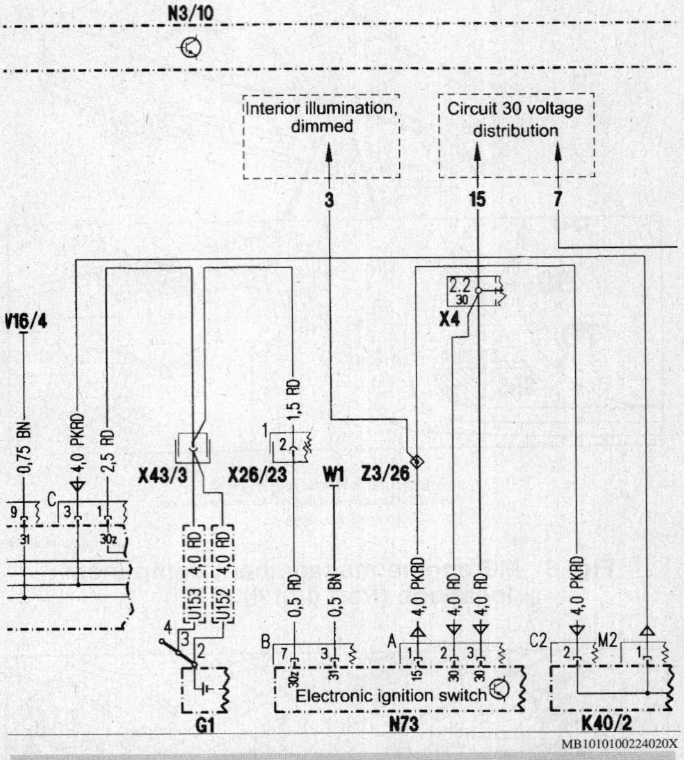

Fig. 8 ME-SFI wiring diagram (Part 2 of 10). C43 & C280 & 1998–2000 CLK320 & 1999–2000 CLK430 engine block

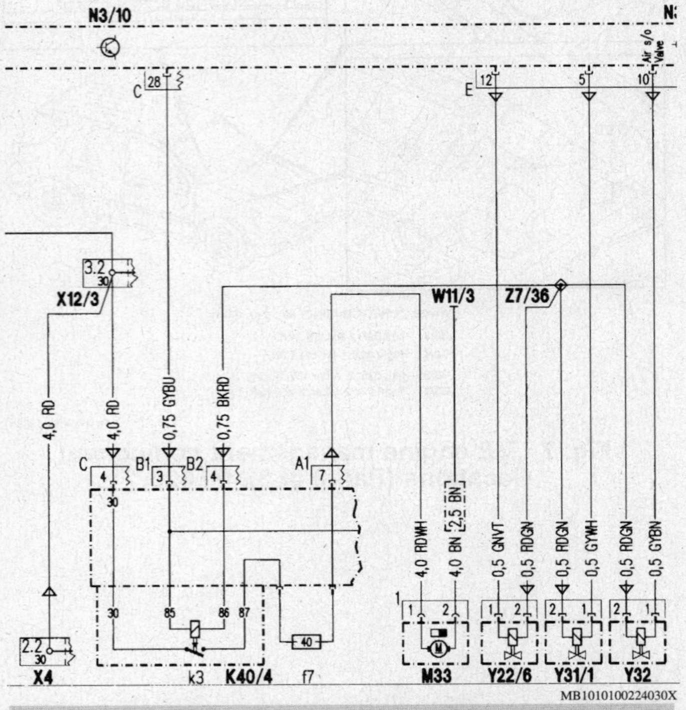

Fig. 8 ME-SFI wiring diagram (Part 3 of 10). C43 & C280 & 1998–2000 CLK320 & 1999–2000 CLK430 engine block

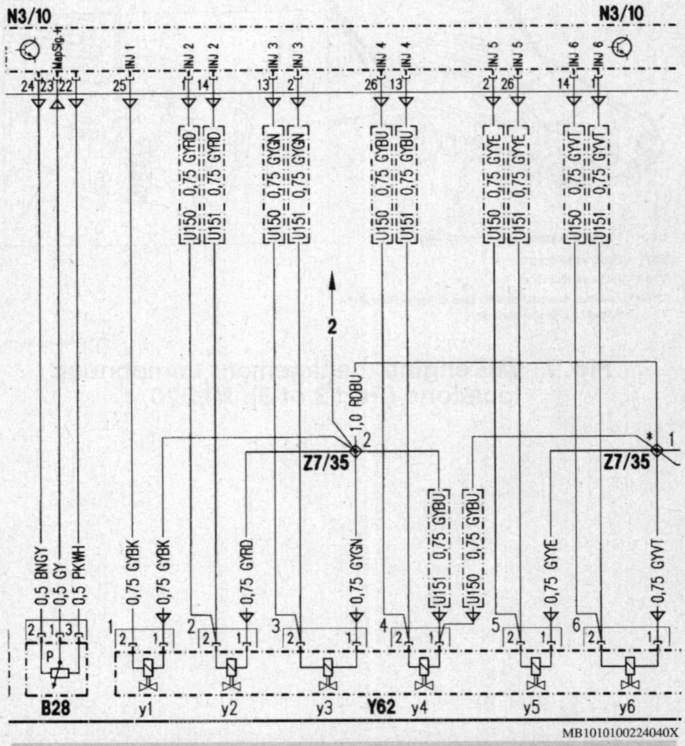

Fig. 8 ME-SFI wiring diagram (Part 4 of 10). C43 & C280 & 1998–2000 CLK320 & 1999–2000 CLK430 engine block

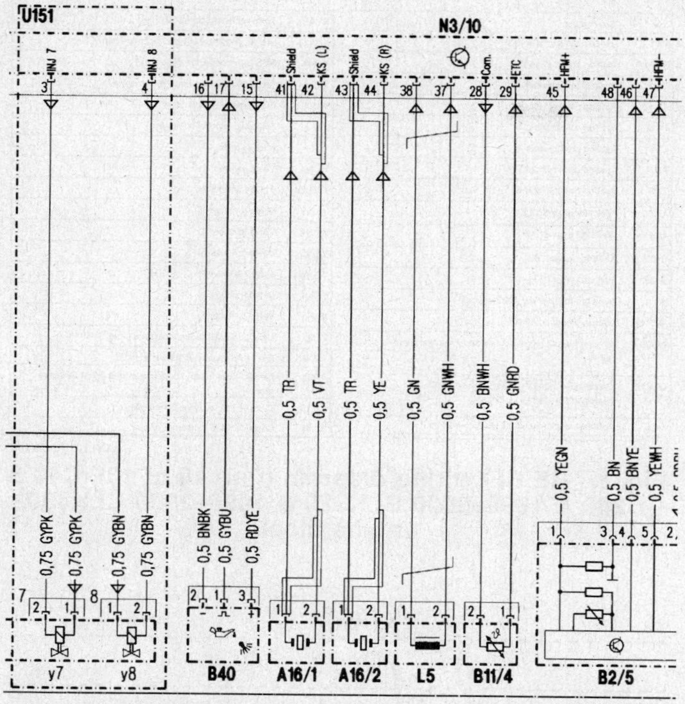

MB1010100224050X

Fig. 8 ME-SFI wiring diagram (Part 5 of 10). C43 & C280 & 1998–2000 CLK320 & 1999–2000 CLK430 engine block

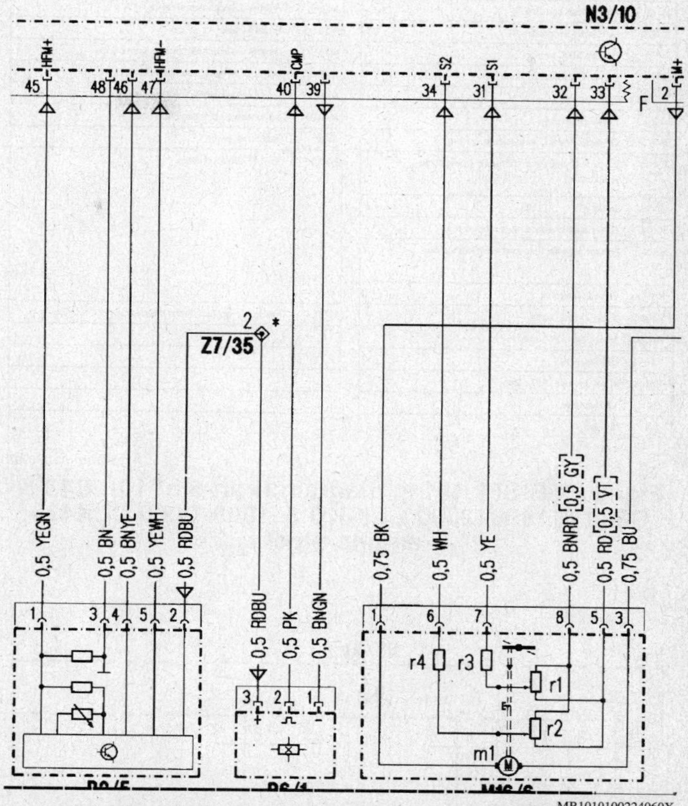

MB1010100224060X

Fig. 8 ME-SFI wiring diagram (Part 6 of 10). C43 & C280 & 1998–2000 CLK320 & 1999–2000 CLK430 engine block

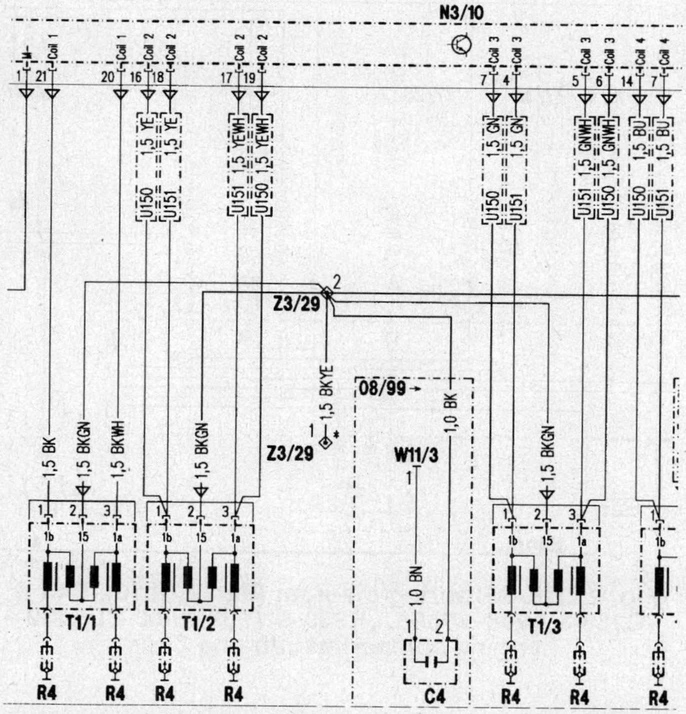

MB1010100224070X

Fig. 8 ME-SFI wiring diagram (Part 7 of 10). C43 & C280 & 1998–2000 CLK320 & 1999–2000 CLK430 engine block

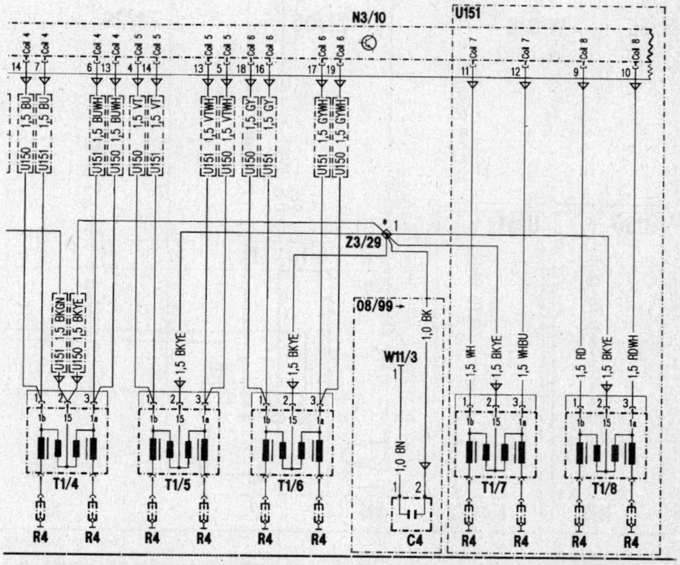

MB1010100224080X

Fig. 8 ME-SFI wiring diagram (Part 8 of 10). C43 & C280 & 1998–2000 CLK320 & 1999–2000 CLK430 engine block

A16/1	Right knock sensor 1
A16/2	Left knock sensor 2
B2/5	Hot film MAF sensor
B6/1	Camshaft Hall-effect sensor
B11/4	ECT sensor
B28	Pressure sensor
B40	Oil sensor (level, temperature, quality)
C4	Electrolytic capacitor connector (radio noise suppressor)
G1	Battery
K40/2	Driver-side fuse and relay module box
K40/4	Passenger-side fuse and relay module box
K40/4f4	Fuse 2, Motronic
K40/4f6	Fuse, ignition coils
K40/4f7	Maxi-fuse, AIR pump
K40/4k2	Starter relay
K40/4k3	Relay module, AIR pump
L5	CKP sensor
M1	Starter

M16/6	Throttle valve control element
M16/6m1	Actuator motor
M16/6r1	Throttle valve actual value potentiometer
M16/6r2	Drive actual value potentiometer
M16/6r3	Actual value potentiometer (wiper 1)
M16/6r4	Actual value potentiometer (wiper 2)
M33	Electric air pump
N3/10	ME-SFI control module
N73	Electronic ignition-starter switch (EIS) control module

MB1010100224090X

Fig. 8 ME-SFI wiring diagram (Part 9 of 10). C43 & C280 & 1998–2000 CLK320 & 1999–2000 CLK430 engine block

R4	Spark plugs
T1/1	Ignition coil (cylinder 1)
T1/2	Ignition coil (cylinder 2)
T1/3	Ignition coil (cylinder 3)
T1/4	Ignition coil (cylinder 4)
T1/5	Ignition coil (cylinder 5)
T1/6	Ignition coil (cylinder 6)
T1/7	Ignition coil (cylinder 7)
T1/8	Ignition coil (cylinder 8)
U150	Valid for engine 112
U151	Valid for engine 113
U152	Valid for model 202
U153	Valid for model 208
W1	Main ground (behind instrument cluster)
W11/3	Ground (engine-left side)
W16/4	Ground (output ground - component compartment - right)
W16/6	Ground (electronics ground - component compartment - right)
X4	Terminal block (circuit 30, left footwell)

X12/3	Terminal block (circuit 30)
X26/23	Engine compartment/cockpit connector
X43/3	REST/CL connector, circuit 30Z
Y22/6	Shifting induction pipe switchover valve
Y31/1	EGR pressure transducer
Y32	Air pump switchover valve
Y62	Fuel Injectors
Y62y1	Valve (cylinder 1)
Y62y2	Valve (cylinder 2)
Y62y3	Valve (cylinder 3)
Y62y4	Valve (cylinder 4)
Y62y5	Valve (cylinder 5)
Y62y6	Valve (cylinder 6)
Y62y7	Valve (cylinder 7)
Y62y8	Valve (cylinder 8)
Z3/26	Circuit 15 (unfused) connector sleeve
Z3/29	Circuit 15 connector sleeve (fused)
Z7/25	Circuit 87 (unfused) connector sleeve (HFM-SFI/base module)
Z7/35	Circuit 87 M1e connector sleeve
Z7/36	Circuit 87 M2e connector sleeve

MB1010100224100X

Fig. 8 ME-SFI wiring diagram (Part 10 of 10). C43 & C280 & 1998–2000 CLK320 & 1999–2000 CLK430 engine block

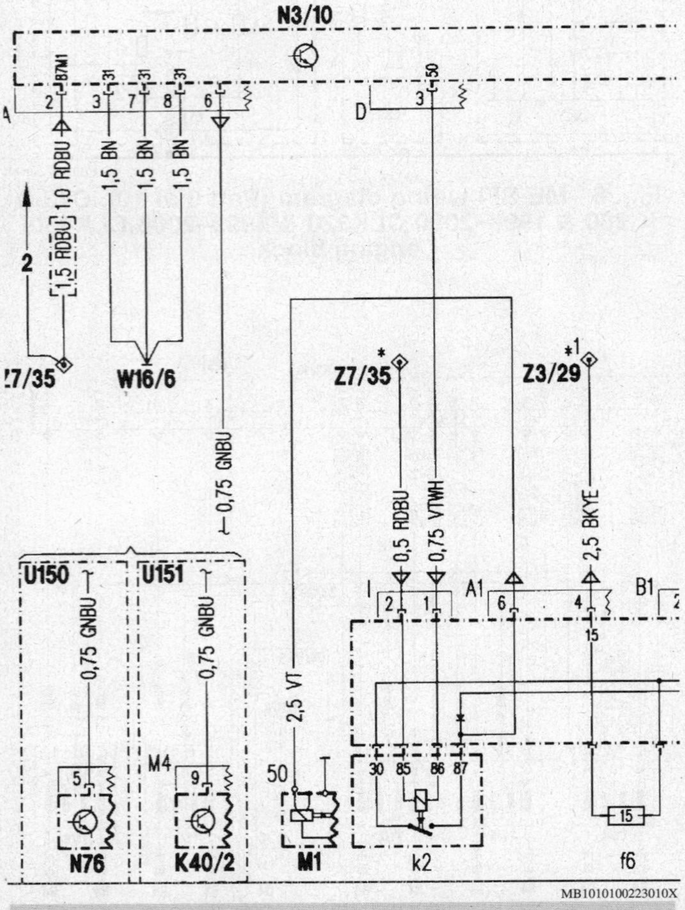

MB1010100223010X

Fig. 9 ME-SFI wiring diagram (Part 1 of 13). C43 & C280 & 1998–2000 CLK320 & 1999–2000 CLK430 engine compartment/frame floor

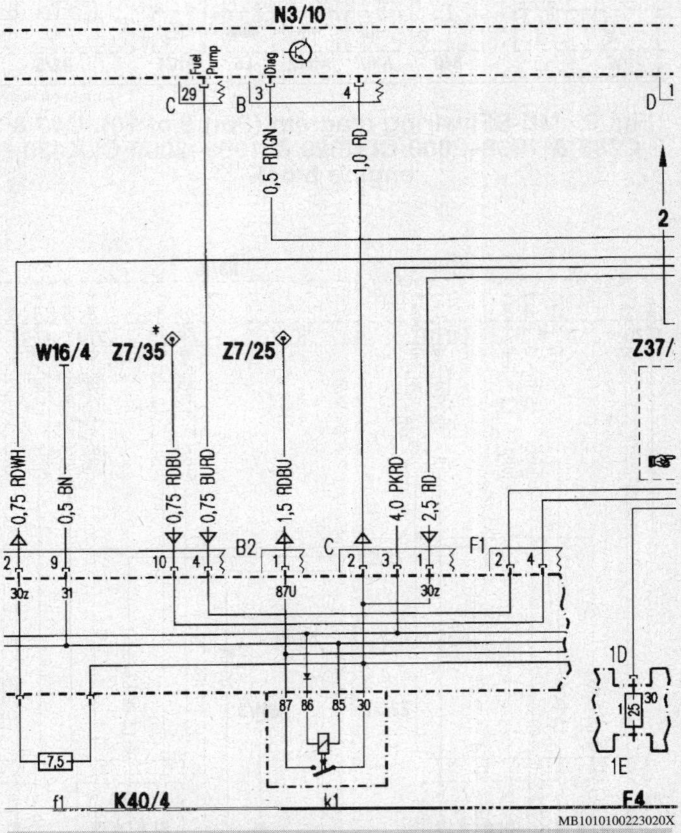

MB1010100223020X

Fig. 9 ME-SFI wiring diagram (Part 2 of 13). C43 & C280 & 1998–2000 CLK320 & 1999–2000 CLK430 engine compartment/frame floor

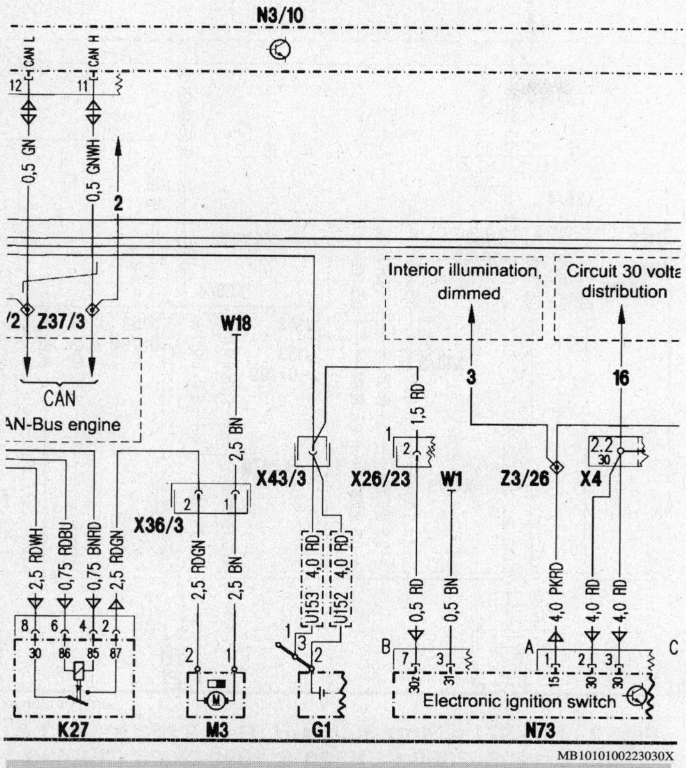

Fig. 9 ME-SFI wiring diagram (Part 3 of 13). C43 & C280 & 1998–2000 CLK320 & 1999–2000 CLK430 engine compartment/frame floor

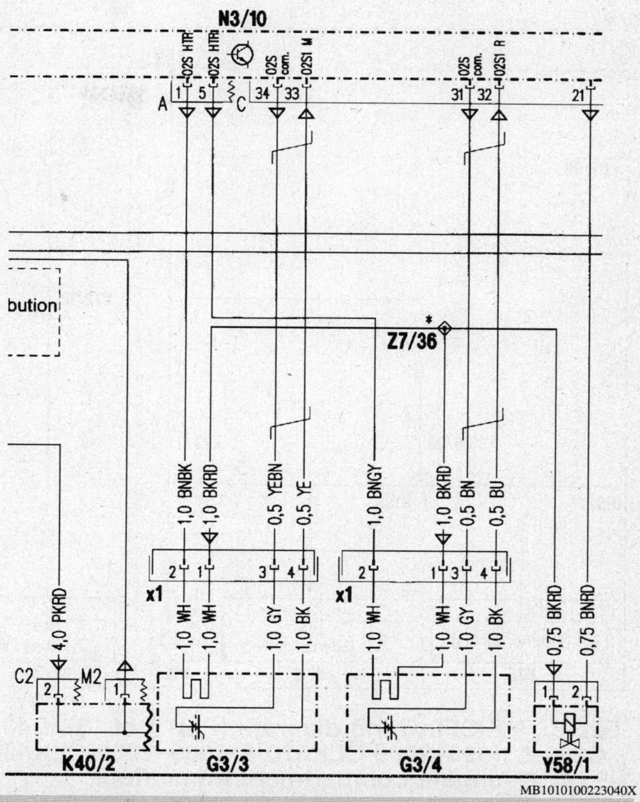

Fig. 9 ME-SFI wiring diagram (Part 4 of 13). C43 & C280 & 1998–2000 CLK320 & 1999–2000 CLK430 engine compartment/frame floor

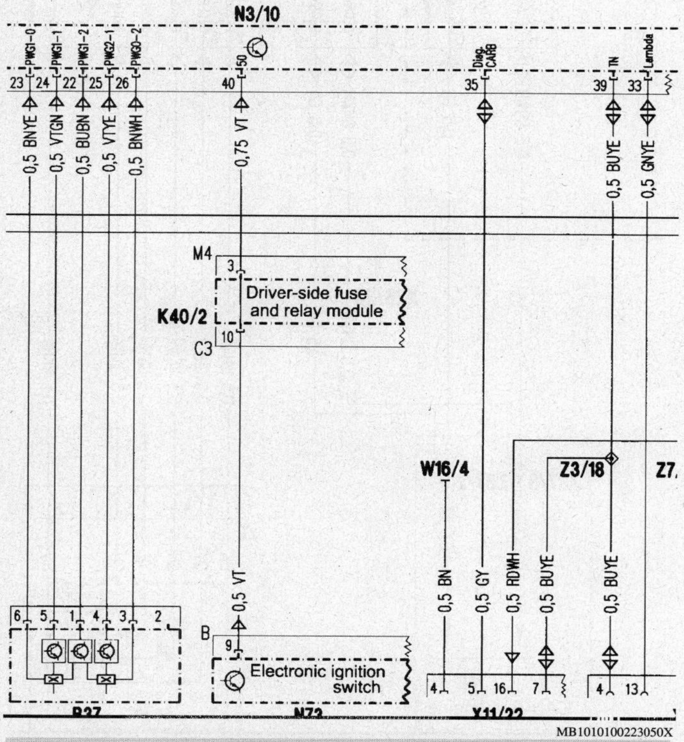

Fig. 9 ME-SFI wiring diagram (Part 5 of 13). C43 & C280 & 1998–2000 CLK320 & 1999–2000 CLK430 engine compartment/frame floor

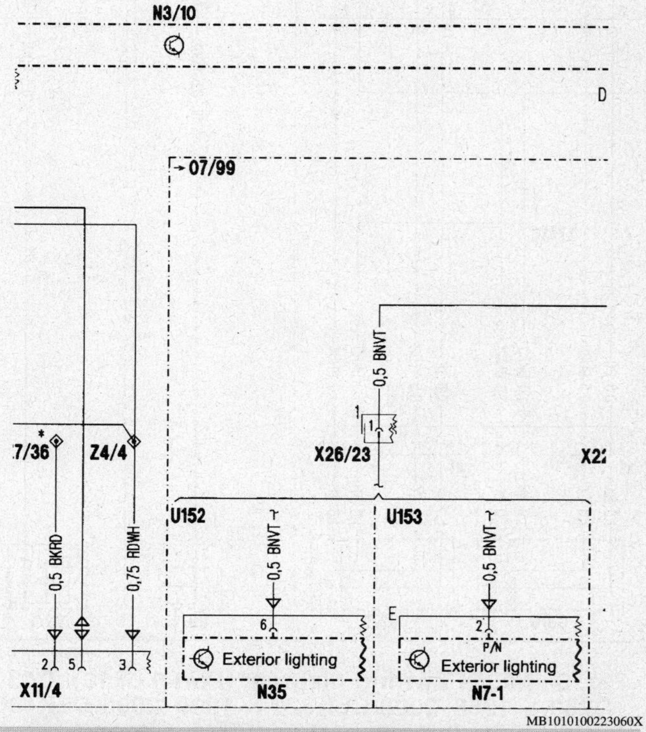

Fig. 9 ME-SFI wiring diagram (Part 6 of 13). C43 & C280 & 1998–2000 CLK320 & 1999–2000 CLK430 engine compartment/frame floor

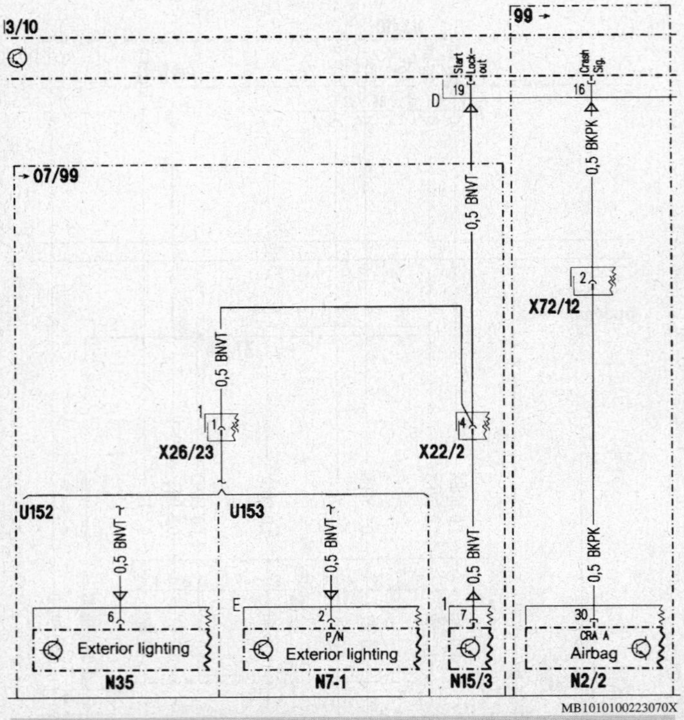

Fig. 9 ME-SFI wiring diagram (Part 7 of 13). C43 & C280 & 1998–2000 CLK320 & 1999–2000 CLK430 engine compartment/frame floor

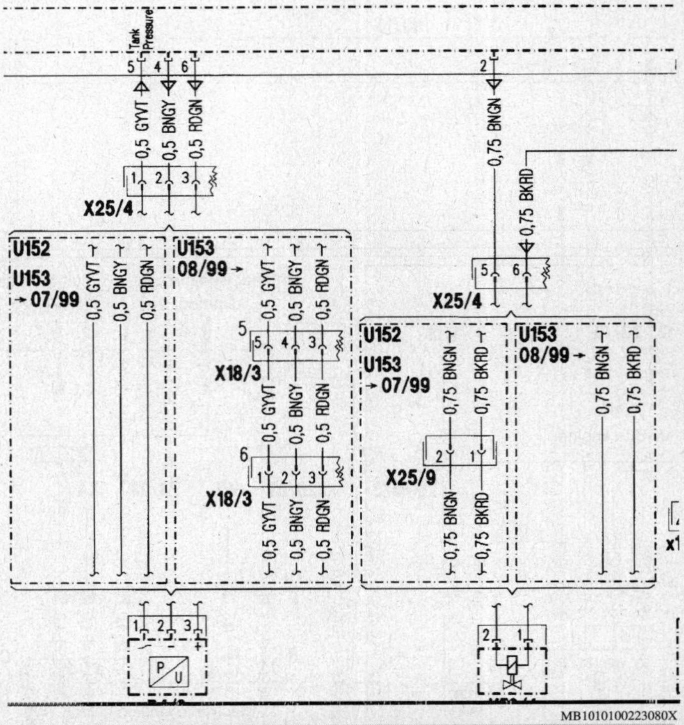

Fig. 9 ME-SFI wiring diagram (Part 8 of 13). C43 & C280 & 1998–2000 CLK320 & 1999–2000 CLK430 engine compartment/frame floor

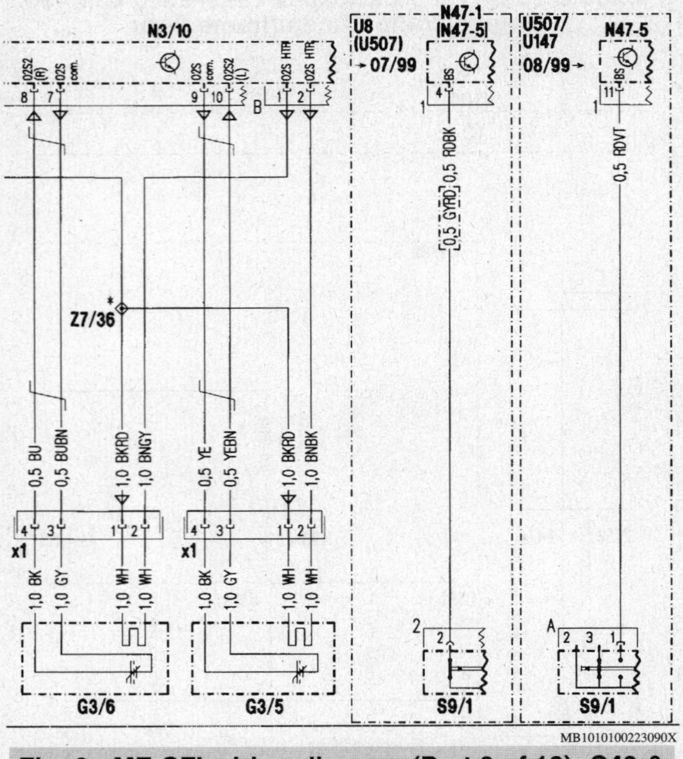

Fig. 9 ME-SFI wiring diagram (Part 9 of 13). C43 & C280 & 1998–2000 CLK320 & 1999–2000 CLK430 engine compartment/frame floor

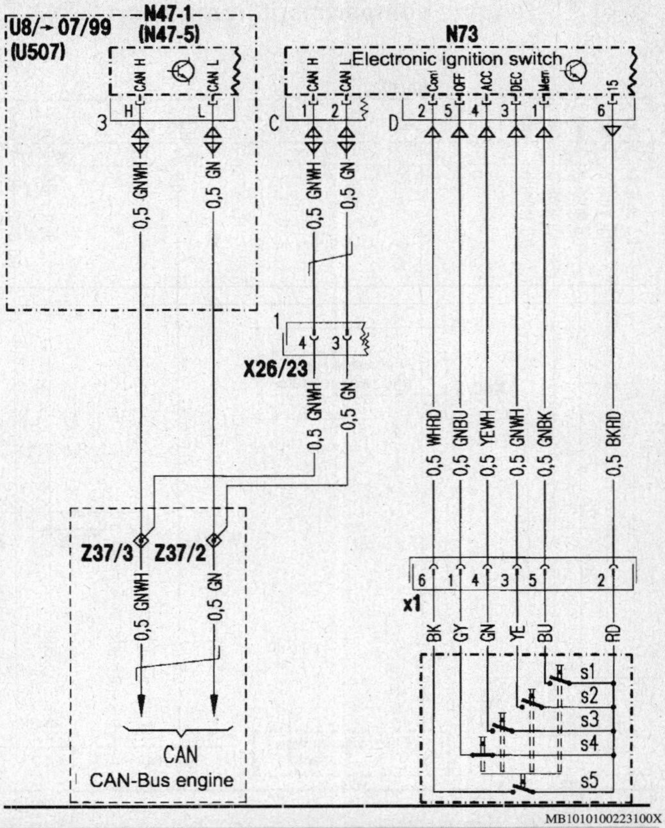

Fig. 9 ME-SFI wiring diagram (Part 10 of 13). C43 & C280 & 1998–2000 CLK320 & 1999–2000 CLK430 engine compartment/frame floor

B43	Fuel tank pressure sensor
B37	Pedal value sensor
F4	Fuse box in trunk
F4F1	Fuse 1
G1	Battery
G3/3	Left O2S 1 (before TWC)
G3/3x1	Left O2S 1 connector (before TWC)
G3/4	Right O2S 1 (before TWC)
G3/4x1	Right O2S 1 connector (before TWC)
G3/5	Left O2S 2 (after TWC)
G3/5x1	Left O2S 2 connector (after TWC)
G3/6	Right O2S 2 (after TWC)
G3/6x1	Right O2S 2 connector (after TWC)
K27	FP relay module
K40/2	Driver-side fuse and relay module box
K40	Passenger-side fuse and relay module box
K40/4F1	Fuse, circuit 30z
K44/F6	Fuse, ignition coils

K40/4k1	Polarity protection relay
K40/4k2	Starter relay
M1	Starter
M3	FP assembly
N2/2	SRS control module
N3/10	ME-SFI control module
N7-1	Illumination control module
N15/3	ETC control module
N35	Daytime running lamp control module
N47-1	ASR/SPS control module
N47-5	ESP/BAS control module

MB1010100223110X

Fig. 9 ME-SFI wiring diagram (Part 11 of 13). C43 & C280 & 1998–2000 CLK320 & 1999–2000 CLK430 engine compartment/frame floor

X11/22	Diagnostic module (OBD II) generic scan tool connector
X18/3	Interior/fuel tank connector
X22/2	AT/engine connector
X25/4	Fuel tank connector (pressure, charcoal filter)
X25/9	Activated charcoal filter connector
X26/23	Engine compartment/cockpit connector
X36/3	FP harness connector (2-pole)
X43/3	REST/CL connector, circuit 30Z
X72/12	Auxiliary heater/crash signal connector
Y58/1	Purge control valve
Y58/4	Activated charcoal canister shutoff valve
Z3/18	Circuit 15 connector sleeve (HFM-SFI, interior/engine)
Z3/26	Circuit 15 (unfused) connector sleeve
Z3/29	Circuit 15 connector sleeve (fused)

Z4/4	Circuit 30Z connector sleeve (solder joint in harness)
Z7/25	Circuit 87 (unfused) connector sleeve (HFM-SFI/base module)
Z7/35	Circuit 87 M1e connector sleeve
Z7/36	Circuit 87 M2e connector sleeve
Z37/2	Engine CAN-Bus (low) connector sleeve
Z37/3	Engine CAN-Bus (high) connector sleeve

MB1010100223130X

Fig. 9 ME-SFI wiring diagram (Part 13 of 13). C43 & C280 & 1998–2000 CLK320 & 1999–2000 CLK430 engine compartment/frame floor

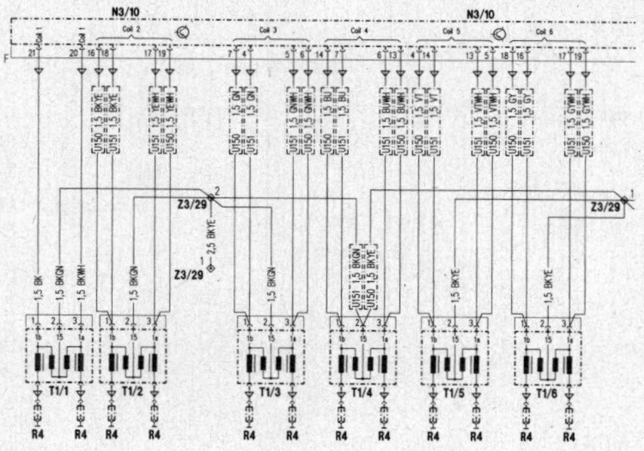

A16/1	Left knock sensor 1
A16/2	Right knock sensor 2
B2/5	Hot film MAF sensor
B6/1	Camshaft Hall-effect sensor
B11/4	ECT sensor
B28	Pressure sensor
B40	Oil sensor (level, temperature, quality)
G1	Battery
K40/4	Passenger-side fuse and relay module box
K40/4f4	Fuse 2, Motronic
K40/4f6	Fuse, ignition coils
K40/4f7	Maxi-fuse, AIR pump
K40/4k2	Starter relay
K40/4k3	Relay module, AIR pump
L5	CKP sensor
M1	Starter
M16/6	Throttle valve actuator
M16/6m1	Actuator motor
M16/6r1	Throttle valve actual value potentiometer

M16/6r2	Drive actual value potentiometer
M33	AIR pump
N3/10	Engine control module (ME-SFI)
N10/1	Signal pickup- and activation module (SAM) left front
N73	Electronic ignition lock control module

MB1019900155010X

Fig. 10 ME-SFI wiring diagram (Part 1 of 5). E55, E320 & E430 engine block

N73	Electronic ignition-starter switch (EIS) control module
N76	Engine/climate control electric cooling fan control module
S9/1	Stop lamp switch (4-pole)
S40	CC pushbutton switch
S40s1	Memory recall
S40s2	Decelerate/set
S40s3	Accelerate/set
S40s4	Off
S40s5	Control contact
S40x1	CC pushbutton switch connector
U8	Valid for ASR
U147	Valid for Bosch system
U150	Valid for engine 112
U151	Valid for engine 113

U152	Valid for model 202
U153	Valid for model 208
U507	Valid for ESP
W1	Main ground (behind instrument cluster)
W16/4	Ground (output ground - component compartment - right)
W16/6	Ground (electronics ground - component compartment - right)
W18	Ground (left front seat crossmember)
X4	Terminal block (circuit 30, left footwell)
X11/4	Diagnostic test clutch

MB1010100223120X

Fig. 9 ME-SFI wiring diagram (Part 12 of 13). C43 & C280 & 1998–2000 CLK320 & 1999–2000 CLK430 engine compartment/frame floor

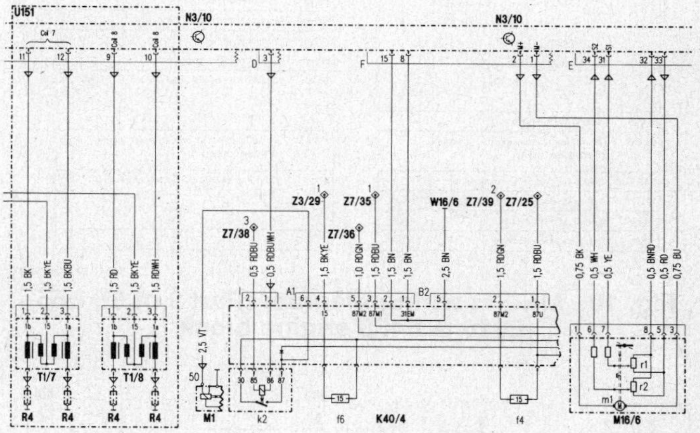

R4	Spark plugs
S40	CC switch
S40s1	Memory recall
S40s2	Decelerate/set
S40s3	Accelerate/set
S40s4	Off
S40s5	Control contact
S40x1	CC switch connector
T1/1	Ignition coil 1
T1/2	Ignition coil 2

T1/3	Ignition coil 3
T1/4	Ignition coil 4
T1/5	Ignition coil 5
T1/6	Ignition coil 6
T1/7	Ignition coil 7
T1/8	Ignition coil 8
U150	Valid for engine 112

MB1019900155020X

Fig. 10 ME-SFI wiring diagram (Part 2 of 5). E55, E320 & E430 engine block

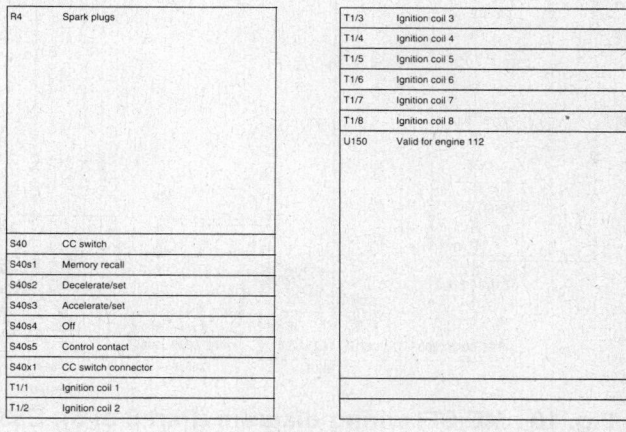

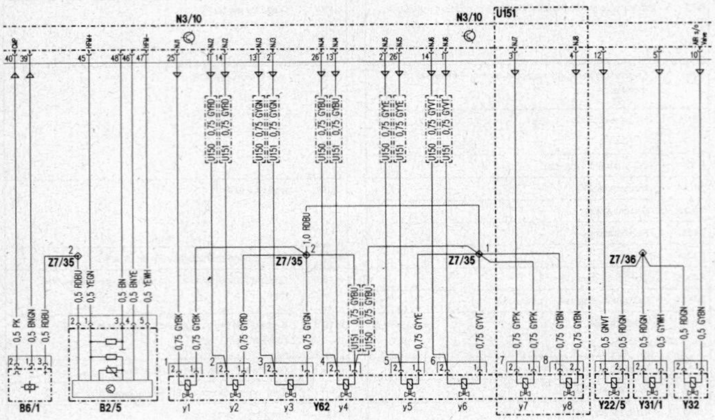

U151	Valid for engine 113	Y31/1	EGR valve vacuum transducer
		Y32	AIR pump switchover valve
		Y62	Injectors
		Y62y1	Injector (cylinder 1)
		Y62y2	Injector (cylinder 2)
		Y62y3	Injector (cylinder 3)
		Y62y4	Injector (cylinder 4)
		Y62y5	Injector (cylinder 5)
		Y62y6	Injector (cylinder 6)
		Y62y7	Injector (cylinder 7)
		Y62y8	Injector (cylinder 8)
		Z3/29	Circuit 15 connector sleeve, (fused)
W11/3	Ground (engine-left side)		
W16/6	Ground (electronics ground - component compartment - right)	Z7/25	Circuit 87 (unfused) connector sleeve (HFM-SFI/base module)
X25/7	Engine compartment/FFS connector	Z7/35	Connector sleeve, circuit 87M, feed from BM (N16/1)
X30/7	Star-point coupler databus (CAN) tie-in connector		
X63/6	CAN-Bus/15u connector		
Y22/5	Intake manifold switchover valve		

MB1019900155030X

Fig. 10 ME-SFI wiring diagram (Part 3 of 5). E55, E320 & E430 engine block

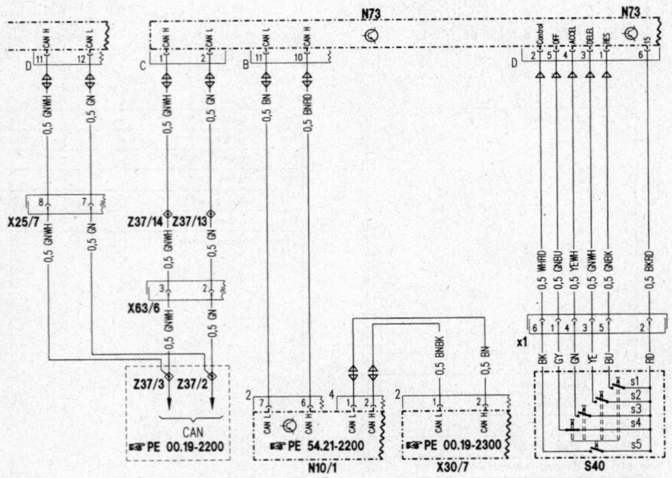

MB1019900155050X

Fig. 10 ME-SFI wiring diagram (Part 5 of 5). E55, E320 & E430 engine block

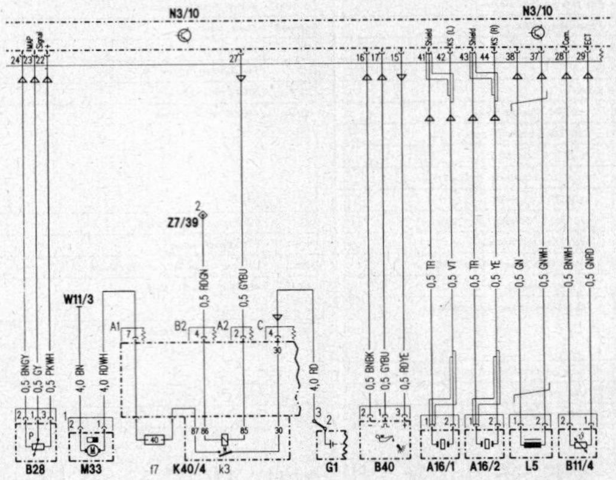

Z7/36	Circuit 87 M2e connector sleeve
Z7/38	Circuit 87 M1i connector sleeve
Z7/39	Circuit 87 M2i connector sleeve
Z37/2	Engine CAN-Bus (low) connector sleeve
Z37/3	Engine CAN-Bus (high) connector sleeve
Z37/13	Engine CAN-Bus (low) connector sleeve
Z37/14	Engine CAN-Bus (high) connector sleeve
	CAN-Bus engine
	CAN-Bus interior
	Driver-side signal pickup- and activation module (SAM)

MB1019900155040X

Fig. 10 ME-SFI wiring diagram (Part 4 of 5). E55, E320 & E430 engine block

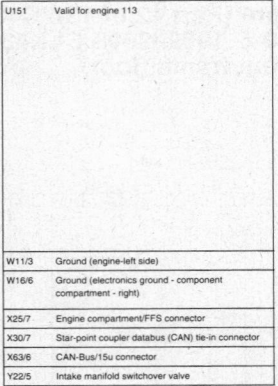

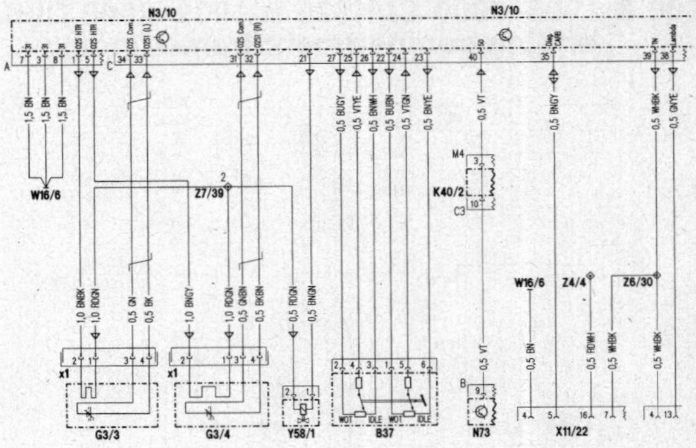

B4/3	Fuel tank pressure sensor	M1	Starter
B37	Pedal value sensor	M3	Fuel pump
F4	Rear fuse box	N3/10	Engine control module (ME-SFI)
F4f6	Fuse 6		
G3/3	Left O2S 1 (before TWC)		
G3/3x1	Left O2S 1 connector (before TWC)		
G3/4	Right O2S 1 (before TWC)		
G3/4x1	Right O2S 1 connector (before TWC)	N15/3	Transmission control module
G3/5	Left O2S 2 (after TWC)	N73	Electronic ignition lock control module
G3/5x1	Left O2S 2 connector (after TWC)	W16/4	Ground (output ground - right wheel housing)
G3/6	Right O2S 2 (after TWC)	W16/6	Ground (electronics ground - component compartment - right)
G3/6x1	Right O2S 2 connector (after TWC)		
K27	FP relay module	W18	Ground (left front seat crossmember)
K40/2	Driver-side fuse and relay module box	X11/4	Data link connector (DTC readout)
K40/4	Passenger-side fuse and relay module box	X11/22	Diagnostic module (OBD II) generic scan tool connector
K40/4f1	Fuse, circuit 30z		
K40/4f5	Fuse 1, Motronic	X25/7	Engine compartment/FFS connector
K40/4f6	Fuse, ignition coils	Y58/1	Purge control valve
K40/4k1	Polarity protection relay	Y58/4	Activated charcoal canister shut-off valve
K40/4k2	Starter relay	Z3/29	Circuit 15 connector sleeve, (fused)

MB1019900155060X

Fig. 11 ME-SFI wiring diagram (Part 1 of 3). E320 & E430 engine compartment/frame-floor (until May 31, 1998)

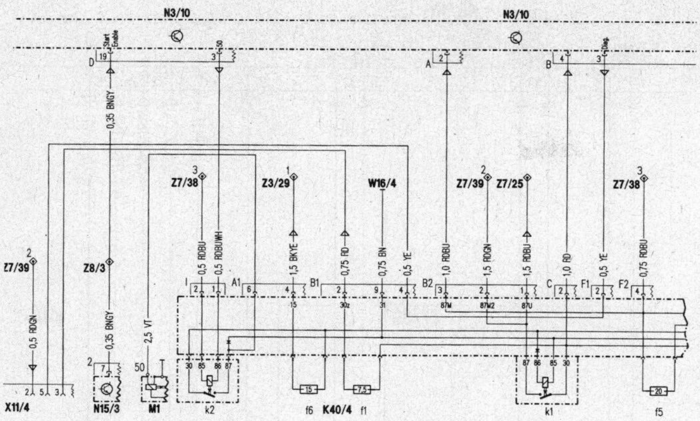

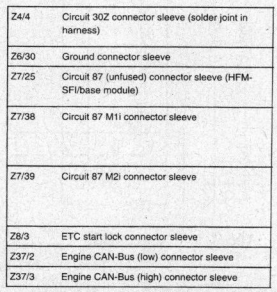

Z4/4	Circuit 30Z connector sleeve (solder joint in harness)
Z6/30	Ground connector sleeve
Z7/25	Circuit 87 (unfused) connector sleeve (HFM-SFI/base module)
Z7/38	Circuit 87 M1i connector sleeve
Z7/39	Circuit 87 M2i connector sleeve
Z8/3	ETC start lock connector sleeve
Z37/2	Engine CAN-Bus (low) connector sleeve
Z37/3	Engine CAN-Bus (high) connector sleeve

MB1019900155070X

Fig. 11 ME-SFI wiring diagram (Part 2 of 3). E320 & E430 engine compartment/frame-floor (until May 31, 1998)

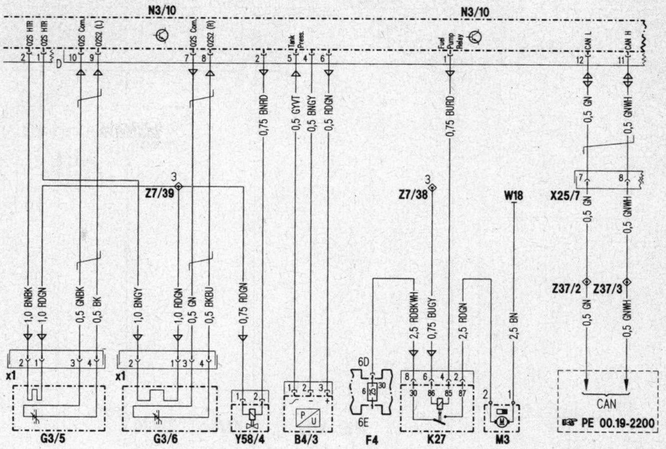

MB1019900155080X

Fig. 11 ME-SFI wiring diagram (Part 3 of 3). E320 & E430 engine compartment/frame-floor (until May 31, 1998)

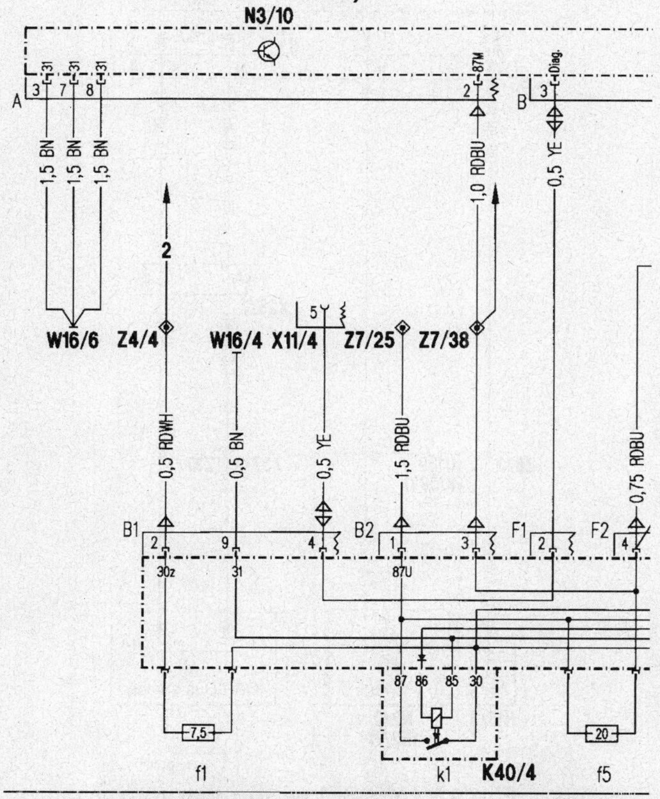

MB1010100237010X

Fig. 12 ME-SFI wiring diagram (Part 1 of 8). E55, E320 & E430 engine compartment/frame-floor (as of June 1, 1998)

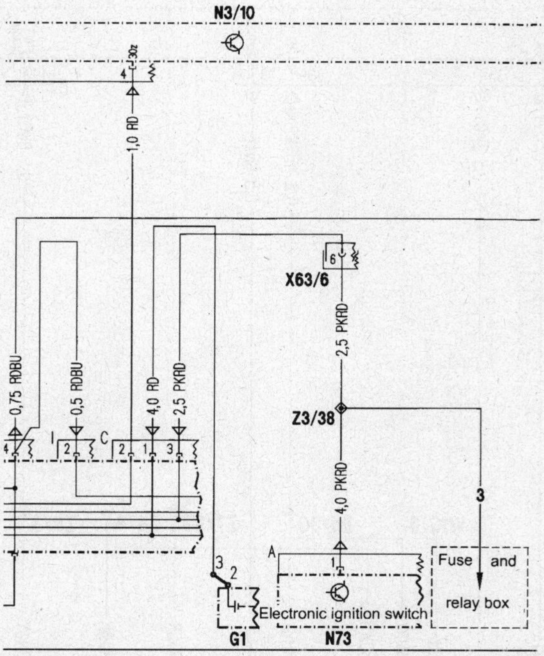

MB1010100237020X

Fig. 12 ME-SFI wiring diagram (Part 2 of 8). E55, E320 & E430 engine compartment/frame-floor (as of June 1, 1998)

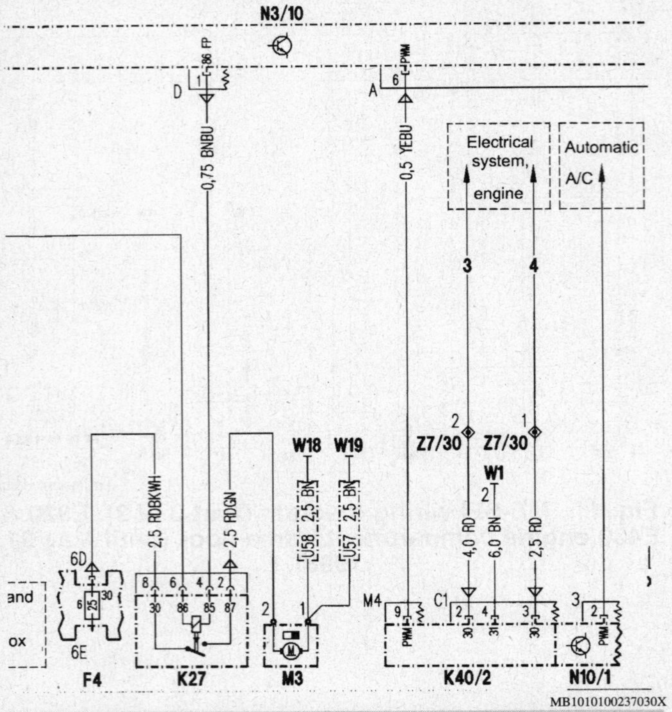

Fig. 12 ME-SFI wiring diagram (Part 3 of 8). E55, E320 & E430 engine compartment/frame-floor (as of June 1, 1998)

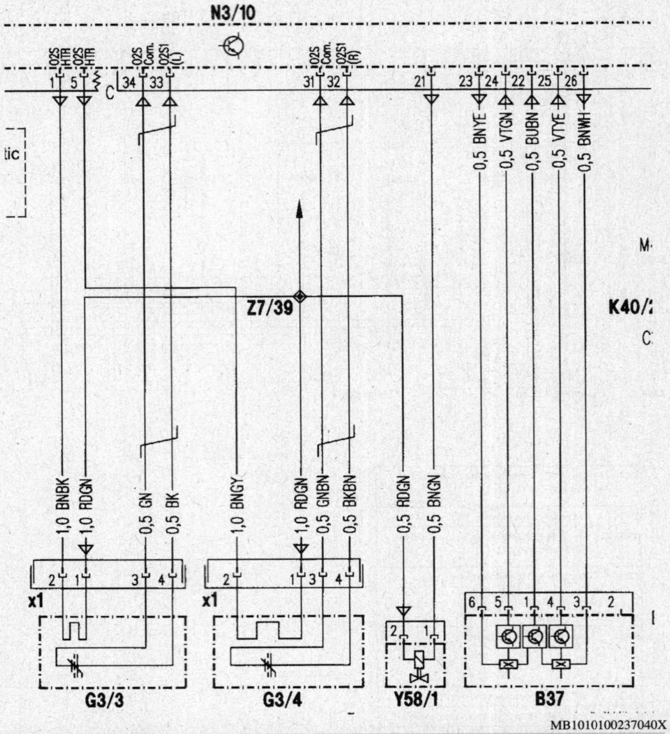

Fig. 12 ME-SFI wiring diagram (Part 4 of 8). E55, E320 & E430 engine compartment/frame-floor (as of June 1, 1998)

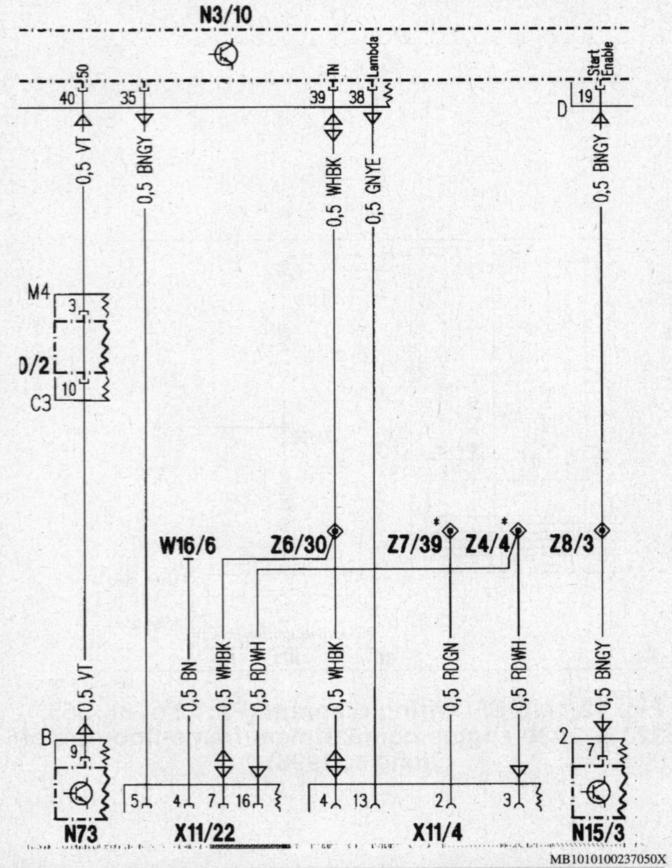

Fig. 12 ME-SFI wiring diagram (Part 5 of 8). E55, E320 & E430 engine compartment/frame-floor (as of June 1, 1998)

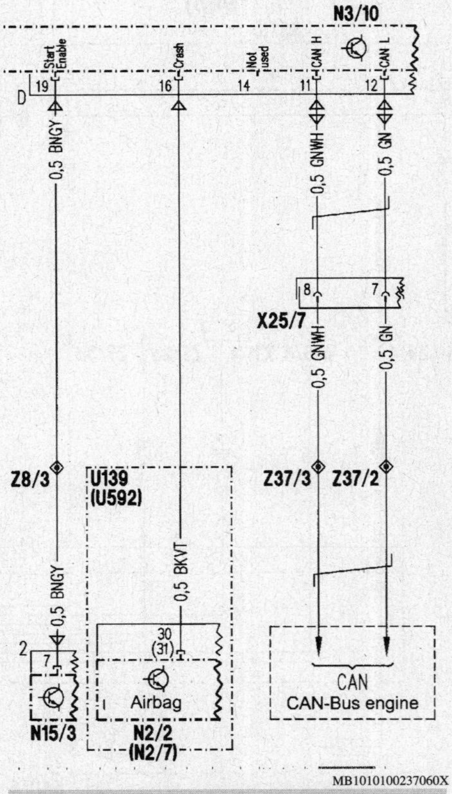

Fig. 12 ME-SFI wiring diagram (Part 6 of 8). E55, E320 & E430 engine compartment/frame-floor (as of June 1, 1998)

B37	Pedal value sensor	N3/10	Engine control module (ME-SFI)
F4	Rear fuse box		
F4f6	Fuse 6		
G1	Battery		
G3/3	Left O2S 1 (before TWC)		
G3/3x1	Left O2S 1 connector (before TWC)	N10/1	Signal pickup- and activation module (SAM) left front
G3/4	Right O2S 1 (before TWC)	N15/3	ETC control module
G3/4x1	Right O2S 1 connector (before TWC)	N73	Electronic ignition-starter switch (EIS) control module
K27	FP relay module		
K40/2	Driver-side fuse and relay module box	U57	Valid for station wagon
		U58	Valid for sedan and limousine
K40/4	Passenger-side fuse and relay module box	U139	Valid for ETR with driver/front passenger airbag
K40/4f1	Fuse, circuit 30z	U592	Valid for curtain (window) airbag
K40/4f5	Fuse 1, Motronic	W1	Main ground (behind instrument cluster)
K40/4k1	Polarity protection relay	W16/4	Ground (output ground - right wheel housing)
M3	Fuel pump	W16/6	Ground (electronics ground - component compartment - right)
N2/2	SRS control module		
N2/7	Restraint system control module	W18	Ground (left front seat crossmember)
		W19	Ground (right front seat crossmember)

MB1010100237070X

Fig. 12 ME-SFI wiring diagram (Part 7 of 8). E55, E320 & E430 engine compartment/frame-floor (as of June 1, 1998)

X11/4	Data link connector (DTC readout)
X11/22	Diagnostic module (OBD II) generic scan tool connector
X25/7	Engine compartment/FFS connector
X63/6	CAN-Bus/15u connector
Y58/1	Purge control valve
Z3/38	Circuit 15 (unfused) connector sleeve
Z4/4	Circuit 30Z connector sleeve (solder joint in harness)
Z6/30	Ground connector sleeve
Z7/25	Circuit 87 (unfused) connector sleeve (HFM-SFI/base module)
Z7/30	Circuit 30 (unfused) connector sleeve
Z7/38	Circuit 87 M1i connector sleeve
Z7/39	Circuit 87 M2i connector sleeve
Z8/3	ETC start lock connector sleeve
Z37/2	Engine CAN-Bus (low) connector sleeve
Z37/3	Engine CAN-Bus (high) connector sleeve

MB1010100237080X

Fig. 12 ME-SFI wiring diagram (Part 8 of 8). E55, E320 & E430 engine compartment/frame-floor (as of June 1, 1998)

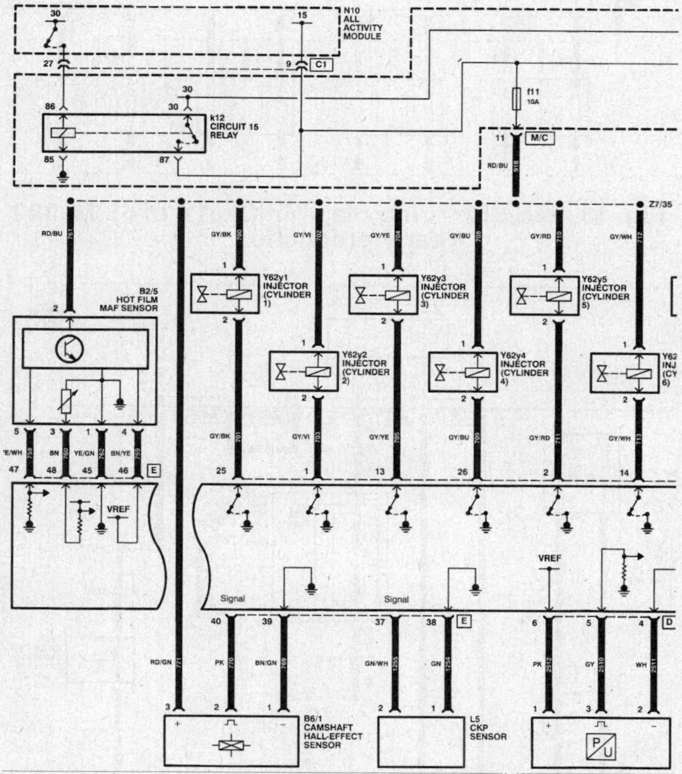

MB1010100239010X

Fig. 13 ME-SFI wiring diagram (Part 1 of 6). ML320 early production

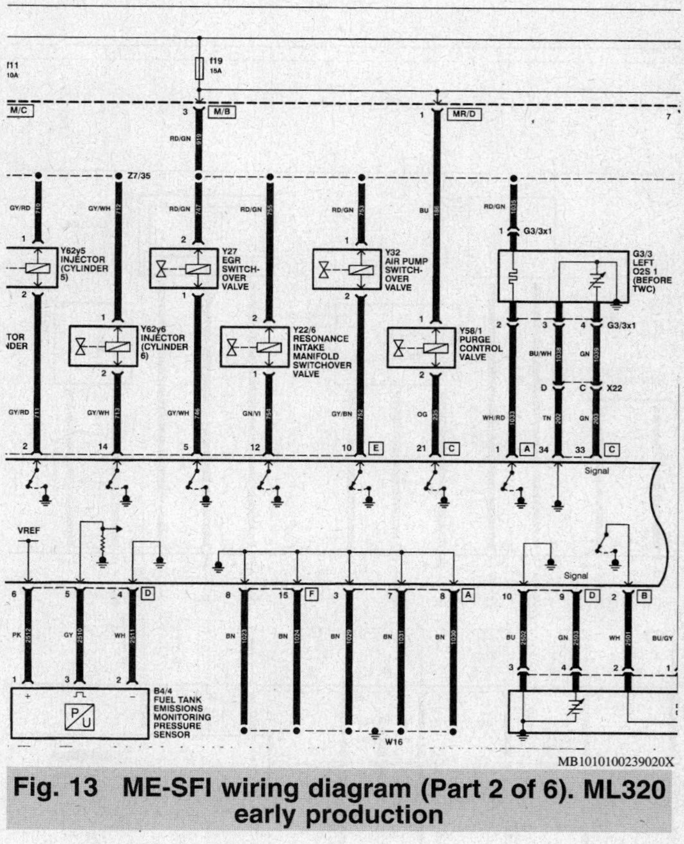

MB1010100239020X

Fig. 13 ME-SFI wiring diagram (Part 2 of 6). ML320 early production

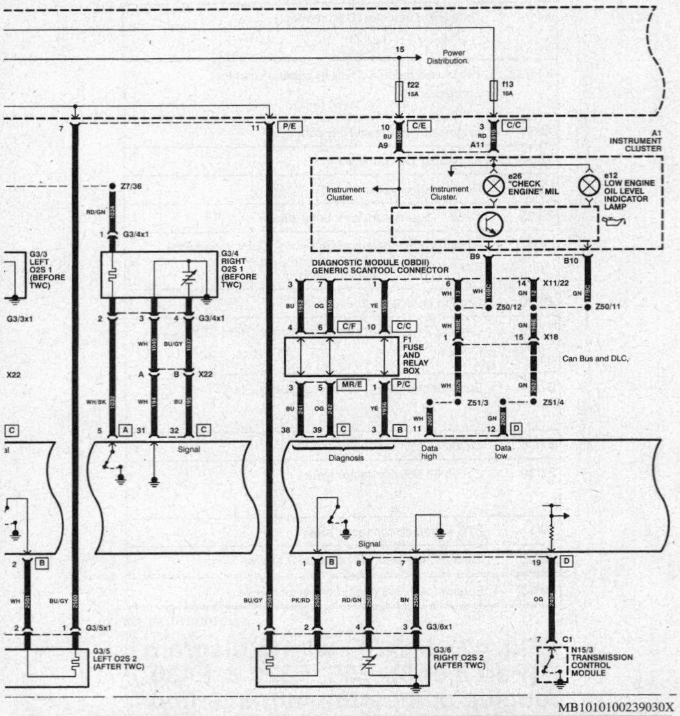

Fig. 13 ME-SFI wiring diagram (Part 3 of 6). ML320 early production

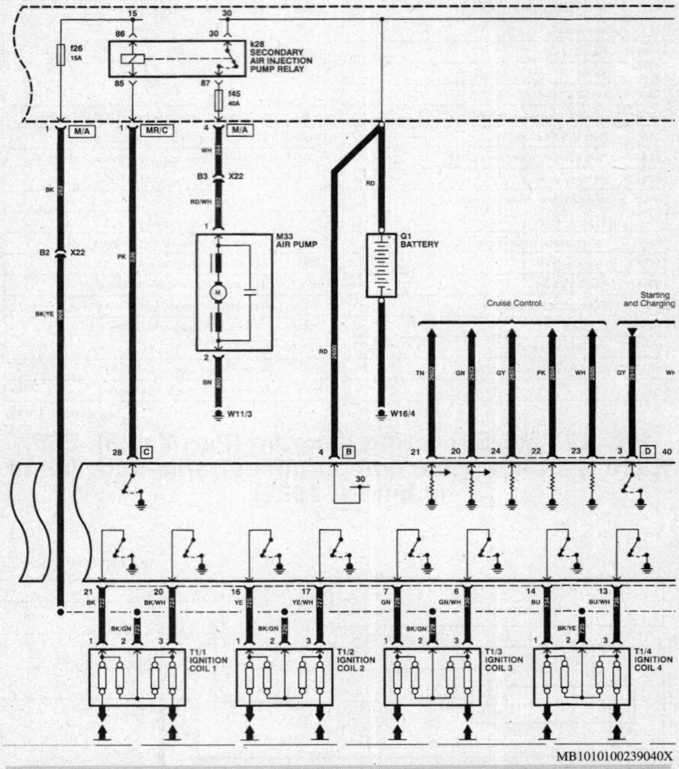

Fig. 13 ME-SFI wiring diagram (Part 4 of 6). ML320 early production

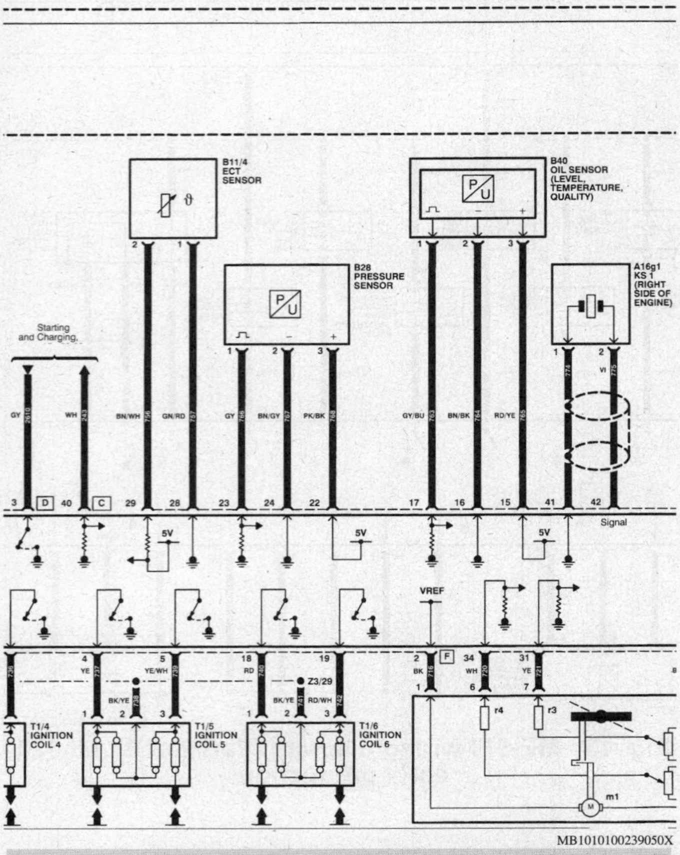

Fig. 13 ME-SFI wiring diagram (Part 5 of 6). ML320 early production

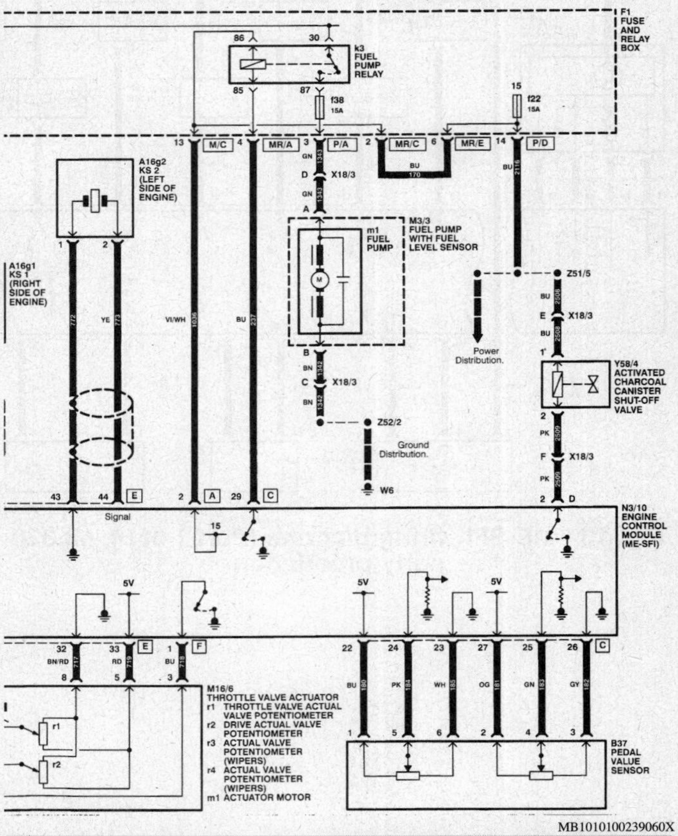

Fig. 13 ME-SFI wiring diagram (Part 6 of 6). ML320 early production

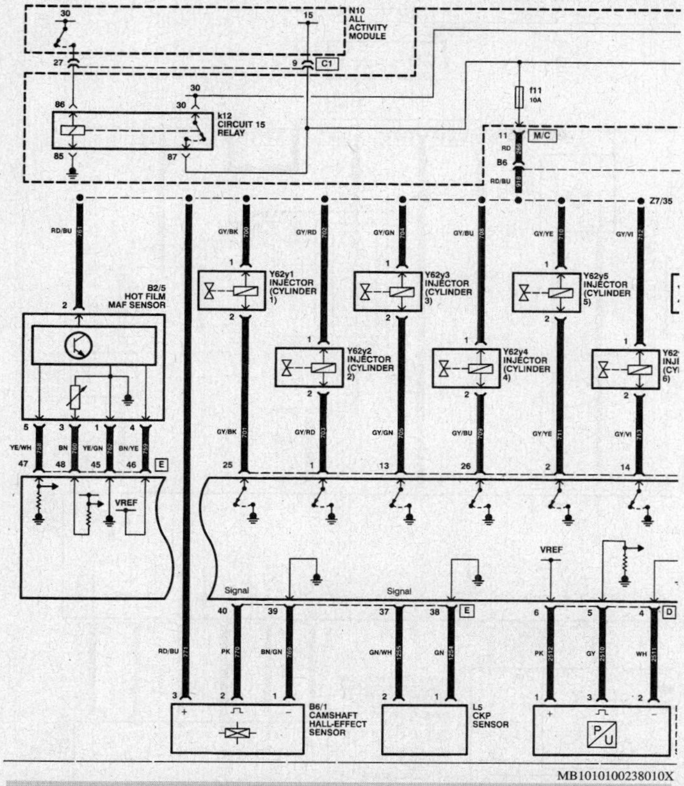

Fig. 14 ME-SFI wiring diagram (Part 1 of 6). ML320 late production

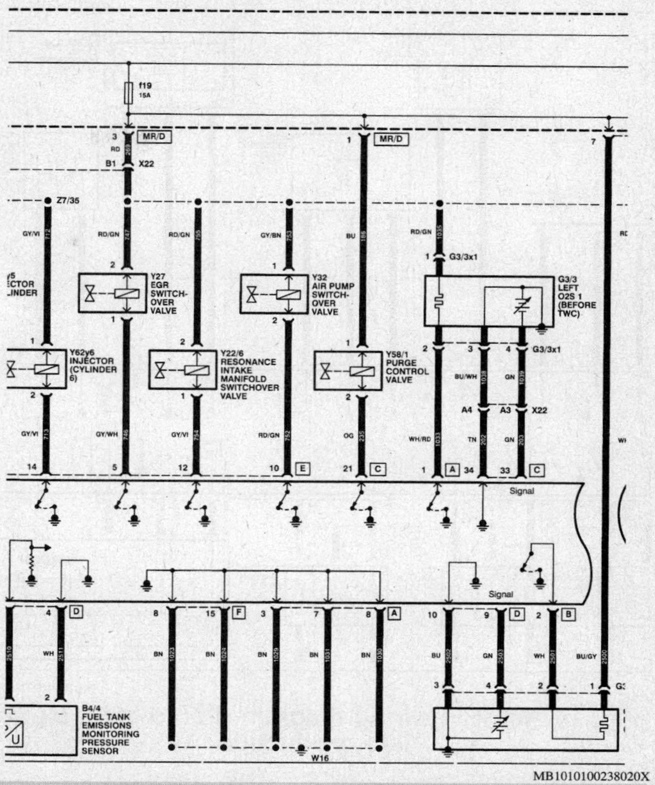

Fig. 14 ME-SFI wiring diagram (Part 2 of 6). ML320 late production

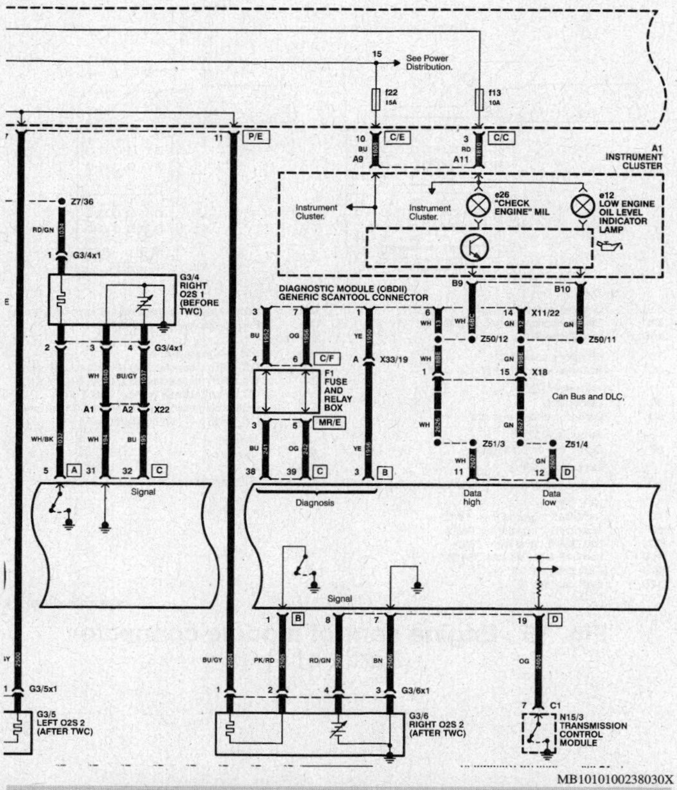

Fig. 14 ME-SFI wiring diagram (Part 3 of 6). ML320 late production

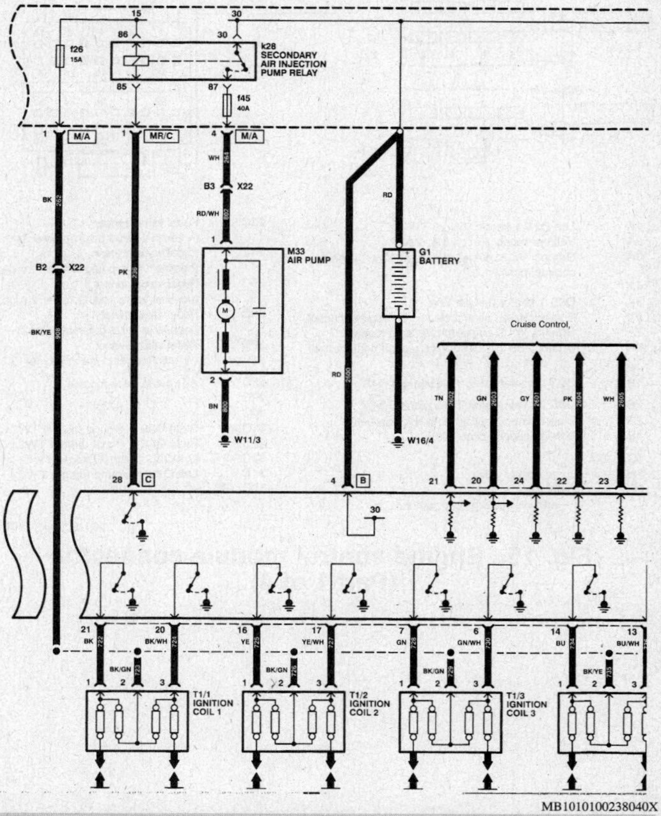

Fig. 14 ME-SFI wiring diagram (Part 4 of 6). ML320 late production

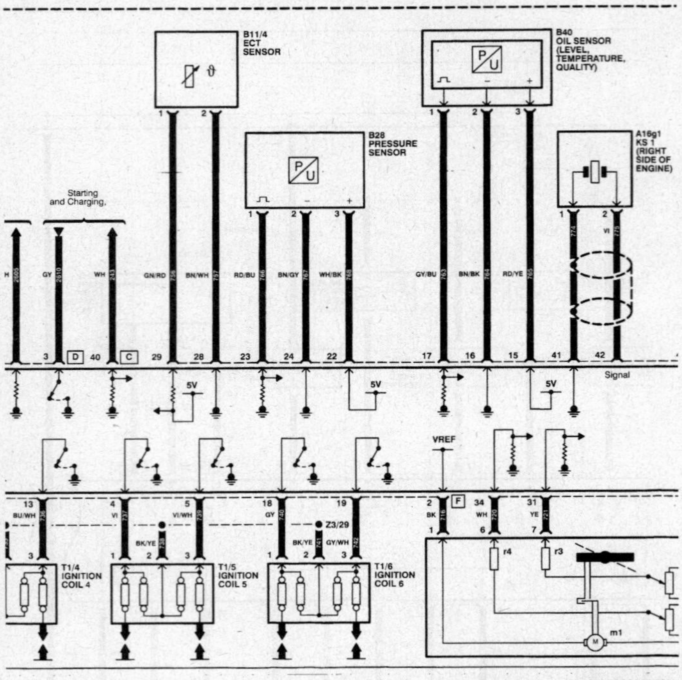

MB1010100238050X

Fig. 14 ME-SFI wiring diagram (Part 5 of 6). ML320 late production

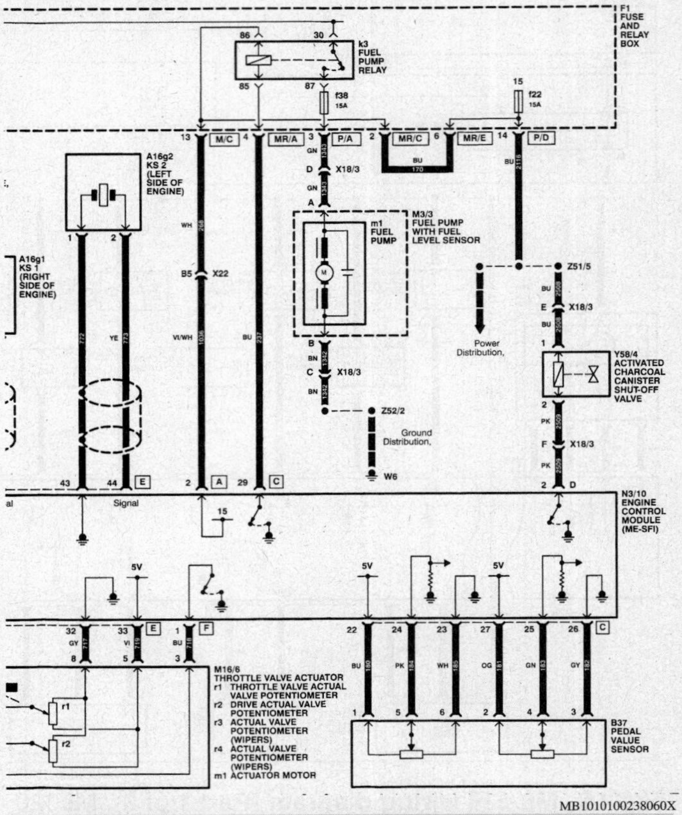

MB1010100238060X

Fig. 14 ME-SFI wiring diagram (Part 6 of 6). ML320 late production

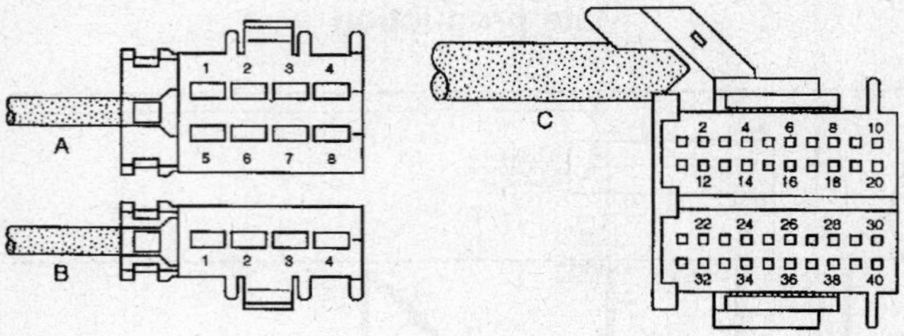

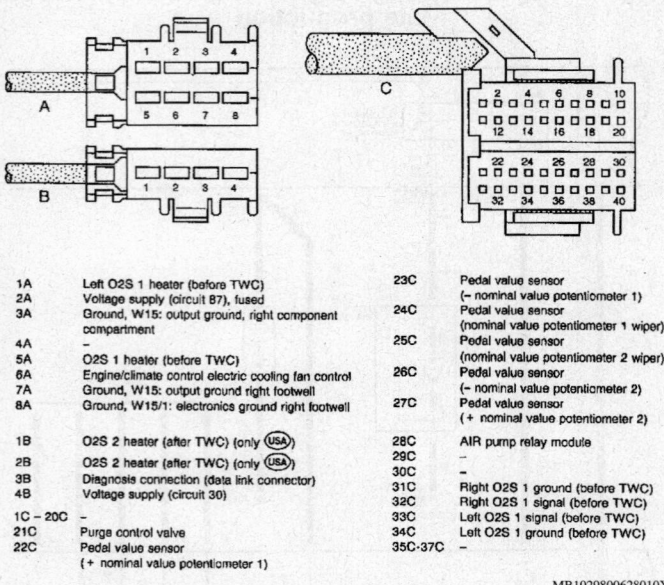

1A	Left O2S 1 heater (before TWC)
2A	Voltage supply (circuit 87), fused
3A	Ground, W15: output ground, right component compartment
4A	-
5A	O2S 1 heater (before TWC)
6A	Engine/climate control electric cooling fan control
7A	Ground, W15: output ground right footwell
8A	Ground, W15/1: electronics ground right footwell
1B	O2S 2 heater (after TWC) (only USA)
2B	O2S 2 heater (after TWC) (only USA)
3B	Diagnosis connection (data link connector)
4B	Voltage supply (circuit 30)
1C – 20C	-
21C	Purge control valve
22C	Pedal value sensor (+ nominal value potentiometer 1)
23C	Pedal value sensor (– nominal value potentiometer 1)
24C	Pedal value sensor (nominal value potentiometer 1 wiper)
25C	Pedal value sensor (nominal value potentiometer 2 wiper)
26C	Pedal value sensor (– nominal value potentiometer 2)
27C	Pedal value sensor (+ nominal value potentiometer 2)
28C	AIR pump relay module
29C	-
30C	-
31C	Right O2S 1 ground (before TWC)
32C	Right O2S 1 signal (before TWC)
33C	Left O2S 1 signal (before TWC)
34C	Left O2S 1 ground (before TWC)
35C-37C	-

MB1029800628010X

Fig. 15 Engine control module connector (Part 1 of 4)

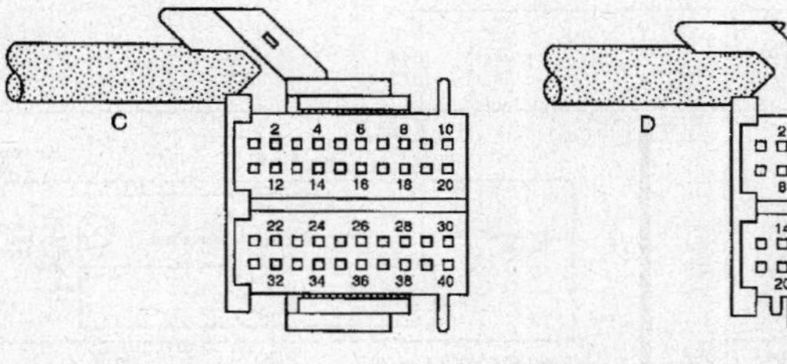

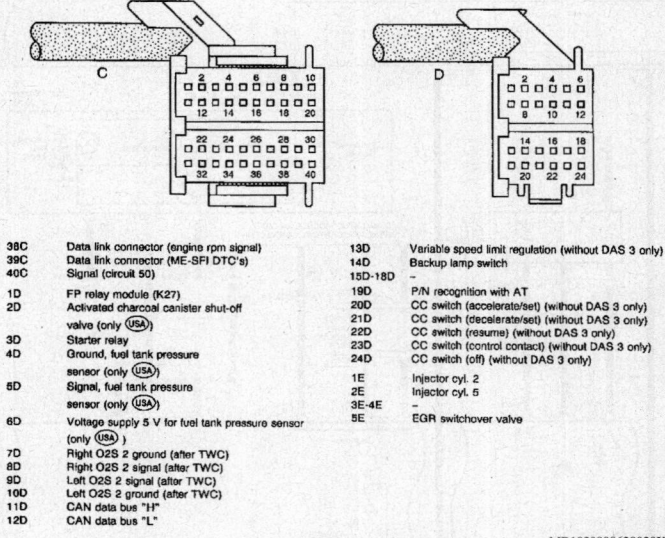

38C	Data link connector (engine rpm signal)
39C	Data link connector (ME-SFI DTC's)
40C	Signal (circuit 50)
1D	FP relay module (K27)
2D	Activated charcoal canister shut-off valve (only USA)
3D	Starter relay
4D	Ground, fuel tank pressure sensor (only USA)
5D	Signal, fuel tank pressure sensor (only USA)
6D	Voltage supply 5 V for fuel tank pressure sensor (only USA)
7D	Right O2S 2 ground (after TWC)
8D	Right O2S 2 signal (after TWC)
9D	Left O2S 2 signal (after TWC)
10D	Left O2S 2 ground (after TWC)
11D	CAN data bus "H"
12D	CAN data bus "L"
13D	Variable speed limit regulation (without DAS 3 only)
14D	Backup lamp switch
15D-18D	-
19D	P/N recognition with AT
20D	CC switch (accelerate/set) (without DAS 3 only)
21D	CC switch (decelerate/set) (without DAS 3 only)
22D	CC switch (resume) (without DAS 3 only)
23D	CC switch (control contact) (without DAS 3 only)
24D	CC switch (off) (without DAS 3 only)
1E	Injector cyl. 2
2E	Injector cyl. 5
3E-4E	-
5E	EGR switchover valve

MB1029800628020X

Fig. 15 Engine control module connector (Part 2 of 4)

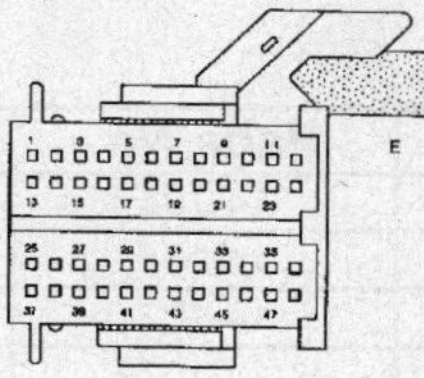

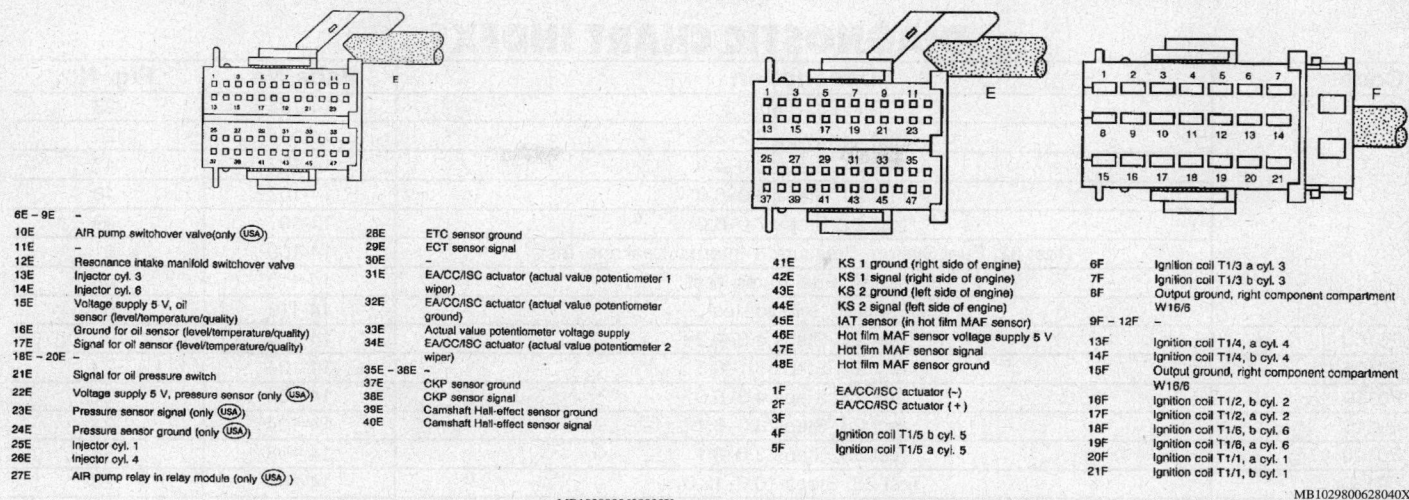

6E – 9E	–
10E	AIR pump switchover valve(only USA)
11E	–
12E	Resonance intake manifold switchover valve
13E	Injector cyl. 3
14E	Injector cyl. 6
15E	Voltage supply 5 V, oil sensor (level/temperature/quality)
16E	Ground for oil sensor (level/temperature/quality)
17E	Signal for oil sensor (level/temperature/quality)
18E – 20E	–
21E	Signal for oil pressure switch
22E	Voltage supply 5 V, pressure sensor (only USA)
23E	Pressure sensor signal (only USA)
24E	Pressure sensor ground (only USA)
25E	Injector cyl. 1
26E	Injector cyl. 4
27E	AIR pump relay in relay module (only USA)
28E	ETC sensor ground
29E	ECT sensor signal
30E	–
31E	EA/CC/ISC actuator (actual value potentiometer 1 wiper)
32E	EA/CC/ISC actuator (actual value potentiometer ground)
33E	Actual value potentiometer voltage supply
34E	EA/CC/ISC actuator (actual value potentiometer 2 wiper)
35E – 36E	–
37E	CKP sensor ground
38E	CKP sensor signal
39E	Camshaft Hall-effect sensor ground
40E	Camshaft Hall-effect sensor signal

MB1029800628030X

Fig. 15 Engine control module connector (Part 3 of 4)

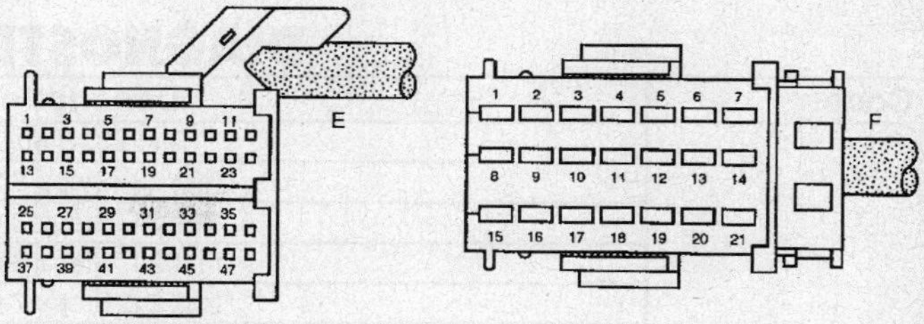

41E	KS 1 ground (right side of engine)
42E	KS 1 signal (right side of engine)
43E	KS 2 ground (left side of engine)
44E	KS 2 signal (left side of engine)
45E	IAT sensor (in hot film MAF sensor)
46E	Hot film MAF sensor voltage supply 5 V
47E	Hot film MAF sensor signal
48E	Hot film MAF sensor ground
1F	EA/CC/ISC actuator (–)
2F	EA/CC/ISC actuator (+)
3F	–
4F	Ignition coil T1/5 b cyl. 5
5F	Ignition coil T1/5 a cyl. 5
6F	Ignition coil T1/3 a cyl. 3
7F	Ignition coil T1/3 b cyl. 3
8F	Output ground, right component compartment W16/6
9F – 12F	–
13F	Ignition coil T1/4, a cyl. 4
14F	Ignition coil T1/4, b cyl. 4
15F	Output ground, right component compartment W16/6
16F	Ignition coil T1/2, b cyl. 2
17F	Ignition coil T1/2, a cyl. 2
18F	Ignition coil T1/6, b cyl. 6
19F	Ignition coil T1/6, a cyl. 6
20F	Ignition coil T1/1, a cyl. 1
21F	Ignition coil T1/1, b cyl. 1

MB1029800628040X

Fig. 15 Engine control module connector (Part 4 of 4)

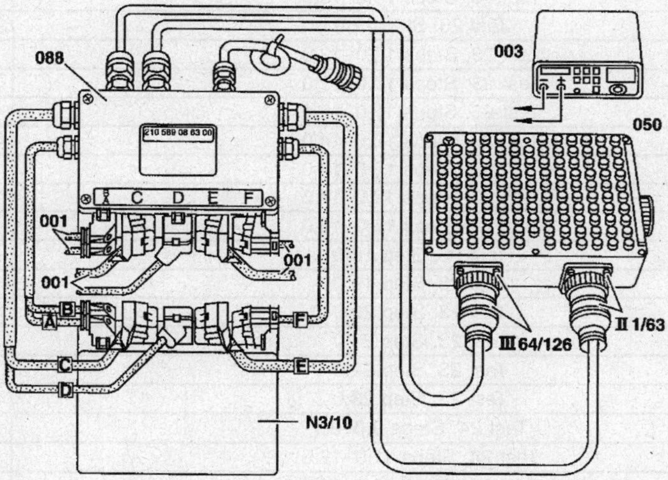

001	Engine control module connectors
003	Digital multimeter
050	Socket box (126-pole)
088	Test cable
N3/10	Engine control module (ME-SFI)

MB1029800627000X

Fig. 16 Test connections

DIAGNOSTIC CHART INDEX

Code	Description	Page No.	Fig. No.
—	Test 23, Step 7.0	14-104	23
	Test 23, Steps 8.2–9.0	14-104	25
	Test 24, Steps 3.0–4.0	14-107	47
	Test 24, Steps 5.0–6.0	14-107	48
	Test 24, Steps 7.0–8.0	14-107	49
	Test 32, Fuel System Pressure & Internal Leakage Test	14-109	61
	Test 34, Fuel Pump Test	14-110	63
	Test 36, Injector test	14-110	65
P0100	Test 23, Steps 4.0–4.2	14-104	20
P0105	Test 23, Steps 5.1–6.0	14-104	22
P0110	Test 23, Steps 4.3–5.0	14-104	21
P0115	Test 23, Steps 8.0–8.1	14-104	24
P0120	Test 25, Steps 3.0–3.1	14-108	58
P0130	Test 23, Steps 10.0–12.0	14-105	26
P0133	Test 23, Steps 10.0–12.0	14-105	26
P0135	Test 23, Steps 10.0–12.0	14-105	26
	Test 23, Steps 12.0–14.0	14-105	27
P0136	Test 23, Steps 15.0–16.0	14-105	28
P0141	Test 23, Step 17.0	14-105	29
P0150	Test 23, Steps 10.0–12.0	14-105	26
P0153	Test 23, Steps 10.0–12.0	14-105	26
P0155	Test 23, Steps 10.0–12.0	14-105	26
	Test 23, Steps 12.0–14.0	14-105	27
P0156	Test 23, Steps 12.0–14.0	14-105	27
P0160	Test 23, Steps 12.0–14.0	14-105	27
P0161	Test 23, Steps 15.0–16.0	14-105	28
P0201	Test 23, Step 18.0	14-105	30
P0202	Test 23, Step 19.0	14-105	31
P0203	Test 23, Step 20.0	14-105	32
P0204	Test 23, Step 21.0	14-105	33
P0205	Test 23, Step 22.0	14-105	34
P0206	Test 23, Step 23.0	14-106	35
P0335	Test 24, Steps 9.0–9.1	14-107	50
P0300	Test 24, Steps 11.0–12.0	14-108	52
	Test 24, Steps 12.1–13.1	14-108	53
	Test 24, Steps 14.0–15.0	14-108	54
	Test 24, Steps 15.1–16.1	14-108	55
	Test 24, Step 17.0	14-108	56
P0301	Test 24, Steps 11.0–12.0	14-108	52
	Test 24, Step 17.0	14-108	56
P0302	Test 24, Steps 11.0–12.0	14-108	52
	Test 24, Step 17.0	14-108	56
P0303	Test 24, Steps 12.1–13.1	14-108	53
	Test 24, Step 17.0	14-108	56
P0304	Test 24, Steps 14.0–15.0	14-108	54
	Test 24, Step 17.0	14-108	56
P0305	Test 24, Steps 14.0–15.0	14-108	54
	Test 24, Step 17.0	14-108	56
P0306	Test 24, Steps 15.1–16.1	14-108	55
	Test 24, Step 17.0	14-108	56
P0341	Test 24, Steps 10.0–10.1	14-108	51
P0400	Test 23, Step 27.0	14-106	38
P0410	Test 23, Step 26.0	14-106	37
P0440	Test 23, Steps 30.0–31.0	14-106	40
P0441	Test 23, Steps 28.0–29.0	14-106	39
	Test 23, Steps 30.0–31.0	14-106	40
P0442	Test 23, Steps 30.0–31.0	14-106	40

Continued

DIAGNOSTIC CHART INDEX—Continued

Code	Description	Page No.	Fig. No.
P0443	Test 23, Steps 28.0–29.0	14-106	39
P0446	Test 23, Steps 32.0–33.1	14-106	41
P0450	Test 23, Steps 32.0–33.1	14-106	41
P0455	Test 23, Steps 30.0–31.0	14-106	40
	Test 23, Steps 32.0–33.1	14-106	41
P0507	Test 25, Steps 1.0–2.1	14-108	57
	Test 25, Steps 3.0–3.1	14-108	58
P0560	Test 23, Steps 1.0–1.1	14-104	17
	Test 23, Steps 1.2–2.2	14-104	18
	Test 24, Steps 1.0–1.1	14-107	45
	Test 24, Steps 1.2–2.2	14-107	46
P0600	Test 23, Steps 34.0–34.2	14-106	42
P0801	Test 23, Steps 36.0–37.0	14-107	44
P0802	Test 23, Steps 28.0–29.0	14-106	39
P1177	Test 23, Steps 35.0–35.1	14-107	43
P1178	Test 23, Steps 35.0–35.1	14-107	43
P1179	Test 23, Steps 35.0–35.1	14-107	43
P1180	Test 23, Steps 35.0–35.1	14-107	43
P1182	Test 23, Steps 3.0–3.1	14-104	19
P1185	Test 23, Steps 35.0–35.1	14-107	43
P1186	Test 25, Steps 3.0–3.1	14-108	58
	Test 25, Steps 4.0–5.0	14-109	59
P1400	Test 23, Step 27.0	14-106	38
P1420	Test 23, Steps 24.0–25.0	14-106	36
P1453	Test 23, Steps 24.0–25.0	14-106	36
P1542	Test 25, Steps 1.0–2.1	14-108	57
P1570	Test 23, Steps 34.0–34.2	14-106	42
P1580	Test 25, Steps 3.0–3.1	14-108	58
	Test 25, Steps 4.0–5.0	14-109	59
P1747	Test 23, Steps 34.0–34.2	14-106	42

⇒		Test scope	Test connection	Test condition	Nominal value	Possible cause/remedy
1.0	P0 560	**Engine control module (ME-SFI) (N3/10)** Voltage supply Circuit 30 U	N3/10 3 (3A) –V– 12 (4B)	Ignition: **ON**	11 – 14 V	⇒ 1.1
1.1		Ground wire, Output ground	N3/10 3 (3A) –V– X11/4 2 7 (7A) –V– X11/4 2 112 (8F) –V– X11/4 2 119 (15F) –V– X11/4 2	Ignition: **ON**	11 – 14 V	Wiring, **Models 202, 208, 210:** Output ground (W16/6), right component compartment. **Model 163:** Ground (W16), component compartment. ⇒ 1.2

MB1029800629000X

Fig. 17 Code P0560: Test 23, Steps 1.0–1.1

⇒		Test scope	Test connection	Test condition	Nominal value	Possible cause/remedy
3.0	P1 182	**Starter relay** **Models 202, 208, 210:** **(K40/4k2) in passenger-side fuse and relay module box (K40/4)** **Model 163:** **(F1k8) in fuse and relay box** Activation	N3/10 35 (8A) –V– 2 (2A)	ECT temperature > 20 °C Vehicle with AT Ignition/starter switch (S2/1): position 3 (start position): crank engine **briefly**	11 – 14 V or if engine does not start in approx. 5 seconds.	⇒ 3.1, Engine control module (N3/10)
3.1		**Starter signal circuit 50**	N3/10 8 (8A) –V– 32 (40C)	Engine: **Start**	11 – 14 V while starting.	Wiring, Ignition/starter switch (S2/1)

MB1029800631000X

Fig. 19 Code P1182: Test 23, Steps 3.0–3.1

⇒		Test scope	Test connection	Test condition	Nominal value	Possible cause/remedy
4.3		**Hot film MAF sensor (B2/5)** Voltage supply 12 V	N3/10 104 (48E) –V– B2/5 2 (2)	Disconnect MAF sensor (B2/5) connector and connect plus of voltmeter to socket 2 (red/blue). Ignition: **ON**	11 – 14 V	Wiring, Passenger-side fuse and relay module (K40/4). or Fuse and relay box (F1f11).
5.0	P0 110	**IAT sensor in hot film MAF sensor (B2/5)** Voltage	N3/10 104 (48E) –V– 101 (45E)	Ignition: **ON**	°C V 10 3.1 20 2.7 30 2.2 40 1.8 50 1.4 60 1.1 ± 5%	⇒ 5.1 N3/10

MB1029800633000X

Fig. 21 Code P0110: Test 23, Steps 4.3–5.0

⇒		Test scope	Test connection	Test condition	Nominal value	Possible cause/remedy
7.0		**FP relay module** **Models 202/208/210: (K27)** **Model 163:** **(F1k3) in fuse and relay box** Activation	N3/10 21 (29C) –V– 2 (2A)	Ignition: **ON**	11 – 14 V for approx. 1 sec. 3)	Wiring, K27 or F1k3, N3/10
				Engine: **Start**	11 – 14 V during cranking and while engine runs.	
		Current draw (K27) or (F1k3)	N3/10 8 (8A) –A– 21 (29C)	Ignition: **ON**	0.1 – 0.3 A	

MB1029800635000X

Fig. 23 Code —: Test 23, Step 7.0

⇒		Test scope	Test connection	Test condition	Nominal value	Possible cause/remedy
8.0	P0 115	**ECT sensor (B11/4)** Voltage	N3/10 84 (28E) –V– 85 (29E)	Ignition: **ON**	°C V 20 3.4 30 2.9 40 2.4 50 1.9 60 1.5 70 1.2 80 0.9 90 0.7 100 0.5 ±5 %	⇒ 8.1, N3/10
8.1		Resistance (B11/4)	N3/10 84 (28E) –Ω– 85 (29E)	Ignition: **OFF** Disconnect connector **E** on engine control module (N3/10).	°C Ω 20 3090 30 2000 40 1330 50 900 60 620 70 440 80 320 90 230 100 170 ±5 %	⇒ 8.2, Wiring.

MB1029800636000X

Fig. 24 Code P0115: Test 23, Steps 8.0–8.1

⇒		Test scope	Test connection	Test condition	Nominal value	Possible cause/remedy
1.2		Voltage supply Circuit 30	N3/10 X11/4 1 –V– 12 (4B)	Ignition: **ON**	11 – 14 V	Wiring, Passenger-side fuse and relay module (K40/4). or Fuse and relay box (F1).
2.0	P0 560	**Engine control module (ME-SFI) (N3/10)** Voltage supply Circuit 87 U	N3/10 8 (8A) –V– 2 (2A)	Ignition: **ON**	11 – 14 V	⇒ 2.1 – 2.2
2.1		Electronics ground	N3/10 8 (8A) –V– X11/4 2	Ignition: **ON**	11 – 14 V	Wiring, **Models 202, 208, 210** Output ground (W16/6), right component compartment. **Model 163:** Ground (W16), component compartment.
2.2		Voltage supply Circuit 87	N3/10 X11/4 1 –V– 12 (2A)	Ignition: **ON** **Model 163:** Connect socket 4 to 16-pole test connector	11 – 14 V	Wiring, Passenger-side fuse and relay module (K40/4). or Fuse and relay box (F1).
				Ignition: **OFF**	< 1 V	

MB1029800630000X

Fig. 18 Code P0560: Test 23, Steps 1.2–2.2

⇒		Test scope	Test connection	Test condition	Nominal value	Possible cause/remedy
4.0	P0 100	**Hot film MAF sensor (B2/5)** Hot film signal	N3/10 104 (48E) –V– 103 (47E)	Ignition: **ON** Engine: **at idle** Engine coolant temperature >70°C	0.9 – 1.1 V 1.3 – 1.7 V 2)	⇒ 4.1 – 4.3, Wiring, Air intake system leak, B2/5
4.1		**Hot film MAF sensor (B2/5)** Voltage supply 5 V	N3/10 104 (48E) –V– B2/5 4	Disconnect MAF sensor (B2/5) connector and measure directly on socket 4 (brown/yellow). Ignition: **ON**	4.7 – 5.2 V	Wiring, N3/10
4.2		**Ground wire for hot film MAF sensor (B2/5)**	B2/5 3 –V– N3/10 102 (46E)	Disconnect MAF sensor (B2/5) connector and measure directly on socket 3 (brown). Ignition: **ON**	4.7 – 5.2 V	Wiring.

MB1029800632000X

Fig. 20 Code P0100: Test 23, Steps 4.0–4.2

⇒		Test scope	Test connection	Test condition	Nominal value	Possible cause/remedy
5.1		IAT sensor Resistance	N3/10 104 (48E) –Ω– 101 (45E)	Ignition: **OFF** Disconnect connector **E** on engine control module (N3/10).	oC Ω 10 3600 20 2420 30 1660 40 1170 50 850 60 600 ± 5%	B2/5
6.0	P0 105	**Only (USA)** **Pressure sensor (B28)** Sensor signal	N3/10 80 (24E) –V– 79 (23E)	Connect vacuum tester to pressure sensor (B28) using Y-fitting		Vacuum line, Wiring, B28, N3/10
				Ignition: **ON**	> 3.5 V	
				Engine: **at idle**	< 2 V and vacuum climbs to > 500 mbar.	
		Pressure sensor (B28) Voltage supply	N3/10 80 (24E) –V– 78 (22E)	Ignition: **ON**	4.7 – 5.3 V	

MB1029800634000X

Fig. 22 Code P0105: Test 23, Steps 5.1–6.0

⇒		Test scope	Test connection	Test condition	Nominal value	Possible cause/remedy
8.2		ECT sensor (B11/4) Resistance	B11/4 1 –Ω– 2	Disconnect connector on ECT sensor (B11/4).	Nominal value, see ⇒ 8.1	B11/4
9.0		**Engine control module (N3/10)** TN-signal output	N3/10 3) 8 (8A) –⊕– 30 (38C)	Engine: **Start** or Engine: **at idle**	Signal	Wiring, N3/10
			N3/10 4) 8 (8A) –V– 30 (38C)		7.5 – 9.0 V	

MB1029800637000X

Fig. 25 Code —: Test 23, Steps 8.2–9.0

⇒		Test scope	Test connection	Test condition	Nominal value	Possible cause/remedy
10.0	P0 150 P0 153	**Left O2S 1** **(before TWC) (G3/3)** O2S signal	N3/10 26 (34C) — V — 25 (33C)	ECT > 80 ° C, run engine at idle for at least two minutes.	fluctuates from – 0.2 V to + 1.0 V, by more than 0.3 V	⇒ 12.0, Wiring, G3/3
11.0	P0 130 P0 133	**Right O2S 1** **(before TWC) (G3/4)** O2S signal	N3/10 23 (31C) — V — 24 (32C)	ECT > 80 ° C, run engine at idle for at least two minutes.	fluctuates from – 0.2 V to + 1.0 V, by more than 0.3 V	⇒ 13.0, Wiring, G3/4
12.0	P0 135 P0 155	**Left O2S 1** **(before TWC) (G3/3)** O2S heater Activation	N3/10 1 (1A) — V — 2 (2A)	Engine: **at idle** ECT > 80° C, run engine at idle for at least 2 minutes.	11 – 14 V	Wiring, G3/3, N3/10
		O2S 1 (G3/3) Current draw	N3/10 3 (3A) — A — 1 (1A)	Disconnect connector **A** on engine control module N3/10 Ignition: **ON**	1.5 – 4.5 A	

MB1029800638000X

Fig. 26 Codes P0130, P0133, P0135, P0150, P0153 & P0155: Test 23, Steps 10.0–12.0

⇒		Test scope	Test connection	Test condition	Nominal value	Possible cause/remedy
15.0	P0 136	**Only (USA)** **Right O2S 2** **(after TWC) (G3/6)** O2S signal	N3/10 39 (7D) — V — 40 (8D)	ECT > 80° C, run engine at 2000-3000 rpm for approx. 2 minutes.		⇒ 17.0, Wiring, G3/6, N3/10
			N3/10 3 (3A) — — 60 (10E) 3 (3A) — — 20 (28C)	Engine: **at idle** Bridge sockets on socket box.	> 550mV Air pump runs. Voltage changes within 60 seconds to < 40 mV	
16.0	P0 161	**Only (USA)** **Left O2S 2** **(after TWC) (G3/5)** O2S heater Activation	N3/10 10 (2B) — V — 2 (2A)	Engine: **at idle** ECT > 80° C, run engine at idle for at least 2 minutes.	11 – 14 V or voltage fluctuates between 1 – 14 V.	Wiring, G3/5, N3/10
		O2S 2 (G3/5) Current draw	N3/10 3 (3A) — A — 10 (2B)	Disconnect connector **B** on engine control module N3/10 Ignition: **ON**	1.5 – 4.5 A	

MB1029800640000X

Fig. 28 Codes P0136 & P0161: Test 23, Steps 15.0–16.0

⇒		Test scope	Test connection	Test condition	Nominal value	Possible cause/remedy
18.0	P0 201	**Injector (Y62y1)** Activation and injection time	N3/10 81 (25E) — — 2 (2A)	**ECT approx. 20° C** at start **ECT approx. 80° C** at idle accelerate briefly	Injection time: approx. 8 ms approx. 3 – 5 ms approx. 14 ms signal	Wiring, Y62y1, N3/10, **Further possibilities:** ECT sensor (B11/4), IAT sensor in hot film MAF sensor (B2/5), O2S 1 (G3/3 or G3/4).
		Resistance (Y62y1)	N3/10 81 (25E) — Ω — 2 (2A)	Ignition: **OFF**	14 – 18 Ω	

MB1029800642000X

Fig. 30 Code P0201: Test 23, Step 18.0

⇒		Test scope	Test connection	Test condition	Nominal value	Possible cause/remedy
20.0	P0 203	**Injector (Y62y3)** Activation and injection time	N3/10 69 (13E) — — 2 (2A)	**ECT approx. 20° C** at start **ECT approx. 80° C** at idle accelerate briefly	Injection time: approx. 8 ms approx. 3 – 5 ms approx. 14 ms signal	Wiring, Y62y3, N3/10 **Further possibilities:** ECT sensor (B11/4), IAT sensor in hot film MAF sensor (B2/5), O2S 1 (G3/3 or G3/4).
		Resistance (Y62y3)	N3/10 69 (13E) — Ω — 2 (2A)	Ignition: **OFF**	14 – 18 Ω	

MB1029800644000X

Fig. 32 Code P0203: Test 23, Step 20.0

⇒		Test scope	Test connection	Test condition	Nominal value	Possible cause/remedy
13.0	P0 135 P0 155	**Right O2S 1** **(after TWC) (G3/4)** O2S heater Activation	N3/10 5 (5A) — V — 2 (2A)	Engine: **at idle** ECT > 80° C, run engine at idle for at least 2 minutes.	11 – 14 V	Wiring, G3/4, N3/10
		O2S 2 (G3/4) Current draw	N3/10 3 (3A) — A — 5 (5A)	Disconnect connector **A** on engine control module N3/10 Ignition: **ON**	1.5 – 4.5 A	
14.0	P0 156 P0 160	**Only (USA)** **Left O2S 2** **(after TWC) (G3/5)** O2S signal	N3/10 42 (10D) — V — 41 (9D)	ECT > 80° C, run engine at 2000-3000 rpm for approx. 2 minutes.		⇒ 16.0, Wiring, G3/5, N3/10
			N3/10 3 (3A) — — 66 (10E) 3 (3A) — — 20 (28C)	Engine: **at idle** Bridge sockets on socket box.	> 550mV Air pump runs. Voltage changes within 60 seconds to < 40 mV	

MB1029800639000X

Fig. 27 Codes P0135, P0155, P0156 & P0160: Test 23, Steps 13.0–14.0

⇒		Test scope	Test connection	Test condition	Nominal value	Possible cause/remedy
17.0	P0 141	**Only (USA)** **Right O2S 2** **(after TWC) (G3/6)** O2S heater Activation	N3/10 9 (1B) — V — 2 (2A)	Engine: **at idle** ECT > 80° C, run engine at idle for at least 2 minutes.	11 – 14 V or voltage fluctuates between 1 – 14 V.	Wiring, G3/6, N3/10
		O2S 2 (G3/6) Current draw	N3/10 3 (3A) — A — 9 (1B)	Disconnect connector **B** on engine control module Ignition: **ON**	1.5 – 4.5 A	

MB1029800641000X

Fig. 29 Code P0141: Test 23, Step 17.0

⇒		Test scope	Test connection	Test condition	Nominal value	Possible cause/remedy
19.0	P0 202	**Injector (Y62y2)** Activation and injection time	N3/10 57 (1E) — — 2 (2A)	**ECT approx. 20° C** at start **ECT approx. 80° C** at idle accelerate briefly	Injection time: approx. 8 ms approx. 3 – 5 ms approx. 14 ms	Wiring, Y62y2, N3/10, **Further possibilities:** ECT sensor (B11/4), IAT sensor in hot film MAF sensor (B2/5), O2S 1 (G3/3 or G3/4).
		Resistance (Y62y2)	N3/10 57 (1E) — Ω — 2 (2A)	Ignition: **OFF**	14 – 18 Ω	

MB1029800643000X

Fig. 31 Code P0202: Test 23, Step 19.0

⇒		Test scope	Test connection	Test condition	Nominal value	Possible cause/remedy
21.0	P0 204	**Injector (Y62y4)** Activation and injection time	N3/10 82 (26E) — — 2 (2A)	**ECT approx. 20° C** at start **ECT approx. 80° C** at idle accelerate briefly	Injection time: approx. 8 ms approx. 3 – 5 ms approx. 14 ms	Wiring, Y62y4, N3/10 **Further possibilities:** ECT sensor (B11/4), IAT sensor in hot film MAF sensor (B2/5), O2S 1 (G3/3 or G3/4).
		Resistance (Y62y4)	N3/10 82 (26E) — Ω — 2 (2A)	Ignition: **OFF**	14 – 18 Ω	

MB1029800645000X

Fig. 33 Code P0204: Test 23, Step 21.0

⇒		Test scope	Test connection	Test condition	Nominal value	Possible cause/remedy
22.0	P0 205	**Injector (Y62y5)** Activation and injection time	N3/10 58 (2E) — — 2 (2A)	**ECT approx. 20° C** at start **ECT approx. 80° C** at idle accelerate briefly	Injection time: approx. 8 ms approx. 3 – 5 ms approx. 14 ms	Wiring, Y62y5, N3/10 **Further possibilities:** ECT sensor (B11/4), IAT sensor in hot film MAF sensor (B2/5), O2S 1 (G3/3 or G3/4).
		Resistance (Y62y5)	N3/10 58 (26E) — Ω — 2 (2A)	Ignition: **OFF**	14 – 18 Ω	

MB1029800646000X

Fig. 34 Code P0205: Test 23, Step 22.0

⇒		Test scope	Test connection	Test condition	Nominal value	Possible cause/remedy
23.0	P0 206	**Injector (Y62y6)** Activation and injection time	N3/10 70 (14E) —(⊕)— 2 (2A)	**ECT approx. 20° C** at start **ECT approx. 80° C** at idle accelerate briefly	Injection time: approx. 8 ms approx. 3 – 5 ms approx. 14 ms	Wiring, Y62y6, N3/10 **Further possibilities:** ECT sensor (B11/4), IAT sensor in hot film MAF sensor (B2/5), O2S 1 (G3/3 or G3/4).
		Resistance (Y62y6)	N3/10 70 (14E) —(Ω)— 2 (2A)	Ignition: **OFF**	14 – 18 Ω	

MB1029800647000X

Fig. 35 Code P0206: Test 23, Step 23.0

⇒		Test scope	Test connection	Test condition	Nominal value	Possible cause/remedy
24.0	P1 453	**Only (USA)** **AIR relay module** **Models 202/208/210: (K17), In Passenger-side fuse and relay module box (K40/4)** **Model 163: In fuse and relay box (F1k28)** Activation	N3/10 20 (28C) —(V)— 2 (2A)	Disconnect ECT sensor (B11/4) connector. Simulate 2.5 kΩ resistance at sockets 1 and 2 with resistance substitution unit. Engine: **at idle**	11 – 14 V for approx. two minutes **and** AIR pump runs.	Wiring, K40/4 or F1k28, N3/10
		Current draw (K40/4) or (F1k28)	N3/10 3 (3A) —(A)— 20 (28C)	Ignition: **ON**	0.1 – 0.3 A	
25.0	P1 420	**Only (USA)** **AIR pump switchover valve (Y32)** Activation	N3/10 66 (10E) —(V)— 2 (2A)	Disconnect ECT sensor (B11/4) connector. Simulate 2.5 kΩ resistance at sockets 1 and 2 with resistance substitution unit. Engine: **at idle**	11 – 14 V for approx. two minutes **and** AIR pump runs.	Wiring, Y32, N3/10
		Current draw (Y32)	N3/10 3 (3A) —(A)— 66 (10E)	Ignition: **ON**	0.3 – 0.5 A	

MB1029800648000X

Fig. 36 Codes P1420 & P1453: Test 23, Steps 24.0–25.0

⇒		Test scope	Test connection	Test condition	Nominal value	Possible cause/remedy
26.0	P0 410	**Only (USA)** **AIR system** (logic chain)	N3/10 23 (31C) —(V)— 24 (32C)	**Note:** The O2S 1 signal before TWC is measured. With ETC > 80°C run engine at idle for at least 2 minutes.	The O2S voltage oscillates in the area of –0.2 V and +1.0 V	Y32 binding, AIR combi valve, AIR pump no output.
			N3/10 3 (3A) ←→ 66 (10E) 3 (3A) ←→ 20 (28C)	Bridge sockets on socket box	AIR pump runs. Voltage changes to < 100 mV within 20 seconds	

MB1029800649000X

Fig. 37 Code P0410: Test 23, Step 26.0

⇒		Test scope	Test connection	Test condition	Nominal value	Possible cause/remedy
27.0	P0 400 P1 400	**EGR valve vacuum transducer (Y31/1)** Activation and vacuum control	N3/10 61 (5E) —(V)— 2 (2A)	**Note regarding test:** This test is not possible on models 163 and 210 **4MATIC** **Note to test connection:** Connect vacuum tester to EGR valve vacuum transducer, after removing the MAF sensor with air box. **Engine: at idle** ETC > 60°C	< 1 V and < 10 mbar vacuum.	Wiring, N3/10, Y31/1
		Current draw (Y31/1)	N3/10 3 (3A) —(A)— 61 (5E)	**Vehicle at approx. 3000/rpm while on dynamometer** Ignition: **ON**	1 – 7 V and 80 – 220 mbar vacuum. 0.3 – 0.5 A	

MB1029800650000X

Fig. 38 Codes P0400 & P1400: Test 23, Step 27.0

⇒		Test scope	Test connection	Test condition	Nominal value	Possible cause/remedy
28.0	P0 802	**Resonance intake manifold switchover valve (Y22/6)** Activation	N3/10 68 (12E) —(V)— 2 (2A)	Engine: **Start** Engine: at idle Engine: accelerate briefly to > approx. 3900 rpm	< 1 V 9 – 14 V and vacuum applied to valve.	Wiring, Y22/6, N3/10
		Current draw (Y22/6)	N3/10 3 (3A) —(A)— 68 (12E)	Ignition: **ON**	0.3 – 0.5 A	
29.0	P0 441 P0 443	**Purge control valve (Y58/1)** Activation	N3/10 13 (21C) —(⊕)— 2 (2A)	Engine: **at idle** and at operating temperature.	After approx. 2 minutes, purge control valve (Y58/1) must noticeably cycle.	⇒ 30.0, Wiring, Y58/1, N3/10
		Current draw (Y58/1)	N3/10 3 (3A) —(A)— 13 (21C)	Ignition: **ON**	0.2 – 0.4 A	

MB1029800651000X

Fig. 39 Codes P0441, P0443 & P0802: Test 23, Steps 28.0–29.0

⇒		Test scope	Test connection	Test condition	Nominal value	Possible cause/remedy
30.0	P0 440 P0 441	**Purge control valve (Y58/1)** Vacuum control		Connect vacuum tester to purge control valve (Y58/1) between purge line to charcoal canister. Engine at operating temperature and at idle.	After approx. 2 minute, > 50 mbar and needle oscillates, Y58/1 must cycle.	Vacuum line, Y58/1
31.0	P0 440 P0 442 P0 455	**Only (USA)** **Purge system** Leaks Activated charcoal canister shut-off valve (Y58/4) activated	N3/10 3 (3A) ←→ 34 (2D)	Disconnect purge line (A) to charcoal canister on purge control valve (Y58/1). Connect vacuum tester to purge line. Ignition: **ON** Apply approx. 25 mbar of vacuum.	After approx. 1 minute, < 5 mbar vacuum loss.	Fuel tank cap, Purge line to charcoal canister, Purge line from charcoal canister to Y58/4, Charcoal canister, Y58/1, Y58/4

MB1029800652000X

Fig. 40 Codes P0440, P0441, P0442 & P0455: Test 23, Steps 30.0–31.0

⇒		Test scope	Test connection	Test condition	Nominal value	Possible cause/remedy
32.0	P0 446	**Only (USA)** **Activated charcoal canister shut-off valve (Y58/4)** Current draw	N3/10 3 (3A) —(A)— 34 (2D)	Ignition: **ON**	0.5 – 0.9 A	Wiring, Y58/4
33.0	P0 450 P0 455	**Only (USA)** **Fuel tank pressure sensor (B4/3)** Sender signal Activated charcoal canister shut-off valve (Y58/4) activated	N3/10 36 (4D) —(V)— 37 (5D) N3/10 3 (3A) ←→ 34 (2D)	Disconnect purge line (A) to charcoal canister on purge control valve (Y58/1). Connect vacuum tester to purge line. Ignition: **ON** Apply approx. 25 mbar of vacuum.	> 2.9 V < 2.3 V	⇒ 33.1, Wiring, Vacuum line, Charcoal canister plugged, B4/3
33.1		**Only (USA)** Fuel tank pressure sensor (B4/3) Voltage supply	N3/10 36 (4D) —(V)— 38 (6D)	Ignition: **ON**	4.7 – 5.3 V	N3/10

MB1029800653000X

Fig. 41 Codes P0446, P0450 & P0455: Test 23, Steps 32.0–33.1

⇒		Test scope	Test connection	Test condition	Nominal value	Possible cause/remedy
34.0	P0 600 P1 570 P1 747	**CAN data bus**	N3/10 43 (11D) —(Ω)— 44 (12D)	Ignition: **OFF**	55 – 65 Ω	⇒ 34.1 – 34.2 Data line.
34.1		**CAN element in DAS control module (N54/1)** Resistance	N3/10 43 (11D) —(Ω)— 44 (12D)	Ignition: **OFF** Disconnect connector **D** from engine control module N3/10.	115 – 125 Ω	Wiring, N54/1
34.2		**CAN element in engine control module (N3/10)** Resistance	N3/10 43 (11D) —(Ω)— 44 (12D)	Ignition: **OFF** Disconnect connector **D** from test cable and reconnect connector **D** to N3/10	115 – 125 Ω	N3/10

MB1029800654000X

Fig. 42 Codes P0600, P1570 & P1747: Test 23, Steps 34.0–34.2

⇒		Test scope	Test connection	Test condition	Nominal value	Possible cause/remedy
35.0	P1 177 P1 178 P1 179 P1 180 P1 185	**Oil sensor (level/ temperature/quality) (B40)**	N3/10[3] 72 (18E) — 73 (17E) N3/10[4] 72 (18E) — 73 (17E)	Test connection note regarding oscillascope: Range: 2V Duration: 50ms Ignition: **ON**	 0.3 – 3 V, voltage jumps	⇒ 35.1, oil level, oil quality, wiring, B40
35.1		Voltage supply (B40)	N3/10 72 (18E) — 71 (15E)	Ignition: **ON**	4.7 – 5.3 V	N3/10

3) Test with oscilloscope.
4) Test with multimeter only if oscilloscope is not available.

MB1029800655000X

Fig. 43 Codes P1177, P1178, P1179, P1180 & P1185: Test 23, Steps 35.0–35.1

⇒		Test scope	Test connection	Test condition	Nominal value	Possible cause/remedy
1.0	P0 560	**Engine control module (N3/10)** Voltage supply circuit 30	N3/10 3 (3A) — 12 (4B)	Ignition: **ON**	11 – 14 V	⇒ 1.1 – 1.2
1.1		Ground wire	N3/10 3 (3A) — X11/4 2 7 (7A) — X11/4 2 112 (8F) — X11/4 2 119 (15F) — X11/4 2	Ignition: **ON** **Model 163:** Connect socket 8 to 16-pole connector.	11 – 14 V	Wiring, **Model 202/208/210:** Output ground (W16/6), right component compartment. **Model 163:** Ground (W16), component compartment. ⇒ 1.2

MB1029800657000X

Fig. 45 Code P0560: Test 24, Steps 1.0–1.1

⇒		Test scope	Test connection	Test condition	Nominal value	Possible cause/remedy
3.0		**Ignition coil (T1/1)** Cylinder 1 Voltage supply Primary coil a Voltage supply Primary coil b	N3/10 3 (3A) — 124 (20F) N3/10 3 (3A) — 125 (21F)	Ignition: **ON**	11 – 14 V	Wiring, Fuses: Fuses in passenger-side fuse and relay module box (K40/4) or fuse and relay box (F1f26), Ignition coil (T1/1).
4.0		**Ignition coil (T1/2)** Cylinder 2 Voltage supply Primary coil a Voltage supply Primary coil b	N3/10 3 (3A) — 121 (17F) N3/10 3 (3A) — 120 (16F)	Ignition: **ON**	11 – 14 V	Wiring, Fuses: Fuses in passenger-side fuse and relay module box (K40/4) or fuse and relay box (F1f26), Ignition coil (T1/2).

MB1029800659000X

Fig. 47 Code —: Test 24, Steps 3.0–4.0

⇒		Test scope	Test connection	Test condition	Nominal value	Possible cause/remedy
7.0		**Ignition coil (T1/5)** Cylinder 5 Voltage supply Primary coil a Voltage supply Primary coil b	N3/10 3 (3A) — 109 (5F) N3/10 3 (3A) — 108 (4F)	Ignition: **ON**	11 – 14 V	Wiring, Fuses: Fuses in passenger-side fuse and relay module box (K40/4), or fuse and relay box (F1f26), Ignition coil (T1/5).
8.0		**Ignition coil (T1/6)** Cylinder 6 Voltage supply Primary coil a Voltage supply Primary coil b	N3/10 3 (3A) — 123 (19F) N3/10 3 (3A) — 122 (18F)	Ignition: **ON**	11 – 14 V	Wiring, Fuses: Fuses in passenger-side fuse and relay module box (K40/4) or fuse and relay box (F1f26), Ignition coil (T1/6).

MB1029800661000X

Fig. 49 Code —: Test 24, Steps 7.0–8.0

⇒		Test scope	Test connection	Test condition	Nominal value	Possible cause/remedy
36.0	P0 801	**With engine/climate control electric cooling fan only** **Engine/climate control electric cooling fan control module (N76)** Activation	N3/10 6 (6A) — 2 (2A)	Engine: **at idle** ECT < 70° C Ignition: **ON** A/C: **ON** ECT > 85° C	 1 – 1.9 V and cooling fan is stationary. 2 – 4 V and cooling fan runs. between 2.5 – 12.5 V and cooling fan speed is based on activation.	Wiring, N76, N3/10
37.0		**Diagnosis line** Activation	N3/10 3 (3A) — 31 (39C)	Ignition: **ON**	11 – 14 V	Wiring, N3/10

MB1029800656000X

Fig. 44 Code P0801: Test 23, Steps 36.0–37.0

⇒		Test scope	Test connection	Test condition	Nominal value	Possible cause/remedy
1.2		Voltage supply circuit 30	N3/10 X11/4 1 — 12 (4B)	Ignition: **ON** **Model 163:** Connect socket 4 to 16-pole connector.	11 – 14 V	Wiring, Passenger-side fuse and relay module box (K40/4) or Fuse and relay box (F1).
2.0	P0 560	**Engine control module (N3/10)** Voltage supply circuit 87	N3/10 8 (8A) — 2 (2A)	Ignition: **ON**	11 – 14 V	⇒ 2.1 – 2.2
2.1		Electronics ground	N3/10 8 (8A) — X11/4 2	Ignition: **ON**	11 – 14 V	Wiring, **Models 202/208/210:** Output ground (W16/6), right component compartment. **Model 163:** Ground (W16), component compartment.
2.2		Voltage supply circuit 87	N3/10 X11/4 1 — 2 (2A)	Ignition: **ON** **Model 163:** Connect socket 4 to 16-pole connector. Ignition: **OFF**	11 – 14 V < 1 V	Wiring, Passenger-side fuse and relay module box (K40/4) or fuse and relay box (F1f22).

MB1029800658000X

Fig. 46 Code P0560: Test 24, Steps 1.2–2.2

⇒		Test scope	Test connection	Test condition	Nominal value	Possible cause/remedy
5.0		**Ignition coil (T1/3)** Cylinder 3 Voltage supply Primary coil a Voltage supply Primary coil b	N3/10 3 (3A) — 110 (6F) N3/10 3 (3A) — 111 (7F)	Ignition: **ON**	11 – 14 V	Wiring, Fuses: Fuses in passenger-side fuse and relay module box (K40/4) or fuse and relay box (F1f26), Ignition coil (T1/3).
6.0		**Ignition coil (T1/4)** Cylinder 4 Voltage supply Primary coil a Voltage supply Primary coil b	N3/10 3 (3A) — 117 (13F) N3/10 3 (3A) — 118 (14F)	Ignition: **ON**	11 – 14 V	Wiring, Fuses: Fuses in passenger-side fuse and relay module box (K40/4) or fuse and relay box (F1f26) Ignition coil (T1/4)

MB1029800660000X

Fig. 48 Code —: Test 24, Steps 5.0–6.0

⇒		Test scope	Test connection	Test condition	Nominal value	Possible cause/remedy
9.0	P0 335	**CKP sensor (L5)** Signal Voltage	N3/10 2) 93 (37E) — 94 (38E) N3/10 3) 93 (37E) — 94 (38E)	Starter: **Crank** Engine: **at idle** Starter: **Crank** Engine: **at idle**	signal > 2.5 V~ > 5 V~ 4)	⇒ 9.1, Teeth on starter ring gear.
9.1		Resistance of CKP sensor (L5)	N3/10 93 (37E) — Ω — 94 (38E)	Ignition: **OFF** Unplug connector E on engine control module (N3/10).	700 – 1400 Ω	Wiring, L5

2) Test with oscilloscope.
3) Test with multimeter only if oscilloscope is unavailable.
4) Voltage increases with increasing rpm.

MB1029800662000X

Fig. 50 Code P0335: Test 24, Steps 9.0–9.1

⇒		Test scope	Test connection	Test condition	Nominal value	Possible cause/remedy
10.0	P0 341	**Camshaft Hall-effect sensor (B6/1)** Hall-effect signal Voltage	N3/10 2) 95 (39E) — 96 (40E) N3/10 3) 96 (40E) — 2 (2A)	Engine: **at idle** Engine: **at idle**	 1.2 – 2.2 V Value changes.	⇒ 10.1, Wiring, B6/1
10.1		Voltage supply to camshaft Hall-effect sensor (B6/1)	B6/1 1 — 3	Ignition: **ON** Disconnect connector from Hall-effect sensor (B6/1) and test directly on sockets 1 (brown/green) and 3 (red/blue) of connector.	11 – 14 V	Wiring.

2) Test with oscilloscope.
3) Test with multimeter only if oscilloscope is unavailable.

MB1029800663000X

Fig. 51 Code P0341: Test 24, Steps 10.0–10.1

⇒		Test scope	Test connection	Test condition	Nominal value	Possible cause/remedy
12.1		Primary winding of T1/2 Primary circuit a and b	N3/10 120 (16F) — 121 (17F)	Ignition: **OFF**	0.9 – 1.6 Ω 6)	Wiring, T1/2
13.0	P0 300 P0 303	**Primary voltage** Ignition coil (T1/3), Cylinder 3 Primary circuit a Primary circuit b	N3/10 110 (6F) — 2 (2A) N3/10 111 (7F) — 2 (2A)	**Test connection Note:** Individual primary pattern Range: 400 V Duration: 100% Starter: **Crank**	200 – 350 V	⇒ 13.1
13.1		Primary winding of T1/3 Primary circuit a and b	N3/10 110 (6F) — 111 (7F)	Ignition: **OFF**	0.9 – 1.6 Ω 6)	Wiring, T1/3

6) The resistance of a single coil at 20° C is approx. 0.6 Ω.

MB1029800665000X

Fig. 53 Codes P0300 & P0303: Test 24, Steps 12.1–13.1

⇒		Test scope	Test connection	Test condition	Nominal value	Possible cause/remedy
15.1		Primary winding of T1/5 Primary circuit a and b	N3/10 108 (4F) — 109 (5F)	Ignition: **OFF**	0.9 – 1.6 Ω 6)	Wiring, T1/5
16.0	P0 300 P0 306	**Primary voltage** Ignition coil (T1/6), Cylinder 6 Primary circuit a Primary circuit b	N3/10 123 (19F) — 2 (2A) N3/10 122 (18F) — 2 (2A)	**Test connection Note:** Individual primary pattern Range: 400 V Duration: 100% Starter: **Crank**	200 – 350 V	⇒ 16.1
16.1		Primary winding of T1/6 Primary circuit a and b	N3/10 122 (18F) — 123 (19F)	Ignition: **OFF**	0.9 – 1.6 Ω 6)	Wiring, T1/6

6) The resistance of a single coil at 20° C is approx. 0.6 Ω.

MB1029800667000X

Fig. 55 Codes P0300 & P0306: Test 24, Steps 15.1–16.1

⇒		Test scope	Test connection	Test condition	Nominal value	Possible cause/remedy
1.0	P1 542 P0 507	**Pedal value sensor (B37)** Signal Nominal value potentiometer 1	N3/10 15 (23C) — 16 (24C)	Ignition: **ON** Accelerator pedal position: CTP WOT with kick-down	 0.2 – 0.5 V 4.3 – 4.8 V	⇒ 1.1, Wiring, B37
1.1		Voltage supply Nominal value potentiometer 2 (Hall-sensor)	N3/10 15 (23C) — 14 (22C)	Ignition: **ON**	4.75 – 5.25 V	Wiring, N3/10
2.0	P1 542 P0 507	**Pedal value sensor (B37)** Signal Nominal value potentiometer 2	N3/10 18 (26C) — 17 (25C)	Ignition: **ON** Accelerator pedal position: CTP WOT with kick-down	 0.1 – 0.4 V 2.1 – 2.5 V	⇒ 2.1, Wiring, B37
2.1		Voltage supply Nominal value potentiometer 2 only up to 08/97 (without Hall-sensor)	N3/10 18 (26C) — 19 (27C)	Ignition: **ON**	2.25 – 2.75 V	Wiring, N3/10

MB1029800669000X

Fig. 57 Codes P0507 & P1542: Test 25, Steps 1.0–2.1

⇒		Test scope	Test connection	Test condition	Nominal value	Possible cause/remedy
11.0	P0 300 P0 301	**Primary voltage** Ignition coil (T1/1), Cylinder 1 Primary circuit a Primary circuit b	N3/10 124 (20F) — 2 (2A) N3/10 125 (21F) — 2 (2A)	**Test connection Note:** Individual primary pattern Range: 400 V Duration: 100% Starter: **Crank**	200 – 350 V	⇒ 11.1
11.1		Primary winding of T1/1 Primary circuit a and b	N3/10 124 (20F) — 125 (21F)	Ignition: **OFF**	0.9 – 1.6 Ω 6)	Wiring, T1/1
12.0	P0 300 P0 302	**Primary voltage** Ignition coil (T1/2), Cylinder 2 Primary circuit a Primary circuit b	N3/10 121 (17F) — 2 (2A) N3/10 120 (16F) — 2 (2A)	**Test connection Note:** Individual primary pattern Range: 400 V Duration: 100% Starter: **Crank**	200 – 350 V	⇒ 12.1

6) The resistance of a single coil at 20° C is approx. 0.6 Ω.

MB1029800664000X

Fig. 52 Codes P0300, P0301 & P0302: Test 24, Steps 11.0–12.0

⇒		Test scope	Test connection	Test condition	Nominal value	Possible cause/remedy
14.0	P0 300 P0 304	**Primary voltage** Ignition coil (T1/4), Cylinder 4 Primary circuit a Primary circuit b	N3/10 117 (13F) — 2 (2A) N3/10 118 (14F) — 2 (2A)	**Test connection Note:** Individual primary pattern Range: 400 V Duration: 100% Starter: **Crank**	200 – 350 V	⇒ 14.1
14.1		Primary winding of T1/4 Primary circuit a and b	N3/10 117 (13F) — 118 (14F)	Ignition: **OFF**	0.9 – 1.6 Ω 6)	Wiring, T1/4
15.0	P0 300 P0 305	**Primary voltage** Ignition coil (T1/5), Cylinder 5 Primary circuit a Primary circuit b	N3/10 109 (5F) — 2 (2A) N3/10 108 (4F) — 2 (2A)	**Test connection Note:** Individual primary pattern Range: 400 V Duration: 100% Starter: **Crank**	200 – 350 V	⇒ 15.1

6) The resistance of a single coil at 20° C is approx. 0.6 Ω.

MB1029800666000X

Fig. 54 Codes P0300, P0304 & P0305: Test 24, Steps 14.0–15.0

⇒		Test scope	Test connection	Test condition	Nominal value	Possible cause/remedy
17.0	P0 300 P0 301 P0 302 P0 303 P0 304 P0 305 P0 306	**Firing voltage** Ignition coil (T1/1) to (T1/6)	Engine analyzer	**Test connection Note:** Individual secondary pattern. Range: 20 kV Duration: 100% Connect kV pick-ups successively to T1/1 through T1/6. Starter: **Crank**	8 – 20 kV 7)	Spark plugs, N3/10

7) The resistance of the secondary winding can not be measured due to an installed diode.

MB1029800668000X

Fig. 56 Codes P0300, P0301, P0302, P0303, P0304, P0305 & P0306: Test 24, Step 17.0

⇒		Test scope	Test connection	Test condition	Nominal value	Possible cause/remedy
3.0	P0 507 P0 120 P1 186 P1 580	**EA/CC/ISC actuator (M16/6)** Signal Actual value potentiometer 1 Actual value potentiometer 2	N3/10 88 (32E) — 87 (31E) N3/10 88 (32E) — 90 (34E)	Ignition: **ON** Accelerator pedal position: CTP WOT or kick-down Accelerator pedal position: CTP WOT or kick-down	 4.0 – 4.6 V < CTP value 0.3 – 0.9 V > CTP value	⇒ 3.1, Wiring, M16/6
3.1		Voltage supply Actual value potentiometers 1 and 2	N3/10 88 (32E) — 89 (33E)	Ignition: **ON**	4.75 – 5.25 V	Wiring, N3/10

MB1029800670000X

Fig. 58 Codes P0120, P0507, P1186 & P1580: Test 25, Steps 3.0–3.1

⇒		Test scope	Test connection	Test condition	Nominal value	Possible cause/remedy
4.0	P1186 P1580	**EA/CC/ISC actuator (M16/6)** Activation of actuator motor	N3/10 105 (1F) — V — 106 (2F)	Ignition: **ON**	0.8 – 2.3 V	Wiring, M16/6, N3/10
				Engine: **at idle** ECT > 70 °C	1.0 – 2.5 V Value oscillates.	
		Actuator motor resistance	N3/10 105 (1F) — Ω — 106 (2F)	Ignition: **OFF**	< 10 Ω	
5.0		**With AT only** **P/N recognition**	N3/10 51 (19D) — V — 2 (2A)	Ignition: **ON** Selector lever position: P/N →	11 – 14 V	Wiring, Test ETC
				R, D, 4, 3, 2, 1 →	< 2.0 V	

MB1029800671000X

Fig. 59 Codes P1186 & P1580: Test 25, Steps 4.0–5.0

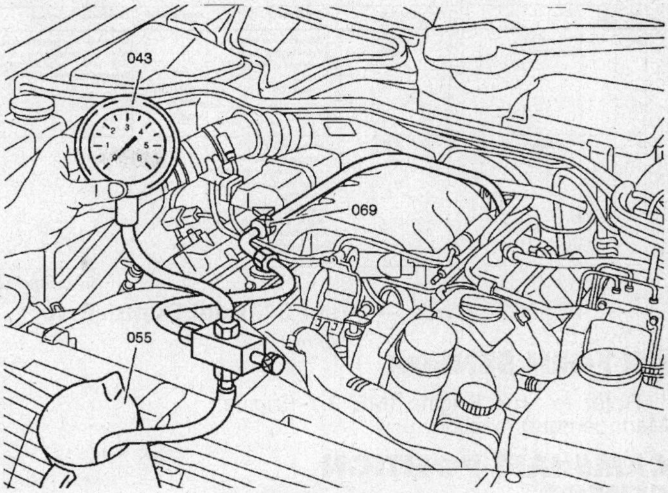

043 Pressure gauge, part no. 103 589 00 21 00
055 Measuring glass
069 Pressure hose, part no. 119 589 04 63 00

MB1029800672000X

Fig. 60 Fuel pressure connection

⇒		Test scope	Test connection	Test condition	Nominal value	Possible cause/remedy
1.0		**Fuel pressure at idle (with vacuum)**	Pressure gauge connected to test connection.	Engine: **at idle** Valve on pressure gauge closed.	3.7 – 4.2 bar	Check fuel pumps □ 34, Diaphragm pressure regulator.
2.0		**Fuel system internal leakage test**	Pressure gauge connected to test connection.	Engine: **OFF**	> 3.0 bar	If the pressure drops quickly: Replace check valve in fuel pumps.
				After 30 minutes	> 2.5 bar	If the pressure drops slowly: check injectors □ 36, Replace diaphragm pressure.

MB1029800673000X

Fig. 61 Code —: Test 32, Fuel System Pressure & Internal Leakage Test

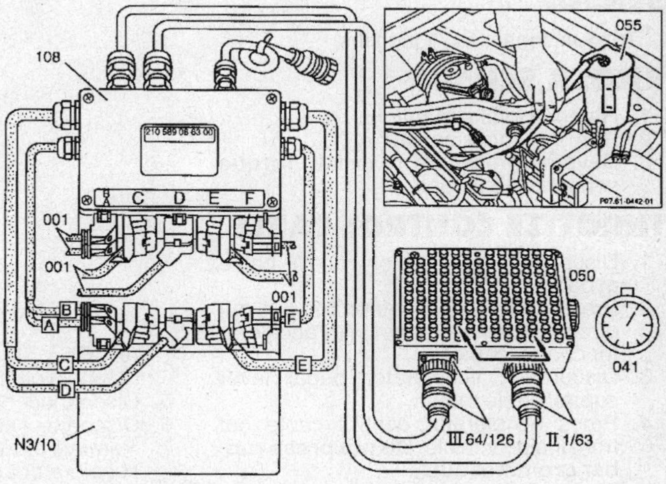

001 Engine control module connectors A–F
041 Stop watch
050 Socket box tester, 126 pole
055 Measuring glass
088 Test cable
N3/10 Engine control module (ME-SFI)

MB1029800674000X

Fig. 62 Fuel pump test connections

SYSTEM SERVICE

Component Replacement

FUEL RAIL

1. **On S430 and 1999–2001 SL500 and 2000–01 CL500 and S500 models,** remove engine face end trim panel.
2. **On all models,** remove cylinder head cover trim panel and resonance housing, then the plastic cover.
3. Release fuel pressure through service valve.
4. Disconnect feed pipe and electric connectors at injectors.
5. Remove mounting bolts and lift fuel rail with injectors from intake manifold.
6. Reverse procedure to install with new oiled oil rings. **Torque** fuel feed pipe to 28 ft. lbs.

FUEL INJECTOR

Refer to "104 Engine (ME 2.1 Engine Management)" section.

HOT FILM MASS AIR FLOW (MAF) SENSOR

C280, E320, E430 & ML320

1. Disconnect electronic accelerator actuator cable, push down on plate with suitable screwdriver and remove air intake manifold lock.
2. Remove righthand crankcase breather pipe and air cleaner.
3. Pull up and out on rubber bush, then remove resonance housing.
4. Remove mounting bolt and air intake pipe.
5. Disconnect electrical connection and remove hot film MAF sensor.
6. Reverse procedure to install.

S430 & 1999–2001 SL500 & 2000–01 CL500 & S500

1. Remove engine front face cover, then the air filter with intake pipes.
2. Disconnect electronic accelerator actuator cable.
3. Disconnect crankcase vent hose from air intake pipe.
4. Push down on air intake pipe lug and remove hot film MAF sensor.
5. Reverse procedure to install.

ML55 & ML430

1. Relieve cooling system pressure by removing reservoir cap.
2. Remove expansion reservoir overflow line, then the coolant lines. Collect spilling coolant in suitable container.
3. Disconnect connector and remove expansion reservoir.
4. Disconnect crankcase ventilation vacuum hose.
5. Disconnect air intake pipe from cylinder head cover.
6. Remove hot film MAF sensor mounting bolt.
7. Pressure air intake pipe lock down using suitable screwdriver and unhook pipe at top.
8. Remove resonance housing.
9. Disconnect connector and remove air intake pipe with MAF sensor.
10. Remove sensor.
11. Reverse procedure to install.

⇒		Test scope	Test connection	Test condition	Nominal value	Possible cause/remedy
1.0		**Fuel pump** Delivery capacity	N3/10 3 (3A) ←→ 21 (29C)	Disconnect fuel return hose from fuel line and place end in measuring glass. Ignition: **ON**	1 liter of fuel within 35 seconds.	Check fuel lines for restrictions (kinks and dents). Replace fuel filter or diaphragm pressure regulator, ⇒ 2.0
2.0		**Fuel pumps** Current draw		**Models 202/208/210:** Remove FP relay module (K27), connect multimeter on sockets 2 and 8. **Model 163:** Remove fuel pump relay (F1k3), connect multimeter on sockets 30 and 87. Ignition: **ON**	4 – 9 A	Fuel pump

MB1029800675000X

Fig. 63 Code —: Test 34, Fuel Pump Test

OXYGEN SENSOR

Refer to "104 Engine (ME 2.1 Engine Management)" section.

CAMSHAFT POSITION SENSOR

If O-ring is faulty, replace camshaft position sensor. **Torque** sensor to 71 inch lbs.

CRANKSHAFT POSITION SENSOR

Torque sensor to 71 inch lbs.

KNOCK SENSOR

1. Remove intake manifold.
2. Remove knock sensor.
3. Reverse procedure to install. **Torque** sensor to 15 ft. lbs.

THROTTLE CONTROL CABLE

1. Disconnect accelerator control cable at ball head.
2. Press plastic clip together and pull out of control lever bracket with accelerator control cable.
3. Disconnect accelerator pedal lever control cable mount.
4. Press accelerator control cable out from inside vehicle. **Do not press rubber grommet out.**
5. Remover control cable from engine compartment.
6. Reverse procedure to install. Adjust cable as outlined under "Adjustments."

ELECTRONIC ACCELERATOR ACTUATOR

1. **On C280, CLK320, E320, E430, ML55, ML320 and ML430 models,** remove cylinder head cover.
2. **On S430 and 1999–2001 SL500 and 2000–01 CL500 and S500 models,** remove engine front cover.
3. **On C43, CLK55, CLK430, E55 and S430 and 1999–2001 SL500 and 2000–01 CL500 and S500 models,** remove air cleaner housing.
4. **On all models,** remove hot film Mass Air Flow (MAF) sensor with intake manifold pipe.
5. Disconnect crankcase ventilation line.
6. Disconnect connector.
7. Remove mounting bolts and electronic accelerator actuator.
8. Disconnect electronic accelerator pedal actuator connector.
9. Reverse procedure to install. **Torque** actuator mounting bolt to 80 inch lbs.

Adjustments

THROTTLE CONTROL CABLE

CLK55, CLK320, CLK430, E55, E320 & E430 & 1999–2001 SL500

1. Check ease of movement, then the condition of relay lever and accelerator control cable.
2. Ensure relay lever rests against Close Throttle Position (CTP) stop.
3. Turn adjusting bolt until no accelerator pedal travel exists as idle, as required.
4. Depress accelerator pedal until it touches kick-down switch.
5. Ensure relay lever rests against Wide Open Throttle (WOT) stop.
6. Turn adjusting bolt until relay lever rests against WOT stop.

ML55, ML320 & ML430

1. Ensure relay lever and accelerator control cable move easily and are in good condition.
2. If relay lever is not resting against Closed Throttle Position (CTP) stop, turn adjusting bolt until it does.
3. Depress accelerator until relay lever rests against Wide Open Throttle (WOT) stop.
4. If lever does not rest against WOT stop, release WOT stop by turning to left, press accelerator unit it makes contact and lock WOT stop in position by turning to right.

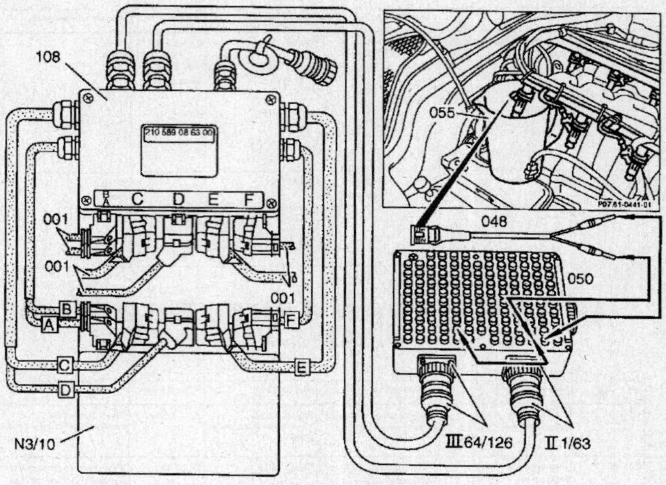

001 Engine control module connectors A–F
048 Self made harness
050 Socket box tester, 126 pole
055 Measuring glass
088 Test cable
N3/10 Engine control module (ME-SFI)

MB1029800676000X

Fig. 64 Injector test connection

⇒		Test scope	Test connection	Test condition	Nominal value	Possible cause/remedy
1.0		**Injectors** Leakage test	N3/10 3 (3A) ←→ 33 (1D)	Fuel rail and fuel injectors removed. Ignition: **ON**	Injectors must not drip.	⇒ 2.0, Replace dripping injectors.
2.0		**Injectors** Operation and spray pattern test	N3/10 3 (3A) ←→ 33 (1D)	Ignition: **ON** Hold each injector (one after another) into a container and, using the self-made test harness, manually activate the injector by connecting harness banana plugs to socket box sockets 3 (–) and 2 (+).	Injectors must spray evenly	Replace defective injectors.

MB1029800677000X

Fig. 65 Code —: Test 36, Injector test

113 Engine (ME 2.0 Engine Management)

NOTE: On Air Bag Equipped Models, Refer To "Air Bag System Precautions" Located In The Front Of This Manual For System Disarming & Arming Procedures.

NOTE: Refer To "Computer Relearn Procedures" Located In The Front Of This Manual When Battery Power To The Computer Has Been Interrupted.

NOTE: Electrical Symbol Identification Located In Front Of This Manual May Be Used As An Aid When Using Wiring Diagrams Found In This Section.

NOTE: Prior To Performing Any Service Listed In This Section Consult Technical Service Bulletin Section For Related Information.

INDEX

	Page No.
Description	14-113
Diagnosis & Testing	14-113
Accessing Diagnostic Trouble Codes	14-113
Generic Scan Tool	14-113
Hand-Held Tester	14-113
Clearing Diagnostic Trouble Codes	14-114
Component Tests	14-114
Fuel Injector	14-114
Fuel Pump	14-114
Components Locations	14-113
Connector Terminal Identification	14-113
Diagnostic Tests	14-114
Diagnostic Trouble Code Interpretation	14-113
Symbol Explanation	14-113
Symptom Related Diagnosis	14-113
Wiring Diagrams	14-113
Diagnostic Chart Index	14-129
Precautions	14-112
Air Bag Systems	14-112
Battery Ground Cable	14-112
Drive Authorization System (DAS)	14-112
ECM Recognition	14-112
ECM Self-Adaptation	14-112
ESP/ASR/ETS/ABS Control Modules	14-113
Ignition System	14-112
Sensor & Fuel Injector Specifications	14-112
System Service	14-137
Adjustments	14-137
Component Replacement	14-137

SENSOR & FUEL INJECTOR SPECIFICATIONS

Temperature, °F	Resistance, Ohms①	Voltage①
ADJUSTABLE CAMSHAFT TIMING SOLENOID		
158	7–12	—
CAMSHAFT POSITION SENSOR		
—	900–1600	—
CRANKSHAFT POSITION (CKP) SENSOR		
	700–1400	
ENGINE COOLANT TEMPERATURE (ECT) SENSOR		
68	3090	3.4
86	2000	2.9
104	1330	2.4
122	900	1.9
140	630	1.5
158	440	1.2
176	320	.9
194	230	.7
212	170	.5
FUEL INJECTOR		
—	14–18	—
INTAKE AIR TEMPERATURE (IAT) SENSOR		
50	3600	3.1
68	2420	2.7
104	1660	2.2
122	1170	1.8
140	850	1.4
158	600	1.1
MASS AIR FLOW (MAF) SENSOR		
158	—	0.9–1.1

① — Tolerance ± 5%

PRECAUTIONS

Air Bag Systems

Refer to "Air Bag System Precautions" in the front of this manual for system disarming and arming procedures.

Battery Ground Cable

Prior to service, disconnect battery ground cable and isolate as required.

Ignition System

1. Both control module coupling must be disconnected or connect with ignition switch in Off position.
2. Do not short circuit ignition coils terminal No. 1.
3. Do not operate the ignition system at starting speed unless the ignition cables are fully connected.
4. Do not conduct are test at starting speed or when engine is running. This includes: holding ignition cable No. 4 at a distance to ground, disconnecting a plug connector or pulling cable No. 4 out of the ignition coils.
5. High output side of ignition system must always carry at least two ohms resistance (spark plug connected).
6. Do not load ignition coil with more than 28,000 volts.
7. Ignition coil iron cores must always be connected to ground. **Use caution, coil cores can be charged with up to 400 volts.**
8. **Do not work on this system if you have a pacemaker.**
9. Ensure engine and ignition switch are in Off position when connecting and disconnecting ignition coil.
10. When working at start speeds during test such as compression check, switch ignition to off position and disconnect control module connector No. 2.

ECM Self-Adaptation

After repair work, the Engine Control Module (ECM) will automatically adapt itself after the vehicle has made approximately 10 trips. A trip includes a vehicle speed of more than 2.5 mph, engine speed of more than 700 RPM and engine shutoff of more than 30 seconds.

However, after fixing a malfunction or installation of a test ECM, the self-adaptation function must be reset as outlined under "Computer Relearn" in "Service Reminder & Warning Lamp Reset Procedures" at the front of this manual.

ECM Recognition

The ECM must be coded for vehicle model, catalytic converter, transmission, cruise control, acceleration slip regulation (ASR), electronic traction system (ETS) and country version with the Hand-Held Tester.

Before replacing the ECM, read and store existing code numbers with the Hand-Held Tester. When the new ECM is installed, enter the stored code numbers from the Hand-Held Tester. If code numbers cannot be read, the corresponding codes number must be obtained from Mercedes-Benz spare parts microfiche and manually entered with a Hand-Held Tester.

Drive Authorization System (DAS)

The DAS can only be activated or deactivated by the electronic ignition key. The ECM, RCL and DAS control module are permanently locked together by an identification code. This code cannot be erased. Trial installation of an ECM or RCL control module from another vehicle is not possible. After 40 starts, a new ECM cannot be used in any other vehicle. The code number and VIN must be entered into the ECM with a Hand-Held Tester.

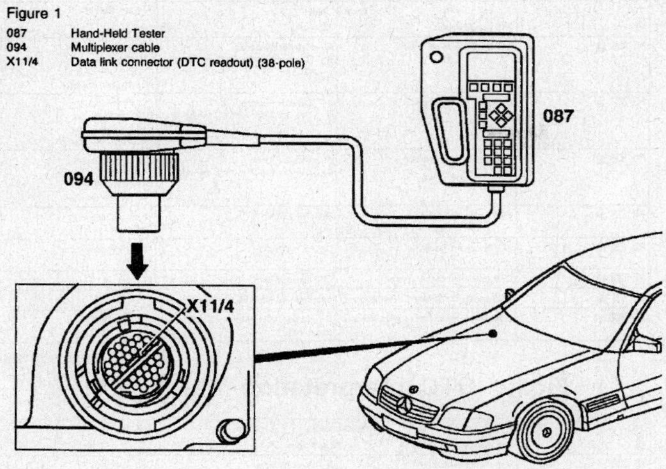

MB1029800678000X

Fig. 1 DLC tool connection

DTC		Possible cause		Test step/Remedy 1)
		SAE nomenclature	Explanation	
P0 133 ■		O2S 1 circuit slow response	A O2S 1 (before C) (G3/4), ageing correction value exceeded B O2S 1 (before TWC) (G3/4), ageing time period too long C O2S 1 (before TWC) (G3/4), ageing O2S 1 sensor response too slow	□ 23⇒ 11.0
P0 135 ■		O2S 1 heater circuit malfunction	O2S 1 heater (before TWC) (G3/4)	□ 23 ⇒ 13.0
P0 136 ■	Only (USA)	O2S 2 circuit malfunction	O2S 2 (after TWC) (G3/6)	□ 23 ⇒ 15.0
P0 141 ■	Only (USA)	O2S 2 heater circuit malfunction	Right O2S 2 heater (after TWC) (G3/6)	□ 23⇒ 17.0
P0 150 ■		O2S 1 circuit malfunction	A O2S 1 heater (before TWC) (G3/3) B O2S 1 heater (before TWC) (G3/3), voltage increase too slow	□ 23⇒ 10.0
P0 153 ■		O2S 1 circuit slow response	A O2S 1 heater (before TWC) (G3/3), ageing correction value exceeded B O2S 1 heater (before TWC) (G3/3), ageing time period too long C O2S 1 heater (before TWC) (G3/3), ageing O2S 1 sensor response too slow	□ 23⇒ 10.0
P0 155 ■		O2S 2 heater circuit malfunction	Left O2S 1 heater (before TWC) (G3/3)	□ 23⇒ 12.0
P0 156 ■	Only (USA)	O2S 2 circuit malfunction	Left O2S 2 (after TWC) (G3/5)	□ 23⇒ 14.0
P0 161 ■	Only (USA)	O2S 2 heater circuit malfunction	Right O2S 2 heater (after TWC) (G3/5)	□ 23⇒ 16.0

MB1029800679020X

Fig. 2 DTC interpretation (Part 2 of 11)

DTC		Possible cause		Test step/Remedy 1)
		SAE nomenclature	Explanation	
–		No malfunction in system		In case of complaint, perform □ 23, 24, 25 or 26 in its entirety
P0 100 ■		MAF circuit malfunction	Hot film MAF sensor (B2/5)	□ 23⇒ 4.0
P0 105 ■	Only (USA)	MAP circuit malfunction	Pressure sensor (B28)	□ 23⇒ 6.0
P0 110 ■		IAT circuit malfunction	IAT sensor (in Hot film MAF sensor B2/5)	□ 23⇒ 5.0
P0 115 ■		ECT circuit malfunction	ECT sensor (B11/4)	□ 23⇒ 8.0
P0 120		Throttle position circuit malfunction	Actual value potentiometer in EA/CC/ISC actuator (M16/6)	□ 26⇒ 3.0
P0 130 ■		O2S 1 circuit malfunction	A. O2S 1 (before TWC) (G3/4) B. O2S 1 (before TWC) (G3/4) voltage increase insufficient	□ 23⇒ 11.0

MB1029800679010X

Fig. 2 DTC interpretation (Part 1 of 11)

DTC	Possible cause		Test step/Remedy 1)
	SAE nomenclature	Explanation	
P0 170 ■	Fuel trim malfunction	A Self adaptation of fuel mixture "partial load", right cylinder bank, at limit from engine control module (N3/10). B Self adaptation of fuel mixture "CTP", right cylinder bank, at limit from engine control module (N3/10).	Intake air leak, injectors, diaphragm pressure regulator, engine wear.
P0 173 ■	Fuel trim malfunction	A Self adaptation of fuel mixture "partial load", left cylinder bank, at limit from engine control module (N3/10). B Self adaptation of fuel mixture "CTP", left cylinder bank, at limit from engine control module (N3/10).	Intake air leak, injectors, diaphragm pressure regulator, engine wear.
P0 201 ■	Injector circuit malfunction - cyl. 1	Injector (Y62y1) – cylinder 1	□ 23⇒ 18.0
P0 202 ■	Injector circuit malfunction - cyl. 2	Injector (Y62y2) – cylinder 2	□ 23⇒ 19.0
P0 203 ■	Injector circuit malfunction - cyl. 3	Injector (Y62y3) – cylinder 3	□ 23 ⇒ 20.0
P0 204 ■	Injector circuit malfunction - cyl. 4	Injector (Y62y4) – cylinder 4	□ 23 ⇒ 21.0
P0 205 ■	Injector circuit malfunction - cyl. 5	Injector (Y62y5) – cylinder 5	□ 23 ⇒ 22.0
P0 206 ■	Injector circuit malfunction - cyl. 6	Injector (Y62y6) – cylinder 6	□ 23 ⇒ 23.0
P0 207 ■	Injector circuit malfunction - cyl. 7	Injector (Y62y7) – cylinder 7	□ 23 ⇒ 24.0
P0 208 ■	Injector circuit malfunction - cyl. 8	Injector (Y62y8) – cylinder 8	□ 23 ⇒ 25.0

MB1029800679030X

Fig. 2 DTC interpretation (Part 3 of 11)

ESP/ASR/ETS/ABS Control Modules

The Electronic Stability Program (ESP), Acceleration Slip Regulation (ASR), Electronic Traction System (ETS) and/or Anti-lock Brake System (ABS) control modules must not be disconnected. The Engine Control Module (ECM) and Transmission Control Module (TCM) rely on those control modules for Vehicle Speed Sensor (VSS) information. To disable brake and engine regulation of those modules, proceed as follows:

1. Turn ignition switch to Off position.
2. Connect Hand-Held Tester adapter to Data Link Connector (DLC).
3. Jump sockets No. 1 and 6.
4. Start engine. MIL must light.
5. If Hand-Held Tester is available, disconnect VSS front axle connector.
6. When testing is complete, connect VSS and erase Diagnostic Trouble Codes with Hand-Held Tester.

DESCRIPTION

Refer to "104 Engine (ME 2.1 Engine Management)" section.

DIAGNOSIS & TESTING

Symbol Explanation

Refer to "104 Engine (ME 2.1 Engine Management)" section for explanations of symbols, connections and steps included in the charts.

Accessing Diagnostic Trouble Codes

GENERIC SCAN TOOL

Follow tool manufacturers instructions and connect suitably programmed scan tool to generic scan tool connection X11/22.

HAND-HELD TESTER

1. Turn ignition switch to Off position.
2. Attach test cable tool No. 965 589 00 40 00, or equivalent, to Hand-Held Tester tool No. 965 589 00 01 00, or equivalent.
3. Connect cable to Data Link Connector (DLC), **Fig. 1**.
4. Turn multiplexer cable locking ring completely to left detent stop.
5. Attach multiplexer cable to data link connector via locking pins.
6. To lock multiplexer cable to connector, turn locking ring to the right.
7. Follow tool manufacturer's instructions.

Diagnostic Trouble Code Interpretation

Refer to **Fig. 2** for DTC interpretation. **Black square items are emission related and may activate MIL during test cycle.**

Symptom Related Diagnosis

Refer to **Fig. 3** for symptom related diagnosis.

Components Locations

Refer to **Figs. 4 through 6** for component locations.

Wiring Diagrams

On C43 and CLK430 models, refer to "112 Engine (ME 2.0 Engine Management)" section for wiring diagrams.

Refer to **Figs. 7 through 9** for wiring diagrams.

Connector Terminal Identification

Refer to **Fig. 10** for engine control module connector terminal identification.

DTC	Possible cause: SAE nomenclature	Possible cause: Explanation	Test step/Remedy [1]
P0 300 ■	Random misfire detected	A Random misfire B Random misfire, TWC damaging	☐ 24 ⇒ 13.0 – 21.0 ☐ 36 ⇒ 1.0 – 2.0 Compression pressure
P0 301 ■	Cylinder 1 misfire detected	A Cylinder 1 misfire B Cylinder 1 misfire, TWC damaging	☐ 24 ⇒ 13.0 ☐ 24 ⇒ 21.0 ☐ 36 ⇒ 1.0 – 2.0 Compression pressure
P0 302 ■	Cylinder 2 misfire detected	A Cylinder 2 misfire B Cylinder 2 misfire, TWC damaging	☐ 24 ⇒ 14.0 ☐ 24 ⇒ 21.0 ☐ 36 ⇒ 2.0 Compression pressure
P0 303 ■	Cylinder 3 misfire detected	A Cylinder 3 misfire B Cylinder 3 misfire, TWC damaging	☐ 24 ⇒ 15.0 ☐ 24 ⇒ 21.0 ☐ 36 ⇒ 1.0 – 2.0 Compression pressure
P0 304 ■	Cylinder 4 misfire detected	A Cylinder 4 misfire B Cylinder 4 misfire, TWC damaging	☐ 24 ⇒ 16.0 ☐ 24 ⇒ 21.0 ☐ 36 ⇒ 1.0 – 2.0 Compression pressure
P0 305 ■	Cylinder 5 misfire detected	A Cylinder 5 misfire B Cylinder 5 misfire, TWC damaging	☐ 24 ⇒ 17.0 ☐ 24 ⇒ 21.0 ☐ 36 ⇒ 1.0 – 2.0 Compression pressure

MB1029800679040X

Fig. 2 DTC interpretation (Part 4 of 11)

DTC	Possible cause: SAE nomenclature	Possible cause: Explanation	Test step/Remedy [1]
P0 306 ■	Cylinder 6 misfire detected	A Cylinder 6 misfire B Cylinder 6 misfire, TWC damaging	☐ 24 ⇒ 18.0 ☐ 24 ⇒ 21.0 ☐ 36 ⇒ 1.0 – 2.0 Compression pressure
P0 307 ■	Cylinder 7 misfire detected	A Cylinder 7 misfire B Cylinder 7 misfire, TWC damaging	☐ 24 ⇒ 19.0 ☐ 24 ⇒ 21.0 ☐ 36 ⇒ 1.0 – 2.0 Compression pressure
P0 308 ■	Cylinder 8 misfire detected	A Cylinder 8 misfire B Cylinder 8 misfire, TWC damaging	☐ 24 ⇒ 20.0 ☐ 24 ⇒ 21.0 ☐ 36 ⇒ 1.0 – 2.0 Compression pressure
P0 325 ■	KS 1 circuit malfunction	Right KS 1 (A16g1)	Wiring, connector, A16g1
P0 330 ■	KS 2 circuit malfunction	Left KS 2 (A16g2)	Wiring, connector, A16g2
P0 335 ■	CKP sensor circuit malfunction	CKP sensor (L5)	☐ 24 ⇒ 11.0
P0 341 ■	CMP sensor circuit range/performance	Camshaft Hall-effect sensor (B6/1)	☐ 24 ⇒ 12.0
P0 400 ■	Exhaust gas recirculation flow malfunction	Exhaust gas recirculation malfunction (logic chain)	☐ 24 ⇒ 29.0

MB1029800679050X

Fig. 2 DTC interpretation (Part 5 of 11)

DTC		Possible cause: SAE nomenclature	Possible cause: Explanation	Test step/Remedy
P0 410 ■	Only (USA)	Air injection system malfunction	AIR system malfunction (logic chain)	☐ 23 ⇒ 26.0– 28.0
P0 422 ■		TWC (right) efficiency below threshold	TWC efficiency below threshold	Replace right TWC
P0 432 ■		TWC (left) efficiency below threshold	TWC efficiency below threshold	Replace left TWC
P0 440 ■	Only (USA)	EVAP system malfunction	EVAP malfunction (logic chain)	☐ 23 ⇒ 32.0 – 33.0
P0 441 ■		EVAP system incorrect purge flow	EVAP not functioning	☐ 23 ⇒ 31.0 – 32.0
P0 442 ■	Only (USA)	EVAP system leak detected (small leak)	EVAP system, small leak	☐ 23 ⇒ 33.0
P0 443 ■		EVAP system purge control valve circuit malfunction	Purge control valve (Y58/1)	☐ 23 ⇒ 31.0
P0 446 ■	Only (USA)	EVAP system vent control malfunction	A. Activated charcoal canister shut-off valve (Y58/4) B. End stage activated charcoal canister shut-off valve (Y58/4) within N3/10	☐ 23 ⇒ 34.0, N3/10
P0 450 ■	Only (USA)	EVAP system pressure sensor malfunction	A. Fuel tank pressure sensor (B4/3) electrical fault B. Fuel tank pressure sensor (B4/3) electrical fluctuations	☐ 23 ⇒ 35.0 Charcoal canister plugged.
P0 455 ■	Only (USA)	EVAP system leak detected (large leak)	EVAP system, large leak Fuel tank pressure sensor (B4/3) (voltage supply)	☐ 23 ⇒ 33.0 ☐ 23 ⇒ 35.0
P0 460		Fuel level sensor circuit low input	Fuel tank level too low	Fill fuel tank

MB1029800679060X

Fig. 2 DTC interpretation (Part 6 of 11)

DTC	Possible cause: SAE nomenclature	Possible cause: Explanation	Test step/Remedy
P0 500	VSS sensor malfunction	A VSS left front B VSS left rear	Test ASR, ESP
P0 507	ISC rpm higher than expected	Idle control system, unplausible	☐ 25 ⇒ 1.0 – 3.0
P0 560	System voltage malfunction	Voltage supply to engine control module (N3/10)	☐ 23 ⇒ 1.0 – 2.0
P0 565	Cruise control switch	CC switch (S40)	☐ 26 ⇒ 2.0
P0 600	Serial communication link malfunction	CAN bus from ESP/SPS control module (N47-5)	☐ 23 ⇒ 36.0
P0 604	Internal control module random Access memory (RAM) error	A Engine control module (N3/10) B Engine control module (N3/10)	(N3/10)
P0 605	Internal control module read only memory (ROM) error	Engine control module (N3/10)	(N3/10)
P0 700 ■	Transmission control system malfunction	Read DTC memory of transmission control module.	Test ETC,
P0 702 ■	Transmission control system electrical	Read DTC memory of transmission control module.	Test ETC,
P0 715 ■	Input/turbine speed sensor circuit malfunction	Read DTC memory of transmission control module.	Test ETC,
P0 720 ■	Output speed sensor circuit malfunction	Read DTC memory of transmission control module.	Test ETC,

MB1029800679070X

Fig. 2 DTC interpretation (Part 7 of 11)

Diagnostic Tests

1. Turn ignition switch to Off position.
2. Connect 126-pole socket box tool No. 129 589 00 21 00, or equivalent, with contact module tool No. 210 589 08 63 00, or equivalent, to Engine Control Module, **Fig. 11.**
3. Connect interior harness connector to test cable connection No. 1 and engine harness connector to test cable connection No. 2.
4. Conduct tests as directed in **Figs. 12 through 58** using suitable multimeter.

Component Tests

FUEL PUMP

1. Connect suitable pressure gauge to test connection, **Fig. 59.**
2. Conduct tests as directed, **Fig. 60.**
3. Connect 126-pole socket box tool No. 129 589 00 21 00, or equivalent, to Engine Control Module (ECM) with test cable tool No. 140 589 46 63 00, or equivalent, **Fig. 61.**
4. Conduct tests as directed, **Fig. 62.**
5. Release fuel pressure and allow fuel to drain into suitable measuring cup.

FUEL INJECTOR

1. Connect 126-pole socket box tool No. 129 589 00 21 00, or equivalent, to Engine Control Module (ECM) with test cable tool No. 140 589 46 63 00, or equivalent, **Fig. 63.**
2. Disconnect injector connectors, then remove fuel rail with injectors. **Do not disconnect fuel feed and return lines.**
3. Connect self-made harness to one injector after another, hold over suitable measuring glass and test as directed, **Fig. 64.**

Clearing Diagnostic Trouble Codes

The Diagnostic Trouble Code (DTC) memory is cleared when the vehicle battery is disconnected.

When a component has been repaired or replaced, the related DTC will be cleared. After three trips the CHECK ENGINE Malfunction Indicator Lamp (MIL) will go out and after 40 warm-up periods the DTC is automatically erased. A trip includes engine running for more than 20 minutes, engine oil temperature of more than 19°F, engine speed of more than 700 RPM and emission related logic chain functions. A warm-up period includes an engine coolant temperature at start-up of less than 95°F and increasing to more than 176°F.

To erase DTCs with a Hand-Held Tester, follow the tool manufacturer's instructions.

DTC	Possible cause: SAE nomenclature	Possible cause: Explanation	Test step/Remedy
P0 730 ■	Incorrect gear ratio	Read DTC memory of transmission control module.	Test ETC,
P0 740 ■	Torque converter clutch circuit malfunction	Read DTC memory of transmission control module.	Test ETC.
P0 743 ■	Torque converter clutch circuit electrical	Read DTC memory of transmission control module.	Test ETC,
P0 748 ■	Pressure control solenoid electrical	Read DTC memory of transmission control module.	Test ETC,
P0 753 ■	Shift solenoid A electrical	Read DTC memory of transmission control module.	Test ETC.
P0 758 ■	Shift solenoid B electrical	Read DTC memory of transmission control module.	Test ETC,
P0 763 ■	Shift solenoid C electrical	Read DTC memory of transmission control module.	Test ETC,
P0 801	Engine/climate control electric cooling fan malfunction	Engine/climate control electric cooling fan (M4/3).	□ 23 ⇒ 38.0

MB1029800679080X

Fig. 2 DTC interpretation (Part 8 of 11)

DTC	Possible cause: SAE nomenclature	Possible cause: Explanation	Test step/Remedy 1)
P1 186	Fuel safety shut-off recognized	EA/CC/ISC actuator (M16/6)	□ 25 ⇒ 3.0 – 4.0, EA/CC/ISC actuator (M16/1) sticks or binds, Check intake system for residue.
P1 386 ■	Knock sensor control from ECM (N3/10) at end stop	Knock sensor regulation from engine control module (N3/10) at end stop	1. Increased knock tendency due to bad fuel, carbon in combustion chamber or mechanical damage.
P1 400 ■	EGR valve vacuum transducer	EGR valve vacuum transducer (Y31/1) faulty	□ 23 ⇒ 29.0
P1 420 ■ only (USA)	AIR pump switchover valve	AIR pump switchover valve (Y32)	□ 23 ⇒ 27.0
P1 453 ■ only (USA)	AIR relay module, AIR pump	Relay module, AIR pump (K40/4k2) in relay module (K40)	□ 23 ⇒ 26.0
P1 491		Refrigerant pressure in A/C system too high	Check automatic A/C system.
P1 542	Pedal value sensor	Pedal value sensor (B37)	□ 25 ⇒ 1.0 – 2.0
P1 570	CAN signal from DAS control module to engine control module	A. Start attempted with "locked" DAS B. CAN signal from DAS control module (N54/1) to engine control module (N3/10) interrupted. C. Engine control module (ME-SFI) and DAS control module are not compatible.	User error, Check correct operation of DAS, □ 23 ⇒ 36.0 Check control modules and part no.

MB1029800679100X

Fig. 2 DTC interpretation (Part 10 of 11)

Complaint/Problem	Possible cause	Test step/Remedy	Actual value Engine test Menu item
Engine starts and accelerates poorly when cold	Injector (Y62) activation and injection duration. Hot film MAF sensor (B2/5). ECT sensor (B11/4). Ignition voltage too low. Intake air leak.	□ 23 ⇒ 18.0 – 25.0 □ 23 ⇒ 4.0 □ 23 ⇒ 8.0 □ 24 ⇒ 21.0 Remedy air leak.	2/7 1/7 3/7 – –
Engine does not start	Voltage supply from engine control module (N3/10) is missing. Malfunction of drive authorization system (DAS) . Fuel pumps defective. No compression due to high oil pressure. Ignition voltage too low.	□ 23 ⇒ 1.0 – 3.0 □ 23 ⇒ 36.0 □ 34 ⇒ 2.0 Check compression and oil pressure. □ 24 ⇒ 21.0	– DAS 1/1 – – –
Engine has uneven idle	Injector (Y62) activation and injection duration. Intake air leak.	□ 23 ⇒ 1.0 – 2.0 Remedy leak.	2/7 –
Engine has insufficient output	TWC flow restricted. O2S 1 (G3/3 or G3/4) (before TWC). ECT sensor (B11/4). Hot film MAF sensor (B2/5).	Check exhaust back pressure, see DM, Engines, Vol. 1, section A, "Engine Output" □ 23 ⇒ 10.0 □ 23 ⇒ 10.0 – 13.0 □ 23 ⇒ 8.0 □ 23 ⇒ 4.0	– – 3/7 1/7, 2/7

MB1029800680010X

Fig. 3 Symptom related diagnosis (Part 1 of 2)

Complaint/Problem	Possible cause	Test step/Remedy 1)	Actual value Engine test Menu item
Engine runs unevenly (shakes)	Injector (Y62) activation and injection duration. Injector leaking, spray pattern. O2S 1 (G3/3 or G3/4) (before TWC). Ignition voltage too low. Compression on one or more cylinders too low. Intake air leak.	□ 23 ⇒ 18.0 – 25.0 □ 36 ⇒ 1.0– 2.0 □ 23 ⇒ 10.0 – 13.0 □ 24 ⇒ 21.0 Check compression. Remedy air leak.	2/7 – 5/7 – – –
Engine runs unevenly (misfiring)	Ignition voltage too low. Hot film MAF sensor (B2/5).	□ 24 ⇒ 21.0 □ 23 ⇒ 4.0	– 1/7
Engine surges after cold start	Intake air leak.	Remedy air leak.	–
Transition failure during warm-up	ECT sensor (B11/4). Hot film MAF sensor (B2/5). Intake air leak.	□ 23 ⇒ 8.0 □ 23 ⇒ 4.0 Remedy air leak.	3/7 1/7 –
Transition failure when warm or increased fuel consumption	O2S 1 (G3/3 or G3/4) (before TWC). Purge control valve (Y58/1) stuck in open position.	□ 23 ⇒ 10.0 – 13.0 □ 23 ⇒ 31.0 – 32.0	5/7 3/7
Engine bucks, jerks	Hot film MAF sensor (B2/5). Ignition voltage too low. O2S 1 (G3/3 or G3/4) (before TWC).	□ 23 ⇒ 4.0 □ 24 ⇒ 21.0 □ 23 ⇒ 10.0 – 13.0	1/7 – 5/7
EA is in "limp-home" mode	Nominal value potentiometer in pedal value sensor (B37). EA/CC/ISC actuator actual value potentiometer.	□ 25 ⇒ 1.0 – 2.0 □ 25 ⇒ 3.0	4/7 4/7

MB1029800680020X

Fig. 3 Symptom related diagnosis (Part 2 of 2)

DTC	Possible cause: SAE nomenclature	Possible cause: Explanation	Test step/Remedy 1)
P0 802	Resonance intake mainfold switchover valve malfunction	Resonance intake mainfold switchover valve (Y22/6).	□ 23 ⇒ 30.0
P0 809	Angle deviation between camshaft and crankshaft	Angle deviation between camshaft and crankshaft.	Check basic adjustment of camshaft.
P0 811	CAN from electronic ignition lock	CAN from electronic ignition lock.	□ 23 ⇒ 36.0
P1 031	O2 sensors (G3/3, G3/4) reversed	O2 sensors (G3/3, G3/4) reversed.	Check proper connection of O2 sensors in ETM.
P1 177	Oil sensor	Oil sensor (level/temperature/quality) (B40), Oil temperature implausible.	□ 23 ⇒ 37.0
P1 178	Oil sensor	Oil sensor (level/temperature/quality) (B40), Oil level implausible.	□ 23 ⇒ 37.0
P1 179	Oil sensor	Oil sensor (level/temperature/quality) (B40), Oil quality implausible.	□ 23 ⇒ 37.0
P1 180	Oil sensor	Oil sensor (level/temperature/quality) (B40), Oil temperature too high.	□ 23 ⇒ 37.0
P1 185	Oil sensor	Oil sensor (level/temperature/quality) (B40), Water in oil.	□ 23 ⇒ 37.0

MB1029800679090X

Fig. 2 DTC interpretation (Part 9 of 11)

DTC	Possible cause: SAE nomenclature	Possible cause: Explanation	Test step/Remedy 1)
P1 580 ■	EA/CC/ISC actuator	EA/CC/ISC actuator (M16/6)	□ 25 ⇒ 3.0 – 4.0
P1 584	Stop lamp switch	Stop lamp switch (S9/1)	Test ETS,
P1 605		Poor road/traction condition recognition signal (via comparison of VSS rpm signals)	Test ASR/ESP
P1 644		Transmission version can not be checked due to low voltage at transmission control module (N15/3)	Test ETC,
P1 747 ■	CAN signal from ETC	A. CAN failure: Transmission protection malfunction from transmission control module (N15/3) B. CAN failure: Instrument cluster	Test ETC. Test instrument cluster (A1),

MB1029800679110X

Fig. 2 DTC interpretation (Part 11 of 11)

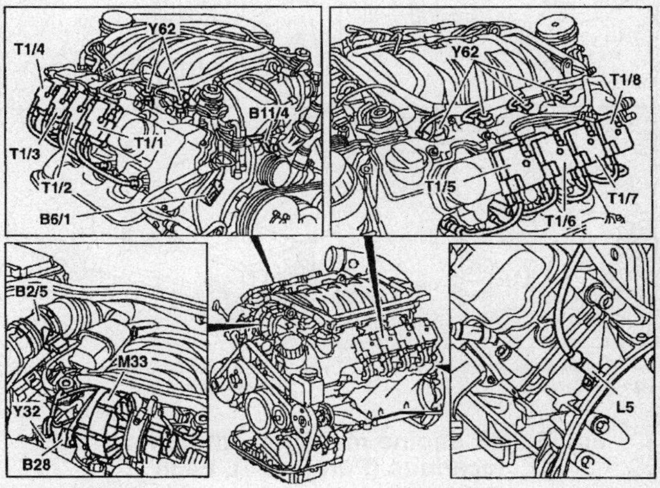

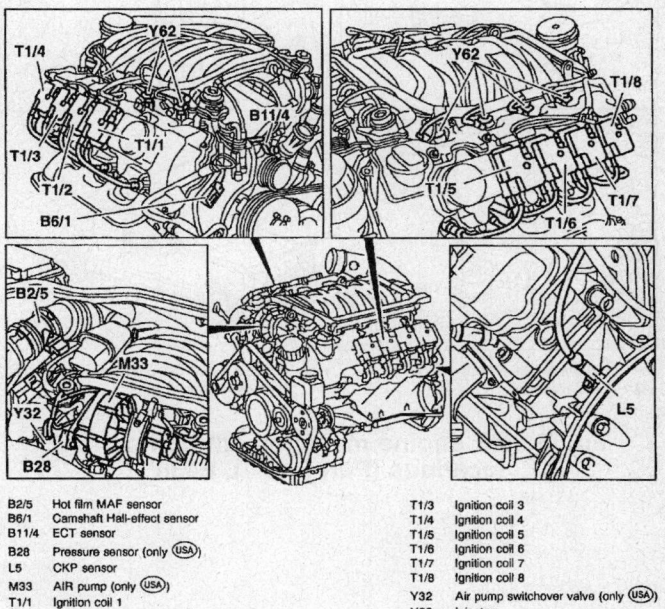

B2/5	Hot film MAF sensor	T1/3	Ignition coil 3
B6/1	Camshaft Hall-effect sensor	T1/4	Ignition coil 4
B11/4	ECT sensor	T1/5	Ignition coil 5
B28	Pressure sensor (only (USA))	T1/6	Ignition coil 6
L5	CKP sensor	T1/7	Ignition coil 7
M33	AIR pump (only (USA))	T1/8	Ignition coil 8
T1/1	Ignition coil 1	Y32	Air pump switchover valve (only (USA))
T1/2	Ignition coil 2	Y62	Injectors

MB1029800681010X

Fig. 4 ME engine management component locations (Part 1 of 2). 113 engine

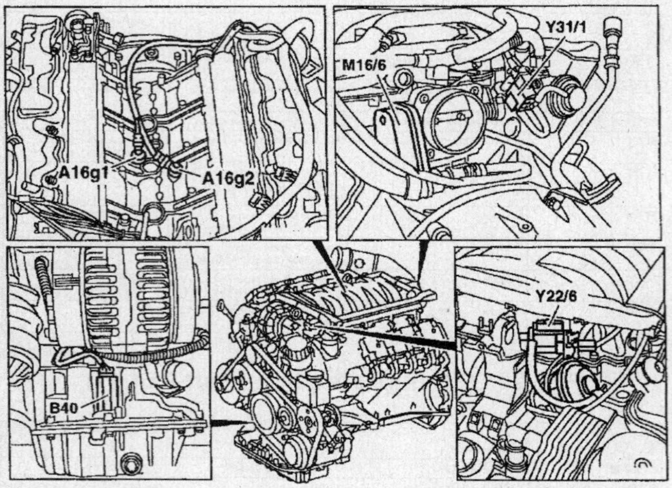

A16g1 KS 1 (right side of engine)
A16g2 KS 2 (left side of engine)
M16/6 EA/CC/ISC actuator
Y22/6 Resonance intake manifold switchover valve
Y31/1 EGR valve vacuum transducer
B40 Oil sensor (level/temperature/quality)

MB1029800681020X

Fig. 4 ME engine management component locations (Part 2 of 2). 113 engine

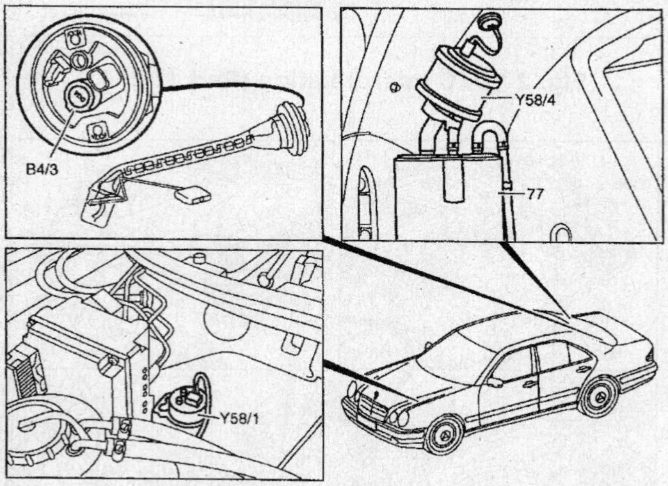

B4/3 Fuel tank pressure sensor (only USA)
Y58/1 Purge control valve
Y58/4 Activated charcoal canister shut-off valve (only USA)
77 Activated charcoal canister

MB1029800682020X

Fig. 5 ME engine management component locations (Part 2 of 4). E430

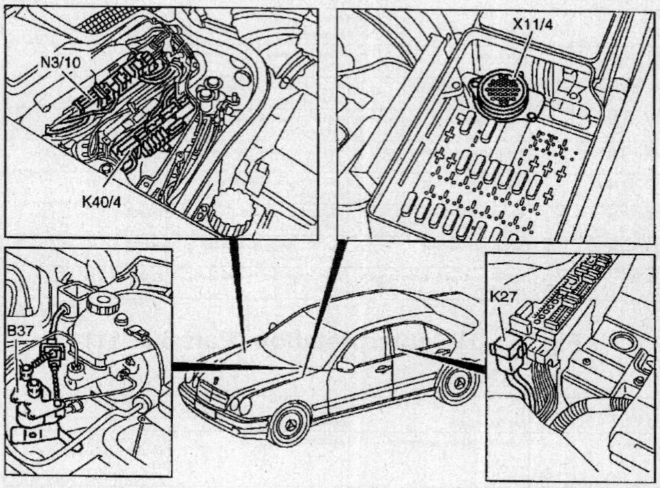

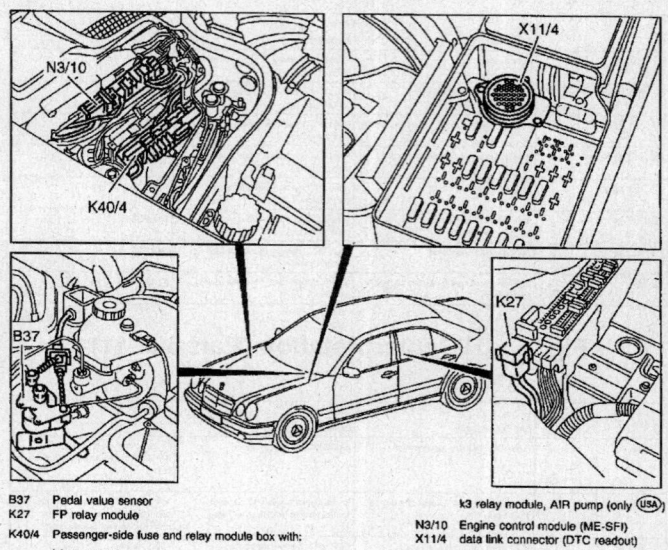

B37 Pedal value sensor
K27 FP relay module
K40/4 Passenger-side fuse and relay module box with:
k2 starter relay
k3 relay module, AIR pump (only USA)
N3/10 Engine control module (ME-SFI)
X11/4 data link connector (DTC readout)

MB1029800682010X

Fig. 5 ME engine management component locations (Part 1 of 4). E430

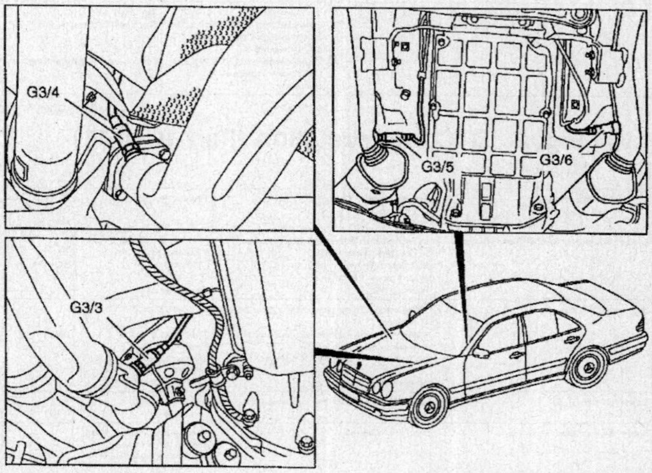

G3/3 Left 02S 1 (before TWC)
G3/4 Right 02S 1 (before TWC)
G3/5 Left 02S 2 (after TWC) (only USA)
G3/6 Right 02s 2 (after TWC) (only USA)

MB1029800682030X

Fig. 5 ME engine management component locations (Part 3 of 4). E430

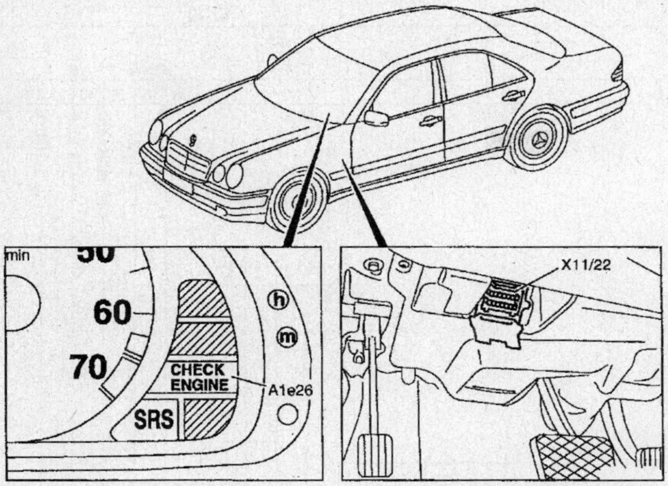

A1e26 "CHECK ENGINE" MIL (only USA)

X11/22 Diagnostic module (OBD II) generic scan tool connector

MB1029800682040X

Fig. 5 ME engine management component locations (Part 4 of 4). E430

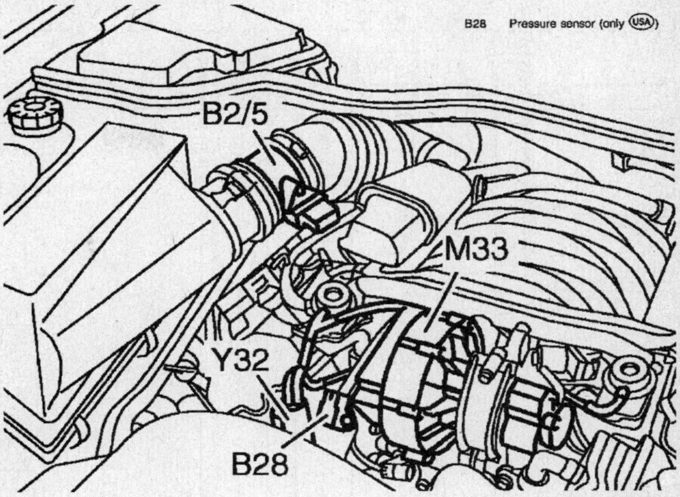

MB1029800683000X

Fig. 6 ME engine management component locations. Pressure sensor

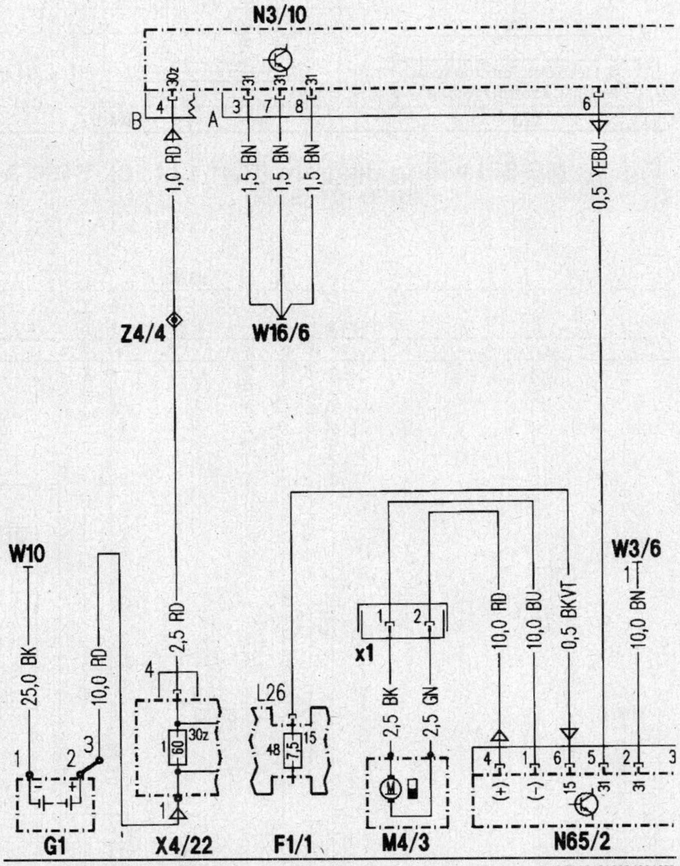

MB1010100240010X

Fig. 7 ME-SFI wiring diagram (Part 1 of 18). S430 & 2000–01 S500

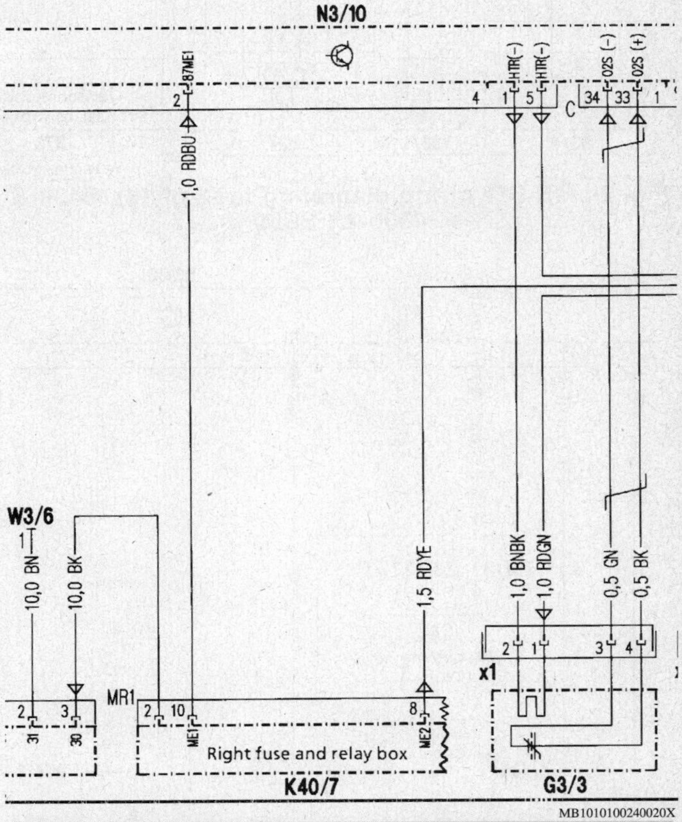

MB1010100240020X

Fig. 7 ME-SFI wiring diagram (Part 2 of 18). S430 & 2000–01 S500

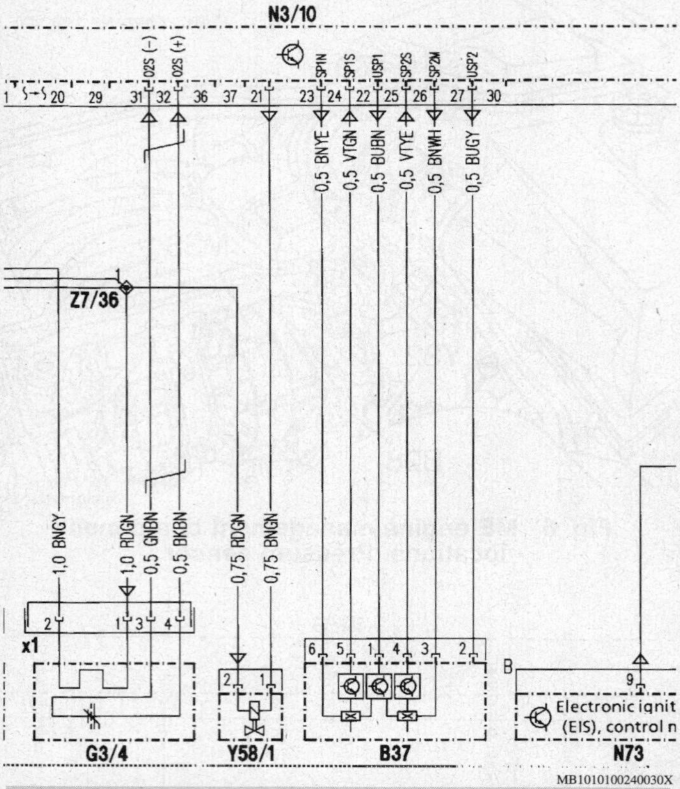

Fig. 7 ME-SFI wiring diagram (Part 3 of 18). S430 & 2000–01 S500

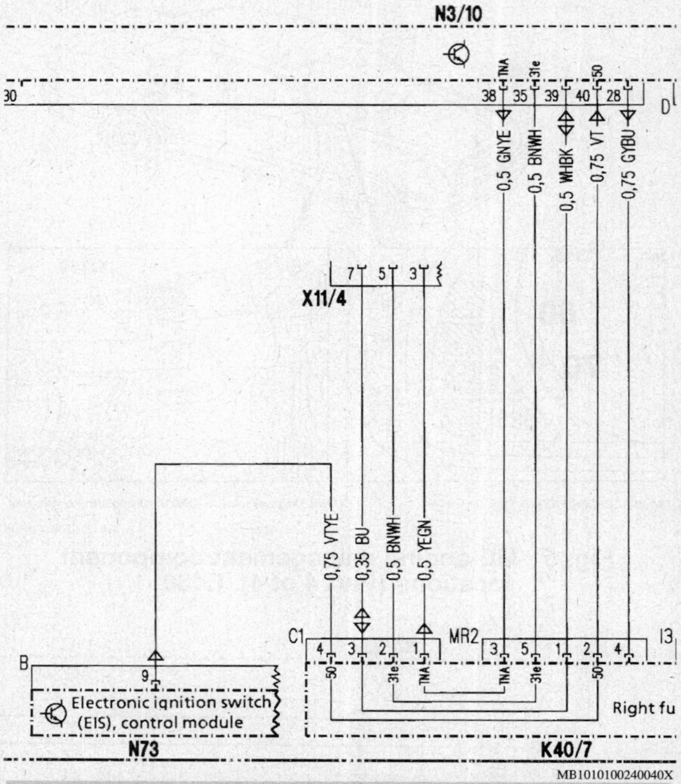

Fig. 7 ME-SFI wiring diagram (Part 4 of 18). S430 & 2000–01 S500

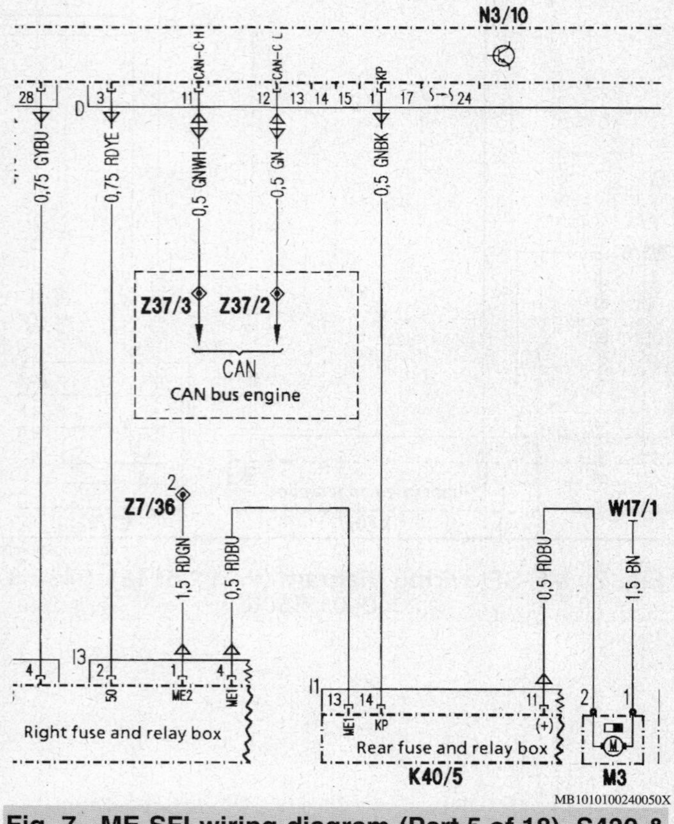

Fig. 7 ME-SFI wiring diagram (Part 5 of 18). S430 & 2000–01 S500

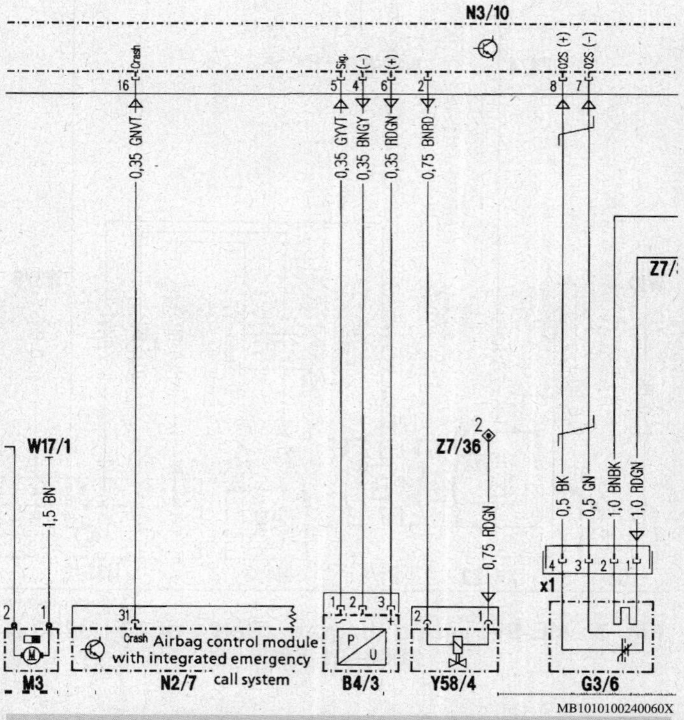

Fig. 7 ME-SFI wiring diagram (Part 6 of 18). S430 & 2000–01 S500

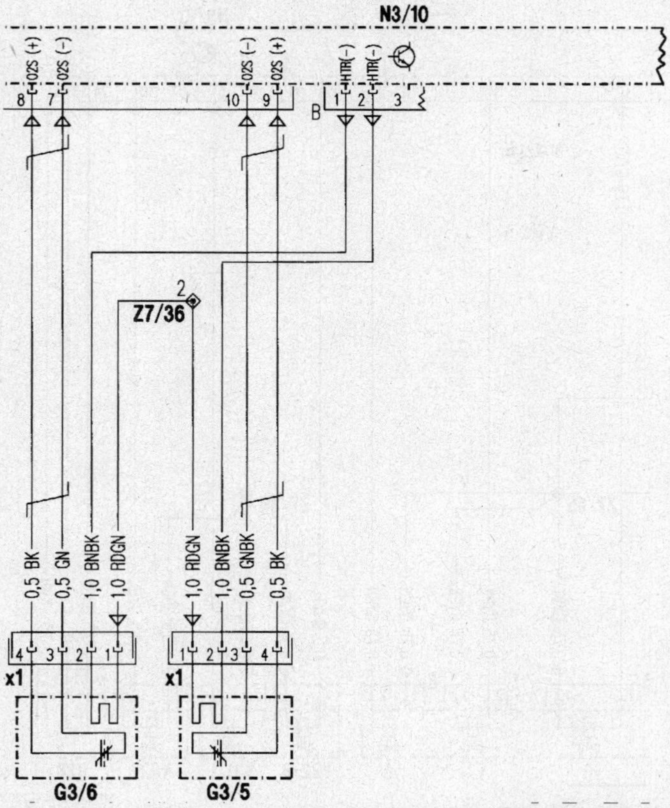

MB1010100240070X

Fig. 7 ME-SFI wiring diagram (Part 7 of 18). S430 & 2000–01 S500

Z4/4	Circuit 30Z connector sleeve (solder joint in harness)
Z7/36	Circuit 87 M2e connector sleeve
Z37/2	Engine CAN-Bus (low) connector sleeve
Z37/3	Engine CAN-Bus (high) connector sleeve

MB1010100240090X

Fig. 7 ME-SFI wiring diagram (Part 9 of 18). S430 & 2000–01 S500

B4/3	Fuel tank pressure sensor
B37	Pedal value sensor
F1/1	Right fuse box
F1/1f48	Fuse 48
G1	Battery
G3/3	Left O2S 1 (before TWC)
G3/3x1	Left O2S 1 connector (before TWC)
G3/4	Right O2S 1 (before TWC)
G3/4x1	Right O2S 1 connector (before TWC)
G3/5	Left O2S 2 (after TWC)
G3/5x1	Left O2S 2 connector (after TWC)
G3/6	Right O2S 2 (after TWC)
G3/6x1	Right O2S 2 connector (after TWC)
K40/5	Rear fuse/relay module
K40/7	Right front fuse/relay module
M3	Fuel pump
M4/3	Engine/climate control electric cooling fan
M4/3x1	Engine/climate control electric cooling fan connector
N2/7	Restraint system control module
N3/10	Engine control module (ME-SFI)
N65/2	Suction cooling fan control module
N73	Electronic ignition-starter switch (EIS) control module
W3/6	Ground (right bottom wheel housing)
W10	Ground (battery)
W16/6	Ground (electronics ground - component compartment - right)
W17/1	Ground (left rear seat)
X4/22	Terminal block and fuse box (circuit 30Z)
X4/22f1	Fuse 1
X11/4	Data link connector (DTC readout)
Y58/1	Purge control valve
Y58/4	Activated charcoal canister shut-off valve

MB1010100240080X

Fig. 7 ME-SFI wiring diagram (Part 8 of 18). S430 & 2000–01 S500

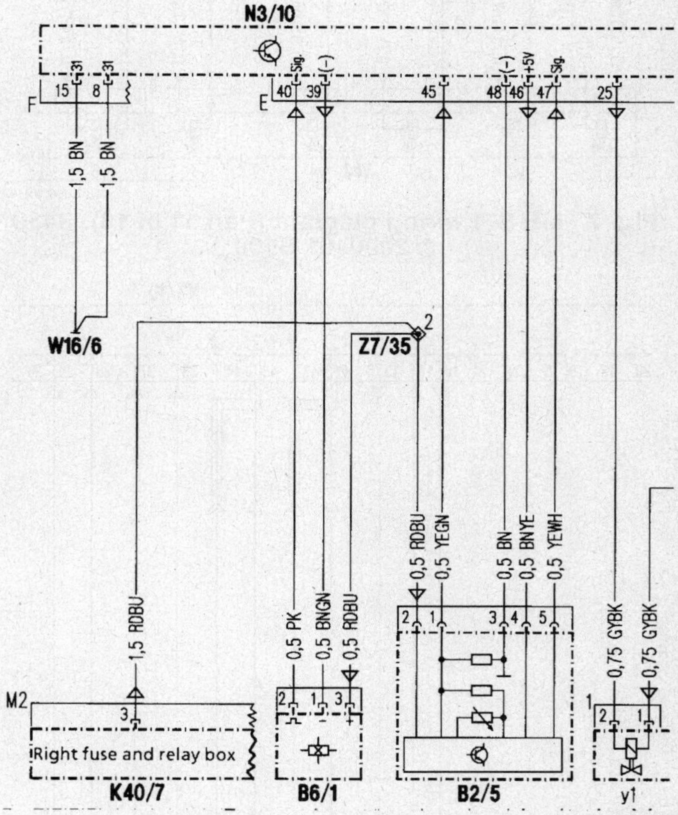

MB1010100240100X

Fig. 7 ME-SFI wiring diagram (Part 10 of 18). S430 & 2000–01 S500

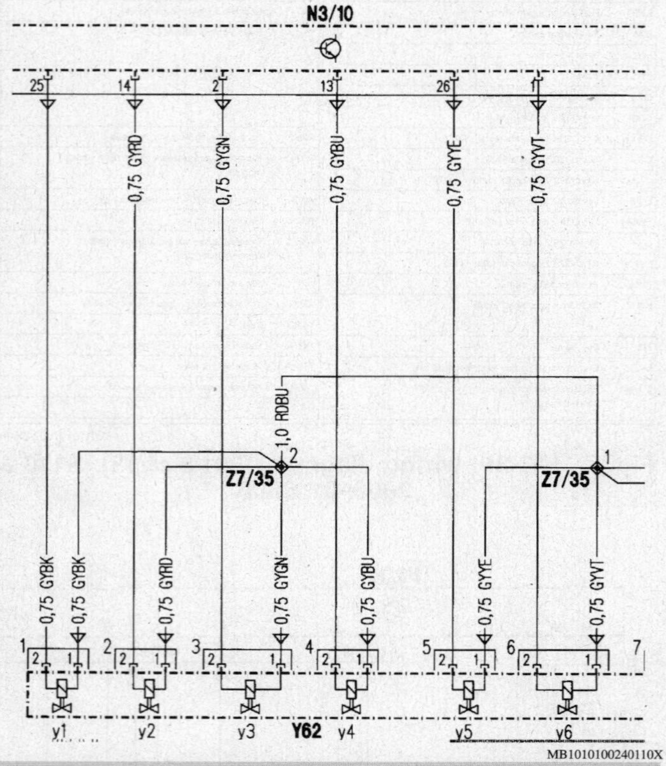

Fig. 7 ME-SFI wiring diagram (Part 11 of 18). S430 & 2000–01 S500

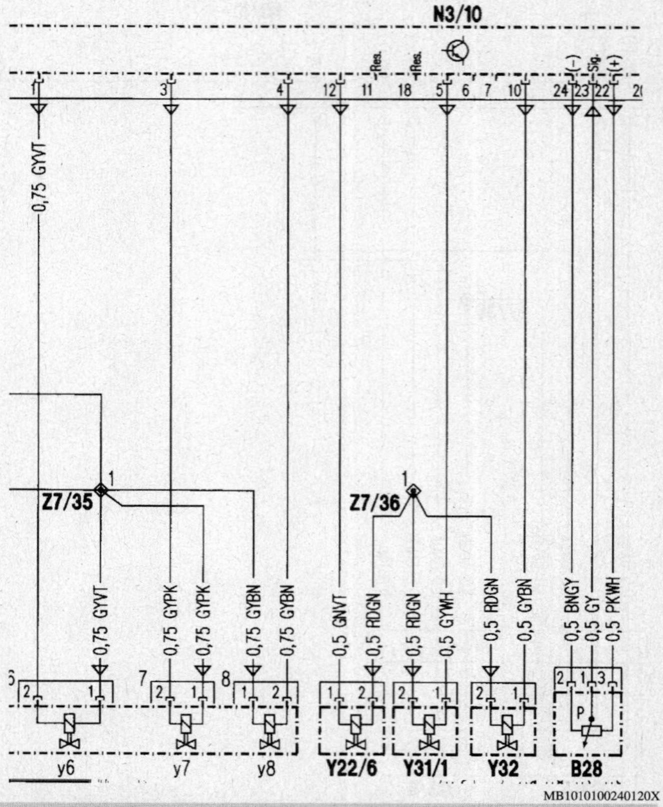

Fig. 7 ME-SFI wiring diagram (Part 12 of 18). S430 & 2000–01 S500

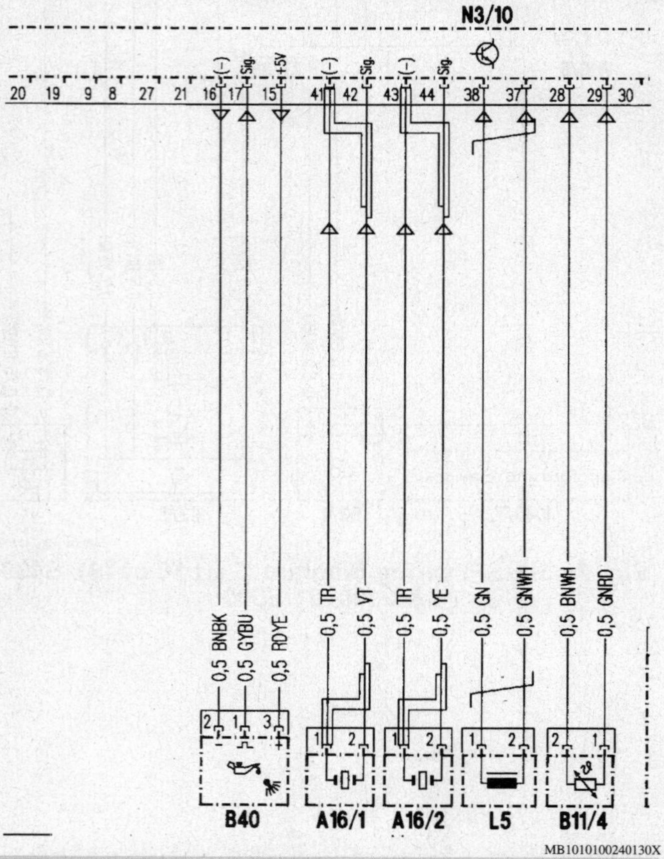

Fig. 7 ME-SFI wiring diagram (Part 13 of 18). S430 & 2000–01 S500

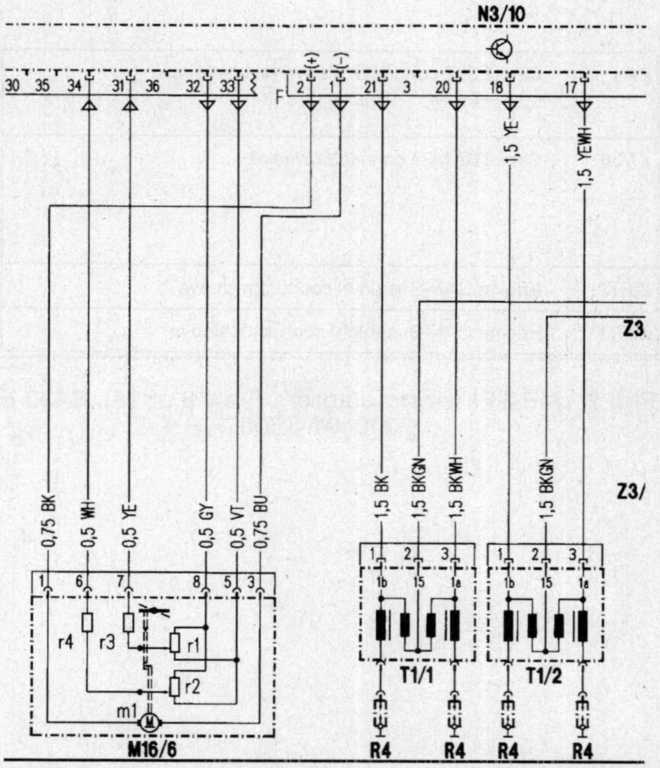

Fig. 7 ME-SFI wiring diagram (Part 14 of 18). S430 & 2000–01 S500

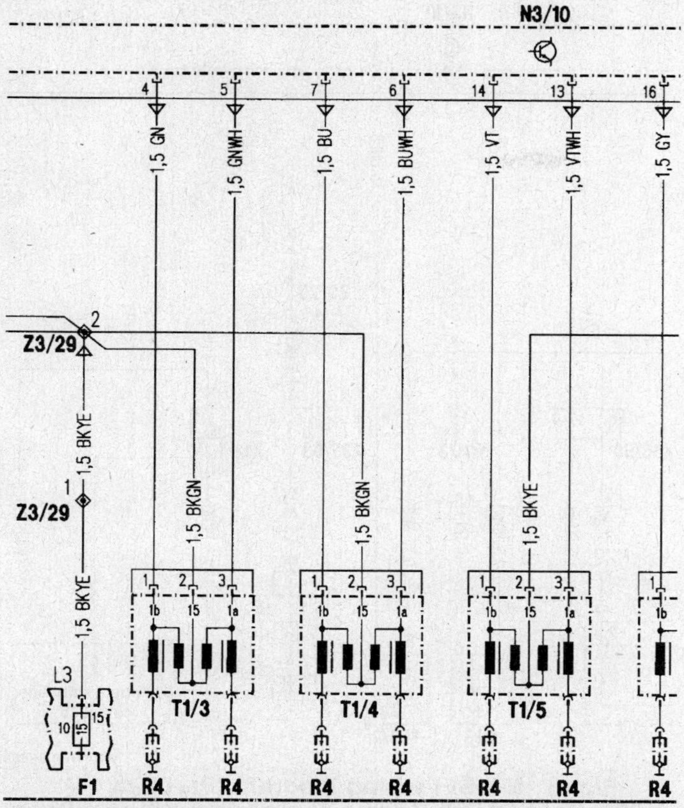

MB1010100240150X

Fig. 7 ME-SFI wiring diagram (Part 15 of 18). S430 & 2000–01 S500

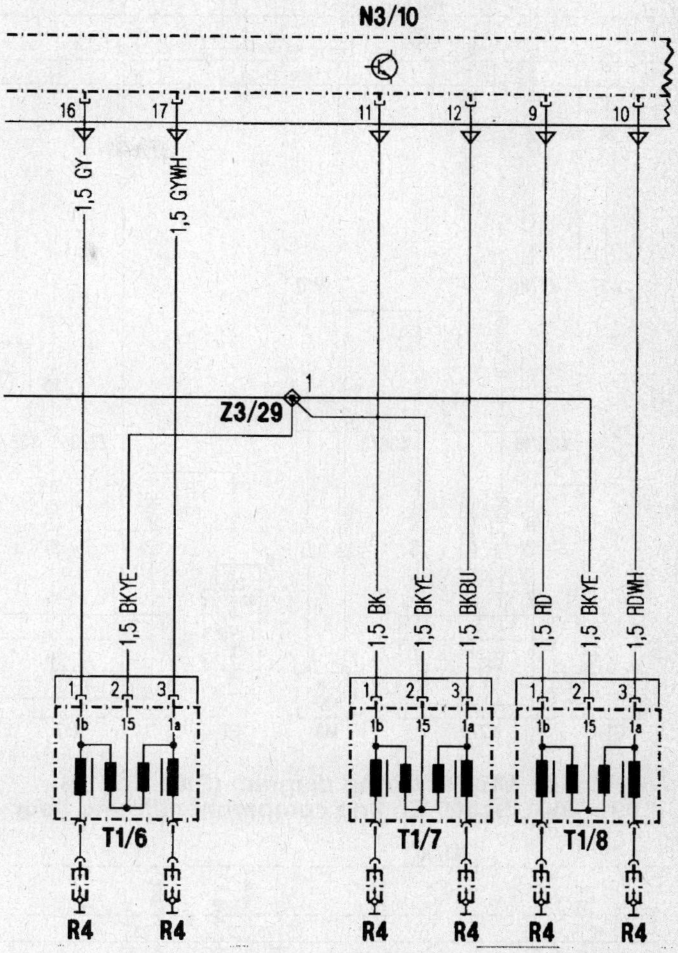

MB1010100240160X

Fig. 7 ME-SFI wiring diagram (Part 16 of 18). S430 & 2000–01 S500

A16/1	Right knock sensor 1
A16/2	Left knock sensor 2
B2/5	Hot film MAF sensor
B6/1	Camshaft Hall-effect sensor
B11/4	ECT sensor
B28	Pressure sensor
B40	Oil sensor (level, temperature, quality)
F1	Left fuse box
F1f10	Fuse 10
K40/7	Right front fuse/relay module
L5	CKP sensor
M16/6	Throttle valve control element
M16/6m1	Actuator motor
M16/6r1	Throttle valve actual value potentiometer
M16/6r2	Drive actual value potentiometer
M16/6r3	Actual value potentiometer (wiper 1)
M16/6r4	Actual value potentiometer (wiper 2)

N3/10	Engine control module (ME-SFI)
R4	Spark plugs
T1/1	Ignition coil (cylinder 1)
T1/2	Ignition coil (cylinder 2)
T1/3	Ignition coil (cylinder 3)
T1/4	Ignition coil (cylinder 4)

MB1010100240170X

Fig. 7 ME-SFI wiring diagram (Part 17 of 18). S430 & 2000–01 S500

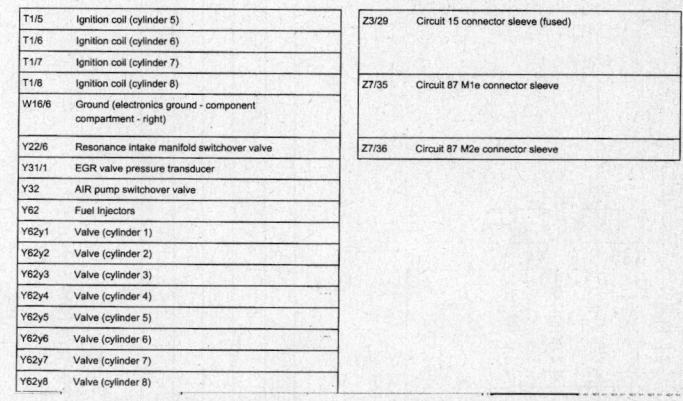

T1/5	Ignition coil (cylinder 5)
T1/6	Ignition coil (cylinder 6)
T1/7	Ignition coil (cylinder 7)
T1/8	Ignition coil (cylinder 8)
W16/6	Ground (electronics ground - component compartment - right)
Y22/6	Resonance intake manifold switchover valve
Y31/1	EGR valve pressure transducer
Y32	AIR pump switchover valve
Y62	Fuel Injectors
Y62y1	Valve (cylinder 1)
Y62y2	Valve (cylinder 2)
Y62y3	Valve (cylinder 3)
Y62y4	Valve (cylinder 4)
Y62y5	Valve (cylinder 5)
Y62y6	Valve (cylinder 6)
Y62y7	Valve (cylinder 7)
Y62y8	Valve (cylinder 8)

Z3/29	Circuit 15 connector sleeve (fused)
Z7/35	Circuit 87 M1e connector sleeve
Z7/36	Circuit 87 M2e connector sleeve

MB1010100240180X

Fig. 7 ME-SFI wiring diagram (Part 18 of 18). S430 & 2000–01 S500

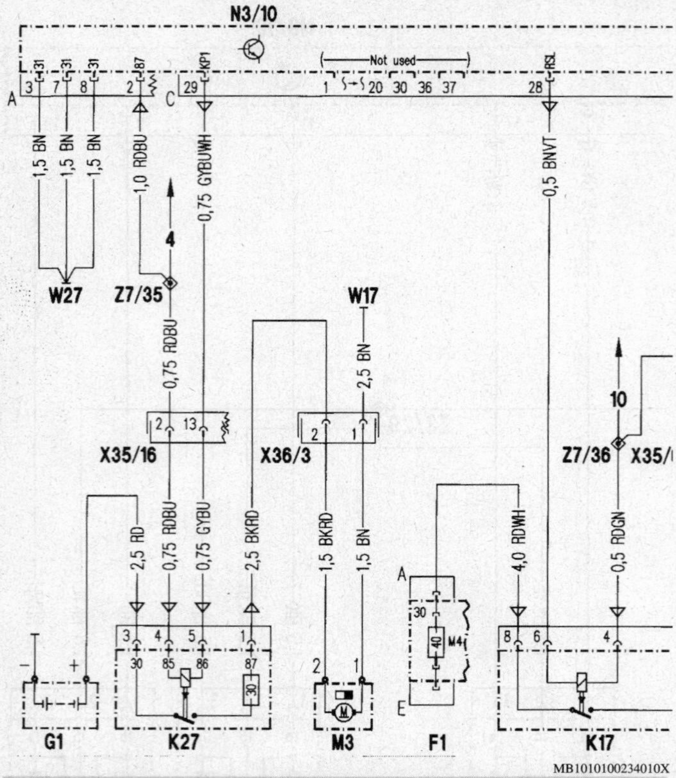

Fig. 8 ME-SFI wiring diagram (Part 1 of 14). 1999–2001 SL500 Engine compartment/frame floor

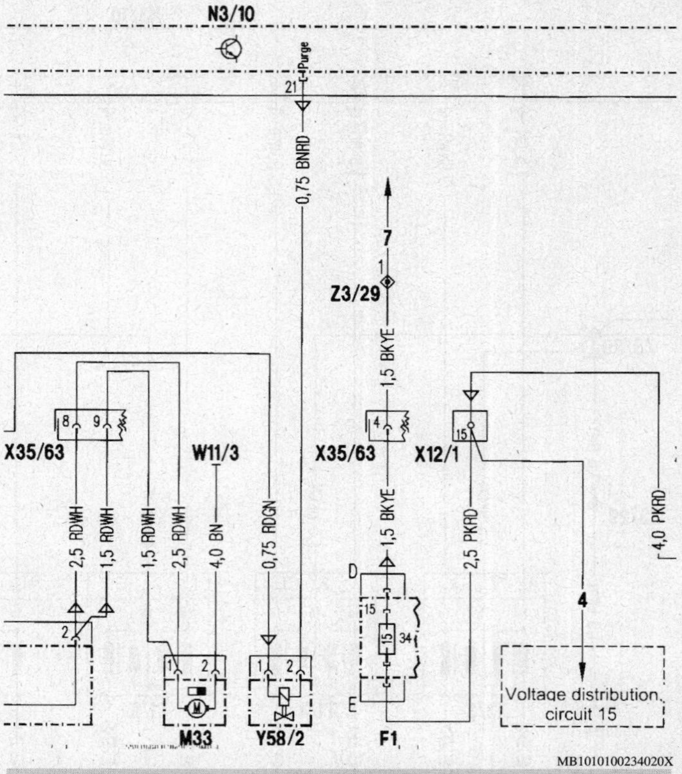

Fig. 8 ME-SFI wiring diagram (Part 2 of 14). 1999–2001 SL500 Engine compartment/frame floor

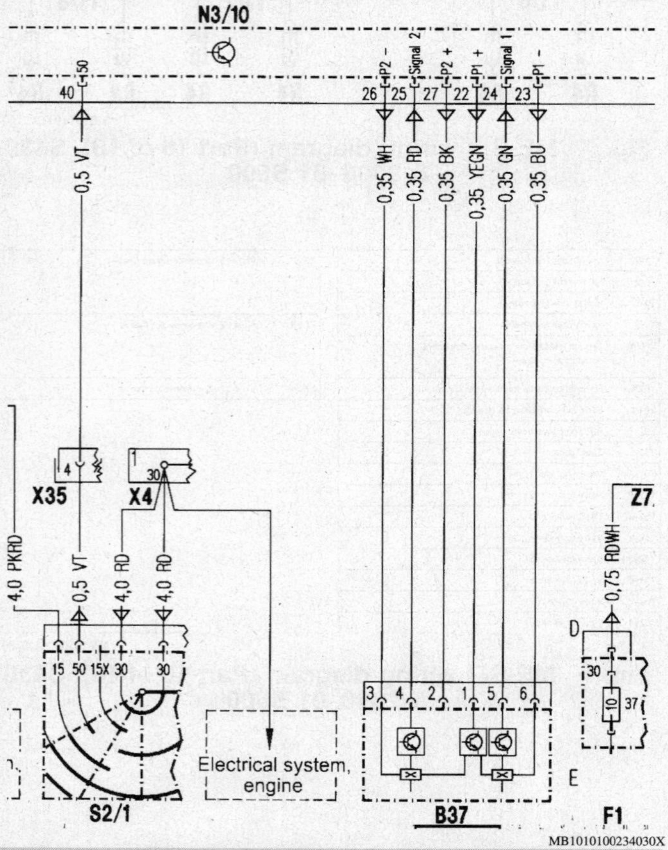

Fig. 8 ME-SFI wiring diagram (Part 3 of 14). 1999–2001 SL500 Engine compartment/frame floor

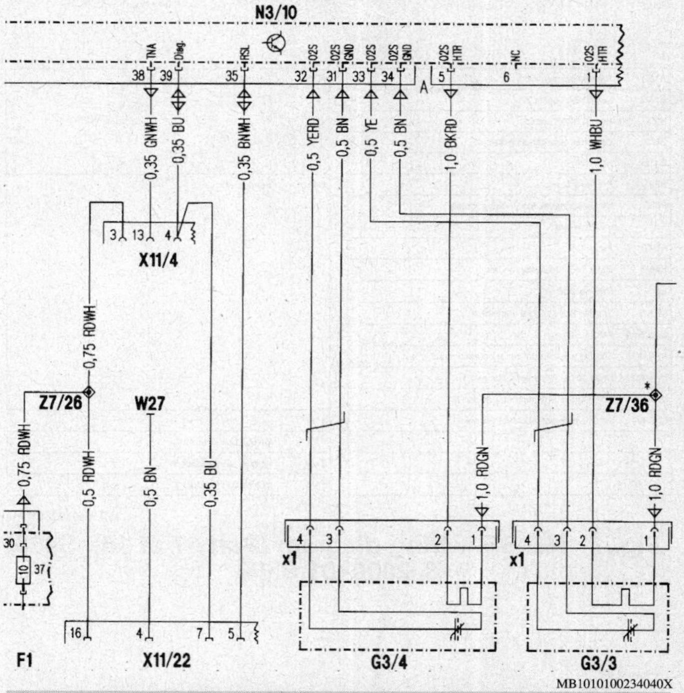

Fig. 8 ME-SFI wiring diagram (Part 4 of 14). 1999–2001 SL500 Engine compartment/frame floor

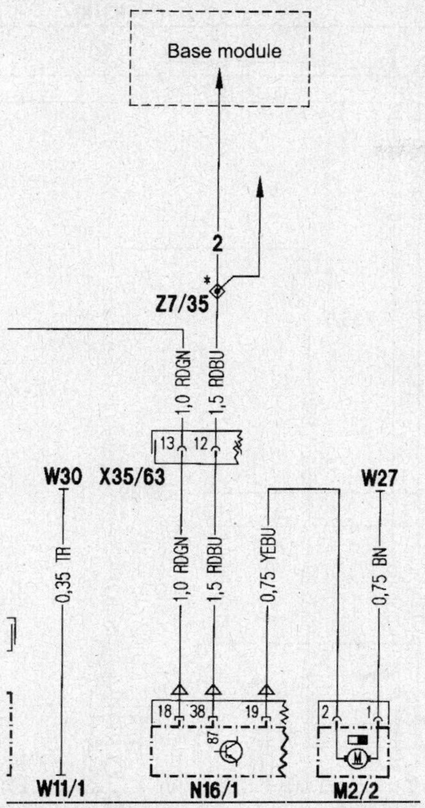

MB1010100234050X

Fig. 8 ME-SFI wiring diagram (Part 5 of 14). 1999–2001 SL500 Engine compartment/frame floor

B37	Pedal value sensor
F1	Fuse and relay box
F1f34	Fuse 34
F1f37	Fuse 37
F1fM4	Maxi-Fuse M4
G1	Battery
G3/3	Left O2S 1 (before TWC)
G3/3x1	Left O2S 1 connector (before TWC)
G3/4	Right O2S 1 (before TWC)
G3/4x1	Right O2S 1 connector (before TWC)
K17	AIR relay module
K27	FP relay module
M2/2	Module box blower motor
M3	FP assembly
M4	Auxiliary fan
M33	Electric air pump
N3/10	ME-SFI control module
N16/1	Base module (BM)
S2/1	Ignition/starter switch
W11/1	Ground (engine - ground strap)
W11/3	Ground (engine-left side)
W17	Ground (right rear seat)
W27	Ground (control module box/module box)
W30	Ground (left front longitudinal frame rail)
X4	Terminal block (circuit 30, fuse and relay box) (2-pole)
X11/4	Diagnostic test clutch
X11/22	Diagnostic module (OBD II) generic scan tool connector
X12/1	Terminal block (circuit 15 unfused)

MB1010100234060X

Fig. 8 ME-SFI wiring diagram (Part 6 of 14). 1999–2001 SL500 Engine compartment/frame floor

X35	Cockpit/module box separation point (12-pole)
X35/16	Module box/taillamp harness separation point (13-pole)
X35/63	Control module box/engine separation point
X36/3	FP harness connector (2-pole)
Y58/2	Left purge control valve (located on right side of engine)
Z3/29	Circuit 15 connector sleeve (fused)
Z7/26	Circuit 30 connector sleeve (solder joint in harness)
Z7/35	Circuit 87 M1e connector sleeve
Z7/36	Circuit 87 M2e connector sleeve

MB1010100234070X

Fig. 8 ME-SFI wiring diagram (Part 7 of 14). 1999–2001 SL500 Engine compartment/frame floor

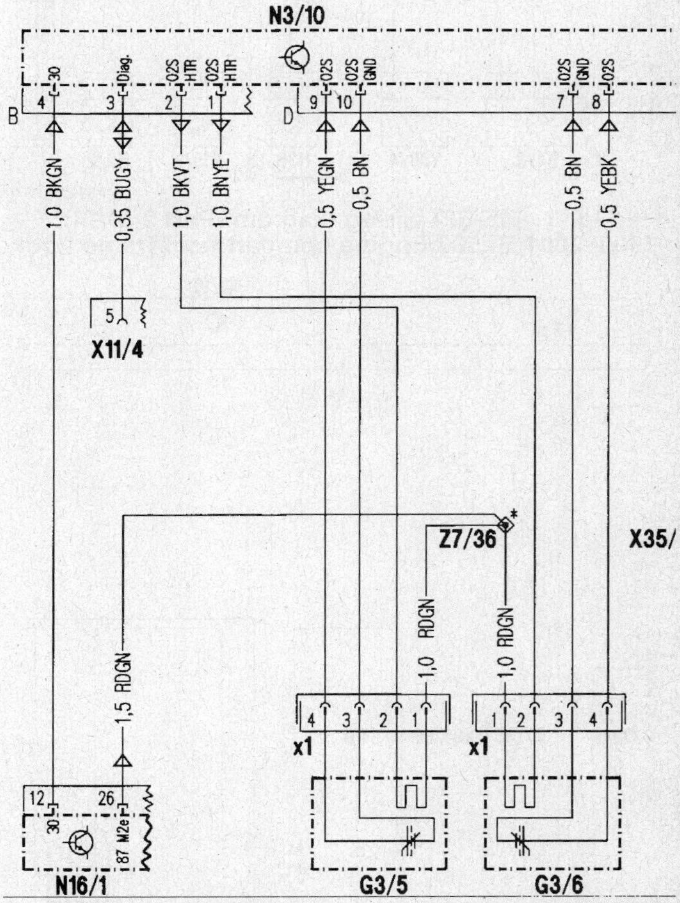

MB1010100235080X

Fig. 8 ME-SFI wiring diagram (Part 8 of 14). 1999–2001 SL500 Engine compartment/frame floor

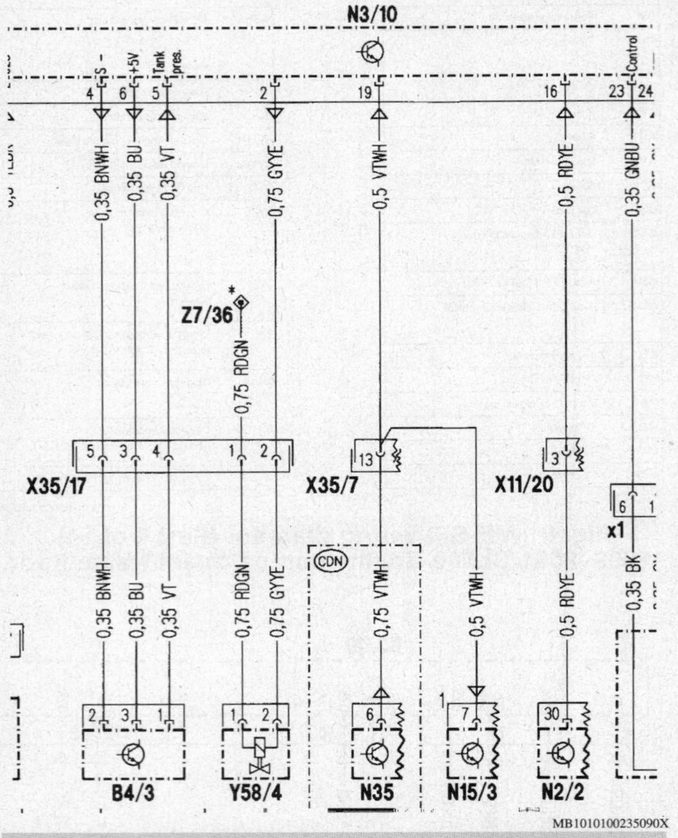

Fig. 8 ME-SFI wiring diagram (Part 9 of 14). 1999–2001 SL500 Engine compartment/frame floor

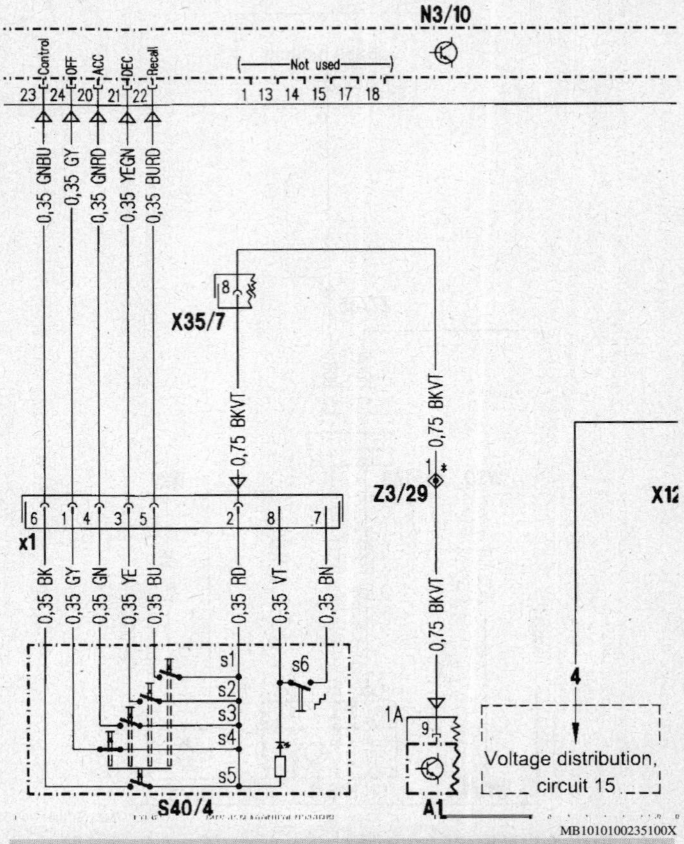

Fig. 8 ME-SFI wiring diagram (Part 10 of 14). 1999–2001 SL500 Engine compartment/frame floor

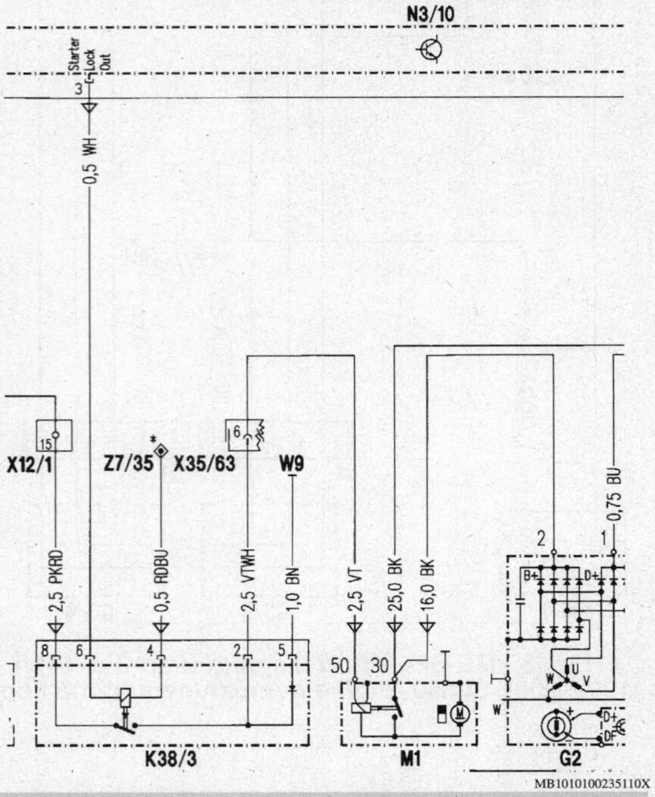

Fig. 8 ME-SFI wiring diagram (Part 11 of 14). 1999–2001 SL500 Engine compartment/frame floor

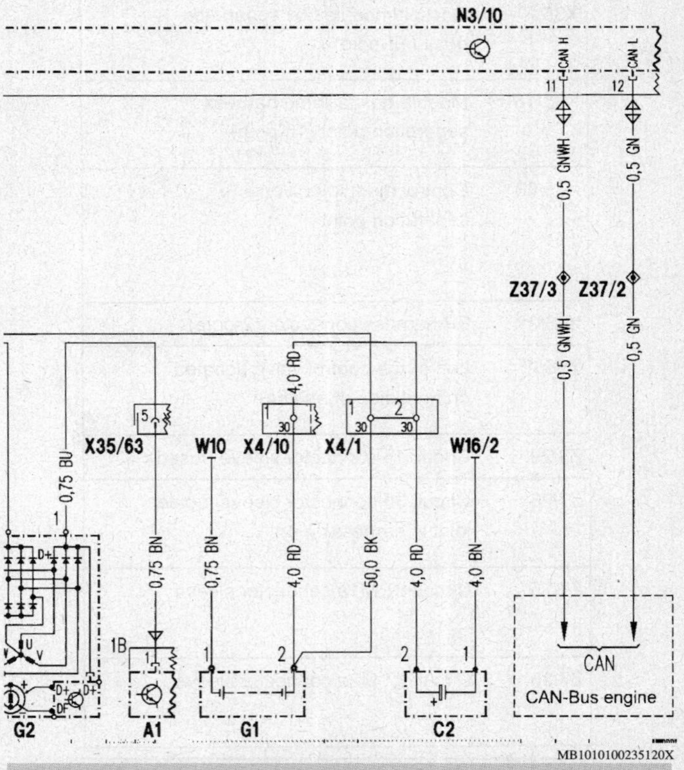

Fig. 8 ME-SFI wiring diagram (Part 12 of 14). 1999–2001 SL500 Engine compartment/frame floor

A1	Instrument cluster
B4/3	Fuel tank pressure sensor
C2	Electrolytic capacitor (generator/battery harness noise suppressor)
G1	Battery
G2	Generator
G3/5	Left O2S 2 (after TWC)
G3/5x1	Left O2S 2 connector (after TWC)
G3/6	Right O2S 2 (after TWC)
G3/6x1	Right O2S 2 connector (after TWC)
K38/3	Starter lock-out relay module
M1	Starter
N2/2	SRS control module
N3/10	ME-SFI control module
N15/3	ETC control module
N16/1	Base module (BM)
N35	Daytime running lamp control module
S40/4	CC with variable speed limitation pushbutton switch
S40/4s1	Memory recall
S40/4s2	Decelerate/set
S40/4s3	Accelerate/set
S40/4s4	Off
S40/4s5	Control contact
S40/4s6	Variable speed
S40/4x1	CC variable pushbutton switch connector
W9	Ground (at left headlamp unit)
W10	Ground (battery)
W16/2	Ground (component compartment - generator/battery harness noise suppressor)
X4/1	Terminal block (circuit 30, interior)

MB1010100235130X

Fig. 8 ME-SFI wiring diagram (Part 13 of 14). 1999–2001 SL500 Engine compartment/frame floor

X4/10	Terminal block (circuit 30/30Ü/61e/87L) (6-pole)
X11/4	Diagnostic test clutch
X11/20	Diagnostic intermediate connector (ATA, RCL, SRS [EDW, IFZ, SRS]) (4-pin, modular cabling
X12/1	Terminal block (circuit 15 unfused)
X35/7	Cockpit/module box separation point (18-pole)
X35/17	Module box/taillamp harness separation point (6-pole)
X35/63	Control module box/engine separation point
Y58/4	Activated charcoal canister shutoff valve
Z3/29	Circuit 15 connector sleeve (fused)
Z7/35	Circuit 87 M1e connector sleeve
Z7/36	Circuit 87 M2e connector sleeve
Z37/2	Engine CAN-Bus (low) connector sleeve
Z37/3	Engine CAN-Bus (high) connector sleeve

MB1010100235140X

Fig. 8 ME-SFI wiring diagram (Part 14 of 14). 1999–2001 SL500 Engine compartment/frame floor

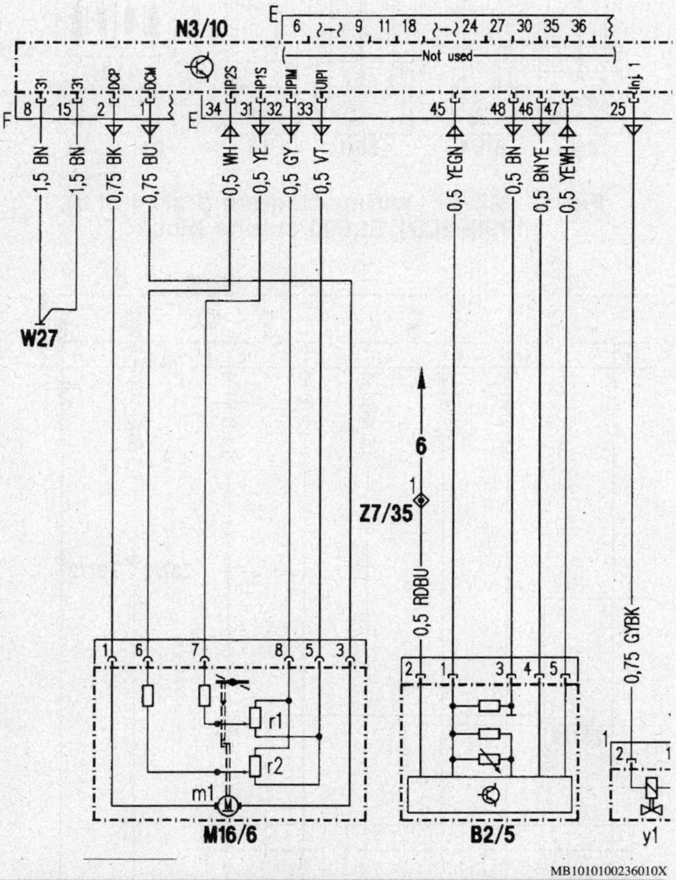

Fig. 9 ME-SFI wiring diagram (Part 1 of 8). 1999–2001 SL500 engine block

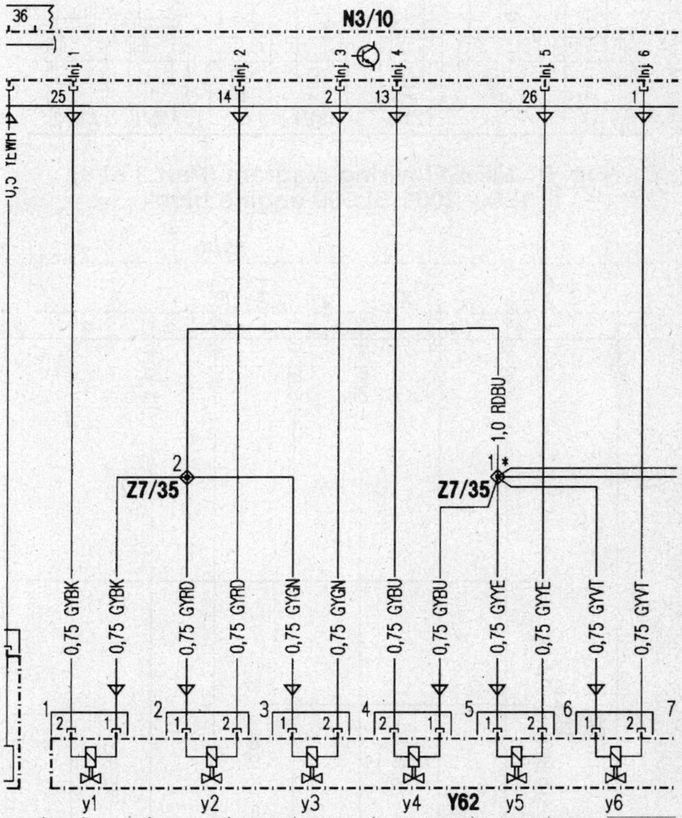

Fig. 9 ME-SFI wiring diagram (Part 2 of 8). 1999–2001 SL500 engine block

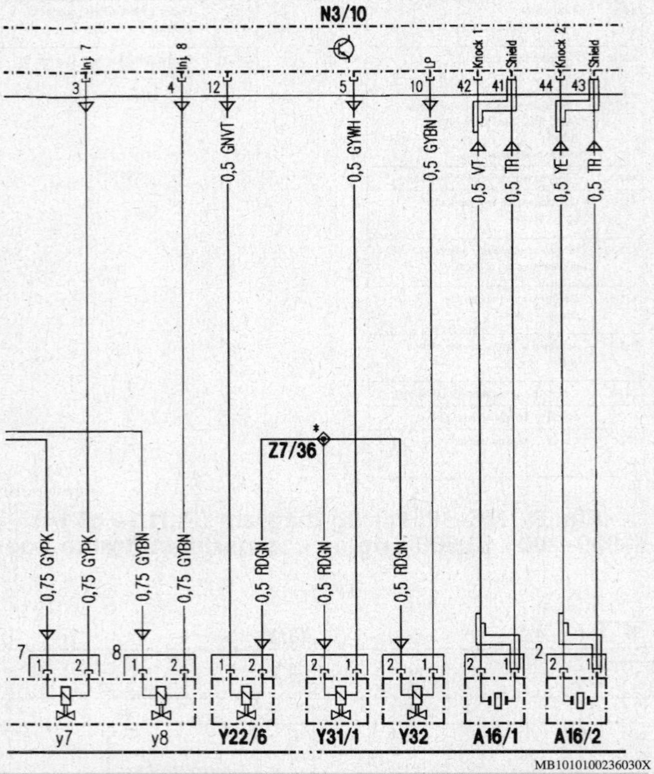

Fig. 9 ME-SFI wiring diagram (Part 3 of 8). 1999–2001 SL500 engine block

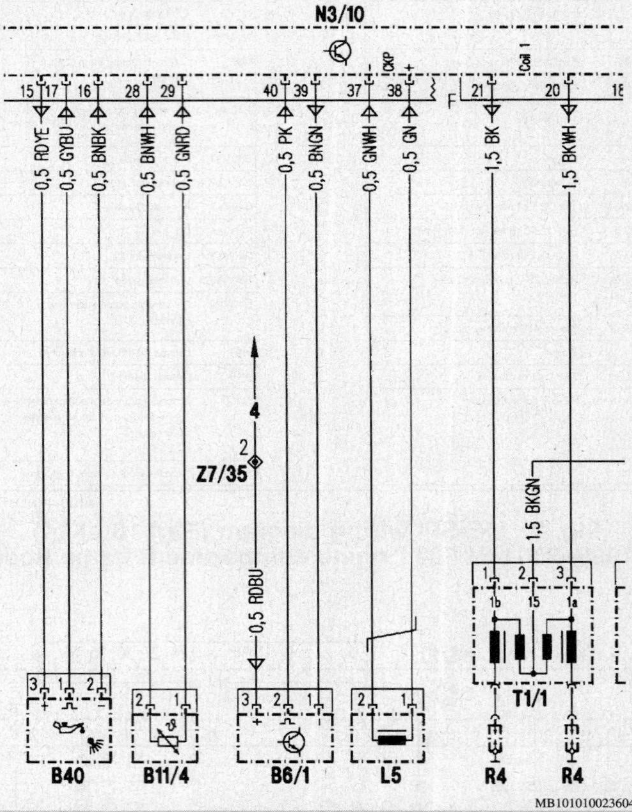

Fig. 9 ME-SFI wiring diagram (Part 4 of 8). 1999–2001 SL500 engine block

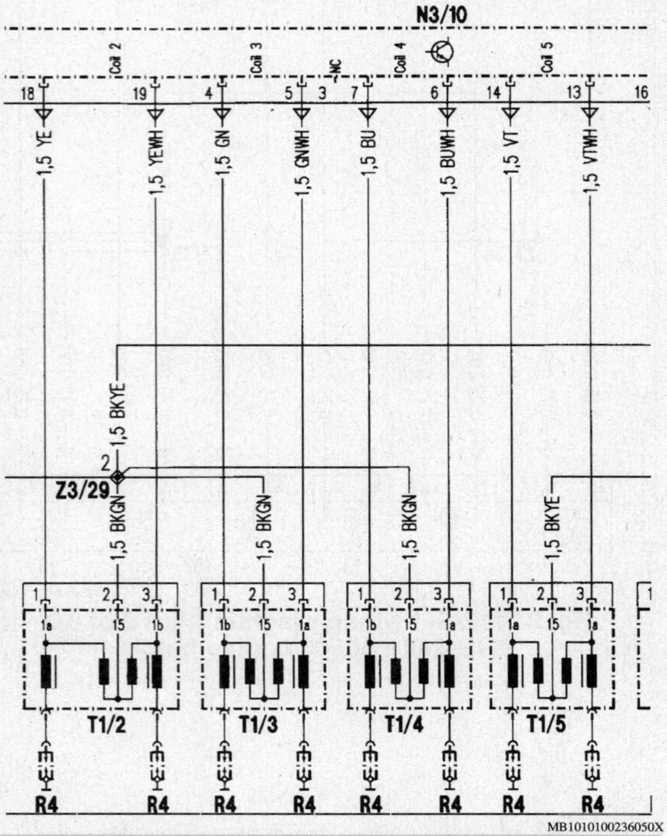

Fig. 9 ME-SFI wiring diagram (Part 5 of 8). 1999–2001 SL500 engine block

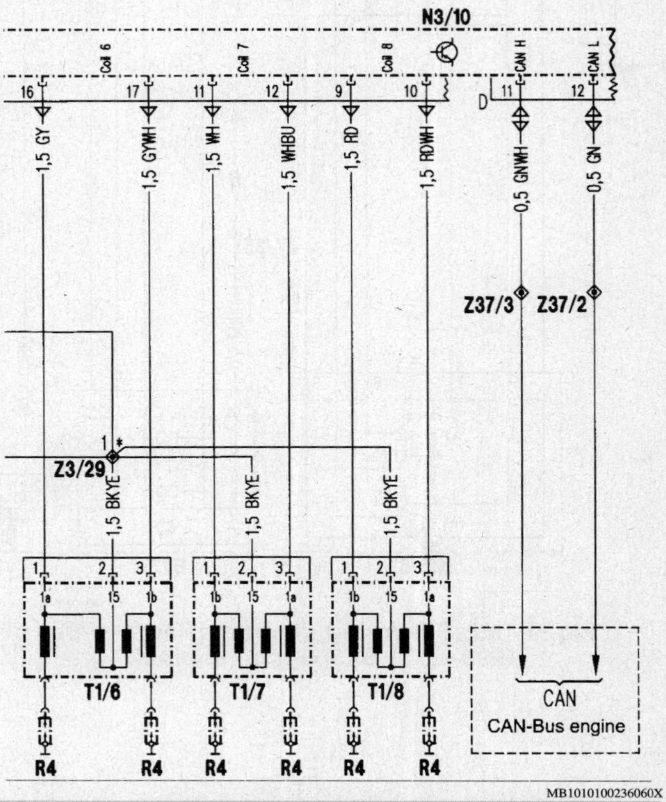

Fig. 9 ME-SFI wiring diagram (Part 6 of 8). 1999–2001 SL500 engine block

A16/1	Right knock sensor 1
A16/2	Left knock sensor 2
B2/5	Hot film MAF sensor
B6/1	Camshaft Hall-effect sensor
B11/4	ECT sensor
B40	Oil sensor (level, temperature, quality)
L5	CKP sensor
M16/6	Throttle valve control element
M16/6m1	Actuator motor
M16/6r1	Throttle valve actual value potentiometer
M16/6r2	Drive actual value potentiometer
N3/10	ME-SFI control module

R4	Spark plugs
T1/1	Ignition coil (cylinder 1)
T1/2	Ignition coil (cylinder 2)
T1/3	Ignition coil (cylinder 3)
T1/4	Ignition coil (cylinder 4)
T1/5	Ignition coil (cylinder 5)
T1/6	Ignition coil (cylinder 6)
T1/7	Ignition coil (cylinder 7)
T1/8	Ignition coil (cylinder 8)
W27	Ground (control module box/module box)

MB1010100236070X

Fig. 9 ME-SFI wiring diagram (Part 7 of 8). 1999–2001 SL500 engine block

Y22/6	Shifting induction pipe switchover valve
Y31/1	EGR pressure transducer
Y32	Air pump switchover valve
Y62	Fuel Injectors
Y62y1	Valve (cylinder 1)
Y62y2	Valve (cylinder 2)
Y62y3	Valve (cylinder 3)
Y62y4	Valve (cylinder 4)
Y62y5	Valve (cylinder 5)
Y62y6	Valve (cylinder 6)
Y62y7	Valve (cylinder 7)
Y62y8	Valve (cylinder 8)
Z3/29	Circuit 15 connector sleeve (fused)
Z7/35	Circuit 87 M1e connector sleeve
Z7/36	Circuit 87 M2e connector sleeve

Z37/2	Engine CAN-Bus (low) connector sleeve
Z37/3	Engine CAN-Bus (high) connector sleeve

MB1010100236080X

Fig. 9 ME-SFI wiring diagram (Part 8 of 8). 1999–2001 SL500 engine block

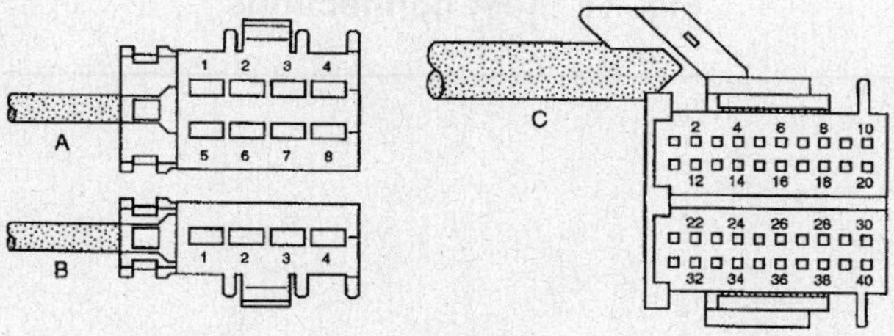

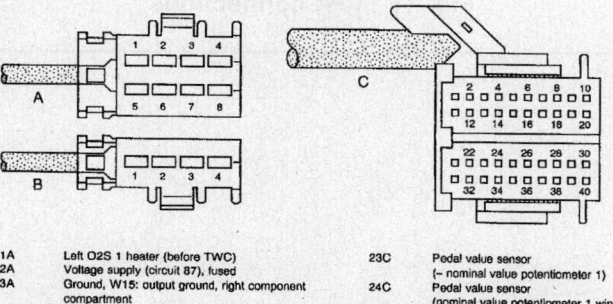

1A	Left O2S 1 heater (before TWC)
2A	Voltage supply (circuit 87), fused
3A	Ground, W15: output ground, right component compartment
4A	–
5A	Right O2S 1 heater (before TWC)
6A	Engine/climate control electric cooling fan control
7A	Ground, W15: output ground right footwell
8A	Ground, W15/1: electronics ground right footwell
1B	Right O2S 2 heater (after TWC) (only USA)
2B	Left O2S 2 heater (after TWC) (only USA)
3B	Diagnosis connection (data link connector)
4B	Voltage supply (circuit 30)
1C - 20C	–
21C	Purge control valve
22C	Pedal value sensor (+ nominal value potentiometer 1)
23C	Pedal value sensor (– nominal value potentiometer 1)
24C	Pedal value sensor (nominal value potentiometer 1 wiper)
25C	Pedal value sensor (nominal value potentiometer 2 wiper)
26C	Pedal value sensor (– nominal value potentiometer 2)
27C	Pedal value sensor (+ nominal value potentiometer 2)
28C	AIR pump relay module
29C	–
30C	–
31C	Right O2S 1 ground (before TWC)
32C	Right O2S 1 signal (before TWC)
33C	Left O2S 1 signal (before TWC)
34C	Left O2S 1 ground (before TWC)
35C-37C	–

MB1029800685010X

Fig. 10 Engine control module engine connector (Part 1 of 4)

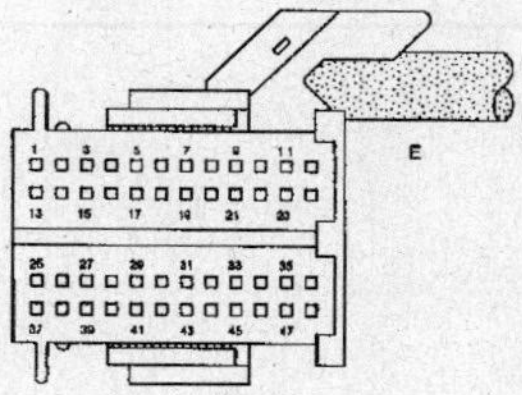

1E	Injector cyl. 6
2E	Injector cyl. 3
3E	Injector cyl. 7
4E	Injector cyl. 8
5E	EGR switch overvalve
6E - 9E	–
10E	AIR pump switchover valve (only USA)
11E	–
12E	Resonance intake manifold switchover valve
13E	Injector cyl. 4
14E	Injector cyl. 2
15E	Voltage supply 5 V, oil sensor (level/temperature/quality)
16E	Ground for oil sensor (level/temperature/quality)
17E	Signal for oil sensor (level/temperature/quality)
18E - 20E	–
21E	Signal for oil pressure switch
22E	Voltage supply 5 V, pressure sensor (only USA)
23E	Pressure sensor signal (only USA)
24E	Pressure sensor ground (only USA)
25E	Injector cyl. 1
26E	Injector cyl. 5
27E	AIR pump relay in relay module (only USA)
28E	ETC sensor ground
29E	ECT sensor signal
30E	–
31E	EA/CC/ISC actuator (actual value potentiometer 1 wiper)
32E	EA/CC/ISC actuator (actual value potentiometer ground)
33E	Actual value potentiometer voltage supply
34E	EA/CC/ISC actuator (actual value potentiometer 2 wiper)
35E – 36E	–
37E	CKP sensor ground
38E	CKP sensor signal
39E	Camshaft Hall-effect sensor ground
40E	Camshaft Hall-effect sensor signal

MB1029800685030X

Fig. 10 Engine control module engine connector (Part 3 of 4)

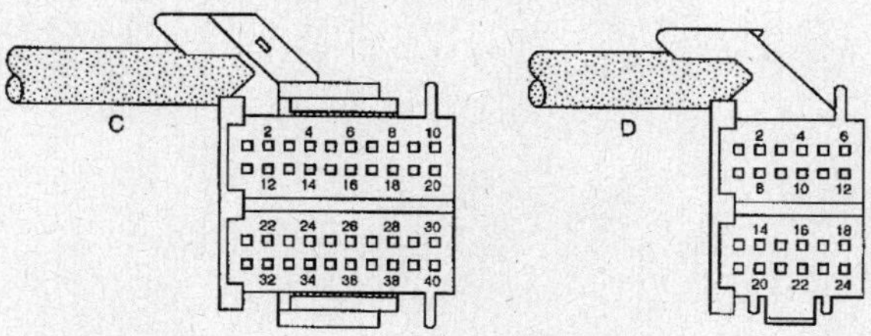

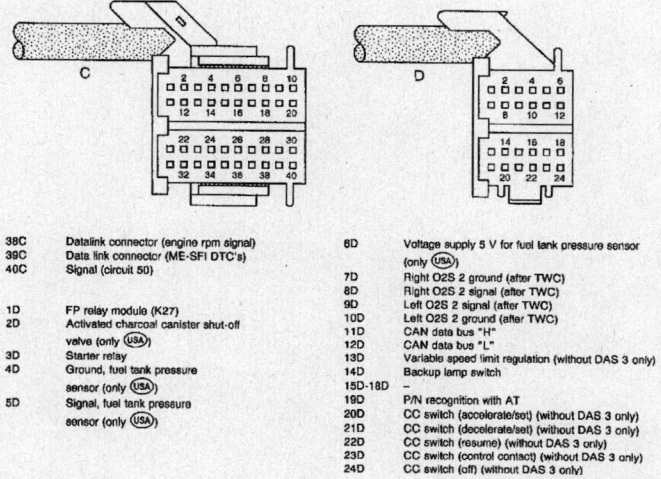

38C	Datalink connector (engine rpm signal)
39C	Data link connector (ME-SFI DTC's)
40C	Signal (circuit 50)
1D	FP relay module (K27)
2D	Activated charcoal canister shut-off valve (only USA)
3D	Starter relay
4D	Ground, fuel tank pressure sensor (only USA)
5D	Signal, fuel tank pressure sensor (only USA)
6D	Voltage supply 5 V for fuel tank pressure sensor (only USA)
7D	Right O2S 2 ground (after TWC)
8D	Right O2S 2 signal (after TWC)
9D	Left O2S 2 signal (after TWC)
10D	Left O2S 2 ground (after TWC)
11D	CAN data bus "H"
12D	CAN data bus "L"
13D	Variable speed limit regulation (without DAS 3 only)
14D	Backup lamp switch
15D-18D	–
19D	P/N recognition with AT
20D	CC switch (accelerate/set) (without DAS 3 only)
21D	CC switch (decelerate/set) (without DAS 3 only)
22D	CC switch (resume) (without DAS 3 only)
23D	CC switch (control contact) (without DAS 3 only)
24D	CC switch (off) (without DAS 3 only)

MB1029800685020X

Fig. 10 Engine control module engine connector (Part 2 of 4)

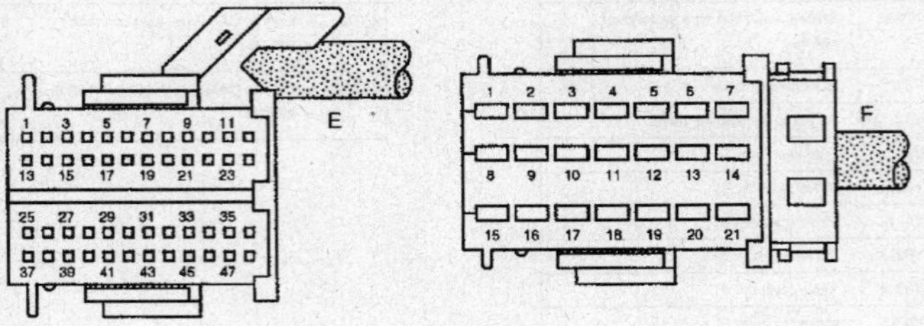

Figure 5

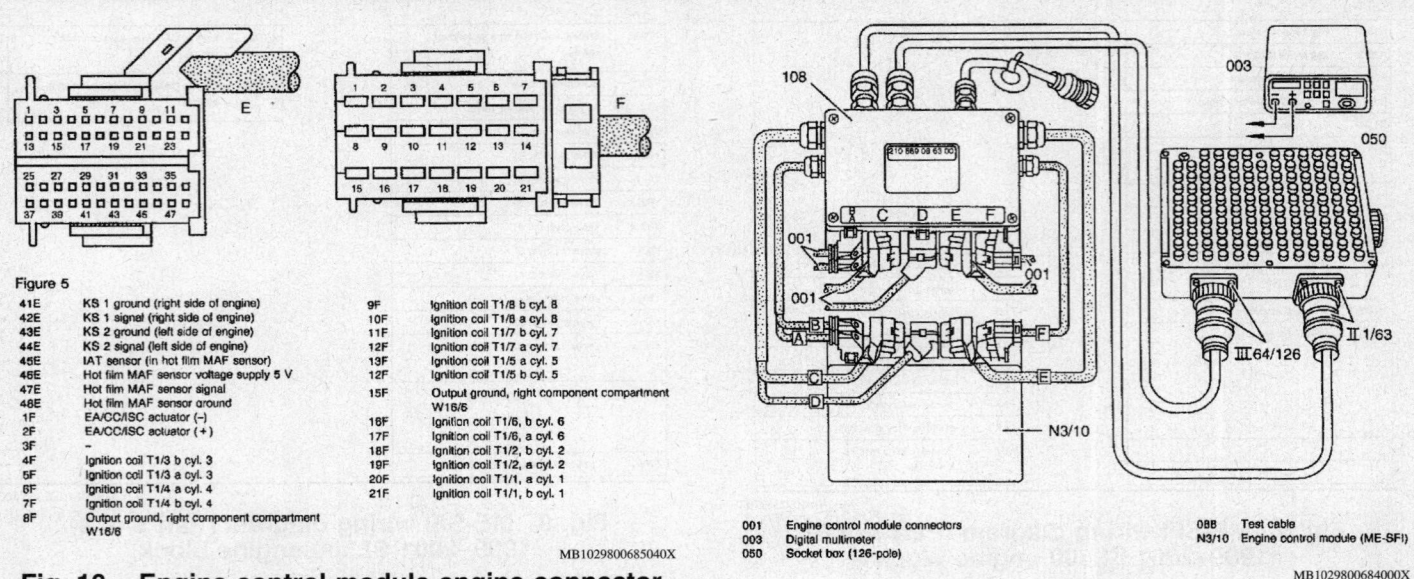

41E	KS 1 ground (right side of engine)	9F	Ignition coil T1/8 b cyl. 8
42E	KS 1 signal (right side of engine)	10F	Ignition coil T1/8 a cyl. 8
43E	KS 2 ground (left side of engine)	11F	Ignition coil T1/7 b cyl. 7
44E	KS 2 signal (left side of engine)	12F	Ignition coil T1/7 a cyl. 7
45E	IAT sensor (in hot film MAF sensor)	13F	Ignition coil T1/5 a cyl. 5
46E	Hot film MAF sensor voltage supply 5 V	12F	Ignition coil T1/5 b cyl. 5
47E	Hot film MAF sensor signal	15F	Output ground, right component compartment W16/6
48E	Hot film MAF sensor ground		
1F	EA/CC/ISC actuator (–)	16F	Ignition coil T1/6, b cyl. 6
2F	EA/CC/ISC actuator (+)	17F	Ignition coil T1/6, a cyl. 6
3F	–	18F	Ignition coil T1/2, b cyl. 2
4F	Ignition coil T1/3 b cyl. 3	19F	Ignition coil T1/2, a cyl. 2
5F	Ignition coil T1/3 a cyl. 3	20F	Ignition coil T1/1, a cyl. 1
6F	Ignition coil T1/4 a cyl. 4	21F	Ignition coil T1/1, b cyl. 1
7F	Ignition coil T1/4 b cyl. 4		
8F	Output ground, right component compartment W16/6		

MB1029800685040X

Fig. 10 Engine control module engine connector (Part 4 of 4)

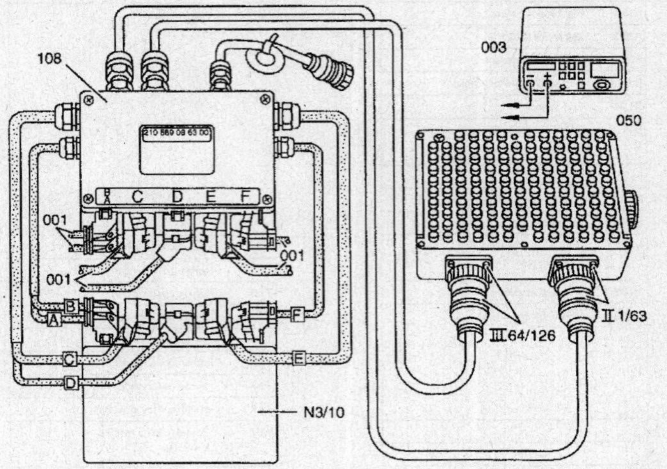

001	Engine control module connectors	088	Test cable
003	Digital multimeter	N3/10	Engine control module (ME-SFI)
050	Socket box (126-pole)		

MB1029800684000X

Fig. 11 Test connections

DIAGNOSTIC CHART INDEX

Code	Description	Page No.	Fig. No.
—	Test 23, Step 7.0	14-131	17
	Test 23, Step 8.2–9.0	14-131	19
	Test 24, Step 3.0–4.0.	14-134	43
	Test 23, Steps 5.0–6.0	14-134	44
	Test 24, Steps 7.0–8.0	14-134	45
	Test 24, Steps 9.0–10.0	14-134	46
	Test 32, Fuel System Pressure & Internal Leakage Test	14-136	60
	Test 34, Fuel Pump Test	14-136	62
	Test 36, Injector Test	14-137	64
P0100	Test 23, Steps 3.1–4.2	14-131	14
P0105	Test 23, Steps 5.1–6.0	14-131	16
P0110	Test 23, Steps 4.3–5.0	14-131	15
P0115	Test 23, Steps 8.0–8.1	14-131	18
P0120	Test 25, Steps 3.0–3.1	14-136	57
P0130	Test 23, Steps 10.0–12.0	14-131	20
P0133	Test 23, Steps 10.0–12.0	14-131	20
P0135	Test 23, Steps 10.0–12.0	14-131	20
	Test 23, Steps 13.0–14.0	14-132	21
P0136	Test 23, Steps 15.0–16.0	14-132	22
P0141	Test 23, Step 17.0	14-132	23
P0150	Test 23, Steps 10.0–12.0	14-131	20
P0153	Test 23, Steps 10.0–12.0	14-131	20
P0155	Test 23, Steps 10.0–12.0	14-131	20
	Test 23, Steps 13.0–14.0	14-132	21
P0156	Test 23, Steps 13.0–14.0	14-132	21
P0160	Test 23, Steps 13.0–14.0	14-132	21
P0161	Test 23, Steps 15.0–16.0	14-132	22
P0201	Test 23, Step 18.0	14-132	24
P0202	Test 23, Step 19.0	14-132	25
P0203	Test 23, Step 20.0	14-132	26
P0204	Test 23, Step 21.0	14-132	27
P0205	Test 23, Step 22.0	14-132	28
P0206	Test 23, Step 23.0	14-132	29
P0207	Test 23, Step 24.0	14-132	30
P0208	Test 23, Step 25.0	14-133	31
P0300	Test 24, Steps 13.0–14.0	14-135	49
	Test 24, Steps 14.1–15.1	14-135	50
	Test 24, Steps 16.0–17.0	14-135	51
	Test 24, Steps 17.1–18.1	14-135	52
	Test 24, Steps 19.0–19.1	14-135	53
	Test 24, Steps 20.0–20.1	14-135	54
	Test 24, Step 21.0	14-135	55
P0301	Test 24, Steps 13.0–14.0	14-135	49
	Test 24, Step 21.0	14-135	55
P0302	Test 24, Steps 13.0–14.0	14-135	49
	Test 24, Step 21.0	14-135	55
P0303	Test 24, Steps 14.1–15.1	14-135	50
	Test 24, Step 21.0	14-135	55
P0304	Test 24, Steps 16.0–17.0	14-135	51
	Test 24, Step 21.0	14-135	55
P0305	Test 24, Steps 16.0–17.0	14-135	51
	Test 24, Step 21.0	14-135	55
P0306	Test 24, Steps 17.1–18.1	14-135	52
	Test 24, Steps 19.0–19.1	14-135	53
	Test 24, Steps 20.0–20.1	14-135	54
	Test 24, Step 21.0	14-135	55
P0307	Test 24, Step 21.0	14-135	55

Continued

DIAGNOSTIC CHART INDEX—Continued

Code	Description	Page No.	Fig. No.
P0308	Test 24, Step 21.0	14-135	55
P0335	Test 24, Steps 11.0–11.1	14-134	47
P0341	Test 24, Steps 12.0–12.1	14-135	48
P0400	Test 23, Step 29.0	14-133	34
P0410	Test 23, Step 28.0	14-133	33
P0420	Test 23, Steps 26.0–27.0	14-133	32
P0440	Test 23, Steps 32.0–33.0	14-133	36
P0441	Test 23, Steps 30.0–31.0	14-133	35
	Test 23, Steps 32.0–33.0	14-133	36
P0442	Test 23, Steps 32.0–33.0	14-133	36
P0443	Test 23, Steps 30.0–31.0	14-133	35
P0446	Test 23, Steps 34.0–35.1	14-133	37
P0450	Test 23, Steps 34.0–35.1	14-133	37
P0453	Test 23, Steps 26.0–27.0	14-133	32
P0455	Test 23, Steps 32.0–33.0	14-133	36
	Test 23, Steps 34.0–35.1	14-133	37
P0507	Test 25, Steps 1.0–2.0	14-136	56
	Test 25, Steps 3.0–3.1	14-136	57
P0560	Test 23, Steps 1.0–1.2	14-131	12
	Test 23, Steps 2.0–3.0	14-131	13
	Test 24, Steps 1.0–1.1	14-134	41
	Test 24, Steps 1.2–2.2	14-134	42
P0600	Test 23, Steps 36.0–36.2	14-133	38
P0801	Test 23, Steps 38.0–39.0	14-134	40
P0802	Test 23, Steps 30.0–31.0	14-133	35
P1177	Test 23, Steps 37.0–37.1	14-134	39
P1178	Test 23, Steps 37.0–37.1	14-134	39
P1179	Test 23, Steps 37.0–37.1	14-134	39
P1180	Test 23, Steps 37.0–37.1	14-134	39
P1182	Test 23, Steps 2.0–3.0	14-131	13
P1185	Test 23, Steps 37.0–37.1	14-134	39
P1186	Test 25, Steps 3.0–3.1	14-136	57
	Test 25, Steps 4.0–5.0	14-136	58
P1400	Test 23, Step 29.0	14-133	34
P1542	Test 25, Steps 1.0–2.0	14-136	56
P1570	Test 23, Steps 36.0–36.2	14-133	38
P1580	Test 25, Steps 3.0–3.1	14-136	57
	Test 25, Steps 4.0–5.0	14-136	58
P1747	Test 23, Steps 36.0–36.2	14-133	38

⇒		Test scope	Test connection	Test condition	Nominal value	Possible cause/remedy
1.0	P0 560	**Engine control module (ME-SFI) (N3/10)** Voltage supply Circuit 30 U	N3/10 3 (3A) –V– 12 (4B)	Ignition: **ON**	11 – 14 V	⇒ 1.1
1.1		Ground wire, Output ground	N3/10 / X11/4 3 (3A) –V– 2 7 (7A) –V– 2 112 (8F) –V– 2 119 (15F) –V– 2	Ignition: **ON**	11 – 14 V	Wiring, Output ground (W16/6), right component compartment, ⇒ 1.2
1.2		Voltage supply Circuit 30	X11/4 / N3/10 1 –V– 12 (4B)	Ignition: **ON**	11 – 14 V	Wiring, **Model 210:** Passenger-side fuse and relay module (K40/4).

MB1029800686000X

Fig. 12 Code P0560: Test 23, Steps 1.0–1.2

⇒		Test scope	Test connection	Test condition	Nominal value	Possible cause/remedy
2.0	P0 560	**Engine control module (ME-SFI) (N3/10)** Voltage supply Circuit 87	N3/10 8 (8A) –V– 2 (2A)	Ignition: **ON**	11 – 14 V	⇒ 2.1 – 2.2
2.1		Electronics ground	N3/10 / X11/4 8 (8A) –V– 2	Ignition: **ON**	11 – 14 V	Wiring, **Model 210:** Output ground (W16/6), right component compartment.
2.2		Voltage supply Circuit 87	X11/4 / N3/10 1 –V– 12 (2A)	Ignition: **ON** Ignition: **OFF**	11 – 14 V < 1 V	Wiring, **Model 210:** Passenger-side fuse and relay module (K40/4).
3.0	P1 182	**Starter relay (K40/4k2): In passenger-side fuse and relay module box (K40/4)** Activation	N3/10 35 (3D) –V– 2 (2A)	ECT temperature > 20 ° C Ignition/starter switch (S2/1): position 3 (start position): crank engine **briefly**	11 – 14 V or if engine does not start in approx. 5 seconds.	⇒ 3.1, Engine control module (N3/10)

MB1029800687000X

Fig. 13 Codes P0560 & P1182: Test 23, Steps 2.0–3.0

⇒		Test scope	Test connection	Test condition	Nominal value	Possible cause/remedy
3.1		**Starter signal circuit 50**	N3/10 8 (8A) –V– 32 (40C)	Engine: **Start**	11 – 14 V while starting.	Wiring, Ignition/starter switch (S2/1).
4.0	P0 100	**Hot film MAF sensor (B2/5)** Hot film signal	N3/10 104 (48E) –V– 103 (47E)	Ignition: **ON** Engine: **at idle** Engine coolant temperature >70°C	0.9 – 1.1 V 1.3 – 1.7 V 2)	⇒ 4.1 – 4.3, Wiring, Air intake system leak, B2/5
4.1		**Hot film MAF sensor (B2/5)** Voltage supply 5 V	N3/10 / B2/5 104 (48E) –V– 4	Disconnect MAF sensor (B2/5) connector and measure directly on socket 4 (brown/yellow). Ignition: **ON**	4.7 – 5.2 V	Wiring, N3/10
4.2		**Ground wire for hot film MAF sensor (B2/5)**	B2/5 / N3/10 3 –V– 102 (46E)	Disconnect MAF sensor (B2/5) connector and measure directly on socket 3 (brown). Ignition: **ON**	4.7 – 5.2 V	Wiring.

2) Increasing rpm, increasing voltage.

MB1029800688000X

Fig. 14 Code P0100: Test 23, Steps 3.1–4.2

⇒		Test scope	Test connection	Test condition	Nominal value	Possible cause/remedy
4.3		**Hot film MAF sensor (B2/5)** Voltage supply 12 V	N3/10 / B2/5 104 (48E) –V– 2 (2)	Disconnect MAF sensor (B2/5) connector and connect plus of voltmeter to socket 2 (red/blue). Ignition: **ON**	11 – 14 V	Wiring, Passenger-side fuse and relay module (K40/4).
5.0	P0 110	**IAT sensor in hot film MAF sensor (B2/5)** Voltage	N3/10 104 (48E) –V– 101 (45E)	Ignition: **ON**	°C V 10 3.1 20 2.7 30 2.2 40 1.8 50 1.4 60 1.1 ± 5%	⇒ 5.1 N3/10

MB1029800689000X

Fig. 15 Code P0110: Test 23, Steps 4.3–5.0

⇒		Test scope	Test connection	Test condition	Nominal value	Possible cause/remedy
5.1		IAT sensor Resistance	N3/10 104 (48E) –Ω– 101 (45E)	Ignition: **OFF** Disconnect connector **E** on engine control module (N3/10).	°C Ω 10 3600 20 2420 30 1660 40 1170 50 850 60 600 ± 5%	B2/5
6.0	P0 105	**Only (USA)** **Pressure sensor (B28)** Sensor signal	N3/10 80 (24E) –V– 79 (22E)	Connect vacuum tester to B28, using the Y-connector. Ignition: **ON** Engine: **at idle**	> 3.5 V < 2 V and vacuum climbs to > 500 mbar.	Vacuum line, Wiring, B28, N3/10
		Pressure sensor (B28) Voltage supply	N3/10 80 (24E) –V– 78 (22E)	Ignition: **ON**	4.7 – 5.3 V	

MB1029800690000X

Fig. 16 Code P0105: Test 23, Steps 5.1–6.0

⇒		Test scope	Test connection	Test condition	Nominal value	Possible cause/remedy
7.0		**FP relay module (K27)** Activation	N3/10 21 (29C) –V– 2 (2A)	Ignition: **ON** Engine: **Start**	11 – 14 V for approx. 1 sec. 3) 11 – 14 V during cranking and while engine runs.	Wiring, K27 or, N3/10
		Current draw (K27)	N3/10 8 (8A) –A– 21 (29C)	Ignition: **ON**	0.1 – 0.3 A	

3) The activation of the FP occurs only once after ignition "ON". For the next activation, the engine must have run briefly.

MB1029800691000X

Fig. 17 Code —: Test 23, Step 7.0

⇒		Test scope	Test connection	Test condition	Nominal value	Possible cause/remedy
8.0	P0 115	**ECT sensor (B11/4)** Voltage	N3/10 84 (28E) –V– 85 (29E)	Ignition: **ON**	°C V 20 3.4 30 2.9 40 2.4 50 1.9 60 1.5 70 1.2 80 0.9 90 0.7 100 0.5 ±5 %	⇒ 8.1, N3/10
8.1		Resistance (B11/4)	N3/10 84 (28E) –Ω– 85 (29E)	Ignition: **OFF** Disconnect connector **E** on engine control module (N3/10).	°C Ω 20 3090 30 2000 40 1330 50 900 60 620 70 440 80 320 90 230 100 170 ±5 %	⇒ 8.2, Wiring.

MB1029800692000X

Fig. 18 Code P0115: Test 23, Steps 8.0–8.1

⇒		Test scope	Test connection	Test condition	Nominal value	Possible cause/remedy
8.2		ECT sensor (B11/4) Resistance	B11/4 1 –Ω– 2	Disconnect connector on ECT sensor (B11/4).	Nominal value, see ⇒ 8.1	B11/4
9.0		**Engine control module (N3/10)** TN-signal output	N3/10 3) 8 (8A) –oscilloscope– 30 (38C) N3/10 4) 8 (8A) –V– 30 (38C)	Engine: **Start** or Engine: **at idle**	Signal: see Figure 2. 7.5 – 9.0 V	Wiring, N3/10

3) Test with oscilloscope.
4) Test with multimeter only if oscilloscope is not available.

MB1029800693000X

Fig. 19 Code —: Test 23, Step 8.2–9.0

⇒		Test scope	Test connection	Test condition	Nominal value	Possible cause/remedy
10.0	P0 150 P0 153	**Left O2S 1 (before TWC) (G3/3)** O2S signal	N3/10 26 (34C) –V– 25 (33C)	ECT > 80 ° C, run engine at idle for at least two minutes.	fluctuates from – 0.2 V to + 1.0 V, by more than 0.3 V	⇒ 12.0, Wiring, G3/3
11.0	P0 130 P0 133	**Right O2S 1 (before TWC) (G3/4)** O2S signal	N3/10 23 (31C) –V– 24 (32C)	ECT > 80 ° C, run engine at idle for at least two minutes.	fluctuates from – 0.2 V to + 1.0 V, by more than 0.3 V	⇒ 13.0, Wiring, G3/4
12.0	P0 135 P0 155	**Left O2S 1 (before TWC) (G3/3)** O2S heater Activation	N3/10 1 (1A) –V– 2 (2A)	Engine: **at idle** ECT > 80° C, run engine at idle for at least 2 minutes.	11 – 14 V	Wiring, G3/3, N3/10
		O2S 1 (G3/3) Current draw	N3/10 3 (3A) –A– 1 (1A)	Disconnect connector **A** on engine control module N3/10 Ignition: **ON**	1.5 – 4.5 A	

MB1029800694000X

Fig. 20 Codes P0130, P0133, P0135. P0150, P0153 & P0155: Test 23, Steps 10.0–12.0

⇒		Test scope	Test connection	Test condition	Nominal value	Possible cause/remedy
13.0	P0 135 P0 155	**Right O2S 1 (before TWC) (G3/4)** O2S heater Activation	N3/10 5 (5A) –(V)– 2 (2A)	Engine: **at idle** ECT > 80° C, run engine at idle for at least 2 minutes.	11 – 14 V	Wiring, G3/4, N3/10
		O2S 2 (G3/4) Current draw	N3/10 3 (3A) –(A)– 5 (5A)	Disconnect connector **A** on engine control module N3/10 Ignition: **ON**	1.5 – 4.5 A	
14.0	P0 156 P0 160	**Only (USA)** **Left O2S 2 (after TWC) (G3/5)** O2S signal	N3/10 42 (10D) –(V)– 41 (9D)	ECT > 80° C, run engine at 2000-3000 rpm for approx. 2 minutes.		⇒ 16.0, Wiring, G3/5, N3/10
			N3/10 3 (3A) ←→ 66 (10E) 3 (3A) ←→ 20 (28C)	Engine: **at idle** Bridge sockets on socket box.	> 550mV Air pump runs. Voltage changes within 60 seconds to < 40 mV	

MB1029800695000X

Fig. 21 Codes P0135, P0155, P0156 & P0160: Test 23, Steps 13.0–14.0

⇒		Test scope	Test connection	Test condition	Nominal value	Possible cause/remedy
15.0	P0 136	**Only (USA)** **Right O2S 2 (after TWC) (G3/6)** O2S signal	N3/10 39 (7D) –(V)– 40 (8D)	ECT > 80° C, run engine at 2000-3000 rpm for approx. 2 minutes.		⇒ 17.0, Wiring, G3/6, N3/10
			N3/10 3 (3A) ←→ 60 (10E) 3 (3A) ←→ 20 (28C)	Engine: **at idle** Bridge sockets on socket box.	> 550mV Air pump runs. Voltage changes within 60 seconds to < 40 mV	
16.0	P0 161	**Only (USA)** **Left O2S 2 (after TWC) (G3/5)** O2S heater Activation	N3/10 10 (2B) –(V)– 2 (2A)	Engine: **at idle** ECT > 80° C, run engine at idle for at least 2 minutes.	11 – 14 V or voltage fluctuates between 1 – 14 V.	Wiring, G3/5, N3/10
		O2S 2 (G3/5) Current draw	N3/10 3 (3A) –(A)– 10 (2B)	Disconnect connector **B** on engine control module N3/10 Ignition: **ON**	1.5 – 4.5 A	

MB1029800696000X

Fig. 22 Codes P0136 & P0161: Test 23, Steps 15.0–16.0

⇒		Test scope	Test connection	Test condition	Nominal value	Possible cause/remedy
17.0	P0 141	**Only (USA)** **Right O2S 2 (after TWC) (G3/6)** O2S heater Activation	N3/10 9 (1B) –(V)– 2 (2A)	Engine: **at idle** ECT > 80° C, run engine at idle for at least 2 minutes.	11 – 14 V or voltage fluctuates between 1 – 14 V.	Wiring, G3/6, N3/10
		O2S 2 (G3/6) Current draw	N3/10 3 (3A) –(A)– 9 (1B)	Disconnect connector **B** on engine control module Ignition: **ON**	1.5 – 4.5 A	

MB1029800697000X

Fig. 23 Code P0141: Test 23, Step 17.0

⇒		Test scope	Test connection	Test condition	Nominal value	Possible cause/remedy
18.0	P0 201	**Injector (Y62y1)** Activation and injection time	N3/10 81 (25E) –(+)– 2 (2A)	**ECT approx. 20° C** at start **ECT approx. 80° C** at idle accelerate briefly	Injection time: approx. 8 ms approx. 3 – 5 ms approx. 14 ms	Wiring, Y62y1, N3/10, **Further possibilities:** ECT sensor (B11/4), IAT sensor in hot film MAF sensor (B2/5), O2S 1 (G3/3 or G3/4).
		Resistance (Y62y1)	N3/10 81 (25E) –(Ω)– 2 (2A)	Ignition: **OFF**	14 – 18 Ω	

MB1029800698000X

Fig. 24 Code P0201: Test 23, Step 18.0

⇒		Test scope	Test connection	Test condition	Nominal value	Possible cause/remedy
19.0	P0 202	**Injector (Y62y2)** Activation and injection time	N3/10 70 (14E) –(+)– 2 (2A)	**ECT approx. 20° C** at start **ECT approx. 80° C** at idle accelerate briefly	Injection time: approx. 8 ms approx. 3 – 5 ms approx. 14 ms	Wiring, Y62y2, N3/10, **Further possibilities:** ECT sensor (B11/4), IAT sensor in hot film MAF sensor (B2/5), O2S 1 (G3/3 or G3/4).
		Resistance (Y62y2)	N3/10 70 (14E) –(Ω)– 2 (2A)	Ignition: **OFF**	14 – 18 Ω	

MB1029800699000X

Fig. 25 Code P0202: Test 23, Step 19.0

⇒		Test scope	Test connection	Test condition	Nominal value	Possible cause/remedy
20.0	P0 203	**Injector (Y62y3)** Activation and injection time	N3/10 58 (2E) –(+)– 2 (2A)	**ECT approx. 20° C** at start **ECT approx. 80° C** at idle accelerate briefly	Injection time: approx. 8 ms approx. 3 – 5 ms approx. 14 ms	Wiring, Y62y3, N3/10 **Further possibilities:** ECT sensor (B11/4), IAT sensor in hot film MAF sensor (B2/5), O2S 1 (G3/3 or G3/4).
		Resistance (Y62y3)	N3/10 58 (2E) –(Ω)– 2 (2A)	Ignition: **OFF**	14 – 18 Ω	

MB1029800700000X

Fig. 26 Code P0203: Test 23, Step 20.0

⇒		Test scope	Test connection	Test condition	Nominal value	Possible cause/remedy
21.0	P0 204	**Injector (Y62y4)** Activation and injection time	N3/10 69 (13E) –(+)– 2 (2A)	**ECT approx. 20° C** at start **ECT approx. 80° C** at idle accelerate briefly	Injection time: approx. 8 ms approx. 3 – 5 ms approx. 14 ms	Wiring, Y62y4, N3/10 **Further possibilities:** ECT sensor (B11/4), IAT sensor in hot film MAF sensor (B2/5), O2S 1 (G3/3 or G3/4).
		Resistance (Y62y4)	N3/10 69 (13E) –(Ω)– 2 (2A)	Ignition: **OFF**	14 – 18 Ω	

MB1029800701000X

Fig. 27 Code P0204: Test 23, Step 21.0

⇒		Test scope	Test connection	Test condition	Nominal value	Possible cause/remedy
22.0	P0 205	**Injector (Y62y5)** Activation and injection time	N3/10 82 (26E) –(+)– 2 (2A)	**ECT approx. 20° C** at start **ECT approx. 80° C** at idle accelerate briefly	Injection time: approx. 8 ms approx. 3 – 5 ms approx. 14 ms	Wiring, Y62y5, N3/10 **Further possibilities:** ECT sensor (B11/4), IAT sensor in hot film MAF sensor (B2/5), O2S 1 (G3/3 or G3/4).
		Resistance (Y62y5)	N3/10 82 (26E) –(Ω)– 2 (2A)	Ignition: **OFF**	14 – 18 Ω	

MB1029800702000X

Fig. 28 Code P0205: Test 23, Step 22.0

⇒		Test scope	Test connection	Test condition	Nominal value	Possible cause/remedy
23.0	P0 206	**Injector (Y62y6)** Activation and injection time	N3/10 57 (1E) –(+)– 2 (2A)	**ECT approx. 20° C** at start **ECT approx. 80° C** at idle accelerate briefly	Injection time: approx. 8 ms approx. 3 – 5 ms approx. 14 ms	Wiring, Y62y6, N3/10 **Further possibilities:** ECT sensor (B11/4), IAT sensor in hot film MAF sensor (B2/5), O2S 1 (G3/3 or G3/4).
		Resistance (Y62y6)	N3/10 57 (1E) –(Ω)– 2 (2A)	Ignition: **OFF**	14 – 18 Ω	

MB1029800703000X

Fig. 29 Code P0206: Test 23, Step 23.0

⇒		Test scope	Test connection	Test condition	Nominal value	Possible cause/remedy
24.0	P0 207	**Injector (Y62y7)** Activation and injection time	N3/10 59 (3E) –(+)– 2 (2A)	**ECT approx. 20° C** at start **ECT approx. 80° C** at idle accelerate briefly	Injection time: approx. 8 ms approx. 3 – 5 ms approx. 14 ms	Wiring, Y62y7, N3/10 **Further possibilities:** ECT sensor (B11/4), IAT sensor in hot film MAF sensor (B2/5), O2S 1 (G3/3 or G3/4).
		Resistance (Y62y7)	N3/10 59 (3E) –(Ω)– 2 (2A)	Ignition: **OFF**	14 – 18 Ω	

MB1029800704000X

Fig. 30 Code P0207: Test 23, Step 24.0

⇒		Test scope	Test connection	Test condition	Nominal value	Possible cause/remedy
25.0	P0 208	**Injector (Y62y8)** Activation and injection time	N3/10 60 (4E) — ⊕ — 2 (2A)	**ECT approx. 20° C** at start **ECT approx. 80° C** at idle accelerate briefly	Injection time: approx. 8 ms approx. 3 – 5 ms approx. 14 ms	Wiring, Y62y8, N3/10 **Further possibilities:** ECT sensor (B11/4), IAT sensor in hot film MAF sensor (B2/5), O2S 1 (G3/3 or G3/4).
		Resistance (Y62y8)	N3/10 60 (4E) — Ω — 2 (2A)	Ignition: **OFF**	14 – 18 Ω	

MB1029800705000X

Fig. 31 Code P0208: Test 23, Step 25.0

⇒		Test scope	Test connection	Test condition	Nominal value	Possible cause/remedy
28.0	P0 410	**Only (USA)** **AIR system** (logic chain)	N3/10 23 (31C) — V — 24 (32C)	**Note:** The O2S 1 signal before TWC is measured. With ETC > 80°C run engine at idle for at least 2 minutes.	The O2S voltage oscillates in the area of –0.2 V and +1.0 V	Y32 binding, AIR combi valve, AIR pump no output.
			N3/10 3 (3A) ←→ 66 (10E) 3 (3A) ←→ 20 (28C)	Bridge sockets on socket box	AIR pump runs. Voltage changes to < 100 mV within 20 seconds	

MB1029800707000X

Fig. 33 Code P0410: Test 23, Step 28.0

⇒		Test scope	Test connection	Test condition	Nominal value	Possible cause/remedy
30.0	P0 802	**Resonance intake manifold switchover valve (Y22/6)** Activation	N3/10 68 (12E) — V — 2 (2A)	Engine: **Start** Engine: **at Idle** Engine: accelerate briefly to > approx. 3900 rpm	< 1 V 9 – 14 V and vacuum applied to valve.	Wiring, Y22/6, N3/10
		Current draw (Y22/6)	N3/10 3 (3A) — A — 68 (12E)	Ignition: **ON**	0.3 – 0.5 A	
31.0	P0 441 P0 443	**Purge control valve (Y58/1)** Activation	N3/10 13 (21C) — ⊕ — 2 (2A)	Engine: **at Idle** and at operating temperature.	After approx. 2 minutes, purge control valve (Y58/1) must noticeably cycle,	⇒ 32.0, Wiring, Y58/1, N3/10
		Current draw (Y58/1)	N3/10 3 (3A) — A — 13 (21C)	Ignition: **ON**	0.2 – 0.4 A	

MB1029800709000X

Fig. 35 Codes P0441, P0443 & P0802: Test 23, Steps 30.0–31.0

⇒		Test scope	Test connection	Test condition	Nominal value	Possible cause/remedy
34.0	P0 446	**Only (USA)** **Activated charcoal canister shut-off valve (Y58/4)** Current draw	N3/10 3 (3A) — A — 34 (2D)	Ignition: **ON**	0.5 – 0.9 A	Wiring, Y58/4
35.0	P0 450 P0 455	**Only (USA)** **Fuel tank pressure sensor (B4/3)** Sender signal	N3/10 36 (4D) — V — 37 (5D)	Disconnect purge line (A) to charcoal canister on purge control valve (Y58/1). Connect vacuum tester to purge line.		⇒ 35.1, Wiring, Vacuum line, Charcoal canister plugged, B4/3
		Activated charcoal canister shut-off valve (Y58/4) activated	N3/10 3 (3A) ←→ 34 (2D)	Ignition: **ON** Apply approx. 25 mbar of vacuum.	> 2.9 V < 2.3 V	
35.1		**Only (USA)** Fuel tank pressure sensor (B4/3) Voltage supply	N3/10 36 (4D) — V — 38 (6D)	Ignition: **ON**	4.7 – 5.3 V	N3/10

MB1029800711000X

Fig. 37 Codes P0446, P0450 & P0455: Test 23, Steps 34.0–35.1

⇒		Test scope	Test connection	Test condition	Nominal value	Possible cause/remedy
26.0	P1 453	Only (USA) **AIR relay module (K17) in Passenger-side fuse and relay module box (K40/4)** Activation	N3/10 20 (28C) — V — 2 (2A)	Disconnect ECT sensor (B11/4) connector. Simulate 2.5 kΩ resistance at sockets 1 and 2 with resistance substitution unit. Engine: **at Idle**	11 – 14 V for approx. two minutes and AIR pump runs.	Wiring, K40/4, N3/10
		Current draw (K40/4)	N3/10 3 (3A) — A — 20 (28C)	Ignition: **ON**	0.1 – 0.3 A	
27.0	P1 420	Only (USA) **AIR pump switchover valve (Y32)** Activation	N3/10 66 (10E) — V — 2 (2A)	Disconnect ECT sensor (B11/4) connector. Simulate 2.5 kΩ resistance at sockets 1 and 2 with resistance substitution unit. Engine: **at Idle**	11 – 14 V for approx. two minutes and AIR pump runs.	Wiring, Y32, N3/10
		Current draw (Y32)	N3/10 3 (3A) — A — 66 (10E)	Ignition: **ON**	0.3 – 0.5 A	

MB1029800706000X

Fig. 32 Codes P0420 & P0453: Test 23, Steps 26.0–27.0

⇒		Test scope	Test connection	Test condition	Nominal value	Possible cause/remedy
29.0	P0 400 P1 400	**EGR valve vacuum transducer (Y31/1)** Activation and vacuum control	N3/10 61 (5E) — V — 2 (2A)	**Note to test connection:** Connect vacuum tester to EGR valve vacuum transducer, after removing the MAF sensor with air box. Engine: **at Idle** ETC > 60°C **Vehicle at approx. 3000/rpm while on dynamometer**	 < 1 V and < 10 mbar vacuum. 1 – 7 V and 80 – 220 mbar vacuum.	Wiring, N3/10, Y31/1
		Current draw (Y31/1)	N3/10 3 (3A) — A — 61 (5E)	Ignition: **ON**	0.3 – 0.5 A	

MB1029800708000X

Fig. 34 Codes P0400 & P1400: Test 23, Step 29.0

⇒		Test scope	Test connection	Test condition	Nominal value	Possible cause/remedy
32.0	P0 440 P0 441	**Purge control valve (Y58/1)** Vacuum control		Connect vacuum tester to purge control valve (Y58/1) between purge line to charcoal canister. Engine at operating temperature and at idle.	After approx. 2 minute, > 50 mbar and needle oscillates, Y58/1 must cycle.	Vacuum line, Y58/1
33.0	P0 440 P0 442 P0 455	**Only (USA)** **Purge system** Leaks		Disconnect purge line (A) to charcoal canister on purge control valve (Y58/1). Connect vacuum tester to purge line.		Fuel tank cap, Purge line to charcoal canister, Purge line from charcoal canister to Y58/4, Charcoal canister, Y58/4.
		Activated charcoal canister shut-off valve (Y58/4) activated	N3/10 3 (3A) ←→ 34 (2D)	Ignition: **ON** Apply approx. 25 mbar of vacuum.	After approx. 1 minute, < 5 mbar vacuum loss.	

MB1029800710000X

Fig. 36 Codes P0440, P0441, P0442 & P0455: Test 23, Steps 32.0–33.0

⇒		Test scope	Test connection	Test condition	Nominal value	Possible cause/remedy
36.0	P0 600 P1 570 P1 747	**CAN data bus**	N3/10 43 (11D) — Ω — 44 (12D)	Ignition: **OFF**	55 – 65 Ω	⇒ 36.1 ⇒1.2 Data line.
36.1		**CAN element in DAS control module (N54/1)** Resistance	N3/10 43 (11D) — Ω — 44 (12D)	Ignition: **OFF** Disconnect connector **D** from engine control module N3/10.	115 – 125 Ω	Wiring, N54/1
36.2		**CAN element in engine control module (N3/10)** Resistance	N3/10 43 (11D) — Ω — 44 (12D)	Ignition: **OFF** Disconnect connector **D** from test cable and reconnect connector **D** to N3/10	115 – 125 Ω	N3/10

MB1029800712000X

Fig. 38 Codes P0600, P1570 & P1747: Test 23, Steps 36.0–36.2

⇒		Test scope	Test connection	Test condition	Nominal value	Possible cause/remedy
37.0	P1177 P1178 P1179 P1180 P1185	**Oil sensor (level/ temperature/quality) (B40)**	N3/10[3] 72 (16E) –(+)– 73 (17E) N3/10[4] 72 (16E) –(V)– 73 (17E)	Test connection note regarding oscillascope: Range: 2V Duration: 50ms Ignition: **ON**	signal 0.3 – 3 V, voltage jumps	⇒ 35.1, oil level, oil quality, wiring, B40
37.1		Voltage supply (B40)	N3/10 72 (16E) –(V)– 71 (15E)	Ignition: **ON**	4.7 – 5.3 V	N3/10

3) Test with oscilloscope.
4) Test with multimeter only if oscilloscope is not available.

MB1029800713000X

Fig. 39 Codes P1177, P1178, P1179, P1180 & P1185: Test 23, Steps 37.0–37.1

⇒		Test scope	Test connection	Test condition	Nominal value	Possible cause/remedy
38.0	P0801	**With engine/climate control electric cooling fan only** **Engine/climate control electric cooling fan control module (N76)** Activation	N3/10 6 (6A) –(V)– 2 (2A)	Engine: **at Idle** ECT < 70° C Ignition: **ON** A/C: **ON** ECT > 85° C	1 – 1.9 V and cooling fan is stationary. 2 – 4 V and cooling fan runs. between 2.5 – 12.5 V and cooling fan speed is based on activation.	Wiring, N76, N3/10
39.0		**Diagnosis line** Activation	N3/10 3 (3A) –(V)– 31 (39C)	Ignition: **ON**	11 – 14 V	Wiring, N3/10

MB1029800714000X

Fig. 40 Code P0801: Test 23, Steps 38.0–39.0

⇒		Test scope	Test connection	Test condition	Nominal value	Possible cause/remedy
1.0	P0560	**Engine control module (N3/10)** Voltage supply circuit 30	N3/10 3 (3A) –(V)– 12 (4B)	Ignition: **ON**	11 – 14 V	⇒ 1.1 – 1.2
1.1		Ground wire	N3/10 3 (3A) –(V)– X11/4 2 7 (7A) –(V)– X11/4 2 112 (6F) –(V)– X11/4 2 119 (15F) –(V)– X11/4 2	Ignition: **ON**	11 – 14 V	Wiring, Output ground (W16/6), right component compartment.

MB1029800715000X

Fig. 41 Code P0560: Test 24, Steps 1.0–1.1

⇒		Test scope	Test connection	Test condition	Nominal value	Possible cause/remedy
1.2		Voltage supply circuit 30	N3/10 X11/4 1 –(V)– 12 (4B)	Ignition: **ON**	11 – 14 V	Wiring, **Model 210:** Passenger-side fuse and relay module box (K40/4).
2.0	P0560	**Engine control module (N3/10)** Voltage supply circuit 87	N3/10 8 (8A) –(V)– 2 (2A)	Ignition: **ON**	11 – 14 V	⇒ 2.1 – 2.2
2.1		Electronics ground	N3/10 8 (8A) –(V)– X11/4 2	Ignition: **ON**	11 – 14 V	Wiring, Output ground (W16/6), right component compartment.
2.2		Voltage supply circuit 87	N3/10 X11/4 1 –(V)– 2 (2A)	Ignition: **ON** Ignition: **OFF**	11 – 14 V < 1 V	Wiring, **Model 210:** Passenger-side fuse and relay module box (K40/4).

MB1029800716000X

Fig. 42 Code P0560: Test 24, Steps 1.2–2.2

⇒		Test scope	Test connection	Test condition	Nominal value	Possible cause/remedy
3.0		**Ignition coil (T1/1)** Cylinder 1 Voltage supply Primary coil a Voltage supply Primary coil b	N3/10 3 (3A) –(V)– 124 (20F) N3/10 3 (3A) –(V)– 125 (21F)	Ignition: **ON**	11 – 14 V	Wiring, Fuses: **Model 210:** In passenger-side fuse and relay module box (K40/4), Ignition coil (T1/1).
4.0		**Ignition coil (T1/2)** Cylinder 2 Voltage supply Primary coil a Voltage supply Primary coil b	N3/10 3 (3A) –(V)– 121 (19F) N3/10 3 (3A) –(V)– 122 (18F)	Ignition: **ON**	11 – 14 V	Wiring, Fuses: **Model 210:** In passenger-side fuse and relay module box (K40/4), Ignition coil (T1/2).

MB1029800717000X

Fig. 43 Code —: Test 24, Step 3.0–4.0.

⇒		Test scope	Test connection	Test condition	Nominal value	Possible cause/remedy
5.0		**Ignition coil (T1/3)** Cylinder 3 Voltage supply Primary coil a Voltage supply Primary coil b	N3/10 3 (3A) –(V)– 109 (5F) N3/10 3 (3A) –(V)– 108 (4F)	Ignition: **ON**	11 – 14 V	Wiring, Fuses: **Model 210:** In passenger-side fuse and relay module box (K40/4), Ignition coil (T1/3).
6.0		**Ignition coil (T1/4)** Cylinder 4 Voltage supply Primary coil a Voltage supply Primary coil b	N3/10 3 (3A) –(V)– 110 (60F) N3/10 3 (3A) –(V)– 111 (7F)	Ignition: **ON**	11 – 14 V	Wiring, Fuses: **Model 210:** In passenger-side fuse and relay module box (K40/4), Ignition coil (T1/4)

MB1029800718000X

Fig. 44 Code —: Test 23, Steps 5.0–6.0

⇒		Test scope	Test connection	Test condition	Nominal value	Possible cause/remedy
7.0		**Ignition coil (T1/5)** Cylinder 5 Voltage supply Primary coil a Voltage supply Primary coil b	N3/10 3 (3A) –(V)– 117 (13F) N3/10 3 (3A) –(V)– 118 (14F)	Ignition: **ON**	11 – 14 V	Wiring, Fuses: **Model 210:** In passenger-side fuse and relay module box (K40/4), Ignition coil (T1/5).
8.0		**Ignition coil (T1/6)** Cylinder 6 Voltage supply Primary coil a Voltage supply Primary coil b	N3/10 3 (3A) –(V)– 121 (17F) N3/10 3 (3A) –(V)– 120 (16F)	Ignition: **ON**	11 – 14 V	Wiring, Fuses: **Model 210:** In passenger-side fuse and relay module box (K40/4), Ignition coil (T1/6).

MB1029800719000X

Fig. 45 Code —: Test 24, Steps 7.0–8.0

⇒		Test scope	Test connection	Test condition	Nominal value	Possible cause/remedy
9.0		**Ignition coil (T1/7)** Cylinder 7 Voltage supply Primary coil a Voltage supply Primary coil b	N3/10 3 (3A) –(V)– 116 (12F) N3/10 3 (3A) –(V)– 115 (11F)	Ignition: **ON**	11 – 14 V	Wiring, Fuses: **Model 210:** In passenger-side fuse and relay module box (K40/4), Ignition coil (T1/7).
10.0		**Ignition coil (T1/8)** Cylinder 8 Voltage supply Primary coil a Voltage supply Primary coil b	N3/10 3 (3A) –(V)– 114 (10F) N3/10 3 (3A) –(V)– 113 (9F)	Ignition: **ON**	11 – 14 V	Wiring, Fuses: **Model 210:** In passenger-side fuse and relay module box (K40/4), Ignition coil (T1/8).

MB1029800720000X

Fig. 46 Code —: Test 24, Steps 9.0–10.0

⇒		Test scope	Test connection	Test condition	Nominal value	Possible cause/remedy
11.0	P0335	**CKP sensor (L5)** Signal Voltage	N3/10[2] 93 (37E) –(+)– 94 (38E) N3/10[3] 93 (37E) –(V)– 94 (38E)	Starter: **Crank** Engine: **at Idle** Starter: **Crank** Engine: **at Idle**	> 2.0 V~ > 5 V~ [4]	⇒ 1.1, Teeth on starter ring gear.
11.1		Resistance of CKP sensor (L5)	N3/10 93 (37E) –(Ω)– 94 (38E)	Ignition: **OFF** Unplug connector E on engine control module (N3/10).	700 – 1400 Ω	Wiring, L5

2) Test with oscilloscope.
3) Test with multimeter only if oscilloscope is unavailable.
4) Voltage increases with increasing rpm.

MB1029800721000X

Fig. 47 Code P0335: Test 24, Steps 11.0–11.1

⇒		Test scope	Test connection	Test condition	Nominal value	Possible cause/remedy
12.0	P0 341	**Camshaft Hall-effect sensor (B6/1)** Hall-effect signal	N3/10[2] 95 (39E) — 96 (40E)	Engine: **at idle**		⇒ 12.1, Wiring, B6/1
		Voltage	N3/10[3] 96 (40E) — 2 (2A)	Engine: **at idle**	1.2 – 2.2 V Value changes.	
12.1		Voltage supply to camshaft Hall-effect sensor (B6/1)	B6/1 1 — 3	Ignition: **ON** Disconnect connector from Hall-effect sensor (B6/1) and test directly on sockets 1 (brown/green) and 3 (red/blue) of connector.	11 – 14 V	Wiring.

2) Test with oscilloscope.
3) Test with multimeter only if oscilloscope is unavailable.

MB1029800722000X

Fig. 48 Code P0341: Test 24, Steps 12.0–12.1

⇒		Test scope	Test connection	Test condition	Nominal value	Possible cause/remedy
13.0	P0 300 P0 301	**Primary voltage** Ignition coil (T1/1), Cylinder 1 Primary circuit a	N3/10 124 (20F) — 2 (2A)	**Test connection Note:** Individual primary pattern Range: 400 V Duration: 100% Starter: **Crank**	200 – 350 V	⇒ 13.1
		Primary circuit b	N3/10 125 (21F) — 2 (2A)			
13.1		Primary winding of T1/1 Primary circuit a and b	N3/10 124 (20F) — 125 (21F)	Ignition: **OFF**	0.9 – 1.6 Ω [6]	Wiring, T1/1
14.0	P0 300 P0 302	**Primary voltage** Ignition coil (T1/2), Cylinder 2 Primary circuit a	N3/10 123 (17F) — 2 (2A)	**Test connection Note:** Individual primary pattern Range: 400 V Duration: 100% Starter: **Crank**	200 – 350 V	⇒ 14.1
		Primary circuit b	N3/10 122 (18F) — 2 (2A)			

6) The resistance of a single coil at 20° C is approx. 0.6 Ω.

MB1029800723000X

Fig. 49 Codes P0300, P0301 & P0302: Test 24, Steps 13.0–14.0

⇒		Test scope	Test connection	Test condition	Nominal value	Possible cause/remedy
14.1		Primary winding of T1/2 Primary circuit a and b	N3/10 122 (18F) — 123 (19F)	Ignition: **OFF**	0.9 – 1.6 Ω [6]	Wiring, T1/2
15.0	P0 300 P0 303	**Primary voltage** Ignition coil (T1/3), Cylinder 3 Primary circuit a	N3/10 109 (5F) — 2 (2A)	**Test connection Note:** Individual primary pattern Range 400 V Duration 100% Starter: **Crank**	200 – 350 V	⇒ 15.1
		Primary circuit b	N3/10 108 (4F) — 2 (2A)			
15.1		Primary winding of T1/3 Primary circuit a and b	N3/10 108 (4F) — 109 (5F)	Ignition: **OFF**	0.9 – 1.6 Ω [6]	Wiring, T1/3

6) The resistance of a single coil at 20° C is approx. 0.6 Ω.

MB1029800724000X

Fig. 50 Codes P0300 & P0303: Test 24, Steps 14.1–15.1

⇒		Test scope	Test connection	Test condition	Nominal value	Possible cause/remedy
16.0	P0 300 P0 304	**Primary voltage** Ignition coil (T1/4), Cylinder 4 Primary circuit a	N3/10 110 (6F) — 2 (2A)	**Test connection Note:** Individual primary pattern Range: 400 V Duration: 100% Starter: **Crank**	200 – 350 V	⇒ 16.1
		Primary circuit b	N3/10 111 (7F) — 2 (2A)			
16.1		Primary winding of T1/4 Primary circuit a and b	N3/10 110 (6F) — 111 (7F)	Ignition: **OFF**	0.9 – 1.6 Ω [6]	Wiring, T1/4
17.0	P0 300 P0 305	**Primary voltage** Ignition coil (T1/5), Cylinder 5 Primary circuit a	N3/10 117 (13F) — 2 (2A)	**Test connection Note:** Individual primary pattern Range: 400 V Duration: 100% Starter: **Crank**	200 – 350 V	⇒ 17.1
		Primary circuit b	N3/10 118 (14F) — 2 (2A)			

6) The resistance of a single coil at 20° C is approx. 0.6 Ω.

MB1029800725000X

Fig. 51 Codes P0300, P0304 & P0305: Test 24, Steps 16.0–17.0

⇒		Test scope	Test connection	Test condition	Nominal value	Possible cause/remedy
17.1		Primary winding of T1/5 Primary circuit a and b	N3/10 117 (13F) — 118 (14F)	Ignition: **OFF**	0.9 – 1.6 Ω [6]	Wiring, T1/5
18.0	P0 300 P0 306	**Primary voltage** Ignition coil (T1/6), Cylinder 6 Primary circuit a	N3/10 121 (17F) — 2 (2A)	**Test connection Note:** Individual primary pattern Range: 400 V Duration: 100% Starter: **Crank**	200 – 350 V	⇒ 18.1
		Primary circuit b	N3/10 120 (16F) — 2 (2A)			
18.1		Primary winding of T1/6 Primary circuit a and b	N3/10 120 (16F) — 121 (17F)	Ignition: **OFF**	0.9 – 1.6 Ω [6]	Wiring, T1/6

6) The resistance of a single coil at 20° C is approx. 0.6 Ω.

MB1029800726000X

Fig. 52 Codes P0300 & P0306: Test 24, Steps 17.1–18.1

⇒		Test scope	Test connection	Test condition	Nominal value	Possible cause/remedy
19.0	P0 300 P0 306	**Primary voltage** Ignition coil (T1/7), Cylinder 7 Primary circuit a	N3/10 116 (12F) — 2 (2A)	**Test connection Note:** Individual primary pattern Range: 400 V Duration: 100% Starter: **Crank**	200 – 350 V	⇒ 19.1
		Primary circuit b	N3/10 115 (11F) — 2 (2A)			
19.1		Primary winding of T1/7 Primary circuit a and b	N3/10 115 (11F) — 116 (12F)	Ignition: **OFF**	0.9 – 1.6 Ω [6]	Wiring, T1/7

6) The resistance of a single coil at 20° C is approx. 0.6 Ω.

MB1029800727000X

Fig. 53 Codes P0300 & P0306: Test 24, Steps 19.0–19.1

⇒		Test scope	Test connection	Test condition	Nominal value	Possible cause/remedy
20.0	P0 300 P0 306	**Primary voltage** Ignition coil (T1/8), Cylinder 8 Primary circuit a	N3/10 114 (10F) — 2 (2A)	**Test connection Note:** Individual primary pattern Range: 400 V Duration: 100% Starter: **Crank**	200 – 350 V	⇒ 20.1
		Primary circuit b	N3/10 113 (9F) — 2 (2A)			
20.1		Primary winding of T1/8 Primary circuit a and b	N3/10 113 (9F) — 114 (10F)	Ignition: **OFF**	0.9 – 1.6 Ω [6]	Wiring, T1/8

6) The resistance of a single coil at 20° C is approx. 0.6 Ω.

MB1029800728000X

Fig. 54 Codes P0300 & P0306: Test 24, Steps 20.0–20.1

⇒		Test scope	Test connection	Test condition	Nominal value	Possible cause/remedy
21.0	P0 300 P0 301 P0 302 P0 303 P0 304 P0 305 P0 306 P0 307 P0 308	**Firing voltage** Ignition coil (T1/1) to (T1/8)	Engine analyzer	**Test connection Note:** Individual secondary pattern. Range: 20 kV Duration: 100% Connect kV pick-ups successively to T1/1 through T1/8. Starter: **Crank**	8 – 20 kV [7]	Spark plugs, N3/10

7) The resistance of the secondary winding can not be measured due to an installed diode.

MB1029800729000X

Fig. 55 Codes P0300, P0301, P0302, P0303, P0304, P0305, P0306, P0307 & P0308: Test 24, Step 21.0

⇒		Test scope	Test connection	Test condition	Nominal value	Possible cause/remedy
1.0	P1 542 P0 507	**Pedal value sensor (B37)** Signal Nominal value potentiometer 1	N3/10 15 (23C) — V — 16 (24C)	Ignition: **ON** Accelerator pedal position: CTP WOT with kick-down	 0.2 – 0.5 V 4.3 – 4.8 V	⇒ 1.1, Wiring, B37
1.1		Voltage supply Nominal value potentiometer 2 (Hall-sensor)	N3/10 15 (23C) — V — 14 (22C)	Ignition: **ON**	4.75 – 5.25 V	Wiring, N3/10
2.0	P1 542 P0 507	**Pedal value sensor (B37)** Signal Nominal value potentiometer 2	N3/10 18 (26C) — V — 17 (25C)	Ignition: **ON** Accelerator pedal position: CTP WOT with kick-down	 0.1 – 0.4 V 2.1 – 2.5 V	⇒ 2.1, Wiring, B37

MB1029800730000X

Fig. 56 Codes P0507 & P1542: Test 25, Steps 1.0–2.0

⇒		Test scope	Test connection	Test condition	Nominal value	Possible cause/remedy
4.0	P1 1186 P1 580	**EA/CC/ISC actuator (M16/6)** Activation of actuator motor	N3/10 105 (1F) — V — 106 (2F)	Ignition: **ON** Engine: **at Idle** ECT > 70 °C	0.8 – 2.3 V 1.0 – 2.5 V Value oscillates.	Wiring, M16/6, N3/10
		Actuator motor resistance	N3/10 105 (1F) — Ω — 106 (2F)	Ignition: **OFF**	< 10 Ω	
5.0		**With AT only** **P/N recognition**	N3/10 51 (19D) — V — 2 (2A)	Ignition: **ON** Selector lever position: P/N → R, D, 4, 3, 2, 1 →	 11 – 14 V < 2.0 V	Wiring, Test ETC, see DM, Chassis & Drivetrain, Vol. 1.

MB1029800732000X

Fig. 58 Codes P1186 & P1580: Test 25, Steps 4.0–5.0

⇒		Test scope	Test connection	Test condition	Nominal value	Possible cause/remedy
1.0		**Fuel pressure at idle (with vacuum)**	Pressure gauge connected to test connection.	Engine: **at Idle**	3.7 – 4.2 bar	Check fuel pumps □ 34, Diaphragm pressure regulator.
2.0		**Fuel system internal leakage test**	Pressure gauge connected to test connection.	Engine: **OFF** After 30 minutes	> 3.0 bar > 2.5 bar	If the pressure drops quickly: Replace check valve in fuel pumps. If the pressure drops slowly: check injectors □ 36, Replace diaphragm pressure.

1) Observe Preparation for Test, see □ 31.

MB1029800734000X

Fig. 60 Code —: Test 32, Fuel System Pressure & Internal Leakage Test

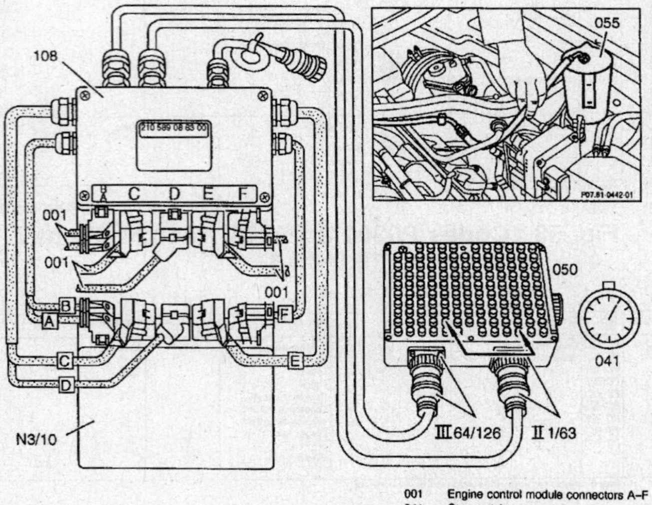

001 Engine control module connectors A–F
041 Stop watch
050 Socket box tester, 126 pole
055 Measuring glass
088 Test cable
N3/10 Engine control module (ME-SFI)

MB1029800735000X

Fig. 61 Fuel pump test connections

⇒		Test scope	Test connection	Test condition	Nominal value	Possible cause/remedy
3.0	P0 507 P0 120 P1 186 P1 580	**EA/CC/ISC actuator (M16/6)** Signal Actual value potentiometer 1	N3/10 88 (32E) — V — 87 (31E)	Ignition: **ON** Accelerator pedal position: CTP WOT or kick-down	 4.0 – 4.6 V < CTP value	⇒ 3.1, Wiring, M16/6
		Actual value potentiometer 2	N3/10 88 (32E) — V — 90 (34E)	Accelerator pedal position: CTP WOT or kick-down	 0.3 – 0.9 V > CTP value	
3.1		Voltage supply Actual value potentiometers 1 and 2	N3/10 88 (32E) — V — 89 (33E)	Ignition: **ON**	4.75 – 5.25 V	Wiring, N3/10

MB1029800731000X

Fig. 57 Codes P0120, P0507, P1186 & P1580: Test 25, Steps 3.0–3.1

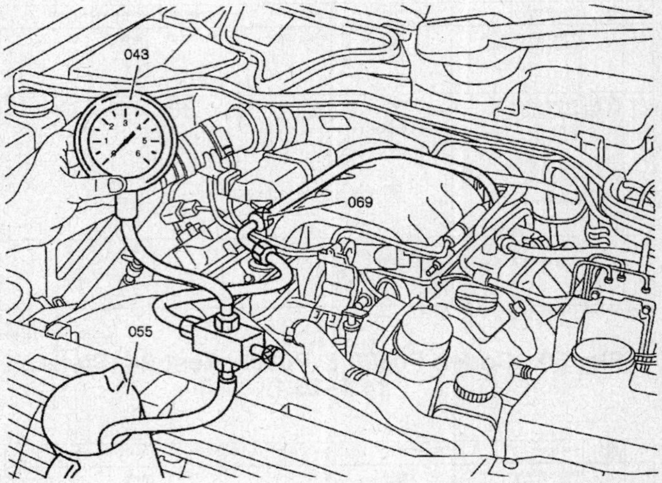

043 Pressure gauge, part no. 103 589 00 21 00
055 Measuring glass
069 Pressure hose, part no. 119 589 04 63 00

MB1029800733000X

Fig. 59 Fuel pressure connection

⇒		Test scope	Test connection	Test condition	Nominal value	Possible cause/remedy
1.0		**Fuel pump** Delivery capacity	N3/10 3 (3A) — 21 (29C)	Disconnect fuel return hose from fuel line and place end in measuring glass. Ignition: **ON**	1 liter of fuel within 35 seconds.	Check fuel lines for restrictions (kinks and dents). Replace fuel filter or fuel pressure regulator.
2.0		**Fuel pumps** Current draw		Remove FP relay module (K27), connect multimeter on sockets 2 and 8. Ignition: **ON**	4 – 9 A	Fuel pump

MB1029800736000X

Fig. 62 Code —: Test 34, Fuel Pump Test

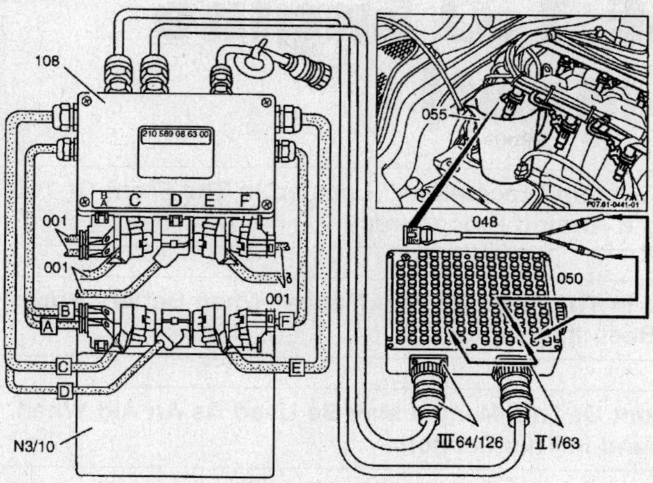

001 Engine control module connectors A–F
048 Self made harness
050 Socket box tester, 126 pole
055 Measuring glass
088 Test cable
N3/10 Engine control module (ME-SFI)

MB1029800737000X

Fig. 63 Injector test connection

⇒		Test scope	Test connection	Test condition	Nominal value	Possible cause/remedy
1.0		**Injectors** Leakage test	N3/10 3 (3A) ←→ 33 (1D)	Fuel rail and fuel injectors removed. Ignition: **ON**	Injectors must not drip.	⇒ 2.0, Replace dripping injectors.
2.0		**Injectors** Operation and spray pattern test	N3/10 3 (3A) ←→ 33 (1D)	Ignition: **ON** Hold each injector (one after another) into a container and, using the self-made test harness, manually activate the injector by connecting harness banana plugs to socket box sockets 3 (–) and 2 (+).	Injectors must spray evenly	Replace defective injectors.

MB1029800738000X

Fig. 64 Code —: Test 36, Injector Test

SYSTEM SERVICE

Component Replacement

Refer to "112 Engine (ME 2.0 Engine Management)" section.

Adjustments

Refer to "104 Engine (ME 2.1 Engine Management)" section.

119 Engine (ME 1.0 Engine Management)

NOTE: On Air Bag Equipped Models, Refer To "Air Bag System Precautions" Located In The Front Of This Manual For System Disarming & Arming Procedures.

NOTE: Refer To "Computer Relearn Procedure" Located In The Front Of This Manual When Battery Power To The Computer Has Been Interrupted.

NOTE: "Electrical Symbol Identification" Located In Front Of This Manual May Be Used As An Aid When Using Wiring Diagrams Found In This Section.

NOTE: Prior To Performing Any Service Listed In This Section Consult Technical Service Bulletin Section For Related Information.

INDEX

Page No.

Description 14-140
Diagnosis & Testing 14-140
Accessing Diagnostic Trouble Codes 14-140
Generic Scan Tool 14-140
Hand-Held Tester 14-140
Clearing Diagnostic Trouble Codes 14-141
Component Tests 14-141
Fuel Injector 14-141
Fuel Pump 14-141
Components Locations 14-140
Connector Terminal Identification 14-141
Diagnostic Tests 14-141
Diagnostic Trouble Code Interpretation 14-140
Symbol Explanation 14-140
Symptom Related Diagnosis 14-140
Wiring Diagrams 14-140
Diagnostic Chart Index 14-154
Precautions 14-139
Air Bag Systems 14-139
Battery Ground Cable 14-139
Drive Authorization System (DAS) 14-139
ECM Recognition 14-139
ECM Self-Adaptation 14-139
ESP/ASR/ETS/ABS Control Modules 14-140
Ignition System 14-139
Throttle Valve Position 14-139
Sensor & Fuel Injector Specifications 14-139
System Service 14-163
Adjustments 14-163
Throttle Control Cable 14-163
Component Replacement 14-163
Crankshaft Position (CKP) Sensor 14-163
Diaphragm Pressure Regulator 14-163
Electronic Accelerator Actuator 14-163
Fuel Injector 14-163
Fuel Rail 14-163
Hot Film Mass Air Flow (MAF) Sensor 14-163
Knock Sensor 14-163
Oxygen Sensor 14-163
Throttle Control Cable 14-163

SENSOR & FUEL INJECTOR SPECIFICATIONS

Temperature, °F	Resistance, Ohms①	Voltage①
CRANKSHAFT POSITION (CKP) SENSOR		
—	700–1400	—
ENGINE COOLANT TEMPERATURE (ECT) SENSOR		
68	2500	3.32–3.68
86	1700	2.94–3.26
104	1170	2.56–2.84
122	830	2.18–2.42
140	600	1.80–2.00
158	435	1.42–1.58
176	325	1.14–1.26
194	245	0.95–1.05
212	185	0.76–0.84
FUEL INJECTOR		
—	14–17	—
INTAKE AIR TEMPERATURE (IAT) SENSOR		
68	6060	2.47–2.73
86	3900	1.99–2.21
104	2600	1.52–1.68
122	1760	1.14–1.26

① — Tolerance ± 5%

PRECAUTIONS

Air Bag Systems

Refer to "Air Bag System Precautions" in the front of this manual for system disarming and arming procedures.

Battery Ground Cable

Prior to service, disconnect battery ground cable and isolate as required.

Ignition System

1. Both control module coupling must be disconnected or connect with ignition switch in Off position.
2. Do not short circuit ignition coils terminal No. 1.
3. Do not operate the ignition system at starting speed unless the ignition cables are fully connected.
4. Do not conduct are test at starting speed or when engine is running. This includes: holding ignition cable No. 4 at a distance to ground, disconnecting a plug connector or pulling cable No. 4 out of the ignition coils.
5. High output side of ignition system must always carry at least two ohms resistance (spark plug connected).
6. Do not load ignition coil with more than 28,000 volts.
7. Ignition coil iron cores must always be connected to ground. **Use caution, coil cores can be charged with up to 400 volts.**
8. **Do not work on this system if you have a pacemaker.**
9. Ensure engine and ignition switch are in Off position when connecting and disconnecting ignition coil.
10. When working at start speeds during test such as compression check, switch ignition to off position and disconnect control module connector No. 2.

ECM Self-Adaptation

After repair work, the Engine Control Module (ECM) will automatically adapt itself after the vehicle has made approximately 10 trips. A trip includes engine running for more than 20 minutes, engine oil temperature of more than 19°F, engine speed of more than 700 RPM and emission related logic chain functions.

However, after fixing a malfunction or installation of a test ECM, the self-adaptation function must be reset as outlined under "Computer Relearn" at the front of this manual.

ECM Recognition

The ECM must be coded for vehicle model, catalytic converter and country version with the Hand-Held Tester.

Before replacing the ECM, read and store existing code numbers with the Hand-Held Tester. When the new ECM is installed, enter the stored code numbers from the Hand-Held Tester. If code numbers cannot be read, the corresponding codes number must be obtained from Mercedes-Benz spare parts microfiche and manually entered with a Hand-Held Tester.

Throttle Valve Position

After replacing the Engine Control Module (ECM) or actuator, the throttle valve mechanical end stop and wide open position must be determined and recorded, allowing data to be erased with a Hand-Held Tester or new data learned.

1. Disconnect and connect battery power supply.
2. With vehicle parked, transmission in P or N position, no pressure on accelerator pedal and ignition switch in Off position, ensure engine coolant temperature is 41–212°F.
3. Turn ignition switch to On position for more than 50 seconds.
4. Turn ignition switch to Off position for more than 10 seconds.
5. If engine runs rough after battery power interruption, proceed as follows:
   a. Ensure engine coolant temperature is more than 176°F.
   b. Drive vehicle on dynamometer with transmission in 4 position or on road in 3 position.
   c. Increase engine speed to more than 3500 RPM and coast until speed is less than 1200 RPM.

Drive Authorization System (DAS)

The DAS can only be activated or deactivated by the electronic ignition key. The ECM, RCL and DAS control module are permanently locked together by an identification code. This code cannot be erased.

087 Hand-Held Tester
094 Multiplexer cable
X11/4 Data link connector (DTC readout) (38-pole)

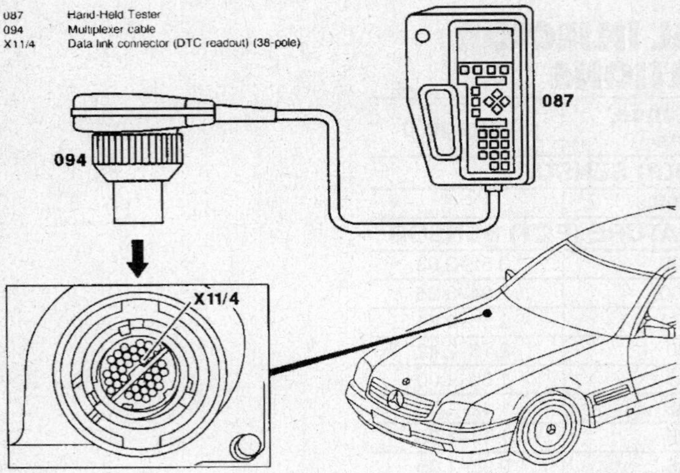

MB1029500278000X

Fig. 1 DLC tool connection

DTC	Possible cause SAE nomenclature	Explanation	Test step/Remedy
P0133 ■	O2S 1 circuit slow response, bank 1 (right)	A Right O2S 1 (before TWC) (G3/4), ageing correction value exceeded B Right O2S 1 (before TWC) (G3/4), ageing time period too long	□ 23⇒ 12.0
P0135 ■	O2S 1 heater circuit malfunction, bank 1 (right)	Right O2S 1 heater (before TWC) (G3/4)	□ 23 ⇒ 13.0
P0136 ■	O2S 2 circuit malfunction, bank 1 (right)	Right O2S 2 (after TWC) (G3/6)	□ 23 ⇒ 15.0
P0141 ■	O2S 2 heater circuit malfunction, bank 1 (right)	Right O2S 2 heater (after TWC) (G3/6)	□ 23⇒ 16.0
P0150 ■	O2S 1 circuit malfunction, bank 2 (left)	Left O2S 1 (before TWC) (G3/3)	□ 23⇒ 11.0
P0153 ■	O2S 1 circuit slow response, bank 2 (left)	A Left O2S 1 (before TWC) (G3/3), ageing correction value exceeded B Left O2S 1 (before TWC) (G3/3), ageing time period too long	□ 23⇒ 11.0
P0155 ■	O2S 1 heater circuit malfunction, bank 2 (left)	Left O2S 1 heater (before TWC) (G3/3)	□ 23⇒ 13.0
P0156 ■	O2S 2 circuit malfunction, bank 2 (left)	Left O2S 2 (after TWC) (G3/5)	□ 23⇒ 14.0
P0161 ■	O2S 2 heater circuit malfunction, bank 2 (left)	Left O2S 2 heater (after TWC) (G3/5)	□ 23⇒ 16.0

MB1029500279020A

Fig. 2 DTC interpretation (Part 2 of 12)

Trial installation of an ECM or RCL control module from another vehicle is not possible. After 40 starts, a new ECM cannot be used in any other vehicle. The code number and VIN must be entered into the ECM with a Hand-Held Tester.

ESP/ASR/ETS/ABS Control Modules

The Electronic Stability Program (ESP), Acceleration Slip Regulation (ASR), Electronic Traction System (ETS) and/or Anti-lock Brake System (ABS) control modules must not be disconnected. The Engine Control Module (ECM) and Transmission Control Module (TCM) rely on those control modules for Vehicle Speed Sensor (VSS) information. To disable brake and engine regulation of those modules, proceed as follows:

1. Turn ignition switch to Off position.
2. Connect Hand-Held Tester adapter to Data Link Connector (DLC).
3. Jump sockets No. 1 and 6.
4. Start engine. MIL must light.
5. If Hand-Held Tester is available, disconnect VSS front axle connector.
6. When testing is complete, connect VSS and erase Diagnostic Trouble Codes with Hand-Held Tester.

DESCRIPTION

Refer to "104 Engine (ME 2.1 Engine Management)" section.

DIAGNOSIS & TESTING

Symbol Explanation

Refer to "104 Engine (ME 2.1 Engine Management)" section for explanations of symbols, connections and steps included in the charts.

Accessing Diagnostic Trouble Codes

GENERIC SCAN TOOL

Follow tool manufacturers instructions and connect suitably programmed scan tool to generic scan tool connection X11/22.

HAND-HELD TESTER

1. Turn ignition switch to Off position.
2. Attach test cable tool No. 965 589 00 40 00, or equivalent, to Hand-Held Tester tool No. 965 589 00 01 00, or equivalent.

DTC	Possible cause SAE nomenclature	Explanation	Test step/Remedy
-	No malfunction in system		In case of complaint, perform □ 23, 24, 25 or 26 in its entirety
P0100 ■	MAF circuit malfunction	Hot film MAF sensor (B2/5)	□ 23⇒ 4.0 - 5.0
P0105 ■	MAP circuit malfunction	Pressure sensor (B28)	□ 23⇒ 6.0
P0110 ■	IAT circuit malfunction	IAT sensor (B17)	□ 23⇒ 9.0
P0115 ■	ECT circuit malfunction	ECT sensor (B11/4)	□ 23⇒ 8.0
P0120	Throttle position circuit malfunction	Actual value potentiometer in EA/CC/ISC actuator (M16/1)	□ 25⇒ 6.0
P0130 ■	O2S 1 circuit malfunction, bank 1 (right)	Right O2S 1 (before TWC) (G3/4)	□ 23⇒ 12.0

MB1029500279010A

Fig. 2 DTC interpretation (Part 1 of 12)

DTC	Possible cause SAE nomenclature	Explanation	Test step/Remedy
P0170 ■	Fuel trim malfunction	A Self adaptation of fuel mixture "partial load" of right cylinder bank at limit from engine control module (N3/10). B Self adaptation of fuel mixture "CTP" of right cylinder bank at limit from engine control module (N3/10).	Intake air leak, injectors, diaphragm pressure regulator, engine wear.
P0173 ■	Fuel trim malfunction	A Self adaptation of fuel mixture "partial load" of left cylinder bank at limit from engine control module (N3/10). B Self adaptation of fuel mixture "CTP" of left cylinder bank at limit from engine control module (N3/10).	Intake air leak, injectors, diaphragm pressure regulator, engine wear.
P0201 ■	Injector circuit malfunction - cyl. 1	Injector (Y62y1) – cylinder 1	□ 23⇒ 17.0
P0202 ■	Injector circuit malfunction - cyl. 2	Injector (Y62y2) – cylinder 2	□ 23⇒ 18.0
P0203 ■	Injector circuit malfunction - cyl. 3	Injector (Y62y3) – cylinder 3	□ 23 ⇒ 19.0
P0204 ■	Injector circuit malfunction - cyl. 4	Injector (Y62y4) – cylinder 4	□ 23 ⇒ 20.0
P0205 ■	Injector circuit malfunction - cyl. 5	Injector (Y62y5) – cylinder 5	□ 23 ⇒ 21.0
P0206 ■	Injector circuit malfunction - cyl. 6	Injector (Y62y6) – cylinder 6	□ 23 ⇒ 22.0
P0207 ■	Injector circuit malfunction - cyl. 7	Injector (Y62y7) – cylinder 7	□ 23 ⇒ 23.0
P0208 ■	Injector circuit malfunction - cyl. 8	Injector (Y62y8) – cylinder 8	□ 23 ⇒ 24.0

MB1029500279030A

Fig. 2 DTC interpretation (Part 3 of 12)

3. Connect cable to Data Link Connector (DLC), **Fig. 1.**
4. Turn multiplexer cable locking ring completely to left detent stop.
5. Attach multiplexer cable to data link connector via locking pins.
6. To lock multiplexer cable to connector, turn locking ring to the right.
7. Follow tool manufacturer's instructions.

Diagnostic Trouble Code Interpretation

Refer to **Fig. 2** for DTC interpretation. **Black square items are emission related and may activate MIL during test cycle.**

Symptom Related Diagnosis

Refer to **Fig. 3** for symptom related diagnosis.

Components Locations

Refer to **Figs. 4 through 6** for component locations.

Wiring Diagrams

Refer to **Figs. 7 through 9** for wiring diagrams.

DTC		Possible cause: SAE nomenclature	Possible cause: Explanation	Test step/Remedy
P0300 ■		Random misfire detected	A Random misfire B Random misfire, TWC damaging	□ 24 ⇒ 22.0 – 29.0 □ 24 ⇒ 30.0 □ 36 ⇒ 1.0 – 2.0 Compression pressure
P0301 ■		Cylinder 1 misfire detected	A Cylinder 1 misfire B Cylinder 1 misfire, TWC damaging	□ 24 ⇒ 22.0 □ 24 ⇒ 30.0 □ 36 ⇒ 1.0 – 2.0 Compression pressure
P0302 ■		Cylinder 2 misfire detected	A Cylinder 2 misfire B Cylinder 2 misfire, TWC damaging	□ 24 ⇒ 23.0 □ 24 ⇒ 30.0 □ 36 ⇒ 1.0 – 2.0 Compression pressure
P0303 ■		Cylinder 3 misfire detected	A Cylinder 3 misfire B Cylinder 3 misfire, TWC damaging	□ 24 ⇒ 24.0 □ 24 ⇒ 30.0 □ 36 ⇒ 1.0 – 2.0 Compression pressure
P0304 ■		Cylinder 4 misfire detected	A Cylinder 4 misfire B Cylinder 4 misfire, TWC damaging	□ 24 ⇒ 25.0 □ 24 ⇒ 30.0 □ 36 ⇒ 1.0 – 2.0 Compression pressure

MB1029500279040A

Fig. 2 DTC interpretation (Part 4 of 12)

DTC		Possible cause: SAE nomenclature	Possible cause: Explanation	Test step/Remedy
P0305 ■		Cylinder 5 misfire detected	A Cylinder 5 misfire B Cylinder 5 misfire, TWC damaging	□ 24 ⇒ 26.0 □ 24 ⇒ 30.0 □ 36 ⇒ 1.0 – 2.0 Compression pressure
P0306 ■		Cylinder 6 misfire detected	A Cylinder 6 misfire B Cylinder 6 misfire, TWC damaging	□ 24 ⇒ 27.0 □ 24 ⇒ 30.0 □ 36 ⇒ 1.0 – 2.0 Compression pressure
P0307 ■		Cylinder 7 misfire detected	A Cylinder 7 misfire B Cylinder 7 misfire, TWC damaging	□ 24 ⇒ 28.0 □ 24 ⇒ 30.0 □ 36 ⇒ 1.0 – 2.0 Compression pressure
P0308 ■		Cylinder 8 misfire detected	A Cylinder 8 misfire B Cylinder 8 misfire, TWC damaging	□ 24 ⇒ 29.0 □ 24 ⇒ 30.0 □ 36 ⇒ 1.0 – 2.0 Compression pressure
P0325 ■		KS 1 circuit malfunction (right side of engine)	Right KS 1 (A16g1)	Wiring, connector, A16 g1
P0330 ■		KS 2 circuit malfunction (left side of engine)	Left KS 2 (A16g2)	Wiring, connector, A16 g2

MB1029500279050A

Fig. 2 DTC interpretation (Part 5 of 12)

DTC		Possible cause: SAE nomenclature	Possible cause: Explanation	Test step/Remedy
P0335 ■		CKP sensor circuit malfunction	CKP sensor (L5)	□ 24 ⇒ 12.0
P0341 ■		CMP sensor circuit range/performance	Camshaft Hall-effect sensor (B6/1)	□ 24 ⇒ 13.0
P0410 ■	Only (USA)	Air injection system malfunction	AIR system malfunction (logic chain)	□ 23 ⇒ 25.0 – 26.0
P0422 ■		TWC efficiency below threshold, right	Right TWC efficiency below threshold	Replace right TWC
P0432 ■		TWC efficiency below threshold, left	Left TWC efficiency below threshold	Replace left TWC
P0440 ■	Only (USA) **Mod.140/210 and 129 as of 09/97**	EVAP system malfunction	EVAP leaking (logic chain)	□ 23 ⇒ 31.0 – 33.0
P0441 ■		EVAP system incorrect purge flow	EVAP not functioning	□ 23 ⇒ 31.0 – 32.0
P0442 ■	Only (USA) **Mod. 140/210 and 129 as of 09/97**	EVAP system leak detected (small leak)	EVAP system, small leak	□ 23 ⇒ 33.0
P0443 ■		EVAP system purge control valve circuit malfunction	Purge control valve (Y58/1)	□ 23 ⇒ 31.0
P0446 ■	Only (USA) **Mod. 140/210 and 129 as of 09/97**	EVAP system vent control malfunction	A Charcoal canister shut-off valve (Y58/4) B End stage of charcoal canister shut-off valve	□ 23 ⇒ 34.0, N3/10

MB1029500279060A

Fig. 2 DTC interpretation (Part 6 of 12)

DTC		Possible cause: SAE nomenclature	Possible cause: Explanation	Test step/Remedy
P0450 ■	Only (USA) **Mod. 140/210 and 129 as of 09/97** Only (USA) **Model 129 up to 08/97**	EVAP system pressure sensor malfunction	Fuel tank pressure sensor (B4/3) Purge monitoring pressure sensor (B4/4)	□ 23 ⇒ 35.0 Charcoal canister plugged. □ 23 ⇒ 36.0
P0455 ■	Only (USA) **Mod. 140/210 and 129 as of 09/97**	EVAP system leak detected (large leak)	EVAP system, large leak Fuel tank press. sensor (B4/3)	□ 23 ⇒ 33.0 □ 23 ⇒ 35.0
P0462		Fuel level sensor circuit low input	Fuel tank level too low	Fill fuel tank
P0500		VSS sensor malfunction	A VSS left front B VSS left rear	□ 25 ⇒ 8.0 □ 25 ⇒ 9.0
P0507		ISC rpm higher than expected	Idle control system	□ 25 ⇒ 4.0 – 7.0
P0560		System voltage malfunction	Voltage supply to engine control module (N3/10)	□ 23 ⇒ 1.0 – 3.0
P0565		Cruise control switch	CC switch (S40)	□ 26 ⇒ 1.0

MB1029500279070A

Fig. 2 DTC interpretation (Part 7 of 12)

Connector Terminal Identification

Refer to **Figs. 10 and 11** for engine control module connector terminal identification.

Diagnostic Tests

1. Turn ignition switch to Off position.
2. Connect 126-pole socket box tool No. 129 589 00 21 00, or equivalent, with contact module tool No. 140 589 46 63 00, or equivalent, to Engine Control Module, **Fig. 12.**
3. Connect interior harness connector to test cable connection No. 1 and engine harness connector to test cable connection No. 2.
4. Conduct tests as directed in **Figs. 13 through 62** using suitable multimeter.

Clearing Diagnostic Trouble Codes

The Diagnostic Trouble Code (DTC) memory is cleared when the vehicle battery is disconnected.

When an component has been repaired or replaced, the related DTC will be cleared. After three trips the CHECK ENGINE Malfunction Indicator Lamp (MIL) will go out and after 40 warm-up periods the DTC is automatically erased. A trip includes engine running for more than 20 minutes, engine oil temperature of more than 19°F, engine speed of more than 700 RPM and emission related logic chain functions. A warm-up period includes an engine coolant temperature at start-up of less than 95°F and increasing to more than 176°F.

To erase DTCs with a Hand-Held Tester, follow the tool manufacturer's instructions.

Component Tests

FUEL PUMP

1. Connect suitable pressure gauge to test connection, **Fig. 63.**
2. Conduct tests as directed, **Fig. 64.**
3. Connect 126-pole socket box tool No. 129 589 00 21 00, or equivalent, to Engine Control Module (ECM) with test cable tool No. 140 589 46 63 00, or equivalent, **Fig. 65.**
4. Conduct tests as directed, **Fig. 66.**
5. Release fuel pressure and allow fuel to drain into suitable measuring cup.

FUEL INJECTOR

1. Connect 126-pole socket box tool No. 129 589 00 21 00, or equivalent, to Engine Control Module (ECM) with test cable tool No. 140 589 46 63 00, or equivalent, **Fig. 67.**
2. Disconnect injector connectors, then remove fuel rail with injectors. **Do not disconnect fuel feed and return lines.**
3. Connect self-made harness to one injector after another, hold over suitable measuring glass and test as directed, **Fig. 68.**

DTC	Possible cause: SAE nomenclature	Possible cause: Explanation	Test step/Remedy
P0600	Serial communication link malfunction	CAN bus from ESP/SPS control module (N47-5)	☐ 23 ⇒ 37.0
P0604	Internal control module random Access memory (RAM) error	A Control module B Control module	(N3/10)
P0605	Internal control module random Access memory (RAM) error	Engine control module (N3/10)	(N3/10)
P0700 ■	Transmission control system malfunction	Read DTC memory of transmission control module	Test ETC
P0702 ■	Transmission control system electrical	Read DTC memory of transmission control module	Test ETC
P0715 ■	Input/turbine speed sensor circuit malfunction	Read DTC memory of transmission control module	Test ETC
P0720 ■	Output speed sensor circuit malfunction	Read DTC memory of transmission control module	Test ETC

MB1029500279080A

Fig. 2 DTC interpretation (Part 8 of 12)

DTC	Possible cause: SAE nomenclature	Possible cause: Explanation	Test step/Remedy
P0730 ■	Incorrect gear ratio	Read DTC memory of transmission control module	Test ETC
P0740 ■	Torque converter clutch system malfunction	Read DTC memory of transmission control module	Test ETC
P0743 ■	Torque converter clutch system electrical	Read DTC memory of transmission control module	Test ETC
P0748 ■	Pressure control solenoid electrical	Read DTC memory of transmission control module	Test ETC
P0753 ■	Shift solenoid A electrical	Read DTC memory of transmission control module	Test ETC
P0758 ■	Shift solenoid B electrical	Read DTC memory of transmission control module	Test ETC
P0763 ■	Shift solenoid C electrical	Read DTC memory of transmission control module	Test ETC

MB1029500279090X

Fig. 2 DTC interpretation (Part 9 of 12)

DTC	Possible cause: SAE nomenclature	Possible cause: Explanation	DTC Description	Test step/Remedy
P0809	Angle deviation between camshaft and crankshaft	Angle deviation between camshaft and crankshaft		Check basic adjustment of camshaft
P1163	Oil level switch	Oil level switch (S43)		☐ 23 ⇒ 39.0
P1 186	Fuel safety shut-off recognized	EA/CC/ISC actuator (M16/6)		☐ 25 ⇒ 3.0 – 4.0, EA/CC/ISC actuator (M16/6) sticks or jammed, Check intake system for residue.
P1386 ■	Knock sensor control from ECM (N3/10) at end stop	Knock sensor control in engine control module (N3/10) hardware failure	☐ 13 ⫸ **41**	1. Increased knock tendency due to bad fuel, carbon in combustion chamber or mechanical damage. 2. Engine control module (N3/10)
P1420 ■ Only USA	AIR pump switchover valve	AIR pump switchover valve (Y32)	☐ 13 ⫸ **42**	☐ 23 ⇒ 26.0
P1453 ■ Only USA	AIR relay module	AIR relay module (K17)	☐ 13 ⫸ **42**	☐ 23 ⇒ 25.0

MB1029500279100X

Fig. 2 DTC interpretation (Part 10 of 12)

DTC	Possible cause: SAE nomenclature	Possible cause: Explanation	DTC Description	Test step/Remedy
P1519 ■	Right adjustable camshaft timing solenoid	Right adjustable camshaft timing solenoid (Y49/2) (logic chain)	☐ 13 ⫸ **43**	☐ 23 ⇒ 28.0
P1522 ■	Left adjustable camshaft timing solenoid	Left adjustable camshaft timing solenoid (Y49/1) (logic chain)	☐ 13 ⫸ **43**	☐ 23 ⇒ 27.0
P1525 ■	Right adjustable camshaft timing solenoid	Right adjustable camshaft timing solenoid (Y49/2)	☐ 13 ⫸ **44**	☐ 23 ⇒ 30.0
P1533 ■	Left adjustable camshaft timing solenoid	Left adjustable camshaft timing solenoid (Y49/1)	☐ 13 ⫸ **44**	☐ 23 ⇒ 29.0
P1542	Pedal value sensor	Pedal value sensor (B37)	☐ 13 ⫸ **45**	☐ 25 ⇒ 4.0 - 5.0

MB1029500279110X

Fig. 2 DTC interpretation (Part 11 of 12)

DTC	Possible cause: SAE nomenclature	Possible cause: Explanation	DTC Description	Test step/Remedy
P1 570 [2]	A. Start attempt performed with RCL locked B. CAN signal from DAS control module to engine control module C. Engine control module (ME-SFI) and DAS control module are not compatible	A. Start attempt performed with RCL locked. B. CAN signal from DAS control module (N54/1) to engine control module (N3/10) interrupted. C. Engine control module (ME-SFI) and DAS control module are not compatible.		Check for correct operation of DAS Check control modules and part no.
P1 580 ■	EA/CC/ISC actuator	EA/CC/ISC actuator (M16/1)	☐ 13 ⫸ **46**	☐ 25 ⇒ 7.0
P1 584	Stop lamp switch	Stop lamp switch (S9/1)		☐ 26 ⇒ 2.0
P1 605 ■	Body acceleration sensor	Body acceleration sensor (B24) (up to 05/96) Poor road/traction condition recognition signal (via comparison of VSS rpm signals) (as of 06/96)	☐ 13 ⫸ **47**	☐ 23 ⇒ 42.0 Test ASR/ESP
P1 747 ■	CAN signal from ETC	CAN signal from ETC (N15/3) interrupted	☐ 13 ⫸ **26**	☐ 23 ⇒ 37.0

[2] The DTC P1 570 can be displayed on model 140 vehicles produced between 09/95 and 11/95 even if no malfunction is present.

MB1029500279120X

Fig. 2 DTC interpretation (Part 12 of 12)

Complaint/Problem	Possible cause	Test step/Remedy	Actual value Engine test Menu item
Engine starts and accelerates poorly when cold	Injector (Y62) control and injection duration. Hot film MAF sensor (B2/5). ECT sensor (B11/4). Ignition voltage too low. Intake air leak.	☐ 23 ⇒ 17.0 – 24.0 ☐ 23 ⇒ 4.0 – 5.0 ☐ 23 ⇒ 8.0 ☐ 24 ⇒ 30.0 Remedy leak.	2/7 1/7 3/7 – –
Engine does not start	No voltage supply from base module (N16/1). Malfunction of drive authorization system (DAS). Fuel pumps defective. No compression, oil pressure too high. Ignition voltage too low.	☐ 23 ⇒ 1.0 – 3.0 ☐ 23 ⇒ 37.0 ☐ 34 ⇒ 2.0 check compression and oil pressure. ☐ 24 ⇒ 30.0	– DAS 1/1 – – –
Engine has uneven idle	Camshaft timing. Injector (Y62) control and injection duration. Intake air leak.	☐ 23 ⇒ 27.0 – 30.0 ☐ 23 ⇒ 17.0 – 24.0 Remedy leak.	2/7 2/7 –
Engine has insufficient output	TWC flow restricted. Left or right O2S 1 (G3/3 or G3/4) (before TWC). ECT sensor (B11/4). Hot film MAF sensor (B2/5). Camshaft timing.	Check exhaust back pressure, see DM, Engines, Vol. 1, section A, "Engine Output" ☐ 23 ⇒ 11.0 – 12.0 ☐ 23 ⇒ 8.0 ☐ 23 ⇒ 4.0 – 5.0 ☐ 23 ⇒ 27.0 – 30.0	– 5/7 3/7 1/7 2/7

MB1029500277010X

Fig. 3 Symptom related diagnosis (Part 1 of 2)

Complaint/Problem	Possible cause	Test step/Remedy	Actual value Engine test Menu item
Engine runs unevenly (shakes)	Injector (Y62) control and injection duration. Injector has leaking, spray pattern. Left or right O2S 1 (G3/3 or G3/4) (before TWC). Ignition voltage too low. Compression on one or more cylinders too low. Intake air leak.	☐ 23 ⇒ 17.0 – 24.0 ☐ 36 ⇒ 1.0 ☐ 23 ⇒ 11.0 – 12.0 ☐ 24 ⇒ 30.0 Check compression. Remedy leak.	2/7 – 5/7 – – –
Engine runs unevenly (misfiring)	Ignition voltage too low. Hot film MAF sensor (B2/5).	☐ 24 ⇒ 30.0 ☐ 23 ⇒ 4.0 – 5.0	– 1/7
Engine surges after cold start	Intake air leak.	Remedy leak.	–
Transition failure during warm-up	ECT sensor (B11/4). Hot film MAF sensor (B2/5). Intake air leak.	☐ 23 ⇒ 8.0 ☐ 23 ⇒ 4.0 – 5.0 Remedy leak.	3/7 1/7 –
Transition failure when warm or with increased fuel consumption	Left or right O2S 1 (G3/3 or G3/4) (before TWC). Purge control valve (Y58/1) stuck in open position.	☐ 23 ⇒ 11.0 – 12.0 ☐ 23 ⇒ 25.0 – 26.0	5/7 3/7
Engine vibrates	Hot film MAF sensor (B2/5). Ignition voltage too low. Left or right O2S 1 (G3/3 or G3/4) (before TWC).	☐ 23 ⇒ 4.0 – 5.0 ☐ 24 ⇒ 30.0 ☐ 23 ⇒ 11.0 – 12.0	1/7 – 5/7
EPC MIL (A1e43) illuminates and EA is in "limp-home" mode	Nominal value potentiometer in pedal value sensor (B37). EA/CC/ISC actuator actual value potentiometer.	☐ 25 ⇒ 4.0 – 5.0 ☐ 25 ⇒ 6.0 – 7.0	4/7 4/7

MB1029500277020X

Fig. 3 Symptom related diagnosis (Part 2 of 2)

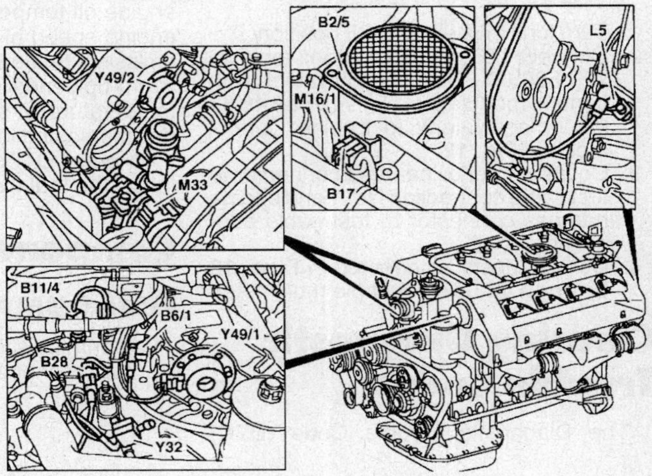

B2/5 Hot film MAF sensor
B6/1 Camshaft Hall-effect sensor
B11/4 ECT sensor
B17 IAT sensor
B28 Pressure sensor
M16/1 EA/CC/ISC actuator
M33 AIR pump
Y32 AIR pump switchover valve
Y49/1 Left adjustable camshaft timing solenoid
Y49/2 Right adjustable camshaft timing solenoid

MB1029500274010X

Fig. 4 ME engine management component locations (Part 1 of 2)

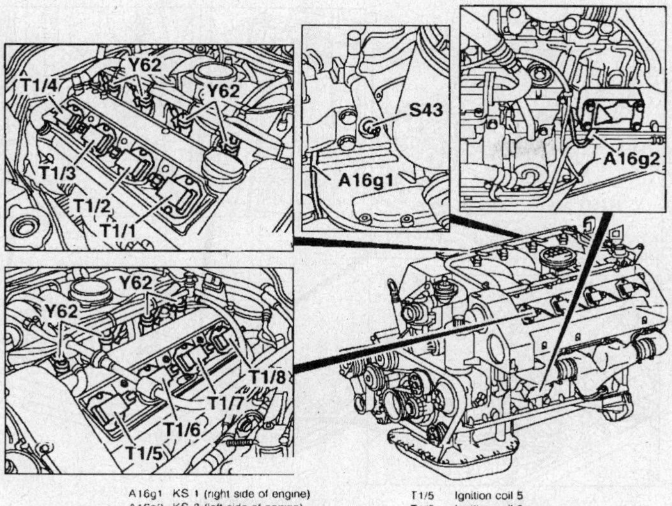

A16g1 KS 1 (right side of engine)
A16g2 KS 2 (left side of engine)
T1/1 Ignition coil 1
T1/2 Ignition coil 2
T1/3 Ignition coil 3
T1/4 Ignition coil 4
T1/5 Ignition coil 5
T1/6 Ignition coil 6
T1/7 Ignition coil 7
T1/8 Ignition coil 8
S43 Oil level switch
Y62 Injectors

MB1029500274020X

Fig. 4 ME engine management component locations (Part 2 of 2)

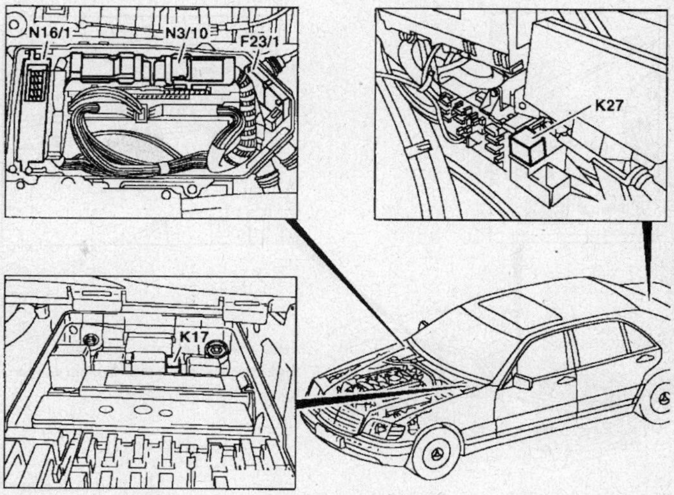

F23/1 Control module box
K17 AIR relay module
K27 FP relay module
N3/10 Engine control module (ME-SFI)
N16/1 Base module (BM)

MB1029500276010X

Fig. 5 ME engine management component locations (Part 1 of 4). S420 & 1998–99 CL500 & S500

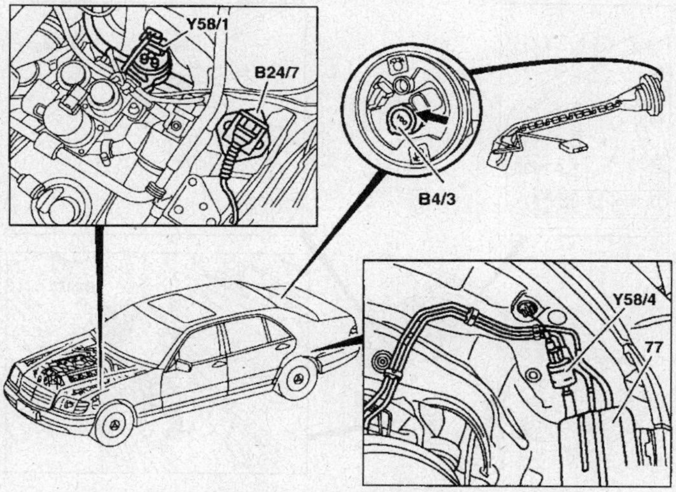

B4/3 Fuel tank pressure sensor
B24/7 Body acceleration sensor
Y58/1 Purge control valve
Y58/4 Activated charcoal canister shut-off valve
77 Active charcoal canister

MB1029500276020X

Fig. 5 ME engine management component locations (Part 2 of 4). S420 & 1998–99 CL500 & S500

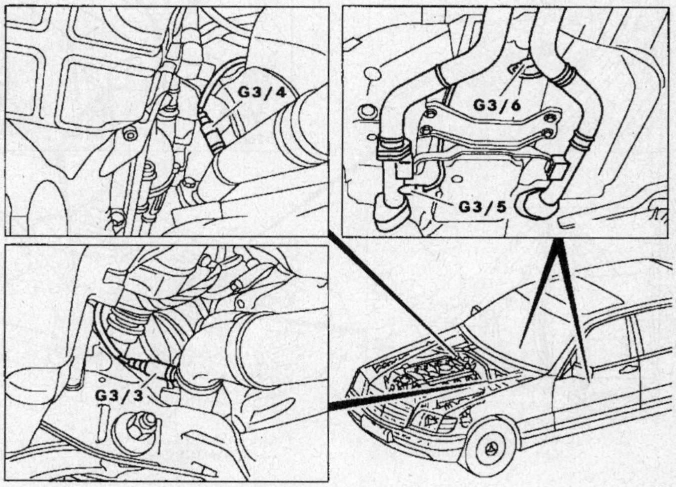

G3/3 Left O2S 1 (before TWC)
G3/4 Right O2S 1 (before TWC)
G3/5 Left O2S 2 (after TWC)
G3/6 Right O2S 2 (after TWC)

MB1029500276030X

Fig. 5 ME engine management component locations (Part 3 of 4). S420 & 1998–99 CL500 & S500

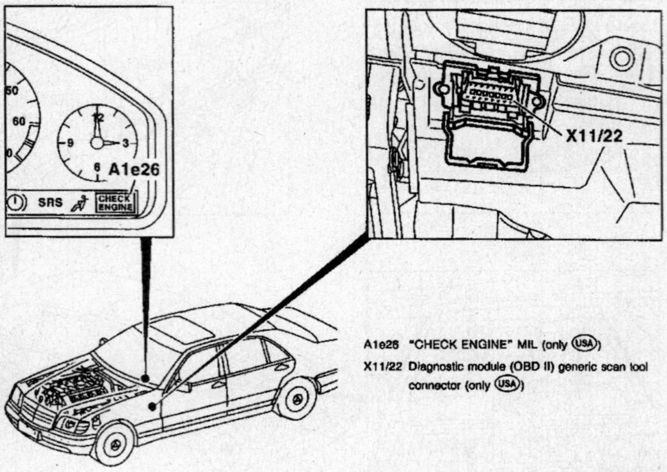

A1e26 "CHECK ENGINE" MIL (only USA)
X11/22 Diagnostic module (OBD II) generic scan tool connector (only USA)

MB1029500276040X

Fig. 5 ME engine management component locations (Part 4 of 4). S420 & 1998–99 CL500 & S500

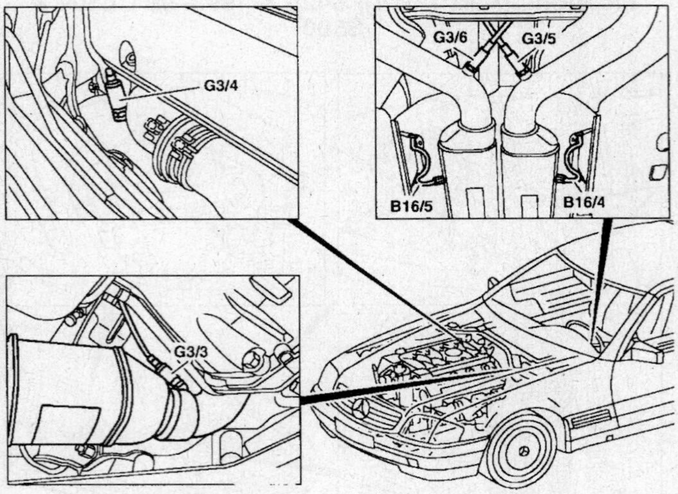

G3/3 Left O2S 1 (before TWC)
G3/4 Right O2S 1 (before TWC)
G3/5 Left O2S 2 (after TWC)
G3/6 Right O2S 2 (after TWC)

MB1029500275020X

Fig. 6 ME engine management component locations (Part 2 of 4). 1998 SL500

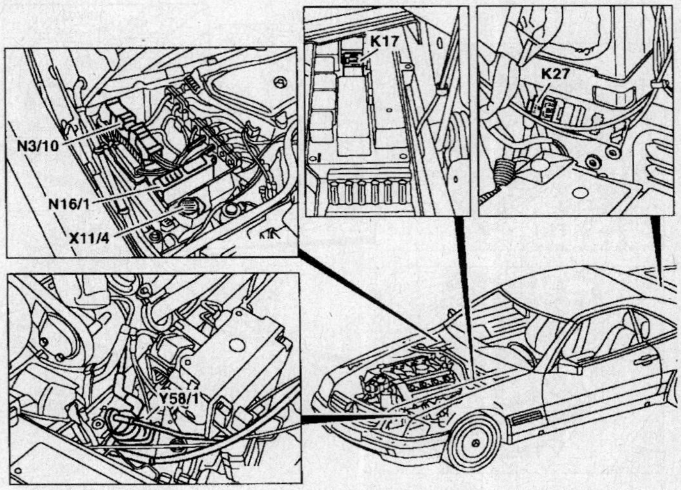

K17 AIR relay module
K27 FP relay module
N3/10 Engine control module (ME-SFI)
N16/1 Base module (BM)
X11/4 Data link connector (DTC readout) (38-pole)
Y58/1 Purge control valve

MB1029500275010X

Fig. 6 ME engine management component locations (Part 1 of 4). 1998 SL500

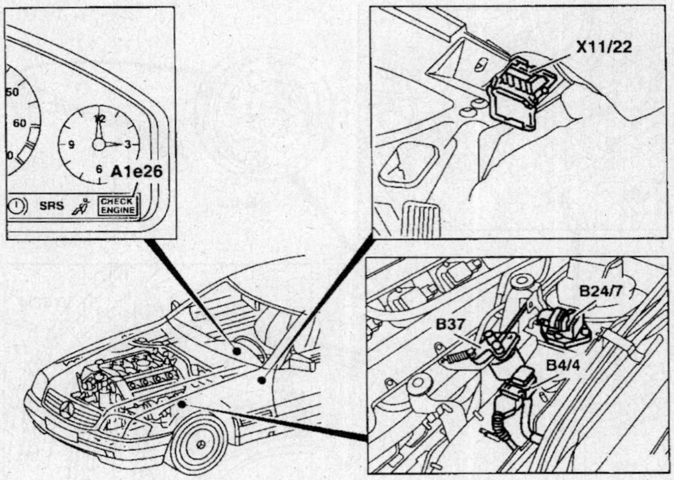

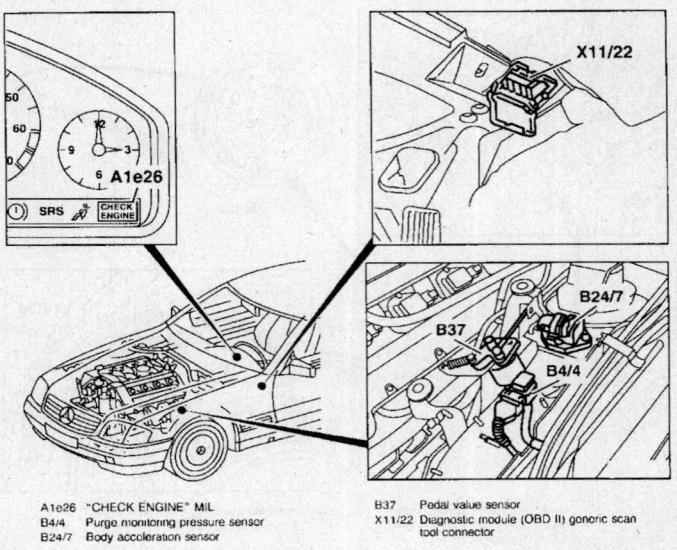

A1e26 "CHECK ENGINE" MIL
B4/4 Purge monitoring pressure sensor
B24/7 Body acceleration sensor
B37 Pedal value sensor
X11/22 Diagnostic module (OBD II) generic scan tool connector

MB1029500275030X

Fig. 6 ME engine management component locations (Part 3 of 4). 1998 SL500

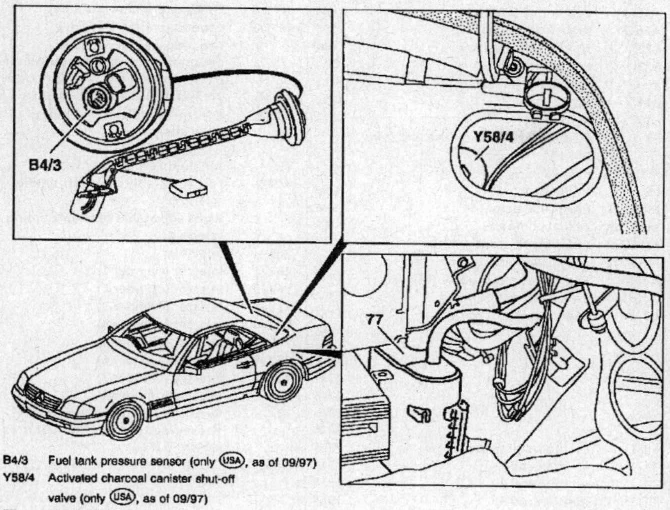

B4/3 Fuel tank pressure sensor (only USA, as of 09/97)
Y58/4 Activated charcoal canister shut-off valve (only USA, as of 09/97)
77 Activated charcoal canister

MB1029500275040X

Fig. 6 ME engine management component locations (Part 4 of 4). 1998 SL500

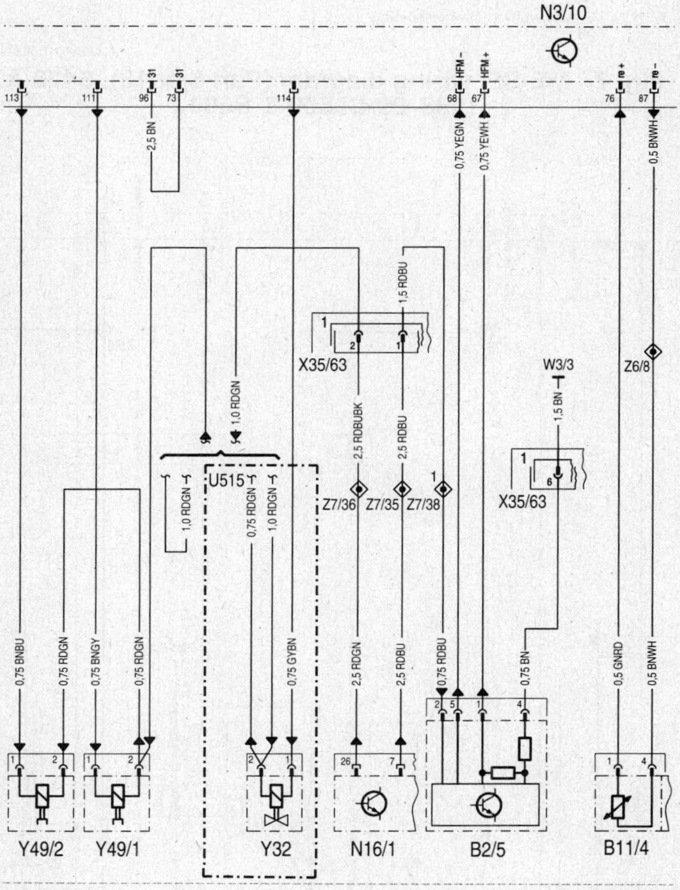

MB1019600153020X

Fig. 7 ME-SFI wiring diagram (Part 2 of 13). S420 & 1998–99 CL500 & S500

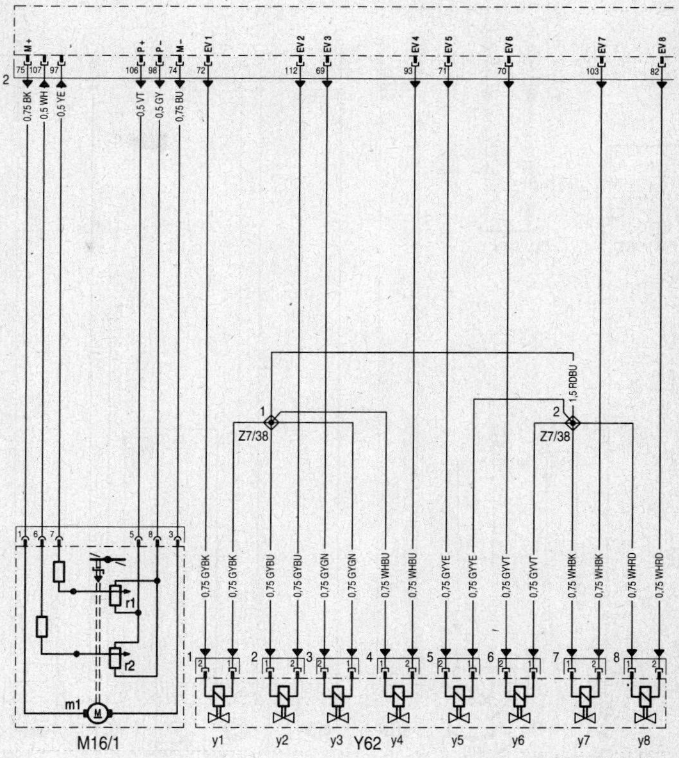

MB1019600153010X

Fig. 7 ME-SFI wiring diagram (Part 1 of 13). S420 & 1998–99 CL500 & S500

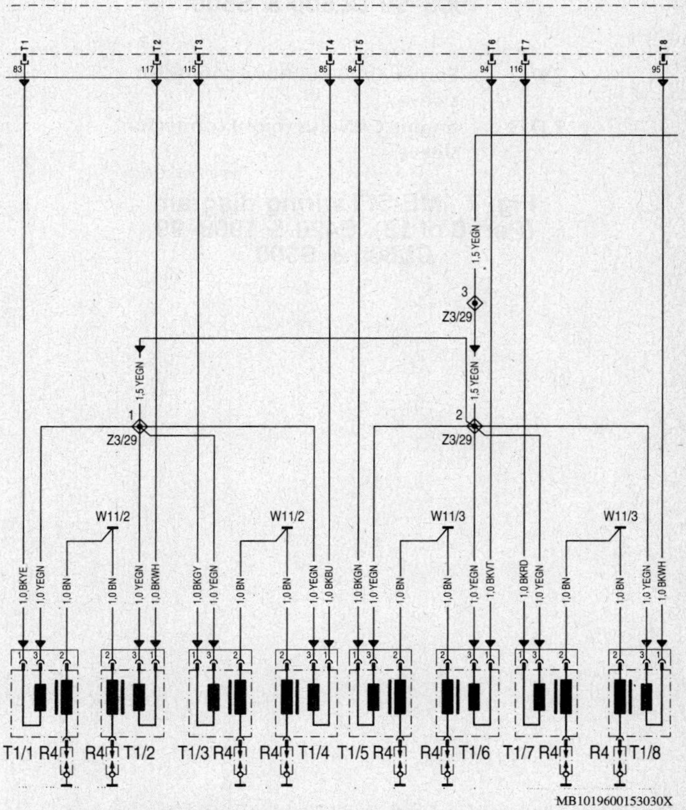

MB1019600153030X

Fig. 7 ME-SFI wiring diagram (Part 3 of 13). S420 & 1998–99 CL500 & S500

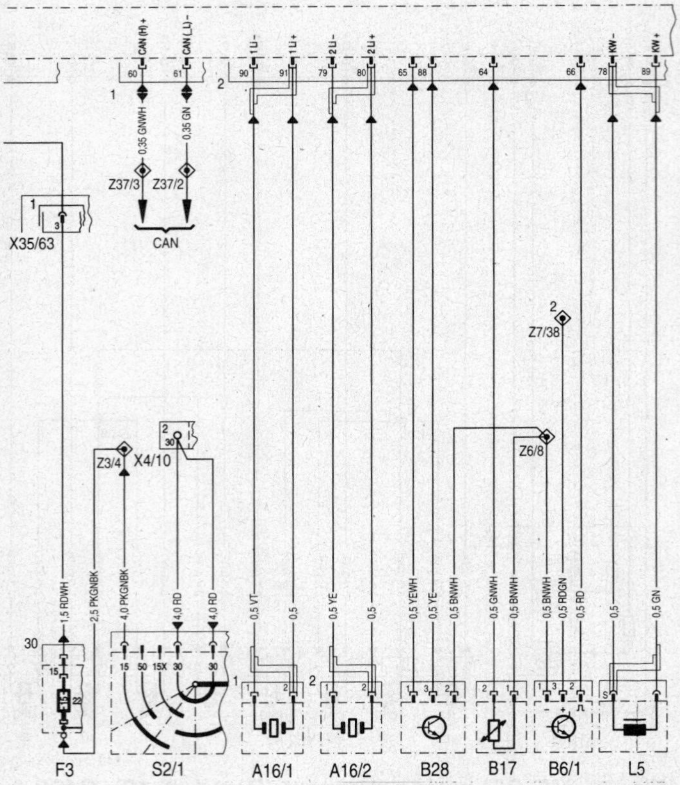

MB1019600153040X

Fig. 7 ME-SFI wiring diagram (Part 4 of 13). S420 & 1998–99 CL500 & S500

Z37/2	Engine CAN-Bus (low) connector sleeve	
Z37/3	Engine CAN-Bus (high) connector sleeve	

MB1019600153060X

Fig. 7 ME-SFI wiring diagram (Part 6 of 13). S420 & 1998–99 CL500 & S500

A16/1	Left knock sensor 1	28M
A16/2	Right knock sensor 2	29M
B2/5	Hot film MAF sensor	14M
B28	Pressure sensor	30M
B6/1	Camshaft Hall-effect sensor	32M
B11/4	ECT sensor	16M
B17	IAT sensor	31M
F3	Fuse box (35-fuse, in fuse and relay box F1)	
F3f22	Fuse 22	26L
L5	CKP sensor	32M
M16/1	EA/CC/ISC actuator	2M
M16/1m1	Actuator motor	1L
M16/1r1	Reference potentiometer	2K
M16/1r2	Actual value potentiometer	2L
N3/10	Engine control module (ME-SFI)	15A
N16/1	Base module (BM)	13M
R4	Spark plugs	17M
		18M
		19M
		20M
		21M
		22M
		23M
		24M
S2/1	Ignition/starter switch	27M
T1/1	Ignition coil 1	17M
T1/2	Ignition coil 2	18M
T1/3	Ignition coil 3	19M
T1/4	Ignition coil 4	20M
T1/5	Ignition coil 5	21M
T1/6	Ignition coil 6	22M
T1/7	Ignition coil 7	23M
T1/8	Ignition coil 8	25M
U515	Valid for secondary air injection (AIR)	
W3/3	Ground (right front wheelhousing - DI)	

W11/2	Ground (engine-right side)
W11/3	Ground (engine-left side)
	Ground location without designation, component grounded directly on engine, chassis or body.
X4/10	Terminal block (circuit 30/30Ü)
X35/63	Control module box/engine separation point
Y32	AIR pump switchover valve
Y49/1	Left adjustable camshaft timing solenoid
Y49/2	Right adjustable camshaft timing solenoid
Y62	Injectors
Y62y1	Injector (cylinder 1)
Y62y2	Injector (cylinder 2)
Y62y3	Injector (cylinder 3)
Y62y4	Injector (cylinder 4)
Y62y5	Injector (cylinder 5)
Y62y6	Injector (cylinder 6)
Y62y7	Injector (cylinder 7)
Y62y8	Injector (cylinder 8)
Z3/4	Circuit 15 (unfused) connector sleeve (feed from ignition/starter switch - S2/1)
Z3/29	Circuit 15 connector sleeve, (fused)
Z6/8	Sensor ground connector sleeve
Z7/35	Connector sleeve, circuit 87M, feed from BM (N16/1)
Z7/36	Circuit 87 M2e connector sleeve
Z7/38	Circuit 87 M1i connector sleeve

MB1019600153050X

Fig. 7 ME-SFI wiring diagram (Part 5 of 13). S420 & 1998–99 CL500 & S500

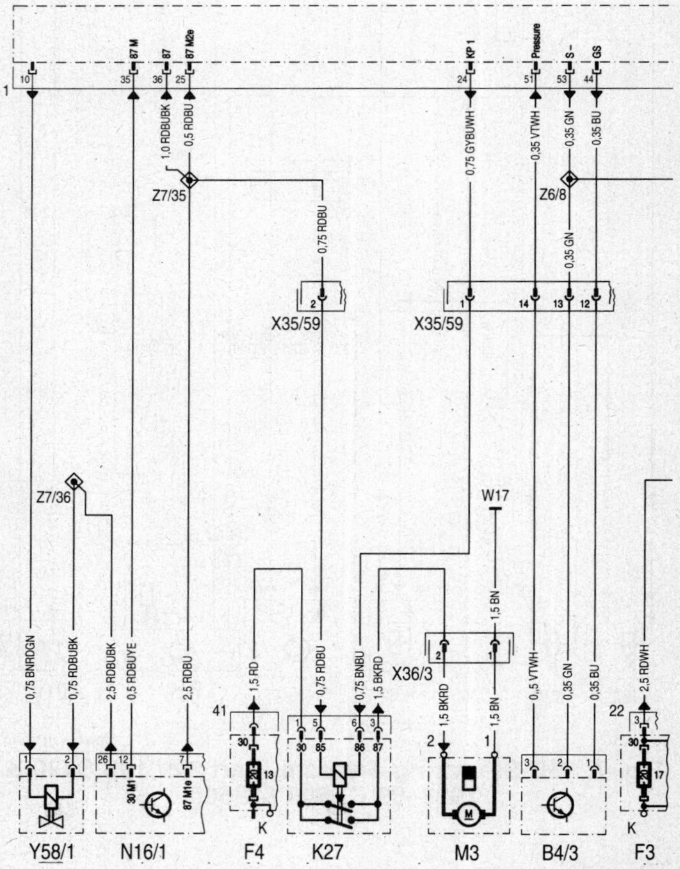

MB1019600153070X

Fig. 7 ME-SFI wiring diagram (Part 7 of 13). S420 & 1998–99 CL500 & S500

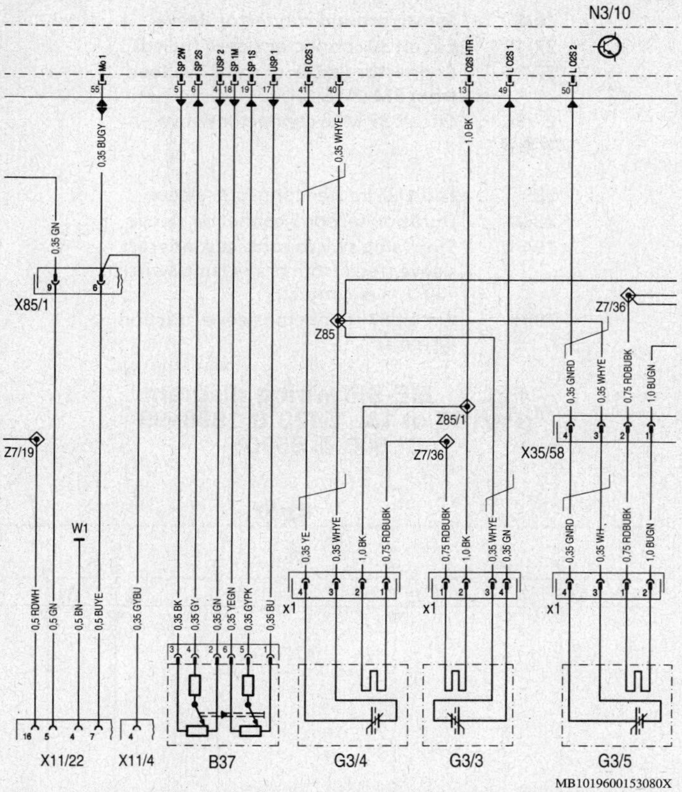

Fig. 7 ME-SFI wiring diagram (Part 8 of 13). S420 & 1998–99 CL500 & S500

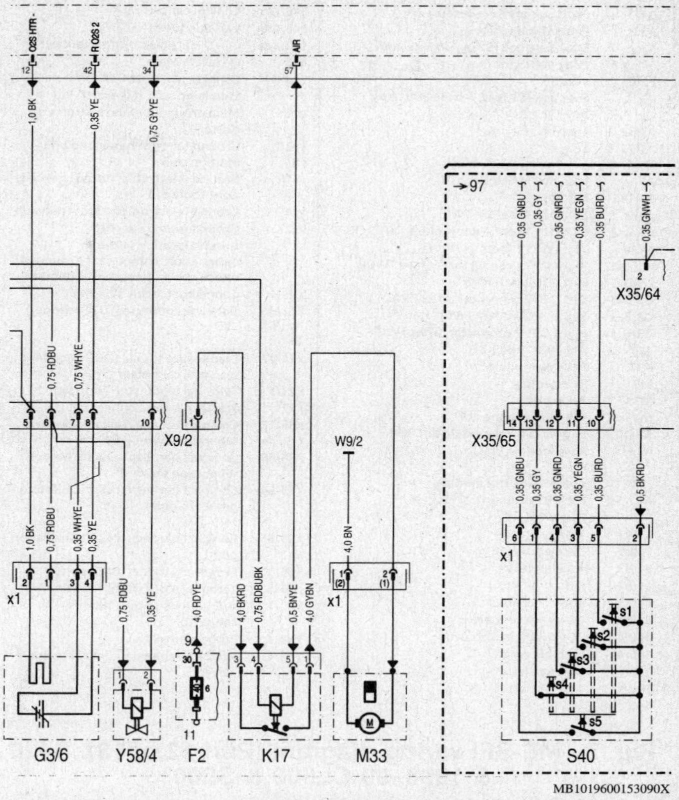

Fig. 7 ME-SFI wiring diagram (Part 9 of 13). S420 & 1998–99 CL500 & S500

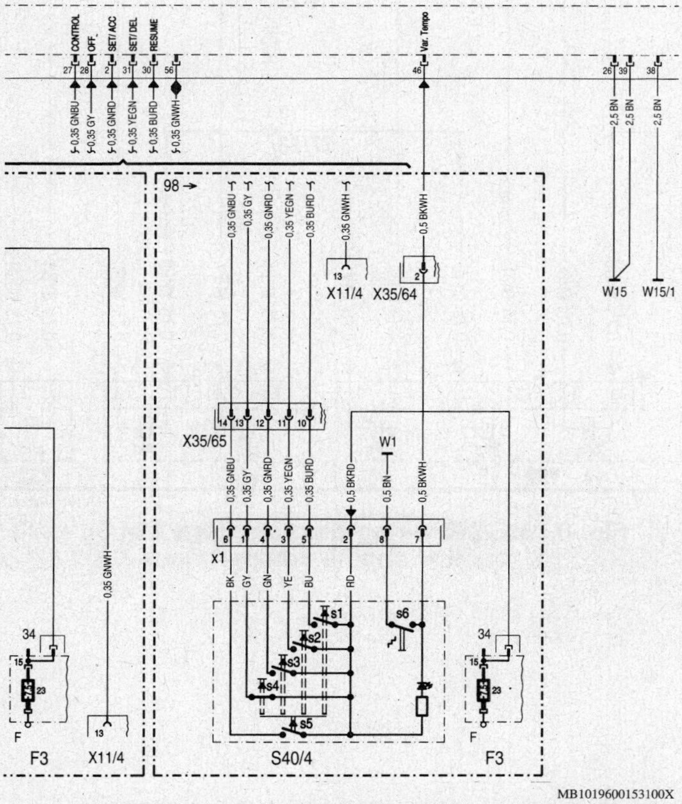

Fig. 7 ME-SFI wiring diagram (Part 10 of 13). S420 & 1998–99 CL500 & S500

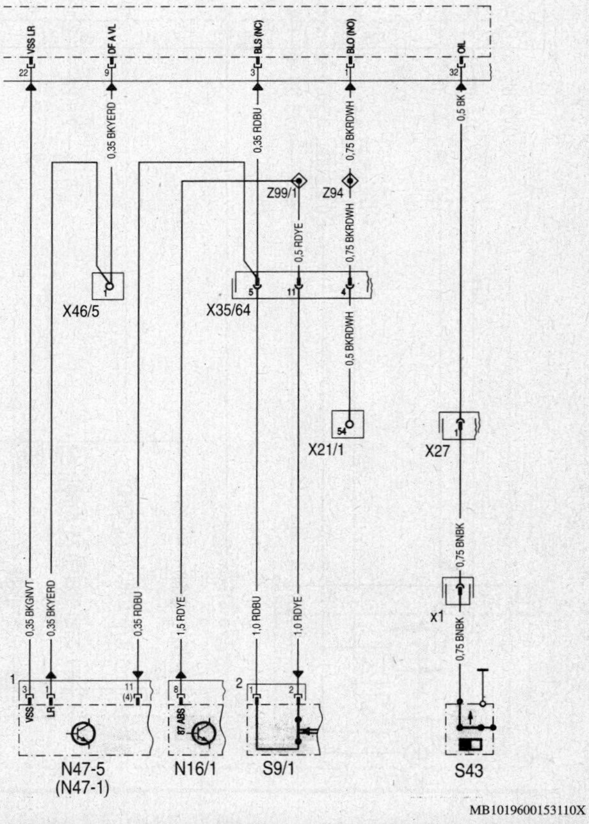

Fig. 7 ME-SFI wiring diagram (Part 11 of 13). S420 & 1998–99 CL500 & S500

B4/3	Fuel tank pressure sensor
B37	Pedal value sensor
F2	Maxi-fuse box (6-fuse, in fuse and relay box F1)
F2f6	Fuse 6
F3	Fuse box (35-fuse, in fuse and relay box F1)
F3f17	Fuse 17
F3f23	Fuse 23
F4	Fuse box in trunk
F4f13	Fuse 13
G3/3	Left O2S 1 (before TWC)
G3/3x1	Left O2S 1 connector (before TWC)
G3/4	Right O2S 1 (before TWC)
G3/4x1	Right O2S 1 connector (before TWC)
G3/5	Left O2S 2 (after TWC)
G3/5x1	Left O2S 2 connector (after TWC)
G3/6	Right O2S 2 (after TWC)
G3/6x1	Right O2S 2 connector (after TWC)
K17	AIR relay module
K27	FP relay module
M3	FP assembly
M33	AIR pump
M33x1	AIR pump connector
N3/10	Engine control module (ME-SFI)
N16/1	Base module (BM)
N47-1	ASR/SPS control module
N47-5	ESP/SPS/BAS control module
S40	CC switch
S40s1	Memory recall
S40s2	Decelerate/set
S40s3	Accelerate/set
S40s4	Off
S40s5	Control contact
S40x1	CC switch connector
S40/4	CC variable pushbutton
S40/4s1	Memory recall
S40/4s2	Decelerate/set
S40/4s3	Accelerate/set
S40/4s4	Off
S40/4s5	Control contact
S40/4s6	Variable speed
S40/4x1	CC variable pushbutton connector
S43	Oil level switch
S43x1	Oil level switch connector
S9/1	Stop lamp switch (4-pole)
W1	Main ground (behind instrument cluster)
W9/2	Ground (at right headlamp unit - ignition coil)
W15	Ground (electronics output ground - right footwell)
W15/1	Ground (electronics - right footwell)
W17	Ground (right rear seat)
	Ground location without designation, component grounded directly on engine, chassis or body.
X9/2	Connector (circuit 30/15)
X11/4	Data link connector (DTC readout)
X11/22	Diagnostic module (OBD II) generic scan tool connector
X21/1	Terminal block (stop lamp switch)
X27	Starter harness connector
X35/58	Compact harness/taillamp harness separation point (10-pole)
X35/59	Compact harness/taillamp harness separation point
X35/64	Compact harness/cockpit separation point (18-pole)
X35/65	Compact harness/cockpit separation point
X36/3	FP harness connector (2-pole)
X46/5	Terminal block (right foot well)
X85/1	A/C harness/engine harness connector
Y58/1	Purge control valve
Y58/4	Activated charcoal canister shut-off valve

MB1019600153120X

Fig. 7 ME-SFI wiring diagram (Part 12 of 13). S420 & 1998–99 CL500 & S500

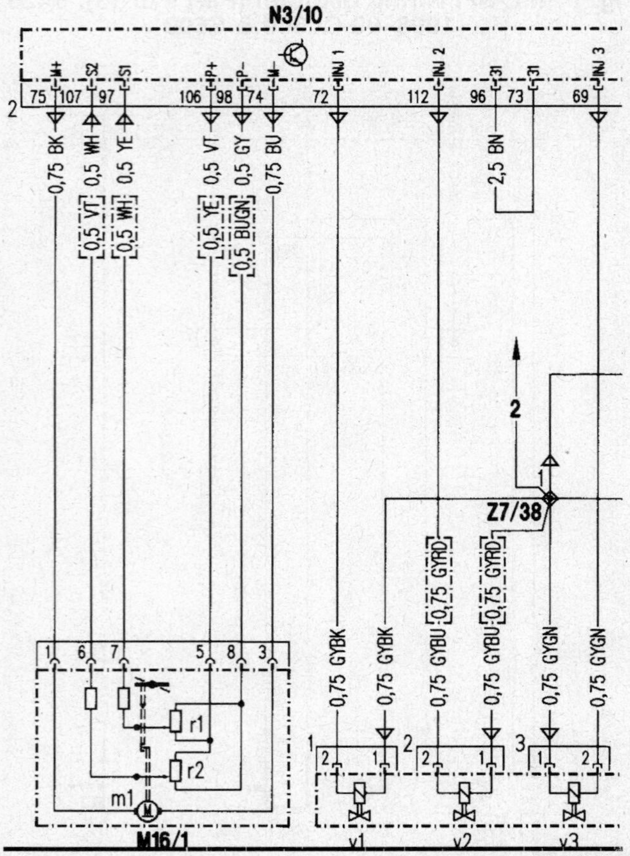

MB1010100228010X

Fig. 8 ME-SFI wiring diagram (Part 1 of 9). 1998 SL500 engine compartment

Z6/8	Sensor ground connector sleeve
Z7/19	Circuit 30 connector sleeve (fused)
Z7/35	Connector sleeve, circuit 87M, feed from BM (N16/1)
Z7/36	Circuit 87 M2e connector sleeve
Z85	Left O2S heater connector sleeve
Z85/1	Duration sensor 1 connector sleeve
Z94	Stop lamp switch contact connector sleeve (feed from brake lamp switch - S9/1, n.o. contact)
Z99/1	Circuit 87 connector sleeve (traction systems)

MB1019600153130X

Fig. 7 ME-SFI wiring diagram (Part 13 of 13). S420 & 1998–99 CL500 & S500

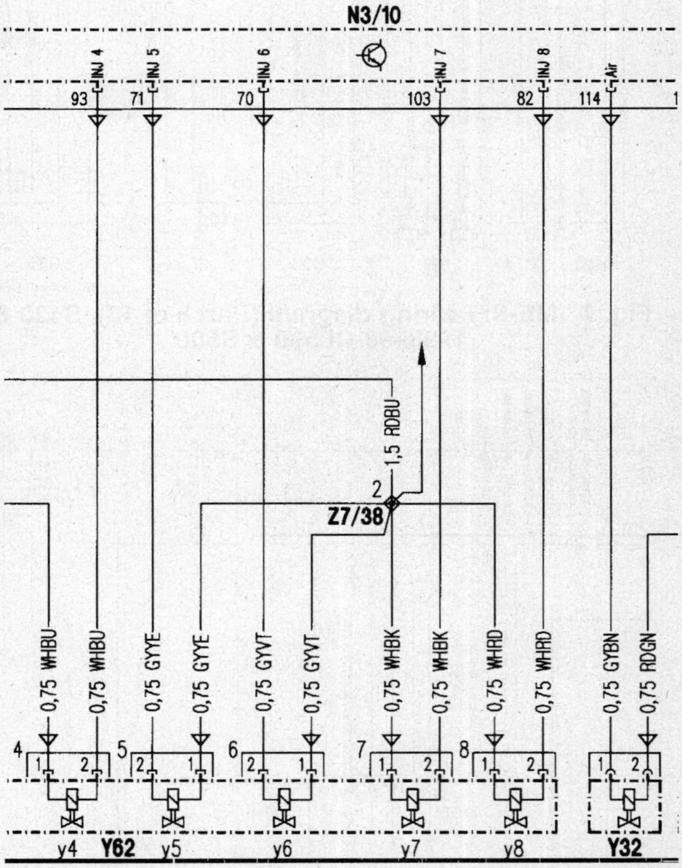

MB1010100228020X

Fig. 8 ME-SFI wiring diagram (Part 2 of 9). 1998 SL500 engine compartment

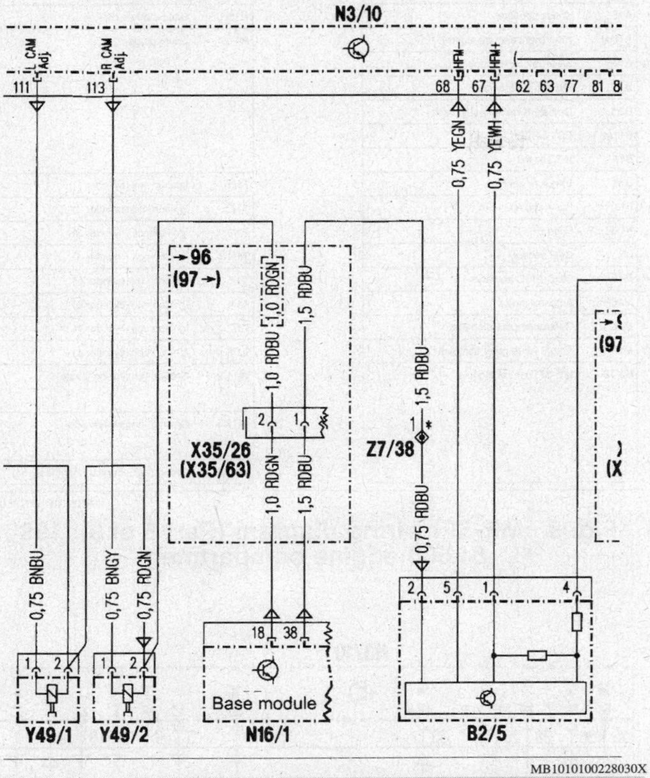

Fig. 8 ME-SFI wiring diagram (Part 3 of 9). 1998 SL500 engine compartment

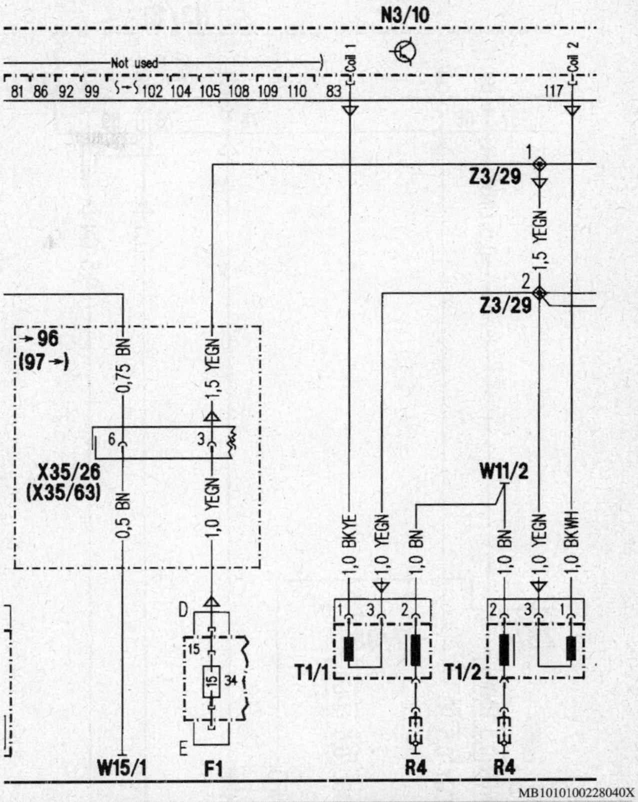

Fig. 8 ME-SFI wiring diagram (Part 4 of 9). 1998 SL500 engine compartment

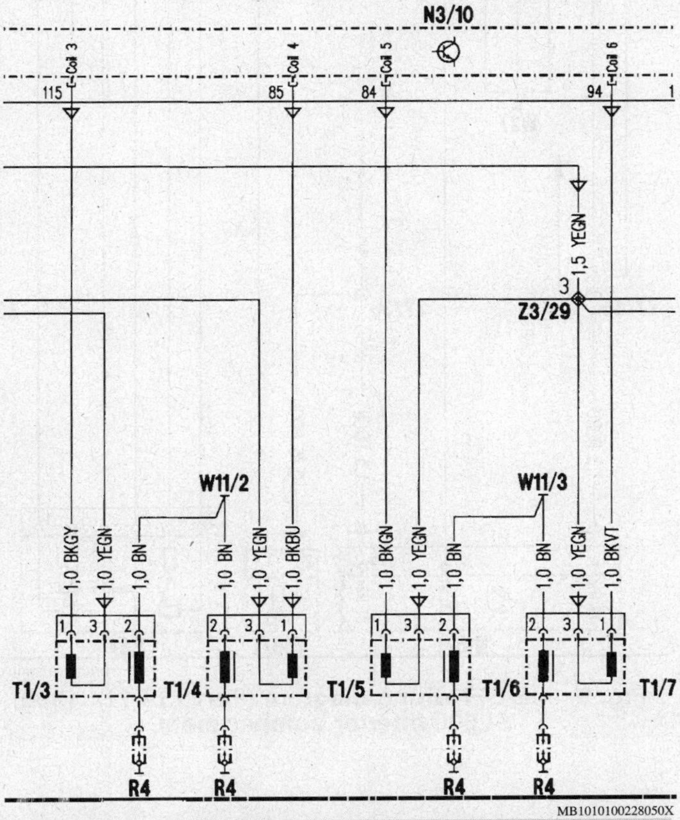

Fig. 8 ME-SFI wiring diagram (Part 5 of 9). 1998 SL500 engine compartment

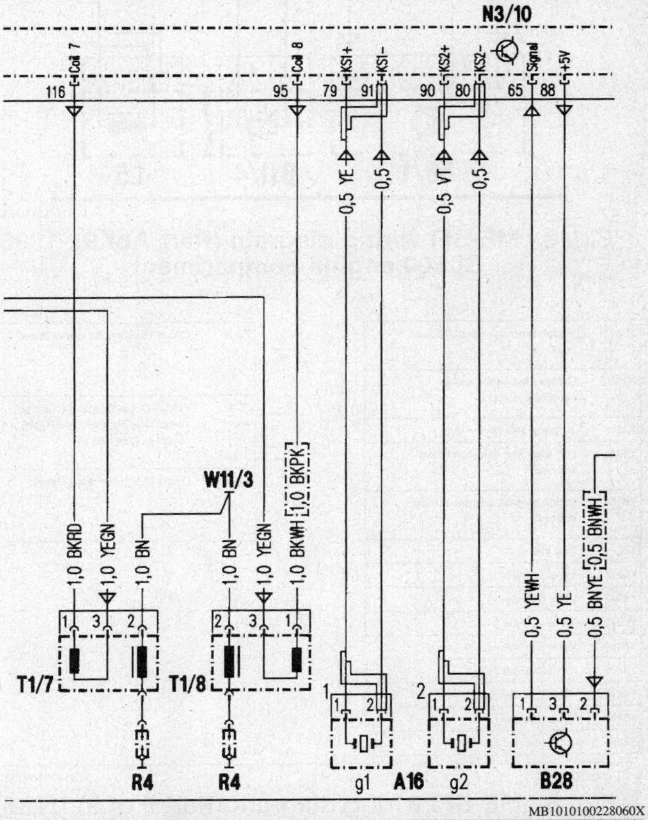

Fig. 8 ME-SFI wiring diagram (Part 6 of 9). 1998 SL500 engine compartment

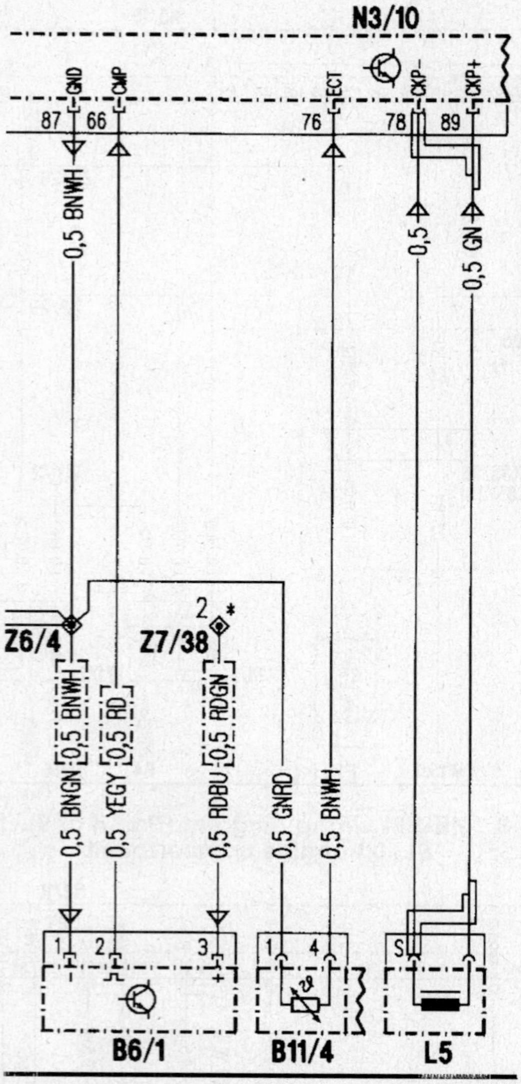

MB1010100228070X

Fig. 8 ME-SFI wiring diagram (Part 7 of 9). 1998 SL500 engine compartment

A16	Knock sensors
A16g1	KS 1 (right side of engine)
A16g2	KS 2 (left side of engine)
B2/5	Hot film MAF sensor
B6/1	Camshaft Hall-effect sensor
B11/4	ECT sensor
B17	IAT sensor
B28	Pressure sensor
F1	Fuse and relay box
F1f34	Fuse 34
L5	CKP sensor
M16/1	EA/CC/ISC actuator
M16/1m1	Actuator motor
M16/1r1	Reference potentiometer
M16/1r2	Actual value potentiometer
N3/10	ME-SFI control module

N16/1	Base module (BM)
R4	Spark plugs
T1/1	Ignition coil (cylinder 1)
T1/2	Ignition coil (cylinder 2)
T1/3	Ignition coil (cylinder 3)
T1/4	Ignition coil (cylinder 4)
T1/5	Ignition coil (cylinder 5)
T1/6	Ignition coil (cylinder 6)
T1/7	Ignition coil (cylinder 7)
T1/8	Ignition coil (cylinder 8)
W11/2	Ground (engine-right side)
W11/3	Ground (engine-left side)
W15/1	Ground (electronics - right footwell)

MB1010100228080X

Fig. 8 ME-SFI wiring diagram (Part 8 of 9). 1998 SL500 engine compartment

X35/26	Module box/engine separation point
X35/63	Control module box/engine separation point
Y32	Air pump switchover valve
Y49/1	Left adjustable camshaft timing solenoid
Y49/2	Right adjustable camshaft timing solenoid
Y62	Fuel Injectors
Y62y1	Valve (cylinder 1)
Y62y2	Valve (cylinder 2)
Y62y3	Valve (cylinder 3)
Y62y4	Valve (cylinder 4)
Y62y5	Valve (cylinder 5)
Y62y6	Valve (cylinder 6)
Y62y7	Valve (cylinder 7)
Y62y8	Valve (cylinder 8)

Z3/29	Circuit 15 connector sleeve (fused)
Z6/4	Left LH-SFI [LH] ground connector sleeve (feed from left LH-SFI [LH] control module - N3/2)
Z7/38	Circuit 87 M1i connector sleeve

MB1010100228090X

Fig. 8 ME-SFI wiring diagram (Part 9 of 9). 1998 SL500 engine compartment

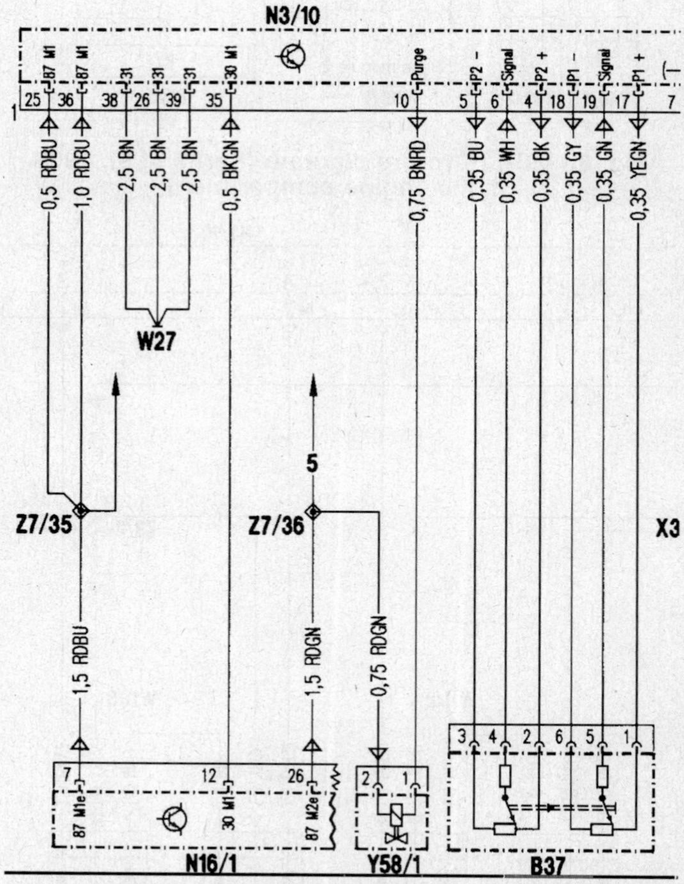

MB1010100229010X

Fig. 9 ME-SFI wiring diagram (Part 1 of 11). 1998 SL500 interior compartment

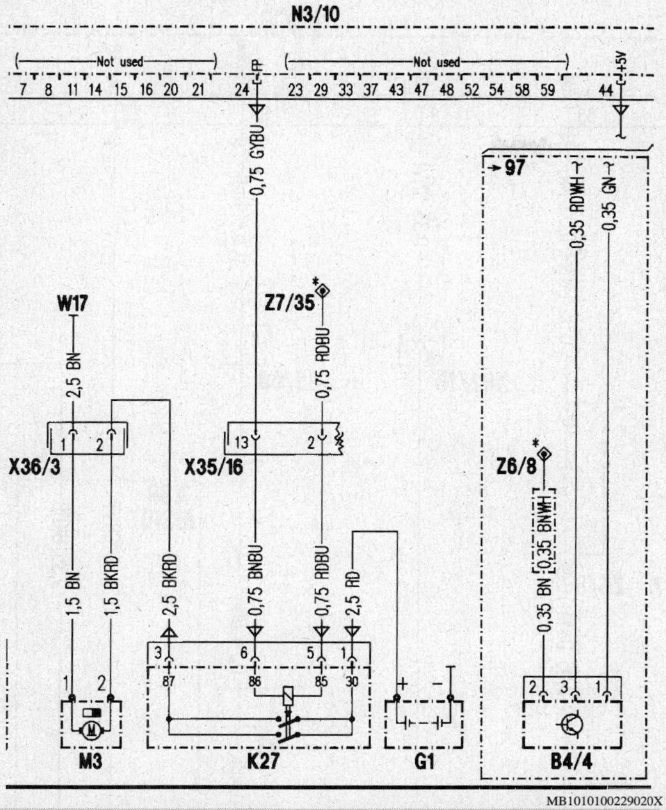

Fig. 9 ME-SFI wiring diagram (Part 2 of 11). 1998 SL500 interior compartment

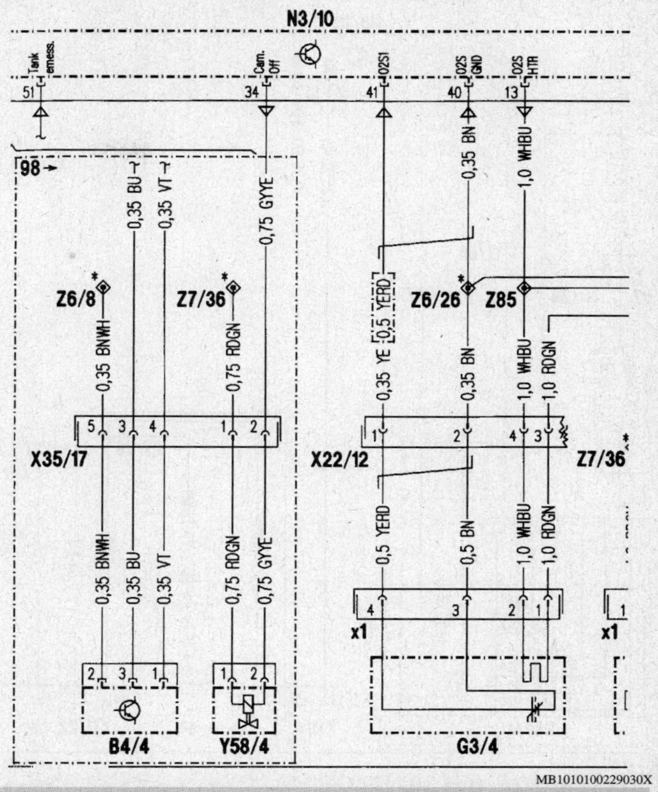

Fig. 9 ME-SFI wiring diagram (Part 3 of 11). 1998 SL500 interior compartment

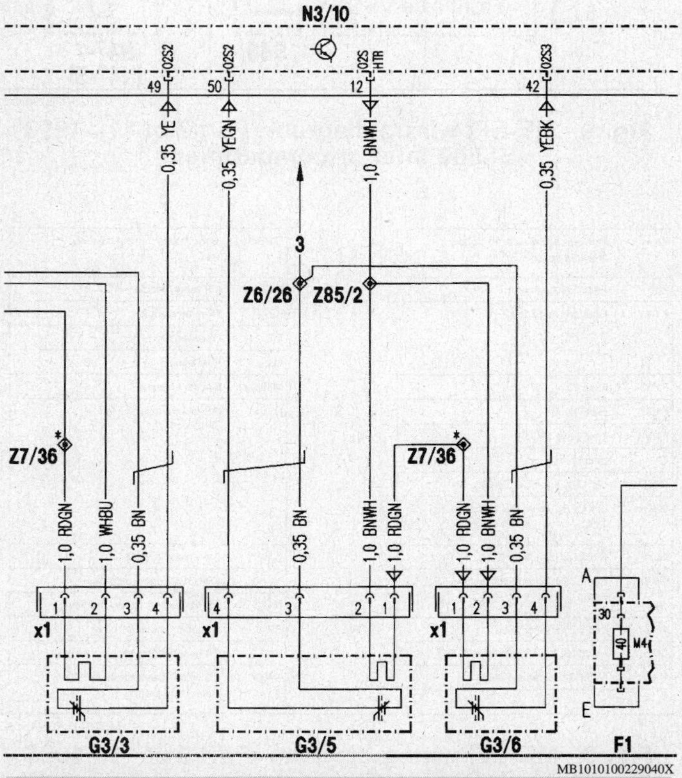

Fig. 9 ME-SFI wiring diagram (Part 4 of 11). 1998 SL500 interior compartment

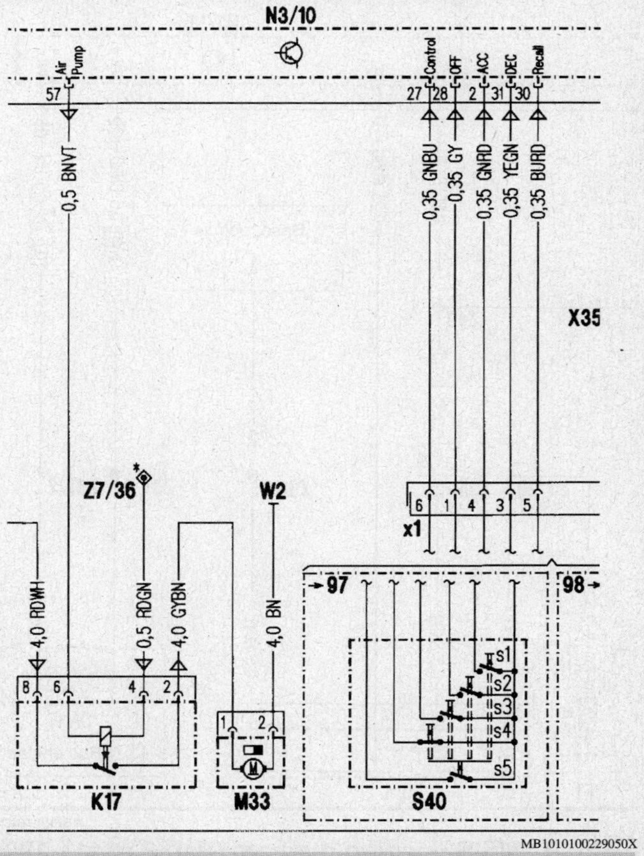

Fig. 9 ME-SFI wiring diagram (Part 5 of 11). 1998 SL500 interior compartment

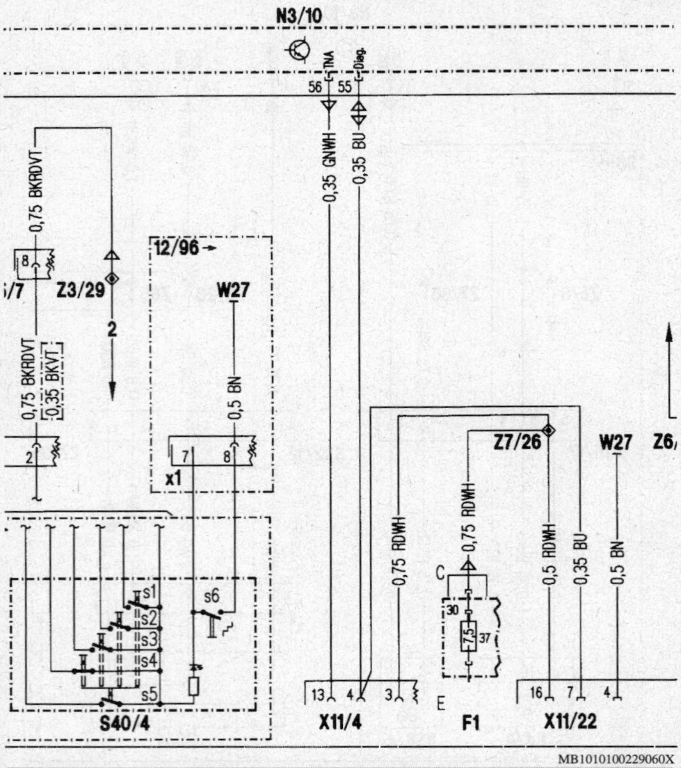

Fig. 9 ME-SFI wiring diagram (Part 6 of 11). 1998 SL500 interior compartment

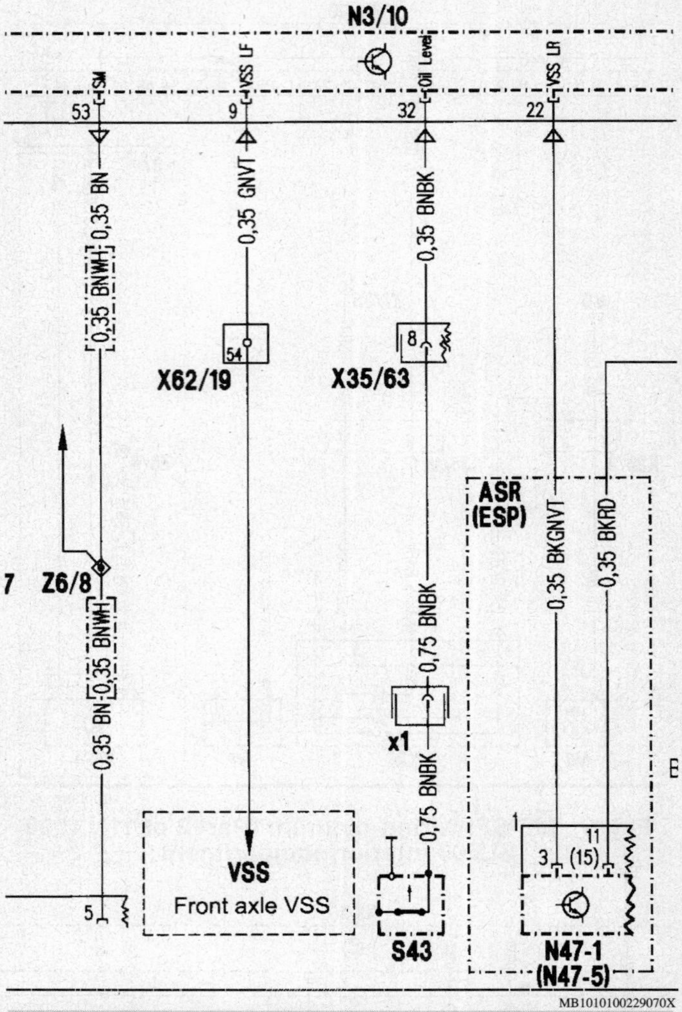

Fig. 9 ME-SFI wiring diagram (Part 7 of 11). 1998 SL500 interior compartment

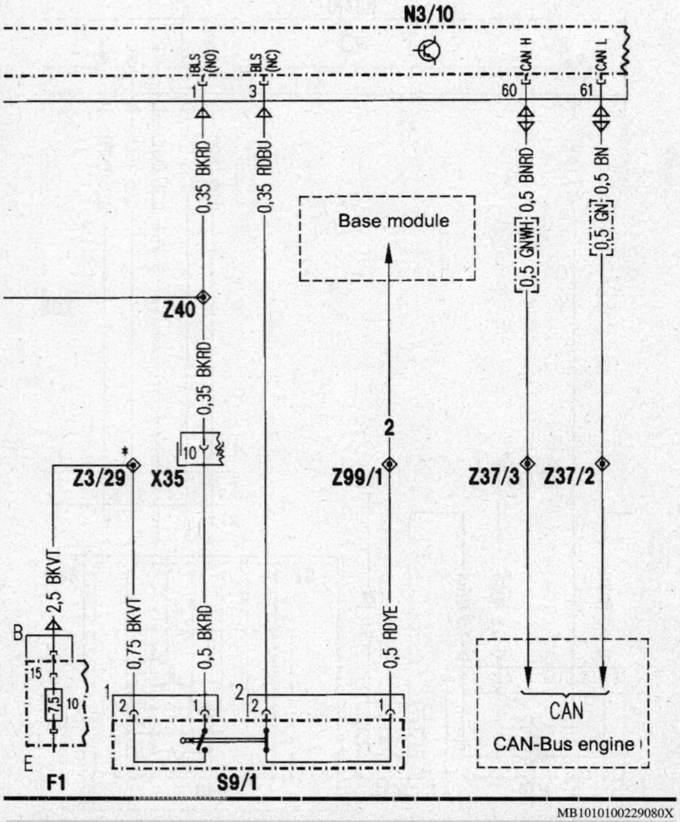

Fig. 9 ME-SFI wiring diagram (Part 8 of 11). 1998 SL500 interior compartment

B4/4	Fuel tank emissions monitoring pressure sensor
B37	Pedal value sensor
F1	Fuse and relay box
F1f10	Fuse 10
F1f37	Fuse 37
F1fM4	Maxi-Fuse M4
G1	Battery
G3/3	Left O2S 1 (before TWC)
G3/3x1	Left O2S 1 connector (before TWC)
G3/4	Right O2S 1 (before TWC)
G3/4x1	Right O2S 1 connector (before TWC)
G3/5	Left O2S 2 (after TWC)
G3/5x1	Left O2S 2 connector (after TWC)
G3/6	Right O2S 2 (after TWC)
G3/6x1	Right O2S 2 connector (after TWC)
K17	AIR relay module
K27	FP relay module
M3	FP assembly
M4	Auxiliary fan
M33	Electric air pump
N3/10	ME-SFI control module
N16/1	Base module (BM)
N47-1	ASR/SPS control module
N47-5	ESP/SPS/BAS control module
S9/1	Stop lamp switch (4-pole)
S40	CC pushbutton switch
S40/4	CC with variable speed limitation pushbutton switch

MB1010100229090X

Fig. 9 ME-SFI wiring diagram (Part 9 of 11). 1998 SL500 interior compartment

S40/4s1	Memory recall
S40/4s2	Decelerate/set
S40/4s3	Accelerate/set
S40/4s4	Off
S40/4s5	Control contact
S40/4s6	Variable speed
S40/4x1	CC variable pushbutton switch connector
S40s1	Memory recall
S40s2	Decelerate/set
S40s3	Accelerate/set
S40s4	Off
S40s5	Control contact
S40x1	CC pushbutton switch connector
S43	Oil level switch
S43x1	Oil level switch connector
W2	Ground (at right headlamp unit)
W17	Ground (right rear seat)

W27	Ground (control module box/module box)
X11/4	Diagnostic test clutch
X11/22	Diagnostic module (OBD II) generic scan tool connector
X22/12	Engine/chassis/ETC connector
X35	Cockpit/module box separation point (12-pole)
X35/7	Cockpit/module box separation point (18-pole)
X35/16	Module box/taillamp harness separation point (13-pole)
X35/17	Module box/taillamp harness separation point (6-pole)
X35/63	Control module box/engine separation point
X36/3	FP harness connector (2-pole)
X62/19	Terminal block (left front VSS sensor - traction systems)

MB1010100229100X

Fig. 9 ME-SFI wiring diagram (Part 10 of 11). 1998 SL500 interior compartment

Y58/1	Purge control valve
Y58/4	Activated charcoal canister shutoff valve
Z3/29	Circuit 15 connector sleeve (fused)
Z6/8	Sensor ground connector sleeve
Z6/26	Sensor ground connector sleeve
Z7/26	Circuit 30 connector sleeve (solder joint in harness)
Z7/35	Circuit 87 M1e connector sleeve
Z7/36	Circuit 87 M2e connector sleeve
Z37/2	Engine CAN-Bus (low) connector sleeve

Z37/3	Engine CAN-Bus (high) connector sleeve
Z40	Stop lamp connector sleeve
Z85	Left O2S heater connector sleeve
Z85/2	Heater diagnostic sensor connector sleeve
Z99/1	Circuit 87 connector sleeve (traction systems)

MB1010100229110X

Fig. 9 ME-SFI wiring diagram (Part 11 of 11). 1998 SL500 interior compartment

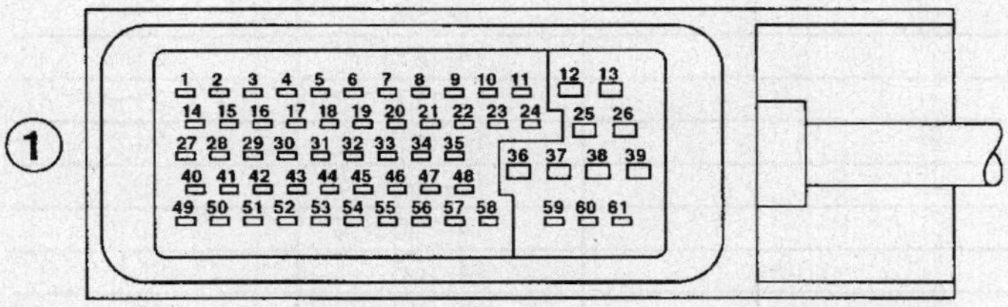

MB1029500283010X

Fig. 10 Engine control module interior connector (Part 1 of 2)

1	Stop lamp switch (S9/1) N.O. contact
2	CC switch (S40), accelerate/set
3	Stop lamp switch (S9/1) N.C. contact
4	Pedal value sensor (B37) nominal potentiometer 2 (+)
5	Pedal value sensor (B37) nominal potentiometer 2 (–)
6	Pedal value sensor (B37) nominal value potentiometer 2 (wiper)
7	–
8	A/C pushbutton control module (N22) (only til 05/96, as of 06/96 via CAN)
9	Left front axle VSS (L6/1)
10	Purge control valve (Y58/1)
11	"CHECK ENGINE" MIL (A1e26) (only til 05/96, as of 06/96 via CAN)
12	O2S 2 (after TWC) heating (G3/5) (G3/6)
13	O2S 1 (before TWC) heating (G3/3) (G3/4)
14–16	–
17	Pedal value sensor (B37) nominal value potentiometer 2 (+)
18	Pedal value sensor (B37) nominal value potentiometer 2 (–)
19	Pedal value sensor (B37) nominal value potentiometer 1 (wiper)
20	–
21	EA warning lamp (A1e39)
22	Left rear axle VSS (L6/3)
23	Tank open signal (only USA, up to 05/96, as of 06/96 via CAN)
24	FP relay module (K27), Model 129/140 Relay module K40, Model 210
25	Voltage supply, (circuit 87M), Model 129/140 from N16/1 Voltage supply, (circuit 87M), Model 210 from K40
26	Output ground (W16), right foot well
27	CC switch (S40), control contact
28	CC switch (S40), off
29	–
30	CC switch (S40), resume
31	CC switch (S40), decelerate/set
32	Oil level switch (S43)
33	Fuel reserve signal (only til 05/96, as of 06/96 via CAN)
34	Activated charcoal canister shut-off valve (Y58/4) (only USA, model 140/210, Model 129 as of 09/97)
35	Voltage supply, circuit 30, Model 129/140 from N16/1 Voltage supply, circuit 30, Model 210 from K40
36	Voltage supply, circuit 87E for EA function
37	–
38	Electronic ground (W15/1), right foot well
39	Output ground (W15), right foot well
40	O2S 1 (before TWC) ground
41	Right O2S 1 (before TWC) signal (G3/4)
42	Right O2S 2 (after TWC) signal (G3/6) (only USA)
43	–
44	Body acceleration sensor (B24), 5V voltage supply, Fuel tank pressure sensor, Model 140/210, Model 129 as of 09/97 (only USA) Purge monitoring pressure sensor, Model 129 up to 08/97
45–46	–
47	*Not applicable to U.S.A. version vehicles*
48	Body acceleration sensor (B24), signal (up to 05/96)
49	Left O2S 1 (before TWC) signal (G3/3)
50	Left O2S 2 (after TWC) signal (G3/5) (only USA)
51	Purge monitoring pressure sensor (B4/4) (only USA, Model 129 up to 08/97) Fuel tank pressure sensor (B4/3) (Model 140/210, Model 129 as of 09/97)
52	–
53	Ground, sensors
54	–
55	Diagnosis output (injection system), DLC (X11/4)
56	Diagnosis output, (engine speed) DLC (X11/4)
57	AIR relay module (K17), Model 129, 140 (only USA)
58	Instrument cluster (fuel consumption signal)
59	–
60	CAN data line "H"
61	CAN data line "L"

MB1029500283020A

Fig. 10 Engine control module interior connector (Part 2 of 2)

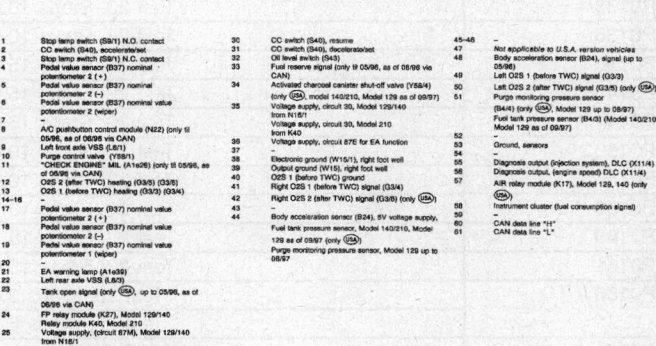

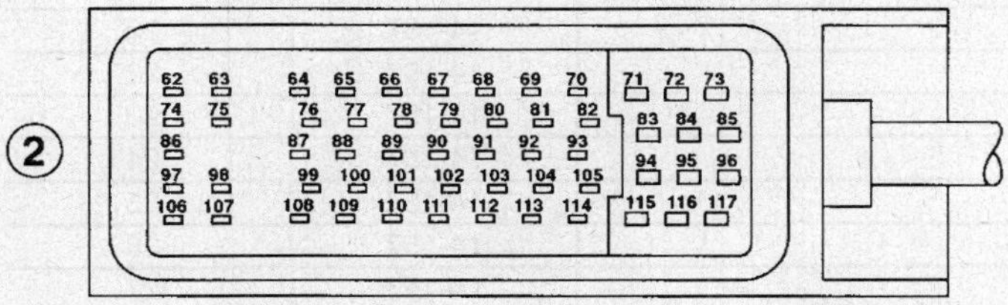

MB1029500284010X

Fig. 11 Engine control module engine connector (Part 1 of 2)

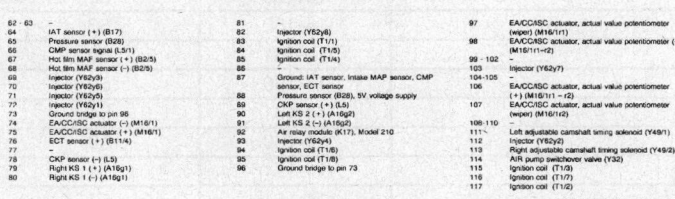

62 - 63	–
64	IAT sensor (+) (B17)
65	Pressure sensor (B28)
66	CMP sensor signal (L5/1)
67	Hot film MAF sensor (+) (B2/5)
68	Hot film MAF sensor (–) (B2/5)
69	Injector (Y62y3)
70	Injector (Y62y6)
71	Injector (Y62y5)
72	Injector (Y62y1)
73	Ground bridge to pin 96
74	EA/CC/ISC actuator (–) (M16/1)
75	EA/CC/ISC actuator (+) (M16/1)
76	ECT sensor (+) (B11/4)
77	–
78	CKP sensor (–) (L5)
79	Right KS 1 (+) (A16g1)
80	Right KS 1 (–) (A16g1)
81	–
82	Injector (Y62y8)
83	Ignition coil (T1/1)
84	Ignition coil (T1/5)
85	Ignition coil (T1/4)
86	–
87	Ground: IAT sensor, Intake MAP sensor, CMP sensor, ECT sensor
88	Pressure sensor (B28), 5V voltage supply
89	CKP sensor (+) (L5)
90	Left KS 2 (+) (A16g2)
91	Left KS 2 (–) (A16g2)
92	Air relay module (K17), Model 210
93	Injector (Y62y4)
94	Ignition coil (T1/6)
95	Ignition coil (T1/8)
96	Ground bridge to pin 73
97	EA/CC/ISC actuator, actual value potentiometer (wiper) (M16/1r1)
98	EA/CC/ISC actuator, actual value potentiometer (- (M16/1r1–r2)
99 - 102	–
103	Injector (Y62y7)
104-105	–
106	EA/CC/ISC actuator, actual value potentiometer (+) (M16/1r1 – r2)
107	EA/CC/ISC actuator, actual value potentiometer (wiper) (M16/1r2)
108-110	–
111	Left adjustable camshaft timing solenoid (Y49/1)
112	Injector (Y62y2)
113	Right adjustable camshaft timing solenoid (Y49/2)
114	AIR pump switchover valve (Y32)
115	Ignition coil (T1/3)
116	Ignition coil (T1/7)
117	Ignition coil (T1/2)

MB1029500284020X

Fig. 11 Engine control module engine connector (Part 2 of 2)

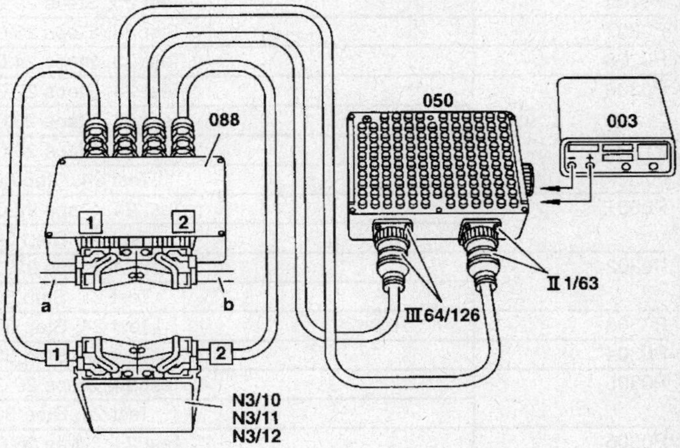

003	Digital multimeter	N3/10	Engine control module (ME-SFI)
050	Socket box (126-pole)	a	Interior harness
088	Test cable	b	Engine harness

MB1029500282000X

Fig. 12 Test connections

DIAGNOSTIC CHART INDEX

Code	Description	Page No.	Fig. No.
—	Test 23, Steps 7.0–7.1	14-156	16
	Test 23, Steps 45.0–47.0	14-159	39
	Test 24, Steps 4.0–6.0	14-159	42
	Test 24, Steps 7.0–9.0	14-159	43
	Test 24, Steps 14.0–15.1	14-160	46
	Test 24, Steps 16.0–17.1	14-160	47
	Test 24, Steps 18.0–19.1	14-160	48
	Test 24, Steps 20.0–21.1	14-160	49
	Test 32, Fuel System Pressure & Internal Leakage Test	14-162	64
	Test 34, Fuel Pump Test	14-162	66
	Test 36, Injector Test	14-162	68
P0100	Test 23, Steps 4.0–5.1	14-156	15
P0105	Test 23, Steps 4.0–5.1	14-156	15
P0110	Test 23, Steps 9.0–9.2	14-156	18
P0115	Test 23, Steps 8.0–8.2	14-156	17
P0120	Test 25, Steps 5.0–6.0	14-161	58
P0130	Test 23, Steps 10.0–13.0	14-156	19
P0133	Test 23, Steps 10.0–13.0	14-156	19
P0135	Test 23, Steps 10.0–13.0	14-156	19
P0136	Test 23, Steps 15.0–16.1	14-157	21
P0140	Test 23, Steps 15.0–16.1	14-157	21
P0141	Test 23, Steps 15.0–16.1	14-157	21
P0150	Test 23, Steps 10.0–13.0	14-156	19
P0155	Test 23, Steps 10.0–13.0	14-156	19
P0156	Test 23, Steps 13.1–14.0	14-156	20
P0160	Test 23, Steps 13.1–14.0	14-156	20
P0161	Test 23, Steps 15.0–16.1	14-157	21
P0186	Test 25, Steps 5.0–6.0	14-161	58
	Test 25, Steps 6.1–8.0	14-161	59
P0201	Test 23, Steps 17.0–18.0	14-157	22
P0202	Test 23, Steps 17.0–18.0	14-157	22
P0203	Test 23, Steps 18.1–19.1	14-157	23
P0204	Test 23, Steps 20.0–20.1	14-157	24
P0205	Test 23, Steps 21.0–21.1	14-157	25
P0206	Test 23, Steps 22.0–22.1	14-157	26
P0207	Test 23, Steps 23.0–23.1	14-157	27
P0208	Test 23, Steps 24.0–24.1	14-157	28
P0300	Test 24, Steps 22.0–23.1	14-160	50
	Test 24, Steps 26.0–27.1	14-160	52
	Test 24, Steps 28.0–29.1	14-160	53
	Test 24, Step 30.0	14-161	54
P0301	Test 24, Steps 22.0–23.1	14-160	50
	Test 24, Step 30.0	14-161	54
P0302	Test 24, Steps 22.0–23.1	14-160	50
	Test 24, Step 30.0	14-161	54
P0303	Test 24, Step 30.0	14-161	54
P0304	Test 24, Step 30.0	14-161	54
P0305	Test 24, Steps 26.0–27.1	14-160	52
	Test 24, Step 30.0	14-161	54
P0306	Test 24, Steps 26.0–27.1	14-160	52
	Test 24, Step 30.0	14-161	54
P0307	Test 24, Steps 28.0–29.1	14-160	53
	Test 24, Step 30.0	14-161	54
P0308	Test 24, Steps 28.0–29.1	14-160	53
	Test 24, Step 30.0	14-161	54
P0335	Test 24, Steps 10.0–12.0	14-159	44
P0341	Test 24, Steps 12.1–13.1	14-159	45

Continued

DIAGNOSTIC CHART INDEX—Continued

Code	Description	Page No.	Fig. No.
P0410	Test 23, Steps 25.0–25.1	14-157	29
	Test 23, Steps 26.0–27.1	14-158	30
P0440	Test 23, Steps 31.0–32.0	14-158	32
	Test 23, Steps 33.0–34.0	14-158	33
P0441	Test 23, Steps 31.0–32.0	14-158	32
P0442	Test 23, Steps 33.0–34.0	14-158	33
P0443	Test 23, Steps 31.0–32.0	14-158	32
P0446	Test 23, Steps 33.0–34.0	14-158	33
P0450	Test 23, Steps 35.0–35.1	14-158	34
	Test 23, Steps 36.0–36.1	14-158	35
P0455	Test 23, Steps 33.0–34.0	14-158	33
	Test 23, Steps 35.0–35.1	14-158	34
P0500	Test 25, Steps 6.1–8.0	14-161	59
	Test 25, Steps 9.0–11.0	14-161	60
	Test 26, Steps 2.0–4.0	14-162	62
P0507	Test 25, Steps 3.0–4.1	14-161	57
	Test 25, Steps 5.0–6.0	14-161	58
P0560	Test 23, Steps 1.0–1.2	14-156	13
	Test 23, Steps 2.0–3.0	14-156	14
	Test 24, Steps 1.0–1.2	14-159	40
	Test 24, Steps 2.0–3.0	14-159	41
	Test 25, Steps 1.0–1.2	14-161	55
	Test 25, Steps 2.0–2.2	14-161	56
	Test 25, Steps 3.0–4.1	14-161	57
P0565	Test 26, Step 1.0	14-161	61
P0600	Test 23, Steps 37.0–37.1	14-158	36
P1163	Test 23, Steps 38.0–41.0	14-158	37
P1420	Test 23, Steps 26.0–27.1	14-158	30
P1437	Test 23, Steps 42.0–44.0	14-159	38
P1444	Test 23, Steps 42.0–44.0	14-159	38
P1453	Test 23, Steps 25.0–25.1	14-157	29
P1519	Test 23, Steps 28.0–30.0	14-158	31
P1522	Test 23, Steps 26.0–27.1	14-158	30
	Test 23, Steps 28.0–30.0	14-158	31
P1525	Test 23, Steps 28.0–30.0	14-158	31
P1533	Test 23, Steps 26.0–27.1	14-158	30
	Test 23, Steps 28.0–30.0	14-158	31
P1542	Test 25, Steps 3.0–4.1	14-161	57
	Test 25, Steps 5.0–6.0	14-161	58
P1570	Test 23, Steps 37.0–37.1	14-158	36
P1580	Test 25, Steps 6.1–8.0	14-161	59
P1584	Test 26, Steps 2.0–4.0	14-162	62
P1605	Test 23, Steps 42.0–44.0	14-159	38
P1747	Test 23, Steps 37.0–37.1	14-158	36

⇒		Test scope	Test connection	Test condition	Nominal value	Possible cause/Remedy
1.0	P0 560	**Engine control module (ME-SFI) (N3/10)** Voltage supply Circuit 30	N3/10 26 —< (V) >— 35 (1.26) (1.35)	Ignition: **ON**	11 – 14 V	⇒ 1.1
1.1		Ground wire	N3/10 X11/4 26 —< (V) >— 2 (1.26) 39 —< (V) >— 2 (1.39)	Ignition: **ON**	11 – 14 V	Wiring, **Model 129:** Ground, module box bracket (W27), **Model 140:** Output ground (W15), right footwell, **Model 210:** Electronic ground (W16/6), right component compartment, ⇒ 1.2
1.2		Voltage supply Circuit 30	X11/4 N3/10 1 —< (V) >— 35 (1.35)	Ignition: **ON**	11 – 14 V	Wiring, **Model 129, 140:** Base module (N16/1) or fuse on base module, **Model 210:** Relay module (K40).

MB1029500285000A

Fig. 13 Code P0560: Test 23, Steps 1.0–1.2

⇒		Test scope	Test connection	Test condition	Nominal value	Possible cause/Remedy
2.0	P0 560	**Engine control module (ME-SFI) (N3/10)** Voltage supply Circuit 87M	N3/10 38 —< (V) >— 25 (1.38) (1.25)	Ignition: **ON**	11 – 14 V	⇒ 2.1
2.1		Electronics ground	N3/10 X11/4 38 —< (V) >— 2 (1.38)	Ignition: **ON**	11 – 14 V	Wiring, **Model 129 and 140:** Electronic ground (W15/1), right footwell, **Model 210:** Electronic ground (W16/6), right component compartment, ⇒ 2.2
2.2		Voltage supply Circuit 87M	X11/4 N3/10 1 —< (V) >— 25 (1.25)	Ignition: **ON** Ignition: **OFF**	11 – 14 V < 1 V	Wiring, **Model 129, 140:** Base module (N16/1) or fuse on base module, **Model 210:** Relay module (K40).
3.0	P0 560	**Engine control module (ME-SFI) (N3/10)** Voltage supply Circuit 87M	N3/10 39 —< (V) >— 36 (1.39) (1.36)	Ignition: **ON** Ignition: **OFF**	11 – 14 V < 1 V	Wiring, **Model 129, 140:** Base module (N16/1) or fuse on base module, **Model 210:** Relay module (K40).

MB1029500286000A

Fig. 14 Code P0560: Test 23, Steps 2.0–3.0

⇒		Test scope	Test connection	Test condition	Nominal value	Possible cause/Remedy
4.0	P0 100	**Hot film MAF sensor (B2/5)** Voltage at hot film	N3/10 68 —< (V) >— 67 (2.68) (2.67)	Engine: **at Idle** Engine coolant temperature >70°C	0.7 – 1.0 V [2]	Wiring ⇒ 5.0, Air intake system leak, B2/5
5.0	P0 100	**Ground wire for hot film MAF sensor (B2/5)**	N3/10 38 —< (Ω) >— 67 (1.38) (2.67)	Ignition: **OFF** Disconnect MAF sensor (B2/5) connector. Bridge sockets 1 and 4.	< 1 Ω	Ground wire.
6.0	P0 105	**Pressure sensor (B28)** Sensor signal	N3/10 87 —< (V) >— 65 (2.87) (2.65)	Connect vacuum tester to pressure sensor (B28) using Y-fitting. Ignition: **ON** Engine: **at Idle**	> 3.5 V < 2 V and pressure climbs to > 500 mbar.	Vacuum line, Wiring, ⇒ 6.1 B28
6.1		Pressure sensor (B28) Voltage supply	N3/10 87 —< (V) >— 88 (2.87) (2.88)	Ignition: **ON**	4.7 – 5.3 V	N3/10

2) Voltage increases with increasing rpm.

MB1029500287000A

Fig. 15 Codes P0100 & P0105: Test 23, Steps 4.0–5.1

⇒		Test scope	Test connection	Test condition	Nominal value	Possible cause/Remedy
7.0		**Model 129, 140** **FP relay module (K27)** **Model 210** **Relay module (K40)** Control signal	N3/10 24 —< (V) >— 25 (1.24) (1.25)	Ignition: **ON** Engine: **Start**	11 – 14 V for approx. 1 sec. 11 – 14 V during cranking and while engine runs.	⇒ 7.1, N3/10
7.1		Current draw K27 or K40	N3/10 26 —< (A) >— 24 (1.26) (1.24)	Ignition: **ON**	0.1 – 0.3 A	Wiring, K27 or K40

MB1029500288000A

Fig. 16 Code —: Test 23, Steps 7.0–7.1

⇒		Test scope	Test connection	Test condition	Nominal value	Possible cause/Remedy
8.0	P0 115	**ECT sensor (B11/4)** Voltage	N3/10 87 —< (V) >— 76 (2.87) (2.76)	Ignition: **ON**	°C V 20 3.5 30 3.1 40 2.7 50 2.3 60 1.9 70 1.5 80 1.2 90 1.0 100 0.8 ±5 %	⇒ 8.1, N3/10
8.1		Resistance (B11/4)	N3/10 87 —< (Ω) >— 76 (2.87) (2.76)	Ignition: **OFF** Disconnect connector 2 on engine control module (N3/10).	°C Ω 20 2500 30 1700 40 1170 50 830 60 600 70 435 80 325 90 245 100 185 ±5 %	Wiring, ⇒ 8.2
8.2		ECT sensor (B11/4) Resistance	B11/4 1 (Ω) 4	Disconnect connector on ECT sensor (B11/4).	Nominal value, see ⇒ 8.1	B11/4

MB1029500289000A

Fig. 17 Code P0115: Test 23, Steps 8.0–8.2

⇒		Test scope	Test connection	Test condition	Nominal value	Possible cause/Remedy
9.0	P0 110	**IAT sensor (B17)** Voltage	N3/10 87 —< (V) >— 64 (2.87) (2.64)	Ignition: **ON**	°C V 10 3.2 20 2.6 30 2.1 40 1.6 50 1.2 60 0.9 70 0.7 ±5 %	⇒ 9.1, N3/10
9.1		Resistance (B17)	N3/10 87 —< (Ω) >— 64 (2.87) (2.64)	Ignition: **OFF** Disconnect connector 2 on engine control module (N3/10).	°C Ω 10 9670 20 6060 30 3900 40 2600 50 1760 60 1220 70 860 ±5 %	Wiring, ⇒ 9.2
9.2		IAT sensor (B17) Resistance	B17 1 (Ω) 2	Disconnect connector from IAT sensor (B17).	Nominal value, see ⇒ 9.1	B17

MB1029500290000A

Fig. 18 Code P0110: Test 23, Steps 9.0–9.2

⇒		Test scope	Test connection	Test condition	Nominal value	Possible cause/Remedy
10.0		**Engine control module (N3/10)** TN-signal output	N3/10 [3] 38 —< (⊕) >— 56 (1.38) (1.56) N3/10 [4] 38 —< (V) >— 56 (1.38) (1.56)	Engine: **Start** or Engine: **at Idle**	Signal: see Figure 2. 5 – 7.5 V	Wiring, N3/10
11.0	P0 150 P0 153	**Left O2S 1 (before TWC) (G3/3)** O2S signal	N3/10 40 —< (V) >— 49 (1.40) (1.49)	ECT > 80 ° C, run engine at idle for at least two minutes.	fluctuates from – 0.2 V to + 1.0 V, by more than 0.3 V	Wiring, G3/3, ⇒ 13.0
12.0	P0 130 P0 133	**Right O2S 1 (before TWC) (G3/4)** O2S signal	N3/10 40 —< (V) >— 41 (1.40) (1.41)	ECT > 80 ° C, run engine at idle for at least two minutes.	fluctuates from – 0.2 V to + 1.0 V, by more than 0.3 V	Wiring, G3/4, ⇒ 13.0
13.0	P0 135 P0 155	**Left O2S 1 (before TWC) (G3/3)** **Right O2S 1 (before TWC) (G3/4)** O2S heater control signal	N3/10 13 —< (V) >— 25 (1.13) (1.25)	ECT > 80 ° C, run engine at idle for at least two minutes.	11 – 14 V	⇒ 13.1, N3/10

3) Test with oscilloscope.
4) Test with multimeter only if oscilloscope is not available.

MB1029500291000A

Fig. 19 Codes P0130, P0133, P0135, P0150 & P0155: Test 23, Steps 10.0–13.0

⇒		Test scope	Test connection	Test condition	Nominal value	Possible cause/Remedy
13.1		O2S 1 (G3/3 and G3/4) Current draw	N3/10 26 —< (A) >— 13 (1.26) (1.13)	Ignition: **ON**	1.2 – 6.8 A [5]	Wiring, G3/3 or G3/4
14.0	P0 156 P0 160	**Left O2S 2 (afterTWC) (G3/5)** O2S signal	N3/10 40 —< (V) >— 50 (1.40) (1.50)	ECT > 80° C, Engine: **Start** Raise and hold engine speed at 2000 – 3000 rpm for approx. three minutes until O2S 2 heater turns on (see HHT). Briefly depress accelerator pedal to WOT.	450 mV constant Voltage changes. Voltage changes by > 100 mV.	Wiring, ⇒ 16.0

5) The current draw for one O2S is 0.6 – 3.4 A.

MB1029500292000A

Fig. 20 Codes P0156 & P0160: Test 23, Steps 13.1–14.0

⇒	Code	Test scope	Test connection	Test condition	Nominal value	Possible cause/Remedy
15.0	P0 136 P0 140	**Right O2S 2** **(afterTWC) (G3/6)** O2S signal	N3/10 40 (1.40) — 42 (1.42)	ECT > 80° C, Engine: **Start** Raise and hold engine speed at 2000 – 3000 rpm for approx. three minutes until O2S 2 heater turns on (see HHT). Briefly depress accelerator pedal to WOT.	450 mV constant Voltage changes. Voltage changes by > 100 mV.	Wiring, ⇒ 16.0
16.0	P0 141 P0 161	**Left O2S 2** **(after TWC) (G3/5)** **Right O2S 2** **(after TWC) (G3/6)** O2S heater control signal	N3/10 12 (1.12) — 25 (1.25)	Engine: **at idle** ECT > 80° C, run engine at idle for at least two minutes.	11 – 14 V	⇒ 16.1, N3/10
16.1		O2S 2 (G3/5 or G3/6) Current draw	N3/10 26 (1.26) — 12 (1.12)	Ignition: **ON**	1.2 – 6.8 A [5]	Wiring, G3/5 or G3/6

[5] The current draw for one O2S is 0.6 – 3.4 A.

MB1029500293000A

Fig. 21 Codes P0136, P0140, P0141 & P0161: Test 23, Steps 15.0–16.1

⇒	Code	Test scope	Test connection	Test condition	Nominal value	Possible cause/Remedy
18.1		Resistance (Y62y2)	N3/10 112 (2.112) — 25 (1.25)	Ignition: **OFF**	14 – 17 Ω	Wiring, Y62y2
19.0	P0 203	**Injector (Y62y3)** Activation and injection duration	N3/10 69 (2.69) — 25 (1.25)	**ECT approx. 20° C** at start **ECT approx. 80° C** at idle accelerate briefly	Injection time: approx. 8 ms approx. 3 – 5 ms approx. 14 ms	⇒ 19.1, N3/10, **Further possibilities:** ECT sensor (B11/4), IAT sensor (B17), O2S 1 (G3/3 or G3/4).
19.1		Resistance (Y62y3)	N3/10 69 (2.69) — 25 (1.25)	Ignition: **OFF**	14 – 17 Ω	Wiring, Y62y3

MB1029500295000A

Fig. 23 Code P0203: Test 23, Steps 18.1–19.1

⇒	Code	Test scope	Test connection	Test condition	Nominal value	Possible cause/Remedy
21.0	P0 205	**Injector (Y62y5)** Activation and injection duration	N3/10 71 (2.71) — 25 (1.25)	**ECT approx. 20° C** at start **ECT approx. 80° C** at idle accelerate briefly	Injection time: approx. 8 ms approx. 3 – 5 ms approx. 14 ms	⇒ 21.1, N3/10 **Further possibilities:** ECT sensor (B11/4), IAT sensor (B17), O2S 1 (G3/3 or G3/4).
21.1		Resistance (Y62y5)	N3/10 71 (2.71) — 25 (1.25)	Ignition: **OFF**	14 – 17 Ω	Wiring, Y62y5

MB1029500297000A

Fig. 25 Code P0205: Test 23, Steps 21.0–21.1

⇒	Code	Test scope	Test connection	Test condition	Nominal value	Possible cause/Remedy
23.0	P0 207	**Injector (Y62y7)** Activation and injection duration	N3/10 103 (2.103) — 25 (1.25)	**ECT approx. 20° C** at start **ECT approx. 80° C** at idle accelerate briefly	Injection time: approx. 8 ms approx. 3 – 5 ms approx. 14 ms	⇒ 23.1, N3/10, **Further possibilities:** ECT sensor (B11/4), IAT sensor (B17), O2S 1 (G3/3 or G3/4).
23.1		Resistance (Y62y7)	N3/10 103 (2.103) — 25 (1.25)	Ignition: **OFF**	14 – 17 Ω	Wiring, Y62y7

MB1029500299000A

Fig. 27 Code P0207: Test 23, Steps 23.0–23.1

⇒	Code	Test scope	Test connection	Test condition	Nominal value	Possible cause/Remedy
17.0	P0 201	**Injector (Y62y1)** Activation and injection duration	N3/10 72 (2.72) — 25 (1.25)	**ECT approx. 20° C** at start **ECT approx. 80° C** at idle accelerate briefly	Injection time: approx. 8 ms approx. 3 – 5 ms approx. 14 ms	⇒ 17.1, N3/10, **Further possibilities:** ECT sensor (B11/4), IAT sensor (B17), O2S 1 (G3/3 or G3/4).
17.1		Resistance (Y62y1)	N3/10 72 (2.72) — 25 (1.25)	Ignition: **OFF**	14 – 17 Ω	Wiring, Y62y1.
18.0	P0 202	**Injector (Y62y2)** Activation and injection duration	N3/10 112 (2.112) — 25 (1.25)	**ECT approx. 20° C** at start **ECT approx. 80° C** at idle accelerate briefly	Injection time: approx. 8 ms approx. 3 – 5 ms approx. 14 ms	⇒ 18.1, N3/10, **Further possibilities:** ECT sensor (B11/4), IAT sensor (B17), O2S 1 (G3/3 or G3/4).

MB1029500294000A

Fig. 22 Codes P0201 & P0202: Test 23, Steps 17.0–18.0

⇒	Code	Test scope	Test connection	Test condition	Nominal value	Possible cause/Remedy
20.0	P0 204	**Injector (Y62y4)** Control signal and injection time	N3/10 93 (2.93) — 25 (1.25)	**ECT approx. 20° C** at start **ECT approx. 80° C** at idle accelerate briefly	Injection time: approx. 8 ms approx. 3 – 5 ms approx. 14 ms	⇒ 20.1, N3/10, **Further possibilities:** ECT sensor (B11/4), IAT sensor (B17), O2S 1 (G3/3 or G3/4).
20.1		Resistance (Y62y4)	N3/10 93 (2.93) — 25 (1.25)	Ignition: **OFF**	14 – 17 Ω	Wiring, Y62y4.

MB1029500296000X

Fig. 24 Code P0204: Test 23, Steps 20.0–20.1

⇒	Code	Test scope	Test connection	Test condition	Nominal value	Possible cause/Remedy
22.0	P0 206	**Injector (Y62y6)** Activation and injection duration	N3/10 70 (2.70) — 25 (1.25)	**ECT approx. 20° C** at start **ECT approx. 80° C** at idle accelerate briefly	Injection time: approx. 8 ms approx. 3 – 5 ms approx. 14 ms	⇒ 22.1, N3/10, **Further possibilities:** ECT sensor (B11/4), IAT sensor (B17), O2S 1 (G3/3 or G3/4).
22.1		Resistance (Y62y6)	N3/10 70 (2.70) — 25 (1.25)	Ignition: **OFF**	14 – 17 Ω	Wiring, Y62y6

MB1029500298000A

Fig. 26 Code P0206: Test 23, Steps 22.0–22.1

⇒	Code	Test scope	Test connection	Test condition	Nominal value	Possible cause/Remedy
24.0	P0 208	**Injector (Y62y8)** Activation and injection duration	N3/10 82 (2.82) — 25 (1.25)	**ECT approx. 20° C** at start **ECT approx. 80° C** at idle accelerate briefly	Injection time: approx. 8 ms approx. 3 – 5 ms approx. 14 ms (signal: see Figures 3 and 4)	⇒ 24.1, N3/10 **Further possibilities:** ECT sensor (B11/4), IAT sensor (B17), O2S 1 (G3/3 or G3/4).
24.1		Resistance (Y62y8)	N3/10 82 (2.82) — 25 (1.25)	Ignition: **OFF**	14 – 17 Ω	Wiring, Y62y8

MB1029500300000A

Fig. 28 Code P0208: Test 23, Steps 24.0–24.1

⇒	Code	Test scope	Test connection	Test condition	Nominal value	Possible cause/Remedy
25.0	P0 410 P1 453	**Only (USA)** **Model 129, 140** **AIR relay module (K17)** **Model 210** **Relay module (K40)** Activation	**Models 129/140** N3/10 57 (1.57) — 25 (1.25) **Model 210** N3/10 92 (2.92) — 25 (1.25)	Disconnect ECT sensor (B11/4) connector. Simulate 2.5 kΩ resistance at sockets 1 and 4 with resistance substitution unit. Engine: **at idle**	11 – 14 V for approx. two minutes and AIR pump runs.	⇒ 25.1, N3/10
25.1		**Model 129, 140** AIR relay module (K17) **Model 210** Relay module (K40) Current draw	**Models 129/140** N3/10 38 (1.38) — 57 (1.57) **Model 210** N3/10 38 (1.38) — 92 (2.92)	Ignition: **ON**	0.1 – 0.3 A	Wiring, K17 or K40

MB1029500301000A

Fig. 29 Codes P0410 & P1453: Test 23, Steps 25.0–25.1

⇒		Test scope	Test connection	Test condition	Nominal value	Possible cause/Remedy
26.0	P0 410 P1 420	**Only** (USA) **AIR pump switchover valve (Y32)** Activation	N3/10 114 (2.114) —(V)— 25 (1.25)	Disconnect ECT sensor (B11/4) connector. Simulate 2.5 kΩ resistance at sockets 1 and 4 with resistance substitution unit. Engine: **at Idle**	11 – 14 V for approx. two minutes **and** AIR pump runs.	26.1, N3/10
26.1		Current draw (Y32)	N3/10 38 (1.38) —(A)— 114 (2.114)	Ignition: **ON**	0.3 – 0.5 A	Wiring, Y32
27.0	P1 522 P1 533	**Left adjustable camshaft timing solenoid (Y49/1)** Current draw	Y49/1 1 —(A)— 2	Connect test cable (102 589 04 63 00) to solenoid. Engine: **Start** and increase engine speed to 3000 rpm.	approx. 1.3 A	⇒ 27.1, ⇒ 29.0, N3/10
27.1		Resistance Y49/1 and Y49/2	N3/10 111 (2.111) —(Ω)— 113 (2.113)	Ignition: **OFF**	14 – 24 Ω 6)	Wiring, Y49/1 or Y49/2

6) The resistance of one solenoid is 7 – 12 Ω.

MB1029500302000A

Fig. 30 Codes P0410, P1420, P1522 & P1533: Test 23, Steps 26.0–27.1

⇒		Test scope	Test connection	Test condition	Nominal value	Possible cause/Remedy
31.0	P0 440 P0 441 P0 443	**Purge control valve (Y58/1)** Activation	N3/10 10 (1.10) —(⊕)— 25 (1.25)	Engine: **at Idle** and at operating temperature.	After approx. 1 minute, purge control valve (Y58/1) must noticeably cycle.	⇒ 31.1, ⇒ 32.0, N3/10
31.1		Current draw (Y58/1)	N3/10 38 (1.38) —(A)— 10 (1.10)	Ignition: **ON**	0.1 – 0.3 A	Wiring, Y58/1
32.0	P0 440 P0 441	**Purge control valve (Y58/1)** Vacuum control		Connect vacuum tester to purge control valve (Y58/1) connector (A). Engine at operating temperature and at idle. Slowly increase engine speed to 3000 rpm.	After approx. 1 minute, > 50 mbar and needle oscillates.	Vacuum line, Y58/1

MB1029500304000A

Fig. 32 Codes P0440, P0441 & P0443: Test 23, Steps 31.0–32.0

⇒		Test scope	Test connection	Test condition	Nominal value	Possible cause/Remedy
35.0	P0 450 P0 455	**Only** (USA)**, Model 140, 210, Model 129 as of 09/97** **Fuel tank pressure sensor (B4/3)** Sender signal Activated charcoal canister shut-off valve (Y58/4) activated	N3/10 53 (1.53) —(V)— 51 (1.51) N3/10 26 (1.26) ←→ 34 (1.34)	Disconnect purge line (A) to charcoal canister on purge control valve (Y58/1). Connect vacuum tester to purge line Ignition: **ON** Apply approx. 25 mbar of vacuum.	 > 3 V < 2.5 V	⇒ 35.1, Wiring, Vacuum line, Charcoal canister plugged, B4/3
35.1		**Only** (USA) Fuel tank pressure sensor (B4/3) Voltage supply	N3/10 53 (1.53) —(V)— 44 (1.44)	Ignition: **ON**	4.7 – 5.3 V	N3/10

MB1029500306000A

Fig. 34 Codes P0450 & P0455: Test 23, Steps 35.0–35.1

⇒		Test scope	Test connection	Test condition	Nominal value	Possible cause/Remedy
37.0	P0 600 P1 570 P1 747	**CAN data bus**	N3/10 60 (1.60) —(Ω)— 61 (1.61)	Ignition: **OFF** Disconnect connector 1 from test cable and measure resistance directly at connector 1 (interior) of engine harness using an ohmmeter. Wire connections see ☐ 22	115 – 125 Ω	⇒ 37.1, Data line.
37.1		**Model 129/140 up to 05/96** **CAN element in RCL control module (N54)** **Model 129/140 as of 06/96 and Model 210.072** **CAN element in DAS control module (N54/1)** Resistance	N54 N54/1 L —(Ω)— H	Ignition: **OFF** Disconnect control module (N54 or N54/1) and test directly at pins of control module	115 – 125 Ω	N54 or N54/1

MB1029500308000A

Fig. 36 Codes P0600, P1570 & P1747: Test 23, Steps 37.0–37.1

⇒		Test scope	Test connection	Test condition	Nominal value	Possible cause/Remedy
28.0	P1 519 P1 525	**Right adjustable camshaft timing solenoid (Y49/2)** Current draw	Y49/2 1 —(A)— 2	Connect test cable (102 589 04 63 00) to solenoid. Engine: **Start** and increase engine speed to 3000 rpm.	approx. 1.3 A	⇒ 28.1, ⇒ 30.0, N3/10
28.1		Resistance Y49/2 and Y49/1	N3/10 113 (2.113) —(Ω)— 111 (2.111)	Ignition: **OFF**	14 – 24 Ω 6)	Wiring, Y49/2 or Y49/1
29.0	P1 522 P1 533	**Left adjustable camshaft timing solenoid (Y49/1)** Mechanical function	N3/10 111 (2.111) ←→ 38 (1.38)	Engine: **at Idle** Bridge sockets on socket box for a maximum of 10 seconds.	Engine runs rough after approx. 5 seconds.	Check function of camshaft adjuster.
30.0	P1 519 P1 525	**Right adjustable camshaft timing solenoid (Y49/2)** Mechanical function	N3/10 113 (2.113) ←→ 38 (1.38)	Engine: **at Idle** Bridge sockets on socket box for a maximum of 10 seconds.	Engine runs rough after approx. 5 seconds.	Check function of camshaft adjuster.

6) The resistance of one solenoid is 7 – 12 Ω.

MB1029500303000A

Fig. 31 Codes P1519, P1522, P1525 & P1533: Test 23, Steps 28.0–30.0

⇒		Test scope	Test connection	Test condition	Nominal value	Possible cause/Remedy
33.0	P0 440 P0 442 P0 455	**Only** (USA)**, Model 140, 210, Model 129 as of 09/97** **Purge system** Leaks Activated charcoal canister shut-off valve (Y58/4) Activated	N3/10 26 (1.26) ←→ 34 (1.34)	Disconnect purge line (A) to charcoal canister on purge control valve (Y58/1). Connect vacuum tester to purge line Ignition: **ON** Apply approx. 25 mbar of vacuum.	After approx. 1 minute, < 5 mbar vacuum loss.	Fuel tank cap, Purge line to charcoal canister, Purge line from charcoal canister to Y58/4, Charcoal canister, Y58/4
34.0	P0 446	**Only** (USA)**, Model 140, 210, Model 129 as of 09/97** **Activated charcoal canister shut-off valve (Y58/4)** Current draw	N3/10 38 (1.38) —(A)— 34 (1.34)	Ignition: **ON**	0.5 – 0.9 A	Wiring, Y58/4

MB1029500305000A

Fig. 33 Codes P0440, P0442, P0446 & P0455: Test 23, Steps 33.0–34.0

⇒		Test scope	Test connection	Test condition	Nominal value	Possible cause/Remedy
36.0	P0 450	**Only** (USA)**, Model 129, up to 08/97** **Purge monitoring pressure sensor (B4/4)** Sender signal	N3/10 53 (1.53) —(V)— 51 (1.51)	Disconnect purge line on purge monitoring pressure sensor (B4/4). Connect vacuum tester to pressure sensor Ignition: **ON** Apply approx. 300 mbar of vacuum.	 > 3.5 V < 3 V	Wiring, ⇒ 36.1, B4/4
36.1		Fuel tank pressure sensor (B4/4) Voltage supply	N3/10 53 (1.53) —(V)— 44 (1.44)	Ignition: **ON**	4.7 – 5.3 V	N3/10

MB1029500307000A

Fig. 35 Code P0450: Test 23, Steps 36.0–36.1

⇒		Test scope	Test connection	Test condition	Nominal value	Possible cause/Remedy
38.0		**CAN element in engine control module (N3/10)** Resistance	N3/10 60 —(Ω)— 61	Ignition: **OFF** Disconnect control module connector 1 (interior) from N3/10 and test directly at control module.	115 – 125 Ω	N3/10
39.0	P1 163	**Oil level switch (S43)**	N3/10 32 (1.32) —(V)— 25 (1.25)	Ignition: **ON** Oil level okay. Oil level low.	 11 – 14 V < 1 V	Wiring, S43
40.0		**Model 129/140 up to 05/96** **Model 210 up to 05/97** **(afterwards via CAN)** **Fuel consumption signal**	N3/10 25 (1.25) —(V)— 58 (1.58)	Engine: **at Idle** and briefly accelerate engine.	> 0.5 V	Wiring, N3/10
41.0		**Diagnosis line** Activation	N3/10 26 (1.26) —(V)— 55 (1.55)	Ignition: **ON**	11 – 14 V	Wiring, N3/10

MB1029500309000A

Fig. 37 Code P1163: Test 23, Steps 38.0–41.0

⇒		Test scope	Test connection	Test condition	Nominal value	Possible cause/Remedy
42.0	P1 605	**(only until 06/96, as of 06/96 deleted)** **Body acceleration sensor (B24)** Sensor signal static	N3/10 53 —(V)— 46 (1.53) (1.48)	Ignition: **ON**	2.35 – 2.65 V	Wiring, ⇒ 42.1, B24
		Sensor signal dynamic	N3/10 53 —(V)— 48 (1.53) (1.48)	Vigorously move left front corner of vehicle by hand.	> 5 mV~ Note: Value changes with movement.	
42.1		Voltage supply (B24/7)	N3/10 53 —(V)— 44 (1.53) (1.44)	Ignition: **ON**	4.7 – 5.3 V	N3/10
43.0	P1 444	***Not applicable to U.S.A. version vehicles***				
44.0	P1 437 P1 444	***Not applicable to U.S.A. version vehicles***				

MB1029500310000A

Fig. 38 Codes P1437, P1444 & P1605: Test 23, Steps 42.0–44.0

⇒		Test scope	Test connection	Test condition	Nominal value	Possible cause/Remedy
1.0	P0 560	**Engine control module (N3/10)** Voltage supply circuit 30	N3/10 26 —(V)— 35 (1.26) (1.35)	Ignition: **ON**	11 – 14 V	⇒ 1.1
1.1		Ground wire	N3/10 26 —(V)— X11/4 2 (1.26); 39 —(V)— 2 (1.39)	Ignition: **ON**	11 – 14 V	Wiring, **Model 129** Ground (W27), module box bracket. **Model 140** Output ground (W15), right footwell. **Model 210** Electronic ground (W16/6), right component compartment, ⇒ 1.2
1.2		Voltage supply circuit 30	X11/4 1 —(V)— N3/10 35 (1.35)	Ignition: **ON**	11 – 14 V	Wire, **Model 129, 140** base module (N16/1) or fuse on base module, **Model 210** relay module (K40).

MB1029500312000A

Fig. 40 Code P0560: Test 24, Steps 1.0–1.2

⇒		Test scope	Test connection	Test condition	Nominal value	Possible cause/Remedy
4.0		**Ignition coil (T1/1)** Voltage supply	N3/10 26 —(V)— 83 (1.26) (2.83)	Ignition: **ON** Starter: **Crank**	11 – 14 V > 10 V	Wiring. Model 210, 129 as of 09/95 and Model 140 as of 06/96 fused as follows: Model 129 fuse 34 Model 140 fuse 22 Model 210 fuse 19
5.0		**Ignition coil (T1/2)** Voltage supply	N3/10 26 —(V)— 117 (1.26) (2.117)	Ignition: **ON** Starter: **Crank**	11 – 14 V > 10 V	Wiring. Model 210, 129 as of 09/95 and Model 140 as of 06/96 fused as follows: Model 129 fuse 34 Model 140 fuse 22 Model 210 fuse 19
6.0		**Ignition coil (T1/3)** Voltage supply	N3/10 26 —(V)— 115 (1.26) (2.115)	Ignition: **ON** Starter: **Crank**	11 – 14 V > 10 V	Wiring. Model 210, 129 as of 09/95 and Model 140 as of 06/96 fused as follows: Model 129 fuse 34 Model 140 fuse 22 Model 210 fuse 19

MB1029500314000A

Fig. 42 Code —: Test 24, Steps 4.0–6.0

⇒		Test scope	Test connection	Test condition	Nominal value	Possible cause/Remedy
10.0		**Ignition coil (T1/7)** Voltage supply	N3/10 26 —(V)— 116 (1.26) (2.116)	Ignition: **ON** Starter: **Crank**	11 – 14 V > 10 V	Wiring. Model 210, 129 as of 09/95 and Model 140 as of 06/96 fused as follows: Model 129 fuse 34 Model 140 fuse 22 Model 210 fuse 19
11.0		**Ignition coil (T1/8)** Voltage supply	N3/10 26 —(V)— 95 (1.26) (2.95)	Ignition: **ON** Starter: **Crank**	11 – 14 V > 10 V	Wiring. Model 210, 129 as of 09/95 and Model 140 as of 06/96 fused as follows: Model 129 fuse 34 Model 140 fuse 22 Model 210 fuse 19
12.0	P0 335	**CKP sensor (L5)**	N3/10 2) 78 —(V)— 89 (2.78) (2.89)	Starter: **Crank** Engine: **at Idle**	Signal, see Figure 1 and 3.	⇒ 12.1, Teeth on starter ring gear.
			N3/10 3) 78 —(V)— 89 (2.78) (2.89)	Starter: **Crank** Engine: **at Idle**	> 2.5 V~ > 5 V~ 4)	

2) Test with oscilloscope.
3) Test with multimeter only if oscilloscope is unavailable.
4) Voltage increases with increasing rpm.

MB1029500316000A

Fig. 44 Code P0335: Test 24, Steps 10.0–12.0

⇒		Test scope	Test connection	Test condition	Nominal value	Possible cause/Remedy
45.0		**Model 140 till 05/96 Model 210 till 05/97 (afterwards via CAN)** **Fuel tank cap open signal**	N3/10 23 —(V)— 25 (1.23) (1.25)	Engine: **at Idle** Tank cap open Tank cap closed after approx. 18 minutes	11 – 14 V < 1 V	Leak in purge system, ⇒ 33.0
46.0		**Model 140 till 05/96 Model 210 till 05/97 (afterwards via CAN)** **"CHECK ENGINE" MIL (A1e26)**	N3/10 11 —(V)— 25 (1.11) (1.25)	Ignition: **ON**	11 – 14 V	N3/10
47.0		**Engine control module (ME-SFI) coding** Bridge	N3/10 73 —(Ω)— 96 (2.73) (2.96)	Ignition: **OFF**	< 1 Ω	Wiring.

MB1029500311000A

Fig. 39 Code —: Test 23, Steps 45.0–47.0

⇒		Test scope	Test connection	Test condition	Nominal value	Possible cause/Remedy
2.0	P0 560	**Engine control module (N3/10)** Voltage supply circuit 87M	N3/10 38 —(V)— 25 (1.38) (1.25)	Ignition: **ON**	11 – 14 V	⇒ 2.1
2.1		Electronics ground	N3/10 38 —(V)— X11/4 2 (1.38)	Ignition: **ON**	11 – 14 V	Wiring, **Model 129, 140** Electronics ground (W15/1), right footwell, **Model 210** Electronics ground (W16/6), right component compartment, ⇒ 2.2
2.2		Voltage supply circuit 87	X11/4 1 —(V)— N3/10 25 (1.25)	Ignition: **ON** Ignition: **OFF**	11 – 14 V < 1 V	Wiring, **Model 129, 140** base module (N16/1) or fuse on base module, **Model 210** relay module (K40).
3.0	P0 560	**Engine control module (N3/10)** Voltage supply circuit 87M	N3/10 39 —(V)— 36 (1.39) (1.36)	Ignition: **ON** Ignition: **OFF**	11 – 14 V < 1 V	Wiring, **Model 129, 140** base module (N16/1) or fuse on base module, **Model 210** relay module (K40).

MB1029500313000A

Fig. 41 Code P0560: Test 24, Steps 2.0–3.0

⇒		Test scope	Test connection	Test condition	Nominal value	Possible cause/Remedy
7.0		**Ignition coil (T1/4)** Voltage supply	N3/10 26 —(V)— 85 (1.26) (2.85)	Ignition: **ON** Starter: **Crank**	11 – 14 V > 10 V	Wiring. Model 210, 129 as of 09/95 and Model 140 as of 06/96 fused as follows: Model 129 fuse 34 Model 140 fuse 22 Model 210 fuse 19
8.0		**Ignition coil (T1/5)** Voltage supply	N3/10 26 —(V)— 84 (1.26) (2.84)	Ignition: **ON** Starter: **Crank**	11 – 14 V > 10 V	Wiring. Model 210, 129 as of 09/95 and Model 140 as of 06/96 fused as follows: Model 129 fuse 34 Model 140 fuse 22 Model 210 fuse 19
9.0		**Ignition coil (T1/6)** Voltage supply	N3/10 26 —(V)— 94 (1.26) (2.94)	Ignition: **ON** Starter: **Crank**	11 – 14 V > 10 V	Wiring. Model 210, 129 as of 09/95 and Model 140 as of 06/96 fused as follows: Model 129 fuse 34 Model 140 fuse 22 Model 210 fuse 19

MB1029500315000A

Fig. 43 Code —: Test 24, Steps 7.0–9.0

⇒		Test scope	Test connection	Test condition	Nominal value	Possible cause/Remedy
12.1		Resistance of CKP sensor (L5)	N3/10 78 —(Ω)— 89 (2.78) (2.89)	Ignition: **OFF** Unplug connector 2 on engine control module (N3/10).	700 – 1400 Ω	L5
13.0	P0 341	**Camshaft Hall-effect sensor (B6/1)** Hall-effect signal	N3/10 2) 87 —(V)— 66 (2.87) (2.66)	Engine: **at Idle**	Signal	⇒ 13.1, B6/1
			N3/10 3) 66 —(V)— 25 (2.66) (1.25)	Engine: **at Idle**	1.2 – 1.7 V Value changes	
13.1		Voltage supply to camshaft Hall-effect sensor (B6/1)	B6/1 1 —(V)— 3	Ignition: **ON** Disconnect connector from Hall-effect sensor (B6/1) and test directly on sockets 1 and 3 of connector.	11 – 14 V	Wiring.

2) Test with oscilloscope.
3) Test with multimeter only if oscilloscope is unavailable.

MB1029500317000A

Fig. 45 Code P0341: Test 24, Steps 12.1–13.1

⇒		Test scope	Test connection	Test condition	Nominal value	Possible cause/Remedy
14.0		**Closing duration for ignition coil (T1/1)**	N3/10 83 (2.83) — 25 (1.25)	Starter: **Crank** Engine: **at Idle**	20 – 100 ms 2 – 4 ms	⇒ 12.0, ⇒ 14.1, N3/10
14.1		Rest current shut-off: T1/1	N3/10 83 (2.83) — 25 (1.25)	Ignition: **ON** Starter: **Crank**	0 V 0.3 – 0.6 V	T1/1, N3/10, < 0.3 V: wire from T1/1 to N3/10, > 0.6 V: T1/1.
15.0		**Closing duration for ignition coil (T1/2)**	N3/10 117 (2.117) — 25 (1.25)	Starter: **Crank** Engine: **at Idle**	20 – 100 ms 2 – 4 ms	⇒ 12.0, ⇒ 15.1, N3/10
15.1		Rest current shut-off: T1/2	N3/10 117 (2.117) — 25 (1.25)	Ignition: **ON** Starter: **Crank**	0 V 0.3 – 0.6 V	T1/2, N3/10, < 0.3 V: wire from T1/2 to N3/10, > 0.6 V: T1/2

MB1029500318000A

Fig. 46 Code —: Test 24, Steps 14.0–15.1

⇒		Test scope	Test connection	Test condition	Nominal value	Possible cause/Remedy
16.0		**Closing duration for ignition coil (T1/3)**	N3/10 115 (2.115) — 25 (1.25)	Starter: **Crank** Engine: **at Idle**	20 – 100 ms 2 – 4 ms	⇒ 12.0, ⇒ 16.1, N3/10
16.1		Rest current shut-off: T1/3	N3/10 115 (2.115) — 25 (1.25)	Ignition: **ON** Starter: **Crank**	0 V 0.3 – 0.6 V	T1/3, N3/10, < 0.3 V: wire from T1/3 to N3/10, > 0.6 V: T1/3.
17.0		**Closing duration for ignition coil (T1/4)**	N3/10 85 (2.85) — 25 (1.25)	Starter: **Crank** Engine: **at Idle**	20 – 100 ms 2 – 4 ms	⇒ 12.0, ⇒ 17.1, N3/10
17.1		Rest current shut-off: T1/4	N3/10 85 (2.85) — 25 (1.25)	Ignition: **ON** Starter: **Crank**	0 V 0.3 – 0.6 V	T1/4, N3/10, < 0.3 V: wire from T1/4 to N3/10, > 0.6 V: T1/4

MB1029500319000A

Fig. 47 Code—: Test 24, Steps 16.0–17.1

⇒		Test scope	Test connection	Test condition	Nominal value	Possible cause/Remedy
18.0		**Closing duration for ignition coil (T1/5)**	N3/10 84 (2.84) — 25 (1.25)	Starter: **Crank** Engine: **at Idle**	20 – 100 ms 2 – 4 ms	⇒ 12.0, ⇒ 18.1, N3/10
18.1		Rest current shut-off: T1/5	N3/10 84 (2.84) — 25 (1.25)	Ignition: **ON** Starter: **Crank**	0 V 0.3 – 0.6 V	T1/5, N3/10, < 0.3 V: wire from T1/5 to N3/10, > 0.6 V: T1/5.
19.0		**Closing duration for ignition coil (T1/6)**	N3/10 94 (2.94) — 25 (1.25)	Starter: **Crank** Engine: **at Idle**	20 – 100 ms 2 – 4 ms	⇒ 12.0, ⇒ 19.1, N3/10
19.1		Rest current shut-off: T1/6	N3/10 94 (2.94) — 25 (1.25)	Ignition: **ON** Starter: **Crank**	0 V 0.3 – 0.6 V	T1/6, N3/10, < 0.3 V: wire from T1/6 to N3/10, > 0.6 V: T1/6

MB1029500320000A

Fig. 48 Code —: Test 24, Steps 18.0–19.1

⇒		Test scope	Test connection	Test condition	Nominal value	Possible cause/Remedy
20.0		**Closing duration for ignition coil (T1/7)**	N3/10 116 (2.116) — 25 (1.25)	Starter: **Crank** Engine: **at Idle**	20 – 100 ms 2 – 4 ms	⇒ 12.0, ⇒ 20.1, N3/10
20.1		Rest current shut-off: T1/7	N3/10 116 (2.116) — 25 (1.25)	Ignition: **ON** Starter: **Crank**	0 V 0.3 – 0.6 V	T1/7, N3/10, < 0.3 V: wire from T1/7 to N3/10, > 0.6 V: T1/7
21.0		**Closing duration for ignition coil (T1/8)**	N3/10 95 (2.95) — 25 (1.25)	Starter: **Crank** Engine: **at Idle**	20 – 100 ms 2 – 4 ms	⇒ 12.0, ⇒ 21.1, N3/10
21.1		Rest current shut-off: T1/8	N3/10 95 (2.95) — 25 (1.25)	Ignition: **ON** Starter: **Crank**	0 V 0.3 – 0.6 V	T1/8, N3/10, < 0.3 V: wire from T1/8 to N3/10, > 0.6 V: T1/8

MB1029500321000A

Fig. 49 Code —: Test 24, Steps 20.0–21.1

⇒		Test scope	Test connection	Test condition	Nominal value	Possible cause/Remedy
22.0	P0 300 P0 301	**Primary voltage** Ignition coil (T1/1)	N3/10 83 (2.83) — 25 (1.25)	**Test connection Note:** Individual primary pattern Range 400 V Duration 100% Starter: **Crank**	200 – 350 V	⇒ 22.1, N3/10
22.1		Primary winding of T1/1 and T1/2	N3/10 83 (2.83) — 117 (2.117)	Ignition: **OFF**	0.9 – 1.4 Ω [6]	Wiring T1/1 or T1/2
23.0	P0 300 P0 302	**Primary voltage** Ignition coil (T1/2)	N3/10 117 (2.117) — 25 (1.25)	**Test connection Note:** Individual primary pattern Range 400 V Duration 100% Starter: **Crank**	200 – 350 V	⇒ 23.1, N3/10
23.1		Primary winding of T1/2 and T1/1	N3/10 117 (2.117) — 83 (2.83)	Ignition: **OFF**	0.9 – 1.4 Ω [6]	Wiring T1/2 or T1/1

[6] The resistance of a single coil is 0.5 – 0.7 Ω

MB1029500322000A

Fig. 50 Codes P0300, P0301 & P0302: Test 24, Steps 22.0–23.1

⇒		Test scope	Test connection	Test condition	Nominal value	Possible cause/Remedy
24.0	P0 300 P0 303	**Primary voltage** Ignition coil (T1/3)	N3/10 115 (2.115) — 25 (1.25)	**Test connection Note:** Individual primary pattern Range 400 V Duration 100% Starter: **Crank**	200 – 350 V	⇒ 24.1, N3/10
24.1		Primary winding of T1/3 and T1/4	N3/10 115 (2.115) — 85 (2.85)	Ignition: **OFF**	0.9 – 1.4 Ω [6]	Wiring T1/3 or T1/4
25.0	P0 300 P0 304	**Primary voltage** Ignition coil (T1/4)	N3/10 85 (2.85) — 25 (1.25)	**Test connection Note:** Individual primary pattern Range 400 V Duration 100% Starter: **Crank**	200 – 350 V	⇒ 25.1, N3/10
25.1		Primary winding of T1/4 and T1/3	N3/10 85 (2.85) — 115 (2.115)	Ignition: **OFF**	0.9 – 1.4 Ω [6]	Wiring T1/4 or T1/3

[6] The resistance of a single coil is 0.5 – 0.7 Ω

MB1029500323000A

Fig. 51 Codes P0300, P0303 & P0304: Test 24, Steps 24.0–25.1

⇒		Test scope	Test connection	Test condition	Nominal value	Possible cause/Remedy
26.0	P0 300 P0 305	**Primary voltage** Ignition coil (T1/5)	N3/10 84 (2.84) — 25 (1.25)	**Test connection Note:** Individual primary pattern Range 400 V Duration 100% Starter: **Crank**	200 – 350 V	⇒ 26.1, N3/10
26.1		Primary winding of T1/5 and T1/6	N3/10 84 (2.84) — 94 (2.94)	Ignition: **OFF**	0.9 – 1.4 Ω [6]	Wiring T1/5 or T1/6
27.0	P0 300 P0 306	**Primary voltage** Ignition coil (T1/6)	N3/10 94 (2.94) — 25 (1.25)	**Test connection Note:** Individual primary pattern Range 400 V Duration 100% Starter: **Crank**	200 – 350 V	⇒ 27.1, N3/10
27.1		Primary winding of T1/6 and T1/5	N3/10 94 (2.94) — 84 (2.84)	Ignition: **OFF**	0.9 – 1.4 Ω [6]	Wiring T1/6 or T1/5

[6] The resistance of a single coil is 0.5 – 0.7 Ω

MB1029500324000A

Fig. 52 Codes P0300, P0305 & P0306: Test 24, Steps 26.0–27.1

⇒		Test scope	Test connection	Test condition	Nominal value	Possible cause/Remedy
28.0	P0 300 P0 307	**Primary voltage** Ignition coil (T1/7)	N3/10 116 (2.116) — 25 (1.25)	**Test connection Note:** Individual primary pattern Range 400 V Duration 100% Starter: **Crank**	200 – 350 V	⇒ 28.1, N3/10
28.1		Primary winding of T1/7 and T1/8	N3/10 116 (2.116) — 95 (2.95)	Ignition: **OFF**	0.9 – 1.4 Ω [6]	Wiring T1/7 or T1/8
29.0	P0 300 P0 308	**Primary voltage** Ignition coil (T1/8)	N3/10 95 (2.95) — 25 (1.25)	**Test connection Note:** Individual primary pattern Range 400 V Duration 100% Starter: **Crank**	200 – 350 V	⇒ 29.1, N3/10
29.1		Primary winding of T1/8 and T1/7	N3/10 95 (2.95) — 116 (2.116)	Ignition: **OFF**	0.9 – 1.4 Ω [6]	Wiring T1/8 or T1/7

[6] The resistance of a single coil is 0.5 – 0.7 Ω

MB1029500325000A

Fig. 53 Codes P0300, P0307 & P0308: Test 24, Steps 28.0–29.1

⇒		Test scope	Test connection	Test condition	Nominal value	Possible cause/Remedy
30.0	P0 300 P0 301 P0 302 P0 303 P0 304 P0 305 P0 306 P0 307 P0 308	**Firing voltage** Ignition coil (T1/1) to (T1/8)	Engine analyzer	**Test connection Note:** Individual secondary pattern Range 20 kV Duration 100% Connect kV pick-ups successively to T1/1 through T1/8. Starter: **Crank**	8 – 20 kV 5)	Spark plugs, T1/1 to T1/8, N3/10

5) The resistance of the secondary winding can not be measured due to an installed diode.

MB1029500326000A

Fig. 54 Codes P0300, P0301, P0302, P0303, P0304, P0305, P0306, P0307 & P0308: Test 24, Step 30.0

⇒		Test scope	Test connection	Test condition	Nominal value	Possible cause/Remedy
2.0	P0 560	**Engine control module (N3/10)** Voltage supply Circuit 87M	N3/10 38 —(V)— 25 (1.38) (1.25)	Ignition: **ON**	11 – 14 V	⇒ 2.1
2.1		Electronic ground	N3/10 X11/4 38 —(V)— 2 (1.38)	Ignition: **ON**	11 – 14 V	Wiring, **Model 129, 140:** Electronic ground (W15), right footwell. **Model 210:** Electronic ground (W16/6), right component compartment, ⇒ 2.2
2.2		Voltage supply Circuit 87M	X11/4 N3/10 1 —(V)— 25 (1.25)	Ignition: **ON**	11 – 14 V	Wiring, **Model 129, 140:** Base module (N16/1) or fuse on base module. **Model 210:** Relay module (K40).

MB1029500328000A

Fig. 56 Code P0560: Test 25, Steps 2.0–2.2

⇒		Test scope	Test connection	Test condition	Nominal value	Possible cause/Remedy
5.0	P1 542 P0 507	**Pedal value sensor (B37)** Signal Nominal value potentiometer 2	N3/10 5 —(V)— 6 (1.5) (1.6)	Ignition: **ON** Accelerator pedal position: CTP WOT	 0.1 – 0.4 V 2.1 – 2.5 V	Wiring, ⇒ 5.1, B37
5.1		Voltage supply Nominal value potentiometer 2	N3/10 5 —(V)— 4 (1.5) (1.4)	Ignition: **ON**	2.25 – 2.75 V	N3/10
6.0	P0 507 P0 120 P0 186	**EA/CC/ISC actuator (M16/1)** Signal Actual value potentiometer 1 Actual value potentiometer 2	N3/10 98 —(V)— 97 (2.98) (2.97) N3/10 98 —(V)— 107 (2.98) (2.107)	Ignition: **ON** Accelerator pedal position: CTP WOT Accelerator pedal position: CTP WOT	 4.0 – 4.6 V < CTP value 0.3 – 0.9 V > CTP value	Wiring, ⇒ 6.1, M16/1

MB1029500330000A

Fig. 58 Codes P0120, P0186, P0507 & P1542: Test 25, Steps 5.0–6.0

⇒		Test scope	Test connection	Test condition	Nominal value	Possible cause/Remedy
9.0	P0 500	**Left rear axle VSS sensor (L6/3)**	N3/10 38 —(V)— 22 (1.38) (1.22)	Raise rear of vehicle. Ignition: **ON** Spin left rear wheel by hand.	4 – 8 V ~	Wiring, ASR or ESP
10.0		**(only until 05/96, as of 06/96 via CAN)** **A/C compressor signal**	N3/10 38 —(V)— 8 (1.38) (1.8)	Engine: **at idle** **Turn A/C system: ON** Move temperature selector wheel to MIN, blower: **ON.**	< 1.0 V 11 – 14 V	Wiring, A/C pushbutton control module (N22).
11.0		**EPC MIL (A1e43)** Activation	N3/10 21 —(V)— 35 (1.21) (1.35)	Ignition: **ON** Engine: **at idle**	11 – 14 V < 1 V	Wiring, Malfunction in actuator or pedal value sensor, N3/10

MB1029500332000A

Fig. 60 Code P0500: Test 25, Steps 9.0–11.0

⇒		Test scope	Test connection	Test condition	Nominal value	Possible cause/Remedy
1.0	P0 560	**Engine control module (N3/10)** Voltage supply Circuit 30	N3/10 26 —(V)— 35 (1.26) (1.35)	Ignition: **ON**	11 – 14 V	⇒ 1.1
1.1		Ground wire	N3/10 X11/4 26 —(V)— 2 (1.26) 39 —(V)— 2 (1.39)	Ignition: **ON**	11 – 14 V	Wiring, **Model 129:** Ground (W27), module box bracket. **Model 140:** Output ground (W15), right footwell. **Model 210:** Electronic ground (W16/6), right component compartment, ⇒ 1.2
1.2		Voltage supply Circuit 30	X11/4 N3/10 1 —(V)— 35 (1.35)	Ignition: **ON**	11 – 14 V	Wiring, **Model 129, 140:** Base module (N16/1) or fuse on base module. **Model 210:** Relay module (K40).

MB1029500327000A

Fig. 55 Code P0560: Test 25, Steps 1.0–1.2

⇒		Test scope	Test connection	Test condition	Nominal value	Possible cause/Remedy
3.0	P0 560	**Engine control module (N3/10)** Voltage supply Circuit 87E	N3/10 39 —(V)— 36 (1.39) (1.36)	Ignition: **ON**	11 – 14 V	Wiring, **Model 129, 140:** Base module (N16/1) or fuse on base module. **Model 210:** Relay module (K40).
4.0	P1 542 P0 507	**Pedal value sensor (B37)** Signal Nominal value potentiometer 1	N3/10 18 —(V)— 19 (1.18) (1.19)	Ignition: **ON** Accelerator pedal position: CTP WOT	 0.2 – 0.5 V 4.3 – 4.8 V	⇒ 4.1, Wiring, B37
4.1		Voltage supply Nominal value potentiometer 1	N3/10 18 —(V)— 17 (1.18) (1.17)	Ignition: **ON**	4.75 – 5.25 V	N3/10

MB1029500329000A

Fig. 57 Codes P0507, P0560 & P1542: Test 25, Steps 3.0–4.1

⇒		Test scope	Test connection	Test condition	Nominal value	Possible cause/Remedy
6.1		Voltage supply Actual value potentiometers 1 and 2	N3/10 98 —(V)— 106 (2.98) (2.106)	Ignition: **ON**	4.75 – 5.25 V	N3/10
7.0	P0 186 P1 580	**EA/CC/ISC actuator (M16/1)** Activation of actuator motor Resistance (actuator motor)	N3/10 74 —(V)— 75 (2.74) (2.75) N3/10 74 —(Ω)— 75 (2.74) (2.75)	Ignition: **ON** Engine: **at idle** ECT > 70 °C Ignition: **OFF**	1.0 – 2.3 V 1.0 – 2.5 V Value oscillates. < 10 Ω	Wiring, M16/1, N3/10
8.0	P0 500	**Left front axle VSS sensor (L6/1)**	N3/10 38 —(V)— 9 (1.38) (1.9)	Raise front of vehicle. Ignition: **ON** Spin left front wheel by hand.	4 – 8 V ~	Wiring, ASR or ESP

MB1029500331000A

Fig. 59 Codes P0186, P0500 & P1580: Test 25, Steps 6.1–8.0

⇒		Test scope	Test connection	Test condition	Nominal value	Possible cause/Remedy
1.0	P0 565	**CC switch (S40)** **V** Decelerate/set **B** Accelerate/set **SP** Memory recall **Off** **Control contact**	N3/10 26 —(V)— 31 (1.26) (1.31) N3/10 26 —(V)— 2 (1.26) (1.2) N3/10 26 —(V)— 30 (1.26) (1.30) N3/10 38 —(V)— 28 (1.38) (1.28) N3/10 38 —(V)— 27 (1.38) (1.27)	Ignition: **ON** CC switch not activated. Decelerate activated. Ignition: **ON** Accelerate activated. Ignition: **ON** Memory activated. Ignition: **ON** Off activated. Ignition: **ON** CC switch not activated. Activate decelerate/accelerate/memory/off	 < 1 V 11 – 14 V 11 – 14 V 11 – 14 V 11 – 14 V < 1 V < 1 V 11 – 14 V	Wiring, S40

MB1029500333000A

Fig. 61 Code P0565: Test 26, Step 1.0

⇒		Test scope	Test connection	Test condition	Nominal value	Possible cause/Remedy
2.0	P1 584	**Stop lamp switch (S9/1)** N.O. contact	N3/10 26 (1.26) —V— 1 (1.1)	Ignition: **ON** Brake pedal not applied. Brake pedal applied.	< 1 V 11 – 14 V	Wiring, S9/1
		N.C. contact	N3/10 26 (1.26) —V— 3 (1.3)	Ignition: **ON** Brake pedal not applied. Brake pedal applied.	11 – 14 V < 1 V	Wiring, S9/1
3.0	P0 500	**Left front axle VSS sensor (L6/1)**	N3/10 38 (1.38) —V— 9 (1.9)	Raise front of vehicle. Ignition: **ON** Spin left front wheel by hand.	4 – 8 V ~	Wiring
4.0	P0 500	**Left rear axle VSS sensor (L6/3)**	N3/10 38 (1.38) —V— 22 (1.22)	Raise rear of vehicle. Ignition: **ON** Spin left rear wheel by hand.	4 – 8 V ~	Wiring

MB1029500334000A

Fig. 62 Codes P0500 & P1584: Test 26, Steps 2.0–4.0

⇒		Test scope	Test connection	Test condition	Nominal value	Possible cause/Remedy
1.0		**Fuel pressure at idle (with vacuum)**	Pressure gauge connected to test connection.	Engine: **at Idle** Valve on pressure gauge closed.	46.4-52.2 psi	Check fuel pumps Replace diaphragm pressure regulator.
2.0		**Fuel pressure at idle (without vacuum)**	Pressure gauge connected to test connection.	Engine: **at Idle** Disconnect vacuum hose from diaphragm pressure regulator.	53.7-60.9 psi	Replace diaphragm pressure regulator.
3.0		**Fuel system leakage**	Pressure gauge connected to test connection.	Engine: **OFF** After 30 minutes	> 43.5 psi > 36.3 psi	If the pressure drops quickly, replace check valve in fuel pumps. If the pressure drops slowly, check injectors Replace diaphragm pressure regulator or O-rings on diaphragm pressure regulator.

MB1029500336000X

Fig. 64 Code —: Test 32, Fuel System Pressure & Internal Leakage Test

⇒		Test scope	Test connection	Test condition	Nominal value	Possible cause/Remedy
1.0		**Fuel pumps** Delivery capacity	N3/10 26 (1.26) ←—→ 24 (1.24)	Disconnect fuel return hose from fuel line and place end in measuring glass. Ignition: **ON**	1 liter of fuel within 35 seconds.	Check fuel lines for restrictions (kinks and dents). Replace fuel filter, ⇒ 2.0
2.0		**Fuel pumps** Current draw Connect multimeter to sockets 1 and 3		Disconnect fuel pumps relay module (K27). Ignition: **ON**	4 – 9 A	Fuel pumps

MB1029500338000A

Fig. 66 Code —: Test 34, Fuel Pump Test

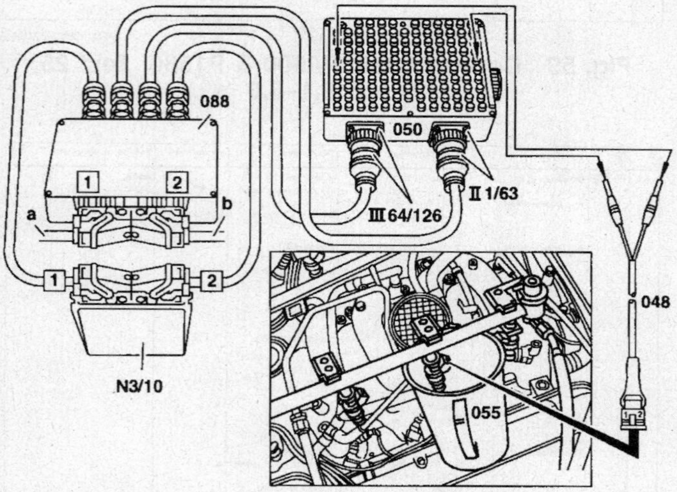

048 Self made harness
050 Socket box tester, 126 pole
055 Measuring glass
088 Test cable
N3/10 Engine control module (ME-SFI)
a Interior wiring harness
b Engine compartment harness

MB1029500339000X

Fig. 67 Injector test connection

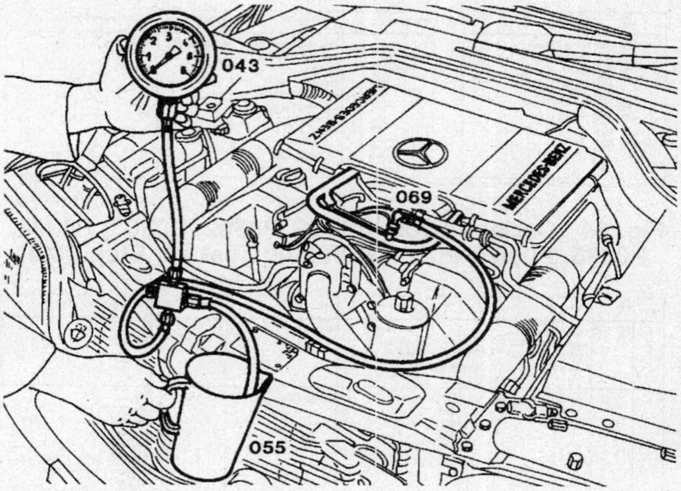

043 Pressure gauge, part no. 103 589 00 21 00
055 Measurement glass
069 Pressure hose, part no. 119 589 04 63 00

MB1029500335000X

Fig. 63 Fuel pressure connection

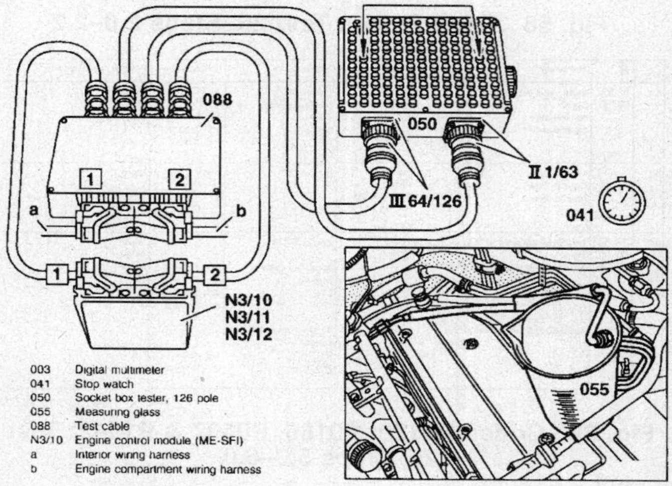

003 Digital multimeter
041 Stop watch
050 Socket box tester, 126 pole
055 Measuring glass
088 Test cable
N3/10 Engine control module (ME-SFI)
a Interior wiring harness
b Engine compartment wiring harness

MB1029500337000X

Fig. 65 Fuel pump test connections

⇒		Test scope	Test connection	Test condition	Nominal value	Possible cause/Remedy
1.0		**Injectors** Leakage test	N3/10 26 (1.26) ←—→ 24 (1.24)	Fuel rail and fuel injectors removed. Ignition: **ON**	Injectors must not drip.	Replace dripping injectors, ⇒ 2.0.
2.0		**Injectors** Operation and spray pattern test	N3/10 26 (1.26) ←—→ 24 (1.24)	Ignition: **ON** Hold each injector (one after another) into a container and, using the self-made test harness, manually activate the injector by connecting harness banana plugs to socket box sockets 38 (–) and 25 (+).	Injectors must spray evenly	Replace defective injectors.

MB1029500340000X

Fig. 68 Code —: Test 36, Injector Test

SYSTEM SERVICE

Component Replacement

FUEL RAIL

1. Relieve fuel pressure through fuel rail service valve.
2. Disconnect brake servo vacuum line.
3. Disconnect crankcase ventilation line.
4. Disconnect pressure regulator vacuum hose.
5. Disconnect fuel feed and return lines. Collect spilled fuel in suitable container.
6. Disconnect injector connectors.
7. Disconnect ME control module.
8. Remove ignition coils lefthand cover.
9. Disconnect cable harness.
10. Remove mounting screws, then pull fuel rail with injection valves out of intake manifold and lead through cable harness.
11. Reverse procedure to install. Lubricate new O-rings with oil.

FUEL INJECTOR

Refer to "104 Engine (ME 2.1 Engine Management)" section.

DIAPHRAGM PRESSURE REGULATOR

Refer to "104 Engine (ME 2.1 Engine Management)" section.

HOT FILM MASS AIR FLOW (MAF) SENSOR

1. Disconnect connector.
2. Remove Intake Air Temperature (IAT) Sensor.
3. Disconnect hose and clip.
4. Remove MAF sensor.
5. Reverse procedure to install.

OXYGEN SENSOR

Refer to "104 Engine (ME 2.1 Engine Management)" section.

CRANKSHAFT POSITION (CKP) SENSOR

1. Disconnect connector.
2. Remove CKP sensor.
3. Reverse procedure to install.

KNOCK SENSOR

1. Remove engine support.
2. Disconnect knock sensor connector.
3. Remove sensor.
4. Reverse procedure to install. **Torque** sensor to 15 ft. lbs.

THROTTLE CONTROL CABLE

1. Disconnect accelerator control cable at ball head.
2. Press plastic clip together and pull out of control lever bracket with accelerator control cable.
3. Disconnect accelerator pedal lever control cable mount.
4. Press accelerator control cable out from inside vehicle. **Do not press rubber grommet out.**
5. Remover control cable from engine compartment.
6. Reverse procedure to install. Adjust cable as outlined under "Adjustments."

ELECTRONIC ACCELERATOR ACTUATOR

1. Remove hot film Mass Air Flow (MAF) sensor.
2. Disconnect clip and hose.
3. Disconnect connector.
4. Remove vent hose.
5. Remove mounting bolts and electronic accelerator actuator.
6. Disconnect electronic accelerator pedal actuator connector.
7. Reverse procedure to install. **Torque** actuator mounting bolt to 18 ft. lbs.

Adjustments

THROTTLE CONTROL CABLE

1. Ensure control bell crank contacts pedal position sensor Closed Throttle Position (CTP) stop. Adjust as required.
2. Ensure ignition switch is in Off position.
3. Press accelerator pedal as far a kickdown switch stop. **Do not operate kickdown switch.**
4. Ensure control bell crank contacts accelerator position sensor Wide Open Throttle (WOT) stop. Adjust as required.

120 Engine (ME 1.0 Engine Management)

NOTE: On Air Bag Equipped Models, Refer To "Air Bag System Precautions" Located In The Front Of This Manual For System Disarming & Arming Procedures.

NOTE: Refer To "Computer Relearn Procedures" Located In The Front Of This Manual When Battery Power To The Computer Has Been Interrupted.

NOTE: "Electrical Symbol Identification" Located In Front Of This Manual May Be Used As An Aid When Using Wiring Diagrams Found In This Section.

NOTE: Prior To Performing Any Service Listed In This Section Consult Technical Service Bulletin Section For Related Information.

INDEX

	Page No.
Description	14-166
Diagnosis & Testing	14-166
Accessing Diagnostic Trouble Codes	14-166
Hand-Held Tester	14-166
Clearing Diagnostic Trouble Codes	14-167
Component Tests	14-167
Fuel Injector	14-167
Fuel Pump	14-167
Components Locations	14-166
Connector Terminal Identification	14-167
Diagnostic Tests	14-167
Diagnostic Trouble Code Interpretation	14-166
Symbol Explanation	14-166
Symptom Related Diagnosis	14-166
Wiring Diagrams	14-167
Diagnostic Chart Index	14-186
Precautions	14-165
Air Bag Systems	14-165
Battery Ground Cable	14-165
Drive Authorization System (DAS)	14-165
ECM Recognition	14-165
ECM Self-Adaptation	14-165
ESP/ASR/ETS/ABS Control Modules	14-166
Ignition System	14-165
Throttle Valve Position	14-165
Sensor & Fuel Injector Specifications	14-165
System Service	14-206
Adjustments	14-206
Accelerator Control Cable	14-206
Component Replacement	14-206
Accelerator Control Cable	14-206
Crankshaft Position (CKP) Sensors	14-206
Electronic Accelerator Actuator	14-206
Fuel Injector	14-206
Fuel Rail	14-206
Hot Film Mass Air Flow (MAF) Sensor	14-206
Knock Sensor	14-206
Oxygen Sensor	14-206
Pressure Regulator	14-206

SENSOR & FUEL INJECTOR SPECIFICATIONS

Temperature, °F	Resistance, Ohms①	Voltage①
CRANKSHAFT POSITION (CKP) SENSOR		
—	700–1400	—
ENGINE COOLANT TEMPERATURE (ECT) SENSOR		
68	2500	3.32–3.68
86	1700	2.94–3.26
104	1170	2.56–2.84
122	830	2.18–2.42
140	600	1.80–2.00
158	435	1.42–1.58
176	325	1.14–1.26
194	245	.95–1.05
212	185	.76–.84
INTAKE AIR TEMPERATURE (IAT) SENSOR		
68	6060	2.47–2.73
86	3900	1.99–2.21
104	2600	1.52–1.68
122	1760	1.14–1.26
FUEL INJECTOR		
—	14–17	—

① — Tolerance ± 5%

PRECAUTIONS

Air Bag Systems

Refer to "Air Bag System Precautions" in the front of this manual for system disarming and arming procedures.

Battery Ground Cable

Prior to service, disconnect battery ground cable and isolate as required.

Ignition System

1. Both control module coupling must be disconnected or connect with ignition switch in Off position.
2. Do not short circuit ignition coils terminal No. 1.
3. Do not operate the ignition system at starting speed unless the ignition cables are fully connected.
4. Do not conduct are test at starting speed or when engine is running. This includes: holding ignition cable No. 4 at a distance to ground, disconnecting a plug connector or pulling cable No. 4 out of the ignition coils.
5. High output side of ignition system must always carry at least two ohms resistance (spark plug connected).
6. Do not load ignition coil with more than 28,000 volts.
7. Ignition coil iron cores must always be connected to ground. **Use caution, coil cores can be charged with up to 400 volts.**
8. **Do not work on this system if you have a pacemaker.**
9. Ensure engine and ignition switch are in Off position when connecting and disconnecting ignition coil.
10. When working at start speeds during test such as compression check, switch ignition to off position and disconnect control module connector No. 2.

ECM Self-Adaptation

After repair work, the Engine Control Module (ECM) will automatically adapt itself after the vehicle has made approximately 10 trips. A trip includes engine running for more than 20 minutes, engine oil temperature of more than 19°F, engine speed of more than 700 RPM and emission related logic chain functions.

However, after fixing a malfunction or installation of a test ECM, the self-adaptation function must be reset as outlined under "Computer Relearn Procedures" at the front of this manual.

ECM Recognition

The ECM must be coded for vehicle model, catalytic converter and country version with the Hand-Held Tester.

Before replacing the ECM, read and store existing code numbers with the Hand-Held Tester. When the new ECM is installed, enter the stored code numbers from the Hand-Held Tester. If code numbers cannot be read, the corresponding codes number must be obtained from Mercedes-Benz spare parts microfiche and manually entered with a Hand-Held Tester.

Throttle Valve Position

After replacing the Engine Control Module (ECM) or actuator, the throttle valve mechanical end stop and wide open position must be determined and recorded, allowing learned data to be erased with a Hand-Held Tester or new data learned.

1. Disconnect and connect battery power supply.
2. With vehicle parked, transmission in P or N position, no pressure on accelerator pedal and ignition switch in Off position, ensure engine coolant temperature is 41–212°F.
3. Turn ignition switch to On position for more than 50 seconds.
4. Turn ignition switch to Off position for more than 10 seconds.
5. If engine runs rough after battery power interruption, proceed as follows:
   a. Ensure engine coolant temperature is more than 176°F.
   b. Drive vehicle on dynamometer with transmission in 4 position or on road in 3 position.
   c. Increase engine speed to more than 3500 RPM and coast until speed is less than 1200 RPM.

Drive Authorization System (DAS)

The DAS can only be activated or deactivated by the electronic ignition key. The ECM, RCL and DAS control module are permanently locked together by an identification code. This code cannot be erased.

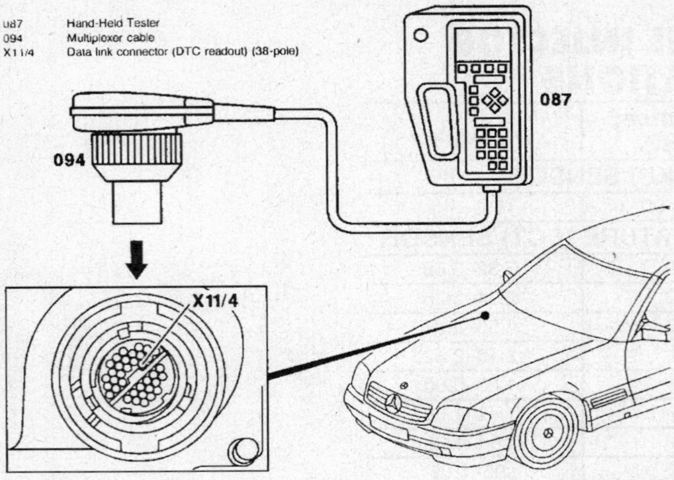

MB1029500393000X

Fig. 1 DLC tool connection. SL600

DTC	Possible cause		DTC Description	Test step/Remedy
	SAE nomenclature	Explanation		
–		No malfunction in system		In case of complaint, perform □ 23, 24, 25 or 26 in its entirety
P0 100 ■	Mass air flow circuit malfunction, bank 1 (right)	Right hot film MAF sensor (B2/7)	□ 13 ≫ 1	□ 23⇒ 4.0 – 5.0
P0 105 ■	MAP circuit malfunction, bank 1 (right)	Right pressure sensor (B28/2)	□ 13 ≫ 2	□ 23⇒ 6.0
P0 110 ■	IAT circuit malfunction, bank 1 (right)	Right IAT sensor (B17/6)	□ 13 ≫ 3	□ 23⇒ 9.0
P0 115 ■	ECT circuit malfunction, bank 1 (right)	Right ECT sensor (B11/10)	□ 13 ≫ 4	□ 23⇒ 8.0
P0 120	Throttle position sensor circuit malfunction, bank 1 (right)	Right EA/CC/ISC actuator (M16/3) (located on left side of engine)	□ 13 ≫ 5	□ 25⇒ 6.0
P0 130 ■	O2S 1 circuit malfunction, bank 1 (right)	Right O2S 1 (before TWC) (G3/4)	□ 13 ≫ 6	□ 23⇒ 11.0

MB1029500394010A

Fig. 2 DTC interpretation (Part 1 of 14)

DTC	Possible cause		DTC Description	Test step/Remedy
	SAE nomenclature	Explanation		
P0 133 ■	O2S 1 circuit slow response, bank 1 (right)	A Right O2S 1 (before TWC) (G3/4), ageing correction value exceeded B Right O2S 1 (before TWC) (G3/4), ageing time period too long	□ 13 ≫ 7	□ 23⇒ 11.0
P0 135 ■	O2S 1 heater circuit malfunction, bank 1 (right)	Right O2S 1 heater (before TWC) (G3/4)	□ 13 ≫ 8	□ 23 ⇒ 12.0
P0 136 ■	O2S 2 circuit malfunction, bank 1 (right)	Right O2S 2 (after TWC) (G3/6)	□ 13 ≫ 6	□ 23 ⇒ 13.0
P0 141 ■	O2S 2 heater circuit malfunction, bank 1 (right)	Right O2S 2 heater (after TWC) (G3/6)	□ 13 ≫ 8	□ 23⇒ 14.0
P0 150 ■	O2S 1 circuit malfunction, bank 2 (left)	Left O2S 1 (before TWC) (G3/3)	□ 13 ≫ 6	□ 23⇒ 11.0
P0 153 ■	O2S 1 circuit slow response, bank 2 (left)	A Left O2S 1 (before TWC) (G3/3), ageing correction value exceeded B Left O2S 1 (before TWC) (G3/3), ageing time period too long	□ 13 ≫ 7	□ 23⇒ 11.0
P0 155 ■	O2S 1 heater circuit malfunction, bank 2 (left)	Left O2S 1 heater (before TWC) (G3/3)	□ 13 ≫ 8	□ 23⇒ 12.0
P0 156 ■	O2S 2 circuit malfunction, bank 2 (left)	Left O2S 2 (after TWC) (G3/5)	□ 13 ≫ 6	□ 23⇒ 13.0
P0 161 ■	O2S 2 heater circuit malfunction, bank 2 (left)	Left O2S 2 heater (after TWC) (G3/5)	□ 13 ≫ 8	□ 23⇒ 14.0

MB1029500394020A

Fig. 2 DTC interpretation (Part 2 of 14)

DTC	Possible cause		DTC Description	Test step/Remedy
	SAE nomenclature	Explanation		
P0 170 ■	Fuel trim malfunction, bank 1 (right)	A Self adaptation of fuel mixture "partial load" at limit from right engine control module (N3/12). B Self adaptation of fuel mixture "CTP" at limit from right engine control module (N3/12).	□ 13 ≫ 9	Intake air leak, injectors, diaphragm pressure regulator, engine wear.
P0 173 ■	Fuel trim malfunction, bank 2 (left)	A Self adaptation of fuel mixture "partial load" at limit from left engine control module (N3/11). B Self adaptation of fuel mixture "CTP" at limit from left engine control module (N3/11).	□ 13 ≫ 9	Intake air leak, injectors, diaphragm pressure regulator, engine wear.
P0 201 ■	Injector circuit malfunction - cyl. 1	Injector (Y64y1) – cylinder 1	□ 13 ≫ 10	□ 23⇒ 15.0
P0 202 ■	Injector circuit malfunction - cyl. 2	Injector (Y64y2) – cylinder 2	□ 13 ≫ 10	□ 23⇒ 16.0
P0 203 ■	Injector circuit malfunction - cyl. 3	Injector (Y64y3) – cylinder 3	□ 13 ≫ 10	□ 23 ⇒ 17.0
P0 204 ■	Injector circuit malfunction - cyl. 4	Injector (Y64y4) – cylinder 4	□ 13 ≫ 10	□ 23 ⇒ 18.0
P0 205 ■	Injector circuit malfunction - cyl. 5	Injector (Y64y5) – cylinder 5	□ 13 ≫ 10	□ 23 ⇒ 19.0
P0 206 ■	Injector circuit malfunction - cyl. 6	Injector (Y64y6) – cylinder 6	□ 13 ≫ 10	□ 23 ⇒ 20.0
P0 207 ■	Injector circuit malfunction - cyl. 7	Injector (Y63y7) – cylinder 7	□ 13 ≫ 10	□ 23 ⇒ 15.0
P0 208 ■	Injector circuit malfunction - cyl. 8	Injector (Y63y8) – cylinder 8	□ 13 ≫ 10	□ 23 ⇒ 16.0
P0 209 ■	Injector circuit malfunction - cyl. 9	Injector (Y63y9) – cylinder 9	□ 13 ≫ 10	□ 23 ⇒ 17.0

MB1029500354030A

Fig. 2 DTC interpretation (Part 3 of 14)

Trial installation of an ECM or RCL control module from another vehicle is not possible. After 40 starts, a new ECM cannot be used in any other vehicle. The code number and VIN must be entered into the ECM with a Hand-Held Tester.

ESP/ASR/ETS/ABS Control Modules

The Electronic Stability Program (ESP), Acceleration Slip Regulation (ASR), Electronic Traction System (ETS) and/or Antilock Brake System (ABS) control modules must not be disconnected. The Engine Control Module (ECM) and Transmission Control Module (TCM) rely on those control modules for Vehicle Speed Sensor (VSS) information. To disable brake and engine regulation of those modules, proceed as follows:

1. Turn ignition switch to Off position.
2. Connect Hand-Held Tester adapter to Data Link Connector (DLC).
3. Jump sockets No. 1 and 6.
4. Start engine, MIL should light.
5. If Hand-Held Tester is available, disconnect VSS front axle connector.
6. When testing is complete, connect VSS and erase Diagnostic Trouble Codes with Hand-Held Tester.

DESCRIPTION

Refer to "104 Engine (ME 2.1 Engine Management)" section.

On 120 engines, two separate fuel injection and ignition system are fitted. One each for the right and lefthand cylinder banks.

DIAGNOSIS & TESTING

Symbol Explanation

Refer to "104 Engine (ME 2.1 Engine Management)" section for explanations of symbols, connections and steps included in the charts.

Accessing Diagnostic Trouble Codes

HAND-HELD TESTER

1. Turn ignition switch to Off position.
2. Attach test cable tool No. 965 589 00 40 00, or equivalent, to Hand-Held Tester tool No. 965 589 00 01 00, or equivalent.
3. Connect cable to Data Link Connector (DLC), **Fig. 1.**
4. Turn multiplexer cable locking ring completely to left detent stop.
5. Attach multiplexer cable to data link connector via locking pins.
6. To lock multiplexer cable to connector, turn locking ring to the right.
7. Follow tool manufacturer's instructions.

Diagnostic Trouble Code Interpretation

Refer to **Fig. 2** for DTC interpretation. **Black square items are emission related and may activate MIL during test cycle.**

Symptom Related Diagnosis

Refer to **Fig. 3** for symptom related diagnosis.

Components Locations

Refer to **Figs. 4 through 6** for component locations.

DTC	Possible cause: SAE nomenclature	Possible cause: Explanation	DTC Description	Test step/Remedy
P0 210 ■	Injector circuit malfunction - cyl. 10	Injector (Y63y10) – cylinder 10	☐ 13 ⊳ **10**	☐ 23 ⇒ 18.0
P0 211 ■	Injector circuit malfunction - cyl. 11	Injector (Y63y11) – cylinder 11	☐ 13 ⊳ **10**	☐ 23 ⇒ 19.0
P0 212 ■	Injector circuit malfunction - cyl. 12	Injector (Y63y12) – cylinder 12	☐ 13 ⊳ **10**	☐ 23 ⇒ 20.0
P0 300 ■	Random misfire detected	A Random misfire B Random misfire, TWC damaging	☐ 13 ⊳ **11**	☐ 24 ⇒ 18.0 – 23.0 ☐ 24 ⇒ 24.0 ☐ 36 ⇒ 1.0 – 2.0 Compression pressure
P0 301 ■	Cylinder 1 misfire detected	A Cylinder 1 misfire B Cylinder 1 misfire, TWC damaging	☐ 13 ⊳ **11**	☐ 24 ⇒ 18.0 ☐ 24 ⇒ 24.0 ☐ 36 ⇒ 1.0 – 2.0 Compression pressure
P0 302 ■	Cylinder 2 misfire detected	A Cylinder 2 misfire B Cylinder 2 misfire, TWC damaging	☐ 13 ⊳ **11**	☐ 24 ⇒ 19.0 ☐ 24 ⇒ 24.0 ☐ 36 ⇒ 1.0 – 2.0 Compression pressure
P0 303 ■	Cylinder 3 misfire detected	A Cylinder 3 misfire B Cylinder 3 misfire, TWC damaging	☐ 13 ⊳ **11**	☐ 24 ⇒ 20.0 ☐ 24 ⇒ 24.0 ☐ 36 ⇒ 1.0 – 2.0 Compression pressure
P0 304 ■	Cylinder 4 misfire detected	A Cylinder 4 misfire B Cylinder 4 misfire, TWC damaging	☐ 13 ⊳ **11**	☐ 24 ⇒ 21.0 ☐ 24 ⇒ 24.0 ☐ 36 ⇒ 1.0 – 2.0 Compression pressure

MB1029500354040A

Fig. 2 DTC interpretation (Part 4 of 14)

DTC	Possible cause: SAE nomenclature	Possible cause: Explanation	DTC Description	Test step/Remedy
P0 305 ■	Cylinder 5 misfire detected	A Cylinder 5 misfire B Cylinder 5 misfire, TWC damaging	☐ 13 ⊳ **11**	☐ 24 ⇒ 22.0 ☐ 24 ⇒ 24.0 ☐ 36 ⇒ 1.0 – 2.0 Compression pressure
P0 306 ■	Cylinder 6 misfire detected	A Cylinder 6 misfire B Cylinder 6 misfire, TWC damaging	☐ 13 ⊳ **11**	☐ 24 ⇒ 23.0 ☐ 24 ⇒ 24.0 ☐ 36 ⇒ 1.0 – 2.0 Compression pressure
P0 307 ■	Cylinder 7 misfire detected	A Cylinder 7 misfire B Cylinder 7 misfire, TWC damaging	☐ 13 ⊳ **11**	☐ 24 ⇒ 18.0 ☐ 24 ⇒ 24.0 ☐ 36 ⇒ 1.0 – 2.0 Compression pressure
P0 308 ■	Cylinder 8 misfire detected	A Cylinder 8 misfire B Cylinder 8 misfire, TWC damaging	☐ 13 ⊳ **11**	☐ 24 ⇒ 19.0 ☐ 24 ⇒ 24.0 ☐ 36 ⇒ 1.0 – 2.0 Compression pressure
P0 309 ■	Cylinder 9 misfire detected	A Cylinder 9 misfire B Cylinder 9 misfire, TWC damaging	☐ 13 ⊳ **11**	☐ 24 ⇒ 20.0 ☐ 24 ⇒ 24.0 ☐ 36 ⇒ 1.0 – 2.0 Compression pressure

MB1029500354050A

Fig. 2 DTC interpretation (Part 5 of 14)

DTC	Possible cause: SAE nomenclature	Possible cause: Explanation	DTC Description	Test step/Remedy
P0 310 ■	Cylinder 10 misfire detected	A Cylinder 10 misfire B Cylinder 10 misfire, TWC damaging	☐ 13 ⊳ **11**	☐ 24 ⇒ 21.0 ☐ 24 ⇒ 24.0 ☐ 36 ⇒ 1.0 – 2.0 Compression pressure
P0 311 ■	Cylinder 11 misfire detected	A Cylinder 11 misfire B Cylinder 11 misfire, TWC damaging	☐ 13 ⊳ **11**	☐ 24 ⇒ 22.0 ☐ 24 ⇒ 24.0 ☐ 36 ⇒ 1.0 – 2.0 Compression pressure
P0 312 ■	Cylinder 12 misfire detected	A Cylinder 12 misfire B Cylinder 12 misfire, TWC damaging	☐ 13 ⊳ **11**	☐ 24 ⇒ 23.0 ☐ 24 ⇒ 24.0 ☐ 36 ⇒ 1.0 – 2.0 Compression pressure
P0 325 ■	KS 1 circuit malfunction (right front)	Right KS 1 (A30g1)	☐ 13 ⊳ **12**	Wiring, connector, A30 g1
P0 330 ■	KS 2 circuit malfunction (right rear)	Right KS 2 (A30g2)	☐ 13 ⊳ **12**	Wiring, connector, A30 g2
P0 335	CKP sensor circuit malfunction, bank 1 (right)	Right CKP sensor (L5/5)	☐ 13 ⊳ **13**	☐ 24 ⇒ 10.0

MB1029500394060A

Fig. 2 DTC interpretation (Part 6 of 14)

DTC		Possible cause: SAE nomenclature	Possible cause: Explanation	DTC Description	Test step/Remedy
P0 341 ■		CMP sensor circuit range/performance, bank1 (right)	Right camshaft Hall-effect sensor (B6/3)	☐ 13 ⊳ **14**	☐ 24 ⇒ 11.0
P0 410 ■		AIR injection system malfunction	AIR system malfunction (logic chain)	☐ 13 ⊳ **15**	☐ 23 ⇒ 21.0 – 22.0 Hose disconnected from actuator.
P0 422 ■		TWC efficiency below threshold, right	Right TWC efficiency below threshold	☐ 13 ⊳ **16**	Replace right TWC
P0 432 ■		TWC efficiency below threshold, left	Left TWC efficiency below threshold	☐ 13 ⊳ **16**	Replace left TWC
P0 440 ■	**Only USA Model 140, Model 129 as of 09/97**	EVAP system malfunction	EVAP malfunction (logic chain)	☐ 13 ⊳ **17**	☐ 23 ⇒ 25.0 – 27.0
P0 441 ■		EVAP system incorrect purge flow	Right EVAP system malfunction	☐ 13 ⊳ **18**	☐ 23 ⇒ 25.0 – 26.0
P0 442 ■	**Only USA Model 140, Model 129 as of 09/97**	EVAP system leak detected (small leak)	EVAP system, small leak	☐ 13 ⊳ **17**	☐ 23 ⇒ 27.0
P0 443 ■		EVAP system purge control valve circuit malfunction, bank 1 (right)	Right purge control valve (Y58/3)	☐ 13 ⊳ **19**	☐ 23 ⇒ 25.0
P0 446 ■	**Only USA Model 140, Model 129 as of 09/97**	EVAP system vent control malfunction	A. Charcoal canister shut-off valve (Y58/4) B. End stage of charcoal canister shut-off valve	☐ 13 ⊳ **20**	☐ 23 ⇒ 28.0

MB1029500394070A

Fig. 2 DTC interpretation (Part 7 of 14)

Wiring Diagrams

Refer to **Figs. 7 through 11** for wiring diagrams.

Connector Terminal Identification

Refer to **Figs. 12 and 13** for engine control module connector terminal identification.

Diagnostic Tests

1. Turn ignition switch to Off position.
2. Connect 126-pole socket box tool No. 129 589 00 21 00, or equivalent, with contact module tool No. 140 589 46 63 00, or equivalent, to Engine Control Module, **Fig. 14.**
3. Connect interior harness connector to test cable connection No. 1 and engine harness connector to test cable connection No. 2.
4. Conduct tests as directed in **Figs. 15 through 62** using suitable multimeter.

Clearing Diagnostic Trouble Codes

The Diagnostic Trouble Code (DTC) memory is cleared when the vehicle battery is disconnected.

When an component has been repaired or replaced, the related DTC will be cleared. After three trips the CHECK ENGINE Malfunction Indicator Lamp (MIL) will go out and after 40 warm-up periods the DTC is automatically erased. A trip includes engine running for more than 20 minutes, engine oil temperature of more than 19°F, engine speed of more than 700 RPM and emission related logic chain functions. A warm-up period includes an engine coolant temperature at start-up of less than 95°F and increasing to more than 176°F.

To erase DTCs with a Hand-Held Tester, follow the tool manufacturer's instructions.

Component Tests

FUEL PUMP

1. Connect suitable pressure gauge to test connection, **Fig. 63.**
2. Conduct tests as directed, **Fig. 64.**
3. Connect 126-pole socket box tool No. 129 589 00 21 00, or equivalent, to Engine Control Module (ECM) with test cable tool No. 140 589 46 63 00, or equivalent, **Fig. 65.**
4. Conduct tests as directed, **Fig. 66.**
5. Release fuel pressure and allow fuel to drain into suitable measuring cup.

FUEL INJECTOR

1. Connect 126-pole socket box tool No. 129 589 00 21 00, or equivalent, to Engine Control Module (ECM) with test cable tool No. 140 589 46 63 00, or equivalent, **Fig. 67.**
2. Remove injector connectors and fuel rail with injectors. **Do not disconnect fuel feed and return lines.**
3. Connect self-made harness to one injector after another, hold over suitable measuring glass and test as directed, **Fig. 68.**

DTC	Possible cause		DTC Description	Test step/Remedy
	SAE nomenclature	Explanation		
P0 450 ■ Only (USA) Model 140, Model 129 as of 09/97	EVAP system pressure sensor malfunction	Fuel tank pressure sensor (B4/3)	□ 13 ≫ **21**	□ 23 ⇒ 29.0 Charcoal canister plugged.
Only (USA) Model 129 up to 08/97		Purge monitoring pressure sensor (B4/4)	□ 13 ≫ **22**	□ 23 ⇒ 30.0
P0 455 ■ Only (USA) Model 140, Model 129 as of 09/97	EVAP system leak detected (large leak)	EVAP system, large leak, Fuel tank pressure sensor (B4/3)	□ 13 ≫ **17**	□ 23 ⇒ 27.0 □ 23 ⇒ 29.0
P0 462	Fuel level sensor circuit low input	Fuel tank level too low		Fill fuel tank
P0 500	VSS sensor malfunction	A VSS left front B VSS left rear	□ 13 ≫ **23**	□ 25 ⇒ 8.0 □ 25 ⇒ 9.0
P0 507 ■	ISC rpm higher than expected	Idle control system	□ 13 ≫ **24**	□ 25 ⇒ 4.0, 5.0, 10.0
P0 560	System voltage malfunction	Voltage supply to right engine control module (N3/12)	□ 13 ≫ **25**	□ 23 ⇒ 1.0 – 3.0
P0 565	Cruise control switch	CC switch (S40)		□ 26 ⇒ 1.0
P0 600	Serial communication link malfunction	CAN bus from ESP/SPS control module (N47-5)	□ 13 ≫ **26**	□ 23 ⇒ 31.0

MB1029500394080A

Fig. 2 DTC interpretation (Part 8 of 14)

DTC	Possible cause		DTC Description	Test step/Remedy
	SAE nomenclature	Explanation		
P0 604	Internal control module random Access memory (RAM) error	A Engine control module left (N3/11) or right (N3/12) B Engine control module left (N3/11) or right (N3/12)		(N3/11) or (N3/12)
P0 605	Internal control module random Access memory (RAM) error	Engine control module left (N3/11) or right (N3/12)		(N3/11) or (N3/12)
P0 700 ■	Transmission control system malfunction	Read DTC memory of transmission control module	□ 13 ≫ **27** □ 13 ≫ **28**	Test ETC,
P0 702 ■	Transmission control system electrical	Read DTC memory of transmission control module	□ 13 ≫ **29** □ 13 ≫ **30**	Test ETC,
P0 715 ■	Input/turbine speed sensor circuit malfunction	Read DTC memory of transmission control module	□ 13 ≫ **31**	Test ETC,
P0 720 ■	Output speed sensor circuit malfunction	Read DTC memory of transmission control module	□ 13 ≫ **32**	Test ETC,
P0 730 ■	Incorrect gear ratio	Read DTC memory of transmission control module	□ 13 ≫ **33**	Test ETC,

MB1029500394090A

Fig. 2 DTC interpretation (Part 9 of 14)

DTC	Possible cause		DTC Description	Test step/Remedy
	SAE nomenclature	Explanation		
P0 740 ■	Torque converter clutch system malfunction	Read DTC memory of transmission control module	□ 13 ≫ **34**	Test ETC
P0 743 ■	Torque converter clutch system electrical	Read DTC memory of transmission control module	□ 13 ≫ **35**	Test ETC
P0 748 ■	Pressure control solenoid electrical	Read DTC memory of transmission control module	□ 13 ≫ **36** □ 13 ≫ **37**	Test ETC
P0 753 ■	Shift solenoid A electrical	Read DTC memory of transmission control module	□ 13 ≫ **38**	Test ETC
P0 758 ■	Shift solenoid B electrical	Read DTC memory of transmission control module	□ 13 ≫ **39**	Test ETC
P0 763 ■	Shift solenoid C electrical	Read DTC memory of transmission control module	□ 13 ≫ **40**	Test ETC
P0 809 ■	Angle deviation between camshaft and crankshaft	Angle deviation between camshaft and crankshaft		Check basic adjustment of camshaft
P1 146 ■	Mass air flow circuit malfunction, bank 2 (left)	Left hot film MAF sensor (B2/6)	□ 13 ≫ **1**	□ 23 ⇒ 4.0 – 5.0

MB1029500394100A

Fig. 2 DTC interpretation (Part 10 of 14)

DTC	Possible cause		DTC Description	Test step/Remedy
	SAE nomenclature	Explanation		
P1 147 ■	ECT circuit malfunction, bank 2 (left)	Left ECT sensor (B11/9)	□ 13 ≫ **4**	□ 23 ⇒ 8.0
P1 148 ■	IAT circuit malfunction, bank 2 (left)	Left IAT sensor (B17/5)	□ 13 ≫ **3**	□ 23 ⇒ 9.0
P1 149 ■	MAP circuit malfunction, bank 2 (left)	Left pressure sensor (B28/1)	□ 13 ≫ **2**	□ 23 ⇒ 6.0
P1 162	Throttle position sensor circuit malfunction, bank 2 (left)	Left EA/CC/ISC actuator actual value potentiometer (M16/4r1, M16/4r2)	□ 13 ≫ **5**	□ 25 ⇒ 6.0
P1 163	Oil level switch	Oil level switch (S43)		□ 23 ⇒ 33.0
P1 186	Fuel safety shut-off recognized	EA/CC/ISC actuator (M16/6)		□ 25 ⇒ 3.0 – 4.0, EA/CC/ISC actuator (M16/6) sticks or jammed, Check intake system for residue.
P1 300	CKP sensor circuit malfunction, bank 2 (left)	Left CKP sensor (L5/4)	□ 13 ≫ **13**	□ 24 ⇒ 10.0
P1 384 ■	KS 1 circuit malfunction (left front)	Left knock sensor 1 (A29g1)	□ 13 ≫ **12**	Wiring, connector, A29g1.
P1 385 ■	KS 2 circuit malfunction (left rear)	Left knock sensor 2 (A29g2)	□ 13 ≫ **12**	Wiring, connector, A29g2.

MB1029500394110A

Fig. 2 DTC interpretation (Part 11 of 14)

DTC	Possible cause		DTC Description	Test step/Remedy
	SAE nomenclature	Explanation		
P1 386 ■	Knock sensor control from ECM (N3/12) at end stop	Knock sensor regulation from right engine control module (N3/12) hardware failure	□ 13 ≫ **41**	1. Increased knock tendency due to bad fuel, carbon in combustion chamber or mechanical damage. 2. Engine control module (N3/12)
P1 397 ■	CMP sensor circuit range/performance, bank2 (left)	Left camshaft Hall-effect sensor (B6/2)	□ 13 ≫ **14**	□ 24 ⇒ 11.0
P1 420 ■	AIR pump switchover valve	AIR pump switchover valve (Y32)	□ 13 ≫ **42**	□ 23 ⇒ 22.0
P1 443 ■	EVAP system malfunction	Left EVAP system malfunction	□ 13 ≫ **18**	□ 23 ⇒ 25.0 – 26.0
P1 453 ■	AIR relay module	AIR relay module (K17)	□ 13 ≫ **42**	□ 23 ⇒ 21.0
P1 463 ■	Left AIR system malfunction	Left AIR system malfunction	□ 13 ≫ **15**	□ 23 ⇒ 21.0 – 22.0 Hose disconnected from actuator.

MB1029500394120A

Fig. 2 DTC interpretation (Part 12 of 14)

DTC	Possible cause		DTC Description	Test step/Remedy
	SAE nomenclature	Explanation		
P1 490 ■	EVAP system purge control valve circuit malfunction, bank 2 (left)	Left purge control valve (Y58/2)	□ 13 ≫ **19**	□ 23 ⇒ 25.0
P1 519 ■	Right adjustable camshaft timing solenoid	Right adjustable camshaft timing solenoid (Y49/2) (logic chain)	□ 13 ≫ **43**	□ 23 ⇒ 23.0– 24.0
P1 522 ■	Left adjustable camshaft timing solenoid	Left adjustable camshaft timing solenoid (Y49/1) (logic chain)	□ 13 ≫ **43**	□ 23 ⇒ 23.0 – 24.0
P1 525 ■	Right adjustable camshaft timing solenoid	Right adjustable camshaft timing solenoid (Y49/2)	□ 13 ≫ **44**	□ 23 ⇒ 23.0 – 24.0
P1 533 ■	Left adjustable camshaft timing solenoid	Left adjustable camshaft timing solenoid (Y49/1)	□ 13 ≫ **44**	□ 23 ⇒ 23.0 – 24.0
P1 542	Pedal value sensor	Pedal value sensor (B37)	□ 13 ≫ **45**	□ 25 ⇒ 4.0 – 5.0
P1 570	CAN signal from DAS control module to right engine control module (N3/12)	CAN signal from DAS control module (N54/1) to right engine control module (N3/12) interrupted.		□ 23 ⇒ 31.0
P1 580 ■	Right EA/CC/ISC actuator	Right EA/CC/ISC actuator (M16/3)	□ 13 ≫ **46**	□ 25 ⇒ 7.0
P1 581 ■	Left EA/CC/ISC actuator	Left EA/CC/ISC actuator (M16/4)	□ 13 ≫ **46**	□ 25 ⇒ 7.0
P1 584	Stop lamp switch	Stop lamp switch (S9/1)		□ 26 ⇒ 2.0
P1 587	Left engine control module voltage supply	Left engine control module (N3/11) voltage supply	□ 13 ≫ **25**	□ 23 ⇒ 1.0 – 3.0

MB1029500394130A

Fig. 2 DTC interpretation (Part 13 of 14)

DTC	Possible cause		DTC Description	Test step/Remedy
	SAE nomenclature	Explanation		
PI 588	CAN signal from RCL control module to left engine control module	CAN signal from RCL to left engine control module (N3/11)		□ 23 ⇒ 31.0
PI 589 ■	Knock sensor control from left engine control module at end stop	Knock sensor regulation from left engine control module (N3/11) hardware failure	□ 13 ⊳ **41**	1. Increased knock tendency due to bad fuel, carbon in combustion chamber or mechanical damage. 2. Engine control module (N3/11)
PI 605 ■	Body acceleration sensor (up to 05/96)	Body acceleration sensor (B24) (up to 05/96) Poor road/traction condition recognition signal (via comparison of VSS rpm signals) (as of 06/96)	□ 13 ⊳ **47**	□ 23 ⇒ 37.0 Test ASR/ESP see DM, Chassis and Drivetrain, Vol. 3, Section 9, 10
PI 632	Engine control module	Left engine control module (N3/11)		(N3/11)
PI 641	Engine control module	A Right CTP signal implausible B Left CTP signal implausible C CAN signal to left engine control module (N3/11) interrupted	□ 13 ⊳ **26**	□ 25 ⇒ 10.0, □ 25 ⇒ 10.0, □ 23 ⇒ 31.0
PI 747 ■	CAN signal from ETC	CAN signal from ETC (N15/3)	□ 13 ⊳ **26**	□ 23 ⇒ 31.0

MB1029500394140A

Fig. 2 DTC interpretation (Part 14 of 14)

Complaint/Problem	Possible cause	Test step/Remedy	Actual value Engine test Menu item
Engine runs unevenly (shakes)	Injector (Y62) control and injection duration. Injector leaking, spray pattern. Left or right O2S 1 (G3/3 or G3/4) (before TWC). Ignition voltage too low. Compression on one or more cylinders too low. Intake air leak.	□ 23 ⇒ 15.0 – 20.0 □ 36 ⇒ 1.0 □ 23 ⇒ 11.0 – 12.0 □ 24 ⇒ 24.0 Check compression. Remedy leak.	2/7 – 5/7 – – –
Engine runs unevenly (misfiring)	Ignition voltage too low. Hot film MAF sensor (B2/6 or B2/7).	□ 24 ⇒ 24.0 □ 23 ⇒ 4.0 – 5.0	– 1/7
Engine surges after cold start	Intake air leak.	Remedy leak.	–
Transition failure during warm-up	ECT sensor (B11/9 or B11/10). Hot film MAF sensor (B2/6 or B2/7). Intake air leak.	□ 23 ⇒ 8.0 □ 23 ⇒ 4.0 – 5.0 Remedy leak.	3/7 1/7 –
Transition failure when warm or with increased fuel consumption	Left or right O2S 1 (G3/3 or G3/4) (before TWC). Purge control valve (Y58/2 or Y58/3) stuck in open position.	□ 23 ⇒ 11.0 – 12.0 □ 23 ⇒ 25.0 – 26.0	5/7 3/7
Engine vibrates	Hot film MAF sensor (B2/6 or B2/7). Ignition voltage too low. Left or right O2S 1 (G3/3 or G3/4) (before TWC).	□ 23 ⇒ 4.0 – 5.0 □ 24 ⇒ 24.0 □ 23 ⇒ 11.0 – 12.0	1/7 – 5/7
EPC MIL (A1e43) illuminates and EA is in "limp-home" mode	Nominal value potentiometer in pedal value sensor (B37). EA/CC/ISC actuator actual value potentiometer.	□ 25 ⇒ 4.0 – 5.0 □ 25 ⇒ 6.0 – 7.0	4/7 4/7

MB1029500395020X

Fig. 3 Symptom related diagnosis (Part 2 of 2)

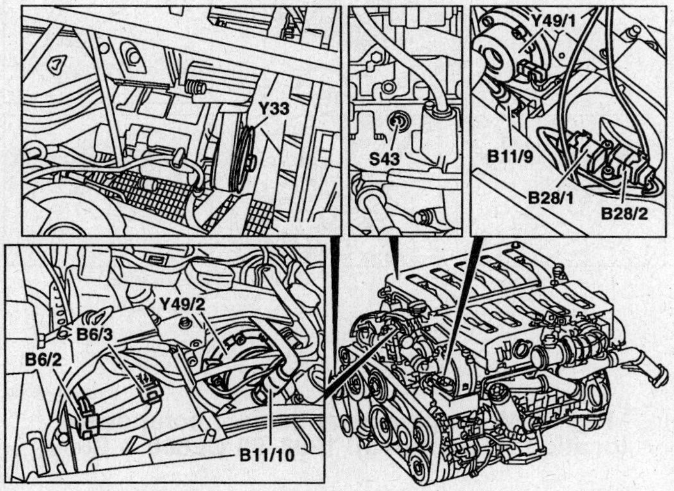

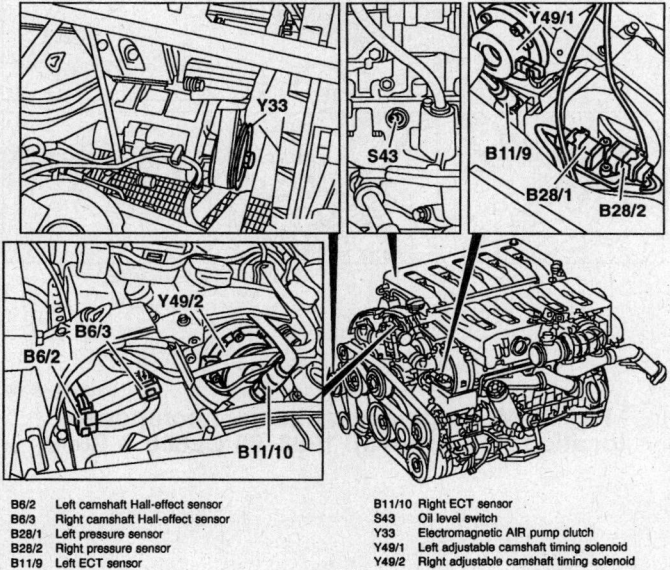

B6/2 Left camshaft Hall-effect sensor
B6/3 Right camshaft Hall-effect sensor
B28/1 Left pressure sensor
B28/2 Right pressure sensor
B11/9 Left ECT sensor
B11/10 Right ECT sensor
S43 Oil level switch
Y33 Electromagnetic AIR pump clutch
Y49/1 Left adjustable camshaft timing solenoid
Y49/2 Right adjustable camshaft timing solenoid

MB1029500388020A

Fig. 4 ME engine management component locations (Part 2 of 3). 120 engine

Complaint/Problem	Possible cause	Test step/Remedy [1]	Actual value Engine test Menu item
Engine starts and accelerates poorly when cold	Injector (Y62) control and injection duration. Hot film MAF sensor (B2/6 or B2/7). ECT sensor (B11/9 or B11/10). Ignition voltage too low. Intake air leak.	□ 23 ⇒ 15.0 – 20.0 □ 23 ⇒ 4.0 – 5.0 □ 23 ⇒ 8.0 □ 24 ⇒ 24.0 Remedy leak.	2/7 1/7 3/7 – –
Engine does not start	No voltage supply from base module (N16/1). Malfunction of drive authorization system (DAS) . Fuel pumps defective. No compression, oil pressure too high. Ignition voltage too low.	□ 23 ⇒ 1.0 – 3.0 □ 23 ⇒ 31.0 □ 34 ⇒ 2.0 check compression and oil pressure. □ 24 ⇒ 24.0	– DAS 1/1 – – –
Engine has uneven idle	Camshaft timing. Injector (Y62) control and injection duration. Intake air leak.	□ 23 ⇒ 23.0 – 24.0 □ 23 ⇒ 15.0 – 20.0 Remedy leak.	2/7 2/7 –
Engine has insufficient output	TWC flow restricted. Left or right O2S 1 (G3/3 or G3/4) (before TWC). ECT sensor (B11/9 or B11/10). Hot film MAF sensor (B2/6 or B2/7). Camshaft timing.	Check exhaust back pressure, see DM, Engines, Vol. 1, section A, "Engine Output" □ 23 ⇒ 11.0 – 12.0 □ 23 ⇒ 8.0 □ 23 ⇒ 4.0 – 5.0 □ 23 ⇒ 23.0 – 24.0	 – 5/7 3/7 1/7 2/7

MB1029500395010X

Fig. 3 Symptom related diagnosis (Part 1 of 2)

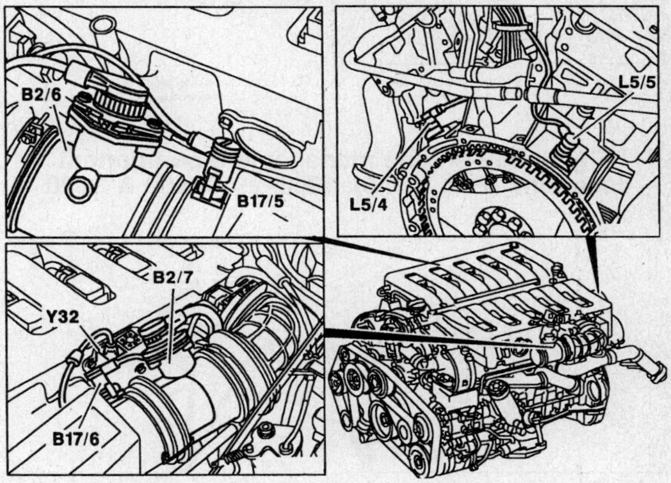

B2/6 Left hot film MAF sensor
B2/7 Right hot film MAF sensor
B17/5 Left IAT sensor
B17/6 Right IAT sensor
L5/4 Left CKP sensor
L5/5 Right CKP sensor
Y32 AIR pump switchover valve

MB1029500388010A

Fig. 4 ME engine management component locations (Part 1 of 3). 120 engine

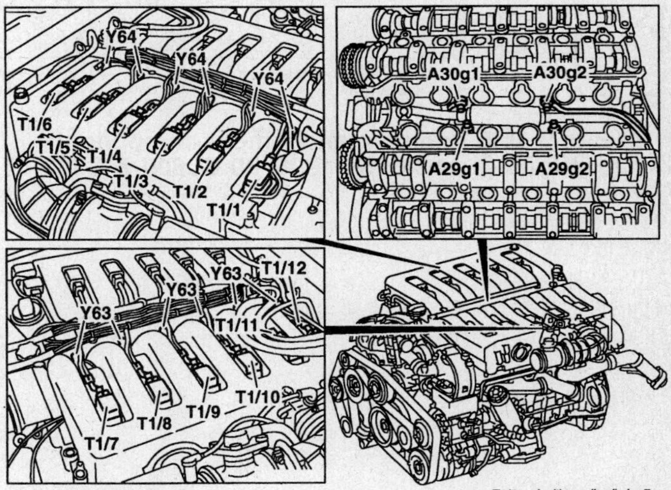

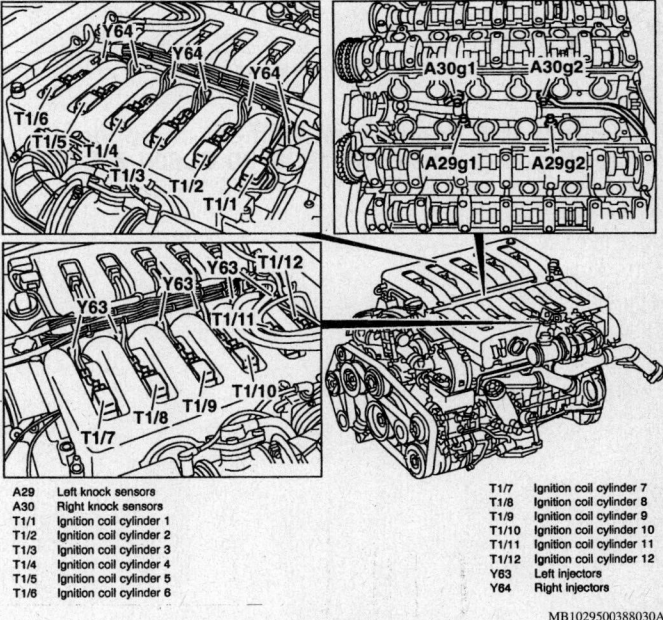

A29 Left knock sensors
A30 Right knock sensors
T1/1 Ignition coil cylinder 1
T1/2 Ignition coil cylinder 2
T1/3 Ignition coil cylinder 3
T1/4 Ignition coil cylinder 4
T1/5 Ignition coil cylinder 5
T1/6 Ignition coil cylinder 6
T1/7 Ignition coil cylinder 7
T1/8 Ignition coil cylinder 8
T1/9 Ignition coil cylinder 9
T1/10 Ignition coil cylinder 10
T1/11 Ignition coil cylinder 11
T1/12 Ignition coil cylinder 12
Y63 Left injectors
Y64 Right injectors

MB1029500388030A

Fig. 4 ME engine management component locations (Part 3 of 3). 120 engine

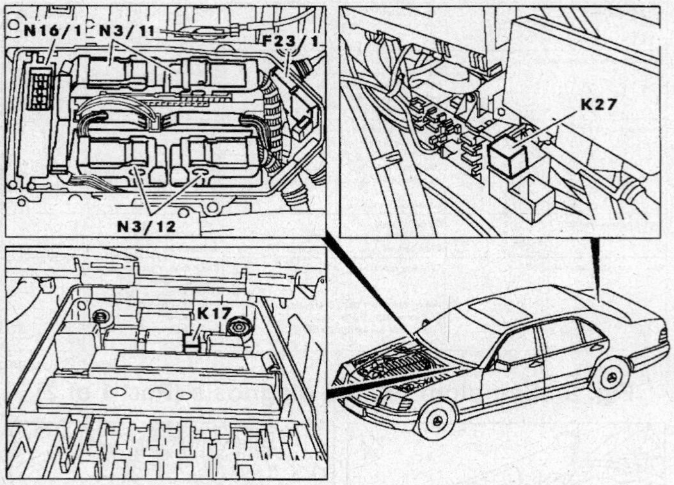

F23/1 Control module box
K17 AIR relay module
K27 FP relay module
N3/11 Left engine control module (ME-SFI)
N3/12 Right engine control module (ME-SFI)
N16/1 Base module

MB1029500390010X

Fig. 5 ME engine management component locations (Part 1 of 5). 1998–99 CL600 & S600

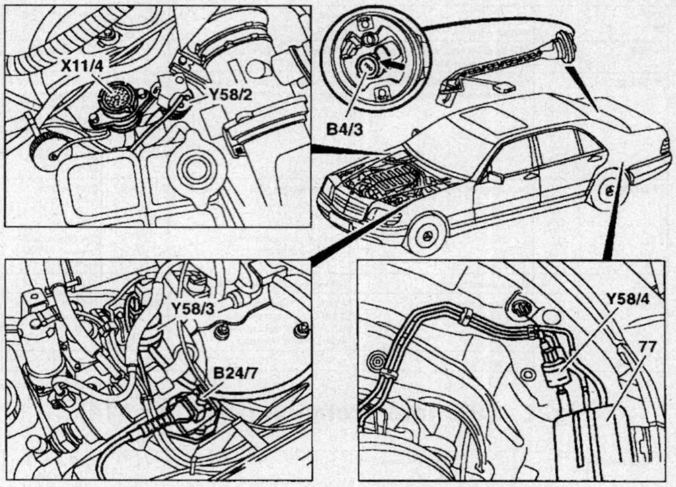

B4/3 Fuel tank pressure sensor
B24/7 Body acceleration sensor
X11/4 Data link connector
Y58/2 Left purge control valve
Y58/3 Right purge control valve
Y58/4 Activated charcoal canister shut-off valve
77 Active charcoal canister

MB1029500390020X

Fig. 5 ME engine management component locations (Part 2 of 5). 1998–99 CL600 & S600

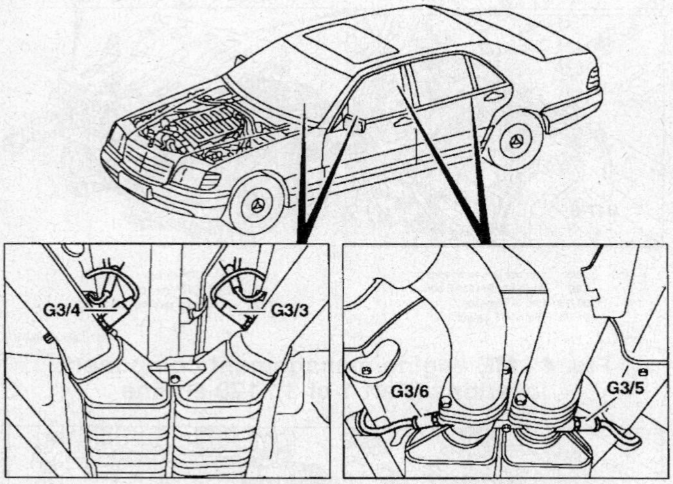

G3/3 Left O2S 1 (before TWC)
G3/4 Right O2S 1 (before TWC)
G3/5 Left O2S 2 (after TWC)
G3/6 Right O2S 2 (after TWC)

MB1029500390030X

Fig. 5 ME engine management component locations (Part 3 of 5). 1998–99 CL600 & S600

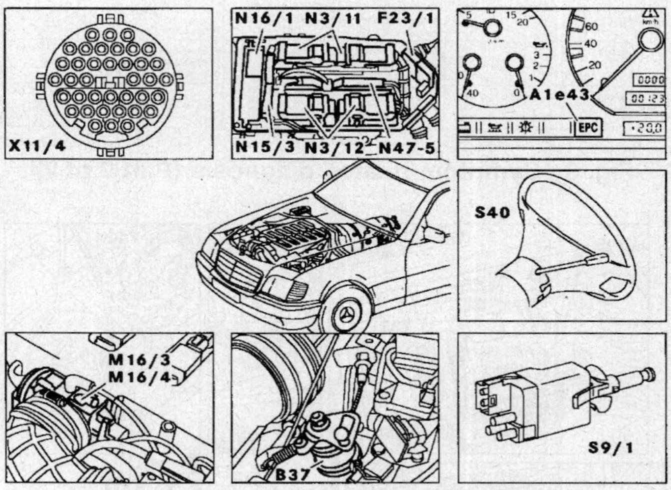

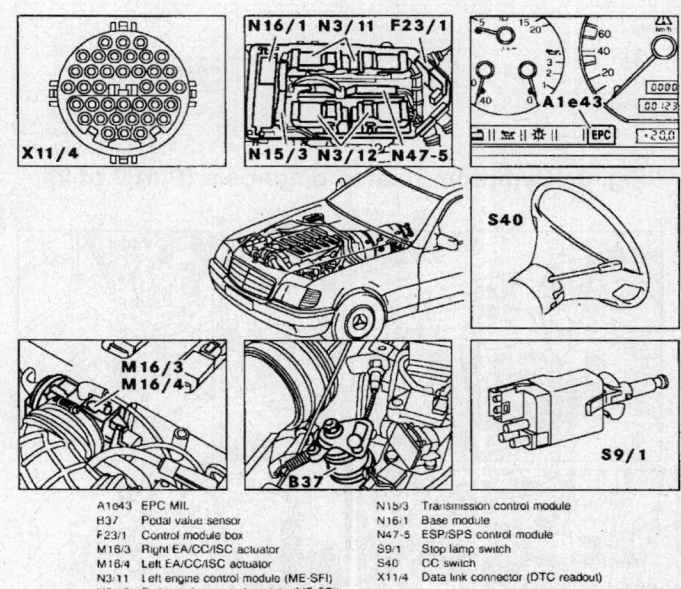

A1e43 EPC MIL
B37 Pedal value sensor
F23/1 Control module box
M16/3 Right EA/CC/ISC actuator
M16/4 Left EA/CC/ISC actuator
N3/11 Left engine control module (ME-SFI)
N3/12 Right engine control module (ME-SFI)
N15/3 Transmission control module
N16/1 Base module
N47-5 ESP/SPS control module
S9/1 Stop lamp switch
S40 CC switch
X11/4 Data link connector (DTC readout)

MB1029500390040X

Fig. 5 ME engine management component locations (Part 4 of 5). 1998–99 CL600 & S600

A1e26 "CHECK ENGINE" MIL (only USA)
X11/22 Diagnostic module (OBD II) generic scan tool connector (only USA)

MB1029500390050X

Fig. 5 ME engine management component locations (Part 5 of 5). 1998–99 CL600 & S600

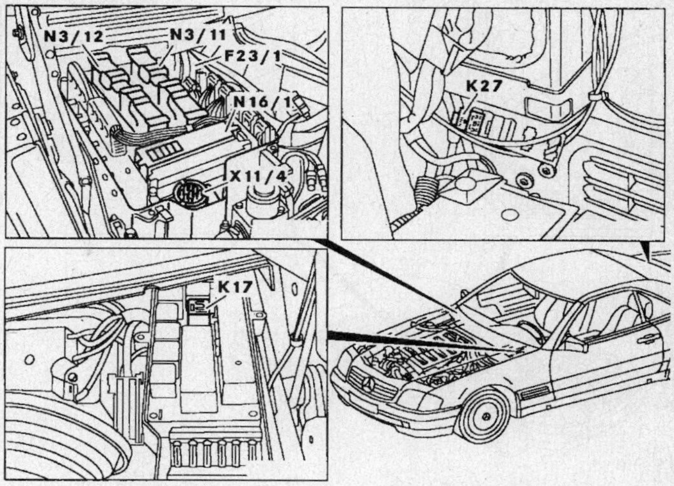

F23/1 Control module box
K17 AIR relay module
K27 FP relay module
N3/11 Left engine control module (ME-SFI)
N3/12 Right engine control module (ME-SFI)
N16/1 Base module
X11/4 Data link connector (DTC readout)

MB1029500389010X

Fig. 6 ME engine management component locations (Part 1 of 5). SL600

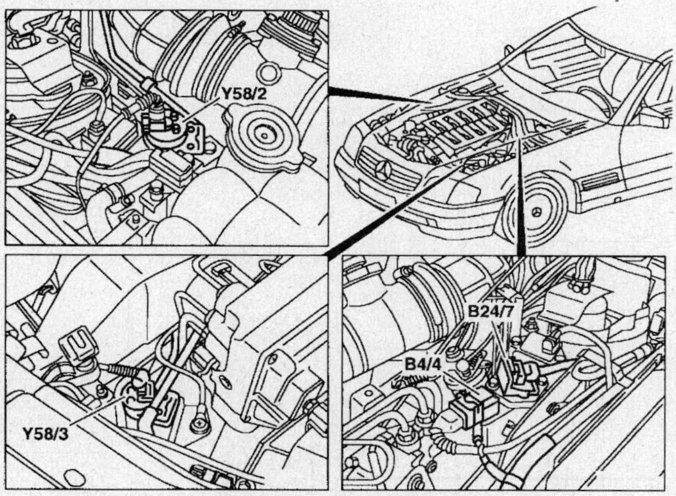

B4/4 Purge control pressure sensor
B24/7 Body acceleration sensor
Y58/2 Left purge control valve
Y58/3 Right purge control valve

MB1029500389020X

Fig. 6 ME engine management component locations (Part 2 of 5). SL600

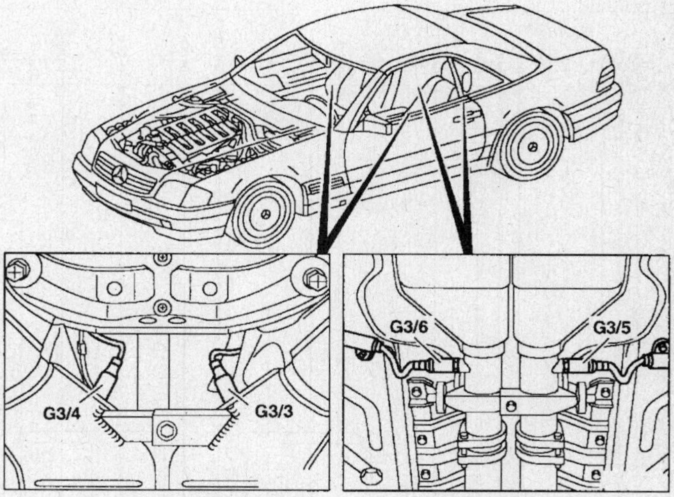

G3/3 Left O2S 1 (before TWC)
G3/4 Right O2S 1 (before TWC)
G3/5 Left O2S 2 (after TWC)
G3/6 Right O2S 2 (after TWC)

MB1029500389030X

Fig. 6 ME engine management component locations (Part 3 of 5). SL600

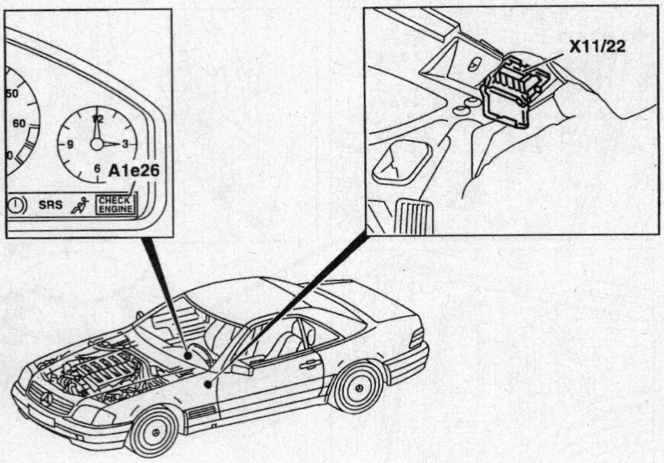

A1e26 "CHECK ENGINE" MIL (only USA)
X11/22 Diagnostic module (OBD II) generic scan tool connector (only USA)

MB1029500389040X

Fig. 6 ME engine management component locations (Part 4 of 5). SL600

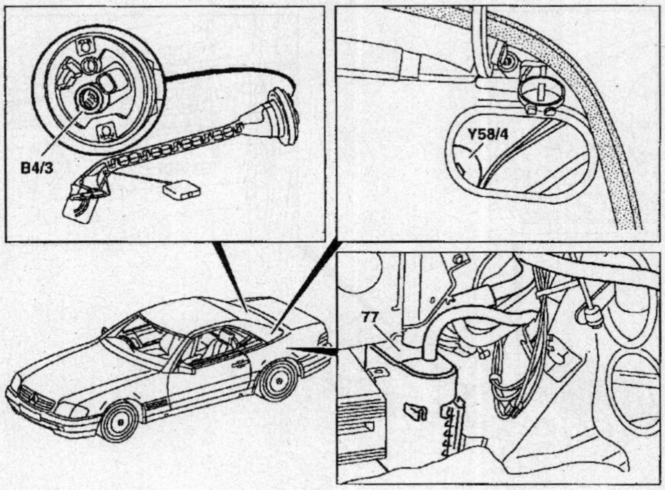

B4/3 Fuel tank pressure sensor (only USA, as of 09/97)
Y58/4 Activated charcoal canister shut-off valve (only USA, as of 09/97)
77 Activated charcoal canister

MB1029500389050X

Fig. 6 ME engine management component locations (Part 5 of 5). SL600

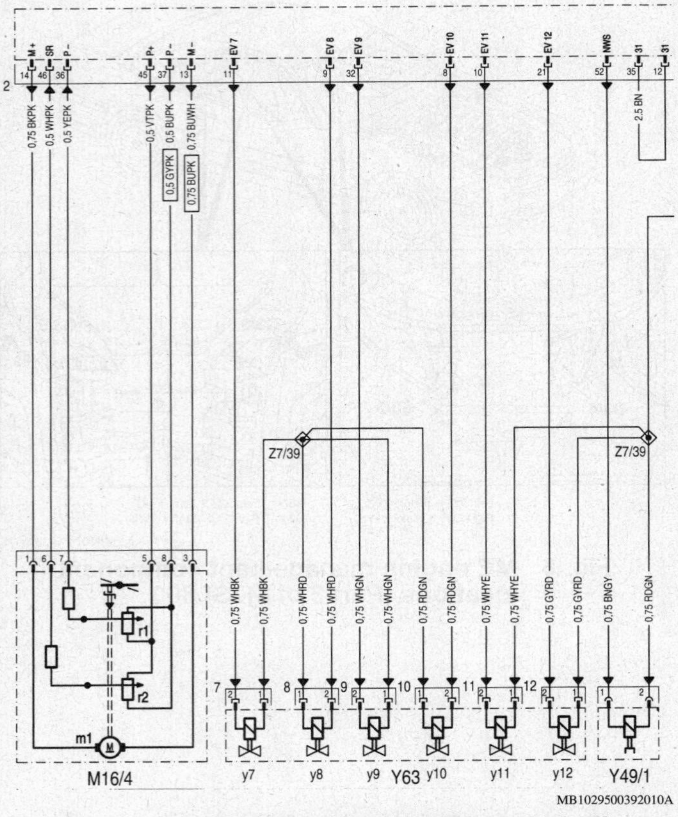

MB1029500392010A

Fig. 7 ME-SFI wiring diagram (Part 1 of 17). 1998–99 CL600 & S600

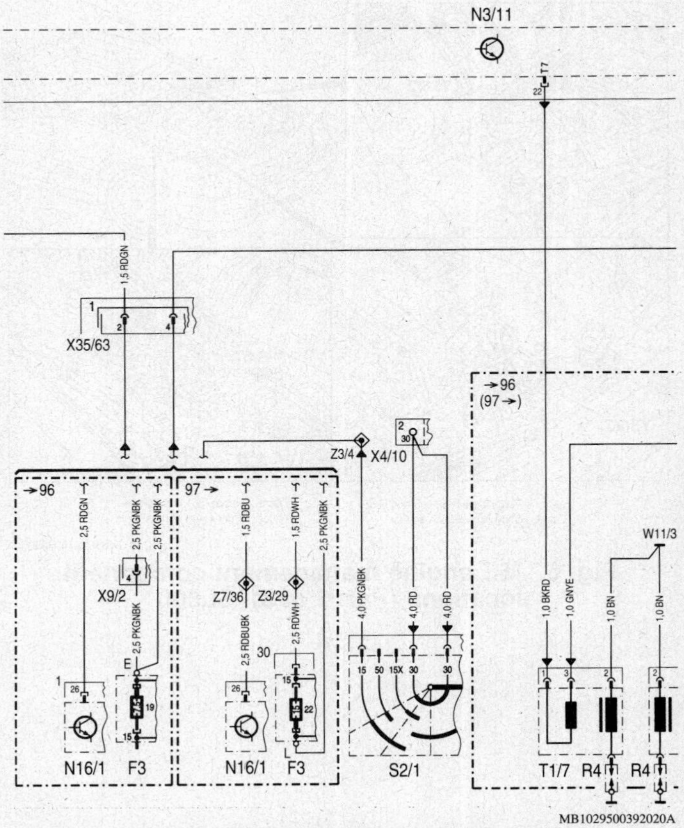

MB1029500392020A

Fig. 7 ME-SFI wiring diagram (Part 2 of 17). 1998–99 CL600 & S600

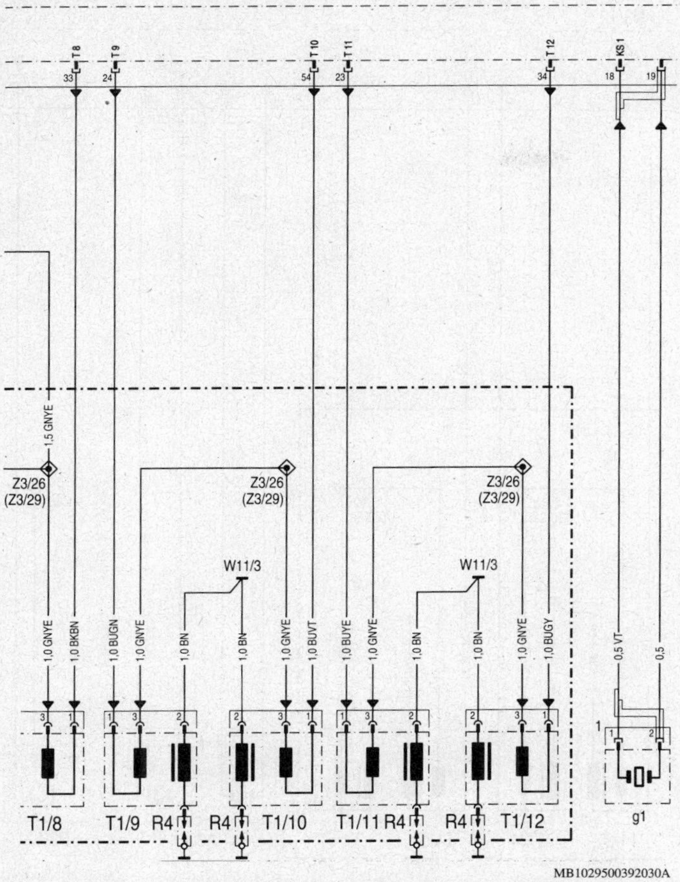

Fig. 7 ME-SFI wiring diagram (Part 3 of 17). 1998–99 CL600 & S600

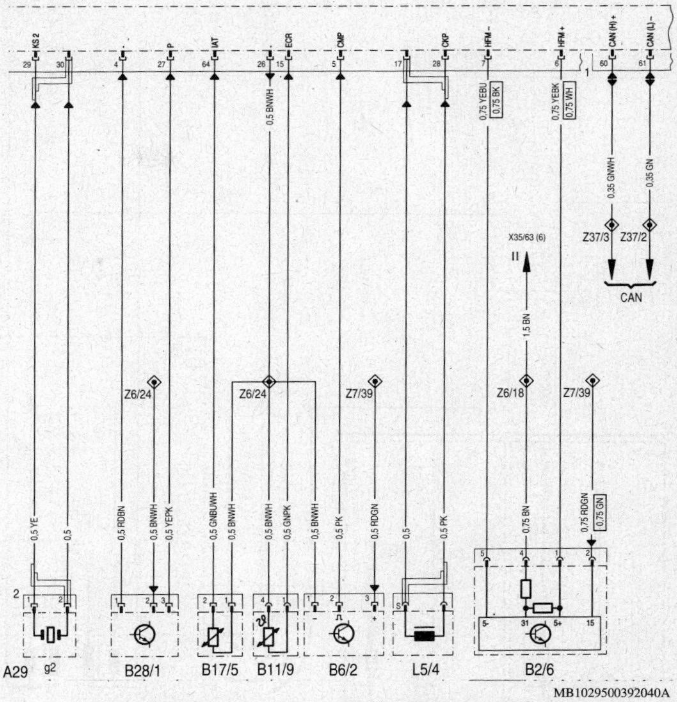

Fig. 7 ME-SFI wiring diagram (Part 4 of 17). 1998–99 CL600 & S600

A29	Left knock sensors
A29g1	Left KS 1
A29g2	Left KS 2
B2/6	Left hot film MAF sensor (located on right side of engine)
B6/2	Left camshaft Hall-effect sensor
B11/9	Left ECT sensor
B17/5	Left IAT sensor (located on right side of engine)
B28/1	Left pressure sensor
F3	Fuse box (35-fuse, in fuse and relay box F1)
F3f19	Fuse 19
F3f22	Fuse 22
L5/4	Left CKP sensor
M16/4	Left EA/CC/ISC actuator (located on right side of engine)
M16/4m1	Actuator motor
M16/4r1	Actual value potentiometer
M16/4r2	Actual value potentiometer
N3/11	Left engine control module (ME-SFI)
N16/1	Base module (BM)
R4	Spark plugs
S2/1	Ignition/starter switch
T1/7	Ignition coil 7
T1/8	Ignition coil 8
T1/9	Ignition coil 9
T1/10	Ignition coil 10
T1/11	Ignition coil 11
T1/12	Ignition coil 12
W11/3	Ground (engine-left side)
	Ground location without designation, component grounded directly on engine, chassis or body.
X4/10	Terminal block (circuit 30/30Ü)
X9/2	Connector (circuit 30/15)
X35/63	Control module box/engine separation point
Y49/1	Left adjustable camshaft timing solenoid
Y63	Left injectors (LH-SFI)
Y63y7	Injector (cylinder 7)
Y63y8	Injector (cylinder 8)
Y63y9	Injector (cylinder 9)
Y63y10	Injector (cylinder 10)
Y63y11	Injector (cylinder 11)
Y63y12	Injector (cylinder 12)
Z3/4	Circuit 15 (unfused) connector sleeve (feed from ignition/starter switch - S2/1)
Z3/26	Circuit 15 (unfused) connector sleeve
Z3/29	Circuit 15 connector sleeve, (fused)
Z6/18	Electronics ground connector sleeve
Z6/24	Left sensor ground connector sleeve
Z7/36	Circuit 87 M2e connector sleeve
Z7/39	Circuit 87 M2i connector sleeve
Z37/2	Engine CAN-Bus (low) connector sleeve
Z37/3	Engine CAN-Bus (high) connector sleeve

MB1029500392050A

Fig. 7 ME-SFI wiring diagram (Part 5 of 17). 1998–99 CL600 & S600

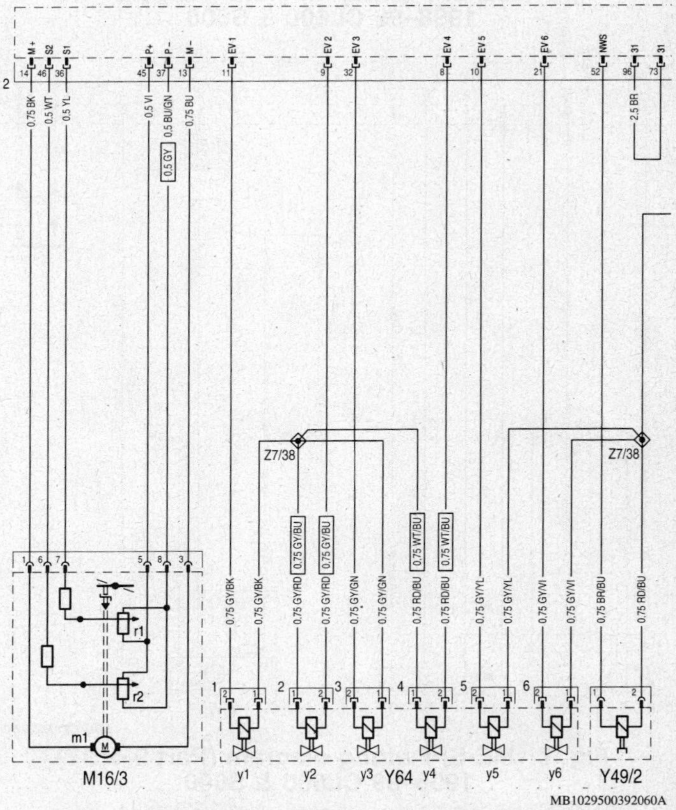

Fig. 7 ME-SFI wiring diagram (Part 6 of 17). 1998–99 CL600 & S600

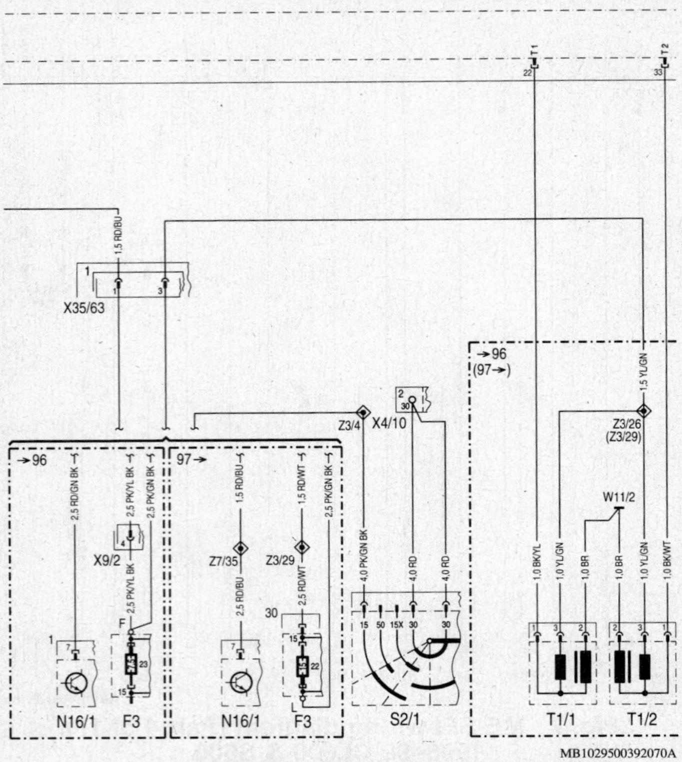

Fig. 7 ME-SFI wiring diagram (Part 7 of 17). 1998–99 CL600 & S600

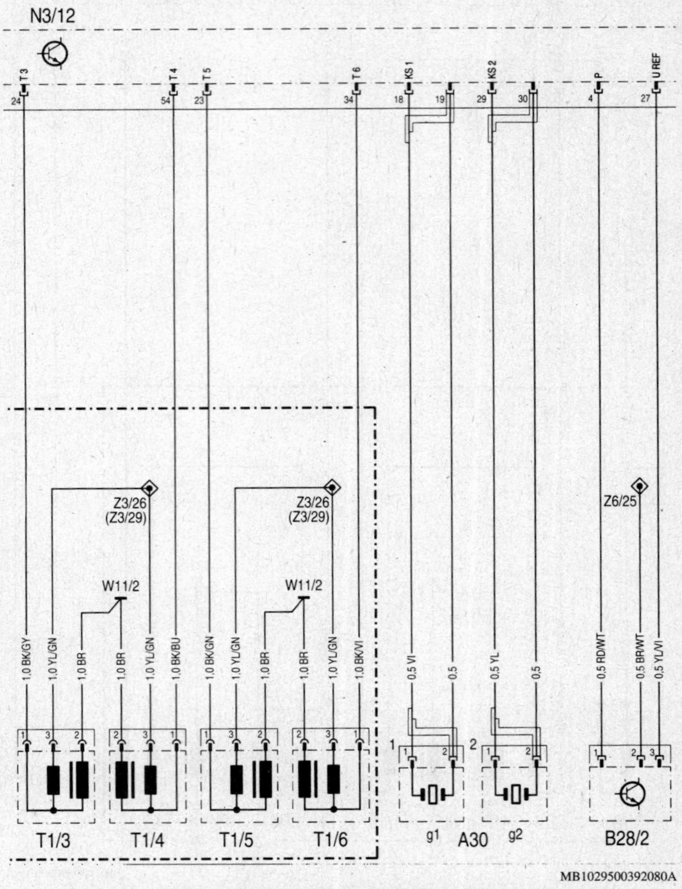

Fig. 7 ME-SFI wiring diagram (Part 8 of 17). 1998–99 CL600 & S600

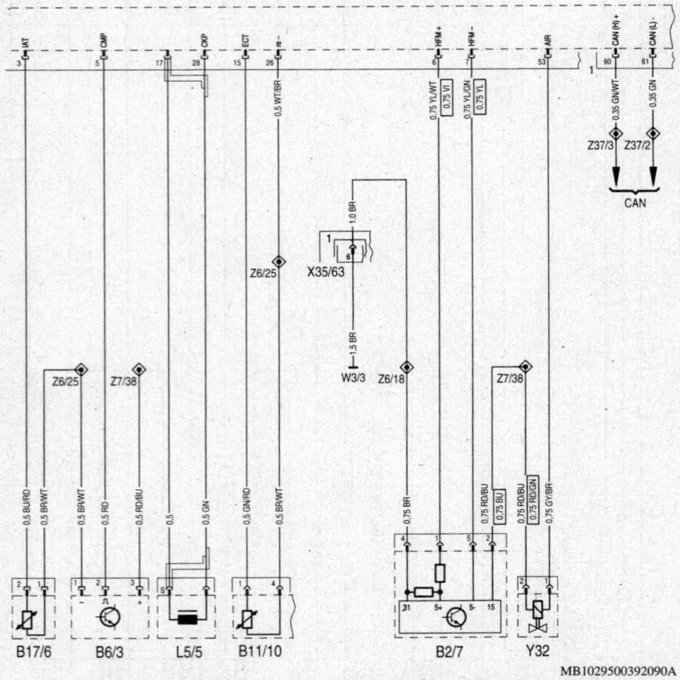

Fig. 7 ME-SFI wiring diagram (Part 9 of 17). 1998–99 CL600 & S600

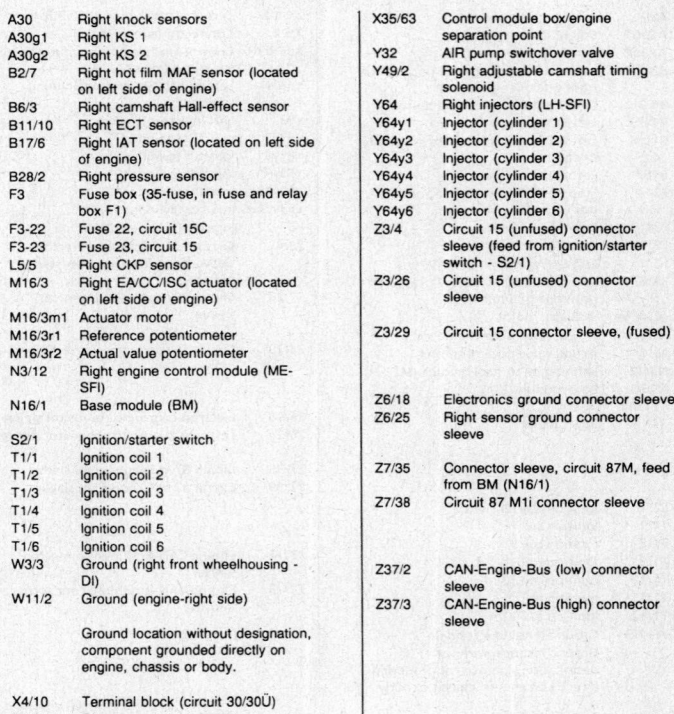

A30	Right knock sensors
A30g1	Right KS 1
A30g2	Right KS 2
B2/7	Right hot film MAF sensor (located on left side of engine)
B6/3	Right camshaft Hall-effect sensor
B11/10	Right ECT sensor
B17/6	Right IAT sensor (located on left side of engine)
B28/2	Right pressure sensor
F3	Fuse box (35-fuse, in fuse and relay box F1)
F3-22	Fuse 22, circuit 15C
F3-23	Fuse 23, circuit 15
L5/5	Right CKP sensor
M16/3	Right EA/CC/ISC actuator (located on left side of engine)
M16/3m1	Actuator motor
M16/3r1	Reference potentiometer
M16/3r2	Actual value potentiometer
N3/12	Right engine control module (ME-SFI)
N16/1	Base module (BM)
S2/1	Ignition/starter switch
T1/1	Ignition coil 1
T1/2	Ignition coil 2
T1/3	Ignition coil 3
T1/4	Ignition coil 4
T1/5	Ignition coil 5
T1/6	Ignition coil 6
W3/3	Ground (right front wheelhousing - DI)
W11/2	Ground (engine-right side)
	Ground location without designation, component grounded directly on engine, chassis or body.
X4/10	Terminal block (circuit 30/30Ü)
X9/2	Connector (circuit 30/15)
X35/63	Control module box/engine separation point
Y32	AIR pump switchover valve
Y49/2	Right adjustable camshaft timing solenoid
Y64	Right injectors (LH-SFI)
Y64y1	Injector (cylinder 1)
Y64y2	Injector (cylinder 2)
Y64y3	Injector (cylinder 3)
Y64y4	Injector (cylinder 4)
Y64y5	Injector (cylinder 5)
Y64y6	Injector (cylinder 6)
Z3/4	Circuit 15 (unfused) connector sleeve (feed from ignition/starter switch - S2/1)
Z3/26	Circuit 15 (unfused) connector sleeve
Z3/29	Circuit 15 connector sleeve, (fused)
Z6/18	Electronics ground connector sleeve
Z6/25	Right sensor ground connector sleeve
Z7/35	Connector sleeve, circuit 87M, feed from BM (N16/1)
Z7/38	Circuit 87 M1i connector sleeve
Z37/2	CAN-Engine-Bus (low) connector sleeve
Z37/3	CAN-Engine-Bus (high) connector sleeve

MB1029500392100A

Fig. 7 ME-SFI wiring diagram (Part 10 of 17). 1998–99 CL600 & S600

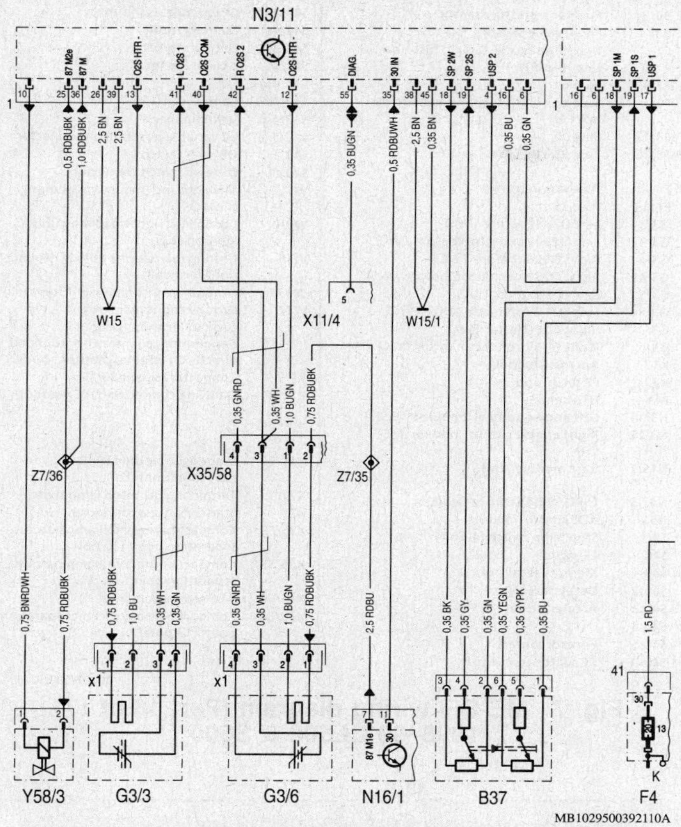

Fig. 7 ME-SFI wiring diagram (Part 11 of 17). 1998–99 CL600 & S600

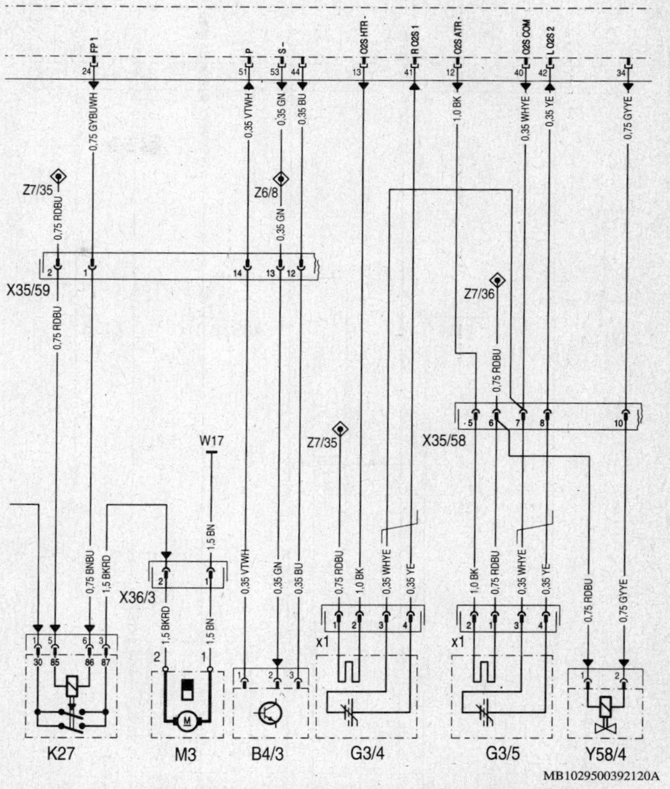

Fig. 7 ME-SFI wiring diagram (Part 12 of 17). 1998–99 CL600 & S600

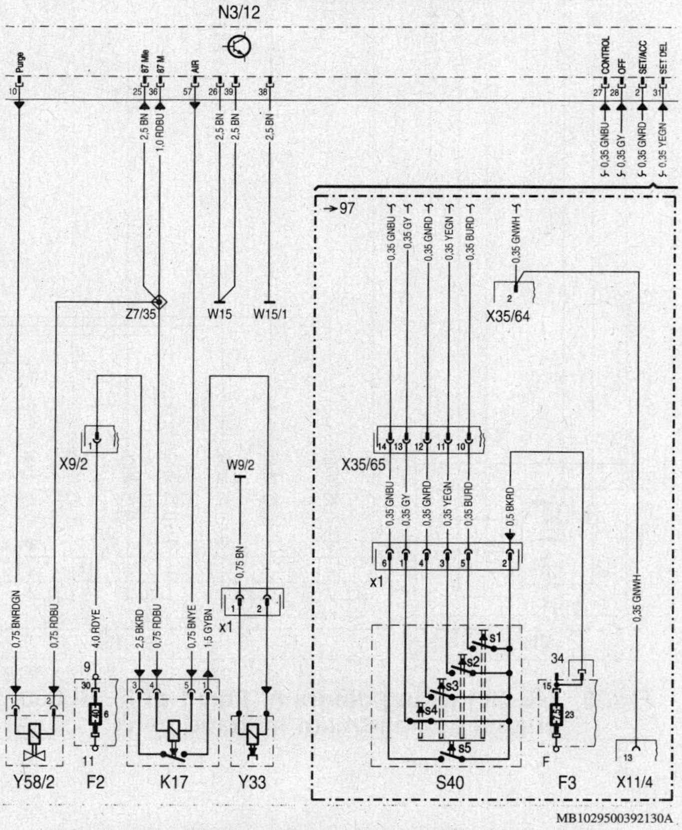

Fig. 7 ME-SFI wiring diagram (Part 13 of 17). 1998–99 CL600 & S600

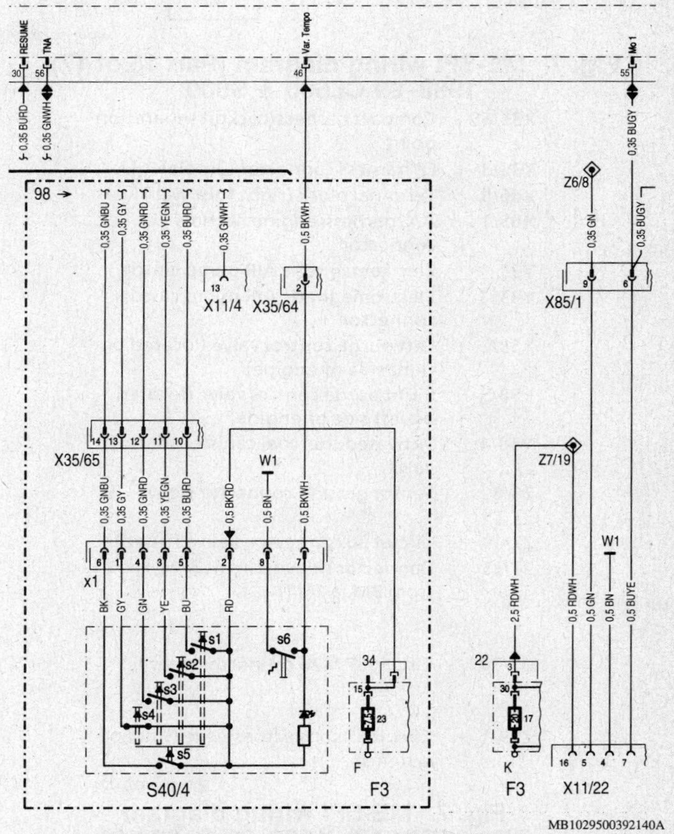

Fig. 7 ME-SFI wiring diagram (Part 14 of 17). 1998–99 CL600 & S600

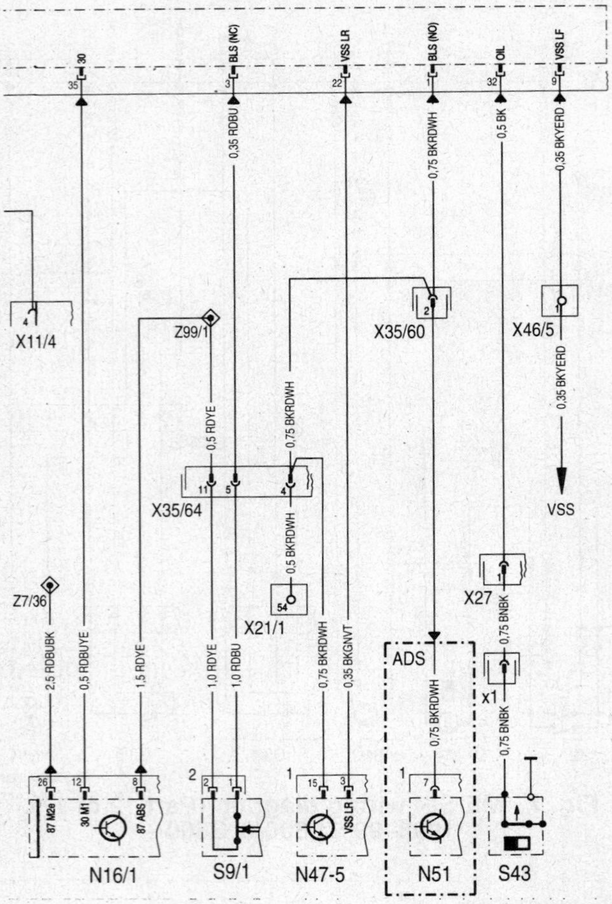

MB1029500392150A

Fig. 7 ME-SFI wiring diagram (Part 15 of 17). 1998–99 CL600 & S600

X35/65	Compact harness/cockpit separation point
X36/3	FP harness connector (2-pole)
X46/5	Terminal block (right foot well)
X85/1	A/C harness/engine harness connector
Y33	Electromagnetic AIR pump clutch
Y33x1	Electromagnetic AIR pump clutch connector
Y58/2	Left purge control valve (located on right side of engine)
Y58/3	Right purge control valve (located on left side of engine)
Y58/4	Activated charcoal canister shut-off valve
Z6/8	Sensor ground connector sleeve
Z7/19	Circuit 30 connector sleeve (fused)
Z7/35	Connector sleeve, circuit 87M, feed from BM (N16/1)
Z7/36	Circuit 87 M2e connector sleeve
Z99/1	Circuit 87 connector sleeve (traction systems)

MB1029500392170A

Fig. 7 ME-SFI wiring diagram (Part 17 of 17). 1998–99 CL600 & S600

B4/3	Fuel tank pressure sensor
B37	Pedal value sensor
F2	Maxi-fuse box (6-fuse, in fuse and relay box F1)
F2f6	Fuse 6
F3	Fuse box (35-fuse, in fuse and relay box F1)
F3f17	Fuse 17
F3f23	Fuse 23
F4	Fuse box in trunk
F4f13	Fuse 13
G3/3	Left O2S 1 (before TWC)
G3/3x1	Left O2S 1 connector (before TWC)
G3/4	Right O2S 1 (before TWC)
G3/4x1	Right O2S 1 connector (before TWC)
G3/5	Left O2S 2 (after TWC)
G3/5x1	Left O2S 2 connector (after TWC)
G3/6	Right O2S 2 (after TWC)
G3/6x1	Right O2S 2 connector (after TWC)
K17	AIR relay module
K27	FP relay module
M3	FP assembly
N3/11	Left engine control module (ME-SFI)
N3/12	Right engine control module (ME-SFI)
N16/1	Base module (BM)
N47-5	ESP/SPS/BAS control module
N51	ADS control module
S9/1	Stop lamp switch (4-pole)
S40	CC switch
S40s1	Memory recall
S40s2	Decelerate/set
S40s3	Accelerate/set
S40s4	Off
S40s5	Control contact
S40x1	CC switch connector
S40/4	CC variable pushbutton
S40/4s1	Memory recall
S40/4s2	Decelerate/set
S40/4s3	Accelerate/set
S40/4s4	Off
S40/4s5	Control contact
S40/4s6	Variable speed
S40/4x1	CC variable pushbutton connector
S43	Oil level switch
S43x1	Oil level switch connector
W1	Main ground (behind instrument cluster)
W9/2	Ground (at right headlamp unit - ignition coil)
W15	Ground (electronics output ground - right footwell)
W15/1	Ground (electronics - right footwell)
W17	Ground (right rear seat)
	Ground location without designation, component grounded directly on engine, chassis or body.
X9/2	Connector (circuit 30/15)
X11/4	Data link connector (DTC readout)
X11/22	Diagnostic module (OBD II) generic scan tool connector
X21/1	Terminal block (stop lamp switch)
X27	Starter harness connector
X35/58	Compact harness/taillamp harness separation point (10-pole)
X35/59	Compact harness/taillamp harness separation point
X35/60	ADS separation point
X35/64	Compact harness/cockpit separation point (18-pole)

MB1029500392160A

Fig. 7 ME-SFI wiring diagram (Part 16 of 17). 1998–99 CL600 & S600

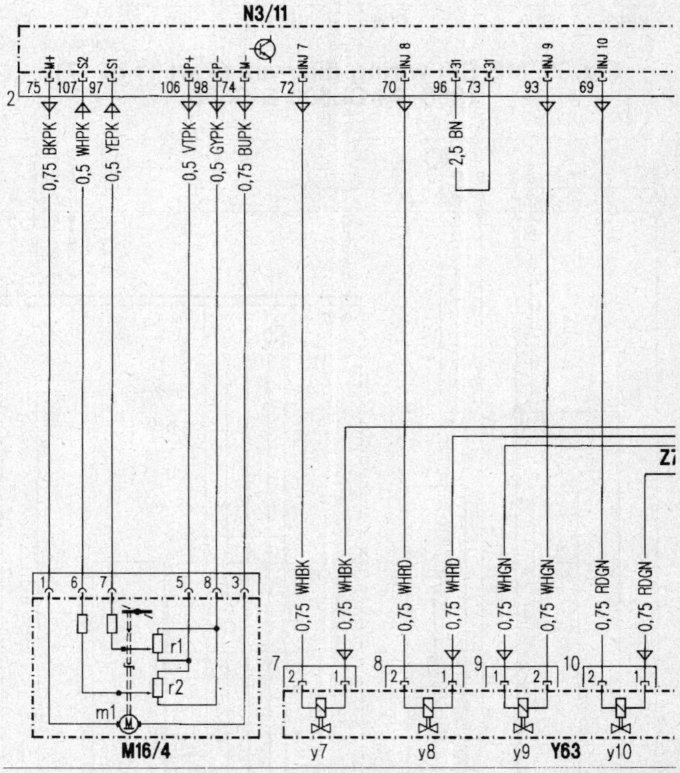

MB1010100230010X

Fig. 8 ME-SFI wiring diagram (Part 1 of 7). SL600 engine compartment lefthand bank

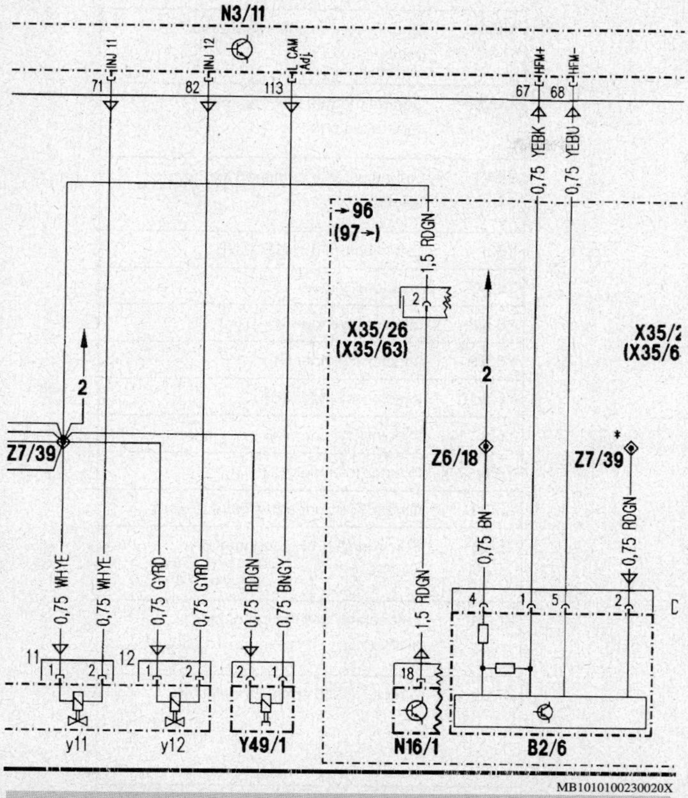

Fig. 8 ME-SFI wiring diagram (Part 2 of 7). SL600 engine compartment lefthand bank

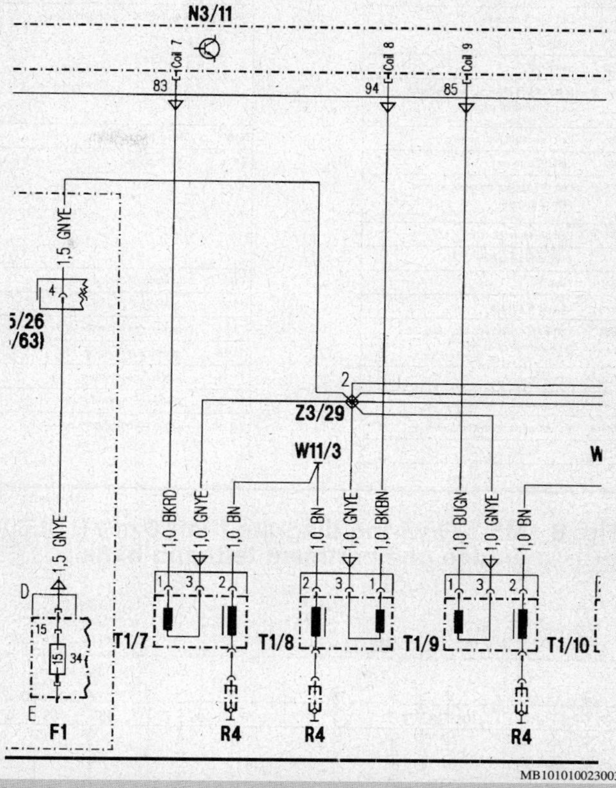

Fig. 8 ME-SFI wiring diagram (Part 3 of 7). SL600 engine compartment lefthand bank

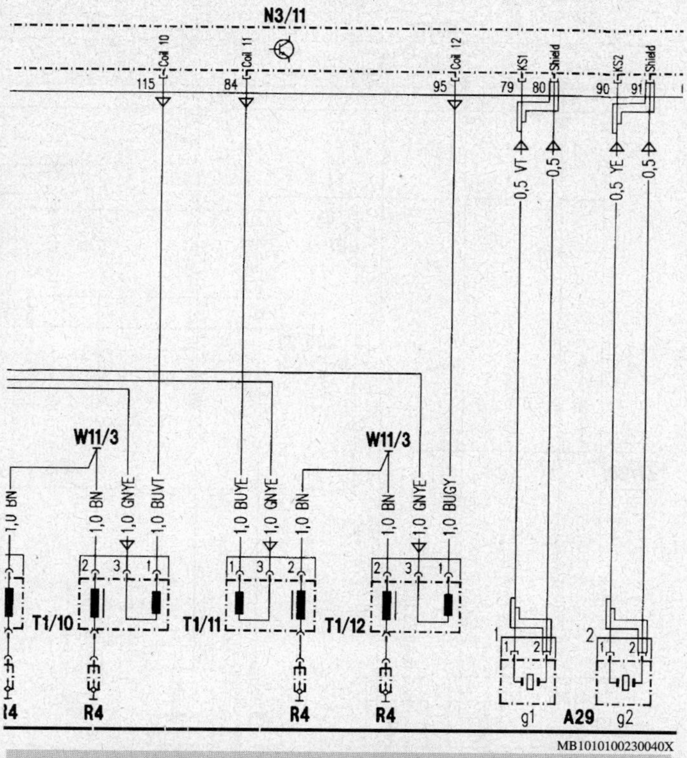

Fig. 8 ME-SFI wiring diagram (Part 4 of 7). SL600 engine compartment lefthand bank

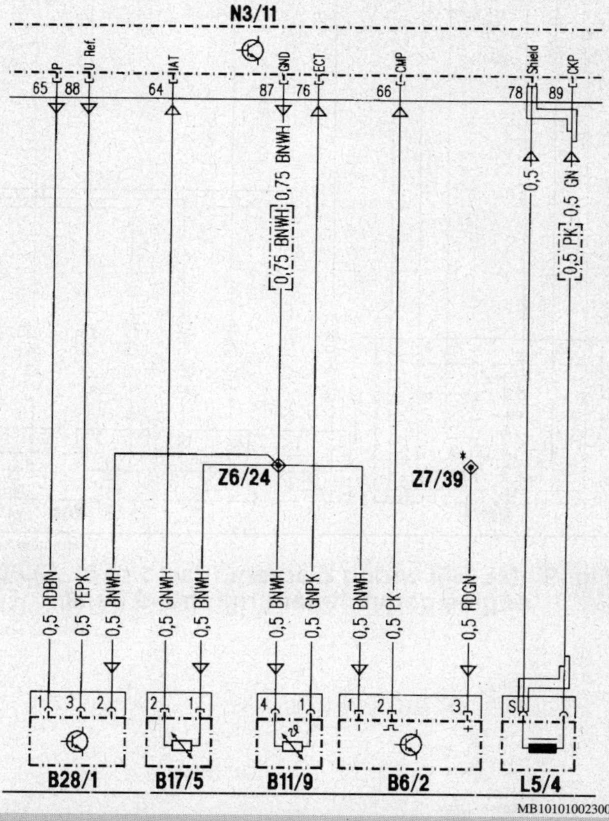

Fig. 8 ME-SFI wiring diagram (Part 5 of 7). SL600 engine compartment lefthand bank

A29	Left knock sensors
A29g1	Left KS 1
A29g2	Left KS 2
B2/6	Left hot film MAF sensor (located on right side of engine)
B6/2	Left camshaft Hall sensor
B11/9	Left ECT sensor
B17/5	Left IAT sensor (located on right side of engine)
B28/1	Left pressure sensor
F1	Fuse and relay box
F1f34	Fuse 34
L5/4	Left CKP sensor
M16/4	Left EA/CC/ISC actuator (located on right side of engine)
M16/4m1	Actuator motor
M16/4r1	Actual value potentiometer
M16/4r2	Actual value potentiometer
N3/11	Left ME-SFI control module
N16/1	Base module (BM)
R4	Spark plugs
T1/7	Ignition coil (cylinder 7)
T1/8	Ignition coil (cylinder 8)
T1/9	Ignition coil (cylinder 9)
T1/10	Ignition coil (cylinder 10)
T1/11	Ignition coil (cylinder 11)
T1/12	Ignition coil (cylinder 12)
W11/3	Ground (engine-left side)

MB1010100230060X

Fig. 8 ME-SFI wiring diagram (Part 6 of 7). SL600 engine compartment lefthand bank

X35/26	Module box/engine separation point
X35/63	Control module box/engine separation point
Y49/1	Left adjustable camshaft timing solenoid
Y63	Left injectors (LH-SFI [LH])
Y63y7	Injector (cylinder 7)
Y63y8	Injector (cylinder 8)
Y63y9	Injector (cylinder 9)
Y63y10	Injector (cylinder 10)
Y63y11	Injector (cylinder 11)
Y63y12	Injector (cylinder 12)
Z3/29	Circuit 15 connector sleeve (fused)
Z6/18	Electronics ground connector sleeve
Z6/24	Left sensor ground connector sleeve
Z7/39	Circuit 87 M2i connector sleeve

MB1010100230070X

Fig. 8 ME-SFI wiring diagram (Part 7 of 7). SL600 engine compartment lefthand bank

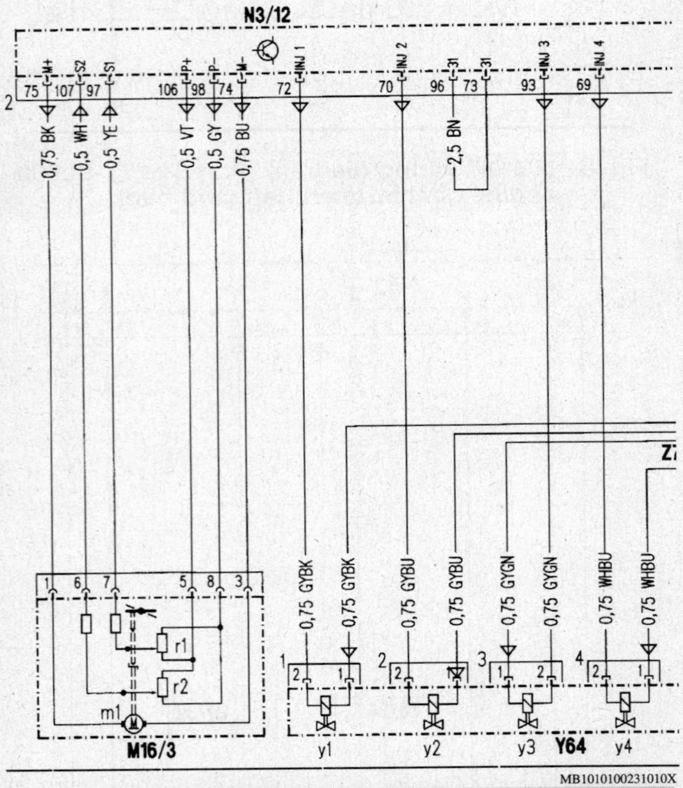

MB1010100231010X

Fig. 9 ME-SFI wiring diagram (Part 1 of 8). SL600 engine compartment righthand bank

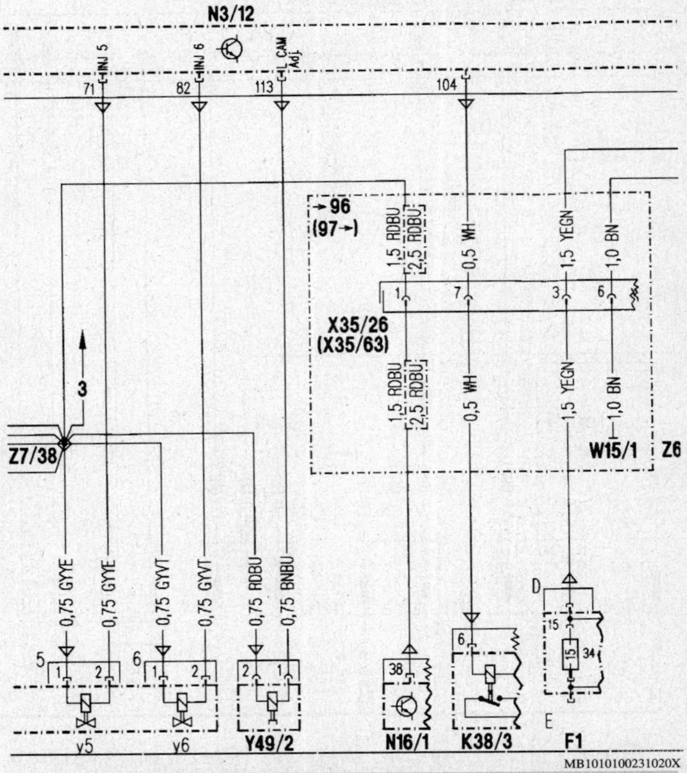

MB1010100231020X

Fig. 9 ME-SFI wiring diagram (Part 2 of 8). SL600 engine compartment righthand bank

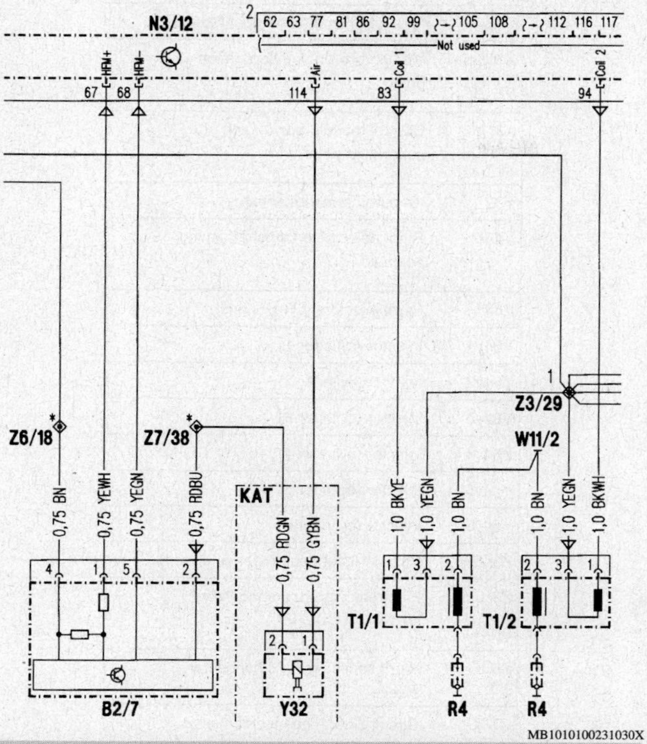

Fig. 9 ME-SFI wiring diagram (Part 3 of 8). SL600 engine compartment righthand bank

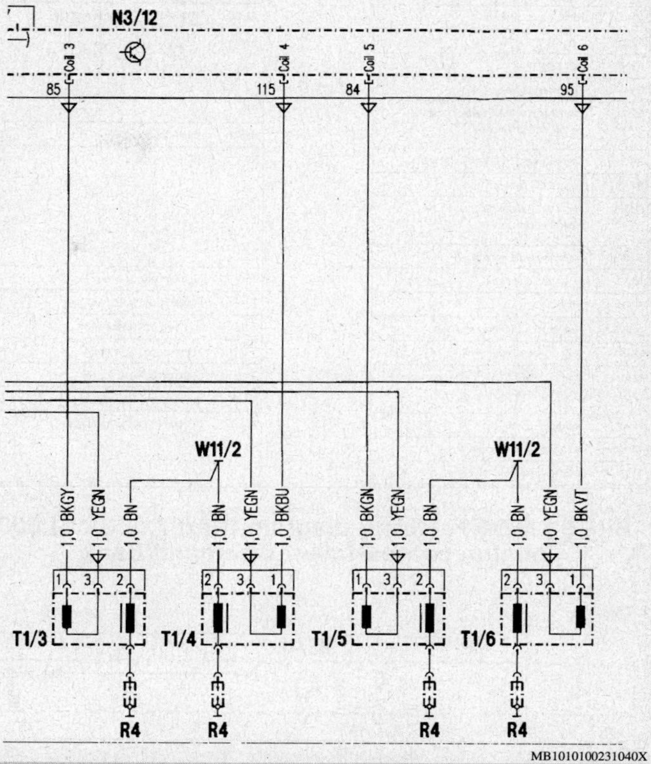

Fig. 9 ME-SFI wiring diagram (Part 4 of 8). SL600 engine compartment righthand bank

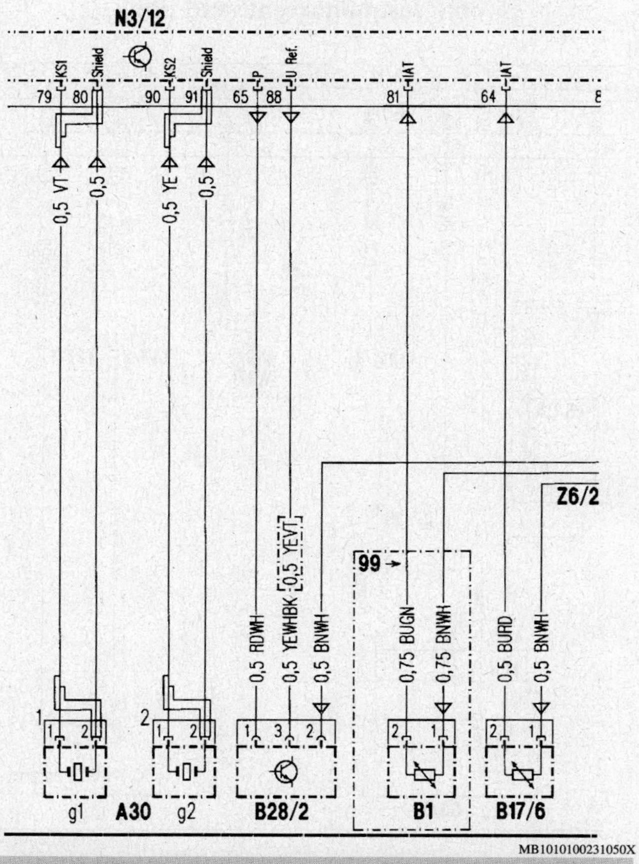

Fig. 9 ME-SFI wiring diagram (Part 5 of 8). SL600 engine compartment righthand bank

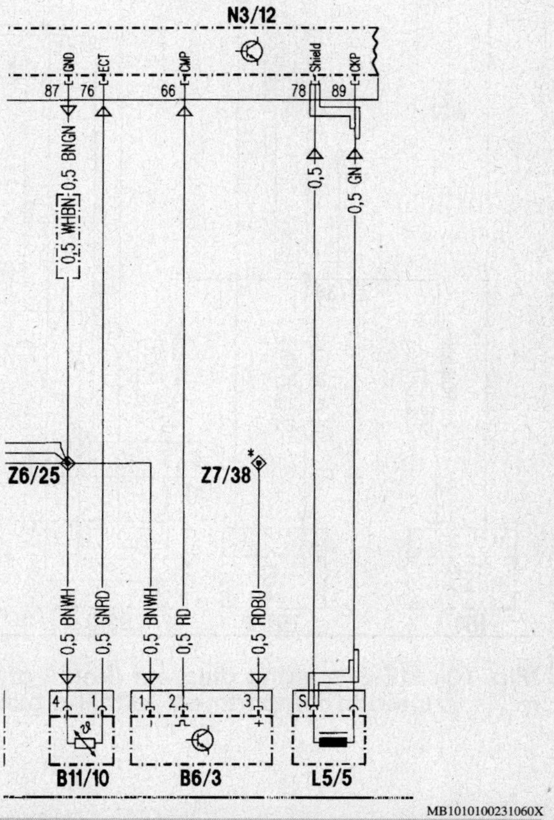

Fig. 9 ME-SFI wiring diagram (Part 6 of 8). SL600 engine compartment righthand bank

A30	Right knock sensors
A30g1	Left KS 1
A30g2	Left KS 2
B1	Oil temperature sensor
B2/7	Right hot film MAF sensor (located on left side of engine)
B6/3	Right camshaft Hall-effect sensor
B11/10	Right ECT sensor
B17/6	Right IAT sensor (located on left side of engine)
B28/2	Right pressure sensor
F1	Fuse and relay box
F1f34	Fuse 34
K38/3	Starter lock-out relay module
L5/5	Right CKP sensor
M16/3	Right EA/CC/ISC actuator (located on left side of engine)
M16/3m1	Actuator motor
M16/3r1	Reference potentiometer
M16/3r2	Actual value potentiometer

N3/12	Right ME-SFI control module
N16/1	Base module (BM)
R4	Spark plugs
T1/1	Ignition coil (cylinder 1)
T1/2	Ignition coil (cylinder 2)
T1/3	Ignition coil (cylinder 3)
T1/4	Ignition coil (cylinder 4)
T1/5	Ignition coil (cylinder 5)
T1/6	Ignition coil (cylinder 6)
W11/2	Ground (engine-right side)

MB1010100231070X

Fig. 9 ME-SFI wiring diagram (Part 7 of 8). SL600 engine compartment righthand bank

W15/1	Ground (electronics - right footwell)
X35/26	Module box/engine separation point
X35/63	Control module box/engine separation point
Y32	Air pump switchover valve
Y49/2	Right adjustable camshaft timing solenoid
Y64	Right injectors (LH-SFI [LH])
Y64y1	Injector (cylinder 1)
Y64y2	Injector (cylinder 2)
Y64y3	Injector (cylinder 3)
Y64y4	Injector (cylinder 4)
Y64y5	Injector (cylinder 5)
Y64y6	Injector (cylinder 6)
Z3/29	Circuit 15 connector sleeve (fused)
Z6/18	Electronics ground connector sleeve
Z6/25	Right sensor ground connector sleeve
Z7/38	Circuit 87 M1i connector sleeve

MB1010100231080X

Fig. 9 ME-SFI wiring diagram (Part 8 of 8). SL600 engine compartment righthand bank

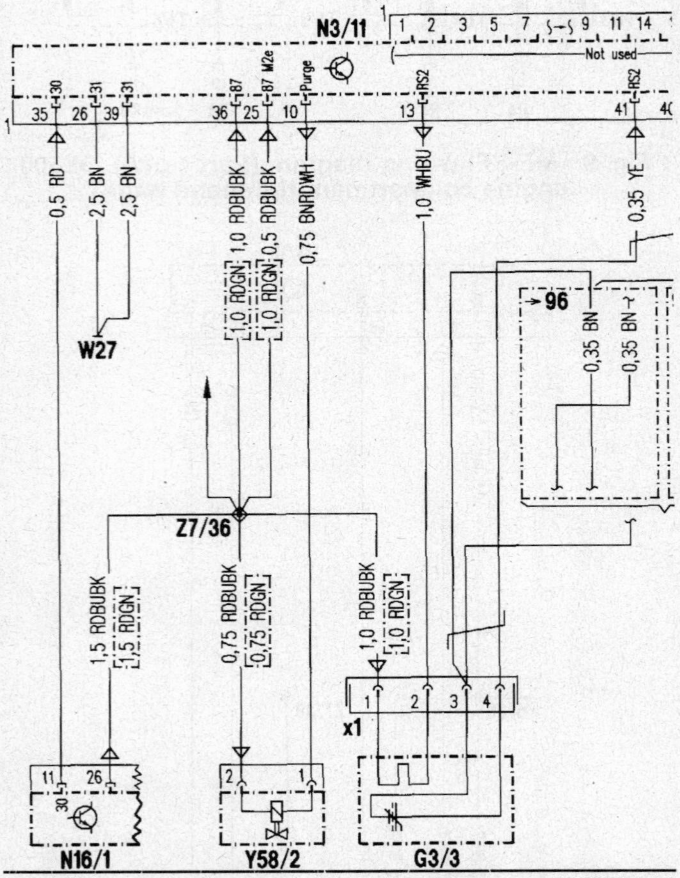

MB1010100233010X

Fig. 10 ME-SFI wiring diagram (Part 1 of 4). SL600 interior compartment lefthand bank

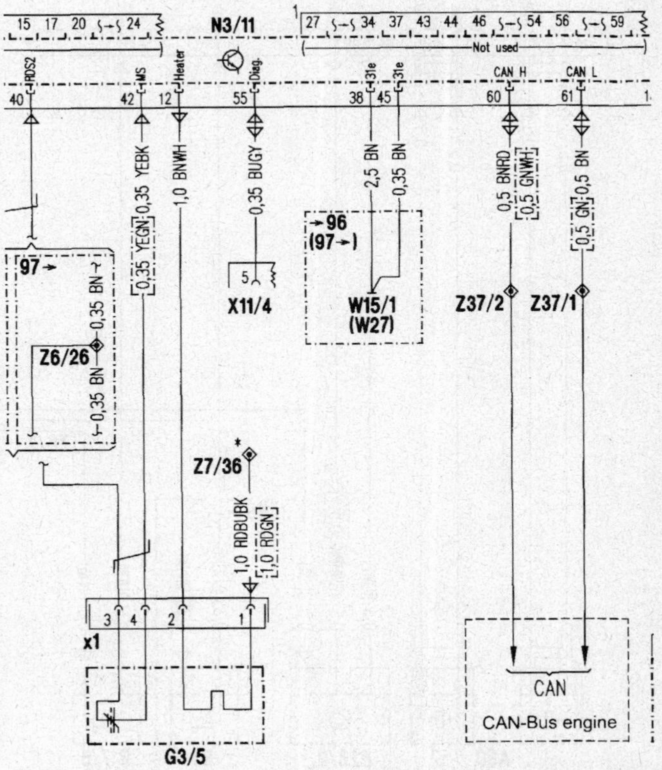

MB1010100233020X

Fig. 10 ME-SFI wiring diagram (Part 2 of 4). SL600 interior compartment lefthand bank

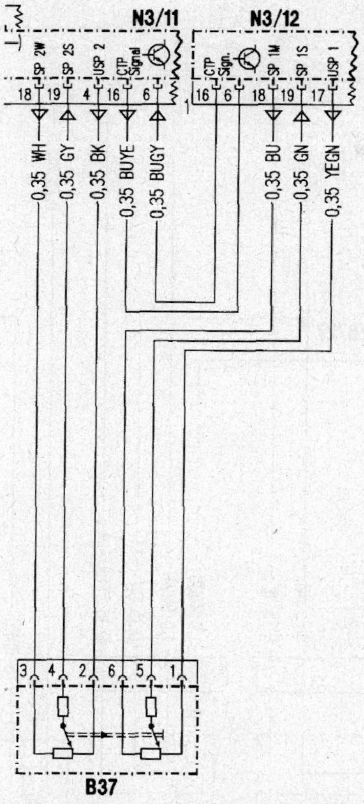

Fig. 10 ME-SFI wiring diagram (Part 3 of 4). SL600 interior compartment lefthand bank

B37	Pedal value sensor	18L
G3/3	Left O2S 1 (before TWC)	6L
G3/3x1	Left O2S 1 connector (before TWC)	5J
G3/5	Left O2S 2 (after TWC)	10L
G3/5x1	Left O2S 2 connector (after TWC)	9J
N3/11	Left ME-SFI control module	5A 11A 18A
N3/12	Right ME-SFI control module	20A
N16/1	Base module (BM)	1L
W15/1	Ground (electronics - right footwell)	13E
W27	Ground (control module box/module box)	2E 13E
X11/4	Diagnostic test clutch	11E
Y58/2	Left purge control valve (located on right side of engine)	4L
Z6/26	Sensor ground connector sleeve	9F
Z7/36	Circuit 87 M2e connector sleeve	3G 11G
Z37/1	CAN-Interior-Bus (high) connector sleeve	15E
Z37/2	Engine CAN-Bus (low) connector sleeve	14E

MB1010100233040X

Fig. 10 ME-SFI wiring diagram (Part 4 of 4). SL600 interior compartment lefthand bank

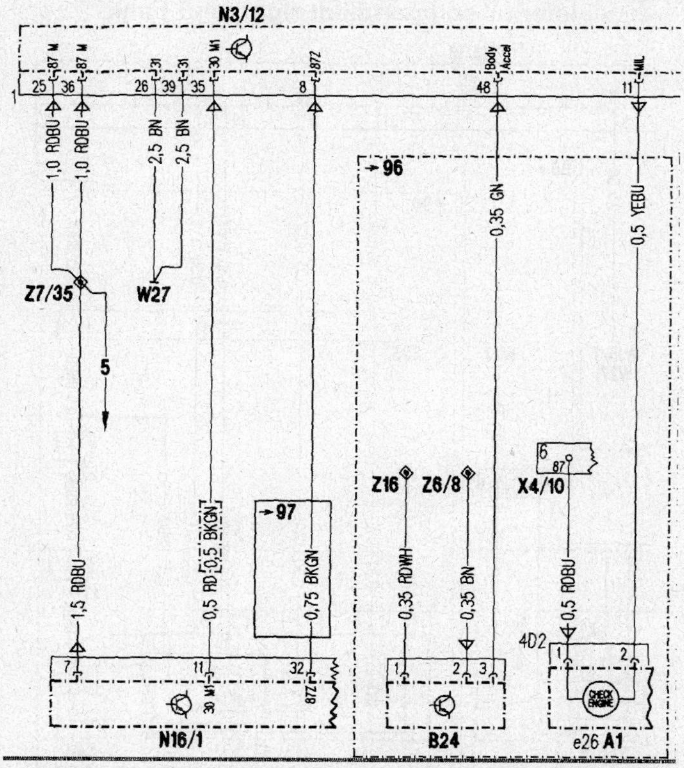

Fig. 11 ME-SFI wiring diagram (Part 1 of 12). SL600 interior compartment righthand bank

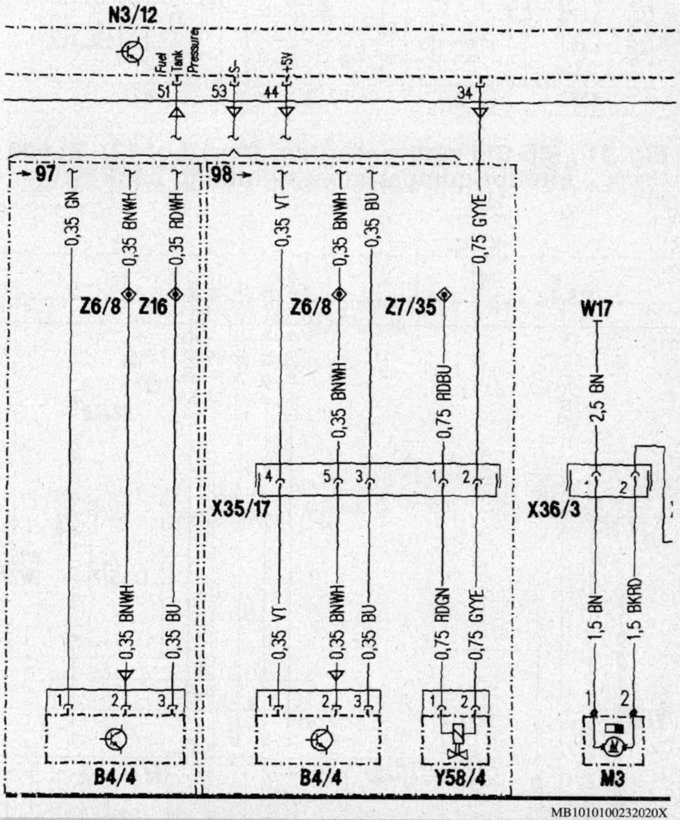

Fig. 11 ME-SFI wiring diagram (Part 2 of 12). SL600 interior compartment righthand bank

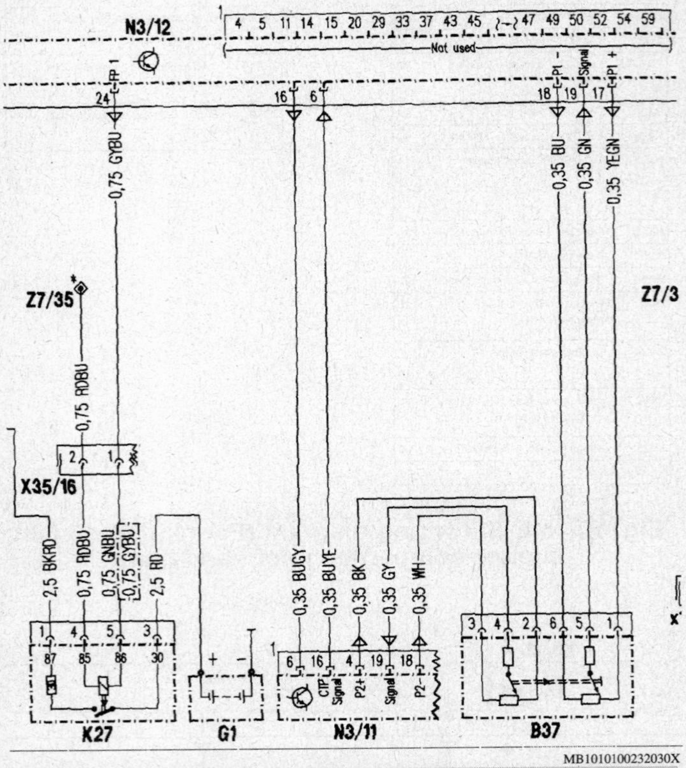

Fig. 11 ME-SFI wiring diagram (Part 3 of 12). SL600 interior compartment righthand bank

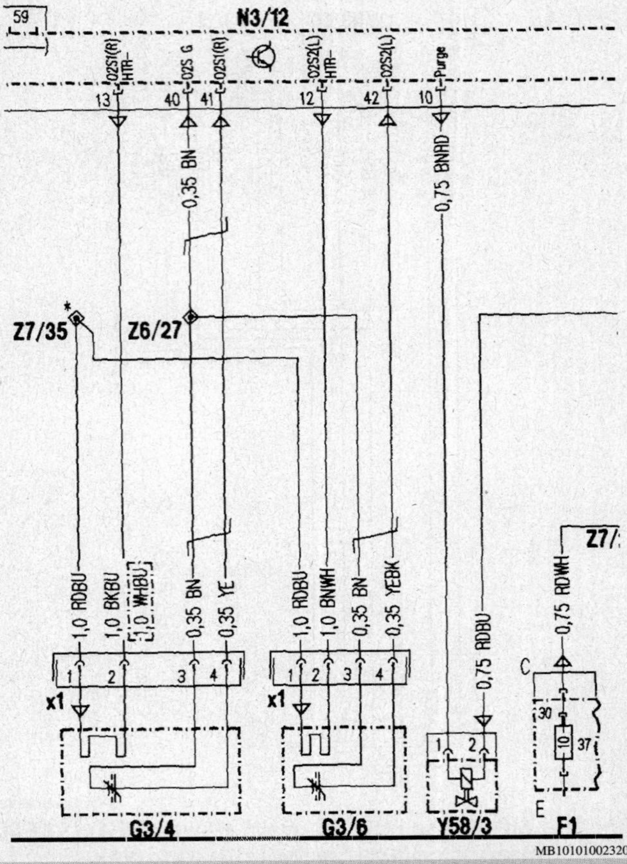

Fig. 11 ME-SFI wiring diagram (Part 4 of 12). SL600 interior compartment righthand bank

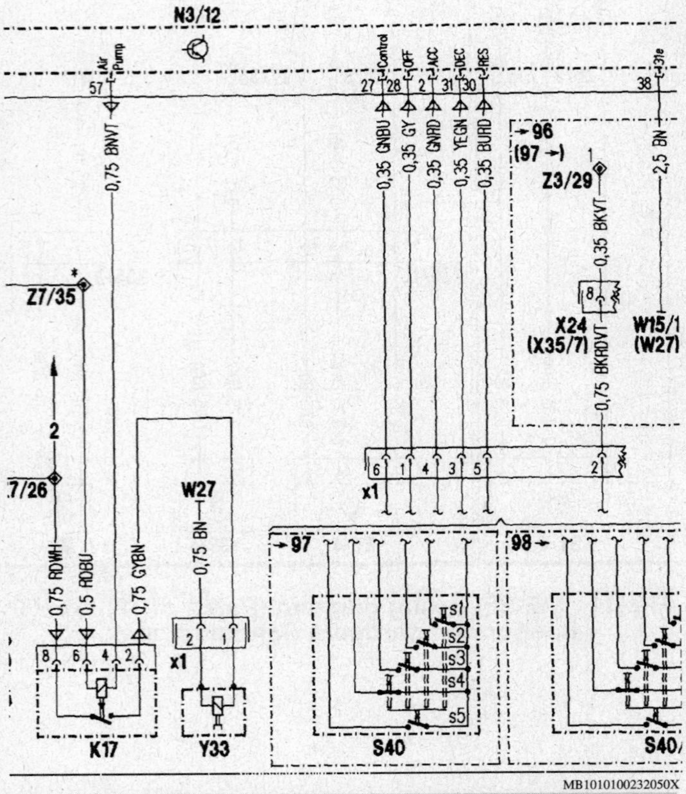

Fig. 11 ME-SFI wiring diagram (Part 5 of 12). SL600 interior compartment righthand bank

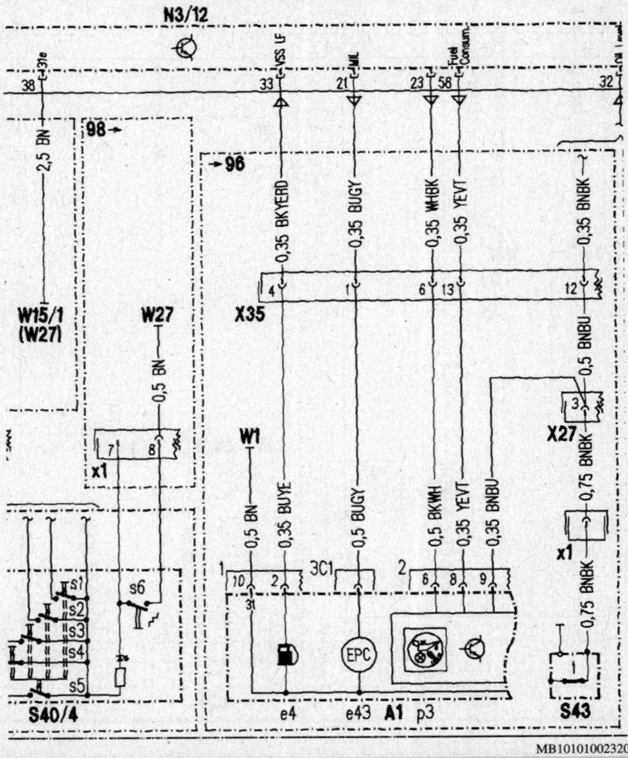

Fig. 11 ME-SFI wiring diagram (Part 6 of 12). SL600 interior compartment righthand bank

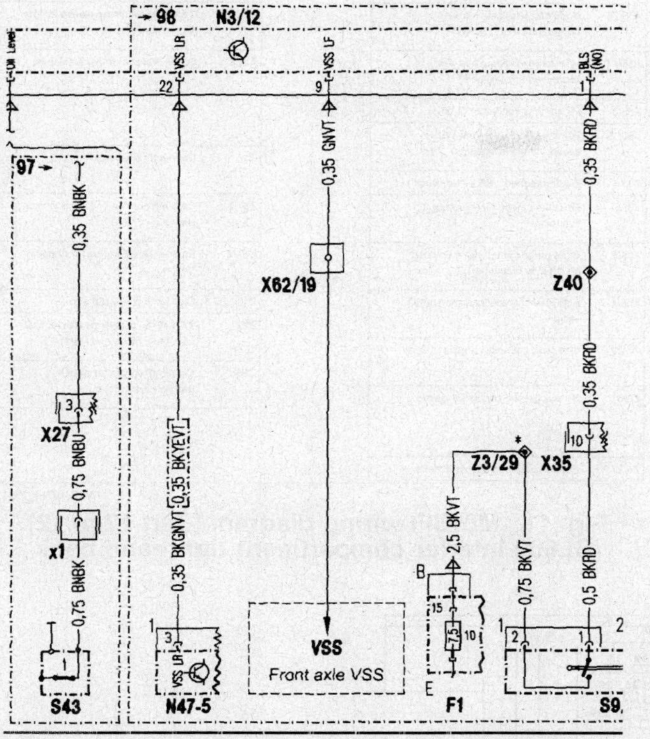

Fig. 11 ME-SFI wiring diagram (Part 7 of 12). SL600 interior compartment righthand bank

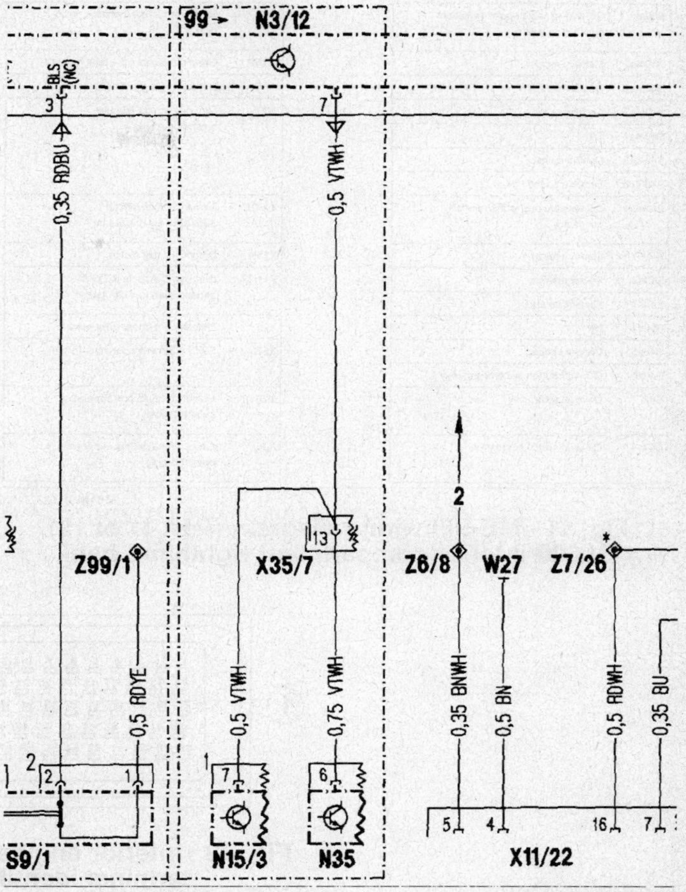

Fig. 11 ME-SFI wiring diagram (Part 8 of 12). SL600 interior compartment righthand bank

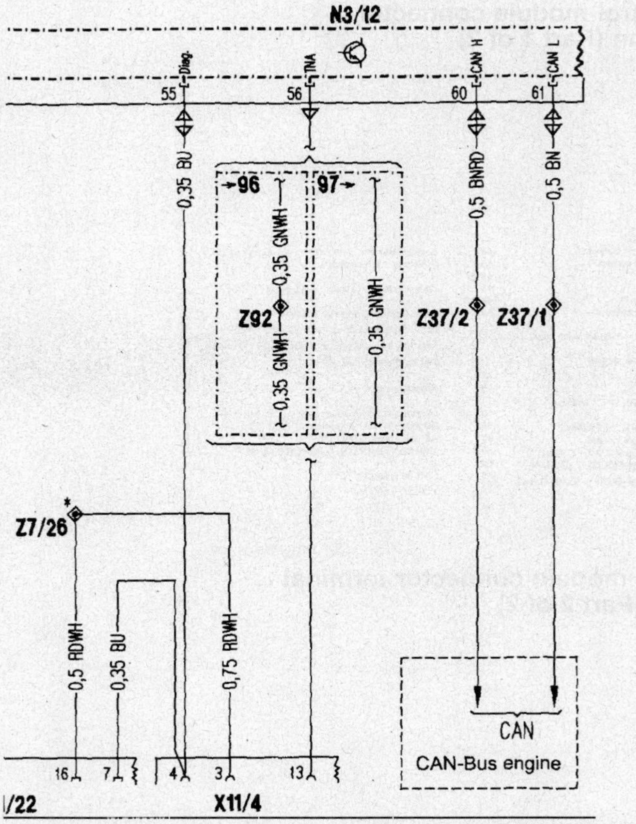

Fig. 11 ME-SFI wiring diagram (Part 9 of 12). SL600 interior compartment righthand bank

A1	Instrument cluster
A1e4	Fuel reserve indicator lamp
A1e26	"CHECK ENGINE" MIL
A1e43	EPC MIL
A1p3	Engine oil pressure gauge with warning lamp
B4/4	Fuel tank emissions monitoring pressure sensor
B24	Body acceleration sensor
B37	Pedal value sensor
F1	Fuse and relay box
F1f10	Fuse 10
F1f37	Fuse 37
G1	Battery
G3/4	Right O2S 1 (before TWC)
G3/4x1	Right O2S 1 connector (before TWC)
G3/6	Right O2S 2 (after TWC)
G3/6x1	Right O2S 2 connector (after TWC)
K17	AIR relay module
K27	FP relay module
M3	FP assembly
N3/11	Left ME-SFI control module
N3/12	Right ME-SFI control module
N15/3	ETC control module
N16/1	Base module (BM)
N35	Daytime running lamp control module
N47-5	ESP/SPS/BAS control module
S9/1	Stop lamp switch (4-pole)
S40	CC pushbutton switch

MB1010100232100X

Fig. 11 ME-SFI wiring diagram (Part 10 of 12). SL600 interior compartment righthand bank

S40/4	CC with variable speed limitation pushbutton switch
S40/4s1	Memory recall
S40/4s2	Decelerate/set
S40/4s3	Accelerate/set
S40/4s4	Off
S40/4s5	Control contact
S40/4s6	Variable speed
S40/4x1	CC variable pushbutton switch connector
S40s1	Memory recall
S40s2	Decelerate/set
S40s3	Accelerate/set
S40s4	Off
S40s5	Control contact
S40x1	CC pushbutton switch connector
S43	Oil level switch
S43x1	Oil level switch connector

W1	Main ground (behind instrument cluster)
W15/1	Ground (electronics - right footwell)
W17	Ground (right rear seat)
W27	Ground (control module box/module box)
X4/10	Terminal block (circuit 30/30Ü/61e/87L) (6-pole)
X11/4	Diagnostic test clutch
X11/22	Diagnostic module (OBD II) generic scan tool connector
X24	Headlamp harness connector
X27	Starter harness connector (5-pole)
X35	Cockpit/module box separation point (12-pole)
X35/7	Cockpit/module box separation point (18-pole)

MB1010100232110X

Fig. 11 ME-SFI wiring diagram (Part 11 of 12). SL600 interior compartment righthand bank

X35/16	Module box/taillamp harness separation point (13-pole)
X35/17	Module box/taillamp harness separation point (6-pole)
X36/3	FP harness connector (2-pole)
X62/19	Terminal block (left front VSS sensor - traction systems)
Y33	Electromagnetic AIR pump clutch
Y33x1	Electromagnetic AIR pump clutch connector
Y58/3	Right purge control valve (located on left side of engine)
Y58/4	Activated charcoal canister shutoff valve
Z3/29	Circuit 15 connector sleeve (fused)
Z6/8	Sensor ground connector sleeve
Z6/27	Sensor ground connector sleeve

Z7/26	Circuit 30 connector sleeve (solder joint in harness)
Z7/35	Circuit 87 M1e connector sleeve
Z16	Connector sleeve 8
Z37/1	CAN-Interior-Bus (high) connector sleeve
Z37/2	Engine CAN-Bus (low) connector sleeve
Z40	Stop lamp connector sleeve
Z92	TNA-signal connector sleeve (feed from base module - N16/1)
Z99/1	Circuit 87 connector sleeve (traction systems)

MB1010100232120X

Fig. 11 ME-SFI wiring diagram (Part 12 of 12). SL600 interior compartment righthand bank

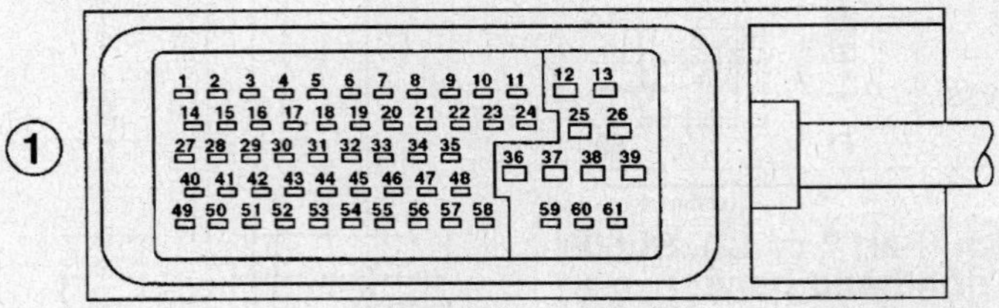

MB1029500397010X

Fig. 12 Interior engine control module connector terminal identification (Part 1 of 2)

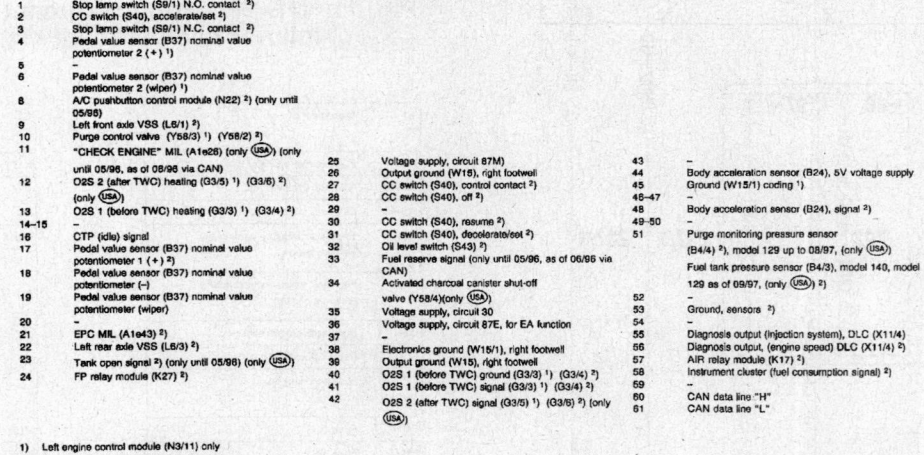

1	Stop lamp switch (S9/1) N.O. contact [2]
2	CC switch (S40), accelerate/set [2]
3	Stop lamp switch (S9/1) N.C. contact [2]
4	Pedal value sensor (B37) nominal value potentiometer 2 (+) [1]
5	–
6	Pedal value sensor (B37) nominal value potentiometer 2 (wiper) [1]
8	A/C pushbutton control module (N22) [2] (only until 05/96)
9	Left front axle VSS (L6/1) [2]
10	Purge control valve (Y58/3) [1] (Y58/2) [2]
11	"CHECK ENGINE" MIL (A1e26) (only USA) (only until 05/96, as of 06/96 via CAN)
12	O2S 2 (after TWC) heating (G3/5) [1] (G3/6) [2] (only USA)
13	O2S 1 (before TWC) heating (G3/3) [1] (G3/4) [2]
14–15	–
16	CTP (idle) signal
17	Pedal value sensor (B37) nominal value potentiometer 1 (+) [2]
18	Pedal value sensor (B37) nominal value potentiometer (–)
19	Pedal value sensor (B37) nominal value potentiometer (wiper)
20	–
21	EPC MIL (A1e43) [2]
22	Left rear axle VSS (L6/3) [2]
23	Tank open signal [2] (only until 05/96) (only USA)
24	FP relay module (K27) [2]
25	Voltage supply, circuit 87M)
26	Output ground (W15), right footwell
27	CC switch (S40), control contact [2]
28	CC switch (S40), off [2]
29	–
30	CC switch (S40), resume [2]
31	CC switch (S40), decelerate/set [2]
32	Oil level switch (S43) [2]
33	Fuel reserve signal (only until 05/96, as of 06/96 via CAN)
34	Activated charcoal canister shut-off valve (Y58/4)(only USA)
35	Voltage supply, circuit 30
36	Voltage supply, circuit 87E, for EA function
37	–
38	Electronics ground (W15/1), right footwell
39	Output ground (W15), right footwell
40	O2S 1 (before TWC) ground (G3/3) [1] (G3/4) [2]
41	O2S 1 (before TWC) signal (G3/3) [1] (G3/4) [2]
42	O2S 2 (after TWC) signal (G3/5) [1] (G3/6) [2] (only USA)
43	–
44	Body acceleration sensor (B24), 5V voltage supply
45	Ground (W15/1) coding [1]
46–47	–
48	Body acceleration sensor (B24), signal [2]
49–50	–
51	Purge monitoring pressure sensor (B4/4) [2], model 129 up to 08/97, (only USA) Fuel tank pressure sensor (B4/3), model 140, model 129 as of 09/97, (only USA) [2]
52	–
53	Ground, sensors [2]
54	–
55	Diagnosis output (injection system), DLC (X11/4)
56	Diagnosis output, (engine speed) DLC (X11/4) [2]
57	AIR relay module (K17) [2]
58	Instrument cluster (fuel consumption signal) [2]
59	–
60	CAN data line "H"
61	CAN data line "L"

1) Left engine control module (N3/11) only
2) Right engine control module (N3/12) only

MB1029500397020A

Fig. 12 Interior engine control module connector terminal identification (Part 2 of 2)

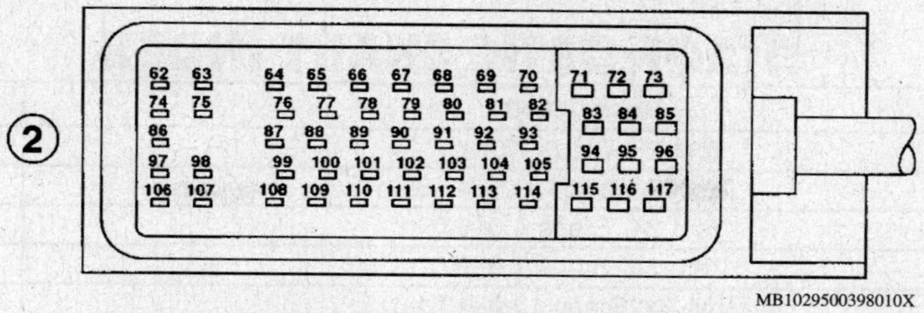

MB1029500398010X

Fig. 13 Engine side engine control module connector terminal identification (Part 1 of 2)

62 - 63	–
64	IAT sensor (+) (B17/6) [1] (B17/5) [2]
65	Pressure sensor (B28/1) [1] (B28/2) [2]
66	CMP sensor signal (L5/2) [1] (L5/3) [2]
67	Hot film MAF sensor (+) (B2/6) [1] (B2/7) [2]
68	Hot film MAF sensor (–) (B2/6) [1] (B2/7) [2]
69	Injector (Y63y10) [1] (Y64y4) [2]
70	Injector (Y63y8) [1] (Y64y2) [2]
71	Injector (Y63y11) [1] (Y64y5) [2]
72	Injector (Y63y7) [1] (Y64y1) [2]
73	Ground bridge to pin 96
74	EA/CC/ISC actuator (–) (M16/4) [1] (M16/3) [2]
75	EA/CC/ISC actuator (+) (M16/4) [1] (M16/3) [2]
76	ECT sensor (+) (B11/9) [1] (B11/10) [2]
77	-
78	CKP sensor (–) (L5/4) [1] (L5/5) [2]
79	Front KS 1 (+) (A29g1) [1] (A30g1) [2]
80	Front KS 1 (–) (A29g1) [1] (A30g1) [2]
81	–
82	Injector (Y63y12) [1] (Y64y6) [2]
83	Ignition coil (T1/7) [1] (T1/1) [2]
84	Ignition coil (T1/11) [1] (T1/5) [2]
85	Ignition coil (T1/9) [1] (T1/3) [2]
86	–
87	Ground: IAT sensor, Intake MAP sensor, CMP sensor, ECT sensor
88	Pressure sensor, 5V voltage supply (B28/1) [1] (B28/2) [2]
89	CKP sensor (+) (L5/4) [1] (L5/5) [2]
90	Rear KS 2 (+) (A29g2) [1] (A30g2) [2]
91	Rear KS 2 (–) (A29g2) [1] (A30g2) [2]
92	–
93	Injector (Y63y9) [1] (Y64y3) [2]
94	Ignition coil (T1/8) [1] (T1/2) [2]
95	Ignition coil (T1/12) [1] (T1/6) [2]
96	Ground bridge to pin 73
97	EA/CC/ISC actuator, actual value potentiometer (wiper) (M16/4r2) [1] (M16/3r2) [2]
98	EA/CC/ISC actuator, actual value potentiometer (–) (M16/4r1–r2) [1] (M16/3r1–r2) [2]
99 - 105	–
106	EA/CC/ISC actuator, actual value potentiometer (+) (M16/4r1) [1] (M16/3r1) [2]
107	EA/CC/ISC actuator, actual value potentiometer (wiper) (M16/4r1–r2) [1] (M16/3r1–r2) [2]
108-112	–
113	Adjustable camshaft timing solenoid (Y49/1) [1] (Y49/2) [2]
114	AIR pump switchover valve (Y32)
115	Ignition coil (T1/10) [1] (T1/4) [2]
116-117	–

1) Left engine control module (N3/11)
2) Right engine control module (N3/12)

MB1029500398020X

Fig. 13 Engine side engine control module connector terminal identification (Part 2 of 2)

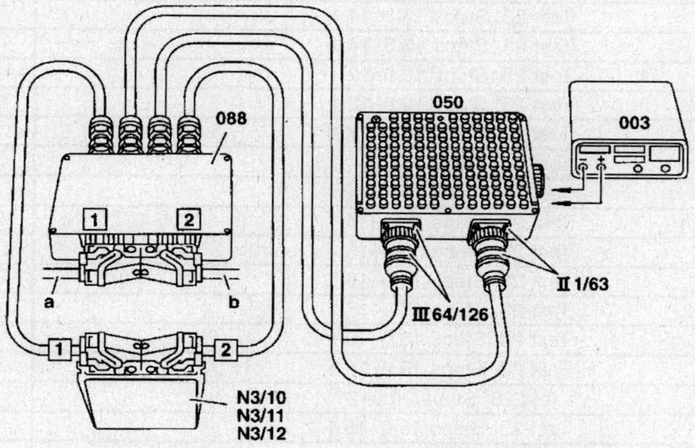

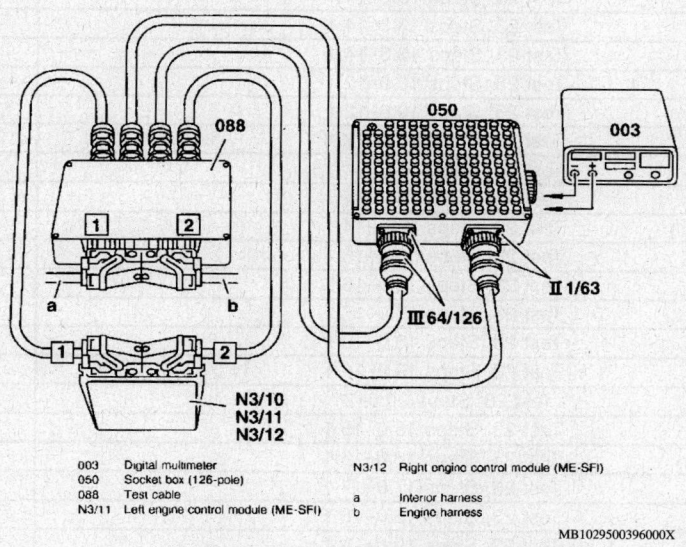

003 Digital multimeter
050 Socket box (126-pole)
088 Test cable
N3/11 Left engine control module (ME-SFI)
N3/12 Right engine control module (ME-SFI)
a Interior harness
b Engine harness

MB1029500396000X

Fig. 14 Test connections

DIAGNOSTIC CHART INDEX

Code	Description	Page No.	Fig. No.
—	Test 23, Steps 7.0–7.1	14-190	18
	Test 23, Steps 39.0–41.0	14-196	38
	Test 24, Steps 4.0–6.0	14-197	41
	Test 24, Steps 7.0–9.0	14-198	42
	Test 24, Steps 12.0–13.1	14-199	45
	Test 24, Steps 14.0–15.1	14-199	46
	Test 24, Steps 16.0–17.1	14-199	47
	Test 25, Steps 16.0–17.0	14-203	59
	Test 32, Fuel System Pressure & Leakage Test	14-205	64
	Test 34, Fuel Pump Test	14-205	66
	Test 36, Fuel Injector Test	14-205	68
P0100	Test 23, Steps 4.0–6.1	14-189	17
P0105	Test 23, Steps 4.0–6.1	14-189	17
P0110	Test 23, Steps 9.0–9.2	14-190	20
P0115	Test 23, Steps 8.0–8.2	14-190	19
P0120	Test 25, Steps 5.0–6.0	14-202	55
P0130	Test 23, Steps 10.0–12.1	14-191	21
P0133	Test 23, Steps 10.0–12.1	14-191	21
P0135	Test 23, Steps 10.0–12.1	14-191	21
	Test 23, Steps 13.0–14.1	14-191	22
P0140	Test 23, Steps 13.0–14.1	14-191	22
P0141	Test 23, Steps 13.0–14.1	14-191	22
P0150	Test 23, Steps 10.0–12.1	14-191	21
P0153	Test 23, Steps 10.0–12.1	14-191	21
P0155	Test 23, Steps 10.0–12.1	14-191	21
P0156	Test 23, Steps 13.0–14.1	14-191	22
P0160	Test 23, Steps 13.0–14.1	14-191	22
P0161	Test 23, Steps 13.0–14.1	14-191	22
P0201	Test 23, Steps 15.0–15.1	14-191	23
P0202	Test 23, Steps 16.0–16.1	14-192	24
P0203	Test 23, Steps 17.0–17.1	14-192	25
P0204	Test 23, Steps 18.0–18.1	14-192	26
P0205	Test 23, Steps 19.0–19.1	14-193	27
P0206	Test 23, Steps 20.0–21	14-193	28
P0207	Test 23, Steps 15.0–15.1	14-191	23
P0208	Test 23, Steps 16.0–16.1	14-192	24
P0209	Test 23, Steps 17.0–17.1	14-192	25
P0210	Test 23, Steps 18.0–18.1	14-192	26
P0211	Test 23, Steps 19.0–19.1	14-193	27
P0212	Test 23, Steps 20.0–21	14-193	28
P0300	Test 24, Steps 18.0–19.1	14-200	48
	Test 24, Steps 20.0–21.1	14-200	49
	Test 24, Steps 22.0–23.1	14-200	50
	Test 24, Step 24.0	14-201	51
P0301	Test 24, Steps 18.0–19.1	14-200	48
	Test 24, Step 24.0	14-201	51
P0302	Test 24, Steps 18.0–19.1	14-200	48
	Test 24, Step 24.0	14-201	51
P0303	Test 24, Steps 20.0–21.1	14-200	49
	Test 24, Step 24.0	14-201	51
P0304	Test 24, Steps 20.0–21.1	14-200	49
	Test 24, Step 24.0	14-201	51
P0305	Test 24, Steps 22.0–23.1	14-200	50
	Test 24, Step 24.0	14-201	51
P0306	Test 24, Steps 22.0–23.1	14-200	50
	Test 24, Step 24.0	14-201	51

Continued

DIAGNOSTIC CHART INDEX—Continued

Code	Description	Page No.	Fig. No.
P0307	Test 24, Steps 18.0–19.1	14-200	48
	Test 24, Step 24.0	14-201	51
P0308	Test 24, Steps 18.0–19.1	14-200	48
	Test 24, Step 24.0	14-201	51
P0309	Test 24, Steps 20.0–21.1	14-200	49
	Test 24, Step 24.0	14-201	51
P0310	Test 24, Steps 20.0–21.1	14-200	49
	Test 24, Step 24.0	14-201	51
P0311	Test 24, Steps 22.0–23.1	14-200	50
	Test 24, Step 24.0	14-201	51
P0312	Test 24, Steps 22.0–23.1	14-200	50
	Test 24, Step 24.0	14-201	51
P0335	Test 24, Steps 10.0–10.1	14-198	43
P0341	Test 24, Steps 11.0–11.1	14-198	44
P0410	Test 23, Steps 20.0–21	14-193	28
	Test 23, Steps 21.1–22.1	14-193	29
P0420	Test 23, Steps 21.1–22.1	14-193	29
P0440	Test 23, Steps 25.0–26.0	14-194	31
	Test 23, Steps 27.0–28.0	14-194	32
P0441	Test 23, Steps 25.0–26.0	14-194	31
P0442	Test 23, Steps 27.0–28.0	14-194	32
P0443	Test 23, Steps 25.0–26.0	14-194	31
P0445	Test 23, Steps 27.0–28.0	14-194	32
P0446	Test 23, Steps 27.0–28.0	14-194	32
P0450	Test 23, Steps 29.0–29.1	14-195	33
	Test 23, Steps 30.0–30.1	14-195	34
P0453	Test 23, Steps 20.0–21	14-193	28
P0455	Test 23, Steps 29.0–29.1	14-195	33
P0463	Test 23, Steps 20.0–21	14-193	28
	Test 23, Steps 21.1–22.1	14-193	29
P0500	Test 25, Steps 6.1–8.0	14-202	56
	Test 25, Steps 9.0–11.0	14-203	57
	Test 26, Steps 2.0–4.0	14-204	61
P0507	Test 25, Steps 3.0–4.1	14-202	54
	Test 25, Steps 5.0–6.0	14-202	55
	Test 25, Steps 9.0–11.0	14-203	57
P0560	Test 23, Steps 1.0–1.2	14-189	15
	Test 23, Steps 2.0–3.0	14-189	16
	Test 24, Steps 1.0–1.2	14-197	39
	Test 24, Steps 2.0–3.0	14-197	40
	Test 25, Steps 1.0–1.2	14-201	52
	Test 25, Steps 2.0–2.2	14-201	53
	Test 25, Steps 3.0–4.1	14-202	54
P0565	Test 26, Steps 1.0–1.4	14-204	60
P0600	Test 23, Steps 31.0–32.0	14-195	35
	Test 25, Steps 12.0–15.0	14-203	58
	Test 26, Steps 5.0–7.0	14-204	62
P1146	Test 23, Steps 4.0–6.1	14-189	17
P1147	Test 23, Steps 8.0–8.2	14-190	19
P1148	Test 23, Steps 9.0–9.2	14-190	20
P1149	Test 23, Steps 4.0–6.1	14-189	17
P1162	Test 25, Steps 5.0–6.0	14-202	55
P1163	Test 23, Steps 33.0–36.0	14-196	36
P1186	Test 25, Steps 5.0–6.0	14-202	55
P1300	Test 24, Steps 10.0–10.1	14-198	43
P1397	Test 24, Steps 11.0–11.1	14-198	44
P1443	Test 23, Steps 25.0–26.0	14-194	31

Continued

DIAGNOSTIC CHART INDEX—Continued

Code	Description	Page No.	Fig. No.
P1477	Test 25, Steps 12.0–15.0	14-203	58
	Test 26, Steps 5.0–7.0	14-204	62
P1490	Test 23, Steps 25.0–26.0	14-194	31
P1519	Test 23, Steps 23.0–24.0	14-194	30
P1522	Test 23, Steps 23.0–24.0	14-194	30
P1525	Test 23, Steps 23.0–24.0	14-194	30
P1533	Test 23, Steps 23.0–24.0	14-194	30
P1542	Test 25, Steps 3.0–4.1	14-202	54
	Test 25, Steps 5.0–6.0	14-202	55
P1570	Test 25, Steps 12.0–15.0	14-203	58
	Test 26, Steps 5.0–7.0	14-204	62
P1580	Test 25, Steps 6.1–8.0	14-202	56
P1581	Test 25, Steps 6.1–8.0	14-202	56
P1584	Test 26, Steps 2.0–4.0	14-204	61
P1587	Test 23, Steps 1.0–1.2	14-189	15
	Test 23, Steps 2.0–3.0	14-189	16
	Test 24, Steps 1.0–1.2	14-197	39
	Test 24, Steps 2.0–3.0	14-197	40
	Test 25, Steps 1.0–1.2	14-201	52
	Test 25, Steps 2.0–2.2	14-201	53
	Test 25, Steps 3.0–4.1	14-202	54
P1605	Test 23, Steps 37.0–37.1	14-196	37
P1641	Test 25, Steps 9.0–11.0	14-203	57

⇒		Test scope	Test connection	Test condition	Nominal value	Possible cause/Remedy
1.0	P0 560 P1 587	**Engine control module (ME-SFI) (N3/11 or N3/12)** Voltage supply Circuit 30	N3/11 N3/12 26 (1.26) — V — 35 (1.35)	Ignition: **ON**	11 – 14 V	⇒ 1.1
1.1		Ground wire	N3/11 N3/12 26 (1.26) — V — X11/4 2 39 (1.39) — V — 2	Ignition: **ON**	11 – 14 V	Wiring, **Model 129:** Ground (W27), module box bracket. **Model 140:** Output ground (W15), right footwell. ⇒ 1.2
1.2		Voltage supply Circuit 30	X11/4 1 — V — N3/11 N3/12 35 (1.35)	Ignition: **ON**	11 – 14 V	Wiring, Base moduel (N16/1) or fuse on base module.

MB1029500399000A

Fig. 15 Codes P0560 & P1587: Test 23, Steps 1.0–1.2

⇒		Test scope	Test connection	Test condition	Nominal value	Possible cause/Remedy
2.0	P0 560 P1 587	**Engine control module (ME-SFI) (N3/11 or N3/12)** Voltage supply Circuit 87M	N3/11 N3/12 38 (1.38) — V — 25 (1.25)	Ignition: **ON**	11 – 14 V	⇒ 2.1
2.1		Electronics ground	N3/11 N3/12 38 (1.38) — V — X11/4 2	Ignition: **ON**	11 – 14 V	Wiring, **Model 129, 140:** Electronics ground (W15/1), right footwell. ⇒ 2.2
2.2		Voltage supply Circuit 87M	X11/4 1 — V — N3/11 N3/12 25 (1.25)	Ignition: **ON** Ignition: **OFF**	11 – 14 V < 1 V	Wiring, Base module (N16/1) or fuse on base module, Ignition/starter switch (S2/1).
3.0	P0 560 P1 587	**Engine control module (ME-SFI) (N3/11 or N3/12)** Voltage supply Circuit 87M	N3/11 N3/12 39 (1.39) — V — 36 (1.36)	Ignition: **ON** Ignition: **OFF**	11 – 14 V < 1 V	Wiring.

MB1029500400000A

Fig. 16 Codes P0560 & P1587: Test 23, Steps 2.0–3.0

⇒		Test scope	Test connection	Test condition	Nominal value	Possible cause/Remedy
4.0	P0 100 P1 146	**Left hot film MAF sensor (B2/6)** **Right hot film MAF sensor (B2/7)** Voltage at hot film	N3/11 N3/12 68 (2.68) — V — 67 (2.67)	Engine: **at Idle** Engine coolant temperature >70°C	0.6 – 0.9 V 1)	Wiring ⇒ 5.0, Air intake system leak, B2/6 or B2/7
5.0	P0 100 P1 146	**Ground wire for hot film MAF sensor (B2/6 or B2/7)**	N3/11 N3/12 38 (1.38) — Ω — 67 (2.67)	Ignition: **OFF** Disconnect MAF sensor (B2/6 or B2/7) connector. Bridge sockets 1 and 4.	< 1 Ω	Ground wire.
6.0	P0 105 P1 149	**Left pressure sensor (B28/1)** **Right pressure sensor (B28/2)** Sender signal	N3/11 N3/12 87 (2.87) — V — 65 (2.65)	Connect vacuum tester to pressure sensor (B28/1 or B28/2) using Y-fitting (Figure 1). Ignition: **ON** Engine: **at Idle**	> 3.5 V < 2 V and pressure climbs to > 500 mbar.	Vacuum line, Wiring, ⇒ 6.1 B28/1 or B28/2
6.1		**Pressure sensor (B28/1 or B28/2)** Voltage supply	N3/11 N3/12 87 (2.87) — V — 88 (2.88)	Ignition: **ON**	4.7 – 5.3 V	N3/11 or N3/12

1) Voltage increases with increasing rpm.

MB1029500401000A

Fig. 17 Codes P0100, P0105, P1146 & P1149: Test 23, Steps 4.0–6.1

⇒		Test scope	Test connection	Test condition	Nominal value	Possible cause/Remedy
7.0		**Right engine control module (N3/12)** **FP relay module (K27)** Control signal	N3/12 24 —((1.24) –V+)— 25 (1.25)	Ignition: **ON** Engine: **Start**	11 – 14 V for approx. 1 sec. 11 – 14 V during cranking and while engine runs.	⇒ 7.1, N3/12
7.1		Current draw (K27)	N3/12 26 —((1.26) –A+)— 24 (1.24)	Ignition: **ON**	0.1 – 0.3 A	Wiring, K27

MB1029500402000A

Fig. 18 Code —: Test 23, Steps 7.0–7.1

⇒		Test scope	Test connection	Test condition	Nominal value	Possible cause/Remedy
8.0	P0 115 P1 147	**Left ECT sensor (B11/9)** **Right ECT sensor (B11/10)** Voltage	N3/11 N3/12 87 —((2.87) –V+)— 76 (2.76)	Ignition: **ON**	°C V 20 3.5 30 3.1 40 2.7 50 2.3 60 1.9 70 1.5 80 1.2 90 1.0 100 0.8 ±5 %	⇒ 8.1, N3/11 or N3/12
8.1		Resistance	N3/11 N3/12 87 —((2.87) –Ω+)— 76 (2.76)	Ignition: **OFF** Disconnect connector 2 on engine control module (N3/11 or N3/12).	°C Ω 20 2500 30 1700 40 1170 50 830 60 600 70 435 80 325 90 245 100 185 ±5 %	Wiring, ⇒ 8.2
8.2		ECT sensor (B11/9 or B11/10) Resistance	B11/9 B11/10 1 –Ω+ 4	Disconnect connector on ECT sensor (B11/9 or B11/10).	Nominal value, see ⇒ 8.1	B11/9 or B11/10

MB1029500403000A

Fig. 19 Codes P0115 & P1147: Test 23, Steps 8.0–8.2

⇒		Test scope	Test connection	Test condition	Nominal value	Possible cause/Remedy
9.0	P0 110 P1 148	**Left IAT sensor (B17/5)** **Right IAT sensor (B17/6)** Voltage	N3/11 N3/12 87 —((2.87) –V+)— 64 (2.64)	Ignition: **ON**	°C V 10 3.2 20 2.6 30 2.1 40 1.6 50 1.2 60 0.9 70 0.7 ±5 %	⇒ 9.1, N3/11 or N3/12
9.1		Resistance (B17/5 or B17/6)	N3/11 N3/12 87 —((2.87) –Ω+)— 64 (2.64)	Ignition: **OFF** Disconnect connector 2 on engine control module (N3/11 or N3/12).	°C Ω 10 9670 20 6060 30 3900 40 2600 50 1760 60 1220 70 860 ±5 %	Wiring, ⇒ 9.2
9.2		IAT sensor (B17/5 or B17/6) Resistance	B17/5 B17/6 1 –Ω+ 2	Disconnect connector from IAT sensor (B17/5 or B17/6).	Nominal value, see ⇒ 9.1	B17/5 or B17/6

MB1029500404000A

Fig. 20 Codes P0110 & P1148: Test 23, Steps 9.0–9.2

⇒	(tester)	Test scope	Test connection	Test condition	Nominal value	Possible cause/Remedy
10.0		**Right engine control module (N3/12)** TN-signal output	N3/12 3) 38 —((+))— 56 (1.38) (1.56) N3/12 4) 38 —((V))— 56 (1.38) (1.56)	Engine: **Start** or Engine: **at Idle**	Signal: see Figure 2. 5 – 7.5 V	Wiring, N3/12
11.0	P0 130 P0 133 P0 150 P0 153	**Left O2S 1** **(before TWC) (G3/3)** **Right O2S 1** **(before TWC) (G3/4)** O2S signal	N3/11 N3/12 40 —((V))— 41 (1.40) (1.41)	ECT > 80 ° C, run engine at idle for at least two minutes.	fluctuates from – 0.2 V to + 1.0 V, by more than 0.3 V	Wiring, G3/3 or G3/4, ⇒ 12.0
12.0	P0 135 P0 155	**Left O2S 1** **(before TWC) (G3/3)** **Right O2S 1** **(before TWC) (G3/4)** O2S heater control signal	N3/11 N3/12 13 —((V))— 25 (1.13) (1.25)	ECT > 80 ° C, run engine at idle for at least two minutes.	11 – 14 V	⇒ 12.1, N3/11 or N3/12
12.1		O2S 1 (G3/3 or G3/4) Current draw	N3/11 N3/12 26 —((A))— 13 (1.26) (1.13)	Ignition: **ON**	0.6 – 3.4 A	Wiring, G3/3 or G3/4

3) Test with oscilloscope.
4) Test with multimeter only if oscilloscope is not available.

MB1029500405000A

Fig. 21 Codes P0130, P0133, P0135, P0150, P0153 & P0155: Test 23, Steps 10.0–12.1

⇒	(tester)	Test scope	Test connection	Test condition	Nominal value	Possible cause/Remedy
13.0.	P0 136 P0 140 P0 156 P0 160	**Left O2S 2** **(afterTWC) (G3/5)** **Right O2S 2** **(afterTWC) (G3/6)** O2S signal	N3/11 N3/12 40 —((V))— 42 (1.40) (1.42)	ECT > 80° C, Engine: **Start** Raise and hold engine speed at 2000 – 3000 rpm for approx. three minutes until O2S 2 heater turns on (see HHT). Briefly depress accelerator pedal to WOT.	450 mV constant Voltage changes. Voltage changes > 100 mV.	Wiring, ⇒ 14.0
14.0	P0 141 P0 161	**Left O2S 2** **(after TWC) (G3/5)** **Right O2S 2** **(after TWC) (G3/6)** O2S heater control signal	N3/11 N3/12 12 —((V))— 25 (1.12) (1.25)	Engine: **at Idle** ECT > 80° C, run engine at idle for at least two minutes.	11 – 14 V	⇒ 14.1, N3/11 or N3/12
14.1		O2S 2 (G3/5 or G3/6) Current draw	N3/11 N3/12 26 —((A))— 12 (1.26) (1.12)	Ignition: **ON**	0.6 – 3.4 A	Wiring, G3/5 or G3/6

MB1029500406000A

Fig. 22 Codes P0135, P0140, P0141, P0156, P0160 & P0161: Test 23, Steps 13.0–14.1

⇒	(tester)	Test scope	Test connection	Test condition	Nominal value	Possible cause/Remedy
15.0	P0 201 P0 207	**Injector (Y64y1, Y63y7)** Control signal and injection time	N3/11 N3/12 72 —((+))— 25 (2.72) (1.25)	**ECT approx. 20° C** at start **ECT approx. 80° C** at idle accelerate briefly	Injection time: approx. 8 ms approx. 3 – 5 ms approx. 14 ms (signals see Figures 3 and 4)	⇒ 15.1, N3/11 or N3/12, **Further possibilities:** ECT sensor (B11/9 or B11/10), IAT sensor (B17/5 or B17/6), O2S 1 (G3/3 or G3/4).
15.1		Resistance	N3/11 N3/12 72 —((Ω))— 25 (2.72) (1.25)	Ignition: **OFF**	14 – 17 Ω	Wiring, Y64y1, Y63y7

MB1029500407000A

Fig. 23 Codes P0201 & P0207: Test 23, Steps 15.0–15.1

⇒		Test scope	Test connection	Test condition	Nominal value	Possible cause/Remedy
16.0	P0 202 P0 208	**Injector (Y64y2, Y63y8)** Control signal and injection time	N3/11 N3/12 70 (2.70) — 25 (1.25)	**ECT approx. 20° C** at start **ECT approx. 80° C** at idle accelerate briefly	Injection time: approx. 8 ms approx. 3 – 5 ms approx. 14 ms (signals see Figures 3 and 4)	⇒ 16.1, N3/11 or N3/12, **Further possibilities:** ECT sensor (B11/9 or B11/10), IAT sensor (B17/5 or B17/6), O2S 1 (G3/3 or G3/4).
16.1		Resistance	N3/11 N3/12 70 (2.70) — 25 (1.25)	Ignition: **OFF**	14 – 17 Ω	Wiring, Y64y2, Y63y8

MB1029500408000A

Fig. 24 Codes P0202 & P0208: Test 23, Steps 16.0–16.1

⇒		Test scope	Test connection	Test condition	Nominal value	Possible cause/Remedy
17.0	P0 203 P0 209	**Injector (Y64y3, Y63y9)** Control signal and injection time	N3/11 N3/12 93 (2.93) — 25 (1.25)	**ECT approx. 20° C** at start **ECT approx. 80° C** at idle accelerate briefly	Injection time: approx. 8 ms approx. 3 – 5 ms approx. 14 ms (signals see Figures 3 and 4)	⇒ 17.1, N3/11 or N3/12, **Further possibilities:** ECT sensor (B11/9 or B11/10), IAT sensor (B17/5 or B17/6), O2S 1 (G3/3 or G3/4).
17.1		Resistance	N3/11 N3/12 93 (2.93) — 25 (1.25)	Ignition: **OFF**	14 – 17 Ω	Wiring, Y64y3, Y63y9

MB1029500409000A

Fig. 25 Codes P0203 & P0209: Test 23, Steps 17.0–17.1

⇒		Test scope	Test connection	Test condition	Nominal value	Possible cause/Remedy
18.0	P0 204 P0 210	**Injector (Y64y4, Y63y10)** Control signal and injection time	N3/11 N3/12 69 (2.69) — 25 (1.25)	**ECT approx. 20° C** at start **ECT approx. 80° C** at idle accelerate briefly	Injection time: approx. 8 ms approx. 3 – 5 ms approx. 14 ms (signals: see Figures 3 and 4).	⇒ 18.1, N3/11 or N3/12 **Further possibilities:** ECT sensor (B11/9 or B11/10), IAT sensor (B17/5 or B17/6), O2S 1 (G3/3 or G3/4).
18.1		Resistance (Y64y4 or Y63y10)	N3/11 N3/12 69 (2.69) — 25 (1.25)	Ignition: **OFF**	14 – 17 Ω	Wiring, Y64y4 or Y63y10

MB1029500410000A

Fig. 26 Codes P0204 & P0210: Test 23, Steps 18.0–18.1

⇒	DTC	Test scope	Test connection	Test condition	Nominal value	Possible cause/Remedy
19.0	P0 205 P0 211	**Injector (Y64y5, Y63y11)** Control signal and injection time	71 (2.71) – N3/11, N3/12 – 25 (1.25)	**ECT approx. 20° C** at start **ECT approx. 80° C** at idle accelerate briefly	Injection time: approx. 8 ms approx. 3 – 5 ms approx. 14 ms (signals: see Figures 3 and 4).	⇒ 19.1, N3/11 or N3/12 **Further possibilities:** ECT sensor (B11/9 or B11/10), IAT sensor (B17/5 or B17/6), O2S 1 (G3/3 or G3/4).
19.1		Resistance (Y64y5 or Y63y11)	71 (2.71) – N3/11, N3/12 – 25 (1.25)	Ignition: **OFF**	14 – 17 Ω	Wiring, Y64y5, Y63y11

MB1029500411000A

Fig. 27 Codes P0205 & P0211: Test 23, Steps 19.0–19.1

⇒	DTC	Test scope	Test connection	Test condition	Nominal value	Possible cause/Remedy
20.0	P0 206 P0 212	**Injector (Y64y6, Y63y12)** Control signal and injection time	82 (2.82) – N3/11, N3/12 – 25 (1.25)	**ECT approx. 20° C** at start **ECT approx. 80° C** at idle accelerate briefly	Injection time: approx. 8 ms approx. 3 – 5 ms approx. 14 ms	⇒ 20.1, N3/11 or N3/12, **Further possibilities:** ECT sensor (B11/9 or B11/10), IAT sensor (B17/5 or B17/6), O2S 2 (G3/3 or G3/4).
20.1		Resistance	82 (2.82) – N3/11, N3/12 – 25 (1.25)	Ignition: **OFF**	14 – 17 Ω	Wiring, Y62y6, Y62y12
21.0	P0 410 P1 453 P1 463	**Right engine control module (N3/12)** **AIR relay module (K17)** Control signal	57 (1.57) – N3/12 – 25 (1.25)	Disconnect right ECT sensor (B11/10) connector. Simulate 2.5 kΩ resistance at sockets 1 and 4 with resistance substitution unit. Engine: **at Idle**	11 – 14 V for approx. two minutes and AIR pump runs.	⇒ 21.1, N3/12

MB1029500412000A

Fig. 28 Codes P0206, P0212, P0410, P0453 & P0463: Test 23, Steps 20.0–21

⇒	DTC	Test scope	Test connection	Test condition	Nominal value	Possible cause/Remedy
21.1		Current draw	38 (1.38) – N3/12 – 57 (1.57)	Ignition: **ON**	0.1 – 0.3 A	Wiring, K17
22.0	P0 410 P1 420 P1 463	**Right engine control module (N3/12)** **AIR pump switchover valve (Y32)** Control signal	114 (2.114) – N3/12 – 25 (1.25)	Disconnect right ECT sensor (B11/10) connector. Simulate 2.5 kΩ resistance at sockets 1 and 4 with resistance substitution unit. Engine: **at Idle**	11 – 14 V for approx. two minutes **and** AIR pump runs.	⇒ 22.1, N3/12
22.1		Current draw	38 (1.38) – N3/12 – 114 (2.114)	Ignition: **ON**	0.3 – 0.5 A	Wiring, Y32

MB1029500413000A

Fig. 29 Codes P0410, P0420 & P0463: Test 23, Steps 21.1–22.1

⇒		Test scope	Test connection	Test condition	Nominal value	Possible cause/Remedy
23.0	P1 519 P1 522 P1 525 P1 533	**Left adjustable camshaft timing solenoid (Y49/1)** **Right adjustable camshaft timing solenoid (Y49/2)** Current draw	Y49/1 Y49/2 1 —(—(A)—)— 2	Connect test cable (102 589 04 63 00) to solenoid. Engine: **Start** and increase engine speed to 3000 rpm.	approx. 1.0 A	⇒ 23.1, ⇒ 24.0, N3/11 or N3/12.
23.1		Resistance Y49/1 or Y49/2	Y49/1 Y49/2 1 — —(Ω)— — 2	Ignition: **OFF** Unplug connector on left or right camshaft timing solenoid (Y49/1 or Y49/2).	7 – 12 Ω	Y49/1 or Y49/2
24.0	P1 519 P1 522 P1 525 P1 533	**Left adjustable camshaft timing solenoid (Y49/1)** **Right adjustable camshaft timing solenoid (Y49/2)** Mechanical function	N3/11 N3/12 113 —(←—→)— 38 (2.113) (1.38)	Engine: **at idle** Bridge sockets on socket box for a maximum of 10 seconds.	Engine runs rough after approx. 5 seconds.	Check function of camshaft adjuster.

MB1029500414000A

Fig. 30 Codes P1519, P1522, P1525 & P1533: Test 23, Steps 23.0–24.0

⇒		Test scope	Test connection	Test condition	Nominal value	Possible cause/Remedy
25.0	P0 440 P0 441 P0 443 P1 443 P1 490	**Left purge control valve (Y58/2)** **Right purge control valve (Y58/3)** Control signal	N3/11 N3/12 10 —(—(f)—)— 25 (1.10) (1.25)	Engine: **at idle** and at operating temperature.	After approx. 1 minute, purge control valve (Y58/2 or Y58/3) must noticeably cycle	⇒ 25.1, ⇒ 26.0, N3/11 or N3/12.
25.1		Current draw	N3/11 N3/12 38 —(—(A)—)— 10 (1.38) (1.10)	Ignition: **ON**	0.1 – 0.3 A	Wiring, Y58/2 or Y58/3.
26.0	P0 440 P0 441 P1 443	**Purge control valve (Y58/2 or Y58/3)** Vacuum control		Connect vacuum tester to purge control valve (Y58/2 or Y58/3) connector (A) Slowly increase engine speed to 3000 rpm and ECT > 80° C.	After approx. 1 minute, > 50 mbar and needle oscillates.	Vacuum line, Y58/2 or Y58/3.

MB1029500415000X

Fig. 31 Codes P0440, P0441, P0443, P1443 & P1490: Test 23, Steps 25.0–26.0

⇒		Test scope	Test connection	Test condition	Nominal value	Possible cause/Remedy
27.0	P0 440 P0 442 P0 445	**Only (USA), Model 140 and 129 as of 09/97** **Right engine control module (N3/12)** **Purge system** Leaks Activated charcoal canister shut-off valve (Y58/4) activated	N3/12 26 —(←—→)— 34 (1.26) (1.34)	Disconnect purge line (A) to charcoal canister on right purge control valve (Y58/3, left side of engine compartment). Connect vacuum tester to purge line Ignition: **ON** Apply approx. 25 mbar of vacuum.	After approx. 1 minute, < 5 mbar vacuum loss.	Fuel tank cap, Purge line to charcoal canister, Purge line from charcoal canister to Y58/4, Charcoal canister, Y58/4
28.0	P0 446	**Only (USA), Model 140 and 129 as of 09/97** **Right engine control module (N3/12)** **Activated charcoal canister shut-off valve (Y58/4)** Current draw	N3/12 38 —(—(A)—)— 34 (1.38) (1.34)	Ignition: **ON**	0.5 – 0.9 A	Wiring, Y58/4

MB1029500416000A

Fig. 32 Codes P0440, P0442, P0445 & P0446: Test 23, Steps 27.0–28.0

⇒		Test scope	Test connection	Test condition	Nominal value	Possible cause/Remedy
29.0	P0 450 P0 455	**Model 140 only** **Fuel tank pressure sensor (B4/3)** Sender signal	N3/12 53 —(V)— 51 (1.53) (1.51)	Disconnect purge line (A) to charcoal canister on right purge control valve (Y58/3, left side of engine compartment). Connect vacuum tester to purge line.		⇒ 29.1, Wiring, Vacuum line, Charcoal canister plugged, B4/3.
		Activated charcoal canister shut-off valve (Y58/4) activated	N3/12 26 ←—→ 34 (1.26) (1.34)	Ignition: **ON**	> 3 v	
				Apply approx. 40 mbar of vacuum.	< 2 V	
29.1		Fuel tank pressure sensor (B4/3) Voltage supply	N3/12 53 —(V)— 44 (1.53) (1.44)	Ignition: **ON**	4.7 – 5.3 V	N3/12.

MB1029500417000X

Fig. 33 Codes P0450 & P0455: Test 23, Steps 29.0–29.1

⇒		Test scope	Test connection	Test condition	Nominal value	Possible cause/Remedy
30.0	P0 450	**Only (USA), Model 129 up to 09/97** **Right engine control module (N3/12)** **Purge monitoring pressure sensor (B4/4)** Sender signal	N3/12 53 —(V)— 51 (1.53) (1.51)	Disconnect purge line (A) to charcoal canister on purge monitoring pressure sensor (B4/4). Connect vacuum tester to purge monitoring pressure sensor		Wiring, ⇒ 30.1, B4/4
				Ignition: **ON**	> 3.5 V	
				Apply approx. 300 mbar of vacuum.	< 3 V	
30.1		Purge monitoring pressure sensor (B4/4) Voltage supply	N3/12 53 —(V)— 44 (1.53) (1.44)	Ignition: **ON**	4.7 – 5.3 V	N3/12

MB1029500418000A

Fig. 34 Code P0450: Test 23, Steps 30.0–30.1

⇒		Test scope	Test connection	Test condition	Nominal value	Possible cause/Remedy
31.0	P0 600 P1 570 P1 747	**CAN data bus**	N3/11 N3/12 60 —(Ω)— 61 (1.60) (1.61)	Ignition: **OFF** Disconnect connector 1 from test cable and measure resistance directly at connector 1 (interior) using an ohmmeter. Wire connections see □ 22.	75 – 85 Ω	⇒ 31.1, Data line.
31.1.		**CAN element in RCL control module (N54)** Resistance **CAN element in DAS control module (N54/1)** Resistance	N54 N54/1 L —(Ω)— H	Ignition: **OFF** Disconnect control module (N54 or N54/1) and test directly at pins.	115 – 125 Ω	N54 or N54/1
32.0		**CAN element in engine control module (N3/11 or N3/12)** Resistance	N3/11 N3/12 60 —(Ω)— 61	Ignition: **OFF** Disconnect connector 1 (interior) from engine control module (N3/11 or N3/12) and test directly at pins.	235 – 245 Ω	N3/11 or N3/12

MB1029500419000A

Fig. 35 Code P0600: Test 23, Steps 31.0–32.0

⇒		Test scope	Test connection	Test condition	Nominal value	Possible cause/Remedy
33.0	P1 163	**Right engine control module (N3/12)** **Oil level switch (S43)**	N3/12 32 —< (1.32) V >— 25 (1.25)	Ignition: **ON** Oil level okay. Oil level low.	 11 – 14 V < 1 V	Wiring, S43
34.0		**Only on right engine control module (N3/12) until 05/96 (as of 06/96 via CAN)** **Fuel consumption signal**	N3/12 25 —< (1.25) V >— 58 (1.58)	Engine: **at idle** and briefly accelerate engine.	> 0.5 V	Wiring, N3/12
35.0		**Diagnosis line** Control	N3/11 N3/12 26 —< (1.26) V >— 55 (1.55)	Ignition: **ON**	11 – 14 V	Wiring, N3/11 or N3/12
36.0		**Only on left engine control module (N3/11)** **Coding**	N3/11 45 —< (1.45) V >— 25 (1.25)	Ignition: **ON**	11 – 14 V	Wiring.

MB1029500420000A

Fig. 36 Code P1163: Test 23, Steps 33.0–36.0

⇒		Test scope	Test connection	Test condition	Nominal value	Possible cause/Remedy
37.0	P1 605	**Body acceleration sensor (B24/7)** Sensor signal static	N3/12 53 —< (1.53) V >— 48 (1.48)	Ignition: **ON**	2.35 – 2.65 V	Wiring, ⇒ 37.1, B24/7.
		Sensor signal dynamic	N3/12 53 —< (1.53) V >— 48 (1.48)	Vigorously move left front corner of vehicle by hand.	> 5 mV~ Note: Value changes with movement.	
37.1		Voltsge supply	N3/12 53 —< (1.53) V >— 44 (1.44)	Ignition: **ON**	4.7 – 5.3 V	N3/12.

MB1029500421000X

Fig. 37 Code P1605: Test 23, Steps 37.0–37.1

⇒		Test scope	Test connection	Test condition	Nominal value	Possible cause/Remedy
39.0		**Only model 140 on right engine control module (N3/12) until 05/96 (as of 06/96 via CAN)** **Fuel tank cap open signal**	N3/12 23 —< (1.23) V >— 25 (1.25)	Engine: **at idle** Tank cap open Tank cap closed after approx. 18 minutes	 11 – 14 V < 1 V	Leak in purge system, ⇒ 27.0
40.0		**Only on right engine control module (N3/12) until 05/96 (as of 06/96 via CAN)** **"CHECK ENGNE" MIL (A1e26)**	N3/12 11 —< (1.11) V >— 25 (1.25)	Ignition: **ON**	11 – 14 V	N3/12
41.0		**Engine control module (ME-SFI) coding** Bridge	N3/11 N3/12 73 —< (2.73) Ω >— 96 (2.96)	Ignition: **OFF**	< 1 Ω	Wiring.

MB1029500422000A

Fig. 38 Code —: Test 23, Steps 39.0–41.0

⇒		Test scope	Test connection	Test condition	Nominal value	Possible cause/Remedy
1.0	P0 560 P1 587	**Left engine control module (N3/11)** **Right engine control module (N3/12)** Voltage supply circuit 30	N3/11 N3/12 26 (1.26) — V — 35 (1.35)	Ignition: **ON**	11 – 14 V	⇒ 1.1
1.1		Ground wire	N3/11 N3/12 26 (1.26) — V — X11/4 2; 39 (1.39) — V — 2	Ignition: **ON**	11 – 14 V	Wiring, **Model 129** Ground (W27), module box bracket. **Model 140** Harness ground (W15), right footwell. ⇒ 1.2
1.2		Voltage supply circuit 30	N3/11 N3/12 X11/4 1 — V — 35 (1.35)	Ignition: **ON**	11 – 14 V	Wire to terminal block X4/10.

MB1029500423000X

Fig. 39 Codes P0560 & P1587: Test 24, Steps 1.0–1.2

⇒		Test scope	Test connection	Test condition	Nominal value	Possible cause/Remedy
2.0	P0 560 P1 587	**Left engine control module (N3/11)** **Right engine control module (N3/12)** Voltage supply circuit 87M	N3/11 N3/12 38 (1.38) — V — 25 (1.25)	Ignition: **ON**	11 – 14 V	⇒ 2.1
2.1		Electronics ground	N3/11 N3/12 38 (1.38) — V — X11/4 2	Ignition: **ON**	11 – 14 V	Wiring, **Model 129 and 140** Electronics ground (W15/1), right footwell ⇒ 2.2
2.2		Voltage supply circuit 87	N3/11 N3/12 X11/4 1 — V — 25 (1.25)	Ignition: **ON** Ignition: **OFF**	11 – 14 V < 1 V	Wiring, Base module (N16/1) or fuse on base module.
3.0	P0 560 P1 587	**Left engine control module (N3/11)** **Right engine control module (N3/12)** Voltage supply circuit 87M	N3/11 N3/12 39 (1.39) — V — 38 (1.38)	Ignition: **ON** Ignition: **OFF**	11 – 14 V < 1 V	Wiring, Base module (N16/1) or fuse on base module, Ignition/starter switch (S2/1).

MB1029500424000A

Fig. 40 Codes P0560 & P1587: Test 24, Steps 2.0–3.0

⇒		Test scope	Test connection	Test condition	Nominal value	Possible cause/Remedy
4.0		**Ignition coil (T1/1 or T1/7)** Voltage supply	N3/11 N3/12 26 (1.26) — V — 83 (2.83)	Ignition: **ON** Starter: **Crank**	11 – 14 V > 10 V	Wiring. Model 129 as of 09/95 and Model 140 as of 06/96 fused as follows: Model 129 fuse 34 Model 140 fuse 22
5.0		**Ignition coil (T1/2 or T1/8)** Voltage supply	N3/11 N3/12 26 (1.26) — V — 94 (2.94)	Ignition: **ON** Starter: **Crank**	11 – 14 V > 10 V	Wiring. Model 129 as of 09/95 and Model 140 as of 06/96 fused as follows: Model 129 fuse 34 Model 140 fuse 22
6.0		**Ignition coil (T1/3 or T1/9)** Voltage supply	N3/11 N3/12 26 (1.26) — V — 85 (2.85)	Ignition: **ON** Starter: **Crank**	11 – 14 V > 10 V	Wiring. Model 129 as of 09/95 and Model 140 as of 06/96 fused as follows: Model 129 fuse 34 Model 140 fuse 22

MB1029500425000A

Fig. 41 Code —: Test 24, Steps 4.0–6.0

⇒		Test scope	Test connection	Test condition	Nominal value	Possible cause/Remedy
7.0		**Ignition coil (T1/4 or T1/10)** Voltage supply	N3/11 N3/12 26 —< (V) >— 115 (1.26) (2.115)	Ignition: **ON**	11 – 14 V	Wiring.
				Starter: **Crank**	> 10 V	Model 129 as of 09/95 and Model 140 as of 06/96 fused as follows: Model 129 fuse 34 Model 140 fuse 22
8.0		**Ignition coil (T1/5 or T1/11)** Voltage supply	N3/11 N3/12 26 —< (V) >— 84 (1.26) (2.84)	Ignition: **ON**	11 – 14 V	Wiring.
				Starter: **Crank**	> 10 V	Model 129 as of 09/95 and Model 140 as of 06/96 fused as follows: Model 129 fuse 34 Model 140 fuse 22
9.0		**Ignition coil (T1/6 or T1/12)** Voltage supply	N3/11 N3/12 26 —< (V) >— 95 (1.26) (2.95)	Ignition: **ON**	11 – 14 V	Wiring.
				Starter: **Crank**	> 10 V	Model 129 as of 09/95 and Model 140 as of 06/96 fused as follows: Model 129 fuse 34 Model 140 fuse 22

MB1029500426000A

Fig. 42 Code —: Test 24, Steps 7.0–9.0

⇒		Test scope	Test connection	Test condition	Nominal value	Possible cause/Remedy
10.0	P0 335 P1 300	**Left CKP sensor (L5/4)** **Right CKP sensor (L5/5)**	N3/11 2) N3/12 2) 78 —< (⊕) >— 89 (2.78) (2.89)	Starter: **Crank**	Signal, see Figure 1.	⇒ 10.1, Teeth on starter ring gear.
				Engine: **at Idle**		
			N3/11 3) N3/12 3) 78 —< (V) >— 89 (2.78) (2.89)	Starter: **Crank**	> 0.5 V~	
				Engine: **at Idle**	> 7 V~ 4)	
10.1		Resistance of CKP sensor (L5/4 or L5/5)	N3/11 N3/12 78 —< (Ω) >— 89 (2.78) (2.89)	Ignition: **OFF** Unplug connector 2 on engine control module (N3/11) or (N3/12).	700 – 1400 Ω	L5/4 or L5/5

2) Test with oscilloscope.
3) Test with multimeter only if oscilloscope is unavailable.
4) Voltage increases with increasing rpm.

MB1029500427000A

Fig. 43 Codes P0335 & P1300: Test 24, Steps 10.0–10.1

⇒		Test scope	Test connection	Test condition	Nominal value	Possible cause/Remedy
11.0	P0 341 P1 397	**Left camshaft Hall-effect sensor (B6/2)** **Right camshaft Hall-effect sensor (B6/3)** Hall-effect signal	N3/11 2) N3/12 2) 87 —< (⊕) >— 66 (2.87) (2.66)	Engine: **at Idle**	Signal, see Figure 2.	⇒ 11.1, B6/2 or B6/3
			N3/11 3) N3/12 3) 66 —< (V) >— 25 (2.66) (1.25)	Engine: **at Idle**	1.3 – 1.7 V Value changes	
11.1		Voltage supply to camshaft Hall-effect sensor (B6/2 or B6/3)	B6/2 B6/3 1 —< (V) >— 3	Ignition: **ON** Disconnect connector from Hall-effect sensor (B6/2 or B6/3) and test directly on sockets 1 and 3 of connector.	11 – 14 V	Wiring.

2) Test with oscilloscope.
3) Test with multimeter only if oscilloscope is unavailable.

MB1029500428000A

Fig. 44 Codes P0341 & P1397: Test 24, Steps 11.0–11.1

⇒		Test scope	Test connection	Test condition	Nominal value	Possible cause/Remedy
12.0		**Closing duration for ignition coil (T1/1 or T1/7)**	83 (2.83) – N3/11, N3/12 (ms) – 25 (1.25)	Starter: **Crank** Engine: **at Idle**	20 – 100 ms 2 – 4 ms	⇒ 10.0, ⇒ 12.1, N3/11 or N3/12
12.1		Rest current shut-off: T1/1 or T1/7	83 (2.83) – N3/11, N3/12 (V) – 25 (1.25)	Ignition: **ON** Starter: **Crank**	0 V 0.3 – 0.5 V	T1/1 or T1/7, N3/11 or N3/12, < 0.3 V: wire from T1/1 to N3/12 or T1/7 to N3/11 open circuit, > 0.5 V: T1/1 or T1/7
13.0		**Closing duration for ignition coil (T1/2 or T1/8)**	94 (2.94) – N3/11, N3/12 (ms) – 25 (1.25)	Starter: **Crank** Engine: **at Idle**	20 – 100 ms 2 – 4 ms	⇒ 13.1, N3/11 or N3/12
13.1		Rest current shut-off: T1/2 or T1/8	94 (2.94) – N3/11, N3/12 (V) – 25 (1.25)	Ignition: **ON** Starter: **Crank**	0 V 0.3 – 0.5 V	T1/2 or T1/8, N3/11 or N3/12, < 0.3 V: wire from T1/2 to N3/12 or T1/8 to N3/11 open circuit, > 0.5 V: T1/2 or T1/8

MB1029500429000A

Fig. 45 Code —: Test 24, Steps 12.0–13.1

⇒		Test scope	Test connection	Test condition	Nominal value	Possible cause/Remedy
14.0		**Closing duration for ignition coil (T1/3 or T1/9)**	85 (2.85) – N3/11, N3/12 (ms) – 25 (1.25)	Starter: **Crank** Engine: **at Idle**	20 – 100 ms 2 – 4 ms	⇒ 14.1, N3/11 or N3/12
14.1		Rest current shut-off: T1/3 or T1/9	85 (2.85) – N3/11, N3/12 (V) – 25 (1.25)	Ignition: **ON** Starter: **Crank**	0 V 0.3 – 0.5 V	T1/3 or T1/9, N3/11 or N3/12, < 0.3 V: wire from T1/3 to N3/12 or T1/9 to N3/11 open circuit, > 0.5 V: T1/3 or T1/9
15.0		**Closing duration for ignition coil (T1/4 or T1/10)**	115 (2.115) – N3/11, N3/12 (ms) – 25 (1.25)	Starter: **Crank** Engine: **at Idle**	20 – 100 ms 2 – 4 ms	⇒ 15.1, N3/11 or N3/12
15.1		Rest current shut-off: T1/4 or T1/10	115 (2.115) – N3/11, N3/12 (V) – 25 (1.25)	Ignition: **ON** Starter: **Crank**	0 V 0.3 – 0.5 V	T1/4 or T1/10, N3/11 or N3/12, < 0.3 V: wire from T1/4 to N3/12 or T1/10 to N3/11 open circuit, > 0.5 V: T1/4 or T1/10

MB1029500430000A

Fig. 46 Code —: Test 24, Steps 14.0–15.1

⇒		Test scope	Test connection	Test condition	Nominal value	Possible cause/Remedy
16.0		**Closing duration for ignition coil (T1/5 or T1/11)**	84 (2.84) – N3/11, N3/12 (ms) – 25 (1.25)	Starter: **Crank** Engine: **at Idle**	20 – 100 ms 2 – 4 ms	⇒ 16.1, N3/11 or N3/12
16.1		Rest current shut-off: T1/5 or T1/11	84 (2.84) – N3/11, N3/12 (V) – 25 (1.25)	Ignition: **ON** Starter: **Crank**	0 V 0.3 – 0.5 V	T1/5 or T1/11, N3/11 or N3/12, < 0.3 V: wire from T1/5 to N3/12 or T1/11 to N3/11 open circuit, > 0.5 V: T1/5 or T1/11
17.0		**Closing duration for ignition coil (T1/6 or T1/12)**	95 (2.95) – N3/11, N3/12 (ms) – 25 (1.25)	Starter: **Crank** Engine: **at Idle**	20 – 100 ms 2 – 4 ms	⇒ 17.1, N3/11 or N3/12
17.1		Rest current shut-off: T1/6 or T1/12	95 (2.95) – N3/11, N3/12 (V) – 25 (1.25)	Ignition: **ON** Starter: **Crank**	0 V 0.3 – 0.5 V	T1/6 or T1/12, N3/11 or N3/12, < 0.3 V: wire from T1/6 to N3/12 or T1/12 to N3/11 open circuit, > 0.5 V: T1/6 or T1/12

MB1029500431000A

Fig. 47 Code —: Test 24, Steps 16.0–17.1

⇒		Test scope	Test connection	Test condition	Nominal value	Possible cause/Remedy
18.0	P0 300 P0 301 P0 307	**Primary voltage** Ignition coil (T1/1 or T1/7)	N3/11 N3/12 83 (2.83) — 25 (1.25)	**Test connection Note:** Individual primary pattern Range 400 V Duration 100% Starter: **Crank**	200 – 350 V	⇒ 18.1, N3/11 or N3/12
18.1		Primary winding of T1/1 and T1/2 or T1/7 and T1/8	N3/11 N3/12 83 (2.83) — 94 (2.94)	Ignition: **OFF**	0.9 – 1.4 Ω [6]	T1/1 or T1/2 and/or T1/7 or T1/8
19.0	P0 300 P0 302 P0 308	**Primary voltage** Ignition coil (T1/2 or T1/8)	N3/11 N3/12 94 (2.94) — 25 (1.25)	**Test connection Note:** Individual primary pattern Range 400 V Duration 100% Starter: **Crank**	200 – 350 V	⇒ 19.1, N3/11 or N3/12
19.1		Primary winding of T1/2 and T1/1 or T1/8 and T1/7	N3/11 N3/12 94 (2.94) — 83 (2.83)	Ignition: **OFF**	0.9 – 1.4 Ω [6]	T1/2 or T1/1 and/or T1/8 or T1/7

[6] The resistance of a single coil is 0.5 – 0.7 Ω

MB1029500432000A

Fig. 48 Codes P0300, P0301, P0302, P0307 & P0308: Test 24, Steps 18.0–19.1

⇒		Test scope	Test connection	Test condition	Nominal value	Possible cause/Remedy
20.0	P0 300 P0 303 P0 309	**Primary voltage** Ignition coil (T1/3 or T1/9)	N3/11 N3/12 85 (2.85) — 25 (1.25)	**Test connection Note:** Individual primary pattern Range 400 V Duration 100% Starter: **Crank**	200 – 350 V	⇒ 20.1, N3/11 or N3/12
20.1		Primary winding of T1/3 and T1/4 or T1/9 and T1/10	N3/11 N3/12 85 (2.85) — 115 (2.115)	Ignition: **OFF**	0.9 – 1.4 Ω [6]	T1/3 or T1/4 and/or T1/9 or T1/10
21.0	P0 300 P0 304 P0 310	**Primary voltage** Ignition coil (T1/4 or T1/10)	N3/11 N3/12 115 (2.115) — 25 (1.25)	**Test connection Note:** Individual primary pattern Range 400 V Duration 100% Starter: **Crank**	200 – 350 V	⇒ 21.1, N3/11 or N3/12
21.1		Primary winding of T1/4 and T1/3 or T1/10 and T1/9	N3/11 N3/12 115 (2.115) — 85 (2.85)	Ignition: **OFF**	0.9 – 1.4 Ω [6]	T1/4 or T1/3 and/or T1/10 or T1/9

[6] The resistance of a single coil is 0.5 – 0.7 Ω

MB1029500433000A

Fig. 49 Codes P0300, P0303, P0304, P0309 & P0310: Test 24, Steps 20.0–21.1

⇒		Test scope	Test connection	Test condition	Nominal value	Possible cause/Remedy
22.0	P0 300 P0 305 P0 311	**Primary voltage** Ignition coil (T1/5 or T1/11)	N3/11 N3/12 84 (2.84) — 25 (1.25)	**Test connection Note:** Individual primary pattern Range 400 V Duration 100% Starter: **Crank**	200 – 350 V	⇒ 22.1, N3/11 or N3/12
22.1		Primary winding of T1/5 and T1/6 or T1/11 and T1/12	N3/11 N3/12 84 (2.84) — 95 (2.95)	Ignition: **OFF**	0.9 – 1.4 Ω [6]	T1/5 or T1/6 and/or T1/11 or T1/12
23.0	P0 300 P0 306 P0 312	**Primary voltage** Ignition coil (T1/6 or T1/12)	N3/11 N3/12 95 (2.95) — 25 (1.25)	**Test connection Note:** Individual primary pattern Range 400 V Duration 100% Starter: **Crank**	200 – 350 V	⇒ 23.1, N3/11 or N3/12
23.1		Primary winding of T1/6 and T1/5 or T1/12 and T1/11	N3/11 N3/12 95 (2.95) — 84 (2.84)	Ignition: **OFF**	0.9 – 1.4 Ω [6]	T1/6 or T1/5 and/or T1/12 or T1/11

[6] The resistance of a single coil is 0.5 – 0.7 Ω

MB1029500434000A

Fig. 50 Codes P0300, P0305, P0306, P0311 & P0312: Test 24, Steps 22.0–23.1

⇒		Test scope	Test connection	Test condition	Nominal value	Possible cause/Remedy
24.0	P0 300 P0 301 P0 302 P0 303 P0 304 P0 305 P0 306 P0 307 P0 308 P0 309 P0 310 P0 311 P0 312	**Firing voltage** Ignition coil (T1/1) to (T1/12)	Engine analyzer (E)	**Test connection Note:** Individual secondary pattern Range 20 kV Duration 100% Connect kV pick-ups successively to T1/1 through T1/12. Starter: **Crank**	8 – 20 kV 5)	Spark plugs, T1/1 to T1/12, N3/11 or N3/12

5) The resistance of the secondary winding can not be measured due to an installed diode.

MB1029500435000A

Fig. 51 Codes P0300, P0301, P0302, P0303, P0304, P0305, P0306, P0307, P0308, P0309, P0310, P0311 & P0312: Test 24, Step 24.0

⇒		Test scope	Test connection	Test condition	Nominal value	Possible cause/Remedy
1.0	P1 587 P0 560	**Left engine control module (N3/11)** **Right engine control module (N3/12)** Voltage supply Circuit 30	N3/11 N3/12 26 —< (V) >— 35 (1.26) (1.35)	Ignition: **ON**	11 – 14 V	⇒ 1.1
1.1		Ground wire	N3/11 N3/12 26 —< (V) >— 2 X11/4 (1.26) 39 —< (V) >— 2 (1.39)	Ignition: **ON**	11 – 14 V	Wiring, **Model 129:** Ground (W27), module box bracket. **Model 140:** Harness ground (W15), right footwell. ⇒ 1.2
1.2		Voltage supply Circuit 30	X11/4 1 —< (V) >— 35 N3/11 N3/12 (1.35)	Ignition: **ON**	11 – 14 V	Wiring, Base module (N16/1) or fuse on base module, Ignition/starter switch (S2/1).

MB1029500436000A

Fig. 52 Codes P0560 & P1587: Test 25, Steps 1.0–1.2

⇒		Test scope	Test connection	Test condition	Nominal value	Possible cause/Remedy
2.0	P1 587 P0 560	**Left engine control module (N3/11)** **Right engine control module (N3/12)** Voltage supply Circuit 87M	N3/11 N3/12 38 —< (V) >— 25 (1.38) (1.25)	Ignition: **ON**	11 – 14 V	⇒ 2.1
2.1		Electronic ground	N3/11 N3/12 38 —< (V) >— 2 X11/4 (1.38)	Ignition: **ON**	11 – 14 V	Wiring, **Model 129, 140:** Electronics ground (W15), right footwell. ⇒ 2.2
2.2		Voltage supply Circuit 87M	X11/4 1 —< (V) >— 25 N3/11 N3/12 (1.25)	Ignition: **ON**	11 – 14 V	Wiring, Base module (N16/1) or fuse on base module, Ignition/starter switch (S2/1).

MB1029500437000A

Fig. 53 Codes P0560 & P1587: Test 25, Steps 2.0–2.2

⇒	[code]	Test scope	Test connection	Test condition	Nominal value	Possible cause/Remedy
3.0	P1 587 P0 560	**Left engine control module (N3/11)** **Right engine control module (N3/12)** Voltage supply Circuit 87E (EA)	N3/11, N3/12 39 (1.39) — V — 36 (1.36)	Ignition: **ON**	11 – 14 V	Wiring, Base module (N16/1) or fuse on base module, Ignition/starter switch (S2/1).
4.0	P1 542 P0 507	**Pedal value sensor (B37)** Signal Nominal value potentiometer 1	N3/12 18 (1.18) — V — 19 (1.19)	Ignition: **ON** Accelerator pedal position: CTP WOT	 0.2 – 0.5 V 4.3 – 4.8 V	⇒ 4.1, Wiring, B37.
4.1		Voltage supply Nominal value potentiometer 1	N3/12 18 (1.18) — V — 17 (1.17)	Ignition: **ON**	5.0 ± 0.25 V	N3/12.

MB1029500438000X

Fig. 54 Codes P0507, P0560, P1542 & P1587, : Test 25, Steps 3.0–4.1

⇒	[code]	Test scope	Test connection	Test condition	Nominal value	Possible cause/Remedy
5.0	P1 542 P0 507	**Only Left engine control module (N3/11)** **Pedal value sensor (B37)** Signal Nominal value potentiometer 2	N3/11 18 (1.18) — V — 19 (1.19)	Ignition: **ON** Accelerator pedal position: CTP WOT	 0.1 – 0.4 V 2.1 – 2.5 V	Wiring, ⇒ 5.1, B37
5.1		Voltage supply Nominal value potentiometer 2	N3/11 18 (1.18) — V — 4 (1.4)	Ignition: **ON**	2.25–2.75 V	N3/11
6.0	P0 507 P0 120 P1 162 P1 186	**Right EA/CC/ISC actuator (M16/3)** **Left EA/CC/ISC actuator (M16/4)** Signal Actual value potentiometer 1 Actual value potentiometer 2	N3/11, N3/12 98 (2.98) — V — 97 (2.97) N3/11, N3/12 98 (2.98) — V — 107 (2.107)	Ignition: **ON** Accelerator pedal position: CTP WOT Accelerator pedal position: CTP WOT	 4.0 – 4.6 V < CTP value 0.3 – 0.9 V > CTP value	Wiring, ⇒ 6.1, M16/4 or M16/3

MB1029500439000A

Fig. 55 Codes P0120, P0507, P1162, P1186 & P1542: Test 25, Steps 5.0–6.0

⇒	[code]	Test scope	Test connection	Test condition	Nominal value	Possible cause/Remedy
6.1		Voltage supply Actual value potentiometers 1 and 2	N3/11, N3/12 98 (2.98) — V — 106 (2.106)	Ignition: **ON**	4.75–5.25 V	N3/11 or N3/12
7.0	P1 580 P1 581	**Right EA/CC/ISC actuator (M16/3)** **Left EA/CC/ISC actuator (M16/4)** Activation of actuator motor Resistance of actuator motor	N3/11, N3/12 74 (2.74) — V — 75 (2.75) N3/11, N3/12 74 (2.74) — Ω — 75 (2.75)	Ignition: **ON** Engine: **at idle** ECT > 70 °C Ignition: **OFF**	1.0 – 2.3 V 1.0 – 2.5 V Value oscillates. < 10 Ω	Wiring, M16/3 or M16/4, N3/11 or N3/12
8.0	P0 500	**Only right engine control module (N3/12)** **Left front axle VSS sensor (L6/1)**	N3/12 38 (1.38) — V — 9 (1.9)	Raise front of vehicle. Ignition: **ON** Spin left front wheel by hand.	4 – 8 V ~	Wiring, ESP.

MB1029500440000A

Fig. 56 Codes P0500, P1580 & P1581: Test 25, Steps 6.1–8.0

⇒		Test scope	Test connection	Test condition	Nominal value	Possible cause/Remedy
9.0	P0 500	**Only right engine control module (N3/12)** **Left rear axle VSS sensor (L6/3)**	N3/12 38 (1.38) — V — 22 (1.22)	Raise rear of vehicle. Ignition: **ON** Spin left rear wheel by hand.	4 – 8 V ~	Wiring, ESP.
10.0	P0 507 P1 641	**CTP (idle) signal**	N3/11 N3/12 38 (1.38) — V — 16 (1.16)	Ignition: **ON** Accelerator pedal position: CTP WOT	 > 4.0 V 2.0 – 3.0 V	Wiring, N3/11 or N3/12
11.0		**Only on right engine control module (N3/12) until 05/96 (as of 06/96 via CAN)** **A/C compressor signal**	N3/12 38 (1.38) — V — 8 (1.8)	Engine: **at idle** Turn A/C system ON, move temperature selector wheel to MIN, blower set to AUTO.	< 1.0 V 11 – 14 V	Wiring, A/C pushbutton control module (N22).

MB1029500441000A

Fig. 57 Codes P0500 & P0507 & P1641: Test 25, Steps 9.0–11.0

⇒		Test scope	Test connection	Test condition	Nominal value	Possible cause/Remedy
12.0		**EPC MIL (A1e43)** Activation	N3/12 21 (1.21) — V — 35 (1.35)	Ignition: **ON** Engine: **at idle**	11 – 14 V < 1.0 V	Wiring, Malfunction in actuators or pedal value sensor, N3/12.
13.0		**Coding**	N3/11 45 (1.45) — V — 25 (1.25)	Ignition: **ON**	11 – 14 V	Wiring.
14.0		**Ground bridge**	N3/11 N3/12 73 (2.73) — Ω — 96 (2.96)	Ignition: **OFF**	< 1 Ω	Wiring.
15.0	P0 600 P1 570 P1 477	**CAN data bus**	N3/11 N3/12 60 (1.60) — Ω — 61 (1.61)	Ignition: **OFF** Disconnect connector 1 from test cable and test directly at connector 1 of engine wiring harness using an ohmmeter.	75 – 85 Ω	Data bus.

MB1029500442000X

Fig. 58 Codes P0600, P1477 & P1570: Test 25, Steps 12.0–15.0

⇒		Test scope	Test connection	Test condition	Nominal value	Possible cause/Remedy
16.0		**Model 129/140 up to 05/96 CAN element in RCL control module (N54)** **Model 129/140 as of 06/96 CAN element in DAS control module (N54/1)** Resistance	N54 N54/1 L — Ω — H	Ignition: **OFF** Disconnect control module (N54 or N54/1) and test directly at control module.	115 – 125 Ω	N54 or N54/1
17.0		**CAN element in engine control module (N3/11 or N3/12)** Resistance	N3/11 N3/12 60 (1.60) — Ω — 61 (1.61)	Ignition: **OFF** Disconnect connector 1 from control module (N3/11 or N3/12) and test directly at control module.	235 – 245 Ω	N3/11 or N3/12

MB1029500443000A

Fig. 59 Code —: Test 25, Steps 16.0–17.0

⇒	Code	Test scope	Test connection	Test condition	Nominal value	Possible cause/Remedy
1.0	P0 565	**CC switch (S40)** **V** Decelerate/set	N3/12 26 — (V) — 31 (1.26) (1.31)	Ignition: **ON** CC switch not activated. Decelerate activated.	< 1 V 11 – 14 V	Wiring, S40
1.1		**B** Accelerate/set	N3/12 26 — (V) — 2 (1.26) (1.2)	Ignition: **ON** Accelerate activated.	11 – 14 V	Wiring, S40
1.2		**SP** Memory recall	N3/12 26 — (V) — 30 (1.26) (1.30)	Ignition: **ON** Memory activated.	11 – 14 V	Wiring, S40
1.3		**Off**	N3/12 38 — (V) — 28 (1.38) (1.28)	Ignition: **ON** CC switch not activated. Off activated.	11 – 14 V < 1 V	Wiring, S40
1.4		**Control contact**	N3/12 38 — (V) — 27 (1.38) (1.27)	Ignition: **ON** CC switch not activated. Activate decelerate/accelerate/memory/off	< 1 V 11 – 14 V	Wiring, S40

MB1029500444000A

Fig. 60 Code P0565: Test 26, Steps 1.0–1.4

⇒	Code	Test scope	Test connection	Test condition	Nominal value	Possible cause/Remedy
2.0	P1 584	**Stop lamp switch (S9/1)** N.O. contact	N3/12 1 — (V) — 26 (1.1) (1.26)	Ignition: **ON** Brake pedal not applied. Brake pedal applied.	< 1 V 11 – 14 V	Wiring, S9/1
2.1		N.C. contact	N3/12 26 — (V) — 3 (1.26) (1.3)	Ignition: **ON** Brake pedal not applied. Brake pedal applied.	11 – 14 V < 1 V	Wiring, S9/1
3.0	P0 500	**Left front axle VSS sensor (L6/1)**	N3/11 38 — (V) — 9 (1.38) (1.9)	Raise front of vehicle. Ignition: **ON** Spin left front wheel by hand.	4 – 8 V ~	Wiring
4.0	P0 500	**Left rear axle VSS sensor (L6/3)**	N3/11 38 — (V) — 22 (1.38) (1.22)	Raise rear of vehicle. Ignition: **ON** Spin left rear wheel by hand.	4 – 8 V ~	Wiring

MB1029500445000A

Fig. 61 Codes P0500 & P1584: Test 26, Steps 2.0–4.0

⇒	Code	Test scope	Test connection	Test condition	Nominal value	Possible cause/Remedy
5.0	P0 600 P1 570 P1 477	**CAN data bus**	N3/11 N3/12 60 — (Ω) — 61 (1.60) (1.61)	Ignition: **OFF** Disconnect connector 1 from test cable and test directly at connector 1 of engine wiring harness using an ohmmeter.	75 – 85 Ω	Data bus.
6.0		**CAN element in RCL control module (N54)** Resistance	N54 L — (Ω) — H	Ignition: **OFF** Disconnect control module (N54) and test directly at control module.	115 – 125 Ω	N54.
7.0		**CAN element in engine control module (N3/11 or N3/12)** Resistance	N3/11 N3/12 60 — (Ω) — 61 (1.60) (1.61)	Ignition: **OFF** Disconnect connector 1 from control module (N3/11 or N3/12) and test directly at control module.	235 – 245 Ω	N3/11 or N3/12.

MB1029500446000A

Fig. 62 Codes P0600, P1477 & P1570: Test 26, Steps 5.0–7.0

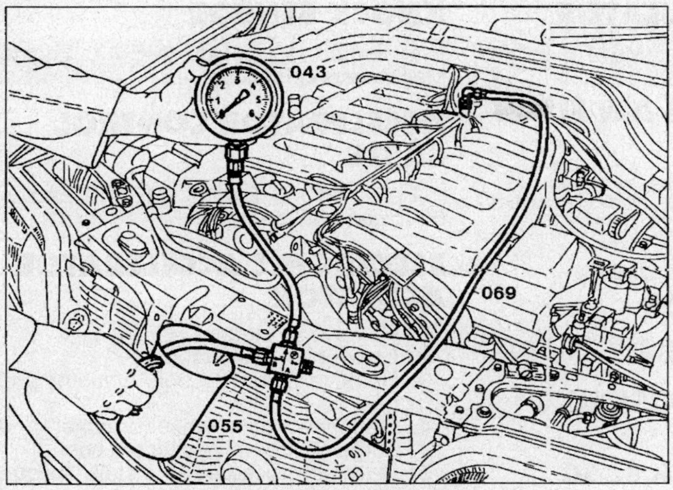

043 Pressure gauge, part no. 103 589 00 21 00
055 Measurement glass
069 Pressure hose, part no. 119 589 04 63 00

MB1029500447000X

Fig. 63 Fuel pressure connections

⇒		Test scope	Test connection	Test condition	Nominal value	Possible cause/Remedy
1.0		**Fuel pressure at idle (with vacuum)**	Pressure gauge connected to test connection.	Engine: **at idle** Valve on pressure gauge closed.	46.4 - 52.2 psi	Check fuel pumps □ 33, Replace diaphragm pressure regulator.
2.0		**Fuel pressure at idle (without vacuum)**	Pressure gauge connected to test connection.	Engine: **at idle** Disconnect vacuum hose from diaphragm pressure regulator.	53.7 - 60.9 psi	Replace diaphragm pressure regulator.
3.0		**Fuel system internal leakage**	Pressure gauge connected to test connection.	Engine: **OFF** After 30 minutes	> 43.5 psi > 36.3 psi	If the pressure drops quickly, replace check valve in fuel pumps. If the pressure drops slowly, check injectors □ 36, Replace diaphragm pressure regulator or O-rings on diaphragm pressure regulator.

MB1029500448000X

Fig. 64 Code —: Test 32, Fuel System Pressure & Leakage Test

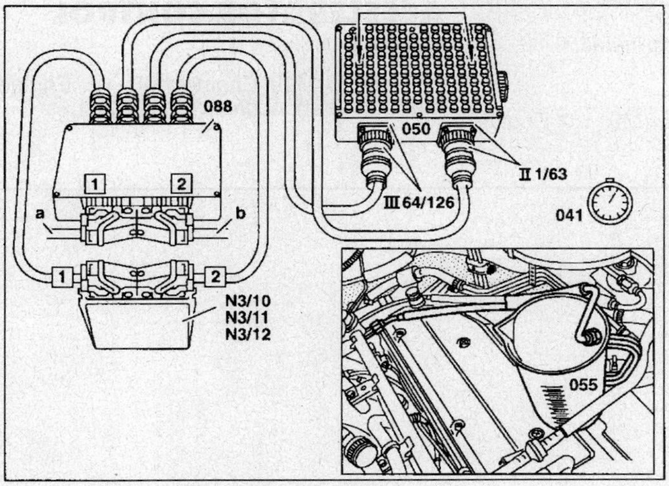

003 Digital multimeter
041 Stop watch
050 Socket box tester, 126 pole
055 Measuring glass
088 Test cable
a Interior wiring harness
b Engine compartment wiring harness

MB1029500449000X

Fig. 65 Fuel pump test connections

⇒		Test scope	Test connection	Test condition	Nominal value	Possible cause/Remedy
1.0		**Fuel pumps** Delivery capacity	N3/12 26 (1.26) ←→ 24 (1.24)	Disconnect fuel return hose from fuel line and place end in measuring glass. Ignition: **ON**	1 liter of fuel within 35 seconds.	Check fuel lines for restrictions (kinks and dents). Replace fuel filter, ⇒ 2.0.
2.0		**Fuel pumps** Current draw Connect multimeter to sockets 1 and 3 (Figure 1)	1 —< >— 3	Disconnect fuel pump relay module (K27). Ignition: **ON**	5 - 9 A	Fuel pumps

MB1029500450000X

Fig. 66 Code —: Test 34, Fuel Pump Test

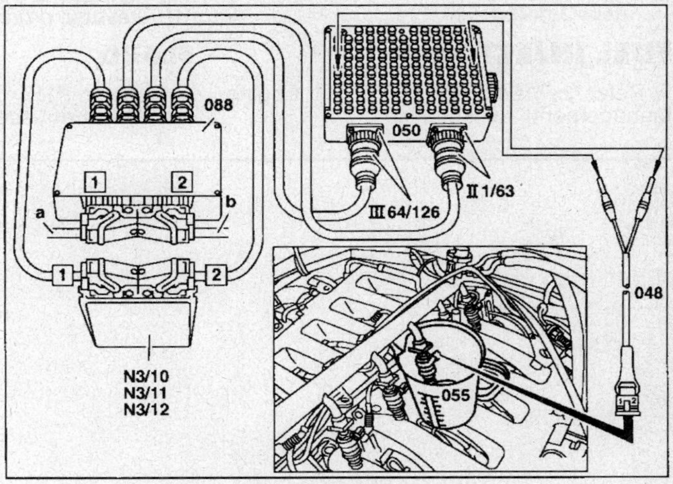

048 Self made harness
050 Socket box tester, 126 pole
055 Measuring glass
088 Test cable
N3/12 Right engine control module (ME-SFI)

MB1029500451000X

Fig. 67 Fuel injector test connections

⇒		Test scope	Test connection	Test condition	Nominal value	Possible cause/Remedy
1.0		**Injectors** Leakage test	N3/12 26 (1.26) ←→ 24 (1.24)	Fuel rail and fuel injectors removed. Ignition: **ON**	Injectors must not drip.	Replace dripping injectors, ⇒ 2.0.
2.0		**Injectors** Operation and spray pattern test	N3/12 26 (1.26) ←→ 24 (1.24)	Ignition: **ON** Hold each injector (one after another) into a container and, using the self-made test harness, manually activate the injector by connecting harness banana plugs to socket box sockets 38 (–) and 25 (+).	Injectors must spray evenly.	Replace defective injectors.

MB1029500452000X

Fig. 68 Code —: Test 36, Fuel Injector Test

SYSTEM SERVICE

Component Replacement

FUEL RAIL

1. Relieve fuel pressure through fuel rail service valve.
2. **On 1998–99 CL600 and S600 models,** remove air inlet plenum.
3. **On all models,** remove cable duct.
4. Disconnect automatic transmission vacuum line at intake manifold.
5. Remove electric wiring straps from fuel rail.
6. Disconnect pressure regulator vacuum line.
7. Disconnect fuel feed and return lines. Collect spilled fuel in suitable container.
8. Disconnect electrical connectors.
9. Remove mounting screws.
10. Pull fuel rail with injection valves from intake manifold.
11. Reverse procedure to install. Lubricate new O-rings

FUEL INJECTOR

Refer to "104 Engine (ME 2.1 Engine Management)" section.

PRESSURE REGULATOR

Refer to "119 Engine (ME 1.0 Engine Management)" section.

HOT FILM MASS AIR FLOW (MAF) SENSOR

1. Disconnect connector.
2. Remove union nut and disconnect hose.
3. Remove sensor.
4. Reverse procedure to install.

OXYGEN SENSOR

Refer to "119 Engine (ME 1.0 Engine Management)" section.

CRANKSHAFT POSITION (CKP) SENSORS

1998–99 CL600 & S600

1. Remove fuel rail as described under "Fuel Rail, Replace."
2. Remove air cleaner.
3. Remove intake manifold.
4. Disconnect control cables.
5. Remove CKP sensors.
6. Reverse procedure to install.

SL600

Refer to "119 Engine (ME 1.0 Engine Management)" section.

KNOCK SENSOR

Refer to "119 Engine (ME 1.0 Engine Management)" section.

ACCELERATOR CONTROL CABLE

Refer to "119 Engine (ME 1.0 Engine Management)" section.

ELECTRONIC ACCELERATOR ACTUATOR

1. Remove air cleaner.
2. Disconnect connector.
3. Remove mounting bolt, actuator and gasket.
4. Disconnect crankcase breather and purge control valve vacuum hose.
5. Reverse procedure to install. **Torque** mounting bolts to 18 ft. lbs.

Adjustments

ACCELERATOR CONTROL CABLE

Refer to "119 Engine (ME 1.0 Engine Management)" section.

606 Diesel Engine

NOTE: On Air Bag Equipped Models, Refer To "Air Bag System Precautions" Located In The Front Of This Manual For System Disarming & Arming Procedures.

NOTE: Refer To "Computer Relearn Procedures" Located In The Front Of This Manual When Battery Power To The Computer Has Been Interrupted.

NOTE: Prior To Performing Any Service Listed In This Section Consult Technical Service Bulletin Section For Related Information.

NOTE: "Electrical Symbol Identification" Located In Front Of This Manual May Be Used As An Aid When Using Wiring Diagrams Found In This Section.

INDEX

	Page No.
Description	14-208
Electronic Diesel System (EDS)	14-208
Pre-Glow & Afterglow System	14-209
Diagnosis & Testing	14-209
Accessing Diagnostic Trouble Codes	14-209
Generic Scan Tool	14-209
Hand-Held Tester	14-209
Impulse Counter Scan Tool	14-209
Clearing Diagnostic Trouble Codes	14-210
Hand-Held Tester	14-210
Impulse Counter Scan Tool	14-210
Components Locations	14-210
Connector Terminal Identification	14-210
Diagnostic Tests	14-210
Diagnostic Trouble Code Interpretation	14-210
Symbol Explanation	14-209
Symptom Related Diagnosis	14-210
Wiring Diagrams	14-210
Diagnostic Chart Index	14-214
Precautions	14-208
Air Bag Systems	14-208
Battery Ground Cable	14-208
Drive Authorization System (DAS)	14-208
ECM Recognition	14-208
Sensor & Fuel Injector Specifications	14-208
System Service	14-221
Adjustments	14-221
TDC Sensor	14-221
Throttle Cable	14-221
Component Service	14-221
Fuel Heat Exchanger	14-221
Fuel Injectors	14-221
Injection Pipes	14-221
Throttle Cable	14-221
Throttle Position Sensor	14-221

SENSOR & FUEL INJECTOR SPECIFICATIONS

Year	Temperature, F°	Resistance, Ohms	Voltage
CRANKSHAFT POSITION (CKP) SENSOR			
1998	—	680–1300	—
ENGINE COOLANT TEMPERATURE①			
1998	68	2,500	3.7
	86	1,700	3.4
	104	1.170	3.0
	122	830	2.6
	140	600	2.1
	158	435	1.8
	176	315	1.5
	194	245	1.2
FUEL RACK POSITION SENSOR			
1998	—	④	2.2–2.7
FUEL TEMPERATURE			
1998	68	2,500	3.9
	86	1,700	3.5
	104	1,170	3.0
	122	830	2.6
IN-LINE FUEL INJECTION (IFI) ACCELERATOR PEDAL POSITION			
1998	—	—	③
INTAKE AIR TEMPERATURE②			
1998	68	6,060	3.8
	86	3,900	3.3
	104	2,600	2.9

① — ±10%.
② — ±5%.
③ — Closed Throttle Position (CTP): 0.3–0.5 volt. Full load position: 3.75–4.75 volts.
④ — Between terminals No. 9 & 46, 20–25 ohms; No. 9 & 20, 40–50 ohms, ±5%.

PRECAUTIONS

Air Bag Systems

Refer to “Air Bag System Precautions” in the front of this manual for system disarming and arming procedures.

Battery Ground Cable

Prior to service, disconnect battery ground cable and isolate as required.

ECM Recognition

The ECM must be coded for vehicle model, ABS, transmission, cruise control, electronic traction system (ETS) and country version with the Hand-Held Tester.

Before replacing the ECM, read and store existing code numbers with the Hand-Held Tester. When the new ECM is installed, enter the stored code numbers from the Hand-Held Tester. If code numbers cannot be read, the corresponding codes number must be obtained from Mercedes-Benz spare parts microfiche and manually entered with a Hand-Held Tester.

Trial installation of an ECM or RCL control module from another vehicle is not possible. After 40 starts, a new ECM cannot be used in any other vehicle. The code number and VIN must be entered into the ECM with a Hand-Held Tester.

Drive Authorization System (DAS)

The DAS is activated by the Remote Central Locking (RCL) infrared remote control transmitter or master key. The ECM and RCL control module are permanently locked together by an identification code. This code cannot be erased. Trial installation of an ECM or RCL control module from another vehicle is not possible. After 40 start, a new ECM cannot be used in any other vehicle. The code number and VIN must be entered into the ECM with a Hand-Held Tester.

DESCRIPTION

ELECTRONIC DIESEL SYSTEM (EDS)

The Electronic Diesel System (EDS) control processes the following functions: electronic idle speed control, exhaust gas recirculation, boost pressure control and system diagnostics. The EDS on the 606 diesel engine differs from that on the older 603 engine in electrical and pneumatic component locations, fuel filter with shutoff valve, fuel preheater, fuel injection lines, prechamber, idle speed control and low pressure fuel circuit. There are additional differences in the emission control system including: resonance intake manifold,

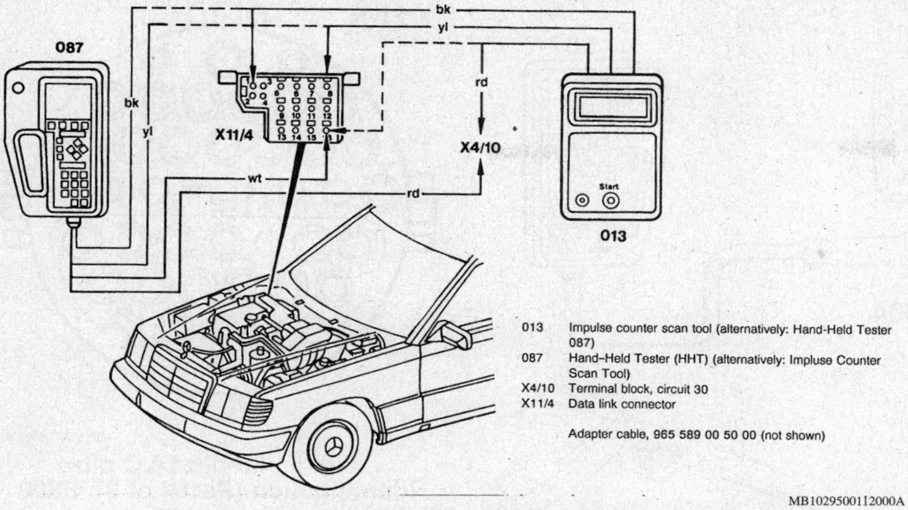

013 Impulse counter scan tool (alternatively: Hand-Held Tester 087)
087 Hand-Held Tester (HHT) (alternatively: Impluse Counter Scan Tool)
X4/10 Terminal block, circuit 30
X11/4 Data link connector

Adapter cable, 965 589 00 50 00 (not shown)

MB1029500112000A

Fig. 1 Tool connection to 16-pin DLC. E300

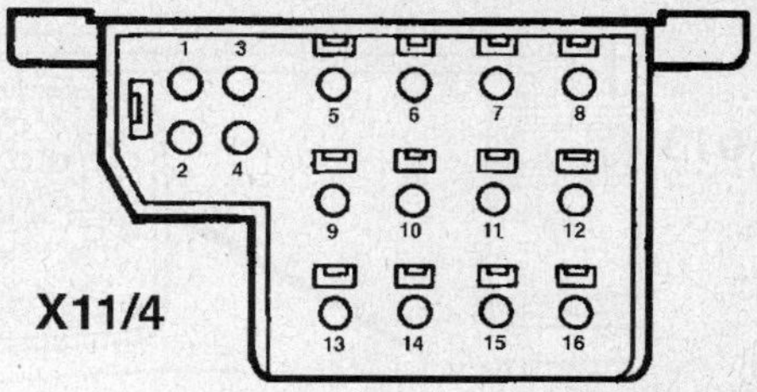

MB1029500113010A

Fig. 2 16-pin DLC connector terminal identification (Part 1 of 2). E300 except California models

1		Ground, circuit 31
2		Not used
3	CFI	Continuous fuel injection (CIS-E)
4	EDS	Electronic diesel system
5	ASD	Automatic locking differential
5		4MATIC
6	AB	Airbag/ETR (SRS)
7	A/C	Air conditioning, Model 124
7	RB	Roll bar, Model 129
8	DI	Distributor ignition
8	HFM-SFI	HFM sequential multiport fuel injection/ignition
9	ADS	Adaptive damping system
9	RB	Roll bar, Model 124
10	RST	Roadster soft top, Model 129
10		TN-signal (Gasoline)
11	ATA	Anti-theft alarm
12	RCL	Remote central locking
13	ETC	Electronic transmission control
14	EA	Electronic accelerator, Model 124
14	CC/ISC	Cruise control/idle speed control, Model 124
14	ESCM	Engine systems control module (MAS), Model 129
15		Not used
16		Circuit 15

MB1029500113020A

Fig. 2 16-pin DLC connector terminal identification (Part 2 of 2). E300 except California models

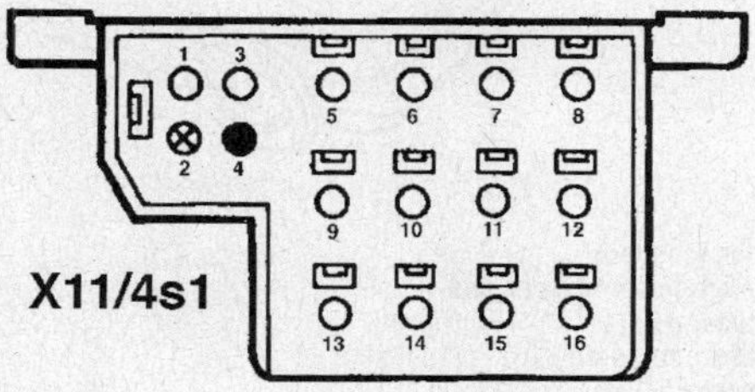

MB1029500114010A

Fig. 3 16-pin DLC connector terminal identification (Part 1 of 2). E300 California models

1		Ground, circuit 31
2	OBD	Pushbutton for on-board diagnostics
3	CFI	Continuous fuel injection (CIS-E)
3	DM	Diagnostic module
4		LED
5	ASD	Automatic locking differential
6	AB	Airbag/ETR (SRS)
7	A/C	Air conditioning, Model 124
7	RB	Roll bar, Model 129
8	DI	Distributor ignition
8	HFM-SFI	HFM sequential multiport fuel injection/ignition
9	ADS	Adaptive damping system
9	RB	Roll bar, Model 124
10	RST	Roadster soft top, Model 129
10		TN-signal (gasoline)
11	ATA	Anti-theft alarm
12	RCL	Remote central locking
13	ETC	Electronic transmission control
14	EA	Electronic accelerator, Model 124
14	CC/ISC	Cruise control/idle speed control, Model 124
14	ESCM	Engine systems control module (MAS), Model 129
15		Not used
16		Circuit 15

MB1029500114020A

Fig. 3 16-pin DLC connector terminal identification (Part 2 of 2). E300 California models

emission control, test program, emission control function diagram, oxidation catalytic converter and barometric sensor.

PRE-GLOW & AFTERGLOW SYSTEM

The pre-glow system consists of a pre-glow time relay, coolant temperature sensor and pin type glow plugs. Pre-glow lasts until the pre-glow indicator lamp goes out, lamp operation is dependent upon coolant temperature. To improve engine warm-up characteristics, glow time (afterglow) may extend a maximum of 60 seconds after engine is running. Glow plugs are continuously monitored by a microprocessor in the pre-glow time relay unit. The pre-glow indicator lamp will illuminate for approximately one minute if one or more of glow plugs fail.

A short circuit protection mechanism is provided for pre-glow system. If a short circuit occurs, current circuit is interrupted. Once short is repaired, relay is operational again. To reset circuit protection, steering lock key must be on Off position.

DIAGNOSIS & TESTING

Symbol Explanation

Refer to "104 Engine (ME 2.1 Engine Management)" section for explanations of symbols, connections and steps included in the charts.

Accessing Diagnostic Trouble Codes

GENERIC SCAN TOOL

Follow tool manufacturers instructions and connect suitably programmed scan tool to generic scan tool connection X11/22.

HAND-HELD TESTER

1. Turn ignition switch to Off position.
2. **On models equipped with 16-pin Data Link Connector (DLC),** connect Hand-Held Tester No. 965 589 00 01 00, or equivalent, as follows:
   a. Attach test cable tool No. 965 589 00 50 00, or equivalent, to tester.
   b. Connect ground circuit 31 black wire to DLC socket No. 1, **Fig. 1.**
   c. Connect voltage circuit 15 white wire to socket No. 16.
   d. Connect circuit 30 red wire to battery positive terminal or X4/10 terminal block circuit 30.
   e. Connect yellow wire to diagnostic output socket of system being tested, **Figs. 2 and 3.**
3. **On models equipped with 38-pin DLC,** connect Hand-Held Tester No. 965 589 00 01 00, or equivalent, as follows:
   a. Connect tester to multiplexer cable tool No. 965 589 00 40 00, or equivalent.
   b. Turn multiplexer cable locking ring completely to left detent stop.
   c. Attach multiplexer cable to data link connector via locking pins, **Fig. 4.**
   d. To lock multiplexer cable to connector, turn locking ring to the right.
4. Follow tool manufacturer's instructions.

IMPULSE COUNTER SCAN TOOL

1. **On models equipped with 16-pin Data Link Connector (DLC),** connect impulse counter scan tool No. 124 589 19 21 00, or equivalent, as follows:
   a. Connect ground circuit 31 black wire to socket No. 1, **Fig. 1.**
   b. Connect ignition circuit 15 white wire to socket No. 16.
   c. Connect yellow wire to diagnostic output socket of system being tested, **Figs. 2 and 3.**
2. **On models equipped with 38-pin data link connector,** connect impulse counter scan tool No. 124 589 19 21

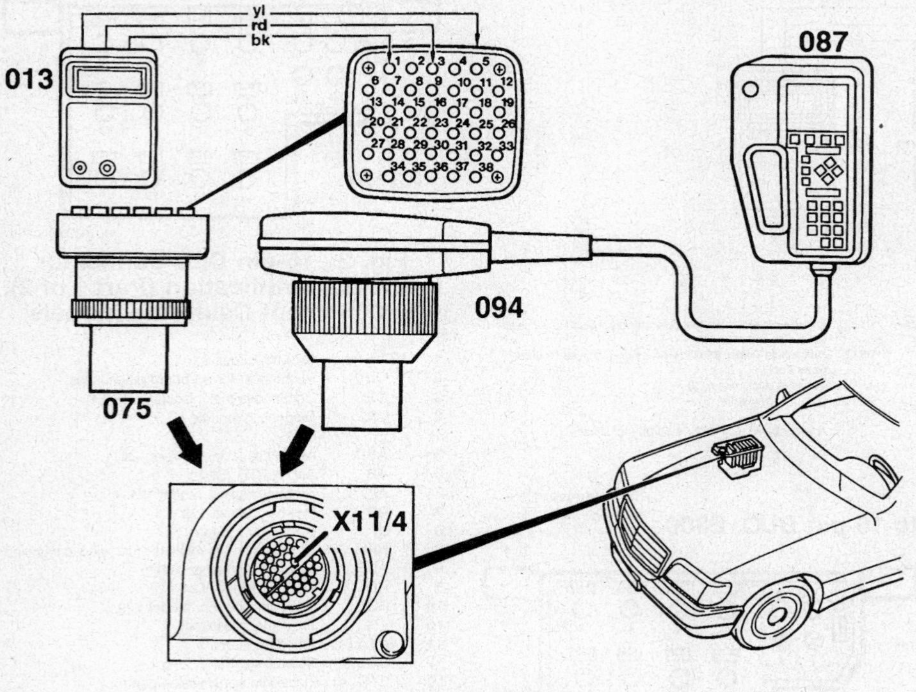

013	Impulse counter scan tool
075	Adaptor for impulse counter scan tool
087	Hand-Held Tester (HHT)
094	Multiplexer, 965 589 00 40
X11/4	Data link connector

MB1029500115000A

Fig. 4 Tool connection to 38-pin DLC. E300

00, or equivalent, as follows:

a. Connect adapter tool No. 140 589 14 63 00, or equivalent, to 38-pin data link connector, **Fig. 4.**
b. Connect voltage circuit 30 red wire to socket No. 3.
c. Connect ground circuit 31 black wire to socket No. 1.
d. Connect yellow wire to diagnostic output socket of system being tested, **Fig. 5.**

3. LED "U-Bat" must light. If LED does not light, check voltage supply and tool fuse.
4. Turn ignition switch to On position, then press scan tool start button for 2–4 seconds.
5. Read and record Diagnostic Trouble Code (DTC) displayed.
6. Press scan tool start button again for 2–4 seconds and record next DTC.
7. Continue to press start button for 2–4 seconds until all diagnostic codes have been displayed. If no other DTCs are stored, first DTC will be displayed, again.

Diagnostic Trouble Code Interpretation

Refer to **Fig 6** for DTC interpretation.

Symptom Related Diagnosis

Refer to **Fig. 7** for symptom related diagnosis.

Components Locations

Refer to **Fig. 8** for system component locations.

Wiring Diagrams

Refer to **Fig. 9** for wiring diagram.

Connector Terminal Identification

Refer to for engine control module connector terminal identification.

Refer to **Fig. 10** for control module connector terminal identification.

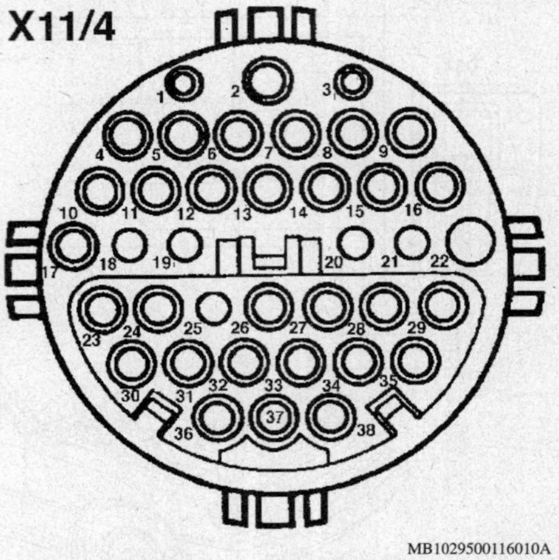

Fig. 5 38-pin DLC pin identification (Part 1 of 3). E300

Diagnostic Tests

1. Turn ignition switch to Off position.
2. Remove In-line Fuel Injection (IFI) connector.
3. Connect 126-pole socket box tool No. 129 589 00 21 00, or equivalent, to IFI control module and connector with test cable tool No. 104 589 00 63 00, or equivalent, **Fig. 11.**
4. Conduct test as directed in **Figs. 12 through 28** using suitable digital multimeter.

Clearing Diagnostic Trouble Codes

The Diagnostic Trouble Codes will be cleared when the effected component has been repaired or replaced.

HAND-HELD TESTER

Follow tool manufacturer's instructions.

IMPULSE COUNTER SCAN TOOL

1. Press start button 2–4 seconds until Diagnostic Trouble Code (DTC) appears.
2. Wait three second, then press start button and hold 6–8 seconds, erasing previously displayed DTC. Erasing must begin within 20 seconds of DTC display. After 20 seconds, DTC can no longer be erased until displayed again.
3. Erase each stored DTC individually.

1		Ground, circuit 31 (W12, W15, electronics ground)
2		Voltage, circuit 87
3		Voltage, circuit 30
4	EDS	Electronic diesel system
4	DFI	Electronic distributor-type fuel injection (Diesel)
4	IFI	Electronic In-line fuel injection (Diesel)
4	HFM-SFI	HFM sequential multiport fuel injection/ignition, Engine 104
4	LH-SFI	LH sequential multiport fuel injection, Engines 104, 119 Engine 120 (right)
4	ME-SFI	ME sequential multiport fuel injection/ignition, Engine 119, Engine 120 (right)
5	LH-SFI	LH sequential multiport fuel injection, Engine 120 (left)
5	ME-SFI	ME sequential multiport fuel injection/ignition, Engine 120 (left)
6	ABS	Anti-lock brake system
6	ETS	Electronic traction system
6	ASR	Acceleration slip regulation
6	ESP	Electronic stability program
7	EA	Electronic accelerator
7	CC/ISC	Cruise control/idle speed control
8	BM	Base module
9	ASD	Automatic locking differential, Models 124, 129, 140
10	ETC	Electronic transmission control
10	ETC	Electronic transmission control (A/T 722.6)
11	ADS	Adaptive damping system
12	SPS	Speed-sensitive power steering
13		TNA-signal (gasoline), LH-SFI engines
13		TN-signal (gasoline), HFM-SFI engines

MB1029500116020A

Fig. 5 38-pin DLC pin identification (Part 2 of 3). E300

DTC	Possible cause	Test step/Remedy
	No malfunction in system	–
P0100	Hot film MAF sensor (B2/5)	☐ 23/13⇒19
P0105	Pressure sensor (B28)	☐ 23/4⇒ 8.0
P0110	IAT sensor (B17)	☐ 23/4⇒ 7.0
P0115	ECT sensor (B11)	☐ 23/3⇒ 6.0
P0180	Fuel temperature sensor (Y1/1b1)	☐ 23/11⇒ 17.0
P0500	VSS	N47-2, 3,
P0600	CAN data bus	☐ 23/14⇒ 20.0
P0700	DTC code ETC	N15/1,
P0703	Stop lamp switch (S9/1)	
P1105	Atmospheric pressure sensor in control module	N3/7
P1220	Fuel quantity actuator (IFI) (Y23/1)	☐ 23/6⇒ 10.0
P1221	CAN communication ASR interrupted	
P1222	IFI accelerator pedal position sensor (R25/2)	☐ 23/7⇒ 12.0

2) The DTC P0600 can be displayed even if no malfunction is present

MB1029800488010X

Fig. 6 DTC interpretation (Part 1 of 3)

DTC	Possible cause	Test step/Remedy
P1617	N3/7 EEPROM or incorrectly coded	N37
P1622	Electrohydraulic shut-off actuator (Y1/1)	☐ 23/11⇒ 16.0
P1630	Drive authorization signal	☐ 23/15⇒ 23.0
P1705	Starter lock-out/backup lamp switch (N15/3)	☐ 23/14⇒ 21.0

MB1029800488030X

Fig. 6 DTC interpretation (Part 3 of 3)

14		On-off ratio, Engine 119 LH-SFI, Engine 120 LH-SFI (right)
15		On-off ratio, Engine 120 LH-SFI (left)
15	IC	Instrument cluster
16	A/C	Air conditioning, Models 124, 140, 202
17	DI	Distributor ignition, Engines 104, 119, Engine 120 (right)
17		TD-speed signal (time division), Model 140
17		TN-speed signal, LH-SFI engines
18	DI	Distributor ignition, Engine 120 (left)
19	DM	Diagnostic module
20	PSE	Pneumatic system equipment, Models 129, 140
20	CCM	Combination control module, Model 210
21	CF	Convenience feature, Model 140
21	RST	Roadster soft top, Model 129
22	RB	Roll bar, Model 129
23	ATA	Anti-theft alarm
24-25		Not used
26	ASD	Automatic locking differential, Model 202
27		Not used
28	PTS	Parktronic system
29		Not used
30	AB	Airbag/ETR (SRS)
31	RCL	Remote central locking
32-33		Not used
34	CNS	Communication and navigation system
35		Not used
36		Not used
37-38		Not used

MB1029500116030A

Fig. 5 38-pin DLC pin identification (Part 3 of 3). E300

DTC	Possible cause	Test step/Remedy
P1223	Fuel rack position sensor (Y23/1l1)	☐ 23/6⇒ 11.0
P1330	Starter operation	☐ 23/15⇒ 24.0
P1335	CKP sensor (IFI) (L5/6)	☐ 23/5⇒ 9.0
P1401	EGR lifting sender (B28/3)	☐ 23/13⇒ 18.0
P1404	EGR valve vacuum transducer (Y31/1)	☐ 23/10⇒ 15.0
P1470	Boost pressure control/pressurecontrol flap vacuum transducer (Y31/5)	☐ 23/9⇒ 14.0
P1480	Preglow control	☐ 23/15⇒ 25.0
P1481	Glow plug failure	☐ 23/16⇒ 27.0
P1482	Preglow control unit (N14/2)	☐ 23/16⇒ 26.0
P1520	Cruise control switch (S40)	☐ 23/8⇒ 13.0
P1610	Voltage supply missing or relay module (K40)	☐ 23/2⇒ 5.0
P1611	Internal reference voltage (2.5 V)	N3/7
P1612	IFI control module (N3/7) voltage, circuit 15	☐ 23/2⇒ 4.0
P1613	IFI control module (N3/7) stabilization	N3/7
P1614	IFI control module (N3/7) microprocessor/fuel calculation	N3/7
P1615	IFI control module (N3/7) supply voltage	☐ 23/1⇒ 1.0

MB1029800488020X

Fig. 6 DTC interpretation (Part 2 of 3)

Complaint/Problem	Possible cause	Test step/Remedy
Preglow indicator lamp does not light with glow/starter switch ON, engine can be started.	Preglow indicator lamp.	A1
Preglow indicator lamp does not light, engine can not be started.	Voltage supply to preglow control module (N14/2) is missing or preglow control module (N14/2) is defective.	☐ 23 ⇒ 23.0 + 24.0
Preglow indicator lamp lights for approx. 1 minute while driving.	Open circuit at glow plugs.	☐ 23 ⇒ 27.0
Preglow indicator lamp lights while driving or lights intermittantly.	Short circuit N14/2. Communication between N3/7 and N14/2 interrupted.	☐ 23 ⇒ 25.0+ 26.0

MB1029800489000X

Fig. 7 Symptom related diagnosis

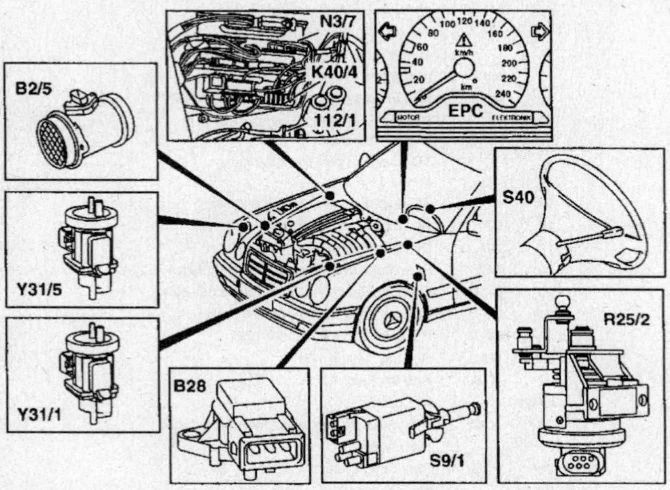

112/1	Ventilation filter for EGR valve vacuum transducer (Y31/1)	N14/2	Preglow control module
A1e43	Does not apply to U.S. vehicles	R25/2	IFI accelerator pedal position sensor
B2/5	Hot film MAF sensor	S40	CC switch
B28	Pressure sensor	Y31/1	EGR valve vacuum tranducer
K40/4	Passenger side fuse and relay module box	Y31/5	Boost pressure control/pressure control flap vacuum transducer
N3/7	IFI control module		

MB1029800490010X

Fig. 8 EDS fuel injection component locations (Part 1 of 3). E300

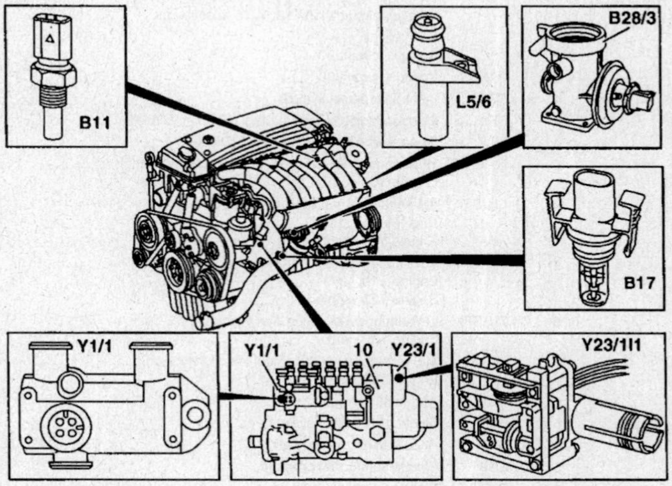

B11	ECT senor	Y1/1	IFI electrohydraulic shut-off actuator
B17	IAT sensor	Y23/1	IFI fuel injection pump
B28/3	EGR lifting sender	Y23/1l1	Fuel rack position sensor
L5/6	CKP sensor (IFI/DFI)		

MB1029800490020X

Fig. 8 EDS fuel injection component locations (Part 2 of 3). E300

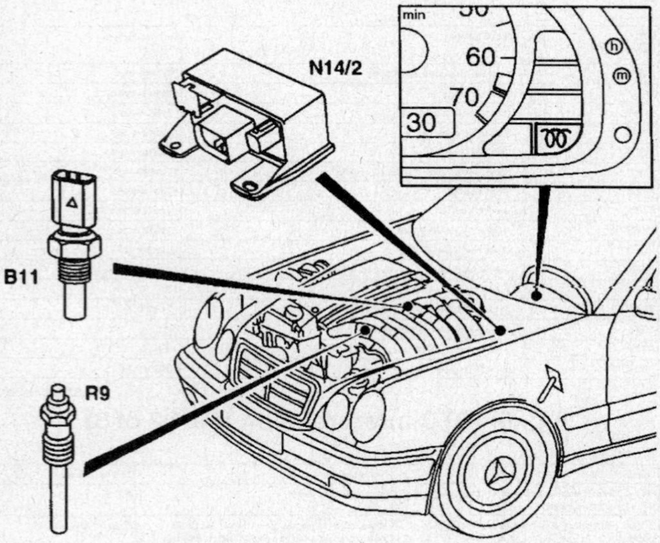

A1e16	Preglow indicator lamp
B11	ECT sensor
N14/2	Preglow output stage module
R9	Glow plugs

MB1029800490030X

Fig. 8 EDS fuel injection component locations (Part 3 of 3). E300

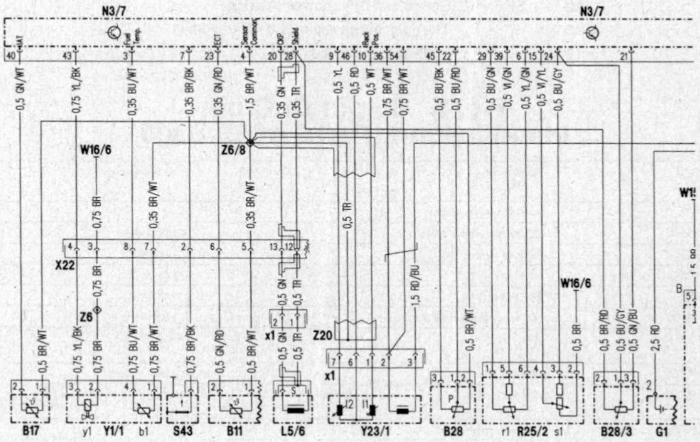

B11	ECT sensor	R25/2	IFI/DFI accelerat or pedal position sensor
B17	IAT sensor	R25/2r1	Reference potentiometer
B28	Pressure sensor	R25/2s1	CTP contact switch
B28/3	EGR lifting sender	S2	Starter switch
F1	Fuse and relay box	S35	Resonance intake manifold switch
F1-17	Fuse 17, circuit 30	S35/1	Resonance intake line switch
G1	Battery	S40	CC switch
K40	Relay module (HFM-SFI, HFM-LP, ME-SFI, EDC, base function)	S40s1	Memory recall
		S40s2	Decelerate/set
K40f5	FP fuse	S40s3	Accelerate/set
K40k8	EDC relay	S40s4	Off
L5/6	CKP sensor (IFI/DFI)	S40s5	Control contact
L5/6x1	CKP sensor connector (IFI/DFI)	S40x1	CC switch connector
M1	Starter	S43	Oil level switch
N3/7	IFI control module	W15/1	Ground (right footwell)
		W16/3	Ground (output ground-left wheel housing)
N14/2	Preglow output		
N15/3	Transmission control module		
R9	Glow plugs		

MB1029900757010X

Fig. 9 EDS wiring diagram (Part 1 of 3). E300

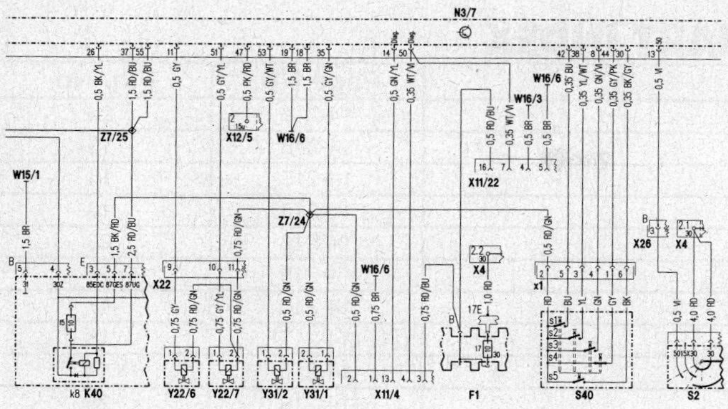

W16/6	Ground (electronics ground - component compartment - right)
X4	Terminal block (circuit 30, left footwell)
X11/4	Data link connector (DTC readout)
X11/22	Diagnostic module (OBD II) generic scan tool connector
X12/3	Terminal block (circuit 30/15 unfused) (2-pole)
X12/5	Terminal block, circuit 15/15R (FFS)
X22	Engine compartment/transmission connector
X22/2	Control module box/engine connector
X22/4	MT/engine connector (4-pole)
X25/7	Engine compartment/FFS connector
X26	Engine compartment/cockpit connector
Y1/1	IFI electrohydraulic shut-off actuator
Y1/1b1	Fuel temperature sensor
Y1/1y1	Actuator

Y22/6	Resonance intake manifold switchover valve
Y22/7	Resonance intake line switchover valve
Y23/1	In-line fuel injection pump
Y23/1l1	Fuel rack position sensor
Y23/1l2	Regulating valve-actual value
Y23/1x1	Fuel quantity actuator (IFI) connector
Y31/1	EGR valve vacuum transducer
Y31/2	Pressure control flap vacuum transducer
Z6	Ground connector sleeve
Z6/8	Sensor ground connector sleeve
Z7/24	Circuit 87 connector sleeve
Z7/25	Circuit 87 (unfused) connector sleeve (HFM-SFI/base module)
Z20	Shielding placed inside insulated tubing
Z37/2	CAN-Engine-Bus (low) connector sleeve
Z37/3	CAN-Engine-Bus (high) connector sleeve

MB1029900757020X

Fig. 9 EDS wiring diagram (Part 2 of 3). E300

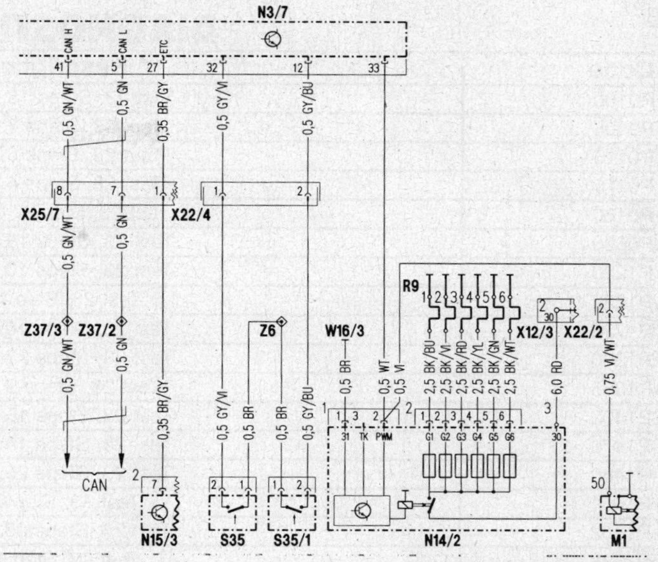

MB1029900757030X

Fig. 9 EDS wiring diagram (Part 3 of 3). E300

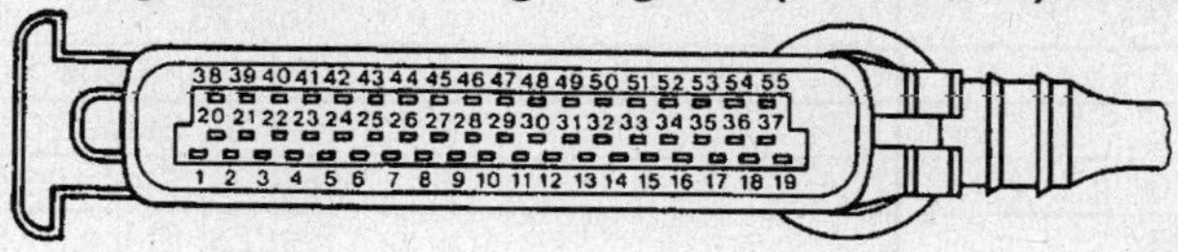

31	Cruise control switch (S40)
32	-
33	Preglow control module ([N14/2] connector 1, socket 2)
34	-
35	EGR valve vacuum transducer ([Y31/1] socket 1)
36	Fuel quantity actuator ([Y23/1] socket 2)
37	Voltage supply, circuit 87UG, unfused (relay module K40 [base function], connector E, socket 5)
38	CC switch ([S40s2] decelerate/set, socket 3)
39	IFI accelerator pedal position sensor ([R25/2] potentiometer, socket 5)
40	IAT sensor ([B17] socket 2)
41	CAN data bus (socket H)
42	CC switch ([S40s1] resume, socket 5)
43	IFI electrohydraulic shut-off actuator ([Y1/1] socket 3)
44	CC switch ([S40s4] off, socket 1)
45	Pressure sensor ([B28] socket 3)
46	Fuel rack position sensor ([Y23/1l1] socket 6)
47	Circuit 15E
48	-
49	-
50	Diagnostic signal (to X11/4, socket 4)
51	-
52	Pressure control flap vacuum transducer ([Y31/2] socket 1)
53	Boost pressure control/pressure control flap vacuum transducer ([Y31/5] socket 1)
54	IFI injection pump ([Y23/1] socket 2)
55	Voltage supply, circuit 87UG, unfused (relay module K40 [base function], connector E, socket 7)

MB1029800491020X

Fig. 10 IFI connector terminal identification (Part 2 of 2)

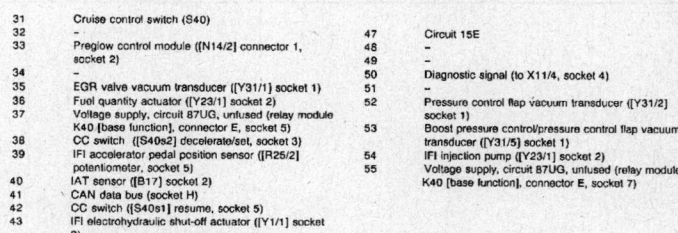

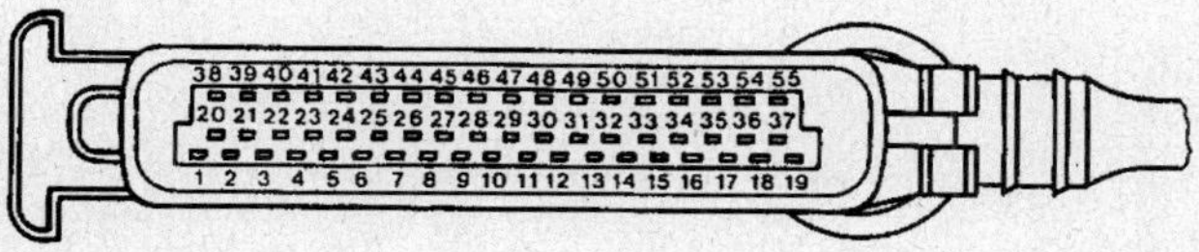

1	-
2	-
3	Fuel temperature sensor (Y1/1b1) in electrohydraulic shut off actuator, socket 4
4	Sensor ground GND
5	CAN data bus (socket L)
6	IFI accelerator pedal position sensor (R25/2) pressure sensor ([B28] socket 6)
7	Oil level switch (S43)
8	CC switch (S40) (accelerate/set, socket 4)
9	Fuel rack position sensor ([Y23/1l1] socket 7)
10	Fuel rack position sensor ([Y23/1l1] socket 1)
11	-
12	-
13	Terminal 50
14	TN-signal
15	IFI accelerator pedal position sensor ([R25/2] CTP switch, socket 4)
16	-
17	Starter relay (K40/4k2)
18	Ground W15 (electronics outut ground - right footwell)
19	Ground W15 (electronics outut ground - right footwell)
20	CKP sensor (L5/6)
21	Hot film MAF sensor ([B2/5] socket 5)
22	Pressure sensor ([B28] socket 1)
23	ECT sensor ([B11] socket 1)
24	IFI accelerator pedal position sensor ([R25/2] CTP switch, socket 3)
25	-
26	Terminal HRL from relay module K40 (connector E, socket 3)
27	P/N signal from transmission control module (N15/3)
28	CKP sensor (L5/6) ground
29	IFI accelerator pedal position sensor ([R25/2] potentiometer socket 1)
30	CC switch ([S40s5] control contact, socket 6)

MB1029800491010X

Fig. 10 IFI connector terminal identification (Part 1 of 2)

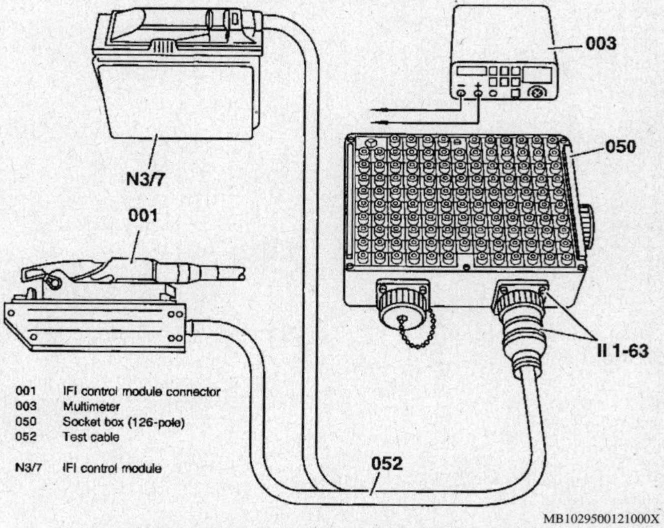

001	IFI control module connector
003	Multimeter
050	Socket box (126-pole)
052	Test cable
N3/7	IFI control module

MB1029500121000X

Fig. 11 IFI socket box connection

DIAGNOSTIC CHART INDEX

Code	Description	Page No.	Fig. No.
P0100	Test 23, Steps 18.0–20.0	14-219	24
P0105	Test 23, Steps 7.1–8.1	14-216	15
P0110	Test 23, Steps 6.1–7.0	14-215	14
P0115	Test 23, Steps 4.0–6.0	14-215	13
P0180	Test 23, Step 17.0–17.2	14-218	23
P0600	Test 23, Steps 18.0–20.0	14-219	24
P1220	Test 23, Steps 10.0–11.1	14-216	17
P1222	Test 23, Step 12.0	14-217	18
P1223	Test 23, Steps 10.0–11.1	14-216	17
P1330	Test 23, Steps 23.0–24.1	14-219	26
P1335	Test 23, Steps 9.0–9.1	14-216	16
P1403	Test 23, Steps 15.0–15.2	14-218	21
P1470	Test 23, Steps 14.0–14.2	14-217	20
P1480	Test 23, Steps 25.0–26.1	14-220	27
P1481	Test 23, Step 27.0	14-220	28
P1482	Test 23, Steps 25.0–26.1	14-220	27
P1520	Test 23, Step 13.0	14-217	19
P1610	Test 23, Steps 4.0–6.0	14-215	13
P1612	Test 23, Steps 4.0–6.0	14-215	13
P1615	Test 23, Steps 1.0–3.0	14-215	12
P1622	Test 23, Steps 16.0–16.2	14-218	22
P1630	Test 23, Steps 23.0–24.1	14-219	26
P1705	Test 23, Steps 21.0–22.1	14-219	25

⇒		Test scope	Test connection	Test condition	Nominal value	Possible cause/Remedy
1.0	P1615	**IFI control module (N3/7)** Voltage supply Circuit 87	N3/7 19 —‹ V ›— 37 18 —‹ V ›— 55	Ignition: **ON**	11 – 14 V 11 – 14 V	⇒ 3.0, Passenger side fuse and relay module box (K40/4), Wiring.
1.1		Power ground, electronic	N3/7 18 —‹ V X12/3 — 19 —‹ V X12/3 —	Ignition: **OFF** X12/3	11 – 14 V	Power ground, electronic
2.0		**Non U.S.A. vehicles only**				
3.0		**Passenger side fuse and relay module box (K40/4)** Voltage supply Terminal 30	K40/4 C ⊥ V ›— 1	Ignition: **OFF** Disconnect connector **C** from the passenger side fuse and relay module box (K40/4)	11 – 14 V	Fuses Wiring/connectors Passenger side fuse and relay module box (K40/4)

MB1029800492000X

Fig. 12 Code P1615: Test 23, Steps 1.0–3.0

⇒		Test scope	Test connection	Test condition	Nominal value	Possible cause/Remedy
4.0	P1612	**Circuit 15U**	N3/7 18 —‹ V ›— 47	Ignition: **ON**	11 – 14 V	Check voltage supply ⇒ 1.0, Wiring/connectors Electronic igintion lock control module (N73) Passenger side fuse and relay module box (K40/4) Starter relay (K40/4k2)
5.0	P1610	**IFI control module (N3/7)** Holding relay activation Terminal HRL	N3/7 26 —‹ V X12/3 —	Ignition: **Engine at CTP (idle)** **Engine**: Shut off	11 – 14 V 11 – 14 V for approx. 4 sec. then < 1 V	Check voltage supply ⇒ 1.0, Wiring/connectors, ⇒ 3.0 Passenger side fuse and relay module box (K40/4) IFI control module (N3/7).
6.0	P0115	**ECT sensor (B11)** Voltage	N3/7 4 —‹ V ›— 23	Ignition: **ON**	°C V 20 3.7 30 3.4 40 3.0 50 2.6 60 2.1 70 1.8 80 1.5 90 1.2 ± 10%	⇒ 6.1 IFI control module (N3/7)

MB1029800493000X

Fig. 13 Codes P0115, P1610 & P1612: Test 23, Steps 4.0–6.0

⇒		Test scope	Test connection	Test condition	Nominal value	Possible cause/Remedy
6.1		Resistance	N3/7 4 —‹ Ω ›— 23	Ignition: **OFF** Disconnect plug on IFI control module (N3/7)	°C Ω 20 2500 30 1700 40 1170 50 830 60 600 70 435 80 325 90 245 ± 10%	⇒ 6.2 Wiring/connectors,
6.2		B11	B11 1 — Ω — 2	Ignition: **OFF** Disconnect plug on ECT sensor (B11)	Nominal values see ⇒ 6.1	B11.
7.0	P0110	**IAT sensor (B17)** Voltage	N3/7 4 —‹ V ›— 40	Engine: **At CTP (idle)**	°C V 20 3.8 30 3.3 40 2.9 ± 5%	⇒ 7.1, IFI control module (N3/7)

MB1029800494000X

Fig. 14 Code P0110: Test 23, Steps 6.1–7.0

⇒		Test scope	Test connection	Test condition	Nominal value	Possible cause/Remedy
7.1		Resistance	4 —(N3/7 Ω)— 40	Ignition: **OFF** Remove plug on IFI control module (N3/7)	°C Ω 20 6060 30 3900 40 2600 ±5%	⇒ 7.2 Wiring/connectors
7.2		B17	Shield or 2 — B17 Ω — 1	Ignition: **OFF** Remove plug on sensor B17	Nominal values see ⇒ 7.1	B17.
8.0	P0105	**(B28) Pressure sensor** **Note for connection:** Connect pressure tester with Y-fitting to pressure sensor	6 —(N3/7 V)— 22	Slowly increase engine speed to 2500 rpm	Voltage: **Rises** Pressure: **Rises**	⇒ 8.1 Pressure line, Pressure sensor (B28)
8.1		Voltage supply B28	6 —(N3/7 V)— 45	Ignition: **ON**	4.8 – 5.2 V	Wiring/connectors, IFI control module (N3/7).

MB1029800495000X

Fig. 15 Code P0105: Test 23, Steps 7.1–8.1

⇒		Test scope	Test connection	Test condition	Nominal value	Possible cause/Remedy
9.0	P1335	**CKP sensor (L5/6)**	28 —(N3/7 2))— 20	Engine: **At CTP (idle)**	Signal see Figure 8	Installation position of CKP sensor (L5/6), Dirt on L5/6 (metal chips), Segments on flywheel, ⇒ 9.1
			28 —(N3/7 1) V)— 20	Engine: **At CTP (idle)**	> 0.8 V~ increasing rpm = increasing voltage	
				Cranking rpm: > 200 rpm	> 0.3 V~	
9.1		Resistance of sensor L5/6	28 —(N3/7 Ω)— 20	Ignition: **OFF** Remove plug on IFI control module (N3/7)	680 – 1300 Ω	Connector L5/6x1 Wiring/connectors Position of CKP sensor (L5/6).

1) Test with multimeter only if oscilloscope is not available.
2) Test with oscilloscope. This test can be performed at idle speed with the Bear DACE engine analyzer. Set time axis to 25 milliseconds, voltage to A/C at 40V.

MB1029800496000X

Fig. 16 Code P1335: Test 23, Steps 9.0–9.1

⇒		Test scope	Test connection	Test condition	Nominal value	Possible cause/Remedy
10.0	P1220	**(Y23/1)** Adjustment solenoid	N3/7 36 —(V)— 37 54 —(V)— 37	Ignition: **ON**	> 4.0 V max. for 30 seconds with a clearly audible click	⇒ 10.1, Engine control module (IFI) (N3/7)
10.1		Resistance	N3/7 36 —(Ω)— 37 54 —(Ω)— 37	Ignition: **OFF** Remove connector on IFI control module (N3/7)	1.0 ± 1.4 Ω 1.0 ± 1.4 Ω	Fuel quantity actuator connector (Y23/1x1) Wiring/connectors, Fuel quantity actuator (Y23/1).
11.0	P1223	**Fuel rack position sensor (Y23/1I1)**	N3/7 19 —(V)— 9 19 —(V)— 10	Ignition: **ON**	2.2 – 2.7 V 2.2 – 2.7 V	⇒ 11.1, Engine control module (IFI) (N3/7).
11.1		Resistance	N3/7 46 —(Ω)— 9 10 —(Ω)— 9	Ignition: **OFF** Remove connector on IFI control module (N3/7)	20 – 25 Ω 40 – 50 Ω	Connector Y23/1x1 Fuel quantity actuator (Y23/1), Wiring/connectors,

MB1029800497000X

Fig. 17 Codes P1220 & P1223: Test 23, Steps 10.0–11.1

⇒		Test scope	Test connection	Test condition	Nominal value	Possible cause/Remedy
12.0	P1222	**IFI accelerator pedal position sensor (R25/2)** Nominal value poteniometer	N3/7 6 —< (V) >— 39	Ignition: **ON** CTP (idle) position: Full load position:	 0.2 ± 0.5 V 3.7 ± 4.8 V	IFI accelerator pedal position sensor (R25/2) Wiring/connectors, IFI control module (N3/7),
		Actual value poteniometer	18 —< (V) >— 15	CTP (idle) position: Full load position:	> 4.5 V <0.5 V	
			15 —< (V) >— 24	CTP(idle) position: Full load position:	<0.5 V > 4.5 V	
			15 —< (V) >— 29	CTP (idle) position: Full load position:	<0.5 V > 4.5 V	

MB1029800498000X

Fig. 18 Code P1222: Test 23, Step 12.0

⇒		Test scope	Test connection	Test condition	Nominal value	Possible cause/Remedy
13.0	P1520	**CC switch (S40)**		Ignition: **ON** Selection: Cruise control actual values		Wiring/connectors, IFI control module (N3/7) CC switch (S40).
		CC switch (S40)		Position: **DECELERATE** Position: **ACCELERATE** Position: **RESUME** Position: **OFF** Switch not actuated	D A R O (No display)	
		Safety contact		Switch not actuated Position: **DECELERATE, ACCELERATE, RESUME, OFF**	ON OFF	

MB1029800499000X

Fig. 19 Code P1520: Test 23, Step 13.0

⇒		Test scope	Test connection	Test condition	Nominal value	Possible cause/Remedy
14.0	P1470	**Boost pressure control/pressure control flap vacuum transducer (Y31/5)** **Test connections:** Connect vacum/pressure tester with Y - fitting, between Y31/5 "OUT" outlet and boost pressure control valve. Intake manifold pressure can be observed using the HHT.	N3/7 53 —< (V) >— 37	Check vacuum at Y31/5 "OUT" outlet Engine: **at CTP** (idle) Accelerate briefly to 3500 rpm	 > 3.5 V >350 mbar < 3 V < 300 mbar Intake manifold pressure rises.	Vent filter dirty □ 31/1, ⇒ 14.1, Vacuum lines, Vacuum supply ⇒ 14.2, Wiring/connectors, IFI control module (N3/7).
14.1		Current draw	N3/7 43 —< (A) >— 53	Ignition: **ON**	0.8 - 1.2 A	Wiring/connectors, Y31/5
14.2		Vacuum supply **Test connections:** Connect vacum/pressure tester with Y - fitting between vacuum supply lines.		Engine: **At CTP (idle)**	>700 mbar	Vacuum lines, Vacuum pump.

MB1029800500000X

Fig. 20 Code P1470: Test 23, Steps 14.0–14.2

⇒		Test scope	Test connection	Test condition	Nominal value	Possible cause/Remedy
15.0	P1403	**EGR valve vacuum transducer (Y31/1)** Vacuum at outlet "OUT" of vacuum transducer		Engine: at **CTP** (idle) Pressure regulating >1000 rpm Accelerate briefly to >3300 rpm	 ON OFF	Vent filter dirty ⇒ 15.1 Vacuum lines, Vacuum supply ⇒ 14.2, Wiring, EGR valve ⇒ 15.2 IFI control module (N3/7).
15.1		Current draw	N3/7 18 —< —(A)— >— 35	Ignition: **ON**	0.8 - 1.2 A	Y31/1
15.2		EGR valve leakage		Ignition: **OFF** Remove vacuum line and connect pressure/vacuum tester. Apply 400 mbar of vacuum to EGR valve.	EGR valve closes audibly	EGR valve.

MB1029800501000X

Fig. 21 Code P1403: Test 23, Steps 15.0–15.2

⇒		Test scope	Test connection	Test condition	Nominal value	Possible cause/Remedy
16.0	P1622	**Electrohydraulic shut-off actuator (Y1/1)** Activation	N3/7 18 —< —(V)— >— 43	Engine: **At CTP (idle)**	11 – 14 V	⇒ 16.1, IFI control module (N3/7).
16.1		Current draw	N3/7 X12/3 43 —< —(A)— —	Ignition: **OFF** Disconnect terminal block circuit 30 (X12/3) at IFI control module (N3/7)	1.4 - 1.6 A Y1/1 clicks audibly	⇒ 16.2 Wiring/connectors,
16.2		Resistance	Y1/1y1 2 —< —(Ω)— >— 3	Ignition: **OFF** Remove plug Y1/1	7.6 ± 8.6 Ω	Electrohydraulic shut-off actuator (Y1/1).

MB1029800502000X

Fig. 22 Code P1622: Test 23, Steps 16.0–16.2

⇒		Test scope	Test connection	Test condition	Nominal value	Possible cause/Remedy
17.0	P0180	**Fuel temperature sensor (Y1/1b1)**	N3/7 4 —< —(V)— >— 3	Engine: **At CTP**	°C V 20 3.9 30 3.5 40 3.0 50 2.6	⇒ 17.1 IFI control moduel (N3/7)
17.1		Resistance	N3/7 4 —< —(Ω)— >— 3	Ignition: **OFF** Remove connector on IFI control module (N3/7)	°C Ω 20 2500 30 1700 40 1170 50 830	⇒ 17.2 Wiring
17.2		Y1/1b1	Y1/1b1 1 — —(Ω)— — 4	Ignition: **OFF** Remove connector on electrohydraulic shut-off actuator (Y1/1)	Nominal values see ⇒ 16.1	Fuel temperature sensor (Y1/1b1), (Replace electrohydraulic shut-off actuator [Y1/1]).

MB1029800503000X

Fig. 23 Code P0180: Test 23, Step 17.0–17.2

⇒	[tester]	Test scope	Test connection	Test condition	Nominal value	Possible cause/Remedy
18.0		**Non U.S. vehicles only**				
19.0	P0100	**Hot film MAF sensor (2/5)**	[tester]	Engine: **at CTP** (idle) Air quantity (Select actual value test, engine test.)	Compare Nominal/Actual value	Unmetered air (air leak), Wiring/connectors, Hot film MAF sensor (B2/5)
20.0	P0600	**CAN data bus** Wire resistance	N3/7 41 –(–Ω–)– 5	Ignition: **OFF**	58 – 62 Ω	Data line, connector, CAN bus

MB1029800504000X

Fig. 24 Codes P0100 & P0600: Test 23, Steps 18.0–20.0

⇒	[tester]	Test scope	Test connection	Test condition	Nominal value	Possible cause/Remedy
21.0	P1705	**P/N signal from transmission control module (N15/3)**	N3/7 18 –(–V–)– 27	Ignition: **OFF** Selector lever: In **P** or **N** pos., Out of **P** or **N** pos.	< 0.5 11 - 14V	Wiring, Ground electronics (right footwell) (W15/1), Transmission control module (N15/3).
22.0	P1705	**Stop lamp switch (S9/1)**	[tester]	Ignition: **ON** Brake pedal position via CAN (Select actual values tests, engine tests): Brake pedal **depressed** Brake pedal **released**	> 6 V **ON** **OFF**	⇒ 22.1 Wiring, CAN - Bus,
22.1		Resistance	S9/1 1 — –Ω– — 4	Ignition: **OFF** Disconnect stop lamp switch connector (S9/1x1): Brake pedal **depressed** Brake pedal **released**	< 1Ω > 100 kΩ	Stop lamp switch (S9/1)

4) Electrohydraulic sut-off actuator clicks audibly.

MB1029800505000X

Fig. 25 Code P1705: Test 23, Steps 21.0–22.1

⇒	[tester]	Test scope	Test connection	Test condition	Nominal value	Possible cause/Remedy
23.0	P1630	**Drive authorization system (DAS)**	[tester]	Ignition: **ON** (Select actual values tests, DAS tests): Start authorization Vehicle locked	Yes No	Incorrect version coding for IFI control module (N3/7), CAN - Bus ⇒ 20.0 IFI control module (N3/7), Electronic ignition lock control module (N73).
24.0	P1330	**Starter control** Activating starter relay (K40/4K2)	N3/7 17 –(–V–)– 55	Engine: **Start**	11 – 14 V while cranking	24.1, Wiring/connectors, Starter relay (K40/4K2) Passenger side fuse and relay module box (K40/4) IFI control module (N3/7).
24.1		Electronic ignition lock control module (N73) terminal 50	N3/7 13 –(–V–)– 55	Engine: **Start**	<1 V while cranking	Wiring/connectors, Driver side fuse and relay module box (K40/2), Electronic ignition lock control module (N73), IFI control module (N3/7).

MB1029800506000X

Fig. 26 Codes P1330 & P1630: Test 23, Steps 23.0–24.1

⇒		Test scope	Test connection	Test condition	Nominal value	Possible cause/Remedy
25.0	P1480	**Preglow control** Communication wire between IFI control module (N3/7) and preglow control module (N14/2) Resistance	N3/7 33 — Ω — N14/2x1 2	Ignition: **OFF** Remove connector (N14/2x1) from preglow control module (N14/2) IFI control module (N3/7) remove.	< 1 Ω	Wiring, IFI control module (N3/7), Preglow control module (N14/2)
26.0	P1482	**Preglow control module (N14/2)** Voltage supply Circuit 30	⊥ — V — N14/2x3	Ignition: **OFF**	11 – 14 V	⇒ 26.1 Preglow control module (N14/2)
26.1		Ground, electronics output ground - right footwell (W15)	⊥ — Ω — N14/2x1 1	Ignition: **OFF** Remove connector (N14/2x1) from preglow control module (N14/2)	< 1 Ω	Ground, electronics output ground - right footwell (W15), Wiring/connectors.

MB1029800507000X

Fig. 27 Codes P1480 & P1482: Test 23, Steps 25.0–26.1

⇒		Test scope	Test connection	Test condition	Nominal value	Possible cause/Remedy
27.0	P1481	**Glow plug failure** Glow plug and wiring test	N14/2x2 ⊥ — A — 1 (2.1) ⊥ — A — 2 (2.2) ⊥ — A — 3 (2.3) ⊥ — A — 4 (2.4) ⊥ — A — 5 (2.5) ⊥ — A — 6 (2.6)	Measure with DC current pickup. Remove windshield washer reservoir, remove cable cover, loosen cable ties, pull back protective sleeve from cable, Turn ignition key for each measurement again to position 2.	8 – 25 A The current draw is dependent on the coolant temperature.	Glow plugs, Wiring, Preglow output (N14/2), IFI control module (N3/7).

MB1029800508000X

Fig. 28 Code P1481: Test 23, Step 27.0

SYSTEM SERVICE

Component Service

FUEL HEAT EXCHANGER

1. Remove charge distribution pipe.
2. Drain approximately two quarts of coolant from cooling system into suitable container.
3. Remove cable duct and fuel heat exchanger mounting bolts.
4. Remove injection pipes and fuel heat exchanger.
5. Reverse procedure to install, noting following:
   a. Replace O-rings and clamps, as required.
   b. Replace cable duct mounting bolt.
   c. **Torque** mounting bolts to 80 inch lbs.

FUEL INJECTORS

1. Remove cylinder head trim panel.
2. Remove leak fuel hoses.
3. Remove injection pipes from injectors and remove injectors.
4. Reverse procedure to install noting following:
   a. Replace injector disks.
   b. **Torque** fuel injectors to 30 ft. lbs.
   c. **Torque** injection pipes to 13–17 ft. lbs.
   d. Ensure cylinder no. 1 leak fuel hose is correctly routed to fuel return hose.

INJECTION PIPES

1. Remove cylinder head trim panel.
2. **On 1998 models,** remove charge air distribution pipe.
3. **On all models,** if replacing individual injection pipes, remove retaining clips and remove mounting bolts.
4. Unscrew union nuts at injection pump and nozzles. Seal off injection pump and nozzles connections.
5. Remove injection pipes.
6. Reverse procedure to install, noting following:
   a. Install new retaining clips.
   b. Ensure cylinder No. 1 leak fuel hose is correctly routed to fuel return hose.
   c. **Torque** injection pipes to 13–17 ft. lbs. and mounting bolts to 80 inch lbs.

THROTTLE POSITION SENSOR

1. Remove return spring.
2. Press off lock washer and unplug electric connection.
3. Remove sensor.
4. Reverse procedure to install.

THROTTLE CABLE

1. Compress plastic clip and pull cable out of accelerator control lever bracket with Bowden cable
2. Pull bracket out with expansion pin, press in and remove Bowden cable mount at accelerator pedal.
3. Press Bowden cable out from inside vehicle. Do not press rubber grommet out.
4. Remove Bowden cable from engine compartment.
5. Reverse procedure to install.

Adjustments

TDC SENSOR

1. Remove water pump belt.
2. Remove cylinder No. 1 shaft cover bush, injection nozzle, glow plug and prechamber.
3. Screw dial gauge holder tool No. 601 589 07 21 00, or equivalent, into cylinder No. 1 prechamber bore and set piston to 10° Before Top Dead Center (BTDC).
4. Set dial gauge tool No. 001 589 53 21 00, or equivalent, with tracer pin into holder and set tracer pin on dial gauge with. 1969 inch preload.
5. Slowly crank engine in rotation direction at front of crankshaft until dial gauge pointer stops at Top Dead Center (TDC) and zero gauge.
6. Slowly crank engine in rotation direction at front of crankshaft until dial gauge pointer reaches 20° After Top Dead Center (ATDC) at. 127 inch. The crankshaft belt pulley or vibration damper pin must be position exactly below the TDC sensor bracket.
7. Insert fixing pin too No. 603 589 01 21 00, or equivalent, into TDC sensor bracket and engage crankshaft belt pulley or vibration damper pin with slot.
8. If pin does not engage, loosen mounting bolt, move bracket until pin engages fixing pin slot and tighten mounting bolt.

THROTTLE CABLE

1. Inspect relay lever and accelerator control cable for easy of movement and condition. Replace as required.
2. Ensure relay level rests against Closed Throttle Position (CTP) stop when accelerator is not depressed.
3. Turn adjusting nut until relay level touches CTP stop or there is no further idle travel in accelerator.
4. Depress accelerator and ensure it touches kickdown switch.
5. Turn adjusting bolt until relay lever touches Wide Open Throttle (WOT) stop. Do not overtension Bowden cable.

Emission Control System Application Charts

Engine Liters	Certification Type		Trans. Type		Computerized Engine Management	Fuel Induction System Type	Ignition Timing, Deg. BTDC @ RPM	TSB	EPA & CARB Emission Recall	Emission Control System SRI	Emission Control Systems								
	CA	FED	A/T	M/T							PCV	ACL	AIS	EGR	EVAP	CAT	SPK	FR	O2S
1998																			
2.3L	X	X	X	—	YES(15)	SFI	(11)	—	—	—	X	—	—	—	X	X(1)	X(6)	X	X(14)
2.3L Turbo	X	X	X	—	YES(15)	SFI	(11)	—	—	—	X	—	—	—	X	X(18)	X(6)	X	X
2.8L	X	X	X	—	YES(16)	SFI	(11)	—	—	X(23)	X	—	—	X(4)	X	X(18)	X(17)	X	X
3.0L(15)	X	X	X	—	YES(12)	FI	—	—	—	—	X	—	—	X(4)	—	—	—	—	—
3.2L	X	X	X	—	YES(16)	SFI	(11)	—	—	X(23)	X	—	—	X(4)	X	X(18)	X(17)	X	X
3.2L	X	X	X	—	YES(15)	SFI	(11)	—	—	—	X	—	X(8)	X(4)	X	X(1)	X(13)	X	X(14)
4.2L	X	X	X	—	YES(10)	SFI	(11)	—	—	—	X	—	—	—	X	X	X(13)	X	X
5.0L	X	X	X	—	YES(10)	SFI	(11)	—	—	—	X	—	X(8)	X(4)	X	X(5)	X(13)	X	X(14)
6.0L	X	X	X	—	YES(10)	SFI	(11)	—	—	—	X	—	X(8)	X(4)	X	X(5)	X(13)	X	X(14)
1999																			
2.3L/140/L4	X	X	X	—	YES(24)(15)	SFI	(11)	—	—	X(23)	X	—	—	—	X	X(2)	X(6)	X	X(14)
2.8L/171/V6	X	X	X	—	YES(24)(16)	SFI	(11)	—	—	X(23)	X	—	—	—	X	X(5)	X(17)	X	X(14)
3.0L/183/L6(25)	X	X	X	—	YES(24)(12)	FI	—	—	—	—	X	—	—	X(4)	—	X(1)	—	—	—
3.2L/196/V6	X	X	X	—	YES(24)(16)	SFI	(11)	—	—	X(23)	X	—	X(8)	X(4)	X	X(5)	X(17)	X	X(29)
3.2L/196/L6	X	X	X	—	YES(24)(15)	SFI	(11)	—	—	X(23)	X	—	X(8)	X(4)	X	X(2)	X(13)	X	X(14)
4.2L/256/V8	X	X	X	—	YES(24)(10)	SFI	(11)	—	—	X(23)	X	—	—	—	X	X(5)	X(13)	X	X(14)
4.3L/260/V8	X	X	X	—	YES(24)(16)	SFI	(11)	—	—	X(23)	X	—	—	—	X	X(5)	X(17)	X	X(29)
5.0L/303/V8 SL500	X	X	X	—	YES(24)(16)	SFI	(11)	—	—	X(23)	X	—	—	—	X	X(5)	X(17)	X	X(29)
5.0L/304/V8 CL500 & S500	X	X	X	—	YES(24)(10)	SFI	(11)	—	—	X(23)	X	—	X(8)	—	X	X(5)	X(13)	X	X(14)
6.0L/365/V12	X	X	X	—	YES(24)(10)	SFI	(11)	—	—	X(23)	X	—	X(8)	—	X	X(5)	X(13)	X	X(14)
2000																			
2.3L/140/L4	X	X	X	—	YES(15)(24)	SFI	(11)	—	—	X(23)	X	—	—	—	X	X(2)	X(24)	X	X(14)
2.8L/171/V6	X	X	X	—	YES(16)(24)	SFI	(11)	—	—	X(23)	X	—	—	—	X	X(18)	X(17)	X	X(14)
3.2L/196/V6	X	X	X	—	YES(16)(24)	SFI	(11)	—	—	X(23)	X	—	X(8)	X(4)	X	X(18)	X(17)	X	X(29)
4.2L/256/V8	X	X	X	—	YES(10)(24)	SFI	(11)	—	—	X(23)	X	—	—	—	X	X(18)	X(13)	X	X(14)
4.3L/260/V8	X	X	X	—	YES(16)(24)	SFI	(11)	—	—	X(23)	X	—	—	—	X	X(18)	X(17)	X	X(29)
5.0L/303/V8	X	X	X	—	YES(16)(24)	SFI	(11)	—	—	X(23)	X	—	—	—	X	X(18)	X(17)	X	X(29)
5.5L/332/V8	X	X	X	—	YES(16)(24)	SFI	(11)	—	—	X(23)	X	—	—	—	X	X(18)	X(17)	X	X(29)
6.0L/365/V12	X	X	X	—	YES(10)(24)	SFI	(11)	—	—	X(23)	X	—	X(8)	—	X	X(5)	X(13)	X	X(14)
2001																			
2.3L/140/L4	X	X	X	X	YES(24)(30)	SFI	(11)	—	—	X(23)	X	—	—	—	X	X(2)	X(17)	X	X(14)
2.6L/159/V6	X	X	X	X	YES(24)(31)	SFI	(11)	—	—	X(23)	X	—	—	—	X	X(18)	X(17)	X	X(14)
3.2L/195/V6	X	X	X	X	YES(24)(31)	SFI	(11)	—	—	X(23)	X	—	X(8)	X(4)	X	X(18)	X(17)	X	X(29)
4.3L/260/V8	X	X	X	—	YES(24)(31)	SFI	(11)	—	—	X(23)	X	—	—	—	X	X(18)	X(17)	X	X(29)
5.0L/303/V8 (Except SL500)	X	X	X	—	YES(24)(31)	SFI	(11)	—	—	X(23)	X	—	—	—	X	X(18)	X(17)	X	X(29)
5.0L/303/V8 (SL500)	X	X	X	—	YES(16)(24)	SFI	(11)	—	—	X(23)	X	—	—	—	X	X(18)	X(17)	X	X(29)
5.4L/332/V8 (Except ML55 AMG)	X	X	X	—	YES(24)(31)	SFI	(11)	—	—	X(23)	X	—	—	—	X	X(18)	X(17)	X	X(29)

Continued

Engine Liters	Certification Type		Trans. Type		Computerized Engine Management	Fuel Induction System Type	Ignition Timing, Deg. BTDC @ RPM	TSB	EPA & CARB Emission Recall	Emission Control System SRI	Emission Control Systems								
	CA	FED	A/T	M/T							PCV	ACL	AIS	EGR	EVAP	CAT	SPK	FR	O2S
5.4L/332/V8 (ML55 AMG)	X	X	X	—	YES⑯㉔	SFI	⑪	—	—	X㉓	X	—	—	—	X	X⑱	X⑰	X	X㉙
5.8L/353/ V12	X	X	X	—	YES㉔㉜	SFI	⑪	—	—	X㉓	X	—	—	—	X	X	X⑰	X	X
6.0L/365/ V12	X	X	X	—	YES㉔㉝	SFI	⑪	—	—	X㉓	X	—	—	—	X	X	X⑰	X	X

X — Equipped
— Not Equipped
① — Type, OC; number of catalytic converters, 1.
② — Type, TWC; number of catalytic converters, 1.
③ — One O2S.
④ — Electronically controlled EGR.
⑤ — SL models, type, TWC; number of catalytic converters, 2. Except SL models, type, TWC; number of catalytic converters, 1. SL models, type, TWC; number of catalytic converters, 2. Except SL models, type, TWC; number of catalytic converters, 1.
⑥ — EI (Electronic Ignition).
⑦ — Electronic Diesel System.
⑧ — Pump type.
⑨ — HFM; OBDII, Motronic.
⑩ — ME-1; OBDII, Bosch Motronic.
⑪ — Refer to emission control information label.
⑫ — EDC.
⑬ — DIS.
⑭ — Two, HO2S.
⑮ — ME-2.1; OBDII.
⑯ — Motronic ME-2.0; OBDII.
⑰ — EI/Phase Shifted Twin Plug Ignition System.
⑱ — Type TWC.
⑲ — E-300.
⑳ — Except E-320.
㉑ — E-320.
㉒ — TLEV.
㉓ — Flexible Service System.
㉔ — Equipped w/MIL.
㉕ — Diesel.
㉖ — Certain S320 models (serial No. 163 478 to 204 398) may have an incorrect ECI label. Source Mercedes-Benz Campaign No. 94–0612.
㉗ — On certain models, the EGR valve (EGR valve with date code 94T174) may stick. Source Mercedes-Benz Campaign No. 95–0131.
㉘ — Injection timing 15° ATDC.
㉙ — Four HO2S.
㉚ — Siemens Engine Control System.
㉛ — Motronic ME-2.8; OBDII.
㉜ — Motronic ME-2.7; Plus Active Cylinder Control.
㉝ — Motronic ME-1.0; Plus Active Cylinder Control.
ACL — Air Cleaner (Thermostatic Air Cleaner)
AIS — Air Injection System
A/T — Automatic Transmission
1 BBL — One Barrel Carburetor
2x2 BBL — Two 2 Barrel Carburetors
4 BBL — Four Barrel Carburetor
BTDC — Before Top Dead Center
CA — California
CAT — Catalytic Converter
CIS — Continuous Injection System
DI — Distributor Ignition
DIS — Distributorless Ignition System.
DLC — Data Link Connector
EDC — Electronic Diesel Control
EGR — Exhaust Gas Recirculation
EVAP — Evaporative Emission Control System
FED — Federal
FI — Fuel Injection
FR — Fillpipe Restrictor
HFM — Hot Film Air Mass Sensor
HO2S — Heated Oxygen Sensor
MFI — Multi-Point Fuel Injection
M/T — Manual Transmission
OBD II — On Board Diagnostics II
OC — Oxidation Catalytic Converter
O2S — Oxygen Sensor
PCV — Positive Crankcase Ventilation
RPM — Revolutions Per Minute
SFI — Sequential Fuel Injection
SPK — Spark Control
SRI — Service Reminder Indicator
TSB — Technical Service Bulletin
TLEV — Transitional Low Emission Vehicle

Vacuum Hose Routings

INDEX

	FIG. NO.	PAGE NO.
Engine Vacuum Hose Routing:		
C43, CL55, CLK55, CLK430, E55, E430, ML55, ML430, S55, S430 & 1999-2001 SL500 & 2000-01 CL500 & S500	1	14-224
C240, C280, C320, CLK320, E320, ML320 & SLK320	2	14-224
E300	3	14-225
S420 & 1998-99 CL500 & S500 & 1998 SL500	4	14-225
SL600 & 1998-99 CL600 & S600	5	14-225
EVAP Emission Control System Vacuum Hose Routing		
C43, CL55, CLK55, CLK430, E55, E430, ML55, ML430, S55 & S430 & 1999-2001 SL500 & 2000-01 CL500 & S500	6	14-225
C240, C280, C320, CLK320, E320, ML320 & SLK320	7	14-226
S420 & 1998-99 CL500 & S500	8	14-226
1998 SL500	9	14-226

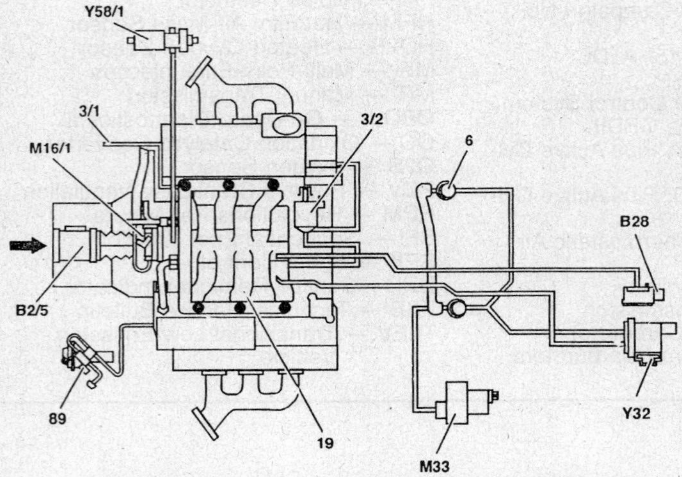

3/1	Connection of remaining consumers	B2/5	Hot film mass air flow sensor
3/2	Vacuum unit of intake manifold control flap	B28	Intake manifold pressure sensor
6	Secondary air injection combination valve	M16/1	Electronic accelerator actuator
19	Intake manifold	M33	Electric air pump
		Y27	EGR switchover valve
		Y32	Air pump switchover valve
		Y58/1	Purge control valve

MB1029900752000X

Fig. 1 Engine vacuum hose routing. C43, CL55, CLK55, CLK430, E55, E430, ML55, ML430, S55 & S430 & 1999–2001 SL500 & 2000–01 CL500 & S500

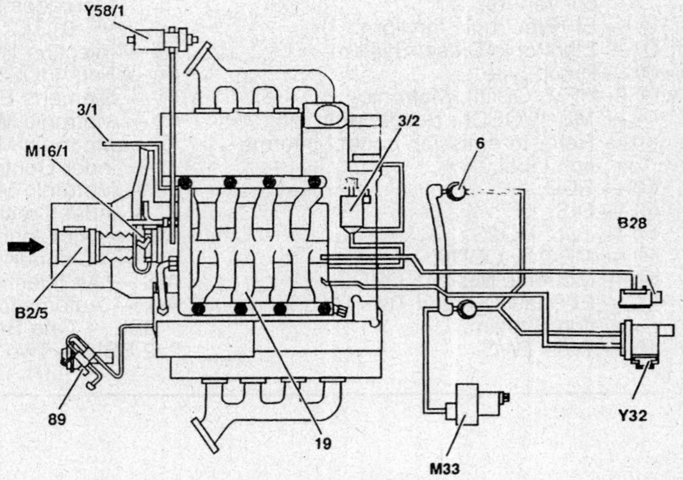

3/1	Connection of remaining consumers	89	EGR valve
3/2	Vacuum unit of intake manifold control flap	B2/5	Hot film mass air flow sensor
6	Secondary air injection combination valve	B28	Intake manifold pressure sensor
19	Intake manifold	M16/1	Electronic accelerator actuator
		M33	Electric air pump
		Y32	Air pump switchover valve
		Y58/1	Purge control valve

MB1029900751000X

Fig. 2 Engine vacuum hose routing. C240, C280, C320, CLK320, E320, ML320 & SLK320

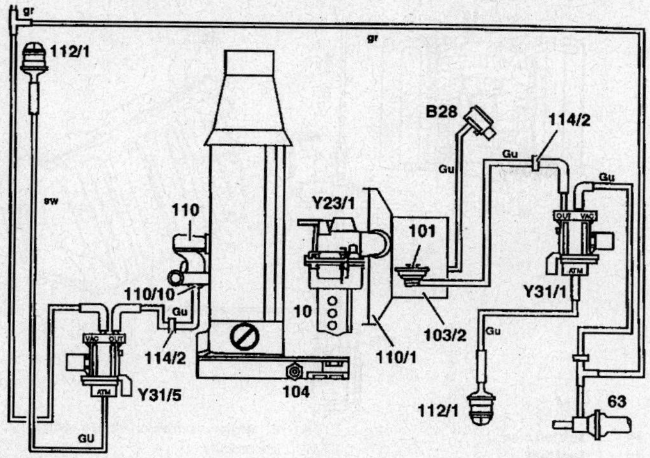

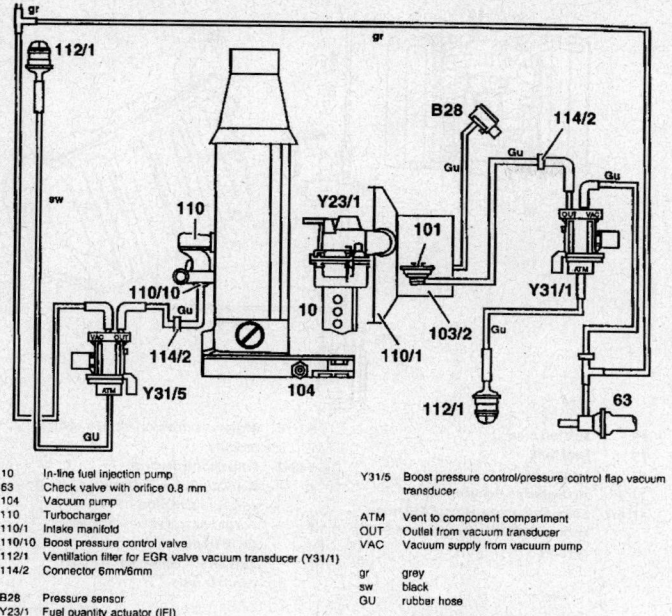

10 In-line fuel injection pump
63 Check valve with orifice 0.8 mm
104 Vacuum pump
110 Turbocharger
110/1 Intake manifold
110/10 Boost pressure control valve
112/1 Ventilation filter for EGR valve vacuum transducer (Y31/1)
114/2 Connector 6mm/6mm

B28 Pressure sensor
Y23/1 Fuel quantity actuator (IFI)
Y31/1 EGR valve vacuum transducer

Y31/5 Boost pressure control/pressure control flap vacuum transducer

ATM Vent to component compartment
OUT Outlet from vacuum transducer
VAC Vacuum supply from vacuum pump

gr grey
sw black
GU rubber hose

c Remaining consumers

MB1029800509000X

Fig. 3 Engine vacuum hose routing. E300

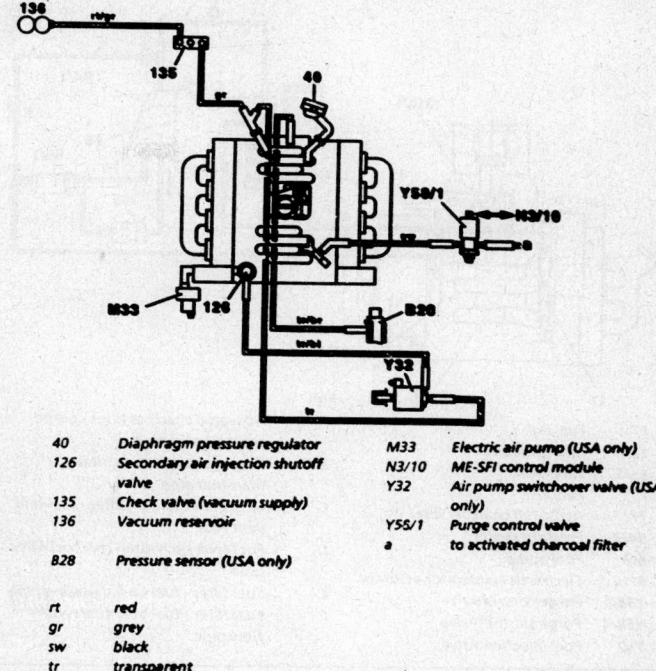

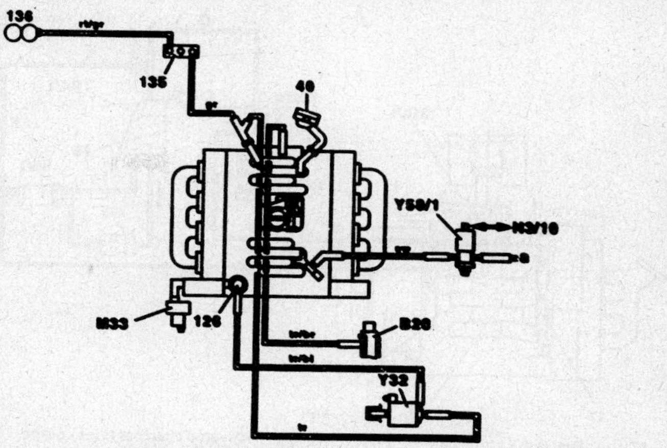

40 Diaphragm pressure regulator
126 Secondary air injection shutoff valve
135 Check valve (vacuum supply)
136 Vacuum reservoir
B28 Pressure sensor (USA only)
M33 Electric air pump (USA only)
N3/10 ME-SFI control module
Y32 Air pump switchover valve (USA only)
Y55/1 Purge control valve
a to activated charcoal filter

rt red
gr grey
sw black
tr transparent

MB1029900748000X

Fig. 4 Engine vacuum hose routing. S420 & 1998–99 CL500 & S500 & 1998 SL500

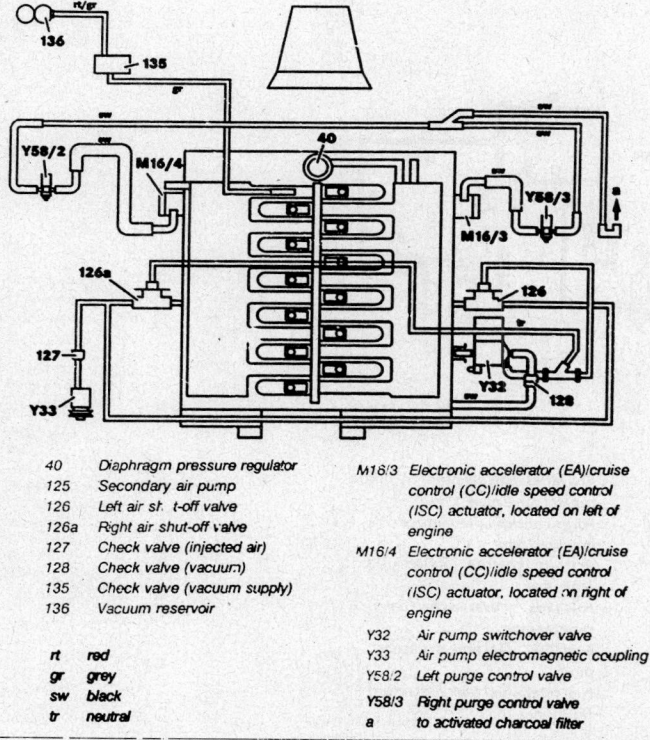

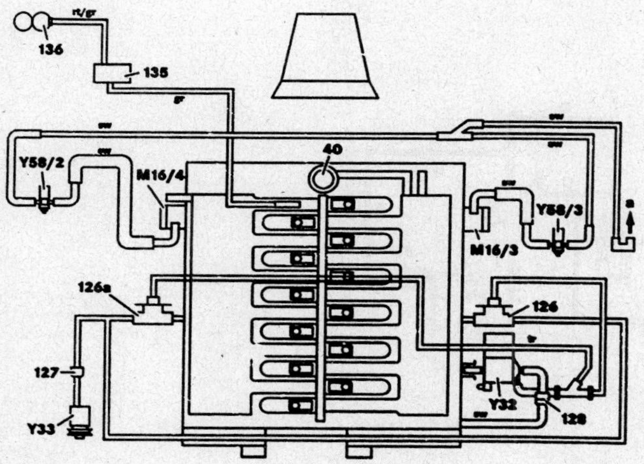

40 Diaphragm pressure regulator
125 Secondary air pump
126 Left air shut-off valve
126a Right air shut-off valve
127 Check valve (injected air)
128 Check valve (vacuum)
135 Check valve (vacuum supply)
136 Vacuum reservoir

rt red
gr grey
sw black
tr neutral

M16/3 Electronic accelerator (EA)/cruise control (CC)/idle speed control (ISC) actuator, located on left of engine
M16/4 Electronic accelerator (EA)/cruise control (CC)/idle speed control (ISC) actuator, located on right of engine
Y32 Air pump switchover valve
Y33 Air pump electromagnetic coupling
Y58/2 Left purge control valve
Y58/3 Right purge control valve
a to activated charcoal filter

MB1029900750000X

Fig. 5 Engine vacuum hose routing. SL600 & 1998–99 CL600, S600

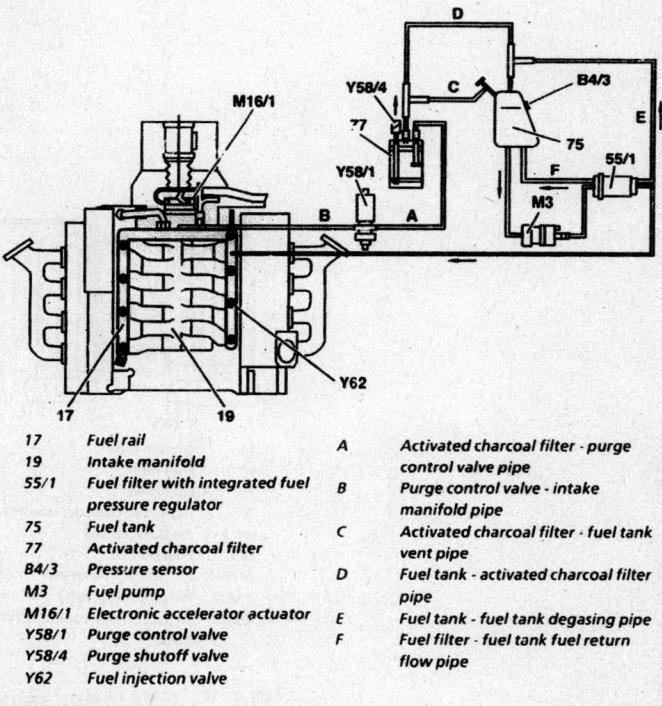

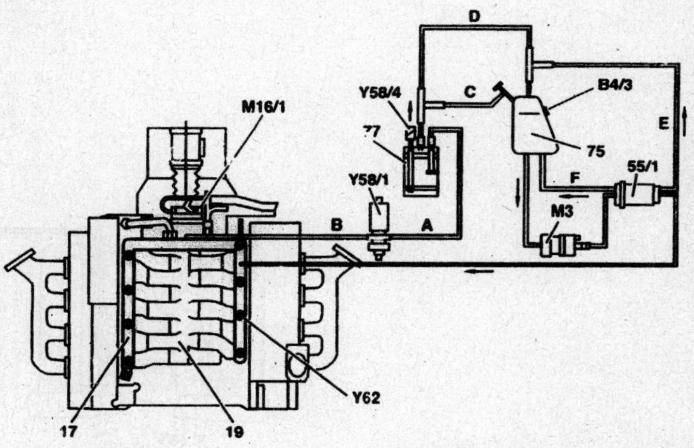

17 Fuel rail
19 Intake manifold
55/1 Fuel filter with integrated fuel pressure regulator
75 Fuel tank
77 Activated charcoal filter
B4/3 Pressure sensor
M3 Fuel pump
M16/1 Electronic accelerator actuator
Y58/1 Purge control valve
Y58/4 Purge shutoff valve
Y62 Fuel injection valve

A Activated charcoal filter - purge control valve pipe
B Purge control valve - intake manifold pipe
C Activated charcoal filter - fuel tank vent pipe
D Fuel tank - activated charcoal filter pipe
E Fuel tank - fuel tank degasing pipe
F Fuel filter - fuel tank fuel return flow pipe

MB1030100115000X

Fig. 6 EVAP emission control system vacuum hose routing. C43, CL55, CLK55, CLK430, E55, E430, ML55, ML430, S55 & S430 & 1999–2001 SL500 & 2000–01 CL500 & S500

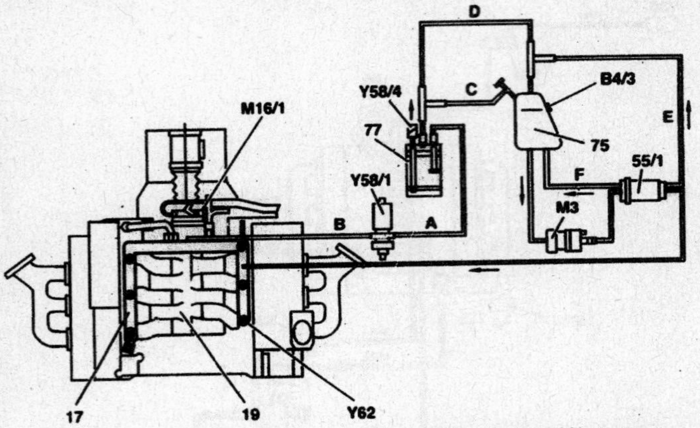

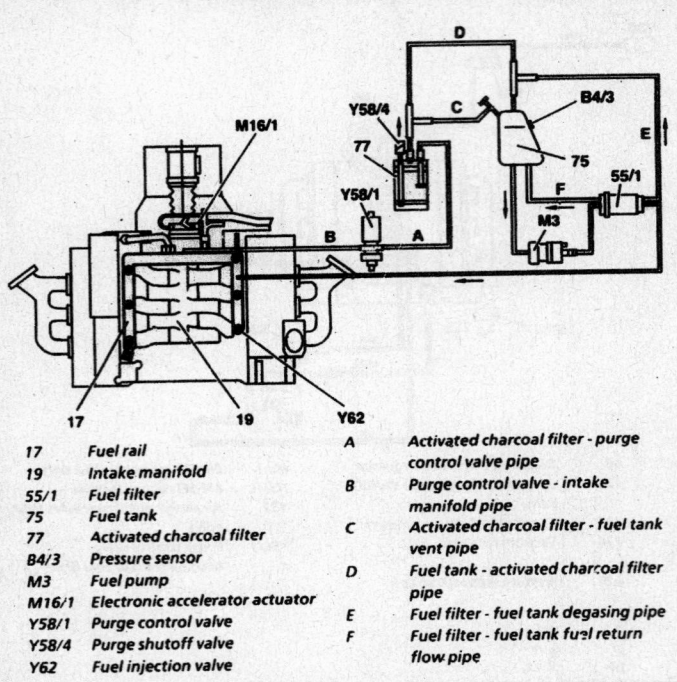

17	Fuel rail	A	Activated charcoal filter - purge control valve pipe
19	Intake manifold	B	Purge control valve - intake manifold pipe
55/1	Fuel filter	C	Activated charcoal filter - fuel tank vent pipe
75	Fuel tank	D	Fuel tank - activated charcoal filter pipe
77	Activated charcoal filter	E	Fuel filter - fuel tank degasing pipe
B4/3	Pressure sensor	F	Fuel filter - fuel tank fuel return flow pipe
M3	Fuel pump		
M16/1	Electronic accelerator actuator		
Y58/1	Purge control valve		
Y58/4	Purge shutoff valve		
Y62	Fuel injection valve		

MB1030100113000X

Fig. 7 EVAP emission control system vacuum hose routing. C240, C280, C320, CLK320, E320, ML320 & SLK320

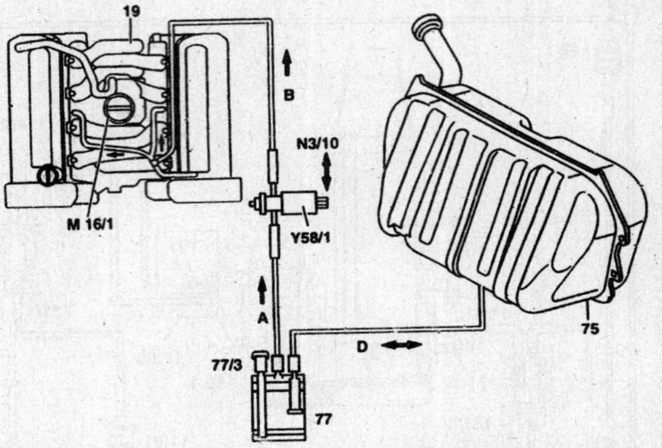

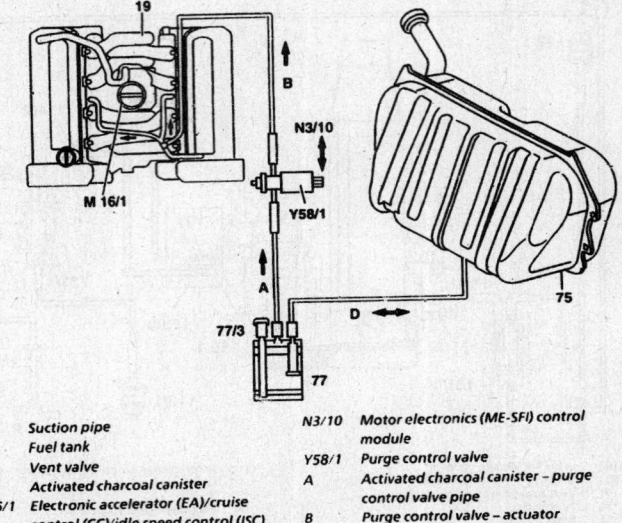

19	Suction pipe	N3/10	Motor electronics (ME-SFI) control module
75	Fuel tank	Y58/1	Purge control valve
76	Vent valve	A	Activated charcoal canister – purge control valve pipe
77	Activated charcoal canister	B	Purge control valve – actuator (M16/1) pipe
M16/1	Electronic accelerator (EA)/cruise control (CC)/idle speed control (ISC) actuator	D	Fuel tank – activated charcoal canister pipe

MB1030100112000X

Fig. 8 EVAP emission control system vacuum hose routing. S420 & 1998–99 CL500 & S500

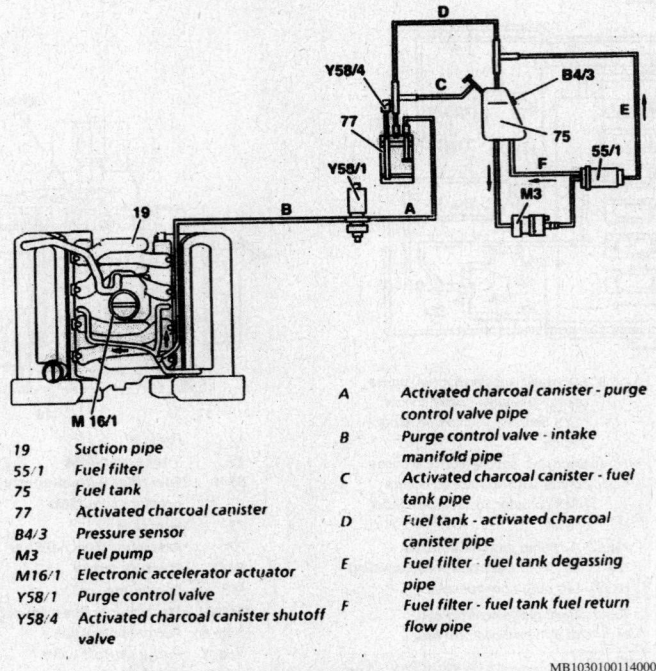

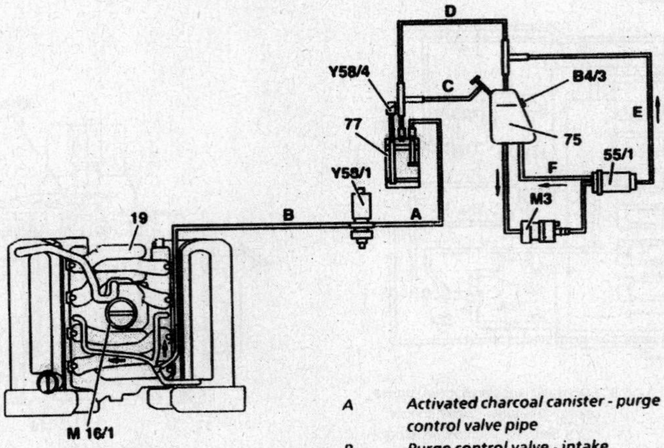

19	Suction pipe	A	Activated charcoal canister - purge control valve pipe
55/1	Fuel filter	B	Purge control valve - intake manifold pipe
75	Fuel tank	C	Activated charcoal canister - fuel tank pipe
77	Activated charcoal canister	D	Fuel tank - activated charcoal canister pipe
B4/3	Pressure sensor	E	Fuel filter - fuel tank degassing pipe
M3	Fuel pump	F	Fuel filter - fuel tank fuel return flow pipe
M16/1	Electronic accelerator actuator		
Y58/1	Purge control valve		
Y58/4	Activated charcoal canister shutoff valve		

MB1030100114000X

Fig. 9 EVAP emission control system vacuum hose routing. 1998 SL500

Emission Controls

NOTE: If Unsure Of The System Used On The Vehicle Being Serviced, Refer To The "Engine Systems Identification Chart." Further Assistance For The Proper Use Of Information Contained In This Section Can Also Be Found In The Front Of This Tabbed Section Under "How To Use This Manual."

NOTE: On Air Bag Equipped Models, Refer To "Air Bag System Precautions" Located In The Front Of This Manual For System Disarming & Arming Procedures.

NOTE: Many Emission System Components Are Interrelated With Fuel Injection System. For Systems And Components Not Covered In This Section, Refer To "Fuel Injection."

INDEX

Page No.

Evaporate (EVAP) Emission Control System 14-228
Description 14-228
System Service 14-228
Component Replacement 14-228
Exhaust Gas Recirculation (EGR) 14-228
Description 14-228
Diagnosis & Testing 14-228
120 Engine 14-228
System Service 14-228
Component Replacement 14-228
Positive Crankcase Ventilation System 14-228
Description 14-228
Secondary Air Injection (AIR) System 14-227
Description 14-227
Diagnosis & Testing 14-227
System Service 14-227
Component Replacement 14-227
Three-Way Catalytic Converter (TWC) 14-228
Description 14-228

SECONDARY AIR INJECTION (AIR) SYSTEM

Description

The air pumps inducts air through a maintenance-free filter and pumps it to the air shutoff valve. The air pump switchover valve switches the intake manifold pressure through to the air shutoff valve. The later opens and the air supplied by the air pump us pumped into the exhaust manifold.

The injected air reacts with the hot exhaust gases in the exhaust passage. An oxidation of carbon monoxide (CO) and hydrocabon (HC) takes place and results in an additional increase in exhaust temperature.

Diagnosis & Testing

1. Inspect magnetic clutch for any visible damage and repair or replace as required.
2. Start engine and run at idle with coolant temperature above 108°F.
3. If magnetic clutch is on, check temperature switch with ohmmeter.
4. If there is continuity, replace temperature switch. If there is no continuity, replace relay.
5. Allow coolant temperature to reach approximately 122°F, and disconnect oxygen sensor and temperature switch connectors, and connect them together.
6. If clutch does not go on, check for voltage at temperature switch connector.
7. If there is voltage, check circuit and replace defective components.
8. Disconnect vacuum line at air injection shutoff valve and connect vacuum gauge to line.
9. Disconnect oxygen sensor.
10. If there is no vacuum, proceed to next step. If there is vacuum, proceed as follows:
    a. Disconnect temperature switch.
    b. If vacuum drops to zero, replace temperature switch.
    c. If vacuum does not drop, check voltage supply relay and switchover valve, replace as required.
    d. Disconnect temperature switch electrical connector and connect connector terminals.
    e. If there is no vacuum, check vacuum hose routing and correct as required.
    f. If there is still no vacuum, check switch over valve and check valve for blockage, correcting as required.
11. Connect vacuum gauge to air injection shutoff valve and check for leakage.
12. Replace valve if there is leakage.
13. Disconnect molded hose on air cleaner and cover lightly with finger.
14. If there is no noticeable intake of air, replace molded hose or air pump as required.
15. If there is only a slightly noticeable intake of air, disconnect white/purple/blue vacuum line from switchover valve and check for vacuum.
16. If there is vacuum, replace air injection shutoff valve.

System Service

COMPONENT REPLACEMENT

AIR PUMP

S320

1. Remove air cleaner.
2. Remove drive belt.
3. Remove thermostat housing.
4. Disconnect hose.
5. Remove mounting bolts and pump.
6. Reverse procedure to install.

C43, C240, C280, C320, CLK320, CLK430, E320, E430, ML320, ML430 & SLK320

1. Remove cylinder head cover or air cleaner.
2. Remove mounting bolts and air hose.
3. Remove air pump.
4. Reverse procedure to install. **Torque** mounting bolts to 80 inch lbs.

S420 & 1998-99 CL500 & S500 & 1998 SL500

1. Disconnect fan shroud.
2. Disconnect righthand front engine mount and raise engine.
3. Remove hose.
4. Remove support mounting bolt and pump.
5. Disconnect electrical connector.

6. Reverse procedure to install. **Torque** mounting bolt to 18 ft. lbs.

S430 & 1999-2001 SL500 & 2000-01 CL 500 & S500

1. Remove engine front end cover.
2. Remove mounting bolts and air hose.
3. Remove air pump.
4. Reverse procedure to install. **Torque** mounting bolts to 106 inch lbs.

EXHAUST GAS RECIRCULATION (EGR)

Description

Exhaust gas is recirculated as a function of the engine control unit map when coolant temperature, engine speed and throttle position criteria are met. The EGR switchover valve is actuated at the ground end and switches vacuum to open the EGR valve. Low-oxygen exhaust is inducted dependent on the throttle valve position resulting in the fuel/air mixture containing less oxygen. The result combustion temperature reduction also reduces formation of NO_x.

Diagnosis & Testing

120 ENGINE

1. Disconnect purge line between charcoal canister and throttle valve housing at charcoal canister.
2. Block hose with finger and slowly increase engine speed to 2000 RPM. There should be no vacuum at idle but vacuum should increase as RPM increases.
3. If vacuum does not increase, check purge connection at throttle valve housing for blockage and check hose for leaks, correcting as required.
4. If vacuum is still not available, disconnect white/purple/black vacuum line from purge valve and accelerate engine to approximately 2000 RPM.
5. If there is vacuum at line, replace purge valve.
6. If there is no vacuum at line, replace thermo valve.

System Service

COMPONENT REPLACEMENT

EGR RECIRCULATION VALVE

C43, C240, C280, C320, CLK320, CLK55, CLK430, E55, E320, E430, S430 & SLK320 & 1999-2001 SL500 & 2000-01 S500

1. **On S430 and 2000–01 CL500 and S500 models,** disconnect front engine trim cover.
2. **On all models,** remove cylinder head cover and air cleaner top.
3. Remove hot film Mass Air Flow (MAF) sensor with air intake pipe.
4. **On C240 and C320 models,** disconnect dipstick guide tube and turn aside.
5. **On all models,** remove EGR valve union nut, then the EGR pipe at intake manifold.
6. Remove EGR mounting bolt and disconnect connector.
7. Remove EGR valve.
8. Reverse procedure to install, noting the following:
   a. Install new gaskets.
   b. Ensure length and routing of vacuum line is correct.
   c. **Torque** EGR valve mounting bolt to 15 ft. lbs.
   d. **Torque** union nut to 17 ft. lbs.
   e. **Torque** EGR pipe mounting bolt to 71 inch lbs.

ML55, ML320 & ML430

1. Remove engine trim panel and air cleaner top.
2. Remove hot film Mass Air Flow (MAF) sensor with intake manifold pipe.
3. Remove EGR valve union nut, then the EGR line at intake manifold.
4. Remove EGR mounting bolt and disconnect connector.
5. Remove EGR valve.
6. Reverse procedure to install, noting the following:
   a. Install new gaskets.
   b. Ensure length and routing of vacuum line is correct.
   c. **Torque** EGR valve mounting bolt to 15 ft. lbs.
   d. **Torque** union nut to 17 ft. lbs.
   e. **Torque** EGR pipe mounting bolt to 71 inch lbs.

POSITIVE CRANKCASE VENTILATION SYSTEM

Description

Engine blow-by gases and crankcase vapors flow across vent insert and connection fitting to cyclone oil separator. They flow through air intake system and into combustion chambers together with intake air.

Oil separated in cyclone oil separator flows through return line and check valve back into oil pan. Check valve ensures no oil vapors from oil pan are drawn into intake system by existing vacuum.

EVAPORATE (EVAP) EMISSION CONTROL SYSTEM

Description

The Evaporative (EVAP) emissions control system prevents fuel vapors escaping into the atmosphere. The vapors are temporarily stored in the activated charcoal filter. When the engine is running, the fuel vapors are drawn from the activated charcoal filter through the purge control valve and into the engine. The purge control valve is actuated by the engine control module in order to control the quantity of vapors purged.

Air is admitted to and released from the fuel tank through the activated charcoal filter.

System Service

COMPONENT REPLACEMENT

ACTIVATED CHARCOAL CANISTER

C43, C230, C280, CLK55, CLK320 & CLK430

1. Remove lefthand rear wheelhouse liner.
2. Disconnect lines.
3. Remove mounting bolt and canister.
4. Reverse procedure to install.

CL500, CL600, S320, S420, S430, S500 & S600

1. Remove lefthand rear wheelhouse liner.
2. Disconnect lines.
3. Remove canister.
4. Reverse procedure to install.

E55, E320 & E430

1. Remove fuel tank and luggage compartment righthand side trim panels.
2. Remove fuel overflow line and vent hose.
3. Remove pressure relief valve.
4. Remove canister.
5. Disconnect lines.
6. Reverse procedure to install. Replace hose clips.

ML55, ML320 & ML430

The activated charcoal canister and fuel tank are replaced as a unit.

SL500 & SL600

1. Remove lefthand side wall trim panel.
2. Disconnect lines.
3. Release and remove canister.
4. Reverse procedure to install.

SLK230 & SLK320

1. Disconnect fuel pump/activated charcoal canister cover.
2. Disconnect lines.
3. Disconnect and remove canister.
4. Reverse procedure to install.

THREE-WAY CATALYTIC CONVERTER (TWC)

Description

The catalytic converter consists of a sandwich design insulated stainless steel housing and a ceramic monolith substrate with the actual catalytic layer. The catalytic coating applied to the substrate consists of platinum and rhodium.

The exhaust gases flow through the catalytic converter and come into contact with the rare metals platinum and rhodium. The resulting platinum promotes oxidation converts carbon monoxide (CO) to carbon dioxide (CO_2) and hydrocarbons (HC) into water (H_2O) and CO_2. As a result of reduction, the rhodium converts oxides of nitrogen (NO_x) into nitrogen (N_2) and CO_2.

The critical factor for the conversion of the pollutants is the residual oxygen content in the exhaust gas. This is determined by the Lambda control. Once the catalytic converter is at its operating temperature and the Lambda control is activated, the oxygen (O_2) sensor signal downstream of the TWC is compared with the O_2 sensor signal upstream.

Technical Service Bulletins

INDEX

Page No.
Engine Runs Rough, Surges Or Does Not Start 14-231
C230, & 1998–99 CL500, CL600, S500, S600 & SL600 & 1998 SL500 14-231
Engine Shakes Or Misses During Acceleration Or Dies While Idling 14-230
Engine Shaking, Missing During Acceleration Or Stalling At Closed Throttle Position 14-230
C230, S320 & SLK230.......... 14-230
Engine Surges Or Runs Irregularly At Idle 14-230
C230, C280, CLK320, E320, ML320, S320, S420 & SLK230 & 1998–99 CL500 & S500 & 1998 SL500 14-230
Engine Vibrates During Warm Up................................ 14-230
1999 C230 & SLK230 14-230
Long Starting Times, Poor Acceleration & Lower Output ... 14-231
C230 & SLK230 14-231

ENGINE VIBRATES DURING WARM UP

1999 C230 & SLK230

On some of these models the engine may hesitate after cold start and have rough 1–2 and 2–3 up shifts during warm up.

This condition may be caused by the engine control module being very lean after cold start causing rough idle and sending incorrect load signals to transmission.

To correct this condition, replace the engine control module, **Fig. 1.**

Model	Control Module No. Old	New
C230	023 545 83 32	023 545 44 32
	023 545 57 32	023 545 44 32
SLK230	023 545 85 32	023 545 46 32
	023 545 14 32	023 545 46 32

Fig. 1 Engine control module replacement

ENGINE SHAKING, MISSING DURING ACCELERATION OR STALLING AT CLOSED THROTTLE POSITION

C230, S320 & SLK230

On some of these models the engine may shake and miss during acceleration or stall at closed throttle position.

This condition may be caused by a defective ignition coil.

To correct this condition, replace ignition coil (Bosch ignition, part No. 000 150 04 80 or Magnetek ignition, part No. 000 150 05 80).

ENGINE SURGES OR RUNS IRREGULARLY AT IDLE

C230, C280, CLK320, E320, ML320, S320, S420 & SLK230 & 1998–99 CL500 & S500 & 1998 SL500

On some of these models the engine may occasionally surge and/or run irregularly at idle. The throttle valve actuator may also be noisy.

This condition may be caused by exceeded production tolerances.

To correct this condition, replace the throttle valve actuator, noting the following:

1. Condition only affects production dates 662XX–769XX.
2. Throttle valve actuators improved as of production date 769XX with test stamp in black lettering on system cover: 01.97.
3. Production date later than 769XX may not have test stamp.
4. Production date is located on white sticker in center column all the way to right, attached to cover side.

ENGINE SHAKES OR MISSES DURING ACCELERATION OR DIES WHILE IDLING

On some of these models the engine may shake or miss during acceleration or die while idling.

This condition may be caused by a damaged Hot Film Mass Air Flow (HFM) sensor.

To correct this condition, replace the HMF sensor, noting the following:

1. Ensure air cleaner gasket is not damaged.
2. Ensure air cleaner cover is not distorted.

3. Ensure air cleaner and housing cover are mounted properly.
4. Ensure intake manifold is clean.

ENGINE RUNS ROUGH, SURGES OR DOES NOT START

C230, & 1998–99 CL500, CL600, S500, S600 & SL600 & 1998 SL500

On some these models the engine may run rough, surge or not start.

These conditions may be caused by inner leak in diaphragm-type fuel pressure regulator.

To correct this condition, check for leak and replace pressure regulator as required.

LONG STARTING TIMES, POOR ACCELERATION & LOWER OUTPUT

C230 & SLK230

Some of these models with vehicle production dates between 43/96 and 47/96, may take a long time to start, have poor acceleration and lower power output. The check engine lamp may be lit. Diagnostic Trouble Code (DTC) P0341 may be set.

These conditions may be caused by a malfunctioning camshaft Hall-effect sensor. To correct this condition, replace camshaft Hall-effect sensor.

Abbreviations & Acronyms

AB: Air Bag
ABS: Anti-lock Brake System
ACSR: Automatic Child Seat recognition
ADS: Adaptive Damping System
AIR: Secondary AIR Injection
AP: Accelerator Pedal
ASD: Automatic Locking Differential
ASR: Acceleration Slip Regulation
BA: Backup Assist
BARO: Barometric Pressure
BAS: Brake Assist
BCAPC: Barometric Pressure-Charge Air Pressure Compensation
BDC: Bottom Dead Center
BLS: Brake Lamp Switch
BM: Body Module
BPC: Barometric Pressure Compensation
CA: Closing Assist
CAN: Controller Area Network
CC: Cruise Control
CCM: Combination Control Module
CKA: Crankshaft Angle
CKP: Crankshaft Position
CLUS: Instrument Cluster
CMP: Camshaft Position
CTP: Closed Throttle Position (Idle)
DAS: Drive Authorization System
DFA: Speed Signal Output
DFAHL: Lefthand rear VSS Output
DFAVL: Lefthand Front VSS Output
DFHL: Lefthand Rear VSS Sensor
DFHR: Righthand Rear VSS Output
DFVL: Lefthand Front VSS Output
DFVL: Lefthand Front VSS Output
DFVR: Righthand Front VSS Output
DI: Distributor Ignition System
DIAG & DIAGN: Diagnostic Connection
DM: Diagnostic Mode
DSV: Drive Authorization System Shut-Off Valve
DTC: Diagnostic Trouble Code
EA: Electronic Accelerator
EBR: Engine Braking Regulation
ECL: Engine Coolant Level
ECT: Engine Coolant Temperature
EDC: Electronic Diesel Control
EDR: Electronic Diesel Regulation
EDS: Electronic Diesel System
EGR: Exhaust Gas Recirculation
EIFI: Electric In-Line Fuel Injection
EPC: Electronic Powertrain Control
ESCM: Engine System Control Module
ESP: Electronic Stability Program
ETC: Electronic Automatic Transmission Control
ETR: Emergency Tensioning Retractor
ETS: Electronic Traction System
EVAP: Evaporative Emission Control System
FP: Fuel Pump
GES: Vehicle Speed Singal
GIM: Governor Impulse Method
HFM-SFI: HFM Sequential Multi-Port Fuel Injection/Ignition System
HHT: Hand-Held Tester
IAT: Intake Air Temperature
IC: Instrument Cluster
IDC: In-Dash Controller
IFI: Electronic In-Line Fuel Injection
ISC: Idle Speed Control
IV: Input Valve
KS: Knock Sensor
KSS: Knock Sensor System
LH-SFI: LH Sequential Multiport Fuel Injection/Ignition System
LSK: Idle Speed Safety Contact
MAF: Mass Air Flow
MAP: Manifold Absolute Pressure
ME-SFI: ME Sequential multi-port Fuel Injection/Ignition System
MIL: Malfunction Indicator Lamp
MSK: Open Throttle Safety Contact
MVA: Manifold Vacuum Assist
O2S: Oxygen (O_2) Sensor
OBD: On-Board Diagnostics
OC: Oxidation Catalytic Converter
OV: Output Valve
PMP: Partial Intake Manifold Preheater
PSE: Pneumatic System Equipment
REST: Residual Engine Heat Utilization
SLO: Starter Lock-Out
SPS: Speed-Sensitive Power Steering
TB: Throttle Body
TC: Turbo Charger
TCM: Transmission Control Module
TDC: Top Dead Center
TIC: Transistorized Ignition System
TWC: Three-Way Catalytic Converter
VAF: Volume Air Flow
VSS Vehicle Speed Sensor
WOT: Wide Open Throttle
4-MATIC: Automatic Controlled Four-wheel Drive

PORSCHE

TABLE OF CONTENTS

Page No.

EMISSIONS:
Abbreviations & Acronyms . . . 15-296
Application Charts . . . 15-290
Emission Controls . . . 15-294
Emission Control System Application Charts . . 15-290
Engine Compartment Reference Diagrams . . . 15-291

ENGINE SYSTEMS IDENTIFICATION . . . 15-2

FUEL SYSTEMS:
Abbreviations & Acronyms . . . 15-296
Electric Fuel Pumps . . . 15-286
Engine Compartment Reference Diagrams . . . 15-291
Fuel Injection . . . 15-6
Technical Service Bulletins . . . 15-295

ENGINE TUNE UP & PERFORMANCE:
Abbreviations & Acronyms . . . 15-296
Specifications . . . 15-2
Technical Service Bulletins . . . 15-295

GENERAL INFORMATION:
Abbreviations & Acronyms . . . 15-296
Air Bag System Precautions . . . 0-12
Air Quality Standards . . . 0-23
Computer Relearn Procedures . . . 0-10
Electrical Symbol & Wire Color Code Identification . . . 0-33
Engine Systems Identification . . . 15-2
How To Use This Manual . . . 0-1
Quick Reference . . . 15-1
Service Reminder & Warning Lamp Reset Procedure . . . 0-14
Technical Service Bulletins . . . 15-295
Vehicle Identification . . . 0-3
Vehicle Lift Points . . . 0-24
Vehicle Maintenance Schedules . . . 0-45

IGNITION SYSTEMS:
Abbreviations & Acronyms . . . 15-296
Engine Compartment Reference Diagrams . . . 15-291
Ignition Systems . . . 15-4
Technical Service Bulletins . . . 15-295

INDUCTION SYSTEMS:
Abbreviations & Acronyms . . . 15-296
Turbochargers . . . 15-288

Quick Reference

Application	Page No.
ACCESSING DIAGNOSTIC TROUBLE CODES	
Motronic 5.2 Fuel Injection System	15-7
Motronic 7.2 Fuel Injection System	15-119
Motronic 7.8 Fuel Injection System	15-204
CLEARING DIAGNOSTIC TROUBLE CODES	
Motronic 5.2 Fuel Injection System	15-7
Motronic 7.2 Fuel Injection System	15-119
Motronic 7.8 Fuel Injection System	15-204
COMPRESSION PRESSURE SPECIFICATIONS	
All	15-3
FUEL PRESSURE SPECIFICATIONS	
All	15-2
SENSOR SPECIFICATIONS	
Motronic 5.2 Fuel Injection System	15-7
Motronic 7.2 Fuel Injection System	15-118
Motronic 7.8 Fuel Injection System	15-203

Engine Systems Identification

The first two characters of the engine number denote engine type. The engine number is stamped on the engine, near the temperature sensor

Engine Code	Engine	Ignition System	Page No.	Fuel System/Computer System	Page No.
1998					
M 96/20	2.5L	DME Ignition w/Dual Knock Sensors	15-4	Motronic (DME) 5.2 Fuel Injection System	15-6
64	3.6L	DME Ignition w/Dual Knock Sensors	15-4	Motronic (DME) 5.2 Fuel Injection System	15-6
1999					
M 96/20	2.5L	DME Ignition w/Dual Knock Sensors	15-4	Motronic (DME) 5.2 Fuel Injection System	15-6
M 96/01	3.4L	DME Ignition w/Dual Knock Sensors	15-4	Motronic (DME) 5.2 Fuel Injection System	15-6
M 96/02	3.4L	DME Ignition w/Dual Knock Sensors	15-4	Motronic (DME) 7.2 Fuel Injection System	15-118
2000–2001					
M 96/20	2.5L	DME Ignition w/Dual Knock Sensors	15-4	Motronic (DME) 5.2 Fuel Injection System	15-6
M 96/20	3.2L	DME Ignition w/Dual Knock Sensors	15-4	Motronic (DME) 5.2 Fuel Injection System	15-6
M 96/02	3.4L	DME Ignition w/Dual Knock Sensors	15-4	Motronic (DME) 7.2 Fuel Injection System	15-118
M 96/02	3.6L	DME Ignition w/Dual Knock Sensors	15-4	Motronic (DME) 7.8 Fuel Injection System	15-203

Tune Up Specifications

Year/Model	Spark Plug Gap Inch	Ignition Timing		Curb Idle Speed		Fuel System Pressure, psi	Valve Clearance, inch
		Firing Order	Timing BTDC	Man. Trans.	Auto. Trans.		
1998							
Boxster	.031	1-6-2-4-3-5	③	790	790D	52–58	①
911	.026	1-6-2-4-3-5	③	800④	750D④	52–58②	①
1999							
2.5L	.031	1-6-2-4-3-5	③	—	—	52–58	①
3.4L	.032	1-6-2-4-3-5	③	660–740	660–740	52–58	①
2000–2001							
2.5L	.031	1-6-2-4-3-5	③	—	—	52–58	①
3.2L	.031	1-6-2-4-3-5	③	—	—	52–58	①
3.4L	.032	1-6-2-4-3-5	③	660–740	660–740	52–58	①
3.6L	.031	1-6-2-4-3-5	③	700–780	700–780	52–58	①

D — Drive
BTDC — Before Top Dead Center
① — Equipped w/hydraulic lash adjusters.
② — Key On, Engine Off.
③ — Controlled by DME (Digital Motor Electronics) control unit.
④ — 880 RPM with A/C.

Engine Tune Up & Performance

NOTE: If Uncertain About The Proper Use Of Information Contained In This Section, Please Refer To "How To Use This Manual" Located In The Front Of This Manual.

NOTE: On Air Bag Equipped Models, Refer To "Air Bag System Precautions" Located In The Front Of This Manual For System Disarming & Arming Procedures.

NOTE: Refer To "Computer Relearn Procedures" Located In The Front Of This Manual When Battery Power To The Computer Has Been Interrupted.

INDEX

	Page No.
Compression Pressures	15-3
Engine Identification	15-3
Idle Speed & Mixture Adjustments	15-3
Idle Mixture	15-3
Idle Speed	15-3
Ignition Timing	15-3
Precautions	15-3
Air Bag Systems	15-3
Battery Ground Cable	15-3
Spark Plugs	15-3
Valves	15-3
Valve Adjustment	15-3
Valve Arrangement	15-3

PRECAUTIONS

Air Bag Systems

Refer to "Air Bag System Precautions" in the front of this manual for system disarming and arming procedures.

Battery Ground Cable

Prior to service, disconnect battery ground cable and isolate as required.

ENGINE IDENTIFICATION

The first two characters of the engine number denote engine type. The engine number is stamped on the engine, near the temperature sensor.

SPARK PLUGS

Spark plugs should be changed every 30,000 miles, or a minimum of once every two years. Refer to Tune Up Specifications charts for spark plug gap. Coat spark plug threads with graphite grease and **torque** to 20 ft. lbs.

COMPRESSION PRESSURES

1. **On models less turbo,** when checking compression, disconnect Digital Motor Electronics (DME) control unit plug located under driver's seat.
2. **On all models,** perform compression test with engine at operating temperature, spark plugs removed and throttle wide open.
3. Compression pressure should be 142–184 psi, with a minimum of 107 psi on any cylinder. Pressure should not vary more than 22 psi between cylinders.

IGNITION TIMING

Refer to Tune Up Specifications charts for correct ignition timing and firing order.

Ignition timing is controlled by the Digital Motor Electronics (DME) control unit and is not adjustable.

IDLE SPEED & MIXTURE ADJUSTMENTS

Refer to Tune Up Specifications charts for curb idle speed specifications.

Idle Speed

Idle speed is controlled by the Digital Motor Electronics (DME) control unit and is not adjustable.

Idle Mixture

Idle speed is controlled by the Digital Motor Electronics (DME) control unit and is not adjustable.

VALVES

Valve Arrangement

Intake valves are on upper part of cylinder head. Exhaust valves are on lower part of cylinder head.

Valve Adjustment

Equipped with hydraulic lash adjusters, no adjustment is necessary.

Ignition Systems

NOTE: If Uncertain About The Proper Use Of Information Contained In This Section, Please Refer To "How To Use This Manual" Located In The Front Of This Manual.

NOTE: On Air Bag Equipped Models, Refer To "Air Bag System Precautions" Located In The Front Of This Manual For System Disarming & Arming Procedures.

NOTE: Refer To "Computer Relearn Procedures" Located In The Front Of This Manual When Battery Power To The Computer Has Been Interrupted.

INDEX

	Page No.
Description	15-4
Diagnosis & Testing	15-5
Precautions	15-4
Air Bag Systems	15-4
Battery Ground Cable	15-4
System	15-4
Troubleshooting	15-4
Engine Does Not Start	15-4
Engine Hesitation	15-4
Engine Knocking During Acceleration	15-4
Erratic Idle	15-4
Hard Starting	15-4
High Fuel Consumption	15-4
Low Power Output	15-4
Misfiring	15-4
Poor Acceleration	15-4

PRECAUTIONS

System

1. Do not attempt to start engine without battery being properly connected.
2. Never disconnect battery while engine is running.
3. Never use a battery booster to start engine. If jump start is required, use only a 12 volt outside battery.
4. Disconnect battery before charging.
5. Before attempting to measure resistance values, ensure ignition is turned off or battery is disconnected.
6. If starter has to be cranked without starting engine, connect terminal 4 of ignition coil to ground with a high voltage lead with a shielding sleeve of at least 2000 ohms, or disconnect electrical connectors of control units.
7. Do not replace ignition coil with a different type.
8. Do not install a shielded capacitor to ignition coil terminals 1 and 15.
9. Do not connect positive battery voltage or a test lamp to ignition coil terminal 1.
10. Do not disconnect high tension lead between coil and distributor while engine is running.
11. Secondary side of ignition system must be shielded with at least 4000 ohms, along with the standard rotor shielding of 1000 ohms. Do not install a rotor of higher resistance for any reason.

Air Bag Systems

Refer to "Air Bag System Precautions" in the front of this manual for system disarming and arming procedures.

Battery Ground Cable

Prior to service, disconnect battery ground cable and isolate as required.

DESCRIPTION

There are five ignition systems available: electronic ignition system, DME electronic ignition with dual knock sensor, DME ignition system with spark control and electronic ignition (DI) system.

TROUBLESHOOTING

Engine Does Not Start

1. Poor electrical connections.
2. Power supply to ECU.
3. Speed/reference mark sensor.
4. Faulty engine temperature sensor.
5. Ignition system.

Hard Starting

1. Poor electrical connections.
2. Speed/reference mark sensor.
3. Faulty engine temperature sensor.
4. Ignition system.

Erratic Idle

1. Faulty engine temperature sensor.
2. Ignition system.

Poor Acceleration

1. Poor electrical connections.
2. Speed/reference mark sensor.
3. Faulty engine temperature sensor.
4. Faulty throttle switch.
5. Ignition system.

Misfiring

1. Poor electrical connections.
2. Power supply to ECU.
3. Speed/reference mark sensor.
4. Faulty charging system.

High Fuel Consumption

1. Load sensor.
2. Faulty engine temperature sensor.
3. Faulty throttle switch.
4. Ignition system.

Low Power Output

1. Poor electrical connections.
2. Speed/reference mark sensor.
3. Load sensor.
4. Faulty temperature sensor Nos. 1 or 2.
5. Faulty throttle switch.
6. Ignition system.
7. Octane loop.

Engine Hesitation

1. Poor electrical connections.
2. Power supply to ECU.
3. Speed/reference mark sensor.
4. Load sensor.
5. Faulty engine temperature sensor.
6. Faulty throttle switch.
7. Ignition system.
8. Faulty charging system.

Engine Knocking During Acceleration

1. Load sensor.
2. Temperature sensor No. 1.

3. Ignition system.

DIAGNOSIS & TESTING

The ignition system is controlled by the Digital Motor Electronic (DME) system. For information on this system, refer to "Fuel Injection."

Fuel Injection

TABLE OF CONTENTS

	Page No.
MOTRONIC (DME) 5.2 FUEL INJECTION SYSTEMS	15-6
MOTRONIC (DME) 7.2 FUEL INJECTION SYSTEMS	15-118
MOTRONIC (DME) 7.8 FUEL INJECTION SYSTEMS	15-203

Motronic (DME) 5.2 Fuel Injection Systems

NOTE: If Unsure Of The System Used On The Vehicle Being Serviced, Refer To The "Engine Systems Identification Chart." Further Assistance For The Proper Use Of Information Contained In This Section Can Also Be Found In The Front Of This Tabbed Section Under "How To Use This Manual."

NOTE: On Air Bag Equipped Models, Refer To "Air Bag System Precautions" Located In The Front Of This Manual For System Disarming & Arming Procedures.

NOTE: Prior To Performing Any Service Operations Listed In This Section, Consult The "Technical Service Bulletins" Section For Related Information.

NOTE: "Electrical Symbol & Wire Color Code Identification" Located In The Front Of This Manual May Be Used As An Aid When Using Wiring Circuits Found In This Section.

NOTE: Refer To "Computer Relearn Procedures" Located In The Front Of This Manual When Battery Power To The Computer Has Been Interrupted.

INDEX

	Page No.
Description	15-7
Diagnosis & Testing	15-7
Accessing Diagnostic Trouble Codes	15-7
Clearing Diagnostic Trouble Codes	15-7
DME Connector Pin Identification	15-7
Boxster	15-7
911	15-7
Diagnostic Tests	15-7
Boxster	15-7
911	15-7
Diagnostic Trouble Code Interpretation	15-7
Boxster	15-7
911	15-7
Wiring Diagrams	15-7
Boxster	15-7
911	15-7
Diagnostic Chart Index	15-23
Precautions	15-7
Air Bag Systems	15-7
Battery Ground Cable	15-7
Sensor & Fuel Injector Specifications	15-7
System Service	15-7
Component Replacement	15-7

SENSOR & FUEL INJECTOR SPECIFICATIONS

Component	Temperature, Degrees F	Value, Ohms
Crankshaft Position Sensor	68	.8–1.0
Engine Compartment Temperature Sensor	68	2200–2600
Engine Coolant Temperature Sensor	32	5000–7000
	68	2000–3000
	140	400–800
EVAP Canister Purge Valve	68	22–30
Fuel Injector	—	11–13
HO2S Heater Element	68	1.8–2.5
Intake Air Temperature Sensor	68	2300–2700
Throttle Position Sensor	—	2000–3000①
	—	700–1400②
Vehicle Speed Sensor	—	1600–1800

① — At idle.
② — At wide open throttle.

PRECAUTIONS

Air Bag Systems

Refer to "Air Bag System Precautions" in the front of this manual for system disarming and arming procedures.

Battery Ground Cable

Prior to service, disconnect battery ground cable and isolate as required.

DESCRIPTION

This system uses a Digital Motor Electronics (DME) control module to manage fuel injection, ignition and electronic engine controls. The DME module, located under the left seat, also features an optimized engine management diagnostic system (OBD II).

Refer to **Fig. 1 through 4** for Motronic 5.2 system component locations.

DIAGNOSIS & TESTING

Accessing Diagnostic Trouble Codes

If a malfunction occurs, the Malfunction Indicator Lamp (Check Engine) will be illuminated. At the same time, the Diagnostic Trouble Code (DTC) is stored in the fault memory of the DME control module. To retrieve stored DTCs, connect system tester 9288, or equivalent OBD II scan tool, to the vehicle diagnostic connector, located under the lefthand side of the instrument panel, left of the steering column, **Fig. 5.**

Diagnostic Trouble Code Interpretation

BOXSTER

Refer to **Fig. 6** for diagnostic trouble code interpretation.

911

1. Refer to **Figs. 7 and 8** for a listing of DTCs. The different fault types are used to indicate the following:
   a. **Fault type 1,** signal implausible/implausible operating range/malfunction.
   b. **Fault type 2,** open circuit/no signal.
   c. **Fault type 3,** short to ground/below lower limit/lean stop.
   d. **Fault type 4,** Short to positive/upper limit exceeded/rich stop.
2. Final column in chart indicates Malfunction Indicator Lamp (MIL) operation. Compare MIL operation as follows:
   a. 0=MIL is not triggered for this fault.
   b. 1=MIL on, emission related fault.
   c. 2=MIL is flashing, fault damaging to TWC.
   d. 3=Only in combination with engine misfire.

Wiring Diagrams

BOXSTER

Refer to **Figs. 9 and 10** for DME wiring circuit.

911

Refer to **Figs. 11 and 12** for DME wiring circuits.

DME Connector Pin Identification

BOXSTER

Refer to **Fig. 13** for connector pin identification.

911

Refer to **Fig. 14** for connector pin identification.

Diagnostic Tests

BOXSTER

Refer to **Figs. 15 through 80** for diagnostic tests.

911

Refer to **Figs. 81 through 151** for diagnostic tests.

Clearing Diagnostic Trouble Codes

If a fault (DTC) has been removed but the fault memory has not been erased, three trips are usually required to switch off the Malfunction indicator lamp (MIL). Erasing diagnostic trouble codes may also be accomplished using the system tester or scan tool. Disconnecting the battery ground cable or control module connector will erase diagnostic trouble codes, but this will require a DME module adaption phase in which the engine must be run for 250 seconds after the battery ground cable or control module is reconnected.

SYSTEM SERVICE

Component Replacement

Refer to **Fig. 1 through 4** for Motronic 5.2 system component locations.

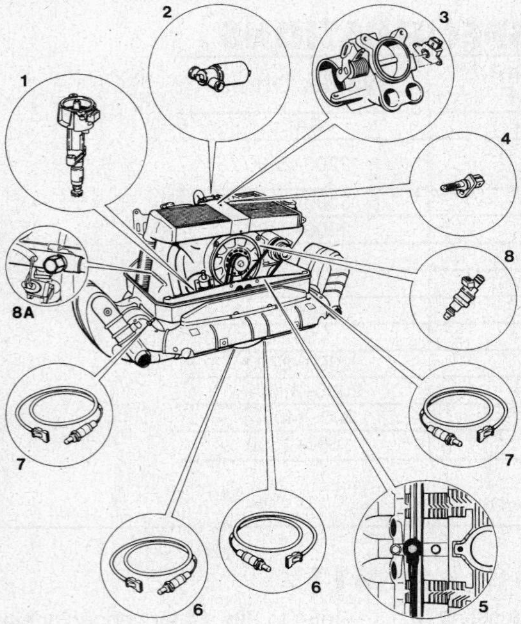

1 - Distributor with Hall sensor
2 - Idle Air control Valve (IACV)
3 - Throttle potentiometer
4 - Intake air temperature sensor
5 - Knock sensor on bridge
6 - Oxygen sensors ahead of catalytic converter
7 - Oxygen sensors behind catalytic converter
8A- Test connection for fuel pressure

PR1029600016010X

Fig. 1 Motronic 5.2 component locations (Part 1 of 2). 1998 911

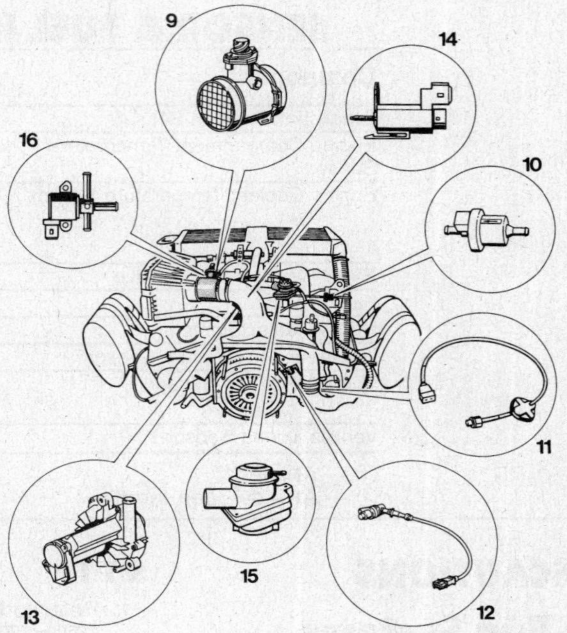

9 - Mass air flow sensor
10 - Tank venting valve
11 - Engine temperature sensor
12 - Rpm/reference mark sensor
13 - Air pump
14 - Secondary air solenoid
15 - Pneumatic switching valve for secondary air
16 - Frequency valve for boost air control

PR1029600016020X

Fig. 1 Motronic 5.2 component locations (Part 2 of 2). 1998 911

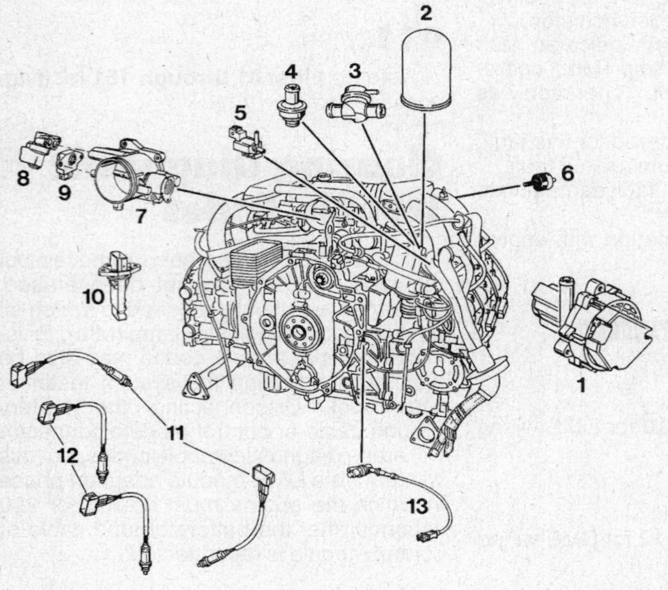

PR1019700079010X

Fig. 2 Motronic 5.2 engine component locations (rear view, Part 1 of 2). Boxster

Designation

1 – Secondary air pump
2 – Vacuum reservoir
3 – Overflow valve
4 – Check valve
5 – Vacuum valve
6 – Check valve
7 – Throttle part
8 – Idle air control valve
9 – Throttle potentiometer
10 – Hot film mass air flow sensor with intake air temperature sensor
11 – Oxygen sensors ahead of the catalytic converter
12 – Oxygen sensors behind the catalytic converter
13 – Pulse sender (reference mark sensor/rpm sender)

PR1019700079020X

Fig. 2 Motronic 5.2 engine component locations (rear view, Part 2 of 2). Boxster

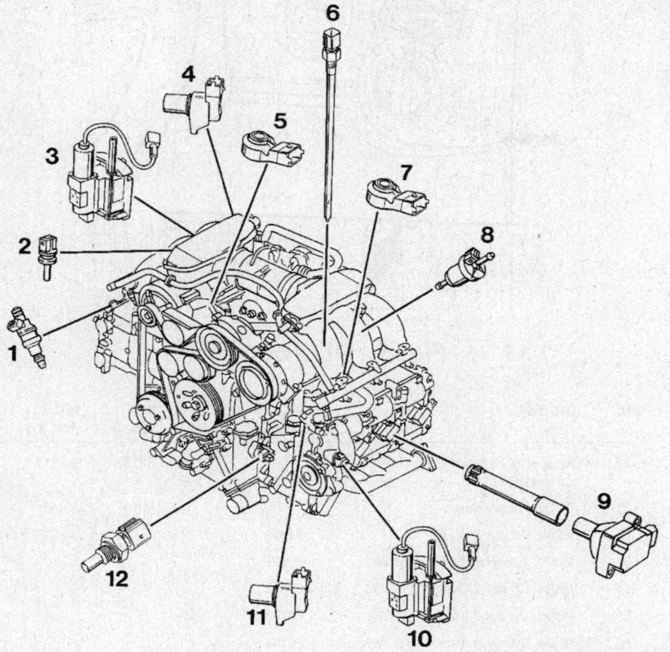

PR1019700080010X

Fig. 3 Motronic 5.2 engine component locations (front view, Part 1 of 2). Boxster

Designation

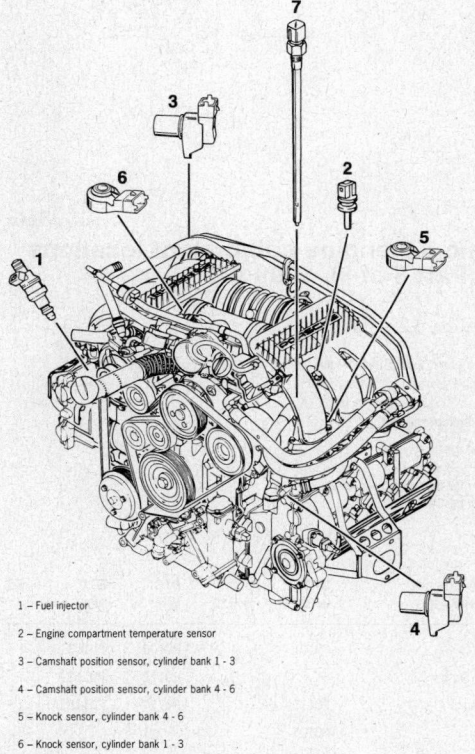

1 – Injection valve

2 – Temperature switch for engine temperature

3 – Tensioning element (camshaft adjuster VarioCam)

4 – Hall-effect sensor

5 – Knock sensor

6 – Oil temperature sender/oil level sensor

7 – Knock sensor

8 – Tank vent (fuel evaporative valve)

9 – Individual coil/spark plug connector

10 – Tensioning element (camshaft adjuster VarioCam)

11 – Hall-effect sensor

12 – Temperature sender (coolant)

PR1019700080020X

Fig. 3 Motronic 5.2 engine component locations (front view, Part 2 of 2). Boxster

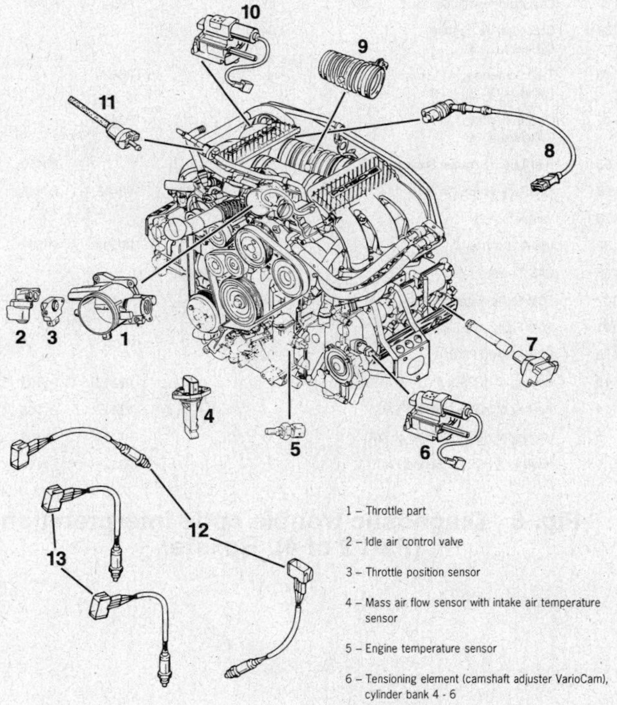

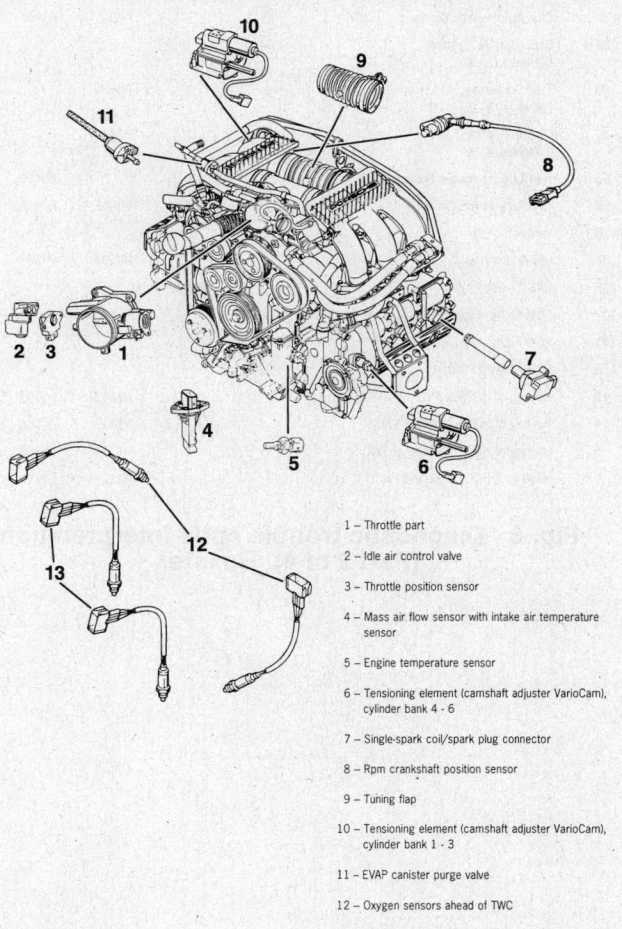

1 – Throttle part

2 – Idle air control valve

3 – Throttle position sensor

4 – Mass air flow sensor with intake air temperature sensor

5 – Engine temperature sensor

6 – Tensioning element (camshaft adjuster VarioCam), cylinder bank 4 - 6

7 – Single-spark coil/spark plug connector

8 – Rpm crankshaft position sensor

9 – Tuning flap

10 – Tensioning element (camshaft adjuster VarioCam), cylinder bank 1 - 3

11 – EVAP canister purge valve

12 – Oxygen sensors ahead of TWC

13 – Oxygen sensors after TWC

PR1029900120010X

Fig. 4 Motronic 5.2 engine component locations (Part 1 of 3). 1999 911

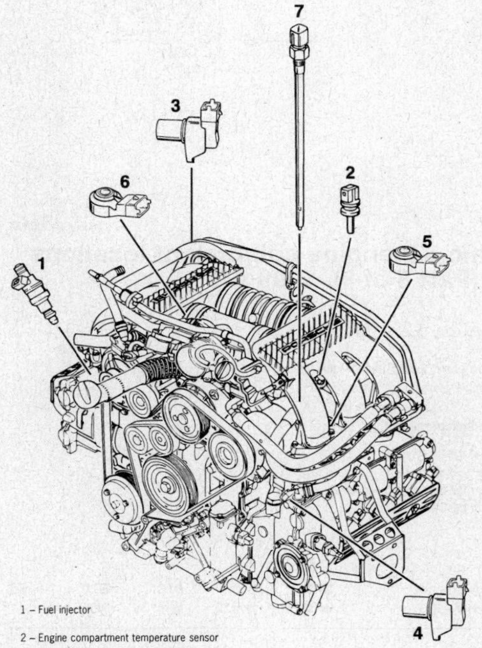

1 – Fuel injector

2 – Engine compartment temperature sensor

3 – Camshaft position sensor, cylinder bank 1 - 3

4 – Camshaft position sensor, cylinder bank 4 - 6

5 – Knock sensor, cylinder bank 4 - 6

6 – Knock sensor, cylinder bank 1 - 3

7 – Oil temperature sensor

PR1029900120020X

Fig. 4 Motronic 5.2 engine component locations (Part 2 of 3). 1999 911

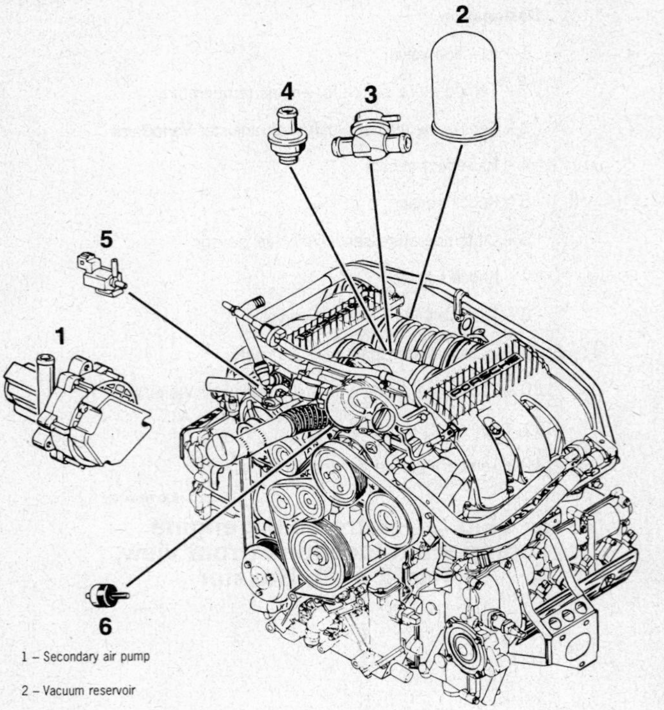

1 – Secondary air pump

2 – Vacuum reservoir

3 – Overflow valve

4 – Non-return valve

5 – Vacuum valve

6 – Non-return valve

PR1029900120030X

Fig. 4 Motronic 5.2 engine component locations (Part 3 of 3). 1999 911

DTC Versions

Version 1 Signal Implausible / Implausible Operating Range / Malfunction
Version 2 Interruption / No Signal
Version 3 Short to Ground / Below Lower Limit / Lean Mixture Limit
Version 4 Short to B+ / Above Upper Limit / Rich Mixture Limit

MIL (Check Engine Malfunction Indicator Light)

0 MIL is not triggered with this fault
1 MIL is on, emissions-relevant fault
2 MIL is blinking, fault harmful to catalytic converter
3 Only in combination with misfires

DTC	DTC Text	DTC vers. 1	DTC vers. 2	DTC vers. 3	DTC vers. 4	MIL
115	Mass Air Flow Sensor	P0101		P0102	P0103	1
124	Intake Air Temperature Sensor			P0112	P0113	1
123	Engine Temperature Sensor	P0115		P0117	P0118	1
117	Throttle Position Sensor	P0123				1
10	HO2S Ahead of TWC Cylinders (1 - 3)	P0130	P0134	P0131	P0132	1
15	Aging of HO2S Ahead of TWC Cylinders (1 - 3)			P0133		1
12	HO2S Behind TWC Cylinders (1 - 3)	P0136	P0140	P0137	P0138	1
17	Aging of O2S Behind TWC Cylinders (1 - 3)			P0139		0
18	HO2S Ahead of TWC Cylinders (4 - 6)	P0150	P0154	P0151	P0152	1
21	Aging of HO2S Ahead of TWC Cylinders (4 - 6)			P0153		1
20	HO2S Behind TWC Cylinders (4 - 6)	P0156	P0160	P0157	P0158	1

PR1019700011010X

Fig. 6 Diagnostic trouble code interpretation (Part 1 of 4). Boxster

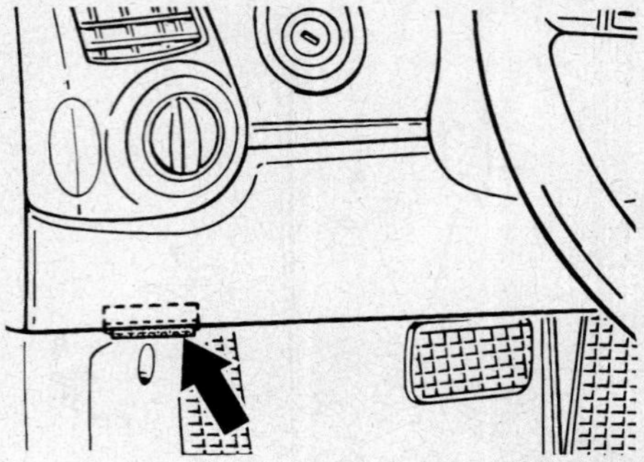

PR1029600045000X

Fig. 5 DLC connector

DTC	DTC Text	DTC vers. 1	DTC vers. 2	DTC vers. 3	DTC vers. 4	MIL
23	Aging of HO2S Behind TWC Cylinders (4 - 6)			P0159		0
125	Oil Temperature Sensor			P0197	P0198	0
75	Misfire, Damaging to TWC	P0300				2
63	Misfire, Cylinder 1, Damaging to TWC	P0301				2
64	Misfire, Cylinder 2, Damaging to TWC	P0302				2
65	Misfire, Cylinder 3, Damaging to TWC	P0303				2
66	Misfire, Cylinder 4, Damaging to TWC	P0304				2
67	Misfire, Cylinder 5, Damaging to TWC	P0305				2
68	Misfire, Cylinder 6, Damaging to TWC	P0306				2
111	Crankshaft Position Sensor	P0336				1
112	Camshaft Position Sensor 1	P0341		P0341	P0341	1
80	Secondary Air System Cylinders (1 - 3)	P0410				1
40	TWC Converting, Cylinders (1 - 3)			P0420		1
45	TWC Converting, Cylinders (4 - 6)			P0430		1
93	Fuel Tank Ventilation System				P0440	1
98	Fuel Tank Ventilation Valve		P0444	P0445	P0445	1
120	Vehicle Speed	P0501				1
32	Idle Air Control			P0506	P0507	1
236	CAN Timeout		P0600			1
102	ECM Faulty (External RAM)	P0603				1
101	ECM Faulty (Internal RAM)	P0604				1
103	ECM Faulty (EPROM)	P0605				1
13	Heating of HO2S 1 Ahead of TWC			P1115	P1102	1
14	Heating of HO2S 1 Behind TWC			P1117	P1105	1
5	Heating of HO2S 2 Ahead of TWC			P1119	P1107	1
4	Heating of HO2S 2 Behind TWC			P1121	P1110	1

PR1019700011020X

Fig. 6 Diagnostic trouble code interpretation (Part 2 of 4). Boxster

DTC	DTC Text	DTC vers. 1	DTC vers. 2	DTC vers. 3	DTC vers. 4	MIL
27	Oxygen Sensing, Area 1 Cylinders (1 - 3)			P1123	P1124	1
35	Oxygen Sensing, Area 1 Cylinders (4 - 6)			P1125	P1126	1
26	Oxygen Sensing, Area 2 Cylinders (1 - 3)			P1127	P1128	1
34	Oxygen Sensing, Area 2 Cylinders (4 - 6)			P1129	P1130	1
121	Load Signal	P1140				1
30	Engine Compartment Temperature Sensor			P1157	P1158	0
150	Fuel Injector, Cylinder 1		P1237	P1225	P1213	1
151	Fuel Injector, Cylinder 2		P1238	P1226	P1214	1
152	Fuel Injector, Cylinder 3		P1239	P1227	P1215	1
153	Fuel Injector, Cylinder 4		P1240	P1228	P1216	1
154	Fuel Injector, Cylinder 5		P1241	P1229	P1217	1
155	Fuel Injector, Cylinder 6		P1242	P1230	P1218	1
301	Airbag Signal	P1265				0
16	Aging of HO2S Ahead of TWC Cylinders (1 - 3)			P1275		0
22	Aging of HO2S Ahead of TWC Cylinders (4 - 6)			P1276		0
50	Misfire, Cylinder 1, Emission Related	P1313				1
51	Misfire, Cylinder 2, Emission Related	P1314				1
52	Misfire, Cylinder 3, Emission Related	P1315				1
53	Misfire, Cylinder 4, Emission Related	P1316				1
54	Misfire, Cylinder 5, Emission Related	P1317				1
55	Misfire, Cylinder 6, Emission Related	P1318				1
62	Misfire Emission Related	P1319				1
325	Timing Chain out of Position, Bank 2			P1324	P1324	1
322	Timing Chain out of Position, Bank 1			P1340	P1340	1
212	Knock Sensor 1	P1384				0

PR1019700011030X

Fig. 6 Diagnostic trouble code interpretation (Part 3 of 4). Boxster

Porsche Decimal malfunction code	Malfunction text	Fault type1	Fault type 2	Fault type 3	Fault type4	Check engine
62	Misfire emission-relevant	P0300	P0300	P0300	P0300	2
50	Misfire Cylinder 1 emission-relevant	P0301	P0301	P0301	P0301	2
51	Misfire Cylinder 2 emission-relevant	P0302	P0302	P0302	P0302	2
52	Misfire Cylinder 3 emission-relevant	P0303	P0303	P0303	P0303	2
53	Misfire Cylinder 4 emission-relevant	P0304	P0304	P0304	P0304	2
54	Misfire Cylinder 5 emission-relevant	P0305	P0305	P0305	P0305	2
55	Misfire Cylinder 6 emission-relevant	P0306	P0306	P0306	P0306	2
75	Misfire damaging to cat. conv.	P0300	P0300	P0300	P0300	3
63	Misfire Cylinder 1 damaging to cat. conv.	P0301	P0301	P0301	P0301	3
64	Misfire Cylinder 2 damaging to cat. conv.	P0302	P0302	P0302	P0302	3
65	Misfire Cylinder 3 damaging to cat. conv.	P0303	P0303	P0303	P0303	3
66	Misfire Cylinder 4 damaging to cat. conv.	P0304	P0304	P0304	P0304	3
67	Misfire Cylinder 5 damaging to cat. conv.	P0305	P0305	P0305	P0305	3
68	Misfire Cylinder 6 damaging to cat. conv.	P0306	P0306	P0306	P0306	3
111	Reference mark sensor	P0336	P0336	P0336	P0336	1
117	Throttle potentiometer	P0123	P0123	P0123	P0123	1

PR1029600017010X

Fig. 7 Diagnostic trouble code identification (Part 1 of 4). 1998 911

DTC	DTC Text	DTC vers. 1	DTC vers. 2	DTC vers. 3	DTC vers. 4	MIL
213	Knock Sensor 2	P1385				0
222	Knock Sensing Test Pulse	P1386				0
113	Camshaft Position Sensor 2	P1397		P1397	P1397	1
208	Secondary Air System Cylinders (4 - 6)	P1411				1
170	A/C Compressor Control		P1455	P1457	P1456	0
167	Fuel Pump Relay End-Stage		P1541	P1501	P1502	1
168	Idle Control Valve Opening Coil		P1514	P1513	P1510	1
178	Camshaft Adjustment, Bank 2			P1539	P1524	1
174	Camshaft Adjustment, Bank 1			P1531	P1530	1
169	Idle Control Valve Closing Coil		P1551	P1552	P1553	1
39	Immobilizer	P1570	P1571			0
8	Misfire with Empty Tank				P1585	3
107	Voltage Supply	P1600		P1600	P1601	1
108	Voltage Supply		P1602			0
105	ECM Faulty (EEPROM)	P1640				1
251	Engine Compartment Purge Fan End-Stage		P1671	P1671	P1671	0
253	Fan End-Stage		P1673	P1673	P1673	0
104	ECM Faulty (DTC Memory)	P1689				0
165	MIL (Check Engine)		P1691	P1692	P1693	1
135	Engine Engagement / Nominal Engine Torque			P1782		0

PR1019700011040X

Fig. 6 Diagnostic trouble code interpretation (Part 4 of 4). Boxster

Porsche Decimal malfunction code	Malfunction text	Fault type 1	Fault type 2	Fault type 3	Fault type 4	Check engine
108	Supply voltage	P1602	P1602	P1602	P1602	0
28	Oxygen sensing Range 1 Cylinder (1-3)	P1136	P1137	P1136	P1137	0
36	Oxygen sensing Range 1 Cylinder (4-6)	P1138	P1139	P1138	P1139	0
150	Injector circuit Cylinder 1	P1237	P1237	P1225	P1213	1
151	Injector circuit Cylinder 2	P1238	P1238	P1226	P1214	1
152	Injector circuit Cylinder 3	P1239	P1239	P1227	P1215	1
153	Injector circuit Cylinder 4	P1240	P1240	P1228	P1216	1
154	Injector circuit Cylinder 5	P1241	P1241	P1229	P1217	1
155	Injector circuit Cylinder 6	P1242	P1242	P1230	P1218	1
26	Oxygen sensing Range 2 Cylinder (1-3)	P1127	P1128	P1127	P1128	2
34	Oxygen sensing Range 2 Cylinder (4-6	P1129	P1130	P1129	P1130	2
104	Control module faulty (Fault memory)	P0604	P0604	P0604	P0604	0
14	OS2 heater 1 behind cat. conv.	P1117	P1117	P1117	P1105	1
4	OS2 heater 2 behind cat. conv.	P1121	P1121	P1121	P1110	1
13	OS2 heater 1 ahead of cat. conv.	P1115	P1115	P1115	P1102	1
5	OS2 heater 2 ahead of cat. conv.	P1119	P1119	P1119	P1107	1
40	Cat. converter efficiency Cylinder (1-3)	P0420	P0420	P0420	P0420	1
45	Cat. converter efficiency Cylinder (4-6)	P0430	P0430	P0430	P0430	1
138	A/C compressor signal	P1458	P1458	P1458	P1458	0
170	A/C compressor control	P1455	P1455	P1457	P1456	0
167	Fuel pump relay final stage	P1541	P1541	P1501	P1502	1
222	Knock control test pulse	P1386	P1386	P1386	P1386	0

PR1029600017020X

Fig. 7 Diagnostic trouble code identification (Part 2 of 4). 1998 911

Porsche Decimal malfunction code	Malfunction text	Fault type 1	Fault type 2	Fault type 3	Fault type 4	Check engine
210	Knock sensor 1	P0326	P0326	P0326	P0326	0
211	Knock sensor 2	P0331	P0331	P0331	P0331	0
17	Sensor ageing behind cat. converter Cylinder (1-3)	P0139	P0139	P0139	P0139	0
23	Sensor ageing behind cat. converter Cylinder (4-6)	P0159	P0159	P0159	P0159	0
15	Sensor ageing ahead of cat. converter Cylinder (1-3)	P0133	P0133	P0133	P0133	1
21	Sensor ageing ahead of cat. converter Cylinder (4-6)	P0153	P0153	P0153	P0153	1
16	Sensor ageing ahead of cat. converter Cylinder (1-3)	P0133	P0133	P0133	P0133	0
22	Sensor ageing ahead of cat. converter Cylinder (4-6)	P0153	P0153	P0153	P0153	0
171	Turbocharger frequency valve	P0236	P0236	P0236	P0236	0
230	Boost pressure curve	P1555	P1555	P1555	P1555	0
231	Boost pressure deviation	P1556	P1557	P1556	P1557	0
121	Load detection	P1140	P1140	P1140	P1140	1
32	Idle control	P0506	P0507	P0506	P0507	1
115	Hot film MAP sensor	P0101	P0102	P0102	P0103	1
12	O2 sensor ahead of cat. converter Cylinder (1-3)	P0136	P0140	P0137	P0138	1
20	O2 sensor ahead of cat. converter Cylinder (4-6)	P0156	P0160	P0157	P0158	1
10	O2 sensor behind cat. converter Cylinder (1-3)	P0130	P0134	P0131	P0132	1
18	O2 sensor behind cat. converter Cylinder (4-6)	P0150	P0154	P0151	P0152	1
165	MIL (Check Engine)	P1691	P1691	P1692	P1693	1
112	Hall-effect sensor	P0341	P0341	P0341	P0341	1

PR1029600017030X

Fig. 7 Diagnostic trouble code identification (Part 3 of 4). 1998 911

Fault text	Fault type 1	Fault type 2	Fault type 3	Fault type 4	MIL
Mass air flow sensor	P0101		P0102	P0103	1
Intake air temperature sensor			P0112	P0113	1
Engine temperature sensor	P0115		P0117	P0118	1
Throttle position sensor			P0122	P0123	1
Oxygen sensor (HO2S) ahead of TWC Cylinders (1 - 3)	P0130	P0134	P0131	P0132	1
Aging of oxygen sensor ahead of TWC Cylinders (1 - 3)			P0133		1
Oxygen sensor after TWC Cylinders (1 - 3)	P0136	P0140	P0137	P0138	1
Aging of oxygen sensor after TWC Cylinders (1 - 3)			P0139		0

PR1029900046010X

Fig. 8 Diagnostic trouble code identification (Part 1 of 5). 1999 911

Porsche Decimal malfunction code	Malfunction text	Fault type 1	Fault type 2	Fault type 3	Fault type 4	Check engine
105	Control module faulty (EEPROM)	P1640	P1640	P1640	P1640	1
101	Control module faulty (internal RAM)	P0604	P0604	P0604	P0604	1
103	Control module faulty (EPROM)	P0605	P0605	P0605	P0605	1
102	Control module faulty (external RAM)	P0604	P0604	P0604	P0604	1
80	Secondary air injection system Cylinder (1-3)	P0410	P0410	P0410	P0410	1
208	Secondary air injection system Cylinder (4-6)	P1411	P1411	P1411	P1411	1
124	Intake air temperature sensor	P0112	P0112	P0112	P0112	1
93	Tank vent system	P0441	P0441	P0441	P0441	1
98	Tank vent valve	P0444	P0444	P0445	P0445	1
123	Engine temperature sensor	P0115	P0117	P0117	P0118	1
27	Oxygen sensing Range 1 Cylinder (1-3)	P1123	P1124	P1123	P1124	2
35	Oxygen sensing Range 1 Cylinder (4-6)	P1125	P1126	P1125	P1126	2
107	Supply voltage	P1600	P1601	P1600	P1601	1
120	Vehicle speed	P0501	P0501	P0501	P0501	1
39	Anti-drive-off feature	P1570	P1571	P1571	P1571	0
168	IACV break winding	P1514	P1514	P1513	P1510	1
169	IACV make winding	P1551	P1551	P1552	P1553	1

PR1029600017040X

Fig. 7 Diagnostic trouble code identification (Part 4 of 4). 1998 911

Fault text	Fault type 1	Fault type 2	Fault type 3	Fault type 4	MIL
Oxygen sensor ahead of TWC Cylinders (4 - 6)	P0150	P0154	P0151	P0152	1
Aging of oxygen sensor ahead of TWC Cylinders (4 - 6)			P0153		1
Oxygen sensor after TWC Cylinders (4 - 6)	P0156	P0160	P0157	P0158	1
Aging of oxygen sensor after TWC Cylinders (4 - 6)			P0159		0
Oil temperature sensor			P0197	P0198	0
Misfire damaging to TWC	P0300				2
Misfire, cylinder 1, damaging to TWC	P0301				2
Misfire, cylinder 2, damaging to TWC	P0302				2
Misfire, cylinder 3, damaging to TWC	P0303				2
Misfire, cylinder 4, damaging to TWC	P0304				2
Misfire, cylinder 5, damaging to TWC	P0305				2
Misfire, cylinder 6, damaging to TWC	P0306				2
Crankshaft position sensor	P0336				1
Camshaft position sensor 1	P0341		P0341	P0341	1
Secondary air injection system Cylinders (1 - 3)	P0410				1
TWC conversion Cylinders (1 - 3)			P0420		1
TWC conversion Cylinders (4 - 6)			P0430		1
Fuel tank ventilation system				P0440	1
Fuel tank ventilation system				P0441	1

PR1029900046020X

Fig. 8 Diagnostic trouble code identification (Part 2 of 5). 1999 911

Fault text	Fault type 1	Fault type 2	Fault type 3	Fault type 4	MIL
Fuel tank ventilation system (micro-leak)			P0442		1
EVAP canister purge valve		P0444	P0445	P0445	1
EVAP canister shutoff valve			P0446		1
EVAP canister shutoff valve		P0447	P0448	P0448	1
Tank pressure sensor	P0450		P0452	P0453	1
Fuel tank ventilation system (major leak)			P0455		1
Vehicle speed	P0501				1
Idle air control			P0506	P0507	1
CAN timeout		P0600			1
Control module faulty (external RAM)	P0603				1
Control module faulty (internal RAM)	P0604				1
Control module faulty (EPROM)	P0605				1
Heating of oxygen sensor 1 ahead of TWC			P1115	P1102	1
Heating of oxygen sensor 1 after TWC			P1117	P1105	1
Heating of oxygen sensor 2 ahead of TWC			P1119	P1107	1
Heating of oxygen sensor 2 after TWC			P1121	P1110	1
Oxygen sensing, area 1 Cylinders (1 - 3)			P1123	P1124	1
Oxygen sensing, area 1 Cylinders (4 - 6)			P1125	P1126	1
Oxygen sensing, area 2 Cylinders (1 - 3)			P1127	P1128	1
Oxygen sensing, area 2 Cylinders (4 - 6)			P1129	P1130	1
Load sensing	P1140				1

PR1029900046030X

Fig. 8 Diagnostic trouble code identification (Part 3 of 5). 1999 911

Fault text	Fault type 1	Fault type 2	Fault type 3	Fault type 4	MIL
Engine compartment temperature sensor			P1157	P1158	0
Fuel injector, cylinder 1		P1237	P1225	P1213	1
Fuel injector, cylinder 2		P1238	P1226	P1214	1
Fuel injector, cylinder 3		P1239	P1227	P1215	1
Fuel injector, cylinder 4		P1240	P1228	P1216	1
Fuel injector, cylinder 5		P1241	P1229	P1217	1
Fuel injector, cylinder 6		P1242	P1230	P1218	1
Airbag signal	P1265				0
Aging of oxygen sensor ahead of TWC Cylinders (1 - 3)			P1275		0
Aging of oxygen sensor ahead of TWC Cylinders (4 - 6)			P1276		0
Misfire, cylinder 1, emission relevant	P1313				1
Misfire, cylinder 2, emission relevant	P1314				1
Misfire, cylinder 3, emission relevant	P1315				1
Misfire, cylinder 4, emission relevant	P1316				1
Misfire, cylinder 5, emission relevant	P1317				1
Misfire, cylinder 6, emission relevant	P1318				1
Misfire, emission relevant	P1319				1
Timing chain out of position, bank 2			P1324	P1324	1
Timing chain out of position, bank 1			P1340	P1340	1
Knock sensor 1	P1384				0
Knock sensor 2	P1385				0
Knock control test pulse	P1386				0
Camshaft position sensor 2	P1397		P1397	P1397	1

PR1029900046040X

Fig. 8 Diagnostic trouble code identification (Part 4 of 5). 1999 911

Fault text	Fault type 1	Fault type 2	Fault type 3	Fault type 4	MIL
Secondary air injection system Cylinders (4 - 6)	P1411				1
A/C compressor control		P1455	P1457	P1456	0
Fuel pump relay output stage		P1541	P1501	P1502	1
Idle air control valve opening coil		P1514	P1513	P1510	1
Tuning flap		P1516	P1515	P1512	0
Camshaft adjustment, bank 2			P1539	P1524	1
Camshaft adjustment, bank 1			P1531	P1530	1
Idle air control valve closing coil		P1551	P1552	P1553	1
Immobilizer	P1570	P1571			0
Misfire with empty fuel tank				P1585	3
Voltage supply	P1600		P1600	P1601	1
Voltage supply		P1602			0
Control module faulty (EEPROM)	P1640				1
Engine compartment purge fan output stage		P1671	P1671	P1671	0
Fan output stage		P1673	P1673	P1673	0
Control module faulty (fault memory)	P1689				0
MIL (Check Engine)		P1691	P1692	P1693	1
Engine engagement / nominal engine torque			P1782		0

PR1029900046050X

Fig. 8 Diagnostic trouble code identification (Part 5 of 5). 1999 911

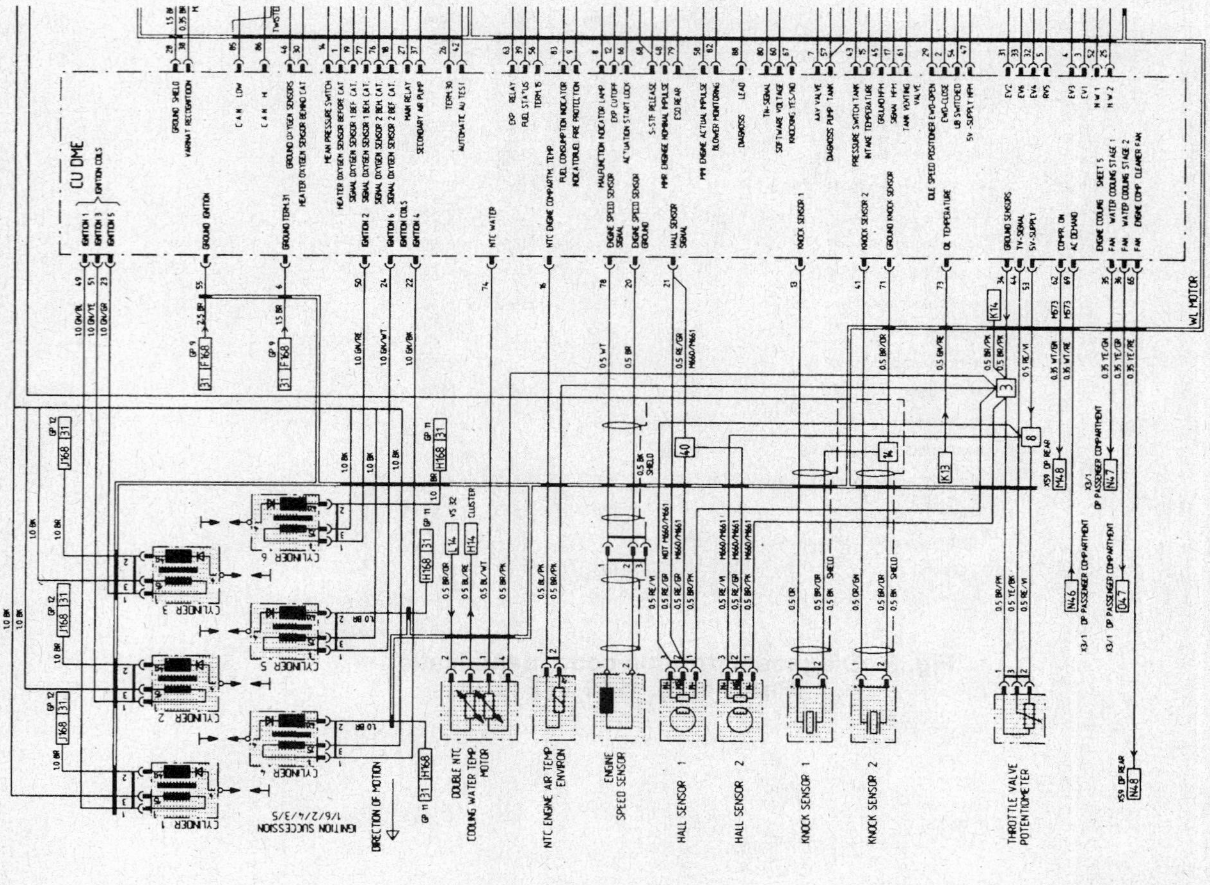

PR1019800008010X

Fig. 9 DME wiring circuit (Part 1 of 3). 1998 Boxster

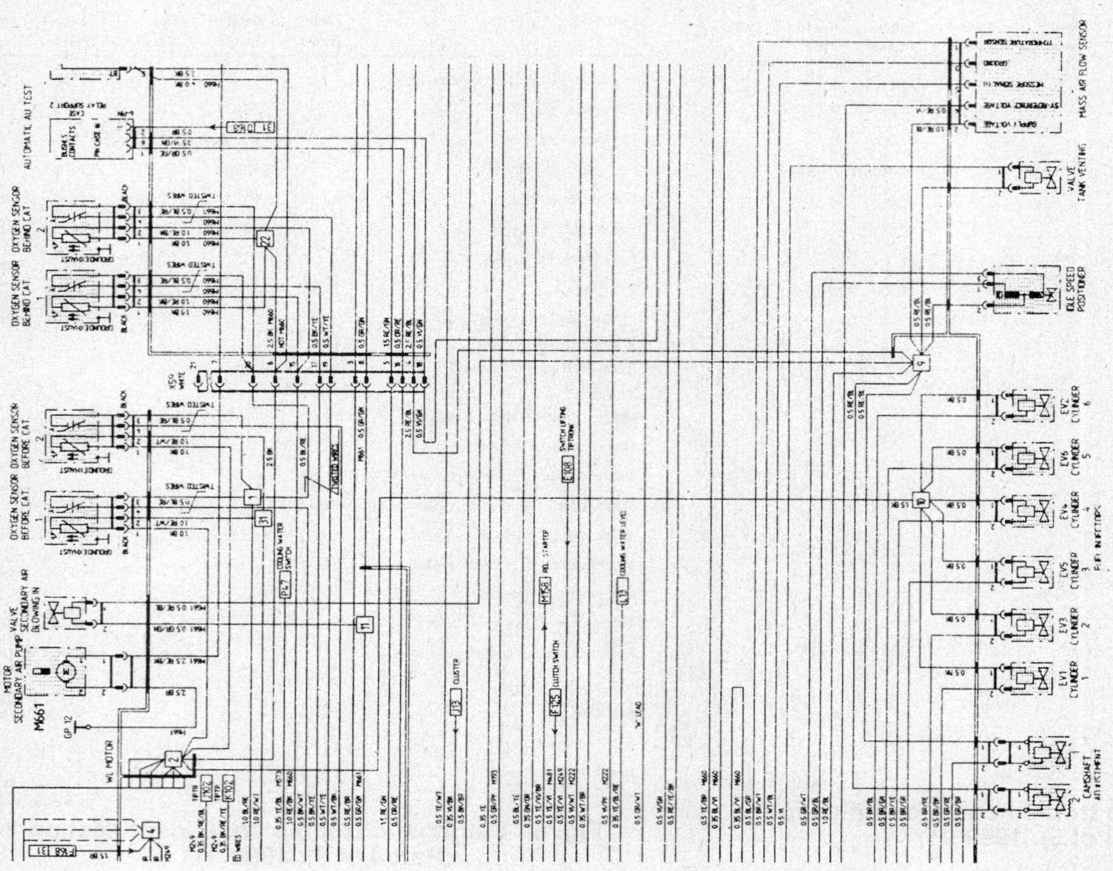

PR1019800008020X

Fig. 9 DME wiring circuit (Part 2 of 3). 1998 Boxster

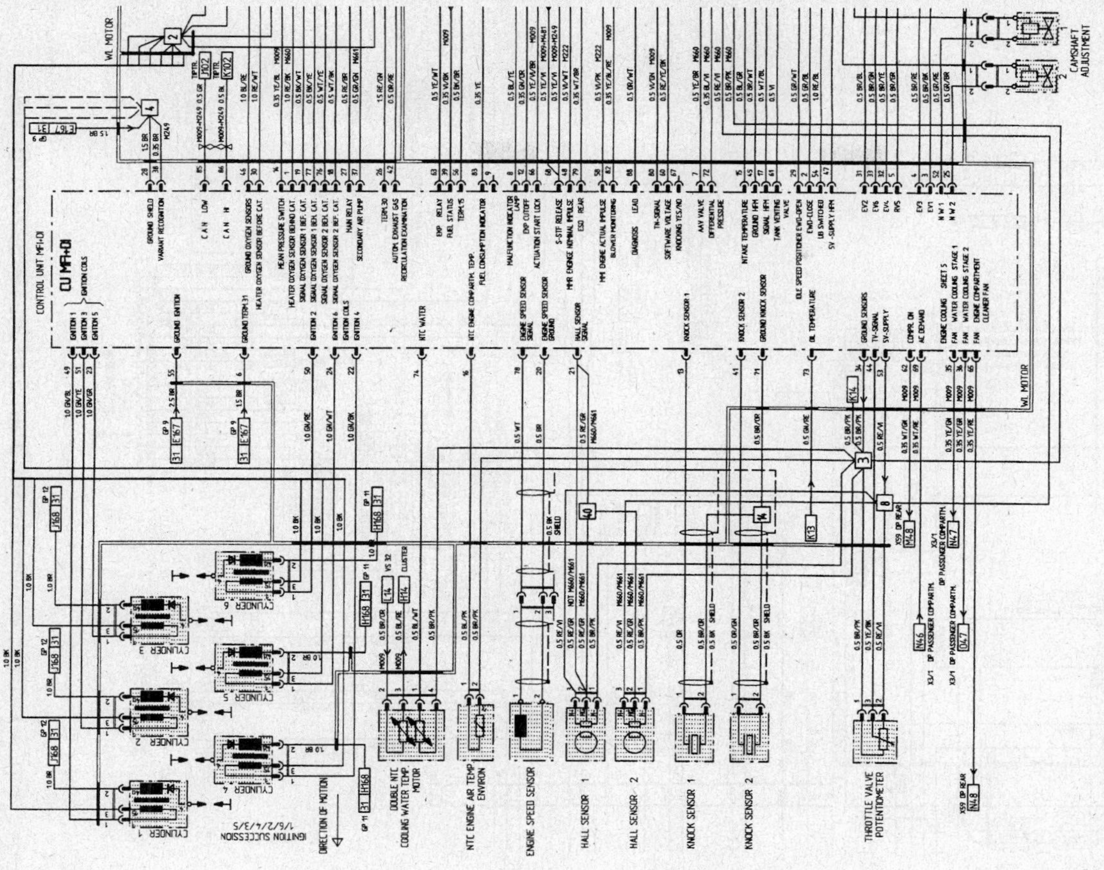

PR1020100334010X

Fig. 10 DME wiring circuit (Part 1 of 3). 1999–2001 Boxster

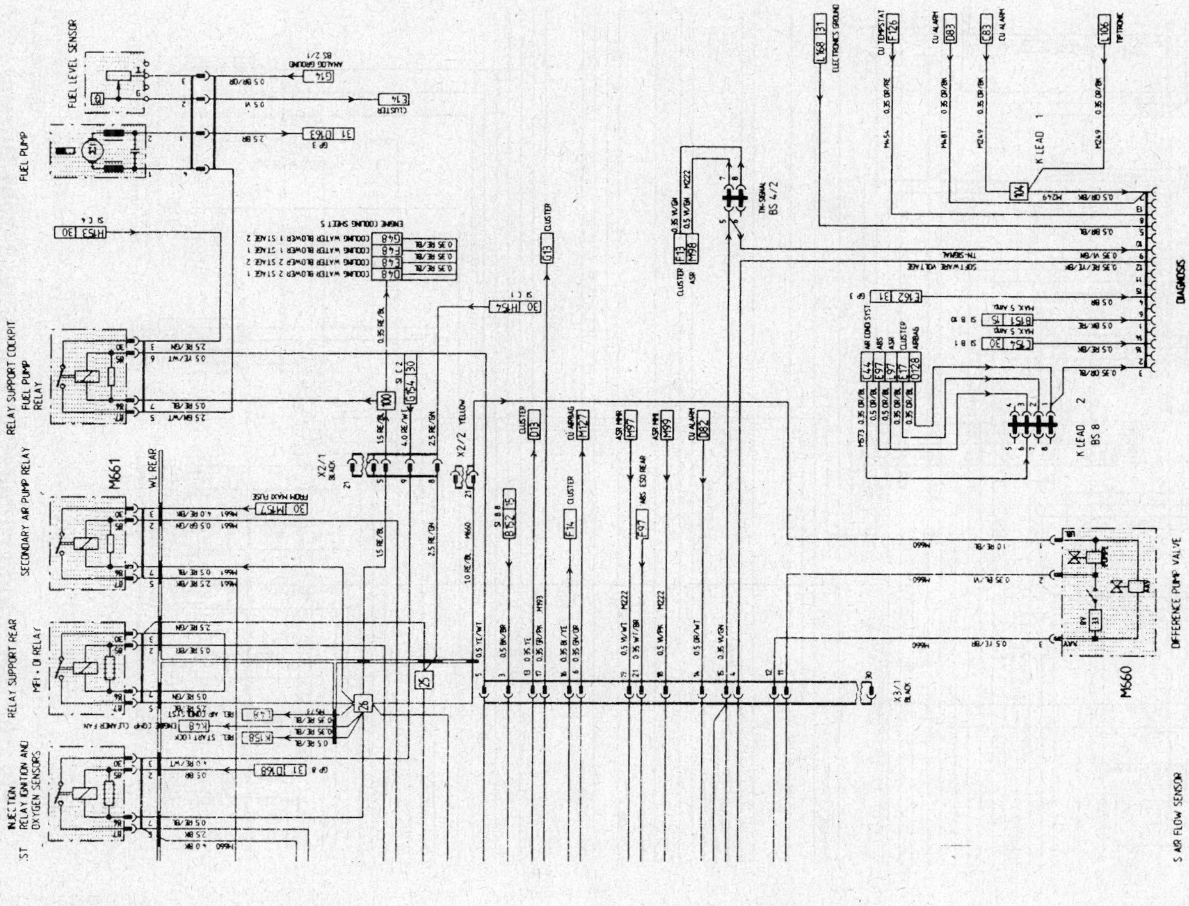

PR1019800008030X

Fig. 9 DME wiring circuit (Part 3 of 3). 1998 Boxster

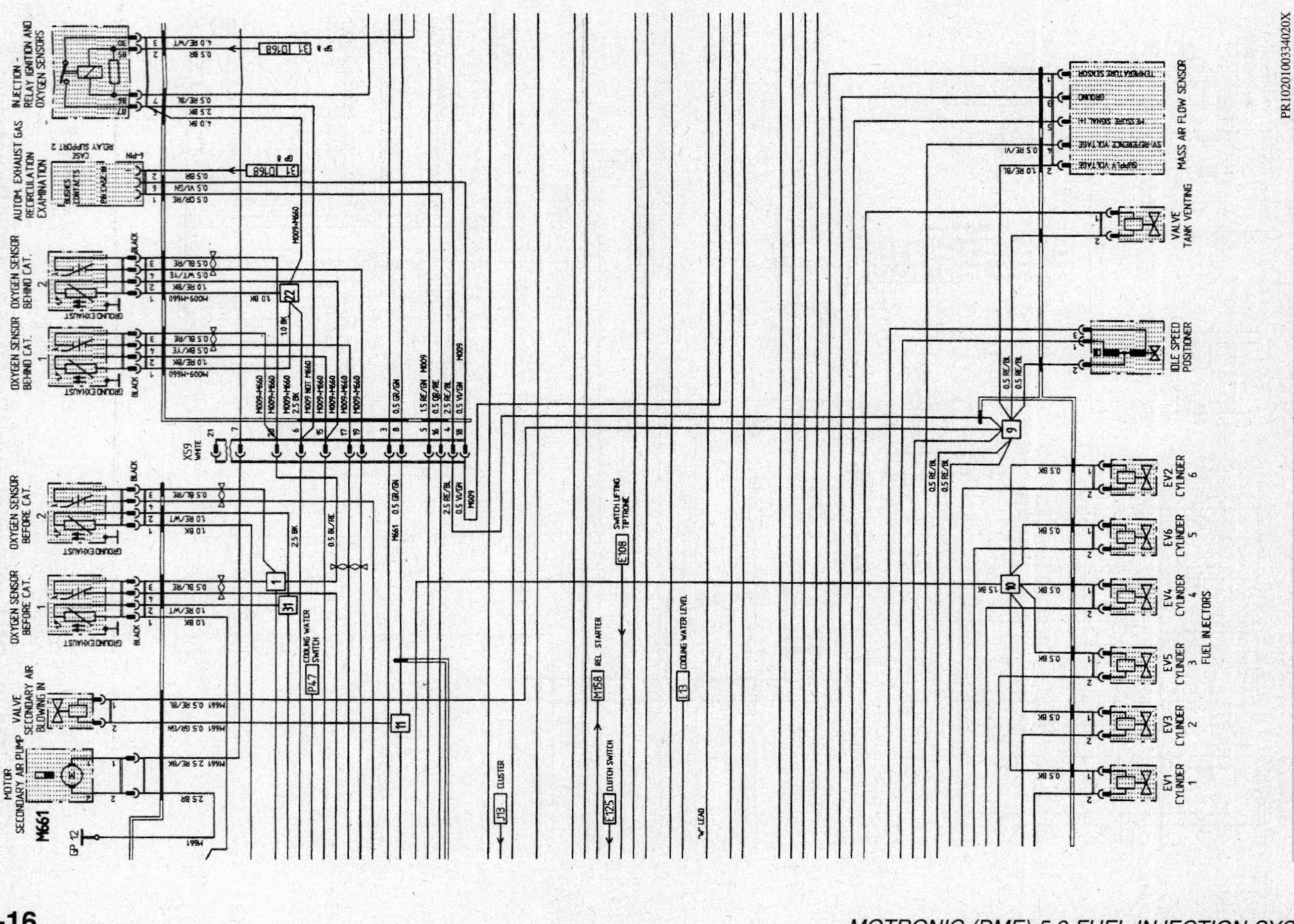

PR102010033402OX

Fig. 10 DME wiring circuit (Part 2 of 3). 1999–2001 Boxster

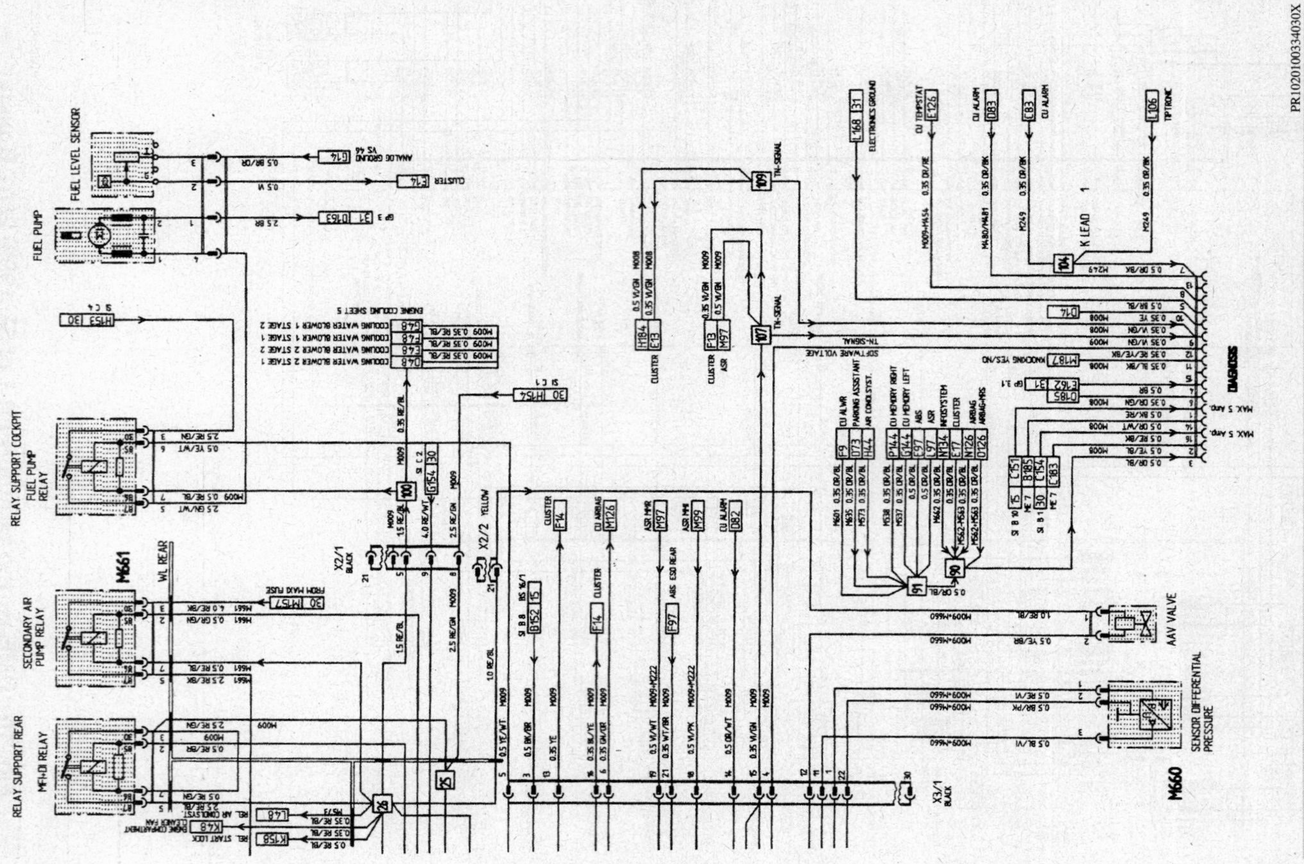

PR102010033403OX

Fig. 10 DME wiring circuit (Part 3 of 3). 1999–2001 Boxster

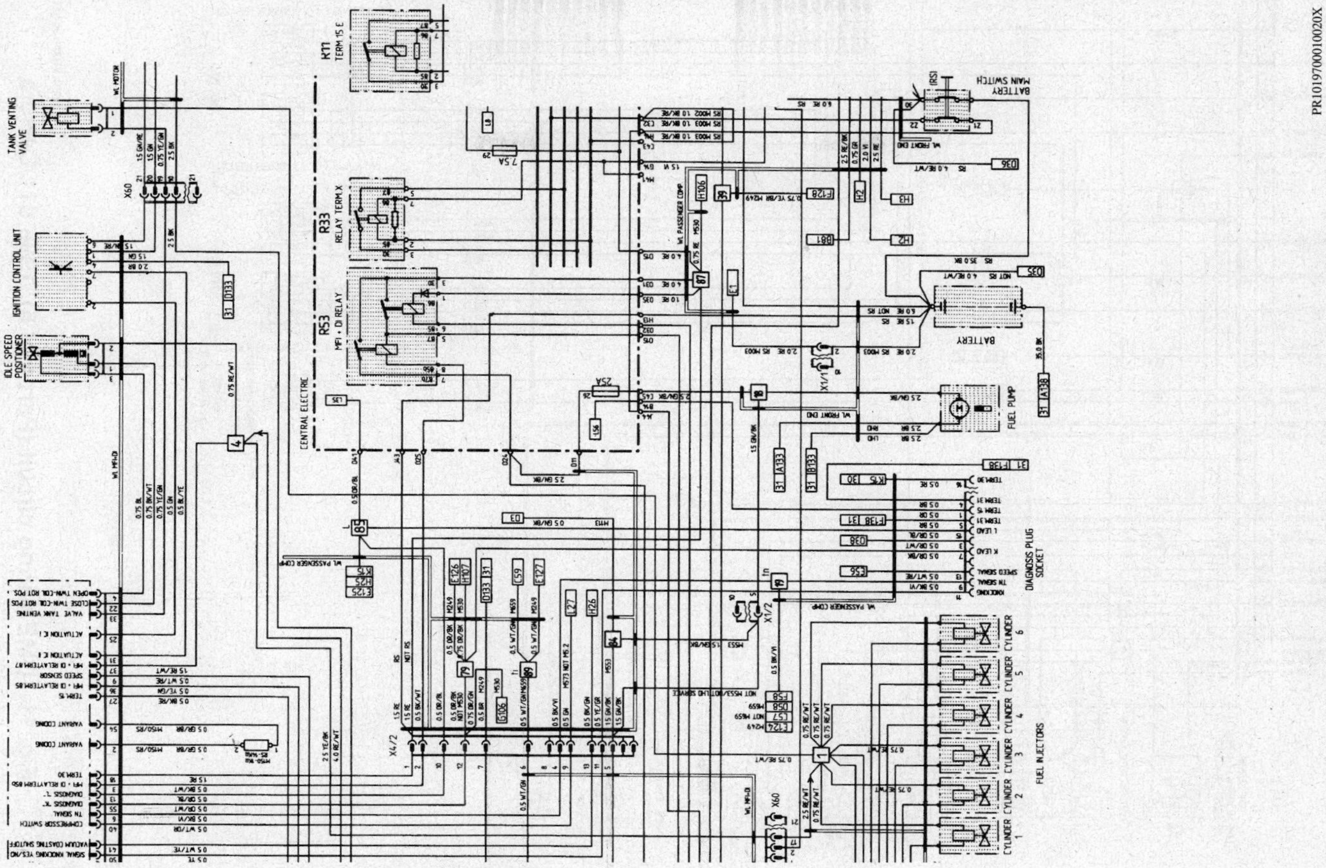

Fig. 11 DME wiring circuit (Part 2 of 6). 1998 911 Carrera

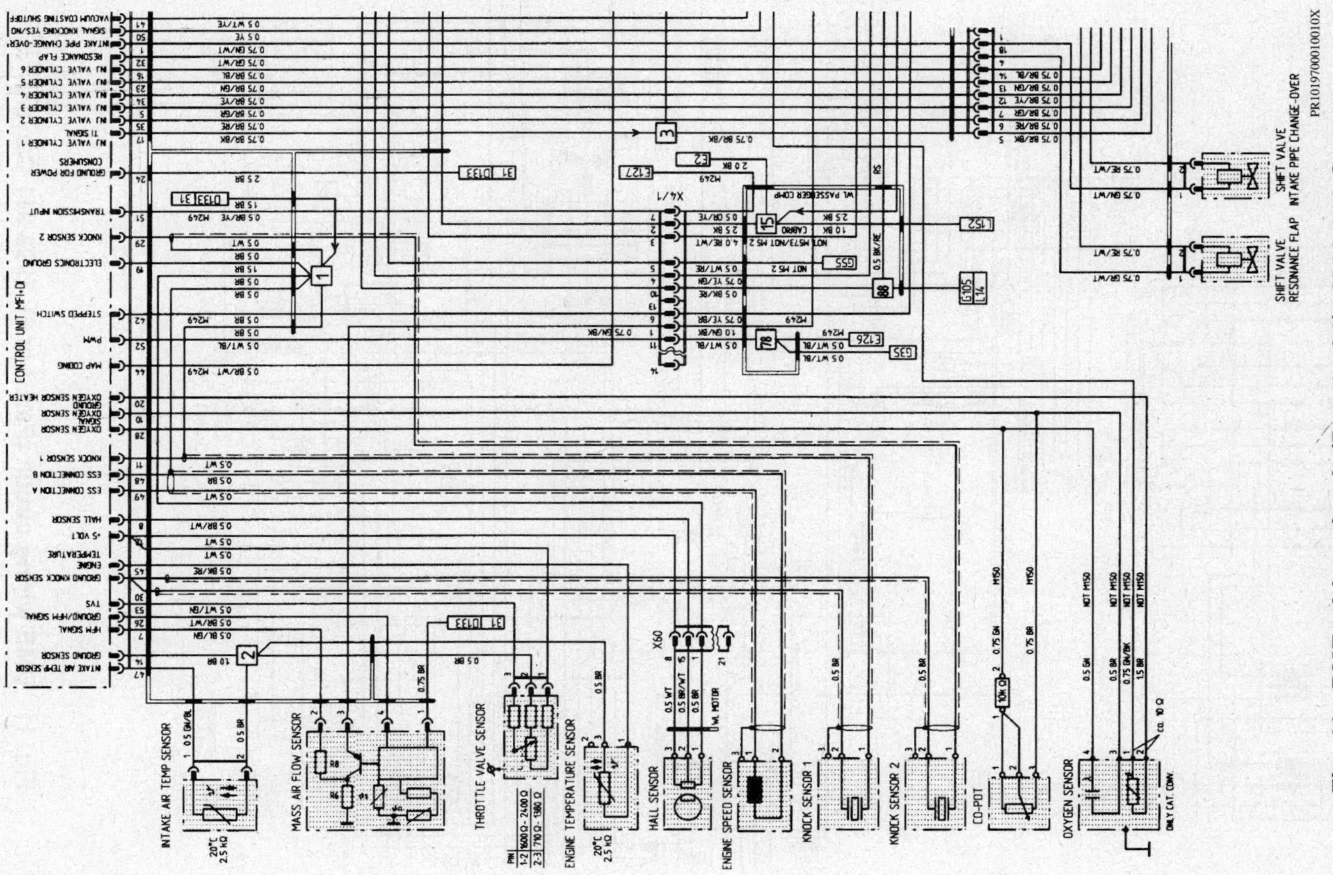

Fig. 11 DME wiring circuit (Part 1 of 6). 1998 911 Carrera

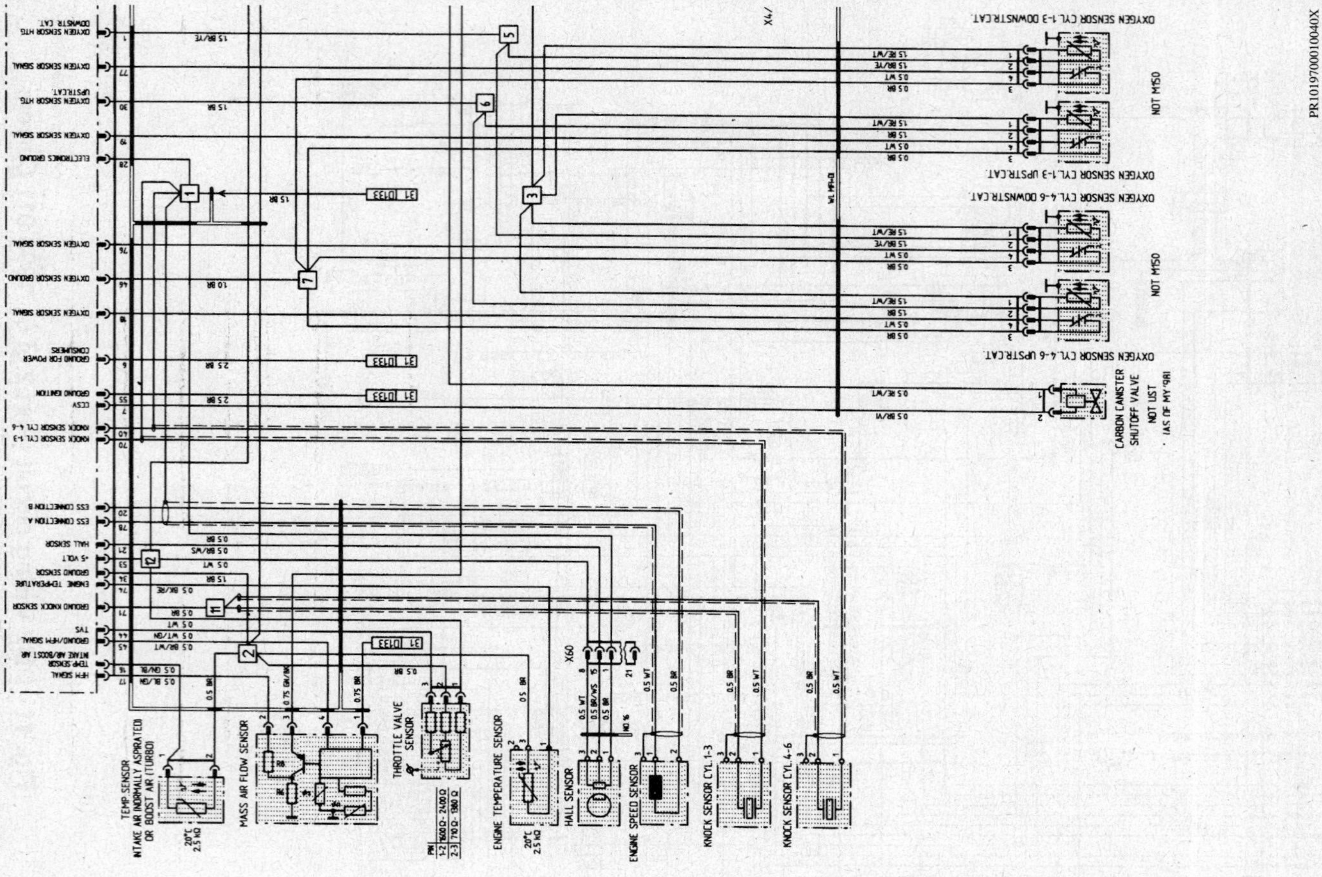

PR1019700010040X

Fig. 11 DME wiring circuit (Part 4 of 6). 1998 911 Carrera

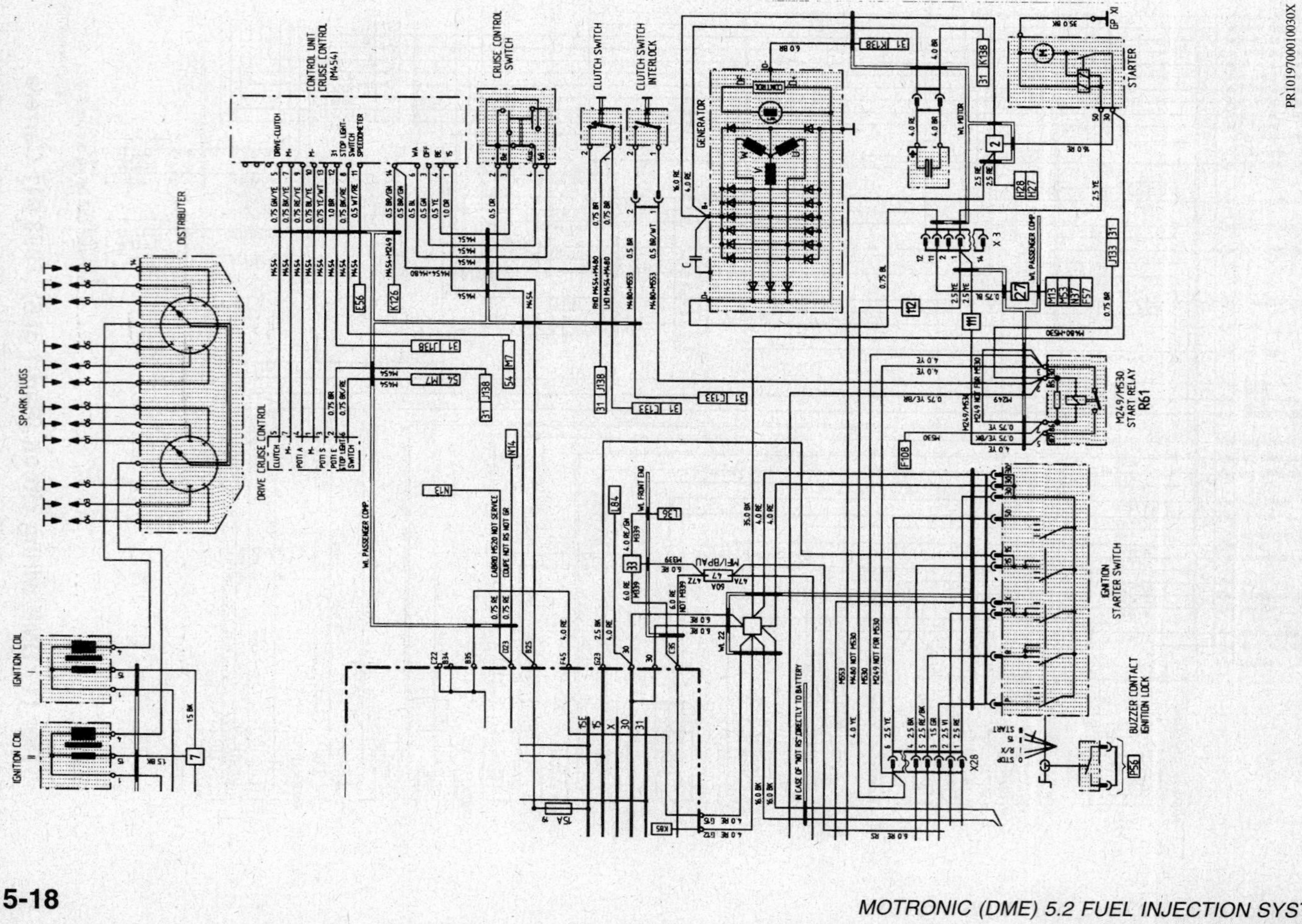

PR1019700010030X

Fig. 11 DME wiring circuit (Part 3 of 6). 1998 911 Carrera

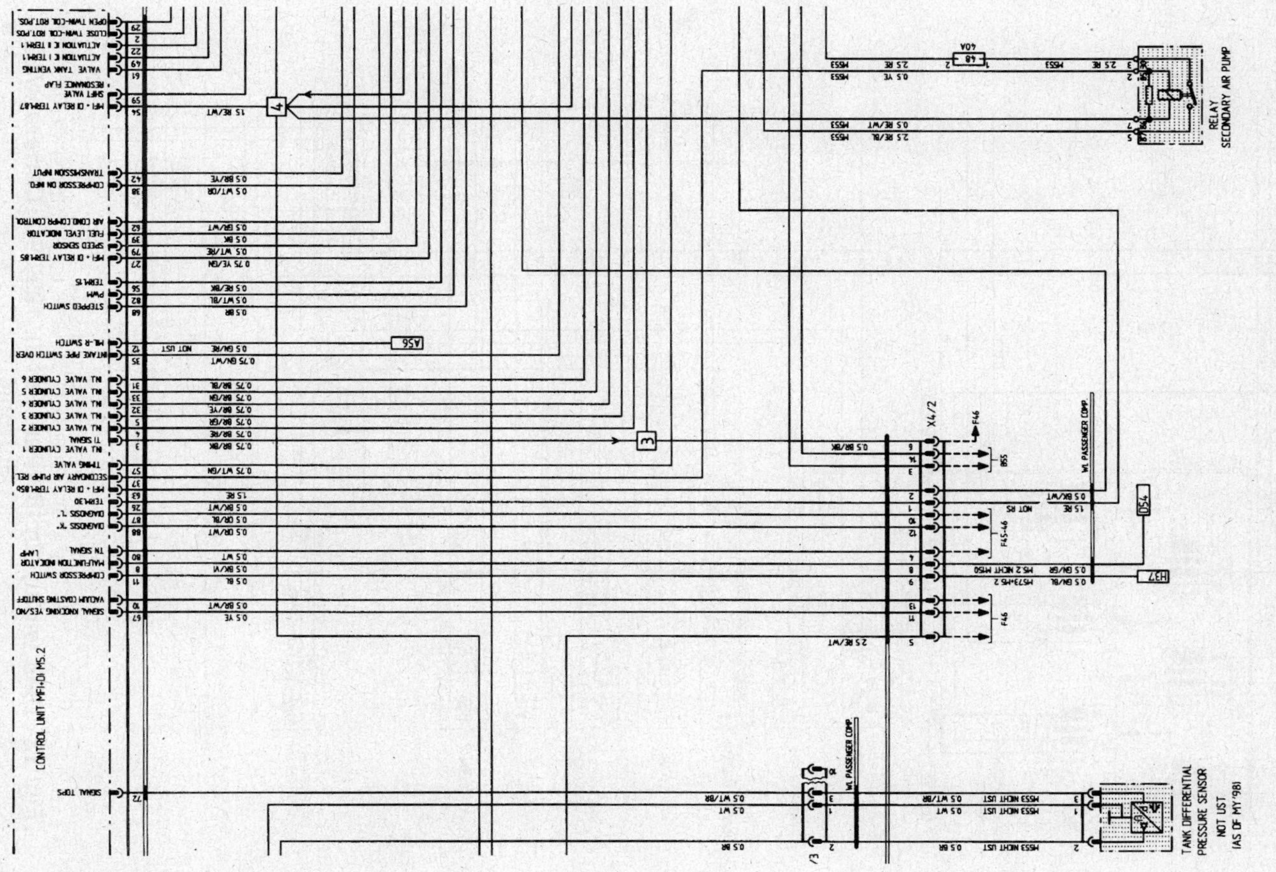

PR10197000100050X

Fig. 11 DME wiring circuit (Part 5 of 6). 1998 911 Carrera

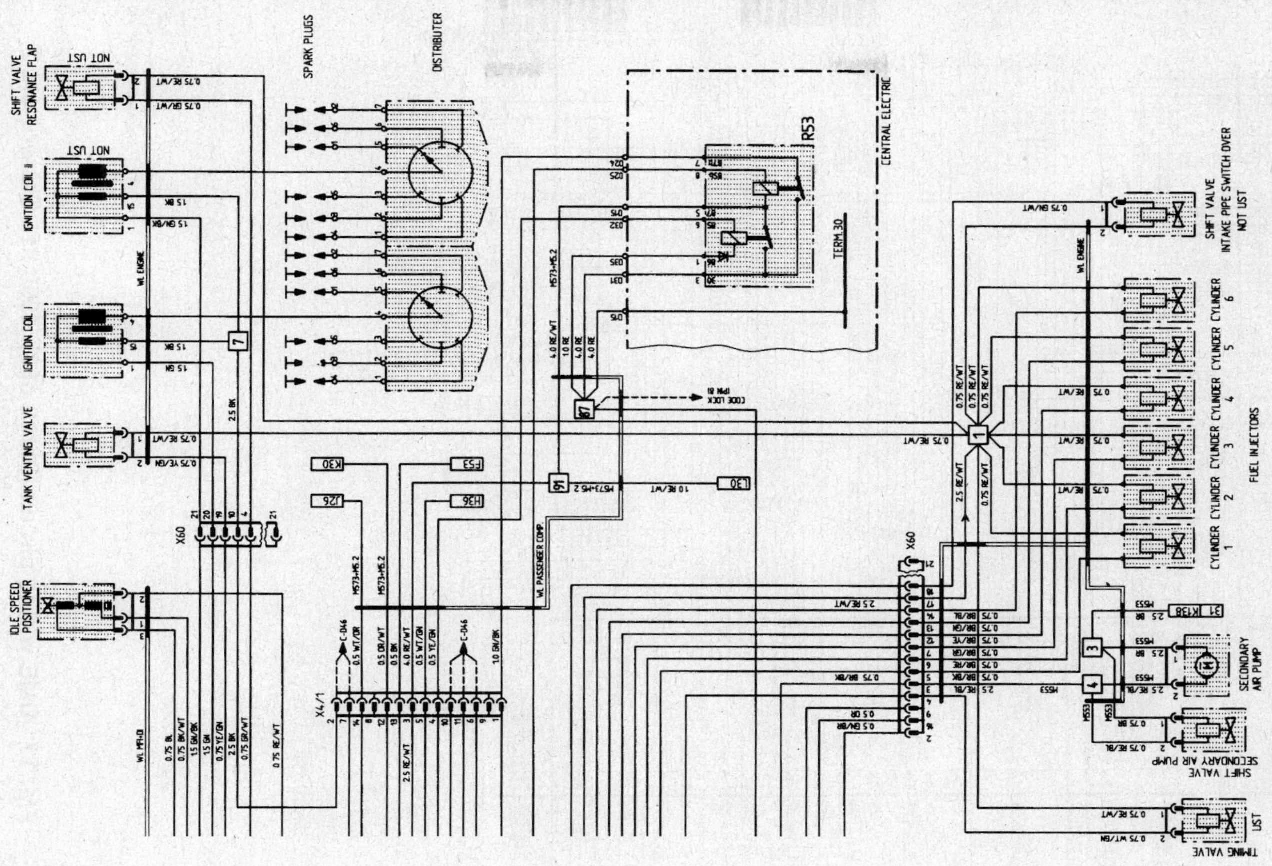

PR10197000100060X

Fig. 11 DME wiring circuit (Part 6 of 6). 1998 911 Carrera

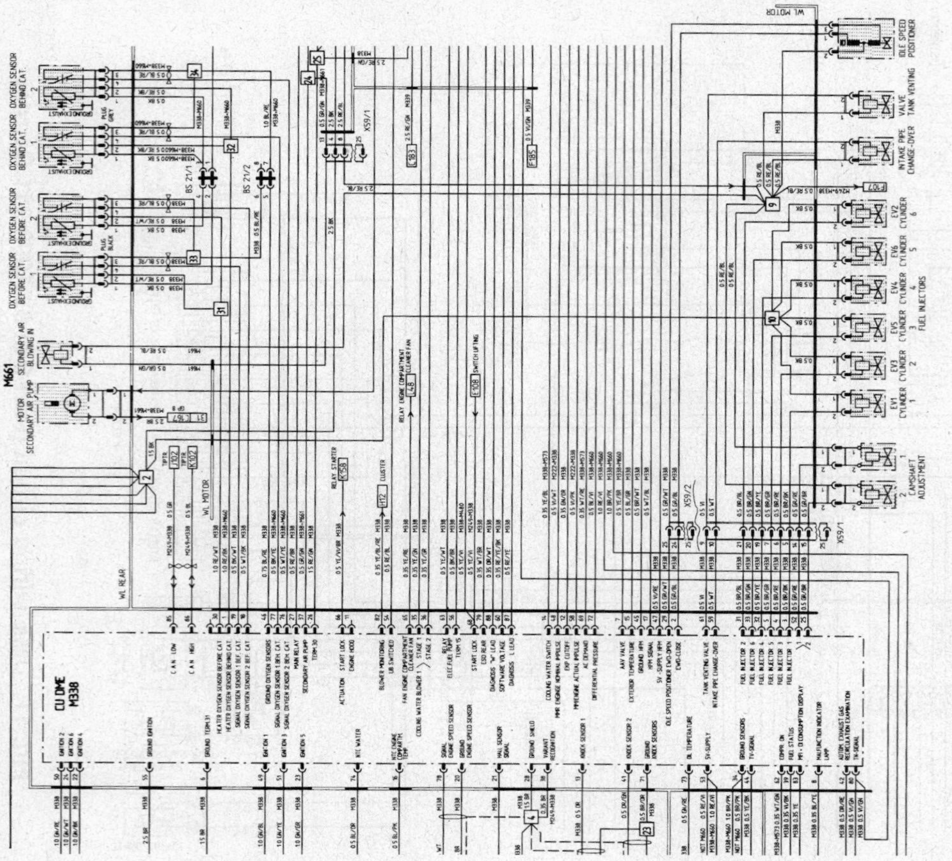

PR101990000902OX

Fig. 12 DME wiring circuit (Part 2 of 3). 1999 911 Carrera w/5.2 Motronic

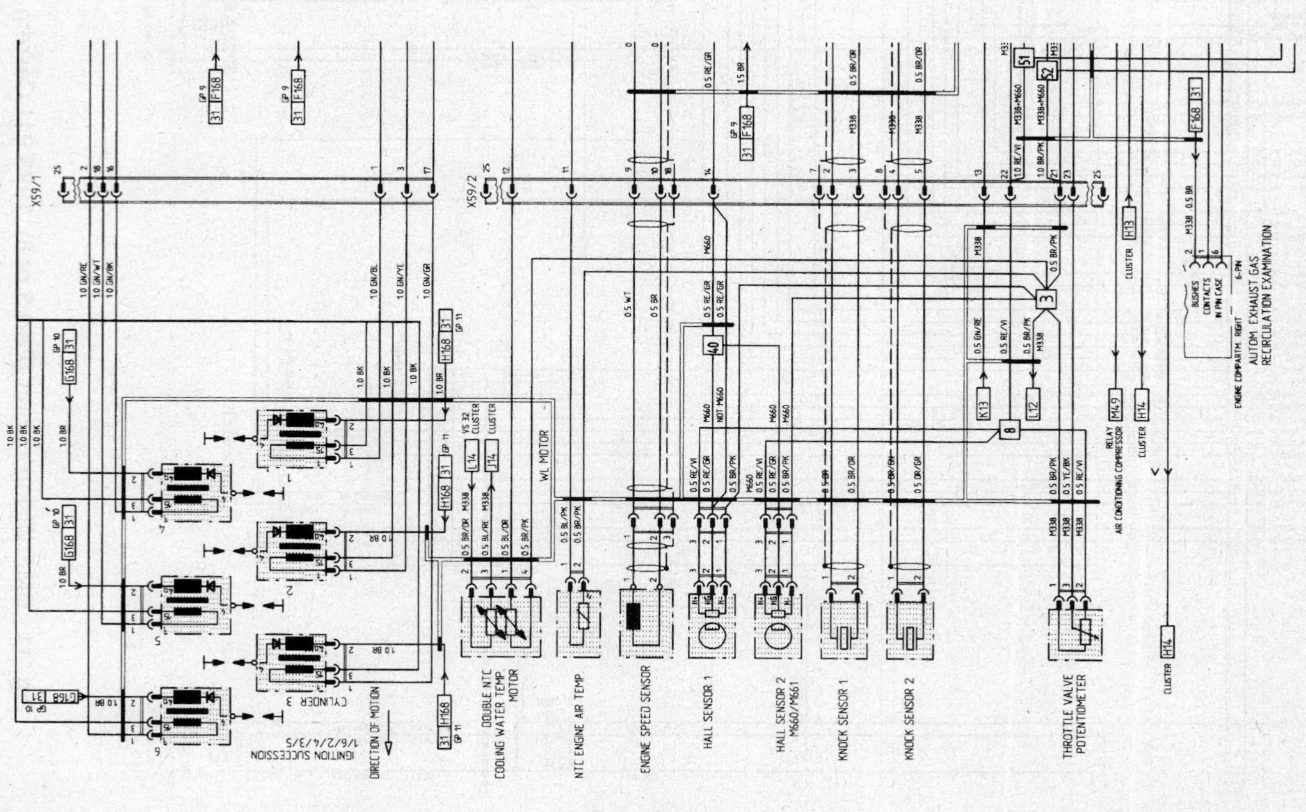

PR101990000901OX

Fig. 12 DME wiring circuit (Part 1 of 3). 1999 911 Carrera w/5.2 Motronic

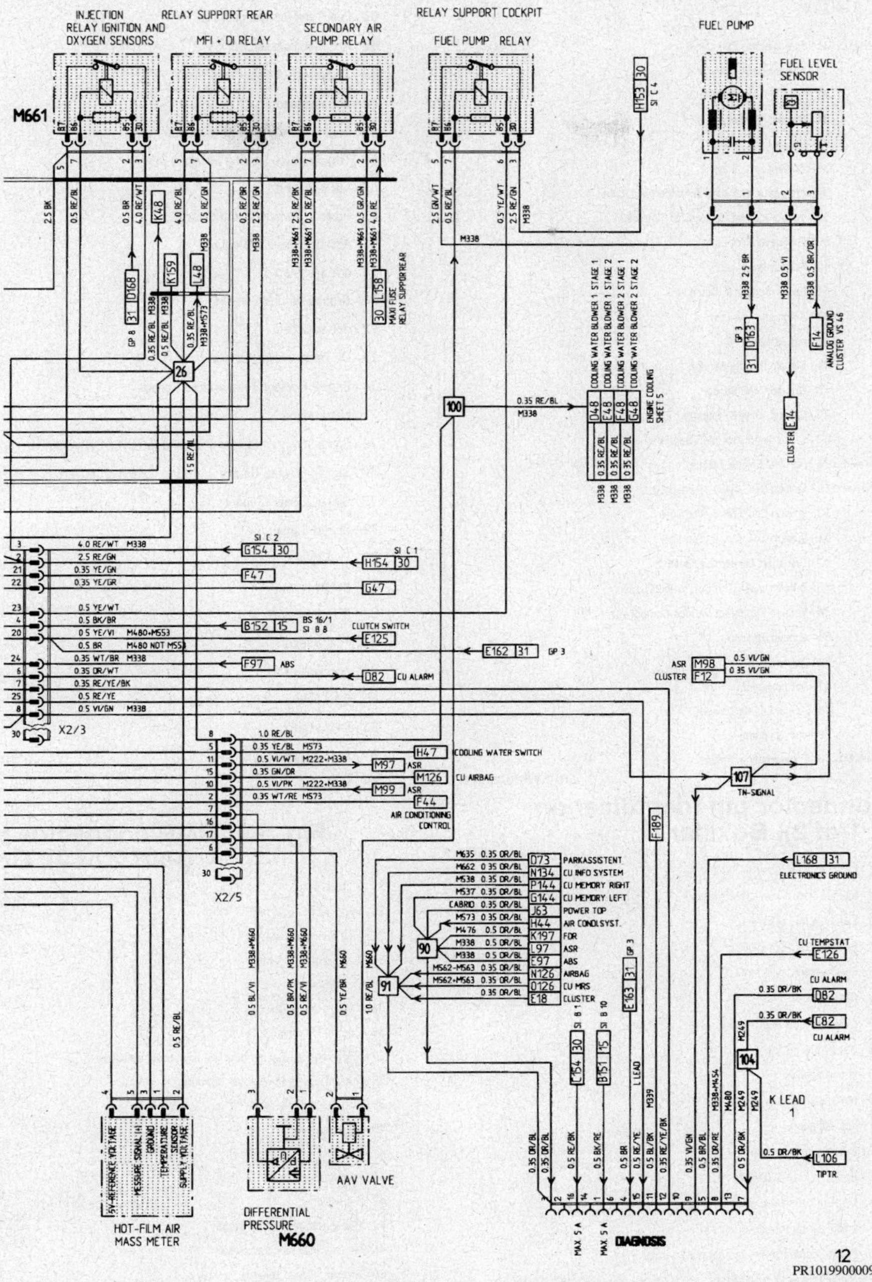

Fig. 12 DME wiring circuit (Part 3 of 3). 1999 911 Carrera w/5.2 Motronic

DME Connector Assignment

1 - Oxygen Sensor Heating Behind Catalytic Converter
2 - Idle Air Control Valve, Closing Coil
3 - Fuel Injector, Cylinder 1
4 - Fuel Injector, Cylinder 2
5 - Fuel Injector, Cylinder 3
6 - Ground
7 - not assigned
8 - Malfunction Indication Light Check Engine
9 - not assigned
10 - not assigned
11 - not assigned
12 - Crash Signal (Airbag)
13 - Knock Sensor 1 (Cyl. 1 - 3)
14 - Medium Pressure Switch (Air Conditioning)
15 - Intake Air Temperature Sensor
16 - Engine Compartment Temperature Sensor
17 - Signal, Mass Air Flow Sensor
18 - Signal, Oxygen Sensor 2 Ahead of Catalytic Converter
19 - Signal, Oxygen Sensor 1 Ahead of Catalytic Converter
20 - Ground, Speed Sender
21 - Signal, Camshaft Position Sensor 1 + 2
22 - Ignition Coil, Cyl. 4, Terminal 1
23 - Ignition Coil, Cyl. 3, Terminal 1
24 - Ignition Coil, Cyl. 5, Terminal 1
25 - Camshaft Adjustment, Bank 2
26 - Terminal 30
27 - Triggering of ECM Relay, Terminal 85
28 - Ground, Electronic System
29 - Idle Air Control Valve, Opening Coil
30 - Oxygen Sensor Heating Ahead of Catalytic Converter
31 - Fuel Injector, Cylinder 6
32 - Fuel Injector, Cylinder 4
33 - Fuel Injector, Cylinder 5
34 - Ground, Sender
35 - Coolant Fan, Stage 1
36 - Coolant Fan, Stage 2
37 - Triggering of Relay, Secondary Air Pump
38 - Version coding (Ground for Tiptronic)
39 - Fuel Level Pilot Light
40 - not assigned
41 - Knock Sensor 2 (Cyl. 4 - 6)
42 - Automatic I/M Test
43 - not assigned
44 - Signal, Throttle Sender
45 - Ground, MAF Sensor
46 - Ground, Oxygen Sensors
47 - 5 Volt Supply for MAF Sensor
48 - Nominal Engine Torque
49 - Ignition Coil, Cyl. 1, Terminal 1
50 - Ignition Coil, Cyl. 6, Terminal 1
51 - Ignition Coil, Cyl. 2, Terminal 1
52 - Camshaft Adjustment, Bank 1
53 - 5 Volt supply, Throttle Position Sensor
54 - Voltage Supply for Various Components
55 - Ground, Ignition
56 - Terminal 15
57 - not assigned
58 - Actual Engine Torque
59 - not assigned
60 - Programming Voltage

PR1019700012010X

Fig. 13 DME connector pin identification (Part 1 of 2). Boxster

61 - Fuel Tank Ventilation Valve
62 - A/C Compressor On
63 - Triggering of Fuel Pump Relay
64 - not assigned
65 - Engine Compartment Purge Fan
66 - Triggering of Starting Interlock Relay
67 - not assigned
68 - Position Switch/Clutch Switch
69 - A/C Compressor Request
70 - not assigned
71 - Ground, Knock Sensors
72 - not assigned
73 - Oil Temperature Sensor
74 - Engine Coolant Temperature Sensor
75 - not assigned
76 - Signal, Oxygen Sensor 2 Behind Catalytic Converter
77 - Signal, Oxygen Sensor 1 Behind Catalytic Converter
78 - Signal, Speed Sender
79 - Speed Signal
80 - T_N Signal
81 - not assigned
82 - Coolant Level
83 - Fuel Gauge
84 - not assigned
85 - CAN Low
86 - CAN High
87 - not assigned
88 - K Wire

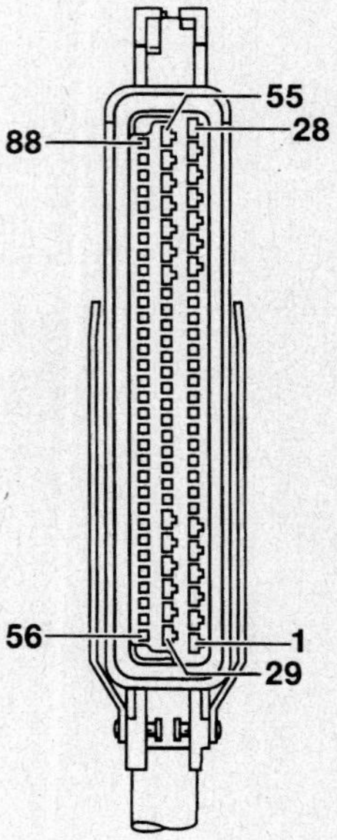

PR1019700012020X

Fig. 13 DME connector pin identification (Part 2 of 2). Boxster

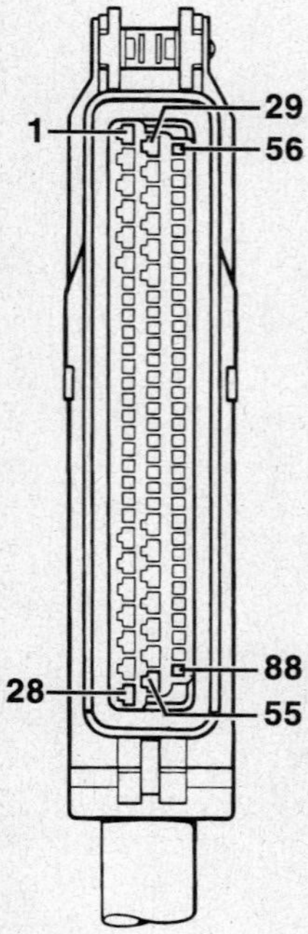

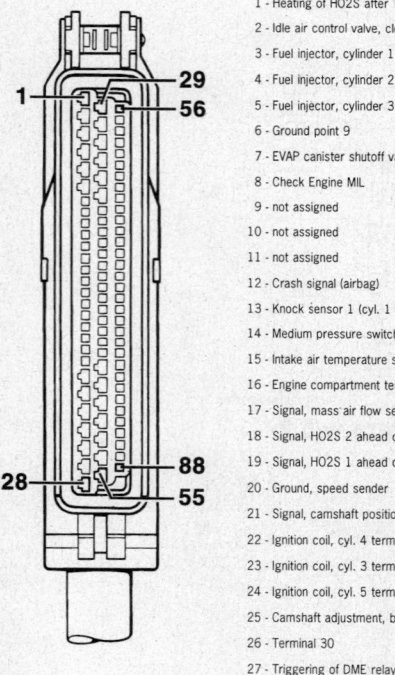

1 - Heating of HO2S after TWC
2 - Idle air control valve, closing coil
3 - Fuel injector, cylinder 1
4 - Fuel injector, cylinder 2
5 - Fuel injector, cylinder 3
6 - Ground point 9
7 - EVAP canister shutoff valve
8 - Check Engine MIL
9 - not assigned
10 - not assigned
11 - not assigned
12 - Crash signal (airbag)
13 - Knock sensor 1 (cyl. 1 - 3)
14 - Medium pressure switch (A/C)
15 - Intake air temperature sensor
16 - Engine compartment temperature sensor
17 - Signal, mass air flow sensor
18 - Signal, HO2S 2 ahead of TWC
19 - Signal, HO2S 1 ahead of TWC
20 - Ground, speed sender
21 - Signal, camshaft position sensor 1 + 2
22 - Ignition coil, cyl. 4 terminal 1
23 - Ignition coil, cyl. 3 terminal 1
24 - Ignition coil, cyl. 5 terminal 1
25 - Camshaft adjustment, bank 2
26 - Terminal 30
27 - Triggering of DME relay, terminal 85
28 - Ground, electronic system (shield)
29 - Idle air control valve opening coil
30 - Heating of HO2S ahead of TWC

PR1029900048010X

Fig. 14 DME connector pin identification (Part 1 of 2). 1999 911

31 - Fuel injector, cylinder 6
32 - Fuel injector, cylinder 4
33 - Fuel injector, cylinder 5
34 - Ground, sender
35 - Coolant fan, stage 1
36 - Coolant fan, stage 2
37 - Triggering of relay (terminal 85), secondary air pump
38 - Version coding (ground for Tiptronic)
39 - Fuel reserve pilot light
40 - not assigned
41 - Knock sensor 2 (cyl. 4 - 6)
42 - Automatic I/M test
43 - not assigned
44 - Signal, throttle position sensor
45 - Ground, mass air flow sensor
46 - Ground, oxygen sensors
47 - 5-volt supply for mass air flow sensor
48 - Nominal engine torque to TC control module
49 - Ignition coil, cyl. 1 terminal 1
50 - Ignition coil, cyl. 6 terminal 1
51 - Ignition coil, cyl. 2 terminal 1
52 - Camshaft adjustment, bank 1
53 - 5-volt supply, throttle position sensor
54 - Voltage supply for various components
55 - Ground, ignition
56 - Terminal 15
57 - not assigned
58 - Actual engine torque from TC control module
59 - Tuning flap (intake manifold switchover)
60 - Programming voltage
61 - EVAP canister purge valve
62 - A/C compressor On
63 - Triggering of fuel pump relay (terminal 85)
64 - not assigned
65 - Relay of engine compartment purge fan (terminal 85)
66 - Start-inhibit relay (terminal 85)
67 - not assigned
68 - Position switch/clutch switch
69 - A/C compressor requirement
70 - not assigned
71 - Ground, knock sensors
72 - Tank pressure sensor
73 - Oil temperature sensor
74 - Engine coolant temperature sensor
75 - not assigned
76 - Signal, HO2S 2 after TWC
77 - Signal, HO2S 1 after TWC
78 - Signal, rpm crankshaft position sensor
79 - Speed signal from ABS control module
80 - Speed signal output
81 - not assigned
82 - Coolant level
83 - Fuel gauge
84 - not assigned
85 - CAN low
86 - CAN high
87 - L wire
88 - K wire

PR1029900048020X

Fig. 14 DME connector pin identification (Part 2 of 2). 1999 911

DIAGNOSTIC CHART INDEX

Code	Description	Page No.	Fig. No.
BOXSTER			
P0101	MAF Sensor Signal Circuit	15-28	15
P0102	MAF Sensor Signal Circuit	15-28	15
P0103	MAF Sensor Signal Circuit	15-28	15
P0112	Intake Air Temperature Circuit	15-28	16
P0113	Intake Air Temperature Circuit	15-28	16
P0115	ECT Sensor Circuit	15-29	17
P0117	ECT Sensor Circuit	15-29	17
P0118	ECT Sensor Circuit	15-29	17
P0123	Throttle Position Sensor Signal Implausible	15-31	18
P0130	O2 Sensor Short Circuit (O2 In Front Of Catalytic Converter, Cyl 1-3)	15-31	19
P0131	O2 Sensor Short Circuit To Ground (O2 In Front Of Catalytic Converter, Cyl 1-3)	15-32	20
P0132	O2 Short Circuit To Power (O2 In Front Of Catalytic Converter, Cyl 1-3)	15-33	21
P0133	Aging of O2 Sensor In Front Of Three Way Catalytic Converter	15-34	22
P0134	O2 Sensor Interruption Of Signal (In Front Of Catalytic Converter, Cyl 1-3)	15-34	23
P0136	O2 Sensor Circuit Short (Behind Catalytic Converter, Cyl	15-35	24
P0137	O2 Sensor Short Circuit To Ground (Behind Catalytic Converter, Cyl 1-3)	15-36	25
P0138	O2 Sensor Short Circuit To Power (Behind Catalytic Converter, Cyl 1-3)	15-37	26
P0139	Aging O2 Sensor After 3 Way Catalytic Converter	15-37	27
P0140	O2 Sensor Interruption Of Signal (Behind Catalytic Converter, Cyl 1-3)	15-38	28
P0150	O2 Sensor Short Circuit Of Wires (In Front Of Catalytic Converter, Cyl 4-6)	15-39	29
P0151	O2 Sensor Short Circuit To Ground (In Front Of Catalytic Converter, Cyl 4-6)	15-40	30
P0152	O2 Sensor Short To Power (In Front Of Catalytic Converter Cyl 4-6)	15-40	31
P0153	Aging of O2 Sensor In Front Of Three Way Catalytic Converter	15-34	22
P0154	O2 Sensor Interruption Of Signal (In Front Of Catalytic Converter, Cyl 4-6)	15-41	32
P0156	O2 Sensor Short Circuit Of Wires (Behind Catalytic Converter, Cyl 4-6)	15-42	33
P0157	O2 Sensor Short Circuit To Ground (Behind Catalytic Converter, Cyl 4-6)	15-43	34
P0158	O2 Sensor Short To Power (Behind Catalytic Converter, Cyl 4-6)	15-43	35
P0159	Aging O2 Sensor After 3 Way Catalytic Converter	15-37	27
P0160	O2 Sensor Interruption Of Signal (Behind Catalytic Converter, Cyl 4-6)	15-44	36
P0197	Oil Temperature Sensor Circuit	15-45	37
P0198	Oil Temperature Sensor Circuit	15-45	37
P0300	Cylinder Misfire	15-46	38
P0301	Cylinder Misfire	15-46	38
P0302	Cylinder Misfire	15-46	38
P0303	Cylinder Misfire	15-46	38
P0304	Cylinder Misfire	15-46	38
P0305	Cylinder Misfire	15-46	38
P0306	Cylinder Misfire	15-46	38
P0336	Crankshaft Position Sensor Not In Specified Range	15-47	39
P0341	Camshaft Position Sensor Short Circuit	15-48	40
P0410	Secondary Air Injection Signal Implausible	15-49	41
P0420	TWC Conversion Too Low	15-51	42
P0430	TWC Conversion Too Low	15-51	42
P0440	Fuel Tank Ventilation Malfunction	15-51	43
P0444	EVAP Canister Purge Valve	15-52	44
P0445	EVAP Canister Purge Valve	15-52	44
P0501	Vehicle Speed Sensor Not In Specified Range	15-53	45
P0506	Idle Air Control Circuit	15-54	46
P0507	Idle Air Control Circuit	15-54	46
P0600	CAN Timeout Signal Implausible	15-54	47
P0603	ECM Faulty	15-55	48
P0604	ECM Faulty	15-55	48
P0605	ECM Faulty	15-55	48
P1102	O2 Sensor Heating Above Upper Limit (In Front Of Catalytic Converter)	15-55	49
P1105	O2 Sensor Heating Above Upper Limit (Behind Catalytic Converter)	15-56	50
P1107	O2 Sensor Heating Above Upper Limit (In Front Of Catalytic Converter)	15-55	49
P1110	O2 Sensor Heating Above Upper Limit (Behind Catalytic Converter)	15-56	50

Continued

DIAGNOSTIC CHART INDEX—Continued

Code	Description	Page No.	Fig. No.
BOXSTER			
P1115	O2 Sensor Heating Below Lower Threshold (Behind Catalytic Converter)	15-56	51
P1117	O2 Sensor Heating Below Lower Threshold	15-57	52
P1119	O2 Sensor Heating Below Lower Threshold (Behind Catalytic Converter)	15-56	51
P1121	O2 Sensor Heating Below Lower Threshold	15-57	52
P1123	O2 Sensor Adaptation Range 1 Lean Limit	15-57	53
P1124	O2 Sensor Adaptation Range 1 Enrichment Limit	15-58	54
P1125	O2 Sensor Adaptation Range 1 Lean Limit	15-57	53
P1126	O2 Sensor Adaptation Range 1 Enrichment Limit	15-58	54
P1127	O2 Sensor adaptation Range 2 Lean Limit	15-59	55
P1128	O2 Sensor Adaptation Range 2 Enrichment Limit	15-60	56
P1129	O2 Sensor adaptation Range 2 Lean Limit	15-59	55
P1130	O2 Sensor Adaptation Range 2 Enrichment Limit	15-60	56
P1140	Load Calculation Signal Implausible	15-61	57
P1157	Engine Compartment Temperature Sensor Short	15-62	58
P1158	Engine Compartment Temperature Sensor Short	15-62	58
P1213	Injector Circuit Cylinder 1	15-63	59
P1214	Injector Circuit Cylinder 2	15-63	60
P1215	Injector Circuit Cylinder 3	15-64	61
P1216	Injector Circuit Cylinder 4	15-64	62
P1217	Injector Circuit Cylinder 5	15-65	63
P1218	Injector Circuit Cylinder 6	15-65	64
P1225	Injector Circuit Cylinder 1	15-63	59
P1226	Injector Circuit Cylinder 2	15-63	60
P1227	Injector Circuit Cylinder 3	15-64	61
P1228	Injector Circuit Cylinder 4	15-64	62
P1229	Injector Circuit Cylinder 5	15-65	63
P1230	Injector Circuit Cylinder 6	15-65	64
P1237	Injector Circuit Cylinder 1	15-63	59
P1238	Injector Circuit Cylinder 2	15-63	60
P1239	Injector Circuit Cylinder 3	15-64	61
P1240	Injector Circuit Cylinder 4	15-64	62
P1241	Injector Circuit Cylinder 5	15-65	63
P1242	Injector Circuit Cylinder 6	15-65	64
P1265	Air Bag Signal Implausible	15-66	65
P1275	Aging Of O2 Sensor In Front Of Three Way Catalytic Converter	15-34	22
P1276	Aging Of O2 Sensor In Front Of Three Way Catalytic Converter	15-34	22
P1313	Cylinder Misfire	15-46	38
P1314	Cylinder Misfire	15-46	38
P1315	Cylinder Misfire	15-46	38
P1316	Cylinder Misfire	15-46	38
P1317	Cylinder Misfire	15-46	38
P1318	Cylinder Misfire	15-46	38
P1319	Cylinder Misfire	15-46	38
P1324	Timing Chain Out Of Position	15-66	66
P1340	Timing Chain Out Of Position	15-66	66
P1384	Knock Sensor Circuit	15-66	67
P1385	Knock Sensor Circuit	15-66	67
P1386	Knock Sensor Circuit	15-66	67
P1397	Camshaft Position Sensor Short Circuit	15-48	40
P1411	Secondary Air Injection Signal Implausible	15-49	41
P1455	A/C Compressor Control	15-67	68
P1456	A/C Compressor Control	15-67	68
P1457	A/C Compressor Control	15-67	68
P1501	End Stage Fuel Pump Relay	15-68	69
P1502	End Stage Fuel Pump Relay	15-68	69
P1510	Idle Control Valve Opening Coil	15-69	70
P1513	Idle Control Valve Opening Coil	15-69	70

Continued

DIAGNOSTIC CHART INDEX—Continued

Code	Description	Page No.	Fig. No.
BOXSTER			
P1514	Idle Control Valve Opening Coil	15-69	70
P1524	Camshaft Adjustment Bank 2	15-70	71
P1530	Camshaft Adjustment Bank 1	15-70	72
P1531	Camshaft Adjustment Bank 1	15-70	72
P1539	Camshaft Adjustment Bank 2	15-70	71
P1541	End Stage Fuel Pump Relay	15-68	69
P1551	Idle Air Control	15-71	73
P1552	Idle Air Control	15-71	73
P1553	Idle Air Control	15-71	73
P1570	Immobilizer Circuit	15-72	74
P1571	Immobilizer Circuit	15-72	74
P1585	Cylinder Misfire	15-46	38
P1600	Power Supply Circuit	15-73	75
P1601	Power Supply Circuit	15-73	75
P1602	Power Supply Interruption	15-73	76
P1640	ECM Faulty	15-55	48
P1671	Engine Compartment Purge Fan End Stage	15-74	77
P1673	Fan End Stage	15-75	78
P1689	ECM Faulty	15-55	48
P1691	Malfunction Indication Light	15-76	79
P1692	Malfunction Indication Light	15-76	79
P1693	Malfunction Indication Light	15-76	79
P1782	Engine Engagement Nominal Engine Torque Short Circuit To Ground	15-77	80
1999 911			
P0101	Mass Air Flow Sensor, Signal Implausible	15-77	81
P0102	Mass Air Flow Sensor, Below Lower Limit	15-77	81
P0103	Mass Air Flow Sensor, Above Upper Limit	15-77	81
P0112	Intake Air Temperature Sensor, Below Lower Limit	15-78	82
P0113	Intake Air Temperature Sensor, Above Upper Limit	15-78	82
P0115	Engine Coolant Temperature Sensor, Signal Implausible	15-79	83
P0117	Engine Coolant Temperature Sensor, Below Lower Limit	15-79	83
P0118	Engine Coolant Temperature Sensor, Above Upper Limit	15-79	83
P0122	Throttle Position Sensor, Below Lower Limit	15-80	84
P0123	Throttle Position Sensor, Above Upper Limit	15-80	84
P0130	Front Oxygen Sensor Cylinders 1–3 Short Circuit Or Limited Voltage Increase	15-81	85
P0131	Front Oxygen Sensor Cylinders 1–3 Short Circuit To Ground Or Incorrect Voltage	15-81	86
P0132	Front Oxygen Sensor Cylinders 1–3 Short Circuit To Battery Positive	15-82	87
P0133	Front Oxygen Sensors Aging	15-82	88
P0134	Front Oxygen Sensor Cylinders 1–3 Signal Interruption	15-82	89
P0136	Rear Oxygen Sensor Cylinders 1–3 Short Circuit	15-83	90
P0137	Rear Oxygen Sensor Cylinders 1–3 Short Circuit To Ground Or Incorrect Voltage	15-84	91
P0138	Rear Oxygen Sensor Cylinders 1–3 Short Circuit To Battery Positive	15-84	92
P0139	Rear Oxygen Sensors Aging	15-85	93
P0140	Rear Oxygen Sensor Cylinders 1–3 Signal Interruption	15-85	94
P0150	Front Oxygen Sensor Cylinders 4–6 Short Circuit Or Limited Voltage Increase	15-86	95
P0151	Front Oxygen Sensor Cylinders 4–6 Short Circuit To Ground Or Incorrect Voltage	15-86	96
P0152	Front Oxygen Sensor Cylinders 4–6 Short Circuit To Battery Positive	15-87	97
P0153	Front Oxygen Sensors Aging	15-82	88
P0154	Front Oxygen Sensor Cylinders 4–6 Signal Interruption	15-87	98
P0156	Rear Oxygen Sensor Cylinders 4–6 Intercore Short Circuit	15-88	99
P0157	Rear Oxygen Sensor Cylinders 4–6 Signal Wire Short Circuit Or Incorrect Voltage	15-88	100
P0158	Rear Oxygen Sensor Cylinders 4–6 Short Circuit To Battery Positive	15-89	101
P0159	Rear Oxygen Sensors Aging	15-85	93
P0160	Rear Oxygen Sensor Cylinders 4–6 Signal Interruption	15-89	102
P0197	Oil Temperature Sensor Short Circuit To Ground	15-90	103
P0198	Oil Temperature Sensor Short Circuit To Battery Positive	15-90	103
P0300	Engine Misfire, Multiple Cylinders	15-91	104

Continued

DIAGNOSTIC CHART INDEX—Continued

Code	Description	Page No.	Fig. No.
1999 911			
P0301	Engine Misfire, Cylinder No. 1	15-91	104
P0302	Engine Misfire, Cylinder No. 2	15-91	104
P0303	Engine Misfire, Cylinder No. 3	15-91	104
P0304	Engine Misfire, Cylinder No. 4	15-91	104
P0305	Engine Misfire, Cylinder No. 5	15-91	104
P0306	Engine Misfire, Cylinder No. 6	15-91	104
P0336	Crankshaft Position Sensor Not In Specified Range	15-91	105
P0341	Camshaft Position Sensor Signal Implausible Or Short Circuit	15-91	106
P0410	Secondary Air Injection Signal Implausible, Cylinders 1-3	15-92	107
P0420	Catalytic Converter Conversion Too Low, Cylinders 1-3	15-93	108
P0430	Catalytic Converter Conversion Too Low, Cylinders 4-6	15-93	108
P0440	Fuel Tank Ventilation System Above Limit	15-93	109
P0441	Fuel Tank Ventilation System, Above Limit	15-94	110
P0442	Fuel Tank Ventilation System, Below Lower Limit	15-94	111
P0444	EVAP Canister Purge Valve, Open Circuit	15-95	112
P0445	EVAP Canister Purge Valve, Short Circuit	15-95	112
P0446	EVAP Canister Shutoff Valve, Below Lower Limit	15-96	113
P0447	EVAP Canister Shutoff Valve, Open Circuit	15-96	114
P0448	EVAP Canister Shutoff Valve, Short Circuit	15-96	114
P0450	Tank Pressure Sensor, Signal Implausible	15-97	115
P0452	Tank Pressure Sensor, Short Circuit To Ground	15-97	115
P0453	Tank Pressure Sensor, Short Circuit To Battery Positive	15-97	115
P0455	Fuel Tank Ventilation System, Below Lower Limit	15-98	116
P0501	Vehicle Speed Not In Specified Range	15-99	117
P0506	Idle Air Control, Idle Speed Too Low	15-100	118
P0507	Idle Air Control, Idle Speed Too High	15-100	118
P0600	CAN Timeout Signal Implausible	15-100	119
P1102	Front Oxygen Sensor Heating 1 Above Limit	15-101	120
P1105	Rear Oxygen Sensor Heating 1 Above Limit	15-101	121
P1107	Front Oxygen Sensor Heating 2 Above Limit	15-101	120
P1110	Rear Oxygen Sensor Heating 2 Above Limit	15-101	121
P1115	Front Oxygen Sensor Heating 1 Below Lower Limit	15-102	122
P1117	Rear Oxygen Sensor Heating 1 Below Lower Limit	15-102	123
P1119	Front Oxygen Sensor Heating 2 Below Lower Limit	15-102	122
P1121	Rear Oxygen Sensor Heating 2 Below Lower Limit	15-102	123
P1123	Oxygen Sensing Adaption Area 1 Lean Threshold	15-103	124
P1124	Oxygen Sensing Adaption Area 1 Rich Threshold	15-103	125
P1125	Oxygen Sensing Adaption Area 1 Lean Threshold	15-103	124
P1126	Oxygen Sensing Adaption Area 1 Rich Threshold	15-103	125
P1127	Oxygen Sensing Adaption Area 2 Lean Threshold	15-103	126
P1128	Oxygen Sensing Adaption Area 2 Rich Threshold	15-103	127
P1129	Oxygen Sensing Adaption Area 2 Lean Threshold	15-103	126
P1130	Oxygen Sensing Adaption Area 2 Rich Threshold	15-103	127
P1140	Load Sensing Signal Implausible	15-104	128
P1157	Engine Compartment Temperature Sensor, Short Circuit To Ground	15-104	129
P1158	Engine Compartment Temperature Sensor Short Circuit To Battery Positive	15-104	129
P1213	Fuel Injector Cylinder 1, Short Circuit To Battery Positive	15-105	130
P1214	Fuel Injector Cylinder 2, Short Circuit To Battery Positive	15-105	131
P1215	Fuel Injector Cylinder 3, Short Circuit To Battery Positive	15-105	132
P1216	Fuel Injector Cylinder 4, Short Circuit To Battery Positive	15-106	133
P1217	Fuel Injector Cylinder 5, Short Circuit To Battery Positive	15-106	134
P1218	Fuel Injector Cylinder 6, Short To Battery Positive	15-107	135
P1225	Fuel Injector Cylinder 1, Short Circuit To Ground	15-105	130
P1226	Fuel Injector Cylinder 2, Short Circuit To Ground	15-105	131
P1227	Fuel Injector Cylinder 3, Short Circuit To Ground	15-105	132
P1228	Fuel Injector Cylinder 4, Short Circuit To Ground	15-106	133
P1229	Fuel Injector Cylinder 5, Short Circuit To Ground	15-106	134

Continued

DIAGNOSTIC CHART INDEX—Continued

Code	Description	Page No.	Fig. No.
1999 911			
P1230	Fuel Injector Cylinder 6, Short Circuit To Ground	15-107	135
P1237	Fuel Injector Cylinder 1, Open Circuit	15-105	130
P1238	Fuel Injector Cylinder 2, Open Circuit	15-105	131
P1239	Fuel Injector Cylinder 3, Open Circuit	15-105	132
P1240	Fuel Injector Cylinder 4, Open Circuit	15-106	133
P1241	Fuel Injector Cylinder 5, Open Circuit	15-106	134
P1242	Fuel Injector Cylinder 6, Open Circuit	15-107	135
P1265	Air Bag Signal Implausible	15-107	136
P1275	Front Oxygen Sensors Aging	15-82	88
P1276	Front Oxygen Sensors Aging	15-82	88
P1313	Engine Misfire, Cylinder No. 1 (Emission Relevant)	15-91	104
P1314	Engine Misfire, Cylinder No. 2 (Emission Relevant)	15-91	104
P1315	Engine Misfire, Cylinder No. 3 (Emission Relevant)	15-91	104
P1316	Engine Misfire, Cylinder No. 4 (Emission Relevant)	15-91	104
P1317	Engine Misfire, Cylinder No. 5 (Emission Relevant)	15-91	104
P1318	Engine Misfire, Cylinder No. 6 (Emission Relevant)	15-91	104
P1319	Engine Misfire, Multiple Cylinders (Emission Relevant)	15-91	104
P1384	Knock Sensor 1, Signal Implausible	15-107	137
P1385	Knock Sensor 2, Signal Implausible	15-107	137
P1386	Knock Control Test Pulse, Signal Implausible	15-107	137
P1397	Camshaft Position Sensor Signal Implausible Or Short Circuit	15-91	106
P1411	Secondary Air Injection Signal Implausible, Cylinders 4-6	15-92	107
P1455	A/C Compressor Control, Open Circuit	15-108	138
P1456	A/C Compressor Control, Above Upper Limit	15-108	138
P1457	A/C Compressor Control, Below Lower Limit	15-108	138
P1501	Fuel Pump Relay Output Stage, Short Circuit To Ground	15-109	139
P1502	Fuel Pump Relay Output Stage, Short Circuit To Battery Positive	15-109	139
P1510	Idle Air Control Valve Opening Coil, Above Upper Limit	15-109	140
P1512	Intake Manifold Switchover 1, Short Circuit To Battery Positive	15-110	141
P1513	Idle Air Control Valve Opening Coil, Below Lower Limit	15-109	140
P1514	Idle Air Control Valve Opening Coil, Open Circuit	15-109	140
P1515	Intake Manifold Switchover 1, Short Circuit To Ground	15-110	141
P1516	Intake Manifold Switchover 1, Open Circuit	15-110	141
P1524	Camshaft Adjustment Bank 2	15-111	142
P1530	Camshaft Adjustment Bank 1	15-112	143
P1531	Camshaft Adjustment Bank 1	15-112	143
P1539	Camshaft Adjustment Bank 2	15-111	142
P1541	Fuel Pump Relay Output Stage, Open Circuit	15-109	139
P1551	Idle Air Control Valve Closing Coil, Open Circuit	15-112	144
P1552	Idle Air Control Valve Closing Coil, Below Lower Limit	15-112	144
P1553	Idle Air Control Valve Closing Coil, Above Upper Limit	15-112	144
P1570	Immobilizer, Implausible Operating Range	15-113	145
P1571	Immobilizer, Open Circuit	15-113	145
P1585	Engine Misfire, Fuel Tank Empty	15-91	104
P1600	Voltage Supply, Signal Implausible	15-114	146
	Voltage Supply, Below Lower Limit	15-114	147
P1601	Voltage Supply, Above Upper Limits	15-114	147
P1602	Voltage Supply, Open Circuit	15-114	148
P1671	Engine Compartment Purge Fan, Open Or Short Circuit	15-115	149
P1673	Fan Output Stage, Open Or Short Circuit	15-116	150
P1691	MIL Lamp, Open Circuit	15-117	151
P1692	MIL Lamp, Short Circuit To Ground	15-117	151
P1693	MIL Lamp, Short Circuit To Battery Positive	15-117	151

Function

The Mass Air Flow Sensor delivers a signal to calculate the intake air mass. The intake air mass is an exact measurement for the load condition of the engine.

Diagnostic conditions

Engine speed is higher than 400 rpm **and** at least 0.8 seconds after starting the engine.

PR101970001300AX

Fig. 15 Codes P0101, P0102 & P0103: MAF Sensor Signal Circuit (Part 1 of 3). Boxster

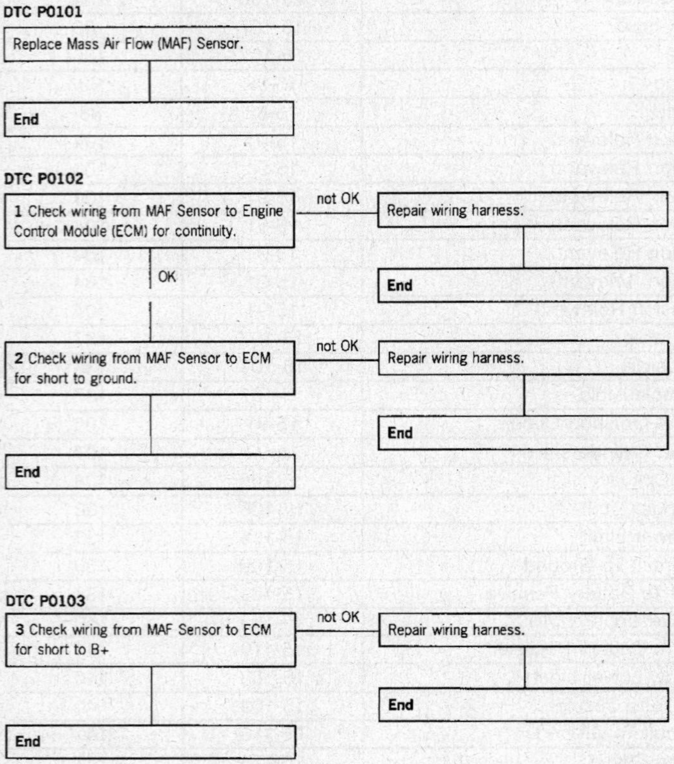

PR101970001300BX

Fig. 15 Codes P0101, P0102 & P0103: MAF Sensor Signal Circuit (Part 3 of 3). Boxster

Function

The Intake Air Temperature Sensor measures the temperature of the intake air. It consists of a variable resistor. The Intake Air Temperature Sensor is integrated in the mass air flow sensor.

Diagnostic condition

P0112
Intake air temperature lower than -42° C and 180 seconds after engine start-up, 10 seconds idling, no load interruption.

P0113
Intake air temperature higher than 140 °C.

Note

A substitute value (20 °C) is used in the event of a fault.

PR101970001400AX

Fig. 16 Codes P0112 & P0113: Intake Air Temperature Circuit (Part 1 of 4). Boxster

1 Check wiring from MAF Sensor to ECM for continuity.

1. Remove MAF Sensor connector.
2. Connect special tool 9616 to wiring harness.
3. Connect ohmmeter to special tool 9616, pin 17 and MAF Sensor connector, pin 5.
   Specified value: 0 - 5 Ω

If meter reads ∞Ω, check wiring harness for chafing and pinching damage.

2 Check wiring from MAF Sensor to ECM for short to ground.

1. Remove MAF Sensor connector.
2. Connect special tool 9616 to wiring harness.
3. Connect ohmmeter to special tool 9616, pin 17 and ground.
   Specified value: ∞Ω

If meter reads 0 - 5 Ω, check wiring for chafing or pinching damage.

3 Check wiring from MAF Sensor to ECM for short to B+.

1. Remove MAF Sensor connector.
2. Connect special tool 9616 to wiring harness.
3. Connect voltmeter to special tool 9616, pin 17 (plus) and ground.
4. Switch ignition on.
5. Specified value: 0 Volt

If meter reads battery voltage, check wiring for chafing or pinching damage.

PR101970001300CX

Fig. 15 Codes P0101, P0102 & P0103: MAF Sensor Signal Circuit (Part 2 of 3). Boxster

1 Check Intake Air Temperature Sensor in mass air flow sensor.

1. Remove mass air flow sensor connector.
2. Connect ohmmeter to mass air flow sensor, pins 1 and 3.
   Specified value: 2.3 - 2.7 kΩ at 20°C

2 Check wiring from ECM to Intake Air Temperature Sensor for continuity.

1. Remove mass air flow sensor connector.
2. Connect special tool 9616 to wiring harness.
3. Connect ohmmeter to special tool 9616, pin 15 and mass air flow sensor connector, pin 1.
   Specified value: 0 - 5 Ω.

If meter reads ∞Ω, check wiring harness for chafing and pinching damage.

3 Check wiring between ECM and Intake Air Temperature Sensor for short circuit to ground.

1. Remove mass air flow sensor connector.
2. Connect special tool 9616 to wiring harness.
3. Connect ohmmeter to special tool 9616, pin 15 and to ground.
   Specified value: ∞ Ω

If meter reads 0 - 5 Ω, check wiring harness for chafing and pinching damage.

PR101970001400BX

Fig. 16 Codes P0112 & P0113: Intake Air Temperature Circuit (Part 2 of 4). Boxster

4 Check wiring from ECM to Intake Air Temperature Sensor for short circuit to B+.

1. Remove mass air flow sensor connector.
2. Connect special tool 9616 to wiring harness.
3. Switch ignition on.
4. Connect voltmeter to special tool 9616, pin 15 (plus) and to ground (minus).
   Specified value: 0 Volt

If meter reads battery voltage, check wiring harness for chafing and pinching damage.

PR101970001400CX

Fig. 16 Codes P0112 & P0113: Intake Air Temperature Circuit (Part 3 of 4). Boxster

Function

The ECT sensor measures the engine temperature by means of a variable resistor.
The engine coolant temperature is required for control of the warm-up phase. In the event of a fault, a calculated substitute characteristic is used.

Diagnostic conditions

P0115
60 seconds after engine start-up, load interruption. A fault is recorded after a debounce time of 0.4 seconds if the measured engine temperature is lower than the calculated engine temperature minus approx. 10° C.

P0117
A fault is recorded after a debounce time of 0.4 seconds if an engine temperature of less than -42° C is measured.

P0118
A fault is recorded after a debounce time of 0.4 seconds if an engine temperature of more than 140° C is measured.

PR101970001500AX

Fig. 17 Codes P0115, P0117 & P0118: ECT Sensor Circuit (Part 1 of 6). Boxster

DTC P0112

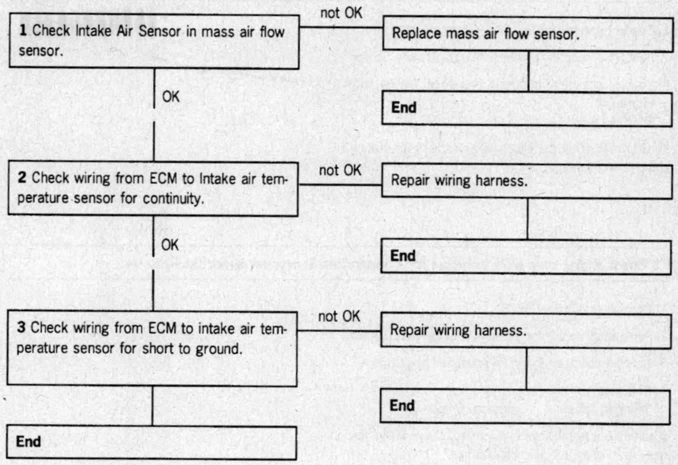

DTC P0113

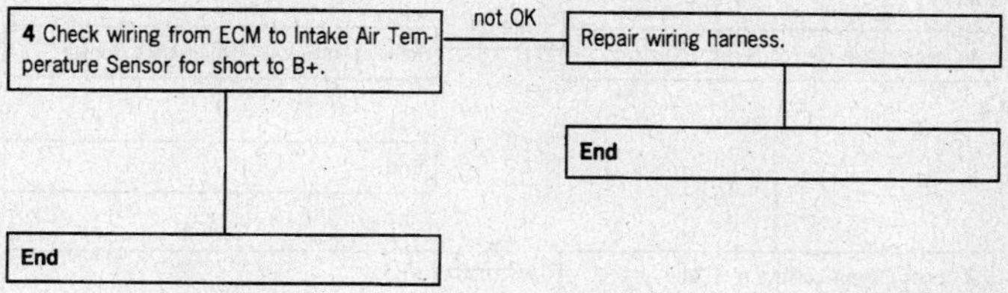

PR101970001400DX

Fig. 16 Codes P0112 & P0113: Intake Air Temperature Circuit (Part 4 of 4). Boxster

1 Check Intake Air Temperature Sensor.

1. Remove connector in the engine compartment.
2. Connect ohmmeter to Intake Air Temperature Sensor connector, pins 1 and 4.
   Specified value: 2 - 3 kΩ at 20°C

2 Check Output Voltage of ECM

1. Connect special tool 9616.
2. Connect voltmeter to pin 74 (plus) and 34 (minus).
3. Ignition on.
   Specific value: approx. 5 V.

3 Check wiring from ECM to Intake Air Temperature Sensor for continuity.

1. Connect special tool 9616 to wiring harness.
2. Remove connector for Intake Air Temperature Sensor.
3. Connect ohmmeter to special tool 9616, pin 34, and temperature sensor connector, pin 4.
   Specified value: 0 - 5 Ω.
4. Connect ohmmeter to special tool 9616, pin 74, and temperature sensor connector, pin 1
   Specified value: 0 - 5 Ω.

PR101970001500BX

Fig. 17 Codes P0115, P0117 & P0118: ECT Sensor Circuit (Part 2 of 6). Boxster

4 Check wiring between ECM and Intake Air Temperature Sensor for short circuit to ground.

1. Connect special tool 9616 to wiring harness.
2. Remove connector for Intake Air Temperature Sensor.
3. Connect ohmmeter to special tool 9616, pin 74, and to ground.
   Specified value: ∞ Ω

If meter reads 0 - 5 Ω, check wiring harness for chafing and pinching damage.

5 Check wiring from ECM to Intake Air Temperature Sensor for short circuit to B+.

1. Connect special tool 9616.
2. Remove connector for Intake Air Temperature Sensor.
3. Connect voltmeter to pin 74 (plus) and to ground.
4. Switch ignition on.
   Specified value: approx. 5 Volt

If battery positive voltage is displayed, check wiring harness for chafing and pinching damage.

PR101970001500CX

Fig. 17 Codes P0115, P0117 & P0118: ECT Sensor Circuit (Part 3 of 6). Boxster

P0115

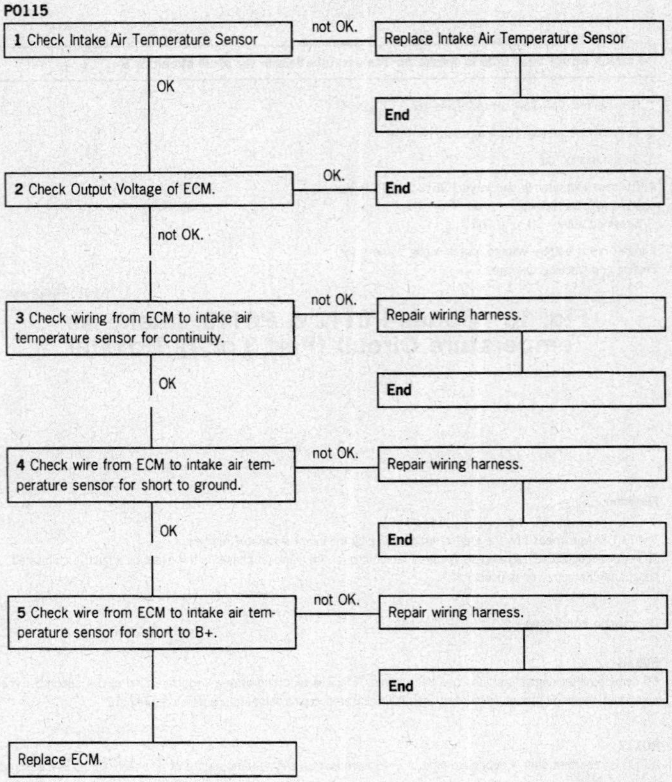

PR101970001500DX

Fig. 17 Codes P0115, P0117 & P0118: ECT Sensor Circuit (Part 4 of 6). Boxster

P0117

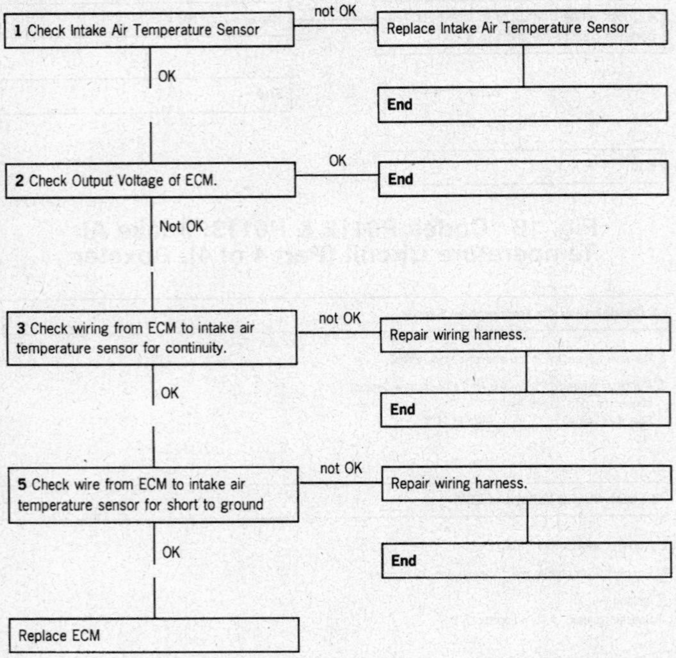

PR101970001500EX

Fig. 17 Codes P0115, P0117 & P0118: ECT Sensor Circuit (Part 5 of 6). Boxster

P0118

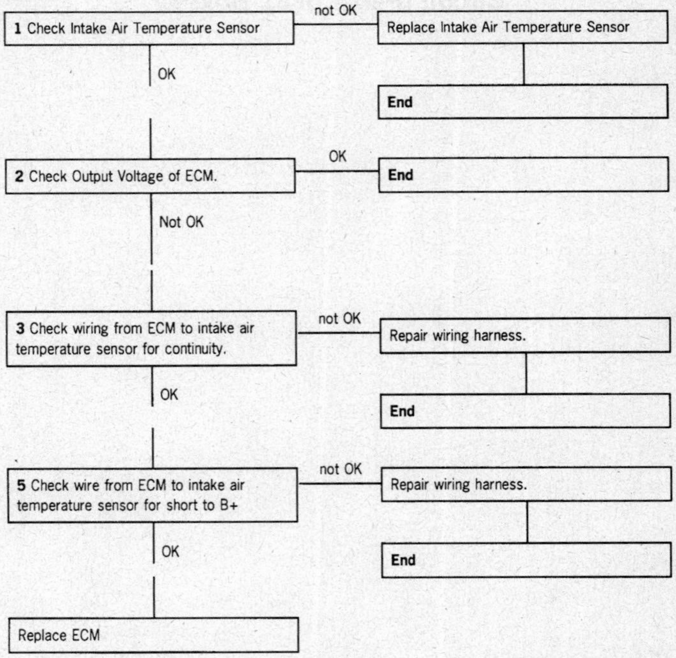

PR101970001500FX

Fig. 17 Codes P0115, P0117 & P0118: ECT Sensor Circuit (Part 6 of 6). Boxster

Function

The TP Sensor determines the position of the throttle valve. The TP Sensor is supplied with + 5 Volt through pin 53 of the Engine Control Module (ECM) and through pin 34 connected to ground. The TP Sensor signal voltage is between approximately 0.5 Volt to approximately 4.7 Volt, depending on the position of the throttle valve.

The idle contact is generated from the voltage value that occurs during the load phase.
The value for the wide open throttle contact is calculated from the value of the generated idle contact.

Diagnostic conditions

P0123
A fault is recognized and stored in the memory if the voltage is below 0.15 Volt or above 4.85 Volt **and** if the engine speed is above 400 rpm.

PR101970001600AX

Fig. 18 Code P0123: Throttle Position Sensor Signal Implausible (Part 1 of 4). Boxster

1 Check voltage supply to TP Sensor.

1. Connect special tool 9616.
2. Connect voltmeter to pin 53 (plus) and 34 (minus).
   Switch on ignition.
   Specified value: approx. 4.5 - 5 Volt

2 Check TP Sensor.

1. Connect special tool 9616 to wiring harness.
2. Connect ohmmeter to pin 44 and pin 53.
   Specified value: approx. 2.0 - 3.0 kΩ

   Fully depress accelerator pedal.
   Specified value: approx. 0.7 - 1.4 kΩ

If there is no display, check directly at the throttle position sensor.

PR101970001600BX

Fig. 18 Code P0123: Throttle Position Sensor Signal Implausible (Part 2 of 4). Boxster

3 Check wiring from TP Sensor to ECM for continuity or short circuit to B+ or ground.

1. Separate disconnection point to TP sensor.
2. Connect special tool 9616 to wiring harness.
3. Connect ohmmeter to disconnection point pin 1 and special tool 9616 pin 34.
   Display: 0 - 5 Ω
4. Connect ohmmeter to disconnection point pin 2 and special tool 9616 pin 53.
   Display: 0 - 5 Ω
5. Connect ohmmeter to disconnection point pin 3 and special tool 9616 pin 44.
   Display: 0 - 5 Ω
6. Connect ohmmeter to disconnection point pin 2 and ground.
   Display: ∞ Ω
7. Connect ohmmeter to disconnection point pin 3 and ground.
   Display: ∞ Ω
8. Connect voltmeter to disconnection point pin 2 and positive.
   Display: 0 Volt
9. Connect voltmeter to disconnection point pin 3 and positive.
   Display: 0 Volt

Check wiring harness for trapped locations and abrasions if battery voltage is displayed for Points 8 and 9.

PR101970001600CX

Fig. 18 Code P0123: Throttle Position Sensor Signal Implausible (Part 3 of 4). Boxster

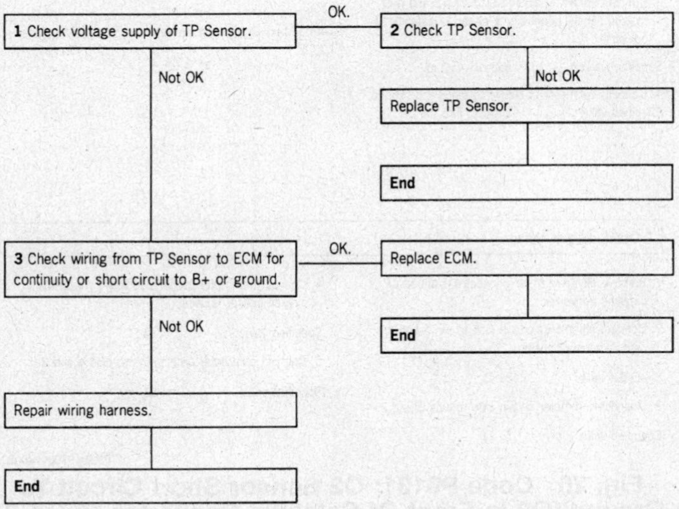

PR101970001600DX

Fig. 18 Code P0123: Throttle Position Sensor Signal Implausible (Part 4 of 4). Boxster

Function

To diagnose the readiness for operation of the oxygen sensors, the position of the sensor voltage is evaluated (in case of certain faults or conditions, the diagnosis is disabled).

Diagnosis Conditions

Diagnostic Trouble Code P0130 is stored on the Engine Control Module (ECM) when a voltage increase of the oxygen sensor between 60 mV and 400 mV for more than 15 seconds is detected by the ECM **and** when the sensor voltage behind the catalytic converter exceeds 350 mV.

The fault also occurs if, with a cold oxygen sensor, the voltage value lies in the range - 40 mV to + 40 mV (intercore short-circuit) or if an intercore short-circuit is present for 15 seconds **and** the sensor voltage behind the catalytic converter is greater than 350 mV.

Conditions for the diagnosis of the oxygen sensor signals:

- Sensor heating is active.
- Oxygen sensing is active.
- Oxygen sensor voltage behind catalytic converter > 350 mV.
- No Secondary Air Injection.
- No diagnosis of tank ventilation system.
- No faults detected for fuel tank ventilation and Secondary Air Injection.

Note

When DTC P0130 is shedded, a non-shedded fault P1115 will be stored as well. This non-shedded fault is not an actual fault.

PR101970001700AX

Fig. 19 Code P0130: O2 Sensor Short Circuit (O2 In Front Of Catalytic Converter, Cyl. 1-3, Part 1 of 3). Boxster

1 Check oxygen sensor.

1. Heat the oxygen sensors (road-test car under load or run engine without load at high engine speed).
2. Connect Porsche System Tester 2 or scan tool and read voltage of oxygen sensor 1 ahead of catalytic converter.

Specified value: Voltage fluctuations between 100 mV and 800 mV.
➡ Oxygen sensor OK.

In case of a displayed value near 0 V, a short circuit between the signal wire and the sensor ground has occurred.

3. Remove oxygen sensor connector 1 ahead of catalytic converter.
4. Connect voltmeter at sleeve to pins 3 and 4.
Specified value: 450 mV.
➡ Replace oxygen sensor.

Specified value: approx. 0 V
➡ Check wiring harness.

If the wiring harness is OK, remove all oxygen sensor connectors and perform measurement of item 4 on all oxygen sensors.

2 Check wiring harness.

1. Remove oxygen sensor connector.
2. Connect special tool 9616 to wiring harness.
3. With ohmmeter measure resistance between special tool 9616 pin 19 and oxygen sensor connector pin 4.

Display: 0 - 5 Ω

4. With ohmmeter measure resistance between special tool 9616 pin 46 and oxygen sensor connector pin 3.

Note:
For this measurement, all other oxygen sensor connectors must be removed.

Display: 0 - 5 Ω

3 Check ECM final stage.

1. Connect special tool 9616.
2. Remove oxygen sensor connector 1 ahead of catalytic converter.
3. Connect voltmeter to pins 19 and 46.
4. Switch ignition on.

Specified value: approx. 450 mV

If reading < 400 mV or > 500 mV: Replace ECM.

PR101970001700BX

Fig. 19 Code P0130: O2 Sensor Short Circuit (O2 In Front Of Catalytic Converter, Cyl. 1-3, Part 2 of 3). Boxster

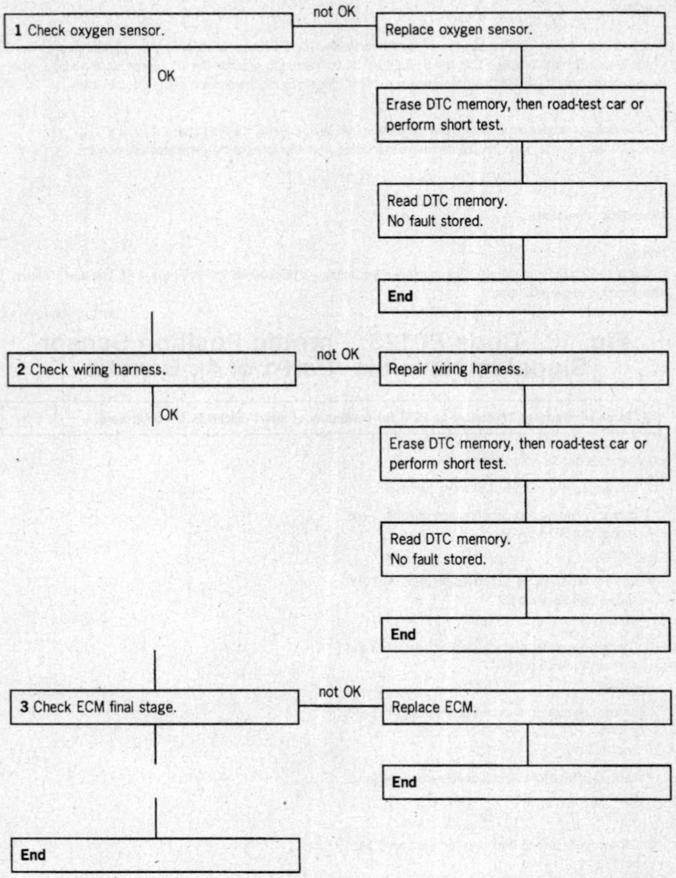

PR101970001700CX

Fig. 19 Code P0130: O2 Sensor Short Circuit (O2 In Front Of Catalytic Converter, Cyl. 1-3, Part 3 of 3). Boxster

Function

To diagnose the readiness for operation of the oxygen sensors, the position of the sensor voltage is evaluated (in case of certain faults or conditions, the diagnosis is disabled).

Diagnosis Conditions

Diagnostic Trouble Code P0131 is stored in the Engine Control Module when the sensor voltage is below - 150 mV.

Conditions for the diagnosis of the oxygen sensor signals:

– Sensor heating is active.

* When these faults occur, the fault codes P1115 and P1119 may be stored in addition; however, these faults are no actual faults.

** When this fault occurs, all the four oxygen sensors are stored.

Note:

When DTC P0131 is stored and faults of the heating of the other three oxygen sensors are displayed, only one oxygen sensor is probably faulty.

PR101970001800AX

Fig. 20 Code P0131: O2 Sensor Short Circuit To Ground (O2 In Front Of Catalytic Converter, Cyl. 1-3, Part 1 of 3). Boxster

1 Check wiring harness.

1. Remove all the four oxygen sensor connectors.
2. Switch ignition on.
3. Connect voltmeter at sleeve to pins 3 and 4 of oxygen sensor connector 1 ahead of catalytic converter.

Specified value: approx. 450 mV

4. Connect voltmeter at sleeve to pin 3 and ground.
Specified value: approx. 720 mV

If the measurement according to items 3 and 4 does not show the specified values, remove ECM connector and check wires for short circuit to ground.

If no short circuit to ground can be detected, replace ECM.

2 Check oxygen sensor.

1. Remove oxygen sensor connector 1 ahead of catalytic converter.
2. Connect ohmmeter on pin side to pin 3 and the oxygen sensor housing.

Specified value: ∞ Ω

3. Connect ohmmeter on pin side to pins 3 and 2.

Specified value: ∞ Ω

4. Connect ohmmeter on pin side to pin 4 and the oxygen sensor housing.

Specified value: ∞ Ω

5. Connect ohmmeter on pin side to pins 4 and 2.

Specified value: ∞ Ω

PR101970001800BX

Fig. 20 Code P0131: O2 Sensor Short Circuit To Ground (O2 In Front Of Catalytic Converter, Cyl. 1-3, Part 2 of 3). Boxster

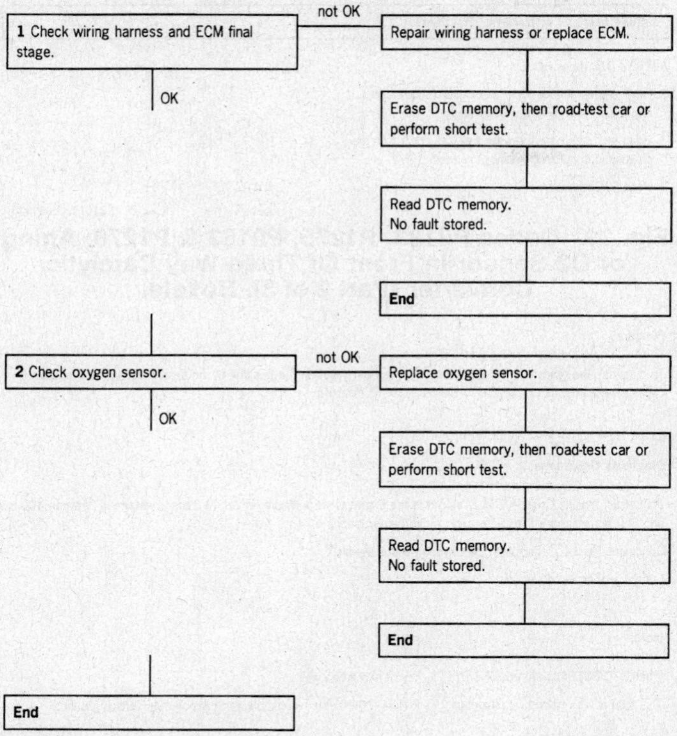

PR101970001800CX

Fig. 20 Code P0131: O2 Sensor Short Circuit To Ground (O2 In Front Of Catalytic Converter, Cyl. 1-3, Part 3 of 3). Boxster

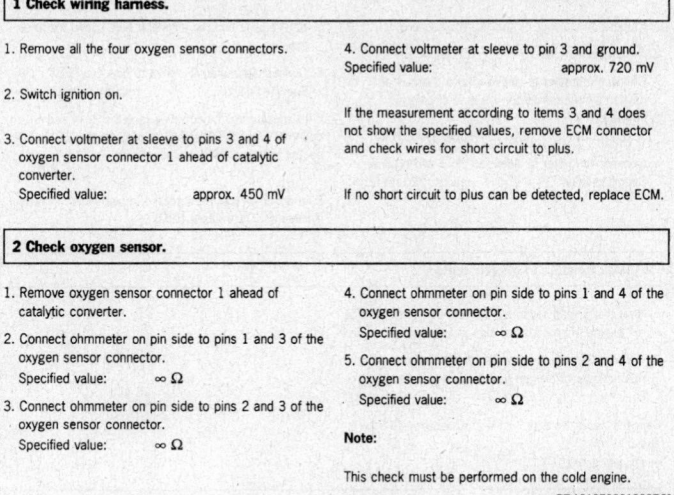

1 Check wiring harness.

1. Remove all the four oxygen sensor connectors.
2. Switch ignition on.
3. Connect voltmeter at sleeve to pins 3 and 4 of oxygen sensor connector 1 ahead of catalytic converter.
   Specified value: approx. 450 mV
4. Connect voltmeter at sleeve to pin 3 and ground.
   Specified value: approx. 720 mV

If the measurement according to items 3 and 4 does not show the specified values, remove ECM connector and check wires for short circuit to plus.

If no short circuit to plus can be detected, replace ECM.

2 Check oxygen sensor.

1. Remove oxygen sensor connector 1 ahead of catalytic converter.
2. Connect ohmmeter on pin side to pins 1 and 3 of the oxygen sensor connector.
   Specified value: ∞ Ω
3. Connect ohmmeter on pin side to pins 2 and 3 of the oxygen sensor connector.
   Specified value: ∞ Ω
4. Connect ohmmeter on pin side to pins 1 and 4 of the oxygen sensor connector.
   Specified value: ∞ Ω
5. Connect ohmmeter on pin side to pins 2 and 4 of the oxygen sensor connector.
   Specified value: ∞ Ω

Note:

This check must be performed on the cold engine.

PR101970001900BX

Fig. 21 Code P0132: O2 Short Circuit To Power (O2 In Front Of Catalytic Converter, Cyl. 1-3, Part 2 of 3). Boxster

Function

To diagnose the readiness for operation of the oxygen sensors, the position of the sensor voltage is evaluated (in case of certain faults or conditions, the diagnosis is disabled).

Diagnosis Conditions

Diagnostic Trouble Code P0132 is stored in the Engine Control Module when the sensor voltage is above 1 V for more than 0.5 seconds without interruptions.

Conditions for the diagnosis of the oxygen sensor signals:

– Sensor heating is active.

Note:

In case of a short circuit to plus at one oxygen sensor, all the four oxygen sensors will be stored. Furthermore, the fault may cause misfires.

PR101970001900AX

Fig. 21 Code P0132: O2 Short Circuit To Power (O2 In Front Of Catalytic Converter, Cyl. 1-3, Part 1 of 3). Boxster

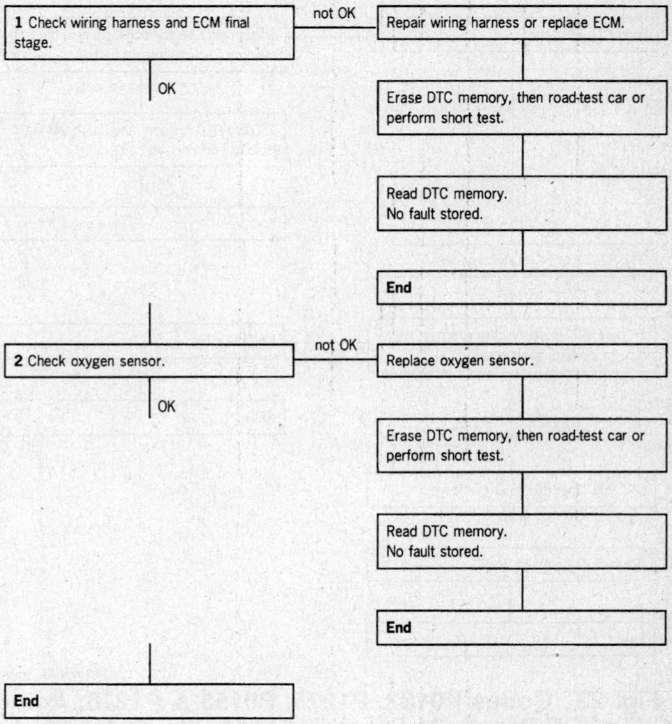

PR101970001900CX

Fig. 21 Code P0132: O2 Short Circuit To Power (O2 In Front Of Catalytic Converter, Cyl. 1-3, Part 3 of 3). Boxster

Function

The diagnosis of "oxygen sensor aging" helps to identify oxygen sensors that exceed emission limits because of aging.

During the diagnosis of oxygen sensor aging, the ECM monitors the length of the time period of the sensor signal.

With an old sensor, the time period is too long, i.e. the diffusion of oxygen into the exhaust gas is more difficult for the sensor. Reasons could be frequent driving in the lower load range (city driving, short distances etc.) or a contaminated sensor.

Diagnosis conditions

Manual transmission
Engine speed between 1400 rpm and 2600 rpm. Engine load between 0.7 ms and 1.5 ms.
Calculated catalytic converter temperature greater than 350° C.
Oxygen sensing active.

Tiptronic
Engine speed between 1200 rpm and 2200 rpm. Engine load between 0.7 ms and 1.8 ms.
Calculated catalytic converter temperature greater than 350° C.
Oxygen sensing active.

No faults for misfire recognition, throttle valve, oxygen sensor heating, hall sender, fuel tank ventilation end stage, voltage supply, mixture adaptation.

PR101970002000AX

Fig. 22 Codes P0133, P1275, P0153 & P1276: Aging of O2 Sensor In Front Of Three Way Catalytic Converter (Part 1 of 3). Boxster

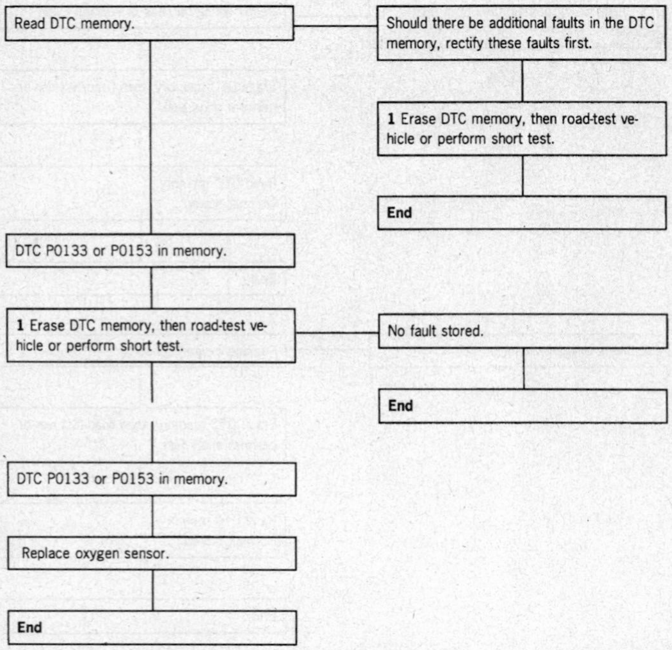

PR101970002000CX

Fig. 22 Codes P0133, P1275, P0153 & P1276: Aging of O2 Sensor In Front Of Three Way Catalytic Converter (Part 3 of 3). Boxster

1 Road test car or perform short test.

1. Erase DTC memory.
2. Heat oxygen sensor (road test vehicle under load, run engine at high rpm with no load).
3. Road test car or perform short test during which the diagnostic conditions must be reached.
4. Read DTC memory.

PR101970002000BX

Fig. 22 Codes P0133, P1275, P0153 & P1276: Aging of O2 Sensor In Front Of Three Way Catalytic Converter (Part 2 of 3). Boxster

Function

To diagnose the readiness for operation of the oxygen sensors, the position of the sensor voltage is evaluated (in case of certain faults or conditions, the diagnosis is disabled).

Diagnosis Conditions

Diagnostic Trouble Code P0134 is stored in the Engine Control Module when the sensor voltage is between 400 mV and 600 mV for more than 5 seconds without interruptions.

Conditions for the diagnosis of the oxygen sensor signals:

Sensor heating is active.

Note:

When DTC P0134 is stored, DTC P1115 may be stored as well.

This fault is also stored simultaneously as P0154 if there is an interruption in the common sensor ground.

PR101970002100AX

Fig. 23 Code P0134: O2 Sensor Interruption Of Signal (In Front Of Catalytic Converter, Cyl. 1–3, Part 1 of 4). Boxster

1 Check wiring harness.

1. Remove all the four oxygen sensor connectors.
2. Switch ignition on.
3. Connect voltmeter at sleeve to pins 3 and 4 of oxygen sensor connector 1 ahead of catalytic converter.
   Specified value: approx. 450 mV
4. Connect voltmeter at sleeve to pin 3 and ground.
   Specified value: approx. 720 mV
5. Start engine and run engine at high speed for three minutes.
6. Connect voltmeter at sleeve to pins 1 and 2.
   Specified value: battery voltage

If the measurement according to items 3, 4, and 6 does not show the specified values, remove ECM connector and check wires for continuity.

If no continuity can be detected, repair wiring harness. If continuity OK, replace ECM.

2 Check function of oxygen sensor.

1. Heat the oxygen sensors (road-test car under load or run engine without load at high engine speed).
2. Connect Porsche System Tester 2 or scan tool and read voltage of oxygen sensor 1 ahead of catalytic converter.

Specified value: Voltage fluctuations between 100 mV and 800 mV.
➡ Oxygen sensor OK.

3 Check oxygen sensor heating.

1. Remove oxygen sensor connector 1 ahead of catalytic converter.
2. Connect ohmmeter on pin side to pins 1 and 2 of the oxygen sensor connector.
   Specified value: 1.8 - 2.5 Ω at 20 °C
3. Connect ohmmeter on pin side to pin 1 and the oxygen sensor housing.
   Specified value: ∞ Ω
4. Connect ohmmeter on pin side to pin 2 and the oxygen sensor housing.
   Specified value: ∞ Ω

PR101970002100BX

Fig. 23 Code P0134: O2 Sensor Interruption Of Signal (In Front Of Catalytic Converter, Cyl. 1–3, Part 2 of 4). Boxster

1 Check wiring harness and ECM final stage.
- not OK → Repair wiring harness or replace ECM. → Erase DTC memory, then road-test car or perform short test. → Read DTC memory. No fault stored. → **End**
- OK ↓

2 Check function of oxygen sensor.
- not OK → Replace oxygen sensor. → Erase DTC memory, then road-test car or perform short test. → Read DTC memory. No fault stored. → **End**
- OK ↓

PR101970002100CX

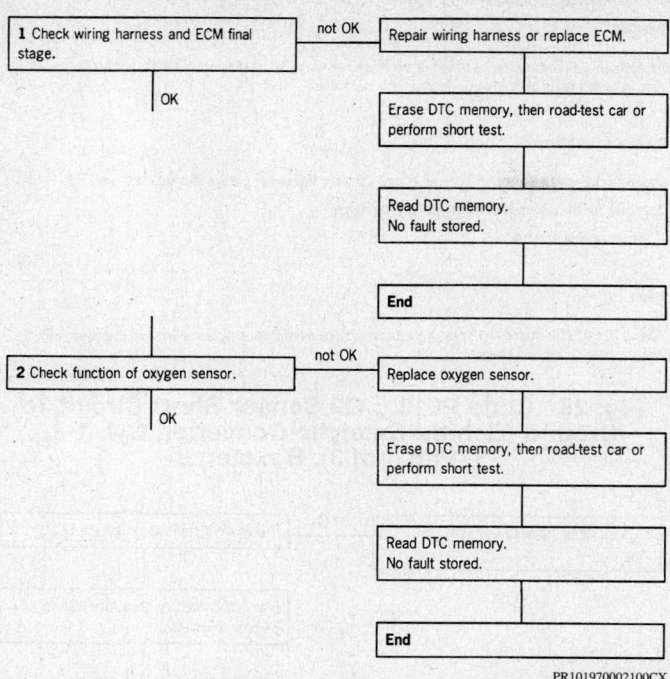

Fig. 23 Code P0134: O2 Sensor Interruption Of Signal (In Front Of Catalytic Converter, Cyl. 103, Part 3 of 4). Boxster

Function

To diagnose the readiness for operation of the oxygen sensors, the position of the sensor voltage is evaluated (in case of certain faults or conditions, the diagnosis is disabled).

Diagnosis Conditions

Diagnostic Trouble Code P0136 is stored in the Engine Control Module when the voltage is between - 40 mV and + 40 mV for more than 200 seconds.

Conditions for the diagnosis of the oxygen sensor signals:

- Sensor heating is active.
- Oxygen sensing behind catalytic converter is active.
- No Secondary Air Injection.
- No faults detected for fuel tank ventilation and Secondary Air Injection.

Note

When DTC P0136 is stored, DTC P1117 (sensor heating) is stored as well.

PR101970002200AX

Fig. 24 Code P0136: O2 Sensor Circuit Short (Behind Catalytic Converter, Cyl. 1-3, Part 1 of 3). Boxster

3 Check oxygen sensor heating.
- not OK → Replace oxygen sensor. → Erase DTC memory, then road-test car or perform short test. → Read DTC memory. No fault stored. → **End**
- OK → **End**

PR101970002100DX

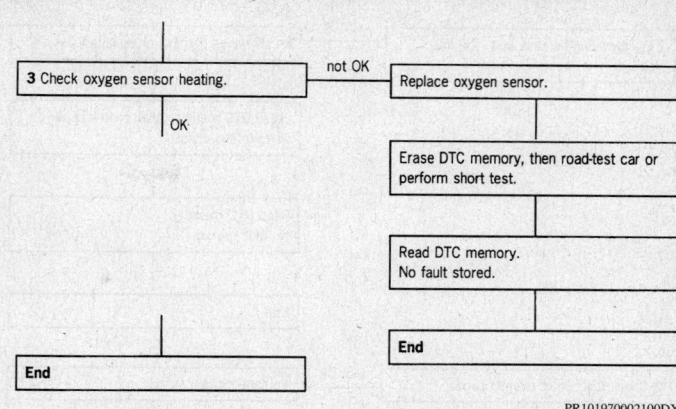

Fig. 23 Code P0134: O2 Sensor Interruption Of Signal (In Front Of Catalytic Converter, Cyl. 103, Part 4 of 4). Boxster

1 Check wiring harness.

1. Remove all oxygen sensor connectors.
2. Connect voltmeter at sleeve to pins 3 and 4 of oxygen sensor connector 1 behind catalytic converter.
3. Switch ignition on.
   Specified value: approx. 450 mV
4. Connect voltmeter at sleeve to pin 3 and ground.
   Specified value: approx. 720 mV

If the measurement according to items 3 and 4 does not show the specified values, remove ECM connector and check wires for short circuit.

If the wires are OK, replace ECM.

2 Check function of oxygen sensor.

1. Heat the oxygen sensors (road-test car under load or run engine without load at high engine speed).
2. Connect Porsche System Tester 2 or scan tool and read voltage of oxygen sensor 1 behind catalytic converter.
3. Change the fuel/air ratio with acceleration bursts.

Specified value: Voltage fluctuations between 100 mV and 800 mV.
➡Oxygen sensor OK.

If the oxygen sensor voltage is approx. 0 Volt, replace oxygen sensor.

PR101970002200BX

Fig. 24 Code P0136: O2 Sensor Circuit Short (Behind Catalytic Converter, Cyl. 1-3, Part 2 of 3). Boxster

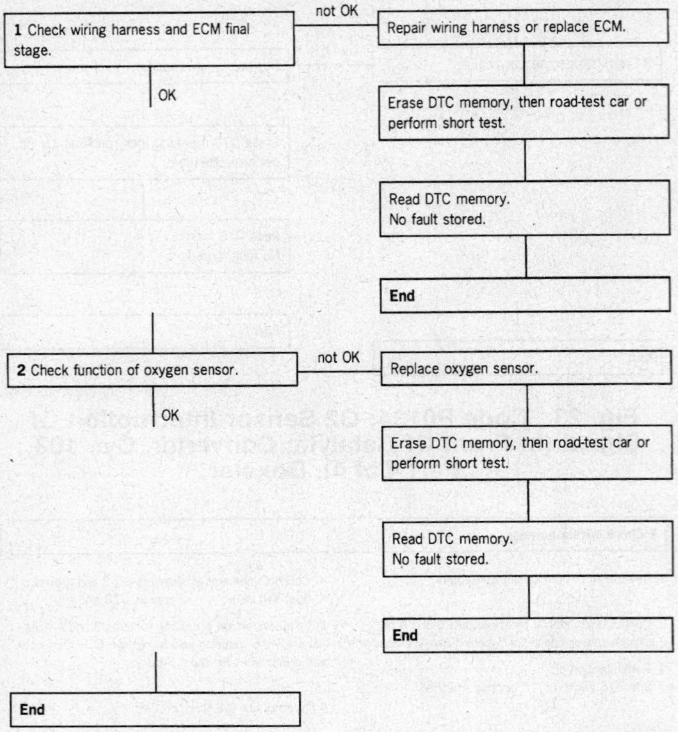

PR101970002200CX

Fig. 24 Code P0136: O2 Sensor Circuit Short (Behind Catalytic Converter, Cyl. 1-3, Part 3 of 3). Boxster

1 Check wiring harness.

1. Remove all the four oxygen sensor connectors.
2. Switch ignition on.
3. Connect voltmeter at sleeve to pins 3 and 4 of oxygen sensor connector 1 behind catalytic converter.
   Specified value: approx. 450 mV
4. Connect voltmeter at sleeve to pin 3 and ground.
   Specified value: approx. 720 mV

If the measurement according to items 3 and 4 does not show the specified values, remove ECM connector and check wires for short circuit to ground.

If no short circuit to ground can be detected, replace ECM.

2 Check oxygen sensor.

1. Remove oxygen sensor connector 1 behind catalytic converter.
2. Connect ohmmeter on pin side to pin 3 and the oxygen sensor housing.

Specified value: ∞ Ω

3. Connect ohmmeter on pin side to pin 4 and the oxygen sensor housing.

Specified value: ∞ Ω

4. Connect ohmmeter on pin side to pins 4 and 2.

Specified value: ∞ Ω

5. Connect ohmmeter on pin side to pins 3 and 2.

Specified value: ∞ Ω

PR101970002300BX

Fig. 25 Code P0137: O2 Sensor Short Circuit To Ground (Behind Catalytic Converter, Cyl. 1-3, Part 2 of 3). Boxster

Function

To diagnose the readiness for operation of the oxygen sensors, the position of the sensor voltage is evaluated (in case of certain faults or conditions, the diagnosis is disabled).

Diagnosis Conditions

Diagnostic Trouble Code P0137 is stored in the ECM when the sensor voltage is below - 150 mV.

Conditions for the diagnosis of the oxygen sensor signals:

– Sensor heating is active.

Note:

When DTC P0137 is stored and faults of the heating of the other three oxygen sensors are displayed, only one oxygen sensor is probably faulty.

PR101970002300AX

Fig. 25 Code P0137: O2 Sensor Short Circuit To Ground (Behind Catalytic Converter, Cyl. 1-3, Part 1 of 3). Boxster

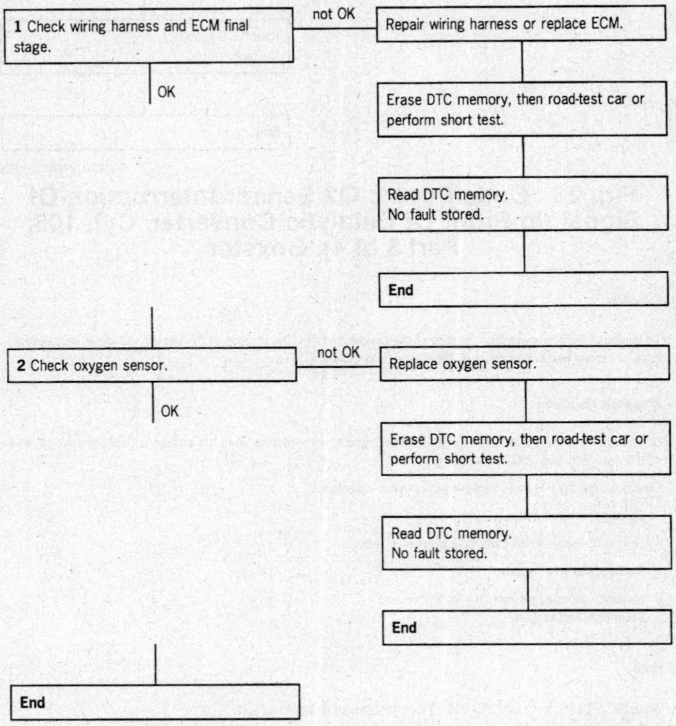

PR101970002300CX

Fig. 25 Code P0137: O2 Sensor Short Circuit To Ground (Behind Catalytic Converter, Cyl. 1-3, Part 3 of 3). Boxster

Function

To diagnose the readiness for operation of the oxygen sensors, the position of the sensor voltage is evaluated (in case of certain faults or conditions, the diagnosis is disabled).

Diagnosis Conditions

Diagnostic Trouble Code P0138 is stored in the Engine Control Module when the sensor voltage is above 1 V for more than 0.5 seconds without interruptions.

Conditions for the diagnosis of the oxygen sensor signals:

– Sensor heating is active.

Note

In case of a short circuit to plus at one oxygen sensor, all the four oxygen sensors will be stored. Furthermore, the fault may cause misfires.

PR101970002400AX

Fig. 26 Code P0138: O2 Sensor Short Circuit To Power (Behind Catalytic Converter, Cyl. 1-3, Part 1 of 3). Boxster

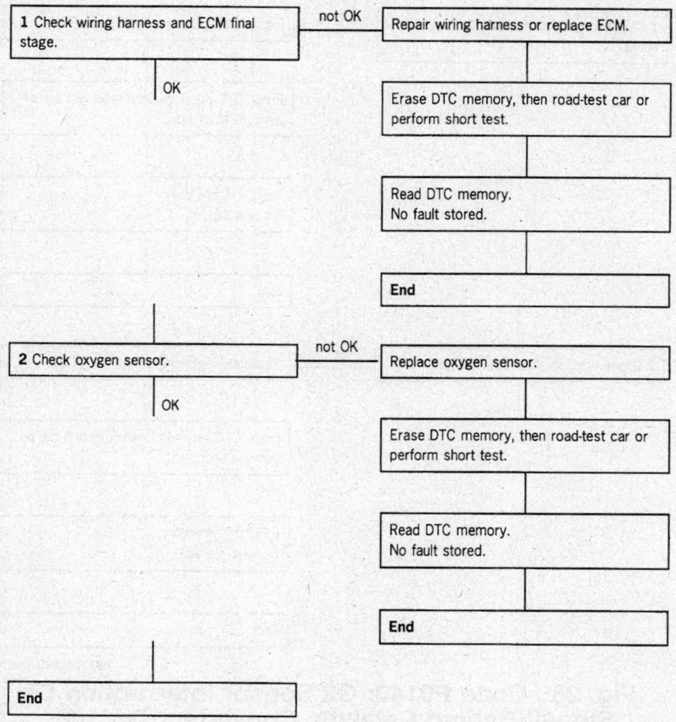

PR101970002400CX

Fig. 26 Code P0138: O2 Sensor Short Circuit To Power (Behind Catalytic Converter, Cyl. 1-3, Part 3 of 3). Boxster

1 Check wiring harness.

1. Remove all the four oxygen sensor connectors.
2. Switch ignition on.
3. Connect voltmeter at sleeve to pins 3 and 4 of oxygen sensor connector 1 behind catalytic converter.
   Specified value: approx. 450 mV
4. Connect voltmeter at sleeve to pin 3 and ground.
   Specified value: approx. 720 mV

If the measurement according to items 3 and 4 does not show the specified values, remove ECM connector and check wires for short circuit to plus.

If no short circuit to plus can be detected, replace ECM.

2 Check oxygen sensor.

1. Remove oxygen sensor connector 1 behind catalytic converter.
2. Connect ohmmeter on pin side to pins 1 and 3 of the oxygen sensor connector.
   Specified value: ∞ Ω
3. Connect ohmmeter on pin side to pins 2 and 3 of the oxygen sensor connector.
   Specified value: ∞ Ω
4. Connect ohmmeter on pin side to pins 1 and 4 of the oxygen sensor connector.
   Specified value: ∞ Ω
5. Connect ohmmeter on pin side to pins 2 and 4 of the oxygen sensor connector.
   Specified value: ∞ Ω

Note

This check must be performed on the cold engine.

PR101970002400BX

Fig. 26 Code P0138: O2 Sensor Short Circuit To Power (Behind Catalytic Converter, Cyl. 1-3, Part 2 of 3). Boxster

Function

The oxygen sensors after the catalytic converter serve the purpose of pilot control of the oxygen sensors ahead of the catalytic converter. This allows correction of any oxygen sensor characteristic displacement ahead of the catalytic converter.

Diagnosis conditions

Engine speed between 720 rpm and 2400 rpm.
Engine load between 0.8 ms and 2.6 ms.
Oxygen sensor heating active.
Oxygen sensing ahead of catalytic converter active.
Calculated catalytic converter temperature > 352° C.
No secondary air injection.
No fuel tank ventilation.
No faults detected for fuel tank ventilation and secondary air injection.

PR101970002500AX

Fig. 27 Codes P0139 & P0159: Aging O2 Sensor After 3 Way Catalytic Converter (Part 1 of 3). Boxster

1 Road test vehicle or perform short test

1. Erase DTC memory.
2. Heat oxygen sensors (road test vehicle under load, run engine under no load at high engine speed).
3. Road test vehicle or perform short test, whereby the diagnosis conditions must be reached.
4. Read DTC memory.

PR101970002500BX

Fig. 27 Codes P0139 & P0159: Aging O2 Sensor After 3 Way Catalytic Converter (Part 2 of 3). Boxster

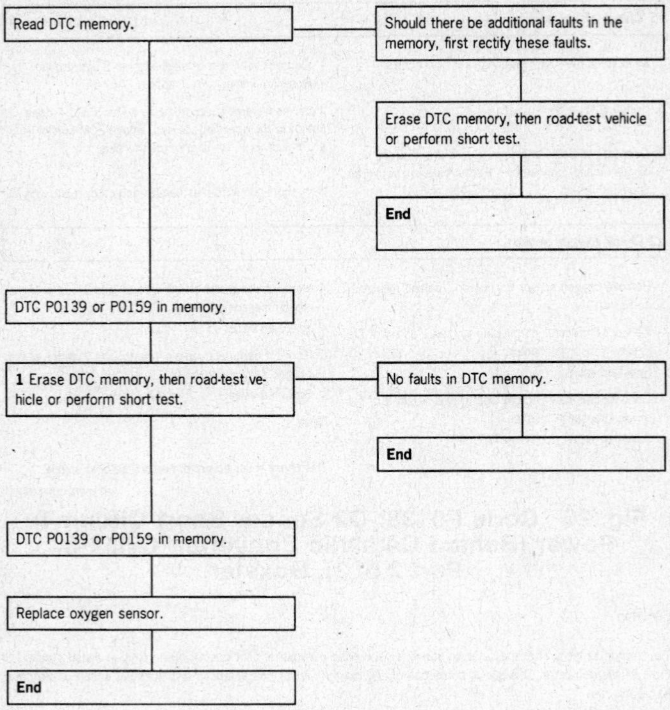

PR101970002500CX

Fig. 27 Codes P0139 & P0159: Aging O2 Sensor After 3 Way Catalytic Converter (Part 3 of 3). Boxster

1 Check wiring harness.

1. Remove all the four oxygen sensor connectors.
2. Switch ignition on.
3. Connect voltmeter at sleeve to pins 3 and 4 of oxygen sensor connector 1 behind catalytic converter.
   Specified value: approx. 450 mV
4. Connect voltmeter at sleeve to pin 3 and ground.
   Specified value: approx. 720 mV
5. Start engine and run engine at high speed for three minutes.
6. Connect voltmeter at sleeve to pins 1 and 2.
   Specified value: battery voltage

If the measurement according to items 3, 4, and 6 does not show the specified values, remove ECM connector and check wires for continuity.

If no continuity can be detected, repair wiring harness. If continuity OK, replace ECM.

2 Check function of oxygen sensor.

1. Heat the oxygen sensors (road-test car under load or run engine without load at high engine speed).
2. Connect Porsche System Tester 2 or scan tool and read voltage of oxygen sensor 1 behind catalytic converter.

Specified value: Voltage fluctuations between 100 mV and 800 mV.
➡ Oxygen sensor OK.

3 Check oxygen sensor heating.

1. Remove oxygen sensor connector 1 behind catalytic converter.
2. Connect ohmmeter on pin side to pins 1 and 2 of the oxygen sensor connector.
   Specified value: 1.8 - 2.5 Ω at 20 °C
3. Connect ohmmeter on pin side to pin 1 and the oxygen sensor housing.
   Specified value: ∞ Ω
4. Connect ohmmeter on pin side to pin 2 and the oxygen sensor housing.
   Specified value: ∞ Ω

PR101970002600BX

Fig. 28 Code P0140: O2 Sensor Interruption Of Signal (Behind Catalytic Converter, Cyl. 103, Part 2 of 4). Boxster

Function

To diagnose the readiness for operation of the oxygen sensors, the position of the sensor voltage is evaluated (in case of certain faults or conditions, the diagnosis is disabled).

Diagnosis Conditions

Diagnostic Trouble Code P0140 is stored in the Engine Control Module when the sensor voltage is between 400 mV and 500 mV for more than 400 seconds without interruptions.

Conditions for the diagnosis of the oxygen sensor signals:

- Sensor heating is active.

Note:

When DTC P0140 is stored, DTC P1117 may be stored as well.

PR101970002600AX

Fig. 28 Code P0140: O2 Sensor Interruption Of Signal (Behind Catalytic Converter, Cyl. 103, Part 1 of 4). Boxster

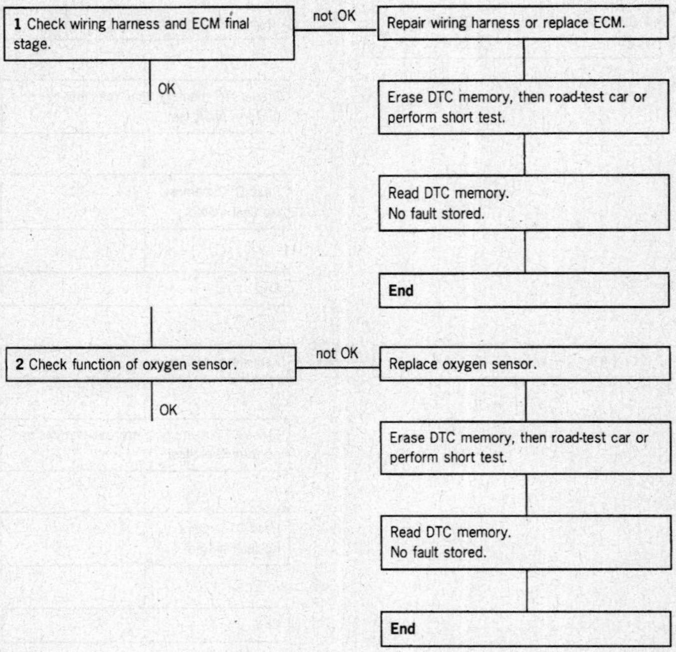

PR101970002600CX

Fig. 28 Code P0140: O2 Sensor Interruption Of Signal (Behind Catalytic Converter, Cyl. 103, Part 3 of 4). Boxster

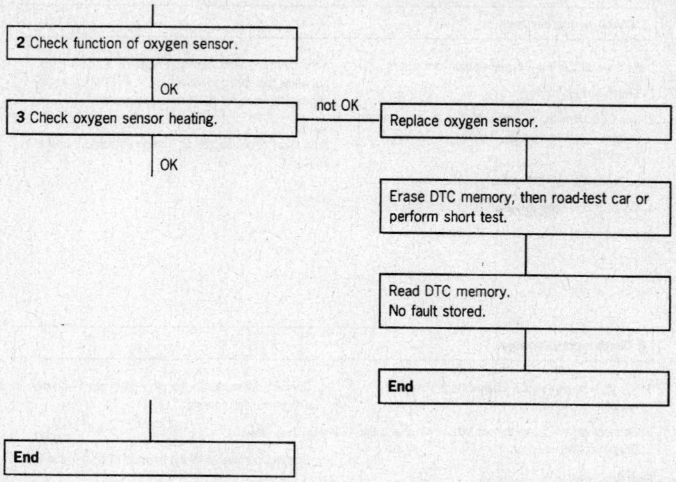

PR101970002600DX

Fig. 28 Code P0140: O2 Sensor Interruption Of Signal (Behind Catalytic Converter, Cyl. 103, Part 4 of 4). Boxster

1 Check oxygen sensor.

1. Heat the oxygen sensors (road-test car under load or run engine without load at high engine speed).
2. Connect Porsche System Tester 2 or scan tool and read voltage of oxygen sensor 2 ahead of catalytic converter.

Specified value: Voltage fluctuations between 100 mV and 800 mV.
➡ Oxygen sensor OK.

In case of a displayed value near 0 V, a short circuit between the signal wire and the sensor ground has occurred.

3. Remove oxygen sensor connector 2 ahead of catalytic converter.
4. Connect voltmeter at sleeve to pins 3 and 4.
Specified value: approx. 450 mV.
➡ Replace oxygen sensor.
Specified value: approx. 0 V
➡ Check wiring harness (check item 2).

If the wiring harness is OK, remove all oxygen sensor connectors and perform measurement of item 4 on all oxygen sensors.

2 Check wiring harness.

1. Remove oxygen sensor connector.
2. Connect special tool 9616 to wiring harness.
3. With ohmmeter measure resistance between special tool 9616 pin 18 and oxygen sensor connector pin 4.
Specified value: 0 - 5 Ω
4. With ohmmeter measure resistance between special tool 9616 pin 46 and oxygen sensor connector pin 3.
Specified value: 0 - 5 Ω

Note

For this measurement, all other oxygen sensor connectors must be removed.

3 Check ECM final stage.

1. Connect special tool 9616.
2. Remove oxygen sensor connector 2 ahead of catalytic converter.
3. Connect voltmeter at sleeve to pins 18 and 46.
4. Switch ignition on.
Specified value: approx. 450 mV

If reading < 400 mV or > 500 mV: Replace ECM.

PR101970002700BX

Fig. 29 Code P0150: O2 Sensor Short Circuit Of Wires (In Front Of Catalytic Converter, Cyl. 4-6, Part 2 of 3). Boxster

Function

To diagnose the readiness for operation of the oxygen sensors, the position of the sensor voltage is evaluated (in case of certain faults or conditions, the diagnosis is disabled).

Diagnosis Conditions

Diagnostic Trouble Code P0150 is stored on the Engine Control Module (ECM) when a voltage increase of the oxygen sensor between 60 mV and 400 mV for more than 15 seconds is detected by the ECM and when the sensor voltage behind the catalytic converter exceeds 350 mV.

The fault also occurs if, with a cold oxygen sensor, the voltage value lies in the range - 40 mV to + 40 mV (intercore short-circuit) or if an intercore short-circuit is present for 15 seconds and the sensor voltage behind the catalytic converter is greater than 350 mV.

Conditions for the diagnosis of the oxygen sensor signals:

- Sensor heating is active.
- Oxygen sensing is active.
- Oxygen sensor voltage behind catalytic converter > 350 mV.
- No Secondary Air Injection.
- No diagnosis of tank ventilation system.
- No faults detected for fuel tank ventilation and Secondary Air Injection.

Note

When DTC P0150 is shedded, a non-shedded fault P1121 will be stored as well. This non-shedded fault is not an actual fault.

PR101970002700AX

Fig. 29 Code P0150: O2 Sensor Short Circuit Of Wires (In Front Of Catalytic Converter, Cyl. 4-6, Part 1 of 3). Boxster

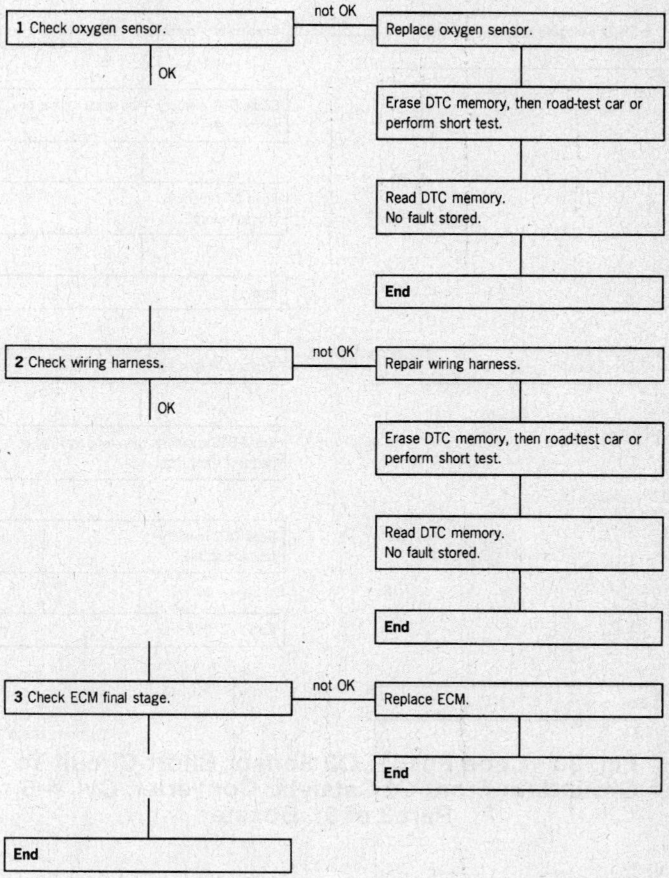

PR101970002700CX

Fig. 29 Code P0150: O2 Sensor Short Circuit Of Wires (In Front Of Catalytic Converter, Cyl. 4-6, Part 3 of 3). Boxster

Function

To diagnose the readiness for operation of the oxygen sensors, the position of the sensor voltage is evaluated (in case of certain faults or conditions, the diagnosis is disabled).

Diagnosis Conditions

Diagnostic Trouble Code P0151 is stored in the Engine Control Module when the sensor voltage is below - 150 mV.

Conditions for the diagnosis of the oxygen sensor signals:

– Sensor heating is active.

DTC No.	Fault conditions	Fault area
P0151	Short circuit of signal wire to ECM ground or housing ground. * Short circuit of sensor ground to ECM ground or housing ground.** Short circuit to ground of ECM final stage.	– Wiring harness – Oxygen sensor – ECM

* When these faults occur, the fault codes P1115 and P1119 may be stored in addition; however, these faults are no actual faults.

** When this fault occurs, all the four oxygen sensors are stored.

Note:

When DTC P0151 is stored and faults of the heating of the other three oxygen sensors are displayed, only one oxygen sensor is probably faulty.

PR101970002800AX

Fig. 30 Code P0151: O2 Sensor Short Circuit To Ground (In Front Of Catalytic Converter, Cyl. 4-6, Part 1 of 3). Boxster

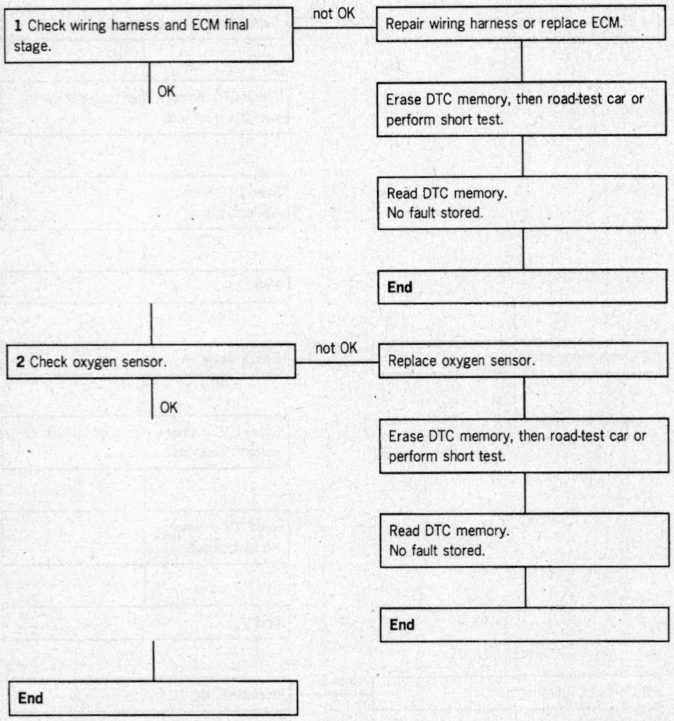

PR101970002800CX

Fig. 30 Code P0151: O2 Sensor Short Circuit To Ground (In Front Of Catalytic Converter, Cyl. 4-6, Part 3 of 3). Boxster

1 Check wiring harness.

1. Remove all the four oxygen sensor connectors.
2. Switch ignition on.
3. Connect voltmeter at sleeve to pins 3 and 4 of oxygen sensor connector 2 ahead of catalytic converter.

Specified value: approx. 450 mV

4. Connect voltmeter at sleeve to pin 3 and ground.

Specified value: approx. 720 mV

If the measurement according to items 3 and 4 does not show the specified values, remove ECM connector and check wires for short circuit to ground.

If no short circuit to ground can be detected, replace ECM.

2 Check oxygen sensor.

1. Remove oxygen sensor connector 2 ahead of catalytic converter.
2. Connect ohmmeter to the pin side of pin 3 and the oxygen sensor housing.

Specified value: ∞ Ω

3. Connect ohmmeter to the pin side of pins 3 and 2.

Specified value: ∞ Ω

4. Connect ohmmeter to the pin side of pin 4 and the oxygen sensor housing.

Specified value: ∞ Ω

5. Connect ohmmeter to the pin side of pins 4 and 2.

Specified value: ∞ Ω

PR101970002800BX

Fig. 30 Code P0151: O2 Sensor Short Circuit To Ground (In Front Of Catalytic Converter, Cyl. 4-6, Part 2 of 3). Boxster

Function

To diagnose the readiness for operation of the oxygen sensors, the position of the sensor voltage is evaluated (in case of certain faults or conditions, the diagnosis is disabled).

Diagnosis Conditions

Diagnostic Trouble Code P0152 is stored in the Engine Control Module when the sensor voltage is above 1 V for more than 0.5 seconds without interruptions.

Conditions for the diagnosis of the oxygen sensor signals:

– Sensor heating is active.

Note

In case of a short circuit to plus at one oxygen sensor, all the four oxygen sensor will be stored. Furthermore, the fault may cause misfires.

PR101970002900AX

Fig. 31 Code P0152: O2 Sensor Short To Power (In Front Of Catalytic Converter Cyl. 4-6, Part 1 of 3). Boxster

1 Check wiring harness.

1. Remove all the four oxygen sensor connectors.
2. Switch ignition on.
3. Connect voltmeter at sleeve to pins 3 and 4 of oxygen sensor connector 2 ahead of catalytic converter.
   Specified value: approx. 450 mV
4. Connect voltmeter at sleeve to pin 3 and ground.
   Specified value: approx. 720 mV

If the measurement according to items 3 and 4 does not show the specified values, remove ECM connector and check wires for short circuit to plus.

If no short circuit to plus can be detected, replace ECM.

2 Check oxygen sensor.

1. Remove oxygen sensor connector 2 ahead of catalytic converter.
2. Connect ohmmeter on pin side to pins 1 and 3 of the oxygen sensor connector.
   Specified value: ∞ Ω
3. Connect ohmmeter on pin side to pins 2 and 3 of the oxygen sensor connector.
   Specified value: ∞ Ω
4. Connect ohmmeter on pin side to pins 1 and 4 of the oxygen sensor connector.
   Specified value: ∞ Ω
5. Connect ohmmeter on pin side to pins 2 and 4 of the oxygen sensor connector.
   Specified value: ∞ Ω

Note

This check must be performed on the cold engine.

PR101970002900BX

Fig. 31 Code P0152: O2 Sensor Short To Power (In Front Of Catalytic Converter Cyl. 4-6, Part 2 of 3). Boxster

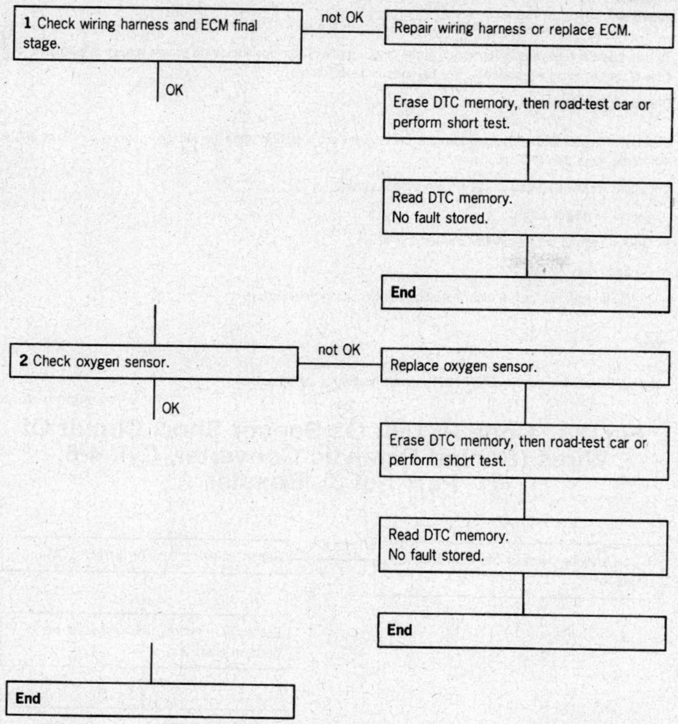

PR101970002900CX

Fig. 31 Code P0152: O2 Sensor Short To Power (In Front Of Catalytic Converter Cyl. 4-6, Part 3 of 3). Boxster

1 Check wiring harness.

1. Remove all the four oxygen sensor connectors.
2. Switch ignition on.
3. Connect voltmeter at sleeve to pins 3 and 4 of oxygen sensor connector 2 ahead of catalytic converter.
   Specified value: approx. 450 mV
4. Connect voltmeter at sleeve to pin 3 and ground.
   Specified value: approx. 720 mV
5. Start engine and run engine at high speed for three minutes.
6. Connect voltmeter at sleeve to pins 1 and 2.
   Specified value: battery voltage

If the measurement according to items 3, 4, and 6 does not show the specified values, remove ECM connector and check wires for continuity.

If no continuity can be detected, repair wiring harness. If continuity OK, replace ECM.

2 Check function of oxygen sensor.

1. Heat the oxygen sensors (road-test car under load or run engine without load at high engine speed).
2. Connect Porsche System Tester 2 or scan tool and read voltage of oxygen sensor 2 ahead of catalytic converter.

Specified value: Voltage fluctuations between 100 mV and 800 mV.
➨ Oxygen sensor OK.

3 Check oxygen sensor heating.

1. Remove oxygen sensor connector 2 ahead of catalytic converter.
2. Connect ohmmeter on pin side to pins 1 and 2 of the oxygen sensor connector.
   Specified value: 1.8 - 2.5 Ω at 20 °C
3. Connect ohmmeter on pin side to pin 1 and the oxygen sensor housing.
   Specified value: ∞ Ω
4. Connect ohmmeter on pin side to pin 2 and the oxygen sensor housing.
   Specified value: ∞ Ω

PR101970003000BX

Fig. 32 Code P0154: O2 Sensor Interruption Of Signal (In Front Of Catalytic Converter, Cyl. 4-6, Part 2 of 4). Boxster

Function

To diagnose the readiness for operation of the oxygen sensors, the position of the sensor voltage is evaluated (in case of certain faults or conditions, the diagnosis is disabled).

Diagnosis Conditions

Diagnostic Trouble Code P0154 is stored in the Engine Control Module when the sensor voltage is between 400 mV and 600 mV for more than 5 seconds without interruptions.

Conditions for the diagnosis of the oxygen sensor signals:

– Sensor heating is active.

Note

When DTC P0154 is stored, DTC P1119 may be stored as well.
This fault is also stored simultaneously as P0134 if there is an interruption in the common sensor ground

PR101970003000AX

Fig. 32 Code P0154: O2 Sensor Interruption Of Signal (In Front Of Catalytic Converter, Cyl. 4-6, Part 1 of 4). Boxster

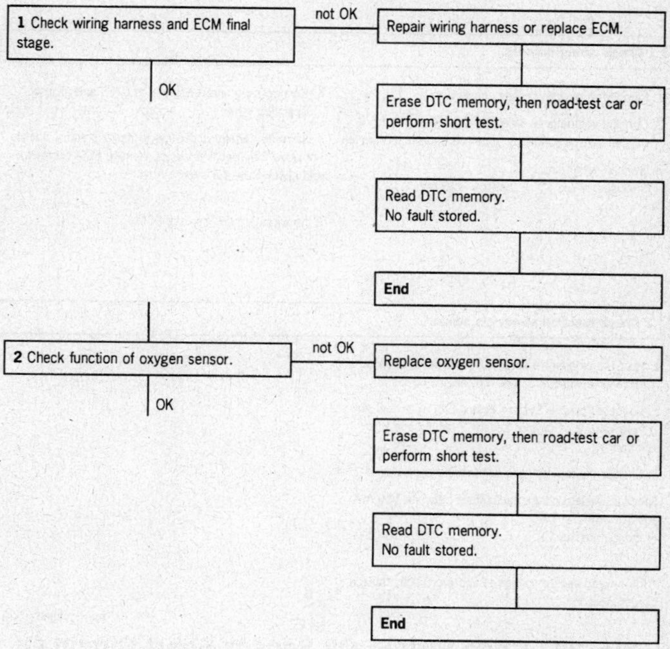

PR101970003000CX

Fig. 32 Code P0154: O2 Sensor Interruption Of Signal (In Front Of Catalytic Converter, Cyl. 4-6, Part 3 of 4). Boxster

3 Check oxygen sensor heating.

- not OK → Replace oxygen sensor. → Erase DTC memory, then road-test car or perform short test. → Read DTC memory. No fault stored. → **End**
- OK → **End**

PR101970003000DX

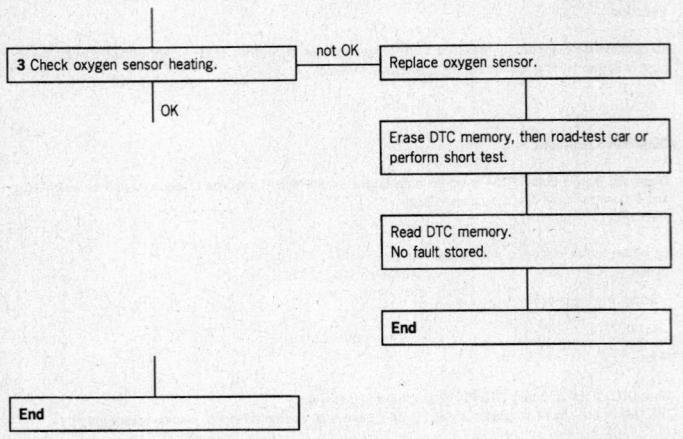

Fig. 32 Code P0154: O2 Sensor Interruption Of Signal (In Front Of Catalytic Converter, Cyl. 4-6, Part 4 of 4). Boxster

1 Check wiring harness.

1. Remove all oxygen sensor connectors.
2. Connect voltmeter at sleeve to pins 3 and 4 of oxygen sensor connector 2 behind catalytic converter.
3. Switch ignition on.
   Specified value: approx. 450 mV
4. Connect voltmeter at sleeve to pin 3 and ground.
   Specified value: approx. 720 mV

If the measurement according to items 3 and 4 does not show the specified values, remove ECM connector and check wires for short circuit.

If the wires are OK, replace ECM.

2 Check function of oxygen sensor.

1. Heat the oxygen sensors (road-test car under load or run engine without load at high engine speed).
2. Connect Porsche System Tester 2 or scan tool and read voltage of oxygen sensor 2 behind catalytic converter.
3. Change the fuel/air ratio with acceleration bursts.

Specified value: Voltage fluctuations between 100 mV and 800 mV.
➡ Oxygen sensor OK.

If the oxygen sensor voltage is approx. 0 Volt, replace oxygen sensor.

PR101970003100BX

Fig. 33 Code P0156: O2 Sensor Short Circuit Of Wires (Behind Catalytic Converter, Cyl. 4-6, Part 2 of 3). Boxster

Function

To diagnose the readiness for operation of the oxygen sensors, the position of the sensor voltage is evaluated (in case of certain faults or conditions, the diagnosis is disabled).

Diagnosis Conditions

Diagnostic Trouble Code P0156 is stored in the Engine Control Module when the voltage is between - 40 mV and + 40 mV for more than 200 seconds.

Conditions for the diagnosis of the oxygen sensor signals:

- Sensor heating is active.
- Oxygen sensing behind catalytic converter is active.
- No Secondary Air Injection.
- No faults detected for fuel tank ventilation and Secondary Air Injection.

Note

When DTC P0156 is stored, DTC P1121 (sensor heating) is stored as well.

PR101970003100AX

Fig. 33 Code P0156: O2 Sensor Short Circuit Of Wires (Behind Catalytic Converter, Cyl. 4-6, Part 1 of 3). Boxster

1 Check wiring harness and ECM final stage.

- not OK → Repair wiring harness or replace ECM. → Erase DTC memory, then road-test car or perform short test. → Read DTC memory. No fault stored. → **End**
- OK ↓

2 Check function of oxygen sensor.

- not OK → Replace oxygen sensor. → Erase DTC memory, then road-test car or perform short test. → Read DTC memory. No fault stored. → **End**
- OK → **End**

PR101970003100CX

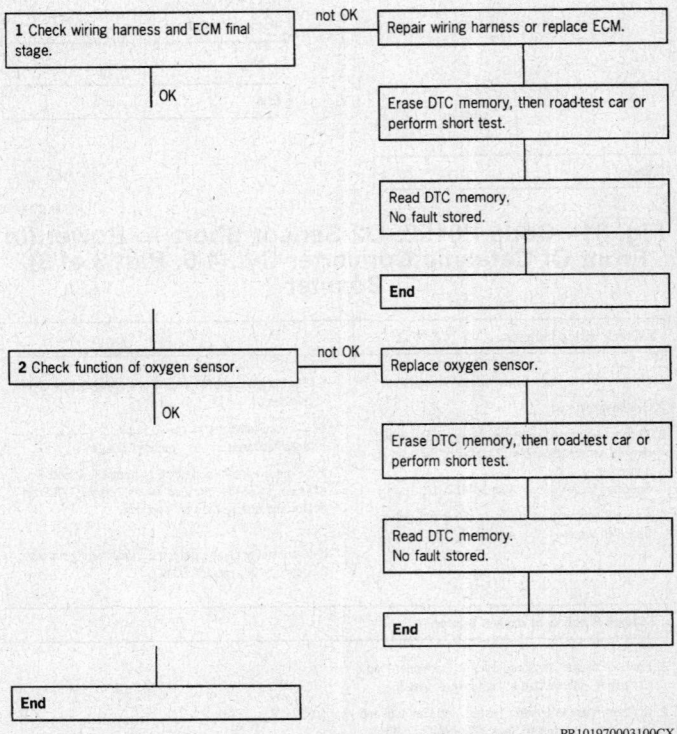

Fig. 33 Code P0156: O2 Sensor Short Circuit Of Wires (Behind Catalytic Converter, Cyl. 4-6, Part 3 of 3). Boxster

Function

To diagnose the readiness for operation of the oxygen sensors, the position of the sensor voltage is evaluated (in case of certain faults or conditions, the diagnosis is disabled).

Diagnosis Conditions

Diagnostic Trouble Code P0157 is stored in the ECM, when the sensor voltage is below - 150 mV.

Conditions for the diagnosis of the oxygen sensor signals:

– Sensor heating is active.

DTC No.	Fault conditions	Fault area
P0157	Short circuit of signal wire to ECM ground or housing ground. * Short circuit of sensor ground to ECM ground or housing ground.** Short circuit to ground of ECM final stage.	– Wiring harness – Oxygen sensor – ECM

* When these faults occur, the fault codes P1115 and P1119 may be stored in addition; however, these faults are no actual faults.

** When this fault occurs, all the four oxygen sensors are stored.

Note

When DTC P0157 is stored and faults of the heating of the other three oxygen sensors are displayed, only one oxygen sensor is probably faulty.

PR101970003200AX

Fig. 34 Code P0157: O2 Sensor Short Circuit To Ground (Behind Catalytic Converter, Cyl. 4-6, Part 1 of 3). Boxster

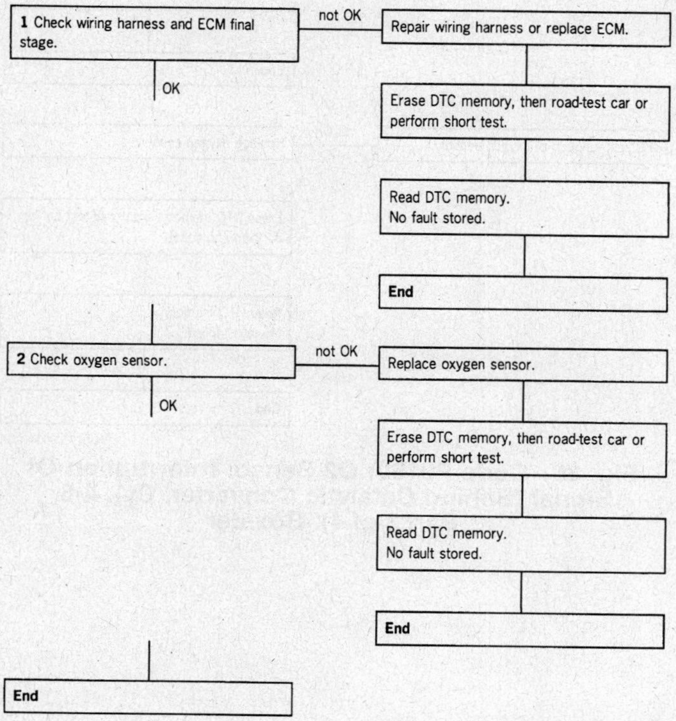

PR101970003200CX

Fig. 34 Code P0157: O2 Sensor Short Circuit To Ground (Behind Catalytic Converter, Cyl. 4-6, Part 3 of 3). Boxster

1 Check wiring harness.

1. Remove all the four oxygen sensor connectors.
2. Switch ignition on.
3. Connect voltmeter at sleeve to pins 3 and 4 of oxygen sensor connector 2 behind catalytic converter.
   Specified value: approx. 450 mV
4. Connect voltmeter at sleeve to pin 3 and ground.
   Specified value: approx. 720 mV

If the measurement according to items 3 and 4 does not show the specified values, remove ECM connector and check wires for short circuit to ground.

If no short circuit to ground can be detected, replace ECM.

2 Check oxygen sensor.

1. Remove oxygen sensor connector 2 behind catalytic converter.
2. Connect ohmmeter on pin side to pin 3 and the oxygen sensor housing.
   Specified value: ∞ Ω
3. Connect ohmmeter on pin side to pin 4 and the oxygen sensor housing.
   Specified value: ∞ Ω
4. Connect ohmmeter on pin side to pins 4 and 2.
   Specified value: ∞ Ω
5. Connect ohmmeter on pin side to pins 3 and 2.
   Specified value: ∞ Ω

PR101970003200BX

Fig. 34 Code P0157: O2 Sensor Short Circuit To Ground (Behind Catalytic Converter, Cyl. 4-6, Part 2 of 3). Boxster

Function

To diagnose the readiness for operation of the oxygen sensors, the position of the sensor voltage is evaluated (in case of certain faults or conditions, the diagnosis is disabled).

Diagnosis Conditions

Diagnostic Trouble Code P0158 is stored in the Engine Control Module when the sensor voltage is above 1 V for more than 0.5 seconds without interruptions.

Conditions for the diagnosis of the oxygen sensor signals:

– Sensor heating is active.

Note

In case of a short circuit to plus at one oxygen sensor, all the four oxygen sensors will be stored. Furthermore, the fault may cause misfires.

PR101970003300AX

Fig. 35 Code P0158: O2 Sensor Short To Power (Behind Catalytic Converter, Cyl. 4-6, Part 1 of 3). Boxster

1 Check wiring harness.

1. Remove all the four oxygen sensor connectors.
2. Switch ignition on.
3. Connect voltmeter at sleeve to pins 3 and 4 of oxygen sensor connector 2 behind catalytic converter.
   Specified value: approx. 450 mV
4. Connect voltmeter at sleeve to pin 3 and ground.
   Specified value: approx. 720 mV

If the measurement according to items 3 and 4 does not show the specified values, remove ECM connector and check wires for short circuit to plus.

If no short circuit to plus can be detected, replace ECM.

2 Check oxygen sensor.

1. Remove oxygen sensor connector 2 behind catalytic converter.
2. Connect ohmmeter on pin side to pins 1 and 3 of the oxygen sensor connector.
   Specified value: ∞ Ω
3. Connect ohmmeter on pin side to pins 2 and 3 of the oxygen sensor connector.
   Specified value: ∞ Ω
4. Connect ohmmeter on pin side to pins 1 and 4 of the oxygen sensor connector.
   Specified value: ∞ Ω
5. Connect ohmmeter on pin side to pins 2 and 4 of the oxygen sensor connector.
   Specified value: ∞ Ω

Note

This check must be performed on the cold engine.

PR101970003300BX

Fig. 35 Code P0158: O2 Sensor Short To Power (Behind Catalytic Converter, Cyl. 4-6, Part 2 of 3). Boxster

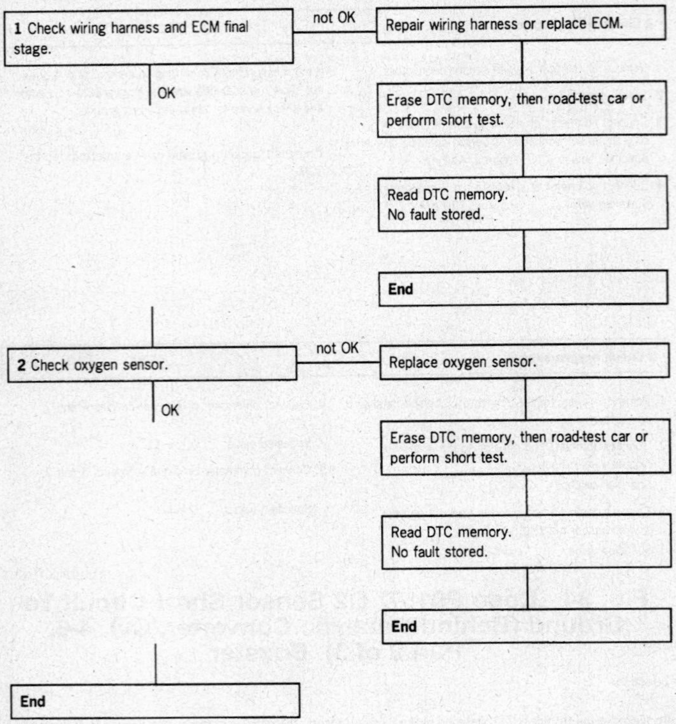

PR101970003300CX

Fig. 35 Code P0158: O2 Sensor Short To Power (Behind Catalytic Converter, Cyl. 4-6, Part 3 of 3). Boxster

1 Check wiring harness.

1. Remove all the four oxygen sensor connectors.
2. Switch ignition on.
3. Connect voltmeter at sleeve to pins 3 and 4 of oxygen sensor connector 2 behind catalytic converter.
   Specified value: approx. 450 mV
4. Connect voltmeter at sleeve to pin 3 and ground.
   Specified value: approx. 720 mV
5. Start engine and run engine at high speed for three minutes.
6. Connect voltmeter at sleeve to pins 1 and 2.
   Specified value: battery voltage

If the measurement according to items 3, 4, and 6 does not show the specified values, remove ECM connector and check wires for continuity.

If no continuity can be detected, repair wiring harness.
If continuity OK, replace ECM.

2 Check function of oxygen sensor.

1. Heat the oxygen sensors (road-test car under load or run engine without load at high engine speed).
2. Connect Porsche System Tester 2 or scan tool and read voltage of oxygen sensor 2 behind catalytic converter.

Specified value: Voltage fluctuations between 100 mV and 800 mV.
➡ Oxygen sensor OK.

3 Check oxygen sensor heating.

1. Remove oxygen sensor connector 2 behind catalytic converter.
2. Connect ohmmeter on pin side to pins 1 and 2 of the oxygen sensor connector.
   Specified value: 1.8 - 2.5 Ω at 20 °C
3. Connect ohmmeter on pin side to pin 1 and the oxygen sensor housing.
   Specified value: ∞ Ω
4. Connect ohmmeter on pin side to pin 2 and the oxygen sensor housing.
   Specified value: ∞ Ω

PR101970003400BX

Fig. 36 Code P0160: O2 Sensor Interruption Of Signal (Behind Catalytic Converter, Cyl. 4-6, Part 2 of 4). Boxster

Function

To diagnose the readiness for operation of the oxygen sensors, the position of the sensor voltage is evaluated (in case of certain faults or conditions, the diagnosis is disabled).

Diagnosis Conditions

Diagnostic Trouble Code P0160 is stored in the Engine Control Module when the sensor voltage is between 400 mV and 500 mV for more than 400 seconds without interruptions.

Conditions for the diagnosis of the oxygen sensor signals:

- Sensor heating is active.

Note

When DTC P0160 is stored, DTC P1121 may be stored as well.

PR101970003400AX

Fig. 36 Code P0160: O2 Sensor Interruption Of Signal (Behind Catalytic Converter, Cyl. 4-6, Part 1 of 4). Boxster

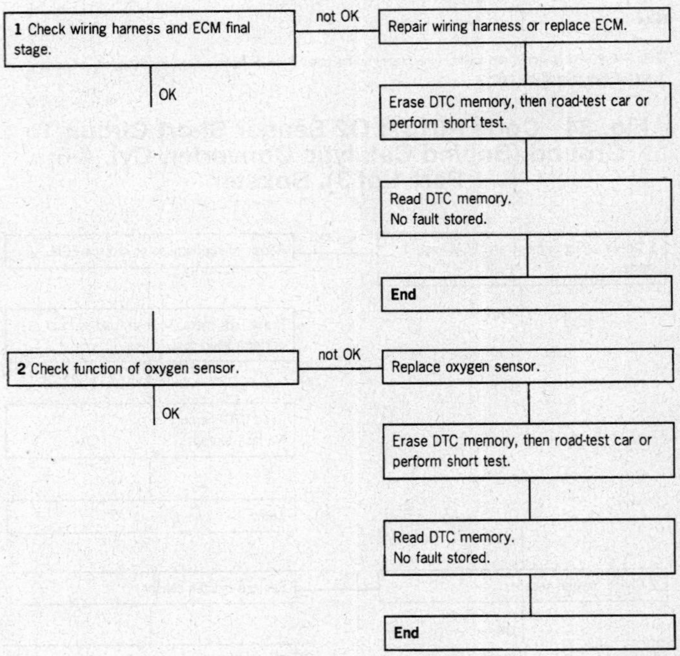

PR101970003400CX

Fig. 36 Code P0160: O2 Sensor Interruption Of Signal (Behind Catalytic Converter, Cyl. 4-6, Part 3 of 4). Boxster

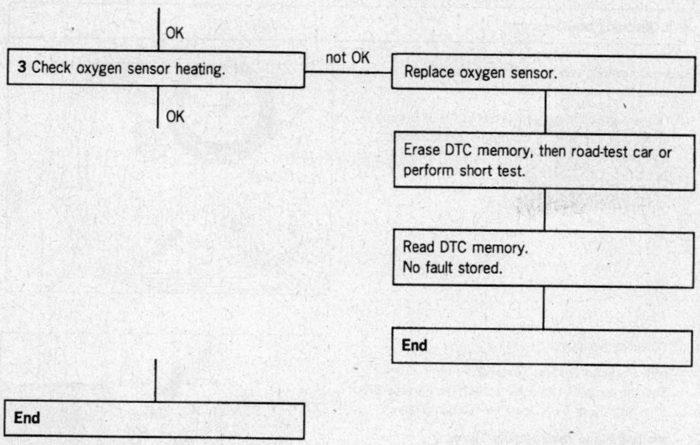

PR101970003400DX

Fig. 36 Code P0160: O2 Sensor Interruption Of Signal (Behind Catalytic Converter, Cyl. 4-6, Part 4 of 4). Boxster

1 Check temperature sensor.

1. Connect special tool 9616 to wiring harness.
2. Connect ohmmeter to pin 34 and pin 73.
   Display: 2.8 – 3.5 kΩ at 60 °C

2 Check wiring from ECM to temperature sensor for continuity.

1. Connect special tool 9616 to wiring harness.
2. Separate connector on the temperature sensor.
3. Connect ohmmeter to pin 34 (special tool 9616) and pin 3 (temperature sensor connector).
   Display: 0 - 5 Ω

   Connect ohmmeter to pin 73 (special tool 9616) and pin 1 (temperature sensor connector).
   Display: 0 - 5 Ω

3 Check wire from ECM to temperature sensor for short to ground.

1. Connect special tool 9616 to wiring harness.
2. Separate connector on the temperature sensor.
3. Connect ohmmeter to pin 73 and ground.
   Display: ∞ Ω

   If 0 - 5 Ω is displayed, check wiring harness for chafing and pinching damage.

4 Check wire from ECM to temperature sensor for short to B+.

1. Connect special tool 9616 to wiring harness.
2. Separate connector on the temperature sensor.
3. Connect voltmeter to pin 73 and ground.
   Switch on ignition.
   Display: 0 Volt

   If battery positive voltage is displayed, check wiring harness for chafing and pinching damage.

PR101970003500BX

Fig. 37 Codes P0197 & P0198: Oil Temperature Sensor Circuit (Part 2 of 4). Boxster

Function

The temperature sensor measures the oil temperature via a variable resistance. The oil temperature is used to control camshaft adjustment.

Diagnosis Conditions

Engine running

Note

A substitute value of 95 °C is used in the event of a malfunction of the temperature sensor.

PR101970003500AX

Fig. 37 Codes P0197 & P0198: Oil Temperature Sensor Circuit (Part 1 of 4). Boxster

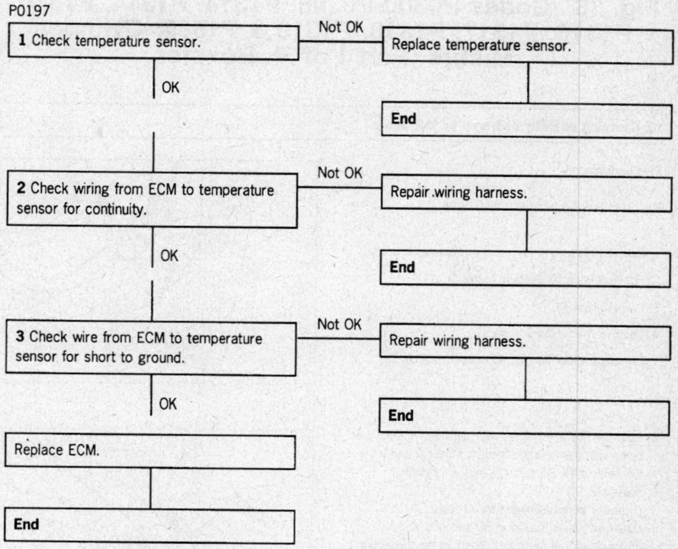

PR101970003500CX

Fig. 37 Codes P0197 & P0198: Oil Temperature Sensor Circuit (Part 3 of 4). Boxster

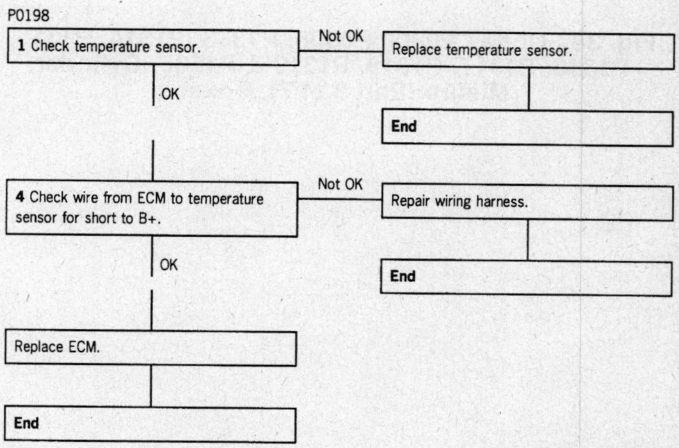

PR101970003500DX

Fig. 37 Codes P0197 & P0198: Oil Temperature Sensor Circuit (Part 4 of 4). Boxster

Function

To detect misfire, the decrease of engine speed is evaluated when no combustion occurs at one or more cylinders.

Faults that are emission related and faults that are damaging to the Three Way Catalytic Converter (TWC) are separate categories.

The engine speed is measured with an inductive sensor that is located above the ring gear of the flywheel.

The ring gear is divides into three segments. For the detection, the difference is calculated by the time measured between the segments. This difference is corrected by a mean value that is developed over several segments to compensate for the engine speed fluctuations caused by driving conditions. If the corrected value is above a specified value which depends on engine speed and engine load, a misfire is detected.

Diagnostic conditions

A cycle of 1,000 crankshaft revolutions each is evaluated (for misfire damaging to the TWC, 200 crank shaft revolutions). The misfire occurrences are compared to a threshold value. If the number of misfire is larger than the threshold value, a fault is recorded in memory.

The Malfunction Indicator Lamp (MIL) is switched on and stays on, when the misfire rate is above the threshold value for two consecutive driving cycles, when the FTP-limit values are exceeded by 1.5 times.

The MIL blinks if the misfire rate may lead to permanent damage to the TWC. The MIL goes back to consultant on when the misfire rate no longer reaches the threshold.

PR101970003600AX

Fig. 38 Codes P0300-P0306, P1313, P1314, P1315, P1316, P1317, P1318, P1319 & P1585: Cylinder Misfire (Part 1 of 7). Boxster

2 Checking quantity delivered by fuel pump

Precondition:

Fuel filter and electrical supply in order.

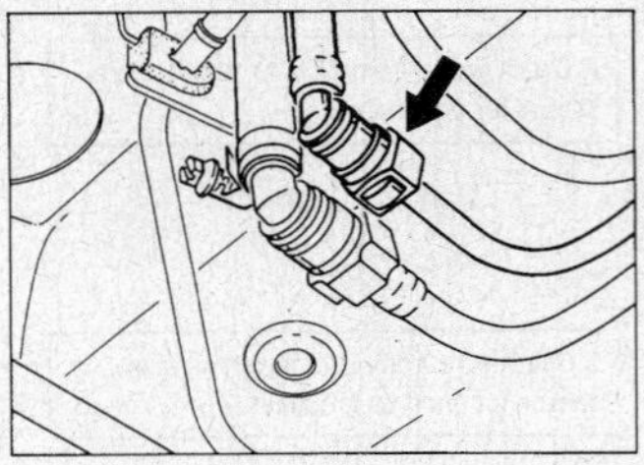

1. Relieve pressure in fuel tank by opening tank cap.
2. Connect Porsche System Tester 2.
3. Raise vehicle.
4. Remove rear underside panel.
5. Disconnect fuel return line. Collect residual fuel.
6. Hold fuel line in a measuring container. Actuate fuel pump with the Porsche System Tester 2 and allow fuel to flow for 30 seconds into a measuring container.
   Quantity supplied must be at least 850 cm³/30 s, i.e. after 30 seconds at least 850 cm³ of fuel must be present in the measuring container.

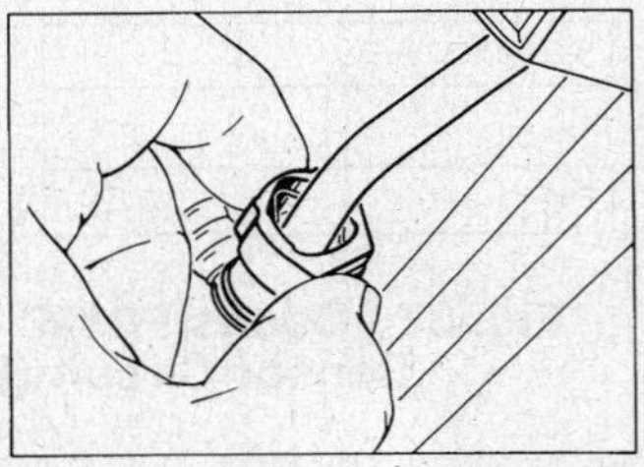

PR101970003600CX

Fig. 38 Codes P0300-P0306, P1313, P1314, P1315, P1316, P1317, P1318, P1319 & P1585: Cylinder Misfire (Part 3 of 7). Boxster

1 Checking fuel pressure.

1. Undo covering cap on test connection of fuel collection pipe and remove.
2. Connect pressure gauge (special tool P 378a) with connecting line (special tool 9559) and connect to test connection.

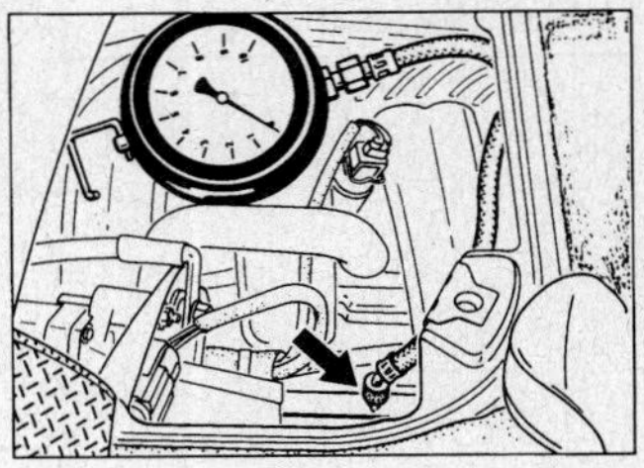

3. Actuating fuel pump:

- **with Porsche System Tester 2.**
  The fuel pump can be actuated with the Porsche System Tester 2 or by bridging the fuel-pump relay.
- **Via fuel-pump relay without Tester.**
  Disconnect fuel-pump relay from the central electrical board and bridge contacts 30 and 87 (identified as 3 and 5 on the central electrical board) with a fused shop-made cable. The fuel pump must now operate or deliver fuel.

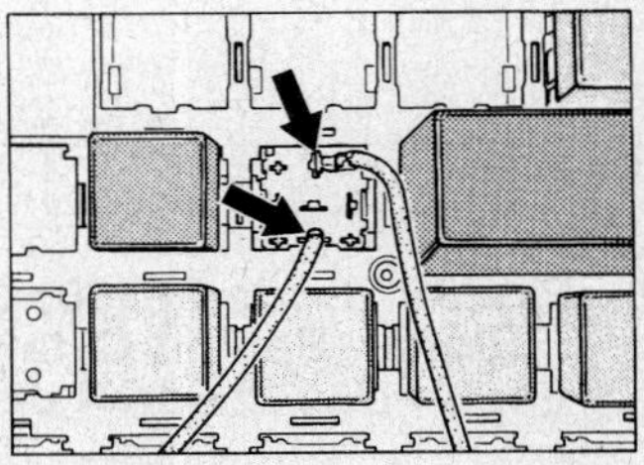

4. Nominal test values

   Stationary engine 3,8 ± 0,2 bar
   Engine idling 3,3 ± 0,2 bar

Note

The seal or sealing ring in the brass closure cap is **not** exchangeable. It must therefore be used only **once**.
Tightening torque of new brass closure cap
2,5 ± 0,5 Nm.(2.0 ± 0.5 ftlb.).

PR101970003600BX

Fig. 38 Codes P0300-P0306, P1313, P1314, P1315, P1316, P1317, P1318, P1319 & P1585: Cylinder Misfire (Part 2 of 7). Boxster

3 Check triggering of fuel injectors.

The fuel injectors can be individually suppressed with the Porsche System Tester 2 in the menu "Drive link active". The engine idle speed decreases if triggering is OK.

If no rpm decrease can be detected, check triggering as follows:

a) Voltage supply

1. Remove connector of fuel injector to be checked.
2. Connect voltmeter between injector connector, cavity 1 and ground.
3. Switch ignition on.
   Specified value: battery voltage

If meter does not read battery voltage, check wiring according to wiring diagram for continuity or short circuit.

b.) Coil resistance of fuel injectors

1. Remove connector of fuel injector to be checked.
2. With ohmmeter, measure resistance between terminals of fuel injector.
   Specified value: 11 - 13 Ω

c.) Injection end stage (minus supply)

1. Connect special tool V.A.G 1315 A/1 between fuel injector and connector.
2. Connect engine tester according to manufacturer's instructions. Connect tester cable with adapter cable.
   Caution:
   Tester cables must not contain ground connections.

PR101970003600DX

Fig. 38 Codes P0300-P0306, P1313, P1314, P1315, P1316, P1317, P1318, P1319 & P1585: Cylinder Misfire (Part 4 of 7). Boxster

3. Start engine: For a perfectly working injector end stage, the following display must be shown at starting rpm.

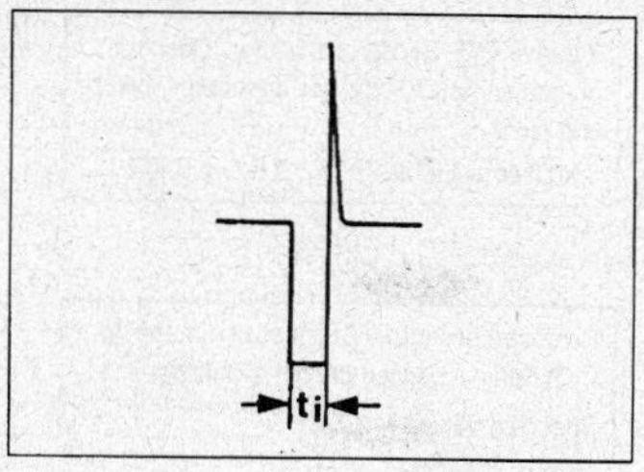

Note

If the engine does not start, or if the idling speed drops, replace tester cable at adapter cable.

PR101970003600EX

Fig. 38 Codes P0300-P0306, P1313, P1314, P1315, P1316, P1317, P1318, P1319 & P1585: Cylinder Misfire (Part 5 of 7). Boxster

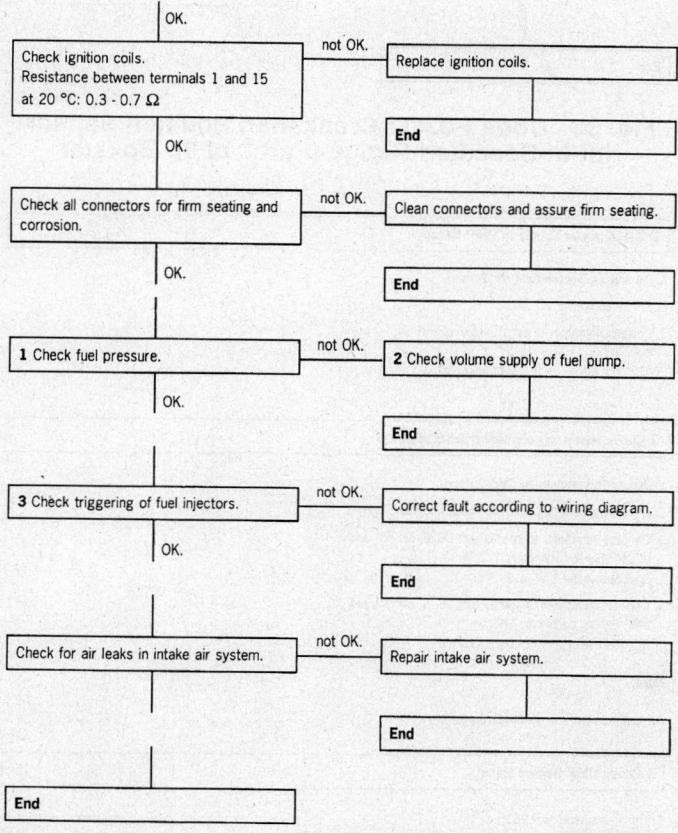

OK.

Check ignition coils. Resistance between terminals 1 and 15 at 20 °C: 0.3 - 0.7 Ω — not OK. → Replace ignition coils. → **End**

OK.

Check all connectors for firm seating and corrosion. — not OK. → Clean connectors and assure firm seating. → **End**

OK.

1 Check fuel pressure. — not OK. → **2** Check volume supply of fuel pump. → **End**

OK.

3 Check triggering of fuel injectors. — not OK. → Correct fault according to wiring diagram. → **End**

OK.

Check for air leaks in intake air system. — not OK. → Repair intake air system. → **End**

End

PR101970003600GX

Fig. 38 Codes P0300-P0306, P1313, P1314, P1315, P1316, P1317, P1318, P1319 & P1585: Cylinder Misfire (Part 7 of 7). Boxster

Test requirements: Engine mechanically OK.

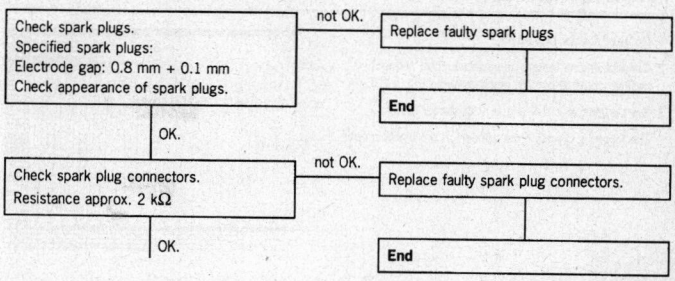

Check spark plugs. Specified spark plugs: Electrode gap: 0.8 mm + 0.1 mm. Check appearance of spark plugs. — not OK. → Replace faulty spark plugs → **End**

OK.

Check spark plug connectors. Resistance approx. 2 kΩ — not OK. → Replace faulty spark plug connectors. → **End**

OK.

PR101970003600FX

Fig. 38 Codes P0300-P0306, P1313, P1314, P1315, P1316, P1317, P1318, P1319 & P1585: Cylinder Misfire (Part 6 of 7). Boxster

Function

To precisely determine the crankshaft position, a Crankshaft Position (CKP) Sensor is needed.

Engine speed and crankshaft position is monitored via an inductive sensor. A larger gear notch in the ring gear serves as reference mark. Through the larger notch, a higher voltage is induced in the sensor.

A soft iron core partially bundles the magnetic field produced by the permanent magnet which then enters the space and closes again through the magnetically conductive parts of the engine. A steel toothed ring moving past the face of the sensor affects the magnetic field. The change in the magnetic field induces an electric charge that is used by the ECM.

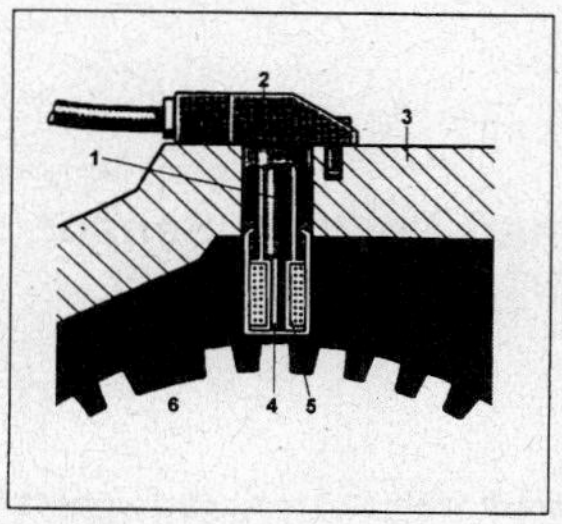

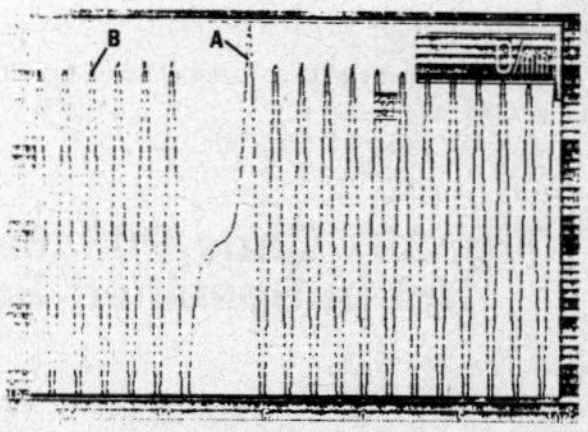

A – Crankshaft Position Sensor signal
B – Engine speed signal

1 – Permanent magnet 2 – Sensor housing 3 – Engine case
4 – Soft iron core 5 – Inductor coil 6 – Reference mark

Diagnostic conditions

A DTC is stored in memory when no Crankshaft Position (CKP) Sensor signal is recognized within 60 crankshaft revolutions **and** when the engine speed is above 500 rpm .

PR101970003700AX

Fig. 39 Code P0336: Crankshaft Position Sensor Not In Specified Range (Part 1 of 3). Boxster

1 Check signal with engine tester.

1. Connect special tool 9616.
2. Connect engine tester. Use special input; connect positive cable to pin 78, negative cable to pin 20.
3. Start engine or crank engine with starter motor.

The following display must appear on the oscilloscope:

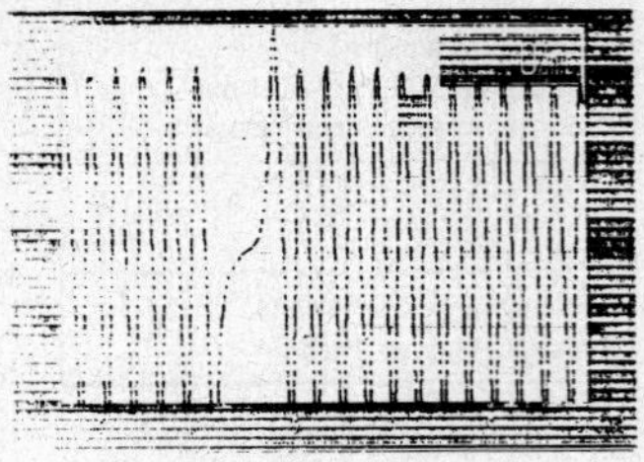

2 Check wiring from CKP Sensor to ECM for breaks and short circuit.

1. Connect special tool 9616 to wiring harness.
2. Remove connector at CKP sensor.
3. Connect ohmmeter to special tool 9616, pin 78, and connector, pin 1.
   Specified value: 0 - 5 Ω
4. Connect ohmmeter to special tool 9616, pin 20, and connector, pin 2.
   Specified value: 0 - 5 Ω
5. Connect ohmmeter to special tool 9616, pin 28, and connector, pin 3.
   Specified value: 0 - 5 Ω
6. Connect ohmmeter to special tool 9616, pin 78, and ground.
   Specified value: ∞ Ω

PR101970003700BX

Fig. 39 Code P0336: Crankshaft Position Sensor Not In Specified Range (Part 2 of 3). Boxster

Function

The CMP sensor 1 signal identifies the first cylinder. If both the crankshaft position (CKP) sensor signal and the CMP sensor signal coincide, this signifies the timing point for cylinder 1. Recognizing cylinder 1 is needed for sequential fuel injection and knock sensing.
The CMP sensor 2 is needed to identify the position of the camshaft for cylinders 4 - 6.

Diagnostic conditions

Engine running

PR101970003800AX

Fig. 40 Codes P0341 & P1397: Camshaft Position Sensor Short Circuit (Part 1 of 5). Boxster

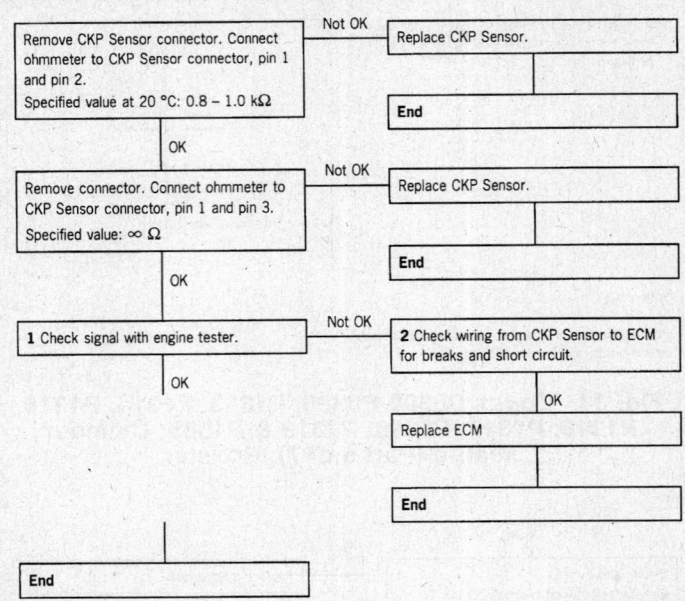

Remove CKP Sensor connector. Connect ohmmeter to CKP Sensor connector, pin 1 and pin 2.
Specified value at 20 °C: 0.8 – 1.0 kΩ
- Not OK → Replace CKP Sensor. → **End**
- OK ↓

Remove connector. Connect ohmmeter to CKP Sensor connector, pin 1 and pin 3.
Specified value: ∞ Ω
- Not OK → Replace CKP Sensor. → **End**
- OK ↓

1 Check signal with engine tester.
- Not OK → **2** Check wiring from CKP Sensor to ECM for breaks and short circuit. → OK → Replace ECM → **End**
- OK ↓

End

PR101970003700CX

Fig. 39 Code P0336: Crankshaft Position Sensor Not In Specified Range (Part 3 of 3). Boxster

1 Check power supply to CMP Sensor.

1. Remove connectors on CMP Sensors.
2. Switch on ignition.
3. Connect voltmeter to pin 1 (negative) and pin 3 (positive).
   Specified value: approx. 5 Volt

2 Check power supply wiring for continuity.

1. Remove connectors on CMP Sensors.
2. Connect special tool 9616 to wiring harness.
3. Connect ohmmeter to special tool 9616, pin 53, and to CMP Sensor connector 1/2, pin 3.
   Specified value: 0 - 5 Ω
4. Connect ohmmeter to special tool 9616, pin 34, and CMP Sensor connector 1/2, pin 1.
   Specified value: 0 - 5 Ω

Note

Perform this test for both CMP Sensors.

3 Check CMP Sensor signal.

1. Connect special tool 9616.
2. Connect engine tester. Use special input; connect positive cable to pin 21, negative cable to pin 34.
3. Start engine.

The following display must appear on the oscilloscope:

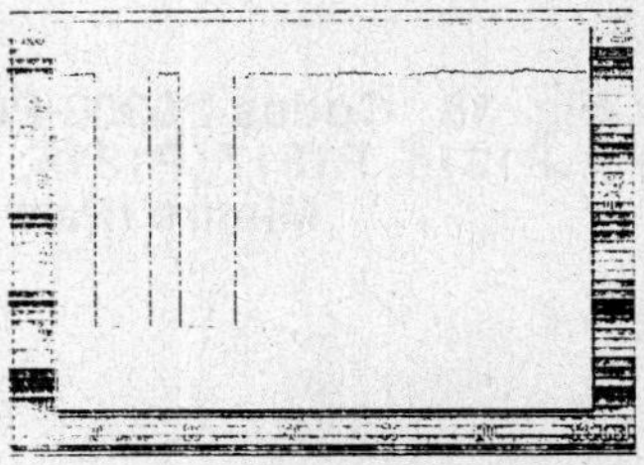

PR101970003800BX

Fig. 40 Codes P0341 & P1397: Camshaft Position Sensor Short Circuit (Part 2 of 5). Boxster

4 Check signal wire from ECM to CMP Sensors.

1. Connect special tool 9616 to wiring harness.
2. Remove connectors on CMP sensors.
3. Connect ohmmeter to special tool 9616, pin 21, and to CMP sensor connector 1/2, pin 2.
   Specified value: 0 - 5 Ω

5 Check signal wire from ECM to CMP Sensors for short circuit to ground.

1. Connect special tool 9616 to wiring harness.
2. Remove connectors on the CMP sensors.
3. Connect ohmmeter to special tool 9616, pin 21, and ground.
   Specified value: ∞ Ω

If 0 - 5 Ω is displayed, check wiring harness for chafing and pinching damage.

6 Check signal wire from ECM to CMP Sensors for short circuit to B+.

1. Connect special tool 9616 to wiring harness.
2. Remove connectors on CMP sensors.
3. Connect voltmeter to special tool 9616, pin 21, and ground.
   Switch on ignition.
   Specified value: 0 Volt

If battery positive voltage is displayed, check wiring harness for chafing and pinching damage.

PR101970003800CX

Fig. 40 Codes P0341 & P1397: Camshaft Position Sensor Short Circuit (Part 3 of 5). Boxster

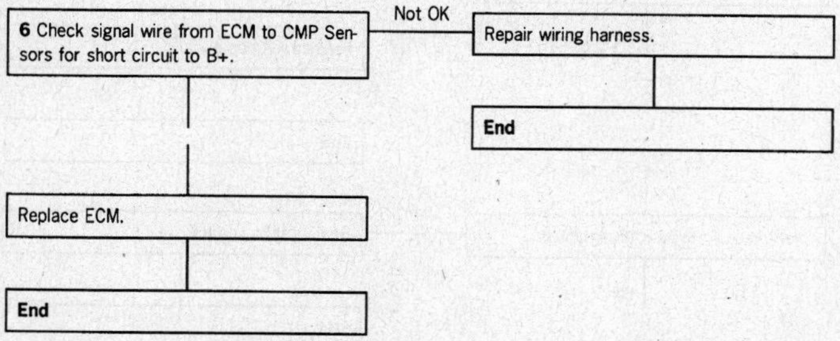

PR101970003800EX

Fig. 40 Codes P0341 & P1397: Camshaft Position Sensor Short Circuit (Part 5 of 5). Boxster

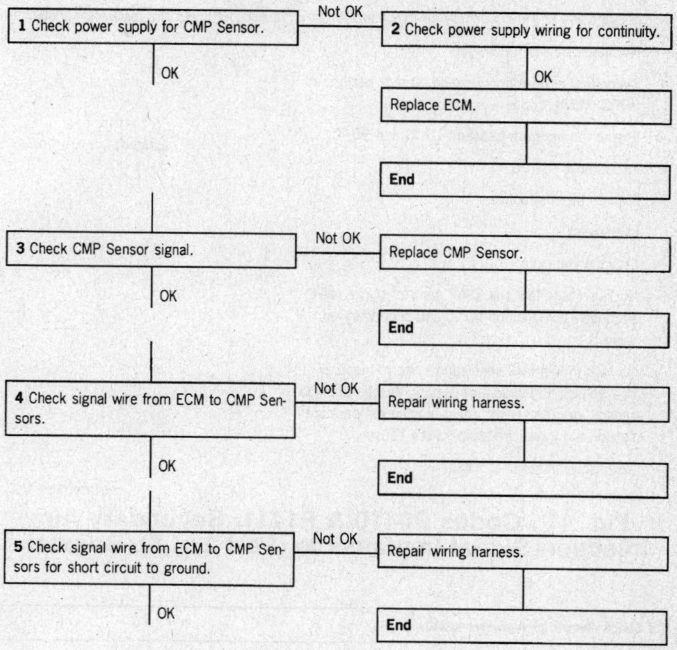

PR101970003800DX

Fig. 40 Codes P0341 & P1397: Camshaft Position Sensor Short Circuit (Part 4 of 5). Boxster

Function

To improve emissions and to heat the three-way catalytic converter (TWC) faster, the secondary air injection pump is activated after the engine is started when the engine is cold, thus blowing secondary air behind the discharge valves. If the engine temperature at start-up is less than –10 °C, the secondary air injection pump is disabled until the engine temperature has reached more than 44 °C. If the engine is started in a temperature range between –10 °C and 60 °C, the secondary air injection system is activated for a time depending on the start-up temperature. The secondary air injection system is deactivated under the following conditions:
Engine load > 4.5 ms
Air mass > 300 kg/h
Engine speed > 3800 rpm

A distinction is made between active and passive diagnosis. With passive diagnosis, testing is performed during the actual secondary air injection function. The sensor voltages ahead of the three-way catalytic converter are evaluated. If passive diagnosis is interrupted, active diagnosis takes place with the engine idling. The secondary air injection pump is switched on for this purpose. The deviation of the oxygen sensors due to the excess oxygen is evaluated.

Diagnosis conditions

Passive diagnosis of the secondary air injection system is carried out under the following conditions:

- Diagnosis has not yet been carried out in this cycle.
- The secondary air injection pump is switched on.
- The time after engine start-up is between 50 seconds and 179 seconds.
- Engine speed is between 680 rpm and 2800 rpm.
- Engine load is between 0.7 ms and 3.0 ms.
- Air mass < 100 kg/h.
- Engine temperature > 30 °C.
- Vehicle must not be at an altitude above 2448 m above sea level.
- No fault at the injection final stages.
- No fault in the voltage supply.
- No fault in fuel tank ventilation.
- No misfires harmful to TWC.
- No fault at Mass Air Flow (MAF) sensor.
- No fault in load recording.
- Oxygen sensors 1 and 2 ahead of TWC are ready for operation.

PR101970003900AX

Fig. 41 Codes P0410 & P1411: Secondary Air Injection Signal Implausible (Part 1 of 5). Boxster

Active diagnosis of the secondary air injection system is carried out under the following conditions:

- No diagnosis with result yet.
- Secondary air injection function already performed in this driving cycle.
- Engine temperature between 10 °C and 95 °C.
- Intake air > –10 °C.
- Oxygen sensing active.
- Idle speed.
- Stationary vehicle.
- No final stage faults in EVAP canister purge valve, secondary air injection pump and secondary air valve.
- No fault in fuel tank ventilation system, mass air flow sensor, in the voltage supply, throttle position sensor, oxygen sensor aging, engine temperature sensor and intake air temperature sensor.
- No misfires harmful to TWC.

PR101970003900BX

Fig. 41 Codes P0410 & P1411: Secondary Air Injection Signal Implausible (Part 2 of 5). Boxster

3 Check electric change-over valve.

1. Remove two-pole connector at change-over valve.
2. Connect voltmeter to pin 1 (positive) and pin 2 (negative).
3. Trigger AIR pump with Porsche System Tester 2.
   Display: Battery positive voltage
4. Remove vacuum hose on change-over valve with the engine running. Check whether vacuum is present.

4 Check air change-over valve and air supply lines.

1. Run engine briefly to produce vacuum.
2. Trigger AIR pump with Porsche System Tester 2.
3. Remove vacuum hose on air change-over valve.

If a vacuum is present at the air change-over valve, check air supply from the AIR pump up to the change-over valve up to the air supply line to the cylinder heads.

Check function of air change-over valve.

PR101970003900DX

Fig. 41 Codes P0410 & P1411: Secondary Air Injection Signal Implausible (Part 4 of 5). Boxster

1 In menu "Drive links", trigger secondary air injection (AIR) pump.

1. Connect and switch on Porsche System Tester 2.
2. Select DME.
3. Call up menu "Drive links".
4. Select AIR pump.
5. Activate AIR pump.

2 Check triggering of AIR pump.

1. Check fuse for AIR pump (on relay carrier 2).
2. Remove relay for AIR pump (on relay carrier 2).
   Connect voltmeter to pin 3 and ground.
   Display: Battery positive voltage

   Connect voltmeter to pin 2 (negative) and pin 7 (positive). Start engine (the ECM relay must pick up).
   Display: Battery positive voltage

If 0 Volt is displayed, check wire from pin 2 to ECM pin 37 for continuity.
Push on relay again.

3. Remove connector on AIR pump.
   Connect voltmeter to pin 1 (positive) and pin 2 (negative). Trigger AIR pump with Porsche System Tester 2.
   Display: Battery positive voltage

PR101970003900CX

Fig. 41 Codes P0410 & P1411: Secondary Air Injection Signal Implausible (Part 3 of 5). Boxster

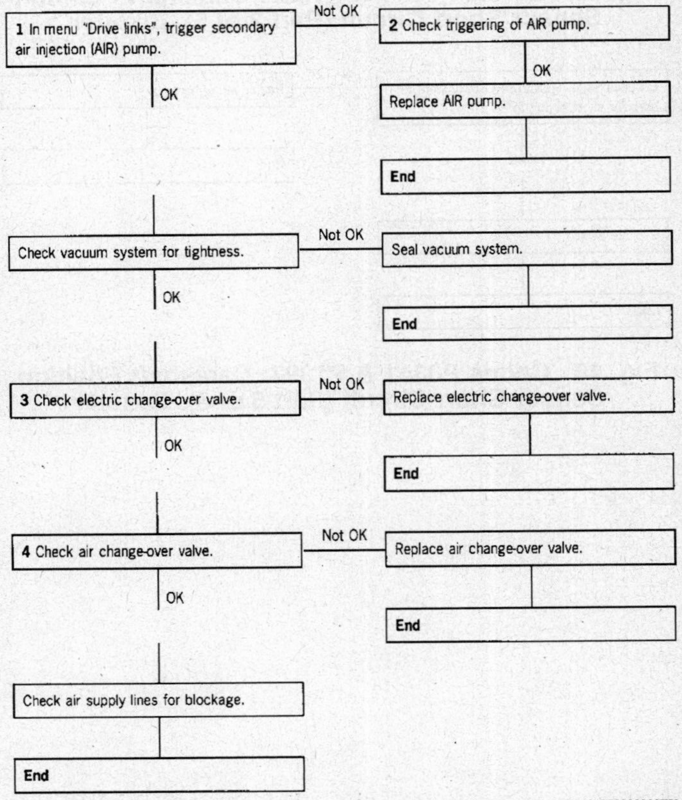

PR101970003900EX

Fig. 41 Codes P0410 & P1411: Secondary Air Injection Signal Implausible (Part 5 of 5). Boxster

Function

In order to assess the conversion efficiency of the catalytic converter, the oxygen absorption efficiency of the converter is established through comparison of the oxygen sensor amplitudes before and after the TWC. The conversion efficiency of the catalytic converter is reduced if the oxygen absorption efficiency is reduced due to converter aging.

Diagnostic procedure

- Catalytic converter temperature > 368° C.
- 4 speed/load ranges must be attained for at least 300 seconds.
- Oxygen sensing is active before catalytic converter.
- Oxygen sensors behind catalytic converter are ready for operation.
- No excessive load of the evaporative emission (EVAP) canister.
- No oxygen sensor heating fault.
- No oxygen sensor aging fault.
- No misfire detection fault.
- No adaptation fault limits exceeded.
- No mass air flow sensor fault.
- No throttle position sensor fault.
- No fault in the fuel tank ventilation system or in the fuel tank ventilation end stage.
- The speed must be in the range between 1080 rpm and 3000 rpm.
- The engine load must be between 0.7 ms and 2.8 ms.

The oxygen absorption efficiency of the catalytic converter is established in 4 speed/load ranges. A fault is detected if the limit values are exceeded in 3 ranges.

Note

If an aged oxygen sensor is signalled together with a catalytic converter fault, perform a test with a new oxygen sensor in order to determine whether the catalytic converter fault will still be signalled.

PR101970004000AX

Fig. 42 Codes P0420 & P0430: TWC Conversion Too Low (Part 1 of 2). Boxster

Function

The fuel vapors from the fuel tank must not escape into the open air. For this reason, the ventilation line of the fuel tank is routed to an evaporative emission filter that retains the fuel vapors. When driving, air is drawn in through the evaporative emission filter which picks up the accumulated fuel vapors and feeds them to the combustion process.

Diagnosis conditions

- Engine at idle.
- Vehicle speed = 0 km/h.
- Oxygen sensing active.
- Time elapsed after engine start-up > 1000 seconds.
- No secondary air injection.
- Engine load < 1.9 ms.
- Air mass < 30 kg/h.
- Engine temperature at time of engine start-up ≥ – 15° C.
- Engine temperature ≥ 60° C.
- The vehicle must not be at an altitude of above 2448 m.
- No faults: Throttle position sensor, idle air control, vehicle speed, EVAP canister purge valve end stage, idle air control valve, mass air flow sensor, load signal, voltage supply and engine temperature.

Note

Fuel tank ventilation diagnosis is aborted if the nominal idle speed changes by more than 60 rpm, the pilot air by more than 0.8 kg/h or the nominal air mass by more than 1.4 kg/h.
Fuel tank ventilation diagnosis can be initiated in the menu "Short test" with the Porsche System Tester 2. As a result, the 1000 seconds after engine start-up are not active.

PR101970004100AX

Fig. 43 Code P0440: Fuel Tank Ventilation Malfunction (Part 1 of 4). Boxster

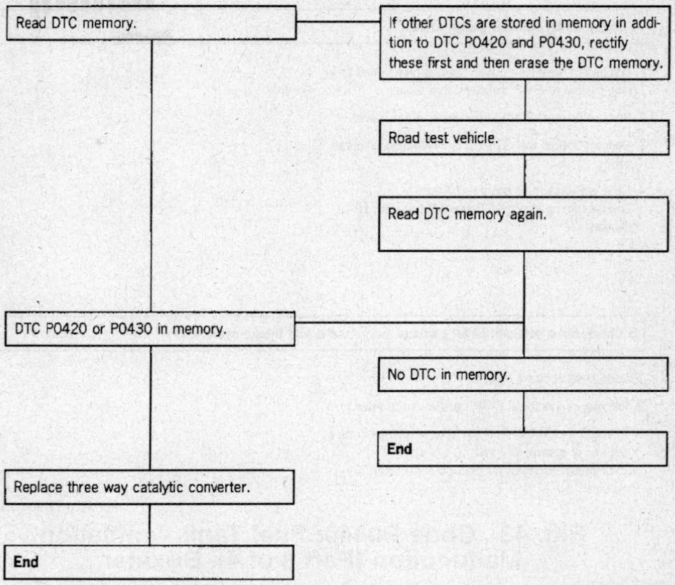

PR101970004000BX

Fig. 42 Codes P0420 & P0430: TWC Conversion Too Low (Part 2 of 2). Boxster

1 Check installation position of EVAP canister purge valve.

Flow through the EVAP canister purge valve is possible in one direction only. The flow direction is indicated by an arrow on the EVAP canister purge valve. When the valve is installed, the flow direction can be checked by way of the position of the electric connector. The connector must point towards the rear.

2 Check triggering of the EVAP canister purge valve.

1. Connect Porsche System Tester 2.
2. In menu "Drive links", select "Tank Vent".
   The EVAP canister purge valve must switch audibly.

3 Check voltage supply and leads.

1. Disconnect connector at EVAP canister purge valve.
2. Connect voltmeter (positive) to pin 1 of the connector and to vehicle ground.
3. Switch on ignition.
   Display: Battery voltage
4. Connect special tool 9616 to wiring harness.
5. Connect ohmmeter to pin 61 and EVAP canister purge valve connector pin 2.
   Display: 0 - 5 Ω

PR101970004100BX

Fig. 43 Code P0440: Fuel Tank Ventilation Malfunction (Part 2 of 4). Boxster

4 Check EVAP canister purge valve.

1. Disconnect hose from EVAP canister purge valve to intake system at EVAP canister purge valve.
2. Remove connector at EVAP canister purge valve.
3. Connect special tool 9160/1 to EVAP canister purge valve.
4. Generate vacuum of approx. 0.7 bar.
   The vacuum must not fall below 0.5 bar after 10 minutes.

5 Check hose between EVAP canister purge valve and intake system.

1. Undo hose at intake system.
2. Remove connector at EVAP canister purge valve.
3. Connect special tool 9160/1 to hose and generate a vacuum of approx. 0.7 bar.
   The vacuum must not fall below 0.5 bar after 10 minutes.

PR101970004100CX

Fig. 43 Code P0440: Fuel Tank Ventilation Malfunction (Part 3 of 4). Boxster

Function

The fuel vapors from the fuel tank must not escape into the open air. For this reason, the ventilation line of the fuel tank is routed to an evaporative emission filter that retains the fuel vapors. When driving, air is drawn in through the evaporative emission filter which picks up the accumulated fuel vapors and feeds them to the combustion process. The EVAP canister purge valve is installed between the evaporative emission (EVAP) canister and intake system. The flow direction through the valve is indicated by an arrow on the plastic housing.
The end stage that controls the EVAP canister purge valve is monitored.

Diagnosis conditions

A fault is detected and stored if the engine speed is over 80 1/min **and** if the battery voltage is between 7.5 Volt and 17 Volt.

PR101970004200AX

Fig. 44 Codes P0444 & P0445: EVAP Canister Purge Valve (Part 1 of 5). Boxster

1 Check voltage supply for EVAP canister purge valve.

1. Remove connector at EVAP canister purge valve.
2. Connect voltmeter (positive) to EVAP canister purge valve connector pin 2 and ground.
3. Switch on ignition.
   Display: Battery positive voltage

2 Check EVAP canister purge valve.

1. Remove connector at EVAP canister purge valve.
2. Connect ohmmeter to EVAP canister purge valve pin 1 and pin 2.
   Display: 26 ± 4 Ω at 20° C.

3 Check control line for EVAP canister purge valve.

1. Remove connector at EVAP canister purge valve.
2. Connect special tool 9616 to wiring harness.
3. Connect ohmmeter to EVAP canister purge valve pin 1 and special tool 9616 pin 61.
   Display: 0 - 5 Ω

PR101970004200BX

Fig. 44 Codes P0444 & P0445: EVAP Canister Purge Valve (Part 2 of 5). Boxster

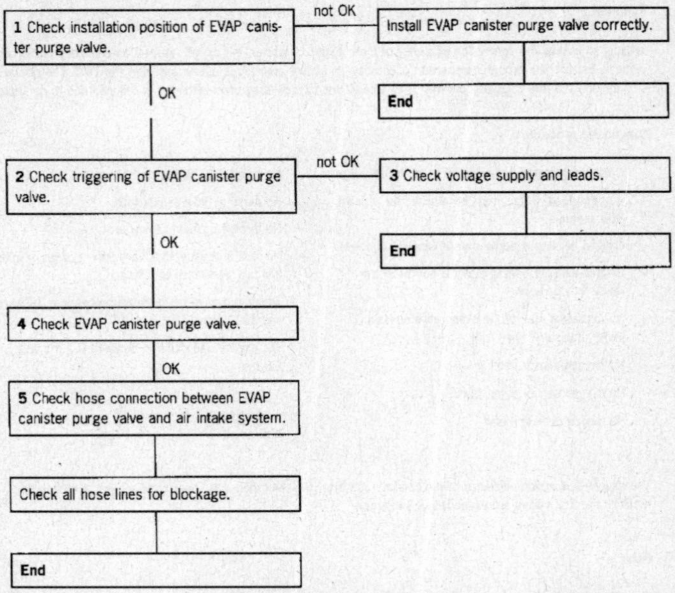

PR101970004100DX

Fig. 43 Code P0440: Fuel Tank Ventilation Malfunction (Part 4 of 4). Boxster

4 Check control line for EVAP canister purge valve for short circuit to B+.

1. Remove connector at EVAP canister purge valve.
2. Connect special tool 9616 to wiring harness.
3. Connect voltmeter (positive) to EVAP canister purge valve connector pin 1 and ground.
4. Switch on ignition.
   Display: 0 Volt

If battery positive voltage is displayed, check wiring harness for chafing and pinching damage.

5 Check control line for EVAP canister purge valve for short circuit to ground.

1. Remove connector at EVAP canister purge valve.
2. Connect special tool 9616 to wiring harness.
3. Connect ohmmeter to EVAP canister purge valve connector pin 1 and ground.
   Display: ∞ Ω

If 0 to 5 Ω is displayed, check wiring harness for chafing and pinching damage.

PR101970004200CX

Fig. 44 Codes P0444 & P0445: EVAP Canister Purge Valve (Part 3 of 5). Boxster

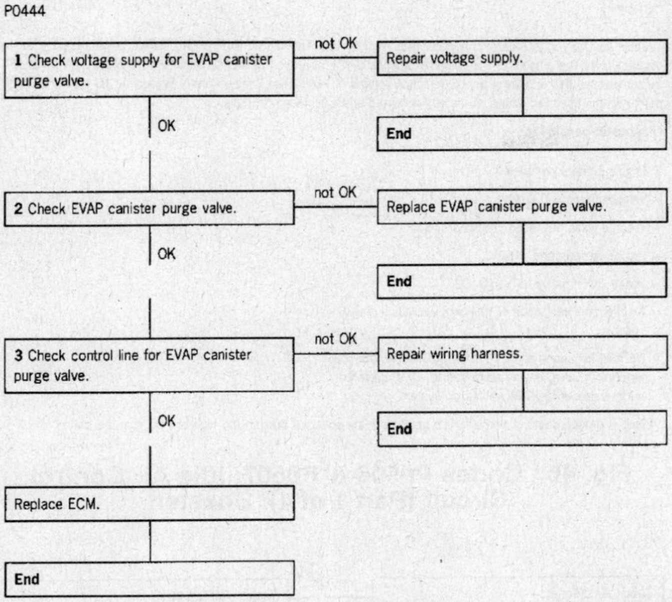

PR101970004200DX

Fig. 44 Code P0444: EVAP Canister Purge Valve (Part 4 of 5). Boxster

Function

The system adaptation and the diagnosis for fuel tank ventilation is performed when the vehicle is stationary and the engine is at idle. The diagnosis for misfire recognition is blocked at very high vehicle speed changes. To recognize the vehicle speed, the speed signal for ABS is used.

Diagnostic conditions

A fault is recognized and stored when the engine speed is above 3000 rpm, the load signal is higher than 3.8 ms, the time since last reading is more than 10 sec., and no speed signal was detected.

PR101970004300AX

Fig. 45 Code P0501: Vehicle Speed Sensor Not In Specified Range (Part 1 of 4). Boxster

1 Read ABS control module fault memory.

1. Connect Porsche System Tester 2 and switch on.
2. Select vehicle type Boxster.
3. Select ABS 5.3 or ABS/TC 5.3.
4. Read fault memory.

2 Check speed sensor with ohmmeter.

1. Remove connector X 2/2.
2. Connect ohmmeter on pin side to pin 1 and pin 2. Specified value: 1.6 - 1.8 kΩ

3 Check speed signal with engine tester.

1. Connect and switch on Porsche System Tester 2.
2. Select vehicle type Boxster and system ABS 5.3 in menu "Actual Values, Rear left speed sensor".
3. Raise vehicle at left rear.
4. By hand, turn left rear wheel in driving direction. The speed must be displayed on the Tester.

PR101970004300BX

Fig. 45 Code P0501: Vehicle Speed Sensor Not In Specified Range (Part 2 of 4). Boxster

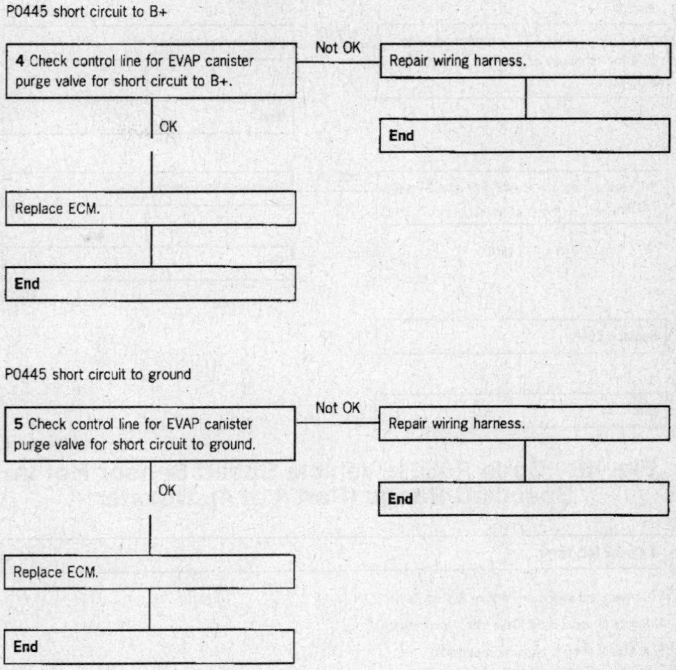

PR101970004200EX

Fig. 44 Code P0445: EVAP Canister Purge Valve (Part 5 of 5). Boxster

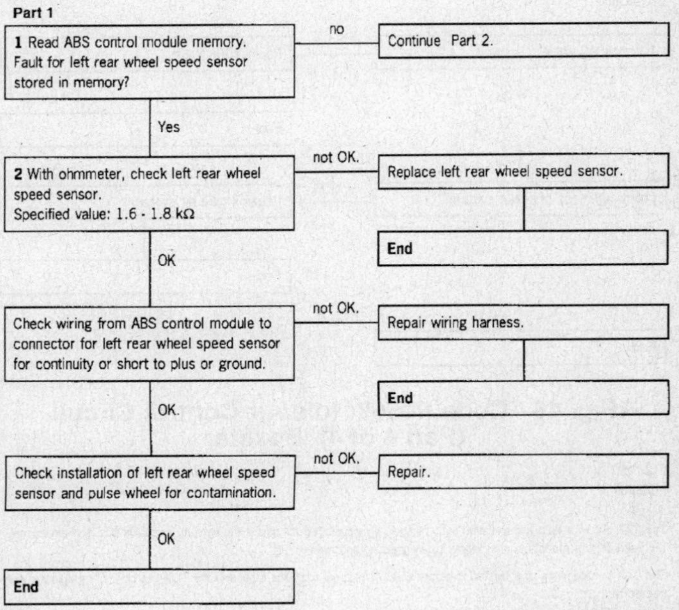

PR101970004300CX

Fig. 45 Code P0501: Vehicle Speed Sensor Not In Specified Range (Part 3 of 4). Boxster

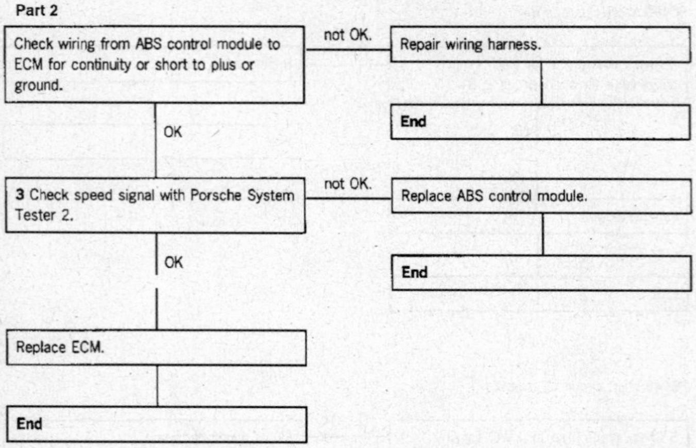
Part 2
Check wiring from ABS control module to ECM for continuity or short to plus or ground.
not OK.
Repair wiring harness.
End
OK
3 Check speed signal with Porsche System Tester 2.
not OK.
Replace ABS control module.
End
OK
Replace ECM.
End

PR101970004300DX

Fig. 45 Code P0501: Vehicle Speed Sensor Not In Specified Range (Part 4 of 4). Boxster

1 Check IAC Valve.

1. Connect and switch on Porsche System Tester 2.
2. Switch to menu point "Drive Links" and activate.
3. A distinct clicking noise must be heard.

PR101970004400BX

Fig. 46 Codes P0506 & P0507: Idle Air Control Circuit (Part 2 of 4). Boxster

DTC P0507

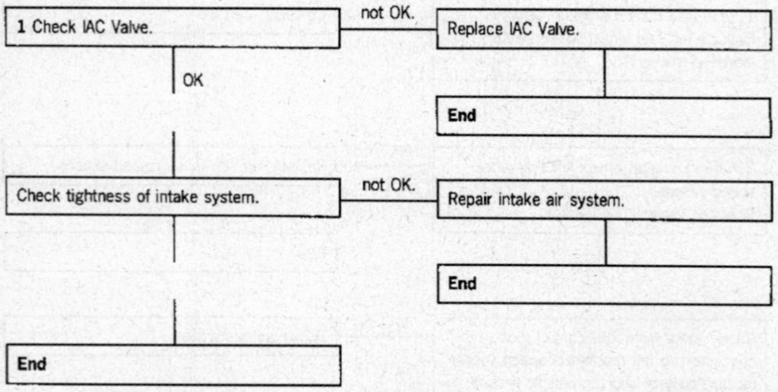
1 Check IAC Valve.
not OK.
Replace IAC Valve.
End
OK
Check tightness of intake system.
not OK.
Repair intake air system.
End
End

PR101970004400DX

Fig. 46 Code P0507: Idle Air Control Circuit (Part 4 of 4). Boxster

Function

The CAN bus is a data transmission system specially developed for use in the vehicle. The CAN bus is bi-directional, i.e. each control module connected to it can transmit and receive.

The CAN bus consists of a twisted two-core wire. At present, only the ECM and the Tiptronic control module are connected to it.

A CAN timeout means that the ECM was unable to establish a connection with the Tiptronic control module.

Diagnostic conditions

- Vehicle with Tiptronic transmission
- Battery positive voltage greater than 7 Volt
- Idle speed

PR101970004500AX

Fig. 47 Code P0600: CAN Timeout Signal Implausible (Part 1 of 4). Boxster

Function

The Idle Air Control (IAC) permits a stable and low idle rpm. The Idle Air Control (IAC) Valve opens a bypass to the throttle valve. The amount of the opening depends on the operation of the IAC Valve. As the Mass Air Flow (MAF) Sensor senses this additional air, the injection volume changes. The Engine Control Module (ECM) makes comparisons with the specified values of the engine speed and adjusts accordingly.

Diagnostic conditions

- Engine start-up completed
- Vehicle speed = 0 km/h
- Throttle valve at Closed Throttle Position
- Engine temperature > 60°C.
- Intake air temperature > -10 °C.
- No fuel tank ventilation or fuel tank ventilation diagnosis.
- No fault for speed signal, throttle position sensor, idle air control valve, engine temperature, EVAP canister purge valve or fuel tank ventilation system.

A fault is detected and stored after 15 seconds if the speed is 50 rpm too high or 200 rpm too low.

PR101970004400AX

Fig. 46 Codes P0506 & P0507: Idle Air Control Circuit (Part 1 of 4). Boxster

DTC P0506

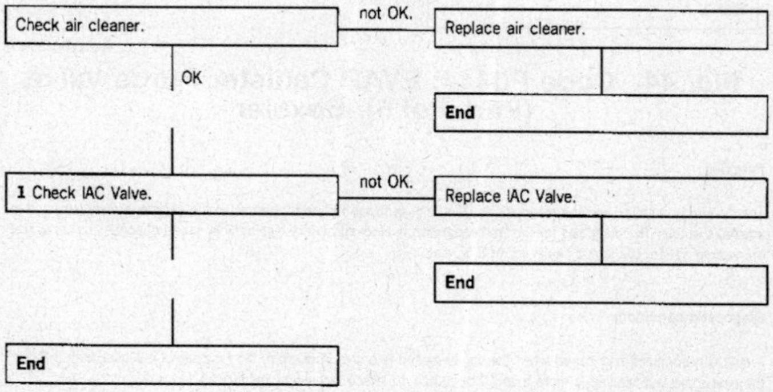
Check air cleaner.
not OK.
Replace air cleaner.
End
OK
1 Check IAC Valve.
not OK.
Replace IAC Valve.
End
End

PR101970004400CX

Fig. 46 Code P0506: Idle Air Control Circuit (Part 3 of 4). Boxster

1 Check CAN bus from ECM to Tiptronic control module for continuity.

1. Remove ECM plug.
2. Remove Tiptronic control module plug.
3. Connect ohmmeter to ECM plug, pin 85, and Tiptronic plug, pin 85.
   Display: 0 - 5 Ω
4. Connect ohmmeter to ECM plug, pin 86, and Tiptronic plug, pin 86.
   Display: 0 - 5 Ω

If ∞ Ω is displayed, check wiring harness for chafing and pinching damage.

2 Check CAN bus from ECM to Tiptronic control module for short to ground.

1. Remove ECM plug.
2. Remove Tiptronic control module plug.
3. Connect special tool 9616 to wiring harness.
4. Connect ohmmeter to special tool 9616, pin 85, and ground.
   Display: ∞ Ω
5. Connect ohmmeter to special tool 9616, pin 86, and ground.
   Display: ∞ Ω

If 0 - 5 Ω is displayed, check wiring harness for chafing and pinching damage.

PR101970004500BX

Fig. 47 Code P0600: CAN Timeout Signal Implausible (Part 2 of 4). Boxster

3 Check CAN bus from ECM to Tiptronic control module for short to B+.

1. Remove ECM plug.
2. Remove Tiptronic control module plug.
3. Connect special tool 9616 to wiring harness.
4. Connect voltmeter to special tool 9616, pin 85, and ground.
   Switch on ignition.
   Display: 0 Volt
5. Connect voltmeter to special tool 9616, pin 86, and ground.
   Switch on ignition.
   Display: 0 Volt

If battery positive voltage is displayed, check wiring harness for chafing and pinching damage.

4 Check CAN bus from ECM to Tiptronic control module for short circuit.

1. Remove ECM plug.
2. Remove Tiptronic control module plug.
3. Connect special tool 9616 to wiring harness.
4. Connect ohmmeter to special tool 9616, pins 85 and 86.
   Display: ∞ Ω

If 0 - 5 Ω is displayed, check wiring harness for chafing and pinching damage.

PR101970004500CX

Fig. 47 Code P0600: CAN Timeout Signal Implausible (Part 3 of 4). Boxster

P0603

ECM faulty

P0604

ECM faulty

P0605

ECM faulty

P1640

ECM faulty

P1689

ECM faulty

Note

These faults concern faults in the Engine Control Module (ECM). If such faults occur, replace the ECM.

PR101970004600OX

Fig. 48 Codes P0603, P0604, P09605, P1640 & P1689: ECM Faulty. Boxster

Function

The oxygen sensor generates a voltage signal at approximately 300 °C that determines the fuel/air mixture. This signal is used for the regulation of the fuel injection. The oxygen sensor is heated to bring it quickly to operating temperature to start oxygen sensing earlier.

Diagnosis Conditions

400 seconds after oxygen sensor heating is on, when no DTC "Oxygen sensor heating - below lower limit" is stored in memory.

PR101970004700AX

Fig. 49 Codes P1102 & P1107: O2 Sensor Heating Above Upper Limit (In Front Of Catalytic Converter, Part 1 of 3). Boxster

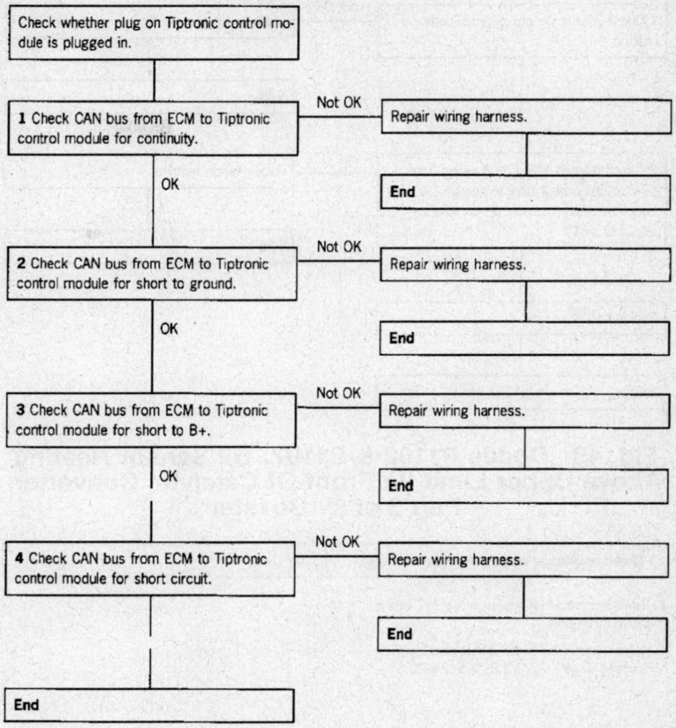

PR101970004500DX

Fig. 47 Code P0600: CAN Timeout Signal Implausible (Part 4 of 4). Boxster

1 Check resistance of oxygen sensor heating.

1. Remove connector of oxygen sensor 1/2 ahead of catalytic converter.
2. Connect ohmmeter on pin side to pins 1 and 2.
   Specified value: 1.8 - 2.5 Ω at 20 °C

2 Check oxygen sensor and wiring from ECM to disconnect oxygen sensor 1/2 ahead of catalytic converter for short circuit to plus.

1. Remove connectors for oxygen sensor 1/2 ahead of catalytic converter.
2. Start engine and run engine at high speed for three minutes.
3. Connect voltmeter at sleeve to pins 1 (plus) and 2 of connector.
   Specified value: battery voltage

   Connect voltmeter at sleeve to pin 2 (plus) and ground.
   Specified value: approx. 0 Volt
4. Turn engine off.
5. Remove ECM connector.
6. Remove ignition, injection and oxygen sensor heating relay and bridge terminals 30 and 87.
7. Connect voltmeter at sleeve to pin 2 (plus) and ground of oxygen sensor connector.
   Specified value: 0 Volt

PR101970004700BX

Fig. 49 Codes P1102 & P1107: O2 Sensor Heating Above Upper Limit (In Front Of Catalytic Converter, Part 2 of 3). Boxster

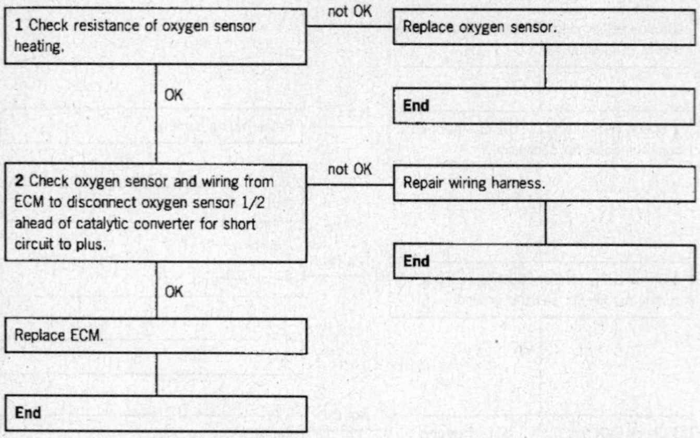

PR101970004700CX

Fig. 49 Codes P1102 & P1107: O2 Sensor Heating Above Upper Limit (In Front Of Catalytic Converter, Part 3 of 3). Boxster

1 Check resistance of oxygen sensor heating.

1. Remove connector of oxygen sensor 1/2 behind catalytic converter.
2. Connect ohmmeter on pin side to pins 1 and 2.
   Specified value: 1.8 - 2.5 Ω at 20 °C

2 Check oxygen sensor and wiring from ECM to disconnect oxygen sensor 1/2 behind catalytic converter for short circuit to plus.

1. Remove connectors for oxygen sensor 1/2 behind catalytic converter.
2. Start engine and run engine at high speed for ten minutes.
3. Connect voltmeter at sleeve to pin 1 (plus) and pin 2 of connector.
   Specified value: battery voltage

   Connect voltmeter at sleeve to pin 2 (plus) and ground.
   Specified value: approx. 0 Volt
4. Turn engine off.
5. Remove ECM connector.
6. Remove ignition, injection and oxygen sensor heating relay and bridge terminals 30 and 87.
7. Connect voltmeter at sleeve to pin 2 (plus) and ground of oxygen sensor connector.
   Specified value: 0 Volt

PR101970004800BX

Fig. 50 Codes P1105 & P1110: O2 Sensor Heating Above Upper Limit (Behind Catalytic Converter, Part 2 of 3). Boxster

Function

The oxygen sensor generates a voltage signal at approximately 300 °C that determines the fuel/air mixture. This signal is used for the regulation of the fuel injection. The oxygen sensor is heated to bring it quickly to operating temperature to start oxygen sensing earlier.

Diagnosis Conditions

During a cold start (sensor readiness after 20 seconds) the time t_1 is measured. t_1 is the time from switching the oxygen sensor heating on until the time an oxygen sensor is operational. Then a time t_2 is calculated ($t_2=2.5*t_1$). t_3 is the time from switching the oxygen sensor heating on until the time the other oxygen sensor is operational. When t_3 is larger than t_2 a fault is recognised.

When a fault is recognised, the resistance comparison of the oxygen sensor heating is blocked. If no fault is recorded, the calculated resistance of the oxygen sensor heating is compared to a threshold after 400 seconds. If the resistance is too high, a fault is recognised for <u>both</u> oxygen sensor heatings.

PR101970004900AX

Fig. 51 Codes P1115 & P1119: O2 Sensor Heating Below Lower Threshold (Behind Catalytic Converter, Part 1 of 4). Boxster

Function

The oxygen sensor generates a voltage signal at approximately 300 °C that determines the fuel/air mixture. This signal is used for the regulation of the fuel injection. The oxygen sensor is heated to bring it quickly to operating temperature to start oxygen sensing earlier.
The oxygen sensors behind the catalytic converter are used to monitor the conversion rate.

Diagnosis Conditions

400 seconds after oxygen sensor heating is on, when no DTC "Oxygen sensor heating - below lower limit" is stored in memory.

PR101970004800AX

Fig. 50 Codes P1105 & P1110: O2 Sensor Heating Above Upper Limit (Behind Catalytic Converter, Part 1 of 3). Boxster

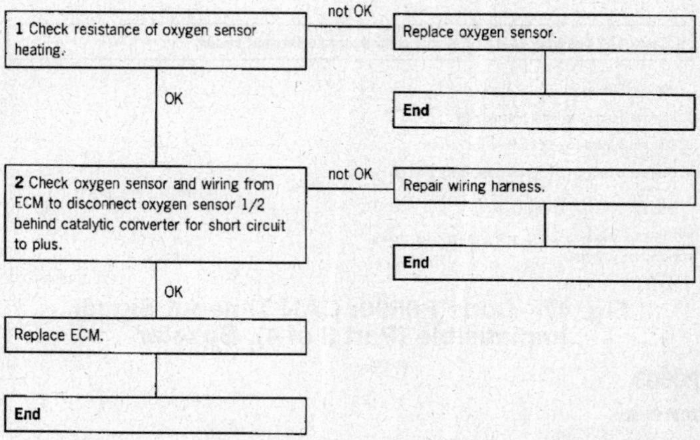

PR101970004800CX

Fig. 50 Codes P1105 & P1110: O2 Sensor Heating Above Upper Limit (Behind Catalytic Converter, Part 3 of 3). Boxster

1 Check resistance of oxygen sensor heating.

1. Remove connector of oxygen sensor 1/2 ahead of catalytic converter.
2. Connect ohmmeter on pin side to pins 1 and 2.
   Specified value: 1.8 - 2.5 Ω at 20 °C
3. Connect ohmmeter on pin side to pin 1 and the oxygen sensor housing.
   Specified value: ∞ Ω

2 Check wiring from ECM to disconnect oxygen sensor 1/2 for continuity, short circuit to plus and short circuit to ground.

1. Remove connector for oxygen sensors 1 and 2 ahead of catalytic converter.
2. Connect special tool 9616 to wiring harness.
3. Connect ohmmeter to special tool 9616 pin 30 and disconnection of oxygen sensors 1/2 ahead of catalytic converter pin 2.

   Specified value: < 1 Ω
4. Connect ohmmeter at sleeve to connector, pin 2, and ground.

   Specified value: ∞ Ω
5. Remove ignition, injection and oxygen sensor heating relay and bridge terminals 30 and 87.
6. Connect voltmeter at sleeve to connector, pin 2, and ground.
   Specified value: 0 Volt

PR101970004900BX

Fig. 51 Codes P1115 & P1119: O2 Sensor Heating Below Lower Threshold (Behind Catalytic Converter, Part 2 of 4). Boxster

3 Check ECM final stage.

1. Remove connectors for oxygen sensors.
2. Start engine and run engine at high speed for three minutes.
3. Connect voltmeter at sleeve to pins 1 (plus) and 2.

Specified value: battery voltage

PR101970004900CX

Fig. 51 Codes P1115 & P1119: O2 Sensor Heating Below Lower Threshold (Behind Catalytic Converter, Part 3 of 4). Boxster

Function

The heated oxygen (H02) sensor generates a current signal starting at approximately 300°C that determines the fuel/air mixture. This signal is used for the regulation of the fuel injection. To assure that the H02 Sensor reaches its operating temperature earlier, the H02 Sensor is heated.

Diagnostic conditions

During a cold start (H02S readiness after 20 seconds) the time t_1 is measured. t_1 is the time from switching the H02S heating on until the time an H02S is operational. Then a time t_2 is calculated ($t_2=2.0*t_1$). t_3 is the time from switching the H02S heating on until the time the other H02S is operational. When t_3 is larger than t_2, a fault is recognized.

When a fault is recognized, the resistance comparison of the heating of the H02S is blocked. If no fault is recorded, the calculated resistance of the H02S heating is compared to a threshold after 400 seconds. If the resistance is too high, a fault is recognized for both H02S.

PR101970005000AX

Fig. 52 Codes P1117 & P1121: O2 Sensor Heating Below Lower Threshold (Part 1 of 4). Boxster

3 Check ECM final stage to B+.

1. Remove connectors to H02S 1 and 2 behind TWC.
2. Start engine and run engine at high speed for ten minutes.
3. Connect voltmeter at sleeve to pins 1 (plus) and 2. Specified value: battery voltage

PR101970005000CX

Fig. 52 Codes P1117 & P1121: O2 Sensor Heating Below Lower Threshold (Part 3 of 4). Boxster

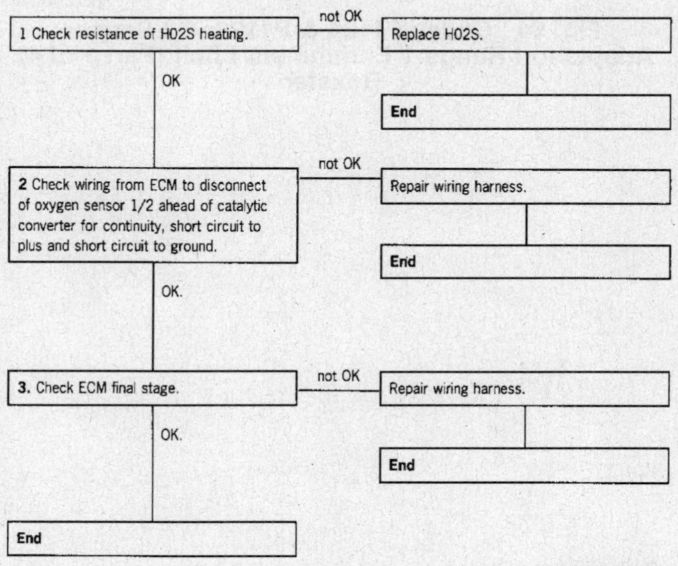

PR101970005000DX

Fig. 52 Codes P1117 & P1121: O2 Sensor Heating Below Lower Threshold (Part 4 of 4). Boxster

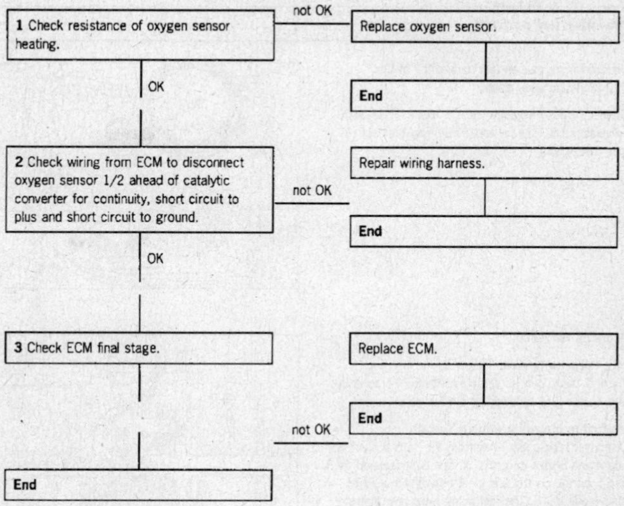

PR101970004900DX

Fig. 51 Codes P1115 & P1119: O2 Sensor Heating Below Lower Threshold (Behind Catalytic Converter, Part 4 of 4). Boxster

1 Check resistance of H02S heating.

1. Remove connector for H02S 1/2 behind TWC.
2. Connect ohmmeter on pin side to pin 1 and pin 2.
   Specified value: 1.8 - 2.5 Ω at 20 °C
3. Connect ohmmeter on pin side to pin 1 and the oxygen sensor housing.
   Specified value: ∞ Ω

2 Check wiring from ECM to disconnect of oxygen sensor 1/2 for continuity, short circuit to plus and short circuit to ground

1. Remove connectors for H02S 1/2 behind TWC.
2. Connect special tool 9616 to wiring harness.
3. Connect ohmmeter to special tool 9616, pin 30 and disconnect of H02S 1/2 behind TWC, pin 2.
   Specified value: < 1 Ω
4. Connect ohmmeter at sleeve to connector, pin 2, and ground.
   Specified value: ∞ Ω
5. Remove ignition, injection and oxygen sensor heating relay and bridge terminals 30 and 87.
6. Connect voltmeter at sleeve to connector, pin 2, and ground.
   Specified value: 0 Volt

PR101970005000BX

Fig. 52 Codes P1117 & P1121: O2 Sensor Heating Below Lower Threshold (Part 2 of 4). Boxster

Function

The adaptive oxygen sensing corrects longer lasting deviations of the fuel/air mixture from λ = 1 through changes of the calculated pilot control within the engine control module and with that the injection time.
Should the correction factor through adaptation exceed a predetermined value, the diagnosis will detect the adaptation limit.
Range 1 covers the engine operating state close to idle.

Diagnosis conditions

- Oxygen sensing is active.
- Time elapsed after engine start-up is 250 to 350 seconds.
- Engine temperature > 62°C.
- Intake air temperature < 90°C.
- Air mass flow < 29 kg/h.
- Engine speed < 880 rpm.

Note

If DTC P1123 or P1125 (oxygen sensing up to lean limit) is in memory, the fuel/air mixture is too rich.

PR101970005100AX

Fig. 53 Codes P1123 & P1125: O2 sensor Adaptation Range 1 Lean Limit (Part 1 of 4). Boxster

1 Checking fuel pressure

1. Undo covering cap on test connection of fuel collection pipe and remove.
2. Connect pressure gauge (special tool P 378a) with connecting line (special tool 9559) and connect to test connection.

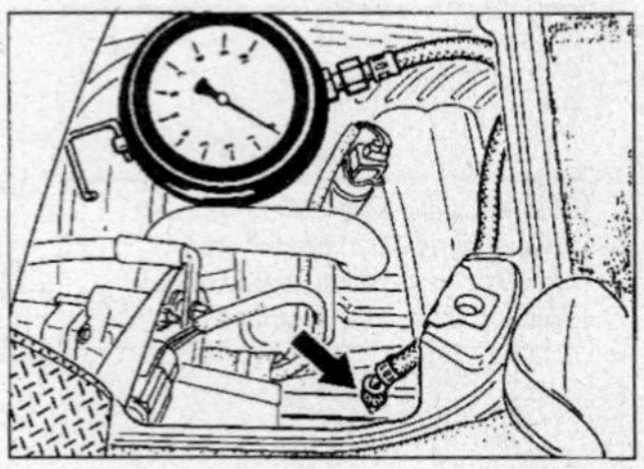

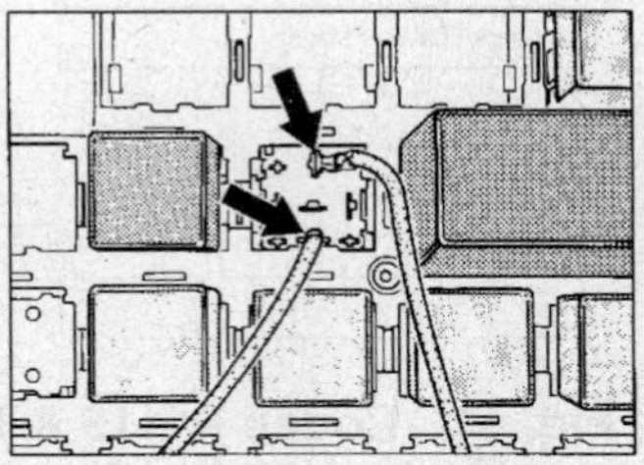

3. Actuating fuel pump
- **with Porsche System Tester 2.** The fuel pump can be actuated with the Porsche System Tester 2 or by bridging the fuel-pump relay.
- **via fuel-pump relay without Tester.** Disconnect fuel-pump relay from the central electrical board and bridge contacts 30 and 87 (identified as 3 and 5 on the central electrical board) with a fused shop-made cable. The fuel pump must now operate or deliver fuel.

4. Nominal test values

Stationary engine 3.8 ± 0.2 bar
Engine idling 3.3 ± 0.2 bar

Note

The seal or sealing ring in the brass closure cap is **not** exchangeable. It must therefore be used only **once**.

Tightening torque of new brass closure cap
2.5 ± 0.5 Nm (2.0 ± 0.5 ftlb.)

PR101970005100BX

Fig. 53 Codes P1123 & P1125: O2 sensor Adaptation Range 1 Lean Limit (Part 2 of 4). Boxster

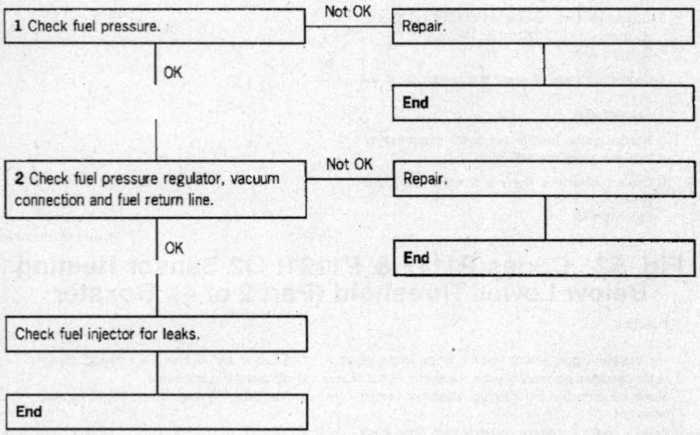

PR101970005100DX

Fig. 53 Codes P1123 & P1125: O2 sensor Adaptation Range 1 Lean Limit (Part 4 of 4). Boxster

2 Check fuel pressure regulator, vacuum connection and fuel return line.

1. Remove vacuum line at fuel pressure regulator.
2. Connect special tool 9103/2 to vacuum hose.
3. Start engine.
   Display: 0.4 - 0.6 bar

If the value is not reached, check vacuum system for leaks and check vacuum line to fuel pressure regulator for restrictions.

4. Check housing of fuel pressure regulator for outside damage.

Replace the fuel pressure regulator if the fuel pressure regulator is damaged with the result that the spring pre-tensioning is increased.

PR101970005100CX

Fig. 53 Codes P1123 & P1125: O2 sensor Adaptation Range 1 Lean Limit (Part 3 of 4). Boxster

Function

The adaptive oxygen sensing corrects longer lasting deviations of the fuel/air mixture from $\lambda = 1$ through changes of the calculated pilot control within the engine control module and with that the injection time.
Should the correction factor through adaptation exceed a predetermined value, the diagnosis will detect the adaptation limit.
Range 1 covers the engine operating state close to idle.

Diagnostic conditions

- Oxygen sensing is active.
- Time elapsed after engine start-up 250 to 350 seconds.
- Engine temperature >62°C.
- Intake air temperature < 90°C.
- Air mass flow < 29 kg/h
- Engine speed < 880 rpm

Note

If DTC P1124 or P1126 (oxygen sensing at enrichment limit) is in the memory, this means that the fuel/air mixture is too lean.
Leakage air ahead of the oxygen sensors can also lead to a fault in adaptation.

PR101970005200AX

Fig. 54 Codes P1124 & P1126: O2 Sensor Adaptation Range 1 Enrichment Limit (Part 1 of 4). Boxster

1 Checking fuel pressure

1. Undo covering cap on test connection of fuel collection pipe and remove.
2. Connect pressure gauge (special tool P 378a) with connecting line (special tool 9559) and connect to test connection.

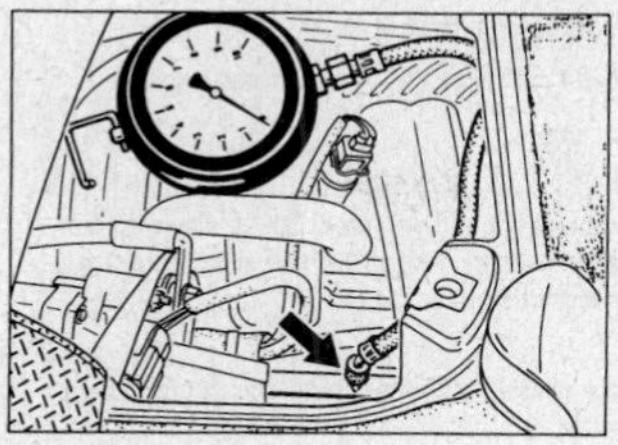

3. Actuating fuel pump

– **with Porsche System Tester 2.**
The fuel pump can be actuated with the Porsche System Tester 2 or by bridging the fuel-pump relay.

– **via fuel pump relay without Tester.**
Disconnect fuel-pump relay from the central electrical board and bridge contacts 30 and 87 (identified as 3 and 5 on the central electrical board) with a fused shop-made cable. The fuel pump must now operate or deliver fuel.

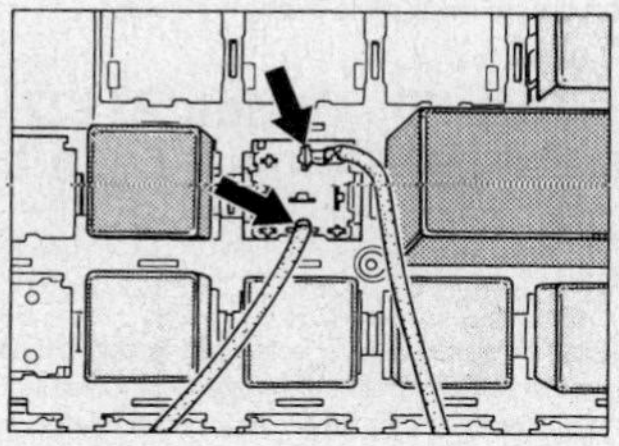

4. Nominal test values

Stationary engine 3.8 ± 0.2 bar
Engine idling 3.3 ± 0.2 bar

Note

The seal or sealing ring in the brass closure cap is **not** exchangeable. It must therefore be used only **once**.

Tightening torque of new brass closure cap
2.5 ± 0.5 Nm (2.0 ± 0.5 ftlb.)

PR101970005200BX

Fig. 54 Codes P1124 & P1126: O2 Sensor Adaptation Range 1 Enrichment Limit (Part 2 of 4). Boxster

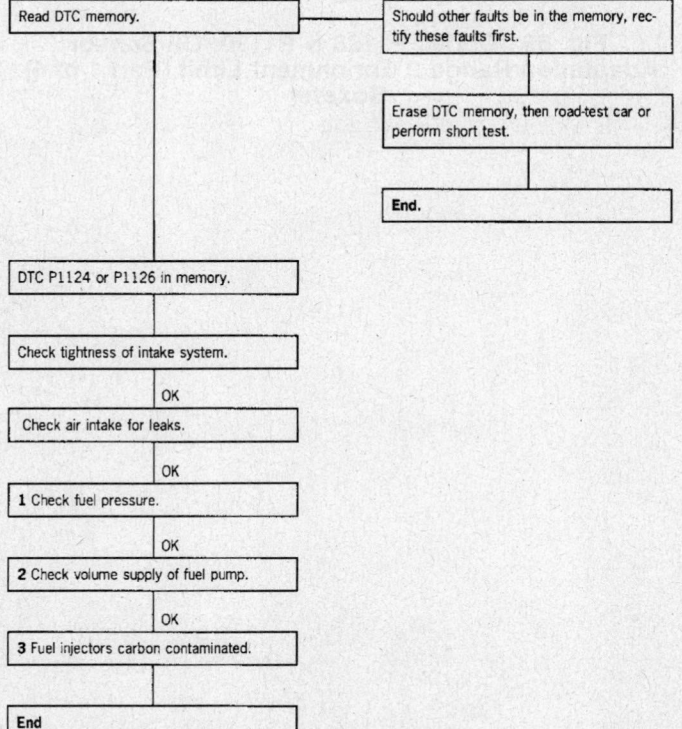

2 Checking volume supply of fuel pump

Precondition:

Fuel filter and electrical supply in order.

1. Relieve pressure in fuel tank by opening tank cap.
2. Connect Porsche System Tester 2.
3. Raise vehicle.
4. Remove rear underside panel.
5. Disconnect fuel return line. Collect residual fuel.

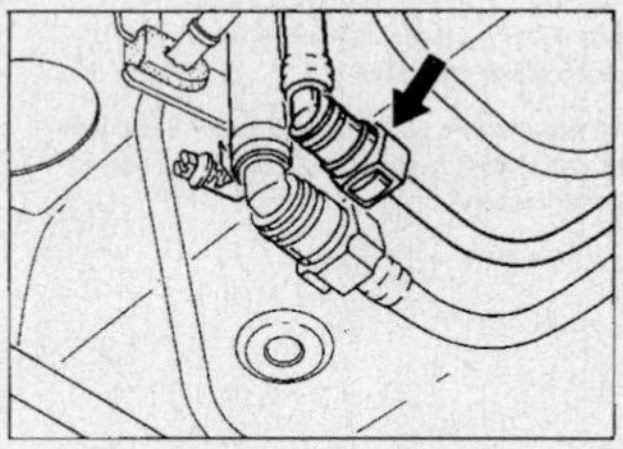

6. Hold fuel line in a measuring container. Actuate fuel pump with the Porsche System Tester 2 and allow fuel to flow for 30 seconds into a measuring container.
Quantity supplied must be at least 850 cm^3/30 s, i.e. after 30 seconds at least 850 cm^3 of fuel must be present in the measuring container.

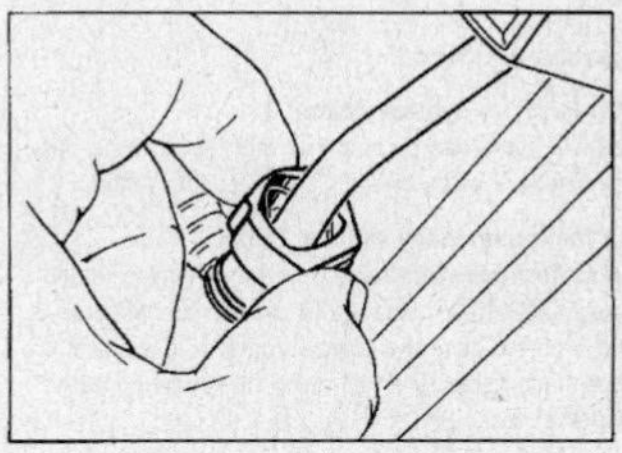

Note

Always observe safety regulations.

3 Fuel injectors contaminated (carbonized).

1. If checkpoints are negative, the fuel injectors may be contaminated (carbonized).
2. Clean fuel injectors (ultrasound cleaning device) or replace.

PR101970005200CX

Fig. 54 Codes P1124 & P1126: O2 Sensor Adaptation Range 1 Enrichment Limit (Part 3 of 4). Boxster

Read DTC memory. → Should other faults be in the memory, rectify these faults first.

Erase DTC memory, then road-test car or perform short test.

End.

DTC P1124 or P1126 in memory.

Check tightness of intake system.

OK

Check air intake for leaks.

OK

1 Check fuel pressure.

OK

2 Check volume supply of fuel pump.

OK

3 Fuel injectors carbon contaminated.

End

PR101970005200DX

Fig. 54 Codes P1124 & P1126: O2 Sensor Adaptation Range 1 Enrichment Limit (Part 4 of 4). Boxster

Function

The adaptive oxygen sensing corrects longer lasting deviations of the fuel/air mixture from $\lambda = 1$ through changes of the calculated pilot control within the engine control module and with that the injection time.
Should the correction factor through adaptation exceed a predetermined value, the diagnosis will detect the adaptation limit.
Range 2 covers the engine operating state close to full load.

Diagnosis conditions

- Oxygen sensing active.
- Time elapsed after engine start-up 250 to 350 seconds.
- Engine temperature > 62°C.
- Intake air temperature < 90°C.
- Air mass flow > 35 kg/h.
- Load signal > 0.95 ms.

Note

If DTC P1127 or P1129 (oxygen sensing at lean limit) is stored in the memory, this means that the fuel/air mixture is too rich.

PR101970005300AX

Fig. 55 Codes P1127 & P1129: O2 Sensor adaptation Range 2 Lean Limit (Part 1 of 4). Boxster

1 Checking fuel pressure

1. Undo covering cap on test connection of fuel collection pipe and remove.
2. Connect pressure gauge (special tool P 378a) with connecting line (special tool 9559) and connect to test connection.

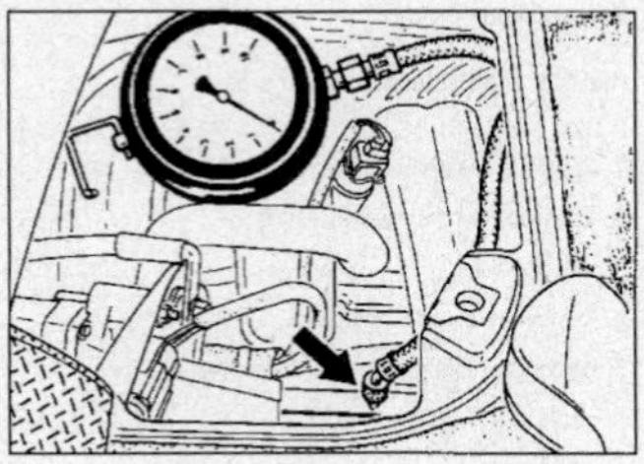

3. Actuating fuel pump

- **with Porsche System Tester 2.** The fuel pump can be actuated with the Porsche System Tester 2 or by bridging the fuel-pump relay.
- **via fuel-pump relay without Tester.** Disconnect fuel-pump relay from the central electrical board and bridge contacts 30 and 87 (identified as 3 and 5 on the central electrical board) with a fused shop-made cable. The fuel pump must now operate or deliver fuel.

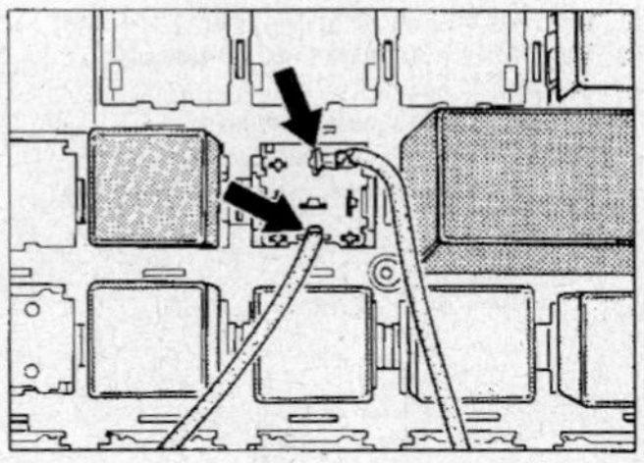

4. Nominal test values

Stationary engine 3.8 ± 0.2 bar
Engine idling 3.3 ± 0.2 bar

Note

The seal or sealing ring in the brass closure cap is **not** exchangeable. It must therefore be used only **once**.

Tightening torque of new brass closure cap
2.5 ± 0.5 Nm (2.0 ± 0.5 ftlb.)

PR101970005300BX

Fig. 55 Codes P1127 & P1129: O2 Sensor adaptation Range 2 Lean Limit (Part 2 of 4). Boxster

1 Check fuel pressure. → Not OK → Repair. → **End**

OK ↓

2 Check fuel pressure regulator, vacuum connection and fuel return line. → Not OK → Repair. → **End**

OK ↓

Check fuel injector for leaks.

End

PR101970005300DX

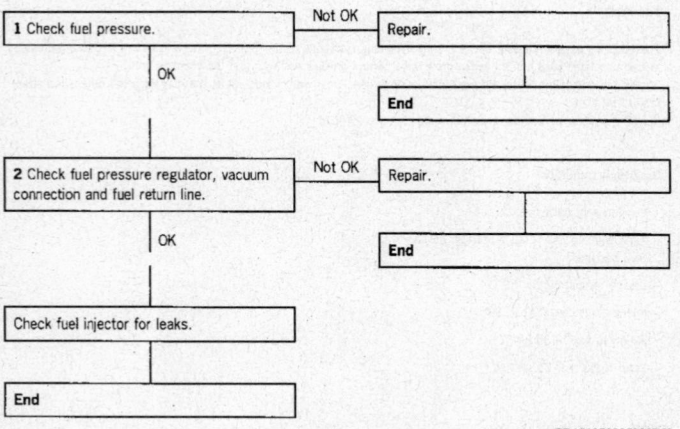

Fig. 55 Codes P1127 & P1129: O2 Sensor adaptation Range 2 Lean Limit (Part 4 of 4). Boxster

2 Check fuel pressure regulator, vacuum connection and fuel return line.

1. Remove vacuum hose at fuel pressure regulator.
2. Connect special tool 9103/2 to vacuum hose.
3. Start engine.
   Display: 0.4 - 0.6 bar

If the value is not attained, check the air intake system for leaks and check vacuum line to fuel pressure regulator for restrictions.

4. Check housing of fuel pressure regulator for outside damage.

Replace the fuel pressure regulator if it is damaged with the result that the spring pre-tensioning is increased.

PR101970005300CX

Fig. 55 Codes P1127 & P1129: O2 Sensor adaptation Range 2 Lean Limit (Part 3 of 4). Boxster

Function

The adaptive oxygen sensing corrects longer lasting deviations of the fuel/air mixture of $\lambda = 1$ through changes of the calculated monitoring within the Engine Control Module (ECM) and with that the injection time.
Should the correction factor through adaptation exceed a predetermined value, the diagnosis will detect the adaptation limit.
Range 2 covers the engine operating state close to idle

Diagnosis condition

- Oxygen sensing system active.
- Time elapsed after engine start-up 250 to 350 sec.
- Engine temperature > 62°C.
- Intake air temperature < 90°C
- Air mass > 35 kg/h
- Load signal > 0.95 ms.

Note

If DTC P1128 or P1130 (oxygen sensing at enrichment limit) is in the memory, this means that the fuel/air mixture is too lean.
Leakage air ahead of the oxygen sensors can also lead to a fault in adaptation.

PR101970005400AX

Fig. 56 Codes P1128 & P1130: O2 Sensor Adaptation Range 2 Enrichment Limit (Part 1 of 4). Boxster

1 Checking fuel pressure.

1. Undo covering cap on test connection of fuel collection pipe and remove.
2. Connect pressure gauge (special tool P 378a) with connecting line (special tool 9559) and connect to test connection.

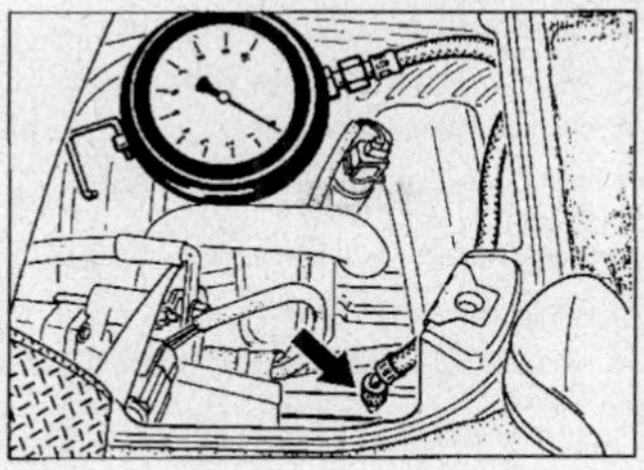

3. Actuating fuel pump:

- **with Porsche System Tester 2.**
  The fuel pump can be actuated with the Porsche System Tester 2 or by bridging the fuel-pump relay.
- **via fuel-pump relay without Tester.**
  Disconnect fuel-pump relay from the central electrical board and bridge contacts 30 and 87 (identified as 3 and 5 on the central electrical board) with a fused shop-made cable. The fuel pump must now operate or deliver fuel.

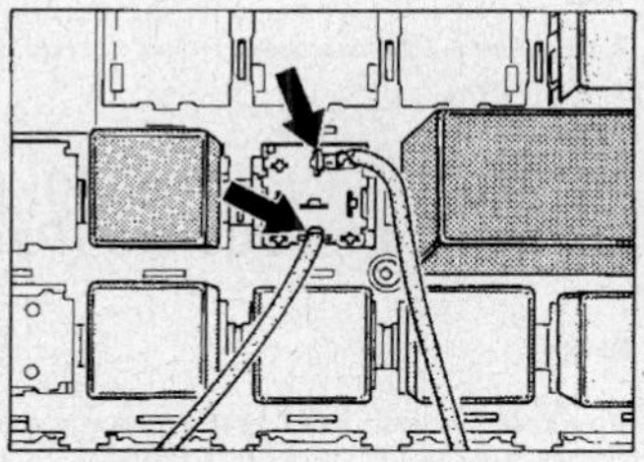

4. Nominal test values

Stationary engine 3.8 ± 0.2 bar
Engine idling 3.3 ± 0.2 bar

Note

The seal or sealing ring in the brass closure cap is **not** exchangeable. It must therefore be used only **once**.

Tightening torque of new brass closure cap
2.5 ± 0.5 Nm.(2.0 ± 0.5 ftlb.).

PR101970005400BX

Fig. 56 Codes P1128 & P1130: O2 Sensor Adaptation Range 2 Enrichment Limit (Part 2 of 4). Boxster

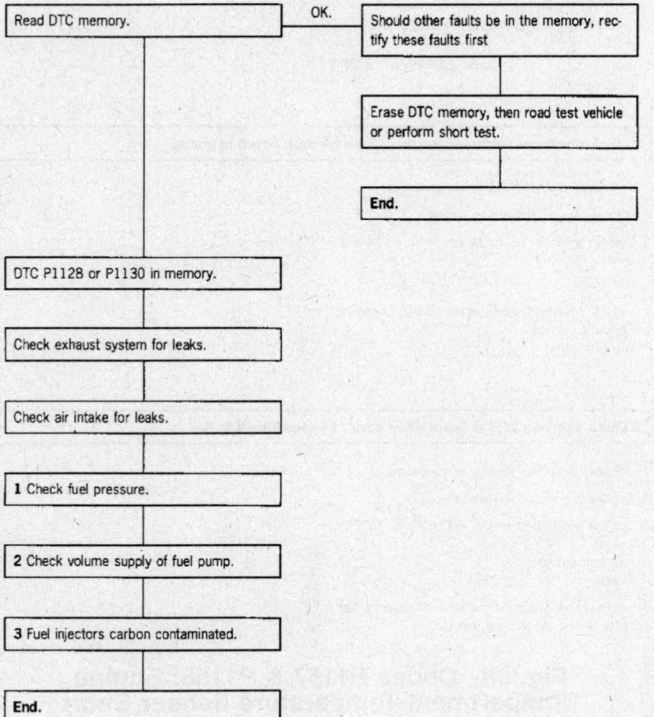

Read DTC memory. — OK. → Should other faults be in the memory, rectify these faults first → Erase DTC memory, then road test vehicle or perform short test. → **End.**

DTC P1128 or P1130 in memory.
↓
Check exhaust system for leaks.
↓
Check air intake for leaks.
↓
1 Check fuel pressure.
↓
2 Check volume supply of fuel pump.
↓
3 Fuel injectors carbon contaminated.
↓
End.

PR101970005400DX

Fig. 56 Codes P1128 & P1130: O2 Sensor Adaptation Range 2 Enrichment Limit (Part 4 of 4). Boxster

2 Checking volume supply of fuel pump

Precondition:

Fuel filter and electrical supply in order.

1. Relieve pressure in fuel tank by opening tank cap.
2. Connect Porsche System Tester 2.
3. Raise vehicle.
4. Remove rear underside panel.
5. Disconnect fuel return line. Collect residual fuel.

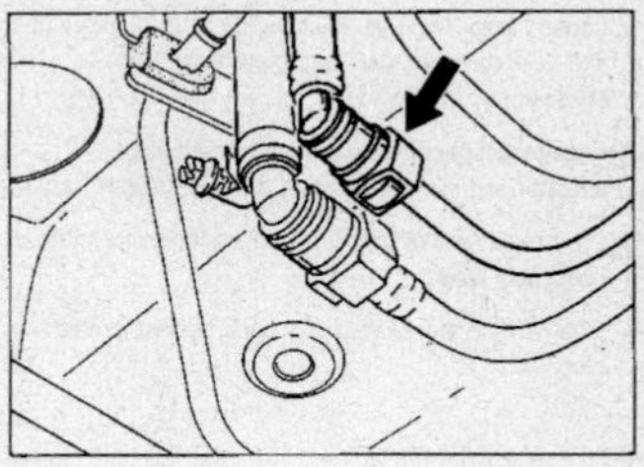

6. Hold fuel line in a measuring container. Actuate fuel pump with the Porsche System Tester 2 and allow fuel to flow for 30 seconds into a measuring container.
   Quantity supplied must be at least 850 cm^3/30 s, i.e. after 30 seconds at least 850 cm^3 of fuel must be present in the measuring container.

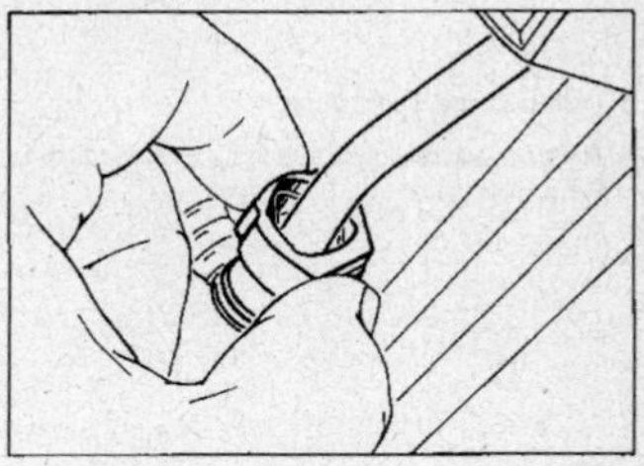

Note

Always observe safety regulations.

3 Fuel injectors contaminated, carbonized.

1. If preceding check points were negative, the fuel injectors may be carbonized.
2. Clean fuel injectors (ultra sound cleaning device) or replace fuel injectors.

PR101970005400CX

Fig. 56 Codes P1128 & P1130: O2 Sensor Adaptation Range 2 Enrichment Limit (Part 3 of 4). Boxster

Function

A load signal is generated to determine the engine load. This signal is calculated from the intake air mass (signal from the mass air flow sensor) and the engine speed. This load signal is corrected by the intake air temperature and a taught altitude factor for the purpose of adaption to the air density.

Diagnostic conditions

- Engine at idle.
- Throttle valve angle between 10° and 60°.
- No fault in mass air flow sensor.
- No fault in throttle position sensor.
- No fault in idle air control valve.
- Speed > 4 km/h
- Time after engine start-up > 240 seconds.
- Time for fault detection > 25 seconds.

PR101970005500AX

Fig. 57 Code P1140: Load Calculation Signal Implausible (Part 1 of 4). Boxster

1 Readjust operating cable for cruise control.

1. Loosen snap ring 1 at adjusting piece 2 (displace it) and push threaded part 3 through along with cruise-control cable.
2. Engage cruise-control cable on cruise-control actuator and clip on adjusting piece 4 (bayonet lock).
3. Unscrew threaded part 5 until the accelerator plate is noticeably pulled.
4. Draw accelerator plate firmly back against its idle stop.

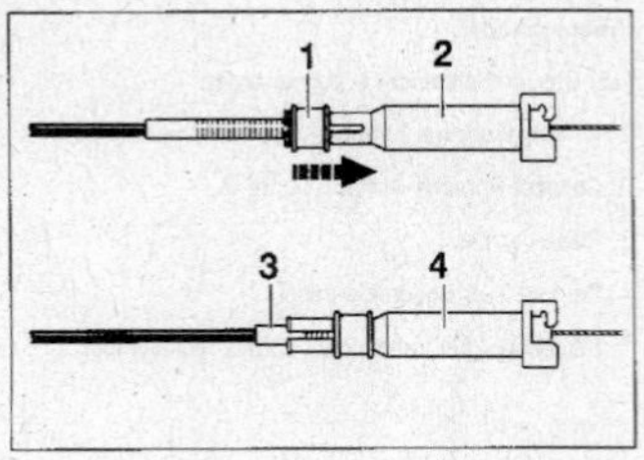

5. Push snap ring 6 back (fixing it).
6. Make fine adjustment by turning the threaded part 7.
   Permissible play: 0 + 1 mm.

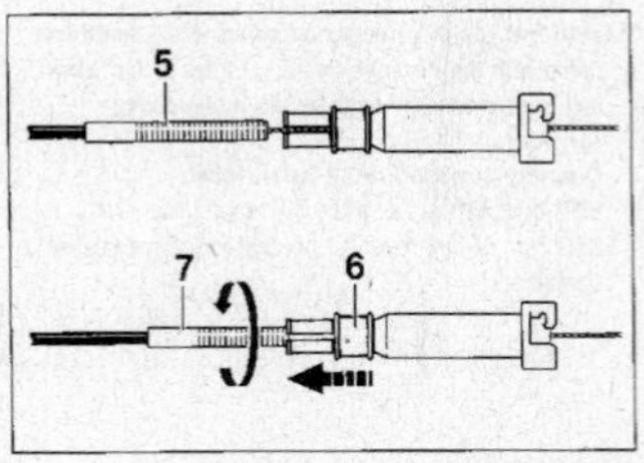

PR101970005500BX

Fig. 57 Code P1140: Load Calculation Signal Implausible (Part 2 of 4). Boxster

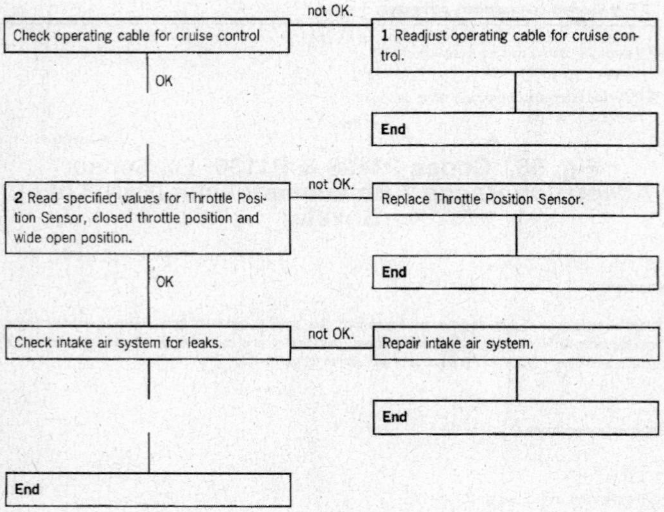

PR101970005500DX

Fig. 57 Code P1140: Load Calculation Signal Implausible (Part 4 of 4). Boxster

2 Read specified values for Throttle Position Sensor.

1. Connect and switch on Porsche System Tester 2.
2. Switch to menu point "Specified values".
3. Select Throttle Position Sensor.
4. Read specified value for closed Throttle Position Sensor.
   Specified value: approximately 0 %
5. Fully depress accelerator pedal.
6. Read specified value for wide open Throttle Position Sensor.
   Specified value: approximately 70 - 80 %

Note

It is important that the value change and not stay fixed at one value.

PR101970005500CX

Fig. 57 Code P1140: Load Calculation Signal Implausible (Part 3 of 4). Boxster

Function

The temperature sensor measures the engine compartment temperature. With these diagnostic trouble codes, the wire from ECM pin 16 to temperature sensor pin 1 is monitored.

Diagnostic conditions

P1157
After a settling time of 2 seconds, a fault is stored if an engine compartment temperature < –42 °C is measured.

P1158
After a settling time of 2 seconds, a fault is stored if an engine compartment temperature > 135 °C is measured.

PR101970005600AX

Fig. 58 Codes P1157 & P1158: Engine Compartment Temperature Sensor Short (Part 1 of 4). Boxster

1 Check temperature sensor.

1. Remove plug on temperature sensor.
2. Connect ohmmeter to temperature sensor, pins 1 and 2.
   Display: approx. 2.2 - 2.6 kΩ at 20 °C

2 Check wire from ECM to temperature sensor for short circuit to ground.

1. Connect special tool 9616 to wiring harness.
2. Remove plug on temperature sensor.
3. Connect ohmmeter to special tool 9616, pin 16 and ground.
   Display: ∞ Ω

If 0 - 5 Ω is displayed, check wiring harness for chafing and pinching damage.

3 Check wire from ECM to temperature sensor for short circuit to B+.

1. Connect special tool 9616 to wiring harness.
2. Remove plug on temperature sensor.
3. Connect voltmeter to special tool 9616, pin 16 and ground.
   Switch on ignition.
   Display: 0 Volt

If battery positive voltage is displayed, check wiring harness for chafing and pinching damage.

PR101970005600BX

Fig. 58 Codes P1157 & P1158: Engine Compartment Temperature Sensor Short (Part 2 of 4). Boxster

4 Check output voltage of ECM.

1. Connect special tool 9616.
2. Remove plug on temperature sensor.
3. Connect voltmeter to pin 16 (positive) and 34 (negative).
   Switch on ignition.
   Display: approx. 5 Volt

PR101970005600CX

Fig. 58 Codes P1157 & P1158: Engine Compartment Temperature Sensor Short (Part 3 of 4). Boxster

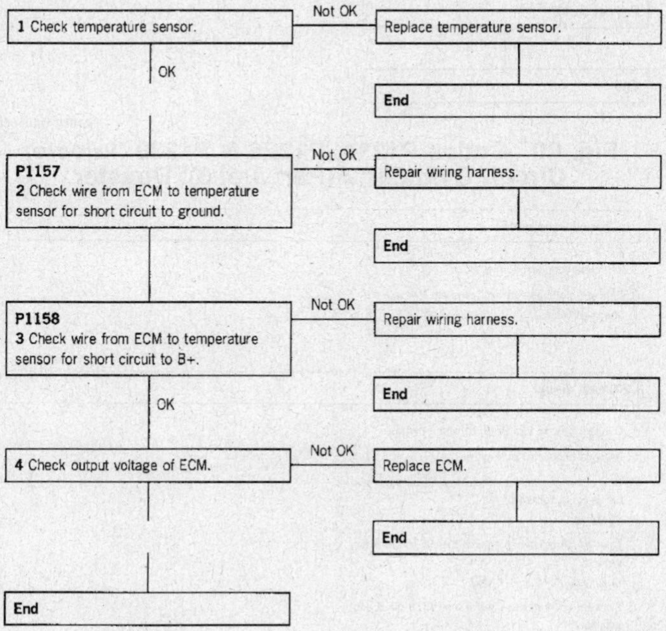

PR101970005600DX

Fig. 58 Codes P1157 & P1158: Engine Compartment Temperature Sensor Short (Part 4 of 4). Boxster

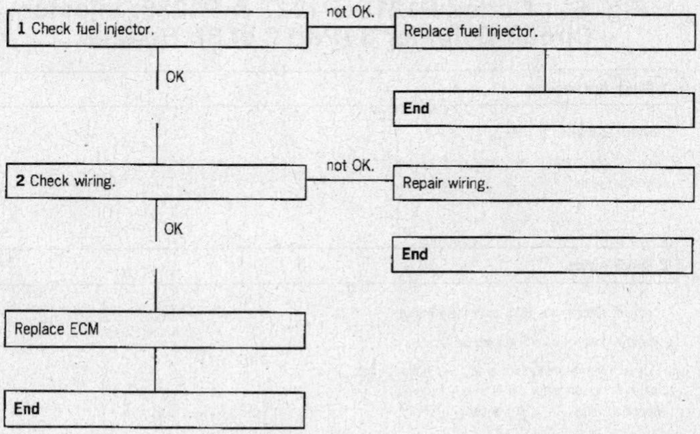

PR101970005700CX

Fig. 59 Codes P1213, P1225 & P1237: Injector Circuit Cylinder 1 (Part 3 of 3). Boxster

Function

The coil of the fuel injector is supplied on one side with B+ (battery voltage) and on the other with ground via an end-stage of the ECM.
For these faults the connection to ground is monitored.

Diagnostic conditions

A fault is recognized and stored in memory when the engine speed is above 80 rpm **and** the battery voltage is between 7.5 Volt and 17 Volt.

PR101970005700AX

Fig. 59 Codes P1213, P1225 & P1237: Injector Circuit Cylinder 1 (Part 1 of 3). Boxster

1 Check fuel injector.

1. Remove connector of injector 1.
2. Connect ohmmeter to pin 1 and pin 2 of injector.
   Specified value: 11 - 13 Ω at 20°C.

2 Check wiring.

1. Connect special tool 9616 to wiring harness.
2. Remove connector on fuel injector.
3. Connect ohmmeter to special tool 9616 pin 3 and fuel injector connector pin 2.
   Specified value: 0 - 5 Ω
4. Connect ohmmeter to special tool 9616 pin 3 and ground.
   Specified value: ∞Ω
5. Connect voltmeter to special tool 9616 pin 3 and ground.
   Ignition on.
   Specified value: 0 Volt

If the measured values are not achieved, check wiring harness for chafing and pinching damage.

PR101970005700BX

Fig. 59 Codes P1213, P1225 & P1237: Injector Circuit Cylinder 1 (Part 2 of 3). Boxster

Function

The coil of the fuel injector is supplied on one side with B+ (battery voltage) and on the other with ground via an end-stage of the ECM.
For these faults the connection to ground is monitored.

Diagnostic conditions

A fault is recognized and stored in memory when the engine speed is above 80 rpm **and** the battery voltage is between 7.5 Volt and 17 Volt.

PR101970005800AX

Fig. 60 Codes P1214, P1226 & P1238: Injector Circuit Cylinder 2 (Part 1 of 3). Boxster

1 Check fuel injector.

1. Remove connector of injector 2.
2. Connect ohmmeter to pin 1 and pin 2 of injector.
   Specified value: 11 - 13 Ω at 20°C.

2 Check wiring.

1. Connect special tool 9616 to wiring harness.
2. Remove connector on fuel injector.
3. Connect ohmmeter to special tool 9616 pin 4 and fuel injector connector pin 2.
   Specified value: 0 - 5 Ω
4. Connect ohmmeter to special tool 9616 pin 4 and ground.
   Specified value: ∞Ω
5. Connect voltmeter to special tool 9616 pin 4 and ground.
   Ignition on.
   Specified value: 0 Volt

If the measured values are not achieved, check wiring harness for chafing and pinching damage.

PR101970005800BX

Fig. 60 Codes P1214, P1226 & P1238: Injector Circuit Cylinder 2 (Part 2 of 3). Boxster

Function

The coil of the fuel injector is supplied on one side with B+ (battery voltage) and on the other with ground via an end-stage of the ECM.
For these faults the connection to ground is monitored.

Diagnostic conditions

A fault is recognized and stored in memory when the engine speed is above 80 rpm **and** the battery voltage is between 7.5 Volt and 17 Volt.

PR101970005900AX

Fig. 61 Codes P1215, P1227 & P1239: Injector Circuit Cylinder 3 (Part 1 of 3). Boxster

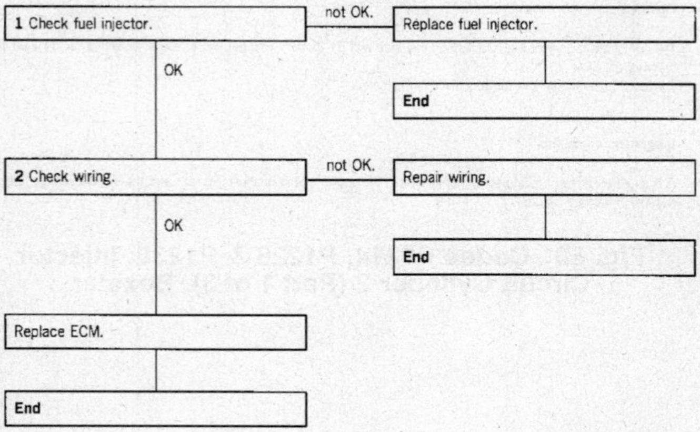

PR101970005900CX

Fig. 61 Codes P1215, P1227 & P1239: Injector Circuit Cylinder 3 (Part 3 of 3). Boxster

Function

The coil of the fuel injector is supplied on one side with B+ (battery voltage) and on the other with ground via an end-stage of the ECM.
For these faults the connection to ground is monitored.

Diagnostic conditions

A fault is recognized and stored in memory when the engine speed is above 80 rpm **and** the battery voltage is between 7.5 Volt and 17 Volt.

PR101970006000AX

Fig. 62 Codes P1216, P1228 & P1240: Injector Circuit Cylinder 4 (Part 1 of 3). Boxster

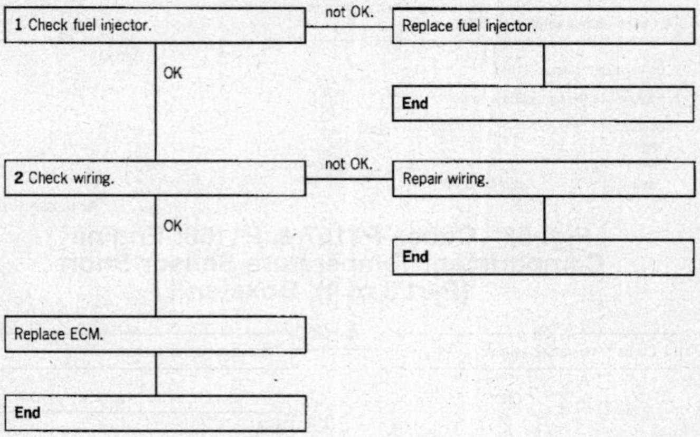

PR101970005800CX

Fig. 60 Codes P1214, P1226 & P1238: Injector Circuit Cylinder 2 (Part 3 of 3). Boxster

1 Check fuel injector.

1. Remove connector of injector 3.
2. Connect ohmmeter to pin 1 and pin 2 of injector.
   Specified value: 11 - 13 Ω at 20°C.

2 Check wiring.

1. Connect special tool 9616 to wiring harness.
2. Remove connector on fuel injector.
3. Connect ohmmeter to special tool 9616 pin 5 and fuel injector connector pin 2.
   Specified value: 0 - 5 Ω
4. Connect ohmmeter to special tool 9616 pin 5 and ground.
   Specified value: ∞Ω
5. Connect voltmeter to special tool 9616 pin 5 and ground.
   Ignition on.
   Specified value: 0 Volt

If the measured values are not achieved, check wiring harness for chafing and pinching damage.

PR101970005900BX

Fig. 61 Codes P1215, P1227 & P1239: Injector Circuit Cylinder 3 (Part 2 of 3). Boxster

1 Check fuel injector.

1. Remove connector of injector 4.
2. Connect ohmmeter to pin 1 and pin 2 of injector.
   Specified value: 11 - 13 Ω at 20°C.

2 Check wiring.

1. Connect special tool 9616 to wiring harness.
2. Remove connector on fuel injector.
3. Connect ohmmeter to special tool 9616 pin 32 and fuel injector connector pin 2.
   Specified value: 0 - 5 Ω
4. Connect ohmmeter to special tool 9616 pin 32 and ground.
   Specified value: ∞Ω
5. Connect voltmeter to special tool 9616 pin 32 and ground.
   Ignition on.
   Specified value: 0 Volt

If the measured values are not achieved, check wiring harness for chafing and pinching damage.

PR101970006000BX

Fig. 62 Codes P1216, P1228 & P1240: Injector Circuit Cylinder 4 (Part 2 of 3). Boxster

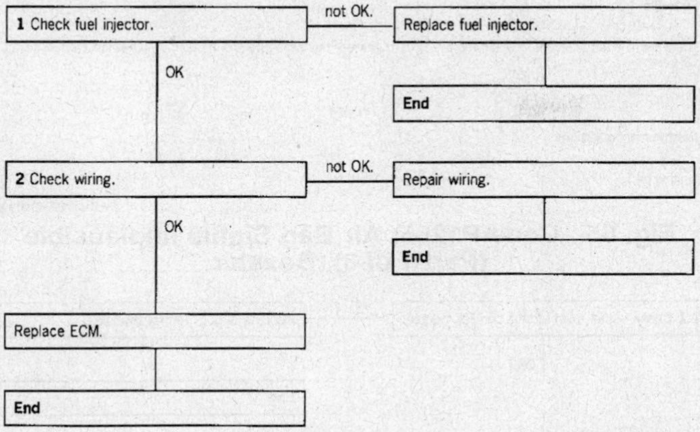

PR101970006000CX

Fig. 62 Codes P1216, P1228 & P1240: Injector Circuit Cylinder 4 (Part 3 of 3). Boxster

1 Check fuel injector.

1. Remove connector of injector 5.
2. Connect ohmmeter to pin 1 and pin 2 of injector.
   Specified value: 11 - 13 Ω at 20°C.

2 Check wiring.

1. Connect special tool 9616 to wiring harness.
2. Remove connector on fuel injector.
3. Connect ohmmeter to special tool 9616 pin 33 and fuel injector connector pin 2.
   Specified value: 0 - 5 Ω
4. Connect ohmmeter to special tool 9616 pin 33 and ground.
   Specified value: ∞Ω
5. Connect voltmeter to special tool 9616 pin 33 and ground.
   Ignition on.
   Specified value: 0 Volt

If the measured values are not achieved, check wiring harness for chafing and pinching damage.

PR101970006100BX

Fig. 63 Codes P1217, P1229 & P1241: Injector Circuit Cylinder 5 (Part 2 of 3). Boxster

Function

The coil of the fuel injector is supplied on one side with B+ (battery voltage) and on the other with ground via an end-stage of the ECM.
For these faults the connection to ground is monitored.

Diagnostic conditions

A fault is recognized and stored in memory when the engine speed is above 80 rpm **and** the battery voltage is between 7.5 Volt and 17 Volt.

PR101970006200AX

Fig. 64 Codes P1218, P1230 & P1242: Injector Circuit Cylinder 6 (Part 1 of 3). Boxster

Function

The coil of the fuel injector is supplied on one side with B+ (battery voltage) and on the other with ground via an end-stage of the ECM.
For these faults the connection to ground is monitored.

Diagnostic conditions

A fault is recognized and stored in memory when the engine speed is above 80 rpm **and** the battery voltage is between 7.5 Volt and 17 Volt.

PR101970006100AX

Fig. 63 Codes P1217, P1229 & P1241: Injector Circuit Cylinder 5 (Part 1 of 3). Boxster

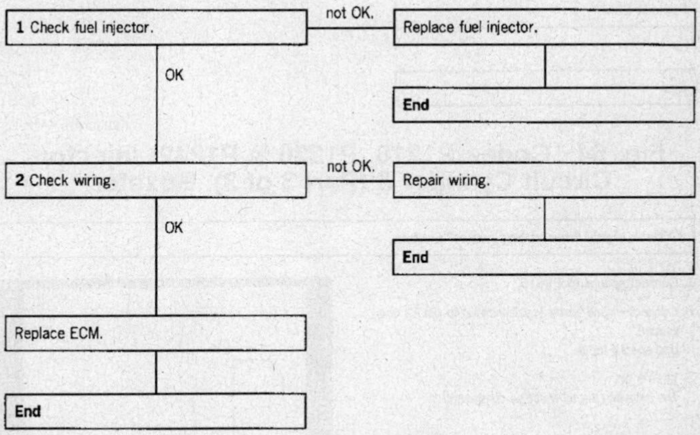

PR101970006100CX

Fig. 63 Codes P1217, P1229 & P1241: Injector Circuit Cylinder 5 (Part 3 of 3). Boxster

1 Check fuel injector.

1. Remove connector of injector 6.
2. Connect ohmmeter to pin 1 and pin 2 of injector.
   Specified value: 11 - 13 Ω at 20°C.

2 Check wiring.

1. Connect special tool 9616 to wiring harness.
2. Remove connector on fuel injector.
3. Connect ohmmeter to special tool 9616 pin 31 and fuel injector connector pin 2.
   Specified value: 0 - 5 Ω
4. Connect ohmmeter to special tool 9616 pin 31 and ground.
   Specified value: ∞Ω
5. Connect voltmeter to special tool 9616 pin 31 and ground.
   Ignition on.
   Specified value: 0 Volt

If the measured values are not achieved, check wiring harness for chafing and pinching damage.

PR101970006200BX

Fig. 64 Codes P1218, P1230 & P1242: Injector Circuit Cylinder 6 (Part 2 of 3). Boxster

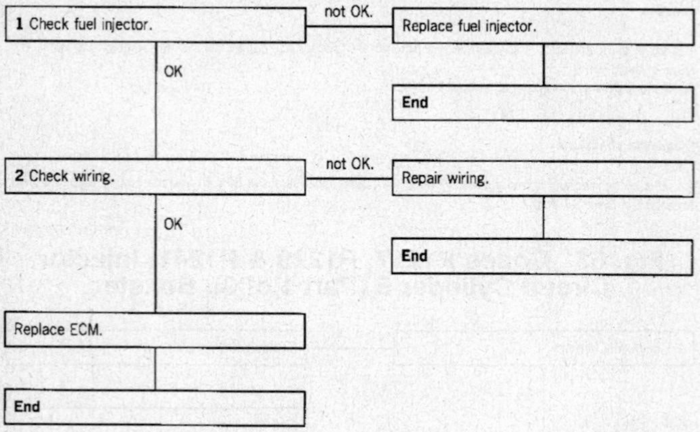

PR101970006200CX

Fig. 64 Codes P1218, P1230 & P1242: Injector Circuit Cylinder 6 (Part 3 of 3). Boxster

1 Check signal from airbag control module.

1. Connect special tool 9616.
2. Connect engine tester (oscilloscope) to pin 12 and ground.
   Use special input.
3. Ignition on.
   The following signal must be displayed:

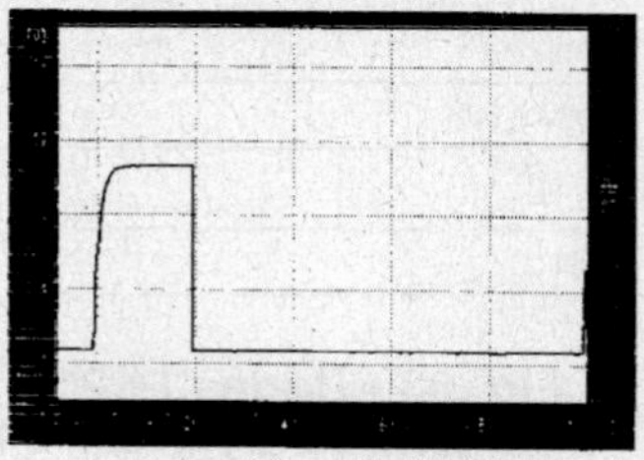

PR101970006300BX

Fig. 65 Code P1265: Air Bag Signal Implausible (Part 2 of 3). Boxster

Function

When the engine is started and the reference mark has been recognized, the control module adapts the camshaft signal with respect to the reference mark, i.e. the software compensates for deviations from a fixed value by angle shifts. The state "Timing chain out of position" is recognised if these adaptation values reach their limits.

Diagnostic conditions

- Engine started.
- Reference mark detected.
- Engine speed < 1 200 rpm.
- Engine temperature > 60 °C.
- No fault in camshaft position sensors.
- Reference mark OK.
- No fault in camshaft adjustment.

PR101970006400AX

Fig. 66 Codes P1324 & P1340: Timing Chain Out Of Position (Part 1 of 2). Boxster

Function

The knock control system is designed to detect knocking combustion and to retard the ignition timing for the knocking cylinder(s). When no further knocking occurs, the ignition timing is advanced again gradually to the specified value. Because of the engine design (opposed-cylinder engine), two knock sensors are needed.

Knock sensor 1 - cylinders 1 to 3
Knock sensor 2 - cylinders 4 to 6

Diagnostic conditions

Engine speed higher than 3600 rpm.

PR101970006500AX

Fig. 67 Codes P1384, P1385 & P1386: Knock Sensor Circuit (Part 1 of 5). Boxster

Function

In the event of an accident in which the airbag is triggered, the airbag control module switches off the fuel pump.

Diagnostic conditions

Ignition on

PR101970006300AX

Fig. 65 Code P1265: Air Bag Signal Implausible (Part 1 of 3). Boxster

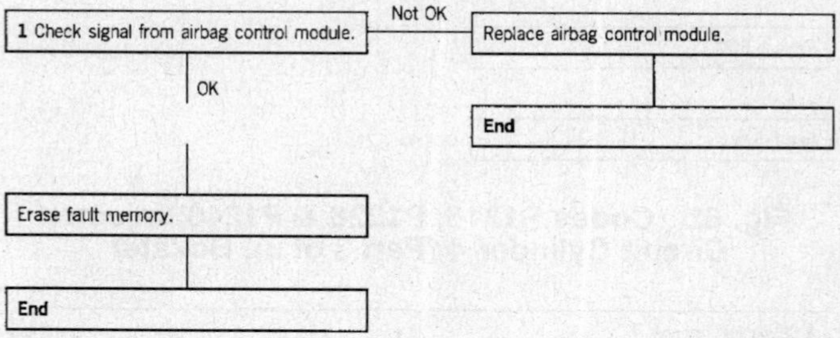

PR101970006300CX

Fig. 65 Code P1265: Air Bag Signal Implausible (Part 3 of 3). Boxster

Note

This fault can be stored only if the engine was disassembled and the allocation of the outlet camshaft with respect to the inlet camshaft was incorrectly set.

PR101970006400BX

Fig. 66 Codes P1324 & P1340: Timing Chain Out Of Position (Part 2 of 2). Boxster

1 Check wiring from ECM to the knock sensors for continuity.

1. Remove knock sensor connectors.
2. Connect special tool 9616 to wiring harness.
3. Connect ohmmeter to special tool 9616, pin 13, and to knock sensor 1 connector, pin 1.
   Display: 0 - 5 Ω
4. Connect ohmmeter to special tool 9616, pin 41, and to knock sensor 2 connector, pin 1.
   Display: 0 - 5 Ω
5. Connect ohmmeter to special tool 9616, pin 71, and to knock sensor 1 connector, pin 2.
   Display: 0 - 5 Ω
6. Connect ohmmeter to special tool 9616, pin 71, and to knock sensor 2 connector, pin 2.
   Display: 0 - 5 Ω

If a resistance of ∞ Ω is displayed in points 3 to 6, check wiring harness for chafing and pinching damage.

2 Check wiring from ECM to knock sensors for short to ground.

1. Remove knock sensor connectors.
2. Connect special tool 9616 to wiring harness.
3. Connect ohmmeter to special tool 9616, pin 13, and ground.
   Display: ∞ Ω
4. Connect ohmmeter to special tool 9616, pin 41, and ground
   Display: ∞ Ω

If a resistance of 0 - 5 Ω is displayed in points 3 and 4, check wiring harness for chafing and pinching damage.

PR101970006500BX

Fig. 67 Codes P1384, P1385 & P1386: Knock Sensor Circuit (Part 2 of 5). Boxster

3 Check wiring from ECM to knock sensors for short to B+.

1. Remove knock sensor connectors.
2. Connect special tool 9616 to wiring harness.
3. Connect voltmeter to special tool 9616, pin 13, and ground.
   Display: 0 Volt
4. Connect voltmeter to special tool 9616, pin 41, and ground.
   Display: 0 Volt
5. Connect voltmeter to special tool 9616, pin 71, and ground.
   Display: 0 Volt

If battery positive voltage is displayed in points 3 to 5, check wiring harness for chafing and pinching damage.

PR101970006500CX

Fig. 67 Codes P1384, P1385 & P1386: Knock Sensor Circuit (Part 3 of 5). Boxster

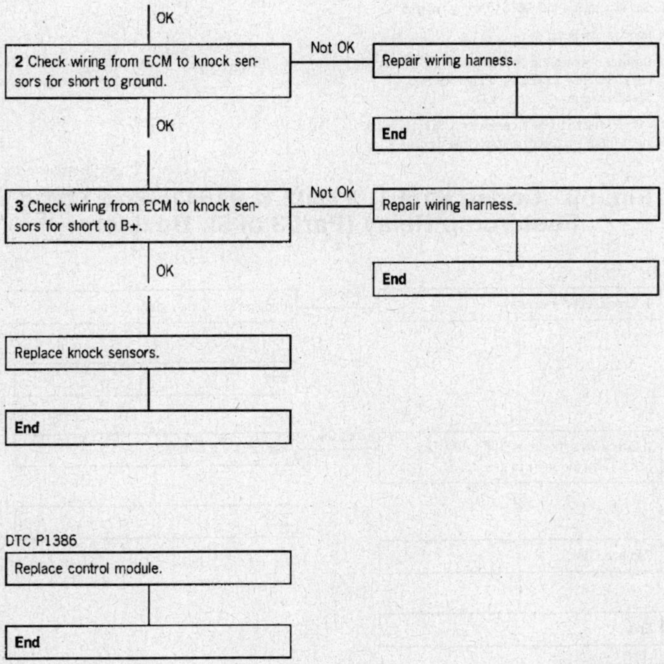

PR101970006500EX

Fig. 67 Codes P1384, P1385 & P1386: Knock Sensor Circuit (Part 5 of 5). Boxster

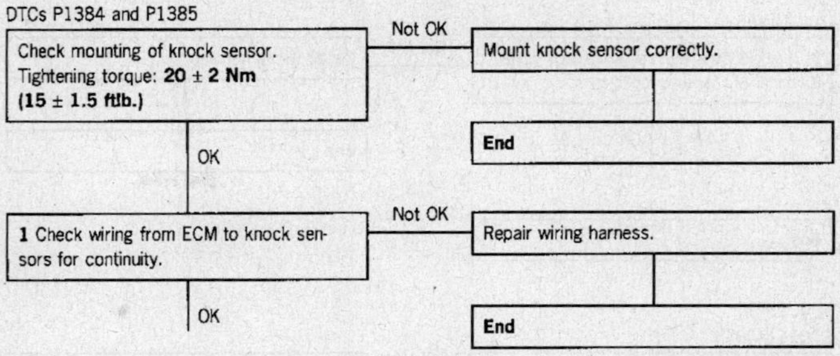

PR101970006500DX

Fig. 67 Codes P1384, P1385 & P1386: Knock Sensor Circuit (Part 4 of 5). Boxster

Function

The magnetic clutch for the A/C compressor is supplied with battery voltage via a relay.
The coil of the relay is supplied with battery voltage by the ECM on one side and with ground by the ECM on the other. The diagnosis only monitors the wiring from the ECM, pin 62 to the A/C relay, terminal 85.

Diagnostic condition

A fault is recognized and stored in memory when the engine speed is above 80 rpm **and** the battery voltage is between 7.5 Volt and 17 Volt.

PR101970006600AX

Fig. 68 Codes P1455, P1456 & P1457: A/C Compressor Control (Part 1 of 3). Boxster

1 Check control wire for A/C relay, pin 2 for interruptions.

1. Remove A/C relay.
2. Connect special tool 9616 to wiring harness.
3. Connect ohmmeter to special tool 9616, pin 62 and to A/C relay pin 2.
   Specified value: 0 - 5 Ω.

Note

The control wire is routed via connector X 59 pin 9.

2 Check control wire for A/C relay, pin 2 for short circuit to B+.

1. Remove A/C relay.
2. Remove control module connector on ECM.
3. Connect voltmeter (plus) to pin 2 at A/C relay and ground.
   Specified value: 0 Volt

If meter reads battery voltage, check wiring harness for chafing and pinching damage.

3 Check control wire for A/C relay, pin 2 (terminal 85) for short circuit to ground.

1. Remove A/C relay.
2. Remove ECM connector.
3. Connect ohmmeter to ground and pin 2 (terminal 85).
   Specified value: ∞ Ω.

If meter reads 0 - 5 Ω, check wiring harness for chafing or pinching damage.

PR101970006600BX

Fig. 68 Codes P1455, P1456 & P1457: A/C Compressor Control (Part 2 of 3). Boxster

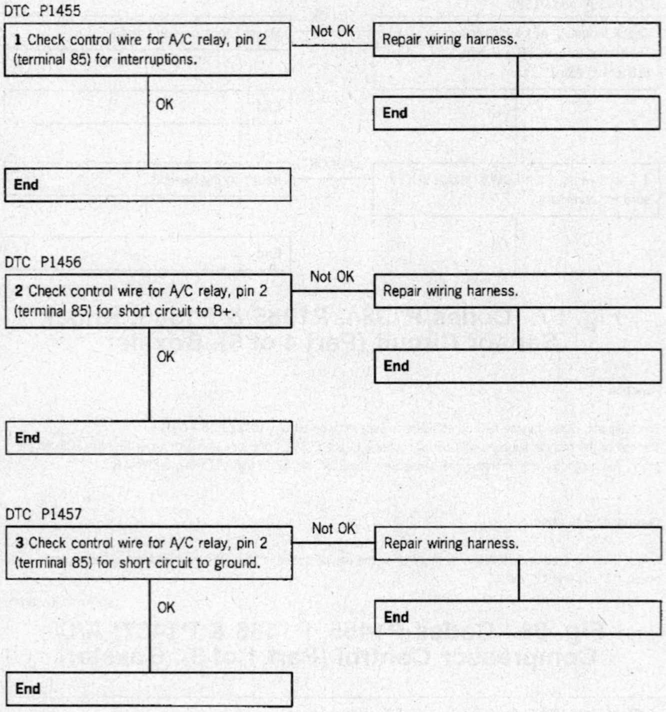

PR101970006600CX

Fig. 68 Codes P1455, P1456 & P1457: A/C Compressor Control (Part 3 of 3). Boxster

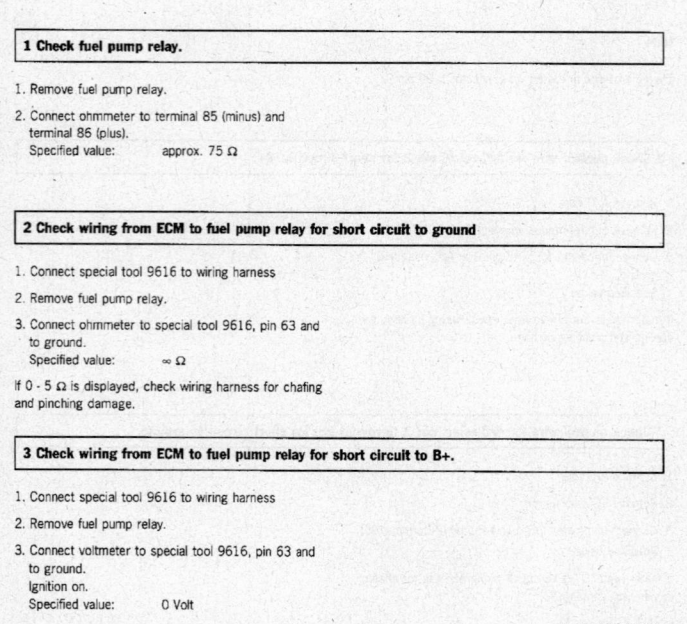

1 Check fuel pump relay.

1. Remove fuel pump relay.
2. Connect ohmmeter to terminal 85 (minus) and terminal 86 (plus).
   Specified value: approx. 75 Ω

2 Check wiring from ECM to fuel pump relay for short circuit to ground

1. Connect special tool 9616 to wiring harness
2. Remove fuel pump relay.
3. Connect ohmmeter to special tool 9616, pin 63 and to ground.
   Specified value: ∞ Ω

If 0 - 5 Ω is displayed, check wiring harness for chafing and pinching damage.

3 Check wiring from ECM to fuel pump relay for short circuit to B+.

1. Connect special tool 9616 to wiring harness
2. Remove fuel pump relay.
3. Connect voltmeter to special tool 9616, pin 63 and to ground.
   Ignition on.
   Specified value: 0 Volt

PR101970006700BX

Fig. 69 Codes P1501, P1502 & P1541: End Stage Fuel Pump Relay (Part 2 of 5). Boxster

Function

To prevent the fuel pump from running with ignition on and engine not running, a safety circuit is integrated in the ECM. Beginning with an engine speed of 25 rpm, the ECM supplies a ground connection to the fuel pump relay.

Diagnostic conditions

P1501 and P1541

A fault is recognized and stored in memory only in the after-run of the ECM program, meaning, when the ignition is switched off after the engine has run.

P1502

A fault is recognized and stored in memory when the engine speed is higher than 80 rpm and the battery voltage is between 7.5 Volt and 17 Volt.

Note

The signal wiring for the fuel pump relay is monitored via terminal 85.

PR101970006700AX

Fig. 69 Codes P1501, P1502 & P1541: End Stage Fuel Pump Relay (Part 1 of 5). Boxster

4 Check wiring from ECM to fuel pump relay for continuity.

1. Connect special tool 9616 to wiring harness
2. Remove fuel pump relay.
3. Connect ohmmeter to special tool 9616, pin 63, and fuel pump relay socket, pin 6 (terminal 85).
   Specified value: 0 - 5 Ω

If ∞ Ω is displayed, check connector X 3/1, pin 5 and wiring harness for chafing and pinching damage.

PR101970006700CX

Fig. 69 Codes P1501, P1502 & P1541: End Stage Fuel Pump Relay (Part 3 of 5). Boxster

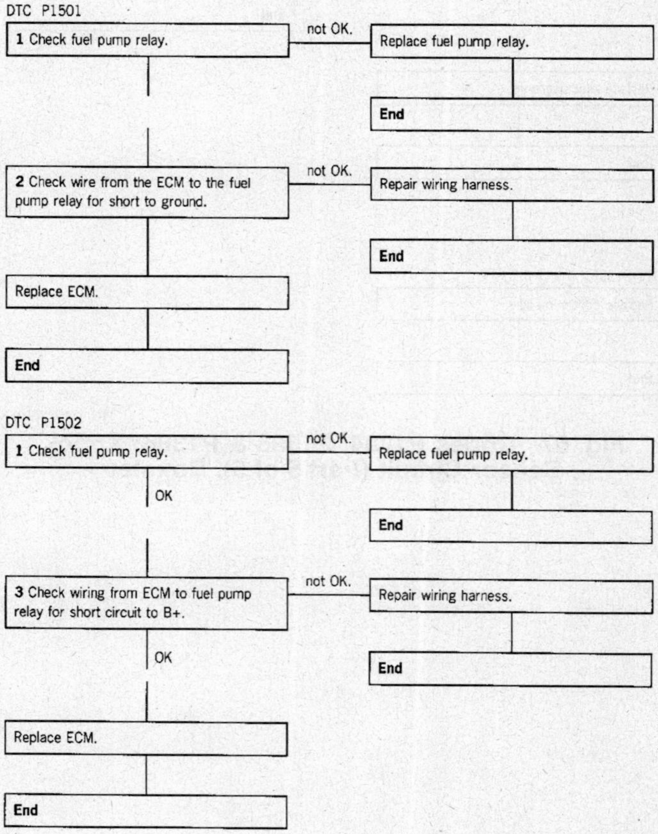

PR101970006700DX

Fig. 69 Codes P1501, P1502 & P1541: End Stage Fuel Pump Relay (Part 4 of 5). Boxster

DTC P1541

1 Check fuel pump relay
- not OK. → Replace fuel pump relay. → End
- OK ↓

4 Check wiring from ECM to fuel pump relay for continuity.
- not OK. → Repair wiring harness. → End
- OK ↓

Replace ECM.

End

PR101970006700EX

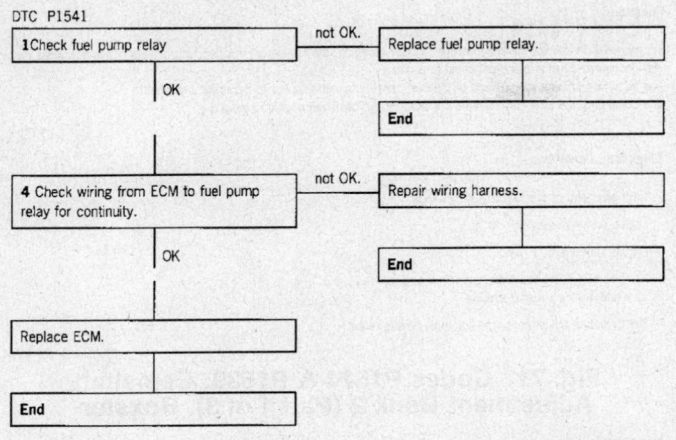

Fig. 69 Codes P1501, P1502 & P1541: End Stage Fuel Pump Relay (Part 5 of 5). Boxster

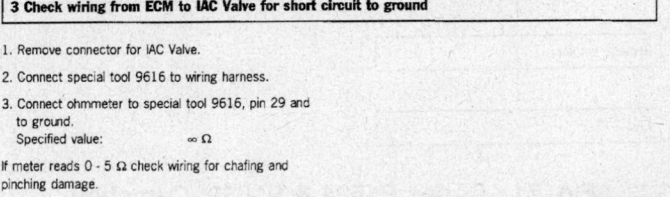

1 Check coil resistance of IAC Valve.

1. Remove connector for IAC Valve.
2. Connect ohmmeter to pin 2 and 1 at IAC Valve.
   Specified value: 16 - 19 Ω at 20 °C.

2 Check wiring from ECM to IAC Valve for short circuit to B+.

1. Remove connector for IAC Valve.
2. Connect special tool 9616 to wiring harness.
3. Connect voltmeter to special tool 9616, pin 29 and to ground.
   Specified value: 0 Volt

If meter reads battery voltage, check wiring for chafing and pinching damage.

3 Check wiring from ECM to IAC Valve for short circuit to ground

1. Remove connector for IAC Valve.
2. Connect special tool 9616 to wiring harness.
3. Connect ohmmeter to special tool 9616, pin 29 and to ground.
   Specified value: ∞ Ω

If meter reads 0 - 5 Ω check wiring for chafing and pinching damage.

PR101970006800BX

Fig. 70 Codes P1510, P1513 & P1514: Idle Control Valve Opening Coil (Part 2 of 5). Boxster

Function

Idle speed control is realized via the idle air control valve. Two coils, the opening coil and closing coil, are integrated in the idle air control valve for this purpose.
In the basic or emergency position, neither of the coils is triggered. To increase the rpm, the opening coil is triggered with a certain pulse duty ratio; the closing coil is triggered to control the rpm.

Diagnostic conditions

A fault is recognized and stored in memory when the engine speed is higher than 80 rpm **and** the battery voltage is between 7.5 Volt and 17 Volt.

Note

If a fault occurs that would lead to very high engine speed, a late adjustment of the ignition angle sets in to act as an engine speed limiter.

PR101970006800AX

Fig. 70 Codes P1510, P1513 & P1514: Idle Control Valve Opening Coil (Part 1 of 5). Boxster

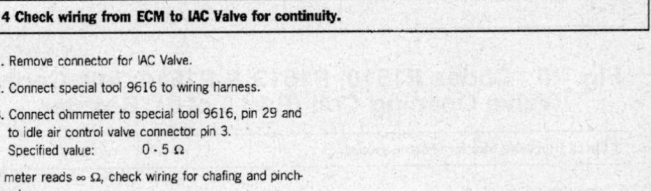

4 Check wiring from ECM to IAC Valve for continuity.

1. Remove connector for IAC Valve.
2. Connect special tool 9616 to wiring harness.
3. Connect ohmmeter to special tool 9616, pin 29 and to idle air control valve connector pin 3.
   Specified value: 0 - 5 Ω

If meter reads ∞ Ω, check wiring for chafing and pinching damage.

PR101970006800CX

Fig. 70 Codes P1510, P1513 & P1514: Idle Control Valve Opening Coil (Part 3 of 5). Boxster

DTC P1510

1 Check coil resistance of IAC Valve.
- not OK → Replace IAC Valve. → End
- OK ↓

2 Check wiring from ECM to IAC Valve for short circuit to B+.
- not OK → Repair wiring harness. → End
- OK ↓

Replace ECM.

End

DTC P1513

1 Check coil resistance of IAC Valve.
- not OK → Replace IAC Valve. → End
- OK ↓

3 Check wiring from ECM to IAC Valve for short circuit to ground
- not OK → Repair wiring harness. → End
- OK ↓

Replace ECM.

End

PR101970006800DX

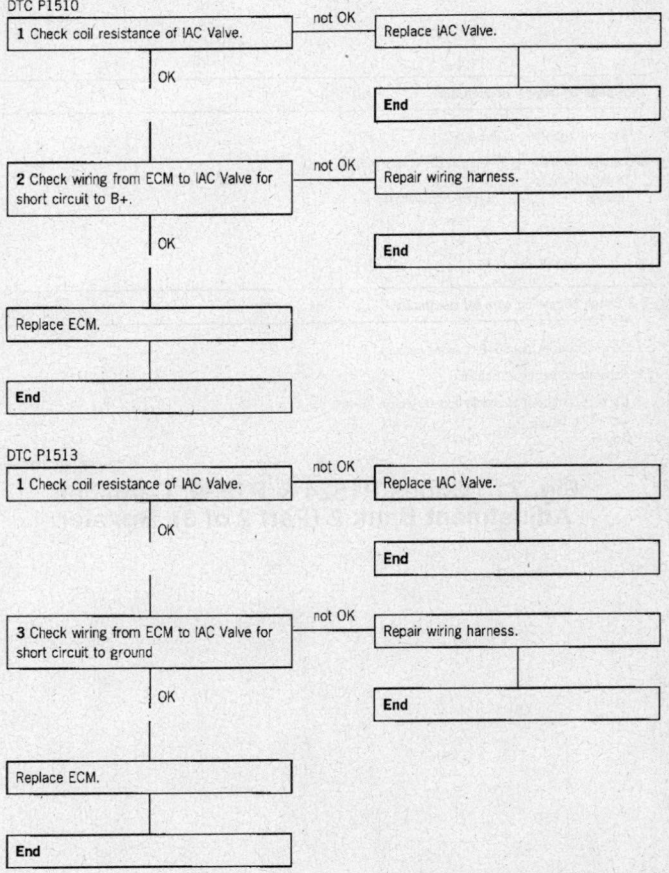

Fig. 70 Codes P1510, P1513 & P1514: Idle Control Valve Opening Coil (Part 4 of 5). Boxster

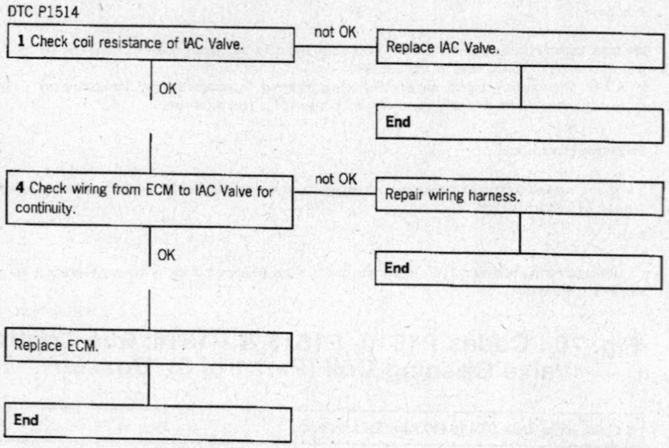

PR101970006800EX

Fig. 70 Codes P1510, P1513 & P1514: Idle Control Valve Opening Coil (Part 5 of 5). Boxster

1 Check triggering wire for short to ground.

1. Connect special tool 9616.
2. Connect ohmmeter to pin 25 and ground.
   Display: $\infty\ \Omega$

If 0 - 5 Ω is displayed, check wiring harness for chafing and pinching damage.

2 Check B+ supply of actuator.

1. Separate connector to actuator.
2. Connect voltmeter to connector, pin 1, and ground.
   Switch on ignition.
   Display: Battery positive voltage

3 Check triggering wire for continuity.

1. Connect special tool 9616 to wiring harness.
2. Separate connector to actuator.
3. Connect ohmmeter to special tool 9616, pin 25, and connector, pin 2.
   Display: 0 - 5 Ω

PR101970006900BX

Fig. 71 Codes P1524 & P1539: Camshaft Adjustment Bank 2 (Part 2 of 3). Boxster

Function

In order to increase torque and improve cylinder charging, the engine is equipped with two VarioCam actuators that are incorporated in the camshaft chain tensioners.
The actuators change the position of the inlet camshafts with respect to the outlet camshafts.
The position of the inlet camshafts is checked by the camshaft position sensors.

Diagnostic conditions

- Time after end of starting > 200 seconds.
- Engine oil temperature > 30 °C.
- Engine speed > 600 rpm.
- No fault with reference mark, camshaft position sensors and engine oil temperature.
- The camshaft adjustment actuator must be triggered.

PR101970006900AX

Fig. 71 Codes P1524 & P1539: Camshaft Adjustment Bank 2 (Part 1 of 3). Boxster

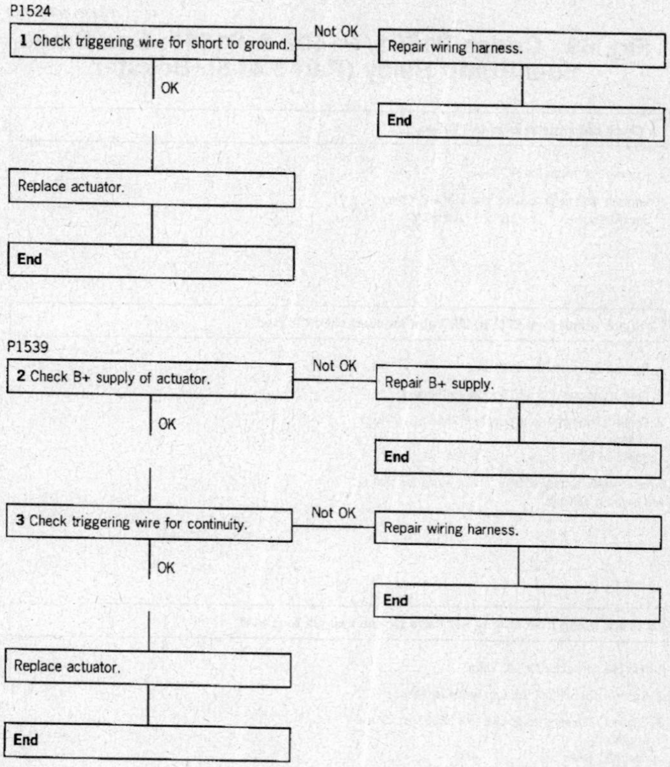

PR101970006900CX

Fig. 71 Codes P1524 & P1539: Camshaft Adjustment Bank 2 (Part 3 of 3). Boxster

Function

In order to increase torque and improve cylinder charging, the engine is equipped with two VarioCam actuators that are incorporated in the camshaft chain tensioners.
The actuators change the position of the inlet camshafts with respect to the outlet camshafts.
The position of the inlet camshafts is checked by the camshaft position sensors.

Diagnostic conditions

- Time after end of starting > 200 seconds.
- Engine oil temperature > 30 °C.
- Engine speed > 600 rpm.
- No fault with reference mark, camshaft position sensors and engine oil temperature.
- The camshaft adjustment actuator must be triggered.

PR101970007000AX

Fig. 72 Codes P1530 & P1531: Camshaft Adjustment Bank 1 (Part 1 of 3). Boxster

1 Check triggering wire for short to ground.

1. Connect special tool 9616.
2. Connect ohmmeter to pin 52 and ground.
   Display: ∞ Ω

If 0 - 5 Ω is displayed, check wiring harness for chafing and pinching damage.

2 Check B+ supply of actuator.

1. Separate connector to actuator.
2. Connect voltmeter to connector, pin 1, and ground.
   Switch on ignition.
   Display: Battery positive voltage

3 Check triggering wire for continuity.

1. Connect special tool 9616 to wiring harness.
2. Separate connector to actuator.
3. Connect ohmmeter to special tool 9616, pin 52, and connector, pin 2.
   Display: 0 - 5 Ω

PR101970007000BX

Fig. 72 Codes P1530 & P1531: Camshaft Adjustment Bank 1 (Part 2 of 3). Boxster

Function

Idle speed control is realized via the idle air control valve. Two coils, the opening coil and closing coil, are integrated in the idle air control valve for this purpose.
In the basic or emergency position, neither of the coils is triggered. To increase the rpm, the opening coil is triggered with a certain pulse duty ratio; the closing coil is triggered to control the rpm.

Diagnostic conditions

A fault is recognized and stored in memory when the engine speed is higher than 80 rpm **and** the battery voltage is between 7.5 Volt and 17 Volt.

Note

If a fault occurs that would lead to very high engine speed, a late adjustment of the ignition angle sets in to act as an engine speed limiter.

PR101970007100AX

Fig. 73 Codes P1551, P1552 & P1553: Idle Air Control (Part 1 of 5). Boxster

1 Check coil resistance of IAC Valve.

1. Remove connector for IAC Valve.
2. Connect ohmmeter to pins 2 and 1 at IAC Valve.
   Specified value: 14 - 17 Ω at 20°C

2 Check wiring from ECM to IAC Valve for continuity.

1. Remove connector for IAC Valve.
2. Connect special tool 9616 to wiring harness.
3. Connect ohmmeter to special tool 9616, pin 2 and to IAC Valve connector, pin 1.
   Specified value: 0 - 5 Ω

If meter reads ∞ Ω, check wiring for chafing and pinching damage.

3 Check wiring from ECM to IAC Valve for short circuit to ground.

1. Remove connector for IAC Valve
2. Connect special tool 9616 to wiring harness.
3. Connect ohmmeter to special tool 9616, pin 2 and to ground.
   Specified value: ∞ Ω

If meter reads 0 - 5 Ω, check wiring for chafing and pinching damage.

PR101970007100BX

Fig. 73 Codes P1551, P1552 & P1553: Idle Air Control (Part 2 of 5). Boxster

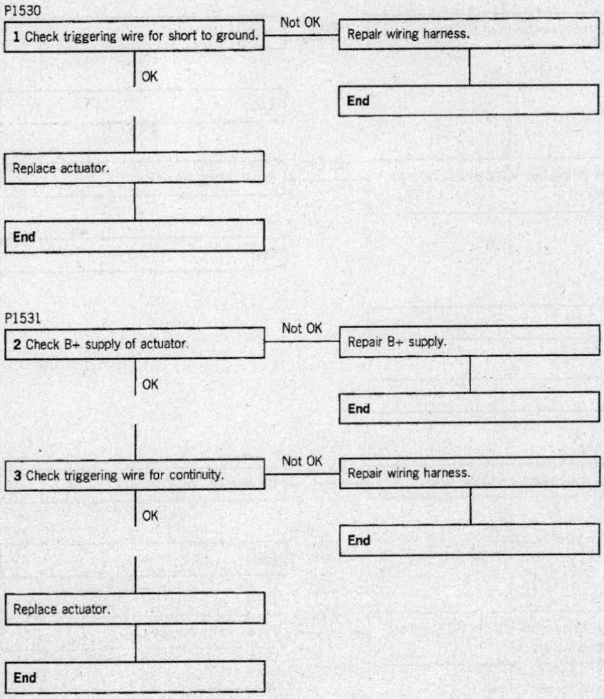

PR101970007000CX

Fig. 72 Codes P1530 & P1531: Camshaft Adjustment Bank 1 (Part 3 of 3). Boxster

4 Check wiring from ECM to IAC Valve for short circuit to B+.

1. Remove connector for IAC Valve.
2. Connect special tool 9616 to wiring harness.
3. Connect voltmeter to special tool 9616, pin 2 and to ground.
   Specified value: 0 Volt

If meter reads battery voltage, check wiring for chafing and pinching damage.

PR101970007100CX

Fig. 73 Codes P1551, P1552 & P1553: Idle Air Control (Part 3 of 5). Boxster

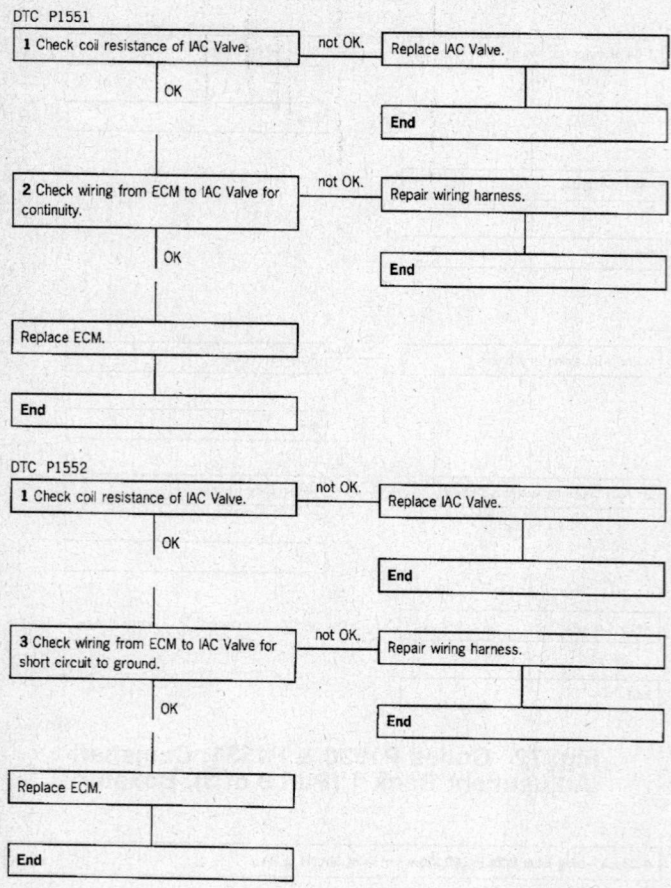

DTC P1551

1 Check coil resistance of IAC Valve.
- not OK. → Replace IAC Valve. → **End**
- OK ↓

2 Check wiring from ECM to IAC Valve for continuity.
- not OK. → Repair wiring harness. → **End**
- OK ↓

Replace ECM. → **End**

DTC P1552

1 Check coil resistance of IAC Valve.
- not OK. → Replace IAC Valve. → **End**
- OK ↓

3 Check wiring from ECM to IAC Valve for short circuit to ground.
- not OK. → Repair wiring harness. → **End**
- OK ↓

Replace ECM. → **End**

PR101970007100DX

Fig. 73 Codes P1551, P1552 & P1553: Idle Air Control (Part 4 of 5). Boxster

Function

During a restart of the engine or the Motronic reset, the ECM communicates with the alarm system control module. The engine can be started when this communication takes place properly. If the communication is interfered with, the engine cannot be started. The starter is not triggered.

Diagnostic conditions

Condition start
Motronic reset

DTC No.	Fault conditions	Fault area
P1570	implausible operating range	– Wiring between ECM and alarm system interrupted.
P1571	Interruption / no signal	– Short circuit to ground or short circuit to B+ – Alarm system control module faulty

PR101970007200AX

Fig. 74 Codes P1570 & P1571: Immobilizer Circuit (Part 1 of 4). Boxster

DTC P1553

1 Check coil resistance of IAC Valve.
- not OK. → Replace IAC Valve. → **End**
- OK ↓

4 Check wiring from ECM to IAC Valve for short circuit to B+.
- not OK. → Repair wiring harness. → **End**
- OK ↓

Replace ECM. → **End**

PR101970007100EX

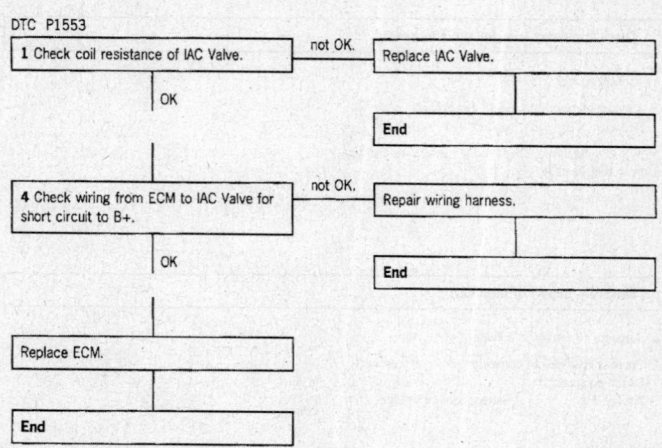

Fig. 73 Codes P1551, P1552 & P1553: Idle Air Control (Part 5 of 5). Boxster

1 Check signal wire for continuity.

1. Remove connector I on alarm control module.
2. Connect special tool 9616 to wiring harness.
3. Connect ohmmeter to special tool 9616, pin 88, and to alarm system connector I/23.
   Display: 0 - 5 Ω

If ∞ Ω is displayed, remove connector X 3/1.

4. Connect ohmmeter to connector X 3/1, pin 14, on cavity side and special tool 9616, pin 88.
   Display: 0 - 5 Ω

If ∞ Ω is displayed, repair wiring harness.

5. Connect ohmmeter to connector X 3/1, pin 14 on pin side, and alarm control module connector I, pin 23.
   Display: 0 - 5 Ω

If ∞ Ω is displayed, repair wiring harness.

2 Check signal wire for short circuit to ground.

1. Remove connector I on alarm control module.
2. Connect special tool 9616 to wiring harness.
3. Connect ohmmeter to special tool 9616, pin 88, and ground.
   Display: ∞ Ω

If 0 - 5 Ω is displayed, check wiring harness for chafing and pinching damage.

PR101970007200BX

Fig. 74 Codes P1570 & P1571: Immobilizer Circuit (Part 2 of 4). Boxster

3 Check signal wire for short circuit to B+.

1. Remove connector I on alarm control module.
2. Connect special tool 9616 to wiring harness.
3. Connect voltmeter to special tool 9616, pin 88, and ground.
   Display: 0 Volt

If battery positive voltage is displayed, check wiring harness for chafing and pinching damage.

PR101970007200CX

Fig. 74 Codes P1570 & P1571: Immobilizer Circuit (Part 3 of 4). Boxster

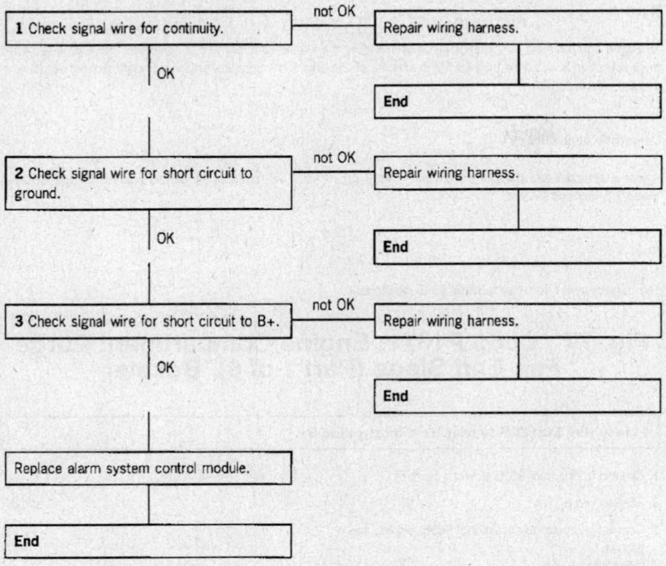

PR101970007200DX

Fig. 74 Codes P1570 & P1571: Immobilizer Circuit (Part 4 of 4). Boxster

1 Check wire, terminal 30, for contact resistances.

1. Remove connector X 59.
2. Connect voltmeter to pin 5 (positive) on pin side and ground.
   Display: Battery positive voltage

If no battery positive voltage is displayed, check wire from connector X 59, pin 5, to current distributor fuse C 1 for continuity. Check connectors for corrosion.

3. Reconnect connector X 59.
4. Connect special tool 9616 to wiring harness.
5. Connect voltmeter to special tool 9616, pin 26 (positive), and ground.
   Display: Battery positive voltage.

If no battery positive voltage is displayed, check wire from special tool 9616, pin 26, to cavity side of connector X 59, pin 5, for continuity. Check connectors for corrosion.

PR101970007300BX

Fig. 75 Codes P1600 & P1601: Power Supply Circuit (Part 2 of 3). Boxster

Function

The memory components are supplied with voltage by terminal 30. If terminal 30 is interrupted (for instance, if the battery is disconnected), the adaptation values are erased.

Diagnostic conditions

No special diagnostic conditions required.

Note

This DTC does not necessarily mean that a fault exists. This DTC is also recorded in memory if the battery is disconnected or the ECM connector is pulled off. In such cases, erase the DTC memory and road test the vehicle.

PR101970007400AX

Fig. 76 Code P1602: Power Supply Interruption (Part 1 of 3). Boxster

The ECM and the RAM cells are supplied with voltage via terminal 30. If the voltage exceeds or falls below the voltage limits, reliable storage of the faults or adaption values is no longer ensured.

Diagnostic conditions

- Speed greater than 0 km/h.
- No error in vehicle speed.

Note

When a fault is recorded in memory, the idle air control adaptation is blocked.

PR101970007300AX

Fig. 75 Codes P1600 & P1601: Power Supply Circuit (Part 1 of 3). Boxster

Diagnostic trouble code P1600 – below lower limit

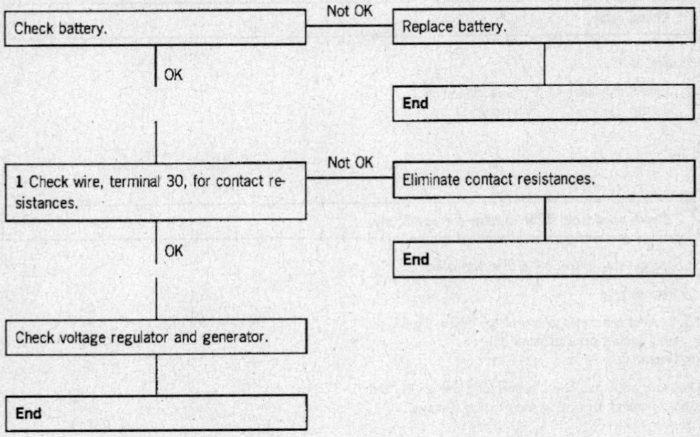

Diagnostic trouble code P1601

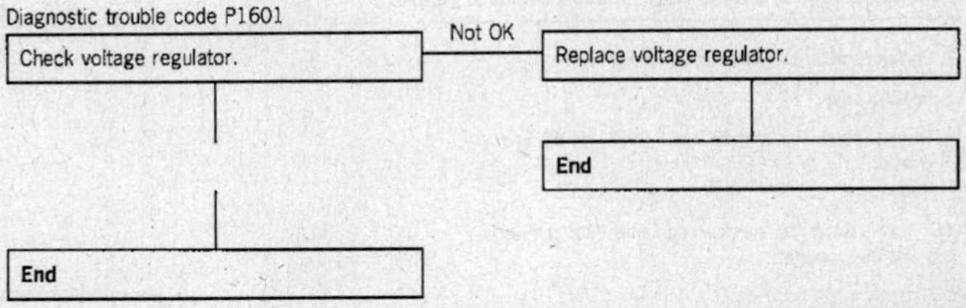

PR101970007300CX

Fig. 75 Codes P1600 & P1601: Power Supply Circuit (Part 3 of 3). Boxster

1 Check wiring for terminal 30 for continuity.

1. Remove connector X 59.
2. Connect voltmeter on pin side to pin 5 (plus) and ground.
   Display: Battery positive voltage

If no battery positive voltage is displayed, check wiring from connector X 59, pin 5, to current distributor fuse C 1, for continuity. Check connectors for corrosion.

3. Reconnect connector X 59.
4. Connect special tool 9616 to wiring harness.
5. Connect voltmeter to special tool 9616, pin 26 (plus) and ground.
   Display: Battery positive voltage.

If no battery positive voltage is displayed, check wiring from special tool 9616, pin 26, to cavity side of connector X 59, pin 5, for continuity. Check connectors for corrosion.

PR101970007400BX

Fig. 76 Code P1602: Power Supply Interruption (Part 2 of 3). Boxster

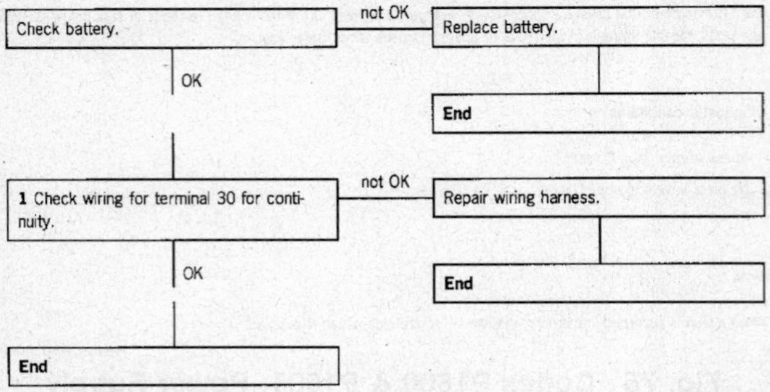

PR101970007400CX

Fig. 76 Code P1602: Power Supply Interruption (Part 3 of 3). Boxster

1 Check relay.

1. Remove relay.
2. Connect ohmmeter to terminals 85 and 86.
   Display: approx. 75 Ω

2 Check wire from ECM to relay for continuity.

1. Connect special tool 9616 to wiring harness.
2. Remove relay.
3. Connect ohmmeter to special tool 9616, pin 65, and relay socket, pin 2 (terminal 85).
   Display: 0 - 5 Ω

If ∞ Ω is displayed, check connector X 59, pin 11, and wiring harness for chafing and pinching damage.

3 Check wire from ECM to relay for short circuit to ground.

1. Connect special tool 9616 to wiring harness.
2. Remove relay.
3. Connect ohmmeter to special tool 9616, pin 65, and ground.
   Display: ∞ Ω

If 0 - 5 Ω is displayed, check wiring harness for chafing and pinching damage.

PR101970007500BX

Fig. 77 Code P1671: Engine Compartment Purge Fan End Stage (Part 2 of 6). Boxster

Open circuit

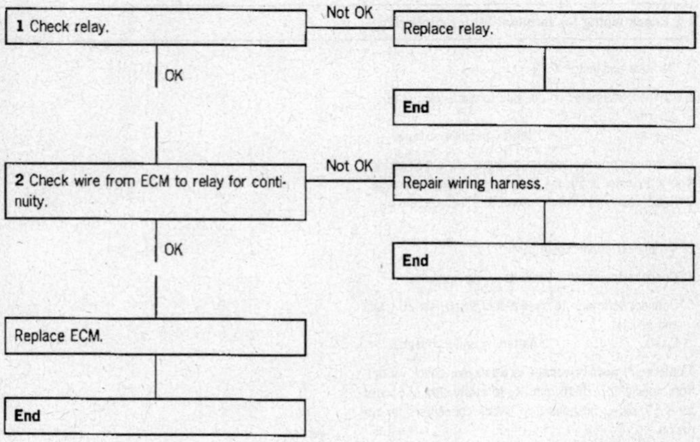

PR101970007500DX

Fig. 77 Code P1671: Engine Compartment Purge Fan End Stage (Part 4 of 6). Boxster

Function

An engine compartment purge fan is installed to reduce the engine compartment temperature. The engine compartment purge fan is activated by the ECM depending on the engine temperature, engine compartment temperature and the vehicle speed.

Diagnostic conditions

A fault is detected and stored if the engine speed is greater than 80 rpm **and** the battery positive voltage lies between 7.5 Volt and 17 Volt.

Note

The triggering wire for relay terminal 85 is monitored.

PR101970007500AX

Fig. 77 Code P1671: Engine Compartment Purge Fan End Stage (Part 1 of 6). Boxster

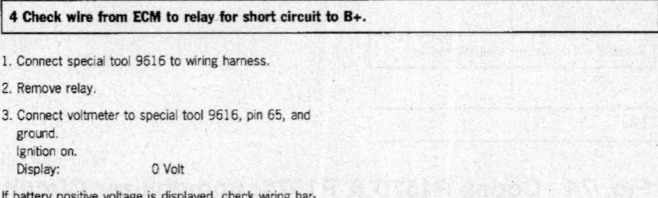

4 Check wire from ECM to relay for short circuit to B+.

1. Connect special tool 9616 to wiring harness.
2. Remove relay.
3. Connect voltmeter to special tool 9616, pin 65, and ground.
   Ignition on.
   Display: 0 Volt

If battery positive voltage is displayed, check wiring harness for chafing and pinching damage.

PR101970007500CX

Fig. 77 Code P1671: Engine Compartment Purge Fan End Stage (Part 3 of 6). Boxster

Short circuit to ground

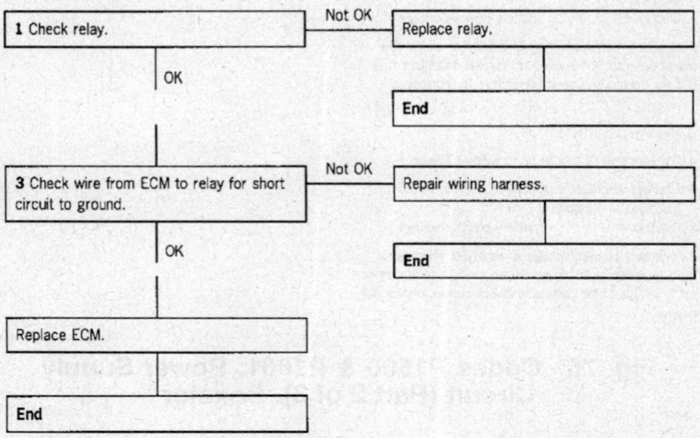

PR101970007500EX

Fig. 77 Code P1671: Engine Compartment Purge Fan End Stage (Part 5 of 6). Boxster

Short circuit to B+

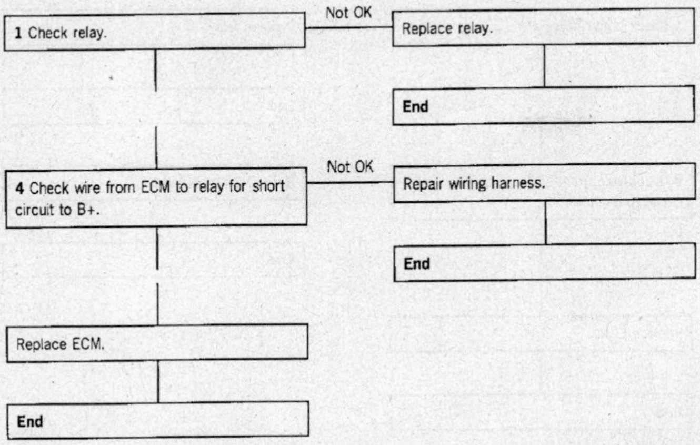

PR101970007500FX

Fig. 77 Code P1671: Engine Compartment Purge Fan End Stage (Part 6 of 6). Boxster

1 Check both relays.

1. Remove relay.
2. Connect ohmmeter to terminals 85 and 86.
   Display: approx. 75 Ω

2 Check wire from ECM to relays for continuity.

1. Connect special tool 9616 to wiring harness.
2. Remove relay, stage 1, coolant blower 1.
3. Remove relay, stage 1, coolant blower 2.
4. Connect ohmmeter to special tool 9616, pin 35, and relay socket, coolant blower 1, pin 2 (terminal 85).
   Display: 0 - 5 Ω
5. Connect ohmmeter to special tool 9616, pin 35, and relay socket, coolant blower 2, pin 2 (terminal 85).
   Display: 0 - 5 Ω

If ∞ Ω is displayed, check connector X 3/1, pin 7, and wiring harness for chafing and pinching damage.

3 Check wire from ECM to relays for short circuit to ground.

1. Connect special tool 9616 to wiring harness.
2. Remove relay, stage 1, coolant blower 1.
3. Remove relay, stage 1, coolant blower 2.
4. Connect ohmmeter to special tool 9616, pin 35, and ground.
   Display: ∞ Ω

If 0 - 5 Ω is displayed, check wiring harness for chafing and pinching damage.

PR101970007600BX

Fig. 78 Code P1673: Fan End Stage (Part 2 of 6). Boxster

Function

Two electric fans are installed to cool the coolant. The electric fans are triggered via two relays by the ECM.

Diagnostic conditions

A fault is recognized and stored if the engine speed is greater than 80 rpm **and** the battery positive voltage lies between 7.5 Volt and 17 Volt.

Note

The triggering power for the relay, stage 1, terminal 85 is monitored.

PR101970007600AX

Fig. 78 Code P1673: Fan End Stage (Part 1 of 6). Boxster

4 Check wire from ECM to relays for short circuit to B+.

1. Connect special tool 9616 to wiring harness.
2. Remove relay, stage 1, coolant blower 1.
3. Remove relay, stage 1, coolant blower 2.
4. Connect voltmeter to special tool 9616, pin 35, and ground.
   Ignition on.
   Display: 0 Volt

If battery positive voltage is displayed, check wiring harness for chafing and pinching damage.

PR101970007600CX

Fig. 78 Code P1673: Fan End Stage (Part 3 of 6). Boxster

Open circuit

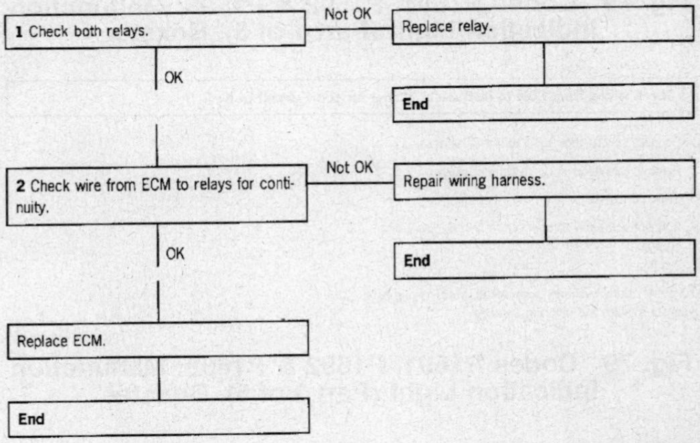

PR101970007600DX

Fig. 78 Code P1673: Fan End Stage (Part 4 of 6). Boxster

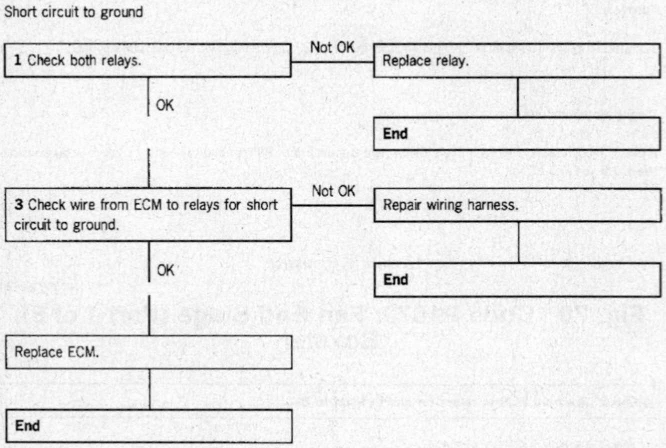

PR101970007600EX

Fig. 78 Code P1673: Fan End Stage (Part 5 of 6). Boxster

Function

The MIL Check engine is on when a fault is recorded in memory of the Engine Control Module (ECM).

Diagnostic conditions

A fault is recognized and recorded when the engine speed is above 80 rpm **and** the battery voltage is between 7.5 Volt and 17 Volt.

PR101970007700AX

Fig. 79 Codes P1691, P1692 & P1693: Malfunction Indication Light (Part 1 of 5). Boxster

3 Check wiring from ECM to instrument cluster for short circuit to B+.

1. Connect special tool 9616 to wiring harness.
2. Remove connector III on instrument cluster.
3. Switch on ignition.
4. Connect voltmeter to special tool 9616, pin 8, and ground.
   Display: 0 Volt

If battery positive voltage is displayed, check wiring harness for chafing and pinching damage.

PR101970007700CX

Fig. 79 Codes P1691, P1692 & P1693: Malfunction Indication Light (Part 3 of 5). Boxster

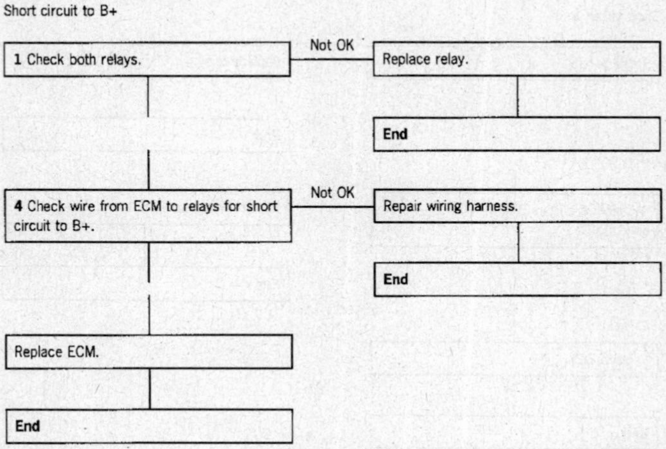

PR101970007600FX

Fig. 78 Code P1673: Fan End Stage (Part 6 of 6). Boxster

1 Check wiring from ECM to instrument cluster for continuity.

1. Connect special tool 9616 to wiring harness.
2. Separate connector X 3/1.
3. Connect ohmmeter to special tool 9616, pin 8, and to X 3/1 on cavity side, pin 16.
   Display: 0 - 5 Ω

If ∞ Ω is displayed, check wiring harness for chafing and pinching damage.

4. Remove connector III on instrument cluster.
5. Connect ohmmeter to X 3/1 on pin side and connector III of instrument cluster, pin 2.
   Display: 0 - 5 Ω

If ∞ Ω is displayed, check wiring harness for chafing and pinching damage.

2 Check wiring from ECM to instrument cluster for short circuit to ground.

1. Connect special tool 9616 to wiring harness.
2. Remove connector III on instrument cluster.
3. Connect ohmmeter to special tool 9616, pin 8, and ground.
   Display: ∞ Ω

If 0 - 5 Ω is displayed, check wiring harness for chafing and pinching damage.

PR101970007700BX

Fig. 79 Codes P1691, P1692 & P1693: Malfunction Indication Light (Part 2 of 5). Boxster

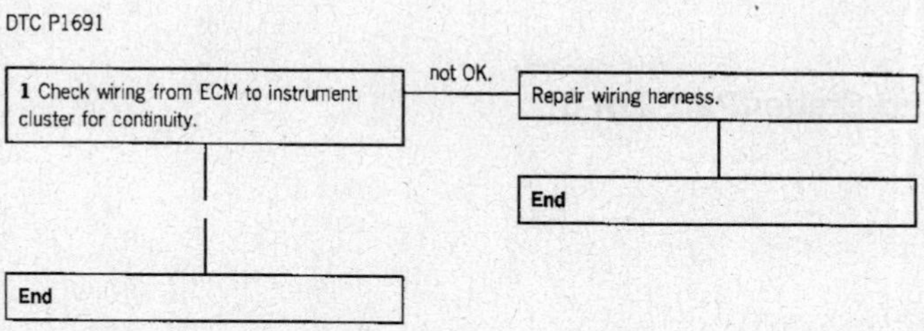

PR101970007700DX

Fig. 79 Codes P1691, P1692 & P1693: Malfunction Indication Light (Part 4 of 5). Boxster

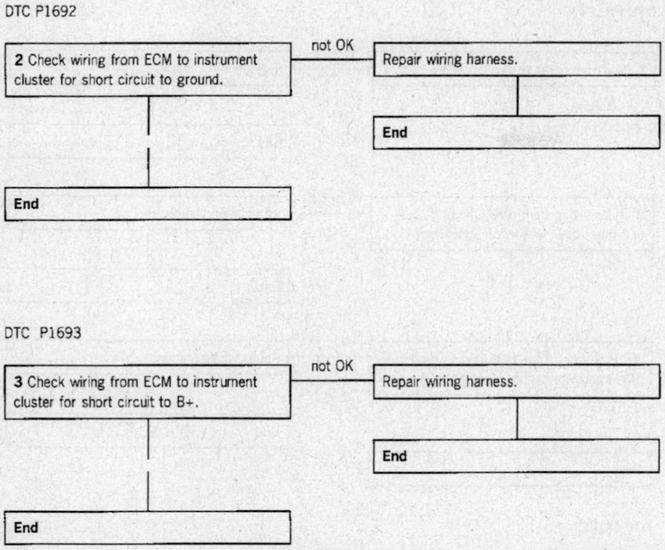

PR101970007700EX

Fig. 79 Codes P1691, P1692 & P1693: Malfunction Indication Light (Part 5 of 5). Boxster

Note

This fault is a control module fault.

The following situations are conceivable:

1. Tiptronic control module faulty.
   Tiptronic control module continues to send a signal for torque reduction although the ECM has reduced the torque.
2. ECM faulty.
   The ECM does not reduce the torque although the Tiptronic control module requests torque reduction. If no signal that the torque was reduced is sent by the ECM, the request remains in the Tiptronic control module and the time of 2.5 seconds is thus exceeded.

An indication of a faulty control module could be an additionally stored checksum error (control module faulty).

PR101970007800BX

Fig. 80 Code P1782: Engine Engagement Nominal Engine Torque Short Circuit To Ground (Part 2 of 2). Boxster

Function

In order to protect the transmission (Tiptronic), the advance angle is reduced for a short time when a gear shift is performed at high speeds and high torques.

Diagnostic conditions

– Tiptronic vehicle

A fault is recognized and stored if the signal for torque reduction is present for longer than approx. 2.5 seconds.

PR101970007800AX

Fig. 80 Code P1782: Engine Engagement Nominal Engine Torque Short Circuit To Ground (Part 1 of 2). Boxster

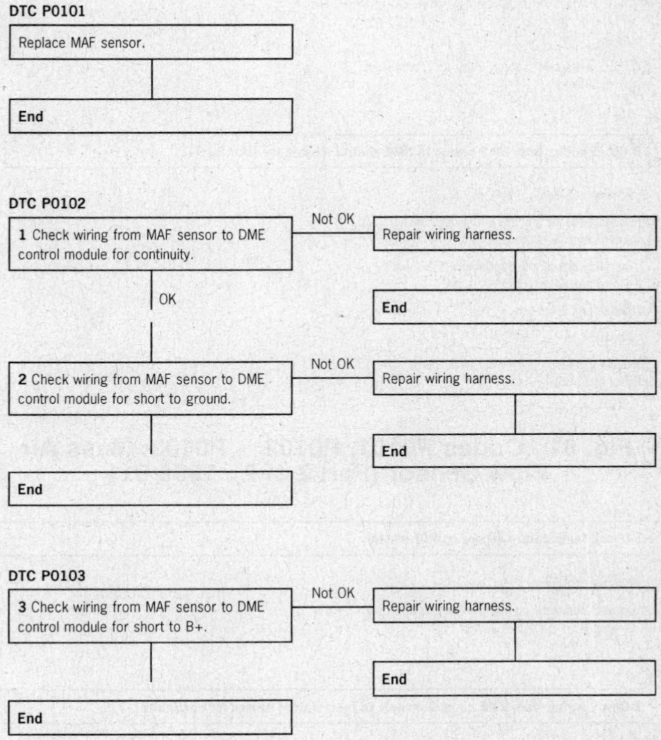

PR1029900049010X

Fig. 81 Codes P0101, P0102 & P0103: Mass Air Flow Sensor (Part 1 of 2). 1999 911

1 Check wiring from MAF sensor to DME control module for continuity.

1. Remove connector of MAF sensor.
2. Connect special tool 9616 to wiring harness (DME control module connector).
3. Connect ohmmeter to special tool 9616, pin 17, and MAF sensor connector, pin 5.
   Display: 0 - 5 Ω

If ∞ Ω is displayed, check wiring harness for chafing and pinching damage.

2 Check wiring from MAF sensor to DME control module for short to ground.

1. Remove connector of MAF sensor.
2. Connect special tool 9616 to wiring harness (DME control module connector).
3. Connect ohmmeter to special tool 9616, pin 17, and to ground, pin 6.
   Display: ∞ Ω

If 0 - 5 Ω is displayed, check wiring for chafing and pinching damage.

3 Check wiring from MAF sensor to DME control module for short to B+.

1. Remove connector of MAF sensor.
2. Connect special tool 9616 to wiring harness (DME control module connector).
3. Connect voltmeter to special tool 9616, pin 17 (B+), and to ground, pin 6.
4. Switch on the ignition.
5. Display: 0 V

If battery voltage is displayed, check wiring harness for chafing and pinching damage.

PR1029900049020X

Fig. 81 Codes P0101, P0102 & P0103: Mass Air Flow Sensor (Part 2 of 2). 1999 911

1 Check temperature sensor in MAF sensor.

1. Remove connector of MAF sensor.
2. Connect ohmmeter to MAF sensor pins 1 and 3.
   Display: 2.3 - 2.7 kΩ at 20 °C

2 Check wiring from DME control module to temperature sensor for continuity.

1. Remove connector of MAF sensor.
2. Connect special tool 9616 to wiring harness (DME control module connector).
3. Connect ohmmeter to special tool 9616, pin 15, and MAF sensor connector, pin 1.
   Display: 0 - 5 Ω.

If ∞ Ω is displayed, check wiring harness for chafing and pinching damage.

3 Check wiring from DME control module to temperature sensor for short to ground.

1. Remove connector of MAF sensor.
2. Connect special tool 9616 to wiring harness (DME control module connector).
3. Connect ohmmeter to special tool 9616, pin 15, and to ground, pin 6.
   Display: ∞ Ω

If 0 - 5 Ω is displayed, check wiring for chafing and pinching damage.

PR1029900050020X

Fig. 82 Codes P0112 & P0113: Intake Air Temperature Sensor (Part 2 of 3). 1999 911

DTC P0112

1 Check temperature sensor in MAF sensor. — Not OK → Replace MAF sensor. → **End**
OK ↓

2 Check wiring from DME control module to temperature sensor for continuity. — Not OK → Repair wiring harness. → **End**
OK ↓

3 Check wiring from DME control module to temperature sensor for short to ground. — Not OK → Repair wiring harness. → **End**
↓
End

DTC P0113

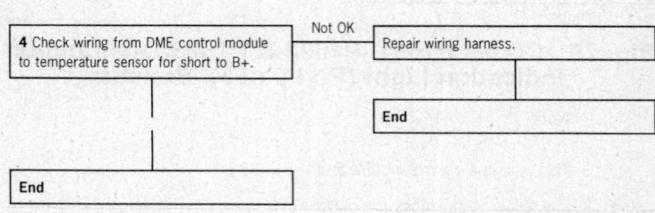

4 Check wiring from DME control module to temperature sensor for short to B+. — Not OK → Repair wiring harness. → **End**
↓
End

PR1029900050010X

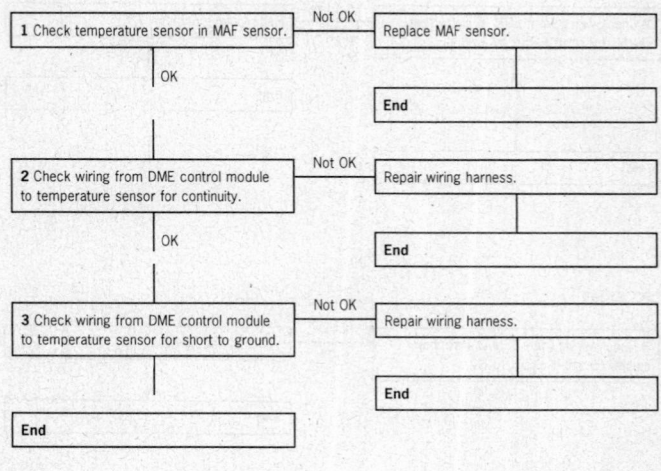

Fig. 82 Codes P0112 & P0113: Intake Air Temperature Sensor (Part 1 of 3). 1999 911

4 Check wiring from DME control module to temperature sensor for short to B+.

1. Remove connector of MAF sensor.
2. Connect special tool 9616 to wiring harness (DME control module connector).
3. Switch on the ignition.
4. Connect voltmeter to special tool 9616, pin 15 (B+), and to ground, pin 6.
   Display: 0 V

If battery voltage is displayed, check wiring harness for chafing and pinching damage.

PR1029900050030X

Fig. 82 Codes P0112 & P0113: Intake Air Temperature Sensor (Part 3 of 3). 1999 911

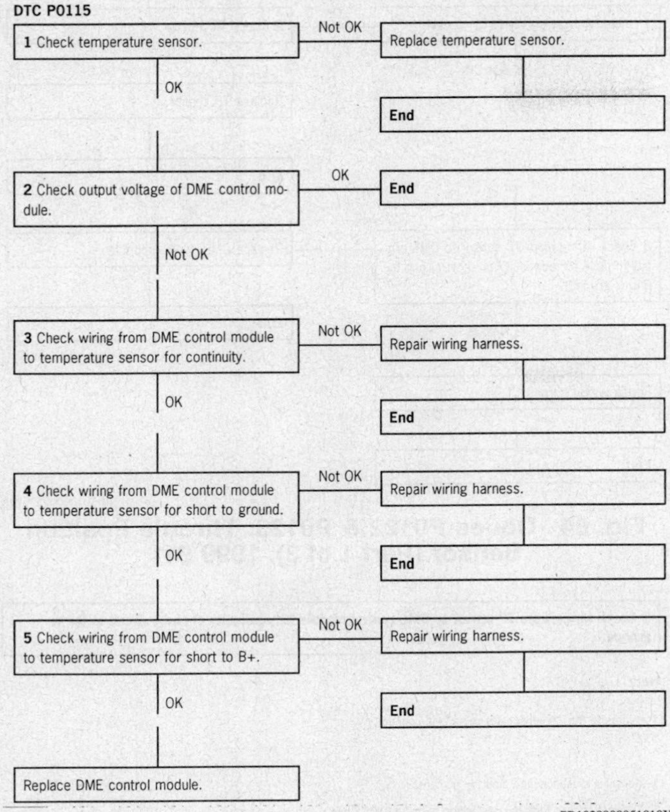

PR1029900051010X

Fig. 83 Codes P0115, P0117 & P0118: Engine Coolant Temperature Sensor (Part 1 of 5). 1999 911

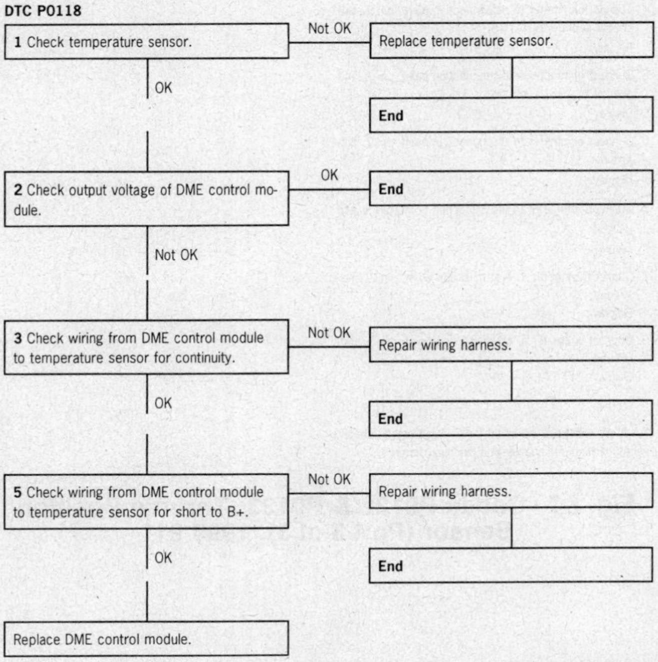

PR1029900051030X

Fig. 83 Codes P0115, P0117 & P0118: Engine Coolant Temperature Sensor (Part 3 of 5). 1999 911

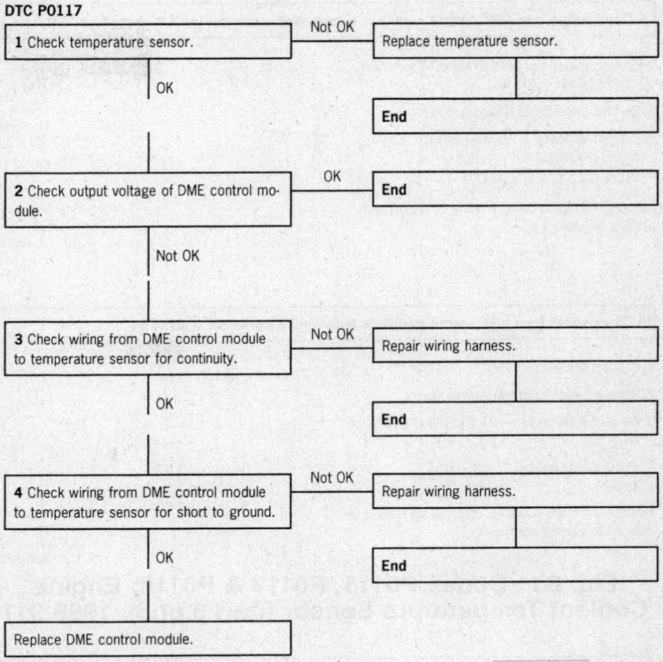

PR1029900051020X

Fig. 83 Codes P0115, P0117 & P0118: Engine Coolant Temperature Sensor (Part 2 of 5). 1999 911

1 Check temperature sensor.

1. Remove connector in engine compartment.
2. Connect ohmmeter to temperature sensor at pins 1 and 4.
   Display: 2 - 3 kΩ at 20 °C.

2 Check output voltage of DME control module.

1. Connect special tool 9616.
2. Connect voltmeter to pin 74 (positive) and 34 (negative).
3. Ignition on.
   Display: approx. 5 V

3 Check wiring from DME control module to temperature sensor for continuity.

1. Connect special tool 9616 to wiring harness (DME control module connector).
2. Remove connector of temperature sensor.
3. Connect ohmmeter to special tool 9616, pin 34, and temperature sensor connector, pin 4.
   Display: 0 - 5 Ω
4. Connect ohmmeter to special tool 9616, pin 74, and temperature sensor connector, pin 1.
   Display: 0 - 5 Ω

PR1029900051040X

Fig. 83 Codes P0115, P0117 & P0118: Engine Coolant Temperature Sensor (Part 4 of 5). 1999 911

4 Check wiring from DME control module to temperature sensor for short to ground.

1. Connect special tool 9616 to wiring harness (DME control module connector).
2. Remove connector of temperature sensor.
3. Connect ohmmeter to special tool 9616, pin 74, and to ground, pin 6.
   Display: ∞ Ω

If 0 - 5 Ω is displayed, check wiring for chafing and pinching damage.

5 Check wiring from DME control module to temperature sensor for short to B+.

1. Connect special tool 9616.
2. Remove connector of temperature sensor.
3. Connect voltmeter to pin 74 (B+) and to ground, pin 6.
4. Switch on the ignition.
   Display: approx. 5 V

If battery voltage is displayed, check wiring harness for chafing and pinching damage.

PR1029900051050X

Fig. 83 Codes P0115, P0117 & P0118: Engine Coolant Temperature Sensor (Part 5 of 5). 1999 911

1 Check voltage supply to TP sensor.

1. Connect special tool 9616.
2. Connect voltmeter to pin 53 (positive) and pin 34 (negative).
   Switch on the ignition.
   Display: approx. 4.5 - 5 volts

2 Check TP sensor.

1. Connect special tool 9616 to wiring harness (DME control module connector).
2. Connect ohmmeter to pin 44 and pin 53.
   Display: approx. 2.0 - 3.0 kΩ

   Fully depress accelerator pedal.
   Display: approx. 0.7 - 1.4 kΩ

If there is no display, check the throttle position sensor directly.

PR1029900052020X

Fig. 84 Codes P0122 & P0123: Throttle Position Sensor (Part 2 of 3). 1999 911

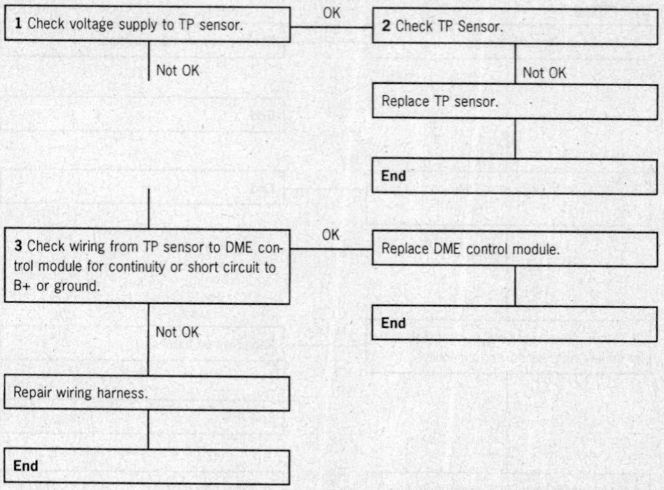

PR1029900052010X

Fig. 84 Codes P0122 & P0123: Throttle Position Sensor (Part 1 of 3). 1999 911

3 Check wiring from TP sensor to DME control module for continuity or short circuit to B+ or ground.

Note

The wires to the TP sensor are routed via connector X 59/2.

1. Separate disconnection point to TP sensor.
2. Connect special tool 9616 to wiring harness (DME control module connector).
3. Connect ohmmeter to disconnection point, pin 1, and special tool 9616, pin 34.
   Display: 0 - 5 Ω
4. Connect ohmmeter to disconnection point, pin 2, and special tool 9616, pin 53.
   Display: 0 - 5 Ω
5. Connect ohmmeter to disconnection point, pin 3, and special tool 9616, pin 44.
   Display: 0 - 5 Ω
6. Connect ohmmeter to disconnection point, pin 2, and ground.
   Display: ∞ Ω
7. Connect ohmmeter to disconnection point, pin 3, and ground.
   Display: ∞ Ω
8. Connect voltmeter to disconnection point, pin 2, and ground.
   Display: 0 V
9. Connect voltmeter to disconnection point, pin 3, and ground.
   Display: 0 V

If battery voltage is indicated for points 8 and 9, check wiring harness for chafing and pinching damage.

PR1029900052030X

Fig. 84 Codes P0122 & P0123: Throttle Position Sensor (Part 3 of 3). 1999 911

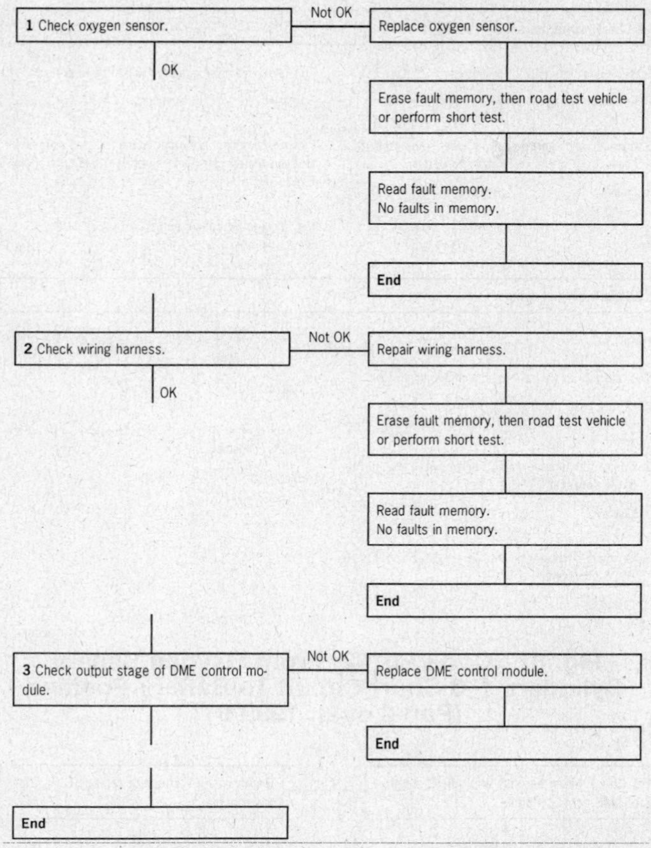

PR1029900053010X

Fig. 85 Code P0130: Front Oxygen Sensor Cylinders 1–3 Short Circuit Or Limited Voltage Increase (Part 1 of 2). 1999 911

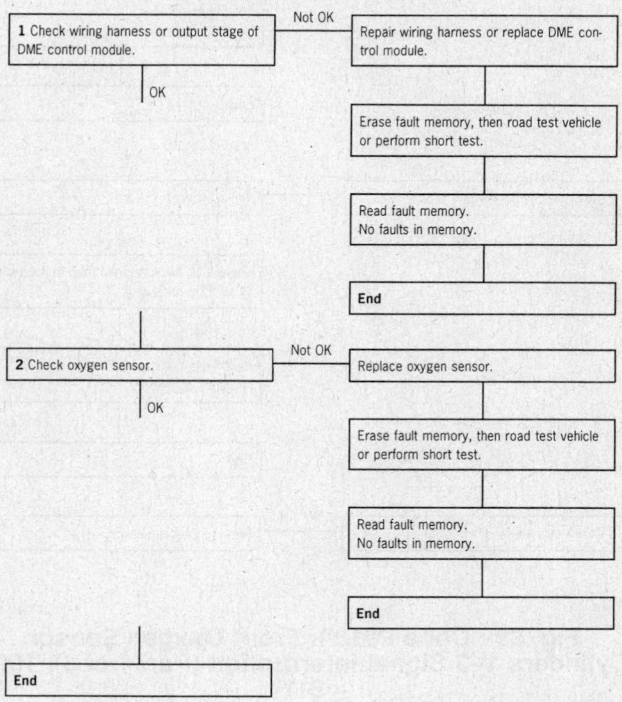

PR1029900054010X

Fig. 86 Code P0131: Front Oxygen Sensor Cylinders 1–3 Short Circuit To Ground Or Incorrect Voltage (Part 1 of 2). 1999 911

1 Check oxygen sensor.

1. Heat the oxygen sensors (road test car under load or run engine without load at high rpm).
2. Connect Porsche System Tester 2 or scan tool and read voltage of oxygen sensor 1 ahead of catalytic converter.

   Display: Voltage fluctuations between 100 mV and 800 mV.
   ➡ Oxygen sensor OK.

If a value around 0 V is displayed, a short circuit has occurred between the signal wire and sensor ground.

3. Remove HO2S connector 1 ahead of catalytic converter.
4. Connect voltmeter at sleeve to pins 3 and 4.

   Display: approx. 450 mV.
   ➡ Replace oxygen sensor.

   Display: approx. 0 V
   ➡ Check wiring harness.

If the wiring harness is OK, remove all oxygen sensor connectors and perform measurement to item 4 on all oxygen sensors.

2 Check wiring harness.

1. Remove all four oxygen sensor connectors.
2. Connect special tool 9616 to wiring harness (DME control module connector).
3. With an ohmmeter, measure resistance between special tool 9616, pin 19, and oxygen sensor connector, pin 4.

   Display: 0 - 5 Ω
4. With an ohmmeter, measure resistance between special tool 9616, pin 46, and oxygen sensor connector, pin 3.

   Display: 0 - 5 Ω

3 Check output stage of DME control module.

1. Connect special tool 9616.
2. Remove HO2S connector 1 ahead of catalytic converter.
3. Connect voltmeter to pins 19 and 46.
4. Switch on the ignition.

   Display: approx. 450 mV

If display shows < 400 mV or > 500 mV, replace DME control module.

PR1029900053020X

Fig. 85 Code P0130: Front Oxygen Sensor Cylinders 1–3 Short Circuit Or Limited Voltage Increase (Part 2 of 2). 1999 911

1 Check wiring harness.

1. Remove all four HO2S connectors.
2. Switch on the ignition.
3. Connect voltmeter at sleeve to pins 3 and 4 of HO2S connector 1 ahead of catalytic converter.

   Display: approx. 450 mV
4. Connect voltmeter at sleeve to pin 3 and ground.

   Display: approx. 720 mV

If the measurement according to items 3 and 4 does not show the specified values, remove DME control module connector and check wiring for short to ground.

If no short to ground can be detected, replace DME control module.

2 Check oxygen sensor.

1. Remove HO2S connector 1 ahead of catalytic converter.
2. Connect ohmmeter on pin side to pin 3 and to HO2S housing.

   Display: ∞ Ω
3. Connect ohmmeter on pin side to pins 3 and 2.

   Display: ∞ Ω
4. Connect ohmmeter on pin side to pin 4 and to HO2S housing.

   Display: ∞ Ω
5. Connect ohmmeter on pin side to pins 4 and 2.

   Display: ∞ Ω

PR1029900054020X

Fig. 86 Code P0131: Front Oxygen Sensor Cylinders 1–3 Short Circuit To Ground Or Incorrect Voltage (Part 2 of 2). 1999 911

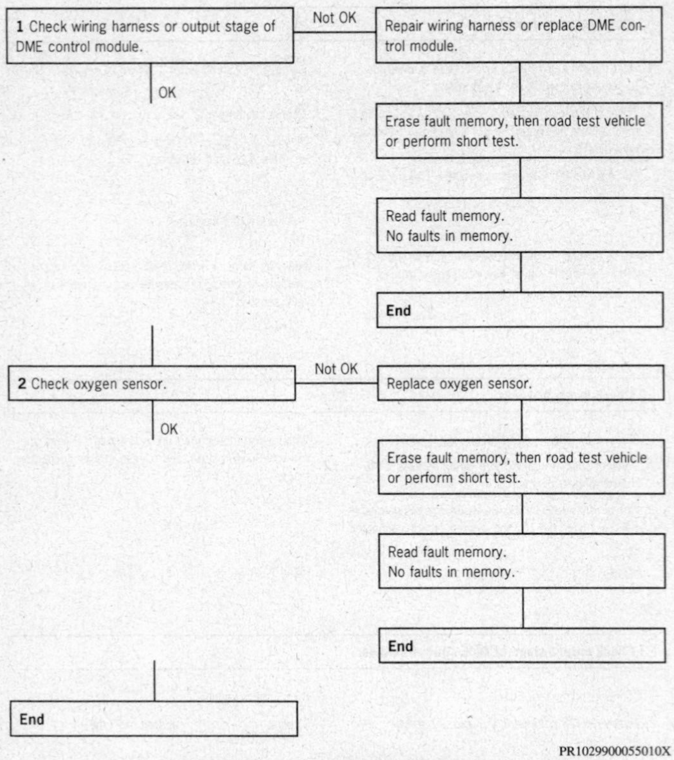

Fig. 87 Code P0132: Front Oxygen Sensor Cylinders 1–3 Short Circuit To Battery Positive (Part 1 of 2). 1999 911

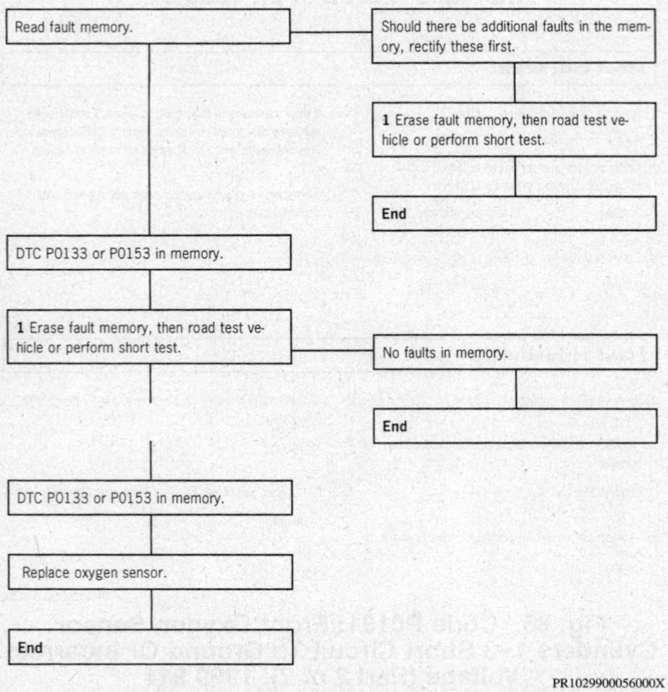

Fig. 88 Codes P0133, P0153, P1275 & P1276: Front Oxygen Sensors Aging. 1999 911

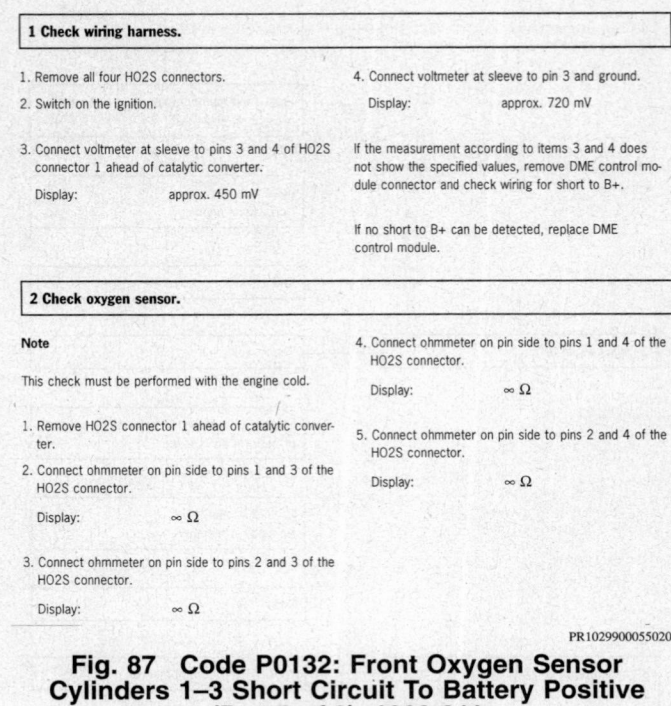

1 Check wiring harness.

1. Remove all four HO2S connectors.
2. Switch on the ignition.
3. Connect voltmeter at sleeve to pins 3 and 4 of HO2S connector 1 ahead of catalytic converter.

   Display: approx. 450 mV

4. Connect voltmeter at sleeve to pin 3 and ground.

   Display: approx. 720 mV

If the measurement according to items 3 and 4 does not show the specified values, remove DME control module connector and check wiring for short to B+.

If no short to B+ can be detected, replace DME control module.

2 Check oxygen sensor.

Note

This check must be performed with the engine cold.

1. Remove HO2S connector 1 ahead of catalytic converter.
2. Connect ohmmeter on pin side to pins 1 and 3 of the HO2S connector.

   Display: ∞ Ω

3. Connect ohmmeter on pin side to pins 2 and 3 of the HO2S connector.

   Display: ∞ Ω

4. Connect ohmmeter on pin side to pins 1 and 4 of the HO2S connector.

   Display: ∞ Ω

5. Connect ohmmeter on pin side to pins 2 and 4 of the HO2S connector.

   Display: ∞ Ω

PR1029900055020X

Fig. 87 Code P0132: Front Oxygen Sensor Cylinders 1–3 Short Circuit To Battery Positive (Part 2 of 2). 1999 911

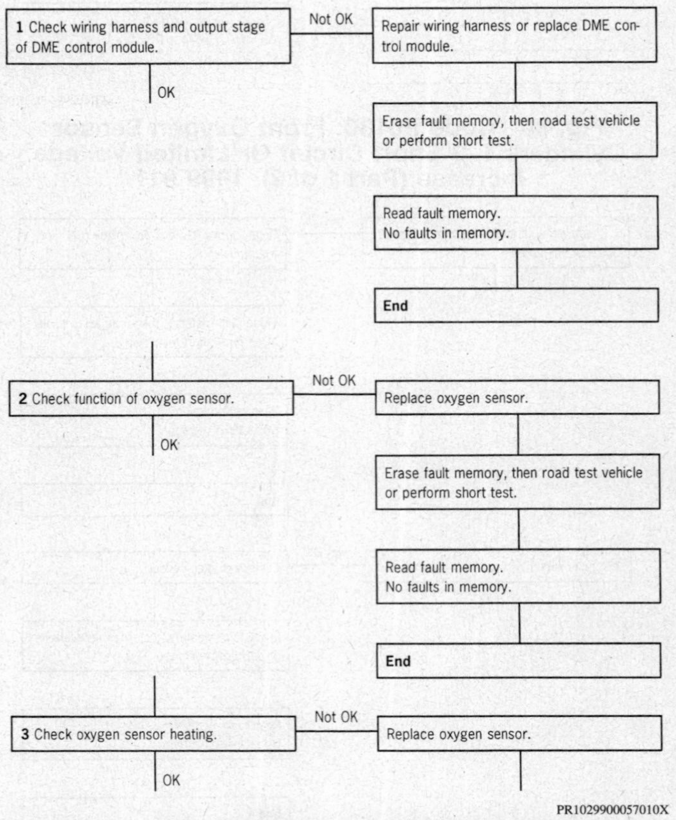

Fig. 89 Code P0134: Front Oxygen Sensor Cylinders 1–3 Signal Interruption (Part 1 of 3). 1999 911

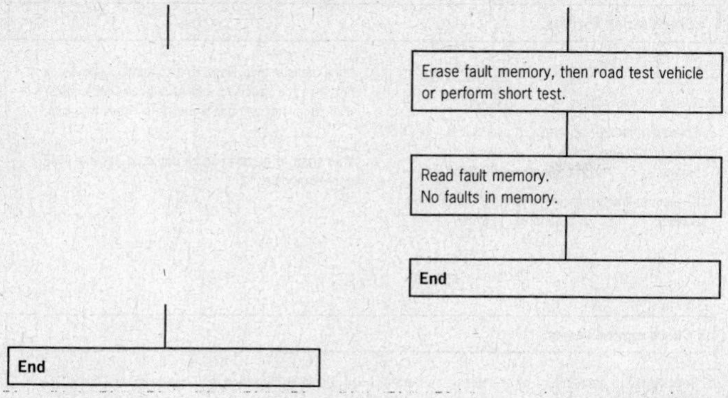

PR1029900057020X

Fig. 89 Code P0134: Front Oxygen Sensor Cylinders 1–3 Signal Interruption (Part 2 of 3). 1999 911

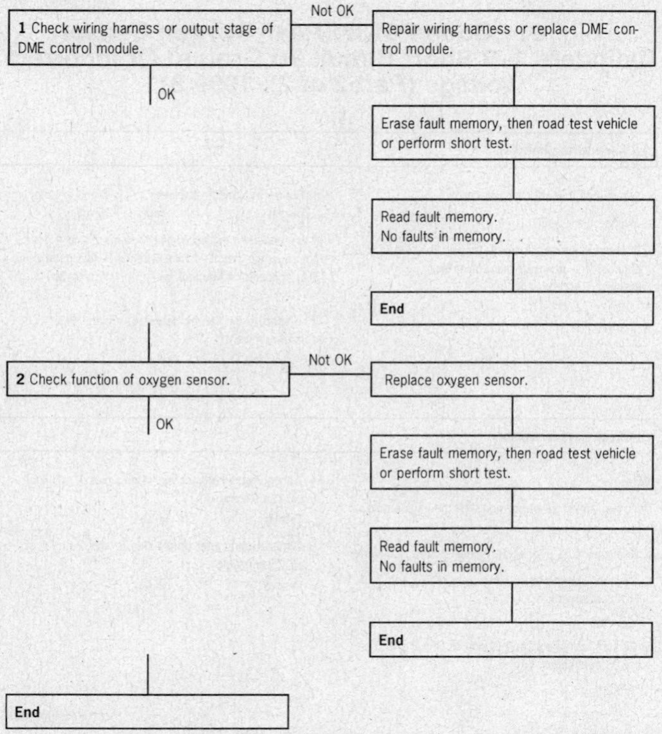

PR1029900058010X

Fig. 90 Code P0136: Rear Oxygen Sensor Cylinders 1–3 Short Circuit (Part 1 of 2). 1999 911

1 Check wiring harness.

1. Remove all four HO2S connectors.
2. Switch on the ignition.
3. Connect voltmeter at sleeve to pins 3 and 4 of HO2S connector 1 ahead of catalytic converter.

   Display: approx. 450 mV

4. Connect voltmeter at sleeve to pin 3 and ground.

   Display: approx. 720 mV

5. Start engine and run at high speed for three minutes.
6. Connect voltmeter at sleeve to pins 1 and 2.

   Display: battery voltage

If the measurement according to items 3, 4 or 6 does not show the specified values, remove DME control module connector and check wiring for continuity.

If no continuity can be detected, repair wiring harness. If continuity exists, replace DME control module.

2 Check function of oxygen sensor.

1. Heat the oxygen sensors (road test car under load or run engine without load at high rpm).
2. Connect Porsche System Tester 2 or scan tool and read voltage of oxygen sensor 1 ahead of catalytic converter.

   Display: Voltage fluctuations between 100 mV and 800 mV.
   ➡Oxygen sensor OK.

3 Check oxygen sensor heating.

1. Remove HO2S connector 1 ahead of catalytic converter.
2. Connect ohmmeter on pin side to pins 1 and 2.

   Display: 1.8 - 2.5 Ω at 20 °C.

3. Connect ohmmeter on pin side to pin 1 and HO2S housing.

   Display: ∞ Ω

4. Connect ohmmeter on pin side to pin 2 and HO2S housing.

   Display: ∞ Ω

PR1029900057030X

Fig. 89 Code P0134: Front Oxygen Sensor Cylinders 1–3 Signal Interruption (Part 3 of 3). 1999 911

1 Check wiring harness.

1. Remove all four HO2S connectors.
2. Connect voltmeter at sleeve to pins 3 and 4 of HO2S connector 1 after catalytic converter.
3. Switch on the ignition.
   Display: approx. 450 mV
4. Connect voltmeter at sleeve to pin 3 and ground.
   Display: approx. 720 mV

If the measurement according to items 3 and 4 does not show the specified values, remove DME control module connector and check wiring for short circuit.

If wiring is OK, replace DME control module.

2 Check function of oxygen sensor.

1. Heat the oxygen sensors (road test car under load or run engine without load at high rpm).
2. Connect Porsche System Tester 2 or scan tool and read voltage of oxygen sensor 1 after catalytic converter.
3. Change the fuel/air ratio with acceleration bursts.
   Display: Voltage fluctuations between 100 mV and 800 mV.
   ➡Oxygen sensor OK.

If the oxygen sensor voltage is approx. 0 V, replace oxygen sensor.

PR1029900058020X

Fig. 90 Code P0136: Rear Oxygen Sensor Cylinders 1–3 Short Circuit (Part 2 of 2). 1999 911

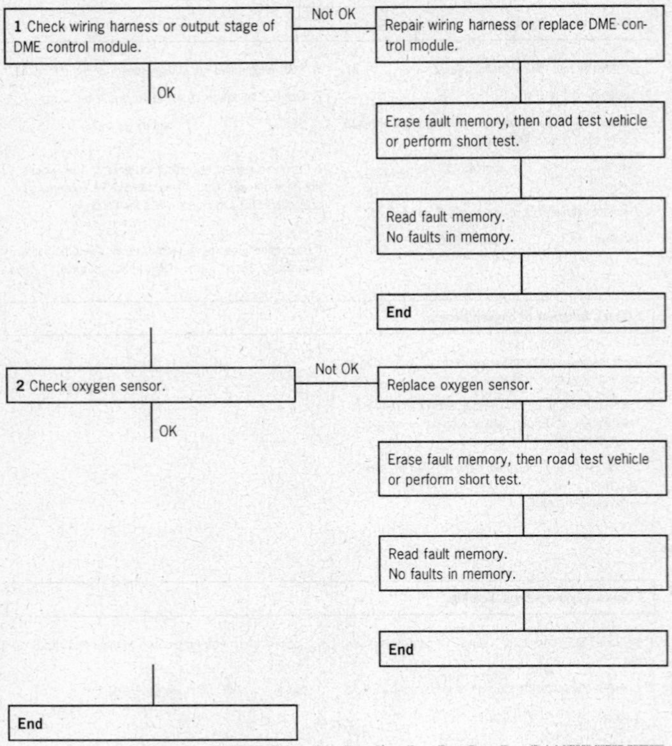

PR1029900059010X

Fig. 91 Code P0137: Rear Oxygen Sensor Cylinders 1–3 Short Circuit To Ground Or Incorrect Voltage (Part 1 of 2). 1999 911

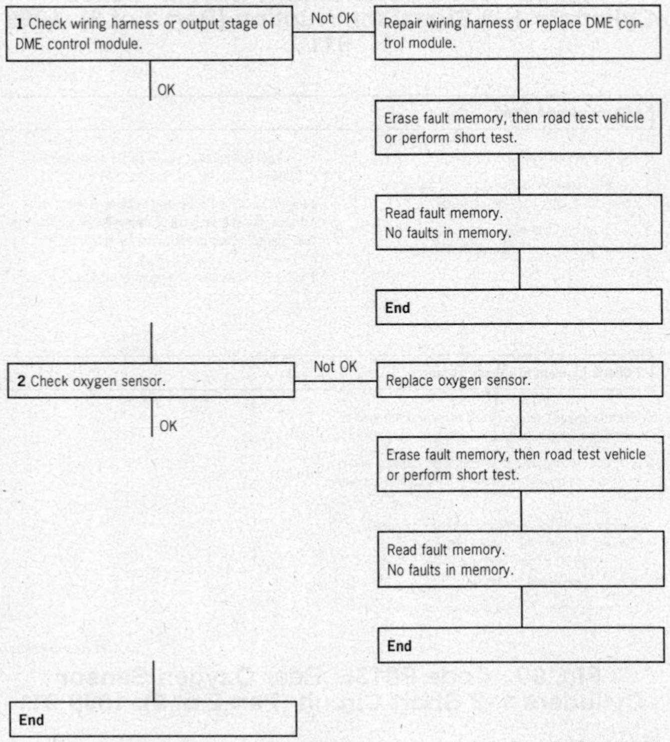

PR1029900060010X

Fig. 92 Code P0138: Rear Oxygen Sensor Cylinders 1–3 Short Circuit To Battery Positive (Part 1 of 2). 1999 911

1 Check wiring harness.

1. Remove all four HO2S connectors.
2. Switch on the ignition.
3. Connect voltmeter at sleeve to pins 3 and 4 of HO2S connector 1 after catalytic converter.
   Display: approx. 450 mV
4. Connect voltmeter at sleeve to pin 3 and ground.
   Display: approx. 720 mV

If the measurement according to items 3 and 4 does not show the specified values, remove DME control module connector and check wiring for short to ground.

If no short to ground can be detected, replace DME control module.

2 Check oxygen sensor.

1. Remove HO2S connector 1 after catalytic converter.
2. Connect ohmmeter on pin side to pin 3 and to HO2S housing.
   Display: ∞ Ω
3. Connect ohmmeter on pin side to pin 4 and to HO2S housing.
   Display: ∞ Ω
4. Connect ohmmeter on pin side to pins 4 and 2.
   Display: ∞ Ω
5. Connect ohmmeter on pin side to pins 3 and 2.
   Display: ∞ Ω

PR1029900059020X

Fig. 91 Code P0137: Rear Oxygen Sensor Cylinders 1–3 Short Circuit To Ground Or Incorrect Voltage (Part 2 of 2). 1999 911

1 Check wiring harness.

1. Remove all four HO2S connectors.
2. Switch on the ignition.
3. Connect voltmeter at sleeve to pins 3 and 4 of HO2S connector 1 after catalytic converter.
   Display: approx. 450 mV
4. Connect voltmeter at sleeve to pin 3 and ground.
   Display: approx. 720 mV

If the measurement according to items 3 and 4 does not show the specified values, remove DME control module connector and check wiring for short to B+.

If no short to B+ can be detected, replace DME control module.

2 Check oxygen sensor.

Note

This check must be performed with the engine cold.

1. Remove HO2S connector 1 after catalytic converter.
2. Connect ohmmeter on pin side to pins 1 and 3 of HO2S connector.
   Display: ∞ Ω
3. Connect ohmmeter on pin side to pins 2 and 3 of HO2S connector.
   Display: ∞ Ω
4. Connect ohmmeter on pin side to pins 1 and 4 of HO2S connector.
   Display: ∞ Ω
5. Connect ohmmeter on pin side to pins 2 and 4 of HO2S connector.
   Display: ∞ Ω

PR1029900060020X

Fig. 92 Code P0138: Rear Oxygen Sensor Cylinders 1–3 Short Circuit To Battery Positive (Part 2 of 2). 1999 911

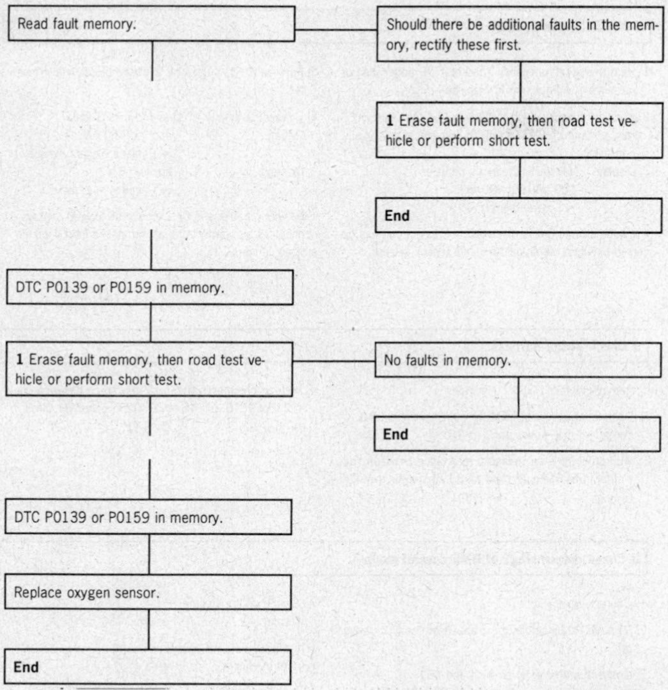

PR1029900061000X

Fig. 93 Codes P0139 & P0159: Rear Oxygen Sensors Aging. 1999 911

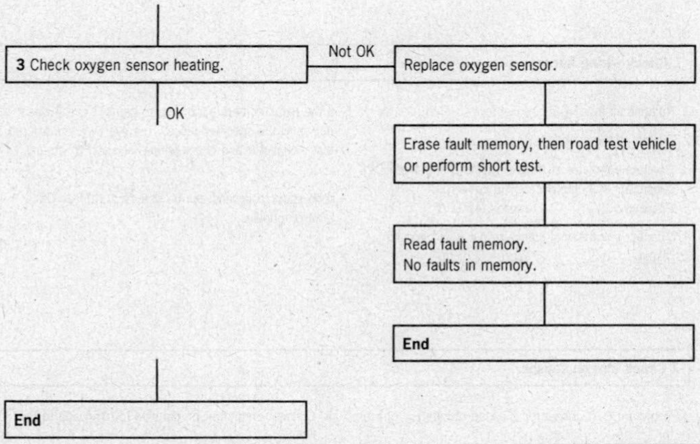

PR1029900062020X

Fig. 94 Code P0140: Rear Oxygen Sensor Cylinders 1–3 Signal Interruption (Part 2 of 3). 1999 911

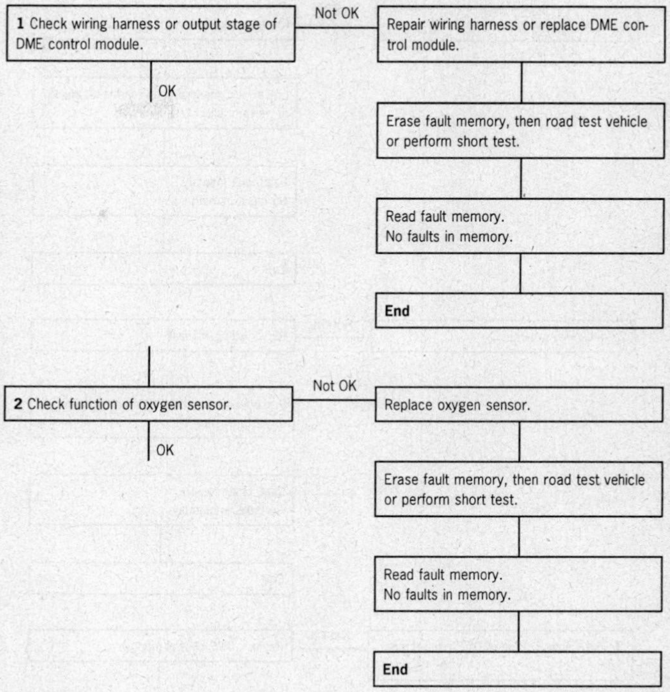

PR1029900062010X

Fig. 94 Code P0140: Rear Oxygen Sensor Cylinders 1–3 Signal Interruption (Part 1 of 3). 1999 911

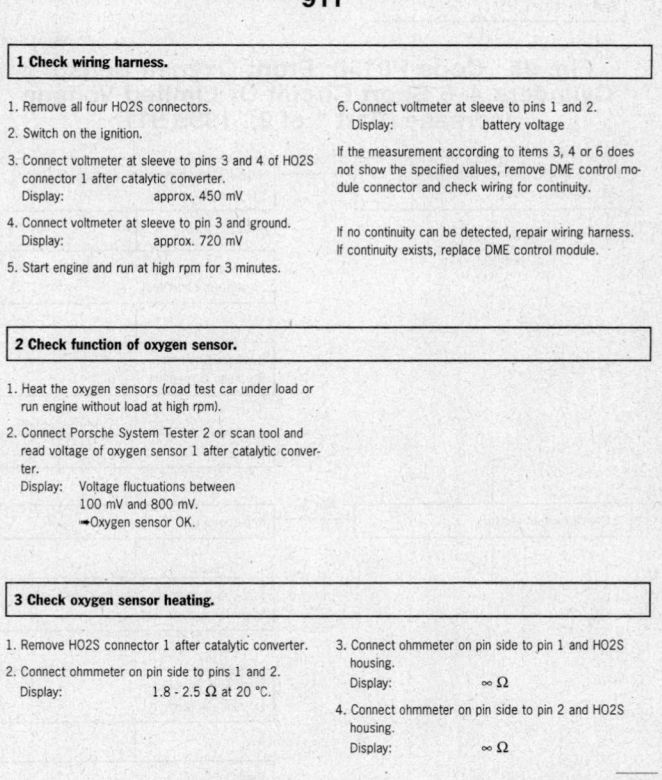

1 Check wiring harness.

1. Remove all four HO2S connectors.
2. Switch on the ignition.
3. Connect voltmeter at sleeve to pins 3 and 4 of HO2S connector 1 after catalytic converter.
   Display: approx. 450 mV
4. Connect voltmeter at sleeve to pin 3 and ground.
   Display: approx. 720 mV
5. Start engine and run at high rpm for 3 minutes.
6. Connect voltmeter at sleeve to pins 1 and 2.
   Display: battery voltage

If the measurement according to items 3, 4 or 6 does not show the specified values, remove DME control module connector and check wiring for continuity.

If no continuity can be detected, repair wiring harness.
If continuity exists, replace DME control module.

2 Check function of oxygen sensor.

1. Heat the oxygen sensors (road test car under load or run engine without load at high rpm).
2. Connect Porsche System Tester 2 or scan tool and read voltage of oxygen sensor 1 after catalytic converter.
   Display: Voltage fluctuations between 100 mV and 800 mV.
   ➡Oxygen sensor OK.

3 Check oxygen sensor heating.

1. Remove HO2S connector 1 after catalytic converter.
2. Connect ohmmeter on pin side to pins 1 and 2.
   Display: 1.8 - 2.5 Ω at 20 °C.
3. Connect ohmmeter on pin side to pin 1 and HO2S housing.
   Display: ∞ Ω
4. Connect ohmmeter on pin side to pin 2 and HO2S housing.
   Display: ∞ Ω

PR1029900062030X

Fig. 94 Code P0140: Rear Oxygen Sensor Cylinders 1–3 Signal Interruption (Part 3 of 3). 1999 911

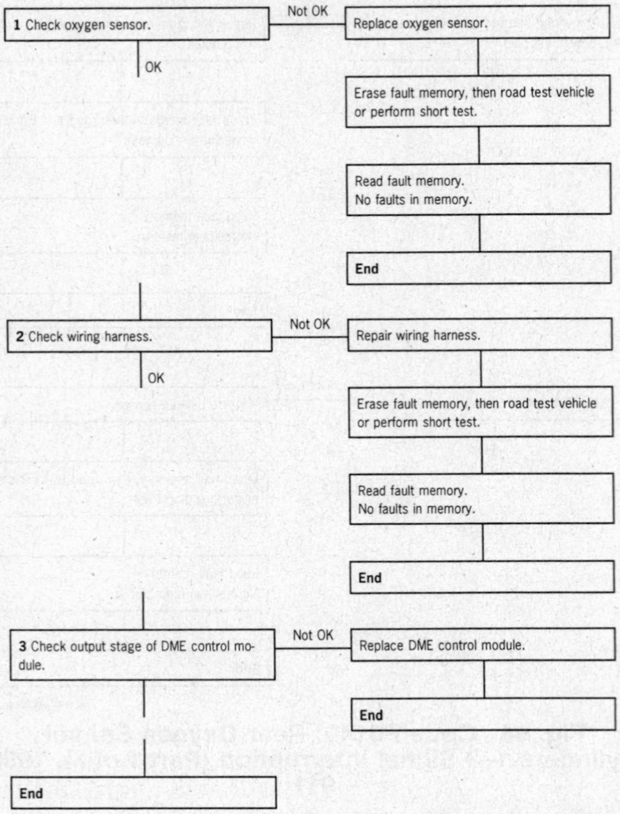

PR1029900063010X

Fig. 95 Code P0150: Front Oxygen Sensor Cylinders 4–6 Short Circuit Or Limited Voltage Increase (Part 1 of 2). 1999 911

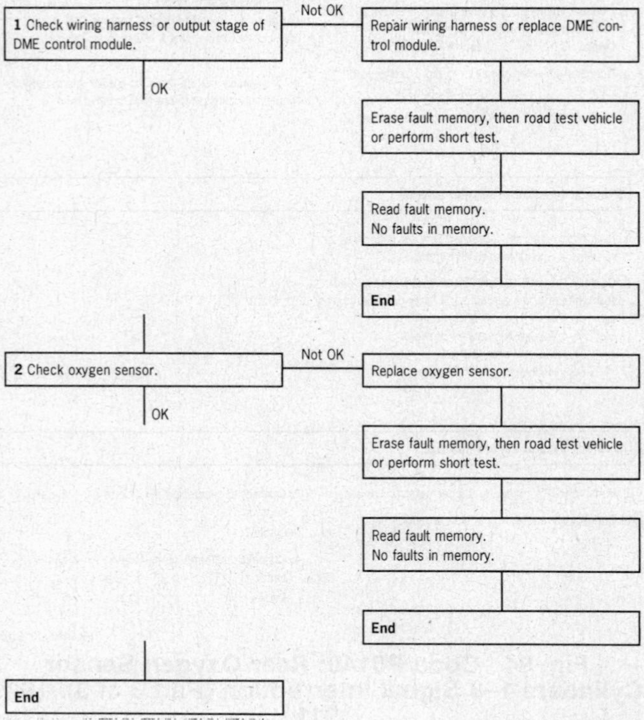

PR1029900064010X

Fig. 96 Code P0151: Front Oxygen Sensor Cylinders 4–6 Short Circuit To Ground Or Incorrect Voltage (Part 1 of 2). 1999 911

1 Check oxygen sensor.

1. Heat the oxygen sensors (road test car under load or run engine without load at high rpm).
2. Connect Porsche System Tester 2 or scan tool and read voltage of oxygen sensor 2 ahead of catalytic converter.
   Display: Voltage fluctuations between 100 mV and 800 mV.
   ➠ Oxygen sensor OK.

If a value around 0 V is displayed, a short circuit has occurred between the signal wire and sensor ground.

3. Remove HO2S connector 2 ahead of catalytic converter.
4. Connect voltmeter at sleeve to pins 3 and 4.
   Display: approx. 450 mV.
   ➠ Replace oxygen sensor.
   Display: approx. 0 V
   ➠ Check wiring harness.

If the wiring harness is OK, remove all oxygen sensor connectors and perform measurement to item 4 on all oxygen sensors.

2 Check wiring harness.

1. Remove all four HO2S connectors.
2. Connect special tool 9616 to wiring harness (DME control module connector).
3. With an ohmmeter, measure resistance between special tool 9616, pin 18, and HO2S connector, pin 4.
   Display: 0 - 5 Ω
4. With an ohmmeter, measure resistance between special tool 9616, pin 46, and HO2S connector, pin 3.
   Display: 0 - 5 Ω

3 Check output stage of DME control module.

1. Connect special tool 9616.
2. Remove HO2S connector 2 ahead of catalytic converter.
3. Connect voltmeter to pins 18 and 46.
4. Switch on the ignition.
   Display: approx. 450 mV

If display shows < 400 mV or > 500 mV, replace DME control module.

PR1029900063020X

Fig. 95 Code P0150: Front Oxygen Sensor Cylinders 4–6 Short Circuit Or Limited Voltage Increase (Part 2 of 2). 1999 911

1 Check wiring harness.

1. Remove all four HO2S connectors.
2. Switch on the ignition.
3. Connect voltmeter at sleeve to pins 3 and 4 of HO2S connector 2 ahead of catalytic converter.
   Display: approx. 450 mV
4. Connect voltmeter at sleeve to pin 3 and ground.
   Display: approx. 720 mV

If the measurement according to items 3 and 4 does not show the specified values, remove DME control module connector and check wiring for short to ground.

If no short to ground can be detected, replace DME control module.

2 Check oxygen sensor.

1. Remove HO2S connector 2 ahead of catalytic converter.
2. Connect ohmmeter on pin side to pin 3 and to HO2S housing.
   Display: ∞ Ω
3. Connect ohmmeter on pin side to pins 3 and 2.
   Display: ∞ Ω
4. Connect ohmmeter on pin side to pin 4 and to HO2S housing.
   Display: ∞ Ω
5. Connect ohmmeter on pin side to pins 4 and 2.
   Display: ∞ Ω

PR1029900064020X

Fig. 96 Code P0151: Front Oxygen Sensor Cylinders 4–6 Short Circuit To Ground Or Incorrect Voltage (Part 2 of 2). 1999 911

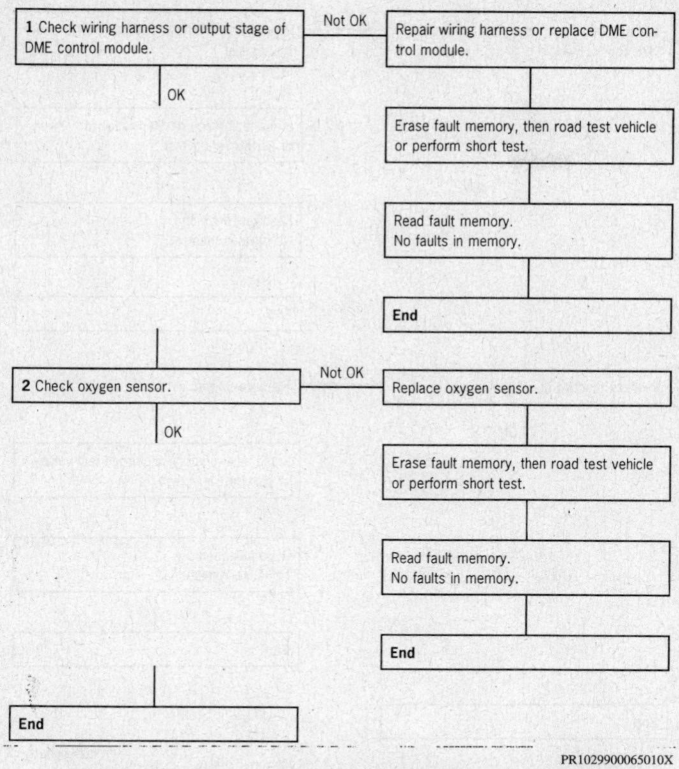

Fig. 97 Code P0152: Front Oxygen Sensor Cylinders 4–6 Short Circuit To Battery Positive (Part 1 of 2). 1999 911

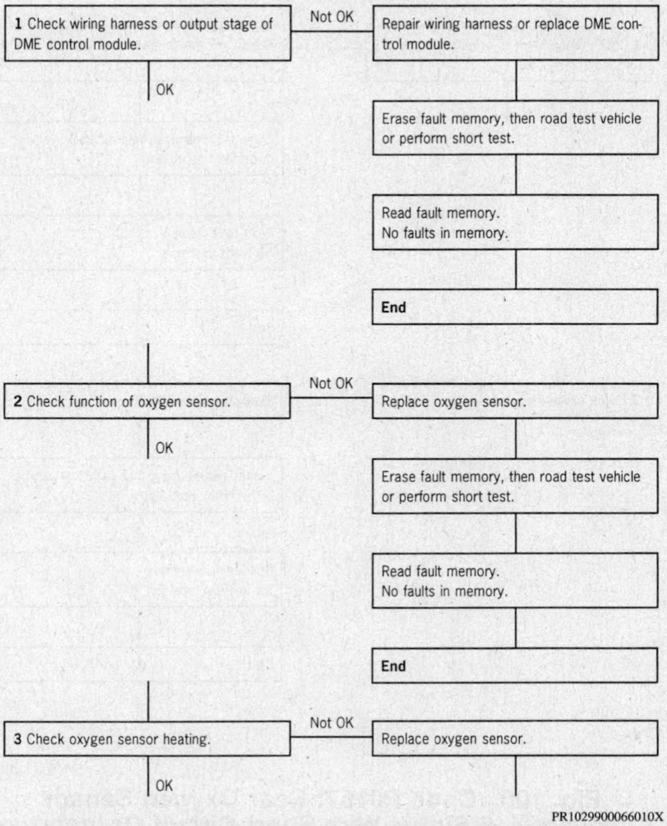

Fig. 98 Code P0154: Front Oxygen Sensor Cylinders 4–6 Signal Interruption (Part 1 of 3). 1999 911

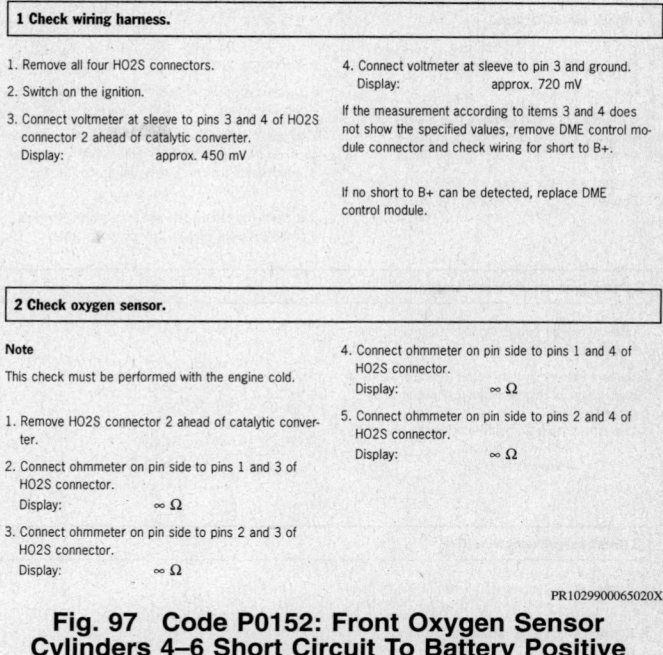

1 Check wiring harness.

1. Remove all four HO2S connectors.
2. Switch on the ignition.
3. Connect voltmeter at sleeve to pins 3 and 4 of HO2S connector 2 ahead of catalytic converter.
   Display: approx. 450 mV
4. Connect voltmeter at sleeve to pin 3 and ground.
   Display: approx. 720 mV

If the measurement according to items 3 and 4 does not show the specified values, remove DME control module connector and check wiring for short to B+.

If no short to B+ can be detected, replace DME control module.

2 Check oxygen sensor.

Note

This check must be performed with the engine cold.

1. Remove HO2S connector 2 ahead of catalytic converter.
2. Connect ohmmeter on pin side to pins 1 and 3 of HO2S connector.
   Display: $\infty\ \Omega$
3. Connect ohmmeter on pin side to pins 2 and 3 of HO2S connector.
   Display: $\infty\ \Omega$
4. Connect ohmmeter on pin side to pins 1 and 4 of HO2S connector.
   Display: $\infty\ \Omega$
5. Connect ohmmeter on pin side to pins 2 and 4 of HO2S connector.
   Display: $\infty\ \Omega$

PR1029900065020X

Fig. 97 Code P0152: Front Oxygen Sensor Cylinders 4–6 Short Circuit To Battery Positive (Part 2 of 2). 1999 911

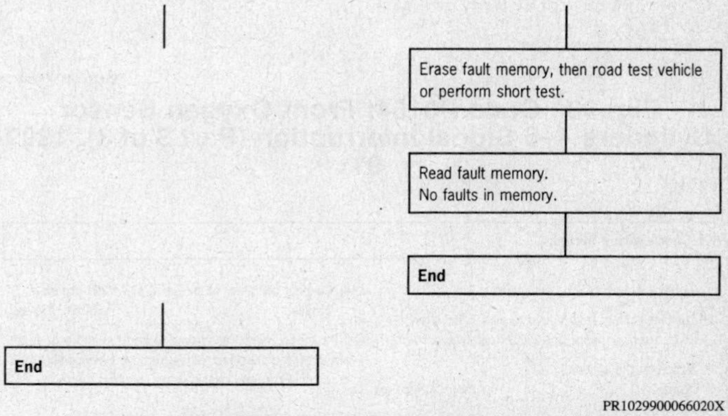

Fig. 98 Code P0154: Front Oxygen Sensor Cylinders 4–6 Signal Interruption (Part 2 of 3). 1999 911

1 Check wiring harness.

1. Remove all four HO2S connectors.
2. Switch on the ignition.
3. Connect voltmeter at sleeve to pins 3 and 4 of HO2S connector 2 ahead of catalytic converter.
   Display: approx. 450 mV
4. Connect voltmeter at sleeve to pin 3 and ground.
   Display: approx. 720 mV
5. Start engine and run at high rpm for 3 minutes.
6. Connect voltmeter at sleeve to pins 1 and 2.
   Display: battery voltage

If the measurement according to items 3, 4 or 6 does not show the specified values, remove DME control module connector and check wiring for continuity.

If no continuity can be detected, repair wiring harness. If continuity exists, replace DME control module.

2 Check function of oxygen sensor.

1. Heat the oxygen sensors (road test car under load or run engine without load at high rpm).
2. Connect Porsche System Tester 2 or scan tool and read voltage of oxygen sensor 2 ahead of catalytic converter.
   Display: Voltage fluctuations between 100 mV and 800 mV.
   ➡Oxygen sensor OK.

3 Check oxygen sensor heating.

1. Remove HO2S connector 2 ahead of catalytic converter.
2. Connect ohmmeter on pin side to pins 1 and 2.
   Display: 1.8 - 2.5 Ω at 20 °C.
3. Connect ohmmeter on pin side to pin 1 and HO2S housing.
   Display: ∞ Ω
4. Connect ohmmeter on pin side to pin 2 and HO2S housing.
   Display: ∞ Ω

PR1029900066030X

Fig. 98 Code P0154: Front Oxygen Sensor Cylinders 4–6 Signal Interruption (Part 3 of 3). 1999 911

1 Check wiring harness.

1. Remove all four HO2S connectors.
2. Connect voltmeter at sleeve to pins 3 and 4 of oxygen sensor connector 2 after catalytic converter.
3. Switch on the ignition.
   Display: approx. 450 mV
4. Connect voltmeter at sleeve to pin 3 and ground.
   Display: approx. 720 mV

If the measurement according to items 3 and 4 does not show the specified values, remove DME control module connector and check wiring for short circuit.

If wiring is OK, replace DME control module.

2 Check function of oxygen sensor.

1. Heat the oxygen sensors (road test car under load or run engine without load at high rpm).
2. Connect Porsche System Tester 2 or scan tool and read voltage of oxygen sensor 2 after catalytic converter.
3. Change the fuel/air ratio with acceleration bursts.
   Display: Voltage fluctuations between 100 mV and 800 mV.
   ➡Oxygen sensor OK.

If the oxygen sensor voltage is approx. 0 V, replace oxygen sensor.

PR1029900067020X

Fig. 99 Code P0156: Rear Oxygen Sensor Cylinders 4–6 Intercore Short Circuit (Part 2 of 2). 1999 911

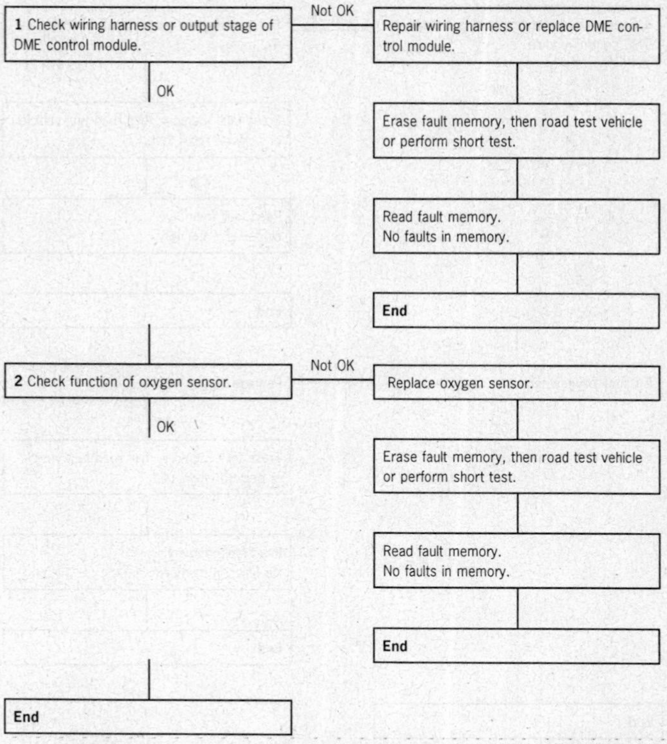

PR1029900067010X

Fig. 99 Code P0156: Rear Oxygen Sensor Cylinders 4–6 Intercore Short Circuit (Part 1 of 2). 1999 911

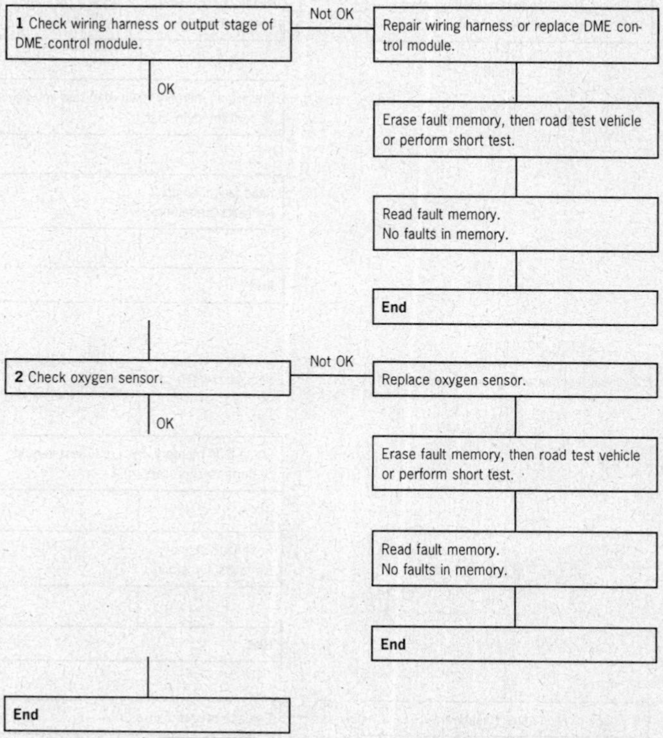

PR1029900068010X

Fig. 100 Code P0157: Rear Oxygen Sensor Cylinders 4–6 Signal Wire Short Circuit Or Incorrect Voltage (Part 1 of 2). 1999 911

1 Check wiring harness.

1. Remove all four HO2S connectors.
2. Switch on the ignition.
3. Connect voltmeter at sleeve to pins 3 and 4 of HO2S connector 2 after catalytic converter.
   Display: approx. 450 mV
4. Connect voltmeter at sleeve to pin 3 and ground.
   Display: approx. 720 mV

If the measurement according to items 3 and 4 does not show the specified values, remove DME control module connector and check wiring for short to ground.

If no short to ground can be detected, replace DME control module.

2 Check oxygen sensor.

1. Remove connector of HO2S 2 after catalytic converter.
2. Connect ohmmeter on pin side to pin 3 and to HO2S housing.
   Display: ∞ Ω
3. Connect ohmmeter on pin side to pin 4 and to HO2S housing.
   Display: ∞ Ω
4. Connect ohmmeter on pin side to pins 4 and 2.
   Display: ∞ Ω
5. Connect ohmmeter on pin side to pins 3 and 2.
   Display: ∞ Ω

PR1029900068020X

Fig. 100 Code P0157: Rear Oxygen Sensor Cylinders 4–6 Signal Wire Short Circuit Or Incorrect Voltage (Part 2 of 2). 1999 911

1 Check wiring harness.

1. Remove all four HO2S connectors.
2. Switch on the ignition.
3. Connect voltmeter at sleeve to pins 3 and 4 of HO2S connector 2 after catalytic converter.
   Display: approx. 450 mV
4. Connect voltmeter at sleeve to pin 3 and ground.
   Display: approx. 720 mV

If the measurement according to items 3 and 4 does not show the specified values, remove DME control module connector and check wiring for short to B+.

If no short to B+ can be detected, replace DME control module.

2 Check oxygen sensor.

Note

This check must be performed with the engine cold.

1. Remove connector of HO2S 2 after catalytic converter.
2. Connect ohmmeter on pin side to pins 1 and 3 of HO2S connector.
   Display: ∞ Ω
3. Connect ohmmeter on pin side to pins 2 and 3 of HO2S connector.
   Display: ∞ Ω
4. Connect ohmmeter on pin side to pins 1 and 4 of HO2S connector.
   Display: ∞ Ω
5. Connect ohmmeter on pin side to pins 2 and 4 of HO2S connector.
   Display: ∞ Ω

PR1029900069020X

Fig. 101 Code P0158: Rear Oxygen Sensor Cylinders 4–6 Short Circuit To Battery Positive (Part 2 of 2). 1999 911

1 Check wiring harness or output stage of DME control module.
- Not OK → Repair wiring harness or replace DME control module. → Erase fault memory, then road test vehicle or perform short test. → Read fault memory. No faults in memory. → **End**
- OK ↓

2 Check oxygen sensor.
- Not OK → Replace oxygen sensor. → Erase fault memory, then road test vehicle or perform short test. → Read fault memory. No faults in memory. → **End**
- OK ↓

End

PR1029900069010X

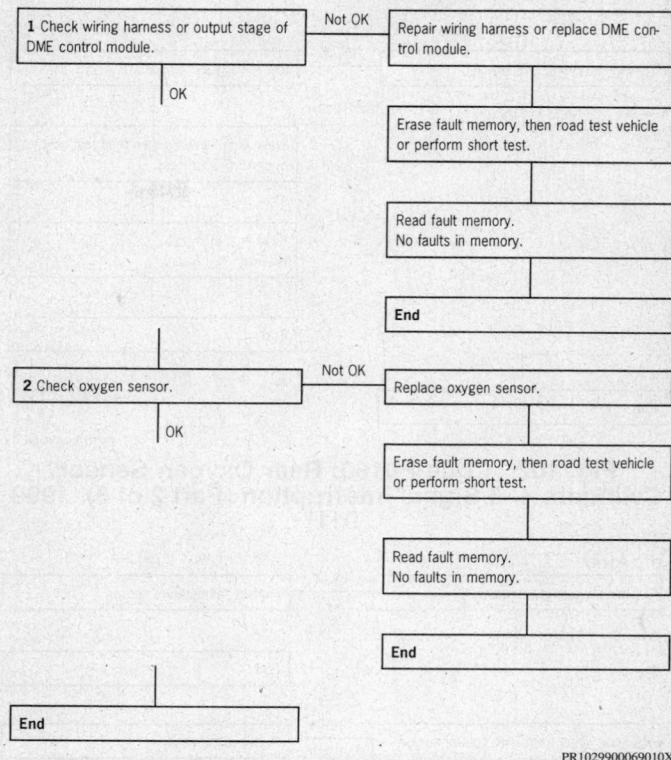

Fig. 101 Code P0158: Rear Oxygen Sensor Cylinders 4–6 Short Circuit To Battery Positive (Part 1 of 2). 1999 911

1 Check wiring harness or output stage of DME control module.
- Not OK → Repair wiring harness or replace DME control module. → Erase fault memory, then road test vehicle or perform short test. → Read fault memory. No faults in memory. → **End**
- OK ↓

2 Check function of oxygen sensor.
- Not OK → Replace oxygen sensor. → Erase fault memory, then road test vehicle or perform short test. → Read fault memory. No faults in memory. → **End**
- OK ↓

PR1029900070010X

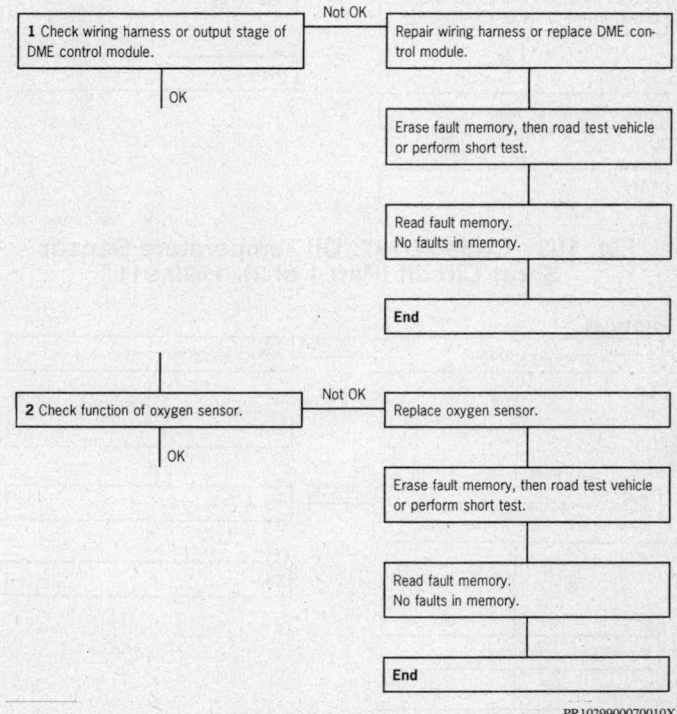

Fig. 102 Code P0160: Rear Oxygen Sensor Cylinders 4–6 Signal Interruption (Part 1 of 3). 1999 911

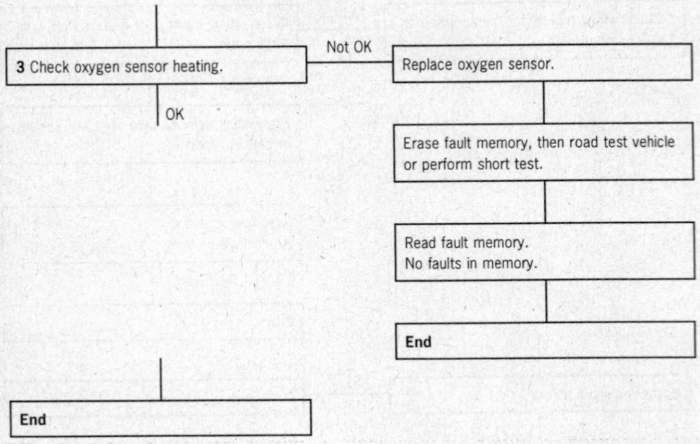

PR1029900070020X

Fig. 102 Code P0160: Rear Oxygen Sensor Cylinders 4–6 Signal Interruption (Part 2 of 3). 1999 911

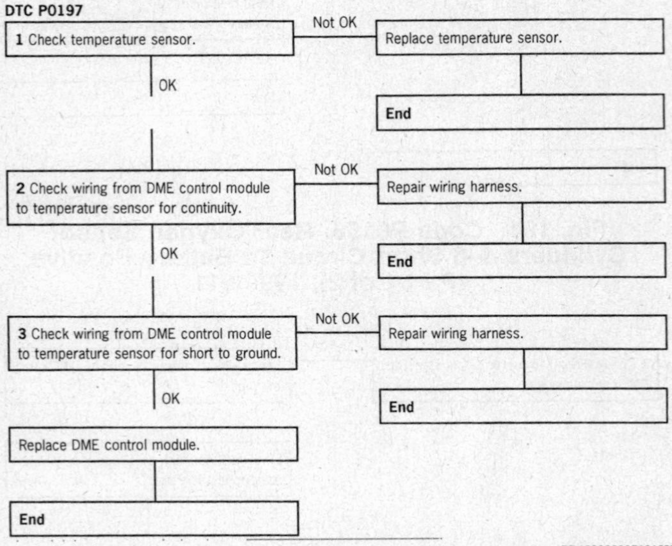

PR1029900071010X

Fig. 103 Code P0197: Oil Temperature Sensor Short Circuit (Part 1 of 3). 1999 911

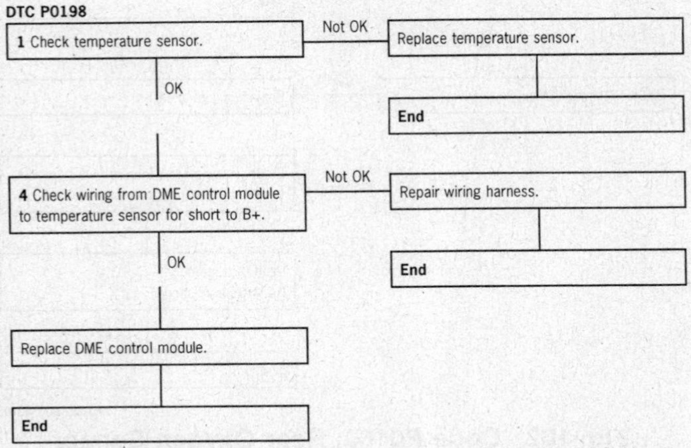

PR1029900071020X

Fig. 103 Code P0198: Oil Temperature Sensor Short Circuit (Part 2 of 3). 1999 911

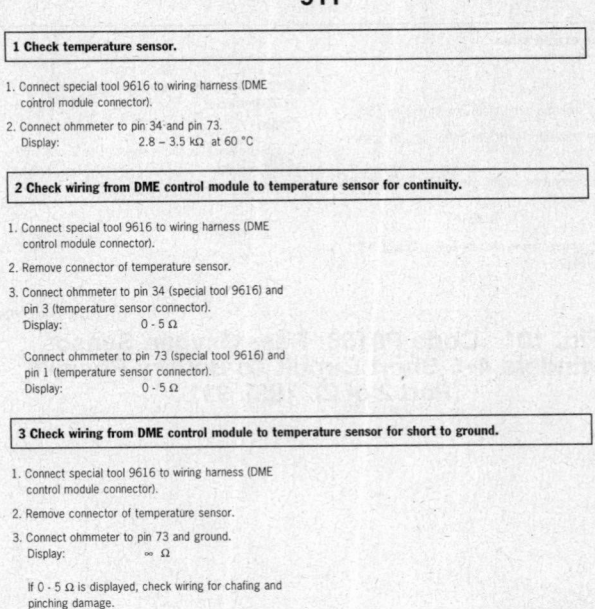

1 Check wiring harness.

1. Remove all four HO2S connectors.
2. Switch on the ignition.
3. Connect voltmeter at sleeve to pins 3 and 4 of HO2S connector 2 after catalytic converter.
   Display: approx. 450 mV
4. Connect voltmeter at sleeve to pin 3 and ground.
   Display: approx. 720 mV
5. Start engine and run at high rpm for 3 minutes.
6. Connect voltmeter at sleeve to pins 1 and 2.
   Display: battery voltage

If the measurement according to items 3, 4 or 6 does not show the specified values, remove DME control module connector and check wiring for continuity.

If no continuity can be detected, repair wiring harness.
If continuity exists, replace DME control module.

2 Check function of oxygen sensor.

1. Heat the oxygen sensors (road test car under load or run engine without load at high rpm).
2. Connect Porsche System Tester 2 or scan tool and read voltage of oxygen sensor 2 after catalytic converter.
   Display: Voltage fluctuations between 100 mV and 800 mV.
   ➜Oxygen sensor OK.

3 Check oxygen sensor heating.

1. Remove connector of HO2S 2 after catalytic converter.
2. Connect ohmmeter on pin side to pins 1 and 2.
   Display: 1.8 - 2.5 Ω at 20 °C.
3. Connect ohmmeter on pin side to pin 1 and HO2S housing.
   Display: ∞ Ω
4. Connect ohmmeter on pin side to pin 2 and HO2S housing.
   Display: ∞ Ω

PR1029900070030X

Fig. 102 Code P0160: Rear Oxygen Sensor Cylinders 4–6 Signal Interruption (Part 3 of 3). 1999 911

1 Check temperature sensor.

1. Connect special tool 9616 to wiring harness (DME control module connector).
2. Connect ohmmeter to pin 34 and pin 73.
   Display: 2.8 – 3.5 kΩ at 60 °C

2 Check wiring from DME control module to temperature sensor for continuity.

1. Connect special tool 9616 to wiring harness (DME control module connector).
2. Remove connector of temperature sensor.
3. Connect ohmmeter to pin 34 (special tool 9616) and pin 3 (temperature sensor connector).
   Display: 0 - 5 Ω

   Connect ohmmeter to pin 73 (special tool 9616) and pin 1 (temperature sensor connector).
   Display: 0 - 5 Ω

3 Check wiring from DME control module to temperature sensor for short to ground.

1. Connect special tool 9616 to wiring harness (DME control module connector).
2. Remove connector of temperature sensor.
3. Connect ohmmeter to pin 73 and ground.
   Display: ∞ Ω

   If 0 - 5 Ω is displayed, check wiring for chafing and pinching damage.

4 Check wiring from DME control module to temperature sensor for short to B+.

1. Connect special tool 9616 to wiring harness (DME control module connector).
2. Remove connector of temperature sensor.
3. Connect voltmeter to pin 73 and ground.
   Switch on the ignition.
   Display: 0 V

   If battery voltage is displayed, check wiring harness for chafing and pinching damage.

PR1029900071030X

Fig. 103 Codes P0197 & P0198: Oil Temperature Sensor Short Circuit (Part 3 of 3). 1999 911

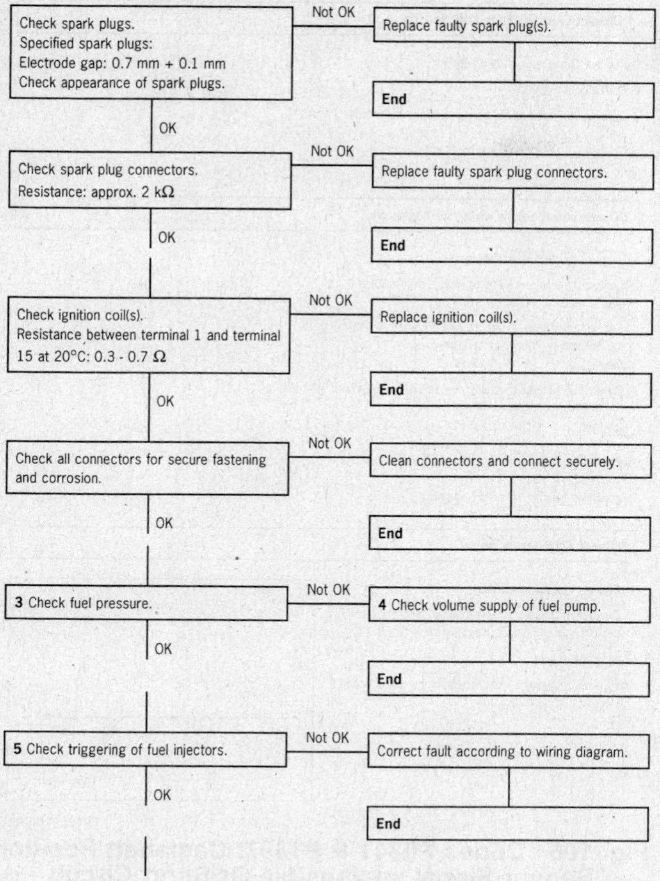

PR1029900072010X

Fig. 104 Codes P0300, P0301, P0302, P0303, P0304, P305, P0306, P1313, P1314, P1315, P1316, P1317, P1318, P1319 & P1585: Engine Misfire (Part 1 of 2). 1999 911

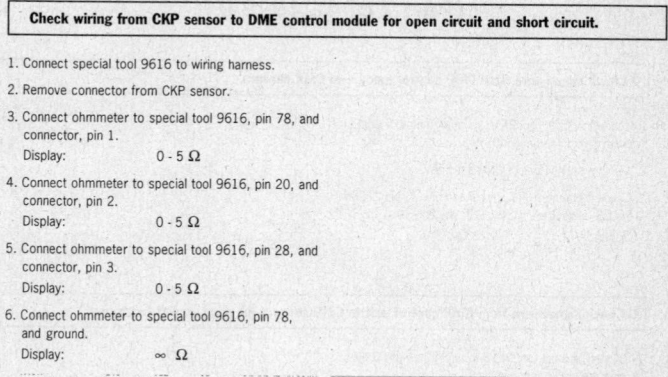

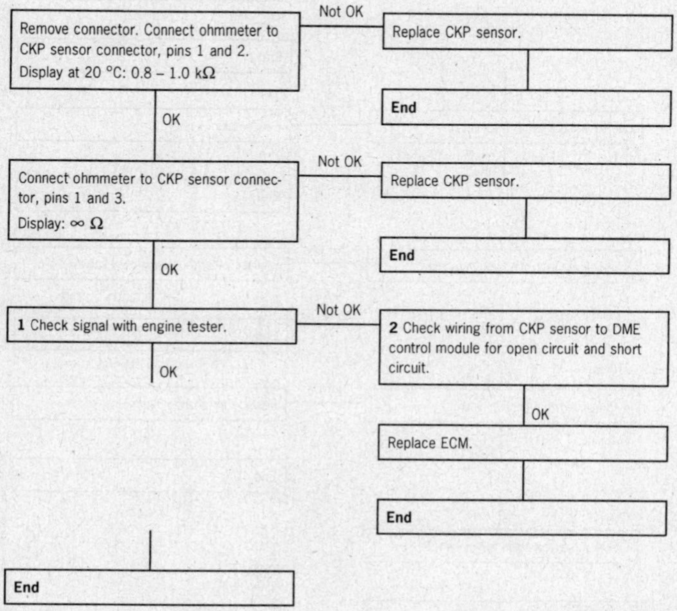

PR1029900073010X

Fig. 105 Code P0336: Crankshaft Position Sensor Not In Specified Range (Part 1 of 2). 1999 911

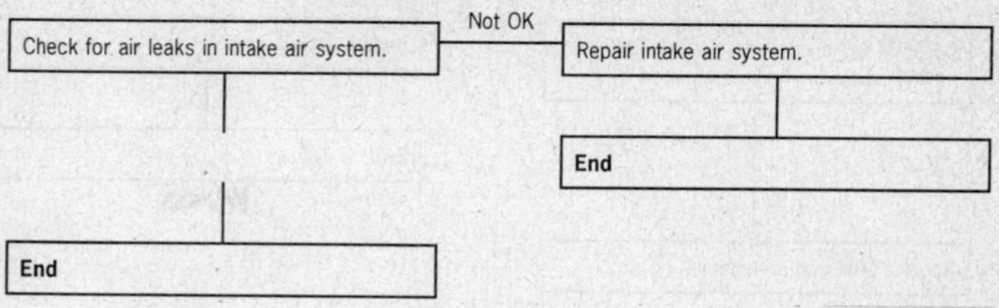

PR1029900072020X

Fig. 104 Codes P0300, P0301, P0302, P0303, P0304, P305, P0306, P1313, P1314, P1315, P1316, P1317, P1318, P1319 & P1585: Engine Misfire (Part 2 of 2). 1999 911

Check wiring from CKP sensor to DME control module for open circuit and short circuit.

1. Connect special tool 9616 to wiring harness.
2. Remove connector from CKP sensor.
3. Connect ohmmeter to special tool 9616, pin 78, and connector, pin 1.
   Display: 0 - 5 Ω
4. Connect ohmmeter to special tool 9616, pin 20, and connector, pin 2.
   Display: 0 - 5 Ω
5. Connect ohmmeter to special tool 9616, pin 28, and connector, pin 3.
   Display: 0 - 5 Ω
6. Connect ohmmeter to special tool 9616, pin 78, and ground.
   Display: ∞ Ω

PR1029900073020X

Fig. 105 Code P0336: Crankshaft Position Sensor Not In Specified Range (Part 2 of 2). 1999 911

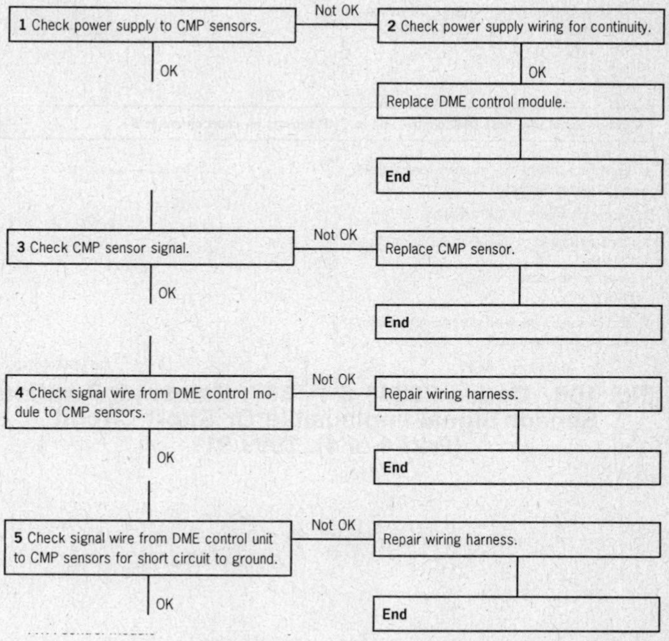

PR1029900074010X

Fig. 106 Codes P0341 & P1397: Camshaft Position Sensor Signal Implausible Or Short Circuit (Part 1 of 4). 1999 911

6 Check signal wire from DME control unit to CMP sensors for short circuit to B+.

Not OK → Repair wiring harness. → End

Replace DME control module.

End

PR1029900074020X

Fig. 106 Codes P0341 & P1397: Camshaft Position Sensor Signal Implausible Or Short Circuit (Part 2 of 4). 1999 911

4 Check signal wire from DME control module to CMP sensors.

1. Connect special tool 9616 to wiring harness (DME control module connector).
2. Remove connectors of CMP sensors.
3. Connect ohmmeter to special tool 9616, pin 21, and to CMP sensor connector 1/2, pin 2.
   Display: 0 - 5 Ω

5 Check signal wire from DME control unit to CMP sensors for short circuit to ground.

1. Connect special tool 9616 to wiring harness (DME control module connector).
2. Remove connectors of CMP sensors.
3. Connect ohmmeter to special tool 9616, pin 21, and ground.
   Display: ∞ Ω

If 0 - 5 Ω is displayed, check wiring for chafing and pinching damage.

6 Check signal wire from DME control unit to CMP sensors for short circuit to B+.

1. Connect special tool 9616 to wiring harness (DME control module connector).
2. Remove connectors of CMP sensors.
3. Connect voltmeter to special tool 9616, pin 21, and ground.
   Switch on the ignition.
   Display: 0 V

If battery voltage is displayed, check wiring harness for chafing and pinching damage.

PR1029900074040X

Fig. 106 Codes P0341 & P1397: Camshaft Position Sensor Signal Implausible Or Short Circuit (Part 4 of 4). 1999 911

1 Check power supply to CMP sensors.

1. Remove connectors of CMP sensors.
2. Switch on the ignition.
3. Connect voltmeter to pin 1 (negative) and pin 3 (positive).
   Display: approx. 5 V

2 Check power supply wiring for continuity.

1. Remove connectors of CMP sensors.
2. Connect special tool 9616 to wiring harness (DME control module connector).
3. Connect ohmmeter to special tool 9616, pin 53, and to CMP sensor connector 1/2, pin 3.
   Display: 0 - 5 Ω
4. Connect ohmmeter to special tool 9616, pin 34, and CMP sensor connector 1/2, pin 1.
   Display: 0 - 5 Ω

Note

Perform this test for both CMP sensors.

3 Check CMP sensor signal.

1. Connect special tool 9616.
2. Connect engine tester. Use special input, connect positive cable to pin 21, negative cable to pin 34.
3. Start the engine.

The following display should appear on the oscilloscope:

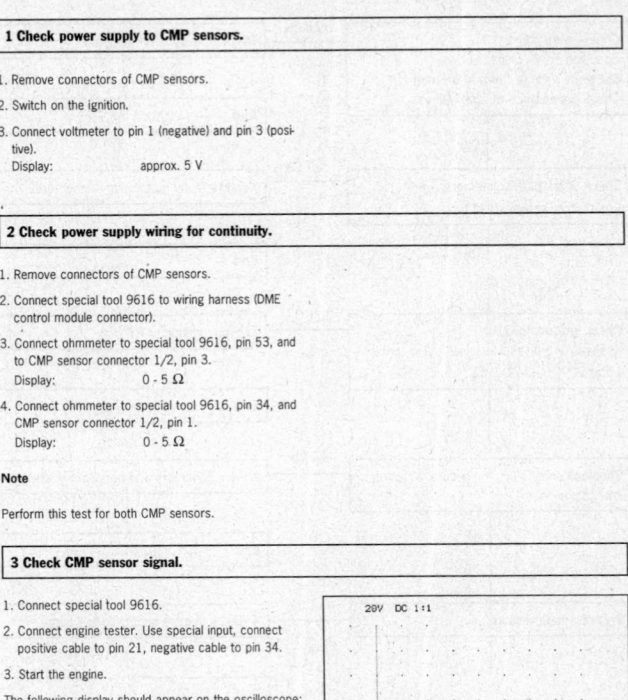

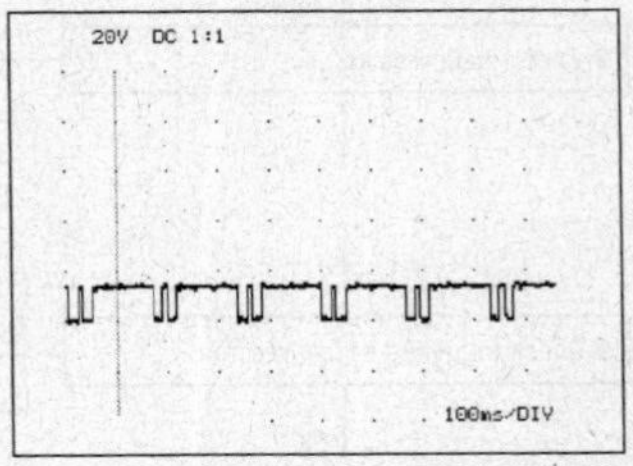

PR1029900074030X

Fig. 106 Codes P0341 & P1397: Camshaft Position Sensor Signal Implausible Or Short Circuit (Part 3 of 4). 1999 911

1 In menu "Drive links", trigger secondary air injection (AIR) pump.

Not OK → **2** Check triggering of AIR pump. → OK → Replace AIR pump. → End

OK

Check vacuum system for leaks.

Not OK → Seal vacuum system. → End

OK

3 Check electric change-over valve.

Not OK → Replace electric change-over valve. → End

OK

4 Check air change-over valve.

Not OK → Replace air change-over valve. → End

OK

Check air supply lines for blockage.

End

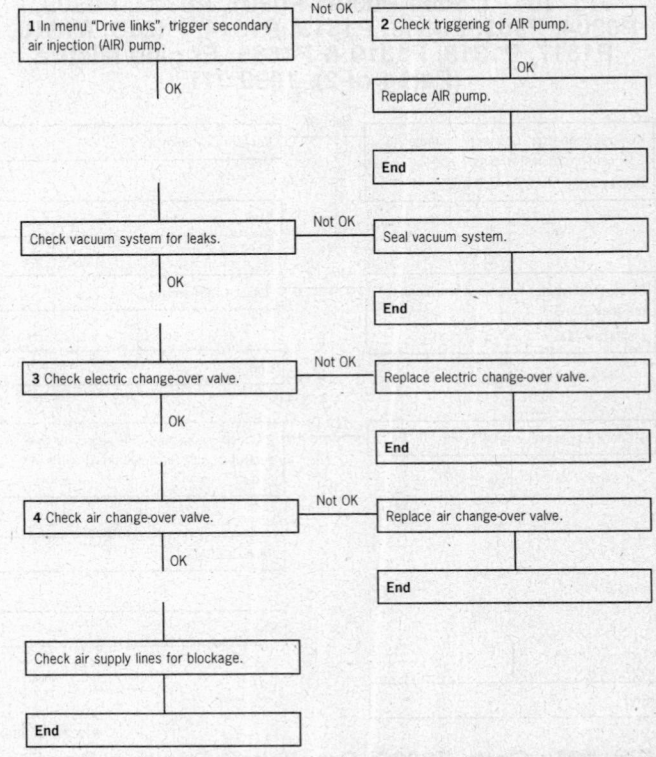

PR1029900075010X

Fig. 107 Codes P0410 & P1411: Secondary Air Injection Signal Implausible (Part 1 of 3). 1999 911

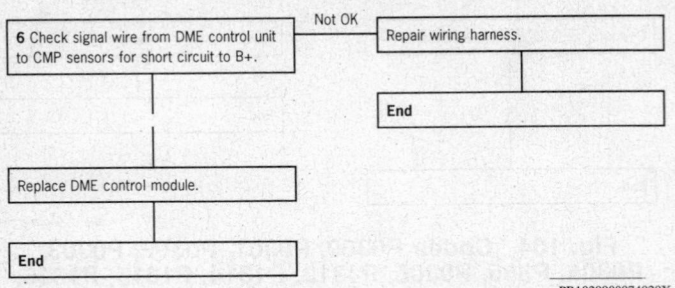

1 In menu "Drive links", trigger secondary air injection (AIR) pump.

1. Connect and switch on Porsche System Tester 2.
2. Select DME.
3. Call up "Drive links" menu.
4. Select AIR pump.
5. Activate AIR pump (audible function).

2 Check triggering of AIR pump.

1. Check fuse (Maxi Fuse) of AIR pump (on relay carrier 2).
2. Remove relay of AIR pump (on relay carrier 2).
   Connect voltmeter to pin 3 and ground.
   Display: battery voltage

   Connect voltmeter to pin 2 (negative) and pin 7 (positive).
   Start engine (the DME relay must pick up).
   Display: battery voltage

If 0 V is indicated, check wire from pin 2 to DME control module, pin 37, for continuity.
Push relay back on.

3. Remove connector of AIR pump.
   Connect voltmeter to pin 1 (positive) and pin 2 (negative).
   Trigger AIR pump with Porsche System Tester 2.
   Display: battery voltage

PR1029900075020X

Fig. 107 Codes P0410 & P1411: Secondary Air Injection Signal Implausible (Part 2 of 3). 1999 911

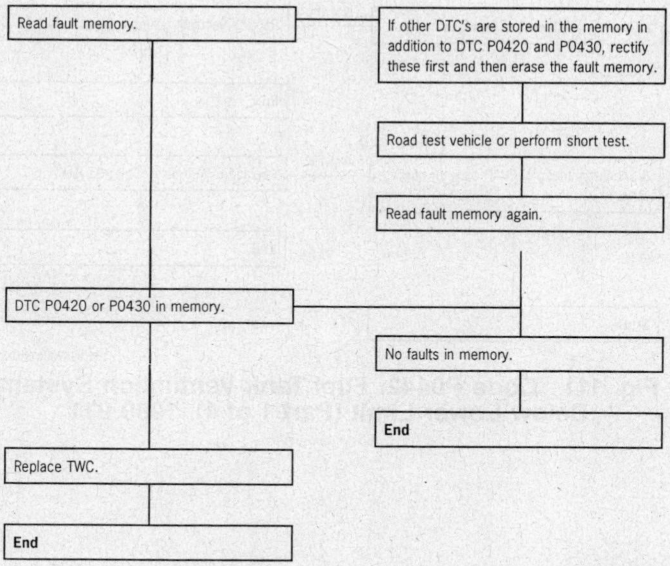

PR1029900076000X

Fig. 108 Codes P0420 & P0430: Catalytic Converter Conversion Too Low. 1999 911

3 Check electric change-over valve.

1. Remove two-pole connector of change-over valve.
2. Connect voltmeter to pin 1 (positive) and pin 2 (negative).
3. Trigger AIR pump with Porsche System Tester 2.
   Display: battery voltage
4. Remove vacuum hose of change-over valve with the engine running. Check whether vacuum is present.

4 Check air change-over valve and air supply lines.

1. Run engine briefly to produce vacuum.
2. Trigger AIR pump with Porsche System Tester 2.
3. Remove vacuum hose of air change-over valve.

If vacuum is present at the air change-over valve, check air supply from the AIR pump to the change-over valve to the air supply line to the cylinder heads.

Check function of air change-over valve.

PR1029900075030X

Fig. 107 Codes P0410 & P1411: Secondary Air Injection Signal Implausible (Part 3 of 3). 1999 911

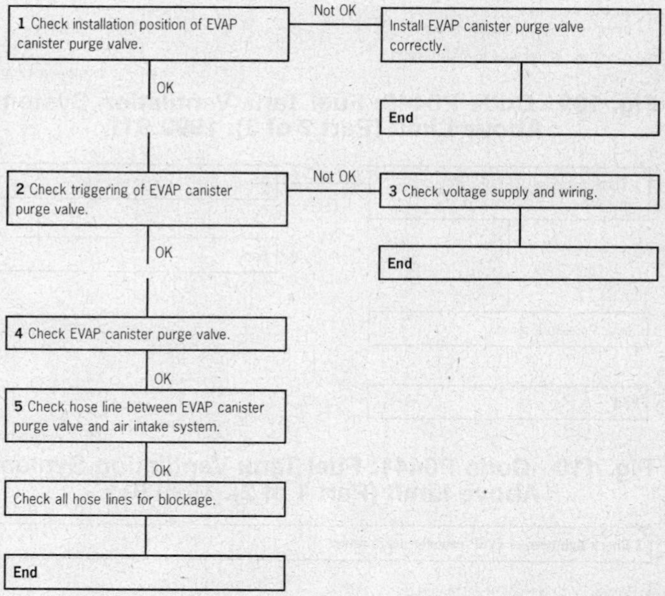

PR1029900077010X

Fig. 109 Code P0440: Fuel Tank Ventilation System Above Limit (Part 1 of 3). 1999 911

1 Check installation position of EVAP canister purge valve.

Flow through the EVAP canister purge valve is possible in one direction only. The flow direction is indicated by an arrow on the EVAP canister purge valve. The arrow must point towards the intake manifold.

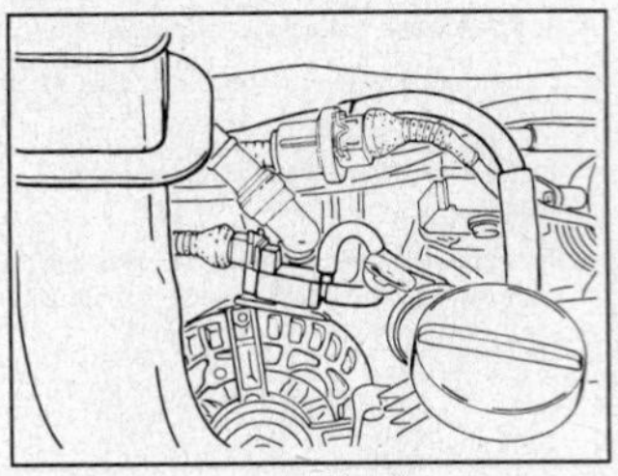

2 Check triggering of EVAP canister purge valve.

1. Connect Porsche System Tester 2.
2. In the `Drive links` menu, select EVAP canister purge valve.
   The EVAP canister purge valve must switch audibly.

3 Check voltage supply and wiring.

1. Remove connector of EVAP canister purge valve.
2. Connect voltmeter (positive) to pin 1 of the connector and to ground.
3. Switch on the ignition.
   Display: battery voltage
4. Connect special tool 9616 to wiring harness.

PR1029900077020X

Fig. 109 Code P0440: Fuel Tank Ventilation System Above Limit (Part 2 of 3). 1999 911

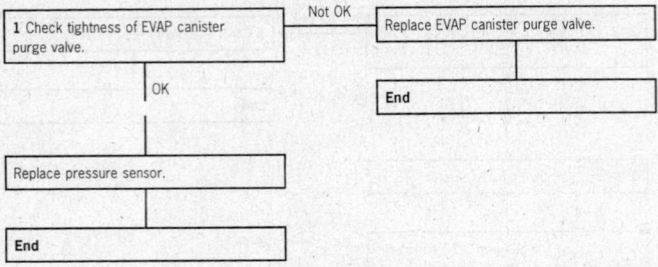

1 Check tightness of EVAP canister purge valve. — Not OK → Replace EVAP canister purge valve. → **End**

OK ↓

Replace pressure sensor. → **End**

PR1029900078010X

Fig. 110 Code P0441: Fuel Tank Ventilation System Above Limit (Part 1 of 2). 1999 911

1 Check tightness of EVAP canister purge valve.

1. Remove front right-hand wheel housing liner.

Note

Before detaching the ventilation lines from the EVAP canister, clean the area around the connections. Dirt must not be allowed to get into the connectors.

2. Detach the ventilation line to the EVAP canister purge valve from the EVAP canister (protective cap).
3. With special tool 9160/1, generate a vacuum of 200 mbar (0.2 bar).

If no vacuum can be built up, replace the EVAP canister purge valve.

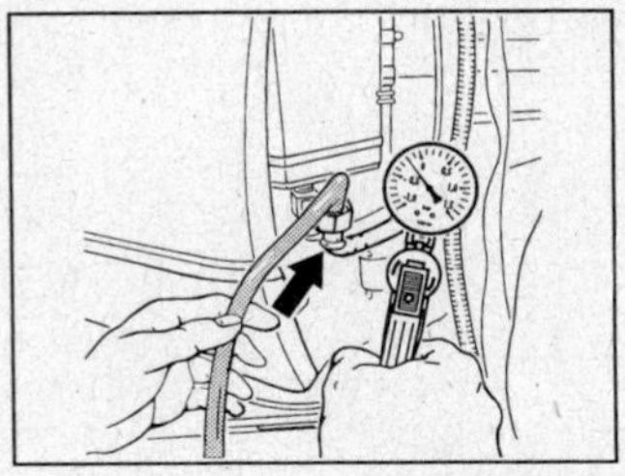

PR1029900078020X

Fig. 110 Code P0441: Fuel Tank Ventilation System Above Limit (Part 2 of 2). 1999 911

5. Connect ohmmeter to pin 61 and EVAP canister purge valve connector, pin 2.
   Display: 0 - 5 Ω

4 Check EVAP canister purge valve.

1. Disconnect hose from EVAP canister purge valve to intake system at EVAP canister purge valve.
2. Remove connector of EVAP canister purge valve.
3. Connect special tool 9160/1 to EVAP canister purge valve.
4. Generate vacuum of approx. 0.7 bar.
   The vacuum must not fall below 0.5 bar after 10 minutes.

5 Check hose line between EVAP canister purge valve and air intake system.

1. Undo hose at intake system.
2. Remove connector of EVAP canister purge valve.
3. Connect special tool 9160/1 to hose and generate a vacuum of approx. 0.7 bar.
   The vacuum must not fall below 0.5 bar after 10 minutes.

PR1029900077030X

Fig. 109 Code P0440: Fuel Tank Ventilation System Above Limit (Part 3 of 3). 1999 911

1 Check tightness of shutoff valve. — Not OK → Replace shutoff valve. → **End**

↓

2 Check ventilation lines for leaks. — Not OK → Replace ventilation lines. → **End**

↓

3 Check tightness of EVAP canister purge valve. — Not OK → Replace EVAP canister purge valve. → **End**

↓

End

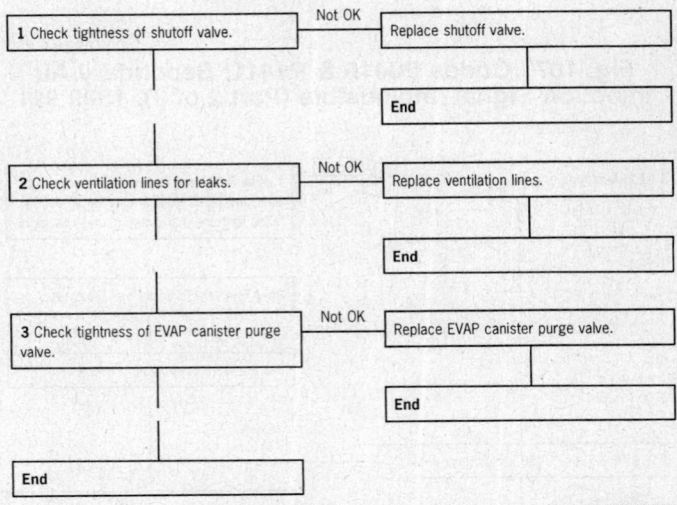

PR1029900079010X

Fig. 111 Code P0442: Fuel Tank Ventilation System Below Lower Limit (Part 1 of 4). 1999 911

1 Check tightness of shutoff valve.

1. Remove front right-hand wheel housing liner.
2. Detach connector of shutoff valve.
3. Detach ventilation line of shutoff valve.
4. Connect shutoff valve to the battery or a separate power supply unit via special tool V.A.G. 1315A/1.

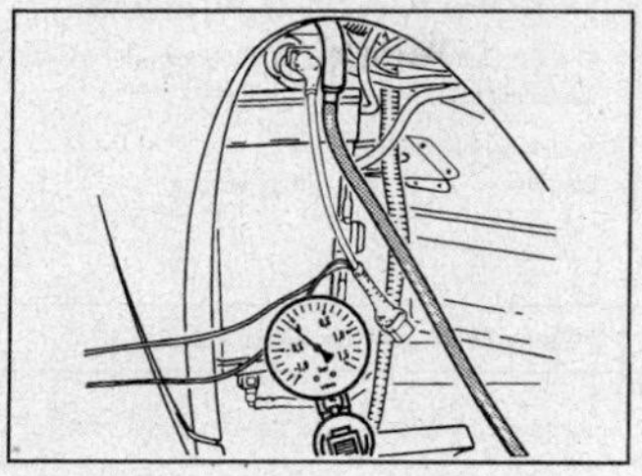

Note

Do not actuate the shutoff valve for more than 5 minutes (overload).

5. Connect special tool 9160/1 to EVAP canister.
6. Using special tool 9160/1, produce 100 mbar (0.1 bar) of vacuum.

Note

Do not produce a vacuum of more than 100 mbar, as otherwise the vacuum will cause the shutoff valve to open.

If no vacuum can be built up, replace the shutoff valve.

Note

Coat the sealing ring of the new shutoff valve with tire fitting lubricant prior to installation.
The shutoff valve can only be installed in one position: with the electrical connection facing upwards.

PR1029900079020X

Fig. 111 Code P0442: Fuel Tank Ventilation System Below Lower Limit (Part 2 of 4). 1999 911

3 Check tightness of EVAP canister purge valve.

Note

Before detaching the ventilation lines from the EVAP canister, clean the area around the connections. Dirt must not be allowed to get into the connectors.

1. Detach the ventilation line to the EVAP canister purge valve from the EVAP canister (protective cap).
2. With special tool 9160/1, generate a vacuum of 200 mbar (0.2 bar).

If no vacuum can be built up, replace the EVAP canister purge valve.

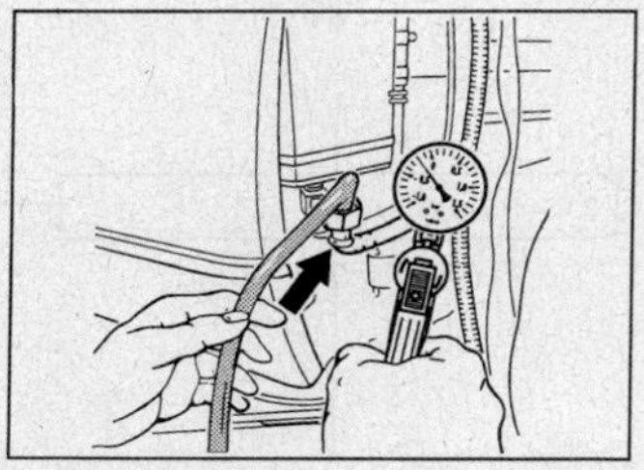

PR1029900079040X

Fig. 111 Code P0442: Fuel Tank Ventilation System Below Lower Limit (Part 4 of 4). 1999 911

2 Check ventilation lines for leaks.

Check the tank system for leaks using an HC tester. To do so, hold the connecting hose of the the HC tester in the spot to be tested. In the case of a leak, the display of the HC tester increases to above 1000 ppm. Values below 50 ppm indicate no leaks.
To test the ventilation lines, guide the connecting hose slowly along them.

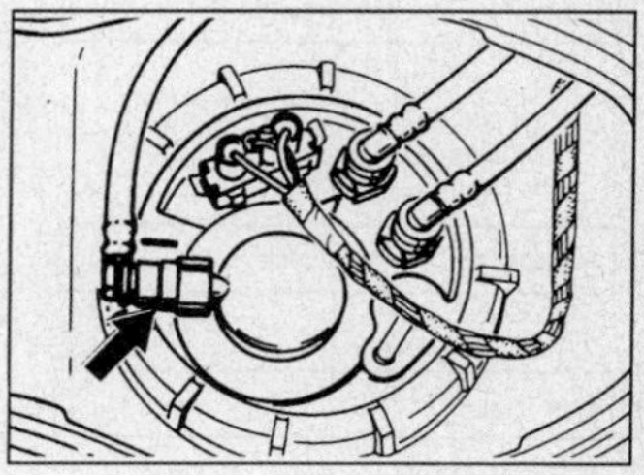

Check the following locations:

1. Tank cap
2. Line connections to EVAP canister
3. EVAP canister
4. Line connection to fuel tank sender unit (445_1_96)
5. Pressure sensor
6. Opening of fuel filler neck into tank
7. Line connection of EVAP canister purge valve (17_98)
8. Ventilation lines:
   a) from EVAP canister to operating purge valve
   b) from operating purge valve to tank
   c) from EVAP canister to EVAP canister purge valve

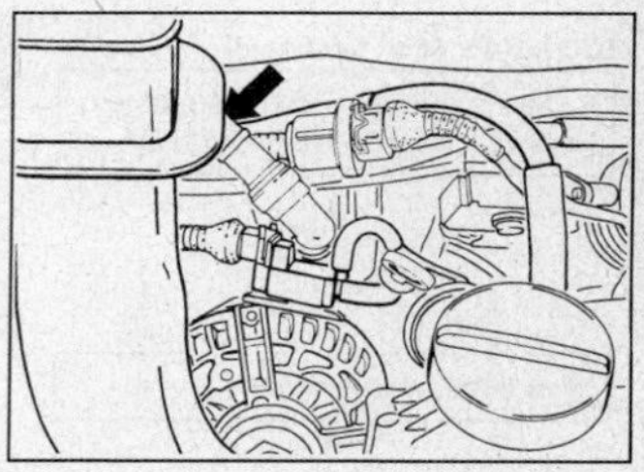

If no leaks are found, a gauge pressure of max. 100 mbar (0.1 bar) can be generated at the EVAP canister at the connection to the tank using special tool 9160/1, in order to increase the escape of fuel vapors.

PR1029900079030X

Fig. 111 Code P0442: Fuel Tank Ventilation System Below Lower Limit (Part 3 of 4). 1999 911

DTC P0444

1 Check voltage supply for EVAP canister purge valve.
- Not OK → Repair voltage supply. → **End**
- OK ↓

2 Check EVAP canister purge valve.
- Not OK → Replace EVAP canister purge valve. → **End**
- OK ↓

3 Check triggering wire for EVAP canister purge valve.
- Not OK → Repair wiring harness. → **End**
- OK ↓

Replace DME control module.

End

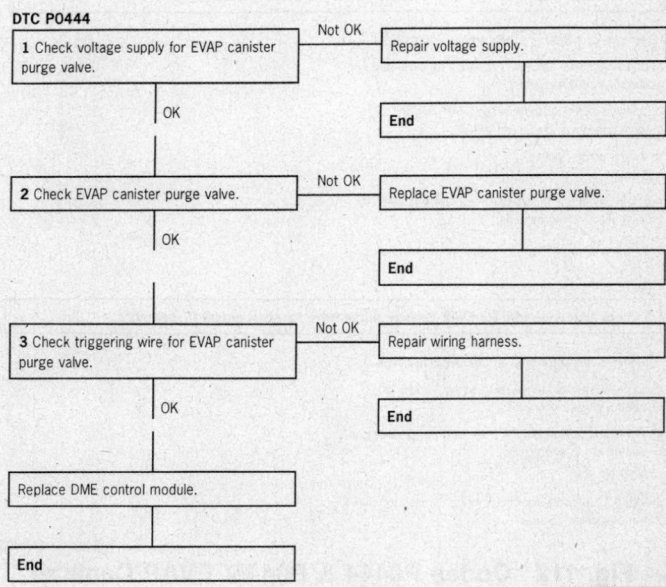

PR1029900080010X

Fig. 112 Code P0444: EVAP Canister Purge Valve Open Or Short Circuit (Part 1 of 4). 1999 911

DTC P0445, Short to B+

4 Check triggering wire for EVAP canister purge valve for short circuit to B+.
- Not OK → Repair wiring harness. → **End**
- OK → Replace DME control module. → **End**

DTC P0445, Short to Ground

5 Check triggering wire for EVAP canister purge valve for short circuit to ground.
- Not OK → Repair wiring harness. → **End**
- OK → Replace DME control module. → **End**

PR1029900080020X

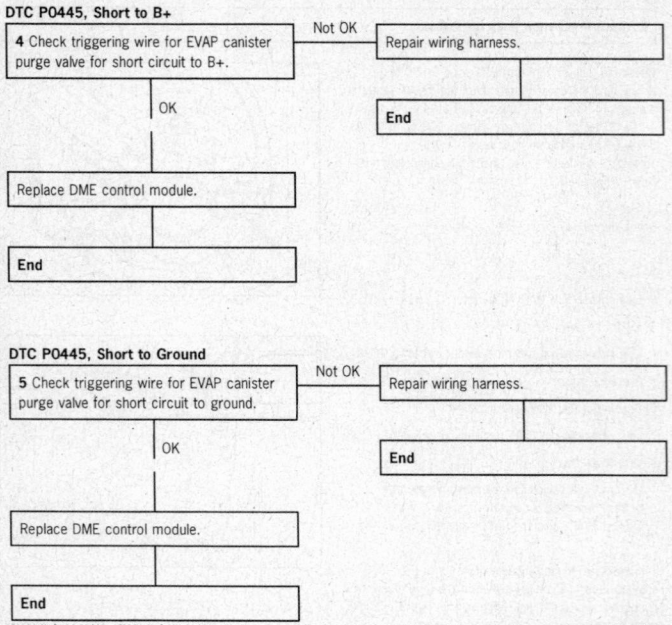

Fig. 112 Code P0445: EVAP Canister Purge Valve Open Or Short Circuit (Part 2 of 4). 1999 911

4 Check triggering wire for EVAP canister purge valve for short circuit to B+.

1. Remove connector of EVAP canister purge valve.
2. Connect special tool 9616 to wiring harness (DME control module connector).
3. Connect voltmeter (positive) to EVAP canister purge valve connector, pin 2, and ground.
4. Switch on the ignition.
   Display: 0 V

If battery voltage is displayed, check wiring harness for chafing and pinching damage.

5 Check triggering wire for EVAP canister purge valve for short circuit to ground.

1. Remove connector of EVAP canister purge valve.
2. Connect special tool 9616 to wiring harness (DME control module connector).
3. Connect ohmmeter to EVAP canister purge valve connector, pin 2, and ground.
   Display: ∞ Ω

If 0 to 5 Ω is displayed, check wiring harness for chafing and pinching damage.

PR1029900080040X

Fig. 112 Codes P0444 & P0445: EVAP Canister Purge Valve Open Or Short Circuit (Part 4 of 4). 1999 911

1 Check purge air line for blockage.
- Not OK → Repair purge air line. → **End**
- OK → Replace EVAP canister. → **End**

PR1029900081000X

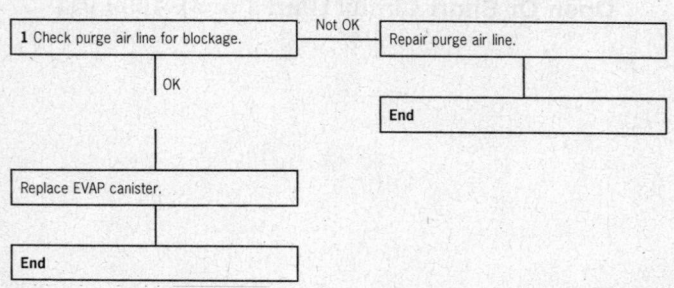

Fig. 113 Code P0446: EVAP Canister Shutoff Valve Below Lower Limit. 1999 911

1 Check voltage supply for EVAP canister purge valve.

1. Remove connector of EVAP canister purge valve.
2. Connect voltmeter (positive) to EVAP canister purge valve connector, pin 1, and ground.
3. Switch on the ignition.
   Display: battery voltage

2 Check EVAP canister purge valve.

1. Remove connector of EVAP canister purge valve.
2. Connect ohmmeter to EVAP canister purge valve pins 1 and 2.
   Display: 26 ± 4 Ω at 20 °C.

3 Check triggering wire for EVAP canister purge valve.

1. Remove connector of EVAP canister purge valve.
2. Connect special tool 9616 to wiring harness (DME control module connector).
3. Connect ohmmeter to EVAP canister purge valve, pin 2, and special tool 9616, pin 61.
   Display: 0 - 5 Ω

PR1029900080030X

Fig. 112 Codes P0444 & P0445: EVAP Canister Purge Valve Open Or Short Circuit (Part 3 of 4). 1999 911

DTC P0447

1 Check voltage supply for shutoff valve.
- Not OK → Repair voltage supply. → **End**
- OK ↓

2 Check shutoff valve.
- Not OK → Replace shutoff valve. → **End**
- OK ↓

3 Check triggering wire for shutoff valve for continuity.
- Not OK → Repair wiring harness. → **End**
- OK → Replace DME control module. → **End**

PR1029900082010X

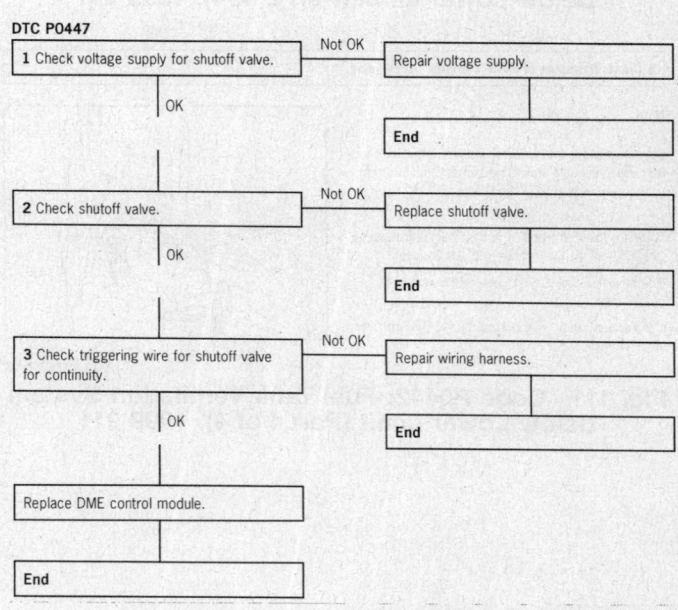

Fig. 114 Codes P0447 & P0448: EVAP Canister Shutoff Valve Open Or Short Circuit (Part 1 of 4). 1999 911

DTC P0448, Short to B+

4 Check triggering wire for shutoff valve for short circuit to B+.

Not OK → Repair wiring harness. → **End**

OK → Replace DME control module. → **End**

DTC P0448, Short to Ground

5 Check triggering wire for shutoff valve for short circuit to ground.

Not OK → Repair wiring harness. → **End**

OK → Replace DME control module. → **End**

PR1029900082020X

Fig. 114 Codes P0447 & P0448: EVAP Canister Shutoff Valve Open Or Short Circuit (Part 2 of 4). 1999 911

4 Check triggering wire for shutoff valve for short circuit to B+.

1. Remove front right-hand wheel housing liner.
2. Remove connector of shutoff valve.
3. Connect special tool 9616 to wiring harness (DME control module connector).
4. Connect voltmeter (positive) to shutoff valve connector, pin 2, and ground.
5. Switch on the ignition.
   Display: 0 V

If battery voltage is indicated, check wiring harness for chafing and pinching damage.

5 Check triggering wire for shutoff valve for short circuit to ground.

1. Remove front right-hand wheel housing liner.
2. Remove connector of shutoff valve.
3. Connect special tool 9616 to wiring harness (DME control module connector).
4. Connect ohmmeter to shutoff valve connector, pin 2, and ground.
   Display: ∞ Ω

If 0 - 5 Ω is displayed, check wiring for chafing and pinching damage.

PR1029900082040X

Fig. 114 Codes P0447 & P0448: EVAP Canister Shutoff Valve Open Or Short Circuit (Part 4 of 4). 1999 911

1 Check voltage supply for shutoff valve.

1. Remove front right-hand wheel housing liner.
2. Remove connector of shutoff valve.
3. Connect voltmeter (positive) to shutoff valve connector, pin 1, and ground.
4. Switch on the ignition.
   Display: battery voltage

2 Check shutoff valve.

1. Remove front right-hand wheel housing liner.
2. Remove connector of shutoff valve.
3. Connect ohmmeter to shutoff valve pins 1 and 2.
   Display: 22 - 26 Ω at 20 °C

3 Check triggering wire for shutoff valve for continuity.

1. Remove front right-hand wheel housing liner.
2. Remove connector of shutoff valve.
3. Connect special tool 9616 to wiring harness (DME control module connector).
4. Connect ohmmeter to shutoff valve, pin 2, and special tool 9616, pin 7.
   Display: 0 - 5 Ω

Note

The wire is routed via connector X 2/5, pin 6.

PR1029900082030X

Fig. 114 Codes P0447 & P0448: EVAP Canister Shutoff Valve Open Or Short Circuit (Part 3 of 4). 1999 911

DTC P0452

1 Check wiring from pressure sensor to DME control module for short to ground.

Not OK → Repair wiring harness. → **End**

→ **End**

DTC P0453

2 Check wiring from pressure sensor to DME control module for short to B+.

Not OK → Repair wiring harness. → **End**

→ **End**

PR1029900083010X

Fig. 115 Codes P0450, P0452 & P0453: Tank Pressure Sensor Signal Implausible Or Short Circuit (Part 1 of 2). 1999 911

1 Check wiring from pressure sensor to DME control module for short to ground.

1. Connect special tool 9616 to wiring harness (DME control module connector).
2. Remove connector of pressure sensor.
3. Connect ohmmeter to special tool 9616, pin 72, and ground.
   Display: ∞ Ω

If 0 - 5 Ω is displayed, check wiring harness for chafing and pinching damage.

2 Check wiring from pressure sensor to DME control module for short to B+.

1. Connect special tool 9616 to wiring harness (DME control module connector).
2. Remove connector of pressure sensor.
3. Connect voltmeter to special tool 9616, pin 72, and ground.
   Display: 0 V

If battery voltage is displayed, check wiring harness for chafing and pinching damage.

PR1029900083020X

Fig. 115 Codes P0450, P0452 & P0453: Tank Pressure Sensor Signal Implausible Or Short Circuit (Part 2 of 2). 1999 911

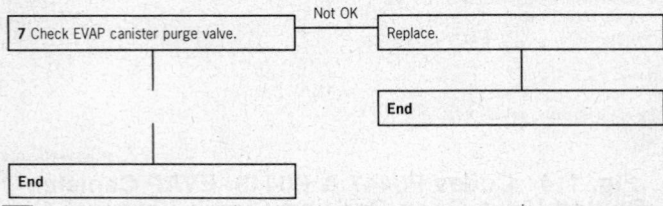

7 Check EVAP canister purge valve. — Not OK → Replace. → **End**

↓

End

PR1029900084020X

Fig. 116 Code P0455: Fuel Tank Ventilation System Below Lower Limit (Part 2 of 6). 1999 911

1 Check tank cap.

1. Check whether the tank cap is present.
2. Check whether the tank cap is correctly screwed on.

2 Check ventilation lines to EVAP canister.

1. Remove front right-hand wheel housing liner.
2. Check whether ventilation lines are attached to the EVAP canister.

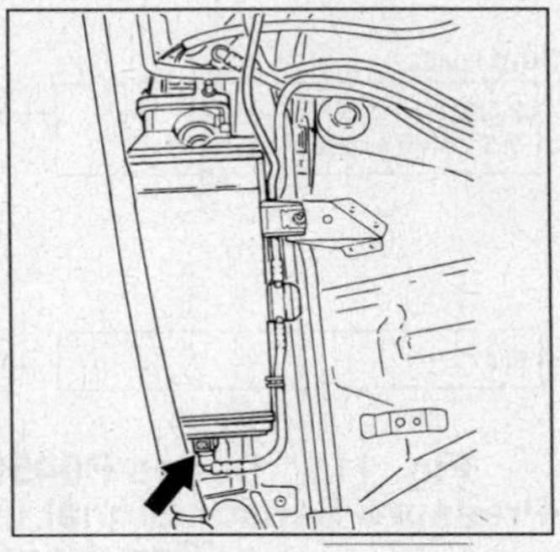

PR1029900084030X

Fig. 116 Code P0455: Fuel Tank Ventilation System Below Lower Limit (Part 3 of 6). 1999 911

Diagnosis Procedure

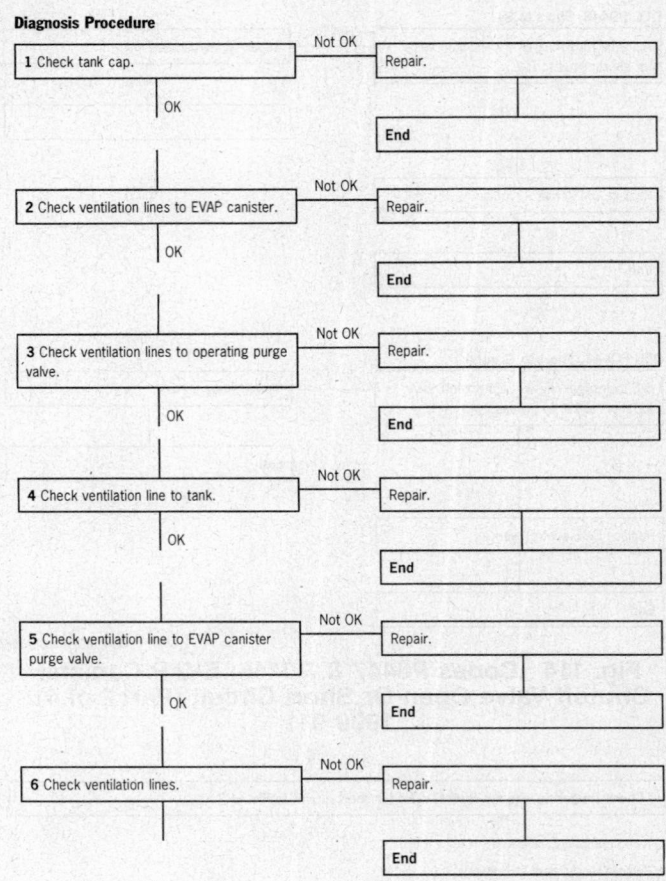

1 Check tank cap. — Not OK → Repair. → **End**

↓ OK

2 Check ventilation lines to EVAP canister. — Not OK → Repair. → **End**

↓ OK

3 Check ventilation lines to operating purge valve. — Not OK → Repair. → **End**

↓ OK

4 Check ventilation line to tank. — Not OK → Repair. → **End**

↓ OK

5 Check ventilation line to EVAP canister purge valve. — Not OK → Repair. → **End**

↓ OK

6 Check ventilation lines. — Not OK → Repair. → **End**

↓

PR1029900084010X

Fig. 116 Code P0455: Fuel Tank Ventilation System Below Lower Limit (Part 1 of 6). 1999 911

3 Check ventilation lines to operating purge valve.

1. Remove front right-hand wheel housing liner.
2. Check whether ventilation lines are attached to the operating purge valve.

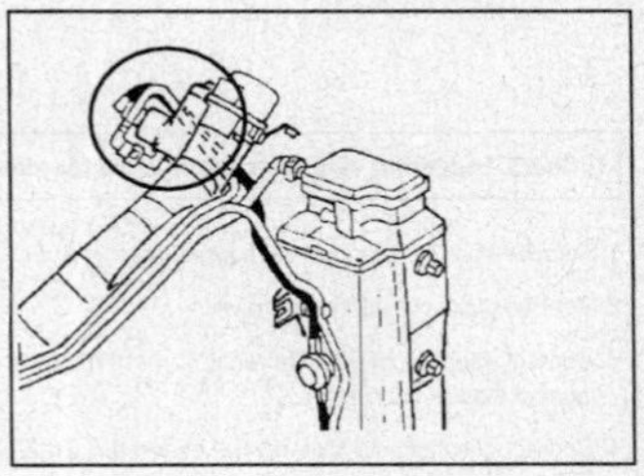

4 Check ventilation line to tank.

1. Remove battery.
2. Remove battery cover.
3. Check whether ventilation line is attached to the fuel tank sender unit.

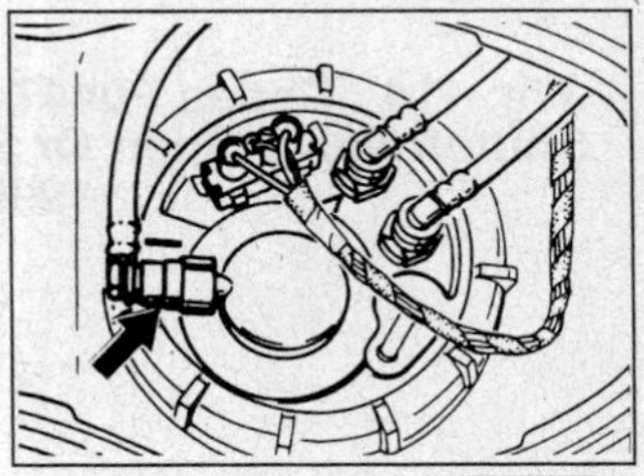

PR1029900084040X

Fig. 116 Code P0455: Fuel Tank Ventilation System Below Lower Limit (Part 4 of 6). 1999 911

5 Check ventilation line to EVAP canister purge valve.

Check whether ventilation line is attached to the EVAP canister purge valve.

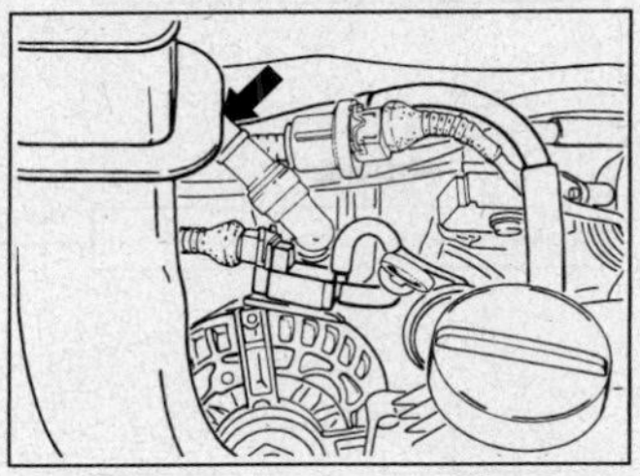

6 Check ventilation lines.

Check whether ventilation lines are:

- cracked
- broken
- interrupted

PR1029900084050X

Fig. 116 Code P0455: Fuel Tank Ventilation System Below Lower Limit (Part 5 of 6). 1999 911

Part 1

1 Read ABS control module fault memory. Is rear left wheel speed sensor fault stored?
- No → Go to Part 2.
- Yes ↓

2 Check wheel speed sensor with ohmmeter. Display: 1.6 - 1.8 kΩ
- Not OK → Replace wheel speed sensor. → **End**
- OK ↓

Check wiring from ABS control module to connector of rear left wheel speed sensor for continuity or short to B+ or ground.
- Not OK → Repair wiring harness. → **End**
- OK ↓

Check rear left wheel speed sensor and pulse wheel installation for dirt.
- Not OK → Repair.
- OK ↓

End

PR1029900085010X

Fig. 117 Code P0501: Vehicle Speed Not In Specified Range (Part 1 of 3). 1999 911

7 Check EVAP canister purge valve.

1. Remove front right-hand wheel housing liner.
2. Clean EVAP canister in the vicinity of the ventilation lines.
3. Detach the ventilation line to the EVAP canister purge valve from the EVAP canister (connection with protective cap).
4. With special tool 9160/1, generate a vacuum of 200 mbar (0.2 bar).

If no vacuum can be built up, replace the EVAP canister purge valve.

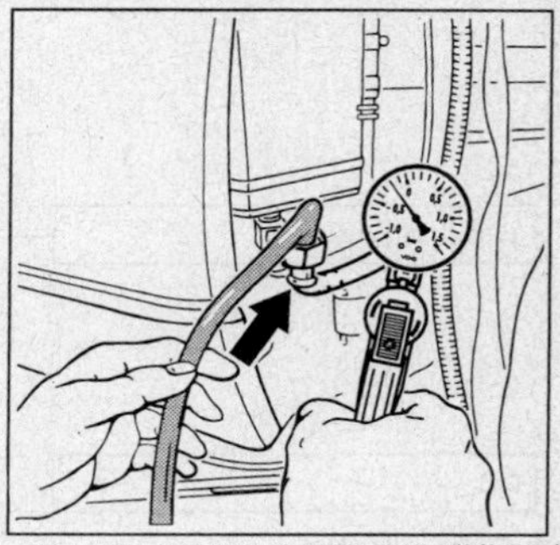

PR1029900084060X

Fig. 116 Code P0455: Fuel Tank Ventilation System Below Lower Limit (Part 6 of 6). 1999 911

Part 2

Check wiring from ABS control module to DME control module for continuity or short to B+ or ground.
- Not OK → Repair wiring harness. → **End**
- OK ↓

3 Check speed signal with Porsche System Tester 2.
- Not OK → Replace ABS control module. → **End**
- OK ↓

Replace DME control module.

End

PR1029900085020X

Fig. 117 Code P0501: Vehicle Speed Not In Specified Range (Part 2 of 3). 1999 911

1 Read ABS control module fault memory.

1. Connect and switch on Porsche System Tester 2.
2. Select vehicle type `911 Carrera (996)`.
3. Select system `ABS 5.3` or `ABS/TC 5.3`.
4. Read fault memory.

2 Check wheel speed sensor with ohmmeter.

1. Remove connector X 2/4.
2. Connect ohmmeter on pin side to pins 1 and 2. Display: 1.6 - 1.8 kΩ

3 Check speed signal with Porsche System Tester 2.

1. Connect and switch on Porsche System Tester 2.
2. Select vehicle type `911 Carrera (996)` and system `ABS 5.3`, menu `Actual values, Rear left wheel speed sensor`.
3. Raise vehicle at rear left.
4. By hand, turn rear left wheel in driving direction. The speed must be displayed on the tester.

PR1029900085030X

Fig. 117 Code P0501: Vehicle Speed Not In Specified Range (Part 3 of 3). 1999 911

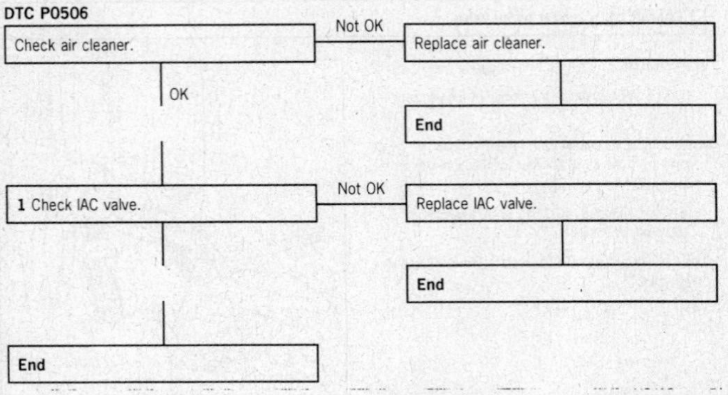
DTC P0506
Check air cleaner.
Not OK
Replace air cleaner.
End
OK
1 Check IAC valve.
Not OK
Replace IAC valve.
End
End

PR1029900086010X

Fig. 118 Codes P0506 & P0507: Idle Air Control, Idle Speed Too High Or Too Low (Part 1 of 2). 1999 911

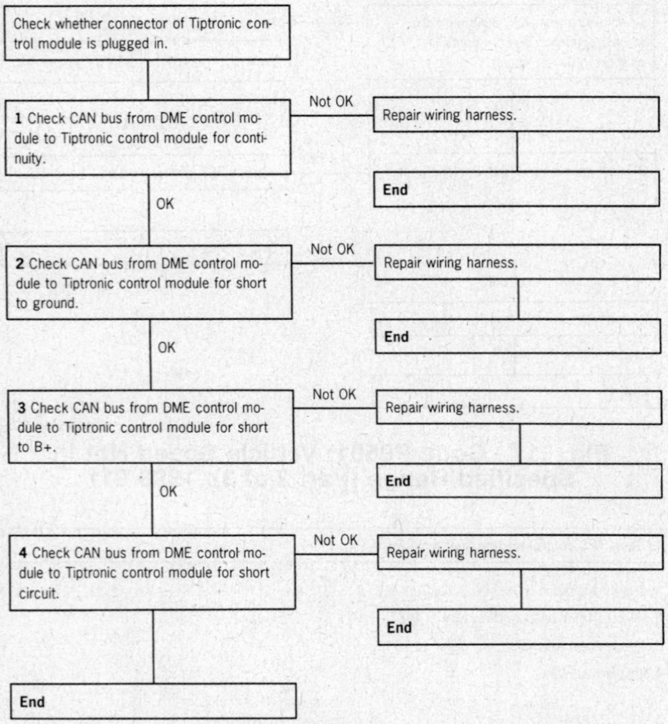
Check whether connector of Tiptronic control module is plugged in.
1 Check CAN bus from DME control module to Tiptronic control module for continuity.
Not OK
Repair wiring harness.
End
OK
2 Check CAN bus from DME control module to Tiptronic control module for short to ground.
Not OK
Repair wiring harness.
End
OK
3 Check CAN bus from DME control module to Tiptronic control module for short to B+.
Not OK
Repair wiring harness.
End
OK
4 Check CAN bus from DME control module to Tiptronic control module for short circuit.
Not OK
Repair wiring harness.
End
End

PR1029900087010X

Fig. 119 Code P0600: CAN Timeout Signal Implausible (Part 1 of 3). 1999 911

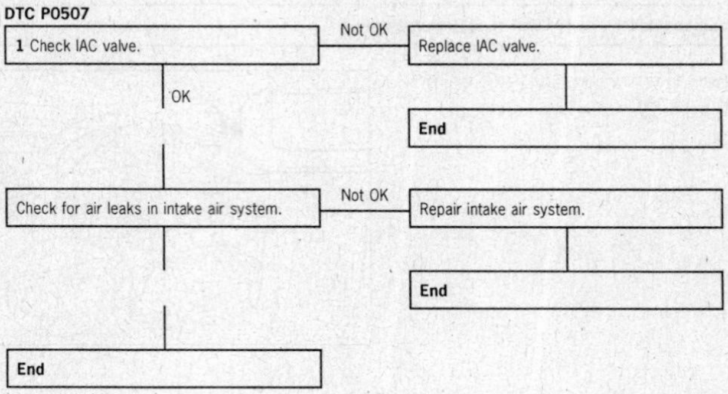
DTC P0507
1 Check IAC valve.
Not OK
Replace IAC valve.
End
OK
Check for air leaks in intake air system.
Not OK
Repair intake air system.
End
End

1 Check IAC valve.

1. Connect and switch on Porsche System Tester 2.
2. In the "Drive links" menu, select and activate `IAC valve`.
3. A distinct clicking noise should be heard.

PR1029900086020X

Fig. 118 Codes P0506 & P0507: Idle Air Control, Idle Speed Too High Or Too Low (Part 2 of 2). 1999 911

1 Check CAN bus from DME control module to Tiptronic control module for continuity.

1. Remove DME control module connector.
2. Remove Tiptronic control module connector.
3. Connect ohmmeter to DME control module connector, pin 85, and Tiptronic control module connector, pin 85.
   Display: 0 - 5 Ω
4. Connect ohmmeter to DME control module connector, pin 86, and Tiptronic control module connector, pin 86.
   Display: 0 - 5 Ω

If ∞ Ω is displayed, check wiring harness for chafing and pinching damage.

2 Check CAN bus from DME control module to Tiptronic control module for short to ground.

1. Remove DME control module connector.
2. Remove Tiptronic control module connector.
3. Connect special tool 9616 to wiring harness (DME control module connector).
4. Connect ohmmeter to special tool 9616, pin 85, and ground.
   Display: ∞ Ω
5. Connect ohmmeter to special tool 9616, pin 86, and ground.
   Display: ∞ Ω

If 0 - 5 Ω is displayed, check wiring for chafing and pinching damage.

PR1029900087020X

Fig. 119 Code P0600: CAN Timeout Signal Implausible (Part 2 of 3). 1999 911

3 Check CAN bus from DME control module to Tiptronic control module for short to B+.

1. Remove DME control module connector.
2. Remove Tiptronic control module connector.
3. Connect special tool 9616 to wiring harness (DME control module connector).
4. Connect voltmeter to special tool 9616, pin 85, and ground.
   Switch on the ignition.
   Display: 0 V
5. Connect voltmeter to special tool 9616, pin 86, and ground.
   Switch on the ignition.
   Display: 0 V

If battery voltage is displayed, check wiring harness for chafing and pinching damage.

4 Check CAN bus from DME control module to Tiptronic control module for short circuit.

1. Remove DME control module connector.
2. Remove Tiptronic control module connector.
3. Connect special tool 9616 to wiring harness (DME control module connector).
4. Connect ohmmeter to special tool 9616, pins 85 and 86.
   Display: ∞ Ω

If 0 - 5 Ω is displayed, check wiring harness for chafing and pinching damage.

PR1029900087030X

Fig. 119 Code P0600: CAN Timeout Signal Implausible (Part 3 of 3). 1999 911

1 Check resistance of HO2S heating.

1. Remove connector of HO2S 1/2 ahead of catalytic converter.
2. Connect ohmmeter on pin side to pins 1 and 2.
   Display: 1.8 - 2.5 Ω at 20 °C.

2 Check HO2S and wiring from DME control module to disconnection points of HO2S 1/2 ahead of catalytic converter for short to B+.

1. Remove connector of HO2S 1/2 ahead of catalytic converter.
2. Start engine and run at high speed for 3 minutes.
3. Connect voltmeter at sleeve to pin 1 (positive) and pin 2 of connector.
   Display: battery voltage

   Connect voltmeter at sleeve to connector, pin 2 (positive), and ground.
   Display: approx. 0 V
4. Switch off engine.
5. Remove DME control module connector.
6. Remove ignition, injection and HO2S heating relay and bridge terminals 30 and 87.
7. Connect voltmeter at sleeve to HO2S connector, pin 2 (positive), and ground.
   Display: 0 V

PR1029900088020X

Fig. 120 Codes P1102 & P1107: Front Oxygen Sensor Heating Above Limit (Part 2 of 2). 1999 911

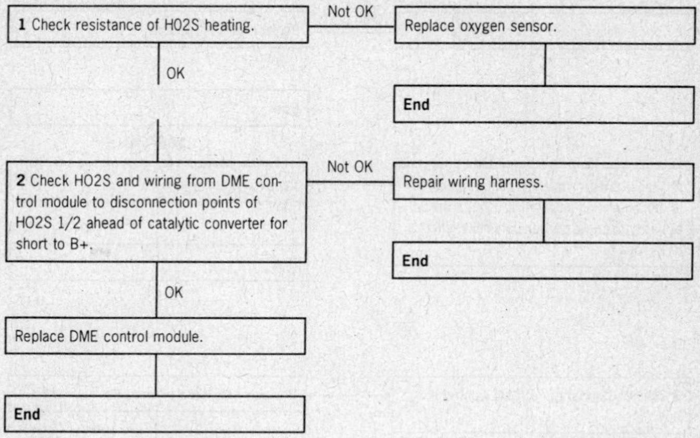

PR1029900088010X

Fig. 120 Codes P1102 & P1107: Front Oxygen Sensor Heating Above Limit (Part 1 of 2). 1999 911

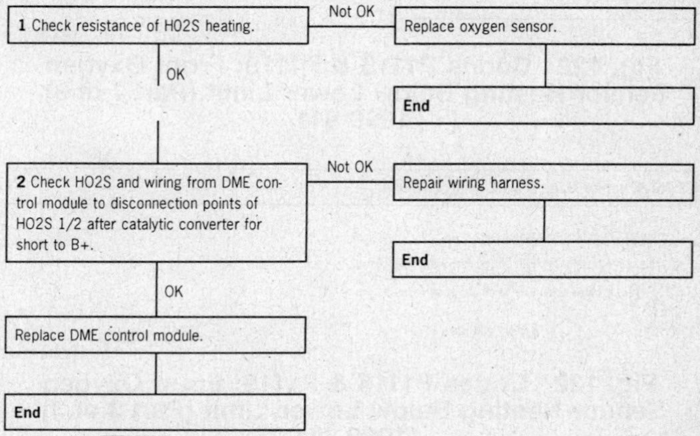

PR1029900089010X

Fig. 121 Codes P1105 & P1110: Rear Oxygen Sensor Heating Above Limit (Part 1 of 2). 1999 911

1 Check resistance of HO2S heating.

1. Remove connector of HO2S 1/2 after catalytic converter.
2. Connect ohmmeter on pin side to pins 1 and 2.
   Display: 1.8 - 2.5 Ω at 20 °C.

2 Check HO2S and wiring from DME control module to disconnection points of HO2S 1/2 ahead of catalytic converter for short to B+.

1. Remove connector of HO2S 1/2 after catalytic converter.
2. Start engine and run at high speed for 3 minutes.
3. Connect voltmeter at sleeve to connector, pin 1 (positive), and pin 2.
   Display: battery voltage

   Connect voltmeter at sleeve to connector, pin 2 (positive), and ground.
   Display: approx. 0 V
4. Switch off engine.
5. Remove DME control module connector.
6. Remove ignition, injection and HO2S heating relay and bridge terminals 30 and 87.
7. Connect voltmeter at sleeve to HO2S connector, pin 2 (positive), and ground.
   Display: 0 V

PR1029900089020X

Fig. 121 Codes P1105 & P1110: Rear Oxygen Sensor Heating Above Limit (Part 2 of 2). 1999 911

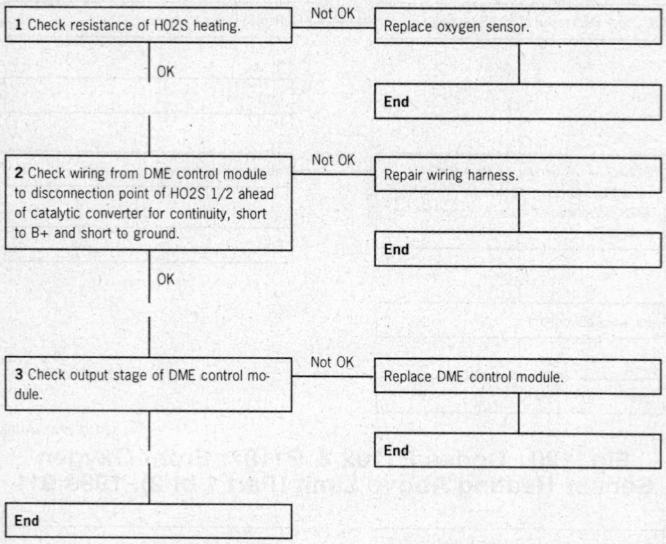

PR1029900090010X

Fig. 122 Codes P1115 & P1119: Front Oxygen Sensor Heating Below Lower Limit (Part 1 of 3). 1999 911

3 Check output stage of DME control module.

1. Remove connectors to oxygen sensors.
2. Start engine and run at high speed for 3 minutes.
3. Connect voltmeter at sleeve to pin 1 (positive) and pin 2.
   Display: battery voltage

PR1029900090030X

Fig. 122 Codes P1115 & P1119: Front Oxygen Sensor Heating Below Lower Limit (Part 3 of 3). 1999 911

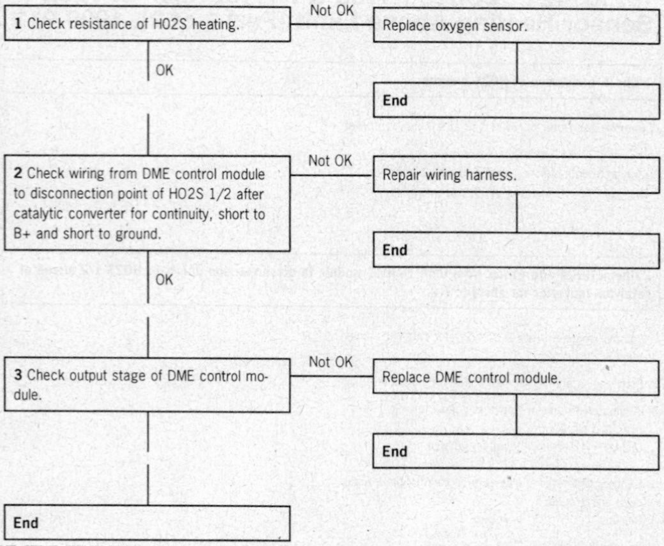

PR1029900091010X

Fig. 123 Codes P1117 & P1121: Rear Oxygen Sensor Heating Below Lower Limit (Part 1 of 3). 1999 911

1 Check resistance of H02S heating.

1. Remove connector of H02S 1/2 ahead of catalytic converter.
2. Connect ohmmeter on pin side to pins 1 and 2.
   Display: 1.8 - 2.5 Ω at 20 °C.
3. Connect ohmmeter on pin side to pin 1 and H02S housing.
   Display: ∞ Ω

2 Check wiring from DME control module to disconnection point of H02S 1/2 for continuity, short to B+ and short to ground.

1. Remove connector of H02S 1 and 2 ahead of catalytic converter.
2. Connect special tool 9616 to wiring harness (DME control module connector).
3. Connect ohmmeter to special tool 9616, pin 30, and disconnection point of H02S 1/2 ahead of catalytic converter, pin 2.
   Display: < 1 Ω
4. Connect ohmmeter at sleeve to connector, pin 2, and ground.
   Display: ∞ Ω
5. Remove ignition, injection and oxygen sensor heating relay and bridge terminals 30 and 87.
6. Connect voltmeter at sleeve to connector, pin 2, and ground.
   Display: 0 V

PR1029900090020X

Fig. 122 Codes P1115 & P1119: Front Oxygen Sensor Heating Below Lower Limit (Part 2 of 3). 1999 911

1 Check resistance of H02S heating.

1. Remove connector of H02S 1/2 after catalytic converter.
2. Connect ohmmeter on pin side to pins 1 and 2.
   Display: 1.8 - 2.5 Ω at 20 °C.
3. Connect ohmmeter on pin side to pin 1 and H02S housing.
   Display: ∞ Ω

2 Check wiring from DME control module to disconnection point of H02S 1/2 for continuity, short to B+ and short to ground.

1. Remove connector of H02S 1 and 2 after catalytic converter.
2. Connect special tool 9616 to wiring harness (DME control module connector).
3. Connect ohmmeter to special tool 9616, pin 30, and disconnection point of H02S 1/2 after catalytic converter, pin 2.
   Display: < 1 Ω
4. Connect ohmmeter at sleeve to connector, pin 2, and ground.
   Display: ∞ Ω
5. Remove ignition, injection and oxygen sensor heating relay and bridge terminals 30 and 87.
6. Connect voltmeter at sleeve to connector, pin 2, and ground.
   Display: 0 V

PR1029900091020X

Fig. 123 Codes P1117 & P1121: Rear Oxygen Sensor Heating Below Lower Limit (Part 2 of 3). 1999 911

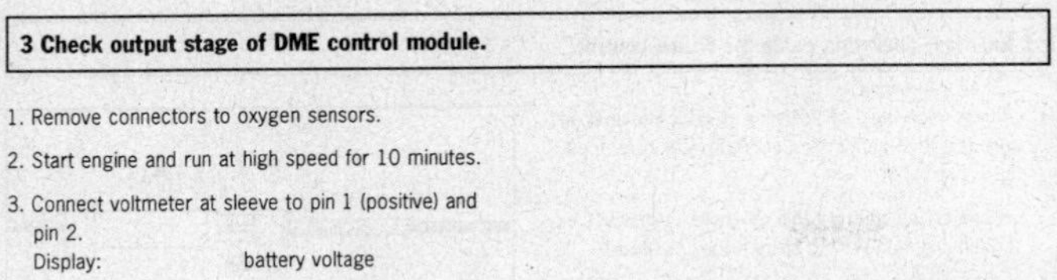

PR1029900091030X

Fig. 123 Codes P1117 & P1121: Rear Oxygen Sensor Heating Below Lower Limit (Part 3 of 3). 1999 911

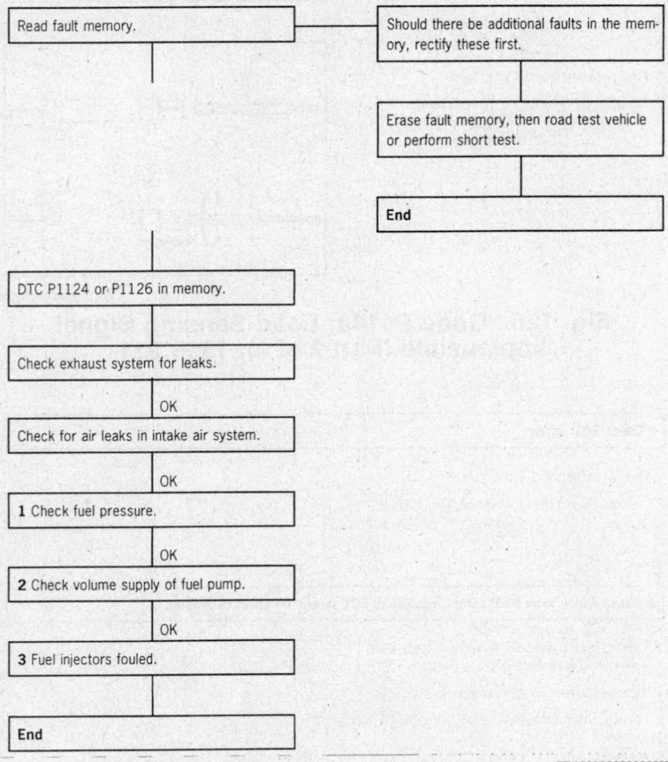

PR1029900093000X

Fig. 125 Codes P1124 & P1126: Oxygen Sensing Adaption Area 1 Rich Threshold. 1999 911

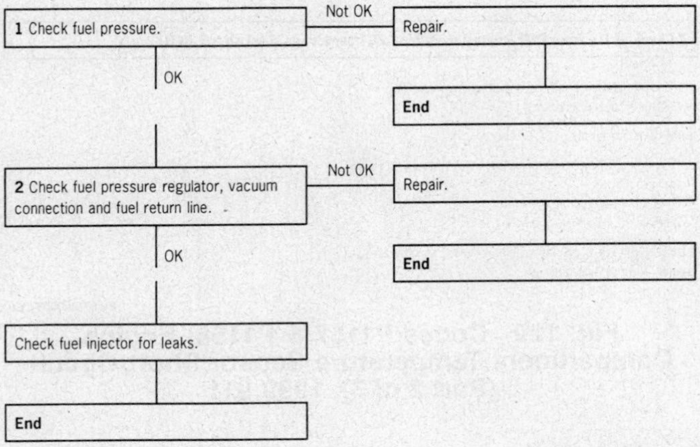

PR1029900094000X

Fig. 126 Code P1127 & P1129: Oxygen Sensing Adaption Area 2 Lean Threshold. 1999 911

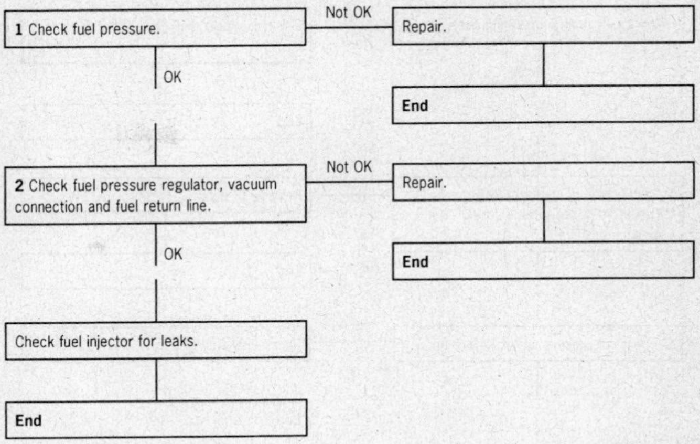

PR1029900092000X

Fig. 124 Codes P1123 & P1125: Oxygen Sensing Adaption Area 1 Lean Threshold . 1999 911

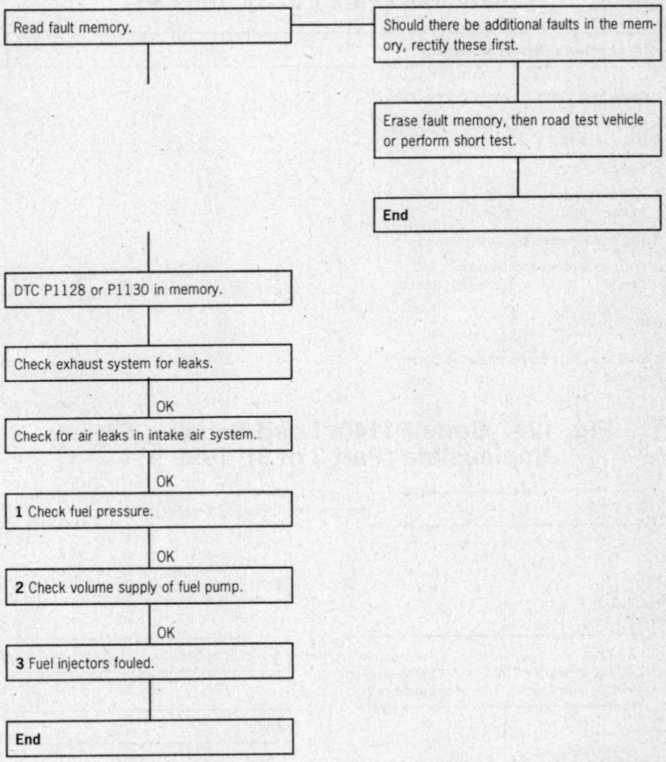

PR1029900095000X

Fig. 127 Codes P1128 & P1130: Oxygen Sensing Adaption Area 2 Rich Threshold. 1999 911

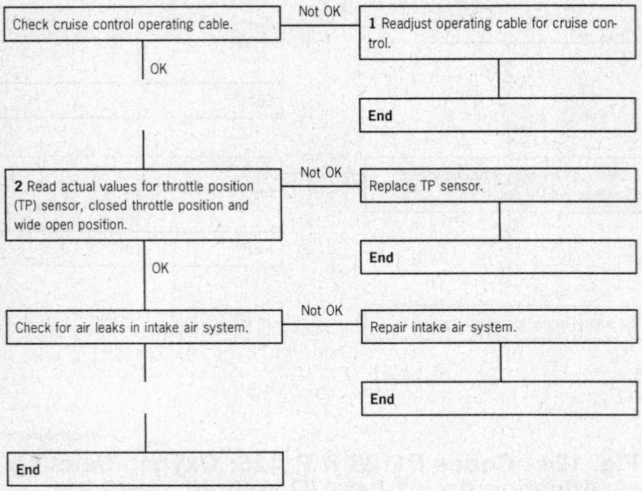

PR1029900096010X

Fig. 128 Code P1140: Load Sensing Signal Implausible (Part 1 of 3). 1999 911

2 Read actual values for TP sensor.

1. Connect and switch on Porsche System Tester 2.
2. Select vehicle type `996, DME, Actual values.`
3. Select TP sensor.
4. Read actual value with throttle valve closed.
   Display: approx. 0 %
5. Fully depress accelerator pedal.
6. Read actual value with throttle valve open.
   Display: approx. 70 - 80 %

Note

It is important that the value changes and does not remain fixed.

PR1029900096030X

Fig. 128 Code P1140: Load Sensing Signal Implausible (Part 3 of 3). 1999 911

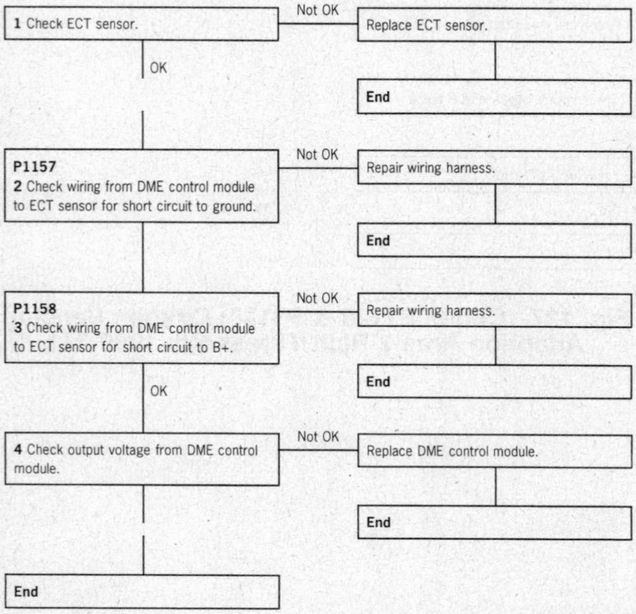

PR1029900097010X

Fig. 129 Codes P1157 & P1158: Engine Compartment Temperature Sensor Short Circuit (Part 1 of 3). 1999 911

1 Readjust operating cable for cruise control.

1. Loosen snap ring 1 at adjusting piece 2 (move it) and push threaded part 3 through along with cruise control cable.
2. Engage cruise control cable on cruise control actuator and clip on adjusting piece 4 (bayonet lock).
3. Unscrew threaded part 5 until the accelerator plate is noticeably pulled.
4. Draw accelerator plate firmly back against its idle stop.

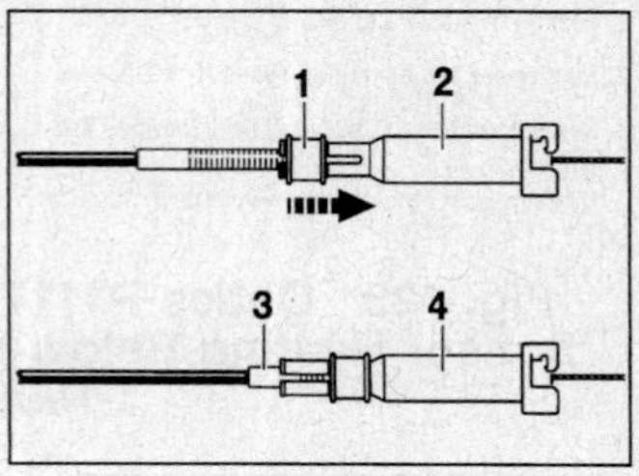

5. Push snap ring 6 back (fix in place).
6. Adjust precisely by turning the threaded part 7.
   Permitted play: 0 + 1 mm.

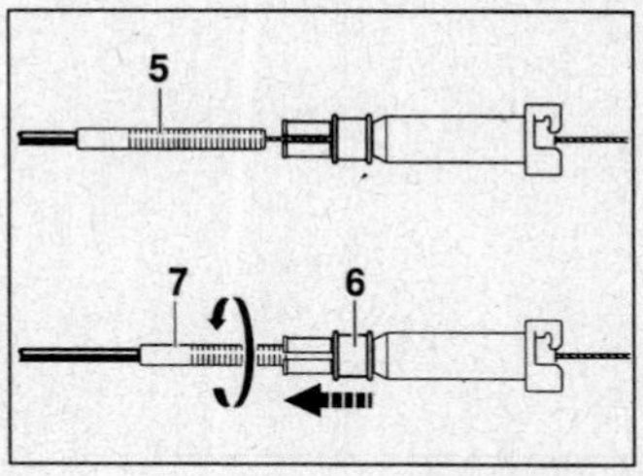

PR1029900096020X

Fig. 128 Code P1140: Load Sensing Signal Implausible (Part 2 of 3). 1999 911

1 Check ECT sensor.

1. Remove connector of ECT sensor.
2. Connect ohmmeter to ECT sensor, pins 1 and 2.
   Display: approx. 2.2 - 2.6 kΩ at 20 °C

2 Check wiring from DME control module to ECT sensor for short to ground.

1. Connect special tool 9616 to wiring harness (DME control module connector).
2. Remove connector of ECT sensor.
3. Connect ohmmeter to special tool 9616, pin 16, and ground.
   Display: ∞ Ω

If 0 - 5 Ω is displayed, check wiring for chafing and pinching damage.

3 Check wiring from DME control module to ECT sensor for short circuit to B+.

1. Connect special tool 9616 to wiring harness (DME control module connector).
2. Remove connector of ECT sensor.
3. Connect voltmeter to special tool 9616, pin 16, and ground.
   Switch on the ignition.
   Display: 0 V

If battery voltage is displayed, check wiring harness for chafing and pinching damage.

PR1029900097020X

Fig. 129 Codes P1157 & P1158: Engine Compartment Temperature Sensor Short Circuit (Part 2 of 3). 1999 911

4 Check output voltage from DME control module.

1. Connect special tool 9616.
2. Remove connector of ECT sensor.
3. Connect voltmeter to pins 16 (positive) and 34 (negative).
   Switch on the ignition.
   Display: approx. 5 V

PR1029900097030X

Fig. 129 Codes P1157 & P1158: Engine Compartment Temperature Sensor Short Circuit (Part 3 of 3). 1999 911

1 Check fuel injector.

1. Remove connector of injector 1.
2. Connect ohmmeter to pins 1 and 2 of injector.
   Display: 11 - 13 Ω at 20 °C.

2 Check wiring harness.

1. Connect special tool 9616 to wiring harness (DME control module connector).
2. Remove connector of fuel injector.
3. Connect ohmmeter to special tool 9616, pin 3, and injector connector, pin 2.
   Display: 0 - 5 Ω
4. Connect ohmmeter to special tool 9616, pin 3, and ground.
   Display: ∞ Ω
5. Connect voltmeter to special tool 9616, pin 3, and ground.
   Ignition on.
   Display: 0 V

If the measured values are not achieved, check wiring harness for chafing and pinching damage.

PR1029900098020X

Fig. 130 Codes P1213, P1225 & P1237: Fuel Injector Cylinder 1 Open Or Short (Part 2 of 2). 1999 911

1 Check fuel injector.

1. Remove connector of injector 2.
2. Connect ohmmeter to pins 1 and 2 of injector.
   Display: 11 - 13 Ω at 20 °C.

2 Check wiring harness.

1. Connect special tool 9616 to wiring harness (DME control module connector).
2. Remove connector of fuel injector.
3. Connect ohmmeter to special tool 9616, pin 4, and injector connector, pin 2.
   Display: 0 - 5 Ω
4. Connect ohmmeter to special tool 9616, pin 4, and ground.
   Display: ∞ Ω
5. Connect voltmeter to special tool 9616, pin 4, and ground.
   Ignition on.
   Display: 0 V

If the measured values are not achieved, check wiring harness for chafing and pinching damage.

PR1029900099020X

Fig. 131 Codes P1214, P1226 & P1238: Fuel Injector Cylinder 2 Open Or Short (Part 2 of 2). 1999 911

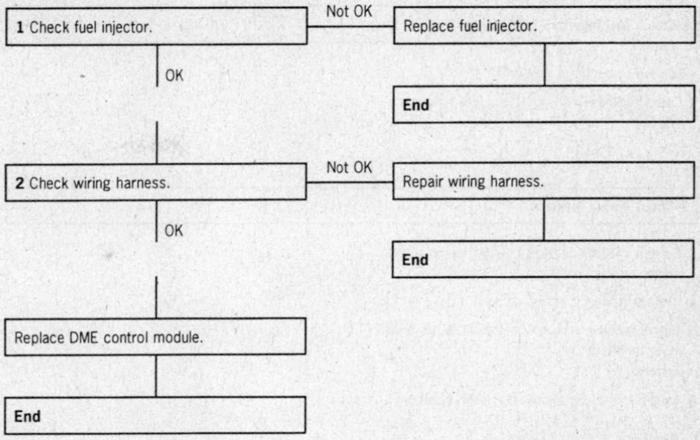

PR1029900098010X

Fig. 130 Codes P1213, P1225 & P1237: Fuel Injector Cylinder 1 Open Or Short (Part 1 of 2). 1999 911

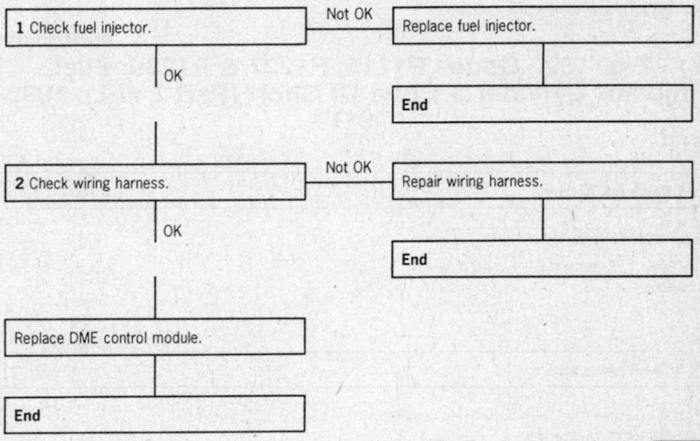

PR1029900099010X

Fig. 131 Codes P1214, P1226 & P1238: Fuel Injector Cylinder 2 Open Or Short (Part 1 of 2). 1999 911

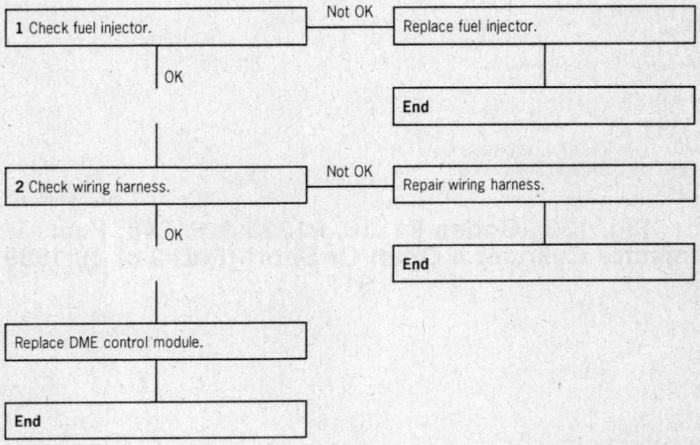

PR1029900100010X

Fig. 132 Codes P1215, P1227 & P1239: Fuel Injector Cylinder 3 Open Or Short (Part 1 of 2). 1999 911

1 Check fuel injector.

1. Remove connector of injector 3.
2. Connect ohmmeter to pins 1 and 2 of injector.
   Display: 11 - 13 Ω at 20 °C.

2 Check wiring harness.

1. Connect special tool 9616 to wiring harness (DME control module connector).
2. Remove connector of fuel injector.
3. Connect ohmmeter to special tool 9616, pin 5, and injector connector, pin 2.
   Display: 0 - 5 Ω
4. Connect ohmmeter to special tool 9616, pin 5, and ground.
   Display: ∞ Ω
5. Connect voltmeter to special tool 9616, pin 5, and ground.
   Ignition on.
   Display: 0 V

If the measured values are not achieved, check wiring harness for chafing and pinching damage.

PR1029900100020X

Fig. 132 Codes P1215, P1227 & P1239: Fuel Injector Cylinder 3 Open Or Short (Part 2 of 2). 1999 911

1 Check fuel injector.

1. Remove connector of injector 4.
2. Connect ohmmeter to pins 1 and 2 of injector.
   Display: 11 - 13 Ω at 20 °C.

2 Check wiring harness.

1. Connect special tool 9616 to wiring harness (DME control module connector).
2. Remove connector of fuel injector.
3. Connect ohmmeter to special tool 9616, pin 32, and injector connector, pin 2.
   Display: 0 - 5 Ω
4. Connect ohmmeter to special tool 9616, pin 32, and ground.
   Display: ∞ Ω
5. Connect voltmeter to special tool 9616, pin 32, and ground.
   Ignition on.
   Display: 0 V

If the measured values are not achieved, check wiring harness for chafing and pinching damage.

PR1029900101020X

Fig. 133 Codes P1216, P1228 & P1240: Fuel Injector Cylinder 4 Open Or Short (Part 2 of 2). 1999 911

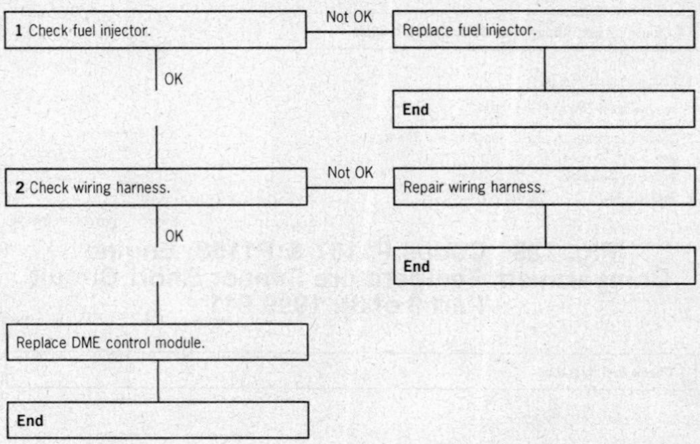

PR1029900101010X

Fig. 133 Codes P1216, P1228 & P1240: Fuel Injector Cylinder 4 Open Or Short (Part 1 of 2). 1999 911

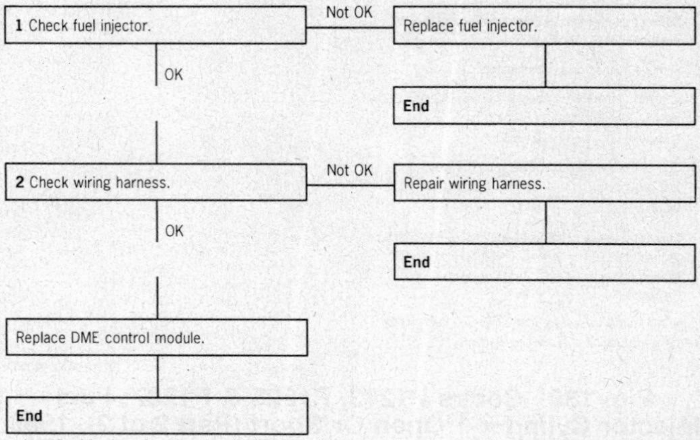

PR1029900102010X

Fig. 134 Codes P1217, P1229 & P1241: Fuel Injector Cylinder 5 Open Or Short (Part 1 of 2). 1999 911

1 Check fuel injector.

1. Remove connector of injector 5.
2. Connect ohmmeter to pins 1 and 2 of injector.
   Display: 11 - 13 Ω at 20 °C.

2 Check wiring harness.

1. Connect special tool 9616 to wiring harness (DME control module connector).
2. Remove connector of fuel injector.
3. Connect ohmmeter to special tool 9616, pin 33, and injector connector, pin 2.
   Display: 0 - 5 Ω
4. Connect ohmmeter to special tool 9616, pin 33, and ground.
   Display: ∞ Ω
5. Connect voltmeter to special tool 9616, pin 33, and ground.
   Ignition on.
   Display: 0 V

If the measured values are not achieved, check wiring harness for chafing and pinching damage.

PR1029900102020X

Fig. 134 Codes P1217, P1229 & P1241: Fuel Injector Cylinder 5 Open Or Short (Part 2 of 2). 1999 911

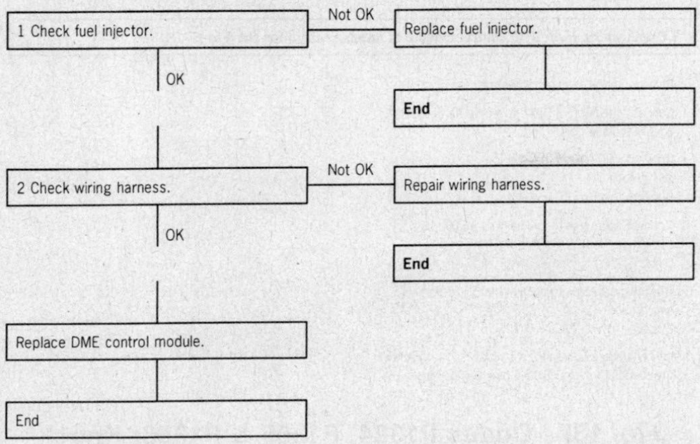

PR1029900103010X

Fig. 135 Code P1218, P1230 & P1242: Fuel Injector Cylinder 6 Open Or Short (Part 1 of 2). 1999 911

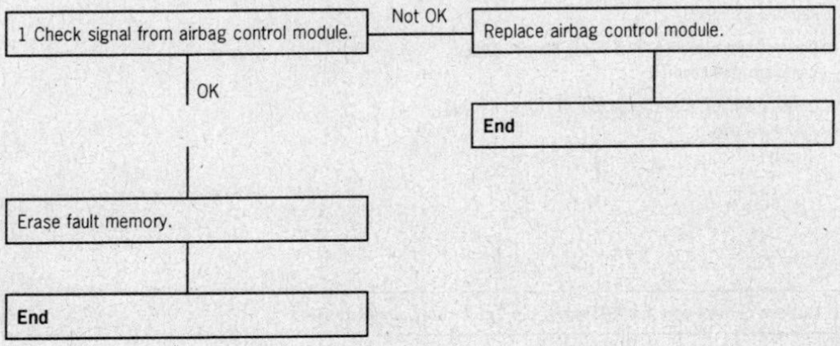

PR1029900104000X

Fig. 136 Code P1265: Air Bag Signal Implausible. 1999 911

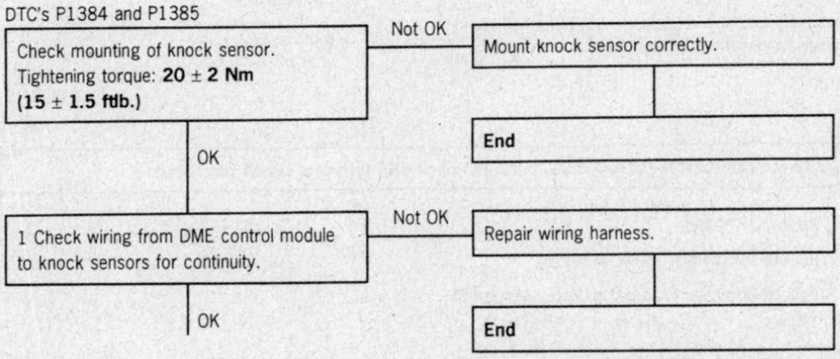

PR1029900105010X

Fig. 137 Codes P1384, P1385 & P1386: Knock Sensor Signal Implausible (Part 1 of 4). 1999 911

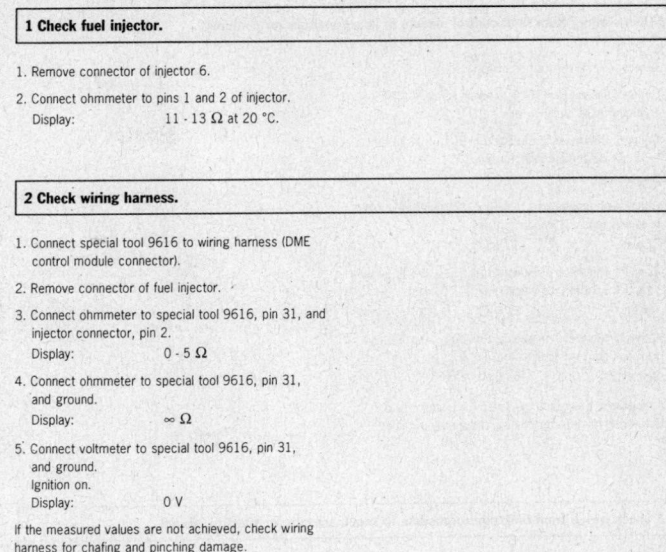

1 Check fuel injector.

1. Remove connector of injector 6.
2. Connect ohmmeter to pins 1 and 2 of injector.
   Display: 11 - 13 Ω at 20 °C.

2 Check wiring harness.

1. Connect special tool 9616 to wiring harness (DME control module connector).
2. Remove connector of fuel injector.
3. Connect ohmmeter to special tool 9616, pin 31, and injector connector, pin 2.
   Display: 0 - 5 Ω
4. Connect ohmmeter to special tool 9616, pin 31, and ground.
   Display: ∞ Ω
5. Connect voltmeter to special tool 9616, pin 31, and ground.
   Ignition on.
   Display: 0 V

If the measured values are not achieved, check wiring harness for chafing and pinching damage.

PR1029900103020X

Fig. 135 Code P1218, P1230 & P1242: Fuel Injector Cylinder 6 Open Or Short (Part 2 of 2). 1999 911

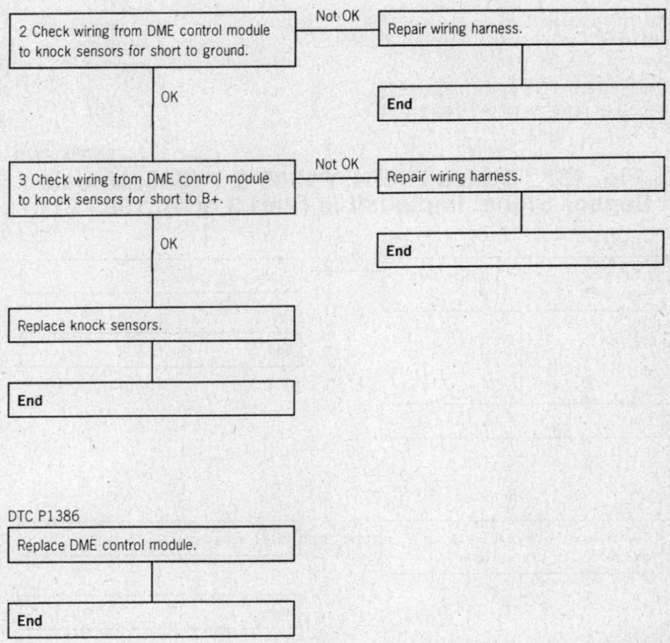

PR1029900105020X

Fig. 137 Codes P1384, P1385 & P1386: Knock Sensor Signal Implausible (Part 2 of 4). 1999 911

1 Check wiring from DME control module to knock sensors for continuity.

1. Remove knock sensor connectors.
2. Connect special tool 9616 to wiring harness (DME control module connector).
3. Connect ohmmeter to special tool 9616, pin 13, and to knock sensor 1 connector, pin 1.
   Display: 0 - 5 Ω
4. Connect ohmmeter to special tool 9616, pin 41, and to knock sensor 2 connector, pin 1.
   Display: 0 - 5 Ω
5. Connect ohmmeter to special tool 9616, pin 71, and to knock sensor 1 connector, pin 2.
   Display: 0 - 5 Ω
6. Connect ohmmeter to special tool 9616, pin 71, and to knock sensor 2 connector, pin 2.
   Display: 0 - 5 Ω

If a resistance of ∞ Ω is displayed for points 3 to 6, check wiring harness for chafing and pinching damage.

2 Check wiring from DME control module to knock sensors for short to ground.

1. Remove knock sensor connectors.
2. Connect special tool 9616 to wiring harness (DME control module connector).
3. Connect ohmmeter to special tool 9616, pin 13, and ground.
   Display: ∞ Ω
4. Connect ohmmeter to special tool 9616, pin 41, and ground.
   Display: ∞ Ω

If a resistance of 0 - 5 Ω is displayed for points 3 and 4, check wiring harness for chafing and pinching damage.

PR1029900105030X

Fig. 137 Codes P1384, P1385 & P1386: Knock Sensor Signal Implausible (Part 3 of 4). 1999 911

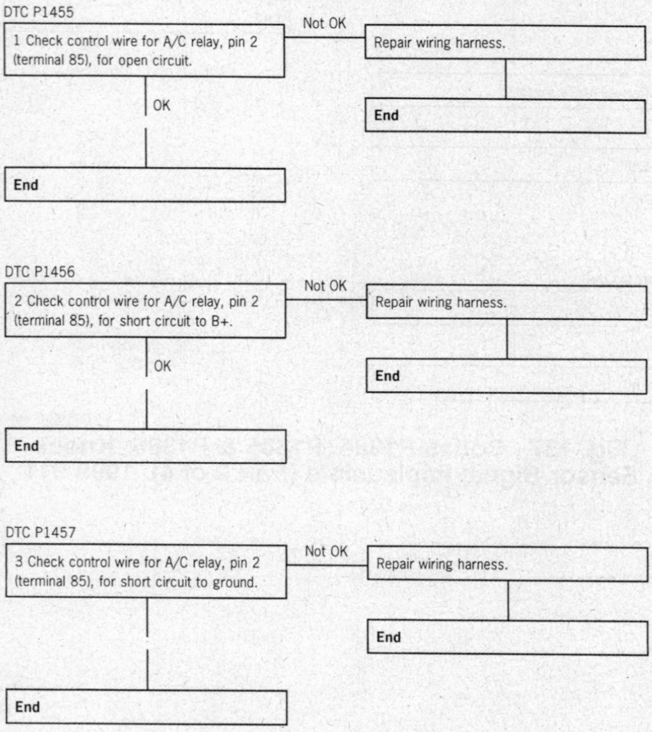

PR1029900106010X

Fig. 138 Codes P1455, P1456 & P1457: A/C Compressor Control (Part 1 of 2). 1999 911

3 Check wiring from DME control module to knock sensors for short to B+.

1. Remove knock sensor connectors.
2. Connect special tool 9616 to wiring harness (DME control module connector).
3. Connect voltmeter to special tool 9616, pin 13, and ground.
   Display: 0 V
4. Connect voltmeter to special tool 9616, pin 41, and ground.
   Display: 0 V
5. Connect voltmeter to special tool 9616, pin 71, and ground.
   Display: 0 V

If battery voltage is displayed for points 3 to 5, check wiring harness for chafing and pinching damage.

PR1029900105040X

Fig. 137 Codes P1384, P1385 & P1386: Knock Sensor Signal Implausible (Part 4 of 4). 1999 911

1 Check control wire for A/C relay, pin 2, for open circuit.

1. Remove A/C relay.
2. Connect special tool 9616 to wiring harness (DME control module connector).
3. Connect ohmmeter to special tool 9616, pin 62, and A/C relay, pin 2.
   Display: 0 - 5 Ω

2 Check control wire for A/C relay, pin 2, for short circuit to B+.

1. Remove A/C relay.
2. Remove DME control module connector.
3. Connect voltmeter (positive) to A/C relay, pin 2, and ground.
   Display: 0 V

If battery voltage is displayed, check wiring harness for chafing and pinching damage.

3 Check control wire for A/C relay, pin 2 (terminal 85), for short circuit to ground.

1. Remove A/C relay.
2. Remove DME control module connector.
3. Connect ohmmeter to ground and pin 2 (terminal 85).
   Display: ∞ Ω

If 0 - 5 Ω is displayed, check wiring harness for chafing and pinching damage.

PR1029900106020X

Fig. 138 Codes P1455, P1456 & P1457: A/C Compressor Control (Part 2 of 2). 1999 911

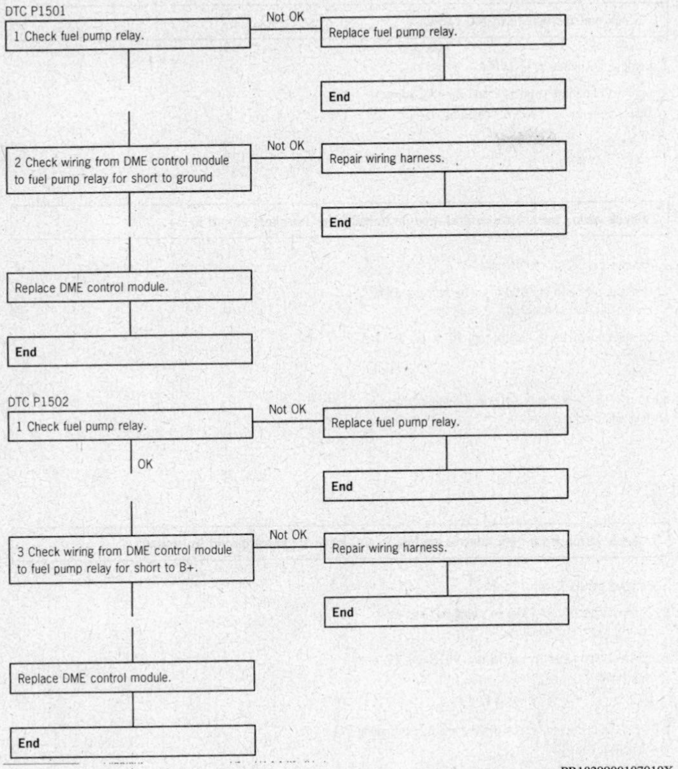

PR1029900107010X

Fig. 139 Codes P1501, P1502 & P1541: Fuel Pump Relay Output Stage Open Or Short Circuit (Part 1 of 4). 1999 911

1 Check fuel pump relay.

1. Remove fuel pump relay.
2. Connect ohmmeter to terminals 85 and 86.
   Display: approx. 75 Ω

2 Check wiring from DME control module to fuel pump relay for short circuit to ground.

1. Connect special tool 9616 to wiring harness (DME control module connector).
2. Remove fuel pump relay.
3. Connect ohmmeter to special tool 9616, pin 63, and ground.
   Display: ∞ Ω

If 0 - 5 Ω is displayed, check wiring for chafing and pinching damage.

3 Check wiring from DME control module to fuel pump relay for short circuit to B+.

1. Connect special tool 9616 to wiring harness (DME control module connector).
2. Remove fuel pump relay.
3. Connect voltmeter to special tool 9616, pin 63, and ground.
   Ignition on.
   Display: 0 V

PR1029900107030X

Fig. 139 Codes P1501, P1502 & P1541: Fuel Pump Relay Output Stage Open Or Short Circuit (Part 3 of 4). 1999 911

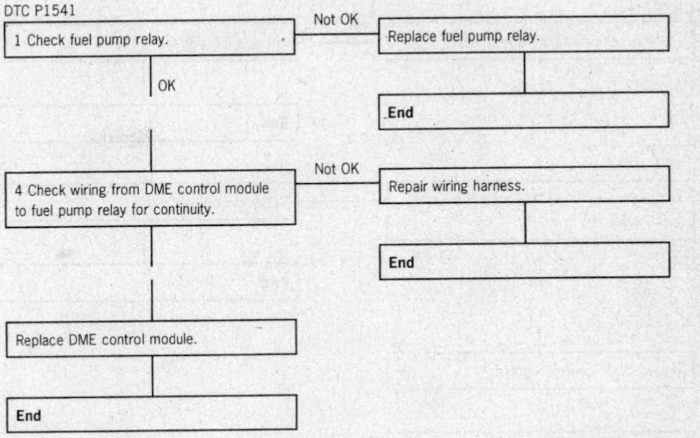

PR1029900107020X

Fig. 139 Codes P1501, P1502 & P1541: Fuel Pump Relay Output Stage Open Or Short Circuit (Part 2 of 4). 1999 911

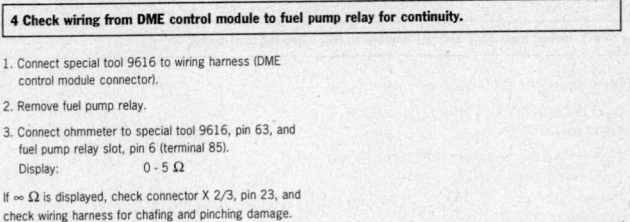

4 Check wiring from DME control module to fuel pump relay for continuity.

1. Connect special tool 9616 to wiring harness (DME control module connector).
2. Remove fuel pump relay.
3. Connect ohmmeter to special tool 9616, pin 63, and fuel pump relay slot, pin 6 (terminal 85).
   Display: 0 - 5 Ω

If ∞ Ω is displayed, check connector X 2/3, pin 23, and check wiring harness for chafing and pinching damage.

PR1029900107040X

Fig. 139 Codes P1501, P1502 & P1541: Fuel Pump Relay Output Stage Open Or Short Circuit (Part 4 of 4). 1999 911

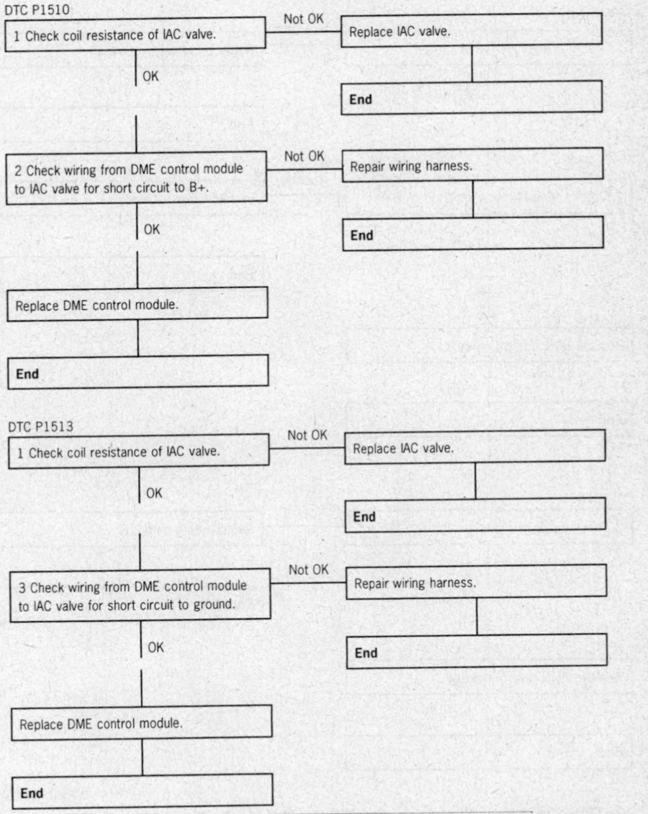

PR1029900108010X

Fig. 140 Codes P1510, P1513 & P1514: Idle Air Control Valve Opening Coil (Part 1 of 4). 1999 911

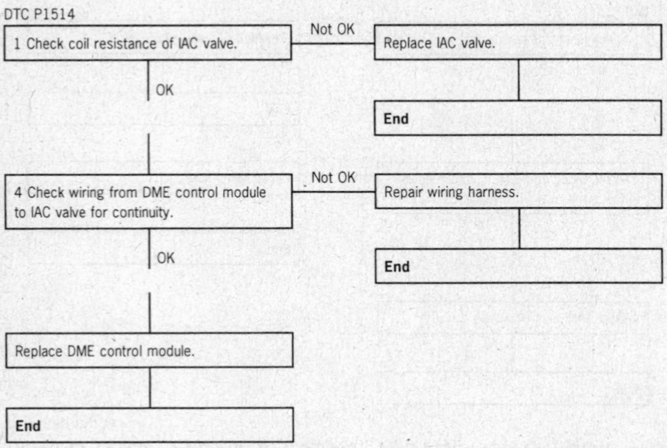

PR1029900108020X

Fig. 140 Codes P1510, P1513 & P1514: Idle Air Control Valve Opening Coil (Part 2 of 4). 1999 911

4 Check wiring from DME control module to IAC valve for continuity.

1. Remove connector of IAC valve.
2. Connect special tool 9616 to wiring harness (DME control module connector).
3. Connect ohmmeter to special tool 9616, pin 29, and to IAC valve connector, pin 3.
   Display: 0 - 5 Ω

If ∞ Ω is displayed, check wiring harness for chafing and pinching damage.

PR1029900108040X

Fig. 140 Codes P1510, P1513 & P1514: Idle Air Control Valve Opening Coil (Part 4 of 4). 1999 911

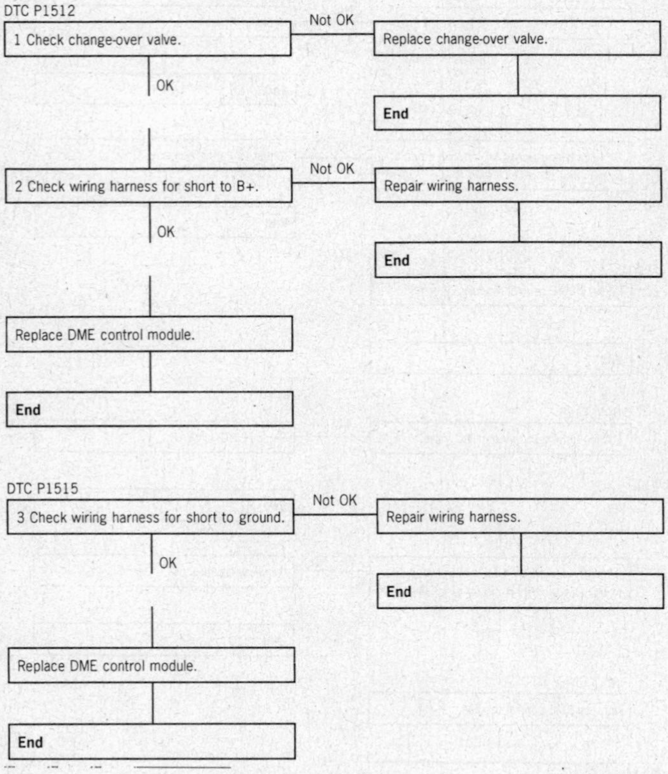

PR1029900109010X

Fig. 141 Codes P1512, P1515 & P1516: Intake Manifold Switchover 1 Open Or Short (Part 1 of 4). 1999 911

1 Check coil resistance of IAC valve.

1. Remove connector of IAC valve.
2. Connect ohmmeter to pins 2 and 3 of IAC valve.
   Display: 16 - 19 Ω at 20 °C.

2 Check wiring from DME control module to IAC valve for short circuit to B+.

1. Remove connector of IAC valve.
2. Connect special tool 9616 to wiring harness (DME control module connector).
3. Connect voltmeter to special tool 9616, pin 29, and to ground.
   Display: 0 V

If battery voltage is displayed, check wiring harness for chafing and pinching damage.

3 Check wiring from DME control module to IAC valve for short circuit to ground.

1. Remove connector of IAC valve.
2. Connect special tool 9616 to wiring harness (DME control module connector).
3. Connect ohmmeter to special tool 9616, pin 29, and to ground.
   Display: ∞ Ω

If 0 - 5 Ω is displayed, check wiring harness for chafing and pinching damage.

PR1029900108030X

Fig. 140 Codes P1510, P1513 & P1514: Idle Air Control Valve Opening Coil (Part 3 of 4). 1999 911

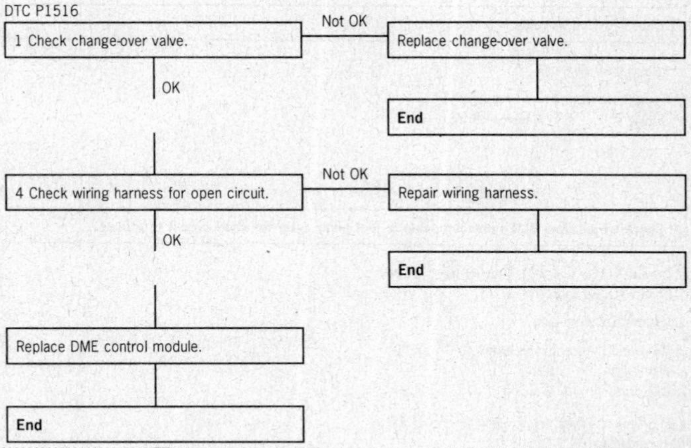

PR1029900109020X

Fig. 141 Codes P1512, P1515 & P1516: Intake Manifold Switchover 1 Open Or Short (Part 2 of 4). 1999 911

1 Check change-over valve.

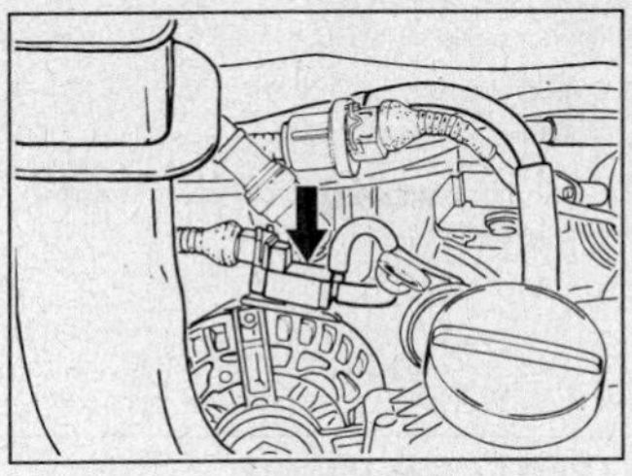

1. Remove connector of change-over valve.
2. Connect special tool V.A.G. 1315 A/1 to change-over valve.
3. Connect ohmmeter to special tool V.A.G. 1315 A/1.
   Display: 28 - 32 Ω at 20 °C.

2 Check wiring harness for short to B+.

1. Remove connector of change-over valve.
2. Connect voltmeter to connector, pin 2 (positive), and ground (negative). Switch on the ignition.
   Display: 0 V

If battery voltage is displayed, check wiring harness for chafing and pinching damage.

3 Check wiring harness for short to ground.

1. Remove connector of change-over valve.
2. Connect ohmmeter to connector, pin 2, and ground.
   Display: ∞ Ω

If 0 - 5 Ω is displayed, check wiring harness for chafing and pinching damage.

PR1029900109030X

Fig. 141 Codes P1512, P1515 & P1516: Intake Manifold Switchover 1 Open Or Short (Part 3 of 4). 1999 911

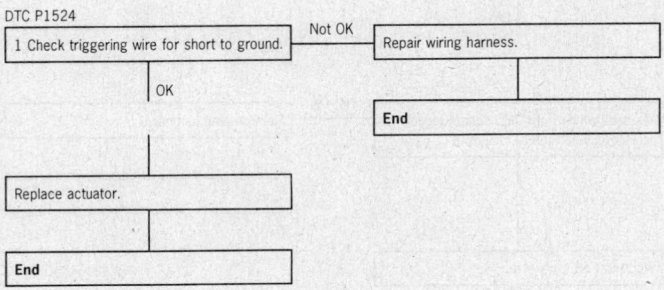

DTC P1524

1 Check triggering wire for short to ground. — Not OK → Repair wiring harness. → End

OK ↓

Replace actuator.

End

DTC P1539

2 Check B+ supply of actuator. — Not OK → Repair B+ supply. → End

OK ↓

3 Check triggering wire for continuity. — Not OK → Repair wiring harness. → End

OK ↓

Replace actuator.

End

PR1029900110010X

Fig. 142 Codes P1524 & P1539: Camshaft Adjustment Bank 2 (Part 1 of 2). 1999 911

4 Check wiring harness for open circuit.

1. Connect special tool 9616 to wiring harness (DME control module connector).
2. Remove connector of change-over valve.
3. Connect ohmmeter to special tool 9616, pin 59, and change-over valve connector, pin 2.
   Display: 0 - 5 Ω

Note

The wire is routed via connector X 59/1, pin 10.

If ∞ Ω is displayed, check connector X59/1, pin 10, for corrosion, and check wiring harness for chafing and pinching damage.

PR1029900109040X

Fig. 141 Codes P1512, P1515 & P1516: Intake Manifold Switchover 1 Open Or Short (Part 4 of 4). 1999 911

1 Check triggering wire for short to ground.

1. Connect special tool 9616.
2. Connect ohmmeter to pin 25 and ground.
   Display: ∞ Ω

If 0 - 5 Ω is displayed, check wiring harness for chafing and pinching damage.

2 Check B+ supply of actuator.

1. Remove connector of actuator.
2. Connect voltmeter to connector, pin 1, and ground. Switch on the ignition.
   Display: battery voltage

3 Check triggering wire for continuity.

1. Connect special tool 9616 to wiring harness (DME control module connector).
2. Remove connector of actuator.
3. Connect ohmmeter to special tool 9616, pin 25, and connector, pin 2.
   Display: 0 - 5 Ω

PR1029900110020X

Fig. 142 Codes P1524 & P1539: Camshaft Adjustment Bank 2 (Part 2 of 2). 1999 911

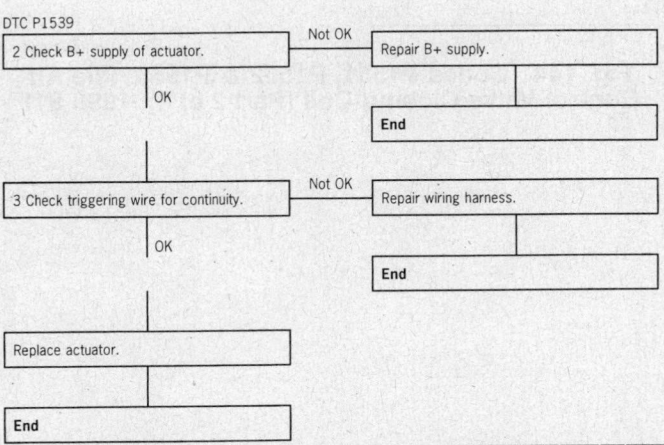

DTC P1530

1 Check triggering wire for short to ground. — Not OK → Repair wiring harness. → End

OK ↓

Replace actuator.

End

DTC P1531

2 Check B+ supply of actuator. — Not OK → Repair B+ supply. → End

OK ↓

3 Check triggering wire for continuity. — Not OK → Repair wiring harness. → End

OK ↓

Replace actuator.

End

PR1029900111010X

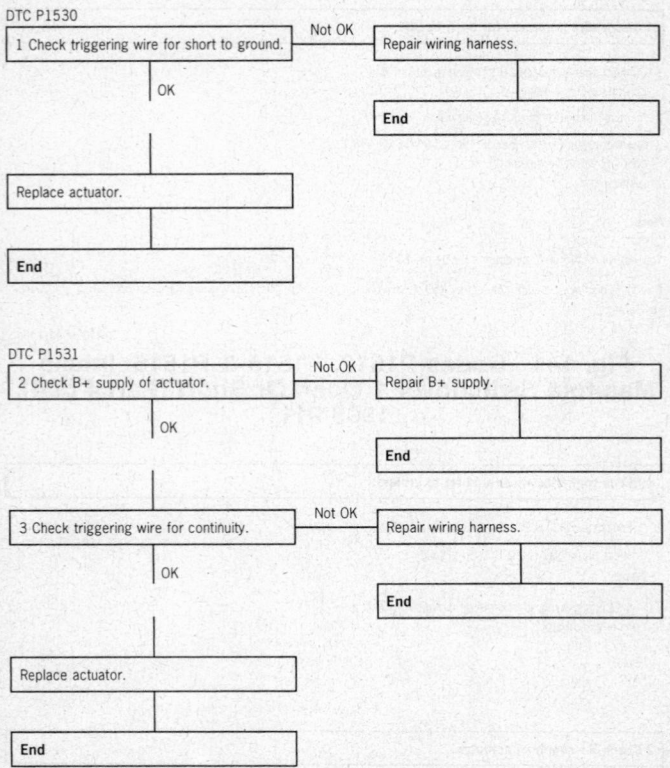

Fig. 143 Codes P1530 & P1531: Camshaft Adjustment Bank 1 (Part 1 of 2). 1999 911

DTC P1551

1 Check coil resistance of IAC valve. — Not OK → Replace IAC valve. → **End**

OK ↓

2 Check wiring from DME control module to IAC valve for continuity. — Not OK → Repair wiring harness. → **End**

OK ↓

Replace DME control module.

End

DTC P1552

1 Check coil resistance of IAC valve. — Not OK → Replace IAC valve. → **End**

OK ↓

3 Check wiring from DME control module to IAC valve for short circuit to ground. — Not OK → Repair wiring harness. → **End**

OK ↓

Replace DME control module.

End

PR1029900112010X

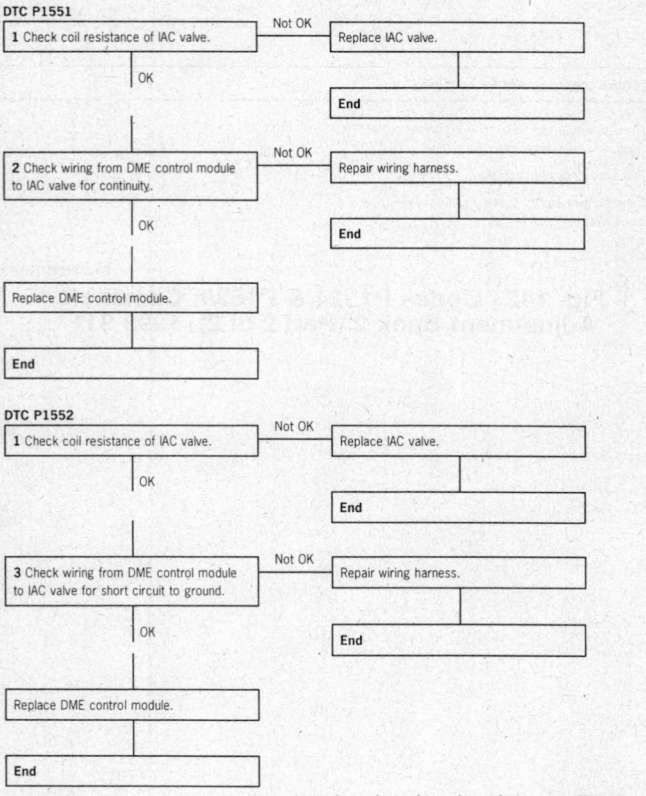

Fig. 144 Codes P1551, P1552 & P1553: Idle Air Control Valve Closing Coil (Part 1 of 4). 1999 911

1 Check triggering wire for short to ground.

1. Connect special tool 9616.
2. Connect ohmmeter to pin 52 and ground.
   Display: $\infty\ \Omega$

If 0 - 5 Ω is displayed, check wiring harness for chafing and pinching damage.

2 Check B+ supply of actuator.

1. Remove connector of actuator.
2. Connect voltmeter to connector, pin 1, and ground.
   Switch on the ignition.
   Display: battery voltage

3 Check triggering wire for continuity.

1. Connect special tool 9616 to wiring harness (DME control module connector).
2. Remove connector of actuator.
3. Connect ohmmeter to special tool 9616, pin 52, and connector, pin 2.
   Display: 0 - 5 Ω

PR1029900111020X

Fig. 143 Codes P1530 & P1531: Camshaft Adjustment Bank 1 (Part 2 of 2). 1999 911

DTC P1553

1 Check coil resistance of IAC valve. — Not OK → Replace IAC valve. → **End**

OK ↓

4 Check wiring from DME control module to IAC valve for short circuit to B+. — Not OK → Repair wiring harness. → **End**

OK ↓

Replace DME control module.

End

PR1029900112020X

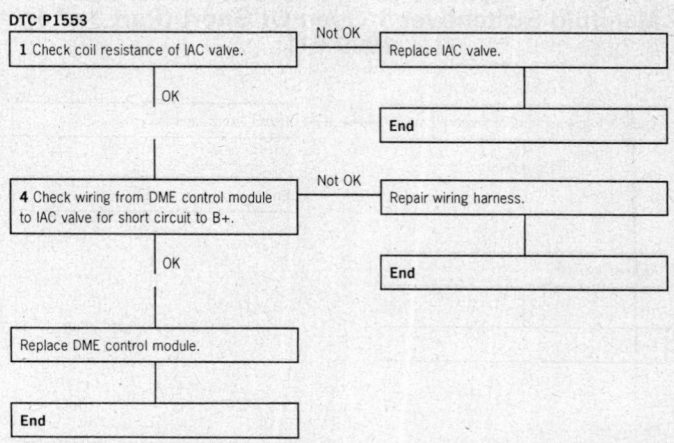

Fig. 144 Codes P1551, P1552 & P1553: Idle Air Control Valve Closing Coil (Part 2 of 4). 1999 911

1 Check coil resistance of IAC valve.

1. Remove connector of IAC valve.
2. Connect ohmmeter to pins 2 and 1 of IAC valve.
   Display: 14 - 17 Ω at 20 °C.

2 Check wiring from DME control module to IAC valve for continuity.

1. Remove connector of IAC valve.
2. Connect special tool 9616 to wiring harness (DME control module connector).
3. Connect ohmmeter to special tool 9616, pin 2, and to IAC valve connector, pin 1.
   Display: 0 - 5 Ω

If ∞ Ω is displayed, check wiring harness for chafing and pinching damage.

3 Check wiring from DME control module to IAC valve for short circuit to ground.

1. Remove connector of IAC valve.
2. Connect special tool 9616 to wiring harness (DME control module connector).
3. Connect ohmmeter to special tool 9616, pin 2, and ground.
   Display: ∞ Ω

If 0 - 5 Ω is displayed, check wiring harness for chafing and pinching damage.

PR1029900112030X

Fig. 144 Codes P1551, P1552 & P1553: Idle Air Control Valve Closing Coil (Part 3 of 4). 1999 911

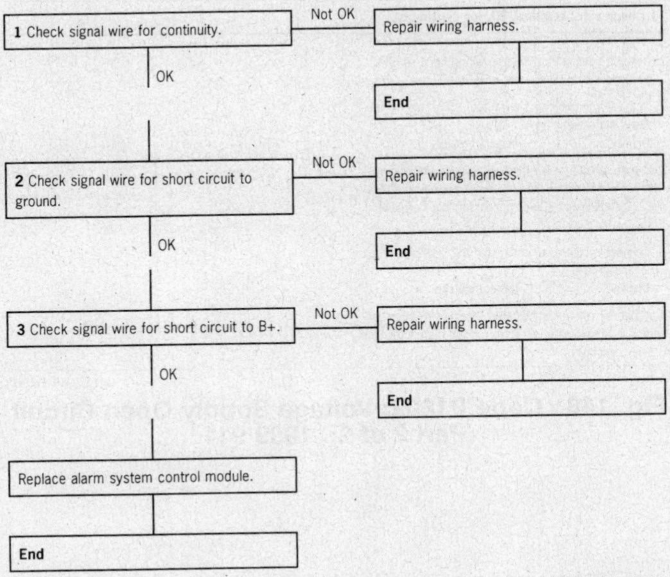

PR1029900113010X

Fig. 145 Codes P1570 & P1571: Immobilizer Implausible Operating Range Or Open Circuit (Part 1 of 3). 1999 911

4 Check wiring from DME control module to IAC valve for short circuit to B+.

1. Remove connector of IAC valve.
2. Connect special tool 9616 to wiring harness (DME control module connector).
3. Connect voltmeter to special tool 9616, pin 2, and ground.
   Display: 0 V

If battery voltage is displayed, check wiring harness for chafing and pinching damage.

PR1029900112040X

Fig. 144 Codes P1551, P1552 & P1553: Idle Air Control Valve Closing Coil (Part 4 of 4). 1999 911

1 Check signal wire for continuity.

1. Remove connector I of alarm system control module.
2. Connect special tool 9616 to wiring harness (DME control module connector).
3. Connect ohmmeter to special tool 9616, pin 88, and to alarm system connector I/23.
   Display: 0 - 5 Ω

If ∞ Ω is displayed, remove connector X 2/3.

4. Connect ohmmeter to connector X 2/3, pin 6, on sleeve side and to special tool 9616, pin 88.
   Display: 0 - 5 Ω

If ∞ Ω is displayed, repair wiring harness.

5. Connect ohmmeter to connector X 2/3, pin 6, on pin side, and to alarm control module connector I, pin 23.
   Display: 0 - 5 Ω

If ∞ Ω is displayed, repair wiring harness.

2 Check signal wire for short circuit to ground.

1. Remove connector I of alarm system control module.
2. Connect special tool 9616 to wiring harness (DME control module connector).
3. Connect ohmmeter to special tool 9616, pin 88, and ground.
   Display: ∞ Ω

If 0 - 5 Ω is displayed, check wiring harness for chafing and pinching damage.

PR1029900113020X

Fig. 145 Codes P1570 & P1571: Immobilizer Implausible Operating Range Or Open Circuit (Part 2 of 3). 1999 911

3 Check signal wire for short circuit to B+.

1. Remove connector I of alarm system control module.
2. Connect special tool 9616 to wiring harness (DME control module connector).
3. Connect voltmeter to special tool 9616, pin 88, and ground.
   Display: 0 V

If battery voltage is displayed, check wiring harness for chafing and pinching damage.

PR1029900113030X

Fig. 145 Codes P1570 & P1571: Immobilizer Implausible Operating Range Or Open Circuit (Part 3 of 3). 1999 911

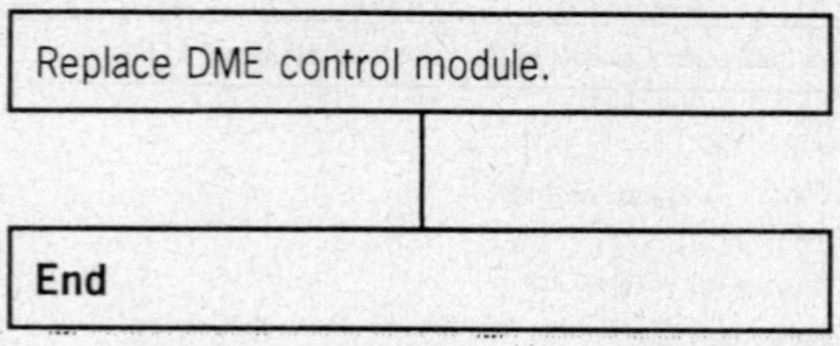

PR1029900114000X

Fig. 146 Code P1600: Voltage Supply Signal Implausible. 1999 911

1 Check wire, terminal 30, for contact resistance.

1. Connect special tool 9616 to wiring harness (DME control module connector).
2. Connect voltmeter to special tool 9616, pin 26 (positive), and ground.
   Display: battery voltage.

If no battery voltage is indicated, check wire from special tool 9616, pin 26, to pin side of connector X 2/3, pin 2, for continuity. Check connectors for corrosion.

3. Check wire from connector X 2/3, sleeve side, to current distributor fuse C 1 for continuity.

PR1029900115020X

Fig. 147 Codes P1600 & P1601: Voltage Supply Below Lower Or Above Upper Limits (Part 2 of 2). 1999 911

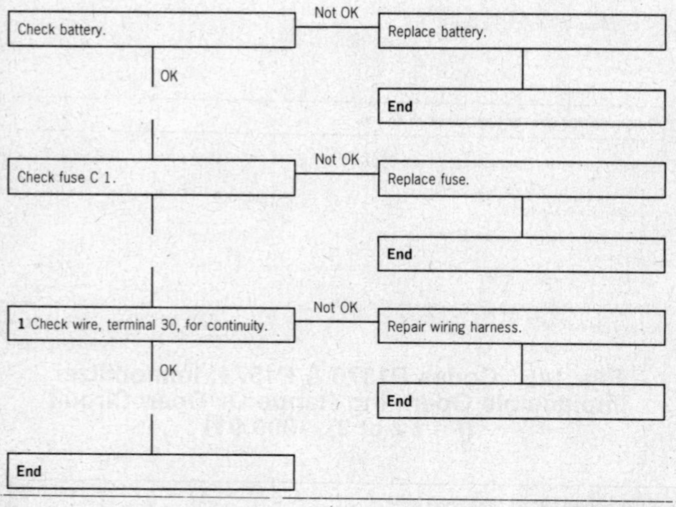

PR1029900116010X

Fig. 148 Code P1602: Voltage Supply Open Circuit (Part 1 of 2). 1999 911

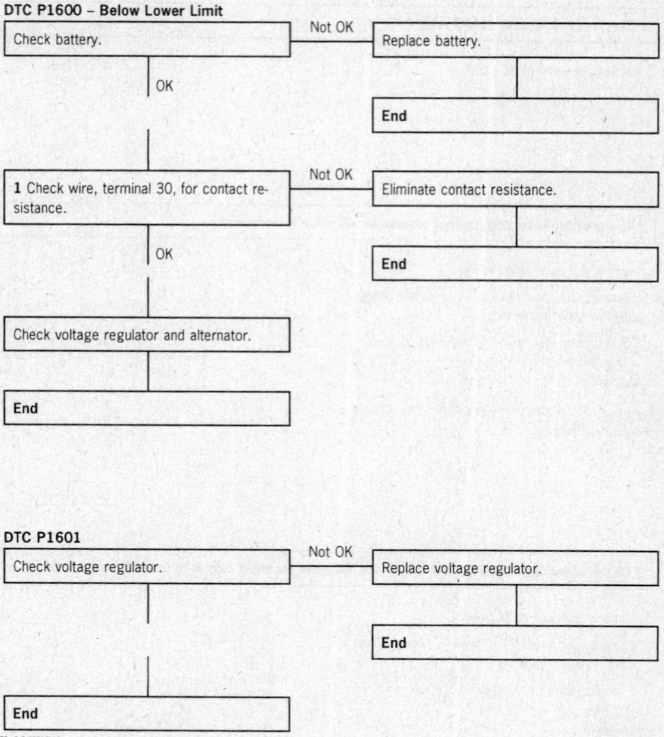

PR1029900115010X

Fig. 147 Codes P1600 & P1601: Voltage Supply Below Lower Or Above Upper Limits (Part 1 of 2). 1999 911

1 Check wire, terminal 30, for continuity.

1. Connect special tool 9616 to wiring harness (DME control module connector).
2. Connect voltmeter to special tool 9616, pin 26 (positive), and ground.
   Display: battery voltage.

If no battery voltage is indicated, check wire from special tool 9616, pin 26, to pin side of connector X 2/3, pin 2, for continuity. Check connectors for corrosion.

3. Connect voltmeter to connector X 2/3 at sleeve, pin 2, and ground.
   Display: battery voltage.

If no battery voltage is indicated, check wire from connector X 2/3 pin side, pin 2, to current distributor fuse C 1 for continuity.

PR1029900116020X

Fig. 148 Code P1602: Voltage Supply Open Circuit (Part 2 of 2). 1999 911

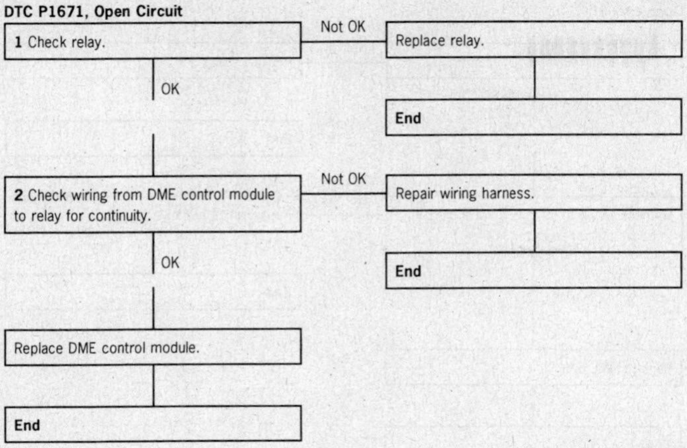

PR1029900117010X

Fig. 149 Code P1671: Engine Compartment Purge Fan Output Stage Open Or Short Circuit (Part 1 of 5). 1999 911

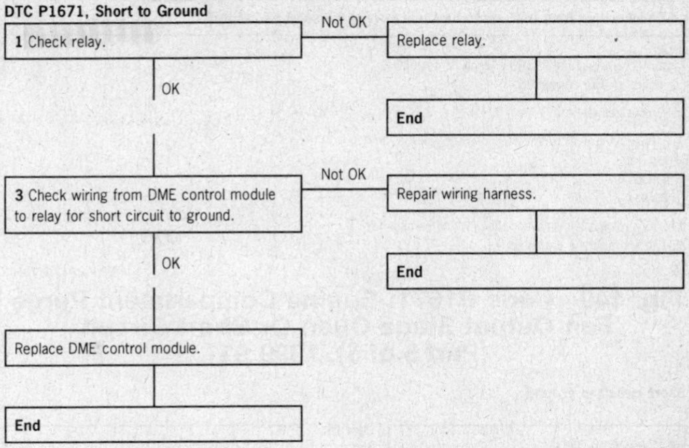

PR1029900117020X

Fig. 149 Code P1671: Engine Compartment Purge Fan Output Stage Open Or Short Circuit (Part 2 of 5). 1999 911

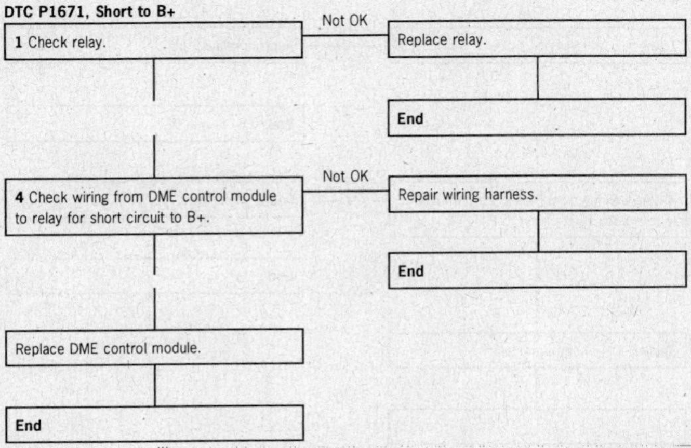

PR1029900117030X

Fig. 149 Code P1671: Engine Compartment Purge Fan Output Stage Open Or Short Circuit (Part 3 of 5). 1999 911

1 Check relay.

1. Remove relay.
2. Connect ohmmeter to terminals 85 and 86.
   Display: approx. 75 Ω

2 Check wiring from DME control module to relay for continuity.

1. Connect special tool 9616 to wiring harness (DME control module connector).
2. Remove relay.
3. Connect ohmmeter to special tool 9616, pin 65, and relay slot, pin 2 (terminal 85).
   Display: 0 - 5 Ω

If ∞ Ω is displayed, check wiring harness for chafing and pinching damage.

3 Check wiring from DME control module to relay for short circuit to ground.

1. Connect special tool 9616 to wiring harness (DME control module connector).
2. Remove relay.
3. Connect ohmmeter to special tool 9616, pin 65, and ground.
   Display: ∞ Ω

If 0 - 5 Ω is displayed, check wiring harness for chafing and pinching damage.

PR1029900117040X

Fig. 149 Code P1671: Engine Compartment Purge Fan Output Stage Open Or Short Circuit (Part 4 of 5). 1999 911

4 Check wiring from DME control module to relay for short circuit to B+.

1. Connect special tool 9616 to wiring harness (DME control module connector).
2. Remove relay.
3. Connect voltmeter to special tool 9616, pin 65, and ground.
   Ignition on.
   Display: 0 V

If battery voltage is displayed, check wiring harness for chafing and pinching damage.

PR1029900117050X

Fig. 149 Code P1671: Engine Compartment Purge Fan Output Stage Open Or Short Circuit (Part 5 of 5). 1999 911

Short circuit to ground

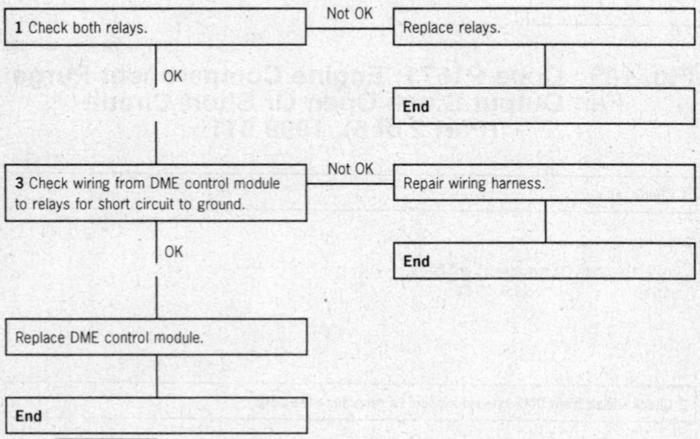

PR1029900118020X

Fig. 150 Code P1673: Fan Output Stage Open Or Short Circuit (Part 2 of 5). 1999 911

1 Check both relays.

1. Remove relays.
2. Connect ohmmeter to terminals 85 and 86.
   Display: approx. 75 Ω

2 Check wiring from DME control module to relays for continuity.

1. Connect special tool 9616 to wiring harness (DME control module connector).
2. Remove relay stage 1 of coolant fan 1.
3. Remove relay stage 1 of coolant fan 2.
4. Connect ohmmeter to special tool 9616, pin 35, and relay slot of coolant fan 1, pin 2 (terminal 85).
   Display: 0 - 5 Ω
5. Connect ohmmeter to special tool 9616, pin 35, and relay slot of coolant fan 2, pin 2 (terminal 85).
   Display: 0 - 5 Ω

If ∞ Ω is displayed, check connector X 2/3, pin 21, and check wiring harness for chafing and pinching damage.

3 Check wiring from DME control module to relays for short circuit to ground.

1. Connect special tool 9616 to wiring harness (DME control module connector).
2. Remove relay stage 1 of coolant fan 1.
3. Remove relay stage 1 of coolant fan 2.
4. Connect ohmmeter to special tool 9616, pin 35, and ground.
   Display: ∞ Ω

If 0 - 5 Ω is displayed, check wiring for chafing and pinching damage.

PR1029900118040X

Fig. 150 Code P1673: Fan Output Stage Open Or Short Circuit (Part 4 of 5). 1999 911

Open circuit

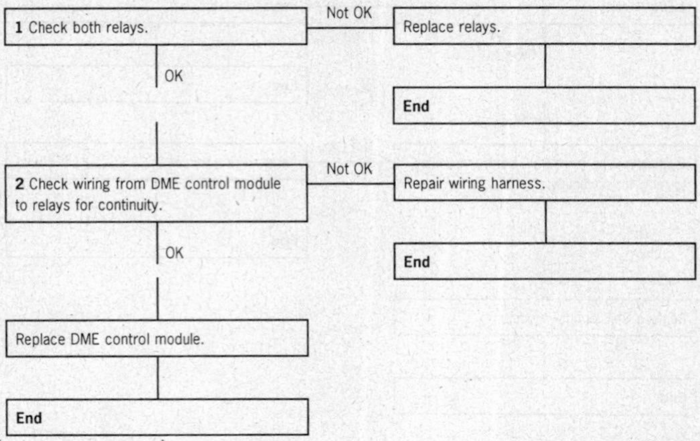

PR1029900118010X

Fig. 150 Code P1673: Fan Output Stage Open Or Short Circuit (Part 1 of 5). 1999 911

Short circuit to B+

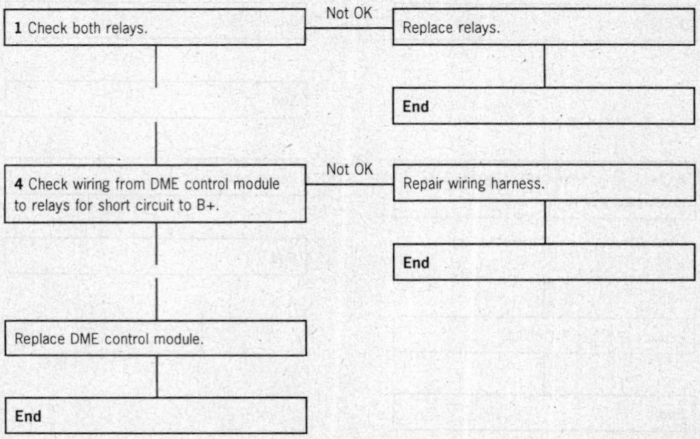

PR1029900118030X

Fig. 150 Code P1673: Fan Output Stage Open Or Short Circuit (Part 3 of 5). 1999 911

4 Check wiring from DME control module to relays for short circuit to B+.

1. Connect special tool 9616 to wiring harness (DME control module connector).
2. Remove relay stage 1 of coolant fan 1.
3. Remove relay stage 1 of coolant fan 2.
4. Connect voltmeter to special tool 9616, pin 35, and ground.
   Ignition on.
   Display: 0 V

If battery voltage is displayed, check wiring harness for chafing and pinching damage.

PR1029900118050X

Fig. 150 Code P1673: Fan Output Stage Open Or Short Circuit (Part 5 of 5). 1999 911

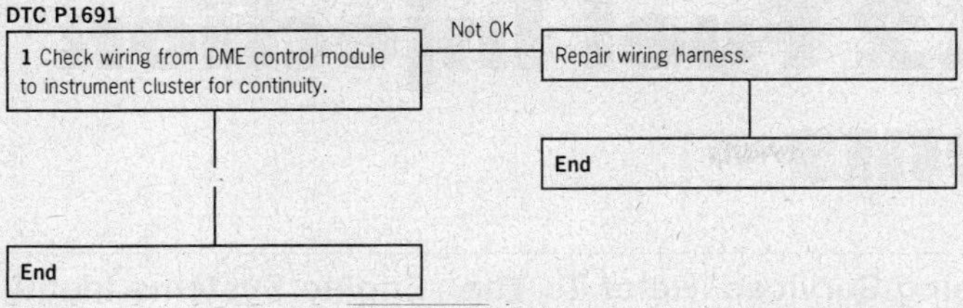

PR1029900119010X

Fig. 151 Codes P1691, P1692 & P1693: MIL Lamp Open Or Short Circuit (Part 1 of 4). 1999 911

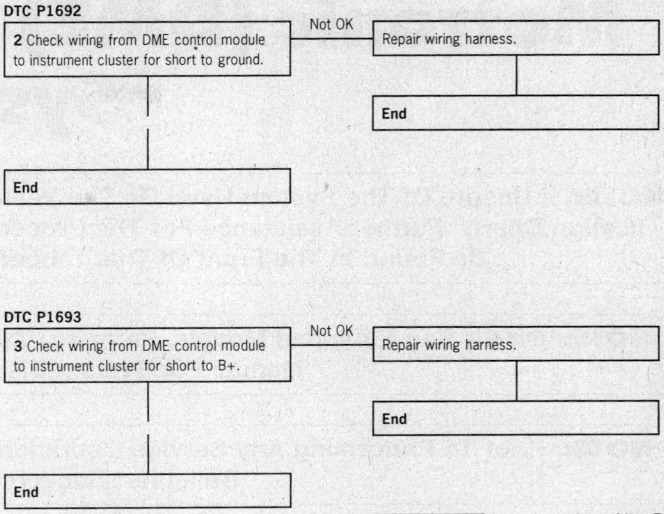

PR1029900119020X

Fig. 151 Codes P1691, P1692 & P1693: MIL Lamp Open Or Short Circuit (Part 2 of 4). 1999 911

1 Check wiring from DME control module to instrument cluster for continuity.

1. Connect special tool 9616 to wiring harness (DME control module connector).
2. Remove connector X 2/3.
3. Connect ohmmeter to special tool 9616, pin 8, and to X 2/3 on pin side, pin 11.
   Display: 0 - 5 Ω

If ∞ Ω is displayed, check wiring harness for chafing and pinching damage.

4. Remove connector III of instrument cluster.
5. Connect ohmmeter to X 2/3 on pin side and to connector III of instrument cluster, pin 2.
   Display: 0 - 5 Ω

If ∞ Ω is displayed, check wiring harness for chafing and pinching damage.

2 Check wiring from DME control module to instrument cluster for short to ground.

1. Connect special tool 9616 to wiring harness (DME control module connector).
2. Remove connector III of instrument cluster.
3. Connect ohmmeter to special tool 9616, pin 8, and ground.
   Display: ∞ Ω

If 0 - 5 Ω is displayed, check wiring harness for chafing and pinching damage.

PR1029900119030X

Fig. 151 Codes P1691, P1692 & P1693: MIL Lamp Open Or Short Circuit (Part 3 of 4). 1999 911

3 Check wiring from DME control module to instrument cluster for short to B+.

1. Connect special tool 9616 to wiring harness (DME control module connector).
2. Remove connector III of instrument cluster.
3. Switch on the ignition.
4. Connect voltmeter to special tool 9616, pin 8, and ground.
   Display: 0 V

If battery voltage is displayed, check wiring harness for chafing and pinching damage.

PR1029900119040X

Fig. 151 Codes P1691, P1692 & P1693: MIL Lamp Open Or Short Circuit (Part 4 of 4). 1999 911

Motronic (DME) 7.2 Fuel Injection Systems

NOTE: If Unsure Of The System Used On The Vehicle Being Serviced, Refer To The "Engine Systems Identification Chart." Further Assistance For The Proper Use Of Information Contained In This Section Can Also Be Found In The Front Of This Tabbed Section Under "How To Use This Manual."

NOTE: On Air Bag Equipped Models, Refer To "Air Bag System Precautions" Located In The Front Of This Manual For System Disarming & Arming Procedures.

NOTE: Prior To Performing Any Service Operations Listed In This Section, Consult The "Technical Service Bulletins" Section For Related Information.

NOTE: "Electrical Symbol & Wire Color Code Identification" Located In The Front Of This Manual May Be Used As An Aid When Using Wiring Circuits Found In This Section.

NOTE: Refer To "Computer Relearn Procedures" Located In The Front Of This Manual When Battery Power To The Computer Has Been Interrupted.

INDEX

Page No.

Description 15-119
Diagnosis & Testing 15-119
Accessing Diagnostic Trouble Codes 15-119
Clearing Diagnostic Trouble Codes 15-119
DME Connector Pin Identification 15-119
Diagnostic Tests 15-119
Diagnostic Trouble Code Interpretation 15-119
Wiring Diagrams 15-119
Diagnostic Chart Index 15-126
Precautions 15-119
Air Bag Systems 15-119
Battery Ground Cable 15-119
Sensor & Fuel Injector Specifications 15-118
System Service 15-119
Component Replacement 15-119

SENSOR & FUEL INJECTOR SPECIFICATIONS

Component	Temperature, Degrees F	Value, Ohms
Crankshaft Position Sensor	68	.8–1.0
Engine Compartment Temperature Sensor	68	2200–2600
Engine Coolant Temperature Sensor	32	5000–7000
	68	2000–3000
	140	400–800
EVAP Canister Purge Valve	68	22–30
Fuel Injector	—	11–13
HO2S Heater Element	68	1.8–2.5
Intake Air Temperature Sensor	68	2300–2700
Vehicle Speed Sensor	—	1600–1800

PRECAUTIONS

Air Bag Systems

Refer to "Air Bag System Precautions" in the front of this manual for system disarming and arming procedures.

Battery Ground Cable

Prior to service, disconnect battery ground cable and isolate as required.

DESCRIPTION

This system uses a Digital Motor Electronics (DME) control module to manage fuel injection, ignition and electronic engine controls. The DME module, located under the left seat, also features an optimized engine management diagnostic system (OBD II).

Refer to **Fig. 1** for Motronic 7.2 system component locations.

DIAGNOSIS & TESTING

Accessing Diagnostic Trouble Codes

If a malfunction occurs, the Malfunction Indicator Lamp (Check Engine) will be illuminated. At the same time, the Diagnostic Trouble Code (DTC) is stored in the fault memory of the DME control module. To retrieve stored DTCs, connect system tester 9288, or equivalent OBD II scan tool, to the vehicle diagnostic connector, located under the lefthand side of the instrument panel, left of the steering column, **Fig. 2.**

Diagnostic Trouble Code Interpretation

1. Refer to **Fig. 3** for a listing of DTCs. The different fault types are used to indicate the following:
   a. **Fault type 1,** signal implausible/implausible operating range/malfunction.
   b. **Fault type 2,** open circuit/no signal.
   c. **Fault type 3,** short to ground/below lower limit/lean stop.
   d. **Fault type 4,** Short to positive/upper limit exceeded/rich stop.
2. Final column in chart indicates Malfunction Indicator Lamp (MIL) operation. Compare MIL operation as follows:
   a. 0=MIL is not triggered for this fault.
   b. 1=MIL on, emission related fault.
   c. 2=MIL is flashing, fault damaging to TWC.
   d. 3=Only in combination with engine misfire.

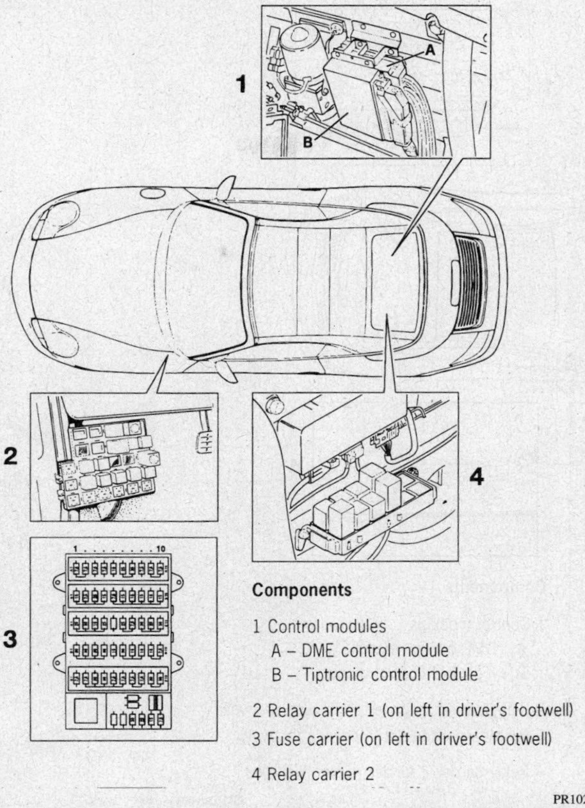

Fig. 1 Motronic 7.2 engine component locations (Part 1 of 4). 1999 911 Carrera 4 convertible

Wiring Diagrams

Refer to **Fig. 4** for DME wiring circuits.

DME Connector Pin Identification

Refer to **Fig. 5** for connector pin identification.

Diagnostic Tests

Refer to **Figs. 6 through 99** for diagnostic tests.

Clearing Diagnostic Trouble Codes

If a fault (DTC) has been removed but the fault memory has not been erased, three trips are usually required to switch off the Malfunction indicator lamp (MIL). Erasing diagnostic trouble codes may also be accomplished using the system tester or scan tool. Disconnecting the battery ground cable or control module connector will erase diagnostic trouble codes, but this will require a DME module adaption phase in which the engine must be run for 250 seconds after the battery ground cable or control module is reconnected.

SYSTEM SERVICE

Component Replacement

Refer to **Fig. 1** for Motronic 7.2 system component locations.

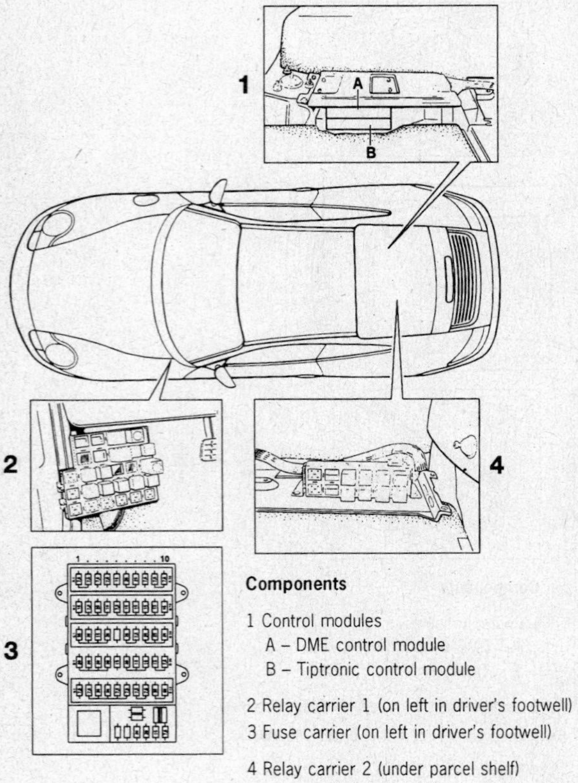

PR1029900121020X

Fig. 1 Motronic 7.2 engine component locations (Part 1 of 4). 1999 911 Carrera 4 coupe

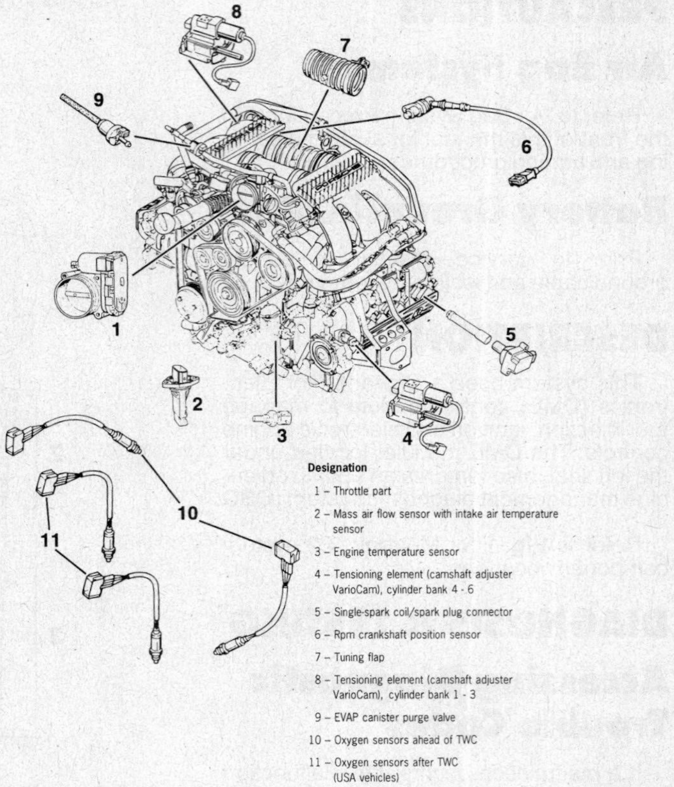

PR1029900121030X

Fig. 1 Motronic 7.2 engine component locations (Part 2 of 4). 1999 911 Carrera 4

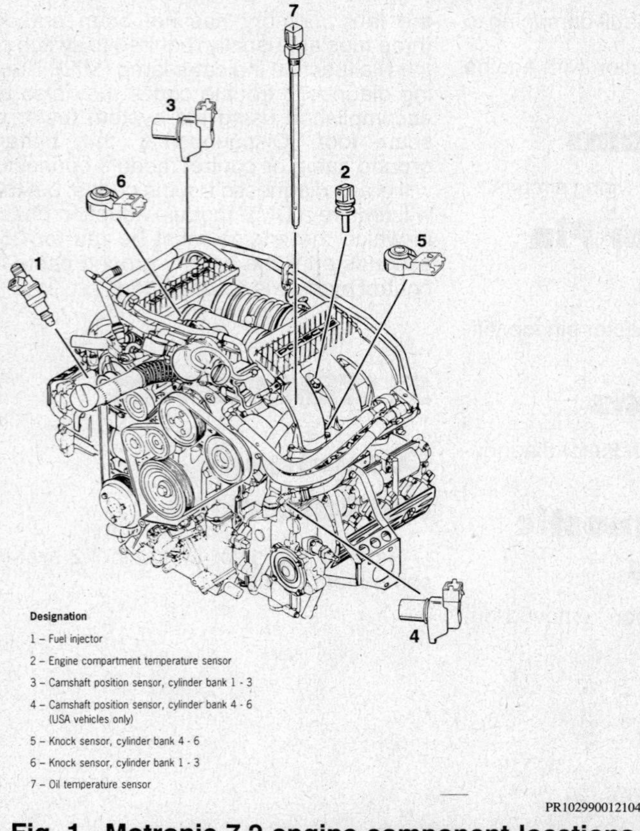

PR1029900121040X

Fig. 1 Motronic 7.2 engine component locations (Part 3 of 4). 1999 911 Carrera 4

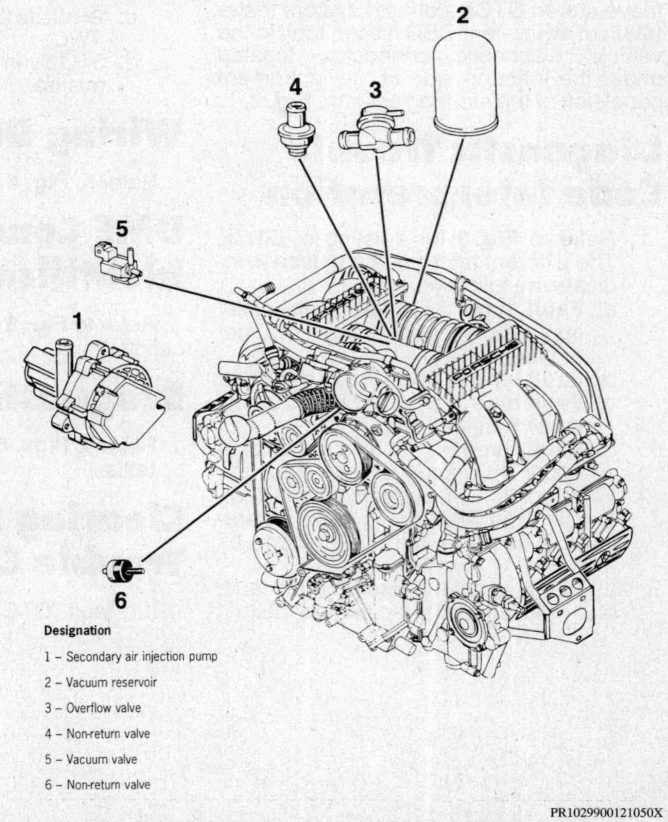

PR1029900121050X

Fig. 1 Motronic 7.2 engine component locations (Part 4 of 4). 1999 911 Carrera 4

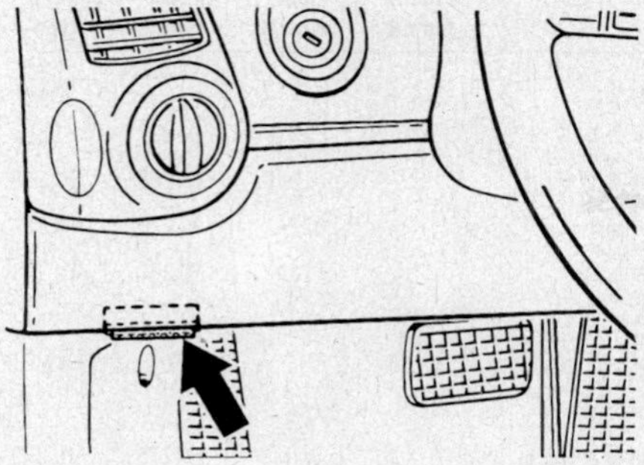

PR1029900122000X

Fig. 2 DLC connector

Fault text	Fault type 1	Fault type 2	Fault type 3	Fault type 4	MIL USA/RoW
Oxygen sensor ahead of TWC, bank 1	P0150	P0154		P0152	1/0
Oxygen sensor aging, period duration, bank 2			P0153	P0153	1/0
Oxygen sensor after TWC, bank 2	P0156	P0160		P0158	1/–
Aging of oxygen sensor after TWC, bank 2	P0159		P0159	P0159	1/–
Oil temperature sensor			P0197	P0198	0/0
Misfire detection (sum total)	P0300 *		P0300 *	P0300 *	1-2/1-2
Misfire, cylinder 1	P0301 *		P0301 *	P0301 *	1-2/1-2
Misfire, cylinder 2	P0302 *		P0302 *	P0302 *	1-2/1-2
Misfire, cylinder 3	P0303 *		P0303 *	P0303 *	1-2/1-2
Misfire, cylinder 4	P0304 *		P0304 *	P0304 *	1-2/1-2
Misfire, cylinder 5	P0305 *		P0305 *	P0305 *	1-2/1-2
Misfire, cylinder 6	P0306 *		P0306 *	P0306 *	1-2/1-2
Knock sensor 1			P0327	P0328	0/0
Knock sensor 2			P0332	P0333	0/0
Engine speed sensor signal		P0336			1/0
Camshaft position sensor 1	P0341		P0342	P0343	1/0
Electric change-over valve		P0413	P0414	P0414	1/0

PR1029900123020X

Fig. 3 Diagnostic trouble code identification (Part 2 of 6). 1999 911 Carrera 4

Fault text	Fault type 1	Fault type 2	Fault type 3	Fault type 4	MIL USA/RoW
Mass air flow sensor			P0102	P0103	1/0
Ambient pressure sensor			P0107	P0108	1/0
Intake air temperature sensor			P0112	P0113	1/0
Engine temperature sensor	P0115	P0117	P0117	P0118	1/0
Throttle valve	P0121				0/0
Oxygen sensor ahead of TWC, bank 1	P0130	P0134		P0132	1/0
Oxygen sensor aging, period duration, bank 1			P0133	P0133	1/0
Oxygen sensor after TWC, bank 1	P0136	P0140		P0138	1/–
Aging of oxygen sensor after TWC, bank 1	P0139		P0139	P0139	1/–

PR1029900123010X

Fig. 3 Diagnostic trouble code identification (Part 1 of 6). 1999 911 Carrera 4

Fault text	Fault type 1	Fault type 2	Fault type 3	Fault type 4	MIL USA/RoW
Secondary air injection system, bank 1	P0410		P0410		1/–
Secondary air injection pump		P0418	P0418	P0418	1/0
TWC conversion, bank 1				P0420	1/–
TWC conversion, bank 2				P0430	1/–
Fuel tank ventilation system				P0440	1/0
Fuel tank ventilation system (micro-leak)			P0442		1/–
EVAP canister purge valve		P0444	P0445	P0445	1/0
EVAP canister shutoff valve (function)			P0446		1/–
EVAP canister shutoff valve (output stage)		P0447	P0448	P0448	1/–
Tank pressure sensor	P0450		P0452	P0453	1/–
Fuel tank ventilation system (major leak)	P0455		P0455		1/–
Fan output stage 1		P0480	P0480	P0480	0/0
Fan output stage 2		P0481	P0481	P0481	0/0
Vehicle speed		P0501			1/0
Idle air control at stop			P0506	P0507	1/0
Voltage supply	P0560		P0562	P0563	1/0
CAN timeout, Tiptronic		P0600			1/0
Control module faulty (RAM)	P0604				1/0
Control module faulty (ROM)	P0605				1/0
MIL (Check Engine)		P0650	P0650	P0650	1/0
Oxygen sensor heating 1 ahead of TWC	P1115	P1115	P1115	P1115	1/0

PR1029900123030X

Fig. 3 Diagnostic trouble code identification (Part 3 of 6). 1999 911 Carrera 4

Fault text	Fault type 1	Fault type 2	Fault type 3	Fault type 4	MIL USA/RoW
Oxygen sensor heating 1 after TWC	P1117	P1117	P1117	P1117	1/–
Oxygen sensor heating 2 after TWC	P1118	P1118	P1118	P1118	1/–
Oxygen sensor heating 2 ahead of TWC	P1119	P1119	P1119	P1119	1/0
Throttle position sensor 1	P1121		P1121	P1121	0/0
Throttle position sensor 2	P1122		P1122	P1122	0/0
Fuel pump relay output stage		P1124	P1124	P1124	1/0
Oxygen sensing adaptation, upper load range, bank 1			P1125	P1125	1/0
Oxygen sensing adaptation, lower load range, bank 1			P1126	P1126	1/0
Oxygen sensing error by means of short test, bank 1			P1127	P1127	3/3
Oxygen sensing adaptation, idle range, bank 1			P1128	P1128	1/0
Oxygen sensing adaptation, idle range, bank 2			P1130	P1130	1/0
Oxygen sensing adaptation, upper load range, bank 2			P1132	P1132	1/0
Oxygen sensing adaptation, lower load range, bank 2			P1133	P1133	1/0
Oxygen sensing error by means of short test, bank 2			P1134	P1134	3/3
Clutch switch	P1137				0/0
Engine compartment temperature			P1157	P1158	0/0
Fuel injector, cylinder 1		P1237	P1225	P1213	1/0

PR1029900123040X

Fig. 3 Diagnostic trouble code identification (Part 4 of 6). 1999 911 Carrera 4

Fault text	Fault type 1	Fault type 2	Fault type 3	Fault type 4	MIL USA/RoW
Fuel injector, cylinder 6		P1238	P1226	P1214	1/0
Fuel injector, cylinder 2		P1239	P1227	P1215	1/0
Fuel injector, cylinder 4		P1240	P1228	P1216	1/0
Fuel injector, cylinder 3		P1241	P1229	P1217	1/0
Fuel injector, cylinder 5		P1242	P1230	P1218	1/0
Accelerator pedal	P1219				1/0
Airbag signal	P1265				0/0
Fuel cutoff function monitor	P1266				1/0
Aging of oxygen sensor ahead of TWC, delay time, bank 1			P1275	P1275	1/0
Aging of oxygen sensor ahead of TWC, delay time, bank 2			P1276	P1276	1/0
Position of camshaft in relation to crankshaft, bank 2			P1324	P1324	1/0
Camshaft adjustment, bank 2	P1325		P1325	P1325	1/0
Position of camshaft in relation to crankshaft, bank 1			P1340	P1340	1/0
Camshaft adjustment, bank 1	P1341		P1341	P1341	1/0
Knock control zero test	P1384				0/0
Knock control offset	P1385				0/0
Knock control test pulse	P1386				0/0
Camshaft position sensor 2	P1397		P1397	P1397	1/–
Secondary air injection system, bank 2	P1411		P1411		1/–
A/C compressor control		P1455	P1457	P1456	0/0

PR1029900123050X

Fig. 3 Diagnostic trouble code identification (Part 5 of 6). 1999 911 Carrera 4

Fault text	Fault type 1	Fault type 2	Fault type 3	Fault type 4	MIL USA/RoW
Throttle jacking unit Output stage	P1501				1/0
Throttle jacking unit Spring test				P1502	1/0
Throttle jacking unit Position error	P1503				1/0
Throttle jacking unit Emergency air position	P1504				0/0
Throttle jacking unit Control range		P1505	P1505	P1505	1/0
Throttle jacking unit Lower mechanical stop	P1506				1/0
Throttle jacking unit Gain adjustment	P1507				1/0
Torque comparison function monitor	P1508				1/0
Torque limiter				P1509	0/0
Immobilizer	P1570	P1571			0/0
Stop light switch	P1574				0/0
Cruise control standby lamp	P1576	P1576	P1576	P1576	0/0
Accelerator pedal potentiometer 1	P1577		P1577	P1577	1/0
Accelerator pedal potentiometer 2	P1578		P1578	P1578	1/0
Crankshaft position sensor	P1579				1/0
CAN timeout, PSM		P1600			0/0
Start enable (output stage)		P1668	P1668	P1668	0/0
Electric change-over valve, variable-length manifold		P1670	P1670	P1670	0/0

PR1029900123060X

Fig. 3 Diagnostic trouble code identification (Part 6 of 6). 1999 911 Carrera 4

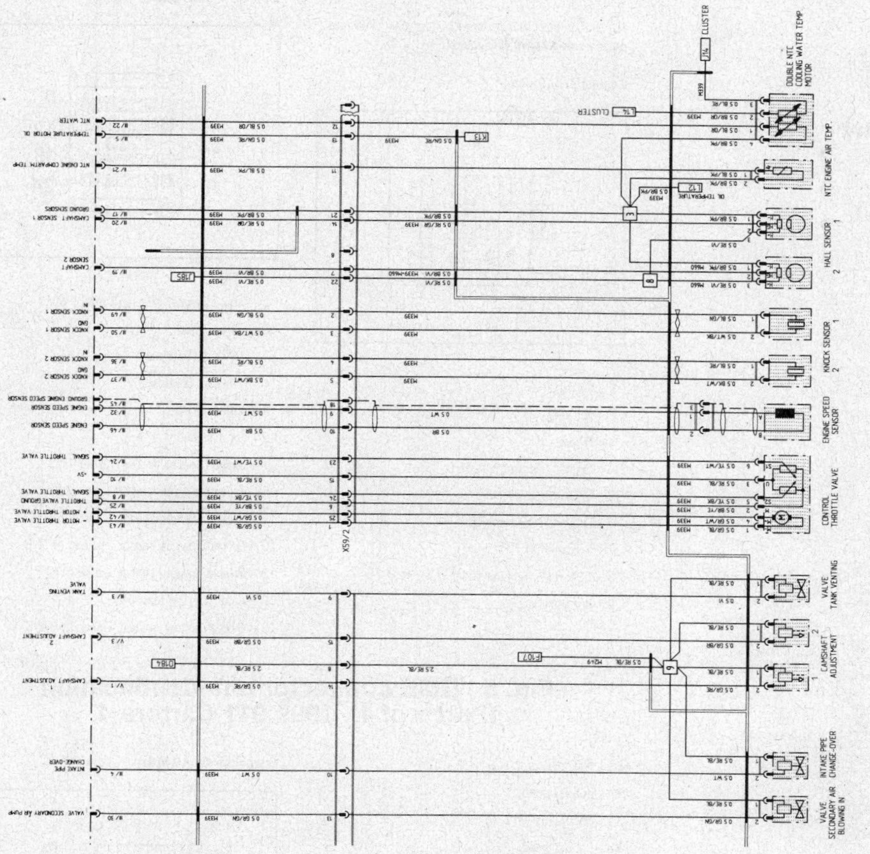

PR1029900124020X

Fig. 4 DME wiring circuit (Part 2 of 3). 1999 911 Carrera 4

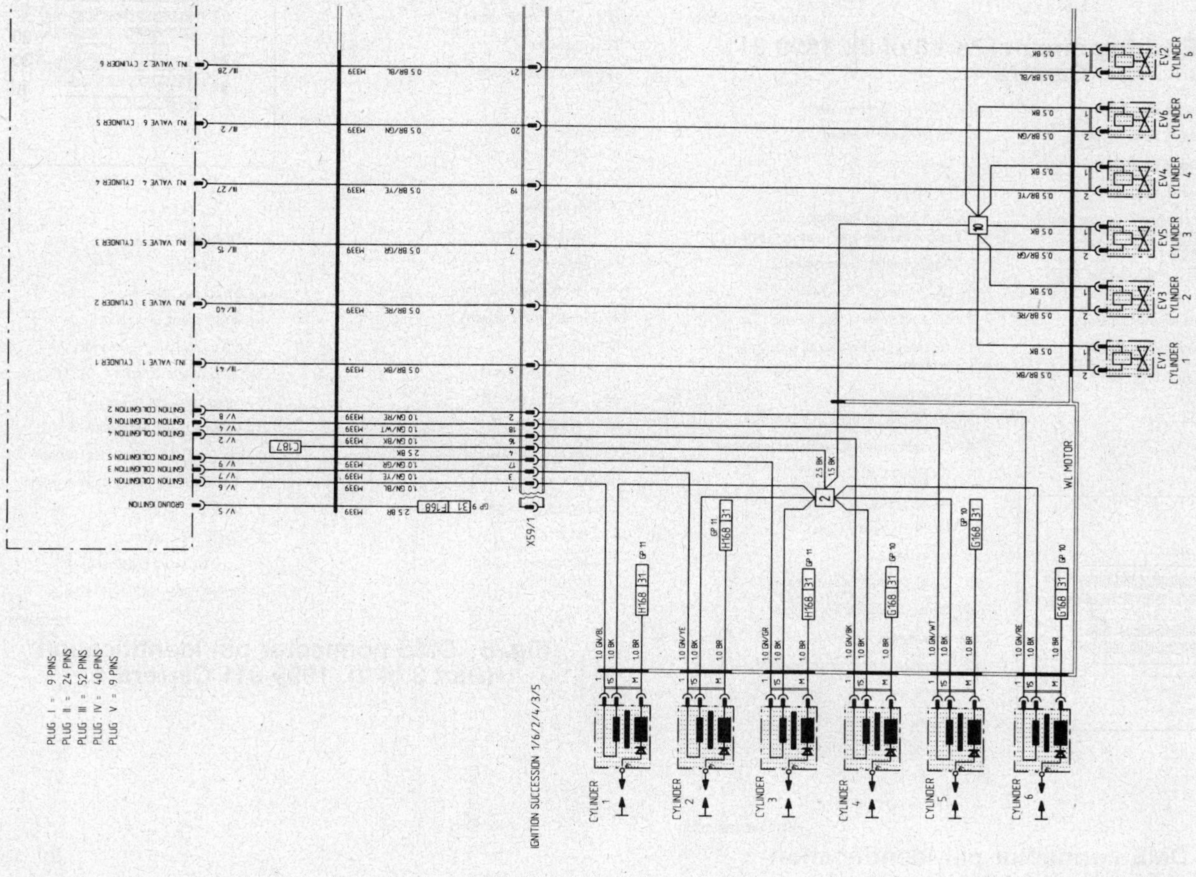

PR1029900124010X

Fig. 4 DME wiring circuit (Part 1 of 3). 1999 911 Carrera 4

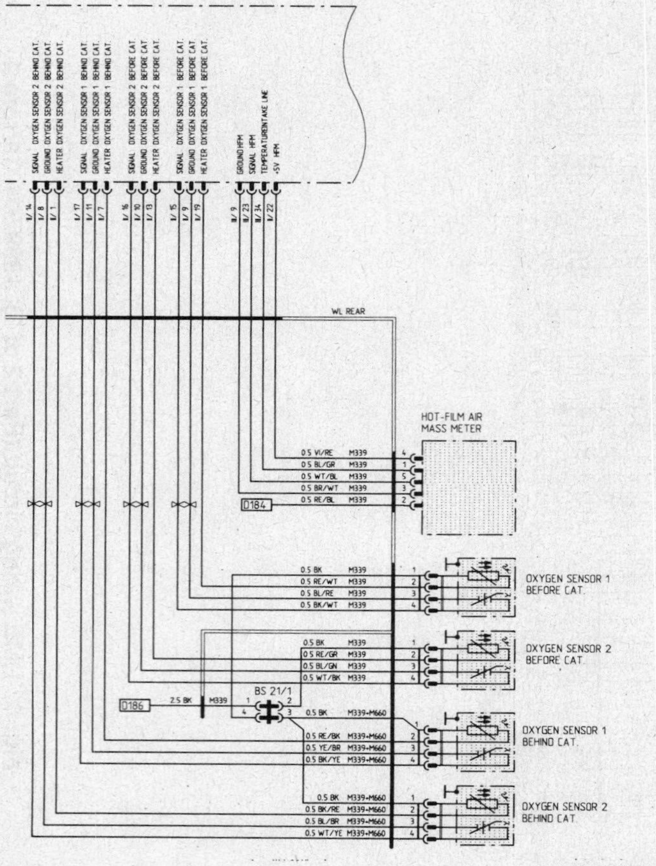

PR1029900124030X

Fig. 4 DME wiring circuit (Part 3 of 3). 1999 911 Carrera 4

14 – Signal, oxygen sensor 2 after TWC
15 – Signal, oxygen sensor 1 ahead of TWC
16 – Signal, oxygen sensor 2 ahead of TWC
17 – Signal, oxygen sensor 1 after TWC
18 – Triggering of A/C compressor relay (terminal 85)
19 – Oxygen sensor heating 1 ahead of TWC
20 – Triggering of engine compartment fan (terminal 85)
21 – Engine compartment temperature sensor
22 – 5-volt supply for mass air flow sensor
23 – Triggering of DME relay (terminal 85)
24 - not assigned

Connector III (52-pole)

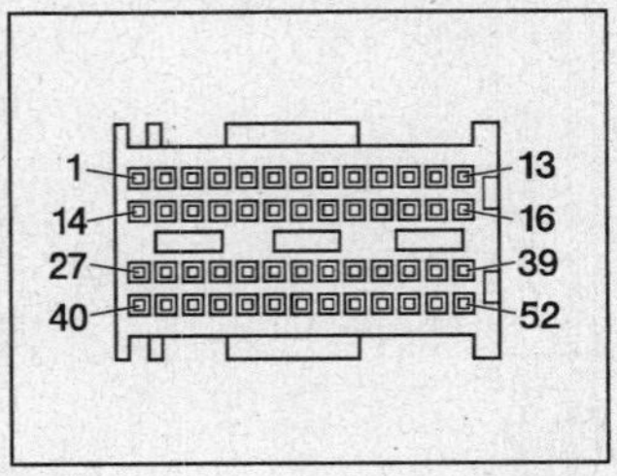

1 – Knocking signal
2 – Fuel injector, cyl. 5
3 – EVAP canister purge valve
4 – Variable-length manifold
5 – Oil temperature sensor
6 – not assigned
7 – 5-volt supply for camshaft position sensor and differential pressure sensor
8 – Signal, throttle position sensor 2
9 – Ground, mass air flow sensor
10 – 5-volt supply for throttle actuation
11 – Triggering of secondary air pump relay (terminal 85)
12 – not assigned
13 – Start enable, Tiptronic (P + N)
14 – Pilot light, engine compartment fan
15 – Fuel injector, cyl. 3
16 – not assigned
17 – Ground, sensors
18 – not assigned
19 – Signal, camshaft position sensor 2
20 – Signal, camshaft position sensor 1
21 – not assigned
22 – Engine coolant temperature sensor
23 – Signal, mass air flow sensor
24 – Signal, throttle position sensor 1
25 – Ground, throttle position sensors 1 + 2
26 – not assigned
27 – Fuel injector, cyl. 4

PR1029900125020X

Fig. 5 DME connector pin identification (Part 2 of 4). 1999 911 Carrera 4

The DME control module has 134 terminals which are divided between five connectors.

Connector I (9-pole)

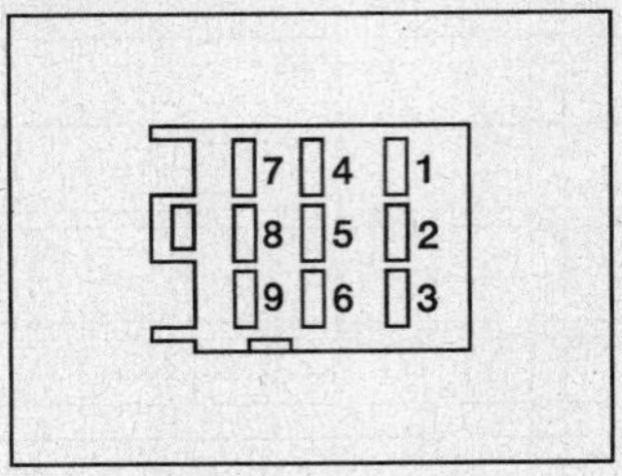

1 – Terminal 15
2 – not assigned
3 – W-wire
4 – Ground, electronic system
5 – Ground, fuel injectors
6 – Ground, output stages
7 – Terminal 30
8 – DME relay (terminal 87)
9 – not assigned

Connector II (24-pole)

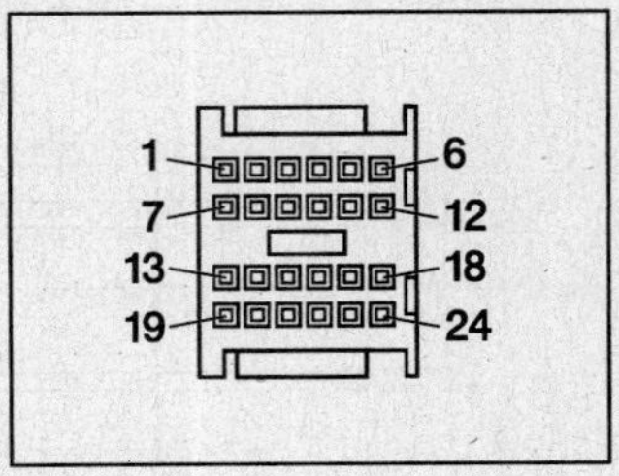

1 – Oxygen sensor heating 2 after TWC
2 – not assigned
3 – CAN low (Tiptronic)
4 – CAN high (Tiptronic)
5 – not assigned
6 – not assigned
7 – Oxygen sensor heating 1 after TWC
8 – Ground, oxygen sensor 2 after TWC
9 – Ground, oxygen sensor 1 ahead of TWC
10 – Ground, oxygen sensor 2 ahead of TWC
11 – Ground, oxygen sensor 1 after TWC
12 – Automatic I/M test
13 – Oxygen sensor heating 2 ahead of TWC

PR1029900125010X

Fig. 5 DME connector pin identification (Part 1 of 4). 1999 911 Carrera 4

28 – Fuel injector, cyl. 6
29 – not assigned
30 – Secondary air valve
31 – not assigned
32 – Signal A, speed sensor
33 – not assigned
34 – Intake air temperature sensor
35 – not assigned
36 – Input, knock sensor 2
37 – Ground, knock sensor 2
38 – not assigned
39 – not assigned
40 – Fuel injector cyl. 2
41 – Fuel injector, cyl. 1
42 – Throttle motor actuator
43 – Throttle motor actuator
44 – not assigned
45 – Shield, speed sensor
46 – Signal B, speed sensor
47 – not assigned
48 – not assigned
49 – Input, knock sensor 1
50 – Ground, knock sensor 1
51 – not assigned
52 – not assigned

Connector IV (40-pole)

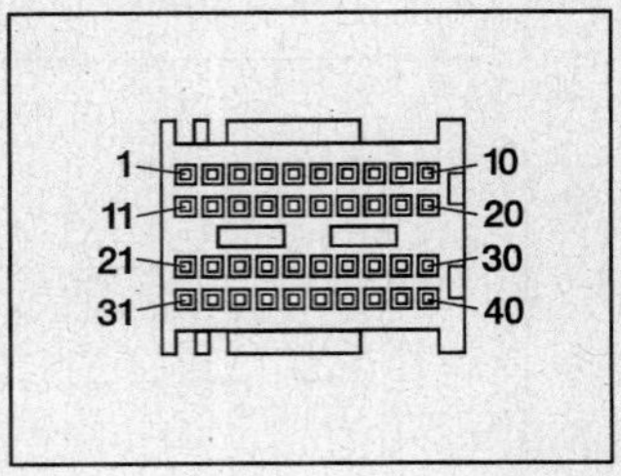

1 – Interlock clutch switch
2 – not assigned
3 – not assigned
4 – Coolant fan, stage 1
5 – Variant coding (ground for Tiptronic)
6 – A/C compressor requirement
7 – Ground, pedal sensor 1
8 – Signal, pedal sensor 1
9 – 5-volt supply for pedal sensor 1
10 – Triggering of fuel pump relay (terminal 85)
11 – Dim information from instrument cluster
12 – Ground, pedal sensor 2
13 – Signal, pedal sensor 2
14 – 5-volt supply for pedal sensor 2
15 – Ground, differential pressure sensor

PR1029900125030X

Fig. 5 DME connector pin identification (Part 3 of 4). 1999 911 Carrera 4

16 – Crash signal (airbag)
17 – Speed signal output
18 – Cruise control pilot light
19 – Cruise control switch "Off"
20 – Coolant fan, stage 2
21 – Signal, differential pressure sensor
22 – Speed signal from ABS control module
23 – Cruise control clutch switch
24 – Stop light switch 1
25 – Cruise control switch "Set"
26 – not assigned
27 – Cruise control switch "Resume"
28 – Stop light switch 2
29 – not assigned
30 – EVAP canister shutoff valve
31 – Check Engine MIL
32 – not assigned
33 – Fuel gauge
34 – Fuel reserve pilot light
35 – not assigned
36 – CAN high (PSM)
37 – CAN low (PSM)
38 – not assigned
39 – Medium pressure switch (A/C)
40 – Start-inhibit relay (terminal 85)

Connector V (9-pole)

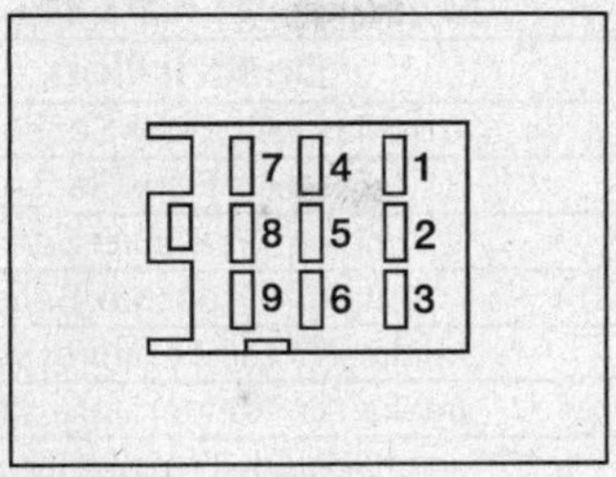

1 – Camshaft adjustment, bank 1
2 – Ignition coil, cyl. 4 (terminal 1)
3 – Camshaft adjustment, bank 2
4 – Ignition coil, cyl. 6 (terminal 1)
5 – Ground
6 – Ignition coil, cyl. 1 (terminal 1)
7 – Ignition coil, cyl. 3 (terminal 1)
8 – Ignition coil, cyl. 2 (terminal 1)
9 – Ignition coil, cyl. 5 (terminal 1)

PR1029900125040X

Fig. 5 DME connector pin identification (Part 4 of 4). 1999 911 Carrera 4

DIAGNOSTIC CHART INDEX

Code	Description	Page No.	Fig. No.
P0102	Mass Air Flow Sensor	15-129	6
P0103	Mass Air Flow Sensor	15-129	6
P0107	Ambient Pressure Sensor	15-129	7
P0108	Ambient Pressure Sensor	15-129	7
P0112	Intake Air Temperature Sensor	15-129	8
P0113	Intake Air Temperature Sensor	15-129	8
P0115	Engine Coolant Temperature Sensor	15-130	9
P0117	Engine Coolant Temperature Sensor	15-130	9
P0118	Engine Coolant Temperature Sensor	15-130	9
P0121	Throttle Valve	15-132	10
P0130	Front Oxygen Sensor Cylinders 1–3, Signal Implausible	15-133	11
P0132	Front Oxygen Sensor Cylinders 1–3, Above Limit	15-134	12
P0133	Front Oxygen Sensors Aging	15-134	13
P0134	Front Oxygen Sensor Cylinders 1–3 Signal Interruption	15-135	14
P0136	Rear Oxygen Sensor Cylinders 1–3 Signal Implausible	15-136	15
P0138	Rear Oxygen Sensor Cylinders 1–3 Above Limit	15-137	16
P0139	Rear Oxygen Sensors Aging	15-137	17
P0140	Rear Oxygen Sensor Cylinders 1–3 Open Circuit	15-138	18
P0150	Front Oxygen Sensor Cylinders 4–6 Signal Implausible	15-138	19
P0152	Front Oxygen Sensor Cylinders 4–6 Above Limit	15-139	20
P0153	Front Oxygen Sensors Aging	15-134	13
P0154	Front Oxygen Sensor Cylinders 4–6 Signal Interruption	15-140	21
P0156	Rear Oxygen Sensor Cylinders 4–6 Signal Implausible	15-141	22
P0158	Rear Oxygen Sensor Cylinders 4–6 Above Limit	15-142	23
P0159	Rear Oxygen Sensors Aging	15-137	17
P0160	Rear Oxygen Sensor Cylinders 4–6 Open Circuit	15-142	24
P0197	Oil Temperature Sensor	15-143	25
P0198	Oil Temperature Sensor	15-143	25
P0300	Engine Misfire	15-144	26
P0301	Engine Misfire	15-144	26
P0302	Engine Misfire	15-144	26
P0303	Engine Misfire	15-144	26
P0304	Engine Misfire	15-144	26
P0305	Engine Misfire	15-144	26
P0306	Engine Misfire	15-144	26
P0327	Knock Sensor No. 1	15-145	27
P0328	Knock Sensor No. 1	15-145	27
P0332	Knock Sensor No. 2	15-146	28
P0333	Knock Sensor No. 2	15-146	28
P0336	Engine Speed Sensor Signal	15-147	29
P0341	Camshaft Position Sensor No. 1	15-148	30
P0342	Camshaft Position Sensor No. 1	15-148	30
P0343	Camshaft Position Sensor No. 1	15-148	30
P0410	Secondary Air Injection System	15-149	31
P0413	Electric Change-Over Valve	15-149	32
P0414	Electric Change-Over Valve	15-149	32
P0418	Secondary Air Injection Pump	15-150	33
P0420	Catalytic Converter Conversion Above Limit	15-151	34
P0430	Catalytic Converter Conversion Above Limit	15-151	34
P0440	Fuel Tank Ventilation System Above Limit	15-151	35
P0442	Fuel Tank Ventilation System Below Lower Limit	15-152	36
P0444	EVAP Canister Purge Valve Open Or Short Circuit	15-153	37
P0445	EVAP Canister Purge Valve Open Or Short Circuit	15-153	37
P0446	EVAP Canister Shutoff Valve Below Limit	15-154	38
P0447	EVAP Canister Shutoff Valve Output Stage	15-154	39
P0448	EVAP Canister Shutoff Valve Output Stage	15-154	39
P0450	Tank Pressure Sensor	15-156	40

Continued

DIAGNOSTIC CHART INDEX—Continued

Code	Description	Page No.	Fig. No.
P0452	Tank Pressure Sensor	15-156	40
P0453	Tank Pressure Sensor	15-156	40
P0455	Fuel Tank Ventilation System Major Leak	15-156	41
P0480	Fan Output Stage No. 1	15-157	42
P0481	Fan Output Stage No. 2	15-159	43
P0482	Fan Output Stage No. 2	15-160	44
P0501	Vehicle Speed Not In Specified Range	15-161	45
P0506	Idle Air Control At Stop	15-162	46
P0507	Idle Air Control At Stop	15-162	46
P0560	Voltage Supply	15-162	47
P0562	Voltage Supply	15-162	47
P0563	Voltage Supply	15-162	47
P0600	CAN Timeout Signal Implausible	15-163	48
P0604	Control Module Faulty	15-164	49
P0605	Control Module Faulty	15-164	49
P0650	Malfunction Indicator Lamp	15-164	50
P1115	Front Oxygen Sensor Heating Bank 1	15-164	51
P1117	Rear Oxygen Sensor Heating Bank 1	15-166	52
P1118	Rear Oxygen Sensor Heating Bank 2	15-167	53
P1119	Front Oxygen Sensor Heating Bank 2	15-168	54
P1121	Throttle Position Sensor No. 1	15-169	55
P1122	Throttle Position Sensor No. 2	15-171	56
P1124	Fuel Pump Relay Output Stage	15-172	57
P1125	Oxygen Sensing Adaption, Upper Load Range Above Limit	15-173	58
	Oxygen Sensing Adaption, Upper Load Range Below Limit	15-175	59
P1126	Oxygen Sensing Adaption, Lower Load Range Above Limit	15-176	60
	Oxygen Sensing Adaption, Lower Load Range Below Limit	15-177	61
P1127	Oxygen Sensing Error By Means Of Short Test Above Limit	15-178	62
P1128	Oxygen Sensing Adaption, Idle Range Above Limit	15-180	64
	Oxygen Sensing Adaption, Idle Range Below Limit	15-181	65
P1130	Oxygen Sensing Adaption, Idle Range Above Limit	15-180	64
	Oxygen Sensing Adaption, Idle Range Below Limit	15-181	65
P1132	Oxygen Sensing Adaption, Upper Load Range Above Limit	15-173	58
	Oxygen Sensing Adaption, Upper Load Range Below Limit	15-175	59
P1133	Oxygen Sensing Adaption, Lower Load Range Above Limit	15-176	60
	Oxygen Sensing Adaption, Lower Load Range Below Limit	15-177	61
P1134	Oxygen Sensing Error By Means Of Short Test Above Limit	15-178	62
	Oxygen Sensing Error By Means Of Short Test Below Limit	15-179	63
P1137	Clutch Switch Signal Implausible	15-182	66
P1157	Engine Compartment Temperature	15-183	67
P1158	Engine Compartment Temperature	15-183	67
P1213	Fuel Injector, Cylinder No. 1	15-183	68
P1214	Fuel Injector, Cylinder No. 6	15-184	69
P1215	Fuel Injector, Cylinder No. 2	15-184	70
P1216	Fuel Injector, Cylinder No. 4	15-185	71
P1217	Fuel Injector, Cylinder No. 3	15-185	72
P1218	Fuel Injector, Cylinder No. 5	15-186	73
P1219	Accelerator Pedal Signal Implausible	15-186	74
P1225	Fuel Injector, Cylinder No. 1	15-183	68
P1226	Fuel Injector, Cylinder No. 6	15-184	69
P1227	Fuel Injector, Cylinder No. 2	15-184	70
P1228	Fuel Injector, Cylinder No. 4	15-185	71
P1229	Fuel Injector, Cylinder No. 3	15-185	72
P1230	Fuel Injector, Cylinder No. 5	15-186	73
P1237	Fuel Injector, Cylinder No. 1	15-183	68
P1238	Fuel Injector, Cylinder No. 6	15-184	69
P1239	Fuel Injector, Cylinder No. 2	15-184	70

Continued

DIAGNOSTIC CHART INDEX—Continued

Code	Description	Page No.	Fig. No.
P1240	Fuel Injector, Cylinder No. 4	15-185	71
P1241	Fuel Injector, Cylinder No. 3	15-185	72
P1242	Fuel Injector, Cylinder No. 5	15-186	73
P1265	Air Bag Signal Implausible	15-187	75
P1266	Fuel Shutoff Function Monitor & Torque Comparison Function Monitor	15-187	76
P1275	Front Oxygen Sensors Aging	15-134	13
P1276	Front Oxygen Sensors Aging	15-134	13
P1325	Camshaft Adjustment, Bank 2	15-187	77
P1341	Camshaft Adjustment, Bank 2	15-188	78
P1384	Knock Control Signal Implausible	15-189	79
P1385	Knock Control Signal Implausible	15-189	79
P1386	Knock Control Signal Implausible	15-189	79
P1397	Camshaft Position Sensor No. 2	15-189	80
P1411	Secondary Air Injection System	15-149	31
P1414	Electric Change-Over Valve	15-149	32
P1455	A/C Compressor Control	15-190	81
P1456	A/C Compressor Control	15-190	81
P1457	A/C Compressor Control	15-190	81
P1501	Throttle Jacking Unit, Output Stage Signal Implausible	15-191	82
P1503	Throttle Jacking Unit, Position Error, Signal Implausible	15-192	84
P1502	Throttle Jacking Unit, Spring Test	15-191	83
P1504	Throttle Jacking Unit, Emergency Air Position, Signal Implausible	15-193	85
P1505	Throttle Jacking Unit, Control Range	15-193	86
P1506	Throttle Jacking Unit, Lower Mechanical Stop	15-194	87
P1507	Throttle Jacking Unit, Gain Adjustment	15-194	88
P1508	Fuel Shutoff Function Monitor & Torque Comparison Function Monitor	15-187	76
P1509	Torque Limiter Above Limit	15-194	89
P1570	Immobilizer Signal Implausible Or Open Circuit	15-195	90
P1571	Immobilizer Signal Implausible Or Open Circuit	15-195	90
P1574	Stop Light Switch Signal Implausible	15-196	91
P1576	Cruise Control Standby Lamp	15-196	92
P1577	Accelerator Pedal Potentiometer 1	15-197	93
P1578	Accelerator Pedal Potentiometer 2	15-198	94
P1579	Crankshaft Position Sensor Not In Specified Range	15-198	95
P1600	CAN Timeout, PSM Signal Implausible	15-199	96
P1668	Start Enable, Output Stage	15-200	97
P1670	Electric Change-Over Valve, Variable-Length Manifold, Output Stage	15-200	98
P1671	Control Module Faulty	15-164	49
P1674	Engine Compartment Purge Fan Output Stage	15-201	99

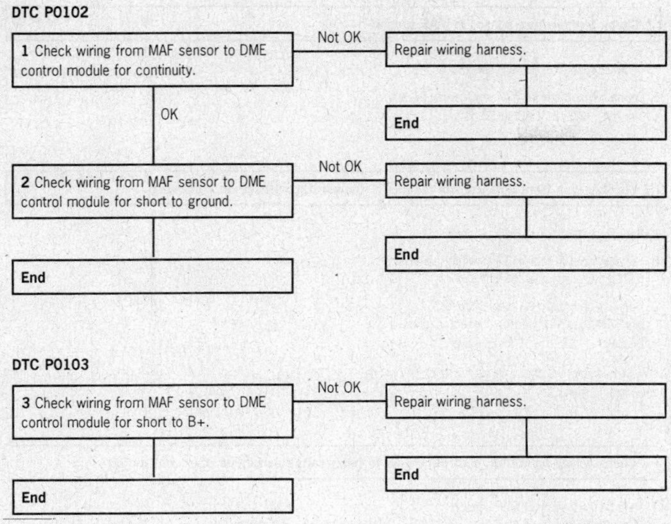

PR1029900126010X

Fig. 6 Codes P0102 & P0103: Mass Air Flow Sensor (Part 1 of 3)

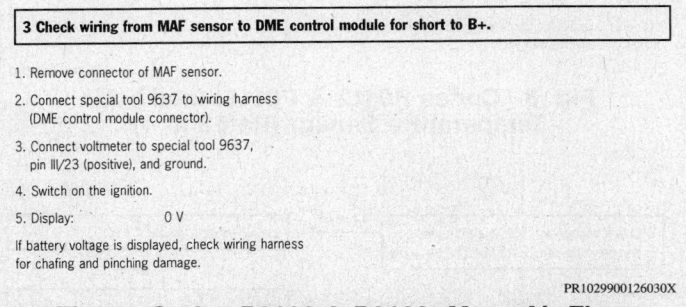

3 Check wiring from MAF sensor to DME control module for short to B+.

1. Remove connector of MAF sensor.
2. Connect special tool 9637 to wiring harness (DME control module connector).
3. Connect voltmeter to special tool 9637, pin III/23 (positive), and ground.
4. Switch on the ignition.
5. Display: 0 V

If battery voltage is displayed, check wiring harness for chafing and pinching damage.

PR1029900126030X

Fig. 6 Codes P0102 & P0103: Mass Air Flow Sensor (Part 3 of 3)

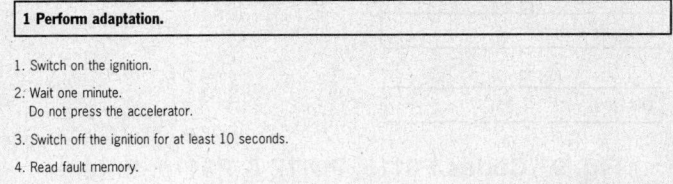

1 Perform adaptation.

1. Switch on the ignition.
2. Wait one minute. Do not press the accelerator.
3. Switch off the ignition for at least 10 seconds.
4. Read fault memory.

PR1029900127020X

Fig. 7 Codes P0107 & P0108: Ambient Pressure Sensor (Part 2 of 2)

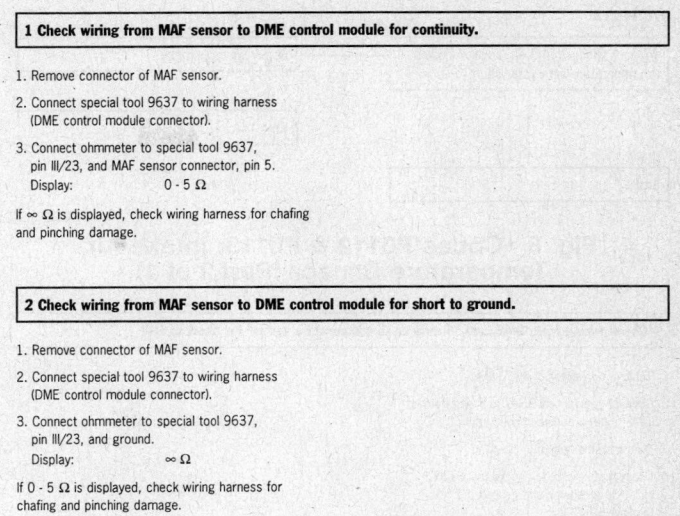

1 Check wiring from MAF sensor to DME control module for continuity.

1. Remove connector of MAF sensor.
2. Connect special tool 9637 to wiring harness (DME control module connector).
3. Connect ohmmeter to special tool 9637, pin III/23, and MAF sensor connector, pin 5. Display: 0 - 5 Ω

If ∞ Ω is displayed, check wiring harness for chafing and pinching damage.

2 Check wiring from MAF sensor to DME control module for short to ground.

1. Remove connector of MAF sensor.
2. Connect special tool 9637 to wiring harness (DME control module connector).
3. Connect ohmmeter to special tool 9637, pin III/23, and ground. Display: ∞ Ω

If 0 - 5 Ω is displayed, check wiring harness for chafing and pinching damage.

PR1029900126020X

Fig. 6 Codes P0102 & P0103: Mass Air Flow Sensor (Part 2 of 3)

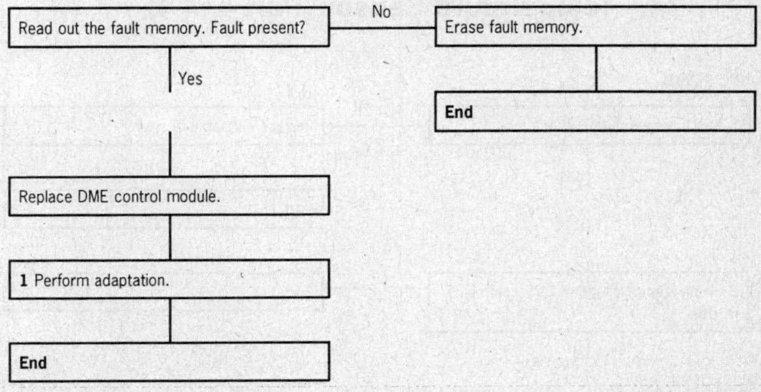

PR1029900127010X

Fig. 7 Codes P0107 & P0108: Ambient Pressure Sensor (Part 1 of 2)

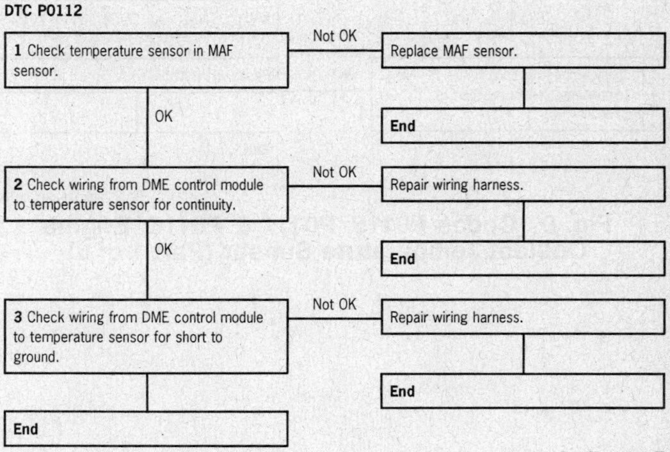

PR1029900128010X

Fig. 8 Codes P0112 & P0113: Intake Air Temperature Sensor (Part 1 of 4)

DTC P0113

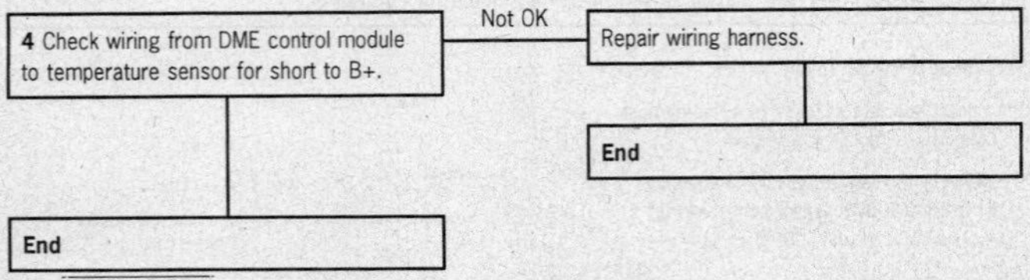

PR1029900128020X

Fig. 8 Codes P0112 & P0113: Intake Air Temperature Sensor (Part 2 of 4)

4 Check wiring from DME control module to temperature sensor for short to B+.

1. Remove connector of MAF sensor.
2. Connect special tool 9637 to wiring harness (DME control module connector).
3. Switch on the ignition.
4. Connect voltmeter to special tool 9637, pin III/34 (positive), and ground.
   Display: 0 V

If battery voltage is displayed, check wiring harness for chafing and pinching damage.

PR1029900128040X

Fig. 8 Codes P0112 & P0113: Intake Air Temperature Sensor (Part 4 of 4)

DTC P0115

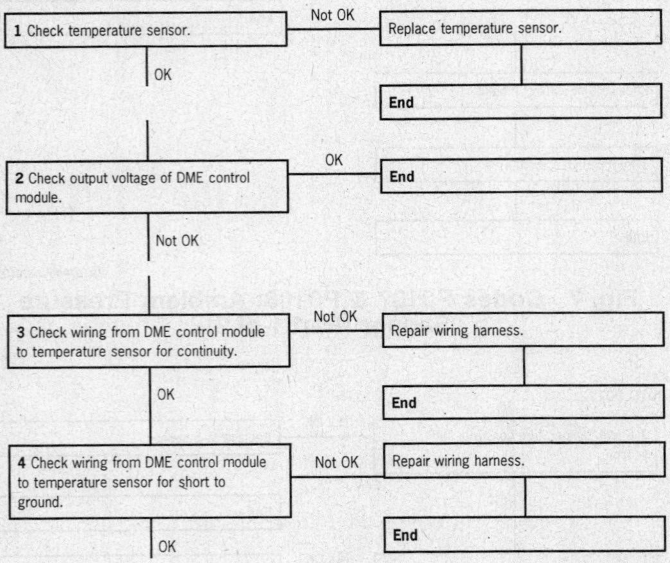

PR1029900129010X

Fig. 9 Codes P0115, P0117 & P0118: Engine Coolant Temperature Sensor (Part 1 of 6)

1 Check temperature sensor in MAF sensor.

1. Remove connector of MAF sensor.
2. Connect ohmmeter to MAF sensor, pins 1 and 3.
   Display: 2.3 - 2.7 kΩ at 20 °C

2 Check wiring from DME control module to temperature sensor for continuity.

1. Remove connector of MAF sensor.
2. Connect special tool 9637 to wiring harness (DME control module connector).
3. Connect ohmmeter to special tool 9637, pin III/34, and MAF sensor connector, pin 1.
   Display: 0 - 5 Ω.

If ∞ Ω is displayed, check wiring harness for chafing and pinching damage.

3 Check wiring from DME control module to temperature sensor for short to ground.

1. Remove connector of MAF sensor.
2. Connect special tool 9637 to wiring harness (DME control module connector).
3. Connect ohmmeter to special tool 9637, pin III/34, and ground.
   Display: ∞ Ω

If 0 - 5 Ω is displayed, check wiring harness for chafing and pinching damage.

PR1029900128030X

Fig. 8 Codes P0112 & P0113: Intake Air Temperature Sensor (Part 3 of 4)

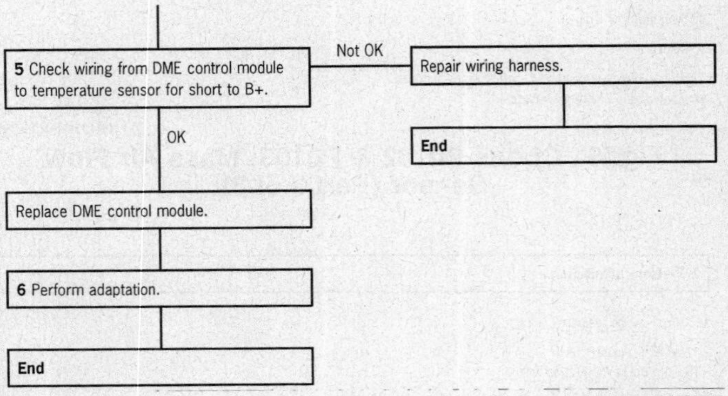

PR1029900129020X

Fig. 9 Codes P0115, P0117 & P0118: Engine Coolant Temperature Sensor (Part 2 of 6)

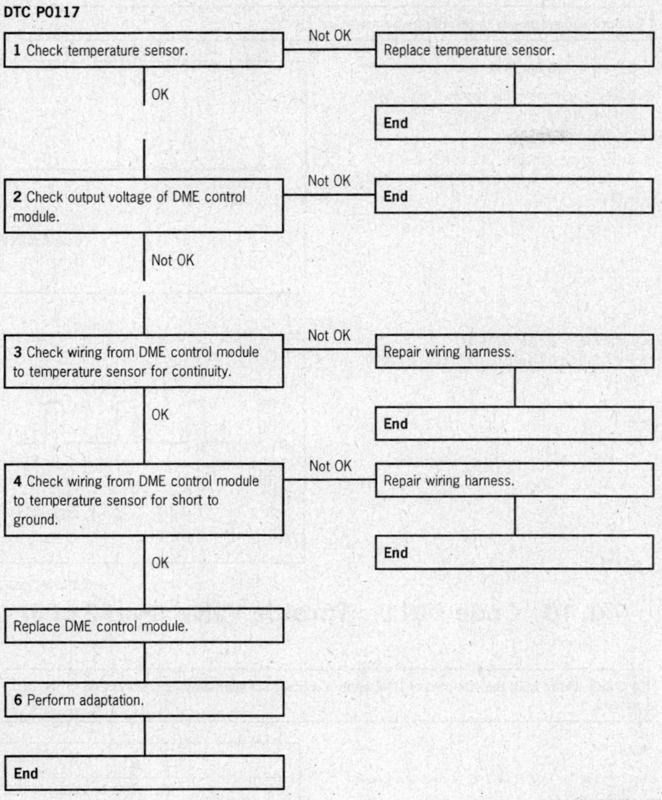

Fig. 9 Codes P0115, P0117 & P0118: Engine Coolant Temperature Sensor (Part 3 of 6)

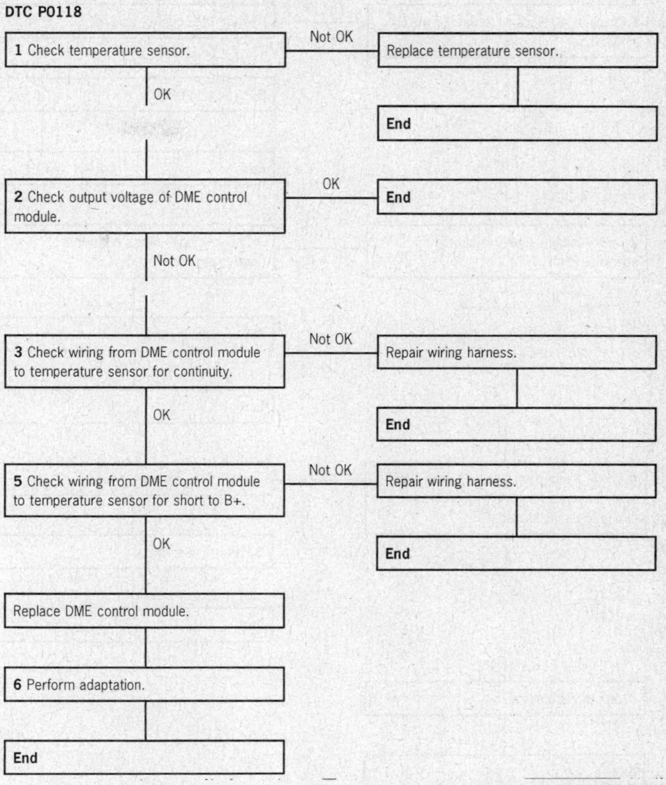

Fig. 9 Codes P0115, P0117 & P0118: Engine Coolant Temperature Sensor (Part 4 of 6)

1 Check temperature sensor.

1. Remove connector in engine compartment.
2. Connect ohmmeter to temperature sensor, pins 1 and 4.
   Display: 2 - 3 kΩ at 20 °C.

2 Check output voltage of DME control module.

1. Connect special tool 9637. Do not connect connector III of vehicle wiring harness.
2. Connect voltmeter to pin III/22 (B+) and III/17 (ground).
3. Ignition on.
   Display: approx. 5 V

3 Check wiring from DME control module to temperature sensor for continuity.

1. Connect special tool 9637 to wiring harness (DME control module connector).
2. Remove connector of temperature sensor.
3. Connect ohmmeter to special tool 9637, pin III/17, and temperature sensor connector, pin 4.
   Display: 0 - 5 Ω
4. Connect ohmmeter to special tool 9637, pin III/22, and temperature sensor connector, pin 1.
   Display: 0 - 5 Ω

PR1029900129050X

Fig. 9 Codes P0115, P0117 & P0118: Engine Coolant Temperature Sensor (Part 5 of 6)

4 Check wiring from DME control module to temperature sensor for short to ground.

1. Connect special tool 9637 to wiring harness (DME control module connector).
2. Remove connector of temperature sensor.
3. Connect ohmmeter to special tool 9637, pin III/22, and ground.
   Display: ∞ Ω

If 0 - 5 Ω is displayed, check wiring for chafing and pinching damage.

5 Check wiring from DME control module to temperature sensor for short to B+.

1. Connect special tool 9637.
2. Remove connector of temperature sensor.
3. Connect voltmeter to pin III/22 (B+) and to ground.
4. Switch on the ignition.
   Display: approx. 5 V

If battery voltage is displayed, check wiring harness for chafing and pinching damage.

6 Perform adaptation.

1. Switch on the ignition.
2. Wait one minute.
   Do not press the accelerator.
3. Switch off the ignition for at least 10 seconds.
4. Read out the fault memory.

PR1029900129060X

Fig. 9 Codes P0115, P0117 & P0118: Engine Coolant Temperature Sensor (Part 6 of 6)

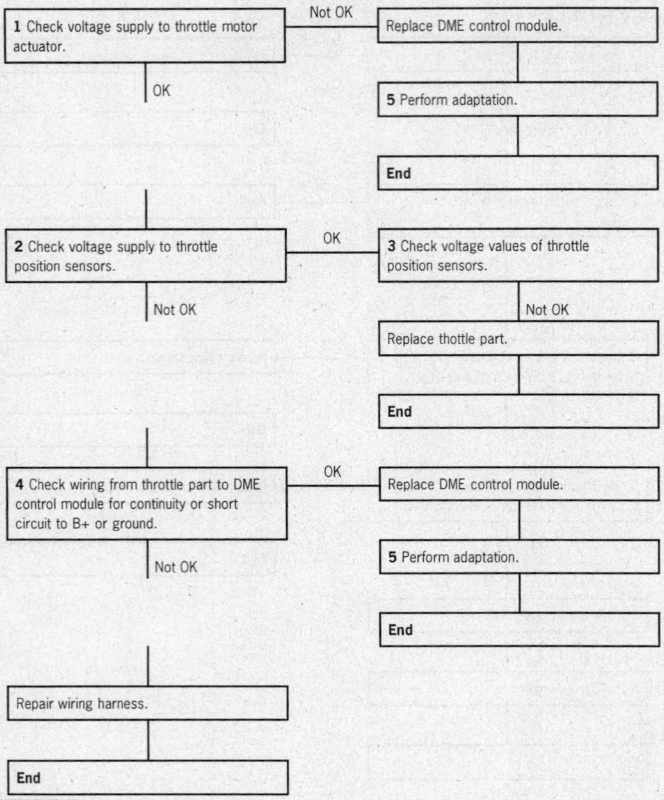

PR1029900130010X

Fig. 10 Code P0121: Throttle Valve (Part 1 of 5)

1 Check voltage supply to throttle motor actuator.

1. Connect special tool 9637.
2. Connect engine tester (oscilloscope) to pin III/42 (positive) and pin III/43 (negative). Use special input.
3. Switch on the ignition. The signal shown in the diagram opposite should appear:

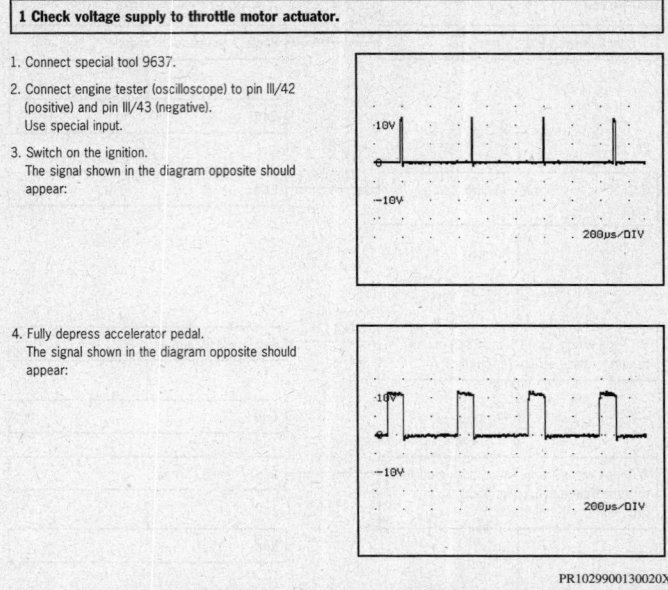

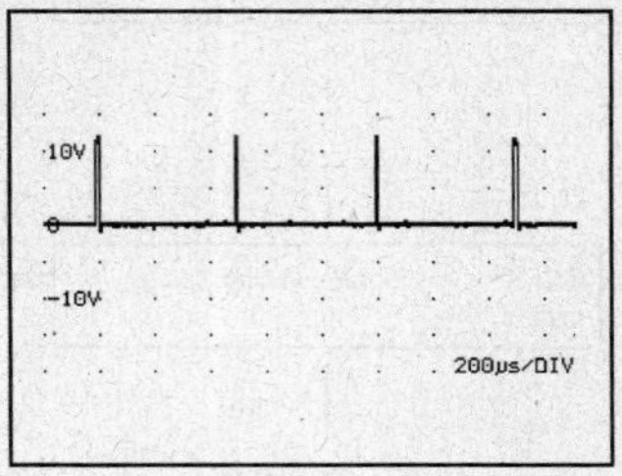

4. Fully depress accelerator pedal. The signal shown in the diagram opposite should appear:

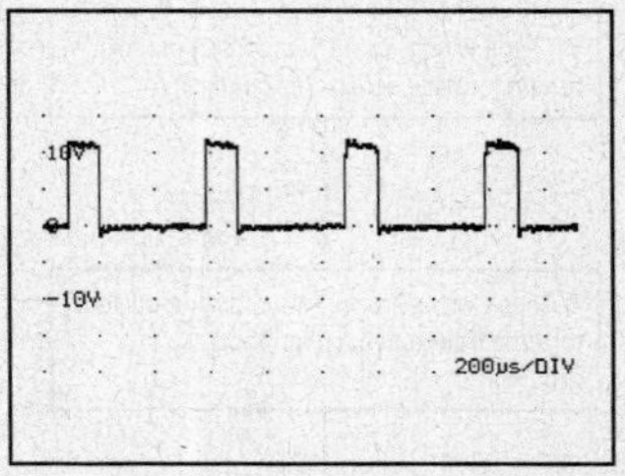

PR1029900130020X

Fig. 10 Code P0121: Throttle Valve (Part 2 of 5)

2 Check voltage supply to throttle position sensors.

1. Connect special tool 9637 to wiring harness (DME control module connector).
2. Connect voltmeter to pin III/10 (positive) and pin III/25.
   Switch on the ignition.
   Display: approx. 5 V

3 Check voltage values of throttle position sensors.

1. Connect special tool 9637.
2. Connect voltmeter to pin III/24 (positive) and pin III/25 (negative).
   Switch on the ignition.
   Display: approx. 0.7 - 0.9 V

   Fully depress accelerator pedal.
   Display: approx. 4.1 - 4.5 V
3. Connect voltmeter to pin III/8 (positive) and pin III/25 (negative).
   Switch on the ignition.
   Display: approx. 4.0 - 4.4 V

   Fully depress accelerator pedal.
   Display: approx. 0.5 - 0.8 V

PR1029900130030X

Fig. 10 Code P0121: Throttle Valve (Part 3 of 5)

4 Check wiring from throttle part to DME control module for continuity or short circuit to B+ or ground.

Note

The wires to the throttle part are routed via connector X 59/2.

1. Separate disconnection point to throttle part.

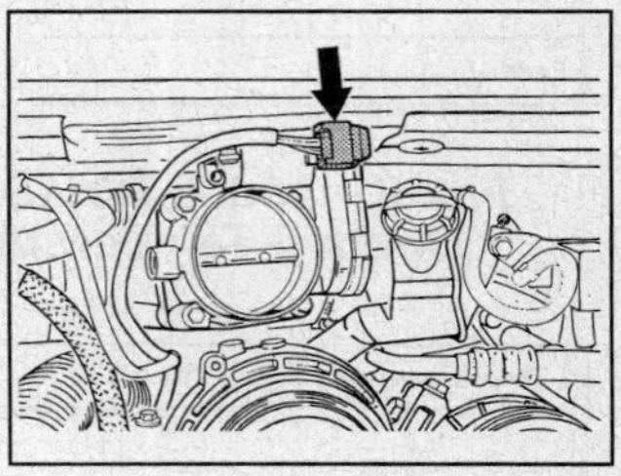

2. Connect special tool 9637 to wiring harness (DME control module connector).
3. Connect ohmmeter to disconnection point, pin 1, and special tool 9637, pin III/43.
   Display: 0 - 5 Ω
4. Connect ohmmeter to disconnection point, pin 2, and special tool 9637, pin III/25.
   Display: 0 - 5 Ω
5. Connect ohmmeter to disconnection point, pin 3, and special tool 9637, pin III/10.
   Display: 0 - 5 Ω
6. Connect ohmmeter to disconnection point, pin 4, and special tool 9637, pin III/42.
   Display: 0 - 5 Ω

PR1029900130040X

Fig. 10 Code P0121: Throttle Valve (Part 4 of 5)

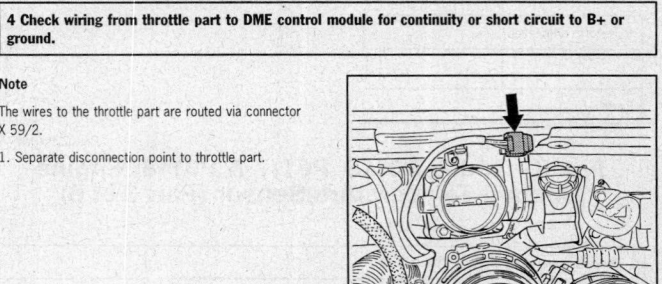

7. Connect ohmmeter to disconnection point, pin 5, and special tool 9637, pin III/8.
   Display: 0 - 5 Ω
8. Connect ohmmeter to disconnection point, pin 6, and special tool 9637, pin III/24.
   Display 0 - 5 Ω
9. Connect ohmmeter to disconnection point, pin 4, and ground.
   Display: ∞ Ω
10. Connect ohmmeter to disconnection point, pin 5, and ground.
   Display: ∞ Ω
11. Connect ohmmeter to disconnection point, pin 6, and ground.
   Display: ∞ Ω
12. Connect voltmeter to disconnection point, pin 4, and ground.
   Switch on the ignition.
   Display: 0 V
13. Connect voltmeter to disconnection point, pin 5, and ground.
   Switch on the ignition.
   Display: 0 V
14. Connect voltmeter to disconnection point, pin 6, and ground.
   Switch on the ignition.
   Display: 0 V

If battery voltage is displayed for points 12 to 14, check wiring harness for chafing and pinching damage.

5 Perform adaptation.

1. Switch on the ignition.
2. Wait one minute.
   Do not press the accelerator.
3. Switch off the ignition for at least 10 seconds.
4. Read out the fault memory.

PR1029900130050X

Fig. 10 Code P0121: Throttle Valve (Part 5 of 5)

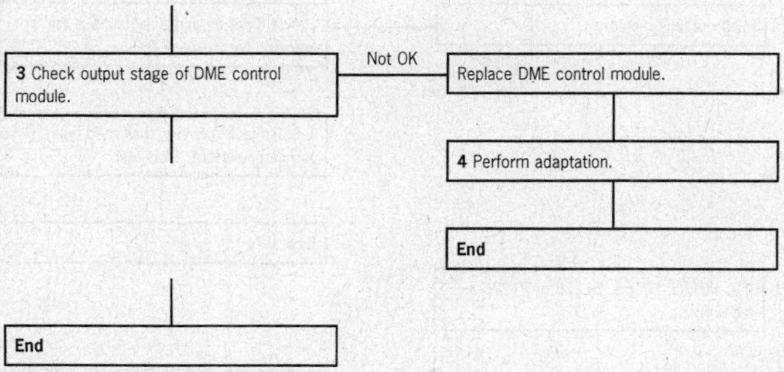

PR1029900131020X

Fig. 11 Code P0130: Front Oxygen Sensor Cylinders 1–3, Signal Implausible (Part 2 of 4)

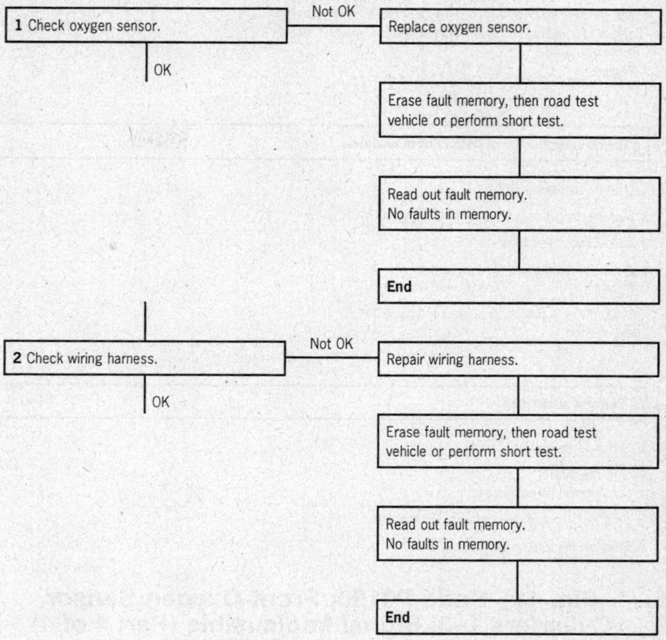

PR1029900131010X

Fig. 11 Code P0130: Front Oxygen Sensor Cylinders 1–3, Signal Implausible (Part 1 of 4)

1 Check oxygen sensor.

1. Heat the oxygen sensors (road test car under load or run engine without load at high rpm).
2. Connect Porsche System Tester 2 or scan tool and read voltage of oxygen sensor 1 ahead of TWC.
   Display: Voltage fluctuations between 100 mV and 800 mV.
   ➠ Oxygen sensor OK.

If a value around 0 V is displayed, a short circuit has occurred between the signal wire and sensor ground.

3. Remove oxygen sensor connector 1 ahead of TWC.
4. Connect voltmeter at sleeve to pins 3 and 4.
   Display: approx. 450 mV.
   ➠ Replace oxygen sensor.

   Display: approx. 0 V
   ➠ Check wiring harness.

2 Check wiring harness.

1. Remove oxygen sensor connector.
2. Connect special tool 9637 to wiring harness (DME control module connector).
3. With an ohmmeter, measure resistance between special tool 9637, pin II/15, and oxygen sensor connector, pin 4.
   Display: 0 - 5 Ω

PR1029900131030X

Fig. 11 Code P0130: Front Oxygen Sensor Cylinders 1–3, Signal Implausible (Part 3 of 4)

4. With an ohmmeter, measure resistance between special tool 9637, pin II/9, and oxygen sensor connector, pin 3.
   Display: 0 - 5 Ω

3 Check output stage of DME control module.

1. Connect special tool 9637.
2. Remove oxygen sensor connector 1 ahead of TWC.
3. Connect voltmeter to pins II/9 and II/15.
4. Switch on the ignition.
   Display: approx. 450 mV

If < 400 mV or > 500 mV is displayed, replace DME control module.

4 Perform adaptation.

1. Switch on the ignition.
2. Wait one minute.
   Do not press the accelerator.
3. Switch off the ignition for at least 10 seconds.
4. Read out the fault memory.

PR1029900131040X

Fig. 11 Code P0130: Front Oxygen Sensor Cylinders 1–3, Signal Implausible (Part 4 of 4)

1 Check wiring harness.

1. Remove oxygen sensor connector 1 ahead of TWC.
2. Switch on the ignition.
3. Connect voltmeter at sleeve to pins 3 and 4 of oxygen sensor connector 1 after TWC.
   Display: approx. 450 mV

If the value is not reached, remove DME control module connector and check wiring for short to B+.

If no short to B+ can be detected, replace DME control module.

2 Check oxygen sensor.

Note

This check must be performed with the engine cold.

1. Remove oxygen sensor connector 1 ahead of TWC.
2. Connect ohmmeter on pin side to pins 1 and 3 of oxygen sensor connector.
   Display: ∞ Ω
3. Connect ohmmeter on pin side to pins 2 and 3 of oxygen sensor connector.
   Display: ∞ Ω
4. Connect ohmmeter on pin side to pins 1 and 4 of oxygen sensor connector.
   Display: ∞ Ω
5. Connect ohmmeter on pin side to pins 2 and 4 of oxygen sensor connector.
   Display: ∞ Ω

PR1029900132020X

Fig. 12 Code P0132: Front Oxygen Sensor Cylinders 1–3, Above Limit (Part 2 of 2)

1 Check wiring harness or output stage of DME control module.
Not OK → Repair wiring harness or replace DME control module.
→ Erase fault memory, then road test vehicle or perform short test.
→ Read out fault memory. No faults in memory.
→ **End**
OK ↓

2 Check oxygen sensor.
Not OK → Replace oxygen sensor.
→ Erase fault memory, then road test vehicle or perform short test.
→ Read out fault memory. No faults in memory.
→ **End**
OK ↓

End

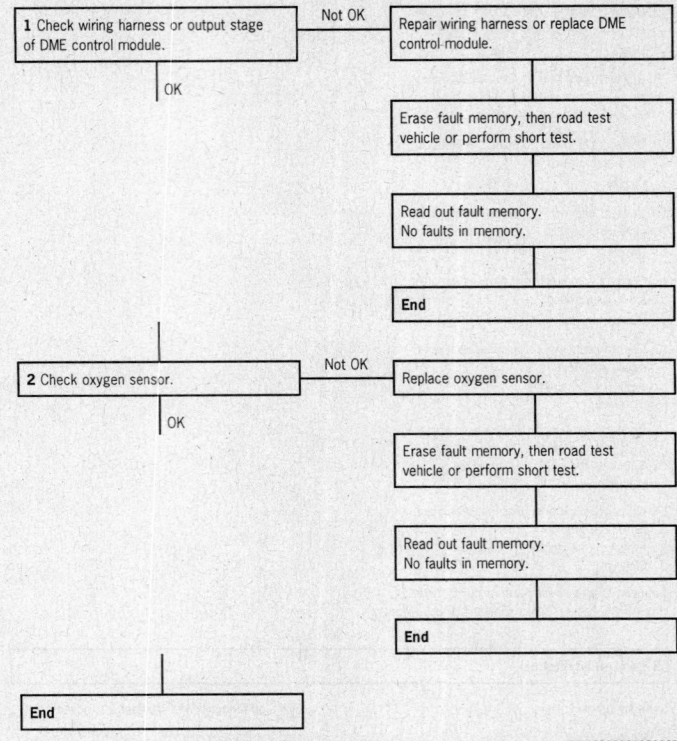

PR1029900132010X

Fig. 12 Code P0132: Front Oxygen Sensor Cylinders 1–3, Above Limit (Part 1 of 2)

Read out fault memory.
→ Should there be additional faults in the memory, rectify these first.
→ **1** Erase fault memory, then road test vehicle or perform short test.
→ **End**

DTC P0133, P0153, P1275 or P1276 in memory.
↓
1 Erase fault memory, then road test vehicle or perform short test.
→ No faults in memory.
→ **End**
↓
DTC P0133, P0153, P1275 or P1276 in memory.
↓
Replace oxygen sensor.
↓
End

PR1029900133010X

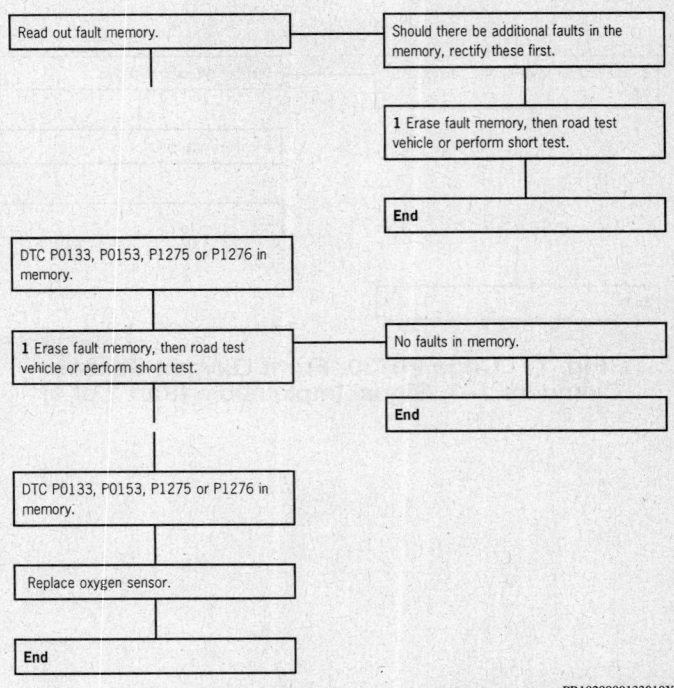

Fig. 13 Codes P0133, P0153, P1275 & P1276: Front Oxygen Sensors Aging (Part 1 of 2)

1 Road test vehicle or perform short test.

1. Erase fault memory.
2. Heat the oxygen sensors (road test car under load, run engine without load at high rpm).
3. Road test vehicle or perform short test, ensuring that the diagnosis conditions are reached.
4. Read out the fault memory.

PR1029900133020X

Fig. 13 Codes P0133, P0153, P1275 & P1276: Front Oxygen Sensors Aging (Part 2 of 2)

3 Check oxygen sensor heating.

Not OK → Replace oxygen sensor. → Erase fault memory, then road test vehicle or perform short test. → Read out fault memory. No faults in memory. → **End**

OK → **End**

PR1029900134020X

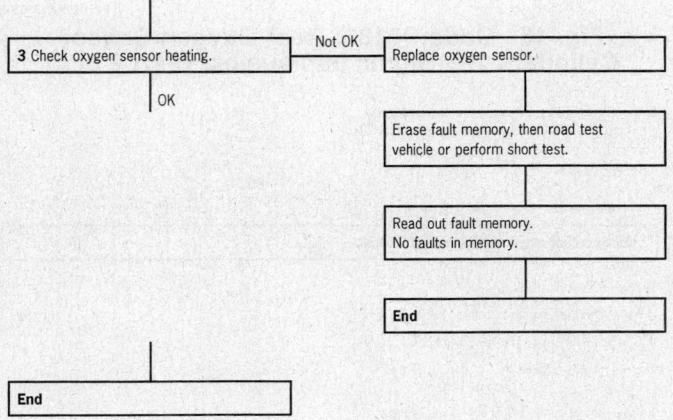

Fig. 14 Code P0134: Front Oxygen Sensor Cylinders 1–3 Signal Interruption (Part 2 of 4)

1 Check wiring harness.

1. Remove oxygen sensor connector 1 ahead of TWC.
2. Switch on the ignition.
3. Connect voltmeter at sleeve to pins 3 and 4 of oxygen sensor connector 1 ahead of TWC.
   Display: approx. 450 mV
4. Start engine and run at high speed for 3 minutes.
5. Connect voltmeter at sleeve to pins 1 and 2.
   Display: battery voltage

If the measurement according to items 3 and 5 does not show the specified values, remove DME control module connector and check wiring for continuity.

If no continuity can be detected, repair wiring harness. If continuity exists, replace DME control module.

2 Check function of oxygen sensor.

1. Heat the oxygen sensors (road test car under load or run engine without load at high rpm).
2. Connect Porsche System Tester 2 or scan tool and read voltage of oxygen sensor 1 ahead of TWC.
   Display: Voltage fluctuations between 100 mV and 800 mV
   ➡ Oxygen sensor OK.

PR1029900134030X

Fig. 14 Code P0134: Front Oxygen Sensor Cylinders 1–3 Signal Interruption (Part 3 of 4)

1 Check wiring harness or output stage of DME control module.

Not OK → Repair wiring harness or replace DME control module. → Erase fault memory, then road test vehicle or perform short test. → Read out fault memory. No faults in memory. → **End**

OK ↓

2 Check function of oxygen sensor.

Not OK → Replace oxygen sensor. → Erase fault memory, then road test vehicle or perform short test. → Read out fault memory. No faults in memory. → **End**

OK ↓

PR1029900134010X

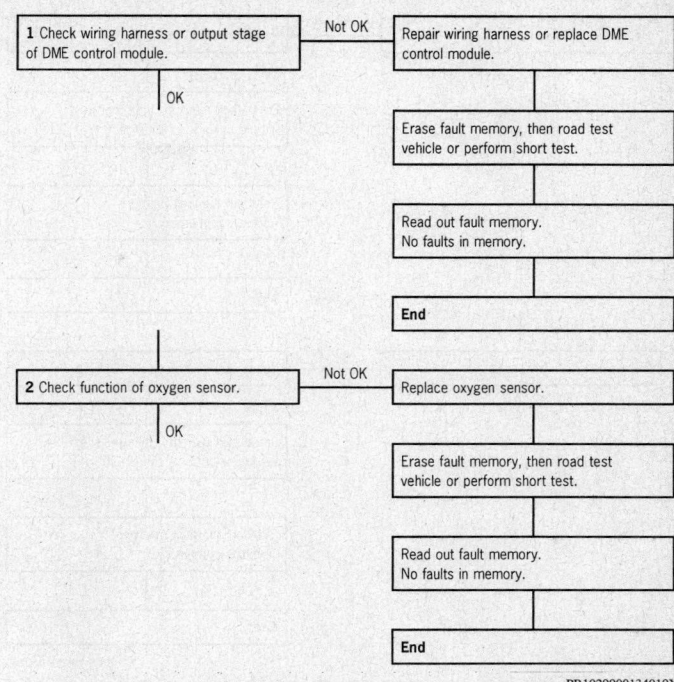

Fig. 14 Code P0134: Front Oxygen Sensor Cylinders 1–3 Signal Interruption (Part 1 of 4)

3 Check oxygen sensor heating.

1. Remove oxygen sensor connector 1 ahead of TWC.
2. Connect ohmmeter on pin side to pins 1 and 2.
   Display: 1.0 - 2.6 Ω at 25 °C.
3. Connect ohmmeter on pin side to pin 1 and oxygen sensor housing.
   Display: ∞ Ω
4. Connect ohmmeter on pin side to pin 2 and oxygen sensor housing.
   Display: ∞ Ω

PR1029900134040X

Fig. 14 Code P0134: Front Oxygen Sensor Cylinders 1–3 Signal Interruption (Part 4 of 4)

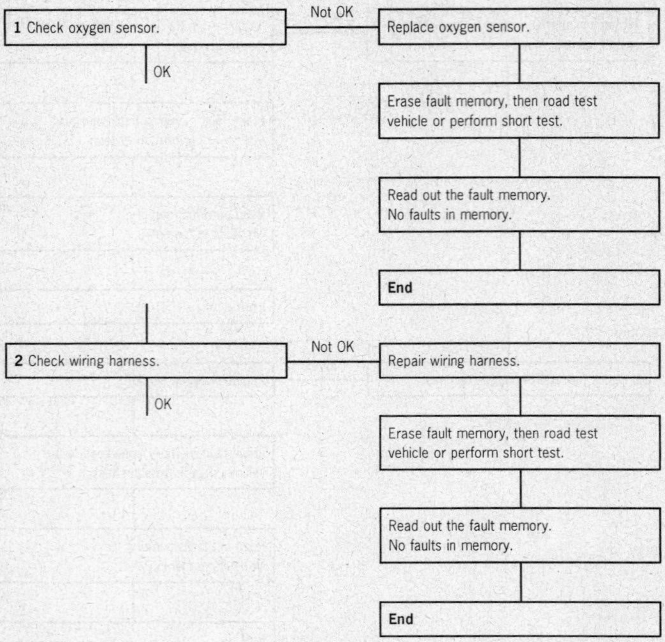

PR1029900135010X

Fig. 15 Code P0136: Rear Oxygen Sensor Cylinders 1–3 Signal Implausible (Part 1 of 4)

1 Check oxygen sensor.

1. Heat the oxygen sensors (road test car under load or run engine without load at high rpm).
2. Connect Porsche System Tester 2 or scan tool and read voltage of oxygen sensor 1 after TWC.
   Display: Voltage fluctuations between 100 mV and 800 mV.
   ➡ Oxygen sensor OK.

If a value around 0 V is displayed, a short circuit has occurred between the signal wire and sensor ground.

3. Remove oxygen sensor connector 1 after TWC.
4. Connect voltmeter at sleeve to pins 3 and 4.
   Display: approx. 450 mV.
   ➡ Replace oxygen sensor.

   Display: approx. 0 V
   ➡ Check wiring harness.

2 Check wiring harness.

1. Remove oxygen sensor connector.
2. Connect special tool 9637 to wiring harness (DME control module connector).
3. With an ohmmeter, measure resistance between special tool 9637, pin II/11, and oxygen sensor connector, pin 3.
   Display: 0 - 5 Ω

PR1029900135030X

Fig. 15 Code P0136: Rear Oxygen Sensor Cylinders 1–3 Signal Implausible (Part 3 of 4)

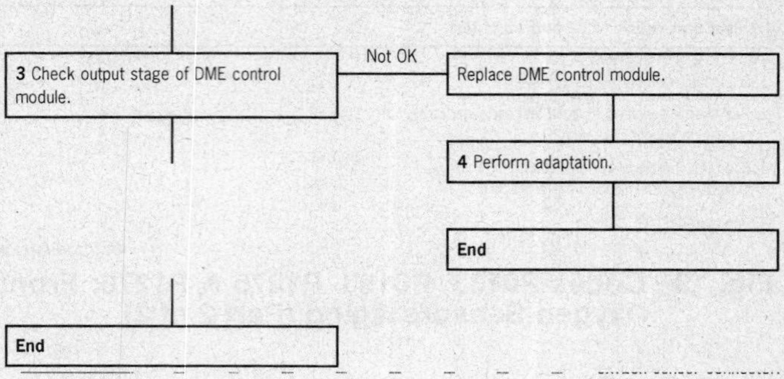

PR1029900135020X

Fig. 15 Code P0136: Rear Oxygen Sensor Cylinders 1–3 Signal Implausible (Part 2 of 4)

4. With an ohmmeter, measure resistance between special tool 9637, pin II/17, and oxygen sensor connector, pin 4.
   Display: 0 - 5 Ω

3 Check output stage of DME control module.

1. Connect special tool 9637.
2. Remove oxygen sensor connector 1 after TWC.
3. Connect voltmeter to pins II/11 and II/17.
4. Switch on the ignition.
   Display: approx. 450 mV

If display shows < 400 mV or > 500 mV, replace DME control module.

4 Perform adaptation.

1. Switch on the ignition.
2. Wait one minute.
   Do not press the accelerator.
3. Switch off the ignition for at least 10 seconds.
4. Read out the fault memory.

PR1029900135040X

Fig. 15 Code P0136: Rear Oxygen Sensor Cylinders 1–3 Signal Implausible (Part 4 of 4)

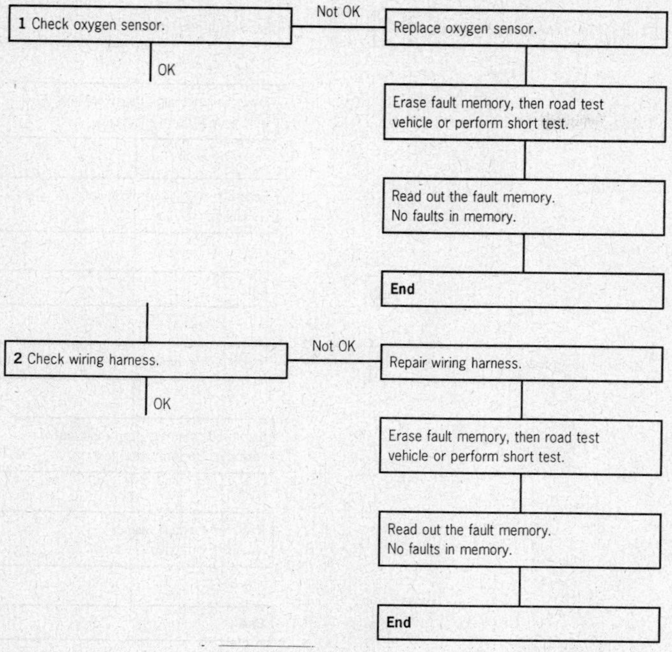

PR1029900136010X

Fig. 16 Code P0138: Rear Oxygen Sensor Cylinders 1–3 Above Limit (Part 1 of 4)

1 Check oxygen sensor.

Note

This check must be performed with the engine cold.

1. Remove oxygen sensor connector 1 after TWC.
2. Connect ohmmeter on pin side to pins 1 and 4 of oxygen sensor connector.
   Display: ∞ Ω

If 0 - 5 Ω is displayed, replace oxygen sensor.

2 Check wiring harness.

1. Remove oxygen sensor connector 1 after TWC.
2. Connect special tool 9637 to wiring harness (DME control module connector).
3. Connect voltmeter to special tool 9637, pin II/17, and ground.
4. Switch on the ignition.
   Display: 0 V

If battery voltage is displayed, check wiring harness for chafing and pinching damage.

PR1029900136030X

Fig. 16 Code P0138: Rear Oxygen Sensor Cylinders 1–3 Above Limit (Part 3 of 4)

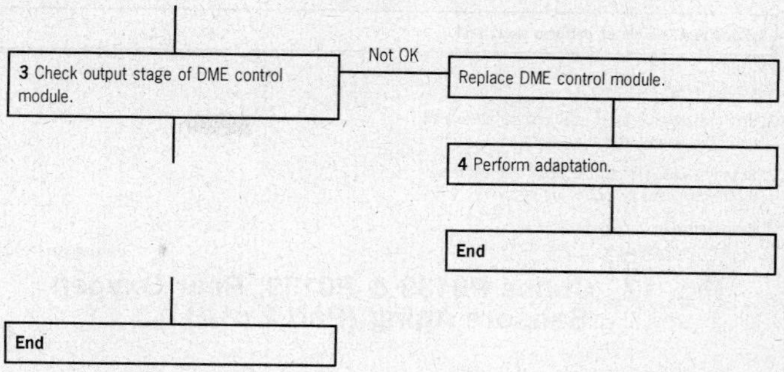

PR1029900136020X

Fig. 16 Code P0138: Rear Oxygen Sensor Cylinders 1–3 Above Limit (Part 2 of 4)

3 Check output stage of DME control module.

1. Connect special tool 9637.
2. Remove oxygen sensor connector 1 after TWC.
3. Connect voltmeter to pins II/11 and II/17.
4. Switch on the ignition.
   Display: approx. 450 mV

If display > 500 mV, replace DME control module.

4 Perform adaptation.

1. Switch on the ignition.
2. Wait one minute.
   Do not press the accelerator.
3. Switch off the ignition for at least 10 seconds.
4. Read out the fault memory.

PR1029900136040X

Fig. 16 Code P0138: Rear Oxygen Sensor Cylinders 1–3 Above Limit (Part 4 of 4)

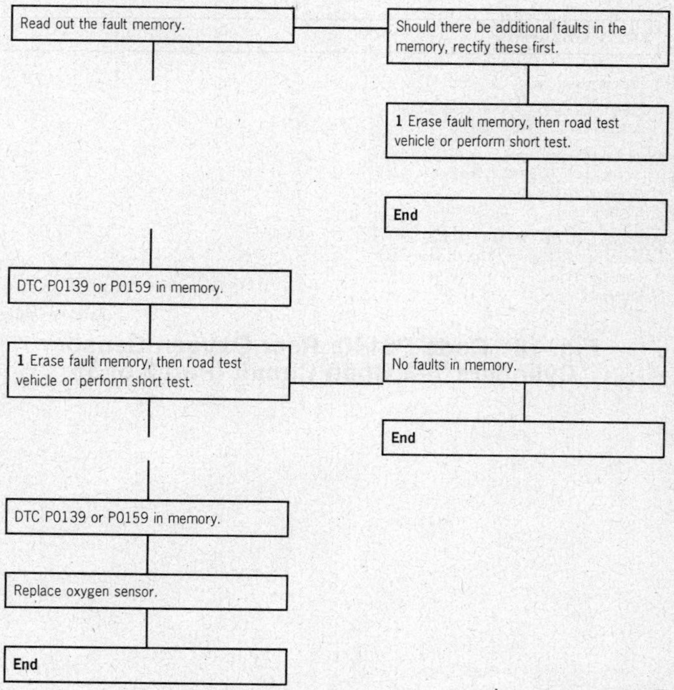

PR1029900137010X

Fig. 17 Codes P0139 & P0159: Rear Oxygen Sensors Aging (Part 1 of 2)

1 Road test vehicle or perform short test.

1. Erase the fault memory.
2. Heat the oxygen sensors (road test car under load, run engine without load at high rpm).
3. Road test vehicle or perform short test, ensuring that the diagnosis conditions are reached.
4. Read out the fault memory.

PR1029900137020X

Fig. 17 Codes P0139 & P0159: Rear Oxygen Sensors Aging (Part 2 of 2)

Check oxygen sensor heating (see DTC P1117).

End

PR1029900138020X

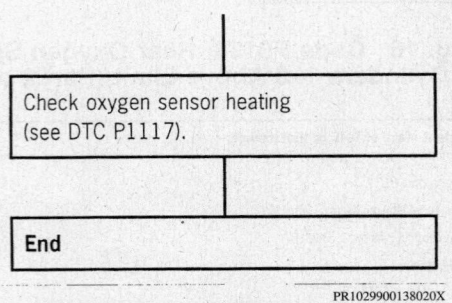

Fig. 18 Code P0140: Rear Oxygen Sensor Cylinders 1–3 Open Circuit (Part 2 of 3)

1 Check function of oxygen sensor.

1. Heat the oxygen sensors (road test car under load or run engine without load at high rpm).
2. Connect Porsche System Tester 2 or scan tool and read voltage of oxygen sensor 1 after TWC.
   Display: Voltage fluctuations between 100 mV and 800 mV.
   ➡ Oxygen sensor OK.

2 Check wiring harness.

1. Remove oxygen sensor connector.
2. Connect special tool 9637 to wiring harness (DME control module connector).
3. With an ohmmeter, measure resistance between special tool 9637, pin II/11, and oxygen sensor connector, pin 3.
   Display: 0 - 5 Ω
4. With an ohmmeter, measure resistance between special tool 9637, pin II/17, and oxygen sensor connector, pin 4.
   Display: 0 - 5 Ω

PR1029900138030X

Fig. 18 Code P0140: Rear Oxygen Sensor Cylinders 1–3 Open Circuit (Part 3 of 3)

1 Check function of oxygen sensor. — Not OK → Replace oxygen sensor. → Erase fault memory, then road test vehicle or perform short test. → Read out the fault memory. No faults in memory. → **End**

OK ↓

2 Check wiring harness. — Not OK → Repair wiring harness. → Erase fault memory, then road test vehicle or perform short test. → Read out the fault memory. No faults in memory. → **End**

OK

PR1029900138010X

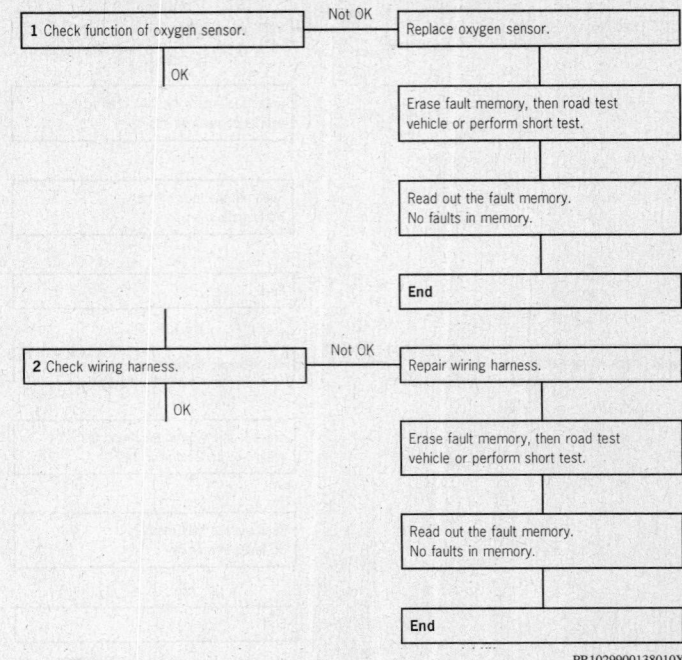

Fig. 18 Code P0140: Rear Oxygen Sensor Cylinders 1–3 Open Circuit (Part 1 of 3)

1 Check oxygen sensor. — Not OK → Replace oxygen sensor. → Erase fault memory, then road test vehicle or perform short test. → Read out fault memory. No faults in memory. → **End**

OK ↓

2 Check wiring harness. — Not OK → Repair wiring harness. → Erase fault memory, then road test vehicle or perform short test. → Read out fault memory. No faults in memory. → **End**

OK

PR1029900139010X

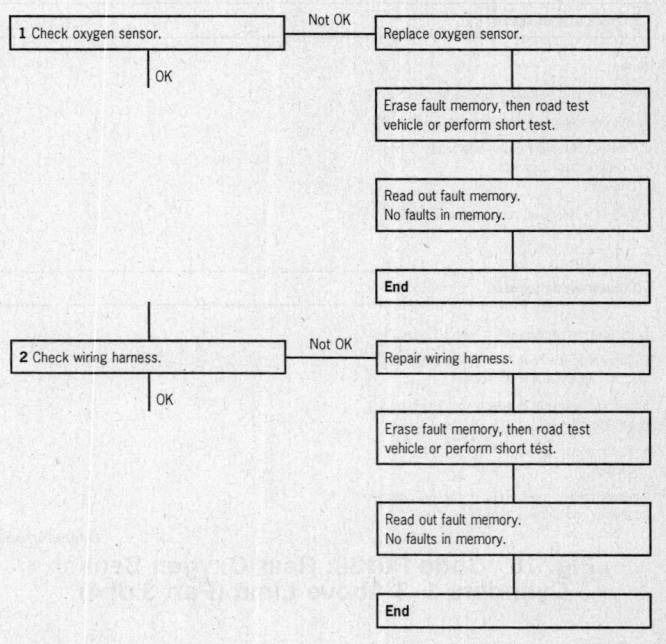

Fig. 19 Code P0150: Front Oxygen Sensor Cylinders 4–6 Signal Implausible (Part 1 of 4)

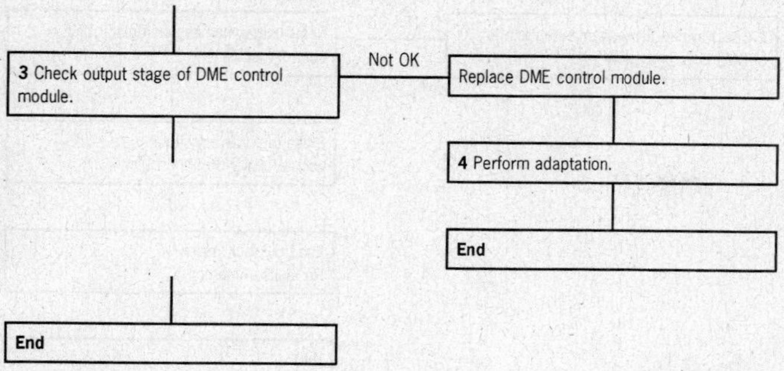

PR1029900139020X

Fig. 19 Code P0150: Front Oxygen Sensor Cylinders 4–6 Signal Implausible (Part 2 of 4)

4. With an ohmmeter, measure resistance between special tool 9637, pin II/10, and oxygen sensor connector, pin 3.
   Display: 0 - 5 Ω

3 Check output stage of DME control module.

1. Connect special tool 9637.
2. Remove oxygen sensor connector 2 ahead of TWC.
3. Connect voltmeter to pins II/10 and II/16.
4. Switch on the ignition.
   Display: approx. 450 mV

If display shows < 400 mV or > 500 mV, replace DME control module.

4 Perform adaptation.

1. Switch on the ignition.
2. Wait one minute.
   Do not press the accelerator.
3. Switch off the ignition for at least 10 seconds.
4. Read out the fault memory.

PR1029900139040X

Fig. 19 Code P0150: Front Oxygen Sensor Cylinders 4–6 Signal Implausible (Part 4 of 4)

1 Check oxygen sensor.

1. Heat the oxygen sensors (road test car under load or run engine without load at high rpm).
2. Connect Porsche System Tester 2 or scan tool and read voltage of oxygen sensor 2 ahead of TWC.
   Display: Voltage fluctuations between 100 mV and 800 mV.
   ➡ Oxygen sensor OK.

If a value around 0 V is displayed, a short circuit has occurred between the signal wire and sensor ground.

3. Remove oxygen sensor connector 2 ahead of TWC.
4. Connect voltmeter with sleeve to pins 3 and 4.
   Display: approx. 450 mV.
   ➡ Replace oxygen sensor.
   Display: approx. 0 V
   ➡ Check wiring harness.

2 Check wiring harness.

1. Remove oxygen sensor connector.
2. Connect special tool 9637 to wiring harness (DME control module connector).
3. With an ohmmeter, measure resistance between special tool 9637, pin II/16, and oxygen sensor connector, pin 4.
   Display: 0 - 5 Ω

PR1029900139030X

Fig. 19 Code P0150: Front Oxygen Sensor Cylinders 4–6 Signal Implausible (Part 3 of 4)

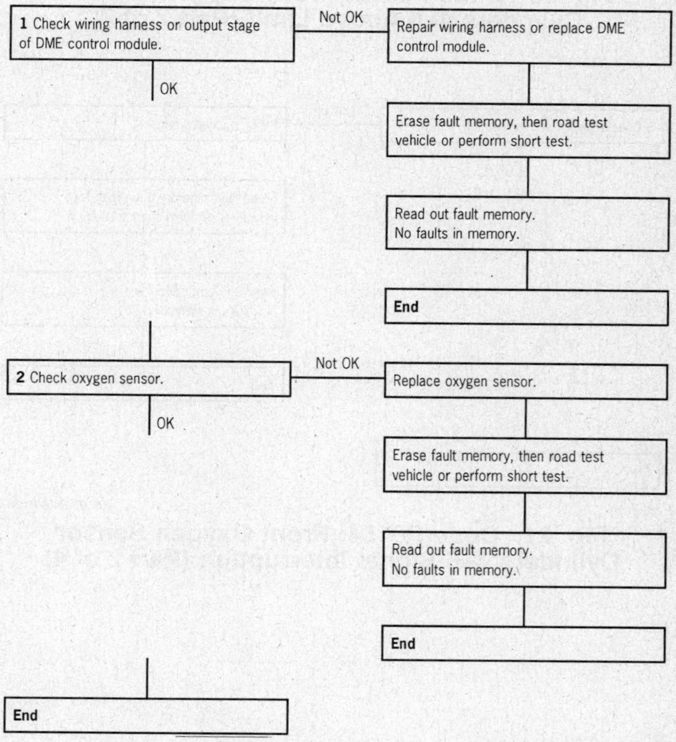

PR1029900140010X

Fig. 20 Code P0152: Front Oxygen Sensor Cylinders 4–6 Above Limit (Part 1 of 2)

1 Check wiring harness.

1. Remove oxygen sensor connector 2 ahead of TWC.
2. Switch on the ignition.
3. Connect voltmeter at sleeve to pins 3 and 4 of oxygen sensor connector 2 ahead of TWC.
   Display: approx. 450 mV

If the value is not reached, remove DME control module connector and check wiring for short to B+.

If no short to B+ can be detected, replace DME control module.

2 Check oxygen sensor.

Note

This check must be performed with the engine cold.

1. Remove oxygen sensor connector 2 ahead of TWC.
2. Connect ohmmeter on pin side to pins 1 and 3 of oxygen sensor connector.
   Display: ∞ Ω
3. Connect ohmmeter on pin side to pins 2 and 3 of oxygen sensor connector.
   Display: ∞ Ω
4. Connect ohmmeter on pin side to pins 1 and 4 of oxygen sensor connector.
   Display: ∞ Ω
5. Connect ohmmeter on pin side to pins 2 and 4 of oxygen sensor connector.
   Display: ∞ Ω

PR1029900140020X

Fig. 20 Code P0152: Front Oxygen Sensor Cylinders 4–6 Above Limit (Part 2 of 2)

3 Check oxygen sensor heating. — Not OK → Replace oxygen sensor. → Erase fault memory, then road test vehicle or perform short test. → Read out fault memory. No faults in memory. → **End**

OK ↓

End

PR1029900141020X

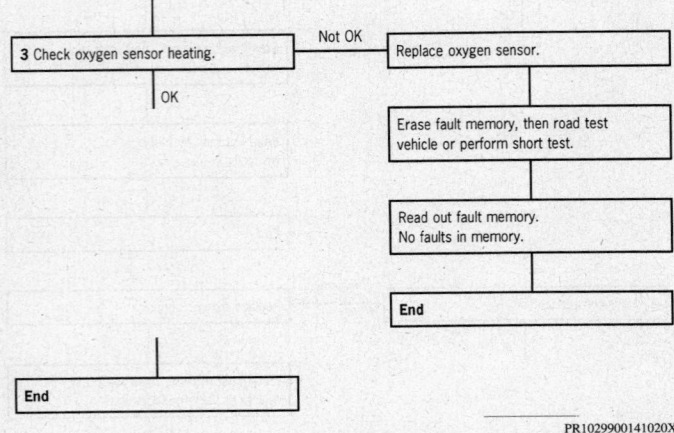

Fig. 21 Code P0154: Front Oxygen Sensor Cylinders 4–6 Signal Interruption (Part 2 of 4)

1 Check wiring harness or output stage of DME control module. — Not OK → Repair wiring harness or replace DME control module. → Erase fault memory, then road test vehicle or perform short test. → Read out fault memory. No faults in memory. → **End**

OK ↓

2 Check function of oxygen sensor. — Not OK → Replace oxygen sensor. → Erase fault memory, then road test vehicle or perform short test. → Read out fault memory. No faults in memory. → **End**

OK ↓

PR1029900141010X

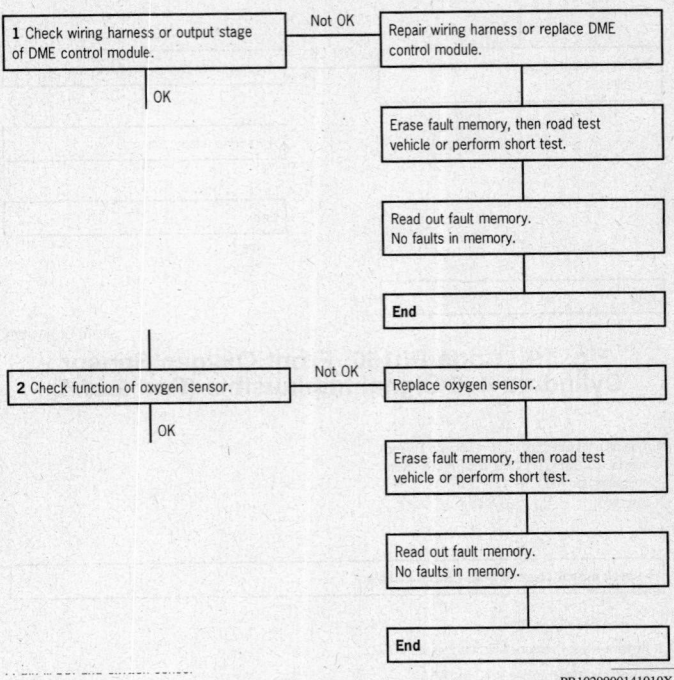

Fig. 21 Code P0154: Front Oxygen Sensor Cylinders 4–6 Signal Interruption (Part 1 of 4)

1 Check wiring harness.

1. Remove oxygen sensor connector 2 ahead of TWC.
2. Switch on the ignition.
3. Connect voltmeter at sleeve to pins 3 and 4 of oxygen sensor connector 2 ahead of TWC.
   Display: approx. 450 mV
4. Start engine and run at high speed for 3 minutes.
5. Connect voltmeter at sleeve to pins 1 and 2.
   Display: battery voltage

If the measurement according to items 3 and 5 does not show the specified values, remove DME control module connector and check wiring for continuity.

If no continuity can be detected, repair wiring harness.
If continuity exists, replace DME control module.

2 Check function of oxygen sensor.

1. Heat the oxygen sensors (road test car under load or run engine without load at high rpm).
2. Connect Porsche System Tester 2 or scan tool and read voltage of oxygen sensor 2 ahead of TWC.
   Display: Voltage fluctuations between 100 mV and 800 mV.
   ➡Oxygen sensor OK.

PR1029900141030X

Fig. 21 Code P0154: Front Oxygen Sensor Cylinders 4–6 Signal Interruption (Part 3 of 4)

3 Check oxygen sensor heating.

1. Remove oxygen sensor connector 2 ahead of TWC.
2. Connect ohmmeter on pin side to pins 1 and 2.
   Display: 1.0 - 2.6 Ω at 25 °C.
3. Connect ohmmeter on pin side to pin 1 and oxygen sensor housing.
   Display: ∞ Ω
4. Connect ohmmeter on pin side to pin 2 and oxygen sensor housing.
   Display: ∞ Ω

PR1029900141040X

Fig. 21 Code P0154: Front Oxygen Sensor Cylinders 4–6 Signal Interruption (Part 4 of 4)

3 Check output stage of DME control module.

Not OK → Replace DME control module. → **4** Perform adaptation. → **End**

(OK) → **End**

PR1029900142020X

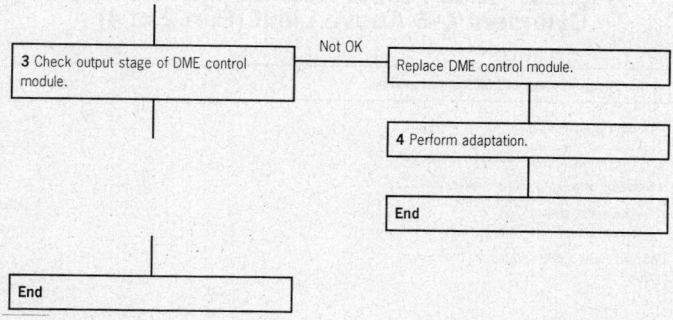

Fig. 22 Code P0156: Rear Oxygen Sensor Cylinders 4–6 Signal Implausible (Part 2 of 4)

1 Check oxygen sensor.

1. Heat the oxygen sensors (road test car under load or run engine without load at high rpm).
2. Connect Porsche System Tester 2 or scan tool and read voltage of oxygen sensor 2 after TWC.
   Display: Voltage fluctuations between 100 mV and 800 mV.
   ➡ Oxygen sensor OK.

If a value around 0 V is displayed, a short circuit has occurred between the signal wire and sensor ground.

3. Remove oxygen sensor connector 2 after TWC.
4. Connect voltmeter at sleeve to pins 3 and 4.
   Display: approx. 450 mV.
   ➡ Replace oxygen sensor.

   Display: approx. 0 V
   ➡ Check wiring harness.

2 Check wiring harness.

1. Remove oxygen sensor connector.
2. Connect special tool 9637 to wiring harness (DME control module connector).
3. With an ohmmeter, measure resistance between special tool 9637, pin II/14, and oxygen sensor connector, pin 4.
   Display: 0 - 5 Ω

PR1029900142030X

Fig. 22 Code P0156: Rear Oxygen Sensor Cylinders 4–6 Signal Implausible (Part 3 of 4)

1 Check oxygen sensor.

Not OK → Replace oxygen sensor. → Erase fault memory, then road test vehicle or perform short test. → Read out the fault memory. No faults in memory. → **End**

OK ↓

2 Check wiring harness.

Not OK → Repair wiring harness. → Erase fault memory, then road test vehicle or perform short test. → Read out the fault memory. No faults in memory. → **End**

OK ↓

PR1029900142010X

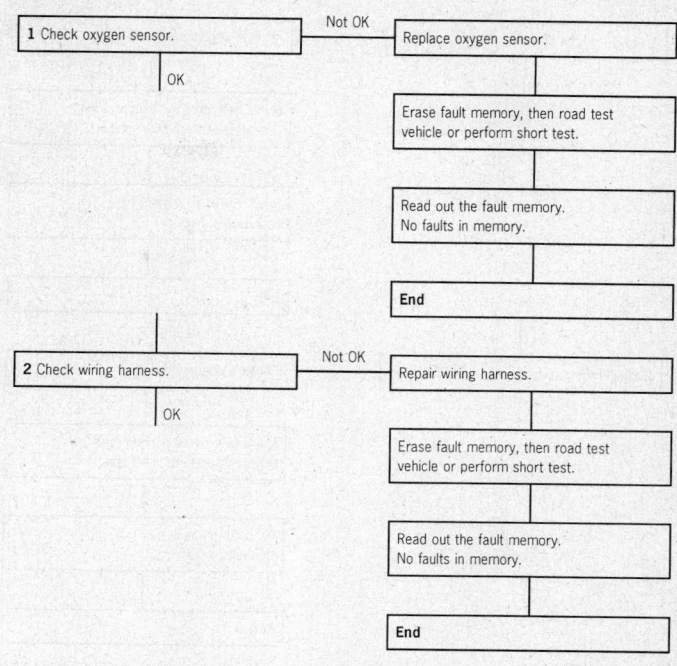

Fig. 22 Code P0156: Rear Oxygen Sensor Cylinders 4–6 Signal Implausible (Part 1 of 4)

4. With an ohmmeter, measure resistance between special tool 9637, pin II/8, and oxygen sensor connector, pin 3.
   Display: 0 - 5 Ω

3 Check output stage of DME control module.

1. Connect special tool 9637.
2. Remove oxygen sensor connector 2 after TWC.
3. Connect voltmeter to pins II/8 and II/14.
4. Switch on the ignition.
   Display: approx. 450 mV

If display shows < 400 mV or > 500 mV, replace DME control module.

4 Perform adaptation.

1. Switch on the ignition.
2. Wait one minute.
   Do not press the accelerator.
3. Switch off the ignition for at least 10 seconds.
4. Read out the fault memory.

PR1029900142040X

Fig. 22 Code P0156: Rear Oxygen Sensor Cylinders 4–6 Signal Implausible (Part 4 of 4)

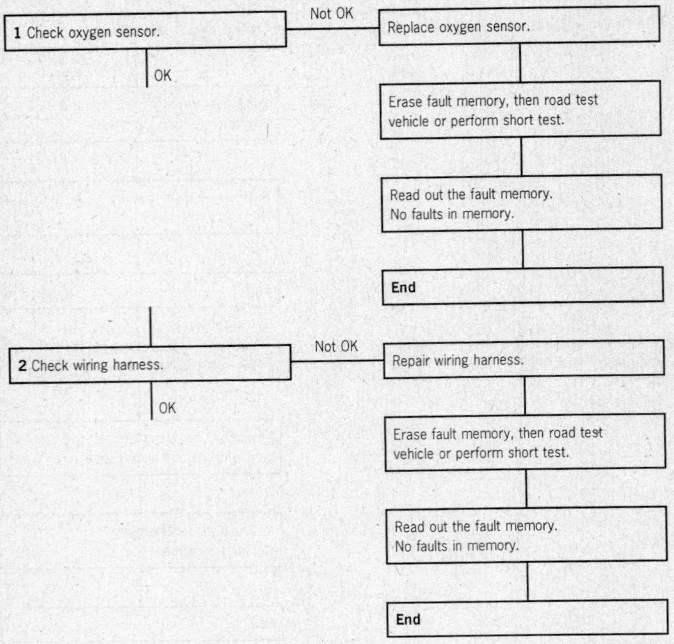

Fig. 23 Code P0158: Rear Oxygen Sensor Cylinders 4–6 Above Limit (Part 1 of 4)

1 Check oxygen sensor.

Note

This check must be performed with the engine cold.

1. Remove oxygen sensor connector 2 after TWC.
2. Connect ohmmeter on pin side to pins 1 and 4 of oxygen sensor connector.
   Display: ∞ Ω

If 0 - 5 Ω is displayed, replace oxygen sensor.

2 Check wiring harness.

1. Remove oxygen sensor connector 2 after TWC.
2. Connect special tool 9637 to wiring harness (DME control module connector).
3. Connect voltmeter to special tool 9637, pin II/14, and ground.
4. Switch on the ignition.
   Display: 0 V

If battery voltage is displayed, check wiring harness for chafing and pinching damage.

PR1029900143030X

Fig. 23 Code P0158: Rear Oxygen Sensor Cylinders 4–6 Above Limit (Part 3 of 4)

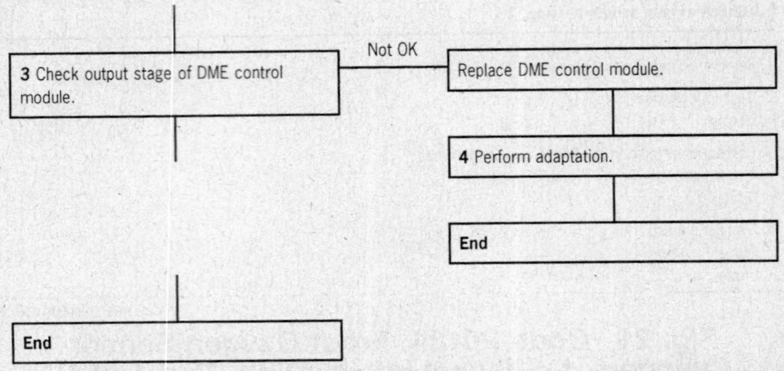

Fig. 23 Code P0158: Rear Oxygen Sensor Cylinders 4–6 Above Limit (Part 2 of 4)

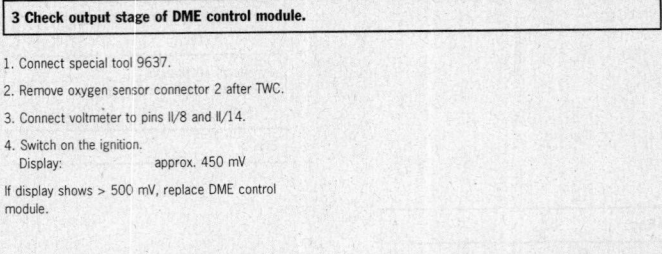

3 Check output stage of DME control module.

1. Connect special tool 9637.
2. Remove oxygen sensor connector 2 after TWC.
3. Connect voltmeter to pins II/8 and II/14.
4. Switch on the ignition.
   Display: approx. 450 mV

If display shows > 500 mV, replace DME control module.

4 Perform adaptation.

1. Switch on the ignition.
2. Wait one minute.
   Do not press the accelerator.
3. Switch off the ignition for at least 10 seconds.
4. Read out the fault memory.

PR1029900143040X

Fig. 23 Code P0158: Rear Oxygen Sensor Cylinders 4–6 Above Limit (Part 4 of 4)

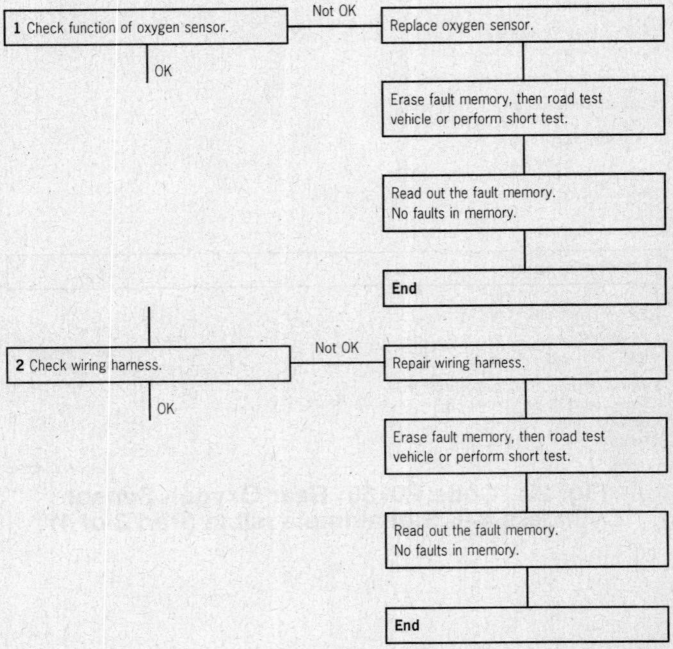

Fig. 24 Code P0160: Rear Oxygen Sensor Cylinders 4–6 Open Circuit (Part 1 of 3)

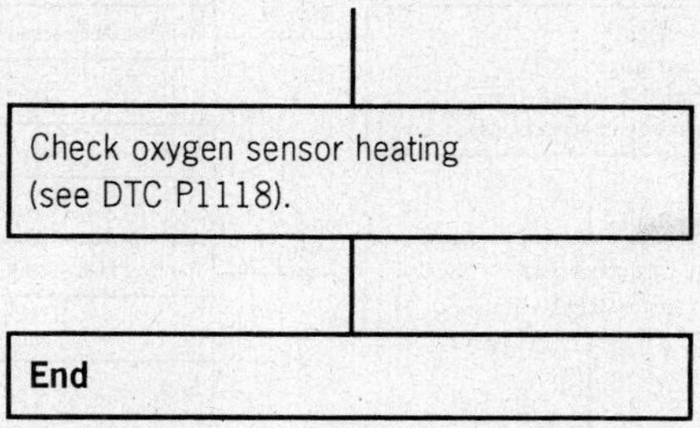

PR1029900144020X

Fig. 24 Code P0160: Rear Oxygen Sensor Cylinders 4–6 Open Circuit (Part 2 of 3)

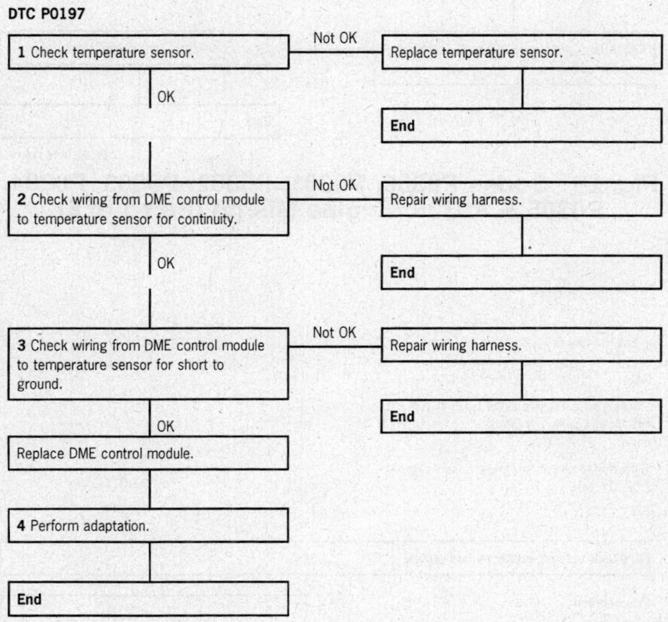

PR1029900145010X

Fig. 25 Codes P0197 & P0198: Oil Temperature Sensor (Part 1 of 4)

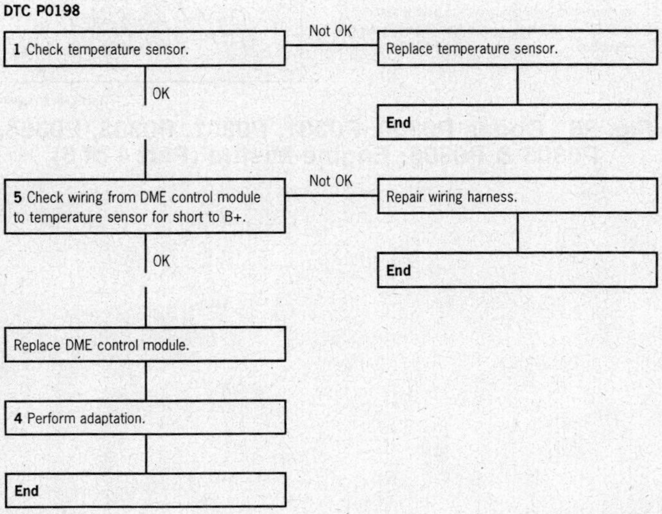

PR1029900145020X

Fig. 25 Codes P0197 & P0198: Oil Temperature Sensor (Part 2 of 4)

1 Check function of oxygen sensor.

1. Heat the oxygen sensors (road test car under load or run engine without load at high rpm).
2. Connect Porsche System Tester 2 or scan tool and read voltage of oxygen sensor 2 after TWC.
   Display: Voltage fluctuations between 100 mV and 800 mV.
   ➡ Oxygen sensor OK.

2 Check wiring harness.

1. Remove oxygen sensor connector.
2. Connect special tool 9637 to wiring harness (DME control module connector).
3. With an ohmmeter, measure resistance between special tool 9637, pin II/8, and oxygen sensor connector, pin 3.
   Display: 0 - 5 Ω
4. With an ohmmeter, measure resistance between special tool 9637, pin II/14, and oxygen sensor connector, pin 4.
   Display: 0 - 5 Ω

PR1029900144030X

Fig. 24 Code P0160: Rear Oxygen Sensor Cylinders 4–6 Open Circuit (Part 3 of 3)

1 Check temperature sensor.

1. Connect special tool 9637 to wiring harness (DME control module connector).
2. Connect ohmmeter to pins III/17 and III/5.
   Display: 2.8 – 3.5 kΩ at 60 °C

2 Check wiring from DME control module to temperature sensor for continuity.

1. Connect special tool 9637 to wiring harness (DME control module connector).
2. Remove connector of temperature sensor.
3. Connect ohmmeter to pin III/17 (special tool 9637) and pin 3 (temperature sensor connector).
   Display: 0 - 5 Ω
4. Connect ohmmeter to pin III/5 (special tool 9637) and pin 1 (temperature sensor connector).
   Display: 0 - 5 Ω

3 Check wiring from DME control module to temperature sensor for short to ground.

1. Connect special tool 9637 to wiring harness (DME control module connector).
2. Remove connector of temperature sensor.
3. Connect ohmmeter to pin III/5 and ground.
   Display: ∞ Ω

If 0 - 5 Ω is displayed, check wiring harness for chafing and pinching damage.

PR1029900145030X

Fig. 25 Codes P0197 & P0198: Oil Temperature Sensor (Part 3 of 4)

4 Perform adaptation.

1. Switch on the ignition.
2. Wait one minute.
   Do not press the accelerator.
3. Switch off the ignition for at least 10 seconds.
4. Read out the fault memory.

5 Check wiring from DME control module to temperature sensor for short to B+.

1. Connect special tool 9637 to wiring harness (DME control module connector).
2. Remove connector of temperature sensor.
3. Connect voltmeter to pin III/5 and ground.
   Switch on the ignition.
   Display: 0 V

If battery voltage is displayed, check wiring harness for chafing and pinching damage.

PR1029900145040X

Fig. 25 Codes P0197 & P0198: Oil Temperature Sensor (Part 4 of 4)

1 Check fuel pressure. — Not OK → 2 Check volume supply of fuel pump. → End

OK ↓

3 Check triggering of fuel injectors. — Not OK → Correct fault according to wiring diagram. → End

OK ↓

Check for air leaks in intake air system. — Not OK → Repair intake air system. → End

↓

End

PR1029900146020X

Fig. 26 Codes P0300, P0301, P0302, P0303, P0304, P0305 & P0306: Engine Misfire (Part 2 of 6)

1 Check fuel pressure.

1. Undo and remove the closure cap of the fuel collection pipe test connection (A/F 13 mm).
2. Connect pressure gauge (special tool P 378a) to connecting line (special tool 9559) and connect to test connection.

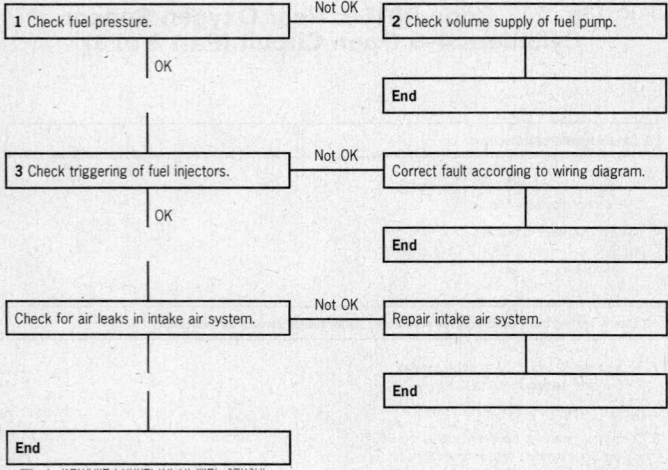

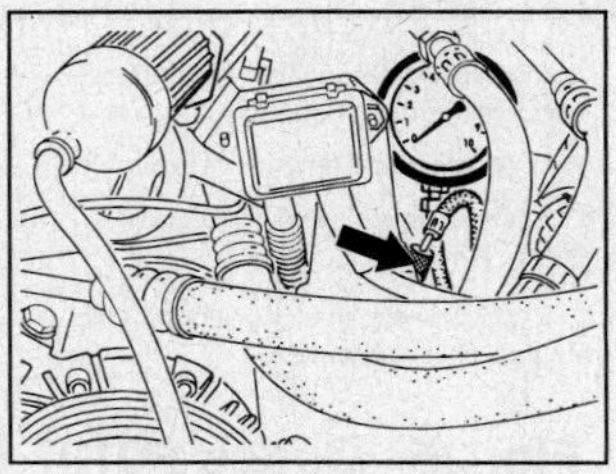

3. Actuate fuel pump, either

– **with Porsche System Tester 2**
The fuel pump can be actuated with the Porsche System Tester 2 or by jumpering the fuel pump relay.

or

– **via fuel pump relay without tester**
Disconnect the fuel pump relay from the central electrical system and jumper plug-in contacts 30 and 87 (identification 3 und 5 on central electrical system) with a fused shop-made cable. The fuel pump must now operate or deliver fuel.

PR1029900146030X

Fig. 26 Codes P0300, P0301, P0302, P0303, P0304, P0305 & P0306: Engine Misfire (Part 3 of 6)

Check spark plugs.
Specified spark plugs:
Electrode gap: 0.7 mm + 0.1 mm
Check appearance of spark plugs. — Not OK → Replace faulty spark plug(s). → End

OK ↓

Check spark plug connectors.
Resistance: approx. 2 kΩ — Not OK → Replace faulty spark plug connectors. → End

OK ↓

Check ignition coil(s).
Resistance between terminals 1 and 15 at 20 °C: 0.3 - 0.7 Ω — Not OK → Replace ignition coil(s). → End

OK ↓

Check all connectors for secure fastening and corrosion. — Not OK → Clean connectors and connect securely. → End

OK ↓

PR1029900146010X

Fig. 26 Codes P0300, P0301, P0302, P0303, P0304, P0305 & P0306: Engine Misfire (Part 1 of 6)

4. Nominal test values

Stationary engine 3.8 ± 0.2 bar
Engine idling 3.3 ± 0.2 bar

Note

The seal or sealing ring in the brass closure cap is **not** exchangeable. It must therefore be used only **once**.

Tightening torque of new brass closure cap 2.5 ± 0.5 Nm.

2 Check volume supply of fuel pump.

Precondition:

Fuel filter and electrical supply OK.

1. Relieve pressure in fuel tank by opening tank cap.
2. Connect Porsche System Tester 2.
3. Remove complete air filter system.
4. Detach fuel return line (A/F 17 mm) from the engine compartment (left), taking care to **hold it fast** (A/F 17 mm). Collect residual fuel. Observe safety regulations.

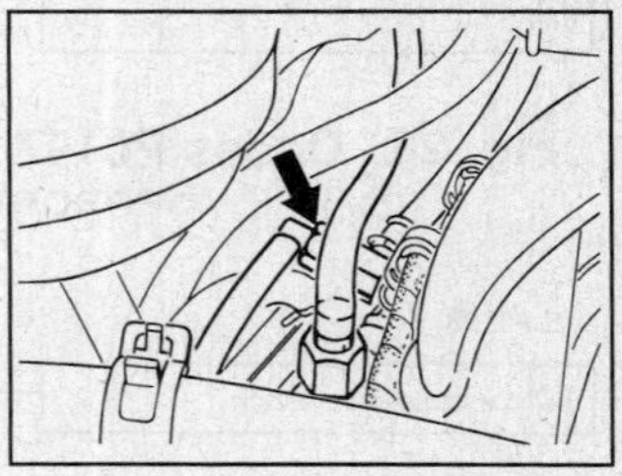

PR1029900146040X

Fig. 26 Codes P0300, P0301, P0302, P0303, P0304, P0305 & P0306: Engine Misfire (Part 4 of 6)

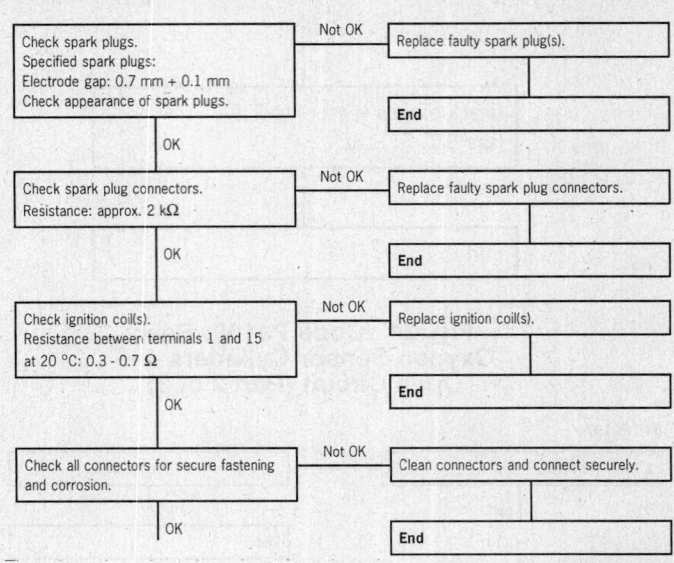

5. Connect fuel hose (shop-made, approx. 1.5 meters long) to the fitting and hold in a measuring container.
6. Actuate fuel pump with the Porsche System Tester 2 and allow fuel to flow into the measuring container for 30 seconds.
   Quantity supplied must be at least 850 cm^3/30 s, i.e. after 30 seconds at least 850 cm^3 of fuel must be in the measuring container.

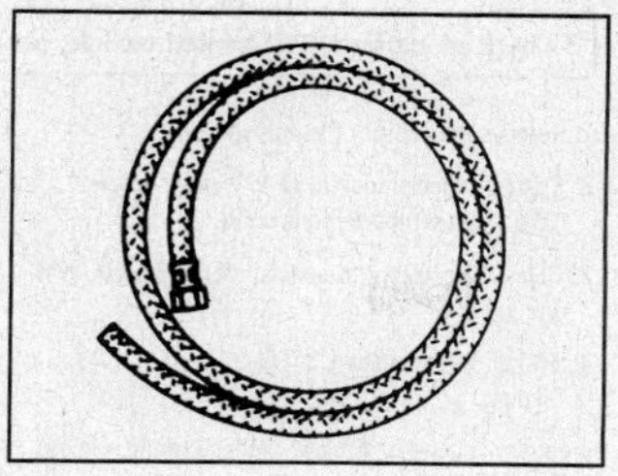

Note

It is essential to observe safety regulations for handling fuel.

3 Check triggering of fuel injectors.

The fuel injectors can be individually suppressed with the Porsche System Tester 2 in the menu "Drive link active". The engine idle speed decreases if triggering is OK.

If no drop in rpm can be detected, check triggering as follows:

a) B+ supply

1. Remove connector of fuel injector to be checked.
2. Connect voltmeter to the valve plug contact, terminal 1, and ground using an auxiliary cable.
3. Switch on the ignition.
   Display: battery voltage

PR1029900146050X

Fig. 26 Codes P0300, P0301, P0302, P0303, P0304, P0305 & P0306: Engine Misfire (Part 5 of 6)

If meter does not read battery voltage, check wiring according to wiring diagram for continuity or short circuit.

b) Coil resistance of fuel injectors

1. Remove connector of fuel injector to be checked.
2. With an ohmmeter, measure resistance between terminals of fuel injector.
   Display: 11 - 13 Ω

c) Injection output stage (negative supply)

1. Connect special tool V.A.G 1315 A/1 between fuel injector and connector.
2. Connect engine tester according to manufacturer's instructions. Connect cable for special input to special tool.

Caution

Tester cables must not be connected to ground.

3. Start the engine. For a perfectly working injector output stage, the following display must be shown at starting rpm.

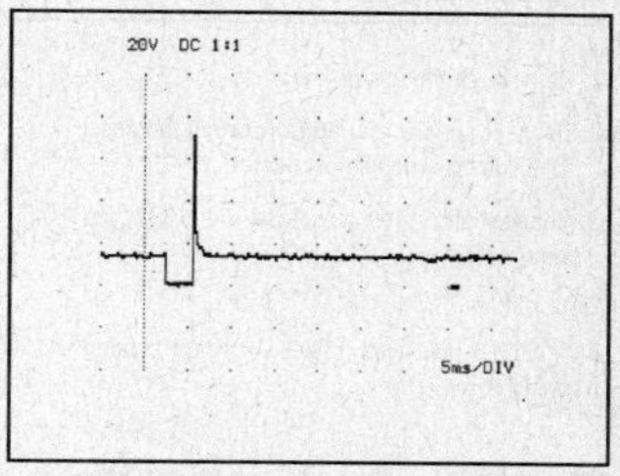

Note

If the engine does not start, or if the idling speed drops, replace tester cable connected to special tool.

PR1029900146060X

Fig. 26 Codes P0300, P0301, P0302, P0303, P0304, P0305 & P0306: Engine Misfire (Part 6 of 6)

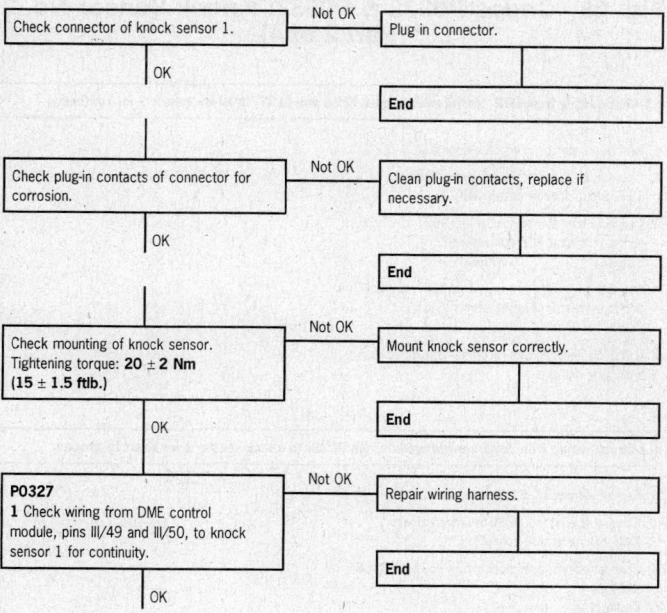

Check connector of knock sensor 1. — Not OK → Plug in connector. → **End**

OK

Check plug-in contacts of connector for corrosion. — Not OK → Clean plug-in contacts, replace if necessary. → **End**

OK

Check mounting of knock sensor. Tightening torque: **20 ± 2 Nm (15 ± 1.5 ftlb.)** — Not OK → Mount knock sensor correctly. → **End**

OK

P0327
1 Check wiring from DME control module, pins III/49 and III/50, to knock sensor 1 for continuity. — Not OK → Repair wiring harness. → **End**

OK

PR1029900147010X

Fig. 27 Codes P0327 & P0328: Knock Sensor No. 1 (Part 1 of 4)

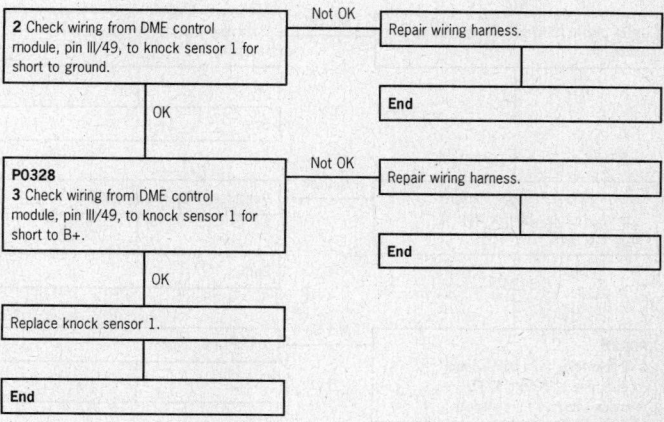

2 Check wiring from DME control module, pin III/49, to knock sensor 1 for short to ground. — Not OK → Repair wiring harness. → **End**

OK

P0328
3 Check wiring from DME control module, pin III/49, to knock sensor 1 for short to B+. — Not OK → Repair wiring harness. → **End**

OK

Replace knock sensor 1. → **End**

PR1029900147020X

Fig. 27 Codes P0327 & P0328: Knock Sensor No. 1 (Part 2 of 4)

1 Check wiring from DME control module, pins III/49 and III/50, to knock sensor 1 for continuity.

1. Remove connector of knock sensor 1.
2. Connect special tool 9637 to wiring harness (DME control module connector).
3. Connect ohmmeter to special tool 9637, pin III/49, and to connector of knock sensor 1, pin 1.
   Display: 0 - 5 Ω
4. Connect ohmmeter to special tool 9637, pin III/50, and to connector of knock sensor 1, pin 2.
   Display: 0 - 5 Ω

If ∞ Ω is displayed, check wiring harness for chafing and pinching damage.

2 Check wiring from DME control module, pin III/49, to knock sensor 1 for short to ground.

1. Remove connector of knock sensor 1.
2. Connect special tool 9637 to wiring harness (DME control module connector).
3. Connect ohmmeter to special tool 9637, pin III/49, and ground.
   Display: ∞ Ω

If 0 - 5 Ω is displayed, check wiring for chafing and pinching damage.

PR1029900147030X

Fig. 27 Codes P0327 & P0328: Knock Sensor No. 1 (Part 3 of 4)

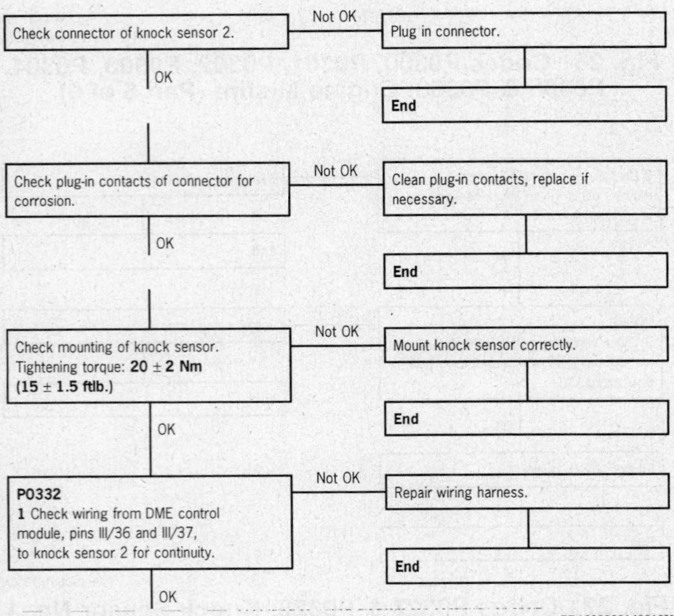

PR1029900148010X

Fig. 28 Codes P0332 & P0333: Knock Sensor No. 2 (Part 1 of 4)

3 Check wiring from DME control module, pin III/49, to knock sensor 1 for short to B+.

1. Remove connector of knock sensor 1.
2. Connect special tool 9637 to wiring harness (DME control module connector).
3. Connect voltmeter to special tool 9637, pin III/49, and ground.
4. Switch on the ignition.
   Display: 0 V

If battery voltage is displayed, check wiring harness for chafing and pinching damage.

PR1029900147040X

Fig. 27 Codes P0327 & P0328: Knock Sensor No. 1 (Part 4 of 4)

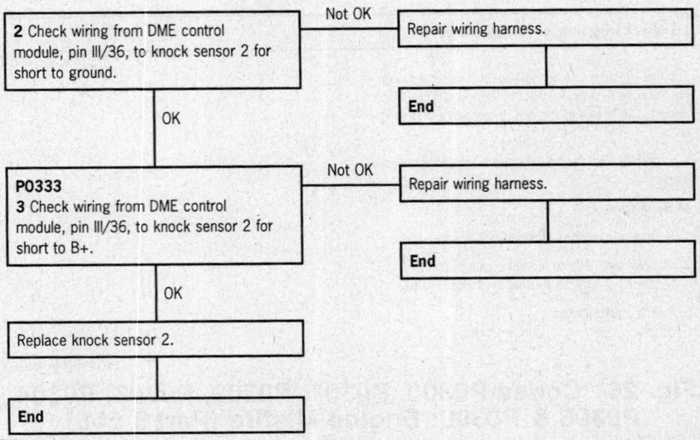

PR1029900148020X

Fig. 28 Codes P0332 & P0333: Knock Sensor No. 2 (Part 2 of 4)

1 Check wiring from DME control module, pins III/36 and III/37, to knock sensor 2 for continuity.

1. Remove connector of knock sensor 2.
2. Connect special tool 9637 to wiring harness (DME control module connector).
3. Connect ohmmeter to special tool 9637, pin III/36, and to connector of knock sensor 2, pin 1.
   Display: 0 - 5 Ω
4. Connect ohmmeter to special tool 9637, pin III/37, and to connector of knock sensor 2, pin 2.
   Display:

If ∞ Ω is displayed, check wiring harness for chafing and pinching damage.

2 Check wiring from DME control module, pin III/36, to knock sensor 2 for short to ground.

1. Remove connector of knock sensor 2.
2. Connect special tool 9637 to wiring harness (DME control module connector).
3. Connect ohmmeter to special tool 9637, pin III/36, and ground.
   Display: ∞ Ω

If 0 - 5 Ω is displayed, check wiring for chafing and pinching damage.

PR1029900148030X

Fig. 28 Codes P0332 & P0333: Knock Sensor No. 2 (Part 3 of 4)

3 Check wiring from DME control module, pin III/36, to knock sensor 2 for short to B+.

1. Remove connector of knock sensor 2.
2. Connect special tool 9637 to wiring harness (DME control module connector).
3. Connect voltmeter to special tool 9637, pin III/36, and ground.
   Display: 0 V

If battery voltage is displayed, check wiring harness for chafing and pinching damage.

PR1029900148040X

Fig. 28 Codes P0332 & P0333: Knock Sensor No. 2 (Part 4 of 4)

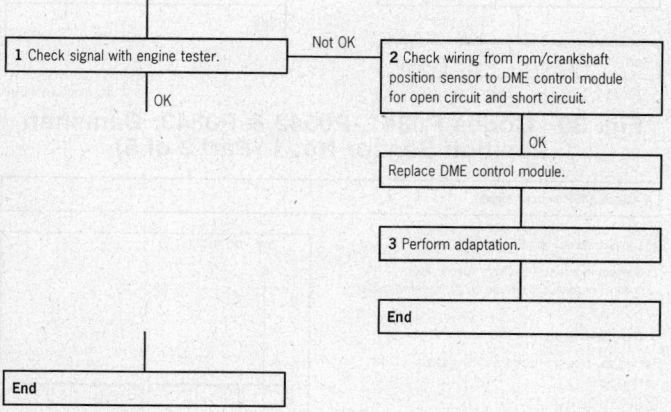

1 Check signal with engine tester. — Not OK → **2** Check wiring from rpm/crankshaft position sensor to DME control module for open circuit and short circuit.

OK → End

2 → OK → Replace DME control module. → **3** Perform adaptation. → End

PR1029900149020X

Fig. 29 Code P0336: Engine Speed Sensor Signal (Part 2 of 4)

1 Check signal with engine tester.

1. Connect special tool 9637.
2. Connect engine tester. Using special input, connect positive cable to pin III/32, negative cable to pin III/46.
3. Start engine or crank engine with starter motor.

The display pictured opposite should appear on the oscilloscope:

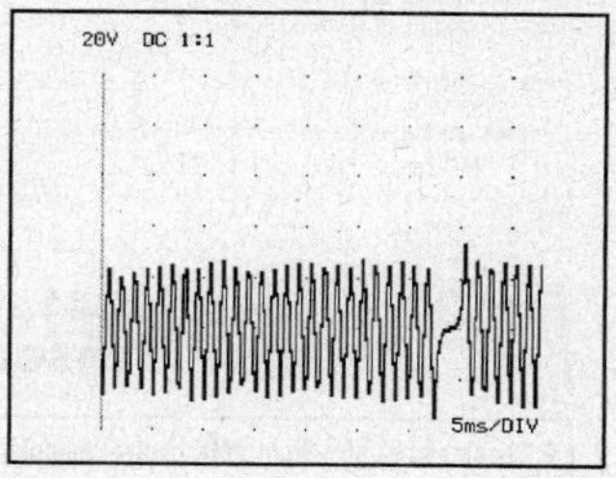

2 Check wiring from rpm/crankshaft position sensor to DME control module for open circuit and short circuit.

1. Connect special tool 9637 to wiring harness.
2. Remove connector of rpm/crankshaft position sensor.

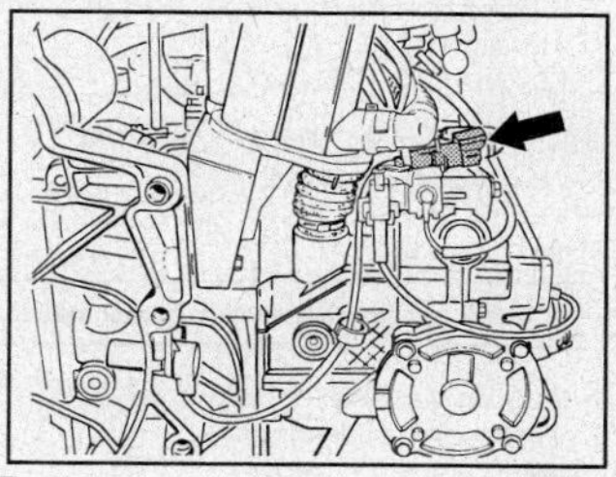

PR1029900149030X

Fig. 29 Code P0336: Engine Speed Sensor Signal (Part 3 of 4)

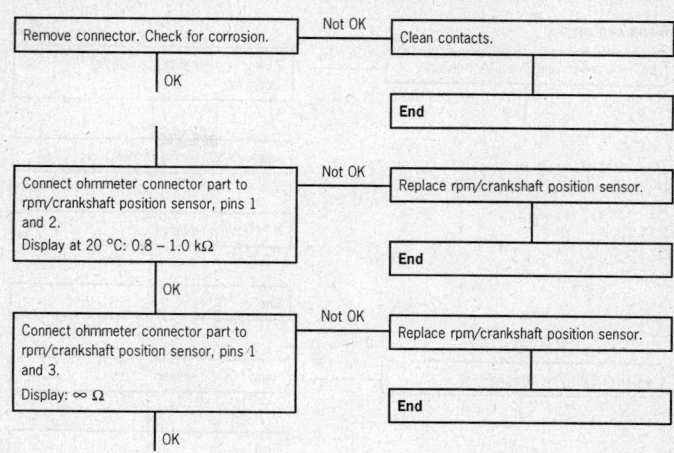

Remove connector. Check for corrosion. — Not OK → Clean contacts. → End

OK ↓

Connect ohmmeter connector part to rpm/crankshaft position sensor, pins 1 and 2.
Display at 20 °C: 0.8 – 1.0 kΩ — Not OK → Replace rpm/crankshaft position sensor. → End

OK ↓

Connect ohmmeter connector part to rpm/crankshaft position sensor, pins 1 and 3.
Display: ∞ Ω — Not OK → Replace rpm/crankshaft position sensor. → End

OK ↓

PR1029900149010X

Fig. 29 Code P0336: Engine Speed Sensor Signal (Part 1 of 4)

3. Connect ohmmeter to special tool 9637, pin III/32, and connector, pin 1.
   Display: 0 - 5 Ω
4. Connect ohmmeter to special tool 9637, pin III/46, and connector, pin 2.
   Display: 0 - 5 Ω
5. Connect ohmmeter to special tool 9637, pin III/45, and connector, pin 3.
   Display: 0 - 5 Ω
6. Connect ohmmeter to special tool 9637, pin III/32, and ground.
   Display: ∞ Ω
7. Connect ohmmeter to special tool 9637, pin III/46, and ground.
   Display: ∞ Ω

3 Perform adaptation.

1. Switch on the ignition.
2. Wait one minute.
   Do not press the accelerator.
3. Switch off the ignition for at least 10 seconds.
4. Read out the fault memory.

PR1029900149040X

Fig. 29 Code P0336: Engine Speed Sensor Signal (Part 4 of 4)

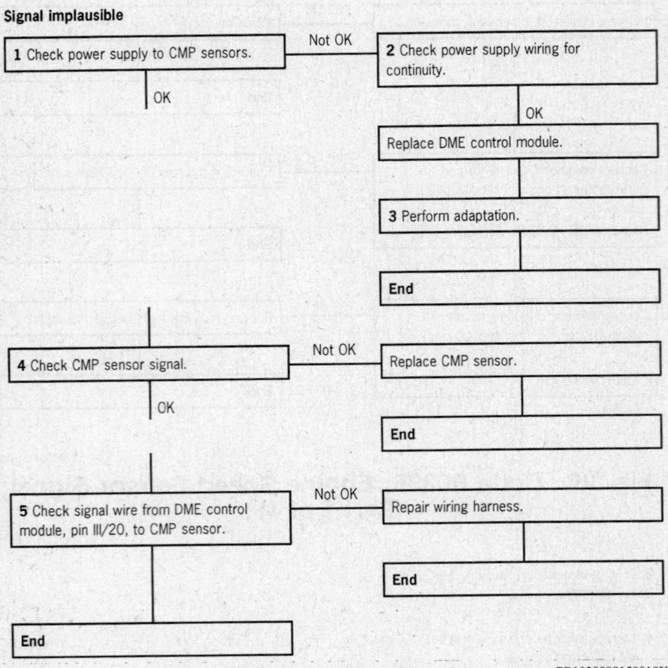

PR1029900150010X

Fig. 30 Codes P0341, P0342 & P0343: Camshaft Position Sensor No. 1 (Part 1 of 5)

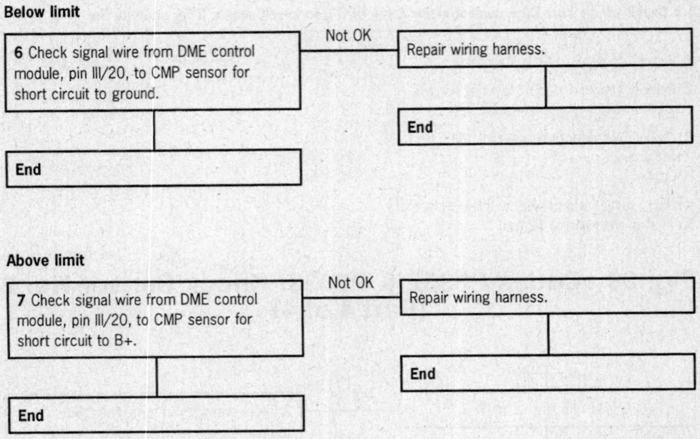

PR1029900150020X

Fig. 30 Codes P0341, P0342 & P0343: Camshaft Position Sensor No. 1 (Part 2 of 5)

1 Check power supply to CMP sensors.

1. Remove connector of CMP sensor 1.
2. Switch on the ignition.
3. Connect voltmeter to pin 1 (negative) and pin 3 (positive).
   Display: approx. 5 V

2 Check power supply wiring for continuity.

1. Remove connector of CMP sensor 1.
2. Connect special tool 9637 to wiring harness (DME control module connector).
3. Connect ohmmeter to special tool 9637, pin III/7, and to CMP sensor connector 1, pin 3.
   Display: 0 - 5 Ω
4. Connect ohmmeter to special tool 9637, pin III/17, and to CMP sensor connector 1, pin 1.
   Display: 0 - 5 Ω

3 Perform adaptation.

1. Switch on the ignition.
2. Wait one minute.
   Do not press the accelerator.
3. Switch off the ignition for at least 10 seconds.
4. Read out the fault memory.

PR1029900150030X

Fig. 30 Codes P0341, P0342 & P0343: Camshaft Position Sensor No. 1 (Part 3 of 5)

4 Check CMP sensor signal.

1. Connect special tool 9637.
2. Connect engine tester. Using special input, connect positive cable to pin III/20, negative cable to pin III/17.
3. Start the engine.

The display pictured opposite should appear on the oscilloscope:

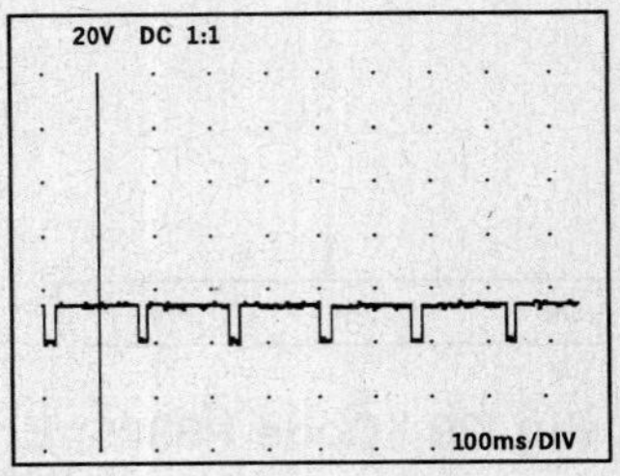

5 Check signal wire from DME control module, pin III/20, to CMP sensor.

1. Connect special tool 9637 to wiring harness (DME control module connector).
2. Remove connector of CMP sensor.
3. Connect ohmmeter to special tool 9637, pin III/20, and to CMP sensor connector 1, pin 2.
   Display: 0 - 5 Ω

PR1029900150040X

Fig. 30 Codes P0341, P0342 & P0343: Camshaft Position Sensor No. 1 (Part 4 of 5)

6 Check signal wire from DME control module, pin III/20, to CMP sensor for short circuit to ground.

1. Connect special tool 9637 to wiring harness (DME control module connector).
2. Remove connector of CMP sensor.
3. Connect ohmmeter to special tool 9637, pin III/20, and ground.
   Display: ∞ Ω

If 0 - 5 Ω is displayed, check wiring harness for chafing and pinching damage.

7 Check signal wire from DME control module, pin III/20, to CMP sensor for short circuit to B+.

1. Connect special tool 9637 to wiring harness (DME control module connector).
2. Remove connector of CMP sensor.
3. Connect voltmeter to special tool 9637, pin III/20, and ground.
   Switch on the ignition.
   Display: 0 V

If battery voltage is displayed, check wiring harness for chafing and pinching damage.

PR1029900150050X

Fig. 30 Codes P0341, P0342 & P0343: Camshaft Position Sensor No. 1 (Part 5 of 5)

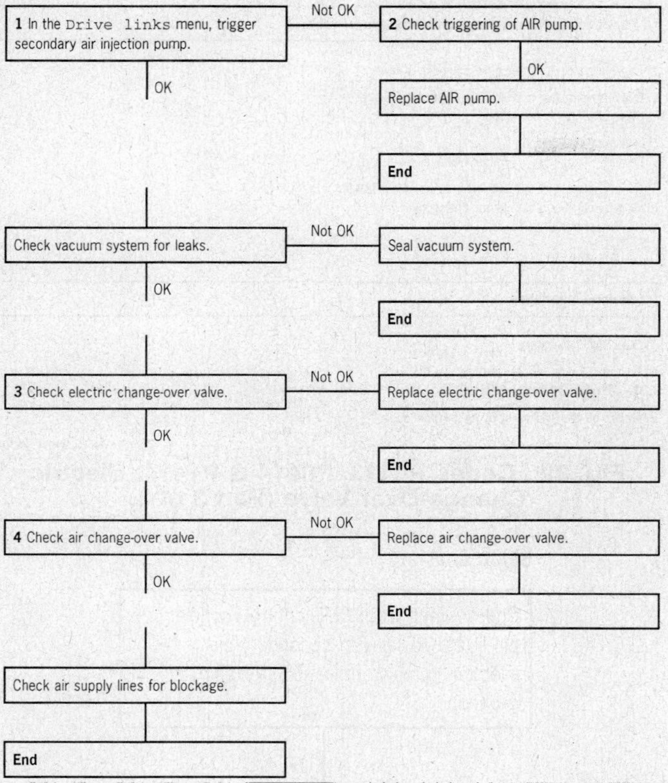

PR1029900151010X

Fig. 31 Codes P0410 & P1411: Secondary Air Injection System (Part 1 of 3)

3 Check electric change-over valve.

1. Remove two-pole connector of electric change-over valve.
2. Connect voltmeter to pin 1 (positive) and pin 2 (negative).
3. Trigger AIR pump with Porsche System Tester 2.
   Display: battery voltage
4. Remove vacuum hose of electric change-over valve with the engine running. Check whether vacuum is present.

4 Check air change-over valve and air supply lines.

1. Run engine briefly to produce vacuum.
2. Trigger AIR pump with Porsche System Tester 2.
3. Remove vacuum hose of air change-over valve.

If vacuum is present at the air change-over valve, check air supply from the AIR pump to the change-over valve up to the air supply line to the cylinder heads.

Check function of air change-over valve.

PR1029900151030X

Fig. 31 Codes P0410 & P1411: Secondary Air Injection System (Part 3 of 3)

1 In the Drive links menu, trigger secondary air injection (AIR) pump.

1. Connect and switch on Porsche System Tester 2.
2. Select `DME`.
3. Call up the `Drive links` menu.
4. Select `AIR pump`.
5. Activate AIR pump (audible function).

2 Check triggering of AIR pump.

1. Check fuse (Maxi Fuse) of AIR pump (on relay carrier 2).
2. Remove relay of AIR pump (on relay carrier 2).
   Connect voltmeter to pin 3 and ground.
   Display: battery voltage

   Connect voltmeter to pin 2 (negative) and pin 7 (positive).
   Start engine (the DME relay must pick up).
   Display: battery voltage

If 0 V is indicated, check wiring from pin 2 to DME control module, pin III/11, for continuity.
Push relay back on.

3. Remove connector of AIR pump.
   Connect voltmeter to pin 1 (positive) and pin 2 (negative).
   Trigger AIR pump with Porsche System Tester 2.
   Display: battery voltage

PR1029900151020X

Fig. 31 Codes P0410 & P1411: Secondary Air Injection System (Part 2 of 3)

P0413

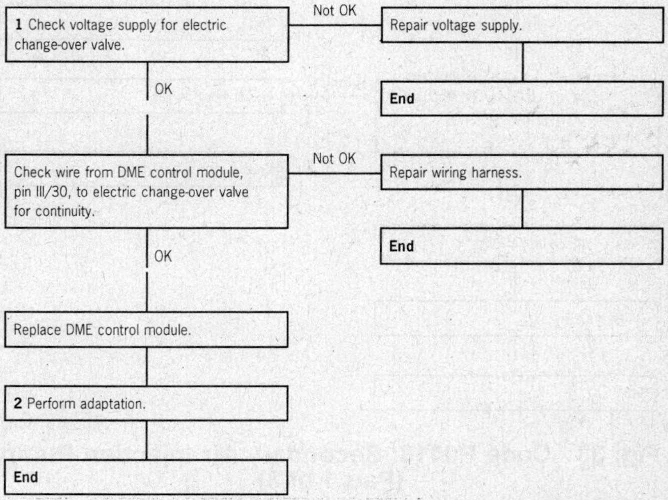

PR1029900152010X

Fig. 32 Codes P0413, P0414 & P1414: Electric Change-Over Valve (Part 1 of 3)

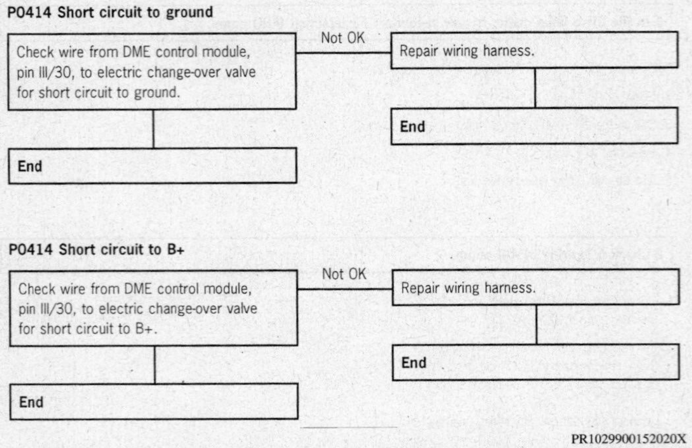

P0414 Short circuit to ground
Check wire from DME control module, pin III/30, to electric change-over valve for short circuit to ground.
Not OK
Repair wiring harness.
End
End
P0414 Short circuit to B+
Check wire from DME control module, pin III/30, to electric change-over valve for short circuit to B+.
Not OK
Repair wiring harness.
End
End
PR1029900152020X

Fig. 32 Codes P0413, P0414 & P1414: Electric Change-Over Valve (Part 2 of 3)

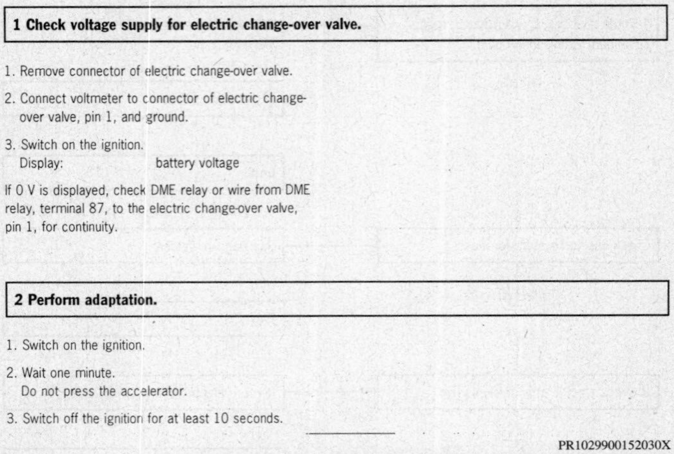

Fig. 32 Codes P0413, P0414 & P1414: Electric Change-Over Valve (Part 3 of 3)

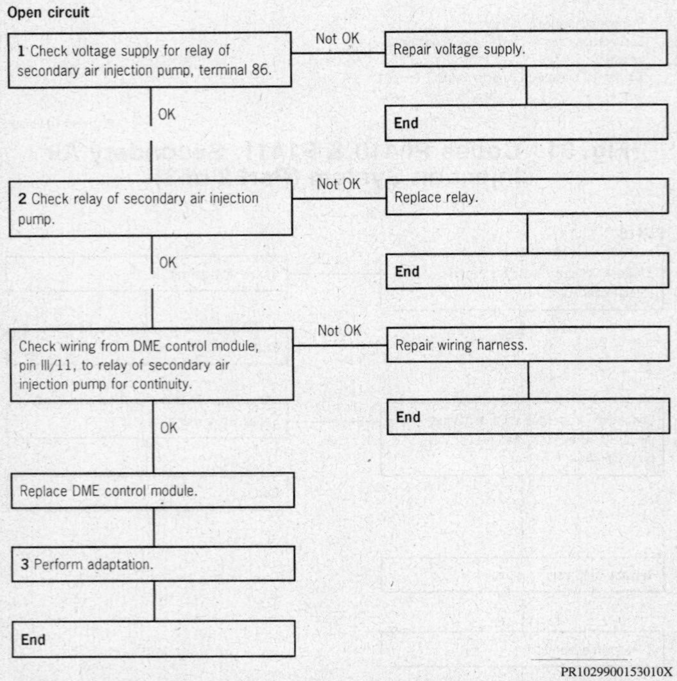

Fig. 33 Code P0418: Secondary Air Injection Pump (Part 1 of 3)

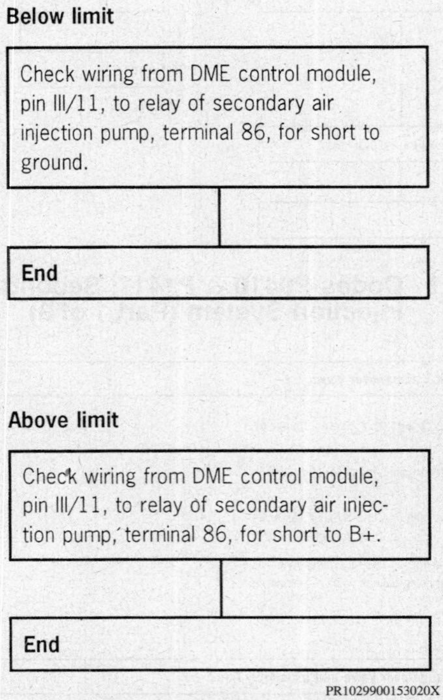

Fig. 33 Code P0418: Secondary Air Injection Pump (Part 2 of 3)

1 Check voltage supply for relay of secondary air injection pump, terminal 86.

1. Remove relay of secondary air injection pump.
2. Connect voltmeter to pin 7 (terminal 86) and ground.
3. Switch on the ignition.
   Display: battery voltage

If 0 V is displayed, check DME relay or wire from DME relay, terminal 87, to relay of secondary air injection pump, terminal 86, for continuity.

2 Check relay of secondary air injection pump.

1. Remove relay of secondary air injection pump.
2. Connect ohmmeter to relay terminals 85 and 86.
   Display: approx. 70 Ω at 25 °C

3 Perform adaptation.

1. Switch on the ignition.
2. Wait one minute.
   Do not press the accelerator.
3. Switch off the ignition for at least 10 seconds.
4. Read out the fault memory.

PR1029900153030X

Fig. 33 Code P0418: Secondary Air Injection Pump (Part 3 of 3)

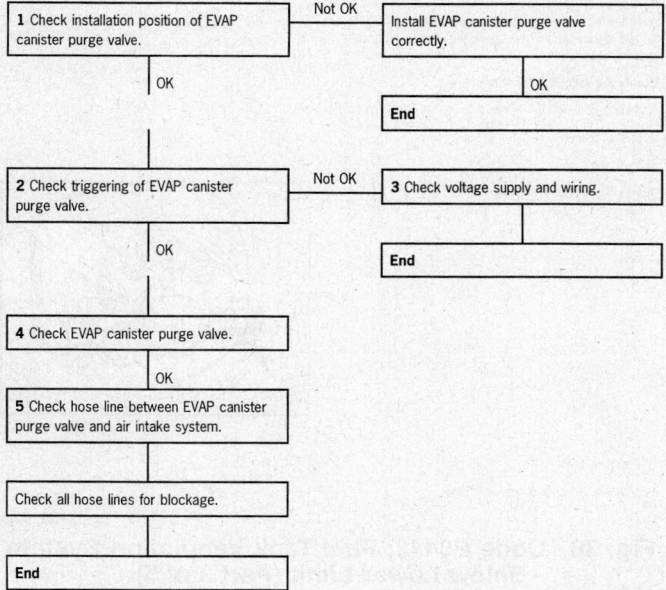

1 Check installation position of EVAP canister purge valve.
- Not OK → Install EVAP canister purge valve correctly. → OK → **End**
- OK ↓

2 Check triggering of EVAP canister purge valve.
- Not OK → 3 Check voltage supply and wiring. → **End**
- OK ↓

4 Check EVAP canister purge valve.
- OK ↓

5 Check hose line between EVAP canister purge valve and air intake system.
↓
Check all hose lines for blockage.
↓
End

PR1029900155010X

Fig. 35 Code P0440: Fuel Tank Ventilation System Above Limit (Part 1 of 3)

Read out the fault memory.
- → If other DTC's are stored in the memory in addition to DTC P0420 and P0430, rectify these first and then erase the fault memory. → Road test vehicle or perform short test. → Read fault memory again. → DTC P0420 or P0430 in memory. / No faults in memory. → **End**
- ↓ DTC P0420 or P0430 in memory.
- ↓ Replace TWC. → **End**

PR1029900154000X

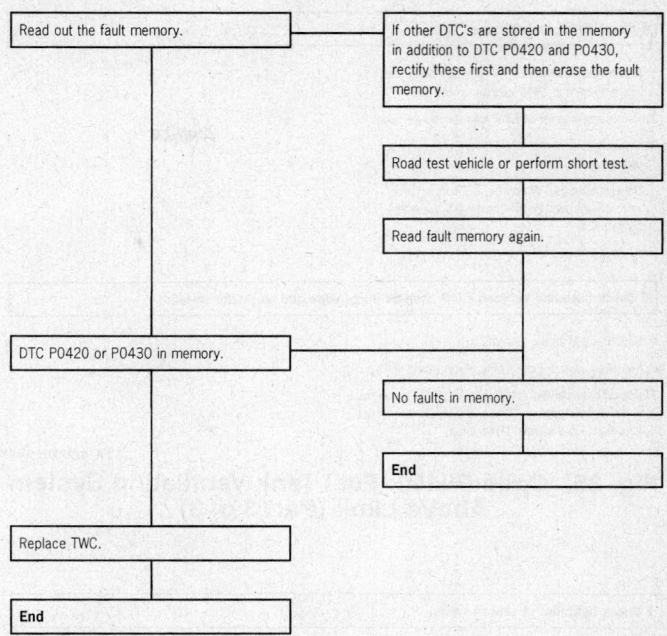

Fig. 34 Codes P0420 & P0430: Catalytic Converter Conversion Above Limit

1 Check installation position of EVAP canister purge valve.

Flow through the EVAP canister purge valve is possible in one direction only. The flow direction is indicated by an arrow on the EVAP canister purge valve. The arrow must point towards the intake manifold.

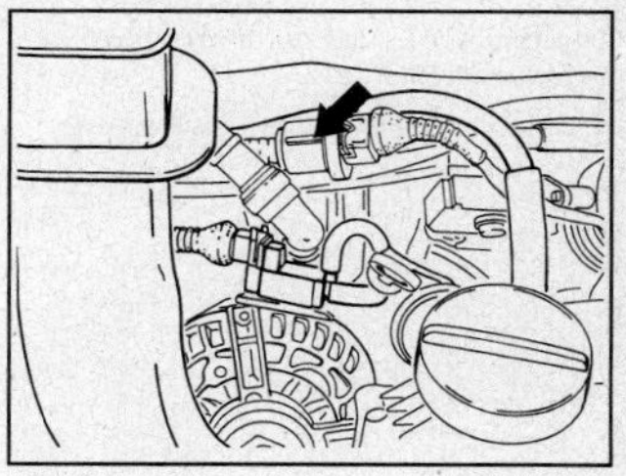

2 Check triggering of EVAP canister purge valve.

1. Connect Porsche System Tester 2.
2. In the "Drive links" menu, select EVAP canister purge valve.
   The EVAP canister purge valve must switch audibly.

3 Check voltage supply and wiring.

1. Remove connector of EVAP canister purge valve.
2. Connect voltmeter (positive) to pin 1 of the connector and to ground.
3. Switch on the ignition.
   Display: battery voltage
4. Connect special tool 9637 to wiring harness.
5. Connect ohmmeter to pin III/3 and EVAP canister purge valve connector, pin 2.
   Display: 0 - 5 Ω

PR1029900155020X

Fig. 35 Code P0440: Fuel Tank Ventilation System Above Limit (Part 2 of 3)

4 Check EVAP canister purge valve.

1. Disconnect hose from EVAP canister purge valve to intake system at EVAP canister purge valve.
2. Remove connector of EVAP canister purge valve.
3. Connect special tool 9160/1 to EVAP canister purge valve.
4. Generate vacuum of approx. 0.7 bar. The vacuum must not fall below 0.5 bar after 10 minutes.

5 Check hose line between EVAP canister purge valve and air intake system.

1. Undo hose at intake system.
2. Remove connector of EVAP canister purge valve.
3. Connect special tool 9160/1 to hose and generate a vacuum of approx. 0.7 bar. The vacuum must not fall below 0.5 bar after 10 minutes.

PR1029900155030X

Fig. 35 Code P0440: Fuel Tank Ventilation System Above Limit (Part 3 of 3)

1 Check tightness of shutoff valve. — Not OK → Replace shutoff valve. → **End**

OK ↓

2 Check ventilation lines for leaks. — Not OK → Replace ventilation lines. → **End**

OK ↓

3 Check tightness of EVAP canister purge valve. — Not OK → Replace EVAP canister purge valve. → **End**

↓

End

PR1029900156010X

Fig. 36 Code P0442: Fuel Tank Ventilation System Below Lower Limit (Part 1 of 5)

1 Check tightness of shutoff valve.

1. Remove front right-hand wheel housing liner.
2. Detach connector of shutoff valve.
3. Detach ventilation line of shutoff valve.
4. Connect shutoff valve to the battery or a separate power supply unit via special tool V.A.G. 1315A/1.

Note

Do not actuate the shutoff valve for more than 5 minutes (overload).

5. Connect special tool 9160/1 to EVAP canister.

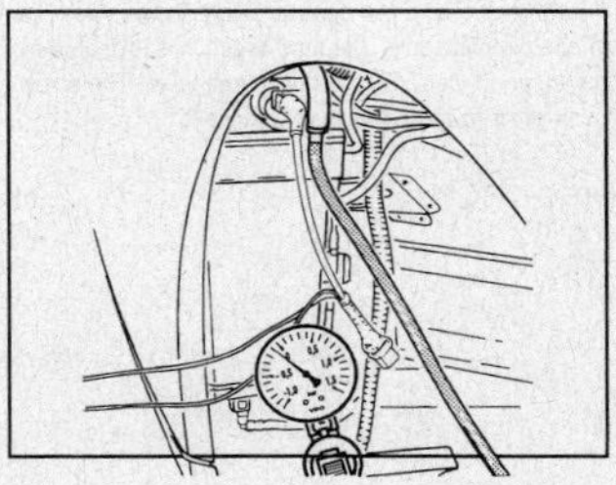

6. Using special tool 9160/1, produce 100 mbar (0.1 bar) of vacuum.

Note

Do not produce a vacuum of more than 100 mbar, as otherwise the vacuum will cause the shutoff valve to open.

If no vacuum can be built up, replace the shutoff valve.

Coat the sealing ring of the new shutoff valve with tyre fitting lubricant prior to installation.
The shutoff valve can only be installed in one position: with the electrical connection facing upwards.

PR1029900156020X

Fig. 36 Code P0442: Fuel Tank Ventilation System Below Lower Limit (Part 2 of 5)

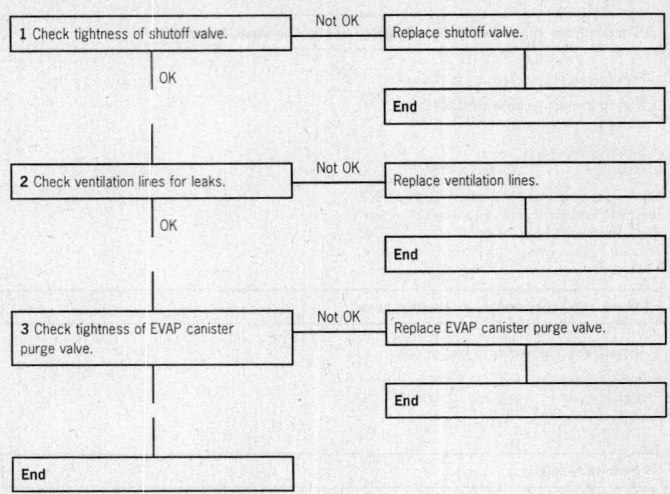

2 Check ventilation lines for leaks.

Check the tank system for leaks using an HC tester. To do so, hold the connecting hose of the the HC tester in the spot to be tested. In the case of a leak, the display of the HC tester increases to above 1000 ppm. Values below 50 ppm indicate no leaks.
To test the ventilation lines, guide the connecting hose slowly along them.

Check the following locations:

1. Tank cap
2. Line connections to EVAP canister
3. EVAP canister
4. Line connection to fuel tank sender unit

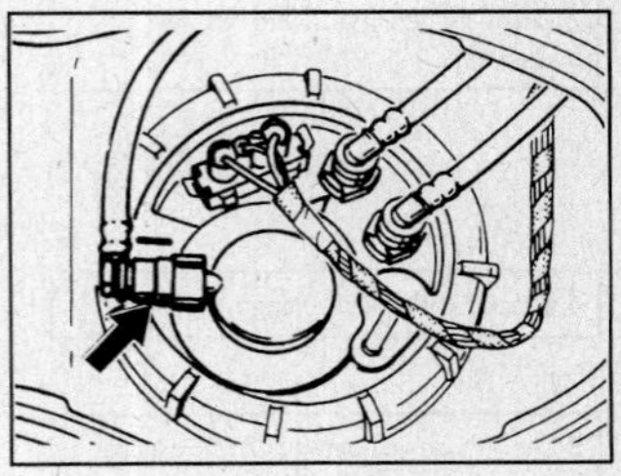

5. Pressure sensor
6. Opening of fuel filler neck into tank

PR1029900156030X

Fig. 36 Code P0442: Fuel Tank Ventilation System Below Lower Limit (Part 3 of 5)

7. Line connection of EVAP canister purge valve

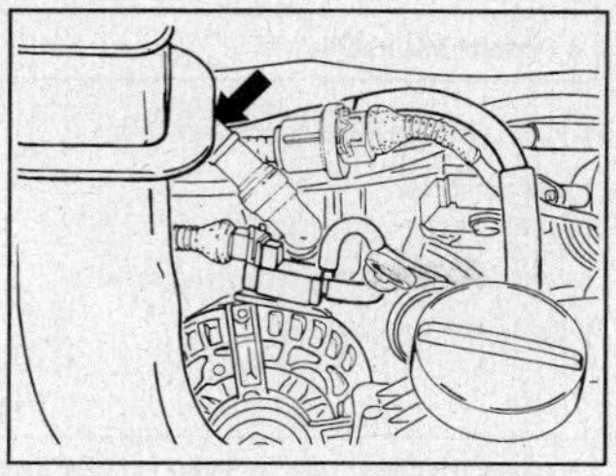

8. Ventilation lines:

a) from EVAP canister to operating purge valve
b) from operating purge valve to tank
c) from EVAP canister to EVAP canister purge valve

If no leaks are found, a gauge pressure of max. 100 mbar (0.1 bar) can be generated at the EVAP canister at the connection to the tank using special tool 9160/1, in order to increase the escape of fuel vapours.

PR1029900156040X

Fig. 36 Code P0442: Fuel Tank Ventilation System Below Lower Limit (Part 4 of 5)

DTC P0444

1 Check voltage supply for EVAP canister purge valve.
- Not OK: Repair voltage supply. → **End**
- OK: ↓

2 Check EVAP canister purge valve.
- Not OK: Replace EVAP canister purge valve. → **End**
- OK: ↓

3 Check triggering wire for EVAP canister purge valve.
- Not OK: Repair wiring harness. → **End**
- OK: ↓

Replace DME control module.

4 Perform adaptation.

End

PR1029900157010X

Fig. 37 Codes P0444 & P0445: EVAP Canister Purge Valve Open Or Short Circuit (Part 1 of 4)

3 Check tightness of EVAP canister purge valve.

Note

Before detaching the ventilation lines from the EVAP canister, clean the area around the connections. Dirt must not be allowed to get into the connectors.

1. Detach the ventilation line to the EVAP canister purge valve from the EVAP canister (protective cap).

2. With special tool 9160/1, generate a vacuum of 200 mbar (0.2 bar).

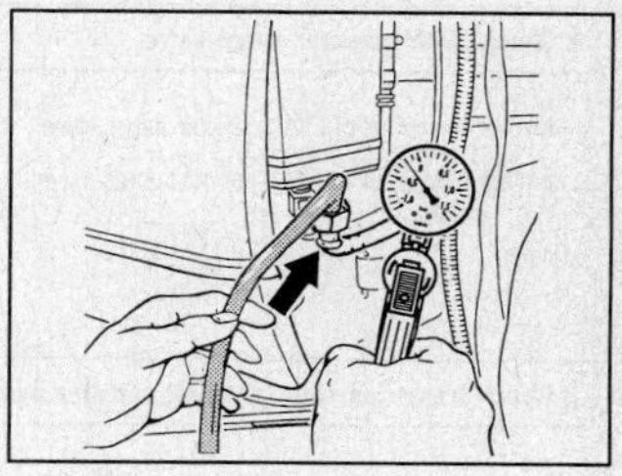

If no vacuum can be built up, replace the EVAP canister purge valve.

PR1029900156050X

Fig. 36 Code P0442: Fuel Tank Ventilation System Below Lower Limit (Part 5 of 5)

DTC P0445, Short to B+

5 Check triggering wire for EVAP canister purge valve for short circuit to B+.
- Not OK: Repair wiring harness. → **End**
- OK: ↓

Replace DME control module.

4 Perform adaptation.

End

DTC P0445, Short to Ground

6 Check triggering wire for EVAP canister purge valve for short circuit to ground.
- Not OK: Repair wiring harness. → **End**
- OK: ↓

Replace DME control module.

4 Perform adaptation.

End

PR1029900157020X

Fig. 37 Codes P0444 & P0445: EVAP Canister Purge Valve Open Or Short Circuit (Part 2 of 4)

1 Check voltage supply for EVAP canister purge valve.

1. Remove connector of EVAP canister purge valve.
2. Connect voltmeter (positive) to EVAP canister purge valve connector, pin 1, and ground.
3. Switch on the ignition.
   Display: battery voltage

2 Check EVAP canister purge valve.

1. Remove connector of EVAP canister purge valve.
2. Connect ohmmeter to EVAP canister purge valve, pins 1 and 2.
   Display: 26 ± 4 Ω at 20 °C.

3 Check triggering wire for EVAP canister purge valve.

1. Remove connector of EVAP canister purge valve.
2. Connect special tool 9637 to wiring harness (DME control module connector).
3. Connect ohmmeter to EVAP canister purge valve, pin 2, and special tool 9637, pin III/3.
   Display: 0 - 5 Ω

PR1029900157030X

Fig. 37 Codes P0444 & P0445: EVAP Canister Purge Valve Open Or Short Circuit (Part 3 of 4)

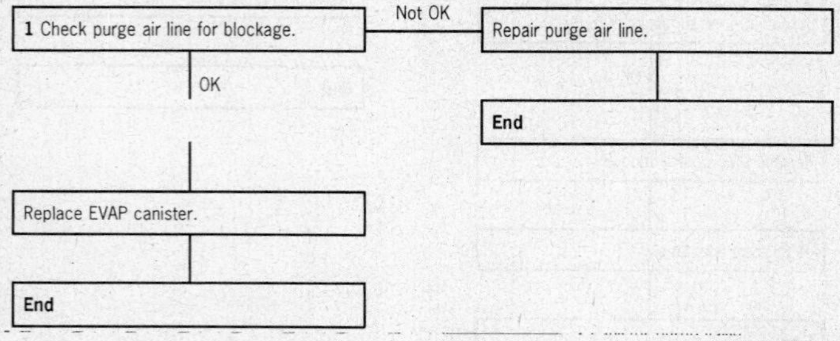

PR1029900158010X

Fig. 38 Code P0446: EVAP Canister Shutoff Valve Below Limit (Part 1 of 2)

1 Check purge air line for blockage.

1. Remove front right-hand wheel housing liner.
2. Detach purge air line (connection face up) from EVAP canister.
3. Blow through purge air line with compressed air.

PR1029900158020X

Fig. 38 Code P0446: EVAP Canister Shutoff Valve Below Limit (Part 2 of 2)

4 Perform adaptation.

1. Switch on the ignition.
2. Wait one minute.
   Do not press the accelerator.
3. Switch off the ignition for at least 10 seconds.
4. Read out the fault memory.

5 Check triggering wire for EVAP canister purge valve for short circuit to B+.

1. Remove connector of EVAP canister purge valve.
2. Connect special tool 9637 to wiring harness (DME control module connector).
3. Connect voltmeter (positive) to EVAP canister purge valve connector, pin 2, and ground.
4. Switch on the ignition.
   Display: 0 V

If battery voltage is displayed, check wiring harness for chafing and pinching damage.

6 Check triggering wire for EVAP canister purge valve for short circuit to ground.

1. Remove connector of EVAP canister purge valve.
2. Connect special tool 9637 to wiring harness (DME control module connector).
3. Connect ohmmeter to EVAP canister purge valve connector, pin 2, and ground.
   Display: ∞ Ω

If 0 to 5 Ω is displayed, check wiring harness for chafing and pinching damage.

PR1029900157040X

Fig. 37 Codes P0444 & P0445: EVAP Canister Purge Valve Open Or Short Circuit (Part 4 of 4)

DTC P0447

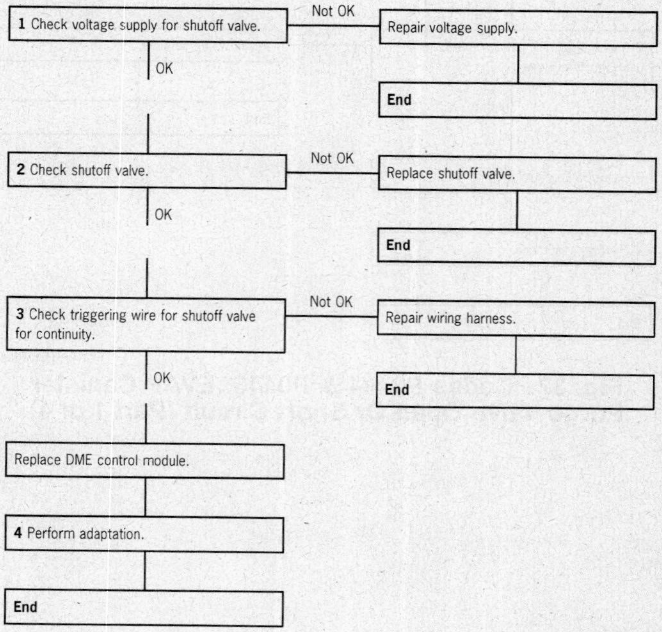

PR1029900159010X

Fig. 39 Codes P0447 & P0448: EVAP Canister Shutoff Valve Output Stage (Part 1 of 5)

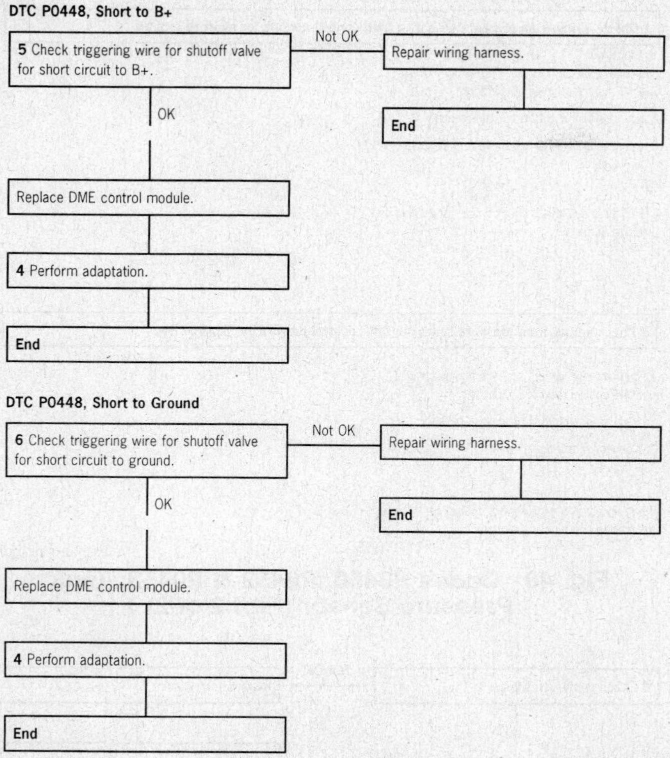

PR1029900159020X

Fig. 39 Codes P0447 & P0448: EVAP Canister Shutoff Valve Output Stage (Part 2 of 5)

4 Perform adaptation.

1. Switch on the ignition.
2. Wait one minute.
   Do not press the accelerator.
3. Switch off the ignition for at least 10 seconds.
4. Read out the fault memory.

5 Check triggering wire for shutoff valve for short circuit to B+.

1. Remove front right-hand wheel housing liner.
2. Remove connector of shutoff valve.
3. Remove DME control module connector.
4. Connect voltmeter (positive) to shutoff valve connector, pin 2, and ground.
5. Switch on the ignition.
   Display: 0 V

If battery voltage is displayed, check wiring harness for chafing and pinching damage.

PR1029900159040X

Fig. 39 Codes P0447 & P0448: EVAP Canister Shutoff Valve Output Stage (Part 4 of 5)

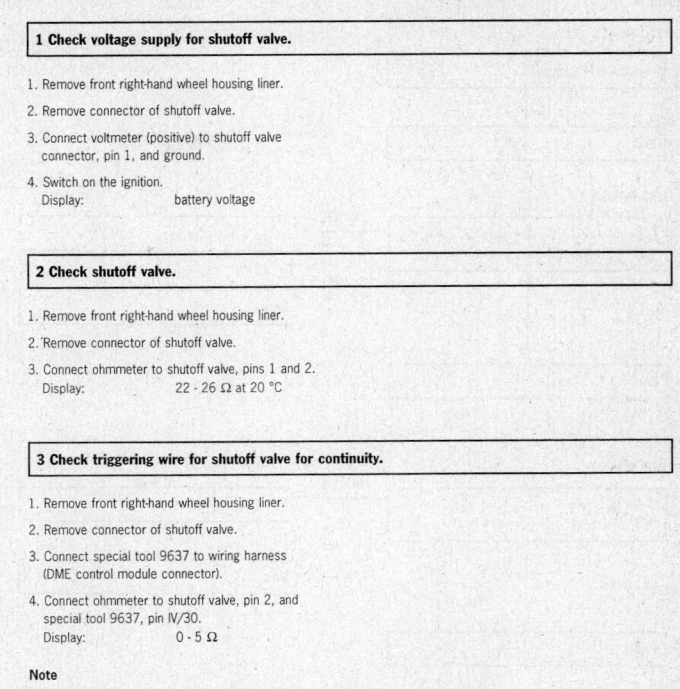

1 Check voltage supply for shutoff valve.

1. Remove front right-hand wheel housing liner.
2. Remove connector of shutoff valve.
3. Connect voltmeter (positive) to shutoff valve connector, pin 1, and ground.
4. Switch on the ignition.
   Display: battery voltage

2 Check shutoff valve.

1. Remove front right-hand wheel housing liner.
2. Remove connector of shutoff valve.
3. Connect ohmmeter to shutoff valve, pins 1 and 2.
   Display: 22 - 26 Ω at 20 °C

3 Check triggering wire for shutoff valve for continuity.

1. Remove front right-hand wheel housing liner.
2. Remove connector of shutoff valve.
3. Connect special tool 9637 to wiring harness (DME control module connector).
4. Connect ohmmeter to shutoff valve, pin 2, and special tool 9637, pin IV/30.
   Display: 0 - 5 Ω

Note

The wire is routed via connector X 2/5, pin 6.

PR1029900159030X

Fig. 39 Codes P0447 & P0448: EVAP Canister Shutoff Valve Output Stage (Part 3 of 5)

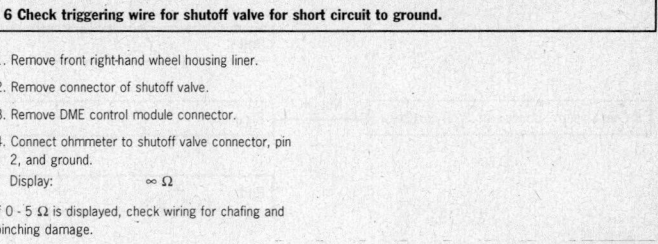

6 Check triggering wire for shutoff valve for short circuit to ground.

1. Remove front right-hand wheel housing liner.
2. Remove connector of shutoff valve.
3. Remove DME control module connector.
4. Connect ohmmeter to shutoff valve connector, pin 2, and ground.
   Display: ∞ Ω

If 0 - 5 Ω is displayed, check wiring for chafing and pinching damage.

PR1029900159050X

Fig. 39 Codes P0447 & P0448: EVAP Canister Shutoff Valve Output Stage (Part 5 of 5)

DTC P0450

Replace pressure sensor.

End

DTC P0452

1 Check wiring from pressure sensor to DME control module for short to ground. — Not OK → Repair wiring harness. → End

End

DTC P0453

2 Check wiring from pressure sensor to DME control module for short to B+. — Not OK → Repair wiring harness. → End

End

PR1029900160010X

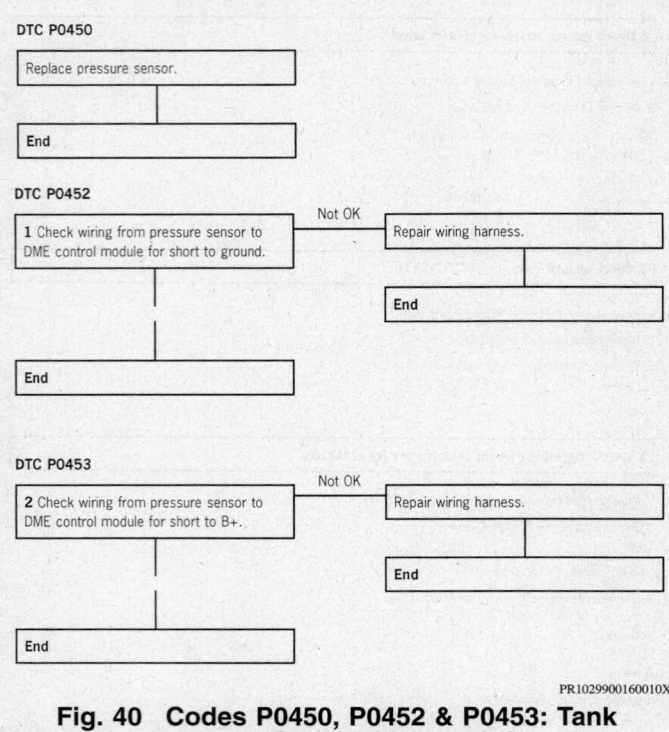

Fig. 40 Codes P0450, P0452 & P0453: Tank Pressure Sensor (Part 1 of 2).

Below limit

1 Check tank cap. — Not OK → Repair. → End

OK

2 Check ventilation lines at EVAP canister. — Not OK → Repair. → End

OK

3 Check ventilation lines at operating purge valve. — Not OK → Repair. → End

OK

4 Check ventilation line at tank. — Not OK → Repair. → End

OK

5 Check ventilation line at EVAP canister purge valve. — Not OK → Repair. → End

OK

PR1029900161010X

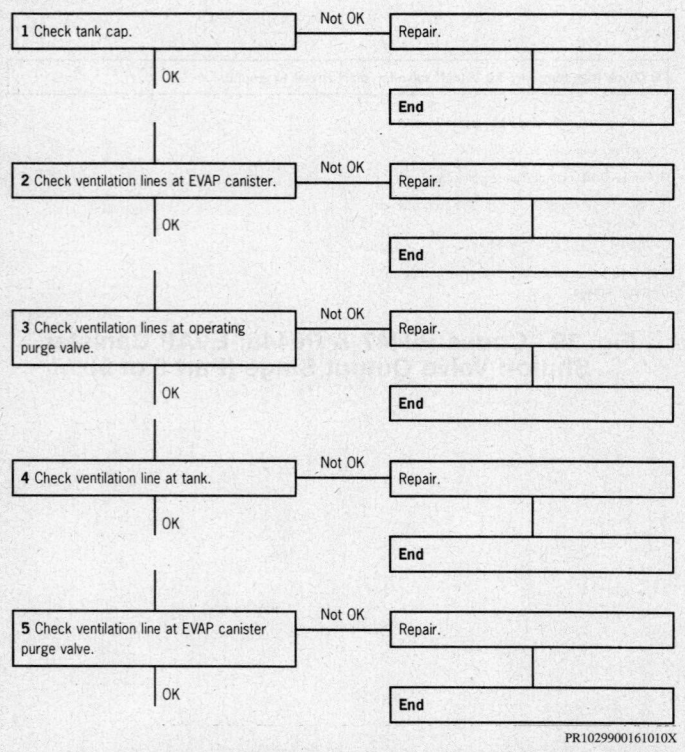

Fig. 41 Code P0455: Fuel Tank Ventilation System Major Leak (Part 1 of 6)

1 Check wiring from pressure sensor to DME control module for short to ground.

1. Connect special tool 9637 to wiring harness (DME control module connector).
2. Remove connector of pressure sensor.
3. Connect ohmmeter to special tool 9637, pin IV/21, and ground.
   Display: ∞ Ω

If 0 - 5 Ω is displayed, check wiring for chafing and pinching damage.

2 Check wiring from pressure sensor to DME control module for short to B+.

1. Connect special tool 9637 to wiring harness (DME control module connector).
2. Remove connector of pressure sensor.
3. Connect voltmeter to special tool 9637, pin IV/21, and ground.
   Display: 0 V

If battery voltage is displayed, check wiring harness for chafing and pinching damage.

PR1029900160020X

Fig. 40 Codes P0450, P0452 & P0453: Tank Pressure Sensor (Part 2 of 2)

6 Check ventilation lines. — Not OK → Repair. → End

OK

7 Check EVAP canister purge valve. — Not OK → Replace EVAP canister purge valve. → End

End

Signal implausible

Replace pressure sensor.

End

PR1029900161020X

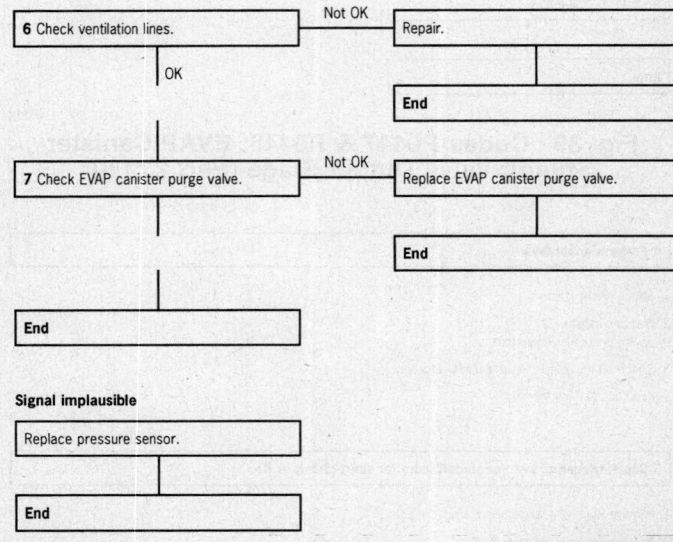

Fig. 41 Code P0455: Fuel Tank Ventilation System Major Leak (Part 2 of 6)

1 Check tank cap.

1. Check whether the tank cap is present.
2. Check whether the tank cap is correctly screwed on.

2 Check ventilation lines at EVAP canister.

1. Remove front right-hand wheel housing liner.
2. Check whether ventilation lines are attached to the EVAP canister.

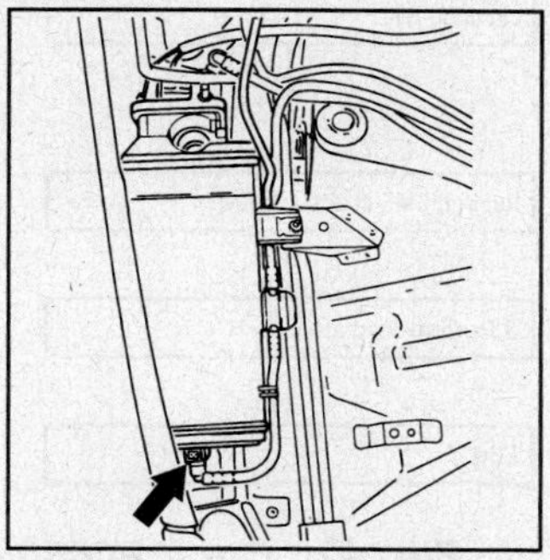

PR1029900161030X

Fig. 41 Code P0455: Fuel Tank Ventilation System Major Leak (Part 3 of 6)

3 Check ventilation lines at operating purge valve.

1. Remove front right-hand wheel housing liner.
2. Check whether ventilation lines are attached to the operating purge valve.

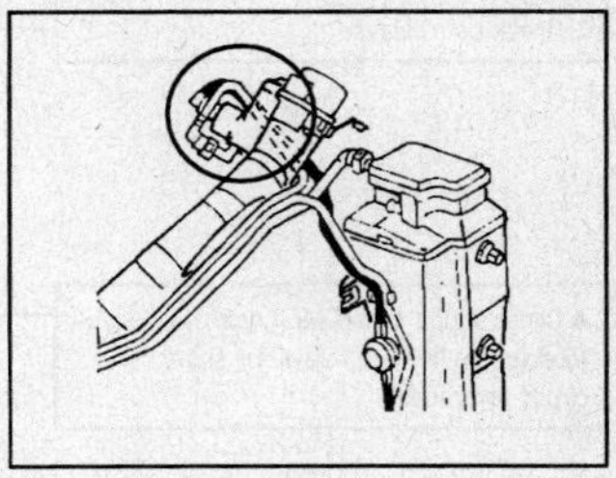

4 Check ventilation line at tank.

1. Remove battery.
2. Remove battery cover.
3. Check whether ventilation line is attached to the fuel tank sender unit.

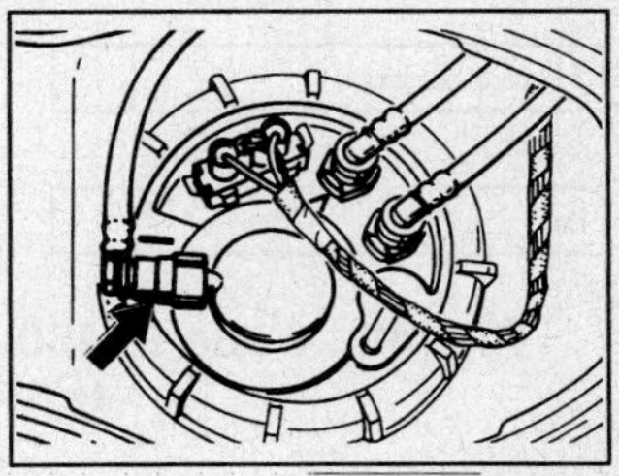

PR1029900161040X

Fig. 41 Code P0455: Fuel Tank Ventilation System Major Leak (Part 4 of 6)

5 Check ventilation line at EVAP canister purge valve.

Check whether ventilation line is attached to the EVAP canister purge valve.

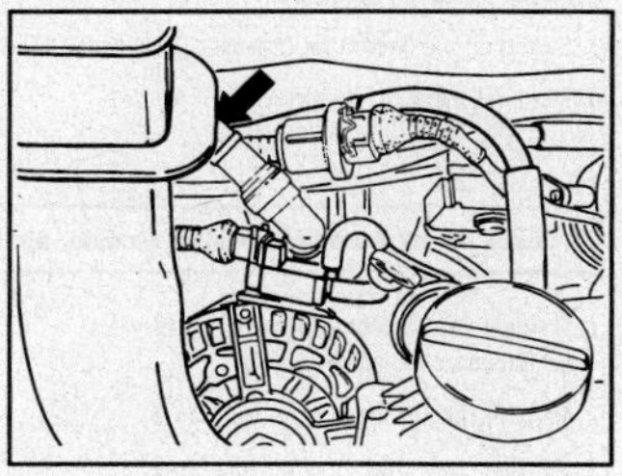

6 Check ventilation lines.

Check whether ventilation lines are:

- cracked
- broken
- interrupted

PR1029900161050X

Fig. 41 Code P0455: Fuel Tank Ventilation System Major Leak (Part 5 of 6)

7 Check EVAP canister purge valve.

1. Remove front right-hand wheel housing liner.
2. Clean EVAP canister in the vicinity of the ventilation lines.
3. Detach the ventilation line to the EVAP canister purge valve at the EVAP canister (connection with protective cap).
4. With special tool 9160/1, generate a vacuum of 200 mbar (0.2 bar).

If no vacuum can be built up, replace the EVAP canister purge valve.

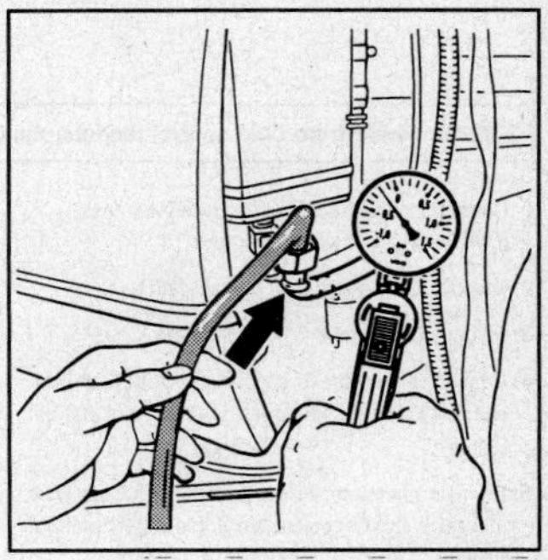

PR1029900161060X

Fig. 41 Code P0455: Fuel Tank Ventilation System Major Leak (Part 6 of 6)

1 Check both relays.
- Not OK → Replace relays. → **End**
- OK ↓

2 Check wiring from DME control module, pin IV/4, to relays for continuity.
- Not OK → Repair wiring harness. → **End**
- OK ↓

Replace DME control module.

3 Perform adaptation.

End

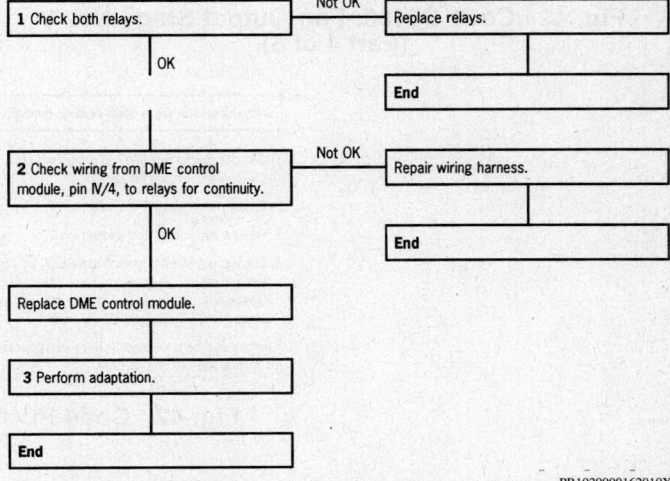

PR1029900162010X

Fig. 42 Code P0480: Fan Output Stage No. 1 (Part 1 of 6)

Short circuit to ground

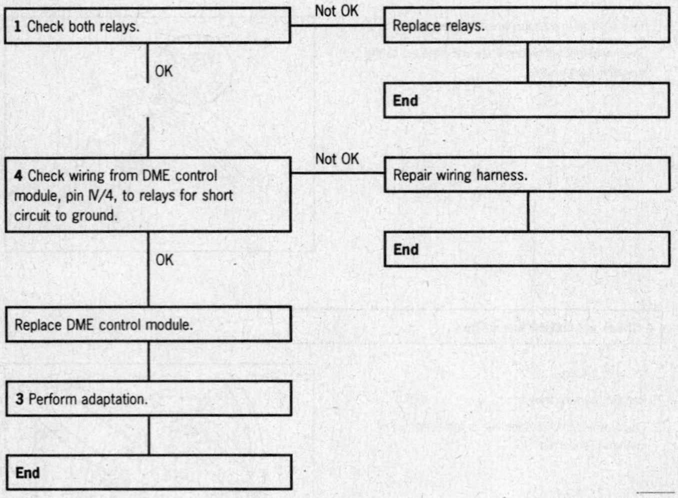

PR1029900162020X

Fig. 42 Code P0480: Fan Output Stage No. 1 (Part 2 of 6)

Short circuit to B+

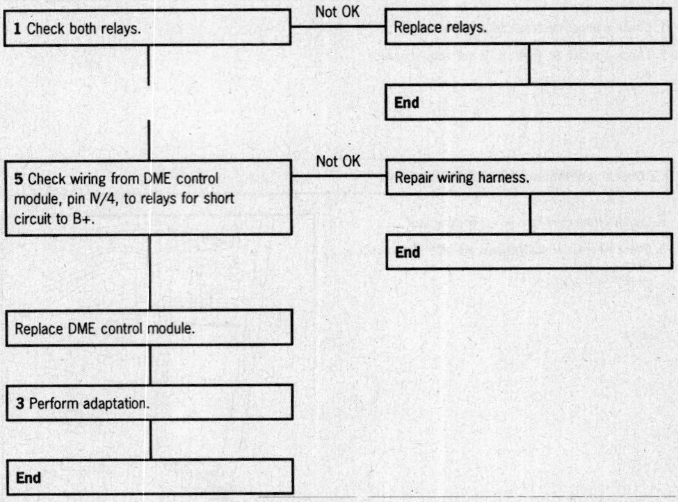

PR1029900162030X

Fig. 42 Code P0480: Fan Output Stage No. 1 (Part 3 of 6)

1 Check both relays.

1. Remove relays.
2. Connect ohmmeter to terminals 85 and 86.
   Display: approx. 75 Ω

2 Check wiring from DME control module, pin IV/4, to relays for continuity.

1. Connect special tool 9637 to wiring harness (DME control module connector).
2. Remove relay stage 1 of coolant fan 1.
3. Remove relay stage 1 of coolant fan 2.
4. Connect ohmmeter to special tool 9637, pin IV/4, and relay slot of coolant fan 1, pin 2 (terminal 85).
   Display: 0 - 5 Ω
5. Connect ohmmeter to special tool 9637, pin IV/4, and relay slot of coolant fan 2, pin 2 (terminal 85).
   Display: 0 - 5 Ω

If ∞ Ω is displayed, check connector X 2/3, pin 21, and check wiring harness for chafing and pinching damage.

PR1029900162040X

Fig. 42 Code P0480: Fan Output Stage No. 1 (Part 4 of 6)

3 Perform adaptation.

1. Switch on the ignition.
2. Wait one minute.
   Do not press the accelerator.
3. Switch off the ignition for at least 10 seconds.
4. Read out the fault memory.

4 Check wiring from DME control module, pin IV/4, to relays for short circuit to ground.

1. Connect special tool 9637 to wiring harness (DME control module connector).
2. Remove relay stage 1 of coolant fan 1.
3. Remove relay stage 1 of coolant fan 2.
4. Connect ohmmeter to special tool 9637, pin IV/4, and ground.
   Display: ∞ Ω

If 0 - 5 Ω is displayed, check wiring for chafing and pinching damage.

PR1029900162050X

Fig. 42 Code P0480: Fan Output Stage No. 1 (Part 5 of 6)

5 Check wiring from DME control module, pin IV/4, to relays for short circuit to B+.

1. Connect special tool 9637 to wiring harness (DME control module connector).
2. Remove relay stage 1 of coolant fan 1.
3. Remove relay stage 1 of coolant fan 2.
4. Connect voltmeter to special tool 9637, pin IV/4, and ground.
   Ignition on.
   Display: 0 V

If battery voltage is displayed, check wiring harness for chafing and pinching damage.

PR1029900162060X

Fig. 42 Code P0480: Fan Output Stage No. 1 (Part 6 of 6)

Open circuit

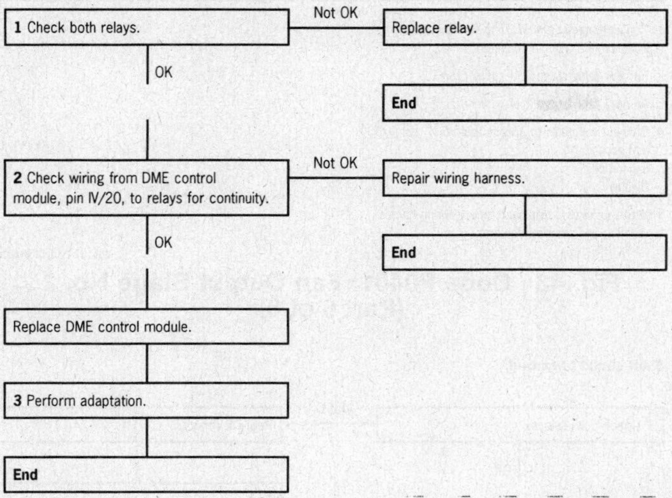

PR1029900163010X

Fig. 43 Code P0481: Fan Output Stage No. 2 (Part 1 of 6)

Short circuit to ground

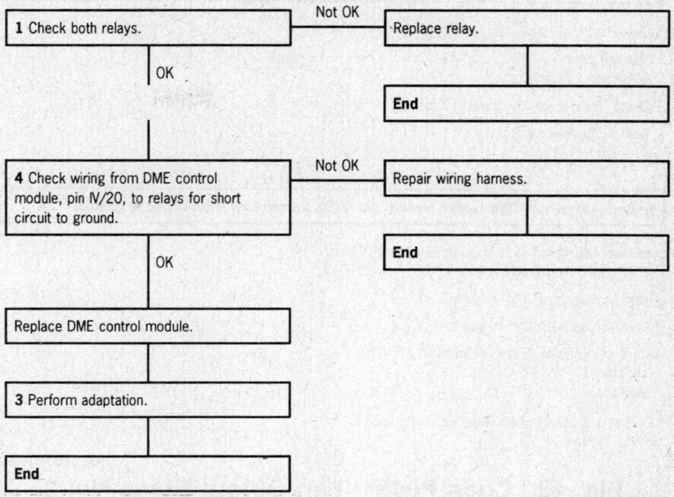

PR1029900163020X

Fig. 43 Code P0481: Fan Output Stage No. 2 (Part 2 of 6)

Short circuit to B+

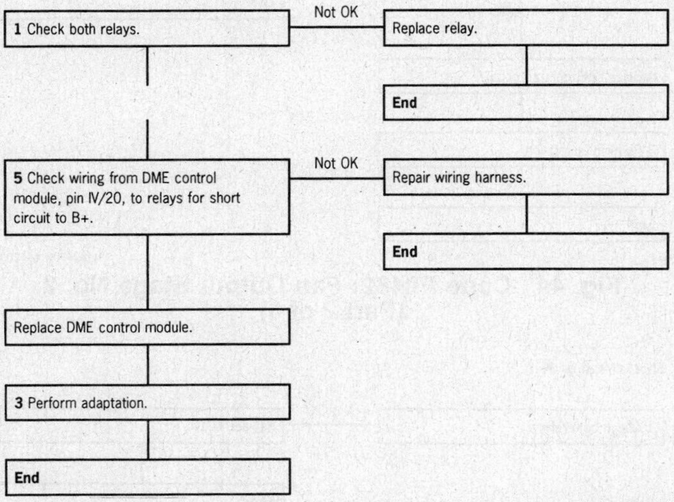

PR1029900163030X

Fig. 43 Code P0481: Fan Output Stage No. 2 (Part 3 of 6)

1 Check both relays.

1. Remove relay.
2. Connect ohmmeter to terminals 85 and 86.
   Display: approx. 75 Ω

2 Check wiring from DME control module, pin IV/20, to relays for continuity.

1. Connect special tool 9637 to wiring harness (DME control module connector).
2. Remove relay stage 2 of coolant fan 1.
3. Remove relay stage 2 of coolant fan 2.
4. Connect ohmmeter to special tool 9637, pin IV/20, and relay slot of coolant fan 1, pin 2 (terminal 85).
   Display: 0 - 5 Ω
5. Connect ohmmeter to special tool 9637, pin IV/20, and relay slot of coolant fan 2, pin 2 (terminal 85).
   Display: 0 - 5 Ω

If ∞ Ω is displayed, check connector X 2/3, pin 22, and wiring harness for chafing and pinching damage.

PR1029900163040X

Fig. 43 Code P0481: Fan Output Stage No. 2 (Part 4 of 6)

3 Perform adaptation.

1. Switch on the ignition.
2. Wait one minute.
   Do not press the accelerator.
3. Switch off the ignition for at least 10 seconds.
4. Read out the fault memory.

4 Check wiring from DME control module, pin IV/20, to relays for short circuit to ground.

1. Connect special tool 9637 to wiring harness (DME control module connector).
2. Remove relay stage 2 of coolant fan 1.
3. Remove relay stage 2 of coolant fan 2.
4. Connect ohmmeter to special tool 9637, pin IV/20, and ground.
   Display: ∞ Ω

If 0 - 5 Ω is displayed, check wiring for chafing and pinching damage.

PR1029900163050X

Fig. 43 Code P0481: Fan Output Stage No. 2 (Part 5 of 6)

Open circuit

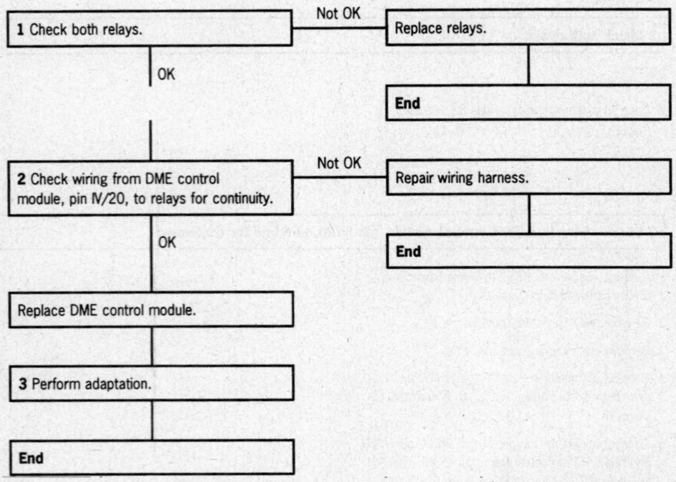

PR1029900164010X

Fig. 44 Code P0482: Fan Output Stage No. 2 (Part 1 of 6)

5 Check wiring from DME control module, pin IV/20, to relays for short circuit to B+.

1. Connect special tool 9637 to wiring harness (DME control module connector).
2. Remove relay stage 2 of coolant fan 1.
3. Remove relay stage 2 of coolant fan 2.
4. Connect voltmeter to special tool 9637, pin IV/20, and ground.
   Ignition on.
   Display: 0 V

If battery voltage is displayed, check wiring harness for chafing and pinching damage.

PR1029900163060X

Fig. 43 Code P0481: Fan Output Stage No. 2 (Part 6 of 6)

Short circuit to ground

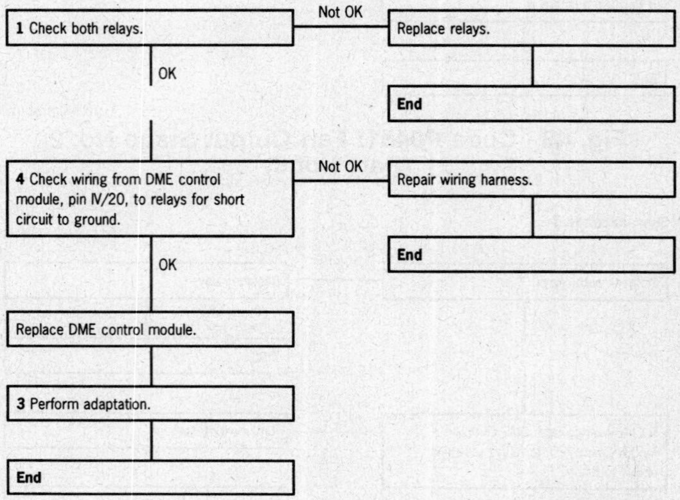

PR1029900164020X

Fig. 44 Code P0482: Fan Output Stage No. 2 (Part 2 of 6)

Short circuit to B+

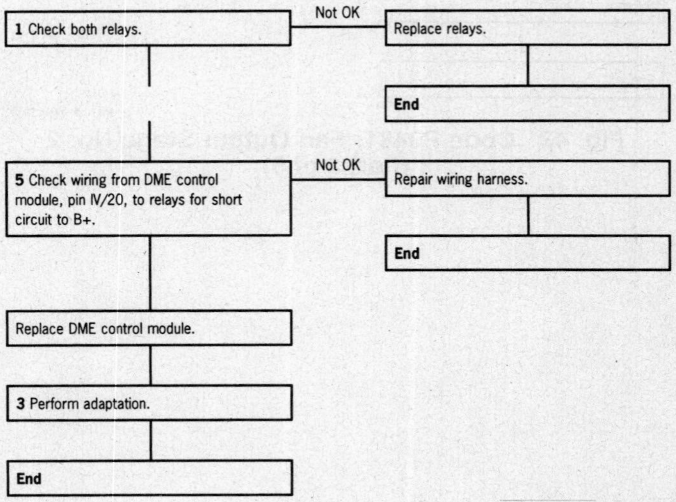

PR1029900164030X

Fig. 44 Code P0482: Fan Output Stage No. 2 (Part 3 of 6)

1 Check both relays.

1. Remove relays.
2. Connect ohmmeter to terminals 85 and 86.
   Display: approx. 75 Ω

2 Check wiring from DME control module, pin IV/20, to relays for continuity.

1. Connect special tool 9637 to wiring harness (DME control module connector).
2. Remove relay stage 2 of coolant fan 1.
3. Remove relay stage 2 of coolant fan 2.
4. Connect ohmmeter to special tool 9637, pin IV/20, and relay slot of coolant fan 1, pin 2 (terminal 85).
   Display: 0 - 5 Ω
5. Connect ohmmeter to special tool 9637, pin IV/20, and relay slot of coolant fan 2, pin 2 (terminal 85).
   Display: 0 - 5 Ω

If ∞ Ω is displayed, check connector X 2/3, pin 22, and check wiring harness for chafing and pinching damage.

PR1029900164040X

Fig. 44 Code P0482: Fan Output Stage No. 2 (Part 4 of 6)

5 Check wiring from DME control module, pin IV/20, to relays for short circuit to B+.

1. Connect special tool 9637 to wiring harness (DME control module connector).
2. Remove relay stage 2 of coolant fan 1.
3. Remove relay stage 2 of coolant fan 2.
4. Connect voltmeter to special tool 9637, pin IV/20, and ground.
   Ignition on.
   Display: 0 V

If battery voltage is displayed, check wiring harness for chafing and pinching damage.

PR1029900164060X

Fig. 44 Code P0482: Fan Output Stage No. 2 (Part 6 of 6)

Part 1

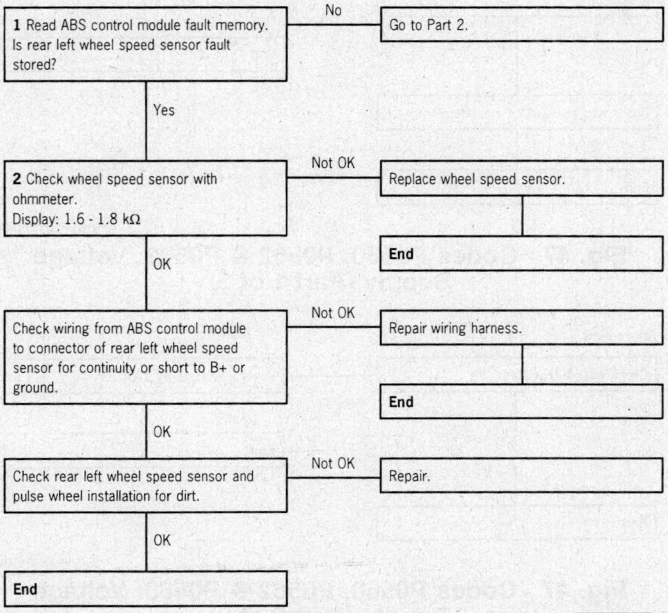

PR1029900165010X

Fig. 45 Code P0501: Vehicle Speed Not In Specified Range (Part 1 of 4)

3 Perform adaptation.

1. Switch on the ignition.
2. Wait one minute.
   Do not press the accelerator.
3. Switch off the ignition for at least 10 seconds.
4. Read out the fault memory.

4 Check wiring from DME control module, pin IV/20, to relays for short circuit to ground.

1. Connect special tool 9637 to wiring harness (DME control module connector).
2. Remove relay stage 2 of coolant fan 1.
3. Remove relay stage 2 of coolant fan 2.
4. Connect ohmmeter to special tool 9637, pin IV/20, and ground.
   Display: ∞ Ω

If 0 - 5 Ω is displayed, check wiring for chafing and pinching damage.

PR1029900164050X

Fig. 44 Code P0482: Fan Output Stage No. 2 (Part 5 of 6)

Part 2

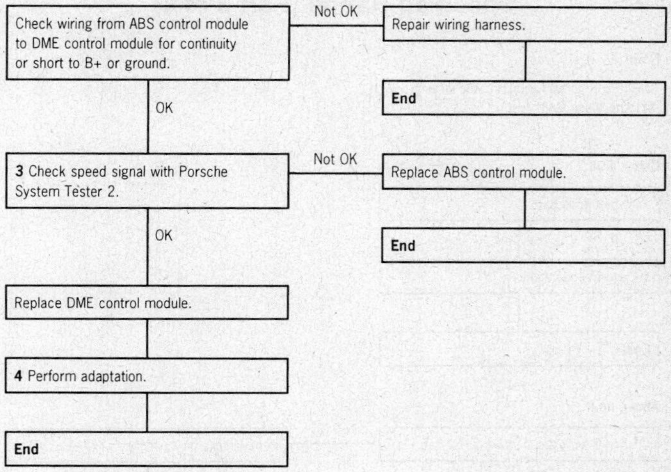

PR1029900165020X

Fig. 45 Code P0501: Vehicle Speed Not In Specified Range (Part 2 of 4)

1 Read ABS control module fault memory.

1. Connect and switch on Porsche System Tester 2.
2. Select vehicle type `911 Carrera (996)`.
3. Select system `ABS 5.3 or ABS/TC 5.3`.
4. Read out the fault memory.

2 Check wheel speed sensor with ohmmeter.

1. Remove connector X 2/4.
2. Connect ohmmeter on pin side to pins 16 and 17.
   Display: 1.6 - 1.8 kΩ

3 Check speed signal with Porsche System Tester 2.

1. Connect and switch on Porsche System Tester 2.
2. Select vehicle type `911 Carrera (996)` and system `ABS 5.3`, menu `Actual values, Rear left wheel speed sensor`.
3. Raise vehicle at rear left.
4. By hand, turn rear left wheel in driving direction.
   The speed must be displayed on the tester.

PR1029900165030X

Fig. 45 Code P0501: Vehicle Speed Not In Specified Range (Part 3 of 4)

Note

If faults are stored for the throttle jacking device, eliminate these faults first.

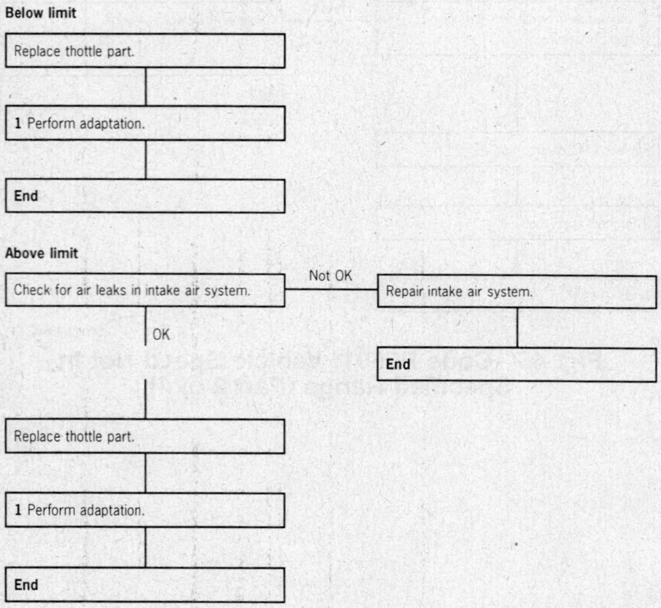

PR1029900166010X

Fig. 46 Codes P0506 & P0507: Idle Air Control At Stop (Part 1 of 2)

4 Perform adaptation.

1. Switch on the ignition.
2. Wait one minute.
   Do not press the accelerator.
3. Switch off the ignition for at least 10 seconds.
4. Read out the fault memory.

PR1029900165040X

Fig. 45 Code P0501: Vehicle Speed Not In Specified Range (Part 4 of 4)

1 Perform adaptation.

1. Switch on the ignition.
2. Wait one minute.
   Do not press the accelerator.
3. Switch off the ignition for at least 10 seconds.
4. Read out the fault memory.

PR1029900166020X

Fig. 46 Codes P0506 & P0507: Idle Air Control At Stop (Part 2 of 2)

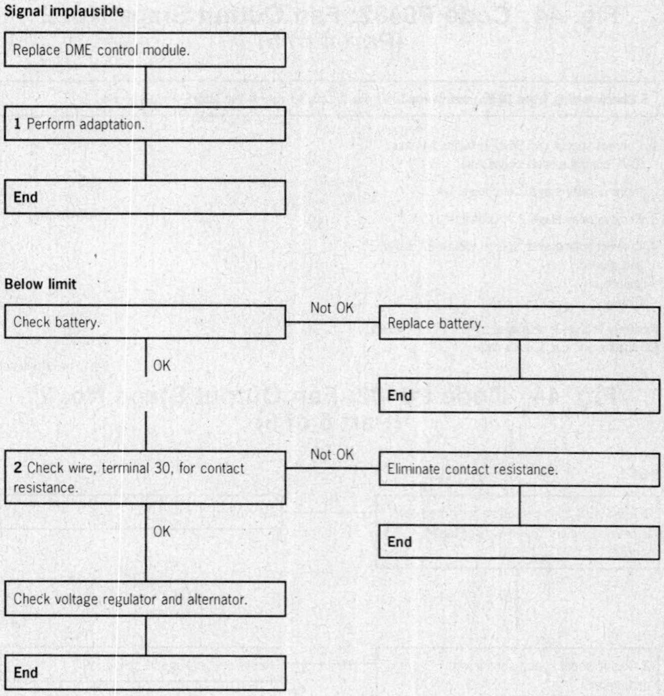

PR1029900167010X

Fig. 47 Codes P0560, P0562 & P0563: Voltage Supply (Part 1 of 3)

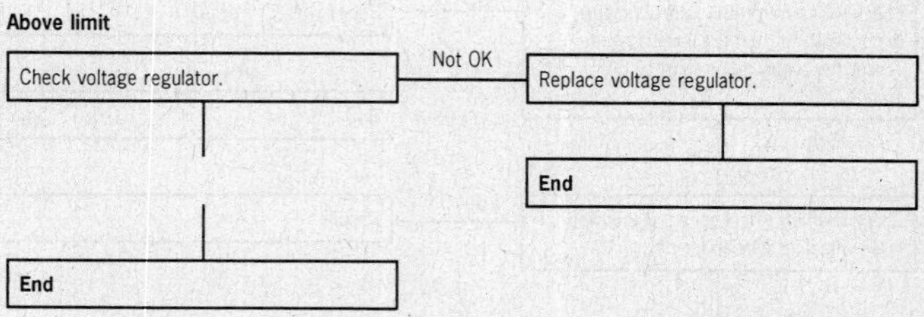

PR1029900167020X

Fig. 47 Codes P0560, P0562 & P0563: Voltage Supply (Part 2 of 3)

1 Perform adaptation.

1. Switch on the ignition.
2. Wait one minute.
   Do not press the accelerator.
3. Switch off the ignition for at least 10 seconds.
4. Read out the fault memory.

2 Check wire, terminal 30, for contact resistance.

1. Connect special tool 9637 to wiring harness (DME control module connector).
2. Connect voltmeter to special tool 9637, pin I/7 (positive), and ground.
   Display: battery voltage

If no battery voltage is indicated, check wire from special tool 9637, pin I/7, to pin side of connector X 2/3, pin 2, for continuity. Check connectors for corrosion.

3. Check wire from connector X 2/3, sleeve side, to current distributor fuse C 1 for continuity.

PR1029900167030X

Fig. 47 Codes P0560, P0562 & P0563: Voltage Supply (Part 3 of 3)

1 Check CAN bus from DME control module to Tiptronic control module for continuity.

1. Remove DME control module connector.
2. Remove Tiptronic control module connector.
3. Connect special tool 9637 to wiring harness (DME control module connector).
4. Connect ohmmeter to special tool 9637, pin II/3, and Tiptronic control module connector, pin 85.
   Display: 0 - 5 Ω
5. Connect ohmmeter to special tool 9637, pin II/4, and Tiptronic control module connector, pin 86.
   Display: 0 - 5 Ω

If ∞ Ω is displayed, check wiring harness for chafing and pinching damage.

2 Check CAN bus from DME control module to Tiptronic control module for short to ground.

1. Remove DME control module connector.
2. Remove Tiptronic control module connector.
3. Connect special tool 9637 to wiring harness (DME control module connector).
4. Connect ohmmeter to special tool 9637, pin II/3, and ground.
   Display: ∞ Ω
5. Connect ohmmeter to special tool 9637, pin II/4, and ground.
   Display: ∞ Ω

If 0 - 5 Ω is displayed, check wiring harness for chafing and pinching damage.

PR1029900168020X

Fig. 48 Code P0600: CAN Timeout Signal Implausible (Part 2 of 3)

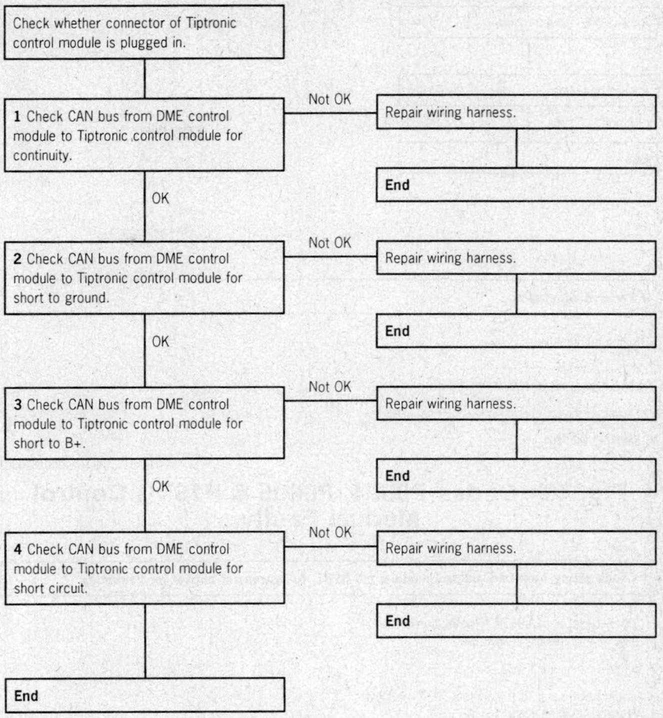

PR1029900168010X

Fig. 48 Code P0600: CAN Timeout Signal Implausible (Part 1 of 3)

3 Check CAN bus from DME control module to Tiptronic control module for short to B+.

1. Remove DME control module connector.
2. Remove Tiptronic control module connector.
3. Connect special tool 9637 to wiring harness (DME control module connector).
4. Connect voltmeter to special tool 9637, pin II/3, and ground.
   Switch on the ignition.
   Display: 0 V
5. Connect voltmeter to special tool 9637, pin II/4, and ground.
   Switch on the ignition.
   Display: 0 V

If battery voltage is displayed, check wiring harness for chafing and pinching damage.

4 Check CAN bus from DME control module to Tiptronic control module for short circuit.

1. Remove DME control module connector.
2. Remove Tiptronic control module connector.
3. Connect special tool 9637 to wiring harness (DME control module connector).
4. Connect ohmmeter to special tool 9637, pins II/3 and II/4.
   Display: ∞ Ω

If 0 - 5 Ω is displayed, check wiring for chafing and pinching damage.

PR1029900168030X

Fig. 48 Code P0600: CAN Timeout Signal Implausible (Part 3 of 3)

Replace DME control module.

1 Perform adaptation.

End

1 Perform adaptation.

1. Switch on the ignition.
2. Wait one minute.
   Do not press the accelerator.
3. Switch off the ignition for at least 10 seconds.
4. Read out the fault memory.

PR1029900169000X

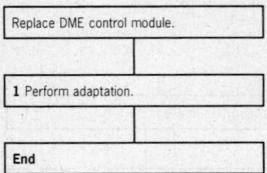

Fig. 49 Codes P0604, P0605 & P1671: Control Module Faulty

1 Check wiring from DME control module, pin IV/31, to instrument cluster for continuity.

1. Connect special tool 9637 to wiring harness (DME control module connector).
2. Remove connector X 2/3.
3. Connect ohmmeter to special tool 9637, pin IV/31, and to X 2/3 on pin side, pin 11.
   Display: 0 - 5 Ω

If ∞ Ω is displayed, check wiring harness for chafing and pinching damage.

4. Remove connector III of instrument cluster.
5. Connect ohmmeter to X 2/3, sleeve side, and to connector III of instrument cluster, pin 2.
   Display: 0 - 5 Ω

If ∞ Ω is displayed, check wiring harness for chafing and pinching damage.

2 Check wiring from DME control module, pin IV/31, to instrument cluster for short to ground.

1. Connect special tool 9637 to wiring harness (DME control module connector).
2. Remove connector III of instrument cluster.
3. Connect ohmmeter to special tool 9637, pin IV/31, and ground.
   Display: ∞ Ω

If 0 - 5 Ω is displayed, check wiring harness for chafing and pinching damage.

PR1029900170020X

Fig. 50 Code P0650: Malfunction Indicator Lamp (Part 2 of 3)

3 Check wiring from DME control module, pin IV/31, to instrument cluster for short to B+.

1. Connect special tool 9637 to wiring harness (DME control module connector).
2. Remove connector III of instrument cluster.
3. Switch on the ignition.
4. Connect voltmeter to special tool 9637, pin IV/31, and ground.
   Display: 0 V

If battery voltage is displayed, check wiring harness for chafing and pinching damage.

PR1029900170030X

Fig. 50 Code P0650: Malfunction Indicator Lamp (Part 3 of 3)

Open circuit

1 Check wiring from DME control module, pin IV/31, to instrument cluster for continuity. — Not OK → Repair wiring harness. → End

End

Below limit

2 Check wiring from DME control module, pin IV/31, to instrument cluster for short to ground. — Not OK → Repair wiring harness. → End

End

Above limit

3 Check wiring from DME control module, pin IV/31, to instrument cluster for short to B+. — Not OK → Repair wiring harness. → End

End

PR1029900170010X

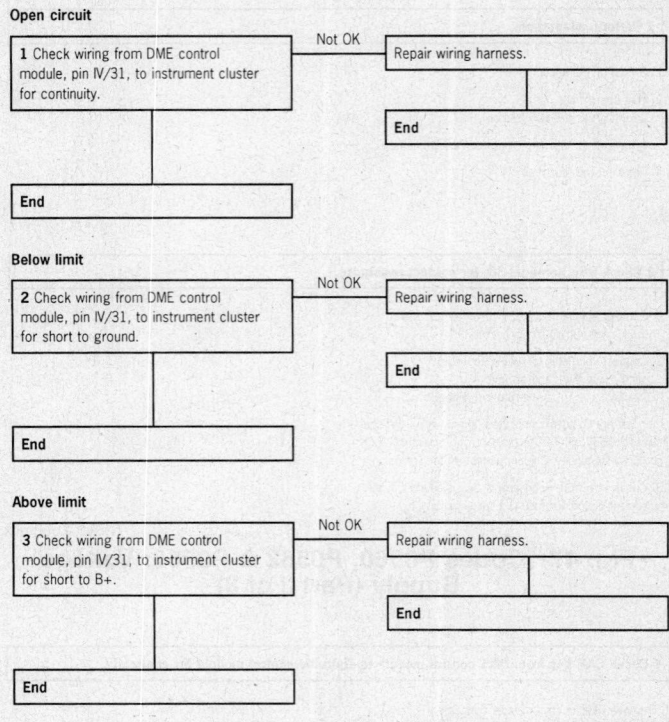

Fig. 50 Code P0650: Malfunction Indicator Lamp (Part 1 of 3)

Above limit

1 Check resistance of oxygen sensor heating. — Not OK → Replace oxygen sensor. → End

OK

Check wiring from DME control module, pin II/19, to disconnection point of oxygen sensor 1 ahead of TWC for short to B+. — Not OK → Repair wiring harness. → End

OK

Replace DME control module.

2 Perform adaptation.

End

PR1029900171010X

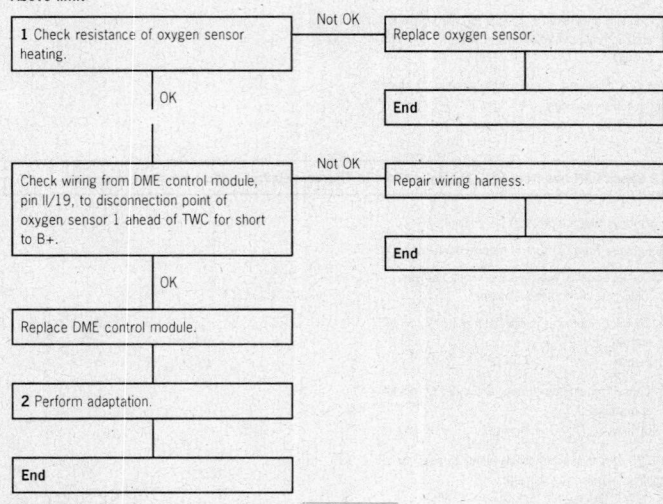

Fig. 51 Code P1115: Front Oxygen Sensor Heating Bank 1 (Part 1 of 6)

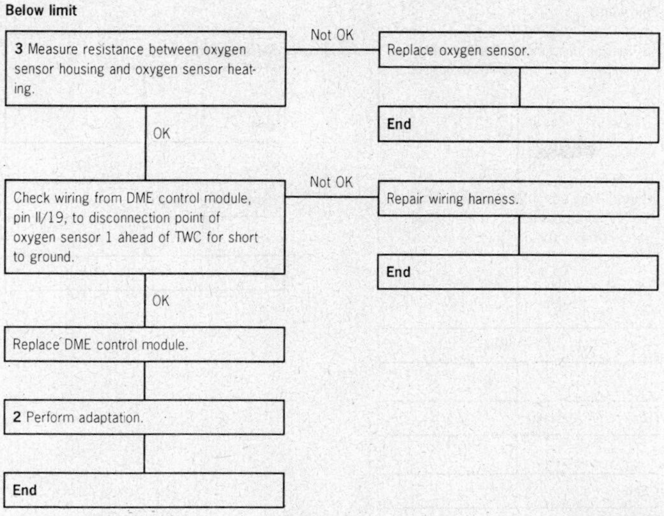

PR1029900171020X

Fig. 51 Code P1115: Front Oxygen Sensor Heating Bank 1 (Part 2 of 6)

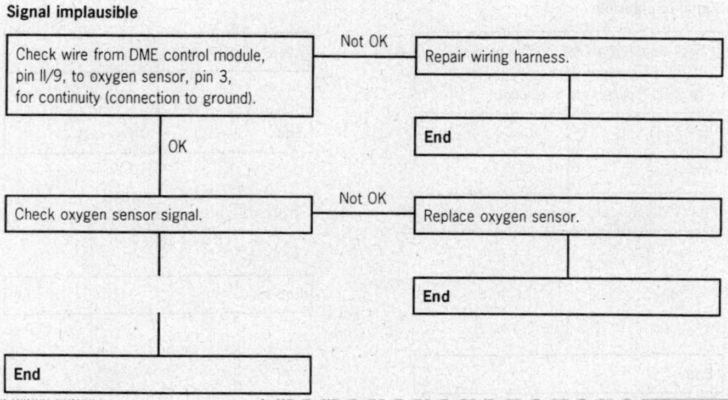

PR1029900171040X

Fig. 51 Code P1115: Front Oxygen Sensor Heating Bank 1 (Part 4 of 6)

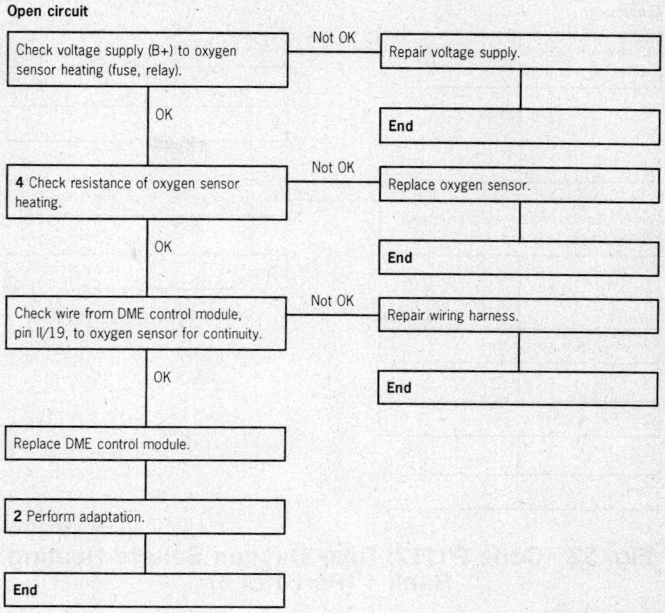

PR1029900171030X

Fig. 51 Code P1115: Front Oxygen Sensor Heating Bank 1 (Part 3 of 6)

1 Check resistance of oxygen sensor heating.

1. Remove connector of oxygen sensor 1 ahead of TWC.
2. Connect ohmmeter on pin side to pins 1 and 2.
   Display: > 1.0 Ω at 25 °C

2 Perform adaptation.

1. Switch on the ignition.
2. Wait one minute.
   Do not press the accelerator.
3. Switch off the ignition for at least 10 seconds.
4. Read out the fault memory.

3 Measure resistance between oxygen sensor housing and oxygen sensor heating.

1. Remove connector of oxygen sensor 1 ahead of TWC.
2. Connect ohmmeter on pin side to oxygen sensor housing and connector, pin 1.
   Display: > 100 Ω
3. Connect ohmmeter on pin side to oxygen sensor housing and connector, pin 2.
   Display: > 100 Ω

PR1029900171050X

Fig. 51 Code P1115: Front Oxygen Sensor Heating Bank 1 (Part 5 of 6)

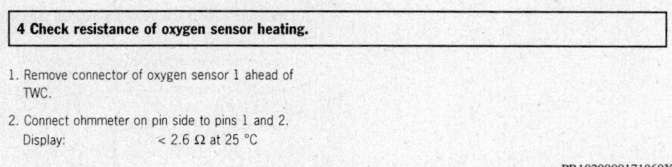

4 Check resistance of oxygen sensor heating.

1. Remove connector of oxygen sensor 1 ahead of TWC.
2. Connect ohmmeter on pin side to pins 1 and 2.
   Display: < 2.6 Ω at 25 °C

PR1029900171060X

Fig. 51 Code P1115: Front Oxygen Sensor Heating Bank 1 (Part 6 of 6)

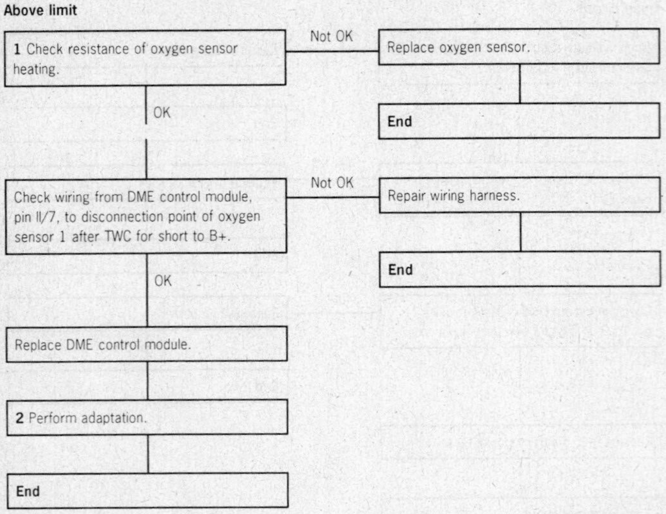

PR1029900172010X

Fig. 52 Code P1117: Rear Oxygen Sensor Heating Bank 1 (Part 1 of 6)

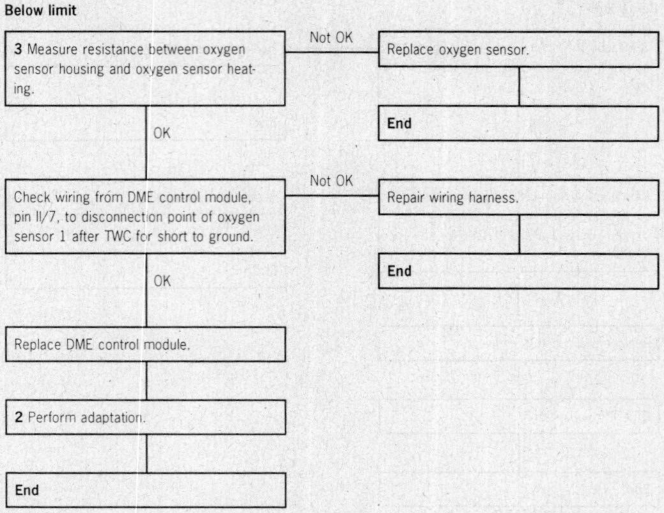

PR1029900172020X

Fig. 52 Code P1117: Rear Oxygen Sensor Heating Bank 1 (Part 2 of 6)

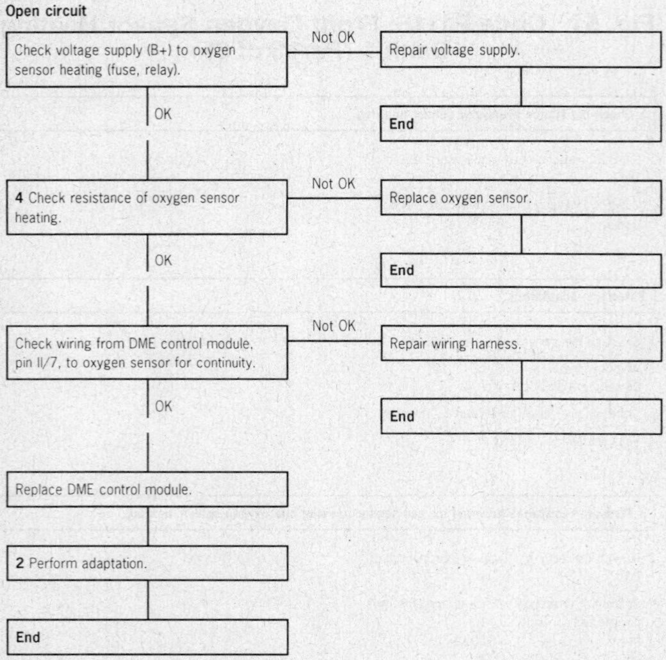

PR1029900172030X

Fig. 52 Code P1117: Rear Oxygen Sensor Heating Bank 1 (Part 3 of 6)

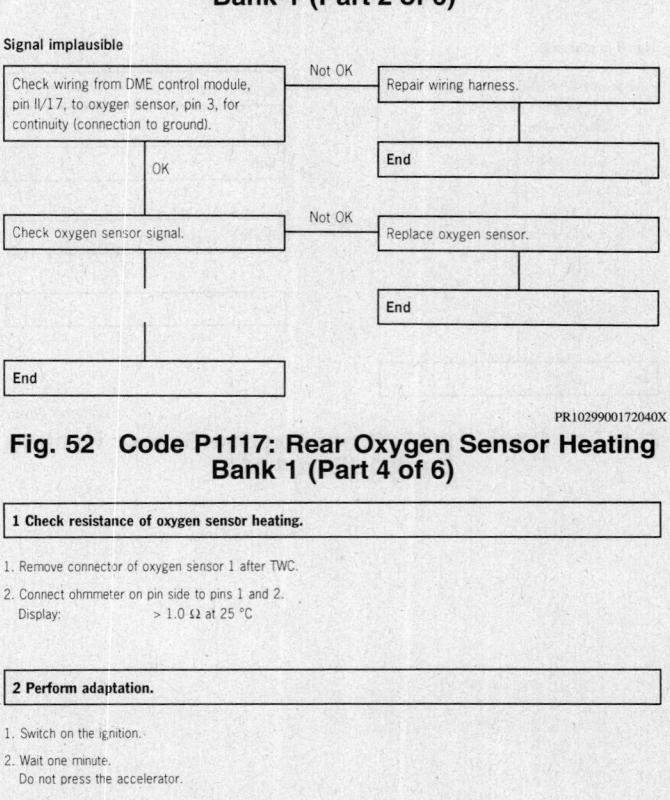

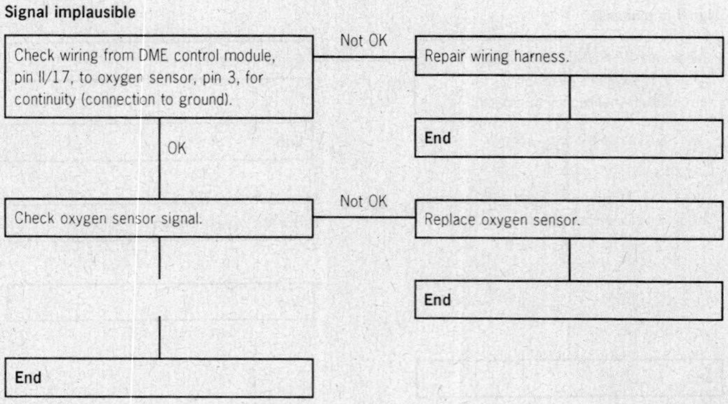

PR1029900172040X

Fig. 52 Code P1117: Rear Oxygen Sensor Heating Bank 1 (Part 4 of 6)

1 Check resistance of oxygen sensor heating.

1. Remove connector of oxygen sensor 1 after TWC.
2. Connect ohmmeter on pin side to pins 1 and 2.
   Display: > 1.0 Ω at 25 °C

2 Perform adaptation.

1. Switch on the ignition.
2. Wait one minute.
   Do not press the accelerator.
3. Switch off the ignition for at least 10 seconds.
4. Read out the fault memory.

3 Measure resistance between oxygen sensor housing and oxygen sensor heating.

1. Remove connector of oxygen sensor 1 after TWC.
2. Connect ohmmeter on pin side to oxygen sensor housing and connector, pin 1.
   Display: > 100 Ω
3. Connect ohmmeter on pin side to oxygen sensor housing and connector, pin 2.
   Display: > 100 Ω

PR1029900172050X

Fig. 52 Code P1117: Rear Oxygen Sensor Heating Bank 1 (Part 5 of 6)

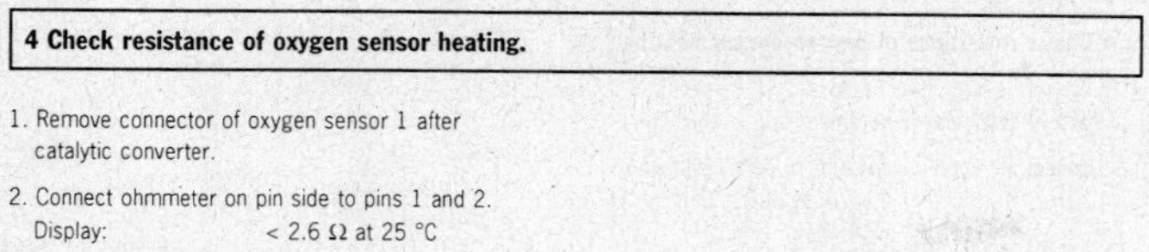

PR1029900172060X

Fig. 52 Code P1117: Rear Oxygen Sensor Heating Bank 1 (Part 6 of 6)

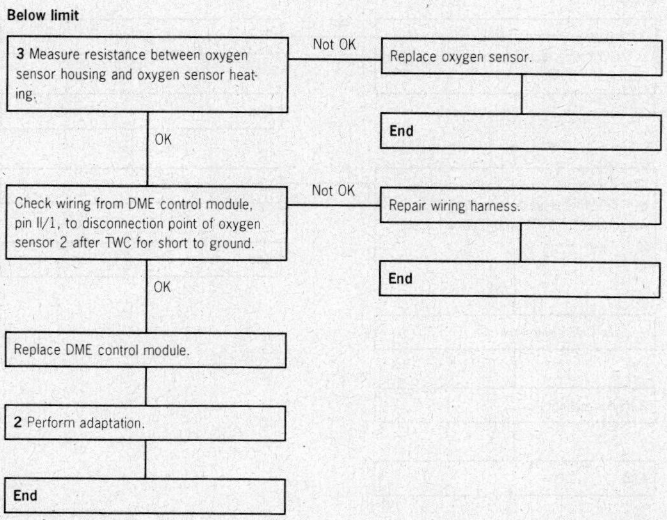

PR1029900173020X

Fig. 53 Code P1118: Rear Oxygen Sensor Heating Bank 2 (Part 2 of 6)

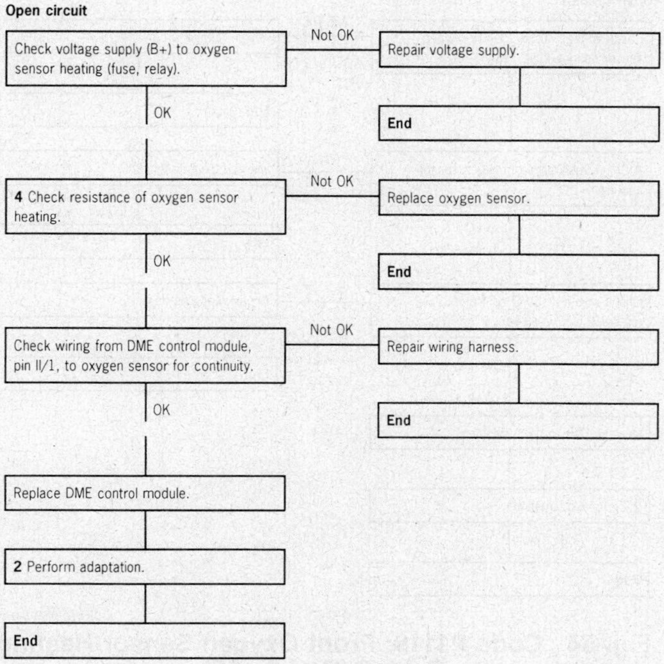

PR1029900173030X

Fig. 53 Code P1118: Rear Oxygen Sensor Heating Bank 2 (Part 3 of 6)

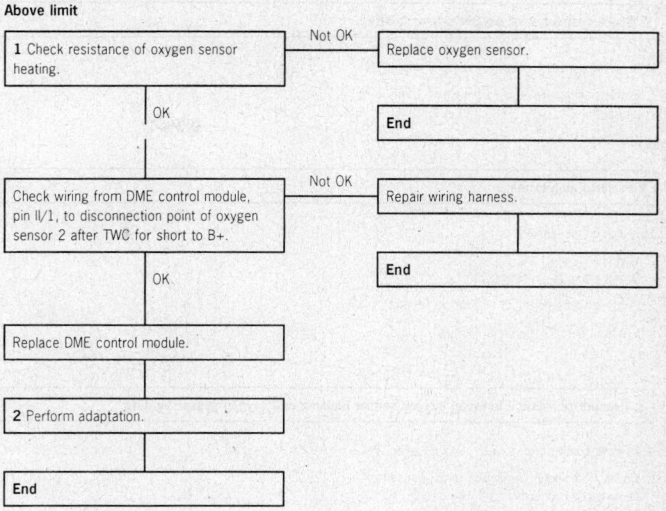

PR1029900173010X

Fig. 53 Code P1118: Rear Oxygen Sensor Heating Bank 2 (Part 1 of 6)

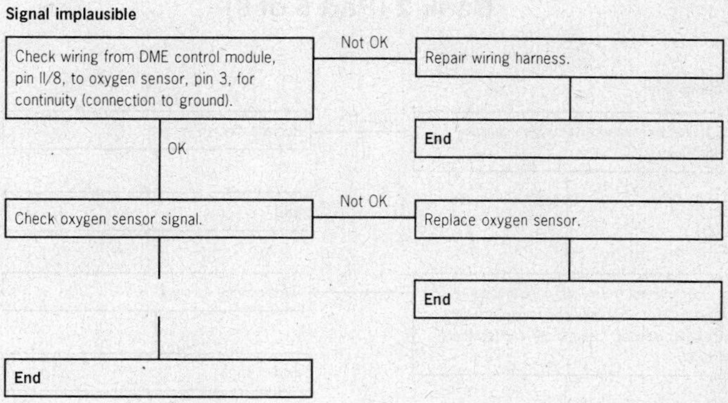

PR1029900173040X

Fig. 53 Code P1118: Rear Oxygen Sensor Heating Bank 2 (Part 4 of 6)

1 Check resistance of oxygen sensor heating.

1. Remove connector of oxygen sensor 2 after TWC.
2. Connect ohmmeter on pin side to pins 1 and 2.
   Display: > 1.0 Ω at 25 °C

2 Perform adaptation.

1. Switch on the ignition.
2. Wait one minute.
   Do not press the accelerator.
3. Switch off the ignition for at least 10 seconds.
4. Read out the fault memory.

3 Measure resistance between oxygen sensor housing and oxygen sensor heating.

1. Remove connector of oxygen sensor 2 after TWC.
2. Connect ohmmeter on pin side to oxygen sensor housing and connector, pin 1.
   Display: > 100 Ω
3. Connect ohmmeter on pin side to oxygen sensor housing and connector, pin 2.
   Display: > 100 Ω

PR1029900173050X

Fig. 53 Code P1118: Rear Oxygen Sensor Heating Bank 2 (Part 5 of 6)

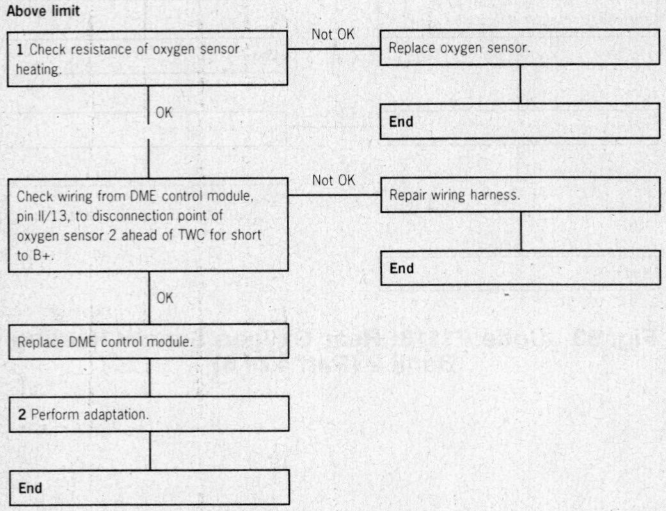

PR1029900174010X

Fig. 54 Code P1119: Front Oxygen Sensor Heating Bank 2 (Part 1 of 6)

4 Check resistance of oxygen sensor heating.

1. Remove connector of oxygen sensor 2 after TWC.
2. Connect ohmmeter on pin side to pins 1 and 2.
   Display: < 2.6 Ω at 25 °C

PR1029900173060X

Fig. 53 Code P1118: Rear Oxygen Sensor Heating Bank 2 (Part 6 of 6)

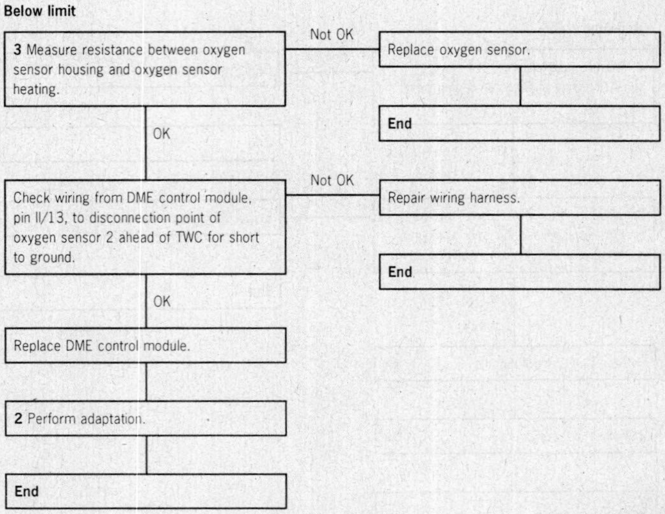

PR1029900174020X

Fig. 54 Code P1119: Front Oxygen Sensor Heating Bank 2 (Part 2 of 6)

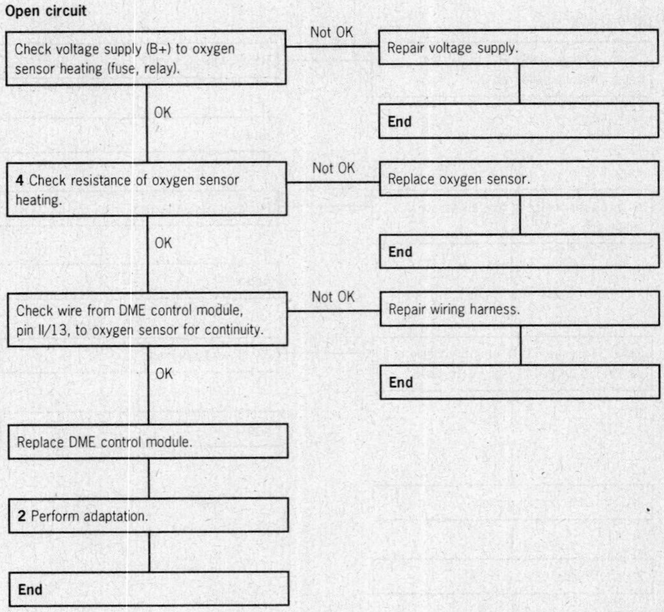

PR1029900174030X

Fig. 54 Code P1119: Front Oxygen Sensor Heating Bank 2 (Part 3 of 6)

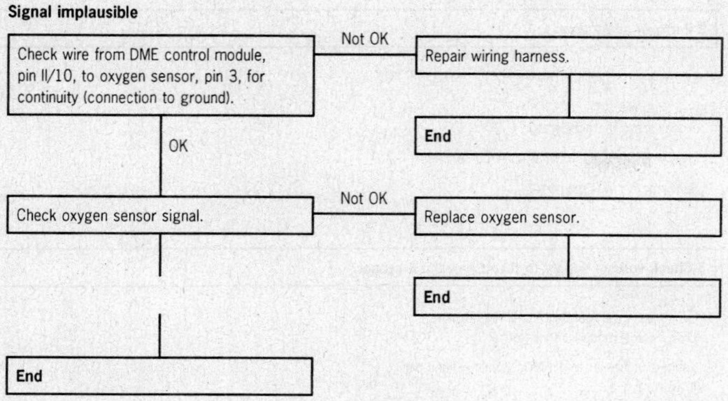

PR1029900174040X

Fig. 54 Code P1119: Front Oxygen Sensor Heating Bank 2 (Part 4 of 6)

4 Check resistance of oxygen sensor heating.

1. Remove connector of oxygen sensor 2 ahead of TWC.
2. Connect ohmmeter on pin side to pins 1 and 2.
   Display: < 2.6 Ω at 25 °C

PR1029900174060X

Fig. 54 Code P1119: Front Oxygen Sensor Heating Bank 2 (Part 6 of 6)

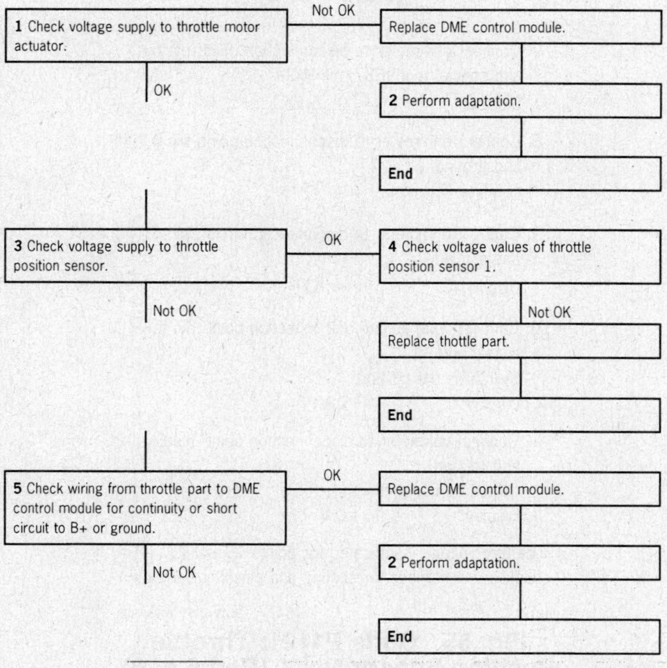

PR1029900175010X

Fig. 55 Code P1121: Throttle Position Sensor No. 1 (Part 1 of 6)

1 Check resistance of oxygen sensor heating.

1. Remove connector of oxygen sensor 2 ahead of TWC.
2. Connect ohmmeter on pin side to pins 1 and 2.
   Display: > 1.0 Ω at 25 °C

2 Perform adaptation.

1. Switch on the ignition.
2. Wait one minute.
   Do not press the accelerator.
3. Switch off the ignition for at least 10 seconds.
4. Read out the fault memory.

3 Measure resistance between oxygen sensor housing and oxygen sensor heating.

1. Remove connector of oxygen sensor 2 ahead of TWC.
2. Connect ohmmeter on pin side to oxygen sensor housing and connector, pin 1.
   Display: > 100 Ω
3. Connect ohmmeter on pin side to oxygen sensor housing and connector, pin 2.
   Display: > 100 Ω

PR1029900174050X

Fig. 54 Code P1119: Front Oxygen Sensor Heating Bank 2 (Part 5 of 6)

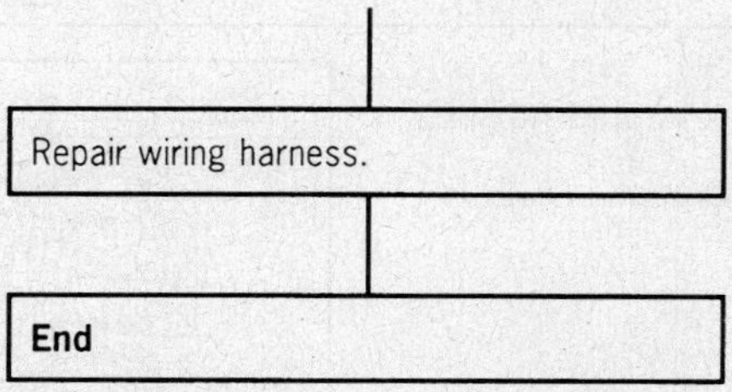

PR1029900175020X

Fig. 55 Code P1121: Throttle Position Sensor No. 1 (Part 2 of 6)

1 Check voltage supply to throttle motor actuator.

1. Connect special tool 9637.
2. Connect engine tester (oscilloscope) to pin III/42 (positive) and pin III/43 (negative). Use special input.
3. Switch on the ignition. The signal shown in the diagram opposite should appear:

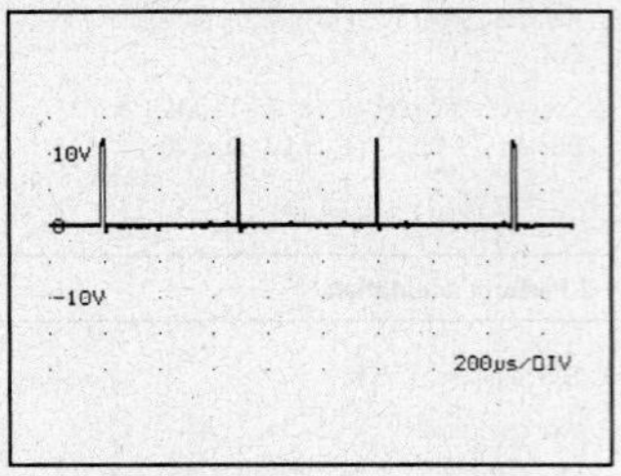

4. Fully depress accelerator pedal. The signal shown in the diagram opposite should appear:

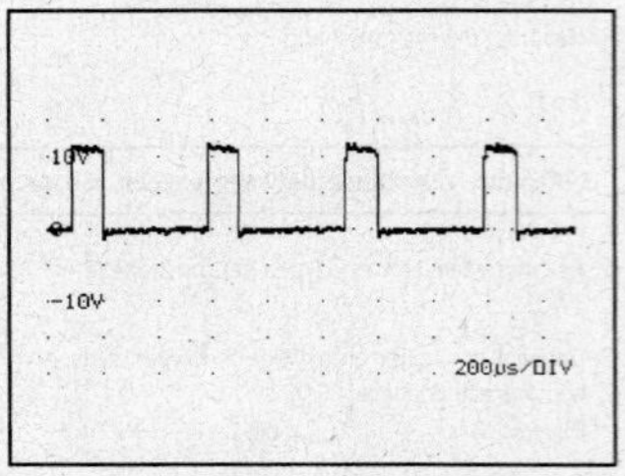

PR1029900175030X

Fig. 55 Code P1121: Throttle Position Sensor No. 1 (Part 3 of 6)

5 Check wiring from throttle part to DME control module for continuity or short circuit to B+ or ground.

Note

The wires to the throttle part are routed via connector X 59/2.

1. Separate disconnection point to throttle part.

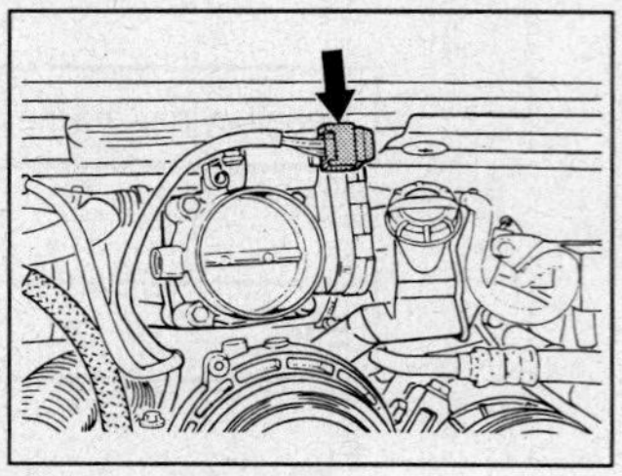

2. Connect special tool 9637 to wiring harness (DME control module connector).
3. Connect ohmmeter to disconnection point, pin 1, and special tool 9637, pin III/43.
   Display: 0 - 5 Ω
4. Connect ohmmeter to disconnection point, pin 2, and special tool 9637, pin III/25.
   Display: 0 - 5 Ω
5. Connect ohmmeter to disconnection point, pin 3, and special tool 9637, pin III/10.
   Display: 0 - 5 Ω
6. Connect ohmmeter to disconnection point, pin 4, and special tool 9637, pin III/42.
   Display: 0 - 5 Ω

PR1029900175050X

Fig. 55 Code P1121: Throttle Position Sensor No. 1 (Part 5 of 6)

2 Perform adaptation.

1. Switch on the ignition.
2. Wait one minute. Do not press the accelerator.
3. Switch off the ignition for at least 10 seconds.
4. Read out the fault memory.

3 Check voltage supply to throttle position sensor.

1. Connect special tool 9637 to wiring harness (DME control module connector).
2. Connect voltmeter to pin III/10 (positive) and pin III/25. Switch on the ignition.
   Display: approx. 5 V

4 Check voltage values of throttle position sensor 1.

1. Connect special tool 9637.
2. Connect voltmeter to pin III/24 (positive) and pin III/25 (negative). Switch on the ignition.
   Display: approx. 0.7 - 0.9 V

   Fully depress accelerator pedal.
   Display: approx. 4.1 - 4.5 V

PR1029900175040X

Fig. 55 Code P1121: Throttle Position Sensor No. 1 (Part 4 of 6)

7. Connect ohmmeter to disconnection point, pin 6, and special tool 9637, pin III/24.
   Display: 0 - 5 Ω
8. Connect ohmmeter to disconnection point, pin 4, and ground.
   Display: ∞ Ω
9. Connect ohmmeter to disconnection point, pin 6, and ground.
   Display: ∞ Ω
10. Connect voltmeter to disconnection point, pin 4, and ground. Switch on the ignition.
    Display: 0 V
11. Connect voltmeter to disconnection point, pin 6, and ground. Switch on the ignition.
    Display: 0 V

If battery voltage is indicated for points 10 and 11, check wiring harness for chafing and pinching damage.

PR1029900175060X

Fig. 55 Code P1121: Throttle Position Sensor No. 1 (Part 6 of 6)

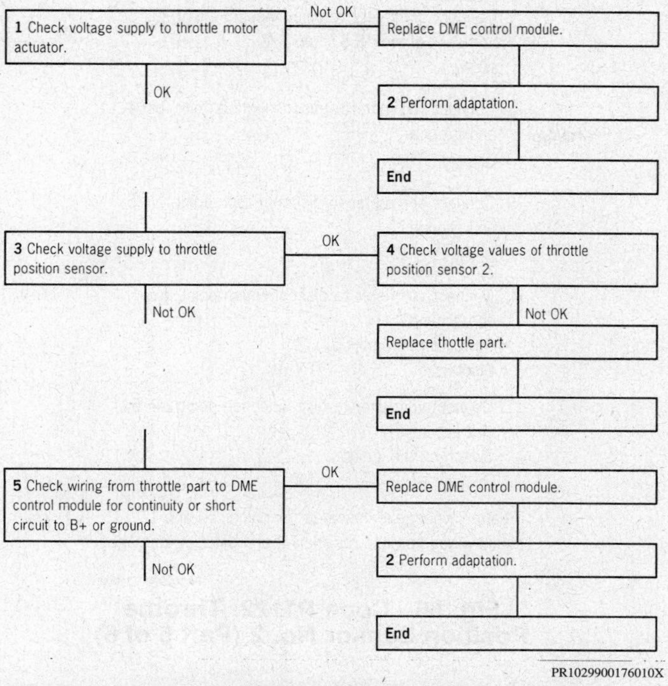

Fig. 56 Code P1122: Throttle Position Sensor No. 2 (Part 1 of 6)

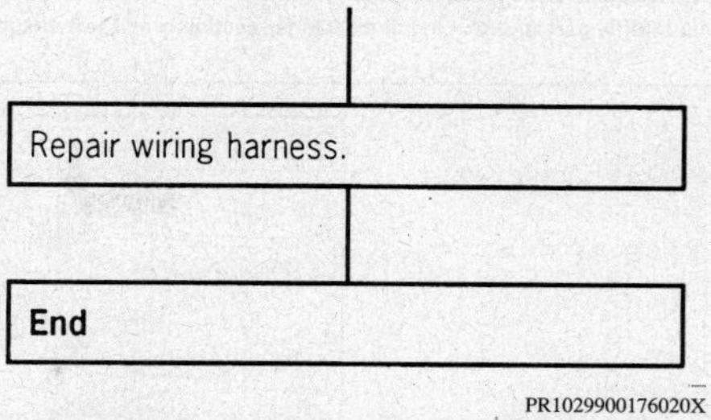

Fig. 56 Code P1122: Throttle Position Sensor No. 2 (Part 2 of 6)

1 Check voltage supply to throttle motor actuator.

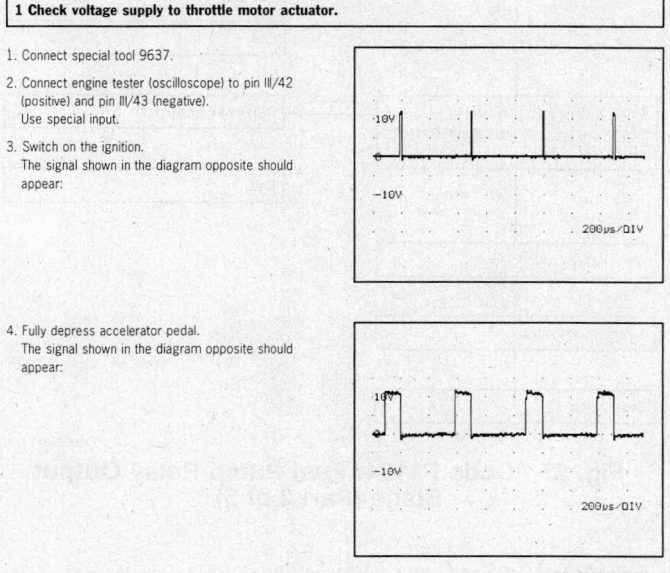

1. Connect special tool 9637.
2. Connect engine tester (oscilloscope) to pin III/42 (positive) and pin III/43 (negative).
   Use special input.
3. Switch on the ignition.
   The signal shown in the diagram opposite should appear:

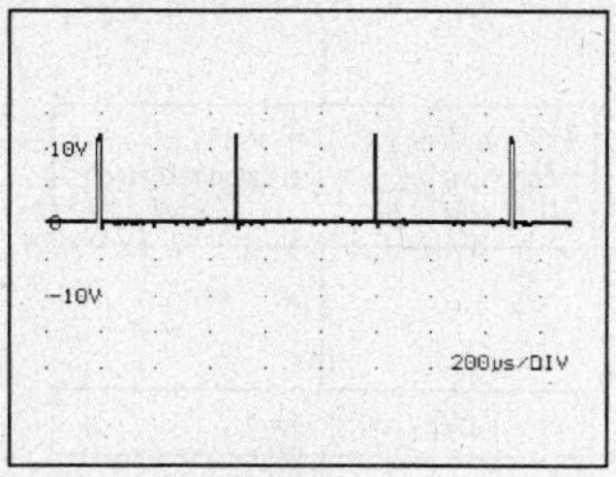

4. Fully depress accelerator pedal.
   The signal shown in the diagram opposite should appear:

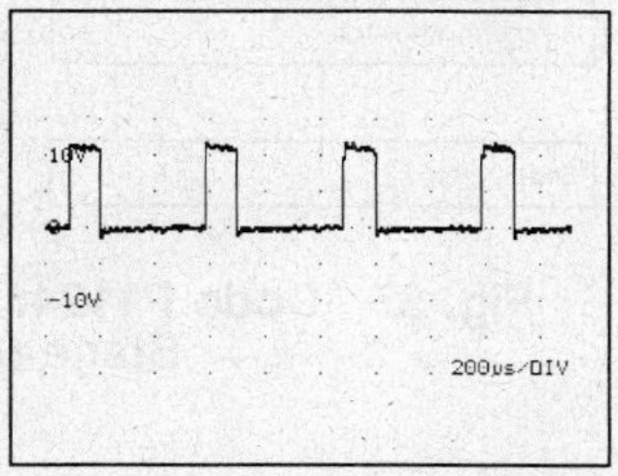

PR1029900176030X

Fig. 56 Code P1122: Throttle Position Sensor No. 2 (Part 3 of 6)

2 Perform adaptation.

1. Switch on the ignition.
2. Wait one minute.
   Do not press the accelerator.
3. Switch off the ignition for at least 10 seconds.
4. Read out the fault memory.

3 Check voltage supply to throttle position sensor.

1. Connect special tool 9637 to wiring harness (DME control module connector).
2. Connect voltmeter to pin III/10 (positive) and pin III/25.
   Switch on the ignition.
   Display: approx. 5 V

4 Check voltage values of throttle position sensor 2.

1. Connect special tool 9637.
2. Connect voltmeter to pin III/8 (positive) and pin III/25 (negative).
   Switch on the ignition.
   Display: approx. 4.0 - 4.4 V

   Fully depress accelerator pedal.
   Display: approx. 0.5 - 0.8 V

PR1029900176040X

Fig. 56 Code P1122: Throttle Position Sensor No. 2 (Part 4 of 6)

5 Check wiring from throttle part to DME control module for continuity or short circuit to B+ or ground.

Note

The wires to the throttle part are routed via connector X 59/2.

1. Separate disconnection point to throttle part.

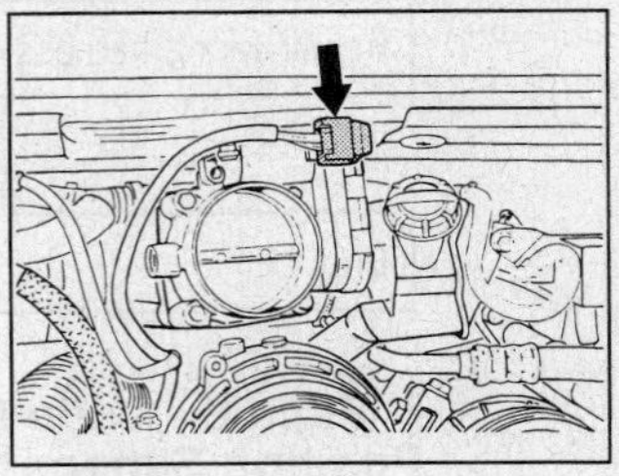

2. Connect special tool 9637 to wiring harness (DME control module connector).
3. Connect ohmmeter to disconnection point, pin 1, and special tool 9637, pin III/43.
   Display: 0 - 5 Ω
4. Connect ohmmeter to disconnection point, pin 2, and special tool 9637, pin III/25.
   Display: 0 - 5 Ω
5. Connect ohmmeter to disconnection point, pin 3, and special tool 9637, pin III/10.
   Display: 0 - 5 Ω
6. Connect ohmmeter to disconnection point, pin 4, and special tool 9637, pin III/42.
   Display: 0 - 5 Ω

PR1029900176050X

Fig. 56 Code P1122: Throttle Position Sensor No. 2 (Part 5 of 6)

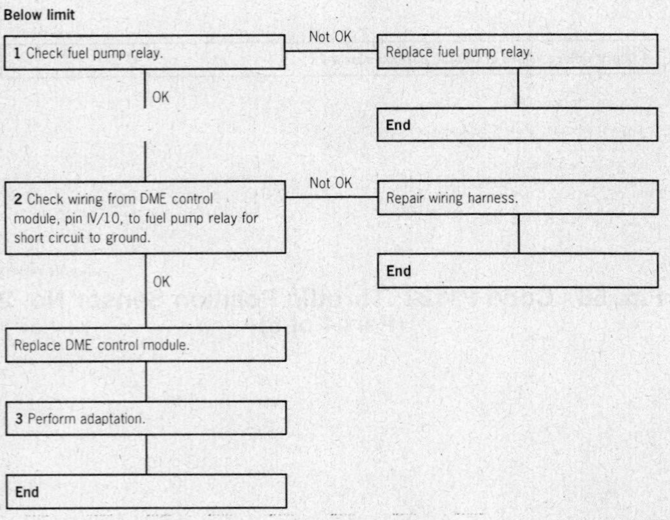

PR1029900177010X

Fig. 57 Code P1124: Fuel Pump Relay Output Stage (Part 1 of 5)

7. Connect ohmmeter to disconnection point, pin 5, and special tool 9637, pin III/8.
   Display: 0 - 5 Ω
8. Connect ohmmeter to disconnection point, pin 4, and ground.
   Display: ∞ Ω
9. Connect ohmmeter to disconnection point, pin 5, and ground.
   Display: ∞ Ω
10. Connect voltmeter to disconnection point, pin 4, and ground.
    Switch on the ignition.
    Display: 0 V
11. Connect voltmeter to disconnection point, pin 5, and ground.
    Switch on the ignition.
    Display: 0 V

If battery voltage is indicated for points 10 and 11, check wiring harness for chafing and pinching damage.

PR1029900176060X

Fig. 56 Code P1122: Throttle Position Sensor No. 2 (Part 6 of 6)

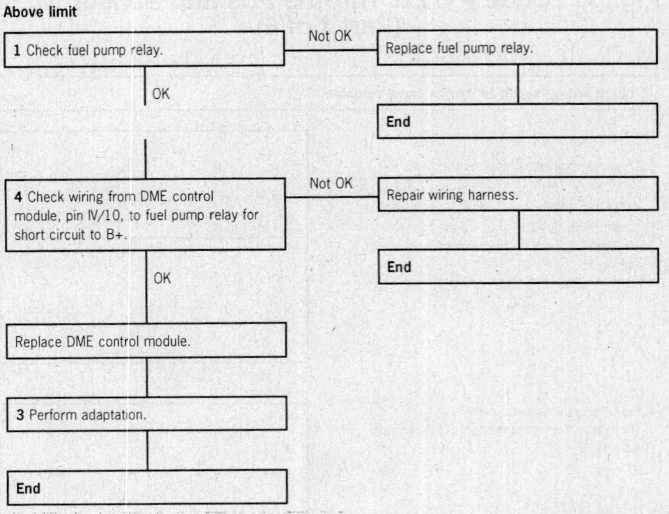

PR1029900177020X

Fig. 57 Code P1124: Fuel Pump Relay Output Stage (Part 2 of 5)

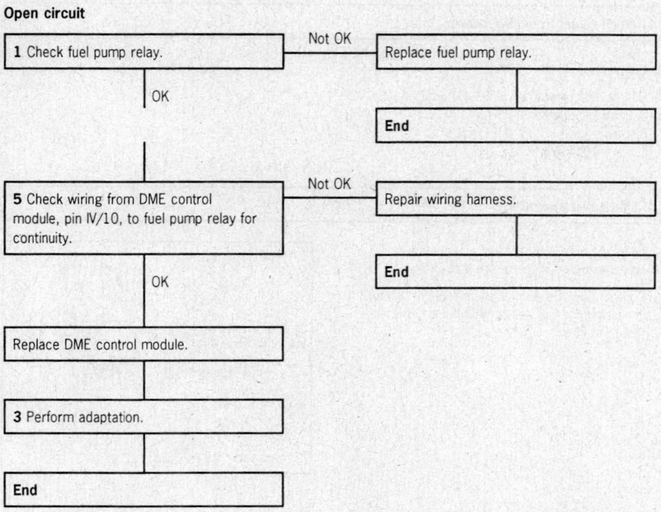

PR1029900177030X

Fig. 57 Code P1124: Fuel Pump Relay Output Stage (Part 3 of 5)

1 Check fuel pump relay.

1. Remove fuel pump relay.
2. Connect ohmmeter to terminals 85 and 86.
   Display: approx. 75 Ω

2 Check wiring from DME control module, pin IV/10, to fuel pump relay for short circuit to ground.

1. Connect special tool 9637 to wiring harness (DME control module connector).
2. Remove fuel pump relay.
3. Connect ohmmeter to special tool 9637, pin IV/10, and ground.
   Display: ∞ Ω

If 0 - 5 Ω is displayed, check wiring harness for chafing and pinching damage.

3 Perform adaptation.

1. Switch on the ignition.
2. Wait one minute.
   Do not press the accelerator.
3. Switch off the ignition for at least 10 seconds.
4. Read out the fault memory.

PR1029900177040X

Fig. 57 Code P1124: Fuel Pump Relay Output Stage (Part 4 of 5)

4 Check wiring from DME control module, pin IV/10, to fuel pump relay for short circuit to B+.

1. Connect special tool 9637 to wiring harness (DME control module connector).
2. Remove fuel pump relay.
3. Connect voltmeter to special tool 9637, pin IV/10, and ground.
   Ignition on.
   Display: 0 V

5 Check wiring from DME control module, pin IV/10, to fuel pump relay for continuity.

1. Connect special tool 9637 to wiring harness (DME control module connector).
2. Remove fuel pump relay.
3. Connect ohmmeter to special tool 9637, pin IV/10, and fuel pump relay slot, pin 6 (terminal 85).
   Display: 0 - 5 Ω

If ∞ Ω is displayed, check connector X 2/3, pin 23, and check wiring harness for chafing and pinching damage.

PR1029900177050X

Fig. 57 Code P1124: Fuel Pump Relay Output Stage (Part 5 of 5)

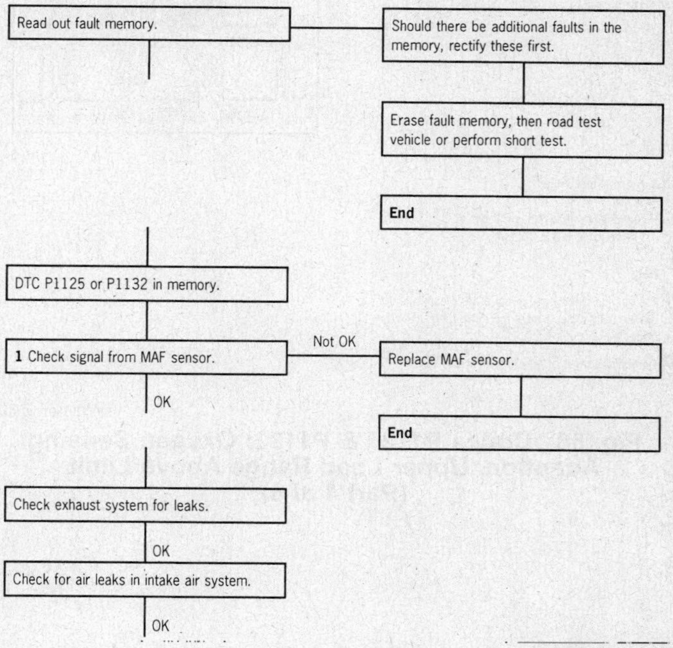

PR1029900178010X

Fig. 58 Codes P1125 & P1132: Oxygen Sensing Adaption, Upper Load Range Above Limit (Part 1 of 6)

2 Check fuel pressure.

OK

3 Check volume supply of fuel pump.

OK

4 Fuel injectors fouled.

End

PR1029900178020X

Fig. 58 Codes P1125 & P1132: Oxygen Sensing Adaption, Upper Load Range Above Limit (Part 2 of 6)

1 Check signal from MAF sensor.

1. Connect special tool 9637.
2. Connect voltmeter to pin III/23 and ground. Switch on the ignition. Display: 0.9 to 1.1 V

2 Check fuel pressure.

1. Undo and remove the closure cap of the fuel collection pipe test connection (A/F 13 mm).
2. Connect pressure gauge (special tool P 378a) to connecting line (special tool 9559) and connect to test connection.

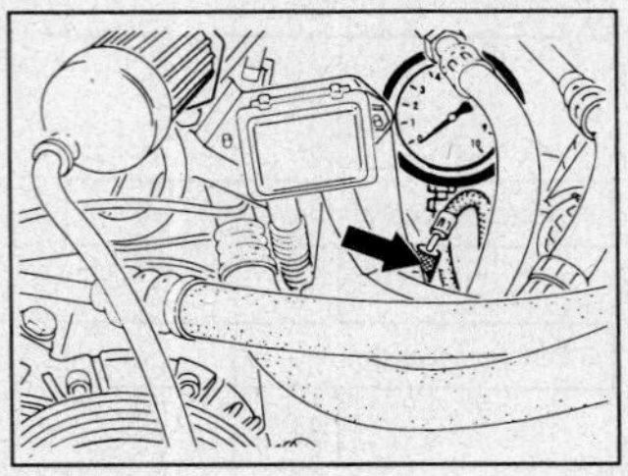

3. Actuate fuel pump, either

– **with Porsche System Tester 2**
The fuel pump can be actuated with the Porsche System Tester 2 or by jumpering the fuel pump relay.

or

PR1029900178030X

Fig. 58 Codes P1125 & P1132: Oxygen Sensing Adaption, Upper Load Range Above Limit (Part 3 of 6)

– **via fuel pump relay without tester**
Disconnect the fuel pump relay from the central electrical system and jumper plug-in contacts 30 and 87 (identification 3 und 5 on central electrical system) with a fused shop-made cable. The fuel pump must now operate or deliver fuel.

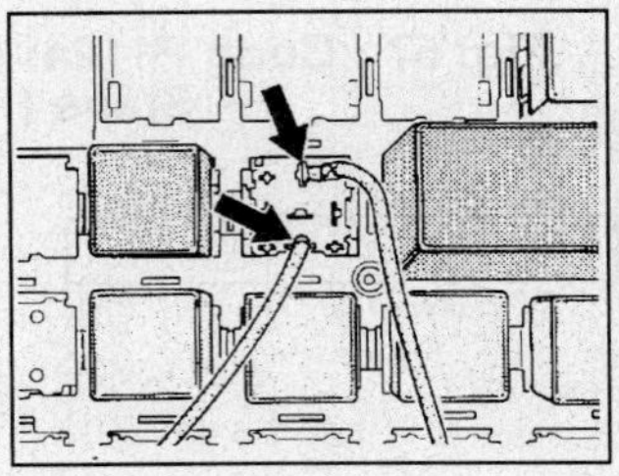

4. Nominal test values

Stationary engine 3.8 ± 0.2 bar
Engine idling 3.3 ± 0.2 bar

Note

The seal or sealing ring in the brass closure cap is **not** exchangeable. It must therefore be used only **once**.

Tightening torque of new brass closure cap 2.5 ± 0.5 Nm.

PR1029900178040X

Fig. 58 Codes P1125 & P1132: Oxygen Sensing Adaption, Upper Load Range Above Limit (Part 4 of 6)

3 Check volume supply of fuel pump.

Precondition:

Fuel filter and electrical supply OK.

1. Relieve pressure in fuel tank by opening tank cap.
2. Connect Porsche System Tester 2.
3. Remove complete air cleaner system.
4. Detach fuel return line from the engine compartment, taking care to **hold it fast.** Collect residual fuel.

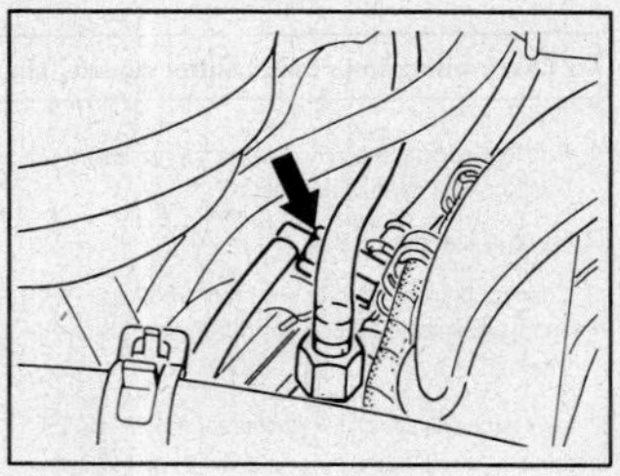

5. Connect fuel hose (shop-made, approx. 1.5 m long) to the fitting and hold in a measuring container.

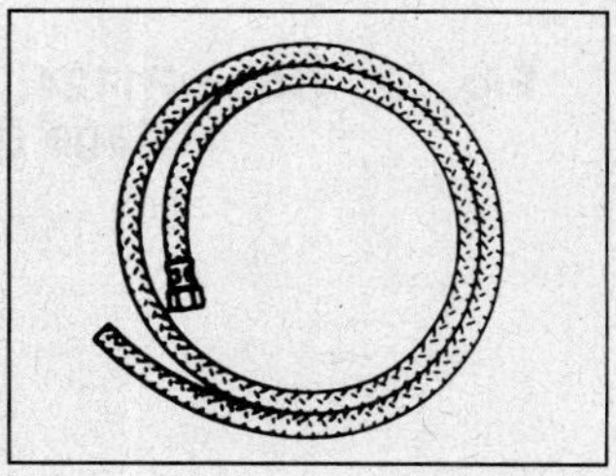

PR1029900178050X

Fig. 58 Codes P1125 & P1132: Oxygen Sensing Adaption, Upper Load Range Above Limit (Part 5 of 6)

6. Actuate fuel pump with the Porsche System Tester 2 and allow fuel to flow into the measuring container for 30 seconds.
Quantity supplied must be at least 850 cm^3/30 s, i.e. after 30 seconds at least 850 cm^3 of fuel must be in the measuring container.

Note

It is essential to observe safety regulations for handling fuel.

4 Fuel injectors fouled.

1. If preceding Check Points were negative, the fuel injectors may be fouled.
2. Clean fuel injectors (ultrasonic cleaning device) or replace them.

PR1029900178060X

Fig. 58 Codes P1125 & P1132: Oxygen Sensing Adaption, Upper Load Range Above Limit (Part 6 of 6)

1 Check signal from MAF sensor.

1. Connect special tool 9637.
2. Connect voltmeter to pin III/23 and ground.
   Switch on the ignition.
   Display: 0.9 to 1.1 V

2 Check fuel pressure.

1. Undo and remove the closure cap of the fuel collection pipe test connection (A/F 13 mm).
2. Connect pressure gauge (special tool P 378a) to connecting line (special tool 9559) and connect to test connection.

PR1029900179020X

Fig. 59 Codes P1125 & P1132: Oxygen Sensing Adaption, Upper Load Range Below Limit (Part 2 of 4)

3. Actuate fuel pump, either

– **with Porsche System Tester 2**
  The fuel pump can be actuated with the Porsche System Tester 2 or by jumpering the fuel pump relay.

  or

– **via fuel pump relay without tester**
  Disconnect the fuel pump relay from the central electrical system and jumper plug-in contacts 30 and 87 (identification 3 und 5 on central electrical system) with a fused shop-made cable. The fuel pump must now operate or deliver fuel.

4. Nominal test values

   Stationary engine 3.8 ± 0.2 bar
   Engine idling 3.3 ± 0.2 bar

Note

The seal or sealing ring in the brass closure cap is **not** exchangeable. It must therefore be used only **once**.

Tightening torque of new brass closure cap 2.5 ± 0.5 Nm.

PR1029900179030X

Fig. 59 Codes P1125 & P1132: Oxygen Sensing Adaption, Upper Load Range Below Limit (Part 3 of 4)

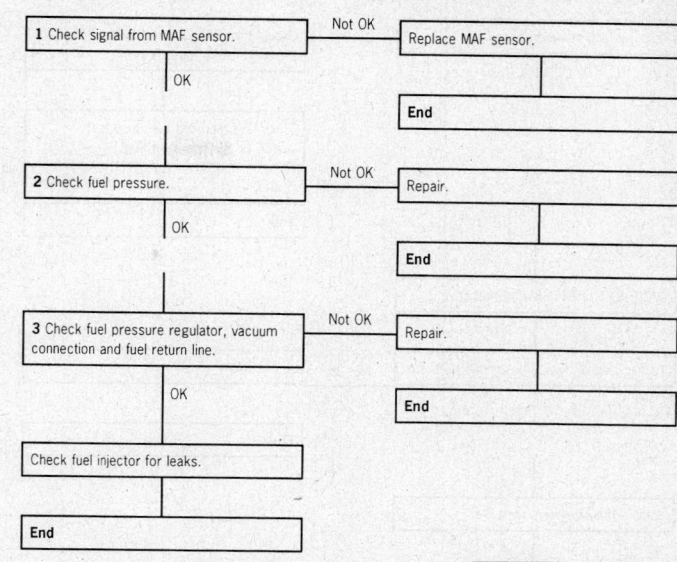

1 Check signal from MAF sensor. — Not OK → Replace MAF sensor. → **End**

OK ↓

2 Check fuel pressure. — Not OK → Repair. → **End**

OK ↓

3 Check fuel pressure regulator, vacuum connection and fuel return line. — Not OK → Repair. → **End**

OK ↓

Check fuel injector for leaks.

↓

End

PR1029900179010X

Fig. 59 Codes P1125 & P1132: Oxygen Sensing Adaption, Upper Load Range Below Limit (Part 1 of 4)

3 Check fuel pressure regulator, vacuum connection and fuel return line.

1. Remove vacuum hose from fuel pressure regulator.
2. Connect special tool 9103/2 to vacuum hose.
3. Start the engine.
   Display: 0.4 - 0.6 bar

If the value is not attained, check the intake air system for leaks and check vacuum line to fuel pressure regulator for restrictions.

4. Check housing of fuel pressure regulator for damage and deformation.

Replace the fuel pressure regulator if it is damaged with the result that the spring pre-tensioning is increased.

PR1029900179040X

Fig. 59 Codes P1125 & P1132: Oxygen Sensing Adaption, Upper Load Range Below Limit (Part 4 of 4)

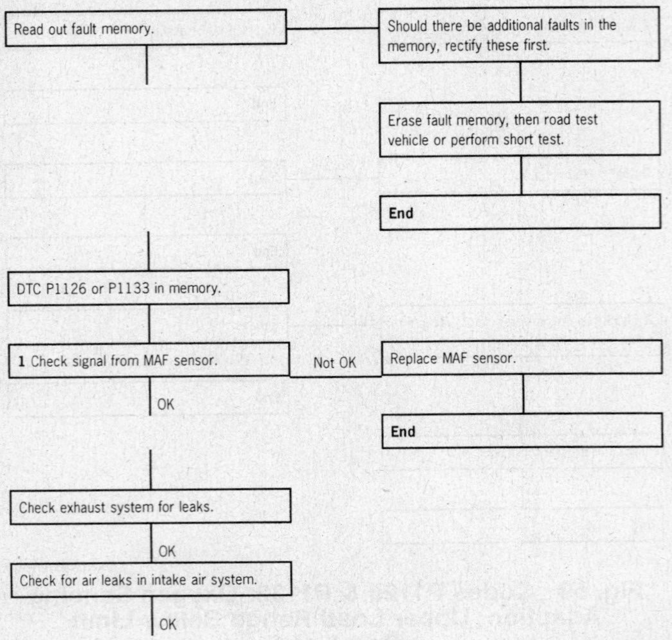

PR1029900180010X

Fig. 60 Code P1126 & P1133: Oxygen Sensing Adaption, Lower Load Range Above Limit (Part 1 of 6)

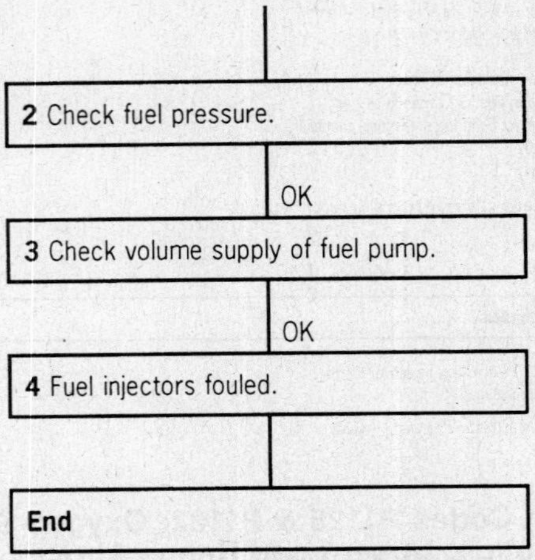

PR1029900180020X

Fig. 60 Code P1126 & P1133: Oxygen Sensing Adaption, Lower Load Range Above Limit (Part 2 of 6)

1 Check signal from MAF sensor.

1. Connect special tool 9637.
2. Connect voltmeter to pin III/23 and ground.
   Switch on the ignition.
   Display: 0.9 to 1.1 V

2 Check fuel pressure.

1. Undo and remove the closure cap of the fuel collection pipe test connection (A/F 13 mm).
2. Connect pressure gauge (special tool P 378a) to connecting line (special tool 9559) and connect to test connection.

3. Actuate fuel pump, either

– **with Porsche System Tester 2**
  The fuel pump can be actuated with the Porsche System Tester 2 or by jumpering the fuel pump relay.

or

PR1029900180030X

Fig. 60 Code P1126 & P1133: Oxygen Sensing Adaption, Lower Load Range Above Limit (Part 3 of 6)

– **via fuel pump relay without tester**
  Disconnect the fuel pump relay from the central electrical system and jumper plug-in contacts 30 and 87 (identification 3 and 5 on central electrical system) with a fused shop-made cable. The fuel pump must now operate or deliver fuel.

4. Nominal test values

   Stationary engine 3.8 ± 0.2 bar
   Engine idling 3.3 ± 0.2 bar

Note

The seal or sealing ring in the brass closure cap is **not** exchangeable. It must therefore be used only **once**.

Tightening torque of new brass closure cap
2.5 ± 0.5 Nm.

PR1029900180040X

Fig. 60 Code P1126 & P1133: Oxygen Sensing Adaption, Lower Load Range Above Limit (Part 4 of 6)

3 Check volume supply of fuel pump.

Precondition:

Fuel filter and electrical supply OK.

1. Relieve pressure in fuel tank by opening tank cap.
2. Connect Porsche System Tester 2.
3. Remove complete air cleaner system.
4. Detach fuel return line from the engine compartment, taking care to **hold it fast.** Collect residual fuel.

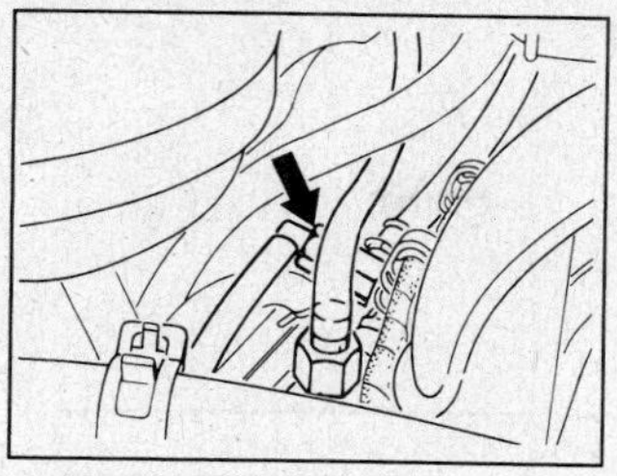

5. Connect fuel hose (shop-made, approx. 1.5 m long) to the fitting and hold in a measuring container.

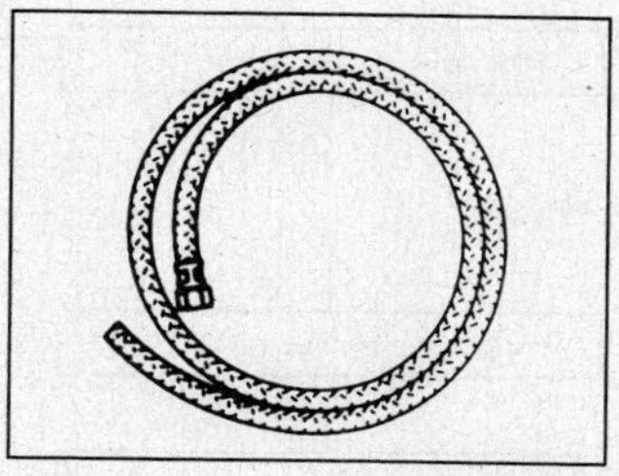

PR1029900180050X

Fig. 60 Code P1126 & P1133: Oxygen Sensing Adaption, Lower Load Range Above Limit (Part 5 of 6)

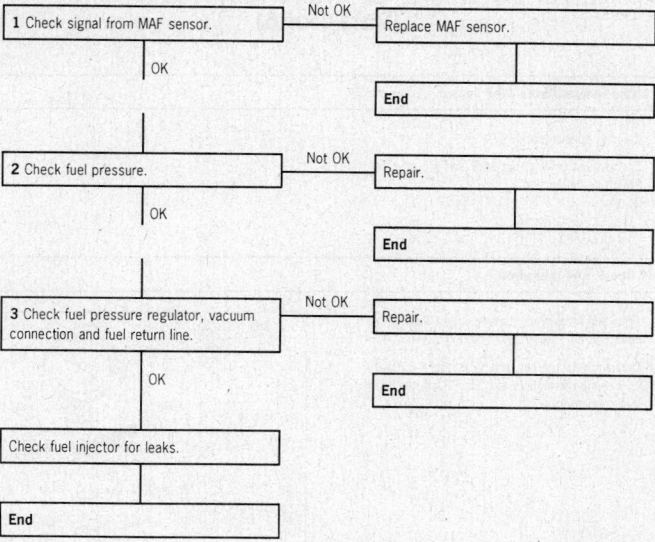

1 Check signal from MAF sensor. — Not OK → Replace MAF sensor. → **End**

↓ OK

2 Check fuel pressure. — Not OK → Repair. → **End**

↓ OK

3 Check fuel pressure regulator, vacuum connection and fuel return line. — Not OK → Repair. → **End**

↓ OK

Check fuel injector for leaks.

End

PR1029900181010X

Fig. 61 Code P1126 & P1133: Oxygen Sensing Adaption, Lower Load Range Below Limit (Part 1 of 4)

6. Actuate fuel pump with the Porsche System Tester 2 and allow fuel to flow into the measuring container for 30 seconds.
Quantity supplied must be at least 850 cm^3/30 s, i.e. after 30 seconds at least 850 cm^3 of fuel must be in the measuring container.

Note

It is essential to observe safety regulations for handling fuel.

4 Fuel injectors fouled.

1. If preceding Check Points were negative, the fuel injectors may be fouled.
2. Clean fuel injectors (ultrasonic cleaning device) or replace them.

PR1029900180060X

Fig. 60 Code P1126 & P1133: Oxygen Sensing Adaption, Lower Load Range Above Limit (Part 6 of 6)

1 Check signal from MAF sensor.

1. Connect special tool 9637.
2. Connect voltmeter to pin III/23 and ground.
Switch on the ignition.
Display: 0.9 to 1.1 V

2 Check fuel pressure.

1. Undo and remove the closure cap of the fuel collection pipe test connection (A/F 13 mm).
2. Connect pressure gauge (special tool P 378a) to connecting line (special tool 9559) and connect to test connection.

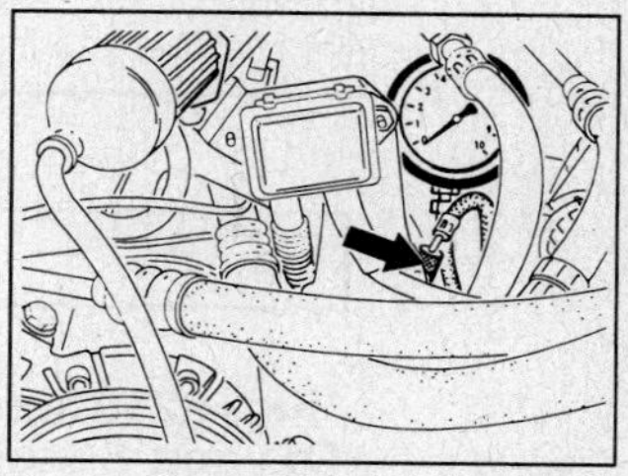

PR1029900181020X

Fig. 61 Code P1126 & P1133: Oxygen Sensing Adaption, Lower Load Range Below Limit (Part 2 of 4)

3. Actuate fuel pump, either

– **with Porsche System Tester 2**
The fuel pump can be actuated with the Porsche System Tester 2 or by jumpering the fuel pump relay.

or

– **via fuel pump relay without tester**
Disconnect the fuel pump relay from the central electrical system and jumper plug-in contacts 30 and 87 (identification 3 and 5 on central electrical system) with a fused shop-made cable. The fuel pump must now operate or deliver fuel.

4. Nominal test values

Stationary engine 3.8 ± 0.2 bar
Engine idling 3.3 ± 0.2 bar

Note

The seal or sealing ring in the brass closure cap is **not** exchangeable. It must therefore be used only **once**.

Tightening torque of new brass closure cap 2.5 ± 0.5 Nm.

PR1029900181030X

Fig. 61 Codes P1126 & P1133: Oxygen Sensing Adaption, Lower Load Range Below Limit (Part 3 of 4)

3 Check fuel pressure regulator, vacuum connection and fuel return line.

1. Remove vacuum hose from fuel pressure regulator.
2. Connect special tool 9103/2 to vacuum hose.
3. Start the engine.
   Display: 0.4 - 0.6 bar

If the value is not attained, check the intake air system for leaks and check vacuum line to fuel pressure regulator for restrictions.

4. Check housing of fuel pressure regulator for damage and deformation.

Replace the fuel pressure regulator if it is damaged with the result that the spring pre-tensioning is increased.

PR1029900181040X

Fig. 61 Codes P1126 & P1133: Oxygen Sensing Adaption, Lower Load Range Below Limit (Part 4 of 4)

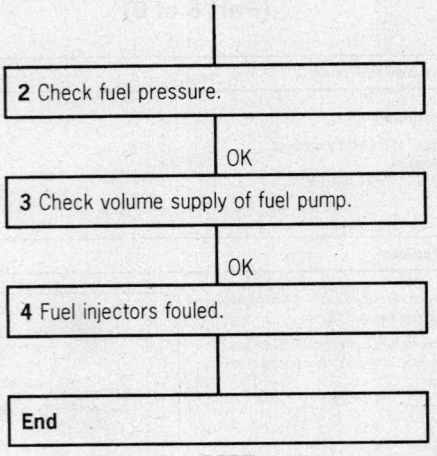

2 Check fuel pressure.

OK

3 Check volume supply of fuel pump.

OK

4 Fuel injectors fouled.

End

PR1029900182020X

Fig. 62 Codes P1127 & P1134: Oxygen Sensing Error By Means Of Short Test Above Limit (Part 2 of 6)

Read out fault memory. → Should there be additional faults in the memory, rectify these first. → Erase fault memory, then road test vehicle or perform short test. → **End**

DTC P1127 or P1134 in memory.

1 Check signal from MAF sensor. — Not OK → Replace MAF sensor. → **End**

OK

Check exhaust system for leaks.

OK

Check for air leaks in intake air system.

OK

PR1029900182010X

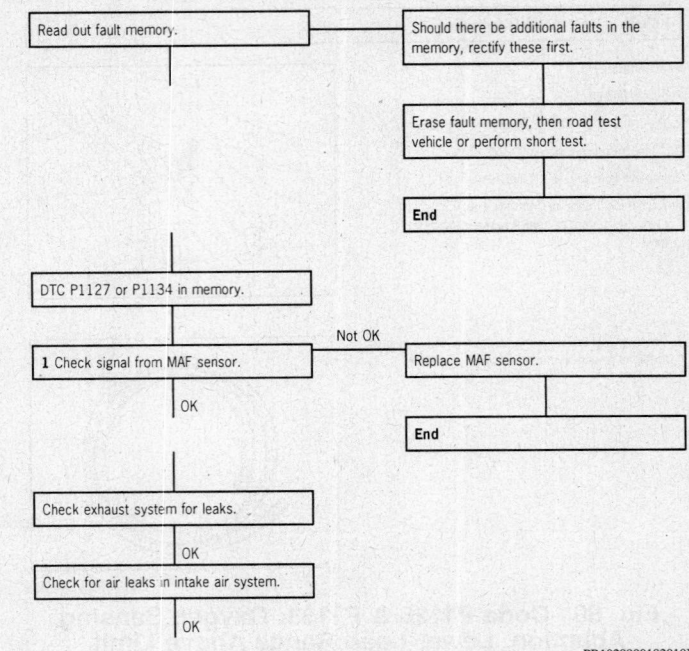

Fig. 62 Codes P1127 & P1134: Oxygen Sensing Error By Means Of Short Test Above Limit (Part 1 of 6)

1 Check signal from MAF sensor.

1. Connect special tool 9637.
2. Connect voltmeter to pin III/23 and ground.
   Switch on the ignition.
   Display: 0.9 to 1.1 V

2 Check fuel pressure.

1. Undo and remove the closure cap of the fuel collection pipe test connection (A/F 13 mm).
2. Connect pressure gauge (special tool P 378a) to connecting line (special tool 9559) and connect to test connection.

3. Actuate fuel pump, either

– **with Porsche System Tester 2**
  The fuel pump can be actuated with the Porsche System Tester 2 or by jumpering the fuel pump relay.

or

PR1029900182030X

Fig. 62 Codes P1127 & P1134: Oxygen Sensing Error By Means Of Short Test Above Limit (Part 3 of 6)

- **via fuel pump relay without tester**
  Disconnect the fuel pump relay from the central electrical system and jumper plug-in contacts 30 and 87 (identification 3 und 5 on central electrical system) with a fused shop-made cable. The fuel pump must now operate or deliver fuel.

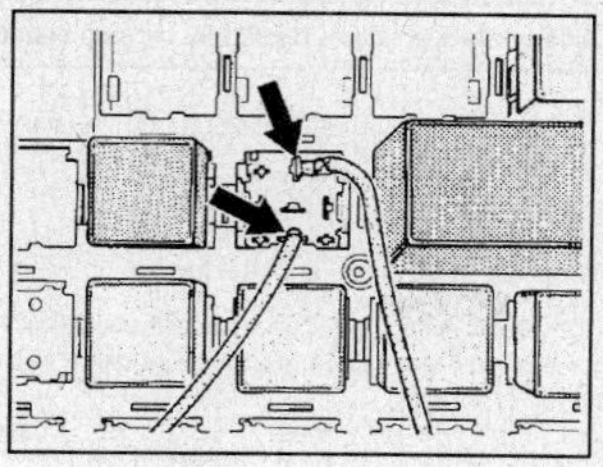

4. Nominal test values

   Stationary engine 3.8 ± 0.2 bar
   Engine idling 3.3 ± 0.2 bar

Note

The seal or sealing ring in the brass closure cap is **not** exchangeable. It must therefore be used only **once**.

Tightening torque of new brass closure cap 2.5 ± 0.5 Nm.

PR1029900182040X

Fig. 62 Codes P1127 & P1134: Oxygen Sensing Error By Means Of Short Test Above Limit (Part 4 of 6)

6. Actuate fuel pump with the Porsche System Tester 2 and allow fuel to flow into the measuring container for 30 seconds.
   Quantity supplied must be at least 850 cm³/30 s, i.e. after 30 seconds at least 850 cm³ of fuel must be in the measuring container.

Note

It is essential to observe safety regulations for handling fuel.

4 Fuel injectors fouled.

1. If preceding Check Points were negative, the fuel injectors may be fouled.
2. Clean fuel injectors (ultrasonic cleaning device) or replace them.

PR1029900182060X

Fig. 62 Codes P1127 & P1134: Oxygen Sensing Error By Means Of Short Test Above Limit (Part 6 of 6)

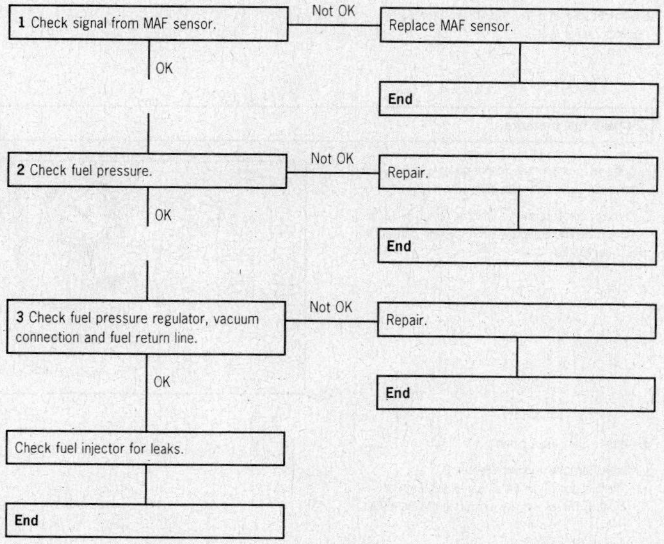

PR1029900183010X

Fig. 63 Codes P1127 & P1134: Oxygen Sensing Error By Means Of Short Test Below Limit (Part 1 of 4)

3 Check volume supply of fuel pump.

Precondition:

Fuel filter and electrical supply OK.

1. Relieve pressure in fuel tank by opening tank cap.
2. Connect Porsche System Tester 2.
3. Remove complete air cleaner system.
4. Detach fuel return line from the engine compartment, taking care to **hold it fast.** Collect residual fuel.

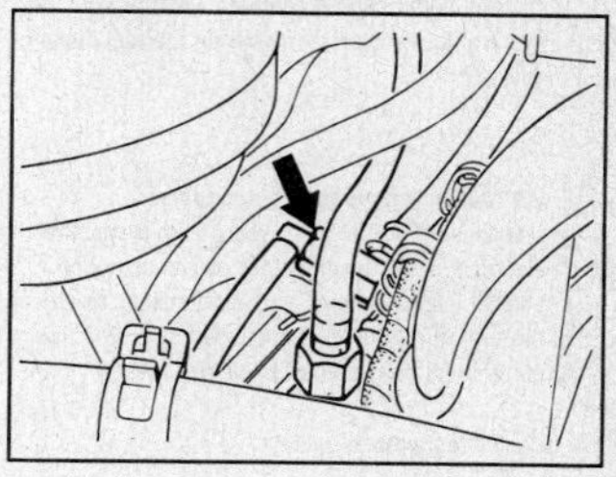

5. Connect fuel hose (shop-made, approx. 1.5 m long) to the fitting and hold in a measuring container.

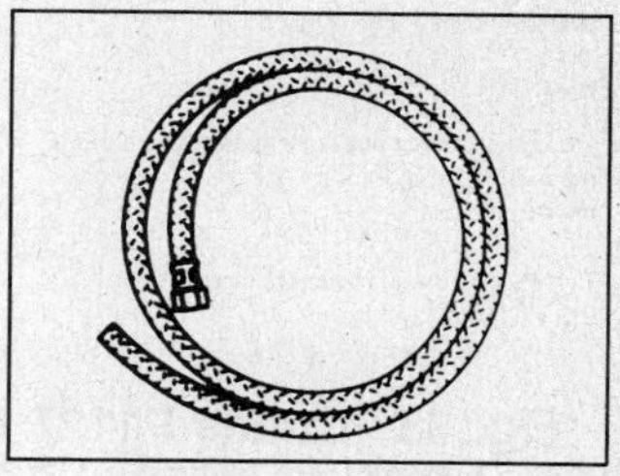

PR1029900182050X

Fig. 62 Codes P1127 & P1134: Oxygen Sensing Error By Means Of Short Test Above Limit (Part 5 of 6)

1 Check signal from MAF sensor.

1. Connect special tool 9637.
2. Connect voltmeter to pin III/23 and ground.
   Switch on the ignition.
   Display: 0.9 to 1.1 V

2 Check fuel pressure.

1. Undo and remove the closure cap of the fuel collection pipe test connection (A/F 13 mm).
2. Connect pressure gauge (special tool P 378a) to connecting line (special tool 9559) and connect to test connection.

PR1029900183020X

Fig. 63 Codes P1127 & P1134: Oxygen Sensing Error By Means Of Short Test Below Limit (Part 2 of 4)

3. Actuate fuel pump, either

- **with Porsche System Tester 2**
  The fuel pump can be actuated with the Porsche System Tester 2 or by jumpering the fuel pump relay.

  or

- **via fuel pump relay without tester**
  Disconnect the fuel pump relay from the central electrical system and jumper plug-in contacts 30 and 87 (identification 3 und 5 on central electrical system) with a fused shop-made cable. The fuel pump must now operate or deliver fuel.

4. Nominal test values

Stationary engine 3.8 ± 0.2 bar
Engine idling 3.3 ± 0.2 bar

Note

The seal or sealing ring in the brass closure cap is **not** exchangeable. It must therefore be used only **once**.

Tightening torque of new brass closure cap
2.5 ± 0.5 Nm.

PR1029900183030X

Fig. 63 Codes P1127 & P1134: Oxygen Sensing Error By Means Of Short Test Below Limit (Part 3 of 4)

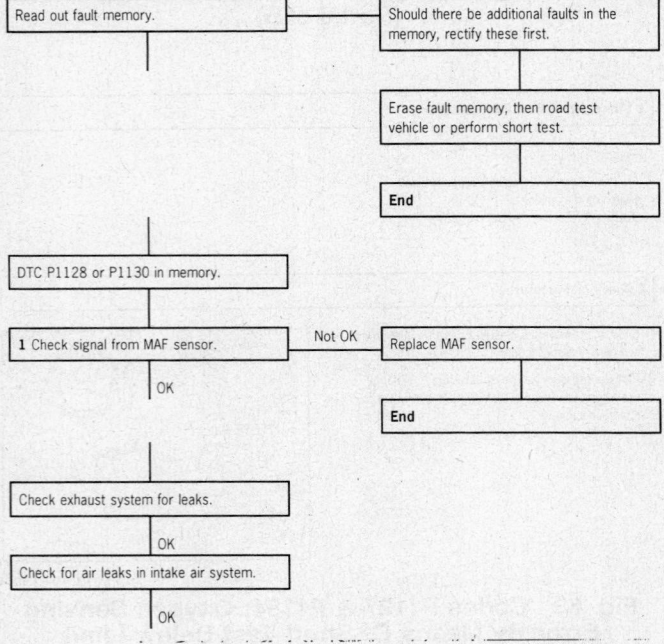

Read out fault memory. → Should there be additional faults in the memory, rectify these first. → Erase fault memory, then road test vehicle or perform short test. → End

DTC P1128 or P1130 in memory.

1 Check signal from MAF sensor. — Not OK → Replace MAF sensor. → End

OK

Check exhaust system for leaks.

OK

Check for air leaks in intake air system.

OK

PR1029900184010X

Fig. 64 Codes P1128 & P1130: Oxygen Sensing Adaption, Idle Range Above Limit (Part 1 of 6)

3 Check fuel pressure regulator, vacuum connection and fuel return line.

1. Remove vacuum hose from fuel pressure regulator.
2. Connect special tool 9103/2 to vacuum hose.
3. Start the engine.
   Display: 0.4 - 0.6 bar

If the value is not attained, check the intake air system for leaks and check vacuum line to fuel pressure regulator for restrictions.

4. Check housing of fuel pressure regulator for damage and deformation.

Replace the fuel pressure regulator if it is damaged with the result that the spring pre-tensioning is increased.

PR1029900183040X

Fig. 63 Codes P1127 & P1134: Oxygen Sensing Error By Means Of Short Test Below Limit (Part 4 of 4)

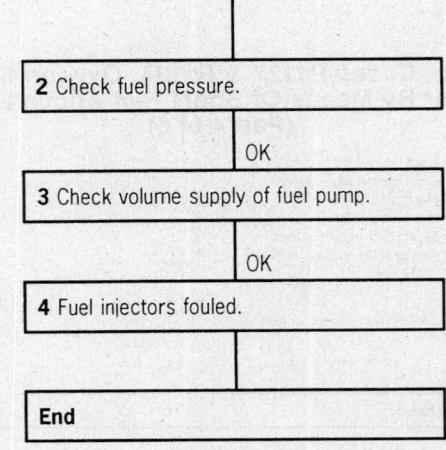

2 Check fuel pressure.

OK

3 Check volume supply of fuel pump.

OK

4 Fuel injectors fouled.

End

PR1029900184020X

Fig. 64 Codes P1128 & P1130: Oxygen Sensing Adaption, Idle Range Above Limit (Part 2 of 6)

1 Check signal from MAF sensor.

1. Connect special tool 9637.
2. Connect voltmeter to pin III/23 and ground.
   Switch on the ignition.
   Display: 0.9 to 1.1 V

2 Check fuel pressure.

1. Undo and remove the closure cap of the fuel collection pipe test connection (A/F 13 mm).
2. Connect pressure gauge (special tool P 378a) to connecting line (special tool 9559) and connect to test connection.

3. Actuate fuel pump, either

- **with Porsche System Tester 2**
  The fuel pump can be actuated with the Porsche System Tester 2 or by jumpering the fuel pump relay.

  or

PR1029900184030X

Fig. 64 Codes P1128 & P1130: Oxygen Sensing Adaption, Idle Range Above Limit (Part 3 of 6)

- **via fuel pump relay without tester**
  Disconnect the fuel pump relay from the central electrical system and jumper plug-in contacts 30 and 87 (identification 3 und 5 on central electrical system) with a fused shop-made cable. The fuel pump must now operate or deliver fuel.

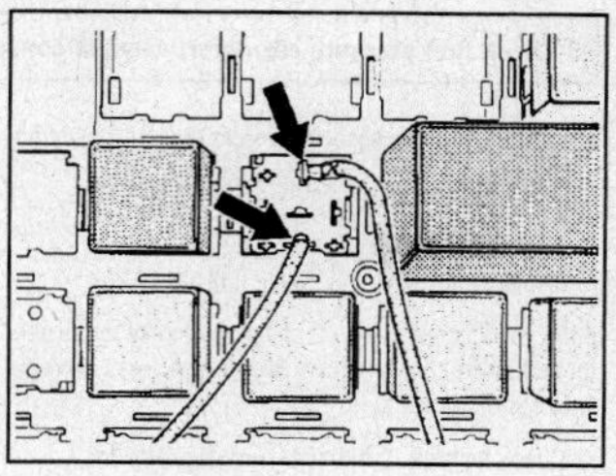

4. Nominal test values

   Stationary engine 3.8 ± 0.2 bar
   Engine idling 3.3 ± 0.2 bar

Note

The seal or sealing ring in the brass closure cap is **not** exchangeable. It must therefore be used only **once**.

Tightening torque of new brass closure cap
2.5 ± 0.5 Nm.

PR1029900184040X

Fig. 64 Codes P1128 & P1130: Oxygen Sensing Adaption, Idle Range Above Limit (Part 4 of 6)

3 Check volume supply of fuel pump.

Precondition:

Fuel filter and electrical supply OK.

1. Relieve pressure in fuel tank by opening tank cap.
2. Connect Porsche System Tester 2.
3. Remove complete air cleaner system.
4. Detach fuel return line from the engine compartment, taking care to **hold it fast**. Collect residual fuel.

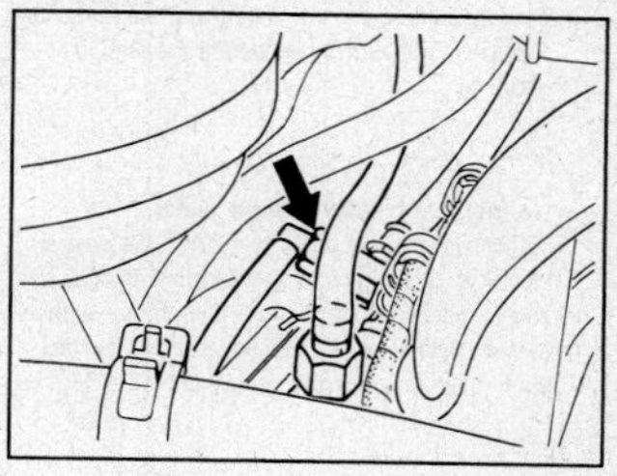

5. Connect fuel hose (shop-made, approx. 1.5 m long) to the fitting and hold in a measuring container.

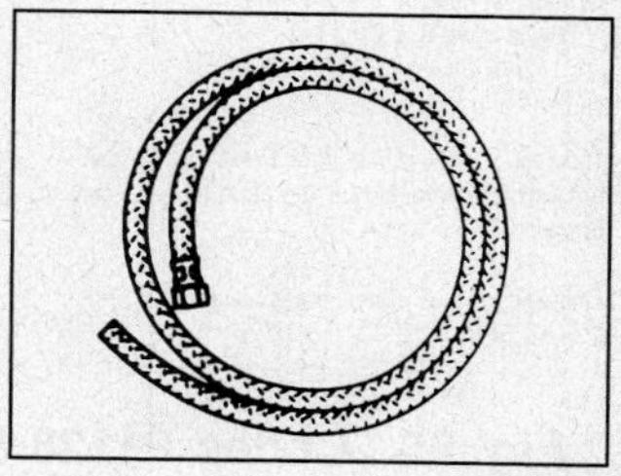

PR1029900184050X

Fig. 64 Codes P1128 & P1130: Oxygen Sensing Adaption, Idle Range Above Limit (Part 5 of 6)

6. Actuate fuel pump with the Porsche System Tester 2 and allow fuel to flow into the measuring container for 30 seconds.
   Quantity supplied must be at least **850 cm^3/30 s**, i.e. after 30 seconds at least 850 cm^3 of fuel must be in the measuring container.

Note

It is essential to observe safety regulations for handling fuel.

4 Fuel injectors fouled.

1. If preceding Check Points were negative, the fuel injectors may be fouled.
2. Clean fuel injectors (ultrasonic cleaning device) or replace them.

PR1029900184060X

Fig. 64 Codes P1128 & P1130: Oxygen Sensing Adaption, Idle Range Above Limit (Part 6 of 6)

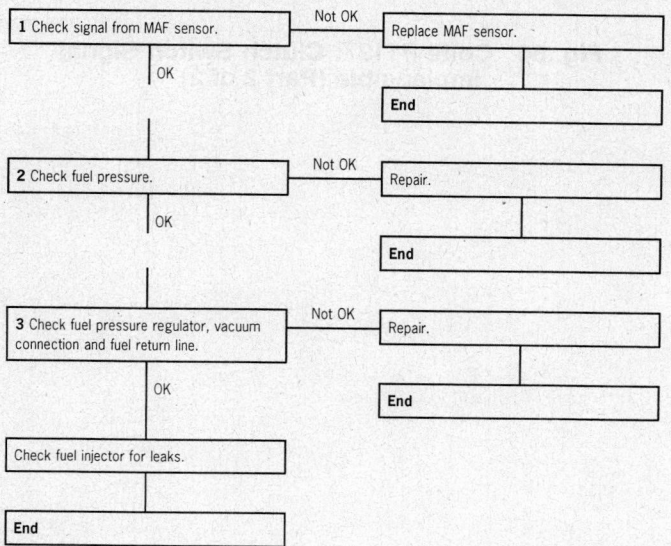

1 Check signal from MAF sensor. — Not OK → Replace MAF sensor. → **End**
OK ↓

2 Check fuel pressure. — Not OK → Repair. → **End**
OK ↓

3 Check fuel pressure regulator, vacuum connection and fuel return line. — Not OK → Repair. → **End**
OK ↓

Check fuel injector for leaks.
↓
End

PR1029900185010X

Fig. 65 Codes P1128 & P1130: Oxygen Sensing Adaption, Idle Range Below Limit (Part 1 of 4)

1 Check signal from MAF sensor.

1. Connect special tool 9637.
2. Connect voltmeter to pin III/23 and ground.
   Switch on the ignition.
   Display: 0.9 to 1.1 V

2 Check fuel pressure.

1. Undo and remove the closure cap of the fuel collection pipe test connection (A/F 13 mm).
2. Connect pressure gauge (special tool P 378a) to connecting line (special tool 9559) and connect to test connection.

PR1029900185020X

Fig. 65 Codes P1128 & P1130: Oxygen Sensing Adaption, Idle Range Below Limit (Part 2 of 4)

3. Actuate fuel pump, either

– **with Porsche System Tester 2**
The fuel pump can be actuated with the Porsche System Tester 2 or by jumpering the fuel pump relay.

or

– **via fuel pump relay without tester**
Disconnect the fuel pump relay from the central electrical system and jumper plug-in contacts 30 and 87 (identification 3 und 5 on central electrical system) with a fused shop-made cable. The fuel pump must now operate or deliver fuel.

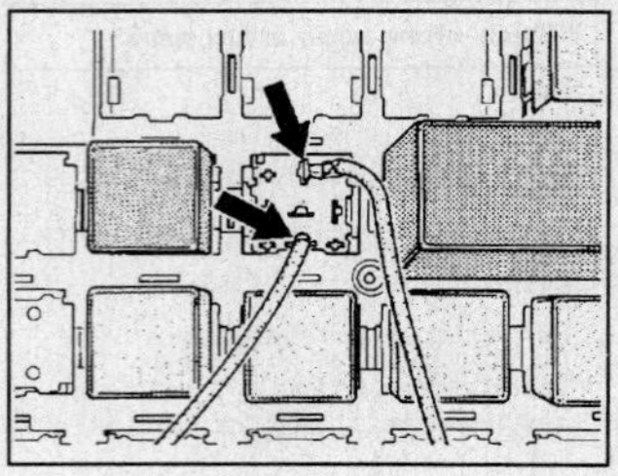

4. Nominal test values

Stationary engine 3.8 ± 0.2 bar
Engine idling 3.3 ± 0.2 bar

Note

The seal or sealing ring in the brass closure cap is **not** exchangeable. It must therefore be used only **once**.

Tightening torque of new brass closure cap
2.5 ± 0.5 Nm.

PR1029900185030X

Fig. 65 Codes P1128 & P1130: Oxygen Sensing Adaption, Idle Range Below Limit (Part 3 of 4)

3 Check fuel pressure regulator, vacuum connection and fuel return line.

1. Remove vacuum hose from fuel pressure regulator.
2. Connect special tool 9103/2 to vacuum hose.
3. Start the engine.
   Display: 0.4 - 0.6 bar

If the value is not attained, check the intake air system for leaks and check vacuum line to fuel pressure regulator for restrictions.

4. Check housing of fuel pressure regulator for damage and deformation.

Replace the fuel pressure regulator if it is damaged with the result that the spring pre-tensioning is increased.

PR1029900185040X

Fig. 65 Codes P1128 & P1130: Oxygen Sensing Adaption, Idle Range Below Limit (Part 4 of 4)

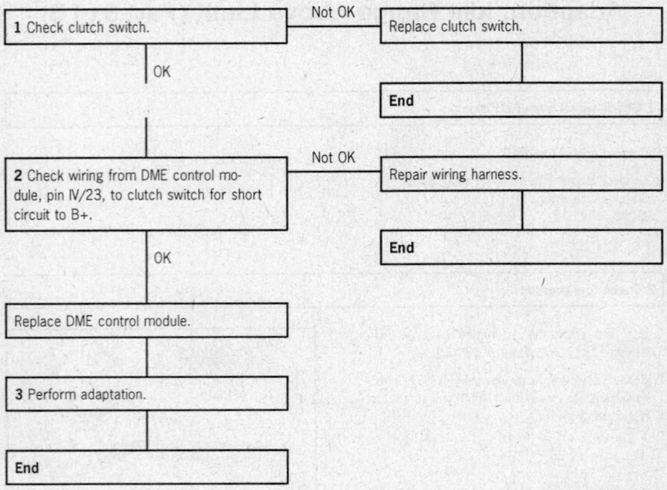

PR1029900186010X

Fig. 66 Code P1137: Clutch Switch Signal Implausible (Part 1 of 2)

1 Check clutch switch.

1. Remove clutch switch.
2. Connect ohmmeter to clutch switch, pins 1 and 4.
   Display: 0 - 5 Ω
3. Actuate clutch switch.
   Display: ∞ Ω

2 Check wiring from DME control module, pin IV/23, to clutch switch for short circuit to B+.

1. Connect special tool 9637 to wiring harness (DME control module connector).
2. Connect voltmeter to pin IV/23 and ground.
3. Switch on the ignition.
   Display: 0 V

If battery voltage is displayed, check wiring harness for chafing and pinching damage.

3 Perform adaptation.

1. Switch on the ignition.
2. Wait one minute.
   Do not press the accelerator.
3. Switch off the ignition for at least 10 seconds.
4. Read out the fault memory.

PR1029900186020X

Fig. 66 Code P1137: Clutch Switch Signal Implausible (Part 2 of 2)

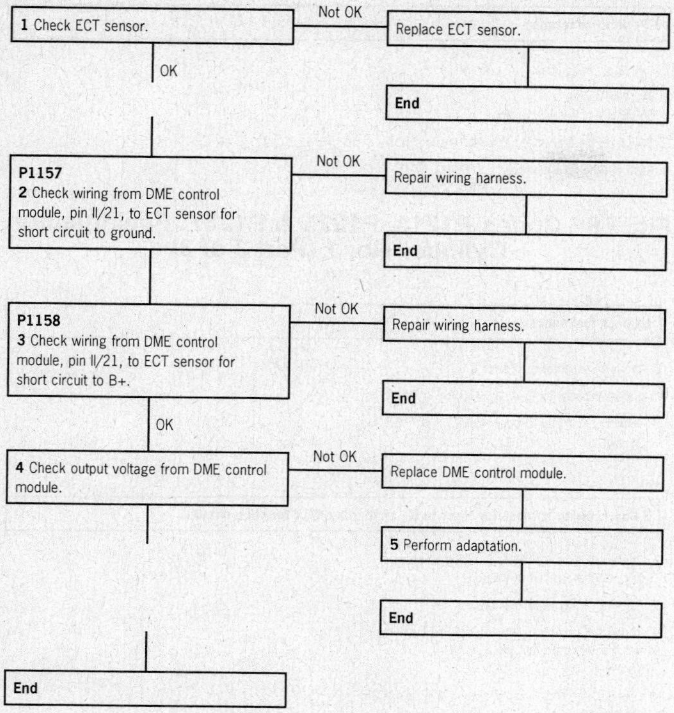

PR1029900187010X

Fig. 67 Codes P1157 & P1158: Engine Compartment Temperature (Part 1 of 3)

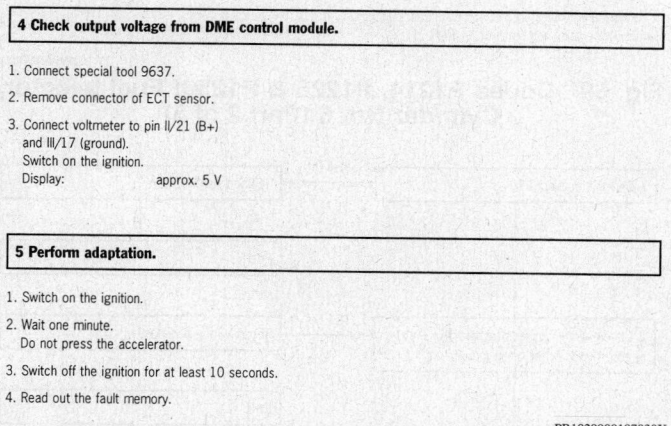

1 Check ECT sensor.

1. Remove connector of ECT sensor.
2. Connect ohmmeter to ECT sensor, pins 1 and 2.
   Display: approx. 2.2 - 2.6 kΩ at 20 °C

2 Check wiring from DME control module, pin II/21, to ECT sensor for short circuit to ground.

1. Connect special tool 9637 to wiring harness (DME control module connector).
2. Remove connector of ECT sensor.
3. Connect ohmmeter to special tool 9637, pin II/21, and ground.
   Display: ∞ Ω

If 0 - 5 Ω is displayed, check wiring harness for chafing and pinching damage.

2 Check wiring from DME control module, pin II/21, to ECT sensor for short circuit to B+.

1. Connect special tool 9637 to wiring harness (DME control module connector).
2. Remove connector of ECT sensor.
3. Connect voltmeter to special tool 9637, pin II/21, and ground.
   Switch on the ignition.
   Display: 0 V

If battery voltage is displayed, check wiring harness for chafing and pinching damage.

PR1029900187020X

Fig. 67 Codes P1157 & P1158: Engine Compartment Temperature (Part 2 of 3)

4 Check output voltage from DME control module.

1. Connect special tool 9637.
2. Remove connector of ECT sensor.
3. Connect voltmeter to pin II/21 (B+) and III/17 (ground).
   Switch on the ignition.
   Display: approx. 5 V

5 Perform adaptation.

1. Switch on the ignition.
2. Wait one minute.
   Do not press the accelerator.
3. Switch off the ignition for at least 10 seconds.
4. Read out the fault memory.

PR1029900187030X

Fig. 67 Codes P1157 & P1158: Engine Compartment Temperature (Part 3 of 3)

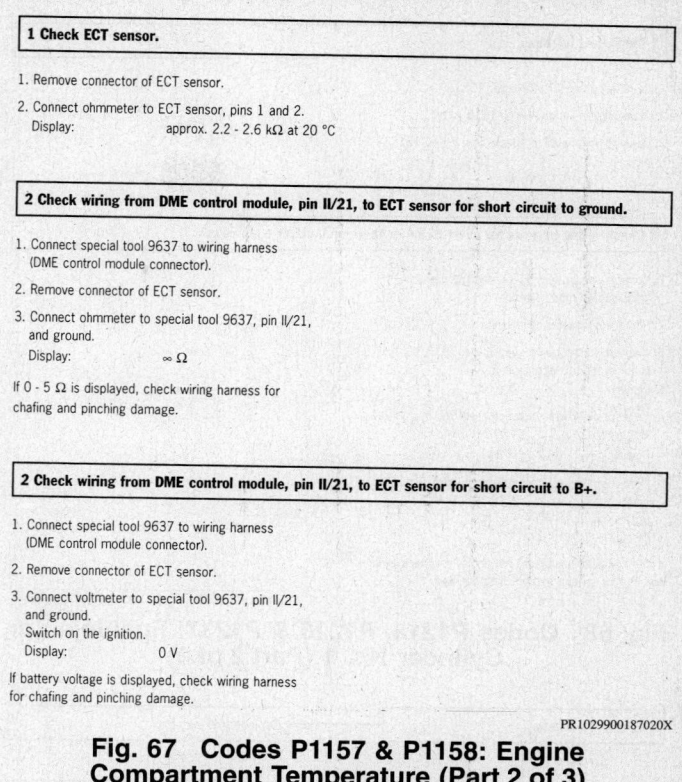

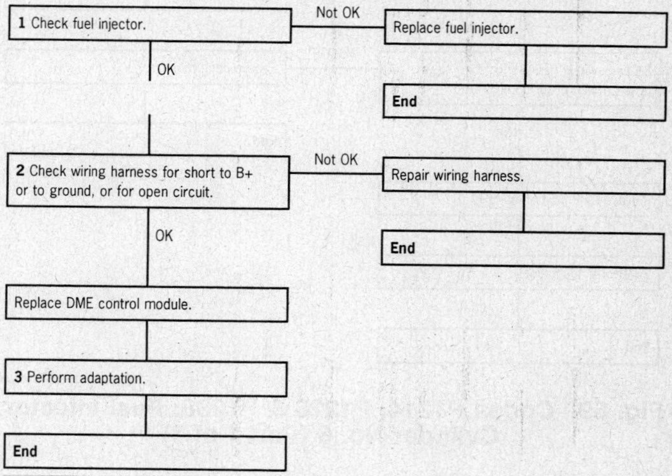

PR1029900188010X

Fig. 68 Codes P1213, P1225 & P1237: Fuel Injector, Cylinder No. 1 (Part 1 of 3)

1 Check fuel injector.

1. Remove connector of injector 1.
2. Connect special tool V.A.G. 1315 A/1.
3. Connect ohmmeter to special tool V.A.G. 1315 A/1.
   Display: 11 - 13 Ω at 20 °C.

2 Check wiring harness for short to B+ or to ground, or for open circuit.

1. Connect special tool 9637 to wiring harness (DME control module connector).
2. Remove connector of fuel injector.
3. Connect ohmmeter to special tool 9637, pin III/41, and injector connector, pin 2.
   Display: 0 - 5 Ω
4. Connect ohmmeter to special tool 9637, pin III/41, and ground.
   Display: ∞ Ω
5. Connect voltmeter to special tool 9637, pin III/41, and ground.
   Ignition on.
   Display: 0 V

If the measured values are not achieved, check wiring harness for chafing and pinching damage.

PR1029900188020X

Fig. 68 Codes P1213, P1225 & P1237: Fuel Injector, Cylinder No. 1 (Part 2 of 3)

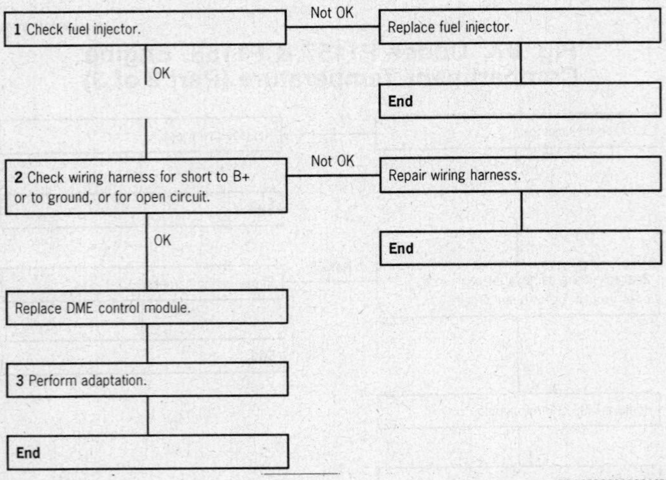

PR1029900189010X

Fig. 69 Codes P1214, P1226 & P1238: Fuel Injector, Cylinder No. 6 (Part 1 of 3)

3 Perform adaptation.

1. Switch on the ignition.
2. Wait one minute.
   Do not press the accelerator.
3. Switch off the ignition for at least 10 seconds.
4. Read out the fault memory.

PR1029900189030X

Fig. 69 Codes P1214, P1226 & P1238: Fuel Injector, Cylinder No. 6 (Part 3 of 3)

3 Perform adaptation.

1. Switch on the ignition.
2. Wait one minute.
   Do not press the accelerator.
3. Switch off the ignition for at least 10 seconds.
4. Read out the fault memory.

PR1029900188030X

Fig. 68 Codes P1213, P1225 & P1237: Fuel Injector, Cylinder No. 1 (Part 3 of 3)

1 Check fuel injector.

1. Remove connector of injector 6.
2. Connect special tool V.A.G. 1315 A/1.
3. Connect ohmmeter to special tool V.A.G. 1315 A/1.
   Display: 11 - 13 Ω at 20 °C.

2 Check wiring harness for short to B+ or to ground, or for open circuit.

1. Connect special tool 9637 to wiring harness (DME control module connector).
2. Remove connector of fuel injector.
3. Connect ohmmeter to special tool 9637, pin III/28, and injector connector, pin 2.
   Display: 0 - 5 Ω
4. Connect ohmmeter to special tool 9637, pin III/28, and ground.
   Display: ∞ Ω
5. Connect voltmeter to special tool 9637, pin III/28, and ground.
   Ignition on.
   Display: 0 V

If the measured values are not achieved, check wiring harness for chafing and pinching damage.

PR1029900189020X

Fig. 69 Codes P1214, P1226 & P1238: Fuel Injector, Cylinder No. 6 (Part 2 of 3)

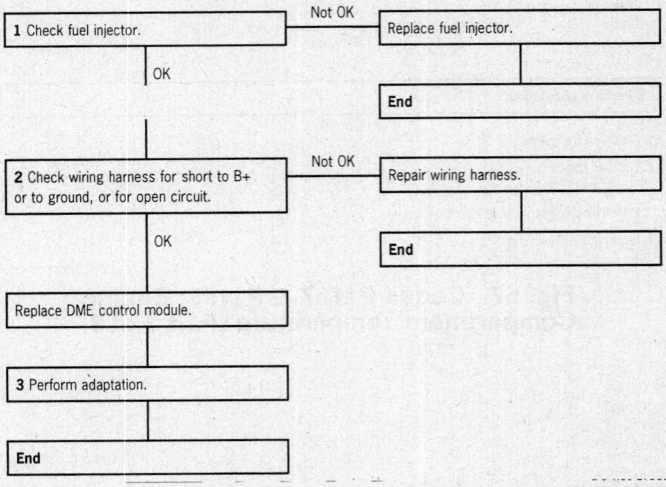

PR1029900190010X

Fig. 70 Codes P1215, P1227 & P1239: Fuel Injector, Cylinder No. 2 (Part 1 of 3)

1 Check fuel injector.

1. Remove connector of injector 2.
2. Connect special tool V.A.G. 1315 A/1.
3. Connect ohmmeter to special tool V.A.G. 1315 A/1.
   Display: 11 - 13 Ω at 20 °C.

2 Check wiring harness for short to B+ or to ground, or for open circuit.

1. Connect special tool 9637 to wiring harness (DME control module connector).
2. Remove connector of fuel injector.
3. Connect ohmmeter to special tool 9637, pin III/40, and injector connector, pin 2.
   Display: 0 - 5 Ω
4. Connect ohmmeter to special tool 9637, pin III/40, and ground.
   Display: ∞ Ω
5. Connect voltmeter to special tool 9637, pin III/40, and ground.
   Ignition on.
   Display: 0 V

If the measured values are not achieved, check wiring harness for chafing and pinching damage.

PR1029900190020X

Fig. 70 Codes P1215, P1227 & P1239: Fuel Injector, Cylinder No. 2 (Part 2 of 3)

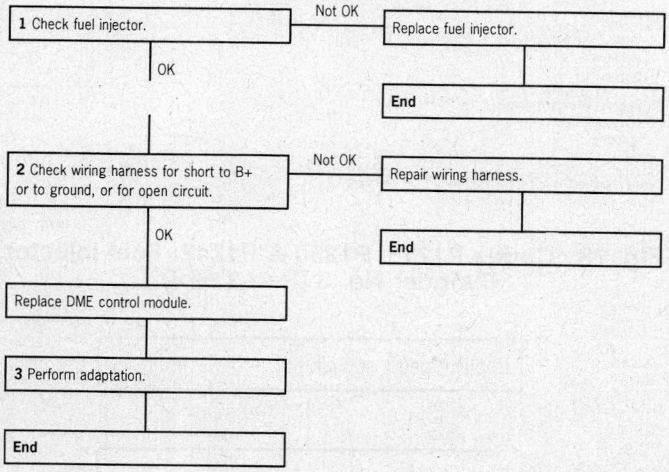

PR1029900191010X

Fig. 71 Codes P1216, P1228 & P1240: Fuel Injector, Cylinder No. 4 (Part 1 of 3)

3 Perform adaptation.

1. Switch on the ignition.
2. Wait one minute.
   Do not press the accelerator.
3. Switch off the ignition for at least 10 seconds.
4. Read out the fault memory.

PR1029900191030X

Fig. 71 Codes P1216, P1228 & P1240: Fuel Injector, Cylinder No. 4 (Part 3 of 3)

3 Perform adaptation.

1. Switch on the ignition.
2. Wait one minute.
   Do not press the accelerator.
3. Switch off the ignition for at least 10 seconds.
4. Read out the fault memory.

PR1029900190030X

Fig. 70 Codes P1215, P1227 & P1239: Fuel Injector, Cylinder No. 2 (Part 3 of 3)

1 Check fuel injector.

1. Remove connector of injector 4.
2. Connect special tool V.A.G. 1315 A/1.
3. Connect ohmmeter to special tool V.A.G. 1315 A/1.
   Display: 11 - 13 Ω at 20 °C.

2 Check wiring harness for short to B+ or to ground, or for open circuit.

1. Connect special tool 9637 to wiring harness (DME control module connector).
2. Remove connector of fuel injector.
3. Connect ohmmeter to special tool 9637, pin III/27, and injector connector, pin 2.
   Display: 0 - 5 Ω
4. Connect ohmmeter to special tool 9637, pin III/27, and ground.
   Display: ∞ Ω
5. Connect voltmeter to special tool 9637, pin III/27, and ground.
   Ignition on.
   Display: 0 V

If the measured values are not achieved, check wiring harness for chafing and pinching damage.

PR1029900191020X

Fig. 71 Codes P1216, P1228 & P1240: Fuel Injector, Cylinder No. 4 (Part 2 of 3)

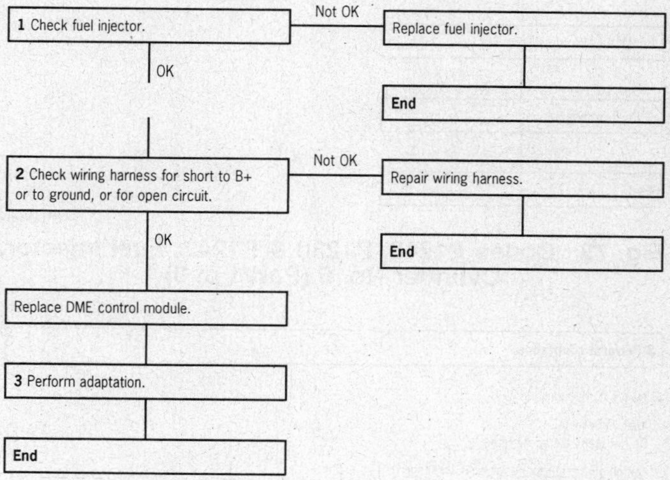

PR1029900192010X

Fig. 72 Codes P1217, P1229 & P1241: Fuel Injector, Cylinder No. 3 (Part 1 of 3)

1 Check fuel injector.

1. Remove connector of injector 3.
2. Connect special tool V.A.G. 1315 A/1.
3. Connect ohmmeter to special tool V.A.G. 1315 A/1.
   Display: 11 - 13 Ω at 20 °C.

2 Check wiring harness for short to B+ or to ground, or for open circuit.

1. Connect special tool 9637 to wiring harness (DME control module connector).
2. Remove connector of fuel injector.
3. Connect ohmmeter to special tool 9637, pin III/15, and injector connector, pin 2.
   Display: 0 - 5 Ω
4. Connect ohmmeter to special tool 9637, pin III/15, and ground.
   Display: ∞ Ω
5. Connect voltmeter to special tool 9637, pin III/15, and ground.
   Ignition on.
   Display: 0 V

If the measured values are not achieved, check wiring harness for chafing and pinching damage.

PR1029900192020X

Fig. 72 Codes P1217, P1229 & P1241: Fuel Injector, Cylinder No. 3 (Part 2 of 3)

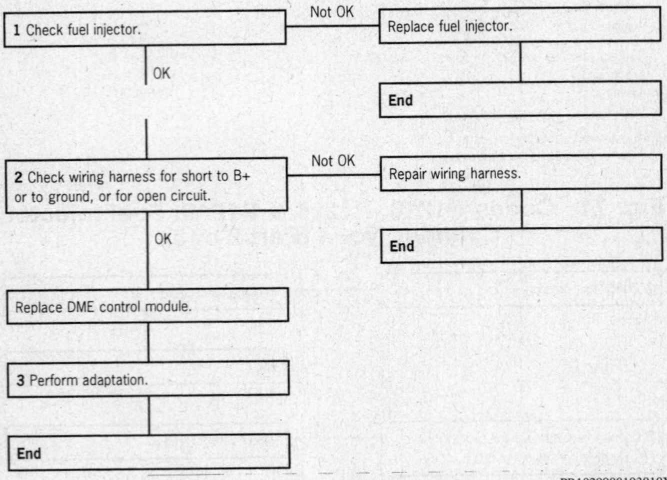

PR1029900193010X

Fig. 73 Codes P1218, P1230 & P1242: Fuel Injector, Cylinder No. 5 (Part 1 of 3)

3 Perform adaptation.

1. Switch on the ignition.
2. Wait one minute.
   Do not press the accelerator.
3. Switch off the ignition for at least 10 seconds.
4. Read out the fault memory.

PR1029900193030X

Fig. 73 Codes P1218, P1230 & P1242: Fuel Injector, Cylinder No. 5 (Part 3 of 3)

3 Perform adaptation.

1. Switch on the ignition.
2. Wait one minute.
   Do not press the accelerator.
3. Switch off the ignition for at least 10 seconds.
4. Read out the fault memory.

PR1029900192030X

Fig. 72 Codes P1217, P1229 & P1241: Fuel Injector, Cylinder No. 3 (Part 3 of 3)

1 Check fuel injector.

1. Remove connector of injector 5.
2. Connect special tool V.A.G. 1315 A/1.
3. Connect ohmmeter to special tool V.A.G. 1315 A/1.
   Display: 11 - 13 Ω at 20 °C.

2 Check wiring harness for short to B+ or to ground, or for open circuit.

1. Connect special tool 9637 to wiring harness (DME control module connector).
2. Remove connector of fuel injector.
3. Connect ohmmeter to special tool 9637, pin III/2, and injector connector, pin 2.
   Display: 0 - 5 Ω
4. Connect ohmmeter to special tool 9637, pin III/2, and ground.
   Display: ∞ Ω
5. Connect voltmeter to special tool 9637, pin III/2, and ground.
   Ignition on.
   Display: 0 V

If the measured values are not achieved, check wiring harness for chafing and pinching damage.

PR1029900193020X

Fig. 73 Codes P1218, P1230 & P1242: Fuel Injector, Cylinder No. 5 (Part 2 of 3)

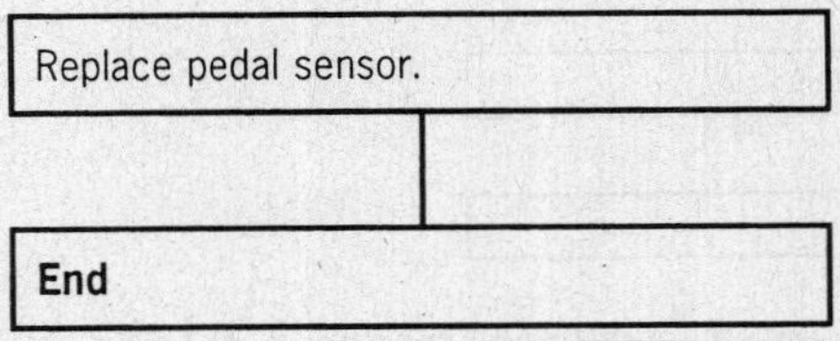

PR1029900194000X

Fig. 74 Code P1219: Accelerator Pedal Signal Implausible

1 Check wiring from airbag control module to DME control module for continuity.
- Not OK → Repair wiring harness. → **End**
- OK ↓

2 Check wiring from airbag control module to DME control module for short to ground.
- Not OK → Repair wiring harness. → **End**
- ↓

3 Check signal from airbag control module.
- Not OK → Replace airbag control module. → **End**
- OK ↓

Erase fault memory.

End

PR1029900195010X

Fig. 75 Code P1265: Air Bag Signal Implausible (Part 1 of 3)

3 Check signal from airbag control module.

1. Connect special tool 9637.
2. Connect engine tester (oscilloscope) to pin IV/16 and ground.
   Use special input.
3. Ignition on.
   The signal shown opposite should be displayed:

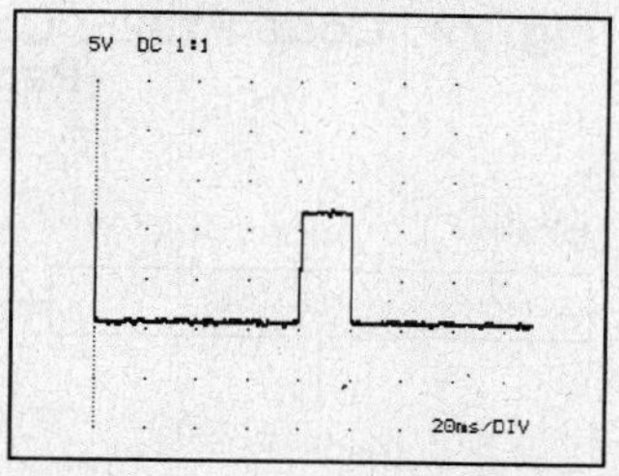

PR1029900195030X

Fig. 75 Code P1265: Air Bag Signal Implausible (Part 3 of 3)

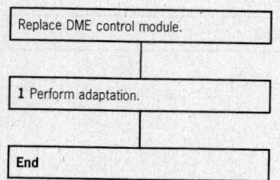

Replace DME control module.

1 Perform adaptation.

End

1 Perform adaptation.

1. Switch on the ignition.
2. Wait one minute.
   Do not press the accelerator.
3. Switch off the ignition for at least 10 seconds.
4. Read out the fault memory.

PR1029900196000X

Fig. 76 Codes P1266 & P1508: Fuel Shutoff Function Monitor & Torque Comparison Function Monitor

1 Check wiring from airbag control module to DME control module for continuity.

1. Connect special tool 9637 to wiring harness (DME control module connector).
2. Remove connector of airbag control module.
3. Connect ohmmeter to special tool 9637, pin IV/16, and airbag connector, pin 24 or 34.
   Display: 0 - 5 Ω

If ∞ Ω is displayed, check connector X2/5 or check wiring harness for chafing and pinching damage.

2 Check wiring from airbag control module to DME control module for short to ground.

1. Connect special tool 9637 to wiring harness (DME control module connector).
2. Remove connector of airbag control module.
3. Connect ohmmeter to special tool 9637, pin IV/16, and ground.
   Display: ∞ Ω

If 0 - 5 Ω is displayed, check wiring harness for chafing and pinching damage.

PR1029900195020X

Fig. 75 Code P1265: Air Bag Signal Implausible (Part 2 of 3)

Below limit

1 Check triggering wire for short to ground.
- Not OK → Repair wiring harness. → **End**
- OK ↓

Replace actuator.

End

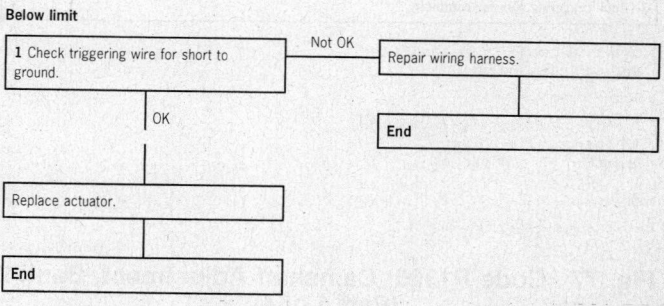

PR1029900197010X

Fig. 77 Code P1325: Camshaft Adjustment, Bank 2 (Part 1 of 4)

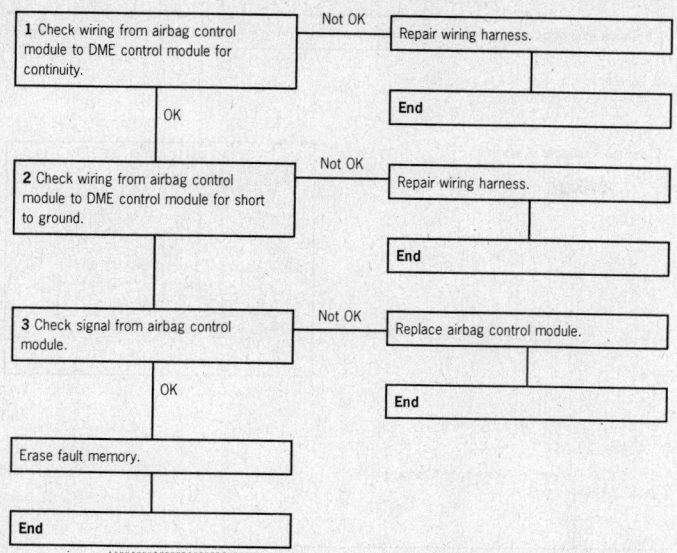

Above limit

2 Check B+ supply of actuator. — Not OK → Repair B+ supply. → End

OK ↓

3 Check triggering wire for continuity. — Not OK → Repair wiring harness. → End

OK ↓

Replace actuator.

End

Signal implausible

Replace actuator.

End

PR1029900197020X

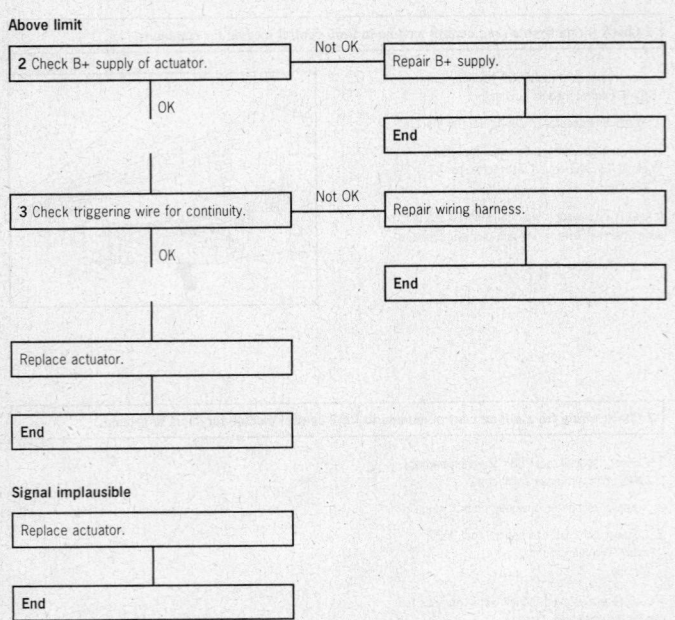

Fig. 77 Code P1325: Camshaft Adjustment, Bank 2 (Part 2 of 4)

3 Check triggering wire for continuity.

1. Connect special tool 9637 to wiring harness (DME control module connector).
2. Remove connector of actuator.
3. Connect ohmmeter to special tool 9637, pin V/3, and connector, pin 2.
   Display: 0 - 5 Ω

Note

The wire is routed via connector X 59/1.

PR1029900197040X

Fig. 77 Code P1325: Camshaft Adjustment, Bank 2 (Part 4 of 4)

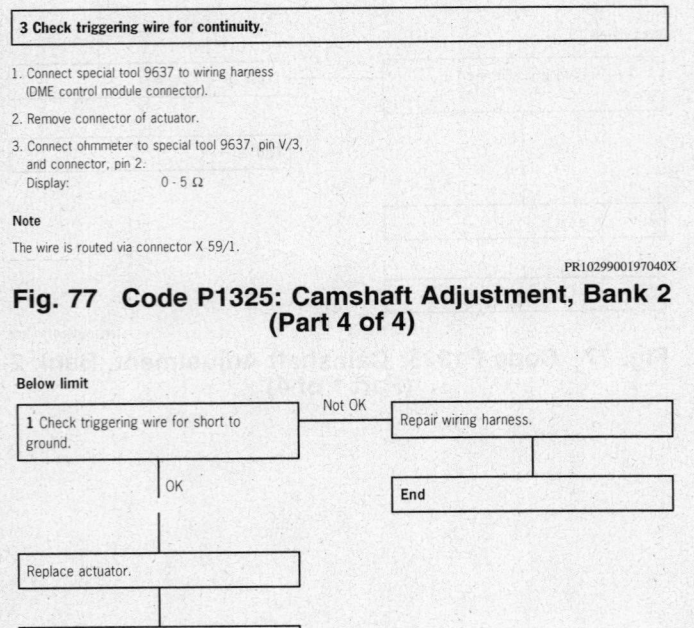

Below limit

1 Check triggering wire for short to ground. — Not OK → Repair wiring harness. → End

OK ↓

Replace actuator.

End

PR1029900198010X

Fig. 78 Code P1341: Camshaft Adjustment, Bank 2 (Part 1 of 4)

1 Check triggering wire for short to ground.

1. Connect special tool 9637 to wiring harness (DME control module connector).
2. Remove connector of actuator.

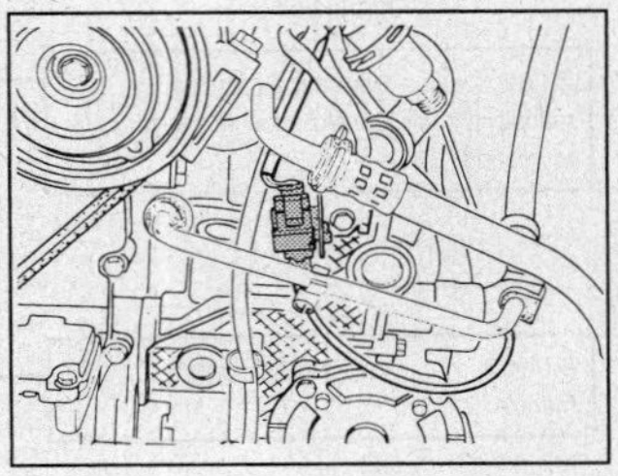

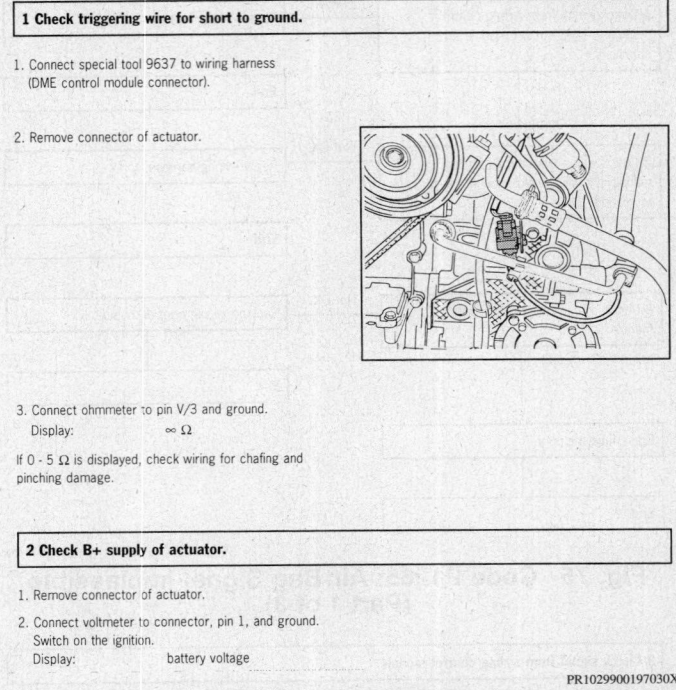

3. Connect ohmmeter to pin V/3 and ground.
   Display: ∞ Ω

If 0 - 5 Ω is displayed, check wiring for chafing and pinching damage.

2 Check B+ supply of actuator.

1. Remove connector of actuator.
2. Connect voltmeter to connector, pin 1, and ground.
   Switch on the ignition.
   Display: battery voltage

PR1029900197030X

Fig. 77 Code P1325: Camshaft Adjustment, Bank 2 (Part 3 of 4)

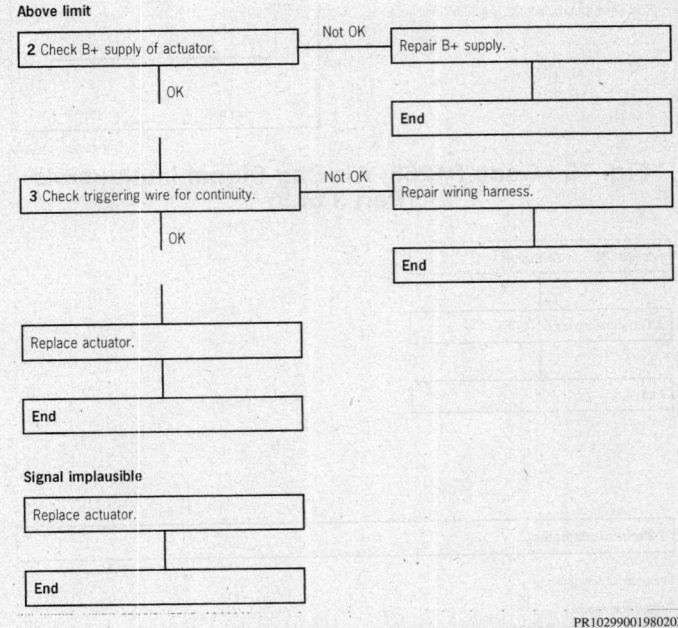

Above limit

2 Check B+ supply of actuator. — Not OK → Repair B+ supply. → End

OK ↓

3 Check triggering wire for continuity. — Not OK → Repair wiring harness. → End

OK ↓

Replace actuator.

End

Signal implausible

Replace actuator.

End

PR1029900198020X

Fig. 78 Code P1341: Camshaft Adjustment, Bank 2 (Part 2 of 4)

1 Check triggering wire for short to ground.

1. Connect special tool 9637 to wiring harness (DME control module connector).
2. Remove connector of actuator.

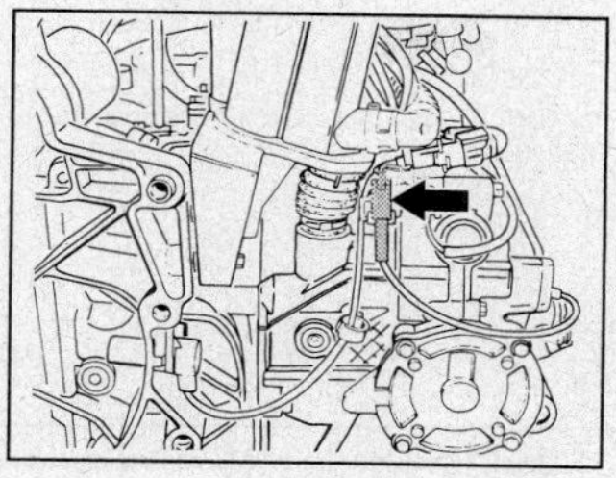

3. Connect ohmmeter to pin V/1 and ground.
   Display: ∞ Ω

If 0 - 5 Ω is displayed, check wiring for chafing and pinching damage.

2 Check B+ supply of actuator.

1. Remove connector of actuator.
2. Connect voltmeter to connector, pin 1, and ground.
   Switch on the ignition.
   Display: battery voltage

PR1029900198030X

Fig. 78 Code P1341: Camshaft Adjustment, Bank 2 (Part 3 of 4)

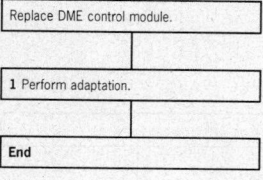

Replace DME control module.

1 Perform adaptation.

End

1 Perform adaptation.

1. Switch on the ignition.
2. Wait one minute.
   Do not press the accelerator.
3. Switch off the ignition for at least 10 seconds.
4. Read out the fault memory.

PR1029900199000X

Fig. 79 Codes P1384, P1385 & P1386: Knock Control Signal Implausible

3 Check triggering wire for continuity.

1. Connect special tool 9637 to wiring harness (DME control module connector).
2. Remove connector of actuator.
3. Connect ohmmeter to special tool 9637, pin V/1, and connector, pin 2.
   Display: 0 - 5 Ω

Note

The wire is routed via connector X 59/1.

PR1029900198040X

Fig. 78 Code P1341: Camshaft Adjustment, Bank 2 (Part 4 of 4)

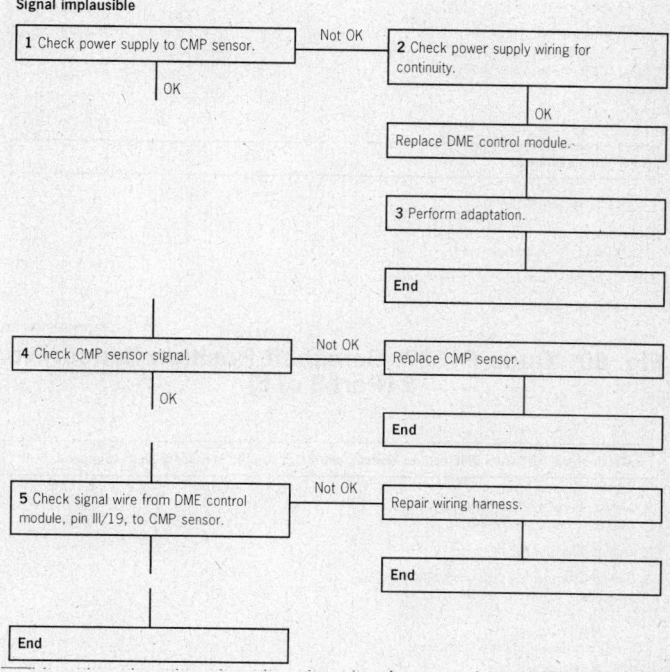

Signal implausible

- **1** Check power supply to CMP sensor.
  - Not OK → **2** Check power supply wiring for continuity.
    - OK → Replace DME control module. → **3** Perform adaptation. → **End**
  - OK → **4** Check CMP sensor signal.
    - Not OK → Replace CMP sensor. → **End**
    - OK → **5** Check signal wire from DME control module, pin III/19, to CMP sensor.
      - Not OK → Repair wiring harness. → **End**
      - → **End**

PR1029900200010X

Fig. 80 Code P1397: Camshaft Position Sensor No. 2 (Part 1 of 5)

Below limit

- **6** Check signal wire from DME control module, pin III/19, to CMP sensor for short to ground.
  - Not OK → Repair wiring harness. → **End**
  - → **End**

Above limit

- **7** Check signal wire from DME control module, pin III/19, to CMP sensor for short circuit to B+.
  - Not OK → Repair wiring harness. → **End**
  - → **End**

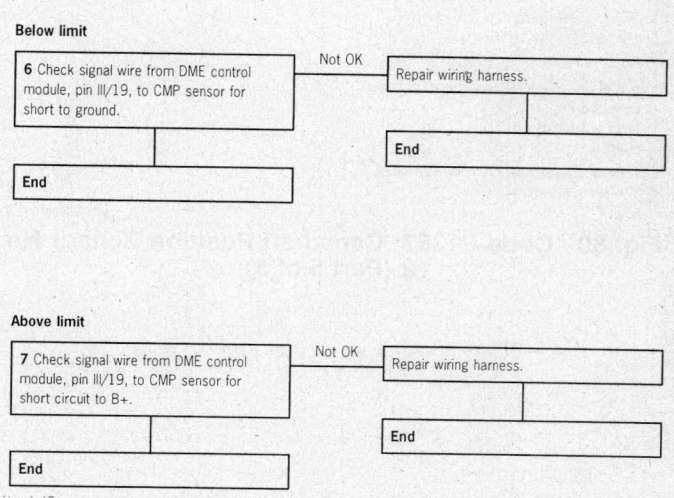

PR1029900200020X

Fig. 80 Code P1397: Camshaft Position Sensor No. 2 (Part 2 of 5)

1 Check power supply to CMP sensor.

1. Remove connector of CMP sensor 2.
2. Switch on the ignition.
3. Connect voltmeter to pin 1 (negative) and pin 3 (positive).
   Display: approx. 5 V

2 Check power supply wiring for continuity.

1. Remove connector of CMP sensor 2.
2. Connect special tool 9637 to wiring harness (DME control module connector).
3. Connect ohmmeter to special tool 9637, pin III/7, and to CMP sensor connector 2, pin 3.
   Display: 0 - 5 Ω
4. Connect ohmmeter to special tool 9637, pin III/17, and to CMP sensor connector 2, pin 1.
   Display: 0 - 5 Ω

3 Perform adaptation.

1. Switch on the ignition.
2. Wait one minute.
   Do not press the accelerator.
3. Switch off the ignition for at least 10 seconds.
4. Read out the fault memory.

PR1029900200030X

Fig. 80 Code P1397: Camshaft Position Sensor No. 2 (Part 3 of 5)

6 Check signal wire from DME control module, pin III/19, to CMP sensor for short to ground.

1. Connect special tool 9637 to wiring harness (DME control module connector).
2. Remove connector of CMP sensor.
3. Connect ohmmeter to special tool 9637, pin III/19, and ground.
   Display: ∞ Ω

If 0 - 5 Ω is displayed, check wiring harness for chafing and pinching damage.

7 Check signal wire from DME control module, pin III/19, to CMP sensor for short circuit to B+.

1. Connect special tool 9637 to wiring harness (DME control module connector).
2. Remove connector of CMP sensor.
3. Connect voltmeter to special tool 9637, pin III/19, and ground.
   Switch on the ignition.
   Display: 0 V

If battery voltage is displayed, check wiring harness for chafing and pinching damage.

PR1029900200050X

Fig. 80 Code P1397: Camshaft Position Sensor No. 2 (Part 5 of 5)

4 Check CMP sensor signal.

1. Connect special tool 9637.
2. Connect engine tester. Using special input, connect positive cable to pin III/19, negative cable to pin III/17.
3. Start the engine.

The display pictured opposite should appear on the oscilloscope:

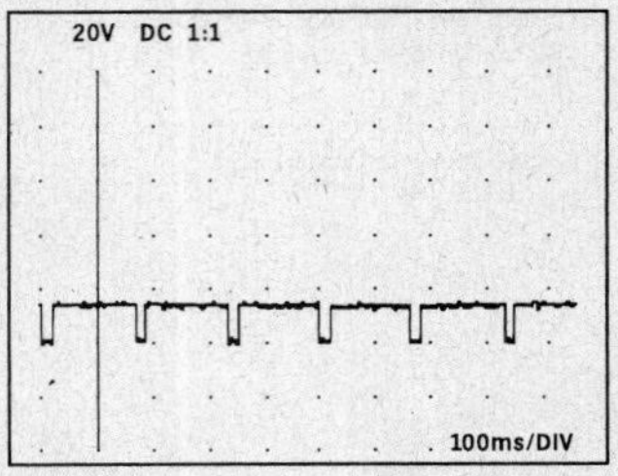

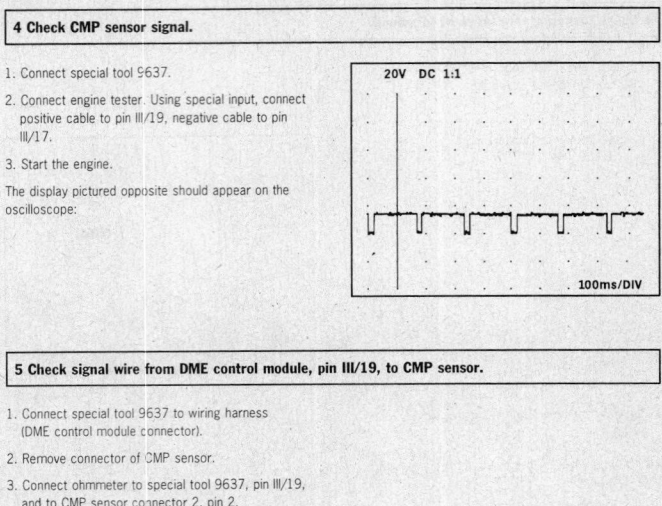

5 Check signal wire from DME control module, pin III/19, to CMP sensor.

1. Connect special tool 9637 to wiring harness (DME control module connector).
2. Remove connector of CMP sensor.
3. Connect ohmmeter to special tool 9637, pin III/19, and to CMP sensor connector 2, pin 2.
   Display: 0 - 5 Ω

PR1029900200040X

Fig. 80 Code P1397: Camshaft Position Sensor No. 2 (Part 4 of 5)

DTC P1455

1 Check control wire for A/C relay, pin 2 (terminal 85), for open circuit.
- Not OK → Repair wiring harness. → **End**
- OK → **End**

DTC P1456

2 Check control wire for A/C relay, pin 2 (terminal 85), for short circuit to B+.
- Not OK → Repair wiring harness. → **End**
- OK → **End**

DTC P1457

3 Check control wire for A/C relay, pin 2 (terminal 85), for short circuit to ground.
- Not OK → Repair wiring harness. → **End**
- OK → **End**

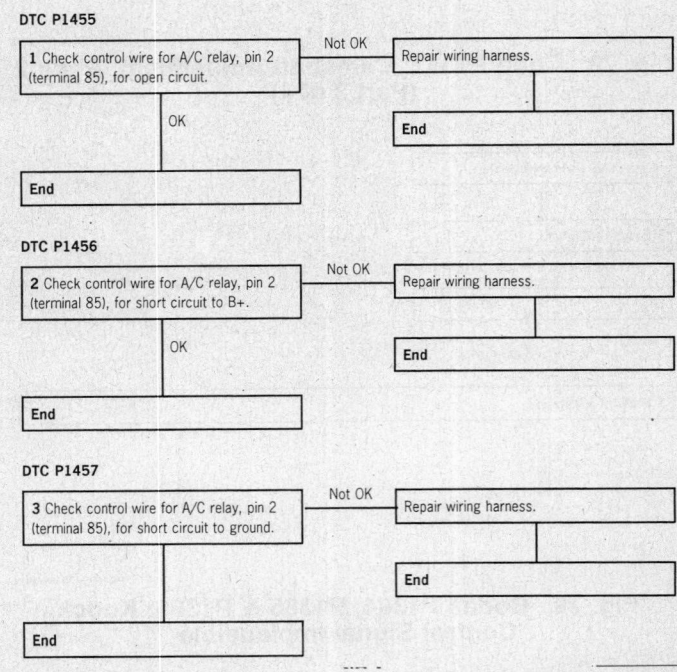

PR1029900201010X

Fig. 81 Codes P1455, P1456 & P1457: A/C Compressor Control (Part 1 of 2)

1 Check control wire for A/C relay, pin 2, for open circuit.

1. Remove A/C relay.
2. Connect special tool 9637 to wiring harness (DME control module connector).
3. Connect ohmmeter to special tool 9637, pin II/18, and A/C relay, pin 2.
   Display: 0 - 5 Ω

2 Check control wire for A/C relay, pin 2, for short circuit to B+.

1. Remove A/C relay.
2. Remove DME control module connector.
3. Connect voltmeter (positive) to A/C relay, pin 2, and ground.
   Display: 0 V

If battery voltage is displayed, check wiring harness for chafing and pinching damage.

3 Check control wire for A/C relay, pin 2 (terminal 85), for short circuit to ground.

1. Remove A/C relay.
2. Remove DME control module connector.
3. Connect ohmmeter to ground and pin 2 (terminal 85).
   Display: ∞ Ω

If 0 - 5 Ω is displayed, check wiring for chafing and pinching damage.

PR1029900201020X

Fig. 81 Codes P1455, P1456 & P1457: A/C Compressor Control (Part 2 of 2)

1 Check wiring from DME control module, pin III/42, to throttle part for short circuit to B+.

1. Connect special tool 9637 to wiring harness (DME control module connector).
2. Connect voltmeter to pin III/42 and ground.
3. Switch on the ignition.
   Display: 0 V

If battery voltage is displayed, check wiring harness for chafing and pinching damage.

2 Check wiring from DME control module, pin III/42, to throttle part for short circuit to ground.

1. Connect special tool 9637 to wiring harness (DME control module connector).
2. Connect ohmmeter to pin III/42 and ground.
   Display: ∞ Ω

If 0 - 5 Ω is displayed, check wiring for chafing and pinching damage.

PR1029900202020X

Fig. 82 Code P1501: Throttle Jacking Unit, Output Stage Signal Implausible (Part 2 of 2)

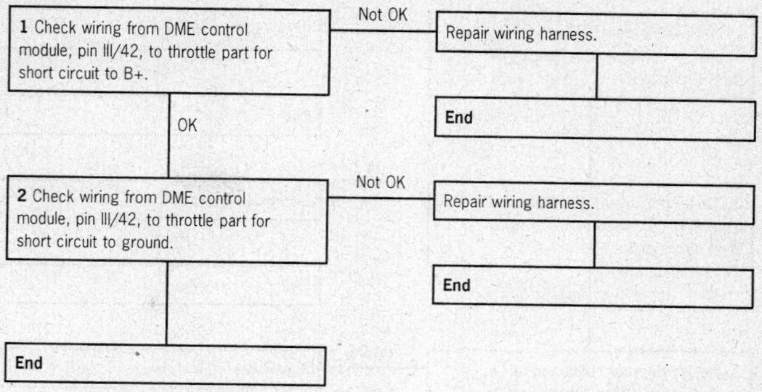

PR1029900202010X

Fig. 82 Code P1501: Throttle Jacking Unit, Output Stage Signal Implausible (Part 1 of 2)

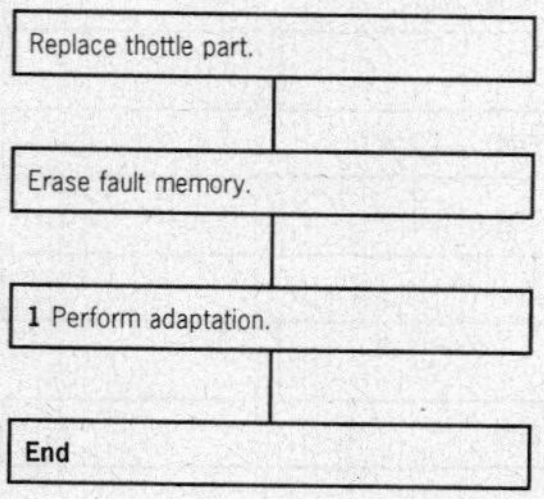

1 Perform adaptation.

1. Switch on the ignition.
2. Wait one minute.
   Do not press the accelerator.
3. Switch off the ignition for at least 10 seconds.
4. Read out the fault memory.

PR1029900203000X

Fig. 83 Code P1502: Throttle Jacking Unit, Spring Test

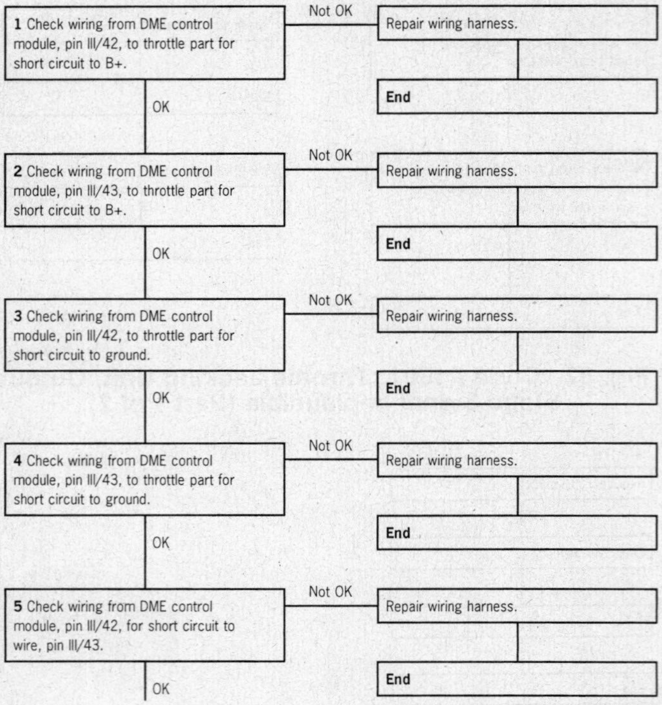

PR1029900204010X

Fig. 84 Code P1503: Throttle Jacking Unit, Position Error, Signal Implausible (Part 1 of 5)

1 Check wiring from DME control module, pin III/42, to throttle part for short circuit to B+.

1. Connect special tool 9637.
2. Connect voltmeter to pin III/42 and ground.
3. Switch on the ignition.
   Display: 0 V

If battery voltage is displayed, check wiring harness for chafing and pinching damage.

2 Check wiring from DME control module, pin III/43, to throttle part for short circuit to B+.

1. Connect special tool 9637.
2. Connect voltmeter to pin III/43 and ground.
3. Switch on the ignition.
   Display: 0 V

If battery voltage is displayed, check wiring harness for chafing and pinching damage.

3 Check wiring from DME control module, pin III/42, to throttle part for short circuit to ground.

1. Connect special tool 9637.
2. Connect voltmeter to pin III/42 and B+.
3. Switch on the ignition.
   Display: 0 V

If battery voltage is displayed, check wiring harness for chafing and pinching damage.

PR1029900204030X

Fig. 84 Code P1503: Throttle Jacking Unit, Position Error, Signal Implausible (Part 3 of 5)

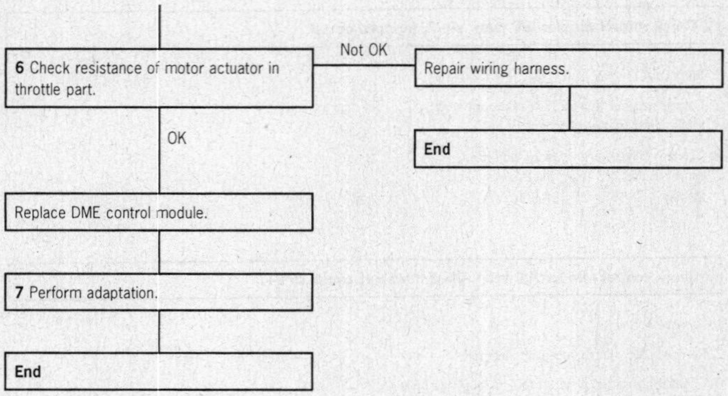

PR1029900204020X

Fig. 84 Code P1503: Throttle Jacking Unit, Position Error, Signal Implausible (Part 2 of 5)

4 Check wiring from DME control module, pin III/43, to throttle part for short circuit to ground.

1. Connect special tool 9637.
2. Connect voltmeter to pin III/43 and B+.
3. Switch on the ignition.
   Display: 0 V

If battery voltage is displayed, check wiring harness for chafing and pinching damage.

5 Check wiring from DME control module, pin III/42, for short circuit to wire, pin III/43.

1. Connect special tool 9637 to wiring harness (DME control module connector).
2. Remove connector of throttle part.

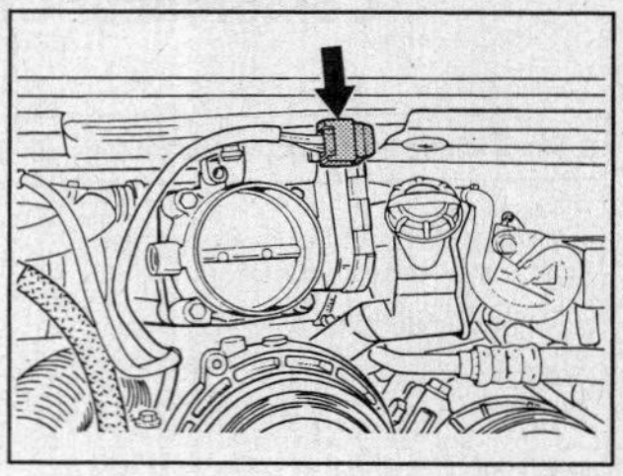

3. Connect ohmmeter to pins III/42 and III/43.
   Display: ∞ Ω

If 0 - 5 Ω is displayed, check wiring harness for chafing and pinching damage.

PR1029900204040X

Fig. 84 Code P1503: Throttle Jacking Unit, Position Error, Signal Implausible (Part 4 of 5)

6 Check resistance of motor actuator in throttle part.

1. Connect special tool 9637 to wiring harness (DME control module connector).
2. Connect ohmmeter to pins III/42 and III/43.
   Display: 1.2 - 1.6 Ω at 20 °C.

7 Perform adaptation.

1. Switch on the ignition.
2. Wait one minute.
   Do not press the accelerator.
3. Switch off the ignition for at least 10 seconds.
4. Read out the fault memory.

PR1029900204050X

Fig. 84 Code P1503: Throttle Jacking Unit, Position Error, Signal Implausible (Part 5 of 5)

1 Perform adaptation. — OK → Replace thottle part. → **1** Perform adaptation. → **End**

End

1 Perform adaptation.

1. Switch on the ignition.
2. Wait one minute.
   Do not press the accelerator.
3. Switch off the ignition for at least 10 seconds.
4. Read out the fault memory.

PR1029900205000X

Fig. 85 Code P1504: Throttle Jacking Unit, Emergency Air Position, Signal Implausible

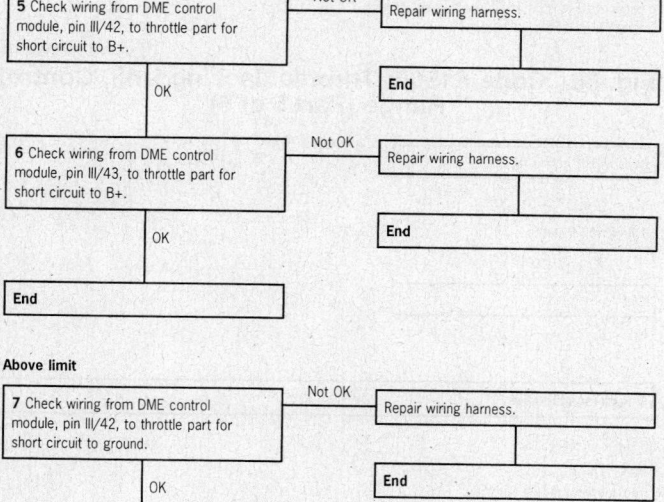

5 Check wiring from DME control module, pin III/42, to throttle part for short circuit to B+.
- Not OK → Repair wiring harness. → **End**
- OK ↓

6 Check wiring from DME control module, pin III/43, to throttle part for short circuit to B+.
- Not OK → Repair wiring harness. → **End**
- OK ↓

End

Above limit

7 Check wiring from DME control module, pin III/42, to throttle part for short circuit to ground.
- Not OK → Repair wiring harness. → **End**
- OK ↓

8 Check wiring from DME control module, pin III/43, to throttle part for short circuit to ground.
- Not OK → Repair wiring harness. → **End**
- OK ↓

End

PR1029900206020X

Fig. 86 Code P1505: Throttle Jacking Unit, Control Range (Part 2 of 5)

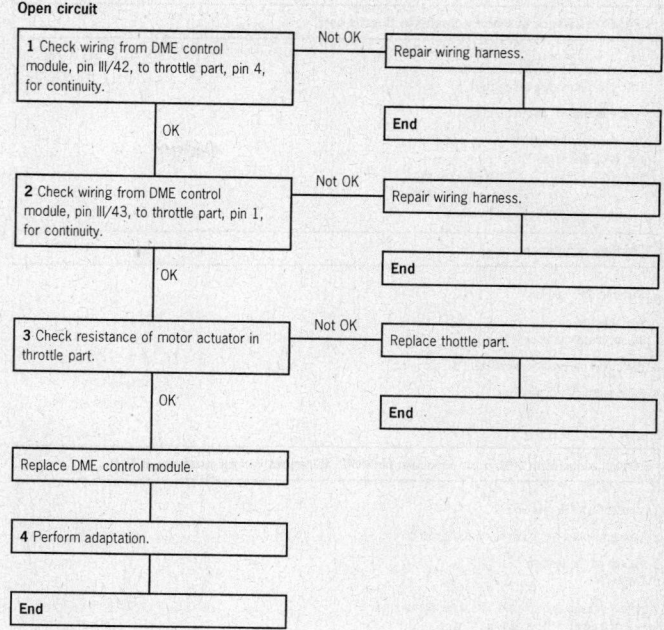

Open circuit

1 Check wiring from DME control module, pin III/42, to throttle part, pin 4, for continuity.
- Not OK → Repair wiring harness. → **End**
- OK ↓

2 Check wiring from DME control module, pin III/43, to throttle part, pin 1, for continuity.
- Not OK → Repair wiring harness. → **End**
- OK ↓

3 Check resistance of motor actuator in throttle part.
- Not OK → Replace thottle part. → **End**
- OK ↓

Replace DME control module.

4 Perform adaptation.

End

PR1029900206010X

Fig. 86 Code P1505: Throttle Jacking Unit, Control Range (Part 1 of 5)

1 Check wiring from DME control module, pin III/42, to throttle part, pin 4, for continuity.

1. Connect special tool 9637 to wiring harness (DME control module connector).
2. Remove connector of throttle part.

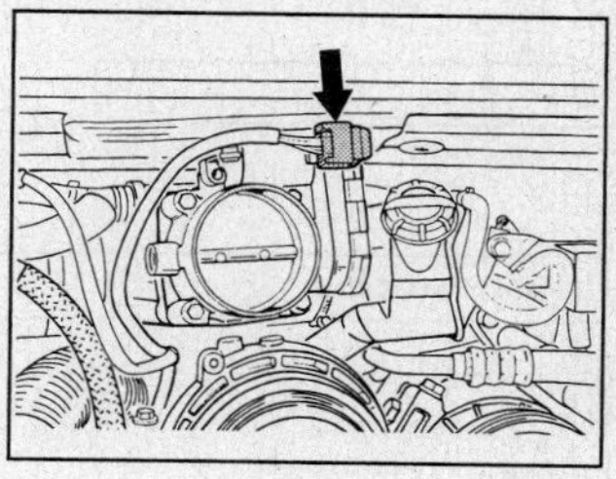

3. Connect ohmmeter to special tool 9637, pin III/42, and throttle part connector, pin 4.
   Display: 0 - 5 Ω

If ∞ Ω is displayed, check wiring harness for chafing and pinching damage.

2 Check wiring from DME control module, pin III/43, to throttle part, pin 1, for continuity.

1. Connect special tool 9637 to wiring harness (DME control module connector).
2. Remove connector of throttle part.
3. Connect ohmmeter to special tool 9637, pin III/43, and throttle part connector, pin 1.
   Display: 0 - 5 Ω

If ∞ Ω is displayed, check wiring harness for chafing and pinching damage.

PR1029900206030X

Fig. 86 Code P1505: Throttle Jacking Unit, Control Range (Part 3 of 5)

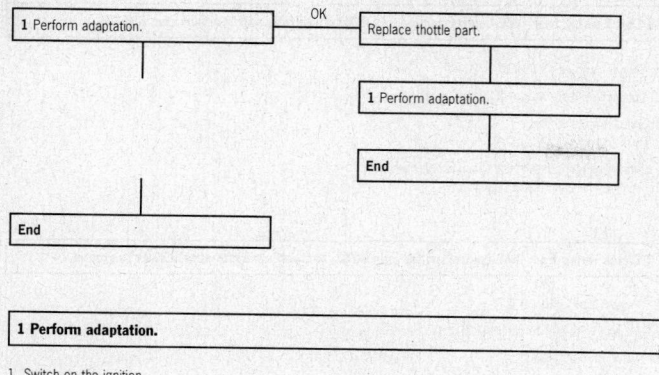

3 Check resistance of motor actuator in throttle part.

1. Connect special tool 9637 to wiring harness (DME control module connector).
2. Plug in connector of throttle part.
3. Connect ohmmeter to special tool 9637, pins III/42 and III/43.
   Display: 1.2 - 1.6 Ω at 20 °C

4 Perform adaptation.

1. Switch on the ignition.
2. Wait one minute.
   Do not press the accelerator.
3. Switch off the ignition for at least 10 seconds.
4. Read out the fault memory.

5 Check wiring from DME control module, pin III/42, to throttle part for short circuit to B+.

1. Connect special tool 9637.
2. Connect voltmeter to pin III/43 and ground.
3. Switch on the ignition.
   Display: 0 V

If battery voltage is displayed, check wiring harness for chafing and pinching damage.

PR1029900206040X

Fig. 86 Code P1505: Throttle Jacking Unit, Control Range (Part 4 of 5)

Diagnosis Procedure

1 Perform adaptation.

End

1 Perform adaptation.

1. Switch on the ignition.
2. Wait one minute.
   Do not press the accelerator.
3. Switch off the ignition for at least 10 seconds.
4. Read out the fault memory.

PR1029900207000X

Fig. 87 Code P1506: Throttle Jacking Unit, Lower Mechanical Stop

6 Check wiring from DME control module, pin III/43, to throttle part for short circuit to B+.

1. Connect special tool 9637.
2. Connect voltmeter to pin III/43 and ground.
3. Switch on the ignition.
   Display: 0 V

If battery voltage is displayed, check wiring harness for chafing and pinching damage.

7 Check wiring from DME control module, pin III/42, to throttle part for short circuit to ground.

1. Connect special tool 9637.
2. Connect voltmeter to pin III/42 and B+.
3. Switch on the ignition.
   Display: 0 V

If battery voltage is displayed, check wiring harness for chafing and pinching damage.

8 Check wiring from DME control module, pin III/43, to throttle part for short circuit to ground.

1. Connect special tool 9637.
2. Connect voltmeter to pin III/42 and B+.
3. Switch on the ignition.
   Display: 0 V

If battery voltage is displayed, check wiring harness for chafing and pinching damage.

PR1029900206050X

Fig. 86 Code P1505: Throttle Jacking Unit, Control Range (Part 5 of 5)

Replace DME control module.

1 Perform adaptation.

End

1 Perform adaptation.

1. Switch on the ignition.
2. Wait one minute.
   Do not press the accelerator.
3. Switch off the ignition for at least 10 seconds.
4. Read out the fault memory.

PR1029900208000X

Fig. 88 Code P1507: Throttle Jacking Unit, Gain Adjustment

Replace DME control module.

1 Perform adaptation.

End

1 Perform adaptation.

1. Switch on the ignition.
2. Wait one minute.
   Do not press the accelerator.
3. Switch off the ignition for at least 10 seconds.
4. Read out the fault memory.

PR1029900209000X

Fig. 89 Code P1509: Torque Limiter Above Limit

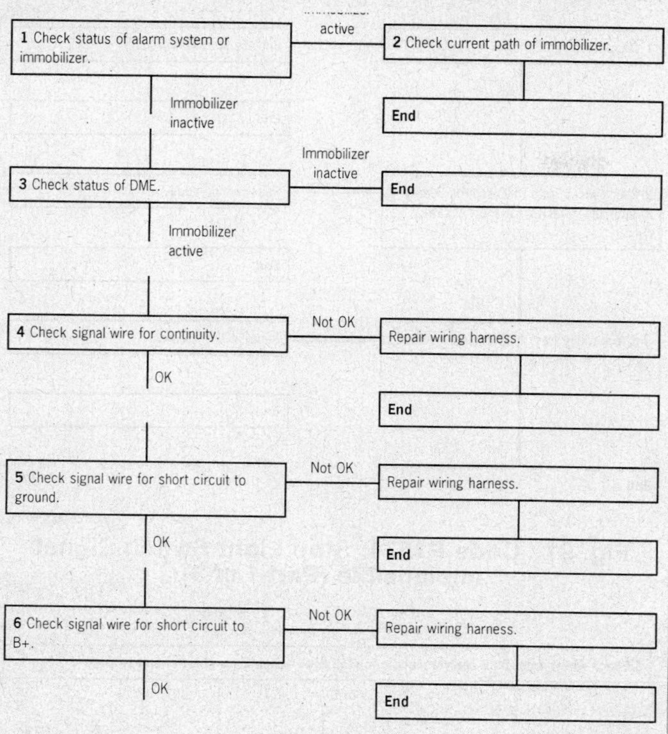

PR1029900210010X

Fig. 90 Codes P1570 & P1571: Immobilizer Signal Implausible Or Open Circuit (Part 1 of 5)

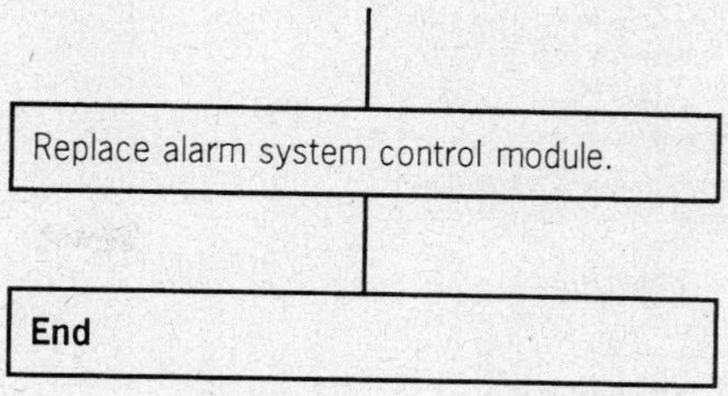

PR1029900210020X

Fig. 90 Codes P1570 & P1571: Immobilizer Signal Implausible Or Open Circuit (Part 2 of 5)

1 Check status of alarm system or immobilizer.

1. Connect and switch on Porsche System Tester 2.
2. Select vehicle type `996`.
3. Select `Alarm system` or `Immobilizer`.
4. Select `Input signals`.
5. Select `Immobilizer`.
6. Read out status.

Note

If the engine is not started, the immobilizer locks again after 30 sec. (status "Immobilizer active"). If necessary, switch ignition off and on again.

2 Check current path of immobilizer.

1. Read out fault memory of alarm system or immobilizer control module. If faults concerning the immobilizer are stored n the memory (teaching Transponder key, status wire, signal converter, etc.), these must be corrected first.

PR1029900210030X

Fig. 90 Codes P1570 & P1571: Immobilizer Signal Implausible Or Open Circuit (Part 3 of 5)

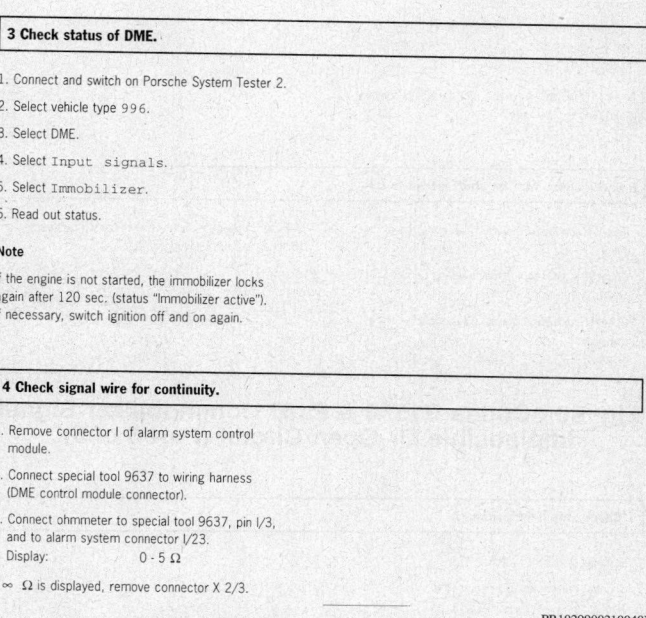

3 Check status of DME.

1. Connect and switch on Porsche System Tester 2.
2. Select vehicle type `996`.
3. Select DME.
4. Select `Input signals`.
5. Select `Immobilizer`.
6. Read out status.

Note

If the engine is not started, the immobilizer locks again after 120 sec. (status "Immobilizer active"). If necessary, switch ignition off and on again.

4 Check signal wire for continuity.

1. Remove connector I of alarm system control module.
2. Connect special tool 9637 to wiring harness (DME control module connector).
3. Connect ohmmeter to special tool 9637, pin I/3, and to alarm system connector I/23.
   Display: 0 - 5 Ω

If ∞ Ω is displayed, remove connector X 2/3.

PR1029900210040X

Fig. 90 Codes P1570 & P1571: Immobilizer Signal Implausible Or Open Circuit (Part 4 of 5)

4. Connect ohmmeter to connector X 2/3, pin 6, on sleeve side, and to special tool 9637, pin I/3.
   Display: 0 - 5 Ω

If ∞ Ω is displayed, repair wiring harness.

5. Connect ohmmeter to connector X 2/3, pin 6, on pin side, and to alarm control module connector I, pin 23.
   Display: 0 - 5 Ω

If ∞ Ω is displayed, repair wiring harness.

5 Check signal wire for short circuit to ground.

1. Remove connector I of alarm system control module.
2. Connect special tool 9637 to wiring harness (DME control module connector).
3. Connect ohmmeter to special tool 9637, pin I/3, and ground.
   Display: ∞ Ω

If 0 - 5 Ω is displayed, check wiring harness for chafing and pinching damage.

6 Check signal wire for short circuit to B+.

1. Remove connector I of alarm system control module.
2. Connect special tool 9637 to wiring harness (DME control module connector).
3. Connect voltmeter to special tool 9637, pin I/3, and ground.
   Display: 0 V

If battery voltage is displayed, check wiring harness for chafing and pinching damage.

PR1029900210050X

Fig. 90 Codes P1570 & P1571: Immobilizer Signal Implausible Or Open Circuit (Part 5 of 5)

1 Check stop light switch.

1. Remove stop light switch.
2. Connect ohmmeter to pins 1 and 4.
   Display: 0 - 5 Ω
3. Actuate stop light switch.
   Display: ∞ Ω
4. Connect ohmmeter to pins 1 and 2.
   Display: ∞ Ω
5. Actuate stop light switch.
   Display: 0 - 5 Ω
6. Install stop light switch.

2 Check wiring from DME control module to stop light switch 1 for short circuit to B+.

1. Connect special tool 9637.
2. Connect voltmeter to pin IV/24 and ground.
3. Switch on the ignition.
   Display: 0 V
4. Actuate brake.
   Display: battery voltage

If battery voltage is displayed for point 3, check wiring harness for chafing and pinching damage.

PR1029900211020X

Fig. 91 Code P1574: Stop Light Switch Signal Implausible (Part 2 of 3)

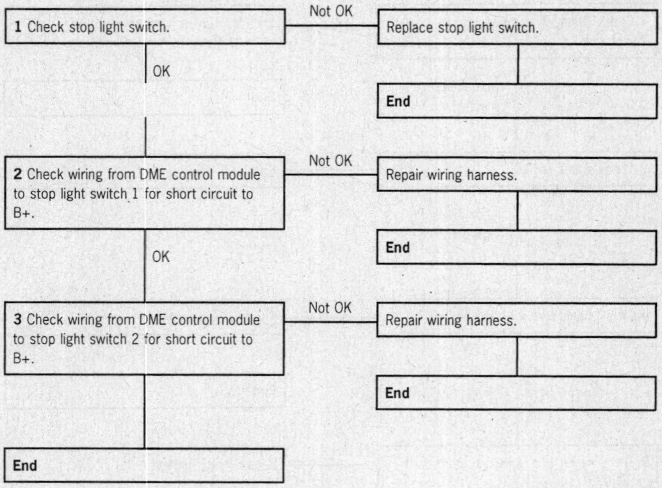

PR1029900211010X

Fig. 91 Code P1574: Stop Light Switch Signal Implausible (Part 1 of 3)

3 Check wiring from DME control module to stop light switch 2 for short circuit to B+.

1. Connect special tool 9637.
2. Connect voltmeter to pin IV/28 and ground.
3. Switch on the ignition.
   Display: battery voltage
4. Actuate brake.
   Display: 0 V

If battery voltage is displayed for point 4, check wiring harness for chafing and pinching damage.

PR1029900211030X

Fig. 91 Code P1574: Stop Light Switch Signal Implausible (Part 3 of 3)

Short circuit to B+

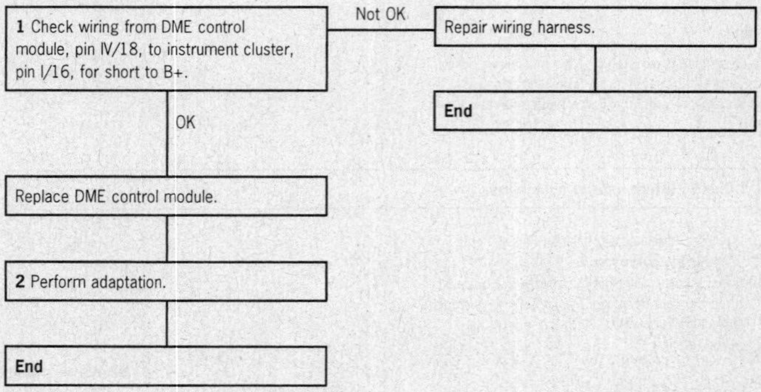

PR1029900212010X

Fig. 92 Code P1576: Cruise Control Standby Lamp (Part 1 of 4)

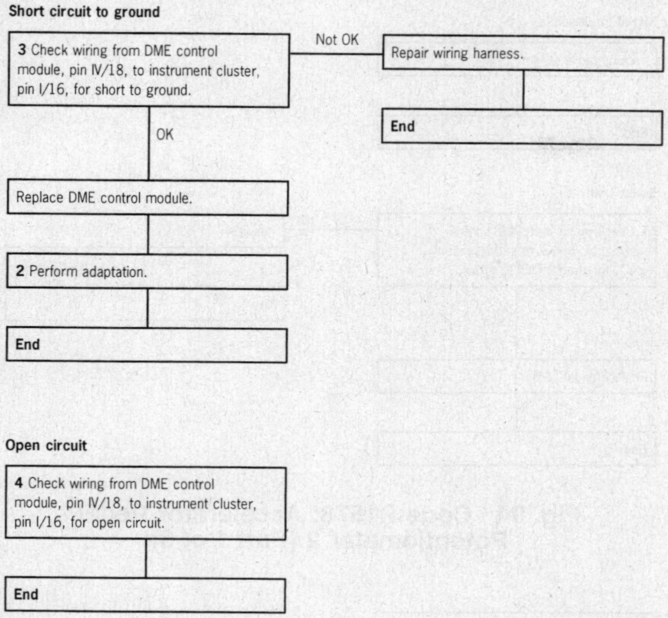

PR1029900212020X

Fig. 92 Code P1576: Cruise Control Standby Lamp (Part 2 of 4)

4 Check wiring from DME control module, pin IV/18, to instrument cluster, pin I/16, for open circuit.

1. Connect special tool 9637 to wiring harness (DME control module connector).
2. Remove connector I of instrument cluster.
3. Connect ohmmeter to special tool 9637, pin IV/18, and to connector I/16 of instrument cluster.
   Display: 0 - 5 Ω

Note

The wire is routed via connector X 2/5.

If ∞ Ω is displayed, check wiring harness for chafing and pinching damage.

PR1029900212040X

Fig. 92 Code P1576: Cruise Control Standby Lamp (Part 4 of 4)

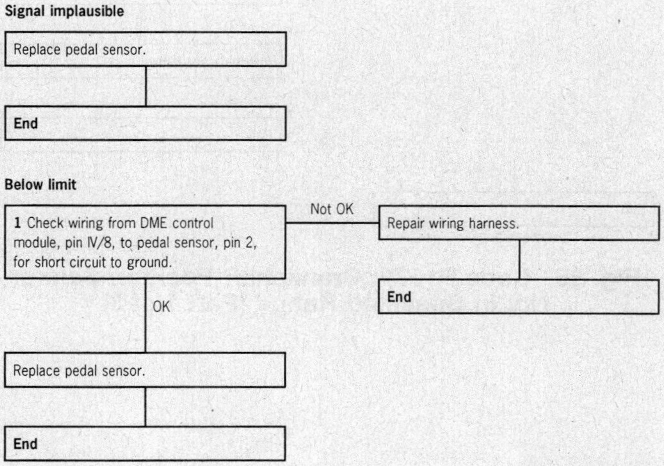

PR1029900213010X

Fig. 93 Code P1577: Accelerator Pedal Potentiometer 1 (Part 1 of 3)

1 Check wiring from DME control module, pin IV/18, to instrument cluster, pin I/16, for short to B+.

1. Connect special tool 9637 to wiring harness (DME control module connector).
2. Connect voltmeter to pin IV/18 and ground.
3. Switch on the ignition.
   Display: 0 V

If battery voltage is displayed, check wiring harness for chafing and pinching damage.

2 Perform adaptation.

1. Switch on the ignition.
2. Wait one minute.
   Do not press the accelerator.
3. Switch off the ignition for at least 10 seconds.
4. Read out the fault memory.

3 Check wiring from DME control module, pin IV/18, to instrument cluster, pin I/16, for short to ground.

1. Connect special tool 9637 to wiring harness (DME control module connector).
2. Connect voltmeter to pin IV/18 and B+.
3. Switch on the ignition.
   Display: 0 V

If battery voltage is displayed, check wiring harness for chafing and pinching damage.

PR1029900212030X

Fig. 92 Code P1576: Cruise Control Standby Lamp (Part 3 of 4)

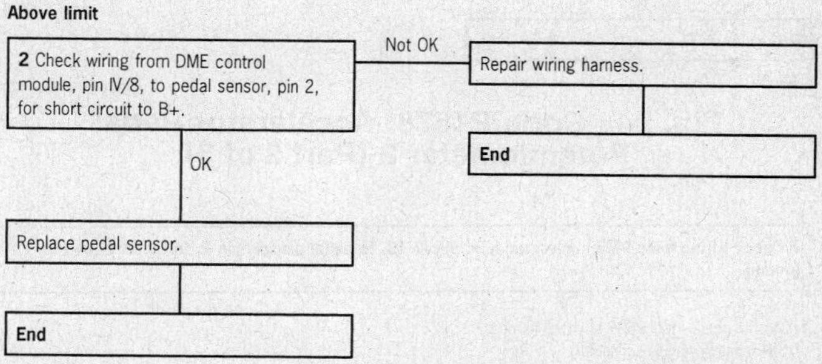

PR1029900213020X

Fig. 93 Code P1577: Accelerator Pedal Potentiometer 1 (Part 2 of 3)

1 Check wiring from DME control module, pin IV/8, to pedal sensor, pin 2, for short circuit to ground.

1. Connect special tool 9637 to wiring harness (DME control module connector).
2. Connect ohmmeter to special tool, pin IV/8, and ground.
   Display: ∞ Ω

If 0 - 5 Ω is displayed, check wiring for chafing and pinching damage.

2 Check wiring from DME control module, pin IV/8, to pedal sensor, pin 2, for short circuit to B+.

1. Connect special tool 9637 to wiring harness (DME control module connector).
2. Connect voltmeter to special tool, pin IV/8, and ground.
3. Switch on the ignition.
   Display: 0 V

If battery voltage is displayed, check wiring harness for chafing and pinching damage.

PR1029900213030X

Fig. 93 Code P1577: Accelerator Pedal Potentiometer 1 (Part 3 of 3)

Above limit

2 Check wiring from DME control module, pin IV/13, to pedal sensor, pin 2, for short circuit to B+.
- Not OK → Repair wiring harness. → **End**
- OK → Replace pedal sensor. → **End**

PR1029900214020X

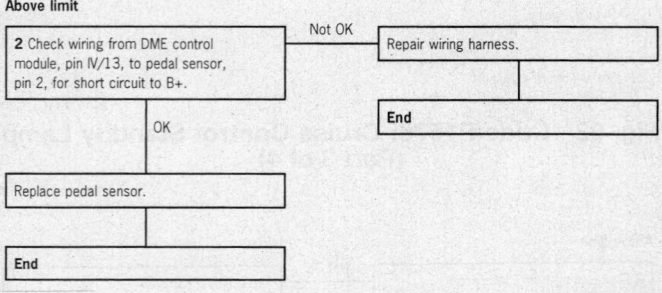

Fig. 94 Code P1578: Accelerator Pedal Potentiometer 2 (Part 2 of 3)

1 Check wiring from DME control module, pin IV/13, to pedal sensor, pin 2, for short circuit to ground.

1. Connect special tool 9637 to wiring harness (DME control module connector).
2. Connect ohmmeter to special tool, pin IV/13, and ground.
   Display: ∞ Ω

If 0 - 5 Ω is displayed, check wiring for chafing and pinching damage.

2 Check wiring from DME control module, pin IV/13, to pedal sensor, pin 2, for short circuit to B+.

1. Connect special tool 9637 to wiring harness (DME control module connector).
2. Connect voltmeter to special tool, pin IV/13, and ground.
3. Switch on the ignition.
   Display: 0 V

If battery voltage is displayed, check wiring harness for chafing and pinching damage.

PR1029900214030X

Fig. 94 Code P1578: Accelerator Pedal Potentiometer 2 (Part 3 of 3)

Signal implausible

Replace pedal sensor. → **End**

Below limit

1 Check wiring from DME control module, pin IV/13, to pedal sensor, pin 2, for short circuit to ground.
- Not OK → Repair wiring harness. → **End**
- OK → Replace pedal sensor. → **End**

PR1029900214010X

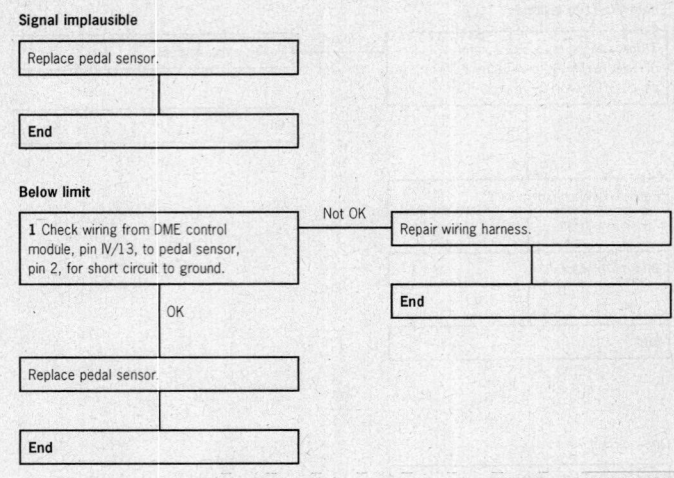

Fig. 94 Code P1578: Accelerator Pedal Potentiometer 2 (Part 1 of 3)

Remove connector.
Check plug-in contacts for corrosion.
Connect ohmmeter connector part to rpm/crankshaft position sensor, pins 1 and 2.
Display at 20 °C: approx. 0.7 - 1.0 kΩ
- Not OK → Replace rpm/crankshaft position sensor. → **End**
- OK ↓

Connect ohmmeter connector part to rpm/crankshaft position sensor, pins 1 and 3.
Display: ∞ Ω
- Not OK → Replace rpm/crankshaft position sensor. → **End**
- OK ↓

1 Check signal with engine tester.
- Not OK → **2** Check wiring from rpm/crankshaft position sensor to DME control module for open circuit and short circuit. → OK → Replace DME control module. → **3** Perform adaptation. → **End**
- OK → **End**

PR1029900215010X

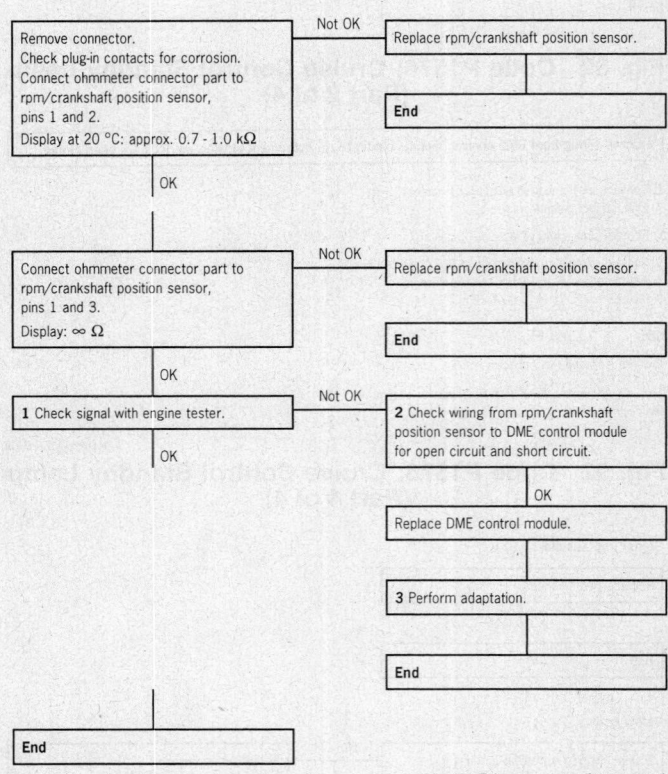

Fig. 95 Code P1579: Crankshaft Position Sensor Not In Specified Range (Part 1 of 3)

1 Check signal with engine tester.

1. Connect special tool 9637.
2. Connect engine tester. Using special input, connect positive cable to pin III/32, negative cable to pin III/46.
3. Start engine or crank engine with starter motor.

The display pictured opposite should appear on the oscilloscope:

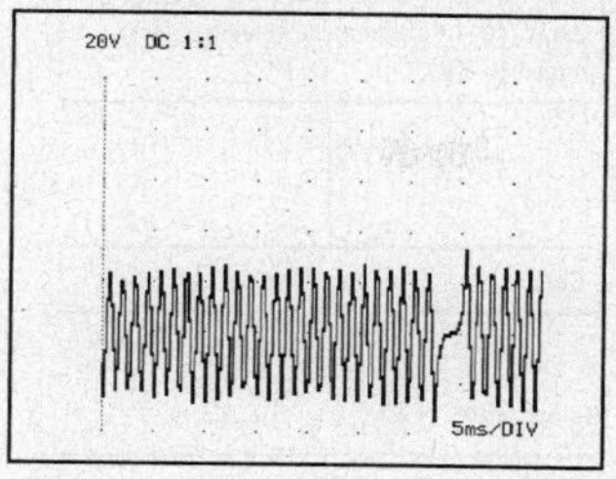

2 Check wiring from crankshaft position sensor to DME control module for open circuit and short circuit.

1. Connect special tool 9637 to wiring harness.
2. Remove connector from crankshaft position sensor.
3. Connect ohmmeter to special tool 9637, pin III/32, and connector, pin 1.
   Display: 0 - 5 Ω
4. Connect ohmmeter to special tool 9637, pin III/46, and connector, pin 2.
   Display: 0 - 5 Ω
5. Connect ohmmeter to special tool 9637, pin III/45, and connector, pin 3.
   Display: 0 - 5 Ω

PR1029900215020X

Fig. 95 Code P1579: Crankshaft Position Sensor Not In Specified Range (Part 2 of 3)

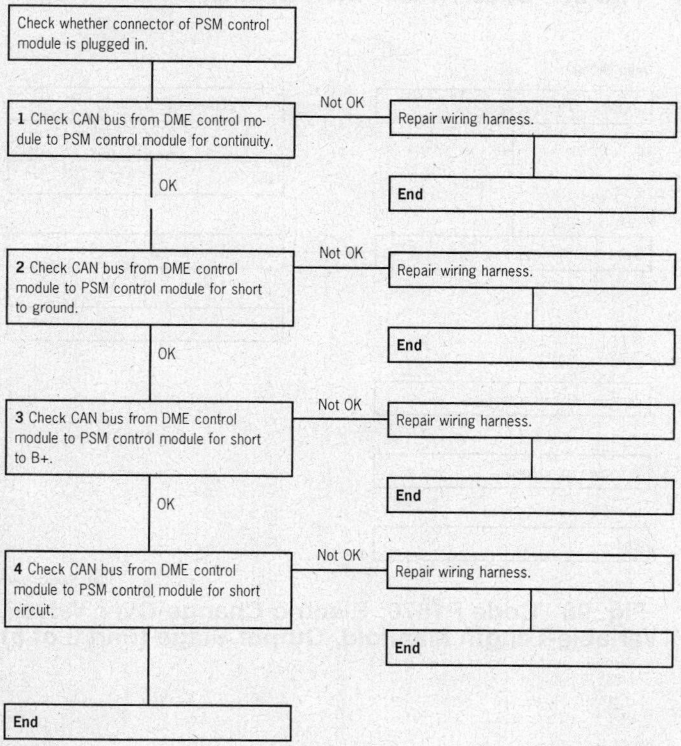

PR1029900216010X

Fig. 96 Code P1600: CAN Timeout, PSM Signal Implausible (Part 1 of 3)

6. Connect ohmmeter to special tool 9637, pins III/32 and III/45.
   Display: ∞Ω

3 Perform adaptation.

1. Switch on the ignition.
2. Wait one minute.
   Do not press the accelerator.
3. Switch off the ignition for at least 10 seconds.
4. Read out the fault memory.

PR1029900215030X

Fig. 95 Code P1579: Crankshaft Position Sensor Not In Specified Range (Part 3 of 3)

1 Check CAN bus from DME control module to PSM control module for continuity.

1. Remove DME control module connector.
2. Remove PSM control module connector.
3. Connect special tool 9637 to wiring harness (DME control module connector).
4. Connect ohmmeter to special tool 9637, pin IV/36, and to PSM control module connector, pin 61.
   Display: 0 - 5 Ω
5. Connect ohmmeter to special tool 9637, pin IV/37, and to PSM control module connector, pin 63.
   Display: 0 - 5 Ω

Note

The wires are routed via two connectors.

If ∞ Ω is displayed, check wiring harness for chafing and pinching damage.

2 Check CAN bus from DME control module to PSM control module for short to ground.

1. Remove DME control module connector.
2. Remove PSM control module connector.
3. Connect special tool 9637 to wiring harness (DME control module connector).
4. Connect ohmmeter to special tool 9637, pin IV/36, and ground.
   Display: ∞ Ω
5. Connect ohmmeter to special tool 9637, pin IV/37, and ground.
   Display: ∞ Ω

If 0 - 5 Ω is displayed, check wiring harness for chafing and pinching damage.

PR1029900216020X

Fig. 96 Code P1600: CAN Timeout, PSM Signal Implausible (Part 2 of 3)

3 Check CAN bus from DME control module to PSM control module for short to B+.

1. Remove DME control module connector.
2. Remove PSM control module connector.
3. Connect special tool 9637 to wiring harness (DME control module connector).
4. Connect voltmeter to special tool 9637, pin IV/36, and ground.
   Switch on the ignition.
   Display: 0 V
5. Connect voltmeter to special tool 9637, pin IV/37, and ground.
   Switch on the ignition.
   Display: 0 V

If battery voltage is displayed, check wiring harness for chafing and pinching damage.

4 Check CAN bus from DME control module to PSM control module for short circuit.

1. Remove DME control module connector.
2. Remove PSM control module connector.
3. Connect special tool 9637 to wiring harness (DME control module connector).
4. Connect ohmmeter to special tool 9637, pins IV/36 and IV/37.
   Display: ∞Ω

If 0 - 5 Ω is displayed, check wiring for chafing and pinching damage.

PR1029900216030X

Fig. 96 Code P1600: CAN Timeout, PSM Signal Implausible (Part 3 of 3)

Above limit

1 Check change-over valve.
- Not OK → Replace change-over valve. → **End**
- OK ↓

2 Check wiring harness for short to B+.
- Not OK → Repair wiring harness. → **End**
- OK ↓

Replace DME control module.

3 Perform adaptation.

End

PR1029900218010X

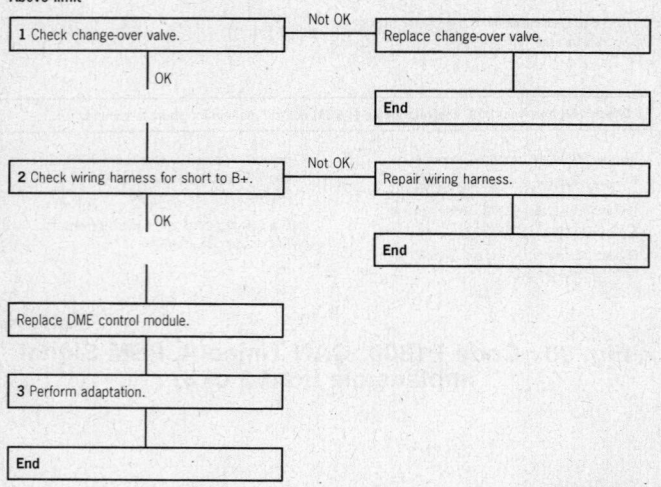

Fig. 98 Code P1670: Electric Change-Over Valve, Variable-Length Manifold, Output Stage (Part 1 of 5)

Below limit

4 Check wiring harness for short to ground.
- Not OK → Repair wiring harness. → **End**
- OK ↓

Replace DME control module.

3 Perform adaptation.

End

PR1029900218020X

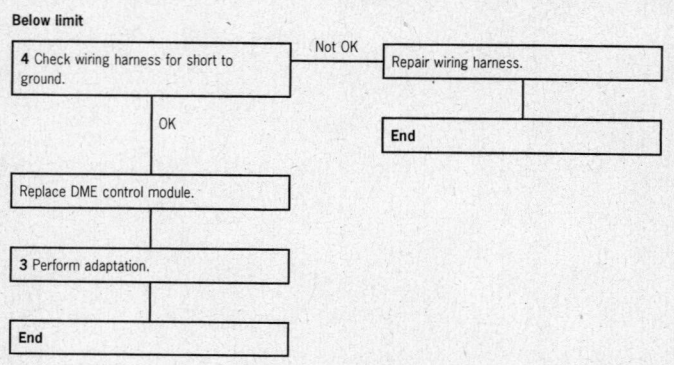

Fig. 98 Code P1670: Electric Change-Over Valve, Variable-Length Manifold, Output Stage (Part 2 of 5)

Above limit

Check wiring from DME control module, pin IV/40, to start enable relay for short circuit to B+.
- Not OK → Repair wiring harness. → **End**

End

Below limit

Check wiring from DME control module, pin IV/40, to start enable relay for short circuit to ground.
- Not OK → Repair wiring harness. → **End**

End

Open circuit

Check wiring from DME control module, pin IV/40, to start enable relay for continuity.
- Not OK → Repair wiring harness. → **End**

End

PR1029900217000X

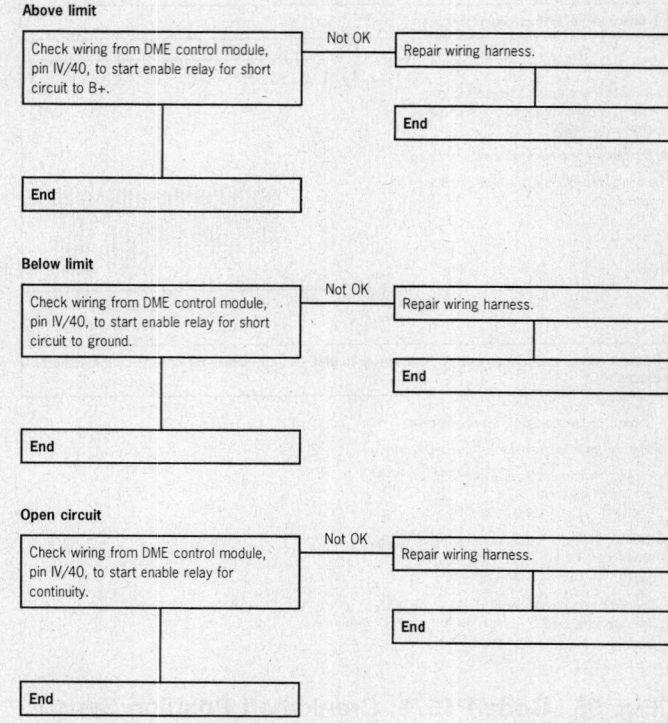

Fig. 97 Code P1668: Start Enable, Output Stage

Open circuit

1 Check change-over valve.
- Not OK → Replace change-over valve. → **End**
- OK ↓

5 Check wiring harness for open circuit.
- Not OK → Repair wiring harness. → **End**
- OK ↓

Replace DME control module.

3 Perform adaptation.

End

PR1029900218030X

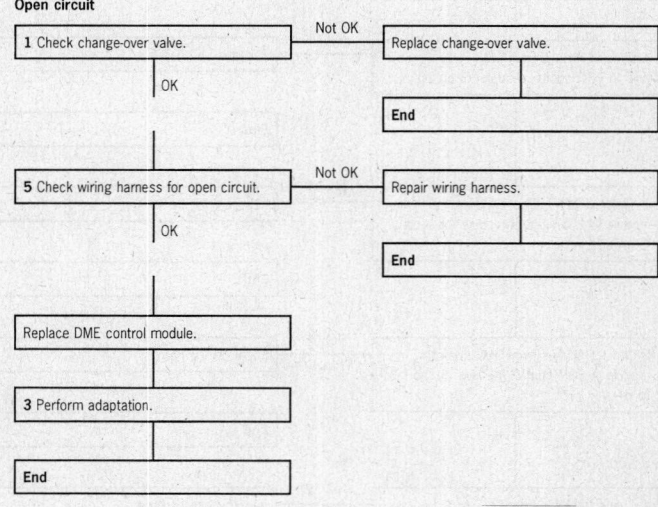

Fig. 98 Code P1670: Electric Change-Over Valve, Variable-Length Manifold, Output Stage (Part 3 of 5)

1 Check change-over valve.

1. Remove connector of change-over valve.
2. Connect special tool V.A.G. 1315 A/1 to change-over valve.
3. Connect ohmmeter to special tool V.A.G. 1315 A/1.
   Display: 28 - 32 Ω at 20 °C.

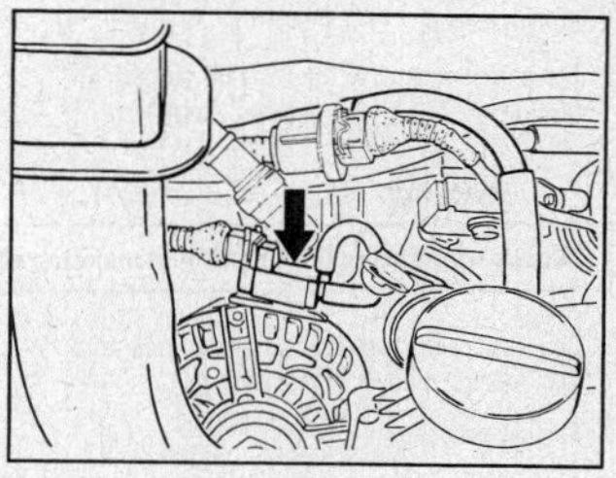

2 Check wiring harness for short to B+.

1. Remove connector of change-over valve.
2. Connect voltmeter to connector, pin 2 (positive), and ground (negative). Switch on the ignition.
   Display: 0 V

If battery voltage is displayed, check wiring harness for chafing and pinching damage.

PR1029900218040X

Fig. 98 Code P1670: Electric Change-Over Valve, Variable-Length Manifold, Output Stage (Part 4 of 5)

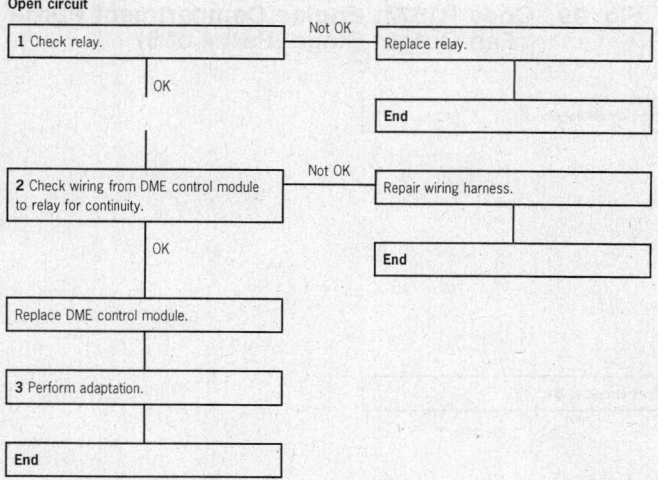

Open circuit

- **1** Check relay. — Not OK → Replace relay. → **End**
- OK ↓
- **2** Check wiring from DME control module to relay for continuity. — Not OK → Repair wiring harness. → **End**
- OK ↓
- Replace DME control module.
- **3** Perform adaptation.
- **End**

PR1029900219010X

Fig. 99 Code P1674: Engine Compartment Purge Fan Output Stage (Part 1 of 5)

3 Perform adaptation.

1. Switch on the ignition.
2. Wait one minute.
   Do not press the accelerator.
3. Switch off the ignition for at least 10 seconds.
4. Read out the fault memory.

4 Check wiring harness for short to ground.

1. Remove connector of change-over valve.
2. Connect ohmmeter to connector, pin 2, and ground.
   Display: ∞ Ω

If 0 - 5 Ω is displayed, check wiring harness for chafing and pinching damage.

5 Check wiring harness for open circuit.

1. Connect special tool 9637 to wiring harness (DME control module connector).
2. Remove connector of change-over valve.
3. Connect ohmmeter to special tool 9637, pin III/4, and change-over valve connector, pin 2.
   Display: 0 - 5 Ω

Note

The wire is routed via connector X 59/1, pin 10. If ∞ Ω is displayed, check connector X59/1, pin 10, for corrosion, and check wiring harness for chafing and pinching damage.

PR1029900218050X

Fig. 98 Code P1670: Electric Change-Over Valve, Variable-Length Manifold, Output Stage (Part 5 of 5)

Short circuit to ground

- **1** Check relay. — Not OK → Replace relay. → **End**
- OK ↓
- **4** Check wiring from DME control module to relay for short circuit to ground. — Not OK → Repair wiring harness. → **End**
- OK ↓
- Replace DME control module.
- **3** Perform adaptation.
- **End**

PR1029900219020X

Fig. 99 Code P1674: Engine Compartment Purge Fan Output Stage (Part 2 of 5)

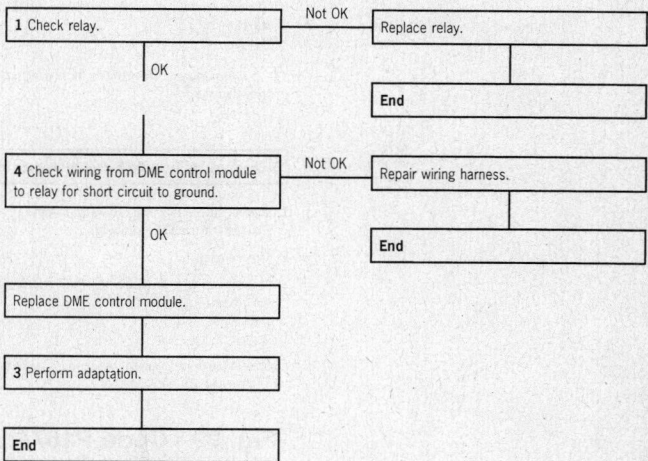

Short circuit to B+

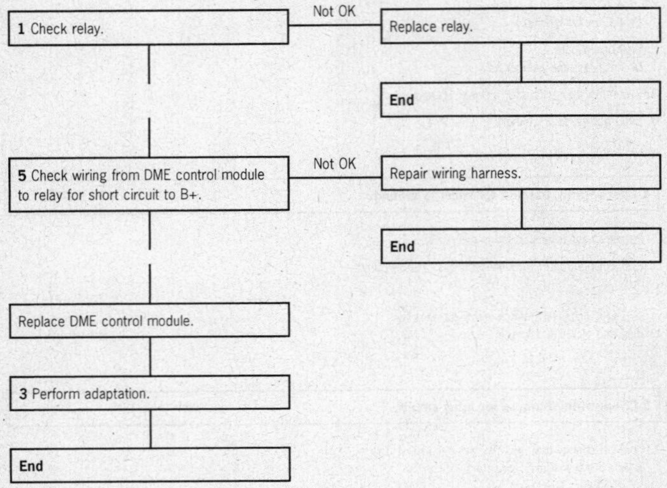

PR1029900219030X

Fig. 99 Code P1674: Engine Compartment Purge Fan Output Stage (Part 3 of 5)

1 Check relay.

1. Remove relay.
2. Connect ohmmeter to terminals 85 and 86.
   Display: approx. 75 Ω

2 Check wiring from DME control module to relay for continuity.

1. Connect special tool 9637 to wiring harness (DME control module connector).
2. Remove relay.
3. Connect ohmmeter to special tool 9637, pin II/20, and relay slot, pin 2 (terminal 85).
   Display: 0 - 5 Ω

If ∞ Ω is displayed, check wiring harness for chafing and pinching damage.

3 Perform adaptation.

1. Switch on the ignition.
2. Wait one minute.
   Do not press the accelerator.
3. Switch off the ignition for at least 10 seconds.
4. Read out the fault memory.

PR1029900219040X

Fig. 99 Code P1674: Engine Compartment Purge Fan Output Stage (Part 4 of 5)

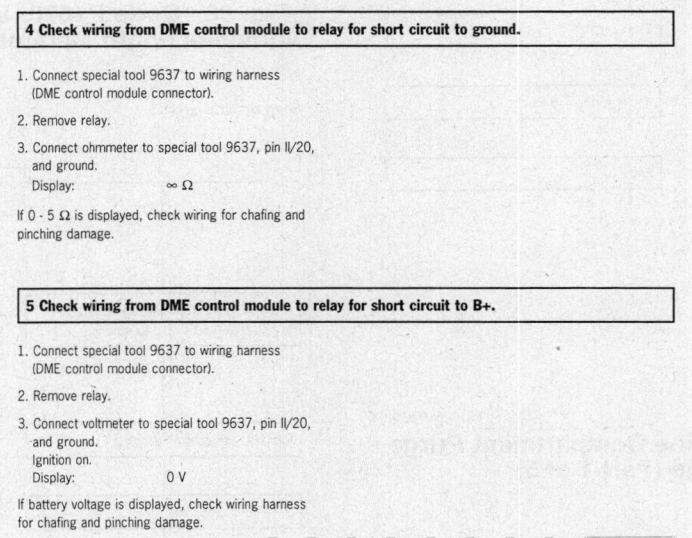

4 Check wiring from DME control module to relay for short circuit to ground.

1. Connect special tool 9637 to wiring harness (DME control module connector).
2. Remove relay.
3. Connect ohmmeter to special tool 9637, pin II/20, and ground.
   Display: ∞ Ω

If 0 - 5 Ω is displayed, check wiring for chafing and pinching damage.

5 Check wiring from DME control module to relay for short circuit to B+.

1. Connect special tool 9637 to wiring harness (DME control module connector).
2. Remove relay.
3. Connect voltmeter to special tool 9637, pin II/20, and ground.
   Ignition on.
   Display: 0 V

If battery voltage is displayed, check wiring harness for chafing and pinching damage.

PR1029900219050X

Fig. 99 Code P1674: Engine Compartment Purge Fan Output Stage (Part 5 of 5)

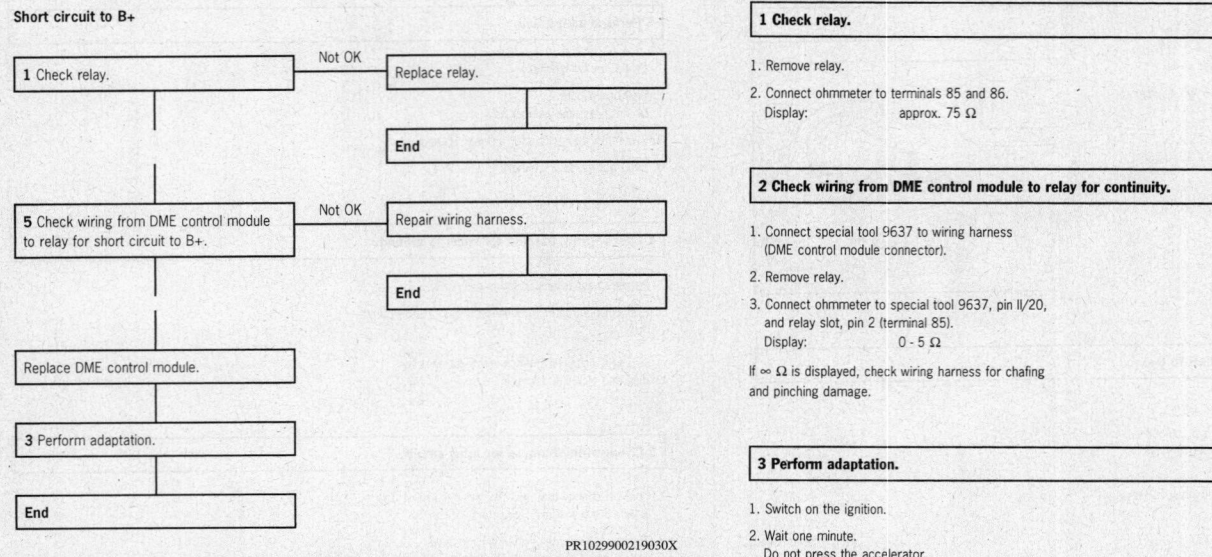

Motronic (DME) 7.8 Fuel Injection Systems

NOTE: If Unsure Of The System Used On The Vehicle Being Serviced, Refer To The "Engine Systems Identification Chart." Further Assistance For The Proper Use Of Information Contained In This Section Can Also Be Found In The Front Of This Tabbed Section Under "How To Use This Manual."

NOTE: On Air Bag Equipped Models, Refer To "Air Bag System Precautions" Located In The Front Of This Manual For System Disarming & Arming Procedures.

NOTE: Prior To Performing Any Service Operations Listed In This Section, Consult The "Technical Service Bulletins" Section For Related Information.

NOTE: "Electrical Symbol & Wire Color Code Identification" Located In The Front Of This Manual May Be Used As An Aid When Using Wiring Circuits Found In This Section.

NOTE: Refer To "Computer Relearn Procedures" Located In The Front Of This Manual When Battery Power To The Computer Has Been Interrupted.

INDEX

Page No.

Description 15-204
Diagnosis & Testing 15-204
Accessing Diagnostic Trouble Codes 15-204
Clearing Diagnostic Trouble Codes 15-204
Diagnostic Tests 15-204
Diagnostic Trouble Code Interpretation 15-204
Wiring Diagrams 15-204
Diagnostic Chart Index 15-210
Precautions 15-204
Air Bag Systems 15-204
Battery Ground Cable 15-204
Sensor & Fuel Injector Specifications 15-203
System Service 15-204
Component Replacement 15-204

SENSOR & FUEL INJECTOR SPECIFICATIONS

Component	Temperature, Degrees F	Value, Ohms
Crankshaft Position Sensor	68	.8–1.0
Engine Compartment Temperature Sensor	68	2200–2600
Engine Coolant Temperature Sensor	32	5000–7000
	68	2000–3000
	140	400–800
EVAP Canister Purge Valve	68	22–30
Fuel Injector	—	11–13
HO2S Heater Element	68	1.8–2.5
Intake Air Temperature Sensor	68	2300–2700
Vehicle Speed Sensor	—	1600–1800

PRECAUTIONS

Air Bag Systems

Refer to "Air Bag System Precautions" in the front of this manual for system disarming and arming procedures.

Battery Ground Cable

Prior to service, disconnect battery ground cable and isolate as required.

DESCRIPTION

This system uses a Digital Motor Electronics (DME) control module to manage fuel injection, ignition and electronic engine controls. The DME module, located under the left seat, also features an optimized engine management diagnostic system (OBD II).

DIAGNOSIS & TESTING

Accessing Diagnostic Trouble Codes

If a malfunction occurs, the Malfunction Indicator Lamp (Check Engine) will be illuminated. At the same time, the Diagnostic Trouble Code (DTC) is stored in the fault memory of the DME control module. To retrieve stored DTCs, connect system tester 9288, or equivalent OBD II scan tool, to the vehicle diagnostic connector, located under the lefthand side of the instrument panel, left of the steering column.

Diagnostic Trouble Code Interpretation

1. Refer to **Fig. 1** for a listing of DTCs.
2. Different fault types are used to indicate the following:
   a. **Fault type 1,** signal implausible/implausible operating range/malfunction.
   b. **Fault type 2,** open circuit/no signal.
   c. **Fault type 3,** short to ground/below lower limit/lean stop.
   d. **Fault type 4,** short to positive/upper limit exceeded/rich stop.

Wiring Diagrams

Refer to **Fig. 2** for DME wiring circuits.

Diagnostic Tests

Refer to **Figs. 3 through 112** for diagnostic tests.

Fault Text	Fault type 1	Fault type 2	Fault type 3	Fault type 4
Mass air flow sensor			P0102	P0103
Ambient pressure sensor	P0107		P0107	P0108
Intake air temperature sensor			P0112	P0113
Engine temperature sensor	P0115	P0117	P0117	P0118
Throttle	P0121			
Oxygen sensor ahead of TWC, bank 1	P0130**	P0134**	P0133**	P0132**
Oxygen sensor after TWC, bank 1	P0136	P0140		P0138
Ageing of oxygen sensor after TWC, bank 1			P0139	P0139
Oxygen sensor heating behind TWC, bank 1		P0141	P0141	P0141
Oxygen sensor ahead of TWC, bank 2	P0150	P0154	P0153	P0152
Oxygen sensor after TWC, bank 2	P0156	P0160		P0158
Ageing of oxygen sensor after TWC, bank 2			P0159	P0159
Oxygen sensor heating behind TWC, bank 2		P0161	P0161	P0161
Oil temperature sensor			P0197	P0198
Pressure sensor, charge pressure	P0235	P0236	P0237	P0238
Misfire detection (sum total)	P0300*		P0300*	P0300*

PR1020100332010X

Fig. 1 Diagnostic trouble code identification (Part 1 of 7)

Clearing Diagnostic Trouble Codes

If a fault (DTC) has been removed but the fault memory has not been erased, three trips are usually required to switch off the Malfunction indicator lamp (MIL). Erasing diagnostic trouble codes may also be accomplished using the system tester or scan tool. Disconnecting the battery ground cable or control module connector will erase diagnostic trouble codes, but this will require a DME module adaption phase in which the engine must be run for 250 seconds after the battery ground cable or control module is reconnected.

SYSTEM SERVICE

Component Replacement

Refer to the "Motronic (DME) 7.2 Fuel Injection Systems" **Fig. 1**, for component locations.

Fault Text	Fault type 1	Fault type 2	Fault type 3	Fault type 4
Misfire detection cylinder 1	P0301		P0301	P0301
Misfire detection cylinder 2	P0302		P0302	P0302
Misfire detection cylinder 3	P0303		P0303	P0303
Misfire detection cylinder 4	P0304		P0304	P0304
Misfire detection cylinder 5	P0305		P0305	P0305
Misfire detection cylinder 6	P0306		P0306	P0306
Knock sensor 1			P0327	P0328
Knock sensor 2			P0332	P0333
Engine speed sensor signal		P0336		
Camshaft position sensor 1	P0341		P0342	P0343
Secondary air system, bank 1	P0410			
Electric change-over valve		P0413	P0414	P0414
Secondary air pump		P0418	P0418	P0418
TWC conversion, bank 1				P0420
TWC conversion, bank 2				P0430
Fuel tank ventilation system (DTESK)				P0440
Fuel tank ventilation system (DTEV)				P0441
Fuel tank ventilation system (micro-leak)			P0442	
EVAP canister purge valve		P0444	P0445	P0445
EVAP canister shutoff valve (function)			P0446	
EVAP canister shutoff valve (output stage)		P0447	P0448	P0448
Pressure sensor, tank	P0450		P0452	P0453
Fuel tank ventilation system (major leak)	P0455		P0455	

PR1020100332020X

Fig. 1 Diagnostic trouble code identification (Part 2 of 7)

Fault Text	Fault type 1	Fault type 2	Fault type 3	Fault type 4
Fan output stage 1		P0480	P0480	P0480
Fan output stage 2		P0481	P0481	P0481
Fan output stage 3		P0482	P0482	P0482
Vehicle speed		P0501		
Idle air control at stop			P0506	P0507
Power supply	P0560		P0562	P0563
CAN timeout Tiptronic		P0600		
EEPROM faulty	P0603	P0603	P0603	P0603
Control module faulty (RAM)	P0604			
Control module faulty (ROM)	P0605			
MIL lamp (via CAN)		P0650		
Tiptronic (CAN distribution transmission position implausible)	P0700			
Tiptronic (gear implausible/transmission slips)	P0701			
Tiptronic control module faulty	P0702			
Fault at unused output stage	P0715			
Tiptronic (CAN: rear right wheel speed)	P0720			
Tiptronic (gear comparison negative)	P0730			
Tiptronic (torque converter clutch)	P0740			
Tiptronic (solenoid valve torque converter)	P0743			
Tiptronic (control solenoid valve, modulating pressure)	P0748			
Tiptronic (solenoid valve 1-2 / 4-5 shift)	P0753			
Tiptronic (solenoid valve 2-3 shift)	P0758			

PR1020100332030X

Fig. 1 Diagnostic trouble code identification (Part 3 of 7)

Fault Text	Fault type 1	Fault type 2	Fault type 3	Fault type 4
Tiptronic (solenoid valve 3-4 shift)	P0763			
Input variables, charge measurement			P1101	P1101
Oxygen sensors ahead of TWC exchanged	P1110			
Heating LSU, inertia fuel shut-off	P1114			
Oxygen sensor heating ahead of catalytic converter, bank 1	P1115	P1115	P1115	P1115
Heating LSU bank 2 inertia fuel shutoff	P1116			
Oxygen sensor heating behind catalytic converter, bank 1	P1117			
Oxygen sensor heating behind catalytic converter, bank 2	P1118			
Oxygen sensor heating ahead of catalytic converter, bank 2	P1119	P1119	P1119	P1119
Throttle position sensor 1	P1121		P1121	P1121
Throttle position sensor 2	P1122		P1122	P1122
Output stage, fuel pump relay		P1124	P1124	P1124
Oxygen sensing adaptation, upper load range, bank 1			P1125	P1125
Oxygen sensing adaptation, lower load range, bank 1			P1126	P1126
Oxygen sensing error by means of short test, bank 1			P1127	P1127
Oxygen sensing adaptation idle range, bank 1			P1128	P1128
Oxygen sensing adaptation idle range, bank 2			P1130	P1130
Oxygen sensing, upper load range, bank 2			P1132	P1132
Oxygen sensing, lower load range, bank 2			P1133	P1133
Oxygen sensing error by means of short test, bank 2			P1134	P1134

PR1020100332040X

Fig. 1 Diagnostic trouble code identification (Part 4 of 7)

Fault Text	Fault type 1	Fault type 2	Fault type 3	Fault type 4
Pressure comparison ambient charge pressure	P1136			
Clutch switch	P1137			
Engine compartment temperature sensor			P1157	P1158
Fuel injector of cylinder 1		P1237	P1225	P1213
Fuel injector of cylinder 6		P1238	P1226	P1214
Fuel injector of cylinder 2		P1239	P1227	P1215
Fuel injector of cylinder 4		P1240	P1228	P1216
Fuel injector of cylinder 3		P1241	P1229	P1217
Fuel injector of cylinder 5		P1242	P1230	P1218
Accelerator pedal	P1219			
Charge pressure control			P1249	P1249
Charge pressure characteristic, upper value exceeded				P1255
Signal from airbag	P1265			
Function monitor fuel shutoff	P1266			
Position of camshaft in relation to crankshaft, bank 2			P1324	P1324
Camshaft adjustment, bank 2	P1325		P1325	P1325
Position of camshaft in relation to crankshaft, bank 1			P1340	P1340
Camshaft adjustment, bank 1	P1341		P1341	P1341
Camshaft adjustment, bank 1, output stage		P1342	P1342	P1342
Camshaft adjustment, bank 2, output stage		P1343	P1343	P1343
Valve lift control output stage bank 1		P1344	P1344	P1344
Valve lift control output stage bank 2		P1345	P1345	P1345
Valve lift control checksum error	P1350		P1350	P1350
Valve lift control, cylinder 1	P1351		P1351	P1351
Valve lift control, cylinder 6	P1352		P1352	P1352

PR1020100332050X

Fig. 1 Diagnostic trouble code identification (Part 5 of 7)

Fault Text	Fault type 1	Fault type 2	Fault type 3	Fault type 4
Valve lift control, cylinder 2	P1353		P1353	P1353
Valve lift control, cylinder 4	P1354		P1354	P1354
Valve lift control, cylinder 3	P1355		P1355	P1355
Valve lift control, cylinder 5	P1356		P1356	P1356
Knock control zero test	P1384			
Knock control offset	P1385			
Knock control test pulse	P1386			
Camshaft position sensor 2	P1397		P1397	P1397
Secondary air system, bank 2	P1411			
A/C compressor control		P1455	P1457	P1456
Throttle jacking unit output stage	P1501			
Throttle jacking unit spring test				P1502
Throttle jacking unit position error	P1503			
Throttle jacking unit emergency air position	P1504			
Throttle jacking unit, control range		P1505	P1505	P1505
Throttle jacking unit lower mechanical stop	P1506			
Throttle jacking unit gain adjustment	P1507			
Function monitor torque comparison	P1508			
Torque limiter				P1509
Throttle jacking unit exchange detection without adaptation	P1510			
Throttle jacking unit abortion of test due to negative influence on ambient condition			P1511	P1511
Ambient temperature (via CAN from instrument cluster)	P1512			

PR1020100332060X

Fig. 1 Diagnostic trouble code identification (Part 6 of 7)

Fault Text	Fault type 1	Fault type 2	Fault type 3	Fault type 4
Throttle jacking unit open spring test			P1513	P1513
Throttle jacking unit re-learn lower mechanical stop	P1514			
Charge pressure control valve output stage	P1548	P1548	P1547	P1546
Immobilizer	P1570	P1571		
Stop light switch	P1574			
Cruise control standby lamp via CAN		P1576		
Accelerator pedal potentiometer 1	P1577		P1577	P1577
Accelerator pedal potentiometer 2	P1578		P1578	P1578
Crankshaft position sensor	P1579			
CAN timeout PSM		P1600		
CAN timeout instrument cluster	P1601	P1601		
Cooling water shutoff valve		P1656	P1656	P1656
Output stage, overrun recirculating air valve		P1657	P1657	P1657
Control module faulty (computer monitoring, reset)	P1671			
Output stage, engine compartment purge fan		P1674	P1674	P1674
Engine purge fan fault				P1675
Tiptronic (voltage supply valves or selector lever)	P1702			
Tiptronic (control solenoid valve, shifting pressure)	P1748			

PR1020100332070X

Fig. 1 Diagnostic trouble code identification (Part 7 of 7)

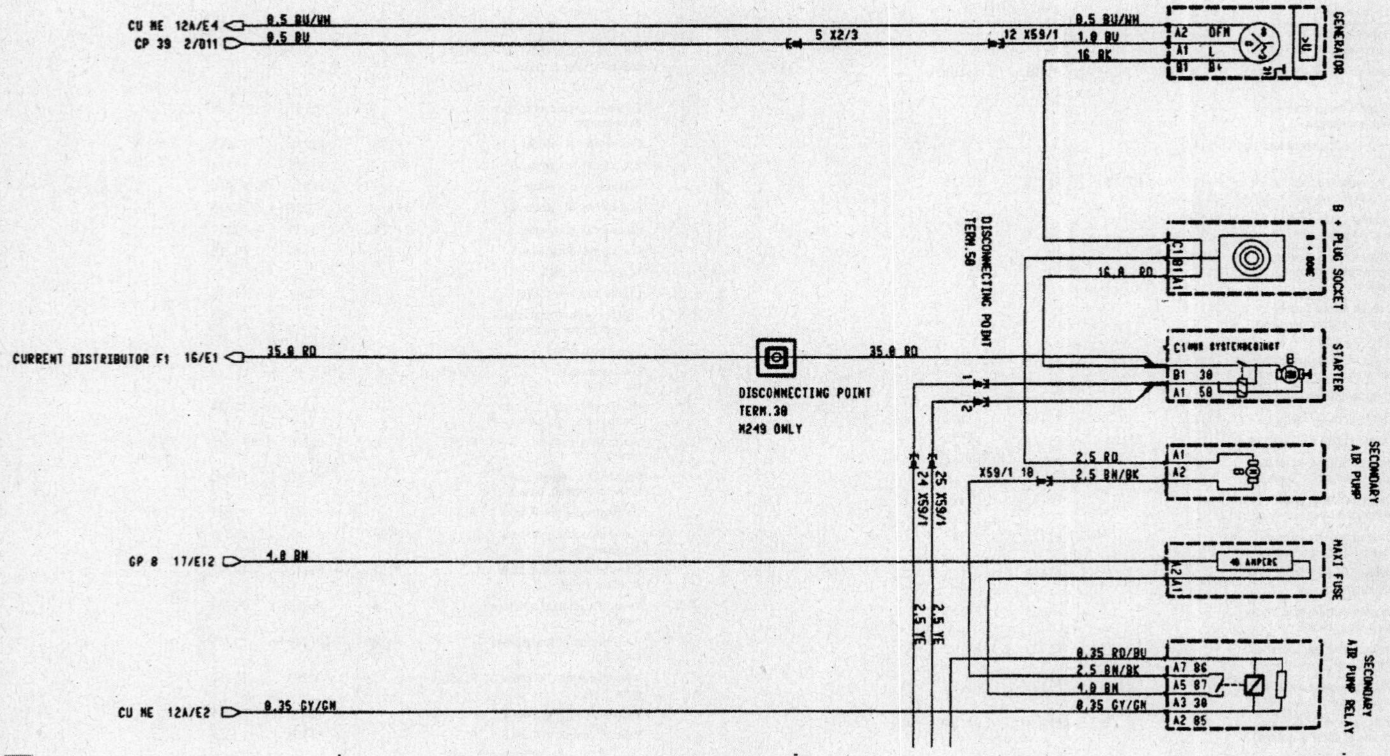

PR1020100333010X

Fig. 2 DME wiring circuit (Part 1 of 6)

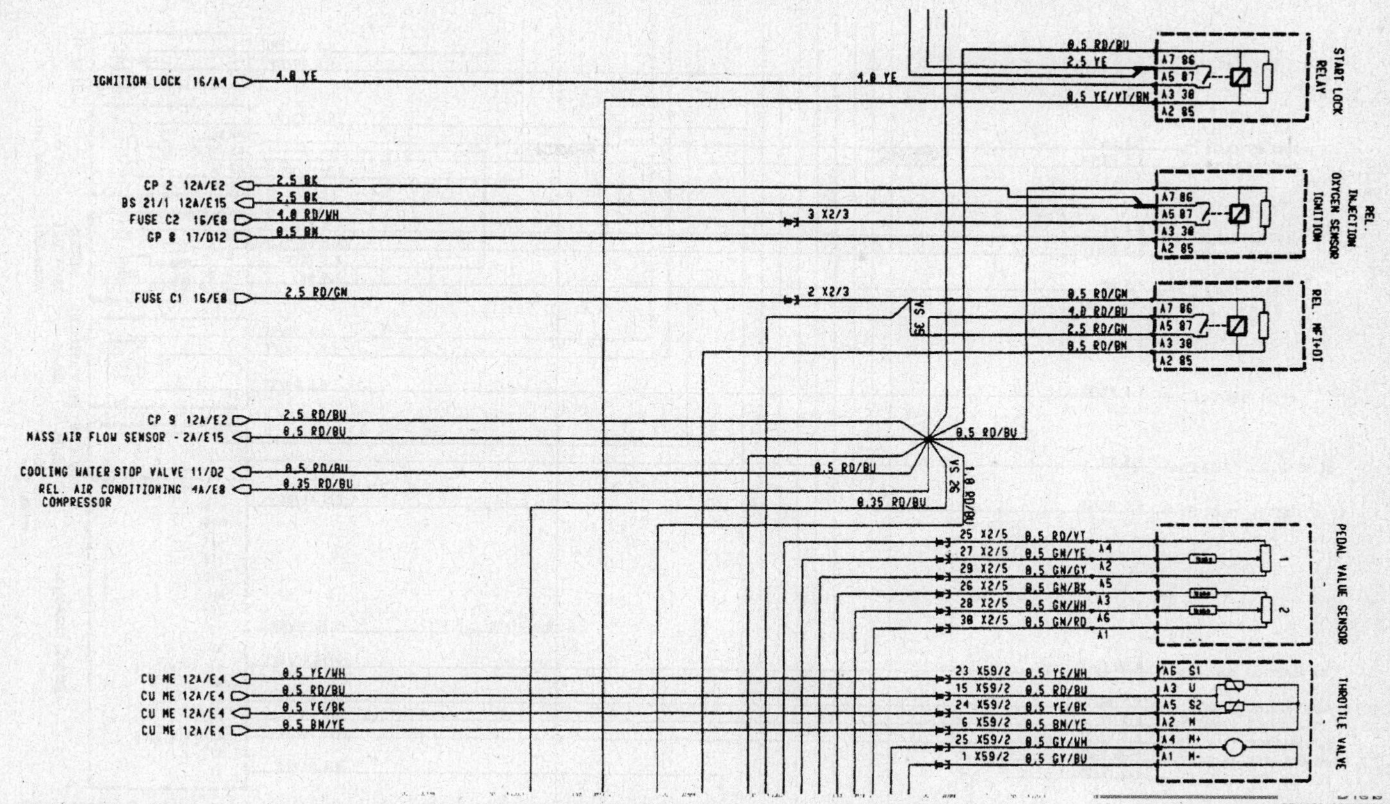
PR1020100333020X

Fig. 2 DME wiring circuit (Part 2 of 6)

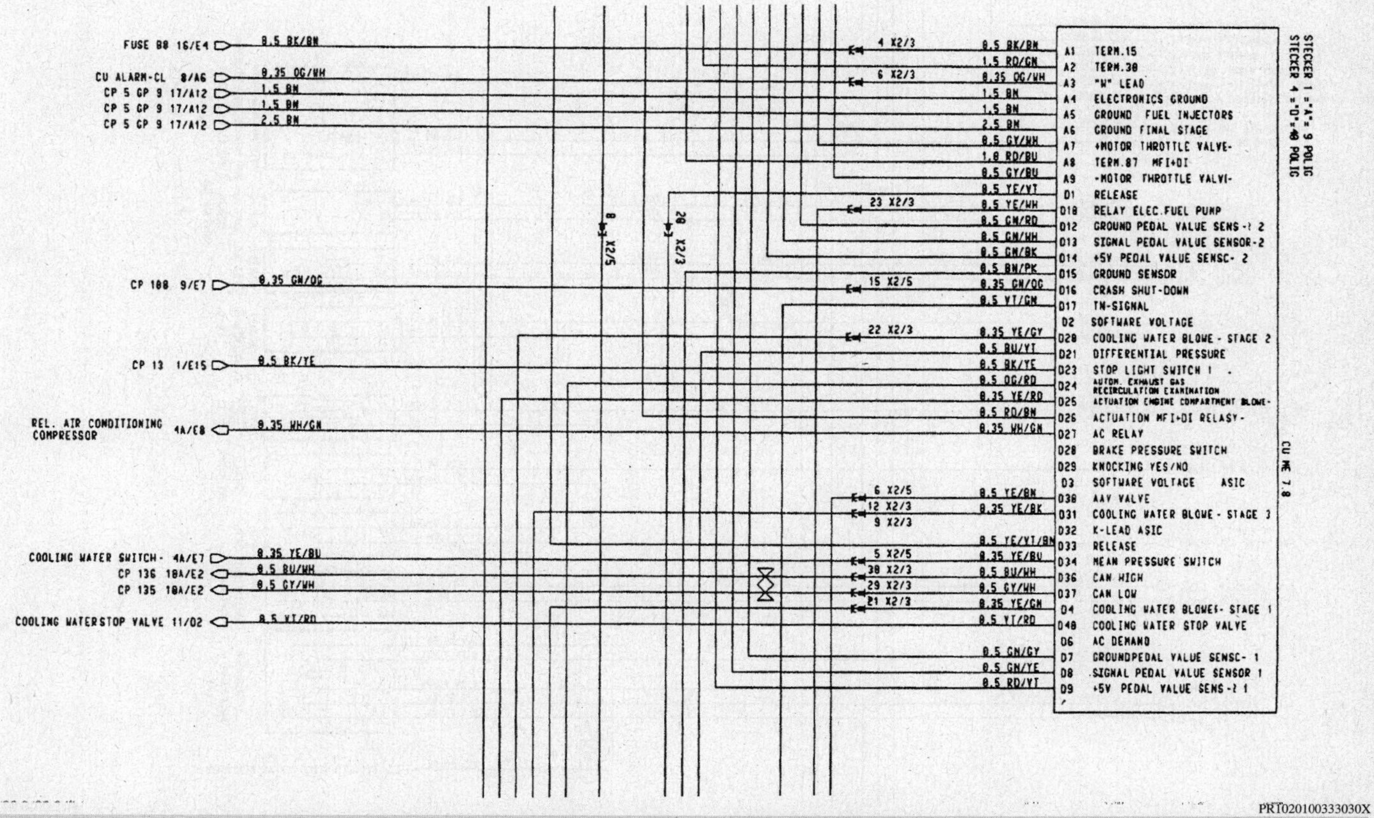
PR1020100333030X

Fig. 2 DME wiring circuit (Part 3 of 6)

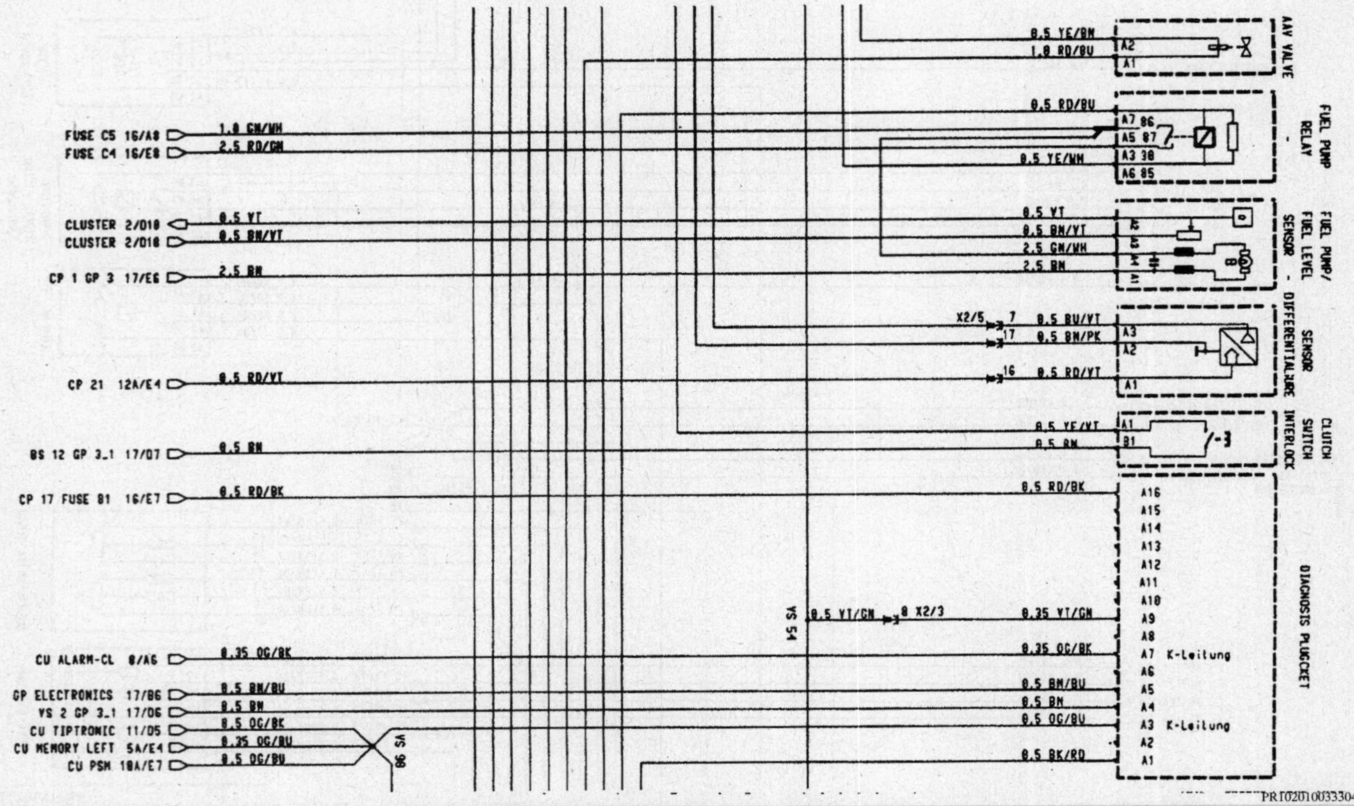

PR1020100333040X

Fig. 2 DME wiring circuit (Part 4 of 6)

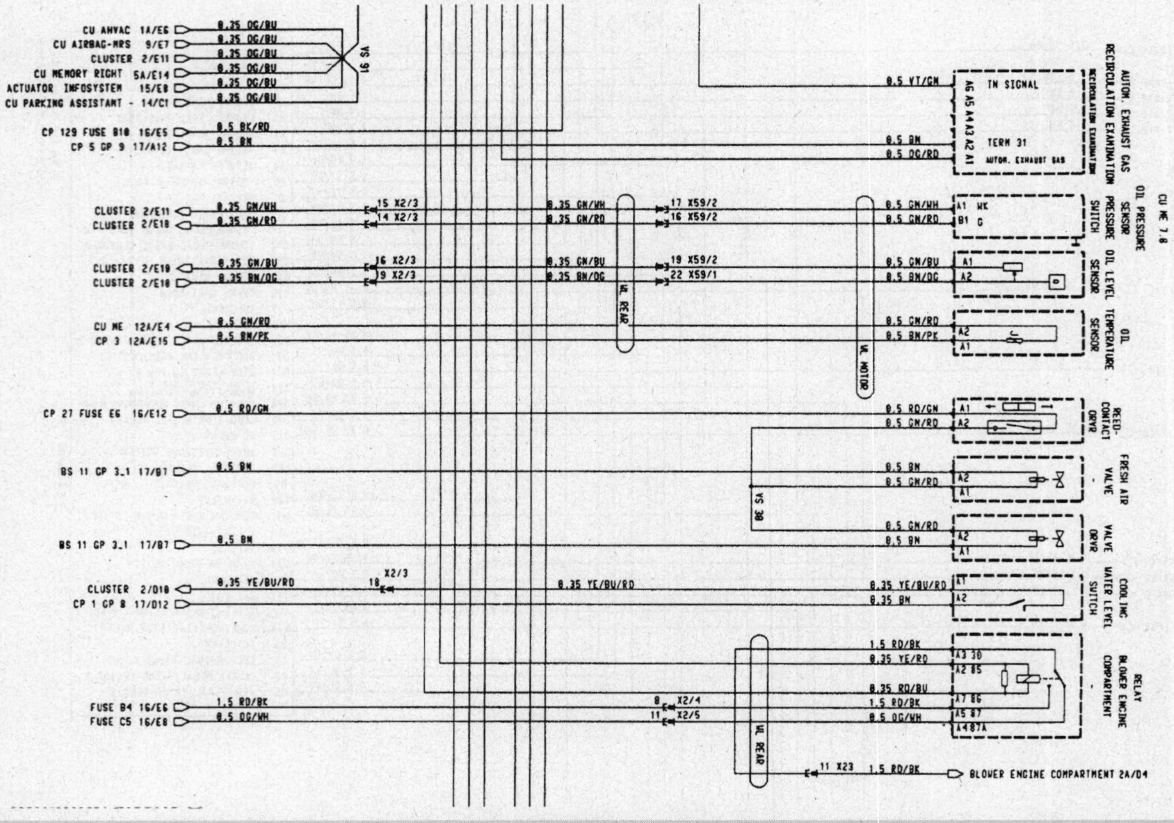

PR1020100333050X

Fig. 2 DME wiring circuit (Part 5 of 6)

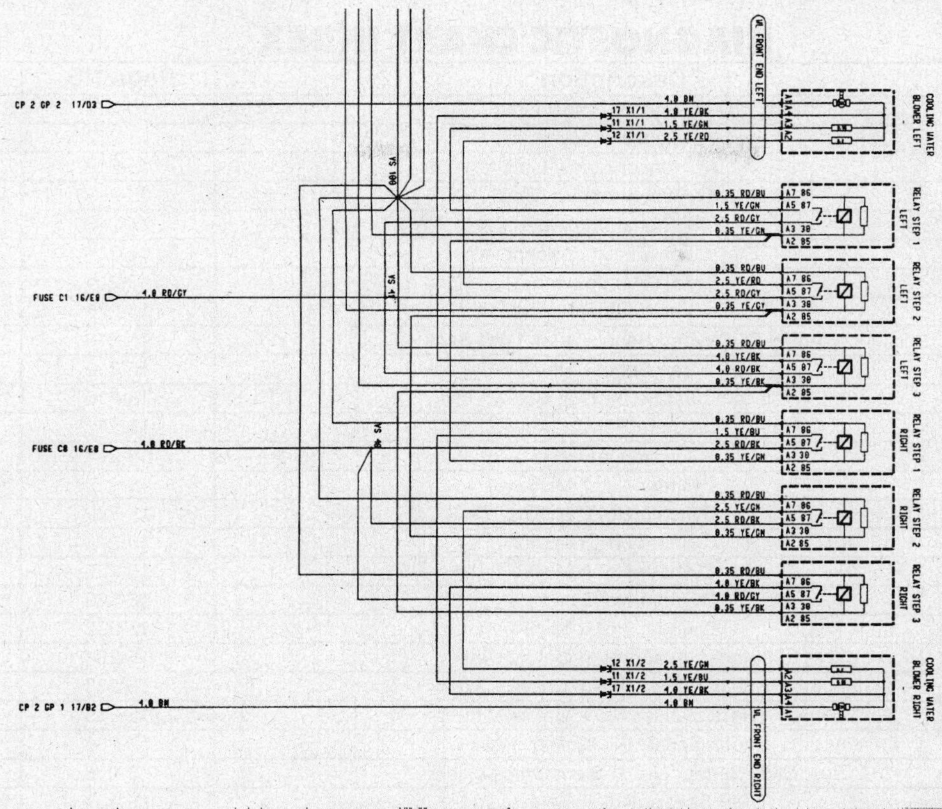

PR1020100333060X

Fig. 2 DME wiring circuit (Part 6 of 6)

DIAGNOSTIC CHART INDEX

Code	Description	Page No.	Fig. No.
P0102	MAF Sensor Below Limit	15-212	3
P0103	MAF Sensor Above Limit	15-212	4
P0112	IAT Sensor Below Limit	15-212	5
P0113	IAT Sensor Above Limit	15-213	6
P0115	ECT Signal Implausible	15-213	7
P0117	ECT Open Circuit, Below Limit	15-214	8
P0118	ECT Above Limit	15-214	9
P0121	Throttle Valve, Signal Implausible	15-215	10
P0139	Aging Of Oxygen Sensor After TWC Bank 1	15-216	11
P0159	Aging Of Oxygen Sensor After TWC Bank 2	15-216	12
P0197	Oil Temperature Sensor, Below Limit	15-216	13
P0198	Oil Temperature Sensor, Above Limit	15-217	14
P0300	Misfire Detection	15-217	15
P0301	Cylinder No. 1 Misfire	15-219	16
P0302	Cylinder No. 2 Misfire	15-222	17
P0303	Cylinder No. 3 Misfire	15-224	18
P0304	Cylinder No. 4 Misfire	15-227	19
P0305	Cylinder No. 5 Misfire	15-229	20
P0306	Cylinder No. 6 Misfire	15-232	21
P0327	Knock Sensor No. 1 Below Limit	15-234	22
P0328	Knock Sensor No. 1 Above Limit	15-235	23
P0332	Knock Sensor No. 2 Below Limit	15-235	24
P0333	Knock Sensor No. 2 Above Limit	15-236	25
P0341	CMP Sensor No. 1, Signal Implausible	15-236	26
P0342	CMP Sensor No. 1, Below Limit	15-237	27
P0342	CMP Sensor No. 1, Above Limit	15-237	28
P0413	Electric Change Over Valve, Open Circuit	15-237	29
P0414	Electric Change Over Valve, Below Limit	15-237	30
P0418	Secondary Air Injection Pipe, Open Circuit	15-238	31
P0420	TWC Conversion Bank No. 1, Above Limit	15-238	32
P0430	TWC Conversion Bank No. 2, Above Limit	15-239	33
P0444	EVAP Canister Purge Valve, Open Circuit	15-240	34
P0445	EVAP Canister Purge Valve, Short Circuit To Battery Positive	15-240	35
P0447	EVAP Canister Shutoff Valve Open	15-241	36
P0448	Canister Shutoff Valve	15-241	37
P0450	Tank Pressure, Signal Implausible	15-242	38
P0452	Tank Pressure Sensor, Below Limit	15-242	39
P0453	Tank Pressure Sensor, Above Limit	15-242	40
P0480	Fan Output Stage 1, Open Circuit	15-242	41
P0481	Fan Output Stage 1, Open Circuit	15-243	42
P0482	Fan Output Stage 3, Open Circuit	15-244	43
P0506	Idle Air Control At Stop, Below Limit	15-245	44
P0507	Idle Air Control At Stop, Above Limit	15-246	45
P0560	Voltage Supply, Signal Implausible	15-246	46
P0562	Voltage Supply, Below Limit	15-246	47
P0563	Voltage Supply, Below Limit	15-246	48
P0600	CAN Timeout Tiptronic	15-247	49
P0604	Control Module Faulty, Signal Implausible	15-247	50
P0605	Control Module Faulty, Signal Implausible	15-247	51
P1101	Input Variables, Charge Measurement Above Or Below Limit	15-248	52
P1121	TP Sensor No. 1	15-248	53
P1122	TP Sensor No. 2	15-249	54
P1124	Fuel Pump Relay Output Stage	15-250	55
P1213	Fuel Injector Cylinder No. 1, Above Limit	15-250	56
P1214	Fuel Injector Cylinder No. 6, Above Limit	15-251	57
P1215	Fuel Injector Cylinder No. 2, Above Limit :	15-251	58
P1216	Fuel Injector Cylinder No. 4, Above Limit	15-252	59

Continued

DIAGNOSTIC CHART INDEX—Continued

Code	Description	Page No.	Fig. No.
P1217	Fuel Injector Cylinder No. 3, Above Limit	15-252	60
P1218	Fuel Injector Cylinder No. 5, Above Limit	15-252	61
P1219	Accelerator Pedal, Signal Implausible	15-253	62
P1225	Fuel Injector Cylinder No. 1, Below Limit	15-253	63
P1226	Fuel Injector Cylinder No. 6, Below Limit	15-253	64
P1227	Fuel Injector Cylinder No. 2, Below Limit	15-254	65
P1228	Fuel Injector Cylinder No. 4, Below Limit	15-254	66
P1229	Fuel Injector Cylinder No. 3, Below Limit	15-254	67
P1230	Fuel Injector Cylinder No. 5, Below Limit	15-255	68
P1237	Fuel Injector Cylinder No. 1, Open Circuit	15-255	69
P1238	Fuel Injector Cylinder No. 6, Open Circuit	15-255	70
P1239	Fuel Injector Cylinder No. 2, Open Circuit	15-256	71
P1240	Fuel Injector Cylinder No. 4, Open Circuit	15-256	72
P1241	Fuel Injector Cylinder No. 3, Open Circuit	15-256	73
P1242	Fuel Injector Cylinder No. 5, Open Circuit	15-257	74
P1265	Air Bag Signal, Signal Implausible	15-257	75
P1266	Fuel Shutoff Function Monitor, Signal Implausible	15-257	76
P1350	Valve Lift Control Checksum Error	15-258	77
P1351	Valve Lift Control Cylinder No. 1, Above Limit	15-260	78
P1352	Valve Lift Control Cylinder No. 6, Above Limit	15-262	79
P1353	Valve Lift Control Cylinder No. 2, Above Limit	15-264	80
P1354	Valve Lift Control Cylinder No. 4, Above Limit	15-267	81
P1355	Valve Lift Control Cylinder No. 3, Above Limit	15-269	82
P1356	Valve Lift Control Cylinder No. 5, Above Limit	15-271	83
P1384	Knock Control Zero Test, Signal Implausible	15-273	84
P1385	Knocfk Control Offset, Signal Implausible	15-274	85
P1386	Knock Control Test Pulse, Signal Implausible	15-274	86
P1397	CMP Sensor No. 2	15-274	87
P1455	A/C Compressor Control, Open Circuit	15-275	88
P1456	A/C Compressor Control, Above Limit	15-275	89
P1457	A/C Compressor Control, Below Limit	15-276	90
P1501	Throttle Jacking Unit, Output Stage, Signal Implausible	15-276	91
P1502	Thottle Jacking Unit, Spring Test, Above Limit	15-276	92
P1503	Throttle Jacking Unit, Position Error, Signal Implausible	15-276	93
P1504	Throttle Jacking Unit, Emergency Air Position, Signal Implausible	15-277	94
P1505	Throttle Jacking Unit, Control Range	15-277	95
P1506	Throttle Jacking Unit Lower Mechanical Stop, Signal Implausible	15-278	96
P1507	Throttle Jacking Unit, Gain Adjustment, Signal Implausible	15-278	97
P1508	Torque Comparison Function Monitor, Signal Implausible	15-278	98
P1510	Throttle Jacking Unit, Exchange Detection Without Adaptation, Signal Implausible	15-279	99
P1511	Throttle Jacking Unit, Abortion Of Test Due To Negative Influence On Ambient Condition	15-279	100
P1513	Throttle Jacking Unit, Spring Test, Above Or Below Limit	15-279	101
P1514	Throttle Jacking Unit Lower Mechanical Stop, Signal Implausible	15-279	102
P1570	39 Immobilizer, Signal Implausible	15-280	103
P1571	39 Immobilizer, Open Circuit Or No Signal	15-280	104
P1574	Stop Lamp Switch, Signal Implausible	15-280	105
P1577	Accelerator Pedal Position Sensor No. 1	15-281	106
P1578	Accelerator Pedal Position Sensor No. 2	15-281	107
P1600	CAN Timeout PSM, Open Circuit	15-282	108
P1601	CAN Timeout Instrument Cluster	15-283	109
P1656	Coolant Shutoff Valve	15-284	110
P1671	Control Module Faulty, Signal Implausible	15-284	111
P1674	Engine Compartment Purge Fan Output Stage	15-285	112

Diagnosis conditions

- Engine running
- Battery voltage greater than 8 V

Possible fault cause

- Open circuit
- Short circuit to ground
- Mass air flow sensor faulty

Note!

In the case of a fault, the PSM is switched off.

Affected terminals

Terminal III/23

Diagnosis/troubleshooting

Work instruction			Display OK	If not OK
1	Check wiring from MAF sensor to DME control module for continuity.	• Remove connector of MAF sensor • Connect special tool 9637 to wiring harness (DME control module connector). • Measure resistance between special tool 9637 Pin III/23 and MAF sensor plug Pin 5	0 - 5 Ω ⇒ Step 2	Repair wiring harness → End
2	Check wiring from MAF sensor to DME control module for short to ground	• Remove connector of MAF sensor • Connect special tool 9637 to wiring harness (DME control module connector). • Measure resistance between special tool 9637 Pin III/23 and ground	∞ Ω ⇒ Step 3	Repair wiring harness → End

PR1020100223010X

Fig. 3 Code P0102: MAF Sensor Below Limit (Part 1 of 2)

Diagnosis conditions

- Engine running
- Battery voltage greater than 8 V

Possible fault cause

- Short circuit to B+
- Mass air flow sensor faulty
- Throttle jacking unit faulty

Note!

In the case of a fault, the PSM is switched off.

Affected terminals

Terminal III/23

Diagnosis/troubleshooting

Work instruction			Display OK	If not OK
1	Check intake air system for leaks		⇒ Step 2	Repair intake air system → End
2	Check wiring from MAF sensor to DME control module for short to B+	• Remove connector of MAF sensor • Connect special tool 9637 to wiring harness (DME control module connector). • Measure voltage between special tool 9637 Pin III/23 and ground • Switch on the ignition	0 V ⇒ Step 3	
3	Check signal from MAF sensor	• Check voltage signal from MAF sensor with 'Ignition on' (with Porsche System Tester 2 in the 'Actual values/mass air flow' menu, or with a voltmeter and special tool 9637).	0.9 to 1.1 V	Replace MAF sensor ⇒ Step 5

PR1020100224010X

Fig. 4 Code P0103: MAF Sensor Above Limit (Part 1 of 2)

Work instruction			Display OK	If not OK
3	Check signal from MAF sensor	• Check voltage signal from MAF sensor with 'Ignition on' (with Porsche System Tester 2 in the 'Actual values/mass air flow' menu, or with a voltmeter and special tool 9637). • Start the engine	0.9 to 1.1 V 1.2 to 1.5 V (at idle speed) → End	Replace MAF sensor ⇒ Step 4
4	Clean air cleaner and replace filter element	• Clean pure air side of air cleaner (extract dirt, do not blow out with compressed air with mass air flow sensor installed) • Replace filter element	→ End	

PR1020100223020X

Fig. 3 Code P0102: MAF Sensor Below Limit (Part 2 of 2)

Work instruction			Display OK	If not OK
3		• Start the engine	1.2 to 1.5 V (at idle speed) ⇒ Step 4	
4	Check and clean throttle jacking unit	• Read out throttle actual value at idling speed (engine at operating temperature, air conditioning switched off)	Less than 4 % → End	Clean throttle jacking unit → End
5	Clean air cleaner and replace filter element	• Clean pure air side of air cleaner (extract dirt, do not blow out with compressed air with mass air flow sensor installed) • Replace filter element		

PR1020100224020X

Fig. 4 Code P0103: MAF Sensor Above Limit (Part 2 of 2)

Diagnosis conditions

- Idle speed
- Time elapsed after engine start-up greater than 5 minutes

Possible fault cause

- Temperature sensor faulty
- Short circuit to B+
- Open circuit

Note!

A substitute value (approx. 60 °C) is used in the event of a fault.

Affected terminals

Terminal III/34

Diagnosis/troubleshooting

Work instruction			Display OK	If not OK
1	Check temperature sensor	• Remove plug of temperature sensor • Measure resistance between temperature sensor Pin 1 and Pin 2	2.3 - 2.7 kΩ (at 20 °C) ⇒ Step 2	Replace temperature sensor → End

PR1020100225010X

Fig. 5 Code P0112: IAT Sensor Below Limit (Part 1 of 2)

Work instruction			Display OK	If not OK
2	Check wiring from DME control module to temperature sensor for continuity	• Remove plug of temperature sensor • Connect special tool 9637 to wiring harness (DME control module connector). • Measure resistance between special tool 9637 Pin III/34 and temperature sensor plug Pin 2	0 - 5 Ω ⇒ Step 3	Repair wiring harness → End
3	Check wiring from DME control module to temperature sensor for short to B+	• Remove plug of temperature sensor • Connect special tool 9637 to wiring harness (DME control module connector). • Switch on the ignition • Measure voltage between special tool 9637 Pin III/34 and ground	0 V → End	Repair wiring harness → End

PR1020100225020X

Fig. 5 Code P0112: IAT Sensor Below Limit (Part 2 of 2)

Diagnosis conditions

- A temperature model is formed. If the measured temperature deviates too much from the calculated temperature, a fault is detected.

Note!

A thermostat which is constantly open can cause the fault P0115.

Possible fault cause

- Thermostat (permanently open)
- Open coolant shutoff valve (only Tiptronic vehicles)
- Wiring
- Temperature sensor faulty
- DME control module faulty

Affected terminals

Terminal III/22 and III/17

Resistance values

0 °C	5.0 - 7.0 kΩ
20 °C	2.0 - 3.0 kΩ
60 °C	0.4 - 0.8 kΩ

Diagnosis/troubleshooting

Work instruction		Display OK	If not OK
1	Check thermostat	⇒ Step 2	Replace thermostat → End
2	Check coolant shutoff valve in Tiptronic vehicles	⇒ Step 3	Replace coolant shutoff valve in Tiptronic vehicles → End

PR1020100227010X

Fig. 7 Code P0115: ECT Signal Implausible (Part 1 of 2)

Diagnosis conditions

- Idle speed
- Time elapsed after engine start-up greater than 2 seconds

Possible fault cause

- Short circuit to ground

Note!

A substitute value (approx. 60 °C) is used in the event of a fault.

Affected terminals

Terminal III/34

Diagnosis/troubleshooting

Work instruction			Display OK	If not OK
1	Check wiring from DME control module to temperature sensor for short to ground	• Remove plug of temperature sensor • Connect special tool 9637 to wiring harness (DME control module connector). • Measure resistance between special tool 9637 Pin III/34 and ground	∞ Ω → End	Repair wiring harness → End

PR1020100226000X

Fig. 6 Code P0113: IAT Sensor Above Limit

Work instruction			Display OK	If not OK
3	Check temperature sensor	• Remove plug connection in engine compartment • Measure resistance between temperature sensor Pin 1 and Pin 4	Approx. 2 - 3 kΩ ⇒ Step 4	Replace temperature sensor → End
4	Check output voltage of DME control module	• Connect special tool 9637. Do not connect connector III of vehicle wiring harness. • Measure voltage between Pin III/22 and III/17 • Ignition on	Approx. 5 V → End	⇒ Step 5
5	Check wiring from DME control module to temperature sensor for continuity	• Connect special tool 9637 to wiring harness (DME control module plug) • Remove plug of temperature sensor • Measure resistance between special tool 9637 Pin III/17 and temperature sensor plug connection Pin 4 • Measure resistance between special tool 9637 Pin III/22 and temperature sensor plug connection Pin 1	0 - 5 Ω ⇒ Step 6	Repair wiring harness → End
6	Check wiring from DME control module to temperature sensor for short to ground	• Connect special tool 9637 to wiring harness (DME control module plug) • Remove plug of temperature sensor • Measure resistance between special tool 9637 Pin III/22 and ground	∞ Ω ⇒ Step 7	Repair wiring harness → End
7	Check wiring from DME control module to temperature sensor for short to B+	• Connect special tool 9637 to wiring harness (DME control module plug) • Remove plug of temperature sensor • Measure voltage between Pin III/22 and ground	Approx. 5 V ⇒ Step 8	Repair wiring harness → End
8	Replace DME control module		⇒ Step 9	→ End
9	Perform adaptation	• Switch on the ignition • Wait one minute. Do not press the accelerator. • Switch off the ignition for at least 10 seconds. • Read out the fault memory	→ End	→ End

PR1020100227020X

Fig. 7 Code P0115: ECT Signal Implausible (Part 2 of 2)

Diagnosis conditions

- A fault is recorded after a debounce time of 0.4 seconds if an engine temperature of less than -45 °C is measured.

Possible fault cause

- Wiring
- Temperature sensor faulty
- DME control module faulty

Affected terminals

Terminal III/22 and III/17

Resistance values

0 °C	5.0 - 7.0 kΩ
20 °C	2.0 - 3.0 kΩ
60 °C	0.4 - 0.8 kΩ

Diagnosis/troubleshooting

Work instruction			Display OK	If not OK
1	Check temperature sensor	• Remove plug connection in engine compartment • Measure resistance between temperature sensor Pin 1 and Pin 4	Approx. 2 - 3 kΩ ⇒ Step 2	Replace temperature sensor → End
2	Check output voltage of DME control module	• Connect special tool 9637. Do not connect connector III of vehicle wiring harness. • Measure voltage between Pin III/22 and III/17 • Ignition on	Approx. 5 V → End	⇒ Step 3

PR1020100228010X

Fig. 8 Code P0117: ECT Open Circuit, Below Limit (Part 1 of 2)

Diagnosis conditions

- A fault is recorded after a debounce time of 0.4 seconds if an engine temperature of more than 140°C is measured.

Possible fault cause

- Wiring
- Temperature sensor faulty
- DME control module faulty

Affected terminals

Terminal III/22 and III/17

Resistance values

0 °C	5.0 - 7.0 kΩ
20 °C	2.0 - 3.0 kΩ
60 °C	0.4 - 0.8 kΩ

Diagnosis/troubleshooting

Work instruction			Display OK	If not OK
1	Check temperature sensor	• Remove plug connection in engine compartment • Measure resistance between temperature sensor Pin 1 and Pin 4	Approx. 2 - 3 kΩ ⇒ Step 1	Replace temperature sensor → End
2	Check output voltage of DME control module	• Connect special tool 9637. Do not connect connector III of vehicle wiring harness. • Measure voltage between Pin III/22 and III/17 • Ignition on	Approx. 5 V → End	⇒ Step 3

PR1020100229010X

Fig. 9 Code P0118: ECT Above Limit (Part 1 of 2)

Work instruction			Display OK	If not OK
3	Check wiring from DME control module to temperature sensor for continuity	• Connect special tool 9637 to wiring harness (DME control module plug) • Remove plug of temperature sensor • Measure resistance between special tool 9637 Pin III/17 and temperature sensor plug connection Pin 4 • Measure resistance between special tool 9637 Pin III/22 and temperature sensor plug connection Pin 1	0 - 5 Ω ⇒ Step 4	Repair wiring harness → End
4	Check wiring from DME control module for short to B+	• Connect special tool 9637 to wiring harness (DME control module plug) • Remove plug of temperature sensor • Measure voltage between Pin III/22 and ground • Switch on the ignition	Approx. 5 V ⇒ Step 5	Repair wiring harness → End
5	Replace DME control module		⇒ Step 6	→ End
6	Perform adaptation	• Switch on the ignition • Wait one minute. Do not press the accelerator. • Switch off the ignition for at least 10 seconds. • Read out the fault memory	→ End	→ End

PR1020100228020X

Fig. 8 Code P0117: ECT Open Circuit, Below Limit (Part 2 of 2)

Work instruction			Display OK	If not OK
3	Check wiring from DME control module to temperature sensor for continuity	• Connect special tool 9637 to wiring harness (DME control module plug) • Remove plug of temperature sensor • Measure resistance between special tool 9637 Pin III/17 and temperature sensor plug connection Pin 4 • Measure resistance between special tool 9637 Pin III/22 and temperature sensor plug connection Pin 1	0 - 5 Ω ⇒ Step 4	Repair wiring harness → End
4	Check wiring from DME control module to temperature sensor for short to ground	• Connect special tool 9637 to wiring harness (DME control module plug) • Remove plug of temperature sensor • Measure resistance between special tool 9637 Pin III/22 and ground	∞ Ω ⇒ Step 5	Repair wiring harness → End
5	Replace DME control module		⇒ Step 6	→ End
6	Perform adaptation	• Switch on the ignition • Wait one minute. Do not press the accelerator. • Switch off the ignition for at least 10 seconds. • Read out the fault memory	→ End	→ End

PR1020100229020X

Fig. 9 Code P0118: ECT Above Limit (Part 2 of 2)

Diagnosis conditions

- Engine running

Possible fault cause

- Open circuit or short circuit in the wiring
- Throttle position sensor faulty
- DME control module faulty

Affected terminals

Terminal I/7, I/9, III/8, III/10, III/24 and III/25

Note!

- *Fault P0121 only appears in conjunction with fault P1121 or P1122.*
- *The system operates in pedal sensor standby mode, i.e. the angle of the accelerator pedal is calculated from the residual position sensor signal.*
- *The opening angle of the throttle valve is limited to 30 %.*
- *The dynamic of the throttle valve is restricted.*

Diagnosis/troubleshooting

Work instruction			Display OK	If not OK
1	Check voltage supply to throttle motor actuator	• Connect special tool 9637 • Connect motor tester (oscilloscope) to Pin I/7 and Pin I/9 • Use special input • Switch on the ignition	See Figure 1	⇒ Step 5
		• Fully depress accelerator pedal	See Figure 2 ⇒ Step 2	

PR1020100230010X

Fig. 10 Code P0121: Throttle Valve, Signal Implausible (Part 1 of 4)

Work instruction			Display OK	If not OK
4		• Measure resistance between disconnection point Pin 1 and special tool 9637 Pin I/9	0 - 5 Ω	Repair wiring harness ⇒ End
		• Measure resistance between disconnection point Pin 2 and special tool 9637 Pin III/25	0 - 5 Ω	
		• Measure resistance between disconnection point Pin 3 and special tool 9637 Pin III/10	0 - 5 Ω	
		• Measure resistance between disconnection point Pin 4 and special tool 9637 Pin I/7	0 - 5 Ω	
		• Measure resistance between disconnection point Pin 5 and special tool 9637 Pin III/8	0 - 5 Ω	
		• Measure resistance between disconnection point Pin 6 and special tool 9637 Pin III/24	0 - 5 Ω	
		• Measure resistance between disconnection point Pin 4 and ground	∞ Ω	
		• Measure resistance between disconnection point Pin 5 and ground	∞ Ω	
		• Measure resistance between disconnection point Pin 6 and ground	∞ Ω	
		• Switch on the ignition • Measure voltage between disconnection point Pin 4 and ground	0 V	
		• Measure voltage between disconnection point Pin 5 and ground	0 V	
		• Measure voltage between disconnection point Pin 6 and ground	0 V ⇒ Step 5	

PR1020100230030X

Fig. 10 Code P0121: Throttle Valve, Signal Implausible (Part 3 of 4)

Figure 1:

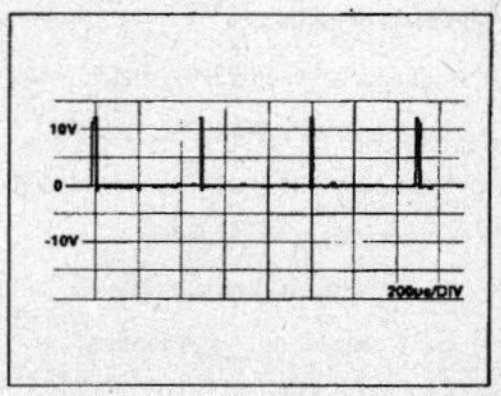

Figure 2:

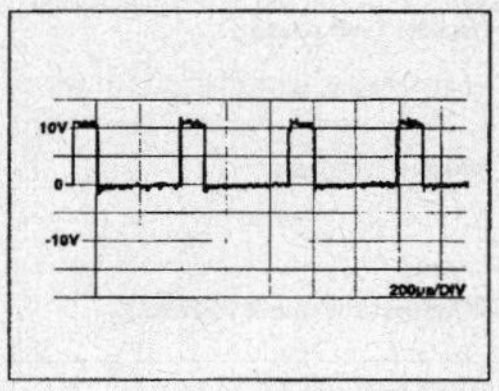

Work instruction			Display OK	If not OK
2	Check TP voltage supply.	• Connect special tool 9637 to wiring harness (DME control module plug) • Measure voltage between Pin III/10 and Pin III/25 • Switch on the ignition	Approx. 5 V ⇒ Step 3	⇒ Step 4
3	Check voltage values of throttle position sensors.	• Connect special tool 9637 • Switch on the ignition		
		• Measure voltage between Pin III/24 and Pin III/25	Approx. 0.7 - 0.9 V	Replace throttle part → End
		• Fully depress accelerator pedal	Approx. 4.1 - 4.5 V	
		• Measure voltage between Pin III/8 and Pin III/25	Approx. 4.0 - 4.4 V	
		• Fully depress accelerator pedal	Approx. 0.5 V → End	
4	Check wiring from throttle part to DME control module for continuity or short circuit to B+ and ground	• Separate disconnection point to throttle part • Connect special tool 9637 to wiring harness (DME control module plug)		

PR1020100230020X

Fig. 10 Code P0121: Throttle Valve, Signal Implausible (Part 2 of 4)

Disconnection point throttle part:

Note!

The wires to the throttle part are routed via connector X 59/2.

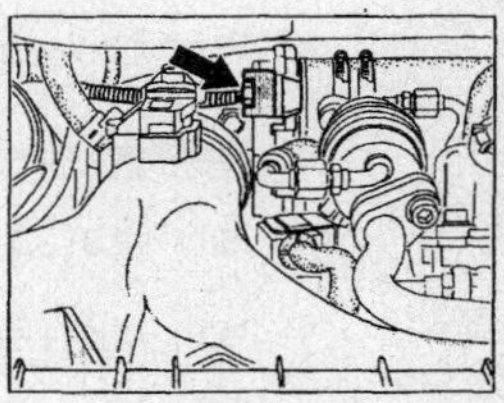

Work instruction			Display OK	If not OK
5	Replace DME control module		⇒ Step 6	
6	Perform adaptation	• Switch on the ignition • Wait one minute • Do not press the accelerator • Switch off the ignition for at least 10 seconds • Read out the fault memory	→ End	→ End

PR1020100230040X

Fig. 10 Code P0121: Throttle Valve, Signal Implausible (Part 4 of 4)

Diagnosis conditions

- Air mass between 25 kg/h and 120 kg/h
- Oxygen sensing after TWC is active
- Basic adaptation has reached steady condition
- No secondary air diagnosis
- No fuel tank ventilation diagnosis
- EVAP canister not highly loaded
- No faults in memory

Possible fault cause

- Implausible signal from oxygen sensor

Affected terminals

-

Diagnosis/troubleshooting

Work instruction			Display OK	If not OK
1	Erase fault memory, then road test vehicle or perform short test	• Erase fault memory • Heat the oxygen sensors (road test car under load, run engine without load at high rpm) • Road test vehicle or perform short test, ensuring that the diagnosis conditions are reached		
2	Read out the fault memory		No fault stored → End	Replace oxygen sensor

PR1020100231000X

Fig. 11 Code P0139: Aging Of Oxygen Sensor After TWC Bank 1

Diagnosis conditions

- Air mass between 25 kg/h and 120 kg/h
- Oxygen sensing after TWC is active
- Basic adaptation has reached steady condition
- No secondary air diagnosis
- No fuel tank ventilation diagnosis
- EVAP canister not highly loaded
- No faults in memory

Possible fault cause

- Implausible signal from oxygen sensor

Affected terminals

-

Diagnosis/troubleshooting

Work instruction			Display OK	If not OK
1	Erase fault memory, then road test vehicle or perform short test	• Erase fault memory • Heat the oxygen sensors (road test car under load, run engine without load at high rpm) • Road test vehicle or perform short test, ensuring that the diagnosis conditions are reached		
2	Read out the fault memory		No fault stored → End	Replace oxygen sensor

PR1020100232000X

Fig. 12 Code P0159: Aging Of Oxygen Sensor After TWC Bank 2

Diagnosis conditions

- Idle speed
- Time elapsed after engine start-up greater than 5 minutes

Possible fault cause

- Temperature sensor faulty
- Wiring harness
- DME control module faulty

Affected terminals

Terminal III/5 and III/17

Resistance values

60 °C	2.8 - 3.5 kΩ
90 °C	1.0 - 1.3 kΩ
120 °C	0.4 - 0.6 kΩ

PR1020100233010X

Fig. 13 Code P0197: Oil Temperature Sensor, Below Limit (Part 1 of 2)

Work instruction			Display OK	If not OK
1	Check temperature sensor	• Connect special tool 9637 to wiring harness (DME control module plug) • Measure resistance between Pin III/17 and Pin III/5	2.8 - 3.5 kΩ (at 60 °C) ⇒ Step 2	Replace temperature sensor → End
2	Check wiring from DME control module to temperature sensor for continuity	• Connect special tool 9637 to wiring harness (DME control module plug) • Remove plug connection of temperature sensor • Measure resistance between special tool 9637 Pin III/17 and temperature sensor plug Pin 2 • Measure resistance between special tool 9637 Pin III/5 and temperature sensor plug Pin 1	0 - 5 Ω ⇒ Step 3	Repair wiring harness → End
3	Check wiring from DME control module to temperature sensor for short to ground	• Connect special tool 9637 to wiring harness (DME control module plug) • Remove plug connection of temperature sensor • Measure resistance between Pin III/5 and ground	∞ Ω ⇒ Step 4	Repair wiring harness → End
4	Replace DME control module		⇒ Step 5	
5	Perform adaptation	• Switch on the ignition • Wait one minute • Do not press the accelerator • Switch off the ignition for at least 10 seconds • Read out the fault memory	→ End	

PR1020100233020X

Fig. 13 Code P0197: Oil Temperature Sensor, Below Limit (Part 2 of 2)

Diagnosis conditions

- Idle speed
- Time elapsed after engine start-up greater than 5 minutes

Possible fault cause

- Temperature sensor faulty
- Wiring harness
- DME control module faulty

Affected terminals

Terminal III/5 and III/17

Resistance values

60 °C	2.8 - 3.5 kΩ
90 °C	1.0 - 1.3 kΩ
120 °C	0.4 - 0.6 kΩ

Diagnosis/troubleshooting

Work instruction			Display OK	If not OK
1	Check temperature sensor	◆ Connect special tool 9637 to wiring harness (DME control module plug) ◆ Measure resistance between Pin III/17 and Pin III/5	2.8 - 3.5 kΩ (at 60 °C) ⇒ Step 2	Replace temperature sensor → End
2	Check wiring from DME control module to temperature sensor for short to B+	◆ Connect special tool 9637 to wiring harness (DME control module plug) ◆ Remove plug connection of temperature sensor ◆ Switch on the ignition ◆ Measure voltage between Pin III/5 and ground	0 V ⇒ Step 3	Repair wiring harness → End

PR1020100234010X

Fig. 14 Code P0198: Oil Temperature Sensor, Above Limit (Part 1 of 2)

Diagnosis conditions

- A cycle of 1,000 crankshaft revolutions is evaluated (for misfire damaging to the TWC, 200 crankshaft revolutions). The misfire rates are compared with a threshold value. If the misfire rate is greater than the threshold value, a fault is recorded in the memory.
- The Check Engine Malfunction Indicator Lamp (MIL) is switched on and stays on when the misfire rate lies above the threshold value at which the emission limit values are exceeded during two consecutive driving cycles (in the case of EOBD 3 driving cycles).
- If the misfire rate may lead to permanent damage to the TWC, the Check Engine MIL flashes. If the misfire rate is no longer reached during the first journey, the MIL goes out. If the rate is reached during the next journey, the MIL flashes. If this misfire rate is subsequently no longer reached, the MIL changes to a continuous light.

Note!

- *When the fuel tank is driven to empty, misfiring can occur. For this reason the fuel level in the tank is also stored in the memory when misfiring occurs. If the tank was nearly empty, there was probably no fault. Erase fault memory and road test vehicle.*
- *In the event of a short circuit to B+ or ground in the oxygen sensors ahead of the TWC, the mixture becomes too lean or too rich. This can cause misfiring. If, in addition, an oxygen sensor signal fault ahead of the TWC is stored in memory, first correct this fault and then road test the vehicle.*

Possible fault cause

- Fault in ignition system
- Fault in injection system
- Flat-base tappets (valve lift fault)
- Mixture too rich
- Mixture too lean
- Mechanical causes:

Valve lifter chattering

PR1020100235010X

Fig. 15 Code P0300: Misfire Detection (Part 1 of 10)

Work instruction			Display OK	If not OK
3	Replace DME control module		⇒ Step 4	
4	Perform adaptation	◆ Switch on the ignition ◆ Wait one minute ◆ Do not press the accelerator ◆ Switch off the ignition for at least 10 seconds ◆ Read out the fault memory	→ End	

PR1020100234020X

Fig. 14 Code P0198: Oil Temperature Sensor, Above Limit (Part 2 of 2)

This is caused by dirt in the valve lifter.

When the Check Engine MIL lights up, a chattering valve lifter may also occur for a certain time. The DME control module registers (sporadic) misfiring at one or more cylinders. The mixture adaptation values are normal.

Remedy:

1 - Remove lifter bores, check for damage and blow out oil passages.

2 - Replace all valve lifters.

3 - During the test drive, listen for valve lifter noises.

Camshaft control times adjusted

The camshaft control times have changed. No chattering noises occur. The DME control module indicates misfiring for the entire cylinder bank 1 or 2. The mixture adaptation values in the idle speed range differ in bank 1 and bank 2, the mixture adaptation values in the upper and lower load ranges are generally normal.

Remedy:

1 - Carry out raw emission measurement:

1. Reset mixture adaptation values (disconnect battery)
2. Disconnect oxygen sensors

If the difference between bank 1 and bank 2 is greater than approx. 0.8 %, then

1 - Set the camshaft control times again.

2 - Road test vehicle. The mixture adaptation values must be normal.

VarioCam does not switch over completely

The VarioCam does not switch over completely from power to torque valve timing.

An indication of this problem is misfiring detected by the DME control module in the range of 1200 - 1500 rpm occurring in an entire bank.

The mixture adaptation values are normal.

Remedy:

1 - Replace VarioCam.

2 - Road test vehicle.

PR1020100235020X

Fig. 15 Code P0300: Misfire Detection (Part 2 of 10)

Other possible fault causes

- worn camshafts
- leaking valves
- faulty piston rings

If opposing cylinders have misfiring, the cause could be the sensor wheel.

If valve lift faults are suspected, perform the system test for large lift and the system test for small lift with the Porsche System Tester 2.

Note!

If the battery was disconnected, at least range 1 of sensor wheel adaptation must be adapted before troubleshooting is carried out; see actual values explanation.

Affected terminals

-

Diagnosis/troubleshooting

Note!

If there is a lot of oil in the engine, check that the oil filler tube and cap are tight.

Work instruction			Display OK	If not OK
1	Check for air leaks in intake air system		⇒ Step 2	Repair intake air system → End
2	Carry out pressure loss test		⇒ Step 3	Repair engine → End
3	Check spark plugs. Specified spark plugs: Electrode gap: 1.6 mm ± 0.2 mm. Check appearance of spark plugs		⇒ Step 4	Replace faulty spark plug(s). → End
4	Check spark plug connectors		Approx. 2 kΩ ⇒ Step 5	Replace faulty spark plug connectors. → End
5	Check ignition coil(s)	• Measure resistance between Pin 1 and Pin 15	0.3 to 0.7 Ω (at 20 °C) ⇒ Step 6	Replace ignition coil(s) → End

PR1020100235030X

Fig. 15 Code P0300: Misfire Detection (Part 3 of 10)

Work instruction			Display OK	If not OK
8	Check volume supply of fuel pump. (Fuel filter and electrical supply OK)	• Relieve pressure in fuel tank by opening tank cap. • Connect Porsche System Tester 2 • Remove complete air filter system • Detach fuel return line (A/F 17 mm) from the engine compartment (left), taking care to hold it fast (A/F 17 mm). • Collect residual fuel • Observe safety regulations • Connect fuel hose (shop-made, approx. 1.5 metres long) to the fitting and hold in a measuring container • Actuate fuel pump with the Porsche System Tester 2 and allow fuel to flow into the measuring container for 30 seconds • Volume supply must be at least 850 cm³/ 30 s, i.e. after 30 seconds at least 850 cm³ of fuel must be in the measuring container.	→ End	

Note!

It is essential to observe safety regulations for handling fuel.

Work instruction			Display OK	If not OK
9	Check triggering of fuel injectors	• The fuel injectors can be individually suppressed with the Porsche System Tester 2 in the menu 'Drive link active'	The engine idle speed decreases if triggering is OK	Check triggering ⇒ Step 9a
9a	B+ supply	• Remove connector of fuel injector to be checked • Measure voltage between valve plug contact Pin 1 and ground • Switch on the ignition	> 11 V ⇒ Step 9b	Check wiring according to wiring diagram for continuity or short circuit → End
9b	Coil resistance of fuel injectors	• Remove connector of fuel injector to be checked • Measure resistance between the terminals of the fuel injector	11 - 13 Ω ⇒ Step 9c	

PR1020100235050X

Fig. 15 Code P0300: Misfire Detection (Part 5 of 10)

Work instruction			Display OK	If not OK
6	Check all connectors for secure fastening and corrosion		⇒ Step 7	Clean plug connections and connect securely. → End
7	Check fuel pressure	• Undo and remove the closure cap of the fuel collection pipe test connection (A/F 13 mm) • Connect pressure gauge (special tool P 378a) to connecting line (special tool 9559) and connect to test connection. • Actuate fuel pump, either with the Porsche System Tester or via a fuel pump relay without tester		⇒ Step 8
		• Nominal test value, stationary engine	3,8 ± 0.2 bar	
		• Nominal test value, engine idling	3,3 ± 0.2 bar ⇒ Step 9	

Note!

The seal or sealing ring in the brass closure cap is not exchangeable. It must therefore be used only once.

Tightening torque of new brass closure cap 2.5 ± 0.5 Nm (2.0 ± 0.5 ftlb.)

PR1020100235040X

Fig. 15 Code P0300: Misfire Detection (Part 4 of 10)

Work instruction			Display OK	If not OK
9c	Injection output stage (negative supply)	• Connect special tool V.A.G 1315 A/1 between fuel injector and connector • Connect engine tester according to manufacturer's instructions. Connect cable for special input to special tool • Start the engine	See Figure ⇒ Step 9d	
9d	• Perform system test for large lift		→ End	

PR1020100235060X

Fig. 15 Code P0300: Misfire Detection (Part 6 of 10)

Figure:

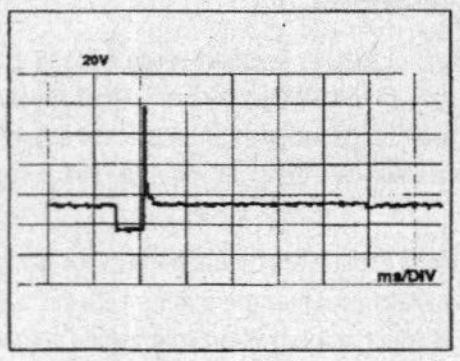

Warning!

Tester cables must not be connected to ground.

Note!

If the engine does not start, or if the idling speed drops, replace tester cable connected to special tool.

Perform system test for large lift

Warning!

Test is carried out while driving. Have a second person operate the Porsche System Tester 2.

During the system test for large lift, the valves remain at large lift, regardless of the type of driving. Faulty switching conditions can be detected by rough running, just like with misfire detection. If a valve is not switched to large lift, the fault type 'over limit' is recorded.

Several cylinders may be stored as faulty, although only one valve on one cylinder is faulty.

In order to guarantee safety during repairs, the flat-base tappets of the inlet valves of the entire cylinder bank should be replaced if a fault occurs.

A faulty flat-base tappet can be detected because the oxygen sensor F_R for this cylinder bank hardly changes the mixture at all given acceleration with wide-open throttle (F_R at 1) and enriches the mixture in the opposite cylinder bank ($F_R > 1$)⇒ see drawing below. Given a difference between F_{R1} and F_{R2} of more than 8 % during acceleration with wide-open throttle, a fault is certainly present.

If the difference is less than 4 %, 1 valve may be faulty on both cylinder banks. In this case, all flat-base tappets of the inlet valves must be replaced.

PR1020100235070X

Fig. 15 Code P0300: Misfire Detection (Part 7 of 10)

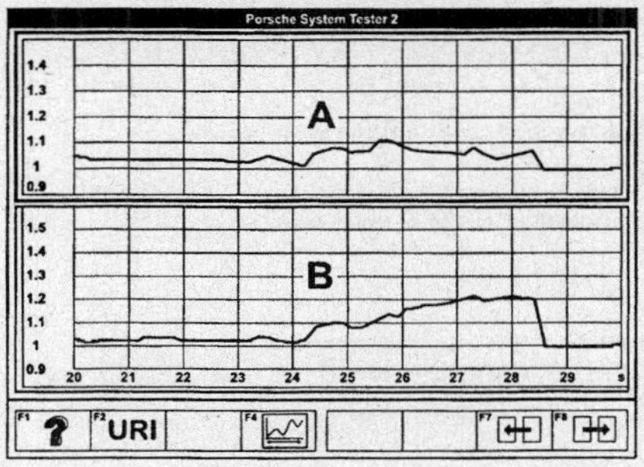

A - Oxygen sensor, bank 1
B - Oxygen sensor, bank 2

1 - **Select system test.**

2 - **Select 'Request large lift'.**

If "Valve diagnosis not ready" appears, a fault may have been stored.

1. Erase the fault memory.

3 - **Activate the system test with the key F8 immediately before acceleration with wide-open throttle.**

The message "Drive link active" then appears.

4 - **Perform acceleration with wide-open throttle in 2nd gear, until "Valve lift diagnosis complete" appears.**

Note!

- *If a fault is detected, it is only recorded in the fault memory after 6,000 ignitions (at idling speed approx. 3 minutes waiting time).*
- *It is important to observe the oxygen sensor during acceleration with wide-open throttle or to record its behaviour with the data logger.*

Continue by performing the system test for small lift

PR1020100235080X

Fig. 15 Code P0300: Misfire Detection (Part 8 of 10)

Perform system test for small lift

Warning!

Test is carried out while driving. Have a second person operate the Porsche System Tester 2.

During the system test for small lift, the valves remain at small lift, regardless of the type of driving. Faulty switching conditions can be detected by rough running, just like with misfire detection. If a valve is not switched to small lift, the fault type 'under limit' is recorded.

Several cylinders may be stored as faulty, although only one valve on one cylinder is faulty.

In order to guarantee safety during repairs, the flat-base tappets of the inlet valves of the entire cylinder bank should be replaced if a fault occurs.

A faulty flat-base tappet can be detected because the oxygen sensor F_R for this cylinder bank enriches the mixture ($F_R > 1$) during acceleration with wide-open throttle ⇒ see drawing below. Difference from the other oxygen sensor > approx. 15 %. In the case of a fault, the flat-base tappets of the inlet valves for the entire cylinder bank must be replaced.

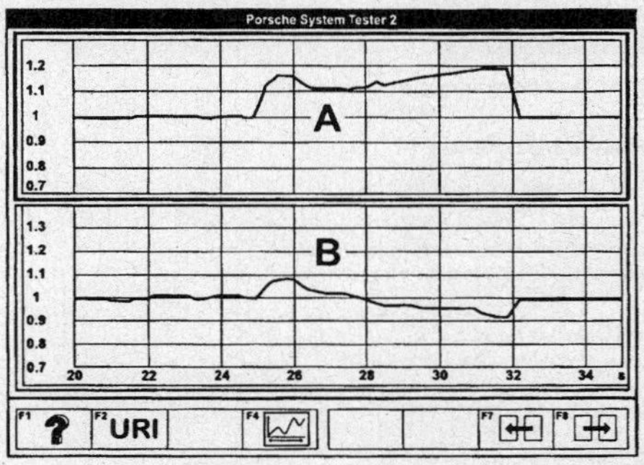

PR1020100235090X

Fig. 15 Code P0300: Misfire Detection (Part 9 of 10)

A - **Oxygen sensor, bank 1**
B - **Oxygen sensor, bank 2**

1 - **Select system test.**

2 - **Select 'Request small lift'.**

If "Valve lift diagnosis not ready" appears, a fault may have been stored.

1. Erase the fault memory.

3 - **Activate the system test with the key F8 immediately before acceleration with wide-open throttle.**

The message "Drive link active" then appears.

Note!

If 'Request small lift' appears, the valves remain at small lift, ie. the performance is reduced dramatically.

4 - **Perform acceleration with wide-open throttle in 2nd gear, until "Valve lift diagnosis complete" (max. 4,000 rpm) appears.**

At speeds above 4,000 rpm, misfires may be stored. Delete the fault memory and repeat the test.

Note!

- *If a fault is detected, it is only recorded in the fault memory after 6,000 ignitions (at idling speed approx. 3 minutes waiting time).*
- *It is important to observe the oxygen sensor during acceleration with wide-open throttle or to record its behaviour with the data logger.*

End

PR1020100235100X

Fig. 15 Code P0300: Misfire Detection (Part 10 of 10)

Diagnosis conditions

- A cycle of 1,000 crankshaft revolutions is evaluated (for misfire damaging to the TWC, 200 crankshaft revolutions). The misfire rates are compared with a threshold value. If the misfire rate is greater than the threshold value, a fault is recorded in the memory.
- The Check Engine Malfunction Indicator Lamp (MIL) is switched on and stays on when the misfire rate lies above the threshold value at which the emission limit values are exceeded during two consecutive driving cycles (in the case of EOBD 3 driving cycles).
- If the misfire rate may lead to permanent damage to the TWC, the Check Engine MIL flashes. If the misfire rate is no longer reached during the first journey, the MIL goes out. If the rate is reached during the next journey, the MIL flashes. If this misfire rate is subsequently no longer reached, the MIL changes to a continuous light.

Note!

- *When the fuel tank is driven to empty, misfiring can occur. For this reason the fuel level in the tank is also stored in the memory when misfiring occurs. If the tank was nearly empty, there was probably no fault. Erase fault memory and road test vehicle.*
- *In the event of a short circuit to B+ or ground in the oxygen sensors ahead of the TWC, the mixture becomes too lean or too rich. This can cause misfiring. If, in addition, an oxygen sensor signal fault ahead of the TWC is stored in memory, first correct this fault and then road test the vehicle.*

Possible fault cause

- Fault in ignition system
- Fault in injection system
- Flat-base tappets (valve lift fault)
- Mixture too rich
- Mixture too lean
- Mechanical causes:

Valve lifter chattering

PR1020100236010X

Fig. 16 Code P0301: Cylinder No. 1 Misfire (Part 1 of 10)

This is caused by dirt in the valve lifter.

When the Check Engine MIL lights up, a chattering valve lifter may also occur for a certain time. The DME control module registers (sporadic) misfiring at one or more cylinders. The mixture adaptation values are normal.

Remedy:

1 - Remove lifter bores, check for damage and blow out oil passages.

2 - Replace all valve lifters.

3 - During the test drive, listen for valve lifter noises.

Camshaft control times adjusted

The camshaft control times have changed. No chattering noises occur. The DME control module indicates misfiring for the entire cylinder bank 1 or 2. The mixture adaptation values in the idle speed range differ in bank 1 and bank 2, the mixture adaptation values in the upper and lower load ranges are generally normal.

Remedy:

1 - Carry out raw emission measurement:

1. Reset mixture adaptation values (disconnect battery)
2. Disconnect oxygen sensors

If the difference between bank 1 and bank 2 is greater than approx. 0.8 %, then

1 - Set the camshaft control times again.

2 - Road test vehicle. The mixture adaptation values must be normal.

VarioCam does not switch over completely

The VarioCam does not switch over completely from power to torque valve timing.

An indication of this problem is misfiring detected by the DME control module in the range of 1200 - 1500 rpm occurring in an entire bank.

The mixture adaptation values are normal.

Remedy:

1 - Replace VarioCam.

2 - Road test vehicle.

PR1020100236020X

Fig. 16 Code P0301: Cylinder No. 1 Misfire (Part 2 of 10)

	Work instruction		Display OK	If not OK
6	Check all connectors for secure fastening and corrosion		⇒ Step 7	Clean plug connections and connect securely. → End
7	Check fuel pressure	• Undo and remove the closure cap of the fuel collection pipe test connection (A/F 13 mm)		⇒ Step 8
		• Connect pressure gauge (special tool P 378a) to connecting line (special tool 9559) and connect to test connection.		
		• Actuate fuel pump, either with the Porsche System Tester or via a fuel pump relay without tester		
		• Nominal test value, stationary engine	3,8 ± 0.2 bar	
		• Nominal test value, engine idling	3,3 ± 0.2 bar ⇒ Step 9	

Note!

The seal or sealing ring in the brass closure cap is not exchangeable. It must therefore be used only once.

Tightening torque of new brass closure cap 2.5 ± 0.5 Nm (2.0 ± 0.5 ftlb.)

PR1020100236040X

Fig. 16 Code P0301: Cylinder No. 1 Misfire (Part 4 of 10)

Other possible fault causes

- worn camshafts
- leaking valves
- faulty piston rings

If opposing cylinders have misfiring, the cause could be the sensor wheel.

If valve lift faults are suspected, perform the system test for large lift and the system test for small lift with the Porsche System Tester 2.

Note!

If the battery was disconnected, at least range 1 of sensor wheel adaptation must be adapted before troubleshooting is carried out; see actual values explanation.

Affected terminals

-

Diagnosis/troubleshooting

Note!

If there is a lot of oil in the engine, check that the oil filler tube and cap are tight.

	Work instruction		Display OK	If not OK
1	Check for air leaks in intake air system		⇒ Step 2	Repair intake air system → End
2	Carry out pressure loss test		⇒ Step 3	Repair engine → End
3	Check spark plugs. Specified spark plugs: Electrode gap: 1.6 mm ± 0.2 mm. Check appearance of spark plugs		⇒ Step 4	Replace faulty spark plug(s). → End
4	Check spark plug connectors		Approx. 2 kΩ ⇒ Step 5	Replace faulty spark plug connectors. → End
5	Check ignition coil(s)	• Measure resistance between Pin 1 and Pin 15	0.3 to 0.7 Ω (at 20 °C) ⇒ Step 6	Replace ignition coil(s) → End

PR1020100236030X

Fig. 16 Code P0301: Cylinder No. 1 Misfire (Part 3 of 10)

	Work instruction		Display OK	If not OK
8	Check volume supply of fuel pump. (Fuel filter and electrical supply OK)	• Relieve pressure in fuel tank by opening tank cap.	→ End	
		• Connect Porsche System Tester 2		
		• Remove complete air filter system		
		• Detach fuel return line (A/F 17 mm) from the engine compartment (left), taking care to hold it fast (A/F 17 mm).		
		• Collect residual fuel		
		• Observe safety regulations		
		• Connect fuel hose (shop-made, approx. 1.5 metres long) to the fitting and hold in a measuring container		
		• Actuate fuel pump with the Porsche System Tester 2 and allow fuel to flow into the measuring container for 30 seconds		
		• Volume supply must be at least 850 cm³/ 30 s, i.e. after 30 seconds at least 850 cm³ of fuel must be in the measuring container.		

Note!

It is essential to observe safety regulations for handling fuel.

	Work instruction		Display OK	If not OK
9	Check triggering of fuel injectors	• The fuel injectors can be individually suppressed with the Porsche System Tester 2 in the menu 'Drive link active'	The engine idle speed decreases if triggering is OK	Check triggering ⇒ Step 9a
9a	B+ supply	• Remove connector of fuel injector to be checked	> 11 V ⇒ Step 9b	Check wiring according to wiring diagram for continuity or short circuit → End
		• Measure voltage between valve plug contact Pin 1 and ground		
		• Switch on the ignition		
9b	Coil resistance of fuel injectors	• Remove connector of fuel injector to be checked	11 - 13 Ω ⇒ Step 9c	
		• Measure resistance between the terminals of the fuel injector		

PR1020100236050X

Fig. 16 Code P0301: Cylinder No. 1 Misfire (Part 5 of 10)

Work instruction			Display OK	If not OK
9c	Injection output stage (negative supply)	♦ Connect special tool V.A.G 1315 A/1 between fuel injector and connector ♦ Connect engine tester according to manufacturer's instructions. Connect cable for special input to special tool ♦ Start the engine	See Figure ⇒ Step 9d	
9d	♦ Perform system test for large lift		→ End	

PR1020100236060X

Fig. 16 Code P0301: Cylinder No. 1 Misfire (Part 6 of 10)

Figure:

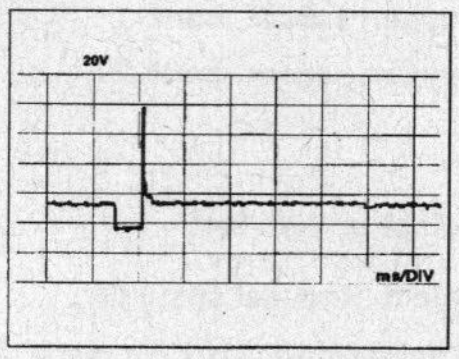

⚠ Warning!

Tester cables must not be connected to ground.

ℹ Note!

If the engine does not start, or if the idling speed drops, replace tester cable connected to special tool.

Perform system test for large lift

⚠ Warning!

Test is carried out while driving. Have a second person operate the Porsche System Tester 2.

During the system test for large lift, the valves remain at large lift, regardless of the type of driving. Faulty switching conditions can be detected by rough running, just like with misfire detection. If a valve is not switched to large lift, the fault type 'over limit' is recorded.

Several cylinders may be stored as faulty, although only one valve on one cylinder is faulty.

In order to guarantee safety during repairs, the flat-base tappets of the inlet valves of the entire cylinder bank should be replaced if a fault occurs.

A faulty flat-base tappet can be detected because the oxygen sensor F_R for this cylinder bank hardly changes the mixture at all given acceleration with wide-open throttle (F_R at 1) and enriches the mixture in the opposite cylinder bank ($F_R > 1$)⇒ see drawing below. Given a difference between F_{R1} and F_{R2} of more than 8 % during acceleration with wide-open throttle, a fault is certainly present.

If the difference is less than 4 %, 1 valve may be faulty on both cylinder banks. In this case, all flat-base tappets of the inlet valves must be replaced.

PR1020100236070X

Fig. 16 Code P0301: Cylinder No. 1 Misfire (Part 7 of 10)

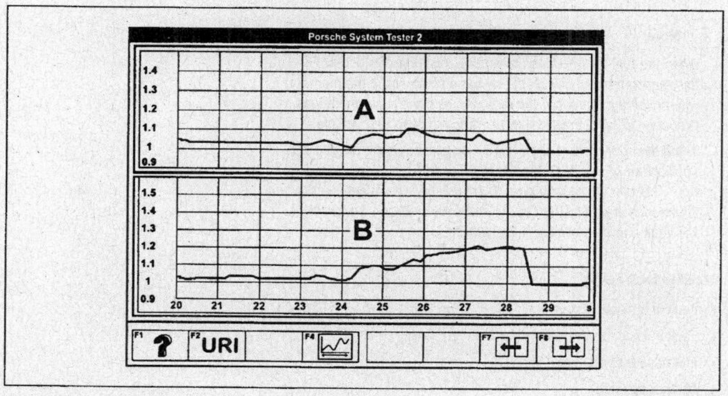

A - Oxygen sensor, bank 1
B - Oxygen sensor, bank 2

1 - Select system test.

2 - Select 'Request large lift'.

If "Valve diagnosis not ready" appears, a fault may have been stored.

1. Erase the fault memory.

3 - Activate the system test with the key F8 immediately before acceleration with wide-open throttle.

The message "Drive link active" then appears.

4 - Perform acceleration with wide-open throttle in 2nd gear, until "Valve lift diagnosis complete" appears.

ℹ Note!

- *If a fault is detected, it is only recorded in the fault memory after 6,000 ignitions (at idling speed approx. 3 minutes waiting time).*
- *It is important to observe the oxygen sensor during acceleration with wide-open throttle or to record its behaviour with the data logger.*

Continue by performing the system test for small lift

PR1020100236080X

Fig. 16 Code P0301: Cylinder No. 1 Misfire (Part 8 of 10)

Perform system test for small lift

⚠ Warning!

Test is carried out while driving. Have a second person operate the Porsche System Tester 2.

During the system test for small lift, the valves remain at small lift, regardless of the type of driving. Faulty switching conditions can be detected by rough running, just like with misfire detection. If a valve is not switched to small lift, the fault type 'under limit' is recorded.

Several cylinders may be stored as faulty, although only one valve on one cylinder is faulty.

In order to guarantee safety during repairs, the flat-base tappets of the inlet valves of the entire cylinder bank should be replaced if a fault occurs.

A faulty flat-base tappet can be detected because the oxygen sensor F_R for this cylinder bank enriches the mixture ($F_R > 1$) during acceleration with wide-open throttle ⇒ see drawing below. Difference from the other oxygen sensor > approx. 15 %. In the case of a fault, the flat-base tappets of the inlet valves for the entire cylinder bank must be replaced.

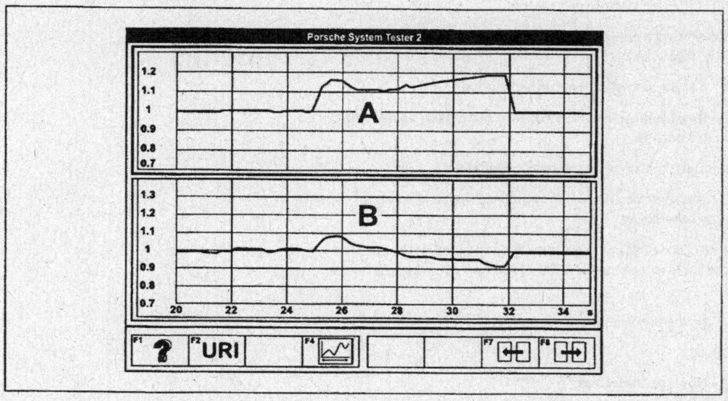

PR1020100236090X

Fig. 16 Code P0301: Cylinder No. 1 Misfire (Part 9 of 10)

A - Oxygen sensor, bank 1

B - Oxygen sensor, bank 2

1 - Select system test.

2 - Select 'Request small lift'.

If "Valve lift diagnosis not ready" appears, a fault may have been stored.

1. Erase the fault memory.

3 - Activate the system test with the key F8 immediately before acceleration with wide-open throttle.

The message "Drive link active" then appears.

Note!

If 'Request small lift' appears, the valves remain at small lift, ie. the performance is reduced dramatically.

4 - Perform acceleration with wide-open throttle in 2nd gear, until "Valve lift diagnosis complete" (max. 4,000 rpm) appears.

At speeds above 4,000 rpm, misfires may be stored. Delete the fault memory and repeat the test.

Note!

- *If a fault is detected, it is only recorded in the fault memory after 6,000 ignitions (at idling speed approx. 3 minutes waiting time).*
- *It is important to observe the oxygen sensor during acceleration with wide-open throttle or to record its behaviour with the data logger.*

End

PR1020100236100X

Fig. 16 Code P0301: Cylinder No. 1 Misfire (Part 10 of 10)

Diagnosis conditions

- A cycle of 1,000 crankshaft revolutions is evaluated (for misfire damaging to the TWC, 200 crankshaft revolutions). The misfire rates are compared with a threshold value. If the misfire rate is greater than the threshold value, a fault is recorded in the memory.
- The Check Engine Malfunction Indicator Lamp (MIL) is switched on and stays on when the misfire rate lies above the threshold value at which the emission limit values are exceeded during two consecutive driving cycles (in the case of EOBD 3 driving cycles).
- If the misfire rate may lead to permanent damage to the TWC, the Check Engine MIL flashes. If the misfire rate is no longer reached during the first journey, the MIL goes out. If the rate is reached during the next journey, the MIL flashes. If this misfire rate is subsequently no longer reached, the MIL changes to a continuous light.

Note!

- *When the fuel tank is driven to empty, misfiring can occur. For this reason the fuel level in the tank is also stored in the memory when misfiring occurs. If the tank was nearly empty, there was probably no fault. Erase fault memory and road test vehicle.*
- *In the event of a short circuit to B+ or ground in the oxygen sensors ahead of the TWC, the mixture becomes too lean or too rich. This can cause misfiring. If, in addition, an oxygen sensor signal fault ahead of the TWC is stored in memory, first correct this fault and then road test the vehicle.*

Possible fault cause

- Fault in ignition system
- Fault in injection system
- Flat-base tappets (valve lift fault)
- Mixture too rich
- Mixture too lean
- Mechanical causes:

Valve lifter chattering

PR1020100237010X

Fig. 17 Code P0302: Cylinder No. 2 Misfire (Part 1 of 10)

This is caused by dirt in the valve lifter.

When the Check Engine MIL lights up, a chattering valve lifter may also occur for a certain time. The DME control module registers (sporadic) misfiring at one or more cylinders. The mixture adaptation values are normal.

Remedy:

1 - Remove lifter bores, check for damage and blow out oil passages.

2 - Replace all valve lifters.

3 - During the test drive, listen for valve lifter noises.

Camshaft control times adjusted

The camshaft control times have changed. No chattering noises occur. The DME control module indicates misfiring for the entire cylinder bank 1 or 2. The mixture adaptation values in the idle speed range differ in bank 1 and bank 2, the mixture adaptation values in the upper and lower load ranges are generally normal.

Remedy:

1 - Carry out raw emission measurement:

1. Reset mixture adaptation values (disconnect battery)
2. Disconnect oxygen sensors

If the difference between bank 1 and bank 2 is greater than approx. 0.8 %, then

1 - Set the camshaft control times again.

2 - Road test vehicle. The mixture adaptation values must be normal.

VarioCam does not switch over completely

The VarioCam does not switch over completely from power to torque valve timing.

An indication of this problem is misfiring detected by the DME control module in the range of 1200 - 1500 rpm occurring in an entire bank.

The mixture adaptation values are normal.

Remedy:

1 - Replace VarioCam.

2 - Road test vehicle.

PR1020100237020X

Fig. 17 Code P0302: Cylinder No. 2 Misfire (Part 2 of 10)

Other possible fault causes

- worn camshafts
- leaking valves
- faulty piston rings

If opposing cylinders have misfiring, the cause could be the sensor wheel.

If valve lift faults are suspected, perform the system test for large lift and the system test for small lift with the Porsche System Tester 2.

Note!

If the battery was disconnected, at least range 1 of sensor wheel adaptation must be adapted before troubleshooting is carried out; see actual values explanation.

Affected terminals

-

Diagnosis/troubleshooting

Note!

If there is a lot of oil in the engine, check that the oil filler tube and cap are tight.

Work instruction			Display OK	If not OK
1	Check for air leaks in intake air system		⇒ Step 2	Repair intake air system → End
2	Carry out pressure loss test		⇒ Step 3	Repair engine → End
3	Check spark plugs. Specified spark plugs: Electrode gap: 1.6 mm ± 0.2 mm. Check appearance of spark plugs		⇒ Step 4	Replace faulty spark plug(s). → End
4	Check spark plug connectors		Approx. 2 kΩ ⇒ Step 5	Replace faulty spark plug connectors. → End
5	Check ignition coil(s)	• Measure resistance between Pin 1 and Pin 15	0.3 to 0.7 Ω (at 20 °C) ⇒ Step 6	Replace ignition coil(s) → End

PR1020100237030X

Fig. 17 Code P0302: Cylinder No. 2 Misfire (Part 3 of 10)

Work instruction		Display OK	If not OK
6	Check all connectors for secure fastening and corrosion	⇒ Step 7	Clean plug connections and connect securely. → End
7	Check fuel pressure	• Undo and remove the closure cap of the fuel collection pipe test connection (A/F 13 mm) • Connect pressure gauge (special tool P 378a) to connecting line (special tool 9559) and connect to test connection. • Actuate fuel pump, either with the Porsche System Tester or via a fuel pump relay without tester		⇒ Step 8
		• Nominal test value, stationary engine	3,8 ± 0.2 bar	
		• Nominal test value, engine idling	3,3 ± 0.2 bar ⇒ Step 9	

Note!

The seal or sealing ring in the brass closure cap is not exchangeable. It must therefore be used only once.

Tightening torque of new brass closure cap 2.5 ± 0.5 Nm (2.0 ± 0.5 ftlb.)

PR1020100237040X

Fig. 17 Code P0302: Cylinder No. 2 Misfire (Part 4 of 10)

Work instruction			Display OK	If not OK
9c	Injection output stage (negative supply)	• Connect special tool V.A.G 1315 A/1 between fuel injector and connector • Connect engine tester according to manufacturer's instructions. Connect cable for special input to special tool • Start the engine	See Figure ⇒ Step 9d	
9d	• Perform system test for large lift		→ End	

PR1020100237060X

Fig. 17 Code P0302: Cylinder No. 2 Misfire (Part 6 of 10)

Figure:

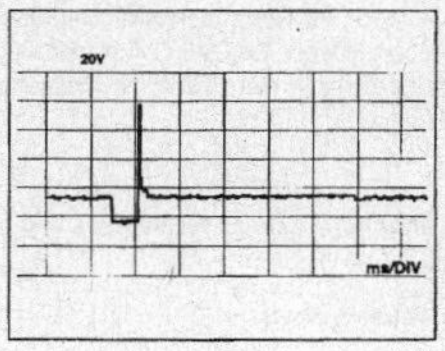

Warning!

Tester cables must not be connected to ground.

Note!

If the engine does not start, or if the idling speed drops, replace tester cable connected to special tool.

Perform system test for large lift

Warning!

Test is carried out while driving. Have a second person operate the Porsche System Tester 2.

During the system test for large lift, the valves remain at large lift, regardless of the type of driving. Faulty switching conditions can be detected by rough running, just like with misfire detection. If a valve is not switched to large lift, the fault type 'over limit' is recorded.

Several cylinders may be stored as faulty, although only one valve on one cylinder is faulty.

In order to guarantee safety during repairs, the flat-base tappets of the inlet valves of the entire cylinder bank should be replaced if a fault occurs.

A faulty flat-base tappet can be detected because the oxygen sensor F_R for this cylinder bank hardly changes the mixture at all given acceleration with wide-open throttle (F_R at 1) and enriches the mixture in the opposite cylinder bank ($F_R > 1$)⇒ see drawing below. Given a difference between F_{R1} and F_{R2} of more than 8 % during acceleration with wide-open throttle, a fault is certainly present.

If the difference is less than 4 %, 1 valve may be faulty on both cylinder banks. In this case, all flat-base tappets of the inlet valves must be replaced.

PR1020100237070X

Fig. 17 Code P0302: Cylinder No. 2 Misfire (Part 7 of 10)

Work instruction			Display OK	If not OK
8	Check volume supply of fuel pump. (Fuel filter and electrical supply OK)	• Relieve pressure in fuel tank by opening tank cap. • Connect Porsche System Tester 2 • Remove complete air filter system • Detach fuel return line (A/F 17 mm) from the engine compartment (left), taking care to hold it fast (A/F 17 mm). • Collect residual fuel • Observe safety regulations • Connect fuel hose (shop-made, approx. 1.5 metres long) to the fitting and hold in a measuring container • Actuate fuel pump with the Porsche System Tester 2 and allow fuel to flow into the measuring container for 30 seconds • Volume supply must be at least 850 cm^3/ 30 s, i.e. after 30 seconds at least 850 cm^3 of fuel must be in the measuring container.	→ End	

Note!

It is essential to observe safety regulations for handling fuel.

Work instruction			Display OK	If not OK
9	Check triggering of fuel injectors	• The fuel injectors can be individually suppressed with the Porsche System Tester 2 in the menu 'Drive link active'	The engine idle speed decreases if triggering is OK	Check triggering ⇒ Step 9a
9a	B+ supply	• Remove connector of fuel injector to be checked • Measure voltage between valve plug contact Pin 1 and ground • Switch on the ignition	> 11 V ⇒ Step 9b	Check wiring according to wiring diagram for continuity or short circuit → End
9b	Coil resistance of fuel injectors	• Remove connector of fuel injector to be checked • Measure resistance between the terminals of the fuel injector	11 - 13 Ω ⇒ Step 9c	

PR1020100237050X

Fig. 17 Code P0302: Cylinder No. 2 Misfire (Part 5 of 10)

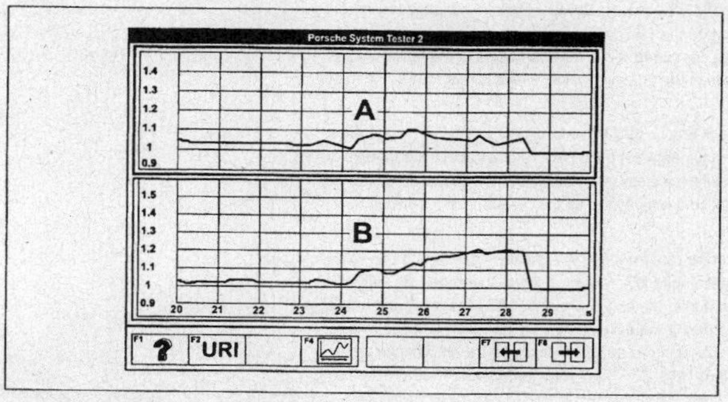

A - Oxygen sensor, bank 1

B - Oxygen sensor, bank 2

1 - Select system test.

2 - Select 'Request large lift'.

If "Valve diagnosis not ready" appears, a fault may have been stored.

1. Erase the fault memory.

3 - Activate the system test with the key F8 immediately before acceleration with wide-open throttle.

The message "Drive link active" then appears.

4 - Perform acceleration with wide-open throttle in 2nd gear, until "Valve lift diagnosis complete" appears.

Note!

- *If a fault is detected, it is only recorded in the fault memory after 6,000 ignitions (at idling speed approx. 3 minutes waiting time).*
- *It is important to observe the oxygen sensor during acceleration with wide-open throttle or to record its behaviour with the data logger.*

Continue by performing the system test for small lift

PR1020100237080X

Fig. 17 Code P0302: Cylinder No. 2 Misfire (Part 8 of 10)

Perform system test for small lift

⚠ **Warning!**

Test is carried out while driving. Have a second person operate the Porsche System Tester 2.

During the system test for small lift, the valves remain at small lift, regardless of the type of driving. Faulty switching conditions can be detected by rough running, just like with misfire detection. If a valve is not switched to small lift, the fault type 'under limit' is recorded.

Several cylinders may be stored as faulty, although only one valve on one cylinder is faulty.

In order to guarantee safety during repairs, the flat-base tappets of the inlet valves of the entire cylinder bank should be replaced if a fault occurs.

A faulty flat-base tappet can be detected because the oxygen sensor F_R for this cylinder bank enriches the mixture ($F_R > 1$) during acceleration with wide-open throttle ⇒ see drawing below. Difference from the other oxygen sensor > approx. 15 %. In the case of a fault, the flat-base tappets of the inlet valves for the entire cylinder bank must be replaced.

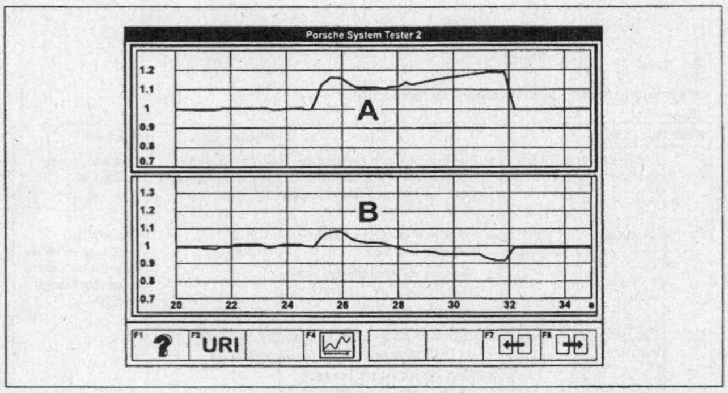

A - Oxygen sensor, bank 1

B - Oxygen sensor, bank 2

1 - **Select system test.**

2 - **Select 'Request small lift'.**

If "Valve lift diagnosis not ready" appears, a fault may have been stored.

1. Erase the fault memory.

3 - **Activate the system test with the key F8 immediately before acceleration with wide-open throttle.**

The message "Drive link active" then appears.

Note!

If 'Request small lift' appears, the valves remain at small lift, ie. the performance is reduced dramatically.

4 - **Perform acceleration with wide-open throttle in 2nd gear, until "Valve lift diagnosis complete" (max. 4,000 rpm) appears.**

At speeds above 4,000 rpm, misfires may be stored. Delete the fault memory and repeat the test.

Note!

- *If a fault is detected, it is only recorded in the fault memory after 6,000 ignitions (at idling speed approx. 3 minutes waiting time).*
- *It is important to observe the oxygen sensor during acceleration with wide-open throttle or to record its behaviour with the data logger.*

End

PR1020100237090X

PR1020100237100X

Fig. 17 Code P0302: Cylinder No. 2 Misfire (Part 9 of 10)

Fig. 17 Code P0302: Cylinder No. 2 Misfire (Part 10 of 10)

Diagnosis conditions

- A cycle of 1,000 crankshaft revolutions is evaluated (for misfire damaging to the TWC, 200 crankshaft revolutions). The misfire rates are compared with a threshold value. If the misfire rate is greater than the threshold value, a fault is recorded in the memory.
- The Check Engine Malfunction Indicator Lamp (MIL) is switched on and stays on when the misfire rate lies above the threshold value at which the emission limit values are exceeded during two consecutive driving cycles (in the case of EOBD 3 driving cycles).
- If the misfire rate may lead to permanent damage to the TWC, the Check Engine MIL flashes. If the misfire rate is no longer reached during the first journey, the MIL goes out. If the rate is reached during the next journey, the MIL flashes. If this misfire rate is subsequently no longer reached, the MIL changes to a continuous light.

Note!

- *When the fuel tank is driven to empty, misfiring can occur. For this reason the fuel level in the tank is also stored in the memory when misfiring occurs. If the tank was nearly empty, there was probably no fault. Erase fault memory and road test vehicle.*
- *In the event of a short circuit to B+ or ground in the oxygen sensors ahead of the TWC, the mixture becomes too lean or too rich. This can cause misfiring. If, in addition, an oxygen sensor signal fault ahead of the TWC is stored in memory, first correct this fault and then road test the vehicle.*

Possible fault cause

- Fault in ignition system
- Fault in injection system
- Flat-base tappets (valve lift fault)
- Mixture too rich
- Mixture too lean
- Mechanical causes:

Valve lifter chattering

This is caused by dirt in the valve lifter.

When the Check Engine MIL lights up, a chattering valve lifter may also occur for a certain time. The DME control module registers (sporadic) misfiring at one or more cylinders. The mixture adaptation values are normal.

Remedy:

1 - **Remove lifter bores, check for damage and blow out oil passages.**

2 - **Replace all valve lifters.**

3 - **During the test drive, listen for valve lifter noises.**

Camshaft control times adjusted

The camshaft control times have changed. No chattering noises occur. The DME control module indicates misfiring for the entire cylinder bank 1 or 2. The mixture adaptation values in the idle speed range differ in bank 1 and bank 2, the mixture adaptation values in the upper and lower load ranges are generally normal.

Remedy:

1 - **Carry out raw emission measurement:**

1. Reset mixture adaptation values (disconnect battery)
2. Disconnect oxygen sensors

If the difference between bank 1 and bank 2 is greater than approx. 0.8 %, then

1 - **Set the camshaft control times again.**

2 - **Road test vehicle. The mixture adaptation values must be normal.**

VarioCam does not switch over completely

The VarioCam does not switch over completely from power to torque valve timing.

An indication of this problem is misfiring detected by the DME control module in the range of 1200 - 1500 rpm occurring in an entire bank.

The mixture adaptation values are normal.

Remedy:

1 - **Replace VarioCam.**

2 - **Road test vehicle.**

PR1020100238010X

PR1020100238020X

Fig. 18 Code P0303: Cylinder No. 3 Misfire (Part 1 of 10)

Fig. 18 Code P0303: Cylinder No. 3 Misfire (Part 2 of 10)

Other possible fault causes

- worn camshafts
- leaking valves
- faulty piston rings

If opposing cylinders have misfiring, the cause could be the sensor wheel.

If valve lift faults are suspected, perform the system test for large lift and the system test for small lift with the Porsche System Tester 2.

Note!

If the battery was disconnected, at least range 1 of sensor wheel adaptation must be adapted before troubleshooting is carried out; see actual values explanation.

Affected terminals

-

Diagnosis/troubleshooting

Note!

If there is a lot of oil in the engine, check that the oil filler tube and cap are tight.

Work instruction			Display OK	If not OK
1	Check for air leaks in intake air system		⇒ Step 2	Repair intake air system → End
2	Carry out pressure loss test		⇒ Step 3	Repair engine → End
3	Check spark plugs. Specified spark plugs: Electrode gap: 1.6 mm ± 0.2 mm. Check appearance of spark plugs		⇒ Step 4	Replace faulty spark plug(s). → End
4	Check spark plug connectors		Approx. 2 kΩ ⇒ Step 5	Replace faulty spark plug connectors. → End
5	Check ignition coil(s)	• Measure resistance between Pin 1 and Pin 15	0.3 to 0.7 Ω (at 20 °C) ⇒ Step 6	Replace ignition coil(s) → End

PR1020100238030X

Fig. 18 Code P0303: Cylinder No. 3 Misfire (Part 3 of 10)

Work instruction			Display OK	If not OK
8	Check volume supply of fuel pump. (Fuel filter and electrical supply OK)	• Relieve pressure in fuel tank by opening tank cap. • Connect Porsche System Tester 2 • Remove complete air filter system • Detach fuel return line (A/F 17 mm) from the engine compartment (left), taking care to hold it fast (A/F 17 mm). • Collect residual fuel • Observe safety regulations • Connect fuel hose (shop-made, approx. 1.5 metres long) to the fitting and hold in a measuring container • Actuate fuel pump with the Porsche System Tester 2 and allow fuel to flow into the measuring container for 30 seconds • Volume supply must be at least 850 cm³/ 30 s, i.e. after 30 seconds at least 850 cm³ of fuel must be in the measuring container.	→ End	

Note!

It is essential to observe safety regulations for handling fuel.

Work instruction			Display OK	If not OK
9	Check triggering of fuel injectors	• The fuel injectors can be individually suppressed with the Porsche System Tester 2 in the menu 'Drive link active'	The engine idle speed decreases if triggering is OK	Check triggering ⇒ Step 9a
9a	B+ supply	• Remove connector of fuel injector to be checked • Measure voltage between valve plug contact Pin 1 and ground • Switch on the ignition	> 11 V ⇒ Step 9b	Check wiring according to wiring diagram for continuity or short circuit → End
9b	Coil resistance of fuel injectors	• Remove connector of fuel injector to be checked • Measure resistance between the terminals of the fuel injector	11 - 13 Ω ⇒ Step 9c	

PR1020100238050X

Fig. 18 Code P0303: Cylinder No. 3 Misfire (Part 5 of 10)

Work instruction			Display OK	If not OK
6	Check all connectors for secure fastening and corrosion		⇒ Step 7	Clean plug connections and connect securely. → End
7	Check fuel pressure	• Undo and remove the closure cap of the fuel collection pipe test connection (A/F 13 mm) • Connect pressure gauge (special tool P 378a) to connecting line (special tool 9559) and connect to test connection. • Actuate fuel pump, either with the Porsche System Tester or via a fuel pump relay without tester		⇒ Step 8
		• Nominal test value, stationary engine	3,8 ± 0.2 bar	
		• Nominal test value, engine idling	3,3 ± 0.2 bar ⇒ Step 9	

Note!

The seal or sealing ring in the brass closure cap is not exchangeable. It must therefore be used only once.

Tightening torque of new brass closure cap 2.5 ± 0.5 Nm (2.0 ± 0.5 ftlb.)

PR1020100238040X

Fig. 18 Code P0303: Cylinder No. 3 Misfire (Part 4 of 10)

Work instruction			Display OK	If not OK
9c	Injection output stage (negative supply)	• Connect special tool V.A.G 1315 A/1 between fuel injector and connector • Connect engine tester according to manufacturer's instructions. Connect cable for special input to special tool • Start the engine	See Figure ⇒ Step 9d	
9d	• Perform system test for large lift		→ End	

PR1020100238060X

Fig. 18 Code P0303: Cylinder No. 3 Misfire (Part 6 of 10)

Figure:

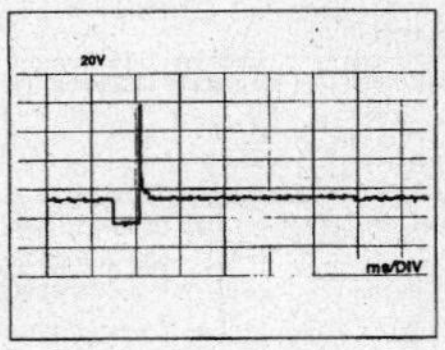

Warning!

Tester cables must not be connected to ground.

Note!

If the engine does not start, or if the idling speed drops, replace tester cable connected to special tool.

Perform system test for large lift

Warning!

Test is carried out while driving. Have a second person operate the Porsche System Tester 2.

During the system test for large lift, the valves remain at large lift, regardless of the type of driving. Faulty switching conditions can be detected by rough running, just like with misfire detection. If a valve is not switched to large lift, the fault type 'over limit' is recorded.

Several cylinders may be stored as faulty, although only one valve on one cylinder is faulty.

In order to guarantee safety during repairs, the flat-base tappets of the inlet valves of the entire cylinder bank should be replaced if a fault occurs.

A faulty flat-base tappet can be detected because the oxygen sensor F_R for this cylinder bank hardly changes the mixture at all given acceleration with wide-open throttle (F_R at 1) and enriches the mixture in the opposite cylinder bank ($F_R > 1$)⇒ see drawing below. Given a difference between F_{R1} and F_{R2} of more than 8 % during acceleration with wide-open throttle, a fault is certainly present.

If the difference is less than 4 %, 1 valve may be faulty on both cylinder banks. In this case, all flat-base tappets of the inlet valves must be replaced.

PR1020100238070X

Fig. 18 Code P0303: Cylinder No. 3 Misfire (Part 7 of 10)

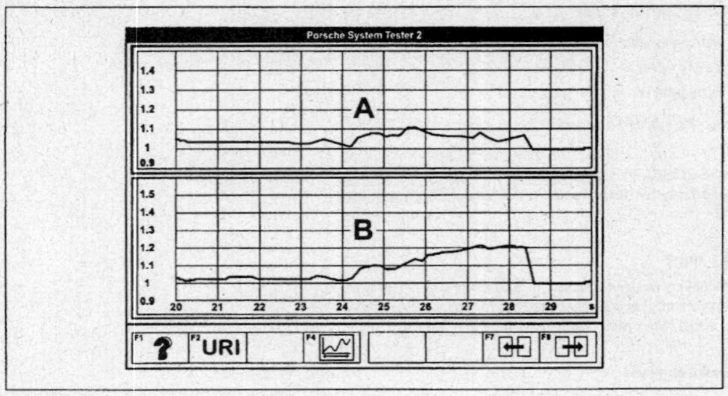

A - Oxygen sensor, bank 1

B - Oxygen sensor, bank 2

1 - Select system test.

2 - Select 'Request large lift'.

If "Valve diagnosis not ready" appears, a fault may have been stored.

1. Erase the fault memory.

3 - Activate the system test with the key F8 immediately before acceleration with wide-open throttle.

The message "Drive link active" then appears.

4 - Perform acceleration with wide-open throttle in 2nd gear, until "Valve lift diagnosis complete" appears.

Note!

- *If a fault is detected, it is only recorded in the fault memory after 6,000 ignitions (at idling speed approx. 3 minutes waiting time).*
- *It is important to observe the oxygen sensor during acceleration with wide-open throttle or to record its behaviour with the data logger.*

Continue by performing the system test for small lift

PR1020100238080X

Fig. 18 Code P0303: Cylinder No. 3 Misfire (Part 8 of 10)

Perform system test for small lift

Warning!

Test is carried out while driving. Have a second person operate the Porsche System Tester 2.

During the system test for small lift, the valves remain at small lift, regardless of the type of driving. Faulty switching conditions can be detected by rough running, just like with misfire detection. If a valve is not switched to small lift, the fault type 'under limit' is recorded.

Several cylinders may be stored as faulty, although only one valve on one cylinder is faulty.

In order to guarantee safety during repairs, the flat-base tappets of the inlet valves of the entire cylinder bank should be replaced if a fault occurs.

A faulty flat-base tappet can be detected because the oxygen sensor F_R for this cylinder bank enriches the mixture ($F_R > 1$) during acceleration with wide-open throttle ⇒ see drawing below. Difference from the other oxygen sensor > approx. 15 %. In the case of a fault, the flat-base tappets of the inlet valves for the entire cylinder bank must be replaced.

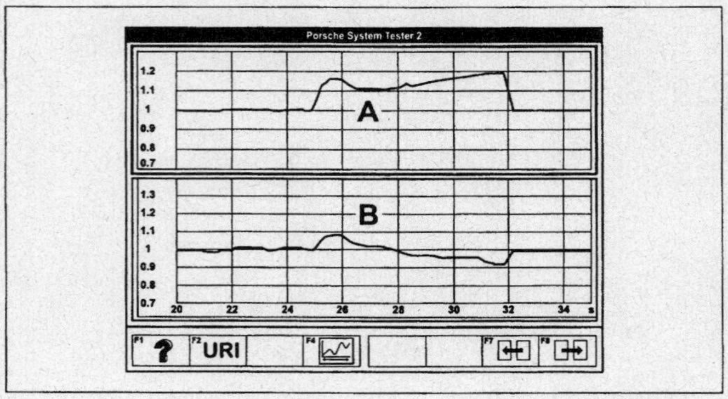

PR1020100238090X

Fig. 18 Code P0303: Cylinder No. 3 Misfire (Part 9 of 10)

A - Oxygen sensor, bank 1

B - Oxygen sensor, bank 2

1 - Select system test.

2 - Select 'Request small lift'.

If "Valve lift diagnosis not ready" appears, a fault may have been stored.

1. Erase the fault memory.

3 - Activate the system test with the key F8 immediately before acceleration with wide-open throttle.

The message "Drive link active" then appears.

Note!

If 'Request small lift' appears, the valves remain at small lift, ie. the performance is reduced dramatically.

4 - Perform acceleration with wide-open throttle in 2nd gear, until "Valve lift diagnosis complete" (max. 4,000 rpm) appears.

At speeds above 4,000 rpm, misfires may be stored. Delete the fault memory and repeat the test.

Note!

- *If a fault is detected, it is only recorded in the fault memory after 6,000 ignitions (at idling speed approx. 3 minutes waiting time).*
- *It is important to observe the oxygen sensor during acceleration with wide-open throttle or to record its behaviour with the data logger.*

End

PR1020100238100X

Fig. 18 Code P0303: Cylinder No. 3 Misfire (Part 10 of 10)

Diagnosis conditions

- A cycle of 1,000 crankshaft revolutions is evaluated (for misfire damaging to the TWC, 200 crankshaft revolutions). The misfire rates are compared with a threshold value. If the misfire rate is greater than the threshold value, a fault is recorded in the memory.
- The Check Engine Malfunction Indicator Lamp (MIL) is switched on and stays on when the misfire rate lies above the threshold value at which the emission limit values are exceeded during two consecutive driving cycles (in the case of EOBD 3 driving cycles).
- If the misfire rate may lead to permanent damage to the TWC, the Check Engine MIL flashes. If the misfire rate is no longer reached during the first journey, the MIL goes out. If the rate is reached during the next journey, the MIL flashes. If this misfire rate is subsequently no longer reached, the MIL changes to a continuous light.

Note!

- *When the fuel tank is driven to empty, misfiring can occur. For this reason the fuel level in the tank is also stored in the memory when misfiring occurs. If the tank was nearly empty, there was probably no fault. Erase fault memory and road test vehicle.*
- *In the event of a short circuit to B+ or ground in the oxygen sensors ahead of the TWC, the mixture becomes too lean or too rich. This can cause misfiring. If, in addition, an oxygen sensor signal fault ahead of the TWC is stored in memory, first correct this fault and then road test the vehicle.*

Possible fault cause

- Fault in ignition system
- Fault in injection system
- Flat-base tappets (valve lift fault)
- Mixture too rich
- Mixture too lean
- Mechanical causes:

Valve lifter chattering

PR1020100239010X

Fig. 19 Code P304: Cylinder No. 4 Misfire (Part 1 of 10)

This is caused by dirt in the valve lifter.

When the Check Engine MIL lights up, a chattering valve lifter may also occur for a certain time. The DME control module registers (sporadic) misfiring at one or more cylinders. The mixture adaptation values are normal.

Remedy:

1 - Remove lifter bores, check for damage and blow out oil passages.

2 - Replace all valve lifters.

3 - During the test drive, listen for valve lifter noises.

Camshaft control times adjusted

The camshaft control times have changed. No chattering noises occur. The DME control module indicates misfiring for the entire cylinder bank 1 or 2. The mixture adaptation values in the idle speed range differ in bank 1 and bank 2, the mixture adaptation values in the upper and lower load ranges are generally normal.

Remedy:

1 - Carry out raw emission measurement:

1. Reset mixture adaptation values (disconnect battery)
2. Disconnect oxygen sensors

If the difference between bank 1 and bank 2 is greater than approx. 0.8 %, then

1 - Set the camshaft control times again.

2 - Road test vehicle. The mixture adaptation values must be normal.

VarioCam does not switch over completely

The VarioCam does not switch over completely from power to torque valve timing.

An indication of this problem is misfiring detected by the DME control module in the range of 1200 - 1500 rpm occurring in an entire bank.

The mixture adaptation values are normal.

Remedy:

1 - Replace VarioCam.

2 - Road test vehicle.

PR1020100239020X

Fig. 19 Code P304: Cylinder No. 4 Misfire (Part 2 of 10)

Other possible fault causes

- worn camshafts
- leaking valves
- faulty piston rings

If opposing cylinders have misfiring, the cause could be the sensor wheel.

If valve lift faults are suspected, perform the system test for large lift and the system test for small lift with the Porsche System Tester 2.

Note!

If the battery was disconnected, at least range 1 of sensor wheel adaptation must be adapted before troubleshooting is carried out; see actual values explanation.

Affected terminals

-

Diagnosis/troubleshooting

Note!

If there is a lot of oil in the engine, check that the oil filler tube and cap are tight.

Work instruction			Display OK	If not OK
1	Check for air leaks in intake air system		⇒ Step 2	Repair intake air system → End
2	Carry out pressure loss test		⇒ Step 3	Repair engine → End
3	Check spark plugs. Specified spark plugs: Electrode gap: 1.6 mm ± 0.2 mm. Check appearance of spark plugs		⇒ Step 4	Replace faulty spark plug(s). → End
4	Check spark plug connectors		Approx. 2 kΩ ⇒ Step 5	Replace faulty spark plug connectors. → End
5	Check ignition coil(s)	• Measure resistance between Pin 1 and Pin 15	0.3 to 0.7 Ω (at 20 °C) ⇒ Step 6	Replace ignition coil(s) → End

PR1020100239030X

Fig. 19 Code P304: Cylinder No. 4 Misfire (Part 3 of 10)

Work instruction			Display OK	If not OK
6	Check all connectors for secure fastening and corrosion		⇒ Step 7	Clean plug connections and connect securely. → End
7	Check fuel pressure	• Undo and remove the closure cap of the fuel collection pipe test connection (A/F 13 mm)		⇒ Step 8
		• Connect pressure gauge (special tool P 378a) to connecting line (special tool 9559) and connect to test connection.		
		• Actuate fuel pump, either with the Porsche System Tester or via a fuel pump relay without tester		
		• Nominal test value, stationary engine	3,8 ± 0.2 bar	
		• Nominal test value, engine idling	3,3 ± 0.2 bar ⇒ Step 9	

Note!

The seal or sealing ring in the brass closure cap is not exchangeable. It must therefore be used only once.

Tightening torque of new brass closure cap 2.5 ± 0.5 Nm (2.0 ± 0.5 ftlb.)

PR1020100239040X

Fig. 19 Code P304: Cylinder No. 4 Misfire (Part 4 of 10)

Work instruction			Display OK	If not OK
8	Check volume supply of fuel pump. (Fuel filter and electrical supply OK)	• Relieve pressure in fuel tank by opening tank cap. • Connect Porsche System Tester 2 • Remove complete air filter system • Detach fuel return line (A/F 17 mm) from the engine compartment (left), taking care to hold it fast (A/F 17 mm). • Collect residual fuel • Observe safety regulations • Connect fuel hose (shop-made, approx. 1.5 metres long) to the fitting and hold in a measuring container • Actuate fuel pump with the Porsche System Tester 2 and allow fuel to flow into the measuring container for 30 seconds • Volume supply must be at least 850 cm³/ 30 s, i.e. after 30 seconds at least 850 cm³ of fuel must be in the measuring container.	→ End	

Note!

It is essential to observe safety regulations for handling fuel.

Work instruction			Display OK	If not OK
9	Check triggering of fuel injectors	• The fuel injectors can be individually suppressed with the Porsche System Tester 2 in the menu 'Drive link active'	The engine idle speed decreases if triggering is OK	Check triggering ⇒ Step 9a
9a	B+ supply	• Remove connector of fuel injector to be checked • Measure voltage between valve plug contact Pin 1 and ground • Switch on the ignition	> 11 V ⇒ Step 9b	Check wiring according to wiring diagram for continuity or short circuit → End
9b	Coil resistance of fuel injectors	• Remove connector of fuel injector to be checked • Measure resistance between the terminals of the fuel injector	11 - 13 Ω ⇒ Step 9c	

PR1020100239050X

Fig. 19 Code P304: Cylinder No. 4 Misfire (Part 5 of 10)

Work instruction			Display OK	If not OK
9c	Injection output stage (negative supply)	• Connect special tool V.A.G 1315 A/1 between fuel injector and connector • Connect engine tester according to manufacturer's instructions. Connect cable for special input to special tool • Start the engine	See Figure ⇒ Step 9d	
9d	• Perform system test for large lift		→ End	

PR1020100239060X

Fig. 19 Code P304: Cylinder No. 4 Misfire (Part 6 of 10)

Figure: ►

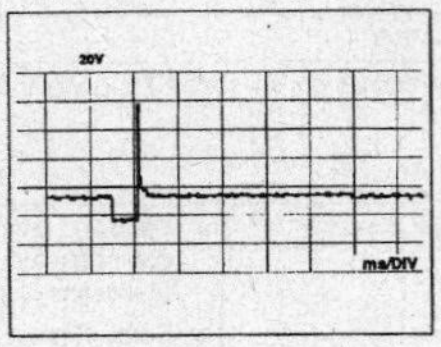

Warning!

Tester cables must not be connected to ground.

Note!

If the engine does not start, or if the idling speed drops, replace tester cable connected to special tool.

Perform system test for large lift

Warning!

Test is carried out while driving. Have a second person operate the Porsche System Tester 2.

During the system test for large lift, the valves remain at large lift, regardless of the type of driving. Faulty switching conditions can be detected by rough running, just like with misfire detection. If a valve is not switched to large lift, the fault type 'over limit' is recorded.

Several cylinders may be stored as faulty, although only one valve on one cylinder is faulty.

In order to guarantee safety during repairs, the flat-base tappets of the inlet valves of the entire cylinder bank should be replaced if a fault occurs.

A faulty flat-base tappet can be detected because the oxygen sensor F_R for this cylinder bank hardly changes the mixture at all given acceleration with wide-open throttle (F_R at 1) and enriches the mixture in the opposite cylinder bank ($F_R > 1$)⇒ see drawing below. Given a difference between F_{R1} and F_{R2} of more than 8 % during acceleration with wide-open throttle, a fault is certainly present.

If the difference is less than 4 %, 1 valve may be faulty on both cylinder banks. In this case, all flat-base tappets of the inlet valves must be replaced.

PR1020100239070X

Fig. 19 Code P304: Cylinder No. 4 Misfire (Part 7 of 10)

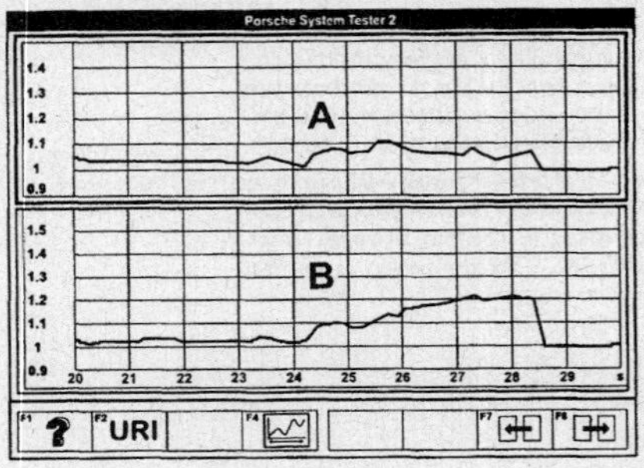

A - Oxygen sensor, bank 1

B - Oxygen sensor, bank 2

1 - Select system test.

2 - Select 'Request large lift'.

If "Valve diagnosis not ready" appears, a fault may have been stored.

1. Erase the fault memory.

3 - Activate the system test with the key [F8] immediately before acceleration with wide-open throttle.

The message "Drive link active" then appears.

4 - Perform acceleration with wide-open throttle in 2nd gear, until "Valve lift diagnosis complete" appears.

Note!

- *If a fault is detected, it is only recorded in the fault memory after 6,000 ignitions (at idling speed approx. 3 minutes waiting time).*
- *It is important to observe the oxygen sensor during acceleration with wide-open throttle or to record its behaviour with the data logger.*

Continue by performing the system test for small lift

PR1020100239080X

Fig. 19 Code P304: Cylinder No. 4 Misfire (Part 8 of 10)

Perform system test for small lift

⚠ **Warning!**

Test is carried out while driving. Have a second person operate the Porsche System Tester 2.

During the system test for small lift, the valves remain at small lift, regardless of the type of driving. Faulty switching conditions can be detected by rough running, just like with misfire detection. If a valve is not switched to small lift, the fault type 'under limit' is recorded.

Several cylinders may be stored as faulty, although only one valve on one cylinder is faulty.

In order to guarantee safety during repairs, the flat-base tappets of the inlet valves of the entire cylinder bank should be replaced if a fault occurs.

A faulty flat-base tappet can be detected because the oxygen sensor F_R for this cylinder bank enriches the mixture ($F_R > 1$) during acceleration with wide-open throttle ⇒ see drawing below. Difference from the other oxygen sensor > approx. 15 %. In the case of a fault, the flat-base tappets of the inlet valves for the entire cylinder bank must be replaced.

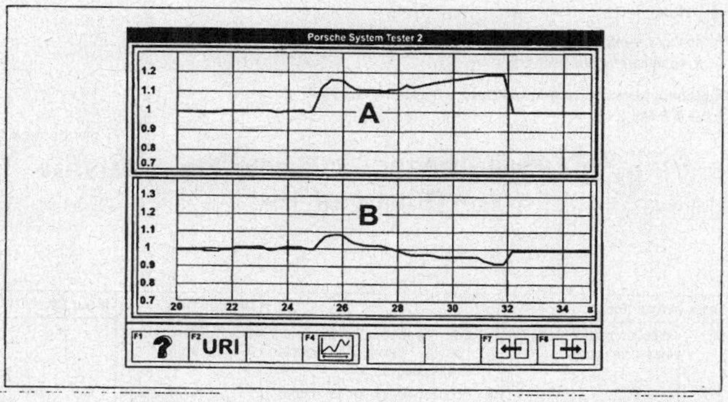

PR1020100239090X

Fig. 19 Code P304: Cylinder No. 4 Misfire (Part 9 of 10)

A - Oxygen sensor, bank 1

B - Oxygen sensor, bank 2

1 - Select system test.

2 - Select 'Request small lift'.

If "Valve lift diagnosis not ready" appears, a fault may have been stored.

1. Erase the fault memory.

3 - Activate the system test with the key [F8] immediately before acceleration with wide-open throttle.

The message "Drive link active" then appears.

Note!

If 'Request small lift' appears, the valves remain at small lift, ie. the performance is reduced dramatically.

4 - Perform acceleration with wide-open throttle in 2nd gear, until "Valve lift diagnosis complete" (max. 4,000 rpm) appears.

At speeds above 4,000 rpm, misfires may be stored. Delete the fault memory and repeat the test.

Note!

- *If a fault is detected, it is only recorded in the fault memory after 6,000 ignitions (at idling speed approx. 3 minutes waiting time).*
- *It is important to observe the oxygen sensor during acceleration with wide-open throttle or to record its behaviour with the data logger.*

End

PR1020100239100X

Fig. 19 Code P304: Cylinder No. 4 Misfire (Part 10 of 10)

Diagnosis conditions

- A cycle of 1,000 crankshaft revolutions is evaluated (for misfire damaging to the TWC, 200 crankshaft revolutions). The misfire rates are compared with a threshold value. If the misfire rate is greater than the threshold value, a fault is recorded in the memory.
- The Check Engine Malfunction Indicator Lamp (MIL) is switched on and stays on when the misfire rate lies above the threshold value at which the emission limit values are exceeded during two consecutive driving cycles (in the case of EOBD 3 driving cycles).
- If the misfire rate may lead to permanent damage to the TWC, the Check Engine MIL flashes. If the misfire rate is no longer reached during the first journey, the MIL goes out. If the rate is reached during the next journey, the MIL flashes. If this misfire rate is subsequently no longer reached, the MIL changes to a continuous light.

Note!

- *When the fuel tank is driven to empty, misfiring can occur. For this reason the fuel level in the tank is also stored in the memory when misfiring occurs. If the tank was nearly empty, there was probably no fault. Erase fault memory and road test vehicle.*
- *In the event of a short circuit to B+ or ground in the oxygen sensors ahead of the TWC, the mixture becomes too lean or too rich. This can cause misfiring. If, in addition, an oxygen sensor signal fault ahead of the TWC is stored in memory, first correct this fault and then road test the vehicle.*

Possible fault cause

- Fault in ignition system
- Fault in injection system
- Flat-base tappets (valve lift fault)
- Mixture too rich
- Mixture too lean
- Mechanical causes:

Valve lifter chattering

PR1020100240010X

Fig. 20 Code P0305: Cylinder No. 5 Misfire (Part 1 of 10)

This is caused by dirt in the valve lifter.

When the Check Engine MIL lights up, a chattering valve lifter may also occur for a certain time. The DME control module registers (sporadic) misfiring at one or more cylinders. The mixture adaptation values are normal.

Remedy:

1 - Remove lifter bores, check for damage and blow out oil passages.

2 - Replace all valve lifters.

3 - During the test drive, listen for valve lifter noises.

Camshaft control times adjusted

The camshaft control times have changed. No chattering noises occur. The DME control module indicates misfiring for the entire cylinder bank 1 or 2. The mixture adaptation values in the idle speed range differ in bank 1 and bank 2, the mixture adaptation values in the upper and lower load ranges are generally normal.

Remedy:

1 - Carry out raw emission measurement:

1. Reset mixture adaptation values (disconnect battery)
2. Disconnect oxygen sensors

If the difference between bank 1 and bank 2 is greater than approx. 0.8 %, then

1 - Set the camshaft control times again.

2 - Road test vehicle. The mixture adaptation values must be normal.

VarioCam does not switch over completely

The VarioCam does not switch over completely from power to torque valve timing.

An indication of this problem is misfiring detected by the DME control module in the range of 1200 - 1500 rpm occurring in an entire bank.

The mixture adaptation values are normal.

Remedy:

1 - Replace VarioCam.

2 - Road test vehicle.

PR1020100240020X

Fig. 20 Code P0305: Cylinder No. 5 Misfire (Part 2 of 10)

Other possible fault causes

- worn camshafts
- leaking valves
- faulty piston rings

If opposing cylinders have misfiring, the cause could be the sensor wheel.

If valve lift faults are suspected, perform the system test for large lift and the system test for small lift with the Porsche System Tester 2.

Note!

If the battery was disconnected, at least range 1 of sensor wheel adaptation must be adapted before troubleshooting is carried out; see actual values explanation.

Affected terminals

Diagnosis/troubleshooting

Note!

If there is a lot of oil in the engine, check that the oil filler tube and cap are tight.

Work instruction			Display OK	If not OK
1	Check for air leaks in intake air system		⇒ Step 2	Repair intake air system → End
2	Carry out pressure loss test		⇒ Step 3	Repair engine → End
3	Check spark plugs. Specified spark plugs: Electrode gap: 1.6 mm ± 0.2 mm. Check appearance of spark plugs		⇒ Step 4	Replace faulty spark plug(s). → End
4	Check spark plug connectors		Approx. 2 kΩ ⇒ Step 5	Replace faulty spark plug connectors. → End
5	Check ignition coil(s)	• Measure resistance between Pin 1 and Pin 15	0.3 to 0.7 Ω (at 20 °C) ⇒ Step 6	Replace ignition coil(s) → End

PR1020100240030X

Fig. 20 Code P0305: Cylinder No. 5 Misfire (Part 3 of 10)

Work instruction			Display OK	If not OK
8	Check volume supply of fuel pump. (Fuel filter and electrical supply OK)	• Relieve pressure in fuel tank by opening tank cap. • Connect Porsche System Tester 2 • Remove complete air filter system • Detach fuel return line (A/F 17 mm) from the engine compartment (left), taking care to hold it fast (A/F 17 mm). • Collect residual fuel • Observe safety regulations • Connect fuel hose (shop-made, approx. 1.5 metres long) to the fitting and hold in a measuring container • Actuate fuel pump with the Porsche System Tester 2 and allow fuel to flow into the measuring container for 30 seconds • Volume supply must be at least 850 cm³/ 30 s, i.e. after 30 seconds at least 850 cm³ of fuel must be in the measuring container.	→ End	

Note!

It is essential to observe safety regulations for handling fuel.

Work instruction			Display OK	If not OK
9	Check triggering of fuel injectors	• The fuel injectors can be individually suppressed with the Porsche System Tester 2 in the menu 'Drive link active'	The engine idle speed decreases if triggering is OK	Check triggering ⇒ Step 9a
9a	B+ supply	• Remove connector of fuel injector to be checked • Measure voltage between valve plug contact Pin 1 and ground • Switch on the ignition	> 11 V ⇒ Step 9b	Check wiring according to wiring diagram for continuity or short circuit → End
9b	Coil resistance of fuel injectors	• Remove connector of fuel injector to be checked • Measure resistance between the terminals of the fuel injector	11 - 13 Ω ⇒ Step 9c	

PR1020100240050X

Fig. 20 Code P0305: Cylinder No. 5 Misfire (Part 5 of 10)

Work instruction			Display OK	If not OK
6	Check all connectors for secure fastening and corrosion		⇒ Step 7	Clean plug connections and connect securely. → End
7	Check fuel pressure	• Undo and remove the closure cap of the fuel collection pipe test connection (A/F 13 mm) • Connect pressure gauge (special tool P 378a) to connecting line (special tool 9559) and connect to test connection. • Actuate fuel pump, either with the Porsche System Tester or via a fuel pump relay without tester		⇒ Step 8
		• Nominal test value, stationary engine	3,8 ± 0.2 bar	
		• Nominal test value, engine idling	3,3 ± 0.2 bar ⇒ Step 9	

Note!

The seal or sealing ring in the brass closure cap is not exchangeable. It must therefore be used only once.

Tightening torque of new brass closure cap 2.5 ± 0.5 Nm (2.0 ± 0.5 ftlb.)

PR1020100240040X

Fig. 20 Code P0305: Cylinder No. 5 Misfire (Part 4 of 10)

Work instruction			Display OK	If not OK
9c	Injection output stage (negative supply)	• Connect special tool V.A.G 1315 A/1 between fuel injector and connector • Connect engine tester according to manufacturer's instructions. Connect cable for special input to special tool • Start the engine	See Figure ⇒ Step 9d	
9d		• Perform system test for large lift	→ End	

PR1020100240060X

Fig. 20 Code P0305: Cylinder No. 5 Misfire (Part 6 of 10)

Figure:

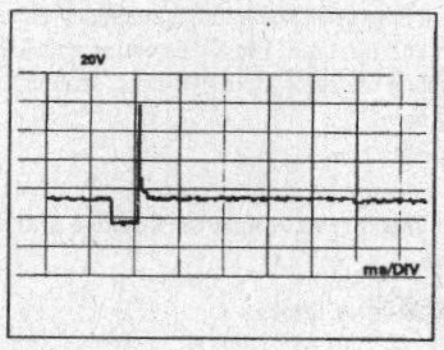

⚠ **Warning!**

Tester cables must not be connected to ground.

Note!

If the engine does not start, or if the idling speed drops, replace tester cable connected to special tool.

Perform system test for large lift

⚠ **Warning!**

Test is carried out while driving. Have a second person operate the Porsche System Tester 2.

During the system test for large lift, the valves remain at large lift, regardless of the type of driving. Faulty switching conditions can be detected by rough running, just like with misfire detection. If a valve is not switched to large lift, the fault type 'over limit' is recorded.

Several cylinders may be stored as faulty, although only one valve on one cylinder is faulty.

In order to guarantee safety during repairs, the flat-base tappets of the inlet valves of the entire cylinder bank should be replaced if a fault occurs.

A faulty flat-base tappet can be detected because the oxygen sensor F_R for this cylinder bank hardly changes the mixture at all given acceleration with wide-open throttle (F_R at 1) and enriches the mixture in the opposite cylinder bank ($F_R > 1$)⇒ see drawing below. Given a difference between F_{R1} and F_{R2} of more than 8 % during acceleration with wide-open throttle, a fault is certainly present.

If the difference is less than 4 %, 1 valve may be faulty on both cylinder banks. In this case, all flat-base tappets of the inlet valves must be replaced.

PR1020100240070X

Fig. 20 Code P0305: Cylinder No. 5 Misfire (Part 7 of 10)

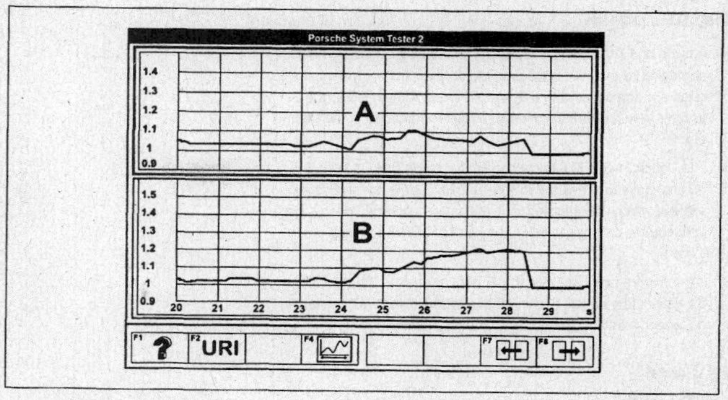

A - Oxygen sensor, bank 1
B - Oxygen sensor, bank 2

1 - Select system test.

2 - Select 'Request large lift'.

If "Valve diagnosis not ready" appears, a fault may have been stored.

1. Erase the fault memory.

3 - Activate the system test with the key [F8] immediately before acceleration with wide-open throttle.

The message "Drive link active" then appears.

4 - Perform acceleration with wide-open throttle in 2nd gear, until "Valve lift diagnosis complete" appears.

Note!

- *If a fault is detected, it is only recorded in the fault memory after 6,000 ignitions (at idling speed approx. 3 minutes waiting time).*
- *It is important to observe the oxygen sensor during acceleration with wide-open throttle or to record its behaviour with the data logger.*

Continue by performing the system test for small lift

PR1020100240080X

Fig. 20 Code P0305: Cylinder No. 5 Misfire (Part 8 of 10)

Perform system test for small lift

⚠ **Warning!**

Test is carried out while driving. Have a second person operate the Porsche System Tester 2.

During the system test for small lift, the valves remain at small lift, regardless of the type of driving. Faulty switching conditions can be detected by rough running, just like with misfire detection. If a valve is not switched to small lift, the fault type 'under limit' is recorded.

Several cylinders may be stored as faulty, although only one valve on one cylinder is faulty.

In order to guarantee safety during repairs, the flat-base tappets of the inlet valves of the entire cylinder bank should be replaced if a fault occurs.

A faulty flat-base tappet can be detected because the oxygen sensor F_R for this cylinder bank enriches the mixture ($F_R > 1$) during acceleration with wide-open throttle ⇒ see drawing below. Difference from the other oxygen sensor > approx. 15 %. In the case of a fault, the flat-base tappets of the inlet valves for the entire cylinder bank must be replaced.

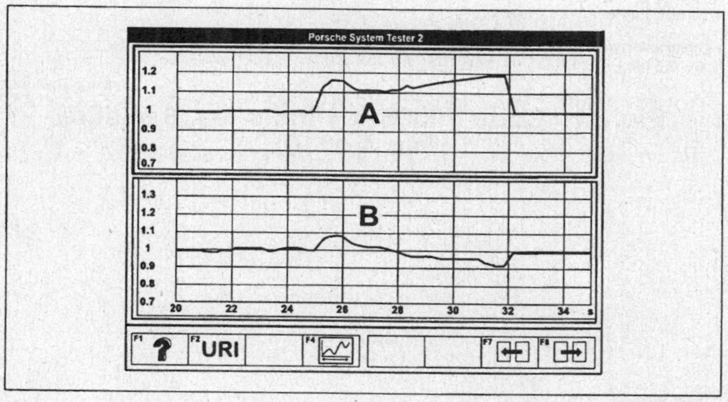

PR1020100240090X

Fig. 20 Code P0305: Cylinder No. 5 Misfire (Part 9 of 10)

A - Oxygen sensor, bank 1
B - Oxygen sensor, bank 2

1 - Select system test.

2 - Select 'Request small lift'.

If "Valve lift diagnosis not ready" appears, a fault may have been stored.

1. Erase the fault memory.

3 - Activate the system test with the key [F8] immediately before acceleration with wide-open throttle.

The message "Drive link active" then appears.

Note!

If 'Request small lift' appears, the valves remain at small lift, ie. the performance is reduced dramatically.

4 - Perform acceleration with wide-open throttle in 2nd gear, until "Valve lift diagnosis complete" (max. 4,000 rpm) appears.

At speeds above 4,000 rpm, misfires may be stored. Delete the fault memory and repeat the test.

Note!

- *If a fault is detected, it is only recorded in the fault memory after 6,000 ignitions (at idling speed approx. 3 minutes waiting time).*
- *It is important to observe the oxygen sensor during acceleration with wide-open throttle or to record its behaviour with the data logger.*

End

PR1020100240100X

Fig. 20 Code P0305: Cylinder No. 5 Misfire (Part 10 of 10)

Diagnosis conditions

- A cycle of 1,000 crankshaft revolutions is evaluated (for misfire damaging to the TWC, 200 crankshaft revolutions). The misfire rates are compared with a threshold value. If the misfire rate is greater than the threshold value, a fault is recorded in the memory.
- The Check Engine Malfunction Indicator Lamp (MIL) is switched on and stays on when the misfire rate lies above the threshold value at which the emission limit values are exceeded during two consecutive driving cycles (in the case of EOBD 3 driving cycles).
- If the misfire rate may lead to permanent damage to the TWC, the Check Engine MIL flashes. If this misfire rate is subsequently no longer reached, the MIL changes to a continuous light.

Note!

- *When the fuel tank is driven to empty, misfiring can occur. For this reason the fuel level in the tank is also stored in the memory when misfiring occurs. If the tank was nearly empty, there was probably no fault. Erase fault memory and road test vehicle.*
- *In the event of a short circuit to B+ or ground in the oxygen sensors ahead of the TWC, the mixture becomes too lean or too rich. This can cause misfiring. If, in addition, an oxygen sensor signal fault ahead of the TWC is stored in memory, first correct this fault and then road test the vehicle.*

Possible fault cause

- Fault in ignition system
- Fault in injection system
- Flat-base tappets (valve lift fault)
- Mixture too rich
- Mixture too lean
- Mechanical causes:

Valve lifter chattering

This is caused by dirt in the valve lifter.

PR1020100241010X

Fig. 21 Code P0306: Cylinder No. 6 Misfire (Part 1 of 10)

When the Check Engine MIL lights up, a chattering valve lifter may also occur for a certain time. The DME control module registers (sporadic) misfiring at one or more cylinders. The mixture adaptation values are normal.

Remedy:

1 - Remove lifter bores, check for damage and blow out oil passages.

2 - Replace all valve lifters.

3 - During the test drive, listen for valve lifter noises.

Camshaft control badly adjusted

The camshaft control has changed. No chattering noises occur. The DME control module indicates misfiring for the entire cylinder bank 1 or 2. The mixture adaptation values in the idle speed range differ in bank 1 and bank 2, the mixture adaptation values in the upper and lower load ranges are generally normal.

Remedy:

1 - Carry out raw emission measurement:

1. Reset mixture adaptation values (disconnect battery)
2. Disconnect oxygen sensors

If the difference between bank 1 and bank 2 is greater than approx. 0.8 %, then

1 - Reset camshaft control.

2 - Road test vehicle. The mixture adaptation values must be normal.

VarioCam does not switch over completely

The VarioCam does not switch over completely from power to torque valve timing.

An indication of this problem is misfiring detected by the DME control module in the range of 1200 - 1500 rpm occurring in an entire bank.

The mixture adaptation values are normal.

Remedy:

1 - Replace VarioCam.

2 - Road test vehicle.

Other possible fault causes

PR1020100241020X

Fig. 21 Code P0306: Cylinder No. 6 Misfire (Part 2 of 10)

- worn camshafts
- leaking valves
- faulty piston rings

If opposing cylinders have misfiring, the cause could be the sensor wheel.

If valve lift faults are suspected, perform the system test for large lift and the system test for small lift with the Porsche System Tester 2.

Note!

If the battery was disconnected, at least range 1 must be adapted before troubleshooting is carried out.

Affected terminals

-

Diagnosis/troubleshooting

Note!

If there is a lot of oil in the engine, check that the oil filler tube and cap are tight.

Work instruction			Display OK	If not OK
1	Check for air leaks in intake air system		⇒ Step 2	Repair intake air system → End
2	Carry out pressure loss test		⇒ Step 3	Repair engine → End
3	Check spark plugs. Specified spark plugs: Electrode gap: 1.6 mm ± 0.2 mm. Check appearance of spark plugs		⇒ Step 4	Replace faulty spark plug(s). → End
4	Check spark plug connectors		Approx. 2 kΩ ⇒ Step 5	Replace faulty spark plug connectors. → End
5	Check ignition coil(s)	• Measure resistance between Pin 1 and Pin 15	0.3 to 0.7 Ω (at 20 °C) ⇒ Step 6	Replace ignition coil(s) → End
6	Check all connectors for secure fastening and corrosion		⇒ Step 7	Clean plug connections and connect securely. → End

PR1020100241030X

Fig. 21 Code P0306: Cylinder No. 6 Misfire (Part 3 of 10)

Work instruction			Display OK	If not OK
7	Check fuel pressure	• Undo and remove the closure cap of the fuel collection pipe test connection (A/F 13 mm) • Connect pressure gauge (special tool P 378a) to connecting line (special tool 9559) and connect to test connection. • Actuate fuel pump, either with the Porsche System Tester or via a fuel pump relay without tester		⇒ Step 8
		• Nominal test value, stationary engine	3,8 ± 0.2 bar	
		• Nominal test value, engine idling	3,3 ± 0.2 bar ⇒ Step 9	

Note!

The seal or sealing ring in the brass closure cap is not exchangeable. It must therefore be used only once.

Tightening torque of new brass closure cap 2.5 ± 0.5 Nm (2.0 ± 0.5 ftlb.)

PR1020100241040X

Fig. 21 Code P0306: Cylinder No. 6 Misfire (Part 4 of 10)

Work instruction			Display OK	If not OK
8	Check volume supply of fuel pump. (Fuel filter and electrical supply OK)	• Relieve pressure in fuel tank by opening tank cap. • Connect Porsche System Tester 2 • Remove complete air filter system • Detach fuel return line (A/F 17 mm) from the engine compartment (left), taking care to hold it fast (A/F 17 mm). • Collect residual fuel • Observe safety regulations • Connect fuel hose (shop-made, approx. 1.5 metres long) to the fitting and hold in a measuring container • Actuate fuel pump with the Porsche System Tester 2 and allow fuel to flow into the measuring container for 30 seconds • Volume supply must be at least 850 cm³/ 30 s, i.e. after 30 seconds at least 850 cm³ of fuel must be in the measuring container.	→ End	

Note!

It is essential to observe safety regulations for handling fuel.

Work instruction			Display OK	If not OK
9	Check triggering of fuel injectors	• The fuel injectors can be individually suppressed with the Porsche System Tester 2 in the menu 'Drive link active'	The engine idle speed decreases if triggering is OK	Check triggering ⇒ Step 9a
9a	B+ supply	• Remove connector of fuel injector to be checked • Measure voltage between valve plug contact Pin 1 and ground • Switch on the ignition	> 11 V ⇒ Step 9b	Check wiring according to wiring diagram for continuity or short circuit → End
9b	Coil resistance of fuel injectors	• Remove connector of fuel injector to be checked • Measure resistance between the terminals of the fuel injector	11 - 13 Ω ⇒ Step 9c	

PR1020100241050X

Fig. 21 Code P0306: Cylinder No. 6 Misfire (Part 5 of 10)

Work instruction			Display OK	If not OK
9c	Injection output stage (negative supply)	• Connect special tool V.A.G 1315 A/1 between fuel injector and connector • Connect engine tester according to manufacturer's instructions. Connect cable for special input to special tool • Start the engine	See Figure ⇒ Step 9d	
9d	• Perform system test for large lift		→ End	

PR1020100241060X

Fig. 21 Code P0306: Cylinder No. 6 Misfire (Part 6 of 10)

Figure:

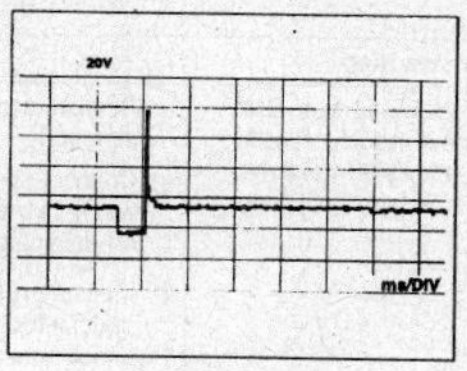

Warning!

Tester cables must not be connected to ground.

Note!

If the engine does not start, or if the idling speed drops, replace tester cable connected to special tool.

Perform system test for large lift

Warning!

Test is carried out while driving. Have a second person operate the Porsche System Tester 2.

System test for large lift means that faults are detected if a valve does not switch to large lift (fault type: above limit).

Several cylinders may be stored as faulty, although only one valve on one cylinder is faulty.

As a rule, only the cylinder bank with the faulty valve can be detected. Therefore in the case of a fault, the flat-base tappets of the inlet valves of the entire cylinder bank must be replaced.

A faulty flat-base tappet can be detected because the oxygen sensor F_R for this cylinder bank hardly changes the mixture at all given acceleration with wide-open throttle (F_R at 1) and enriches the mixture in the opposite cylinder bank ($F_R > 1$)⇒ see drawing below. Given a difference between F_{R1} and F_{R2} of more than 8 % during acceleration with wide-open throttle, a fault is certainly present.

If the difference is less than 4 %, 1 valve may be faulty on both cylinder banks. In this case, all flat-base tappets of the inlet valves must be replaced.

PR1020100241070X

Fig. 21 Code P0306: Cylinder No. 6 Misfire (Part 7 of 10)

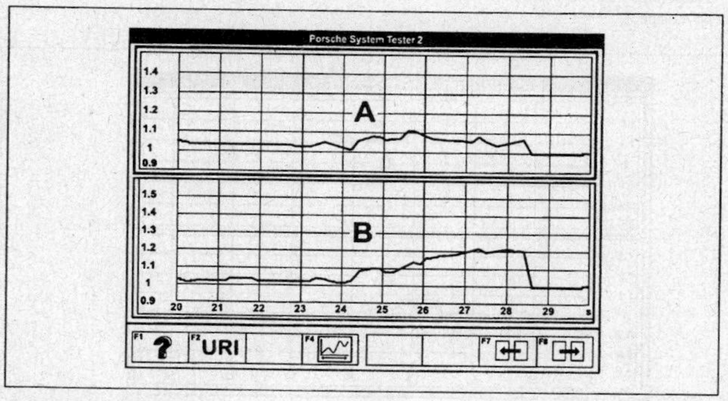

A - Oxygen sensor, bank 1
B - Oxygen sensor, bank 2

1 - **Select system test.**

2 - **Select 'Request large lift'.**

If "Valve diagnosis not ready" appears, a fault may have been stored.

1. Erase the fault memory.

3 - **Activate the system test with the key F8 immediately before acceleration with wide-open throttle.**

The message "Drive link active" then appears.

4 - **Perform acceleration with wide-open throttle in 2nd gear, until "Valve lift diagnosis complete" appears.**

Note!

- *If a fault is detected, it is only recorded in the fault memory after 6,000 ignitions (at idling speed approx. 3 minutes waiting time).*
- *It is important to observe the oxygen sensor during acceleration with wide-open throttle or to record its behaviour with the data logger.*

Continue by performing the system test for small lift

PR1020100241080X

Fig. 21 Code P0306: Cylinder No. 6 Misfire (Part 8 of 10)

Perform system test for small lift

⚠ **Warning!**

Test is carried out while driving. Have a second person operate the Porsche System Tester 2.

System test for small lift means that faults are detected if a valve remains jammed at large lift (fault type: below limit).

Several cylinders may be stored as faulty, although only one valve on one cylinder is faulty. As a rule, only the cylinder bank with the faulty valve can be detected. Therefore in the case of a fault, the flat-base tappets of the inlet valves of the entire cylinder bank must be replaced.

A faulty flat-base tappet can be detected because the oxygen sensor F_R for this cylinder bank enriches the mixture (F_R > 1) during acceleration with wide-open throttle ⇒ see drawing below. Difference from the other oxygen sensor > approx. 15 %. In the case of a fault, the flat-base tappets of the inlet valves for the entire cylinder bank must be replaced.

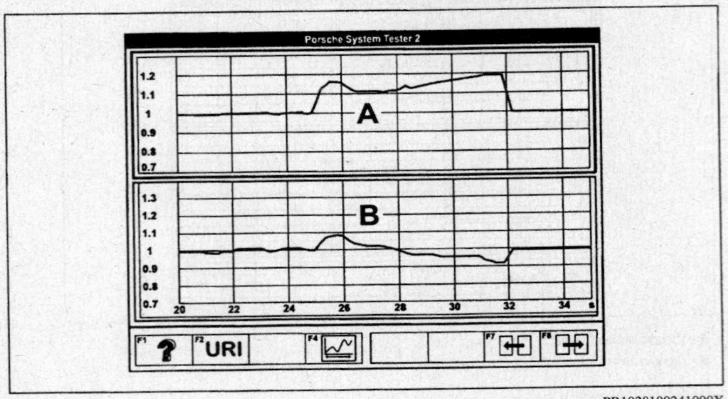

PR1020100241090X

Fig. 21 Code P0306: Cylinder No. 6 Misfire (Part 9 of 10)

A - Oxygen sensor, bank 1

B - Oxygen sensor, bank 2

1 - Select system test.

2 - Select 'Request small lift'.

If "Valve lift diagnosis not ready" appears, a fault may have been stored.

1. Erase the fault memory.

3 - Activate the system test with the key [F8] immediately before acceleration with wide-open throttle.

The message "Drive link active" then appears.

Note!

If 'Request small lift' appears, the valves remain at small lift, ie. the performance is reduced dramatically.

4 - Perform acceleration with wide-open throttle in 2nd gear, until "Valve lift diagnosis complete" (max. 4,000 rpm) appears.

At speeds above 4,000 rpm, misfires may be stored. Delete the fault memory and repeat the test.

Note!

- *If a fault is detected, it is only recorded in the fault memory after 6,000 ignitions (at idling speed approx. 3 minutes waiting time).*
- *It is important to observe the oxygen sensor during acceleration with wide-open throttle or to record its behaviour with the data logger.*

End

PR1020100241100X

Fig. 21 Code P0306: Cylinder No. 6 Misfire (Part 10 of 10)

Diagnosis conditions

- Engine speed more than 3600 rpm
- Engine load greater than 45 %

Possible fault cause

- Break in wiring or short to ground
- Contact corrosion on the connector
- Knock sensor loose
- Short circuit to B+
- Knock sensor

Note!

- *When a fault is stored, the ignition angle is retarded for all cylinders in the range in which knock control is active.*
- *Knock control adaptation is inactive.*
- *If knock control becomes active here, this may indicate engine damage (increased noise level)*

Affected terminals

Terminal III/49 and III/50

Diagnosis/troubleshooting

	Work instruction	Display OK	If not OK
1	Check plug connection of knock sensor 1	⇒ Step 2	Connect plug connection → End
2	Check plug-in contacts of connector for corrosion	⇒ Step 3	Clean plug-in contacts, replace if necessary. → End
3	Check mounting of knock sensor. Tightening torque: 20 ± 2 Nm (15 ± 1.5 ftlb.)	⇒ Step 4	Mount knock sensor correctly. → End

PR1020100242010X

Fig. 22 Code P0327: Knock Sensor No. 1 Below Limit (Part 1 of 2)

Work instruction			Display OK	If not OK
4	Check wiring from DME control module, Pins III/49 and III/50 to knock sensor 1 for continuity	♦ Remove connector of knock sensor 1 ♦ Connect special tool 9637 to wiring harness (DME control module plug)		Repair wiring harness → End
		♦ Measure resistance between special tool 9637 Pin III/49 and knock sensor plug connection Pin 1	0 - 5 Ω	
		♦ Measure resistance between special tool 9637 Pin III/50 and knock sensor plug connection Pin 2	0 - 5 Ω ⇒ Step 5	
5	Check wiring from DME control module, Pin III/49, to knock sensor 1 for short to ground	♦ Remove connector of knock sensor 1 ♦ Connect special tool 9637 to wiring harness (DME control module plug) ♦ Measure resistance between special tool 9637 Pin III/49 and ground	∞ Ω ⇒ Step 6	Repair wiring harness → End
6	Replace knock sensor 1		→ End	

PR1020100242020X

Fig. 22 Code P0327: Knock Sensor No. 1 Below Limit (Part 2 of 2)

Diagnosis conditions

- Engine speed more than 3600 rpm
- Engine load greater than 45 %

Possible fault cause

- Short circuit to B+
- Contact corrosion on the connector
- Knock sensor loose
- Short circuit to B+
- Knock sensor

Note!

- *When a fault is stored, the ignition angle is retarded for all cylinders in the range in which knock control is active.*
- *Knock control adaptation is inactive.*
- *If knock control becomes active here, this may indicate engine damage (increased noise level)*

Affected terminals

Terminal III/49 and III/50

Diagnosis/troubleshooting

	Work instruction	Display OK	If not OK
1	Check plug connection of knock sensor 1	⇒ Step 2	Connect plug connection → End
2	Check plug-in contacts of connector for corrosion	⇒ Step 3	Clean plug-in contacts, replace if necessary. → End
3	Check mounting of knock sensor. Tightening torque: 20 ± 2 Nm (15 ± 1.5 ftlb.)	⇒ Step 4	Mount knock sensor correctly. → End

PR1020100243010X

Fig. 23 Code P0328: Knock Sensor No. 1 Above Limit (Part 1 of 2)

Diagnosis conditions

- Engine speed more than 3600 rpm
- Engine load greater than 45 %

Possible fault cause

- Break in wiring or short to ground
- Contact corrosion on the connector
- Knock sensor loose
- Short circuit to B+
- Knock sensor

Note!

- *When a fault is stored, the ignition angle is retarded for all cylinders in the range in which knock control is active.*
- *Knock control adaptation is inactive.*
- *If knock control becomes active here, this may indicate engine damage (increased noise level)*

Affected terminals

Terminal III/36 and III/37

Diagnosis/troubleshooting

	Work instruction	Display OK	If not OK
1	Check plug connection of knock sensor 2	⇒ Step 2	Connect plug connection → End
2	Check plug-in contacts of connector for corrosion	⇒ Step 3	Clean plug-in contacts, replace if necessary. → End
3	Check mounting of knock sensor. Tightening torque: 20 ± 2 Nm (15 ± 1.5 ftlb.)	⇒ Step 4	Mount knock sensor correctly. → End

PR1020100244010X

Fig. 24 Code P0332: Knock Sensor No. 2 Below Limit (Part 1 of 2)

	Work instruction		Display OK	If not OK
4	Check wiring from DME control module, Pins III/49 and III/50 to knock sensor 1 for continuity	• Remove connector of knock sensor 1 • Connect special tool 9637 to wiring harness (DME control module plug) • Measure resistance between special tool 9637 Pin III/49 and knock sensor plug connection Pin 1 • Measure resistance between special tool 9637 Pin III/50 and knock sensor plug connection Pin 2	0 - 5 Ω 0 - 5 Ω ⇒ Step 5	Repair wiring harness → End
5	Check wiring from DME control module, Pin III/49, to knock sensor 1 for short to B+	• Remove connector of knock sensor 1 • Connect special tool 9637 to wiring harness (DME control module plug) • Switch on the ignition • Measure voltage between special tool 9637 Pin III/49 and ground	0 V ⇒ Step 6	Repair wiring harness → End
6	Replace knock sensor 1		→ End	

PR1020100243020X

Fig. 23 Code P0328: Knock Sensor No. 1 Above Limit (Part 2 of 2)

	Work instruction		Display OK	If not OK
4	Check wiring from DME control module, Pins III/36 and III/37 to knock sensor 2 for continuity	• Remove connector of knock sensor 2 • Connect special tool 9637 to wiring harness (DME control module plug) • Measure resistance between special tool 9637 Pin III/36 and knock sensor plug connection Pin 2 • Measure resistance between special tool 9637 Pin III/37 and knock sensor plug connection Pin 2	0 - 5 Ω 0 - 5 Ω ⇒ Step 5	Repair wiring harness → End
5	Check wiring from DME control module, Pin III/36, to knock sensor 2 for short to ground	• Remove connector of knock sensor 2 • Connect special tool 9637 to wiring harness (DME control module plug) • Measure resistance between special tool 9637 Pin III/36 and ground	∞ Ω ⇒ Step 6	Repair wiring harness → End
6	Replace knock sensor 2		→ End	

PR1020100244020X

Fig. 24 Code P0332: Knock Sensor No. 2 Below Limit (Part 2 of 2)

Diagnosis conditions

- Engine speed more than 3600 rpm
- Engine load greater than 45 %

Possible fault cause

- Short circuit to B+
- Contact corrosion on the connector
- Knock sensor loose
- Short circuit to B+
- Knock sensor

Note!

- *When a fault is stored, the ignition angle is retarded for all cylinders in the range in which knock control is active.*
- *Knock control adaptation is inactive.*
- *If knock control becomes active here, this may indicate engine damage (increased noise level)*

Affected terminals

Terminal III/36 and III/37

Diagnosis/troubleshooting

Work instruction		Display OK	If not OK
1	Check plug connection of knock sensor 2	⇒ Step 2	Connect plug connection → End
2	Check plug-in contacts of connector for corrosion	⇒ Step 3	Clean plug-in contacts, replace if necessary. → End
3	Check mounting of knock sensor. Tightening torque: 20 ± 2 Nm (15 ± 1.5 ftlb.)	⇒ Step 4	Mount knock sensor correctly. → End

PR1020100245010X

Fig. 25 Code P0333: Knock Sensor No. 2 Above Limit (Part 1 of 2)

Diagnosis conditions

- Engine running

Possible fault cause

- Loose contact
- Camshaft position sensor

Note!

- *If both CMP sensor signals are missing, the start will take at least 10 seconds.*
- *For safety reasons, the ignition timing is retarded.*

Affected terminals

Terminals III/7, III/12 and III/17

Diagnosis/troubleshooting

Work instruction			Display OK	If not OK
1	Check CMP voltage supply	• Remove connector of CMP sensor 1 • Switch on the ignition • Measure voltage between Pin 1 and Pin 3	Approx. 5 V ⇒ Step 5	⇒ Step 2
2	Check power supply wiring for continuity	• Remove connector of CMP sensor 1 • Connect special tool 9637 to wiring harness (DME control module plug) • Measure resistance between special tool 9637 Pin III/7 and CMP sensor 1 plug Pin 3 • Measure resistance between special tool 9637 Pin III/17 and CMP sensor 1 plug Pin 1	0 - 5 Ω ⇒ Step 3	
3	Replace DME control module		⇒ Step 4	

PR1020100246010X

Fig. 26 Code P0341: CMP Sensor No. 1, Signal Implausible (Part 1 of 3)

Work instruction			Display OK	If not OK
4	Check wiring from DME control module, Pins III/36 and III/37 to knock sensor 2 for continuity	• Remove connector of knock sensor 2 • Connect special tool 9637 to wiring harness (DME control module plug) • Measure resistance between special tool 9637 Pin III/36 and knock sensor plug connection Pin 1 • Measure resistance between special tool 9637 Pin III/37 and knock sensor plug connection Pin 2	0 - 5 Ω 0 - 5 Ω ⇒ Step 5	Repair wiring harness → End
5	Check wiring from DME control module, Pin III/36, to knock sensor 2 for short to B+	• Remove connector of knock sensor 2 • Connect special tool 9637 to wiring harness (DME control module plug) • Switch on the ignition • Measure voltage between special tool 9637 Pin III/38 and ground	0 V ⇒ Step 6	Repair wiring harness → End
6	Replace knock sensor 2		→ End	

PR1020100245020X

Fig. 25 Code P0333: Knock Sensor No. 2 Above Limit (Part 2 of 2)

Work instruction			Display OK	If not OK
4	Perform adaptation	• Switch on the ignition • Wait one minute • Do not press the accelerator • Switch off the ignition for at least 10 seconds • Read out the fault memory	→ End	
5	Check CMP sensor signal	• Connect special tool 9637 • Connect engine tester; use special input • Positive cable to Pin III/12 • Negative cable to Pin III/17 • Start the engine	See Figure 1 ⇒ Step 6	Replace CMP sensor → End

PR1020100246020X

Fig. 26 Code P0341: CMP Sensor No. 1, Signal Implausible (Part 2 of 3)

Figure 1:

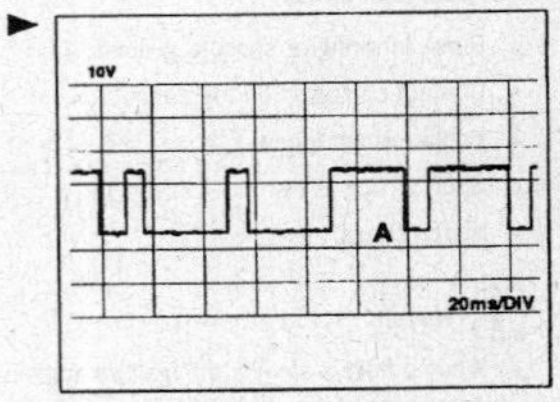

Work instruction			Display OK	If not OK
6	Check signal wire from DME control module, Pin III/12, to CMP sensor	• Connect special tool 9637 to wiring harness (DME control module plug) • Remove connector of CMP sensor 1 • Measure resistance between special tool 9637 Pin III/12 and CMP sensor 1 plug Pin 2	0 - 5 Ω → End	Repair wiring harness → End

PR1020100246030X

Fig. 26 Code P0341: CMP Sensor No. 1, Signal Implausible (Part 3 of 3)

Diagnosis conditions

- Engine running

Possible fault cause

- Short circuit to ground

Note!

- *If both CMP sensor signals are missing, the start will take at least 10 seconds.*
- *For safety reasons, the ignition timing is retarded.*

Affected terminals

Terminal III/12

Diagnosis/troubleshooting

Work instruction			Display OK	If not OK
1	Check signal wire from DME control module, Pin III/12, to CMP sensor for short to ground	• Connect special tool 9637 to wiring harness (DME control module plug) • Remove connector of CMP sensor 1 • Measure resistance between special tool 9637 Pin III/12 and ground	∞ Ω → End	Repair wiring harness → End

PR1020100247000X

Fig. 27 Code P0342: CMP Sensor No. 1, Below Limit

Diagnosis conditions

- Engine running

Possible fault cause

- Short circuit to B+

Note!

- *If both CMP sensor signals are missing, the start will take at least 10 seconds.*
- *For safety reasons, the ignition timing is retarded.*

Affected terminals

Terminal III/12

Diagnosis/troubleshooting

Work instruction			Display OK	If not OK
1	Check signal wire from DME control module, Pin III/12, to CMP sensor for short to B+	• Connect special tool 9637 to wiring harness (DME control module plug) • Remove connector of CMP sensor 1 • Switch on the ignition • Measure voltage between special tool 9637 Pin III/12 and ground	0 V → End	Repair wiring harness → End

PR1020100248000X

Fig. 28 Code P0342: CMP Sensor No. 1, Above Limit

Diagnosis conditions

- Engine running
- Battery voltage greater than 7 V

Possible fault cause

- Wiring harness
- Electric change-over valve
- DME control module faulty

Note!

The triggering wire for the electric change-over valve is monitored.

Affected terminals

Terminal III/14

Diagnosis/troubleshooting

Work instruction			Display OK	If not OK
1	Check voltage supply for electric change-over valve	• Remove connector of electric change-over valve • Measure voltage between electric change-over valve Pin 1 and ground • Switch on the ignition	> 11 V ⇒ Step 2	Repair voltage supply → End
2	Check electric change-over valve	• Remove connector of electric change-over valve • Measure resistance at electric change-over valve between Pin 1 and Pin 2	30 Ω at 20 °C ⇒ Step 3	Replace electric change-over valve → End
3	Check wire from DME control module, Pin III/14, to electric change-over valve for continuity	• Remove connector of electric change-over valve • Measure resistance between DME control module Pin III/14 and electric change-over valve plug Pin 2	0 - 5 Ω ⇒ Step 4	Repair wiring harness → End

PR1020100249010X

Fig. 29 Code P0413: Electric Change Over Valve, Open Circuit (Part 1 of 2)

Work instruction			Display OK	If not OK
4	Replace DME control module		⇒ Step 5	
5	Perform adaptation	• Switch on the ignition • Wait one minute. Do not press the accelerator • Switch off the ignition for at least 10 seconds • Read out the fault memory	→ End	

PR1020100249020X

Fig. 29 Code P0413: Electric Change Over Valve, Open Circuit (Part 2 of 2)

below limit

Diagnosis conditions

- Engine running
- Battery voltage greater than 7 V

Possible fault cause

- Short circuit to ground

Note!

The triggering wire for the electric change-over valve is monitored.

Affected terminals

Terminal III/14

Diagnosis/troubleshooting

Work instruction			Display OK	If not OK
1	Check wire from DME control module, Pin III/14, to electric change-over valve for short circuit to ground	• Remove connector of electric change-over valve • Measure resistance between DME control module Pin III/14 and electric change-over valve plug Pin 2	∞ Ω → End	Repair wiring harness → End

above limit

Diagnosis conditions

- Engine running
- Battery voltage greater than 7 V

Possible fault cause

- Short circuit to B+

Note!

The triggering wire for the electric change-over valve is monitored.

PR1020100250010X

Fig. 30 Code P0414: Electric Change Over Valve, Below Limit (Part 1 of 2)

Work instruction		Display OK	If not OK
1 Check wire from DME control module, Pin III/14, to electric change-over valve for short circuit to B+	♦ Remove connector of electric change-over valve ♦ Measure voltage between DME control module Pin III/14 and electric change-over valve plug Pin 2	0 V → End	Repair wiring harness → End

PR1020100250020X

Fig. 30 Code P0414: Electric Change Over Valve, Below Limit (Part 2 of 2)

Secondary air injection pump - below limit

Diagnosis conditions

- Engine running
- Battery voltage greater than 7 V

Possible fault cause

- Short circuit to ground

Affected terminals

Terminal III/11

Diagnosis/troubleshooting

Work instruction		Display OK	If not OK
1 Check wiring from DME control module, Pin III/11, to relay of secondary air injection pump Pin 85 for short to ground	♦ Remove relay for secondary air injection pump ♦ Measure voltage between DME control module Pin III/11 and B+ ♦ Switch on the ignition	0 V → End	Repair wiring harness → End

Secondary air injection pump - above limit

Diagnosis conditions

- Engine running
- Battery voltage greater than 7 V

Possible fault cause

- Short circuit to B+

Affected terminals

Terminal III/11

PR1020100251020X

Fig. 31 Code P0418: Secondary Air Injection Pipe, Open Circuit (Part 2 of 3)

Work instruction		Display OK	If not OK
1 Check wiring from DME control module, Pin III/11, to relay of secondary air injection pump Pin 85 for short to B+	♦ Remove relay for secondary air injection pump ♦ Measure voltage between DME control module Pin III/11 and ground	0 V → End	Repair wiring harness → End

PR1020100251030X

Fig. 31 Code P0418: Secondary Air Injection Pipe, Open Circuit (Part 3 of 3)

Secondary air injection pump - open circuit

Diagnosis conditions

- Engine running
- Battery voltage greater than 7 V

Possible fault cause

- Wiring harness
- Relay faulty
- DME control module faulty

Affected terminals

Terminal III/11

Diagnosis/troubleshooting

Work instruction		Display OK	If not OK
1 Check voltage supply for relay of secondary air injection pump, terminal 86	♦ Remove relay of secondary air injection pump ♦ Measure voltage between Pin 7 and ground ♦ Switch on the ignition	> 11 V ⇒ Step 2	Repair voltage supply → End
2 Check relay for secondary air injection pump	♦ Remove relay for secondary air injection pump ♦ Measure resistance between relay Pin 85 and Pin 86	Approx. 70 Ω (at 25 °C)	Replace relay → End
3 Check wiring from DME control module, Pin III/11, to relay of secondary air injection pump for continuity	♦ Remove connector of electric change-over valve ♦ Measure resistance between DME control module Pin III/11 and relay of secondary air injection pump	0 - 5 Ω ⇒ Step 4	Repair wiring harness → End
4 Replace DME control module		⇒ Step 5	
5 Perform adaptation	♦ Switch on the ignition ♦ Wait one minute ♦ Do not press the accelerator ♦ Switch off the ignition for at least 10 seconds ♦ Read out the fault memory	→ End	

PR1020100251010X

Fig. 31 Code P0418: Secondary Air Injection Pipe, Open Circuit (Part 1 of 3)

Diagnosis conditions

- TWC temperature 420 - 600 °C
- 85 seconds within rpm/load range (cumulative)
- EVAP canister burden < 8
- Speed 1280 - 2440 rpm
- 20 - 40 % engine load (relative air charge)
- Oxygen sensing ahead of TWC is active
- Oxygen sensing after TWC ready for operation
- Engine starting temperature > - 20 °C
- No faults in memory

Possible fault cause

- Oxygen sensor ahead of and after TWC exchanged
- Valve lift fault
- Aged oxygen sensor after TWC
- TWC faulty

Affected terminals

-

Diagnosis/troubleshooting

Note!

If an ageing oxygen sensor is recorded in conjunction with a fault in the TWC, a check must be performed with a new oxygen sensor to see whether a TWC fault is still indicated.

Work instruction		Display OK	If not OK
1 Check whether the oxygen sensors ahead of and after the TWC have been exchanged			

PR1020100252010X

Fig. 32 Code P0420: TWC Conversion Bank No. 1, Above Limit (Part 1 of 4)

Work instruction		Display OK	If not OK
2 Perform system test for small lift	See below		
3 Replace TWC			

Perform system test for small lift

⚠ **Warning!**

Test is carried out while driving. Have a second person operate the Porsche System Tester 2.

During the system test for small lift, the valves remain at small lift, regardless of the type of driving. Faulty switching conditions can be detected by rough running, just like with misfire detection. If a valve is not switched to small lift, the fault type 'under limit' is recorded.

Several cylinders may be stored as faulty, although only 1 valve on one cylinder is faulty.

In order to guarantee safety during repairs, the flat-base tappets of the inlet valves of the entire cylinder bank should be replaced if a fault occurs.

A faulty flat-base tappet can be detected because the oxygen sensor F_R for this cylinder bank enriches the mixture ($F_R > 1$) during acceleration with wide-open throttle ⇒ see drawing below. Difference from the other oxygen sensor > approx. 15 %. In the case of a fault, the flat-base tappets of the inlet valves for the entire cylinder bank must be replaced.

PR1020100252020X

Fig. 32 Code P0420: TWC Conversion Bank No. 1, Above Limit (Part 2 of 4)

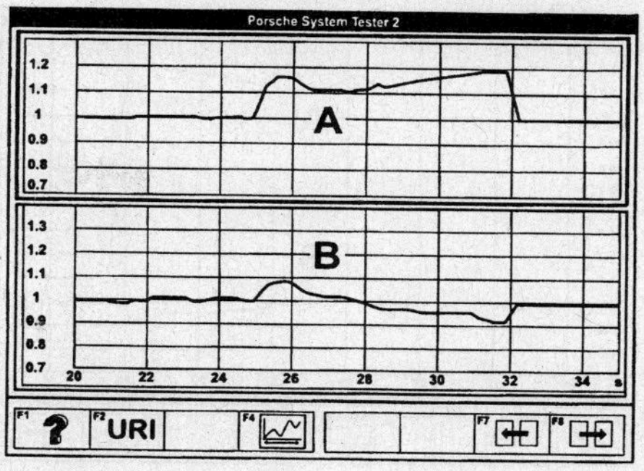

A - Oxygen sensor, bank 1
B - Oxygen sensor, bank 2

1 - Select system test.

2 - Select 'Request small lift'.

If "Valve lift diagnosis not ready" appears, a fault may have been stored.

1. Erase the fault memory.

3 - Activate the system test with the key [F8] immediately before acceleration with wide-open throttle.

The message "Drive link active" then appears.

ℹ **Note!**

If 'Request small lift' appears, the valves remain at small lift, ie. the performance is reduced dramatically.

4 - Perform acceleration with wide-open throttle in 2nd gear, until "Valve lift diagnosis complete" (max. 4,000 rpm) appears.

At speeds above 4,000 rpm, misfires may be stored. Delete the fault memory and repeat the test.

PR1020100252030X

Fig. 32 Code P0420: TWC Conversion Bank No. 1, Above Limit (Part 3 of 4)

ℹ **Note!**

- *If a fault is detected, it is only recorded in the fault memory after 6,000 ignitions (at idling speed approx. 3 minutes waiting time).*
- *It is important to observe the oxygen sensor during acceleration with wide-open throttle or to record its behaviour with the data logger.*

PR1020100252040X

Fig. 32 Code P0420: TWC Conversion Bank No. 1, Above Limit (Part 4 of 4)

Diagnosis conditions

- TWC temperature 420 - 600 °C
- 85 seconds within rpm/load range (cumulative)
- EVAP canister burden < 8
- Speed 1280 - 2440 rpm
- 20 - 40 % engine load (relative air charge)
- Oxygen sensing ahead of TWC is active
- Oxygen sensing after TWC ready for operation
- Engine starting temperature > - 20 °C
- No faults in memory

Possible fault cause

- Oxygen sensor ahead of and after TWC exchanged
- Valve lift fault
- Aged oxygen sensor after TWC
- TWC faulty

Affected terminals

-

Diagnosis/troubleshooting

ℹ **Note!**

If an ageing oxygen sensor is recorded in conjunction with a fault in the TWC, a check must be performed with a new oxygen sensor to see whether a TWC fault is still indicated.

Work instruction		Display OK	If not OK
1 Check whether the oxygen sensors ahead of and after the TWC have been exchanged			

PR1020100253010X

Fig. 33 Code P0430: TWC Conversion Bank No. 2, Above Limit (Part 1 of 4)

Work instruction		Display OK	If not OK
2 Perform system test for small lift	See below		
3 Replace TWC			

Perform system test for small lift

⚠ **Warning!**

Test is carried out while driving. Have a second person operate the Porsche System Tester 2.

During the system test for small lift, the valves remain at small lift, regardless of the type of driving. Faulty switching conditions can be detected by rough running, just like with misfire detection. If a valve is not switched to small lift, the fault type 'under limit' is recorded.

Several cylinders may be stored as faulty, although only 1 valve on one cylinder is faulty.

In order to guarantee safety during repairs, the flat-base tappets of the inlet valves of the entire cylinder bank should be replaced if a fault occurs.

A faulty flat-base tappet can be detected because the oxygen sensor F_R for this cylinder bank enriches the mixture ($F_R > 1$) during acceleration with wide-open throttle ⇒ see drawing below. Difference from the other oxygen sensor > approx. 15 %. In the case of a fault, the flat-base tappets of the inlet valves for the entire cylinder bank must be replaced.

PR1020100253020X

Fig. 33 Code P0430: TWC Conversion Bank No. 2, Above Limit (Part 2 of 4)

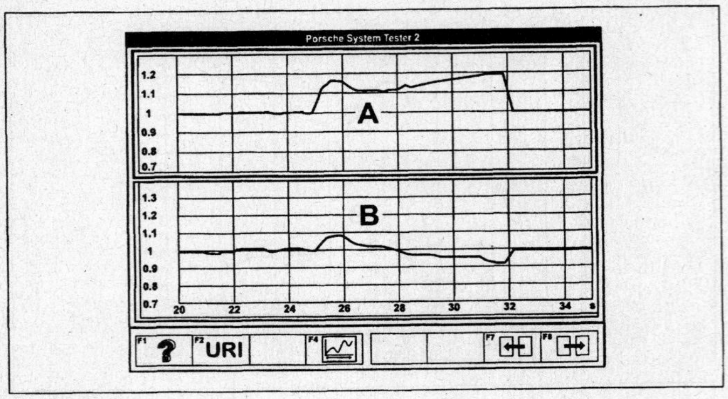

A - Oxygen sensor, bank 1
B - Oxygen sensor, bank 2

1 - Select system test.

2 - Select 'Request small lift'.

If "Valve lift diagnosis not ready" appears, a fault may have been stored.

1. Erase the fault memory.

3 - Activate the system test with the key F8 immediately before acceleration with wide-open throttle.

The message "Drive link active" then appears.

Note!

If 'Request small lift' appears, the valves remain at small lift, ie. the performance is reduced dramatically.

4 - Perform acceleration with wide-open throttle in 2nd gear, until "Valve lift diagnosis complete" (max. 4,000 rpm) appears.

At speeds above 4,000 rpm, misfires may be stored. Delete the fault memory and repeat the test.

PR1020100253030X

Fig. 33 Code P0430: TWC Conversion Bank No. 2, Above Limit (Part 3 of 4)

Diagnosis conditions

- Engine running
- Battery voltage greater than 7 V

Possible fault cause

- Wiring harness
- EVAP canister purge valve
- DME control module

Affected terminals

Terminal III/3

Diagnosis/troubleshooting

Work instruction			Display OK	If not OK
1	Check voltage supply for EVAP canister purge valve	• Remove connector of EVAP canister purge valve • Measure voltage between EVAP canister purge valve plug Pin 1 and ground • Switch on the ignition	> 11 V ⇒ Step 2	Repair voltage supply → End
2	Check EVAP canister purge valve	• Remove connector of EVAP canister purge valve • Measure resistance between EVAP canister purge valve Pin 1 and Pin 2	26 ± 4 Ω (at 20 °C) ⇒ Step 3	Check EVAP canister purge valve → End
3	Check triggering wire for EVAP canister purge valve	• Remove connector of EVAP canister purge valve • Connect special tool 9637 to wiring harness (DME control module plug) • Measure resistance between EVAP canister purge valve Pin 2 and special tool 9637 Pin III/3	0 - 5 Ω ⇒ Step 4	Repair wiring harness → End

PR1020100254010X

Fig. 34 Code P0444: EVAP Canister Purge Valve, Open Circuit (Part 1 of 2)

Note!

- *If a fault is detected, it is only recorded in the fault memory after 6,000 ignitions (at idling speed approx. 3 minutes waiting time).*
- *It is important to observe the oxygen sensor during acceleration with wide-open throttle or to record its behaviour with the data logger.*

PR1020100253040X

Fig. 33 Code P0430: TWC Conversion Bank No. 2, Above Limit (Part 4 of 4)

Work instruction			Display OK	If not OK
4	Replace DME control module		⇒ Step 5	
5	Perform adaptation	• Switch on the ignition • Wait one minute • Do not press the accelerator • Switch off the ignition for at least 10 seconds • Read out the fault memory	→ End	

PR1020100254020X

Fig. 34 Code P0444: EVAP Canister Purge Valve, Open Circuit (Part 2 of 2)

short circuit to B+

Diagnosis conditions

- Engine running
- Battery voltage greater than 7 V

Possible fault cause

- Wiring harness
- DME control module faulty

Affected terminals

Terminal III/3 and IV/26

Diagnosis/troubleshooting

Work instruction			Display OK	If not OK
1	Check triggering wire for EVAP canister purge valve for short circuit to B+	• Remove connector of EVAP canister purge valve • Connect special tool 9637 to wiring harness (DME control module plug) • Measure voltage between special tool 9637 Pin III/3 and ground • Switch on the ignition	0 V ⇒ Step 2	Repair wiring harness → End
2	Replace DME control module		⇒ Step 3	
3	Perform adaptation	• Switch on the ignition • Wait one minute • Do not press the accelerator • Switch off the ignition for at least 10 seconds • Read out the fault memory	→ End	

PR1020100255010X

Fig. 35 Code P0445: EVAP Canister Purge Valve, Short Circuit To Battery Positive (Part 1 of 2)

short circuit to B+

Diagnosis conditions

- Engine running
- Battery voltage greater than 7 V

Possible fault cause

- Wiring harness
- DME control module faulty

Affected terminals

Terminal III/3 and IV/26

Diagnosis/troubleshooting

Work instruction			Display OK	If not OK
1	Check triggering wire for EVAP canister purge valve for short circuit to B+	• Remove connector of EVAP canister purge valve • Connect special tool 9637 to wiring harness (DME control module plug) • Measure voltage between special tool 9637 Pin III/3 and ground • Switch on the ignition	0 V ⇒ Step 2	Repair wiring harness → End
2	Replace DME control module		⇒ Step 3	
3	Perform adaptation	• Switch on the ignition • Wait one minute • Do not press the accelerator • Switch off the ignition for at least 10 seconds • Read out the fault memory	→ End	

PR1020100255020X

Fig. 35 Code P0445: EVAP Canister Purge Valve, Short Circuit To Battery Positive (Part 2 of 2)

Work instruction			Display OK	If not OK
2	Check shutoff valve	• Remove front right-hand wheel housing liner • Remove connector of shutoff valve • Measure resistance between shutoff valve Pin 1 and Pin 2	22 - 26 Ω (at 20 °C) ⇒ Step 3	Replace shutoff valve → End
3	Check triggering wire for shutoff valve for continuity	• Remove front right-hand wheel housing liner • Remove connector of shutoff valve • Connect special tool 9637 to wiring harness (DME control module plug) • Measure resistance between shutoff valve Pin 1 and special tool 9637 plug IV Pin 30	0 - 5 Ω ⇒ Step 3	Repair wiring harness → End

Note!

The wire is routed via connector X 2/5, Pin 6.

Work instruction			Display OK	If not OK
4	Replace DME control module		⇒ Step 4	
5	Perform adaptation	• Switch on the ignition • Wait one minute • Do not press the accelerator • Switch off the ignition for at least 10 seconds • Read out the fault memory	→ End	

PR1020100256020X

Fig. 36 Code P0447: EVAP Canister Shutoff Valve Open (Part 2 of 2)

Diagnosis conditions

- Engine running
- Battery voltage greater than 7 V
- Fuel tank ventilation active

Possible fault cause

- Wiring harness
- Shutoff valve faulty
- DME control module faulty

Note!

Fuel tank ventilation can be activated with the Porsche System Tester 2 in the 'Short test' menu.

Affected terminals

Terminal IV/30

Diagnosis/troubleshooting

Work instruction			Display OK	If not OK
1	Check voltage supply for shutoff valve	• Remove front right-hand wheel housing liner • Remove connector of shutoff valve • Measure voltage between shutoff valve plug Pin 2 and ground • Switch on the ignition	> 11 V ⇒ Step 2	Repair voltage supply → End

PR1020100256010X

Fig. 36 Code P0447: EVAP Canister Shutoff Valve Open (Part 1 of 2)

Diagnosis conditions

- Engine running
- Battery voltage greater than 7 V
- Fuel tank ventilation active

Possible fault cause

- Wiring harness
- DME control module faulty

Note!

Fuel tank ventilation can be activated with the Porsche System Tester 2 in the 'Short test' menu.

Affected terminals

Terminal IV/30

Diagnosis/troubleshooting

Work instruction			Display OK	If not OK
1	Check triggering wire for shutoff valve for short to B+	• Remove front right-hand wheel housing liner • Remove connector of shutoff valve • Remove DME control module connector • Measure voltage between shutoff valve plug Pin 1 and ground • Switch on the ignition	0 V ⇒ Step 2	Repair wiring harness → End
2	Replace DME control module		⇒ Step 3	
3	Perform adaptation	• Switch on the ignition • Wait one minute • Do not press the accelerator • Switch off the ignition for at least 10 seconds • Read out the fault memory	→ End	

PR1020100257010X

Fig. 37 Code P0448: Canister Shutoff Valve (Part 1 of 2)

under limit

Diagnosis conditions

- Engine running
- Battery voltage greater than 7 V
- Fuel tank ventilation active

Possible fault cause

- Wiring harness
- DME control module faulty

Note!

Fuel tank ventilation can be activated with the Porsche System Tester 2 in the 'Short test' menu.

Affected terminals

Terminal IV/30

Diagnosis/troubleshooting

Work instruction			Display OK	If not OK
1	Check triggering wire for shutoff valve for short to ground	• Remove front right-hand wheel housing liner • Remove connector of shutoff valve • Remove DME control module connector • Measure resistance between shutoff valve plug Pin 1 and ground • Switch on the ignition	∞ Ω ⇒ Step 2	Repair wiring harness → End
2	Replace DME control module		⇒ Step 3	
3	Perform adaptation	• Switch on the ignition • Wait one minute • Do not press the accelerator • Switch off the ignition for at least 10 seconds • Read out the fault memory	→ End	

PR1020100257020X

Fig. 37 Code P0448: Canister Shutoff Valve (Part 2 of 2)

Diagnosis conditions

- Ignition on

Possible fault cause

- Short circuit to ground

Affected terminals

Terminal IV/21

Diagnosis/troubleshooting

Work instruction			Display OK	If not OK
1	Check wiring from pressure sensor to DME control module for short to ground	• Connect special tool 9637 to wiring harness (DME control module plug) • Remove connector of pressure sensor • Measure resistance between special tool 9637 Pin IV/21 and ground	∞ Ω → End	Repair wiring harness → End

PR1020100259000X

Fig. 39 Code P0452: Tank Pressure Sensor, Below Limit

Diagnosis conditions

- Ignition on

Possible fault cause

- Pressure sensor

Affected terminals

Diagnosis/troubleshooting

Work instruction		Display OK	If not OK
1	Replace pressure sensor	→ End	

PR1020100258000X

Fig. 38 Code P0450: Tank Pressure, Signal Implausible

Diagnosis conditions

- Ignition on

Possible fault cause

- Short circuit to B+

Affected terminals

Terminal IV/21

Diagnosis/troubleshooting

Work instruction			Display OK	If not OK
1	Check wiring from pressure sensor to DME control module for short to B+	• Connect special tool 9637 to wiring harness (DME control module plug) • Remove connector of pressure sensor • Measure voltage between special tool Pin IV/21 and ground	0 V → End	Repair wiring harness → End

PR1020100260000X

Fig. 40 Code P0453: Tank Pressure Sensor, Above Limit

Diagnosis conditions

- Engine running
- Battery voltage greater than 7 V
- Intake air temperature greater than 9 °C
- Air conditioning switched on and off once

Note!

The triggering wire for relays stage 1, terminal 85, is monitored

Possible fault cause

- Open circuit
- Relay faulty
- DME control module faulty

Affected terminals

Terminal IV/4

Diagnosis/troubleshooting

Work instruction			Display OK	If not OK
1	Check both relays	• Remove relay • Measure resistance between Pin 85 and Pin 86	Approx. 75 Ω ⇒ Step 2	Replace relay → End
2	Check wiring from DME control module, plug IV Pin 4, to relays for continuity	• Connect special tool 9637 to wiring harness (DME control module plug) • Remove relay stage 1 of coolant fan 1 • Remove relay stage 2 of coolant fan 1 • Measure resistance between special tool 9637 plug IV Pin 4 and relay slot of coolant fan 1 plug Pin 2	0 - 5 Ω	Repair wiring harness → End

PR1020100261010X

Fig. 41 Code P0480: Fan Output Stage 1, Open Circuit (Part 1 of 4)

Work instruction			Display OK	If not OK
2		♦ Measure resistance between special tool 9637 plug IV Pin 4 and relay slot of coolant fan 2 plug Pin 2	0 - 5 Ω ⇒ Step 3	Check plug connection X 2/3, Pin 21, and check wiring harness for chafing and pinching damage
3	Replace DME control module		⇒ Step 4	
4	Perform adaptation	♦ Switch on the ignition ♦ Wait one minute ♦ Do not press the accelerator ♦ Switch off the ignition for at least 10 seconds ♦ Read out the fault memory	→ End	

below limit

Diagnosis conditions

- Engine running
- Battery voltage greater than 7 V
- Intake air temperature greater than 9 °C
- Air conditioning switched on and off once

Note!

The triggering wire for relays stage 1, terminal 85, is monitored

Possible fault cause

- Short circuit to ground
- Relay faulty
- DME control module faulty

Affected terminals

Terminal IV/4

PR1020100261020X

Fig. 41 Code P0480: Fan Output Stage 1, Open Circuit (Part 2 of 4)

Work instruction			Display OK	If not OK
1	Check both relays	♦ Remove relay ♦ Measure resistance between Pin 85 and Pin 86	Approx. 75 Ω ⇒ Step 2	Replace relay → End
2	Check wiring from DME control module, plug IV Pin 4, to relays for short to ground	♦ Connect special tool 9637 to wiring harness (DME control module plug) ♦ Remove relay stage 1 of coolant fan 1 ♦ Remove relay stage 2 of coolant fan 1 ♦ Measure resistance between special tool 9637 plug IV Pin 4 and ground	∞ Ω ⇒ Step 3	Repair wiring harness → End
3	Replace DME control module		⇒ Step 4	
4	Perform adaptation	♦ Switch on the ignition ♦ Wait one minute ♦ Do not press the accelerator ♦ Switch off the ignition for at least 10 seconds ♦ Read out the fault memory	→ End	

above limit

Diagnosis conditions

- Engine running
- Battery voltage greater than 7 V
- Intake air temperature greater than 9 °C
- Air conditioning switched on and off once

Note!

The triggering wire for relays stage 1, terminal 85, is monitored

Possible fault cause

- Short circuit to B+
- Relay faulty
- DME control module faulty

PR1020100261030X

Fig. 41 Code P0480: Fan Output Stage 1, Open Circuit (Part 3 of 4)

Work instruction			Display OK	If not OK
1	Check both relays	♦ Remove relay ♦ Measure resistance between Pin 85 and Pin 86	Approx. 75 Ω ⇒ Step 2	Replace relay → End
2	Check wiring from DME control module, plug IV Pin 4, to relays for short to B+	♦ Connect special tool 9637 to wiring harness (DME control module plug) ♦ Remove relay stage 1 of coolant fan 1 ♦ Remove relay stage 2 of coolant fan 1 ♦ Measure voltage between special tool 9637 plug IV Pin 4 and ground ♦ Ignition on	0 V ⇒ Step 3	Repair wiring harness → End
3	Replace DME control module		⇒ Step 4	
4	Perform adaptation	♦ Switch on the ignition ♦ Wait one minute ♦ Do not press the accelerator ♦ Switch off the ignition for at least 10 seconds ♦ Read out the fault memory	→ End	

PR1020100261040X

Fig. 41 Code P0480: Fan Output Stage 1, Open Circuit (Part 4 of 4)

open circuit

Diagnosis conditions

- Engine running
- Battery voltage greater than 7 V
- Medium pressure switch (air conditioning) active or engine temperature greater than 105 °C
- Air conditioning switched on and off once

Note!

The triggering wire for relays stage 2, terminal 85, is monitored

Possible fault cause

- Open circuit
- Relay faulty
- DME control module faulty

Affected terminals

Terminal IV/20

Diagnosis/troubleshooting

Work instruction			Display OK	If not OK
1	Check both relays	♦ Remove relay ♦ Measure resistance between Pin 85 and Pin 86	Approx. 75 Ω ⇒ Step 2	Replace relay → End
2	Check wiring from DME control module, plug IV Pin 20, to relays for continuity	♦ Connect special tool 9637 to wiring harness (DME control module plug) ♦ Remove relay stage 2 of coolant fan 1 ♦ Remove relay stage 2 of coolant fan 2 ♦ Measure resistance between special tool 9637 plug IV Pin 20 and relay slot of coolant fan 1 plug Pin 2	0 - 5 Ω	Repair wiring harness → End

PR1020100262010X

Fig. 42 Code P0481: Fan Output Stage 1, Open Circuit (Part 1 of 4)

Work instruction			Display OK	If not OK
2		• Measure resistance between special tool 9637 plug IV Pin 20 and relay slot of coolant fan 2 plug Pin 2	0 - 5 Ω ⇒ Step 3	Check plug connection X 2/3, Pin 22, and check wiring harness for chafing and pinching damage
3	Replace DME control module		⇒ Step 4	
4	Perform adaptation	• Switch on the ignition • Wait one minute • Do not press the accelerator • Switch off the ignition for at least 10 seconds • Read out the fault memory	→ End	

below limit

Diagnosis conditions

- Engine running
- Battery voltage greater than 7 V
- Medium pressure switch (air conditioning) active or engine temperature greater than 105 °C
- Air conditioning switched on and off once

Note!

The triggering wire for relays stage 2, terminal 85, is monitored

Possible fault cause

- Short circuit to ground
- Relay faulty
- DME control module faulty

Affected terminals

Terminal IV/20

PR1020100262020X

Fig. 42 Code P0481: Fan Output Stage 1, Open Circuit (Part 2 of 4)

Work instruction			Display OK	If not OK
1	Check both relays	• Remove relay • Measure resistance between Pin 85 and Pin 86	Approx. 75 Ω ⇒ Step 2	Replace relay → End
2	Check wiring from DME control module, plug IV Pin 20, to relays for short to ground	• Connect special tool 9637 to wiring harness (DME control module plug) • Remove relay stage 2 of coolant fan 1 • Remove relay stage 2 of coolant fan 2 • Measure resistance between special tool 9637 plug IV Pin 20 and ground	∞ Ω ⇒ Step 3	Repair wiring harness → End
3	Replace DME control module		⇒ Step 4	
4	Perform adaptation	• Switch on the ignition • Wait one minute • Do not press the accelerator • Switch off the ignition for at least 10 seconds • Read out the fault memory	→ End	

above limit

Diagnosis conditions

- Engine running
- Battery voltage greater than 7 V
- Medium pressure switch (air conditioning) active or engine temperature greater than 105 °C
- Air conditioning switched on and off once

Note!

The triggering wire for relays stage 2, terminal 85, is monitored

Possible fault cause

- Short circuit to B+
- Relay faulty
- DME control module faulty

PR1020100262030X

Fig. 42 Code P0481: Fan Output Stage 1, Open Circuit (Part 3 of 4)

Work instruction			Display OK	If not OK
1	Check both relays	• Remove relay • Measure resistance between Pin 85 and Pin 86	Approx. 75 Ω ⇒ Step 2	Replace relay → End
2	Check wiring from DME control module, plug IV Pin 20, to relays for short to B+	• Connect special tool 9637 to wiring harness (DME control module plug) • Remove relay stage 2 of coolant fan 1 • Remove relay stage 2 of coolant fan 2 • Measure voltage between special tool 9637 plug IV Pin 20 and ground • Ignition on	0 V ⇒ Step 3	Repair wiring harness → End
3	Replace DME control module		⇒ Step 4	
4	Perform adaptation	• Switch on the ignition • Wait one minute • Do not press the accelerator • Switch off the ignition for at least 10 seconds • Read out the fault memory	→ End	

PR1020100262040X

Fig. 42 Code P0481: Fan Output Stage 1, Open Circuit (Part 4 of 4)

Diagnosis conditions

- Engine running
- Battery voltage greater than 7 V
- Engine temperature greater than 108 °C
- Vehicle speed greater than 25 km/h (15 mph)
- Engine speed more than 1000 rpm

Note!

The triggering wire for relays stage 3, terminal 85, is monitored.

Possible fault cause

- Open circuit
- Relay faulty
- DME control module faulty

Affected terminals

Terminal IV/31

Diagnosis/troubleshooting

Work instruction			Display OK	If not OK
1	Check both relays	• Remove relay • Measure resistance between Pin 85 and Pin 86	Approx. 75 Ω ⇒ Step 2	Replace relay → End
2	Check wiring from DME control module, plug IV Pin 31, to relays for continuity	• Connect special tool 9637 to wiring harness (DME control module plug) • Remove relay stage 3 of coolant fan 1 • Remove relay stage 3 of coolant fan 2 • Measure resistance between special tool 9637 plug IV Pin 31 and relay slot of coolant fan 1 plug Pin 2	0 - 5 Ω	Repair wiring harness → End

PR1020100263010X

Fig. 43 Code P0482: Fan Output Stage 3, Open Circuit (Part 1 of 4)

Work instruction			Display OK	If not OK
2		• Measure resistance between special tool 9637 plug IV Pin 31 and relay slot of coolant fan 2 plug Pin 2	0 - 5 Ω ⇒ Step 3	Check plug connection X 2/3, Pin 12, and check wiring harness for chafing and pinching damage
3	Replace DME control module		⇒ Step 4	
4	Perform adaptation	• Switch on the ignition • Wait one minute • Do not press the accelerator • Switch off the ignition for at least 10 seconds • Read out the fault memory	→ End	

below limit

Diagnosis conditions

- Engine running
- Battery voltage greater than 7 V
- Engine temperature greater than 108 °C
- Vehicle speed greater than 25 km/h (15 mph)
- Engine speed more than 1000 rpm

Note!

The triggering wire for relays stage 3, terminal 85, is monitored.

Possible fault cause

- Short circuit to ground
- Relay faulty
- DME control module faulty

Affected terminals

Terminal IV/31

PR1020100263020X

Fig. 43 Code P0482: Fan Output Stage 3, Open Circuit (Part 2 of 4)

Work instruction			Display OK	If not OK
1	Check both relays	• Remove relay • Measure resistance between Pin 85 and Pin 86	Approx. 75 Ω ⇒ Step 2	Replace relay → End
2	Check wiring from DME control module, plug IV Pin 20, to relays for short to B+	• Connect special tool 9637 to wiring harness (DME control module plug) • Remove relay stage 3 of coolant fan 1 • Remove relay stage 3 of coolant fan 2 • Measure voltage between special tool 9637 plug IV Pin 31 and ground • Ignition on	0 V ⇒ Step 3	Repair wiring harness → End
3	Replace DME control module		⇒ Step 4	
4	Perform adaptation	• Switch on the ignition • Wait one minute • Do not press the accelerator • Switch off the ignition for at least 10 seconds • Read out the fault memory	→ End	

PR1020100263040X

Fig. 43 Code P0482: Fan Output Stage 3, Open Circuit (Part 4 of 4)

Diagnosis/troubleshooting

Work instruction			Display OK	If not OK
1	Check both relays	• Remove relay • Measure resistance between Pin 85 and Pin 86	Approx. 75 Ω ⇒ Step 2	Replace relay → End
2	Check wiring from DME control module, plug IV Pin 31, to relays for short to ground	• Connect special tool 9637 to wiring harness (DME control module plug) • Remove relay stage 3 of coolant fan 1 • Remove relay stage 3 of coolant fan 2 • Measure resistance between special tool 9637 plug IV Pin 31 and ground	∞ Ω ⇒ Step 3	Repair wiring harness → End
3	Replace DME control module		⇒ Step 4	
4	Perform adaptation	• Switch on the ignition • Wait one minute • Do not press the accelerator • Switch off the ignition for at least 10 seconds • Read out the fault memory	→ End	

above limit

Diagnosis conditions

- Engine running
- Battery voltage greater than 7 V
- Engine temperature greater than 108 °C
- Vehicle speed greater than 25 km/h (15 mph)
- Engine speed more than 1000 rpm

Note!

The triggering wire for relays stage 3, terminal 85, is monitored.

Possible fault cause

- Short circuit to B+
- Relay faulty
- DME control module faulty

PR1020100263030X

Fig. 43 Code P0482: Fan Output Stage 3, Open Circuit (Part 3 of 4)

below limit

Diagnosis conditions

- Start-up ended
- Speed = 0 km/h
- Throttle valve in idle position
- Engine temperature > 60 °C
- Intake air temperature > -10 °C
- No fuel tank ventilation or tank ventilation diagnosis
- No secondary air diagnosis
- Altitude correction factor > 0.75
- No faults in speed signal, throttle position sensor, engine temperature, EVAP canister purge valve or tank ventilation system

Possible fault cause

- Throttle is jammed

Affected terminals

-

Diagnosis/troubleshooting

Note!

If faults are stored for the throttle jacking device, eliminate these faults first.

Work instruction			Display OK	If not OK
1	Replace throttle part			
2	Perform adaptation	• Switch on the ignition • Wait one minute. Do not press the accelerator • Switch off the ignition for at least 10 seconds • Read out the fault memory		

PR1020100264000X

Fig. 44 Code P0506: Idle Air Control At Stop, Below Limit

above limit

Diagnosis conditions

- Start-up ended
- Speed = 0 km/h
- Throttle valve in idle position
- Engine temperature > 60 °C
- Intake air temperature > -10 °C
- No fuel tank ventilation or tank ventilation diagnosis
- No secondary air diagnosis
- Altitude correction factor > 0.75
- No faults in speed signal, throttle position sensor, engine temperature, EVAP canister purge valve or tank ventilation system

Possible fault cause

- Throttle is jammed
- Leaks in intake air system

Affected terminals

-

Diagnosis/troubleshooting

Work instruction			Display OK	If not OK
1	Check for air leaks in intake air system		→ End	→ Step 2
2	Replace throttle part			
3	Perform adaptation	• Switch on the ignition • Wait one minute. Do not press the accelerator • Switch off the ignition for at least 10 seconds • Read out the fault memory		

PR1020100265000X

Fig. 45 Code P0507: Idle Air Control At Stop, Above Limit

Diagnosis conditions

- Vehicle speed greater than 0 km/h (0 mph)
- No fault in vehicle speed
- Time elapsed after start-up 60 sec.

Possible fault cause

- Battery
- Contact resistance

Affected terminals

Terminal II/2

Diagnosis/troubleshooting

Work instruction			Display OK	If not OK
1	Check battery		⇒ Step 2	Replace battery → End
2	Check wire, terminal 30, for contact resistance	• Connect special tool 9637 to wiring harness (DME control module plug) • Measure voltage between special tool 9637 Pin I/2 and ground	> 11 V ⇒ Step 4	⇒ Step 3
3		• Check wire from special tool 9637, Pin I/2, to pin side of connector X 2/3, Pin 2, for continuity • Check connector for corrosion	0 - 5 Ω ⇒ Step 4	
4		• Check wire from connector X 2/3, sleeve side, to current distributor fuse C 1 for continuity	0 - 5Ω ⇒ Step 5	Remedy contact resistance → End
5	Check voltage regulator and alternator		→ End	

PR1020100267000X

Fig. 47 Code P0562: Voltage Supply, Below Limit

Diagnosis conditions

- Vehicle speed greater than 0 km/h (0 mph)
- No fault in vehicle speed
- Time elapsed after start-up 60 sec.

Possible fault cause

- DME control module

Affected terminals

Terminal II/2

Diagnosis/troubleshooting

Note!

In case of a fault, a replacement value of 14.06 V is used.

Work instruction			Display OK	If not OK
1	Replace DME control module		⇒ Step 2	
2	Perform adaptation	• Switch on the ignition • Wait one minute • Do not press the accelerator • Switch off the ignition for at least 10 seconds • Read out the fault memory	→ End	→ End

PR1020100266000X

Fig. 46 Code P0560: Voltage Supply, Signal Implausible

Diagnosis conditions

- Vehicle speed greater than 0 km/h (0 mph)
- No fault in vehicle speed
- Time elapsed after start-up 60 sec.

Possible fault cause

- Voltage regulator

Affected terminals

Terminal II/2

Diagnosis/troubleshooting

Work instruction		Display OK	If not OK
1	Check voltage regulator	→ End	Replace voltage regulator → End

PR1020100268000X

Fig. 48 Code P0563: Voltage Supply, Below Limit

Diagnosis conditions

- Vehicle with Tiptronic transmission
- Battery voltage greater than 10 V
- Ignition on

Possible fault cause

- Wiring harness
- Tiptronic control module not connected
- Tiptronic control module faulty

Note!

- *If all CAN bus faults are stored, there must be a short circuit in the CAN bus wiring.*
- *If one CAN bus fault is stored, the cruise control system is out of order.*
- *CAN bus faults may be caused by a control module reset. The fault is then indicated as "Not present".*

Affected terminals

Terminal II/3 and II/4

Diagnosis/troubleshooting

Work instruction			Display OK	If not OK
1	Check whether connector of Tiptronic control module is plugged in.		⇒ Step 2	
2	Check CAN bus from DME control module to Tiptronic control module for continuity	• Remove DME control module connector		Repair wiring harness → End
		• Remove Tiptronic control module connector		
		• Connect special tool 9637 to wiring harness (DME control module plug)		
		• Measure resistance between special tool 9637 plug II Pin 3 and Tiptronic control module plug Pin 85	0 - 5 Ω	

PR1020100269010X

Fig. 49 Code P0600: CAN Timeout Tiptronic (Part 1 of 2)

Work instruction			Display OK	If not OK
2		• Measure resistance between special tool 9637 plug II Pin 4 and Tiptronic control module plug Pin 86	0 - 5 Ω ⇒ Step 3	
3	Check CAN bus from DME control module to Tiptronic control module for short to ground	• Remove DME control module connector	⇒ Step 4	Repair wiring harness → End
		• Remove Tiptronic control module connector		
		• Connect special tool 9637 to wiring harness (DME control module plug)		
		• Measure resistance between special tool 9637 plug II Pin 3 and ground	∞ Ω	
		• Measure resistance between special tool 9637 plug II Pin 4 and ground	∞ Ω ⇒ Step 4	
4	Check CAN bus from DME control module to Tiptronic control module for short to B+	• Remove DME control module connector	⇒ Step 5	Repair wiring harness → End
		• Remove Tiptronic control module connector		
		• Connect special tool 9637 to wiring harness (DME control module plug)		
		• Measure voltage between special tool 9637 plug II Pin 3 and ground	0 V	
		• Switch on the ignition		
		• Measure voltage between special tool 9637 plug II Pin 4 and ground	0 V ⇒ Step 5	
		• Switch on the ignition		
5	Check CAN bus from DME control module to Tiptronic control module for short circuit	• Remove DME control module connector	∞ Ω → End	Repair wiring harness → End
		• Remove Tiptronic control module connector		
		• Connect special tool 9637 to wiring harness (DME control module plug)		
		• Measure resistance between special tool 9637 plug II Pin 3 and plug II Pin 4		

PR1020100269020X

Fig. 49 Code P0600: CAN Timeout Tiptronic (Part 2 of 2)

Diagnosis conditions

- Ignition on

Possible fault cause

- DME control module faulty

Affected terminals

-

Diagnosis/troubleshooting

Note!

If no fault is present, delete the fault memory.

Work instruction			Display OK	If not OK
1	Replace DME control module		⇒ Step 2	
2	Perform adaptation	• Switch on the ignition • Wait one minute • Do not press the accelerator • Switch off the ignition for at least 10 seconds • Read out the fault memory	→ End	→ End

PR1020100269030X

Fig. 50 Code P0604: Control Module Faulty, Signal Implausible

Diagnosis conditions

- Ignition on

Possible fault cause

- DME control module faulty

Affected terminals

Diagnosis/troubleshooting

Note!

If no fault is present, delete the fault memory.

Work instruction			Display OK	If not OK
1	Replace DME control module		⇒ Step 2	
2	Perform adaptation	• Switch on the ignition • Wait one minute • Do not press the accelerator • Switch off the ignition for at least 10 seconds • Read out the fault memory	→ End	→ End

PR1020100270000X

Fig. 51 Code P0605: Control Module Faulty, Signal Implausible

Diagnosis conditions

- Engine running

Possible fault cause

- Heavily soiled throttle
- Throttle damaged
- Mass air flow sensor

Affected terminals

-

Diagnosis/troubleshooting

Note!

In case of a defect in the MAF sensor, this fault must also be stored in the fault memory.

Work instruction			Display OK	If not OK
1	Check throttle (visual inspection)		⇒ Step 2	Clean throttle → End
2	Check voltage signal of MAF sensor	• Ignition on • Measure voltage between special tool 9637 Pin III/23 and ground • In the Porsche System Tester 2, select the menu point"Actual values/mass air flow"	0.9 to 1.1 V	
		• Start the engine	1.2 to 1.5 V at idle speed	

PR1020100271000X

Fig. 52 Code P1101: Input Variables, Charge Measurement Above Or Below Limit

Figure 1:

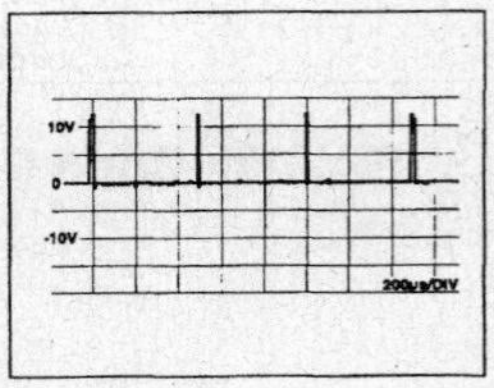

Figure 2:

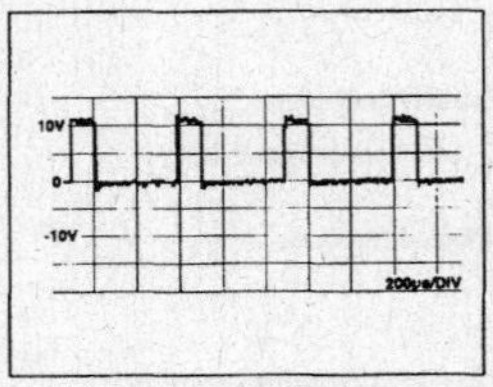

Work instruction			Display OK	If not OK
2	Check TP sensor voltage supply	• Connect special tool 9637 to wiring harness (DME control module plug) • Switch on the ignition • Measure voltage between Pin III/10 and Pin III/25	Approx. 5 V ⇒ Step 3	⇒ Step 4
3	Check voltage values of throttle position sensor 1	• Connect special tool 9637 • Switch on the ignition • Measure voltage between Pin III/24 and Pin III/25 • Fully depress accelerator pedal • Measure voltage between Pin III/24 and Pin III/25	Approx. 0.7 - 0.9 V Approx. 4.1 - 4.5 V	Replace throttle part ⇒ Step 6
4	Check wiring from throttle part to DME control module for continuity or short circuit to B+ and ground	• Separate disconnection point to throttle part. • Connect special tool 9637 to wiring harness (DME control module plug)		Repair wiring harness → End

PR1020100272020X

Fig. 53 Code P1121: TP Sensor No. 1 (Part 2 of 4)

Diagnosis conditions

- Engine running

Possible fault cause

- Open circuit in wiring
- Short circuit in wiring
- Throttle position sensor faulty
- DME control module faulty

Affected terminals

Terminal I/7, I/9, III/10, III/24 and III/25

Diagnosis/troubleshooting

Work instruction			Display OK	If not OK
1	Check voltage supply to throttle motor actuator	• Connect special tool 9637 • Connect motor tester (oscilloscope) to Pin I/7 and Pin I/9 • Use special input • Switch on the ignition • See Figure 1 • Fully depress accelerator pedal	See Figure 1 See Figure 2 ⇒ Step 2	⇒ Step 5

PR1020100272010X

Fig. 53 Code P1121: TP Sensor No. 1 (Part 1 of 4)

Work instruction			Display OK	If not OK
4		• Measure resistance between disconnection point Pin 1 and special tool 9637 Pin I/9	0 - 5 Ω	
		• Measure resistance between disconnection point Pin 2 and special tool 9637 Pin III/25	0 - 5 Ω	
		• Measure resistance between disconnection point Pin 3 and special tool 9637 Pin III/10	0 - 5 Ω	
		• Measure resistance between disconnection point Pin 4 and special tool 9637 Pin I/7	0 - 5 Ω	
		• Measure resistance between disconnection point Pin 6 and special tool 9637 Pin III/24	0 - 5 Ω	
		• Measure resistance between disconnection point Pin 4 and ground	∞ Ω	
		• Measure resistance between disconnection point Pin 6 and ground	∞ Ω	
		• Switch on the ignition • Measure voltage between disconnection point Pin 4 and ground	0 V	
		• Switch on the ignition • Measure voltage between disconnection point Pin 6 and ground	0 V ⇒ Step 5	

PR1020100272030X

Fig. 53 Code P1121: TP Sensor No. 1 (Part 3 of 4)

Disconnection point throttle part:

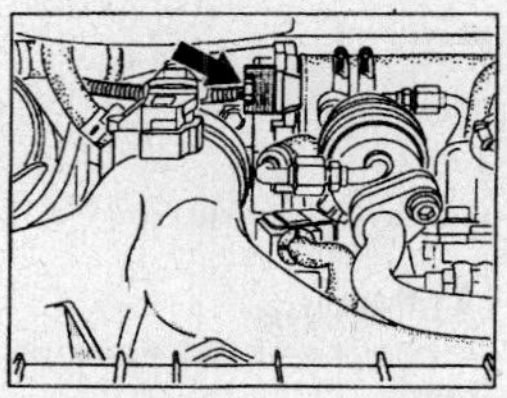

Note!

The wires to the throttle part are routed via connector X 59/2.

Work instruction			Display OK	If not OK
5	Replace DME control module		⇒ Step 6	
6	Perform adaptation	• Switch on the ignition • Wait one minute • Do not press the accelerator • Switch off the ignition for at least 10 seconds • Read out the fault memory	→ End	→ End

PR1020100272040X

Fig. 53 Code P1121: TP Sensor No. 1 (Part 4 of 4)

Figure 1:

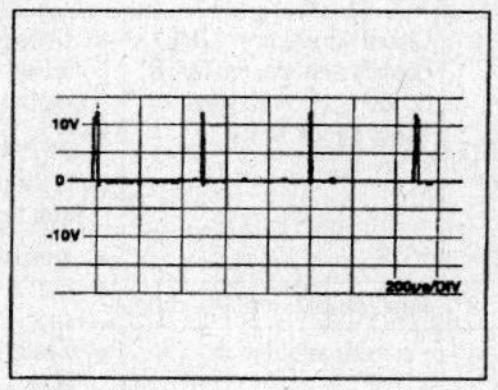

Figure 2:

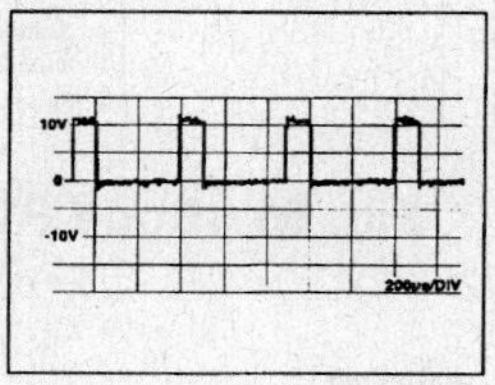

Work instruction			Display OK	If not OK
2	Check TP sensor voltage supply	• Connect special tool 9637 to wiring harness (DME control module plug) • Switch on the ignition • Measure voltage between Pin III/10 and Pin III/25	Approx. 5 V ⇒ Step 3	⇒ Step 4
3	Check voltage values of throttle position sensor 2	• Connect special tool 9637 • Switch on the ignition • Measure voltage between Pin III/8 and Pin III/25 • Fully depress accelerator pedal • Measure voltage between Pin III/8 and Pin III/25	Approx. 4.0 - 4.4 V Approx. 0.5 - 0.8 V	Replace throttle part ⇒ Step 6
4	Check wiring from throttle part to DME control module for continuity or short circuit to B+ and ground	• Separate disconnection point to throttle part. • Connect special tool 9637 to wiring harness (DME control module plug)		Repair wiring harness → End

PR1020100273020X

Fig. 54 Code P1122: TP Sensor No. 2 (Part 2 of 4)

Diagnosis conditions

- Engine running

Possible fault cause

- Open circuit in wiring
- Short circuit in wiring
- Throttle position sensor faulty
- DME control module faulty

Affected terminals

Terminal I/7, I/9, III/10, III/24 and III/25

Diagnosis/troubleshooting

Work instruction			Display OK	If not OK
1	Check voltage supply to throttle motor actuator	• Connect special tool 9637 • Connect motor tester (oscilloscope) to Pin I/7 and Pin I/9 • Use special input • Switch on the ignition • Fully depress accelerator pedal	See Figure 1 See Figure 2 ⇒ Step 2	⇒ Step 5

PR1020100273010X

Fig. 54 Code P1122: TP Sensor No. 2 (Part 1 of 4)

Work instruction			Display OK	If not OK
4		• Measure resistance between disconnection point Pin 1 and special tool 9637 Pin I/9	0 - 5 Ω	
		• Measure resistance between disconnection point Pin 2 and special tool 9637 Pin III/25	0 - 5 Ω	
		• Measure resistance between disconnection point Pin 3 and special tool 9637 Pin III/10	0 - 5 Ω	
		• Measure resistance between disconnection point Pin 4 and special tool 9637 Pin I/7	0 - 5 Ω	
		• Measure resistance between disconnection point Pin 5 and special tool 9637 Pin III/8	0 - 5 Ω	
		• Measure resistance between Pin 4 and ground	∞ Ω	
		• Measure resistance between disconnection point Pin 5 and ground	∞ Ω	
		• Switch on the ignition • Measure voltage between disconnection point Pin 4 and ground	0 V	
		• Switch on the ignition • Measure voltage between disconnection point Pin 5 and ground	0 V ⇒ Step 5	

PR1020100273030X

Fig. 54 Code P1122: TP Sensor No. 2 (Part 3 of 4)

Disconnection point throttle part:

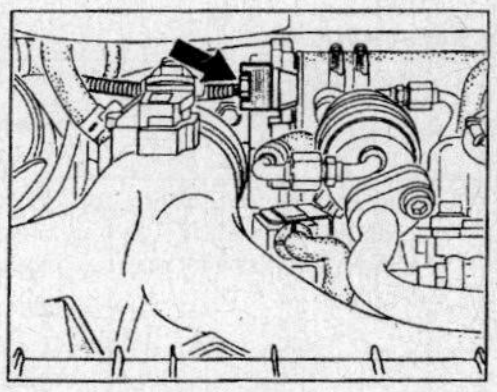

Note!

The wires to the throttle part are routed via connector X 59/2.

Work instruction			Display OK	If not OK
5	Replace DME control module		⇒ Step 6	
6	Perform adaptation	• Switch on the ignition • Wait one minute • Do not press the accelerator • Switch off the ignition for at least 10 seconds • Read out the fault memory	→ End	→ End

PR1020100273040X

Fig. 54 Code P1122: TP Sensor No. 2 (Part 4 of 4)

Diagnosis conditions

- Engine started

Note!

The triggering wire for the fuel pump relay, terminal 85, is monitored.

Possible fault cause

- Fuel pump relay
- Short circuit to ground
- DME control module

Affected terminals

Terminal IV/10

Diagnosis/troubleshooting

Work instruction			Display OK	If not OK
1	Check fuel pump relay	• Remove fuel pump relay • Measure resistance between Pin 85 and Pin 86	Approx. 75 Ω ⇒ Step 2	Replace fuel pump relay → End
2	Check wiring from DME control module, Pin IV/10, to fuel pump relay for short circuit to ground	• Connect special tool 9637 to wiring harness (DME control module plug) • Remove fuel pump relay • Measure resistance between special tool 9637 Pin IV/10 and ground	∞ Ω ⇒ Step 3	Repair wiring harness → End
3	Replace DME control module		⇒ Step 4	
4	Perform adaptation	• Switch on the ignition • Wait one minute • Do not press the accelerator • Switch off the ignition for at least 10 seconds • Read out the fault memory	→ End	

PR1020100274010X

Fig. 55 Code P1124: Fuel Pump Relay Output Stage (Part 1 of 3)

open circuit

Diagnosis conditions

- Engine started

Note!

The triggering wire for the fuel pump relay, terminal 85, is monitored.

Possible fault cause

- Fuel pump relay
- Open circuit
- DME control module

Affected terminals

Terminal IV/10

Diagnosis/troubleshooting

Work instruction			Display OK	If not OK
1	Check fuel pump relay	• Remove fuel pump relay • Measure resistance between Pin 85 and Pin 86	Approx. 75 Ω ⇒ Step 2	Replace fuel pump relay → End
2	Check wiring from DME control module, Pin IV/10, to fuel pump relay for continuity	• Connect special tool 9637 to wiring harness (DME control module plug) • Remove fuel pump relay • Measure resistance between special tool 9637, Pin IV/10, and fuel pump relay slot, Pin 6 (terminal 85)	0 - 5 Ω ⇒ Step 3	Check plug connection X 2/3 and wiring harness → End
3	Replace DME control module		⇒ Step 4	
4	Perform adaptation	• Switch on the ignition • Wait one minute • Do not press the accelerator • Switch off the ignition for at least 10 seconds • Read out the fault memory	→ End	

PR1020100274030X

Fig. 55 Code P1124: Fuel Pump Relay Output Stage (Part 3 of 3)

above limit

Diagnosis conditions

- Engine running
- Battery voltage greater than 7 V

Note!

The triggering wire for the fuel pump relay, terminal 85, is monitored.

Possible fault cause

- Fuel pump relay
- Short circuit to B+
- DME control module

Affected terminals

Terminal IV/10

Diagnosis/troubleshooting

Work instruction			Display OK	If not OK
1	Check fuel pump relay	• Remove fuel pump relay • Measure resistance between Pin 85 and Pin 86	Approx. 75 Ω ⇒ Step 2	Replace fuel pump relay → End
2	Check wiring from DME control module, Pin IV/10, to fuel pump relay for short circuit to B+	• Connect special tool 9637 to wiring harness (DME control module plug) • Remove fuel pump relay • Measure voltage between special tool Pin IV/10 and ground • Ignition on	0 V ⇒ Step 3	Repair wiring harness → End
3	Replace DME control module		⇒ Step 4	
4	Perform adaptation	• Switch on the ignition • Wait one minute • Do not press the accelerator • Switch off the ignition for at least 10 seconds • Read out the fault memory	→ End	

PR1020100274020X

Fig. 55 Code P1124: Fuel Pump Relay Output Stage (Part 2 of 3)

above limit

Diagnosis conditions

- Engine running
- Battery voltage greater than 7 V

Possible fault cause

- Fuel injector (coil) short circuit
- Short circuit to B+ in wiring
- DME control module

Affected terminals

Terminal III/41

Note!

Short to B+ causes the fuel injector to be continually closed.

Diagnosis/troubleshooting

Work instruction			Display OK	If not OK
1	Check fuel injector	• Remove connector of fuel injector 3 • Connect special tool V.A.G. 1315 A/1 • Measure resistance at special tool V.A.G. 1315 A/1	11 - 13 Ω (at 20 °C) ⇒ Step 2	Replace fuel injector → End
2	Check wiring harness for short to B+	• Connect special tool 9637 to wiring harness (DME control module plug) • Remove connector of fuel injector • Measure voltage between special tool 9637 Pin III/41 and ground • Ignition on	0 V ⇒ Step 3	Repair wiring harness → End

PR1020100275010X

Fig. 56 Code P1213: Fuel Injector Cylinder No. 1, Above Limit (Part 1 of 2)

Work instruction			Display OK	If not OK
3	Replace DME control module		⇒ Step 4	
4	Perform adaptation	• Switch on the ignition • Wait one minute • Do not press the accelerator • Switch off the ignition for at least 10 seconds • Read out the fault memory	→ End	

PR1020100275020X

Fig. 56 Code P1213: Fuel Injector Cylinder No. 1, Above Limit (Part 2 of 2)

Work instruction			Display OK	If not OK
3	Replace DME control module		⇒ Step 4	
4	Perform adaptation	• Switch on the ignition • Wait one minute • Do not press the accelerator • Switch off the ignition for at least 10 seconds • Read out the fault memory	→ End	

PR1020100276020X

Fig. 57 Code P1214: Fuel Injector Cylinder No. 6, Above Limit (Part 2 of 2)

Diagnosis conditions

- Engine running
- Battery voltage greater than 7 V

Possible fault cause

- Fuel injector (coil) short circuit
- Short circuit to B+ in wiring
- DME control module

Affected terminals

Terminal III/40

Note!

Short to B+ causes the fuel injector to be continually closed.

Diagnosis/troubleshooting

Work instruction			Display OK	If not OK
1	Check fuel injector	• Remove connector of fuel injector 3 • Connect special tool V.A.G. 1315 A/1 • Measure resistance at special tool V.A.G. 1315 A/1	11 - 13 Ω (at 20 °C) ⇒ Step 2	Replace fuel injector → End
2	Check wiring harness for short to B+	• Connect special tool 9637 to wiring harness (DME control module plug) • Remove connector of fuel injector • Measure voltage between special tool 9637 Pin III/40 and ground • Ignition on	0 V ⇒ Step 3	Repair wiring harness → End

PR1020100277010X

Fig. 58 Code P1215: Fuel Injector Cylinder No. 2, Above Limit (Part 1 of 2)

Diagnosis conditions

- Engine running
- Battery voltage greater than 7 V

Possible fault cause

- Fuel injector (coil) short circuit
- Short circuit to B+ in wiring
- DME control module

Affected terminals

Terminal III/28

Note!

Short to B+ causes the fuel injector to be continually closed.

Diagnosis/troubleshooting

Work instruction			Display OK	If not OK
1	Check fuel injector	• Remove connector of fuel injector 3 • Connect special tool V.A.G. 1315 A/1 • Measure resistance at special tool V.A.G. 1315 A/1	11 - 13 Ω (at 20 °C) ⇒ Step 2	Replace fuel injector → End
2	Check wiring harness for short to B+	• Connect special tool 9637 to wiring harness (DME control module plug) • Remove connector of fuel injector • Measure voltage between special tool 9637 Pin III/28 and ground • Ignition on	0 V ⇒ Step 3	Repair wiring harness → End

PR1020100276010X

Fig. 57 Code P1214: Fuel Injector Cylinder No. 6, Above Limit (Part 1 of 2)

Work instruction			Display OK	If not OK
3	Replace DME control module		⇒ Step 4	
4	Perform adaptation	• Switch on the ignition • Wait one minute • Do not press the accelerator • Switch off the ignition for at least 10 seconds • Read out the fault memory	→ End	

PR1020100277020X

Fig. 58 Code P1215: Fuel Injector Cylinder No. 2, Above Limit (Part 2 of 2)

Diagnosis conditions

- Engine running
- Battery voltage greater than 7 V

Possible fault cause

- Fuel injector (coil) short circuit
- Short circuit to B+ in wiring
- DME control module

Affected terminals

Terminal III/27

Note!

Short to B+ causes the fuel injector to be continually closed.

Diagnosis/troubleshooting

Work instruction			Display OK	If not OK
1	Check fuel injector	• Remove connector of fuel injector 3 • Connect special tool V.A.G. 1315 A/1 • Measure resistance at special tool V.A.G. 1315 A/1	11 - 13 Ω (at 20 °C) ⇒ Step 2	Replace fuel injector → End
2	Check wiring harness for short to B+	• Connect special tool 9637 to wiring harness (DME control module plug) • Remove connector of fuel injector • Measure voltage between special tool 9637 Pin III/27 and ground • Ignition on	0 V ⇒ Step 3	Repair wiring harness → End

PR1020100278010X

Fig. 59 Code P1216: Fuel Injector Cylinder No. 4, Above Limit (Part 1 of 2)

Diagnosis conditions

- Engine running
- Battery voltage greater than 7 V

Possible fault cause

- Fuel injector (coil) short circuit
- Short circuit to B+ in wiring
- DME control module

Affected terminals

Terminal III/15

Note!

Short to B+ causes the fuel injector to be continually closed.

Diagnosis/troubleshooting

Work instruction			Display OK	If not OK
1	Check fuel injector	• Remove connector of fuel injector 3 • Connect special tool V.A.G. 1315 A/1 • Measure resistance at special tool V.A.G. 1315 A/1	11 - 13 Ω (at 20 °C) ⇒ Step 2	Replace fuel injector → End
2	Check wiring harness for short to B+	• Connect special tool 9637 to wiring harness (DME control module plug) • Remove connector of fuel injector • Measure voltage between special tool 9637 Pin III/15 and ground • Ignition on	0 V ⇒ Step 3	Repair wiring harness → End

PR1020100279010X

Fig. 60 Code P1217: Fuel Injector Cylinder No. 3, Above Limit (Part 1 of 2)

Work instruction			Display OK	If not OK
3	Replace DME control module		⇒ Step 4	
4	Perform adaptation	• Switch on the ignition • Wait one minute • Do not press the accelerator • Switch off the ignition for at least 10 seconds • Read out the fault memory	→ End	

PR1020100278020X

Fig. 59 Code P1216: Fuel Injector Cylinder No. 4, Above Limit (Part 2 of 2)

Work instruction			Display OK	If not OK
3	Replace DME control module		⇒ Step 4	
4	Perform adaptation	• Switch on the ignition • Wait one minute • Do not press the accelerator • Switch off the ignition for at least 10 seconds • Read out the fault memory	→ End	

PR1020100279020X

Fig. 60 Code P1217: Fuel Injector Cylinder No. 3, Above Limit (Part 2 of 2)

Diagnosis conditions

- Engine running
- Battery voltage greater than 7 V

Possible fault cause

- Fuel injector (coil) short circuit
- Short circuit to B+ in wiring
- DME control module

Affected terminals

Terminal III/2

Note!

Short to B+ causes the fuel injector to be continually closed.

Diagnosis/troubleshooting

Work instruction			Display OK	If not OK
1	Check fuel injector	• Remove connector of fuel injector 3 • Connect special tool V.A.G. 1315 A/1 • Measure resistance at special tool V.A.G. 1315 A/1	11 - 13 Ω (at 20 °C) ⇒ Step 2	Replace fuel injector → End
2	Check wiring harness for short to B+	• Connect special tool 9637 to wiring harness (DME control module plug) • Remove connector of fuel injector • Measure voltage between special tool 9637 Pin III/2 and ground • Ignition on	0 V ⇒ Step 3	Repair wiring harness → End

PR1020100280010X

Fig. 61 Code P1218: Fuel Injector Cylinder No. 5, Above Limit (Part 1 of 2)

Work instruction			Display OK	If not OK
3	Replace DME control module		⇒ Step 4	
4	Perform adaptation	• Switch on the ignition • Wait one minute • Do not press the accelerator • Switch off the ignition for at least 10 seconds • Read out the fault memory	→ End	

PR1020100280020X

Fig. 61 Code P1218: Fuel Injector Cylinder No. 5, Above Limit (Part 2 of 2)

Diagnosis conditions

- Ignition on (approx. 30 sec.)
- Battery voltage greater than 7 V

Possible fault cause

- Pedal sensor

Affected terminals

Note!

- *The system operates in pedal sensor standby mode, i.e. the angle of the accelerator pedal is calculated from the residual position sensor signal.*
- *The maximum pedal value is limited to 30 %.*
- *The dynamic is limited.*
- *The fault code only appears together with P1577 or P1578.*
- *The pedal value is reset to zero by actuating the brake.*

Diagnosis/troubleshooting

	Work instruction	Display OK	If not OK
1	Replace pedal sensor	→ End	

PR1020100281000X

Fig. 62 Code P1219: Accelerator Pedal, Signal Implausible

	Work instruction		Display OK	If not OK
3	Replace DME control module		⇒ Step 4	
4	Perform adaptation	• Switch on the ignition • Wait one minute • Do not press the accelerator • Switch off the ignition for at least 10 seconds • Read out the fault memory	→ End	

PR1020100282020X

Fig. 63 Code P1225: Fuel Injector Cylinder No. 1, Below Limit (Part 2 of 2)

Diagnosis conditions

- Engine running
- Battery voltage greater than 7 V

Possible fault cause

- Short circuit to ground in wiring
- DME control module

Affected terminals

Terminal III/28

Note!

Short to ground causes the fuel injector to be permanently open.

Diagnosis/troubleshooting

	Work instruction		Display OK	If not OK
1	Check fuel injector	• Remove connector of fuel injector 3 • Connect special tool V.A.G. 1315 A/1 • Measure resistance at special tool V.A.G. 1315 A/1	11 - 13 Ω (at 20 °C) ⇒ Step 2	Replace fuel injector → End
2	Check wiring harness for short to ground	• Connect special tool 9637 to wiring harness (DME control module plug) • Remove connector of fuel injector • Measure resistance between special tool 9637 Pin III/28 and ground	∞ Ω ⇒ Step 3	Repair wiring harness → End

PR1020100283010X

Fig. 64 Code P1226: Fuel Injector Cylinder No. 6, Below Limit (Part 1 of 2)

Diagnosis conditions

- Engine running
- Battery voltage greater than 7 V

Possible fault cause

- Short circuit to ground in wiring
- DME control module

Affected terminals

Terminal III/41

Note!

Short to ground causes the fuel injector to be permanently open.

Diagnosis/troubleshooting

	Work instruction		Display OK	If not OK
1	Check fuel injector	• Remove connector of fuel injector 3 • Connect special tool V.A.G. 1315 A/1 • Measure resistance at special tool V.A.G. 1315 A/1	11 - 13 Ω (at 20 °C) ⇒ Step 2	Replace fuel injector → End
2	Check wiring harness for short to ground	• Connect special tool 9637 to wiring harness (DME control module plug) • Remove connector of fuel injector • Measure resistance between special tool 9637 Pin III/41 and ground	∞ Ω ⇒ Step 3	Repair wiring harness → End

PR1020100282010X

Fig. 63 Code P1225: Fuel Injector Cylinder No. 1, Below Limit (Part 1 of 2)

	Work instruction		Display OK	If not OK
3	Replace DME control module		⇒ Step 4	
4	Perform adaptation	• Switch on the ignition • Wait one minute • Do not press the accelerator • Switch off the ignition for at least 10 seconds • Read out the fault memory	→ End	

PR1020100283020X

Fig. 64 Code P1226: Fuel Injector Cylinder No. 6, Below Limit (Part 2 of 2)

Diagnosis conditions

- Engine running
- Battery voltage greater than 7 V

Possible fault cause

- Short circuit to ground in wiring
- DME control module

Affected terminals

Terminal III/40

Note!

Short to ground causes the fuel injector to be permanently open.

Diagnosis/troubleshooting

Work instruction			Display OK	If not OK
1	Check fuel injector	• Remove connector of fuel injector 3 • Connect special tool V.A.G. 1315 A/1 • Measure resistance at special tool V.A.G. 1315 A/1	11 - 13 Ω (at 20 °C) ⇒ Step 2	Replace fuel injector → End
2	Check wiring harness for short to ground	• Connect special tool 9637 to wiring harness (DME control module plug) • Remove connector of fuel injector • Measure resistance between special tool 9637 Pin III/28 and ground	∞ Ω ⇒ Step 3	Repair wiring harness → End

PR1020100284010X

Fig. 65 Code P1227: Fuel Injector Cylinder No. 2, Below Limit (Part 1 of 2)

Diagnosis conditions

- Engine running
- Battery voltage greater than 7 V

Possible fault cause

- Short circuit to ground in wiring
- DME control module

Affected terminals

Terminal III/27

Note!

Short to ground causes the fuel injector to be permanently open.

Diagnosis/troubleshooting

Work instruction			Display OK	If not OK
1	Check fuel injector	• Remove connector of fuel injector 3 • Connect special tool V.A.G. 1315 A/1 • Measure resistance at special tool V.A.G. 1315 A/1	11 - 13 Ω (at 20 °C) ⇒ Step 2	Replace fuel injector → End
2	Check wiring harness for short to ground	• Connect special tool 9637 to wiring harness (DME control module plug) • Remove connector of fuel injector • Measure resistance between special tool 9637 Pin III/27 and ground	∞ Ω ⇒ Step 3	Repair wiring harness → End

PR1020100285010X

Fig. 66 Code P1228: Fuel Injector Cylinder No. 4, Below Limit (Part 1 of 2)

Work instruction			Display OK	If not OK
3	Replace DME control module		⇒ Step 4	
4	Perform adaptation	• Switch on the ignition • Wait one minute • Do not press the accelerator • Switch off the ignition for at least 10 seconds • Read out the fault memory	→ End	

PR1020100284020X

Fig. 65 Code P1227: Fuel Injector Cylinder No. 2, Below Limit (Part 2 of 2)

Work instruction			Display OK	If not OK
3	Replace DME control module		⇒ Step 4	
4	Perform adaptation	• Switch on the ignition • Wait one minute • Do not press the accelerator • Switch off the ignition for at least 10 seconds • Read out the fault memory	→ End	

PR1020100285020X

Fig. 66 Code P1228: Fuel Injector Cylinder No. 4, Below Limit (Part 2 of 2)

Diagnosis conditions

- Engine running
- Battery voltage greater than 7 V

Possible fault cause

- Short circuit to ground in wiring
- DME control module

Affected terminals

Terminal III/15

Note!

Short to ground causes the fuel injector to be permanently open.

Diagnosis/troubleshooting

Work instruction			Display OK	If not OK
1	Check fuel injector	• Remove connector of fuel injector 3 • Connect special tool V.A.G. 1315 A/1 • Measure resistance at special tool V.A.G. 1315 A/1	11 - 13 Ω (at 20 °C) ⇒ Step 2	Replace fuel injector → End
2	Check wiring harness for short to ground	• Connect special tool 9637 to wiring harness (DME control module plug) • Remove connector of fuel injector • Measure resistance between special tool 9637 Pin III/15 and ground	∞ Ω ⇒ Step 3	Repair wiring harness → End

PR1020100286010X

Fig. 67 Code P1229: Fuel Injector Cylinder No. 3, Below Limit (Part 1 of 2)

Work instruction			Display OK	If not OK
3	Replace DME control module		⇒ Step 4	
4	Perform adaptation	• Switch on the ignition • Wait one minute • Do not press the accelerator • Switch off the ignition for at least 10 seconds • Read out the fault memory	→ End	

PR1020100286020X

Fig. 67 Code P1229: Fuel Injector Cylinder No. 3, Below Limit (Part 2 of 2)

Diagnosis conditions

- Engine running
- Battery voltage greater than 7 V

Possible fault cause

- Short circuit to ground in wiring
- DME control module

Affected terminals

Terminal III/2

Note!

Short to ground causes the fuel injector to be permanently open.

Diagnosis/troubleshooting

Work instruction			Display OK	If not OK
1	Check fuel injector	• Remove connector of fuel injector 3 • Connect special tool V.A.G. 1315 A/1 • Measure resistance at special tool V.A.G. 1315 A/1	11 - 13 Ω (at 20 °C) ⇒ Step 2	Replace fuel injector → End
2	Check wiring harness for short to ground	• Connect special tool 9637 to wiring harness (DME control module plug) • Remove connector of fuel injector • Measure resistance between special tool 9637 Pin III/2 and ground	∞ Ω ⇒ Step 3	Repair wiring harness → End

PR1020100287010X

Fig. 68 Code P1230: Fuel Injector Cylinder No. 5, Below Limit (Part 1 of 2)

Diagnosis conditions

- Engine running
- Battery voltage greater than 7 V

Possible fault cause

- Fuel injector (coil) open circuit
- Open circuit in wiring
- DME control module

Affected terminals

Terminal III/41

Note!

Open circuit causes the fuel injector to be continually closed.

Diagnosis/troubleshooting

Work instruction			Display OK	If not OK
1	Check fuel injector	• Remove connector of fuel injector 3 • Connect special tool V.A.G. 1315 A/1 • Measure resistance at special tool V.A.G. 1315 A/1	11 - 13 Ω (at 20 °C) ⇒ Step 2	Replace fuel injector → End
2	Check wiring harness for open circuit	• Connect special tool 9637 to wiring harness (DME control module plug) • Remove connector of fuel injector • Measure resistance between special tool 9637 Pin III/41 and fuel injector plug Pin 2	0 - 5 Ω ⇒ Step 3	Repair wiring harness → End

PR1020100288010X

Fig. 69 Code P1237: Fuel Injector Cylinder No. 1, Open Circuit (Part 1 of 2)

Work instruction			Display OK	If not OK
3	Replace DME control module		⇒ Step 4	
4	Perform adaptation	• Switch on the ignition • Wait one minute • Do not press the accelerator • Switch off the ignition for at least 10 seconds • Read out the fault memory	→ End	

PR1020100287020X

Fig. 68 Code P1230: Fuel Injector Cylinder No. 5, Below Limit (Part 2 of 2)

Work instruction			Display OK	If not OK
3	Replace DME control module		⇒ Step 4	
4	Perform adaptation	• Switch on the ignition • Wait one minute • Do not press the accelerator • Switch off the ignition for at least 10 seconds • Read out the fault memory	→ End	

PR1020100288020X

Fig. 69 Code P1237: Fuel Injector Cylinder No. 1, Open Circuit (Part 2 of 2)

Diagnosis conditions

- Engine running
- Battery voltage greater than 7 V

Possible fault cause

- Fuel injector (coil) open circuit
- Open circuit in wiring
- DME control module

Affected terminals

Terminal III/28

Note!

Open circuit causes the fuel injector to be continually closed.

Diagnosis/troubleshooting

Work instruction			Display OK	If not OK
1	Check fuel injector	• Remove connector of fuel injector 3 • Connect special tool V.A.G. 1315 A/1 • Measure resistance at special tool V.A.G. 1315 A/1	11 - 13 Ω (at 20 °C) ⇒ Step 2	Replace fuel injector → End
2	Check wiring harness for open circuit	• Connect special tool 9637 to wiring harness (DME control module plug) • Remove connector of fuel injector • Measure resistance between special tool 9637 Pin III/28 and fuel injector plug Pin 2	0 - 5 Ω ⇒ Step 3	Repair wiring harness → End

PR1020100289010X

Fig. 70 Code P1238: Fuel Injector Cylinder No. 6, Open Circuit (Part 1 of 2)

Work instruction			Display OK	If not OK
3	Replace DME control module		⇒ Step 4	
4	Perform adaptation	• Switch on the ignition • Wait one minute • Do not press the accelerator • Switch off the ignition for at least 10 seconds • Read out the fault memory	→ End	

PR1020100289020X

Fig. 70 Code P1238: Fuel Injector Cylinder No. 6, Open Circuit (Part 2 of 2)

Diagnosis conditions

- Engine running
- Battery voltage greater than 7 V

Possible fault cause

- Fuel injector (coil) open circuit
- Open circuit in wiring
- DME control module

Affected terminals

Terminal III/40

Note!

Open circuit causes the fuel injector to be continually closed.

Diagnosis/troubleshooting

Work instruction			Display OK	If not OK
1	Check fuel injector	• Remove connector of fuel injector 3 • Connect special tool V.A.G. 1315 A/1 • Measure resistance at special tool V.A.G. 1315 A/1	11 - 13 Ω (at 20 °C) ⇒ Step 2	Replace fuel injector → End
2	Check wiring harness for open circuit	• Connect special tool 9637 to wiring harness (DME control module plug) • Remove connector of fuel injector • Measure resistance between special tool 9637 Pin III/40 and fuel injector plug Pin 2	0 - 5 Ω ⇒ Step 3	Repair wiring harness → End

PR1020100290010X

Fig. 71 Code P1239: Fuel Injector Cylinder No. 2, Open Circuit (Part 1 of 2)

Diagnosis conditions

- Engine running
- Battery voltage greater than 7 V

Possible fault cause

- Fuel injector (coil) open circuit
- Open circuit in wiring
- DME control module

Affected terminals

Terminal III/27

Note!

Open circuit causes the fuel injector to be continually closed.

Diagnosis/troubleshooting

Work instruction			Display OK	If not OK
1	Check fuel injector	• Remove connector of fuel injector 3 • Connect special tool V.A.G. 1315 A/1 • Measure resistance at special tool V.A.G. 1315 A/1	11 - 13 Ω (at 20 °C) ⇒ Step 2	Replace fuel injector → End
2	Check wiring harness for open circuit	• Connect special tool 9637 to wiring harness (DME control module plug) • Remove connector of fuel injector • Measure resistance between special tool 9637 Pin III/27 and fuel injector plug Pin 2	0 - 5 Ω ⇒ Step 3	Repair wiring harness → End

PR1020100291010X

Fig. 72 Code P1240: Fuel Injector Cylinder No. 4, Open Circuit (Part 1 of 2)

Work instruction			Display OK	If not OK
3	Replace DME control module			⇒ Step 4
4	Perform adaptation	• Switch on the ignition • Wait one minute • Do not press the accelerator • Switch off the ignition for at least 10 seconds • Read out the fault memory	→ End	

PR1020100290020X

Fig. 71 Code P1239: Fuel Injector Cylinder No. 2, Open Circuit (Part 2 of 2)

Work instruction			Display OK	If not OK
3	Replace DME control module		⇒ Step 4	
4	Perform adaptation	• Switch on the ignition • Wait one minute • Do not press the accelerator • Switch off the ignition for at least 10 seconds • Read out the fault memory	→ End	

PR1020100291020X

Fig. 72 Code P1240: Fuel Injector Cylinder No. 4, Open Circuit (Part 2 of 2)

Diagnosis conditions

- Engine running
- Battery voltage greater than 7 V

Possible fault cause

- Fuel injector (coil) open circuit
- Open circuit in wiring
- DME control module

Affected terminals

Terminal III/15

Note!

Open circuit causes the fuel injector to be continually closed.

Diagnosis/troubleshooting

Work instruction			Display OK	If not OK
1	Check fuel injector	• Remove connector of fuel injector 3 • Connect special tool V.A.G. 1315 A/1 • Measure resistance at special tool V.A.G. 1315 A/1	11 - 13 Ω (at 20 °C) ⇒ Step 2	Replace fuel injector → End
2	Check wiring harness for open circuit	• Connect special tool 9637 to wiring harness (DME control module plug) • Remove connector of fuel injector • Measure resistance between special tool 9637 Pin III/15 and fuel injector plug Pin 2	0 - 5 Ω ⇒ Step 3	Repair wiring harness → End

PR1020100292010X

Fig. 73 Code P1241: Fuel Injector Cylinder No. 3, Open Circuit (Part 1 of 2)

Work instruction			Display OK	If not OK
3	Replace DME control module		⇒ Step 4	
4	Perform adaptation	• Switch on the ignition • Wait one minute • Do not press the accelerator • Switch off the ignition for at least 10 seconds • Read out the fault memory	→ End	

PR1020100292020X

Fig. 73 Code P1241: Fuel Injector Cylinder No. 3, Open Circuit (Part 2 of 2)

Diagnosis conditions

- Engine running
- Battery voltage greater than 7 V

Possible fault cause

- Fuel injector (coil) open circuit
- Open circuit in wiring
- DME control module

Affected terminals

Terminal III/2

Note!

Open circuit causes the fuel injector to be continually closed.

Diagnosis/troubleshooting

Work instruction			Display OK	If not OK
1	Check fuel injector	♦ Remove connector of fuel injector 3 ♦ Connect special tool V.A.G. 1315 A/1 ♦ Measure resistance at special tool V.A.G. 1315 A/1	11 - 13 Ω (at 20 °C) ⇒ Step 2	Replace fuel injector → End
2	Check wiring harness for open circuit	♦ Connect special tool 9637 to wiring harness (DME control module plug) ♦ Remove connector of fuel injector ♦ Measure resistance between special tool 9637 Pin III/2 and fuel injector plug Pin 2	0 - 5 Ω ⇒ Step 3	Repair wiring harness → End

PR1020100293010X

Fig. 74 Code P1242: Fuel Injector Cylinder No. 5, Open Circuit (Part 1 of 2)

Diagnosis conditions

- Ignition on

Possible fault cause

- Airbag control module
- Open circuit
- Short circuit to ground

Affected terminals

Terminal 34 and IV/16

Diagnosis/troubleshooting

Work instruction			Display OK	If not OK
1	Check wiring from airbag control module to DME control module for continuity	♦ Connect special tool 9637 to wiring harness (DME control module plug) ♦ Remove connector of airbag control module ♦ Measure resistance between special tool 9637 Pin IV/16 and airbag plug Pin 34	0 - 5 Ω ⇒ Step 2	Check disconnection point X2/5 or check wiring harness for chafing and pinching damage → End

PR1020100294010X

Fig. 75 Code P1265: Air Bag Signal, Signal Implausible (Part 1 of 3)

Oscilloscope display: ►

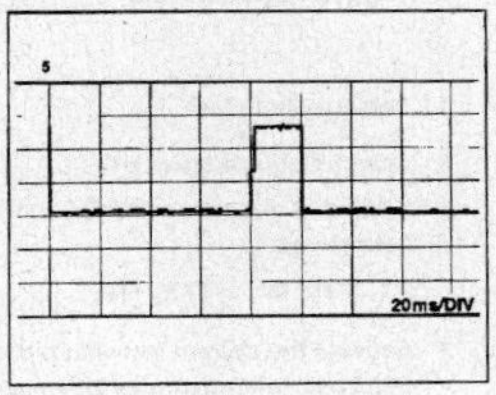

Work instruction		Display OK	If not OK
4	Erase fault memory	→ End	→ End

PR1020100294030X

Fig. 75 Code P1265: Air Bag Signal, Signal Implausible (Part 3 of 3)

Work instruction			Display OK	If not OK
3	Replace DME control module		⇒ Step 4	
4	Perform adaptation	♦ Switch on the ignition ♦ Wait one minute ♦ Do not press the accelerator ♦ Switch off the ignition for at least 10 seconds ♦ Read out the fault memory	→ End	

PR1020100293020X

Fig. 74 Code P1242: Fuel Injector Cylinder No. 5, Open Circuit (Part 2 of 2)

Airbag control module: ►

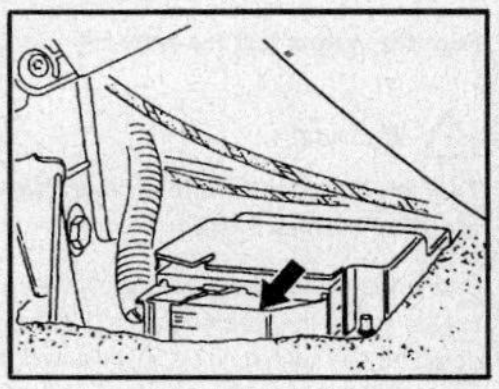

Work instruction			Display OK	If not OK
2	Check wiring from airbag control module to DME control module for short circuit to ground	♦ Connect special tool 9637 to wiring harness (DME control module plug) ♦ Remove connector of airbag control module ♦ Measure resistance between special tool 9637 Pin IV/16 and ground	∞ Ω ⇒ Step 3	Repair wiring harness → End
3	Check signal from airbag control module	♦ Connect special tool 9637 ♦ Connect engine tester (oscilloscope) to Pin IV/16 and ground ♦ Use special input ♦ Ignition on	⇒ Step 4	Replace airbag control module →

PR1020100294020X

Fig. 75 Code P1265: Air Bag Signal, Signal Implausible (Part 2 of 3)

Diagnosis conditions

- Engine speed > 1,120 rpm

Possible fault cause

- DME control module faulty

Affected terminals

Diagnosis/troubleshooting

Work instruction			Display OK	If not OK
1	Replace DME control module		⇒ Step 2	
2	Perform adaptation	♦ Switch on the ignition ♦ Wait one minute ♦ Do not press the accelerator ♦ Switch off the ignition for at least 10 seconds ♦ Read out the fault memory	→ End	→ End

PR1020100295000X

Fig. 76 Code P1266: Fuel Shutoff Function Monitor, Signal Implausible

Diagnosis conditions

- Speed between 5,280 and 6,520 rpm
- Load between 125 and 190 %
- Acceleration with wide-open throttle

Possible fault cause

- A valve does not switch to large lift
- Several valves (various cylinders) do not switch to large lift

Affected terminals

Diagnosis/troubleshooting

Perform system test for large lift

⚠ **Warning!**

Test is carried out while driving. Have a second person operate the Porsche System Tester 2.

During the system test for large lift, the valves remain at large lift, regardless of the type of driving. Faulty switching conditions can be detected by rough running, just like with misfire detection. If a valve is not switched to large lift, the fault type 'over limit' is recorded.

Several cylinders may be stored as faulty, although only 1 valve on one cylinder is faulty.

In order to guarantee safety during repairs, the flat-base tappets of the inlet valves of the entire cylinder bank should be replaced if a fault occurs.

A faulty flat-base tappet can be detected because the oxygen sensor F_R for this cylinder bank does not change the mixture at all given acceleration with wide-open throttle (F_R at 1) and enriches the mixture in the opposite cylinder bank ($F_R > 1$)⇒ see drawing below. Given a difference between F_{R1} and F_{R2} of more than 8 %, a fault is certainly present.

PR1020100296010X

Fig. 77 Code P1350: Valve Lift Control Checksum Error (Part 1 of 9)

If the difference is less than 4 %, 1 valve may be faulty on both cylinder banks. In this case, all flat-base tappets of the inlet valves must be replaced.

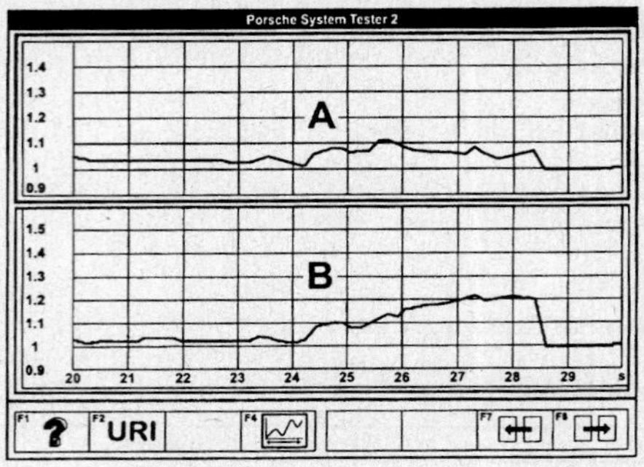

A - **Oxygen sensor, bank 1**
B - **Oxygen sensor, bank 2**

1 - **Select system test.**
2 - **Select 'Request large lift'.**
   If "Valve diagnosis not ready" appears, a fault may have been stored.
   1. Erase the fault memory.
3 - **Activate the system test with the key** F8 **immediately before acceleration with wide-open throttle.**
   The message "Drive link active" then appears.
4 - **Perform acceleration with wide-open throttle in 2nd gear, until "Valve lift diagnosis complete" appears.**

PR1020100296020X

Fig. 77 Code P1350: Valve Lift Control Checksum Error (Part 2 of 9)

Note!

- *If a fault is detected, it is only recorded in the fault memory after 6,000 ignitions (at idling speed approx. 3 minutes waiting time).*
- *It is important to observe the oxygen sensor during acceleration with wide-open throttle or to record its behaviour with the data logger.*
- *If misfires are stored, diagnose misfires.*

Diagnosis conditions

- Speed between 2,000 and 3,320 rpm
- Load between 45 and 70 %
- Acceleration with wide-open throttle

Possible fault cause

- A valve does not switch to small lift
- Several valves (various cylinders) do not switch to small lift

Affected terminals

Diagnosis/troubleshooting

Perform system test for small lift

⚠ **Warning!**

Test is carried out while driving. Have a second person operate the Porsche System Tester 2.

During the system test for small lift, the valves remain at small lift, regardless of the type of driving. Faulty switching conditions can be detected by rough running, just like with misfire detection. If a valve is not switched to small lift, the fault type 'under limit' is recorded.

Several cylinders may be stored as faulty, although only 1 valve on one cylinder is faulty.

In order to guarantee safety during repairs, the flat-base tappets of the inlet valves of the entire cylinder bank should be replaced if a fault occurs.

PR1020100296030X

Fig. 77 Code P1350: Valve Lift Control Checksum Error (Part 3 of 9)

A faulty flat-base tappet can be detected because the oxygen sensor F_R for this cylinder bank enriches the mixture ($F_R > 1$) during acceleration with wide-open throttle ⇒ see drawing below. Difference from the other oxygen sensor > approx. 15 %. In the case of a fault, the flat-base tappets of the inlet valves for the entire cylinder bank must be replaced.

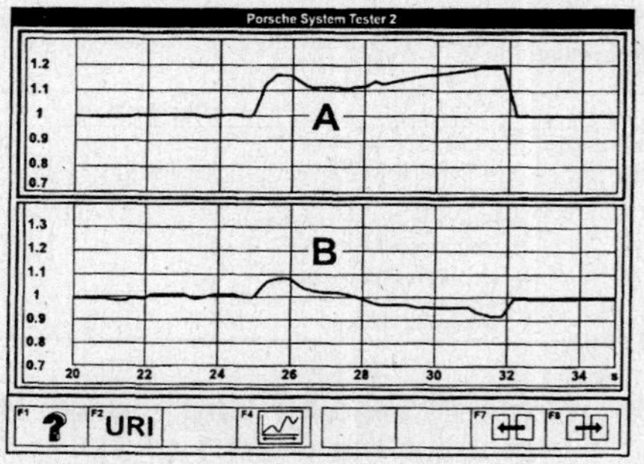

A - **Oxygen sensor, bank 1**
B - **Oxygen sensor, bank 2**

1 - **Select system test.**
2 - **Select 'Request small lift'.**
   If "Valve lift diagnosis not ready" appears, a fault may have been stored.
   1. Erase the fault memory.
3 - **Activate the system test with the key** F8 **immediately before acceleration with wide-open throttle.**
   The message "Drive link active" then appears.

Note!

If 'Request small lift' appears, the valves remain at small lift, ie. the performance is reduced dramatically.

PR1020100296040X

Fig. 77 Code P1350: Valve Lift Control Checksum Error (Part 4 of 9)

4 - Perform acceleration with wide-open throttle in 2nd gear, until "Valve lift diagnosis complete" (max. 4,000 rpm) appears.

If misfires are stored, perform the system test again.

Note!

- *If a fault is detected, it is only recorded in the fault memory after 6,000 ignitions (at idling speed approx. 3 minutes waiting time).*
- *It is important to observe the oxygen sensor during acceleration with wide-open throttle or to record its behaviour with the data logger.*

- signal implau sible

Diagnosis conditions

- Speed between 2,000 and 3,320 rpm and between 5,280 and 6,520 rpm
- Load between 45 and 70 % and between 125 and 190 %
- Acceleration with wide-open throttle

Possible fault cause

- A valve does not switch to large lift
- Several valves (various cylinders) do not switch to large lift

and

- A valve does not switch to small lift
- Several valves (various cylinders) do not switch to small lift

Affected terminals

Diagnosis/troubleshooting

Perform system test for large lift

Warning!

Test is carried out while driving. Have a second person operate the Porsche System Tester 2.

PR1020100296050X

Fig. 77 Code P1350: Valve Lift Control Checksum Error (Part 5 of 9)

During the system test for large lift, the valves remain at large lift, regardless of the type of driving. Faulty switching conditions can be detected by rough running, just like with misfire detection. If a valve is not switched to large lift, the fault type 'over limit' is recorded.

Several cylinders may be stored as faulty, although only 1 valve on one cylinder is faulty.

In order to guarantee safety during repairs, the flat-base tappets of the inlet valves of the entire cylinder bank should be replaced if a fault occurs.

A faulty flat-base tappet can be detected because the oxygen sensor F_R for this cylinder bank does not change the mixture at all given acceleration with wide-open throttle (F_R at 1) and enriches the mixture in the opposite cylinder bank ($F_R > 1$)⇒ see drawing below. Given a difference between F_{R1} and F_{R2} of more than 8 %, a fault is certainly present.

If the difference is less than 4 %, 1 valve may be faulty on both cylinder banks. In this case, all flat-base tappets of the inlet valves must be replaced.

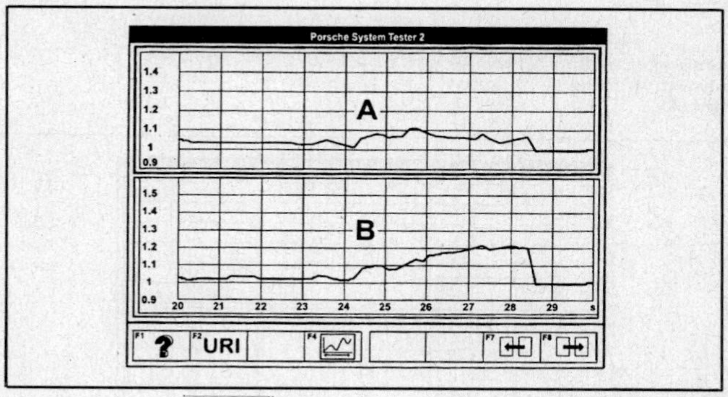

PR1020100296060X

Fig. 77 Code P1350: Valve Lift Control Checksum Error (Part 6 of 9)

A - Oxygen sensor, bank 1
B - Oxygen sensor, bank 2

1 - Select system test.

2 - Select 'Request large lift'.

If "Valve diagnosis not ready" appears, a fault may have been stored.

1. Erase the fault memory.

3 - Activate the system test with the key F8 immediately before acceleration with wide-open throttle.

The message "Drive link active" then appears.

4 - Perform acceleration with wide-open throttle in 2nd gear, until "Valve lift diagnosis complete" appears.

Note!

- *If a fault is detected, it is only recorded in the fault memory after 6,000 ignitions (at idling speed approx. 3 minutes waiting time).*
- *It is important to observe the oxygen sensor during acceleration with wide-open throttle or to record its behaviour with the data logger.*

Perform system test for small lift

Warning!

Test is carried out while driving. Have a second person operate the Porsche System Tester 2.

During the system test for small lift, the valves remain at small lift, regardless of the type of driving. Faulty switching conditions can be detected by rough running, just like with misfire detection. If a valve is not switched to small lift, the fault type 'under limit' is recorded.

Several cylinders may be stored as faulty, although only 1 valve on one cylinder is faulty.

In order to guarantee safety during repairs, the flat-base tappets of the inlet valves of the entire cylinder bank should be replaced if a fault occurs.

A faulty flat-base tappet can be detected because the oxygen sensor F_R for this cylinder bank enriches the mixture ($F_R > 1$) during acceleration with wide-open throttle ⇒ see drawing below. Difference from the other oxygen sensor > approx. 15 %. In the case of a fault, the flat-base tappets of the inlet valves for the entire cylinder bank must be replaced.

PR1020100296070X

Fig. 77 Code P1350: Valve Lift Control Checksum Error (Part 7 of 9)

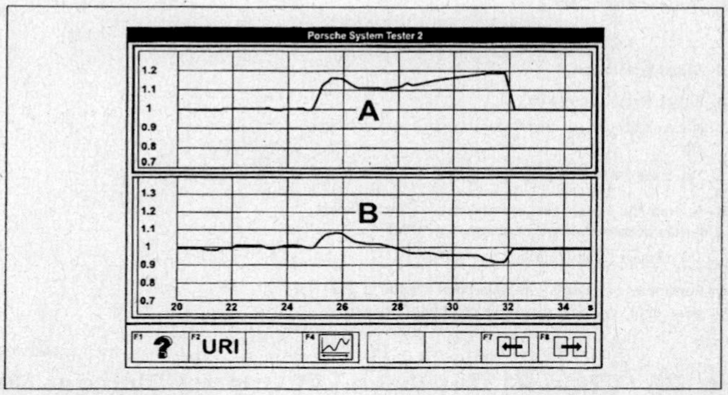

A - Oxygen sensor, bank 1
B - Oxygen sensor, bank 2

1 - Select system test.

2 - Select 'Request small lift'.

If "Valve lift diagnosis not ready" appears, a fault may have been stored.

1. Erase the fault memory.

3 - Activate the system test with the key F8 immediately before acceleration with wide-open throttle.

The message "Drive link active" then appears.

Note!

If 'Request small lift' appears, the valves remain at small lift, ie. the performance is reduced dramatically.

4 - Perform acceleration with wide-open throttle in 2nd gear, until "Valve lift diagnosis complete" (max. 4,000 rpm) appears.

PR1020100296080X

Fig. 77 Code P1350: Valve Lift Control Checksum Error (Part 8 of 9)

If misfires are stored, perform the system test again.

Note!

- *If a fault is detected, it is only recorded in the fault memory after 6,000 ignitions (at idling speed approx. 3 minutes waiting time).*
- *It is important to observe the oxygen sensor during acceleration with wide-open throttle or to record its behaviour with the data logger.*

PR1020100296090X

Fig. 77 Code P1350: Valve Lift Control Checksum Error (Part 9 of 9)

If the difference is less than 4 %, 1 valve may be faulty on both cylinder banks. In this case, all flat-base tappets of the inlet valves must be replaced.

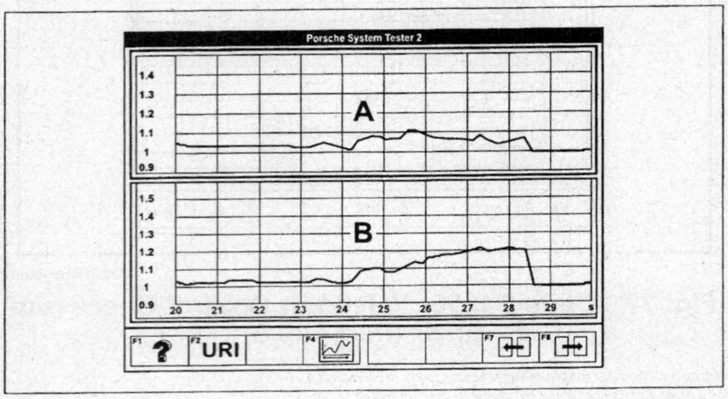

A - Oxygen sensor, bank 1
B - Oxygen sensor, bank 2

1 - Select system test.

2 - Select 'Request large lift'.

If "Valve diagnosis not ready" appears, a fault may have been stored.

1. Erase the fault memory.

3 - Activate the system test with the key F8 immediately before acceleration with wide-open throttle.

The message "Drive link active" then appears.

4 - Perform acceleration with wide-open throttle in 2nd gear, until "Valve lift diagnosis complete" appears.

PR1020100297020X

Fig. 78 Code P1351: Valve Lift Control Cylinder No. 1, Above Limit (Part 2 of 9)

Diagnosis conditions

- Speed between 5,280 and 6,520 rpm
- Load between 125 and 190 %
- Acceleration with wide-open throttle

Possible fault cause

- A valve does not switch to large lift
- Several valves (various cylinders) do not switch to large lift

Affected terminals

Diagnosis/troubleshooting

Perform system test for large lift

Warning!

Test is carried out while driving. Have a second person operate the Porsche System Tester 2.

During the system test for large lift, the valves remain at large lift, regardless of the type of driving. Faulty switching conditions can be detected by rough running, just like with misfire detection. If a valve is not switched to large lift, the fault type 'over limit' is recorded.

Several cylinders may be stored as faulty, although only 1 valve on one cylinder is faulty.

In order to guarantee safety during repairs, the flat-base tappets of the inlet valves of the entire cylinder bank should be replaced if a fault occurs.

A faulty flat-base tappet can be detected because the oxygen sensor F_R for this cylinder bank hardly changes the mixture at all given acceleration with wide-open throttle (F_R at 1) and enriches the mixture in the opposite cylinder bank ($F_R > 1$)⇒ see drawing below. Given a difference between F_{R1} and F_{R2} of more than 8 % during acceleration with wide-open throttle, a fault is certainly present.

PR1020100297010X

Fig. 78 Code P1351: Valve Lift Control Cylinder No. 1, Above Limit (Part 1 of 9)

Note!

- *If a fault is detected, it is only recorded in the fault memory after 6,000 ignitions (at idling speed approx. 3 minutes waiting time).*
- *It is important to observe the oxygen sensor during acceleration with wide-open throttle or to record its behaviour with the data logger.*
- *If misfires are stored, diagnose misfire.*

below limit

Diagnosis conditions

- Speed between 2,000 and 3,320 rpm
- Load between 45 and 70 %
- Acceleration with wide-open throttle

Possible fault cause

- A valve does not switch to small lift
- Several valves (various cylinders) do not switch to small lift

Affected terminals

Diagnosis/troubleshooting

Perform system test for small lift

Warning!

Test is carried out while driving. Have a second person operate the Porsche System Tester 2.

During the system test for small lift, the valves remain at small lift, regardless of the type of driving. Faulty switching conditions can be detected by rough running, just like with misfire detection. If a valve is not switched to small lift, the fault type 'under limit' is recorded.

Several cylinders may be stored as faulty, although only 1 valve on one cylinder is faulty.

In order to guarantee safety during repairs, the flat-base tappets of the inlet valves of the entire cylinder bank should be replaced if a fault occurs.

PR1020100297030X

Fig. 78 Code P1351: Valve Lift Control Cylinder No. 1, Above Limit (Part 3 of 9)

A faulty flat-base tappet can be detected because the oxygen sensor F_R for this cylinder bank enriches the mixture (F_R > 1) during acceleration with wide-open throttle ⇒ see drawing below. Difference from the other oxygen sensor > approx. 15 %. In the case of a fault, the flat-base tappets of the inlet valves for the entire cylinder bank must be replaced.

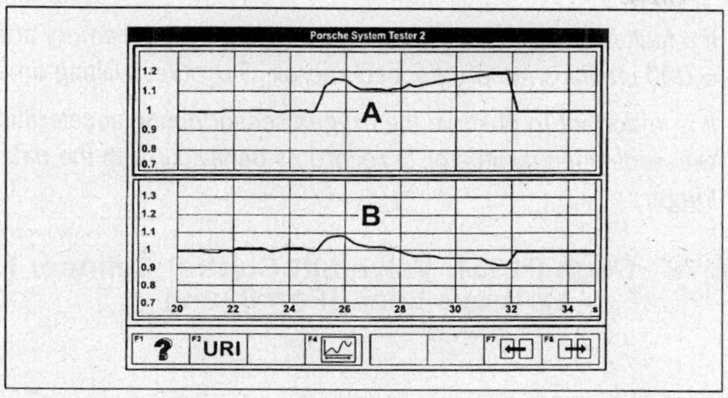

A - Oxygen sensor, bank 1
B - Oxygen sensor, bank 2

1 - Select system test.

2 - Select 'Request small lift'.

If "Valve lift diagnosis not ready" appears, a fault may have been stored.

1. Erase the fault memory.

3 - Activate the system test with the key (F8) immediately before acceleration with wide-open throttle.

The message "Drive link active" then appears.

Note!

If 'Request small lift' appears, the valves remain at small lift, ie. the performance is reduced dramatically.

PR1020100297040X

Fig. 78 Code P1351: Valve Lift Control Cylinder No. 1, Above Limit (Part 4 of 9)

4 - Perform acceleration with wide-open throttle in 2nd gear, until "Valve lift diagnosis complete" (max. 4,000 rpm) appears.

At speeds above 4,000 rpm, misfires may be stored. Delete the fault memory and repeat the test.

Note!

- *If a fault is detected, it is only recorded in the fault memory after 6,000 ignitions (at idling speed approx. 3 minutes waiting time).*
- *It is important to observe the oxygen sensor during acceleration with wide-open throttle or to record its behaviour with the data logger.*

signal implausible

Diagnosis conditions

- Speed between 2,000 and 3,320 rpm and between 5,280 and 6,520 rpm
- Load between 45 and 70 % and between 125 and 190 %
- Acceleration with wide-open throttle

Possible fault cause

- A valve does not switch to large lift
- Several valves (various cylinders) do not switch to large lift

and

- A valve does not switch to small lift
- Several valves (various cylinders) do not switch to small lift

Affected terminals

Diagnosis/troubleshooting

Perform system test for large lift

Warning!

Test is carried out while driving. Have a second person operate the Porsche System Tester 2.

PR1020100297050X

Fig. 78 Code P1351: Valve Lift Control Cylinder No. 1, Above Limit (Part 5 of 9)

During the system test for large lift, the valves remain at large lift, regardless of the type of driving. Faulty switching conditions can be detected by rough running, just like with misfire detection. If a valve is not switched to large lift, the fault type 'over limit' is recorded.

Several cylinders may be stored as faulty, although only 1 valve on one cylinder is faulty.

In order to guarantee safety during repairs, the flat-base tappets of the inlet valves of the entire cylinder bank should be replaced if a fault occurs.

A faulty flat-base tappet can be detected because the oxygen sensor F_R for this cylinder bank hardly changes the mixture at all given acceleration with wide-open throttle (F_R at 1) and enriches the mixture in the opposite cylinder bank (F_R > 1)⇒ see drawing below. Given a difference between F_{R1} and F_{R2} of more than 8 % during acceleration with wide-open throttle, a fault is certainly present.

If the difference is less than 4 %, 1 valve may be faulty on both cylinder banks. In this case, all flat-base tappets of the inlet valves must be replaced.

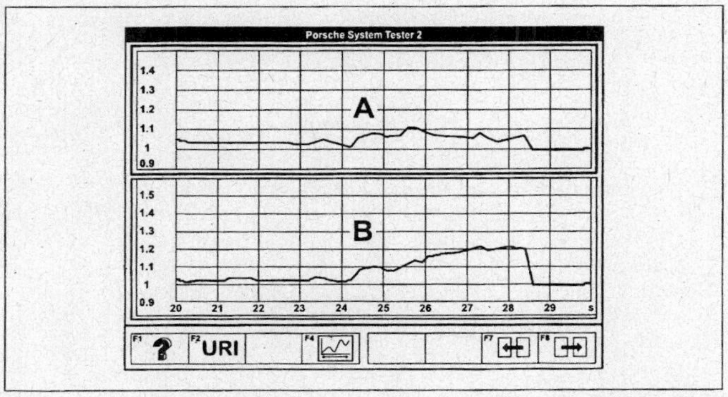

PR1020100297060X

Fig. 78 Code P1351: Valve Lift Control Cylinder No. 1, Above Limit (Part 6 of 9)

A - Oxygen sensor, bank 1
B - Oxygen sensor, bank 2

1 - Select system test.

2 - Select 'Request large lift'.

If "Valve diagnosis not ready" appears, a fault may have been stored.

1. Erase the fault memory.

3 - Activate the system test with the key (F8) immediately before acceleration with wide-open throttle.

The message "Drive link active" then appears.

4 - Perform acceleration with wide-open throttle in 2nd gear, until "Valve lift diagnosis complete" appears.

Note!

- *If a fault is detected, it is only recorded in the fault memory after 6,000 ignitions (at idling speed approx. 3 minutes waiting time).*
- *It is important to observe the oxygen sensor during acceleration with wide-open throttle or to record its behaviour with the data logger.*
- *If misfires are stored, diagnose misfires.*

Perform system test for small lift

Warning!

Test is carried out while driving. Have a second person operate the Porsche System Tester 2.

During the system test for small lift, the valves remain at small lift, regardless of the type of driving. Faulty switching conditions can be detected by rough running, just like with misfire detection. If a valve is not switched to small lift, the fault type 'under limit' is recorded.

Several cylinders may be stored as faulty, although only 1 valve on one cylinder is faulty.

In order to guarantee safety during repairs, the flat-base tappets of the inlet valves of the entire cylinder bank should be replaced if a fault occurs.

A faulty flat-base tappet can be detected because the oxygen sensor F_R for this cylinder bank enriches the mixture (F_R > 1) during

PR1020100297070X

Fig. 78 Code P1351: Valve Lift Control Cylinder No. 1, Above Limit (Part 7 of 9)

acceleration with wide-open throttle ⇒ see drawing below. Difference from the other oxygen sensor > approx. 15 %. In the case of a fault, the flat-base tappets of the inlet valves for the entire cylinder bank must be replaced.

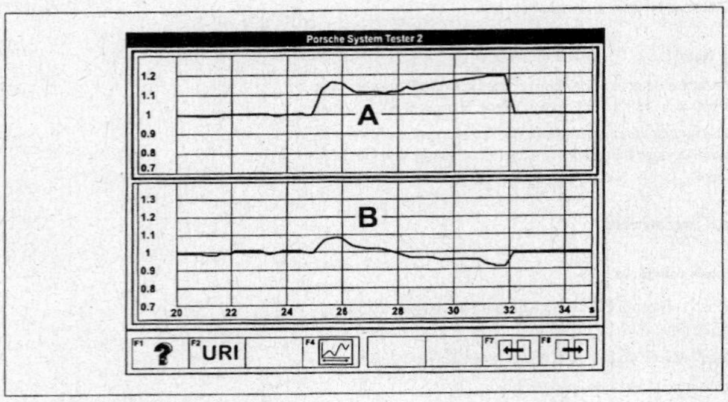

A - Oxygen sensor, bank 1
B - Oxygen sensor, bank 2

1 - Select system test.

2 - Select 'Request small lift'.

If "Valve lift diagnosis not ready" appears, a fault may have been stored.

1. Erase the fault memory.

3 - Activate the system test with the key [F8] immediately before acceleration with wide-open throttle.

The message "Drive link active" then appears.

Note!

If 'Request small lift' appears, the valves remain at small lift, ie. the performance is reduced dramatically.

4 - Perform acceleration with wide-open throttle in 2nd gear, until "Valve lift diagnosis complete" (max. 4,000 rpm) appears.

PR1020100297080X

Fig. 78 Code P1351: Valve Lift Control Cylinder No. 1, Above Limit (Part 8 of 9)

above limit

Diagnosis conditions

- Speed between 5,280 and 6,520 rpm
- Load between 125 and 190 %
- Acceleration with wide-open throttle

Possible fault cause

- A valve does not switch to large lift
- Several valves (various cylinders) do not switch to large lift

Affected terminals

-

Diagnosis/troubleshooting

Perform system test for large lift

Warning!

Test is carried out while driving. Have a second person operate the Porsche System Tester 2.

During the system test for large lift, the valves remain at large lift, regardless of the type of driving. Faulty switching conditions can be detected by rough running, just like with misfire detection. If a valve is not switched to large lift, the fault type 'over limit' is recorded.

Several cylinders may be stored as faulty, although only 1 valve on one cylinder is faulty.

In order to guarantee safety during repairs, the flat-base tappets of the inlet valves of the entire cylinder bank should be replaced if a fault occurs.

A faulty flat-base tappet can be detected because the oxygen sensor F_R for this cylinder bank hardly changes the mixture at all given acceleration with wide-open throttle (F_R at 1) and enriches the mixture in the opposite cylinder bank ($F_R > 1$)⇒ see drawing below. Given a difference between F_{R1} and F_{R2} of more than 8 % during acceleration with wide-open throttle, a fault is certainly present.

PR1020100298010X

Fig. 79 Code P1352: Valve Lift Control Cylinder No. 6, Above Limit (Part 1 of 9)

At speeds above 4,000 rpm, misfires may be stored. Delete the fault memory and repeat the test.

Note!

- *If a fault is detected, it is only recorded in the fault memory after 6,000 ignitions (at idling speed approx. 3 minutes waiting time).*
- *It is important to observe the oxygen sensor during acceleration with wide-open throttle or to record its behaviour with the data logger.*

PR1020100297090X

Fig. 78 Code P1351: Valve Lift Control Cylinder No. 1, Above Limit (Part 9 of 9)

If the difference is less than 4 %, 1 valve may be faulty on both cylinder banks. In this case, all flat-base tappets of the inlet valves must be replaced.

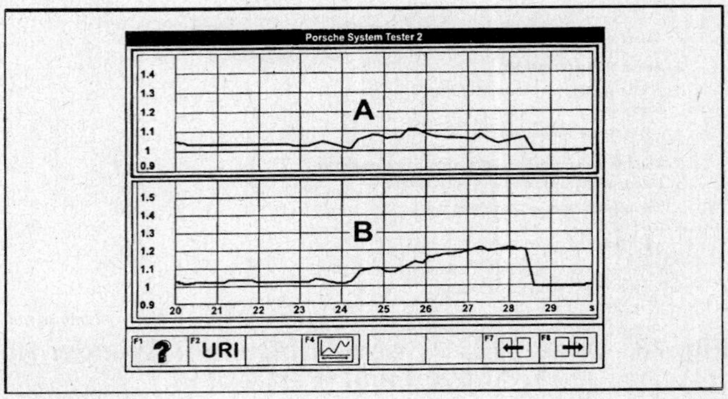

A - Oxygen sensor, bank 1
B - Oxygen sensor, bank 2

1 - Select system test.

2 - Select 'Request large lift'.

If "Valve diagnosis not ready" appears, a fault may have been stored.

1. Erase the fault memory.

3 - Activate the system test with the key [F8] immediately before acceleration with wide-open throttle.

The message "Drive link active" then appears.

4 - Perform acceleration with wide-open throttle in 2nd gear, until "Valve lift diagnosis complete" appears.

PR1020100298020X

Fig. 79 Code P1352: Valve Lift Control Cylinder No. 6, Above Limit (Part 2 of 9)

Note!

- *If a fault is detected, it is only recorded in the fault memory after 6,000 ignitions (at idling speed approx. 3 minutes waiting time).*
- *It is important to observe the oxygen sensor during acceleration with wide-open throttle or to record its behaviour with the data logger.*
- *If misfires are stored, diagnose misfire.*

below limit

Diagnosis conditions

- Speed between 2,000 and 3,320 rpm
- Load between 45 and 70 %
- Acceleration with wide-open throttle

Possible fault cause

- A valve does not switch to small lift
- Several valves (various cylinders) do not switch to small lift

Affected terminals

Diagnosis/troubleshooting

Perform system test for small lift

Warning!

Test is carried out while driving. Have a second person operate the Porsche System Tester 2.

During the system test for small lift, the valves remain at small lift, regardless of the type of driving. Faulty switching conditions can be detected by rough running, just like with misfire detection. If a valve is not switched to small lift, the fault type 'under limit' is recorded.

Several cylinders may be stored as faulty, although only 1 valve on one cylinder is faulty.

In order to guarantee safety during repairs, the flat-base tappets of the inlet valves of the entire cylinder bank should be replaced if a fault occurs.

PR1020100298030X

Fig. 79 Code P1352: Valve Lift Control Cylinder No. 6, Above Limit (Part 3 of 9)

A faulty flat-base tappet can be detected because the oxygen sensor F_R for this cylinder bank enriches the mixture ($F_R > 1$) during acceleration with wide-open throttle ⇒ see drawing below. Difference from the other oxygen sensor > approx. 15 %. In the case of a fault, the flat-base tappets of the inlet valves for the entire cylinder bank must be replaced.

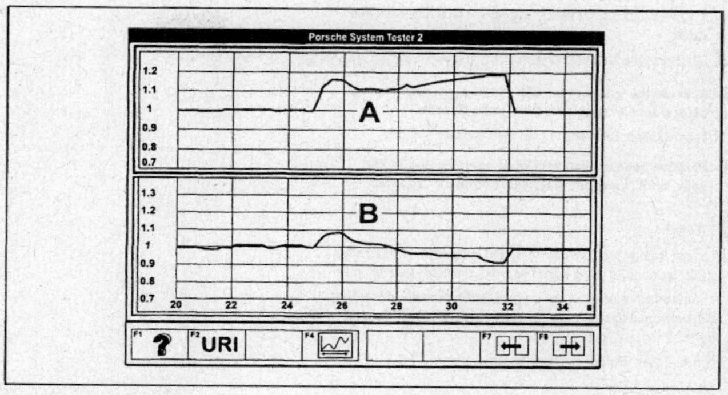

A - Oxygen sensor, bank 1
B - Oxygen sensor, bank 2

1 - Select system test.

2 - Select 'Request small lift'.

If 'Valve lift diagnosis not ready' appears, a fault may have been stored.

1. Erase the fault memory.

3 - Activate the system test with the key F8 immediately before acceleration with wide-open throttle.

The message "Drive link active" then appears.

Note!

If 'Request small lift' appears, the valves remain at small lift, ie. the performance is reduced dramatically.

PR1020100298040X

Fig. 79 Code P1352: Valve Lift Control Cylinder No. 6, Above Limit (Part 4 of 9)

4 - Perform acceleration with wide-open throttle in 2nd gear, until "Valve lift diagnosis complete" (max. 4,000 rpm) appears.

At speeds above 4,000 rpm, misfires may be stored. Delete the fault memory and repeat the test.

Note!

- *If a fault is detected, it is only recorded in the fault memory after 6,000 ignitions (at idling speed approx. 3 minutes waiting time).*
- *It is important to observe the oxygen sensor during acceleration with wide-open throttle or to record its behaviour with the data logger.*

signal implausible

Diagnosis conditions

- Speed between 2,000 and 3,320 rpm and between 5,280 and 6,520 rpm
- Load between 45 and 70 % and between 125 and 190 %
- Acceleration with wide-open throttle

Possible fault cause

- A valve does not switch to large lift
- Several valves (various cylinders) do not switch to large lift

and

- A valve does not switch to small lift
- Several valves (various cylinders) do not switch to small lift

Affected terminals

Diagnosis/troubleshooting

Perform system test for large lift

Warning!

Test is carried out while driving. Have a second person operate the Porsche System Tester 2.

PR1020100298050X

Fig. 79 Code P1352: Valve Lift Control Cylinder No. 6, Above Limit (Part 5 of 9)

During the system test for large lift, the valves remain at large lift, regardless of the type of driving. Faulty switching conditions can be detected by rough running, just like with misfire detection. If a valve is not switched to large lift, the fault type 'over limit' is recorded.

Several cylinders may be stored as faulty, although only 1 valve on one cylinder is faulty.

In order to guarantee safety during repairs, the flat-base tappets of the inlet valves of the entire cylinder bank should be replaced if a fault occurs.

A faulty flat-base tappet can be detected because the oxygen sensor F_R for this cylinder bank hardly changes the mixture at all given acceleration with wide-open throttle (F_R at 1) and enriches the mixture in the opposite cylinder bank ($F_R > 1$)⇒ see drawing below. Given a difference between F_{R1} and F_{R2} of more than 8 % during acceleration with wide-open throttle, a fault is certainly present.

If the difference is less than 4 %, 1 valve may be faulty on both cylinder banks. In this case, all flat-base tappets of the inlet valves must be replaced.

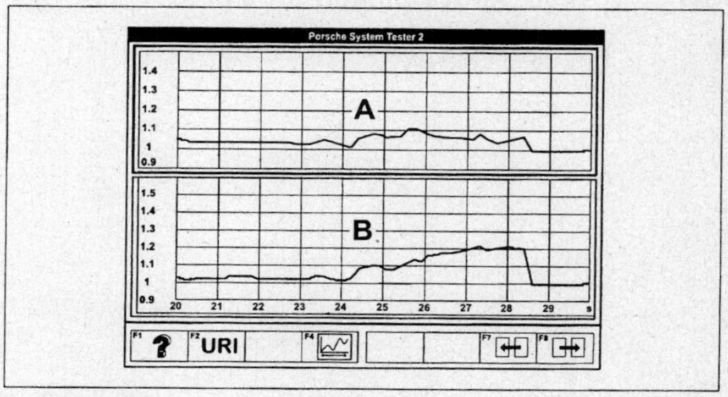

PR1020100298060X

Fig. 79 Code P1352: Valve Lift Control Cylinder No. 6, Above Limit (Part 6 of 9)

A - Oxygen sensor, bank 1
B - Oxygen sensor, bank 2

1 - Select system test.

2 - Select 'Request large lift'.

If "Valve diagnosis not ready" appears, a fault may have been stored.

1. Erase the fault memory.

3 - Activate the system test with the key [F8] immediately before acceleration with wide-open throttle.

The message "Drive link active" then appears.

4 - Perform acceleration with wide-open throttle in 2nd gear, until "Valve lift diagnosis complete" appears.

Note!

- *If a fault is detected, it is only recorded in the fault memory after 6,000 ignitions (at idling speed approx. 3 minutes waiting time).*
- *It is important to observe the oxygen sensor during acceleration with wide-open throttle or to record its behaviour with the data logger.*
- *If misfires are stored, diagnose misfire.*

Perform system test for small lift

Warning!

Test is carried out while driving. Have a second person operate the Porsche System Tester 2.

During the system test for small lift, the valves remain at small lift, regardless of the type of driving. Faulty switching conditions can be detected by rough running, just like with misfire detection. If a valve is not switched to small lift, the fault type 'under limit' is recorded.

Several cylinders may be stored as faulty, although only 1 valve on one cylinder is faulty.

In order to guarantee safety during repairs, the flat-base tappets of the inlet valves of the entire cylinder bank should be replaced if a fault occurs.

A faulty flat-base tappet can be detected because the oxygen sensor F_R for this cylinder bank enriches the mixture ($F_R > 1$) during

PR1020100298070X

Fig. 79 Code P1352: Valve Lift Control Cylinder No. 6, Above Limit (Part 7 of 9)

At speeds above 4,000 rpm, misfires may be stored. Delete the fault memory and repeat the test.

Note!

- *If a fault is detected, it is only recorded in the fault memory after 6,000 ignitions (at idling speed approx. 3 minutes waiting time).*
- *It is important to observe the oxygen sensor during acceleration with wide-open throttle or to record its behaviour with the data logger.*

PR1020100298090X

Fig. 79 Code P1352: Valve Lift Control Cylinder No. 6, Above Limit (Part 9 of 9)

acceleration with wide-open throttle ⇒ see drawing below. Difference from the other oxygen sensor > approx. 15 %. In the case of a fault, the flat-base tappets of the inlet valves for the entire cylinder bank must be replaced.

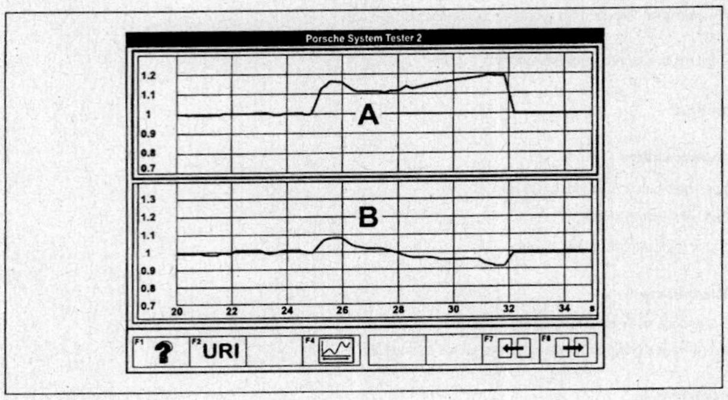

A - Oxygen sensor, bank 1
B - Oxygen sensor, bank 2

1 - Select system test.

2 - Select 'Request small lift'.

If "Valve lift diagnosis not ready" appears, a fault may have been stored.

1. Erase the fault memory.

3 - Activate the system test with the key [F8] immediately before acceleration with wide-open throttle.

The message "Drive link active" then appears.

Note!

If 'Request small lift' appears, the valves remain at small lift, ie. the performance is reduced dramatically.

4 - Perform acceleration with wide-open throttle in 2nd gear, until "Valve lift diagnosis complete" (max. 4,000 rpm) appears.

PR1020100298080X

Fig. 79 Code P1352: Valve Lift Control Cylinder No. 6, Above Limit (Part 8 of 9)

above limit

Diagnosis conditions

- Speed between 5,280 and 6,520 rpm
- Load between 125 and 190 %
- Acceleration with wide-open throttle

Possible fault cause

- A valve does not switch to large lift
- Several valves (various cylinders) do not switch to large lift

Affected terminals

Diagnosis/troubleshooting

Perform system test for large lift

Warning!

Test is carried out while driving. Have a second person operate the Porsche System Tester 2.

During the system test for large lift, the valves remain at large lift, regardless of the type of driving. Faulty switching conditions can be detected by rough running, just like with misfire detection. If a valve is not switched to large lift, the fault type 'over limit' is recorded.

Several cylinders may be stored as faulty, although only 1 valve on one cylinder is faulty.

In order to guarantee safety during repairs, the flat-base tappets of the inlet valves of the entire cylinder bank should be replaced if a fault occurs.

A faulty flat-base tappet can be detected because the oxygen sensor F_R for this cylinder bank hardly changes the mixture at all given acceleration with wide-open throttle (F_R at 1) and enriches the mixture in the opposite cylinder bank ($F_R > 1$)⇒ see drawing below. Given a difference between F_{R1} and F_{R2} of more than 8 % during acceleration with wide-open throttle, a fault is certainly present.

PR1020100299010X

Fig. 80 Code P1353: Valve Lift Control Cylinder No. 2, Above Limit (Part 1 of 9)

If the difference is less than 4 %, 1 valve may be faulty on both cylinder banks. In this case, all flat-base tappets of the inlet valves must be replaced.

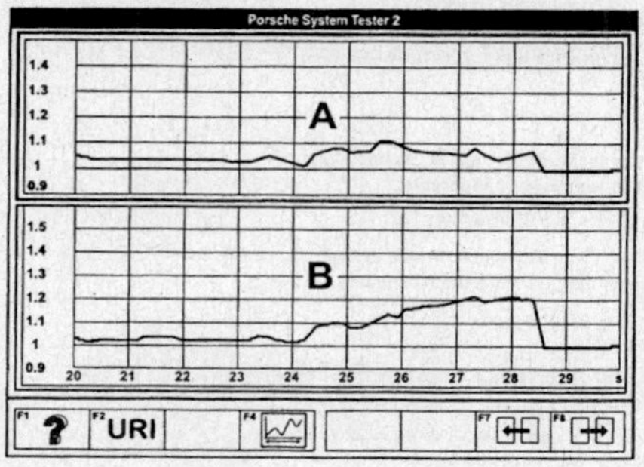

A - Oxygen sensor, bank 1
B - Oxygen sensor, bank 2

1 - **Select system test.**

2 - **Select 'Request large lift'.**

If "Valve diagnosis not ready" appears, a fault may have been stored.

1. Erase the fault memory.

3 - **Activate the system test with the key F8 immediately before acceleration with wide-open throttle.**

The message "Drive link active" then appears.

4 - **Perform acceleration with wide-open throttle in 2nd gear, until "Valve lift diagnosis complete" appears.**

PR1020100299020X

Fig. 80 Code P1353: Valve Lift Control Cylinder No. 2, Above Limit (Part 2 of 9)

A faulty flat-base tappet can be detected because the oxygen sensor F_R for this cylinder bank enriches the mixture ($F_R > 1$) during acceleration with wide-open throttle ⇒ see drawing below. Difference from the other oxygen sensor > approx. 15 %. In the case of a fault, the flat-base tappets of the inlet valves for the entire cylinder bank must be replaced.

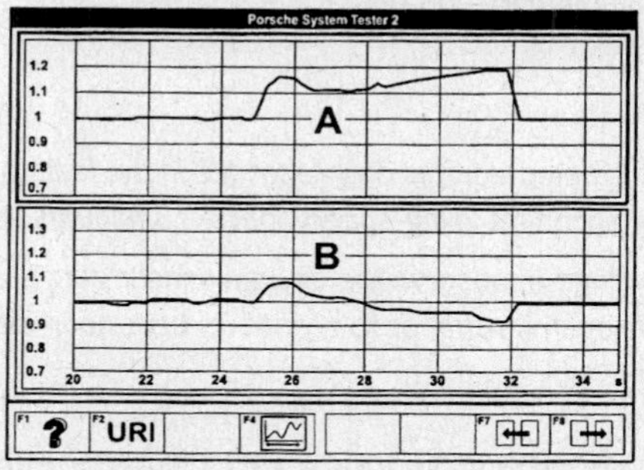

A - Oxygen sensor, bank 1
B - Oxygen sensor, bank 2

1 - **Select system test.**

2 - **Select 'Request small lift'.**

If "Valve lift diagnosis not ready" appears, a fault may have been stored.

1. Erase the fault memory.

3 - **Activate the system test with the key F8 immediately before acceleration with wide-open throttle.**

The message "Drive link active" then appears.

Note!

If 'Request small lift' appears, the valves remain at small lift, ie. the performance is reduced dramatically.

PR1020100299040X

Fig. 80 Code P1353: Valve Lift Control Cylinder No. 2, Above Limit (Part 4 of 9)

Note!

- *If a fault is detected, it is only recorded in the fault memory after 6,000 ignitions (at idling speed approx. 3 minutes waiting time).*
- *It is important to observe the oxygen sensor during acceleration with wide-open throttle or to record its behaviour with the data logger.*
- *If misfires are stored, diagnose misfire.*

below limit

Diagnosis conditions

- Speed between 2,000 and 3,320 rpm
- Load between 45 and 70 %
- Acceleration with wide-open throttle

Possible fault cause

- A valve does not switch to small lift
- Several valves (various cylinders) do not switch to small lift

Affected terminals

Diagnosis/troubleshooting

Perform system test for small lift

Warning!

Test is carried out while driving. Have a second person operate the Porsche System Tester 2.

During the system test for small lift, the valves remain at small lift, regardless of the type of driving. Faulty switching conditions can be detected by rough running, just like with misfire detection. If a valve is not switched to small lift, the fault type 'under limit' is recorded.

Several cylinders may be stored as faulty, although only 1 valve on one cylinder is faulty.

In order to guarantee safety during repairs, the flat-base tappets of the inlet valves of the entire cylinder bank should be replaced if a fault occurs.

PR1020100299030X

Fig. 80 Code P1353: Valve Lift Control Cylinder No. 2, Above Limit (Part 3 of 9)

4 - **Perform acceleration with wide-open throttle in 2nd gear, until "Valve lift diagnosis complete" (max. 4,000 rpm) appears.**

At speeds above 4,000 rpm, misfires may be stored. Delete the fault memory and repeat the test.

Note!

- *If a fault is detected, it is only recorded in the fault memory after 6,000 ignitions (at idling speed approx. 3 minutes waiting time).*
- *It is important to observe the oxygen sensor during acceleration with wide-open throttle or to record its behaviour with the data logger.*

signal implausible

Diagnosis conditions

- Speed between 2,000 and 3,320 rpm and between 5,280 and 6,520 rpm
- Load between 45 and 70 % and between 125 and 190 %
- Acceleration with wide-open throttle

Possible fault cause

- A valve does not switch to large lift
- Several valves (various cylinders) do not switch to large lift

and

- A valve does not switch to small lift
- Several valves (various cylinders) do not switch to small lift

Affected terminals

Diagnosis/troubleshooting

Perform system test for large lift

Warning!

Test is carried out while driving. Have a second person operate the Porsche System Tester 2.

PR1020100299050X

Fig. 80 Code P1353: Valve Lift Control Cylinder No. 2, Above Limit (Part 5 of 9)

During the system test for large lift, the valves remain at large lift, regardless of the type of driving. Faulty switching conditions can be detected by rough running, just like with misfire detection. If a valve is not switched to large lift, the fault type 'over limit' is recorded.

Several cylinders may be stored as faulty, although only 1 valve on one cylinder is faulty.

In order to guarantee safety during repairs, the flat-base tappets of the inlet valves of the entire cylinder bank should be replaced if a fault occurs.

A faulty flat-base tappet can be detected because the oxygen sensor F_R for this cylinder bank hardly changes the mixture at all given acceleration with wide-open throttle (F_R at 1) and enriches the mixture in the opposite cylinder bank ($F_R > 1$)⇒ see drawing below. Given a difference between F_{R1} and F_{R2} of more than 8 % during acceleration with wide-open throttle, a fault is certainly present.

If the difference is less than 4 %, 1 valve may be faulty on both cylinder banks. In this case, all flat-base tappets of the inlet valves must be replaced.

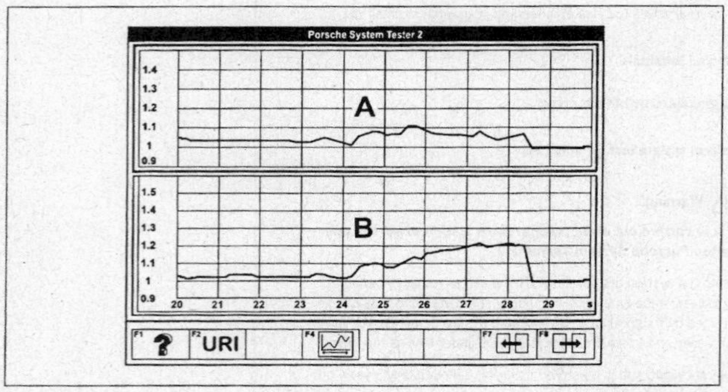

PR1020100299060X

Fig. 80 Code P1353: Valve Lift Control Cylinder No. 2, Above Limit (Part 6 of 9)

A - Oxygen sensor, bank 1

B - Oxygen sensor, bank 2

1 - Select system test.

2 - Select 'Request large lift'.

If "Valve diagnosis not ready" appears, a fault may have been stored.

1. Erase the fault memory.

3 - Activate the system test with the key F8 immediately before acceleration with wide-open throttle.

The message "Drive link active" then appears.

4 - Perform acceleration with wide-open throttle in 2nd gear, until "Valve lift diagnosis complete" appears.

Note!

- *If a fault is detected, it is only recorded in the fault memory after 6,000 ignitions (at idling speed approx. 3 minutes waiting time).*
- *It is important to observe the oxygen sensor during acceleration with wide-open throttle or to record its behaviour with the data logger.*
- *If misfires are stored, diagnose misfire.*

Perform system test for small lift

Warning!

Test is carried out while driving. Have a second person operate the Porsche System Tester 2.

During the system test for small lift, the valves remain at small lift, regardless of the type of driving. Faulty switching conditions can be detected by rough running, just like with misfire detection. If a valve is not switched to small lift, the fault type 'under limit' is recorded.

Several cylinders may be stored as faulty, although only 1 valve on one cylinder is faulty.

In order to guarantee safety during repairs, the flat-base tappets of the inlet valves of the entire cylinder bank should be replaced if a fault occurs.

A faulty flat-base tappet can be detected because the oxygen sensor F_R for this cylinder bank enriches the mixture ($F_R > 1$) during

PR1020100299070X

Fig. 80 Code P1353: Valve Lift Control Cylinder No. 2, Above Limit (Part 7 of 9)

acceleration with wide-open throttle ⇒ see drawing below. Difference from the other oxygen sensor > approx. 15 %. In the case of a fault, the flat-base tappets of the inlet valves for the entire cylinder bank must be replaced.

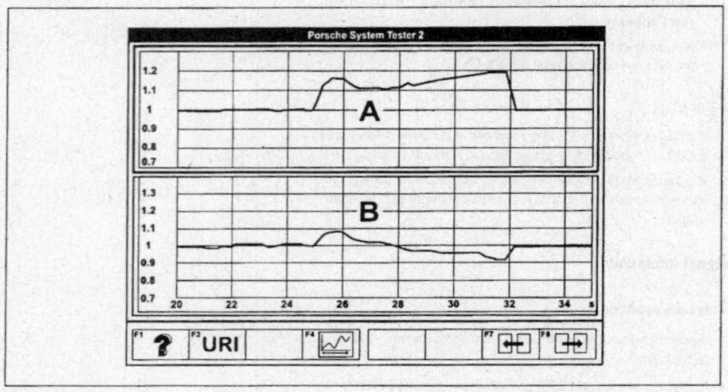

A - Oxygen sensor, bank 1

B - Oxygen sensor, bank 2

1 - Select system test.

2 - Select 'Request small lift'.

If "Valve lift diagnosis not ready" appears, a fault may have been stored.

1. Erase the fault memory.

3 - Activate the system test with the key F8 immediately before acceleration with wide-open throttle.

The message "Drive link active" then appears.

Note!

If 'Request small lift' appears, the valves remain at small lift, ie. the performance is reduced dramatically.

4 - Perform acceleration with wide-open throttle in 2nd gear, until "Valve lift diagnosis complete" (max. 4,000 rpm) appears.

PR1020100299080X

Fig. 80 Code P1353: Valve Lift Control Cylinder No. 2, Above Limit (Part 8 of 9)

At speeds above 4,000 rpm, misfires may be stored. Delete the fault memory and repeat the test.

Note!

- *If a fault is detected, it is only recorded in the fault memory after 6,000 ignitions (at idling speed approx. 3 minutes waiting time).*
- *It is important to observe the oxygen sensor during acceleration with wide-open throttle or to record its behaviour with the data logger.*

PR1020100299090X

Fig. 80 Code P1353: Valve Lift Control Cylinder No. 2, Above Limit (Part 9 of 9)

above limit

Diagnosis conditions

- Speed between 5,280 and 6,520 rpm
- Load between 125 and 190 %
- Acceleration with wide-open throttle

Possible fault cause

- A valve does not switch to large lift
- Several valves (various cylinders) do not switch to large lift

Affected terminals

Diagnosis/troubleshooting

Perform system test for large lift

⚠ Warning!

Test is carried out while driving. Have a second person operate the Porsche System Tester 2.

During the system test for large lift, the valves remain at large lift, regardless of the type of driving. Faulty switching conditions can be detected by rough running, just like with misfire detection. If a valve is not switched to large lift, the fault type 'over limit' is recorded.

Several cylinders may be stored as faulty, although only 1 valve on one cylinder is faulty.

In order to guarantee safety during repairs, the flat-base tappets of the inlet valves of the entire cylinder bank should be replaced if a fault occurs.

A faulty flat-base tappet can be detected because the oxygen sensor F_R for this cylinder bank hardly changes the mixture at all given acceleration with wide-open throttle (F_R at 1) and enriches the mixture in the opposite cylinder bank ($F_R > 1$)⇒ see drawing below. Given a difference between F_{R1} and F_{R2} of more than 8 % during acceleration with wide-open throttle, a fault is certainly present.

PR1020100300010X

Fig. 81 Code P1354: Valve Lift Control Cylinder No. 4, Above Limit (Part 1 of 9)

If the difference is less than 4 %, 1 valve may be faulty on both cylinder banks. In this case, all flat-base tappets of the inlet valves must be replaced.

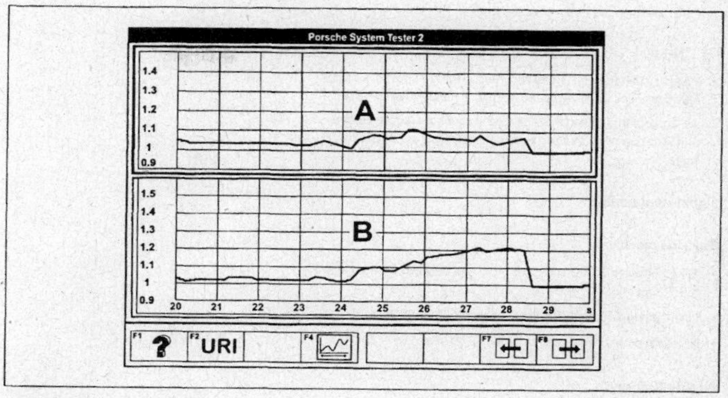

A - Oxygen sensor, bank 1
B - Oxygen sensor, bank 2

1 - Select system test.

2 - Select 'Request large lift'.

If "Valve diagnosis not ready" appears, a fault may have been stored.

1. Erase the fault memory.

3 - Activate the system test with the key [F8] immediately before acceleration with wide-open throttle.

The message "Drive link active" then appears.

4 - Perform acceleration with wide-open throttle in 2nd gear, until "Valve lift diagnosis complete" appears.

PR1020100300020X

Fig. 81 Code P1354: Valve Lift Control Cylinder No. 4, Above Limit (Part 2 of 9)

ℹ Note!

- *If a fault is detected, it is only recorded in the fault memory after 6,000 ignitions (at idling speed approx. 3 minutes waiting time).*
- *It is important to observe the oxygen sensor during acceleration with wide-open throttle or to record its behaviour with the data logger.*
- *If misfires are stored, diagnose misfire.*

below limit

Diagnosis conditions

- Speed between 2,000 and 3,320 rpm
- Load between 45 and 70 %
- Acceleration with wide-open throttle

Possible fault cause

- A valve does not switch to small lift
- Several valves (various cylinders) do not switch to small lift

Affected terminals

Diagnosis/troubleshooting

Perform system test for small lift

⚠ Warning!

Test is carried out while driving. Have a second person operate the Porsche System Tester 2.

During the system test for small lift, the valves remain at small lift, regardless of the type of driving. Faulty switching conditions can be detected by rough running, just like with misfire detection. If a valve is not switched to small lift, the fault type 'under limit' is recorded.

Several cylinders may be stored as faulty, although only 1 valve on one cylinder is faulty.

In order to guarantee safety during repairs, the flat-base tappets of the inlet valves of the entire cylinder bank should be replaced if a fault occurs.

PR1020100300030X

Fig. 81 Code P1354: Valve Lift Control Cylinder No. 4, Above Limit (Part 3 of 9)

A faulty flat-base tappet can be detected because the oxygen sensor F_R for this cylinder bank enriches the mixture ($F_R > 1$) during acceleration with wide-open throttle ⇒ see drawing below. Difference from the other oxygen sensor > approx. 15 %. In the case of a fault, the flat-base tappets of the inlet valves for the entire cylinder bank must be replaced.

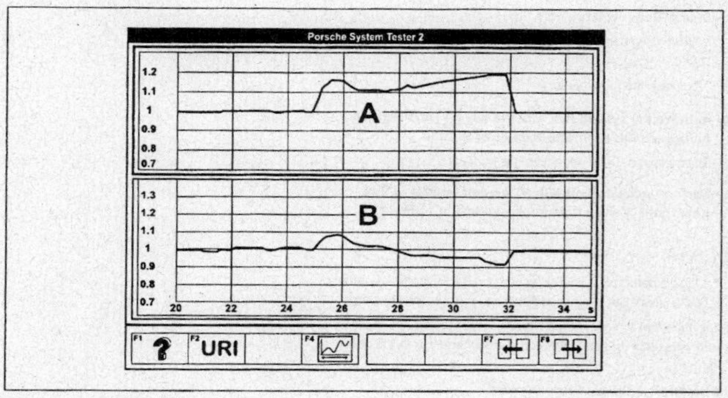

A - Oxygen sensor, bank 1
B - Oxygen sensor, bank 2

1 - Select system test.

2 - Select 'Request small lift'.

If "Valve lift diagnosis not ready" appears, a fault may have been stored.

1. Erase the fault memory.

3 - Activate the system test with the key [F8] immediately before acceleration with wide-open throttle.

The message "Drive link active" then appears.

ℹ Note!

If 'Request small lift' appears, the valves remain at small lift, ie. the performance is reduced dramatically.

PR1020100300040X

Fig. 81 Code P1354: Valve Lift Control Cylinder No. 4, Above Limit (Part 4 of 9)

4 - **Perform acceleration with wide-open throttle in 2nd gear, until "Valve lift diagnosis complete" (max. 4,000 rpm) appears.**

At speeds above 4,000 rpm, misfires may be stored. Delete the fault memory and repeat the test.

Note!

- *If a fault is detected, it is only recorded in the fault memory after 6,000 ignitions (at idling speed approx. 3 minutes waiting time).*
- *It is important to observe the oxygen sensor during acceleration with wide-open throttle or to record its behaviour with the data logger.*

signal implausible

Diagnosis conditions

- Speed between 2,000 and 3,320 rpm and between 5,280 and 6,520 rpm
- Load between 45 and 70 % and between 125 and 190 %
- Acceleration with wide-open throttle

Possible fault cause

- A valve does not switch to large lift
- Several valves (various cylinders) do not switch to large lift

and

- A valve does not switch to small lift
- Several valves (various cylinders) do not switch to small lift

Affected terminals

-

Diagnosis/troubleshooting

Perform system test for large lift

Warning!

Test is carried out while driving. Have a second person operate the Porsche System Tester 2.

PR1020100300050X

Fig. 81 Code P1354: Valve Lift Control Cylinder No. 4, Above Limit (Part 5 of 9)

During the system test for large lift, the valves remain at large lift, regardless of the type of driving. Faulty switching conditions can be detected by rough running, just like with misfire detection. If a valve is not switched to large lift, the fault type 'over limit' is recorded.

Several cylinders may be stored as faulty, although only 1 valve on one cylinder is faulty.

In order to guarantee safety during repairs, the flat-base tappets of the inlet valves of the entire cylinder bank should be replaced if a fault occurs.

A faulty flat-base tappet can be detected because the oxygen sensor F_R for this cylinder bank hardly changes the mixture at all given acceleration with wide-open throttle (F_R at 1) and enriches the mixture in the opposite cylinder bank ($F_R > 1$)⇒ see drawing below. Given a difference between F_{R1} and F_{R2} of more than 8 % during acceleration with wide-open throttle, a fault is certainly present.

If the difference is less than 4 %, 1 valve may be faulty on both cylinder banks. In this case, all flat-base tappets of the inlet valves must be replaced.

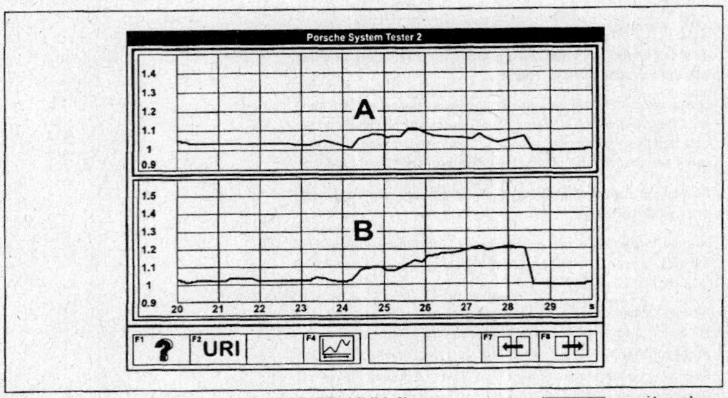

PR1020100300060X

Fig. 81 Code P1354: Valve Lift Control Cylinder No. 4, Above Limit (Part 6 of 9)

A - **Oxygen sensor, bank 1**
B - **Oxygen sensor, bank 2**

1 - **Select system test.**

2 - **Select 'Request large lift'.**

If "Valve diagnosis not ready" appears, a fault may have been stored.

1. Erase the fault memory.

3 - **Activate the system test with the key F8 immediately before acceleration with wide-open throttle.**

The message "Drive link active" then appears.

4 - **Perform acceleration with wide-open throttle in 2nd gear, until "Valve lift diagnosis complete" appears.**

Note!

- *If a fault is detected, it is only recorded in the fault memory after 6,000 ignitions (at idling speed approx. 3 minutes waiting time).*
- *It is important to observe the oxygen sensor during acceleration with wide-open throttle or to record its behaviour with the data logger.*
- *If misfires are stored, diagnose misfire.*

Perform system test for small lift

Warning!

Test is carried out while driving. Have a second person operate the Porsche System Tester 2.

During the system test for small lift, the valves remain at small lift, regardless of the type of driving. Faulty switching conditions can be detected by rough running, just like with misfire detection. If a valve is not switched to small lift, the fault type 'under limit' is recorded.

Several cylinders may be stored as faulty, although only 1 valve on one cylinder is faulty.

In order to guarantee safety during repairs, the flat-base tappets of the inlet valves of the entire cylinder bank should be replaced if a fault occurs.

A faulty flat-base tappet can be detected because the oxygen sensor F_R for this cylinder bank enriches the mixture ($F_R > 1$) during

PR1020100300070X

Fig. 81 Code P1354: Valve Lift Control Cylinder No. 4, Above Limit (Part 7 of 9)

acceleration with wide-open throttle ⇒ see drawing below. Difference from the other oxygen sensor > approx. 15 %. In the case of a fault, the flat-base tappets of the inlet valves for the entire cylinder bank must be replaced.

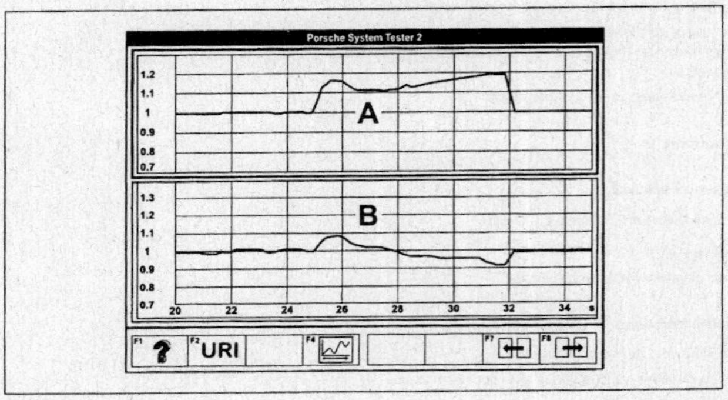

A - **Oxygen sensor, bank 1**
B - **Oxygen sensor, bank 2**

1 - **Select system test.**

2 - **Select 'Request small lift'.**

If "Valve lift diagnosis not ready" appears, a fault may have been stored.

1. Erase the fault memory.

3 - **Activate the system test with the key F8 immediately before acceleration with wide-open throttle.**

The message "Drive link active" then appears.

Note!

If 'Request small lift' appears, the valves remain at small lift, ie. the performance is reduced dramatically.

4 - **Perform acceleration with wide-open throttle in 2nd gear, until "Valve lift diagnosis complete" (max. 4,000 rpm) appears.**

PR1020100300080X

Fig. 81 Code P1354: Valve Lift Control Cylinder No. 4, Above Limit (Part 8 of 9)

At speeds above 4,000 rpm, misfires may be stored. Delete the fault memory and repeat the test.

Note!

- *If a fault is detected, it is only recorded in the fault memory after 6,000 ignitions (at idling speed approx. 3 minutes waiting time).*
- *It is important to observe the oxygen sensor during acceleration with wide-open throttle or to record its behaviour with the data logger.*

PR1020100300090X

Fig. 81 Code P1354: Valve Lift Control Cylinder No. 4, Above Limit (Part 9 of 9)

If the difference is less than 4 %, 1 valve may be faulty on both cylinder banks. In this case, all flat-base tappets of the inlet valves must be replaced.

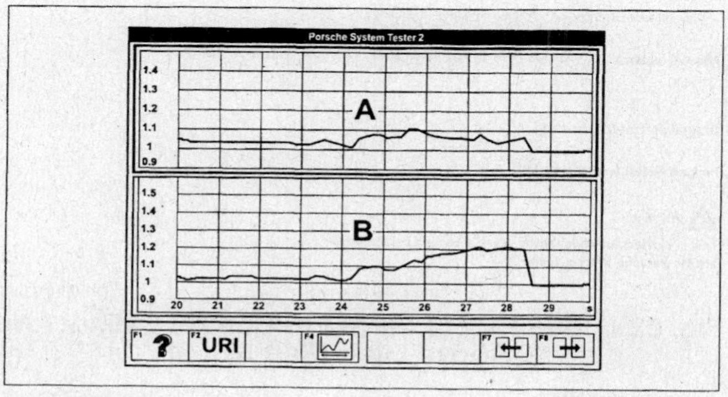

A - Oxygen sensor, bank 1
B - Oxygen sensor, bank 2

1 - **Select system test.**

2 - **Select 'Request large lift'.**

If "Valve diagnosis not ready" appears, a fault may have been stored.

1. Erase the fault memory.

3 - **Activate the system test with the key F8 immediately before acceleration with wide-open throttle.**

The message "Drive link active" then appears.

4 - **Perform acceleration with wide-open throttle in 2nd gear, until "Valve lift diagnosis complete" appears.**

PR1020100301020X

Fig. 82 Code P1355: Valve Lift Control Cylinder No. 3, Above Limit (Part 2 of 9)

above limit

Diagnosis conditions

- Speed between 5,280 and 6,520 rpm
- Load between 125 and 190 %
- Acceleration with wide-open throttle

Possible fault cause

- A valve does not switch to large lift
- Several valves (various cylinders) do not switch to large lift

Affected terminals

-

Diagnosis/troubleshooting

Perform system test for large lift

Warning!

Test is carried out while driving. Have a second person operate the Porsche System Tester 2.

During the system test for large lift, the valves remain at large lift, regardless of the type of driving. Faulty switching conditions can be detected by rough running, just like with misfire detection. If a valve is not switched to large lift, the fault type 'over limit' is recorded.

Several cylinders may be stored as faulty, although only 1 valve on one cylinder is faulty.

In order to guarantee safety during repairs, the flat-base tappets of the inlet valves of the entire cylinder bank should be replaced if a fault occurs.

A faulty flat-base tappet can be detected because the oxygen sensor F_R for this cylinder bank hardly changes the mixture at all given acceleration with wide-open throttle (F_R at 1) and enriches the mixture in the opposite cylinder bank ($F_R > 1$)⇒ see drawing below. Given a difference between F_{R1} and F_{R2} of more than 8 % during acceleration with wide-open throttle, a fault is certainly present.

PR1020100301010X

Fig. 82 Code P1355: Valve Lift Control Cylinder No. 3, Above Limit (Part 1 of 9)

Note!

- *If a fault is detected, it is only recorded in the fault memory after 6,000 ignitions (at idling speed approx. 3 minutes waiting time).*
- *It is important to observe the oxygen sensor during acceleration with wide-open throttle or to record its behaviour with the data logger.*
- *If misfires are stored, diagnose misfire.*

631 Valve lift control, cylinder 3 - below limit

Diagnosis conditions

- Speed between 2,000 and 3,320 rpm
- Load between 45 and 70 %
- Acceleration with wide-open throttle

Possible fault cause

- A valve does not switch to small lift
- Several valves (various cylinders) do not switch to small lift

Affected terminals

Diagnosis/troubleshooting

Perform system test for small lift

Warning!

Test is carried out while driving. Have a second person operate the Porsche System Tester 2.

During the system test for small lift, the valves remain at small lift, regardless of the type of driving. Faulty switching conditions can be detected by rough running, just like with misfire detection. If a valve is not switched to small lift, the fault type 'under limit' is recorded.

Several cylinders may be stored as faulty, although only 1 valve on one cylinder is faulty.

In order to guarantee safety during repairs, the flat-base tappets of the inlet valves of the entire cylinder bank should be replaced if a fault occurs.

PR1020100301030X

Fig. 82 Code P1355: Valve Lift Control Cylinder No. 3, Above Limit (Part 3 of 9)

A faulty flat-base tappet can be detected because the oxygen sensor F_R for this cylinder bank enriches the mixture ($F_R > 1$) during acceleration with wide-open throttle ⇒ see drawing below. Difference from the other oxygen sensor > approx. 15 %. In the case of a fault, the flat-base tappets of the inlet valves for the entire cylinder bank must be replaced.

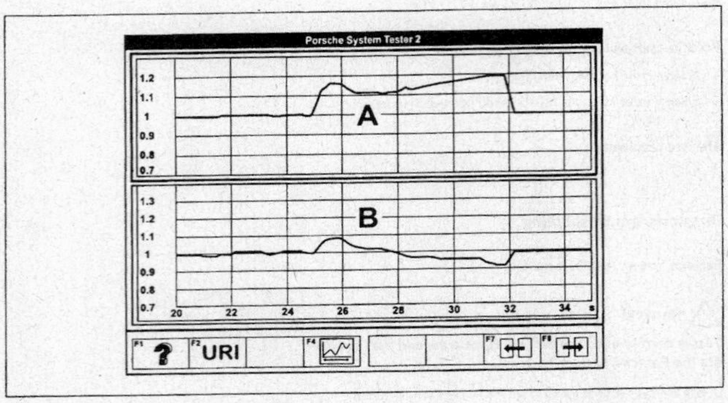

A - Oxygen sensor, bank 1
B - Oxygen sensor, bank 2

1 - Select system test.

2 - Select 'Request small lift'.

If "Valve lift diagnosis not ready" appears, a fault may have been stored.

1. Erase the fault memory.

3 - Activate the system test with the key F8 immediately before acceleration with wide-open throttle.

The message "Drive link active" then appears.

Note!

If 'Request small lift' appears, the valves remain at small lift, ie. the performance is reduced dramatically.

PR1020100301040X

Fig. 82 Code P1355: Valve Lift Control Cylinder No. 3, Above Limit (Part 4 of 9)

4 - Perform acceleration with wide-open throttle in 2nd gear, until "Valve lift diagnosis complete" (max. 4,000 rpm) appears.

At speeds above 4,000 rpm, misfires may be stored. Delete the fault memory and repeat the test.

Note!

- *If a fault is detected, it is only recorded in the fault memory after 6,000 ignitions (at idling speed approx. 3 minutes waiting time).*
- *It is important to observe the oxygen sensor during acceleration with wide-open throttle or to record its behaviour with the data logger.*

signal implausible

Diagnosis conditions

- Speed between 2,000 and 3,320 rpm and between 5,280 and 6,520 rpm
- Load between 45 and 70 % and between 125 and 190 %
- Acceleration with wide-open throttle

Possible fault cause

- A valve does not switch to large lift
- Several valves (various cylinders) do not switch to large lift

and

- A valve does not switch to small lift
- Several valves (various cylinders) do not switch to small lift

Affected terminals

Diagnosis/troubleshooting

Perform system test for large lift

Warning!

Test is carried out while driving. Have a second person operate the Porsche System Tester 2.

PR1020100301050X

Fig. 82 Code P1355: Valve Lift Control Cylinder No. 3, Above Limit (Part 5 of 9)

During the system test for large lift, the valves remain at large lift, regardless of the type of driving. Faulty switching conditions can be detected by rough running, just like with misfire detection. If a valve is not switched to large lift, the fault type 'over limit' is recorded.

Several cylinders may be stored as faulty, although only 1 valve on one cylinder is faulty.

In order to guarantee safety during repairs, the flat-base tappets of the inlet valves of the entire cylinder bank should be replaced if a fault occurs.

A faulty flat-base tappet can be detected because the oxygen sensor F_R for this cylinder bank hardly changes the mixture at all given acceleration with wide-open throttle (F_R at 1) and enriches the mixture in the opposite cylinder bank ($F_R > 1$)⇒ see drawing below. Given a difference between F_{R1} and F_{R2} of more than 8 % during acceleration with wide-open throttle, a fault is certainly present.

If the difference is less than 4 %, 1 valve may be faulty on both cylinder banks. In this case, all flat-base tappets of the inlet valves must be replaced.

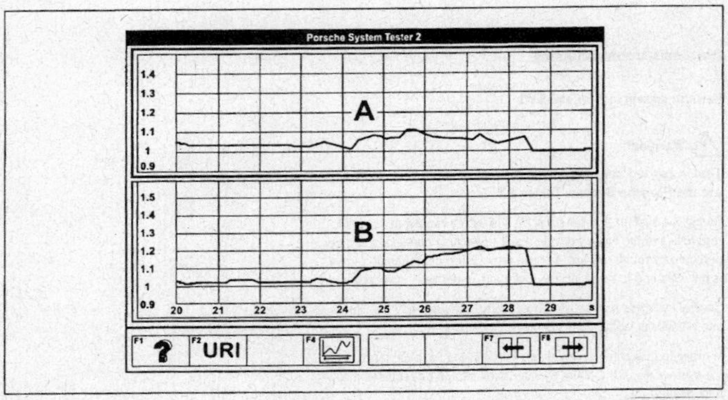

PR1020100301060X

Fig. 82 Code P1355: Valve Lift Control Cylinder No. 3, Above Limit (Part 6 of 9)

A - Oxygen sensor, bank 1
B - Oxygen sensor, bank 2

1 - Select system test.

2 - Select 'Request large lift'.

If "Valve diagnosis not ready" appears, a fault may have been stored.

1. Erase the fault memory.

3 - Activate the system test with the key F8 immediately before acceleration with wide-open throttle.

The message "Drive link active" then appears.

4 - Perform acceleration with wide-open throttle in 2nd gear, until "Valve lift diagnosis complete" appears.

Note!

- *If a fault is detected, it is only recorded in the fault memory after 6,000 ignitions (at idling speed approx. 3 minutes waiting time).*
- *It is important to observe the oxygen sensor during acceleration with wide-open throttle or to record its behaviour with the data logger.*
- *If misfires are stored, diagnose misfire.*

Perform system test for small lift

Warning!

Test is carried out while driving. Have a second person operate the Porsche System Tester 2.

During the system test for small lift, the valves remain at small lift, regardless of the type of driving. Faulty switching conditions can be detected by rough running, just like with misfire detection. If a valve is not switched to small lift, the fault type 'under limit' is recorded.

Several cylinders may be stored as faulty, although only 1 valve on one cylinder is faulty.

In order to guarantee safety during repairs, the flat-base tappets of the inlet valves of the entire cylinder bank should be replaced if a fault occurs.

A faulty flat-base tappet can be detected because the oxygen sensor F_R for this cylinder bank enriches the mixture ($F_R > 1$) during

PR1020100301070X

Fig. 82 Code P1355: Valve Lift Control Cylinder No. 3, Above Limit (Part 7 of 9)

acceleration with wide-open throttle ⇒ see drawing below. Difference from the other oxygen sensor > approx. 15 %. In the case of a fault, the flat-base tappets of the inlet valves for the entire cylinder bank must be replaced.

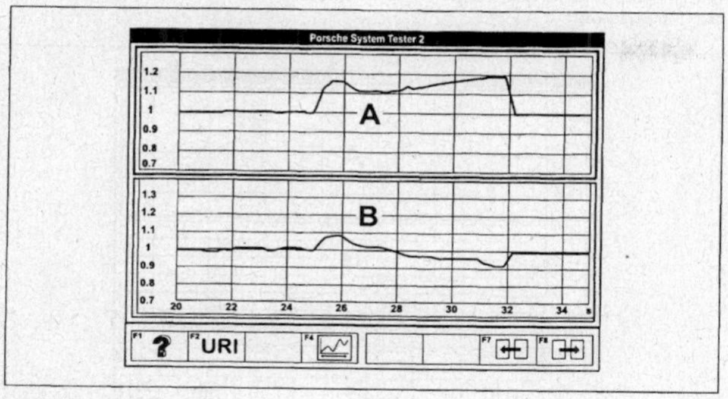

A - Oxygen sensor, bank 1

B - Oxygen sensor, bank 2

1 - Select system test.

2 - Select 'Request small lift'.

If "Valve lift diagnosis not ready" appears, a fault may have been stored.

1. Erase the fault memory.

3 - Activate the system test with the key F8 **immediately before acceleration with wide-open throttle.**

The message "Drive link active" then appears.

Note!

If 'Request small lift' appears, the valves remain at small lift, ie. the performance is reduced dramatically.

4 - Perform acceleration with wide-open throttle in 2nd gear, until "Valve lift diagnosis complete" (max. 4,000 rpm) appears.

PR1020100301080X

Fig. 82 Code P1355: Valve Lift Control Cylinder No. 3, Above Limit (Part 8 of 9)

At speeds above 4,000 rpm, misfires may be stored. Delete the fault memory and repeat the test.

Note!

- *If a fault is detected, it is only recorded in the fault memory after 6,000 ignitions (at idling speed approx. 3 minutes waiting time).*
- *It is important to observe the oxygen sensor during acceleration with wide-open throttle or to record its behaviour with the data logger.*

PR1020100301090X

Fig. 82 Code P1355: Valve Lift Control Cylinder No. 3, Above Limit (Part 9 of 9)

above limit

Diagnosis conditions

- Speed between 5,280 and 6,520 rpm
- Load between 125 and 190 %
- Acceleration with wide-open throttle

Possible fault cause

- A valve does not switch to large lift
- Several valves (various cylinders) do not switch to large lift

Affected terminals

-

Diagnosis/troubleshooting

Perform system test for large lift

Warning!

Test is carried out while driving. Have a second person operate the Porsche System Tester 2.

During the system test for large lift, the valves remain at large lift, regardless of the type of driving. Faulty switching conditions can be detected by rough running, just like with misfire detection. If a valve is not switched to large lift, the fault type 'over limit' is recorded.

Several cylinders may be stored as faulty, although only 1 valve on one cylinder is faulty.

In order to guarantee safety during repairs, the flat-base tappets of the inlet valves of the entire cylinder bank should be replaced if a fault occurs.

A faulty flat-base tappet can be detected because the oxygen sensor F_R for this cylinder bank hardly changes the mixture at all given acceleration with wide-open throttle (F_R at 1) and enriches the mixture in the opposite cylinder bank ($F_R > 1$)⇒ see drawing below. Given a difference between F_{R1} and F_{R2} of more than 8 % during acceleration with wide-open throttle, a fault is certainly present.

PR1020100302010X

Fig. 83 Code P1356: Valve Lift Control Cylinder No. 5, Above Limit (Part 1 of 9)

If the difference is less than 4 %, 1 valve may be faulty on both cylinder banks. In this case, all flat-base tappets of the inlet valves must be replaced.

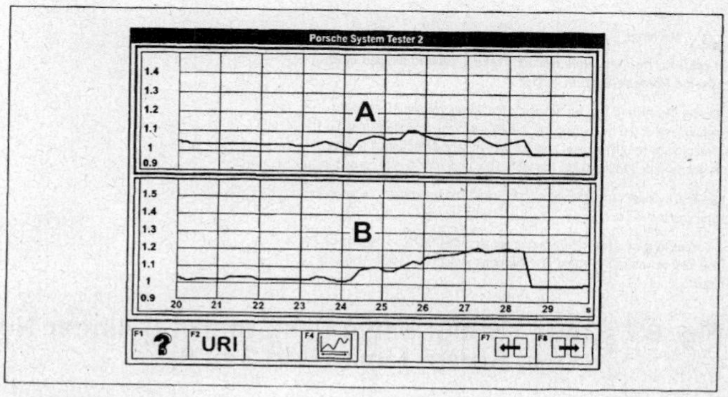

A - Oxygen sensor, bank 1

B - Oxygen sensor, bank 2

1 - Select system test.

2 - Select 'Request large lift'.

If "Valve diagnosis not ready" appears, a fault may have been stored.

1. Erase the fault memory.

3 - Activate the system test with the key F8 **immediately before acceleration with wide-open throttle.**

The message "Drive link active" then appears.

4 - Perform acceleration with wide-open throttle in 2nd gear, until "Valve lift diagnosis complete" appears.

PR1020100302020X

Fig. 83 Code P1356: Valve Lift Control Cylinder No. 5, Above Limit (Part 2 of 9)

Note!

- *If a fault is detected, it is only recorded in the fault memory after 6,000 ignitions (at idling speed approx. 3 minutes waiting time).*
- *It is important to observe the oxygen sensor during acceleration with wide-open throttle or to record its behaviour with the data logger.*
- *If misfires are stored, diagnose misfire.*

below limit

Diagnosis conditions

- Speed between 2,000 and 3,320 rpm
- Load between 45 and 70 %
- Acceleration with wide-open throttle

Possible fault cause

- A valve does not switch to small lift
- Several valves (various cylinders) do not switch to small lift

Affected terminals

-

Diagnosis/troubleshooting

Perform system test for small lift

Warning!

Test is carried out while driving. Have a second person operate the Porsche System Tester 2.

During the system test for small lift, the valves remain at small lift, regardless of the type of driving. Faulty switching conditions can be detected by rough running, just like with misfire detection. If a valve is not switched to small lift, the fault type 'under limit' is recorded.

Several cylinders may be stored as faulty, although only 1 valve on one cylinder is faulty.

In order to guarantee safety during repairs, the flat-base tappets of the inlet valves of the entire cylinder bank should be replaced if a fault occurs.

PR1020100302030X

Fig. 83 Code P1356: Valve Lift Control Cylinder No. 5, Above Limit (Part 3 of 9)

A faulty flat-base tappet can be detected because the oxygen sensor F_R for this cylinder bank enriches the mixture ($F_R > 1$) during acceleration with wide-open throttle ⇒ see drawing below. Difference from the other oxygen sensor > approx. 15 %. In the case of a fault, the flat-base tappets of the inlet valves for the entire cylinder bank must be replaced.

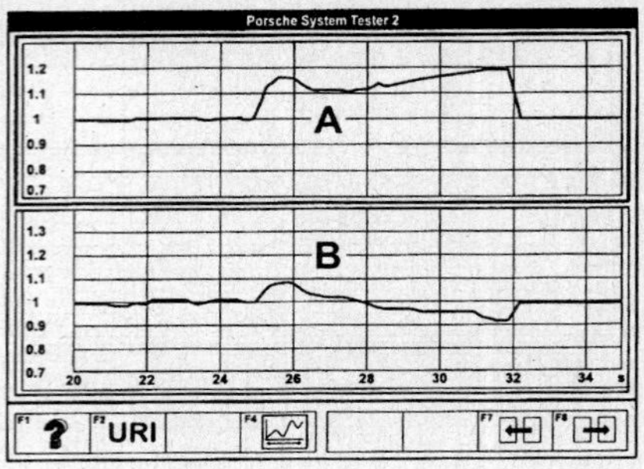

A - Oxygen sensor, bank 1
B - Oxygen sensor, bank 2

1 - Select system test.

2 - Select 'Request small lift'.

If "Valve lift diagnosis not ready" appears, a fault may have been stored.

1. Erase the fault memory.

3 - Activate the system test with the key F8 immediately before acceleration with wide-open throttle.

The message "Drive link active" then appears.

Note!

If 'Request small lift' appears, the valves remain at small lift, ie. the performance is reduced dramatically.

PR1020100302040X

Fig. 83 Code P1356: Valve Lift Control Cylinder No. 5, Above Limit (Part 4 of 9)

4 - Perform acceleration with wide-open throttle in 2nd gear, until "Valve lift diagnosis complete" (max. 4,000 rpm) appears.

At speeds above 4,000 rpm, misfires may be stored. Delete the fault memory and repeat the test.

Note!

- *If a fault is detected, it is only recorded in the fault memory after 6,000 ignitions (at idling speed approx. 3 minutes waiting time).*
- *It is important to observe the oxygen sensor during acceleration with wide-open throttle or to record its behaviour with the data logger.*

signal implausible

Diagnosis conditions

- Speed between 2,000 and 3,320 rpm and between 5,280 and 6,520 rpm
- Load between 45 and 70 % and between 125 and 190 %
- Acceleration with wide-open throttle

Possible fault cause

- A valve does not switch to large lift
- Several valves (various cylinders) do not switch to large lift

and

- A valve does not switch to small lift
- Several valves (various cylinders) do not switch to small lift

Affected terminals

Diagnosis/troubleshooting

Perform system test for large lift

Warning!

Test is carried out while driving. Have a second person operate the Porsche System Tester 2.

PR1020100302050X

Fig. 83 Code P1356: Valve Lift Control Cylinder No. 5, Above Limit (Part 5 of 9)

During the system test for large lift, the valves remain at large lift, regardless of the type of driving. Faulty switching conditions can be detected by rough running, just like with misfire detection. If a valve is not switched to large lift, the fault type 'over limit' is recorded.

Several cylinders may be stored as faulty, although only 1 valve on one cylinder is faulty.

In order to guarantee safety during repairs, the flat-base tappets of the inlet valves of the entire cylinder bank should be replaced if a fault occurs.

A faulty flat-base tappet can be detected because the oxygen sensor F_R for this cylinder bank hardly changes the mixture at all given acceleration with wide-open throttle (F_R at 1) and enriches the mixture in the opposite cylinder bank ($F_R > 1$)⇒ see drawing below. Given a difference between F_{R1} and F_{R2} of more than 8 % during acceleration with wide-open throttle, a fault is certainly present.

If the difference is less than 4 %, 1 valve may be faulty on both cylinder banks. In this case, all flat-base tappets of the inlet valves must be replaced.

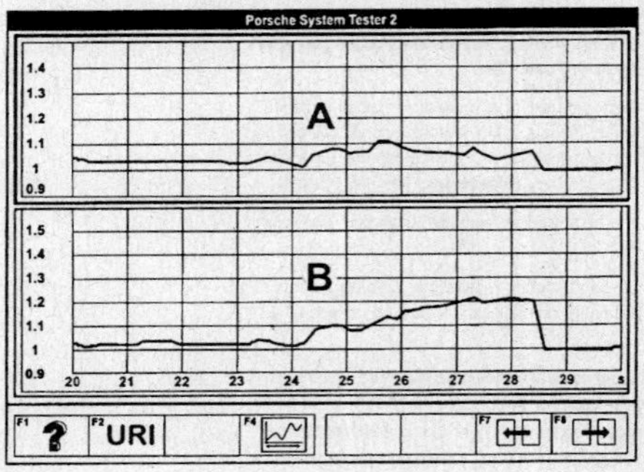

PR1020100302060X

Fig. 83 Code P1356: Valve Lift Control Cylinder No. 5, Above Limit (Part 6 of 9)

A - Oxygen sensor, bank 1

B - Oxygen sensor, bank 2

1 - Select system test.

2 - Select 'Request large lift'.

If "Valve diagnosis not ready" appears, a fault may have been stored.

1. Erase the fault memory.

3 - Activate the system test with the key F8 immediately before acceleration with wide-open throttle.

The message "Drive link active" then appears.

4 - Perform acceleration with wide-open throttle in 2nd gear, until "Valve lift diagnosis complete" appears.

Note!

- *If a fault is detected, it is only recorded in the fault memory after 6,000 ignitions (at idling speed approx. 3 minutes waiting time).*
- *It is important to observe the oxygen sensor during acceleration with wide-open throttle or to record its behaviour with the data logger.*
- *If misfires are stored, diagnose misfire.*

Perform system test for small lift

Warning!

Test is carried out while driving. Have a second person operate the Porsche System Tester 2.

During the system test for small lift, the valves remain at small lift, regardless of the type of driving. Faulty switching conditions can be detected by rough running, just like with misfire detection. If a valve is not switched to small lift, the fault type 'under limit' is recorded.

Several cylinders may be stored as faulty, although only 1 valve on one cylinder is faulty.

In order to guarantee safety during repairs, the flat-base tappets of the inlet valves of the entire cylinder bank should be replaced if a fault occurs.

A faulty flat-base tappet can be detected because the oxygen sensor F_R for this cylinder bank enriches the mixture (F_R > 1) during

PR1020100302070X

Fig. 83 Code P1356: Valve Lift Control Cylinder No. 5, Above Limit (Part 7 of 9)

At speeds above 4,000 rpm, misfires may be stored. Delete the fault memory and repeat the test.

Note!

- *If a fault is detected, it is only recorded in the fault memory after 6,000 ignitions (at idling speed approx. 3 minutes waiting time).*
- *It is important to observe the oxygen sensor during acceleration with wide-open throttle or to record its behaviour with the data logger.*

PR1020100302090X

Fig. 83 Code P1356: Valve Lift Control Cylinder No. 5, Above Limit (Part 9 of 9)

acceleration with wide-open throttle ⇒ see drawing below. Difference from the other oxygen sensor > approx. 15 %. In the case of a fault, the flat-base tappets of the inlet valves for the entire cylinder bank must be replaced.

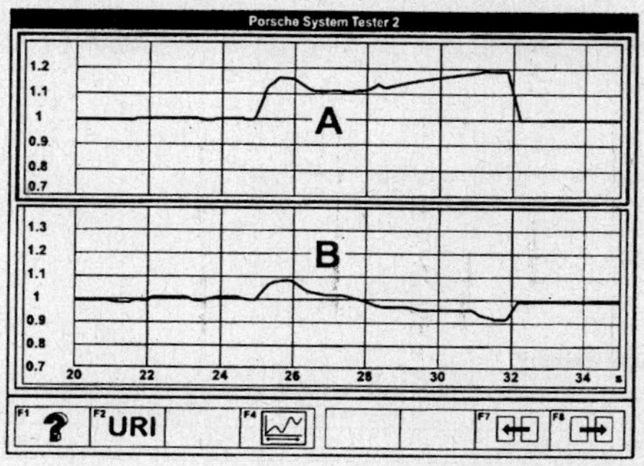

A - Oxygen sensor, bank 1

B - Oxygen sensor, bank 2

1 - Select system test.

2 - Select 'Request small lift'.

If "Valve lift diagnosis not ready" appears, a fault may have been stored.

1. Erase the fault memory.

3 - Activate the system test with the key F8 immediately before acceleration with wide-open throttle.

The message "Drive link active" then appears.

Note!

If 'Request small lift' appears, the valves remain at small lift, ie. the performance is reduced dramatically.

4 - Perform acceleration with wide-open throttle in 2nd gear, until "Valve lift diagnosis complete" (max. 4,000 rpm) appears.

PR1020100302080X

Fig. 83 Code P1356: Valve Lift Control Cylinder No. 5, Above Limit (Part 8 of 9)

Diagnosis conditions

- Engine speed less than 5,600 rpm
- Knock control active
- Engine load greater than 45 %

Possible fault cause

- DME control module

Note!

When a fault is stored, the ignition angle is retarded for all cylinders in the range in which knock control is active.

Affected terminals

Diagnosis/troubleshooting

Work instruction			Display OK	If not OK
1	Replace DME control module		⇒ Step 2	
2	Perform adaptation	• Switch on the ignition • Wait one minute • Do not press the accelerator • Switch off the ignition for at least 10 seconds • Read out the fault memory	→ End	

PR1020100303000X

Fig. 84 Code P1384: Knock Control Zero Test, Signal Implausible

Diagnosis conditions

- Engine speed less than 5,600 rpm
- Knock control active
- Engine load greater than 45 %

Possible fault cause

- DME control module

Note!

When a fault is stored, the ignition angle is retarded for all cylinders in the range in which knock control is active.

Affected terminals

Diagnosis/troubleshooting

Work instruction			Display OK	If not OK
1	Replace DME control module		⇒ Step 2	
2	Perform adaptation	• Switch on the ignition • Wait one minute • Do not press the accelerator • Switch off the ignition for at least 10 seconds • Read out the fault memory	→ End	

PR1020100304000X

Fig. 85 Code P1385: Knock Control Offset, Signal Implausible

Diagnosis conditions

- Engine speed less than 5,600 rpm
- Knock control active
- Engine load greater than 45 %

Possible fault cause

- DME control module

Note!

When a fault is stored, the ignition angle is retarded for all cylinders in the range in which knock control is active.

Affected terminals

Diagnosis/troubleshooting

Work instruction			Display OK	If not OK
1	Replace DME control module		⇒ Step 2	
2	Perform adaptation	• Switch on the ignition • Wait one minute • Do not press the accelerator • Switch off the ignition for at least 10 seconds • Read out the fault memory	→ End	

PR1020100305000X

Fig. 86 Code P1386: Knock Control Test Pulse, Signal Implausible

signal implausible

Diagnosis conditions

- Engine running

Possible fault cause

- Loose contact
- Camshaft position sensor

Note!

- *If both CMP sensor signals are missing, the start will take at least 10 seconds.*
- *For safety reasons, the ignition timing is retarded.*

Affected terminals

Terminals III/7, III/17 and III/18

Diagnosis/troubleshooting

Work instruction			Display OK	If not OK
1	Check CMP sensor voltage supply	• Remove connector of CMP sensor 2 • Switch on the ignition • Measure voltage between Pin 1 and Pin 3	Approx. 5 V ⇒ Step 5	⇒ Step 2
2	Check power supply wiring for continuity	• Remove connector of CMP sensor 2 • Connect special tool 9637 to wiring harness (DME control module plug) • Measure resistance between special tool 9637 Pin III/7 and CMP sensor 2 plug Pin 3 • Measure resistance between special tool 9637 Pin III/17 and CMP sensor 2 plug Pin 1	0 - 5 Ω ⇒ Step 3	
3	Replace DME control module		⇒ Step 4	

PR1020100306010X

Fig. 87 Code P1397: CMP Sensor No. 2 (Part 1 of 4)

Work instruction			Display OK	If not OK
4	Perform adaptation	• Switch on the ignition • Wait one minute • Do not press the accelerator • Switch off the ignition for at least 10 seconds • Read out the fault memory	→ End	
5	Check CMP sensor signal	• Connect special tool 9637 • Connect engine tester; use special input • Positive cable to Pin III/18 • Negative cable to Pin III/17 • Start the engine	See Figure 1 ⇒ Step 6	Replace CMP sensor → End

PR1020100306020X

Fig. 87 Code P1397: CMP Sensor No. 2 (Part 2 of 4)

Figure 1:

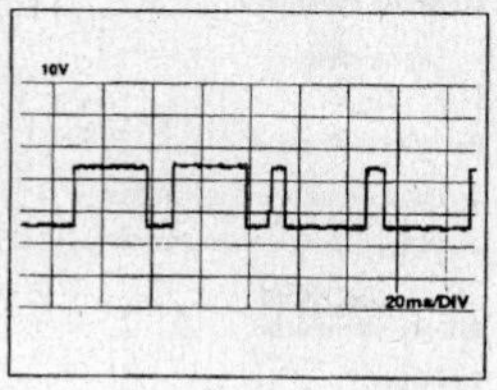

Work instruction			Display OK	If not OK
6	Check signal wire from DME control module, Pin III/18, to CMP sensor	• Connect special tool 9637 to wiring harness (DME control module plug) • Remove connector of CMP sensor 2 • Measure resistance between special tool 9637 Pin III/18 and CMP sensor 2 plug Pin 2	0 - 5 Ω → End	Repair wiring harness → End

below limit

Diagnosis conditions

- Engine running

Possible fault cause

- Short circuit to ground

Note!

- *If both CMP sensor signals are missing, the start will take at least 10 seconds.*
- *For safety reasons, the ignition timing is retarded.*

Affected terminals

Terminal III/18

PR1020100306030X

Fig. 87 Code P1397: CMP Sensor No. 2 (Part 3 of 4)

Diagnosis conditions

- Engine running
- Battery voltage greater than 7 V
- Air conditioning on

Possible fault cause

- A/C relay
- Open circuit in wiring

Affected terminals

Terminal IV/27

Diagnosis/troubleshooting

Work instruction			Display OK	If not OK
1	Check A/C relay	• Remove A/C relay • Measure resistance between Pin 85 and Pin 86	Approx. 75 Ω ⇒ Step 2	Replace A/C relay → End
2	Check control wire for A/C relay, Pin 2 (terminal 85), for open circuit	• Remove A/C relay • Connect special tool 9637 to wiring harness (DME control module plug) • Measure resistance between special tool 9637 Pin IV/27 and A/C relay plug Pin 2	0 - 5 Ω → End	Repair wiring harness → End

PR1020100307000X

Fig. 88 Code P1455: A/C Compressor Control, Open Circuit

Diagnosis/troubleshooting

Work instruction			Display OK	If not OK
1	Check signal wire from DME control module, Pin III/18, to CMP sensor for short to ground	• Connect special tool 9637 to wiring harness (DME control module plug) • Remove connector of CMP sensor 2 • Measure resistance between special tool 9637 Pin III/18 and ground	∞ Ω → End	Repair wiring harness → End

above limit

Diagnosis conditions

- Engine running

Possible fault cause

- Short circuit to B+

Note!

- *If both CMP sensor signals are missing, the start will take at least 10 seconds.*
- *For safety reasons, the ignition timing is retarded.*

Affected terminals

Terminal III/18

Diagnosis/troubleshooting

Work instruction			Display OK	If not OK
1	Check signal wire from DME control module, Pin III/18, to CMP sensor for short to B+	• Connect special tool 9637 to wiring harness (DME control module plug) • Remove connector of CMP sensor 2 • Switch on the ignition • Measure voltage between special tool 9637 Pin III/18 and ground	0 V → End	Repair wiring harness → End

PR1020100306040X

Fig. 87 Code P1397: CMP Sensor No. 2 (Part 4 of 4)

Diagnosis conditions

- Engine running
- Battery voltage greater than 7 V
- Air conditioning on

Possible fault cause

- Short circuit to B+ in wiring

Affected terminals

Terminal IV/27

Diagnosis/troubleshooting

Work instruction			Display OK	If not OK
1	Check control wire for A/C relay, Pin 2 (terminal 85), for short circuit to B+	• Remove A/C relay • Remove DME control module connector • Measure voltage between A/C relay Pin 2 and ground • Ignition on	0 V → End	Repair wiring harness → End

PR1020100308000X

Fig. 89 Code P1456: A/C Compressor Control, Above Limit

Diagnosis conditions

- Engine running
- Battery voltage greater than 7 V
- Air conditioning on

Possible fault cause

- Short circuit to ground in wiring

Affected terminals

Terminal IV/27

Diagnosis/troubleshooting

Work instruction			Display OK	If not OK
1	Check control wire for A/C relay, Pin 2 (terminal 85), for short circuit to ground	• Remove A/C relay • Remove DME control module connector • Measure resistance between Pin 2 (terminal 85) and ground	∞ Ω → End	Repair wiring harness → End

PR1020100309000X

Fig. 90 Code P1457: A/C Compressor Control, Below Limit

Diagnosis conditions

- Ignition on (approx. 30 sec.)
- Stationary vehicle
- Engine not running
- Engine temperature greater than 5 °C
- Intake air temperature greater than 5 °C

Possible fault cause

- Throttle part

Affected terminals

Diagnosis/troubleshooting

Work instruction			Display OK	If not OK
1	Replace throttle part		⇒ Step 2	
2	Erase fault memory		⇒ Step 3	
3	Perform adaptation	• Switch on the ignition • Wait one minute • Actuate accelerator pedal • Switch off the ignition for at least 10 seconds • Read out the fault memory	→ End	→ End

PR1020100311000X

Fig. 92 Code P1502: Throttle Jacking Unit, Spring Test, Above Limit

Diagnosis conditions

- Engine idling

Possible fault cause

- Short circuit in wiring harness
- DME control module output stage faulty

Affected terminals

Terminal I/7

Note!

The vehicle is in emergency air function mode, i.e. the engine is turning at approx. 1200 rpm.

Diagnosis/troubleshooting

Work instruction			Display OK	If not OK
1	Check wiring from DME control module Pin I/7 to the throttle jacking unit for short circuit to B+	• Connect special tool 9637 to wiring harness (DME control module plug) • Measure voltage between Pin I/7 and ground • Switch on the ignition	0 V ⇒ Step 2	Repair wiring harness → End
2	Check wiring from DME control module Pin I/7 to the throttle jacking unit for short circuit to ground	• Connect special tool 9637 to wiring harness (DME control module plug) • Measure resistance between Pin I/7 and ground	∞ Ω → End	Repair wiring harness → End

PR1020100310000X

Fig. 91 Code P1501: Throttle Jacking Unit, Output Stage, Signal Implausible

Diagnosis conditions

- Driving with changing pedal position

Possible fault cause

- Short circuit in wiring harness
- Sluggish throttle

Affected terminals

Terminal I/9 and I/7

Note!

The vehicle is in emergency air function mode, i.e. the engine is turning at approx. 1200 rpm.

Diagnosis/troubleshooting

Work instruction			Display OK	If not OK
1	Check wiring from DME control module Pin I/7 to the throttle jacking unit for short circuit to B+	• Connect special tool 9637 • Measure voltage between Pin I/7 and ground • Switch on the ignition	0 V ⇒ Step 2	Repair wiring harness → End
2	Check wiring from DME control module Pin I/9 to the throttle jacking unit for short circuit to B+	• Connect special tool 9637 • Measure voltage between Pin I/9 and ground • Switch on the ignition	0 V ⇒ Step 3	Repair wiring harness → End
3	Check wiring from DME control module Pin I/7 to the throttle part for short circuit to ground	• Connect special tool 9637 • Measure voltage between Pin I/7 and ground • Switch on the ignition	0 V ⇒ Step 4	Repair wiring harness → End

PR1020100312010X

Fig. 93 Code P1503: Throttle Jacking Unit, Position Error, Signal Implausible (Part 1 of 3)

Work instruction			Display OK	If not OK
4	Check wiring from DME control module Pin I/9 to the throttle part for short circuit to ground	• Connect special tool 9637 • Measure voltage between Pin I/9 and B+ • Switch on the ignition	0 V ⇒ Step 5	Repair wiring harness → End
5	Check wiring from DME control module, Pin I/7, for short circuit to wire, Pin I/9	• Connect special tool 9637 to wiring harness (DME control module plug) • Remove connector of throttle part • Measure resistance between Pin I/7 and Pin I/9	∞ Ω ⇒ Step 6	Repair wiring harness → End

PR1020100312020X

Fig. 93 Code P1503: Throttle Jacking Unit, Position Error, Signal Implausible (Part 2 of 3)

Diagnosis conditions

- Ignition on (approx. 30 sec.)

Possible fault cause

- No adaptation performed
- Throttle part

Affected terminals

Note!

The fault is entered during the adaptation phase.

Diagnosis/troubleshooting

Work instruction			Display OK	If not OK
1	Perform adaptation	• Switch on the ignition • Wait one minute • Do not press the accelerator • Switch off the ignition for at least 10 seconds • Read out the fault memory	Fault entered ⇒ Step 2	→ End
2	Replace throttle part		⇒ Step 3	
3	Perform adaptation	• Switch on the ignition • Wait one minute • Actuate accelerator pedal • Switch off the ignition for at least 10 seconds • Read out the fault memory	→ End	→ End

PR1020100313000X

Fig. 94 Code P1504: Throttle Jacking Unit, Emergency Air Position, Signal Implausible

open circuit

Diagnosis conditions

- Driving with changing pedal position

Possible fault cause

- Open circuit
- Short circuit to B+

Affected terminals

Terminal I/7 and I/9

Diagnosis/troubleshooting

Work instruction			Display OK	If not OK
1	Check wiring from DME control module Pin I/7 to the throttle part for continuity	• Connect special tool 9637 to wiring harness (DME control module plug) • Remove connector of throttle part • Measure resistance between special tool 9637 Pin I/7 and throttle part plug connection Pin 4	0 - 5 Ω ⇒ Step 2	Repair wiring harness → End

PR1020100314010X

Fig. 95 Code P1505: Throttle Jacking Unit, Control Range (Part 1 of 4)

Remove connector of throttle part: ►

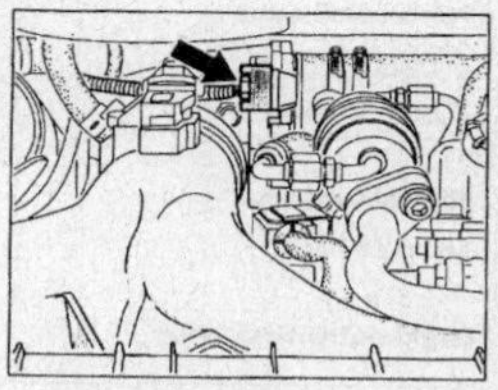

Work instruction			Display OK	If not OK
6	Check resistance of motor actuator in throttle part	• Connect special tool 9637 to wiring harness (DME control module plug) • Measure resistance between Pin I/7 and Pin I/9	1,2 - 1,6 Ω (at 20 °C) ⇒ Step 7	Replace throttle part ⇒ Step 8
7	Replace DME control module		⇒ Step 8	
8	Perform adaptation	• Switch on the ignition • Wait one minute • Do not press the accelerator • Switch off the ignition for at least 10 seconds • Read out the fault memory	→ End	→ End

PR1020100312030X

Fig. 93 Code P1503: Throttle Jacking Unit, Position Error, Signal Implausible (Part 3 of 3)

Remove connector of throttle part: ►

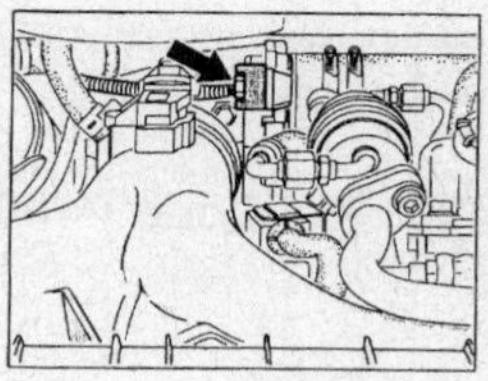

Work instruction			Display OK	If not OK
2	Check wiring from DME control module Pin I/9 to the throttle part for continuity	• Connect special tool 9637 to wiring harness (DME control module plug) • Remove connector of throttle part • Measure resistance between special tool 9637 Pin I/9 and throttle part plug connection Pin 1	0 - 5 Ω ⇒ Step 3	Repair wiring harness → End
3	Check resistance of motor actuator in throttle part	• Connect special tool 9637 to wiring harness (DME control module plug) • Measure resistance between special tool 9637 Pin I/7 and Pin I/9	1.2 to 1.6 Ω (at 20 °C) ⇒ Step 4	Replace throttle part → End
4	Replace DME control module		⇒ Step 5	
5	Perform adaptation	• Switch on the ignition • Wait one minute • Do not actuate accelerator pedal • Switch off the ignition for at least 10 seconds • Read out the fault memory	→ End	→ End

below limit

Diagnosis conditions

- Driving with changing pedal position

PR1020100314020X

Fig. 95 Code P1505: Throttle Jacking Unit, Control Range (Part 2 of 4)

Possible fault cause

- Open circuit
- Short circuit to B+

Affected terminals

Terminal I/7 and I/9

Diagnosis/troubleshooting

Work instruction			Display OK	If not OK
1	Check wiring from DME control module, Pin I/7, to throttle part for short circuit to B+	• Connect special tool 9637 • Measure voltage between Pin I/ 7 and ground • Switch on the ignition	0 V ⇒ Step 2	Repair wiring harness → End
2	Check wiring from DME control module, Pin I/9, to throttle part for short circuit to B+	• Connect special tool 9637 • Measure voltage between Pin I/ 9 and ground • Switch on the ignition	0 V → End	Repair wiring harness → End

above limit

Diagnosis conditions

- Driving with changing pedal position

Possible fault cause

- Short circuit to ground
- Short circuit triggering wire
- Sluggish throttle

Affected terminals

Terminal I/7 and I/9

PR1020100314030X

Fig. 95 Code P1505: Throttle Jacking Unit, Control Range (Part 3 of 4)

Diagnosis conditions

- Ignition on (approx. 30 sec.)
- Stationary vehicle
- Engine not running
- Engine temperature between 5 and 100 °C
- Intake air temperature between 5 and 100 °C
- Battery voltage greater than 10 V
- Pedal value less than 0.8 %

Possible fault cause

- No adaptation performed

Affected terminals

Diagnosis/troubleshooting

Work instruction			Display OK	If not OK
1	Perform adaptation	• Switch on the ignition • Wait one minute • Do not press the accelerator • Switch off the ignition for at least 10 seconds • Read out the fault memory	→ End	Fault is being entered ⇒ Step 2
2	Replace throttle part		⇒ Step 1	

PR1020100315000X

Fig. 96 Code P1506: Throttle Jacking Unit Lower Mechanical Stop, Signal Implausible

Work instruction			Display OK	If not OK
1	Check wiring from DME control module, Pin I/7, to throttle part for short circuit to ground	• Connect special tool 9637 • Measure voltage between Pin I/ 7 and B+ • Switch on the ignition	0 V ⇒ Step 2	Repair wiring harness → End
2	Check wiring from DME control module, Pin I/9, to throttle part for short circuit to ground	• Connect special tool 9637 • Measure voltage between Pin I/ 9 and B+ • Switch on the ignition	0 V → End	Repair wiring harness → End

PR1020100314040X

Fig. 95 Code P1505: Throttle Jacking Unit, Control Range (Part 4 of 4)

Diagnosis conditions

- Ignition on (approx. 30 sec.)
- Stationary vehicle
- Engine not running
- Engine temperature between 5 and 100 °C
- Intake air temperature between 5 and 100 °C
- Battery voltage greater than 10 V
- Pedal value less than 0.8 %

Possible fault cause

- DME control module faulty

Affected terminals

Diagnosis/troubleshooting

Work instruction			Display OK	If not OK
1	Replace DME control module		⇒ Step 2	
2	Perform adaptation	• Switch on the ignition • Wait one minute • Do not press the accelerator • Switch off the ignition for at least 10 seconds • Read out the fault memory	→ End	→ End

PR1020100316000X

Fig. 97 Code P1507: Throttle Jacking Unit, Gain Adjustment, Signal Implausible

Diagnosis conditions

- Engine speed greater than 1,120 rpm

Possible fault cause

- DME control module faulty

Affected terminals

Diagnosis/troubleshooting

Work instruction			Display OK	If not OK
1	Replace DME control module		⇒ Step 2	
2	Perform adaptation	• Switch on the ignition • Wait one minute • Do not press the accelerator • Switch off the ignition for at least 10 seconds • Read out the fault memory	→ End	→ End

PR1020100317000X

Fig. 98 Code P1508: Torque Comparison Function Monitor, Signal Implausible

Diagnosis conditions

- Ignition on
- Stationary vehicle
- Engine not running
- Engine temperature between 5 and 100 °C
- Intake air temperature between 5 and 100 °C
- Battery voltage greater than 10 V
- Pedal value less than 0.8 %

Possible fault cause

- No new adaptation after replacement of throttle part

Affected terminals

Diagnosis/troubleshooting

Work instruction			Display OK	If not OK
1	Perform adaptation	• Switch on the ignition • Wait one minute • Actuate accelerator pedal • Switch off the ignition for at least 10 seconds • Read out the fault memory	→ End	→ End

PR1020100318000X

Fig. 99 Code P1510: Throttle Jacking Unit, Exchange Detection Without Adaptation, Signal Implausible

Diagnosis conditions

- Ignition on (approx. 30 sec.)
- Stationary vehicle
- Engine not running
- Engine temperature greater than 5 °C
- Intake air temperature greater than 5 °C

Possible fault cause

- Throttle part

Affected terminals

Diagnosis/troubleshooting

Work instruction			Display OK	If not OK
1	Replace throttle part		⇒ Step 2	
2	Erase fault memory		⇒ Step 3	
3	Perform adaptation	• Switch on the ignition • Wait one minute • Do not press the accelerator • Switch off the ignition for at least 10 seconds • Read out the fault memory	→ End	→ End

PR1020100320000X

Fig. 101 Code P1513: Throttle Jacking Unit, Spring Test, Above Or Below Limit

Diagnosis conditions

- Ignition on

Possible fault cause

- Starting the vehicle during adaptation after replacement of throttle part

Affected terminals

Diagnosis/troubleshooting

Work instruction			Display OK	If not OK
1	Perform adaptation	• Switch on the ignition • Wait one minute Do not press the accelerator • Switch off the ignition for at least 10 seconds • Read out the fault memory	→ End	→ End
2				

PR1020100319000X

Fig. 100 Code P1511: Throttle Jacking Unit, Abortion Of Test Due To Negative Influence On Ambient Condition

Diagnosis conditions

- Ignition on

Possible fault cause

- No adaptation values available despite repeated adaptations

Affected terminals

Diagnosis/troubleshooting

Work instruction			Display OK	If not OK
1	Replace throttle part		⇒ Step 2	
2	Perform adaptation	• Switch on the ignition • Wait one minute Do not press the accelerator • Switch off the ignition for at least 10 seconds • Read out the fault memory	→ End	→ End

PR1020100321000X

Fig. 102 Code P1514: Throttle Jacking Unit Lower Mechanical Stop, Signal Implausible

Diagnosis conditions

- Start condition
- Motronic reset

Possible fault cause

- Open circuit in wiring between DME control module and alarm system
- Short circuit to ground or short circuit to B+
- Alarm system control module faulty

Affected terminals

Diagnosis/troubleshooting

Work instruction			Display OK	If not OK
1	Check signal wire for continuity	• Remove connector I of alarm system control module • Connect special tool 9637 to wiring harness (DME control module plug) • Measure resistance between special tool 9637 Pin I/3 and alarm system control module plug Pin I/23	0 - 5 Ω ⇒ Step 3	⇒ Step 2
2	Remove connector X 2/3	• Measure resistance between plug connection X 2/3 bushing 6 and special tool 9637 Pin I/3 • Measure resistance between plug connection X 2/3 Pin 6 and alarm system control module plug I Pin 23	0 - 5 Ω ⇒ Step 3	Repair wiring harness → End

PR1020100322010X

Fig. 103 Code P1570: 39 Immobilizer, Signal Implausible (Part 1 of 2)

Work instruction			Display OK	If not OK
3	Check signal wire for short circuit to ground	• Remove connector I of alarm system control module • Connect special tool 9637 to wiring harness (DME control module plug) • Measure resistance between special tool 9637 Pin I/3 and ground	∞ Ω ⇒ Step 4	Repair wiring harness → End
4	Check signal wire for short circuit to B+	• Remove connector I of alarm system control module • Connect special tool 9637 to wiring harness (DME control module plug) • Measure voltage between special tool 9637 Pin I/3 and ground	0 V ⇒ Step 4	Repair wiring harness → End
5	Replace alarm system control module.		→ End	→ End

PR1020100322020X

Fig. 103 Code P1570: 39 Immobilizer, Signal Implausible (Part 2 of 2)

Diagnosis conditions

- Start condition
- Motronic reset

Possible fault cause

- Open circuit in wiring between DME control module and alarm system
- Short circuit to ground or short circuit to B+
- Alarm system control module faulty

Affected terminals

Diagnosis/troubleshooting

Work instruction			Display OK	If not OK
1	Check signal wire for continuity	• Remove connector I of alarm system control module • Connect special tool 9637 to wiring harness (DME control module plug) • Measure resistance between special tool 9637 Pin I/3 and alarm system control module plug Pin I/23	0 - 5 Ω ⇒ Step 3	⇒ Step 2
2	Remove connector X 2/3	• Measure resistance between plug connection X 2/3 bushing 6 and special tool 9637 Pin I/3 • Measure resistance between plug connection X 2/3 Pin 6 and alarm system control module plug I Pin 23	0 - 5 Ω ⇒ Step 3	Repair wiring harness → End

PR1020100323010X

Fig. 104 Code P1571: 39 Immobilizer, Open Circuit Or No Signal (Part 1 of 2)

Work instruction			Display OK	If not OK
3	Check signal wire for short circuit to ground	• Remove connector I of alarm system control module • Connect special tool 9637 to wiring harness (DME control module plug) • Measure resistance between special tool 9637 Pin I/3 and ground	∞ Ω ⇒ Step 4	Repair wiring harness → End
4	Check signal wire for short circuit to B+	• Remove connector I of alarm system control module • Connect special tool 9637 to wiring harness (DME control module plug) • Measure voltage between special tool 9637 Pin I/3 and ground	0 V ⇒ Step 4	Repair wiring harness → End
5	Replace alarm system control module.		→ End	→ End

PR1020100323020X

Fig. 104 Code P1571: 39 Immobilizer, Open Circuit Or No Signal (Part 2 of 2)

Diagnosis conditions

- Ignition on

Possible fault cause

- Stop light switch
- Wiring harness

Note!

The DME control module receives the signals from the stop light switches via CAN bus.

Affected terminals

Diagnosis/troubleshooting

Work instruction			Display OK	If not OK
1	Check stop light switch	• Remove stop light switch • Measure resistance between Pin 1 and Pin 4 • Actuate stop light switch • Measure resistance between Pin 1 and Pin 2 • Actuate stop light switch • Install stop light switch	0 - 5 Ω ∞ Ω ∞ Ω 0 - 5 Ω ⇒ Step 2	Replace stop light switch → End
2	Check wiring from PSM control module to stop light switch 1 for short circuit to B+	• Remove PSM control module connector • Measure voltage between Pin 32 and ground • Switch on the ignition • Actuate brake	0 V Battery voltage ⇒ Step 3	Repair wiring harness → End

PR1020100324010X

Fig. 105 Code P1574: Stop Lamp Switch, Signal Implausible (Part 1 of 2)

Work instruction			Display OK	If not OK
3	Check wiring from PSM control module to stop light switch 2 for short circuit to B+	• Remove PSM control module connector • Measure voltage between Pin 37 and ground • Switch on the ignition	Battery voltage	Repair wiring harness → End
		• Actuate brake	0 V → End	

PR1020100324020X

Fig. 105 Code P1574: Stop Lamp Switch, Signal Implausible (Part 2 of 2)

Affected terminals

Terminal IV/8

Note!

- *The system operates in pedal sensor standby mode, i.e. the angle of the accelerator pedal is calculated from the residual position sensor signal.*
- *The maximum pedal value is limited to 30 %.*
- *The dynamic is limited.*

Diagnosis/troubleshooting

Work instruction			Display OK	If not OK
1	Check wiring from DME control module, Pin IV/8, to pedal sensor, Pin 2, for short circuit to ground	• Connect special tool 9637 to wiring harness (DME control module plug) • Measure resistance between special tool Pin IV/8 and ground	∞ Ω ⇒ Step 2	Repair wiring harness → End
2	Replace pedal sensor		→ End	→ End

above limit

Diagnosis conditions

- Ignition on (approx. 30 sec.)
- Battery voltage greater than 7 V

Possible fault cause

- Short circuit to B+
- Pedal sensor

Affected terminals

Terminal IV/8

Note!

- *The system operates in pedal sensor standby mode, i.e. the angle of the accelerator pedal is calculated from the residual position sensor signal.*
- *The maximum pedal value is limited to 30 %.*
- *The dynamic is limited.*

PR1020100325020X

Fig. 106 Code P1577: Accelerator Pedal Position Sensor No. 1 (Part 2 of 3)

Work instruction			Display OK	If not OK
1	Check wiring from DME control module, Pin IV/8, to pedal sensor, Pin 2, for short circuit to B+	• Connect special tool 9637 to wiring harness (DME control module plug) • Switch on the ignition • Measure voltage between special tool Pin IV/8 and ground	0 V ⇒ Step 2	Repair wiring harness → End
2	Replace pedal sensor		→ End	→ End

PR1020100325030X

Fig. 106 Code P1577: Accelerator Pedal Position Sensor No. 1 (Part 3 of 3)

Diagnosis conditions

- Ignition on (approx. 30 sec.)
- Battery voltage greater than 7 V

Possible fault cause

- Pedal sensor

Affected terminals

Note!

- *The system operates in pedal sensor standby mode, i.e. the angle of the accelerator pedal is calculated from the residual position sensor signal.*
- *The maximum pedal value is limited to 30 %.*
- *The dynamic is limited.*

Diagnosis/troubleshooting

Work instruction		Display OK	If not OK
1	Replace pedal sensor	→ End	→ End

below limit

Diagnosis conditions

- Ignition on (approx. 30 sec.)
- Battery voltage greater than 7 V

Possible fault cause

- Short circuit to ground
- Pedal sensor

PR1020100325010X

Fig. 106 Code P1577: Accelerator Pedal Position Sensor No. 1 (Part 1 of 3)

Diagnosis conditions

- Ignition on (approx. 30 sec.)
- Battery voltage greater than 7 V

Possible fault cause

- Pedal sensor

Affected terminals

Note!

- *The system operates in pedal sensor standby mode, i.e. the angle of the accelerator pedal is calculated from the residual position sensor signal.*
- *The maximum pedal value is limited to 30 %.*
- *The dynamic is limited.*

Diagnosis/troubleshooting

Work instruction		Display OK	If not OK
1	Replace pedal sensor	→ End	→ End

Diagnosis conditions

- Ignition on (approx. 30 sec.)
- Battery voltage greater than 7 V

Possible fault cause

- Short circuit to ground
- Pedal sensor

PR1020100326010X

Fig. 107 Code P1578: Accelerator Pedal Position Sensor No. 2 (Part 1 of 3)

Affected terminals

Terminal IV/13

Note!

- *The system operates in pedal sensor standby mode, i.e. the angle of the accelerator pedal is calculated from the residual position sensor signal.*
- *The maximum pedal value is limited to 30 %.*
- *The dynamic is limited.*

Diagnosis/troubleshooting

Work instruction			Display OK	If not OK
1	Check wiring from DME control module, Pin IV/13, to pedal sensor, Pin 2, for short circuit to ground	• Connect special tool 9637 to wiring harness (DME control module plug) • Measure resistance between special tool Pin IV/13 and ground	∞ Ω ⇒ Step 2	Repair wiring harness → End
2	Replace pedal sensor		→ End	→ End

Diagnosis conditions

- Ignition on (approx. 30 sec.)
- Battery voltage greater than 7 V

Possible fault cause

- Short circuit to B+
- Pedal sensor

Affected terminals

Terminal IV/13

PR1020100326020X

Fig. 107 Code P1578: Accelerator Pedal Position Sensor No. 2 (Part 2 of 3)

Diagnosis conditions

- Vehicle has PSM
- Battery voltage greater than 10 V
- Ignition on

Possible fault cause

- Wiring harness
- PSM control module not connected
- PSM control module faulty

Note!

- *If all CAN bus faults are stored, there must be a short circuit in the CAN bus wiring.*
- *If one CAN bus fault is stored, the cruise control system is out of order.*
- *CAN bus faults may be caused by a control module reset. The fault is then indicated as "Not present".*

Affected terminals

Terminal IV/36 and IV/37

Diagnosis/troubleshooting

Work instruction			Display OK	If not OK
1	Check whether connector of PSM control module is plugged in.		⇒ Step 2	
2	Check CAN bus from DME control module to PSM control module for continuity	• Remove DME control module connector • Remove plug I from instrument cluster • Remove PSM control module connector • Connect special tool 9637 to wiring harness (DME control module plug)		Repair wiring harness → End

PR1020100327010X

Fig. 108 Code P1600: CAN Timeout PSM, Open Circuit (Part 1 of 3)

Note!

- *The system operates in pedal sensor standby mode, i.e. the angle of the accelerator pedal is calculated from the residual position sensor signal.*
- *The maximum pedal value is limited to 30 %.*
- *The dynamic is limited.*

Diagnosis/troubleshooting

Work instruction			Display OK	If not OK
1	Check wiring from DME control module, Pin IV/13, to pedal sensor, Pin 2, for short circuit to B+	• Connect special tool 9637 to wiring harness (DME control module plug) • Switch on the ignition • Measure voltage between special tool Pin IV/13 and ground	0 V ⇒ Step 2	Repair wiring harness → End
2	Replace pedal sensor		→ End	→ End

PR1020100326030X

Fig. 107 Code P1578: Accelerator Pedal Position Sensor No. 2 (Part 3 of 3)

Work instruction			Display OK	If not OK
2		• Measure resistance between special tool plug IV Pin 36 and PSM control module plug Pin 61 • Measure resistance between special tool 9637 plug IV Pin 37 and PSM control module plug Pin 63	0 - 5 Ω 0 - 5 Ω ⇒ Step 3	

Note!

The wires are routed via two connectors.

Work instruction			Display OK	If not OK
3	Check CAN bus from DME control module to PSM control module for short circuit to ground	• Remove DME control module connector • Remove plug I from instrument cluster • Remove PSM control module connector • Connect special tool 9637 to wiring harness (DME control module plug) • Measure resistance between special tool 9637 plug IV Pin 36 and ground • Measure resistance between special tool plug IV Pin 37 and ground	 ∞ Ω ∞ Ω ⇒ Step 4	Repair wiring harness → End

Note!

The wires are also routed to the instrument cluster.

PR1020100327020X

Fig. 108 Code P1600: CAN Timeout PSM, Open Circuit (Part 2 of 3)

Work instruction			Display OK	If not OK
4	Check CAN bus from DME control module to PSM control module for short circuit to B+	• Remove DME control module connector • Remove plug I from instrument cluster • Remove PSM control module connector • Connect special tool 9637 to wiring harness (DME control module plug)		Repair wiring harness → End
		• Measure voltage between special tool 9637 plug IV Pin 36 and ground • Switch on the ignition	0 V	
		• Measure voltage between special tool 9637 plug IV Pin 37 and ground • Switch on the ignition	0 V ⇒ Step 5	
5	Check CAN bus from DME control module to PSM control module for short circuit	• Remove DME control module connector • Remove plug I from instrument cluster • Remove PSM control module connector • Connect special tool 9637 to wiring harness (DME control module plug) • Measure resistance between special tool 9637 plug IV Pin 36 and plug IV Pin 37	∞ Ω → End	Repair wiring harness → End

PR1020100327030X

Fig. 108 Code P1600: CAN Timeout PSM, Open Circuit (Part 3 of 3)

Note!

- *If all CAN bus faults are stored, there must be a short circuit in the CAN bus wiring.*
- *If one CAN bus fault is stored, the cruise control system is out of order.*
- *CAN bus faults may be caused by a control module reset. The fault is then indicated as "Not present".*

Affected terminals

Terminal I/15 and I/31

Diagnosis/troubleshooting

Work instruction			Display OK	If not OK
1	Check whether connector of instrument cluster is plugged in		⇒ Step 2	
2	Check CAN bus from DME control module to instrument cluster for continuity	• Remove DME control module connector • Remove plug I from instrument cluster • Remove PSM control module connector • Connect special tool 9637 to wiring harness (DME control module plug)		Repair wiring harness → End
		• Measure resistance between special tool 9637 plug IV Pin 36 and instrument cluster plug I Pin 15	0 - 5 Ω	
		• Measure resistance between special tool plug IV Pin 37 and instrument cluster plug I Pin 31	0 - 5 Ω ⇒ Step 3	
3	Check CAN bus from DME control module to instrument cluster for short circuit to ground	• Remove DME control module connector • Remove plug I from instrument cluster • Remove PSM control module connector • Connect special tool 9637 to wiring harness (DME control module plug)		Repair wiring harness → End

PR1020100328020X

Fig. 109 Code P1601: CAN Timeout Instrument Cluster (Part 2 of 3)

Diagnosis conditions

- Battery voltage greater than 10 V
- Ignition on

Possible fault cause

- Instrument cluster faulty

Note!

- *If one CAN bus fault is stored, the cruise control system is out of order.*
- *CAN bus faults may be caused by a control module reset. The fault is then indicated as "Not present".*

Affected terminals

Diagnosis/troubleshooting

Replace instrument cluster.

open circuit

Diagnosis conditions

- Battery voltage greater than 10 V
- Ignition on

Possible fault cause

- Wiring harness faulty
- Plug on instrument cluster not connected
- Instrument cluster faulty

PR1020100328010X

Fig. 109 Code P1601: CAN Timeout Instrument Cluster (Part 1 of 3)

Work instruction			Display OK	If not OK
3		• Measure resistance between special tool 9637 plug IV Pin 36 and ground	∞ Ω	
		• Measure resistance between special tool 9637 plug IV Pin 37 and ground	∞ Ω ⇒ Step 4	

Note!

The wires are also routed to the PSM control module.

Work instruction			Display OK	If not OK
4	Check CAN bus from DME control module to instrument cluster for short circuit to B+	• Remove DME control module connector • Remove plug I from instrument cluster • Remove PSM control module connector • Connect special tool 9637 to wiring harness (DME control module plug)	⇒ Step 5	Repair wiring harness → End
		• Measure voltage between special tool 9637 plug IV Pin 36 and ground • Switch on the ignition	0 V	
		• Measure voltage between special tool 9637 plug IV Pin 37 and ground • Switch on the ignition	0 V ⇒ Step 5	
5	Check CAN bus from DME control module to instrument cluster for short circuit	• Remove DME control module connector • Remove plug I from instrument cluster • Remove PSM control module connector • Connect special tool 9637 to wiring harness (DME control module plug) • Measure resistance between special tool 9637 plug IV Pin 36 and plug IV Pin 37	∞ Ω → End	Repair wiring harness → End

PR1020100328030X

Fig. 109 Code P1601: CAN Timeout Instrument Cluster (Part 3 of 3)

Diagnosis conditions

- Engine running
- Battery voltage greater than 7 V
- Coolant temperature greater than 90 °C or ATF temperature > 85 °C

Possible fault cause

- Wiring harness
- DME control module
- Coolant shutoff valve

Affected terminals

Terminal IV/40

Diagnosis/troubleshooting

	Work instruction		Display OK	If not OK
1	Check coolant shutoff valve for continuity	• Remove connector of coolant shutoff valve • Measure resistance at coolant shutoff valve between Pin 1 and Pin 2	Approx. 20 - 30 Ω ⇒ Step 2	Replace coolant shutoff valve → End
2	Check wiring from DME control module to coolant shutoff valve for continuity	• Connect special tool 9637 to wiring harness (DME control module plug) • Remove connector of coolant shutoff valve • Measure resistance between special tool 9637 plug IV Pin 40 and coolant shutoff valve plug Pin 2	0 - 5 Ω ⇒ Step 3	Repair wiring harness → End
3	Replace DME control module		⇒ Step 4	
4	Perform adaptation	• Switch on the ignition • Wait one minute • Do not press the accelerator • Switch off the ignition for at least 10 seconds • Read out the fault memory	→ End	

PR1020100329010X

Fig. 110 Code P1656: Coolant Shutoff Valve (Part 1 of 3)

above limit

Diagnosis conditions

- Engine running
- Battery voltage greater than 7 V

Possible fault cause

- Wiring harness
- DME control module

Affected terminals

Terminal IV/40

Diagnosis/troubleshooting

	Work instruction		Display OK	If not OK
1	Check wiring from DME control module to coolant shutoff valve for short circuit to B+	• Connect special tool 9637 to wiring harness (DME control module plug) • Remove connector of coolant shutoff valve • Measure voltage between special tool 9637 plug IV Pin 40 and ground • Switch on the ignition	0 V ⇒ Step 2	Repair wiring harness → End
2	Replace DME control module		⇒ Step 3	
3	Perform adaptation	• Switch on the ignition • Wait one minute • Do not press the accelerator • Switch off the ignition for at least 10 seconds • Read out the fault memory	→ End	

PR1020100329030X

Fig. 110 Code P1656: Coolant Shutoff Valve (Part 3 of 3)

Diagnosis conditions

- Engine running
- Battery voltage greater than 7 V
- Coolant temperature greater than 90 °C or ATF temperature > 85 °C

Possible fault cause

- Wiring harness
- DME control module

Affected terminals

Terminal IV/40

Diagnosis/troubleshooting

	Work instruction		Display OK	If not OK
1	Check wiring from DME control module to colant shutoff valve for short to ground	• Connect special tool 9637 to wiring harness (DME control module plug) • Remove connector of coolant shutoff valve • Measure resistance between special tool 9637 plug IV Pin 40 and coolant shutoff valve plug Pin 2	∞ Ω ⇒ Step 2	Repair wiring harness → End
2	Replace DME control module		⇒ Step 3	
3	Perform adaptation	• Switch on the ignition • Wait one minute • Do not press the accelerator • Switch off the ignition for at least 10 seconds • Read out the fault memory	→ End	

PR1020100329020X

Fig. 110 Code P1656: Coolant Shutoff Valve (Part 2 of 3)

Diagnosis conditions

- Ignition on

Possible fault cause

- Undervoltage
- DME control module faulty

This fault may be entered if the control module has been operated with undervoltage.

Affected terminals

I/1

Diagnosis/troubleshooting

Note!

If no fault is present, delete the fault memory.

	Work instruction		Display OK	If not OK
1	Check voltage supply, terminal 15	• Measure voltage between Pin I/1 and ground	> 11 V ⇒ Step 2	
2	Replace DME control module		⇒ Step 3	
3	Perform adaptation	• Switch on the ignition • Wait one minute • Do not press the accelerator • Switch off the ignition for at least 10 seconds • Read out the fault memory	→ End	→ End

PR1020100330000X

Fig. 111 Code P1671: Control Module Faulty, Signal Implausible

open circuit

Diagnosis conditions

- Engine running
- Battery voltage greater than 7 V
- Engine compartment purge fan switched on once
- Engine compartment temperature greater than 75 °C
- Front and rear lids closed

Note!

The triggering wire for relay terminal 85 is monitored.

The rear lid may be opened to speed up the warming process. In order to proceed with the diagnosis, the rear lid must then be closed.

Possible fault cause

- Open circuit
- Relay faulty
- DME control module faulty

Affected terminals

Terminal II/20

Diagnosis/troubleshooting

Work instruction			Display OK	If not OK
1	Check relay	• Remove relay • Measure resistance between Pin 85 and Pin 86	Approx. 75 Ω ⇒ Step 2	Replace relay → End
2	Check wiring from DME control module to relay for continuity	• Connect special tool 9637 to wiring harness (DME control module plug) • Remove relay • Measure resistance between special tool 9637, plug II Pin 20, and relay slot, Pin 2 (terminal 85)	0 - 5 Ω ⇒ Step 3	Repair wiring harness → End

PR1020100331010X

Fig. 112 Code P1674: Engine Compartment Purge Fan Output Stage (Part 1 of 4)

Diagnosis/troubleshooting

Work instruction			Display OK	If not OK
1	Check relay	• Remove relay • Measure resistance between Pin 85 and Pin 86	Approx. 75 Ω ⇒ Step 2	Replace relay → End
2	Check wiring from DME control module to relay for short to ground	• Connect special tool 9637 to wiring harness (DME control module plug) • Remove relay • Measure resistance between special tool 9637 plug II Pin 20 and ground	∞ Ω ⇒ Step 3	Repair wiring harness → End
3	Replace DME control module		⇒ Step 4	
4	Perform adaptation	• Switch on the ignition • Wait one minute • Do not press the accelerator • Switch off the ignition for at least 10 seconds • Read out the fault memory	→ End	

Diagnosis conditions

- Engine running
- Battery voltage greater than 7 V
- Engine compartment purge fan switched on once
- Engine compartment temperature greater than 75 °C
- Front and rear lids closed

Note!

The triggering wire for relay terminal 85 is monitored.

The rear lid may be opened to speed up the warming process. In order to proceed with the diagnosis, the rear lid must then be closed.

Possible fault cause

- Short circuit to B+

PR1020100331030X

Fig. 112 Code P1674: Engine Compartment Purge Fan Output Stage (Part 3 of 4)

Work instruction			Display OK	If not OK
3	Replace DME control module		⇒ Step 4	
4	Perform adaptation	• Switch on the ignition • Wait one minute • Do not press the accelerator • Switch off the ignition for at least 10 seconds • Read out the fault memory	→ End	

short circuit to ground

Diagnosis conditions

- Engine running
- Battery voltage greater than 7 V
- Engine compartment purge fan switched on once
- Engine compartment temperature greater than 75 °C
- Front and rear lids closed

Note!

The triggering wire for relay terminal 85 is monitored.

The rear lid may be opened to speed up the warming process. In order to proceed with the diagnosis, the rear lid must then be closed.

Possible fault cause

- Short circuit to ground
- Relay faulty
- DME control module faulty

Affected terminals

Terminal II/20

PR1020100331020X

Fig. 112 Code P1674: Engine Compartment Purge Fan Output Stage (Part 2 of 4)

- Relay faulty
- DME control module faulty

Affected terminals

Terminal II/20

Diagnosis/troubleshooting

Work instruction			Display OK	If not OK
1	Check relay	• Remove relay • Measure resistance between Pin 85 and Pin 86	Approx. 75 Ω ⇒ Step 2	Replace relay → End
2	Check wiring from DME control module to relay for short circuit to B+	• Connect special tool 9637 to wiring harness (DME control module plug) • Remove relay • Measure voltage between special tool 9637 plug II Pin 20 and ground • Switch on the ignition	0 V ⇒ Step 3	Repair wiring harness → End
3	Replace DME control module		⇒ Step 4	
4	Perform adaptation	• Switch on the ignition • Wait one minute • Do not press the accelerator • Switch off the ignition for at least 10 seconds • Read out the fault memory	→ End	

PR1020100331040X

Fig. 112 Code P1674: Engine Compartment Purge Fan Output Stage (Part 4 of 4)

Electric Fuel Pumps

NOTE: If Uncertain About The Proper Use Of Information Contained In This Section, Please Refer To "How To Use This Manual" Located In The Front Of This Manual.

NOTE: On Air Bag Equipped Models, Refer To "Air Bag System Precautions" Located In The Front Of This Manual For System Disarming & Arming Procedures.

NOTE: Refer To "Computer Relearn Procedures" Located In The Front Of This Manual When Battery Power To The Computer Has Been Interrupted.

INDEX

	Page No.
Diagnosis & Testing	15-286
Fuel Delivery Rate	15-287
Boxster	15-287
911 Turbo	15-287
911	15-287
Operation Check	15-286
911 Carrera	15-286
Pressure Test	15-286
Boxster	15-286
911	15-286
Fuel Pump Relay Location	15-286
Boxster	15-286
911	15-286
Fuel Pump Replacement	15-287
Boxster	15-287
Installation	15-287
Removal	15-287
911 w/3.4L Engine	15-288
911 w/3.6L Engine	15-287
1998	15-287
Fuel Pump Specifications	15-288
Precautions	15-286
Air Bag Systems	15-286
Battery Ground Cable	15-286

PRECAUTIONS

Air Bag Systems

Refer to "Air Bag System Precautions" in the front of this manual for system disarming and arming procedures.

Battery Ground Cable

Prior to service, disconnect battery ground cable and isolate as required.

FUEL PUMP RELAY LOCATION

911

The fuel pump relay is located in the relay center on the lefthand side of the engine compartment.

Boxster

The relay is located in the central electrical board.

DIAGNOSIS & TESTING

Operation Check

911 CARRERA

1. Operate starter while listening for fuel pump operation. If fuel pump is not operating, proceed to step 2.
2. Check fuse No. 16, replace as necessary.

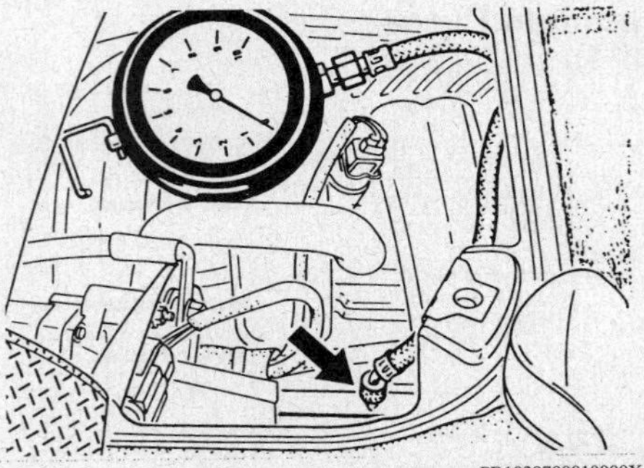

Fig. 1 Test connection. Boxster

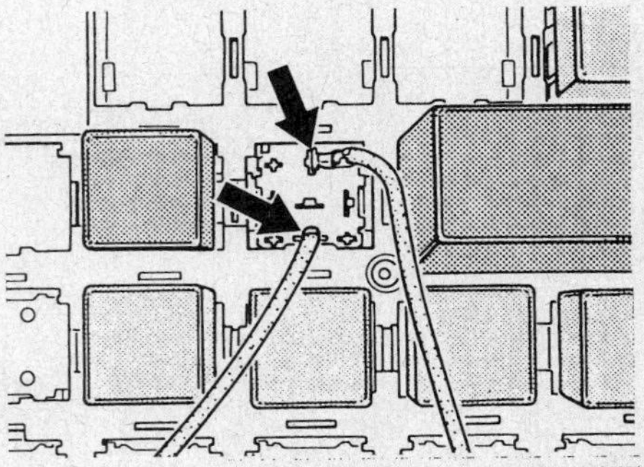

Fig. 2 Fuel pump relay contacts. Boxster

3. If fuse is satisfactory, jump voltage from fuse No. 17 to fuse No. 16 with a jumper wire.
4. If pump still does not operate, pump or wiring is faulty.

Pressure Test

BOXSTER

1. Remove cover cap from test connection on fuel collection pipe.
2. Connect pressure gauge tool No. P378a with connecting line tool No. 9559, or equivalents, to test connection, **Fig. 1**.
3. Actuate fuel pump with Porsche System Tester 2 or disconnect fuel pump relay from the central electrical board and bridge contacts 30 and 87 (identified as 3 and 5 of the central electrical board) with a fused jumper as shown in **Fig. 2.**
4. Pressure with engine off should be 52–58 psi and pressure with engine idling should be 42–48 psi.
5. Replace sealing ring in brass closure cap. **Torque** new brass cap to 24 inch lbs.

911

1. Remove test port cap nut from fuel distribution line. **Do not allow fuel to spill on hot engine. Also ensure sealing ball does not fall out of capped nut.**
2. Connect fuel pressure gauge to test connection.
3. Bridge fuses 16 and 17 with a jumper wire. Fuel pump should operate.
4. Check fuel pressure gauge. Correct reading pressure is approximately 36 psi.
5. Remove jumper wire and fuel pressure gauge.
6. Install test port cap nut. **Torque** cap nut to 108 inch lbs.

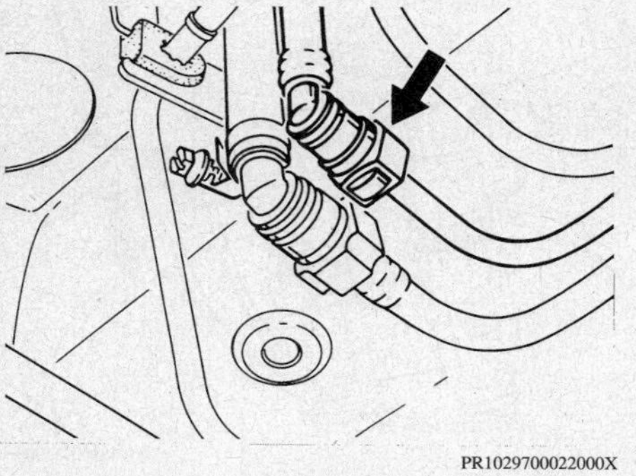

Fig. 3 Fuel line connections. Boxster

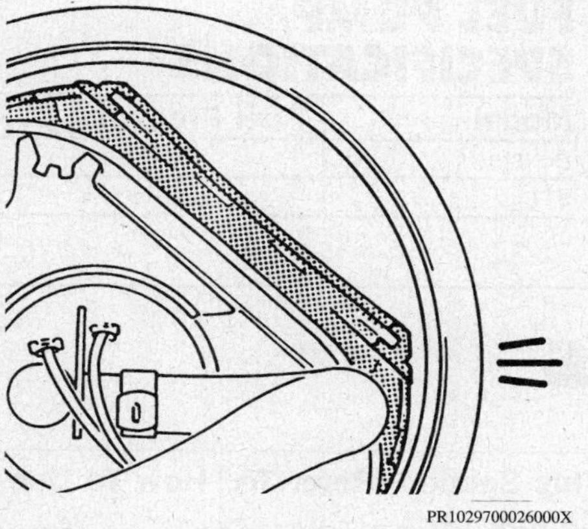

Fig. 6 Fuel pump installation. Boxster

Fuel Delivery Rate

BOXSTER

1. Relieve pressure in fuel tank by opening tank cap.
2. Connect Porsche System tester 2.
3. Raise and support vehicle.
4. Remove rear underside panel.
5. Disconnect fuel return line and collect residual fuel, **Fig. 3.**
6. Hold fuel line in a measuring container. Actuate fuel pump with the Porsche System Tester 2 and allow fuel to flow for 30 seconds into a measuring container. Fuel pump should pump a minimum of 52 cubic inches of fuel within 30 seconds.

911

1. Remove test port cap nut from fuel distribution line. **Do not allow fuel to spill on hot engine. Also ensure sealing ball does not fall out of capped nut.**
2. Connect one end of a length of fuel hose to test connection and place other end in suitable measuring container.
3. Bridge fuses 16 and 17 with a jumper wire. Fuel pump should run.
4. Let fuel run into container for 30 seconds.
5. Fuel pump should pump fuel at a minimum of 50 cubic inches in 30 seconds.
6. Remove jumper wire and fuel hose.
7. Install test port cap nut. **Torque** cap

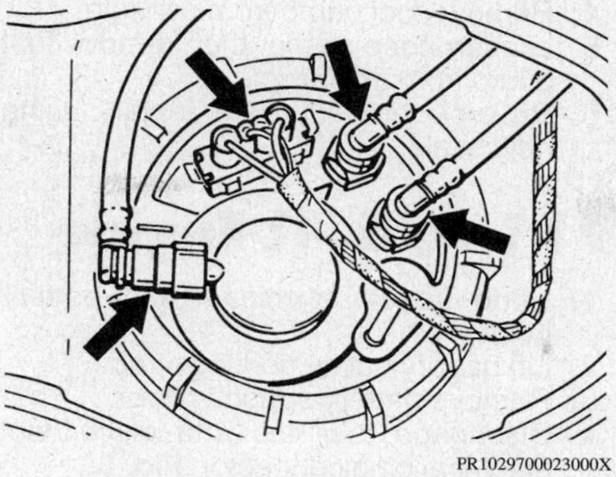

Fig. 4 Fuel pump. Boxster

nut to 9 ft. lbs.

911 TURBO

Prior to checking fuel pump delivery rate, ensure fuel filter is clean, electrical connections are satisfactory and fuel pump voltage is at least 11.5 volts.

1. Disconnect the fuel return line at left side of engine compartment.
2. Install a section of fuel hose onto fuel return line, and position hose end in a graduated container of at least 1500cc capacity.
3. Bridge both fuel pump relay terminals 30 and 87, or pull out air sensor contact plug.
4. Switch ignition on for 30 seconds. Pumps should deliver 92 cubic inches of fuel.
5. If delivery rate is not within specifications, proceed as follows:
   a. Remove fuel inlet line from rear fuel pump.
   b. Connect pressure gauge between fuel inlet line and rear fuel pump.
   c. Bridge both fuel pump relay terminals 30 and 87, or pull out air sensor contact plug.
   d. Switch ignition on, then read pressure gauge. Pressure should be between 29 and 58 psi. If pressure is less than 29 psi, the front pump is defective. If pressure is more than 58 psi, the rear pump is defective.
   e. Replace pump as necessary.

FUEL PUMP REPLACEMENT

Boxster

REMOVAL

1. Remove battery, then the battery support cover.
2. Disconnect fuel line and electrical connector, **Fig. 4.**
3. Remove union nut with VW union nut wrench tool No. 3217, or equivalent, **Fig. 5.**
4. Remove residual fuel.
5. Lift fuel gauge, then disconnect electrical connector and fuel pipes.
6. Turn fuel pump to the left approximately 15° and remove from fuel tank.

INSTALLATION

1. Position fuel pump so edge of pump

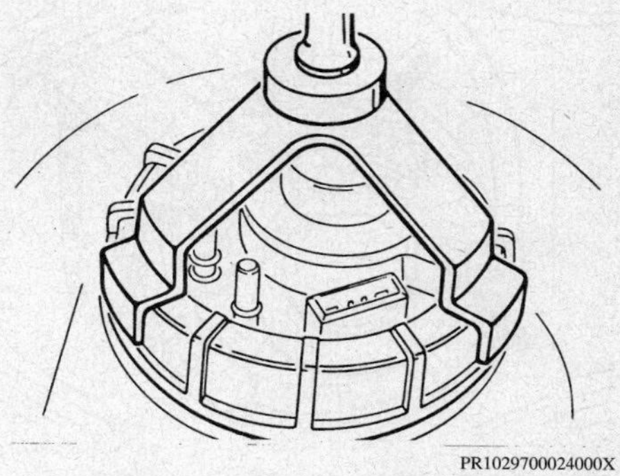

Fig. 5 Union nut removal. Boxster

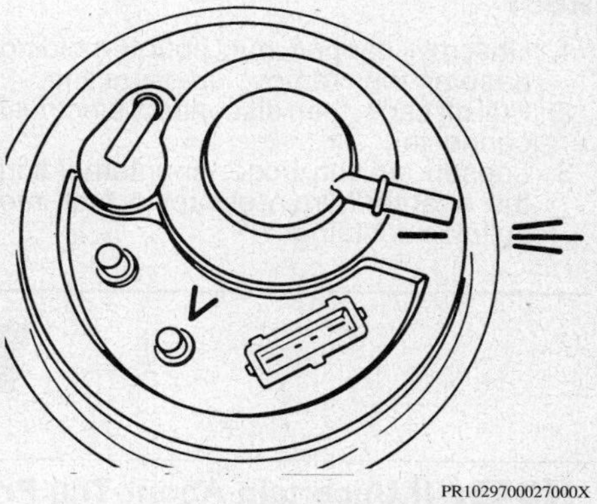

Fig. 7 Fuel pump markings. Boxster

housing faces fuel tank sending unit, **Fig. 6.**

2. Place fuel pump on tank floor bayonet fixture and turn pump to right as far as the stop, ensure pump is properly seated by pulling it up.
3. Install fuel tank sending unit and turn until marking on sending unit matches marking on fuel tank, **Fig. 7.**
4. Tighten union nut with union nut wrench tool No. 3217, or equivalent. **Torque** new union nut with new sealing ring to 52 ft. lbs.
5. Attach fuel lines and electrical connectors until lines audibly engage. **Correct engagement must be checked with a gentle pull.** The color-coded plug (green) must be fitted to connection identified with "V."

911 w/3.6L Engine

1998

Front

1. Remove shield from underneath vehicle.
2. Pinch fuel suction hose with a clamp, then loosen attaching clamp and disconnect suction hose from pump.
3. Pull off caps, then disconnect electrical connector.
4. Unscrew capped nut, counterholding adapter, then remove pressure line.
5. Loosen strap, then remove fuel pump.
6. Reverse procedure to install, using new seals.

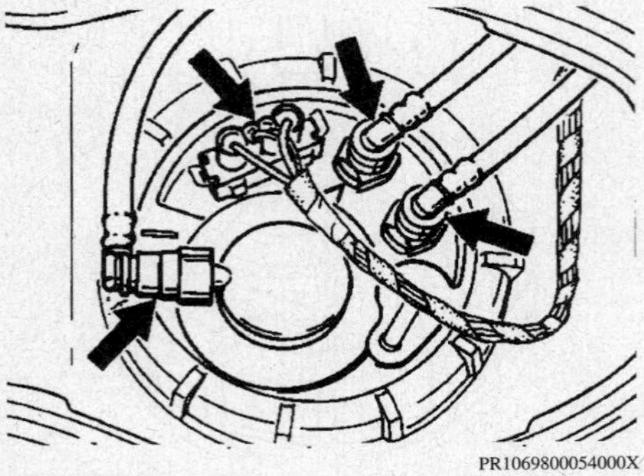

Fig. 8 Sending unit connections. 1999–2001 911 w/3.4L engine

Rear

1. Unscrew capped nut, counterholding adapter, then remove pressure line.
2. Pull off caps, then disconnect electrical connector.
3. Loosen suction hose, counterholding the adapter. Drain escaping fuel into suitable container.
4. Remove fuel pump from console.
5. Loosen hose clamp, then remove fuel pump from holder.
6. Reverse procedure to install, using new seals.

911 w/3.4L Engine

1. Undo battery terminals and battery holder.
2. Lift battery out by holding strap.
3. Remove battery support cover.
4. Disengage fuel line and disconnect electrical plug connector, **Fig. 8.**
5. Undo union nut using union nut remover tool No. 3217 or equivalent.
6. Lift fuel tank sending unit and disconnect electrical connector and fuel pipes, **Fig. 9.**
7. Using a suitable fuel proof glove, hold fuel pump fastened to tank floor, turn it to left (approximately. 15°) and remove fuel pump.
8. Reverse procedure to install.

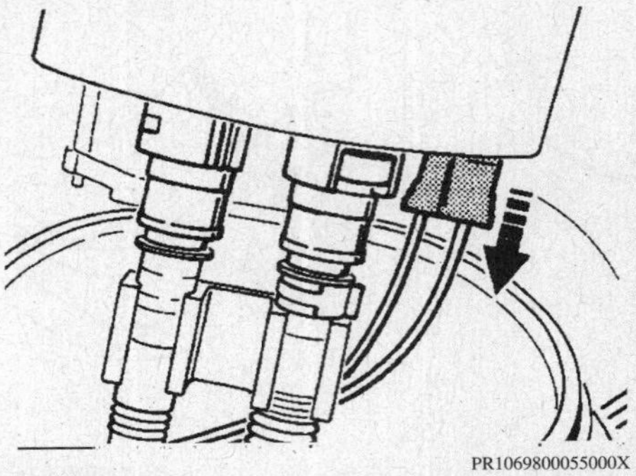

Fig. 9 Fuel pump connections. 1999–2001 911 w/3.4L engine

FUEL PUMP SPECIFICATIONS

Model	Fuel Pressure, psi
Boxster	52–58
911	52–58

Turbochargers

NOTE: If Uncertain About The Proper Use Of Information Contained In This Section, Refer To "How To Use This Manual" Located In The Front Of This Manual.

NOTE: On Air Bag Equipped Models, Refer To "Air Bag System Precautions" Located In The Front Of This Manual For System Disarming & Arming Procedures.

NOTE: Refer To "Computer Relearn Procedures" Located In The Front Of This Manual When Battery Power To The Computer Has Been Interrupted.

INDEX

Page No.

Description 15-288
Diagnosis & Testing 15-288
Component Testing 15-288
Boost Pressure Control Switch.......................15-289
Boost Pressure 15-288
Turbocharger Shaft Endplay ..15-289
Turbocharger Turbine Radial Play.........................15-289
Wastegate Operation 15-289
Precautions......................15-288
Air Bag Systems................15-288
Battery Ground Cable...........15-288
System Service..................15-289
Component Replacement 15-289
Intercooler 15-289
Turbocharger Oil Pump 15-289
Turbocharger 15-289
Wastegate 15-289

DESCRIPTION

The turbocharger is an exhaust driven device that compresses the air/fuel mixture to augment engine power.

By way of a connecting shaft, a turbine spun by exhaust gases spins an intake air impeller. As the throttle is opened and exhaust flow intensifies, the turbine and impeller spin more quickly. The result of increased impeller action, high pressure in the intake manifold produces a denser mixture that yields more power in the firing stroke.

Intake manifold pressure (boost) is regulated by a wastegate valve. This valve bypasses a portion of the exhaust gases around the turbine at a predetermined point in the cycle, limiting the boost pressure and reducing the risk of engine damage.

PRECAUTIONS

Air Bag Systems

Refer to "Air Bag System Precautions" in the front of this manual for system disarming and arming procedures.

Battery Ground Cable

Prior to service, disconnect battery ground cable and isolate as required.

DIAGNOSIS & TESTING

Component Testing

BOOST PRESSURE

1. Disconnect boost pressure control switch electrical connector, then the

switch. Switch is located behind pop-off valve housing.
2. Using necessary threaded adapters, connect a pressure gauge to boost pressure control switch port. Ensure pressure gauge hose is long enough to reach passenger seat.
3. With assistant in passenger seat, drive vehicle with engine operating at 4500–5500 RPM in first or second gear, using brake to limit RPM. Have assistant read off maximum boost. **Boost pressure can only be checked during acceleration. Perform test as quickly as possible to prevent overheating brakes.**
4. Maximum boost is 10–12 psi.

BOOST PRESSURE CONTROL SWITCH

1. Disconnect boost pressure control switch electrical connector, then the switch. Switch is located behind pop-off valve housing.
2. Carefully clamp boost pressure control switch in a vise.
3. Connect ohmmeter between switch housing and connecting terminal. Ohmmeter should indicate 0 ohms.
4. Install tubeless tire rubber valve stem, minus valve core, on threads of switch.
5. Connect air hose to pressure gauge.
6. Slowly raise air pressure. When pressure reaches approximately 21.75 psi, ensure ohmmeter reads infinity.
7. Slowly drop air pressure. When pressure drops to 16–20 psi, ensure ohmmeter reads 0 ohms.
8. If switch does not perform as outlined, replace switch.

WASTEGATE OPERATION

1. Disconnect control line to wastegate.
2. With engine running at idle speed, ensure vacuum is present at control line.
3. Increase engine speed. As engine speed increases, control line vacuum should change to boost pressure.
4. Plug control line, then carefully apply compressed air to control line opening in wastegate while listening for sound of wastegate opening. **Do not apply more than 21 psi of air pressure to wastegate.**

TURBOCHARGER SHAFT ENDPLAY

1. Install a dial gauge and holder.
2. Set dial gauge on end of turbine wheel shaft.
3. Press rotor shaft against dial gauge and note reading.
4. Press rotor shaft in opposite direction and note reading.
5. Difference between two readings is endplay, which should not exceed .013 inch on 911 Turbo models.

TURBOCHARGER TURBINE RADIAL PLAY

Radial play is checked on turbine end only.

1. Set a dial gauge on face of hub.
2. Press turbine wheel to one side, and note value.
3. Press turbine wheel in opposite direction and note value.
4. Difference between two readings is radial play, which should not exceed .025 inch.

SYSTEM SERVICE

Component Replacement

WASTEGATE

1. Disconnect vent line and control line from wastegate.
2. Unlock, then remove wastegate attaching nuts.
3. Remove wastegate, upper gasket, heat guard and lower gasket.
4. Reverse procedure to install. Use new gaskets, seals, nuts and lockplates.

TURBOCHARGER OIL PUMP

1. Remove oil pump guard at exhaust pipe.
2. Disconnect oil pump inlet and pressure lines.
3. Remove oil pump attaching bolts, then the oil pump.
4. Reverse procedure to install, noting the following:
   a. Use new gasket.
   b. Install oil pump shaft pin between camshaft keys. **Left side camshaft keys must be protruding .315 inch (8 mm) beyond camshaft face. Key slots must be positioned properly to avoid oil pump pin from resting in a slot.**

INTERCOOLER

1. Loosen hose clamps from right side of intercooler, then remove hoses.
2. Disconnect hose between wastegate and intercooler at intercooler, then remove intercooler attaching bolts.
3. Remove intercooler, then the turbo outlet duct to intercooler.
4. Reverse procedure to install, noting the following:
   a. Inspect O-rings and replace if necessary.
   b. Prior to installation, lubricate O-rings with silicone grease, or equivalent.

TURBOCHARGER

1. Disconnect hose between turbo outlet and turbo outlet duct, then the oil line from engine.
2. Loosen rear apron attaching screws, then the rear apron and seal.
3. Loosen clamp between bypass line and muffler, then attaching nuts between turbo and muffler.
4. Loosen muffler clamp, then remove muffler.
5. Disconnect hose between turbo inlet line and turbo, then slide hose to left and allow oil to drain into oil trap.
6. Disconnect oil return line at oil trap, then loosen oil trap drain tube located under turbo and remove trap.
7. Remove turbo to exhaust pipe attaching bolts and turbo attaching bolts, then the turbo unit.
8. Reverse procedure to install, noting the following:
   a. Install new oil drain plug seals, self-locking nuts and gaskets.
   b. After installation, lubricate turbo with 2–4cc of engine oil.
   c. Prior to starting engine, the turbo lubricating oil must be pumped for 30 seconds. This can be accomplished by disconnecting the boost pressure control switch wiring connector and turning engine over with the starter for 30 seconds.

Emission Control System Application Charts

Model	Certification Type		Trans. Type		Computerized Engine Management	Fuel Induction System Type	Ignition Timing, Deg. BTDC @RPM	EPA & CARB Emission Recall	Emission Control System SRI	Emission Control Systems								
	CA	FED	A/T	M/T						PCV	ACL	AIS	EGR	EVAP	CAT	SPK	FR	O2S
1998																		
2.5L/151/6	X	X	X	X	YES(5)(9)(10)	SFI	(12)	—	—	X	—	X(6)	—	X	X(8)	X(2)	X	X(7)
3.6L/220/6	X	X	X	X	YES(10)	SFI	(12)	—	X	X	—	X(6)	—	X	X(14)	X(11)	X	X(13)
1999																		
2.5L/151/6	X	X	X	X	YES(5)(9)(10)	SFI	(12)	—	—	X	—	X(6)	—	X	X(8)	X(2)	X	X(7)
3.4L/207/6 911	X	X	X	X	YES(5)(9)(10)	SFI	(12)	—	—	X	—	X(6)	—	X	X(8)	X(2)	X	X(7)
2000–01																		
2.7L/164/6	X	X	X	X	YES(4)(5)(10)	SFI	(12)	—	—	X	—	X(6)	—	X	X(8)	X(2)	X	X(7)
3.2L/194/6	X	X	X	X	YES(4)(5)(10)	SFI	(12)	—	—	X	—	X(6)	—	X	X(8)	X(2)	X	X(7)
3.4L/207/6	X	X	X	X	YES(4)(5)(10)	SFI	(12)	—	—	X	—	X(6)	—	X	X(8)	X(2)	X	X(7)
3.6L/220/6 Turbo	X	X	X	X	YES(3)(5)(10)	SFI	(12)	—	—	X	—	—	—	X	X(1)	X(2)	X	X

X — Equipped
— Not Equipped
(1) — Type, WU-TWC & TWC, number of catalytic converters, 4.
(2) — COP ignition system.
(3) — Bosch M7.8.
(4) — Bosch M7.2.
(5) — Vario Cam valve timing.
(6) — Electric pump type.
(7) — Four HO2S.
(8) — Type, TWC; number of catalytic converters, 2
(9) — Bosch M5.2
(10) — OBD II.
(11) — DI/DME.
(12) — Controlled by Digital Motor Electronic (Motronic) control.
(13) — One O2S.
(14) — TWC (Three Way Catalytic Converter).

ACL — Air Cleaner (Thermostatic Air Cleaner)
AIS — Air Injection System
A/T — Automatic Transmission
BTDC — Before Top Dead Center
CA — California
CARB — Carburetor
CAT — Catalytic Converter
COP — Coil On Plug Ignition System
DI — Distributor Ignition.
DLC — Data Link Connector
DME — Digital Motor Electronics
EGR — Exhaust Gas Recirculation
EI — Electronic Ignition
EVAP — Evaporative Emission Control System
FED — Federal
FR — Fillpipe Restrictor
MFI — Multi-Port Fuel Injection
MIL — Malfunction Indicator Lamp (Check Engine, Service Engine Soon Lamp)
M/T — Manual Transmission
OBD II — On Board Diagnostics II
OC — Oxidation Catalytic Converter
O2S — Oxygen Sensor
PCV — Positive Crankcase Ventilation
RPM — Revolutions Per Minute
SFI — Sequential Fuel Injection
SPK — Spark Control
SRI — Service Reminder Indicator
TDC — Top Dead Center
TSB — Technical Service Bulletin
TWC — Three Way Catalytic Converter

Engine Compartment Reference Diagrams

INDEX

	PAGE NO.	FIG. NO.
BOXSTER	15-292	2
911:		
1998:		
Non-Turbo	15-291	1
1999:		
3.4L Engine	15-293	3

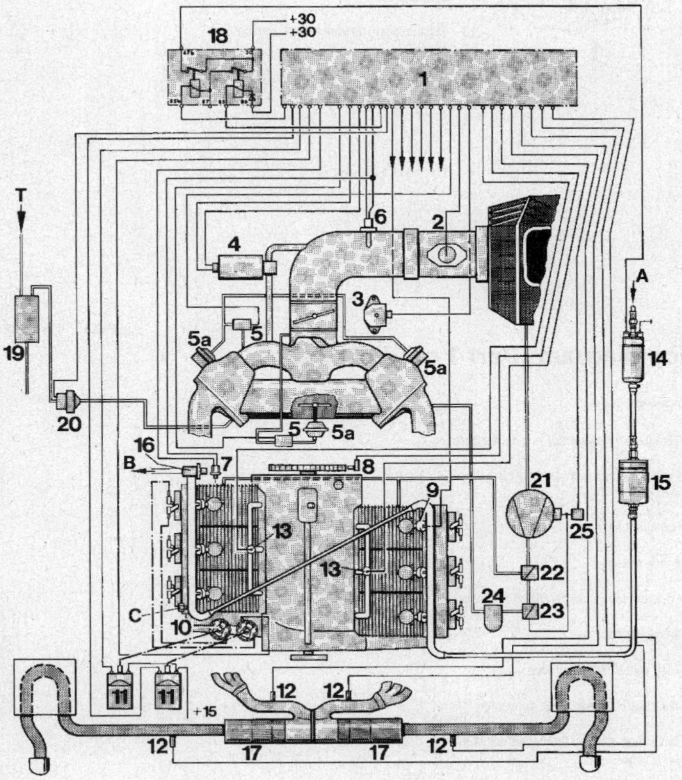

PR101960000400AX

Fig. 1 Engine compartment reference diagram (Part 1 of 2). 1998 911 Non-Turbo

1 - DME control module
2 - Mass air flow sensor
3 - Throttle potentiometer
4 - Idle Air Control Valve (IACV)
5 - Solenoid valve
5a - Diaphragm valve
6 - Intake air temperature sensor
7 - Engine temperature sensor
8 - Rpm reference mark sensor
9 - Injection valve
10 - Twin distributor with Hall-effect sensor
11 - Ignition coil
12 - Oxygen sensor
13 - Knock sensor
14 - Fuel pump
15 - Fuel filter
16 - Fuel pressure regulator
17 - Catalytic converter
18 - DME relay
19 - Carbon canister
20 - Tank venting valve
21 - Secondary air pump
22 - Pneumatic valve
23 - Solenoid valve
24 - Vacuum tank

A - From tank
B - Return line to tank
C - Fuel pressure test connection
T - Tank venting line

PR101960000400BX

Fig. 1 Engine compartment reference diagram (Part 2 of 2). 1998 911 Non-Turbo

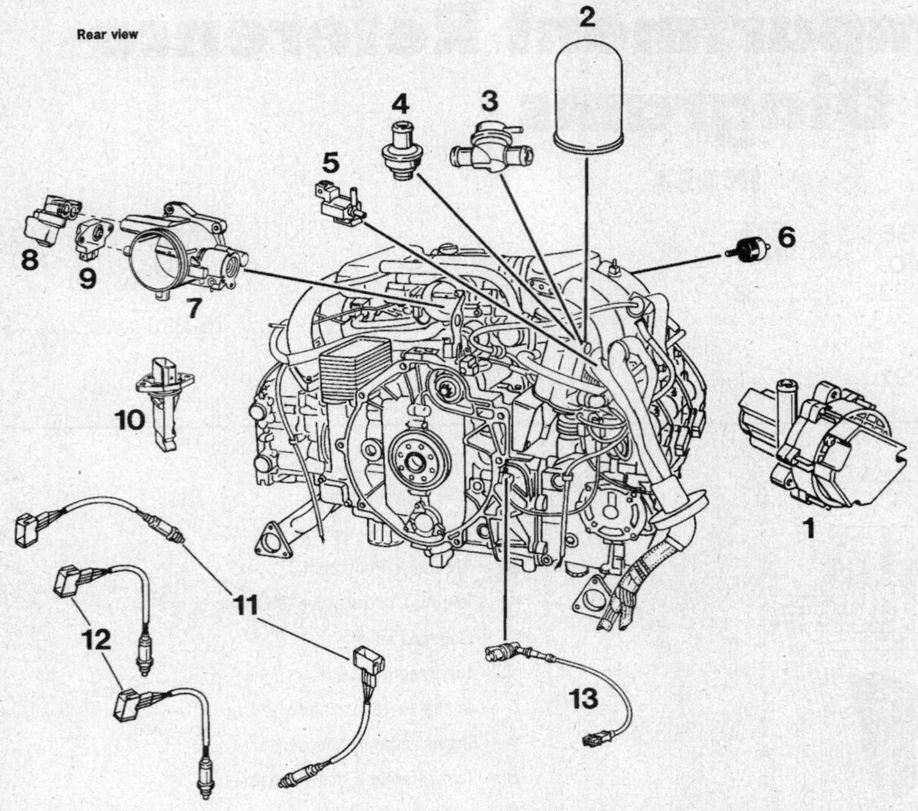

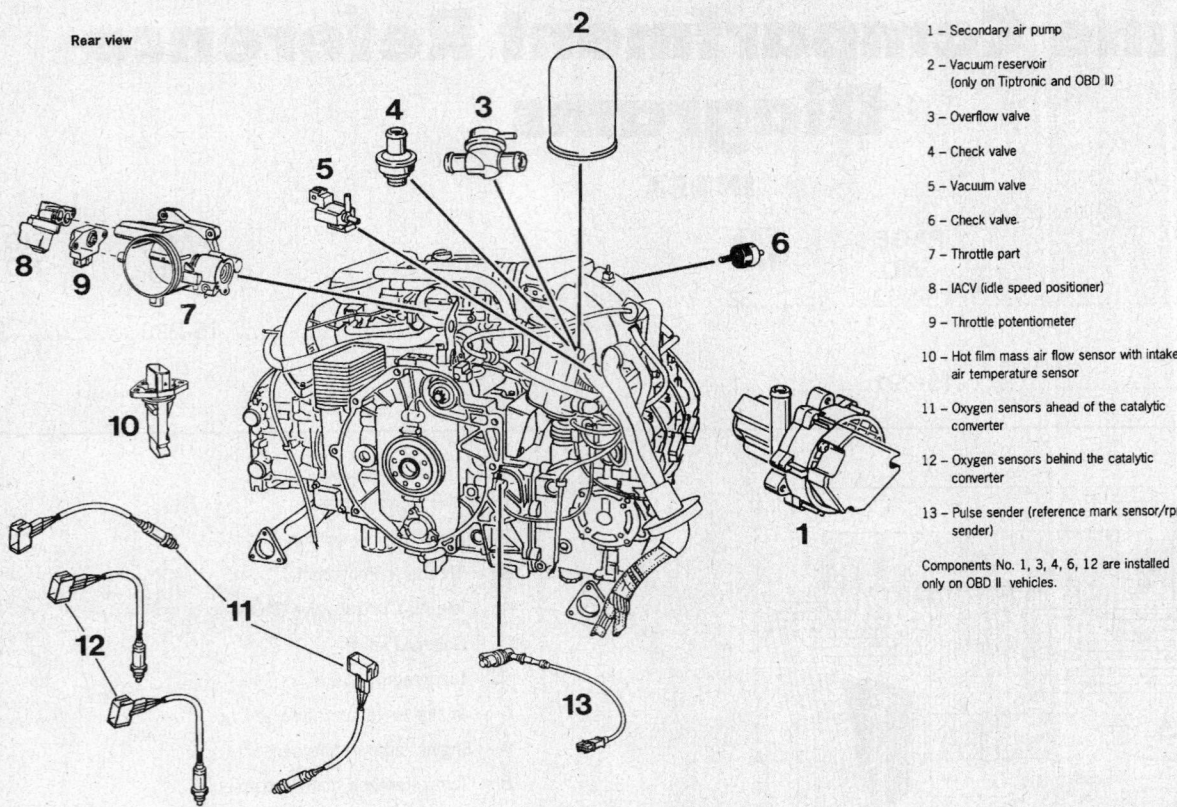

1 – Secondary air pump

2 – Vacuum reservoir (only on Tiptronic and OBD II)

3 – Overflow valve

4 – Check valve

5 – Vacuum valve

6 – Check valve

7 – Throttle part

8 – IACV (idle speed positioner)

9 – Throttle potentiometer

10 – Hot film mass air flow sensor with intake air temperature sensor

11 – Oxygen sensors ahead of the catalytic converter

12 – Oxygen sensors behind the catalytic converter

13 – Pulse sender (reference mark sensor/rpm sender)

Components No. 1, 3, 4, 6, 12 are installed only on OBD II vehicles.

PRA019700001010X

Fig. 2 Engine compartment reference diagram (Part 1 of 2). Boxster

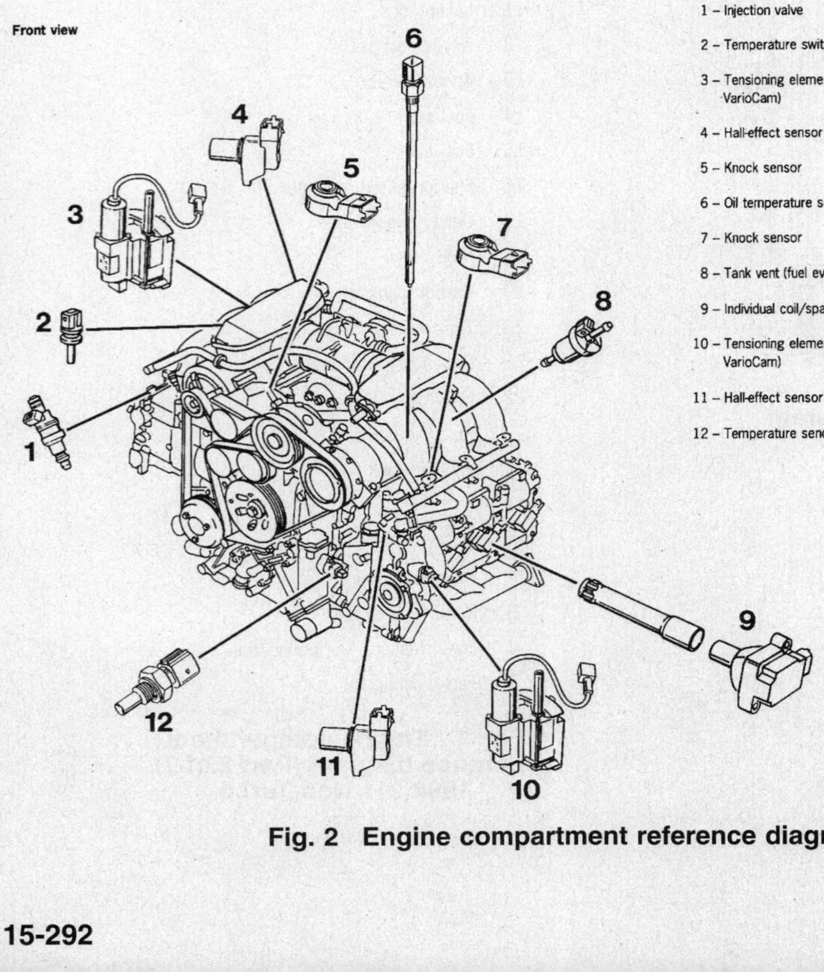

1 – Injection valve

2 – Temperature switch for engine temperature

3 – Tensioning element (camshaft adjuster VarioCam)

4 – Hall-effect sensor

5 – Knock sensor

6 – Oil temperature sender/oil level sensor

7 – Knock sensor

8 – Tank vent (fuel evaporative valve)

9 – Individual coil/spark plug connector

10 – Tensioning element (camshaft adjuster VarioCam)

11 – Hall-effect sensor

12 – Temperature sender (coolant)

PRA019700001020X

Fig. 2 Engine compartment reference diagram (Part 2 of 2). Boxster

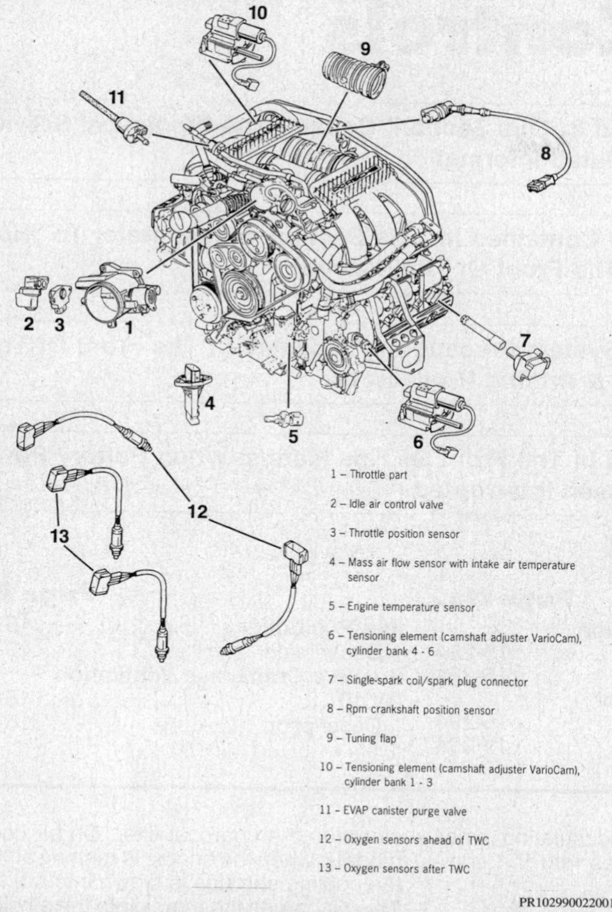

Fig. 3 Engine compartment reference diagram (Part 1 of 3). 1999 911 w/3.4L Engine

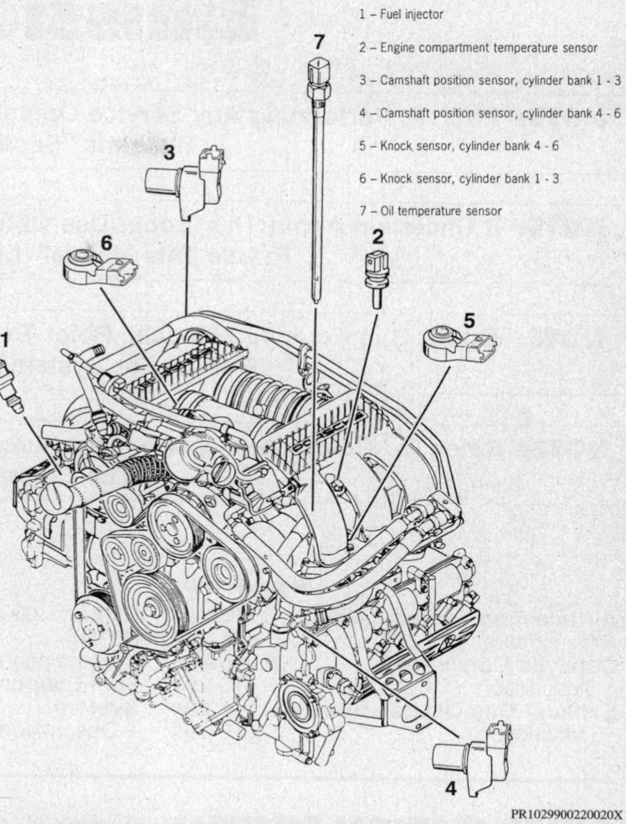

Fig. 3 Engine compartment reference diagram (Part 2 of 3). 1999 911 w/3.4L Engine

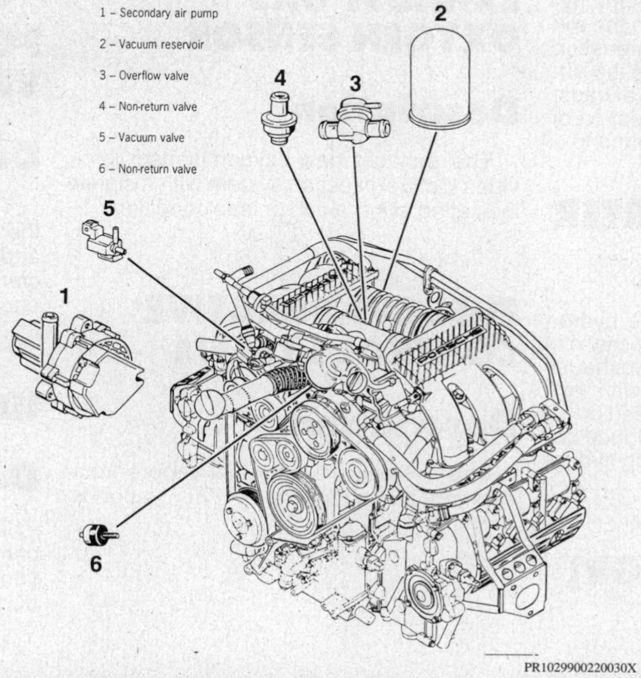

Fig. 3 Engine compartment reference diagram (Part 3 of 3). 1999 911 w/3.4L Engine

Emission Controls

NOTE: Prior To Performing Any Service Operations Listed In This Section, Consult The "Technical Service Bulletins" Section For Related Information.

NOTE: If Uncertain About The Proper Use Of Information Contained In This Section, Please Refer To "How To Use This Manual" Located In The Front Of This Manual.

NOTE: On Air Bag Equipped Models, Refer To "Air Bag System Precautions" Located In The Front Of This Manual For System Disarming & Arming Procedures.

NOTE: Refer To "Computer Relearn Procedures" Located In The Front Of This Manual When Battery Power To The Computer Has Been Interrupted.

INDEX

	Page No.
Air Injection System (AIS)	15-294
Description	15-294
Catalytic Converter	15-294
Description	15-294
Exhaust Gas Oxygen Sensor	15-294
Description	15-294
Exhaust Gas Recirculation (EGR)	15-294
Description	15-294
Fuel Evaporative Control System	15-294
Description	15-294
Idle Positioner	15-294
Description	15-294
Positive Crankcase Ventilation (PCV)	15-294
Description	15-294

AIR INJECTION SYSTEM (AIS)

Description

The air injection system reduces the hydrocarbon and carbon monoxide in the exhaust gases by continuing the combustion of unburned gases after they leave the engine. Fresh air is injected into the exhaust stream which results in further oxidation of both the hydrocarbons and carbon monoxide.

CATALYTIC CONVERTER

Description

The catalytic converter reduces hydrocarbons and carbon monoxide in the exhaust by oxidizing these exhaust components. Models equipped with exhaust gas oxygen sensors are equipped with three-way catalysts which reduce nitrogen oxides in addition to oxidizing hydrocarbons and carbon monoxide.

EXHAUST GAS RECIRCULATION (EGR)

Description

The EGR system reduces the formation of nitrogen oxides by recirculating small amounts of exhaust gases into the combustion cycle.

EXHAUST GAS OXYGEN SENSOR

Description

The exhaust gas oxygen sensor provides the fuel injection system with a signal indicating either a rich or lean condition.

FUEL EVAPORATIVE CONTROL SYSTEM

Description

This system prevents fuel vapors from entering the atmosphere. Fuel vapor is stored in the charcoal filter. On air cooled models, when the engine is running air from the cooling shrouds is blown into the filter. This air carries the fumes into the air cleaner where they are drawn into the engine.

POSITIVE CRANKCASE VENTILATION (PCV)

Description

This system recirculates emissions from the crankcase to the oil tank (if equipped) and from there to the intake system. The crankcase vapors are then drawn into the engine and burned.

IDLE POSITIONER

Description

This device opens the throttle slightly according to intake manifold vacuum to prevent an increase in hydrocarbon emissions during deceleration.

Technical Service Bulletins

INDEX

	Page No.
Check Engine Light On, Engine Misfire	15-295
Boxster	15-295
Oxygen Sensor Connections	15-295
3.6L Engine	15-295
Codes P0130–P0160	15-295
Sulfur Like Smell From Exhaust System	15-295
Boxster	15-295

OXYGEN SENSOR CONNECTIONS

3.6L Engine

CODES P0130–P0160

Malfunction of the oxygen sensor system and/or incorrect failure modes in the control unit memory, results in the MIL coming on. This condition will occur if the connector in the engine compartment for the oxygen sensor is cleaned or treated with contact cleaners or other sprays, oils, grease, water etc. The reference air for the oxygen sensor is pulled through the cable harness electrical connector. Cleaners or sprays will cause contamination of the reference air and/or limit the amount of reference air that reaches the oxygen sensor. This will create faults in the oxygen sensor system and may ruin the oxygen sensor.

Before attempting diagnosis of the oxygen sensor's performance, disconnect the affected sensor and test drive the vehicle until it reaches operating temperature, then run engine at 3500–4000 RPM for approximately 10 minutes. This should burn off any sensor contamination which may have occurred, and yield better test results.

SULFUR LIKE SMELL FROM EXHAUST SYSTEM

Boxster

Some vehicles may exhibit a sulfur or rotten egg smell from the exhaust system.

Sulfur found in gasoline is normally converted during combustion and catalytic after treatment processes into sulfur dioxide (SO2). Under certain operating conditions, hydrogen sulfide (H2S) is formed instead of sulfur dioxide. This depends largely on two factors, sulfur content of the fuel and operating condition of the catalytic converter.

If you have a sulfur or rotten egg smell, you should do the following:

1. Ensure there are no faults stored in the engine control module.
2. Ensure engine and fuel systems are operating properly.
3. If no problems are found with these systems, advise a change to a different brand of fuel.

CHECK ENGINE LIGHT ON, ENGINE MISFIRE

Boxster

Some of these vehicles may have a illuminated check engine light, engine misfire and misfire codes. These conditions may be caused by damage or excessive irregularities in the valve tappet guides.

To determine if the valve tappet guides are the problem. Inspect ignition system for possible causes of the engine misfire. If ignition system is working correctly, remove valve tappets and inspect guides for damage or irregularities, replace as necessary.

Abbreviations & Acronyms

ACL: Air Cleaner (Thermostatic Air Cleaner)
AIS: Air Injection System
AT: Automatic Transmission
AWD: All-Wheel Dive
BTDC: Before Top Dead Center
CA: California
CARB: Carburetor
CAT: Catalytic Converter
CO: Carbon Monoxide
DI: Distributor Ignition
DLC: Data Link Connector
DME: Digital Motor Electronics
DTC: Diagnostic Trouble Code
ECU: Electronic Control Unit
EGR: Exhaust Gas Recirculation
EVAP: Evaporative Emission Control System
FED: Federal
FR: Fillpipe Restrictor
IACV: Idle Air Control Valve
IAT: Intake Air Temperature
MAP: Manifoled Air Pressure
MFI: Multi-Port Fuel Injection
MIL: Malfunction Indicator Lamp
MT: Manual Transmission
OC: Oxidation Catalytic Converter
O2S: Oxygen Sensor
PCV: Positive Crankcase Ventilation
PROM: Programmable Read Only Memory
RPM: Revolutions Per Minute
RWD: Rear Wheel Dive
SPK: Spark Control
SRI: Service Reminder Indicator
TDC: Top Dead Center
TSB: Technical Service Bulletin
TWC: Three-Way Catalytic Converter

SAAB

TABLE OF CONTENTS

	Page No.
EMISSIONS:	
Abbreviations & Acronyms	16-182
Application Charts	16-175
Emissions Controls	16-179
Emission Control System Application Chart	16-175
Engine Compartment Reference Diagrams	16-176
ENGINE SYSTEMS IDENTIFICATION	16-2
FUEL SYSTEMS:	
Abbreviations & Acronyms	16-182
Electric Fuel Pumps	16-166
Engine Compartment Reference Diagrams	16-176
Fuel Injection	16-8
ENGINE TUNE UP & PERFORMANCE:	
Abbreviations & Acronyms	16-182
Specifications	16-2
Technical Service Bulletins	16-181
V6 Gasoline Engine	16-5
4 Cylinder Gasoline Engine	16-4
GENERAL INFORMATION:	
Abbreviations & Acronyms	16-182
Air Bag System Precautions	0-12
Air Quality Standards	0-23
Computer Relearn Procedures	0-10
Electrical Symbol & Wire Color Code Identification	0-33
Engine System Identification	16-2
How To Use This Manual	0-1
Quick Reference	16-1
Service Reminder & Warning Lamp Reset Procedure	0-14
Vehicle Identification	0-3
Vehicle Lift Points	0-24
Vehicle Maintenance Schedules	0-45
IGNITION SYSTEMS:	
Abbreviations & Acronyms	16-182
Engine Compartment Reference Diagrams	16-176
Ignition Systems	16-6
INDUCTION SYSTEMS:	
Abbreviations & Acronyms	16-182
Technical Service Bulletins	16-181
Turbochargers	16-168

Quick Reference

Application	Page No.
ACCESSING DIAGNOSTIC TROUBLE CODES	
Bosch Motronic 4.1 Injection System	16-8
Saab Trionic Injection System	16-40
CLEARING DIAGNOSTIC TROUBLE CODES	
Bosch Motronic 4.1 Injection System	16-37
Saab Trionic Injection System	16-43
DIAGNOSTIC CHART INDEX	
Saab Trionic Injection System	16-51
FUEL PRESSURE SPECIFICATIONS	
Bosch Motronic 4.1 Injection System	16-2
Saab Trionic Injection System	16-2
SENSOR & FUEL INJECTOR SPECIFICATIONS	
Bosch Motronic 4.1 Injection System	16-9
Saab Trionic Injection System	16-40

Engine Systems Identification

Engine Code	Engine	Fuel System	Page No.	Ignition System	Page No.	Computer System	Page No.
1998							
J	2.0L	Saab Trionic System	16-40	Distributorless Ignition System	16-6	Saab Trionic System	16-40
B	2.3L④	Bosch Motronic System 4.1 System	16-8	Distributorless Ignition System	16-6	Bosch Motronic System 4.1 System	16-8
R	2.3L③	Saab Trionic System	16-40	Distributorless Ignition System	16-6	Saab Trionic System	16-40
1999–2001							
N	2.0L①	Saab Trionic System	16-40	Distributorless Ignition System	16-6	Saab Trionic System	16-40
P	2.0L②	Saab Trionic System	16-40	Distributorless Ignition System	16-6	Saab Trionic System	16-40
E	2.3L①	Saab Trionic System	16-40	Distributorless Ignition System	16-6	Saab Trionic System	16-40
Z	3.0L	Saab Trionic System	16-40	Distributorless Ignition System	16-6	Saab Trionic System	16-40

① — Turbo.
② — High power output turbo.
③ — 9000.
④ — 900.

Tune Up Specifications

Year & Engine	Spark Plug Gap, Inch	Ignition Timing			Curb Idle Speed		Fast Idle Speed		Fuel Pressure, psi	Valve Lash, Inch	
		Firing Order	Timing, °BTDC	Timing Mark Fig.	Man. Trans.	Auto. Trans.③	Man. Trans.	Auto. Trans.		Intake	Exhaust
1998											
2.0L	.040	②	④	—	④	④	④	④	—	①	①
2.3L	.023	②	④	—	④	④	④	④	—	①	①
2.3L Turbo	.040	②	④	—	④	④	④	④	—	①	①
1999–2001											
2.0L	.023	②	④	—	④	④	④	④	43	①	①
2.3L	.023	②	④	—	④	④	④	④	43	①	①
2.3L	.040	②	④	—	④	④	④	④	43	①	①
3.0L	.040	⑤	④	—	④	④	④	④	43	①	①

BTDC — Before Top Dead Center
N — Neutral
① — Equipped w/hydraulic valve lash adjusters.
② — Firing order, 1-3-4-2.
③ — When adjusting idle speed, set parking brake & chock drive wheels.
④ — Controlled by electronic control unit.
⑤ — Firing order 1-2-3-4-5-6.

Engine Tune Up & Performance

NOTE: If Unsure Of The System Used On The Vehicle Being Serviced, Refer To "The Engine Systems Identification Chart." Further Assistance For The Proper Use Of Information Contained In This Section Can Also Be Found In The Front Of This Tabbed Section Under "How To Use This Manual."

NOTE: On Air Bag Equipped Models, Refer To "Air Bag System Precautions" Located In The Front Of This Manual For System Disarming & Arming Procedures.

NOTE: Refer To "Computer Relearn Procedures" Located In The Front Of This Manual When Battery Power To The Computer Has Been Interrupted.

NOTE: Prior To Performing Any Service Operations Listed In This Section, Consult The "Technical Service Bulletins" Section For Related Information.

TABLE OF CONTENTS

	Page No.
V6 GASOLINE ENGINE	16-5
4 CYLINDER GASOLINE ENGINE	16-4

4 Cylinder Gasoline Engine

INDEX

	Page No.
Fuel Injector Cleaning	16-4
Idle Speed & Mixture Adjustments	16-4
Curb Idle Speed	16-4
Throttle Valve	16-4
Ignition Timing	16-4
Sensor Adjustments	16-4
Throttle Position Sensor	16-4
Spark Plugs	16-4
Valves	16-4
Valve Adjustment	16-4
Valve Arrangement	16-4

SPARK PLUGS

Spark plugs should be replaced at 30,000 mile intervals under normal driving conditions.Torque spark plugs to 20 ft. lbs. Refer to "Gasoline Engine Tune Up Specifications" chart for correct spark plug gap.

On models equipped with turbo engine and electronic ignition ((EI) direct ignition system (DI/APC)), a resistor type spark plug must be used.

IGNITION TIMING

Ignition timing is controlled by the engine management system and is not adjustable. Refer to "Gasoline Engine Tune Up Specifications" for ignition timing specifications.

IDLE SPEED & MIXTURE ADJUSTMENTS

Idle speed adjustments are not required as part of recommended service. Refer to "Gasoline Engine Tune Up Specifications" chart for curb idle speed settings.

Curb Idle Speed

THROTTLE VALVE

Basic idle setting must always be done with engine cold (68°F or less). If engine is at normal operating temperature, the gap between throttle plate and throttle housing will be too wide for proper adjustment.

1. Loosen mounting screws for throttle position switch. Rotate switch to point where it no longer acts on throttle plate.
2. Slacken throttle cable.
3. Using throttle stop screw adjuster tool No. 83 94 322, or equivalent, loosen locknut on throttle stop screw, then turn screw until throttle plate is fully closed.
4. Turn screw ½ turn clockwise and tighten locknut. Ensure screw setting does not change.
5. Adjust throttle position switch back to its normal position with contact (pins 1 and 2) closed at idle. Tighten switch mounting screws.
6. To check throttle position switch setting, listen for click as throttle plate moves from idle position.

VALVES

Valve Arrangement

Intake valves are located on the front side of the engine and the exhaust valves are located on the rear side of the engine.

Valve Adjustment

On these engines valve lash is maintained by the hydraulic cam follower, no adjustment is necessary.

FUEL INJECTOR CLEANING

Use caution when cleaning fuel injectors. The atomization of fuel raises the possibility of fire. Cleaning with compressed air is not recommended.

1. Depressurize cleaner tank, using pressure relief pull ring.
2. Remove pump and cap assembly from cleaner/tester tank, then connect discharge hose to fuel rail access fitting. Fully open inline valve.
3. Energize electric fuel pump. Hold push button valve open, draining 1½ quarts of fuel into cleaner tank.
4. Turn off fuel pump.
5. Add three ounces Kent-Moore fuel injector cleaner, or equivalent, to cleaner tank.
6. Bleed discharge hose by opening push button valve, then install pump and cap assembly into cleaner tank, turning clockwise.
7. Pump until pressure indicates 30 psi, or pressure relief valve opens.
8. Remove fuel pump fuse to disable fuel pump.
9. Start and run engine at approximately 3000 RPM for 15–30 minutes, then decrease RPM to idle and shut ignition off.
10. Close off access fitting valve and bleed discharge by opening push button valve.
11. Remove and close off return line, then energize fuel pump.
12. Immediately run engine for five minutes at 2000 RPM to flush cleaner from fuel rail and injectors.
13. If injectors have more than 2.0 psi drop in injector balance test, repeat cleaning procedure.
14. If injectors are not within specifications after second cleaning, replace fuel system components as necessary.

SENSOR ADJUSTMENTS

Throttle Position Sensor

Refer to "Idle Speed & Mixture Adjustments."

V6 Gasoline Engine

INDEX

	Page No.
Fuel Injector Cleaning	16-5
Idle Speed Adjustment	16-5
Ignition Timing	16-5
Sensor Adjustments	16-5
Throttle Position Sensor	16-5
Spark Plugs	16-5
Valves	16-5
Valve Adjustment	16-5

SPARK PLUGS

Spark plugs should be replaced at 40,000 mile intervals under normal driving conditions. Torque spark plugs to 25 ft. lbs. Refer to "Gasoline Engine Tune Up Specifications" chart for correct spark plug gap.

IGNITION TIMING

Ignition timing is controlled by the engine management system and is not adjustable. Refer to "Tune-Up specifications" for ignition timing specifications.

IDLE SPEED ADJUSTMENT

Idle speed adjustments are not required as part of recommended service. Refer to "Gasoline Engine Tune Up Specifications" chart for curb idle speed settings.

VALVES

Valve Adjustment

Valve lash is maintained by the hydraulic cam follower. No adjustments are necessary.

FUEL INJECTOR CLEANING

Use caution when cleaning fuel injectors on vehicle. The atomization of fuel raises the possibility of fire. Cleaning with compressed air is not recommended.

1. Depressurize cleaner tank, using pressure relief pull ring.
2. Remove pump and cap assembly from cleaner/tester tank, then connect discharge hose to fuel rail access fitting. Fully open inline valve.
3. Energize vehicle electric fuel pump. Hold push button valve open, draining 1½ quarts of fuel into cleaner tank.
4. Turn off fuel pump.
5. Add 3 ounces Kent-Moore fuel injector cleaner or equivalent to cleaner tank.
6. Bleed discharge hose by opening push button valve, then install pump and cap assembly into cleaner tank, turning clockwise.
7. Pump until pressure indicates (30 psi) or pressure relief valve opens.
8. Remove fuel pump fuse to disable fuel pump.
9. Start engine and run approximately 3000 RPM for 15–30 minutes, then decrease RPM to idle and shut ignition off.
10. Close off access fitting valve and bleed discharge by opening push button valve.
11. Remove and close off return line, then energize fuel pump.
12. Immediately run engine for five minutes at 2000 RPM to flush cleaner from fuel rail and injectors.
13. If injectors have more than 2 psi drop in injector balance test, repeat cleaning procedure.
14. If injectors are not within specifications after second cleaning, replace as necessary.

SENSOR ADJUSTMENTS

Throttle Position Sensor

Idle speed adjustments are not required as part of recommended service. Refer to "Gasoline Engine Tune Up Specifications" chart for curb idle speed settings.

Ignition Systems

NOTE: If Unsure Of The System Used On The Vehicle Being Serviced, Refer To "The Engine Systems Identification Chart." Further Assistance For The Proper Use Of Information Contained In This Section Can Also Be Found In The Front Of This Tabbed Section Under "How To Use This Manual."

NOTE: On Air Bag Equipped Models, Refer To "Air Bag System Precautions" Located In The Front Of This Manual For System Disarming & Arming Procedures.

NOTE: Refer To "Computer Relearn Procedures" Located In The Front Of This Manual When Battery Power To The Computer Has Been Interrupted.

NOTE: Prior To Performing Any Service Operations Listed In This Section, Consult The "Technical Service Bulletins" Section For Related Information.

INDEX

	Page No.
Description	16-6
Components	16-7
Engine Control Module (ECM)	16-7
Ignition Discharge Module	16-7
System Operation	16-6
Bosch Motronic	16-6
Saab Trionic	16-6
Diagnosis & Testing	16-7
Precautions	16-6
Air Bag Systems	16-6
Battery Ground Cable	16-6
Throttle Position Adaptation	16-6
Saab Trionic	16-6
System Service	16-7
Component Replacement	16-7
Engine Control Module (ECM)	16-7
Ignition Discharge Module	16-7

PRECAUTIONS

Air Bag Systems

Refer to "Air Bag System Precautions" in the front of this manual for system disarming and arming procedures.

Battery Ground Cable

Prior to service, disconnect battery ground cable and isolate as required.

Throttle Position Adaptation

SAAB TRIONIC

After replacing the throttle position sensor, adjusting the throttle position or replacing the ECM on vehicles equipped with the Saab clutch control module, the throttle position must be adapted before the vehicle can be driven. Adapt throttle position as follows:

1. Turn ignition switch on, then connect ISAT scan tool and contact Trionic system.
2. Select "IDLING ADAPTATION" command on "ACTIVATE" menu. **Do not touch accelerator pedal.**
3. Select "IDLING" command on "READ ON/OFF" menu.
4. ISAT must show "YES" when accelerator is not pressed.

DESCRIPTION

The distributorless ignition system is controlled by the engine management system. Both the Bosch Motronic system and the Saab Trionic system control ignition, fuel injection and engine knock.

System Operation

BOSCH MOTRONIC

High voltage for the ignition spark is generated in the module containing three ignition coils. Each ignition coil supplies two spark plugs simultaneously with high tension to produce a good spark. Ignition coil No. 1 causes a spark to be produced simultaneously in cylinders Nos. 2 and 5, ignition coil No. 2 in cylinders Nos. 3 and 6, and ignition coil No. 3 in cylinders Nos. 1 and 4. The firing order is 1-2-3-4-5-6.

The control module and a reference signal from the crankshaft position sensor ensure the correct timing information is supplied to the righthand ignition coil.

Depending on engine temperature, idling speed varies between 600 and 800 RPM. At idling speed, the ignition timing normally varies between about 8–12°, depending on engine speed and operating temperature.

In conjunction with upshifts or downshifts on vehicles with automatic transaxle, engine torque is limited by retarding the ignition to -10°, provided it is already less than this.

Ignition timing is determined by the control module on the basis of engine speed, engine load and, if applicable, engine knocking.

SAAB TRIONIC

The Saab Trionic ignition system is a capacitive ignition system, consisting of four ignition coils and electronics built into the ignition discharge module. The ignition coils are controlled by the electronics in the ignition discharge module, which are regulated by low-level outputs from the Engine Control Module (ECM).

When the engine is cranked, the ignition system produces a spark on two spark plugs simultaneously, Nos. 1 and 4 or 2 and 3, for a number of consecutive complete combustion processes. With this information and signals from the crankshaft position sensor, the system can synchronize spark generation and fuel injection to the correct cylinder.

To improve starting performance when

the engine temperature is below 0°C, the ignition system generates a large number of sparks in a quick succession (multi-spark function), while the starter motor is engaged (10°BTDC–20°ATDC).

The Saab Trionic does not have a conventional knock sensor. Instead, the ignition discharge module analyzes the ionization currents for all the cylinders and sends signals to the ECM. This function is adaptive with respect to interfering fuel additives.

Components

ENGINE CONTROL MODULE (ECM)

The ECM is located behind the panel by the righthand A pillar.

The ECM receives input signals from various sensors, including information on engine load, temperature, engine RPM, exhaust gas composition, knocking, etc. The module uses this information to control both ignition and fuel injection. The Saab Trionic ECM also controls boost pressure.

IGNITION DISCHARGE MODULE

Bosch Motronic

The ignition discharge module integrates three ignition coils. On the basis of information on engine speed and load supplied by the ECM, pins 1, 20 and 21 ground circuit to integrated ignition coils.

The output signal on pin 1 triggers the ignition coil for cylinders 1 and 4, while the output signal on pin 20 triggers the ignition coil for cylinders 2 and 5 and the output signal on pin 21 triggers the ignition coil for cylinders 3 and 6.

Saab Trionic

The ignition discharge module is mounted on the valve cover over the spark plugs. There are four ignition coils in the ignition discharge module. The secondary windings are directly connected to the spark plugs.

DIAGNOSIS & TESTING

For diagnosis and testing the Bosch Motronic or Saab Trionic ignition system, refer to "Fuel Injection."

SYSTEM SERVICE

Component Replacement

ENGINE CONTROL MODULE (ECM)

1. Turn off ignition.
2. Remove glove compartment.
3. Fold back carpet and remove central locking system relay.
4. Disconnect module electrical connector, then remove ECM.
5. Reverse procedure to install. On models equipped with Saab Trionic system, adapt throttle position as outlined under "Precautions."

IGNITION DISCHARGE MODULE

Saab Trionic

1. Disconnect electrical connector.
2. Remove mounting bolts and module.
3. To replace spring, proceed as follows:
   a. Turn ignition discharge module up and down, then remove screws.
   b. Lift off black lower part of ignition discharge module.
   c. Pry off old spring with screwdriver, then install new spring.
4. Install module and mounting bolts.
5. Connect electrical connector.

Fuel Injection

TABLE OF CONTENTS

	Page No.		Page No.
BOSCH MOTRONIC 4.1 INJECTION SYSTEM	16-8	**SAAB TRIONIC INJECTION SYSTEM**	16-40

Bosch Motronic 4.1 Injection System

NOTE: If Unsure Of The System Used On The Vehicle Being Serviced, Refer To "The Engine Systems Identification Chart." Further Assistance For The Proper Use Of Information Contained In This Section Can Also Be Found In The Front Of This Tabbed Section Under "How To Use This Manual."

NOTE: On Air Bag Equipped Models, Refer To "Air Bag System Precautions" Located In The Front Of This Manual For System Disarming & Arming Procedures.

NOTE: Refer To "Computer Relearn Procedures" Located In The Front Of This Manual When Battery Power To The Computer Has Been Interrupted.

NOTE: Prior To Performing Any Service Operations Listed In This Section, Consult The "Technical Service Bulletins" Section For Related Information.

NOTE: "Electrical Symbol & Wire Color Code Identification" Located In The Front Of This Manual May Be Used As An Aid When Using Wiring Circuits Found In This Section.

INDEX

	Page No.
Description	16-9
Diagnosis & Testing	16-10
Accessing Diagnostic Trouble Codes	16-10
Clearing Diagnostic Trouble Codes	16-37
Component Testing	16-37
Ignition Coil	16-37
Main Relay	16-37
Connector Terminal Identification	16-10
Diagnostic Tests	16-10
Code P0116: Temperature Sensor	16-12
Code P0155: Front Heated Oxygen Sensor	16-17
Code P0161: Rear Heated Oxygen Sensor	16-21
Code P0300: Random Misfire	16-22
Code P0327: Knock Sensor	16-24
Code P0328: Knock Sensor	16-24
Code P0332: Knock Sensor	16-24
Code P0333: Knock Sensor	16-25
Code P0341: Camshaft Position Sensor	16-25
Code P0422: Three-Way Catalytic Converter Rear Bank	16-27
Code P0432: Three-Way Catalytic Converter Front Bank	16-27
Code P0440: EVAP Valve Control	16-27
Code P0441: EVAP Canister Purge Valve Low Flow	16-28
Code P0450: Tank Pressure Sensor	16-29
Code P0501: Vehicle Speed Signal	16-30
Code P1140: Mass Air Flow Sensor/Throttle Position Sensor	16-32
Code P1386: ECM Knock Sensor Circuitry	16-34
Code P1551: Idle Air Control (IAC) Valve	16-35
Code P1585: Fuel Tank Low Level	16-35
Code P1611: Check Engine	16-35
Code P1614: Check Engine	16-36
Code P1624: Check Engine	16-36
Code P1664: Shift Up	16-36
Code P1669: TCS Signal Active	16-36
Code P1782: Torque Reduction	16-37
Code —: Prior To Replacing Electronic Control Module (ECM)	16-37
Codes P0102 & P0103: Mass Air Flow Sensor	16-10
Codes P0112 & P0113: Intake Air Temperature Sensor	16-11
Codes P0117 & P0118: Temperature Sensor	16-13
Codes P0122 & P0123: Throttle Position Sensor	16-14
Codes P0130, P0131, P0132, P0133 & P0134: Front Heated Oxygen Sensor	16-15
Codes P0136, P0137, P0138, P0139 & P0140: Rear Heated Oxygen Sensor	16-16
Codes P0150, P0151, P0152, P0153 & P0154: Front	

Page No.

Heated Oxygen Sensor 16-16
Codes P0156, P0157, P0158, P0159 & P0160: Rear Heated Oxygen Sensor 16-17
Codes P0301, P0302, P0303 & P0304: Misfire 16-23
Codes P0335, P0336 & P1396: Crankshaft Position Sensor 16-25
Codes P0410 & P0411: Secondary Air Injection 16-25
Codes P0412, P0413 & P0414: Secondary Air Injection 16-27
Codes P0442 & P0455: Purge System Leak 16-28
Codes P0446, P0447 & P0448: EVAP Shut-Off Valve 16-29
Codes P0452 & P0453: Fuel Tank Pressure Sensor 16-29
Codes P0506 & P0507: Idling Speed 16-30
Codes P0560 & P1602: Battery Voltage 16-30
Codes P0562 & P0563: Battery Voltage 16-30
Codes P0601 & P0604: ECM Internal Fault 16-31
Codes P1102 & P1115: Preheating Of Front H02S (Rear Bank) 16-31
Codes P1105 & P1117: Rear H02S (Rear Bank)........... 16-31
Codes P1123, P1124, P1125, P1126, P1127, P1128, P1129 & P1130: Adaptation Malfunction 16-32
Codes P1136, P1137, P1138 & P1139: Adaption 16-32
Codes P1170, P1171 & P1172: Variable Intake Manifold Outer Flap 16-33
Codes P1213, P1214, P1215, P1216, P1217, P1218, P1225, P1226, P1227, P1228, P1229 & P1230: Injectors 1, 2, 3 & 4 16-33
Codes P1237, P1238, P1239, P1240, P1241 & P1242: Injectors 1, 2, 3, 4, 5 & 6 16-34
Codes P1410, P1425 & P1426: EVAP Canister Purge Valve 16-34
Codes P1501, 1502 & 1541: Pump Relay 16-34
Codes P1510, 1513, 1514, 1551, 1552 & 1553: Idle Air Control Valve 16-35
Codes P1512, P1515 & P1516: Variable Intake Manifold Inner Flap 16-35
Codes P1655, P1657, P1660 & P1662: Control Module Output 16-36
Codes P1691, P1692, P1693: Check Engine (MIL) 16-36
Diagnostic Trouble Code Interpretation 16-10
Preliminary Check 16-10
Wiring Diagrams 16-10
Precautions 16-9
Air Bag Systems 16-9
Battery Ground Cable 16-9
Sensor & Fuel Injector Specifications 16-9
System Service 16-38
Component Replacement 16-38
Camshaft Position (CMP) Sensor 16-38
Crankshaft Position (CKP) Sensor 16-38
Engine Control Module (ECM) 16-38
Engine Coolant Temperature (ECT) Sensor 16-38
Idle Air Control (IAC) Valve ... 16-38
Injector 16-39
Secondary Air Injection Pump & Filter 16-39
Throttle Body 16-39

SENSOR & FUEL INJECTOR SPECIFICATIONS

Sensor	Voltage	Resistance
Crankshaft Position (CKP)	—	770–950 Ohms @ 68°F
Camshaft Position (CMP)	0 Or 12 Volts	—
Engine Coolant Temperature (ECT)	—	295–365 Ohms @ 176°F
Fuel Injector (2.3L Non-Turbo)	—	14.5 Ohms @ 68°F
Fuel Injector (2.3LTurbo)	—	12 Ohms @ 68°F
Heated Oxygen Sensor (HO2S)	—	1.8–2.5 Ohms @ 68°F
Intake Air Temperature (IAT)	—	2.1–2.9 kOhms @ 68°F
	—	295–365 Ohms @ 176°F
Knock Sensor (KS)	5 mVolts AC @ Idle	—
	100 mVolts AC When Striking Retaining Bolt	—
Mass Air Flow (MAF)	2.2–2.6 Volts @ 33 G/S	—
	3.9–4.6 Volts @ 133 G/S	—
Manifold Absolute Pressure (MAP)	2.4 Volts @ 18 PSI	—
	3.3 Volts @ 25 PSI	—

CTP — Closed Throttle Position
G/S — Grams Per Second
WOT — Wide Open Throttle

PRECAUTIONS

Air Bag Systems

Refer to "Air Bag System Precautions" in the front of this manual for system disarming and arming procedures.

Battery Ground Cable

Prior to service, disconnect battery ground cable and isolate as required.

DESCRIPTION

The Bosch Motronic system controls ignition, fuel injection and air intake when the vehicle is idling.

The Bosch Motronic system is a combination of a conventional electronic fuel injection system and an electronic ignition system with a knock sensor. The injection system features sequential injection while

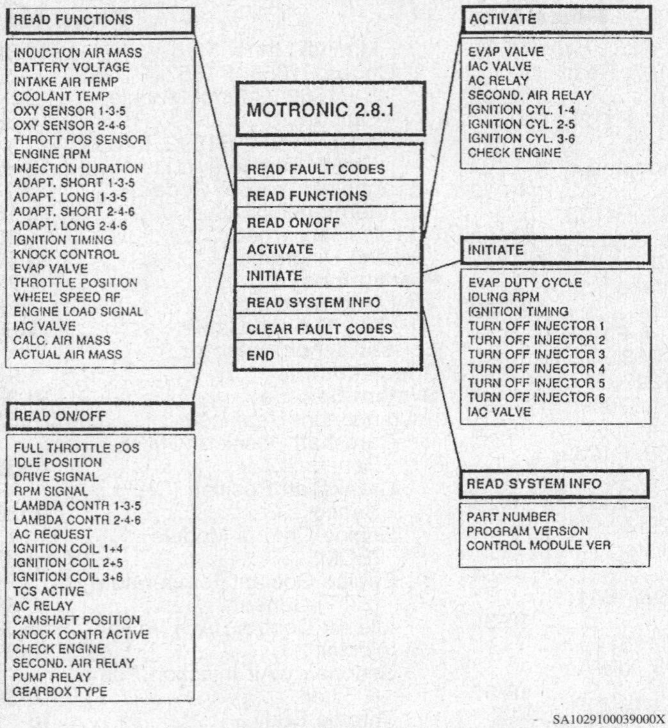

Fig. 1 Command code system menu structure

Diagnostic trouble code (SAE)	Faulty function/component	CHECK ENGINE	ISAT ST display text
P0102	Mass air flow sensor. Control module input low, open circuit or shorting to ground.	On	FAULT XX P0102 INDUCTION AIR MASS BREAK/SHORT TO GROUND
P0103	Mass air flow sensor. Control module input high, shorting to battery positive (B+).	On	FAULT XX P0103 INDUCTION AIR MASS SHORTING TO B+
P0112	Intake air temperature sensor, control module input. Shorting to ground.	On	FAULT XX P0112 INTAKE AIR TEMP SHORT TO GROUND
P0113	Intake air temperature sensor, control module input. Open circuit or shorting to battery positive (B+).	On	FAULT XX P0113 INTAKE AIR TEMP BREAK/SHORT TO B+
P0116	Engine coolant temperature sensor Temperature increase on start of engine less than that calculated by control module.	On	FAULT XX P0116 COOLANT TEMP INPUT FAULTY
P0117	Engine coolant temperature sensor, control module input. Shorting to ground.	On	FAULT XX P0117 COOLANT TEMP SHORT TO GROUND
P0118	Engine coolant temperature sensor, control module input. Open circuit or shorting to battery positive (B+).	On	FAULT XX P0118 COOLANT TEMP BREAK/SHORT TO B+
P0122	Throttle position sensor, control module input. Shorting to ground.	On	FAULT XX P0122 THROTTLE POSITION SHORT TO GROUND
P0123	Throttle position sensor, control module input. Open circuit or shorting to battery positive (B+).	On	FAULT XX P0123 THROTTLE POSITION BREAK/SHORT TO B+
P0130	Front heated oxygen sensor, bank 1. Defective.	On	FAULT XX P0130 02S BANK1 SENSOR1 FUNCTION INCORRECT
P0131	Front heated oxygen sensor, bank 1, control module input. Shorting to ground.	On	FAULT XX P0131 02S BANK1 SENSOR1 SHORT TO GROUND
P0132	Front heated oxygen sensor, bank 1, control module input. Shorting to battery positive (B+).	On	FAULT XX P0132 02S BANK1 SENSOR1 SHORT TO B+
P0133	Front heated oxygen sensor, bank 1. Alternating between rich and lean too slow.	On	FAULT XX P0133 02S BANK1 SENSOR1 LOW FREQUENCY
P0134	Front heated oxygen sensor, bank 1, control module input. Open circuit.	On	FAULT XX P0134 02S BANK1 SENSOR1 OPEN CIRCUIT

SA1029700190010X

Fig. 2 Diagnostic trouble code identification (Part 1 of 10)

the power output stage of the ignition system is integrated in the control module.

Fuel injection is sequential, following the firing order of the engine. Injection duration is determined by the control module on basis of engine load (received from the mass air flow sensor), engine RPM (received from the crankshaft sensor), engine temperature, oxygen sensors, etc.

DIAGNOSIS & TESTING

Preliminary Check

Before beginning diagnosis, check the following items:

1. Inspect fuses.
2. Inspect connectors for corrosion on pins and contact surfaces, excessive play, looseness or other items that may cause poor contact or deterioration in conductivity.
3. Before connecting BOB into circuit, first check voltage supply to pin 37 and ensure pins 2, 14 and 24 are properly grounded.
4. Check how long main relay remains on after ignition has been switched off. Relay should operate for an additional five seconds or so if temperature is approximately 68°F, or about 30 seconds if temperature is below 32°F.

Accessing Diagnostic Trouble Codes

Connect a suitable ISAT scan tool to diagnostics socket pin 50, located under the dashboard on the lefthand side of the vehicle. To access diagnostic trouble codes, select "READ FAULT CODES" from main menu, **Fig. 1.**

Diagnostic Trouble Code Interpretation

Refer to **Fig. 2** for diagnostic trouble code identification.

Wiring Diagrams

Refer to **Fig. 3** for wiring diagrams.

Connector Terminal Identification

Refer to **Fig. 4** for ECM connector terminal identification.

Refer to **Figs. 5 through 27** for component connector terminal identification.

Diagnostic Tests

CODES P0102 & P0103: MASS AIR FLOW SENSOR

Fault Symptoms

Conditions: CHECK ENGINE lamp (MIL) ON. Engine reluctant to start, impaired driveability and high fuel consumption. DTC P0102 is set and engine speed above 400 RPM and intake air mass less than .03V/1.11 g/s; DTC P0103 is set engine speed 1000 RPM and intake air mass greater than 3.2 V/84.5 g/s.

Slightly higher values may occur as result of temporary short circuits and breaks in the wiring. Jiggle the wiring at several points and in different directions to ascertain whether the wiring harness, including any connectors, is causing trouble. Observe the multi-meter, scan tool or test lamp while doing this.

Inspect MAF performance with scan tool as follows:

Diagnostic trouble code (SAE)	Faulty function/component	CHECK ENGINE	ISAT ST display text
P0136	Rear heated oxygen sensor, bank 1. Defective.	On	FAULT XX P0136 02S BANK1 SENSOR2 FUNCTION INCORRECT
P0137	Rear heated oxygen sensor, bank 1, control module input. Shorting to ground.	On	FAULT XX P0137 02S BANK1 SENSOR2 SHORT TO GROUND
P0138	Rear heated oxygen sensor, bank 1, control module input. Shorting to battery positive (B+).	On	FAULT XX P0138 02S BANK1 SENSOR2 SHORT TO B+
P0139	Rear heated oxygen sensor, bank 1. Alternating between rich and lean too slow.	On	FAULT XX P0139 02S BANK1 SENSOR2 LOW FREQUENCY
P0140	Rear heated oxygen sensor, bank 1, control module input. Open circuit.	On	FAULT XX P0140 02S BANK1 SENSOR2 OPEN CIRCUIT
P0150	Front heated oxygen sensor, bank 2. Defective.	On	FAULT XX P0150 02S BANK2 SENSOR1 FUNCTION INCORRECT
P0151	Front heated oxygen sensor, bank 2, control module input. Shorting to ground.	On	FAULT XX P0151 02S BANK2 SENSOR1 SHORT TO GROUND
P0152	Front heated oxygen sensor, bank 2, control module input. Shorting to battery positive (B+).	On	FAULT XX P0152 02S BANK2 SENSOR1 SHORT TO B+
P0153	Front heated oxygen sensor, bank 2. Alternating between rich and lean too slow.	On	FAULT XX P0153 02S BANK2 SENSOR1 LOW FREQUENCY
P0154	Front heated oxygen sensor, bank 2, control module input. Open circuit.	On	FAULT XX P0154 02S BANK2 SENSOR1 OPEN CIRCUIT
P0155	Front heated oxygen sensor, bank 2, control module input. Current in preheating circuit too high.	On	FAULT XX P0155 02S BANK2 SENSOR1 PREHEATING HIGH CURRENT
P0156	Rear heated oxygen sensor, bank 2. Defective.	On	FAULT XX P0156 02S BANK2 SENSOR2 FUNCTION INCORRECT
P0157	Rear heated oxygen sensor, bank 2, control module input. Shorting to ground.	On	FAULT XX P0157 02S BANK2 SENSOR2 SHORT TO GROUND
P0158	Rear heated oxygen sensor, bank 2, control module input. Shorting to battery positive (B+).	On	FAULT XX P0158 02S BANK2 SENSOR2 SHORT TO B+
P0159	Rear heated oxygen sensor, bank 2. Alternating between rich and lean too slow.	On	FAULT XX P0159 02S BANK2 SENSOR2 LOW FREQUENCY

SA1029700190020X

Fig. 2 Diagnostic trouble code identification (Part 2 of 10)

Diagnostic trouble code (SAE)	Faulty function/component	CHECK ENGINE	ISAT ST display text
P0160	Rear heated oxygen sensor, bank 2, control module input. Open circuit.	On	FAULT XX P0160 02S BANK2 SENSOR2 OPEN CIRCUIT
P0161	Rear heated oxygen sensor, bank 2, control module input. Current in preheating circuit too high.	On	FAULT XX P0161 02S BANK2 SENSOR2 PREHEATING HIGH CURRENT
P0300	Random misfiring in one of the cylinders.	On	FAULT XX P0300 MISFIRING
P0301	Misfiring in cylinder 1.	On	FAULT XX P0301 MISFIRE CYL 1
P0302	Misfiring in cylinder 2.	On	FAULT XX P0302 MISFIRE CYL 2
P0303	Misfiring in cylinder 3.	On	FAULT XX P0303 MISFIRE CYL 3
P0304	Misfiring in cylinder 4.	On	FAULT XX P0304 MISFIRE CYL 4
P0305	Misfiring in cylinder 5.	On	FAULT XX P0305 MISFIRE CYL 5
P0306	Misfiring in cylinder 6.	On	FAULT XX P0306 MISFIRE CYL 6
P0327	Knock sensor, bank 1, control module input. Open circuit or shorting to ground or battery positive (B+).	On	FAULT XX P0327 KNOCK SENSOR BANK1 BREAK/SHORTING
P0332	Knock sensor, bank 2, control module input. Open circuit or shorting to ground or battery positive (B+).	On	FAULT XX P0332 KNOCK SENSOR BANK2 BREAK/SHORTING
P0335	Crankshaft position sensor, control module input. No signals.		FAULT XX P0335 CRANKSHAFT POS. NO INPUT
P0336	Crankshaft position sensor, control module input. Malfunctioning, gap in slotted ring undefinable.		FAULT XX P0336 CRANKSHAFT POS. INPUT INCORRECT
P0341	Camshaft position sensor, control module input. Defective.	On	FAULT XX P0341 CAMSHAFT POSITION INPUT INCORRECT
P0410	Secondary air injection. Incorrect air flow.	On	FAULT XX P0410 SECONDARY AIR FLOW INCORRECT
P0411	Secondary air injection. Air flow too weak.	On	FAULT XX P0411 SECONDARY AIR FLOW LOW
P0412	Secondary air injection control valve, control module output. Shorting to battery positive (B+).	On	FAULT XX P0412 SECONDARY AIR VALVE SHORT TO B+

SA1029700190030X

Fig. 2 Diagnostic trouble code identification (Part 3 of 10)

1. Connect scan tool, start engine, then select "READ FUNCTIONS," and "MASS AIR FLOW SENSOR."
2. Inspect scan tool functions as follows:
   a. All electrical equipment OFF.
   b. Transmission selector lever in N or P position.
   c. With engine at idling speed, approximately .8 volts.
   d. With engine at 2500 RPM and no load, approximately 1.5 volts.

Diagnostic Procedure

1. Inspect mass air flow sensor ground connection and power supply as follows:
   a. Disconnect mass air flow sensor four pin electrical connector, then turn ignition switch to On position.
   b. Connect test lamp to battery positive and pin 1, battery positive and pin 2, pin 3 and battery ground.
   c. Test lamp should light in all three cases.
   d. If test lamp lights, proceed to next step.
   e. If test lamp did not light, repair or replace wire in question and proceed to final inspection.
2. Inspect control module's mass air flow sensor input as follows:
   a. Connect conventional 1.5 volt battery with battery positive pole to pin 4 and battery ground pole to pin 2.
   b. Connect scan tool, then turn ignition switch to On, then select "READ FUNCTIONS," then "MASS AIR FLOW SENSOR."
   c. Scan tool should read approximately 1.5 volts.
   d. If all reading are within specifications, replace mass air flow sensor and proceed to next step.
   e. If not within specifications, inspect wire in question and repair or replace as necessary, then proceed to next step.
3. Final inspection as follows:
   a. Clear diagnostic trouble codes.
   b. Implement drive cycle. Drive vehicle at varying engine loads and RPM for five minutes.
   c. If DTC is present, refer to "Code —: Prior To Replacing Electronic Control Module (ECM)."
   d. If DTC is not present, fault was corrected.

CODES P0112 & P0113: INTAKE AIR TEMPERATURE SENSOR

Fault Symptoms

Conditions: CHECK ENGINE lamp (MIL) ON. DTC P0112 set and intake air temperature above 140°C for more than 2 seconds. DTC P0113 set and engine running for 180 seconds, then idling for more than 10 seconds, and intake air temperature below -40°C for more than 2 seconds.

1. Determine temperature sensor performance with scan tool as follows:
   a. Connect scan tool.
   b. Turn ignition switch to ON position.
   c. Select "READ FUNCTIONS," then "INTAKE AIR TEMP."
   d. Ensure intake air temperature sensor is in proper working order, scan tool should show current intake air temperature.
   e. Inspect wiring for intermittent faults.

Diagnostic trouble code (SAE)	Faulty function/component	CHECK ENGINE	ISAT ST display text
P0413	Secondary air injection control valve, control module output. Open circuit.	On	FAULT XX P0413 SECONDARY AIR VALVE BREAK
P0414	Secondary air injection control valve, control module output. Shorting to ground.	On	FAULT XX P0414 SECONDARY AIR VALVE SHORT TO GROUND
P0422	Three way catalytic converter, bank 1. Defective.	On	FAULT XX P0422 CATALYTIC CONVERTER BANK1 FUNCTION INCORRECT
P0432	Three way catalytic converter, bank 2 Defective.	On	FAULT XX P0432 CATALYTIC CONVERTER BANK2 FUNCTION INCORRECT
P0441	EVAP system. Defective.	On	FAULT XX P0441 EVAP FLOW INCORRECT
P0442	EVAP system. Slight leakage.	On	FAULT XX P0442 EVAP LEAKAGE SMALL
P0446	EVAP shut–off valve, control module output. Shorting to battery positive (B+) and EVAP malfunctioning.		FAULT XX P0446 EVAP SHUTOFF VALVE FUNCTION INCORRECT
P0447	EVAP shut–off valve, control module output. Open circuit.		FAULT XX P0447 EVAP SHUTOFF VALVE OPEN CIRCUIT
P0448	EVAP shut–off valve, control module output. Shorting to ground.		FAULT XX P0448 EVAP SHUTOFF VALVE SHORT TO GROUND
P0452	Fuel tank pressure sensor, control module input. Shorting to ground.	On	FAULT XX P0452 TANK PRESSURE SENSOR SHORT TO GROUND
P0453	Fuel tank pressure sensor, control module input. Open circuit or shorting to battery positive (B+).	On	FAULT XX P0453 TANK PRESSURE SENSOR BREAK/SHORT TO B+
P0455	EVAP system. Large leak.	On	FAULT XX P0455 EVAP LEAKAGE LARGE
P0501	Vehicle speed, input signal to control module. Incorrect signal.	On	FAULT XX P0501 CAR SPEED SIGNAL INCORRECT
P0562	Battery voltage. Low voltage level.		FAULT XX P0562 BATTERY VOLTAGE LOW VOLTAGE
P0563	Battery voltage. High voltage level.		FAULT XX P0563 BATTERY VOLTAGE HIGH VOLTAGE

SA1029700190040X

Fig. 2 Diagnostic trouble code identification (Part 4 of 10)

Diagnostic trouble code (SAE)	Faulty function/component	CHECK ENGINE	ISAT ST display text
P0601	Control module, internal fault. Defective read memory.	On	FAULT XX P0601 CONTROL MODULE INTERNAL FAULT INTERNAL ROM
P0604	Control module, internal fault. Defective write memory.	On	FAULT XX P0604 CONTROL MODULE INTERNAL FAULT INTERNAL RAM
P1102	Front heated oxygen sensor, bank 1, control module input. Current in preheating circuit much too high.	On	FAULT XX P1102 02S BANK1 SENSOR1 PREHEATING HIGH CURRENT
P1105	Rear heated oxygen sensor, bank 1, control module input. Current in preheating circuit much too high.	On	FAULT XX P1105 02S BANK1 SENSOR2 PREHEATING HIGH CURRENT
P1115	Front heated oxygen sensor, bank 1, control module input. Current in preheating circuit much too low.	On	FAULT XX P1115 02S BANK1 SENSOR1 PREHEATING LOW CURRENT
P1117	Rear heated oxygen sensor, bank 1, control module input. Current in preheating circuit much too low.	On	FAULT XX P1117 02S BANK1 SENSOR2 PREHEATING LOW CURRENT
P1123	Additive adaptation, bank 1. Min value.	On	FAULT XX P1123 ADD.ADAPTION BANK1 MINIMAL VALUE
P1124	Additive adaptation, bank 1. Max value.	On	FAULT XX P1124 ADD.ADAPTION BANK1 MAXIMAL VALUE
P1125	Additive adaptation, bank 2. Min value.	On	FAULT XX P1125 ADD.ADAPTION BANK2 MINIMAL VALUE
P1126	Additive adaptation, bank 2. Max value.	On	FAULT XX P1126 ADD.ADAPTION BANK2 MAXIMAL VALUE
P1127	Multiplicative adaptation, bank 1. Min value.	On	FAULT XX P1127 MULT.ADAPTION BANK1 MINIMAL VALUE
P1128	Multiplicative adaptation, bank 1. Max value.	On	FAULT XX P1128 MULT.ADAPTION BANK1 MAXIMAL VALUE
P1129	Multiplicative adaptation, bank 2. Min value.	On	FAULT XX P1129 MULT.ADAPTION BANK2 MINIMAL VALUE
P1130	Multiplicative adaptation, bank 2. Max value.	On	FAULT XX P1130 MULT.ADAPTION BANK2 MAXIMAL VALUE

SA1029700190050X

Fig. 2 Diagnostic trouble code identification (Part 5 of 10)

Diagnostic Procedure

1. Inspect temperature sensor ground as follows:
   a. Disconnect temperature sensor two pin electrical connector.
   b. Connect test lamp to battery positive and pin 2.
   c. If test lamp lights, proceed to next step.
   d. If test lamp does not light, check circuit for open or short, repair or replace as necessary and proceed to step 3.
2. Inspect control module temperature sensor input as follows:
   a. Connect scan tool and turn ignition switch to ON position.
   b. Select "READ FUNCTIONS" and "INTAKE AIR TEMP."
   c. Scan tool should show reading of approximately 5 volts.
   d. Connect jumper wire between pins 1 and 2 of temperature sensor connector.
   e. Scan tool should show reading of zero volts.
   f. If readings are as specified, replace temperature sensor and proceed to step 3.
   g. If readings are not as specified, check circuit for an open or short circuit, repair or replace as necessary, then proceed to step 3.
3. Clear all DTC's, then drive vehicle at varying engine loads and RPMs for five minutes.
4. If DTC is present, refer to "Electronic Control Module (ECM)" under "Component Replacement."
5. If DTC is not present, fault was corrected.

CODE P0116: TEMPERATURE SENSOR

Fault Symptoms

Conditions: CHECK ENGINE lamp (MIL) on. DTC P0116 set and coolant temperature is 10° C below calculated engine temperature. The DTC is generated as a result of connection of a non-approved external parking heater; or ice formation in cooling system; a fault in coolant temperature sensor or its circuit or a defective thermostat. Inspect the wiring harness. Intermittent short circuits and breaks in wiring. Jiggle wiring at several points and in different directions to ascertain whether wiring harness, including any connectors are causing the trouble. Observe multimeter, scan tool or test lamp.

Diagnostic Procedure

1. Determine freezing point as follows:
   a. If freezing point is within specifications, proceed to next step.
   b. If freezing point is not within specifications, rectify fault and proceed to step 4.
2. Inspect thermostat as follows:
   a. Engine should be cool enough to touch.
   b. Connect scan tool and contact EDU.
   c. Select "READ FUNCTIONS" and "COOLANT TEMPERATURE."
   d. Start engine and warm up to idling speed. Determine engine temperature of coolant reaches approximately 92° C (198° F) and thermostat opens.

Diagnostic trouble code (SAE)	Faulty function/component	CHECK ENGINE	ISAT ST display text
P1213	Injector, cylinder 1, control module output. Shorting to battery positive (B+).		FAULT XX P1213 INJECTOR CYL 1 SHORT TO B+
P1214	Injector, cylinder 2, control module output. Shorting to battery positive (B+).		FAULT XX P1214 INJECTOR CYL 2 SHORT TO B+
P1215	Injector, cylinder 3, control module output. Shorting to battery positive (B+).		FAULT XX P1215 INJECTOR CYL 3 SHORT TO B+
P1216	Injector, cylinder 4, control module output. Shorting to battery positive (B+).		FAULT XX P1216 INJECTOR CYL 4 SHORT TO B+
P1217	Injector, cylinder 5, control module output. Shorting to battery positive (B+).		FAULT XX P1217 INJECTOR CYL 5 SHORT TO B+
P1218	Injector, cylinder 6, control module output. Shorting to battery positive (B+).		FAULT XX P1218 INJECTOR CYL 6 SHORT TO B+
P1225	Injector, cylinder 1, control module output. Open circuit or shorting to ground.		FAULT XX P1225 INJECTOR CYL 1 BREAK/SHORT TO GROUND
P1226	Injector, cylinder 2, control module output. Open circuit or shorting to ground.		FAULT XX P1226 INJECTOR CYL 2 BREAK/SHORT TO GROUND
P1227	Injector, cylinder 3, control module output. Open circuit or shorting to ground.		FAULT XX P1227 INJECTOR CYL 3 BREAK/SHORT TO GROUND
P1228	Injector, cylinder 4, control module output. Open circuit or shorting to ground.		FAULT XX P1228 INJECTOR CYL 4 BREAK/SHORT TO GROUND
P1229	Injector, cylinder 5, control module output. Open circuit or shorting to ground.		FAULT XX P1229 INJECTOR CYL 5 BREAK/SHORT TO GROUND
P1230	Injector, cylinder 6, control module output. Open circuit or shorting to ground.		FAULT XX P1230 INJECTOR CYL 6 BREAK/SHORT TO GROUND
P1386	Control module, electronic circuitry for processing knock sensor signals. Internal fault.		FAULT XX P1386 CONTROL MODULE INTERNAL FAULT KNOCK CONTROL
P1396	Crankshaft position sensor, control module input. Malfunctioning, slotted ring has too many ribs.		FAULT XX P1396 CRANKSHAFT POS. INPUT INCORRECT

SA1029700190060X

Fig. 2 Diagnostic trouble code identification (Part 6 of 10)

Diagnostic trouble code (SAE)	Faulty function/component	CHECK ENGINE	ISAT ST display text
P1410	EVAP canister purge valve, control module output. Shorting to battery positive (B+).		FAULT XX P1410 EVAP VALVE SHORT TO B+
P1425	EVAP canister purge valve, control module output. Shorting to ground.		FAULT XX P1425 EVAP VALVE SHORT TO GROUND
P1426	EVAP canister purge valve, control module output. Open circuit.		FAULT XX P1426 EVAP VALVE OPEN CIRCUIT
P1501	Fuel pump relay, control module output. Shorting to ground.		FAULT XX P1501 FUEL PUMP OUTPUT STAGE SHORT TO GROUND
P1502	Fuel pump relay, control module output. Shorting to battery positive (B+).		FAULT XX P1502 FUEL PUMP OUTPUT STAGE SHORT TO B+
P1510	Idle air control valve, open function, control module output. Shorting to battery positive (B+).		FAULT XX P1510 IAC VALVE OPEN SHORT TO B+
P1513	Idle air control valve, open function, control module output. Shorting to ground.		FAULT XX P1513 IAC VALVE OPEN SHORT TO GROUND
P1514	Idle air control valve, open function, control module output. Open circuit.		FAULT XX P1514 IAC VALVE OPEN OPEN CIRCUIT
P1541	Fuel pump relay, control module output. Open circuit.		FAULT XX P1541 FUEL PUMP OUTPUT STAGE OPEN CIRCUIT
P1551	Idle air control valve, close function, control module output. Open circuit.		FAULT XX P1551 IAC VALVE CLOSED OPEN CIRCUIT
P1552	Idle air control valve, close function, control module output. Shorting to ground.		FAULT XX P1552 IAC VALVE CLOSED SHORT TO GROUND
P1553	Idle air control valve, close function, control module output. Shorting to battery positive (B+).		FAULT XX P1553 IAC VALVE CLOSED SHORT TO B+
P1585	Fuel level less than 10 litres.		FAULT XX P1585 TANK LEVEL LOW VOLUME
P1611	CHECK ENGINE request, input signal to control module. Shorting to ground.	On	FAULT XX P1611 CHECK ENGINE REQUEST SHORT TO GROUND
P1624	The automatic transmission has a stored emission–related fault.	On	FAULT XX P1624 CHECK ENG. REQUEST REPLY TCM

SA1029700190070X

Fig. 2 Diagnostic trouble code identification (Part 7 of 10)

e. Coolant temperature should remain relatively constant at this temperature for minute or so.
f. If thermostat operates as specified, proceed to next step.
g. If thermostat does not operate as specified, replace thermostat and proceed to step 4.

3. Inspect coolant temperature sensor as follows:
   a. Run engine at idling speed.
   b. Connect scan tool.
   c. Establish communication with Motronic system.
   d. Select "READ FUNCTIONS" and "COOLANT TEMPERATURE."
   e. Record temperature.
   f. Establish communication with EDU.
   g. Select "READ VALUES," then "COOLANT TEMPERATURE."
   h. Temperature readings should not differ by more than maximum 9° F.
   i. If temperature readings are within specifications, proceed to step 4.
   j. If temperature readings are not within specifications, see fault diagnosis procedure for DTC's P0117 and P0118.
4. Clear all DTC's's, then start and run engine until radiator fan turns On.
5. Disconnect temperature sensor connector from EDU so radiator fan will run continuously.
6. Ensure coolant temperature in system drops to and stabilizes at approximately 198° F.
7. If coolant temperature drops and stabilizes, refer to "Electronic Control Module (ECM)" under "Component Replacement."
8. If coolant temperature does not drop and stabilize, clear all DTC's from temperature sensor in EDU and diagnose cooling system.

CODES P0117 & P0118: TEMPERATURE SENSOR

Fault Symptoms

Conditions: CHECK ENGINE lamp (MIL) On. CHECK ENGINE lamp (MIL) ON. Impaired driveability. Engine reluctant to start. DTC P0117 set and engine temperature lower than -40°C for more than one second; DTC P0118 set and Engine temperature higher than 140°C for more than one second. Inspect wiring. Intermittent faults may occur as a result of temporary short circuits and breaks in wiring. Jiggle wiring at several points and in different directions to ascertain whether wiring harness, including any connectors, is causing the trouble. Observe multimeter, scan tool or test lamp.

1. Determine temperature sensor performance with scan tool as follows:
   a. Connect scan tool.
   b. Turn ignition switch to ON position.
   c. Select "READ FUNCTIONS," then "COOLANT TEMPERATURE."
   d. If temperature sensor is in proper working order, scan tool should show current temperature of coolant.

Diagnostic Procedure

1. Inspect temperature sensor grounding as follows:
   a. Disconnect temperature sensor two pin electrical connector.
   b. Connect test lamp to battery positive and pin 2.
   c. If test lamp lights, proceed to step 2.
   d. If test lamp does not light, check circuit for an open of short, repair or replace as necessary and proceed to step 3.
2. Check control module temperature sensor input as follows:
   a. Connect scan tool.
   b. Turn ignition switch to ON position.

Diagnostic trouble code (SAE)	Faulty function/component	CHECK ENGINE	ISAT ST display text
P1664	Shift up, output signal from control module. Malfunction.		FAULT XX P1664 SHIFT-UP FUNCTION INCORRECT
P1669	TCS active, input signal to control module. Open circuit or shorting to ground or battery positive (B+).		FAULT XX P1669 TCS SIGNAL BREAK/SHORTING
P1691	CHECK ENGINE, output signal from control module. Open circuit.	On	FAULT XX P1691 CHECK ENGINE OPEN CIRCUIT
P1692	CHECK ENGINE, output signal from control module. Shorting to ground.	On	FAULT XX P1692 CHECK ENGINE SHORT TO GROUND
P1693	CHECK ENGINE, output signal from control module. Shorting to battery positive (B+).	On	FAULT XX P1693 CHECK ENGINE SHORT TO B+

SA1029700190080X

Fig. 2 Diagnostic trouble code identification (Part 8 of 10)

Type	DTC	Faulty function/component
P	0328	Knock sensor circuit. Input high, bank 1.
P	0333	Knock sensor circuit. Input high, bank 2.
P	0440	Tank venting. Function not OK.
P	0450	Tank pressure sensor. Function not OK.
P	0506	Idle speed control. Idle speed too low
P	0507	Idle Speed Control. Idle speed too fast.
P	0560	Power supply. Malfunction.
P	1136	Additive adaptation. Min. value, fuel/air mixture too rich, bank 1.
P	1137	Additive adaptation. Max. value, fuel-air mixture too lean, bank 1.
P	1138	Additive adaptation. Min. value, fuel-air mixture too lean, bank 2.
P	1139	Additive adaption. Max. value, fuel-air mixture too rich, bank 2.
P	1140	Mass air flow sensor or throttle position sensor. Malfunction.
P	1237	Injector circuit, cylinder 1. Break/shorting to ground.

SA1029700190090X

Fig. 2 Diagnostic trouble code identification (Part 9 of 10)

c. Select "READ FUNCTIONS" , then "COOLANT TEMPERATURE."
d. Scan tool should show reading of approximately 5 volts.
e. Connect jumper wire between pins 1 and 2 of temperature sensor connector.
f. Scan tool should read zero volts.
g. If readings are as specified, replace temperature sensor and proceed to step 3.
h. If reading are not as specified, check circuit for an open or short, repair or replace as necessary, then proceed step 3.

3. Clear all DTC's, then drive vehicle at varying engine loads and RPMs for five minutes.
4. If DTC is present, refer to "Electronic Control Module (ECM)" under "Component Replacement."
5. If DTC is not present, fault was corrected.

CODES P0122 & P0123: THROTTLE POSITION SENSOR

Fault Symptoms

Conditions: CHECK ENGINE lamp (MIL) ON. DTC P0122 voltage lower than .2 volts set and engine speed higher than 480 RPM for more than two seconds; DTC P0123 voltage higher than 4.85 volts set and engine speed higher than 480 RPM for more than two seconds.

1. Using scan tool determine performance of throttle position sensor as follows:
   a. Connect scan tool.
   b. Turn ignition switch to On position.
   c. Select "READ FUNCTIONS," then "THROTT POS SENSOR."
   d. If throttle position sensor is satisfactory, scan tool should show current throttle position from unactuated to fully depressed accelerator .5–4.5 volts.
   e. Inspect wiring for intermittent faults.

Diagnostic Procedure

1. Inspect throttle position sensor ground connection and power supply as follows:
   a. Disconnect throttle position sensor three pin electrical connector.
   b. Turn ignition switch to ON position.
   c. Measure voltage readings at connector pin 2 to battery ground. Voltage should be approximately 5 volts.
   d. Measure battery positive to pin 1, voltage should be approximately 12 volts.
   e. If voltage readings are within specifications, proceed to step 2.
   f. If voltage reading are not as specified, check circuits for open or short, repair or replace as necessary, then proceed step 3.
2. Inspect control module throttle position input as follows:
   a. Connect scan tool and turn ignition switch to ON position.
   b. Select "READ FUNCTIONS," then "THROTT POS SENSOR."
   c. Scan tool should show reading of approximately 5 volts.
   d. Connect jumper wire between pins 1 and 3 of throttle position sensor connector.
   e. Scan tool should show zero volts.
   f. If readings are as specified, replace throttle position sensor and proceed to step 3.
   g. If reading are not as specified, check circuit for an open or short, repair or replace as necessary, then proceed to step 3.
3. Clear all DTC's, then drive vehicle at varying engine loads and RPMs for five minutes.
4. If DTC is present, refer to "Electronic Control Module (ECM)" under "Component Replacement."

5. If DTC is not present, fault was corrected.

CODES P0130, P0131, P0132, P0133 & P0134: FRONT HEATED OXYGEN SENSOR

Fault Symptoms

Conditions: CHECK ENGINE lamp (MIL) ON. Any other DTCs, such as misfiring, closed loop, adaptation. DTC P0130 is set and sensor voltage .06–.4 volts and sensor No. 2 exceeds .5 volts for longer than 20 seconds; DTC P0131 is set and sensor voltage less than -.15 volts for longer than .2 seconds; DTC P0132 is set and sensor voltage exceeds 1.1 volts for longer than .2 seconds; DTC P0133 set and engine speed, 1400–2640 RPM, partial load, 1.45–3 ms, oxygen sensor frequency below 2 Hz and exhaust temperature higher than 352°C; DTC P0124 set and sensor voltage .4–.6 volts for longer than 3.5 seconds and sensor voltage for sensors Nos. 1 and 2 higher than .2 volts on fuel shutoff for longer than 1 second. Use the following procedure to check oxygen sensor operation.

1. Connect suitable scan tool and select "READ FUNCTIONS," then "OXY SENSOR BANK 1."
2. Read "OXY SENSOR FRONT."
3. With closed loop system active, scan tool reading should fluctuates between .1 and .9 volts.
4. Inspect wiring diagram for intermittent faults.
5. If reference ground or voltage of oxygen sensor is shorted to battery positive in wiring harness or oxygen sensors. DTC's P0132, P0152, P0138 and P0158 will usually appear.
6. If reference ground of oxygen sensors through pin 46 is shorted to battery ground in wiring harness or oxygen sensor. DTC's P0131, P0151, P0137 and P0157 will usually appear.
7. Check oxygen sensor preheating element performance as follows:
   a. A faulty preheating element will be most noticeable at idle speed.
   b. If DTCs for an open circuit and preheating are indicated, DTC for preheating should be repaired first.
   c. After repairing fault, inspect performance of oxygen sensor.

Diagnostic Procedure

1. Connect suitable scan tool and check for DTCs.
2. If DTC P1115 is present, refer to "Code P1115."
3. If DTC P0132, P0152, P0138 or P0158 are present, proceed as follows:
   a. Check for shorted wires to battery positive in oxygen sensors circuits connected to pin 18, 19, 76, 77 or 46 in wiring harness or oxygen sensors.
   b. Inspect insulation of oxygen sensors.
   c. Disconnect four four-pin oxygen sensor connectors.
   d. Measure resistance of between oxygen sensor connector pins 1 and 3, then between pins 1 to 4.
   e. If resistance is infinite, inspect wires connected to control module pin 18, 19, 76, 77 or 46, repair or replace as necessary and proceed to step 5.
   f. If resistance is not infinite, replace defective oxygen sensor and proceed to step 7.
4. If DTC P0131, P0151, P0137 or P0157 is present, proceed as follows:
   a. Check wire connected to pin 46 of control module for short to battery ground in wiring harness or oxygen sensors.
   b. Check for shorted wires to battery positive in oxygen sensors circuits connected to pin 18, 19, 76, 77 or 46 in wiring harness or oxygen sensors.
   c. Inspect insulation of oxygen sensors.
   d. Disconnect four four-pin oxygen sensor connector.
   e. Measure resistance between pins 1 to 3, then between pins 1 to 4.
   f. If resistance is infinite, inspect wires connected to control module pins 18, 19, 76, 77 or 46, repair or replace as necessary, then proceed to step 5.
   g. If resistance is not infinite, replace defective oxygen sensor and proceed to step 7.
5. Inspect control module sensor ground as follows:
   a. Disconnect four pin oxygen sensor connector.
   b. Turn ignition switch to ON position.
   c. Measure voltage between connector pin 3 and ground.
   d. If voltage is .7 volts, proceed to step 6.
   e. If voltage is not .7 volts, check circuit for an open of short, repair or replace as necessary, then proceed to step 7.
6. Inspect control module sensor input as follows:

P	1238	Injector circuit, cylinder 2. Break/shorting to ground.
P	1239	Injector circuit, cylinder 3. Break/shorting to ground.
P	1240	Injector circuit, cylinder 4. Break/shorting to ground.
P	1241	Injector circuit, cylinder 5. Break/shorting to ground.
P	1242	Injector circuit, cylinder 6. Break/shorting to ground.
P	1551	Idle air control valve. Closing. No continuity.
P	1602	No +30 when +15 present.
P	1614	CHECK ENGINE request. Break/short circuit B+.
P	1655	Control module pins NOT used are connected to B+.
P	1657	Control module pin NOT used is connected to battery positive (B +).
P	1660	Control module pin NOT used is connected to battery positive (B+).
P	1662	Control module pin NOT used is connected to battery positive (B+).
P	1782	Torque limitation. Break/shorting to ground.

SA1029700190100X

Fig. 2 Diagnostic trouble code identification (Part 10 of 10)

a. Connect scan tool and turn ignition switch to ON position.
b. Select "READ FUNCTIONS," then "OXY SENSOR BANK 1."
c. Read "OXY SENSOR FRONT."
d. Scan tool should show reading of approximately .45 volts.
e. Connect jumper wire between oxygen sensor connector pins 3 and 4.
f. If voltage is zero, replace oxygen sensor and proceed to step 7.
g. If voltage is not zero, check circuit for an open or short, repair or replace as necessary and proceed to step 7.

7. Clear all DTC's, then drive vehicle at varying engine loads and RPMs for five minutes.
8. Connect scan tool and select "ON OFF," then "DIAGNOSTIC STATUS," then "OXY SENSOR BANK 1."
9. Read "OXY SENSOR FRONT."
10. If scan tool reads "NOT READY," repeat driving cycle.
11. If DTC is present, refer to "Electronic Control Module (ECM)" under "Component Replacement."
12. If DTC is not present, fault was corrected.

CODES P0136, P0137, P0138, P0139 & P0140: REAR HEATED OXYGEN SENSOR

Fault Symptoms

Conditions: CHECK ENGINE lamp (MIL) ON. Any other DTCs, such as misfiring, closed loop, adaptation. For all DTCs, preheating shall have been active for more than 200 seconds after starting. The closed loop system should be active.

DTC P0136 is set when sensor voltage is -.04 to +.04 volts for longer than 225 seconds. DTC P0137 is set when sensor voltage is -.15 volts for longer than .2 seconds. DTC P0138 is set when sensor voltage exceeds 1.1 volts for longer than .2 seconds. DTC P0139 is set when sensor voltage is low despite maximum closed loop or sensor voltage is high despite maximum closed loop weakening. DTC P0140 is set when sensor voltage is .4–.5 volts for longer than 11 minutes. Use the following procedure to determine oxygen sensor performance.

1. Connect suitable scan tool and select "READ FUNCTIONS," then "OXY SENSOR BANK 1."
2. Read "OXYGEN SENSOR 2."
3. At full load, scan tool should show reading higher than .7 volts.
4. At fuel shutoff, scan tool should show reading of approximately zero volts.
5. Inspect wiring for intermittent faults.
6. If reference ground or voltage of oxygen sensors is shorted to battery positive in wiring harness or oxygen sensor, DTCs P0132, P0152, P0138 and P0158 will usually be generated.
7. If reference ground of oxygen sensors via pin 46 is shorted to battery ground in wiring harness or oxygen sensor, DTCs P0131, P0151, P0137 and P0157 will usually be generated.
8. If preheating element of any oxygen sensor develops fault, performance of sensor will deteriorate. This will be particularly noticeable at idle speed. DTC indicating that sensor is unserviceable could then be generated. If DTCs are generated for both open circuit and preheating, DTC for preheating should be repaired first.

Diagnostic Procedure

1. Using scan tool obtain all DTCs.
2. If DTC P1117 exists, carry out fault diagnosis and final inspection as outlined under DTC P1117.
3. If DTC P0138, P0132, P0152 or P0158 exist, proceed as follows:
   a. Disconnect oxygen sensor four 4 pin connector.
   b. Measure resistance between pins 1 and 3, then between pins 1 and 4.
   c. If resistance is infinite, check wires connected to control module pins 18, 19, 76, 77 or 46 for an open or short circuit. If circuit is satisfactory, proceed to step 4. If circuit is not satisfactory, repair or replace as necessary and proceed to step 5.
   d. If resistance is not infinite, replace oxygen sensor and proceed to step 7.
4. If DTC P0131, P0151, P0137 or P0157 exist, proceed as follows:
   a. Disconnect oxygen sensor four-pin connector.
   b. Measure resistance between connector pin 3 and ground, then between pin 4 and ground.
   c. If resistance is infinite, inspect wire connected to pin 46 of control module for short to ground. If circuit is satisfactory, proceed to step 4. If circuit is not satisfactory, repair or replace as necessary, then proceed to step 5.
   d. If resistance is not infinite, replace defective oxygen sensor and proceed to step 7.
5. Inspect control module sensor ground as follows:
   a. Disconnect oxygen sensor four-pin connector.
   b. Turn ignition switch to ON position.
   c. Measure voltage between connector pin 3 and ground.
   d. If voltage is .7 volts, proceed to step 6.
   e. If voltage is not .7 volts, check circuit for an open or short, repair or replace as necessary, then proceed to step 7.
6. Inspect control module sensor input as follows:
   a. Connect scan tool and turn ignition switch to ON position.
   b. Select "READ FUNCTIONS," then "OXY SENSOR BANK 1."
   c. Read "OXYGEN SENSOR 2."
   d. Scan tool should indicate .45 volts.
   e. Connect suitable jumper wire between oxygen sensor connector pins 3 and 4.
   f. Scan tool should indicate zero volts.
   g. If voltage readings are as specified, replace oxygen sensor and proceed to step 7.
   h. If voltage readings are not as specified, check circuits for an open or short, repair or replace as necessary, then proceed to step 7.
7. Clear all DTC's, then drive vehicle at varying engine loads and RPMs for five minutes.
8. Connect scan tool and select "ON OFF," then "DIAGNOSTIC STATUS," then "OXY SENSOR BANK 1."
9. Read "OXYGEN SENSOR 2."
10. If scan tool reads "NOT READY," repeat driving cycle.
11. If DTC is present, refer to "Electronic Control Module (ECM)" under "Component Replacement."
12. If DTC is not present, fault was corrected.

CODES P0150, P0151, P0152, P0153 & P0154: FRONT HEATED OXYGEN SENSOR

Fault Symptoms

Conditions: CHECK ENGINE lamp (MIL) ON. Any other DTCs, such as misfiring, closed loop, adaptation. For all DTCs, preheating shall have been active for more than 200 seconds after starting. The closed loop system should be active. DTC P0150 set and sensor voltage .06–.4 volts and sensor No. 2 voltage exceeds .5 volts for longer than 20 seconds.

DTC P0151 is set when sensor voltage is less than -.15 volts for longer than .2 seconds. DTC P0152 is set when sensor voltage exceeds 1.1 volts for longer than .2 seconds. DTC P0153 is set when engine speed at 1400–2640 RPM, partial load is 1.45–3 ms and oxygen sensor frequency is below 2 Hz and exhaust temperature is higher than 352°C. DTC P0154 is set when sensor voltage is .4–.6 volts for longer than 3.5 seconds, sensor voltage for sensors Nos. 1 and 2 is higher than .2 volts on fuel shutoff for longer than one second.

1. Inspect oxygen sensor performance with scan tool as follows:
   a. Select "READ FUNCTIONS," then "OXY SENSOR BANK 2."
   b. Read "OXY SENSOR FRONT."
   c. With closed loop system active, scan tool should alternate between .1 and .9 volts.
2. Inspect wiring for intermittent faults.
3. Determine if reference ground or voltage of oxygen sensors is shorted to battery positive in wiring harness or in oxygen sensors, all these DTCs will usually be generated: DTC's P0132, P0152, P0138 and P0158.
4. If reference ground of oxygen sensors via pin 46 is shorted to battery ground in wiring harness or oxygen sensors, all following DTCs will usually be generated: DTC's P0131, P0151, P0137 and P0157.
5. If preheating element of any oxygen sensor develops fault, performance of sensor will deteriorate. This will be particularly noticeable at idling speed. DTC indicating sensor is unserviceable could then be generated. DTCs

that are generated indicate fault is an open circuit. If DTCs are generated for both open circuit and preheating, trouble code for preheating should be attended to first. Following this, performance of oxygen sensor should be inspected.

Diagnostic Procedure

1. Determine other DTCs in system as follows:
   a. Using scan tool obtain all DTCs.
   b. If DTC P0155 is set, carry out fault diagnosis and final inspection as outlined under DTC P0155.
   c. If DTC P0152 and any of these DTCs are set: DTC's P0132, P0138 or P0158, proceed to next step.
   d. If DTC P0151 and these DTCs are set: DTC's P0131, P0137 or P0157, proceed to step 3.
   e. If not, proceed to step 4.
2. Inspect shorting to battery positive as follows:
   a. Determine if oxygen sensors wires connected to pin 18, 19, 76, 77 or 46 are shorted to battery positive in wiring harness or oxygen sensors.
   b. Inspect insulation of oxygen sensors.
   c. Disconnect four four-pin oxygen sensor connectors.
   d. Measure resistance of sensors at pins 1 to 3 and pins 1 to 4, OL (infinite resistance).
   e. If all readings are within specifications, inspect wires connected to control module pin 18, 19, 76, 77 or 46 and repair or replace as necessary, then proceed to final inspection.
   f. If not, replace defective oxygen sensor, then proceed to final inspection.
3. Inspect shorting to battery ground as follows:
   a. Determine if wire connected to pin 46 of control module is shorted to battery ground in wiring harness or oxygen sensors.
   b. Inspect insulation of oxygen sensors.
   c. Disconnect four four-pin oxygen sensor connectors.
   d. Measure resistance of sensors at pin 3 to ground and pin 4 to ground. Resistance should read, OL, (infinite resistance).
   e. If all readings are within specifications, inspect wire connected to pin 46 of control module for shorting to ground and repair or replace as necessary, then proceed to final inspection.
   f. If not, replace defective oxygen sensor, then proceed to final inspection.
4. Inspect control module sensor ground as follows:
   a. Disconnect four-pin oxygen sensor connectors.
   b. Turn ignition switch to ON position.
   c. Measure voltage reading on connector between pin 3 and ground. Reading should be .7 volts.
   d. If reading is within specifications, proceed to next step.
   e. If not, inspect wire in question and repair or replace as necessary, then proceed to final inspection.
5. Inspect control module sensor input as follows:
   a. Connect scan tool.
   b. Turn ignition switch to On position.
   c. Select "READ FUNCTIONS," then "OXY SENSOR BANK 2."
   d. Read "OXY SENSOR FRONT."
   e. Scan tool should show reading of approximately .45 volts.
   f. Connect jumper wire between pins 3 and 4 in oxygen sensor connector.
   g. Scan tool should show reading of approximately zero.
   h. If all readings are within specifications, replace oxygen sensor, then proceed to final inspection.
   i. If not, inspect wires in question and repair or replace as necessary, then proceed to final inspection.
6. Final inspection.
   a. Clear all DTC's.
   b. Drive vehicle at varying engine loads and RPMs for five minutes.
   c. Connect scan tool.
   d. Select "ON OFF," then "DIAGNOSTIC STATUS," then "OXY SENSOR BANK 2."
   e. Read "OXY SENSOR FRONT."
   f. If scan tool reads "NOT READY," repeat driving cycle.
   g. If DTC is present, refer to "Electronic Control Module (ECM)" under "Component Replacement."
   h. If DTC is not present, fault was corrected.

CODE P0155: FRONT HEATED OXYGEN SENSOR

Fault Symptoms

Conditions: CHECK ENGINE lamp (MIL) ON. Preheating circuit resistance greater than ten ohms after three minutes. If an oxygen sensor attains operative status for times faster than another one, the other one is identified as defective. Preheating circuit resistance less than 2.5 ohms after 3 minutes.

If scan tool shows DTCs P1115, P1117, P0155 and P0161, probable cause is as follows:

1. Fuse 28 defective.
2. Due to wire from crimped connection J37 via fuse 28 and connector H70–1 to crimped connection J129.
3. Inspect wiring for intermittent faults.

Diagnostic Procedure

1. Inspection fuses as follows:
   a. Determine if fuse 28 is intact.
   b. If so, proceed to step 3.
   c. If not, replace fuse and proceed to next step.
2. Measure resistance of oxygen sensor preheating elements as follows:
   a. Engine should have been turned OFF for at least five minutes.
   b. Disconnect four-pin oxygen sensor connectors.
   c. Measure resistance of four sensors, pins 1 & 2, 1.8–4,0 ohms.
   d. If resistance readings are within specifications, measure resistance. If necessary repair or replace wire between pin 1 in each of four oxygen sensor connectors and fuse 28, then proceed to final inspection.
   e. If not, replace defective oxygen sensor and proceed to final inspection.
3. Inspect preheating element power supply as follows:
   a. Disconnect oxygen sensor four pin electrical connector.
   b. Start engine and run it at idling speed.
   c. Connect test lamp to pin 1 and battery ground.
   d. Test lamp should light.
   e. If so, continue with next step.
   f. If not, repair or replace wire in question and proceed to final inspection.
4. Inspect preheating circuit ground connection as follows:
   a. With engine running at idling speed, connect test lamp to battery positive and pin 2.
   b. If test lamp is on or flashing, replace sensor and proceed to final inspection.
   c. If not, inspect wire in question and repair or replace as necessary, then proceed to final inspection.
5. Final inspection as follows:
   a. Clear all DTC's.
   b. Drive vehicle at varying engine loads and RPMs for five minutes.
   c. If DTC is present, refer to "Electronic Control Module (ECM)" under "Component Replacement."
   d. If DTC is not present, fault was corrected.

CODES P0156, P0157, P0158, P0159 & P0160: REAR HEATED OXYGEN SENSOR

Fault Symptoms

Conditions: CHECK ENGINE lamp (MIL) on. Determine any other DTCs, such as misfiring, closed loop, adaptation. For all DTCs, preheating shall have been active for more than 200 seconds after starting. The closed loop system should be active.

DTC P0156 is set and sensor voltage -.04 to .04 volts exist for longer than 225 seconds. DTC P0157 is set and sensor voltage -.5 volts for longer than .2 seconds. DTC P0158 is set and sensor voltage exceeds 1.1 volts for longer than .2 seconds. DTC P0159 is set and sensor voltage low despite maximum closed loop. Sensor voltage high despite maximum closed loop weakening. P0160 set and voltage .4–.5 volts for longer than 11 minutes. Determine oxygen sensor performance with a scan tool as follows:

1. Select "READ FUNCTIONS," then "OXY SENSOR BANK 2."
2. Read "OXYGEN SENSOR 2."
3. At full load scan tool should show reading higher than .7 volts.
4. At fuel shutoff scan tool should show

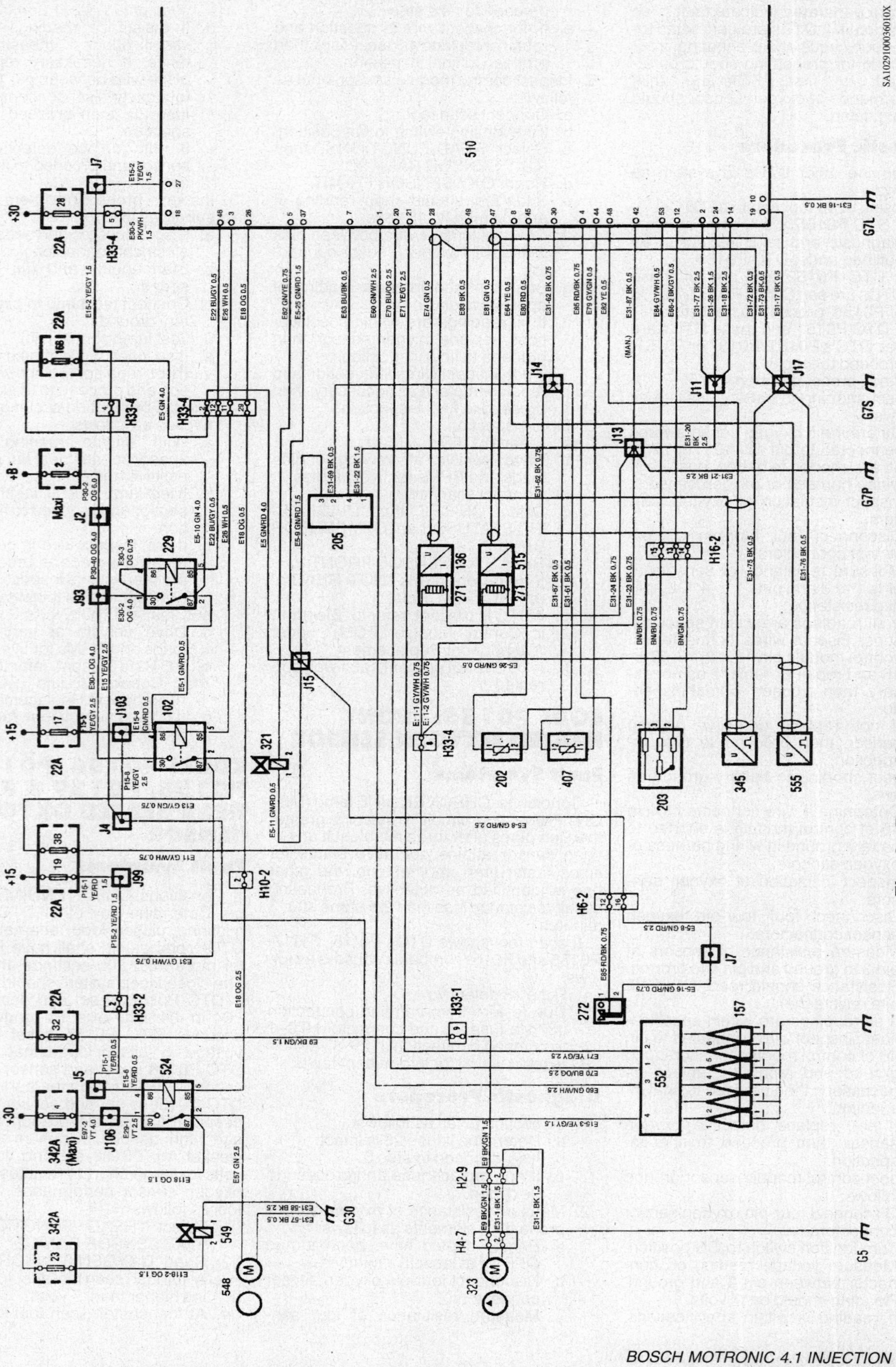

Fig. 3 Bosch Motronic wiring diagram (Part 1 of 3)

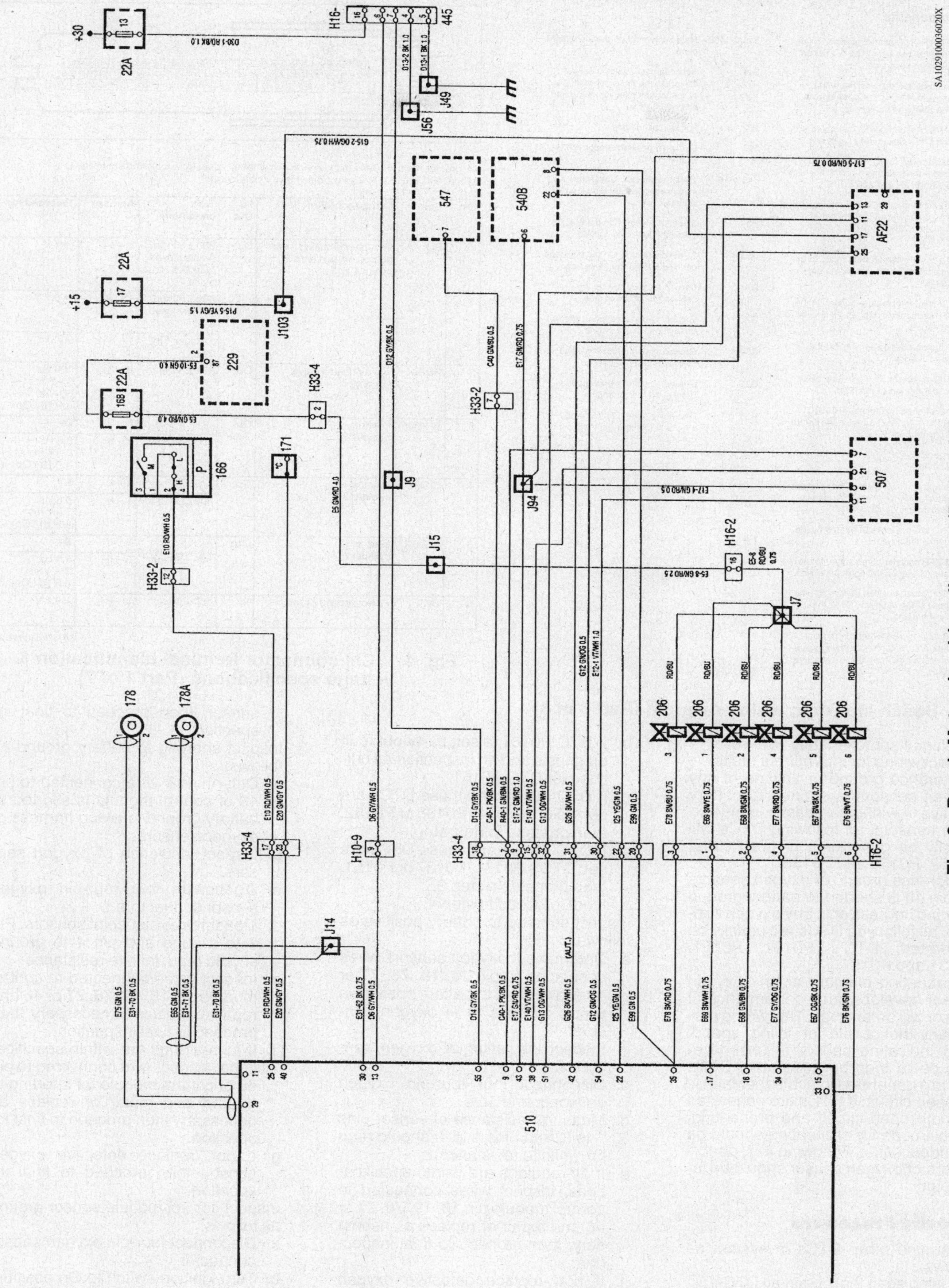

Fig. 3 Bosch Motronic wiring diagram (Part 2 of 3)

List of components

510	MOTRONIC control module. Inside the side trim below the A pillar on the right-hand side.	540A, 540B	Main instrument. In the instrument panel.
502	Automatic transmission control module. Behind the glove box on the bulkhead partition.	549	Secondary air injection control valve. On the hose between the secondary air injection pump and non-return valve.
547	ABS control module. Integrated with the brake unit in the engine bay.	552	Ignition coil module
229	Main relay. In the main fuse box under the instrument panel. Location 22BL (LHD) and 22B:I (RHD).	555	Camshaft position sensor. Under the engine cover.
102	Fuel pump relay. In the main fuse box under the instrument panel. Location 22B:I (LHD) and 22B:F (RHD).	445 (H16-1)	16-pin connector. Under the instrument panel by the steering column.
524	Secondary air injection relay. In the main fuse box in the engine bay (342:B).	H33-2	33-pin connector. On the bracket below the left-hand A pillar.
202	Coolant temperature sensor. In the intake manifold, top left- hand side of engine.	H33-4	33-pin connector. On the bulkhead partition behind the glove box.
203	Throttle position sensor. On the throttle body.	G5	Grounding point. Under the rear seat on the left-hand side.
178	Knock sensor. In the engine block under the intake manifold.	G7L	Grounding point, oxygen sensor. Bracket on rear of engine.
171	Anti-freeze thermostat A/C-ACC. Behind the ACC panel in the centre console.	G7P	Grounding point, power ground. Bracket on rear of engine.
206	Injectors. On top of the intake manifold.	G7S	Grounding point, signal ground. Bracket on rear of engine.
205	Mass air flow sensor. On the intake manifold between the air cleaner and throttle body.	G30	Grounding point. On left-hand structural member behind the battery.
272	IAC valve. Centrally located by the intake manifold.		
321	EVAP canister purge valve. In the engine bay on the right- hand side.		
345	Crankshaft position sensor. On the front of the engine block at the flywheel end.		
166	Pressure monitor for the radiator fan, A/C-ACC. On the drying agent container between the radiator and grille.		

SA1029100036030X

Fig. 3 Bosch Motronic wiring diagram (Part 3 of 3)

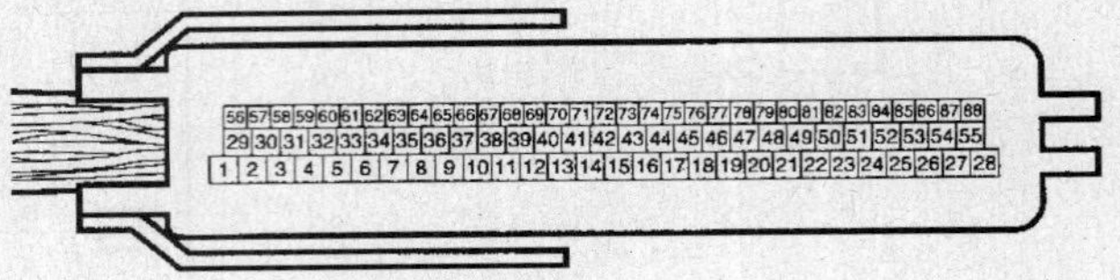

> = greater than; < = less than; ≈ = approximately equal to; ~ = alternating current
(LP: LOGIC PROBE P = select pulse; p = visible pulses).

Pin	Colour	Component/Function	In/ Out	Test conditions	Across	Test reading
1	BU	Ground/preheating, rear heated oxygen sensor, banks 1 and 2	Out	800 ± 50 rpm Active closed loop at 5 Hz pulse	1 – 34	≈ 7 V
				800 ± 50 rpm Active closed loop	1 – 34	≈ 0.7 V
				Remove fuse 38	1 – 34	0 V
2	RD/BK	Idle air control valve (closing)	Out	800 ± 50 rpm	2 – 34	100 Hz 6 – 8 ms (–) 60 – 80% (–) (LP **HI** LOp)
3	BN/WH	Injector cylinder 1	Out		3 – 6	B+
				800 ± 50 rpm	3 – 6	6.6 Hz 2 – 4 ms (LP **HI** LOp)
4	BK/RD	Injector cylinder 3	Out		4 – 6	B+
				800 ± 50 rpm	4 – 6	6.6 Hz 2 – 4 ms (LP **HI** LOp)
5	OG/BK	Injector cylinder 5	Out		5 – 6	B+
				800 ± 50 rpm	5 – 6	6.6 Hz 2 – 4 ms (LP **HI** LOp)
6	BK	Power ground / injectors	In	800 ± 50 rpm	6 – B–	< 0.1 V

SA1029700191010X

Fig. 4 ECM connector terminal identification & voltage specifications (Part 1 of 7)

reading of approximately zero volts.
5. Inspect wiring for intermittent faults.
6. If reference ground or voltage of any oxygen sensors is shorted to battery positive in wiring harness or in any oxygen sensors, all following DTCs will usually be generated: DTC's P0132, P0152, P0138 and P0158.
7. If reference ground of oxygen sensors via pin 46 is shorted to battery ground in wiring harness or in any oxygen sensors, all following DTCs will usually be generated: DTC's P0131, P0151, P0137 and P0157.
8. If preheating element of any oxygen sensor develops fault, performance of sensor will deteriorate. This will be particularly noticeable at idling speed. DTC indicating sensor is unserviceable could then be generated. DTCs that are generated indicate that fault is an open circuit. If DTCs are generated for both open circuit and preheating, trouble code for preheating should be attended to first. Following this, performance of oxygen sensor should be inspected.

Diagnostic Procedure

1. Determine other DTCs in system as follows:
   a. Using scan tool obtain all DTCs.
   b. If DTC P0161 is set, carry out fault diagnosis and an inspection as outlined for DTC P0161.
   c. If DTC P0158 and these DTCs are set: DTC's P0132, P0138 or P0152, then proceed to next step.
   d. If DTC P0157 and these DTCs are set: DTC's P0131, P0137 or P0151, then proceed to step 3.
   e. If not, proceed to step 4.
2. Inspect shorting to battery positive as follows:
   a. Determine if oxygen sensors wires connected to pin 18, 19, 76, 77 or 46 are shorted to battery positive in wiring harness or in oxygen sensors:
   b. Inspect insulation of oxygen sensors.
   c. Disconnect four four-pin oxygen sensor connectors.
   d. Measure resistance of sensor pins 1 to 3, and pins 1 to 4, should read OL (infinite resistance).
   e. If all readings are within specifications, inspect wires connected to control module pin 18, 19, 76, 77 or 46 and repair or replace as necessary, then proceed to final inspection.
   f. If not, replace defective oxygen sensor, then proceed to final inspection.
3. Inspect shorting to battery ground as follows:
   a. Determine if wire connected to pin 46 of control module is shorted to battery ground in wiring harness or oxygen sensors.
   b. Inspect insulation of oxygen sensors.
   c. Disconnect four four-pin oxygen sensor connectors.
   d. Measure resistance of sensors. Pin 3 to ground and pin 4 to ground should read, infinite resistance.
   e. Inspect wires connected to control module pin 18, 19, 76, 77 or 46 and repair or replace as necessary, then proceed to final inspection.
   f. If all readings are within specifications, inspect wire connected to pin 46 of control module for shorting to ground and repair or replace as necessary, then proceed to final inspection.
   g. If not, replace defective oxygen sensor, then proceed to final inspection.
4. Inspect control module sensor ground as follows:
   a. Disconnect four-pin oxygen sensor connector.
   b. Turn ignition switch to On position.

Pin	Colour	Component/Function	In/ Out	Test conditions	Across	Test reading
7		Not used				
8	YE/GN	CHECK ENGINE	Out	CHECK ENGINE on	8 – 34	≈ 0 V
				800 ± 50 rpm CHECK ENGINE out	8 – 34	B+
9		Not used				
10		Not used				
11	GN/BK	Radiator fan	In	Radiator fan not active	11 – 28	B+
				Radiator fan active	11 – 28	≈ 0.5 V
12	GN/GY	A/C in	In	A/C ON	12 – 28	B+
				A/C OFF	12 – 28	0 V
13		Not used				
14		Not used				
15		Not used				
16	GY/GN	Intake air temperature sensor	In	Air temp. about 25°C (77°F)	16 – 71	≈ 3.4 V See also technical data
17	BU/BN	Mass air flow sensor	In	800 ± 50 rpm A/C and all electrical equipment off	17 – 45	≈ 0.8 V
				2500 ± 50 rpm A/C and all electrical equipment off. No load.	17 – 45	≈ 1.2 V
				Wide open throttle, max revs A/C and all electrical equipment off. No load.	17 – 45	≈ 3.9 V

SA1029700191020X

Fig. 4 ECM connector terminal identification & voltage specifications (Part 2 of 7)

Pin	Colour	Component/Function	In/ Out	Test conditions	Across	Test reading
18	YE	Front heated oxygen sensor, cylinder bank 2	In	800 ± 50 rpm active closed loop	18 – 46	0.1 – 0.9 V
19	GN	Front heated oxygen sensor, cylinder bank 1	In	800 ± 50 rpm active closed loop	19 – 46	0.1 – 0.9 V
20	YE	Reference ground, crankshaft position sensor	In		26 – 20	B+
21	OG/WH	Shifting signal (torque reduction)	In	Active	21 – 28	100 Hz
22		Not used				
23		Not used				
24		Not used				
25		Not used				
26	PK/WK	+30	In	800 ±50 rpm	B+ – 26	<0.5 V
27	BU/GY	Main relay	Out		B+ to 27	B+
				Ignition OFF	B+ to 27	0 V
28	BK	Ground, control module circuitry	In	800 ±50 rpm	28 – B–	<0.1 V
29	BK	Idle air control valve (opening)	Out		29 – 34	100 Hz 20 – 40% (–) 2 – 4 ms (–) (LP HI LOp)
30	BU	Ground/oxygen sensor preheating, banks 1 and 2	In	800 ± 50 rpm Active closed loop at 5 Hz pulse	30 – 34	≈ 7 V
				800 ± 50 rpm Active closed loop	30 – 34	≈ 0.7 V
				Remove fuse 38	30 – 34	0 V

SA1029700191030X

Fig. 4 ECM connector terminal identification & voltage specifications (Part 3 of 7)

c. Measure voltage reading on relevant connector between pin 3 and ground, voltage should read 7 V.
d. If yes, proceed to next step.
e. If not, inspect wire in question and repair or replace as necessary, then proceed to final inspection.

5. Inspect control module sensor input as follows:
   a. Connect scan tool.
   b. Turn ignition switch to On position.
   c. Select “READ FUNCTIONS,” then “OXY SENSOR BANK 2.”
   d. Scan tool should show reading of approximately .45 V.
   e. Connect jumper wire between pins 3 and 4 in oxygen sensor connector.
   f. Scan tool should show reading of approximately zero volts.
   g. If all readings are within specifications, then proceed to final inspection.
   h. If not, inspect wires in question and repair or replace as necessary, then proceed to final inspection.
6. final inspection as follows:
   a. Clear all DTC’s.
   b. Drive vehicle at varying engine loads and RPMs for five minutes.
   c. Connect scan tool.
   d. Select “ON OFF,” then “OXY SENSOR BANK 2.”
   e. If scan tool reads “NOT READY,” repeat driving cycle.
   f. If DTC is present, refer to “Electronic Control Module (ECM)” under “Component Replacement.”
   g. If DTC is not present, fault was corrected.

CODE P0161: REAR HEATED OXYGEN SENSOR

Fault Symptoms

Conditions: CHECK ENGINE lamp (MIL) ON. Preheating circuit resistance greater than ten ohms after three minutes. If an oxygen sensor attains operative status four times faster than another one, the other one is identified as defective. Preheating Circuit resistance less than 2.5 ohms after 3 minutes. If scan tool shows DTCs P1115, P1117, P0155 and P0161, the cause of the trouble is because fuse 28 has blown, due to wire from connector J37 via fuse 28 and connector H70–1 to connector J29. Inspect wiring for intermittent faults.

Diagnostic Procedure

1. Inspect fuses as follows:
   a. Determine if fuse 38 is intact.
   b. If so, continue with step 3.
   c. If not, replace fuse and proceed to next step.
2. Measure resistance of oxygen sensor preheating elements.
   a. Engine should have been switched off for at least five minutes.
   b. Disconnect four four-pin oxygen sensor connectors.
   c. Measure resistance of four sensors as follows:
   d. Pins 3 and 4, 1.8–4.0 ohms
   e. If resistance readings are within specifications, inspect and if necessary repair or replace wire between pin 1 in each of four oxygen sensor connectors and fuse 28, then proceed to final inspection.
   f. If not, replace defective oxygen sensor and proceed to final inspection.
3. Inspect preheating element power supply as follows:
   a. Disconnect oxygen sensor four pin electrical connector.
   b. Start engine and run it at idling speed.
   c. Connect test lamp to pin 1 and battery ground.
   d. Test lamp should light.
   e. If so, continue with next step.
   f. If not, repair or replace wire in question and proceed to final inspection.
4. Inspect preheating circuit ground connection as follows:
   a. With engine running at idling speed, connect test lamp to battery positive and pin 2.
   b. Test lamp should light or start flashing, if so, replace sensor and proceed to final inspection.
   c. If not, inspect wire in question and repair or replace as necessary, then proceed to final inspection.
5. Final inspection.
   a. Clear all DTC’s.
   b. Drive vehicle at varying engine loads and RPMs for five minutes.

Pin	Colour	Component/Function	In/ Out	Test conditions	Across	Test reading
31	GN/BN	Injector, cylinder 2	Out		31 – 6	B+
				800 ± 50 rpm	31 – 6	6.6 Hz 2 – 4 ms (LP **HI** LOp)
32	GY/OG	Injector, cylinder 4	Out		32 – 6	B+
				800 ± 50 rpm	32 – 6	6.6 Hz 2 – 4 ms (LP **HI** LOp)
33	BK/GN	Injector, cylinder 6	Out		33 – 6	B+
				800 ± 50 rpm	33 – 6	6.6 Hz 2 – 4 ms (LP **HI** LOp)
34	BK	Ground, other output stages	In	800 ± 50 rpm	34 – B–	<0.1 V
35		Not used				
36	RD/WH	A/C Relay	Out	800 ± 50 rpm A/C ON	26 – 36	B+
				800 ± 50 rpm A/C OFF	26 – 36	≈0 V
37	OG	Relay, secondary air injection pump	Out	Active	37 – 34	≈0.5 V
				Not active	37 – 34	B+
38	YE/RD	Camshaft position sensor	In	800 ± 50 rpm	38 – 71	≈7 Hz ≈11% (–) (LP **HI** LOp)
39	BU/GN	CHECK ENGINE request from TCM	In	When ignition switched ON	56 – 39	B+ for 1 s (LP LOp)
40	GN	Front knock sensor	In	4000 rpm	40 – 71	>30 mV a.c.
41		Not used				
42		Not used				
43		Not used				
44	GY/WH	Throttle position sensor	In	Idling	44 – 71	≈0.5 V
				Wide open throttle	44 – 71	≈4.5 V see also technical data
45	GN	Reference ground, mass air flow sensor	In	800 ± 50 rpm	45 – B–	<0,1 V
46	BK	Reference ground, oxygen sensors	In	800 ± 50 rpm Active closed loop	46 – 34	≈0.7 V

SA1029700191040X

Fig. 4 ECM connector terminal identification & voltage specifications (Part 4 of 7)

Pin	Colour	Component/Function	In/ Out	Test conditions	Across	Test reading
47		Not used				
48		Not used				
49	GN/WH	Ignition coil, cylinders 1 & 4	Out	800 ± 50 rpm	49 – 55	≈7% (–) (LP **HI** LOp)
50	BU/OG	Ignition coil, cylinders 1 & 4	Out	800 ± 50 rpm	50 – 55	≈7% (–) (LP **HI** LOp)
51	YE/GY	Ignition coil, cylinders 3 & 6	Out	800 ± 50 rpm	51 – 55	≈ 7% (–) (LP **HI** LOp)
52		Not used				
53	WH/BK	Power supply, throttle position sensor and fuel tank pressure sensor	Out		53 – 71	5 V
54	GN/RD	Power supply from main relay	In		B+ to 54	<0.5 V
55	BK	Power ground, ignition	In	800 ± 50 rpm	55 to B–	<0.1 V
56	YE/GY	+15 (via anti–theft alarm control module)	In		B+ to 56	<0.5 V
57		Not used				
58		Not used				
59		Not used				
60		Not used				
61	GN/YE	EVAP canister purge valve	Out	800 ± 50 rpm, see page 54 for operating conditions	61 – 34	7.5 Hz 15 Hz 30 Hz (LP **HI** LOp)
62	BU	Secondary air injection control valve	Out	Active	62 – 34	≈0.5 V
				Not active	62 – 34	≈B+
63	WH	Fuel pump relay	Out		63 – 34	≈B+
				800 ± 50 rpm	63 – 34	<0.5 V

SA1029700191050X

Fig. 4 ECM connector terminal identification & voltage specifications (Part 5 of 7)

c. Determine if DTC has recurred.
d. If yes, refer to "Electronic Control Module (ECM)" under "Component Replacement."
e. If not, procedures to rectify fault were correct.

CODE P0300: RANDOM MISFIRE

Fault Symptoms

Conditions: CHECK ENGINE lamp (MIL) ON. Poor running while misfiring. Any other DTCs. During the course of each cylinder's power stroke the rotational speed of the crankshaft increases temporarily. This causes momentary increases in pulse frequency from the crankshaft position sensor. These frequencies are evaluated by the control module and any misfiring is recorded. How large a proportion of misfires is required for exhaust emissions to reach prohibited levels, or for the catalytic converter to be damaged, is specified in a load and RPM dependent matrix or map in the control module's memory. A DTC will be generated if the number of misfires exceeds the matrix figure.

1. Possible cause of misfiring are as follows:
   a. Low fuel level in tank. DTC P1585 will generate.
   b. Fuel system malfunction.
   c. Low fuel level.
   d. Continuously open purge valve.
   e. Air leakage after mass air flow sensor.
   f. Defective/clogged injectors.
   g. Ignition system malfunction.
   h. Defective or incorrect spark plugs.
   i. Defective ignition coil module, HT wires.
   j. Basic engine malfunction.
   k. Poor compression.
   l. Malfunction of common components:
   m. Mass air flow sensor.
   n. Main relay/pump relay.
   o. Engine coolant temperature sensor.
   p. Inspect wiring for intermittent faults.

Diagnostic Procedure

1. Determine additional DTCs as follows:
   a. Using scan tool obtain all DTCs.
   b. If scan tool shows any other DTC's, continue fault diagnosis according to diagnostic procedure for relevant DTC.
   c. If not, proceed to next step.
2. Determine basic causes of fault as follows:
   a. Using scan tool to ensure engine coolant temperature correct.
   b. Ensure mass air flow sensor performance is correct.
   c. Ensure scan tool shows following air mass as function of engine RPM.
   d. At idling speed, approximately .8 volts
   e. At 2500 RPM (no load), approximately 1.5 volts
   f. If fault has been found, rectify fault and proceed to final inspection.
   g. If not, proceed to next step.
3. Inspect spark plugs as follows:
   a. Remove and visually inspect spark plugs.
   b. If spark plugs are satisfactory, continue with next step.
   c. If not, electrode gaps are wider than .0551 inch. Replace spark plugs and proceed to final inspection.
4. Inspect HT cables as follows:
   a. Measure resistance of all HT cables as follows:
   b. HT cables Nos. 1–3–5, should read 7–9 kohms.
   c. HT cables Nos. 2–4–6, should read 2–6 kohms.
5. Inspect performance of ignition coil module as follows:
   a. Install test spark plug, in cylinders Nos. 1 and 4.
   b. Connect spark plugs to ground using test cable assembly tool No. 86 10 867 or equivalent.
   c. Turn ignition switch to ON position.
   d. Select "ACTIVATE," then "IGNITION CYL 1–4."
   e. Ensure spark is produced on each activated spark plug.
   f. Repeat with "IGNITION CYL 2–5" and "IGNITION CYL 3–6.,"

Pin	Colour	Component/Function	In/ Out	Test conditions	Across	Test reading
64	BU/YE	SHIFT UP lamp	Out	Shift up ON	64 – 34	≈0 V
				Shift up OUT	64 – 34	≈B+
65	GN	Shut–off valve, evaporative emission canister	Out	800 ± 50 rpm Not active	65 – 34	≈B+
				800 ± 50 rpm Active	65 – 34	<0.5 V
66		Not used				
67		Not used				
68	VT/WH	TCS test	In	Test signal	68 – 34	31 Hz
				TCS active when driving	68 – 34	62 Hz
69	BK/WH	D/R input	In	P, N, Manual	69 – 28	≈0 V
				R, D, 3, 2, 1	69 – 28	≈B+
70	GN	Rear knock sensor	In	4000 rpm	70 – 71	>30 mV a.c.
71	BK	Sensor ground	Out	800 ± 50 rpm	71 to B–	<0.1 V
72	BU	Fuel tank pressure sensor	In	Filler cap removed	72 – 71	0 kPa ≈2.5 V See also technical data
73	YE	Low fuel level	In	Fuel level lamp ON	73 – 71	≈0 V
				Fuel level lamp OUT	73 – 71	≈5 V
74	RD	Engine coolant temperature sensor	In	Engine temp. 90°C (194°F)	74 – 71	≈1.0 V See also technical data
75		Not used				
76	GN	Rear heated oxygen sensor Cylinder bank 2	In	800 ± 50 rpm active closed loop	76 – 46	0.1 – 0.9 V
77	GN	Rear heated oxygen sensor Cylinder bank 1	In	800 ± 50 rpm active closed loop	77 – 46	0.1 – 0.9 V

SA1029700191060X

Fig. 4 ECM connector terminal identification & voltage specifications (Part 6 of 7)

Pin	Colour	Component/Function	In/ Out	Test conditions	Across	Test reading
78	BK	Crankshaft position sensor/Signal input	In	Starter motor cranking	78 – 20	≈2 – 5 V a.c. 150 – 250 Hz
				800 ± 50 rpm	78 – 20	≈5 – 10 V a.c. ≈775 Hz
79	PK/BK	Car speed from RH front wheel	In	Rotate wheel slowly	79 – 28	0/about 12 V (LP HIp LOp)
				Rotate wheel 1/2 rev/s	79 – 28	≈15 Hz 50% (LP HIp LOp)
80	GN/RD	Engine speed	Out	800 ± 50 rpm	80 – 28	≈6.5 V ≈40 Hz
81		Not used				
82	GN/OG	Throttle position signal	Out		82 – 28	0.25 – 1 V
				800 ± 50 rpm	82 – 28	≈160 Hz ≈9% (+) ≈0.5 ms (+) (LP HIp LO)
83		Not used				
84		Not used				
85		Not used				
86		Not used				
87		Not used				
88	GY/BK	Diagnostics lead (K)	In/ Out	ISAT scan tool not connected	88 – 34	0 V
				ISAT scan tool connected	88 – 34	B+

SA1029700191070X

Fig. 4 ECM connector terminal identification & voltage specifications (Part 7 of 7)

g. Command will activate each ignition coil for 30 seconds.
h. If spark is produced, continue with step 7.
i. If not, proceed to next step.

6. Inspect control module outputs to ignition coil module as follows:
   a. Disconnect ignition coil module four pin electrical connector.
   b. Connect test lamp to pins 4 and 3 (cyl. 1–4).
   c. Select "ACTIVATE," then "IGNITION CYL 1–4."
   d. Repeat test procedure for other cylinders with test lamp connected to pins 4 and 1 on cylinders Nos. 2–5 and pins 4 and 2 on cylinders Nos. 3–6.
   e. Select "IGNITION CYL 2–5," then "IGNITION CYL 3–6."
   f. Command activates relevant ignition coil at frequency of .5 Hz for 30 seconds. If test lamp should flashes, replace ignition coil module and proceed to final inspection.
   g. If not, rectify wire in question and proceed to final inspection.
7. Inspect compression as follows:
   a. Perform compression test on each cylinder.
   b. If compression test is satisfactory, replace all spark plugs and proceed to next step.
   c. If not, continue fault diagnosis as outlined under "Compression Pressures" in "Engine Performance & Tune Up" section.
8. Inspect fuel system as follows:
   a. Measure fuel pressure and fuel flow readings on fuel pump and all injectors.
   b. If fuel system satisfactory, continue with final inspection.
   c. If not, rectify fault and proceed to final inspection.
9. Final inspection: If control module power supply has been disconnected, control module must adapt crankshaft position sensor, perform final inspection as follows:
   a. Drive vehicle in 2nd gear up to 6000 RPM.
   b. Release accelerator completely so that fuel shutoff takes place and allows engine speed to drop to 2000 RPM.
   c. Repeat five times
   d. Clear all DTC's.
   e. While engine is warming up drive vehicle at varying engine loads and RPMs. Make point of driving with engine at high RPMs.
   f. If DTC is present, refer to "Electronic Control Module (ECM)" under "Component Replacement."
   g. If DTC is not present, fault was corrected.

CODES P0301, P0302, P0303 & P0304: MISFIRE

Fault Symptoms

Conditions: CHECK ENGINE lamp (MIL) ON. Runs rough and misfires. Additional DTCs are set. During the course of each cylinder's power stroke the rotational speed of the crankshaft increases temporarily. This causes momentary increases in pulse frequency from the crankshaft position sensor. These frequencies are evaluated by the control module and any misfiring is recorded. How large a proportion of misfires is required for exhaust emissions to reach prohibited levels, or for the catalytic converter to be damaged, is specified in a load and RPM dependent matrix or map in the control module's memory. A DTC will be generated if the number of misfires exceeds the matrix figure. Cause of misfiring could be low fuel level in tank. This will be indicated by DTC P1585 being set.

Injectors and ignition coils can be activated using a scan tool. Select "ACTIVATE," then "INJECTOR 1" (2, 3, 4, 5 or 6) and "IGNITION CYL 1–4" (2–5 or 3–6). The cause of the DTC could be as follows:

1. Defective spark plug, HT cable or ignition coil.
2. Defective/clogged injector.
3. Poor compression in basic engine.
4. Inspect wiring for intermittent faults

Diagnostic Procedure

1. Determine other DTCs in system as follows:
   a. Using scan tool obtain all DTCs.
   b. If scan tool shows DTC P1585, P1213–P1230 and P0300 together with at least two of these DTCs: P0301, P0302, P0303 or P0304, then proceed with fault diagnosis as outlined under DTC P0300.
   c. Continue fault diagnosis according to diagnostic procedure for relevant DTC.
   d. If not, proceed to next step.
2. Inspect performance of ignition coil module as follows:
   a. Install test spark plug, part No. 86 11 386, in relevant cylinder using

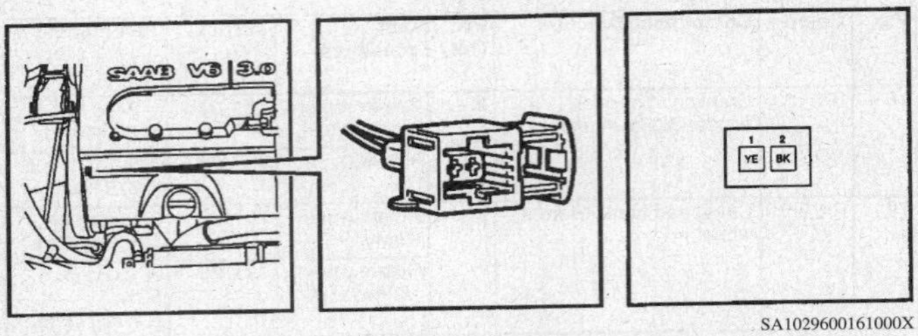

SA1029600161000X

Fig. 5 Knock sensor connector terminal identification

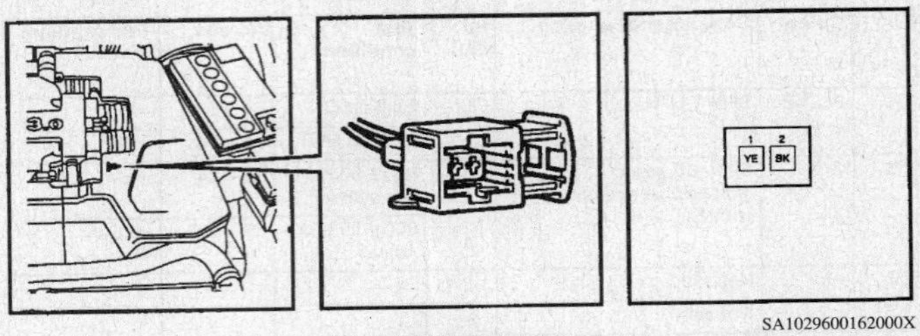

SA1029600162000X

Fig. 6 Engine coolant temperature sensor connector terminal identification

"new" HT cable.

b. Connect spark plug to ground using test cable assembly tool No. 86 10 867 or equivalent.
c. Turn ignition switch to ON position.
d. Select "ACTIVATE" on scan tool, then "IGNITION CYL X-Y." Command activates ignition coil at frequency of .5 Hz for 30 seconds.
e. Ensure activated spark plug produces spark.
f. If spark is produced continue with next step.
g. If not, proceed to next step.

3. Inspect relevant HT cable as follows:
   a. Install test spark plug, part No. 86 11 386, in relevant cylinder. Use existing HT cable.
   b. Ground plug, using test cable tool No. 86 10 867 or equivalent.
   c. Turn ignition switch to ON position.
   d. Select "ACTIVATE," then "IGNITION CYL X-Y." Command activates ignition coil at frequency of .5 Hz for 30 seconds.
   e. Ensure activated spark plug produces spark.
   f. If so, continue with next step.
   g. If not, replace relevant HT cable, then proceed to final inspection.
4. Inspect spark plugs as follows:
   a. Remove and visually inspect spark plug.
   b. If plug is satisfactory, continue with next step.
   c. If not, electrode gap is wider than .0551 inch or otherwise obviously wrong. replace spark plugs and proceed to final inspection
5. Inspect compression as follows:
   a. Perform compression test on relevant cylinder.
   b. If compression is satisfactory, continue with next step.
   c. If not, continue fault diagnosis as outlined under "Compression Pressures" in "Engine Performance & Tune Up" section.
6. Inspect fuel flow capacity of relevant injector as follows:
   a. If fuel flow capacity is satisfactory, continue with final inspection.
   b. If not, replace injector, then proceed to final inspection.
7. Final inspection as follows:
   a. Clear all DTC's.
   b. Implement drive cycle.
   c. While engine is warming up, drive vehicle at varying engine loads and RPMs. Drive with engine at high RPMs.
   d. If DTC is present, refer to "Electronic Control Module (ECM)" under "Component Replacement."
   e. If DTC is not present, fault was corrected.

CODE P0327: KNOCK SENSOR

Fault Symptoms

Conditions: CHECK ENGINE lamp (MIL) ON. Engine performance may be down, continuous retardation of the ignition timing. Engine temperature above 45°C. Engine speed above 2000 RPM. Voltage variations too small compared to engine RPM.

Diagnostic Procedure

1. Inspect knock sensor ground connection as follows:
   a. Disconnect knock sensor two pin connector.
   b. Connect test lamp to battery positive and pin 2.
   c. Test lamp should light.
   d. If so, continue with next step.
   e. If not, repair or replace wire between pin 2 and crimped connection J134, then proceed to final inspection.
2. Inspect control module knock sensor input as follows:
   a. Measure resistance reading at connector contacts (toward control module).
   b. Turn ignition switch to OFF position.
   c. Measure resistance reading across pins 1 and 2 in two pin electrical connector.
   d. Resistance should be approximately one Mohms.
   e. If reading is satisfactory, determine if knock sensor mounting bolt is loose.
   f. If so, **torque** bolt to 16 ft. lbs., then proceed to final inspection.
   g. If not, replace knock sensor, then proceed to final inspection.
   h. If still not satisfactory, inspect wire in question and repair or replace as necessary, then proceed to final inspection.
3. Final inspection as follows:
   a. Clear all DTC's.
   b. Drive vehicle at varying engine loads and RPMs for five minutes.
   c. If DTC is present, refer to "Electronic Control Module (ECM)" under "Component Replacement."
   d. If DTC is not present, fault was corrected.

CODE P0328: KNOCK SENSOR

Fault Symptoms

Conditions: Engine performance may be down, continuous retardation of the ignition timing. Engine temperature above 45°C. Engine speed above 2000 RPM. Excessive voltage compared to engine RPM.

Diagnostic Procedure

Refer to "Code P0327" for procedure.

CODE P0332: KNOCK SENSOR

Fault Symptoms

Conditions: CHECK ENGINE lamp (MIL) ON. Engine performance may be down, continuous retardation of ignition timing. Engine temperature above 45°C. Engine speed above 2000 RPM. Voltage variations too small compared to engine RPM.

Diagnostic Procedure

1. Inspect knock sensor two pin connector as follows:
   a. Connect test lamp to battery positive and pin 2.
   b. Test lamp should light.
   c. If so, continue with next step.
   d. If not, repair or replace wire between pin 2 and crimped connection J134, then proceed to final inspection.
2. Inspect control modules knock sensor input as follows:
   a. Measure resistance reading at connector contacts (toward control module).
   b. Turn ignition switch to OFF position.
   c. Measure resistance reading across pins 1 and 2 in two pin electrical connector.
   d. Resistance should be approximately 1 Mohm.
   e. If reading if is satisfactory, determine if bolt securing knock sensor is loose.
   f. If so, **torque** bolt to 16 ft. lbs., then proceed to final inspection.
   g. If not, replace knock sensor, then proceed to final inspection.
   h. If still not satisfactory, inspect wire in question and repair or replace as necessary, then proceed to final inspection.

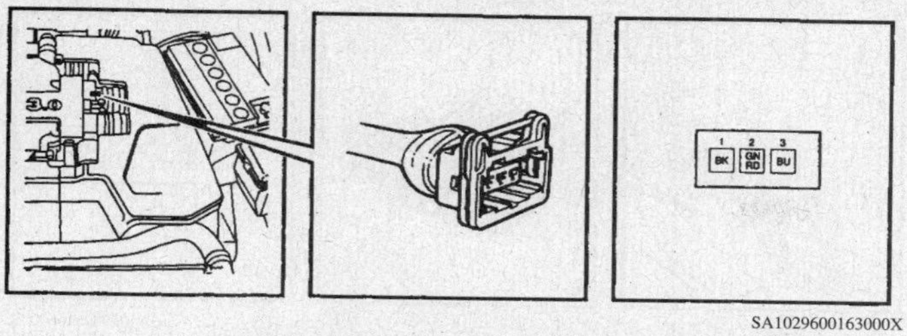

SA1029600163000X

Fig. 7 Throttle position sensor connector terminal identification

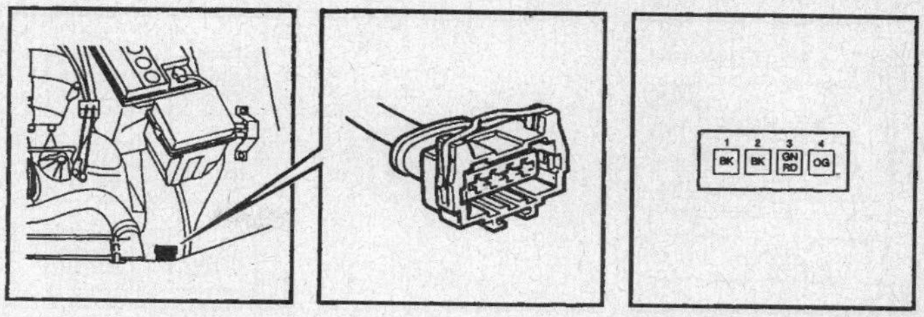

SA1029600164000X

Fig. 8 Mass air flow sensor connector terminal identification

3. Final inspection as follows:
   a. Clear all DTC's.
   b. Drive vehicle at varying engine loads and RPMs for five minutes.
   c. Determine if DTC has recurred.
   d. If DTC is present, refer to "Electronic Control Module (ECM)" under "Component Replacement."
   e. If DTC is not present, fault was corrected.

CODE P0333: KNOCK SENSOR

Fault Symptoms

Conditions: Engine performance may be down, continuous retardation of the ignition timing. Engine temperature above 45°C. Engine speed above 2000 RPM. Excessive voltage compared to engine RPM.

Diagnostic Procedure

Refer to "Code P0332" for procedure.

CODES P0335, P0336 & P1396: CRANKSHAFT POSITION SENSOR

Fault Symptoms

1. Conditions: Engine fails to start or misfires. Other DTCs (misfiring).
2. DTC P0335 sets and no voltage signal from crankshaft position sensor, even though camshaft position sensor has detected eight crankshaft revolutions.
3. DTC P0336 engine speed above 500 RPM. Gap not found in slotted ring which is missing two ribs.
4. DTC P1396 engine speed above 500 RPM. One rib too many detected on slotted ring. DTC may be generated if slotted ring mounted on crankshaft is damaged.
5. Inspect wiring for intermittent faults.

Diagnostic Procedure

1. Measure resistance of crankshaft position sensor as follows:
   a. Disconnect crankshaft position sensor four pin electrical connector.
   b. Measure resistance reading at contacts of sensor connector.
   c. Pins 1–2 should read 770–950 ohms
   d. Inspect for possible stray currents between signal wire and screened wire. Take readings across pins 1 and 3.
   e. Nominal resistance is infinite (OL = Overload).
   f. If readings are satisfactory, continue with next step.
   g. If not, replace crankshaft position sensor and proceed to final inspection.
2. Inspect mounting of crankshaft position sensor as follows:
   a. Remove crankshaft position sensor and inspect:
   b. Ensure sensor tip is clean and that no metal filings are present.
   c. Ensure slotted ring is firmly secured to crankshaft.
   d. While rotating crankshaft, ensure slotted ring is not skewed, buckled or otherwise damaged.
   e. Remove any metal filings, etc. from sensor.
   f. If slotted ring is damaged, refer to "Crankshaft Position Sensor Replacement" as outlined under "System Service" in this section.
   g. If not, proceed to next step.
3. Inspect crankshaft position sensor ground and screened connection. Connect test lamp to connector as follows:
   a. Battery positive and pin 2.
   b. Battery positive and pin 3.
   c. Test lamp should light in both cases.
   d. If so, continue with next step.
   e. If not, inspect and if necessary repair or replace relevant wire between pin 2 and control module pin 20 and pin 3 and crimped connection J135.
   f. Proceed to final inspection.
4. Inspect control module sensor input as
   a. Turn ignition switch to ON position.
   b. Measure voltage readings at connector, Pin 1 to battery ground should read approximately .9 volts.
   c. If wire is satisfactory, replace crankshaft position sensor, then proceed to final inspection.
   d. If not, repair or replace wire, then proceed to final inspection.
5. Final inspection as follows:
   a. Clear all DTC's.
   b. Drive vehicle at varying engine loads and RPMs for five minutes.
   c. If DTC is present, refer to "Electronic Control Module (ECM)" under "Component Replacement."
   d. If DTC is not present, fault was corrected.

CODE P0341: CAMSHAFT POSITION SENSOR

Fault Symptoms

Conditions: CHECK ENGINE lamp (MIL) ON. Engine performance poor due to continuous retardation of ignition timing. DTC P0341 set and engine running. The positions of the camshaft and crankshaft do not coincide for longer than one second. Inspect wiring for intermittent faults.

Diagnostic Procedure

1. Inspect camshaft position sensor power supply and connection to ground as follows:
   a. Disconnect position sensor three pin electrical connector.
   b. Turn ignition switch to ON position.
   c. Connect test lamp to pin 1 and battery ground, then battery positive and pin 3.
   d. Test lamp should light.
   e. If so, proceed to next step.
   f. If not, repair or replace wire in question and proceed to final inspection.
2. Inspect control module position sensor input as follows:
   a. Turn ignition switch to ON position.
   b. Measure voltage readings at connector pin 2 and battery ground, reading should be approximately 12 volts.
   c. If voltage is satisfactory, replace position sensor and proceed to final inspection.
   d. If not, inspect wire in question and repair or replace as necessary, then proceed with final inspection.
3. Final inspection as follows:
   a. Clear all DTC's.
   b. Implementation of driving cycle:
   c. Drive vehicle at varying engine loads and RPMs for five minutes.
   d. Check for DTC.
   e. If DTC is present, refer to "Electronic Control Module (ECM)" under "Component Replacement."
   f. If DTC is not present, fault was corrected.

CODES P0410 & P0411: SECONDARY AIR INJECTION

Fault Symptoms

Conditions: CHECK ENGINE lamp (MIL)

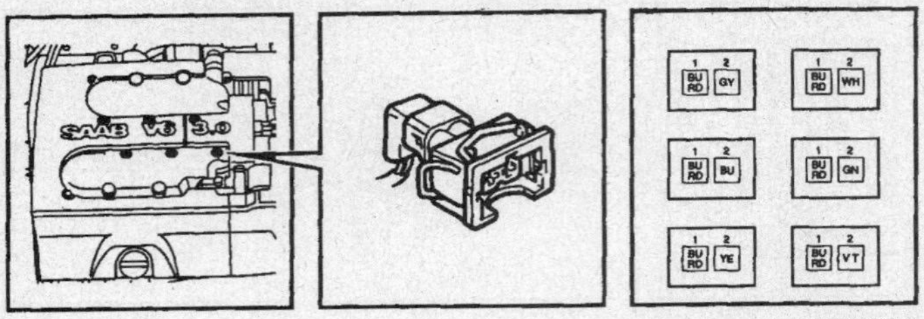

SA1029600165000X

Fig. 9 Injector connector terminal identification

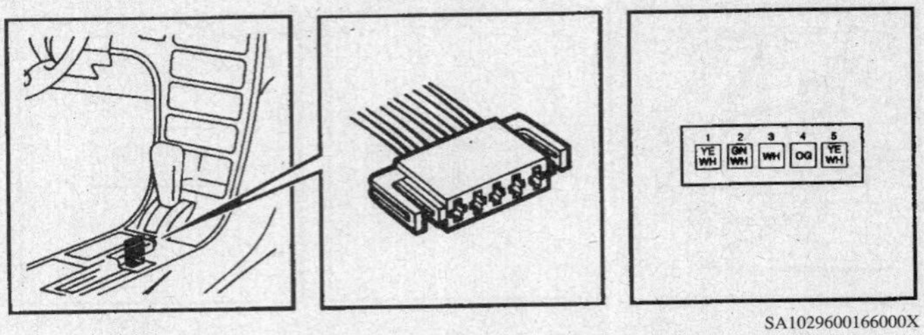

SA1029600166000X

Fig. 10 Transmission range switch connector terminal identification

ON. Secondary air injection system activated at start of this trip. Diagnosis not yet performed this trip. Vehicle speed zero mph. Idling, closed loop active, engine coolant temperature between 10 and 65°C. Intake air temperature above 10°C. Conditions for DTC generation: DTC P0410 (large flow) set and closed loop greater than 25% for 20 seconds. DTC P0411 (small flow) set and secondary air injection pump active and closed loop increases by less than 15 percentage points within 12 seconds. The secondary air injection pump relay can be activated with a scan tool.

1. Select "ACTIVATE," then "SECOND. AIR RELAY."
2. Command activates relay at frequency of .5 Hz for 30 seconds.
3. Inspect wiring for intermittent faults.

Diagnostic Procedure

1. Inspect these fuses:
   a. Maxi fuse No. 1 and fuse 13 at fuse box in engine compartment.
   b. If fuses are intact, proceed to next step.
   c. If not, replace fuse.
   d. Activate secondary air injection pump relay by means of scan tool. If pump works, proceed to final inspection. If maxi fuse 1 blows when relay is activated, proceed to step 9.
   e. If fuse 13 blows when relay is activated, proceed to step 8.
2. Inspect performance of secondary air injection pump and control valve as follows:
   a. If pump and control valve are working, proceed to step 7.
   b. If not, pump and control valve are both inoperative, then proceed to next step.
   c. If not, only pump is out of order, proceed to step 6.
   d. If not, only control valve is out of order, proceed to step 8.
3. Inspect relay socket power supply as follows:
   a. Remove secondary air injection pump relay.
   b. Turn ignition switch to ON position.
   c. Connect test lamp to relay socket pin 30 and battery ground.
   d. Connect test lamp to relay socket pin 86 and battery ground.
   e. Test lamp should light up.
   f. If test lamp lit in both cases, proceed to next step.
   g. If not, inspect relevant wire and repair or replace as necessary, then proceed to final inspection.
4. Inspect control module output as follows:
   a. Connect test lamp to pins 86 and 85 of relay socket.
   b. Connect scan tool.
   c. Turn ignition switch to ON position.
   d. Select "ACTIVATE," then "SECOND. AIR RELAY."
   e. Test lamp should flash at frequency of .5 Hz for 30 seconds.
   f. If test lamp is flashing, proceed to next step.
   g. If not, inspect relevant wire and repair or replace as necessary, then proceed to final inspection.
5. Inspect relay as follows:
   a. Connect jumper wire between relay socket pins 30 and 87.
   b. Pump and control valve should be activated.
   c. If pump and control valve are activated, replace relay and proceed to final inspection.
   d. If pump is not activated, proceed to step 6.
   e. If still not activated, inspect control valve wiring. Inspect wiring between relay socket pin 87 via fuse 13 and control valve to crimped connection J123.
   f. If wiring is satisfactory, replace control valve, then proceed to final inspection.
6. Inspect secondary air injection pump as follows:
   a. Disconnect pump two pin electrical connector.
   b. Connect test lamp to pins 1 and 2 in female connector.
   c. Connect jumper wire between relay socket pins 30 and 87.
   d. If test lamp is lit, replace pump and proceed to final inspection.
   e. If not, inspect and if necessary repair or replace wire between relay socket pin 87 and pin of pumps two pin electrical connector.
   f. Inspect pin 2 of two pin electrical connector and grounding point G30, then continue with final inspection.
7. Inspect hose system as follows:
   a. Disconnect one hose connected to exhaust manifold non-return valves.
   b. Remove hose between intake manifold and secondary air injection control valve and connect vacuum pump to hose.
   c. Turn ignition switch to ON position.
   d. Select "ACTIVATE," then "SECOND. AIR RELAY."
   e. Pump should work but it should not blow air into thick hose.
   f. Using vacuum pump create vacuum.
   g. Pump should now blow air at hose.
   h. If system satisfactory, ensure all hoses are correctly fitted, then proceed to final inspection.
   i. If control valve is tight, replace it.
   j. If control valve opens, replace vacuum valve
8. Inspect secondary air injection control valve as follows:
   a. Disconnect control valve two pin electrical connector.
   b. Connect test lamp to pins 2 and 1 of connector.
   c. Connect scan tool.
   d. Turn ignition switch to ON position.
   e. Select "ACTIVATE," then "SECOND. AIR RELAY."
   f. Test lamp should flash at frequency of .5 Hz for 30 seconds.
   g. If test lamp flashes, replace control valve, then proceed to final inspection.
   h. If not, inspect wiring between pin 87 or relay socket via fuse 13 to crimped connection J123. Repair or replace as necessary, then proceed to final inspection.
9. Inspect secondary air injection pump for shorting as follows:
   a. Disconnect pump two pin electrical connector.
   b. Turn ignition switch to ON position.
   c. Select "ACTIVATE," then "SECOND. AIR RELAY."
   d. If fuse blows again, inspect and if necessary repair or replace wiring between maxi fuse 1 and pin 2 of pump two pin electrical connector.
   e. If not, replace secondary air injection pump.
10. Final inspection as follows:
    a. Using scan tool activate diagnosis of secondary air injection system. For diagnosis to be possible, these conditions must be fulfilled:
    b. Secondary air injection system activated at start of this trip.
    c. Diagnosis not yet performed this trip.
    d. Speed zero mph.
    e. Idling.
11. Perform diagnosis as follows:
    a. Connect scan tool.
    b. Clear fault codes.
    c. Select "INITIATE," then "SLS DIAGNOSIS."
    d. Wait for approximately two minutes or until scan tool reads "READY."

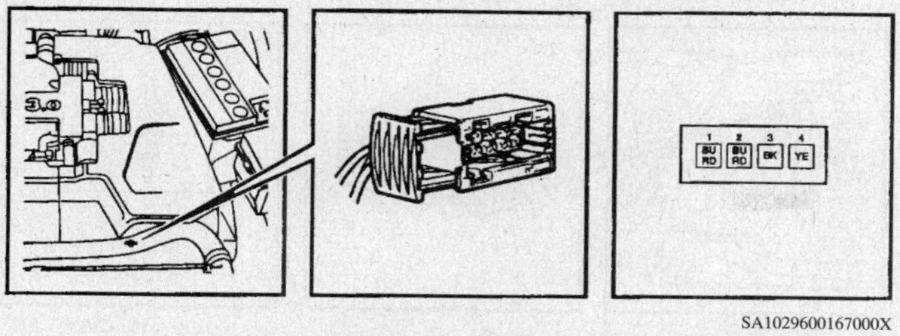

SA1029600167000X

Fig. 11 Front HO2S front cylinder bank connector terminal identification

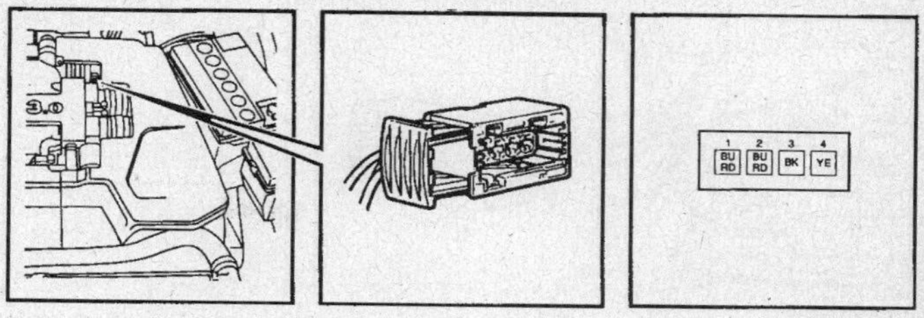

SA1029600168000X

Fig. 12 Rear HO2S front cylinder bank connector terminal identification

e. Obtain readout of DTC.
f. If DTC is present, refer to "Electronic Control Module (ECM)" under "Component Replacement."
g. If DTC is not present, fault was corrected.

CODES P0412, P0413 & P0414: SECONDARY AIR INJECTION

Fault Symptoms

Conditions: CHECK ENGINE lamp (MIL) on. P0412: engine speed above 80 RPM, battery voltage 7.15–17 V, shorting to battery positive (+) terminal. P0413: Engine speed above 380 RPM, battery voltage 7.15–17 V, open circuit. P0414: engine speed above 80 RPM, battery voltage 7.15–17 V, shorting to battery ground (-) terminal.

Diagnostic Procedure

1. Inspect secondary air injection control valve's power supply as follows:
   a. Disconnect secondary air injection control valve's two-pin connector.
   b. Turn ignition switch to ON position.
   c. Connect test lamp to pin 1 and battery ground (-) terminal, test lamp should light up.
   d. If connection lit up, then proceed to next step.
   e. If not, check fuses 19 and 12 in engine bay's main fuse box. Repair fault and proceed to final inspection.
2. Inspect ECM's secondary air injection control valve output as follows:
   a. Connect scan tool, then turn ignition switch to ON position.
   b. Connect test lamp to battery positive (+) terminal
   c. Select "ACTIVATE" and "SECONDARY AIR VALUE."
   d. Test lamp should flash at frequency of .5 Hz for 30 seconds.
   e. If test lamp flashed, change secondary air injection control valve, then proceed to final inspection.
   f. If not, check lead in question, repair fault, then proceed to final inspection.
3. Final inspection as follows:
   a. Clear all DTC's, then start implementation of driving cycle, varying engine loads and RPM for five minutes.
   b. Evaluate driving cycle, check for DTC's.
   c. If DTC is present, refer to "Electronic Control Module (ECM)" under "Component Replacement."
   d. If DTC is not present, fault was corrected.

CODE P0422: THREE-WAY CATALYTIC CONVERTER REAR BANK

Fault Symptoms

Conditions: CHECK ENGINE lamp (MIL) ON. Voltage signal changes from rear heated oxygen sensor are compared with voltage signal changes from front heated oxygen sensor and corrected in respect of engine load and RPM. Vehicle speed 70 km/h for three minutes and 20 seconds. Gentle acceleration from idling speed up to 2000–2500 RPM for a total of three minutes and 20 seconds.

Temporary or permanent decreases in capacity of three-way catalytic converter may be caused by, leaded fuel or fuel with high sulfur content, fuel additives, additives in engine oil if oil consumption is abnormal.

Inspect wiring harness for intermittently open or short circuits.

Diagnostic Procedure

1. Inspect exhaust system as follows:
   a. Start engine and operate at idle.
   b. Inspect exhaust system for leakage between engine and rear heated oxygen sensor.
   c. If leakage exist, correct defect, then proceed to final inspection.
   d. If no leakage exist, replace catalytic converter and proceed to next step.
2. Inspect fuel system as follows:
   a. Inspect fuel pressure and fuel pump flow capacity.
   b. If within specifications, proceed to final inspection.
   c. If not within specifications, correct defect, then proceed to final inspection
3. Final inspection.
   a. Clear all DTC's.

CODE P0432: THREE-WAY CATALYTIC CONVERTER FRONT BANK

Fault Symptoms

Conditions: CHECK ENGINE lamp (MIL) ON. Voltage signal changes from rear heated oxygen sensor are compared with voltage signal changes from front heated oxygen sensor and corrected in respect of engine load and RPM. Vehicle speed 70 km/h for three minutes and 20 seconds. Gentle acceleration from idling speed up to 2000–2500 RPM for a total of three minutes and 20 seconds.

Temporary or permanent decreases in capacity of three-way catalytic converter may be caused by, leaded fuel or fuel with high sulfur content, fuel additives, additives in engine oil if oil consumption is abnormal.

Inspect wiring harness for intermittent open or short circuits.

Diagnostic Procedure

1. Inspect exhaust system as follows:
   a. Start engine and operate at idle.
   b. Inspect exhaust system for leakage between engine and rear heated oxygen sensor.
   c. If leakage exist, correct defect, then proceed to final inspection.
   d. If no leakage exist, replace catalytic converter and proceed to next step.
2. Inspect fuel system as follows:
   a. Inspect fuel pressure and fuel pump flow capacity.
   b. If within specifications, proceed to final inspection.
   c. If not within specifications, correct defect, then proceed to final inspection.
3. Final inspection:
   a. Clear all DTC's.

CODE P0440: EVAP VALVE CONTROL

Fault Symptoms

Conditions: CHECK ENGINE lamp (MIL) on. Intake air temperature above 21°F, engine temperature above 21°F, 1000 seconds since starting, vehicle speed zero mph. The evaporative canister's inlet air is shut off and the purge valve is not active, the pressure in the tank continues to drop.

Diagnostic Procedure

1. Inspect purge valve air flow as follows:
   a. Check that purge valve is closed and does not leak when not supplied with current.
   b. Check that purge valve opens when supplied with current.
   c. If purge valve functions properly, proceed to next step.
   d. If purge valve does not function properly, replace purge valve and proceed to final inspection.
2. Inspect shutoff valve as follows:
   a. Disconnect hose from roll over valve and connect pressure gauge to hose.

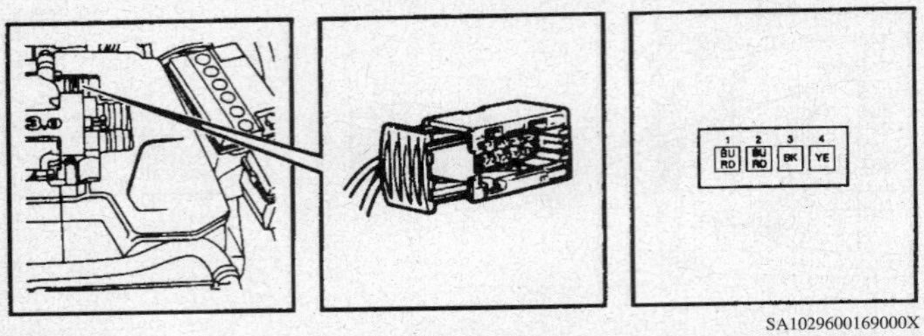

SA1029600169000X

Fig. 13 Front HO2S rear cylinder bank connector terminal identification

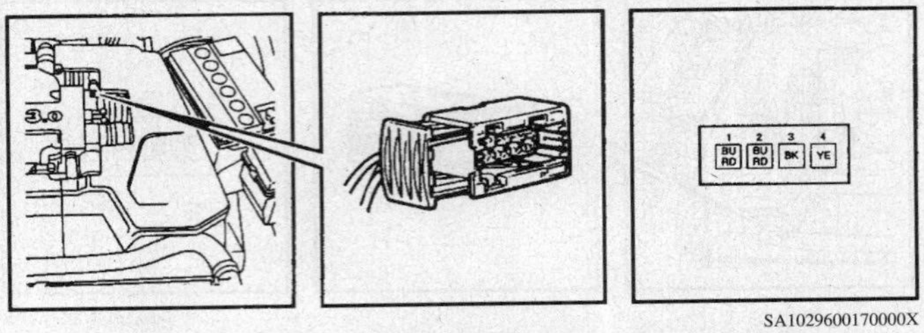

SA1029600170000X

Fig. 14 Rear HO2S rear cylinder bank connector terminal identification

b. Disconnect shutoff valve's electrical connector.
c. Start engine and wait until venting starts, reading should show 0 kPa.
d. Connect shutoff valve (male connector) to battery for about five seconds, pressure gauge should show falling pressure when shutoff valve is supplied with current and 0 kPa when not supplied with current.
e. If shutoff valve functions properly, proceed to final inspection.
f. If shutoff valve does not function properly, replace shutoff valve and proceed to final inspection.

3. Final inspection as follows: **If gasoline evaporation is excessive or canister is saturated, stop testing and repair fault. If not indicated, proceed as follows:**
   a. Start and run engine at 4000 RPM for two minutes.
   b. Shutoff engine and wait ten seconds, then repeat procedure.
   c. Using scan tool, check for recurrence of DTC.
   d. If DTC is present, refer to "Electronic Control Module (ECM)" under "Component Replacement."
   e. If DTC is not present, fault is corrected.

CODE P0441: EVAP CANISTER PURGE VALVE LOW FLOW

Fault Symptoms

Conditions: CHECK ENGINE lamp (MIL) on. Any other DTC's such as closed loop system, misfiring or etc. Vehicle speed zero km/h, idling, engine coolant temperature above 60° C and diagnosis not yet performed this trip. Fault diagnosis pertains to mechanical malfunction. Inspect vacuum hoses for pinch or kink.

Diagnostic Procedure

1. Inspect purge valve air flow as follows:
   a. Disconnect purge valve two pin electrical connector.
   b. Disconnect hose at EVAP emissions canister side of valve.
   c. Start engine, then using pressure gauge on vacuum pump, determine if air is sucked into purge valve.
   d. If air is sucked in to purge valve, proceed to final inspection.
   e. If air is not sucked into purge valve, proceed to next step.
2. Inspect purge valve as follows:
   a. With engine in Off position, connect purge valve two pin electrical connector.
   b. Start engine and operate until engine coolant temperature exceeds 104°F.
   c. Determine if air is sucked into valve in pulses.
   d. If valve is pulsing, proceed to next step.
   e. **After engine start-up, purge valve is active for 220 seconds and idle for 130 seconds. Following this, valve is not active at regular intervals and time will depend on ECM's fuel adaptation.** If valve is not pulsing , replace valve and proceed to final inspection.
3. Inspect purge flow from EVAP emission canister as follow:
   a. Connect pressure vacuum pump to hose from EVAP emission canister.
   b. Ensure steady purge flow is obtained from EVAP emission canister.
   c. If purge flow is steady, proceed to final inspection.
   d. If purge flow is not steady repair or replace purge hose, replace EVAP canister and if necessary proceed to final inspection.
4. Final inspection:
   a. Clear all DTC's
   b. Drive car at varying engine loads and RPM for five minutes.
   c. If DTC is present, refer to "Electronic Control Module (ECM)" under "Component Replacement."
   d. If DTC is not present, fault is corrected.

CODES P0442 & P0455: PURGE SYSTEM LEAK

Fault Symptoms

Conditions: CHECK ENGINE lamp (MIL) ON. Inlet temperature above -6.7° C, 1000 seconds after starting, engine temperature above -6.7° C, vehicle speed zero mph, idling.

Diagnostic Procedure

1. Inspect fuel filler cap.
   a. Check whether fuel filler cap was installed properly when fault was detected.
   b. Inspect fuel filler cap seal and sealing surfaces
   c. If fuel filler cap is in proper working condition, then proceed to next step.
   d. If not, repair fault then proceed to final inspection.
2. Inspect for fuel leakage.
   a. Fill gas tank up to filler pipe.
   b. Visual check to see whether gasoline is leaking from tank, filler pipe or breather pipe.
   c. If any leaks are present, repair fault then proceed to final inspection.
   d. If not, proceed to next step.
3. Inspect purge valve.
   a. Check that purge valve is closed when it receives no current and opens when current is applied.
   b. If purge valve opened, then proceed to next step.
   c. If not, change purge valve then proceed to final inspection.
4. Inspect purging circuit
   a. Turn ignition switch to Off position.
   b. Unplug connector from evaporative emission canister's shutoff valve.
   c. Connect shutoff valve (male connector) to battery's positive (+) terminal.
   d. Connect pressure/vacuum pump and pressure gauge to evaporative emission canister's hose.
   e. Remove fuel filler cap and cover hole in roll over valve.
   f. Reduce pressure to .1 bar for at 10 seconds, by means of pressure/vacuum pump.
   g. If pressure raised, leakage is contained in evaporative emission canister, including connected lines, or shutoff valve. Repair fault, then proceed to final inspection.
   h. If not, change fuel filler cap, then proceed to final inspection.
5. Final inspection. **If gasoline evaporation is excessive or canister is saturated, stop testing and repair fault. If not indicated, proceed as follows:**
   a. Start and run engine at 4000 RPM for two minutes.
   b. Shutoff engine and wait ten seconds, then repeat procedure.
   c. Using scan tool, check for recurrence of DTC.
   d. If yes, refer to "Electronic Control Module (ECM)" under "Component Replacement."
   e. If not, procedures to rectify fault

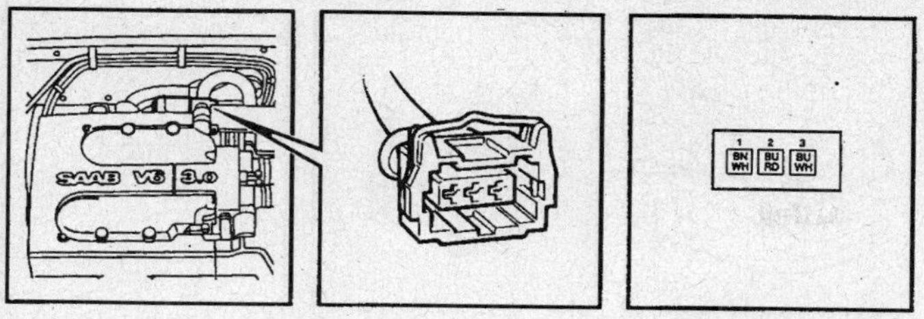

SA1029600171000X

Fig. 15 Idle air control valve connector terminal identification

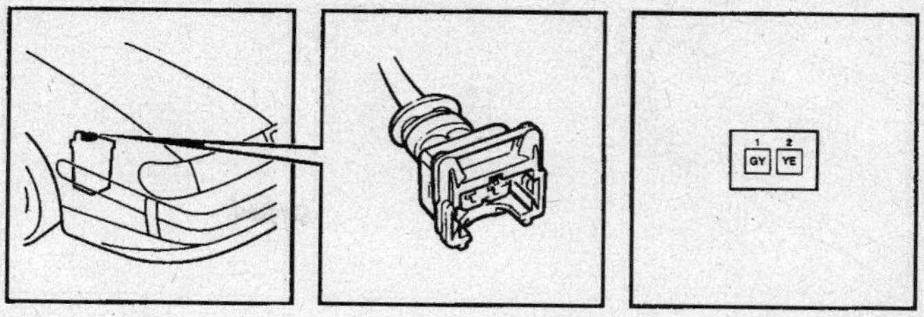

SA1029600172000X

Fig. 16 EVAP canister purge valve connector terminal identification

were correct.

CODES P0446, P0447 & P0448: EVAP SHUT-OFF VALVE

Fault Symptoms

Conditions: P0446: engine speed above 80 RPM, battery voltage 7.15–17 V, shorting to battery positive (+) terminal. P0447: Engine speed above 80 RPM, battery voltage 7.15–17 V, open circuit. P0448: engine speed above 80 RPM, battery voltage 7.15–17 V, shorting to battery ground (-) terminal.

Diagnostic Procedure

1. Inspect shutoff valve's power supply as follows:
   a. Disconnect valve's two-pin connector.
   b. Turn ignition switch to ON position.
   c. Connect test lamp to pin 1 and battery ground (-) terminal, test lamp should light up.
   d. If test lamp lit up, proceed to next step.
   e. If not, check lead between pin 1 and crimped connection J15, then proceed to final inspection.
2. Inspect control module's shutoff valve output as follows:
   a. Connect test lamp to battery positive (+) terminal and pin 2 of two-pin connector.
   b. Connect scan tool, then select "ACTIVATE" and "EVAP SHUTOFF VALVE."
   c. Test lamp should flash at frequency of .5 Hz for 30 seconds.
   d. If test lamp flashed, then proceed to final inspection.
   e. If not, check and repair lead between pin 65 of control module and pin 2 of two-pin connector, then proceed to final inspection.
3. Final inspection as follows: **If gasoline evaporation is excessive or canister is saturated, stop testing and repair fault. If not indicated, proceed as follows:**
   a. Start and run engine at 4000 RPM for two minutes.
   b. Shutoff engine and wait ten seconds, then repeat procedure.
   c. Using scan tool, check for recurrence of DTC.
   d. If yes, refer to "Electronic Control Module (ECM)" under "Component Replacement."
   e. If not, procedures to rectify fault were correct.

CODE P0450: TANK PRESSURE SENSOR

Fault Symptoms

Conditions: CHECK ENGINE lamp (MIL) on. Coolant temperature below 95°F, less than 10 seconds since starting, idling, tank pressure higher than 1.4 kPa.

Diagnostic Procedure

1. Inspect pressure sensor's connection to ground and power supply as follows:
   a. Disconnect pressure sensor's four-pin connector.
   b. Turn ignition switch to ON position.
   c. Take voltage reading on connector contacts (male connector): pin 1 and good ground point, about five volts
   d. Pins 1 and 2, about five volts
   e. If voltage is within specifications, then proceed to next step.
   f. If not, repair fault, then proceed to final inspection.
2. Inspect control module's pressure sensor input as follows:
   a. Connect scan tool, then turn ignition switch to ON position.
   b. Select "READ FUNCTIONS" and "TANK PRESSURE."
   c. Scan tool should show reading of about 2.9 kPa.
   d. Connect jumper lead between pins 2 and 3 of pressure sensor's connector.
   e. Scan tool should show reading of about –2.9 kPa.
   f. If readings are in specifications, then proceed to final inspection.
   g. If not, repair fault, then proceed to final inspection.
3. Final inspection as follows:
   a. Clear all DTC's.
   b. Coolant temperature should be below 35° C (95°F).
   c. Start engine and run it at idling speed for about one minute.
   d. Using scan tool, check for recurrence of DTC.
   e. If yes, refer to "Electronic Control Module (ECM)" under "Component Replacement."
   f. If not, procedures to rectify fault were correct.

CODES P0452 & P0453: FUEL TANK PRESSURE SENSOR

Fault Symptoms

Conditions: CHECK ENGINE lamp (MIL) ON. P0452: ignition switch in ON position, tank pressure below -3 kPa for more than .5 seconds. P0453: ignition switch in ON position, tank pressure above 3 kPa for more than .5 seconds.

Diagnostic Procedure

1. Inspect pressure sensor's connection to ground and power supply as follows:
   a. Disconnect pressure sensor's four-pin connector.
   b. Turn ignition switch to ON position.
   c. Take voltage reading on connector contacts (male connector): pin 1 and good ground point, about five volts
   d. Pins 1 and 2, about five volts
   e. If voltage is within specifications, then proceed to next step.
   f. If not, repair fault, then proceed to final inspection.
2. Inspect control module's pressure sensor input as follows:
   a. Connect scan tool, then turn ignition switch to ON position.
   b. Select "READ FUNCTIONS" and "TANK PRESSURE."
   c. Scan tool should show reading of about 2.9 kPa.
   d. Connect jumper lead between pins 2 and 3 of pressure sensor's connector.
   e. Scan tool should show reading of about –2.9 kPa.
   f. If readings are in specifications, then proceed to final inspection.
   g. If not, repair fault, then proceed to final inspection.
3. Final inspection as follows:
   a. Clear all DTC's, then start implementation of driving cycle, varying engine loads and RPM for five minutes.
   b. Evaluate driving cycle, check DTC's for recurrence.
   c. If yes, refer to "Electronic Control Module (ECM)" under "Component Replacement."
   d. If not, procedures to rectify fault were correct.

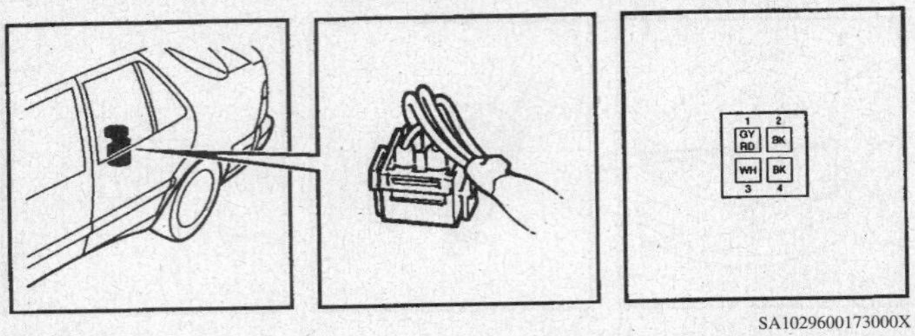

Fig. 17 Fuel pump connector terminal identification

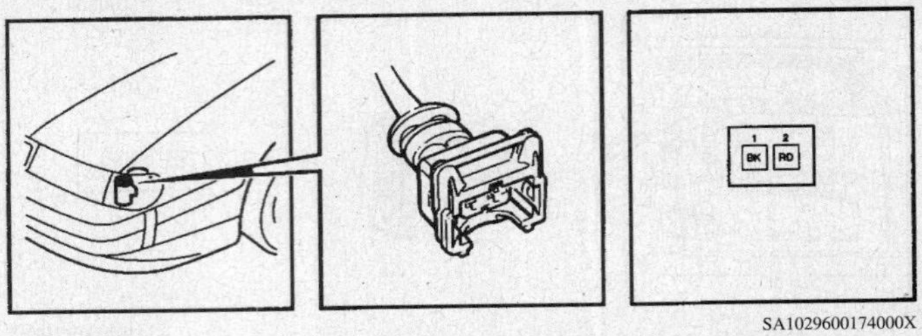

Fig. 18 Secondary air injection control valve connector terminal identification

CODE P0501: VEHICLE SPEED SIGNAL

Fault Symptoms

Conditions: CHECK ENGINE lamp (MIL) ON. ABS warning lamp may be ON. DTC P0501, engine speed above 2000 RPM, engine load for more than three seconds, vehicle speed slower than 10 km/h for more than seven seconds.

1. Select "READ FUNCTIONS" and "CAR SPEED."
2. Scan tool will show actual wheel speed. Drive vehicle and compare scan tool display with vehicle speedometer.
3. Inspect wiring harness for intermittent short or open circuit faults.

Diagnostic Procedure

1. Inspect ABS DTC's.
   a. Connect scan tool, then turn ignition switch to ON position.
   b. Select "ABS" and obtain DTC reading if any.
   c. DTC's for righthand front wheel sensor are 44222, 2422B and 24222.
   d. If scan tool shows DTC's for righthand front wheel speed sensor, refer to diagnosis and testing as outlined under "Anti-Lock Brakes" section.
   e. If no righthand front wheel speed sensor DTC's are shown, proceed to next step.
2. Inspect wheel speed signal as follows:
   a. Disconnect ECM 88 pin connector.
   b. Turn ignition switch to ON position.
   c. Perform frequency measurement between pins 26–79, measurement should read approximately 14 Hz.
   d. If within specifications, proceed to final inspection.
   e. If not within specifications, inspect wire between pin No. 11 of ABS control module and pin 79 of ECM for short and continuity. Repair or replace as required. If wire is satisfactory, refer to diagnosis and testing as outlined under "Anti-Lock Brakes" section.
3. Final inspection:
   a. Clear all DTC's
   b. Drive car at varying engine loads and RPM for five minutes.
   c. Determine if DTC recurred.
   d. If yes, refer to "Electronic Control Module (ECM)" under "Component Replacement."
   e. If not, procedures to rectify fault were correct.

CODES P0506 & P0507: IDLING SPEED

Fault Symptoms

Conditions: Fast or slow idle speed, idle speed sensitive to load change, misfiring. P0506: Vehicle speed zero mph, coolant temperature above 80° C (176°F), purging (EVAP) not active, engine speed more than 200 RPM below requested revs. P0507: Vehicle speed zero mph, coolant temperature above 80° C (176°F), purging (EVAP) not active, engine speed more than 100 RPM above requested revs.

Diagnostic Procedure

1. Inspect air supply as follows:
   a. Check that hoses to and from IAC valve are correctly fitted and not kinked or pinched, which could result in more/less air being supplied.
   b. Check operation of throttle valve.
   c. If valve is within specifications, then proceed to next step.
   d. If not, repair fault, then proceed to step 3.
2. Inspect idle air control valve's power supply as follows:
   a. Disconnect valve's three-pin connector, then turn ignition switch to ON position.
   b. Connect test lamp to pin 2 and battery ground (-) terminal.
   c. Test lamp should light up.
   d. If test lamp lit up, proceed to step 3.
   e. If not, repair lead between three-pin connector and crimped connection J111, then proceed to final inspection.
3. Inspect control module's output as follows:
   a. Connect test lamp to female connector between battery positive (+) terminal and pin 1.
   b. Connect scan tool, then turn ignition switch to ON position.
   c. Select "ACTIVATE" and "IAC VALVE."
   d. Test lamp should flash at frequency of .5 Hz for 30 seconds.
   e. Repeat procedure using battery positive (+) terminal and pin 3.
   f. If test lamp flashed, replace idle air control valve then proceed to final inspection.
   g. If not, repair fault, then proceed to final inspection.
4. Final inspection as follows:
   a. Clear all DTC's, then start implementation of driving cycle: engine attained normal operating temperature, and varying engine loads and RPM for five minutes.
   b. Turn engine Off, then start engine and run it at idling speed for about 45 seconds, repeat three times.
   c. Evaluate driving cycle, check DTC's for recurrence.
   d. If yes, refer to "Electronic Control Module (ECM)" under "Component Replacement."
   e. If not, procedures to rectify fault were correct.

CODES P0560 & P1602: BATTERY VOLTAGE

Fault Symptoms

Conditions: Malfunctioning. P0560: battery voltage lower than 2.5 volts. P1602: No +30 current when +15 current is Off.

Diagnostic Procedure

Using a test lamp, multimeter or scan tool, jiggle leads and inline connectors at several points and in different directions to find faults in wiring harness. If wiring fault is indicated, repair the fault.

CODES P0562 & P0563: BATTERY VOLTAGE

Fault Symptoms

Conditions: No fault symptoms present. DTC P0562, battery voltage lower than 10 volts for more than 60 seconds after starting engine. DTC P0563, battery voltage higher than 16 volts for more than 60 seconds after starting engine.

1. If battery voltage is lower than 10 volts or higher than 16 volts for 60 seconds, consequential fault may set which is too low or too high battery voltage.
2. Inspect wiring for intermittent open or short circuits.

Diagnostic Procedure

1. Inspect additional DTC's as follows:
   a. Using scan tool obtain DTC readouts.
   b. If scan tool shows other DTC's, proceed to final inspection.
   c. If no other codes are shown, inspect battery voltage and ECM ground connection and power supply, then proceed to final inspection.
2. Final inspection:
   a. Clear all DTC's
   b. Drive car at varying engine loads and RPM for five minutes.

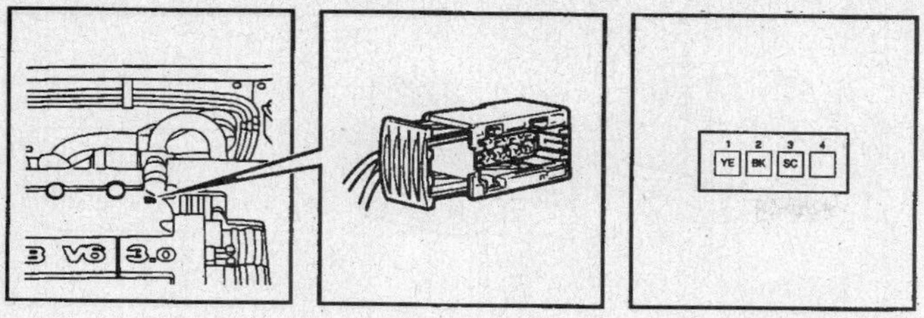

SA1029600176000X

Fig. 20 Crankshaft position sensor connector terminal identification

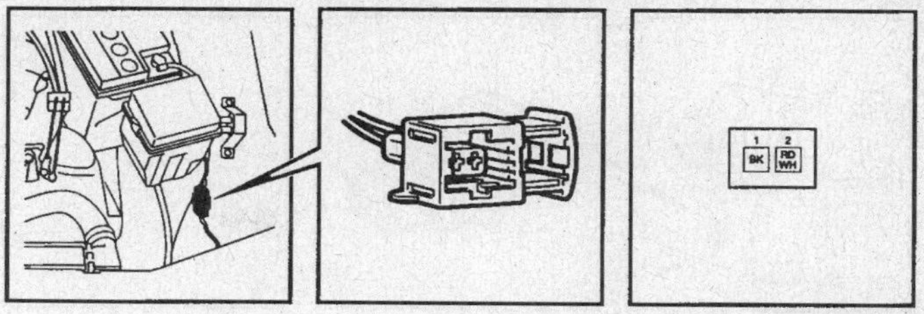

SA1029600175000X

Fig. 19 Secondary air injection pump connector terminal identification

c. Determine if DTC recurred.
d. If yes, refer to "Electronic Control Module (ECM)" under "Component Replacement."
e. If not, procedures to rectify fault were correct.

CODES P0601 & P0604: ECM INTERNAL FAULT

Fault Symptoms

CHECK ENGINE lamp (MIL) ON. Depending upon which internal memory or program is at fault, various fault symptoms may be affected. When ignition is turned to the ON position, the ECM program does not coincide with that programmed by the manufacturer.

Diagnostic Procedure

1. Inspect DTC generation as follows:
   a. Clear all DTC's
   b. Drive car at varying engine loads and RPM for five minutes.
   c. Determine if DTC recurred.
   d. If DTC recur, proceed to next step.
   e. If DTC does not recur, end of test.
2. Inspect ECM power supply and ground connection as follows:
   a. Remove ECM.
   b. Inspect electrical connector for corrosion and socket fit.
   c. Inspect ECM power supply and ground connection within connector.
   d. If inspections are satisfactory, install ECM, then proceed to final inspection.
3. Final inspection:
   a. Clear all DTC's.
   b. Drive car at varying engine loads and RPM for five minutes.
   c. Determine if DTC recurred.
   d. If yes, refer to "Electronic Control Module (ECM)" under "Component Replacement."
   e. If not, procedures to rectify fault were correct.

CODES P1102 & P1115: PREHEATING OF FRONT H02S (REAR BANK)

Fault Symptoms

Conditions: CHECK ENGINE lamp ON. Preheating circuit resistance higher than 10 ohms after three minutes. If one oxygen sensor reaches operative status four times faster than another oxygen sensor, the other oxygen sensor is identified as defective. Preheating circuit resistance lower than 2.5 ohms after three minutes.

1. If scan tool reads DTC's P1115, P1117, P0155 and P0161, check fuse 28 for defect. Inspect wire from J37 connector via fuse 28 and pin 8 of H70–1 connector to J129 connector.

Diagnostic Procedure

1. Inspect fuses as follows:
   a. If fuse 28 is intact proceed to step 3.
   b. If fuse is not intact, replace fuse, then proceed to next step.
2. Inspect resistance of oxygen sensor preheating elements.
   a. Turn engine Off and let sit for five minutes.
   b. Disconnect four pin oxygen sensor electrical connectors.
   c. Measure resistance of four sensors, pins 1 and 2, resistance should be 1.8–4.0 ohms.
   d. If resistance is within specifications, repair or replace wire between pin No. 1 of each of two oxygen sensor electrical connectors and fuse No. 28. Proceed to final inspection.
   e. If resistance is not within specifications, replace defective oxygen sensor, then proceed to final inspection.
3. Inspect preheating element power supply as follows:
   a. Disconnect oxygen sensor four pin electrical connector.
   b. Turn ignition switch to ON position.
   c. Connect test lamp to pin No. 1 and battery ground.
   d. If test lamp lights, proceed to final inspection.
   e. If test lamp does not light, repair or replace wire in question, then proceed to final inspection.
4. Inspect preheating circuit connections to ground as follows:
   a. Run engine at idle speed.
   b. Connect test lamp to battery positive and pin No. 2.
   c. If test lamp lights or begins flashing, replace sensor, then proceed with final inspection.
   d. If test lamp does not light, inspect wire in question, repair or replace, then proceed to final inspection.
5. Final inspection:
   a. Clear all DTC's.
   b. Drive car at varying engine loads and RPM for five minutes.
   c. Determine if DTC recurred.
   d. If yes, refer to "Electronic Control Module (ECM)" under "Component Replacement."
   e. If not, procedures to rectify fault were correct.

CODES P1105 & P1117: REAR H02S (REAR BANK)

Fault Symptoms

Conditions: CHECK ENGINE lamp ON. Preheating circuit resistance higher than 10 ohms after three minutes. If one oxygen sensor reaches operative status four times faster than another oxygen sensor, the other oxygen sensor is identified as defective. Preheating circuit resistance lower than 2.5 ohms after three minutes.

1. If scan tool reads DTC's P1115, P1116, P0155 and P0161, check fuse 38 for defect. Inspect wire from pin 87 of fuel pump relay to fuse 38 and pin 8 of H33-4 connector to J13 connector.

Diagnostic Procedure

1. Inspect fuses as follows:
   a. If fuse 38 is intact, proceed to step 3.
   b. If fuse is not intact, replace fuse, then proceed to next step.
2. Inspect resistance of oxygen sensor preheating elements.
   a. Turn engine Off and let sit for five minutes.
   b. Disconnect four pin oxygen sensor electrical connectors.
   c. Measure resistance of four sensors, pins 1 and 2, resistance should be 1.8–4.0 ohms.
   d. If resistance is within specifications, repair or replace wire between pin No. 1 of each of two oxygen sensor electrical connectors and fuse No. 38. Proceed to final inspection.
   e. If resistance is not within specifications, replace defective oxygen sensor, then proceed to final inspection.
3. Inspect preheating element power supply as follows:
   a. Start engine and operate at idle speed.
   b. Connect test lamp to pin No. 1 and battery ground.
   c. If test lamp lights, proceed to final inspection.
   d. If test lamp does not light, repair or replace wire in question, then proceed to final inspection.
4. Inspect preheating circuit connections to ground as follows:

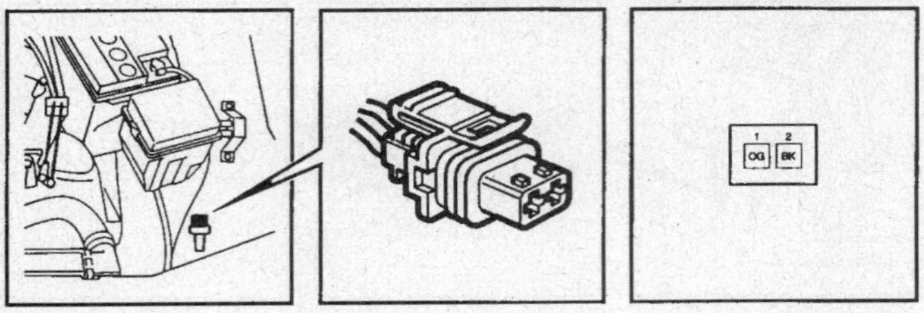

SA1029600177000X

Fig. 21 Intake air temperature sensor connector terminal identification

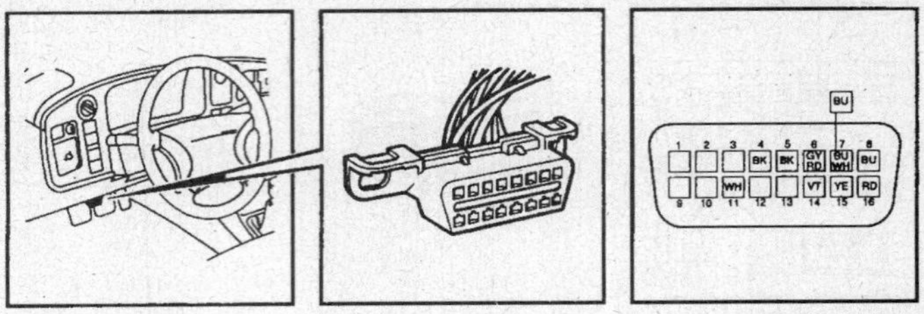

SA1029600178000X

Fig. 22 DLC connector terminal identification

a. Run engine at idle speed.
b. Connect test lamp to battery positive and pin No. 2.
c. If test lamp lights or begins flashing, replace sensor, then proceed with final inspection.
d. If test lamp does not light, inspect wire in question, repair or replace, then proceed to final inspection.

5. Final inspection:
a. Clear all DTC's
b. Drive car at varying engine loads and RPM for five minutes.
c. Determine if DTC recurred.
d. If yes, refer to "Electronic Control Module (ECM)" under "Component Replacement."
e. If not, procedures to rectify fault were correct.

CODES P1123, P1124, P1125, P1126, P1127, P1128, P1129 & P1130: ADAPTATION MALFUNCTION

Fault Symptoms

Conditions: CHECK ENGINE lamp (MIL) ON. Impaired driveability, hunting idle. Any other DTC's, such as low fuel level, mass air flow sensor, or misfiring.

P1123, additive adaptation. Rear bank less than +.485 ms. DTC P1124, additive adaptation. Rear bank greater than +.485 ms. DTC P1125, additive adaptation. Front bank less than +.485 ms. DTC P1126, additive adaptation. Front bank greater than +.485 ms.

Conditions: DTC P1127, multiplicative adaptation. Rear bank less than -18.5%. Conditions: DTC P1128, multiplicative adaptation. Rear bank greater than +23%. Conditions: DTC P1129, multiplicative adaptation. Front bank less than -18.5%. Conditions: DTC P1129, multiplicative adaptation. Front bank greater than +23%. If adaptation malfunction has set as a result of low fuel level, DTC P1585 will set.

1. Using scan tool select "READ FUNCTIONS" and "ADDITIVE ADAPTION," then "MULTIPL ADAPTION."
2. Current multiplicative adaptation is shown in percentage (±25%).
3. Current additive adaptation is shown in milliseconds ms (±.512).
4. Check wiring harness for intermittent open or short circuits.

Diagnostic Procedure

1. Check other DTC's in system as follows:
a. Using scan tool obtain DTC's.
b. If other DTC's are set continue with relevant diagnostic procedure, refer to "Diagnostic Chart Index," then proceed to final inspection.
c. If no other DTC's are set proceed to next step.
2. Check for air leakage as follows:
a. Ensure no air leakage exist in intake system after mass air flow sensor. Inspect all vacuum hoses and crankcase breather hose.
b. Inspect all system connected to intake system for air leakage.
c. Inspect EVAP canister purge valve for leakage under zero current conditions.
d. If all inspections prove satisfactory, proceed to next step.
e. If not satisfactory, correct fault and proceed to final inspection.
3. Inspect performance of mass air flow sensor as follows:
a. Connect scan tool, then start engine.
b. Select "READ FUNCTIONS" and "MASS AIR FLOW SENSOR."
c. Ensure scan tool shows air mass as function of engine RPM, idling speed approximately .8 volts and at 2500 RPM with no load approximately 1.5 volts. Slightly higher readings can be expected for cold engine.
d. If all reading are satisfactory, proceed to next step.
e. If reading are not satisfactory, replace mass air flow sensor and proceed to final inspection.
4. Additional inspections are as follows:
a. Inspect secondary air injection system is operating satisfactory.
b. Ensure fuel pressure is correct.
c. Ensure air leakage does not occur in exhaust system ahead of oxygen sensors or at exhaust manifold.
d. Ensure injector are not clogged.
e. If all inspections are satisfactory proceed to final inspection.
f. If inspections are not satisfactory correct fault and proceed to final inspection.
5. Final inspection as follows:
a. Clear all DTC's
b. Drive car at varying engine loads and RPM for five minutes.
c. Determine if DTC recurred.
d. If yes, refer to "Electronic Control Module (ECM)" under "Component Replacement."
e. If not, procedures to rectify fault were correct.

CODES P1136, P1137, P1138 & P1139: ADAPTION

Fault Symptoms

Conditions: Driveability, possible malfunctioning. P1136: Additive adaptation/fuel injection, bank 1 less than -.45 ms. P1137: Additive adaptation/fuel injection, bank 1 greater than -.29 ms. P1138: Additive adaptation/fuel injection, bank 2 less than -.45 ms. P1139: Additive adaptation/fuel injection, bank 2 greater than -.29 ms.

Diagnostic Procedure

Using a test lamp, multimeter or scan tool, jiggle leads and inline connectors at several points and in different directions to find faults in wiring harness. If wiring fault is indicated, repair the fault.

CODE P1140: MASS AIR FLOW SENSOR/THROTTLE POSITION SENSOR

Fault Symptoms

Conditions: CHECK ENGINE lamp (MIL) ON, performance down/reduced driveability. Coolant temperature above 60° C (140°F), engine speed higher than 1320 RPM, more than 35 seconds since starting, mass air flow sensor's valve does not coincide with valve from throttle position sensor for more than seven seconds.

Diagnostic Procedure

Using a test lamp, multimeter or scan tool, jiggle leads and inline connectors at several points and in different directions to find faults in wiring harness. If wiring fault is indicated, repair the fault.

1. Inspect fuel adaptation as follows:
a. Connect scan tool, then check whether additive adaptation is higher than ±.2 ms and multiplicative adaptation is higher than ±10%.
b. If any exceeded specifications, proceed to next step.
c. If not, proceed to step 5
2. Inspect for air leakage as follows:
a. Inspect hoses/connections between mass air flow sensor and throttle body for leakage.
b. If no leaks were found, proceed to next step.
c. If leaks were found, repair fault,

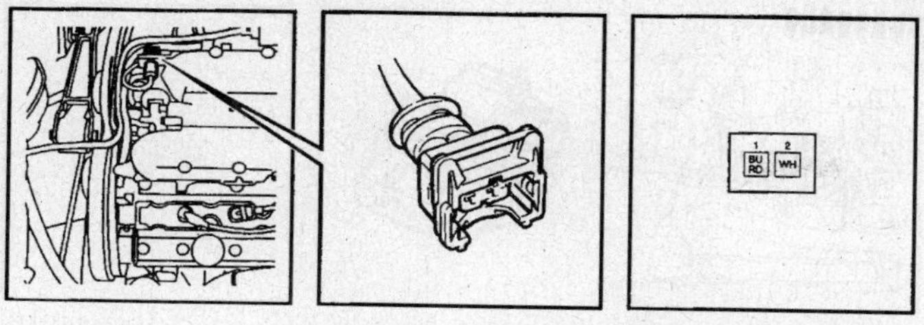

SA1029600179000X

Fig. 23 Variable intake manifold inner flap connector terminal identification

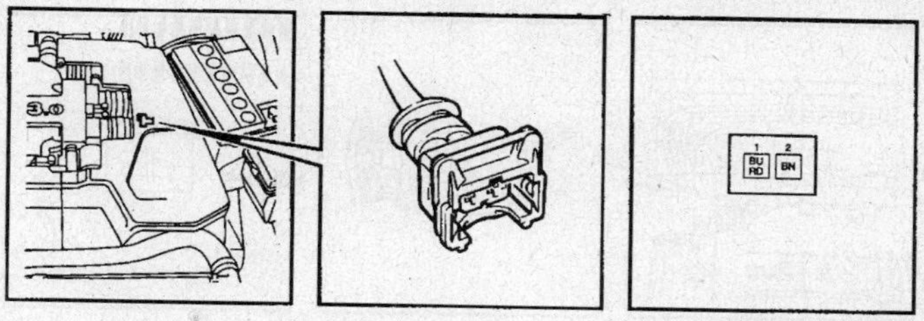

SA1029600180000X

Fig. 24 Variable intake manifold outer flap connector terminal identification

then proceed to final inspection.

3. Inspect mass air flow sensor's ground connection and power supply as follows:
   a. Disconnect mass air flow sensor's four-pin connector, then turn ignition switch to ON position.
   b. Connect test lamp to connector between: battery positive (+) terminal and pin 1; battery positive (+) terminal and pin 2; battery negative (-) terminal and pin 3.
   c. Test lamp should light up in all three cases.
   d. If test lamp lit up in all three cases, then proceed to next step.
   e. If not, repair fault, then proceed to final inspection.
4. Inspect control module's mass air flow sensor input as follows:
   a. Connect conventional 1.5 V battery (in good ground condition), battery positive (+) to pin 4; battery ground (-) to pin 2.
   b. Connect scan tool, then turn ignition switch to ON position
   c. Select "MASS AIR FLOW SENSOR," it should show reading of 1.5 V.
   d. If reading was in specifications, replace mass air flow sensor then proceed to final inspection.
   e. If not, repair fault, then proceed to final inspection.
5. Inspect throttle position sensor's ground connection and power supply as follows:
   a. Connect multimeter.
   b. Disconnect throttle position sensor's three-pin connector, then turn ignition to ON position.
   c. Take resistance reading in connector, pin 1 and battery ground (-) terminal, with reading of about 5 V.
   d. Take resistance reading in connector, pin 2 and battery positive (+) terminal, with reading of about 12 V.
   e. If readings are within specifications, then proceed to next step.
   f. If not, repair fault, then proceed to final inspection.
6. Inspect control module's throttle position sensor input as follows:
   a. Connect scan tool, then turn ignition switch to ON position.
   b. Select "THROTT POS SENSOR," it should show reading of 5 V.
   c. Connect jumper lead in throttle position sensor's connector between pins 2 and 3.
   d. Scan tool should show reading of 0 V.
   e. If both readings are within specifications, replace throttle position sensor then proceed to final inspection.
   f. If not, repair fault, then proceed to final inspection.
7. Final inspection as follows:
   a. Clear all DTC's, then start implementation of driving cycle, varying engine loads and RPM for five minutes.
   b. Evaluate driving cycle, check DTC's for recurrence.
   c. If yes, refer to "Electronic Control Module (ECM)" under "Component Replacement."
   d. If not, procedures to rectify fault were correct.

CODES P1170, P1171 & P1172: VARIABLE INTAKE MANIFOLD OUTER FLAP

Fault Symptoms

Conditions: CHECK ENGINE (MIL) lamp ON and impaired performance. Engine speed higher than 80 RPM and battery voltage 7.5–17 volts. DTC P1170 is set, open circuit. DTC P1171 is set, shorting to battery ground. DTC P1172 is set, shorting to battery positive.

1. Select "ACTIVATE" and "VARIABLE INTAKE," then "OUTER FLAP."
2. Command activates outer flap for 30 seconds.
3. Check wiring for intermittent short or open circuits.

Diagnostic Procedure

1. Check solenoid valve power supply as follows:
   a. Disconnect solenoid valve two pin electrical connector.
   b. Turn ignition switch to ON position.
   c. Connect test lamp to pin No. 1 and battery ground.
   d. If test lamp lights proceed to next step.
   e. If not repair or replace wire between connector J128 and pin No. 1 of two pin connector, then proceed to final inspection.
2. Check ECM output to solenoid valve as follows:
   a. Connect test lamp to battery positive and pin No. 2 of solenoid valve two pin connector.
   b. Connect scan tool, turn ignition switch to ON position.
   c. Select "ACTIVATE" and "VARIABLE INTAKE," then "OUTER FLAP."
   d. If test lamp flashes for 30 seconds, replace solenoid valve, then proceed to final inspection.
   e. If not repair or replace wire in question, then proceed to final inspection.
3. Final inspection:
   a. Clear all DTC's
   b. Drive car at varying engine loads and RPM for five minutes.
   c. Determine if DTC recurred.
   d. If yes, refer to "Electronic Control Module (ECM)" under "Component Replacement."
   e. If not, procedures to rectify fault were correct.

CODES P1213, P1214, P1215, P1216, P1217, P1218, P1225, P1226, P1227, P1228, P1229 & P1230: INJECTORS 1, 2, 3 & 4

Fault Symptoms

Conditions: Any other DTC such as misfiring adaptation, etc. Engine speed higher than 80 RPM, battery voltage 7.5–17 volts with following DTC's set; P1213, P1214, P1215, P1216, P1217 and P1218, shorting to battery positive.

Engine speed higher than 80 RPM, battery voltage 7.5–17 volts with following DTC's set; P1225, P1226, P1227, P1228, P1229 and P1230, shorting to battery negative.

1. Using scan tool activate injector in question.
2. Select "ACTIVATE" and "INJECTOR 1, 2, 3, 4, 5, or 6."
3. Check for intermittent wiring harness short or open circuits.

Diagnostic Procedure

1. Check injector power supply as follows:
   a. Disconnect injector two pin electrical connector, then turn ignition switch to ON position.
   b. Connect test lamp to pin No. 1 and battery ground.
   c. If test lamp lights continue with next step.
   d. If not repair or replace wire between pin No. 1 of two pin connector and J125 connector, then continue with final inspection.

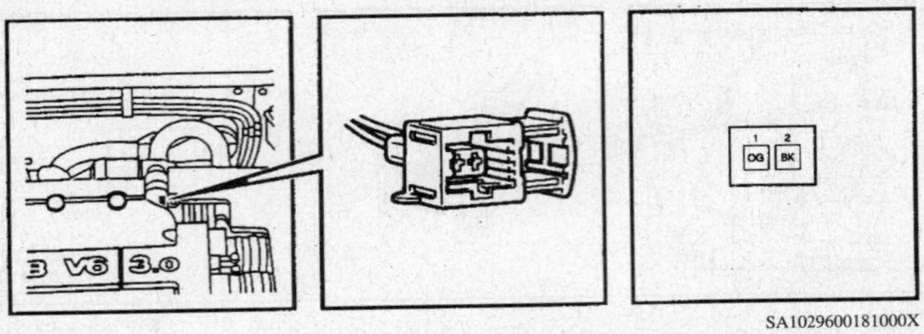

SA1029600181000X

Fig. 25 Knock sensor rear cylinder bank connector terminal identification

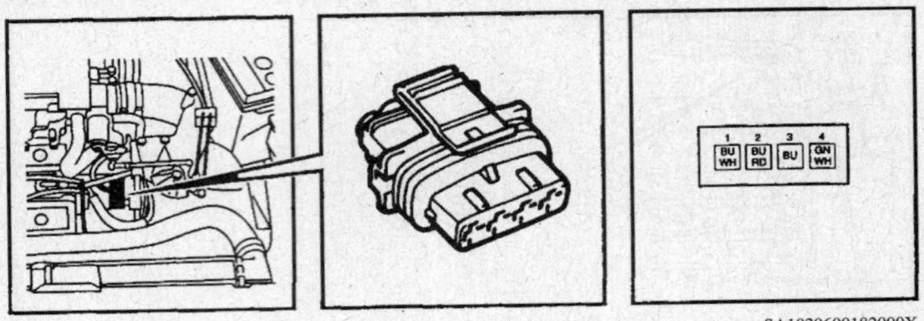

SA1029600182000X

Fig. 26 Ignition control module connector terminal identification

2. Check ECM output to injector as follows:
   a. Connect test lamp between battery positive and pin No. 2 of injector female electrical connector.
   b. Connect scan tool, turn ignition switch to ON position.
   c. Select "ACTIVATE" and "INJECTOR 1, 2, 3, 4, 5, or 6."
   d. If test lamp is flashing change injector, then proceed to final inspection.
   e. If not flashing, repair or replace wire in question, then proceed to final inspection.
3. Final inspection:
   a. Clear all DTC's
   b. Drive car at varying engine loads and RPM for five minutes.
   c. Determine if DTC recurred.
   d. If yes, refer to "Electronic Control Module (ECM)" under "Component Replacement."
   e. If not, procedures to rectify fault were correct.

CODES P1237, P1238, P1239, P1240, P1241 & P1242: INJECTORS 1, 2, 3, 4, 5 & 6

Fault Symptoms

Conditions: Any other DTC such as misfiring adaption, etc. Engine speed higher than 80 RPM, battery voltage 7.5–17 volts with following DTC's set; P1213, P1214, P1215, P1216, P1217 and P1218, break.

Diagnostic Procedure

Refer to "Codes P1213, P1214, P1215, P1216, P1217, P1218, P1225, P1226, P1227, P1228, P1229 & P1230" for procedure.

CODE P1386: ECM KNOCK SENSOR CIRCUITRY

Fault Symptoms

Conditions: Poor engine performance due to retarded ignition timing. Conditions: Fault in ECM's internal knock sensor signal circuits.

Diagnostic Procedure

1. Final inspection as follows:
   a. Clear all DTC's
   b. Drive car at varying engine loads and RPM for five minutes.
   c. Determine if DTC recurred.
   d. If yes, refer to "Electronic Control Module (ECM)" under "Component Replacement."
   e. If not, procedures to rectify fault were correct.

CODES P1410, P1425 & P1426: EVAP CANISTER PURGE VALVE

Fault Symptoms

Conditions: Any DTC such as adaption, misfiring etc. Conditions: Engine speed higher than 80 RPM and battery voltage 7.5–17 volts; DTC P1410 shorting to battery positive; DTC P1425 shorting to battery negative; DTC P1426 open circuit.

1. Using scan tool, select "ACTIVATE" and "EVAP VALVE."
2. EVAP valve will click when activated.
3. Check for intermittent wiring harness open or short circuits.

Diagnostic Procedure

1. Check EVAP valve power supply.
   a. Disconnect EVAP valve two pin electrical connector.
   b. Turn ignition switch to ON position.
   c. Connect test lamp to pin No. 1 and battery ground.
   d. If test lamp lights continue with next step.
   e. If not, repair or replace wire between J37 connector and pin No. 1, then continue with final inspection.
2. Check ECM output to EVAP valve.
   a. Connect test lamp to battery positive and pin No. 2 of female connector.
   b. Connect scan tool, then turn ignition switch to ON.
   c. Select "ACTIVATE" and "EVAP VALVE."
   d. If test lamp flashes for 30 seconds, replace EVAP valve and continue with final inspection.
   e. If not flashing, repair or replace wire in question, then continue with final inspection.
3. Final inspection:
   a. Clear all DTC's
   b. Start engine run at idle speed until coolant temperature exceeds 140°F.
   c. Drive car at varying engine loads and RPM for five minutes.
   d. Determine if DTC recurred.
   e. If yes, refer to "Electronic Control Module (ECM)" under "Component Replacement."
   f. If not, procedures to rectify fault were correct.

CODES P1501, 1502 & 1541: PUMP RELAY

Fault Symptoms

Conditions: Engine fails to start. Engine misfires occasionally. Various other DTC's set, such as adaption misfiring etc. Conditions: DTC P1501 is set and ignition switch in Off position. Fuel pump relay turned Off by ECM. Battery voltage 7.5–17 volts. Shorting to battery ground; DTC P1502 is set and engine speed is higher than 80 RPM. Battery voltage 7.5–17 volts. Shorting to battery positive; DTC P1541 is set and ignition switch is Off. Fuel pump relay turned Off by ECM. Battery voltage is 7.5–17 volts. Open circuit.

1. Using scan tool select "ACTIVATE" and "PUMP RELAY."
2. Ensure anti-theft alarm is operative as wire between main relay and pump relay is via alarm.
3. Check for intermittent short or open wiring.

Diagnostic Procedure

1. Check pump relay control voltage as follows:
   a. Remove fuel pump relay.
   b. Connect test lamp to pin No. 86 of relay socket and good ground.
   c. If test lamp lights, then continue with next step.
   d. If not repair or replace wire from anti-theft alarm between pin 86 of pump relay socket and pin No. 87 of main relay socket, then continue with final inspection.
2. Check ECM output to fuel pump relay as follows:
   a. Connect test lamp to pins No. 86 and No. 85 of relay socket.
   b. Connect scan tool, then turn ignition switch to ON.
   c. Select "ACTIVATE" and "PUMP RELAY."
   d. If test lamp flashes change fuel pump relay, then continue with final inspection.
   e. If not repair or replace wire between pin No. 85 of pump relay socket and pin No. 63 of ECM.
3. Final inspection:
   a. Clear all DTC's.
   b. Drive car at varying engine loads and RPM for five minutes.
   c. Determine if DTC recurred.
   d. If yes, refer to "Electronic Control Module (ECM)" under "Component Replacement."

e. If not, procedures to rectify fault were correct.

CODES P1510, 1513, 1514, 1551, 1552 & 1553: IDLE AIR CONTROL VALVE

Fault Symptoms

Conditions: Low, high or hunting idle speed. Idle speed sensitive to load changes. Engine speed higher than 80 RPM, battery voltage 7.5–17 volts. DTC P1510 is set, shorting to battery positive. DTC P1513 is set, shorting to ground. DTC P1514 is set, open circuit. DTC P1551 is set, open circuit. DTC P1552 is set, shorting to ground. DTC P1553 is set, shorting to battery positive.

1. Using scan tool select "ACTIVATE" and "IAC VALVE."
2. Check wiring harness for intermittent open or short circuits.

Diagnostic Procedure

1. Check idle air control valve power supply.
   a. Disconnect valve three pin electrical connector.
   b. Turn ignition switch to ON position.
   c. Connect test lamp to pin No. 2 and battery negative.
   d. If test lamp lights continue with next step.
   e. If not, repair or replace wire between three pin connector and J128 crimped connector, then continue with final inspection.
2. Check control module outputs to IAC valve.
   a. Connect test lamp to battery positive and pin No. 1 of IAC female connector.
   b. Connect scan tool, then turn ignition switch ON.
   c. Select "ACTIVATE" and "IAC VALVE."
   d. Repeat procedure with test lamp connected to battery positive and pin No. 3 of female connector.
   e. If test lamp lights in both cases, change IAC valve, then continue with final inspection.
   f. If not, repair or replace wire in question, then continue with final inspection.
3. Final inspection:
   a. Clear all DTC's
   b. Drive car at varying engine loads and RPM for five minutes.
   c. Determine if DTC recurred.
   d. If DTC recurred, refer to "Electronic Control Module (ECM)" under "Component Replacement."
   e. If not, procedures to rectify fault were correct.

CODES P1512, P1515 & P1516: VARIABLE INTAKE MANIFOLD INNER FLAP

Fault Symptoms

"Check Engine" (MIL) lamp ON and impaired performance.

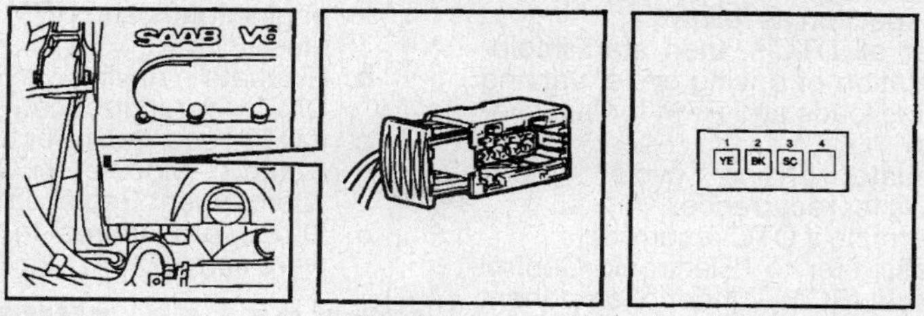

SA1029600183000X

Fig. 27 Camshaft position sensor connector terminal identification

1. Conditions: Engine speed higher than 80 RPM, battery voltage 7.5–17 volt. DTC P1512 set, shorting to battery positive; DTC P1515 set, shorting to battery negative. DTC P1516 set, open circuit.
2. Using scan tool, multi-meter, or test lamp, check for intermittent short or open wiring diagrams.

Diagnostic Procedure

1. Check solenoid valve power supply.
   a. Disconnect solenoid valve two pin electrical connector.
   b. Turn ignition switch to ON position.
   c. Connect test lamp to pin No. 1 and battery ground.
   d. If test lamp is lit continue with next step.
   e. If not, check wire crimp connection J128 and pin 1 of two pin connector. Continue with final inspection.
2. Check control module output to solenoid valve
   a. Connect test lamp to battery positive and pin No. 2 of solenoid valve electrical connector.
   b. Connect scan tool, then turn ignition switch to ON position.
   c. Select "ACTIVATE," "VARIABLE INTAKE," and "INNER FLAP."
   d. Test lamp should flash for approximately 30 seconds.
   e. If test lamp is flashing, change solenoid valve, then continue with final inspection.
   f. If not repair or replace appropriate wire, then continue with final inspection.
3. Final inspection:
   a. Clear all DTC's
   b. Drive car at varying engine loads and RPM for five minutes.
   c. Determine if DTC recurred.
   d. If DTC recurred, refer to "Electronic Control Module (ECM)" under "Component Replacement."
   e. If not, procedures to rectify fault were correct.

CODE P1551: IDLE AIR CONTROL (IAC) VALVE

Fault Symptoms

Conditions: CHECK ENGINE lamp (MIL) ON, fast or slow engine RPM, idling speed sensitive to lead changes. Engine speed higher than 80 RPM, battery voltage 7.5–17 V, open circuit (closing).

Diagnostic Procedure

Refer to "Code P1510" for procedure.

CODE P1585: FUEL TANK LOW LEVEL

Fault Symptoms

Conditions: Less than 10 liters of fuel in tank when one of the following DTC's is set; P0300, P0301–P0306. If fuel tank has less than 10 liters of fuel fault will occur and indicate the same to prevent unnecessary fault diagnosis.

1. Check for intermittent short or open circuits in wiring harness.

Diagnostic Procedure

1. Check additional DTC's.
   a. Using scan tool obtain all DTC's.
   b. If these DTC's set, P0300, P0301–P0306, then fuel level was low when DTC set.
2. Final inspection for appropriate DTC.

CODE P1611: CHECK ENGINE

Fault Symptoms

Conditions: CHECK ENGINE lamp (MIL) ON. Ignition switch in ON position, short circuit to ground for more than 1.8 seconds.

Diagnostic Procedure

1. Inspect wiring as follows:
   a. Check continuity of lead between pin 39 of Motronic control module and pin 5 of transmission control module.
   b. If continuity is within specifications, proceed to next step.
   c. If not, repair fault, then proceed to final inspection.
2. Inspect TCM output stage as follows:
   a. Turn ignition switch to Off position.
   b. Disconnect Motronic control module connector.
   c. Connect test lamp to sockets 26 and 39 of female connector.
   d. Connect scan tool.
   e. Turn ignition switch to ON position.
   f. Select "AUT TRANSMISSION," "ACTIVATE" and "CHECK ENGINE."
   g. Test lamp should light up for one second, when ignition switch is in ON position.
   h. If test lamp lit up for one second, proceed to final inspection.
   i. If not, repair fault, then proceed to final inspection.

3. Final inspection as follows:
   a. Clear all DTC's, then start implementation of driving cycle, varying engine loads and RPM for five minutes.
   b. Evaluate driving cycle, check DTC's for recurrence.
   c. Determine if DTC recurred.
   d. If yes, refer to "Electronic Control Module (ECM)" under "Component Replacement."
   e. If not, procedures to rectify fault were correct.

CODE P1614: CHECK ENGINE

Fault Symptoms

Conditions: CHECK ENGINE lamp (MIL) ON. No test pulses from TCM when ignition ON, Voltage less than 2.5 volts.

Diagnostic Procedure

Refer to "Code P1611" for procedure.

CODE P1624: CHECK ENGINE

Fault Symptoms

Conditions: CHECK ENGINE lamp (MIL) ON, CHECK GEARBOX lamp ON, transmission is in limp-home mode. Transmission control module (TCM) has recorded an emission related fault.

Diagnostic Procedure

Using a test lamp, multimeter or scan tool, jiggle wiring harness at several points and in different directions to ascertain whether wiring harness, including any connectors are causing DTC. If wiring fault is indicated, repair the fault. If not, a transmission fault is indicated.

CODES P1655, P1657, P1660 & P1662: CONTROL MODULE OUTPUT

Fault Symptoms

Conditions: A control module output which should not be used is connected.

Diagnostic Procedure

1. Inspect control module connection as follows:
   a. Refer to **Fig. 4,** to check pins which should not be used and are connected.
   b. If connections are appropriate, then proceed to next step.
   c. If not, repair fault, then proceed to final inspection.
2. Inspect control module version as follows:
   a. Ensure correct control module version is fitted.
   b. If correct version is fitted, then proceed to final inspection.
   c. If not, replace control module with correct version, then proceed to final inspection.
3. Final inspection as follows:
   a. Clear all DTC's, then start implementation of driving cycle, varying engine loads and RPM for five minutes.
   b. Evaluate driving cycle, check DTC's for recurrence.
   c. If DTC recurred, refer to "Electronic Control Module (ECM)" under "Component Replacement."
   d. If not, procedures to rectify fault were correct.

CODE P1664: SHIFT UP

Fault Symptoms

Conditions: SHIFT UP lamp is ON continuously or out of order. Short circuit to battery ground (-) terminal and lamp not activated, short circuit to battery positive (+) terminal and lamp is activated, ignition switched ON and lamp activated, voltage five volts

Diagnostic Procedure

1. Inspect bulb as follows:
   a. Inspect condition of bulb.
   b. If bulb is in working condition, proceed to next step.
   c. If not, repair fault, then proceed to final inspection.
2. Inspect control module connection as follows:
   a. Disconnect main instrument display panel connector.
   b. Connect test lamp to battery positive (+) terminal and pin 39.
   c. Connect scan tool.
   d. Turn ignition switch to ON position.
   e. Select "ACTIVATE" and "SHIFT UP LAMP."
   f. Lamp should flash at frequency of .5 Hz for 30 seconds.
   g. If lamp flashed, fault is indicated in main instrument display panel
   h. If not, repair fault, then proceed to final inspection.
3. Final inspection as follows:
   a. Clear all DTC's, then start implementation of driving cycle, varying engine loads and RPM for five minutes.
   b. Evaluate driving cycle, check DTC's for recurrence.
   c. If DTC recurred, refer to "Electronic Control Module (ECM)" under "Component Replacement."
   d. If not, procedures to rectify fault were correct.

CODE P1669: TCS SIGNAL ACTIVE

Fault Symptoms

Conditions: Slight effect on emissions. No test signal from TCS when starting or TCS active signal constantly high or pulses are longer than 2.5 seconds. TCS and Motronic system interaction can be monitored with ISAT scan tool.

1. Using scan tool select "TCS," "ACTIVATE," then "DISCONN ENRICHMENT."
2. TCS will send battery positive signal for disconnection of full-load enrichment.
3. Using multi-meter, scan tool or test lamp, check wiring for intermittent faults.

Diagnostic Procedure

1. Check for additional DTC's as follows:
   a. Using ISAT scan tool obtain all DTC's in TCS.
   b. Check for DTC's B1406, B1407 or B1408. These DTC's will cause TCS OFF lamp to light.
   c. Does scan tool show any TCS DTC's?
   d. If yes, refer to "Traction Control System" for procedures.
   e. If no, continue with next step.
2. Check TCS signal as follows:
   a. Start engine and operate at idle speed.
   b. Select "TCS," and "ACTIVATE," then "DISCONN ENRICHMENT"
   c. TCS control module will send battery positive signal for disconnection of full-load enrichment. Motronic system will interpret signal as fuel shutoff and stop engine.
   d. If engine has stopped, continue with final inspection.
   e. If not, continue with next step.
3. Check wire between TCS and Motronic control module.
   a. Check wire between Motronic control module pin 68 and TCS control module pin 21 for continuity.
   b. If wire is satisfactory continue with next step.
   c. If not repair or replace wire, then continue with final inspection.
4. Check TCS control module output signal.
   a. Remove Motronic control module.
   b. Connect voltmeter to pins No. 68 and No. 28 of ECM electrical connector.
   c. Select "TCS" AND "ACTIVATE," AND "DISCONN ENRICHMENT."
   d. ON position reading should be approximately 12 volts.
   e. Off position reading should be approximately zero volts.
   f. If voltage readings are satisfactory, continue with final inspection.
   g. If not continue fault diagnosis, refer to "Traction Control System."
5. Final check proceed as follows:
   a. Clear all DTC's's.
   b. Drive vehicle at varying engine loads and RPM for five minutes.
   c. Determine if DTC has recurred.
   d. If yes, refer to "Electronic Control Module (ECM)" under "Component Replacement."
   e. If not, procedure to rectify fault were correct.

CODES P1691, P1692, P1693: CHECK ENGINE (MIL)

Fault Symptoms

Conditions: CHECK ENGINE lamp (MIL) is ON continuously or inoperative. Engine speed higher than 80 RPM, battery voltage 7.5–17 volts; DTC P1691 open circuit, DTC P1692 shorting to ground, and DTC P1693 shorting to battery positive .

1. MIL can be activated with ISAT scan tool. Select "Activate" and "CHECK ENGINE LAMP."
2. Select "EDU," "READ VALUES," and "CHECK ENGINE LAMP." "ON" or "Off" status of lamp will be shown.
3. Check intermittent faults by jiggling wiring at several points in different directions to simulate temporary short or open wire circuits. Observe multimeter or ISAT scan tool while moving wiring to pinpoint wiring harness trouble.

Diagnostic Procedure

1. Check control module output as follows:
   a. Disconnect EDU control module electrical connector.
   b. Connect test lamp to pin 12 of EDU connector and battery negative.
   c. Connect ISAT scan tool and select "ACTIVATE," then "CHECK ENGINE LAMP."
   d. Lamp should flash for 30 seconds.
   e. If lamp is flashing inspect EDU programmable trip computer, then continue with final inspection.
   f. If not, repair of replace wire between pin 12 of EDU connector and pin 8 of Motronic control module connector, then continue with final inspection.
2. Final inspection:
   a. Clear all DTC's's.
   b. Drive car at varying engine loads and RPM for five minutes.
   c. Check if DTC has recurred.
   d. If yes, refer to "Electronic Control Module (ECM)" under "Component Replacement." procedure.
   e. If not, procedures to rectify fault were correct.

CODE P1782: TORQUE REDUCTION

Fault Symptoms

Conditions: CHECK ENGINE lamp (MIL) ON, transmission's emergency program active. Less than 2 V for more than two seconds.

Diagnostic Procedure

1. Inspect output signal from TCM as follows:
   a. Turn ignition switch to OFF position.
   b. Disconnect Motronic control module connector.
   c. Connect test lamp to Motronic control module's connector between pins 26 and 21.
   d. Turn ignition switch to ON position, then connect scan tool.
   e. Select "AUT TRANSMISSION, ACTIVATE, TORQUE LIMITATION," and "AUTO/MANUAL."
   f. Test lamp should flash or light up continuously.
   g. If yes, proceed to final inspection.
   h. If not, proceed to next step.
2. Inspect wiring as follows:
   a. Disconnect transmission control module connector.
   b. Check for continuity in lead between pin 13 of transmission control module and pin 21 of Motronic control module.
   c. Check lead for open circuit and shorting.
   d. If yes, transmission fault is indicated.
   e. If not, repair fault, then proceed to final inspection.
3. Final inspection as follows:
   a. Clear all DTC's's.
   b. Drive car at varying engine loads and RPM for five minutes.
   c. Check if DTC has recurred.
   d. If yes, refer to "Electronic Control Module (ECM)" under "Component Replacement."
   e. If not, procedures to rectify fault were correct.

CODE —: PRIOR TO REPLACING ELECTRONIC CONTROL MODULE (ECM)

After all test and checks have been completed in accordance with diagnostic procedures for the appropriate DTC, or by manual fault diagnosis, without any faults having been found, it can be assumed that the ECM is at fault. Before pinpointing the ECM as the cause of the fault, proceed as follows:

1. Check all points in diagnostic procedure have been performed completely.
2. Review and understand wiring diagram of circuit in question.
3. When removing or installing ECM, be aware that electrostatic discharge may damage ECM. Refer to "Precautions" prior to performing service on ECM.
4. Check all grounds and ECM power supply. Ensure power ground and sensor ground are electrically separated from each other.
5. Connect BOB or SIM, if diagnostic procedure gives desired result.
6. Give careful thought prior to replacing ECM.

Clearing Diagnostic Trouble Codes

Component Testing

IGNITION COIL

Engine Misfires Or Fails To Start

1. If possible, start engine and use ISAT commands "IGNITION COIL 1+4," "IGNITION COIL 2+5" and "IGNITION COIL 3+6" in "READ ON/OFF" menu.
2. If control module sends trigger signals from pin 1 (cyl. 1+4), pin 20 (cyl. 2+5) and pin 21 (cyl. 3+6), ISAT should show "ACTIVE" when each command is used. If ISAT shows "INACTIVE," replace ECM.
3. Remove HT lead from any spark plug in cylinders 2, 4 or 6, and connect to test spark plug with wide gap.
4. Ground spark plug and use ISAT commands "FIRING CYL 1-4," "FIRING CYL 2-5" and "FIRING CYL 3-6," in "ACTIVATE" menu.
5. Spark plugs corresponding to relevant commands should now produce spark. If not, an ignition coil is not producing ignition current. Check leads between pins 1, 20 or 21 of control unit and pins 3, 1 or 2 of ignition coils. If no ignition coils produce ignition current, check if pin 4 on coils receives current from fuse 17.
6. Disconnect ignition coil four-pin connector and use voltmeter to take readings across pins 4 and 1, 4 and 2, and 4 and 3. With ignition switch in Drive position, voltmeter should show about 12 volts. Engage starter motor. Voltage should fluctuate between 4 and 6 volts.
7. If readings are satisfactory, proceed to next step. If readings are not satisfactory, proceed as follows:
   a. Check resistance of primary circuit in ignition coils by taking reading across pins 4 and 1, 4 and 2, and 4 and 3. Correct resistance is about 1 ohm.
   b. Check secondary windings by measuring resistance across HT lead outlets for spark plugs 1+4 and 2+5. Correct resistance is about 12,000 ohms. If resistance is not satisfactory, change ignition coil.
8. If no diagnostic trouble codes have been generated in Bosch Motronic system, ensure ECM is supplied with correct voltage and ground connection is good. Also ensure crankshaft position sensor is in satisfactory working order.

MAIN RELAY

Check main relay operation as follows:

1. Turn ignition switch to Drive position and measure voltage across pin 2 of IAC valve and ground, or across pin 3 of mass air flow sensor and ground, to check if relay has been energized.
2. If current is present, relay is satisfactory if it releases about five seconds after ignition has been switched off. If no current is present, proceed to following step.
3. Lower relay holder under dashboard, then connect jumper lead between ground and pin 85 of relay.
4. Check if relay has been energized by checking for current on pin 87 of relay. If relay has been energized, proceed to next step. If relay has not been energized, proceed as follows:
   a. Check whether current is present on pins 86 and 30 of relay from maxi-fuse 2.
   b. If it is, remove relay and measure resistance across pins 85 and 86 of relay coil. Correct resistance is about 60 ohms. If resistance is not satisfactory, replace relay.
5. Check lead between pin 85 of relay and pin 46 of ECM for continuity.
6. With ignition switch in Drive position, check whether current is supplied to pin 27 of control module from fuse 17.
7. If it is, and control module does not ground pin 46, replace ECM.

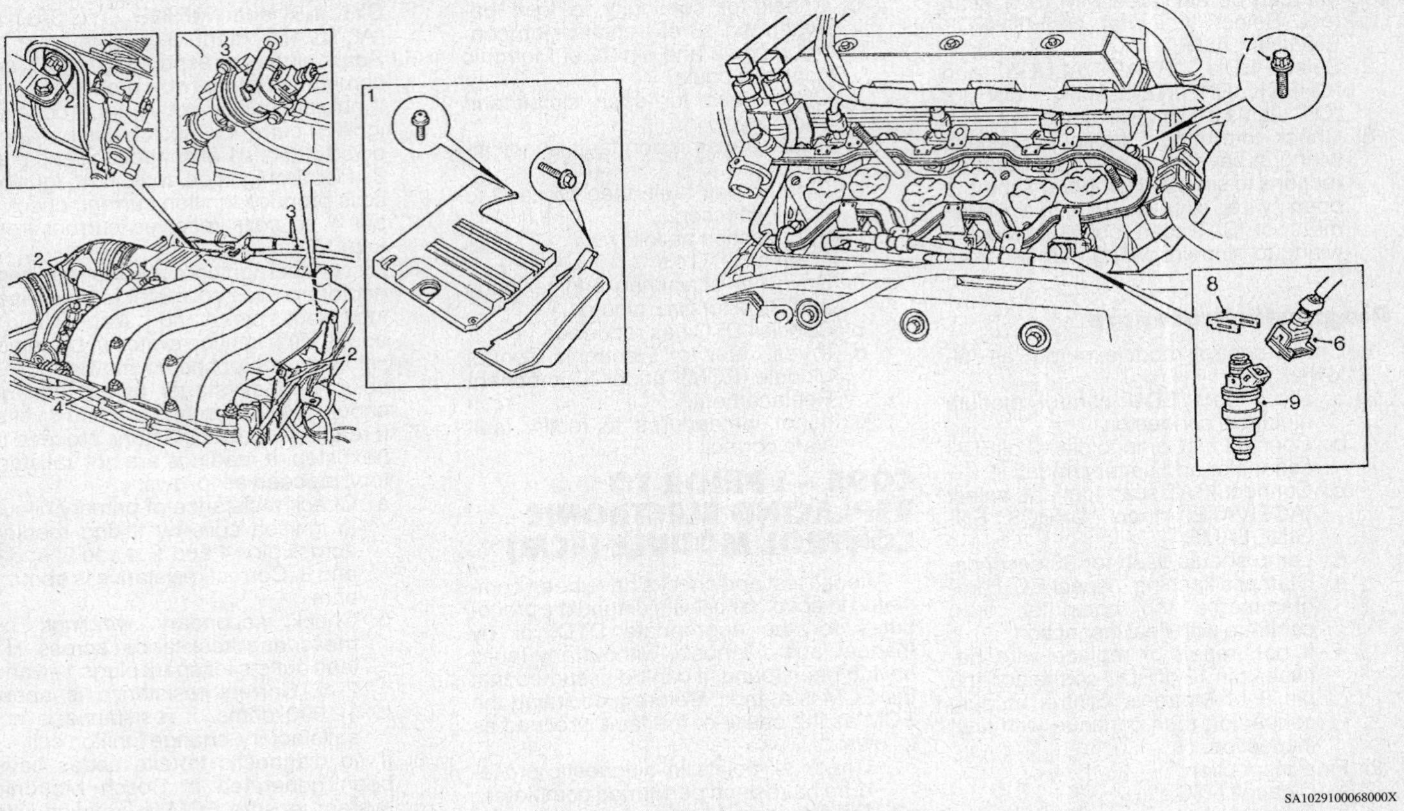

Fig. 28 Fuel injector replacement

SYSTEM SERVICE

Component Replacement

ENGINE CONTROL MODULE (ECM)

1. Before replacing the ECM, perform the following checks:
   a. Ensure every point in fault diagnosis program of relevant diagnostic trouble code has been carried out.
   b. Study wiring diagram of circuit in question and ensure you understand how it works.
   c. Check all grounding points. Ensure power ground and signal ground are electrically separate.
   d. Check voltage supplied to ECM.
   e. Check fuses.
   f. Inspect connectors for corrosion on pins and contact surfaces, excessive play, looseness or anything else which may cause poor contact or deterioration in conductivity.
   g. Check how long main relay remains on after ignition has been switched off. Relay should operate for an additional five seconds or so if temperature is approximately 68°F, or about 30 seconds if temperature is below 32°F.
2. Turn off ignition.
3. Remove glove compartment.
4. Fold back carpet and remove central locking system relay.
5. Disconnect module electrical connector, then remove ECM.
6. Reverse procedure to install.

ENGINE COOLANT TEMPERATURE (ECT) SENSOR

1. Open expansion tank cap to release cooling system pressure, then screw cap back on.
2. Remove engine cover(s).
3. Disconnect sensor electrical connector, then the sensor.
4. Reverse procedure to install.

CRANKSHAFT POSITION (CKP) SENSOR

The CKP sensor is located at the flywheel end of the engine block.

1. Remove engine covers.
2. Disconnect CKP sensor electrical connector.
3. Remove wiring, noting routing and fastening points.
4. Raise and support vehicle
5. Remove sensor bolt, then the sensor, noting position of sealing ring.
6. Reverse procedure to install, noting the following:
   a. Clean sensor seating and fit sealing ring in seating.
   b. **Torque** sensor bolt to 72 inch lbs.

CAMSHAFT POSITION (CMP) SENSOR

1. Remove engine covers, then disconnect CMP sensor electrical connector.
2. Remove sensor bolts, then the sensor.
3. Reverse procedure to install.

IDLE AIR CONTROL (IAC) VALVE

1. Remove engine covers.
2. Release hose clips on rubber duct, then disconnect IAC valve hose and rear knock sensor electrical connector from duct.
3. Remove rubber duct, then disconnect intake manifold retaining stay and cable conduits.
4. Disconnect throttle and cruise control cables form throttle lever and bracket, then the crankcase ventilation and brake servo vacuum hoses.
5. Remove intake manifold upper half nuts, then raise upper half of intake manifold and support with rubber mallet. **Plug intake manifolds with paper or rags to prevent screws from falling into cylinders.**
6. Disconnect valve electrical connector.
7. Remove valve bolts and pull valve with rubber seal straight down.
8. Disconnect hose from valve and remove rubber seal.
9. Reverse procedure to install, noting the following:
   a. Smear petroleum jelly on new valve

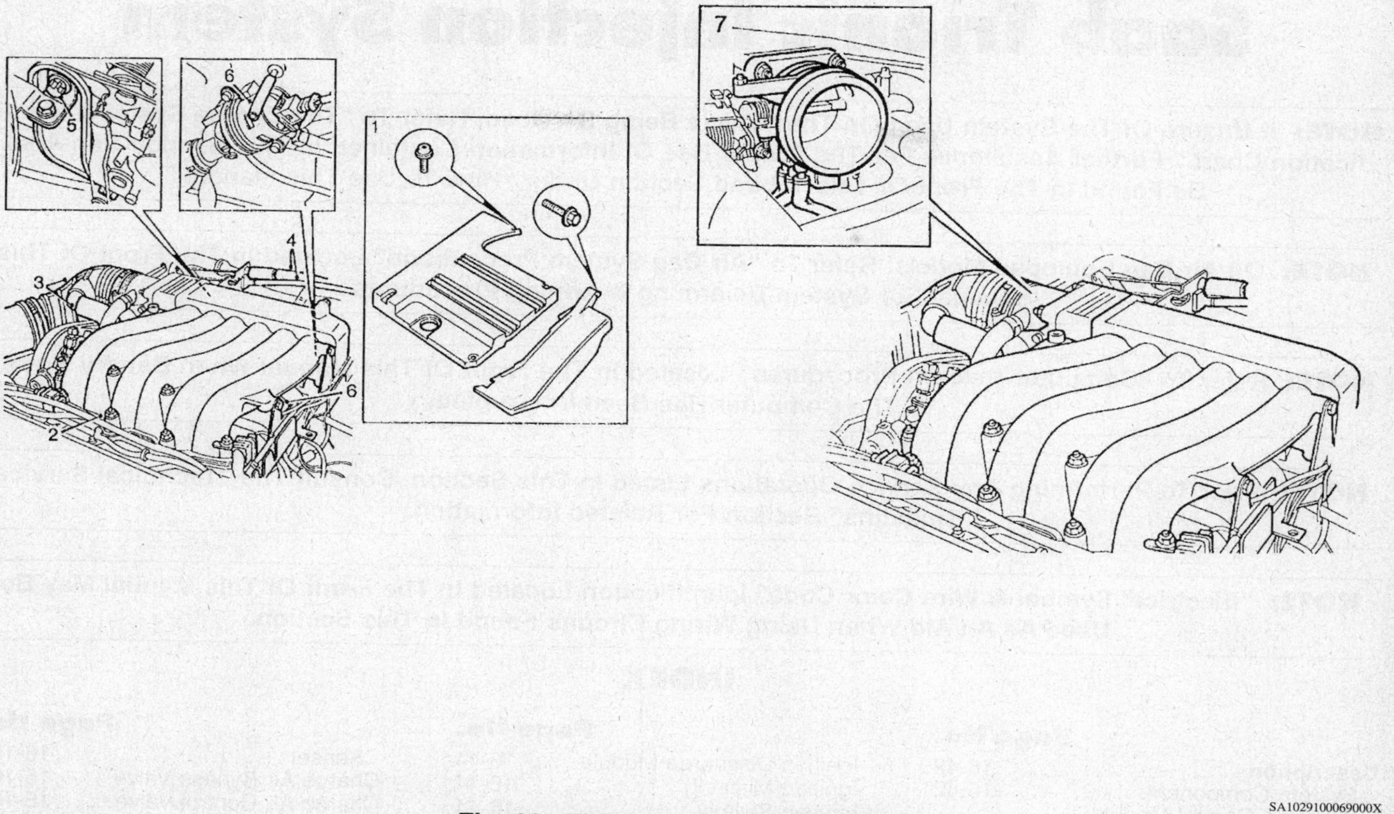

Fig. 29 Throttle body replacement

seal before installing.

b. Clean intake manifold mating surfaces if necessary, then install new gasket.
c. Tighten intake manifold upper half nuts, starting with middle ones and continuing alternately toward outer ends. **Torque** nuts to 15 ft. lbs.
d. **Torque** retaining stay to 15 ft. lbs.
e. Ensure pressure regulator vacuum hose is connected to front nipple on throttle body, in front of butterfly.

INJECTOR

Refer to **Fig. 28** when replacing injectors.

1. Remove engine covers (1).
2. Release hose clips on rubber duct, then disconnect IAC valve hose and knock sensor electrical connector from duct.
3. Remove rubber duct, then disconnect intake manifold retaining stay and cable conduits (2).
4. Disconnect throttle and cruise control cables from throttle lever and bracket (3), then the crankcase ventilation and brake servo vacuum hose.
5. Remove upper intake manifold nuts, then raise intake manifold upper half and support with rubber mallet. **Plug intake manifolds with paper or rags to prevent screws from falling into cylinders.**
6. Disconnect all electrical connectors from injectors (6).
7. Remove fuel rail bolts (7), then ease fuel rail loose with screwdriver.
8. Remove retaining clip (8) from injector(s) to be inspected or replaced.
9. Wrap injector in cloth to catch any dripping fuel, then remove injector (9) from fuel rail.
10. Reverse procedure to install, noting the following:
    a. Smear injector O-rings with petroleum jelly to aid in installation.
    b. Clean intake manifold mating surface if necessary, then install new gasket.
    c. **Torque** intake manifold upper nuts, starting with nuts in middle and continuing alternately toward outer ends of manifold, to 15 ft. lbs.
    d. **Torque** retaining stay to 15 ft. lbs.

THROTTLE BODY

Refer to **Fig. 29** when replacing the Bosch Motronic throttle body.

1. Remove engine covers (1), then the upper intake manifold nuts (2).
2. Release hose clips on rubber duct (3), then disconnect IAC valve hose and rear knock sensor electrical connector from duct.
3. Remove rubber duct.
4. Unhook accelerator and cruise control cables from throttle lever and bracket (4).
5. Release intake manifold retaining stay by removing upper bolt (5) and loosening lower bolt.
6. Remove cable conduit (6) and disconnect hose from nipple on lefthand side under manifold.
7. Lift up upper half of intake manifold and rest it on stud in lower half, or support with rubber mallet.
8. Remove main throttle and TCS throttle nuts, then the main throttle (7).
9. Disconnect hoses.
10. Reverse procedure to install, noting the following:
    a. Install new gasket on TCS throttle body. Ensure holes match up.
    b. **Torque** main throttle and TCS throttle nuts to 72 inch lbs.
    c. **Torque** intake manifold upper nuts, starting with nuts in middle and continuing alternately toward outer ends of manifold, to 15 ft. lbs.
    d. **Torque** retaining stay to 15 ft. lbs.

SECONDARY AIR INJECTION PUMP & FILTER

1. Remove lower section and lower half on lefthand side of spoiler.
2. Remove pump bolts, then disconnect electrical connector and hoses.
3. Remove pump.
4. Remove filter bolt, then the filter with hose.
5. Reverse procedure to install.

Saab Trionic Injection System

NOTE: If Unsure Of The System Used On The Vehicle Being Serviced, Refer To "The Engine Systems Identification Chart." Further Assistance For The Proper Use Of Information Contained In This Section Can Also Be Found In The Front Of This Tabbed Section Under "How To Use This Manual."

NOTE: On Air Bag Equipped Models, Refer To "Air Bag System Precautions" Located In The Front Of This Manual For System Disarming & Arming Procedures.

NOTE: Refer To "Computer Relearn Procedures" Located In The Front Of This Manual When Battery Power To The Computer Has Been Interrupted.

NOTE: Prior To Performing Any Service Operations Listed In This Section, Consult The "Technical Service Bulletins" Section For Related Information.

NOTE: "Electrical Symbol & Wire Color Code" Identification Located In The Front Of This Manual May Be Used As An Aid When Using Wiring Circuits Found In This Section.

INDEX

Page No.

Description 16-42
System Components 16-42
Engine Control Module (ECM) 16-42
Engine Coolant Temperature (ECT) Sensor 16-42
Fuel Injector 16-42
Idle Air Control (IAC) Valve ... 16-43
Intake Air Temperature (IAT) Sensor 16-43
Manifold Absolute Pressure (MAP) Sensor 16-42
Throttle Position Sensor 16-43
System Operation............... 16-42
Diagnosis & Testing 16-43
Accessing Diagnostic Trouble Codes 16-43
Clearing Diagnostic Trouble Codes 16-43
Component Testing 16-43
A/C Relay 16-43
Boost Pressure Control 16-43
Brake Light Switch............ 16-44
Cruise Control 16-44
Drive Input Signal From Automatic Transaxle.......... 16-44
Fuel Pump & Relay............ 16-44
Ignition - Engine Fails To Start 16-44
Ignition Discharge Module 16-44
Ignition Misfiring 16-44
Ignition Switch 16-44
Injectors 16-44
Main Relay 16-44
Malfunction Indicator & Shift Up Lamps..................... 16-44
Transaxle Switch 16-44
Diagnostic Tests 16-43
Diagnostic Trouble Code Interpretation 16-43
Wiring Diagrams................ 16-43
Diagnostic Chart Index 16-51
Precautions......................... 16-42
Air Bag Systems................ 16-42
Battery Ground Cable........... 16-42
Throttle Position Adaptation..... 16-42
900 16-42
Sensor & Fuel Injector Specifications 16-40
System Service.................. 16-161
Adjustments 16-164
Base Charging Pressure 16-164
Charging Pressure Adaption .. 16-165
Limp-Home Solenoid.......... 16-165
Throttle Plate 16-165
Component Replacement 16-162
Charge Air Absolute Pressure Sensor 16-164
Charge Air Bypass Valve...... 16-164
Charge Air Control Valve...... 16-164
Crankshaft Position (CKP) Sensor 16-163
Engine Control Module (ECM) 16-162
Engine Coolant Temperature (ECT) Sensor 16-162
Heated Oxygen Sensor 16-164
Injectors 16-163
Intake Air Temperature (IAT) Sensor 16-164
Limp-Home Solenoid.......... 16-164
Manifold Absolute Pressure (MAP) Sensor 16-164
Mass Air Flow (MAF) Sensor.. 16-164
Throttle Body 16-163
Component Service.............. 16-161
Base Charge Pressure Inspection 16-161
Boost Pressure Control Valve (APC Solenoid) Inspection .. 16-162
Injector Flow Capacity Inspection 16-161
Inspection Of Wastegate 16-162
Membrane Housing Unit Inspection 16-162

SENSOR & FUEL INJECTOR SPECIFICATIONS

Sensor	Voltage	Resistance
2.0L & 2.3L		
Camshaft Position (CMP)	0 Or 12 Volts	—
Charge Air Absolute Pressure	2.1 Volts @ 14.50 psi	—
	3.3 Volts @ 25.38 psi	—
Crankshaft Position (CKP)	—	485–595 Ohms @ 68°F(1)
	—	770–850 Ohms @ 68°F(2)

Continued

SENSOR & FUEL INJECTOR SPECIFICATIONS—Continued

Sensor	Voltage	Resistance
2.0L & 2.3L		
Engine Coolant Temperature (ECT)	—	2.1–2.9 kOhms @ 68°F
	—	295–365 Ohms @ 176°F
Fuel Injector (Non-Turbo)	—	14.5 Ohms @ 68°F
Fuel Injector (Turbo)	—	12 Ohms @ 68°F①
	—	15.15–16.75 Ohms @ 68°F②
Heated Oxygen Sensor (HO2S)	—	Terminals 1 & 2, 1.8–2.5 Ohms @ 68°F①
	—	Terminals 1 & 2, 1.7–2.5 Ohms @ 68°F②
Intake Air Temperature (IAT)	—	2.1–2.9 kOhms @ 68°F
	—	295–365 Ohms @ 176°F
Knock Sensor (KS)	5 mVolts AC @ Idle	—
	100 mVolts AC When Striking Retaining Bolt	
Manifold Absolute Pressure (MAP)	1.9 Volts @ 14.50 psi①	—
	3.3 Volts @ 25.38 psi①	—
	2.1 Volts @ 14.50 psi②	—
	3.3 Volts @ 25.38 psi②	—
Mass Air Flow (MAF)	.8 Volt @ 4 G/S①	—
	3.9 Volts @ 130 G/S①	—
	2355 Hz @ 5 G/S②	—
	8158 Hz @ 140 G/S②	—
Throttle Position (TP)	—	Terminals 2 & 3, .8–1.2 kOhms @ Idle①
	—	Terminals 2 & 3, 2–3 kOhms @ WOT①
	Terminals 6 & 8, .065–1.090 Volts @ CTP②	—
	Terminals 8 & 9, .025–1.070 Volts @ WOT②	—
3.0L		
Charge Air Absolute Pressure	2.1 Volts @ 14.50 psi	—
	3.3 Volts @ 25.38 psi	—
Crankshaft Position (CKP)	—	770–850 Ohms @ 68°F
Engine Coolant Temperature (ECT)	—	2.1–2.9 kOhms @ 68°F
	—	295–365 Ohms @ 176°F
Fuel Injector	—	15.55–16.35 Ohms @ 68°F
Heated Oxygen Sensor (HO2S)	—	Terminals 1 & 2, 1.7–2.5 Ohms @ 68°F
Intake Air Temperature (IAT)	—	2.1–2.9 kOhms @ 68°F
	—	295–365 Ohms @ 176°F
Mass Air Flow (MAF)	—	2355 Hz @ 5 G/S
	—	8158 Hz @ 140 G/S
Manifold Absolute Pressure (MAP)	2.1 Volts @ 14.50 psi	—
	3.3 Volts @ 25.38 psi	—
Throttle Position (TP)	Terminals 6 & 8, .065–1.090 Volts @ CTP	—
	Terminals 8 & 9, .025–1.070 @ WOT	—

CTP — Closed Throttle Position
G/S — Grams Per Second
WOT — Wide Open Throttle
① — 1998.
② — 1999–2001.

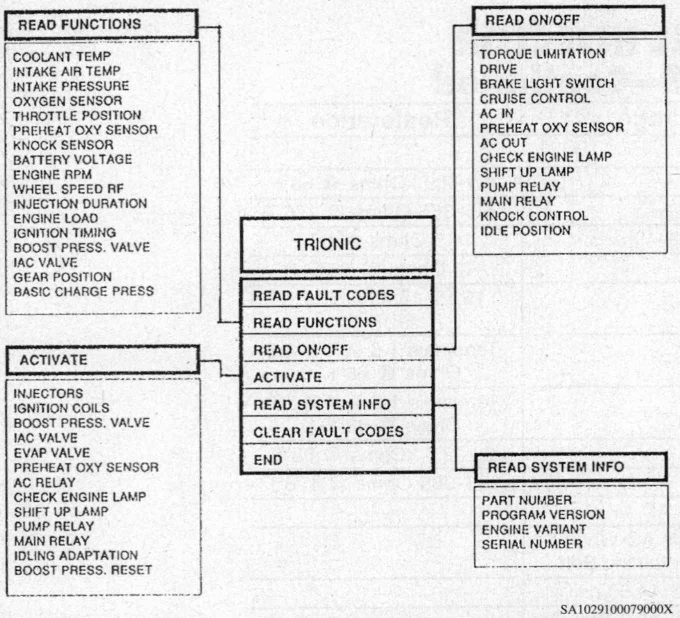

Fig. 1 Command code system menu structure

Diagnostic Trouble Code (SAE)	Faulty function/component	Conditions
P0131	O2S1, Bank 1 Low voltage (Added from start of production)	Short term fuel trim >25% for more than 20 sec. O2S2 shows **rich** mixture at same time.
P0132	O2S1, Bank 1 High voltage (Extended diagnosis from start of production)	Short term fuel trim <-25% for more than 20 sec. O2S2 shows **lean** mixture at same time.
P1651	RAM fault (occurs on early M96)	
P1652	ROM fault (occurs on early M96)	

SA1029700192000X

Fig. 2 DTC interpretation (Part 1 of 6). 9-3 & 900

PRECAUTIONS

Air Bag Systems

Refer to "Air Bag System Precautions" in the front of this manual for system disarming and arming procedures.

Battery Ground Cable

Prior to service, disconnect battery ground cable and isolate as required.

Throttle Position Adaptation

900

After replacing the throttle position sensor, adjusting the throttle position or replacing the ECM on vehicles equipped with the Saab clutch control module, the throttle position must be adapted before the vehicle can be driven. Adapt throttle position as follows:

1. Turn ignition switch on, then connect ISAT scan tool and contact Trionic.
2. Select "IDLING ADAPTATION" command on "ACTIVATE" menu. **Do not touch accelerator pedal.**
3. Select "IDLING" command on "READ ON/OFF" menu.
4. ISAT must show "YES" when accelerator is not pressed.

DESCRIPTION

The distributorless ignition system is controlled by the engine management system. The Saab Trionic system controls ignition, fuel injection and boost pressure from a single engine control module.

The Saab Trionic system provides fuel injection, ignition, boost pressure control, diagnostic capability, emission control and combustion analysis.

System Operation

Fuel injection in the Saab Trionic system is sequential, meaning the fuel injection follows the engine's firing order. This system permits each individual injector to be controlled and regulated individually by the engine control module.

Each cylinder can be supplied with precisely the right amount of fuel, depending on the pressure in the intake manifold, intake air temperature, engine speed, engine coolant temperature, oxygen content of the exhaust gases, any knocking and throttle position.

The Saab Trionic system also has a pre-injection feature. When the ignition switch is turned to the Drive position, the main and fuel pump relays open to inject a small amount of fuel onto the intake valves. This open time is determined by the engine coolant temperature. This pre-injection results in a shorter starting time.

On 900 models, the Saab Trionic system regulates the boost pressure by controlling a solenoid valve connected to the turbo wastegate. The actual boost pressure is read with the pressure sensor.

The boost pressure is calculated by the control module based on engine speed, throttle plate position, gear currently engaged and any knocking.

On 9000 models, the Saab Trionic system contains a secondary air injection system. This helps the catalytic converter to work more quickly and efficiently after a cold start. Ambient air is pumped into the exhaust manifold where the oxygen in the air starts a chemical combustion process together with CO, HC and NOx pollutants. This generates heat so the catalytic converter can start operating effectively more quickly.

The control module starts the air pump only if the signals from the coolant temperature sensor and intake air temperature sensor are 41–95°F. If necessary, the air pump starts immediately after the engine starts.

System Components

ENGINE COOLANT TEMPERATURE (ECT) SENSOR

The ECT sensor provides the ECM with information on the temperature of the engine coolant. The value is used to determine the fuel injection time in pre-injection and for cold starting, and to produce a richer fuel/air mixture during warm-up.

MANIFOLD ABSOLUTE PRESSURE (MAP) SENSOR

The MAP sensor contains a pressure-sensitive ceramic sensing device, an amplifier and a circuit for temperature compensation. It is connected by a short special hose to the engine intake manifold after the throttle. The ECM uses intake manifold pressure and temperature information to calculate the engine load (how great an air mass each cylinder draws in). The fuel injection time is proportional to the air mass drawn in.

FUEL INJECTOR

The Saab Trionic system contains solenoid type injectors with needles and seats. The injectors open when current flows through them, and close when current is broken to activate a powerful spring.

The injectors are precisely set, with two jets on each intake valve. Therefore, service to the jets must be done in pairs in special mounts between cylinders 1-2 and cylinders 3-4.

Injectors receive their voltage from the main relay, while the ECM grounds the injectors.

ENGINE CONTROL MODULE (ECM)

The ECM is located behind the panel by the righthand A pillar.

The ECM receives input signals from various sensors, including information on engine load, temperature, engine RPM, exhaust gas composition, knocking, etc. The module uses this information to control ignition, fuel injection and boost pressure.

Diagnostic trouble code (SAE)	Malfunction/faulty component	CHECK ENGINE	Text displayed on ISAT
P0105	Manifold absolute pressure sensor. Overall DTC for pressure sensor function	on	FAULT XX P0105 INTAKE PRESSURE FUNCTION INCORRECT
P0106	Manifold absolute pressure sensor. Vacuum hose, leakage. Malfunctions, sensor	on	FAULT XX P0106 INTAKE PRESSURE INCORRECT
P0107	Manifold absolute pressure sensor. ECM input shorting to ground	on	FAULT XX P0107 INTAKE PRESSURE SHORT TO GROUND
P0108	Manifold absolute pressure sensor. ECM input shorting to Batt+ or open circuit	on	FAULT XX P0108 INTAKE PRESSURE OPEN CIRCUIT SHORT TO BATT+
P0110	Manifold absolute pressure sensor. Overall DTC for temperature sensor function	on	FAULT XX P0110 INDUCTION AIR TEMP FUNCTION INCORRECT
P0112	Manifold absolute pressure sensor, induction air. ECM input shorting to ground	on	FAULT XX P0112 INDUCTION AIR TEMP SHORT TO GROUND
P0113	Induction air temperature sensor. ECM input shorting to Batt+ or open circuit	on	FAULT XX P0113 INDUCTION AIR TEMP OPEN CIRCUIT SHORT TO BATT+
P0115	Coolant temperature sensor. Overall DTC for temperature sensor function	on	FAULT XX P0115 COOLANT TEMPERATURE FUNCTION FAULTY
P0117	Coolant temperature sensor. ECM input shorting to ground	on	FAULT XX P0117 COOLANT TEMPERATURE SHORT TO GROUND

SA1029100080010X

Fig. 2 DTC interpretation (Part 2 of 6). 9-3 & 900

Diagnostic trouble code (SAE)	Malfunction/faulty component	CHECK ENGINE	Text displayed on ISAT
P0118	Coolant temperature sensor. ECM input shorting to Batt+ or open circuit	on	FAULT XX P0118 COOLANT TEMPERATURE OPEN CIRCUIT SHORT TO BATT+
P0120	Throttle position sensor. Overall DTC for throttle position sensor function	on	FAULT XX P0120 THROTTLE POSITION FUNCTION INCORRECT
P0121	Throttle position sensor. Malfunction in sensor	on	FAULT XX P0121 THROTTLE POSITION INPUT INCORRECT
P0122	Throttle position sensor. ECM input shorting to ground	on	FAULT XX P0122 THROTTLE POSITION SHORT TO GROUND
P0123	Throttle position sensor. ECM input shorting to Batt+ or open circuit	on	FAULT XX P0123 THROTTLE POSITION OPEN CIRCUIT SHORT TO BATT+
P0130	Oxygen sensor. Overall DTC for oxygen sensor function	on	FAULT XX P0130 OXYGEN SENSOR FUNCTION INCORRECT
P0131	Oxygen sensor. Max leaner mixture	on	FAULT XX P0131 OXYGEN SENSOR LEAN
P0132	Oxygen sensor. Max richer mixture	on	FAULT XX P0132 OXYGEN SENSOR RICH
P0135	Preheating, oxygen sensor. Current outside limits	on	FAULT XX P0135 OXYGEN SENSOR NO PREHEATING
P0170	Adaptation. Overall DTC for adaptation function	on	FAULT XX P0170 ADAPTATION FUNCTION INCORRECT
P0171	Adaptation. Lean mixture	on	FAULT XX P0171 ADAPTATION LEAN
P0172	Adaptation. Rich mixture	on	FAULT XX P0172 ADAPTATION RICH

SA1029100080020X

Fig. 2 DTC interpretation (Part 3 of 6). 9-3 & 900

THROTTLE POSITION SENSOR

The TP sensor consists of a potentiometer connected to the throttle plate shaft. This sensor sends information to the ECM concerning idling, partly open throttle and wide open throttle.

At wide open throttle, both the oxygen sensor and fuel injection is switched off. A richer fuel mixture is produced during acceleration and a leaner mixture is produced during deceleration. The maximum boost pressure also depends on the throttle position.

IDLE AIR CONTROL (IAC) VALVE

When the accelerator is in rest position and the throttle butterfly is closed, the engine can only obtain air from the IAC valve. The ECM regulates the degree of valve opening in order to maintain a constant idling speed. The valve opens when the A/C is turned on or when D or R is selected, to compensate for an idle speed drop.

INTAKE AIR TEMPERATURE (IAT) SENSOR

The IAT sensor is located in the intake manifold in front of the throttle. The air temperature value is used with the pressure inside the intake manifold to determine the density of the air drawn in and, essentially, the engine load.

DIAGNOSIS & TESTING

At the start of diagnosis, note the following:

1. Do not forget to check fuses.
2. Inspect connectors for corrosion on pins and contact surfaces, excessive play, looseness or anything else which may cause poor contact or deterioration in conductivity.

Accessing Diagnostic Trouble Codes

The new EPROM developed for the ISAT tool uses a new command code system, EPROM. It contains a system of menus in clear text, enabling the user to select the desired command directly on the keypad. The EPROM consists of eight main menus, each with submenus, **Fig. 1**.

Connect a suitable ISAT tool to diagnostics socket pin 50, located under the dashboard on the lefthand side of the vehicle. To access the diagnostic trouble codes, select "READ FAULT CODES" from main menu, **Fig. 1**.

Diagnostic Trouble Code Interpretation

Refer to **Figs. 2 through 4** for Diagnostic Trouble Code (DTC) interpretation.

Wiring Diagrams

Refer to **Figs. 5 through 9** for wiring diagrams.

Diagnostic Tests

Refer to **Figs. 10 through 139** for diagnostic trouble code diagnosis and repair.

Clearing Diagnostic Trouble Codes

To clear diagnostic trouble codes, select "CLEAR FAULT CODES" from the main menu, **Fig. 1**, or disconnect ECM electrical connector for at least five minutes.

Component Testing

A/C RELAY

9000

Refer to **Fig. 140** for A/C relay diagnosis.

BOOST PRESSURE CONTROL

Refer to **Figs. 141 and 142** for boost pressure control diagnosis.

DTC	Fault
P0442	EVAP. Small Leakage in System.
P0451	EVAP Tank Pressure Sensor. Performance Problem.
P0452	EVAP Tank Pressure Sensor Circuit. Short to Ground.
P0453	EVAP Tank Pressure Sensor Circuit. Open / Short to B+.
P0455	EVAP. Serious Leakage in System.

SA1019900016000X

Fig. 2 DTC interpretation (Part 4 of 6). 9-3

Diagnostic trouble code (SAE)	Malfunction/faulty component	CHECK ENGINE	Text displayed on ISAT
P0325	Knock signal from ignition discharge module faulty (N.B. There is no knock sensor)	—	FAULT XX P0325 KNOCK SENSOR OPEN CIRCUIT
P0335	Crankshaft position sensor. Malfunction	—	FAULT XX P0335 CRANKSHAFT POS SENS FUNCTION INCORRECT
P0443	EVAP valve. Overall DTC for EVAP function	on	FAULT XX P0443 EVAP VALVE FUNCTION INCORRECT
P0444	EVAP valve. ECM output open circuit	on	FAULT XX P0444 EVAP VALVE OPEN CIRCUIT
P0445	EVAP valve. ECM output shorting to ground	on	FAULT XX P0445 EVAP VALVE SHORT TO GROUND
P0500	Wheel speed FR. Input signal from ABS. Overall DTC for wheel speed	—	FAULT XX P0500 WHEEL SPEED FR FUNCTION INCORRECT
P0501	Wheel speed FR. Input signal outside limits	—	WHEEL XX P0501 WHEEL SPEED FR SIGNAL INCORRECT
P0502	Wheel speed FR. No input signal	—	FAULT XX P0502 WHEEL SPEED FR OPEN CIRCUIT
P0505	Idle air control valve. Malfunction	—	FAULT XX P0505 IAC VALVE FUNCTION INCORRECT
P0605	Control module. Internal fault	—	FAULT XX P0605 CONTROL MODULE INTERNAL FAULT
P1500	Battery voltage. Outside limits	—	FAULT XX P1500 BATTERY VOLTAGE VOLTAGE INCORRECT

SA1029100080030X

Fig. 2 DTC interpretation (Part 5 of 6). 9-3 & 900

BRAKE LIGHT SWITCH

Refer to **Figs. 143 and 144** for brake light switch diagnosis.

CRUISE CONTROL

9000 Less TCS

Refer to **Fig. 145** for cruise control diagnosis.

DRIVE INPUT SIGNAL FROM AUTOMATIC TRANSAXLE

900

Refer to **Fig. 146** for drive input signal from automatic transaxle diagnosis.

FUEL PUMP & RELAY

Refer to **Figs. 147 and 148** for fuel pump and relay diagnosis.

IGNITION DISCHARGE MODULE

9000

Refer to **Fig. 149** for ignition discharge module diagnosis.

IGNITION MISFIRING

900

Refer to **Fig. 150** for ignition misfiring diagnosis.

IGNITION SWITCH

9000

Refer to **Fig. 151** for ignition switch diagnosis.

IGNITION - ENGINE FAILS TO START

900

Refer to **Fig. 152** for engine fails to start diagnosis.

INJECTORS

Refer to **Figs. 153 and 154** for injector diagnosis.

MAIN RELAY

Refer to **Figs. 155 and 156** for main relay diagnosis.

MALFUNCTION INDICATOR & SHIFT UP LAMPS

Refer to **Figs. 157 through 160** for malfunction indicator and Shift Up lamp diagnosis.

TRANSAXLE SWITCH

9000

Refer to **Fig. 161** for transaxle switch diagnosis.

Diagnostic Trouble Code (SAE)	Faulty function/component	CHECK ENGINE	Text on diagnostic tool display
P0106	Manifold absolute pressure sensor.	On	FAULT XX P0106 MANIFOLD ABSOLUTE PRESSURE SENSOR INPUT INCORRECT
P0121	Throttle position sensor.	On	FAULT XX P0121 THROTT POS SENSOR MALFUNCTION
P0440	EVAP vent system.	On	FAULT XX P0440 EVAP-SYSTEM MALFUNCTION
P0451	Tank pressure sensor	On	FAULT XX P0451 EVAP PRESSURE SENSOR INPUT INCORRECT
P0452	Tank pressure sensor	On	FAULT XX P0452 EVAP PRESSURE SENSOR INPUT LOW
P0453	Tank pressure sensor	On	FAULT XX P0453 EVAP PRESSURE SENSOR INPUT HIGH

SA1029100080040X

Fig. 2 DTC interpretation (Part 6 of 6). 9-3 & 900

DTC	Fault
P1530	Pedal Position Sensor 1 and 2 Circuit. Sum Out of Range.
P1531	Pedal Position Sensor 1 and 2 Circuit. Adapted Sum Out of Range.
P1532	Pedal Position Sensor 1 and 2 Circuit. Control Module Inputs Shorted to Each other.
P1601	Internal Control Module. Malfunction.
P1603	Internal Control Module. Malfunction.
P1604	Internal Control Module. Malfunction.
P1605	Internal Control Module. Malfunction.
P1606	Internal Control Module. Malfunction.
P1607	Internal Control Module. Malfunction.
P1608	Internal Control Module. Malfunction.
P1609	Internal Control Module. Malfunction.
P1610	Internal Control Module. Malfunction.
P1611	Internal Control Module. Malfunction.
P1613	Internal Control Module. Malfunction.
P1614	Internal Control Module. Malfunction.
P1621	Internal Control Module. Malfunction.
P1632	Internal Control Module. Malfunction.
P1633	Internal Control Module. Malfunction.
P1640	Main Relay Circuit. No Voltage to Control Module pin 1.
P1652	Main Relay Coil Circuit. Open / Short to Ground.
P1653	Main Relay Coil Circuit. Short to B+.
P1654	Fuel Pump Relay Coil Circuit. Open / Short to Ground.
P1655	Fuel Pump Relay Coil Circuit. Short to B+.
P1656	A/C Relay Coil Circuit. Open / Short to Ground.
P1657	A/C Relay Coil Circuit. Short to B+.
P1658	Charge Air Bypass Valve Circuit. Open / Short to Ground.
P1659	Charge Air Bypass Valve Circuit. Short to B+.
P1662	Charge Air Control Valve Circuit. Open / Short to Ground.
P1663	Charge Air Control Valve Circuit. Short to B+.
P1670	Throttle Limphome Relay Coil Circuit. Open / Short to Ground.
P1671	Throttle Limphome Relay Coil Circuit. Short to B+.
P1676	Injector Circuit. Open / Short to Ground or B+.
P1901	No Bus Data From DICE. See Fault Tracing 3:5 Bus and Diagnostic Communication.
P1902	No Bus Data From TWICE. See Fault Tracing 3:5 Bus and Diagnostic Communication.
P1908	No Bus Data From MIU. See Fault Tracing 3:5 Bus and Diagnostic Communication.
P1923	No Bus Data From TCM. See Fault Tracing 3:5 Bus and Diagnostic Communication.

SA1019900015020X

Fig. 3 DTC interpretation (Part 2 of 2). 9-5

DTC	Fault
P0100	Mass Air Flow Circuit. No Signal.
P0102	Mass Air Flow Circuit. Low Input.
P0103	Mass Air Flow Circuit. High Input.
P0107	Manifold Absolute Pressure Sensor Circuit. Open / Short to Ground.
P0108	Manifold Absolute Pressure Sensor Circuit. Short to B+.
P0112	Intake Air Temperature Sensor Circuit. Short to Ground.
P0113	Intake Air Temperature Sensor Circuit. Short to B+ / Open Circuit.
P0117	Engine Coolant Temperature Sensor Circuit. Short to Ground.
P0118	Engine Coolant Temperature Sensor Circuit. Short to B+ / Open circuit.
P0132	O2S Circuit. High Voltage. Sensor 1.
P0134	O2S Circuit. No Activity Detected. Sensor 1.
P0171	Long Term Fuel Trim Multiplicative. Max Value, Air/Fuel too Lean.
P0172	Long Term Fuel Trim Multiplicative. Min Value, Air/Fuel too Rich.
P0327	Knock Sensor Circuit. Low Input, Bank 1.
P0328	Knock Sensor Circuit. High Input, Bank 1.
P0337	Crankshaft Position Sensor. No Input.
P0340	Camshaft Position Sensor. Malfunction.
P0444	EVAP Purge Valve Circuit. Open / Short to Ground.
P0445	EVAP Purge Valve Circuit. Short to B+.
P0502	Vehicle Speed. No input signal.
P0605	Internal Control Module. Malfunction.
P1107	Charge Air Absolute Pressure Sensor Circuit. Short to Ground / Open.
P1108	Charge Air Absolute Pressure Sensor Circuit. Short to B+.
P1135	O2S Heater Circuit. Current too Low, Sensor 1.
P1136	O2S Heater Circuit. Current too High, Sensor 1.
P1171	Short Term Fuel Trim. Max Value, Air/Fuel too Lean.
P1172	Short Term Fuel Trim. Min Value, Air/Fuel too Rich.
P1181	Long Term Fuel Trim Additive. Max Value, Air/Fuel too Lean.
P1182	Long Term Fuel Trim Additive. Min Value, Air/Fuel too Rich.
P1230	Throttle Position Sensor 1 and 2 Circuit. Sum Out of Range.
P1240	Throttle Motor Circuit. Shorted.
P1251	Throttle Motor. Full PWM in Closing Direction. NOTE. May set if Mechanism is not Reseted.
P1252	Throttle Motor. Full PWM in Open Direction and no Motor Current.
P1253	Throttle Motor. Full PWM in Open Direction During Cranking.
P1260	Throttle Return Spring. Too Low Force. NOTE: May set if Mechanism is not Reseted
P1261	Throttle Binding.
P1263	Throttle moved manually when engine was running. NOTE. May set if Mechanism is not Reseted.
P1264	Throttle Open when Pedal is Released.
P1310	Ignition Discharge Module. Not Powered, Bank 1.
P1460	Immobilizer Active. NOTE. If new T7, MIU or TWICE module, program code in TWICE.

SA1019900015010X

Fig. 3 DTC interpretation (Part 1 of 2). 9-5

DTC (SAE)	Malfunction/faulty component	CHECK ENGINE	ISAT ST display text
P0105	Manifold absolute pressure sensor. All–embracing diagnostic trouble code for pressure sensor operation.	on	FAULT XX P0105 INTAKE PRESSURE FUNCTION INCORRECT
P0106	Manifold absolute pressure sensor. Vacuum hose leakage. Sensor malfunction.	on	FAULT XX P0106 INTAKE PRESSURE INPUT INCORRECT
P0107	Manifold absolute pressure sensor. Control module input shorting to ground.	on	FAULT XX P0107 INTAKE PRESSURE SHORT TO GROUND
P0108	Manifold absolute pressure sensor. Control module input shorting to battery positive (B+) or open circuit.	on	FAULT XX P0108 INTAKE PRESSURE OPEN CIRCUIT/ SHORTING TO B+
P0110	Intake air temperature sensor. All–embracing diagnostic trouble code for temperature sensor operation.	on	FAULT XX P0110 INTAKE AIR TEMP FUNCTION INCORRECT
P0112	Intake air temperature sensor. Control module input shorting to ground.	on	FAULT XX P0112 INTAKE AIR TEMP SHORT TO GROUND
P0113	Intake air temperature sensor. Control module input shorting to battery positive (B+) or open circuit.	on	FAULT XX P0113 INTAKE AIR TEMP OPEN CIRCUIT/ SHORTING TO B+
P0115	Engine coolant temperature sensor. All–embracingdiagnostic trouble code for temperature sensor operation.	on	FAULT XX P0115 COOLANT TEMPERATURE FUNCTION INCORRECT
P0117	Engine coolant temperature sensor. Control module input shorting to ground.	on	FAULT XX P0117 COOLANT TEMPERATURE SHORT TO GROUND
P0118	Engine coolant temperature sensor. Control module input shorting to battery positive (B+) or open circuit.	on	FAULT XX P0118 COOLANT TEMPERATURE OPEN CIRCUIT/ SHORTING TO B+
P0120	Throttle position sensor. All–embracing diagnostic trouble code for throttle position sensor operation.	on	FAULT XX P0120 THROTTLE POSITION FUNCTION INCORRECT
P0121	Throttle position sensor. Sensor malfunction.	on	FAULT XX P0121 THROTTLE POSITION INPUT INCORRECT
P0122	Throttle position sensor. Control module input shorting to ground.	on	FAULT XX P0122 THROTTLE POSITION SHORT TO GROUND

SA1029600193010X

Fig. 4 DTC interpretation (Part 1 of 5). 9000

DTC (SAE)	Malfunction/faulty component	CHECK ENGINE	ISAT ST display text
P0123	Throttle position sensor. Control module input shorting to battery positive (B+) or open circuit.	on	FAULT XX P0123 THROTTLE POSITION OPEN CIRCUIT/ SHORTING TO B+
P0125	Engine coolant temperature sensor. Insufficient temperature increase.	on	FAULT XX P0125 COOLANT TEMPERATURE TEMP. INCREASE SLOW
P0130	Front heated oxygen sensor. All–embracing diagnostic trouble code for oxygen sensor operation.	on	FAULT XX P0130 O2S 1 FUNCTION INCORRECT
P0132	Front heated oxygen sensor. Shorting to battery positive (B+).	on	FAULT XX P0132 O2S 1 SHORTING TO B+
P0133	Front heated oxygen sensor. Poor response to change in fuel–airmixture.	on	FAULT XX P0133 O2S 1 LOW FREQUENCY
P0135	Heating, front heated oxygen sensor. Current outside limits.	on	FAULT XX P0135 O2S 1 NO PREHEATING
P0136	Rear heated oxygen sensor. All–embracing diagnostic trouble code for oxygen sensor operation.	on	FAULT XX P0136 O2S 2 FUNCTION INCORRECT
P0138	Rear heated oxygen sensor. Shorting to battery positive (B+).	on	FAULT XX P0138 O2S 2 SHORTING TO B+
P0140	Rear heated oxygen sensor. Shorting to ground or open circuit.	on	FAULT XX P0140 O2S 2 OPEN CIRCUIT/ SHORT TO GROUND
P0141	Heating, rear heated oxygen sensor. Current outside limits.	on	FAULT XX P0141 O2S 2 NO PREHEATING
P0170	Adaptation. All–embracingdiagnostic trouble code for the adaptation function.	on	FAULT XX P0170 ADAPTATION FUNCTION INCORRECT
P0171	Adaptation. Lean mixture.	on	FAULT XX P0171 ADAPTATION LEAN
P0172	Adaptation. Rich mixture.	on	FAULT XX P0172 ADAPTATION RICH

SA1029600193020X

Fig. 4 DTC interpretation (Part 2 of 5). 9000

DTC (SAE)	Malfunction/faulty component	CHECK ENGINE	ISAT ST display text
P0500	Car speed. Input signal from main instrument display panel's speedometer. All–embracingdiagnostic trouble code for wheel speed.	on	FAULT XX P0500 CAR SPEED FUNCTION INCORRECT
P0501	Car speed. Input signal outside limits.	on	FAULT XX P0501 CAR SPEED SIGNAL INCORRECT
P0502	Car speed. No input signal.	on	FAULT XX P0502 CAR SPEED OPEN CIRCUIT
P0505	Idle speed control. Malfunction.	on	FAULT XX P0505 IDLE POSITION FUNCTION INCORRECT
P0506	Idle speed control. Idling speed too low.	on	FAULT XX P0506 IDLE POSITION ENGINE RPM LOW
P0507	Idle speed control. Idling speed too high.	on	FAULT XX P0507 IDLE POSITION ENGINE RPM HIGH
P0605	Control module. Internal fault, program fault.	on	FAULT XX P0605 CONTROL MODULE INTERNAL FAULT
P1170	Closed loop. Malfunction.	on	FAULT XX P1170 LAMBDA CONTROL FUNCTION INCORRECT
P1171	Closed loop. Lean mixture.	on	FAULT XX P1171 LAMBDA CONTROL LEAN
P1172	Closed loop. Rich mixture.	on	FAULT XX P1172 LAMBDA CONTROL RICH
P1416	Tank level. Low level in conjunction with misfiring or fault in fuel system.		FAULT XX P1416 TANK LEVEL LOW LEVEL
P1549	Boost pressure control. Malfunction.	on	FAULT XX P1549 BOOST PRESSURE FUNCTION INCORRECT
P1576	Brake light switch. Shorting to battery positive (B+).	on	FAULT XX P1576 BRAKE LIGHT SWITCH SHORTING TO B+
P1577	Brake light switch. Open circuit.	on	FAULT XX P1577 BRAKE LIGHT SWITCH OPEN CIRCUIT

SA1029600193040X

Fig. 4 DTC interpretation (Part 4 of 5). 9000

DTC (SAE)	Malfunction/faulty component	CHECK ENGINE	ISAT ST display text
P0300	Misfiring, randomly in several cylinders.	on	FAULT XX P0300 MISFIRING
P0301	Misfiring, cylinder 1	on	FAULT XX P0301 MISFIRING CYLINDER 1
P0302	Misfiring, cylinder 2	on	FAULT XX P0302 MISFIRING CYLINDER 2
P0303	Misfiring, cylinder 3	on	FAULT XX P0303 MISFIRING CYLINDER 3
P0304	Misfiring, cylinder 4	on	FAULT XX P0304 MISFIRING CYLINDER 4
P0327	No knocking signal from ignition discharge module.	on	FAULT XX P0327 KNOCK SENSOR OPEN CIRCUIT SHORTING TO B+/GROUND
P0335	Crankshaft position sensor. Malfunction.	on	FAULT XX P0335 CRANKSHAFT POS SENS FUNCTION INCORRECT
P0340	Camshaft positive sensor. Malfunction.	on	FAULT XX P0340 CAMSHAFT POSITION FUNCTION INCORRECT
P0441	Evaporative emission purge valve. Low flow.	on	FAULT XX P0441 EVAP–VALVE FLOW INCORRECT
P0443	Evaporative emission purge valve. All–embracing diagnostic trouble code for EVAP function.	on	FAULT XX P0443 EVAP–VALVE FUNCTION INCORRECT
P0444	Evaporative emission purge valve. Control module output, open circuit.	on	FAULT XX P0444 EVAP–VALVE OPEN CIRCUIT
P0445	Evaporative emission purge valve. Control module output shorting to ground.	on	FAULT XX P0445 EVAP–VALVE SHORT TO GROUND

SA1029600193030X

Fig. 4 DTC interpretation (Part 3 of 5). 9000

Diagnostic Trouble Code (SAE)	Faulty function/component	Conditions
P0131	O2S1, Bank 1 Low voltage (Added from start of production)	Short term fuel trim >25% below for more than 20 sec. O2S2 shows **rich** mixture at same time.
P0132	O2S1, Bank 1 High voltage (Extended diagnosis from start of production)	Short term fuel trim <-25% below for more than 20 sec. O2S2 shows **lean** mixture at same time.
P1651	RAM fault (occurs on early M96)	
P1652	ROM fault (occurs on early M96)	

SA1029600193050X

Fig. 4 DTC interpretation (Part 5 of 5). 9000

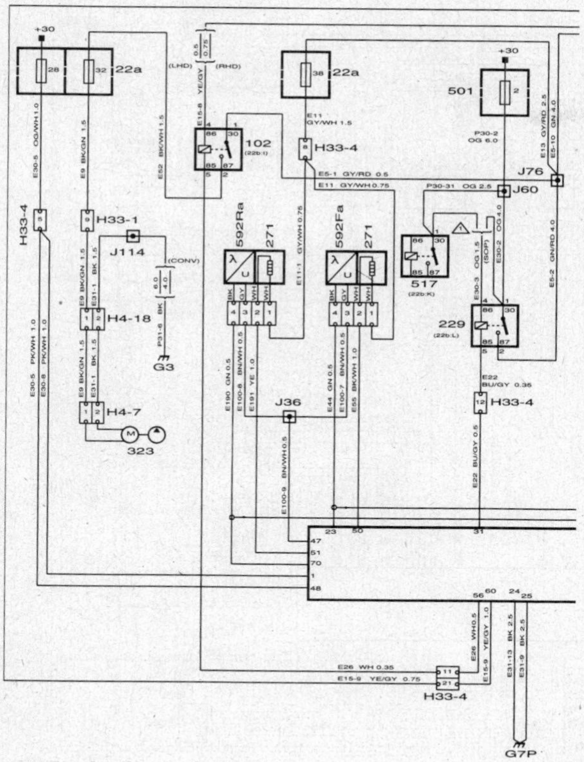

SA1019900012010X

Fig. 5 Trionic wiring diagram (Part 1 of 3). 9-3

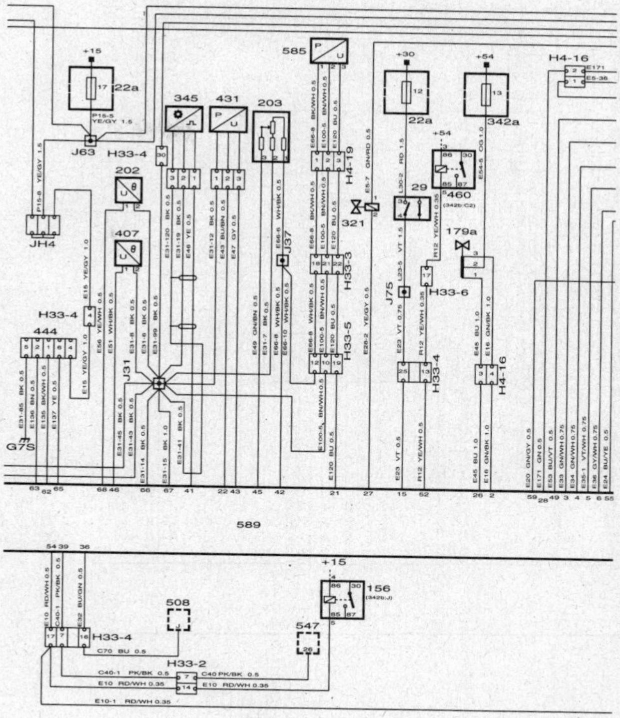

SA1019900012020X

Fig. 5 Trionic wiring diagram (Part 2 of 3). 9-3

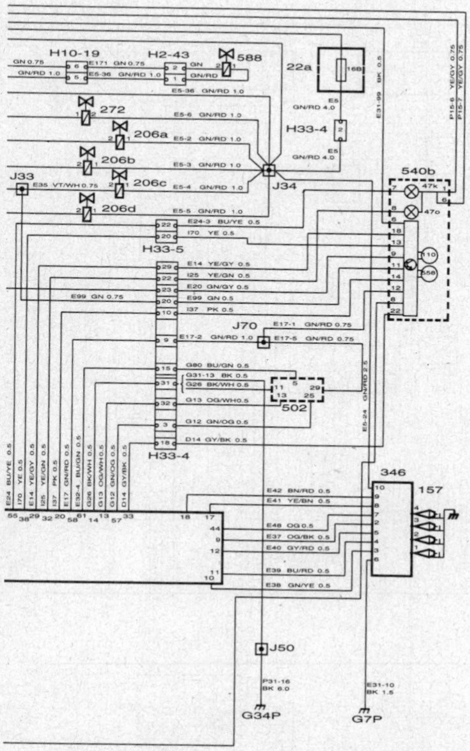

SA1019900012030X

Fig. 5 Trionic wiring diagram (Part 3 of 3). 9-3

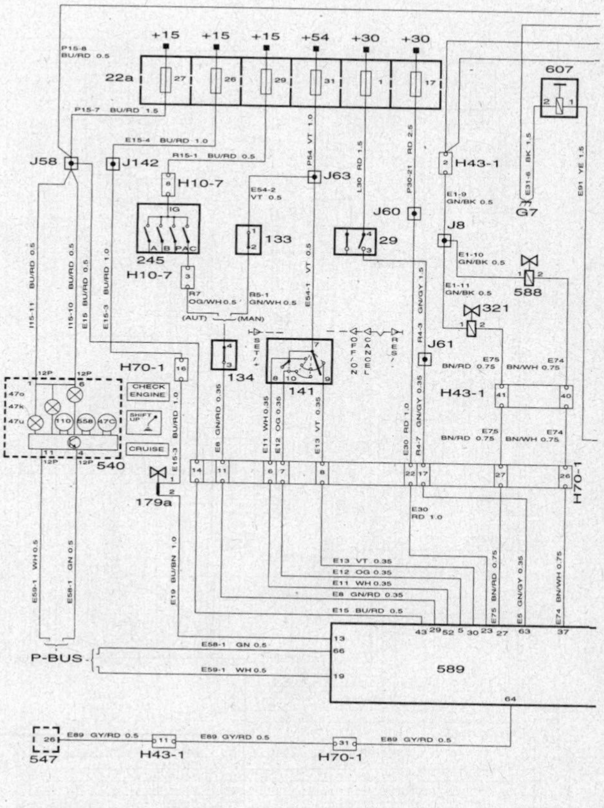

SA1019900013010X

Fig. 6 Trionic wiring diagram (Part 1 of 3). 9-5 w/2.3L engine

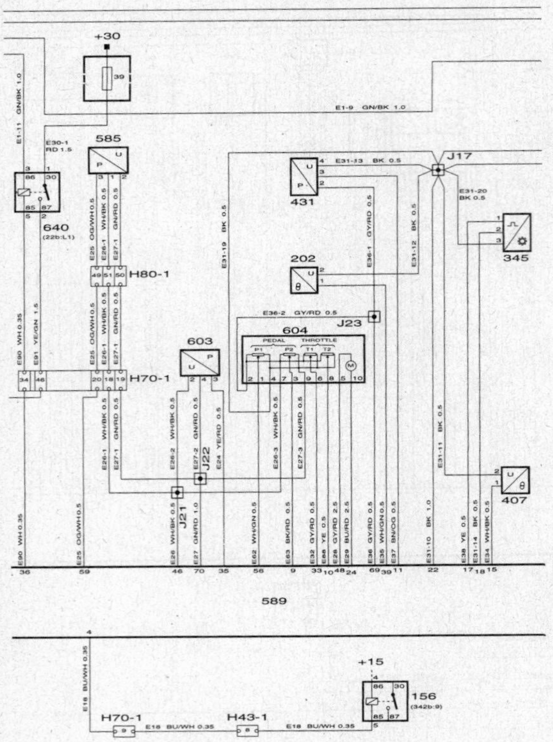

SA1019900013020X

Fig. 6 Trionic wiring diagram (Part 2 of 3). 9-5 w/2.3L engine

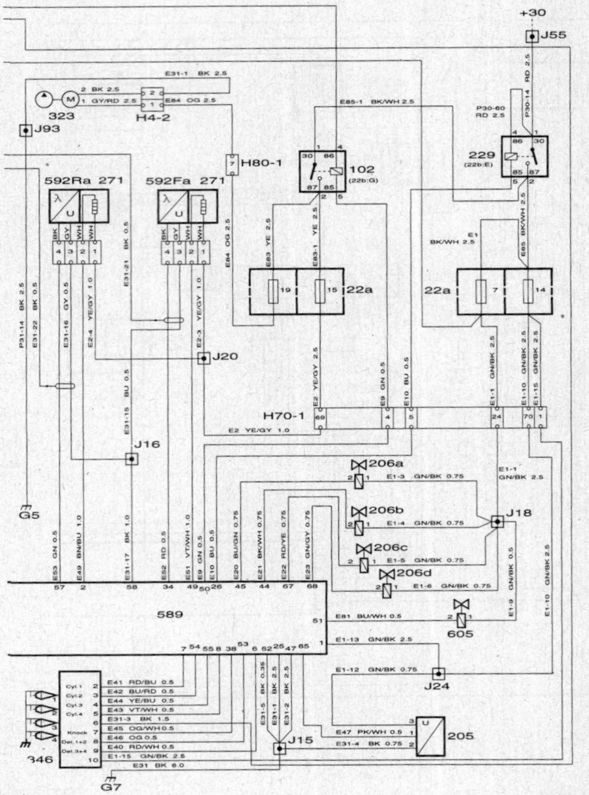

SA1019900013030X

Fig. 6 Trionic wiring diagram (Part 3 of 3). 9-5 w/2.3L engine

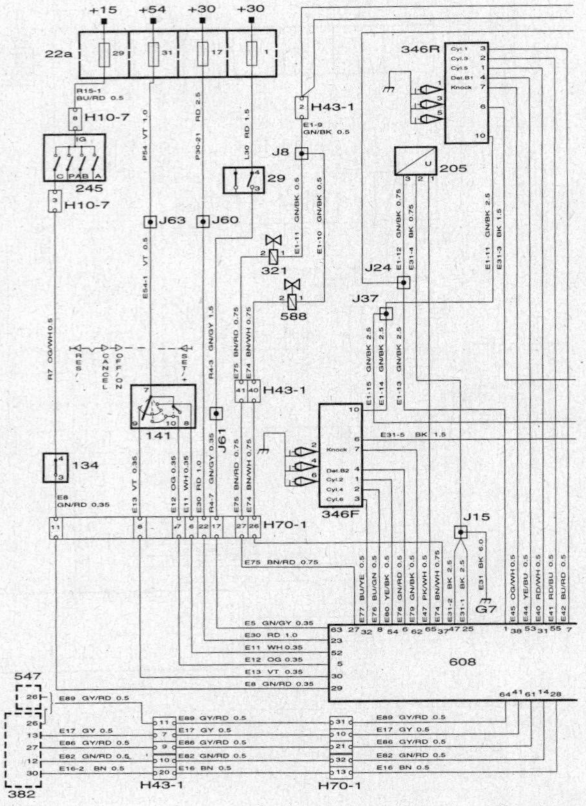

SA1019900014010X

Fig. 7 Trionic wiring diagram (Part 1 of 3). 9-5 w/3.0L engine

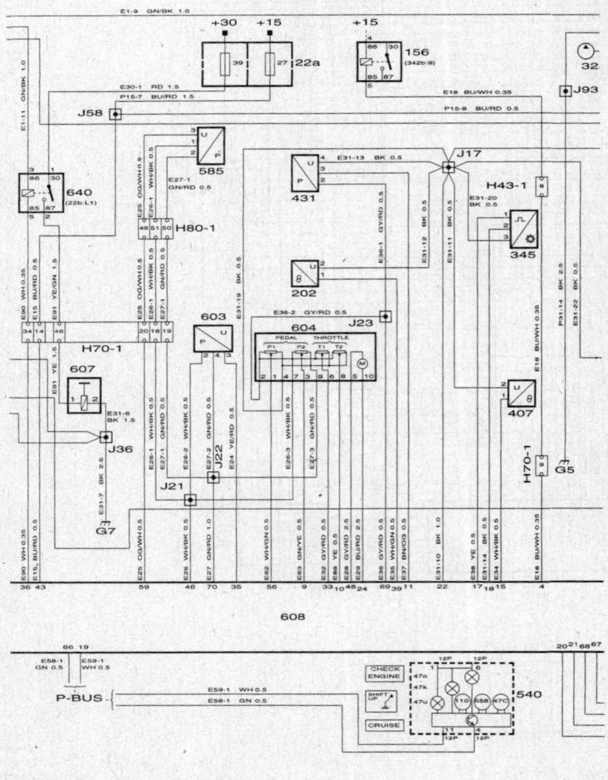

SA1019900014020X

Fig. 7 Trionic wiring diagram (Part 2 of 3). 9-5 w/3.0L engine

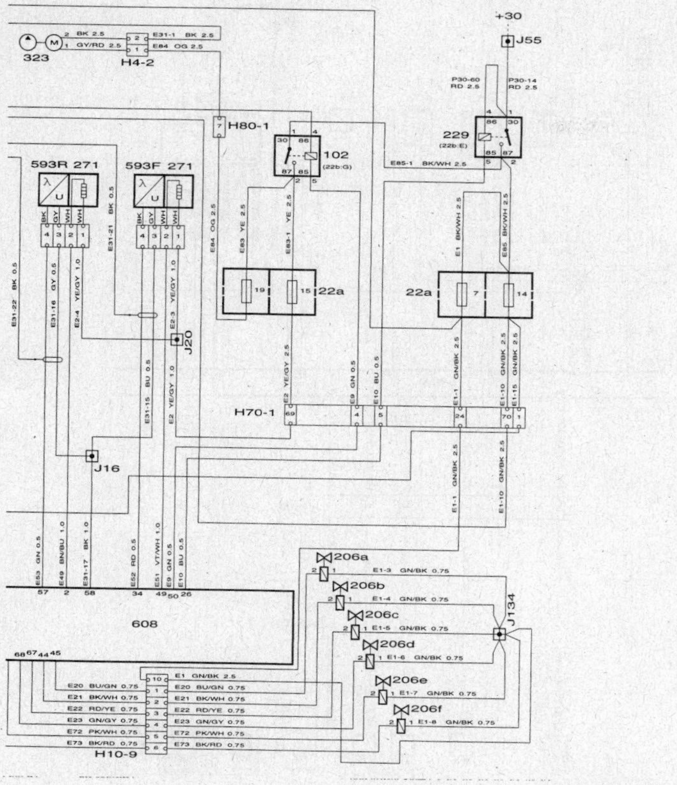

SA1019900014030X

Fig. 7 Trionic wiring diagram (Part 3 of 3). 9-5 w/3.0L engine

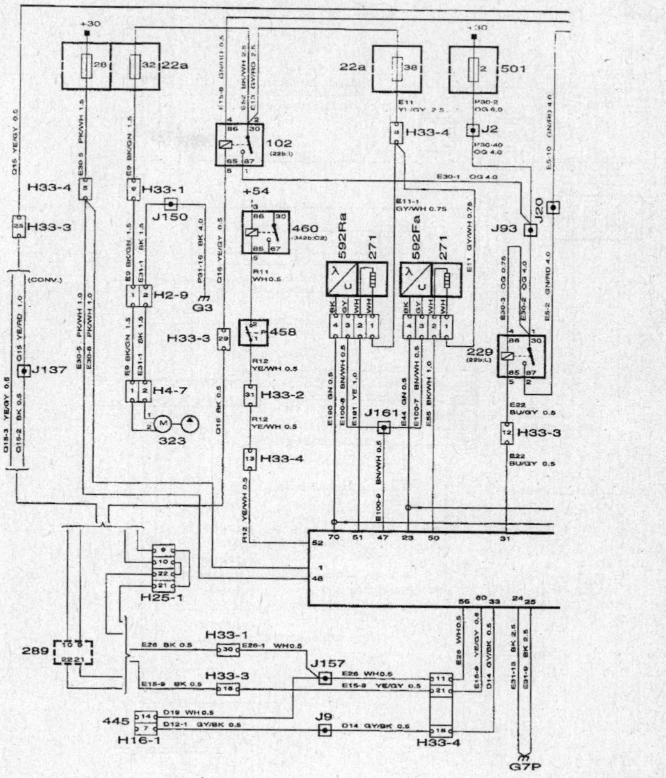

SA1029600209010X

Fig. 8 Trionic wiring diagram (Part 1 of 3). 900

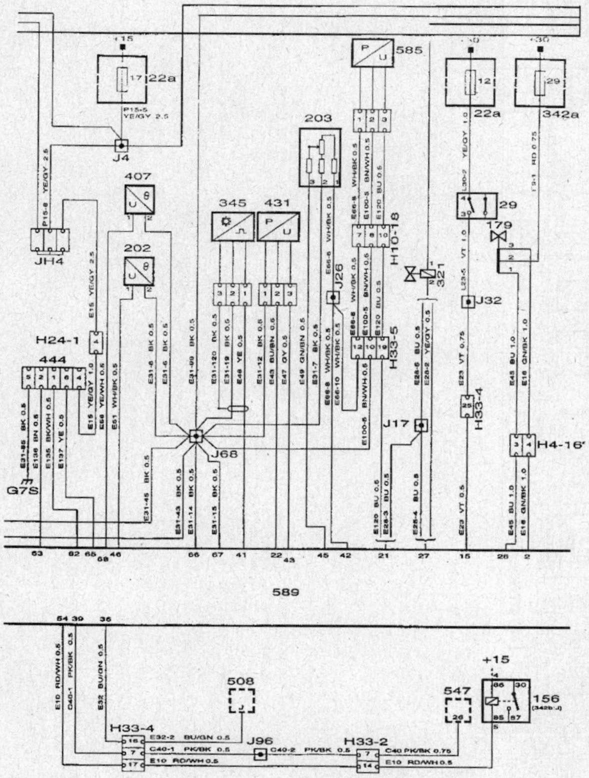

SA1029600209020X

Fig. 8 Trionic wiring diagram (Part 2 of 3). 900

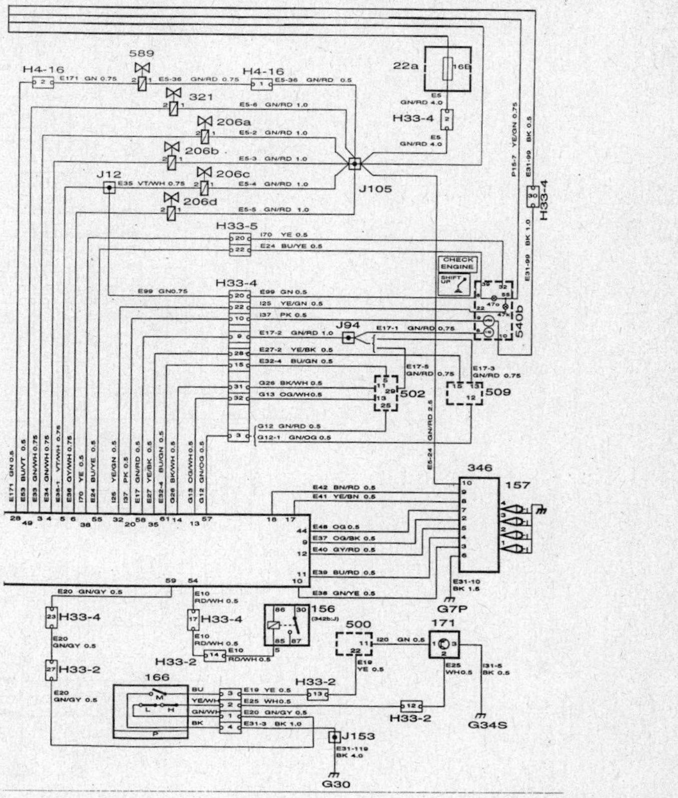

SA1029600209030X

Fig. 8 Trionic wiring diagram (Part 3 of 3). 900

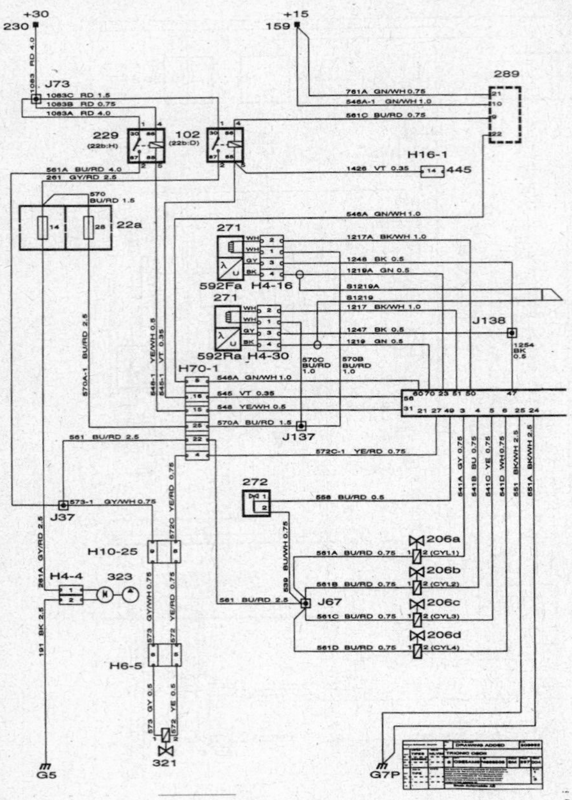

SA1029600210010X

Fig. 9 Trionic wiring diagram (Part 1 of 3). 9000

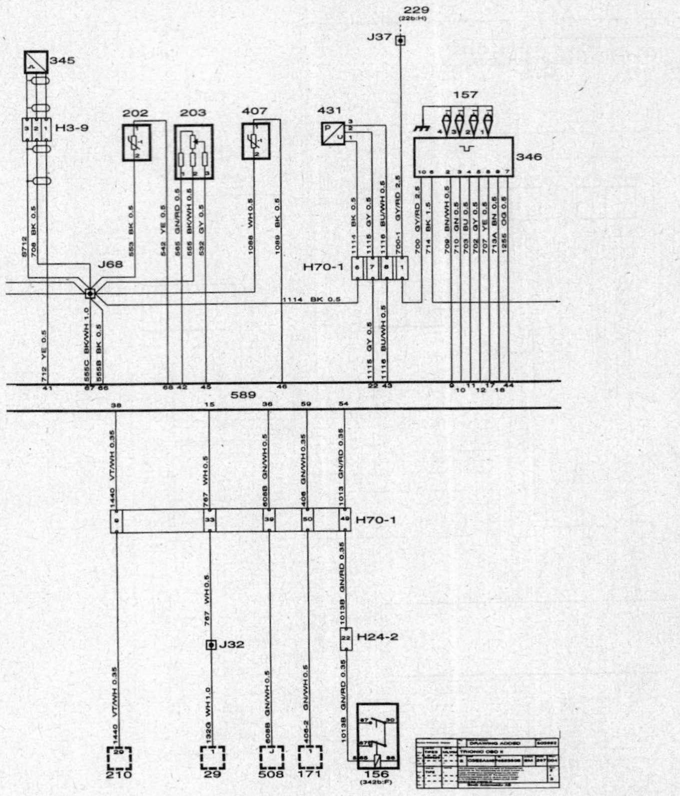

SA1029600210020X

Fig. 9 Trionic wiring diagram (Part 2 of 3). 9000

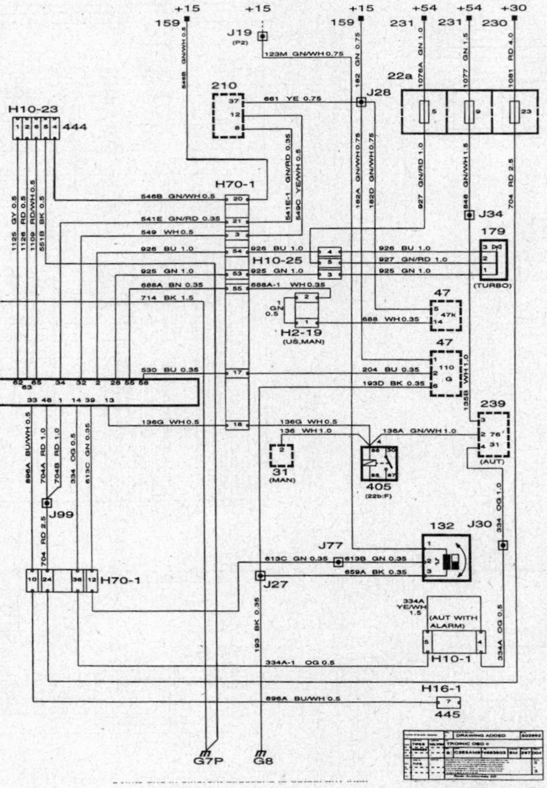

SA1029600210030X

Fig. 9 Trionic wiring diagram (Part 3 of 3). 9000

DIAGNOSTIC CHART INDEX

Code	Description	Page No.	Fig. No.
9.3			
—	A/C Fault Diagnosis	16-69	31
—	Engine Fails To Start, Quick Test w/Test Lamp	16-55	10
—	Poor Driveability Fault Diagnosis	16-68	29
—	Poor Performance Fault Diagnosis	16-69	30
P0105	Manifold Absolute Pressure Sensor	16-55	11
P0106	Manifold Absolute Pressure Sensor	16-55	11
P0107	Manifold Absolute Pressure Sensor	16-55	11
P0108	Manifold Absolute Pressure Sensor	16-55	11
P0110	Intake Air Temperature Sensor	16-56	12
P0112	Intake Air Temperature Sensor	16-56	12
P0113	Intake Air Temperature Sensor	16-56	12
P0115	Engine Coolant Temperature Sensor	16-57	13
P0117	Engine Coolant Temperature Sensor	16-57	13
P0118	Engine Coolant Temperature Sensor	16-57	13
P0120	Throttle Position Sensor	16-57	14
P0121	Throttle Position Sensor	16-57	14
P0122	Throttle Position Sensor	16-57	14
P0123	Throttle Position Sensor	16-57	14
P0130	Oxygen Sensor	16-58	15
P0131	Oxygen Sensor	16-58	15
P0132	Oxygen Sensor	16-58	15
P0135	Preheating Of Heated Oxygen Sensor	16-59	16
P0170	Adaptation Faulty	16-60	17
P0171	Adaptation Faulty	16-60	17
P0172	Adaptation Faulty	16-60	17
P0325	Knock Sensor	16-60	18
P0335	Crankshaft Position Sensor	16-61	19
P0442	EVAP Small Leakage In System	16-62	20
P0443	Evaporation Emission Canister Purge Valve (EVAP Valve)	16-62	21
P0444	Evaporation Emission Canister Purge Valve (EVAP Valve)	16-62	21
P0445	Evaporation Emission Canister Purge Valve (EVAP Valve)	16-62	21
P0451	EVAP Tank Pressure Sensor Performance Problem	16-63	22
P0453	EVAP Tank Pressure Sensor Circuit Open/Short To B+	16-64	23
P0455	EVAP Serious Leakage In System	16-65	24
P0500	Vehicle Speed Signal	16-66	25
P0501	Vehicle Speed Signal	16-66	25
P0502	Vehicle Speed Signal	16-66	25
P0505	Idle Air Control Valve	16-67	26
P0605	ECM	16-68	27
P1500	Battery Voltage Too High Or Low	16-68	28
9.5			
—	Car Fails To Start	16-70	32
—	Cruise Control Does Not Work	16-76	35
—	Idling Speed Too Fast	16-75	34
—	Misfire	16-71	33
P0100	Mass Air Flow Circuit No Signal	16-79	36
P0102	Mass Air Flow Circuit Low Input	16-80	37
P0103	Mass Air Flow Circuit High Output	16-81	38
P0107	Manifold Absolute Pressure Sensor Circuit Open/Short To Ground	16-81	39
P0108	Manifold Absolute Pressure Sensor Circuit Short To B+	16-83	40
P0112	Intake Air Temperature Sensor Circuit Short To Ground	16-83	41
P0113	Intake Air Temperature Sensor Circuit Short To B+/Open Circuit	16-84	42
P0117	Engine Coolant Temperature Sensor Circuit Short To Ground	16-84	43
P0118	Engine Coolant Temperature Sensor Circuit Short To B+/Open Circuit	16-85	44
P0132	O2S Circuit High Voltage Sensor 1	16-85	45
P0134	O2S Circuit No Activity Detected Sensor 1	16-87	46

Continued

DIAGNOSTIC CHART INDEX—Continued

Code	Description	Page No.	Fig. No.
9.5			
P0171	Long Term Fuel Trim Multiplicative Max Valve Air/Fuel Too Lean	16-87	47
P0172	Long Term Fuel Trim Multiplicative Min Value Air/Fuel Too Rich	16-88	48
P0327	Knock Sensor Circuit Low Input Bank 1	16-90	49
P0328	Knock Sensor Circuit High Input Bank 1	16-91	50
P0337	Crankshaft Position Sensor No Input	16-91	51
P0340	Camshaft Position Sensor Malfunction	16-92	52
P0444	EVAP Purge Valve Circuit Open/Short To Ground	16-94	53
P0445	EVAP Purge Valve Circuit Short To B+	16-95	54
P0502	Vehicle Speed No Input Signal	16-95	55
P0605	Internal Control Module Malfunction	16-96	56
P1107	Charge Air Absolute Pressure Sensor Circuit Short To Ground/Open	16-97	57
P1108	Charge Air Absolute Pressure Sensor Circuit Short To B+	16-98	58
P1135	O2S Heater Circuit Current Too Low Sensor 1	16-98	59
P1136	O2S Heater Circuit Current Too High Sensor 1	16-99	60
P1171	Short Term Fuel Trim Max Value Air/Fuel Too Lean	16-99	61
P1172	Short Term Fuel Trim Min Value Air/Fuel Too Rich.	16-100	62
P1181	Long Term Fuel Trim Additive Max Value Air/Fuel Too Lean	16-100	63
P1182	Long Term Fuel Trim Additive Min Valve Air/Fuel Too Rich	16-101	64
P1230	Throttle Position Sensor 1 & 2 Circuit Sum Out Of Range	16-101	65
P1240	Throttle Motor Circuit Shorted	16-103	66
P1251	Throttle Motor Full PWM in Closing Direction	16-104	67
P1252	Throttle Motor Full PWM In Open Direction & No Motor Current	16-105	68
P1253	Throttle Motor Full PWM In Open Direction During Cranking	16-106	69
P1260	Throttle Return Spring Too Low Force	16-107	70
P1261	Throttle Binding	16-107	71
P1263	Throttle Moved Manually When Engine Was Running	16-108	72
P1264	Throttle Open When Pedal Is Released	16-109	73
P1310	Ignition Discharge Module Not Powered Bank 1	16-109	74
P1460	Immobilizer Active	16-110	75
P1530	Pedal Position Sensor 1 & 2 Circuit Sum Out of Range	16-110	76
P1531	Pedal Position Sensor 1 & 2 Circuit Adapted Sum Out Of Range	16-112	77
P1532	Pedal Position Sensor 1 & 2 Circuit Control Module Inputs Shorted To Each Other	16-112	78
P1601	Internal Control Module Malfunction	16-113	79
P1603	Internal Control Module Malfunction	16-113	80
P1604	Internal Control Module Malfunction	16-113	81
P1605	Internal Control Module Malfunction	16-114	82
P1606	Internal Control Module Malfunction	16-114	83
P1607	Internal Control Module Malfunction	16-114	84
P1608	Internal Control Module Malfunction	16-114	85
P1609	Internal Control Module Malfunction	16-114	86
P1610	Internal Control Module Malfunction	16-115	87
P1611	Internal Control Module Malfunction	16-115	88
P1613	Internal Control Module Malfunction	16-115	89
P1614	Internal Control Module Malfunction	16-115	90
P1621	Internal Control Module Malfunction	16-115	91
P1632	Internal Control Module Malfunction	16-115	92
P1633	Internal Control Module Malfunction	16-116	93
P1640	Main Relay Circuit No Voltage To Control Module Pin 1	16-116	94
P1652	Main Relay Coil Circuit Open/Shorted To Ground	16-117	95
P1653	Main Relay Coil Circuit Short To B+	16-118	96
P1654	Fuel Pump Relay Coil Circuit Open/Short To Ground	16-118	97
P1655	Fuel Pump Relay Coil Circuit Short To B+	16-119	98
	Fuel Pump Relay Coil Circuit Shorted To B+	16-120	99
P1657	A/C Relay Coil Circuit Short To B+	16-121	100
P1658	Charge Air Bypass Valve Circuit Open/Short To Ground	16-121	101
P1659	Charge Air Bypass Valve Circuit Short to B+	16-122	102

Continued

DIAGNOSTIC CHART INDEX—Continued

Code	Description	Page No.	Fig. No.
9.5			
P1662	Charge Air Control Valve Circuit Open/Short To Ground	16-122	103
P1663	Charge Air Control Valve Circuit Short To B+.	16-123	104
P1670	Throttle Limp-Home Relay Coil Circuit Open/Short To Ground	16-123	105
P1671	Throttle Limp-Home Relay Coil Circuit Short To B+	16-125	106
P1676	Injector Circuit Open/Short To Ground Or B+	16-125	107
P1901	No Bus Data From DICE	16-126	108
P1902	No Bus Data From TWICE	16-126	109
P1908	No Bus Data From MIU	16-126	110
P1923	No Bus Data From TCM	16-127	111
900			
—	A/C Fault Diagnosis	16-69	31
—	Engine Fails To Start, Quick Test w/Test Lamp	16-55	10
—	Poor Driveability Fault Diagnosis	16-68	29
—	Poor Performance Fault Diagnosis	16-69	30
P0105	Manifold Absolute Pressure Sensor	16-55	11
P0106	Manifold Absolute Pressure Sensor	16-55	11
P0107	Manifold Absolute Pressure Sensor	16-55	11
P0108	Manifold Absolute Pressure Sensor	16-55	11
P0110	Intake Air Temperature Sensor	16-56	12
P0112	Intake Air Temperature Sensor	16-56	12
P0113	Intake Air Temperature Sensor	16-56	12
P0115	Engine Coolant Temperature Sensor	16-57	13
P0117	Engine Coolant Temperature Sensor	16-57	13
P0118	Engine Coolant Temperature Sensor	16-57	13
P0120	Throttle Position Sensor	16-57	14
P0121	Throttle Position Sensor	16-57	14
P0122	Throttle Position Sensor	16-57	14
P0123	Throttle Position Sensor	16-57	14
P0130	Oxygen Sensor	16-58	15
P0131	Oxygen Sensor	16-58	15
P0132	Oxygen Sensor	16-58	15
P0135	Preheating Of Heated Oxygen Sensor	16-59	16
P0170	Adaptation Faulty	16-60	17
P0171	Adaptation Faulty	16-60	17
P0172	Adaptation Faulty	16-60	17
P0325	Knock Sensor	16-60	18
P0335	Crankshaft Position Sensor	16-61	19
P0443	Evaporation Emission Canister Purge Valve (EVAP Valve)	16-62	21
P0444	Evaporation Emission Canister Purge Valve (EVAP Valve)	16-62	21
P0445	Evaporation Emission Canister Purge Valve (EVAP Valve)	16-62	21
P0500	Vehicle Speed Signal	16-66	25
P0501	Vehicle Speed Signal	16-66	25
P0502	Vehicle Speed Signal	16-66	25
P0505	Idle Air Control Valve	16-67	26
P0605	ECM	16-68	27
P1500	Battery Voltage Too High Or Low	16-68	28
9000			
—	A/C Activation Inspection (Less TCS)	16-147	138
—	A/C Activation Inspection (w/TCS)	16-147	139
—	Torque Limiting Function Inspection	16-146	137
—	Torque Limitation Input Signal From Automatic Transaxle Fault Diagnosis	16-146	136
P0105	Manifold Absolute Pressure Sensor	16-127	112
P0106	Manifold Absolute Pressure Sensor	16-127	112
P0107	Manifold Absolute Pressure Sensor	16-127	112
P0108	Manifold Absolute Pressure Sensor	16-127	112
P0110	Intake Air Temperature Sensor	16-128	113

Continued

DIAGNOSTIC CHART INDEX—Continued

Code	Description	Page No.	Fig. No.
9000			
P0112	Intake Air Temperature Sensor	16-128	113
P0113	Intake Air Temperature Sensor	16-128	113
P0115	Engine Coolant Temperature Sensor	16-129	114
P0117	Engine Coolant Temperature Sensor	16-129	114
P0118	Engine Coolant Temperature Sensor	16-129	114
P0120	Throttle Position Sensor	16-129	115
P0121	Throttle Position Sensor	16-129	115
P0122	Throttle Position Sensor	16-129	115
P0123	Throttle Position Sensor	16-129	115
P0125	Engine Coolant Temperature Sensor	16-130	116
P0130	Front Heated Oxygen Sensor	16-131	117
P0131	Front Heated Oxygen Sensor	16-131	117
P0132	Front Heated Oxygen Sensor	16-131	117
P0133	Front Heated Oxygen Sensor	16-131	117
P0135	Preheating Of Heated Oxygen Sensor	16-131	118
P0136	Rear Heated Oxygen Sensor	16-132	119
P0138	Rear Heated Oxygen Sensor	16-132	119
P0140	Rear Heated Oxygen Sensor	16-132	119
P0141	Rear Heated Oxygen Sensor	16-133	120
P0170	Incorrect Fuel-Air Mixture	16-133	121
P0171	Incorrect Fuel-Air Mixture	16-133	121
P0172	Incorrect Fuel-Air Mixture	16-133	121
P0300	Random Cylinder Misfiring	16-134	122
P0301	Misfiring Cylinder	16-135	123
P0302	Misfiring Cylinder	16-135	123
P0303	Misfiring Cylinder	16-135	123
P0304	Misfiring Cylinder	16-135	123
P0327	Knock Sensor	16-137	124
P0335	Crankshaft Position Sensor	16-138	125
P0340	Camshaft Position Sensor	16-139	126
P0441	EVAP Emission Purge Valve	16-139	127
P0443	Canister Purge Valve (ELCD)	16-140	128
P0444	Canister Purge Valve (ELCD)	16-140	128
P0445	Canister Purge Valve (ELCD)	16-140	128
P0500	Vehicle Speed Signal Absent	16-141	129
P0501	Vehicle Speed Signal Absent	16-141	129
P0502	Vehicle Speed Signal Absent	16-141	129
P0505	Idle Speed Control	16-141	130
P0506	Idle Speed Control	16-141	130
P0507	Idle Speed Control	16-141	130
P0605	Control Module	16-142	131
P1170	Lambda Control	16-143	132
P1171	Lambda Control	16-143	132
P1172	Lambda Control	16-143	132
P1416	Fuel Tank Level	16-144	133
P1549	Boost Pressure Control	16-144	134
P1576	Brake Light Switch	16-145	135
P1577	Brake Light Switch	16-145	135

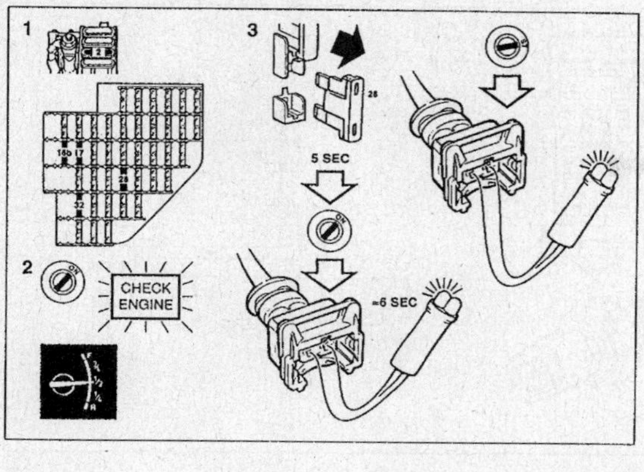

1

Check the following fuses:

- maxi fuse no. 2 (+30 supply to ECM, main relay and fuel pump relay)
- 28 (+30 supply to ECM)
- 17 (+15 supply to ECM)
- 32 (fuel pump relay supply to fuel pump)
- 16B (main relay supply to injectors and ignition discharge module)

2

Ignition switched on. Check that the malfunction indicator lamp (CHECK ENGINE) lights up with a steady glow for approx. 3 seonds. Also check the fuel level.

- if the malfunction indicator lamp is not lit, there is no +15 supply to the ECM
- if the malfunction indicator lamp is lit dimly or flashes, there is no +30 supply or ground to the ECM (in this fault a buzzing sound can also be heard from the main and fuel pump relays at the same time as the tachometer is moving upwards on the scale)

3

The main relay supplies the injectors and ignition discharge module with power. The function of the main relay should therefore be checked as follows:

- connect the test lamp to the connector of the IAC valve
- Switch off the ignition and remove fuse 28 for 5 seconds
- refit fuse 28
- ignition switched on - check that the test lamp is lit for approx. 6 seconds and then goes out. If this does not happen see "Main Relay, Component Diagnosis."
- when the test lamp has gone out, run the starter motor, the test lamp must then light up again. If not, the ECM does not have information from the crankshaft position sensor

SA1029100081010X

Fig. 10 Code —: Engine Fails To Start, Quick Test w/Test Lamp (Part 1 of 2). 9-3 & 900

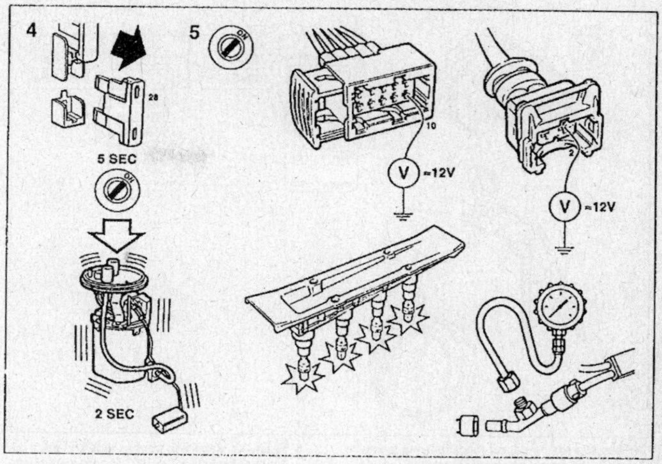

4

The fuel pump relay supplies the fuel pump with power. The function of the fuel pump relay should therefore be checked as follows:

- switch off the ignition and remove fuse 28 for 5 seconds
- refit fuse 28
- ignition switched on - listen to find out whether the fuel pump is working. The fuel pump must operate for approx. 2 seconds.

If this does not happen, see "Fuel Pump and Relay, Component Diagnosis."

5

Check the following:

- as described in 3, that the power supply from the main relay reaches the ignition discharge module and injectors. If this does not happen, carry out fault diagnosis on the leads to crimped connection J67.
- that the ignition discharge module produces sparks.
- that there is fuel pressure.

SA1029100081020X

Fig. 10 Code —: Engine Fails To Start, Quick Test w/Test Lamp (Part 2 of 2). 9-3 & 900

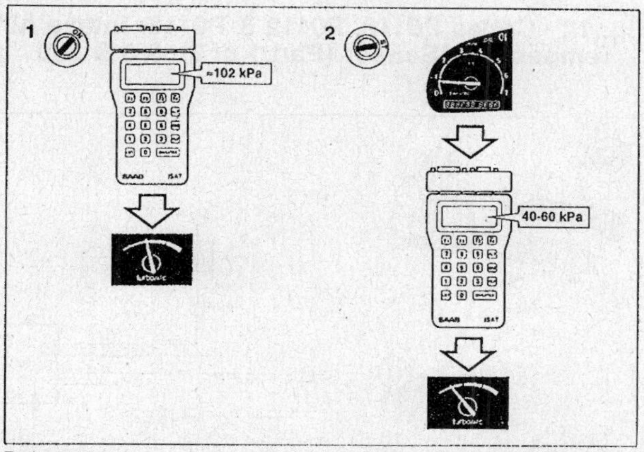

Fault symptom

The malfunction indicator lamp is on.
Deterioration in drivability, basic charging pressure.
Any other diagnostic trouble codes (oxygen sensor, adaptation).
AC compressor not working
Pressure gauge displays implausible values

Conditions

- in case of short circuit/open circuit, diagnostic trouble code appears after 2 seconds
- in case of an implausible pressure value, diagnostic trouble code appears after 2 minutes
- if the hose has been disconnected, diagnostic trouble code appears when fuel shut-off occurs during engine braking

diagnostic procedure

1 Use the ISAT and the turbo pressure gauge in the main instrument to check pressure sensor operation.

Ignition switched on.

Connect ISAT and select the "INTAKE PRESSURE" command on the "READ FUNCTIONS" menu.

If pressure sensor function is OK, the ISAT must display approx. 102 kPa (N.B. the value depends on air pressure) and the turbo/APC needle must be in the area between the white and orange sections of the turbo pressure gauge.

If the measured value is incorrect, continue with point 3.

If the measured value is correct, continue with point 2.

2 Checking of pressure sensor function continues. Start the engine and run it at idling speed. If pressure function is OK, the ISAT must display approx. 40-60 kP and the turbo/APC needle must be in the middle of the white section of the turbo pressure gauge.

If the measured value is faulty, check and if necessary replace the vacuum hose between the pressure sensor and the intake manifold. If the fault persists, replace the pressure sensor.

If the measured value is correct, continue with point 4.

SA1029100082010X

Fig. 11 Codes P0105, P0106, P0107 & P0108: Manifold Absolute Pressure Sensor (Part 1 of 3). 9-3 & 900

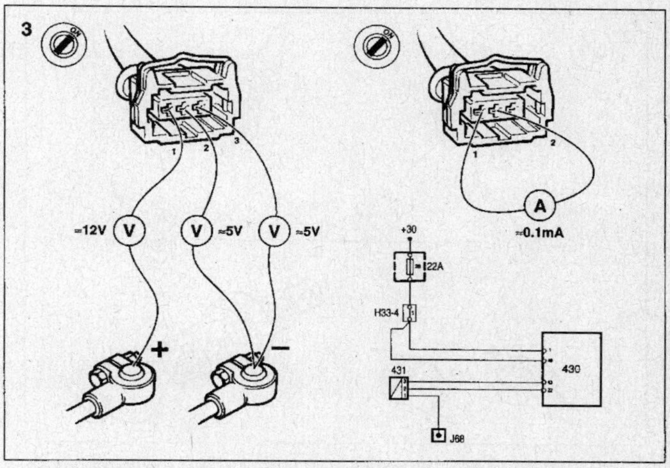

3 Check the electrical interface in the pressure sensor connector.

Disconnect the 3-pole connector.

Measure the voltage in the female connector.

- pin 3 to Batt - ________ approx. 5 V
- pin 2 to Batt - ________ approx. 5 V
- Batt+ to pin 1 ________ approx. 12 V

Carry out current measurement (mA) in

- pin 2 to pin 1 ______ approx. 0.1 mA

The measurements above are to show whether ECM including wiring as far as the pressure sensor are operating correctly.

If all the measured values are correct, continue with action 4.

If any measured value is incorrect, continue with action 5.

SA1029100082020X

Fig. 11 Codes P0105, P0106, P0107 & P0108: Manifold Absolute Pressure Sensor (Part 2 of 3). 9-3 & 900

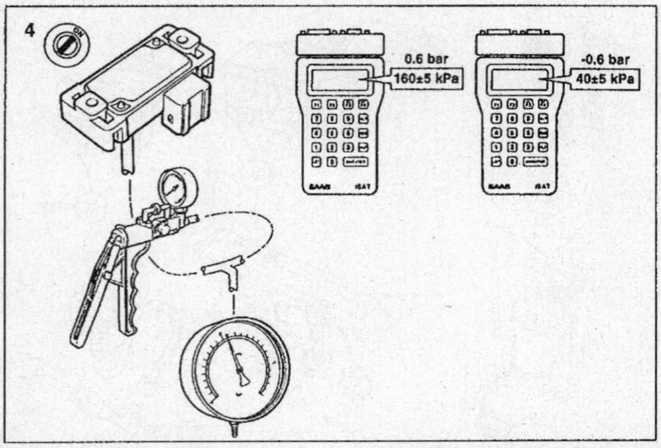

4 Check pressure sensor function using pressure gauge and a pressure/vacuum pump.

Generate a positive pressure of 0.6 bar and a negative pressure of -0.6 bar. The ISAT must display 160±5 kPa and 40±5 respectively (the ISAT may display slightly lower values when measuring at high altitude).

If any measured value is incorrect, replace the pressure sensor.

If the measured values are correct, continue with action 6.

5 Carry out continuity measurement on the wiring between the ECM and the 3-pole connector of the pressure sensor.

Check the wires for open circuits/short circuits and any stray currents.

If the measured values are correct, continue with action 6.

6 Erase the diagnostic trouble code and drive the car to see whether the DTC is generated again.

If the diagnostic trouble code is registered, **replace ECM.**

If the diagnostic trouble code is not registered, the action taken is correct. Otherwise the fault is intermittent in nature.

SA1029100082030X

Fig. 11 Codes P0105, P0106, P0107 & P0108: Manifold Absolute Pressure Sensor (Part 3 of 3). 9-3 & 900

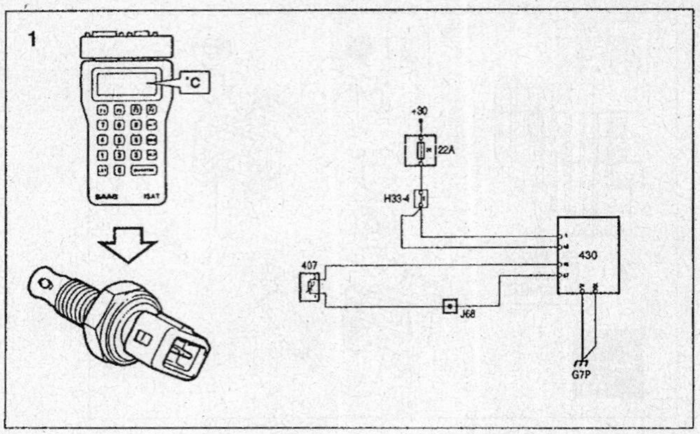

Fault symptom

The malfunction indicator lamp is on.

Conditions

If there is a short circuit/open circuit, a DTC will be generated after 5 seconds.

Diagnostic procedure

1 Check the operation of the temperature sensor using an ISAT scan tool.

Ignition switched on.

Connect the ISAT scan tool and select the "INTAKE AIR TEMP" command on the "READ FUNCTIONS" menu.
The ISAT scan tool must show the intake manifold temperature.

Note that the ECM adopts the substitute value of 8°C in the event of an internal temperature sensor fault. This value is shown on the ISAT where appropriate.

If the measured value is correct, continue with point 5.

If the measured value is incorrect, continue with point 2.

SA1029100083010X

Fig. 12 Codes P0110, P0112 & P0113: Intake Air Temperature Sensor (Part 1 of 3). 9-3 & 900

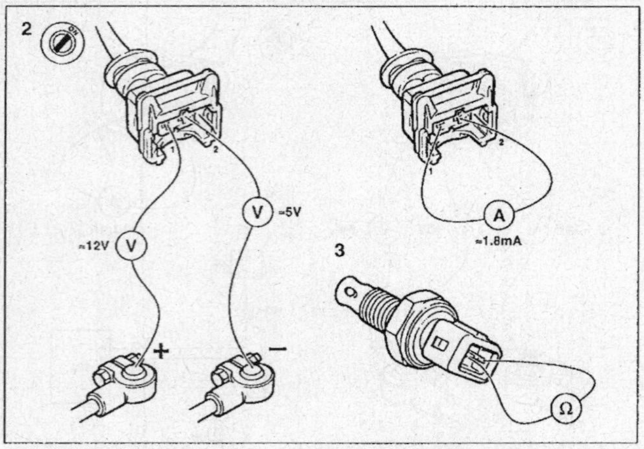

2 Check the electrical interface in the temperature sensor connector. Unplug the 2-pole connector.

Measure the voltage in the female connector.

- pin 2 to Batt - ______ approx. 5 V
- Batt+ to pin 1 ______ approx. 12 V

Measure the current (mA) in the female connector.

- pin 2 to pin 1 ____ approx. 1.8 mA

The measurements above are to show whether ECM including wiring up to the temperature sensor are operating correctly.

If all the measured values are correct, continue with point 3.

If any measured value is incorrect, continue with point 4.

3 Check the resistance of the temperature sensor. Carry out Ω measurement in the temperature sensor connector.

The nominal resistance value is:

°C	°F	Resistance (kΩ)
- 30	- 22	20 - 30
- 10	14	7,0 - 11,4
20	68	2,1 - 2,9
40	104	1,0 - 1,3
60	140	0,565 - 0,670
80	176	0,295 - 0,365
90	194	0,24 - 0,26

If the measured value is incorrect, fit a new the temperature sensor.

If the measured value is correct, continue with point 5.

SA1029100083020X

Fig. 12 Codes P0110, P0112 & P0113: Intake Air Temperature Sensor (Part 2 of 3). 9-3 & 900

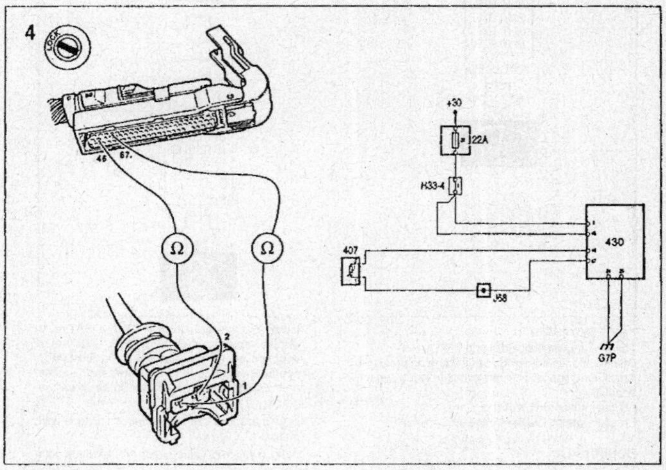

4 Check the continuity of the wiring between the ECM and the 2-pole connector of the temperature sensor.

Check the leads for open circuits, short circuits and any stray current.

If the measured values are correct, continue with point 5.

5 Erase the diagnostic trouble code and drive the car to see whether the DTC is generated again.

If the diagnostic trouble code is registered, **replace ECM.**

If the diagnostic trouble code is not registered, the action taken is correct. Otherwise the fault is intermittent in nature.

SA1029100083030X

Fig. 12 Codes P0110, P0112 & P0113: Intake Air Temperature Sensor (Part 3 of 3). 9-3 & 900

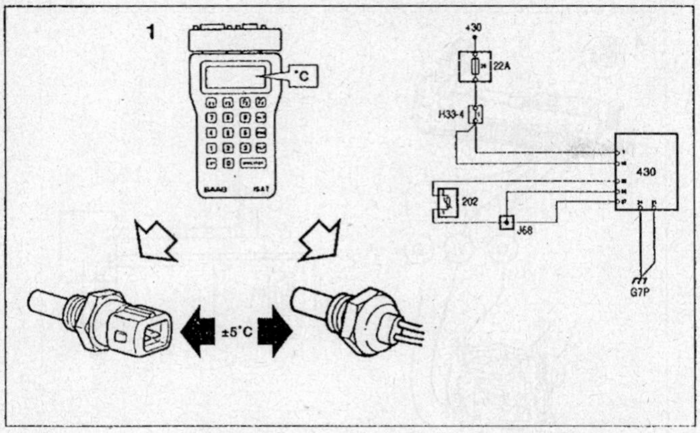

Symptom of fault

The malfunction indicator lamp is on.
Deterioration in drivability.
Difficult to start engine from cold.

Conditions

If there is a short circuit/open circuit, a DTC will be generated after 5 seconds.

Diagnostic procedure

1 Check the operation of the temperature sensor using an ISAT scan tool.

Ignition switched on.

Connect the ISAT scan tool and select the "COOLANT TEMP" command on the "READ FUNCTIONS" menu.

The ISAT display depends on the prevailing engine temperature.

Note that the ECM adopts the substitute value of 26°C if there is an internal temperature sensor fault. This value is shown on the ISAT where appropriate.

"ICE" can be selected on the ISAT and the "COOLANT TEMP" command on the "READ VALUES" menu for reference. Because of tolerances in the two temperature sensors, the ISAT scan tool readings may differ by ±5°C.

If the measured value is correct, continue with point 5.

If the measured value is incorrect, continue with point 2.

SA1029100084010X

Fig. 13 Codes P0115, P0117 & P0118: Engine Coolant Temperature Sensor (Part 1 of 3). 9-3 & 900

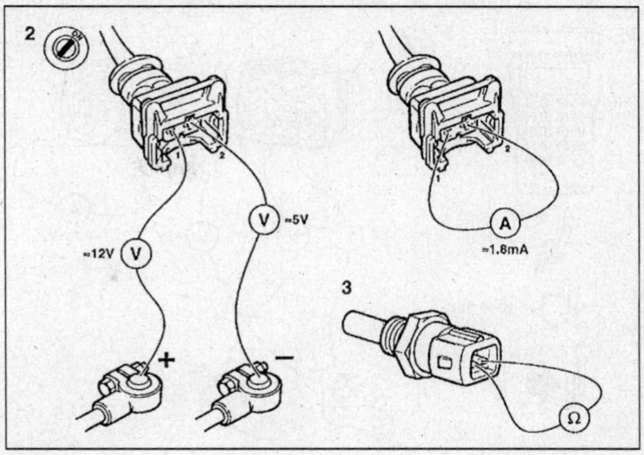

2 Check the electrical interface in the temperature sensor connector. Unplug the 2-pole connector.

Measure the voltage in the female connector.

- pin 2 to Batt - ______ approx. 5 V
- Batt+ to pin 1 ______ approx. 12 V

Measure the current (mA) in the female connector.

- pin 2 to pin 1 ____ approx. 1.8 mA

The measurements above are to show whether ECM including wiring as far as the temperature sensor are operating correctly.

If all the measured values are correct, continue with point 3.

If any measured value is incorrect, continue with point 4.

3 Check the resistance of the temperature sensor. Carry out Ω measurement in the temperature sensor's connector.

The nominal resistance values are:

°C	°F	Resistance (kΩ)
- 30	- 22	20 - 30
- 10	14	7,0 - 11,4
20	68	2,1 - 2,9
40	104	1,0 - 1,3
60	140	0,565 - 0,670
80	176	0,295 - 0,365
90	194	0,24 - 0,26
110	230	0,14 - 0,16

If the measured value is incorrect, fit a new the temperature sensor.

If the measured value is correct, continue with point 5.

SA1029100084020X

Fig. 13 Codes P0115, P0117 & P0118: Engine Coolant Temperature Sensor (Part 2 of 3). 9-3 & 900

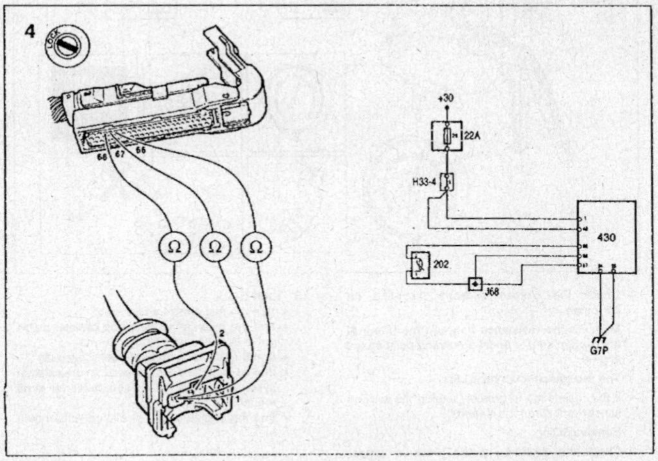

4 Check the continuity of the wiring between the ECM and the 2-pole connector of the temperature sensor.

Check the leads for open circuits, short circuits and any stray current.

If the measured values are correct, continue with point 5.

5 Erase the diagnostic trouble code and drive the car to see whether the DTC is generated again.

If the diagnostic trouble code is registered, replace ECM.

If the diagnostic trouble code is not registered, the action taken is correct. Otherwise the fault is intermittent in nature.

SA1029100084030X

Fig. 13 Codes P0115, P0117 & P0118: Engine Coolant Temperature Sensor (Part 3 of 3). 9-3 & 900

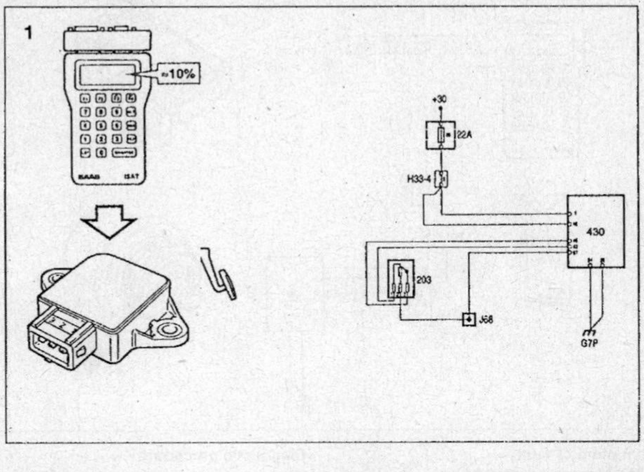

Fault symptom

The malfunction indicator lamp is on.
High idling.
AC compressor not working.
Any other diagnostic trouble codes (throttle position in clutch control module or automatic transmission)

Conditions

If there is a short circuit/open circuit, a DTC will be generated after 5 seconds.

Diagnostic procedure

1 Check the operation of the throttle position sensor an the ISAT scan tool.

Ignition switched on.

Connect the ISAT scan tool and select the "THROTTLE POSITION" command on the "READ FUNCTIONS" menu.

If the ISAT shows a value around 2 % or 99 %, continue with point 3.

If the value is around 10 %, continue with point 2.

Important

The ISAT shows the voltage of the throttle position sensor in % of 5 V, not to be confused with PWM.

⚠ WARNING

If there is a fault in the throttle position sensor, the clutch control module may put the clutch in the operating position as soon as 1st, 2nd or Reverse gear has been selected, and the car will start to move.

⚠ WARNING

Idling adaptation must be carried out after a new throttle position sensor has been fitted

SA1029100085010X

Fig. 14 Codes P0120, P0121, P0122 & P0123: Throttle Position Sensor (Part 1 of 3). 9-3 & 900

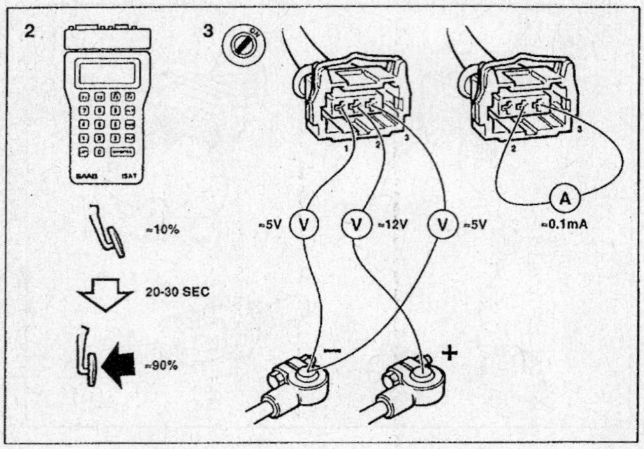

2 Activate the accelerator pedal very slowly, it should take about 20-30 seconds to move the accelerator pedal from the non-depressed position to the fully depressed position. Observe the display on the ISAT scan tool during the activation process.

The ISAT must nominally increase continuously from approx. 10 % to approx. 90 %. Any break in continuity will produce 99 % for a short time.

If the measured value is incorrect, fit a new throttle position sensor.

If the measured value is correct, continue with point 5.

3 Check the electrical interface in the throttle position sensor's connector. Unplug the 3-pole connector.

Measure the voltage in the female connector.

- pin 1 to Batt - ______ approx. 5 V
- pin 3 to Batt - ______ approx. 5 V
- Batt+ to pin 2 ______ approx. 12 V

Measure the current (mA) in the female connector.

- pin 3 to pin 2 ____ approx. 0.1 mA

The measurements above are to show whether ECM including wiring as far as the throttle position sensor are operating correctly.

If all the measured values are correct, fit a new throttle position sensor.

If any measured value is incorrect, continue with point 4.

SA1029100085020X

Fig. 14 Codes P0120, P0121, P0122 & P0123: Throttle Position Sensor (Part 2 of 3). 9-3 & 900

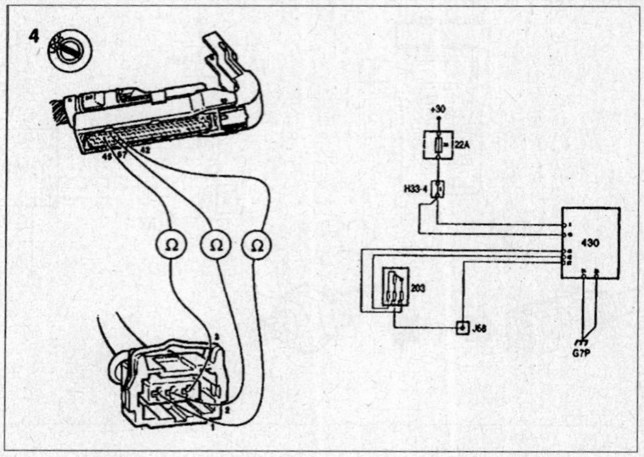

4 Check the continuity of the wiring between the ECM and the 3-pole connector of the throttle position sensor for open circuits, short circuits and any stray current.

If the measured values are correct, continue with point 5.

5 Erase the diagnostic trouble code and drive the car to see whether the DTC is generated again.

If the diagnostic trouble code is registered, replace ECM.

If the diagnostic trouble code is not registered, the action taken is correct. Otherwise the fault is intermittent in nature.

SA1029100085030X

Fig. 14 Codes P0120, P0121, P0122 & P0123: Throttle Position Sensor (Part 3 of 3). 9-3 & 900

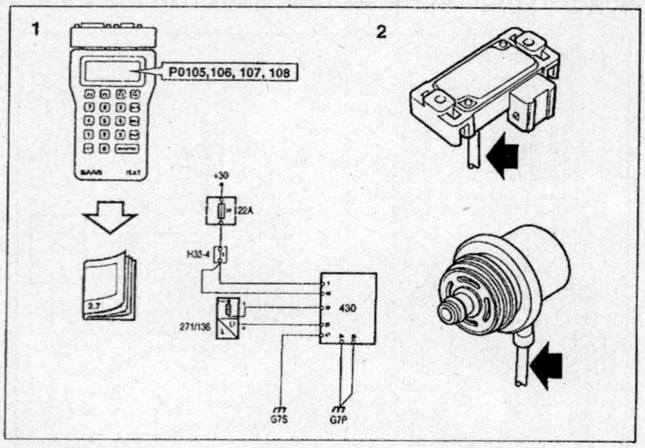

Symptom of fault

The malfunction indicator lamp is on.

Any other diagnostic trouble codes (pressure sensor).

Faults on the oxygen sensor rarely cause drivability problems. On the other hand, other faults which lead to a DTC on the oxygen sensor can cause drivability problems, depending on type.

Conditions

The oxygen sensor indicates lean mixture/low voltage or rich mixture/high voltage for than 30 seconds.

Diagnostic procedure

Important

A DTC may be generated if the fuel tank is driven empty.

1 Check other diagnostic trouble codes in Trionic. Read out all DTCs with an ISAT scan tool.

P0105, P0106, P0107, P0108 is displayed, manifold absolute pressure sensor, start fault diagnosis there.

2 Check that there is no leak of air at the following places:
- the hose between the pressure sensor and the intake manifold
- the hose between the fuel pressure regulator and the intake manifold

Important

Contact spray or grease must not be used on the oxygen sensor's connector.

SA1029100086010X

Fig. 15 Codes P0130, P0131 & P0132: Oxygen Sensor (Part 1 of 4). 9-3 & 900

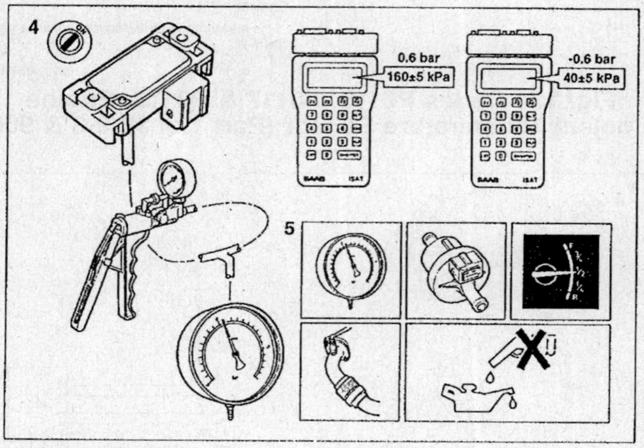

3 Check the oxygen sensor's mounting for corrosion.

Measure the resistance between the frame of the oxygen sensor and a grounding point on the engine.

The resistance must be <0.5Ω.

If the resistance is greater, unplug the oxygen sensor and clean the threads.

Removal/fitting

4 Check the operation of the pressure sensor using a pressure gauge and a pressure/vacuum pump.

Ignition switched on.

Generate a positive pressure of 0.6 bar and a negative pressure of -0.6 bar.

Connect an ISAT scan tool. The ISAT scan tool must show 160±5 kPa and 40±5 kPa respectively in the "READ FUNCTIONS" menu and the "INTAKE PRESSURE" command (the ISAT scan tool may show slightly lower values when measuring at high altitude).

The measurement is intended to detect any shift in the operating range of the pressure sensor.

5 Then check
- that the fuel pressure is correct
- that the evaporative emission canister purge valve is not constantly open
- that the fuel tank has not been driven dry
- that air leakage does not occur in the exhaust system ahead of the oxygen sensor or at its mount
- that the engine oil is not diluted with engine fuel

SA1029100086020X

Fig. 15 Codes P0130, P0131 & P0132: Oxygen Sensor (Part 2 of 4). 9-3 & 900

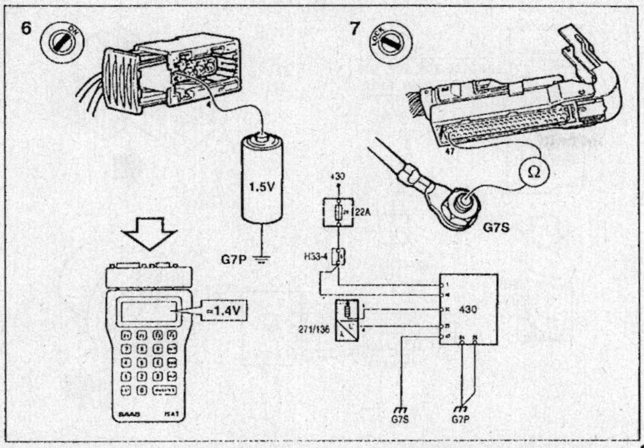

6 Check the electrical interface in the oxygen sensor's connector.
Unplug the 4-pole connector.
Replace the oxygen sensor with a conventional 1.5 V battery which is in good condition.
Connect the + pole of the battery to pin 4 on the female connector.
Connect the - pole of the battery to safe grounding point on the engine.
Ignition switched on.
With the ISAT connected and with the "OXYGEN SENSOR" command on the "READ FUNCTIONS" meny, check the operation of the ECM including wiring as far as the oxygen sensor.
The ISAT must show approx. 1.4 V.

A discontinuity in the oxygen sensor's reference ground from grounding point G7S to pin 47 on the ECM leads to a value of approx. 0.5 V being shown on the ISAT.

If the measured value is approx. 0.5 V, continue with point 7.

If the measured value is approx. 1.4 V, continue with point 8.

If the measured value is neither 0.5 V nor 1.4 V, continue with point 9.

7 Check the lead between G7S and pin 47 on the ECM for discontinuity or shorting.

Important

Contact spray or grease must not be used on the oxygen sensor's connector.

SA1029100086030X

Fig. 15 Codes P0130, P0131 & P0132: Oxygen Sensor (Part 3 of 4). 9-3 & 900

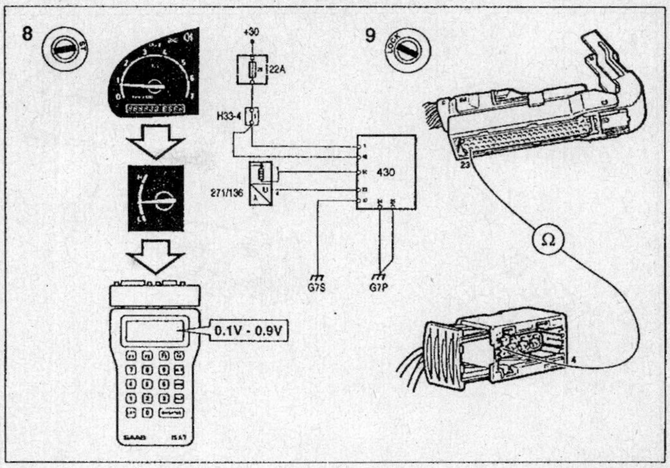

8 Connect oxygen sensor.
Start the engine and leave it run until it has reached operating temperature.
With an ISAT scan tool in the "READ FUNCTIONS" menu and the "OXYGEN SENSOR" command, read off the sensor voltage, which must fluctuate between approx. 0.1 V and approx. 0.9 V.
If the measured value is incorrect, fit a new oxygen sensor.
If the measured value is correct, continue with point 10.

9 Check the lead between pin 4 on the oxygen sensor and pin 23 on the ECM for discontinuity and shorting.

10 Erase the diagnostic trouble code and drive the car to see whether the DTC is generated again.
If the diagnostic trouble code is registered, **replace ECM.**
If the diagnostic trouble code is not registered, the action taken is correct. Otherwise the fault is intermittent in nature.

SA1029100086040X

Fig. 15 Codes P0130, P0131 & P0132: Oxygen Sensor (Part 4 of 4). 9-3 & 900

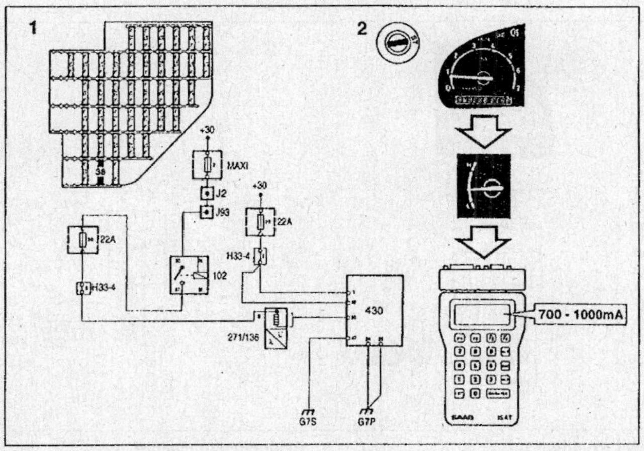

Fault symptom

The malfunction indicator lamp is on.

Conditions

The preheating current is less than 500 mA or more than 2300 mA for 5 seconds.

Diagnostic procedure

1 Check fuse 38.

2 Connect an ISAT scan tool.
Start the engine and run it at idling speed.
The prevailing current consumption for the oxygen sensor's preheating circuit is shown on the ISAT menu "READ FUNCTIONS" and with the PREHEAT OXY SENSOR" command.
The nominal value when the engine is warmed up is 700-1000 mA.
If the measured value is correct, continue with point 6.
If the measured value is incorrect, continue with point 3.

SA1029100087010X

Fig. 16 Code P0135: Preheating Of Heated Oxygen Sensor (Part 1 of 3). 9-3 & 900

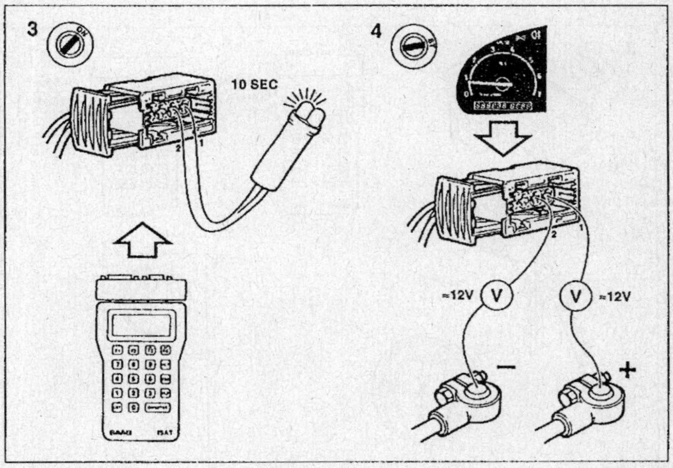

3 Switch off the engine.
Unplug the 4-pole connector of the oxygen sensor.
Connect the test lamp between the oxygen sensor's connector (female), pin 2 to pin 1.
Ignition switched on.
Select the "PREHEAT OXY SENSOR" command on the "ACTIVATE" menu. Preheating is now activated for 10 seconds. If you want a longer activation time, repeat the command.
During the activation time, the test lamp lights up with a steady glow.
If the test lamp comes on, fit a new oxygen sensor.
If the test lamp does not come on, continue with point 4.

4 Start the engine and run it at idling speed.
Measure the voltage in the oxygen sensor's connector (female).
- Batt+ to pin 1 ______ approx. 12 V
- pin 2 to Batt - ______ approx. 12 V

If there is no voltage on pin 2, continue with pin 5.
If there is no voltage on pin 1, continue with point 6.

SA1029100087020X

Fig. 16 Code P0135: Preheating Of Heated Oxygen Sensor (Part 2 of 3). 9-3 & 900

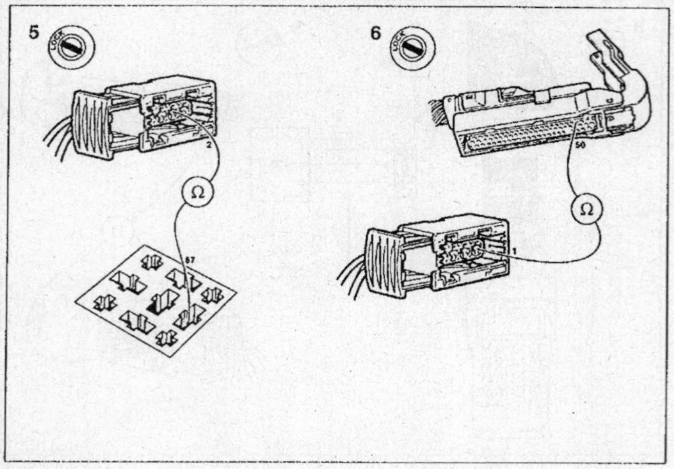

5 Check the continuity of the circuit between pin 2 of the oxygen sensor's connector and pin 87 of the fuel pump relay.

6 Check the lead between pin 1 on the oxygen sensor's connector and pin 50 on the ECM for discontinuity and shorting.

7 Erase the diagnostic trouble code and drive the car to see whether the DTC is generated again.

If the diagnostic trouble code is registered, replace ECM.

If the diagnostic trouble code is not registered, the action taken is correct. Otherwise the fault is intermittent in nature.

SA1029100087030X

Fig. 16 Code P0135: Preheating Of Heated Oxygen Sensor (Part 3 of 3). 9-3 & 900

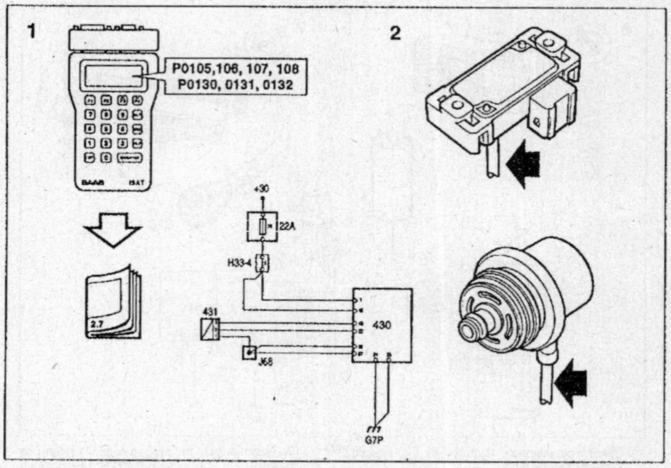

Symptom of fault

The malfunction indicator lamp is on.
Deterioration in drivability, unsteady idling.
Any other diagnostic trouble codes (pressure sensor, oxygen sensor).

Conditions

The ECM has increased or decreased the injection times to the maximum without it being possible to achieve lambda = 1.0.

Diagnostic procedure

1 Check other diagnostic trouble codes in Trionic.

Read out all the diagnostic trouble codes with the ISAT scan tool.

If P0105, P0106, P0107, P0108 appears on the display, manifold absolute pressure sensor, start fault diagnosis there.

If P0130, P0131, P0132 appears on the display, oxygen sensor, start fault diagnosis there.

2 Check that no air leakage occurs at the following places:

- the hose between the pressure sensor and the intake manifold
- the hose between the fuel pressure regulator and the intake manifold

SA1029100088010X

Fig. 17 Codes P0170, P0171 & P0172: Adaptation Faulty (Part 1 of 2). 9-3 & 900

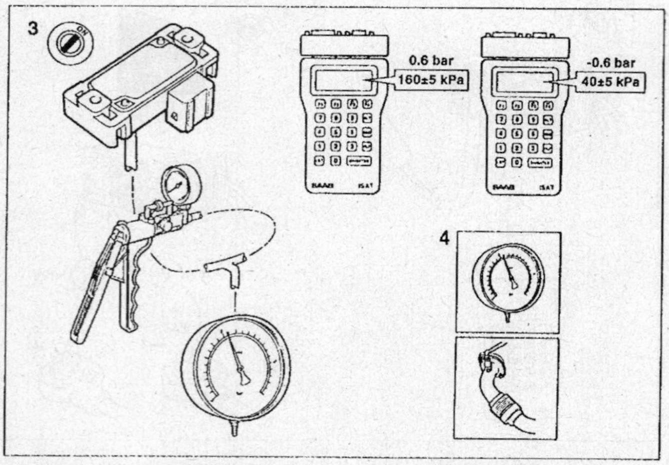

3 Check the operation of the pressure sensor using a pressure gauge and a pressure/vacuum pump.

Ignition switched on.

Generate a positive pressure of 0.6 bar and a negative pressure of -0.6 bar.

With the ISAT scan tool connected and in the "READ FUNCTIONS" menu and the "INTAKE PRESSURE" command, the ISAT scan tool must show 160±5 kPa and 40±5 kPa respectively (the ISAT may show slightly lower values when measuring at high altitude).

The measurement is intended to detect any shift in the operating range of the pressure sensor.

4 Then check

- that the fuel pressure is correct
  that no air leakage occurs in the exhaust system ahead of the oxygen sensor or at its mount.

5 Erase the diagnostic trouble code and drive the car to see whether the DTC is generated again.

If the diagnostic trouble code is registered, replace ECM.

If the diagnostic trouble code is not registered, the action taken is correct. Otherwise the fault is intermittent in nature.

SA1029100088020X

Fig. 17 Codes P0170, P0171 & P0172: Adaptation Faulty (Part 2 of 2). 9-3 & 900

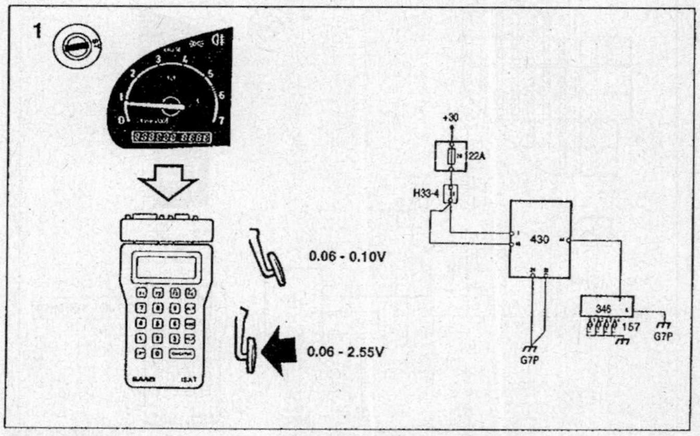

Fault symptom

The car only runs at basic charging pressure, timing continuously retarded.

Note

Saab Trionic does not have a conventional knock sensor. The signal comes from the ignition discharge module.

Conditions

No knocking signal for 10 seconds.

Diagnostic procedure

1 Connect an ISAT scan tool.

Start the engine.

Select the "KNOCK SENSOR" command on the ISAT scan tool menu "READ FUNCTIONS". The ISAT scan tool must show a number between 0 and 2.55 V, depending on the level of the knocking signal.

At idling speed the ISAT must show 0.06-0.10 V.

With a fast accelerator setting, the display on the ISAT may vary between 0.06-2.55 V.

The measurement must show that a signal is present.

If there is a discontinuity in the signal lead, 0.06 V is normally shown regardless of the accelerator setting.

If there is a knocking signal, continue with point 3.

If there is no knocking signal, continue with point 2.

SA1029100089010X

Fig. 18 Code P0325: Knock Sensor (Part 1 of 2). 9-3 & 900

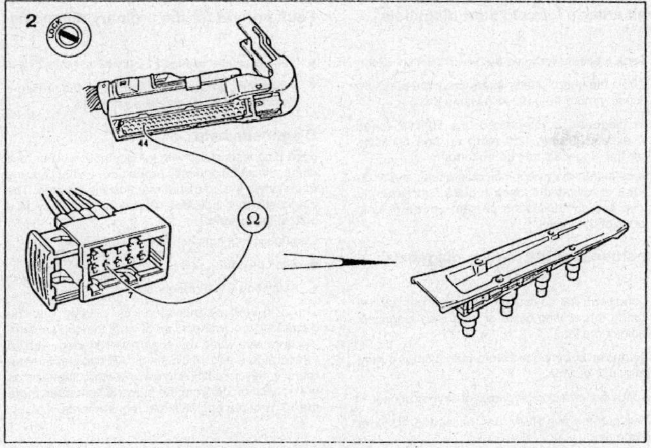

2 Check the lead between connecting pin 7 on the ignition discharge module and pin 44 on the ECM for open circuit, short circuit and any stray current.

If any measured value is incorrect, check and if necessary remedy the fault in the wiring. Pay special attention to the backing-out of connector sleeves and connector pins.

If the measured value is correct, continue with point 3.

3 Erase the diagnostic trouble code and drive the car to see whether the DTC is generated again.

If the diagnostic trouble code is generated again, fit a new ignition discharge module and then drive the car to see whether the diagnostic trouble code is generated again.

If the diagnostic trouble code is generated again, fit a new ignition discharge module and then drive the car to see whether the diagnostic trouble code is generated again. If the diagnostic trouble code recurs, replace ECM, after refitting the ignition discharge module.

If the diagnostic trouble code is not registered, the action taken is correct. Otherwise the fault is intermittent in nature.

SA1029100089020X

Fig. 18 Code P0325: Knock Sensor (Part 2 of 2). 9-3 & 900

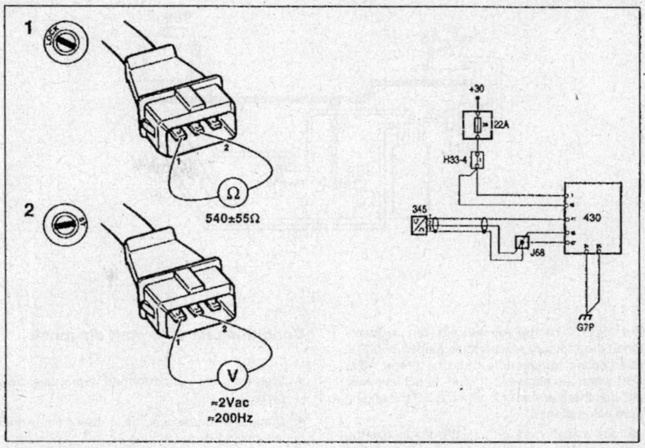

Symptom of fault

The engine fails to start or misfires.

Conditions

The sensor reads the wrong number of ribs (teeth) per crankshaft rotation.

Diagnostic procedure

1 Unplug the 3-pole connector of the crankshaft position sensor.

Check the resistance of the crankshaft position sensor. Measure Ω in the sensor's connector (male), between pins 1 and 2.

The nominal resistance value is 540±55 Ω.

2 Crank the starter motor and at the same time measure the output from the crankshaft position sensor. Connect the voltmeter to the sensor's connector (male), between pins 1 and 2.

Nominal values are approx. 2 V ac and approx. 200 Hz.

If the measured value is correct, continue with point 4.

If the measured value is incorrect, continue with point 3.

SA1029100090010X

Fig. 19 Code P0335: Crankshaft Position Sensor (Part 1 of 3). 9-3 & 900

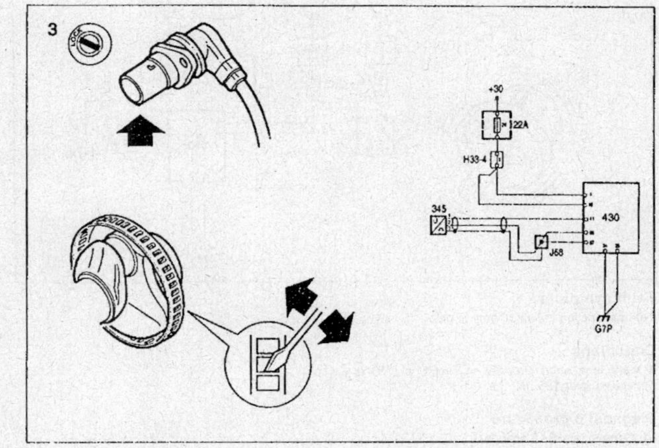

3 Remove the crankshaft position sensor.

Check

- that the sensor point is not fouled with metal chips.
- that the perforated disc is firmly attached to the crankshaft by carefully prising with a screwdriver

Brush off any metal chips.

If the perforated disc is not fixed, service as necessary.

If there is no relevant cause for the fault, fit a new crankshaft position sensor.

SA1029100090020X

Fig. 19 Code P0335: Crankshaft Position Sensor (Part 2 of 3). 9-3 & 900

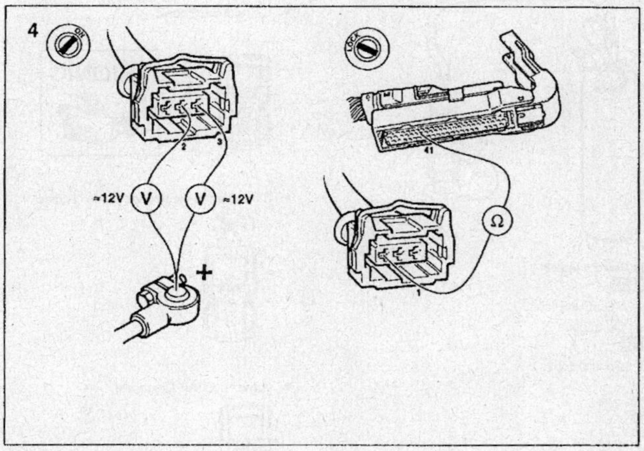

4 Check the ground and screening connection of the crankshaft position sensor.

Unplug the crankshaft position sensor's connector.

Measure the voltage between

- Batt+ and pin 2 ________ 12 V
- Batt+ and pin 3 ________ 12 V

Check the lead between pin 1 and pin 41 of the ECM for open circuit, short circuit and any stray current.

5 Erase the diagnostic trouble code and drive the car to see whether the DTC is generated again.

If the diagnostic trouble code is registerec replace ECM.

If the diagnostic trouble code is not registered, the action taken is correct. Otherwise the fault is intermittent in nature.

SA1029100090030X

Fig. 19 Code P0335: Crankshaft Position Sensor (Part 3 of 3). 9-3 & 900

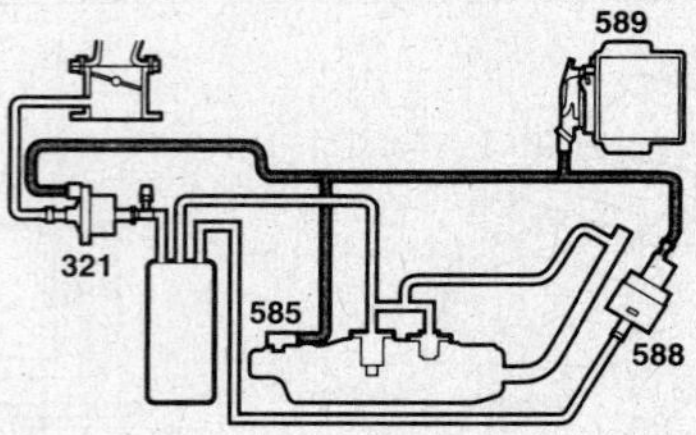

Before this DTC can be set, the cold start diagnosis and then the ordinary must first be carried out. The engine coolant temperature must be below 40°C (104°F) when the engine is started, to achieve this. A DTC can therefore **not** be generated if the engine is warm when started.

To perform a final check on a rectified fault, use the activating command on the diagnostics tool so that the cold start test is performed irrespective of the starting temperature.

Fault symptoms

CHECK ENGINE comes on after two driving cycles.

Possible smell of petrol.

Conditions for cold start diagnosis

- Diagnosis not yet performed during this driving cycle.
- Diagnosis commenced more than 8 times during this driving cycle.
- Engine coolant temperature below 40°C (104°F) when engine was started.
- Idling speed.
- Car stationary for more than 5 s.
- Max. one change of status of the brake light switch.
- Additional fuel from purge is less than 7 % of the engine's fuel requirements.

When the conditions above are fulfilled, the diagnosis will start by closing the shut-off valve and setting the purge valve PWM to 15 %. The additional fuel from the purge is allowed to be 13 % of that required by the engine.

SA1019900017010X

Fig. 20 Code P0442: EVAP Small Leakage In System (Part 1 of 3). 9-3

Fault criteria for cold start diagnosis

- Tank pressure reduced by 0.6 kPa within 23 s.
- When the purge is later interrupted, the pressure rises by more than 0.3 kPa within 9 s.

If the diagnosis is interrupted, the vehicle speed must exceed 4 km/h (2.5 mph) on one occasion before the diagnosis can be restarted.

If the cold start diagnosis indicates a leak, the shut-off valve is activated 4 times in quick succession to remove any contamination present on the sealing surfaces of the valve.

Conditions for the regular diagnosis

- Conditions for cold start diagnosis not fulfilled during this driving cycle or cold start diagnosis indicated a leak.
- Diagnosis commenced more than 8 times during this driving cycle.
- Approved transition diagnosis of oxygen sensor 1.
- The purge valve PWM has exceeded 40 % at some time.
- Idling speed.
- Car stationary for more than 5 s.
- Max. one change of status of the brake light switch.
- Additional fuel from purge is less than 7 % of the engine's fuel requirements.

When the conditions above are fulfilled, the diagnosis will start by closing the shut-off valve and setting the purge valve PWM to 15 %. The additional fuel from the purge is allowed to be 13 % of that required by the engine.

Fault criteria for the ordinary diagnosis

- Tank pressure reduced by 0.6 kPa within 23 s.
- When the purge is later interrupted, the pressure rises by more than 0.3 kPa within 9 s.

Diagnostic help

Fault diagnosis starts with leak detection. After fault diagnosis and diagnostic procedure, a final check is made when the cold start diagnosis is initiated. The diagnostic tool indicates whether or not there is a leak in the system.

Diagnostic tool functions related to this fault are:

- Tank pressure, unit kPa.
- Activating EVAP diagnosis.

The cold start diagnosis can be initiated with the diagnostic tool irrespective of what the coolant temperature was when the engine was started. At high temperatures and when the EVAP canister is saturated, it may be difficult to carry out the diagnosis as the additional fuel from the purge is then often more than 7 % of the engine's fuel requirements.

SA1019900017020X

Fig. 20 Code P0442: EVAP Small Leakage In System (Part 2 of 3). 9-3

Diagnostic procedure

1. Leakage check

Implement the method 'Checking for leaks in the evaporative emission system', see 53.

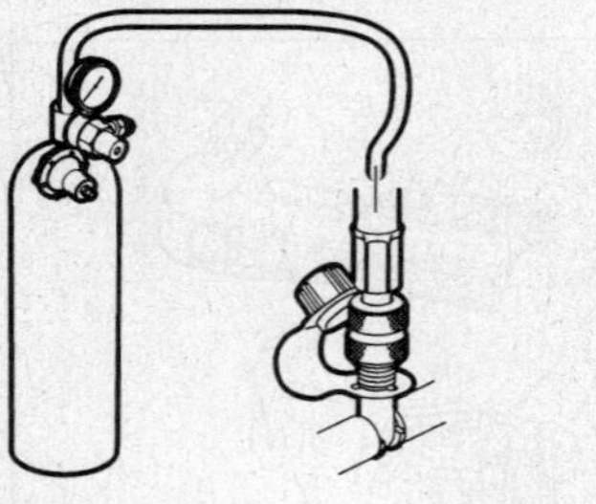

Is there a leak?

YES

- Rectify the fault.
- Go to point 2.

NO

- Go to point 2.

2. Initiate EVAP diagnosis.

- Turn the ignition switch to the ON position.

- Contact the Trionic.

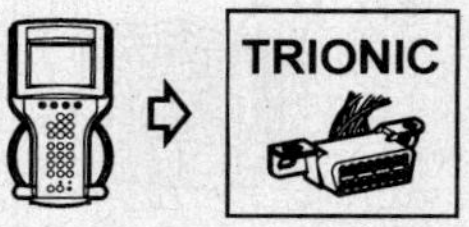

- Clear diagnostic trouble codes: Trionic

- Activate: EVAP Diagnosis.

LEAK

- Fault not rectified.

NO LEAK

- The steps taken to rectify the fault were correct.

SA1019900017030X

Fig. 20 Code P0442: EVAP Small Leakage In System (Part 3 of 3). 9-3

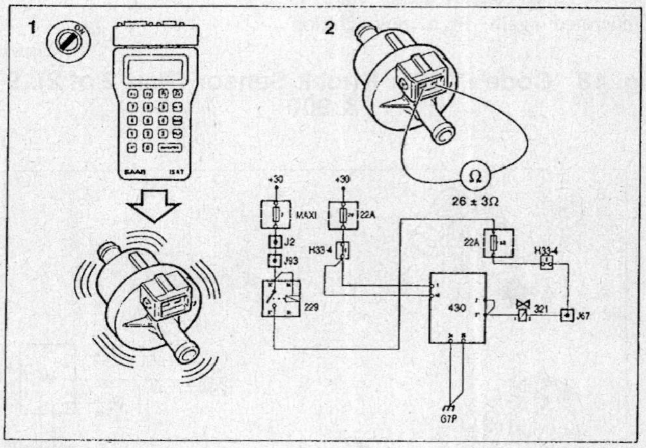

Fault symptom

The malfunction indicator lamp is on.

Conditions

If there is a short circuit/open circuit, a DTC is generated after 125 ms.

Diagnostic procedure

1 Connect an ISAT scan tool. Ignition switched on.

Select the "EVAP VALVE" command on the ISAT scan tool menu "ACTIVATE". The command activates the valve at a frequency of 8 Hz for 10 seconds.

Listen for the sound of the valve working.

If a longer activation time is need, the command must be repeated again.

If the valve clicks, continue with point 2.
If the valve does not click, continue with point 3.

2 Check the resistance of the valve. The correct value is 26±3Ω.

If the value is incorrect, fit a new valve.

If the value is correct, continue with point 6.

SA1029100091010X

Fig. 21 Codes P0443, P0444 & P0445: Evaporation Emission Canister Purge Valve (EVAP Valve, Part 1 of 3). 9-3 & 900

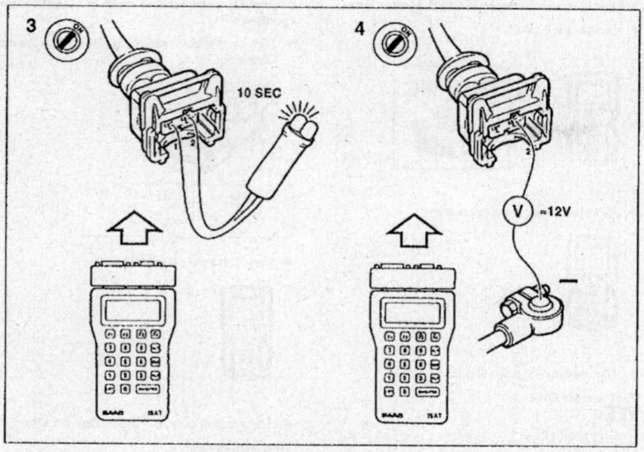

3 Unplug the 2-pole connector of the purge valve.
Connect the test lamp to pins 1 and 2 of the female connector.
Activate with ISAT scan tool command "EVAP VALVE".
The test lamp must flash at a frequency of 8 Hz for 10 seconds.
If the test lamp flashes, suspect an electrical fault in the purge valve.
Check the resistance of the valve. The correct value is 26±3 Ω.
If the value is incorrect, fit a new valve.
If the value is correct, continue with point 6.
If the test lamp does not flash or shines with steady glow, continue with point 4.

4 Measure the voltage in the purge valve's connector (female).
Ignition switched on.
Activate with ISAT scan tool command "EVAP VALVE"
- pin 2 to Batt - ______ approx. 12 V

If there is no voltage in pin 2, the fault is located in the lead between pin 2 and crimped connection J67.
If there is voltage in pin 2, continue with point 5.

SA1029100091020X

Fig. 21 Codes P0443, P0444 & P0445: Evaporation Emission Canister Purge Valve (EVAP Valve, Part 2 of 3). 9-3 & 900

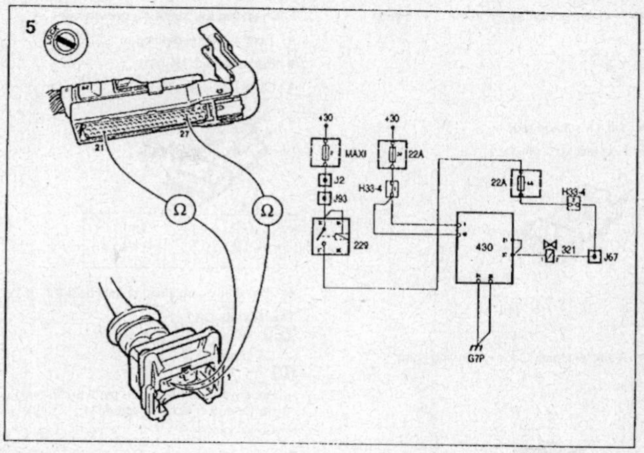

5 Check the lead between pin 2 and pins 21 and 27 of the ECM for discontinuity and shorting.
6 Erase the diagnostic trouble code and drive the car to see whether the DTC is generated again.
If the diagnostic trouble code is registered, replace ECM.

If the diagnostic trouble code is not registered, the action taken is correct. Otherwise the fault is intermittent in nature.

SA1029100091030X

Fig. 21 Codes P0443, P0444 & P0445: Evaporation Emission Canister Purge Valve (EVAP Valve, Part 3 of 3). 9-3 & 900

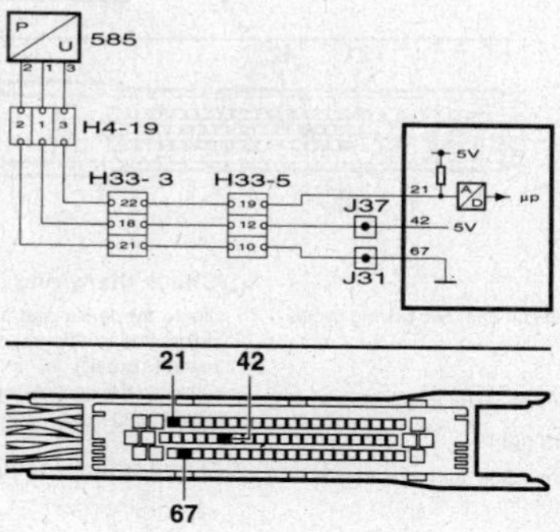

Fault symptoms

CHECK ENGINE comes on after two driving cycles.

Conditions

The following conditions apply for this DTC:

- Ignition switch in ON position.
- Vehicle speed = 0 km/h.
- Pressure variation greater than ± 0.5 kPa.
- Deviates more than 25 times during 5 s.

Diagnostic help

Fault diagnosis concerns electrical faults in connected leads or in the sensor.

Diagnostic tool functions related to this fault are:

- EVAP tank pressure sensor value, unit kPa.

When the fuel level is below the sensor and the filler cap has been removed, the value should be approx. 0 kPa.

Check the wiring

Jiggle the leads and in-line connectors at various points and in different directions to detect any intermittent breaks or short circuits in the wiring. Observe the multimeter, test lamp or diagnostic tool while doing this.

Diagnostic procedure

See "Code P0452."

SA1019900018010X

Fig. 22 Code P0451: EVAP Tank Pressure Sensor Performance Problem (Part 1 of 5). 9-3

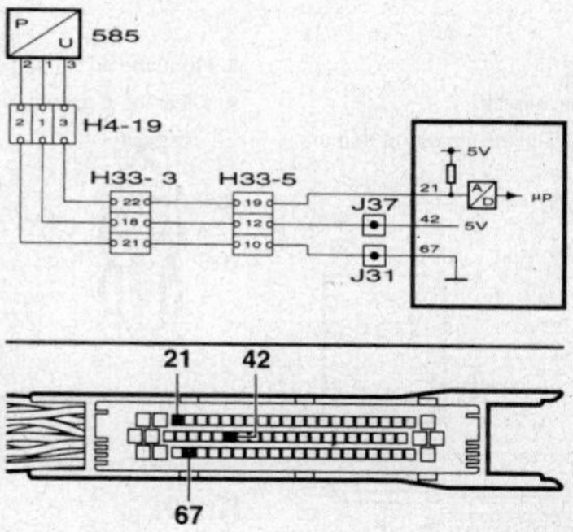

Fault symptoms

CHECK ENGINE comes on after two driving cycles.

Conditions

The following conditions apply for this DTC:

- Ignition switch in ON position.
- Voltage below 0.1 V for more than 5 s.

Diagnostic help

Fault diagnosis concerns electrical faults in connected leads or in the sensor.

Diagnostic tool functions related to this fault are:

- EVAP tank pressure sensor value, unit kPa.

When the fuel level is below the sensor and the filler cap has been removed, the value should be approx. 0 kPa.

Check the wiring

Jiggle the leads and in-line connectors at various points and in different directions to detect any intermittent breaks or short circuits in the wiring. Observe the multimeter, test lamp or diagnostic tool while doing this.

Diagnostic procedure

1. Checking the sensor's power supply

- Unplug connector: H4-19.

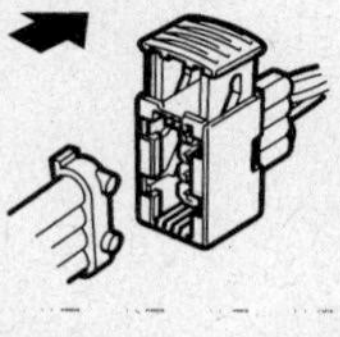

SA1019900018020X

Fig. 22 Code P0451: EVAP Tank Pressure Sensor Performance Problem (Part 2 of 5). 9-3

- Turn the ignition switch to the ON position.

- Take a voltage reading.
- Red test lead: H4-19:1.

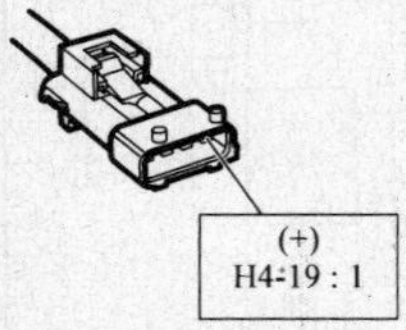

- Black test lead: Good grounding point.

- The reading obtained should be 4.9V - 5.1V.

Test results OK?

YES

– Go to point 2.

NO

– Rectify the lead between pin 1 in the male connector and crimp connector J37.
– Go to point 6.

2. Checking the sensor's grounding

- Take a voltage reading.
- Red test lead: H4-19:1.
- Black test lead: H4-19:2.

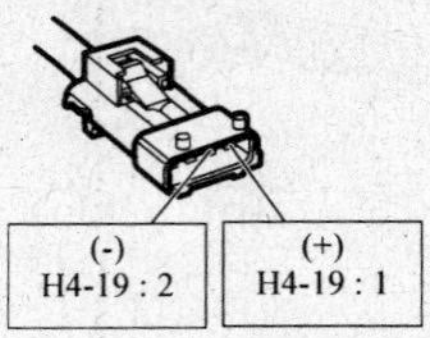

- The reading obtained should be 4.9V - 5.1V.

Test results OK?

YES

– Go to point 3.

NO

– Rectify the lead between pin 2 in the male connector and crimp connector J31.
– Go to point 6.

SA1019900018030X

Fig. 22 Code P0451: EVAP Tank Pressure Sensor Performance Problem (Part 3 of 5). 9-3

3. Checking the control module's sensor input

- Contact the Trionic.

- Read the value: Tank pressure.

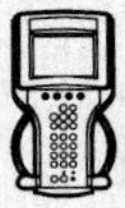

- The reading obtained should be: 3.1 kPa.

Test results OK?

YES

– Go to point 4.

NO

– Rectify the lead between pin 3 on the male connector of the tank pressure sensor and the pin 21 on the control module.
– Go to point 6.

4. Checking the control module's sensor input (continued)

- Fit a jumper lead across pins 2 and 3 on the male connector.

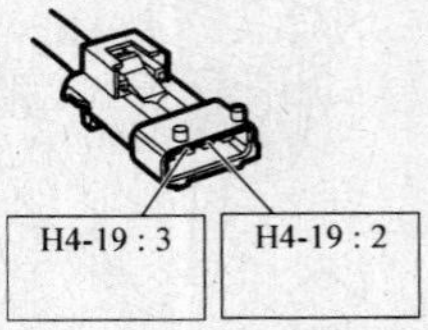

- Read the value: Tank pressure.

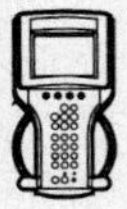

- The reading obtained should be: -3.1 kPa

Test results OK?

YES

– Go to point 5.

NO

– Rectify the lead between pin 3 on the male connector of the tank pressure sensor and the pin 21 on the control module.
– Go to point 6.

SA1019900018040X

Fig. 22 Code P0451: EVAP Tank Pressure Sensor Performance Problem (Part 4 of 5). 9-3

5. Checking the wiring

- Remove the fuel tank, see 59.
- Check the leads between the connector and the pressure sensor.

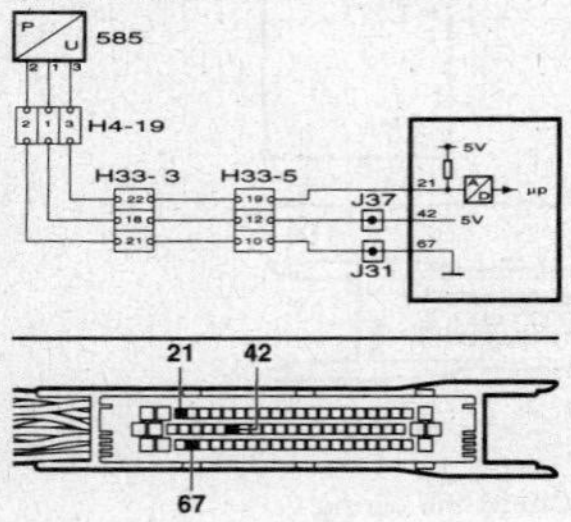

Are the leads OK?

YES

– Replace: EVAP tank pressure sensor.
– Go to point 6.

NO

– Repair or replace the faulty lead.
– Go to point 6.

6. Final check

- Clear the diagnostic trouble codes in all systems.

- Carry out a driving cycle:
- Drive the car under varying engine loads and at different engine rpm for five minutes.

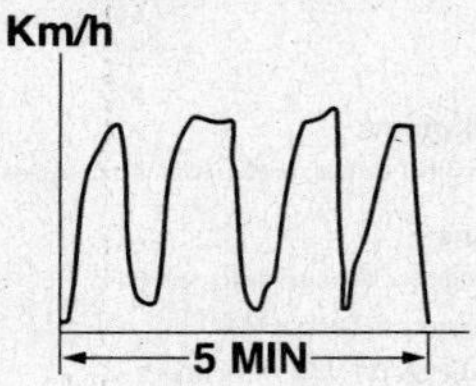

- Evaluate the driving cycle:
- Check that the diagnostic trouble code has not recurred.

Test results OK?

YES

– The steps taken to rectify the fault were correct.

NO

– See "Engine Control Module" under "Component Replacement".

SA1019900018050X

Fig. 22 Code P0451: EVAP Tank Pressure Sensor Performance Problem (Part 5 of 5). 9-3

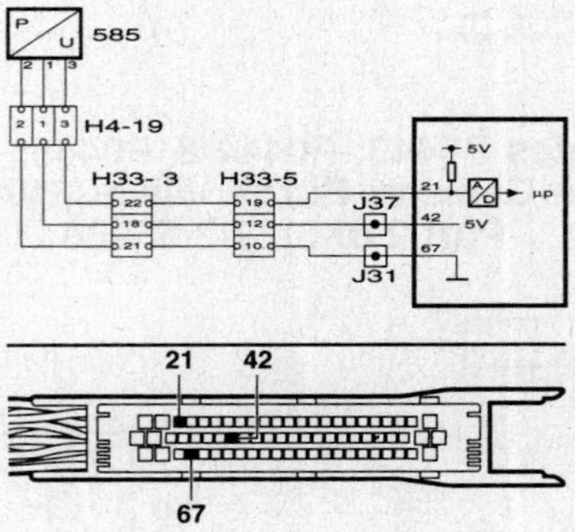

Fault symptoms

CHECK ENGINE comes on after two driving cycles.

Conditions

The following conditions apply for this DTC:

- Ignition switch in ON position.
- Voltage greater than 4.96 V for more than 5 s.

Diagnostic help

Fault diagnosis concerns electrical faults in connected leads or in the sensor.

Diagnostic tool functions related to this fault are:

- EVAP tank pressure sensor value, unit kPa.

When the fuel level is below the sensor and the filler cap has been removed, the value should be approx. 0 kPa.

Check the wiring

Jiggle the leads and in-line connectors at various points and in different directions to detect any intermittent breaks or short circuits in the wiring. Observe the multimeter, test lamp or diagnostic tool while doing this.

Diagnostic procedure

See "Code P0452"

SA1019900019000X

Fig. 23 Code P0453: EVAP Tank Pressure Sensor Circuit Open/Short To B+. 9-3

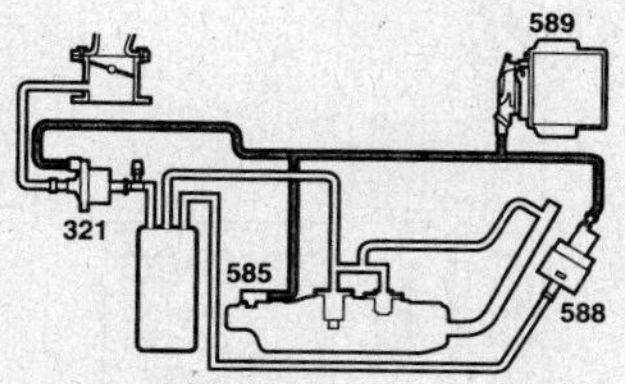

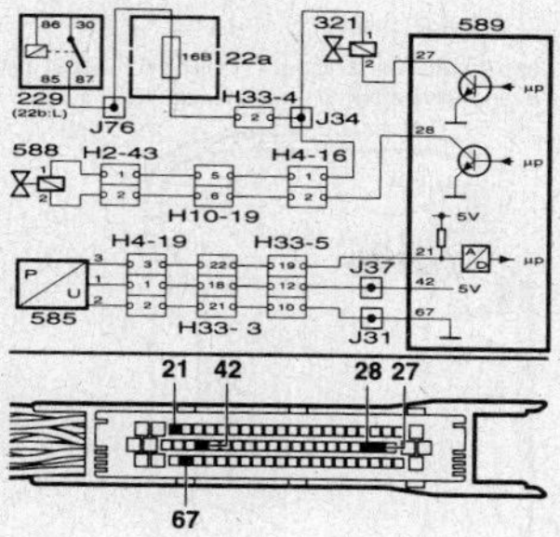

Before this DTC can be set, the cold start diagnosis and then the ordinary must first be carried out. The engine coolant temperature must be below 40°C (104°F) when the engine is started, to achieve this. A DTC can therefore **not** be generated if the engine is warm when started.

To perform a final check on a rectified fault, use the activating command on the diagnostics tool so that the cold start test is performed irrespective of the starting temperature.

Fault symptoms

CHECK ENGINE comes on after two driving cycles.

Possible smell of petrol.

Conditions for cold start diagnosis

- Diagnosis not yet performed during this driving cycle.
- Diagnosis commenced more than 8 times during this driving cycle.
- Engine coolant temperature below 40°C (104°F) when engine was started.
- Idling speed.
- Car stationary for more than 5 s.
- Max. one change of status of the brake light switch.
- Additional fuel from purge is less than 7 % of the engine's fuel requirements.

When the conditions above are fulfilled, the diagnosis will start by closing the shut-off valve and setting the purge valve PWM to 15 %. The additional fuel from the purge is allowed to be 13 % of that required by the engine.

SA1019900020010X

Fig. 24 Code P0455: EVAP Serious Leakage In System (Part 1 of 6). 9-3

Fault criteria for cold start diagnosis

- Tank pressure cannot be reduced by 0.6 kPa during 23 s.

If the diagnosis is interrupted, the vehicle speed must exceed 4 km/h (2.5 mph) on one occasion before the diagnosis can be restarted.

If the cold start diagnosis indicates a leak, the shut-off valve is activated 4 times in quick succession to remove any contamination present on the sealing surfaces of the valve.

Conditions for the regular diagnosis

- Conditions for cold start diagnosis not fulfilled during this driving cycle or cold start diagnosis indicated a leak.
- Diagnosis commenced more than 8 times during this driving cycle.
- Approved transition diagnosis of oxygen sensor 1.
- The purge valve PWM has exceeded 40 % at some time.
- Idling speed.
- Car stationary for more than 5 s.
- Max. one change of status of the brake light switch.
- Additional fuel from purge is less than 7 % of the engine's fuel requirements.

When the conditions above have been fulfilled, the diagnosis will start by closing the shut-off valve and setting the purge valve PWM ratio to 15 %. The additional fuel from the purge is allowed to be 13 % of that required by the engine.

Fault criteria for the ordinary diagnosis

- Tank pressure cannot be reduced by 0.6 kPa during 23 s.

Diagnostic help

Fault diagnosis starts by checking the electric function of the purge valve and the shut-off valve. If these are OK, leak detection is done. After fault diagnosis and diagnostic procedure have been performed, a final check is carried out when the cold start diagnosis is initiated. The diagnostics tool indicates whether or not there is a leak.

Diagnostic tool functions related to this fault are:

- Tank pressure, unit kPa.
- Activating EVAP purge valve.
- Activating EVAP shut-off valve.
- Activating EVAP diagnosis.

The cold start diagnosis can be initiated with the diagnostic tool irrespective of what the coolant temperature was when the engine was started. At high temperatures and when the EVAP canister is saturated, it may be difficult to carry out the diagnosis as the additional fuel from the purge is then often more than 7 % of the engine's fuel requirements.

Check the wiring

Jiggle the leads and in-line connectors at various points and in different directions to detect any intermittent breaks or short circuits in the wiring. Observe the multimeter, test lamp or diagnostic tool while doing this.

SA1019900020020X

Fig. 24 Code P0455: EVAP Serious Leakage In System (Part 2 of 6). 9-3

Diagnostic procedure

1. Checking the electric function of the shut-off valve

- Turn the ignition switch to the ON position.

- Contact the Trionic.

- Activate: Shut-off valve EVAP venting (ON).
- A sound should be heard from the valve which is located in the right-hand rear wheel housing.

Test results OK?

YES

- Go to point 2.

NO

- Go to point 5.

2. Checking the electric function of the EVAP purge valve

- Activate: EVAP purge valve (max. 60 s) (Trionic): 30%.
- A sound should be heard from the valve.

Test results OK?

YES

- Go to point 7.

NO

- Go to point 3.

3. Checking the valve's power supply

- Unplug the connector: EVAP canister purge valve: (321)

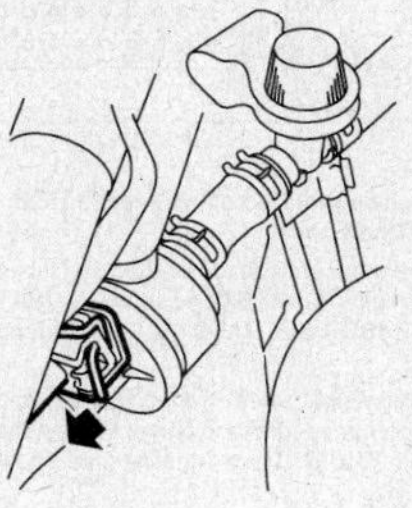

SA1019900020030X

Fig. 24 Code P0455: EVAP Serious Leakage In System (Part 3 of 6). 9-3

- Connect test lamp 86 11 857 to pin 1 of the female connector and a good grounding point.

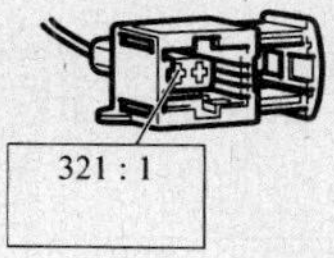

- Activate: EVAP purge valve (max. 60 s) (Trionic): 30%.
- The lamp should light.

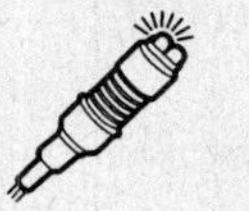

Test results OK?

YES

- Go to point 4.

NO

- Rectify the lead between pin 1 in the female connector and fuse 16B in the dashboard fuse box.
- Go to point 8.

4. Checking the valve's control module output

- Connect test lamp 86 11 857 to pins 1 and 2 of the female connector.

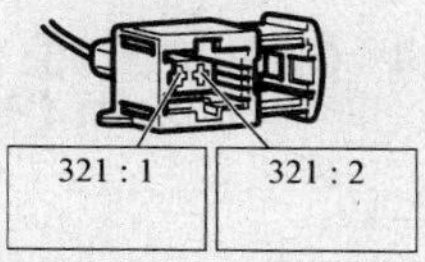

- Activate: EVAP purge valve (max. 60 s) (Trionic): 30%.
- The test lamp should flash.

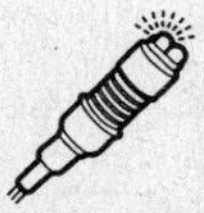

Test results OK?

YES

- Change: EVAP canister purge valve
- Go to point 8.

NO

- Rectify the lead between pin 2 in the female connector and pin 27 on the control module.
- Go to point 8.

SA1019900020040X

Fig. 24 Code P0455: EVAP Serious Leakage In System (Part 4 of 6). 9-3

5. Checking the valve's power supply

- Unplug connector: Solenoid valve, EVAP shut-off: (588).

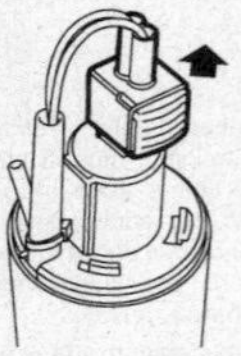

- Connect test lamp 86 11 857 to pin 1 of the female connector and a good grounding point.

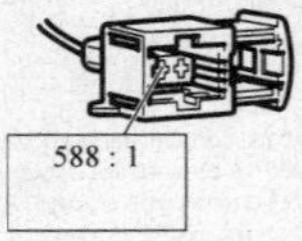

- Activate: Shut-off valve EVAP venting (ON).
- The lamp should light.

Test results OK?

YES

– Go to point 6.

NO

– Rectify the lead between pin 1 in the female connector and fuse 16B in the dashboard fuse box.
– Go to point 8.

6. Checking the valve's control module output

- Connect test lamp 86 11 857 to pins 1 and 2 of the female connector.

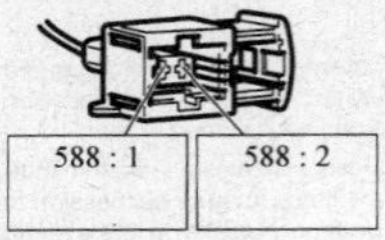

- Activate: Shut-off valve EVAP venting (ON).
- The lamp should light.

Test results OK?

YES

– Change: Solenoid valve, EVAP shut-off.
– Go to point 8.

NO

– Rectify the lead between pin 2 in the female connector and pin 28 on the control module.
– Go to point 8.

SA1019900020050X

Fig. 24 Code P0455: EVAP Serious Leakage In System (Part 5 of 6). 9-3

7. Leakage check

Implement the method 'Checking for leaks in the evaporative emission system', see 53.

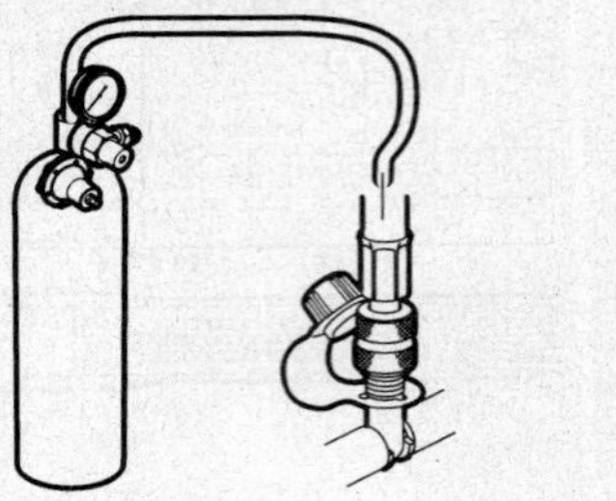

Is there a leak?

YES

– Rectify the fault.
– Go to point 8.

NO

– Go to point 8.

8. Initiate EVAP diagnosis.

- Turn the ignition switch to the ON position.

- Contact the Trionic.

- Clear diagnostic trouble codes: Trionic

- Activate: EVAP Diagnosis.

LEAK

– Fault not rectified.

NO LEAK

– The steps taken to rectify the fault were correct.

SA1019900020060X

Fig. 24 Code P0455: EVAP Serious Leakage In System (Part 6 of 6). 9-3

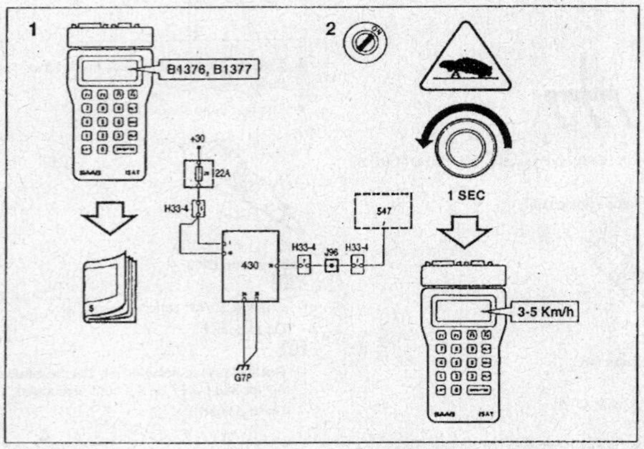

Fault symptom

The SHIFT UP lamp fails to work (certain markets).
Fuel shut-off in all gears.
Low boost pressure in 3rd, 4th and 5th gears, manual transmission.
Possibly ABS warning lamp on.

Conditions

- brake pedal not operated
- engine speed >2000 rpm
- boost pressure >0.3 bar
- no speed signal during the course of 4 seconds

Diagnostic procedure

1 Connect an ISAT scan tool.
Ignition switched on.
Connect the ISAT scan tool to the ABS system and read out diagnostic trouble codes. If diagnostic trouble codes B1376, B1377 are displayed, remedy these faults first

Diagnostic trouble codes in Trionic may be secondary faults.

2 Raid the front assembly of the car with a jack.
Ignition switched on
Select "WHEEL SPEED FR" on the ISAT scan tool menu "READ FUNCTIONS".
Rotate the front right wheel at approx. 1/2 revolution per second. The ISAT scan tool must show 3-5 km/h.
If the measured value is correct, continue with point 5.
If the measured value is incorrect, continue with point 3.

Note

If the ECM for the Saab 9000 has been fitted, a diagnostic trouble code for vehicle speed signal will be generated.
On cars with automatic transmission the diagnostic trouble code may be generated if there is no input from the brake light switch.

SA1029100092010X

Fig. 25 Codes P0500, P0501 & P0502: Vehicle Speed Signal (Part 1 of 3). 9-3 & 900

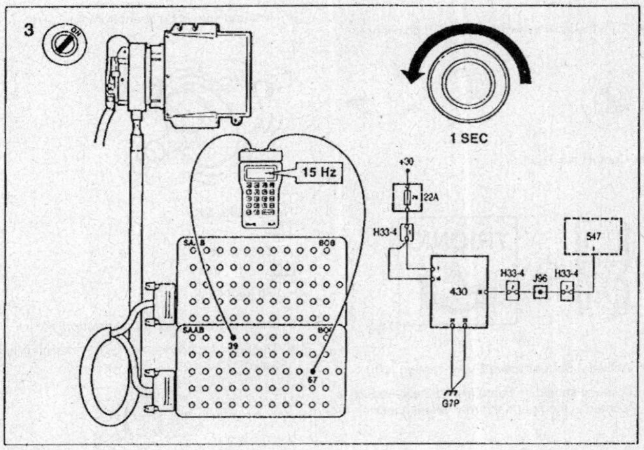

3 With the ignition switched off, connect a BOB.
Ignition switched on.
Connect the measuring leads of the ISAT scan tool between pins 39 and 67 and select the ISAT menu "MEASURING" and the submenu "PULSE".
Rotate the front right wheel manually at approx. 1/2 revolution per second and check that pulses are present. The ISAT scan tool should show approx. 15 Hz.
If the measured value is correct, continue with point 5.
If the measured value is incorrect, continue with point 4.

SA1029100092020X

Fig. 25 Codes P0500, P0501 & P0502: Vehicle Speed Signal (Part 2 of 3). 9-3 & 900

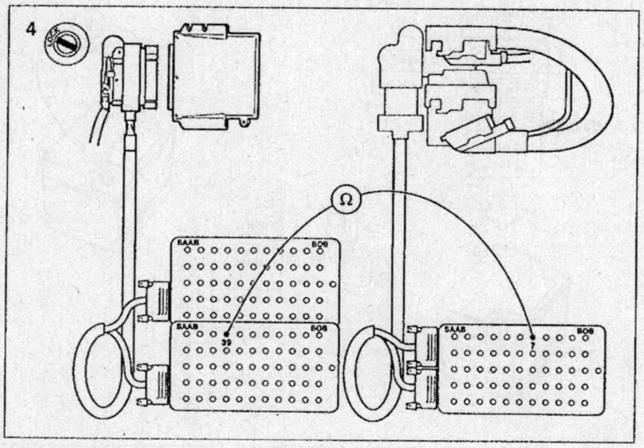

4 Check the lead between pin 7 of the ABS ECM and pin 39 of the Trionic ECM for discontinuity/shorting.

If the lead is OK, continue fault diagnosis Brakes

5 Erase the diagnostic trouble code and drive the car to see whether the DTC is generated again.

If the diagnostic trouble code is registered, replace ECM.

If the diagnostic trouble code is not registered, the action taken is correct. Otherwise the fault is intermittent in nature.

SA1029100092030X

Fig. 25 Codes P0500, P0501 & P0502: Vehicle Speed Signal (Part 3 of 3). 9-3 & 900

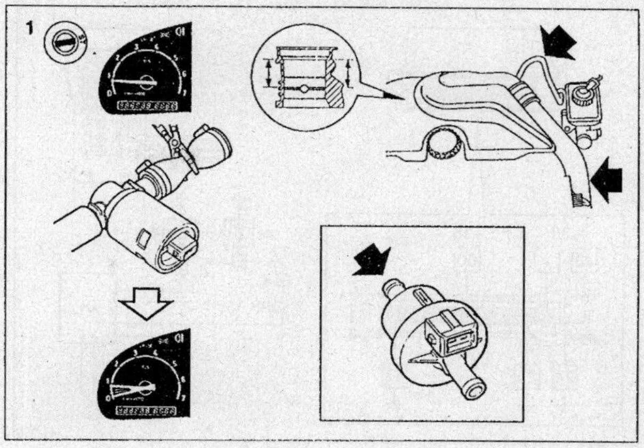

Symptom of fault

Low, high or unsteady idling speed.
Idling speed sensitive to changes in load.

Conditions

- the throttle position sensor indicates idling
- the engine speed is more than 1200 rpm or less than 700 rpm
- normal idling speed cannot be achieved.

Diagnostic procedure

1 Check whether air leakage occurs as follows:

Start the engine and run it at idling speed. Restrict the air flow through the idle air control valve by clamping the air hose with grips.

The idling speed must drop sharply.

If the idling speed is reduced, continue with point 2.

If the idling speed is not reduced, continue fault diagnosis by checking the following:

- air leakage (after the throttle)
- incorrectly adjusted throttle
- faulty brake servo
- purge valve has stuck in the open position

SA1029100093010X

Fig. 26 Code P0505: Idle Air Control Valve (Part 1 of 3). 9-3 & 900

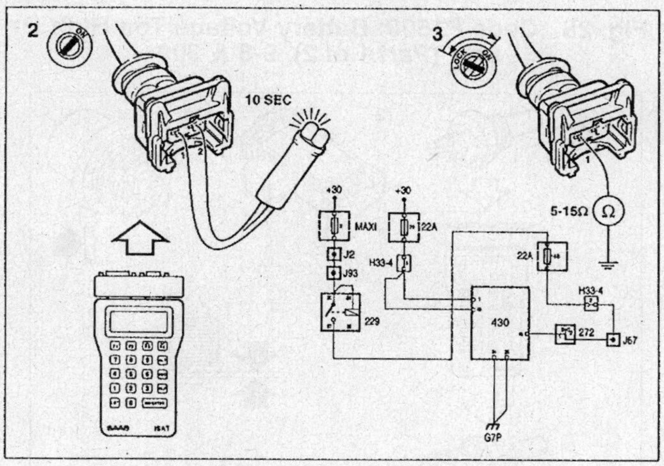

2 Switch off the engine. Ignition switched on.

Unplug the connector of the idle air control valve. Connect the test lamp to the idle air control valve (female connector).

Connect the ISAT scan tool. Select "IAC VALVE" on the "ACTIVATE" menu. The test lamp is activated for 10 seconds, during which it must shine with a steady glow.

If the test lamp does not comes on, continue with point 3.
If the test lamp does not come on, continue with point 5.

3 Check the continuity between the idle air control valve and the ECM.

Measure Ω between the female connector of the idle air control valve, pin 1 and safe grounding point on the engine.

Read the resistance value after the ignition has beeen turned on and then switched off.

The resistance value must be 5-15 Ω.

If the resistance value is correct, the fault is located in the lead between pin 2 and crimped connection J67.

If the resistance value is incorrect, continue with point 4.

SA1029100093020X

Fig. 26 Code P0505: Idle Air Control Valve (Part 2 of 3). 9-3 & 900

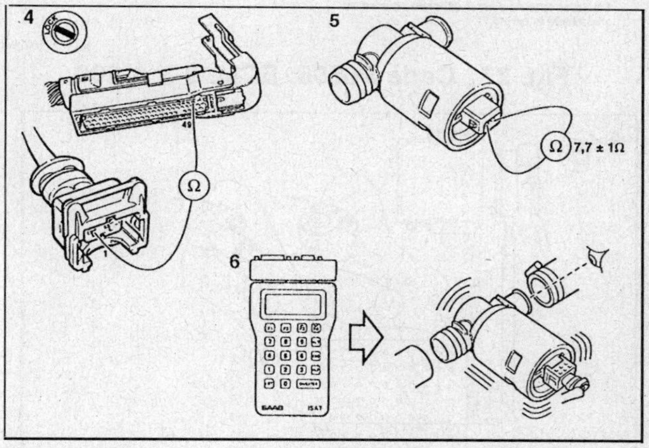

4 Check the lead between pin 1 and pin 49 of the ECM for shorting and discontinuity.

5 Measure the resistance of the idle air control valve. The nominal resistance is 7,7±1 Ω.

If the resistance value is incorrect, fit a new valve.

If the resistance value is correct, continue with point 6.

6 Unplug the valve's air hoses.

Connect the electrical connector of the idle air control valve.

Select "IAC VALVE" on the ISAT menu "ACTIVATE". Activation takes place for 10 seconds. If a longer activation time is required, the command must be repeated.

Check visually that the slide turns without a tendency to seize.

If the slide seizes or sticks, fit a new idle air control valve.
If the idle air control valve operates normally, continue with point 7.

7 Erase the diagnostic trouble code and drive the car to see whether the DTC is generated again.

If the diagnostic trouble code is registered, **replace ECM.**

If the diagnostic trouble code is not registered, the action taken is correct. Otherwise the fault is intermittent in nature.

SA1029100093030X

Fig. 26 Code P0505: Idle Air Control Valve (Part 3 of 3). 9-3 & 900

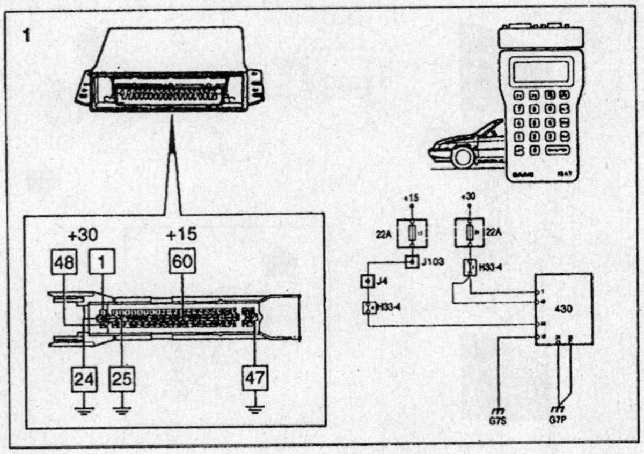

Symptom of fault

Undefinable (different functions may be affected depending on internal memory fault/ program fault).

Conditions

When the ignition is switched on, the ECM's program does not correspond to that originally programmed.

Diagnostic procedure

1 Erase the diagnostic trouble code and drive the car to see whether the DTC is generated again.

If the diagnostic trouble code is registered, remove the ECM and check its connector, particularly for backing-out of contact sleeves. Check the ground and voltage supply of the ECM.

Refit the ECM, erase the diagnostic trouble code and drive the car again.

If the diagnostic trouble code recurs, replace ECM.

If the diagnostic trouble code is not registered, the action taken is correct. Otherwise the fault is intermittent in nature.

SA1029100094000X

Fig. 27 Code P0605: ECM. 9-3 & 900

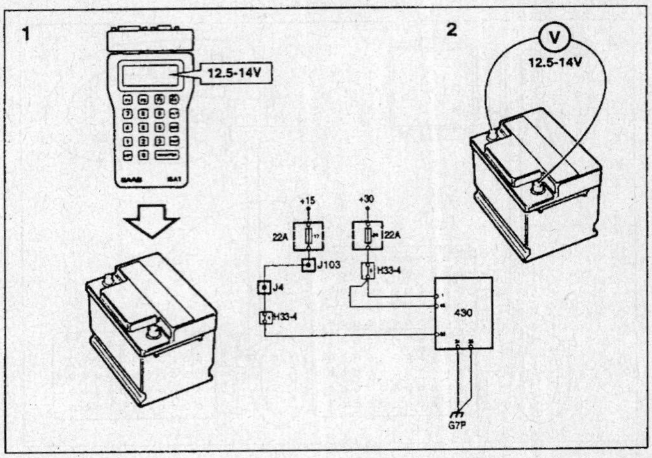

Symptom of fault

Possible drivability problems.

Conditions

- engine speed >2000 rpm
- +15 <8 V or >16 V for 30 seconds.

Note

The fault diagnosis presupposes that the condition of the battery and its connections has been checked.

Diagnostic procedure

1 Connect an ISAT scan tool.

Start the engine and run it at idling speed. Select the "BATTERY VOLTAGE" command on the ISAT menu "READ FUNCTIONS". The ISAT must show 12.5 - 14.0 V.

2 Measure the battery voltage directly across the poles of the battery.

The voltage value must be 12.5 - 14.0 V.

Compare the reading with the ISAT reading. The difference must be <0.5 V.

If the difference is <0.5 V, continue with point 4.

If the difference is >0.5 V, disconnect grounding point G7P, clean the contact surfaces and refit, then repeat point 2.

If the voltage difference is still >0.5 V, continue with point 3.

SA1029100095010X

Fig. 28 Code P1500: Battery Voltage Too High Or Low (Part 1 of 2). 9-3 & 900

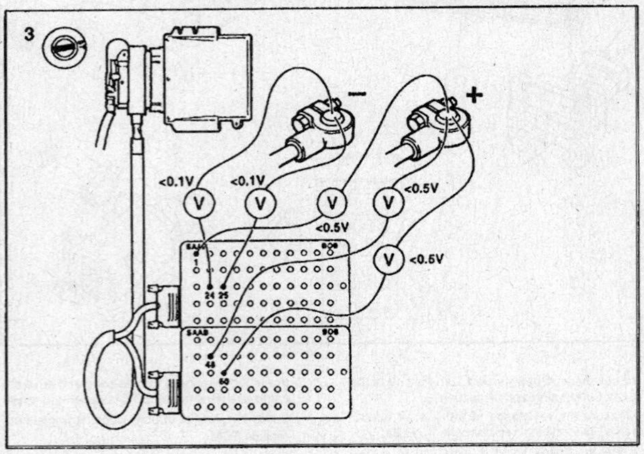

3 With the ignition switched off, connect a BOB.

Start the engine.

Check battery voltage and ground connection by measuring voltage.

- Batt+ - pin 1 ________ <0.5 V
- Batt+ – pin 48 ________ <0.5 V
- Batt+ –pin 60 ________ <0.5 V
- pin 24 – Batt - ________ <0.1 V
- pin 25 – Batt - ________ <0.1 V

If any voltage value is incorrect, check and if necessary remedy the fault in the wiring.

If the voltage values are correct, continue with point 4.

4 Erase the diagnostic trouble code and drive the car to check whether the DTC is generated again.

If the diagnostic trouble code is registered, replace ECM.

If the diagnostic trouble code is not registered, the action taken is correct. Otherwise the fault is intermittent in nature.

SA1029100095020X

Fig. 28 Code P1500: Battery Voltage Too High Or Low (Part 2 of 2). 9-3 & 900

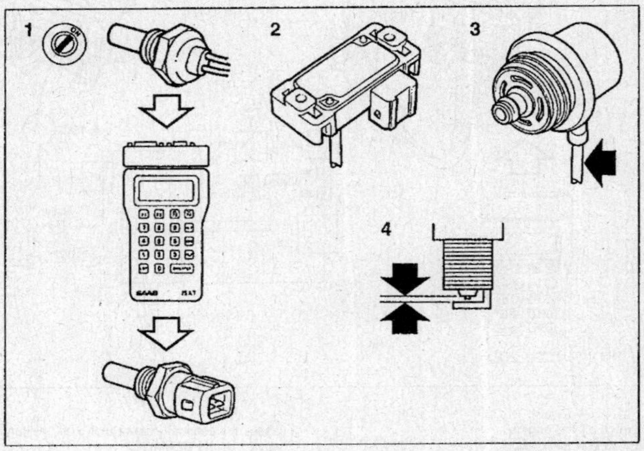

General fault diagnosis for poor drivability is difficult to carry out.

However, a number of tips are given below.

1 Cold-starting and warming-up problems can be caused by the coolant temperature sensor indicating an engine temperature that is too high.

Use an ISAT and read off the coolant temperature in Trionic, then contact ICE and use the ICE's coolant temperature as a reference. The difference between these two temperature readings may be ±5°C because of tolerances.

If Trionic does not have a reference ground from crimped connection J68 to pin 66, Trionic shows a coolant temperature that is approx. 20°C too high even if the temperature sensor is OK.

2 If the pressure sensor does not produce a correct voltage throughout the pressure range, this too can cause drivability problems.

Check also the hose to the pressure sensor for leaks.

3 Check the hose to the fuel pressure regulator for leaks.

4 The electrode gap of the spark plugs is of great significance to the running of the engine.

A gap that is too large causes misfiring at full load.

A gap that is too small causes unsteady idling.

5 Check the colour of the insulator base of the spark plugs. If any spark plug has a distinctly lighter colour, this may be due to this cylinder receiving a fuel/air mixture that is too lean.

If so, carry out flow measurement on the injectors.

SA1029100118000X

Fig. 29 Code —: Poor Driveability Fault Diagnosis. 9-3 & 900

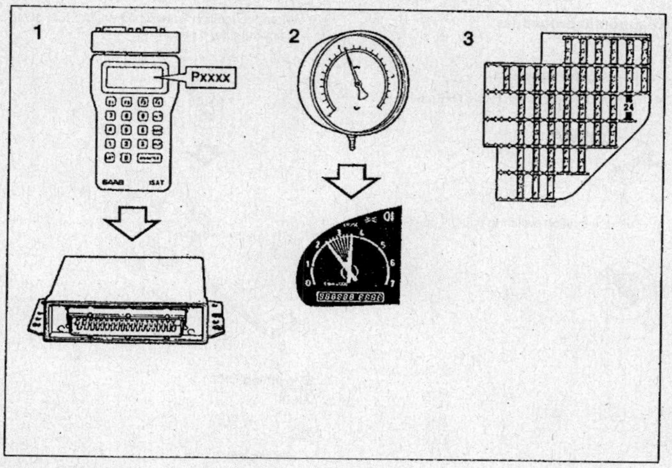

General fault diagnosis for poor performance is difficult to carry out.

However, a number of tips are given below.

1 First read out any diagnostic trouble codes in Trionic and take remedial action if necessary.

2 Check the basic charging pressure and max. boost pressure, and use an ISAT to check that the pressure sensor value corersponds to that of the pressure gauge.

Note that the B204L engine in the Saab 900 only has max. boost pressure in 3rd, 4th and 5th gears (manual transmission).

3 Check fuse 24 to the boost pressure control valve. If the fuse is blown, first check the resistance of the valve.

A fuse that is too strong combined with a short-circuited valve can interfere with the ECM.

SA1029100119010X

Fig. 30 Code —: Poor Performance Fault Diagnosis (Part 1 of 3). 9-3 & 900

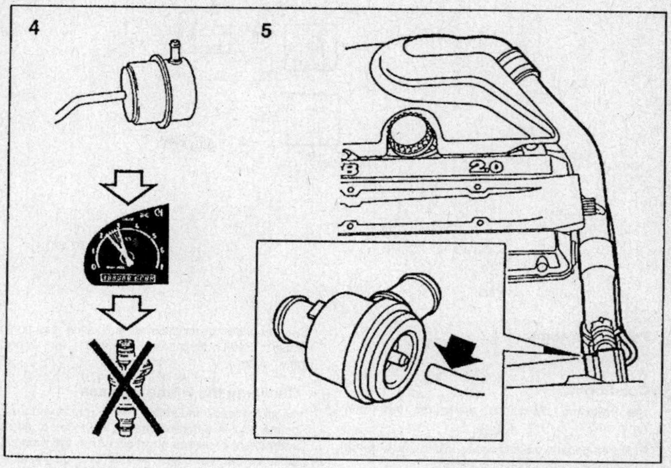

4 Faults in the basic engine, intake, exhaust or turbo systems can be easily detected.

Disconnect the hose to the wastegate. At wide open throttle, the pressure switch function must operate before approx. 3000 rpm. If so, faults in the above system can probably be ruled out. Activate "RESET BOOST PRESSURE" with an ISAT after this test.

5 Leaks between the compressor outlet and throttle body or in the by-pass valve or its regulating hose cause low boost pressure. Activate "RESET BOOST PRESSURE" with the ISAT after repairing the leak.

SA1029100119020X

Fig. 30 Code —: Poor Performance Fault Diagnosis (Part 2 of 3). 9-3 & 900

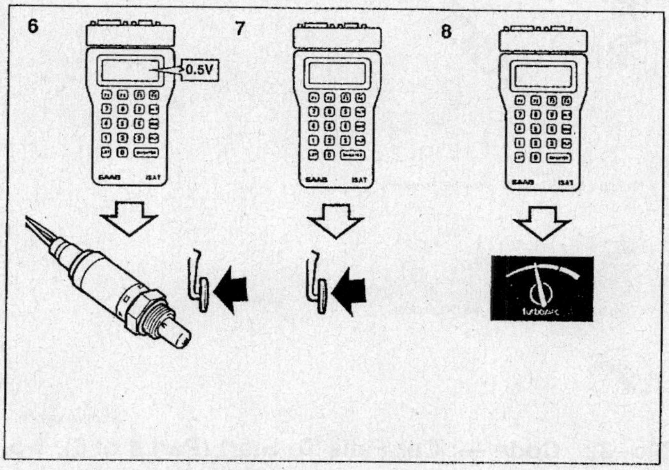

6 A fuel flow that is too low from the fuel pump or through the injectors is noticeable when driving at wide open throttle.

Connect an ISAT and read off the voltage in the oxygen sensor.

When driving at wide open throttle, this must be >0.5 V. If so, faults in the above systems can probably be ruled out.

7 If the ECM for any reason initiates basic charging pressure, this can be observed using an ISAT. Select "READ FUNCTIONS" and the "BASIC CHARGING PRESSURE" command. When driving at wide open throttle, the ISAT will show the cause, if any. If the ISAT shows that knocking is occurring, the cause may be poor fuel quality.

8 A subjective assessment that the car's performance is inadequate may be reinforced by too low a value being shown on the pressure gauge of the main instrument. Carry out adjustment in MIU 2 (main instrument 2) using an ISAT if necessary.

SA1029100119030X

Fig. 30 Code —: Poor Performance Fault Diagnosis (Part 3 of 3). 9-3 & 900

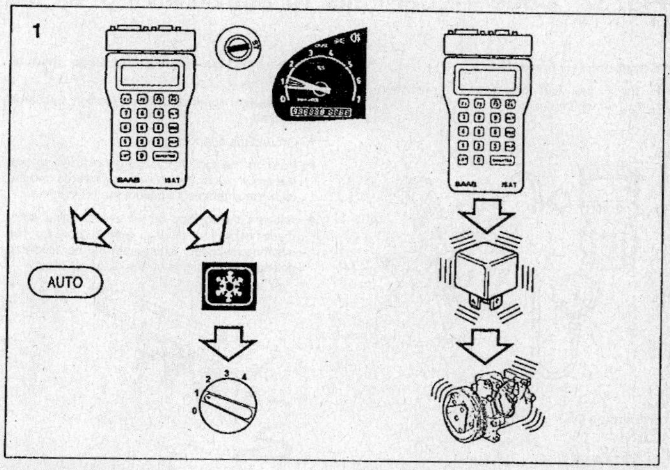

Symptom of fault

The AC compressor does not work.

Conditions

For the Trionic system to activate the AC compressor, the engine must have been started and the pressure sensor and throttle position sensor must be OK.

Diagnostic procedure

1 Start the engine.

Connect an ISAT scan tool.

Contact the Trionic system. Select "READ ON/OFF" and the command "AC IN" in the ISAT.

Activate the compressor from the facia:

- manual AC: fan ON and AC button depressed
- ACC: select AUTO position

Note that the anti-freeze thermostat periodically breaks the signal between ICE and Trionic.

The ISAT must show ON and the engine speed must rise. If this does not happen, the fault is before Trionic.

Stop the engine, then switch the ignition on again.

2 Select "ACTIVATE" and the "AC OUT" command in the ISAT.

Both the AC relay and the compressor coupling must now be audible.

If not, the fault is after Trionic.

SA1029100122000X

Fig. 31 Code —: A/C Fault Diagnosis. 9-3 & 900

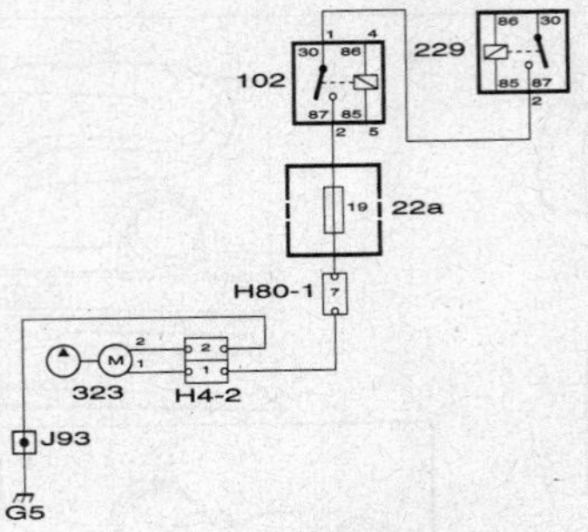

Fault symptoms

Car fails to start.

Conditions

The following conditions apply for this fault symptom:

- No diagnostic trouble codes in the car with the symptom description in question.
- There is petrol in the tank.
- Starter motor is in working order.

Diagnostic help

Most of the functions that can prevent the engine from being started are monitored by self-diagnosis and therefore generate a diagnostic trouble code if they develop a fault. Consequently, this fault diagnosis concerns faults that can prevent the engine from being started but are not monitored.

First check that the fuel pump is in working order and delivers pressure. Then check the ignition discharge module and spark plugs.

Diagnostic tool functions related to this fault are:

- Activation of fuel pump relay.
- Activation of ignition trigger.

See also the description of activating functions under "Fault diagnosis, general" for more information.

Checking the wiring harness

Jiggle the leads and in-line connectors at various points and in different directions to detect any intermittent breaks or short circuits in the wiring. Observe the multimeter, test lamp or diagnostic tool while doing this.

SA1019900097010X

Fig. 32 Code —: Car Fails To Start (Part 1 of 6). 9-5

Diagnostic procedure

1. Checking the fuel pump

- Turn the ignition switch to the OFF position.

- Turn the ignition switch to the ON position.

- When the ignition is switched on, the fuel pump is activated for 1 second.

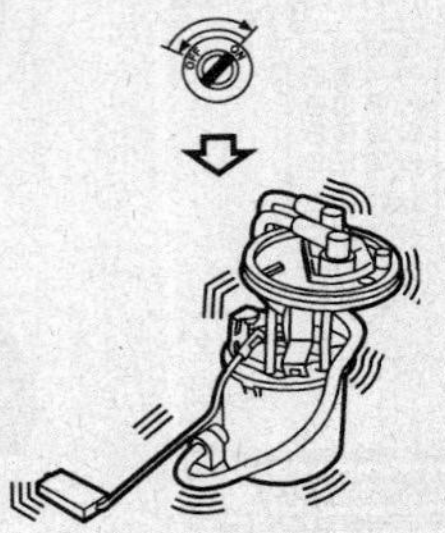

Everything OK?

YES

- Go to point 2.

NO

- Go to point 4.

SA1019900097020X

Fig. 32 Code —: Car Fails To Start (Part 2 of 6). 9-5

2. Checking fuel pressure

- Check the fuel pressure as described in 'Adjustment/replacement'.

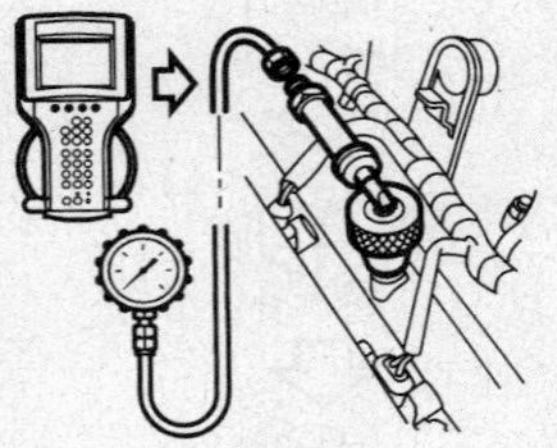

Everything OK?

YES

- Go to point 3.

NO

- Adjust.

- Go to point 7.

3. Checking the ignition discharge module, continued

- Fit the test spark plug in the ignition discharge module.
- Ground the spark plugs.
- Position the ignition discharge module so that the spark plugs are inclined downwards and the oil in the ignition coils covers the HT outputs.
- Activate the ignition trigger by selecting automatic activation of the ignition coil for the misfiring cylinder. Choose from the following activation commands on the diagnostic tool:

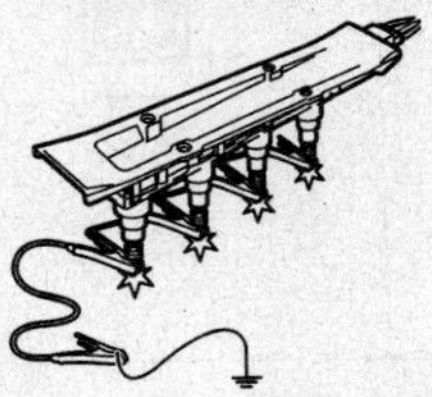

- Ignition coil, cyl. 1
- Ignition coil, cyl. 2
- Ignition coil, cyl. 3
- Ignition coil, cyl. 4
- Check whether the relevant test spark plug produces a spark. If necessary, compare it by activating another ignition coil.

Everything OK?

YES

- Change: Spark plugs
- Go to point 7.

NO

- Change: Ignition discharge module
- Go to point 7.

SA1019900097030X

Fig. 32 Code —: Car Fails To Start (Part 3 of 6). 9-5

4. Checking the pump relay output

- Remove fuse No. 19

- Connect test lamp 86 11 857 to the upper pin and a good grounding point.

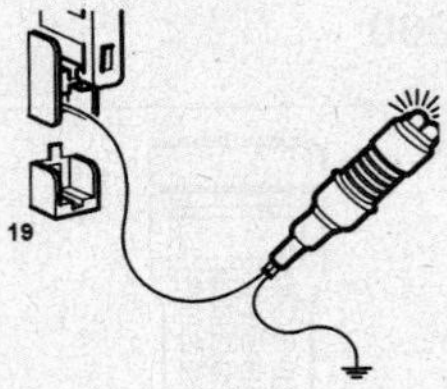

- Turn the ignition switch to the OFF position.

- Turn the ignition switch to the ON position.

- The test lamp should light for 1 second.

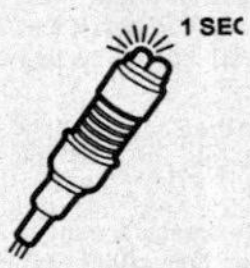

- Check fuse 19 at the same time and change it if necessary.

Everything OK?

YES

- Go to point 5.

NO

- Repair or replace the faulty lead or relay.
- Go to point 7.

SA1019900097040X

Fig. 32 Code —: Car Fails To Start (Part 4 of 6). 9-5

5. Check the lead to the pump

- Unplug the connector: Fuel pump: (323)

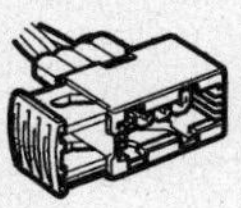

- Connect test lamp 86 11 857 to pins 1 and 2 of the female connector.

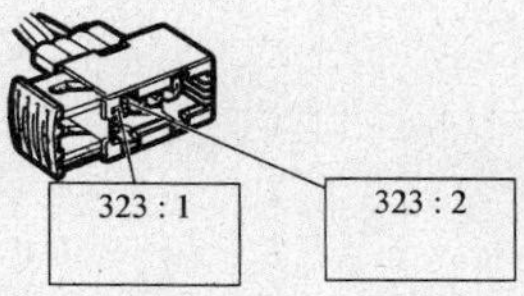

- Turn the ignition switch to the OFF position.

- Turn the ignition switch to the ON position.

- The test lamp should light for 1 second.

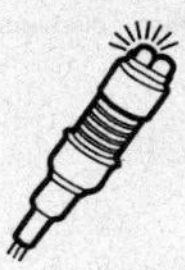

Everything OK?

YES

- Go to point 6.

NO

- The lead from fuse No. 19 to pin No. 1, or from grounding point G5 to pin No. 2, is faulty.
- Go to point 7.

SA1019900097050X

Fig. 32 Code —: Car Fails To Start (Part 5 of 6). 9-5

6. Checking the wiring harness up to the fuel pump

- Check the short wiring harness as far as the pump.

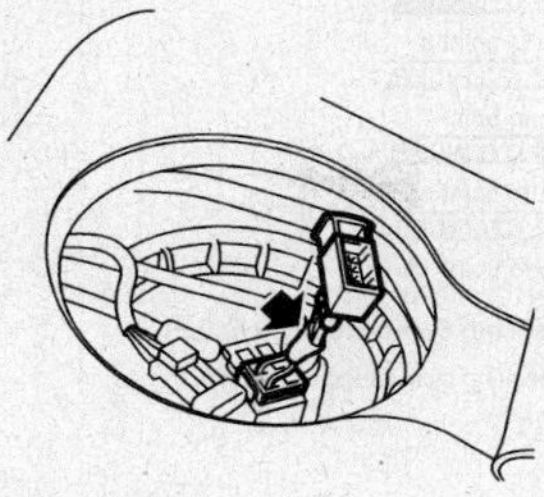

Everything OK?

YES

- Change: Fuel pump
- Go to point 7.

NO

- Repair or replace the faulty lead.
- Go to point 7.

7. Final check

- Clear the diagnostic trouble codes in all systems.

- Carry out a functionality test.

Everything OK?

YES

- The steps taken to rectify the fault were correct.

NO

- See **"Engine Control Module (ECM)" under "Component Replacement"**

SA1019900097060X

Fig. 32 Code —: Car Fails To Start (Part 6 of 6). 9-5

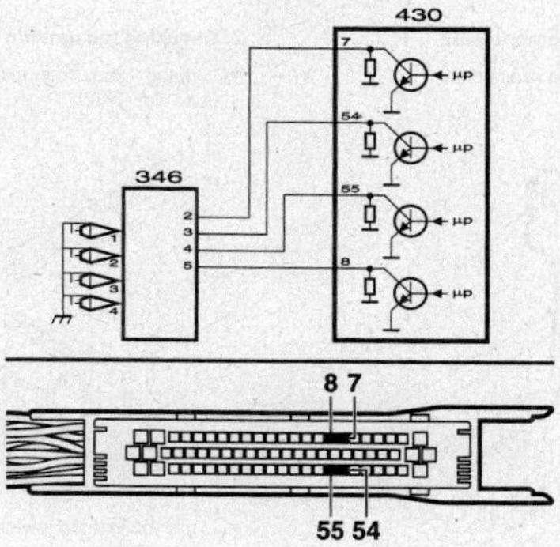

Fault symptoms

Misfiring.

Conditions

The following conditions apply for this fault symptom:

- No diagnostic trouble codes in the car with the symptom description in question.

Diagnostic help

Start fault diagnosis by changing the spark plugs and then use the misfire counters to determine whether one or more cylinders are misfiring.

If only one cylinder is misfiring, concentrate fault diagnosis on that cylinder and check the compression, the ignition trigger from the control module, the ignition discharge module, and finally the injector.

If several cylinders are misfiring, check components and cylinders that are common to all the cylinders. First carry out a general check of the leads, connectors and hoses, and then a thorough check of the compression, ignition and fuel system.

Diagnostic tool functions related to this fault are:

- Misfiring, cylinder 1.
- Misfiring, cylinder 2.
- Misfiring, cylinder 3.
- Misfiring, cylinder 4.
- Multiplicative adaptation, in %
- Additive adaptation, in mg/c.
- Closed loop, in %.
- Purge adaptation, in %.
- Mass air flow deviation from that calculated, in %.
- Activation of misfire counter zeroizing.
- Activation of ignition trigger.
- Activation of injector test.
- Activation of pump test.

SA1019900098010X

Fig. 33 Code —: Misfire (Part 1 of 17). 9-5

See also the description of activating functions under "Fault diagnosis, general" for more information.

Checking the wiring harness

Jiggle the leads and in-line connectors at various points and in different directions to detect any intermittent breaks or short circuits in the wiring. Observe the multimeter, test lamp or diagnostic tool while doing this.

Diagnostic procedure

1. Component replacement

- Change all spark plugs.

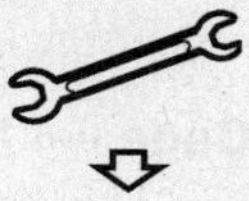

- Turn the ignition switch to the ON position.

- Contact the Trionic.

- Activate: Zeroize misfiring counters

SA1019900098020X

Fig. 33 Code —: Misfire (Part 2 of 17). 9-5

- Carry out a road test in the load and rpm ranges in which the engine misfires.
- Obtain the following readouts with the diagnostic tool:

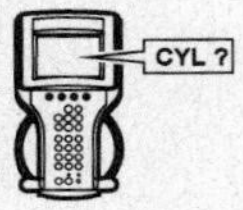

- Misfiring, cylinder 1.
- Misfiring, cylinder 2.
- Misfiring, cylinder 3.
- Misfiring, cylinder 4.

Note
A few regularly-spaced misfires may occur without this indicating the presence of a fault.

- Specify the number of cylinders that have misfired.

ONE CYLINDER.
– Go to point 2.
SEVERAL CYLINDERS.
– Go to point 19.

2. Choice of cylinder

- Specify the cylinder in which combustion is to be checked:

NO. 1 CYLINDER
– Go to point 3.
NO. 2 CYLINDER
– Go to point 7.
NO. 3 CYLINDER
– Go to point 11.
NO. 4 CYLINDER
– Go to point 15.

3. Checking cylinder compression

- Checking cylinder compression.

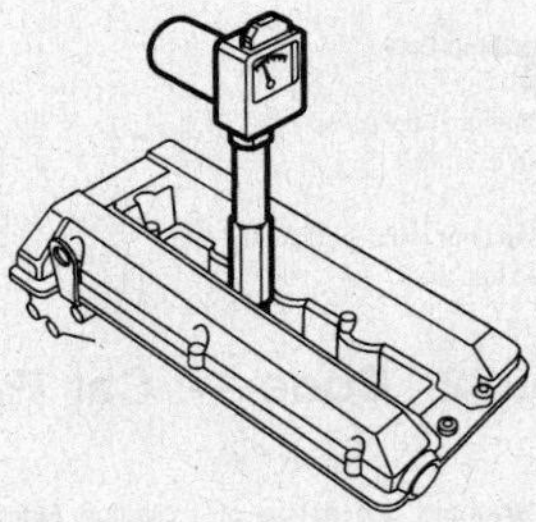

Everything OK?
YES
– Go to point 4.
NO
– Rectify the fault.
– Go to point 33.

SA1019900098030X

Fig. 33 Code —: Misfire (Part 3 of 17). 9-5

4. Checking the ignition coil for cylinder 1

- Unplug the connector: Ignition discharge module: (346)

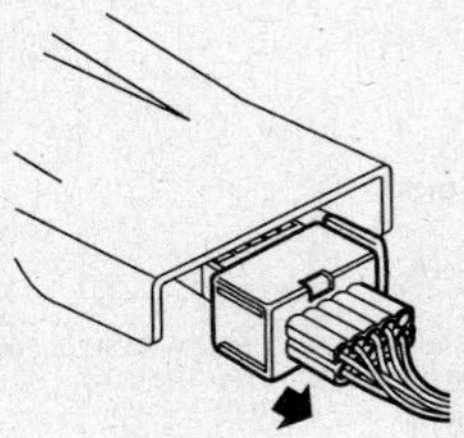

- Turn the ignition switch to the ON position.

- Connect test lamp 86 11 857 to pins 10 and 2 of the female connector.

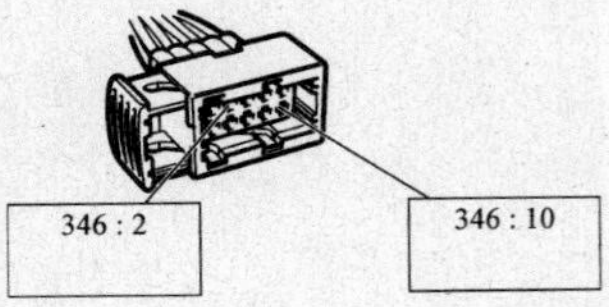

- Activate: Ignition oil, cyl. 1

- The test lamp should light

Everything OK?
YES
– Go to point 5.
NO
– The ignition trigger lead to the ignition discharge module is faulty.
– Go to point 33.

SA1019900098040X

Fig. 33 Code —: Misfire (Part 4 of 17). 9-5

5. Checking the ignition discharge module

- Check visually that:
- the four rubber seals are intact
- the four contact springs are OK
- the connector is free from corrosion and moisture

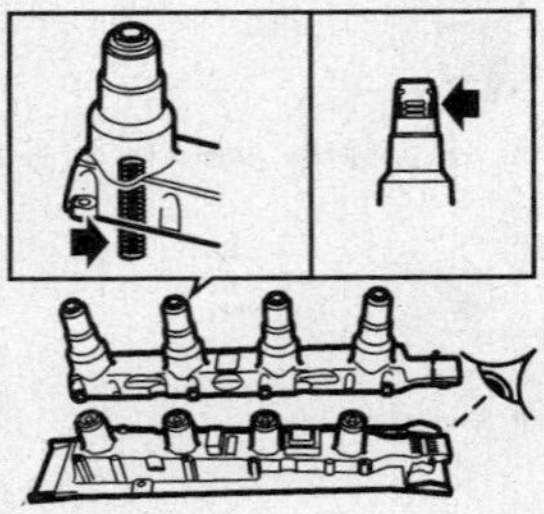

Everything OK?
YES
– Go to point 6.
NO
– Rectify the fault.
– Go to point 33.

6. Checking the ignition discharge module, continued

- Fit the test spark plug in the ignition discharge module.
- Ground the spark plugs.
- Position the ignition discharge module so that the spark plugs are inclined downwards and the oil in the ignition coils covers the HT outputs.
- Activate: Ignition oil, cyl. 1

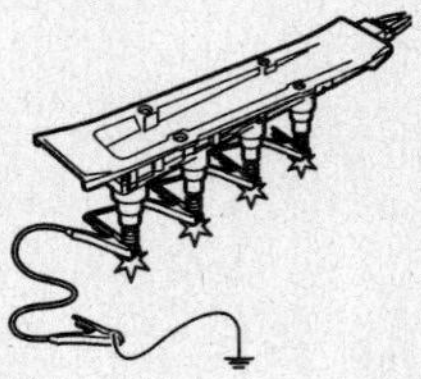

- Select automatic activation.
- Check whether the relevant test spark plug produces a spark. If necessary, compare it by activating another ignition coil.

Everything OK?
YES
– Check the injector as described in 'Checking injector flow capacity'.
– Go to point 33.
NO
– Change: Ignition discharge module
– Go to point 33.

SA1019900098050X

Fig. 33 Code —: Misfire (Part 5 of 17). 9-5

7. Checking cylinder compression

- Checking cylinder compression.

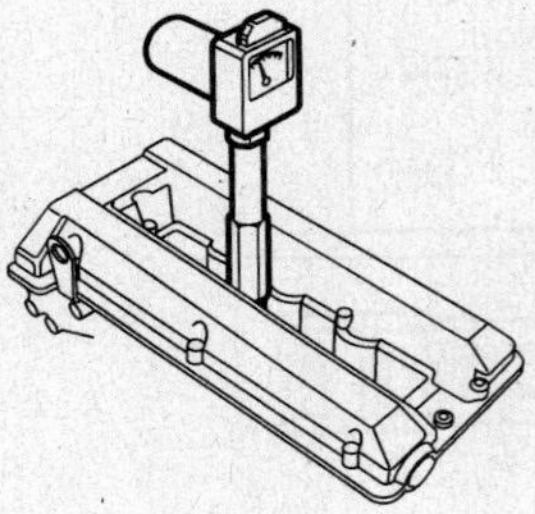

Everything OK?
YES
– Go to point 8.
NO
– Rectify the fault.
– Go to point 33.

8. Checking the ignition coil for cylinder 2

- Unplug the connector: Ignition discharge module: (346)

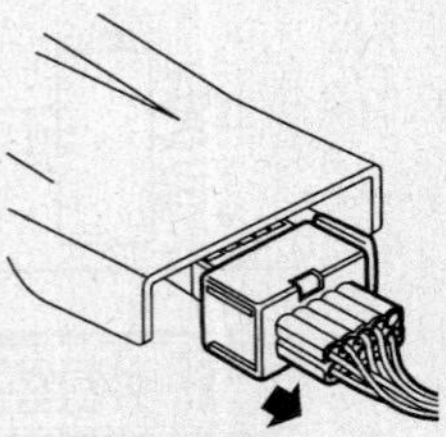

- Turn the ignition switch to the ON position.

- Connect test lamp 86 11 857 to pins 10 and 3 of the female connector.

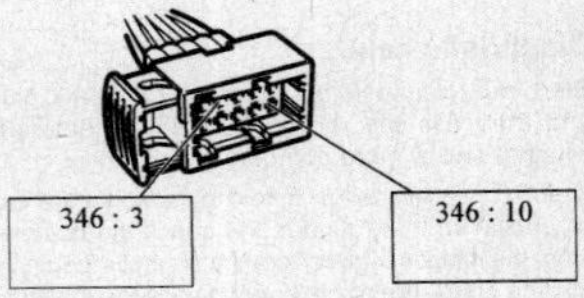

- Activate: Ignition coil, cyl. 2

SA1019900098060X

Fig. 33 Code —: Misfire (Part 6 of 17). 9-5

- The test lamp should light

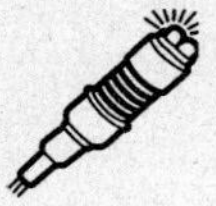

Everything OK?

YES

– Go to point 9.

NO

– The ignition trigger lead to the ignition discharge module is faulty.
– Go to point 33.

9. Checking the ignition discharge module

- Check visually that:
- the four rubber seals are intact
- the four contact springs are OK
- the connector is free from corrosion and moisture

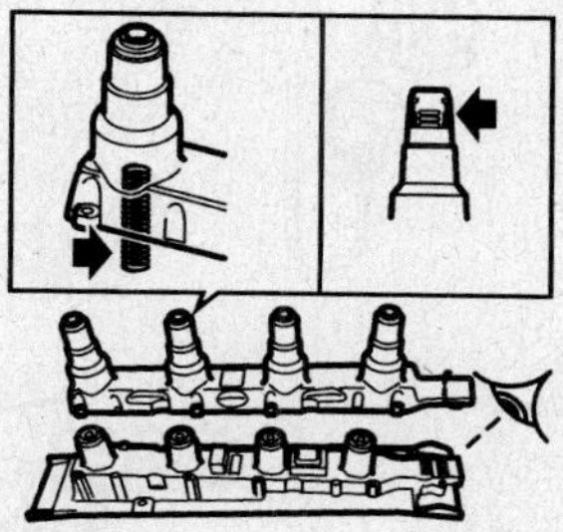

Everything OK?

YES

– Go to point 10.

NO

– Rectify the fault.
– Go to point 33.

SA1019900098070X

Fig. 33 Code —: Misfire (Part 7 of 17). 9-5

Diagnostic tool functions related to this fault are:

- Atmosphere absolute pressure, in kPa.
- Charge air absolute pressure, in kPa
- Manifold absolute pressure, in kPa.
- Mass air flow, deviation from requested, in %.
- Mass air flow, deviation from calculated, in %.
- Engine torque used at current rpm, in %.
- Charge air adaptation, in %.
- All readings in the "MASS AIR FLOW REQUEST" group.
- Activation of the charge air control valve.

See also description of test readings and activation under "Fault diagnosis, general" for more information.

Checking the wiring harness

Jiggle the leads and in-line connectors at various points and in different directions to detect any intermittent breaks or short circuits in the wiring. Observe the multimeter, test lamp or diagnostic tool while doing this.

Diagnostic procedure

1. Checking the manifold absolute pressure sensor

- Turn the ignition switch to the ON position.

- Contact the Trionic.

- Obtain readings for the absolute pressure sensors as described in the instructions below. If any reading differs by more than 10 kPa from the others, the sensor is defective and should be changed.

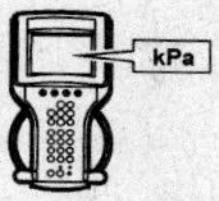

- Reading: Intake manifold Absolute pressure (Trionic).
- Reading: Charge air Absolute pressure (Trionic).
- Reading: Atmosphere Absolute pressure (Trionic).
- The manifold absolute pressure sensor does not affect engine performance but the mass air flow sensor value will be compared with the MAP sensor value later on in the course of fault diagnosis.
- The manifold absolute pressure sensor in the control module will affect engine performance if it shows too low a value.

SA1019900098080X

Fig. 33 Code —: Misfire (Part 8 of 17). 9-5

- Drive the car in top gear with a steady, high engine load.

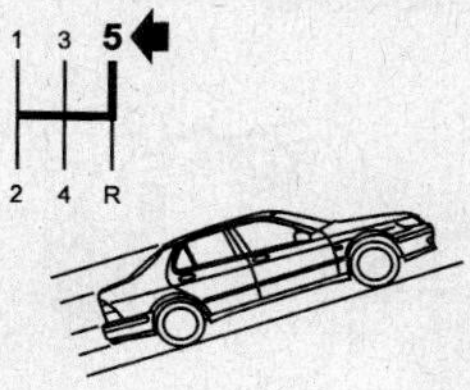

- Driving uphill is recommended.
- Test value: Mass air flow Deviation from Computed value (Trionic).
- State what the diagnostic tool shows:

15% TO 25%

– Go to point 2.

OTHER VALUE

– Go to point 3.

2. Checking air leakage before throttle valve

- Check for the presence of an air leak, using the method described in 'Checking for leaks in the intake system'.

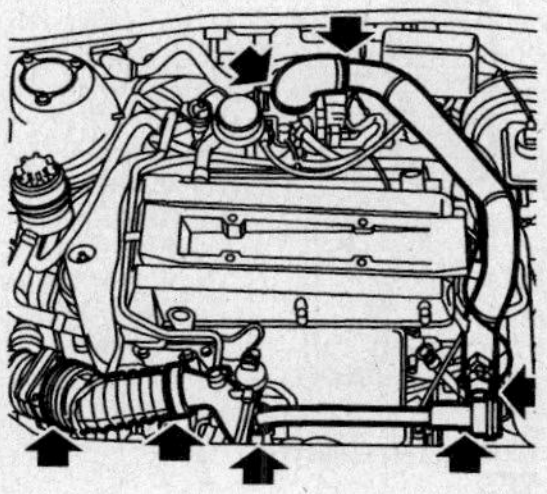

Everything OK?

YES

– Change: Mass air flow sensor
– Go to point 15.

NO

– Rectify the fault.
– Go to point 15.

SA1019900098090X

Fig. 33 Code —: Misfire (Part 9 of 17). 9-5

3. Checking mass air flow variation

- Test reading: Mass air flow, deviation from requested (Trionic).
- Drive the car at wide open throttle from a low engine speed.

>2000

- Driving uphill is recommended.
- When engine speed exceeds 2000 rpm, the value should stabilize at +/- 5%.

Everything OK?

YES

– Go to point 4.

NO

– Go to point 13.

4. Checking the mass air flow limiter

- Drive the car at wide open throttle. With a manual gearbox, engage 2nd gear or higher.

- Driving uphill is recommended.
- Obtain the following readouts with the diagnostic tool:

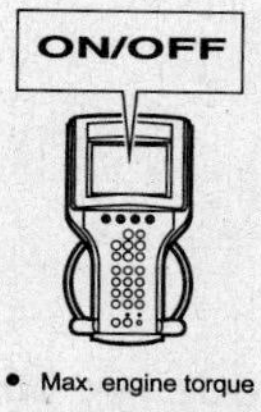

- Max. engine torque
- Manual gearbox
- Automatic transmission (Bus from TCM)
- Specify whether any mass air flow limitation is active.

ONE

– Go to point 8.

NONE

– Go to point 5.

SA1019900098100X

Fig. 33 Code —: Misfire (Part 10 of 17). 9-5

5. Checking the mass air flow limiter, continued

- Obtain the following readout with the diagnostic tool:

- Knock control

Is knock control active?

YES

– Go to point 6.

NO

– Go to point 8.

6. Checking engine torque

- It is not easy to say how much knocking can be permitted as this will depend on the circumstances. The tendency to knock is increased by the following factors: low octane rating, high coolant temperature, high outside temperature, high altitude, and high engine load.
- The fact that knock control reduces engine torque by less than 15% is considered normal under ordinary operating conditions.

- Drive the car at wide open throttle. With a manual gearbox, engage 2nd gear or higher.

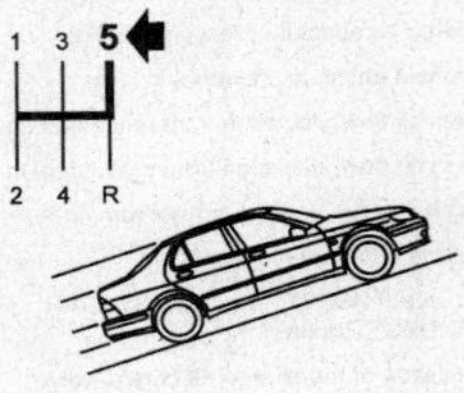

- Driving uphill is recommended.
- Obtain the following readout with the diagnostic tool:
- Max. engine torque at current engine rpm
- When engine speed exceeds 2000 rpm, the value should stabilize at above 85%.

Everything OK?

YES

– Go to point 15.

NO

– The cause of the poor power output is intensified knock control.
– Check the condition and heat range of the spark plugs.
– Check the type of petrol used. The octane rating indicates the petrol's resistance to knocking.
– Go to point 7.

SA1019900098110X

Fig. 33 Code —: Misfire (Part 11 of 17). 9-5

7. Checking engine torque

- Check the fuel pressure, pressure response and flow rate.

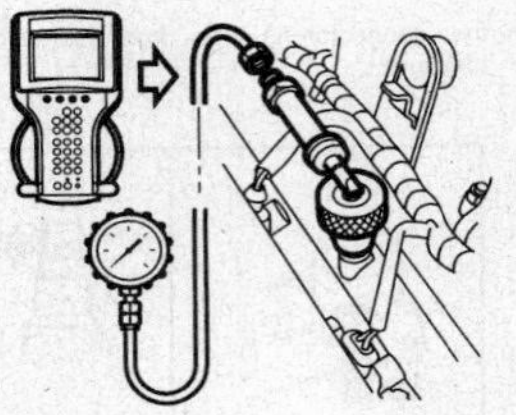

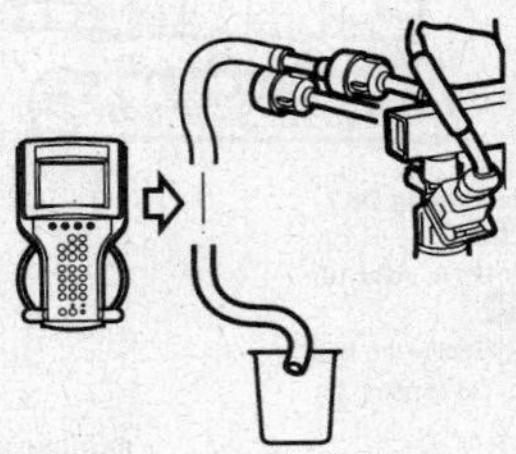

- If necessary, try changing the ignition discharge module.

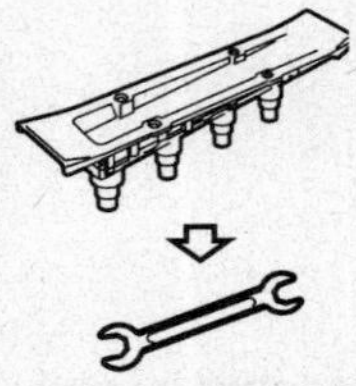

- Clear the diagnostic trouble codes in all systems.

- Carry out a functionality test.

Everything OK?

YES

– The steps taken to rectify the fault were correct.

NO

– See 'Before changing a control module'.

SA1019900098120X

Fig. 33 Code —: Misfire (Part 12 of 17). 9-5

10. Checking injector flow rate

- Check the injector flow rate capacity.

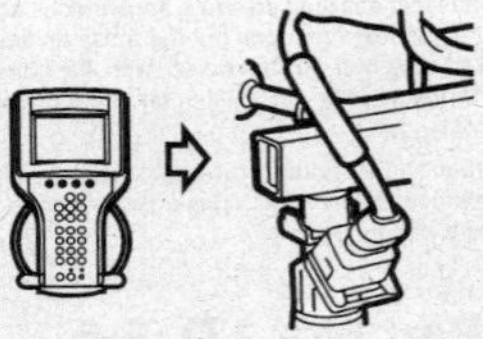

Are the injectors' flow rates OK?

YES

– Go to point 11.

NO

– Follow the diagnostic procedure described in the 'Adjustment/replacement' section of the 'Fuel system' service category.
– Go to point 11.

11. Final check, fuel fault

- Clear diagnostic trouble codes: Trionic

- Unplug the connector: EVAP canister purge valve: (321)

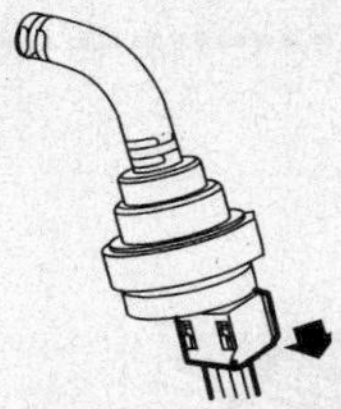

- Connect a test lamp to the female connector.
- Start the engine and run it at idling speed until the coolant temperature exceeds 75 degrees C.

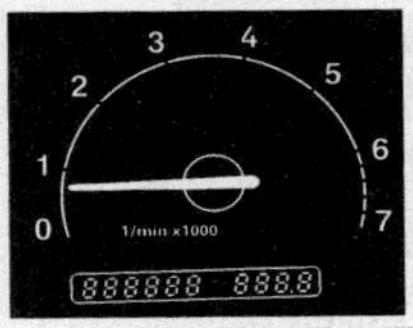

SA1019900098140X

Fig. 33 Code —: Misfire (Part 14 of 17). 9-5

8. Checking the fuel supply

- Check the fuel pressure as described in 'Adjustment/replacement'.

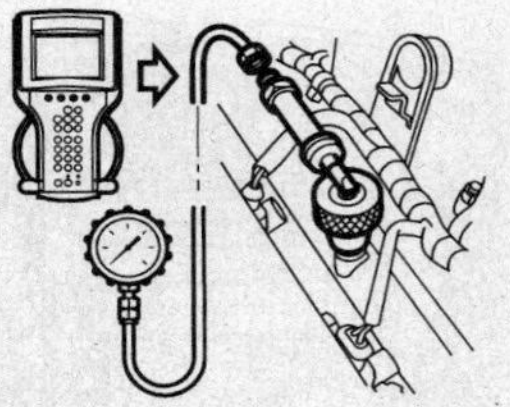

Is the fuel pressure OK?

YES

– Go to point 9

NO

– Adjust.

– Go to point 11.

9. Checking the fuel pump flow rate

- Check the fuel pump flow rate as described in 'Adjustment/replacement'.

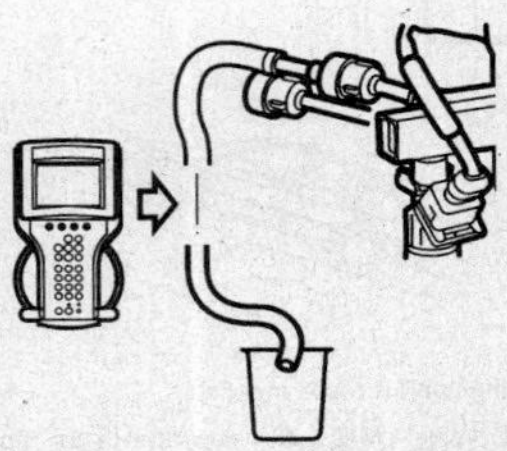

Is the fuel pump flow rate OK?

YES

– Go to point 10.

NO

– Adjust.

– Go to point 11.

SA1019900098130X

Fig. 33 Code —: Misfire (Part 13 of 17). 9-5

- Test value: Purging Adaptation (Trionic)
- State what the diagnostic tool shows:

-15% TO +15%

– Go to point 12.

OTHER VALUE

– Turn the ignition switch to the OFF position.
– Plug in the connector.
– EVAP canister purge valve
– See 'Before changing a control module'.

12. Final check, fuel fault, continued

- Turn the ignition switch to the OFF position.

- Plug in the connector.
- EVAP canister purge valve
- Drive the car at a speed of 60-100 km/h with a steady throttle opening and the engine running at 1500-2750 rpm.

- Wait until the value is fully stabilized.
- Test value:
- Multiplicative adaptation
- State what the diagnostic tool shows:

-15% TO +15%

– The steps taken to rectify the fault were correct.

OTHER VALUE

– See 'Before changing a control module'.

SA1019900098150X

Fig. 33 Code —: Misfire (Part 15 of 17). 9-5

13. Checking charge air control valve

- Disconnect the hose marked 'W' from the charge air control valve.

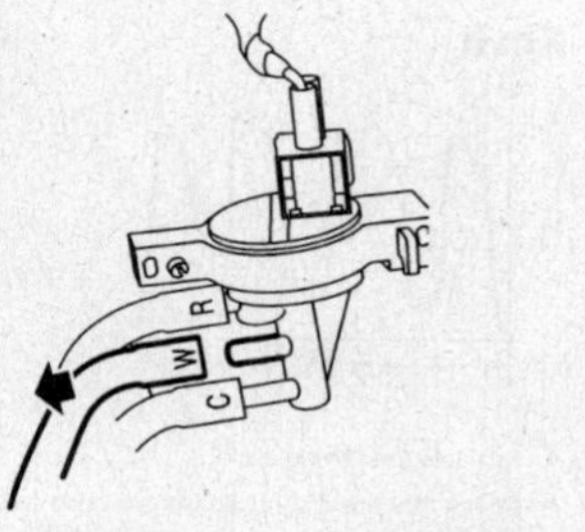

- When driving at wide open throttle from a low engine speed, fuel shut-off should occur before 3000 rpm.

Does fuel shut-off occur?

YES

- Go to point 14.

NO

- Go to point 16.

14. Checking air hoses

- Check to make sure that the charge air control valve's three control hoses are in good condition and correctly connected.

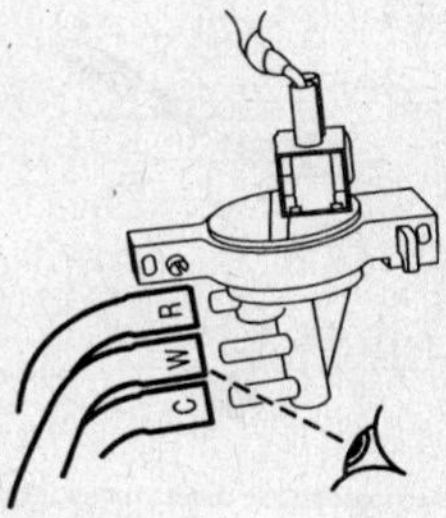

Everything OK?

YES

- Change: Charge air control valve
- Go to point 15.

NO

- Repair or replace the faulty hose.
- Go to point 15.

SA1019900098160X

Fig. 33 Code —: Misfire (Part 16 of 17). 9-5

15. Final check

- Clear the diagnostic trouble codes in all systems.

- Carry out a functionality test.

Everything OK?

YES

- The steps taken to rectify the fault were correct.

NO

- See 'Before changing a control module'.

16. Checking mechanical faults

- Check whether:
- the air supply for the turbocharger or air filter is clogged
- the turbocharger is defective
- the exhaust system or three-way catalytic converter is clogged
- the basic engine has a mechanical fault.

Everything OK?

YES

- Go to point 15.

NO

- Rectify the fault.
- Go to point 15.

SA1019900098170X

Fig. 33 Code —: Misfire (Part 17 of 17). 9-5

Fault symptoms

Idling speed too fast.

Conditions

The following conditions apply for this fault symptom:

- No diagnostic trouble codes in the car with the symptom description in question.

Note

Idling speed is always higher with a cold engine and for a short period after starting.

Diagnostic help

First check that the pedal arm returns completely. Then check that the throttle body is not in limp-home mode without this being detected by the control module. This may happen if a fault has occurred in the throttle and the diagnostic trouble codes are cleared, or if the current supplied to the control module is cut off without the mechanism having been reset. After that, check for air leaks after the throttle valve. The additive fuel adaptation generally exceeds 4 mg/c in the event of such a fault. A considerable negative adaptation generally indicates that the EVAP canister purge valve has stuck in the open position.

Diagnostic tool functions related to this fault are:

- Idle speed control, ON/OFF.
- Idling speed difference, in rpm.
- Additive adaptation, in mg/c.

See also the description of test values under "Fault diagnosis, general" for more information.

Checking the wiring harness

Jiggle the leads and in-line connectors at various points and in different directions to detect any intermittent breaks or short circuits in the wiring. Observe the multimeter, test lamp or diagnostic tool while doing this.

SA1019900099010X

Fig. 34 Code —: Idling Speed Too Fast (Part 1 of 4). 9-5

Diagnostic procedure

1. Checking pedal arm

- Check that the pedal arm returns fully when the accelerator is released. No external objects, such as hoses and cables, must obstruct the movement of the pedal arm.

Everything OK?

YES

- Go to point 2.

NO

- If necessary, adjust the throttle cable as described in 'Adjusting the throttle cable'.
- Go to point 2.

2. Checking mechanical Limp-home

- The fault can arise if the throttle valve is in the mechanical limp-home position without the control module knowing it.
- Turn the ignition switch to the OFF position.

- Wait 10 seconds to be sure that the throttle valve motor is without current. Then turn the pedal arm and check that the throttle valve arm does NOT follow its movement.

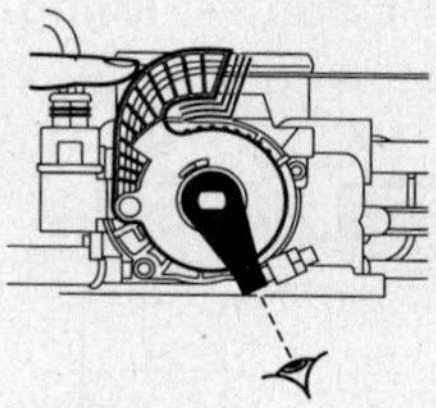

Everything OK?

YES

- Go to point 3.

NO

- Go to point 4.

SA1019900099020X

Fig. 34 Code —: Idling Speed Too Fast (Part 2 of 4). 9-5

3. Rectifying air leakage after the throttle valve

- Possible air leakage points are:
- vacuum hoses
- purge valve
- faulty brake servo

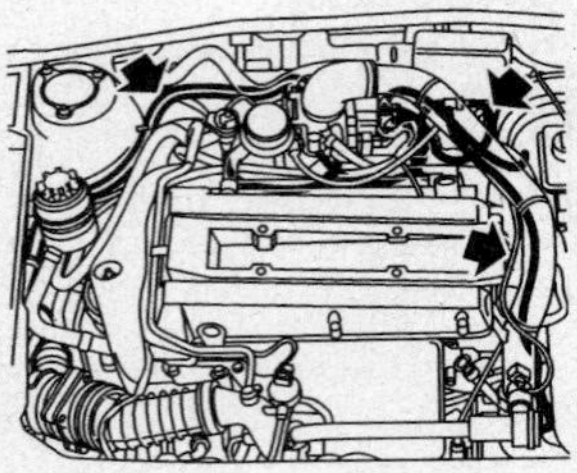

- Clear the diagnostic trouble codes in all systems.

- Carry out a functionality test.

Everything OK?

YES

– The steps taken to rectify the fault were correct.

NO

– See "**Engine Control Module (ECM)**" under "**Component Replacement**"

4. Resetting the limp-home mechanism

- Turn the ignition switch to the ON position.

- Clear diagnostic trouble codes: Trionic

- Turn the ignition switch to the OFF position.

SA1019900099030X

Fig. 34 Code —: Idling Speed Too Fast (Part 3 of 4). 9-5

- Wait for 10 seconds.
- Reset the limp-home mechanism as described in the 'Adjustment and replacement' section.

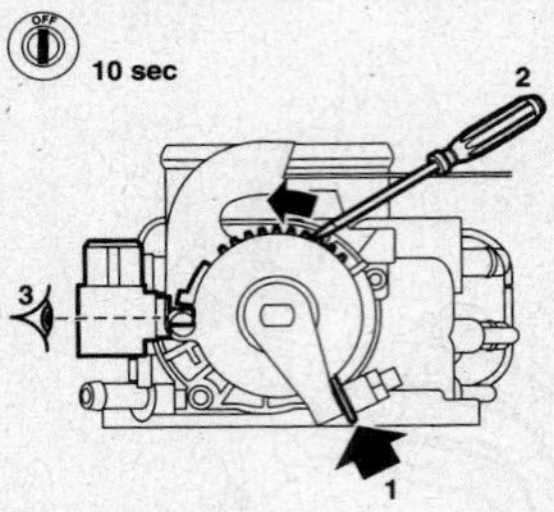

- Clear the diagnostic trouble codes in all systems.

- Carry out a driving cycle:
- Drive the car under varying engine loads and at different engine rpm for five minutes.

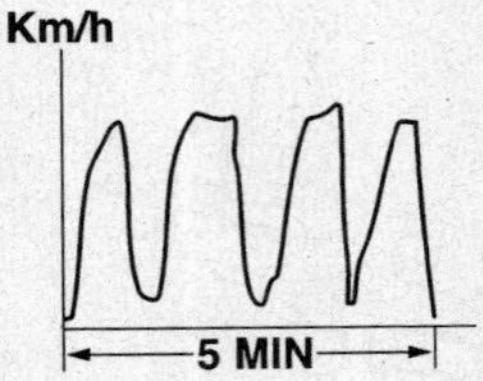

- Evaluate the driving cycle:
- Check that the diagnostic trouble code has not recurred.

Everything OK?

YES

– The steps taken to rectify the fault were correct.

NO

– See "**Engine Control Module (ECM)**" under "**Component Replacement**"

SA1019900099040X

Fig. 34 Code —: Idling Speed Too Fast (Part 4 of 4). 9-5

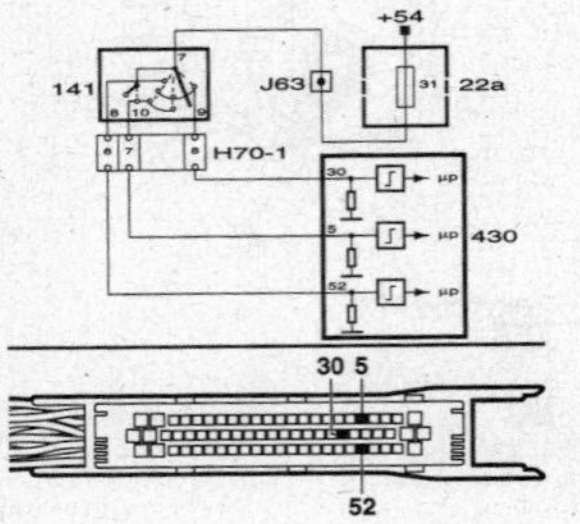

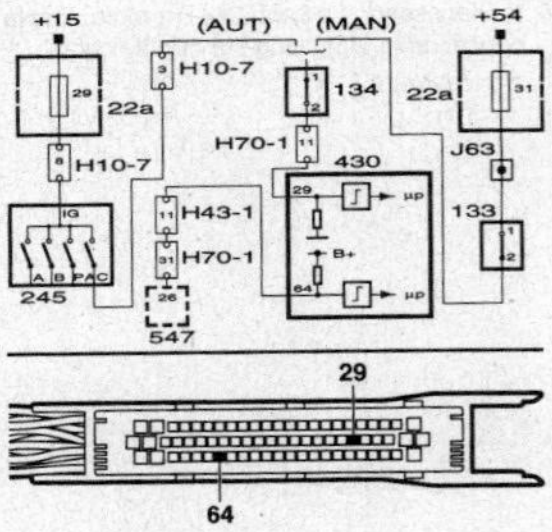

Fault symptoms

Cruise Control does not work.

Conditions

The following conditions apply for this fault symptom:

- No diagnostic trouble codes in the car with the symptom description in question.

Diagnostic help

Drive the car and activate the cruise control while using the diagnostic tool to check the conditions for cruise control at the same time. Start fault diagnosis on the condition that cannot be met.

The diagnostic tool menu also contains a group of test readings called "REASON CC WAS SWITCHED OFF". The readings are from the last time the cruise control was operative and show the cause of it being turned off. The readings are stored as long as the control module is supplied with current, which make them suitable for diagnosing intermittent faults.

Diagnostic tool functions related to this fault are:

- Cruise control A, ON/OFF.
- Cruise control B, ON/OFF.
- Cruise control C, ON/OFF.
- Clutch or brake pedal switch, ON/OFF.
- Brake lights (bus from TWICE), ON/OFF.
- Vehicle Speed (lead from ABS), in km/h.
- Vehicle speed (bus from MIU), in km/h.
- All readings under "CONDITIONS FOR CRUISE CONTROL" group.
- All readings under "REASON CC WAS SWITCHED OFF" group.

See also the description of test values under "Fault diagnosis, general" for more information.

Checking the wiring harness

Jiggle the leads and in-line connectors at various points and in different directions to detect any intermittent breaks or short circuits in the wiring. Observe the multimeter, test lamp or diagnostic tool while doing this.

SA1019900100010X

Fig. 35 Code —: Cruise Control Does Not Work (Part 1 of 12). 9-5

Diagnostic procedure

1. Checking a missing condition

- Turn the ignition switch to the ON position.

- Contact the Trionic.

- Obtain readings of all values in the group:
- CONDITIONS FOR CRUISE CONTROL
- Start the engine and run it at idling speed.

- Depress the brake pedal for a second or so.
- Drive the car at speeds above 40 km/h.

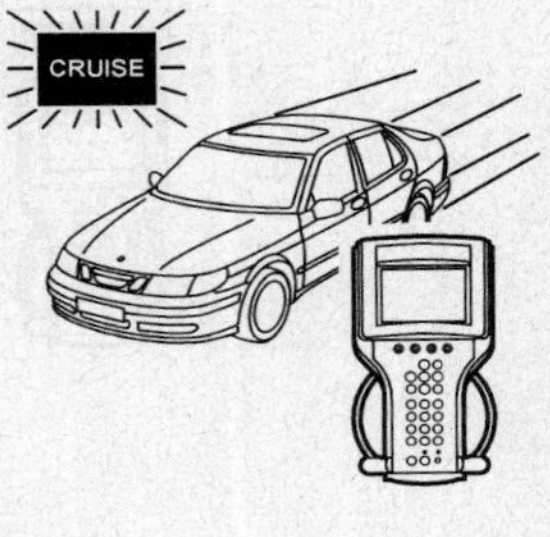

- Move the cruise control switch to 'ON/OFF' and then release it.
- All the test readings should show 'ON'.
- Disregard the test reading "All Inputs Allow Cruise Control", which always shows "OFF" until all the conditions have been met.

Note

Disregard the test reading "All Inputs Allow Cruise Control", which always shows "OFF" until all the conditions have been met.

Everything OK?

YES

– Go to point 2.

NO

– See the description of test readings under 'Fault diagnosis, general' for information on the reason for the fault and suggested fault diagnosis for the test reading that showed 'OFF'.

– Go to point 2.

SA1019900100020X

Fig. 35 Code —: Cruise Control Does Not Work (Part 2 of 12). 9-5

Diagnostic tool functions related to this fault are:

- Atmosphere absolute pressure, in kPa.
- Charge air absolute pressure, in kPa
- Manifold absolute pressure, in kPa.
- Mass air flow, deviation from requested, in %.
- Mass air flow, deviation from calculated, in %.
- Engine torque used at current rpm, in %.
- Charge air adaptation, in %.
- All readings in the "MASS AIR FLOW REQUEST" group.
- Activation of the charge air control valve.

See also description of test readings and activation under "Fault diagnosis, general" for more information.

Checking the wiring harness

Jiggle the leads and in-line connectors at various points and in different directions to detect any intermittent breaks or short circuits in the wiring. Observe the multimeter, test lamp or diagnostic tool while doing this.

Diagnostic procedure

1. Checking the manifold absolute pressure sensor

- Turn the ignition switch to the ON position.

- Contact the Trionic.

- Obtain readings for the absolute pressure sensors as described in the instructions below. If any reading differs by more than 10 kPa from the others, the sensor is defective and should be changed.

- Reading: Intake manifold Absolute pressure (Trionic).
- Reading: Charge air Absolute pressure (Trionic).
- Reading: Atmosphere Absolute pressure (Trionic).
- The manifold absolute pressure sensor does not affect engine performance but the mass air flow sensor value will be compared with the MAP sensor value later on in the course of fault diagnosis.
- The manifold absolute pressure sensor in the control module will affect engine performance if it shows too low a value.

SA1019900100030X

Fig. 35 Code —: Cruise Control Does Not Work (Part 3 of 12). 9-5

- Drive the car in top gear with a steady, high engine load.

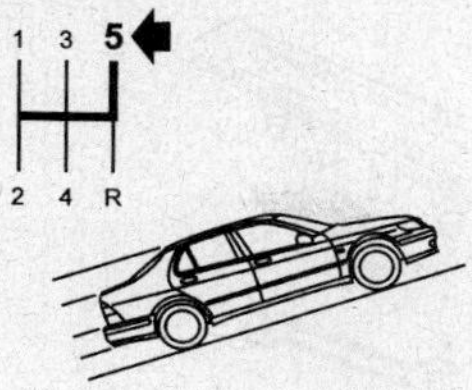

- Driving uphill is recommended.
- Test value: Mass air flow Deviation from Computed value (Trionic).
- State what the diagnostic tool shows:

<u>**15% TO 25%**</u>

– Go to point 2.

<u>**OTHER VALUE**</u>

– Go to point 3.

2. Checking air leakage before throttle valve

- Check for the presence of an air leak, using the method described in 'Checking for leaks in the intake system'.

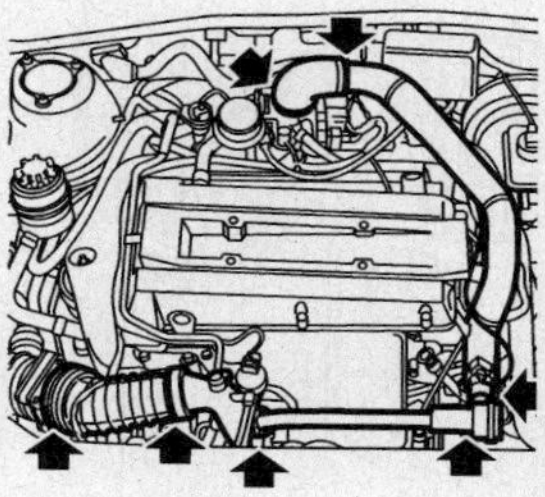

Everything OK?

<u>**YES**</u>

– Change: Mass air flow sensor

– Go to point 15.

<u>**NO**</u>

– Rectify the fault.

– Go to point 15.

SA1019900100040X

Fig. 35 Code —: Cruise Control Does Not Work (Part 4 of 12). 9-5

3. Checking mass air flow variation

- Test reading: Mass air flow, deviation from requested (Trionic).
- Drive the car at wide open throttle from a low engine speed.

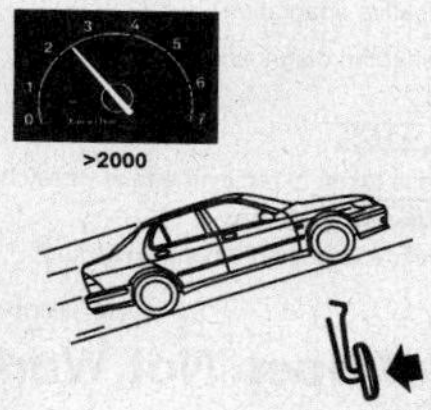

- Driving uphill is recommended.
- When engine speed exceeds 2000 rpm, the value should stabilize at +/- 5%.

Everything OK?

<u>**YES**</u>

– Go to point 4.

<u>**NO**</u>

– Go to point 13.

4. Checking the mass air flow limiter

- Drive the car at wide open throttle. With a manual gearbox, engage 2nd gear or higher.

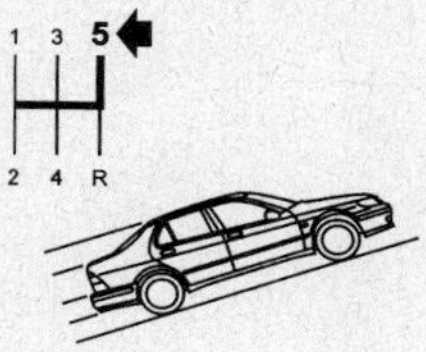

- Driving uphill is recommended.
- Obtain the following readouts with the diagnostic tool:

- Max. engine torque
- Manual gearbox
- Automatic transmission (Bus from TCM)
- Specify whether any mass air flow limitation is active.

<u>**ONE**</u>

– Go to point 8.

<u>**NONE**</u>

– Go to point 5.

SA1019900100050X

Fig. 35 Code —: Cruise Control Does Not Work (Part 5 of 12). 9-5

5. Checking the mass air flow limiter, continued

- Obtain the following readout with the diagnostic tool:

- Knock control

Is knock control active?

<u>**YES**</u>

– Go to point 6.

<u>**NO**</u>

– Go to point 8.

6. Checking engine torque

- It is not easy to say how much knocking can be permitted as this will depend on the circumstances. The tendency to knock is increased by the following factors: low octane rating, high coolant temperature, high outside temperature, high altitude, and high engine load.
- The fact that knock control reduces engine torque by less than 15% is considered normal under ordinary operating conditions.

- Drive the car at wide open throttle. With a manual gearbox, engage 2nd gear or higher.

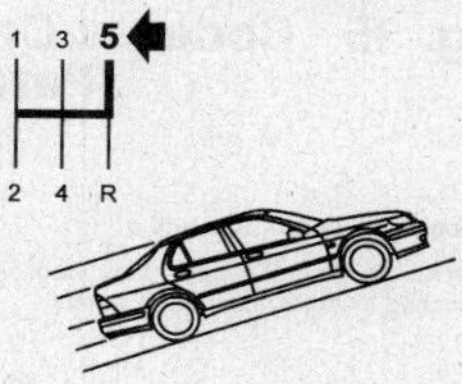

- Driving uphill is recommended.
- Obtain the following readout with the diagnostic tool:
- Max. engine torque at current engine rpm
- When engine speed exceeds 2000 rpm, the value should stabilize at above 85%.

Everything OK?

<u>**YES**</u>

– Go to point 15.

<u>**NO**</u>

– The cause of the poor power output is intensified knock control.

– Check the condition and heat range of the spark plugs.

– Check the type of petrol used. The octane rating indicates the petrol's resistance to knocking.

– Go to point 7.

SA1019900100060X

Fig. 35 Code —: Cruise Control Does Not Work (Part 6 of 12). 9-5

7. Checking engine torque

- Check the fuel pressure, pressure response and flow rate.

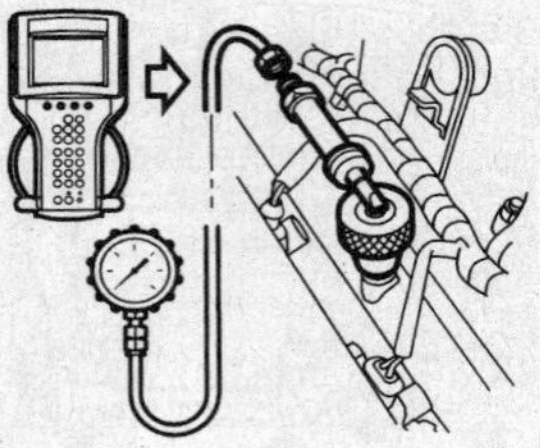

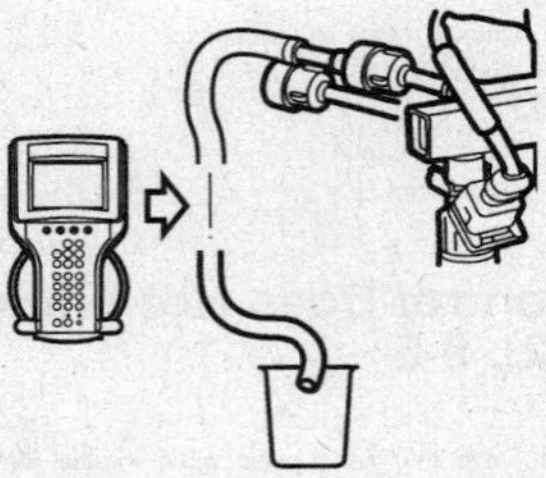

- If necessary, try changing the ignition discharge module.

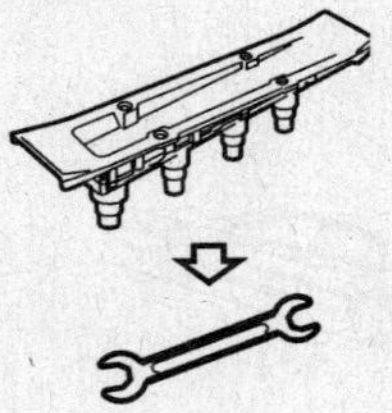

- Clear the diagnostic trouble codes in all systems.

- Carry out a functionality test.

Everything OK?
YES
– The steps taken to rectify the fault were correct.
NO
– See 'Before changing a control module'.

SA1019900100070X

Fig. 35 Code —: Cruise Control Does Not Work (Part 7 of 12). 9-5

8. Checking the fuel supply

- Check the fuel pressure as described in 'Adjustment/replacement'.

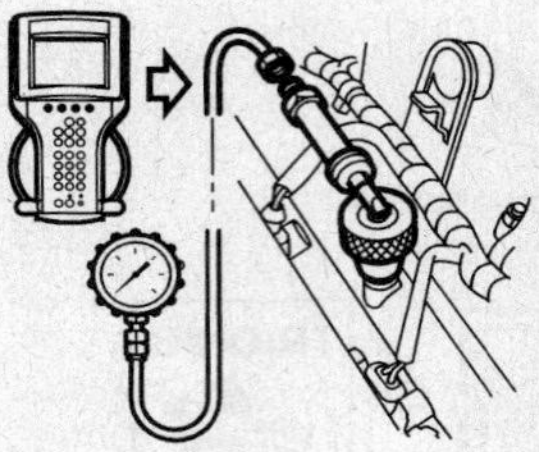

Is the fuel pressure OK?
YES
– Go to point 9.
NO
– Follow the diagnostic procedure described in the 'Adjustment/replacement' section of the 'Fuel system' service category.
– Go to point 11.

9. Checking the fuel pump flow rate

- Check the fuel pump flow rate as described in 'Adjustment/replacement'.

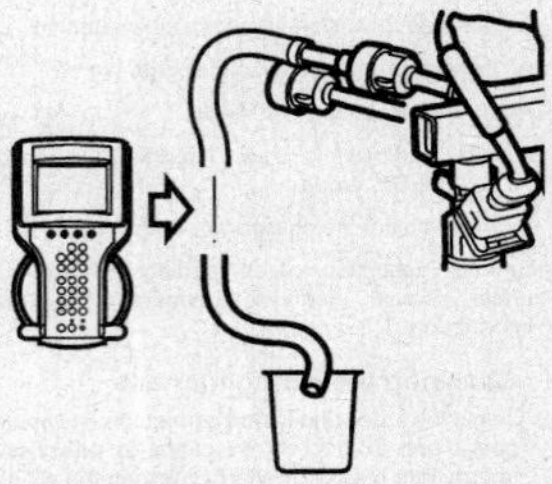

Is the fuel pump flow rate OK?
YES
– Go to point 10.
NO
– Adjust.

– Go to point 11.

SA1019900100080X

Fig. 35 Code —: Cruise Control Does Not Work (Part 8 of 12). 9-5

10. Checking injector flow rate

- Check the injector flow rate capacity as described in 'Adjustment/replacement'.

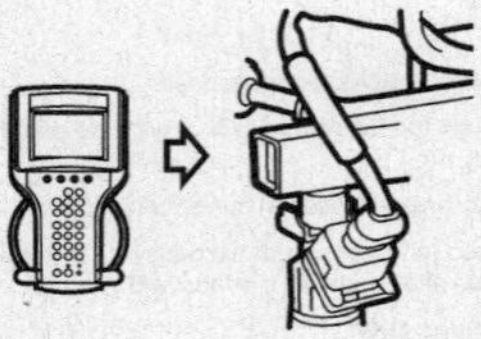

Are the injectors' flow rates OK?
YES
– Go to point 11.
NO
– Adjust.

– Go to point 11.

11. Final check, fuel fault

- Clear diagnostic trouble codes: Trionic

- Unplug the connector: EVAP canister purge valve: (321)

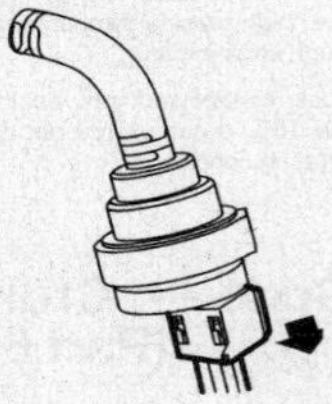

- Connect a test lamp to the female connector.
- Start the engine and run it at idling speed until the coolant temperature exceeds 75 degrees C.

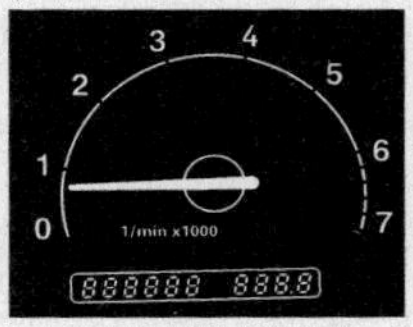

SA1019900100090X

Fig. 35 Code —: Cruise Control Does Not Work (Part 9 of 12). 9-5

- Test value: Purging Adaptation (Trionic)
- State what the diagnostic tool shows:

-15% TO +15%
– Go to point 12.
OTHER VALUE
– Turn the ignition switch to the OFF position.
– Plug in the connector.
– EVAP canister purge valve
– See **"Engine Control Module (ECM)" under "Component Replacement"**

12. Final check, fuel fault, continued

- Turn the ignition switch to the OFF position.

- Plug in the connector.
- EVAP canister purge valve
- Drive the car at a speed of 60-100 km/h with a steady throttle opening and the engine running at 1500-2750 rpm.

- Wait until the value is fully stabilized.
- Test value:
- Multiplicative adaptation
- State what the diagnostic tool shows:

-15% TO +15%
– The steps taken to rectify the fault were correct.
OTHER VALUE
– See 'Before changing a control module'.

SA1019900100100X

Fig. 35 Code —: Cruise Control Does Not Work (Part 10 of 12). 9-5

13. Checking charge air control valve

- Disconnect the hose marked 'W' from the charge air control valve.

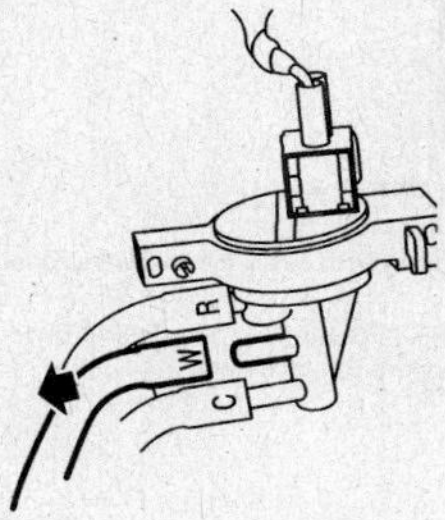

- When driving at wide open throttle from a low engine speed, fuel shut-off should occur before 3000 rpm.

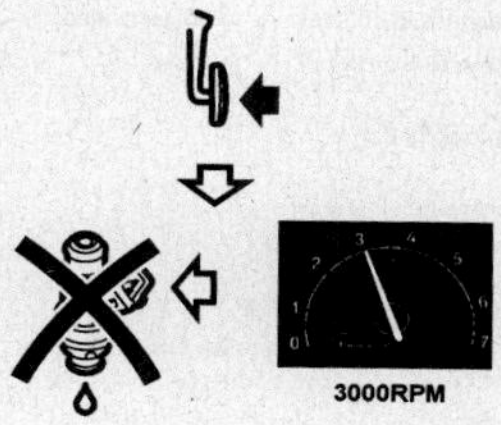

Does fuel shut-off occur?

YES

– Go to point 14.

NO

– Go to point 16.

14. Checking air hoses

- Check to make sure that the charge air control valve's three control hoses are in good condition and correctly connected.

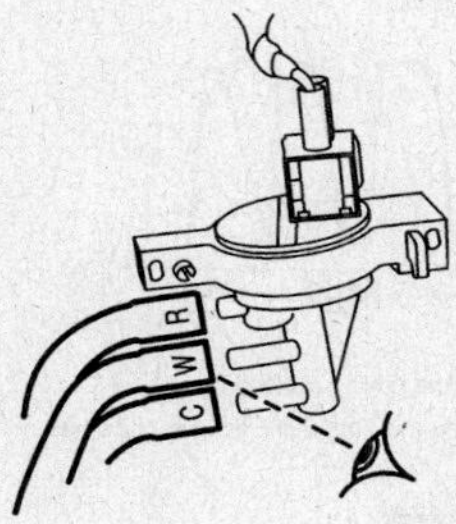

Everything OK?

YES

– Change: Charge air control valve

– Go to point 15.

NO

– Repair or replace the faulty hose.

– Go to point 15.

SA1019900100110X

Fig. 35 Code —: Cruise Control Does Not Work (Part 11 of 12). 9-5

15. Final check

- Clear the diagnostic trouble codes in all systems.

- Carry out a functionality test.

Everything OK?

YES

– The steps taken to rectify the fault were correct.

NO

– See **"Engine Control Module (ECM)" under "Component Replacement"**

16. Checking mechanical faults

- Check whether:
- the air supply for the turbocharger or air filter is clogged
- the turbocharger is defective
- the exhaust system or three-way catalytic converter is clogged
- the basic engine has a mechanical fault.

Everything OK?

YES

– Go to point 15.

NO

– Rectify the fault.

– Go to point 15.

SA1019900100120X

Fig. 35 Code —: Cruise Control Does Not Work (Part 12 of 12). 9-5

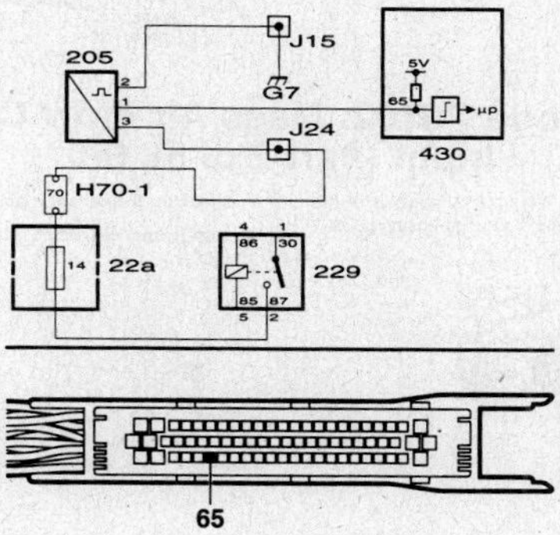

Fault symptoms

- CHECK ENGINE comes on after two driving cycles.
- Engine speed drops slower than normal when the accelerator is released.
- Possible misfiring before DTC is generated.

Conditions

The following conditions apply for this DTC:

- Crankshaft rotating and main relay voltage exceeds 10 V.
- No frequency for more than 0.5 s.

Diagnostic help

Fault diagnosis concerns electrical faults in connected leads or in the sensor.

Diagnostic tool functions related to this fault are:

- Mass air flow sensor reading, in g/s.
- Mass air flow deviation from that calculated, in %.

See also the description of test values under "Fault diagnosis, general" for more information.

Checking the wiring harness

Jiggle the leads and in-line connectors at various points and in different directions to detect any intermittent breaks or short circuits in the wiring. Observe the multimeter, test lamp or diagnostic tool while doing this.

SA1019900021010X

Fig. 36 Code P0100: Mass Air Flow Circuit No Signal (Part 1 of 4). 9-5

Diagnostic procedure

1. Checking the sensor's power supply

- Turn the ignition switch to the ON position.

- Unplug the connector: Mass air flow sensor: (205)

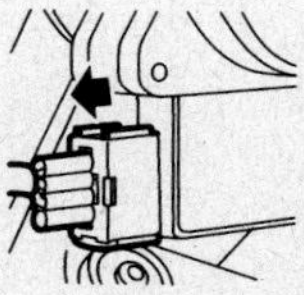

- Connect test lamp 86 11 857 to pin 3 of the female connector and a good grounding point.

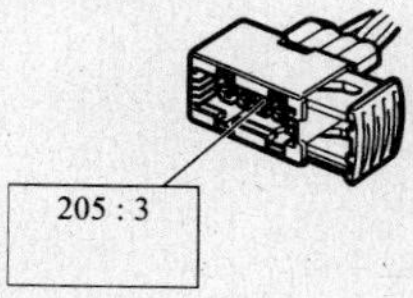

- The test lamp should light.

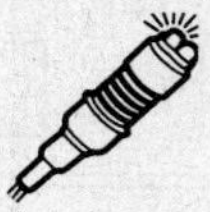

Everything OK?

YES

– Go to point 2.

NO

– The lead from crimp connection J24 to pin 3 of the female connector is faulty.

– Go to point 4.

SA1019900021020X

Fig. 36 Code P0100: Mass Air Flow Circuit No Signal (Part 2 of 4). 9-5

2. Checking the sensor's grounding

- Connect test lamp 86 11 857 to pins 3 and 2 of the female connector.

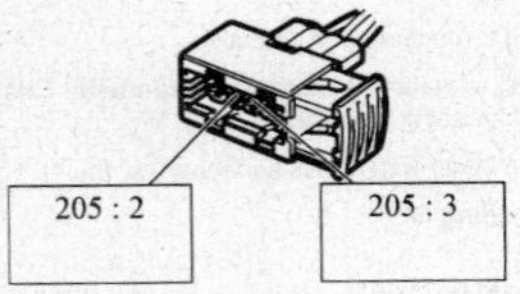

- The test lamp should light.

Everything OK?

YES

– Go to point 3.

NO

– The lead from crimp connection J15 to pin 2 of the female connector is faulty.

– Go to point 4.

3. Checking the control module's sensor input

- Take a voltage reading.
- Red test lead: Mass air flow sensor: 1
- Black test lead: Mass air flow sensor: 2

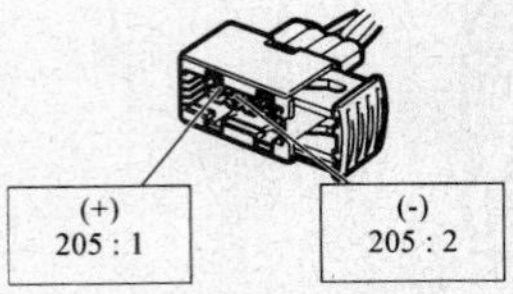

- The reading obtained should be 4.9 V - 5.1 V.

Everything OK?

YES

– Change: Mass air flow sensor

– Go to point 4.

NO

– The lead from pin 1 of the female connector to pin 65 of the control module is faulty.

– Go to point 4.

4. Final check

- Clear the diagnostic trouble codes in all systems.

SA1019900021030X

Fig. 36 Code P0100: Mass Air Flow Circuit No Signal (Part 3 of 4). 9-5

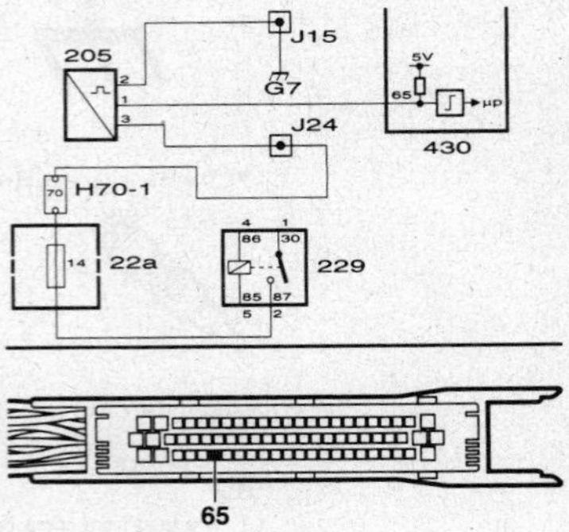

Fault symptoms

- CHECK ENGINE comes on after two driving cycles.
- Engine speed drops slower than normal when the accelerator is released.
- Possible misfiring before DTC is generated.

Conditions

The following conditions apply for this DTC.

- Crankshaft rotating and main relay voltage exceeds 10 V.
- Frequency lower than 500 Hz for more than 0.5 s.

Diagnostic help

The mass air flow sensor sends pulses to the control module but the frequency is too low. The sensor is supplied with current and connected to the control module input.

In most cases, this DTC indicates an internal fault in the sensor but can also be caused by a large leak between the sensor and the throttle. For example, the DTC can be generated if the sensor is removed.

Diagnostic tool functions related to this fault are:

- Mass air flow sensor reading, in g/s.
- Mass air flow deviation from that calculated, in %.

See also the description of test values under "Fault diagnosis, general" for more information.

Checking the wiring harness

Jiggle the leads and in-line connectors at various points and in different directions to detect any intermittent breaks or short circuits in the wiring. Observe the multimeter, test lamp or diagnostic tool while doing this.

SA1019900022010X

Fig. 37 Code P0102: Mass Air Flow Circuit Low Input (Part 1 of 5). 9-5

- Carry out a driving cycle:
- Drive the car under varying engine loads and at different engine rpm for five minutes.

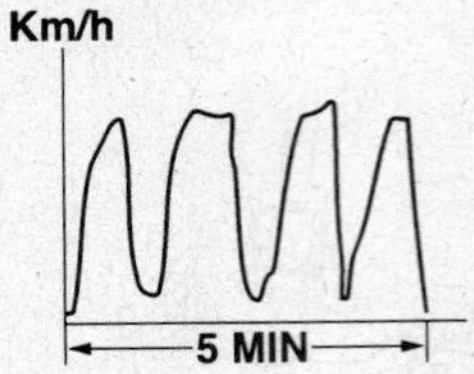

- Evaluate the driving cycle:
- Check that the diagnostic trouble code has not recurred.

Everything OK?

YES

– The steps taken to rectify the fault were correct.

NO

– See "Engine Control Module (ECM)" under "Component Replacement."

SA1019900021040X

Fig. 36 Code P0100: Mass Air Flow Circuit No Signal (Part 4 of 4). 9-5

Diagnostic procedure

1. Checking air leakage

- Check that no major air leakage occurs between the mass air flow sensor and compressor.

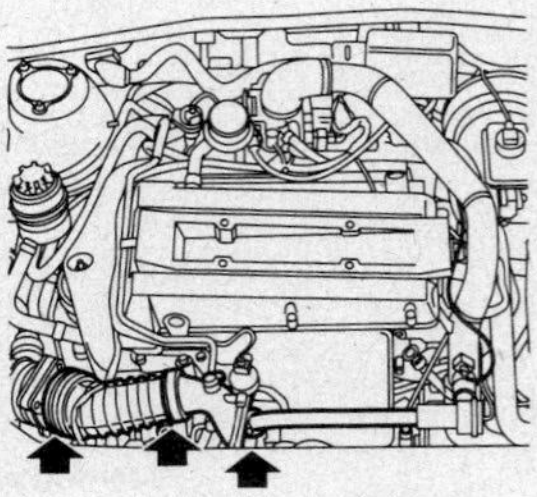

- The air leak must correspond to a 20 mm hole for a diagnostic trouble code to be generated.

Is the system airtight?

YES

– Go to point 2.

NO

– Rectify the air leakage.

– Go to point 5.

2. Checking the sensor's power supply

- Turn the ignition switch to the ON position.

- Unplug the connector: Mass air flow sensor: (205)

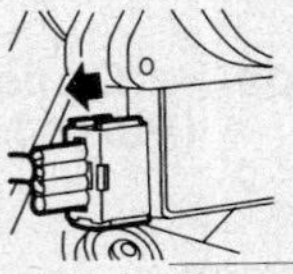

SA1019900022020X

Fig. 37 Code P0102: Mass Air Flow Circuit Low Input (Part 2 of 5). 9-5

- Connect test lamp 86 11 857 to pin 3 of the female connector and a good grounding point.

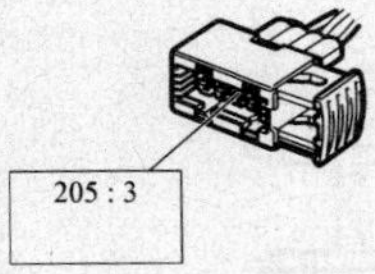

- The test lamp should light.

Everything OK?

YES

– Go to point 3.

NO

– The lead from crimp connection J24 to pin 3 of the female connector is faulty.

– Go to point 5.

3. Checking the sensor's power supply

- Unplug the connector: Mass air flow sensor: (205)

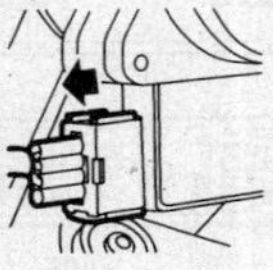

- Connect test lamp 86 11 857 to pins 3 and 2 of the female connector.

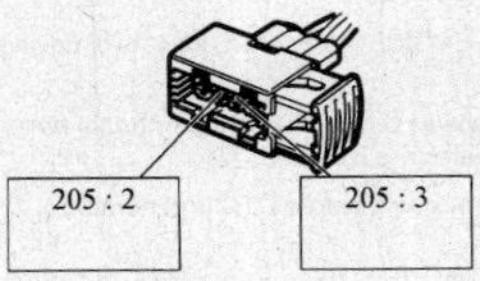

- The test lamp should light.

Everything OK?

YES

– Go to point 4.

NO

– The lead from crimp connection J15 to pin 2 of the female connector is faulty.

– Go to point 5.

SA1019900022030X

Fig. 37 Code P0102: Mass Air Flow Circuit Low Input (Part 3 of 5). 9-5

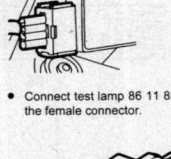

4. Checking the control module's sensor input

- Take a voltage reading.
- Red test lead: Mass air flow sensor: 1
- Black test lead: Mass air flow sensor: 2

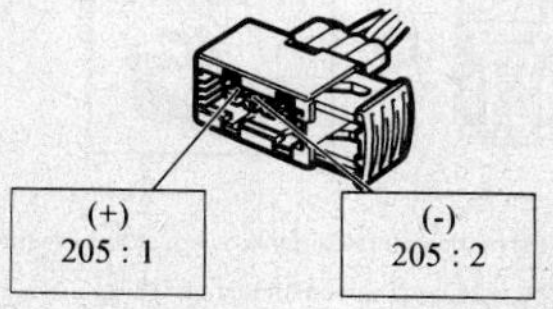

- The reading obtained should be 4.9 V - 5.1 V.

Everything OK?

YES

- Change: Mass air flow sensor
- Go to point 5.

NO

- The lead from pin 1 of the female connector to pin 65 of the control module is faulty.
- Go to point 5.

5. Final check

- Clear the diagnostic trouble codes in all systems.

- Carry out a driving cycle:
- Drive the car under varying engine loads and at different engine rpm for five minutes.

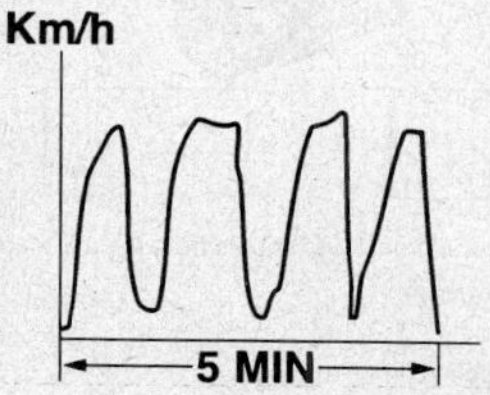

SA1019900022040X

Fig. 37 Code P0102: Mass Air Flow Circuit Low Input (Part 4 of 5). 9-5

- Evaluate the driving cycle:
- Check that the diagnostic trouble code has not recurred.

Everything OK?

YES

- The steps taken to rectify the fault were correct.

NO

- See "Engine Control Module (ECM)" under "Component Replacement."

SA1019900022050X

Fig. 37 Code P0102: Mass Air Flow Circuit Low Input (Part 5 of 5). 9-5

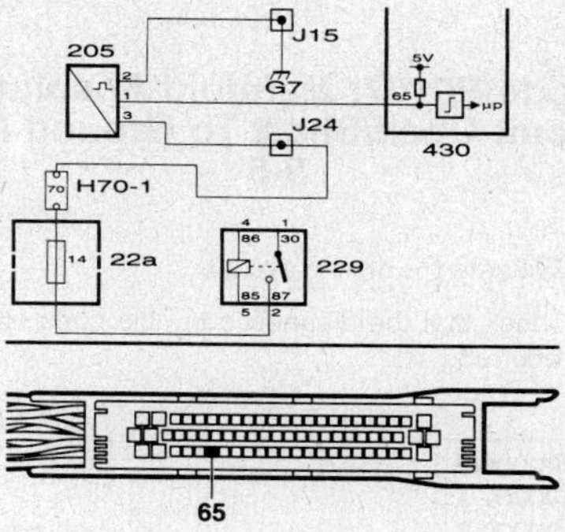

Fault symptoms

- CHECK ENGINE comes on after two driving cycles.
- Engine speed drops slower than normal when the accelerator is released.
- Possible misfiring before DTC is generated.

Conditions

The following conditions apply for this DTC:

- Crankshaft rotating and main relay voltage exceeds 10 V.
- Frequency higher than 15 kHz for more than 0.5 s.

Diagnostic help

The mass air flow sensor sends pulses to the control module but the frequency is too high. The sensor is supplied with current and is connected to the control module input. This DTC indicates an internal fault in the sensor.

Diagnostic tool functions related to this fault are:

- Mass air flow sensor reading, in g/s.
- Mass air flow deviation from that calculated, in %.

See also the description of test values under "Fault diagnosis, general" for more information.

Checking the wiring harness

Jiggle the leads and in-line connectors at various points and in different directions to detect any intermittent breaks or short circuits in the wiring. Observe the multimeter, test lamp or diagnostic tool while doing this.

Diagnostic procedure

See Code P0100.

SA1019900023000X

Fig. 38 Code P0103: Mass Air Flow Circuit High Output. 9-5

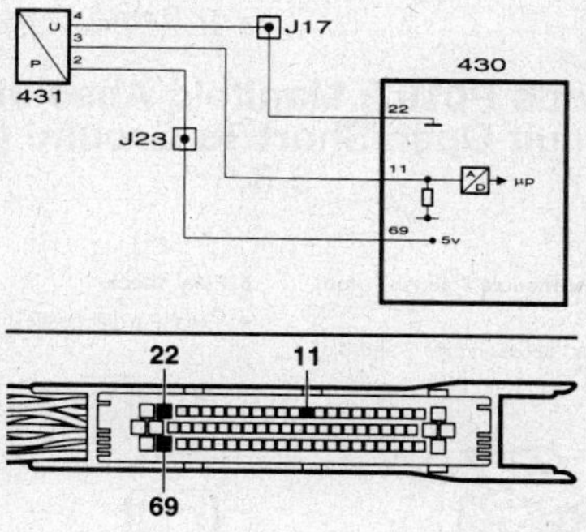

Fault symptoms

- CHECK ENGINE comes on after two driving cycles.
- Engine speed drops slower than normal when the accelerator is released.
- Possible misfiring before DTC is generated.

Conditions

The following conditions apply for this DTC:

- Engine has started and the voltage is lower than 0.185 V for more than 5 s.

Diagnostic help

Fault diagnosis concerns electrical faults in connected leads or in the sensor.

Diagnostic tool functions related to this fault are:

- Pressure sensor reading, in kPa. With the engine switched off, this reading should be the same as those for the other two pressure sensors. Permissible variance is 10 kPa.

See also the description of test values under "Fault diagnosis, general" for more information.

Checking the wiring harness

Jiggle the leads and in-line connectors at various points and in different directions to detect any intermittent breaks or short circuits in the wiring. Observe the multimeter, test lamp or diagnostic tool while doing this.

SA1019900024010X

Fig. 39 Code P0107: Manifold Absolute Pressure Sensor Circuit Open/Short To Ground (Part 1 of 5). 9-5

Diagnostic procedure

1. Checking the sensor's grounding

- Unplug the connector: Manifold absolute pressure sensor: (431)

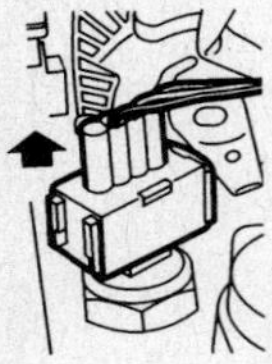

- Connect test lamp 86 11 857 to B+ and pin 4 of the female connector.

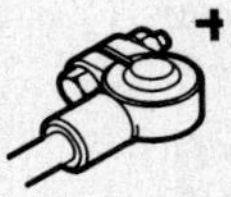

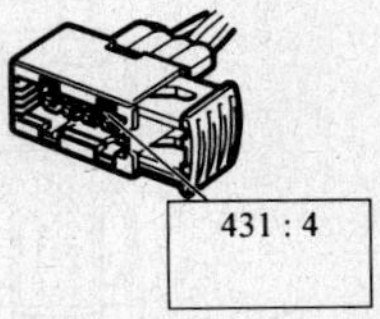

- The test lamp should light.

Everything OK?

YES

– Go to point 2.

NO

– One of the leads from pins 22 and 70 of the control module to pin 4 of the female connector is faulty. (The leads from pins 22 and 70 of the control module are connected together internally in the throttle body.)

– Go to point 5.

SA1019900024020X

Fig. 39 Code P0107: Manifold Absolute Pressure Sensor Circuit Open/Short To Ground (Part 2 of 5). 9-5

2. Checking the sensor's power supply

- Turn the ignition switch to the ON position.

- Take a voltage reading.
- Red test lead: Manifold absolute pressure sensor: 2
- Black test lead: manifold absolute pressure sensor: 4

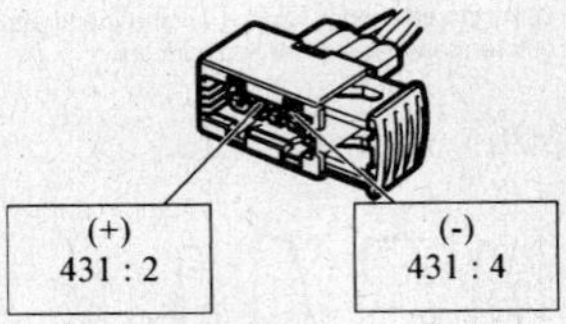

- The reading obtained should be 4.9 V - 5.1 V.

Everything OK?

YES

– Go to point 3.

NO

– The lead from pins 69 and 46 of the control module to pin 4 of the female connector is faulty. (The leads from pins 69 and 46 of the control module are connected together internally in the throttle body.)

– Go to point 5.

3. Checking the control module's sensor input

- Contact the Trionic.

- Test reading: Intake manifold Absolute pressure.
- The reading obtained should be 0 kPa

Everything OK?

YES

– Go to point 4.

NO

– The lead from pin 3 of the female connector to pin 11 of the control module is faulty.

– Go to point 5.

SA1019900024030X

Fig. 39 Code P0107: Manifold Absolute Pressure Sensor Circuit Open/Short To Ground (Part 3 of 5). 9-5

4. Checking the control module's sensor input (continued)

- Connect a jumper lead between pins 2 and 3 of the female connector.

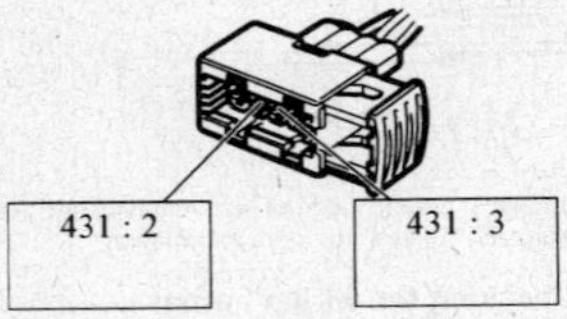

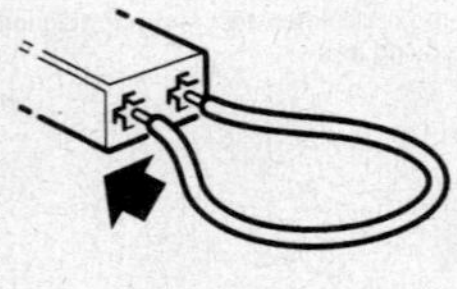

- Test reading: Intake manifold Absolute pressure.
- The reading should be 250 kPa

Everything OK?

YES

– Change: Manifold absolute pressure sensor

– Go to point 5.

NO

– The lead from pin 3 of the female connector to pin 11 of the control module is faulty.

– Go to point 5.

5. Final check

- Clear the diagnostic trouble codes in all systems.

- Carry out a driving cycle:
- Drive the car under varying engine loads and at different engine rpm for five minutes.

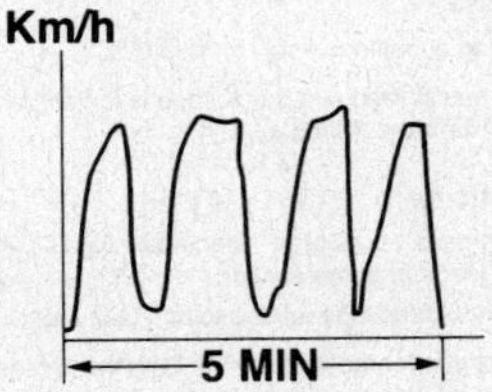

SA1019900024040X

Fig. 39 Code P0107: Manifold Absolute Pressure Sensor Circuit Open/Short To Ground (Part 4 of 5). 9-5

- Evaluate the driving cycle:
- Check that the diagnostic trouble code has not recurred.

Everything OK?

YES

– The steps taken to rectify the fault were correct.

NO

– See "Engine Control Module (ECM)" under "Component Replacement."

SA1019900024050X

Fig. 39 Code P0107: Manifold Absolute Pressure Sensor Circuit Open/Short To Ground (Part 5 of 5). 9-5

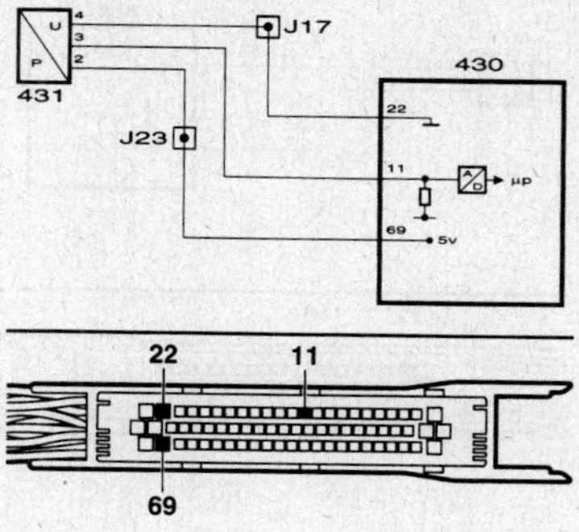

Fault symptoms

- CHECK ENGINE comes on after two driving cycles.
- Engine speed drops slower than normal when the accelerator is released.
- Possible misfiring before DTC is generated.

Conditions

The following conditions apply for this DTC:

- Engine has started and the voltage is higher than 4.815 V for more than 5 s.

Diagnostic help

Fault diagnosis concerns electrical faults in connected leads or in the sensor.

Diagnostic tool functions related to this fault are:

- Pressure sensor reading, in kPa. With the engine switched off, this reading should be the same as those for the other two pressure sensors. Permissible variance is 10 kPa.

See also the description of test values under "Fault diagnosis, general" for more information.

Checking the wiring harness

Jiggle the leads and in-line connectors at various points and in different directions to detect any intermittent breaks or short circuits in the wiring. Observe the multimeter, test lamp or diagnostic tool while doing this.

Diagnostic procedure

See Code P0107.

SA1019900025000X

Fig. 40 Code P0108: Manifold Absolute Pressure Sensor Circuit Short To B+. 9-5

Diagnostic procedure

1. Checking the sensor's grounding

- Unplug the connector: Intake air temperature sensor: (407)

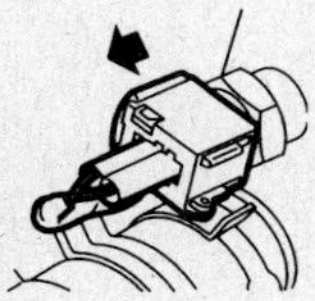

- Connect test lamp 86 11 857 to B+ and pin 2 of the female connector.

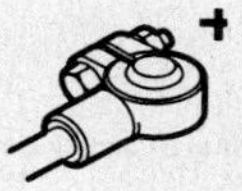

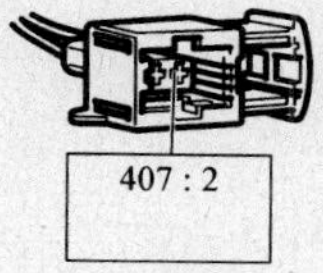

- The test lamp should light.

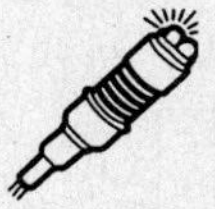

Everything OK?

YES

– Go to point 2.

NO

– The lead from crimp connection J17 to pin 2 of the female connector is faulty.
– Go to point 4.

SA1019900026020X

Fig. 41 Code P0112: Intake Air Temperature Sensor Circuit Short To Ground (Part 2 of 4). 9-5

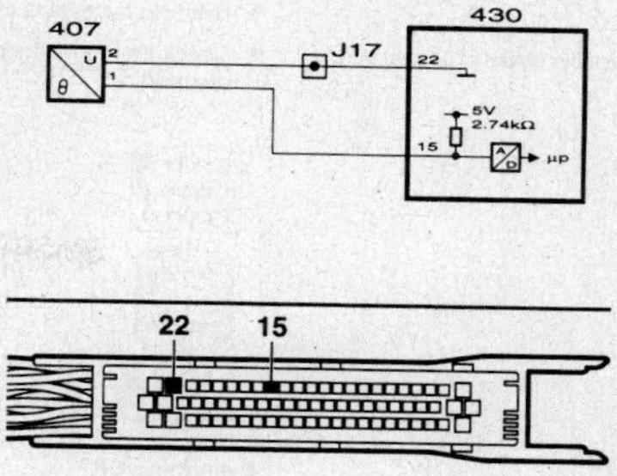

Fault symptoms

CHECK ENGINE comes on after two driving cycles.

Conditions

The following conditions apply for this DTC:

- Engine has started and the voltage is lower than 0.125 V for more than 5 s.

Diagnostic help

Fault diagnosis concerns electrical faults in connected leads or in the sensor.

Diagnostic tool functions related to this fault are:

- Temperature sensor reading, in °C.

See also the description of test values under "Fault diagnosis, general" for more information.

Checking the wiring harness

Jiggle the leads and in-line connectors at various points and in different directions to detect any intermittent breaks or short circuits in the wiring. Observe the multimeter, test lamp or diagnostic tool while doing this.

SA1019900026010X

Fig. 41 Code P0112: Intake Air Temperature Sensor Circuit Short To Ground (Part 1 of 4). 9-5

2. Checking the control module's sensor input

- Turn the ignition switch to the ON position.

- Contact the Trionic.

- Test reading: Intake air temperature.
- The reading obtained should be -40°C

Everything OK?

YES

– Go to point 3.

NO

– The lead from pin 1 of the female connector to pin 15 of the control module is faulty.
– Go to point 4.

3. Checking the control module sensor input (continued)

- Connect a jumper lead between pins 1 and 2 of the female connector.

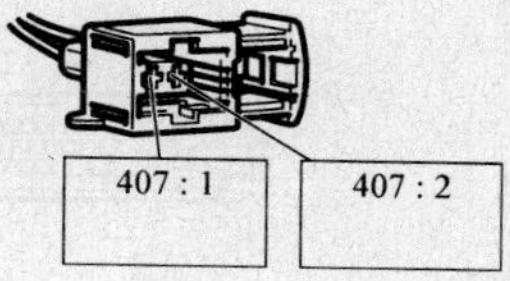

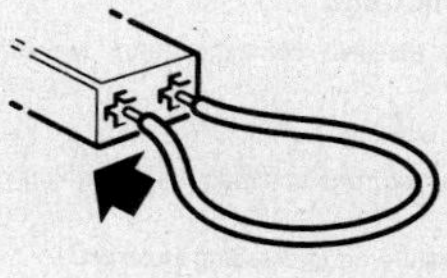

- Test reading: Intake air temperature.
- The reading obtained should be 139°C

Everything OK?

YES

– Change: Intake air temperature sensor
– Go to point 4.

NO

– The lead from pin 1 of the female connector to pin 15 of the control module is faulty.
– Go to point 4.

SA1019900026030X

Fig. 41 Code P0112: Intake Air Temperature Sensor Circuit Short To Ground (Part 3 of 4). 9-5

4. Final check

- Clear the diagnostic trouble codes in all systems.

- Carry out a driving cycle:
- Drive the car under varying engine loads and at different engine rpm for five minutes.

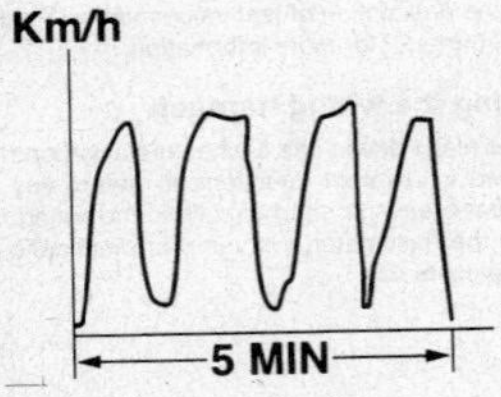

- Evaluate the driving cycle:
- Check that the diagnostic trouble code has not recurred.

Everything OK?

YES

– The steps taken to rectify the fault were correct.

NO

– See "Engine Control Module (ECM)" under "Component Replacement."

SA1019900026040X

Fig. 41 Code P0112: Intake Air Temperature Sensor Circuit Short To Ground (Part 4 of 4). 9-5

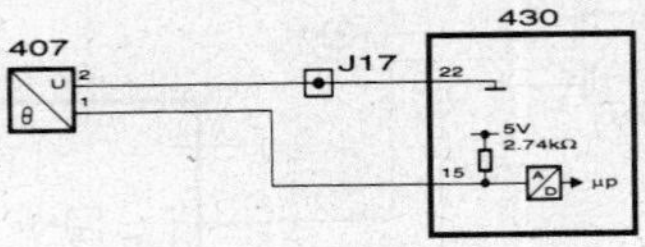

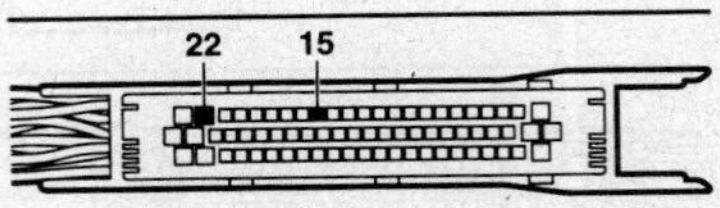

Fault symptoms

CHECK ENGINE comes on after two driving cycles.

Conditions

The following conditions apply for this DTC:

- Engine has started and the voltage is higher than 4.664 V for more than 5 s.

Diagnostic help

Fault diagnosis concerns electrical faults in connected leads or in the sensor.

Diagnostic tool functions related to this fault are:

- Temperature sensor reading, in °C.

See also the description of test values under "Fault diagnosis, general" for more information.

Checking the wiring harness

Jiggle the leads and in-line connectors at various points and in different directions to detect any intermittent breaks or short circuits in the wiring. Observe the multimeter, test lamp or diagnostic tool while doing this.

Diagnostic procedure

See Code P0112.

SA1019900027000X

Fig. 42 Code P0113: Intake Air Temperature Sensor Circuit Short To B+/Open Circuit. 9-5

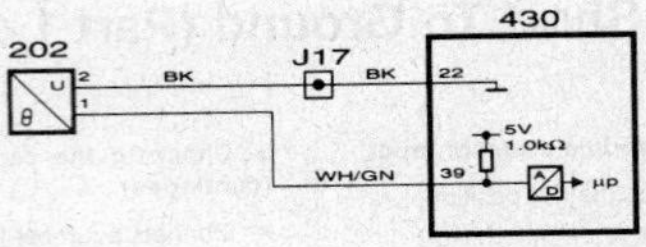

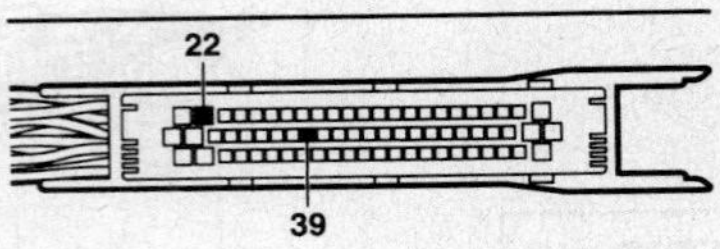

Fault symptoms

- CHECK ENGINE comes on after two driving cycles.
- A/C not working.
- Radiator fan runs continuously when ignition is ON.
- Temperature gauge reading incorrect.
- Possible misfiring before DTC is generated.

Conditions

The following conditions apply for this DTC:

- Engine has started and the voltage is lower than 0.224 V for more than 5 s.

Diagnostic help

Fault diagnosis concerns electrical faults in connected leads or in the sensor.

Diagnostic tool functions related to this fault are:

- Temperature sensor reading, in °C.

See also the description of test values under "Fault diagnosis, general" for more information.

Checking the wiring harness

Jiggle the leads and in-line connectors at various points and in different directions to detect any intermittent breaks or short circuits in the wiring. Observe the multimeter, test lamp or diagnostic tool while doing this.

SA1019900028010X

Fig. 43 Code P0117: Engine Coolant Temperature Sensor Circuit Short To Ground (Part 1 of 4). 9-5

Diagnostic procedure

1. Checking the sensor's grounding

- Unplug the connector: Coolant temperature sensor: (202)

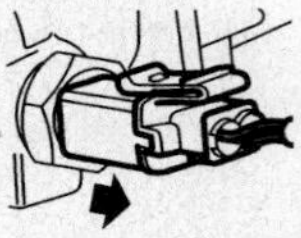

- Connect test lamp 86 11 857 to B+ and pin 2 of the female connector (black).

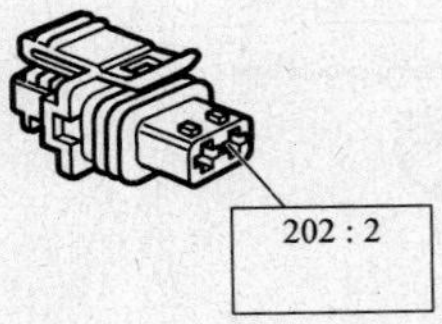

- The test lamp should light.

Everything OK?

YES

– Go to point 2.

NO

– The lead from crimp connection 17 (black) to pin 2 of the female connector is faulty.

– Go to point 4.

SA1019900028020X

Fig. 43 Code P0117: Engine Coolant Temperature Sensor Circuit Short To Ground (Part 2 of 4). 9-5

2. Checking the control module's sensor input

- Turn the ignition switch to the ON position.

- Test reading: Coolant temperature.
- The reading obtained should be -40°C

Everything OK?

YES

– Go to point 3.

NO

– The lead from pin 1 (white/green) of the female connector to pin 39 of the control module is faulty.

– Go to point 4.

3. Checking the control module sensor input (continued)

- Connect a jumper lead between pins 1 and 2 of the female connector.

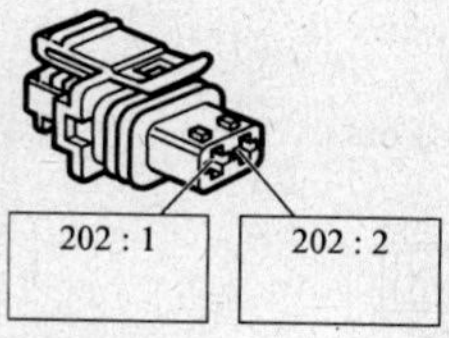

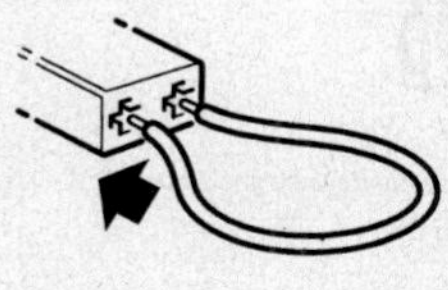

- Test reading: Coolant temperature.
- The reading obtained should be 150°C

Everything OK?

YES

– Change: Coolant temperature sensor

– Go to point 4.

NO

– The lead from pin 1 (white/green) of the female connector to pin 39 of the control module is faulty.

– Go to point 4.

SA1019900028030X

Fig. 43 Code P0117: Engine Coolant Temperature Sensor Circuit Short To Ground (Part 3 of 4). 9-5

4. Final check

- Clear the diagnostic trouble codes in all systems.

- Carry out a driving cycle:
- Drive the car under varying engine loads and at different engine rpm for five minutes.

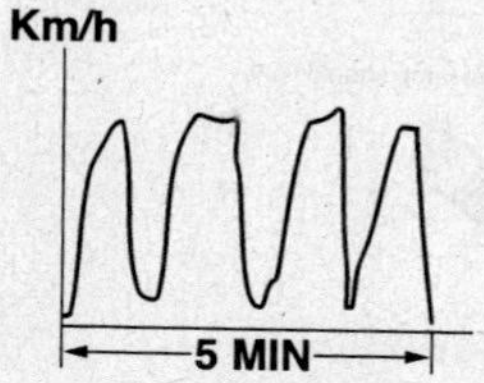

- Evaluate the driving cycle:
- Check that the diagnostic trouble code has not recurred.

Everything OK?

YES

– The steps taken to rectify the fault were correct.

NO

– See "Component Replacement", Engine Control Module (ECM).

SA1019900028040X

Fig. 43 Code P0117: Engine Coolant Temperature Sensor Circuit Short To Ground (Part 4 of 4). 9-5

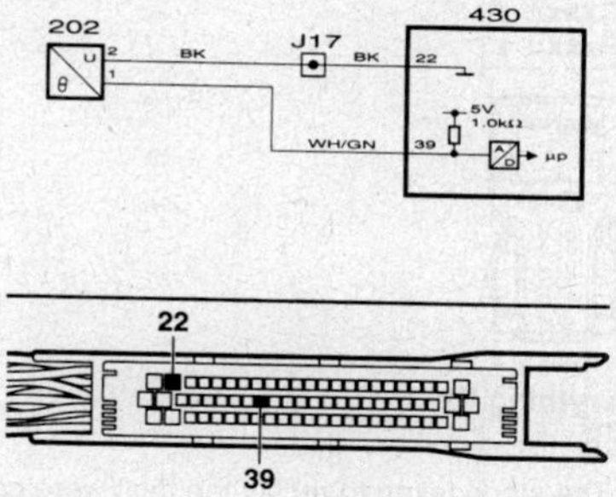

Fault symptoms

- CHECK ENGINE comes on after two driving cycles.
- A/C not working.
- Radiator fan runs continuously when ignition is ON.
- Temperature gauge reading incorrect.
- Possible misfiring before DTC is generated.

Conditions

The following conditions apply for this DTC:

- Engine has started and the voltage is higher than 4.910 V for more than 5 s.

Diagnostic help

Fault diagnosis concerns electrical faults in connected leads or in the sensor.

Diagnostic tool functions related to this fault are:

- Temperature sensor reading, in °C.

See also the description of test values under "Fault diagnosis, general" for more information.

Checking the wiring harness

Jiggle the leads and in-line connectors at various points and in different directions to detect any intermittent breaks or short circuits in the wiring. Observe the multimeter, test lamp or diagnostic tool while doing this.

Diagnostic procedure

See Code P0117.

SA1019900029000X

Fig. 44 Code P0118: Engine Coolant Temperature Sensor Circuit Short To B+/Open Circuit. 9-5

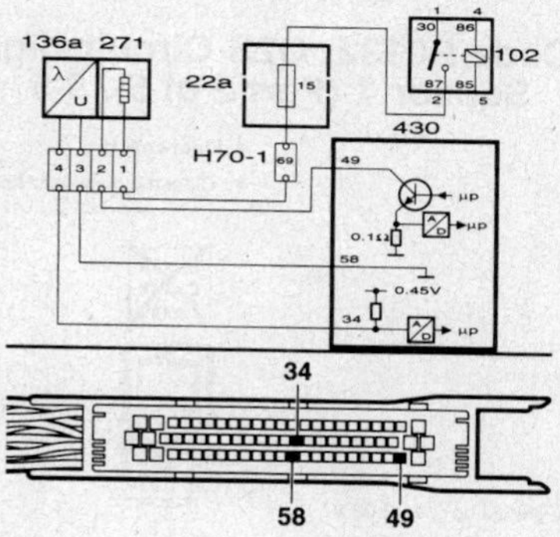

Fault symptoms

- CHECK ENGINE comes on after two driving cycles
- Possible misfiring before DTC is generated.

Conditions

The following conditions apply for this DTC:

- Engine has started and the voltage has been higher than 1.5 V for more than 2 seconds.

Diagnostic help

Fault diagnosis concerns electrical faults in connected leads or in the sensor.

Diagnostic tool functions related to this fault are:

- Heated oxygen sensor reading, in V.

See also the description of test values under "Fault diagnosis, general" for more information.

Checking the wiring harness

Jiggle the leads and in-line connectors at various points and in different directions to detect any intermittent breaks or short circuits in the wiring. Observe the multimeter, test lamp or diagnostic tool while doing this.

SA1019900030010X

Fig. 45 Code P0132: O2S Circuit High Voltage Sensor 1 (Part 1 of 5). 9-5

Diagnostic procedure

1. Checking the sensor's grounding

- Unplug the connector: Heated oxygen sensor: (136a)

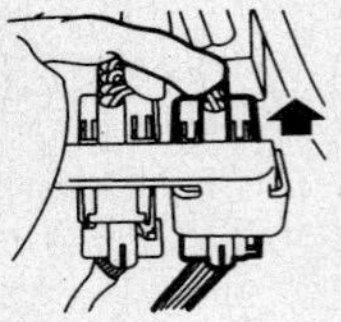

- Connect test lamp 86 11 857 to B+ and pin 3 of the female connector.

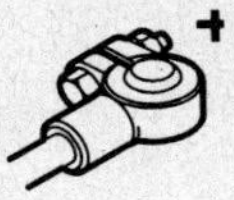

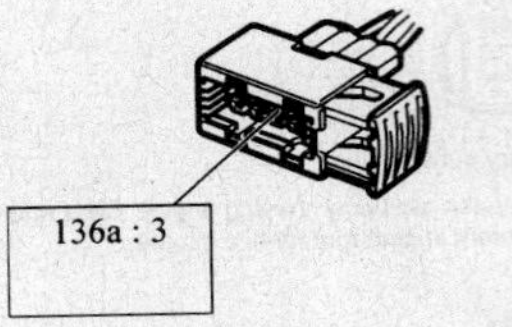

- The test lamp should light.

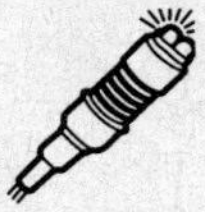

Everything OK?

YES

– Go to point 2.

NO

– The lead from pin 58 of the control module to pin 3 of the female connector is faulty.
– Go to point 4.

SA1019900030020X

Fig. 45 Code P0132: O2S Circuit High Voltage Sensor 1 (Part 2 of 5). 9-5

2. Checking the control module's sensor input

- Turn the ignition switch to the ON position.

- Test reading: O2S 1.

- The reading obtained should be 0.4 V - 0.5 V

Everything OK?

YES

– Go to point 3.

NO

– The lead from pin 4 of the female connector to pin 34 of the control module is faulty.
– Go to point 4.

3. Checking the control module sensor input (continued)

- Connect a jumper lead between pins 3 and 4 of the female connector.

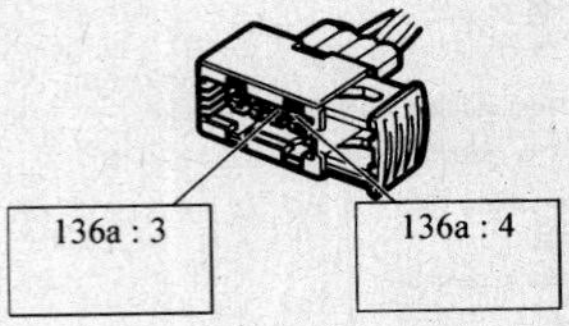

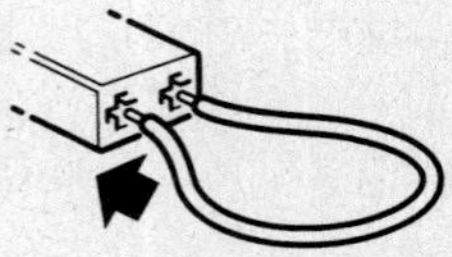

SA1019900030030X

Fig. 45 Code P0132: O2S Circuit High Voltage Sensor 1 (Part 3 of 5). 9-5

- Test reading: O2S 1.

- The reading obtained should be 0 V - 0.02 V.

Everything OK?

YES

– Change: Heated oxygen sensor
– Go to point 4.

NO

– The lead from pin 4 of the female connector to pin 34 of the control module is faulty.
– Go to point 4.

4. Final check

- Clear the diagnostic trouble codes in all systems.

- Carry out a driving cycle:
- Drive the car under varying engine loads and at different engine rpm for five minutes.

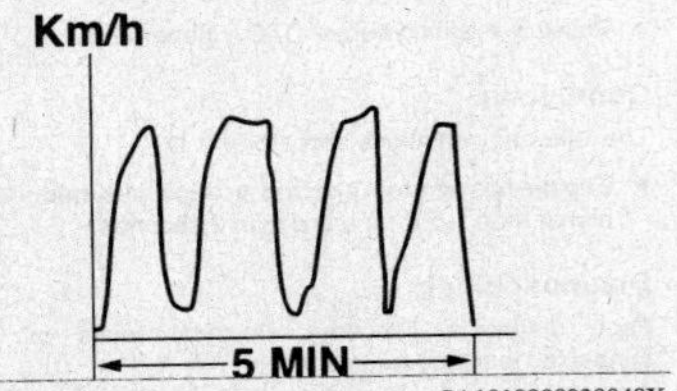

SA1019900030040X

Fig. 45 Code P0132: O2S Circuit High Voltage Sensor 1 (Part 4 of 5). 9-5

- Evaluate the driving cycle:
- Check that the diagnostic trouble code has not recurred.

Everything OK?

YES

– The steps taken to rectify the fault were correct.

NO

– See "Engine Control Module (ECM)" under "Component Replacement."

SA1019900030050X

Fig. 45 Code P0132: O2S Circuit High Voltage Sensor 1 (Part 5 of 5). 9-5

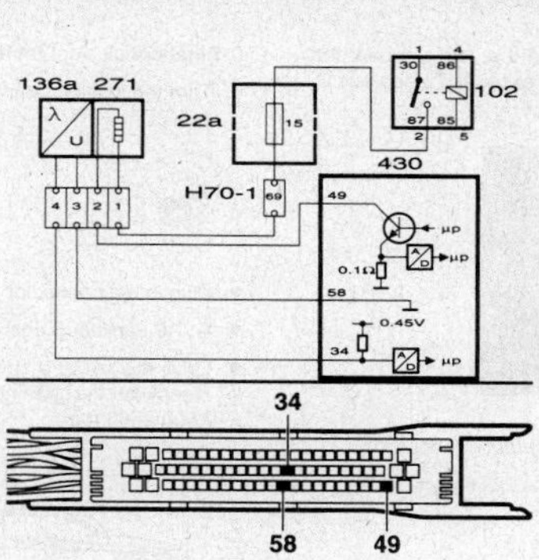

Fault symptoms

- CHECK ENGINE comes on after two driving cycles
- Possible misfiring before DTC is generated.

Conditions

The following conditions apply for this DTC:

- Engine has started and pre-heating has been active for 8 min.
- The voltage has not been outside the range of 0.4 - 0.6 V.

Or:

- Closed loop control is active and the voltage has not been outside the range of 0.4 - 0.6 V for 10 seconds.

Diagnostic help

Fault diagnosis concerns electrical faults in connected leads or in the sensor.

Diagnostic tool functions related to this fault are:

- Heated oxygen sensor reading, in V.

See also the description of test values under "Fault diagnosis, general" for more information.

Checking the wiring harness

Jiggle the leads and in-line connectors at various points and in different directions to detect any intermittent breaks or short circuits in the wiring. Observe the multimeter, test lamp or diagnostic tool while doing this.

Diagnostic procedure

See Code P0132.

SA1019900031000X

Fig. 46 Code P0134: O2S Circuit No Activity Detected Sensor 1. 9-5

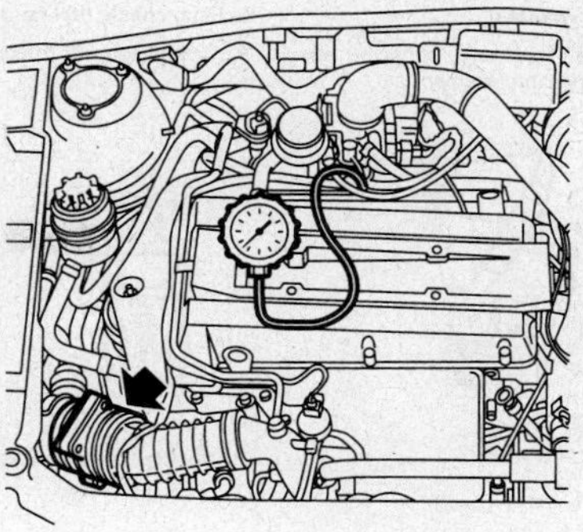

Fault symptoms

- CHECK ENGINE comes on after two driving cycles.
- Engine may stop after starting, uneven running and misfiring.

Conditions

The following conditions apply for this DTC.

- Engine has started and closed loop control is active.
- Multiplicative adaptation exceeds 25 % for more than 30 s.

Note

P1171, P0171 and P1181 may be generated if the heated oxygen sensor input is shorted to ground as there is no diagnosis for this event.

Diagnostic help

Under partial load the engine's fuel requirement is 25 % higher than that calculated by the control module on the basis of information from the mass air flow sensor.

When carrying out fault diagnosis, first determine whether the pressure sensor readings are approximately the same when the ignition is ON, as the mass air flow sensor is later compared with the intake air pressure. If the pressure sensors are OK but the mass air flow sensor reading is incorrect, the mass air flow sensor must be replaced. Air leaks will not generate this DTC.

If the mass air flow is OK, then the fuel supply must be checked, i.e. pressure, pressure response, pump flow and then the injectors.

Diagnostic tool functions related to this fault are:

- O2S 1, in V
- Multiplicative adaptation, in %
- Closed loop, in %.
- Purge adaptation, in %.
- Mass air flow deviation from that calculated, in %.

See also the description of test values under "Fault diagnosis, general" for more information.

Checking the wiring harness

Jiggle the leads and in-line connectors at various points and in different directions to detect any intermittent breaks or short circuits in the wiring. Observe the multimeter, test lamp or diagnostic tool while doing this.

SA1019900032010X

Fig. 47 Code P0171: Long Term Fuel Trim Multiplicative Max Valve Air/Fuel Too Lean (Part 1 of 5). 9-5

Diagnostic procedure

1. Checking the manifold absolute pressure sensor

- Turn the ignition switch to the ON position.

- Contact the Trionic.

- Obtain readings for the absolute pressure sensors as described in the instructions below. If any reading differs by more than 10 kPa from the others, the sensor is defective and should be changed.

- Reading: Intake manifold Absolute pressure (Trionic).
- Reading: Charge air Absolute pressure (Trionic).
- Reading: Atmosphere Absolute pressure (Trionic).
- The manifold absolute pressure sensor value will be compared with the mass air flow sensor value later on in the course of fault diagnosis.
- Drive the car in top gear with a steady, high engine load.

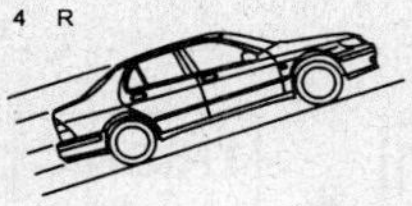

- Driving uphill is recommended.
- Test value: Mass air flow Deviation from Computed value (Trionic).
- State what the diagnostic tool shows:

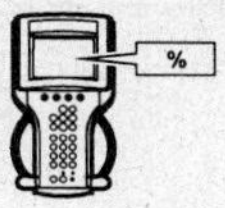

-15% TO -25%

- Change: Mass air flow sensor
- Go to point 5.

OTHER VALUE

- Go to point 2.

SA1019900032020X

Fig. 47 Code P0171: Long Term Fuel Trim Multiplicative Max Valve Air/Fuel Too Lean (Part 2 of 5). 9-5

2. Checking the fuel supply

- Check the fuel pressure as described in 'Adjustment/replacement'.

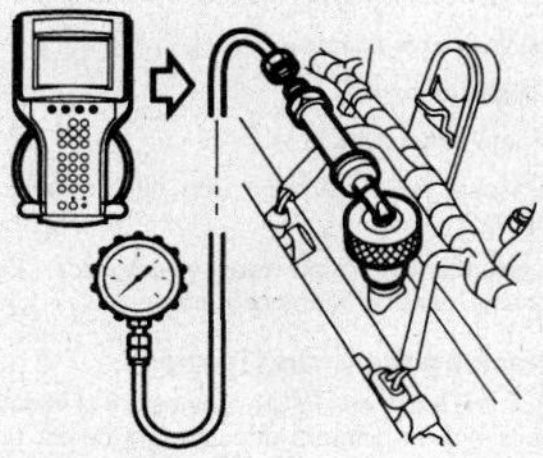

Is the fuel pressure OK?

YES

- Go to point 3.

NO

- Follow the diagnostic procedure described in the 'Adjustment/replacement' section of the 'Fuel system' service category.
- Go to point 5.

3. Checking the fuel pump flow rate

- Check the fuel pump flow rate as described in 'Adjustment/replacement'.

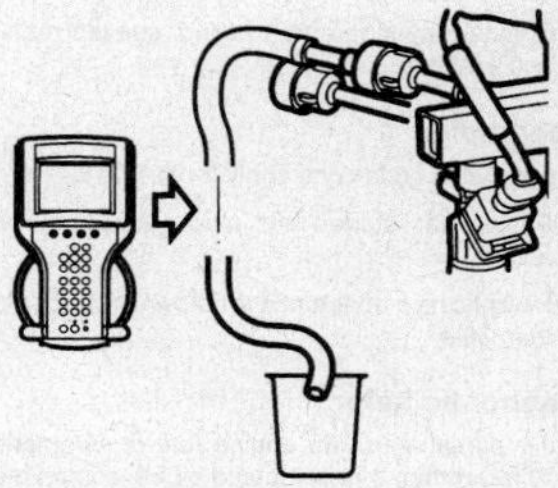

Is the fuel pump flow rate OK?

YES

- Go to point 4.

NO

- 'Adjust
- Go to point 5.

SA1019900032030X

Fig. 47 Code P0171: Long Term Fuel Trim Multiplicative Max Valve Air/Fuel Too Lean (Part 3 of 5). 9-5

4. Checking injector flow rate

- Check the injector flow rate capacity as described in 'Adjustment/replacement'.

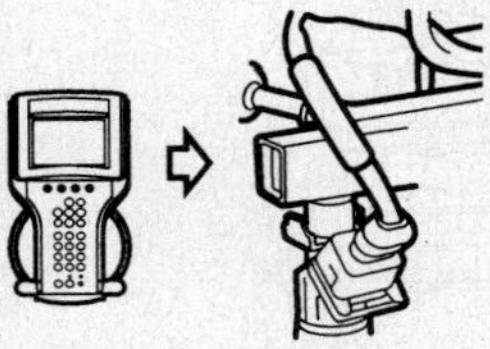

Are the injectors' flow rates OK?

YES

– Go to point 5.

NO

– Follow the diagnostic procedure described in the 'Adjustment/replacement' section of the 'Fuel system' service category.

– Go to point 5.

5. Final check, fuel fault

- Clear diagnostic trouble codes: Trionic

- Unplug the connector: EVAP canister purge valve: (321)

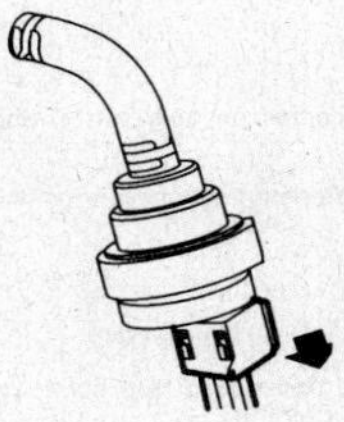

- Connect a test lamp to the female connector.

SA1019900032040X

Fig. 47 Code P0171: Long Term Fuel Trim Multiplicative Max Valve Air/Fuel Too Lean (Part 4 of 5). 9-5

- Start the engine and run it at idling speed until the coolant temperature exceeds 75 degrees C.

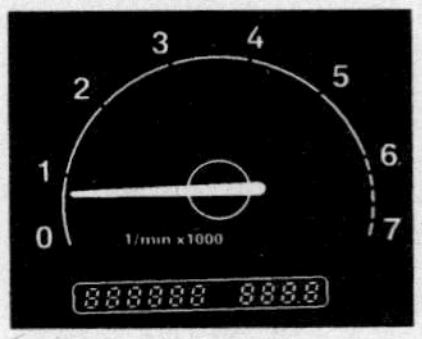

- Test value: Purging Adaptation (Trionic)
- State what the diagnostic tool shows:

-15% TO +15%

– Go to point 6.

OTHER VALUE

– Turn the ignition switch to the OFF position.

– Plug in the connector.

– EVAP canister purge valve

– See "Engine Control Module (ECM)" under "Component Replacement."

6. Final check, fuel fault, continued

- Turn the ignition switch to the OFF position.

- Plug in the connector.
- EVAP canister purge valve
- Drive the car at a speed of 60-100 km/h with a steady throttle opening and the engine running at 1500-2750 rpm.

- Wait until the value is fully stabilized.
- Test value:
- Multiplicative adaptation
- State what the diagnostic tool shows:

-15% TO +15%

– The steps taken to rectify the fault were correct.

OTHER VALUE

– See "Engine Control Module (ECM)" under "Component Replacement."

SA1019900032050X

Fig. 47 Code P0171: Long Term Fuel Trim Multiplicative Max Valve Air/Fuel Too Lean (Part 5 of 5). 9-5

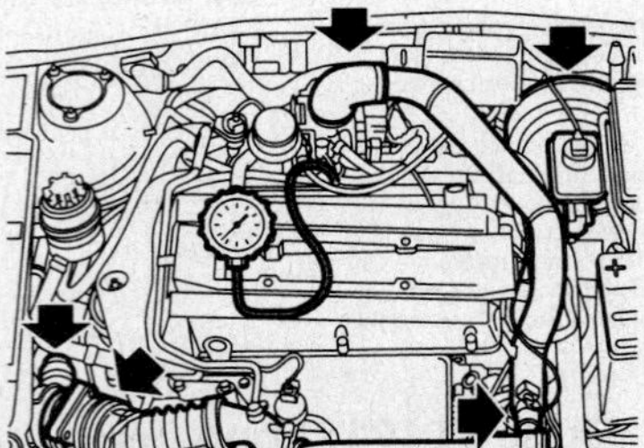

Fault symptoms

- CHECK ENGINE comes on after two driving cycles.
- Engine may stop after starting, uneven running and misfiring.

Conditions

The following conditions apply for this DTC:

- Engine has started and closed loop control is active.
- Multiplicative adaptation is below -25 % for more than 30 s.

Diagnostic help

Under partial load, the engine fuel requirement is 25 % lower than that computed by the control module on the basis of information from the mass air flow sensor.

Fault diagnosis first determines if the pressure sensor readings are approximately the same when the ignition is ON, as the mass air flow sensor is later compared with the intake air pressure. If the pressure sensors are OK but the mass air flow sensor reading is incorrect, first check for air leaks between the compressor and throttle and then change the mass air flow sensor.

If the mass air flow is OK, then the fuel supply must be checked, i.e. pressure, pressure response, pump flow and then the injectors.

Diagnostic tool functions related to this fault are:

- Multiplicative adaptation, in %
- Closed loop, in %.
- Purge adaptation, in %.
- Mass air flow deviation from that calculated, in %.

See also the description of test values under "Fault diagnosis, general" for more information.

Checking the wiring harness

Jiggle the leads and in-line connectors at various points and in different directions to detect any intermittent breaks or short circuits in the wiring. Observe the multimeter, test lamp or diagnostic tool while doing this.

SA1019900033010X

Fig. 48 Code P0172: Long Term Fuel Trim Multiplicative Min Value Air/Fuel Too Rich (Part 1 of 8). 9-5

Diagnostic procedure

1. Checking the manifold absolute pressure sensor

- Turn the ignition switch to the ON position.

- Contact the Trionic.

- Obtain readings for the absolute pressure sensors as described in the instructions below. If any reading differs by more than 10 kPa from the others, the sensor is defective and should be changed.

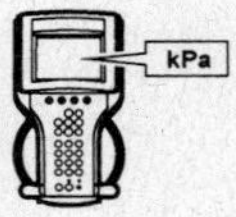

- Reading: Intake manifold Absolute pressure (Trionic).
- Reading: Charge air Absolute pressure (Trionic).
- Reading: Atmosphere Absolute pressure (Trionic).
- The manifold absolute pressure sensor value will be compared with the mass air flow sensor value later on in the course of fault diagnosis.

- Unplug the connector: EVAP canister purge valve: (321)

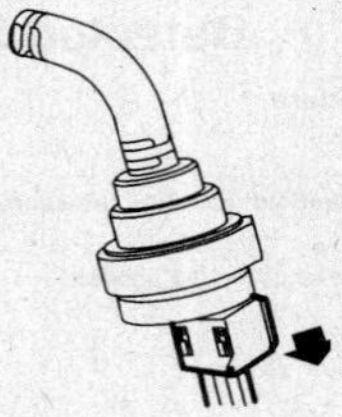

- Connect a test lamp to the female connector.

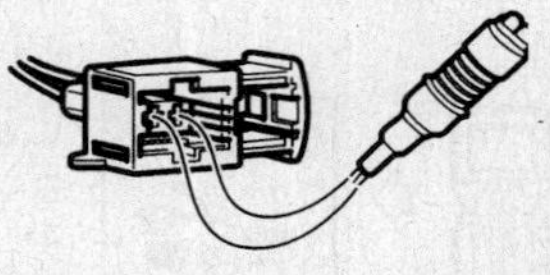

- Start the engine and run it at idling speed.

- Turn off the A/C.
- Test value: Mass air flow Deviation from Computed value (Trionic).

SA1019900033020X

Fig. 48 Code P0172: Long Term Fuel Trim Multiplicative Min Value Air/Fuel Too Rich (Part 2 of 8). 9-5

- State what the diagnostic tool shows:

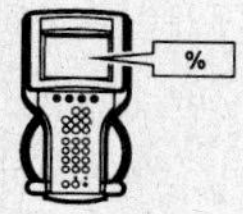

-15% TO -25%

– Go to point 2.

OTHER VALUE

– Go to point 3.

2. Checking for air leakage after throttle valve

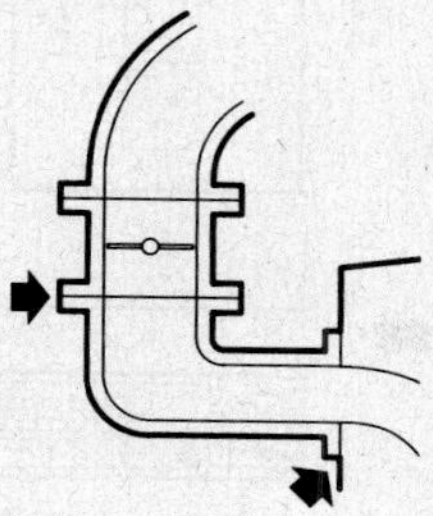

- Check whether:
- the purge valve is airtight
- the brake servo is faulty
- crankcase ventilation is airtight.
- Check that no air leakage occurs in the vacuum hoses.

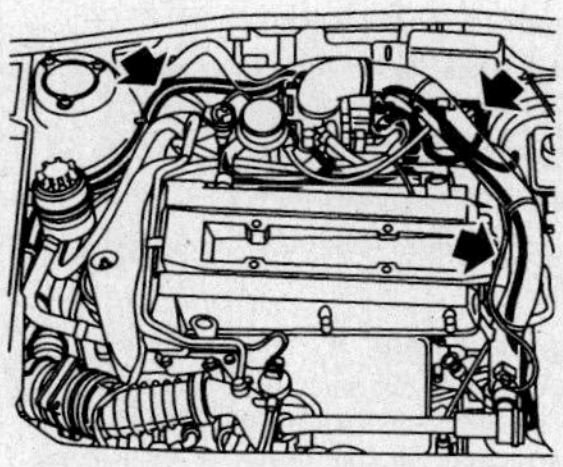

- Pinch off one hose at a time and observe the diagnostic tool's display to determine whether there is a leak. It is OK if crankcase ventilation gives an increment of about 5% via the thin hose.

SA1019900033030X

Fig. 48 Code P0172: Long Term Fuel Trim Multiplicative Min Value Air/Fuel Too Rich (Part 3 of 8). 9-5

- Test value: Mass air flow Deviation from Computed value (Trionic).
- State what the diagnostic tool shows:

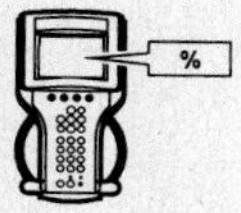

15% TO 25%

– Go to point 4.

OTHER VALUE

– Go to point 5.

4. Checking for air leakage before throttle valve

- Check for the presence of an air leak, using the method described in 'Checking for leaks in the intake system'.

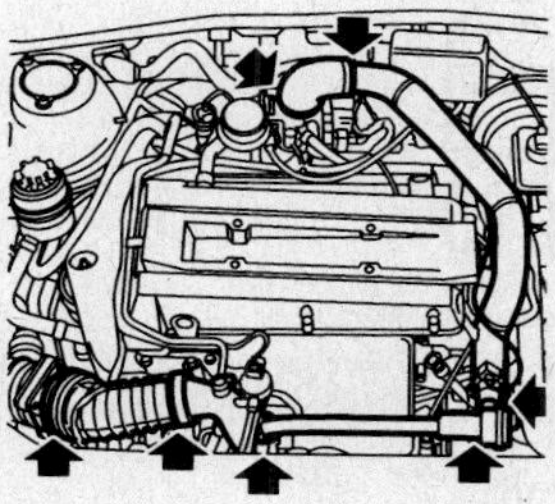

Is the system airtight?

YES

– Change: Mass air flow sensor

– Go to point 8.

NO

– Rectify the fault.

– Go to point 8.

SA1019900033050X

Fig. 48 Code P0172: Long Term Fuel Trim Multiplicative Min Value Air/Fuel Too Rich (Part 5 of 8). 9-5

- The other hoses must not give any noticeable increment. Note that the evap canister purge valve's electrical connection must be disconnected for this check.

Is the system airtight?

YES

– Plug in the connector:

– EVAP canister purge valve

– Change: Mass air flow sensor

– Go to point 8.

NO

– Plug in the connector:

– EVAP canister purge valve

– Rectify the fault.

– Go to point 8.

3. Checking the mass air flow under partial load

- Turn the ignition switch to the OFF position.

- Plug in the connector:
- EVAP canister purge valve
- Drive the car in top gear with a steady, high engine load.

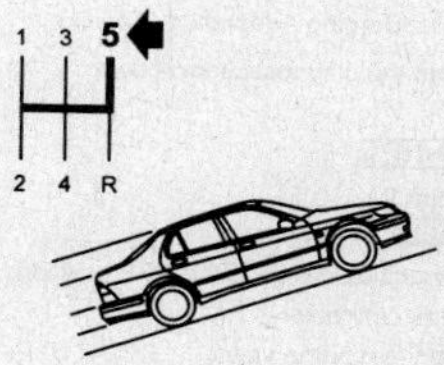

- Driving uphill is recommended.

SA1019900033040X

Fig. 48 Code P0172: Long Term Fuel Trim Multiplicative Min Value Air/Fuel Too Rich (Part 4 of 8). 9-5

5. Checking the fuel supply

- Check the fuel pressure as described in 'Adjustment/replacement'.

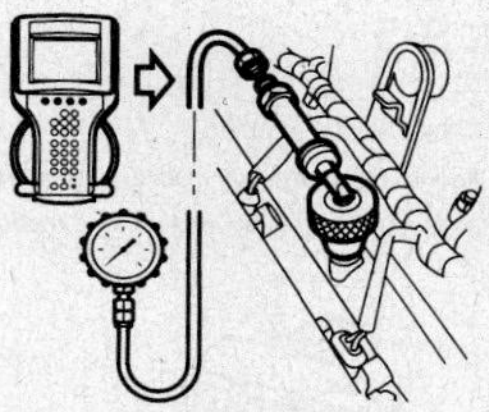

Is the fuel pressure OK?

YES

– Go to point 6.

NO

– Follow the diagnostic procedure described in the 'Adjustment/replacement' section of the 'Fuel system' service category.

– Go to point 8.

6. Checking the fuel pump flow rate

- Check the fuel pump flow rate as described in 'Adjustment/replacement'.

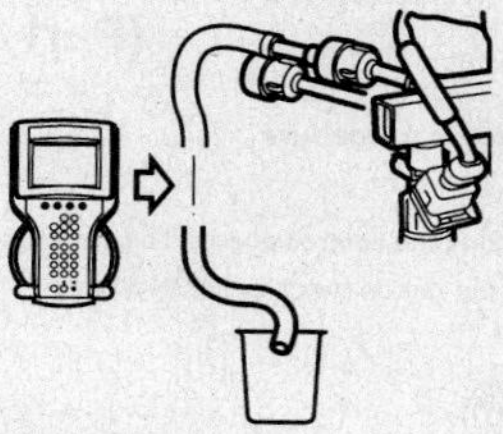

Is the fuel pump flow rate OK?

YES

– Go to point 7.

NO

– 'Adjust

– Go to point 8.

SA1019900033060X

Fig. 48 Code P0172: Long Term Fuel Trim Multiplicative Min Value Air/Fuel Too Rich (Part 6 of 8). 9-5

7. Checking injector flow rate

- Check the injector flow rate capacity as described in 'Adjustment/replacement'.

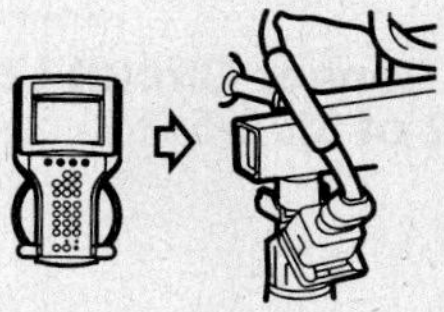

Are the injectors' flow rates OK?

YES

– Go to point 8.

NO

– Follow the diagnostic procedure described in the 'Adjustment/replacement' section of the 'Fuel system' service category.

– Go to point 8.

8. Final check, fuel fault

- Clear diagnostic trouble codes: Trionic

- Unplug the connector: EVAP canister purge valve: (321)

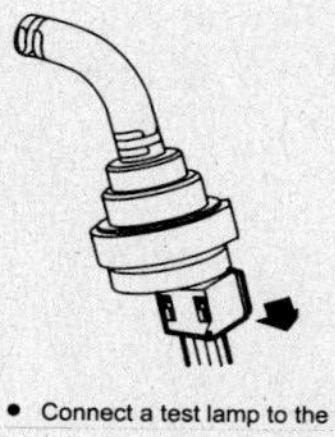

- Connect a test lamp to the female connector.

SA1019900033070X

Fig. 48 Code P0172: Long Term Fuel Trim Multiplicative Min Value Air/Fuel Too Rich (Part 7 of 8). 9-5

- Start the engine and run it at idling speed until the coolant temperature exceeds 75 degrees C.

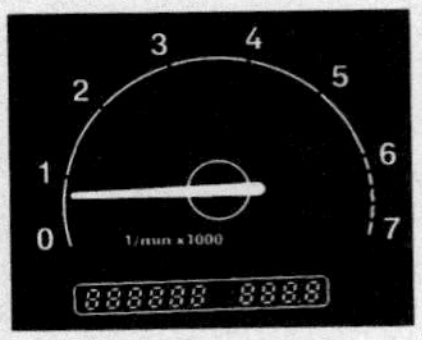

- Test value: Purging Adaptation (Trionic)
- State what the diagnostic tool shows:

-15% TO +15%

– Go to point 9.

OTHER VALUE

– Turn the ignition switch to the OFF position.
– Plug in the connector.
– EVAP canister purge valve
– See "Engine Control Module (ECM)" under "Component Replacement."

9. Final check, fuel fault, continued

- Turn the ignition switch to the OFF position.

- Plug in the connector.
- EVAP canister purge valve
- Drive the car at a speed of 60-100 km/h with a steady throttle opening and the engine running at 1500-2750 rpm.

- Wait until the value is fully stabilized.
- Test value:
- Multiplicative adaptation
- State what the diagnostic tool shows:

-15% TO +15%

– The steps taken to rectify the fault were correct.

OTHER VALUE

– See "Engine Control Module (ECM)" under "Component Replacement."

SA1019900033080X

Fig. 48 Code P0172: Long Term Fuel Trim Multiplicative Min Value Air/Fuel Too Rich (Part 8 of 8). 9-5

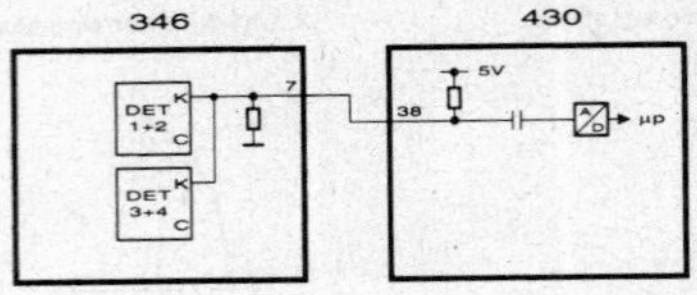

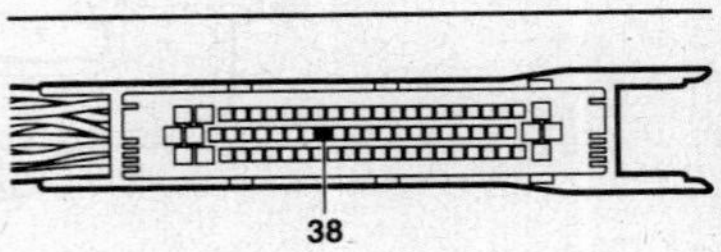

Fault symptoms

- CHECK ENGINE comes on after two driving cycles.
- Limited torque.

Conditions

The following conditions apply for this DTC:

- Engine has started and engine speed exceeds 800 rpm.
- Engine coolant temperature exceeds 60 °C.
- Main relay voltage exceeds 11 V.
- Knock voltage below 0.25 V on sparking for 25 ignitions.

Diagnostic help

Fault diagnosis concerns electrical faults in connecting cables or in the ignition discharge module.

Diagnostic tool functions related to this fault are:

- Knock sensor reading, in V.

Note

The knock sensor is an internal ignition discharge module function. There is no external sensor.

See also the description of test values under "Fault diagnosis, general" for more information.

Checking the wiring harness

Jiggle the leads and in-line connectors at various points and in different directions to detect any intermittent breaks or short circuits in the wiring. Observe the multimeter, test lamp or diagnostic tool while doing this.

SA1019900034010X

Fig. 49 Code P0327: Knock Sensor Circuit Low Input Bank 1 (Part 1 of 3). 9-5

Diagnostic procedure

1. Checking the control module's signal input

- Turn the ignition switch to the ON position.

- Unplug the connector: Ignition discharge module: (346)

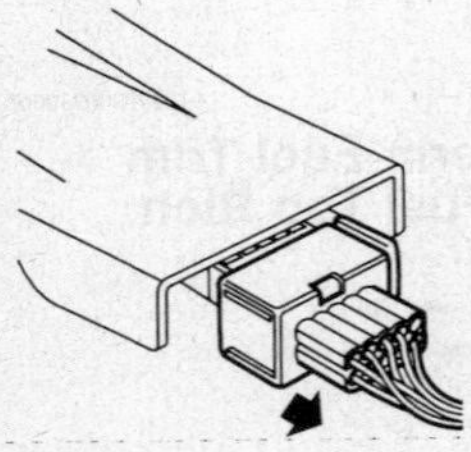

- Take a voltage reading.
- Red test lead: Ignition discharge module: 6
- Black test lead: Ignition discharge module: 7

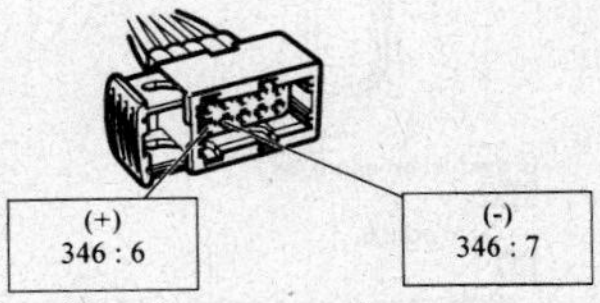

- The reading obtained should be 4.9 V - 5.1 V.

Everything OK?

YES

– Change: Ignition discharge module
– Go to point 2.

NO

– The lead from pin 7 of the female connector to pin 38 of the control module is faulty.
– Go to point 2.

SA1019900034020X

Fig. 49 Code P0327: Knock Sensor Circuit Low Input Bank 1 (Part 2 of 3). 9-5

2. Final check

- Clear the diagnostic trouble codes in all systems.

- Carry out a driving cycle:
- Drive the car under varying engine loads and at different engine rpm for five minutes.

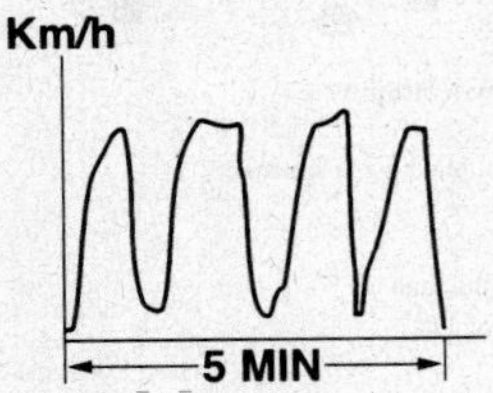

- Evaluate the driving cycle:
- Check that the diagnostic trouble code has not recurred.

Everything OK?

YES

– The steps taken to rectify the fault were correct.

NO

– See "Engine Control Module (ECM)" under "Component Replacement."

SA1019900034030X

Fig. 49 Code P0327: Knock Sensor Circuit Low Input Bank 1 (Part 3 of 3). 9-5

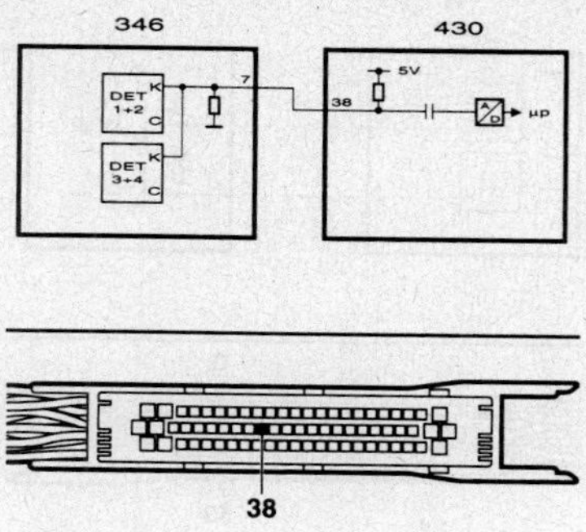

Fault symptoms

- CHECK ENGINE comes on after two driving cycles.
- Limited torque.

Conditions

The following conditions apply for this DTC:

- Engine has started and engine speed exceeds 800 rpm.
- Engine coolant temperature exceeds 60 °C.
- Main relay voltage exceeds 11 V.
- Fuel shut-off is active.
- Knock voltage is below 2 V after sparking for 25 ignitions.

Diagnostic help

Fault diagnosis concerns electrical faults in connecting cables or in the ignition discharge module.

Diagnostic tool functions related to this fault are:

- Knock sensor reading, in V.

Note

The knock sensor is an internal ignition discharge module function. There is no external sensor.

See also the description of test values under "Fault diagnosis, general" for more information.

Checking the wiring harness

Jiggle the leads and in-line connectors at various points and in different directions to detect any intermittent breaks or short circuits in the wiring. Observe the multimeter, test lamp or diagnostic tool while doing this.

Diagnostic procedure

See "Code P0327."

SA1019900035000X

Fig. 50 Code P0328: Knock Sensor Circuit High Input Bank 1. 9-5

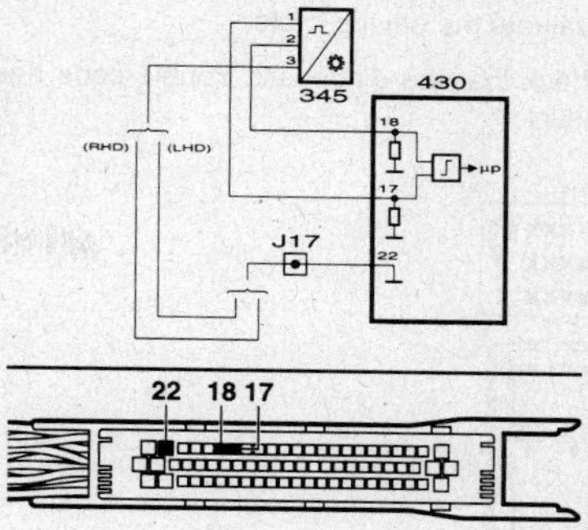

Fault symptoms

- The engine cannot be started if the fault is permanent.
- Possible misfiring before DTC is generated.

Conditions

The following conditions apply for this DTC:

- Ignition ON and crankshaft stationary.
- Immobilizer inactive.
- Ignition switch in ST position.
- Main relay voltage drops by more than 0.8 V.
- Conditions satisfied for 5 s.

Diagnostic help

Fault diagnosis concerns electrical faults in connected leads or in the sensor.

Diagnostic tool functions related to this fault are:

- Engine speed, in rpm.

See also the description of test values under "Fault diagnosis, general" for more information.

Checking the wiring harness

Jiggle the leads and in-line connectors at various points and in different directions to detect any intermittent breaks or short circuits in the wiring. Observe the multimeter, test lamp or diagnostic tool while doing this.

SA1019900036010X

Fig. 51 Code P0337: Crankshaft Position Sensor No Input (Part 1 of 4). 9-5

Diagnostic procedure

1. Checking sensor input

- Turn the ignition switch to the OFF position.

- Unplug the connector: Crankshaft position sensor: (345)

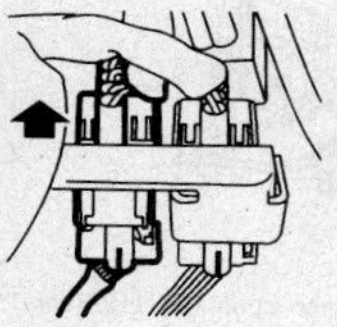

- Take a resistance reading
- Red test lead: Crankshaft position sensor: 1
- Black test lead: Crankshaft position sensor: 2

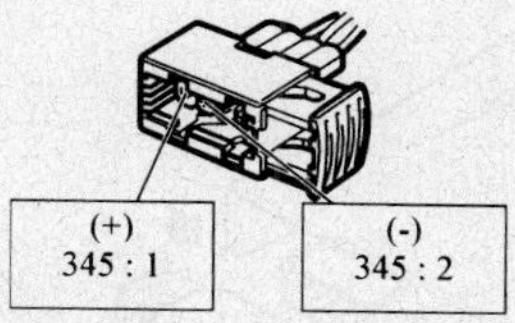

- The reading obtained should be 150 kohm - 250 kohm

Everything OK?

YES

- Go to point 2.

NO

- One of the following leads is faulty. Either the lead from pin 1 of the female connector to pin 17 of the control module or the lead from pin 2 of the female connector to pin 18 of the control module.
- Go to point 3.

SA1019900036020X

Fig. 51 Code P0337: Crankshaft Position Sensor No Input (Part 2 of 4). 9-5

2. Checking the screened lead

- Connect test lamp 86 11 857 to B+ and pin 3 of the female connector.

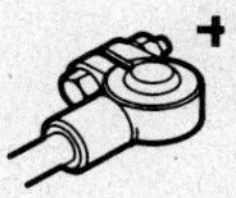

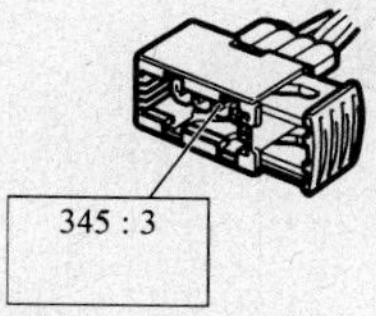

- The test lamp should light.

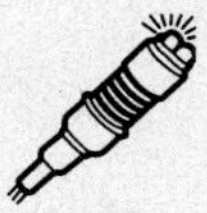

Everything OK?

YES

- Change: Crankshaft position sensor
- Go to point 3.

NO

- The lead from crimp connection J17 to pin 3 of the female connector is faulty.
- Go to point 3.

3. Final check

- Clear the diagnostic trouble codes in all systems.

- Carry out a driving cycle:
- Drive the car under varying engine loads and at different engine rpm for five minutes.

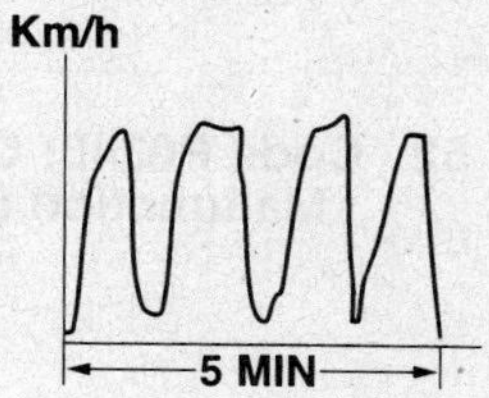

SA1019900036030X

Fig. 51 Code P0337: Crankshaft Position Sensor No Input (Part 3 of 4). 9-5

- Evaluate the driving cycle:
- Check that the diagnostic trouble code has not recurred.

Everything OK?

YES

– The steps taken to rectify the fault were correct.

NO

– See "Engine Control Module (ECM)" under "Component Replacement."

SA1019900036040X

Fig. 51 Code P0337: Crankshaft Position Sensor No Input (Part 4 of 4). 9-5

- See whether any of the following diagnostic trouble codes have been recorded:

- Diagnostic trouble codes P0100-0134
- Diagnostic trouble codes P0171-0172
- Diagnostic trouble codes P0300-0306
- Diagnostic trouble codes P0336-0337
- Diagnostic trouble codes P0443-0445
- Diagnostic trouble codes P1171-1172
- Diagnostic trouble codes P1181-1182
- Diagnostic trouble codes P1300-1306
- Diagnostic trouble codes P1312-1324

Have any of the above diagnostic trouble codes been recorded?

YES

– Change: Spark plugs

– Then continue fault diagnosis for the relevant diagnostic trouble code

NO

– Go to point 2.

2. Checking the control module's signal input for cylinders 1+2/cylinder bank 1

- Unplug the connector: Ignition discharge module: (346)

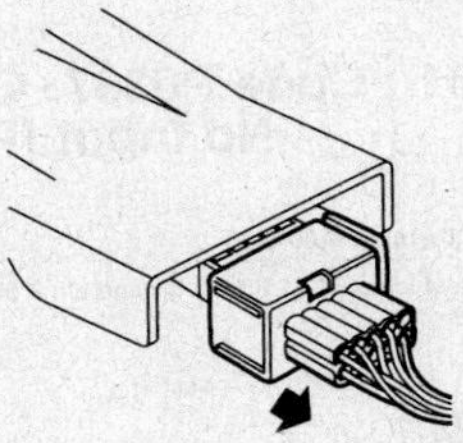

- Extract pins 8 and 9.

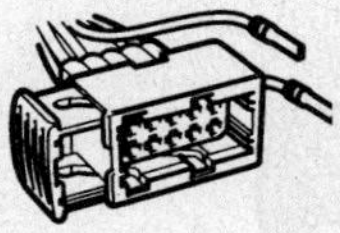

SA1019900037020X

Fig. 52 Code P0340: Camshaft Position Sensor Malfunction (Part 2 of 7). 9-5

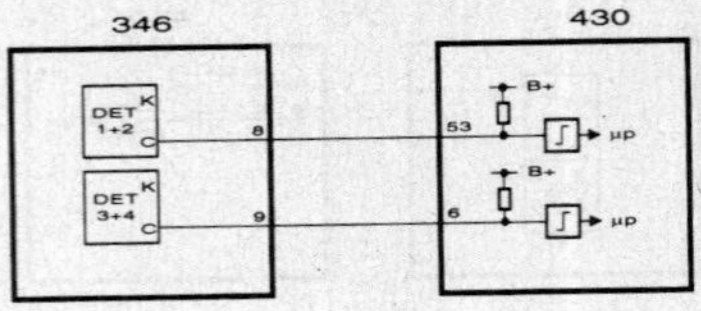

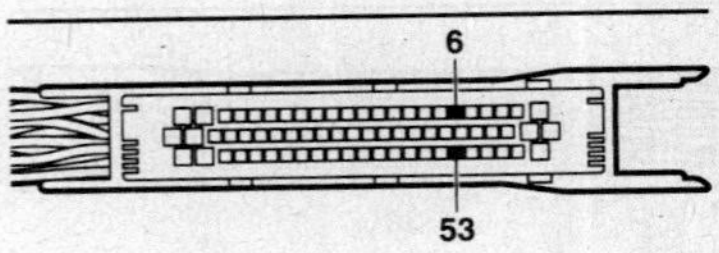

Fault symptoms

- CHECK ENGINE comes on after two driving cycles.

Conditions

The following conditions apply for this DTC:

- Engine has started and main relay voltage exceeds 11 V.
- 1000 ignitions have occurred since start.
- Ignition timing and fuel injection have not been synchronized with the camshaft position.

Diagnostic help

Fault diagnosis concerns electrical faults in connecting cables, sooty or defective spark plugs, or in the ignition discharge module.

Diagnostic tool functions related to this fault are:

- Camshaft position synchronized, ON/OFF.
- Combustion signal cyl. 1+2/bank 1, in %
- Combustion signal cyl. 3+4/Bank 2, in %

See also the description of test values under "Fault diagnosis, general" for more information.

Diagnostic procedure

1. Checking additional diagnostic trouble codes

- Contact the Trionic.

SA1019900037010X

Fig. 52 Code P0340: Camshaft Position Sensor Malfunction (Part 1 of 7). 9-5

- Plug in the connector.
- Ignition discharge module (346)

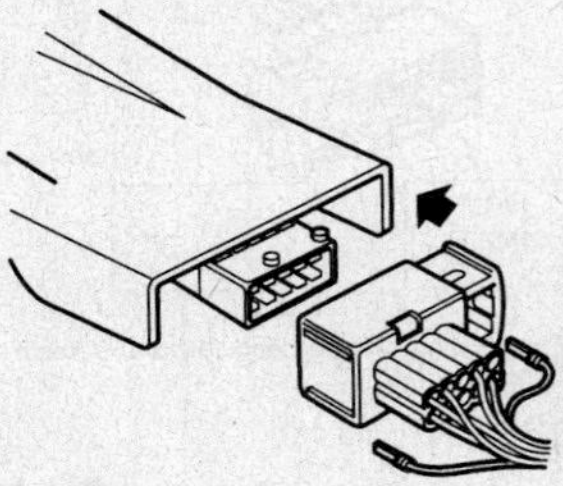

- Start the engine and run it at idling speed.

- Test value: Combustion signal Cyl. 1+2/Bank 1.
- The reading obtained should be 100%

Everything OK?

YES

– Go to point 3.

NO

– The lead from pin 8 of the female connector to pin 53 of the control module is faulty.

– Go to point 8.

3. Checking the control module's signal input for cylinders 1+2/cylinder bank 1 (continued)

- Connect a jumper lead between pin 8 (which is loose) and a good grounding point.

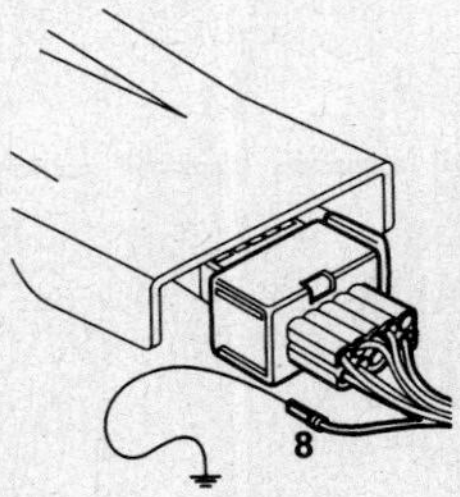

- Test value: Combustion signal Cyl. 1+2/Bank 1.
- The reading obtained should be 0%

Everything OK?

YES

– Go to point 4.

NO

– The lead from pin 8 of the female connector to pin 53 of the control module is faulty.

– Go to point 8.

SA1019900037030X

Fig. 52 Code P0340: Camshaft Position Sensor Malfunction (Part 3 of 7). 9-5

4. Checking the control module's signal input for cylinders 3+4/cylinder bank 2

- Test value: Combustion signal Cyl. 3+4/Bank 2.
- The reading obtained should be 100%

Everything OK?

YES

– Go to point 5.

NO

– The lead from pin 9 of the female connector to pin 6 of the control module is faulty.

– Go to point 8.

5. Checking the control module's signal input for cylinders 3+4/cylinder bank 2 (continued)

- Connect a jumper lead between pin 9 (which is loose) and a good grounding point.

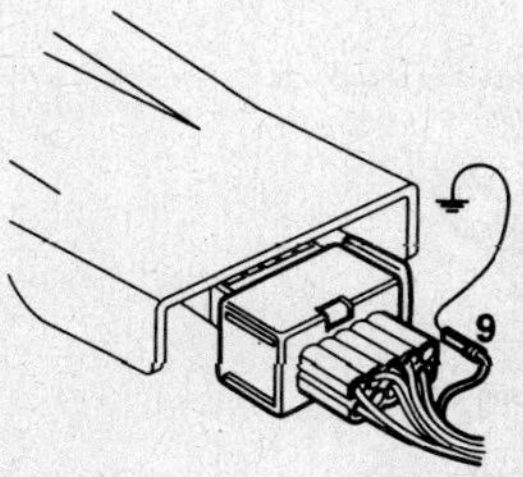

- Test value: Combustion signal Cyl. 3+4/Bank 2.
- The reading obtained should be 0%

Everything OK?

YES

– Go to point 6.

NO

– The lead from pin 9 of the female connector to pin 6 of the control module is faulty.

– Go to point 8.

6. Component replacement

- Change: Spark plugs

- Clear diagnostic trouble codes: Trionic

- Start the engine and run it at idling speed.

SA1019900037040X

Fig. 52 Code P0340: Camshaft Position Sensor Malfunction (Part 4 of 7). 9-5

- Turn off the A/C.

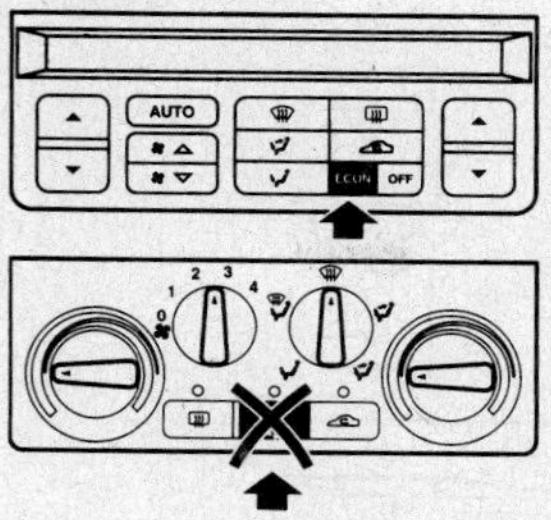

- Run the engine until the radiator fan starts
- Switch off the engine.

- Start the engine and run it at idling speed for 6 minutes

Has the diagnostic trouble code recurred?

YES

– Go to point 7.

NO

– The steps taken to rectify the fault were correct.

7. Component replacement

- Change: Ignition discharge module

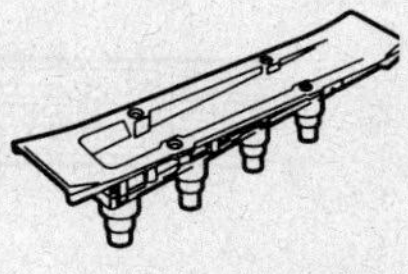

- Clear diagnostic trouble codes: Trionic

- Start the engine and run it at idling speed.

SA1019900037050X

Fig. 52 Code P0340: Camshaft Position Sensor Malfunction (Part 5 of 7). 9-5

- Turn off the A/C.

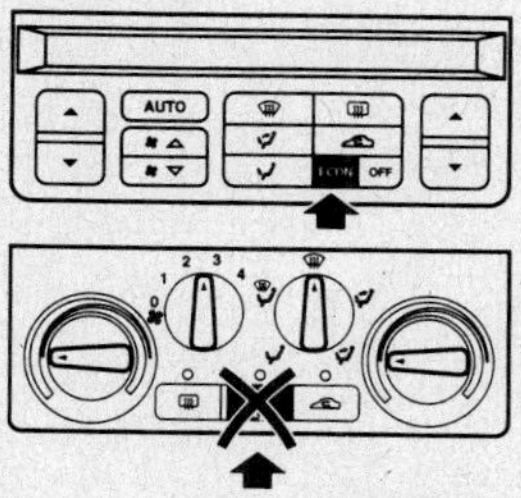

- Run the engine until the radiator fan starts
- Switch off the engine.

- Start the engine and run it at idling speed for 6 minutes

Has the diagnostic trouble code recurred?

YES

- Proceed as described in "Engine Control Module (ECM)" under "Component Replacement," and then, if necessary:

– Change: Control module, Trionic T7

NO

– The steps taken to rectify the fault were correct.

8. Final check

- Clear the diagnostic trouble codes in all systems.

- Carry out a driving cycle:
- Drive the car under varying engine loads and at different engine rpm for five minutes.

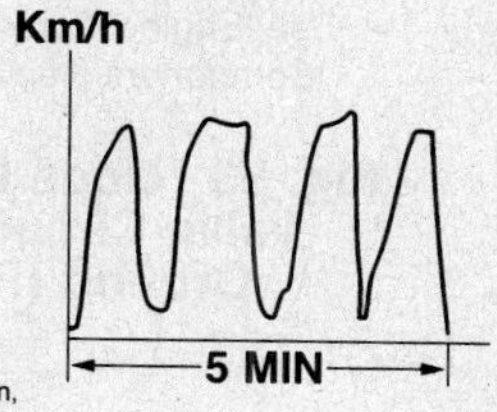

SA1019900037060X

Fig. 52 Code P0340: Camshaft Position Sensor Malfunction (Part 6 of 7). 9-5

- Evaluate the driving cycle:
- Check that the diagnostic trouble code has not recurred.

Everything OK?

YES

– The steps taken to rectify the fault were correct.

NO

– See "Engine Control Module (ECM)" under "Component Replacement."

SA1019900037070X

Fig. 52 Code P0340: Camshaft Position Sensor Malfunction (Part 7 of 7). 9-5

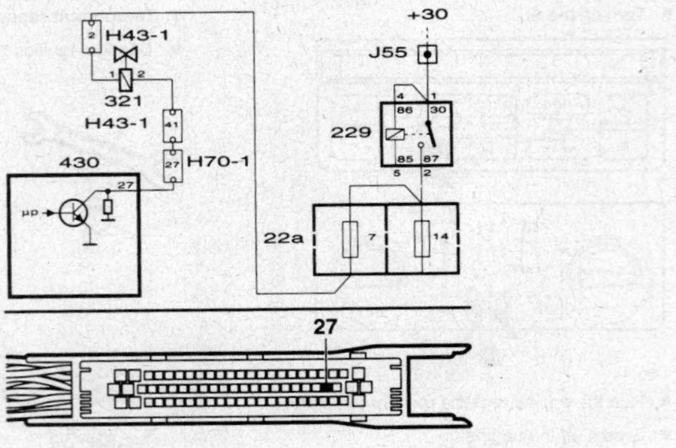

Fault symptoms

- CHECK ENGINE comes on after two driving cycles.
- Possible smell of petrol and misfiring.

Conditions

The following fault symptoms apply for this DTC:

- Engine has started and main relay voltage exceeds 10 V.
- Output voltage is below 2 V while output is inactive.
- Conditions met within 10 periods that must occur within 60 seconds (it normally takes 1 second for the DTC to be generated).

Checking the wiring harness

Jiggle the leads and in-line connectors at various points and in different directions to detect any intermittent breaks or short circuits in the wiring. Observe the multimeter, test lamp or diagnostic tool while doing this.

Diagnostic help

Fault diagnosis concerns electrical faults in connecting cables or in the valve.

Diagnostic tool functions related to this fault are:

- Activating the valve output.

See also the description of activating functions under "Fault diagnosis, general" for more information.

SA1019900038010X

Fig. 53 Code P0444: EVAP Purge Valve Circuit Open/Short To Ground (Part 1 of 4). 9-5

Diagnostic procedure

1. Checking the valve's power supply

- Unplug the connector: EVAP canister purge valve: (321)

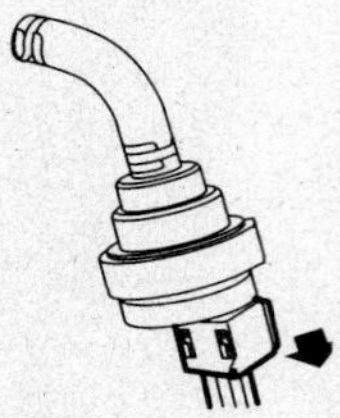

- Turn the ignition switch to the ON position.

- Connect test lamp 86 11 857 to pin 1 of the female connector and a good grounding point.

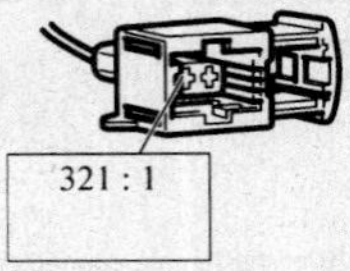

- The test lamp should light.

Everything OK?

YES

- Go to point 2.

NO

- The lead from fuse 7 to pin 1 of the female connector is faulty.
- Go to point 3.

SA1019900038020X

Fig. 53 Code P0444: EVAP Purge Valve Circuit Open/Short To Ground (Part 2 of 4). 9-5

2. Checking the valve's control module output

- Connect test lamp 86 11 857 to pins 1 and 2 of the female connector.

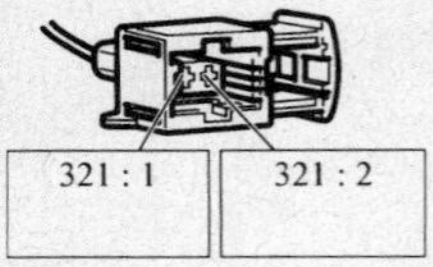

- Activate:
- Evap canister purge valve (Trionic): 100%

- The test lamp should light

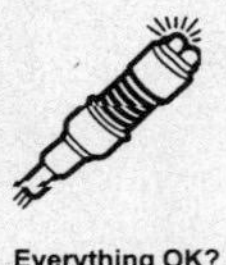

Everything OK?

YES

- Change: Evap canister purge valve
- Go to point 3.

NO

- The lead from pin 27 of the control module to pin 2 of the female connector is faulty.
- Go to point 3.

3. Final check

- Clear the diagnostic trouble codes in all systems.

- Carry out a driving cycle:
- Drive the car under varying engine loads and at different engine rpm for five minutes.

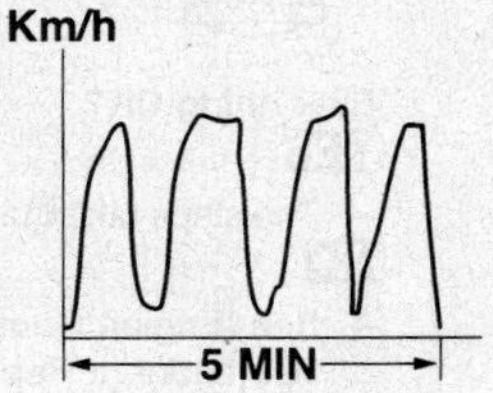

SA1019900038030X

Fig. 53 Code P0444: EVAP Purge Valve Circuit Open/Short To Ground (Part 3 of 4). 9-5

- Evaluate the driving cycle:
- Check that the diagnostic trouble code has not recurred.

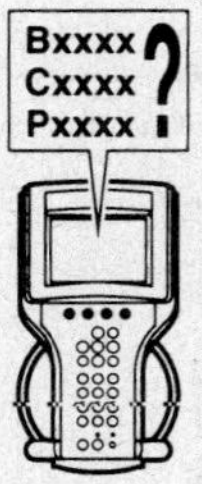

Everything OK?

YES

- The steps taken to rectify the fault were correct.

NO

- See "Engine Control Module (ECM)" under "Component Replacement."

SA1019900038040X

Fig. 53 Code P0444: EVAP Purge Valve Circuit Open/Short To Ground (Part 4 of 4). 9-5

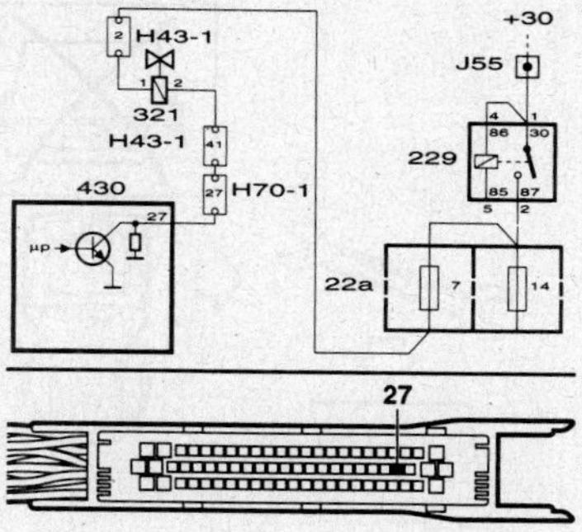

Fault symptoms

- CHECK ENGINE comes on after two driving cycles.
- Possible smell of petrol.

Conditions

The following conditions apply for this DTC:

- Engine has started and main relay voltage exceeds 10 V.
- Output voltage exceeds 2 V when output active.
- Conditions met within 10 periods that must occur within 60 seconds (it normally takes 1 second for the DTC to be generated when purging is active).

Diagnostic help

Fault diagnosis concerns electrical faults in connecting cables or in the valve.

Diagnostic tool functions related to this fault are:

- Activating the valve output.

See also the description of activating functions under "Fault diagnosis, general" for more information.

Checking the wiring harness

Jiggle the leads and in-line connectors at various points and in different directions to detect any intermittent breaks or short circuits in the wiring. Observe the multimeter, test lamp or diagnostic tool while doing this.

Diagnostic procedure

See Code P0444

SA1019900039000X

Fig. 54 Code P0445: EVAP Purge Valve Circuit Short To B+. 9-5

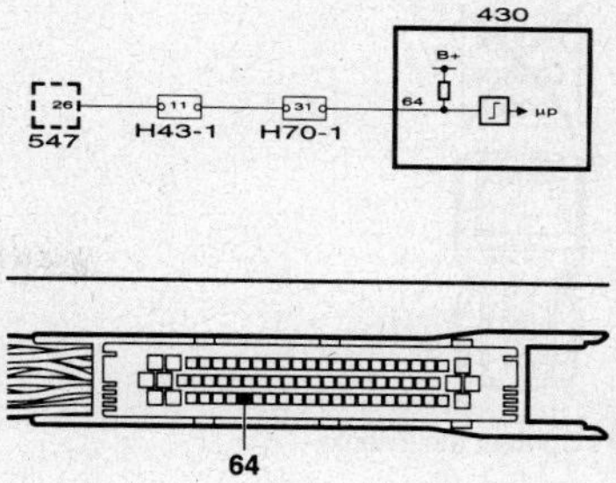

Fault symptoms

- CHECK ENGINE comes on after two driving cycles.
- Cruise control inoperative.

Conditions

The following conditions apply for this DTC:

- Engine has started and vehicle stationary.
- Brake pedal not depressed.
- Engine speed exceeds 2000 rpm.
- Load exceeds 500 mg/c for more than 5 s.
- After which, 17 minutes with vehicle stationary.
- On cars with automatic transmission, the selector lever must be in a position other than P or N.

Diagnostic help

Fault diagnosis concerns electrical faults in connecting cables (first check whether there is a fault in the ABS).

Diagnostic tool functions related to this fault are:

- Vehicle Speed (Lead from ABS), in km/h.

See also the description of test values under "Fault diagnosis, general" for more information.

Checking the wiring harness

Jiggle the leads and in-line connectors at various points and in different directions to detect any intermittent breaks or short circuits in the wiring. Observe the multimeter, test lamp or diagnostic tool while doing this.

SA1019900040010X

Fig. 55 Code P0502: Vehicle Speed No Input Signal (Part 1 of 4). 9-5

Diagnostic procedure

1. Checking diagnostic trouble codes in the ABS

- Contact the ABS.

- Obtain readouts of diagnostic trouble codes in the ABS.

Is diagnostic trouble code C1376 or C1377 present?

YES

- See fault diagnosis in the 'Brakes ABS' service category.
- Go to point 4.

NO

- Go to point 2.

2. Checking the wheel speed signal

- Jack up the front of the car.

- Unplug the connector: Trionic control module: (430)

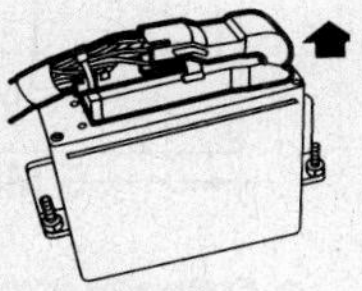

- Turn the ignition switch to the ON position.

- Connect test lamp 86 11 857 to pins 23 and 64 of the female connector.

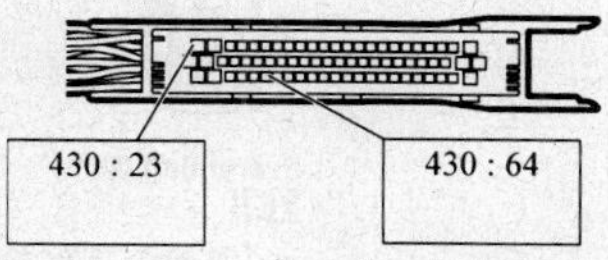

SA1019900040020X

Fig. 55 Code P0502: Vehicle Speed No Input Signal (Part 2 of 4). 9-5

- Spin the RH front wheel.

- The test lamp should flash.

Everything OK?

YES

- Go to point 4.

NO

- Go to point 3.

3. Checking the lead

- Check the lead from pin 26 of the ABS control module to pin 64 of the Trionic control module.

Everything OK?

YES

- Proceed as described in 'Before changing a control module' and then, if necessary:
- Change: ABS control module
- Go to point 4.

NO

- The lead from pin 26 of the ABS control module to pin 64 of the Trionic control module is faulty.
- Go to point 4.

SA1019900040030X

Fig. 55 Code P0502: Vehicle Speed No Input Signal (Part 3 of 4). 9-5

- Contact the Trionic.

- Test reading: Vehicle speed (Lead from ABS) (Trionic).
- Drive the car and check that the test reading corresponds to that indicated by the speedometer.

Everything OK?

YES

– The steps taken to rectify the fault were correct.

NO

– See "Engine Control Module (ECM)" under "Component Replacement"

SA1019900040040X

Fig. 55 Code P0502: Vehicle Speed No Input Signal (Part 4 of 4). 9-5

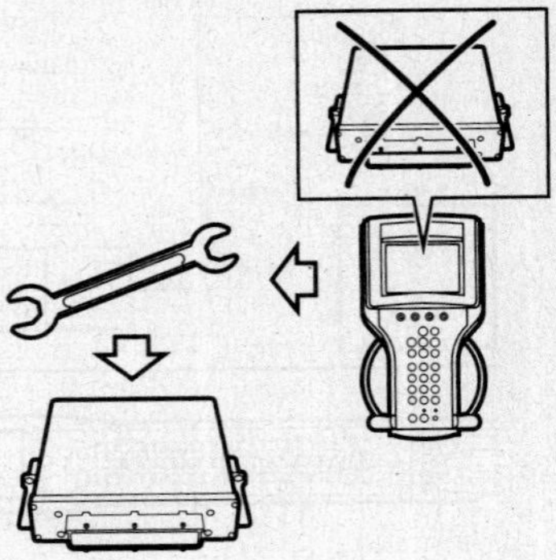

Fault symptoms

- Fuel shut-off activated.

Conditions

The following conditions apply for this DTC:

- Ignition ON and incorrect programming of flash memory.

Diagnostic help

The flash memory has been incorrectly programmed, which means that the control module must be replaced if it cannot be reprogrammed.

Checking the wiring harness

Jiggle the leads and in-line connectors at various points and in different directions to detect any intermittent breaks or short circuits in the wiring. Observe the multimeter, test lamp or diagnostic tool while doing this.

Diagnostic procedure

1. Component replacement

- Change: Control module, Trionic T7

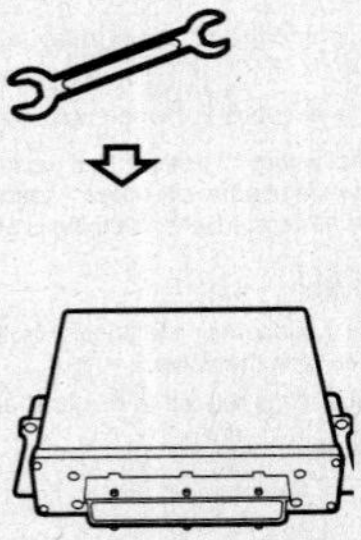

SA1019900041010X

Fig. 56 Code P0605: Internal Control Module Malfunction (Part 1 of 3). 9-5

- Turn the ignition switch to the ON position.

- Clear diagnostic trouble codes: Trionic

- Turn the ignition switch to the OFF position.

- Wait for 10 seconds.
- Reset the limp-home mechanism as described in the 'Adjustment and replacement' section.

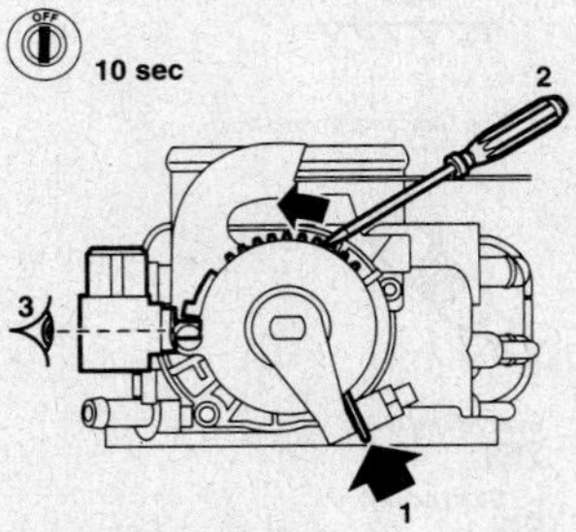

- Clear the diagnostic trouble codes in all systems.

SA1019900041020X

Fig. 56 Code P0605: Internal Control Module Malfunction (Part 2 of 3). 9-5

- Carry out a driving cycle:
- Drive the car under varying engine loads and at different engine rpm for five minutes.

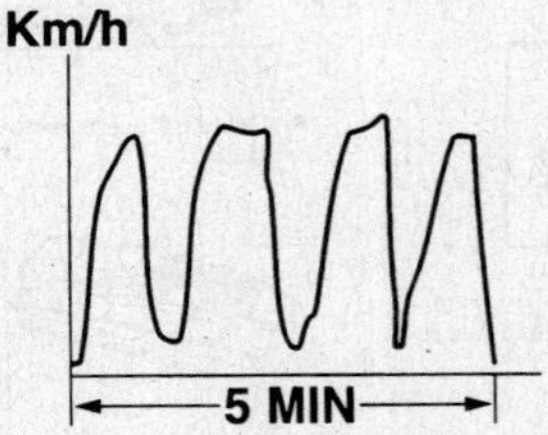

- Evaluate the driving cycle:
- Check that the diagnostic trouble code has not recurred.

Everything OK?

YES

– The steps taken to rectify the fault were correct.

NO

– See "Engine Control Module (ECM)" under "Component Replacement"

SA1019900041030X

Fig. 56 Code P0605: Internal Control Module Malfunction (Part 3 of 3). 9-5

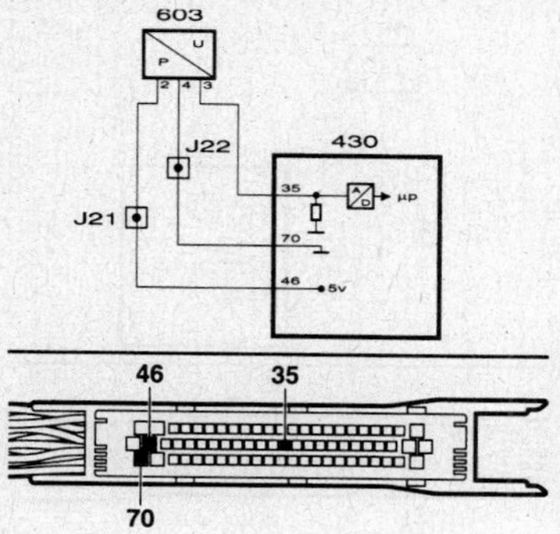

Fault symptoms

- CHECK ENGINE comes on after two driving cycles.
- Engine speed drops slower than normal when the accelerator is released.

Conditions

The following conditions apply for this DTC:

- Engine has started and the voltage is lower than 0.185 V for more than 5 s.

Diagnostic help

Fault diagnosis concerns electrical faults in connecting cables or in the sensor.

Diagnostic tool functions related to this fault are:

- Pressure sensor reading, in kPa.

With the engine switched off, the reading should correspond with those of the other two pressure sensors. Permissible difference is 10 kPa.

See also the description of test values under "Fault diagnosis, general" for more information.

Checking the wiring harness

Jiggle the leads and in-line connectors at various points and in different directions to detect any intermittent breaks or short circuits in the wiring. Observe the multimeter, test lamp or diagnostic tool while doing this.

SA1019900042010X

Fig. 57 Code P1107: Charge Air Absolute Pressure Sensor Circuit Short To Ground/Open (Part 1 of 5). 9-5

Diagnostic procedure

1. Checking the hose

- Check the hose between the pressure sensor and intake manifold.

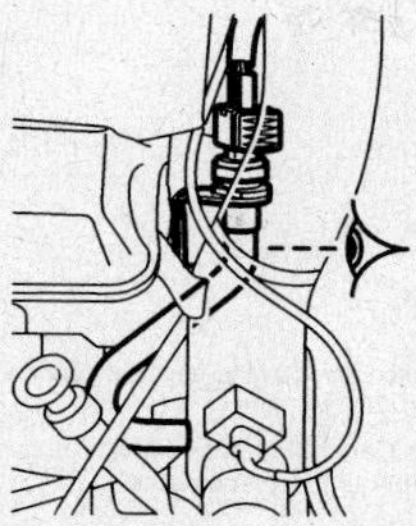

Everything OK?

YES

- Go to point 2.

NO

- Repair or replace the faulty hose.
- Go to point 6.

2. Checking the sensor's grounding

- Unplug the connector: Charge air absolute pressure sensor: (603)

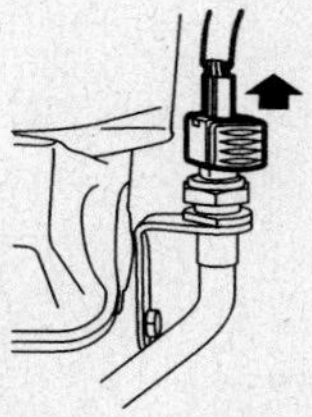

- Connect test lamp 86 11 857 to B+ and pin 4 of the female connector.

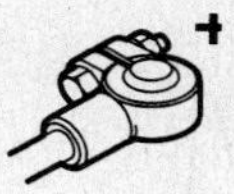

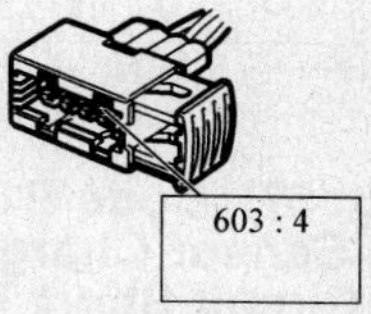

SA1019900042020X

Fig. 57 Code P1107: Charge Air Absolute Pressure Sensor Circuit Short To Ground/Open (Part 2 of 5). 9-5

- The test lamp should light.

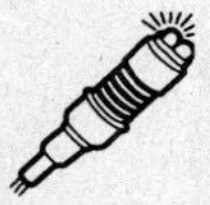

Everything OK?

YES

- Go to point 3.

NO

- One of the leads from pins 70 and 22 of the control module to pin 4 of the female connector is faulty. (The leads from pins 70 and 22 of the control module are connected together internally in the throttle body.)
- Go to point 6.

3. Checking the sensor's power supply

- Turn the ignition switch to the ON position.

- Take a voltage reading.
- Red test lead: Charge air absolute pressure sensor: 2
- Black test lead: Charge air absolute pressure sensor: 4

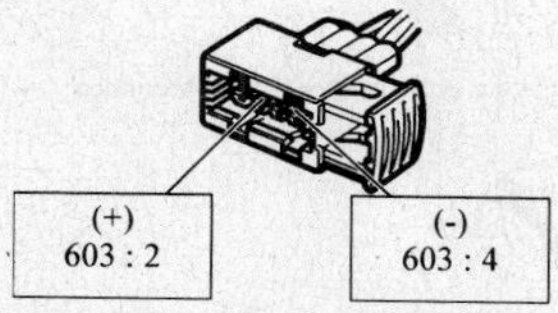

- The reading obtained should be 4.9 V - 5.1 V.

Everything OK?

YES

- Go to point 4.

NO

- One of the leads from pins 46 and 69 of the control module to pin 4 of the female connector is faulty. (The leads from pins 46 and 69 of the control module are connected together internally in the throttle body.)
- Go to point 6.

SA1019900042030X

Fig. 57 Code P1107: Charge Air Absolute Pressure Sensor Circuit Short To Ground/Open (Part 3 of 5). 9-5

4. Checking the control module's sensor input

- Contact the Trionic.

- Test reading: Charge air absolute pressure.
- The reading obtained should be 0 kPa

Everything OK?

YES

- Go to point 5.

NO

- The lead from pin 3 of the female connector to pin 35 of the control module is faulty.
- Go to point 6.

5. Checking control module sensor input (continued)

- Connect a jumper lead between pins 2 and 3

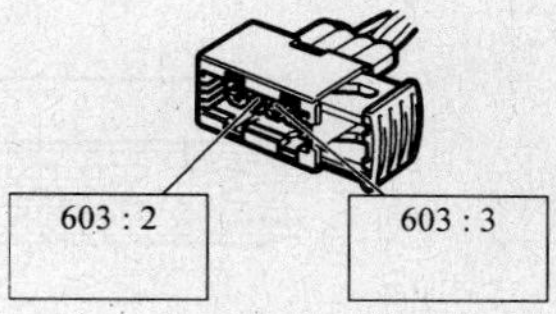

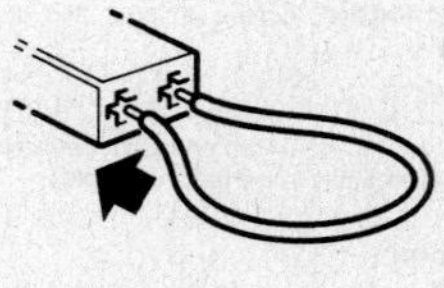

- Test reading: Charge air absolute pressure.
- The reading should be 250 kPa

Everything OK?

YES

- Change: Charge air absolute pressure sensor
- Go to point 6.

NO

- The lead from pin 3 of the female connector to pin 35 of the control module is faulty.
- Go to point 6.

SA1019900042040X

Fig. 57 Code P1107: Charge Air Absolute Pressure Sensor Circuit Short To Ground/Open (Part 4 of 5). 9-5

6. Final check

- Clear the diagnostic trouble codes in all systems.

- Carry out a driving cycle:
- Drive the car under varying engine loads and at different engine rpm for five minutes.

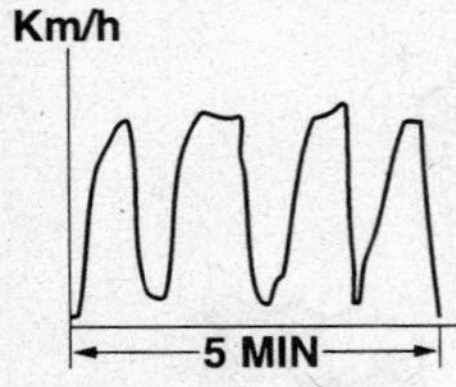

- Evaluate the driving cycle:
- Check that the diagnostic trouble code has not recurred.

Everything OK?

YES

– The steps taken to rectify the fault were correct.

NO

– See "Engine Control Module (ECM)" under "Component Replacements"

SA1019900042050X

Fig. 57 Code P1107: Charge Air Absolute Pressure Sensor Charge Air Absolute Pressure Sensor Circuit Short To Ground/Open (Part 5 of 5). 9-5

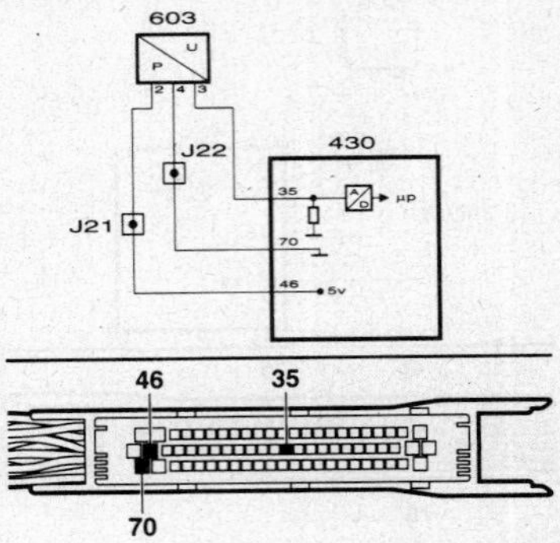

Fault symptoms

- CHECK ENGINE comes on after two driving cycles.
- Engine speed drops slower than normal when the accelerator is released.

Conditions

The following conditions apply for this DTC:

- Engine has started and the voltage is higher than 4.815 V for more than 5 s.

Diagnostic help

Fault diagnosis concerns electrical faults in connecting cables or in the sensor.

Diagnostic tool functions related to this fault are:

- Pressure sensor reading, in kPa.

With the engine switched off, the reading should correspond with those of the other two pressure sensors. Permissible difference is 10 kPa.

See also the description of test values under "Fault diagnosis, general" for more information.

Checking the wiring harness

Jiggle the leads and in-line connectors at various points and in different directions to detect any intermittent breaks or short circuits in the wiring. Observe the multimeter, test lamp or diagnostic tool while doing this.

Diagnostic procedure

See Code P1107

SA1019900043000X

Fig. 58 Code P1108: Charge Air Absolute Pressure Sensor Circuit Short To B+. 9-5

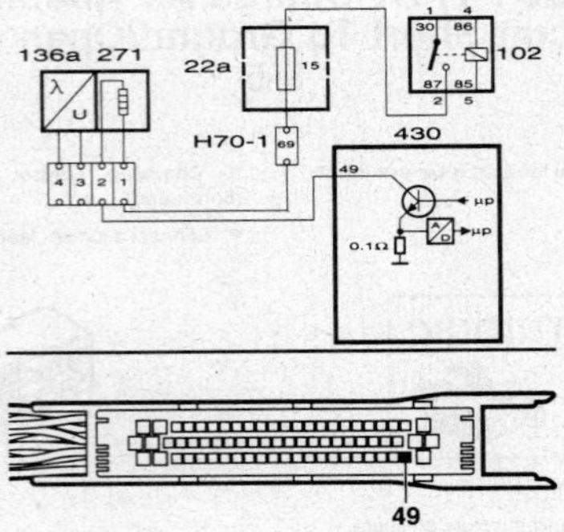

Fault symptoms

- CHECK ENGINE comes on after two driving cycles.

Note

If the engine has backfired or cannot be started, the fault is probably in the fuel pump relay.

Conditions

The following conditions apply for this DTC:

- Engine has started and output voltage is below 2 V when the output is inactive. Conditions met for 5 s.

Or:

- Preheating has been active for more than 60 s.
- Current is below 500 mA for 5 s.

Diagnostic help

Fault diagnosis concerns electrical faults in connecting cables or in the sensor.

Diagnostic tool functions related to this fault are:

- Activation of output for preheating.

See also the description of test values under "Fault diagnosis, general" for more information.

Checking the wiring harness

Jiggle the leads and in-line connectors at various points and in different directions to detect any intermittent breaks or short circuits in the wiring. Observe the multimeter, test lamp or diagnostic tool while doing this.

SA1019900044010X

Fig. 59 Code P1135: O2S Heater Circuit Current Too Low Sensor 1 (Part 1 of 4). 9-5

Diagnostic procedure

1. Checking the sensor preheating power supply

- Unplug the connector: Heated oxygen sensor: (136a)

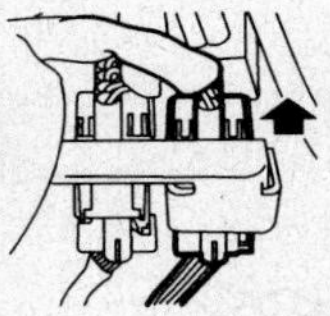

- Turn the ignition switch to the ON position.

- Contact the Trionic.

- Connect test lamp 86 11 857 to pin 1 of the female connector and a good grounding point.

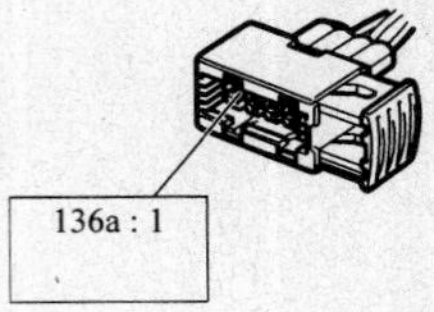

- Activate: Fuel pump relay (ON)

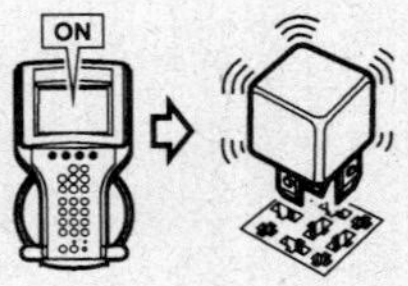

SA1019900044020X

Fig. 59 Code P1135: O2S Heater Circuit Current Too Low Sensor 1 (Part 2 of 4). 9-5

- The test lamp should light

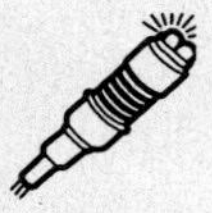

Everything OK?

YES

- Go to point 2.

NO

- The lead from pin 2 (87) of the relay holder via fuse 15 to pin 1 of the female connector is faulty.
- Go to point 3.

2. Checking the sensor preheating control module output

- Connect test lamp 86 11 857 to pins 1 and 2 of the female connector.

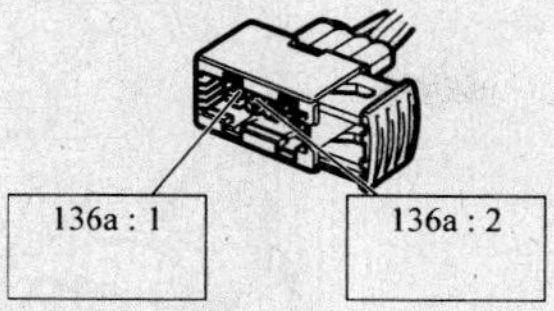

- Activate: Preheating O2S 1 (ON)

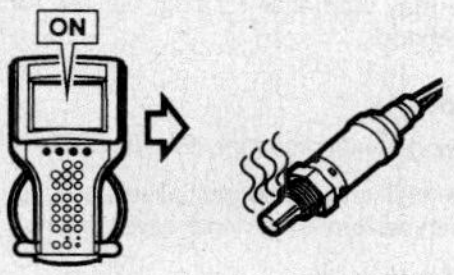

- The test lamp should light

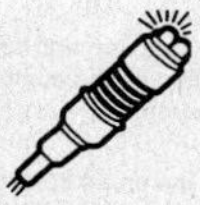

Everything OK?

YES

- Change: Heated oxygen sensor
- Go to point 3.

NO

- The lead from pin 49 of the control module to pin 2 of the female connector is faulty.
- Go to point 3.

SA1019900044030X

Fig. 59 Code P1135: O2S Heater Circuit Current Too Low Sensor 1 (Part 3 of 4). 9-5

3. Final check

- Clear the diagnostic trouble codes in all systems.

- Carry out a driving cycle:
- Drive the car under varying engine loads and at different engine rpm for five minutes.

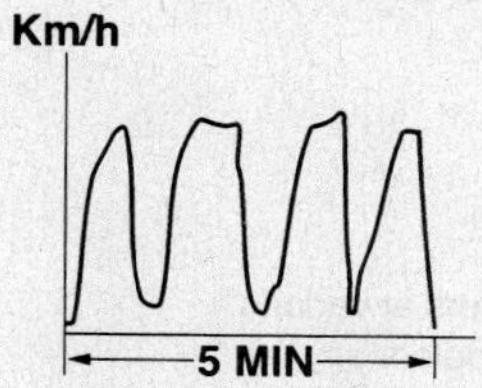

- Evaluate the driving cycle:
- Check that the diagnostic trouble code has not recurred.

Everything OK?

YES

- The steps taken to rectify the fault were correct.

NO

- See "Engine Control Module (ECM)" under "Component Replacement"

SA1019900044040X

Fig. 59 Code P1135: O2S Heater Circuit Current Too Low Sensor 1 (Part 4 of 4). 9-5

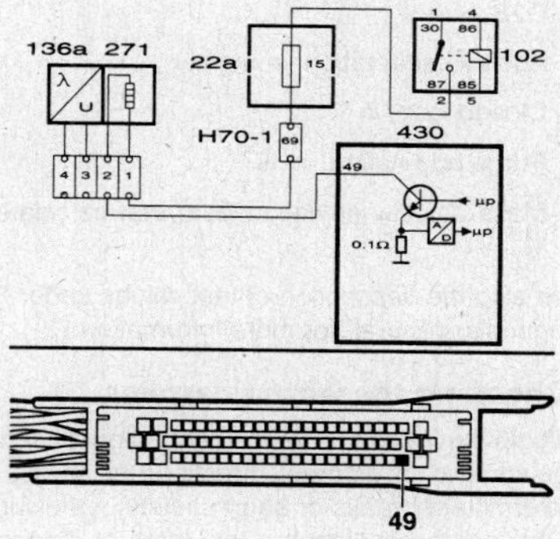

Fault symptoms

- CHECK ENGINE comes on after two driving cycles.

Conditions

The following conditions apply for this DTC:

- Engine has started and output voltage exceeds 2 V when output inactive. Conditions met for 5 s.

Or:

- Preheating has been active for more than 60 s.
- Current exceeds 2300 mA for 5 s.

Diagnostic help

Fault diagnosis concerns electrical faults in connecting cables or in the sensor.

Diagnostic tool functions related to this fault are:

- Activation of output for preheating.

See also the description of test values under "Fault diagnosis, general" for more information.

Checking the wiring harness

Jiggle the leads and in-line connectors at various points and in different directions to detect any intermittent breaks or short circuits in the wiring. Observe the multimeter, test lamp or diagnostic tool while doing this.

Diagnostic procedure

See Code P1135

SA1019900045000X

Fig. 60 Code P1136: O2S Heater Circuit Current Too High Sensor 1. 9-5

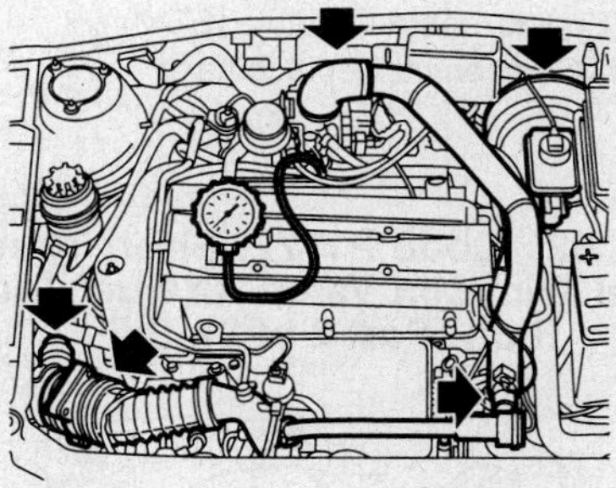

Fault symptoms

- Engine may stop after starting, run unevenly and misfire, or idle speed too fast.

Conditions

The following conditions apply for this DTC:

- Engine has started and multiplicative adaptation has been performed during present driving cycle.
- Closed loop active.
- Closed loop control exceeds 25 % for more than 20 s.

Note

P1171, P0171 and P1181 may be generated if the heated oxygen sensor input is shorted to ground as there is no diagnosis for this event.

Diagnostic help

At some time, the engine's fuel requirement has been 25 % higher than that computed by the control module on the basis of information from the mass air flow sensor.

Fault diagnosis first determines whether the pressure sensor readings are approximately the same when the ignition is ON, as the mass air flow sensor is later compared with the intake air pressure. If the pressure sensors are OK but the mass air flow sensor reading is incorrect, first check for any air leaks after the throttle and after that, replace the sensor.

If the mass air flow is OK, then the fuel supply must be checked, i.e. pressure, pressure response, pump flow and then the injectors.

Diagnostic tool functions related to this fault are:

- O2S 1, in V
- Closed loop, in %.
- Multiplicative adaptation, in %
- Additive adaptation, in mg/c.
- Purge adaptation, in %.
- Mass air flow deviation from that calculated, in %.

Checking the wiring harness

Jiggle the leads and in-line connectors at various points and in different directions to detect any intermittent breaks or short circuits in the wiring. Observe the multimeter, test lamp or diagnostic tool while doing this.

Diagnostic procedure

See Code P0172

SA1019900046010X

Fig. 61 Code P1171: Short Term Fuel Trim Max Value Air/Fuel Too Lean (Part 1 of 2). 9-5

Checking the wiring harness

Jiggle the leads and in-line connectors at various points and in different directions to detect any intermittent breaks or short circuits in the wiring. Observe the mulitmeter, test lamp or diagnostic tool while doing this.

Diagnostic procedure

See Code P0172

SA1019900046020X

Fig. 61 Code P1171: Short Term Fuel Trim Max Value Air/Fuel Too Lean (Part 2 of 2). 9-5

Checking the wiring harness

Jiggle the leads and in-line connectors at various points and in different directions to detect any intermittent breaks or short circuits in the wiring. Observe the mulitmeter, test lamp or diagnostic tool while doing this.

Diagnostic procedure

See "Engine Control Module (ECM)" under "Component Replacement"

SA1019900047020X

Fig. 62 Code P1172: Short Term Fuel Trim Min Value Air/Fuel Too Rich (Part 2 of 2). 9-5

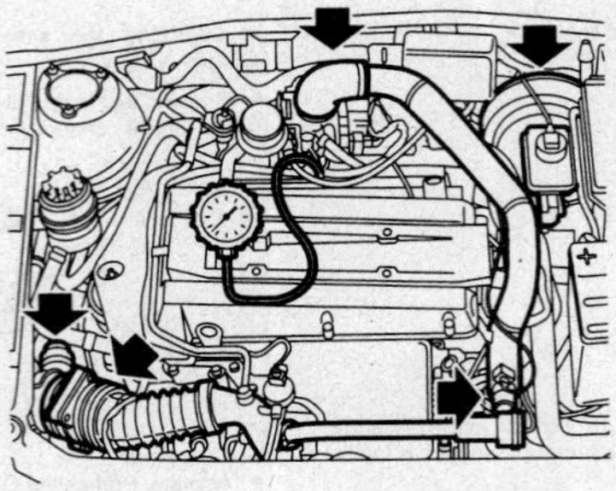

Fault symptoms

- Engine may stop after starting, uneven running and misfiring.

Conditions

The following conditions apply for this DTC:

- Engine has started and multiplicative adaptation has been performed during present driving cycle.
- Closed loop active.
- Closed loop control below -25 % for more than 20 s.

Diagnostic help

At some time, the engine's fuel requirement has been 25 % lower than that computed by the control module on the basis of information from the mass air flow sensor.

Fault diagnosis first determines if the pressure sensor readings are approximately the same when the ignition is ON, as the mass air flow sensor is later compared with the intake air pressure. If the pressure sensors are OK but the mass air flow sensor reading is incorrect, first check for air leaks between the compressor and throttle and then change the mass air flow sensor.

If the mass air flow is OK, then the fuel supply must be checked, i.e. pressure, pressure response, pump flow and then the injectors.

Diagnostic tool functions related to this fault are:

- Closed loop control, in %.
- Multiplicative adaptation, in %
- Additive adaptation, in mg/c.
- Purge adaptation, in %.
- Mass air flow deviation from that calculated, in %.

Checking the wiring harness

Jiggle the leads and in-line connectors at various points and in different directions to detect any intermittent breaks or short circuits in the wiring. Observe the multimeter, test lamp or diagnostic tool while doing this.

Diagnostic procedure

See "Engine Control Module (ECM)" under "Component Replacement"

SA1019900047010X

Fig. 62 Code P1172: Short Term Fuel Trim Min Value Air/Fuel Too Rich (Part 1 of 2). 9-5

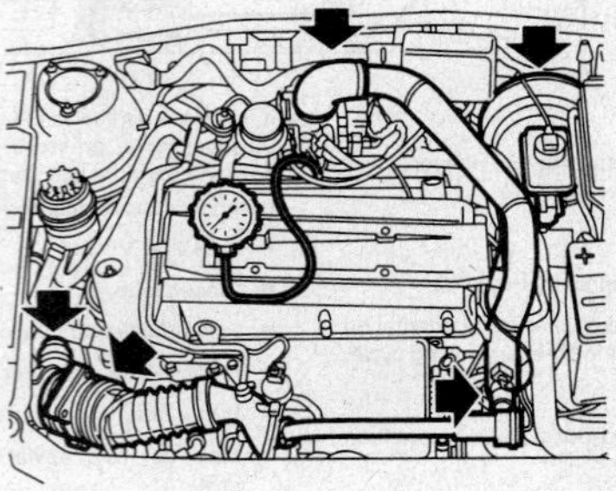

Fault symptoms

- CHECK ENGINE comes on after two driving cycles.
- Engine may stop after starting, run unevenly and misfire, or idle speed too fast.

Conditions

The following conditions apply for this DTC:

- Engine has started and closed loop control is active.
- Additive adaptation above 10 mg/c for more than 30 s.

Note

The condition for additive adaptation is that a multiplicative adaptation has first been performed during the present driving cycle.

Diagnostic help

At idling speed, the engine's fuel requirement has been 25 % higher than that computed by the control module on the basis of information from the mass air flow sensor.

Fault diagnosis first determines whether the pressure sensor readings are approximately the same when the ignition is ON, as the mass air flow sensor is later compared with the intake air pressure. If the pressure sensors are OK but the mass air flow sensor reading is incorrect, first check for any air leaks after the throttle and after that, replace the sensor.

If the mass air flow is OK, then the fuel supply must be checked, i.e. pressure, pressure response, pump flow and then the injectors.

Note

P1171, P0171 and P1181 may be generated if the heated oxygen sensor input is shorted to ground, as there is no diagnosis for this event.

SA1019900048010X

Fig. 63 Code P1181: Long Term Fuel Trim Additive Max Value Air/Fuel Too Lean (Part 1 of 2). 9-5

Diagnostic tool functions related to this fault are:

- O2S 1, in V
- Additive adaptation, in mg/c.
- Closed loop, in %.
- Purge adaptation, in %.
- Mass air flow deviation from that calculated, in %.

See also the description of test values under "Fault diagnosis, general" for more information.

Checking the wiring harness

Jiggle the leads and in-line connectors at various points and in different directions to detect any intermittent breaks or short circuits in the wiring. Observe the multimeter, test lamp or diagnostic tool while doing this.

Diagnostic procedure

See Code P0172

SA1019900048020X

Fig. 63 Code P1181: Long Term Fuel Trim Additive Max Value Air/Fuel Too Lean (Part 2 of 2). 9-5

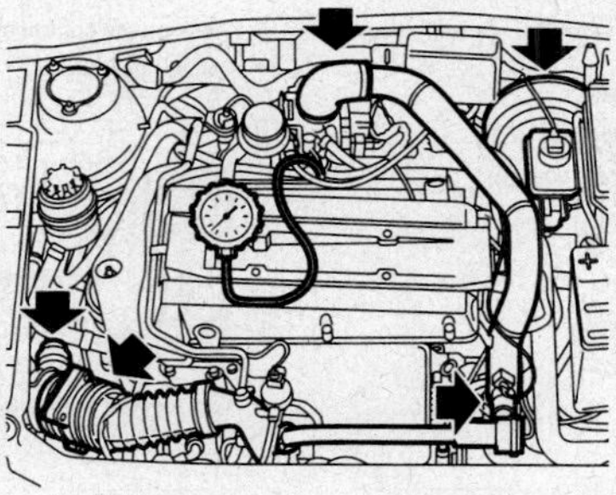

Fault symptoms

- CHECK ENGINE comes on after two driving cycles.
- Engine may stop after starting, uneven running and misfiring.

Conditions

The following conditions apply for this DTC:

- Engine has started and closed loop control is active.
- Additive adaptation below -10 mg/c for more than 30 s.

Note

The condition for additive adaptation is that a multiplicative adaptation has first been performed during the present driving cycle.

Diagnostic help

At idling speed, the engine's fuel requirement has been 25 % higher than that computed by the control module on the basis of information from the mass air flow sensor.

Fault diagnosis first determines if the pressure sensor readings are approximately the same when the ignition is ON, as the mass air flow sensor is later compared with the intake air pressure. If the pressure sensors are OK but the mass air flow sensor reading is incorrect, first check for air leaks between the compressor and throttle and then change the mass air flow sensor.

If the mass air flow is OK, then the fuel supply must be checked, i.e. pressure, pressure response, pump flow and then the injectors.

Diagnostic tool functions related to this fault are:

- Additive adaptation, in mg/c.
- Closed loop, in %.
- Purge adaptation, in %.
- Mass air flow deviation from that calculated, in %.

Checking the wiring harness

Jiggle the leads and in-line connectors at various points and in different directions to detect any intermittent breaks or short circuits in the wiring. Observe the multimeter, test lamp or diagnostic tool while doing this.

Diagnostic procedure

See Code P0172

SA1019900049010X

Fig. 64 Code P1182: Long Term Fuel Trim Additive Min Valve Air/Fuel Too Rich (Part 1 of 2). 9-5

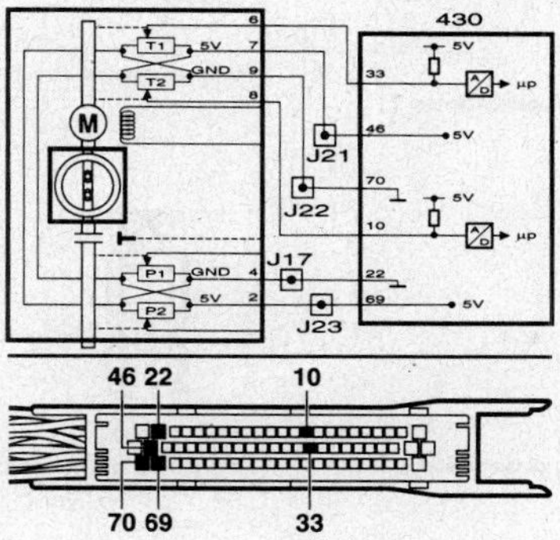

Fault symptoms

- CHECK ENGINE lights up straight away.
- Throttle control in limp-home mode.
- Incorrect idle speed.
- Cruise control inoperative.

Conditions

The following conditions apply for this DTC:

- Ignition ON and the aggregate voltage of throttle position sensors 1 and 2 is above 5.7 V or below 4.59 V.

Diagnostic help

Fault diagnosis concerns electrical faults in connecting cables or in any of the sensors.

Diagnostic tool functions related to this fault are:

- Throttle position sensor 1, in V.
- Throttle position sensor 2, in V.

See also the description of test values under "Fault diagnosis, general" for more information.

Checking the wiring harness

Jiggle the leads and in-line connectors at various points and in different directions to detect any intermittent breaks or short circuits in the wiring. Observe the multimeter, test lamp or diagnostic tool while doing this.

SA1019900050010X

Fig. 65 Code P1230: Throttle Position Sensor 1 & 2 Circuit Sum Out Of Range (Part 1 of 7). 9-5

Checking the wiring harness

Jiggle the leads and in-line connectors at various points and in different directions to detect any intermittent breaks or short circuits in the wiring. Observe the mulitmeter, test lamp or diagnostic tool while doing this.

Diagnostic procedure

See Code P0172

SA1019900049020X

Fig. 64 Code P1182: Long Term Fuel Trim Additive Min Valve Air/Fuel Too Rich (Part 2 of 2). 9-5

Diagnostic procedure

1. Checking the sensor's grounding

- Unplug the connector: Throttle body: (604)

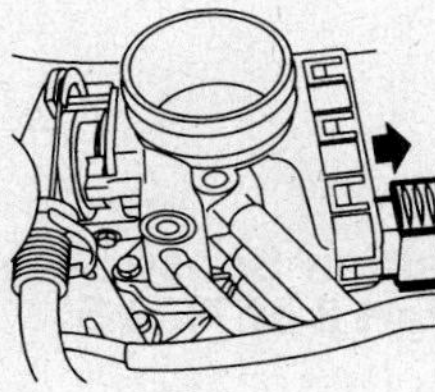

- Connect test lamp 86 11 857 to B+ and pin 9 of the female connector.

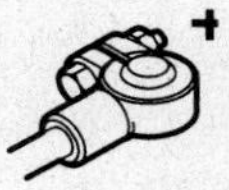

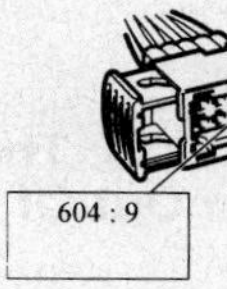

- The test lamp should light.

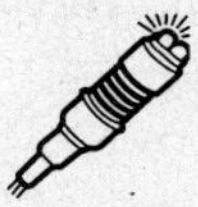

Everything OK?

YES

- Go to point 2.

NO

- The lead from pin 70 of the control module to pin 9 of the female connector is faulty.
- Go to point 9.

SA1019900050020X

Fig. 65 Code P1230: Throttle Position Sensor 1 & 2 Circuit Sum Out Of Range (Part 2 of 7). 9-5

2. Checking the sensor's grounding (continued)

- Connect test lamp 86 11 857 to B+ and pin 4 of the female connector.

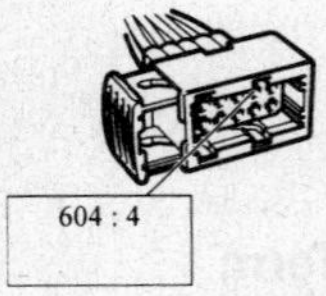

- The test lamp should light.

Everything OK?

YES

- Go to point 3.

NO

- The lead from pin 22 of the control module to pin 4 of the female connector is faulty.
- Go to point 10.

3. Checking the sensor's power supply

- Turn the ignition switch to the ON position.

- Take a voltage reading.
- Red test lead: Throttle body: 7
- Black test lead: Throttle body: 9

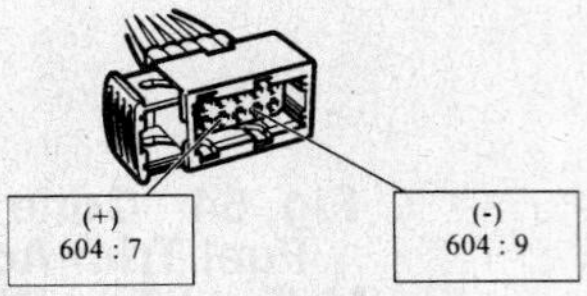

- The reading obtained should be 4.9 V - 5.1 V.

Everything OK?

YES

- Go to point 4.

NO

- The lead from pin 46 of the control module to pin 7 of the female connector is faulty.
- Go to point 9.

SA1019900050030X

Fig. 65 Code P1230: Throttle Position Sensor 1 & 2 Circuit Sum Out Of Range (Part 3 of 7). 9-5

4. Checking the sensor's power supply (continued)

- Take a voltage reading.
- Red test lead: Throttle body: 2
- Black test lead: Throttle body: 9

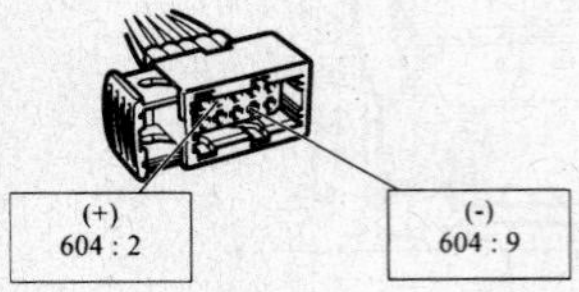

- The reading obtained should be 4.9 V - 5.1 V.

Everything OK?

YES

- Go to point 5.

NO

- The lead from pin 69 of the control module to pin 2 of the female connector is faulty.
- Go to point 10.

5. Checking the control module's sensor input 1

- Contact the Trionic.

- Test reading: Throttle position sensor 1.

- The voltage reading obtained should be 4.95 V - 5 V.

Everything OK?

YES

- Go to point 6.

NO

- The lead from pin 6 of the female connector to pin 33 of the control module is faulty.
- Go to point 9.

SA1019900050040X

Fig. 65 Code P1230: Throttle Position Sensor 1 & 2 Circuit Sum Out Of Range (Part 4 of 7). 9-5

6. Checking the control module's sensor input 1, continued

- Connect a jumper lead between pins 6 and 9 of the female connector.

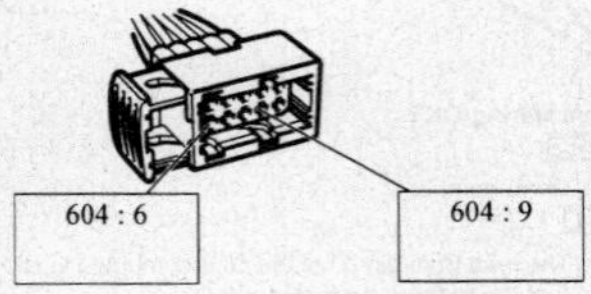

- Test reading: Throttle position sensor 1.

- The voltage reading obtained should be 0 V - 0.05 V.

Everything OK?

YES

- Go to point 7.

NO

- The lead from pin 6 of the female connector to pin 33 of the control module is faulty.
- Go to point 9.

7. Checking the control module's sensor input 2

- Test reading: Throttle position sensor 2.

- The voltage reading obtained should be 4.95 V - 5 V.

Everything OK?

YES

- Go to point 8.

NO

- The lead from pin 8 of the female connector to pin 10 of the control module is faulty.
- Go to point 9.

SA1019900050050X

Fig. 65 Code P1230: Throttle Position Sensor 1 & 2 Circuit Sum Out Of Range (Part 5 of 7). 9-5

8. Checking the control module's sensor input 2, continued

- Connect a jumper lead between pins 8 and 9 of the female connector.

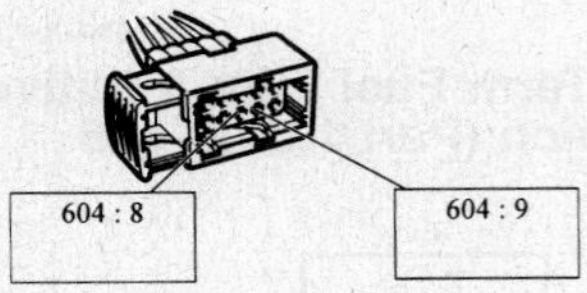

- Test reading: Throttle position sensor 2.

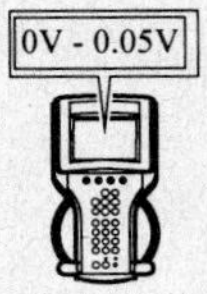

- The voltage reading obtained should be 0 V - 0.05 V.

Everything OK?

YES

- Change: Throttle body
- Go to point 9.

NO

- The lead from pin 8 of the female connector to pin 10 of the control module is faulty.
- Go to point 9.

9. Resetting the limp-home mechanism

- Next time the ignition switch is turned to the ON position the limp-home solenoid will be activated. The throttle valve will then assume the mechanical limp-home position. It is therefore important to reset the limp-home mechanism AFTER all diagnostic trouble codes have been cleared.
- Turn the ignition switch to the ON position.

- Clear diagnostic trouble codes: Trionic

- Turn the ignition switch to the OFF position.

SA1019900050060X

Fig. 65 Code P1230: Throttle Position Sensor 1 & 2 Circuit Sum Out Of Range (Part 6 of 7). 9-5

- Wait for 10 seconds.
- Reset the limp-home mechanism as described in the 'Adjustment and replacement' section.

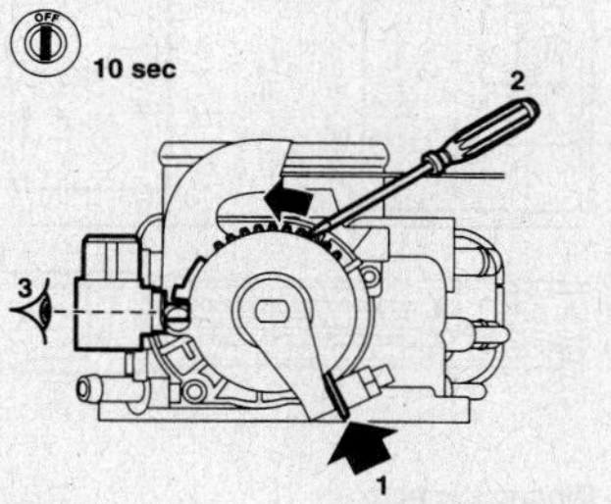

- Clear the diagnostic trouble codes in all systems.

- Carry out a driving cycle:
- Drive the car under varying engine loads and at different engine rpm for five minutes.

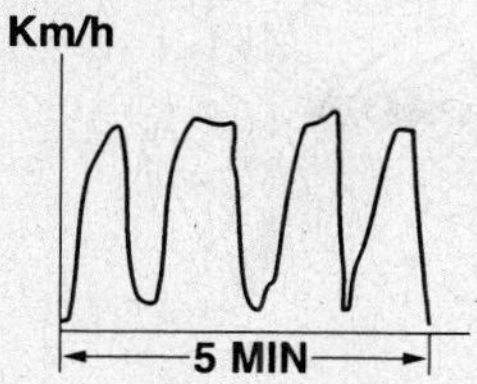

- Evaluate the driving cycle:
- Check that the diagnostic trouble code has not recurred.

Everything OK?

YES

– The steps taken to rectify the fault were correct.

NO

– See "Engine Control Module (ECM)" under "Component Replacement"

SA1019900050070X

Fig. 65 Code P1230: Throttle Position Sensor 1 & 2 Circuit Sum Out Of Range (Part 7 of 7). 9-5

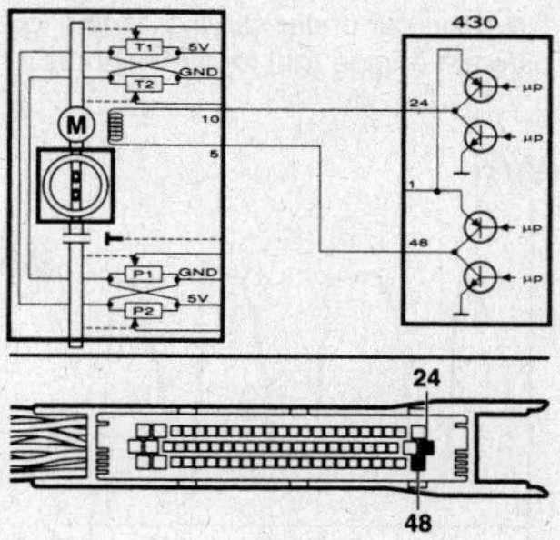

Fault symptoms

- CHECK ENGINE comes on after two driving cycles.
- Inexact throttle control.
- Cruise control inoperative.

Conditions

The following conditions apply for this DTC:

- Ignition ON and motor current exceeds 8 A during the positive or negative portion of the PWM period.
- Condition met for 3 minutes.

Diagnostic help

This DTC is generated when the lead from control module pin 48 is shorted to B+.

Diagnostic tool functions related to this fault are:

- Activation of output for throttle motor.

See also the description of activating functions under "Fault diagnosis, general" for more information.

Checking the wiring harness

Jiggle the leads and in-line connectors at various points and in different directions to detect any intermittent breaks or short circuits in the wiring. Observe the multimeter, test lamp or diagnostic tool while doing this.

SA1019900051010X

Fig. 66 Code P1240: Throttle Motor Circuit Shorted (Part 1 of 4). 9-5

Diagnostic procedure

1. Checking the control module's throttle motor output

- Turn the ignition switch to the ON position.

- Contact the Trionic.

- Activate: Throttle Motor PWM Test (30 s)
- The test lamp should alternate between red and green.

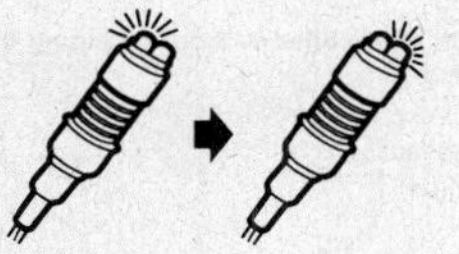

Everything OK?

YES

– Change: Throttle body

– Next time the ignition switch is turned to the ON position the limp-home solenoid will be activated. The throttle valve will then assume the mechanical limp-home position. It is therefore important to reset the limp-home mechanism AFTER all diagnostic trouble codes have been cleared.

– Go to point 2.

NO

– One of the two throttle motor leads is faulty. Either the lead between pin 24 of the control module and pin 10 of the female connector, or the lead between pin 48 of the control module and pin 5 of the female connector.

– Go to point 2.

SA1019900051020X

Fig. 66 Code P1240: Throttle Motor Circuit Shorted (Part 2 of 4). 9-5

2. Resetting the limp-home mechanism

- Turn the ignition switch to the ON position.

- Clear diagnostic trouble codes: Trionic

- Turn the ignition switch to the OFF position.

- Wait for 10 seconds.
- Reset the limp-home mechanism as described in the 'Adjustment and replacement' section.

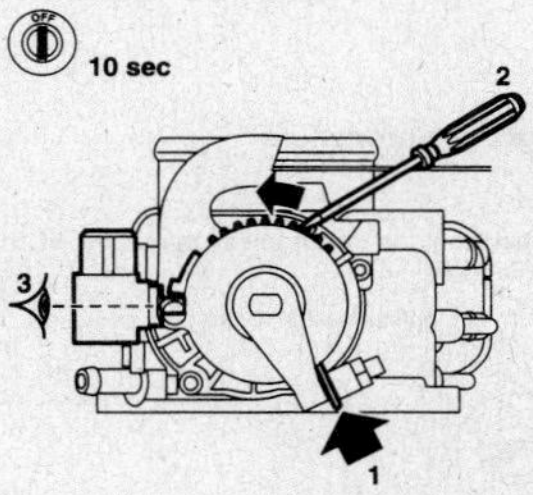

- Clear the diagnostic trouble codes in all systems.

- Carry out a driving cycle:

SA1019900051030X

Fig. 66 Code P1240: Throttle Motor Circuit Shorted (Part 3 of 4). 9-5

- Drive the car under varying engine loads and at different engine rpm for five minutes.

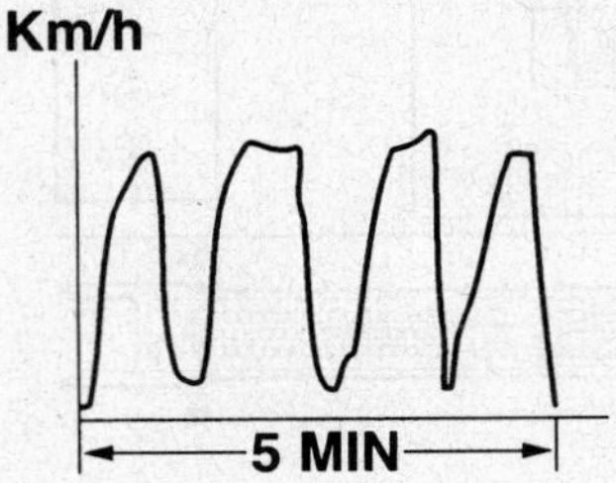

- Evaluate the driving cycle:
- Check that the diagnostic trouble code has not recurred.

Everything OK?
YES
– The steps taken to rectify the fault were correct.
NO
– See "Engine Control Module (ECM)" under "Component Replacement"

SA1019900051040X

Fig. 66 Code P1240: Throttle Motor Circuit Shorted (Part 4 of 4). 9-5

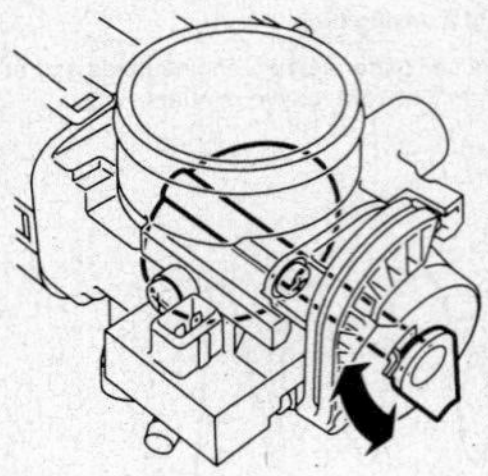

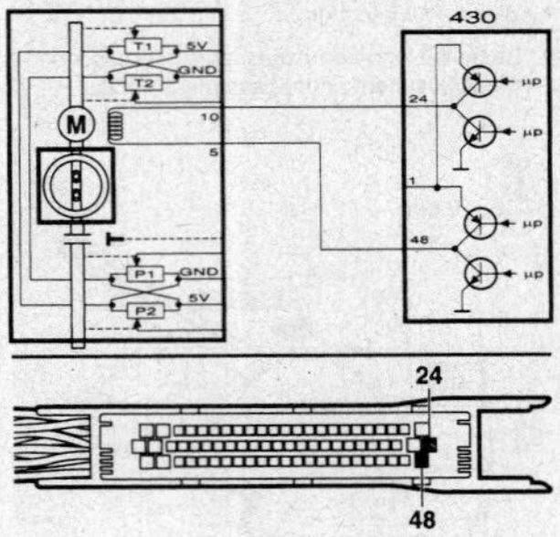

Fault symptoms
- CHECK ENGINE lights up straight away.
- Throttle control in limp-home mode.
- Incorrect idle speed.
- Cruise control inoperative.

Conditions
The following conditions apply for this DTC:
- Engine has started.
- Car is moving.
- Throttle motor is receiving 100% PWM in closing direction.

Or:
- Less than 5 seconds since engine was started.
- Throttle motor is receiving 100% PWM in closing direction.

Diagnostic help
A mechanical fault is preventing the throttle from closing.

Checking the wiring harness
Jiggle the leads and in-line connectors at various points and in different directions to detect any intermittent breaks or short circuits in the wiring. Observe the multimeter, test lamp or diagnostic tool while doing this.

SA1019900052010X

Fig. 67 Code P1251: Throttle Motor Full PWM in Closing Direction (Part 1 of 4). 9-5

Diagnostic procedure

1. Checking the mechanical operation of the throttle valve
- Turn the ignition switch to the OFF position.

- Wait for 10 seconds.
- Open and close the throttle valve by hand.

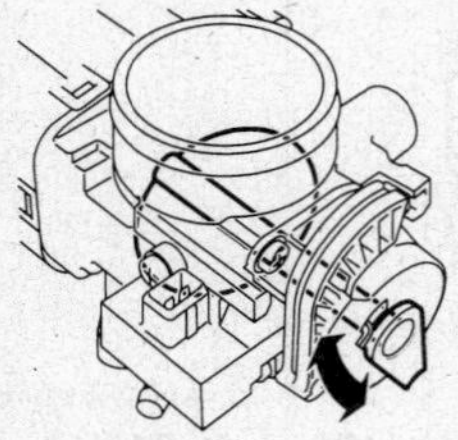

- The throttle valve should not bind in any position.
- The spring should return the throttle valve to the stop screw.
- No external objects, hoses, cables, etc. should obstruct the movement of the throttle arm.

Everything OK?
YES
– Go to point 2.
NO
– Go to point 3.

2. Checking the control module's throttle motor output
- Turn the ignition switch to the ON position.

- Activate: Throttle Motor PWM Test (30 s)
- Follow the diagnostic tool's instructions.
- The test lamp should alternate between red and green.

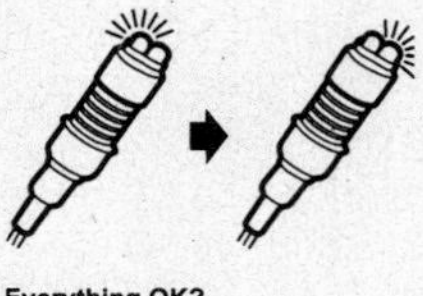

Everything OK?
YES
– Change: Throttle body
– Next time the ignition switch is turned to the ON position the limp-home solenoid will be activated. The throttle valve will then assume the mechanical limp-home position. It is therefore important to reset the limp-home mechanism AFTER all diagnostic trouble codes have been cleared.
– Go to point 4.
NO
– One of the two throttle motor leads is faulty. Either the lead between pin 24 of the control module and pin 10 of the female connector, or the lead between pin 48 of the control module and pin 5 of the female connector.
– Go to point 4.

SA1019900052020X

Fig. 67 Code P1251: Throttle Motor Full PWM in Closing Direction (Part 2 of 4). 9-5

3. Checking the mechanical operation of the throttle valve (continued)

Can the fault be rectified without changing the throttle body?
YES
– Rectify the fault.
– Go to point 4.
NO
– Change: Throttle body
– Next time the ignition switch is turned to the ON position the limp-home solenoid will be activated. The throttle valve will then assume the mechanical limp-home position. It is therefore important to reset the limp-home mechanism AFTER all diagnostic trouble codes have been cleared.
– Go to point 4.

4. Resetting the limp-home mechanism
- Turn the ignition switch to the ON position.

- Clear diagnostic trouble codes: Trionic

- Turn the ignition switch to the OFF position.

SA1019900052030X

Fig. 67 Code P1251: Throttle Motor Full PWM in Closing Direction (Part 3 of 4). 9-5

- Wait for 10 seconds.
- Reset the limp-home mechanism as described in the 'Adjustment and replacement' section.

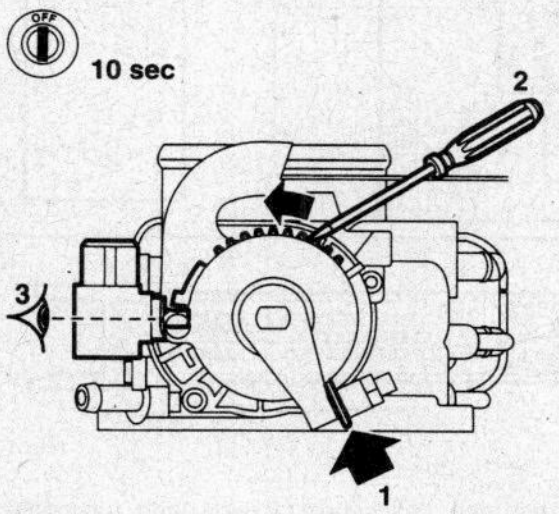

- Clear the diagnostic trouble codes in all systems.

- Carry out a driving cycle:
- Drive the car under varying engine loads and at different engine rpm for five minutes.

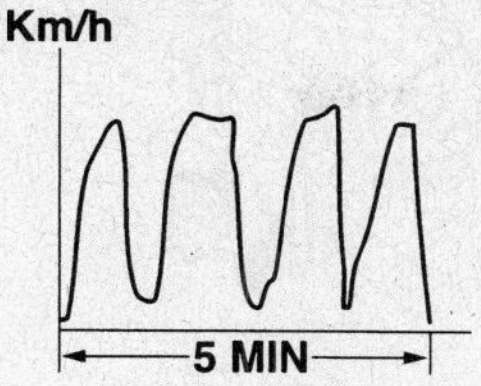

- Evaluate the driving cycle:
- Check that the diagnostic trouble code has not recurred.

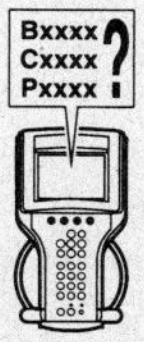

Everything OK?

YES

– The steps taken to rectify the fault were correct.

NO

– See "Engine Control Module (ECM)" under "Component Replacement"

SA1019900052040X

Fig. 67 Code P1251: Throttle Motor Full PWM in Closing Direction (Part 4 of 4). 9-5

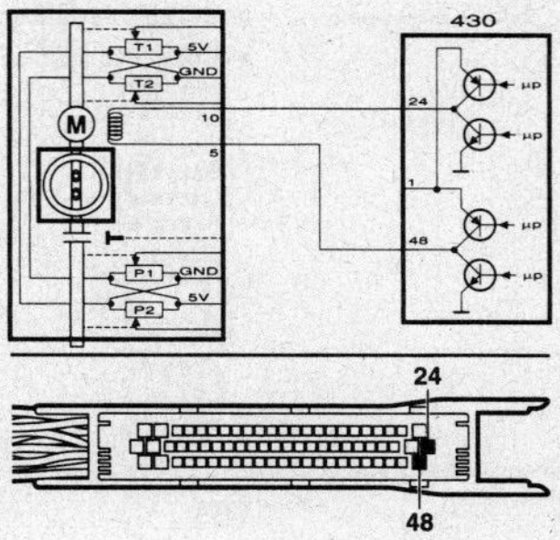

Fault symptoms

- CHECK ENGINE lights up straight away.
- Throttle control in limp-home mode.
- Incorrect idle speed.
- Cruise control inoperative.

Conditions

The following conditions apply for this DTC:

- Crankshaft rotating and main relay voltage exceeds 10 V.
- Throttle motor is receiving 100 % PWM in opening direction but no current.

Diagnostic help

An electrical fault in the throttle motor circuit is preventing the throttle from opening. The main relay voltage supplied to the control module is OK.

Diagnostic tool functions related to this fault are:

- Activation of output for throttle motor.

See also the description of activating functions under "Fault diagnosis, general" for more information.

Checking the wiring harness

Jiggle the leads and in-line connectors at various points and in different directions to detect any intermittent breaks or short circuits in the wiring. Observe the multimeter, test lamp or diagnostic tool while doing this.

SA1019900053010X

Fig. 68 Code P1252: Throttle Motor Full PWM In Open Direction & No Motor Current (Part 1 of 4). 9-5

Diagnostic procedure

1. Checking the control module's throttle motor output

- Turn the ignition switch to the ON position.

- Contact the Trionic.

- Activate: Throttle Motor PWM Test (30 s)
- Follow the diagnostic tool's instructions.
- The test lamp should alternate between red and green.

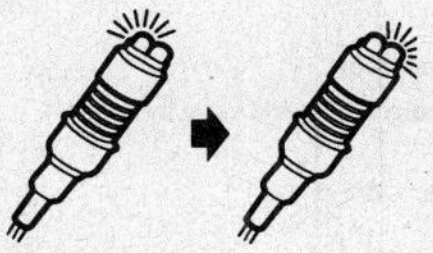

Everything OK?

YES

– Change: Throttle body
– Next time the ignition switch is turned to the ON position the limp-home solenoid will be activated. The throttle valve will then assume the mechanical limp-home position. It is therefore important to reset the limp-home mechanism AFTER all diagnostic trouble codes have been cleared.
– Go to point 2.

NO

– One of the two throttle motor leads is faulty. Either the lead between pin 24 of the control module and pin 10 of the female connector, or the lead between pin 48 of the control module and pin 5 of the female connector.
– Go to point 2.

SA1019900053020X

Fig. 68 Code P1252: Throttle Motor Full PWM In Open Direction & No Motor Current (Part 2 of 4). 9-5

2. Resetting the limp-home mechanism

- Turn the ignition switch to the ON position.

- Clear diagnostic trouble codes: Trionic

- Turn the ignition switch to the OFF position.

- Wait for 10 seconds.
- Reset the limp-home mechanism as described in the 'Adjustment and replacement' section.

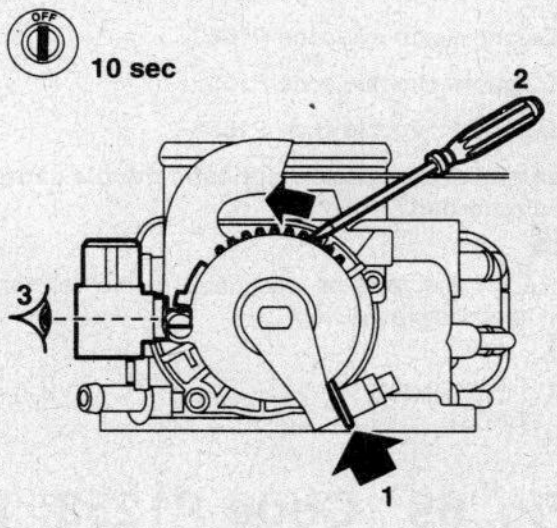

SA1019900053030X

Fig. 68 Code P1252: Throttle Motor Full PWM In Open Direction & No Motor Current (Part 3 of 4). 9-5

- Clear the diagnostic trouble codes in all systems.

- Carry out a driving cycle:
- Drive the car under varying engine loads and at different engine rpm for five minutes.

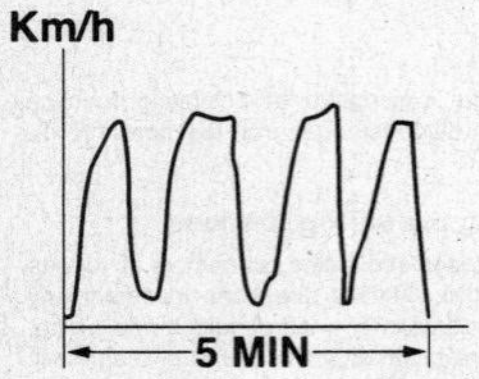

- Evaluate the driving cycle:
- Check that the diagnostic trouble code has not recurred.

Everything OK?

<u>YES</u>

– The steps taken to rectify the fault were correct.

<u>NO</u>

– See "Engine Control Module (ECM)" under "Component Replacement"

SA1019900053040X

Fig. 68 Code P1252: Throttle Motor Full PWM In Open Direction & No Motor Current (Part 4 of 4). 9-5

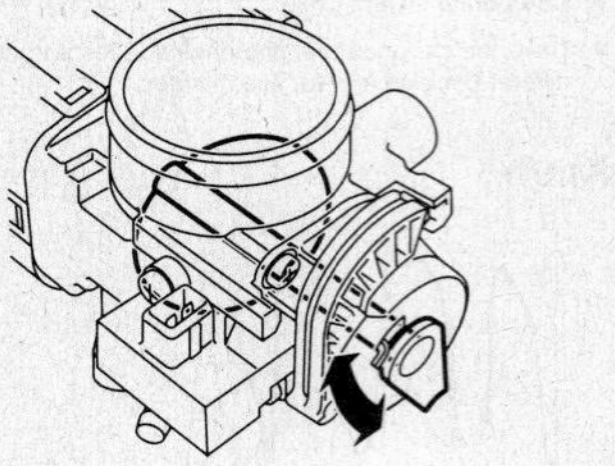

Fault symptoms

- CHECK ENGINE lights up straight away.
- Throttle control in limp-home mode.
- Incorrect idle speed.
- Cruise control inoperative.

Conditions

The following conditions apply for this DTC:

- Crankshaft is rotating but motor has not yet started.
- Main relay voltage exceeds 5 V.
- Throttle motor is receiving 100 % PWM in opening direction.

Diagnostic help

A mechanical or electrical fault is preventing the throttle from opening during starter motor cranking. The main relay voltage supplied to the control module is OK.

Diagnostic tool functions related to this fault are:

- Activation of output for throttle motor.

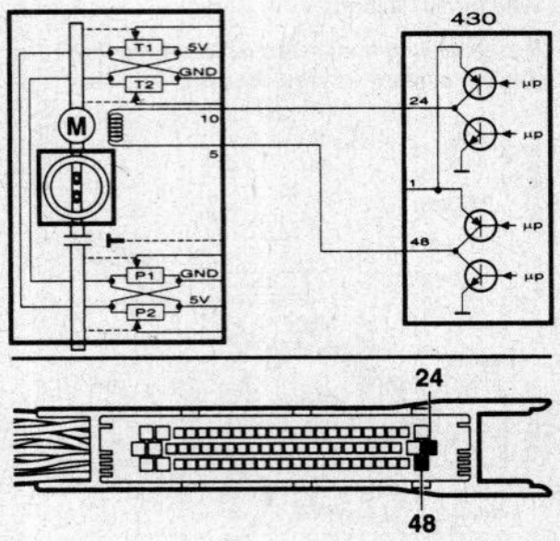

See also the description of activating functions under "Fault diagnosis, general" for more information.

Checking the wiring harness

Jiggle the leads and in-line connectors at various points and in different directions to detect any intermittent breaks or short circuits in the wiring. Observe the multimeter, test lamp or diagnostic tool while doing this.

SA1019900054010X

Fig. 69 Code P1253: Throttle Motor Full PWM In Open Direction During Cranking (Part 1 of 5). 9-5

Diagnostic procedure

1. Checking additional diagnostic trouble codes

- Contact the Trionic.

- See whether any of the following diagnostic trouble codes have been recorded:
- Diagnostic trouble code P1640
- Diagnostic trouble code P1652
- Diagnostic trouble code P1653

Have any of the above diagnostic trouble codes been recorded?

<u>YES</u>

– Rectify the fault as described in the relevant diagnostic procedure.

<u>NO</u>

– Go to point 2.

2. Checking the mechanical operation of the throttle valve

- Turn the ignition switch to the OFF position.

SA1019900054020X

Fig. 69 Code P1253: Throttle Motor Full PWM In Open Direction During Cranking (Part 2 of 5). 9-5

- Wait for 10 seconds.
- Open and close the throttle valve by hand.

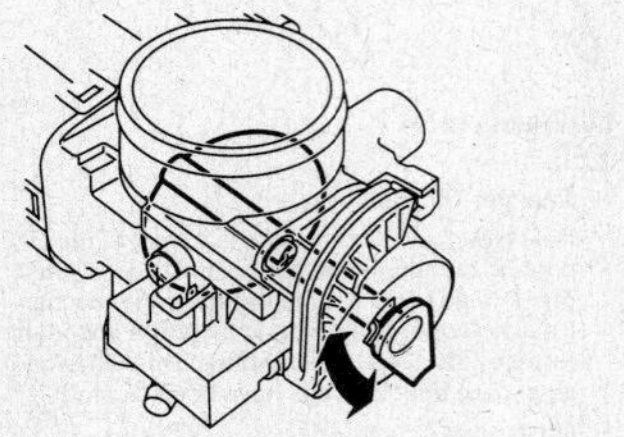

- The throttle valve should not bind in any position.
- The spring should return the throttle valve to the stop screw.
- No external objects, hoses, cables, etc. should obstruct the movement of the throttle arm.

Everything OK?

<u>YES</u>

– Go to point 3.

<u>NO</u>

– Go to point 4.

3. Checking the control module's throttle motor output

- Turn the ignition switch to the ON position.

- Activate: Throttle Motor PWM Test (30 s)
- Follow the diagnostic tool's instructions.
- The test lamp should alternate between red and green.

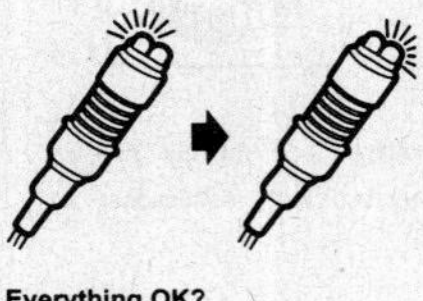

Everything OK?

<u>YES</u>

– Change: Throttle body

– Next time the ignition switch is turned to the ON position the limp-home solenoid will be activated. The throttle valve will then assume the mechanical limp-home position. It is therefore important to reset the limp-home mechanism AFTER all diagnostic trouble codes have been cleared.

– Go to point 5.

<u>NO</u>

– One of the two throttle motor leads is faulty. Either the lead between pin 24 of the control module and pin 10 of the female connector, or the lead between pin 48 of the control module and pin 5 of the female connector.

– Go to point 5.

SA1019900054030X

Fig. 69 Code P1253: Throttle Motor Full PWM In Open Direction During Cranking (Part 3 of 5). 9-5

4. Checking the mechanical operation of the throttle valve (continued)

Can the fault be rectified without changing the throttle body?

YES

– Rectify the fault.

– Go to point 5.

NO

– Change: Throttle body

– Next time the ignition switch is turned to the ON position the limp-home solenoid will be activated. The throttle valve will then assume the mechanical limp-home position. It is therefore important to reset the limp-home mechanism AFTER all diagnostic trouble codes have been cleared.

– Go to point 5.

5. Resetting the limp-home mechanism

- Turn the ignition switch to the ON position.

- Clear diagnostic trouble codes: Trionic

- Turn the ignition switch to the OFF position.

- Reset the limp-home mechanism as described in the 'Adjustment and replacement' section.
- Wait for 10 seconds.

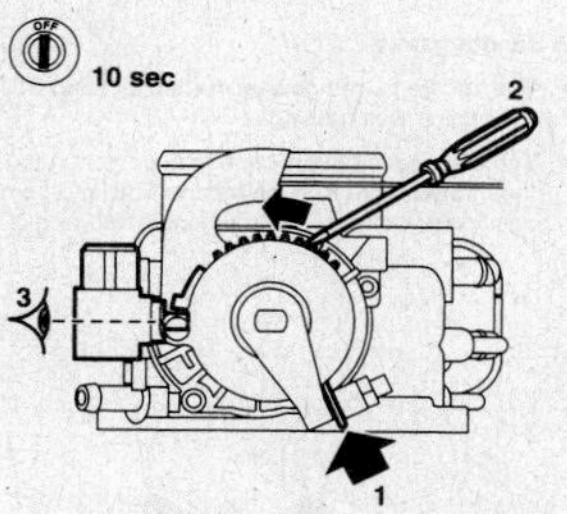

- Clear the diagnostic trouble codes in all systems.

SA1019900054040X

Fig. 69 Code P1253: Throttle Motor Full PWM In Open Direction During Cranking (Part 4 of 5). 9-5

- Carry out a driving cycle:
- Drive the car under varying engine loads and at different engine rpm for five minutes.

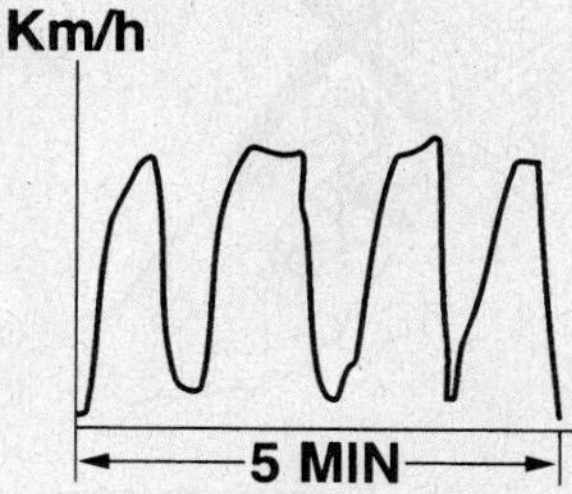

- Evaluate the driving cycle:
- Check that the diagnostic trouble code has not recurred.

Everything OK?

YES

– The steps taken to rectify the fault were correct.

NO

– See "Engine Control Module (ECM)" under "Component Replacement"

SA1019900054050X

Fig. 69 Code P1253: Throttle Motor Full PWM In Open Direction During Cranking (Part 5 of 5). 9-5

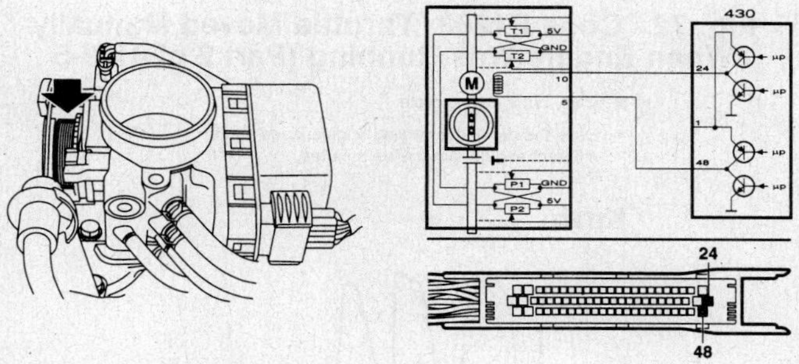

Fault symptoms

- CHECK ENGINE comes on after two driving cycles.

Conditions

The following conditions apply for this DTC:

- Ignition ON.
- Throttle motor receiving close to 0 % PWM in opening direction for 4 seconds.

Diagnostic help

Throttle return spring is too weak.

Checking the wiring harness

Jiggle the leads and in-line connectors at various points and in different directions to detect any intermittent breaks or short circuits in the wiring. Observe the multimeter, test lamp or diagnostic tool while doing this.

Diagnostic procedure

See Code P1251

SA1019900055000X

Fig. 70 Code P1260: Throttle Return Spring Too Low Force. 9-5

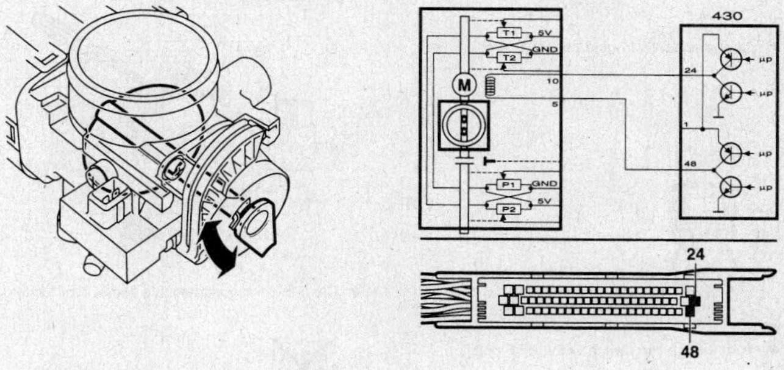

Fault symptoms

- CHECK ENGINE lights up straight away.
- Throttle control in limp-home mode.
- Fuel shut-off activated.
- Main relay inoperative.

Conditions

The following conditions apply for this DTC:

- Engine has started and throttle control is already in limp-home mode due to another DTC.
- Mass air flow per combustion is greater than requested.

Diagnostic help

A mechanical fault is preventing the throttle from closing. P1251 and P1264 have been generated and throttle control is in limp-home mode. The throttle has been open since then, in spite of the driver having released the accelerator.

> ⚠ **WARNING**
> The car must not be driven until the fault has been rectified.

Checking the wiring harness

Jiggle the leads and in-line connectors at various points and in different directions to detect any intermittent breaks or short circuits in the wiring. Observe the multimeter, test lamp or diagnostic tool while doing this.

Diagnostic procedure

See Code P1251

SA1019900056000X

Fig. 71 Code P1261: Throttle Binding. 9-5

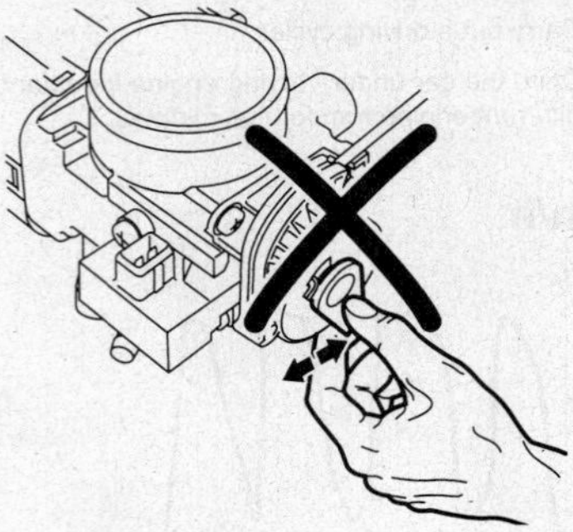

Fault symptoms

- Fuel shut-off activated.

Conditions

The following conditions apply for this DTC:

- Engine has started and been running for at least 5 seconds.
- No vehicle speed.
- Throttle motor is receiving 100% PWM in closing direction.

Diagnostic help

The DTC does not indicate a fault; it is merely an information code. Avoid moving the throttle arm. If you want to increase engine rpm while servicing the engine, move the pedal arm instead.

Checking the wiring harness

Jiggle the leads and in-line connectors at various points and in different directions to detect any intermittent breaks or short circuits in the wiring. Observe the multimeter, test lamp or diagnostic tool while doing this.

Diagnostic procedure

1. Checking additional diagnostic trouble codes

- Contact the Trionic.

SA1019900057010X

Fig. 72 Code P1263: Throttle Moved Manually When Engine Was Running (Part 1 of 4). 9-5

- See whether the following diagnostic trouble code has been recorded:
- Diagnostic trouble code P1251

Has the above diagnostic trouble code been recorded?

YES

- Rectify the fault as described in the relevant diagnostic procedure.
- Go to point 3.

NO

- Go to point 2.

2. Handling fault

- The throttle valve has been turned by hand while the engine was running.
- The diagnostic trouble code may be generated if the throttle valve is in the mechanical limp-home position without the control module knowing it.

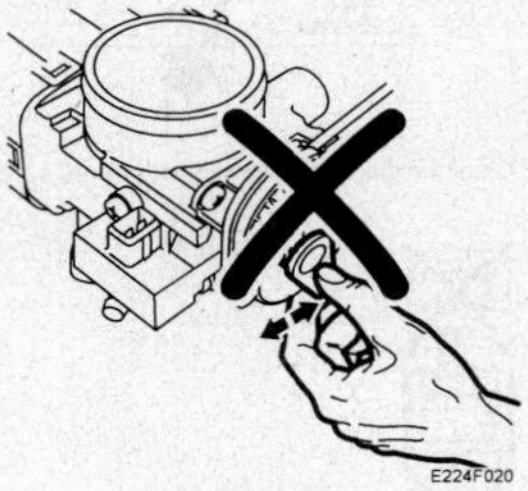

- Turn the ignition switch to the OFF position.

- Switch off the ignition and wait 10 seconds to ensure that the throttle motor will be without current.

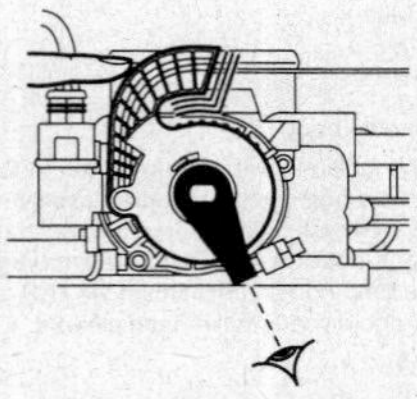

- Turn the pedal arm and check whether the throttle arm follows its movement.

Everything OK?

YES

- Clear diagnostic trouble codes: Trionic

NO

- Go to point 3.

SA1019900057020X

Fig. 72 Code P1263: Throttle Moved Manually When Engine Was Running (Part 2 of 4). 9-5

3. Resetting the limp-home mechanism

- Turn the ignition switch to the ON position.

- Clear diagnostic trouble codes: Trionic

- Turn the ignition switch to the OFF position.

- Wait for 10 seconds.
- Reset the limp-home mechanism as described in the 'Adjustment and replacement' section.

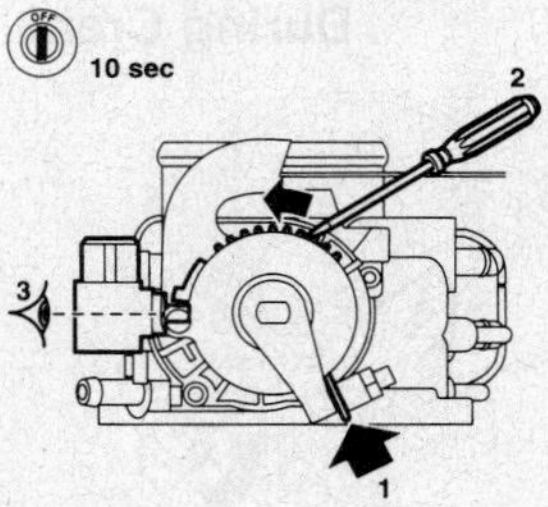

- Clear the diagnostic trouble codes in all systems.

SA1019900057030X

Fig. 72 Code P1263: Throttle Moved Manually When Engine Was Running (Part 3 of 4). 9-5

- Carry out a driving cycle:
- Drive the car under varying engine loads and at different engine rpm for five minutes.

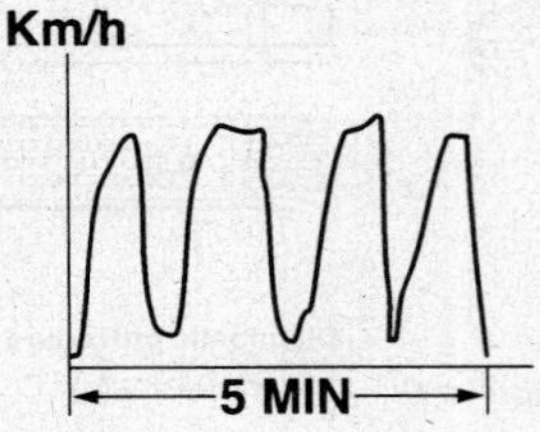

- Evaluate the driving cycle:
- Check that the diagnostic trouble code has not recurred.

Everything OK?

YES

- The steps taken to rectify the fault were correct.

NO

- See "Engine Control Module (ECM)" under "Component Replacement"

SA1019900057040X

Fig. 72 Code P1263: Throttle Moved Manually When Engine Was Running (Part 4 of 4). 9-5

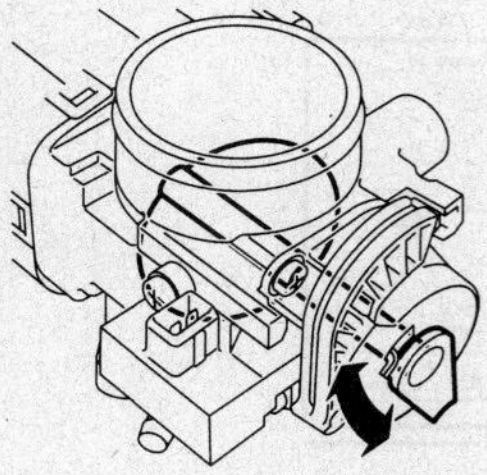

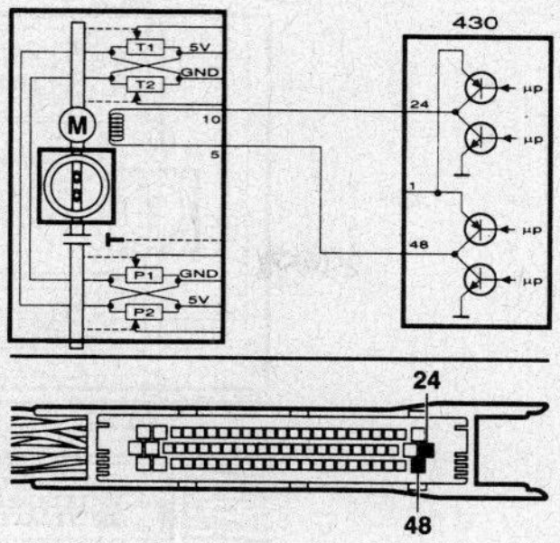

Fault symptoms

- CHECK ENGINE lights up straight away.
- Throttle control in limp-home mode.
- Incorrect idle speed.
- Cruise control inoperative.

Conditions

The following conditions apply for this DTC:

- Engine has started.
- Throttle position exceeds the maximum allowed when pedal is released.

Diagnostic help

The throttle has been open in spite of the driver having released the accelerator. A mechanical fault is preventing the throttle from closing.

Checking the wiring harness

Jiggle the leads and in-line connectors at various points and in different directions to detect any intermittent breaks or short circuits in the wiring. Observe the multimeter, test lamp or diagnostic tool while doing this.

Diagnostic procedure

See Code P1261

SA1019900058000X

Fig. 73 Code P1264: Throttle Open When Pedal Is Released. 9-5

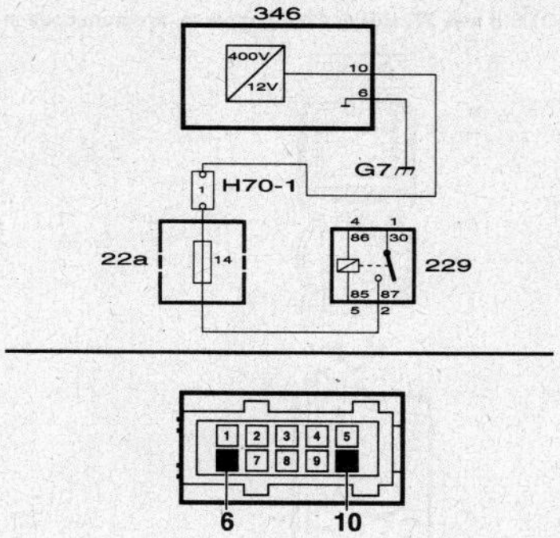

Fault symptoms

- Possible misfiring before DTC is generated.
- Engine fails to start.
- Fuel shut-off

Conditions

The following conditions apply for this DTC:

- Crankshaft rotating and main relay voltage exceeds 10 V.
- Voltage on all ignition trigger outputs is below 2 V for 1 second.

Diagnostic help

The DTC is generated when the ignition discharge module is not supplied with current.

Checking the wiring harness

Jiggle the leads and in-line connectors at various points and in different directions to detect any intermittent breaks or short circuits in the wiring. Observe the multimeter, test lamp or diagnostic tool while doing this.

Diagnostic procedure

1. Checking the ignition discharge module's power supply

- Unplug the connector: Ignition discharge module: (346)

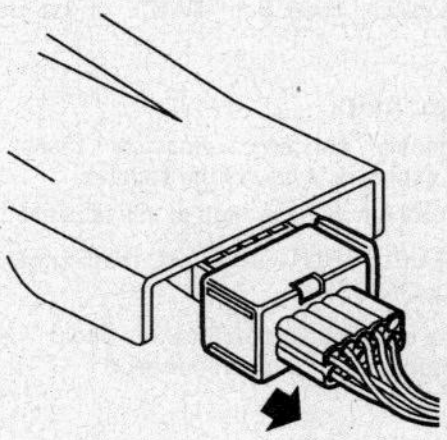

SA1019900059010X

Fig. 74 Code P1310: Ignition Discharge Module Not Powered Bank 1 (Part 1 of 3). 9-5

- Turn the ignition switch to the ON position.

- Connect test lamp 86 11 857 to pin 10 of the female connector and a good grounding point.

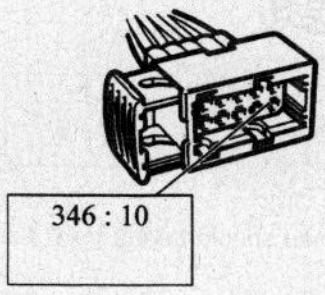

- The test lamp should light.

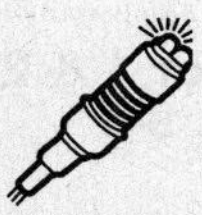

Everything OK?

YES

- Go to point 2.

NO

- The lead from fuse 14 to pin 10 of the female connector is faulty.
- Go to point 3.

2. Checking the grounding of the ignition discharge module

- Connect test lamp 86 11 857 to pins 10 and 6.

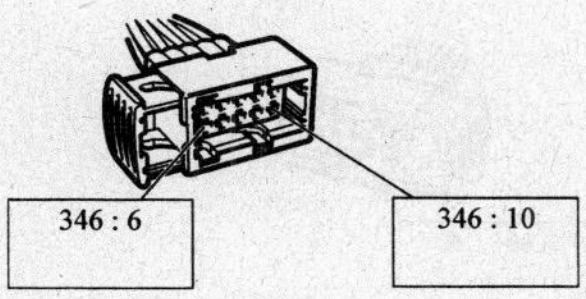

- The test lamp should light.

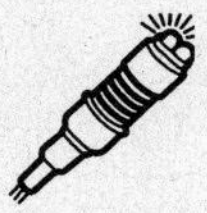

Everything OK?

YES

- Change: Ignition discharge module
- Go to point 3.

NO

- The lead from grounding point G7 to pin 6 of the female connector is faulty.
- Go to point 3.

SA1019900059020X

Fig. 74 Code P1310: Ignition Discharge Module Not Powered Bank 1 (Part 2 of 3). 9-5

3. Final check

- Clear the diagnostic trouble codes in all systems.

- Carry out a driving cycle:
- Drive the car under varying engine loads and at different engine rpm for five minutes.

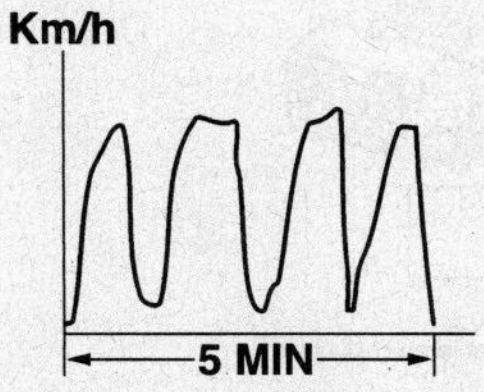

- Evaluate the driving cycle:
- Check that the diagnostic trouble code has not recurred.

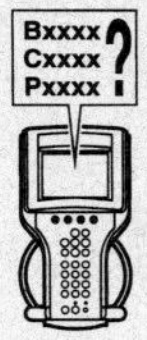

Everything OK?

YES

- The steps taken to rectify the fault were correct.

NO

- See "Engine Control Module (ECM)" under "Component Replacement."

SA1019900059030X

Fig. 74 Code P1310: Ignition Discharge Module Not Powered Bank 1 (Part 3 of 3). 9-5

Immobilizer Active. NOTE. If new T7, MIU or TWICE module, program code in TWICE.

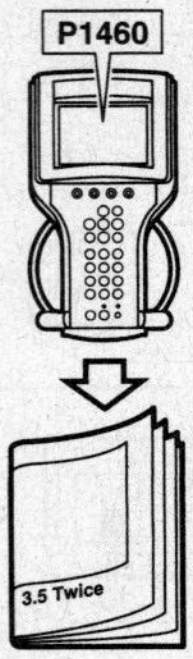

Fault symptoms

- Engine fails to start.

Conditions

The following conditions apply for this DTC:

- Ignition ON and main relay voltage above 10 V.
- No immobilizer code from TWICE or incorrect code.

Diagnostic help

Fault diagnosis concerns electrical faults in connecting cables or in any of the sensors.

Diagnostic tool functions related to this fault are:

- Group FUEL SHUT-OFF, test reading: DTC detected, ON/OFF.

See also the description of test values under "Fault diagnosis, general" for more information.

Note
If a new control module (Trionic T7, TWICE or MIU) is fitted, the immobilizer code must be programmed in TWICE.

Checking the wiring harness

Jiggle the leads and in-line connectors at various points and in different directions to detect any intermittent breaks or short circuits in the wiring. Observe the multimeter, test lamp or diagnostic tool while doing this.

Diagnostic procedure

0. Reference

- See fault diagnosis service category 'Fault diagnosis TWICE/Anti-theft alarm'.

SA1019900060000X

Fig. 75 Code P1460: Immobilizer Active. 9-5

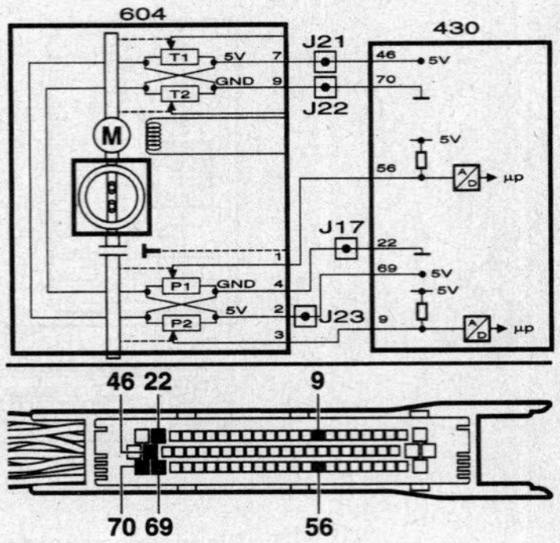

Fault symptoms

- CHECK ENGINE lights up straight away.
- Throttle control in limp-home mode.
- Fuel shut-off at engine speeds above 2200 rpm.
- Incorrect idle speed.
- Cruise control inoperative.

Conditions

The following conditions apply for this DTC:

- Ignition switch in ON position.
- The aggregate of the voltages from pedal position sensors 1 and 2 is above 5.55 V or below 4.45 V.

Diagnostic help

Fault diagnosis concerns electrical faults in connecting cables or in any of the sensors.

Diagnostic tool functions related to this fault are:

- Pedal position sensor 1, in V.
- Pedal position sensor 2, in V.

See also the description of test values under "Fault diagnosis, general" for more information.

Checking the wiring harness

Jiggle the leads and in-line connectors at various points and in different directions to detect any intermittent breaks or short circuits in the wiring. Observe the multimeter, test lamp or diagnostic tool while doing this.

SA1019900061010X

Fig. 76 Code P1530: Pedal Position Sensor 1 & 2 Circuit Sum Out of Range (Part 1 of 8). 9-5

Diagnostic procedure

1. Checking the sensor's grounding

- Unplug the connector: Throttle body: (604)

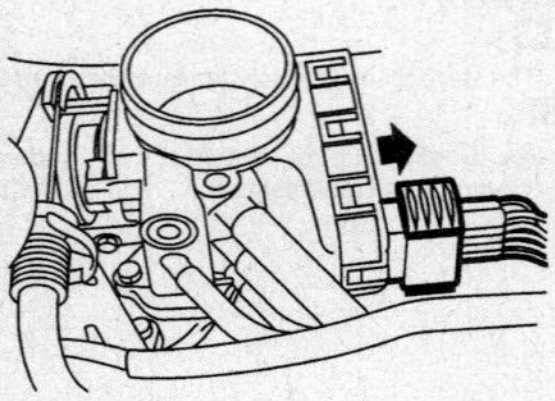

- Connect test lamp 86 11 857 to B+ and pin 9 of the female connector.

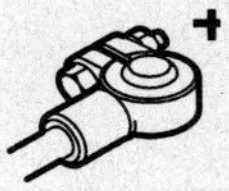

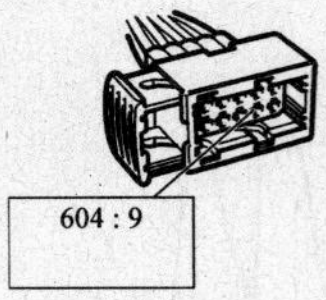

- The test lamp should light.

Everything OK?

YES

– Go to point 2.

NO

– The lead from pin 70 of the control module to pin 9 of the female connector is faulty.

– Go to point 9.

SA1019900061020X

Fig. 76 Code P1530: Pedal Position Sensor 1 & 2 Circuit Sum Out of Range (Part 2 of 8). 9-5

2. Checking the sensor's grounding (continued)

- Connect test lamp 86 11 857 to B+ and pin 4 of the female connector.

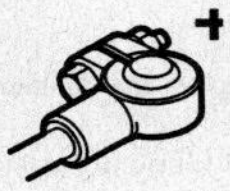

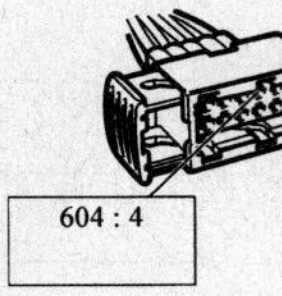

- The test lamp should light.

Everything OK?

YES

– Go to point 3.

NO

– The lead from pin 22 of the control module to pin 4 of the female connector is faulty.

– Go to point 9.

3. Checking the sensor's power supply

- Turn the ignition switch to the ON position.

- Take a voltage reading.
- Red test lead: Throttle body: 7
- Black test lead: Throttle body: 9

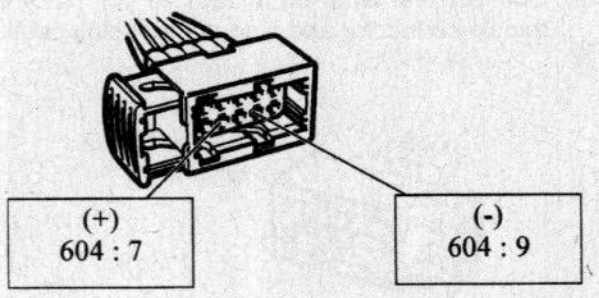

- The reading obtained should be 4.9 V - 5.1 V.

Everything OK?

YES

– Go to point 4.

NO

– The lead from pin 46 of the control module to pin 7 of the female connector is faulty.

– Go to point 9.

SA1019900061030X

Fig. 76 Code P1530: Pedal Position Sensor 1 & 2 Circuit Sum Out of Range (Part 3 of 8). 9-5

4. Checking the sensor's power supply (continued)

- Take a voltage reading.
- Red test lead: Throttle body: 2
- Black test lead: Throttle body: 9

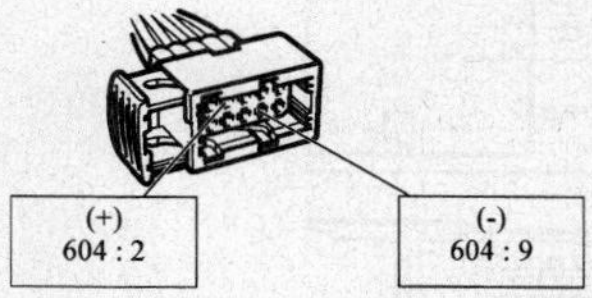

- The reading obtained should be 4.9 V - 5.1 V.

Everything OK?

YES

– Go to point 5.

NO

– The lead from pin 69 of the control module to pin 2 of the female connector is faulty.

– Go to point 9.

5. Checking the control module's sensor input 1

- Contact the Trionic.

- Test reading: Pedal position sensor 1.

- The voltage reading obtained should be 4.95 V - 5 V.

Everything OK?

YES

– Go to point 6.

NO

– The lead from pin 1 of the female connector to pin 56 of the control module is faulty.

– Go to point 9.

SA1019900061040X

Fig. 76 Code P1530: Pedal Position Sensor 1 & 2 Circuit Sum Out of Range (Part 4 of 8). 9-5

6. Checking the control module's sensor input 1, continued

- Connect a jumper lead between pins 1 and 9 of the female connector.

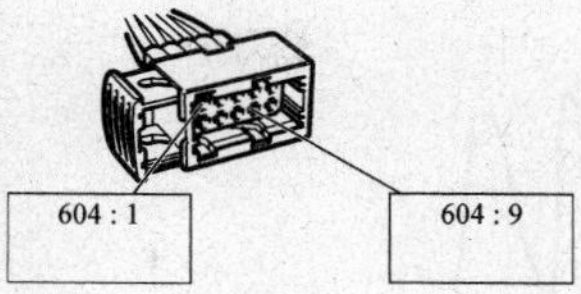

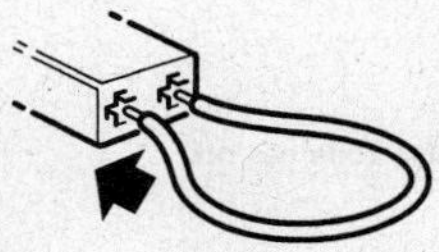

- Test reading: Pedal position sensor 1.

- The voltage reading obtained should be 0 V - 0.05 V.

Everything OK?

YES

– Go to point 7.

NO

– The lead from pin 1 of the female connector to pin 56 of the control module is faulty.

– Go to point 9.

7. Checking the control module's sensor input 2

- Test reading: Pedal position sensor 2.

- The voltage reading obtained should be 4.95 V - 5 V.

Everything OK?

YES

– Go to point 8.

NO

– The lead from pin 3 of the female connector to pin 9 of the control module is faulty.

– Go to point 9.

SA1019900061050X

Fig. 76 Code P1530: Pedal Position Sensor 1 & 2 Circuit Sum Out of Range (Part 5 of 8). 9-5

8. Checking the control module's sensor input 2, continued

- Connect a jumper lead between pins 3 and 9 of the female connector.

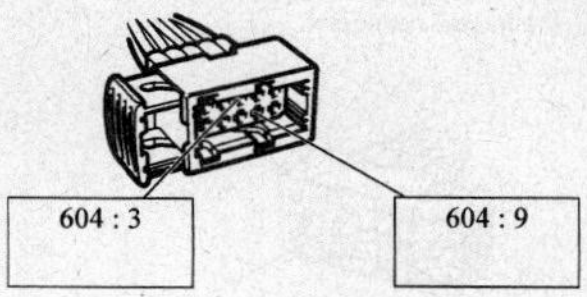

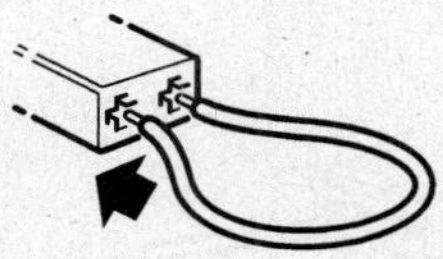

- Test reading: Pedal position sensor 2.

- The voltage reading obtained should be 0 V - 0.05 V.

Everything OK?

YES

– Change: Throttle body

– Next time the ignition switch is turned to the ON position the limp-home solenoid will be activated. The throttle valve will then assume the mechanical limp-home position. It is therefore important to reset the limp-home mechanism AFTER all diagnostic trouble codes have been cleared.

– Go to point 9.

NO

– The lead from pin 3 of the female connector to pin 9 of the control module is faulty.

– Go to point 9.

SA1019900061060X

Fig. 76 Code P1530: Pedal Position Sensor 1 & 2 Circuit Sum Out of Range (Part 6 of 8). 9-5

9. Resetting the limp-home mechanism

- Turn the ignition switch to the ON position.

- Clear diagnostic trouble codes: Trionic

- Turn the ignition switch to the OFF position.

- Wait for 10 seconds.
- Reset the limp-home mechanism as described in the 'Adjustment and replacement' section.

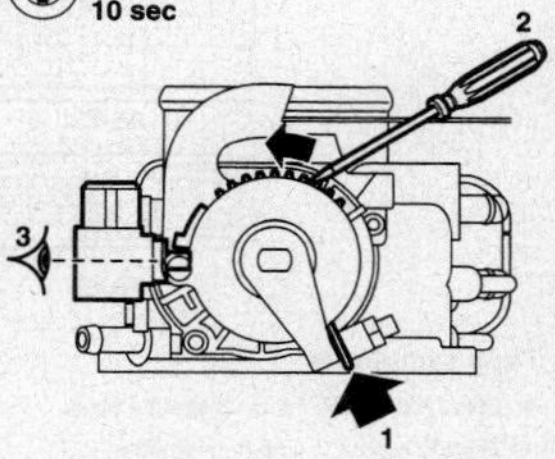

- Clear the diagnostic trouble codes in all systems.

SA1019900061070X

Fig. 76 Code P1530: Pedal Position Sensor 1 & 2 Circuit Sum Out of Range (Part 7 of 8). 9-5

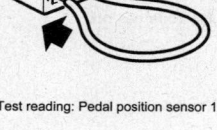

- Carry out a driving cycle:
- Drive the car under varying engine loads and at different engine rpm for five minutes.

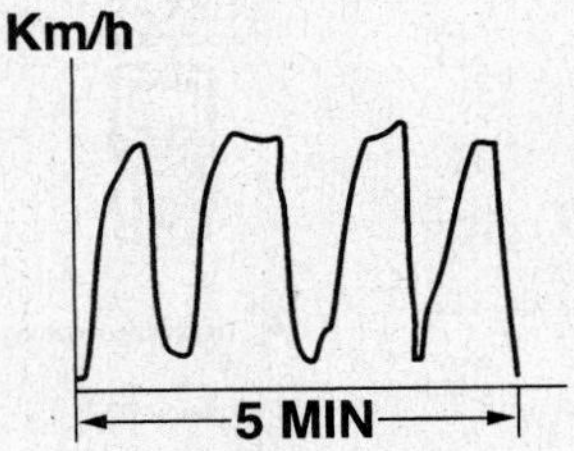

- Evaluate the driving cycle:
- Check that the diagnostic trouble code has not recurred.

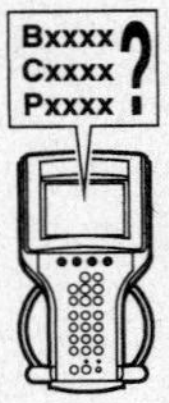

Everything OK?

YES

– The steps taken to rectify the fault were correct.

NO

– See **"Engine Control Module (ECM)" under "Component Replacement"**.

SA1019900061080X

Fig. 76 Code P1530: Pedal Position Sensor 1 & 2 Circuit Sum Out of Range (Part 8 of 8). 9-5

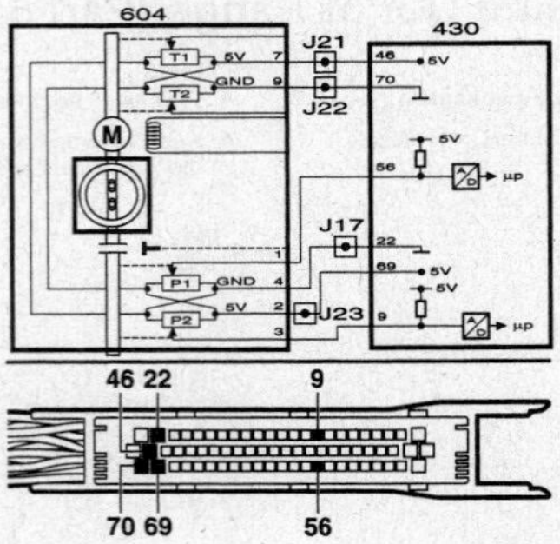

Fault symptoms

- CHECK ENGINE lights up straight away.
- Throttle control in limp-home mode.
- Fuel shut-off at engine speeds above 2200 rpm.
- Incorrect idle speed.
- Cruise control inoperative.

Conditions

The following conditions apply for this DTC:

- Ignition switch in ON position.
- Pedal completely released.
- The aggregate of the voltages from pedal position sensors 1 and 2 exceeds the adapted aggregate by more than 6 %.

Diagnostic help

Fault diagnosis concerns electrical faults in connecting cables or in any of the sensors.

Diagnostic tool functions related to this fault are:

- Pedal position sensor 1, in V.
- Pedal position sensor 2, in V.

See also the description of test values under "Fault diagnosis, general" for more information.

Checking the wiring harness

Jiggle the leads and in-line connectors at various points and in different directions to detect any intermittent breaks or short circuits in the wiring. Observe the multimeter, test lamp or diagnostic tool while doing this.

Diagnostic procedure

See Code P1530.

SA1019900062000X

Fig. 77 Code P1531: Pedal Position Sensor 1 & 2 Circuit Adapted Sum Out Of Range. 9-5

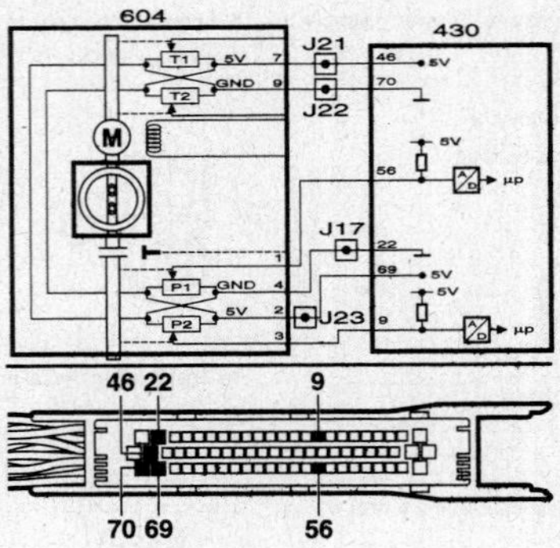

Fault symptoms

- CHECK ENGINE lights up straight away.
- Throttle control in limp-home mode.
- Fuel shut-off at engine speeds above 2200 rpm.
- Incorrect idle speed.
- Cruise control inoperative.

Conditions

The following conditions apply for this DTC:

- Ignition switch in ON position.
- Pulses from the control module input for pedal position sensor 2 are detected on the control module input for pedal position sensor 1.

Diagnostic help

Fault diagnosis concerns electrical faults in connecting cables or in any of the sensors.

Diagnostic tool functions related to this fault are:

- Pedal position sensor 1, in V.
- Pedal position sensor 2, in V.

See also the description of test values under "Fault diagnosis, general" for more information.

Checking the wiring harness

Jiggle the leads and in-line connectors at various points and in different directions to detect any intermittent breaks or short circuits in the wiring. Observe the multimeter, test lamp or diagnostic tool while doing this.

SA1019900063010X

Fig. 78 Code P1532: Pedal Position Sensor 1 & 2 Circuit Control Module Inputs Shorted To Each Other (Part 1 of 4). 9-5

Diagnostic procedure

1. Checking the control module's sensor input

- Unplug the connector: Throttle body: (604)

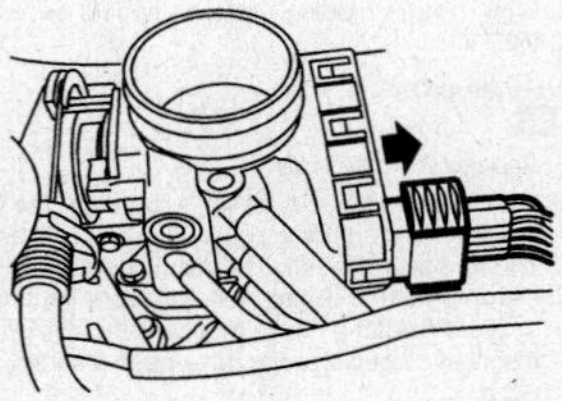

- Connect a jumper lead between pins 1 and 9 of the female connector.

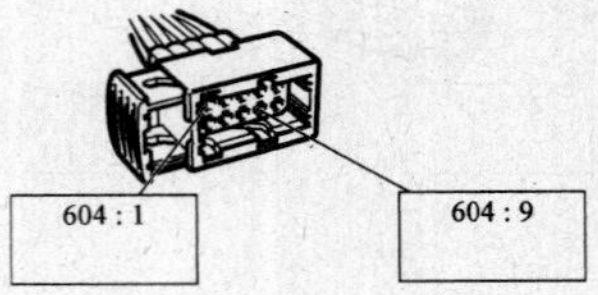

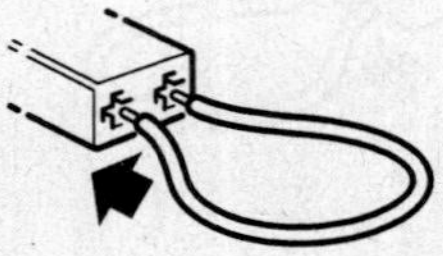

- Turn the ignition switch to the ON position.

- Contact the Trionic.

SA1019900063020X

Fig. 78 Code P1532: Pedal Position Sensor 1 & 2 Circuit Control Module Inputs Shorted To Each Other (Part 2 of 4). 9-5

- Test reading: Pedal position sensor 2.

- The voltage reading obtained should be 4.95 V - 5 V.

Everything OK?

YES

– Change: Throttle body

– Next time the ignition switch is turned to the ON position the limp-home solenoid will be activated. The throttle valve will then assume the mechanical limp-home position. It is therefore important to reset the limp-home mechanism AFTER all diagnostic trouble codes have been cleared.

– Go to point 2.

NO

– Shorting between the sensor leads from pins 1 and 3 of the throttle body.

– Go to point 2.

2. Resetting the limp-home mechanism

- Turn the ignition switch to the ON position.

- Clear diagnostic trouble codes: Trionic

- Turn the ignition switch to the OFF position.

SA1019900063030X

Fig. 78 Code P1532: Pedal Position Sensor 1 & 2 Circuit Control Module Inputs Shorted To Each Other (Part 3 of 4). 9-5

- Wait for 10 seconds.
- Reset the limp-home mechanism as described in the 'Adjustment and replacement' section.

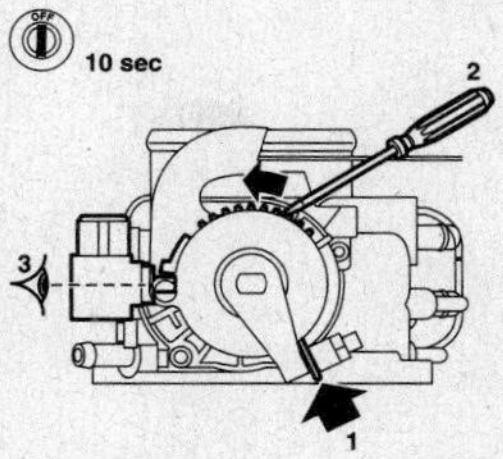

- Clear the diagnostic trouble codes in all systems.

- Carry out a driving cycle:
- Drive the car under varying engine loads and at different engine rpm for five minutes.

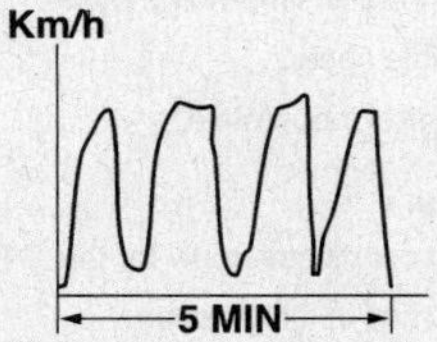

- Evaluate the driving cycle:
- Check that the diagnostic trouble code has not recurred.

Everything OK?

YES

– The steps taken to rectify the fault were correct.

NO

– See **"Engine Control Module (ECM)" under "Component Replacement"**.

SA1019900063040X

Fig. 78 Code P1532: Pedal Position Sensor 1 & 2 Circuit Control Module Inputs Shorted To Each Other (Part 4 of 4). 9-5

Fault symptoms

- CHECK ENGINE comes on after two driving cycles.

Diagnostic procedure

See Code P0605.

Conditions

The following conditions apply for this DTC:

- Ignition switch in ON position.
- No pulses are generated to the control module input for pedal position sensor 2.

Diagnostic help

Fault diagnosis concerns an internal fault in the control module.

Checking the wiring harness

Jiggle the leads and in-line connectors at various points and in different directions to detect any intermittent breaks or short circuits in the wiring. Observe the multimeter, test lamp or diagnostic tool while doing this.

SA1019900064000X

Fig. 79 Code P1601: Internal Control Module Malfunction. 9-5

Fault symptoms

- CHECK ENGINE lights up straight away.
- Throttle control in limp-home mode.
- Incorrect idle speed.
- Cruise control inoperative.

Diagnostic procedure

See Code P0605.

Conditions

The following conditions apply for this DTC:

- Ignition switch in ON position.
- ROM faulty in processor 592.

Diagnostic help

Fault diagnosis concerns an internal fault in the control module.

Checking the wiring harness

Jiggle the leads and in-line connectors at various points and in different directions to detect any intermittent breaks or short circuits in the wiring. Observe the multimeter, test lamp or diagnostic tool while doing this.

SA1019900065000X

Fig. 80 Code P1603: Internal Control Module Malfunction. 9-5

Fault symptoms

- CHECK ENGINE lights up straight away.
- Throttle control in limp-home mode.
- Incorrect idle speed.
- Cruise control inoperative.

Diagnostic procedure

See Code P0605.

Conditions

The following conditions apply for this DTC:

- Ignition switch in ON position.
- ROM faulty in processor 339.

Diagnostic help

Fault diagnosis concerns an internal fault in the control module.

Checking the wiring harness

Jiggle the leads and in-line connectors at various points and in different directions to detect any intermittent breaks or short circuits in the wiring. Observe the multimeter, test lamp or diagnostic tool while doing this.

SA1019900066000X

Fig. 81 Code P1604: Internal Control Module Malfunction. 9-5

Fault symptoms

- CHECK ENGINE lights up straight away.
- Throttle control in limp-home mode.
- Incorrect idle speed.
- Cruise control inoperative.

Diagnostic procedure

See Code P0605.

Conditions

The following conditions apply for this DTC:

- Ignition switch in ON position.
- Serial communication fault between processors 339 and 592.

Diagnostic help

Fault diagnosis concerns an internal fault in the control module.

Checking the wiring harness

Jiggle the leads and in-line connectors at various points and in different directions to detect any intermittent breaks or short circuits in the wiring. Observe the multimeter, test lamp or diagnostic tool while doing this.

SA1019900067000X

Fig. 82 Code P1605: Internal Control Module Malfunction. 9-5

Fault symptoms

- CHECK ENGINE lights up straight away.
- Throttle control in limp-home mode.
- Incorrect idle speed.
- Cruise control inoperative.

Diagnostic procedure

See Code P0605.

Conditions

The following conditions apply for this DTC:

- Ignition switch in ON position.
- Serial communication fault between processors 592 and 339.

Diagnostic help

Fault diagnosis concerns an internal fault in the control module.

Checking the wiring harness

Jiggle the leads and in-line connectors at various points and in different directions to detect any intermittent breaks or short circuits in the wiring. Observe the multimeter, test lamp or diagnostic tool while doing this.

SA1019900077000X

Fig. 84 Code P1607: Internal Control Module Malfunction. 9-5

Fault symptoms

- CHECK ENGINE lights up straight away.
- Throttle control in limp-home mode.
- Incorrect idle speed.
- Cruise control inoperative.

Diagnostic procedure

See Code P0605.

Conditions

The following conditions apply for this DTC:

- Ignition switch in ON position.
- Program fault in processor 339.

Diagnostic help

Fault diagnosis concerns an internal fault in the control module.

Checking the wiring harness

Jiggle the leads and in-line connectors at various points and in different directions to detect any intermittent breaks or short circuits in the wiring. Observe the multimeter, test lamp or diagnostic tool while doing this.

SA1019900068000X

Fig. 83 Code P1606: Internal Control Module Malfunction. 9-5

Fault symptoms

- CHECK ENGINE lights up straight away.
- Throttle control in limp-home mode.
- Incorrect idle speed.
- Cruise control inoperative.

Diagnostic procedure

See Code P0605.

Conditions

The following conditions apply for this DTC:

- Ignition switch in ON position.
- Program fault in processor 592.

Diagnostic help

Fault diagnosis concerns an internal fault in the control module.

Checking the wiring harness

Jiggle the leads and in-line connectors at various points and in different directions to detect any intermittent breaks or short circuits in the wiring. Observe the multimeter, test lamp or diagnostic tool while doing this.

SA1019900078000X

Fig. 85 Code P1608: Internal Control Module Malfunction. 9-5

Fault symptoms

- CHECK ENGINE comes on after two driving cycles.

Diagnostic procedure

See Code P0605.

Conditions

The following conditions apply for this DTC:

- Ignition switch in OFF position.
- Main relay still activated (for 10 seconds).
- Current for the throttle motor cannot be completely cut off.

Diagnostic help

Fault diagnosis concerns an internal fault in the control module.

Checking the wiring harness

Jiggle the leads and in-line connectors at various points and in different directions to detect any intermittent breaks or short circuits in the wiring. Observe the multimeter, test lamp or diagnostic tool while doing this.

SA1019900069000X

Fig. 86 Code P1609: Internal Control Module Malfunction. 9-5

Fault symptoms

- CHECK ENGINE lights up straight away.
- Throttle control in limp-home mode.
- Fuel shut-off at engine speeds above 2200 rpm.
- Incorrect idle speed.
- Cruise control inoperative.

Conditions

The following conditions apply for this DTC:

- Ignition switch in ON position.
- Pedal position differs between processors 592 and 339.

Diagnostic help

Fault diagnosis concerns an internal fault in the control module.

Checking the wiring harness

Jiggle the leads and in-line connectors at various points and in different directions to detect any intermittent breaks or short circuits in the wiring. Observe the multimeter, test lamp or diagnostic tool while doing this.

Diagnostic procedure

See Code P0605.

SA1019900071000X

Fig. 87 Code P1610: Internal Control Module Malfunction. 9-5

Fault symptoms

- CHECK ENGINE lights up straight away.
- Throttle control in limp-home mode.
- Incorrect idle speed.
- Cruise control inoperative.

Conditions

The following conditions apply for this DTC:

- Ignition switch in ON position.
- ROM for important mass air flow control functions is faulty.

Diagnostic help

Fault diagnosis concerns an internal fault in the control module.

Checking the wiring harness

Jiggle the leads and in-line connectors at various points and in different directions to detect any intermittent breaks or short circuits in the wiring. Observe the multimeter, test lamp or diagnostic tool while doing this.

Diagnostic procedure

See Code P0605.

SA1019900070000X

Fig. 89 Code P1613: Internal Control Module Malfunction. 9-5

Fault symptoms

- CHECK ENGINE lights up straight away.
- Throttle control in limp-home mode.
- Incorrect idle speed.
- Cruise control inoperative.

Conditions

The following conditions apply for this DTC:

- Ignition switch in ON position.
- Stack error in processor 339.

Diagnostic help

Fault diagnosis concerns an internal fault in the control module.

Checking the wiring harness

Jiggle the leads and in-line connectors at various points and in different directions to detect any intermittent breaks or short circuits in the wiring. Observe the multimeter, test lamp or diagnostic tool while doing this.

Diagnostic procedure

See Code P0605.

SA1019900074000X

Fig. 91 Code P1621: Internal Control Module Malfunction. 9-5

Fault symptoms

- CHECK ENGINE lights up straight away.
- Throttle control in limp-home mode.
- Fuel shut-off activated.
- Main relay inoperative.

Conditions

The following conditions apply for this DTC:

- Engine has started.
- Throttle control already in limp-home mode.
- Current for the throttle motor cannot be completely cut off.

Diagnostic help

Fault diagnosis concerns an internal fault in the control module.

Checking the wiring harness

Jiggle the leads and in-line connectors at various points and in different directions to detect any intermittent breaks or short circuits in the wiring. Observe the multimeter, test lamp or diagnostic tool while doing this.

Diagnostic procedure

See Code P0605.

SA1019900072000X

Fig. 88 Code P1611: Internal Control Module Malfunction. 9-5

Fault symptoms

- Cruise control inoperative.

Conditions

The following conditions apply for this DTC:

- Ignition ON and processor 339 allows engagement of cruise control.
- Processor 592 does not allow engagement of cruise control.

Diagnostic help

Fault diagnosis concerns an internal fault in the control module.

Checking the wiring harness

Jiggle the leads and in-line connectors at various points and in different directions to detect any intermittent breaks or short circuits in the wiring. Observe the multimeter, test lamp or diagnostic tool while doing this.

Diagnostic procedure

See Code P0605.

SA1019900073000X

Fig. 90 Code P1614: Internal Control Module Malfunction. 9-5

Fault symptoms

- CHECK ENGINE comes on after two driving cycles.
- Possibly limited performance before DTC is generated.

Conditions

The following conditions apply for this DTC:

- Engine has started.
- Voltage from atmosphere absolute pressure sensor is lower than 0.2 V for more than 5 seconds.

Diagnostic help

Fault diagnosis concerns an internal control module fault as the sensor is mounted in the control module.

Diagnostic tool functions related to this fault are:

- Pressure sensor reading, in kPa.

With the engine switched off, the reading should correspond with those of the other two pressure sensors. Permissible difference: 10 kPa.

See also the description of test values under "Fault diagnosis, general" for more information.

Checking the wiring harness

Jiggle the leads and in-line connectors at various points and in different directions to detect any intermittent breaks or short circuits in the wiring. Observe the multimeter, test lamp or diagnostic tool while doing this.

Diagnostic procedure

See Code P0605.

SA1019900075000X

Fig. 92 Code P1632: Internal Control Module Malfunction. 9-5

Fault symptoms

- CHECK ENGINE comes on after two driving cycles.

Conditions

The following conditions apply for this DTC:

- Engine has started.
- Voltage from atmosphere absolute pressure sensor higher than 4.92 V for more than 5 seconds.

Diagnostic help

Fault diagnosis concerns an internal control module fault as the sensor is mounted in the control module.

Diagnostic tool functions related to this fault are:

- Pressure sensor reading, in kPa.

With the engine switched off, the reading should correspond with those of the other two pressure sensors. Permissible difference: 10 kPa.

See also the description of test values under "Fault diagnosis, general" for more information.

Checking the wiring harness

Jiggle the leads and in-line connectors at various points and in different directions to detect any intermittent breaks or short circuits in the wiring. Observe the multimeter, test lamp or diagnostic tool while doing this.

Diagnostic procedure

See Code P0605.

SA1019900076000X

Fig. 93 Code P1633: Internal Control Module Malfunction. 9-5

Diagnostic procedure

1. Checking the relay power supply.

- Remove the component: Main relay for engine management system

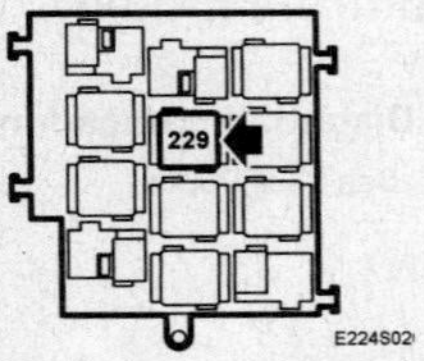

- Turn the ignition switch to the ON position.

- Connect test lamp 86 11 857 to pin 4 (86) of the relay holder and a good grounding point.

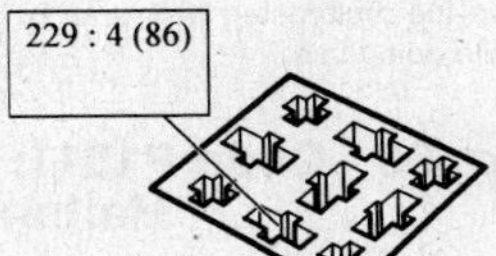

- The test lamp should light.

Everything OK?

YES

- Go to point 2.

NO

- The lead from +30 to pin 4 (86) of the relay holder is faulty.
- Go to point 4.

SA1019900079020X

Fig. 94 Code P1640: Main Relay Circuit No Voltage To Control Module Pin 1 (Part 2 of 5). 9-5

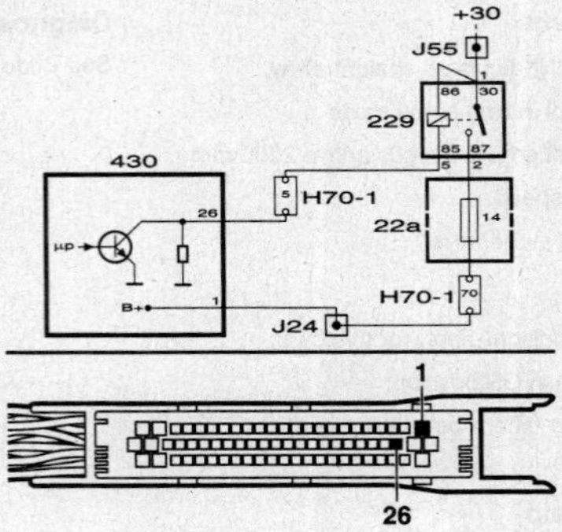

Fault symptoms

- CHECK ENGINE lights up straight away.
- Engine fails to start.
- Possible misfiring before DTC is generated.

Conditions

The following conditions apply for this DTC:

- Crankshaft rotating and main relay voltage below 5 V for 1 second.

Diagnostic help

Fault diagnosis concerns electrical faults in connecting cables or in the relay.

Diagnostic tool functions related to this fault are:

- Main relay voltage, in V.

See also the description of test values under "Fault diagnosis, general" for more information.

Checking the wiring harness

Jiggle the leads and in-line connectors at various points and in different directions to detect any intermittent breaks or short circuits in the wiring. Observe the multimeter, test lamp or diagnostic tool while doing this.

SA1019900079010X

Fig. 94 Code P1640: Main Relay Circuit No Voltage To Control Module Pin 1 (Part 1 of 5). 9-5

2. Checking the relay's control module output

- Connect test lamp 86 11 857 to pins 4 (86) and 5 (85) of the relay holder.

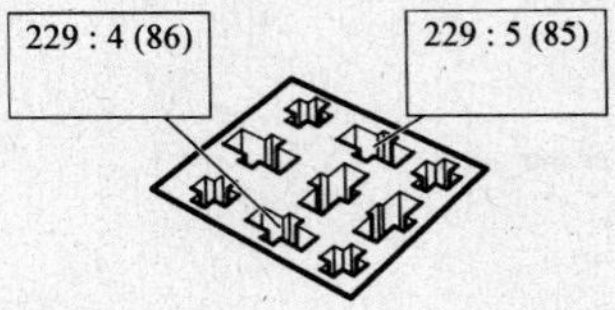

- The test lamp should light.

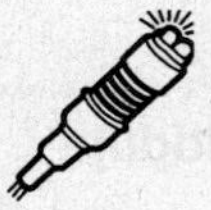

Everything OK?

YES

- Go to point 3.

NO

- The lead from pin 26 of the control module to pin 5 (85) of the relay holder is faulty.
- Go to point 4.

3. Checking the fuse

- Check fuse 14 and change it, if necessary.

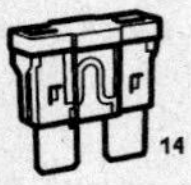

- Connect a jumper lead between pin 1 (30) and pin 2 (87).

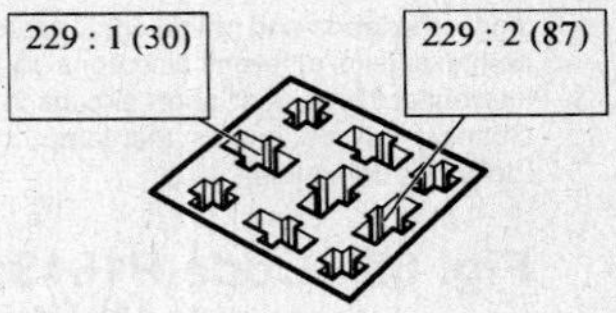

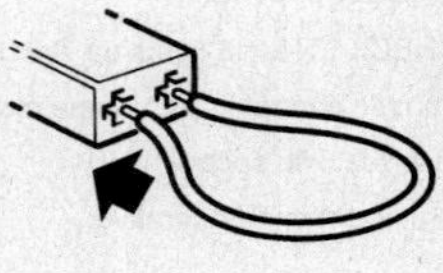

- Contact the Trionic.

SA1019900079030X

Fig. 94 Code P1640: Main Relay Circuit No Voltage To Control Module Pin 1 (Part 3 of 5). 9-5

- Test reading: Main relay voltage.

- The reading obtained should be B+.

Everything OK?

YES

- Change: Main relay for engine management system
- Go to point 4.

NO

- The lead from pin 2 (87) of the relay holder via fuse 14 to pin 1 of the control module is faulty.
- Go to point 4.

4. Final check

- Clear the diagnostic trouble codes in all systems.

- Carry out a driving cycle:
- Drive the car under varying engine loads and at different engine rpm for five minutes.

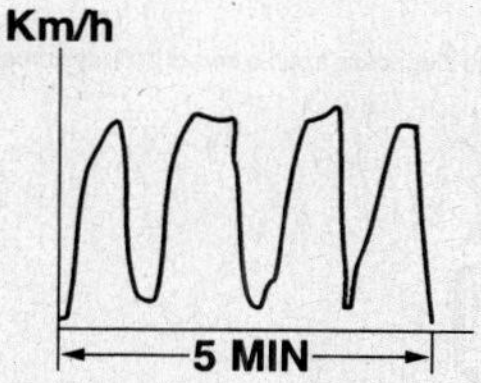

SA1019900079040X

Fig. 94 Code P1640: Main Relay Circuit No Voltage To Control Module Pin 1 (Part 4 of 5). 9-5

- Evaluate the driving cycle:
- Check that the diagnostic trouble code has not recurred.

Everything OK?

YES

- The steps taken to rectify the fault were correct.

NO

- See "Engine Control Module (ECM)" under "Component Replacement"

SA1019900079050X

Fig. 94 Code P1640: Main Relay Circuit No Voltage To Control Module Pin 1 (Part 5 of 5). 9-5

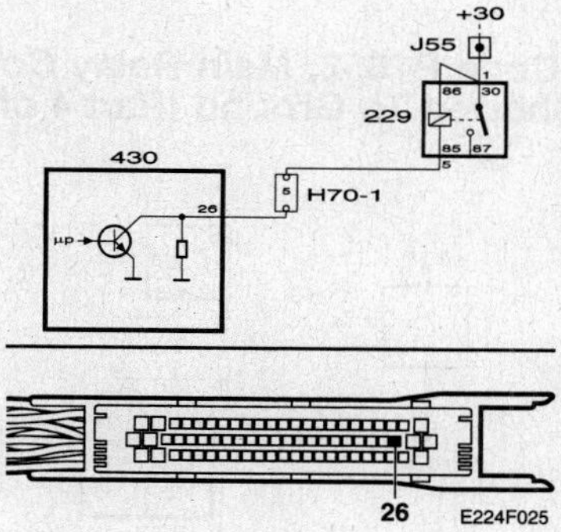

Fault symptoms

- CHECK ENGINE lights up straight away.
- Engine fails to start.
- Possible misfiring before DTC is generated.

Conditions

The following conditions apply for this DTC:

- Crankshaft rotating and output voltage below 2 V when the output is inactive.
- Conditions are met for 0.5 seconds.

Diagnostic help

Fault diagnosis concerns electrical faults in connecting cables or in the relay.

Diagnostic tool functions related to this fault are:

- Activation of output for main relay.

See also the description of activating functions under "Fault diagnosis, general" for more information.

Checking the wiring harness

Jiggle the leads and in-line connectors at various points and in different directions to detect any intermittent breaks or short circuits in the wiring. Observe the multimeter, test lamp or diagnostic tool while doing this.

SA1019900080010X

Fig. 95 Code P1652: Main Relay Coil Circuit Open/Shorted To Ground (Part 1 of 4). 9-5

Diagnostic procedure

1. Checking the relay power supply.

- Remove the component: Main relay for engine management system

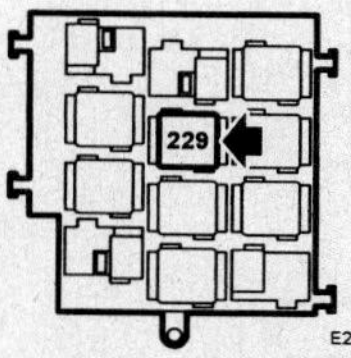

- Turn the ignition switch to the ON position.

- Connect test lamp 86 11 857 to pin 4 (86) of the relay holder and a good grounding point.

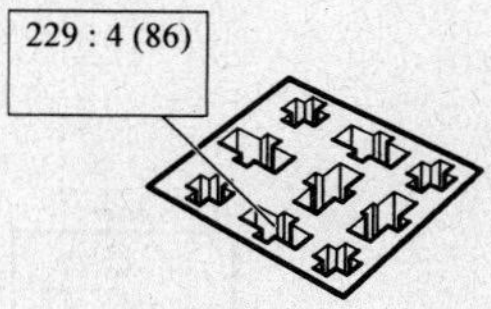

- The test lamp should light.

Everything OK?

YES

- Go to point 2.

NO

- The lead from +30 to pin 4 (86) of the relay holder is faulty.
- Go to point 3.

SA1019900080020X

Fig. 95 Code P1652: Main Relay Coil Circuit Open/Shorted To Ground (Part 2 of 4). 9-5

2. Checking the relay's control module output

- Connect test lamp 86 11 857 to pins 4 (86) and 5 (85) of the relay holder.

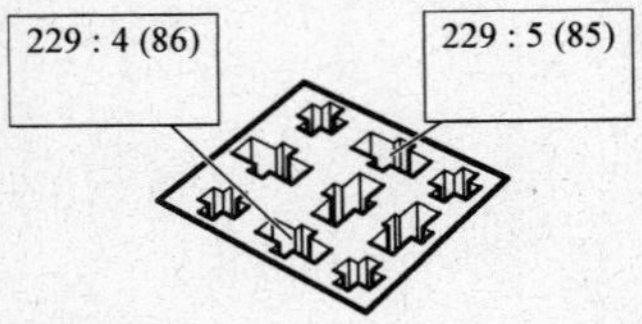

- The test lamp should light.

Everything OK?

YES

– Change: Main relay for engine management system

– Go to point 3.

NO

– The lead from pin 26 of the control module to pin 5 (85) of the relay holder is faulty.

– Go to point 3.

3. Resetting the limp-home mechanism

- Turn the ignition switch to the ON position.

- Clear diagnostic trouble codes: Trionic

- Turn the ignition switch to the OFF position.

SA1019900080030X

Fig. 95 Code P1652: Main Relay Coil Circuit Open/Shorted To Ground (Part 3 of 4). 9-5

- Wait for 10 seconds.
- Reset the limp-home mechanism as described in the 'Adjustment and replacement' section.

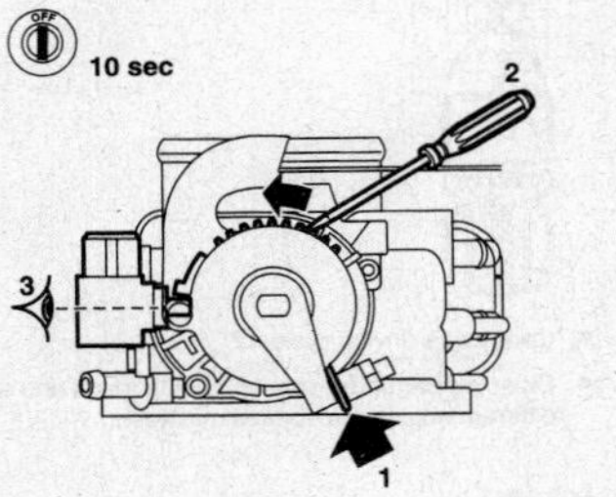

- Clear the diagnostic trouble codes in all systems.

- Carry out a driving cycle:
- Drive the car under varying engine loads and at different engine rpm for five minutes.

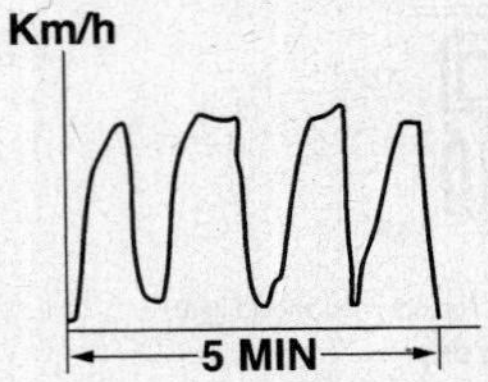

- Evaluate the driving cycle:
- Check that the diagnostic trouble code has not recurred.

Everything OK?

YES

– The steps taken to rectify the fault were correct.

NO

– See "Engine Control Module (ECM)" under "Component Replacement"

SA1019900080040X

Fig. 95 Code P1652: Main Relay Coil Circuit Open/Shorted To Ground (Part 4 of 4). 9-5

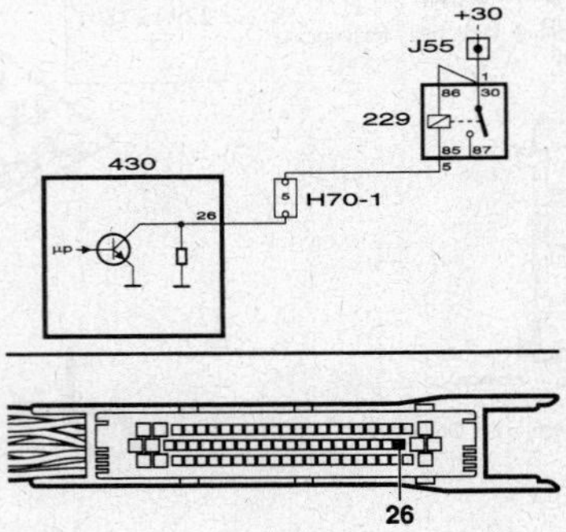

Fault symptoms

- CHECK ENGINE lights up straight away.
- Engine fails to start.
- Possible misfiring before DTC is generated.

Conditions

The following conditions apply for this DTC:

- Crankshaft rotating and output voltage above 2 V when the output is active.
- Conditions are met for 0.5 seconds.

Diagnostic help

Fault diagnosis concerns electrical faults in connecting cables or in the relay.

Diagnostic tool functions related to this fault are:

- Activation of output for main relay.

See also the description of activating functions under "Fault diagnosis, general" for more information.

Checking the wiring harness

Jiggle the leads and in-line connectors at various points and in different directions to detect any intermittent breaks or short circuits in the wiring. Observe the multimeter, test lamp or diagnostic tool while doing this.

Diagnostic procedure

See Code P1652 .

SA1019900081000X

Fig. 96 Code P1653: Main Relay Coil Circuit Short To B+. 9-5

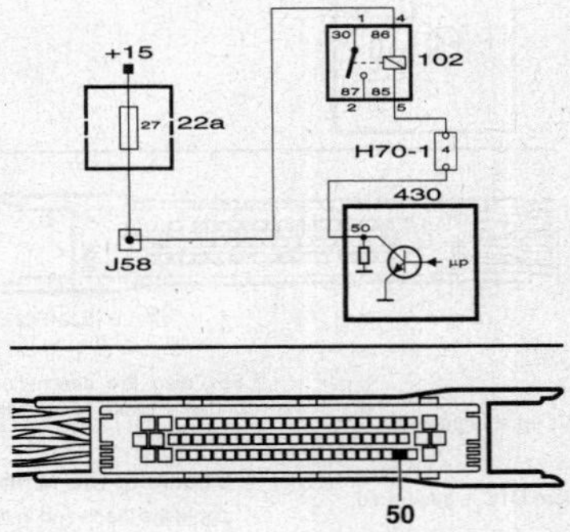

Fault symptoms

- Engine fails to start.
- If the fault occurred while the engine was running, P1135 may be generated as a consequential fault.

Conditions

The following conditions apply for this DTC:

- Ignition ON and main relay voltage above 10 V.
- Output voltage is below 2 V when the output is inactive.
- Conditions are met for 1 second.

Diagnostic help

Fault diagnosis concerns electrical faults in connecting cables or in the relay.

Diagnostic tool functions related to this fault are:

- Activation of output for fuel pump relay.

See also the description of activating functions under "Fault diagnosis, general" for more information.

Checking the wiring harness

Jiggle the leads and in-line connectors at various points and in different directions to detect any intermittent breaks or short circuits in the wiring. Observe the multimeter, test lamp or diagnostic tool while doing this.

SA1019900082010X

Fig. 97 Code P1654: Fuel Pump Relay Coil Circuit Open/Short To Ground (Part 1 of 4). 9-5

Diagnostic procedure

1. Checking the relay power supply.

- Remove component: Fuel pump relay

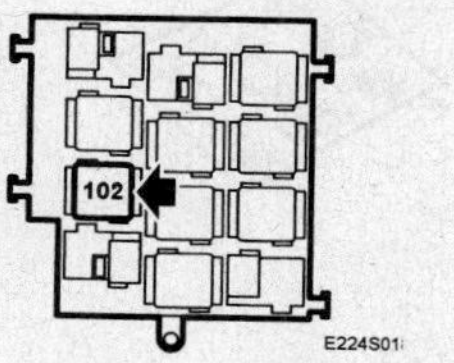

- Turn the ignition switch to the ON position.

- Connect test lamp 86 11 857 to pin 4 (86) of the relay holder and a good grounding point.

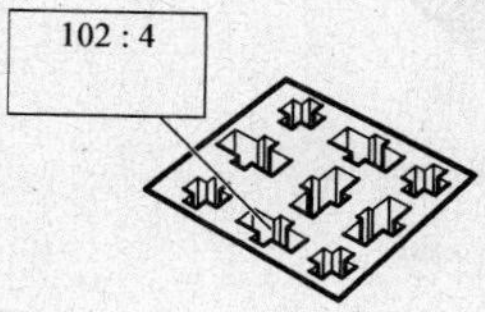

- The test lamp should light.

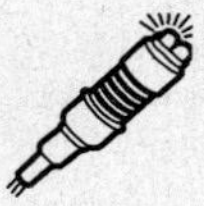

Everything OK?

YES

– Go to point 2.

NO

– The lead from crimp connection J58 to pin 4 (86) of the relay holder is faulty.

– Go to point 3.

SA1019900082020X

Fig. 97 Code P1654: Fuel Pump Relay Coil Circuit Open/Short To Ground (Part 2 of 4). 9-5

2. Checking the relay's control module output

- Connect test lamp 86 11 857 to pins 4 (86) and 5 (85) of the relay holder.

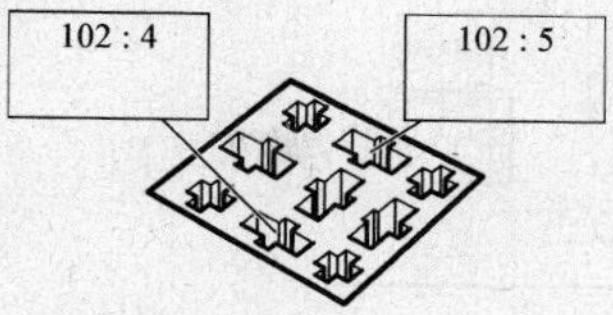

- Activate: Fuel pump relay (ON)

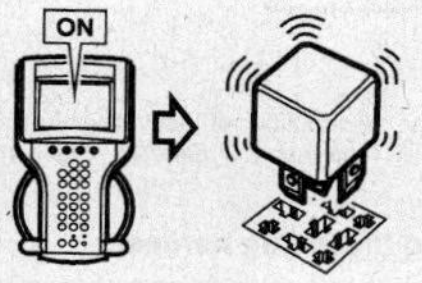

- The test lamp should light.

Everything OK?

YES

– Change: Fuel pump relay

– Go to point 3.

NO

– The lead from pin 50 of the control module to pin 5 (85) of the relay holder is faulty.

– Go to point 3.

3. Final check

- Clear the diagnostic trouble codes in all systems.

- Carry out a driving cycle:
- Drive the car under varying engine loads and at different engine rpm for five minutes.

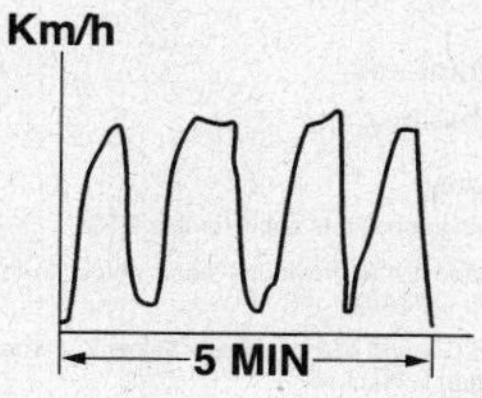

SA1019900082030X

Fig. 97 Code P1654: Fuel Pump Relay Coil Circuit Open/Short To Ground (Part 3 of 4). 9-5

- Evaluate the driving cycle:
- Check that the diagnostic trouble code has not recurred.

Everything OK?

YES

– The steps taken to rectify the fault were correct.

NO

– See "**Engine Control Module (ECM)**" under "**Component Replacement**"

SA1019900082040X

Fig. 97 Code P1654: Fuel Pump Relay Coil Circuit Open/Short To Ground (Part 4 of 4). 9-5

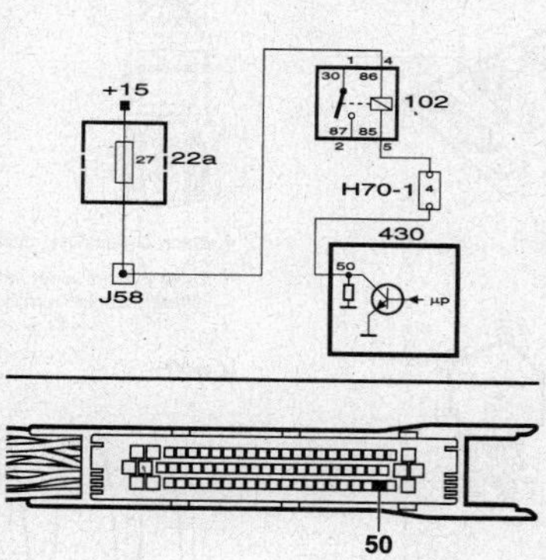

Fault symptoms

- Engine fails to start.
- If the fault occurred while the engine was running, P1135 may be generated as a consequential fault.

Conditions

The following conditions apply for this DTC:

- Ignition ON and main relay voltage above 10 V.
- Output voltage above 2 V when output is active.
- Conditions are met for 1 second.

Diagnostic help

Fault diagnosis concerns electrical faults in connecting cables or in the relay.

Diagnostic tool functions related to this fault are:

- Activation of output for fuel pump relay.

See also the description of activating functions under "Fault diagnosis, general" for more information.

Checking the wiring harness

Jiggle the leads and in-line connectors at various points and in different directions to detect any intermittent breaks or short circuits in the wiring. Observe the multimeter, test lamp or diagnostic tool while doing this.

Diagnostic procedure

See Code P1654.

SA1019900083000X

Fig. 98 Code P1655: Fuel Pump Relay Coil Circuit Short To B+. 9-5

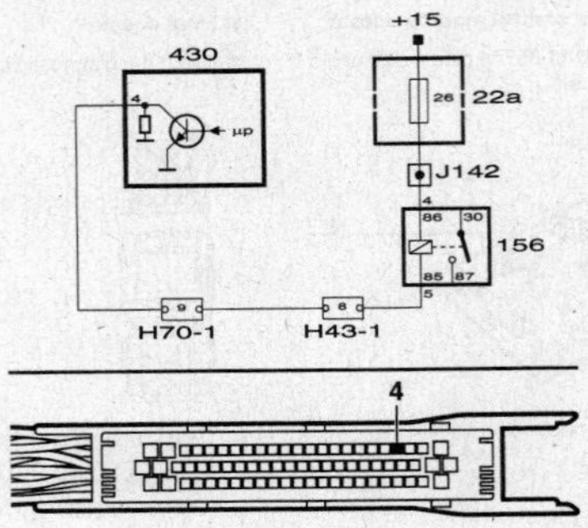

Fault symptoms

- A/C not working.

Conditions

The following conditions apply for this DTC:

- A/C request has previously been output to the bus (car with A/C).
- Ignition ON and output voltage below 2 V when the output is inactive.
- Conditions are met for 1 second.

Diagnostic help

Fault diagnosis concerns electrical faults in connecting cables or in the relay.

Diagnostic tool functions related to this fault are:

- Activation of output for A/C relay.

See also the description of activating functions under "Fault diagnosis, general" for more information.

Checking the wiring harness

Jiggle the leads and in-line connectors at various points and in different directions to detect any intermittent breaks or short circuits in the wiring. Observe the multimeter, test lamp or diagnostic tool while doing this.

SA1019900084010X

Fig. 99 Code P1655: Fuel Pump Relay Coil Circuit Shorted To B+ (Part 1 of 4). 9-5

Diagnostic procedure

1. Checking the relay power supply.

- Remove component: A/C compressor relay

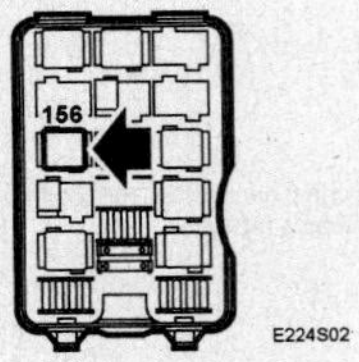

- Turn the ignition switch to the ON position.

- Connect test lamp 86 11 857 to pin 4 (86) of the relay holder and a good grounding point.

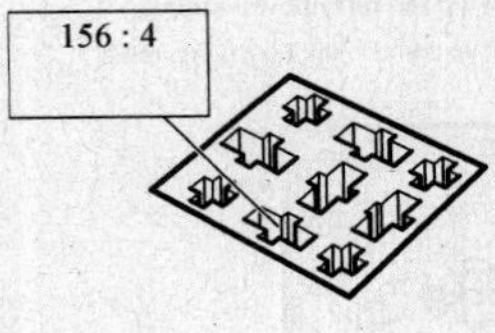

- The test lamp should light.

Everything OK?

YES

– Go to point 2.

NO

– The lead from +15 via fuse 26 to pin 4 (86) of the relay holder is faulty.

– Go to point 3.

SA1019900084020X

Fig. 99 Code P1655: Fuel Pump Relay Coil Circuit Shorted To B+ (Part 2 of 4). 9-5

2. Checking the relay's control module output

- Connect test lamp 86 11 857 to pins 4 (86) and 5 (85) of the relay holder.

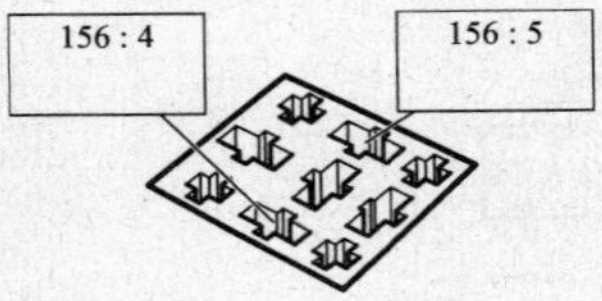

- Activate: A/C relay (ON)

- The test lamp should light

Everything OK?

YES

– Change: A/C compressor relay

– Go to point 3.

NO

– The lead from pin 4 of the control module to pin 5 (85) of the relay holder is faulty.

– Go to point 3.

3. Final check

- Clear the diagnostic trouble codes in all systems.

- Carry out a driving cycle:
- Drive the car under varying engine loads and at different engine rpm for five minutes.

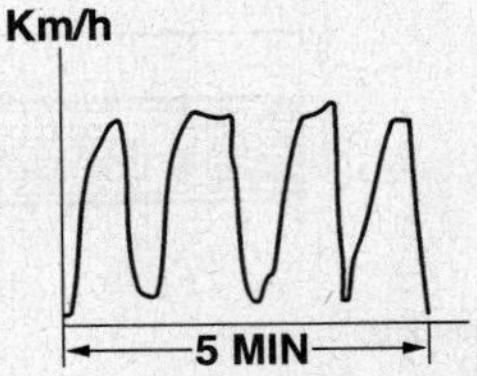

SA1019900084030X

Fig. 99 Code P1655: Fuel Pump Relay Coil Circuit Shorted To B+ (Part 3 of 4). 9-5

- Evaluate the driving cycle:
- Check that the diagnostic trouble code has not recurred.

Everything OK?

YES

– The steps taken to rectify the fault were correct.

NO

– See "**Engine Control Module (ECM)**" under "**Component Replacement**"

SA1019900084040X

Fig. 99 Code P1655: Fuel Pump Relay Coil Circuit Shorted To B+ (Part 4 of 4). 9-5

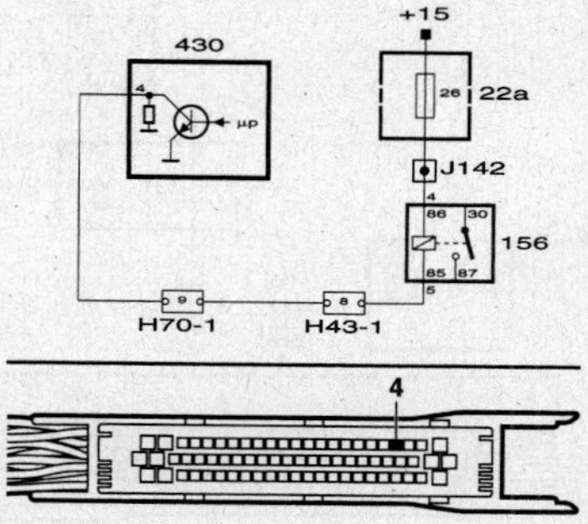

Fault symptoms

- A/C not working.

Conditions

The following conditions apply for this DTC:

- A/C request has previously been output to the bus (car with A/C).
- Ignition ON and output voltage above 2 V when the output is active.
- Conditions are met for 1 second.

Diagnostic help

Fault diagnosis concerns electrical faults in connecting cables or in the relay.

Diagnostic tool functions related to this fault are:

- Activation of output for A/C relay.

See also the description of activating functions under "Fault diagnosis, general" for more information.

Checking the wiring harness

Jiggle the leads and in-line connectors at various points and in different directions to detect any intermittent breaks or short circuits in the wiring. Observe the multimeter, test lamp or diagnostic tool while doing this.

Diagnostic procedure

See Code P1656.

SA1019900085000X

Fig. 100 Code P1657: A/C Relay Coil Circuit Short To B+. 9-5

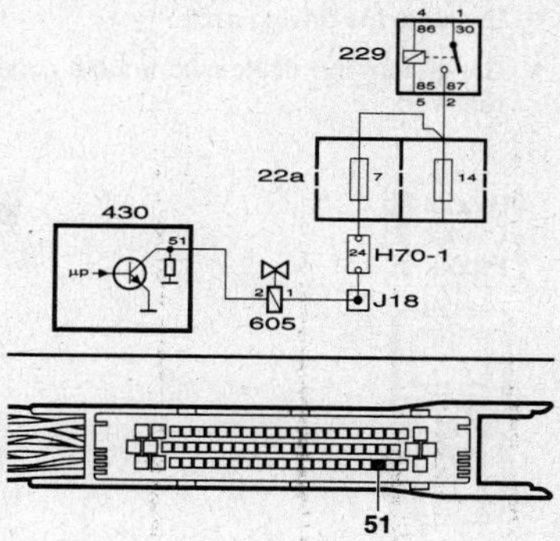

Fault symptoms

- CHECK ENGINE comes on after two driving cycles.
- Possible noise when accelerator released.

Conditions

The following conditions apply for this DTC:

- Engine has started and main relay voltage exceeds 10 V.
- Output voltage is below 2 V when the output is inactive.
- Conditions are met for 1 second.

Diagnostic help

Fault diagnosis concerns electrical faults in connecting cables or in the valve.

Diagnostic tool functions related to this fault are:

- Activating the valve output.

See also the description of activating functions under "Fault diagnosis, general" for more information.

Checking the wiring harness

Jiggle the leads and in-line connectors at various points and in different directions to detect any intermittent breaks or short circuits in the wiring. Observe the multimeter, test lamp or diagnostic tool while doing this.

SA1019900086010X

Fig. 101 Code P1658: Charge Air Bypass Valve Circuit Open/Short To Ground (Part 1 of 4). 9-5

Diagnostic procedure

1. Checking the valve's power supply

- Unplug connector: Charge air bypass valve: (605)

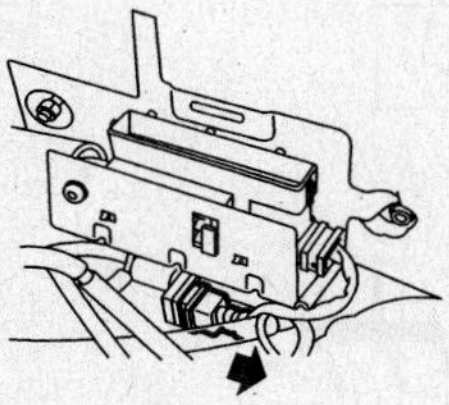

- Turn the ignition switch to the ON position.

- Connect test lamp 86 11 857 to pin 1 of the female connector and a good grounding point.

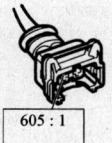

605 : 1

- The test lamp should light.

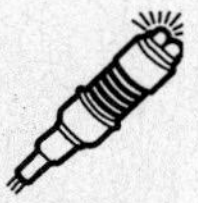

Everything OK?

YES

- Go to point 2.

NO

- The lead from crimp connection J18 to pin 1 of the female connector is faulty.
- Go to point 3.

SA1019900086020X

Fig. 101 Code P1658: Charge Air Bypass Valve Circuit Open/Short To Ground (Part 2 of 4). 9-5

2. Checking the valve's control module output

- Connect test lamp 86 11 857 to pins 1 and 2 of the female connector.

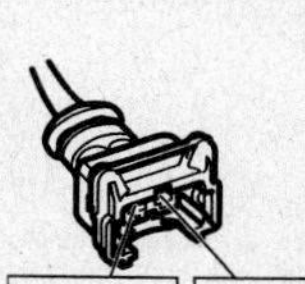

605 : 1 | 605 : 2

- Activate: Charge air bypass valve (ON)

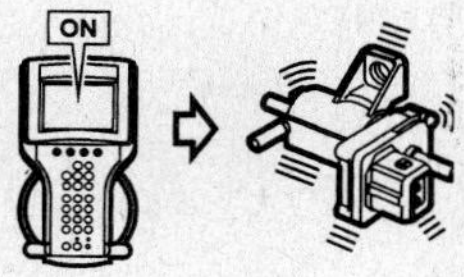

- The test lamp should light

Everything OK?

YES

- Change: Charge air bypass valve
- Go to point 3.

NO

- The lead from pin 51 of the control module to pin 2 of the female connector is faulty.
- Go to point 3.

3. Final check

- Clear the diagnostic trouble codes in all systems.

- Carry out a driving cycle:
- Drive the car under varying engine loads and at different engine rpm for five minutes.

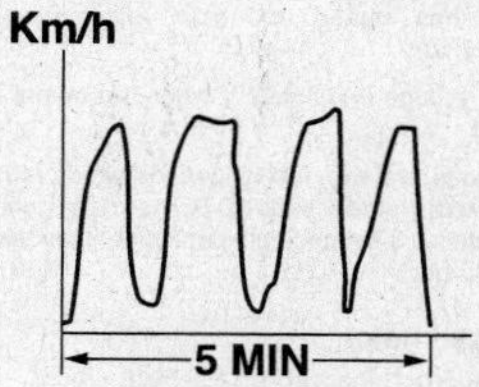

SA1019900086030X

Fig. 101 Code P1658: Charge Air Bypass Valve Circuit Open/Short To Ground (Part 3 of 4). 9-5

- Evaluate the driving cycle:
- Check that the diagnostic trouble code has not recurred.

Everything OK?

YES

– The steps taken to rectify the fault were correct.

NO

– See **"Engine Control Module (ECM)" under "Component Replacement"**

SA1019900086040X

Fig. 101 Code P1658: Charge Air Bypass Valve Circuit Open/Short To Ground (Part 4 of 4). 9-5

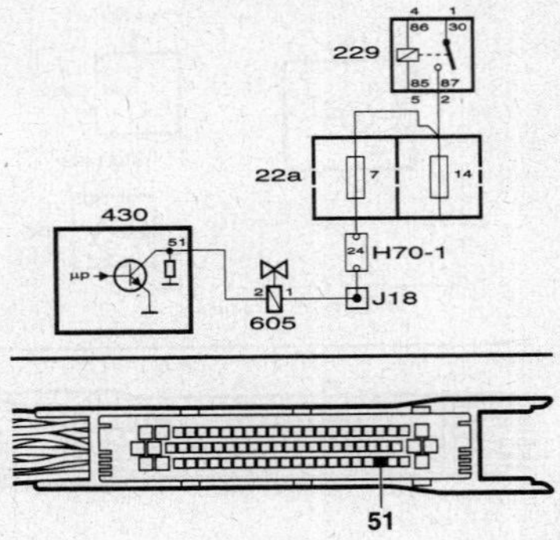

Fault symptoms

- CHECK ENGINE comes on after two driving cycles.

Conditions

The following conditions apply for this DTC:

- Engine has started and main relay voltage exceeds 10 V.
- Output voltage above 2 V when output is active.
- Conditions are met for 1 second.

Diagnostic help

Fault diagnosis concerns electrical faults in connecting cables or in the valve.

Diagnostic tool functions related to this fault are:

- Activating the valve output.

See also the description of activating functions under "Fault diagnosis, general" for more information.

Checking the wiring harness

Jiggle the leads and in-line connectors at various points and in different directions to detect any intermittent breaks or short circuits in the wiring. Observe the multimeter, test lamp or diagnostic tool while doing this.

Diagnostic procedure

See Code P1658 .

SA1019900087000X

Fig. 102 Code P1659: Charge Air Bypass Valve Circuit Short to B+. 9-5

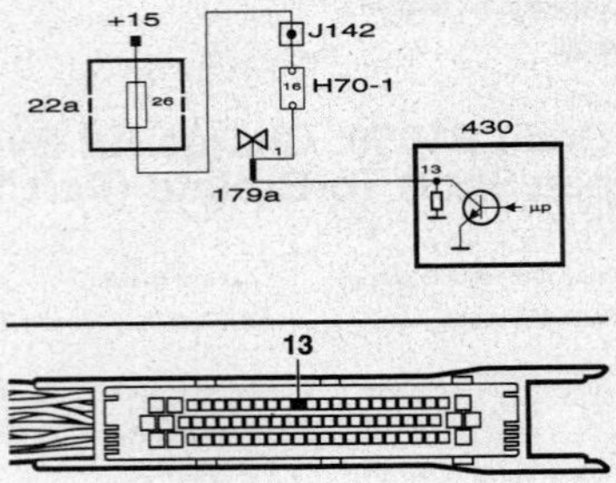

Fault symptoms

- CHECK ENGINE comes on after two driving cycles.
- Torque too low or fuel shut-off during acceleration.

Conditions

The following conditions apply for this DTC:

- Engine has started and main relay voltage exceeds 10 V.
- Output voltage is below 2 V when the output is inactive.
- Conditions are met for 10 periods which must occur within 60 seconds (DTC normally generated after 0.3 seconds but can sometimes take much longer).

Diagnostic help

Fault diagnosis concerns electrical faults in connecting cables or in the valve.

Diagnostic tool functions related to this fault are:

- Activating the valve output.

See also the description of activating functions under "Fault diagnosis, general" for more information.

Checking the wiring harness

Jiggle the leads and in-line connectors at various points and in different directions to detect any intermittent breaks or short circuits in the wiring. Observe the multimeter, test lamp or diagnostic tool while doing this.

SA1019900088010X

Fig. 103 Code P1662: Charge Air Control Valve Circuit Open/Short To Ground (Part 1 of 4). 9-5

Diagnostic procedure

1. Checking the valve's power supply

- Unplug connector: Charge air control valve: (179a)

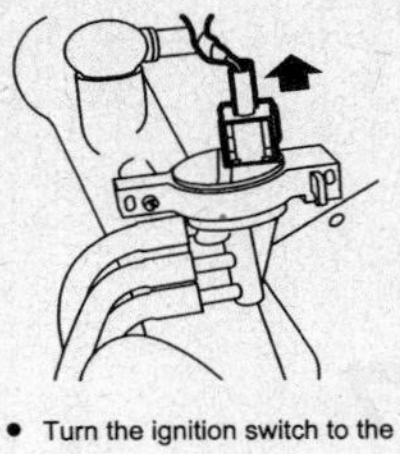

- Turn the ignition switch to the ON position.

- Connect test lamp 86 11 857 to pin 1 of the female connector and a good grounding point.

- The test lamp should light.

Everything OK?

YES

– Go to point 2.

NO

– The lead from +15 via fuse 26 to pin 1 of the female connector is faulty.

– Go to point 3.

SA1019900088020X

Fig. 103 Code P1662: Charge Air Control Valve Circuit Open/Short To Ground (Part 2 of 4). 9-5

2. Checking the valve's control module output

- Connect test lamp 86 11 857 to pins 1 and 2 of the female connector.

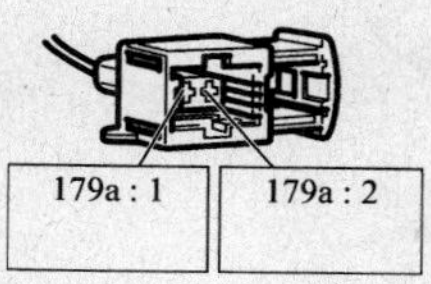

- Activate:
- Charge air control valve (Trionic): 100%

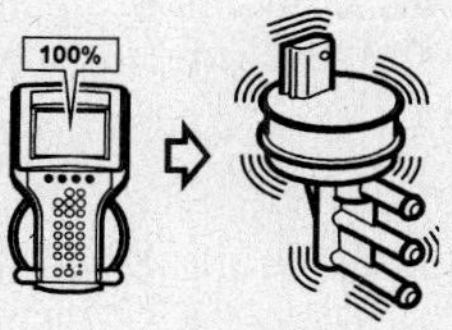

- The test lamp should light

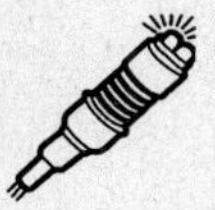

Everything OK?

YES

- Change: Charge air control valve
- Go to point 3.

NO

- The lead from pin 13 of the control module to pin 2 of the female connector is faulty.
- Go to point 3.

3. Final check

- Clear the diagnostic trouble codes in all systems.

- Carry out a driving cycle:
- Drive the car under varying engine loads and at different engine rpm for five minutes.

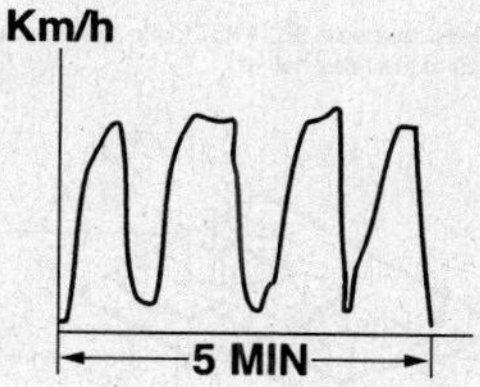

SA1019900088030X

Fig. 103 Code P1662: Charge Air Control Valve Circuit Open/Short To Ground (Part 3 of 4). 9-5

- Evaluate the driving cycle:
- Check that the diagnostic trouble code has not recurred.

Everything OK?

YES

- The steps taken to rectify the fault were correct.

NO

- See "**Engine Control Module (ECM)**" under "**Component Replacement**"

SA1019900088040X

Fig. 103 Code P1662: Charge Air Control Valve Circuit Open/Short To Ground (Part 4 of 4). 9-5

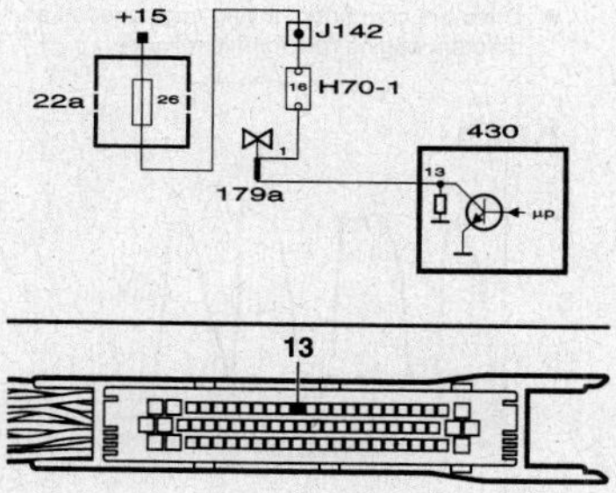

Fault symptoms

- CHECK ENGINE comes on after two driving cycles.
- Torque too low.

Conditions

The following conditions apply for this DTC:

- Engine has started and main relay voltage exceeds 10 V.
- Output voltage above 2 V when output is active.
- Conditions are met for 10 periods which must occur within 60 seconds (DTC normally generated after 0.3 seconds but can sometimes take much longer).

Diagnostic help

Fault diagnosis concerns electrical faults in connecting cables or in the valve.

Diagnostic tool functions related to this fault are:

- Activating the valve output.

See also the description of activating functions under "Fault diagnosis, general" for more information.

Checking the wiring harness

Jiggle the leads and in-line connectors at various points and in different directions to detect any intermittent breaks or short circuits in the wiring. Observe the multimeter, test lamp or diagnostic tool while doing this.

Diagnostic procedure

See Code P1662.

SA1019900089000X

Fig. 104 Code P1663: Charge Air Control Valve Circuit Short To B+. 9-5

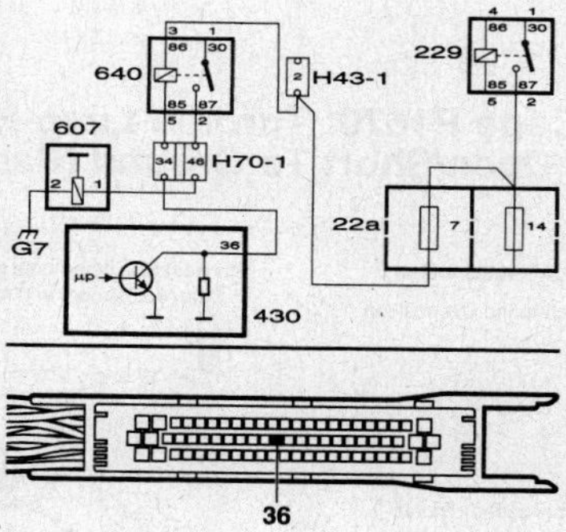

Fault symptoms

- CHECK ENGINE comes on after two driving cycles.
- Throttle control may go into mechanical limp-home mode, and P1251, P1260 or P1263 could then be generated as a secondary fault.

Conditions

The following conditions apply for this DTC:

- Engine has started and main relay voltage exceeds 10 V.
- Output voltage is below 2 V when the output is inactive.
- Conditions are met for 1 second.

Diagnostic help

Fault diagnosis concerns electrical faults in connecting cables or in the relay.

See also the description of activating functions under "Fault diagnosis, general" for more information.

Checking the wiring harness

Jiggle the leads and in-line connectors at various points and in different directions to detect any intermittent breaks or short circuits in the wiring. Observe the multimeter, test lamp or diagnostic tool while doing this.

SA1019900090010X

Fig. 105 Code P1670: Throttle Limp-Home Relay Coil Circuit Open/Short To Ground (Part 1 of 5). 9-5

Diagnostic procedure

1. Checking the relay power supply.

- Remove component: Relay, limp-home solenoid

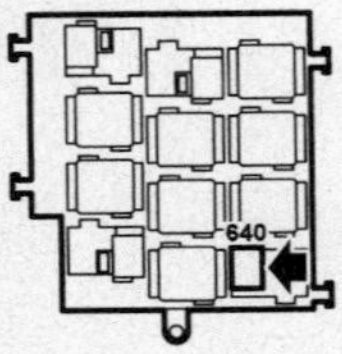

- Turn the ignition switch to the ON position.

- Connect test lamp 86 11 857 to pin 3 (86) of the relay holder and a good grounding point.

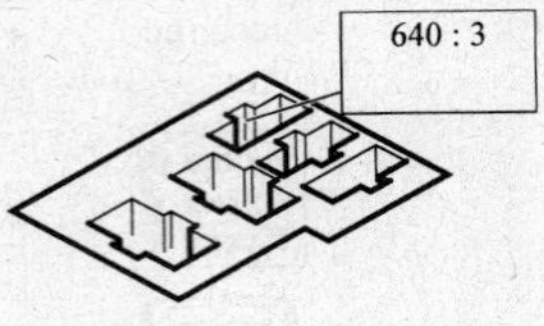

- The test lamp should light.

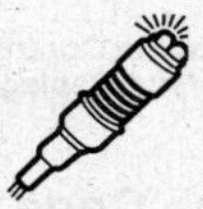

Everything OK?
YES
- Go to point 2.

NO
- The lead from fuse 7 to pin 3 (86) of the relay holder is faulty.
- Go to point 3.

SA1019900090020X

Fig. 105 Code P1670: Throttle Limp-Home Relay Coil Circuit Open/Short To Ground (Part 2 of 5). 9-5

2. Checking the relay's control module output

- Unplug the throttle body connector so that the control module will generate a diagnostic trouble code. The limp-home relay will then be activated next time the ignition is switched on.

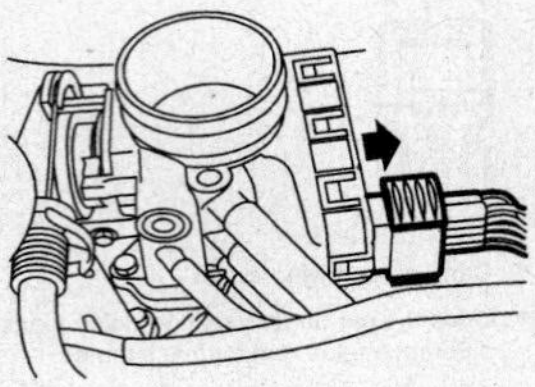

- Connect test lamp 86 11 857 to pin 3 (86) and pin 5 (85) of the relay holder.

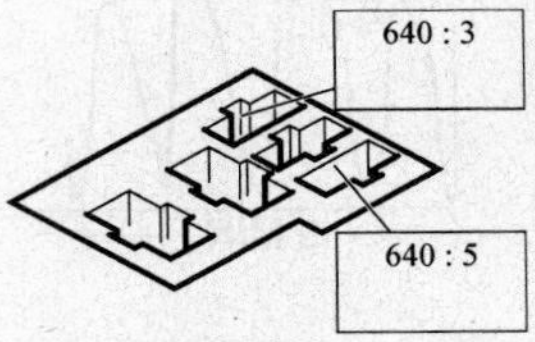

- Turn the ignition switch to the OFF position.

- Turn the ignition switch to the ON position.

- The test lamp should flash 5 times.

Everything OK?
YES
- Change: Relay, limp-home solenoid
- Go to point 3.

NO
- The lead from pin 36 of the control module to pin 5 (85) of the relay holder is faulty.
- Go to point 3.

SA1019900090030X

Fig. 105 Code P1670: Throttle Limp-Home Relay Coil Circuit Open/Short To Ground (Part 3 of 5). 9-5

3. Resetting the limp-home mechanism

- Turn the ignition switch to the ON position.

- Clear diagnostic trouble codes: Trionic

- Turn the ignition switch to the OFF position.

- Reset the limp-home mechanism as described in the 'Adjustment and replacement' section.

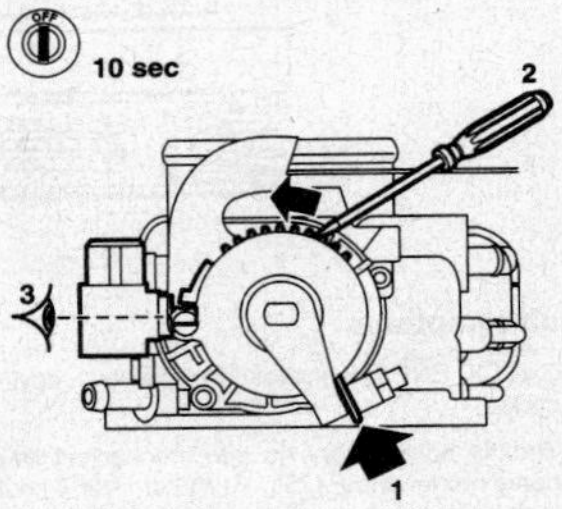

- Clear the diagnostic trouble codes in all systems.

SA1019900090040X

Fig. 105 Code P1670: Throttle Limp-Home Relay Coil Circuit Open/Short To Ground (Part 4 of 5). 9-5

- Carry out a driving cycle:
- Drive the car under varying engine loads and at different engine rpm for five minutes.

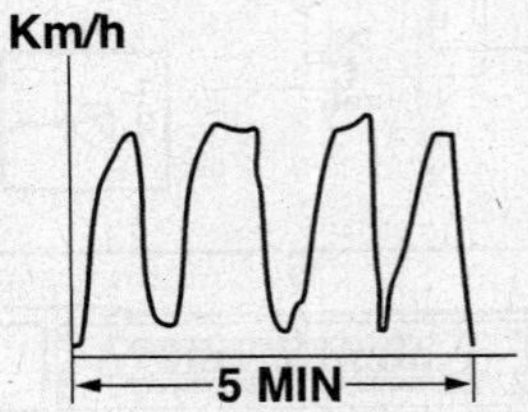

- Evaluate the driving cycle:
- Check that the diagnostic trouble code has not recurred.

Everything OK?
YES
- The steps taken to rectify the fault were correct.

NO
- See **"Engine Control Module (ECM)"** under **"Component Replacement"**

SA1019900090050X

Fig. 105 Code P1670: Throttle Limp-Home Relay Coil Circuit Open/Short To Ground (Part 5 of 5). 9-5

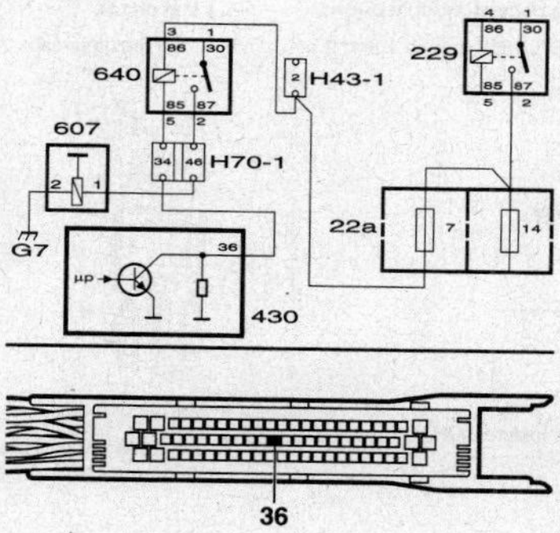

Fault symptoms

- CHECK ENGINE comes on after two driving cycles.

Conditions

The following conditions apply for this DTC:

- Engine has started and main relay voltage exceeds 10 V.
- Output voltage above 2 V when output is active.
- Conditions are met for 1 second.

Diagnostic help

Fault diagnosis concerns electrical faults in connecting cables or in the relay.

Diagnostic tool functions related to this fault are:

- Activation of output for relay, limp-home solenoid.

See also the description of activating functions under "Fault diagnosis, general" for more information.

Diagnostic procedure

See Code P1670.

SA1019900091000X

Fig. 106 Code P1671: Throttle Limp-Home Relay Coil Circuit Short To B+. 9-5

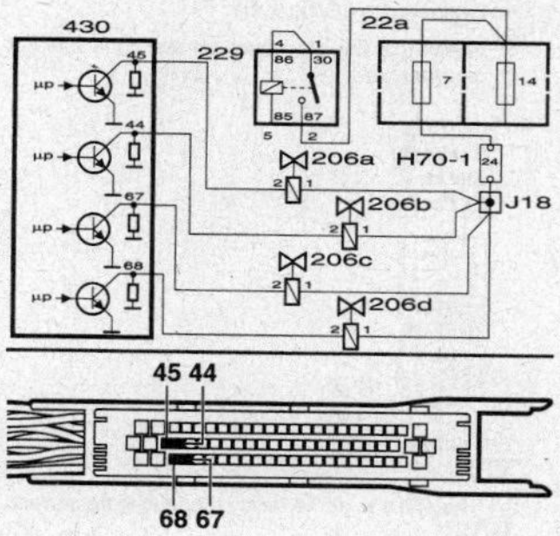

Fault symptoms

- Engine misfires or will not start.

Conditions

The following conditions apply for this DTC:

- Crankshaft rotating and main relay voltage exceeds 10 V.
- Voltage on one of the outputs is below 2 V when the output is inactive, or above 2 V when the output is active.
- Conditions are met for 1 second.

Diagnostic help

Fault diagnosis concerns electrical faults in connecting cables or in one of the valves.

Diagnostic tool functions related to this fault are:

- Activation of outputs for all valves.

See also the description of activating functions under "Fault diagnosis, general" for more information.

Checking the wiring harness

Jiggle the leads and in-line connectors at various points and in different directions to detect any intermittent breaks or short circuits in the wiring. Observe the multimeter, test lamp or diagnostic tool while doing this.

SA1019900092010X

Fig. 107 Code P1676: Injector Circuit Open/Short To Ground Or B+ (Part 1 of 5). 9-5

Diagnostic procedure

1. Checking the fuse

- Check fuse 7 and change it, if necessary.

- Turn the ignition switch to the ON position.

- Activate all injectors, one at a time, to identify the defective circuit. Listen for the sound made by the injectors.

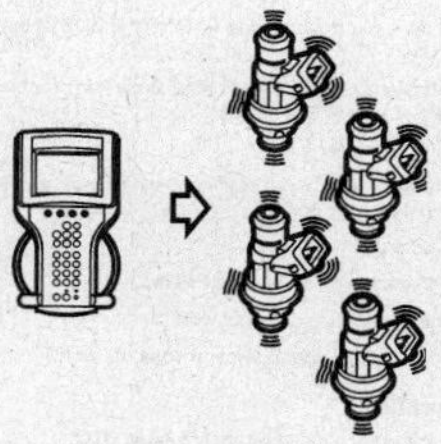

NO INJECTOR CAN BE HEARD.

- The lead from fuse 7 to crimp connection J18 is faulty.
- Go to point 4.

ONE INJECTOR CANNOT BE HEARD.

- Go to point 2.

SA1019900092020X

Fig. 107 Code P1676: Injector Circuit Open/Short To Ground Or B+ (Part 2 of 5). 9-5

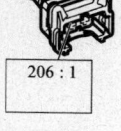

2. Checking the valve's power supply

- Unplug the connector from the injector concerned.

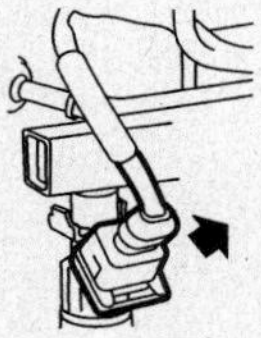

- Connect test lamp 86 11 857 to pin 1 of the female connector and a good grounding point.

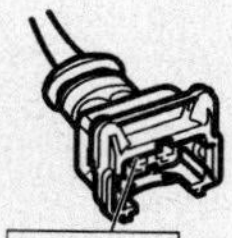

206 : 1

- The test lamp should light.

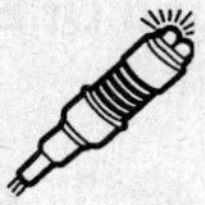

Everything OK?

YES

- Go to point 3.

NO

- The lead from crimp connection J18 to pin 1 of the female connector is faulty.
- Go to point 4.

SA1019900092030X

Fig. 107 Code P1676: Injector Circuit Open/Short To Ground Or B+ (Part 3 of 5). 9-5

- Evaluate the driving cycle:
- Check that the diagnostic trouble code has not recurred.

Everything OK?

YES

– The steps taken to rectify the fault were correct.

NO

– See **"Engine Control Module (ECM)" under "Component Replacement"**

SA1019900092050X

Fig. 107 Code P1676: Injector Circuit Open/Short To Ground Or B+ (Part 5 of 5). 9-5

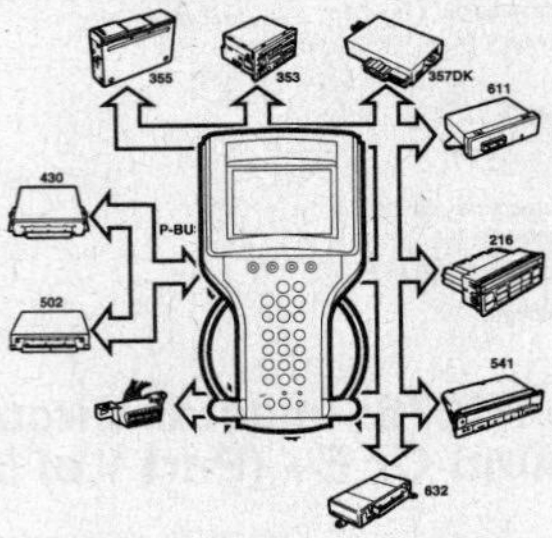

Fault symptoms

Some of the following symptoms may perhaps be observed:

- Diagnostic trouble code P1921 or P1902 in the TCM.
- Additional diagnostic trouble codes in Trionic (P1902, P1923 or P1908).
- A/C not working.
- Radiator fan runs continuously or not at all (coolant may boil).
- Radio does not work.
- Direction indicators do not work.
- Interior lighting does not work.
- Intermittent wiper operation does not work.

Conditions

The following conditions apply for this DTC:

- Engine has started and no communication for more than 10 seconds.

Diagnostic help

Fault diagnosis concerns intermittent electrical faults in the power supply for the sending control module or in a bus lead.

Checking the wiring harness

Jiggle the leads and in-line connectors at various points and in different directions to detect any intermittent breaks or short circuits in the wiring. Observe the multimeter, test lamp or diagnostic tool while doing this.

Diagnostic procedure

0. Reference

SA1019900093000X

Fig. 108 Code P1901: No Bus Data From DICE. 9-5

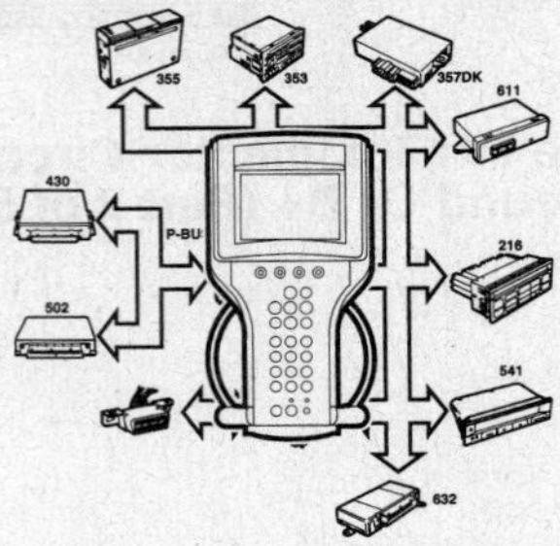

Fault symptoms

Some of the following symptoms may perhaps be observed:

- Additional diagnostic trouble codes in the Trionic (P1901, P1923 or P1908).
- Additional diagnostic trouble code in the TCM (P1921).
- Engine fails to start.
- Cruise Control does not work.
- Radio does not work.
- Central locking system does not work.
- Remote control does not work.

Conditions

The following conditions apply for this DTC:

- Engine has started and no communication for more than 10 seconds.

Diagnostic help

Fault diagnosis concerns intermittent electrical faults in the power supply for the sending control module or in a bus lead.

Checking the wiring harness

Jiggle the leads and in-line connectors at various points and in different directions to detect any intermittent breaks or short circuits in the wiring. Observe the multimeter, test lamp or diagnostic tool while doing this.

Diagnostic procedure

0. Reference

SA1019900094000X

Fig. 109 Code P1902: No Bus Data From TWICE. 9-5

3. Checking the valve's control module output

- Connect test lamp 86 11 857 to pins 1 and 2 of the female connector.

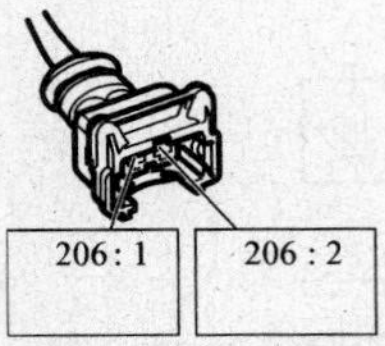

- Activate: Activate the injector (ON)

- The test lamp should light

Everything OK?

YES

– Change: Injector

– Go to point 4.

NO

– The lead from the control module output concerned to pin 2 of the female connector is faulty.

– Go to point 4.

4. Final check

- Clear the diagnostic trouble codes in all systems.

- Carry out a driving cycle:
- Drive the car under varying engine loads and at different engine rpm for five minutes.

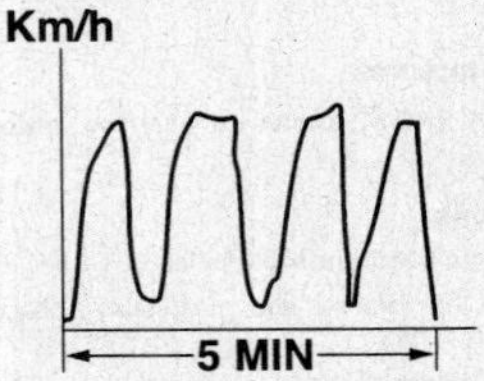

SA1019900092040X

Fig. 107 Code P1676: Injector Circuit Open/Short To Ground Or B+ (Part 4 of 5). 9-5

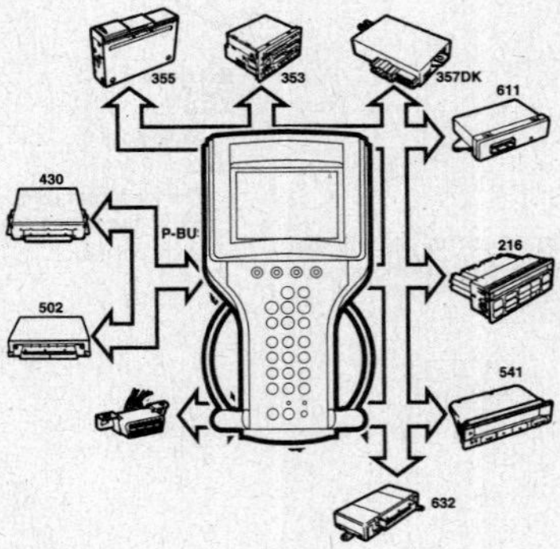

Fault symptoms

Some of the following symptoms may perhaps be observed:

- Additional diagnostic trouble codes in the TCM (P1902 or P1923).
- Additional diagnostic trouble codes in the Trionic (P1901, P1902 or P1923).
- Engine fails to start.
- Cruise Control does not work.
- A/C not working.
- Radiator fan runs continuously.
- Main instrument unit gauges not working.

Conditions

The following conditions apply for this DTC:

- Engine has started and no communication for more than 3 seconds.

Diagnostic help

Fault diagnosis concerns intermittent electrical faults in the power supply for the sending control module or in a bus lead.

Checking the wiring harness

Jiggle the leads and in-line connectors at various points and in different directions to detect any intermittent breaks or short circuits in the wiring. Observe the multimeter, test lamp or diagnostic tool while doing this.

Diagnostic procedure

0. Reference

SA1019900095000X

Fig. 110 Code P1908: No Bus Data From MIU. 9-5

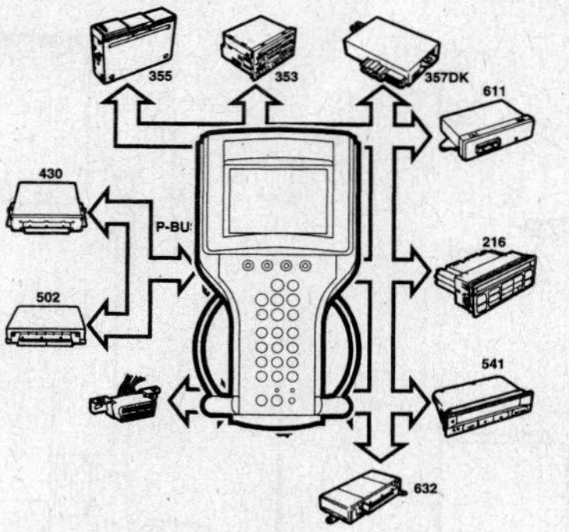

Fault symptoms

Some of the following symptoms may perhaps be observed:

- Diagnostic trouble code P1921 or P1902 in TCM (if the TCM can be contacted).
- Additional diagnostic trouble codes in the Trionic (P1901, P1902 or P1908).
- Engine fails to start.
- Automatic transmission in limp-home mode.
- CHECK GEARBOX

Conditions

The following conditions apply for this DTC:

- The TCM has been present on the bus at some time previously.
- Engine has started and no communication for more than 3 seconds.

Diagnostic help

Fault diagnosis concerns intermittent electrical faults in the power supply for the sending control module or in a bus lead.

Checking the wiring harness

Jiggle the leads and in-line connectors at various points and in different directions to detect any intermittent breaks or short circuits in the wiring. Observe the multimeter, test lamp or diagnostic tool while doing this.

Diagnostic procedure

0. Reference

SA1019900096000X

Fig. 111 Code P1923: No Bus Data From TCM. 9-5

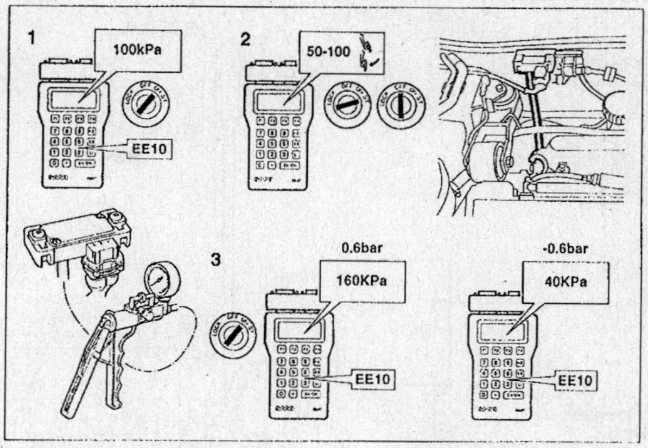

Fault symptom

MIL (CHECK ENGINE lamp) on, performance down (basic charging pressure only)

Diagnostic procedure

1 Check the operation of the manifold absolute pressure (MAP) sensor by entering command code EE10 on the ISAT scan tool.

At atmospheric pressure the correct pressure should be 100 kPa. If it is not, proceed to point 5.

2 If the pressure is correct, start the engine and check whether it changes at different throttle openings.

If not, inspect the hose between the MAP sensor and the intake manifold.

3 If the hose is OK, connect pressure measuring equipment 8393514 and a pressure/vacuum pump to the hose. With the ignition switch in the Drive position, pump up a pressure of 0.6 bar. Enter command code EE10 on the ISAT scan tool once again and check the result, which should now be 160 kPa.

Create a negative pressure of -0.6 bar and repeat the checking procedure. The ISAT scan tool should now show 40 kPa.

If the wrong values are obtained, continue as described below.

SA1029100103010X

Fig. 112 Codes P0105, P0106, P0107 & P0108: Manifold Absolute Pressure Sensor (Part 1 of 3). 9000

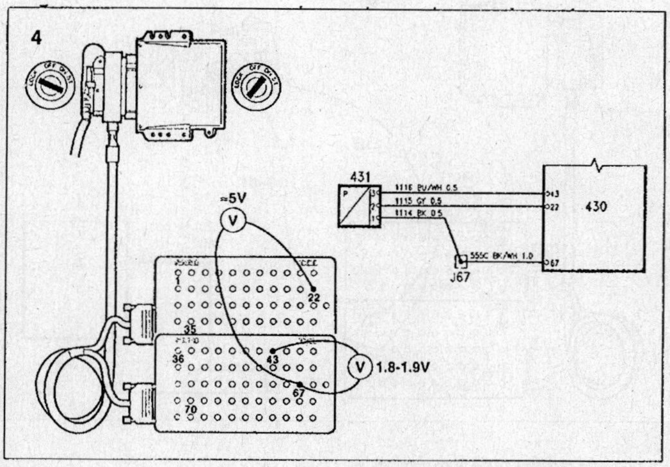

4 Switch off the ignition and connect a BOB.

With the ignition switch in the Drive position, check the signal voltage on pin 22 by taking a measurement across 22 and 67. At atmospheric pressure the voltage should be about 1.8-1.9 V.

Also check that supply voltage is present on pin 43 by measuring across 43 and 67. The supply voltage should be about 5 V.

If the supply voltage is completely wrong or absent, replace the ECM.

SA1029100103020X

Fig. 112 Codes P0105, P0106, P0107 & P0108: Manifold Absolute Pressure Sensor (Part 2 of 3). 9000

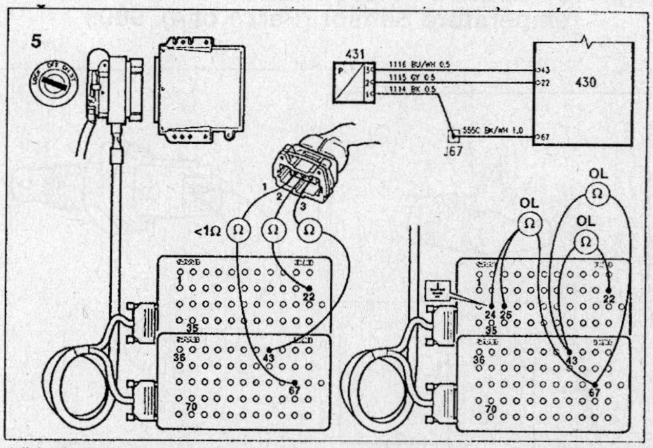

5 If the signal voltage is wrong or absent, switch off the ignition and disconnect the ECM from the test cable. Also unplug the connector from the MAP sensor.

Check the leads for continuity by measuring the resistance as follows:

- across pin 43 of the ECM and pin 3 of the MAP sensor connector
- across pin 22 of the ECM and pin 2 of the MAP sensor connector
- across pin 67 of the ECM and pin 1 of the MAP sensor connector

In every case the resistance should be less than 1 ohm.

Check the leads for continuity by measuring the resistance as follows:

- across pins 43 and 22 of the ECM
- across pins 67 and 43 of the ECM
- across pins 67 and 24/25 of the ECM

In every case the resistance should be "OL".

6 If the connectors and wiring are OK, replace the MAP sensor.

> **CONDITION**
> When road testing and checking the car after remedying a fault, vary the engine rpm for at least two minutes.

7 Erase any DTCs and drive the car to see whether the DTC is generated afresh. If it is, replace ECM.

SA1029100103030X

Fig. 112 Codes P0105, P0106, P0107 & P0108: Manifold Absolute Pressure Sensor (Part 3 of 3). 9000

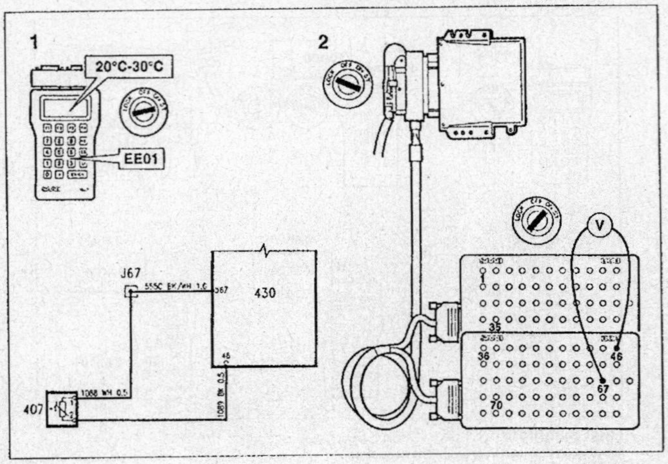

Fault symptom

MIL (CHECK ENGINE lamp) on, deterioration in adjustment of idling speed to compensate for load changes (e.g. engagement of A/C)

Diagnostic procedure

1 Check the operation of the intake air temperature (IAT) sensor by entering command code EE01 on the ISAT scan tool. Start the engine and read the temperature when it is idling. If the ambient temperature is +20°C, for instance, the ISAT scan tool should show a temperature of between +20° and +30°C.

If it does not, continue with the next point.

2 With the ignition switched off, connect a BOB to the ECM.

Turn the ignition switch to the Drive position and measure the signal voltage from the IAT sensor across pins 46 and 67. Depending on the temperature, the voltage should be as shown in the table

SA1029100104010X

Fig. 113 Codes P0110, P0112 & P0113: Intake Air Temperature Sensor (Part 1 of 4). 9000

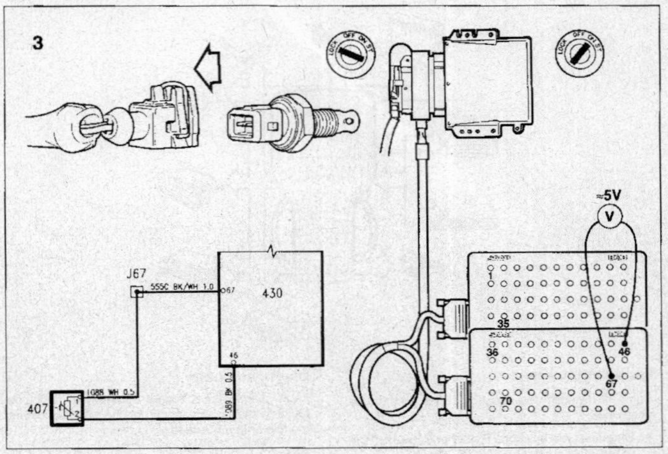

If the voltage is not in accordance with the table, continue as described below. If it is, continue with point 4.

3 Unplug the connector from the IAT sensor. With the ignition switch still in the Drive position, check the voltage once again across pins 46 and 67.

The correct voltage is about 5 V.

If the voltage measured differs from this figure, replace ECM.

C°	F°	Voltage (V)	Resistance (kohm)
-30	-22	approx. 4.5	20-30
-10	14	approx. 3.9	8.3-10.6
20	68	approx. 3.2	2.3-2.7
40	104	approx. 1.5	1.0-1.3
60	140	approx. 0.9	0.56-0.67
80	176	approx. 0.7	0.30-0.36

SA1029100104020X

Fig. 113 Codes P0110, P0112 & P0113: Intake Air Temperature Sensor (Part 2 of 4). 9000

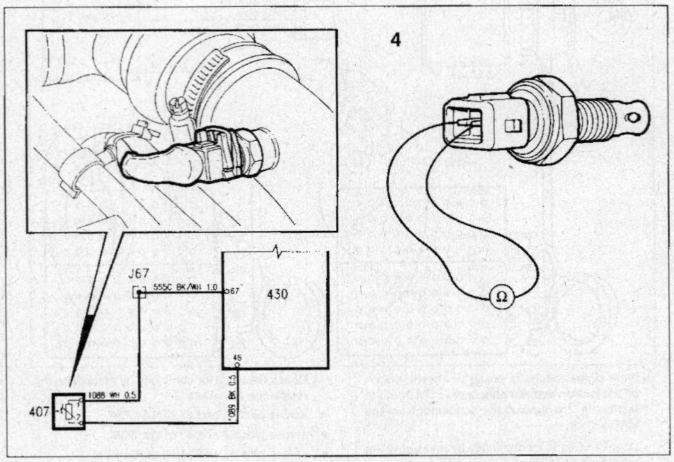

4 Check the resistance of the IAT sensor by taking a measurement across the connecting pins of the sensor.

The resistance should be as shown in the table.

If the resistance is not as shown in the table, fit a new intake air temperature sensor.

C°	F°	Voltage (V)	Resistance (kohm)
-30	-22	approx. 4.5	20-30
-10	14	approx. 3.9	8.3-10.6
20	68	approx. 3.2	2.3-2.7
40	104	approx. 1.5	1.0-1.3
60	140	approx. 0.9	0.56-0.67
80	176	approx. 0,7	0.30-0.36

SA1029100104030X

Fig. 113 Codes P0110, P0112 & P0113: Intake Air Temperature Sensor (Part 3 of 4). 9000

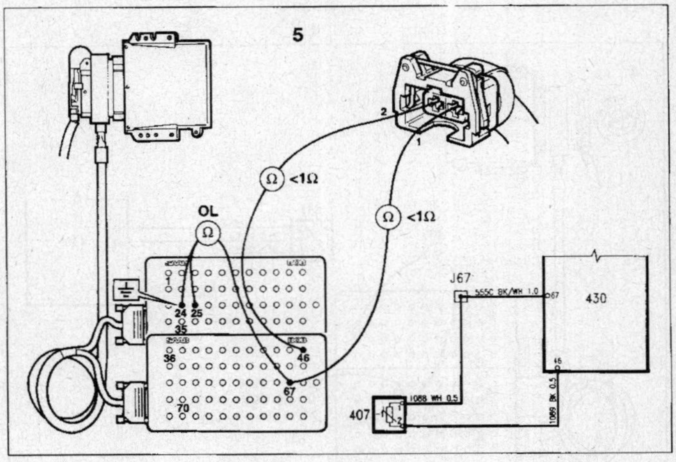

5 Check the continuity of the leads from pins 46 and 67 of the ECM to pins 2 and 1 of the IAT sensor's connector.

Also check that the power ground and signal ground are well separated (resistance OL)

CONDITION

A DTC will be generated if the signal voltage is lower than 0.06 V or higher than 4.96 V for longer than five seconds.

6 Erase any DTCs and drive the car to see whether the fault code is generated afresh. If it is, replace ECM.

SA1029100104040X

Fig. 113 Codes P0110, P0112 & P0113: Intake Air Temperature Sensor (Part 4 of 4). 9000

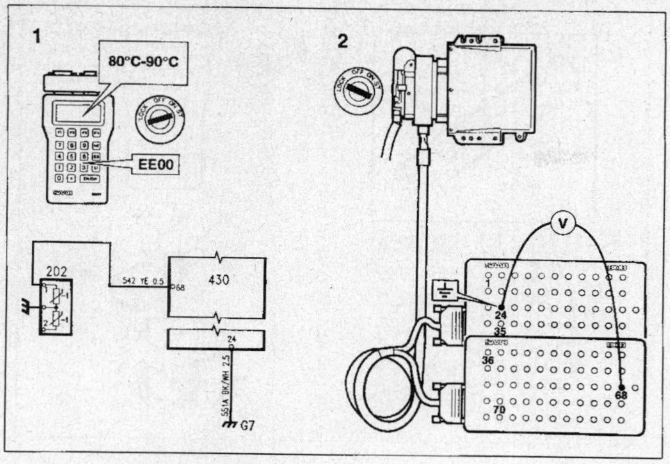

Fault symptom

MIL (CHECK ENGINE lamp) on, poor drivability

Diagnostic procedure

1 Check the operation of the engine coolant temperature (ECT) sensor by entering command code EE00 on the ISAT scan tool.

If it is working correctly, the ISAT scan tool should show a temperature of about 80-95°C when the engine is warmed-up.

2 With the ignition switched off, connect a BOB to the ECM.

Check the signal voltage from the ECT sensor by taking a measurement across pins 68 and 24.

Depending on engine temperature, the voltage should be as shown in the table.

C°	F°	Voltage (V)	Resistance (kohm)
-30	-22	approx. 4.5	20-30
-10	14	approx. 3.9	8.3-10.6
20	68	approx. 3.2	2.3-2.7
40	104	approx. 1.5	1.0-1.3
60	140	approx. 0.9	0.56-0.67
80	176	approx. 0.7	0.30-0.36

SA1029100105010X

Fig. 114 Codes P0115, P0117 & P0118: Engine Coolant Temperature Sensor (Part 1 of 3). 9000

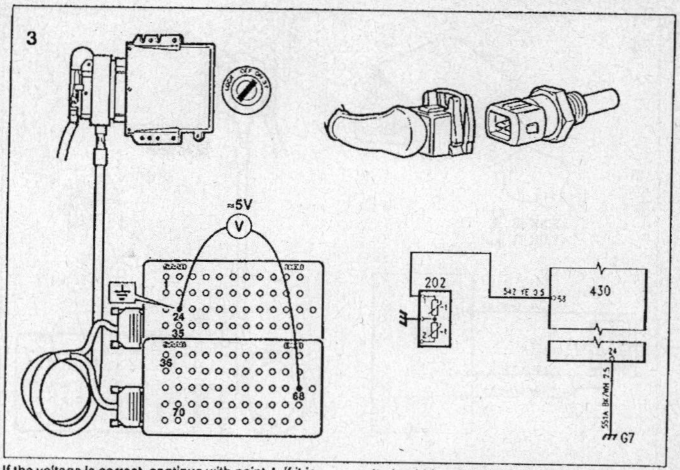

If the voltage is correct, continue with point 4. If it is not, continue as described below.

Note:

On cars equipped with TCS the engine coolant temperature sensor has two circuits, one for ETS and one for SFI. When diagnosing faults it is therefore important to remember that pin 1 corresponds to SFI and pin 2 to ETS.

3 With the ECT sensor's connector unplugged and with the ignition switch in the Drive position, check the voltage across pins 68 and 24 once again.

It should be about 5 V. If it is not, turn to page 149.

4 With the ignition switched off and the ECM unplugged, check the continuity of the lead between pin 68 of the ECM and pin 1 of the sensor's connector. Also check that the sensor body is in good connection with signal ground (24/25).

Remedy any faults in the wiring or continue with the next point.

SA1029100105020X

Fig. 114 Codes P0115, P0117 & P0118: Engine Coolant Temperature Sensor (Part 2 of 3). 9000

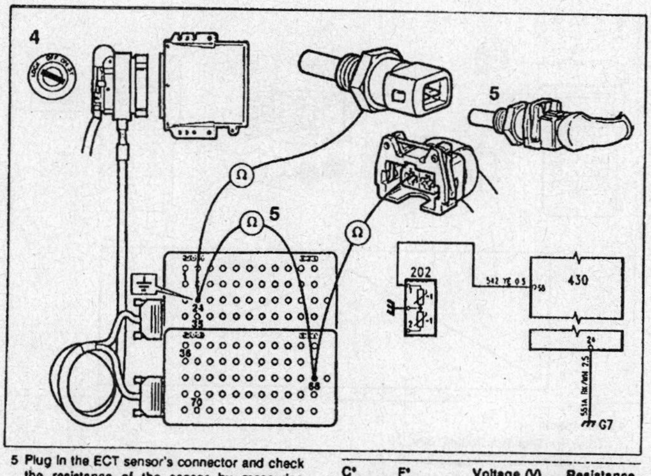

5 Plug in the ECT sensor's connector and check the resistance of the sensor by measuring across sockets 68 and 24 on the BOB.

The correct resistance should be as shown in the table.

If the resistance is not correct, replace the ECT sensor.

C°	F°	Voltage (V)	Resistance (kohm)
-30	-22	approx. 4.5	20-30
-10	14	approx. 3.9	8.3-10.6
20	68	approx. 3.2	2.3-2.7
40	104	approx. 1.5	1.0-1.3
60	140	approx. 0.9	0.56-0.67
80	176	approx. 0.7	0.30-0.36

CONDITION

A DTC will be generated if the signal voltage is lower than 0.06 V or higher than 4.70 V for at least five seconds.

6 Erase any DTCs and drive the car to check whether the DTC is generated afresh. If it is, replace ECM.

SA1029100105030X

Fig. 114 Codes P0115, P0117 & P0118: Engine Coolant Temperature Sensor (Part 3 of 3). 9000

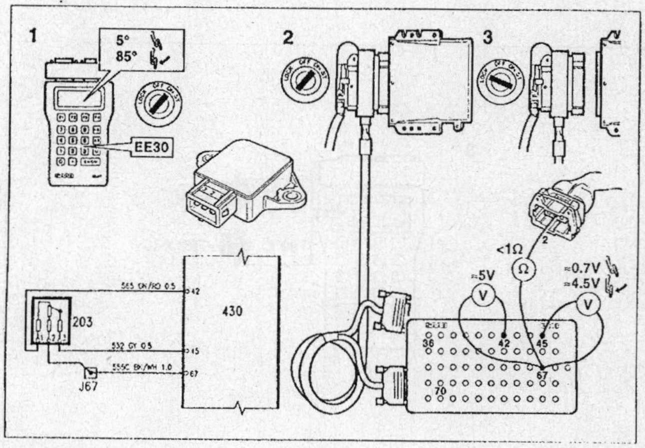

Fault symptom

MIL (CHECK ENGINE lamp) on, unsteady idling

Diagnostic procedure

1 Check the operation of the throttle position (TP) sensor by entering command code EE30 on the ISAT scan tool.

With the ignition switch in the Drive position, check that the correct throttle angle is displayed: about 5° when idling and gradually increasing as the throttle is opened to about 85° at wide open throttle.

2 Switch off the ignition and connect a BOB to the ECM.

Check the signal voltage from the TP sensor by taking a measurement across pins 45 and 67. The correct voltage is about 0.7 V in the idling position and about 4.5 V in the wide open throttle position. If the voltage is not correct, continue with point 4.

Also check the supply voltage to the sensor by taking a measurement across pins 42 and 67. The correct voltage here is about 5 V. If the voltage is not correct, continue with the next point.

3 Switch off the ignition and disconnect the ECM. Also unplug the connector from the TP sensor. Check that there is a signal ground connection between the sensor and the ECM by measuring the resistance across socket 67 on the BOB and pin 2 of the TP sensor connector. The resistance should be less than 1 ohm.

If the resistance is not correct, remedy leads and/or connectors.

If the wiring is OK, replace ECM.

SA1029100106010X

Fig. 115 Codes P0120, P0121, P0122 & P0123: Throttle Position Sensor (Part 1 of 2). 9000

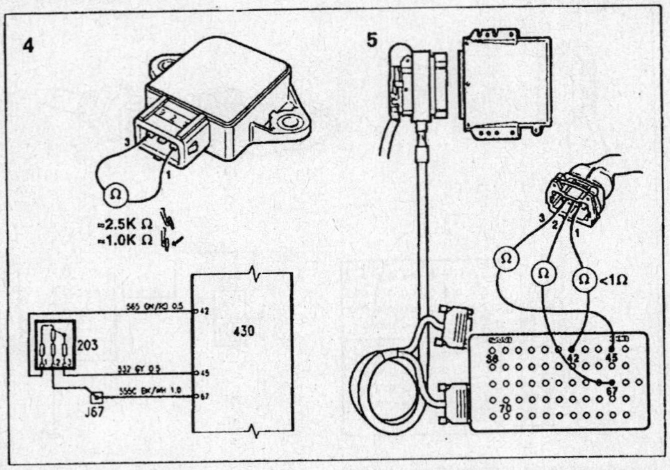

4 Check the resistance by taking a measurement straight across pins 1 and 3 of the TP sensor. The resistance should decrease gradually, without jumps or interruptions, from about 2.5 kohm in the idling position to about 1.0 kohm in the wide open throttle position.

If the resistance is not correct, replace the TP sensor.

If the TP sensor is OK, continue with the next point.

5 Check the wiring for continuity between the ECM and the TP sensor. Remedy any faults in the wiring.

If the wiring is OK, continue as described below.

CONDITION

For a DTC to be generated, the throttle signal must be less than 0.20 V or more than 4.96 V for at least five seconds.

6 Erase any DTCs and drive the car to see whether any DTC is generated afresh. If this is the case, replace ECM.

SA1029100106020X

Fig. 115 Codes P0120, P0121, P0122 & P0123: Throttle Position Sensor (Part 2 of 2). 9000

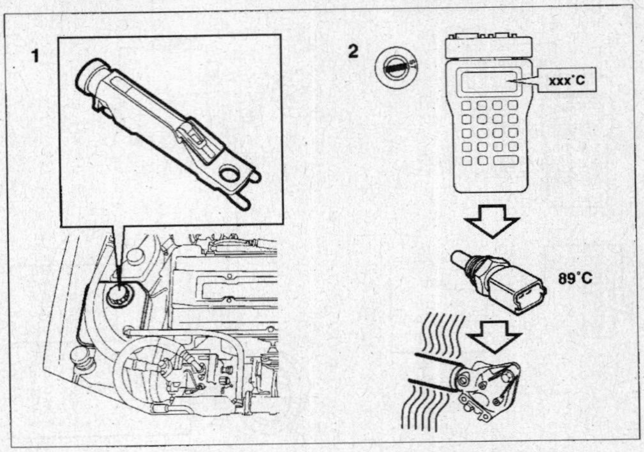

Diagnostic procedure

1 Check the anti–freeze

At ambient temperatures below 0°C (32°F), check the freezing point of the coolant.

Is the freezing point OK?

YES Continue with point 2.

NO Rectify the fault and proceed to point 4.

2 Check the thermostat

The engine should be cold enough to allow a hand to be placed on the cylinder head without discomfort.

- Connect an ISAT scan tool and contact the EDU.
- Select "READ VALUES".
- Select "COOLANT TEMPERATURE".
- Start the engine and warm it up at idling speed. Feel the upper radiator hose, near the thermostat, to check that it quickly becomes hot when the coolant reaches a temperature of about 89°C (192°F) and the thermostat opens.

Following this, the coolant temperature should remain fairly constant at about 89°C (192°F) for a minute or so.

Is the thermostat OK?

YES Continue with point 3.

NO Change the thermostat and proceed to point 4.

SA1029600194010X

Fig. 116 Code P0125: Engine Coolant Temperature Sensor (Part 1 of 3). 9000

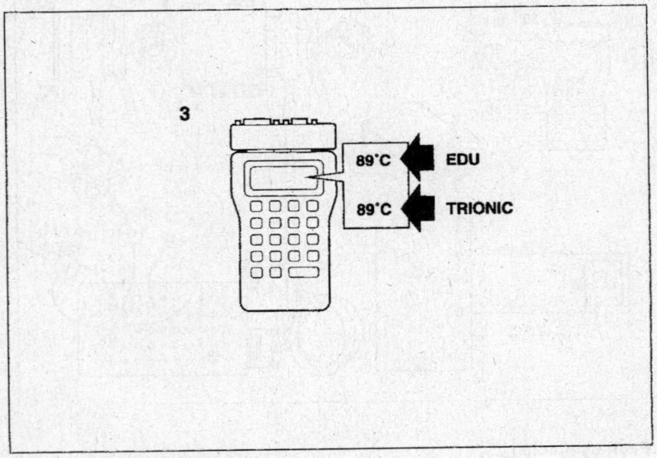

3 Check the coolant temperature sensor

- Engine running at idling speed.
- Connect an ISAT scan tool.
- Contact the Trionic system.
- Select "READ FUNCTIONS".
- Select "COOLANT TEMPERATURE".
- Note the temperature.
- Contact the EDU.
- Select "READ VALUES".
- Select "COOLANT TEMPERATURE".
- Note the temperature.

The difference between the two temperature readings should not be more than 5°C (9°F).

Are the readings OK?

YES Continue with point 4.

NO See fault diagnosis for diagnostic trouble codes P0115, P0117 and P0118.

SA1029600194020X

Fig. 116 Code P0125: Engine Coolant Temperature Sensor (Part 2 of 3). 9000

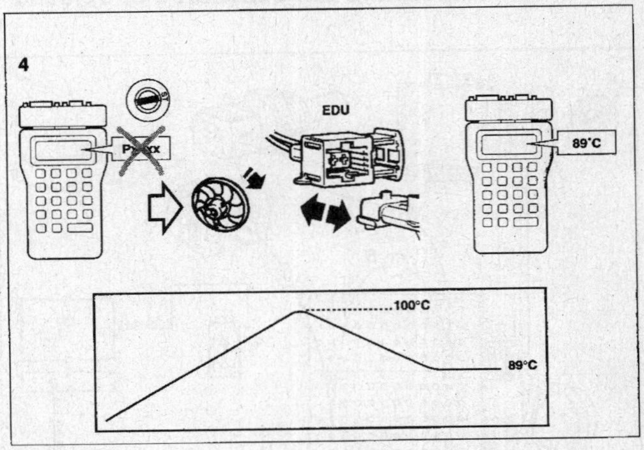

4 Final check:

- Clear the diagnostic trouble code.
- Implementation of driving cycle:
  Warm up the engine at idling speed until the radiator fan cuts in.
- Evaluation of driving cycle:
  Unplug the temperature sensor's connector from the EDU so that the radiator fan will run continuously.
  Check that the coolant temperature in the Trionic system drops to and stabilizes at about 89°C (192°F).

Is the function OK?

YES Replace ECM.

NO The remedial measure taken was correct.

- Clear the diagnostic trouble code for the temperature sensor in the EDU.

SA1029600194030X

Fig. 116 Code P0125: Engine Coolant Temperature Sensor (Part 3 of 3). 9000

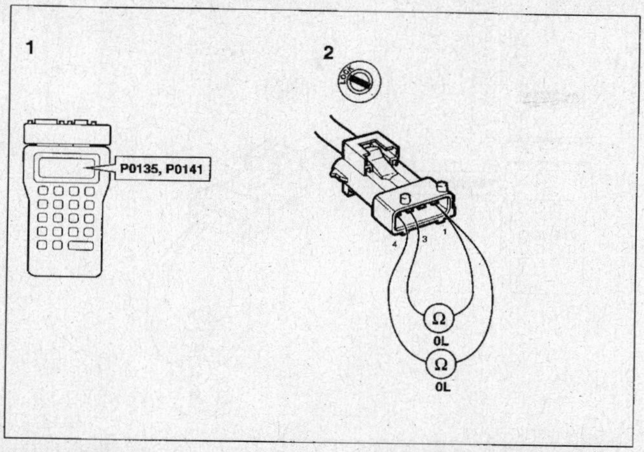

Diagnostic procedure

1 Check additional diagnostic trouble codes in the Trionic system

– Obtain readouts of all diagnostic trouble codes using the ISAT scan tool.

Are P0132 and P0138 present?

YES Continue with point 2.

NO Continue with point 3.

2 One of the oxygen sensor leads connected to electronic control module pin 23, 70 or 47 is short–circuited to battery positive (B+) in the wiring harness or in one of the oxygen sensors.

Check the insulation of the oxygen sensors.

– Unplug the 4–pin connectors of both oxygen sensors.

– Check the resistance of both sensors
- pins 1–3 ____________________OL (OverLoad = infinite resistance)
- pins 1–4____________________OL (OverLoad = infinite resistance)

Are all readings OK?

YES Rectify the lead between the connectors of both sensors and pin 23, 70 or 47 of the electronic control module and then proceed to point 4.

NO Change the relevant oxygen sensor and proceed to point 4.

SA1029600195010X

Fig. 117 Codes P0130, P0131, P0132 & P0133: Front Heated Oxygen Sensor (Part 1 of 3). 9000

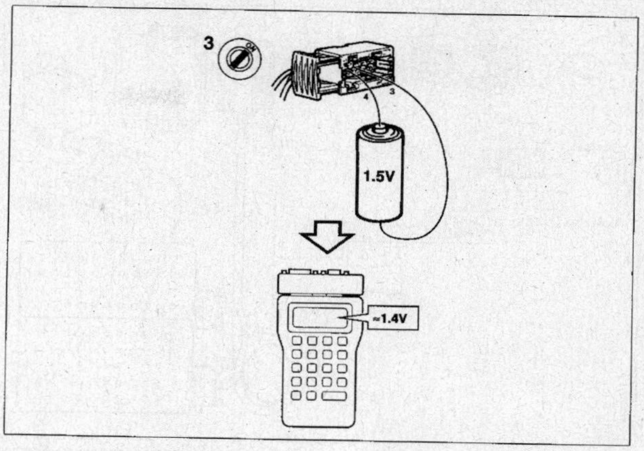

3 Check the oxygen sensor's electrical interfaces

– Unplug the oxygen sensor's 4–pinconnector.

– Replace the sensor with a conventional 1.5 V battery in good condition.

– Connect the battery's positive (+) pole to pin 4 of the connector.

– Connect the battery's – positive (+) pole to pin 3 of the connector.

– Ignition switch in ON position.

– Connect an ISAT scan tool.

– Select "READ FUNCTIONS".

– Select "O2S 1".

Does the ISAT scan tool show about "1.4 V"?

YES Change the oxygen sensor and continue with point 4.

NO Check the leads between:

pin 4 of the connector and pin 23 of the control module and between

pin 3 of the connector and pin 47 of the control module for continuity or shorting and repair or replace them as necessary.

Then continue with point 4.

SA1029600195020X

Fig. 117 Codes P0130, P0131, P0132 & P0133: Front Heated Oxygen Sensor (Part 2 of 3). 9000

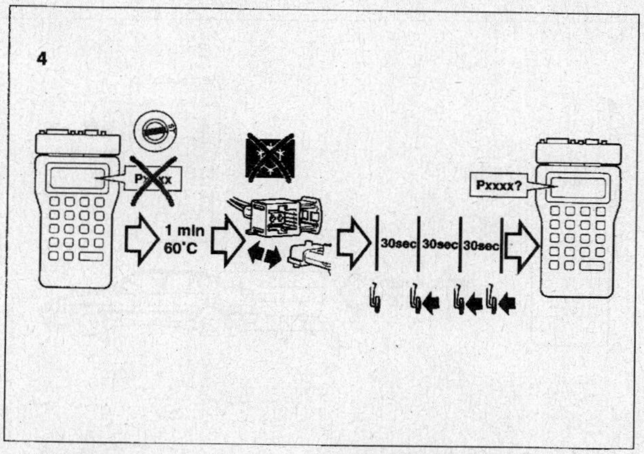

4 Final check:

– Clear the diagnostic trouble code.

– Implementation of driving cycle:
- Ignition switch in the ON position, A/C switched off and temperature sensor unplugged from the EDU so that the radiator fan runs continuously.
- Start the engine and run it at idling speed until the temperature of the coolant exceeds 60°C (140°F) or for at least 1 minute if this temperature is reached earlier.
- Depress the accelerator for a second or so and then let the engine run at idling speed for 30 seconds. Do this twice again.

– Evaluation of driving cycle:

– Connect an ISAT scan tool.

– Select "ON/OFF".

– Select "DIAGNOSTIC STATUS".

– Select "O2S 1".

Does the ISAT scan tool show "NOT READY"?

YES Repeat the driving cycle.

NO Check whether the diagnostic trouble code has recurred.

Has the diagnostic trouble code recurred?

YES Replace PCM.

NO The remedial measure taken was correct.

– Plug the temperature sensor into the EDU.

– Clear the diagnostic trouble code for the temperature sensor in the EDU.

SA1029600195030X

Fig. 117 Codes P0130, P0131, P0132 & P0133: Front Heated Oxygen Sensor (Part 3 of 3). 9000

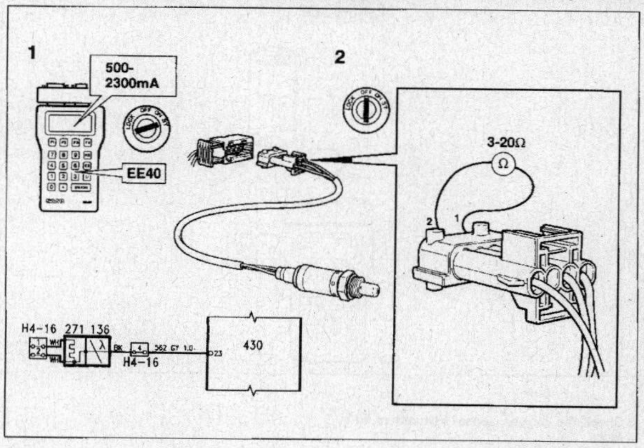

Fault symptom

MIL (CHECK ENGINE lamp) on

Diagnostic procedure

1 Connect an ISAT scan tool. Start the engine and run it at idling speed.

Enter command code EE40 and check the preheating current consumption. The current may vary between about 500 and 2300 mA.

If the current consumption is OK, continue with point 4. If it is not OK, continue with the next point.

2 Switch off the engine. Unplug the connector (H4-16) in the wiring between the sensor and the car's wiring harness and check the resistance across pins 1 and 2 of the sensor's connector.

The correct resistance is 3-20 ohms.

If the resistance is not correct, replace the heated oxygen sensor.

If the resistance is OK, continue with the next point.

SA1029100109010X

Fig. 118 Code P0135: Preheating Of Heated Oxygen Sensor (Part 1 of 2). 9000

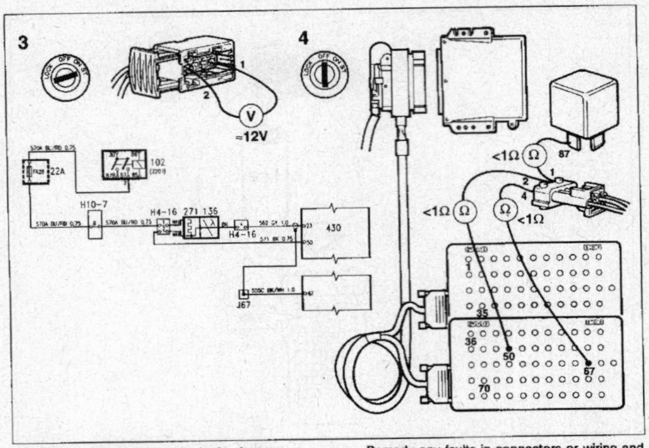

3 Start the engine and check whether battery positive voltage is present across pins 1 and 2 of connector H4-16 on the supply side.

If battery positive voltage is present, turn to page 149 for further diagnostic instructions.

If there is no voltage, check whether battery positive voltage is present on pin 87B of the pump relay, see points 4 and 5 on page 123.

If battery positive voltage is present on pin 87B of the pump relay, continue by checking the wiring as described below.

4 Switch off the engine and connect a BOB to the ECM wiring harness. The ECM should be disconnected.

Check the wiring for continuity from the sensor connector and ground screening to pins 50 and 67 of the ECM and also between pin 87B of the pump relay and the connector of the sensor.

Remedy any faults in connectors or wiring and continue as described below.

CONDITION

With the engine running, preheating should be activated for longer than 60 seconds or current consumption should be lower than 500 mA or higher than 2300 mA for longer than 60 seconds.

5 Erase any DTCs and drive the car to see whether a DTC is generated afresh. If it is, replace ECM.

SA1029100109020X

Fig. 118 Code P0135: Preheating Of Heated Oxygen Sensor (Part 2 of 2). 9000

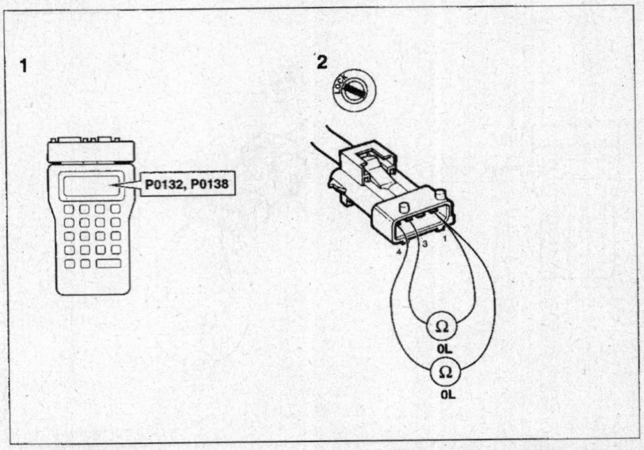

Diagnostic procedure

1 Check additional diagnostic trouble codes in the Trionic system

– Obtain readouts of all diagnostic trouble codes using the ISAT scan tool.

Are P0132 and P0138 present?

YES Continue with point 2.

NO Continue with point 3.

2 One of the oxygen sensor leads connected to electronic control module pin 23, 70 or 47 is short–circuited to battery positive (B+) in the wiring harness or in one of the oxygen sensors.

Check the insulation of the oxygen sensors.

– Unplug the 4–pin connectors of both oxygen sensors.
– Check the resistance of both sensors
  - pins 1–3 ____ OL (OverLoad = infinite resistance)
  - pins 1–4 ____ OL (OverLoad = infinite resistance)

Are all readings OK?

YES Rectify the lead between the connectors of both sensors and pin 23, 70 or 47 of the electronic control module and then proceed to point 4.

NO Change the relevant oxygen sensor and proceed to point 4.

SA1029600196010X

Fig. 119 Codes P0136, P0138 & P0140: Rear Heated Oxygen Sensor (Part 1 of 3). 9000

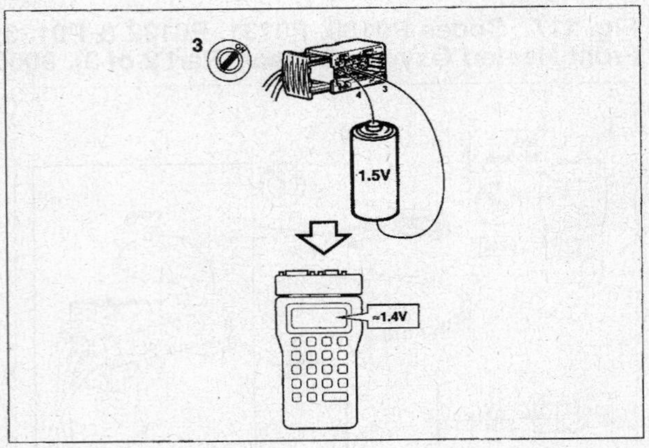

3 Check the oxygen sensor's electrical interfaces

– Unplug the oxygen sensor's 4–pinconnector.
– Replace the sensor with a conventional 1.5 V battery in good condition.
– Connect the battery's positive (+) pole to pin 4 of the connector.
– Connect the battery's negative (-) pole pole to pin 3 of the connector.
– Ignition switch in ON position.
– Connect an ISAT scan tool.
– Select "READ FUNCTIONS".
– Select "O2S 2".

Does the ISAT scan tool show about "1.4 V"?

YES Change the oxygen sensor and continue with point 4.

NO Check the leads between:
pin 4 of the connector and pin 70 of the control module and between
pin 3 of the connector and pin 47 of the control module for continuity or shorting and repair or replace them as necessary.
Then continue with point 4.

SA1029600196020X

Fig. 119 Codes P0136, P0138 & P0140: Rear Heated Oxygen Sensor (Part 2 of 3). 9000

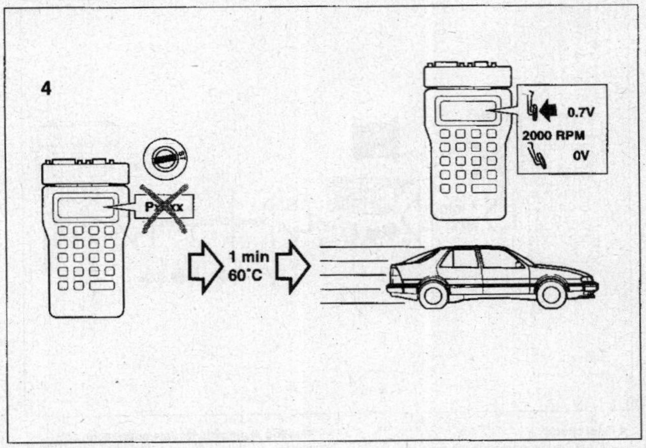

4 Final check:

– Clear the diagnostic trouble code.
– Implementation of driving cycle:
  Start the engine and run it at idling speed until the temperature of the coolant exceeds 60°C (140°F) or for at least 1 minute if this temperature is reached earlier.
– Connect an ISAT scan tool.
– Select "READ FUNCTIONS".
– Select "O2S 2".
– Drive the car and check that the ISAT scan tool readings are:
  - > 0.7 V at full load
  - about 0 V at fuel shut–of in connection with engine braking (manual gearbox: 2nd, 3rd, 4th or 5th and engine speed above 2000 rpm).

Are the readings OK?

YES Replace ECM.

NO The remedial measure taken was correct.

SA1029600196030X

Fig. 119 Codes P0136, P0138 & P0140: Rear Heated Oxygen Sensor (Part 3 of 3). 9000

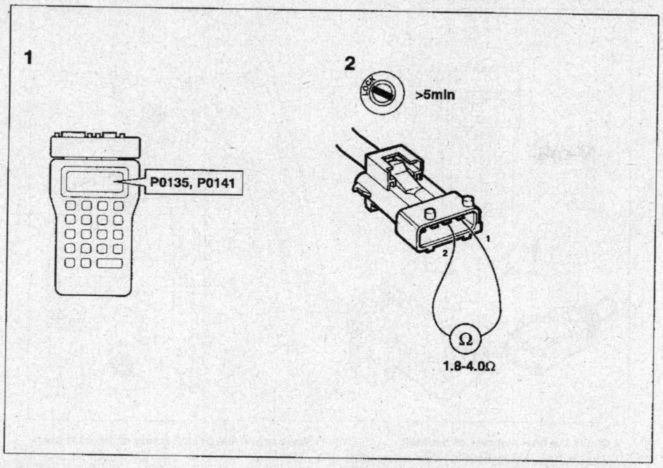

Diagnostic procedure

1 Check additional diagnostic trouble codes in the Trionic system

– Obtain readouts of all diagnostic trouble codes using the ISAT scan tool.

Are P0135 and P0141 present?

YES Continue with point 2.

NO Continue with point 3.

2 Check the oxygen sensors' heating circuit resistance

The engine should have been switched off for at least 5 minutes.

– Check fuse 28 and change it if necessary.
– Unplug the 4–pin connectors of both oxygen sensors.
– Check the resistance of both sensors:
pins 1–2 ____________________ 1.8–4.0 ohms

Are the resistance readings OK?

YES Repair or replace the leads between pin 1 of the connectors of both oxygen sensors and fuse 28. Then continue with point 4.

NO Change the relevant oxygen sensor and proceed to point 4.

SA1029600197010X

Fig. 120 Code P0141: Rear Heated Oxygen Sensor (Part 1 of 3). 9000

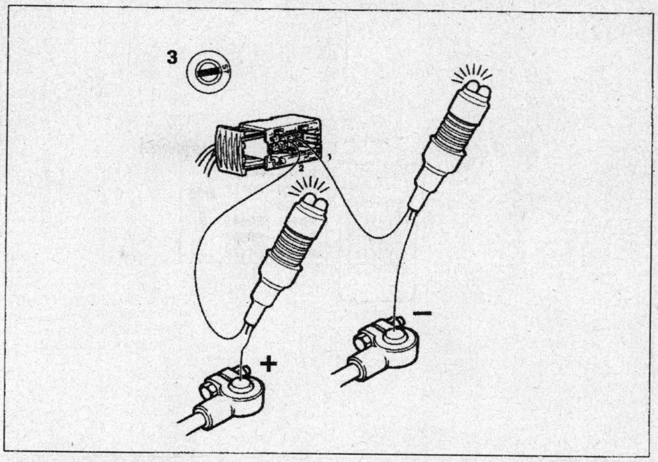

3 Check the heating circuit ground connection and power supply

– Unplug the oxygen sensor's 4–pin connector.
– Start the engine and run it at idling speed until the coolant temperature is above 50°C (122° F).
– Connect the test lamp to:
• pin 1 and B –
• B+ and pin 2

Does the test lamp light up in both cases?

YES Change the sensor and continue with point 4.

NO Rectify the lead in question and proceed to point 4.

SA1029600197020X

Fig. 120 Code P0141: Rear Heated Oxygen Sensor (Part 2 of 3). 9000

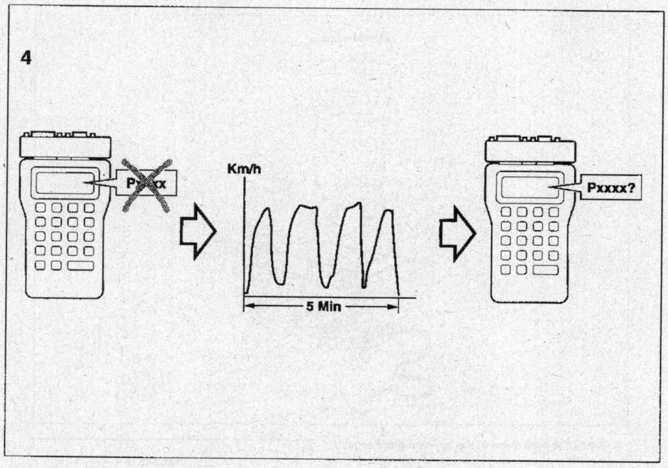

4 Final check:

– Clear the diagnostic trouble code.
– Implementation of driving cycle:
Drive the car at varying loads and engine rpm for 5 minutes.
– Evaluation of driving cycle:
Check whether the diagnostic trouble code has recurred.

Has the diagnostic trouble code recurred?

YES Replace ECM.

NO The remedial measure taken was correct.

SA1029600197030X

Fig. 120 Code P0141: Rear Heated Oxygen Sensor (Part 3 of 3). 9000

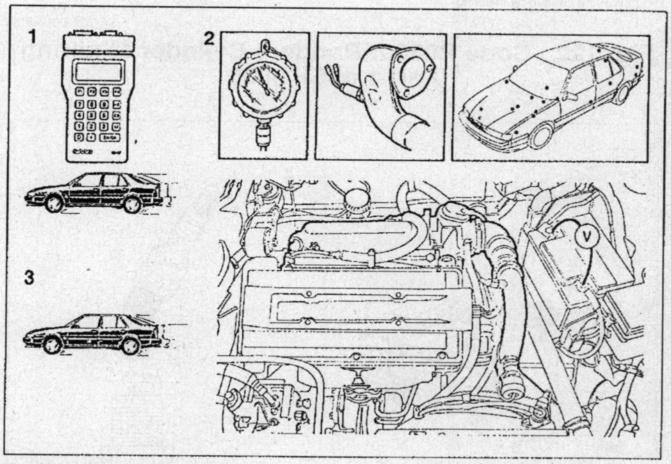

Fault symptom

MIL (CHECK ENGINE lamp) on, unsteady idling, high fuel consumption, poor drivability.

Diagnostic procedure

If any other DTCs are stored in the ISAT scan tool, they should be dealt with first.

1 Erase any DTCs and drive the car to see whether any DTC is generated afresh. If this is the case, continue as described below.

Note:
During the car's running-in period (up to 500 km), any of the above DTCs may be generated even though no actual fault exists.
In such case, carry out an extra careful check if the DTC is generated afresh after being erased.

2 Check the following points:

• that the correct types of component are fitted in the fuel system
• that there is no leakage of air in the intake system
• that the fuel pressure is correct
• that battery positive voltage is correct
• that there are no leaks in the exhaust system in front of the heated oxygen sensor
• that the ground points in the system are OK

3 If no faults can be found when carrying out the above checks, erase any DTCs and drive the car to check whether the DTC is generated afresh. If

If it is, replace ECM.

SA1029100107000X

Fig. 121 Codes P0170, P0171 & P0172: Incorrect Fuel-Air Mixture. 9000

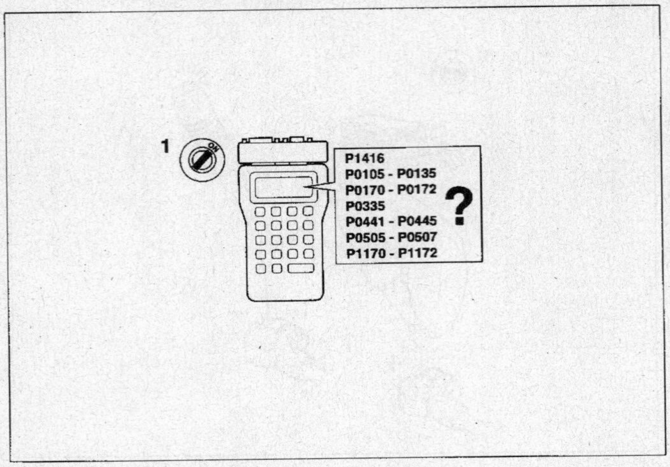

Diagnostic procedure

1 Check additional Trionic diagnostic trouble codes

– Obtain readouts of all diagnostic trouble codes using the ISAT scan tool.
– P1416
– P0105 – P0135
– P0170 – P0172
– P0335
– P0441 – P0445
– P0505 – P0507
– P1170 – P1172

Are any of the above diagnostic trouble codes present?

YES Continue fault diagnosis for the relevant diagnostic trouble code.

NO Continue with point 2.

Note

P1171 may be caused by misfiring.

SA1029600198010X

Fig. 122 Code P0300: Random Cylinder Misfiring (Part 1 of 6). 9000

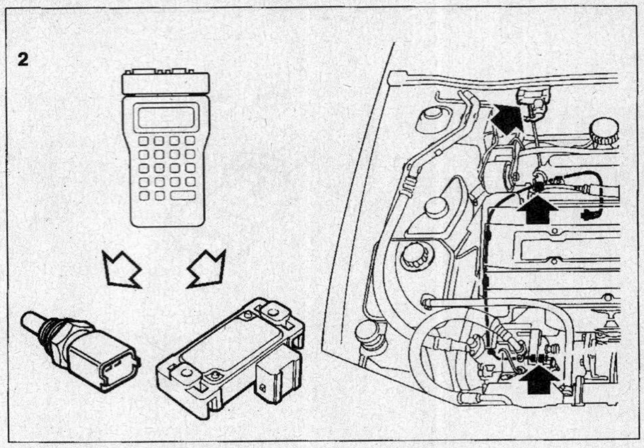

2 Check the basic causes of the fault

– Inspect the vacuum hose between the pressure sensor and intake manifold.
– Check the pressure sensor's electrical connections for moisture and corrosion. Also check that the seal in the female connector is present and undamaged.
– Inspect the vacuum hose between the fuel pressure regulator and intake manifold.
– Using an ISAT scan tool, check that the coolant temperature is plausible.
– Using an ISAT scan tool, check that the operation of the pressure sensor is plausible:

With the ignition switch in the ON position, the reading obtained on the ISAT scan tool should be about 102 kPa (NOTE: the reading is dependent on air pressure).

With the engine idling, the reading obtained on the ISAT scan tool should be 40–60 kPa.

– Check the wiring connected to the front heated oxygen sensor for shorting, continuity and chafing of the insulation.
– Check the front heated oxygen sensor's connector for moisture and corrosion.

Have any of the basic causes of the fault been found?

YES Rectify the fault and proceed to point 8.

NO Continue with point 3.

SA1029600198020X

Fig. 122 Code P0300: Random Cylinder Misfiring (Part 2 of 6). 9000

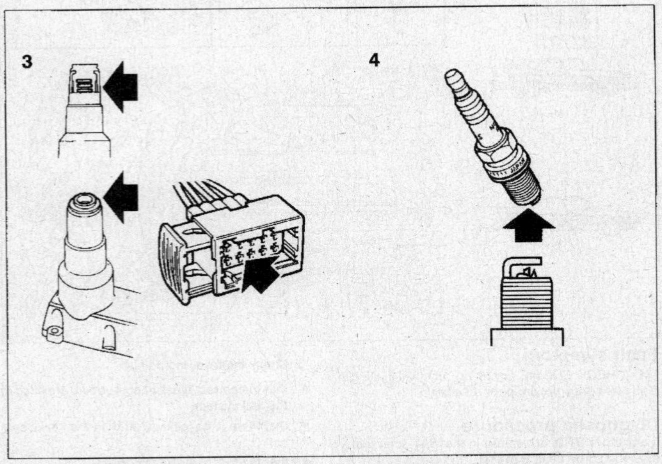

3 Check the condition of the ignition discharge module

– Remove the ignition discharge module from the camshaft cover.
– Check visually:
  - that the four rubber seals for the spark plugs are in good condition.
  - that no contact spring for the spark plugs is missing or that spring travel is inadequate.
  - the connector for moisture and corrosion.

Is the ignition discharge module OK?

YES Continue with point 4.

NO Rectify the fault and proceed to point 4.

4 Check the spark plugs

– Remove the spark plugs and check their condition visually.

Are the plugs OK?

YES Continue with point 5.

NO The electrode gap is wider than 1.4 mm or is otherwise obviously incorrect.
Change the spark plugs and proceed to point 8.

SA1029600198030X

Fig. 122 Code P0300: Random Cylinder Misfiring (Part 3 of 6). 9000

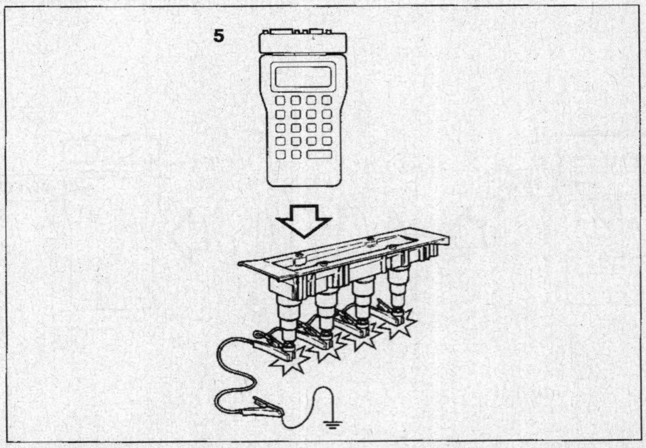

5 Check the operation of the ignition discharge module

– Fit test spark plugs (part No. 86 11 386) in the ignition discharge module.
– Ground the spark plugs using test cable 86 10 867.
– Activate each separate ignition coil, using the ISAT scan tool.
– Ignition switch in ON position.
– Select "ACTIVATE".
– Select "IGNITION COILS"
– Select "IGNITION CYL 1", "CYL 2", "CYL 3" and "CYL 4".

Activation of an ignition coil takes place for 10 seconds at 200 Hz. If a longer activation time is required, the command must be repeated.

– Check that each activated spark plug produces a spark.

Is a spark produced?

YES Continue with point 6.

NO Change the ignition discharge module and proceed to point 8.

⚠ WARNING

The electronic ignition system generates up to 40,000 Volts. Such voltages can prove fatal to people with weak hearts or those who are fitted with a pacemaker. All due caution should therefore be observed when carrying out any work involving the ignition system.

Important

The ignition discharge module must be positioned with the ignition coils facing down during the test so that the transformer oil will provide good insulation in the high–voltage part of the ignition coils.

SA1029600198040X

Fig. 122 Code P0300: Random Cylinder Misfiring (Part 4 of 6). 9000

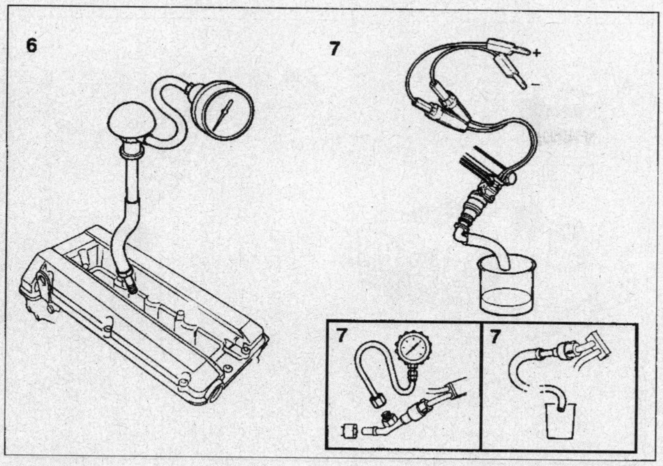

6 Check the compression

– Check the compression of each cylinder.

Is compression OK?

YES Change all spark plugs and continue with point 7.

NO Continue fault diagnosis

7 Check the fuel system

– Carry out fuel pressure and fuel flow measurement on the fuel pump and all the injectors.

Is the fuel system OK?

YES Continue with point 8.

NO Rectify the fault and proceed to point 8.

SA1029600198050X

Fig. 122 Code P0300: Random Cylinder Misfiring (Part 5 of 6). 9000

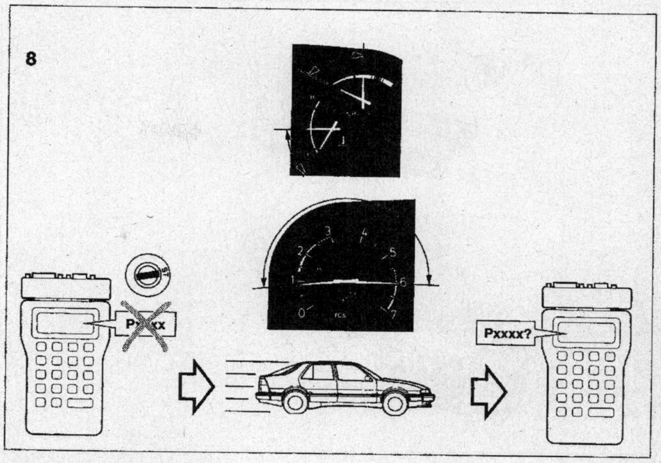

8 Final check:

– Clear the diagnostic trouble code.

– Implementation of driving cycle:
Drive the car at different engine rpm and varying loads, especially at high revs, while the engine is warming up.

– Evaluation of driving cycle:
Check whether the diagnostic trouble code has recurred.

Has the diagnostic trouble code recurred?

YES Replace ECM.

NO The remedial measure taken was correct.

SA1029600198060X

Fig. 122 Code P0300: Random Cylinder Misfiring (Part 6 of 6). 9000

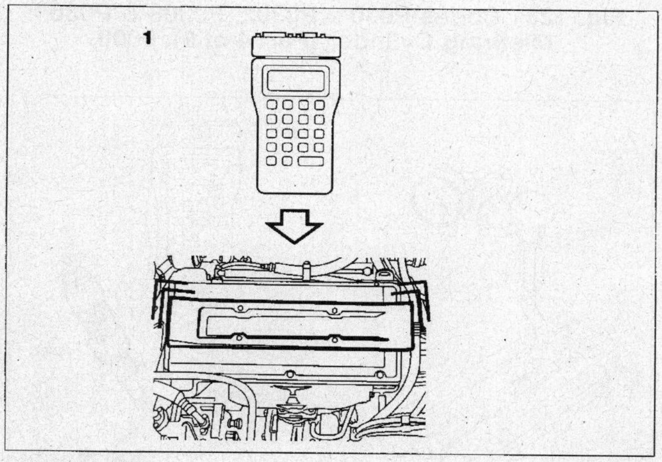

Diagnostic procedure

1 Check the operation of the ignition coil concerned

– Connect an ISAT scan tool.

– Ignition switch in ON position.

– Select "ACTIVATE".

– Select "IGNITION COILS"

– Select "IGNITION CYL 1", "CYL 2", "CYL 3" or "CYL 4".

– Select the cylinder concerned.

Activation of an ignition coil takes place for 10 seconds at 200 Hz. If a longer activation time is required, the command must be repeated.

– Listen for the sound of each ignition coil operating.

Is the ignition coil in question operating?

YES Proceed to point 4.

NO Continue with point 2.

SA1029600199010X

Fig. 123 Codes P0301, P0302, P0303 & P0304: Misfiring Cylinder (Part 1 of 9). 9000

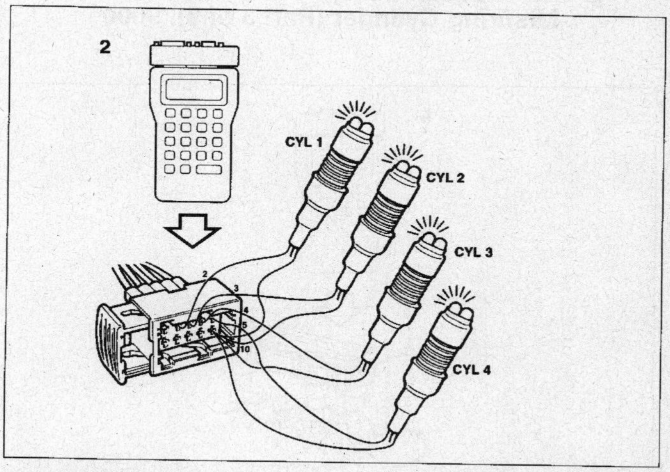

2 Check the trigger lead of the ignition coil concerned

– Unplug the ignition discharge module's 10–pin connector.

– Ignition switch in ON position.

– Connect the test lamp to pin 10 and the trigger lead of the ignition coil in question, see table below.

– Then activate the ignition coil concerned by means of an ISAT scan tool command.

Trigger lead, cylinder No.	10–pin connector, pin No.
1	2
2	3
3	4
4	5

The test lamp should light up for 10 seconds, during which time it should flicker (go out repeatedly for extremely brief periods). In the event of uncertainty, repeat the command.

Does the test lamp light up and start flickering?

YES Change the ignition discharge module and proceed to point 12.

NO The test lamp does not light up or remains on continuously. Continue with point 3.

SA1029600199020X

Fig. 123 Codes P0301, P0302, P0303 & P0304: Misfiring Cylinder (Part 2 of 9). 9000

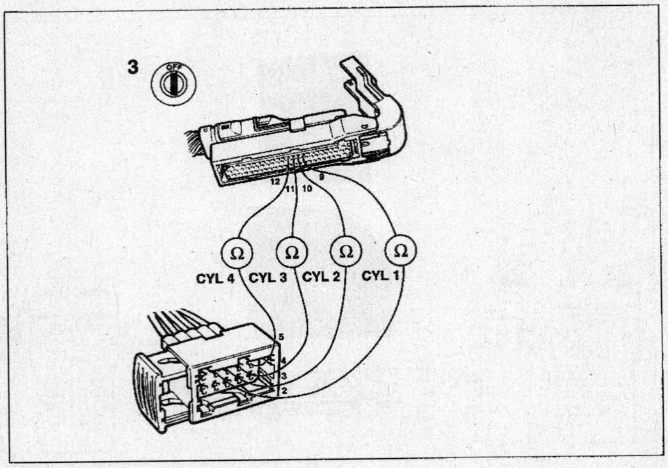

3 Check the trigger lead in question

- Check the trigger lead in question for continuity, see table below.
- Check the lead for continuity/shorting.

Trigger lead, cylinder No.	10–pin connector, pin No.	Control module, pin No.
1	2	9
2	3	10
3	4	11
4	5	12

Is the lead OK?

YES Continue with point 4.

NO Rectify the fault and proceed to point 12.

SA1029600199030X

Fig. 123 Codes P0301, P0302, P0303 & P0304: Misfiring Cylinder (Part 3 of 9). 9000

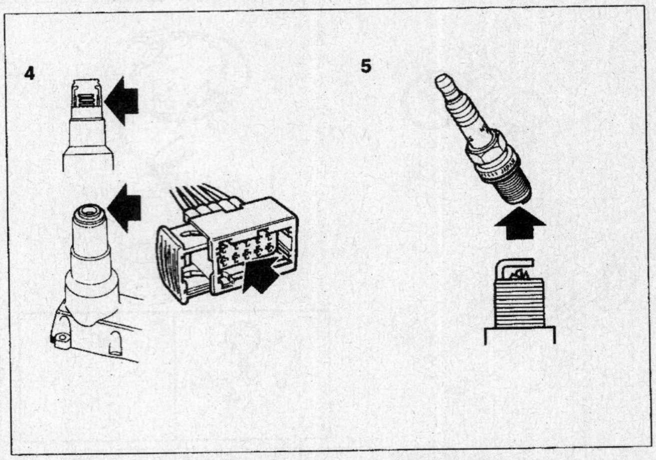

4 Check the condition of the ignition discharge module

- Remove the ignition discharge module from the camshaft cover.
- Check visually:
  - that the four rubber seals for the spark plugs are in good condition.
  - that no contact spring for the spark plugs is missing or that spring travel is inadequate.
  - the connector for moisture and corrosion.

Is the ignition discharge module OK?

YES Continue with point 5.

NO Rectify the fault and proceed to point 5.

5 Check the spark plugs

- Remove the spark plugs and check their condition visually.

Are the plugs OK?

YES Continue with point 6.

NO The electrode gap is wider than 1.4 mm or is otherwise obviously incorrect. Change the spark plugs and proceed to point 12.

SA1029600199040X

Fig. 123 Codes P0301, P0302, P0303 & P0304: Misfiring Cylinder (Part 4 of 9). 9000

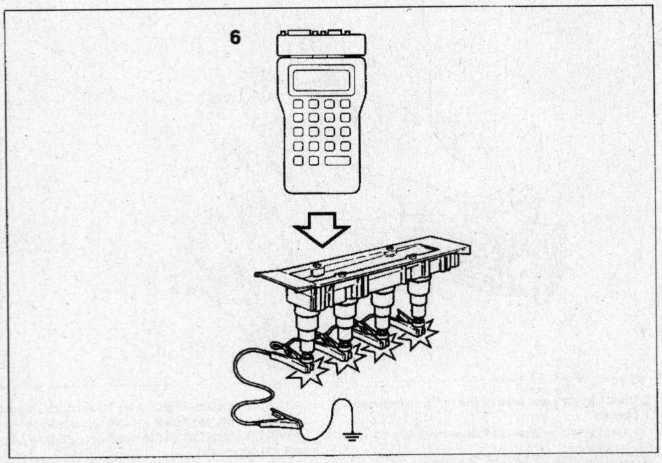

WARNING

The electronic ignition system generates up to 40,000 Volts. Such voltages can prove fatal to people with weak hearts or those who are fitted with a pacemaker. All due caution should therefore be observed when carrying out any work involving the ignition system.

Important

The ignition discharge module must be positioned with the ignition coils facing down during the test so that the transformer oil will provide good insulation in the high–voltage part of the ignition coils.

6 Check the operation of the ignition discharge module

- Fit a test spark plug (part No. 86 11 386) in the relevant spark plug socket.
- Ground the plug using test cable 86 10 867.
- Ignition switch in ON position.
- Activate the ignition coil concerned, using the ISAT scan tool.
- Check that the activated spark plug produces a spark.

Is a spark produced?

YES Continue with point 7.

NO Change the ignition discharge module and proceed to point 12.

SA1029600199050X

Fig. 123 Codes P0301, P0302, P0303 & P0304: Misfiring Cylinder (Part 5 of 9). 9000

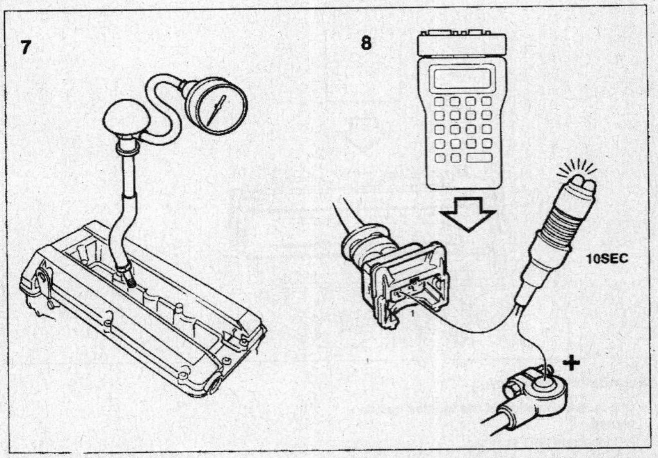

7 Check the compression

- Check the compression of each cylinder.

Is compression OK?

YES Change all spark plugs and continue with point 8.

NO Continue fault diagnosis

8 Check the power supply (B+) of the injector concerned

- Check the voltage by connecting the test lamp to pin 1 of the relevant injector's connector and B–
- Connect an ISAT scan tool.
- Select "ACTIVATE".
- Select "INJECTOR CYL 1", CYL 2, CYL 3 OR CYL 4.

The test lamp should light up for 10 seconds during activation.

Is the test lamp on?

YES Continue with point 9.

NO The fault is in the lead between pin 1 and crimped connection J67. Rectify the fault and proceed to point 12.

SA1029600199060X

Fig. 123 Codes P0301, P0302, P0303 & P0304: Misfiring Cylinder (Part 6 of 9). 9000

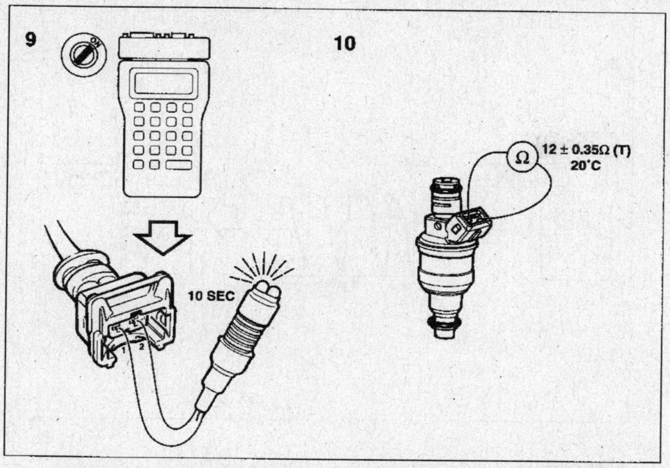

9 Check the relevant injector's control module output

- Unplug the relevant injector's connector.
- Connect the test lamp to pins 1 and 2 of the injector's connector.
- Ignition switch in the ON position.
- Activate the relevant injector using the ISAT scan tool and the activation command "INJECTOR CYL 1", CYL 2, CYL 3 OR CYL 4.

The test lamp should flash at a frequency of 10 Hz for 10 seconds. Repeat the command in the event of uncertainty.

Does the test lamp flash?

YES Continue with point 10.

NO The test lamp flashes or remains on continuously. Check and, if necessary, rectify the lead between pin 2 and the relevant control module output.
If the lead is OK, proceed to point 12.

10 Check the resistance of the relevant injector

- Take a resistance reading across pins 1 and 2 of the relevant injector's connector.
  Nominal resistance is: 12 ± 0.35 ohms at 20° C (68°F).

Is the resistance reading OK?

YES Continue with point 11.

NO Change the injector and proceed to point 12.

SA1029600199070X

Fig. 123 Codes P0301, P0302, P0303 & P0304: Misfiring Cylinder (Part 7 of 9). 9000

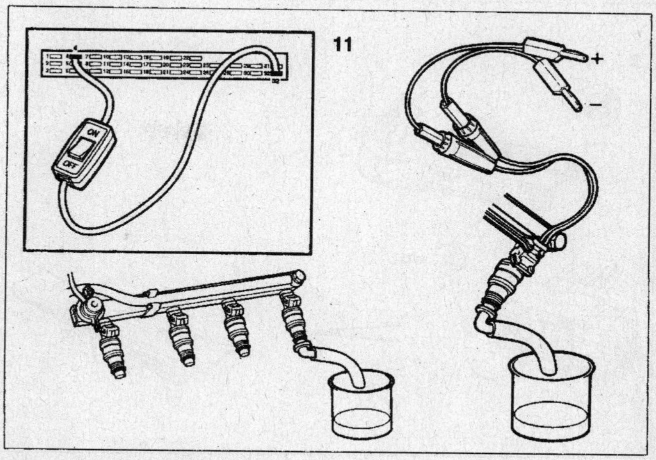

11 Check the relevant injector's fuel delivery flow

- Measure the delivery flow.

Is the delivery flow OK?

YES Continue with point 12.

NO Change the injector and proceed to point 12.

SA1029600199080X

Fig. 123 Codes P0301, P0302, P0303 & P0304: Misfiring Cylinder (Part 8 of 9). 9000

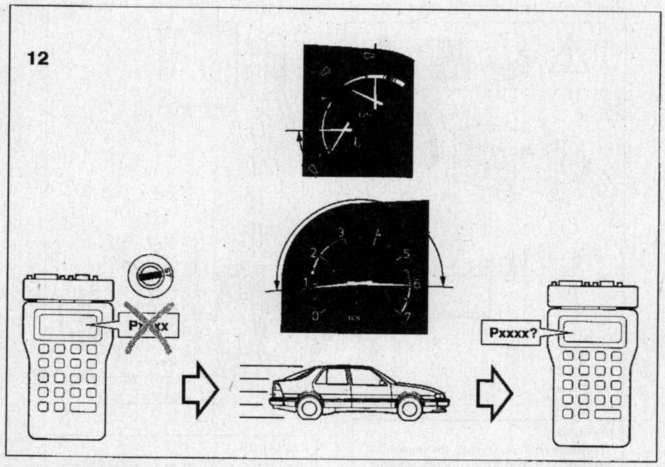

12 Final check:

- Clear the diagnostic trouble code.
- Implementation of driving cycle:
  Drive the car at different engine rpm and varying loads, especially at high revs, while the engine is warming up.
- Evaluation of driving cycle:
  Check whether the diagnostic trouble code has recurred.

Has the diagnostic trouble code recurred?

YES Replace ECM.

NO The remedial measure taken was correct.

SA1029600199090X

Fig. 123 Codes P0301, P0302, P0303 & P0304: Misfiring Cylinder (Part 9 of 9). 9000

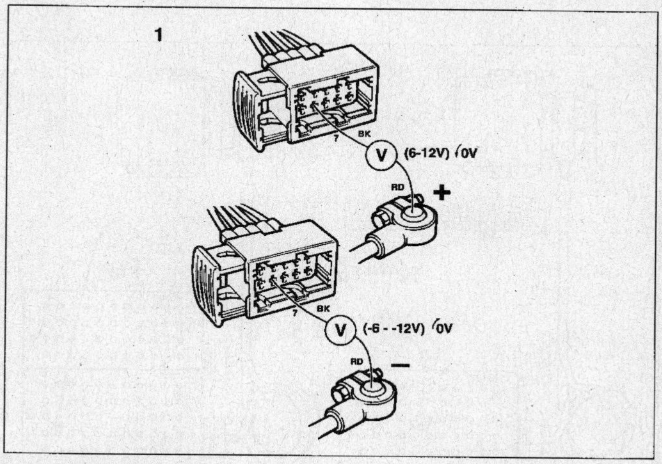

Diagnostic procedure

1 Check the electrical interface

- Ignition switch in ON position.
- Unplug the ignition discharge module's 10-pin connector.
- Connect a multimeter, set for d.c. voltage, to
  - connector pin 7 and battery positive (B+)
  - B – connector pin 7 and battery negative (B–)
  The multimeter should be connected alternately to battery positive (B+) and battery negative (B –).

When connected to battery positive (B+), the meter should indicate a positive voltage (about 6–12 V) which rapidly drops to 0 V.

When connected to battery negative (B–), the meter should indicate a negative voltage (about –6 to –12 V) which rapidly rises to 0 V.

Are the readings obtained OK?

YES Continue with point 3.

NO Continue with point 2.

SA1029600200010X

Fig. 124 Code P0327: Knock Sensor (Part 1 of 3). 9000

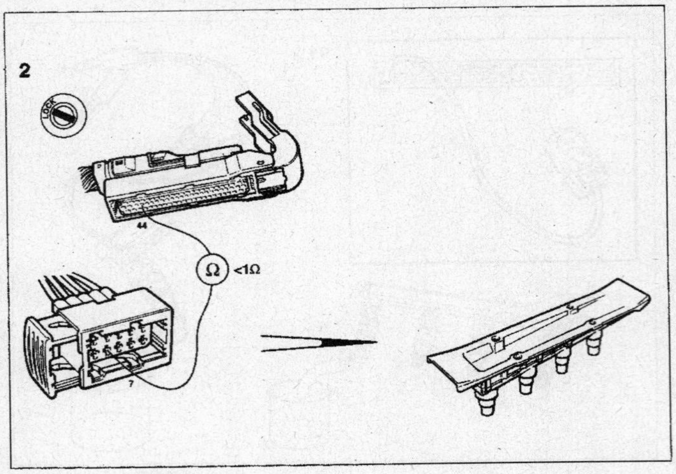

2 Check the knock signal's lead

- Check the continuity of the lead between pin 7 of the ignition discharge module and pin 44 of the control module.
- Check the lead for open circuit and shorting.

Are the test readings OK?

YES Continue with point 3.

NO Rectify the fault and proceed to point 3.

SA1029600200020X

Fig. 124 Code P0327: Knock Sensor (Part 2 of 3). 9000

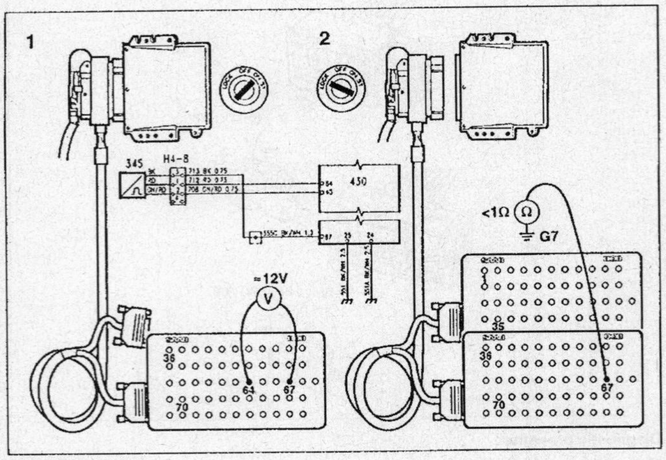

Fault symptom

Engine fails to start/will not run/misfires

Diagnostic procedure

1 Connect a BOB to the ECM. Turn the ignition switch to the Drive position and check whether battery positive voltage is present across pins 64 and 67 of the ECM.

If the voltage is OK, continue with point 3. If not, go to point 2.

2 Switch off the ignition and disconnect the ECM. Check that the correct ground is present on pin 67 by measuring the resistance to grounding point G7 on the intake manifold. The resistance should be less than 1 ohm. If it is not, check and remedy the wiring or connectors.

If the wiring is OK, replace ECM.

SA1029100110010X

Fig. 125 Code P0335: Crankshaft Position Sensor (Part 1 of 2). 9000

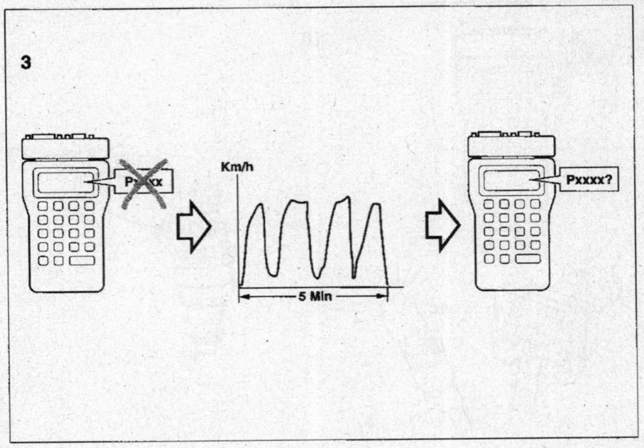

3 Final check:

- Clear the diagnostic trouble code.
- Implementation of driving cycle:
  Drive the car at varying engine loads and rpm for 5 minutes.
- Evaluation of driving cycle:
  Check whether the diagnostic trouble code has recurred.

Has the diagnostic trouble code recurred?

YES Try fitting a replacement ignition discharge module and, after a repetition of the driving cycle, check whether the diagnostic trouble code is generated afresh.

NO The remedial measure taken was correct.

Has the diagnostic trouble code been generated afresh after changing the ignition discharge module?

YES Refit the original ignition discharge module and replace ECM.

NO Scrap the original ignition discharge module.
The remedial measure taken was correct.

SA1029600200030X

Fig. 124 Code P0327: Knock Sensor (Part 3 of 3). 9000

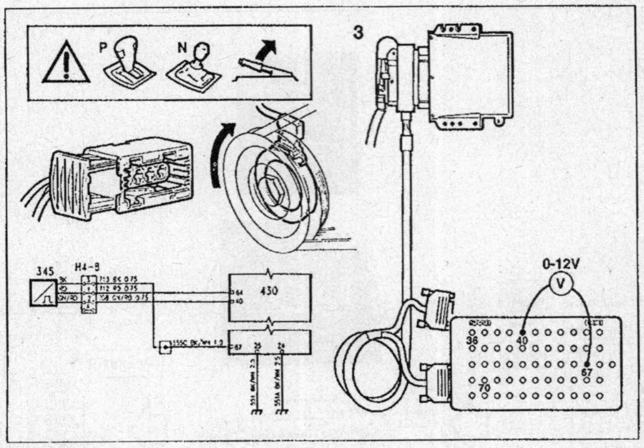

WARNING
When rotating the crankshaft, the selector lever must be in the P position (or the gear lever in neutral) and the handbrake must be applied hard.

CONDITION
For the above DTC to be generated, the engine must be running.

3 Check the voltage across pins 40 and 67 of the ECM while rotating the crankshaft by means of tool 83 94 561. The voltage should alternate between 0 V and battery positive voltage.

If it does not, check the wiring between the ECM and the crankshaft position sensor for continuity.

Remedy any faults in the wiring or connectors.

If the wiring is OK, replace the crankshaft position sensor.

If no fault can be found after carrying out the above checks, replace ECM.

Note:
If the fault persists, it may in such case prove impossible to drive the car.

SA1029100110020X

Fig. 125 Code P0335: Crankshaft Position Sensor (Part 2 of 2). 9000

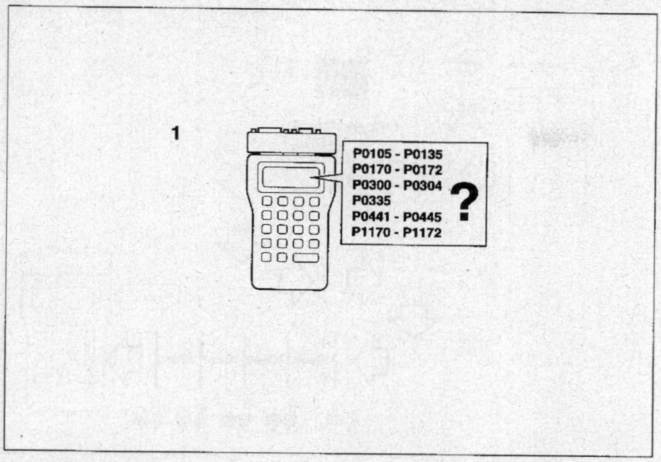

Diagnostic procedure

1 Check additional diagnostic trouble codes in the Trionic system

– Obtain readouts of all diagnostic trouble codes using the ISAT scan tool.
- P0105 – P0135
- P0170 – P0172
- P0300 – P0304
- P0335
- P0441 – P0445
- P1170 – P1172

Are any of the above diagnostic trouble codes present?

YES Continue fault diagnosis as described for the appropriate diagnostic trouble code.

NO Continue with point 2.

SA1029600201010X

Fig. 126 Code P0340: Camshaft Position Sensor (Part 1 of 3). 9000

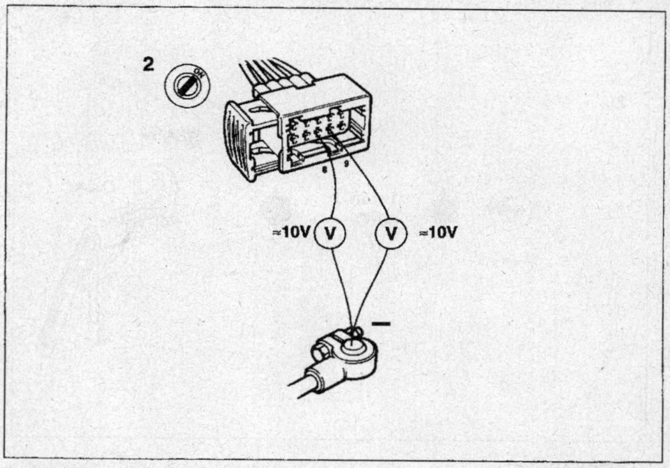

2 Check the ignition discharge module's connections

– Unplug the ignition discharge module's 10–pin connector.

– Ignition switch in ON position.

– Take voltage readings on the female connector sockets
pin 8 to battery negative (B– +
pin 9 to battery negative (B– +

The readings obtained should be about 10 V.

Are the readings OK?

YES Change the spark plugs and continue with point 3.

NO Rectify the lead in question and proceed to point 3.

SA1029600201020X

Fig. 126 Code P0340: Camshaft Position Sensor (Part 2 of 3). 9000

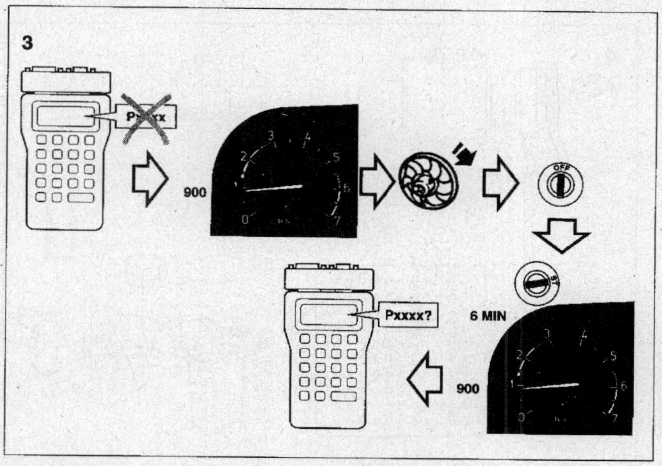

3 Final check:

– Clear the diagnostic trouble code.

– Implementation of driving cycle:
- Run the engine at idling speed until the radiator fan starts, then switch off the engine.
- Start the engine and run it at idling speed for 6 minutes.

– Evaluation of the driving cycle:
Check whether the diagnostic trouble code has recurred.

Has the diagnostic trouble code recurred?

YES Try fitting a replacement ignition discharge module and, after a repetition of the driving cycle, check whether the diagnostic trouble code is generated afresh.

NO The remedial measure taken was correct.

Is the diagnostic trouble code generated afresh after the ignition discharge module has been changed?

YES Refit the original ignition discharge module and replace ECM.

NO Scrap the original ignition discharge module.
The remedial measure taken was correct.

SA1029600201030X

Fig. 126 Code P0340: Camshaft Position Sensor (Part 3 of 3). 9000

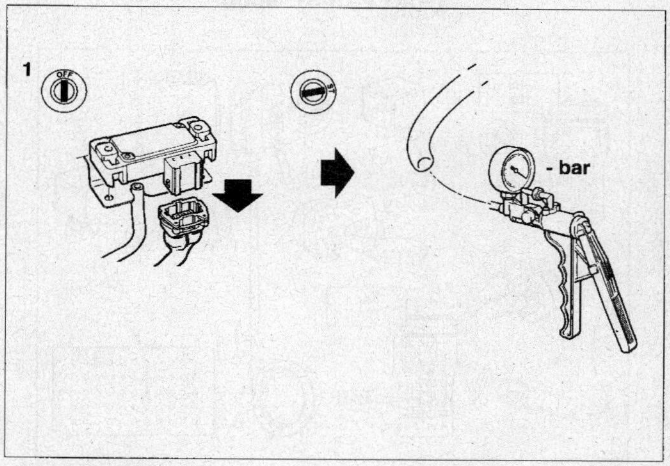

Diagnostic procedure

1 Check the valve

– Ignition switch in the OFF position.

– Disconnect the purge valve hose from the intake manifold.

– Connect the pressure/vacuum pump and create a vacuum. The pressure must not rise.

Does the pressure rise?

YES Repair or replace the hose connected to the valve or the valve itself.
Continue with point 3.

NO Ignition switch in the OFF position.
Continue with point 2.

SA1029600202010X

Fig. 127 Code P0441: EVAP Emission Purge Valve (Part 1 of 3). 9000

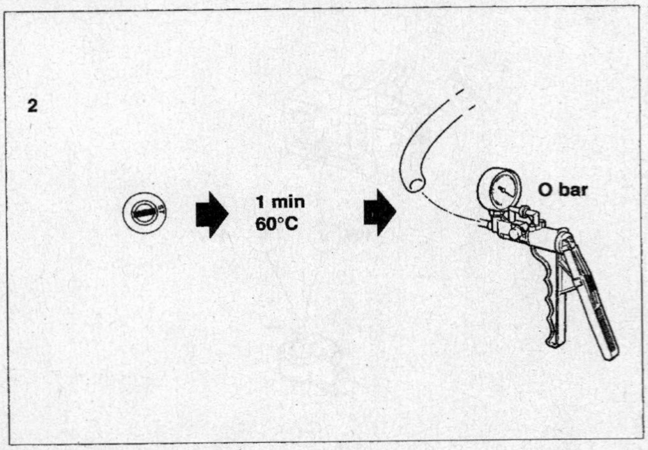

2 Check the air flow

- Start the engine and run it at idling speed until the temperature of the coolant exceeds 60°C (140°F) or for at least 1 minute if this temperature is reached earlier.
- Connect the pressure/vacuum pump to the hose again and create a vacuum.

A steady flow should now be obtained from the evaporative emission canister via the valve (the sound of the valve pulsating can also be heard in the hose).

Is a steady flow obtained?

YES Reconnect the hose and continue with point 3.

NO Repair or replace the hose. Change the valve or evaporative emission canister if necessary, and continue with point 3.

Note

The purge valve is active for 4 1/2 minutes and then idle for 1/2 minute, and so on.

SA1029600202020X

Fig. 127 Code P0441: EVAP Emission Purge Valve (Part 2 of 3). 9000

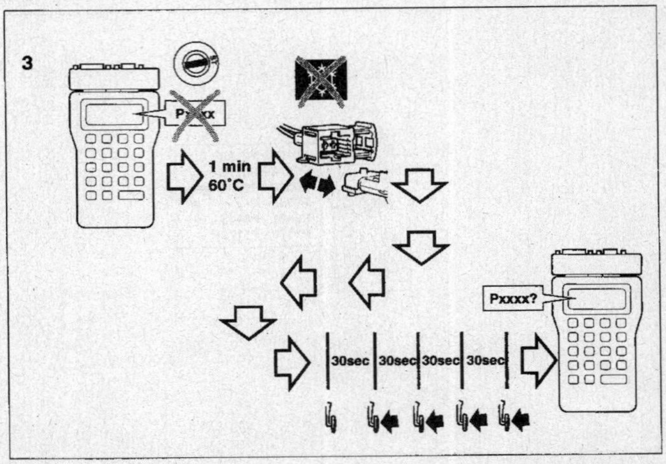

3 Final check:

- Clear the diagnostic trouble code.
- Perform a driving cycle:
  - Ignition switch in the ON position, A/C switched off and temperature sensor unplugged from the EDU so that the radiator fan runs continuously.
  - Start the engine and run it at idling speed until the temperature of the coolant exceeds 60°C (140°F) or for at least 1 minute if this temperature is reached earlier.
  - Depress the accelerator a second or two and then run the engine at idling speed for 30 seconds. Repeat three times.
- Evaluation of the driving cycle:
- Connect an ISAT scan tool.
- Select "READ ON/OFF".
- Select "DIAGNOSTIC STATUS".
- Select "EVAP"

Does the ISAT scan tool show "NOT READY"?

YES Repeat the driving cycle.

NO Check whether the diagnostic trouble code has recurred.

Has the diagnostic trouble code recurred?

YES Replace ECM.

NO The remedial measure taken was correct.

- Plug the temperature sensor into the EDU.
- Clear the diagnostic trouble code for the temperature sensor in the EDU.

SA1029600202030X

Fig. 127 Code P0441: EVAP Emission Purge Valve (Part 3 of 3). 9000

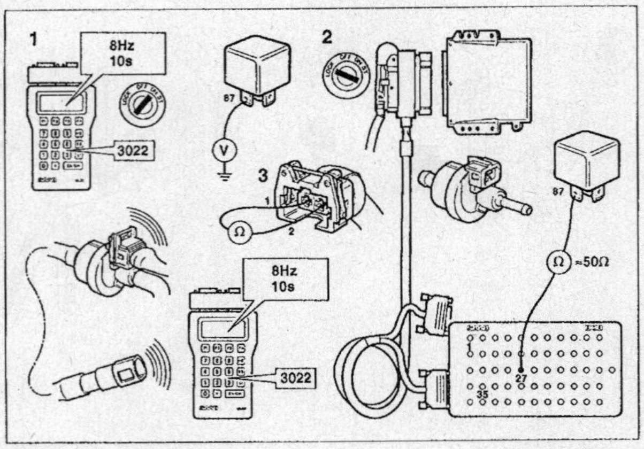

Fault symptom

MIL (CHECK ENGINE lamp) on.

Diagnostic procedure

1 Connect an ISAT scan tool, contact the system and enter command code 3022. The canister purge valve should now be activated with 8 Hz for 10 seconds. Listen for the sound of the valve working. If it is, continue as necessary with physical inspection of the valve as described below.

Disconnect the valve's hose connection to the intake manifold. Listen for the sound of the valve opening and closing (pulsing).

If nothing can be heard, proceed to point 2.

2 Check whether voltage is present on terminal 87 of the main relay.

3 Disconnect the wiring from the valve and check whether the 8 Hz signal (approx. 6.5 V) is present across pins 1 and 2 of the connector when command code 3022 is entered.

If there is no signal, continue with point 4. If the signal is present, check the resistance of the valve coil (including wiring) as described below.

With the wiring connected to the valve, the ignition switched off and a BOB connected to the ECM wiring harness (ECM disconnected), check the resistance of the circuit between pin 27 of the ECM and pin 87 of the main relay. The resistance should be about 50 ohms.

If the resistance is correct, replace ECM

If the resistance is not correct, go to point 5.

SA1029100111010X

Fig. 128 Codes P0443, P0444 & P0445: Canister Purge Valve (ELCD, Part 1 of 2). 9000

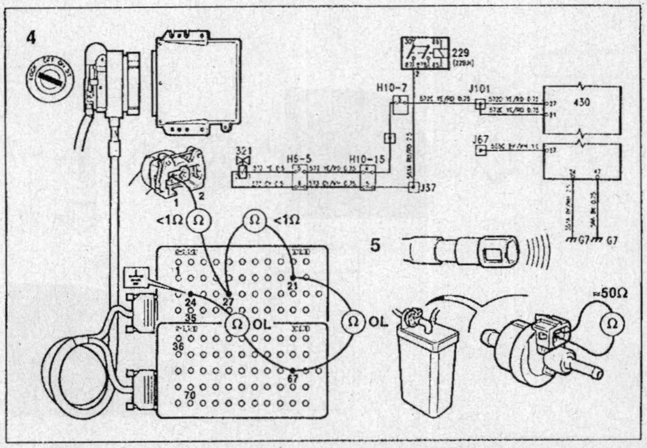

4 Check the wiring to the canister purge valve for continuity/shorting to ground by measuring the resistance across:

- Pin 27 of the ECM and pin 1 of the valve's connector. The resistance should be less than 1 ohm.
- Pins 27 and 21 of the ECM. The resistance should be less than 1 ohm.
- Pins 21 and 67 of the ECM. The resistance should be OL.
- Pins 67 and 24 of the ECM. The resistance should be OL (signal ground and power ground should be electrically separate).

If the resistances measured are incorrect, first check connectors H10-7, H10-15 and H6-5. If these are OK, the fault is in the wiring.

If the wiring and connectors are OK, check the valve as described below.

5 Remove the right-hand fender (wing) liner. Unplug the valve's connector and check the resistance of the valve by measuring directly across the valve pins. The correct resistance is about 50 ohms.

If the resistance is not about 50 ohms, replace the canister purge valve.

CONDITION

For any of the above DTCs to be generated, the engine must be running and the valve activated.

6 Erase any DTCs and drive the car to see whether the DTC is generated afresh.

replace ECM.

SA1029100111020X

Fig. 128 Codes P0443, P0444 & P0445: Canister Purge Valve (ELCD, Part 2 of 2). 9000

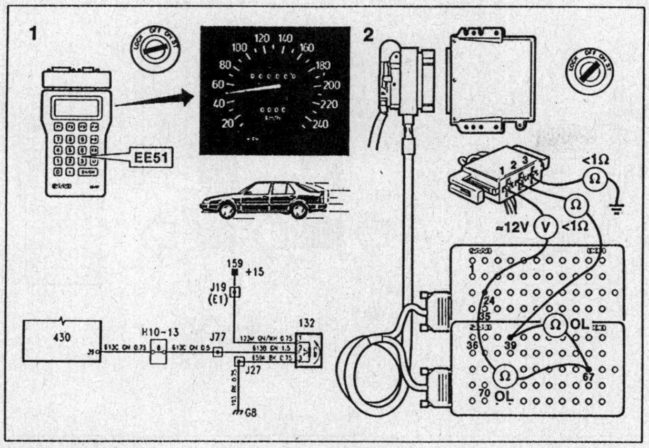

Fault symptom

No fault symptoms noticeable

Diagnostic procedure

1 Connect an ISAT scan tool, contact the SFI system and enter command code EE51.

Drive the car, read off the speed on the ISAT's display and compare it with the speedometer reading. (If the speedometer does not work, go directly to "Checking the speedometer".

In the event of a discrepancy in the speed readings, continue as described below.

2 Connect a BOB to the ECM wiring harness (ECM disconnected). Disconnect the wiring from the vehicle speed sensor (132).

Check the lead between pin 39 of the ECM and pin 2 of the speed sensor's connector for continuity/shorting to ground.

Also check that signal ground (pin 67) and power ground (pin 24) are separated (resistance: OL).

Remedy any faults in the wiring and/or connectors.

If the wiring is OK, turn the ignition switch to the Drive position and check that battery positive voltage is present on pin 1 of the speedometer and that pin 3 is correctly connected to ground. If not, check the wiring to +15 or to grounding point G8.

If the speedometer voltage and ground connection are OK, continue as described below.

SA1029100113010X

Fig. 129 Codes P0500, P0501 & P0502: Vehicle Speed Signal Absent (Part 1 of 2). 9000

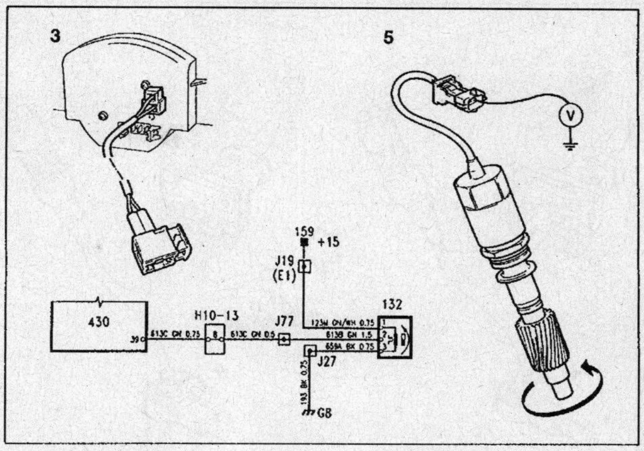

3 Check the circuit between the vehicle speed sensor and speedometer for continuity or shorting to ground.

Remedy any fault in the wiring or continue as described below.

4 Change the speedometer.

5 Remove the vehicle speed sensor from the gearbox. Rotate the sensor by hand and check that voltage pulses are obtained on pin 2 (AC range ≈ 0.5 V). If no pulses are generated, replace the vehicle speed sensor.

6 Erase any DTCs and drive the car to see whether the DTC is generated afresh.

If it is, replace ECM.

CONDITION

For any of the above DTCs to be generated, the engine must be running and one or other of the following must occur:

- indicated speed exceeds 250 km/h for 20 consecutive readings
- engine speed higher than 2000 rpm, brakes not applied and indicated speed 0 km/h for at least four seconds
- indicated speed increases to more than 50 km/h for one second or decreases (without the brakes being applied) by an equal amount.

SA1029100113020X

Fig. 129 Codes P0500, P0501 & P0502: Vehicle Speed Signal Absent (Part 2 of 2). 9000

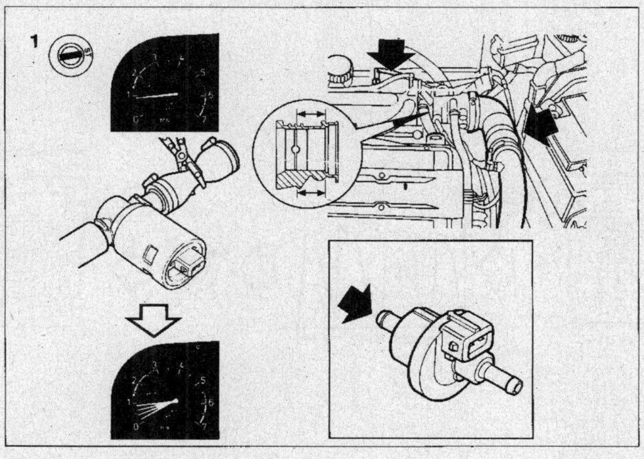

Diagnostic procedure

1 Check for air leakage

- Check whether air leakage occurs, as follows:
- Start the engine and run it at idling speed.
- Constrict the flow of air through the idle air control valve by pinching off the air hose using a pair of pliers.

Idling speed should drop drastically.

Has idling speed dropped?

YES Continue with point 2.

NO Continue fault diagnosis by carrying out the following checks:
- air leakage (after throttle)
- poorly adjusted throttle
- defective brake servo
- purge valve fastened in open position

Rectify as necessary and then continue with point 4.

SA1029600203010X

Fig. 130 Codes P0505, P0506 & P0507: Idle Speed Control (Part 1 of 4). 9000

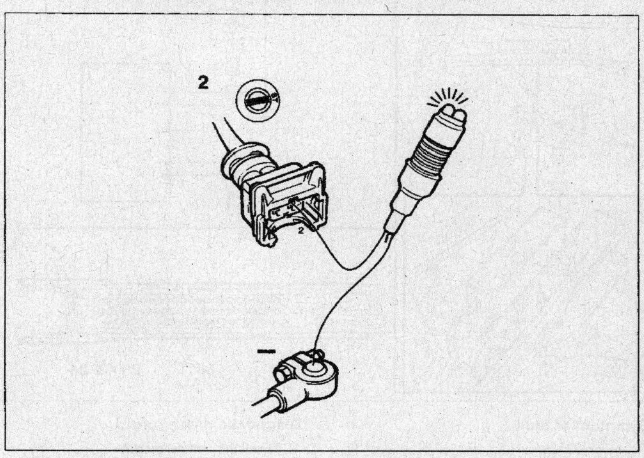

2 Check the idle air control valve's power supply

- Switch off the engine.
- Unplug the idle air control valve's 2-pin connector.
- Start the engine and run it at idling speed.
- Connect the test lamp to pin 2 of the female connector and a good grounding point on the engine.

The test lamp should light up.

Is the test lamp on?

YES Continue with point 3.

NO Repair or replace the lead between pin 2 of the connector and crimped connection J67. Then continue with point 4.

SA1029600203020X

Fig. 130 Codes P0505, P0506 & P0507: Idle Speed Control (Part 2 of 4). 9000

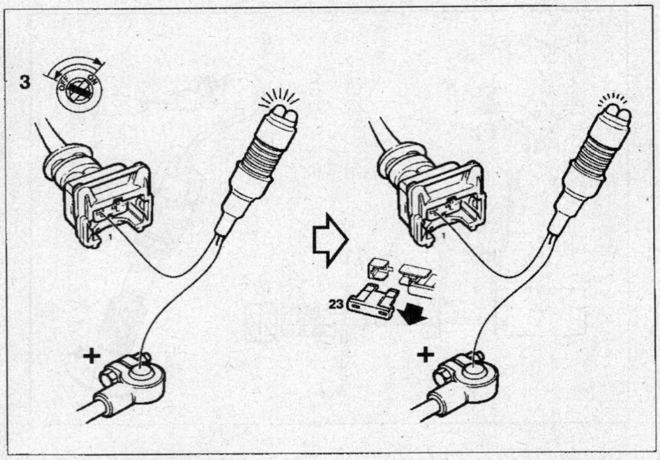

3 Check the lead between the idle air control valve and the control module

- Switch off the engine.
- Turn the ignition switch to the ON position and then back to the OFF position.
- Connect the test lamp to pin 1 of the female connector and battery positive (B+).

The test lamp should light up.

- Remove fuse 23. The test lamp should now shine weakly or go out altogether.

Has the test lamp gone out or nearly so?

YES Change the idle air control valve and continue with point 4.

NO Check the lead between pin 1 of the connector and pin 49 of the control module for continuity and shorting. Rectify if necessary. Then continue with point 4.

SA1029600203030X

Fig. 130 Codes P0505, P0506 & P0507: Idle Speed Control (Part 3 of 4). 9000

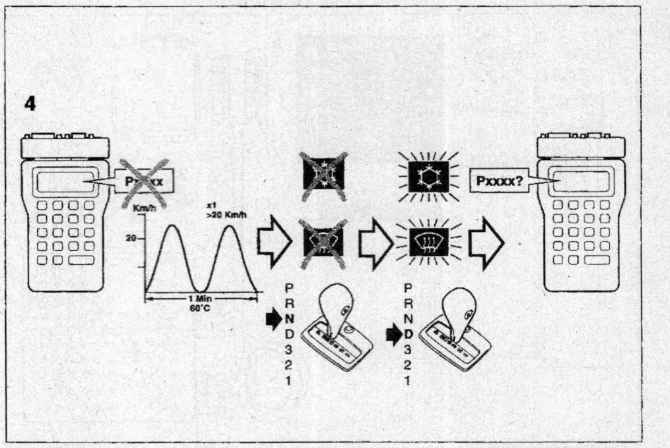

4 Final check:

- Clear the diagnostic trouble code.
- Perform a driving cycle:
  - Drive the car at varying engine loads and rpm until the coolant temperature rises above 60°C (140°F), but for at least 1 minute if this temperature is reached earlier.
  - Car speed should exceed 12 mph (20 km/h) at some time during the driving cycle.
  - Stop the car, apply the handbrake and run the engine at idling speed.
  - Switch off the A/C and all electrical equipment. If the car has automatic transmission, select position P. Allow the engine to stabilize its idling speed for 10 sec.
  - Switch on the A/C and all electrical equipment. If the car has automatic transmission, select position D. Allow the engine to stabilize its idling speed for 10 sec.
- Evaluation of driving cycle: Check whether the diagnostic trouble code has recurred.

Has the diagnostic trouble code recurred?

YES Replace PCM.

NO The remedial measure taken was correct.

SA1029600203040X

Fig. 130 Codes P0505, P0506 & P0507: Idle Speed Control (Part 4 of 4). 9000

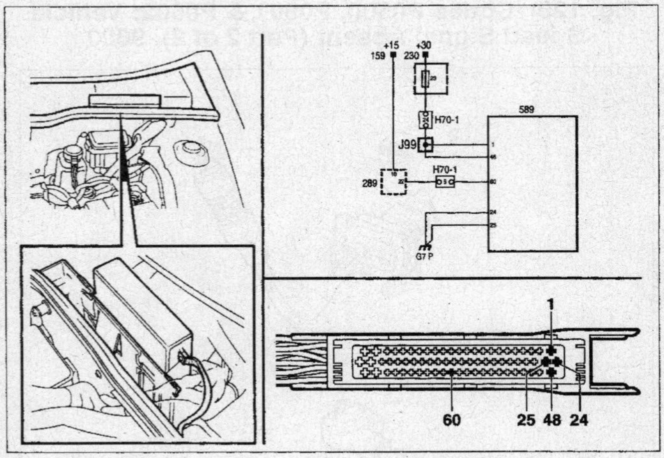

Symptom of fault

The CHECK ENGINE lamp (MIL) is on. Undefinable (different functions may be affected, depending on the internal memory fault and/or program fault).

Conditions

When the ignition is switched on the control module's program does not coincide with that programmed by the supplier.

Diagnostic procedure

1 Check the control module

- If the diagnostic trouble code is generated, remove the control module and check its connector. Pay particular attention to possible socket slide–out.
- Check the control module's ground connection and power supply. See diagnostic trouble code P1500.
- Rectify as necessary and then continue with point 2.

SA1029600204010X

Fig. 131 Code P0605: Control Module (Part 1 of 2). 9000

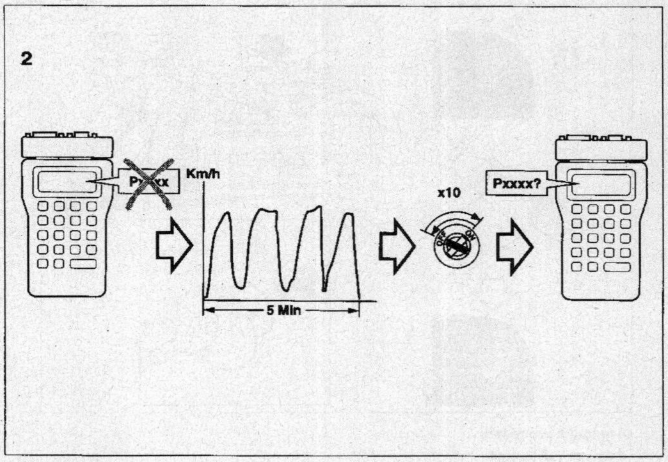

2 Final check:

- Clear the diagnostic trouble code.
- Perform a driving cycle:
  - Drive the car at varying loads and engine rpm for 5 minutes.
  - Turn the ignition switch ON and OFF 10 times.
- Evaluation of driving cycle: Check whether the diagnostic trouble code has recurred.

Has the diagnostic trouble code recurred?

YES Replace ECM.

NO The remedial measure taken was correct.

SA1029600204020X

Fig. 131 Code P0605: Control Module (Part 2 of 2). 9000

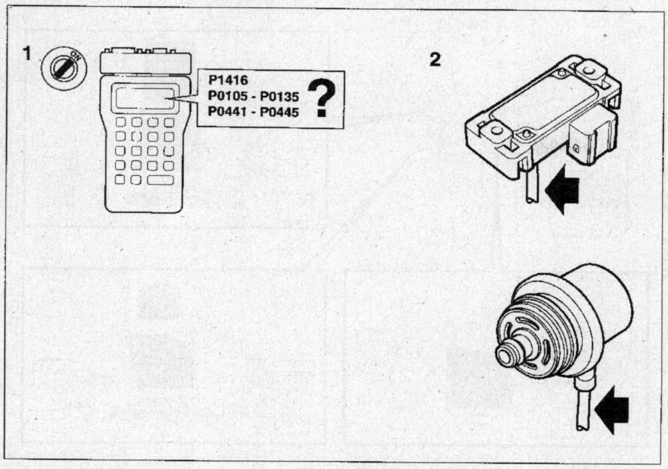

Diagnostic procedure

1 **Check additional diagnostic trouble codes in the Trionic system**
– Obtain readouts of all diagnostic trouble codes using the ISAT scan tool.
- P1416
- P0105 – P0135
- P0441 – P0445

Are any of the above diagnostic trouble codes present?

YES Continue fault diagnosis for the relevant diagnostic trouble code.

NO Continue with point 2.

Note

P1171 may be caused by misfiring.

2 **Check for air leakage**
– Check that no air leakage occurs at the following points:
- the hose between the pressure sensor and intake manifold
- the hose between the fuel pressure regulator and intake manifold

SA1029600205010X

Fig. 132 Codes P1170, P1171 & P1172: Lambda Control (Part 1 of 5). 9000

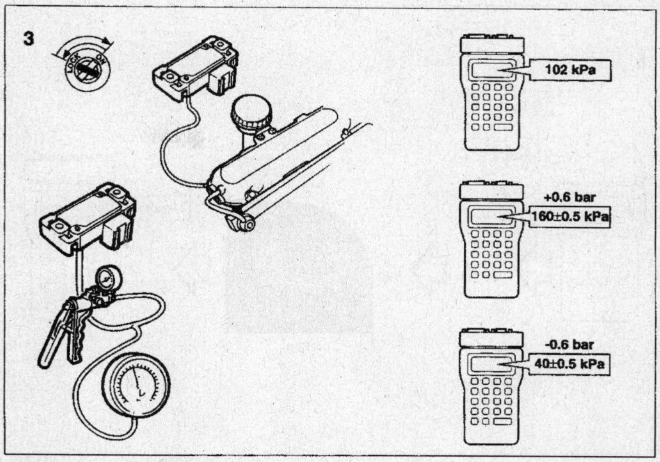

3 **Check pressure sensor operation**
– Turn the ignition switch to the ON position and then back to the OFF position.
– Connect an ISAT scan tool.
– Select "READ FUNCTIONS".
– Select "INTAKE PRESSURE".

The ISAT scan tool should show a reading of about 102 kPa (NOTE: the reading is dependent on air pressure).
First build up a pressure of 0.6 bar and then create a vacuum of – 0.6 bar. Use a pressure gauge and a pressure/vacuum pump.
The ISAT scan tool should show readings of 160± 5 kPa and 40± 5 kPa respectively (the ISAT scan tool readings may be somewhat lower at high altitudes).
This test is intended to detect any shift in the operating range of the pressure sensor.

Are the readings OK?

YES Continue with point 4.

NO Change the pressure sensor and continue with point 6.

SA1029600205020X

Fig. 132 Codes P1170, P1171 & P1172: Lambda Control (Part 2 of 5). 9000

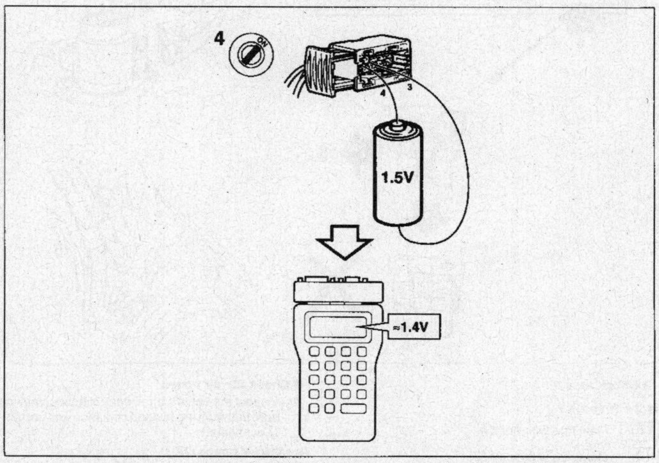

4 **Check the front heated oxygen sensor's electrical interface**
– Unplug the oxygen sensor's 4–pinconnector.
– Replace the oxygen sensor with a conventional 1.5 V dry battery in good condition.
– Connect the battery's positive (+) pole to pin 4 of the connector.
– Connect the battery's -positive (+) pole to pin 3 of the connector.
– Ignition switch in ON position.
– Connect an ISAT scan tool.
– Select "READ FUNCTIONS".
– Select "O2S 1".

Read off the voltage shown on the ISAT scan tool.

Does the ISAT scan tool show about "1.4 V"?

JA Plug in the oxygen sensor and continue with point 5,

NEJ Check the leads between pin 4 of the connector and pin 23 of the control module and between pin 3 of the connector and pin 47 of the control module for continuity and shorting. Rectify as necessary.
Then continue with point 6.

SA1029600205030X

Fig. 132 Codes P1170, P1171 & P1172: Lambda Control (Part 3 of 5). 9000

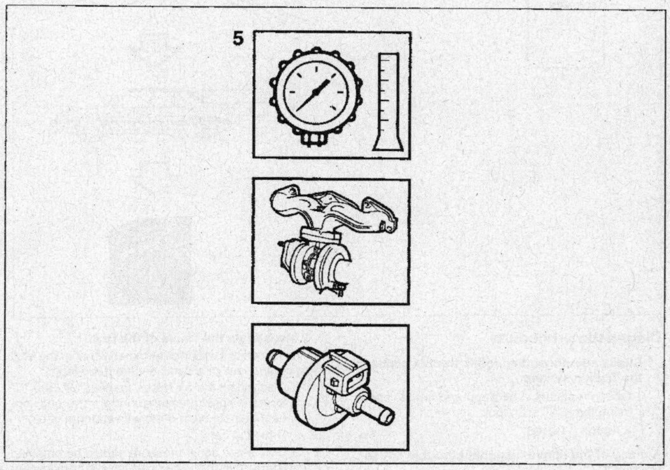

5 **Check**
- fuel pressure and flow
- that the EVAP canister purge valve closes when no current is applied to it
- that there is no air leakage in the exhaust system ahead of the front heated oxygen sensor or its mounting

Is there a relevant cause of the fault?

YES Rectify the fault and proceed to point 6.

NO Change the front heated oxygen sensor and continue with point 6.

SA1029600205040X

Fig. 132 Codes P1170, P1171 & P1172: Lambda Control (Part 4 of 5). 9000

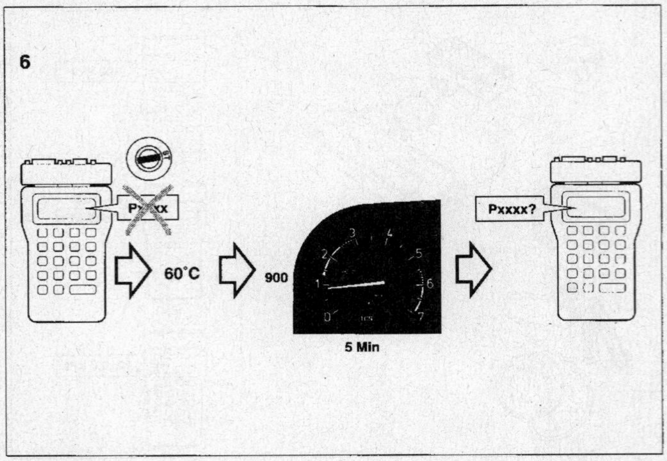

6 Final check

- Clear the diagnostic trouble code.
- Perform a driving cycle:
  - Start the engine and run it at idling speed until the temperature of the coolant reaches 60°C (140°).
  - Run the engine at idling speed for another 5 minutes.
- Evaluation of driving cycle: Check whether the diagnostic trouble code has recurred.

Has the diagnostic trouble code recurred?

YES Replace ECM.

NO The remedial measure taken was correct.

SA1029600205050X

Fig. 132 Codes P1170, P1171 & P1172: Lambda Control (Part 5 of 5). 9000

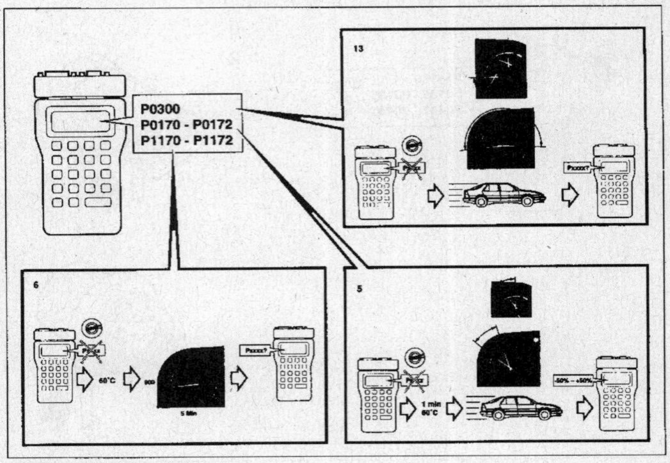

Diagnostic procedure

1 Check other diagnostic trouble codes in the Trionic system

- Obtain readouts of all diagnostic trouble codes using the ISAT scan tool.

When any of the following diagnostic trouble codes is generated, the reason is probably because the fuel level was low at the time.

- P0300 P0170 – P0172
- P1170 – P1172

2 Perform a final check for the relevant diagnostic trouble code.

SA1029600206000X

Fig. 133 Code P1416: Fuel Tank Level. 9000

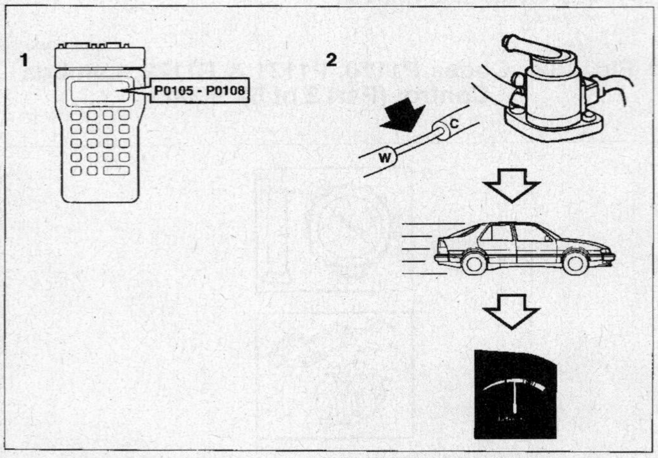

Diagnostic procedure

1 Check additional diagnostic trouble codes in the Trionic system

- Obtain readouts of all diagnostic trouble codes using the ISAT scan tool.
  - P0105 – P0108

Are any of the above diagnostic trouble codes present?

YES Continue fault diagnosis as described for the appropriate diagnostic trouble code.

NO Continue with point 2.

2 Investigate the cause of the fault

In the following it will be determined whether the fault is a control fault or a basic engine/turbo fault.

- Disconnect the air hoses marked "W" and "C" from the boost pressure control valve and connect them to each other with a length of pipe.
- Drive the car.
- Only basic boost pressure should be obtained when driving at wide open throttle from low engine rpm and when opening the throttle suddenly at higher engine rpm.

Is only basic boost pressure obtained?

YES Continue with point 3.

NO Check and, if necessary, rectify the following:

- Binding wastegate
- Defective diaphragm unit
- Defective or incorrectly connected control hoses
- Incorrectly adjusted basic boost pressure

Rectify as necessary and continue with point 9.

SA1029600207010X

Fig. 134 Code P1549: Boost Pressure Control (Part 1 of 5). 9000

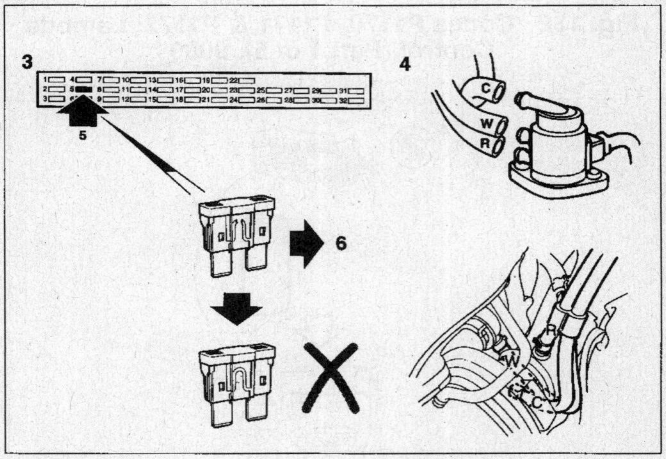

3 Check fuse 5

Is the fuse OK?

YES Continue with point 4.

NO Continue with point 6.

4 Check the air hoses

- Inspect the valve's three control hoses, making sure that they are in good condition and correctly connected.

Are the air hoses OK?

YES Continue with point 5.

NO Rectify the fault and continue with point 9.

SA1029600207020X

Fig. 134 Code P1549: Boost Pressure Control (Part 2 of 5). 9000

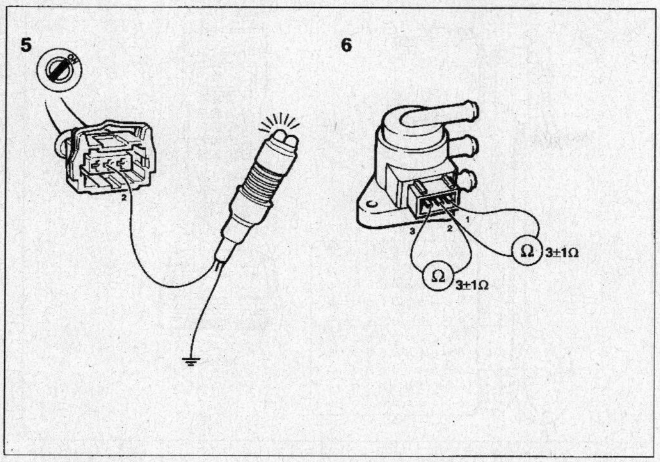

5 Check the power supply

– Ignition switch in ON position.
– Check that the valve is supplied with power (+54 circuit) by connecting a test lamp to pin 2 of the valve's connector and a good grounding point.

Is the test lamp on?

YES Continue with point 6.

NO Repair or replace the lead between pin 2 of the connector and fuse 5. Then continue with point 9.

6 Check the resistance of the valve

– Take resistance readings in the valve's connector across:
  - Pins 1 and 2
  - Pins 2 and 3

Nominal resistance is 3 ± 1 ohm in both cases.

Are the readings OK?

YES Continue with point 7.

NO Change the boost pressure control valve and continue with point 9.

Important
If there is a short circuit in any winding the control module will probably also be damaged. If a new valve is then fitted it will inevitably be rendered unserviceable. In the event of a short circuit, both valve and control module must therefore be changed at the same time.

If necessary, change fuse 5 afterwards.

SA1029600207030X

Fig. 134 Code P1549: Boost Pressure Control (Part 3 of 5). 9000

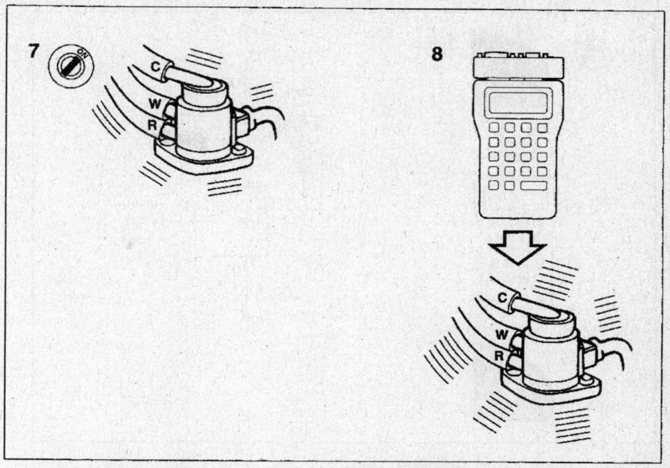

7 Check the lead connected to pin 3 of the valve

– Ignition switch in ON position.
– Plug in the valve's connector. A weak buzzing sound should be heard.

Can a sound be heard?

YES Continue with point 8.

NO Check the lead between pin 3 of the valve's connector and pin 2 of the control module. Repair or replace the lead if necessary. Continue with point 9.

8 Check the lead connected to pin 1 of the valve

– Ignition switch in ON position.
– Plug in the valve's connector.
– Select "ACTIVATE".
– Select "BOOST PRESS. VALVE".

A loud buzzing sound should be heard.

Can a sound be heard?

YES Change the boost pressure control valve and continue with point 9.

NO Check the lead between pin 1 of the valve's connector and pin 26 of the control module. Repair or replace the lead if necessary. Continue with point 9.

SA1029600207040X

Fig. 134 Code P1549: Boost Pressure Control (Part 4 of 5). 9000

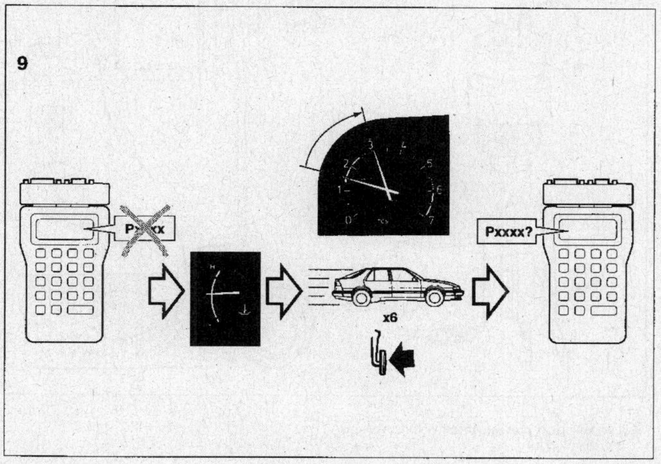

9 Final check:

– Clear the diagnostic trouble code.
– Perform a driving cycle:
  - Warm up the engine.
  - Accelerate at wide open throttle from 1500 rpm to at least 3000 rpm 6 times.
– Evaluation of the driving cycle:
  Check whether the diagnostic trouble code has recurred and whether the pressure switch has opened during the driving cycle.

Has the diagnostic trouble code recurred or has the pressure switch opened during the driving cycle?

YES Replace ECM.

NO The remedial measure taken was correct.

SA1029600207050X

Fig. 134 Code P1549: Boost Pressure Control (Part 5 of 5). 9000

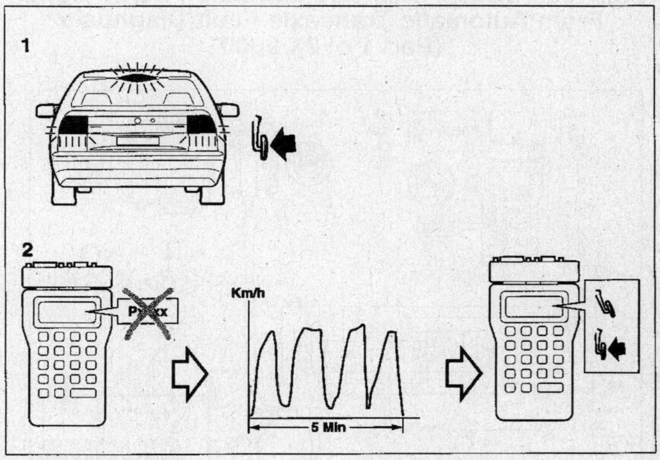

Diagnostic procedure

1 Check the brake lights

– Check whether the brake lights come on when the brake pedal is depressed.

Do the brake lights work?

YES Check the lead between pin 15 of the control module and crimped connection J32. Repair or replace the lead if necessary. Continue with point 2.

NO Continue fault diagnosis

Then carry out a final check in accordance with point 2.

2 Final check:

– Clear the diagnostic trouble code.
– Implementation of driving cycle:
  Drive the car at varying engine loads and rpm for 5 minutes.
– Evaluation of driving cycle:
– Connect an ISAT scan tool.
– Select "READ ON/OFF".
– Select "BRAKE LIGHT SWITCH".

The ISAT scan tool display should read "ON" when the brake pedal is depressed.

Does the display read "OFF"?

YES Proceed to page 282.

NO The remedial measure taken was correct.

SA1029600208000X

Fig. 135 Codes P1576 & P1577: Brake Light Switch. 9000

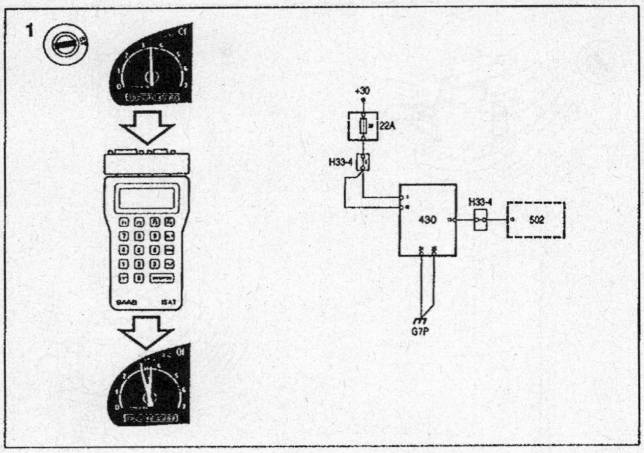

Symptom of fault
Rough gear-changes

Diagnostic procedure

1 Connect an ISAT scan tool.
Maintain a constant engine speed of 3500 rpm. Select "AUT TRANSMISSION", "ACTIVATE" menu and the command "TORQUE LIMITATION" in the ISAT.
The engine speed must drop sharply and then stabilize at 3500 rpm. Repeat this process periodically for approx. 30 seconds.
If this function works, the Trionic ECM is OK. The cause of the rough gear-changes must be in the gearbox.

If the function does not work, continue with point 2.

SA1029100120010X

Fig. 136 Code —: Torque Limitation Input Signal From Automatic Transaxle Fault Diagnosis (Part 1 of 2). 9000

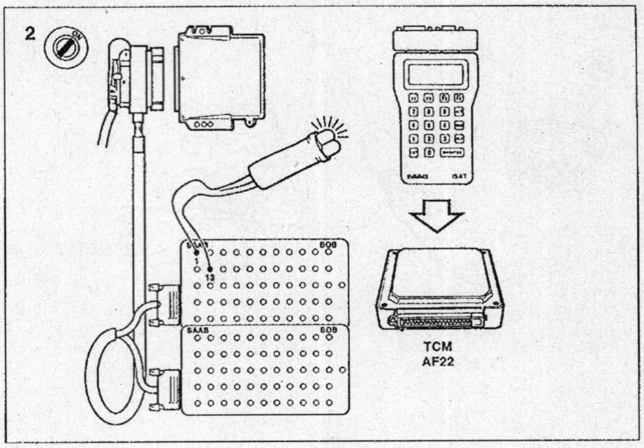

2 Connect a BOB.
The Trionic ECM must not be connected.
Connect the test lamp between pins 1 and 13.
Select "AUT TRANSMISSION", the "ACTIVATE" menu and the "TORQUE LIMITATION" command in the ISAT.
The test lamp must flash.
If the test lamp flashes, continue
If the test lamp does not flash, check and if necessary remedy the fault in the lead between Trionic, pin 13 and pin 13 of the transmission control module.

If the lead is OK, diagnose automatic transaxle.

SA1029100120020X

Fig. 136 Code —: Torque Limitation Input Signal From Automatic Transaxle Fault Diagnosis (Part 2 of 2). 9000

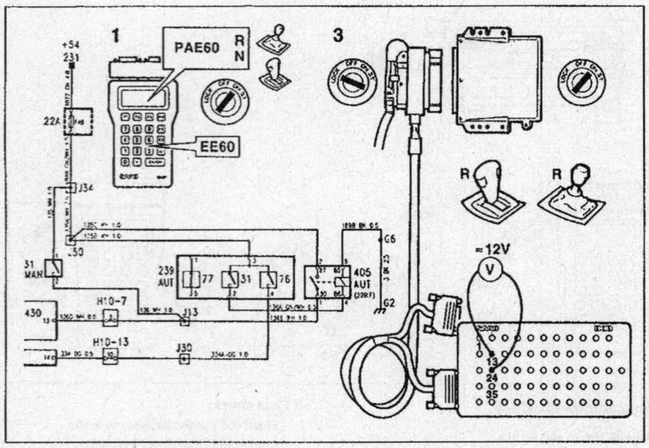

1 Connect an ISAT scan tool, contact the SFI system and enter command code EE60.
The status of the system is displayed on the ISAT:

- With reverse gear selected→ PAE60-ON.
If not, go to point 2.
- With the gear lever in neutral or the selector lever in the N position → PAE60-OFF.
If not, go to point 6.

2 Check whether fuse FA9 is intact.

3 With the ignition switched off, connect a BOB to the ECM wiring harness (ECM disconnected) and check (with the ignition switch turned to the Drive position) whether battery positive voltage is present on pin 13 of the ECM (reverse gear selected).

If voltage is present, replace ECM.

SA1029100121010X

Fig. 137 Code —: Torque Limiting Function Inspection (Part 1 of 3). 9000

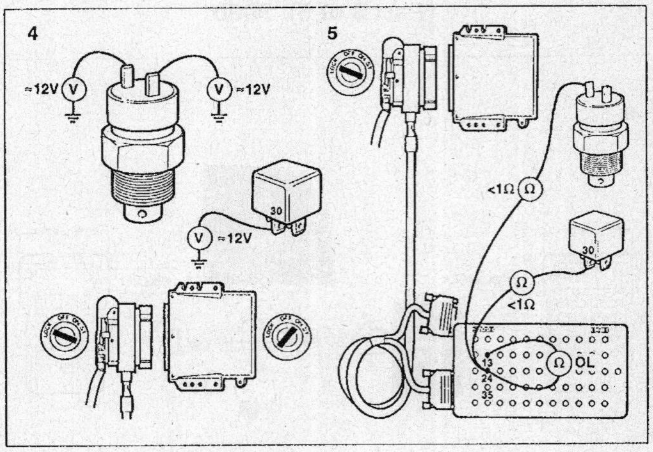

4 If no voltage is present, check whether voltage is present up to:

- **Manual:** Terminal 1 of the reversing light switch, and also terminal 2 when the switch is activated. If it is not, replace the switch or, alternatively, check the lead from terminal 1 of the switch to the fuse.
- **Automatic:** Terminal 30 of the reversing light switch when the switch is activated.
If it is not, check the operation of the selector lever and the reversing light relay

5 With the ignition switched off, use a BOB to check the lead to pin 13 of the ECM for continuity/shorting to ground. Take remedial action if the lead is faulty.

SA1029100121020X

Fig. 137 Code —: Torque Limiting Function Inspection (Part 2 of 3). 9000

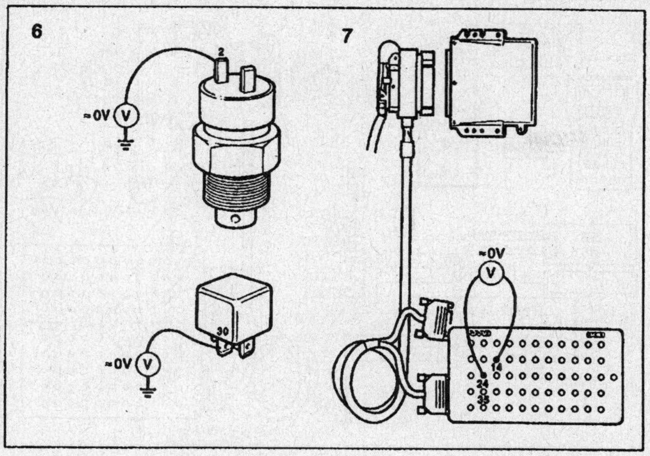

6 **Manual:** Check that pin 2 of the brake light switch is not live when the switch is not activated. If it is, replace the brake light switch.

Automatic: Check that pin 30 of the reversing light relay is not live when the relay is not activated. If it is, check the operation of the selector lever and the reversing light relay

7 With the ignition switched off, connect the BOB to the ECM wiring harness (ECM disconnected).

Turn the ignition switch to the Drive position and check the lead to pin 14 of the ECM for shorting to battery positive voltage. Take remedial action if the cable is faulty.

If the cable is OK, replace ECM.

SA1029100121030X

Fig. 137 Code —: Torque Limiting Function Inspection (Part 3 of 3). 9000

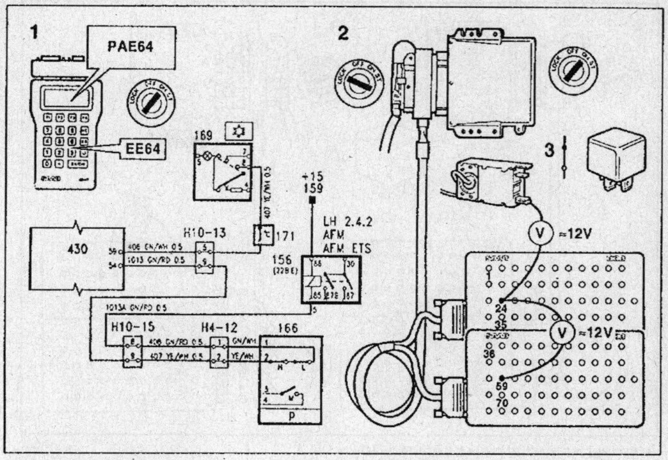

1 Connect an ISAT scan tool, contact the SFI system and enter command code EE64.

The status of the system is displayed on the ISAT:

- A/C compressor switched on@PAE64-ON. If not, go to point 2.
- A/C compressor switched off@PAE64-OFF. If not, go to point 5.

2 Check whether the A/C function is OK. If it is not, connect a BOB to the ECM. Turn the ignition switch to the Drive position and, with the A/C function activated, check whether voltage is present on pin 59 of the ECM.

If it is, replace ECM.

3 If no voltage is present, check whether voltage passes through the anti-freeze thermostat when the A/C compressor is working. If it does not, check the A/C function

SA1029100123010X

Fig. 138 Code —: A/C Activation Inspection (Part 1 of 2). 9000 less TCS

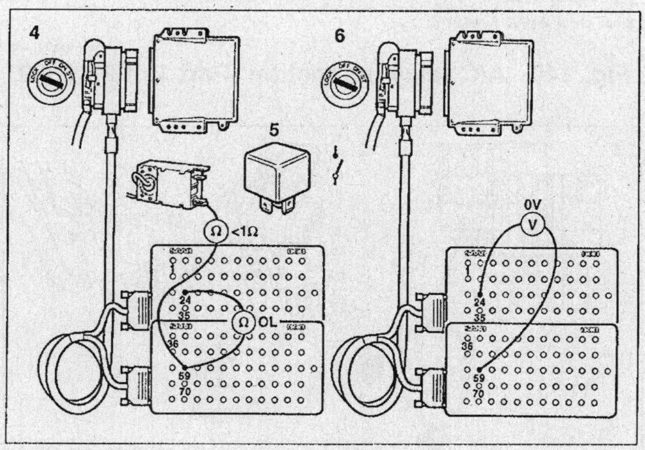

4 If voltage is present, disconnect the ECM, switch the ignition off and use the BOB to check the lead to pin 59 of the ECM for continuity/shorting to ground.

Take remedial action if the lead and/or connectors are faulty.

5 Check that no voltage is applied to the anti-freeze thermostat when the A/C function is not activated.

If it is, check the A/C function

6 If no voltage is applied to the anti-freeze thermostat, use the BOB (ECM disconnected) to check the lead to the ECM for shorting to battery positive voltage or to any component connected to the lead.

Take remedial action in the event of a faulty lead and/or connector, or any component through which voltage is applied to the lead.

If the lead is OK, replace ECM.

SA1029100123020X

Fig. 138 Code —: A/C Activation Inspection (Part 2 of 2). 9000 less TCS

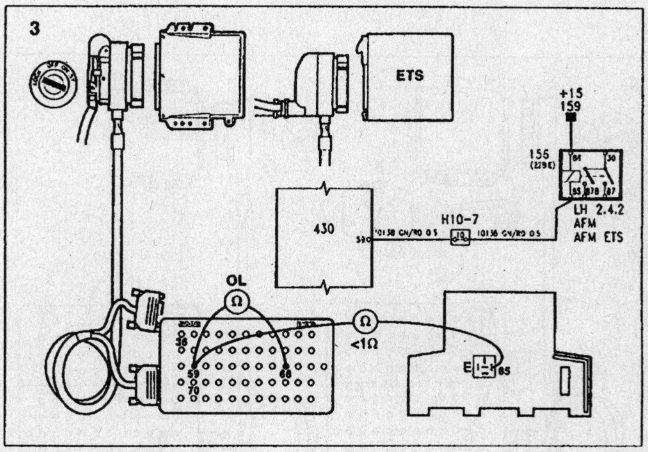

3 **With the ignition switched off, connect a BOB to the ECM wiring harness (ECM disconnected). Also unplug the ETS control module's connector.**

Check the lead between pin 59 of the ECM and pin 85 of the A/C relay for continuity/shorting to ground.

Remedy any faulty leads/connectors.

4 **If malfunctioning of the A/C relay persists in spite of the above checks,** replace ECM

SA1029100124010X

Fig. 139 Code —: A/C Activation inspection (Part 1 of 2). 9000 w/TCS

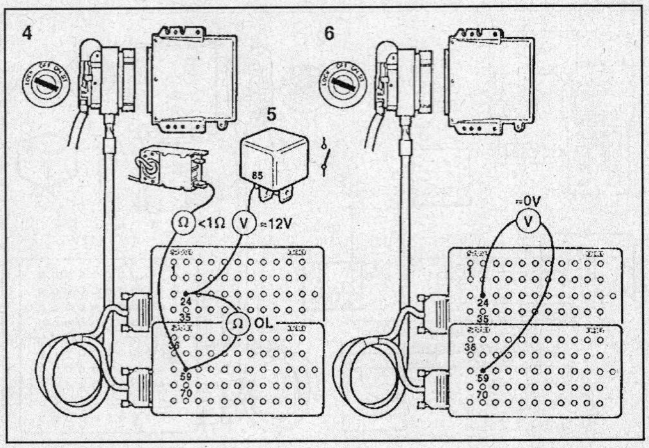

4 If voltage is present, disconnect the ECM, switch off the ignition and check the lead to pin 59 of the ECM for continuity/shorting to ground. Take remedial action if the wiring is faulty.

5 Check whether the voltage applied to pin 85 of the A/C relay is about 12 V when the A/C function is not activated.

If it is not, check the relay and A/C function

6 If no voltage is applied to the relay, use the BOB (ECM disconnected) to check the lead to the ECM for shorting to battery positive voltage or to any component connected to the lead.

Take remedial action in the event of a faulty lead and/or connector, or any component through which voltage is applied to the lead.

If the lead is OK, replace ECM.

SA1029100124020X

Fig. 139 Code —: A/C Activation inspection (Part 2 of 2). 9000 w/TCS

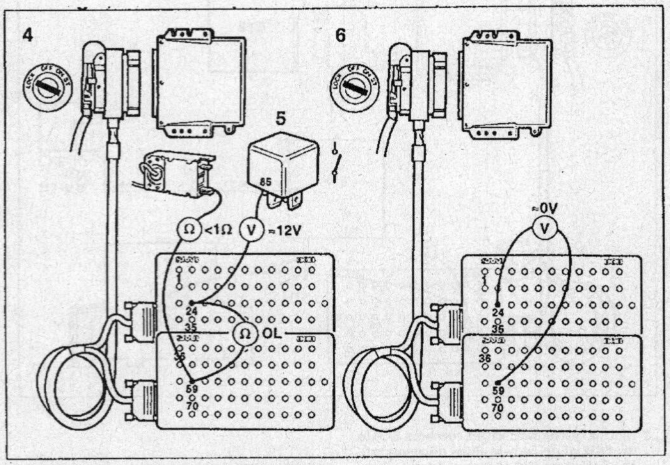

4 If voltage is present, disconnect the ECM, switch off the ignition and check the lead to pin 59 of the ECM for continuity/shorting to ground. Take remedial action if the wiring is faulty.

5 Check whether the voltage applied to pin 85 of the A/C relay is about 12 V when the A/C function is not activated.

If it is not, check the relay and A/C function

6 If no voltage is applied to the relay, use the BOB (ECM disconnected) to check the lead to the ECM for shorting to battery positive voltage or to any component connected to the lead.

Take remedial action in the event of a faulty lead and/or connector, or any component through which voltage is applied to the lead.

If the lead is OK, replace ECM.

SA1029100125020X

Fig. 140 A/C relay inspection (Part 2 of 2). 9000

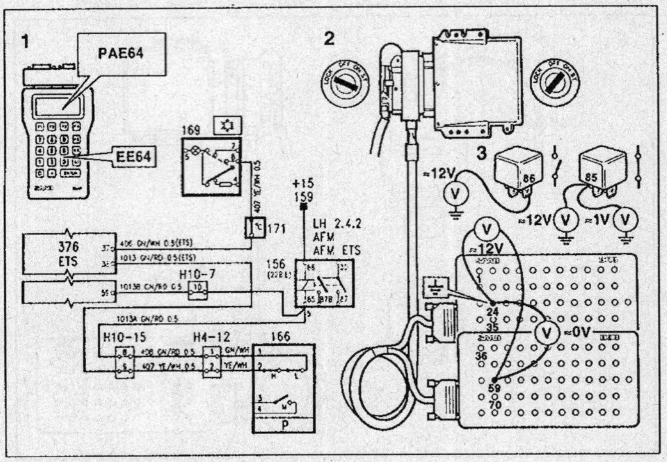

1 Connect an ISAT scan tool, contact the SFI system and (with the engine running) enter command code EE64.

The status of the system is displayed on the ISAT:

- A/C compressor switched off → PAE64-ON. If not, go to point 2.
- A/C compressor switched off → PAE64-OFF. If not, go to point 5.

2 Check whether the A/C function is OK.

If it is not, connect a BOB to the ECM and check whether battery positive voltage is present on pin 59 of the ECM when the A/C compressor is working.

If the voltage is present, replace ECM.

3 If not, check whether voltage is present on pin 86 of the A/C relay and that the voltage applied to pin 85 is about 1 V when the relay is in the operated condition (A/C compressor working).

(With the A/C compressor disconnected the voltage on pin 85 is about 12 V.)

If not, check the A/C function

SA1029100125010X

Fig. 140 A/C relay inspection (Part 1 of 2). 9000

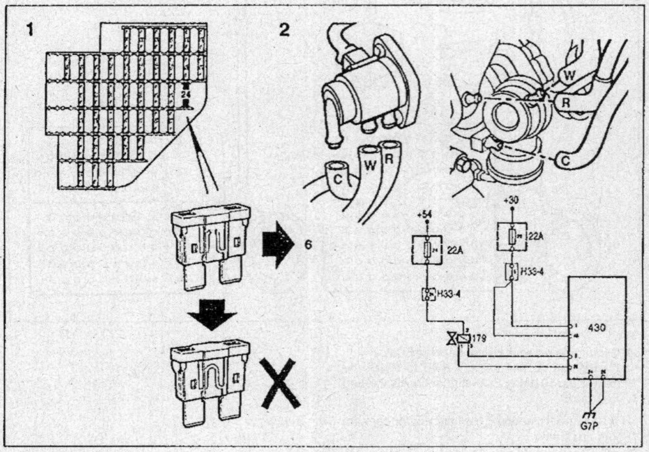

1 Check fuse 24.

If the fuse is blown, do not insert a new one but go to point 6.

2 Check the three regulating hoses of the valve are OK and correctly connected.

SA1029100126010X

Fig. 141 Boost pressure control operation inspection (Part 1 of 5). 900

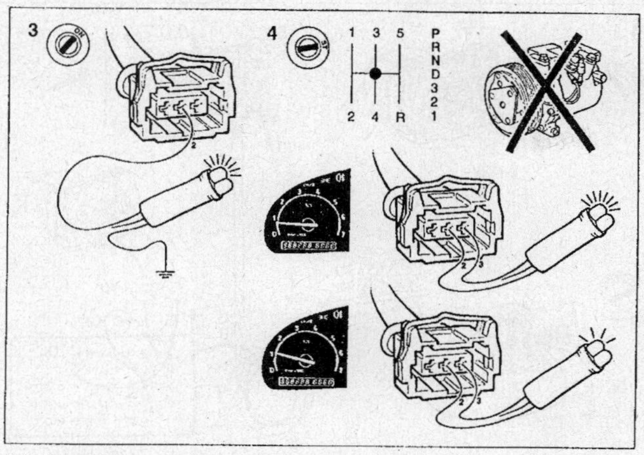

3 Ignition switched on.

Check that the valve receives a +54 supply by connecting the test lamp between the valve's connector, pin 2 and ground. The lamp must then light up.

If the lamp does not light up, check the lead between pin 2 and fuse 24.

4 Apply the handbrake.

Put the gear lever/selector lever in the N/P position. Start the engine, switch off AC/ACC and allow the engine speed to stabilize below 1000 rpm. Connect the test lamp between pins 2 and 3.

The lamp must then light up.

Increase the engine speed to just over 1000 rpm. The lamp must then shine considerably less brightly.

If the lamp does not light up with a steady glow regardless of whether the engine speed is below or above 1000 rpm, check the lead between pin 3 and pin 2 on the ECM for discontinuity/shorting.

If the lead is OK, replace ECM.

SA1029100126020X

Fig. 141 Boost pressure control operation inspection (Part 2 of 5). 900

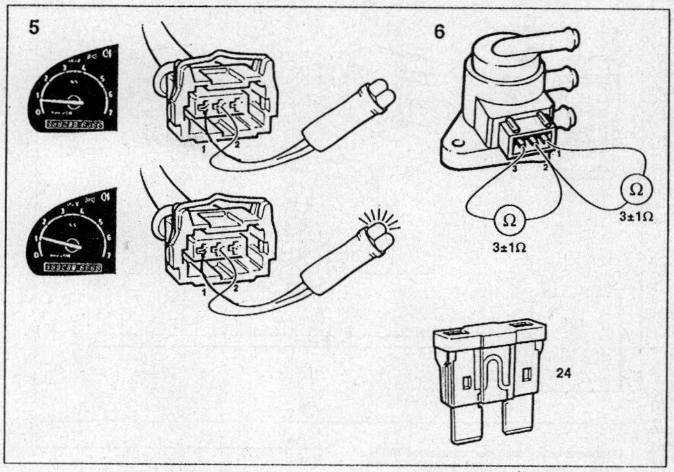

5 Connect the test lamp between pins 2 and 1. When the speed is below 1000 rpm, the lamp must go out.

Increase the engine speed to just over 1000 rpm. The lamp must then come on.

If the lamp does not light up or lights up with a steady glow, regardless of whether the engine speed is below or above 1000 rpm, check the lead between pin 1 and pin 26 of the ECM for discontinuity/shorting.

If the lead is OK, replace ECM.

6 Measure the resistance of the valve between pins 2 and 3 and between pins 2 and 1. The value in both cases must be 3±1Ω.

If the value is incorrect, fit a new valve.

If necessary, then replace fuse 24.

SA1029100126030X

Fig. 141 Boost pressure control operation inspection (Part 3 of 5). 900

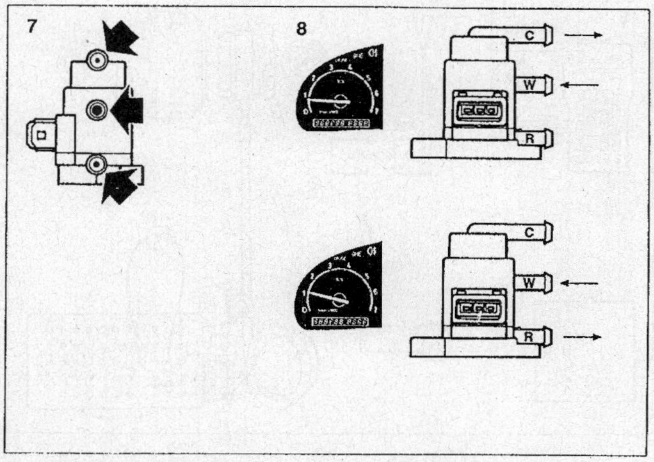

7 Disconnect the valve and check visually that its ports are not obstructed.

If so, fit a new valve.

8 Connect the valve's connector.

Start the engine and allow engine speed to stabilize below 1000 rpm.

Blow into connection W to establish that only connections W and C are joined.

Increase engine speed to just over 1000 rpm. Blow into connection W to establish that only connections W and R are joined.

If the result of the above test is incorrect, fit a new valve.

SA1029100126040X

Fig. 141 Boost pressure control operation inspection (Part 4 of 5). 900

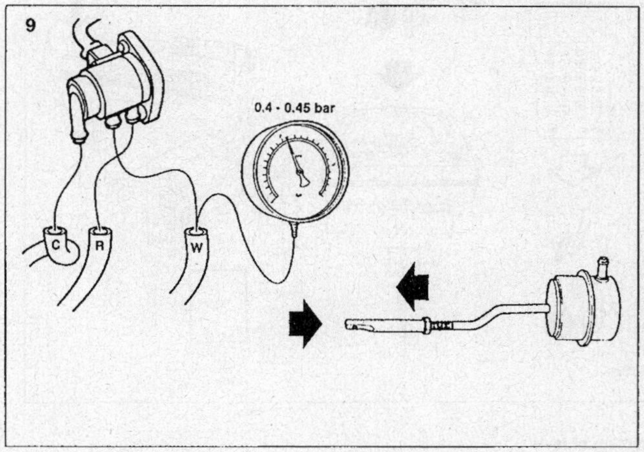

9 Stop the engine.

Check by blowing into hoses R and C that they are clear of obstructions.

Connect a pressure/vacuum pump to the hose marked W.

Generate a positive pressure. The regulating bar of the wastegate must start to move at 0.4-0.45 bar and the membrane housing unit must be pressure-tight.

SA1029100126050X

Fig. 141 Boost pressure control operation inspection (Part 5 of 5). 900

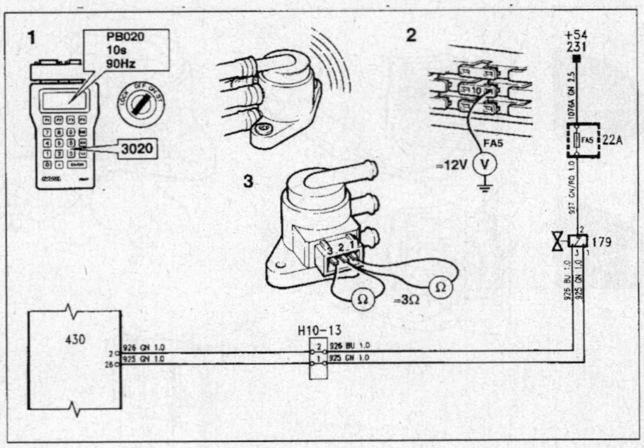

1 Connect an ISAT scan tool, contact the SFI system and enter command code 3020.

Check that the boost pressure control (BPC) valve is working by listening to it (note: low noise level!) or by feeling it vibrating (at a frequency of 8 Hz).

(A physical check of the BPC valve can be carried out as follows: blow into the valve connection to check whether the washer between the valve's poles has jammed, e.g. due to a coating of oil from the crankcase ventilation system. If the BPC valve is faulty, replace it.)

2 If it is not, turn the ignition switch to the Drive position and check that fuse FA5 is intact and that voltage is present up to the fuse holder.

3 Unplug the valve's connector and check the resistance across pins 1 and 2 and also across pins 2 and 3 of the valve. In both cases the resistance should be about 3 ohms.

If it is not, replace the boost pressure control valve.

Note:
When command code 30XX has been used, the car cannot be started for the following 12 minutes. Use command code **FF00** to clear the function, following which the car can be started.

SA1029100127010X

Fig. 142 Boost pressure control valve (APC solenoid) inspection (Part 1 of 2). 9000

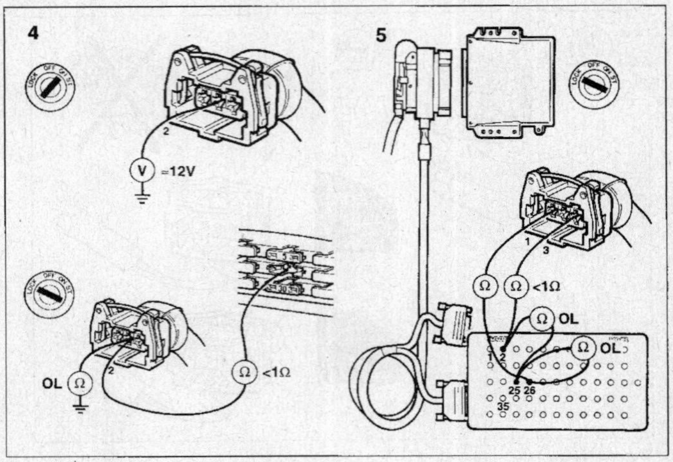

4 If the BPC valve is OK, turn the ignition switch to the Drive position and check that battery positive voltage is present on pin 2 of the valve's connector.

If it is not, switch off the ignition and check the lead between pin 2 of the valve's connector and the fuse holder (fuse removed) for continuity/shorting to ground.

5 With the ignition switched off, connect a BOB to the ECM wiring harness (ECM disconnected).

Check the wiring from pins 2 and 26 of the ECM to pins 3 and 1 of the BPC valve's connector for continuity/shorting to ground.

Remedy faulty wiring and/or connectors or continue as described below.

6 If problems/fault symptoms persist in spite of the above checks and possible road testing, **replace ECM.**

Note
If repeated pressure monitor operation has been caused by excessive boost pressure (such as due to a defective solenoid valve), maximum negative adaption will be obtained. This means that normal maximum boost pressure will not be attained. To attain maximum boost pressure, disconnect and reconnect the control module and carry out adaption.

SA1029100127020X

Fig. 142 Boost pressure control valve (APC solenoid) inspection (Part 2 of 2). 9000

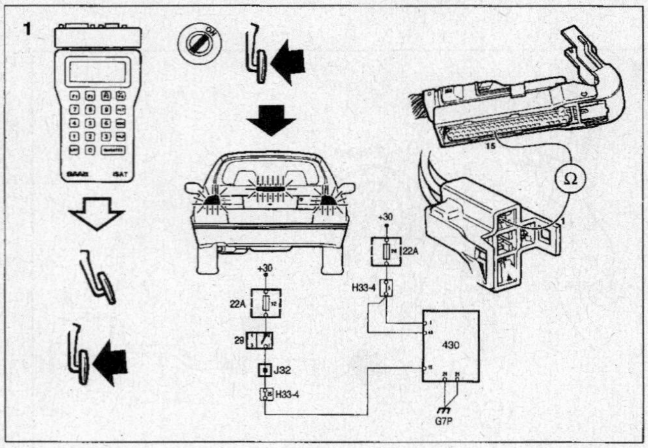

Symptom of fault
Full boost pressure even when the brake pedal is activated.

Diagnostic procedure

1 Connect an ISAT scan tool.
Ignition switched on.
Select "BRAKE LIGHT SWITCH" in the ISAT menu "READ ON/OFF".
Check the brake light switch by depressing and releasing the brake pedal.
If the ISAT shows the correct value, continue.
If the ISAT shows an incorrect value, check that the brake light works when the pedal is depressed.
If the brake light works, the fault is located in the lead between pin 15 of the ECM and crimped connection J67.
If the brake light does not work, diagnose electrical system.

SA1029100128000X

Fig. 143 Input from brake light switch fault diagnosis. 900

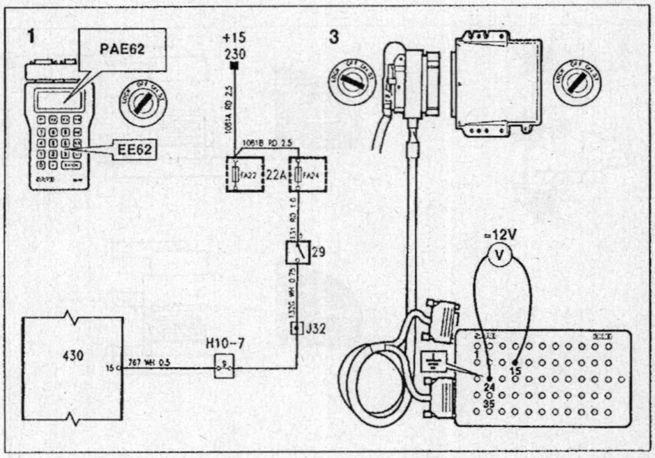

1 Connect an ISAT scan tool, contact the SFI system and enter command code EE62.

The status of the system is displayed on the ISAT:

- Brake pedal depressed → PAE62-ON. If not, go to point 2.
- Brake pedal not depressed→ PAE62-OFF. If not, go to point 5.

2 Check whether fuse FA24 is intact. Also check whether the brake lights work. Change the fuse if it has blown. Take remedial action if the brake lights do not work.

If the fuse is OK, continue as described below.

3 With the ignition switched off, connect a BOB to the ECM wiring harness (ECM disconnected).

With the ignition switch in the Drive position, check whether battery positive voltage is present on pin 15 of the ECM when the brake pedal is depressed.

If it is, **replace ECM**

If it is not, continue as described below.

SA1029100129010X

Fig. 144 Brake light switch operation inspection (Part 1 of 2). 9000

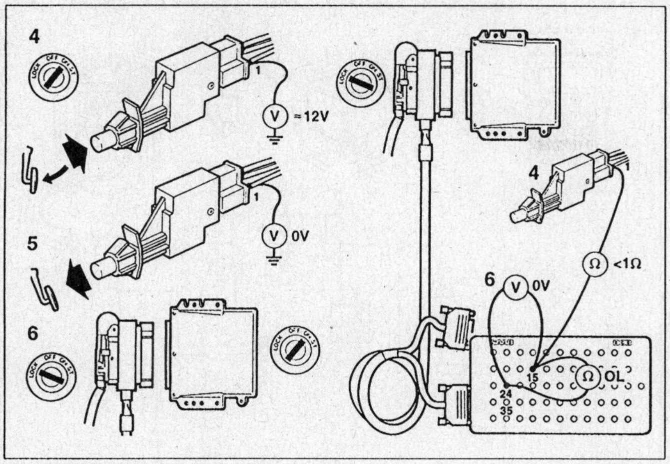

4 Check whether voltage is present on pin 1 of the brake light switch when the switch is activated. If it is not, replace the brake light switch.

If the switch is OK, check the lead to pin 15 of the ECM (ignition switched off) for continuity/shorting to ground.

Take remedial action if the wiring/connectors are faulty.

5 Check whether voltage is present on pin 1 of the brake light switch when the switch is not activated. If voltage is present, replace the brake light switch.

If the switch is OK, continue as described below.

6 With the ignition switched off, connect the BOB to the ECM wiring harness (ECM disconnected).

Turn the ignition switch to the Drive position and check the lead to pin 15 of the ECM for shorting to battery positive voltage.

Take remedial action in the event of faulty wiring/connectors or any component connected to grounding point J32 which might be the cause of voltage being applied to the circuit.

If the wiring is OK, replace ECM.

SA1029100129020X

Fig. 144 Brake light switch operation inspection (Part 2 of 2). 9000

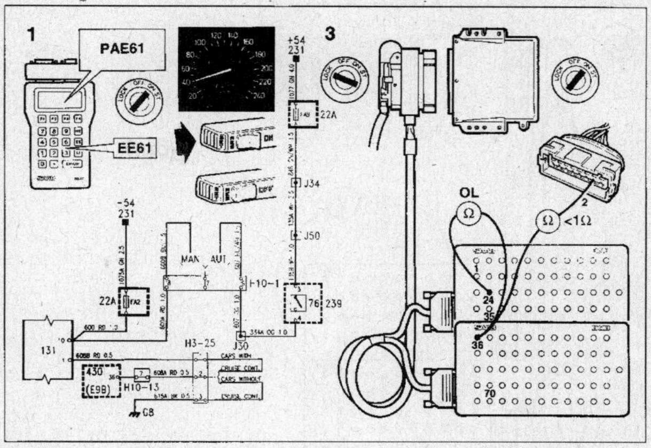

1 Connect an ISAT scan tool, contact the AFM system and enter command code EE61.

The status of the system is displayed on the ISAT:

- With the Cruise Control in the "ON" position (the car must be driven faster than 40 km/h with the SET button depressed) → PAE63-ON. If not, go to point 2.
- With the Cruise Control in the "OFF" position→ PAE63-OFF. If not, go to point 5.

2 Check fuse FA2 (manual) or FA9 (automatic). Also check whether the Cruise Control is in working order.

If it is not, replace the fuse or carry out a fault diagnosis of the Cruise Control system.

If the Cruise Control system is OK, continue as described below.

3 With the ignition switched OFF, connect the BOB to the ECM wiring harness (ECM disconnected) and check the lead to pin 36 of the ECM for continuity/shorting to ground.

Take remedial action if the cable is faulty.

SA1029100130010X

Fig. 145 Cruise control inspection (Part 1 of 2). 9000 less TCS

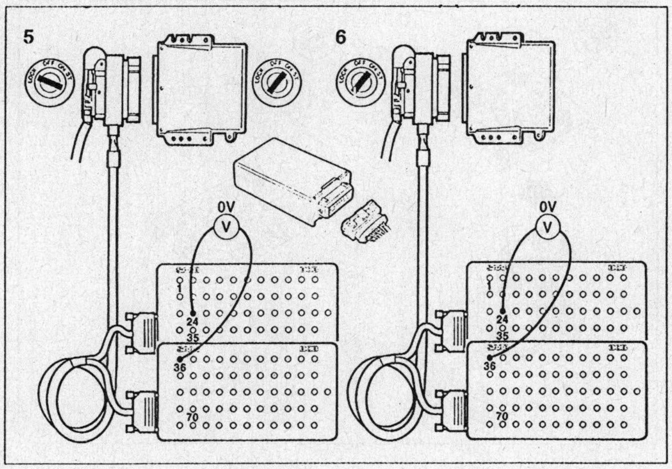

4 If the cable is OK, for further diagnostic instructions.

5 With the ignition switched off, connect the BOB to the ECM wiring harness (ECM disconnected). Turn the ignition switch to the Drive position and check whether voltage is present on pin 36 of the ECM.

If it is not, replace ECM.

If it is, continue as described below.

6 Unplug the connector from the control module of the Cruise Control system and check whether voltage is still present on pin 36. If it is, carry out a fault diagnosis of the Cruise Control system

If voltage is still present on pin 36 of the ECM, check the lead to it for shorting to battery positive voltage.

Take remedial action if the wiring is faulty.

7 **Replace ECM.**

SA1029100130020X

Fig. 145 Cruise control inspection (Part 2 of 2). 9000 less TCS

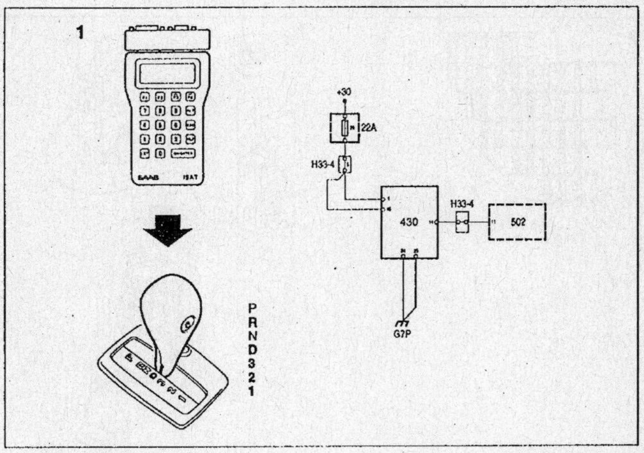

Symptom of fault

Reduction in engine idling speed when the selector lever is moved from P or N.

Diagnostic procedure

1 Connect an ISAT scan tool.
Ignition switched on.
Select the "DRIVE" command in the ISAT menu "READ FUNCTIONS".

Check that an input signal is present by moving the selector lever from P and N to another gear position.

If the ISAT scan tool shows the correct value, continue with diagnostic trouble code P0505

If the ISAT shows an incorrect value, continue with point 2.

SA1029100131010X

Fig. 146 Drive input signal from automatic transaxle fault diagnosis (Part 1 of 2). 900

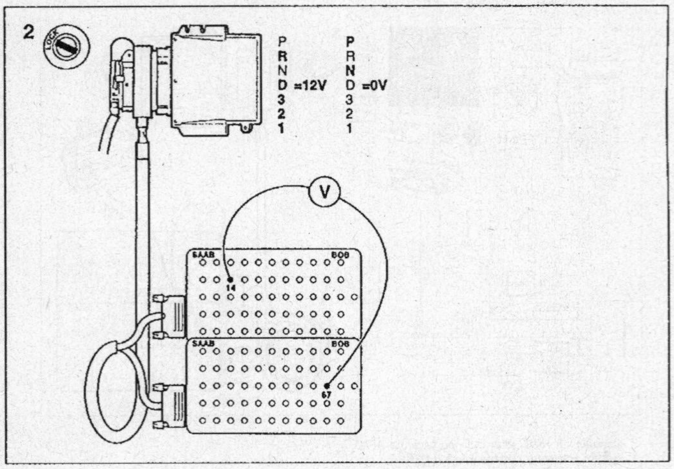

2 Connect a BOB to the Trionic ECM. Measure the voltage in pin 14, input signal from automatic transmission.

The nominal value is 0 V with the selector lever in position P or N and 12 V with the selector lever in positions R, D, 3, 2 or 1.

If the voltage measurement shows correct values,

If the voltage measurement shows incorrect values, check and if necessary remedy the fault in the lead between pin 14 of the Trionic ECM and pin 11 of the transmission control module.

if the lead is OK, diagnose automatic transaxle.

SA1029100131020X

Fig. 146 Drive input signal from automatic transaxle fault diagnosis (Part 2 of 2). 900

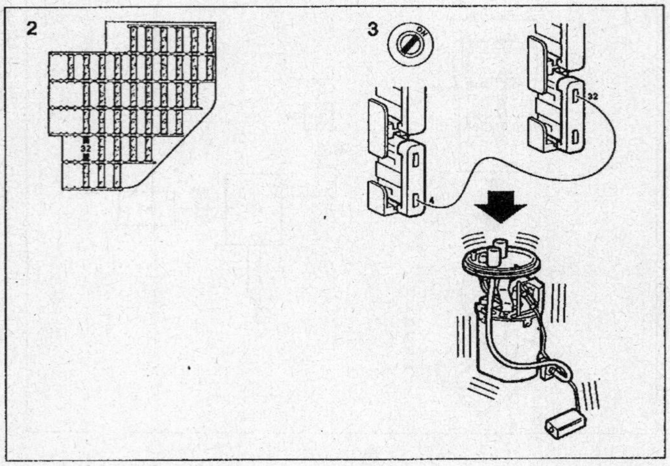

2 Check and if necessary replace fuse 32.

If the fuse is intact, continue with point 3.

If the fuse blows on repeated ISAT activation of the fuel pump relay, continue with point 6.

3 Apply power to the fuel pump. Connect a jumper lead between fuses 4 and 32, and listen for the sound of the pump working.

If the pump is working, continue with point 4.

If the pump is not working, continue with point 5.

SA1029100132020X

Fig. 147 Fuel pump relay/fuel pump fault diagnosis (Part 2 of 6). 900

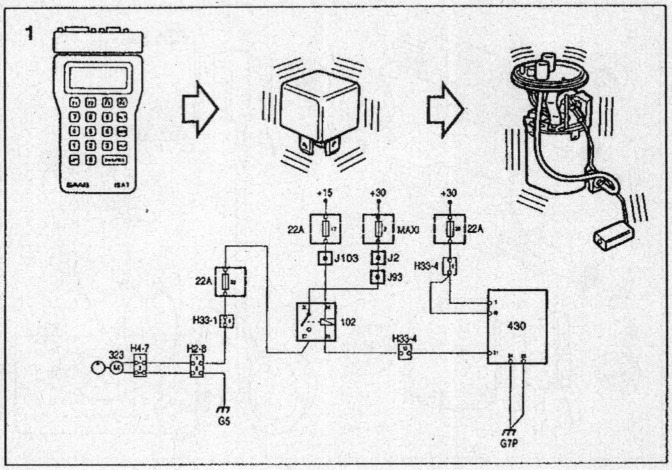

Symptom of fault

The engine fails to start

Diagnostic procedure

1 Connect an ISAT scan tool.

Ignition switched on.

Select the "PUMP RELAY" command in the ISAT menu "ACTIVATE". Activation of the relay takes place for 10 seconds at 1 Hz. If a longer activation time is required, the command must be repeated.

Listen for the sound of the fuel pump relay and fuel pump working. Both must be heard at 1 Hz.

If only the relay can be heard, continue with point 2.

If neither the relay nor the pump can be heard, continue with point 7.

SA1029100132010X

Fig. 147 Fuel pump relay/fuel pump fault diagnosis (Part 1 of 6). 900

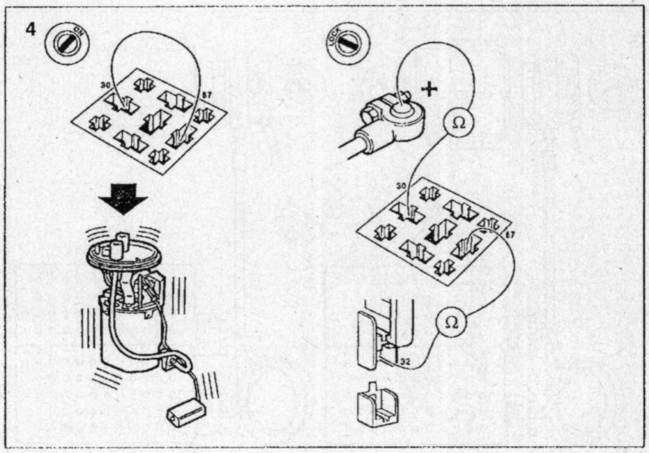

4 Disconnect the fuel pump relay.

Connect a jumper lead between pin 30 and pin 87 on the relay base.

If the fuel pump is now working, fit a new fuel pump relay.

If the pump is not working, check and if necessary remedy faults in the lead between pin 87 and fuse 32 and the lead between pin 30 and Batt+.

SA1029100132030X

Fig. 147 Fuel pump relay/fuel pump fault diagnosis (Part 3 of 6). 900

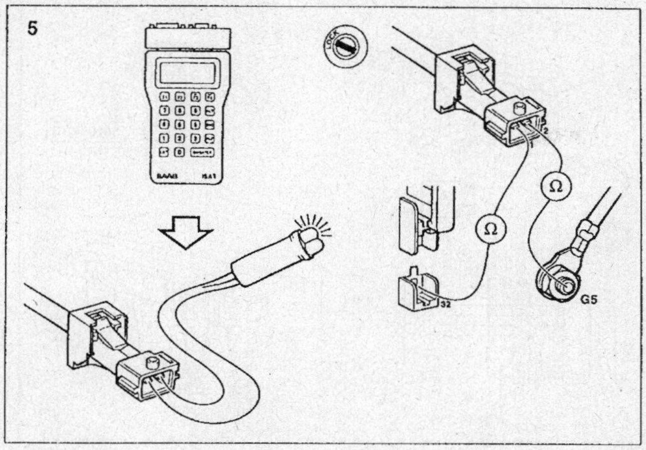

5 Unplug connector H2-9 to the fuel pump.

The connector is located under the rear seat. Note that the connector with thick cables is the correct one. The other one is connected to the level sensor.

Connect the test lamp between both pins of the 2-pole male connector .

Select the "PUMP RELAY" command with the ISAT scan tool. The test lamp must flash at 1 Hz.

If the test lamp flashes, replace the fuel pump and the wiring between H4-7 and H2-9, or just the wiring.

If the test lamp does not flash, check and if necessary remedy faults firstly between pin 2 and grounding point G5 and secondly the lead between pin 1 and fuse 32.

SA1029100132040X

Fig. 147 Fuel pump relay/fuel pump fault diagnosis (Part 4 of 6). 900

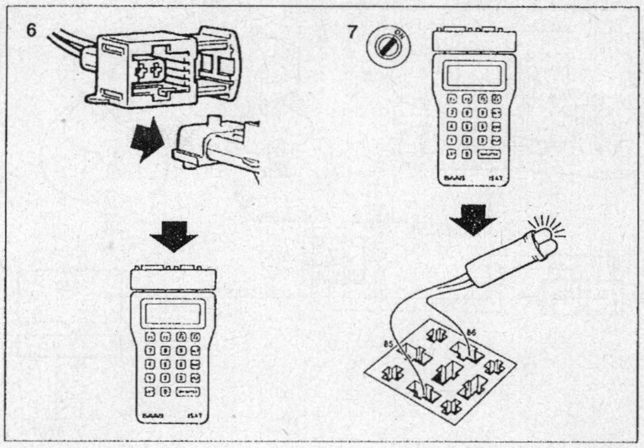

6 Unplug the connector H2-9 to the fuel pump. The connector is located under the rear seat. Note that the connector with thick cables is the correct one. The other connector is connected to the level sensor.

Replace fuse 32 and repeat the ISAT command "PUMP RELAY".

If the fuse blows, check and if necessary remedy the fault in the wiring between fuse 32 and pin 1 in connector H2-9. If the fuse remains intact, replace the fuel pump and the wiring between H4-7 and H2-9, or just the wiring.

7 Disconnect the fuel pump relay.

Connect the test lamp in the relay base between pins 85 and 86.
Ignition switched on

Select "PUMP RELAY" with the ISAT scan tool again. The test lamp must flash at 1 Hz.

If the test lamp flashes, fit a new fuel pump relay.

If the test lamp does not flash, continue with point 8.

SA1029100132050X

Fig. 147 Fuel pump relay/fuel pump fault diagnosis (Part 5 of 6). 900

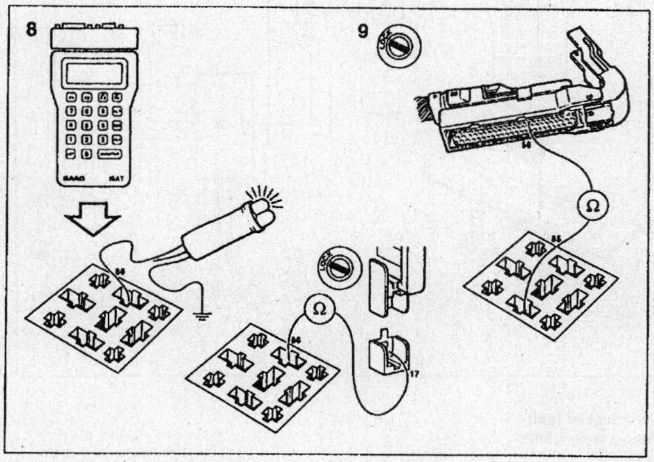

8 Connect the test lamp between the relay base, pin 86 and safe grounding point.

If the test lamp does not light up, check and if necessary remedy the fault in the lead between pin 86 and fuse 17.

Diagnose electrical system.

If the test lamp lights up, continue with point 9.

9 Check and if necessary remedy the fault in the lead between pin 85 and pin 56 of the ECM.

If the lead is OK, replace ECM.

SA1029100132060X

Fig. 147 Fuel pump relay/fuel pump fault diagnosis (Part 6 of 6). 900

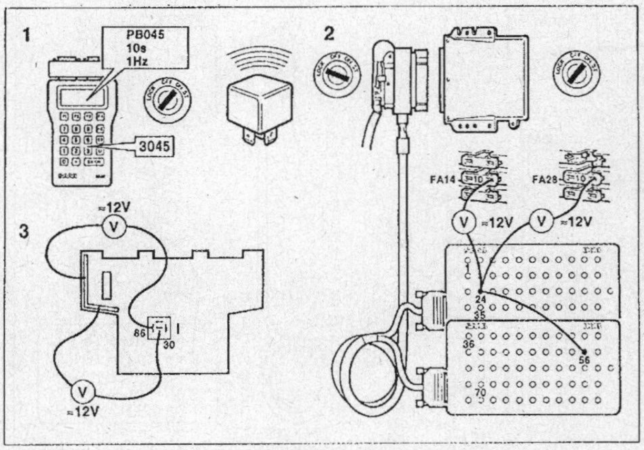

1 Connect an ISAT scan tool, contact the SFI system and enter command code 3045.

Check that the relay is activated at a frequency of 1 Hz (for 10 seconds).

2 With the ignition switched off, connect a BOB to the ECM wiring harness (ECM disconnected). Check operation of the relay as follows:

Turn the ignition switch to the Drive position and connect a jumper cable across terminals 56 and 24 of the BOB. Check whether the relay is energized by measuring the voltage at fuse positions 14 and 28.

If the relay operates, continue with point 6.

If the relay operates but fastens in the energized condition, go to point 5.

If the relay does not operate, continue as described below.

3 Check whether battery positive voltage is present up to pins 86 and 30 of the relay.

Note:
When command code 30XX has been used, the car cannot be started for the following 12 minutes. Use command code FF00 to clear the function, following which the car can be started.

SA1029100133010X

Fig. 148 Fuel pump relay inspection (Part 1 of 2). 9000

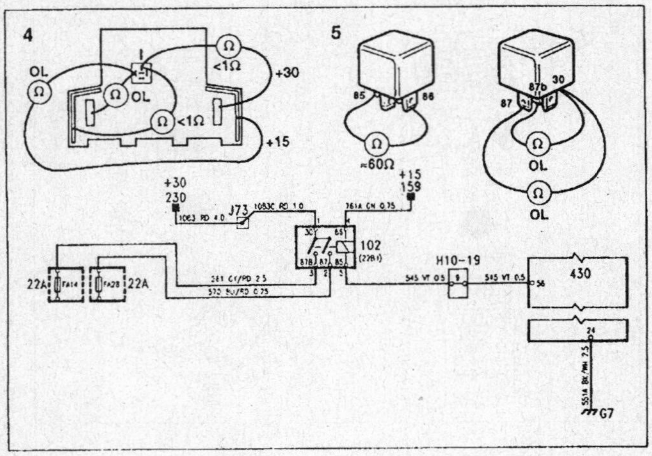

4 If battery positive voltage is not present on terminals 86 and 30, check the supply cables from the + 15 and + 30 terminals for continuity/ shorting to ground.

If the cables are OK, check whether the resistance across terminals 85 and 86 of the relay is about 60 ohms.

If it is not, replace the relay.

5 Check the resistance across terminals 30 and 87 and 87B of the relay. When the relay is not energized the resistance should be about 0 ohms and when energized less than 1 ohm.

If the relay is faulty, replace it.

6 If the fault persists in spite of the above checks, replace ECM.

SA1029100133020X

Fig. 148 Fuel pump relay inspection (Part 2 of 2). 9000

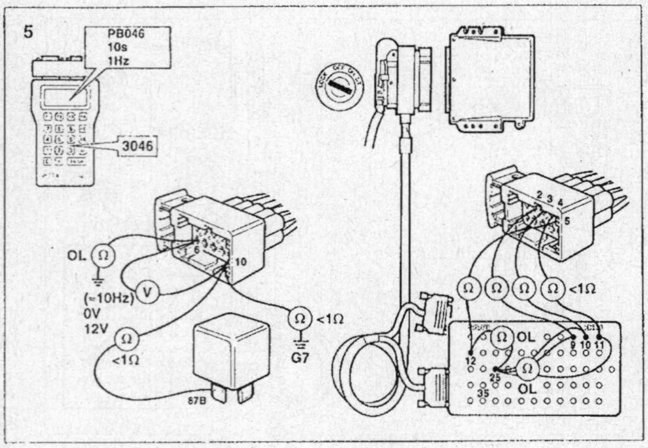

5 Unplug the connector from the IDM.

Enter command code 3046 and check that battery positive voltage is obtained (1 Hz pulses) across pins 10 and 6 of the connector.

If it is not, check the lead between pin 10 of the cartridge's connector and pin 87B of the main relay and also the lead between pin 6 of the cartridge's connector and grounding point G7 for continuity/shorting to ground.

Repair any faulty wiring and/or connectors, or check the main relay

6 With the ignition switched off, connect a BOB to the SFI wiring (the ECM should be disconnected).

Check the trigger/ignition cable for the relevant cylinder for continuity/shorting to ground as follows:

- Pin 9 of the ECM and pin 2 of the IDM connector
- Pin 10 of the ECM and pin 3 of the IDM connector
- Pin 11 of the ECM and pin 4 of the IDM connector
- Pin 12 of the ECM and pin 5 of the IDM connector

7 Remedy any faulty cables. If the cables are OK, try a new ignition discharge module.

8

If the fault nonetheless persists when road testing/checking, replace ECM.

SA1029100134020X

Fig. 149 Ignition discharge module inspection (Part 2 of 2). 9000

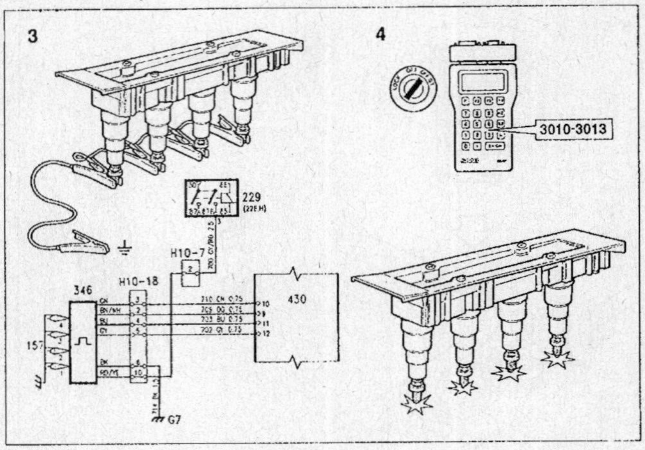

1 Remove the ignition discharge module (IDM) from the cylinder head.

2 Fit spark plugs in the spark plug connections.

3 Ground the spark plugs, using cable 86 10 867.

4 Connect an ISAT scan tool, contact the SFI system and enter command code 3010-3013.

Check that the activated spark plug produces a spark. If a spark is produced, continue with point 6.

If no spark is produced by any spark plug, continue as described below.

Note:

When command code 30XX has been used, the car cannot be started for the following 12 minutes. Use command code FF00 to clear the function, following which the car can be started.

SA1029100134010X

Fig. 149 Ignition discharge module inspection (Part 1 of 2). 9000

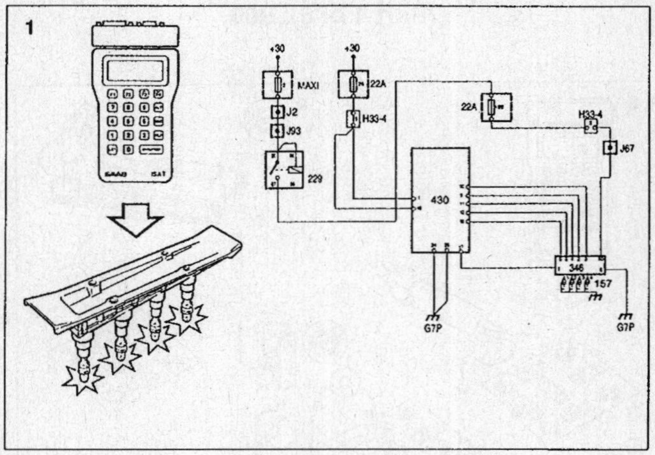

Symptom of fault

Misfiring in any cylinder.

Diagnostic procedure

1 Connect an ISAT scan tool.

Ignition switched on.

Select each individual ignition coil in the ISAT menu "ACTIVATE" with the submenu "IGNITION COILS".

Activation of an ignition coil takes place for 10 seconds at 200 Hz. If a longer activation time is required, the command must be repeated.

Listen for the sound of each individual ignition coil operating.

If all the ignition coils are working, continue with point 4.

If any ignition coil is not working, continue with point 2.

SA1029100135010X

Fig. 150 Ignition misfiring fault diagnosis (Part 1 of 4). 900

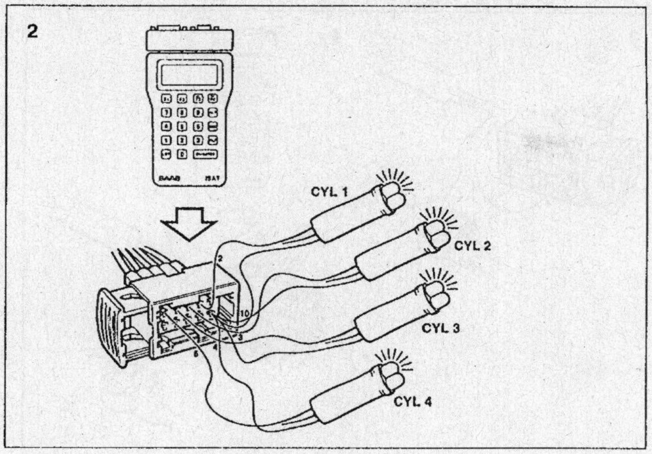

2 With the ignition switched off, unplug the 10-pole connector of the ignition discharge module.

Ignition switched on.

Connect the test lamp between 10 and the trigger cable of the relevant ignition coil. Activate the ignition coil concerned with the ISAT command.

The test lamp must light up with extremely short interruptions for 10 seconds. In the event of uncertainty, repeat the command.

If the test lamp lights up with extremely short interruptions, fit a new ignition discharge module.

If the test lamp does not light up or lights up with a steady glow, continue with point 3.

SA1029100135020X

Fig. 150 Ignition misfiring fault diagnosis (Part 2 of 4). 900

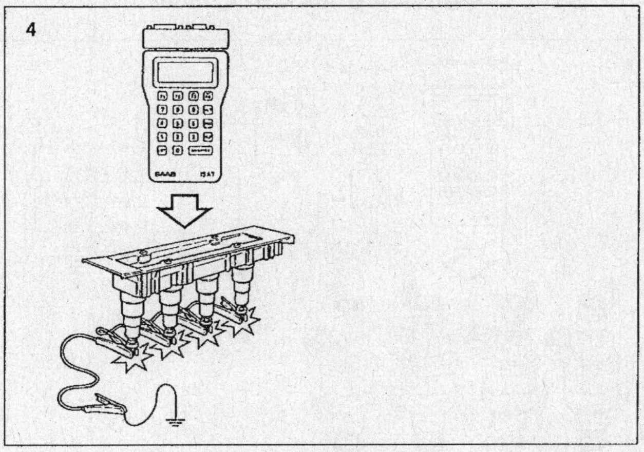

4 Check the operation of the ignition discharge module.

Disconnect the ignition discharge module from the camshaft cover.

Fit a test spark plug (part no. 86 11 386) in the spark plug connection concerned. Ground the spark plug with cable 8610867. Activate each individual ignition coil with an ISAT scan tool. Check that a spark is produced on the activated spark plug.

If no spark is produced, fit a new ignition discharge module.

If a spark is produced, fit a new spark plug.

5 Drive the car to check whether the fault symptoms persist. If so, replace ECM.

⚠ WARNING - HIGH VOLTAGE

The electronic ignition system generates voltages of 40,000 Volts. This voltage can prove fatal to people with weak hearts or those who are fitted with pacemakers. The ignition system should therefore be treated with great respect.

CAUTION

The ignition discharge module must be positioned with the ignition coils facing down during the test so that the transformer oil is insulating the high-voltage part of the ignition coils.

SA1029100135040X

Fig. 150 Ignition misfiring fault diagnosis (Part 4 of 4). 900

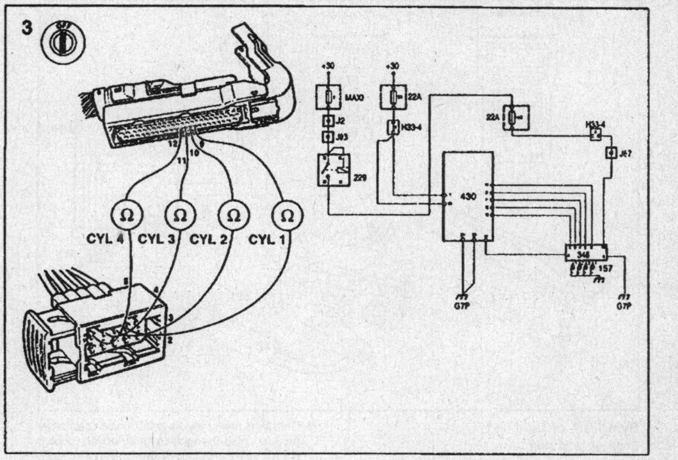

3 **Check the relevant trigger cable for continuity/shorting.**

If the cable is OK, replace ECM.

SA1029100135030X

Fig. 150 Ignition misfiring fault diagnosis (Part 3 of 4). 900

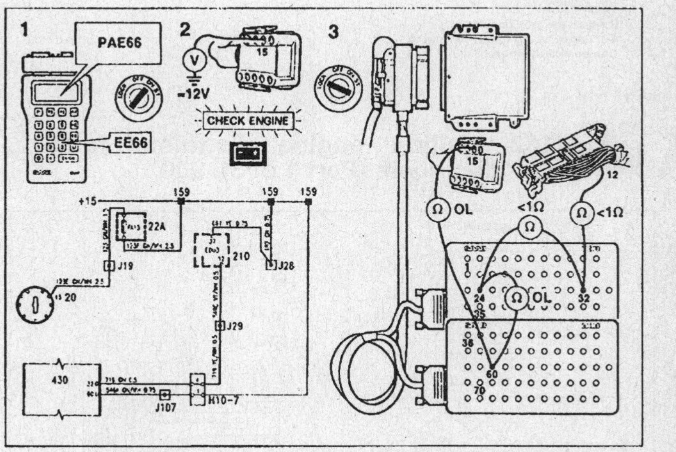

1 Connect an ISAT scan tool, contact the SFI system and enter command code EE66. The status of the system will be displayed on the ISAT scan tool. With the ignition switched on, the display should show PAE66 ON.

If no communication can be established with the system, continue with point 4.

2 Check whether voltage is present on terminal 15 of the ignition switch when it is in the Drive position (look at the warning lamps or take a measurement directly on the +15 terminal).

If voltage is not present, the ignition switch is faulty and must be remedied. If voltage is present on terminal 15, continue as described below.

3 Connect a BOB to the ECM wiring harness (ECM disconnected) and, with the ignition switched off, check the lead to pin 60 of the ECM for continuity/shorting to ground.

If the lead is not OK, remedy the fault or replace ECM.

4 With the ignition still switched off, check the lead to pin 32 of the ECM for continuity/shorting to ground.

If lead is not OK, remedy the fault or check the malfunction indicator lamp (MIL). Refer to "Malfunction Indicator and Shift Up Lamp, Component Diagnosis."

If the MIL (CHECK ENGINE lamp) is OK, replace ECM.

SA1029100136000X

Fig. 151 Ignition switch inspection. 9000

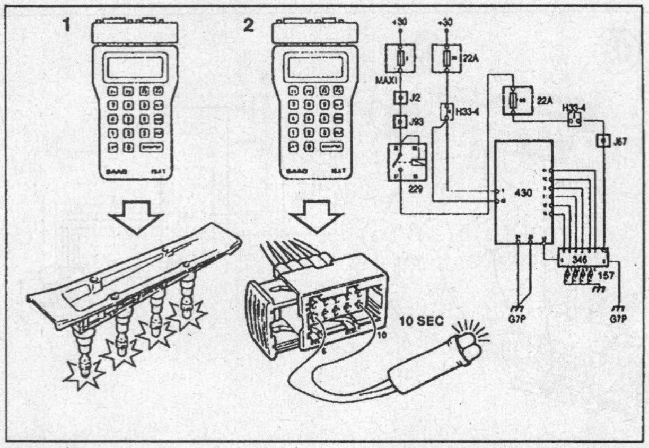

Symptom of fault
Engine fails to start.

Diagnostic procedure

1 Connect an ISAT scan tool.

Ignition switched on.

Select each individual in the ISAT menu "ACTIVATE" with the submenu "IGNITION COILS".

Activation of an ignition coil takes place for 10 seconds at 200 Hz. If a longer activation time is required, the command must be repeated.

Listen for the sound of each ignition coil operating.

If all the ignition coils are working, continue with point 5.

If no ignition coil is working is working, continue with point 2.

If any of the ignition coils are working, refer to "Ignition Misfiring, Component Diagnosis."

2 Check the power supply to the ignition discharge module. With the ignition switched off, unplug the 10-pole connector of the ignition discharge module.

Ignition switched on.

Connect the test lamp between pins 10 and 6 in the ignition discharge module's connector.

Activate one of the ignition coils with the ISAT scan tool. The purpose of the activation is to make the main relay operate.

The test lamp must light up with a steady glow.

If the test lamp lights up, try out a new ignition discharge module.

If the test lamp does not light up, continue with point 3.

SA1029100137010X

Fig. 152 Ignition - engine fails to start fault diagnosis (Part 1 of 3). 900

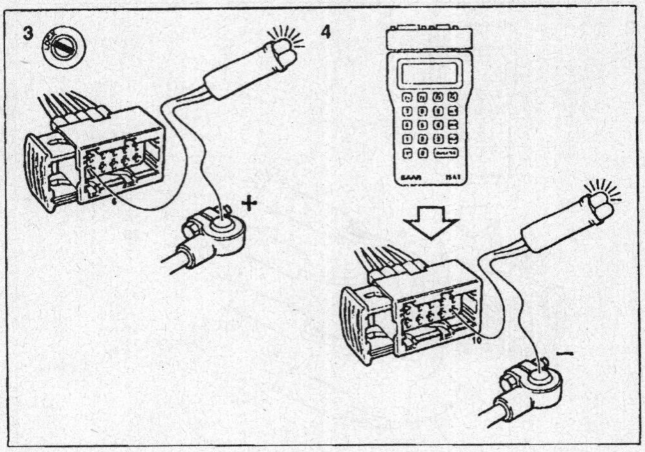

3 The ignition discharge module does not have any power supply, 12V or ground.

Check the continuity to ground.

Connect the test lamp between Batt+ and pin 6 in the ignition discharge module's connector.

The test lamp must light up with a steady glow.

If the test lamp does not light up, check and if necessary remedy the fault in the wiring including grounding point G7P.

If the test lamp lights up with a steady glow, continue with point 4.

4 The ignition discharge module does not have a 12V supply.

Check the continuity to Batt+ .

Connect the test lamp between the ignition discharge module's connector, pin 10 and Batt.

Activate one of the ignition coils with the ISAT scan tool. The purpose of the activation is to make the main relay operate.

The test lamp must light up with a steady glow.

If the test lamp lights up, continue with point 6.

If the test lamp does not light up, refer to "Main Relay, Component Diagnosis."

SA1029100137020X

Fig. 152 Ignition - engine fails to start fault diagnosis (Part 2 of 3). 900

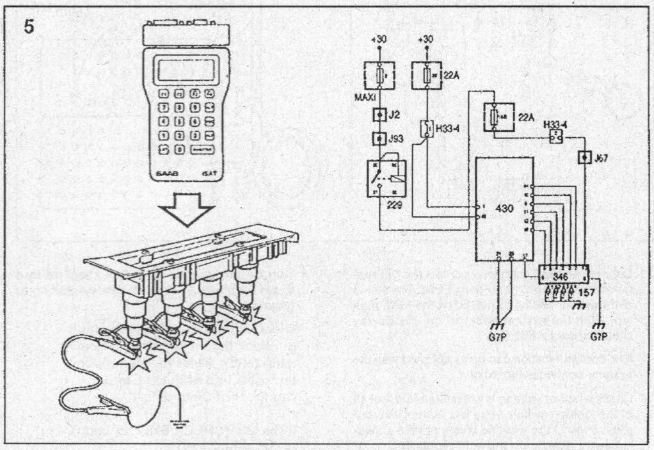

5 Check the operation of the ignition discharge module.

Disconnect the ignition discharge module from the camshaft cover.

Fit a test spark plug (part no. 8611386) in the spark plug terminal concerned. Ground the spark plug with cable 8610867. Activate each individual ignition coil with the ISAT scan tool. Check that sparks are produced on the activated spark plug.

If sparks are not produced, fit a new ignition discharge module.

If sparks are produced, fit a new spark plug.

6 Drive the car to check whether the fault symptoms persist.

replace ECM

CAUTION

The ignition discharge module must be positioned with the ignition coils facing down during the test so that the transformer oil is insulating the high-voltage part of the ignition coils.

⚠ WARNING - HIGH VOLTAGE

The electronic ignition system generates voltages of 40,000 Volts. This voltage can prove fatal to people with weak hearts or those who are fitted with pacemakers. The ignition system should therefore be treated with great respect.

SA1029100137030X

Fig. 152 Ignition - engine fails to start fault diagnosis (Part 3 of 3). 900

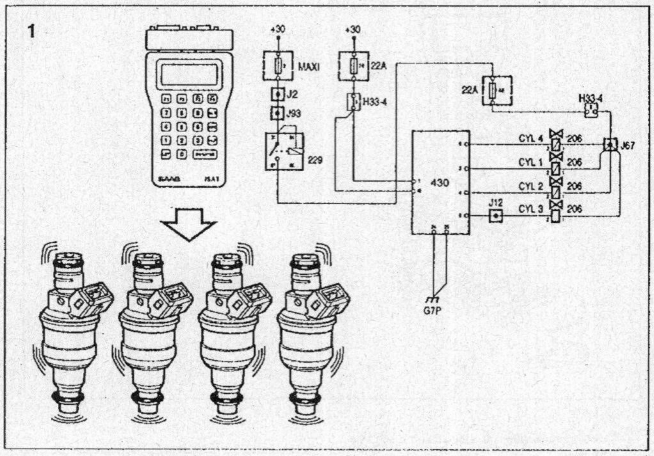

Symptom of fault
The engine is running on 3 cylinders.

Diagnostic procedure

1 Connect an ISAT scan tool.

Ignition switched on.

Select each individual valve in the ISAT menu "ACTIVATE" with the submenu "INJECTORS".

The valve is activated for 10 seconds at 10Hz. If a longer activation time is required, the command must be repeated.

Listen for the sound of each individual injector operating.

If all the injectors are working, continue with point 5.

If any injector is not working, continue with point 2.

SA1029100138010X

Fig. 153 Fuel injector fault diagnosis (Part 1 of 3). 900

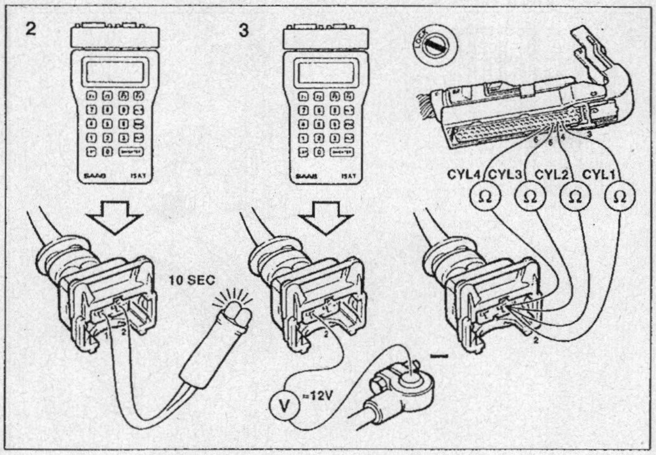

2 Unplug the connector of the injector concerned. Connect the test lamp to the injector's connector (female).

Activate the injector concerned with the ISAT scan tool and the activating command "INJECTOR CYL 1, 2, 3 or 4".

The test lamp must flash at a frequency of 10 Hz for 10 seconds. Repeat the command in the event of uncertainty.

If the test lamp flashes, continue with point 4.

If the test lamp does not flash, continue with point 3.

3 Check that the relevant injector receives a 12V supply.

Measure the volage by connecting the voltmeter between the connector of the relevant injector, pin 1 and Batt-.

Activate the relevant injector with the ISAT scan tool and the activating command "INJECTOR CYL 1, 2, 3 or 4."

The voltmeter must show approx. 12 V.

If the voltage is incorrect, the fault is located in the lead between pin 1 and crimped connection J67.

If the voltage is correct, check the lead between pin 2 and the relevant ECM output.

SA1029100138020X

Fig. 153 Fuel injector fault diagnosis (Part 2 of 3). 900

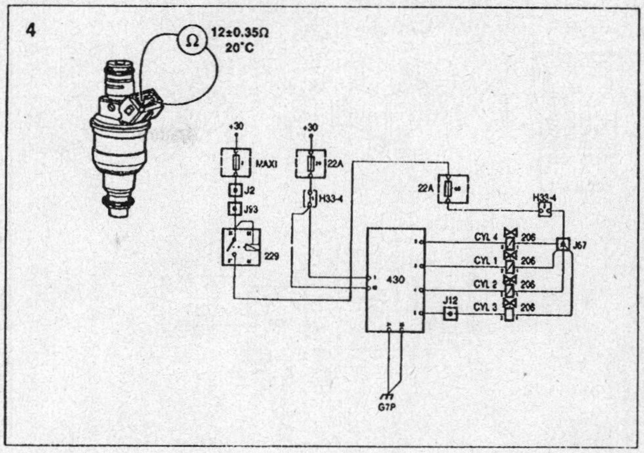

4 Check the resistance of the relevant injector. Measure Ω in the injector's connector between pins 1 and 2.

The nominal resistance is 12±0,35 Ω at 20°C. If the resistance is incorrect, fit a new injector. If the resistance is correct, continue with point 5.

5 Measure flow.

If the flow measurement is incorrect, fit a new injector.

If the flow measurement is correct, continue with point 6.

6 Drive the car to check whether the fault symptoms persist. If so, replace ECM.

SA1029100138030X

Fig. 153 Fuel injector fault diagnosis (Part 3 of 3). 900

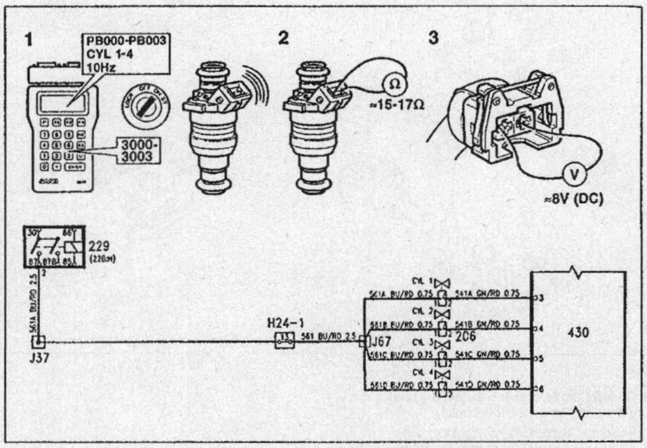

1 Connect an ISAT scan tool, contact the SFI system, enter command code 3000-3003 and check by listening to the sound of each injector that they are all working (10 Hz, 10 seconds). If not, continue as described below.

2 Unplug the connector of the relevant injector and check the injector's resistance. Do this by taking a measurement directly across connecting pins 1 and 2 of the injector.

The correct resistance is 15-17 ohms (@20°C).

If the resistance is different, fit a new injector.

If the resistance is OK, continue with the next point.

3 Turn the ignition switch to the Drive position and enter command code 3000-3003. Check that voltage pulses (10 Hz) (approx. 8 V DC) can be measured across pins 1 and 2 of the connector of the relevant injector.

If voltage is present, continue with point 6.

If there are no voltage pulses on any of the injector connections, continue as described below.

Note:
When command code 30XX has been used, the car cannot be started for the following 12 minutes. Use command code FF00 to clear the function, following which the car can be started.

SA1029100139010X

Fig. 154 Injector inspection (Part 1 of 2). 9000

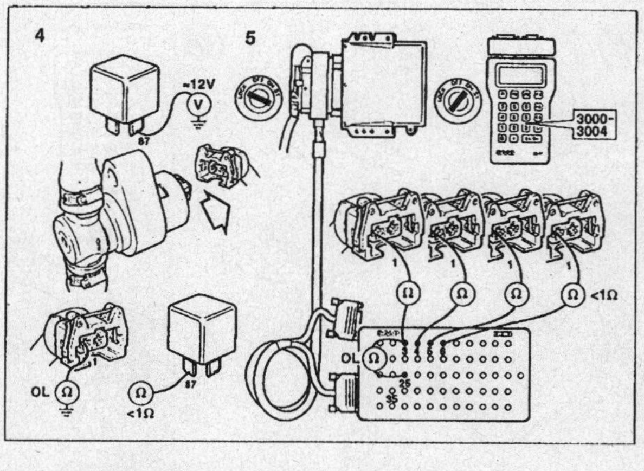

4 Check that battery positive voltage is present on pin 87 of the main relay when command code 3000-3003 is activated.

If it is not, refer to "Main Relay, Component Diagnosis."

If voltage is present, check the wiring (unplug the connector for the IAC valve, where appropriate) between pin 1 of the valve connector and terminal 87 of the main relay for continuity/shorting to ground.

Remedy faulty wiring and connectors or continue with point 6.

5 With the ignition switched off, connect a BOB to the ECM and wiring. Check the wiring for continuity/shorting to ground between pins 3, 4, 5 and 6 of the ECM and pin 1 of the relevant injector connector.

Remedy any faulty wiring or continue as described below.

6 Drive the car to check whether the fault symptoms persist. If so, replace ECM.

SA1029100139020X

Fig. 154 Injector inspection (Part 2 of 2). 9000

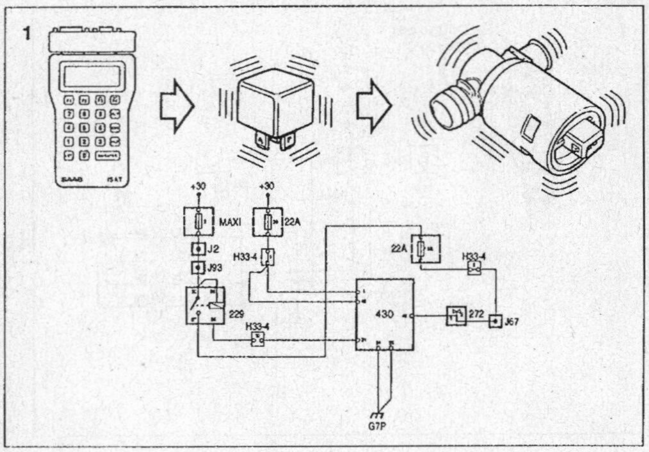

Symptom of fault
The engine fails to start

Diagnostic procedure

1 Connect an ISAT scan tool.
Ignition switched on.

Select the command "MAIN RELAY" in the ISAT menu "ACTIVATE". Activation of the main relay takes place for 10 seconds at 1 Hz. If a longer activation time is required, the command must be repeated.

Listen for the sound of the main relay and the idle air control valve operating. Both must click at 1 Hz.

If only the main relay clicks, continue with point 2.

If neither the main relay nor the idle air control valve clicks, continue with point 5.

SA1029100140010X

Fig. 155 Main relay fault diagnosis (Part 1 of 4). 900

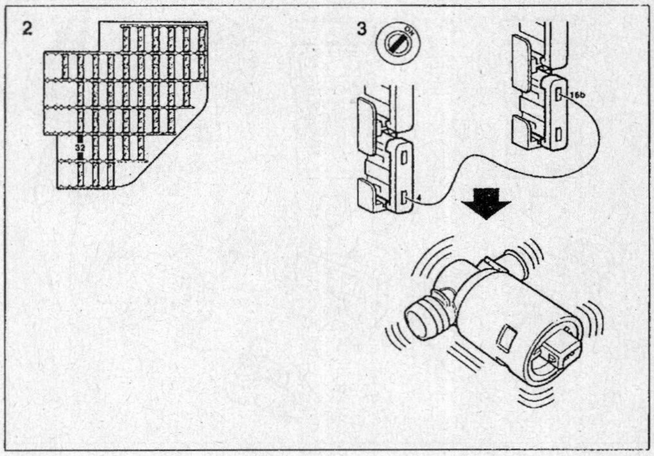

2 Check and if necessary replace fuse 16 B.

3 Apply power to the IAC valve. Connect a jumper lead between fuses 4 and 16 B.

If the idle air control valve does not click, the fault is located in the lead between fuse 16 B and crimped connection J67.

If the idle air control valve clicks, continue with point 4.

SA1029100140020X

Fig. 155 Main relay fault diagnosis (Part 2 of 4). 900

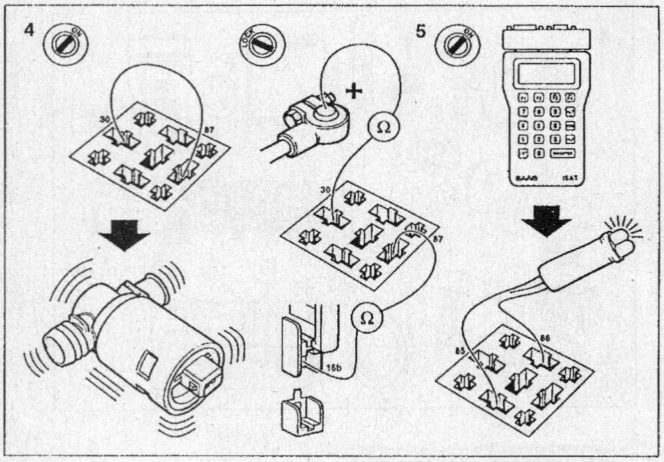

4 Disconnect the main relay.

Connect a jumper lead between pins 30 and 87 on the relay base.

If the idle air control valve clicks, fit a new main relay.

If the idle air control valve does not click, check and if necessary remedy faults in the lead between pin 87 and fuse 16 B and the lead between pin 30 and Batt+ .

5 Disconnect the main relay.

Connect the test lamp in the relay base between pins 85 and 86.
Ignition switched on

Select "MAIN RELAY" again with the ISAT scan tool.

If the test lamp flashes, fit a new main relay.

If the test lamp does not flash, continue with point 6.

SA1029100140030X

Fig. 155 Main relay fault diagnosis (Part 3 of 4). 900

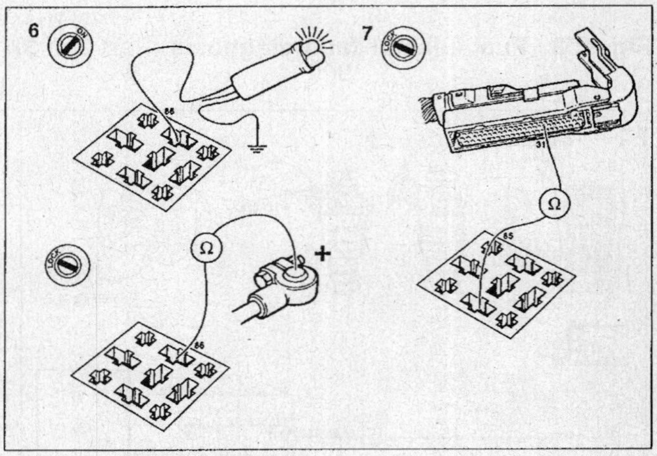

6 Connect the test lamp between the relay base, pin 86 and safe grounding point.

If the test lamp does not light up, check and if necessary remedy the fault in the lead between pin 86 and Batt+.

If the test lamp lights up, continue with point 7.

7 Check and if necessary remedy the fault in the lead between pin 85 and pin 31 of the ECM.

If the lead is OK, replace ECM.

SA1029100140040X

Fig. 155 Main relay fault diagnosis (Part 4 of 4). 900

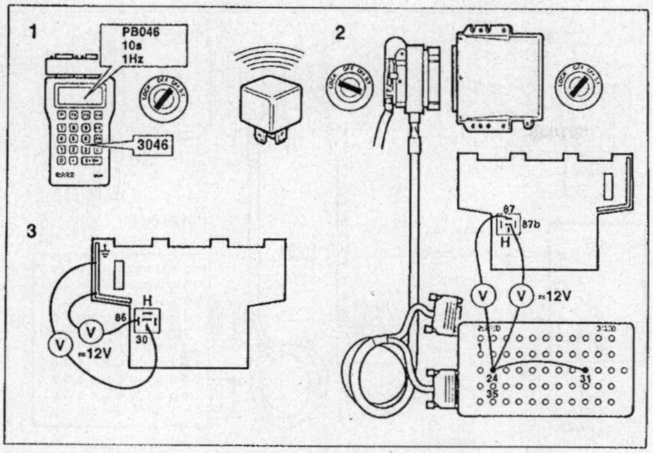

1 Connect an ISAT scan tool, contact the SFI system and enter command code 3046.

Check whether the relay is energized at a frequency of 1 Hz (for 10 seconds).

2 With the ignition switched off, connect a BOB to the ECM. Check the operation of the relay as follows:

Turn the ignition switch to the Drive position and connect a jumper cable between terminals 31 and 24 of the BOB. Check whether the relay is energized by measuring the voltage at pins 87 and 87B.

If the relay operates, continue with point 6.

If the relay operates but fastens in the energized condition, go to point 5.

If the relay does not work, continue as described below.

3 Check that battery positive voltage is present up to pins 86 and 30 of the relay.

Note:
When command code 30XX has been used, the car cannot be started for the following 12 minutes. Use command code FF00 to clear the function, following which the car can be started.

SA1029100141010X

Fig. 156 Main relay inspection (Part 1 of 2). 9000

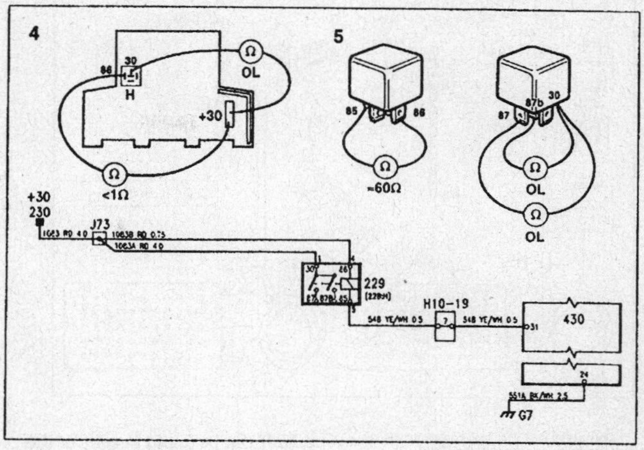

4 If battery positive voltage is not present on pins 86 and 30, check the supply cables from the +30 terminal for continuity/shorting to ground.

If the cables are OK, check that the resistance across terminals 85 and 86 of the relay is about 60 ohms.

If it is not, replace the relay.

5 Check the resistance across terminals 30 and 87 and 87B of the relay. When the relay is not energized the resistance should be about 0 ohms and when energized less than 1 ohm.

If the relay is faulty, replace it.

6 If the fault persists in spite of the above checks, replace ECM.

SA1029100141020X

Fig. 156 Main relay inspection (Part 2 of 2). 9000

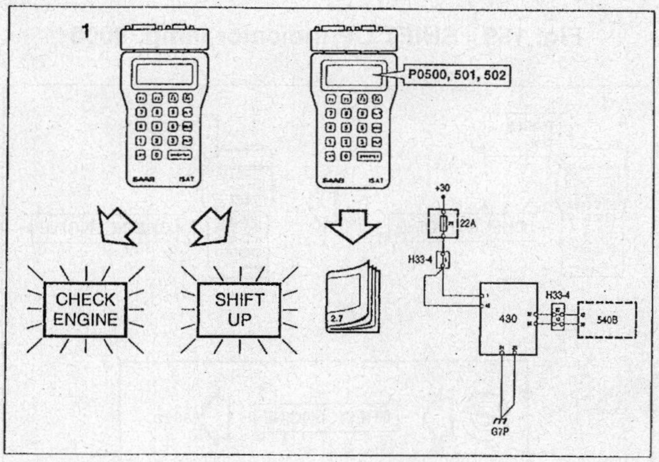

Symptom of fault

The lamps do not light up or shine constantly. Note that the operation of both lamps is tested for 3 seconds when the ignition is switched on.

Diagnostic procedure

1 Activate the lamp concerned by selecting the CHECK ENGINE lamp or SHIFT UP lamp in the ISAT menu "ACTIVATE".

If the lamps do not work, check first that the lamps are intact.

If the lamps work, the SHIFT UP lamp concerned must first be checked for any diagnostic trouble code for wheel speed (P0500, P0501, P0502) and remedial action taken if necessary.

SA1029100142010X

Fig. 157 Malfunction indicator & SHIFT UP lamps (Part 1 of 2). 900

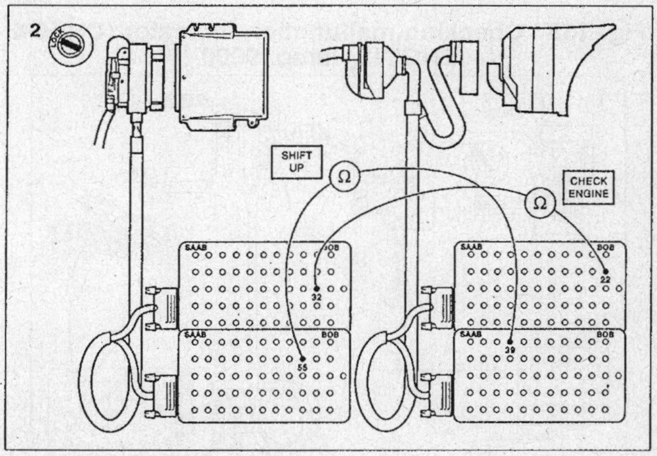

2 Check and if necessary remedy the fault in the lead between the Trionic ECM and the main instrument.

Malfunction indicator lamp: Trionic ECM pin 32 to main instrument pin 22.

SHIFT UP lamp: Trionic ECM pin 55 to main instrument pin 39.

SA1029100142020X

Fig. 157 Malfunction indicator & SHIFT UP lamps (Part 2 of 2). 900

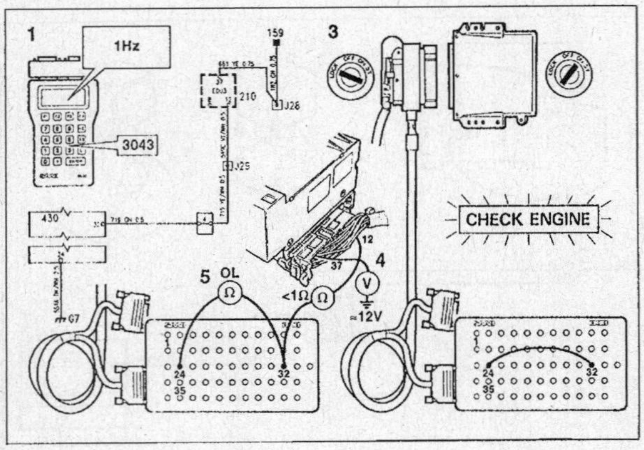

1 Connect an ISAT scan tool, contact the SFI system and enter command code 3043.

Check whether the malfunction indicator lamp (MIL) flashes (at a frequency of 1 Hz).

2 If it does not, check whether the EDU is programmed for the type of car in question

3 With the ignition switched off, connect a BOB to the ECM and cable.

Turn the ignition switch to the Drive position, connect a jumper cable between terminals 32 and 24 of the BOB and check whether the MIL lights up. If it does, continue with point 6.

If it does not, continue as described below.

4 Check whether voltage is present up to pin 37 of the EDU. If it is, the EDU is faulty and must be replaced.

If it is not, check the lead from the +15 voltage supply.

5 Remove the jumper cable and, with the ignition switched off, check the lead between pin 12 of the EDU and pin 32 of the control module for continuity/shorting to ground. Take remedial action if the lead is faulty.

If no fault can be found in spite of the above checks, replace ECM.

Note:

When command code 30XX has been used, the car cannot be started for the following 12 minutes. Use command code FF00 to clear the function, following which the car can be started.

SA1029100143000X

Fig. 158 Checking malfunction indicator (CHECK ENGINE) lamp. 9000

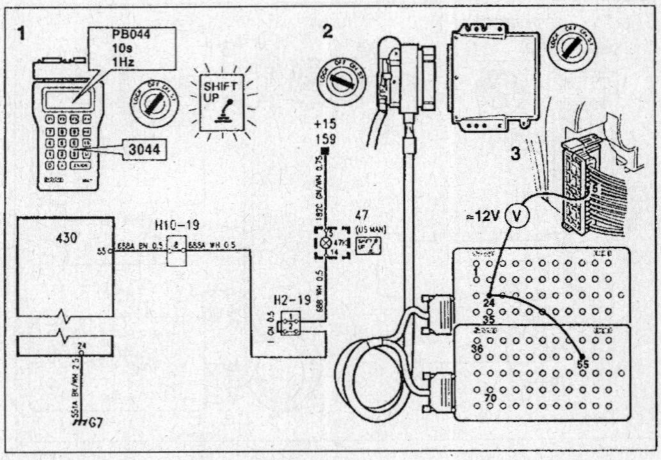

1 Connect an ISAT scan tool, contact the SFI system and enter command code 3044.

Check whether the lamp flashes (at a frequency of 1 Hz).

2 If it does not, switch off the ignition and connect a BOB to the ECM wiring harness (ECM disconnected).

Turn the ignition switch to the Drive position and connect a jumper cable between terminals 55 and 24 of the BOB.

If the lamp lights up, continue with point 4.

3 If the lamp does not light up, remove the main instrument display panel and - with the ignition switch in the Drive position - check whether battery voltage is present on terminal 5 of the SHIFT UP lamp (black connector on the right-hand side of the instrument).

If voltage is present, replace the instrument unit.

If it is not, check the +15 supply voltage lead.

4 **If the fault persists in spite of the above checks, replace ECM.**

Note:

When command code 30XX has been used, the car cannot be started for the following 12 minutes. Use command code FF00 to clear the function, following which the car can be started.

SA1029100144000X

Fig. 159 SHIFT UP indicator lamp. 9000

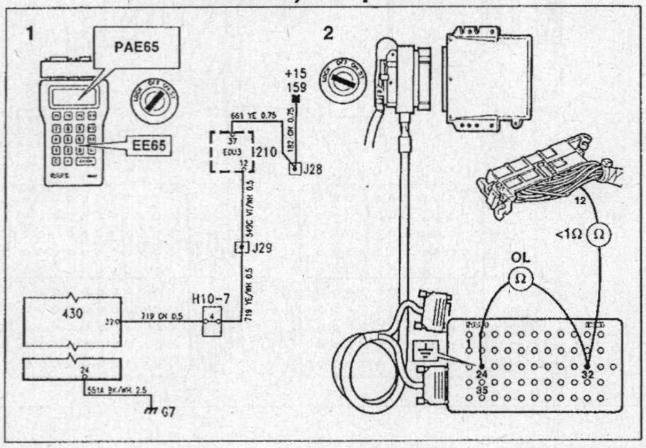

1 Connect an ISAT scan tool, contact the SFI system and enter command code EE65.

Compare the status of the system as displayed on the ISAT scan tool with the malfunction indicator lamp (MIL) in the car, according to the following table:

ISAT	MIL	Action
PAE65 OFF	On	See point 2
PAE65 OFF	Out	OK, no action
PAE65 ON	On *)	See point 4
PAE65 ON	Out	See point 5

**) MIL (CHECK ENGINE lamp) illuminated more than 3 seconds after ignition ON.*

2 With the ignition switched off, connect a BOB to the ECM wiring harness (ECM disconnected) and check the lead to pin 32 of the ECM for continuity/shorting to ground.

If the lead is faulty, remedy it.

SA1029100145010X

Fig. 160 Malfunction indicator (CHECK ENGINE) lamp function inspection (Part 1 of 2). 9000

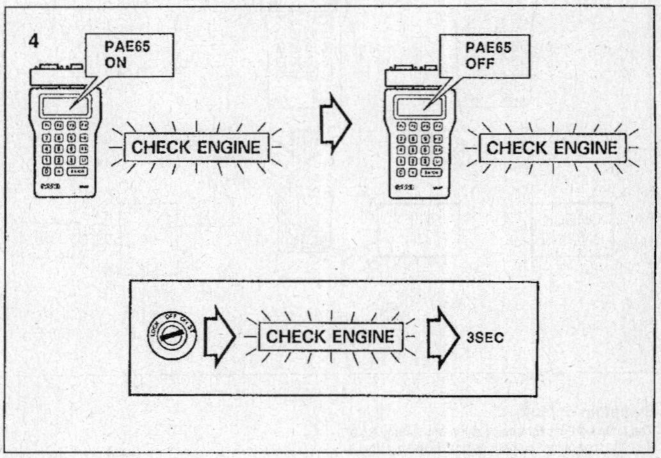

3 If the lead is OK, further diagnostic instructions.

4 PAE65-ON displayed by the ISAT scan tool at the same time as the MIL is illuminated indicates a fault in the SFI system. Use the ISAT to ascertain any faults in the SFI system, remedy the faults and then erase the DTCs.

Check as described in point 1 that PAE65-OFF is now displayed on the ISAT scan tool when the MIL is out.

5 Check the MIL

SA1029100145020X

Fig. 160 Malfunction indicator (CHECK ENGINE) lamp function inspection (Part 2 of 2). 9000

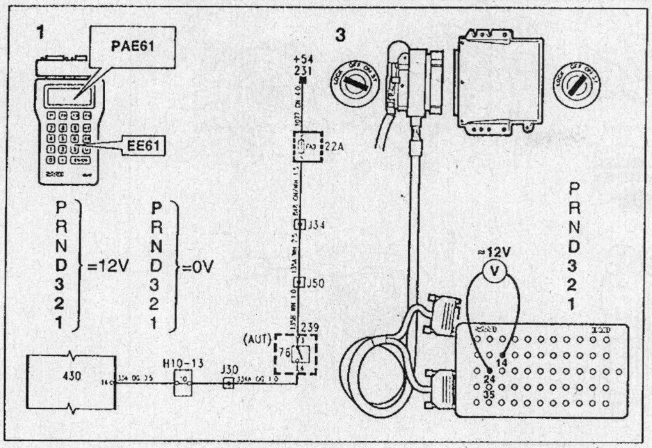

1 Connect an ISAT scan tool, contact the AFM system and enter command code EE61.

The status of the system is displayed on the ISAT:

- Selector lever in position D, R, 1, 2 or 3@PAE61-ON. If not, go to point 2.
- Selector lever in position N or P@PAE61-OFF. If not, go to point 6.

2 Check fuse FA9.

3 With the ignition switched off, connect the BOB to the ECM wiring harness (ECM disconnected).

Turn the ignition switch to the Drive position and check whether voltage is present on pin 14 of the ECM (selector lever in position D, R, 1, 2 or 3).

If it is, replace ECM.

If it is not, continue as described below.

SA1029100146010X

Fig. 161 Transaxle range switch operation inspection (Part 1 of 2). 9000 w/automatic transaxle

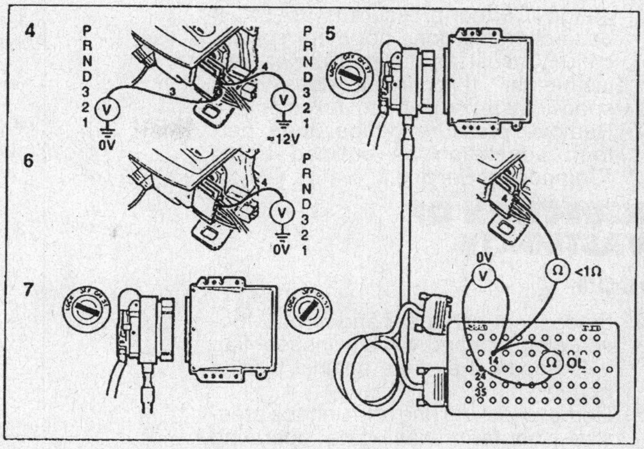

4 Check whether voltage is present on pin 3 of the transmission range switch (selector lever switch) and also on pin 4 when the switch is activated.

If voltage is present on pin 3 but not on pin 4, replace the switch.

If no voltage is present on pin 3, check the lead from pin 3 to fuse FA9 for continuity.

5 If the switch and lead above are OK, switch off the ignition and use the BOB to check the lead to pin 14 of the ECM for continuity/shorting.

Take remedial action if the wiring and/or connectors are faulty.

6 Check whether pin 4 of the transmission range switch is live when the switch is not activated (selector lever in position N or P). If it is, replace the transmission range switch.

7 If the switch is OK, turn off the ignition and connect the BOB to the ECM wiring harness (ECM disconnected).

Turn the ignition switch to the Drive position and check the lead to pin 14 of the ECM for shorting to battery positive voltage.

Take remedial action in regard to faulty wiring/connectors/components causing the short circuit.

8 If the wiring is OK, replace ECM.

SA1029100146020X

Fig. 161 Transaxle range switch operation inspection (Part 2 of 2). 9000 w/automatic transaxle

SYSTEM SERVICE

Component Service

INJECTOR FLOW CAPACITY INSPECTION

900

1. Remove fuel-injection rail and fuel injectors as outlined under "Component Replacement."
2. Start fuel pump by connecting jumper cable between fuses 4 and 32 with jumper lead tool No. 83 93 886, or equivalent. Check for leaking injectors.
3. Place injectors, one at a time, over measuring glass and connect injector to battery voltage using cable tool Nos. 86 11 410 and 86 11 345, or equivalents.
4. Activate valve for 30 seconds, then check amount of fuel in measuring glass. Amount should be 162–190 ml. Maximum allowable difference between injectors is 18 ml.
5. Replace any faulty injectors.
6. Install fuel-injection rail and injectors as outlined under "Component Replacement."

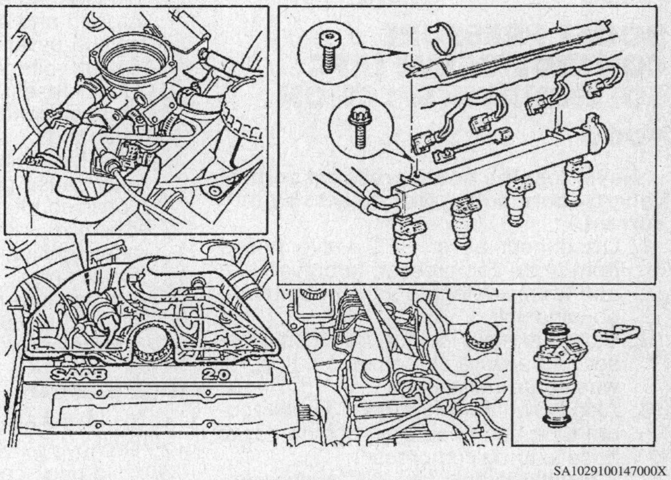

SA1029100147000X

Fig. 162 Fuel injector inspection. 900

BASE CHARGE PRESSURE INSPECTION

9000

1. Ensure motor is thoroughly warmed up.
2. Place suitable pressure gauge vertically, to reduce risk of incorrect indications.
3. Pull hose through recess in front door post to engine compartment, then connect it to nipple between intake manifold and PCV fitting.
4. With third gear as starting position (or gear position 3 on automatic transaxle) and engine speed less than 1500 RPM, do full-throttle acceleration.
5. When engine speed approaches 3000 RPM, brake while continuing to depress accelerator pedal so full load is achieved at 3000 RPM.

6. Read base charging pressure on gauge. Correct pressure is 5.7 psi. If base charging does not meet specification, adjust as outlined under "Adjustments." If charging does meet specification, proceed to next step.
7. Remove pressure gauge, then perform adaptation as outlined under "Component Service."

INSPECTION OF WASTEGATE

9000

1. Disconnect exhaust bend from turbocharging unit and visually inspect flap valve contact surface against turbine housing.
2. Remove locking ring and unhook pressure rod form wastegate operating arm.
3. Ensure operating arm can easily be moved.

MEMBRANE HOUSING UNIT INSPECTION

9000

1. Ensure pressure rod can be moved easily.
2. Inspect membrane and spring by introducing pressure through unit connecting nipple.
3. Ensure rod can be pushed out without any tendency to seize. Release pressure and ensure rod retracts into unit.
4. Replace faulty membrane housing unit.

BOOST PRESSURE CONTROL VALVE (APC SOLENOID) INSPECTION

9000

Never test the boost pressure control valve by connecting it directly to battery current.

1. Disconnect all of BPC valve hoses from turbo compressor, turbo vacuum and from wastegate valve membrane housing unit.
2. Blow into hose leading from compressor and ensure air comes out hose to wastegate valve.
3. Also blow into return hose form vacuum tube and ensure air comes out of hose to turbo compressor.
4. A throttle is built into BPC valve connection to turbo compressor, resulting in this opening being more prone to deposits of dirt, etc., than others. Inspect and ensure throttle is not restricted. If hole is too small and deposits cannot be removed, replace BPC valve.

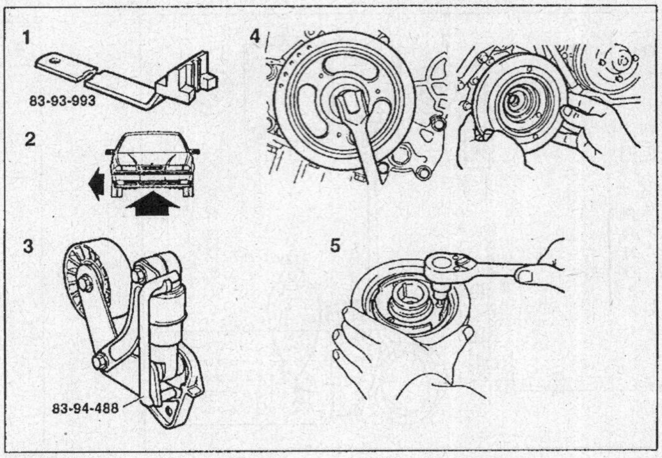

Aperture plate

To remove

1 Fit special tool 83 93 993 to lock the flywheel.
2 Raise the car, remove the right-hand front wheel and dismantle the wing liner.
3 Compress the belt tensioner and secure it by means of clamp 83 94 488.
4 Remove the multigroove belt and dismantle the crankshaft pulley.
5 Remove the aperture plate.

To fit

Assemble in reverse order.

Belt pulley tightening torque: 190 Nm (140 lbf ft)

SA1029100148000X

Fig. 163 Fuel injector inspection. 9000

Component Replacement

ENGINE CONTROL MODULE (ECM)

Before replacing the ECM, perform the following checks:

1. Ensure every point in fault diagnosis program of relevant diagnostic trouble code has been carried out.
2. Study wiring diagram of circuit in question and ensure you understand how it works.
3. Check all grounding points. If already checked, check again. Ensure power ground and signal ground are electrically separate.
4. Check voltage supplied to ECM.
5. Check fuses.
6. Inspect connectors for corrosion on pins and contact surfaces, excessive play, looseness or anything else which may cause poor contact or deterioration in conductivity.
7. Check how long main relay remains on after ignition has been switched off. Relay should operate for an additional five seconds or so if temperature is approximately 68°F, or about 30 seconds if temperature is below 32°F.

9-3 & 900

1. Turn off ignition.
2. Remove glove compartment.
3. Fold back carpet and remove central locking system relay.
4. Disconnect module electrical connector, then remove ECM.
5. Reverse procedure to install. Adapt throttle position as outlined under "Precautions."

9-5

1. Remove wiper spindle caps, then remove mounting nuts and wiper arms using puller tool No. 85 80 144, or equivalent.
2. Remove wiper spindle rubber seals, windshield cover panel short side mounting screws and rubber seal.
3. Remove cover panel.
4. remove mounting nuts and control module cover.
5. Disconnect electrical connect, then remove mounting nuts and control module.
6. Reverse procedure to install.

9000

1. Remove cover over space between bulkhead panels.
2. Pull back locking spring and pull ECM slightly upward, then loosen ground braid and lift ECM completely out.
3. Disconnect electrical connector after releasing catch.
4. Reverse procedure to install. Match new ECM part number against technical data.

ENGINE COOLANT TEMPERATURE (ECT) SENSOR

9-3 & 900

1. Open expansion tank cap to release cooling system pressure, then screw cap back on.
2. Remove engine cover(s).
3. Disconnect sensor electrical connector, then the sensor.
4. Reverse procedure to install. Top off cooling system as necessary.

9-5

1. Release cooling system pressure by carefully loosening expansion tank filler cap. Tighten cap when pressure has been released.
2. Disconnect connector.
3. Remove ECT sensor.
4. Reverse procedure to install, noting the following:
   a. Spray connector with Kontakt 61, or equivalent contact cleaner.

b. Install new sealing washer as required.
c. Lubricate threads with Molykote 1000, or equivalent.
d. **Torque** sensor to 115 inch lbs.

CRANKSHAFT POSITION (CKP) SENSOR

9-3 & 900

The CKP sensor is located at the flywheel end of the engine block.

1. Remove engine covers.
2. **Remove turbo pressure rod and plug turbo discharge hose.**
3. Disconnect CKP sensor electrical connector.
4. Remove wiring, noting routing and fastening points.
5. Raise and support vehicle
6. Remove sensor bolt, then the sensor, noting position of sealing ring.
7. Reverse procedure to install, noting the following:
   a. Clean sensor seating and fit sealing ring in seating.
   b. **Torque** sensor bolt to 6 ft. lbs.

9-5

1. Remove exhaust manifold heat shield.
2. Remove mounting nut and sensor heat shield, then the CKP sensor and O-ring.
3. Disconnect water hose clip and electrical connector.
4. Reverse procedure to install, noting the following:
   a. Smear O-ring with clean motor oil.
   b. Spray connect with Kontakt 61, or equivalent contact cleaner.
   c. Apply Molykote 1000, or equivalent, to mounting bolts.
   d. **Torque** sensor to 36 ft. lbs.

9000

1. Install flywheel locking tool No. 83 93 993, or equivalent, to lock flywheel.
2. raise and support vehicle, then remove righthand front wheel.
3. Remove righthand front fender lining.
4. Compress belt tensioner and secure with clamp tool No. 83 94 488, or equivalent.
5. Remove multigroove belt, then disassemble crankshaft pulley.
6. Remove tensioning roller.
7. Loosen alternator bolts and pull halfway out, then swing alternator rearward.
8. Remove two hall-effect sensor bolts.
9. Remove clips holding wiring, then disconnect electrical connector and remove sensor with wiring. One clip is on coolant pipe at rear of engine block.
10. Reverse procedure to install, noting the following:
    a. Use Loctite 270 or equivalent to lock retaining bolts for hall-effect sensor and crankshaft pulley.
    b. **Torque** belt pulley to 140 ft. lbs.

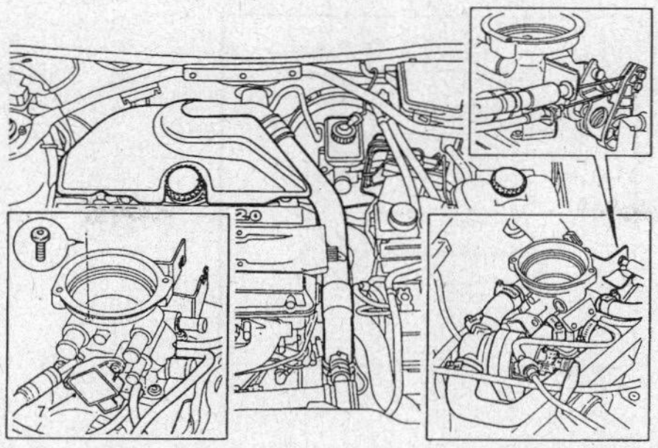

SA1029100149000X

Fig. 164 Throttle body replacement

INJECTORS

9-3 & 900

Refer to **Fig. 162** when replacing injectors.

1. Run fuel system dry as follows:
   a. Start engine and remove fuse 32 while engine is running.
   b. Do not switch off ignition until engine stops.
2. Remove engine cover, then disconnect crankcase ventilation hose and idle air control valve with hoses.
3. Remove dipstick bracket and throttle and cruise control cables.
4. Remove cable groove bolts and fuel injection rail screws.
5. Carefully lift up fuel injection rail with injectors. **Ensure you have paper to soak up escaped fuel from fuel injection rail and injectors.**
6. Reverse procedure to install. Lubricate O-rings with petroleum jelly to ease installation.

9-5

1. Relieve fuel pressure.
2. Remove engine cover.
3. Disconnect crankcase breather hose.
4. Remove mounting bolts and dipstick with filler tunnel. Plug tube.
5. Remove mounting bolts and disconnect throttle cable with holder. Disconnect cable from pedal arm and bend aside.
6. Loosen clips and twist throttle body hose aside.
7. Remove and bend rearward wiring holder by loosening upper front and removing rear mounting bolts.
8. Disconnect ignition discharge module, injector, manifold absolute pressure sensor, mass air flow sensor and charge air control valve electrical connectors.
9. Disconnect fuel rail wiring and bend aside.
10. Secure each injector to fuel rail with suitable cable tie.
11. Remove fuel rail by removing mounting bolts, disconnect pressure regulator vacuum hose and pry loose with two suitable crowbars. Plug nozzle holes.
12. Reverse procedure to install. Spray connector with Kontakt 61, or equivalent contact cleaner.

9000

Refer to **Fig. 163** when replacing fuel injectors.

1. Remove lock mount and loosen injector contact pieces (1).
2. Check placement, then remove holders for injectors (2).
3. Remove injectors as required.
4. Reverse procedure to install, noting the following:
   a. Grease O-rings with petroleum jelly.
   b. Ensure correct contact piece is connected to its respective injector.

THROTTLE BODY

9-3 & 900

Refer to **Fig. 164** when replacing throttle body.

1. Remove engine cover.
2. Remove connecting pipe from throttle pipe, then disconnect throttle and cruise control cables.
3. Unscrew expansion tank cover to release cooling system pressure.
4. Remove idle air control valve.
5. Disconnect coolant hoses from throttle body, then the other hoses from throttle body.
6. Remove throttle position sensor.
7. Remove throttle body bolts, then the throttle body.
8. Reverse procedure to install, noting the following:
   a. **Torque** throttle body bolts to 72 inch lbs.
   b. Check setting of throttle plate. If necessary, adjust by loosening two bolts and moving mount in desired direction.
   c. Check throttle body operation, then adapt throttle position as outlined under "Precautions."

9-5

1. Turn ignition switch to Off position, then remove engine cover.
2. Release cooling system pressure by loosening expansion tank filler cap. Tighten cap when pressure is released.
3. Pinch throttle body coolant hoses using suit clamps.
4. Disconnect bypass valve and preheating hoses.
5. Loosen turbocharger delivery pipe to cylinder head mounting bolt.
6. Disconnect hose clips and bend turbocharger delivery pipe up. Remove rubber bend.
7. Disconnect throttle cable from body's pedal arm.
8. Disconnect limp-home solenoid and throttle body electrical connectors.
9. Remove mounting bolts and throttle body. Disconnect hose under limp-home solenoid.
10. Reverse procedure to install, noting the following:
    a. Spray connector with Kontakt 61, or equivalent contact cleaner.
    b. Replace rubber seal between throttle body and intake manifold as required.

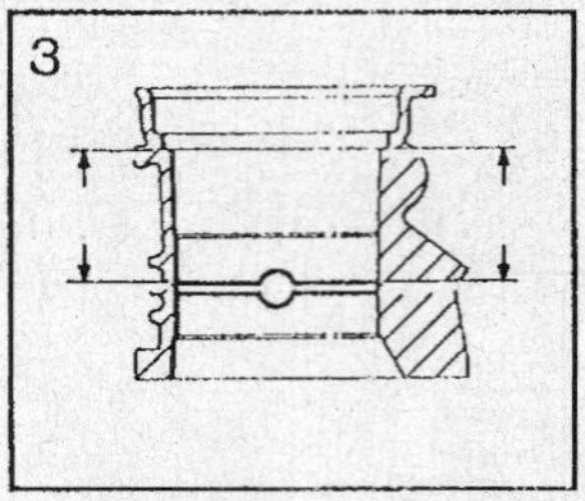

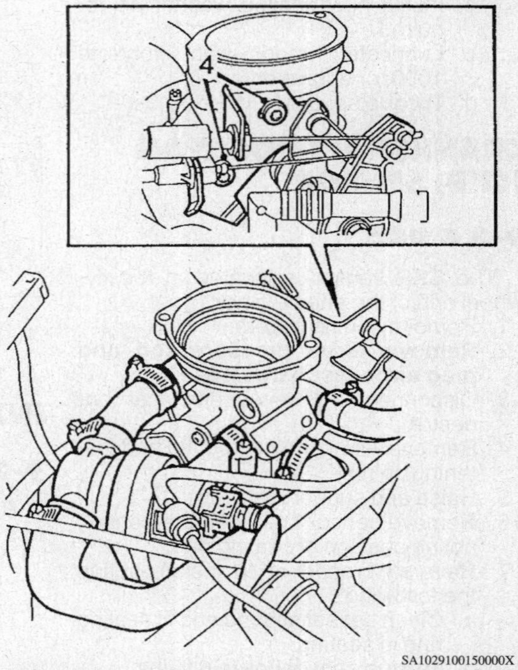

Fig. 165 Throttle plate adjustment

c. Coat rubber seal sparingly with suitable petroleum jelly.
d. **Torque** mounting bolts to 88 inch lbs.

MANIFOLD ABSOLUTE PRESSURE (MAP) SENSOR

9-5

1. Remove engine cover.
2. Disconnect connector.
3. Remove MAP sensor.
4. Reverse procedure to install, noting the following:
   a. Spray connector with Kontakt 61, or equivalent contact cleaner.
   b. Install new sealing washer.
   c. Lubricate threads with Molykote 1000, or equivalent.
   d. **Torque** MAP sensor to 12 ft. lbs.

CHARGE AIR ABSOLUTE PRESSURE SENSOR

9-5

1. Disconnect ignition discharge module connector and place aside.
2. Disconnect electrical connector.
3. Remove charge air absolute pressure sensor.
4. Reverse procedure to install, noting the following:
   a. Spray connector with Kontakt 61, or equivalent contact cleaner.
   b. Install new sealing washer as required.
   c. Lubricate threads with Molykote 1000, or equivalent.
   d. **Torque** sensor to 12 ft. lbs.

INTAKE AIR TEMPERATURE (IAT) SENSOR

9-5

1. Disconnect connector.
2. Remove IAT sensor.
3. Reverse procedure to install, noting the following:
   a. Spray connector with Kontakt 61, or equivalent contact cleaner.
   b. Install new sealing washer as required.
   c. Lubricate threads with Molykote 1000, or equivalent.
   d. **Torque** sensor to 62 inch lbs.

MASS AIR FLOW (MAF) SENSOR

9-5

1. Disconnect connector.
2. Loosen hose clips.
3. Remove MAF sensor.
4. Reverse procedure to install. Spray connector with Kontakt 61, or equivalent contact cleaner.

LIMP-HOME SOLENOID

9-5

1. Remove engine cover.
2. Remove lower mounting screw using suitable magnetic T15 bit.
3. Disconnect electrical connector.
4. Remove upper mounting screw and limp-home solenoid.
5. Reverse procedure to install, noting the following:
   a. Spray connector with Kontakt 61, or equivalent contact cleaner.
   b. **Torque** mounting screws to 22 inch lbs.
   c. Reset solenoid as described under "Adjustments."

CHARGE AIR CONTROL VALVE

9-5

1. Disconnect connector.
2. Mark hose for installation and disconnect.
3. Remove charge air control valve from expanding pin and sheet metal bracket.
4. Reverse procedure to install. Spray connector with Kontakt 61, or equivalent contact cleaner.

CHARGE AIR BYPASS VALVE

9-5

1. Remove cover and disconnect connectors.
2. Remove mounting nuts and windshield cover panel sealing strip.
3. Remove retaining panel by carefully pulling up and unhooking edge from bulkhead partition.
4. Disconnect connector, then mark vacuum hoses for installation and disconnect.
5. Remove valve by drilling out pop rivets and disconnecting holder.
6. Reverse procedure to install. Spray connector with Kontakt 61, or equivalent contact cleaner.

HEATED OXYGEN SENSOR

9-5

1. Remove engine cover.
2. Disconnect crankshaft position sensor and oxygen sensor connectors.
3. Remove oxygen sensor.
4. Reverse procedure to install, noting the following:
   a. Spray connector with Kontakt 61, or equivalent contact cleaner.
   b. Smear threads with Molykote 1000, or equivalent.
   c. **Torque** sensor to 37 ft. lbs.

Adjustments

BASE CHARGING PRESSURE

The base charging pressure is the starting position for the Trionic system's pressure regulating function. Therefore, it must be adjusted to the correct level.

The maximum boost pressure is continuously adapted to the relevant basic charging pressure through the adaptive function. **Increasing the basic charging pressure above the stated value will not lead to a higher boost pressure because the adaptive function adjusts the maximum boost pressure down to the nominal value.**

When adjusting the end piece on the pressure rod, it is important to hold the rod firmly so it does not damage the membrane. When adjusting the pressure rod length, place grips used as a counterstay as close to thread as possible. Turn end piece carefully so ridges do not appear on the rod. If ridges form on the rod, binding could occur in the membrane housing unit bearing, destroying the system's charging pressure regulating capacity.

1. Raise and support vehicle.

2. Remove locking ring and release pressure rod from boost pressure regulator operating arm.
3. Adjust base charging pressure noting the following:
   a. If too low pressure is measured, screw in end piece.
   b. If too high pressure is measured, loosen end piece.
   c. **On 900 models,** one revolution results in change in basic charging pressure of approximately .29 psi.
   d. **On 9000 models,** one revolution results in change in basic charging pressure of approximately .43 psi.
   e. Base charging pressure should be 5.69 psi. **Boost pressure regulator must never have prestressing of less than 2 inch (two turns), even if the basic charging pressure can be adjusted so it is approximately 5.69 psi.**
4. Connect pressure rod to operating rod, then fit locking ring.
5. Lower vehicle.

CHARGING PRESSURE ADAPTION

9000

Adaption of maximum charging pressure occurs continuously during normal driving. If the ECM is replaced or other steps are taken which affect the level of adaption, a system adaption may be conducted as follows in order to speed adaption and achieve maximum performance more quickly.

The engine should be thoroughly warmed-up. The base charging pressure should be adjusted to the correct value. Use good-quality, high-octane fuel.

1. **On models equipped with manual transaxle,** at full-throttle in as high gear as possible, accelerate from 2000 RPM to 3500 RPM.
2. **On models equipped with automatic transaxle,** accelerate from 3000 RPM to 4500 RPM with as much throttle as possible without kickdown function activating.
3. **On all models,** minimum time for passage of adaption area (2750–3250 RPM on models equipped with manual transaxle, 2750–4250 RPM on models equipped with automatic transaxle) should be longer than three seconds. Adaption may be performed on upward incline.
4. Repeat sequence until maximum nominal charging pressure, with regard to fuel quality, etc., is achieved. If repeated pressure monitor operation has been caused by excessive charging pressure (possibly due to defective solenoid valve), maximum negative adaption will be obtained. This means normal maximum charging pressure will not be obtained. To attain maximum charging pressure, disconnect and reconnect control module and repeat this procedure.

THROTTLE PLATE

9-3 & 900

Refer to **Fig. 165** when adjusting throttle plate.

1. Remove engine cover.
2. Disconnect turbo delivery pipe from throttle body.
3. Check setting of throttle plate (3). If necessary, adjust by loosening screws (4) and moving mount in appropriate direction.
4. Install delivery pipe and cover.
5. Adapt throttle position as outlined under "Precautions."

LIMP-HOME SOLENOID

9-5

1. Remove engine cover.
2. Turn ignition switch to On position.
3. Connect suitable scan tool to Diagnostic Link Connector (DLC) and clear Diagnostic Trouble Codes (DTC).
4. Turn ignition switch to Off position and wait 10 seconds.
5. Carefully push solenoid spring end towards throttle body.
6. Turn black toothed disc counterclockwise to stop (click) using suitable screwdriver.
7. Turn pedal arm clockwise.
8. Ensure throttle arm does not follow pedal arm.

Electric Fuel Pumps

NOTE: If Unsure Of The System Used On The Vehicle Being Serviced, Refer To "The Engine Systems Identification Chart." Further Assistance For The Proper Use Of Information Contained In This Section Can Also Be Found In The Front Of This Tabbed Section Under "How To Use This Manual."

NOTE: On Air Bag Equipped Models, Refer To "Air Bag System Precautions" Located In The Front Of This Manual For System Disarming & Arming Procedures.

NOTE: Refer To "Computer Relearn Procedures" Located In The Front Of This Manual When Battery Power To The Computer Has Been Interrupted.

NOTE: Prior To Performing Any Service Operations Listed In This Section, Consult The "Technical Service Bulletins" Section For Related Information.

INDEX

	Page No.
Diagnosis & Testing	16-166
Fuel Pressure Relief	16-166
9-3 & 9-5	16-166
9000	16-166
900	16-166
Fuel Pump Relay Location	16-166
Fuel Pump Replacement	16-166
9-3 & 9-5	16-166
9000	16-167
Bosch Non Ejector Type Pump	16-167
Walbro Ejector Type Pump	16-167
900	16-166
Precautions	16-166
Air Bag Systems	16-166
Battery Ground Cable	16-166

PRECAUTIONS

Air Bag Systems

Refer to "Air Bag System Precautions" in the front of this manual for system disarming and arming procedures.

Battery Ground Cable

Prior to service, disconnect battery ground cable and isolate as required.

FUEL PUMP RELAY LOCATION

Refer to **Figs. 1 through 5** for fuel pump relay locations.

FUEL PRESSURE RELIEF

9-3 & 9-5

Remove fuse No. 19, then start the engine and allow it to run until it stalls.

900

Remove fuse No. 32, then start the engine and allow it to run until it stalls.

9000

Remove fuse No. 14, then start the engine and allow it to run until it stalls.

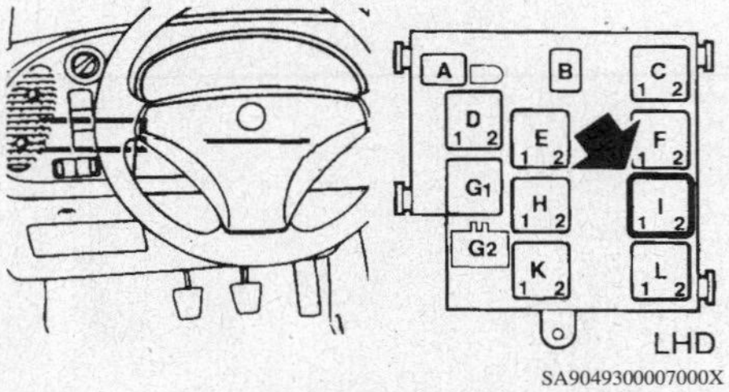

Fig. 1 Fuel pump relay location. 9-3

DIAGNOSIS & TESTING

Refer to "Fuel Injection" for system and line pressure tests.

FUEL PUMP REPLACEMENT

9-3 & 9-5

1. Relieve fuel pressure.
2. Raise rear seat cushions and fold carpeting out of way.
3. Remove fuel pump cover and disconnect electrical connector.
4. Disconnect non-return fuel line valves from pump.
5. Remove screw ring using fuel tank wrench tool No. 83 94 462, or equivalent.
6. Hold suitable cloth ready to catch spilling fuel, then lift pump approximately two inches, turn clockwise 80° and remove.
7. Reverse procedure to install, noting the following:
   a. Install new O-rings smeared with suitable non-acidic petroleum jelly.
   b. Lubricate screw ring threads with suitable non-acidic petroleum jelly.
   c. **Torque** screw ring to 55 ft. lbs.
   d. Spray connector with Kontakt 61, or suitable contact cleaner.

900

1. Empty fuel tank, then raise and support vehicle. **Ensure righthand rear support is placed as far out as possible so as not to obstruct work.**
2. Disconnect rubber hoses from fuel tank and plug tank using fuel tank plugs tool No. 83 94 777, or equivalent.
3. Disconnect fuel filter clamp.
4. Support tank with pillar lift, then remove metal strap nuts and unhook metal clamps.
5. Carefully lower tank, righthand side first, until top is visible.
6. Disconnect pressure and return lines from pump.
7. Remove screw ring from top of fuel pump using fuel pump tool No. 83 94 462, or equivalent.
8. Raise pump until top is about 1.97 inches above tank, then turn pump 80° clockwise and carefully remove.
9. Reverse procedure to install, noting the following:

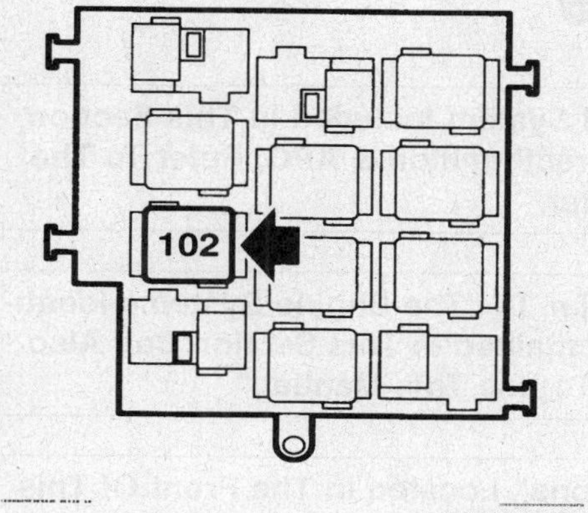

Fig. 2 Fuel pump relay location. 9-5

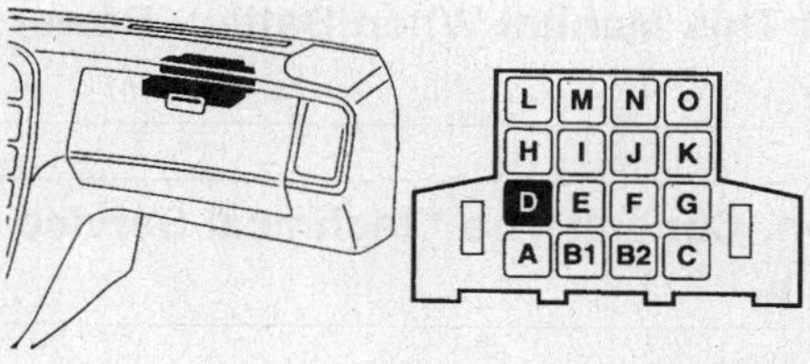

Fig. 5 Fuel pump relay location. 9000 series

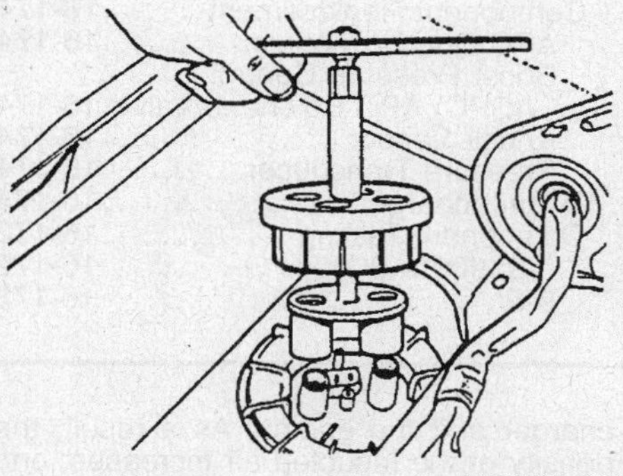

Fig. 8 Fuel pump tool installation. 9000 w/Walbro Ejector type pump

a. Install new O-ring in groove on fuel tank.
b. Ensure marks on tank and pump are aligned.

9000

BOSCH NON EJECTOR TYPE PUMP

1. Lift up rear section of luggage compartment floor, then remove two floor panel screws and lift out floor panel.
2. Using an Allen wrench, loosen two bayonet attaching screws, then remove fuel pump cover.
3. Disconnect electrical connectors from fuel pump, feed pump and fuel gauge transmitter.

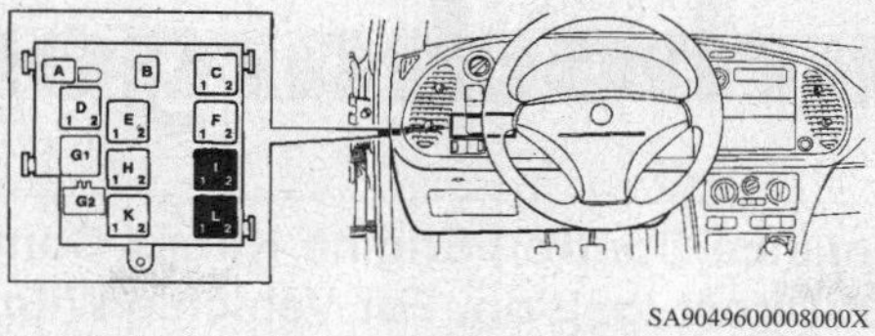

Fig. 3 Fuel pump relay location. 900 series w/Motronic fuel system

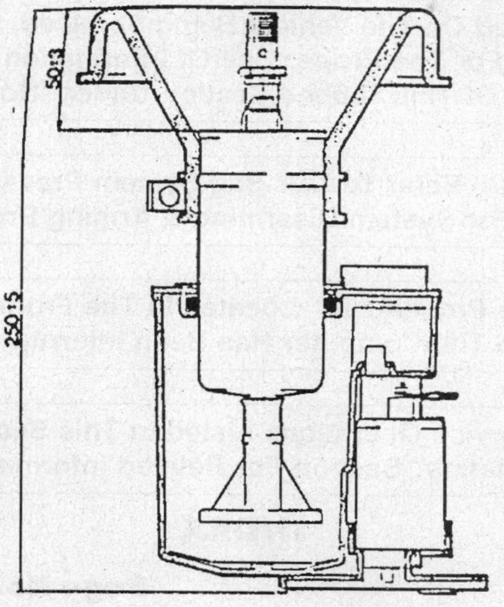

Fig. 6 Fuel pump installation. 9000 w/Bosch Non Ejector type pump

4. Loosen, then remove fuel pipe banjo coupling. Retain washers.
5. Remove fuel pump rubber collar clip.
6. Remove fuel pump and suction reservoir.
7. Reverse procedure to install, noting the following:
   a. Install fuel pump in rubber collar so lip of collar is 1.97 inches above top edge of pump, **Fig. 6.**
   b. Ensure relief valve on reservoir is turned 35–55° from mark as shown, **Fig. 7.**
   c. Adjust overall length of fuel pump to 9.84 inches, **Fig. 6.**

WALBRO EJECTOR TYPE PUMP

1. Lift up rear section of luggage compartment floor, then remove two floor panel screws and lift out floor panel.
2. Remove pump cover, then disconnect wiring harness.
3. Disconnect fuel lines. Position lines aside.
4. Install fuel pump tool No. 83 94 397, or equivalent, **Fig. 8.**
5. Install chain through load securing eyes, **Fig. 9,** then tighten chain.
6. Loosen screw top, then remove tool.
7. Remove screw top, then the seal.
8. Remove fuel pump from fuel tank, tilting top to right.

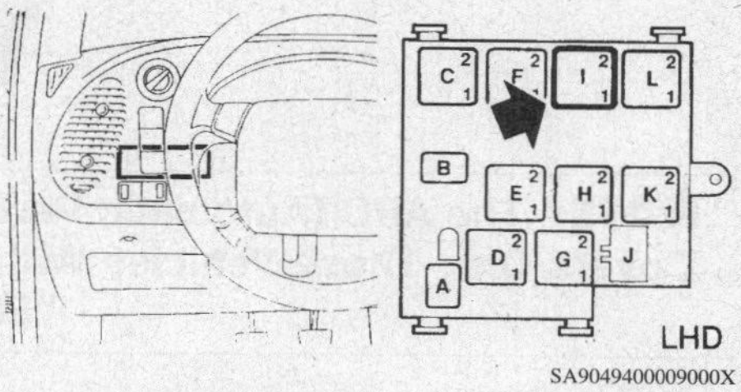

Fig. 4 Fuel pump relay location. 900 series w/Trionic fuel system

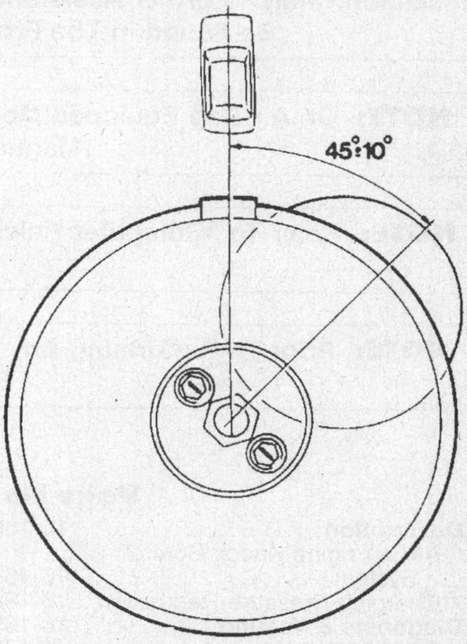

Fig. 7 Fuel pump relief valve position. 9000 w/Bosch Non Ejector type pump

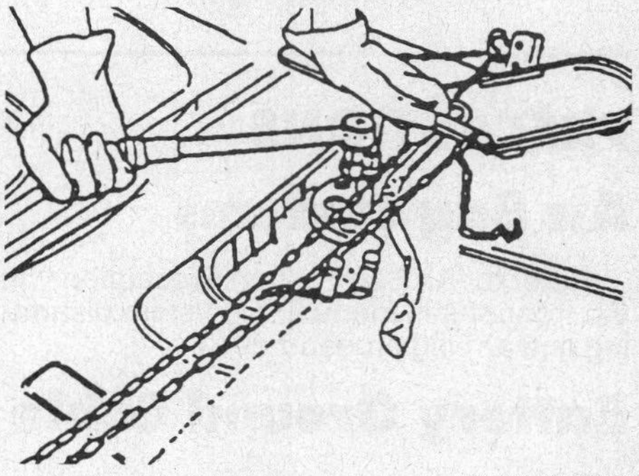

Fig. 9 Load securing chain installation. 9000 w/Walbro Ejector type pump

9. Reverse procedure to install, noting the following:
   a. Ensure bottom of pump is between ribs on bottom of tank.
   b. Ensure mark on top of pump aligns with mark on top of tank.
   c. Using fuel pump tool No. 83 94 397, or equivalent, **torque** screw top to 40 ft. lbs. Do not allow pump to turn when tightening screw top.

Turbochargers

NOTE: The APC (Automatic Performance Control) Engine Knock Control System Included In This Section Covers Only Those Vehicles Without Direct Ignition. For Vehicles With Direct Ignition & APC, Refer To The "Electronic Ignition" Section Of This Chapter.

NOTE: If Unsure Of The System Used On The Vehicle Being Serviced, Refer To "The Engine Systems Identification Chart." Further Assistance For The Proper Use Of Information Contained In This Section Can Also Be Found In The Front Of This Tabbed Section Under "How To Use This Manual."

NOTE: On Air Bag Equipped Models, Refer To "Air Bag System Precautions" Located In The Front Of This Manual For System Disarming & Arming Procedures.

NOTE: Refer To "Computer Relearn Procedures" Located In The Front Of This Manual When Battery Power To The Computer Has Been Interrupted.

NOTE: Prior To Performing Any Service Operations Listed In This Section, Consult The "Technical Service Bulletins" Section For Related Information.

INDEX

Page No.

Description 16-168
APC (Engine Knock Control) System 16-169
Charging Pressure Regulation .. 16-168
Diagnosis & Testing 16-169
9-3, 900 & 9000 16-169
APC System Knock Control Test 16-171
APC System Test 16-170
Basic Pressure Test 16-170
Charging Pressure Test 16-169
9-5 16-171
Charging Pressure 16-171
Precautions 16-168
Air Bag Systems 16-168
Battery Ground Cable 16-168
System Service 16-172
Component Adjustment 16-173
9-3, 900 & 9000 16-173
9-5 16-173
Component Replacement 16-174
APC Control Module 16-174
Boost Pressure Control ((BPC) APC Solenoid) Valve. 16-174
Knock Sensor 16-174
Pressure Transducer 16-174
Turbocharger 16-174
Component Testing 16-172
9-3, 900 & 9000 16-172
9-5 16-173

PRECAUTIONS

Air Bag Systems

Refer to "Air Bag System Precautions" in the front of this manual for system disarming and arming procedures.

Battery Ground Cable

Prior to service, disconnect battery ground cable and isolate as required.

DESCRIPTION

The turbocharger provides improved charging on the induction stroke, which produces more effective combustion of the mixture and an increase in power output. Effectively the engine achieves performance that is comparable to that of a larger engine, while maintaining the advantages of a smaller engine, **Fig. 1.**

Turbocharging is achieved by means of a turbo compressor. This unit utilizes the exhaust gases from the engine to drive the compressor. Exhaust gas flows through a turbine wheel mounted on the same shaft as the compressor impeller. Energy from the exhaust gas velocity is thus transferred to the compressor located in the induction system. The impeller acts on the inducted air causing an increase in charging pressure in the combustion chamber, **Fig. 2.**

The 9-5 3.0L uses asymmetric tubrocharging which means the exhaust gases from only three cylinders (2-4-6) drive the turbo, while all six cylinders are charged.

This system increases torque at engine speeds during normal driving conditions, in contrast to those designed to increase performance only at full throttle. The turbine shaft rotates at high speeds and must be very accurately balanced. The shaft rotates in floating sliding contact bearings. These bearings utilize high pressure oil as the contact surface for the shaft. A special line supplies lubricating oil from the pump. Oil is returned to the sump through a large bore pipe. Sealing between the shaft and the bearing housing consists of sealing rings installed in grooves.

The system also incorporates an Charge Air Cooler (CAC) intercooler, reducing the temperature of the air between the turbocharger and the engine. As a result, the density of the inducted air increases, and the air admitted into the engine contains more oxygen. This allows more fuel to be injected and burned efficiently, increasing engine power. The air is cooled by approximately 110°F in the CAC (intercooler), which also reduces thermal stress on the engine.

The turbo unit is water cooled, **Fig. 3.** This lowers temperature of bearing housing by about 212°F, reducing the chance of burned components.

Charging Pressure Regulation

Charging pressure in the intake manifold is principally controlled by engine speed and load. Charging pressure is limited under high loads by a charge pressure regulator. The charge pressure regulator is located on the exhaust side of the engine and controls the exhaust gas flow through a bypass duct at the side of the turbine.

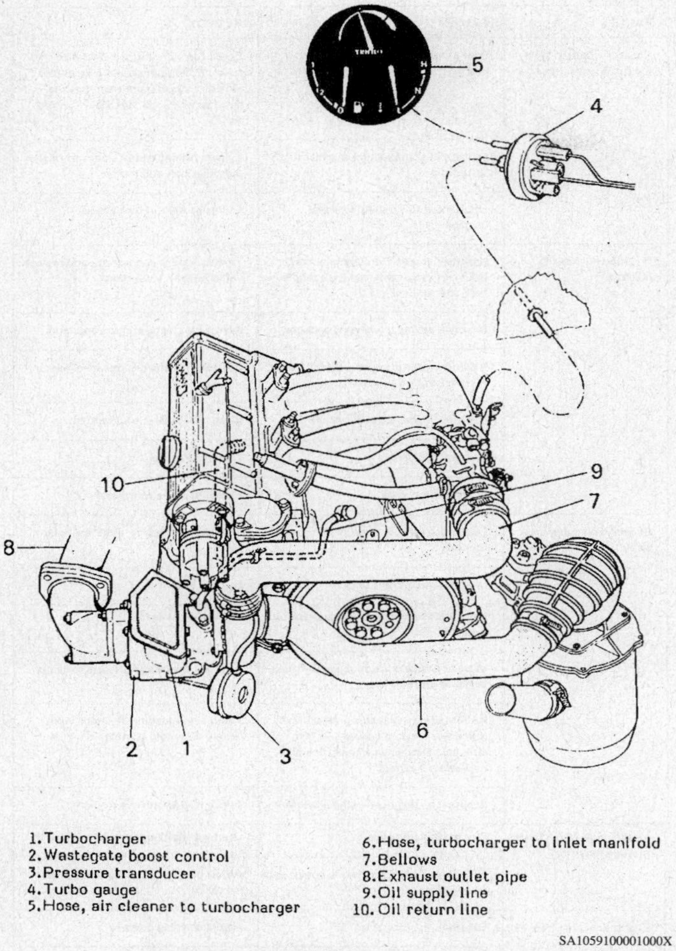

Fig. 1 Turbocharger system

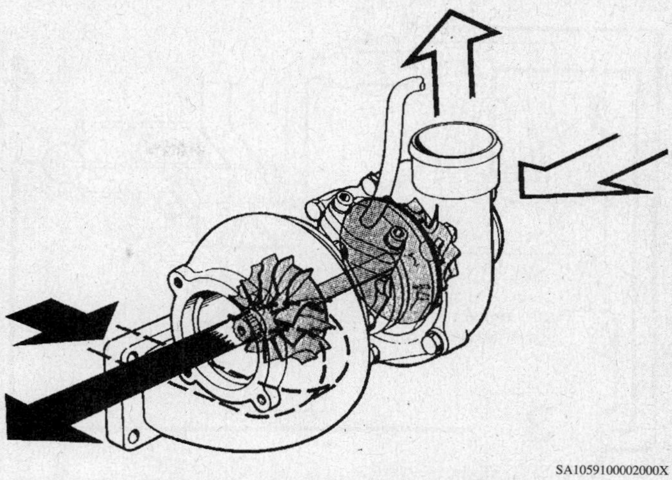

Fig. 2 Turbo compressor operation

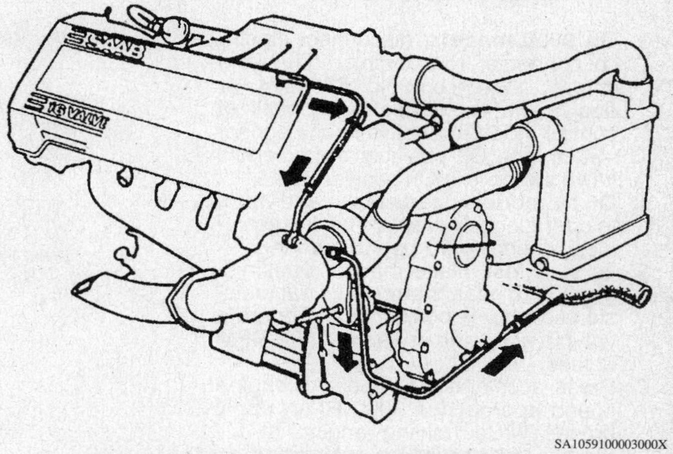

Fig. 3 Water-cooled turbocharger

The charging pressure regulator valve (wastegate) is closed when the load on the engine is normal or less. As the load increases and the charging pressure approaches the maximum preset limit, the wastegate opens allowing some of the exhaust gases to pass through the bypass duct thereby decreasing the load on the turbine.

The charging pressure regulator is a flap valve which closes or opens the bypass duct at the side of the turbine impeller. The flap valve is actuated by a rod from a diaphragm capsule located at the compressor housing. A spring in the diaphragm capsule closes the flap. The diaphragm is activated by pressure from the compressor. When pressure in the compressor is greater than that of the spring, the flap is opened releasing gas pressure from the side of the turbine thus reducing the load to which it is subjected. This in turn reduces compressor pressure.

In the event of a stuck charge pressure regulator, an overpressure relief system is provided to prevent overloading the engine. The overpressure switch is located under the dashboard on the same mounting bracket as the flasher relay. The fuel pump relay also has an extra function that cuts off the fuel pump if engine speed exceeds 6000 RPM.

APC (Engine Knock Control) System

This system automatically adapts to available fuel quality, limiting engine knock by continuously adjusting boost pressure. The APC system, **Fig. 4,** consists of a knock sensor (1), pressure transducer (2), electronic control module (3), and solenoid valve (4). The knock sensor, mounted on engine block, senses engine vibration and produces a voltage signal proportional to the vibration. The pressure transducer senses intake manifold pressure downstream of the throttle and produces a voltage signal proportional to boost pressure. The control module monitors knock sensor and pressure transducer signals and engine RPM, in order to control solenoid valve operation. The solenoid valve regulates control pressure signals to the boost pressure regulator depending upon electrical signals from the control module.

With engine running, the solenoid valve oscillates at a fixed frequency, opening and closing one time each 1/12 second (one cycle). Boost pressure is regulated by varying pulse width, which is the ratio between the amount of time the valve is closed to the amount of time the valve is open during one cycle. Pulse width is controlled by signals from the control module.

When the solenoid valve is closed, full control pressure reaches the pressure regulator, and boost is controlled at a basic setting. When valve is open, control pressure is vented through a calibrated orifice to the compressor intake, and the regulator allows boost to increase.

DIAGNOSIS & TESTING

9-3, 900 & 9000

CHARGING PRESSURE TEST

Charging pressure (maximum boost) is measured while vehicle is being test driven. During road test, also observe engine performance for signs of abnormal operation. Pressure is measured using a suitable gauge connected to the intake manifold.

1. Connect suitable pressure gauge to vacuum connector beside expansion tank or inline in hose between manifold and pressure switch using T connector.
2. Run gauge hose into passenger compartment. Position gauge vertically on instrument panel and ensure hose is not pinched.

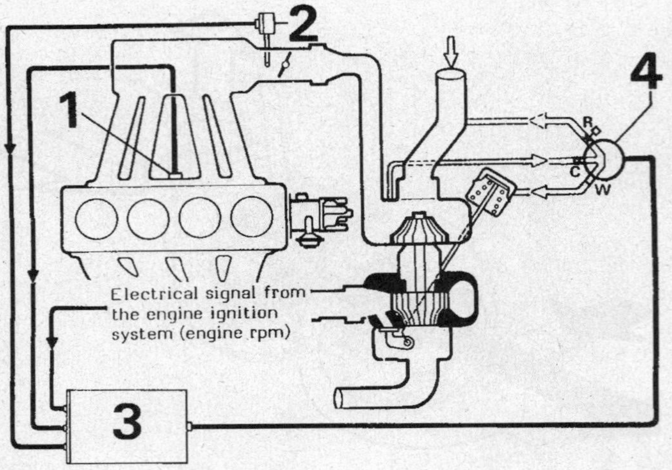

SA1059100004000X

Fig. 4 APC knock control system

3. **On 9000 models,** disconnect electrical connector from control module and connect switch box No. 8394074, or equivalent, to connector on back of control module. Ensure knock sensor switch is in Off position and solenoid valve switch is in On position.
4. **On all models,** start engine and warm to operating temperature by driving vehicle, noting vehicle performance.
5. To start test, place manual transmission in 3rd gear or automatic transmission selector in position 1 and operate vehicle at engine speed of 1500 RPM or less.
6. Press accelerator to floor. As engine speed approaches 3000 RPM, apply brakes while holding engine at full throttle. **Test must be performed as quickly as possible to avoid excessive heat build-up in brake system. If test must be repeated, drive vehicle ½–¾ mile to allow brakes to cool.**
7. Read boost pressure at 3000 RPM with engine under full load. **Boost pressure may surge above maximum limit when engine is first accelerated.**
8. **On 9-3 and 900 models,** gauge reading should be 10.1–11.6 psi.
9. **On 9000 models,** gauge reading should be 11.6–13.0 psi.
10. **On all models,** if readings are not within specifications, or performance is unsatisfactory, refer to troubleshooting charts, **Fig. 5.**

BASIC PRESSURE TEST

Basic pressure (minimum boost) must be within specifications to ensure proper engine operation.

1. Connect suitable pressure gauge to vacuum connector beside expansion tank or inline in hose between manifold and pressure switch, run gauge hose into passenger compartment, mount gauge on instrument panel, and ensure hose is not pinched.
2. Disconnect wiring harness connector to Boost Pressure Control Valve ((BPC valve) APC solenoid valve).
3. To start test, place manual transmission in 3rd gear or automatic transmission selector in position 1 and operate vehicle at engine speed of 1500 RPM or less.
4. Press accelerator to floor. As engine speed approaches 3000 RPM, apply brakes while holding engine at full throttle. **Test must be performed as quickly as possible to avoid excessive heat build-up in brake system. If test must be repeated, drive vehicle ½–¾ mile to allow brakes to cool.**
5. Read boost pressure at 3000 RPM with engine under full load. **Boost pressure may surge above maximum limit when engine is first accelerated.**
6. **On 9-3 and 900 models,** basic boost reading should be 5.26–6.1 psi.
7. **On 9000 models,** basic boost reading should be 4.6–5.4 psi.
8. **On all models,** if readings are not within specifications, adjust pressure regulator. If problem persists, refer to troubleshooting charts, **Fig. 5.**

FAULT	CAUSE	REMEDY
Noise or vibration from the turbo compressor	Poor lubrication of the turbo shaft bearing	Check the oil pressure and flow to the turbo. If the fault should persist after remedial action (permanent bearing damage) exchange the turbo compressor.
	Leakage in the induction or exhaust system	Tighten leaking connections and replace defective seals and gaskets
	Unbalanced turbo shaft owing to damage	Exchange the turbo compressor
Insufficient charging pressure	Leakage between the compressor and cylinder head or between the cylinder head and turbine	Tighten leaking connections and replace defective seals and gaskets
	Incorrect setting of charging pressure	Adjust the charge pressure regulator
	Valve in charge pressure regulator sticks in open position	Overhaul the charge pressure regulator
	Partially clogged exhaust system	Clean or replace exhaust system
	Clogged air cleaner	Change cartridge
	Binding turbo shaft	Exchange turbo compressor
Excessive charging pressure	Leakage at exhaust pressure line connections	Tighten; if necessary, replace nipples
	Clogged exhaust pressure line	Remove and clean
	Damaged diaphragm in charge pressure regulator	Replace diaphragm
	Valve in charge pressure regulator sticks in closed position	Overhaul the charge pressure regulator
	Ice formation in exhaust pressure line. (Excessive pressure occurs 1–2 min after cold start when ambient temperature below freezing)	Avoid heavy loading of engine immediately after cold starting
	Incorrect setting of charging pressure	Adjust charge pressure regulator
Metallic noise from charge pressure regulator	Play in regulator valve	Overhaul the charge pressure regulator
	Spring insufficiently offset in charge pressure regulator	Adjust position of spring (replace as necessary)
Engine knocking (pinking)	Excessive charging pressure	Adjust charging pressure
	Unsuitable fuel (octane too low)	Change fuel
	Ignition setting too far advanced	Adjust timing
Oil leakage at turbo shaft seals (oil fumes in exhaust)	Poor return flow from turbo: – Clogged return line – Excessive crankcase pressure	Check return line Check crankcase ventilation
	Turbo unit seals damaged	Exchange turbo compressor

SA1059100005010X

Fig. 5 Turbocharger troubleshooting chart (Part 1 of 3)

APC SYSTEM TEST

1. Disconnect hose to pressure transducer at manifold and plug manifold fitting.
2. Using T connector, connect pressure gauge No. 8393514, or equivalent, and suitable pressure pump to pressure transducer hose.
3. Start engine and run at fast idle until it reaches normal operating temperature
4. **On 9-3 and 900 models,** set engine to run at 2000 RPM
5. **On 9000 models,** set engine to run at 2100 RPM.
6. **On all models,** apply 7.25 psi pressure to pressure transducer and observe system operation.

Symptoms	Possible causes	Remedy
Maximum boost pressure too low (low engine output).	Enrichment at wide open throttle/high engine speed (> 3800 rpm) not functioning	Check pulse relation, Lambda System. Correct as necessary.
	Ignition timing malfunctioning	Check basic timing setting, function of ignition retard system and camshaft timing. Correct as necessary.
	Incorrectly adjusted basic pressure.	Check the basic setting of the boost pressure regulator.
	Loose or oxidized electrical connections in the APC-System	Check electrical connections of control unit, bulkhead connector, pressure transducer (2 connections) fuel pump relay, knock detector plug and common ground in the engine compartment.
		Also check for broken wires in the knock detector-to-control unit, pressure switch-to-control unit, or fuel pump relay-to-control unit, wiring. Rectify if required.
	Faulty knock detector.	Test system with known good knock detector. If symptoms disappear, knock detector was at fault. Replace.
	Faulty pressure transducer.	Check the pressure transducer. Replace the pressure transducer if required.
	Solenoid valve does not open.	Check the solenoid valve. Replace faulty solenoid valve.
	Faulty control unit.	Test system with known good knock control unit. If symptoms disappear, control unit was at fault. Replace.
	The knock detector registers abnormal engine vibrations.	Connect the test wiring harness with the service box (83 93 548) Set the switch to "On". If the LED flashes when driving under light load listen for abnormal engine noise. If the engine sounds normal try a new knock detector.
	Faulty spring or sticking rod in the diaphragm unit.	Try a new diaphragm unit.

SA1059100005020X

Fig. 5 Turbocharger troubleshooting chart (Part 2 of 3)

Symptoms	Possible causes	Remedy
Boost pressure too high (also covers violent changes in boost pressure during acceleration). Pressure switch cuts out.	Leak in turbocompressor - to - solenoid hose.	Check for leaks. Replace faulty hose.
	Leak in solenoid valve - to - diaphragm unit hose.	Check for leaks. Replace faulty hose.
	Leak in diaphragm unit.	Check for leaks. Replace faulty diaphragm unit.
	Ruptured diaphragm unit.	Check for leaks. Replace faulty diaphragm unit. Check the mounting of the diaphragm unit housing on the bracket. Replace faulty diaphragm unit.
	Leak in hose to pressure transducer.	Check for leaks. Replace hose.
	Faulty pressure transducer.	Check pressure transducer. Replace faulty pressure transducer.
	Solenoid valve does not shut due to sticking valve spool.	Replace faulty solenoid valve.
	Blocked orifice in the solenoid hose connection to the turbocompressor	NOTE. Can be temperature-sensitive. Check and clean orifice as necessary.
	Incorrect basic boost pressure setting.	Check the basic setting of the boost pressure regulator with the car on the road. Adjust as necessary.
	Short circuit in the pressure transducer signal circuit.	Check the wiring between pressure transducer and the control unit. Rectify short circuit.
	Faulty control unit.	Test system with known good control unit. If symptoms disappear, control unit was at fault. Replace.
	Shaft sticking in the boost pressure regulator valve.	Remove the seal and clip. Unhook the diaphragm unit push rod from the regulator valve lever stud. Check that the valve shaft rotates easily. Replace faulty boost pressure regulator valve.
	Sticking diaphragm unit push rod bushing.	Replace diaphragm unit.

SA1059100005030X

Fig. 5 Turbocharger troubleshooting chart (Part 3 of 3)

7. Solenoid valve should begin to operate, identified by chattering sound.
8. If solenoid valve does not operate, refer to troubleshooting chart, **Fig. 6.**
9. Release pressure and return engine to curb idle speed. Solenoid should not operate.
10. If solenoid continues to operate, refer to troubleshooting chart, **Fig. 6.**

APC SYSTEM KNOCK CONTROL TEST

1. Connect suitable pressure gauge and service harness with knock sensor switch No. 8393548, or equivalent, on 900 models, or No. 8394074, or equivalent, on 9000 models, to vehicle.
2. Set switch in ON position, and run gauge hose into passenger compartment. Position gauge vertically on instrument panel and ensure hose is not pinched.
3. **On 9000 models,** disconnect electrical connector from control module and connect switch box No. 8394074, or equivalent, to connector on back of control module. Ensure knock sensor switch is in Off position and solenoid valve switch is in ON position.
4. **On all models,** start engine and warm to operating temperature by driving vehicle, noting vehicle performance.
5. To start test, place manual transmission in 3rd gear or automatic transmission selector in position 1 and operate vehicle at engine speed of 1500 RPM or less.
6. Press accelerator to floor. As engine speed approaches 3000 RPM, apply brakes while holding engine at full throttle. **Test must be performed as quickly as possible to avoid excessive heat build-up in brake system. If test must be repeated, drive vehicle ½–¾ mile to allow brakes to cool.**
7. Read boost pressure at 3000 RPM with engine under full load. **Boost pressure may surge above maximum limit when engine is first accelerated.**
8. **On 9-3 and 900 models,** gauge reading should be 10.1–11.6 psi.
9. **On 9000 models,** gauge reading should be 11.6–13.0 psi.
10. **On all models,** observe gauge while listening for sound of engine ping or knock.
11. If system is operating properly, gauge reading should drop approximately 1.4 psi whenever knocking occurs.
12. If engine is held at 3000 RPM at full load, gauge reading should rise approximately 1.4 psi at 3 second intervals, until engine begins to knock. Then reading should drop approximately 1.4 psi whenever knocking occurs.
13. If system fails to perform as outlined, refer to troubleshooting chart, **Fig. 6.**

9-5

CHARGING PRESSURE

1. Remove bypass pipe with valve.
2. Remove mounting nut, clips and exhaust manifold heat shield.
3. Loosen turbo outlet hose and install plug tool No. 83 94 595, or equivalent.
4. Disconnect throttle body air pipe and remove hose elbow.
5. Install 1.9687 inch length of 1.9687 I.D. hose on pipe.
6. Install plug tool No. 83 95 030, or equivalent, into turbo pressure pipe.
7. Connect pressure gauge tool No. 83 93 514, or equivalent.
8. Connect pressure/vacuum pump tool No. 30 14 883, or equivalent, to bypass valve.
9. Pump pressure to approximately 14.5 psi.
10. Connect pressure/vacuum pump tool No. 30 14 883, or equivalent, to bypass valve.
11. Pump pressure to approximately 14.5 psi.
12. Connect suitable pressure gun to pressure gauge and carefully create 14.5 psi pressure.
13. If pressure drops more than 1.45 psi in 30 seconds, or if there is an audible

Solenoid valve not functioning when APC system tested in car.	The control unit has no voltage between terminal 14 (+) and 6 ground (-). NOTE. The wiring terminal should remanin connected to the control unit during the measurement.	Check that fuse 19 has not blown. Remove any oxidation present. Check the wiring in the connectors at distributor panel (fuse box) and control unit. Check that the (+) and ground (-) wires are undamaged. Rectify as required.
	Loose connector on knock detector. Broken wire between knock detector and control unit.	Check electrical connection at the connectors (in the engine compartment and on the control unit). Rectify as required.
	Knock detector not properly tightened.	Check tightness. See under Removing and refitting of component parts, knock detector
	Faulty knock detector.	Test system with known good knock detector. If symptoms disappear, knock detector was at fault.
	Solenoid valve not functioning despite supply greater than 5 volts. NOTE. The solenoid electrical connector is to remain connected.	Check the solenoid valve. See under Checking of component parts, checking of solenoid valve.
	Faulty pressure transducer.	Check the pressure switch. See under "Checking of component parts, pressure transducer.
	Faulty control unit.	Test system with known good control unit. If symptoms disappear control unit was at fault. Replace.

SA1059100006010X

Fig. 6 APC system troubleshooting chart (Part 1 of 3)

hissing sound, inspect hoses, pipes and connections for leak.

14. Inspect hoses and pipes for leak using suitable compressed air gun.
15. Remove charge air cooler.
16. Install inlet and outlet hoses on charge air cooler, then plug one hose. Connect suitable pressure gauge to other hose.
17. Connect suitable compressed air gun to pressure gauge and carefully create 14.5 psi pressure.
18. If pressure drops more than 1.45 psi in 30 seconds, or if there is an audible hissing sound, inspect hoses, pipes and connections for leak.
19. Inspect hoses and pipes for leak using leak detection fluid No. 30 20 385, or equivalent.
20. Reverse procedure to install, noting the following:
    a. Install new O-rings greased with suitable non-acidic petroleum jelly.
    b. Spray connects with Kontakt 61, or equivalent contact cleaner.
    c. Coat mounting studs with Molykote 1000, or equivalent.
    d. **Torque** bypass pipe and intake pipe bolts and hose clips to 71 inch lbs.
    e. **Torque** heat shield mounting nut to 15 ft. lbs.

SYSTEM SERVICE

Component Testing

9-3, 900 & 9000

PRESSURE SWITCH

1. Start engine and allow to idle.
2. Disconnect hose to pressure switch at intake manifold and connect test gauge No. 8392813, or equivalent, together with suitable pump (coolant system pressure tester), to pressure switch hose, **Fig. 7.**

Symptoms	Possible causes	Remedy
Solenoid valve active at idling speed. (Irregular chattering sound.)	Idling speed too low.	Increase idling speed to 875 ± 50 rpm approx.
	Broken wire between pressure transducer and control unit.	Check the wiring. Rectify as required.
	Faulty pressure transducer.	Check the pressure transducer. See "Checking of the pressure transducer". Replace faulty pressure transducer.
	Bad contact/broken wire between knock detector and control unit.	Check the electrical connections at the connector in the engine compartment and at the control unit. Check that the wiring between the knock detector and the control unit is unbroken. Rectify as required.
	Knock detector not properly tightened.	Check tightness. See "Removing and refitting of component parts, knock detector".
	Faulty knock detector.	Test system with known good knock detector. If symptoms disappear, knock detector was at fault. Replace
	Faulty control unit.	Test system with known good control unit. If symptoms disappear, control unit was at fault. Replace.

SA1059100006020X

Fig. 6 APC system troubleshooting chart (Part 2 of 3)

Symptoms	Possible causes	Remedy
Normal boost pressure, but no pressure reduction despite intensive knocking/pinking.	APC system not functioning.	See "Checking of the APC system knock control".
	Bad contact in the knock detector wiring.	Check the connector between the knock detector and the car wiring harness.
	Knock detector not properly tightened.	Check tightness. See "Removing and refitting of component parts, knock detector".
	Faulty knock detector.	Test system with known good knock detector. If symptoms disappear, knock detector was at fault. Replace.
	Faulty control unit.	Test system with known good control unit. If symptoms disappear, control unit was at fault. Replace.
	Bearing sticking in the boost pressure regulator valve.	Remove the seal and clip. Unhook the diaphragm unit push rod from the regulator valve lever stud. Check that the valve shaft rotates easily. Replace faulty boost pressure regulator valve.
	Diaphragm unit rod bushing sticking.	Replace diaphragm unit.

SA1059100006030X

Fig. 6 APC system troubleshooting chart (Part 3 of 3)

3. Increase pressure to switch using pump and note pressure at which engine cuts out.
4. If cut out pressure is not 15.3–16.7 psi, replace switch.

PRESSURE TRANSDUCER

1. **On 9-3 and 900 models,** remove pressure transducer, then connect suitable air pump to hose fitting and connect ohmmeter to transducer terminals.
2. **On 9000 models,** proceed as follows:
    a. Remove lower lefthand instrument panel and disconnect electrical connector from APC control module.
    b. Connect suitable air pump with pressure gauge to hose from pressure transducer, then connect ohmmeter across black/white and green/red wire terminals in APC connector.
3. **On all models,** ohmmeter should read 5–13 ohms at atmospheric pressure.
4. Apply 14.4 psi pressure to transducer with pump, then gradually reduce applied pressure to 8.7 psi, while tapping transducer lightly with hammer.
5. Ohmmeter should read 83–93 ohms at 8.7 psi.
6. If readings are not within specifications, transducer is defective.

BOOST PRESSURE CONTROL ((BPC) APC SOLENOID) VALVE

1. Disconnect wiring harness connector to solenoid, and disconnect hose to solenoid R fitting at turbocharger inlet.
2. Using jumper wires, connect battery voltage across solenoid terminals.
3. Solenoid should open with an audible click. Check that air passes through valve by blowing through disconnected hose.
4. Disconnect jumper wires. Solenoid should close valve and no air should pass through valve.
5. Check orifice inside solenoid valve C fitting. Orifice should be approximately .10 inch in diameter and free from dirt or obstruction.
6. If solenoid fails to operate as specified,

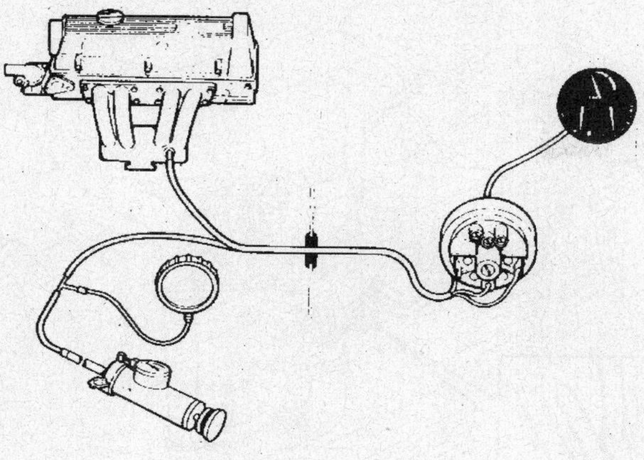

Fig. 7 Pressure switch test connections. 900 models

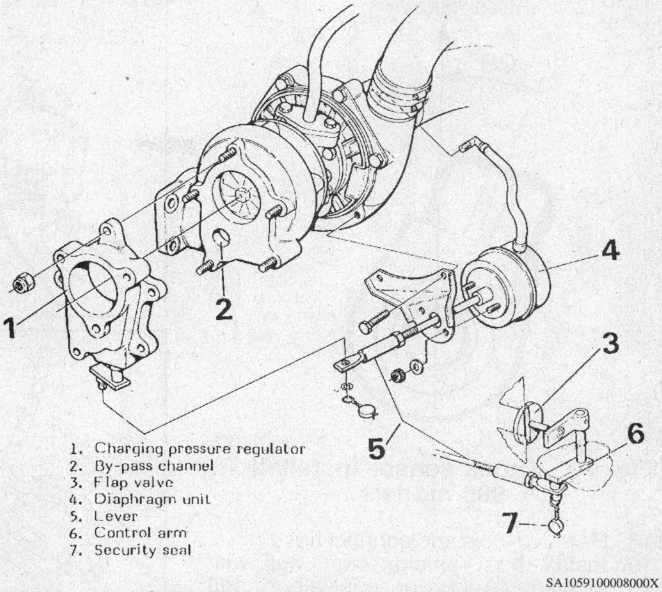

Fig. 8 Exploded view of charge pressure regulator assembly

Symptoms	Possible causes	Remedy
Not possible to adjust basic pressure according to instructions.	Faulty boost pressure regulator valve.	Remove the exhaust elbow. Visually check that the valve flap is in contact with the valve body. Remove the seal and clip. Unhook the diaphragm unit push rod from the boost pressure regulator valve. Check that the valve shaft rotates freely. Replace faulty boost pressure regulator valve.
	Sticking diaphragm unit pushrod bushing	Check that the diaphragm unit push rod moves freely. Replace faulty diaphragm unit.
	Blocked orifice in the solenoid valve hose connection to the turbocompressor (connection "C").	NOTE Can be temperature-sensitive. Clean orifice.

SA1059100009000X

Fig. 9 Pressure regulator troubleshooting chart

or if orifice is not as specified, solenoid valve must be replaced.

TURBO PRESSURE GAUGE

Check gauge by following the same procedure used for checking the pressure switch. At maximum charging pressure, needle should be within the wide orange zone. At the pressure switch actuating pressure, needle should be in front of the limit between the orange and the red zones.

9-5

BYPASS VALVE

1. Disconnect charge air bypass valve vacuum hose.
2. Connect pressure/vacuum pump tool No. 30 14 883, or equivalent, and create vacuum in valve.
3. Ensure diaphragm is intact.
4. Repeat previous steps using pressure instead of vacuum.
5. Connect hose.

Component Adjustment

9-3, 900 & 9000

CHARGING PRESSURE

After test driving the vehicle, if reading on pressure gauge deviates from the specified value, adjustments based on the readings recorded should be performed using the following procedure. Pressure regulator and diaphragm assembly, **Fig. 8,** should be connected to turbocharger during adjustment.

1. Rotate pressure regulator lever to closed position, disconnect diaphragm pushrod, and adjust rod so that it easily fits over pin on regulator lever without forcing diaphragm return spring. **Diaphragm pushrod must be prevented from turning when adjusting end piece.**
2. Turn end piece on diaphragm pushrod 3.5 turns inward, tighten locknut, then reconnect pushrod to pressure regulator lever.
3. Perform "Basic Pressure Test" as previously outlined.
4. If boost readings are not as specified in tests, readjust diaphragm pushrod. **Rotate diaphragm pushrod clockwise to increase basic pressure or counterclockwise to decrease pressure.**
5. Perform basic pressure test again. If pressure cannot be adjusted to specifications, refer to Pressure Regulator Troubleshooting Chart, **Fig. 9.**

9-5

2.3L ENGINE

Basic Charging Pressure

1. Remove bypass pipe with valve.
2. Remove mounting nut, clips and exhaust manifold heat shield.
3. Remove operating arm clip using circlip tool No. 83 94 538, or equivalent.
4. Hold pushrod with suitable pliers and remove locknut using suitable locknut wrench.
5. Hold operating arm and disconnect pushrod. Secure arm from jumping.
6. Move boost pressure control valve operating arm to closed position, then adjust end piece for easy pushrod installation.
7. Disconnect pushrod from operating arm's pin.
8. Turn end piece approximately two turns to obtained .0787 inch pretension.
9. Connect pushrod to pin and retaining ring.
10. Loosen diaphragm housing hose.
11. Connect pressure/vacuum pump tool No. 30 24 883 and pressure gauge tool No. 83 93 514, or equivalents, to diaphragm unit.
12. Carefully pump up pressure so control rod moves and adjusts boost pressure.
13. When control rod begins to move, pressure should be 4.21–5.08 psi.
14. If pressure is too low, shorten rod until pressure is 4.64 psi.
15. If unable to adjust basic charging pressure, refer to "Wastegate Valve."
16. Remove pushrod and coat operating arm pin with Molykote 1000, or equivalent.
17. Install pushrod and clip, then grip rod with suitable pliers and lock nut.

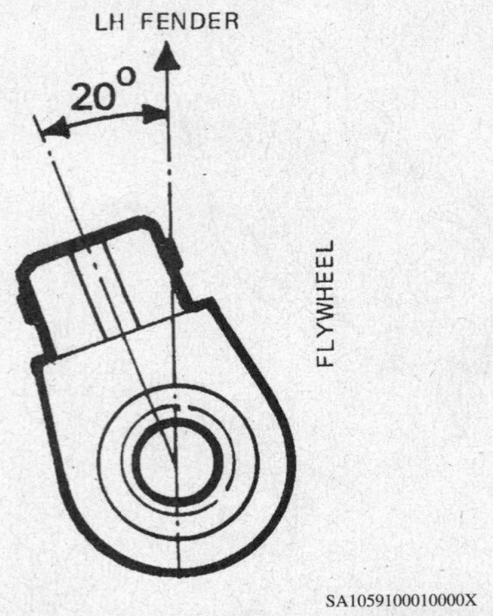

Fig. 10 Knock sensor installation. 900 models

18. Remove tools and connect hose.
19. Install heat shield, coat nut with Molykote 1000, or equivalent, and **torque** mounting screw to 15 ft. lbs.
20. Grease O-ring with suitable non-acidic petroleum jelly, install bypass pipe and **torque** to 71 inch lbs.

Wastegate Valve

1. Disconnect turbocharger pressure pipe hose clip and bend bypass pipe aside.
2. Remove mounting nut, clips and exhaust manifold heat shield.
3. Apply suitable oil and remove front exhaust system mounting nuts from turbocharger. **Front exhaust system must bend more than 7° out of line.**
4. Remove clip and disconnect valve control arm pushrod.
5. Ensure flap valve firmly abuts turbine housing. Remove carbon deposits, etc.
6. Ensure arm moves easily.
7. Connect pushrod and lock clip.
8. Grease studs with Molykote 1000, or equivalent, then install front exhaust system and tighten nuts alternately until **torque** is 18 ft. lbs.
9. Install heat shield (press lefthand holder first), coat nut with Molykote 1000, or equivalent, and **torque** mounting screw to 15 ft. lbs.
10. Grease new O-ring with suitable non-acidic petroleum jelly, connect bypass valve with pipe, and **torque** clip to 71 inch lbs.

Component Replacement

APC CONTROL MODULE

900

1. Fold rear seat back forward.
2. Disconnect wiring harness connector to control module.
3. Remove screws securing unit to floor and remove control module.
4. Reverse procedure to install. Ensure tamper-proof seal is in place.

9000

1. Remove lower lefthand instrument panel shroud.
2. Disconnect electrical connectors from control module, cruise control module, pressure switch and windshield wiper delay relay.
3. Carefully remove control module mounting bracket, then the control module from bracket.
4. Reverse procedure to install, ensuring tamper-proof seal is in place.

KNOCK SENSOR

900 & 9000

1. Disconnect wiring harness connector at sensor.
2. Remove bolt securing sensor to engine block below intake manifold and remove sensor.
3. Clean block and sensor mating surfaces.
4. **On 9-3 and 900 models,** position sensor, **Fig. 10,** and **torque** bolt to 15 ft. lbs.
5. **On 9000 models, torque** bolt to 11 ft. lbs.
6. **On all models,** reconnect wiring harness connector and battery cable.

PRESSURE TRANSDUCER

900

1. Remove rubber bellows between front and rear center console, and remove front console.
2. Remove lefthand lower dash panel and remove three screws securing relay and transducer bracket to body member.
3. Disconnect wiring harness connector and pressure hose from transducer.
4. Remove retaining screws and remove transducer from bracket.
5. Reverse procedure to install.

9000

1. Remove APC control module bracket as previously described.
2. Disconnect electrical connectors from pressure transducer, then remove transducer from mounting bracket.
3. Reverse procedure to install.

BOOST PRESSURE CONTROL ((BPC) APC SOLENOID) VALVE

900

1. Disconnect wiring harness connector to valve.
2. Disconnect pressure hoses from valve, noting position for reassembly.
3. Remove screws securing solenoid bracket righthand side of radiator support and remove valve.
4. Reverse procedure to install. Ensure hoses are properly connected, **Fig. 11.**

9000

1. Disconnect electrical connector from valve.
2. Disconnect hoses from valve connections, noting position for reassembly.
3. Remove solenoid valve screws, then the valve.
4. Reverse procedure to install. Ensure hoses are properly connected, **Fig. 11.**

TURBOCHARGER

Refer to appropriate engine section.

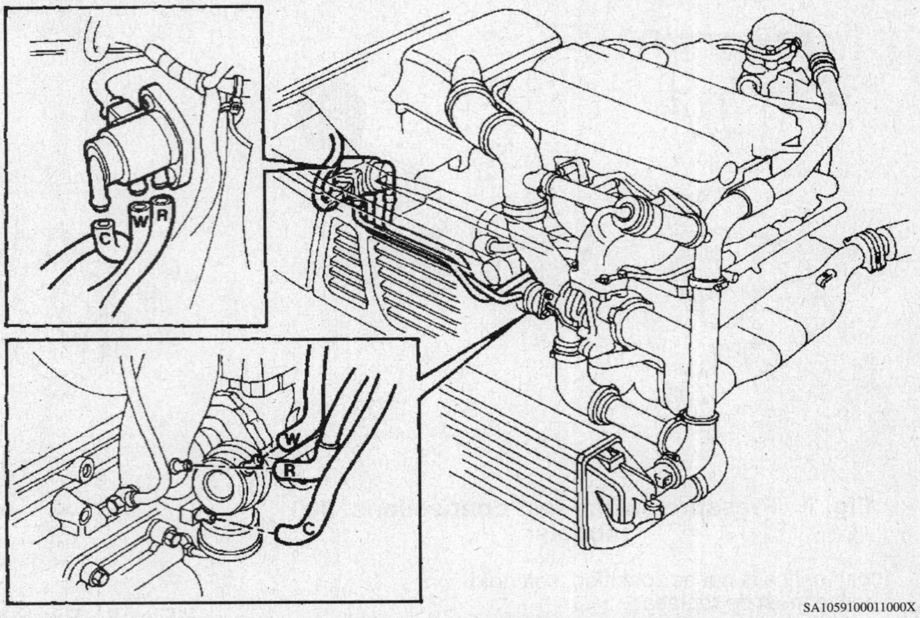

Fig. 11 Solenoid valve hose connections. 900 models

Emission Control System Application Charts

Engine Liters/ CID/ Type	Certification Type		Trans. Type		Computerized Engine Management	Fuel Induction System Type	Ignition Timing, Deg. BTDC @RPM	EPA & CARB Emission Recall	Emission Control System SRI	Emission Control Systems								
	CA	FED	A/T	M/T						PCV	ACL	AIS	EGR	EVAP	CAT	SPK	FR	O2S
1998																		
2.0L/121/L4 Turbo	X	X	X	X	YES⑤	SFI	④	—	—	X	—	—	—	X①	X⑩	X③	X	X⑨
2.3L/140/L4	X	X	X	X	YES⑦	SFI	④	—	—	X	—	X⑧	—	X①	X⑩	X③	X	X⑥
2.3L/140/L4 Turbo	X	X	X	X	YES⑤	SFI	④	—	—	X	—	—	—	X①	X⑩	X③	X	X⑨
1999–2001																		
2.0L/121/L4 Turbo	X	X	X	X	YES⑤	SFI	④	—	—	X	—	—	—	X②	X⑩	X③	X	X⑥
2.3L/140/L4 Turbo	X	X	X	X	YES⑤	SFI	④	—	—	X	—	—	—	X②	X⑩	X③	X	X⑥
3.0L/180/V6 Turbo	X	X	X	X	YES⑤	SFI	④	—	—	X	—	—	—	X②	X⑩	X③	X	X⑥

X — Equipped
— Not Equipped
① — EVAP canister is located behind the front right wheel housing liner.
② — On 9-3 models, EVAP canister to rear of fuel tank. On 9-5 models, EVAP canister is located behind the front right wheel housing liner.
③ — DIS.
④ — Electronically controlled.
⑤ — Trionic System. Equipped w/MIL.
⑥ — One HO2S.
⑦ — Motronic System. Equipped w/MIL.
⑧ — Pump type.
⑨ — Two HO2S.
⑩ — Type, TWC; number of catalytic converters, 1.

ACL — Air Cleaner (Thermostatic Air Cleaner)
AIS — Air Injection System
A/T — Automatic Transmission
BTDC — Before Top Dead Center
CA — California
CARB — Carburetor
CAT — Catalytic Converter
DI — Distributor Ignition.
DIS — Distributorless Ignition System
DLC — Data Link Connector
EGR — Exhaust Gas Recirculation
EI — Electronic Ignition.
EVAP — Evaporative Emission Control System
FED — Federal

FR — Fillpipe Restrictor
HO — High Output
LPT — Light Pressure Turbo
MFI — Multiport Fuel Injection
MIL — Malfunction Indicator Lamp (Check Engine, Service Engine Soon Lamp)
M/T — Manual Transmission
OBD II — On Board Diagnostics II
O2S — Oxygen Sensor
PCV — Positive Crankcase Ventilation
RPM — Revolutions Per Minute
SFI — Sequential Fuel Injection
SPK — Spark Control
SRI — Service Reminder Indicator
TWC — Three Way Catalytic Converter

Engine Compartment Reference Diagrams

INDEX

	PAGE NO.	FIG. NO.
9-3	16-177	2
9-5	16-178	3
900:		
Motronic 4.1	16-177	1
Trionic	16-177	2
9000	16-177	2

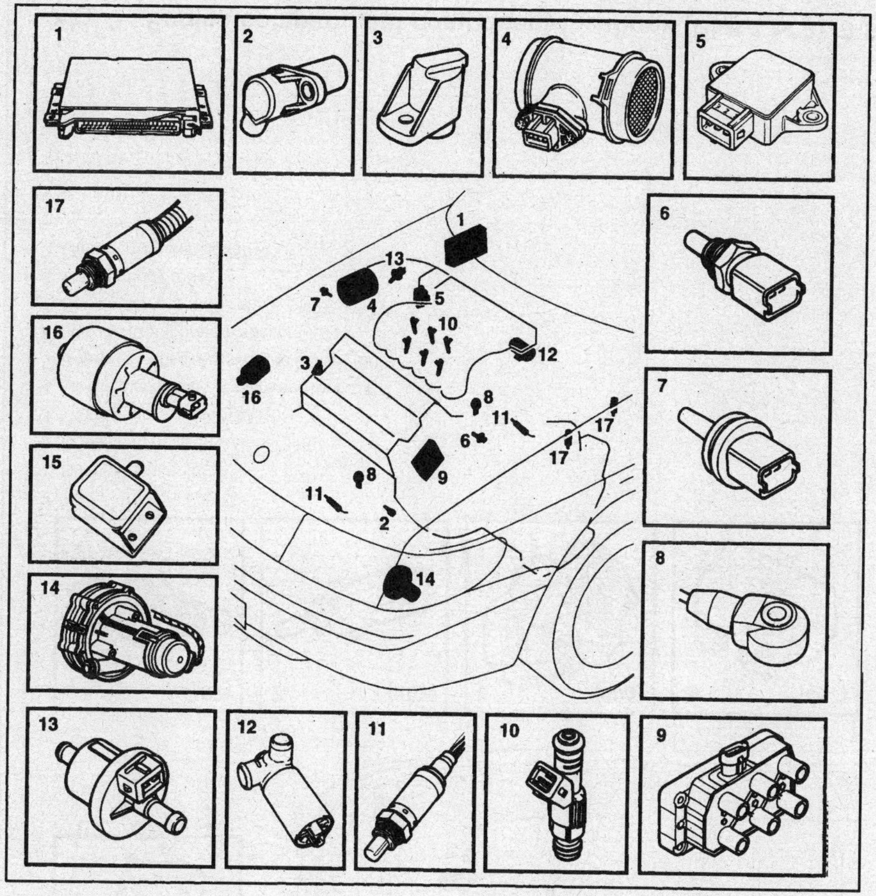

1 Engine control module
2 Crankshaft position sensor
3 Camshaft position sensor
4 Mass air flow sensor
5 Throttle position sensor
6 Engine coolant temperature sensor
7 Intake air temperature sensor
8 Knock sensors (2)
9 Ignition coil module with 3 ignition coils
10 Injectors (6)
11 Oxygen sensors (2 before the three way catalytic converters)
12 Idle air control valve
13 EVAP canister purge valve
14 Secondary air injection pump
15 Fuel tank pressure sensor, mounted in the fuel tank (not shown in illustration)
16 Shut–off valve, evaporative emission canister
17 Oxygen sensors (2 after the three way catalytic converters)

SA1019600008000X

Fig. 1 Engine compartment component locations. 900 series w/Motronic 4.1

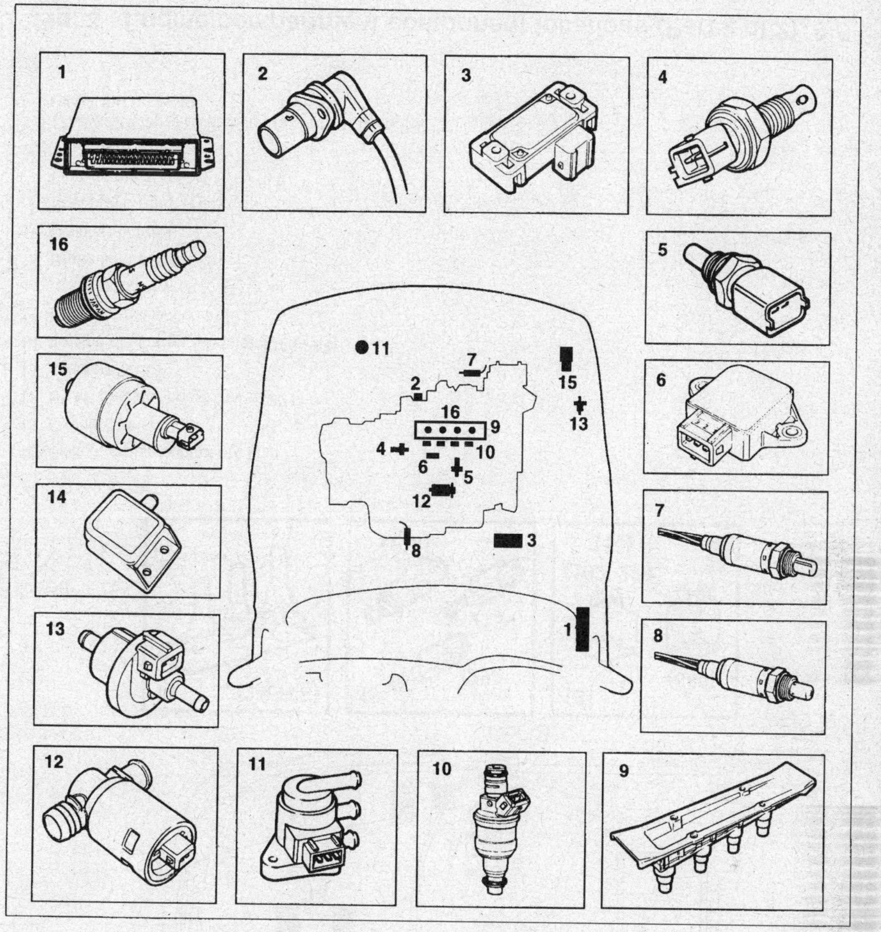

1 Engine control module
2 Crankshaft position sensor
3 Manifold absolute pressure sensor
4 Intake air temperature sensor
5 Temperature sensor, engine coolant
6 Throttle position sensor
7 Front heated oxygen sensor (before three way catalytic converter)
8 Rear heated oxygen sensor (after three way catalytic converter)
9 Ignition discharge module
10 Injectors, 4
11 Boost pressure control valve
12 Idle air control valve
13 EVAP canister purge valve
14 Pressure sensor, fuel tank
15 Shut–of valve, evaporative emission canister
16 Spark plugs

SA1019600010000X

Fig. 2 Engine compartment component locations. 9-3, 900 & 9000 w/Trionic

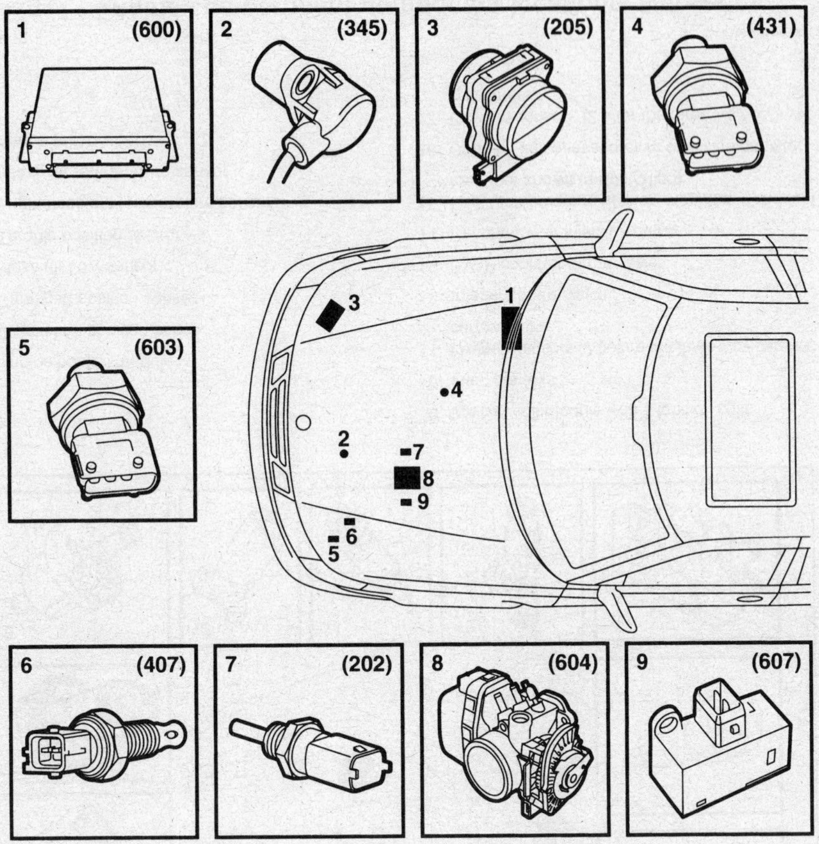

1 Control module (600)
2 Crankshaft position sensor (345)
3 Mass air flow sensor (205)
4 Manifold absolute pressure sensor (431)
5 Charge air absolute pressure sensor (603)
6 Intake air temperature sensor (407)
7 Coolant temperature sensor (202)
8 Throttle body (604)
9 Limp-home solenoid (607)

SA1019900011010X

Fig. 3 Engine compartment component locations (Part 1 of 2). 9-5

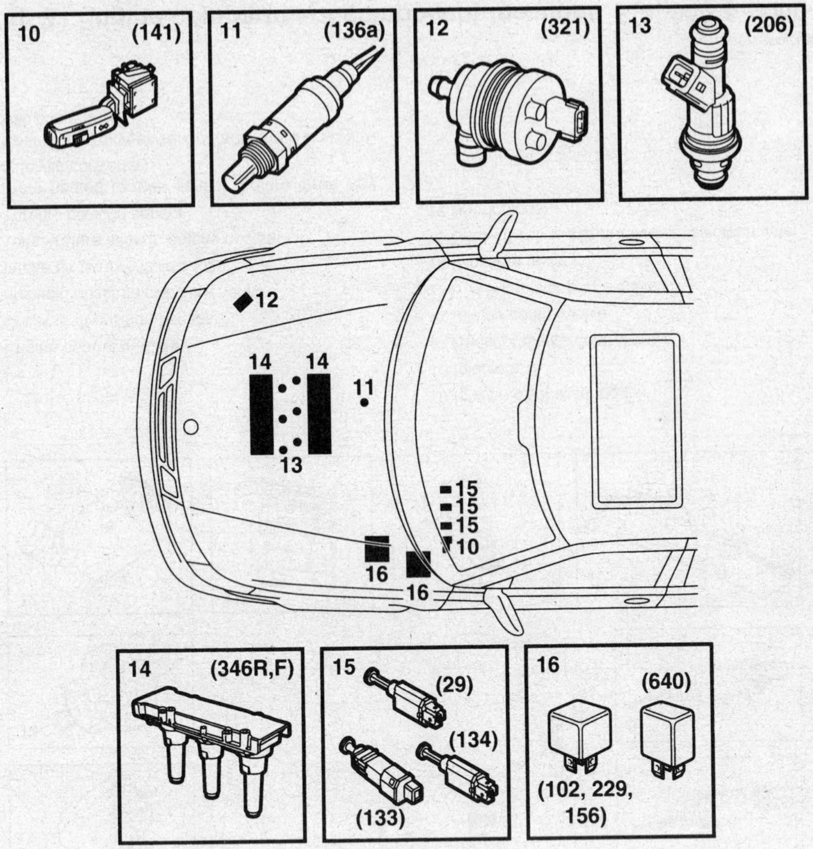

10 Switch, cruise control (141)
11 Oxygen sensor (136a)
12 EVAP canister purge valve (321)
13 Injectors (206)
14 Ignition discharge modules (346 F/R)
15 Clutch pedal switch (133)
Brake pedal switch (134)
Brake light switch (29)
16 Main relay (229)
Fuel pump relay (102)
Limp-home solenoid relay (640)
A/C relay (156)
(The A/C relay is located in the main relay board under the bonnet.)

SA1019900011020X

Fig. 3 Engine compartment component locations (Part 2 of 2). 9-5

Emission Controls

NOTE: If Unsure Of The System Used On The Vehicle Being Serviced, Refer To "The Engine Systems Identification Chart." Further Assistance For The Proper Use Of Information Contained In This Section Can Also Be Found In The Front Of This Tabbed Section Under "How To Use This Manual."

NOTE: On Air Bag Equipped Models, Refer To "Air Bag System Precautions" Located In The Front Of This Manual For System Disarming & Arming Procedures.

NOTE: Refer To "Computer Relearn Procedures" Located In The Front Of This Manual When Battery Power To The Computer Has Been Interrupted.

NOTE: Prior To Performing Any Service Operations Listed In This Section, Consult The "Technical Service Bulletins" Section For Related Information.

INDEX

	Page No.
Evaporative Emission System (Evaporative Emission Control System)	16-179
Exhaust Gas Recirculation System	16-179
Description	16-179
Inspection	16-179
System Service	16-180
Positive Crankcase Ventilation (PCV) System	16-179
Three Way Catalytic Converter ((TWC) Catalytic Converter)	16-180

POSITIVE CRANKCASE VENTILATION (PCV) SYSTEM

The crankcase ventilation system consists of a three-way nipple in the cylinder head cover, from which a small diameter hose runs to the intake manifold and a larger diameter hose runs to either the air cleaner or turbocharger air inlet. The nipple contains an orifice plate which regulates vacuum applied to the crankcase. During normal operation, manifold vacuum is applied to the crankcase and blow-by gasses are drawn into the intake manifold through the smaller hose. However, when crankcase pressure is too low, air is drawn from the air cleaner through the nipple, then to intake manifold. During full load operation, vacuum created in the air cleaner or turbocharger inlet pipe overcomes intake manifold vacuum and blow-by gasses are drawn into the intake stream through the large diameter hose.

EVAPORATIVE EMISSION SYSTEM (EVAPORATIVE EMISSION CONTROL SYSTEM)

This system consists of a charcoal canister and vapor lines. Fuel vapor is vented through a vapor line to charcoal canister located in engine compartment, where fuel vapor is stored until engine is started. When engine is started, fuel vapor is carried by fresh air drawn through canister to air cleaner by means of a hose, then through carburetor and into combustion chamber.

The ECM opens an electronically controlled relief valve located in the fuel vent line, to vent fuel vapors which accumulate in the fuel tank.

EXHAUST GAS RECIRCULATION SYSTEM

Description

The opening of the EGR valve is controlled by two vacuum sources on the throttle body. When the throttle blade is closed (idle), both ports are exposed to atmospheric pressure. This vacuum is partially bled off through port 1 which is still exposed to atmospheric pressure. This reduces the vacuum signal to the EGR valve causing it to open less than it would otherwise. As the throttle blade opens further, port 1 is also exposed to manifold vacuum. At this point the EGR valve opens completely. A thermostatic vacuum switch shuts off vacuum to the EGR valve at coolant temperatures below 112°F to improve cold driveability.

Inspection

1. Connect tachometer following manufacturer's instructions, start engine and run until it reaches normal operating temperature.
2. Gradually increase engine speed while observing EGR valve diaphragm.
3. EGR valve should begin to open at approximately 1900 RPM.
4. If valve fails to open, disconnect vacuum hose from PCV valve at EGR valve, and plug hose.
5. Apply vacuum to EGR valve using suitable pump.
6. If engine begins to run rough (EGR valve opening), valve is operating properly.

System Service

1. Remove throttle body assembly, EGR pipe and valve.
2. Clean opening in intake manifold using .4 inch drill bit. Remove any carbon deposits from intake manifold.
3. Clean EGR pipe and dry with compressed air.
4. Using wire brush clean inlet and outlet of EGR valve taking care not to damage valve pintle.
5. Using vacuum pump, apply vacuum to hold valve open. Rinse valve with suitable solvent and dry with compressed air.
6. Using new gasket, install EGR valve and pipe. Connect vacuum hose.
7. Install throttle body.

THREE WAY CATALYTIC CONVERTER ((TWC) CATALYTIC CONVERTER)

Final filtering of the exhaust gasses is accomplished by a three-way type catalytic converter. The catalytic converter is located between the engine and the muffler. The converter incorporates a ceramic material insert of honeycomb design. The walls are coated with platinum and rhodium.

Technical Service Bulletins

INDEX

	Page No.
Fuel Damper Noise	16-181
9000	16-181
Non-Turbo	16-181
Turbo	16-181
Hooting Noise	16-181
900 & 9000	16-181
Poor Driveability Or Stalling	16-181
900 & 9000	16-181

POOR DRIVEABILITY OR STALLING

900 & 9000

On some of these models equipped with turbochargers, there may be a driveability problem or engine stalling condition.

This condition may be caused by a leaking diaphragm within the air bypass valve. To correct this condition, proceed as follows:

1. Park vehicle and turn ignition switch to Off position.
2. Disconnect bypass valve vacuum hose from intake manifold nipple.
3. Connect vacuum pump to hose and pump down valve.
4. If valve will not hold vacuum, diaphragm is leaking. Replace bypass valve as required.

HOOTING NOISE

900 & 9000

On some of these models equipped with 16-Valve Turbocharged Engines, there may be a hooting noise at partly open throttle.

This condition may be caused by the diaphragm in the bypass valve oscillating. To correct this condition install revised valve.

FUEL DAMPER NOISE

9000

On some of these models equipped with 2.3L engine, there may be a noise when idling with a hot engine and/or when starting from cold. It may sound as if the fuel lines are knocking against the undercarriage of the vehicle. The noise will disappear once the engine has warmed up.

This condition may be caused by fuel pulsation. To correct this condition, install revised new fuel damper (part No. 41 64 232) as follows:

TURBO

1. Relieve fuel pressure.
2. Disconnect return line at fuel distribution pipe.
3. Remove two-inch section of hose. 5.7 inches up from end of return line using suitable sharp knife,
4. Install two spring clips on rubber hose, then the damper. Adjust spring clips to correct position.
5. Connect return line. Ensure there is sufficient clearance around damper and fuel line.

NON-TURBO

1. Relieve fuel pressure
2. Remove inlet hose from throttle housing, then disconnect return line at pressure regulator.
3. Cut 5.5–6 inches of plastic hose using suitable sharp knife.
4. Install connecting nipples in plastic hoses using fuel line grip tool No. 83 94 546, or equivalent.
5. Connect rubber hoses and install spring clips.
6. Install pulsator and adjust spring clips to correct position.
7. Connect return line. Ensure there is sufficient clearance around damper and fuel line.

Abbreviations & Acronyms

A/C: Air Conditioning
AIC: Automatic Idle Control Valve
APC: Automatic Performance Control
BPC: Boost Pressure Control Valve
CAC: Charge Air Cooler
CKP: Crankshaft Position Sensor
CP: Canister Purge Valve
DI: Distributorless Ignition System
DLC: Data Link Connector
DTC: Diagnostic Trouble Code
ECM: Engine Control Module
ECT: Engine Coolant Temperature Sensor
EI: Electronic Ignition
ETS: Electronic Throttle System
EVAP: Evaporative Emission System
HO2S: Heated Oxygen Sensor
IAC: Idle Air Control Valve
IAT: Intake Air Temperature Sensor
ICM: Ignition Control Module
IDM: Ignition Discharge Module
LH: Lambda
MAF: Mass Air Flow Sensor
MAP: Manifold Absolute Pressure Sensor
MFI: LH Multi-Port Fuel Injection System
MIL: Malfunction Indicator Lamp
TP Sensor: Throttle Position Sensor
TP Switch: Throttle Position Switch
TWC: Three Way Catalytic Converter

VOLKSWAGEN

TABLE OF CONTENTS

Page No.

EMISSIONS:
Abbreviations & Acronyms 17-216
Application Charts 17-200
Emission Controls 17-211
Emission Control System Application Chart ... 17-200
Engine Compartment Reference Diagrams 17-202
Technical Service Bulletins 17-214
Vacuum Hose Routings 17-202

ENGINE SYSTEMS IDENTIFICATION 17-2

FUEL SYSTEMS:
Abbreviations & Acronyms 17-216
Electric Fuel Pumps 17-30
Engine Compartment Reference Diagrams 17-202
Fuel Injection 17-17
Technical Service Bulletins 17-214

ENGINE TUNE UP & PERFORMANCE:
Abbreviations & Acronyms 17-216
Specifications 17-3

Page No.
Technical Service Bulletins 17-214
V6 Gasoline Engine 17-6
4 Cylinder Diesel Engine 17-7
4 Cylinder Gasoline Engine 17-5

GENERAL INFORMATION:
Abbreviations & Acronyms 17-216
Air Bag System Precautions 0-12
Air Quality Standards 0-23
Computer Relearn Procedures 0-10
Electrical Symbol & Wire Color Code Identification 0-33
Engine Systems Identification 17-2
How To Use This Manual 0-1
Quick Reference 17-1
Service Reminder & Warning Lamp Reset Procedure 0-14
Technical Service Bulletins 17-214
Vehicle Identification 0-3
Vehicle Lift Points 0-24
Vehicle Maintenance Schedules 0-45

IGNITION SYSTEMS:
Abbreviations & Acronyms 17-216
Engine Compartment Reference Diagrams 17-202
Ignition Systems 17-9
Technical Service Bulletins 17-214

Quick Reference

Application	Page No.
ACCESSING DIAGNOSTIC TROUBLE CODES	
Motronic Fuel Injection	17-20
TDI Diesel Fuel Injection	17-26
CLEARING DIAGNOSTIC TROUBLE CODES	
Motronic Fuel Injection	17-20
TDI Diesel Fuel Injection	17-26
COMPRESSION PRESSURE SPECIFICATIONS	
Inline 4 Cylinder Diesel Engine	17-7
Inline 4 Cylinder Gasoline Engine	17-5
V6 Gasoline Engine	17-6
FUEL PRESSURE SPECIFICATIONS	
Except Diesel Engine	17-3
SENSOR & FUEL INJECTOR SPECIFICATIONS	
Diesel Turbo Direct Injection (TDI)	17-25
Motronic Fuel Injection	17-19

Engine Systems Identification

Note: The engine code is stamped on the engine.

Engine Liter	Eng-ine Code	Fuel System	Page No.	Ignition System	Page No.	Computer System	Page No.
1998							
1.8L	AEB	Motronic Fuel Injection	17-18	Digital Electronic w/Dual Knock Sensor	17-9	Motronic M3.8.2	17-34
1.9L	ALH	Turbo Direct Injection Diesel	17-25	—	—	Turbo Direct Injection Diesel	17-168
2.0L	AEG	Motronic Fuel Injection	17-18	Digital Electronic w/Knock Sensor	17-9	Motronic M5.9.2	17-34
2.8L	AAA	Motronic Fuel Injection	17-18	Digital Electronic w/Dual Knock Sensor	17-9	Motronic	17-34
2.8L	AHA	Motronic Fuel Injection	17-18	Digital Electronic w/Dual Knock Sensor	17-9	Motronic 5.9.2	17-34
1999							
1.8L	AEB	Motronic Fuel Injection	17-18	Digital Electronic w/Dual Knock Sensor	17-9	Motronic M3.8.2	17-34
1.9L	ALH	Turbo Direct Injection Diesel	17-25	—	—	Turbo Direct Injection Diesel	17-168
2.0L	AEG	Motronic Fuel Injection	17-18	Digital Electronic w/Knock Sensor	17-9	Motronic M5.9.2	17-34
2.8L	AFP	Motronic Fuel Injection	17-18	Digital Electronic w/Dual Knock Sensor	17-9	Motronic ME7.1	17-34
2.8L	AHA	Motronic Fuel Injection	17-18	Digital Electronic w/Dual Knock Sensor	17-9	Motronic M5.9.2	17-34
2000							
1.8L	AEB	Motronic Fuel Injection	17-18	Digital Electronic w/Dual Knock Sensor	17-9	Motronic M3.8.2	17-34
1.8L	APH	Motronic Fuel Injection	17-18	Digital Electronic w/Dual Knock Sensor	17-9	Motronic M3.8.5	17-34
1.8L	ATW	Motronic Fuel Injection	17-18	Digital Electronic w/Dual Knock Sensor	17-9	Motronic ME7.5	17-34
1.8L	AWD	Motronic Fuel Injection	17-18	Digital Electronic w/Dual Knock Sensor	17-9	Motronic ME7.5	17-34
1.8L	AWW	Motronic Fuel Injection	17-18	Digital Electronic w/Dual Knock Sensor	17-9	Motronic ME7.5	17-34
1.9L	ALH	Turbo Direct Injection Diesel	17-25	—	—	Turbo Direct Injection Diesel	17-168
2.0L	AEG	Motronic Fuel Injection	17-18	Digital Electronic w/Knock Sensor	17-9	Motronic M5.9.2	17-34
2.8L	AFP	Motronic Fuel Injection	17-18	Digital Electronic w/Dual Knock Sensor	17-9	Motronic ME7.1	17-34
2.8L	AHA	Motronic Fuel Injection	17-18	Digital Electronic w/Dual Knock Sensor	17-9	Motronic M5.9.2	17-34
2.8L	ATQ	Motronic Fuel Injection	17-18	Digital Electronic w/Dual Knock Sensor	17-9	Motronic M5.9.2	17-34
2001							
1.8L	AEB	Motronic Fuel Injection	17-18	Digital Electronic w/Dual Knock Sensor	17-9	Motronic M3.8.2	17-34
1.8L	APH	Motronic Fuel Injection	17-18	Digital Electronic w/Dual Knock Sensor	17-9	Motronic M3.8.5	17-34
1.8L	ATW	Motronic Fuel Injection	17-18	Digital Electronic w/Dual Knock Sensor	17-9	Motronic ME7.5	17-34
1.8L	AWD	Motronic Fuel Injection	17-18	Digital Electronic w/Dual Knock Sensor	17-9	Motronic ME7.5	17-34
1.8L	AWW	Motronic Fuel Injection	17-18	Digital Electronic w/Dual Knock Sensor	17-9	Motronic ME7.5	17-34
1.9L	ALH	Turbo Direct Injection Diesel	17-25	—	—	Turbo Direct Injection Diesel	17-168
2.0L	AEG	Motronic Fuel Injection	17-18	Digital Electronic w/Knock Sensor	17-9	Motronic M5.9.2	17-34
2.8L	AFP	Motronic Fuel Injection	17-18	Digital Electronic w/Dual Knock Sensor	17-9	Motronic ME7.1	17-34
2.8L	AHA	Motronic Fuel Injection	17-18	Digital Electronic w/Dual Knock Sensor	17-9	Motronic M5.9.2	17-34
2.8L	ATQ	Motronic Fuel Injection	17-18	Digital Electronic w/Dual Knock Sensor	17-9	Motronic M5.9.2	17-

34

Tune Up Specifications

TABLE OF CONTENTS

Page No.
DIESEL ENGINE PERFORMANCE SPECIFICATIONS 17-4
GASOLINE ENGINE TUNE UP SPECIFICATIONS 17-3

Gasoline Engine Tune Up Specifications

Year & Engine, Liter	Spark Plug Gap, Inch	Ignition Timing			Curb Idle Speed, RPM		Fuel System Pressure, psi	Valve Lash	
		Firing Order	Timing, °BTDC	Timing Mark Fig.	Man. Trans.	Auto. Trans.		Intake	Exhaust
1998									
1.8L⑦	.039	1-3-4-2	①	—	820–900②	820–900N②	50.76	③	③
2.0L⑧	.039	1-3-4-2	①	—	760–880②	760–880N②	51.45	③	③
2.0L⑨	.032	1-3-4-2	12①	—	800–880②	800–880N②⑤	36.3	③	③
2.8L⑩	.028	1-5-3-6-2-4	6 ①	—	650–750②④	650–750N②④	36.3	③	③
2.8L⑪	.063	1-4-3-6-2-5	①	—	⑥	⑥	51.45	③	③
1999									
1.8L⑦	.039	1-3-4-2	①	—	820–920②	820–920N②	50.76	③	③
2.0L⑧	.039	1-3-4-2	①	—	740–820②	740–820N②	51.45	③	③
2.0L⑨	.032	1-3-4-2	12①	—	800–880②	800–880N②⑤	36.3	③	③
2.8L⑩	.028	1-5-3-6-2-4	①	—	680–720②④	680–720N②④	36.3	③	③
2.8L⑪	.063	1-4-3-6-2-5	①	—	⑥	⑥	51.45	③	③
2000									
1.8L⑦	.039	1-3-4-2	①	—	820–920②	820–920N②	50.76	③	③
2.0L⑧	.039	1-3-4-2	①	—	740–820②	740–820N②	51.45	③	③
2.0L⑨	.032	1-3-4-2	12①	—	800–880②	800–880N②⑤	36.3	③	③
2.8L⑩	.028	1-5-3-6-2-4	①	—	680–720②④	680–720N②④	36.3	③	③
2.8L⑪	.063	1-4-3-6-2-5	①	—	⑥	⑥	51.45	③	③
2001									
1.8L⑦	.039	1-3-4-2	①	—	820–920②	820–920N②	50.76	③	③
2.0L⑧	.039	1-3-4-2	①	—	740–820②	740–820N②	51.45	③	③
2.0L⑨	.032	1-3-4-2	12①	—	800–880②	800–880N②⑤	36.3	③	③
2.8L⑩	.028	1-5-3-6-2-4	①	—	680–720②④	680–720N②④	36.3	③	③
2.8L⑪	.063	1-4-3-6-2-5	①	—	⑥	⑥	51.45	③	③

BTDC — Before Top Dead Center
D — Drive
N — Neutral
① — Not adjustable. Controlled by ECM.
② — Not adjustable.
③ — Equipped w/hydraulic valve lash adjusters. No adjustment required.
④ — When battery voltage drops below 10.5 volts, idle speed will be raised to 900 RPM by ECM.
⑤ — 640–720D.
⑥ — FWD, 740–860 RPM; AWD, 620–740 RPM.
⑦ — Turbo.
⑧ — New Beetle.
⑨ — Cabrio, Golf, GTI & Jetta.
⑩ — Two-valve engine: EuroVan, Golf, GTI & Jetta.
⑪ — Five-valve engine: Passat.

Diesel Engine Performance Specifications

Engine Liter	Firing Order	Injection Pump Timing	Cylinder Compression			Fuel Injectors		Idle Speed	Max. Speed @ Zero Load, RPM	Valve Lash
			Cranking Pressure, psi	Limit. psi	Maximum Variation	Spray Test , psi	Leak Test, psi③			
1998–99										
1.9L	1-3-4-2	①④	363–450	276	73	3191–3336②	2176	④	④	⑤
2000										
1.9L	1-3-4-2	①④	363–450	276	73	3191–3336②	2176	④	④	⑤
2001										
1.9L	1-3-4-2	①④	363–450	276	73	3191–3336②	2176	④	④	⑤

① — Refer to "Injection Pump Timing" procedure in "4 Cylinder Diesel Engine Performance."

② — Opening pressure new, wear limit 2901 psi.

③ — Maintain pressure for 10 seconds with no fuel leakage.

④ — Computer controlled.

⑤ — Hydraulic lifters. No adjustment required.

Engine Tune Up & Performance

TABLE OF CONTENTS

	Page No.		Page No.
V6 GASOLINE ENGINES	17-6	4 CYLINDER GASOLINE ENGINE	17-5
4 CYLINDER DIESEL ENGINE (TDI)	17-7		

4 Cylinder Gasoline Engine

NOTE: If Unsure Of The System Used On The Vehicle Being Serviced, Refer To The "Engine Systems Identification Chart." Further Assistance For The Proper Use Of Information Contained In This Section Can Also Be Found In The Front Of This Tabbed Section Under "How To Use This Manual."

NOTE: On Air Bag Equipped Models, Refer To "Air Bag System Precautions" Located In The Front Of This Manual For System Disarming & Arming Procedures.

NOTE: Prior To Performing Any Service Operations Listed In This Section, Consult The "Technical Service Bulletins" Section For Related Information.

INDEX

	Page No.		Page No.		Page No.
Compression Pressures	17-5	Ignition Timing	17-5	Valves	17-5
Idle Speed & Mixture Adjustments	17-5	Ignition Wire Resistance	17-5	Valve Adjustment	17-5
		Spark Plugs	17-5		

SPARK PLUGS

On all models except Cabrio, spark plugs should be replaced every 40,000 miles under normal driving conditions.

On Cabrio models, spark plugs should be replaced every 20,000 miles under normal driving conditions.

On all models, refer to "Tune Up Specifications" for spark plug gap. **Torque** spark plugs to 14 ft. lbs.

IGNITION WIRE RESISTANCE

Proper ignition wire resistance value is 4000–8000 ohms.

COMPRESSION PRESSURES

1. Perform compression test with engine at operating temperature, spark plugs removed, coolant temperature at least 176°F and throttle plate completely open.
2. Disconnect power output stage of ignition coil high tension wire from distributor cap and connect to suitable ground.
3. Disconnect CMP sensor Hall sender electrical connector.
4. Connect compression tester tool Nos. VAG 1381 and VAG 1763, or equivalents, per manufacturer's instructions.
5. Crank engine until compression tester shows no further increase in pressure.
6. **On AEB, AEG, ALH, APH, AWD and AWW engines,** compression should be 145–189 psi with maximum difference between highest and lowest cylinder of 44 psi. Minimum compression should be 109 psi.
7. **On ATW engines,** compression should be 131–189 psi with a maximum difference of 44 psi. Minimum compression should be 102 psi.

IGNITION TIMING

Ignition timing is not adjustable on these models. Refer to the "Computerized Engine Controls" section.

IDLE SPEED & MIXTURE ADJUSTMENTS

Fuel mixture and idle are not adjustable on these models.

VALVES

Valve Adjustment

Valve lash is maintained by hydraulic cam followers. Adjustment is not required.

V6 Gasoline Engine

NOTE: If Unsure Of The System Used On The Vehicle Being Serviced, Refer To The "Engine Systems Identification Chart." Further Assistance For The Proper Use Of Information Contained In This Section Can Also Be Found In The Front Of This Tabbed Section Under "How To Use This Manual."

NOTE: On Air Bag Equipped Models, Refer To "Air Bag System Precautions" Located In The Front Of This Manual For System Disarming & Arming Procedures.

NOTE: Prior To Performing Any Service Operations Listed In This Section, Consult The "Technical Service Bulletins" Section For Related Information.

INDEX

	Page No.
Compression Pressures	17-6
Idle Speed & Mixture Adjustments	17-6
Ignition Timing	17-6
Ignition Wire Resistance	17-6
Spark Plugs	17-6
Valves	17-6
Valve Adjustment	17-6

SPARK PLUGS

Spark plugs should be replaced every 40,000 miles under normal driving conditions. Refer to "Tune Up Specifications" for spark plug gap.

On all models except Passat, torque spark plugs to 18 ft. lbs.

On Passat models, torque spark plugs to 22 ft. lbs.

IGNITION WIRE RESISTANCE

Proper ignition wire resistance value is 4000–6000 ohms.

COMPRESSION PRESSURES

1. Perform compression test with coolant temperature at minimum of 176°F, throttle plate completely open, fuse No. 18 removed and CMP sensor Hall electrical sender connector disconnected.
2. Connect compression tester tool No. VAG 1381 and VAG 1763, or equivalents.
3. Crank engine until gauge reaches highest level.
4. **On EuroVan, Golf, GTI and Jetta models,**compression should be 145–189 psi with maximum difference between cylinders of 44 psi. Minimum compression is 109 psi.
5. **On Passat models,** compression should be 131–203 psi with maximum difference between cylinders of 44 psi. Minimum compression is 109 psi.

IGNITION TIMING

Ignition timing is electronically controlled and cannot be adjusted. If ignition timing is not within specification, refer to appropriate "Computerized Engine Controls" section.

IDLE SPEED & MIXTURE ADJUSTMENTS

Idle speed and CO content are electronically controlled and cannot be adjusted. If idle speed or CO content are not within specification, refer to the appropriate "Computerized Engine Controls" section.

VALVES

Valve Adjustment

These engines are equipped with hydraulic valve lifters. No adjustment is required.

4 Cylinder Diesel Engine (TDI)

NOTE: If Unsure Of The System Used On The Vehicle Being Serviced, Refer To The "Engine Systems Identification Chart." Further Assistance For The Proper Use Of Information Contained In This Section Can Also Be Found In The Front Of This Tabbed Section Under "How To Use This Manual."

NOTE: On Air Bag Equipped Models, Refer To "Air Bag System Precautions" Located In The Front Of This Manual For System Disarming & Arming Procedures.

NOTE: Prior To Performing Any Service Operations Listed In This Section, Consult The "Technical Service Bulletins" Section For Related Information.

INDEX

	Page No.
Compression Pressures	17-7
Glow Plugs	17-7
Inspection	17-7
Idle Speed Adjustment	17-8
Injection Pump Timing	17-7
Injector Nozzle Pressure	17-7
Valves	17-8
Valve Adjustment	17-8
Valve Arrangement	17-8

GLOW PLUGS

Inspection

1. Turn ignition Off.
2. Disconnect glow plug harness connectors.
3. Connect suitable diode test lamp to battery positive terminal using suitable jumper wire.
4. Touch test probe to each glow plug.
5. If diode does not light, replace glow plug.
6. **Torque** glow plugs to 11 ft. lbs.

COMPRESSION PRESSURES

1. Disconnect fuel cutoff valve on diesel injection pump.
2. Disconnect quantity adjuster harness electrical connector on diesel injection pump.
3. Remove all glow plugs using suitable flexible wrench.
4. Screw in adapter tool No. VAG 1381/12, or equivalent, in place of glow plugs.
5. Attach compression test tool No. VAG 1381 and VAG 1763, or equivalent, to adapter.
6. Measure compression while operating starter until display shows no further increase in pressure.
7. Proper compression is 363–450 psi, with 73 psi maximum difference between highest and lowest cylinder. Minimum compression is 280 psi.

INJECTION PUMP TIMING

1. Connect scan tool No. VAG 1551, or equivalent, to Data Link Connector (DCL), **Fig. 1.**

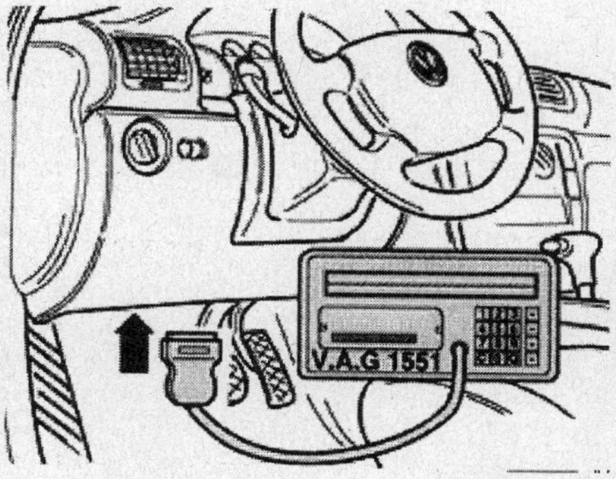

VW1029800150000X

Fig. 1 DLC location

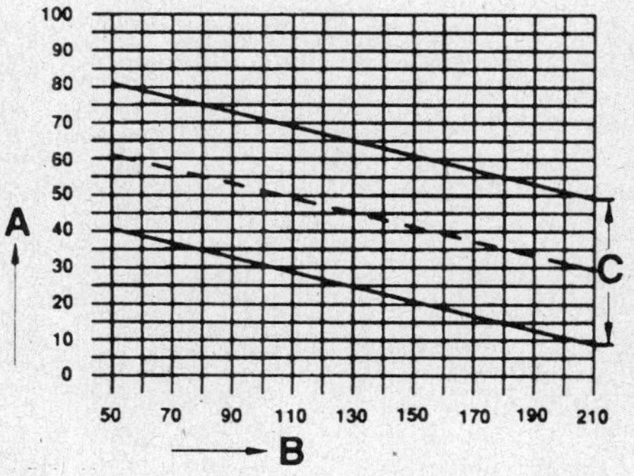

VW1029600072000X

Fig. 2 Temperature correction table for injection pump timing

2. With engine running at closed throttle idle, select "Engine Electronics" with "Address Word 01" on scan tool.
3. Select function 04, "Basic Setting," then press Q button to confirm input.
4. Enter 0, 0, 0 then press Q button to confirm input.
5. Observe coolant temperature in Display Field 7.
6. Injection timing is dependent on fuel temperature. Refer to table in **Fig. 2,** where A equals injection timing and B equals fuel temperature. Zone C of table is acceptable range with no adjustment required. At B=90°C, A should be 34–73 within Zone C.
7. If adjustment is required, proceed as follows:
   a. Turn ignition Off.
   b. Remove upper timing belt cover.
   c. Loosen two injection pump sprocket bolts. **Do not loosen hub center nut. If this is loosened the injection pump basic setting will be altered and cannot be reset with usual workshop equipment.**
   d. Position a suitable 22 MM wrench onto hub nut to counter-hold pump shaft.
   e. Loosen third injection pump sprocket bolt and turn pump shaft slightly. If timing was retarded, move shaft to the left. If timing was advanced, move shaft to the right.
   f. Secure injection pump, then inspect timing. If required, repeat procedure until Zone C mean value is obtained.
   g. **Torque** pump mounting bolts to 18 ft. lbs.
8. Install upper belt cover, then remove scan tool.

INJECTOR NOZZLE PRESSURE

These engines are equipped with dual spring injectors. The fuel injection occurs in two stages. Faulty injectors must be exchanged. No repairs or adjustments are possible.

1. Install suspect injector into injector test unit tool No. VAG 1322 with pressure line tool No. VAG 1322/2, **Fig. 3,** or equivalents.

2. Move pump lever down slowly.
3. When spray begins note opening pressure, which should be 3190–3335 psi on new injectors. Minimum allowable pressure is 2900 psi.
4. Turn pressure gauge on.
5. Move pump lever down slowly and maintain a pressure of approximately 2175 psi for 10 seconds. Ensure fuel does not leak from nozzle tip.
6. Replace any injector that fails inspections.

Remove injection nozzle, then connect suitable tester and gauge according to manufacturer's instructions.

New injector nozzle pressure should be 3191–3336 psi. Wear limit is 2901 psi.

Spray pattern should be uniform and injected at proper angle of injector being tested.

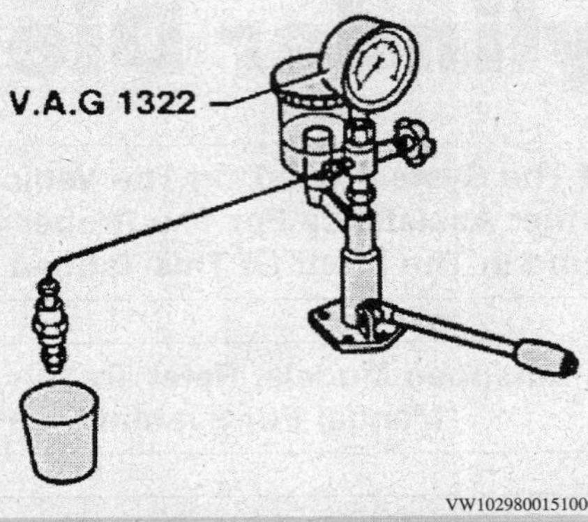

Fig. 3 Fuel injector test tool setup

IDLE SPEED ADJUSTMENT

Engine idle speed is computer controlled and cannot be adjusted.

VALVES

Valve Arrangement

All:............................ E-I-E-I-I-E-I-E

Valve Adjustment

Valve lash is maintained by hydraulic cam followers. No adjustment is required.

Ignition Systems

NOTE: If Unsure Of The System Used On The Vehicle Being Serviced, Refer To The "Engine Systems Identification Chart." Further Assistance For The Proper Use Of Information Contained In This Section Can Also Be Found In The Front Of This Tabbed Section Under "How To Use This Manual."

NOTE: On Air Bag Equipped Models, Refer To "Air Bag System Precautions" Located In The Front Of This Manual For System Disarming & Arming Procedures.

NOTE: Prior To Performing Any Service Operations Listed In This Section, Consult The "Technical Service Bulletins" Section For Related Information.

INDEX

	Page No.
Description	17-9
Diagnosis & Testing	17-9
Component Testing	17-9
Camshaft Position (CMP) Sensor	17-9
Ignition Coil	17-10
Knock Sensor	17-12
Precautions	17-9
Air Bag Systems	17-9
Audio Coded Anti-Theft System	17-9
Battery Ground Cable	17-9
System Service	17-15
Component Replacement	17-15
Camshaft Position (CMP) Sensor	17-15
Ignition Coil	17-15
Knock Sensor	17-16

PRECAUTIONS

Air Bag Systems

Refer to "Air Bag System Precautions" in the front of this manual for system disarming and arming procedures.

Audio Coded Anti-Theft System

Do not use computer memory saver tool. Using the tool will keep the air bag system charged and may cause accidental air bag unit activation.

Obtain the security code from the vehicle operator prior to disconnecting the battery or removing the radio. Refer to the owner's manual for security code disarming and arming procedures.

Battery Ground Cable

Prior to service, disconnect battery ground cable and isolate as required.

DESCRIPTION

The ignition system uses camshaft position and crankshaft position sensors to send signals to the Engine Control Module (ECM). These signals along with other engine sensor information are used to obtain optimum spark timing. The ECM sends this signal to the multiple coil unit to create a spark for the proper cylinder.

Refer to **Figs. 1 through 5** for ignition system component location and identification.

DIAGNOSIS & TESTING

Component Testing

CAMSHAFT POSITION (CMP) SENSOR

1.8L ENGINE

1. Remove engine cover as required.
2. Disconnect CMP sensor electrical connector.
3. Turn ignition On.
4. Measure voltage between harness connector terminals 1 and 3 using a suitable voltmeter. There should be at least 4.5 volts.
5. If there is no voltage, turn ignition Off.
6. Connect test box tool No. VAG 1598/31, or equivalent, to ECM wiring harness connector. **ECM must remain disconnected.**
7. Inspect for open circuits as follows:
   a. Between CMP sensor electrical connector terminal 1 and test box socket 98.
   b. Terminal 2 and socket 86.
   c. Terminal 3 and socket 108.
   d. Maximum resistance for opens is 1.5 ohms.
8. Inspect wires for shorts between each other. Ohmmeter should read infinity.
9. Repair any fault conditions as required.
10. If wiring is satisfactory and there is voltage at CMP connector terminals 1 and 3, replace CMP sensor.
11. If wiring is satisfactory but there is no voltage at CMP connector terminals 1 and 3, replace ECM.

2.0L ENGINE

1. Remove engine cover as required.
2. Disconnect CMP sensor electrical connector.
3. Turn ignition On.
4. Measure voltage between harness connector terminals 1 and 3 using a suitable voltmeter. There should be at least 4.5 volts.
5. If there is no voltage, turn ignition Off.
6. Connect test box tool No. VAG 1598/31, or equivalent, to ECM wiring harness connector.
7. Inspect for open circuits as follows:
   a. Between CMP sensor electrical connector terminal 1 and test box socket 62.
   b. Terminal 2 and socket 76.
   c. Terminal 3 and socket 67.
   d. Maximum resistance for opens is 1.5 ohms.
8. Repair any fault conditions as required.
9. Inspect wires for shorts between each other. Ohmmeter should read infinity.
10. If wiring is satisfactory and there is voltage at CMP connector terminals 1 and 3, replace CMP sensor.
11. If wiring is satisfactory but there is no voltage at CMP connector terminals 1 and 3, replace ECM.

2.8L ENGINE

1. Disconnect CMP sensor electrical connector.
2. Turn ignition On.
3. Measure voltage between harness connector terminals 1 and 3 using a suitable voltmeter. There should be at least 4.5 volts.
4. If there is no voltage, turn ignition Off.

5. Connect test box tool No. VAG 1598/31, or equivalent, to ECM wiring harness connector. **ECM must remain disconnected.**
6. Inspect for open circuits or shorts as follows:
   a. Between CMP sensor electrical connector terminal 1 and test box socket 98.
   b. Terminal 2 and socket 86.
   c. Terminal 3 and socket 108.
   d. Maximum resistance for opens is 1.5 ohms.
7. Inspect wires for shorts between each other. Ohmmeter should read infinity.
8. Repair any fault conditions as required.
9. If wiring is satisfactory and there is voltage at CMP connector terminals 1 and 3, replace CMP sensor.
10. If wiring is satisfactory but there is no voltage at CMP connector terminals 1 and 3, replace ECM.

IGNITION COIL

1.8L ENGINE

1. Disconnect coil electrical connector, **Fig. 6.**
2. Turn ignition On.
3. Connect a suitable voltmeter voltage between harness connector terminals 1 and 2, then between terminals 2 and 4.
4. Measure voltage, which should be at least 11.5 volts.
5. If there is no voltage, turn ignition Off.
6. Inspect wiring between connector terminal 1 and relay plate for open circuit using a suitable ohmmeter. Maximum resistance is 1.5 ohms.
7. Inspect wiring for open circuit between connector terminal 2 and ground, then between terminal 4 and ground. Maximum resistance is 1.5 ohms.
8. If wiring is satisfactory, remove fuse 32. This cuts voltage supply to injectors.
9. Connect voltage tester tool No. VAG 1527B, or equivalent, to connector terminals 2 and 3.
10. Crank engine and observe LED, which should flicker.
11. If LED flickers and supply voltage is satisfactory, replace ignition coils.
12. If LED does not flicker, connect test box tool No. VAG 1598/31, or equivalent, to ECM wiring harness connector. **ECM must remain disconnected.**
13. Inspect for open circuits or shorts as follows:
    a. Cylinder 1 terminal 3 and test box socket 102.
    b. Cylinder 2 terminal 3 and socket 95.
    c. Cylinder 3 terminal 3 and socket 103.
    d. Cylinder 4 terminal 3 and socket 94.
    e. Maximum resistance is 1.5 ohms.
14. If wiring is satisfactory, replace ECM.

2.0L ENGINE

1. Disconnect ignition coil power output stage 5-pin harness connector, spark plug connector and ignition wires.
2. Measure ignition wires' resistance, which should be 4000–8000 ohms.

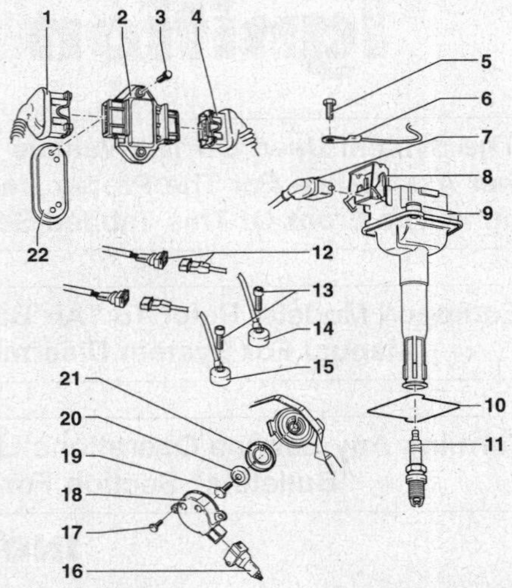

1 Five-Pin Harness Connector
2 Ignition Coil Power Output Stage
3 Mounting Bolt
4 Four-Pin Harness Connector
5 Mounting Bolt
6 Ground Wire
7 Three-Pin Harness Connector
8 Connector Lock
9 Ignition Coils
10 Oil Seal
11 Spark Plug
12 Three-Pin Harness Connector
13 Mounting Bolt
14 Knock Sensor 1
15 Knock Sensor 2
16 Three-Pin Harness Connector
17 Mounting Bolt
18 Camshaft Position (CMP) Sensor
19 Mounting Bolt
20 Conical Washer
21 Hood
22 Heat Sink

VW1119800015000A

Fig. 1 Ignition system components. 1998 1.8L engine

3. With ignition cables connected, measure ignition coils' secondary resistance between spark plug connectors. If resistance is not 8000–14,000 ohms, replace ignition coils and power output stage.
4. Measure voltage between connector terminals Nos. 2 and 4, **Fig. 7.**
5. Turn ignition On. There should be 11.5 volts minimum.
6. If voltage is not as specified, proceed as follows:
   a. Measure resistance between 4-pin connector terminal No. 2 and fuse/relay panel.
   b. Measure resistance between terminal No. 4 and ground.
   c. If resistance is not less than 1.5 ohms, repair open circuit as required.
7. Remove fuse 32.
8. Turn ignition Off.
9. Connect LED tester tool No. VAG 1527B, or equivalent, between connect terminal Nos. 1 and 4.
10. Crank engine. LED should flicker.
11. Repeat procedure using terminals Nos. 3 and 4.
12. Turn ignition Off.
13. If LED flickers and there is voltage between terminal Nos. 2 and 4, replace ignition coils.
14. If LED does not flicker, connect test box tool No. VAG 1598/31, or equivalent, to ECM harness connector.
15. Measure resistance as follows:
    a. Between connector terminal No. 1 and test box socket 71.
    b. Between terminal No. 3 and socket 78.
    c. If resistance is not less than 1.5 ohms, inspect wiring for open circuit.
16. If wiring is satisfactory and there is voltage between terminals Nos. 2 and 4, replace ECM.
17. Measure secondary wiring resistance as follows:
    a. Between terminal No. 4 and cylinders No. 1 and 4.
    b. Between terminal 4 and cylinders No. 2 and 3.
    c. If resistance is not 4000–8000 ohms, replace ignition coils.

2.8L ENGINE

1998 Golf, GTI & Jetta

1. Turn ignition Off, then disconnect ignition coil 5-pin harness connector.
2. Measure voltage between connector terminal Nos. 1 and 5 with ignition On, **Fig. 8.**
3. If measurement is not 9–14.5 volts, proceed as follows:
   a. Measure resistance between connector terminals No. 1 and ground.
   b. Measure resistance between terminal No. 5 and fuse/relay panel.
   c. If resistance is not less than 1.5 ohms, inspect and repair wiring as required.
4. Remove fuse 18.
5. Connect LED tester tool No. VAG 1527B, or equivalent, between connector terminals No. 2 and 5.
6. Crank engine. LED should flicker.
7. Repeat procedure for terminals Nos. 3 and 5, then Nos. 4 and 5.
8. Turn ignition Off.

9. If LED did not flicker, replace ECM.
10. If LED flickered, connect test box tool No. VAG 1598/31, or equivalent, to ECM wiring harness and measure resistance as follows:
    a. Between connector terminal No. 2 and test box socket No. 8.
    b. Between terminal No. 3 and socket No. 60.
    c. Between terminal No. 4 and socket No. 52.
    d. If resistance is not less than 1.5 ohms, inspect wiring for open circuit.
    e. Between terminal No. 2 and socket No. 60.
    f. Between terminal No. 2 and socket No. 52.
    g. Between terminal No. 3 and socket No. 52.
    h. If resistance is not infinite, inspect wiring for short circuit.
11. If wiring is satisfactory and there is voltage between terminals No. 1 and 5, replace ignition coil.
12. Measure resistance as follows:
    a. Between connector terminal No. 4 and cylinders Nos. 1 and 6.
    b. Between terminal No. 4 and cylinders Nos. 3 and 4.
    c. Between terminal No. 4 and cylinders Nos. 2 and 5.
    d. If secondary resistance is 4000–6000 ohms, replace ignition coil.

EuroVan & 1999–2001 Golf, GTI & Jetta

1. Turn ignition Off, then disconnect ignition coil 5-pin harness connector.
2. Measure voltage between connector terminals No. 2 and 4 with ignition On.
3. If measurement is not at least 11.5 volts, proceed as follows:
    a. Measure resistance between terminal 5 and relay plate.
    b. Measure resistance between connector terminal 1 and ground.
    c. If resistance is not less than 1.5 ohms, inspect wiring for open circuit.
4. Remove fuse 32.
5. Connect LED tester tool No. VAG 1527B, or equivalent, between connector terminals Nos. 2 and 5.
6. Crank engine. LED should flicker.
7. Repeat procedure for terminals Nos. 3 and 5, then Nos. 4 and 5.
8. Turn ignition Off.
9. If LED did not flicker, inspect and repair wiring as required.
10. If LED flickered and there is voltage as specified, replace ignition coil.
11. Connect test box tool No. VAG 1598/31, or equivalent, to ECM wiring harness, then measure resistance as follows:
    a. Between connector terminal 2 and test box socket 102.
    b. Between terminal 3 and socket 94.
    c. Between terminal 4 and socket 103.
    d. If resistance is not less than 1.5 ohms, inspect wiring for open circuit.
    e. Inspect wires for short to one another and repair as required.
12. If wiring is satisfactory and there is voltage between terminals Nos. 1 and 5, replace ECM.
13. Measure resistance as follows:
    a. Between connector terminal 4 and cylinders 1 and 6.
    b. Between terminal 4 and cylinders Nos. 3 and 4.
    c. Between terminal 4 and cylinders Nos. 2 and 5.
    d. If secondary resistance is 3600–4400 ohms, replace ignition coil.

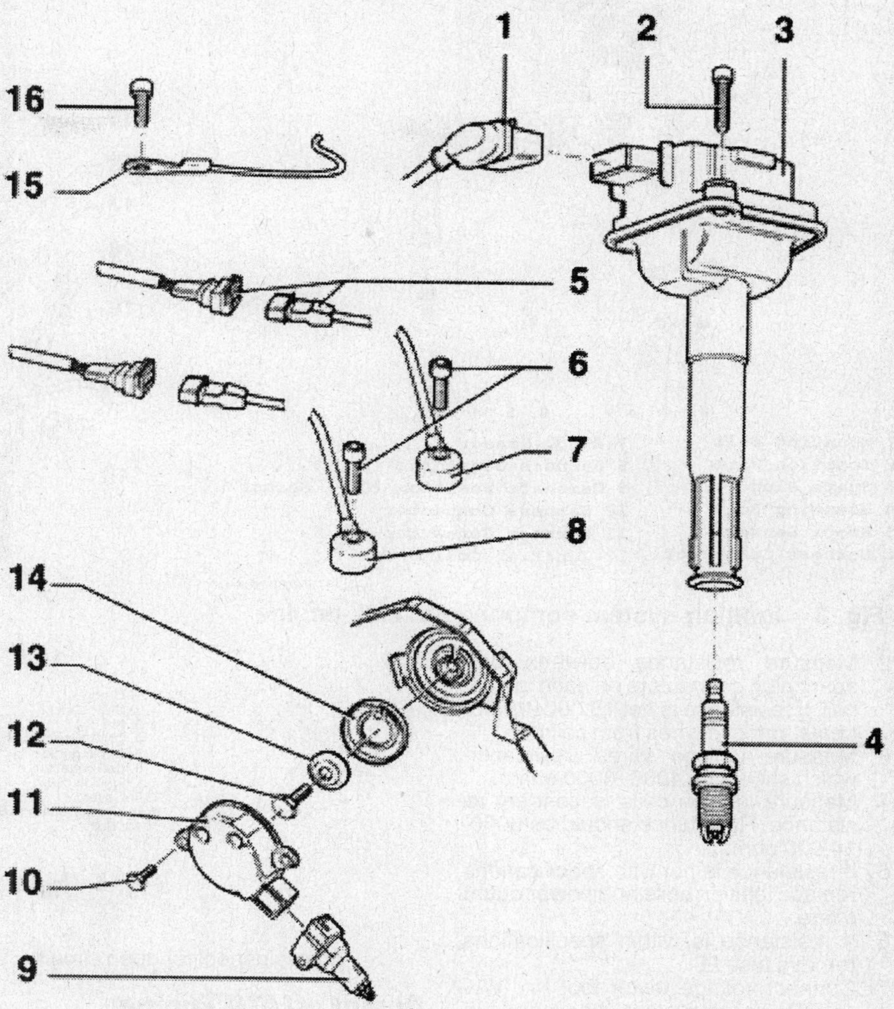

1. Black 4-pin connector
2. Bolt
3. Ignition coil w/output stage
4. Spark plug
5. Knock sensor 3-pin connector
6. Bolts
7. Knock sensor 1
8. Knock sensor 2
9. Camshaft Position (CMP) sensor 2 connector
10. Bolt
11. CMP sensor 2
12. Bolt
13. Washer
14. Hood
15. Ground wire
16. Bolt

VW1119900019000X

Fig. 2 Ignition system components. 1999–2001 1.8L engine

Passat w/AHA Engine

1. Disconnect ignition coil 5-pin connector, then remove ignition wires from spark plugs.

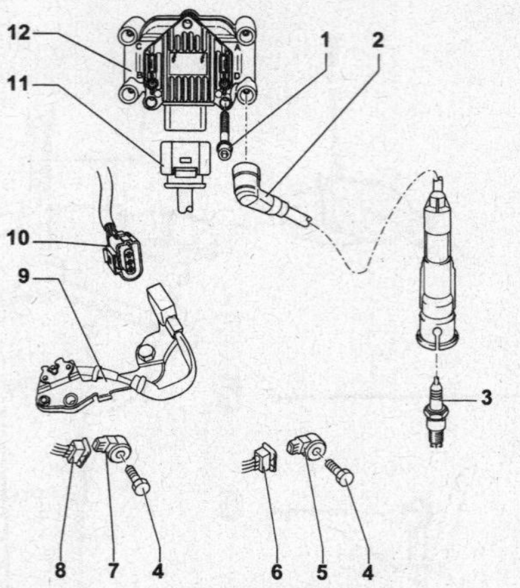

1 Mounting Bolt
2 Ignition Wire
3 Spark Plug
4 Mounting Bolt
5 Knock Sensor 2
6 Harness Connector
7 Knock Sensor 1
8 Harness Connector
9 Camshaft Position (CMP) Sesnor
10 Harness Connector
11 Harness Connector
12 Ignition Coil

VW1119800016000A

Fig. 3 Ignition system components. 2.0L engine

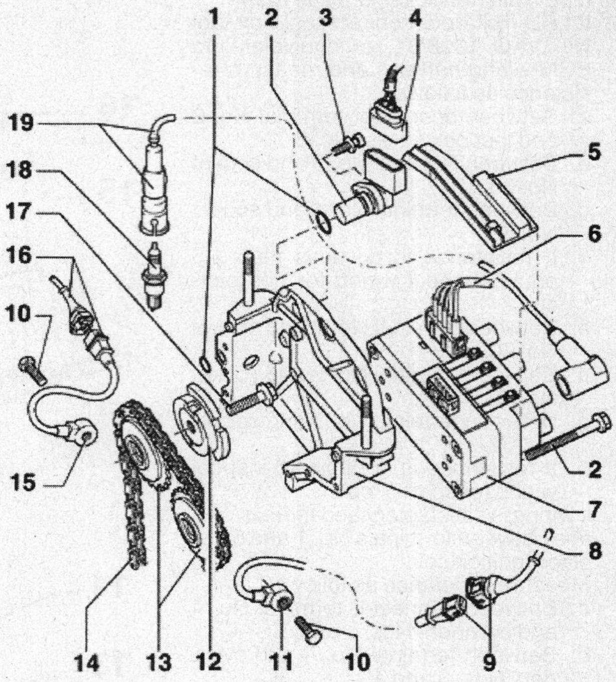

1. O-ring
2. CMP sensor
3. Bolt
4. CMP sensor connector
5. Cable guide
6. Coil conector
7. Ignition coil
8. Cover
9. Knock Sensor (KS) 2 connector
10. Bolt
11. KS 2
12. CMP trigger wheel
13. Camshaft sprockets
14. Timing chain
15. 11. Knock Sensor (KS) 1
16. KS 2 connector
17. Bolt
18. Spark plug
19. Spark plug wire

VW1119900020000X

Fig. 4 Ignition system components. EuroVan, Golf, GTI & Jetta w/2.8L engine

2. Measure resistance between both spark plug connectors on each ignition coil. If resistance is not 18,000–25,000 ohms, remove wires from coils.
3. Measure ignition wires' resistance, which should be 4000–6000 ohms.
4. Measure ignition coils' secondary resistance. Resistance should be 8000–14,000 ohms.
5. If resistance is not with specifications, replace ignition coils and power output stage.
6. If resistance is within specifications, remove fuse 28.
7. Connect voltage tester tool No. VAG 1527B, or equivalent, between connector terminals Nos. 2 and 3.
8. Operate start. LED should flash.
9. Repeat procedure between terminals Nos. 2 and 4, then Nos. 2 and 5.
10. If LED does not flash, connect test box tool No. VAG 1598/31, or equivalent, to ECM harness connector and measure resistance as follows:
    a. Between connector terminal No. 3 and text box socket No. 71.
    b. Between terminal No. 4 and socket No. 78.
    c. Between terminal No. 5 and socket No. 70.
    d. Inspect for short circuits between connector terminals.
    e. If resistance is not less than 1.5 ohms, replace ECM.
    f. If resistance is within specifications, replace ignition coils and power output stage.
11. Measure voltage across connector terminals Nos. 1 and 2 with ignition On.
12. If measurement is not at least 11.5 volts, turn ignition Off and proceed as follows:
    a. Measure resistance between terminal No. 2 and ground.
    b. Measure resistance between terminal No. 1 and relay panel.
    c. If resistance is not less than 1.5 ohms, inspect for open circuit.

Passat w/ATQ Engine

1. Ensure battery is fully charged.
2. Disconnect ignition coil 5-pin electrical connectors.
3. Disconnect spark plug wires at spark plugs.
4. Measure resistance between two coil spark plug connectors using a suitable ohmmeter, which should be 1600–2700 ohms. Repeat test on other two coils.
5. If resistances do not meet specifications, disconnect spark plug wires at coils.
6. Measure spark plug wire resistances, which should be 3000–7000 ohms.
7. Measure coil secondary resistances, which should be 8000–14,000 ohms.
8. Turn ignition On.
9. Measure voltage between coil connector terminals 1 and 2, **Fig. 9,** using a suitable voltmeter. There should be at least 11.5 volts.
10. If there is no voltage, turn ignition Off.
11. Inspect for open circuits in wiring using a suitable ohmmeter between connector terminal 2 and ground, then between terminal 1 and relay carrier. Maximum resistance is 1.5 ohms.
12. Disconnect fuel injector electrical connectors.
13. Connect diode test lamp tool No. VAG 1527, or equivalent, to connector terminals 2 and 3.
14. Crank engine. LED should flicker.
15. Repeat test between terminals 2 and 4, then between terminals 2 and 5.
16. If LED flickers and supply voltage is satisfactory, replace ignition coils.
17. If LED does not flicker, connect test box tool No. VAG 1598/31, or equivalent, to ECM wiring harness connector. **ECM must remain disconnected.**
18. Inspect for open circuits as follows:
    a. Righthand front cylinder head terminal 3 and socket 102.
    b. Terminal 4 and socket 103.
    c. Terminal 5 and socket 94.
    d. Maximum resistance is 1.5 ohms.
19. Inspect wires for shorts between each other. Ohmmeter should read infinity.
20. If wiring is satisfactory and there is voltage between terminals 1 and 2, replace ECM.
21. If voltage supply and activation are satisfactory, replace ignition coils.

KNOCK SENSOR

1.8L AEB ENGINE

1. Disconnect knock sensor 3-pin connectors.
2. Measure resistance as follows:
    a. Between knock sensor connection terminal Nos. 1 and 2.
    b. Between terminal Nos. 1 and 3.

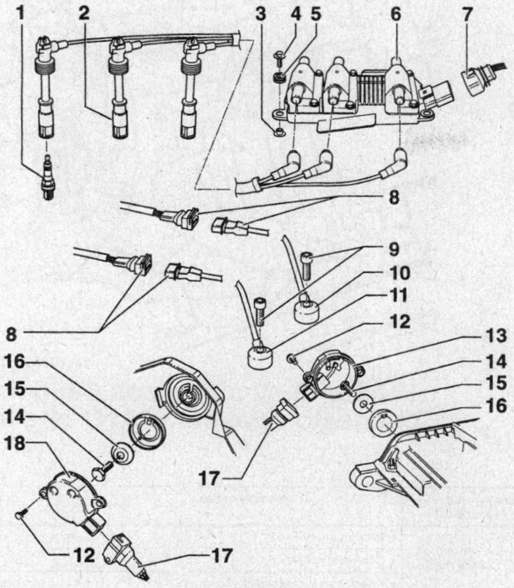

1 Spark Plug
2 Spark Plug Connector
3 Spacer Sleeve
4 Mounting Bolt
5 Rubber Grommet
6 Ignition Coils
7 Harness Connector
8 Harness Connector
9 Mounting Bolt
10 Knock Sensor 2
11 Knock Sensor 1
12 Mounting Bolt
13 Camshaft Position (CMP) Sensor 1
14 Mounting Bolt
15 Washer
16 Rotor
17 Harness Connector
18 Camshaft Position (CMP) Sensor 2

VW1119900018000X

Fig. 5 Ignition system components. Passat w/2.8L engine

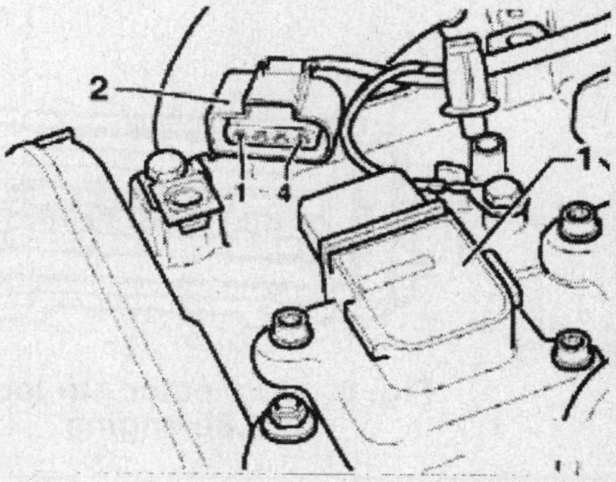

VW1119800021000X

Fig. 6 Ignition coil inspection. Golf, Jetta & GTI w/1.8L engine

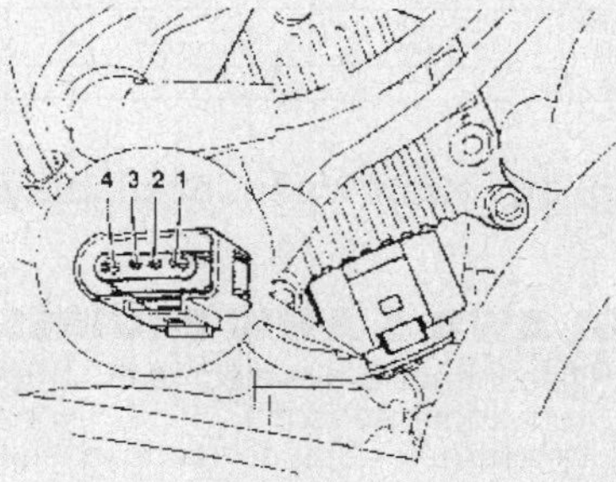

VW1119800017000X

Fig. 7 Connector pin location. 2.0L engine

   c. Between terminal Nos. 2 and 3.
   d. If resistance is not infinite, replace knock sensor.
3. Connect test box tool No. VAG 1598/31, or equivalent, to ECM harness connector.
4. Measure resistance as follows:
   a. Knock sensor 1 wiring resistance between connector terminal No. 1 and test box socket No. 68.
   b. Knock sensor 1 between terminal No. 2 and socket No. 67.
   c. Knock sensor 1 between terminal No. 3 and socket No. 2.
   d. Knock sensor 2 between terminal No. 1 and socket No. 60.
   e. Knock sensor 2 between terminal No. 2 and socket No. 67.
   f. Knock sensor 2 between terminal No. 3 and socket No. 2.
   g. If resistance is not at least 1.5 ohms, inspect wiring for open circuit.
   h. Measure resistance between socket Nos. 67 and 68. Resistance should be infinite.
   i. If resistance is not infinite, inspect wiring for short circuit.
5. If wiring is satisfactory, loosen knock sensor, then **torque** to 15 ft. lbs.
6. If fault condition is still present, replace knock sensor.

1.8L ATW ENGINE

1. Connect scan tool No. VAG 1551/1552, or equivalent, to DLC.
2. Press buttons 0 and 1 to insert "Engine Electronics" address word 01.
3. Ensure engine is running and at idle.
4. Press buttons 0 and 8 to select "Read Measuring Value Block" function 08, then press "Q" to confirm input.
5. Press buttons 0, 2 and 0 to input Display Group number 20, then press "Q" to confirm input.
6. Road test vehicle and compare scan tool display with display readings in **Fig. 10. Have a second technician operate scan tool while on road test.**
7. If knock sensor display values are not as specified in **Fig. 10,** refer to **Fig. 11** for possible causes of knock sensor system fault.
8. If knock sensor values are within specification, proceed as follows:
   a. If DTC memory has been erased, generate new readiness code.
   b. Press right arrow button to advance program sequence.
   c. Press buttons 0 and 6 to select "End Output" function 06, then press "Q" to confirm input.
9. Disconnect knock sensor electrical connector.
10. Measure resistance of the following knock sensor terminals using a suitable ohmmeter and connector test kit tool No. VW 1594, or equivalent, **Fig. 12,** as follows:
    a. Terminal 1 to 2.
    b. Terminals 1 and 2 to 3.
11. Ohmmeter should indicated an infinite reading.
12. If resistance is as specified, proceed as follows:
    a. Connect test box tool No. VAG 1598/31, or equivalent, to Motronic ECM harness connector.
    b. Inspect wiring harness for open circuit between test box and knock sensor electrical connector, **Fig. 13,** using a suitable ohmmeter. Inspect the following pins: connector terminal 1 to test box pins 60 and 68; terminal 2 to pin 67; terminal 3 to pin 2. Maximum resistance is 1.5 ohms.
    c. Inspect knock sensor wiring for short circuit using a suitable ohmmeter. Inspect the following pins: connector terminals 2 and 3 to test box pin 60 and 68; connector terminal 3 to test box pin 67. Ohmmeter should give infinite reading.
13. If wiring inspection is satisfactory, proceed as follows:
    a. Loosen knock sensor, then **torque** to 15 ft. lbs.
    b. If fault condition still exists, replace knock sensor.
    c. If DTC memory has been erased, generate new readiness code.

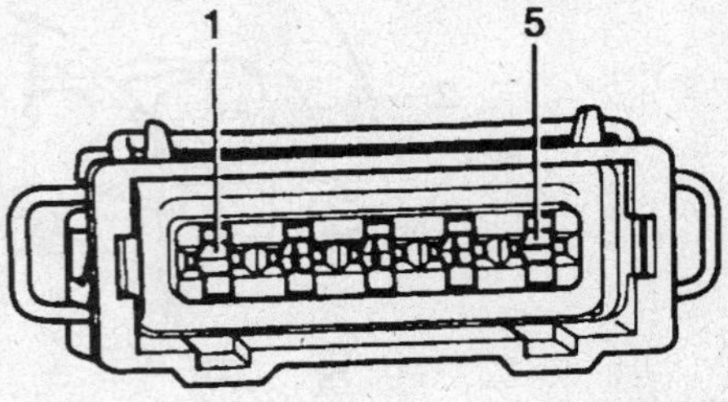

Fig. 8 Connector pin location. 2.8L engine

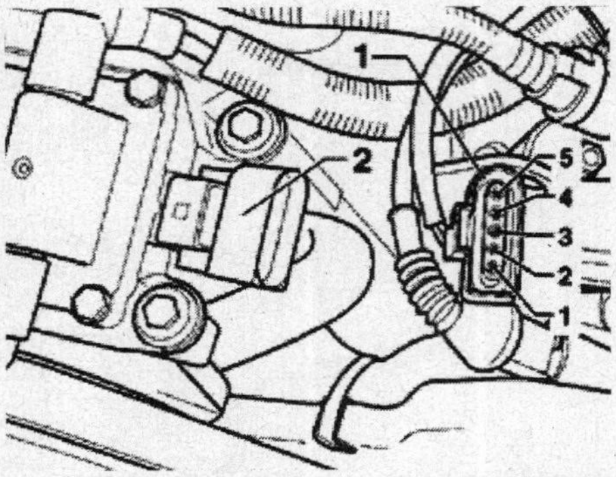

Fig. 9 Ignition coil 5-pin connector. Passat w/ATQ engine

	Display groups 1	2	3	4
Display group 20: Knock sensor system				
Display	xx.x °	xx.x °	xx.x °	xx.x °
Indicates	Timing correction, cylinder 1	Timing correction, cylinder 2	Timing correction cylinder 3	Timing correction, cylinder 4
Range	0.0°–15.0° (crankshaft)	0.0°–15.0° (crankshaft)	0.0°–15.0° (crankshaft)	0.0°–15.0° (crankshaft)
Specified value	0.0°–10.0° (crankshaft)	0.0°–10.0° (crankshaft)	0.0°–10.0° (crankshaft)	0.0°–10.0° (crankshaft)

AD1119800018000X

Fig. 10 Knock sensor display values. 1.8L engine

Display group: 20 Display fields: 1–4	Possible cause	Correcting action
All cylinders retarded more than 10° (crankshaft)	• Knock sensor faulty	– Inspect knock sensor and wiring.
	• Connector corroded	
	• Knock sensor incorrectly torqued	– Loosen knock sensor and re-tighten to 20 Nm (15 ft lb)
	• Components loose on engine	– Tighten components
	• Poor fuel quality	– Change fuel
One cylinder reading is very different from the others	• Connector corroded	Inspect wiring
	• Engine damage	– Check compression
	• Components loose on engine	– Tighten components

AD1119800019000X

Fig. 11 Knock sensor fault chart

1.8L AWD & AWW ENGINES

1. Disconnect 3-pin electrical connector from knock sensor 1.
2. Measure resistance using a suitable ohmmeter between terminals 1 and 2, 1 and 3, then 2 and 3. Ohmmeter should read infinity.
3. Disconnect 3-pin electrical connector from knock sensor 2.
4. Measure resistance between terminals 1 and 2, 1 and 3, then 2 and 3. Ohmmeter should read infinity.
5. If resistances do not meet specifications, replace knock sensor.
6. If resistances are as specified, connect test box tool No. VAG 1598/3, or equivalent, to ECM wiring harness. **ECM must remain disconnected.**
7. Inspect wiring between test box and 3-pin connector for open circuits as follows:
   a. Knock sensor 1 terminal 1 and test box socket 106.
   b. Sensor 1 terminal 2 and socket 99.
   c. Sensor 1 terminal 3 and socket 108.
   d. Knock sensor 2 terminal 1 and test box socket 107.
   e. Sensor 2 terminal 2 and socket 99.
   f. Sensor 2 terminal 3 and socket 108.
   g. Maximum resistance is 1.5 ohms.
8. Inspect wires for shorts between each other. Ohmmeter should read infinity.
9. If wiring is satisfactory, loosen knock sensor, then **torque** to 15 ft. lbs.
10. If fault condition is still present, replace knock sensor.

2.0L ENGINE

1998 Cabrio, Golf, GTI & Jetta

1. Disconnect knock sensor 3-pin connector.
2. Measure resistance as follows:
   a. Between knock sensor connection terminals Nos. 1 and 2.
   b. Between terminals Nos. 1 and 3.
   c. Between terminals Nos. 2 and 3.
   d. If resistance is not infinite, replace knock sensor.
3. Connect test box tool No. VAG 1598/31, or equivalent, to ECM harness connector.
4. Measure resistance as follows:
   a. Between connector terminal No. 1 and test box socket No. 34.
   b. Between terminal No. 2 and socket No. 33.
   c. Between terminal No. 3 and socket No. 56.
   d. If resistance is not less than 1.5 ohms, inspect wiring for open circuit.
   e. Between terminal No. 3 and socket No. 34
   f. Between terminal No. 3 and socket No. 33.
   g. Between terminal No. 2 and socket No. 34.
   h. If resistance is not infinite, inspect wiring for short circuit.
5. If wiring is satisfactory, loosen knock sensor, then **torque** to 15 ft. lbs.
6. If fault condition is still present, replace knock sensor.

New Beetle & 1999–2001 Cabrio, Golf, GTI & Jetta

1. Disconnect knock sensor 2-pin connector.
2. Measure resistance between knock sensor connection terminals and if not infinite, replace knock sensor.
3. Connect test box tool No. VAG 1598/31, or equivalent, to ECM harness connector and measure resistance as follows:
   a. Between knock sensor 1 connector terminal No. 1 and test box socket No. 68.
   b. Between terminal No. 2 and socket No. 67.
   c. Between knock sensor 2 terminal No. 1 and socket No. 60.
   d. Between terminal No. 2 and socket No. 67.
   e. If resistance is not at least 1.5 ohms, inspect wiring for open circuit.
   f. Between socket Nos. 67 and 60.
   g. Between socket Nos. 67 and 68.
   h. If resistance is not infinite, inspect wiring for short circuit.
4. If wiring is satisfactory, loosen knock sensor, then **torque** to 15 ft. lbs.
5. If condition is still present, replace knock sensor.

2.8L ENGINE

EuroVan & 1998 Golf, GTI & Jetta

1. Disconnect knock sensor 3-pin connector.
2. Measure resistance as follows:
   a. Between knock sensor connector terminal Nos. 1 and 2.
   b. Between terminals Nos. 1 and 3.
   c. Between terminals Nos. 2 and 3.
   d. If resistance is not infinite, replace knock sensor.
3. Connect test box tool No. VAG 1598/

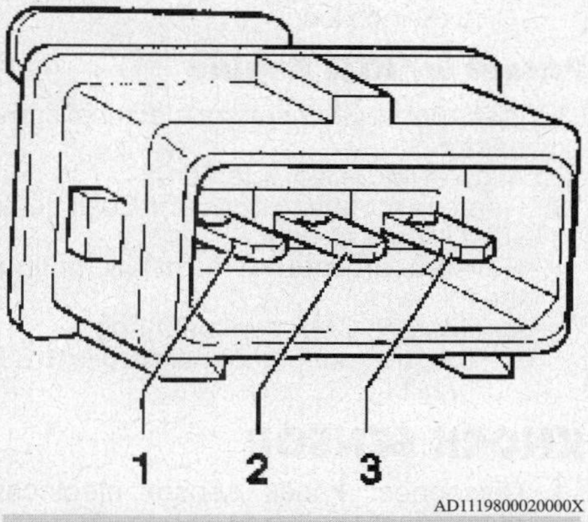

Fig. 12 Knock sensor terminal inspection

31, or equivalent, to ECM harness connector and measure resistance as follows:
   a. Between knock sensor 1 connector terminal No. 1 and test box socket No. 34.
   b. Between terminal No. 2 and socket No. 33.
   c. Between terminal No. 3 and socket No. 56.
   d. Between knock sensor 2 connector terminal No. 1 and test box socket No. 57.
   e. Between terminal No. 2 and socket No. 33.
   f. Between terminal No. 3 and socket No. 56.
   g. If resistance is not less than 1.5 ohms, inspect wiring for open circuit.
   h. Between knock sensor 1 terminal No. 3 and test box socket No. 34.
   i. Between terminal No. 3 and socket No. 33.
   j. Between terminal No. 2 and socket No. 34.
   k. Between knock sensor 2 terminal No. 3 and test box socket No. 57.
   l. Between terminal No. 3 and socket No. 33.
   m. Between terminal No. 2 and socket No. 57.
   n. If resistance is not infinite, inspect wiring for short circuit.
4. If wiring is satisfactory, loosen knock sensor, then **torque** to 15 ft. lbs.
5. If fault condition is still present, replace knock sensor.

1999-2001 Golf, GTI & Jetta

1. Disconnect knock sensor 3-pin connector.
2. Measure resistance as follows:
   a. Between knock sensor connector terminal Nos. 1 and 2.
   b. Between terminal Nos. 1 and 3.
   c. Between terminal Nos. 2 and 3.
   d. If resistance is not infinite, replace knock sensor.
3. Connect test box tool No. VAG 1598/31, or equivalent, to ECM harness connector. **ECM must remain disconnected.**
4. Measure resistance as follows:
   a. Between knock sensor 1 connector terminal No. 1 and test box socket No. 106.
   b. Between terminal 2 and socket 99.
   c. Between terminal 3 and socket 108.
   d. Between knock sensor 2 connector terminal No. 1 and test box socket No. 107.
   e. Between terminal 2 and socket 99.
   f. Between terminal 3 and socket 108.
   g. If resistance is not less than 1.5 ohms, inspect wiring for open circuit.
   h. Measure resistance between wires. If resistance is not infinite, inspect wiring for short circuit.
5. If wiring is satisfactory, loosen knock sensor, then **torque** to 15 ft. lbs.
6. If fault condition is still present, replace knock sensor.

Passat w/AHA Engine

1. Disconnect knock sensor 3-pin connector.
2. Measure resistance as follows:
   a. Between knock sensor connection terminal Nos. 1 and 2.
   b. Between terminal Nos. 1 and 3.
   c. Between terminal Nos. 2 and 3.
   d. If resistance is not infinite, replace knock sensor.
3. Connect test box tool No. VAG 1598/31, or equivalent, to ECM harness connector. **ECM must remain disconnected.**
4. Measure resistance as follows:
   a. Between knock sensor 1 connector terminal No. 1 and test box socket No. 68.
   b. Between terminal No. 2 and socket No. 67.
   c. Between terminal No. 3 and socket No. 67.
   d. Between knock sensor 2 connector terminal No. 1 and test box socket No. 60.
   e. Between terminal No. 2 and socket No. 67.
   f. Between terminal No. 3 and socket No. 67.
   g. If resistance is not less than 1.5 ohms, inspect wiring for open circuit.
   h. Measure resistance between test box socket No. 67 and socket No. 60, then No. 68.
   i. If resistance is not infinite, inspect wiring for short circuit.
5. If wiring is satisfactory, loosen knock sensor, then **torque** to 15 ft. lbs.
6. If fault condition is still present, replace knock sensor.

Passat w/ATQ Engine

1. Disconnect knock sensor 3-pin connector.
2. Measure resistance as follows:
   a. Between knock sensor connector terminal Nos. 1 and 2.
   b. Between terminal Nos. 1 and 3.
   c. Between terminal Nos. 2 and 3.
   d. If resistance is not infinite, replace knock sensor.

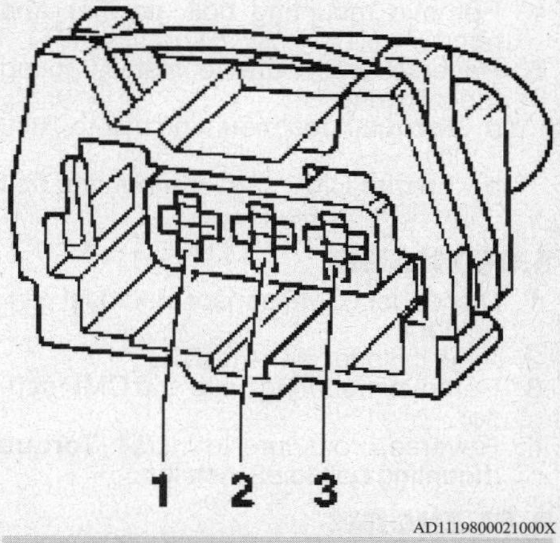

Fig. 13 Knock sensor electrical connector

3. Connect test box tool No. VAG 1598/31, or equivalent, to ECM harness connector. **ECM must remain disconnected.**
4. Measure resistance as follows:
   a. Between knock sensor 1 connector terminal No. 1 and test box socket No. 106.
   b. Between terminal 2 and socket 99.
   c. Between terminal 3 and socket 108.
   d. Between knock sensor 2 connector terminal No. 1 and test box socket No. 107.
   e. Between terminal 2 and socket 99.
   f. Between terminal 3 and socket 108.
   g. If resistance is not less than 1.5 ohms, inspect wiring for open circuit.
   h. Measure resistance between wires. If resistance is not infinite, inspect wiring for short circuit.
5. If wiring is satisfactory, loosen knock sensor, then **torque** to 15 ft. lbs.
6. If fault condition is still present, replace knock sensor.

SYSTEM SERVICE

Component Replacement

IGNITION COIL

1. Disconnect electrical connectors.
2. Remove mounting screws and ignition coil.
3. Reverse procedure to install. Tighten ignition coil mounting bolts securely.

CAMSHAFT POSITION (CMP) SENSOR

1.8L ENGINE

1. Disconnect CMP sensor electrical connector.
2. Align No. 1 cylinder to TDC.
3. Remove mounting bolts and CMP sensor.

4. Remove mounting bolt, washer and hood.
5. Reverse procedure to install, noting the following:
   a. **Torque** hood mounting bolt to 18 ft. lbs.
   b. **Torque** CMP sensor mounting bolt to 89 inch lbs.

2.0L ENGINE

1. Disconnect CMP sensor electrical connector.
2. Align cylinder No. 1 to TDC.
3. Remove mounting bolts and CMP sensor.
4. Reverse procedure to install. **Torque** mounting bolt to 89 inch lbs.

2.8L ENGINE

EuroVan, Golf, GTI & Jetta

1. Disconnect CMP sensor electrical connector.
2. Align cylinder No. 1 to TDC.
3. Remove mounting bolts and CMP sensor. Discard O-ring.
4. Reverse procedure to install, noting the following:
   a. Replace CMP sensor O-ring.
   b. **Torque** mounting bolts to 89 inch lbs.

Passat w/AHA Engine

1. Disconnect electrical connector.
2. Align cylinder No. 1 to TDC.
3. Remove mounting bolts and CMP sensor.
4. Remove mounting bolt, washer and hood.
5. Reverse procedure to install, noting the following:
   a. **Torque** hood mounting bolt to 18 ft. lbs.
   b. **Torque** CMP sensor mounting bolt to 89 inch lbs.

Passat w/ATQ Engine

1. Disconnect CMP sensor electrical connector.
2. Align cylinder No. 1 to TDC.
3. Remove mounting bolts and CMP sensor. Discard O-ring.
4. Reverse procedure to install, noting the following:
   a. Replace CMP sensor O-ring.
   b. **Torque** sensor mounting bolts to 89 inch lbs.

KNOCK SENSOR

1. Disconnect knock sensor electrical connector.
2. Remove mounting bolt and knock sensor.
3. Reverse proceed to install. **Torque** mounting bolt to 15 ft. lbs.

Fuel Injection

NOTE: If Unsure Of The System Used On The Vehicle Being Serviced, Refer To The "Engine Systems Identification Chart." Further Assistance For The Proper Use Of Information Contained In This Section Can Also Be Found In The Front Of This Tabbed Section Under "How To Use This Manual."

NOTE: On Air Bag Equipped Models, Refer To "Air Bag System Precautions" Located In The Front Of This Manual For System Disarming & Arming Procedures.

NOTE: Prior To Performing Any Service Operations Listed In This Section, Consult The "Technical Service Bulletins" Section For Related Information.

NOTE: Refer To The "Electronic Ignition" Or "Computerized Engine Controls" Section For Related Diagnostic Information Not Found In This Section.

NOTE: "Electrical Symbol & Wire Color Code Identification" Located In The Front Of This Manual May Be Used As An Aid When Using wiring diagrams Found In This Section.

NOTE: Refer To "Computer Relearn Procedures" Located In The Front Of This Manual When Battery Power To The Computer Has Been Interrupted.

TABLE OF CONTENTS

	Page No.
MOTRONIC FUEL INJECTION	17-18
TDI DIESEL FUEL INJECTION	17-25

Motronic Fuel Injection

NOTE: On Air Bag Equipped Models, Refer To "Air Bag System Precautions" Located In The Front Of This Manual For System Disarming & Arming Procedures.

NOTE: If Unsure Of The System Used On The Vehicle Being Serviced, Refer To The "Engine Systems Identification" Chart Located At The Beginning Of This Chapter.

NOTE: Prior To Performing Any Service Operations Listed In This Section Consult The Technical Service Bulletin Section For Related Information.

NOTE: Refer To The "Electronic Ignition" Or "Computerized Engine Controls" Section For Related Diagnostic Information Not Found In This Section.

INDEX

	Page No.
Description	17-20
Diagnosis & Testing	17-20
Accessing Diagnostic Trouble Codes	17-20
Clearing Diagnostic Trouble Codes	17-20
Component Testing	17-20
Closed Throttle Position (CTP) Switch	17-22
Fuel Pressure Regulator	17-22
Throttle Body Control Module	17-20
Diagnostic Tests	17-20
Diagnostic Trouble Code Interpretation	17-20
Wiring Diagrams	17-20
Precautions	17-20
Air Bag Systems	17-20
Audio Coded Anti-Theft System	17-20
Battery Ground Cable	17-20
Sensor & Fuel Injector Specifications	17-19
System Service	17-23
Component Replacement	17-23
Fuel Injector	17-23

SENSOR & FUEL INJECTOR SPECIFICATIONS

Sensor	Temperature, Degrees F	Resistance, Ohms
1.8L ENGINE		
Engine Coolant Temperature & Intake Air Temperature	86	1500–2000
	176	275–375
Fuel Injector	—	12–15
Oxygen①	—	5–20
2.0L ENGINE 1998 CABRIO, GOLF, GTI & JETTA		
Engine Coolant Temperature & Intake Air Temperature	86	1500–2000
	176	275–375
Fuel Injector	—	15–22
Oxygen①	—	0–24
2.0L ENGINE 1999–2001 CABRIO, GOLF, GTI & JETTA		
Engine Coolant Temperature & Intake Air Temperature	86	1500–2000
	176	275–375
Fuel Injector	—	14–18
Oxygen①	—	0–24
2.0L ENGINE NEW BEETLE		
Engine Coolant Temperature & Intake Air Temperature	86	1500–2000
	176	275–375
Fuel Injector	—	14–16
Oxygen①	—	0–24
2.8L ENGINE 1998 GOLF, GTI & JETTA		
Engine Coolant Temperature & Intake Air Temperature	86	1500–2000
	176	275–375
Fuel Injector	—	15–21.5
Heated Oxygen	68	20
Input Speed	—	800–900
2.8L ENGINE 1999–2001 GOLF, GTI & JETTA		
Engine Coolant Temperature & Intake Air Temperature	86	1500–2000
	176	275–375
Fuel Injector	—	13–19
Heated Oxygen	68	20
Input Speed	—	800–900
2.8L AHA ENGINE PASSAT		
Engine Coolant Temperature & Intake Air Temperature	86	1500–2000
	176	275–375
Fuel Injector	—	14–16
Heated Oxygen	68	20
Input Speed	—	800–900
2.8L ATQ ENGINE PASSAT		
Engine Coolant Temperature & Intake Air Temperature	86	1500–2000
	176	275–375
Fuel Injector	—	14–16
HO2S Heater	—	2–9 Ohms
IAT	86	1500–2000 Ohms
	176	275–375 Ohms

① — At idle speed.

PRECAUTIONS

Air Bag Systems

Refer to "Air Bag System Precautions" in the front of this manual for system disarming and arming procedures.

Audio Coded Anti-Theft System

Do not use computer memory saver tool. Using the tool will keep the air bag system charged and may cause accidental air bag unit activation.

Obtain the security code from the vehicle operator prior to disconnecting the battery or removing the radio. Refer to the owner's manual for security code disarming and arming procedures.

Battery Ground Cable

Prior to service, disconnect battery ground cable and isolate as required.

DESCRIPTION

The Motronic system uses an electronic control module (ECM) and various sensors located on and around the engine to accurately control fuel injection and electronic ignition.

DIAGNOSIS & TESTING

Accessing Diagnostic Trouble Codes

Refer to "Computerized Engine Controls" to access diagnostic trouble codes.

Diagnostic Trouble Code Interpretation

Refer to "Computerized Engine Controls" for diagnostic trouble code interpretation.

Wiring Diagrams

Refer to "Computerized Engine Controls" for wiring diagrams.

Diagnostic Tests

Refer to "Computerized Engine Controls" for diagnostic tests.

Clearing Diagnostic Trouble Codes

Refer to "Computerized Engine Controls" to clear diagnostic trouble codes.

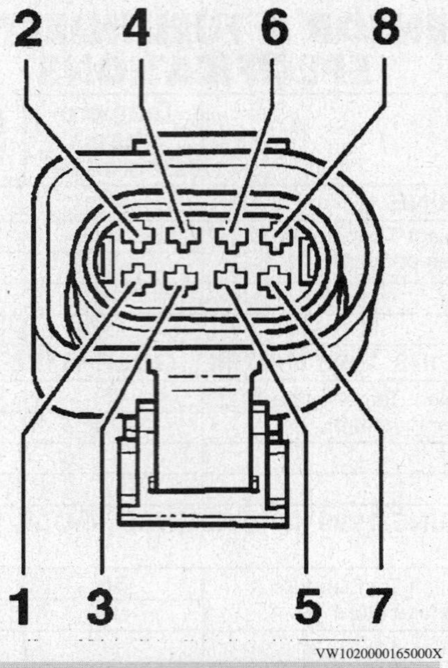

Fig. 1 Throttle body control module 8-pin connector. 1.8L engine

Component Testing

THROTTLE BODY CONTROL MODULE

1.8L ENGINE

1. Disconnect throttle body control module 8-pin harness connector, **Fig. 1.**
2. Measure resistance between connector terminals Nos. 1 and 2, which should be 3–200 ohms.
3. Connect suitable voltage tester between connector terminal Nos. 4 and 7.
4. Turn ignition On. There should be at least 4.5 volts.
5. Measure voltage between terminal Nos. 3 and 7, which should be at least nine volts.
6. Turn ignition Off.
7. Connect test box tool No. VAG 1598/31, or equivalent, to Engine Control Module (ECM) harness connector.
8. Measure resistance as follows:
   a. Between harness connector terminal No. 1 and test box socket No. 66
   b. Between terminal No. 2 and socket No. 59.
   c. Between terminal No. 3 and socket No. 69.
   d. Between terminal No. 4 and socket No. 62.
   e. Between terminal No. 5 and socket No. 75.
   f. Between terminal No. 7 and socket No. 67.
   g. Between terminal No. 8 and socket No. 74.
   h. If resistance is not less than 1.5 ohms, inspect wiring for open circuit.
   i. Measure resistance between wires. If resistance is not infinite, inspect wiring for short circuit.
9. If wiring is satisfactory, inspect ECM voltage supply.

2.0L ENGINE

1998 Cabrio, Golf, GTI & Jetta

1. Disconnect throttle valve control module 8-pin connector.
2. Measure voltage between connector terminals Nos. 3 and 7 with ignition On. There should be 9–14.5 volts.
3. Measure voltage between connector terminals Nos. 4 and 7. There should be 4–6 volts.
4. Turn ignition Off.
5. Connect test box tool No. 1598/18, or equivalent, to ECM wiring harness and measure resistance as follows:
   a. Between connector terminal No. 3 and test box socket No. 10.
   b. Between terminal No. 4 and socket No. 41
   c. Between terminal No. 7 and socket No. 33.
   d. If resistance is not less than 1.5 ohms, inspect wiring for open circuit.
   e. Between connector terminal No. 7 and test box socket No. 10.
   f. Between terminal No. 7 and socket No. 41.
   g. Between terminal No. 4 and socket No. 33.
   h. If resistance is not infinite, inspect wiring for short circuit.
   i. Between test box sockets Nos. 1 and 40.
   j. If resistance is not infinite, inspect wiring for short circuit to ground.
6. Connect suitable voltmeter, turn ignition On and inspect for short circuit to battery voltage.
7. Disconnect throttle valve control module 8-pin connector.
8. If measurement is more than five volts, proceed as follows:
   a. Measure resistance between test box sockets Nos. 40 and 41.
   b. If resistance is not infinite, inspect for short circuit.
9. If measurement is approximately battery voltage, inspect connector terminal No. 5 wiring for short circuit to battery voltage.
10. If voltage was not present, proceed as follows:
    a. Measure resistance between connector terminal No. 5 and test box socket No. 40.
    b. If resistance is not less than 1.5 ohms, inspect for open circuit.
11. Connect connector.
12. If no wiring malfunction was found, replace throttle valve control module.

1999–2001 Cabrio, Golf, GTI & Jetta

1. Disconnect throttle valve control module 8-pin connector.
2. **On models equipped with cruise control,** connect suitable voltmeter between connector terminals Nos. 2 and 5.

3. **On models less cruise control,** connect suitable voltmeter between connector terminals Nos. 4 and 7.
4. **On all models,** turn ignition On. There should be at least 4.5 volts.
5. Turn ignition Off.
6. **On models equipped with cruise control,** connect voltmeter between connector terminals Nos. 2 and 6.
7. **On models less cruise control,** connect voltmeter between connector terminals Nos. 3 and 7.
8. **On all models,** turn ignition On. There should be at least nine volts.
9. Turn ignition Off.
10. If resistance is not as specified, connect test box tool No. 1598/31, or equivalent, to ECM wiring harness.
11. **On models equipped with cruise control,** measure resistance between connector terminals and test box sockets as follows:
    a. Terminal No. 1 and socket No. 74.
    b. Terminal No. 2 and socket No. 67.
    c. Terminal No. 4 and socket No. 75.
    d. Terminal No. 5 and socket No. 62.
    e. Terminal No. 6 and socket No. 69.
    f. Terminal No. 7 and socket No. 59.
    g. Terminal No. 8 and socket No. 66.
12. **On models less cruise control,** measure resistance between connector terminals and test box sockets as follows:
    a. Terminal No. 1 and socket No. 66.
    b. Terminal No. 2 and socket No. 59.
    c. Terminal No. 4 and socket No. 69.
    d. Terminal No. 5 and socket No. 62.
    e. Terminal No. 6 and socket No. 75.
    f. Terminal No. 7 and socket No. 67.
    g. Terminal No. 8 and socket No. 74.
13. **On all models,** if resistance is not less than 1.5 ohms, inspect wiring for open circuit.
14. Inspect wires for short to one another. Resistance should be infinite.
15. If no wiring malfunction was found, replace throttle valve control module.

New Beetle

1. Disconnect throttle valve control module 8-pin connector.
2. Measure voltage between connector terminals Nos. 2 and 5 with ignition On. There should be at least 4.5 volts.
3. Turn ignition Off.
4. Measure voltage between connector terminals Nos. 2 and 6 with ignition On. There should be at least 9 volts.
5. Turn ignition Off.
6. If resistance is not as specified, connect test box tool No. 1598/31, or equivalent, to ECM wiring harness.
7. Measure resistance between connector terminals and test box sockets as follows:
    a. Terminal No. 1 and socket No. 74.
    b. Terminal No. 2 and socket No. 67.
    c. Terminal No. 4 and socket No. 75.
    d. Terminal No. 5 and socket No. 62.
    e. Terminal No. 6 and socket No. 69.
    f. Terminal No. 7 and socket No. 59.
    g. Terminal No. 8 and socket No. 66.
8. If resistance is not than 1.5 ohms, inspect wiring for open circuit and repair as required.
9. Inspect wires for short to one another. Resistance should be infinite.
10. If no wiring malfunction was found, replace throttle valve control module.

2.8L ENGINE

1998 Golf, GTI & Jetta

Refer to "2.0L Engine" "1998 Cabrio, Golf, GTI & Jetta."

EuroVan & 1999-2001 Golf, GTI & Jetta

1. Disconnect throttle valve control module 6-pin connector.
2. Turn ignition On and measure voltage between connector terminals Nos. 2 and 6. There should be at least 4.5 volts.
3. Measure voltage between connector terminal No. 2 and ground. There should be at least 4.5 volts.
4. Turn ignition Off.
5. If measurements are not within specifications, connect test box tool No. 1598/31, or equivalent, to ECM wiring harness and measure resistance as follows:
    a. Between connector terminal No. 1 and test box socket No. 92.
    b. Between terminal No. 2 and socket No. 83.
    c. Between terminal No. 3 and socket No. 117.
    d. Between terminal No. 4 and socket No. 84.
    e. Between terminal No. 5 and socket No. 118.
    f. Between terminal No. 6 and socket No. 91.
    g. If resistance is not less than 1.5 ohms, inspect wiring for open circuit.
    h. Inspect wires for short to one another. Resistance should be infinite.
    i. Inspect wires for short circuit to battery voltage or ground. Resistance should be infinite.
6. If no wiring malfunction was found, replace throttle valve control module.

Passat w/AHA Engine

1. Connect scan tool No. VAG 1551, or equivalent, to DLC.
2. Start engine, then select Engine Control Module (ECM) by pressing "Address Word 01."
3. Press buttons 0 and 8 to select "Read Measuring Value Block" function 08.
4. Press Q button to confirm input.
5. Press 0, 0 and 5 for "Display Group Number 5."
6. Press Q button to confirm input.
7. Observe Closed Throttle Position (CTP) switch Display Field 4, which should read "Throttle Closed Idle" and "Throttle Slightly Open Part Throttle."
8. If displayed values meet specifications, press right arrow button, 0 and 6 to select "End Output" function 06, then Q button to confirm input.
9. If displayed values do not meet specifications, turn ignition Off.
10. Disconnect throttle valve control module 8-pin electrical connector.
11. Bridge connector terminals 3 and 7 using adapter cables from connector test kit tool No. VW 1594, or equivalent, and observe display.
12. When display shows idle:
    a. Press right arrow button.
    b. Press 0 and 6 to select "End Output" function 06.
    c. Press Q button to confirm input.
    d. Turn ignition Off.
    e. Replace throttle valve control module.
13. When display shows part throttle:
    a. Press right arrow button.
    b. Press 0 and 6 to select "End Output" function 06.
    c. Press Q button to confirm input.
    d. Turn ignition Off.
14. Inspect voltage supply to throttle valve control module and wiring to ECM as follows:
    a. Disconnect throttle valve control module 8-pin electrical connector.
    b. Connect suitable voltmeter between harness connector terminals 4 and 7.
    c. Turn ignition On and measure voltage. There should be at least 4.5 volts.
    d. Measure voltage between harness connector terminals 3 and 7. There should be at least nine volts.
15. Turn ignition Off.
16. Connect test box tool No. VAG 1598/31, or equivalent, to ECM wiring harness. **ECM must remain disconnected.**
17. Inspect wiring for open circuits as follows:
    a. Connector terminal 1 and test box socket 66.
    b. Terminal 2 and socket 59.
    c. Terminal 3 and socket 69.
    d. Terminal 4 and socket 62.
    e. Terminal 5 and socket 75.
    f. Terminal 7 and socket 67.
    g. Terminal 8 and socket 74.
    h. Maximum resistance is 1.5 ohms.
18. Inspect for short circuits between wires. Ohmmeter should read infinity.
19. Repair wiring as required.
20. If wiring is satisfactory, proceed as follows:
    a. Inspect fuse 32 and replace if required.
    b. Inspect charging system operation and repair if required.
    c. Connect scan tool No. VAG 1551, or equivalent, to DLC.
    d. Start engine, then select Engine Control Module (ECM) by pressing "Address Word 01."
    e. Press buttons 0 and 8 to select "Read Measuring Value Block" function 08.
    f. Press Q button to confirm input.
    g. Press 0, 0 and 4 for "Display Group Number 4."
    h. Press Q to exit from input mode.
    i. Read voltage indicated in Display Field 2, which should be at least 11.5 volts.
    j. Press right arrow button.
    k. Press buttons 0 and 6 to select

"End Data Transfer" function 06.
l. Press Q button to confirm input.
m. Turn ignition Off.

21. If voltage does not meet specifications, turn ignition On and measure voltages between test box sockets 2 and 3, then between sockets 1 and 2. There should be at least 11.5 volts at each location.
22. If voltages do not meet specifications, inspect wiring connections to relay carrier and repair as required.
23. If wiring is satisfactory but fault condition is still present, an ECM voltage interruption may be the cause and ECM will require adaptation to throttle valve control module. Proceed as follows:
    a. Turn ignition On for at least 10 seconds.
    b. Turn ignition Off.
    c. Ensure throttle is in fully closed position.
    d. Ensure speed control system is properly adjusted.
    e. Turn ignition On, then select Engine Control Module (ECM) by pressing "Address Word 01."
    f. Press buttons 0 and 4 to select "Basic Setting" function 04.
    g. Press Q button to confirm input.
    h. Press buttons 0, 6 and 0 to select "Display Group Number 60."
    i. Press Q button to confirm input.
    j. After pressing Q button, throttle valve actuator will be turned on without current."When 1 - 4 = Display Fields" is indicated on display, ECM to throttle valve control module adaptation has been successfully completed. To store values, turn ignition Off.
24. If fault condition is still present, replace ECM.

Passat w/ATQ Engine

1. Disconnect throttle valve control module 6-pin electrical connector.
2. Measure resistance between module terminals 3 and 5 using a suitable ohmmeter, which should be 3–200 ohms.
3. If resistance is not as specified, replace throttle valve control module.
4. If resistance meets specifications, connect a suitable voltmeter to harness connector terminals 2 and 6.
5. Turn ignition On and measure voltage, which should be at least 4.5 volts.
6. If voltage is not as specified, turn ignition Off.
7. Connect test box tool No. VAG 1598/31, or equivalent, to ECM wiring harness. **ECM must remain disconnected.**
8. Inspect wiring for open circuits as follows:
    a. Connector terminal 1 and test box socket 92.
    b. Terminal 2 and socket 83.
    c. Terminal 3 and socket 117.
    d. Terminal 4 and socket 84.
    e. Terminal 5 and socket 118.
    f. Terminal 6 and socket 91.
    g. Maximum resistance is 1.5 ohms.
9. Inspect for short circuits between wires.
10. Repair wiring as required.
11. If wiring is satisfactory, proceed as follows:
    a. Inspect fuse 32 and replace if required.
    b. Inspect charging system operation and repair if required.
    c. Connect scan tool No. VAG 1551, or equivalent, to DLC.
    d. Start engine, then select Engine Control Module (ECM) by pressing "Address Word 01."
    e. Press buttons 0 and 8 to select "Read Measuring Value Block" function 08.
    f. Press Q button to confirm input.
    g. Press 0, 0 and 4 for "Display Group Number 4."
    h. Press Q to exit from input mode.
    i. Read voltage indicated in Display Field 2, which should be at least 11.5 volts.
    j. Press right arrow button.
    k. Press buttons 0 and 6 to select "End Data Transfer" function 06.
    l. Press Q button to confirm input.
    m. Turn ignition Off.
12. If voltage does not meet specifications, connect test box tool No. 1598/31, or equivalent, to ECM wiring harness. **ECM must remain disconnected.**
13. Turn ignition On.
14. Measure voltages between following test box sockets:
    a. 1 and 62.
    b. 2 and 62.
    c. 1 and 3.
    d. 2 and 3.
    e. There should be at least 11.5 volts at each location.
15. If voltages do not meet specifications, inspect wiring connections to relay carrier and repair as required.
16. If wiring is satisfactory but fault condition is still present, an ECM voltage interruption may be the cause and ECM will require adaptation to throttle valve control module. Proceed as follows:
    a. Turn ignition On for at least 10 seconds.
    b. Turn ignition Off.
    c. Ensure throttle is in fully closed position.
    d. Ensure speed control system is properly adjusted.
    e. Turn ignition On, then select Engine Control Module (ECM) by pressing "Address Word 01."
    f. Press buttons 0 and 4 to select "Basic Setting" function 04.
    g. Press Q button to confirm input.
    h. Press buttons 0, 6 and 0 to select "Display group number 60."
    i. Press Q button to confirm input.
    j. After pressing Q button, throttle valve actuator will be turned on without current."When 1 - 4 = Display Fields" is indicated on display, ECM to throttle valve control module adaptation has been successfully completed. To store values, turn ignition Off.
17. If fault condition is still present, replace ECM.

CLOSED THROTTLE POSITION (CTP) SWITCH

2.0L ENGINE

1998 Cabrio, Golf, GTI & Jetta

1. Turn ignition Off and connect test box tool No. 1598/18, or equivalent, to ECM wiring harness.
2. With throttle valve closed, measure resistance at test box sockets Nos. 10 and 33. Resistance should be not more than five ohms.
3. Slowly open throttle valve. Resistance should increase to infinite.
4. If resistance is not within specifications, proceed as follows:
    a. Disconnect throttle valve control module 8-pin connector.
    b. Measure resistance between connector terminal No. 3 and test box socket No. 10, then terminal No. 7 and socket No. 33.
    c. Resistance should not be more than 1.5 ohms.
    d. Measure resistance between connector terminal No. 7 and test box socket No. 10.
    e. Resistance should be infinite.
    f. If resistance is not within specifications, inspect wiring and repair as required.
    g. Connect connector.
5. If no wiring malfunction is found, replace throttle valve control module.

2.8L ENGINE

1998 Golf, GTI & Jetta

Refer to "2.0L Engine" under "1998 Cabrio, Golf, GTI & Jetta."

FUEL PRESSURE REGULATOR

1.8L ENGINE

1. Open fuel supply line union and catch escaping gasoline with suitable cloth.
2. Connect pressure tester tool No. VAG 1318, or equivalent, between fuel supply line and fuel rail using adapter tool No. VAG 1318/6 and /7, or equivalents.
3. Open pressure gauge shutoff valve.
4. Start and idle engine. Fuel pressure reading should be approximately 51 psi.
5. Disconnect fuel pressure regulator vacuum hose. Pressure reading should increase to approximately 58 psi.
6. Turn ignition Off and monitor gauge for 10 minutes. Pressure should remain at more than 29 psi.
7. If pressure reading drops below 29 psi, proceed as follows:
    a. Start engine and allow pressure to build.
    b. Turn ignition Off and at same time close pressure valve.
    c. If pressure does not drop, inspect fuel pump check valve. Repair or replace as required.

d. If pressure drops, open tester shutoff valve.
e. With handle in direction of flow, start engine and idle.
f. After pressure has built up, turn ignition Off and at same time pinch off return hose.
g. If pressure drops, inspect fuel manifold O-ring and fuel injectors for leaks.
h. Ensure pressure tester does not leak.

2.0L ENGINE

Cabrio, Golf, GTI & Jetta

1. Open fuel supply line union and catch escaping gasoline with suitable cloth.
2. Connect pressure tester tool No. VAG 1318 between fuel supply line and fuel rail using adapter tool No. VAG 1318/10, /11 and /16, or equivalents.
3. Open pressure gauge shutoff valve.
4. Start and idle engine. Fuel pressure reading should be approximately 36 psi.
5. Disconnect fuel pressure regulator vacuum hose. Pressure reading should increase to approximately 44 psi.
6. Turn ignition Off and monitor gauge for 10 minutes. Pressure should remain at more than 29 psi.
7. If pressure reading drops below 29 psi, proceed as follows:
   a. Start engine and allow pressure to build.
   b. Turn ignition Off and at same time close pressure valve.
   c. If pressure does not drop, inspect fuel pump check valve. Repair or replace as required.
   d. If pressure drops, open tester shutoff valve.
   e. With handle in direction of flow, start engine and idle.
   f. After pressure has built up, turn ignition Off and at same time pinch off return hose.
   g. If pressure drops, inspect fuel manifold O-ring and fuel injectors for leaks.
   h. Ensure pressure tester does not leak.

New Beetle

1. Open fuel supply line union and catch escaping gasoline with suitable cloth.
2. Connect pressure tester tool No. VAG 1318 between fuel supply line and fuel rail using adapter tool No. VAG 1318/10, /11 and /16, or equivalents.
3. Open pressure gauge shutoff valve.
4. Start and idle engine. Fuel pressure reading should be approximately 51 psi.
5. Disconnect fuel pressure regulator vacuum hose. Pressure reading should increase to approximately 58 psi.
6. Turn ignition Off and monitor gauge for 10 minutes. Pressure should remain at more than 29 psi.
7. If pressure reading drops below 29 psi, proceed as follows:
   a. Start engine and allow pressure to build.
   b. Turn ignition Off and at same time close pressure valve.
   c. If pressure does not drop, inspect fuel pump check valve. Repair or replace as required.
   d. If pressure drops, open tester shutoff valve.
   e. With handle in direction of flow, start engine and idle.
   f. After pressure has built up, turn ignition Off and at same time pinch off return hose.
   g. If pressure drops, inspect fuel manifold O-ring and fuel injectors for leaks.
   h. Ensure pressure tester does not leak.

2.8L ENGINE

EuroVan, Golf, GTI & Jetta

Refer to "2.0L Engine" "Cabrio, Golf, GTI & Jetta."

Passat w/AHA Engine

Refer to "2.0L Engine" "New Beetle."

Passat w/ATQ Engine

1. Open fuel supply line union and catch escaping gasoline with suitable cloth.
2. Connect pressure tester tool No. VAG 1318 between fuel supply line and fuel rail using adapter tool No. VAG 1318/7, /10 and /13, or equivalents.
3. Open pressure gauge shutoff valve.
4. Start and idle engine. Fuel pressure reading should be approximately 51 psi.
5. Disconnect fuel pressure regulator vacuum hose. Pressure reading should increase to approximately 58 psi.
6. Turn ignition Off and monitor gauge for 10 minutes. Pressure should remain at more than 32 psi.
7. If pressure reading drops below 29 psi, proceed as follows:
   a. Start engine and allow pressure to build.
   b. Turn ignition Off and at same time close pressure valve.
   c. If pressure does not drop, inspect fuel pump check valve. Repair or replace as required.
   d. If pressure drops, open tester shutoff valve.
   e. With handle in direction of flow, start engine and idle.
   f. After pressure has built up, turn ignition Off and at same time pinch off return hose.
   g. If pressure drops, inspect fuel manifold O-ring and fuel injectors for leaks.
   h. Ensure pressure tester does not leak.

SYSTEM SERVICE

Component Replacement

FUEL INJECTOR

1.8L ENGINE

1. Remove clip, strainer and fuel pressure regulator.
2. Remove fuel injectors.
3. Reverse procedure to install using new O-ring seals.

2.0L ENGINE

1998 Cabrio, Golf, GTI & Jetta

Refer to "1.8L Engine."

1999-2001 Cabrio, Golf, GTI & Jetta

1. Remove fuel pressure regulator.
2. Remove vacuum, air line and air hoses.
3. Remove fuel injectors. Discard O-rings.
4. Reverse procedure to install. Always use new O-rings.

New Beetle

Refer to "1.8L Engine."

2.8L ENGINE

1998 Golf, GTI & Jetta

1. Remove ignition wire guides and suction hose from hot wire Mass Air Flow (MAF) sensor.
2. Disconnect hose to EVAP solenoid valve at throttle body.
3. Disconnect harness connector from throttle position sensor.
4. Disconnect idle speed control valve and accelerator cable from throttle body and plug.
5. Disconnect connector hose from heated tube.
6. Disconnect fuel lines at cylinder head cover and remove from fuel rail.
7. Disconnect vacuum hose from fuel pressure regulator.
8. Remove intake manifold upper section.
9. Disconnect lines to fuel injectors from wiring guide.
10. Remove wiring guide, fuel injectors and fuel rail as an assembly.
11. Reverse procedure to install, noting the following:
    a. Lightly lubricate O-rings to ease installation.
    b. **Torque** fuel rail mounting bolts to 89 inch lbs.

EuroVan & 1999-2001 Golf, GTI & Jetta

1. Remove cable guide.
2. Remove mounting bolts and fuel rail.
3. Disconnect fuel lines.

4. Remove fuel injectors. Discard O-rings.
5. Reverse procedure to install, noting the following:
   a. Install new O-rings.
   b. **Torque** fuel rail mounting bolts to 89 inch lbs.

Passat

1. Disconnect fuel and vacuum lines.
2. Remove fuel rail.
3. Remove clips and fuel injectors.
4. Reverse procedure to install. Install new O-rings.

TDI Diesel Fuel Injection

NOTE: On Air Bag Equipped Models, Refer To "Air Bag System Precautions" Located In The Front Of This Manual For System Disarming & Arming Procedures.

NOTE: If Unsure Of The System Used On The Vehicle Being Serviced, Refer To The "Engine Systems Identification" Chart Located At The Beginning Of This Chapter.

NOTE: Prior To Performing Any Service Operations Listed In This Section Consult The Technical Service Bulletin Section For Related Information.

NOTE: Refer To The "Electronic Ignition" Or "Computerized Engine Controls" Section For Related Diagnostic Information Not Found In This Section.

NOTE: Refer To "Computer Relearn Procedures" Located In The Front Of This Manual When Battery Power To The Computer Has Been Interrupted.

INDEX

Page No.

Description 17-26
Diagnosis & Testing 17-26
Accessing Diagnostic Trouble Codes 17-26
Clearing Diagnostic Trouble Codes 17-26
Component Testing 17-26
Fuel Temperature Sensor 17-26
Glow Plugs 17-26
Injection Timing Control Range 17-27
Injectors 17-26
Modulating Piston Displacement Sensor 17-26
Needle Lift Sensor 17-26
Quantity Adjuster 17-26
Diagnostic Tests 17-26
Diagnostic Trouble Code Interpretation 17-26
Wiring Diagrams 17-26
Precautions 17-26
Air Bag Systems 17-26
Audio Coded Anti-Theft System 17-26
Battery Ground Cable 17-26
Sensor & Fuel Injector Specifications 17-25
System Service 17-27
Adjustments 17-29
Injection Pump Timing 17-29
Component Replacement 17-27
Fuel Injector 17-27
Fuel Temperature Sensor 17-29
Injection Pump 17-27
Throttle Position (TP) Sensor 17-28

SENSOR & FUEL INJECTOR SPECIFICATIONS

Sensor	Temperature, Degrees F.	Resistance, Ohms
Cold Start	—	12–20
Engine Coolant Temperature	86	1500–2000
	176	275–375
Engine Speed (RPM)	—	1000–1500
Fuel Temperature	86	1500–2000
	176	275–375
Intake Air Temperature	86	1500–2000
	176	275–375
Mass Air Flow	176	240–340 mg/H
Modulating Position Displacement	—	5–8
Needle Lift	—	80–120
Throttle Position	—	1000–1500 @ CTP
	—	1500–2500 @ WOT

PRECAUTIONS

Air Bag Systems

Refer to "Air Bag System Precautions" in the front of this manual for system disarming and arming procedures.

Audio Coded Anti-Theft System

Do not use computer memory saver tool. Using the tool will keep the air bag system charged and may cause accidental air bag unit activation.

Obtain the security code from the vehicle operator prior to disconnecting the battery or removing the radio. Refer to the owner's manual for security code disarming and arming procedures.

Battery Ground Cable

Prior to service, disconnect battery ground cable and isolate as required.

DESCRIPTION

The Turbo Direct Injection (TDI) engine management system uses an Electronic Control Module (ECM) and various engine and vehicle sensors to allow accurate electronic management of fuel injection and turbocharger boost.

DIAGNOSIS & TESTING

Accessing Diagnostic Trouble Codes

Refer to "Computerized Engine Controls" to access diagnostic trouble codes.

Diagnostic Trouble Code Interpretation

Refer to "Computerized Engine Controls" for diagnostic trouble code interpretation.

Wiring Diagrams

Refer to "Computerized Engine Controls" for wiring diagrams.

Diagnostic Tests

Refer to "Computerized Engine Controls" for diagnostic tests.

Clearing Diagnostic Trouble Codes

Refer to "Computerized Engine Controls" to clear diagnostic trouble codes.

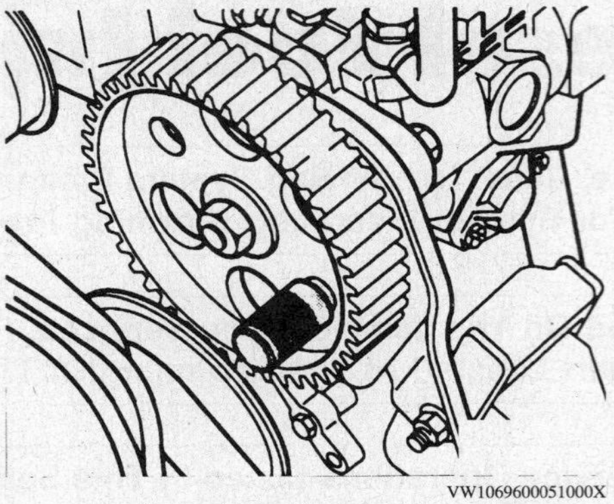

Fig. 1 Timing belt installation. 1998 Jetta

Component Testing

INJECTORS

Refer to "Injector Nozzle Pressure" under "Engine Tune Up & Performance."

GLOW PLUGS

Refer to "Glow Plugs" under "Engine Tune Up & Performance."

QUANTITY ADJUSTER

1998 Jetta

1. Disconnect injection pump connector.
2. Measure resistance between pins Nos. 2 and 3 using a suitable ohmmeter, which should be 12–20 ohms.
3. If resistance does not meet specifications, replace cold start injector.
4. If resistance is as specified, connect test box adapter tool No. VAG 1598/18, or equivalent, to ECM wiring harness and measure resistance as follows:
   a. Between connector terminal No. 2 and test box socket No. 51.
   b. Between terminal No. 3 and socket 68.
   c. If resistance is not less than 1.5 ohms, inspect for open circuit.
   d. Inspect for shorts between wires. Resistance should be infinite.
5. If no malfunctions are found, replace Direct Fuel Injection (DFI) Engine Control Module (ECM).

New Beetle & 1999–2001 Golf & Jetta

1. Disconnect quantity adjust 10-pin connector.
2. Measure resistance between terminals Nos. 5 and 6, which should be .5–2.5 ohms.
3. If resistance does not meet specifications, replace injection pump.
4. If resistance is as specified, connect test box tool No. 1598/31, or equivalent, to ECM wiring harness and measure resistance as follows:
   a. Between connect terminal No. 5 and test box socket No. 2.
   b. Between terminal No. 5 and socket No. 28.
   c. Between terminal No. 6 and socket No. 59.
   d. Between terminal No. 6 and socket No. 66.
   e. Between terminal No. 6 and socket No. 88.
   f. If resistance is not less than 1.5 ohms, inspect for open circuit.
   g. Inspect for shorts between wires. Resistance should be infinite.
5. If no malfunctions are found, replace ECM.

FUEL TEMPERATURE SENSOR

New Beetle & 1999–2001 Golf & Jetta

1. Disconnect fuel temperature sensor 10-pin connector.
2. Measure resistance between terminals Nos. 4 and 7.
3. If resistance is not as specified under "Sensor & Fuel Injector Specifications," replace injection pump.
4. If resistance is as specified, connect test box tool No. 1598/31, or equivalent, to ECM wiring harness and measure resistance as follows:
   a. Between connect terminal No. 4 and test box socket No. 76.
   b. Between terminal No. 7 and socket No. 28.
   c. If resistance is not less than 1.5 ohms, inspect for open circuit.
   d. Inspect for shorts between wires. Resistance should be infinite.
5. If no malfunctions are found, replace ECM.

MODULATING PISTON DISPLACEMENT SENSOR

New Beetle & 1999–2001 Golf & Jetta

1. Disconnect modulating piston displacement sensor 10-pin connector.
2. Measure resistance using a suitable ohmmeter between connector terminals Nos. 1 and 2, then between terminals Nos. 2 and 3.
3. If resistance is not 5–8 ohms, replace injection pump.
4. If resistance is 5–8 ohms, connect test box tool No. 1598/31, or equivalent, to ECM wiring harness.
5. Measure resistance as follows:
   a. Between connector terminal No. 1 and test box socket No. 56.
   b. Between terminal No. 2 and socket No. 56.
   c. Between terminal No. 3 and socket No. 64.
6. If resistance is not less than 1.5 ohms, inspect for open circuit.
7. Inspect for shorts between wires. Resistance should be infinite.
8. If no malfunctions are found, replace ECM.

NEEDLE LIFT SENSOR

New Beetle & 1999–2001 Golf & Jetta

1. Disconnect needle lift sensor 2-pin connector.
2. Measure resistance using a suitable

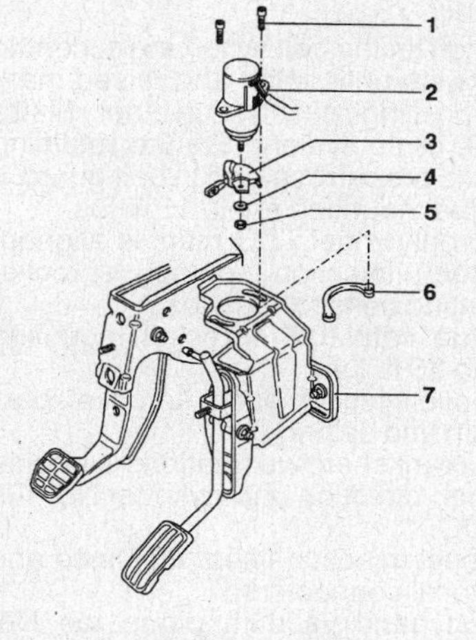

1 - Mounting Bolts

2 - Throttle Position sensor G79

- And/or pedal cluster cover require removal

3 - Cable cam

4 - Spring washer

5 - Plunger Nut

6 - Threaded piece

7 - Mounting bracket

VW1029800152000X

Fig. 2 Throttle Position (TP) sensor replacement. New Beetle

ohmmeter between terminals, which should be 80–120 ohms.

3. If resistance does not meet specifications, replace injector No. 3 with needle lift sensor.
4. If resistance is as specified, connect test box tool No. 1598/31, or equivalent, to ECM wiring harness, then measure resistance as follows:
   a. Between connect terminal No. 1 and test box socket No. 62.
   b. Between terminal No. 2 and socket No. 55.
   c. If resistance is not less than 1.5 ohms, inspect for open circuit.
   d. Inspect for shorts between wires. Resistance should be infinite.
5. If no malfunctions are found, replace ECM.

INJECTION TIMING CONTROL RANGE

New Beetle & 1999–2001 Golf & Jetta

1. Disconnect injection pump 10-pin connector.
2. Measure resistance using a suitable ohmmeter between terminals Nos. 2 and 3, which should be 12–20 ohms.
3. If resistance does not meet specifications, replace cold start injector.
4. If resistance is as specified, connect test box tool No. 1598/31, or equivalent, to ECM wiring harness and measure resistance as follows:
   a. Between connect terminal No. 9 and test box socket No. 79.
   b. Between terminal No. 10 and socket No. 2.
   c. Between terminal No. 10 and socket No. 28.
   d. If resistance is not less than 1.5 ohms, inspect for open circuit.
   e. Inspect for shorts between wires. Resistance should be infinite.
5. If no malfunctions are found, replace ECM.

SYSTEM SERVICE

Component Replacement

FUEL INJECTOR

1. Remove injection lines with injection line wrench tool No. 3035, or equivalent.
2. Remove fuel line cluster as assembly. **Do not alter line shape or routing.**
3. Remove mounting nut, retainer and injector.
4. Reverse procedure to install, noting the following:
   a. Replace heat shield between cylinder head and injector.
   b. Ensure injector is properly seated.
   c. **Torque** injector mounting nut to 15 ft. lbs.
   d. **Torque** injector line to 18 ft. lbs.

INJECTION PUMP

1998 JETTA

Removal

1. Remove air cleaner, upper timing belt guard and valve cover.
2. Turn crankshaft to cylinder No. 1 TDC and lock camshaft with setting bar tool No. 2065B, or equivalent.
3. Remove idler roller and tensioning roller nut.
4. Lock injection pump sprocket with lock pin tool No. 2064, or equivalent.
5. Relieve timing belt tension, then remove camshaft and injection pump sprockets using puller tool No. 3032, or equivalent.
6. Remove high pressure fuel lines using injector line wrench tool No. 3035, or equivalent. Cover openings with suitable cloth.
7. Disconnect fuel cutoff valve and cold start injector connector, then the quantity adjuster connector.
8. Remove mounting bolts and injector pump.

Installation

1. Install injection pump into mounting bracket, then tighten rear support mounting bolt and nut.
2. Align injection pump to central position in mounting bracket elongated holes and hand tighten mounting bolts.
3. Install injection pump sprocket, lock in position with lock pin tool No. 2064, or equivalent, and **torque** mounting nut to 41 inch lbs.
4. Loosen camshaft sprocket mounting bolt ½ turn, place drift through belt guard rear hole and release camshaft sprocket from taper by tapping with suitable hammer.
5. Remove camshaft sprocket.
6. Ensure flywheel TDC and reference marks align.
7. Install timing belt on injection pump and tensioning roller.
8. Fit camshaft sprocket into belt and install.
9. Install idler roller.
10. Remove injection pump sprocket locking pin.
11. Tension timing belt by turning eccentric clockwise until notch and raised mark align, using pin wench tool No. Matra V159, or equivalent, **Fig. 1.**
12. **Torque** mounting nut to 15 ft. lbs.
13. Ensure flywheel TDC mark is aligned.
14. **Torque** camshaft sprocket mounting bolt to 33 ft. lbs.
15. Remove setting bar.
16. Fill injection pump with clean diesel fuel through return line fitting.
17. Connect injection lines, fuel lines and electrical connectors.
18. Install timing belt guard, valve cover and air cleaner.
19. Set injection timing as outlined under "Engine Tune Up & Performance."

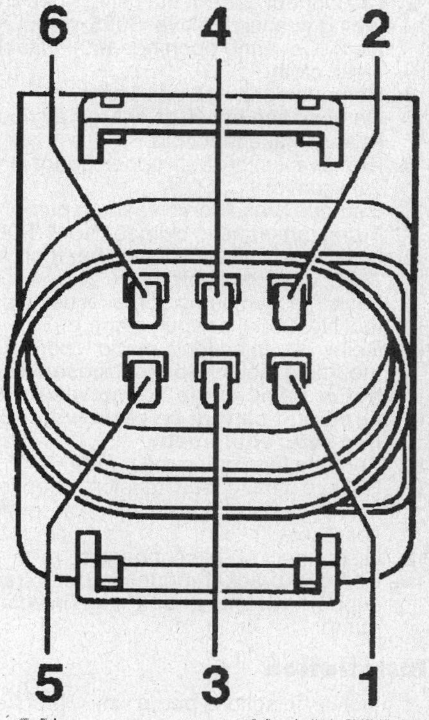

VW1029800153000X

Fig. 3 TP sensor connector terminal identification. New Beetle

1999–2001 GOLF & JETTA

Removal

1. Remove engine cover.

2. Disconnect fuel lines using fuel line tubing wrench tool No. 3035, or equivalent. Covering openings with suitable clean cloth.
3. Remove righthand headlamp.
4. Remove line between charge air cooler and intake manifold.
5. Remove timing belt upper guard and valve cover.
6. Remove brake servo vacuum pump.
7. Turn crankshaft to cylinder No. 1 TDC.
8. Lock camshaft with setting bar tool No. 3418, or equivalent.
9. Lock injection pump sprocket using pin tool No. 3359, or equivalent.
10. Remove injection pump sprocket mounting bolts. **Do not loosen hub nut or basic pump timing will be altered and cannot be reset with normal shop equipment.**
11. Remove tensioning roller nut.
12. Relieve timing belt tension, then remove camshaft and injection pump sprockets.
13. Disconnect 10-pin connector.
14. Remove bracket mounting bolts, rear support mounting bolt and injection pump.

Installation

1. Install injection pump into bracket, then tighten rear support mounting nut. **Torque** mounting bolts to 18 ft. lbs.
2. Install injection pump sprocket using new mounting bolts. **Do not tighten just yet.**
3. Lock sprocket using locking pin tool No. 3359, or equivalent.
4. Align injection pump sprocket to central position in elongated holes.
5. Hold camshaft sprocket with counterhold tool No. 3036, or equivalent, and loosen camshaft sprocket mounting bolt one turn.
6. Remove camshaft sprocket using two-arm puller tool No. T40001, or equivalent, while counter-holding with suitable open end wrench.
7. Ensure flywheel TDC and reference marks align.
8. Install camshaft sprocket with timing belt and locate with mounting bolt.
9. **On models equipped with manual transmission,** tension timing belt using suitable two-hole pin wrench on eccentric, turning clockwise until notch and raised mark align.
10. **On models equipped with automatic transmission,** tension timing belt using suitable hexagon key until notch and indicator align.
11. **On all models,** if eccentric is turned too far, the tensioning roller must be relieved and tensioned. **Eccentric must never be turned back.** Ensure tensioning roller seats properly in rear timing belt guard.
12. **Torque** mounting nut to 15 ft. lbs.
13. Ensure flywheel TDC mark is aligned.
14. **Torque** injection pump sprocket mounting bolts to 15 ft. lbs.
15. Hold camshaft sprocket with counterhold tool No. 3036, or equivalent, then **torque** mounting bolt to 33 ft. lbs.
16. Remove injection pump sprocket locking pin and setting bar.
17. Turn crankshaft two rotations in engine rotation direction until cylinder No. 1 is at TDC.
18. Connect injection lines, fuel lines and electrical connectors.
19. Attach hand vacuum pump too No. VAG 1390 to injection pump return/supply opening with adapter tool No. 1318/10, or equivalents, with approximately 40 inches of transparent plastic hose.
20. Operate pump until fuel flows out of return/supply opening. **Do not draw fuel into vacuum pump.**
21. Remove adapter and connect return/supply line.
22. Install vacuum pump and **torque** mounting bolts to 15 ft. lbs.
23. Install valve cover and **torque** mounting bolts to 89 inch lbs.
24. Set injection timing as outlined under "Engine Tune Up & Performance."
25. Tight injection pump sprocket mounting bolts an addition 90°.

NEW BEETLE

Removal

1. Disconnect fuel lines using fuel line tubing wrench tool No. 3035, or equivalent. Covering openings with suitable clean cloth.
2. Remove line between charge air cooler and intake manifold.
3. Remove timing belt upper guard and valve cover.
4. Remove brake servo vacuum pump.
5. Turn crankshaft to cylinder No. 1 TDC.
6. Lock camshaft with setting bar tool No. 3418, or equivalent.
7. Remove injection pump sprocket mounting bolts. **Do not loosen hub nut or basic pump timing will be altered and cannot be reset with normal shop equipment.**
8. Remove tensioning roller nut.
9. Relieve timing belt tension, then remove camshaft and injection pump sprockets.
10. Disconnect quantity adjuster harness connector.
11. Remove bracket mounting bolts, rear support mounting bolt and injection pump.

Installation

1. Install injection pump into bracket, then tighten rear support mounting nut. **Torque** mounting bolts to 18 ft. lbs.
2. Install injection pump sprocket using new mounting bolts. **Do not tighten just yet.**
3. Align injection pump sprocket to central position in elongated holes and lock sprocket using locking pin tool No. 3359, or equivalent.
4. Loosen camshaft sprocket mounting bolt ½ turn, place drift through belt guard rear hole and release camshaft sprocket from taper by tapping with suitable hammer.
5. Remove camshaft sprocket.
6. Ensure flywheel TDC and reference marks align.
7. Install timing belt on injection pump and tensioning roller.
8. Fit camshaft sprocket into belt and install.
9. Tension timing belt by turning eccentric clockwise until notch and raised mark align, using pin wench tool Matra V159, or equivalent. Ensure retaining hook is properly seated in belt guard.
10. **Torque** mounting nut to 15 ft. lbs.
11. Ensure flywheel TDC mark is aligned.
12. **Torque** injection pump sprocket mounting bolts to 15 ft. lbs.
13. **Torque** camshaft sprocket mounting bolt to 33 ft. lbs.
14. Remove injection pump sprocket locking pin and setting bar.
15. Turn crankshaft two rotations in engine rotation direction until cylinder No. 1 is at TDC.
16. Connect injection lines, fuel lines and electrical connectors.
17. Attach hand vacuum pump too No. VAG 1390 to injection pump return/supply opening with adapter tool No. 1318/10, or equivalents, with approximately 40 inches of transparent plastic hose.
18. Operate pump until fuel flows out of return/supply opening. **Do not draw fuel into vacuum pump.**
19. Remove adapter and connect return/supply line.
20. Install valve cover and vacuum pump.
21. Set injection timing as outlined under "Engine Tune Up & Performance."
22. Rotate injection pump sprocket mounting bolts an addition 90°.

THROTTLE POSITION (TP) SENSOR

GOLF & JETTA

1. Disconnect TP sensor electrical connectors.
2. Remove TP sensor mounting nuts, then the sensor.
3. Reverse procedure to install. **Torque** sensor mounting nuts to 84 inch lbs.

NEW BEETLE

Removal

1. Disconnect TP sensor electrical connector.
2. Make suitable alignment marks for use during installation.
3. Remove TP sensor plunger nut, **Fig. 2.**
4. Remove TP sensor mounting bolts, then the sensor.

Installation

1. Align marks made during removal.
2. **Torque** TP sensor mounting bolts and plunger nut to 84 inch lbs.
3. Connect scan tool No. VAG 1551, or equivalent, to DLC.
4. Turn ignition On.
5. Press 0 and 1 buttons to select Address Word 01: "Engine Electronics."
6. Press 0 and 8 to select Function 08: "Read Measuring Value Block."
7. Press Q button to enter input.
8. Press 0 0 2 to select "Display Group 2."
9. Observe throttle position in Display Zone 2, which should be 0%. **Do not depress accelerator pedal.**

10. Observe Closed Throttle Position switch display in Display Zone 3. Center position must show a 1, appearing as 0**1** 0.
11. Slowly depress accelerator pedal until fully depressed and observe Display Zones 2 and 3. Throttle Position value in Zone 2 must increase continuously to 100% at WOT. Zone 3 center digit must change to a zero, appearing as 0**0** 0.
12. If End specification value is not achieved, proceed as follows:
    a. Press right arrow button.
    b. Press 0 and 6 buttons to select Function 06: "End Transfer."
    c. Press Q button to enter input.
    d. Turn ignition Off.
    e. Depress accelerator pedal by hand until accelerator pedal lies against accelerator pedal stop. **On models equipped with A/T,** the pressure point or stop from kickdown switch must be felt before WOT is reached.
    f. If accelerator pedal stop is not obtained or kickdown switch pressure point cannot be felt, sensor in bracket slots as required. **Torque** bolts to 84 inch lbs.
13. If display does not change or is erratic, proceed as follows:
    a. Press right arrow button.
    b. Press 0 and 6 buttons to select Function 06: "End Transfer."
    c. Press Q button to enter input.
    d. Turn ignition Off.
    e. Disconnect TP sensor 6-pin electrical connector, **Fig. 3.**
    f. Measure sensor resistance using a suitable ohmmeter between connector terminals 1 and 3, which should be 800–1400 ohms at CTP.
    g. Measure sensor resistance between connector terminals 2 and 3, which should be 800–1400 ohms at CTP.
    h. Measure sensor resistance between connector terminals 4 and 6, which should be 800–1200 ohms at CTP and infinity at WOT.
    i. **On models equipped with A/T,** measure sensor resistance between connector terminals 5 and 6, which should be infinity at CTP and 800–1200 ohms at WOT.
14. **On all models,** if resistances do not meet specifications, replace TP sensor.
15. If resistances are as specified, connect test box tool No. VAG 1598/22, or equivalent, to ECM harness connector.
16. **On 1998–99 models,** inspect for open circuits as follows:
    a. Connector terminal 1 and test box socket 24.
    b. Terminal 2 and socket 11.
    c. Terminal 3 and socket 23.
    d. Terminal 4 and socket 12.
    e. Terminal 6 and socket 25.
    f. **On models equipped with A/T,** terminal 5 and socket 8.
    g. Maximum resistance is 1.5 ohms.
17. **On 2000–01 models,** inspect for open circuits as follows:
    a. Connector terminal 1 and test box socket 63.
    b. Terminal 2 and socket 12.
    c. Terminal 3 and socket 50.
    d. Terminal 4 and socket 69.
    e. **On models equipped with A/T,** terminal 5 and socket 51.
    f. **On all models,** terminal 6 and socket 70.
    g. Maximum resistance is 1.5 ohms.
18. Inspect wires for shorts to one another, to vehicle ground and to battery voltage. Ohmmeter should read infinity.
19. If wiring is satisfactory, replace ECM.

FUEL TEMPERATURE SENSOR

1. Remove pump cover.
2. Remove mounting bolts and sensor.
3. Reverse procedure to install.

Adjustments

INJECTION PUMP TIMING

Refer to "Engine Tune Up & Performance" for pump timing procedures.

Electric Fuel Pumps

NOTE: If Unsure Of The System Used On The Vehicle Being Serviced, Refer To The "Engine Systems Identification Chart." Further Assistance For The Proper Use Of Information Contained In This Section Can Also Be Found In The Front Of This Tabbed Section Under "How To Use This Manual."

NOTE: On Air Bag Equipped Models, Refer To "Air Bag System Precautions" Located In The Front Of This Manual For System Disarming & Arming Procedures.

NOTE: Prior To Performing Any Service Operations Listed In This Section, Consult The "Technical Service Bulletins" Section For Related Information.

INDEX

	Page No.
Diagnosis & Testing	17-30
Check Valve Test	17-32
EuroVan, New Beetle & Passat w/1.8L Engine & 1999–2001 Cabrio, Golf & Jetta	17-32
Passat w/2.8L Engine	17-32
1998 Cabrio, Golf, GTI & Jetta w/2.0L Engine	17-32
1998 GTI & Jetta w/2.8L Engine	17-32
Fuel Pump Delivery Rate Test	17-30
EuroVan & 1999–2001 Cabrio, Golf & Jetta	17-31
New Beetle w/1.8L Engine & Passat	17-31
1998 Cabrio, Golf, GTI & Jetta w/2.0L engine	17-30
1998 GTI & Jetta w/2.8L Engine	17-31
Fuel Pump Test	17-30
Fuel Pressure Relief	17-30
Fuel Pump Relay Location	17-30
Fuel Pump Replacement	17-32
Precautions	17-30
Air Bag Systems	17-30
Audio Coded Anti-Theft System	17-30
Battery Ground Cable	17-30

PRECAUTIONS

Air Bag Systems

Refer to "Air Bag System Precautions" in the front of this manual for system disarming and arming procedures.

Audio Coded Anti-Theft System

Do not use computer memory saver tool. Using the tool will keep the air bag system charged and may cause accidental air bag unit activation.

Obtain the security code from the vehicle operator prior to disconnecting the battery or removing the radio. Refer to the owner's manual for security code disarming and arming procedures.

Battery Ground Cable

Prior to service, disconnect battery ground cable and isolate as required.

FUEL PUMP RELAY LOCATION

The fuel pump relay is located in the underhood engine compartment fuse/relay box.

FUEL PRESSURE RELIEF

1. Obtain audio coded anti-theft code.
2. Disconnect and isolate battery ground cable.
3. Remove fuel filler cap to release fuel tank vapor pressure.
4. Locate suitable fuel line connection where fuel under pressure may be caught and collected.
5. Wrap shop towel around fuel line connection to be opened, then place suitable container under connection.
6. Carefully open fuel line connection and allow fuel to drain into container as pressure is relieved. Discard any seals.
7. **Do not install fuel filler cap while fuel line is opened.** After period of time vapor pressure will build and push more fuel from connection.
8. Replace any seals used at fuel line connection.
9. Connect battery ground cable, then reset audio coded anti-theft system.

DIAGNOSIS & TESTING

Fuel Pump Test

1. **On 1998 Cabrio, Golf, GTI and Jetta models,** ensure fuse No. 18 and battery are operating properly.
2. **On EuroVan, New Beetle, Passat and 1999–2001 Cabrio, Golf, GTI and Jetta models,** ensure fuse No. 28 and battery are operating properly.
3. **On all models,** turn ignition On. Fuel pump must be heard for approximately one second.
4. If fuel pump is not heard, remove fuel pump relay from fuse/relay panel.
5. Connect remote control tool No. VAG 1348/3A with adapter cable tool No. 1348/3, or equivalents, between relay contact and battery positive terminal.
6. Operate remote control switch. If fuel pump operates, inspect fuel pump relay.
7. If fuel pump does not operate, remove cover plate in luggage compartment and disconnect fuel tank flange electrical connector.
8. Connect LED tester tool No. US 1115, or equivalent, to connector outer terminals.
9. Operate remote control.
10. If LED does not light, inspect wiring for an open circuit.
11. If LED lights, remove fuel pump access flange using wrench tool No. 3217, or equivalent, and inspect wiring between flange and fuel pump.
12. If wiring is satisfactory, replace fuel pump.

Fuel Pump Delivery Rate Test

1998 CABRIO, GOLF, GTI & JETTA w/2.0L ENGINE

1. Connect remote control tool No. VAG 1348/3A, with adapter cable tool No. 1348/3, or equivalents, between relay contact and battery positive terminal.
2. Remove fuel filler cap.
3. Disconnect fuel supply line from fuel rail.
4. Connect pressure gauge tool No. 1318, with adapter tool No. 1318/10, or

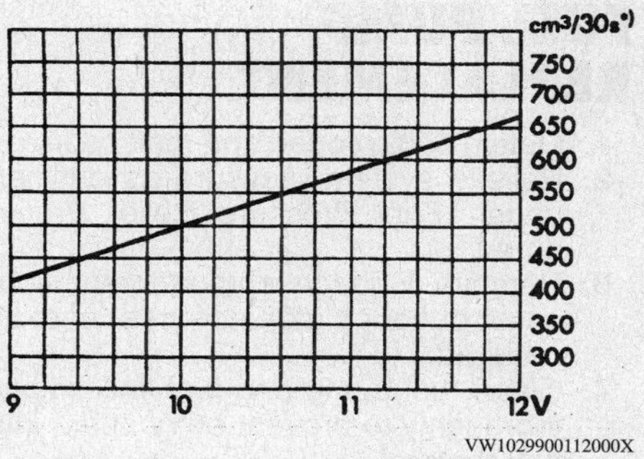

Fig. 1 Fuel pump quantity. 1998 Cabrio, Golf, GTI & Jetta w/2.0L engine

equivalents, to fuel supply line.
5. Connect hose tool No. VAG 1318/1, or equivalent, to pressure gauge and hold in suitable measuring container.
6. Open pressure gauge shutoff valve.
7. Operate fuel pump with remote control, then slowly close shutoff valve until pressure is 44 psi. **Do not change shutoff valve position.**
8. Empty measuring container.
9. Operate remote control for 30 seconds.
10. Compare fuel quantity with specified values, **Fig. 1,** noting the following:
    a. Minimum fuel amount in cm^3/30 seconds.
    b. Voltage at fuel pump with engine Off and fuel pump running should be approximately two volts less than battery voltage.
11. If fuel quantity is not as specified, inspect for kinked or plugged fuel line, plugged fuel filter or fuel pump malfunction.

1998 GTI & JETTA w/2.8L ENGINE

1. Connect remote control tool No. VAG 1348/3A, with adapter cable tool No. 1348/3, or equivalents, between relay contact and battery positive terminal.
2. Remove fuel filler cap.
3. Disconnect fuel supply line from fuel rail.
4. Connect pressure gauge tool No. 1318, with adapter tool No. 1318/10, or equivalents, to fuel supply line.
5. Connect hose tool No. VAG 1318/1, or equivalent, to pressure gauge and hold in suitable measuring container.
6. Open pressure gauge shutoff valve.
7. Operate fuel pump with remote control, then slowly close shutoff valve until pressure is 44 psi. **Do not change shutoff valve position.**
8. Empty measuring container.
9. Operate remote control for 30 seconds.
10. Compare fuel quantity with specified values, **Fig. 2,** noting the following:
    a. Minimum fuel amount in cm^3/30 seconds.
    b. Voltage at fuel pump with engine Off and fuel pump running should be approximately two volts less than battery voltage.
11. If fuel quantity is not as specified, in-

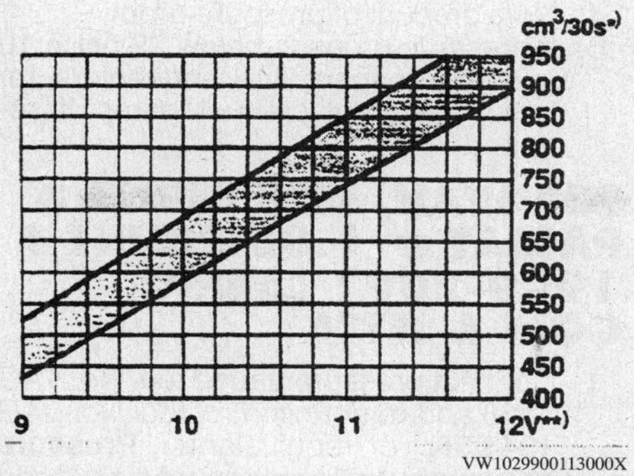

Fig. 2 Fuel pump quantity. 1998 GTI & Jetta w/2.8L engine

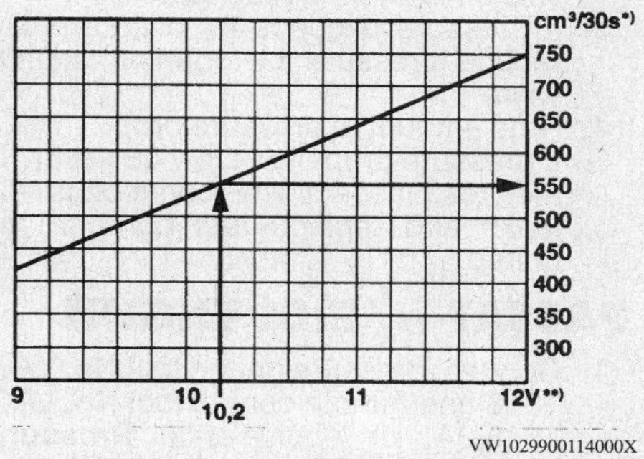

Fig. 4 Fuel pump quantity. New Beetle w/1.8L engine & Passat

spect for kinked or plugged fuel line, plugged fuel filter or fuel pump malfunction.

EUROVAN & 1999–2001 CABRIO, GOLF & JETTA

1. Connect remote control tool No. VAG 1348/3A with adapter cable tool No. 1348/3, or equivalents, between relay contact and battery positive terminal.
2. Remove fuel filler cap and intake manifold cover.
3. Disconnect fuel supply line from fuel rail.
4. Connect pressure gauge tool No. 1318 with adapter tool No. 1318/12, or equivalents, to fuel supply line.
5. Connect hose tool No. VAG 1318/1, or equivalent, to pressure gauge and hold in suitable measuring container.
6. Open pressure gauge shutoff valve.
7. Operate fuel pump with remote control, then slowly close shutoff valve until pressure is 44 psi. **Do not change shutoff valve position.**
8. Empty measuring container.
9. Measure battery voltage.
10. Operate remote control for 30 seconds.
11. Compare fuel quantity with specified values, **Fig. 3,** noting the following:
    a. Minimum fuel amount in cm^3/30 seconds.
    b. Voltage at fuel pump with engine Off and fuel pump running should be approximately two volts less than battery voltage.
12. If minimum delivery rate is not as specified, inspect for kinked or plug fuel line.

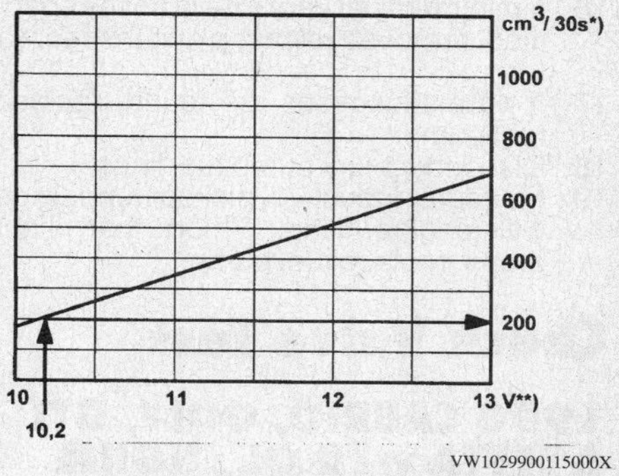

Fig. 3 Fuel pump quantity. EuroVan & 1999–2001 Cabrio, Golf & Jetta

13. Disconnect fuel filter inlet hose and connect pressure gauge to hose.
14. Repeat delivery rate procedure.
15. If minimum delivery rate is as specified, replace fuel filter.
16. If minimum delivery rate is not as specified, remove fuel pump and inspect filter.
17. If no malfunctions are found, replace fuel pump.
18. Disconnect fuel pump fuel lines.
19. Measure inductive pickup amperage with engine idling. If more than eight amps, replace fuel pump.

NEW BEETLE w/1.8L ENGINE & PASSAT

1. Connect remote control tool No. VAG 1348/3A with adapter cable tool No. 1348/3, or equivalents, between relay contact and battery positive terminal.
2. Remove fuel filler cap and intake manifold cover.
3. Disconnect fuel supply line from fuel rail.
4. Connect pressure gauge tool No. 1318 with adapter tool No. 1318/12, or equivalents, to fuel supply line.
5. Connect hose tool No. VAG 1318/1, or equivalent, to pressure gauge and hold in suitable measuring container.
6. Open pressure gauge shutoff valve.
7. Operate fuel pump with remote control, then slowly close shutoff valve until pressure is 44 psi. **Do not change shutoff valve position.**
8. Empty measuring container.
9. Measure battery voltage.
10. Operate remote control for 30 seconds.
11. Compare fuel quantity with specified values, **Fig. 4,** noting the following:
    a. Minimum fuel amount in cm^3/30 seconds.
    b. Voltage at fuel pump with engine off and fuel pump running should be approximately two volts less than battery voltage.
12. If minimum delivery rate is not as specified, inspect for kinked or plugged fuel line.
13. Disconnect fuel filter inlet hose and connect pressure gauge to hose.
14. Repeat delivery rate procedure.
15. If minimum delivery rate is as specified, replace fuel filter.

16. If minimum delivery rate is not as specified, remove fuel pump and inspect filter.
17. If no malfunctions are found, replace fuel pump.
18. Disconnect fuel pump fuel lines.
19. Measure inductive pickup amperage with engine idling. If more than eight amps, replace fuel pump.

Check Valve Test

1998 CABRIO, GOLF, GTI & JETTA w/2.0L ENGINE

1. Connect pressure gauge tool No. VAG 1318 and remote control tool No. VAG 1348/3A, or equivalents. **Pressure gauge shutoff lever must be closed prior to installation.**
2. Activate remote control for brief intervals until 44 psi is reached.
3. If pressure exceeds 44 psi, carefully reduce pressure by opening shutoff valve.
4. Note amount of pressure drop.
5. If pressure drops to below 29 psi in 10 minutes, inspect line connectors for leaks and replace fuel pump if required.

1998 GTI & JETTA w/2.8L ENGINE

1. Connect pressure gauge tool No. VAG 1318 and remote control tool No. VAG 1348/3A, or equivalents. **Pressure gauge shutoff lever must be closed prior to installation.**
2. Activate remote control for brief intervals until 44 psi is reached.
3. If pressure exceeds 44 psi, carefully reduce pressure by opening shutoff valve.
4. Note amount of pressure drop.
5. If pressure drops to below 29 psi in 10 minutes, inspect line connectors for leaks and replace fuel pump if required.

EUROVAN, NEW BEETLE & PASSAT w/1.8L ENGINE & 1999-2001 CABRIO, GOLF & JETTA

1. Connect pressure gauge tool No. VAG 1318 and remote control tool No. VAG 1348/3A, or equivalents. **Pressure gauge shutoff lever must be closed prior to installation.**
2. Activate remote control for brief intervals until 44 psi is reached.
3. If pressure exceeds 44 psi, carefully reduce pressure by opening shutoff valve.
4. Note amount of pressure drop.
5. If pressure drops to below 36 psi in 10 minutes, inspect line connectors for leaks and replace fuel pump if required.

PASSAT w/2.8L ENGINE

1. Connect pressure gauge tool No. VAG 1318 and remote control tool No. VAG 1348/3A, or equivalents. **Pressure gauge shutoff lever must be closed prior to installation.**
2. Activate remote control for brief intervals until 58 psi is reached.
3. If pressure exceeds 58 psi, carefully reduce pressure by opening shutoff valve.
4. Note amount of pressure drop.
5. If pressure drops to below 32 psi (cold engine) or 44 psi (warm engine) in 10 minutes, inspect line connectors for leaks and replace fuel pump if required.

FUEL PUMP REPLACEMENT

1. Obtain audio coded anti-theft code.
2. Relieve system pressure as outlined under "Fuel Pressure Relief Procedure."
3. Remove luggage compartment floor cover or floor plate under rear seat as required.
4. Clean fuel pump and fuel line unions thoroughly to prevent entry of dirt into fuel system.
5. Disconnect electrical connectors and fuel lines.
6. Note fuel pump and sender unit flange to tank alignment marks for assembly reference.
7. **On Cabrio, EuroVan, Golf, Jetta, GTI and New Beetle models,** remove fuel pump flange retaining union nut using wrench tool No. 3217, or equivalent. Discard seal.
8. **On Passat models,** remove fuel pump flange retaining union nut using wrench tool No. 3087, or equivalent. Discard seal.
9. **On all models,** note orientation, then remove fuel pump module by rotating counterclockwise using wrench tool No. 3307, or equivalent, to disengage.
10. Reverse procedure to install, noting the following:
    a. Use caution not to damage fuel level sender float arm.
    b. Coat flange seal with fuel when installing.
    c. Ensure flange fitting marks align with fuel tank marks.
    d. Ensure access port cover is properly sealed.

Computerized Engine Controls

NOTE: If Unsure Of The System Used On The Vehicle Being Serviced, Refer To The "Engine Systems Identification Chart." Further Assistance For The Proper Use Of Information Contained In This Section Can Also Be Found In The Front Of This Tabbed Section Under "How To Use This Manual."

NOTE: On Air Bag Equipped Models, Refer To "Air Bag System Precautions" Located In The Front Of This Manual For System Disarming & Arming Procedures.

NOTE: Prior To Performing Any Service Operations Listed In This Section, Consult The "Technical Service Bulletins" Section For Related Information.

NOTE: "Electrical Symbol & Wire Color Code Identification" Located In The Front Of This Manual May Be Used As An Aid When Using wiring diagrams Found In This Section.

NOTE: Refer To The "Fuel Injection" Or "Electronic Ignition" Sections For Related Diagnostic Information Not Found In This Section. Also, Refer To The "Fuel Injection" Section For System wiring diagrams.

NOTE: Refer To "Computer Relearn Procedures" Located In The Front Of This Manual When Battery Power To The Computer Has Been Interrupted.

TABLE OF CONTENTS

	Page No.
DIESEL TURBO DIRECT INJECTION (TDI)	17-168
MOTRONIC	17-34

Motronic

NOTE: If Unsure Of The System Used On The Vehicle Being Serviced, Refer To The "Engine Systems Identification Chart." Further Assistance For The Proper Use Of Information Contained In This Section Can Also Be Found In The Front Of This Tabbed Section Under "How To Use This Manual."

NOTE: On Air Bag Equipped Models, Refer To "Air Bag System Precautions" Located In The Front Of This Manual For System Disarming & Arming Procedures.

NOTE: Prior To Performing Any Service Operations Listed In This Section, Consult The "Technical Service Bulletins" Section For Related Information.

NOTE: "Electrical Symbol & Wire Color Code Identification" Located In The Front Of This Manual May Be Used As An Aid When Using wiring diagrams Found In This Section.

NOTE: Refer To The "Fuel Injection" Or "Electronic Ignition" Sections For Related Diagnostic Information Not Found In This Section. Also, Refer To The "Fuel Injection" Section For System wiring diagrams.

NOTE: Refer To "Computer Relearn Procedures" Located In The Front Of This Manual When Battery Power To The Computer Has Been Interrupted.

INDEX

Page No.

Description 17-36
Diagnosis & Testing 17-36
Accessing Diagnostic Trouble Codes 17-36
Clearing Diagnostic Trouble Codes 17-36
Component Testing 17-36
A/C Compressor Signal 17-49
Barometric Sensor 17-47
Brake Lamp Switch 17-51
CAN-Bus 17-49
Clutch Pedal Switch 17-51
Engine Control Module (ECM) 17-48
Engine Coolant Temperature (ECT) Sensor 17-42
Engine Speed (RPM) Sensor . 17-45
Heated Oxygen Sensor (HO2S) Control 17-36
Intake Air Preheating 17-49
Intake Air Temperature (IAT) Sensor 17-44
Intake Manifold Turning (IMT) Valve 17-47
Mass Air Flow (MAF) Sensor .. 17-41
Oxygen Sensor (O2S) Heating 17-39
Transmission Range Selection 17-50
Vehicle Speed Sensor (VSS) . 17-47
Diagnostic Tests 17-36
New Beetle & 1998–2001 Cabrio, Golf, GTI, Jetta & Passat 17-36
1998 Cabrio, Golf, GTI & Jetta w/2.0L Engine 17-36
1998 Golf, GTI & Jetta w/2.8L Engine 17-36
Diagnostic Trouble Code Interpretation 17-36
Wiring Diagrams 17-36
Diagnostic Chart Index 17-121
Precautions 17-36
Air Bag Systems 17-36
Audio Coded Anti-Theft System . 17-36
Battery Ground Cable 17-36
Sensor & Fuel Injector Specifications 17-35

SENSOR & FUEL INJECTOR SPECIFICATIONS

Sensor	Temperature, Degrees F	Resistance, Ohms
1.8L ENGINE		
Engine Coolant Temperature & Intake Air Temperature	86	1500–2000
	176	275–375
Fuel Injector	—	12–15
Oxygen①	—	5–20
2.0L ENGINE 1998 CABRIO, GOLF, GTI & JETTA		
Engine Coolant Temperature & Intake Air Temperature	86	1500–2000
	176	275–375
Fuel Injector	—	15–22
Oxygen①	—	0–24
2.0L ENGINE 1999–2001 CABRIO, GOLF, GTI & JETTA		
Engine Coolant Temperature & Intake Air Temperature	86	1500–2000
	176	275–375
Fuel Injector	—	14–18
Oxygen①	—	0–24
2.0L ENGINE NEW BEETLE		
Engine Coolant Temperature & Intake Air Temperature	86	1500–2000
	176	275–375
Fuel Injector	—	14–16
Oxygen①	—	0–24
2.8L ENGINE 1998 GOLF, GTI & JETTA		
Engine Coolant Temperature & Intake Air Temperature	86	1500–2000
	176	275–375
Fuel Injector	—	15–21.5
Heated Oxygen	68	20
Input Speed	—	800–900
2.8L ENGINE 1999–2001 GOLF, GTI & JETTA		
Engine Coolant Temperature & Intake Air Temperature	86	1500–2000
	176	275–375
Fuel Injector	—	13–19
Heated Oxygen	68	20
Input Speed	—	800–900
2.8L AHA ENGINE PASSAT		
Engine Coolant Temperature & Intake Air Temperature	86	1500–2000
	176	275–375
Fuel Injector	—	14–16
Heated Oxygen	68	20
Input Speed	—	800–900
2.8L ATQ ENGINE PASSAT		
Engine Coolant Temperature & Intake Air Temperature	86	1500–2000
	176	275–375
Fuel Injector	—	14–16
HO2S Heater	—	2–9 Ohms
IAT	86	1500–2000 Ohms
	176	275–375 Ohms

① — At idle speed.

PRECAUTIONS

Air Bag Systems

Refer to "Air Bag System Precautions" in the front of this manual for system disarming and arming procedures.

Audio Coded Anti-Theft System

Do not use computer memory saver tool. Using the tool will keep the air bag system charged and may cause accidental air bag unit activation.

Obtain the security code from the vehicle operator prior to disconnecting the battery or removing the radio. Refer to the owner's manual for security code disarming and arming procedures.

Battery Ground Cable

Prior to service, disconnect battery ground cable and isolate as required.

DESCRIPTION

The Motronic system provides central microprocessor control of both the ignition and fuel injection. An ECU monitors engine and vehicle operating conditions through a variety of sensors in order to determine proper ignition timing and air/fuel mixture for efficient engine operation.

An important feature of these systems is the self-diagnostic memory. Diagnostic Trouble Code (DTC) memory is a self-diagnostic function that refers to the vehicles capability to detect and store problems that occur during vehicle operation. If malfunctions occur at monitored sensors or components, a related Diagnostic Trouble Code (DTC) will be stored in control unit memory, for later retrieval.

DIAGNOSIS & TESTING

Accessing Diagnostic Trouble Codes

Connect suitably programmed scan tool to Diagnostic Link Connector (DLC), **Figs. 1 through 4.** Follow scan tool manufacturer's instructions to access Diagnostic Trouble Codes (DTCs).

Diagnostic Trouble Code Interpretation

Refer to **Figs. 5 through 15** for DTC interpretation table.

Wiring Diagrams

Refer to **Figs. 16 through 130** for wiring diagrams.

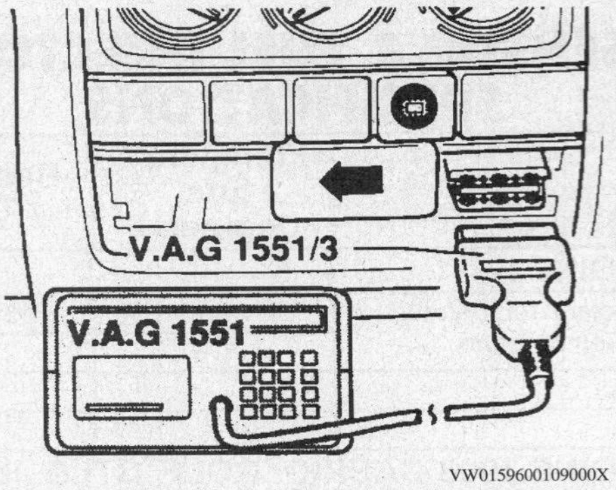

Fig. 1 Scan tool connection. 1998 Cabrio, Golf, GTI & Jetta

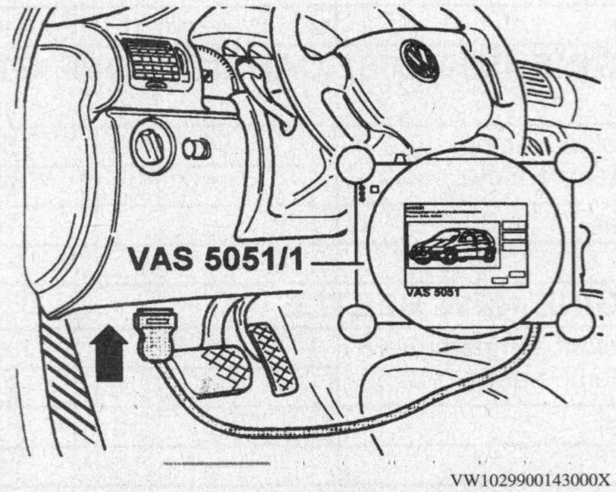

Fig. 2 Scan tool connection. 1999–2001 Cabrio, Golf, GTI & Jetta

Diagnostic Tests

1998 CABRIO, GOLF, GTI & JETTA w/2.0L ENGINE

This procedure has been revised by a Technical Service Bulletin.

Refer to **Figs. 131 through 203** for diagnostic tests.

1998 GOLF, GTI & JETTA w/2.8L ENGINE

Refer to **Figs. 204 through 288** for diagnostic tests.

NEW BEETLE & 1998-2001 CABRIO, GOLF, GTI, JETTA & PASSAT

Refer to "Component Testing."

Clearing Diagnostic Trouble Codes

Follow scan tool manufacturer's instruction to clear stored DTCs.

Component Testing

HEATED OXYGEN SENSOR (HO2S) CONTROL

1998 CABRIO, GOLF, GTI & JETTA

Before Three-Way Catalytic Converter

1. Disconnect HO2S 4-pin connector before three-way catalytic converter.
2. Measure voltage between connector terminals Nos. 3 and 4 with ignition On.
3. If measurement is .4–.5 volts, replace HO2S.
4. If measurement is not .4–.5 volts, connect test box tool No. 1598/18, or equivalent, to ECM wiring harness and measure resistance as follows:
   a. Between connector terminal No. 3 and test box socket No. 42.
   b. Between terminal No. 4 and socket 20.
   c. If resistance is not less than 1.5 ohms, inspect wiring for open circuit.
   d. Between terminal No. 4 and socket 42.
   e. If resistance is not infinite, inspect wiring for short circuits.
   f. Between connector terminal No. 4 and test box socket No. 56.
   g. Between terminal No. 3 and socket 56.
   h. If resistance is not infinite, inspect wiring shielding for short circuit.
5. If no wiring malfunction is found, replace ECM.

After Three-Way Catalytic Converter

1. Disconnect HO2S 4-pin connector after three-way catalytic converter.
2. Measure voltage between connector terminals Nos. 3 and 4 with ignition On.
3. Turn ignition Off.
4. If measurement is .4–.5 volts, replace HO2S.
5. If measurement is not .4–.5 volts, connect test box tool No. 1598/18, or equivalent, to ECM wiring harness and measure resistance as follows:
   a. Between connector terminal No. 3 and test box socket No. 58.
   b. Between terminal No. 4 and socket 13.
   c. If resistance is not less than 1.5 ohms, inspect wiring for open circuit.
   d. Measure resistance between connector terminal No. 4 and test box socket No. 58.
   e. If resistance is not infinite, inspect wiring for short circuits.
   f. Between connector terminal No. 4 and test box socket No. 56.
   g. Between terminal No. 3 and socket 56.

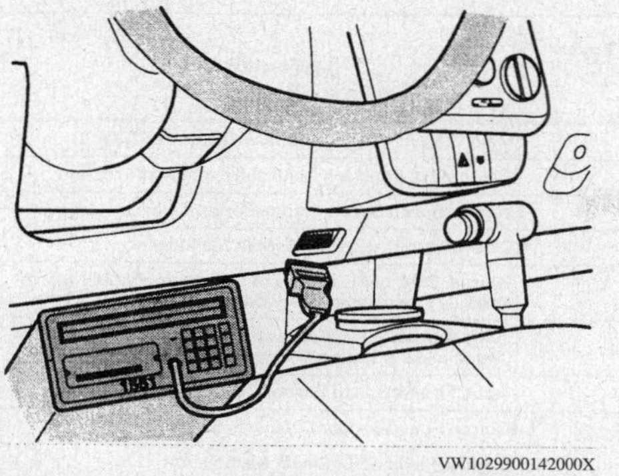

Fig. 3 Scan tool connection. New Beetle

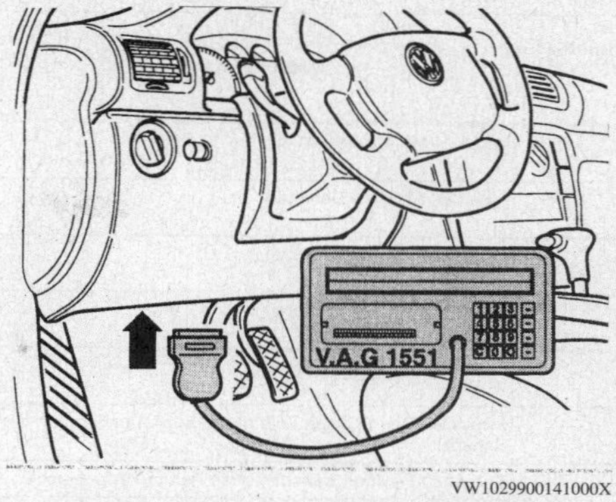

Fig. 4 Scan tool connection. Passat

Diagnostic Trouble Code (DTC) SAE		Malfunction text	MIL switch-on conditions
P0102		Mass or Volume Air Flow Circuit Low Input	2 trips
P0103		Mass or Volume Air Flow Circuit High Input	2 trips
P0112		Intake Air Temperature Circuit Low Input	5 secs
P0113		Intake Air Temperature Circuit High input	5 secs.
P0117		Engine Coolant Temperature Circuit Low Input	5 secs.
P0118		Engine Coolant Temperature Circuit High Input	5 secs.
P0120		Throttle Position Sensor A Circuit Malfunction	5 secs.
P0121		Throttle Position Sensor A Circuit Range/Performance Problem	5 secs.
P0122		Throttle Position Sensor A Circuit Low Input	5 secs.
P0125		Insufficient Coolant Temperature for Closed Loop Fuel Control	2 trips

VW1029900135010X

Fig. 5 Motronic DTC interpretation chart (Part 1 of 6). 1998 Cabrio, Golf, GTI & Jetta w/2.0L engine

Diagnostic Trouble Code (DTC) SAE		Malfunction text	MIL switch-on conditions
P0131		O_2 Sensor Circuit Low Voltage (Bank 1 Sensor 1)	2 trips
P0132		O_2 Sensor Circuit High Voltage (Bank 1 Sensor 1)	2 trips
P0133		O_2 Sensor Circuit Slow Response (Bank 1 Sensor 1)	2 trips
P0134		O_2 Sensor Circuit No Activity Detected (Bank 1 Sensor 1)	2 trips
P0135		O_2 Sensor Heater Circuit Malfunction (Bank 1 Sensor 1)	2 trips
P0137		O_2 Sensor Circuit Low Voltage (Bank 1 Sensor 2)	2 trips
P0138		O_2 Sensor Circuit High Voltage (Bank 1 Sensor 2)	2 trips
P0140		O_2 Sensor Circuit No Activity Detected (Bank 1 Sensor 2)	2 trips
P0141		O_2 Sensor Heater Circuit Malfunction (Bank 1 Sensor 2)	2 trips
P0171		System too Lean (Bank 1)	2 trips
P0172		System too Rich (Bank 1)	2 trips

VW1029900135020X

Fig. 5 Motronic DTC interpretation chart (Part 2 of 6). 1998 Cabrio, Golf, GTI & Jetta w/2.0L engine

h. If resistance is not infinite, inspect wiring shielding for short circuit.

6. If no wiring malfunction is found, replace ECM.

NEW BEETLE & 1999–2001 CABRIO, GOLF, GTI & JETTA W/2.0L ENGINE

Before Three-Way Catalytic Converter

1. Disconnect HO2S 4-pin connector before three-way catalytic converter.
2. Inspect for continuity between harness connector terminals Nos. 1 and 2. If resistance at room temperature is not 1–5 ohms, replace HO2S. If there is continuity, proceed to next step.
3. Measure voltage between connector terminals Nos. 1 and 2 with engine idling. There should be 11–14.5 volts.
4. Turn ignition Off.
5. If voltage was not present, connect test box tool No. 1598/31, or equivalent, to ECM wiring harness and measure resistance as follows:
   a. Between connector terminal No. 2 and test box socket No. 27.
   b. Between terminal No. 1 and fuel pump relay.
   c. If resistance is not less than 1.5 ohms, inspect wiring for open circuit.

After Three-Way Catalytic Converter

1. Disconnect HO2S 4-pin connector after three-way catalytic converter.
2. Inspect for continuity between harness connector terminals Nos. 1 and 2. If resistance at room temperature is not 1–5 ohms, replace HO2S. If there is continuity, proceed to next step.
3. Measure voltage between connector terminals Nos. 1 and 2 with engine idling. There should be 11–14.5 volts.
4. Turn ignition Off.
5. If voltage was not present, connect test box tool No. 1598/31, or equivalent, to ECM wiring harness and measure resistance as follows:
   a. Between connector terminal No. 2 and test box socket No. 28.
   b. If resistance is not less than 1.5 ohms, inspect wiring for open circuit.
   c. Between terminal No. 1 and fuel pump relay.
   d. If resistance is not less than 1.5 ohms, inspect wiring for open circuit.

1999–2001 GTI & JETTA w/2.8L ENGINE

Before Three-Way Catalytic Converter

1. Disconnect HO2S 6-pin connector before three-way catalytic converter.
2. Measure voltage between connector terminals Nos. 3 and 4 with engine idling. There should be 11–14.5 volts.
3. Turn ignition Off.
4. If voltage was not present, connect test box tool No. 1598/31, or equivalent, to ECM wiring harness.
5. Measure resistance between connector terminal No. 4 and test box socket No. 5.
6. If resistance is not less than 1.5 ohms, inspect wiring for open circuit.
7. Measure resistance between terminal No. 3 and fuel pump relay.
8. If resistance is not less than 1.5 ohms, inspect wiring for open circuit.

After Three-Way Catalytic Converter

1. Disconnect HO2S 4-pin connector after three-way catalytic converter.
2. Measure voltage between connector terminals Nos. 1 and 2 with engine idling. There should be 11–14.5 volts.
3. Turn ignition Off.
4. If voltage was not present, connect test box tool No. 1598/31, or equivalent, to ECM wiring harness.
5. Measure resistance between connector terminal No. 2 and test box socket No. 63.
6. If resistance is not less than 1.5 ohms, inspect wiring for open circuit.

Diagnostic Trouble Code (DTC) SAE		Malfunction text	MIL switch-on conditions
P0300		Random Misfire Detected	2 trips / flashes [1]
P0301		Cylinder 1 Misfire Detected	2 trips / flashes [1]
P0302		Cylinder 2 Misfire Detected	2 trips / flashes [1]
P0303		Cylinder 3 Misfire Detected	2 trips / flashes [1]
P0304		Cylinder 4 Misfire Detected	2 trips / flashes [1]
P0327		Knock Sensor 1 Circuit Low Input (Bank 1 or Single Sensor)	5 secs.
P0341		Camshaft Position Sensor Circuit Range/Performance	5 secs.

[1] MIL may come on immediately or after 2 trips, may flash or be continuously illuminated depending on the type of misfire.

VW1029900135030X

Fig. 5 Motronic DTC interpretation chart (Part 3 of 6). 1998 Cabrio, Golf, GTI & Jetta w/2.0L engine

Diagnostic Trouble Code (DTC) SAE		Malfunction text	MIL switch-on conditions
P1127		Long Term Fuel Trim mul.(B1) System too Rich	2 trips
P1128		Long Term Fuel Trim mul.(B1) System too Lean	2 trips
P1213		Cyl.1 Fuel Injector Circ. Short to B+	5 secs.
P1214		Cyl.2 Fuel Injector Circ. Short to B+	5 secs.
P1215		Cyl.3 Fuel Injector Circ. Short to B+	5 secs.
P1216		Cyl.4 Fuel Injector Circ. Short to B+	5 secs.
P1225		Injector Circ.Cyl.1 Short to Ground	5 secs.
P1226		Injector Circ.Cyl.2 Short to Ground	5 secs.
P1227		Injector Circ.Cyl.3 Short to Ground	5 secs.
P1228		Injector Circ.Cyl.4 Short to Ground	5 secs.
P1237		Injector Circ.Cyl.1 Open Circuit	5 secs.
P1238		Injector Circ.Cyl.2 Open Circuit	5 secs.
P1239		Injector Circ.Cyl.3 Open Circuit	5 secs.
P1240		Injector Circ.Cyl.4 Open Circuit	5 secs.

VW1029900135050X

Fig. 5 Motronic DTC interpretation chart (Part 5 of 6). 1998 Cabrio, Golf, GTI & Jetta w/2.0L engine

Diagnostic Trouble Code (DTC) SAE		Malfunction text	MIL switch-on conditions
P0422		Main Catalyst Efficiency Below Threshold (Bank 1)	2 trips
P0440		Evaporative Emission Control System Malfunction	2 trips
P0501		Vehicle Speed Sensor Range/Performance	2 trips
P0510		Closed Throttle Position Switch Malfunction	2 trips
P0605		Internal Control Module Read Only Memory (ROM) Error (Module Identification Defined by SAE J1979)	2 trips
P0605		Internal Control Module Read Only Memory (ROM) Error (Module Identification Defined by SAE J1979)	2 trips
P0715		Input/Turbine Speed Sensor Circuit Malfunction	2 trips
P0722		Output Speed Sensor Circuit No Signal	2 trips
P0725		Engine Speed Input Circuit Malfunction	2 trips
P0748		Pressure Control Solenoid Electrical	2 trips
P0753		Shift Solenoid A Electrical	2 trips
P0758		Shift Solenoid B Electrical	2 trips
P0763		Shift Solenoid C Electrical	2 trips
P0768		Shift Solenoid D Electrical	2 trips
P0773		Shift Solenoid E Electrical	2 trips

VW1029900135040X

Fig. 5 Motronic DTC interpretation chart (Part 4 of 6). 1998 Cabrio, Golf, GTI & Jetta w/2.0L engine

Diagnostic Trouble Code (DTC) SAE		Malfunction text	MIL switch-on conditions
P1340		Camshaft/Crankshaft Pos.Sens.Signals Out of Sequence	5 secs.
P1410		Tank Ventilation Valve Short to B+	5 secs.
P1425		Tank Vent. Valve Short to Ground	5 secs.
P1426		Tank Vent. Valve Open	5 secs.
P1500		Fuel Pump Relay Circ. Electrical Malfunction	5 secs.
P1502		Fuel Pump Relay Circ. Short to B+	5 secs.
P1543		Throttle Actuation Potentiometer Signal too Low	5 secs.
P1544		Throttle Actuation Potentiometer Signal too High	5 secs.
P1580		Throttle Actuator (B1) Malfunction	5 secs.
P1582		Idle Adaptation at Limit	5 secs.
P1611		MIL Call-up Circ./Transm.Control Module Short to Ground	5 secs.
P1613		MIL Call-up Circ.Open Short to B+	5 secs.
P1778		Solenoid EV7 Electrical Malfunction	2 trips
P1780		Engine Intervention Readable	2 trips

VW1029900135060X

Fig. 5 Motronic DTC interpretation chart (Part 6 of 6). 1998 Cabrio, Golf, GTI & Jetta w/2.0L engine

7. Measure resistance between terminal No. 4 and fuel pump relay.
8. If resistance is not less than 1.5 ohms, inspect wiring for open circuit.

PASSAT w/1.8L ENGINE

Before Three-Way Catalytic Converter

1. Disconnect HO2S 4-pin connector.
2. Measure voltage between connector terminals Nos. 3 and 4 with ignition On. There should be .4–.5 volts.
3. Turn ignition Off.
4. If voltage is not as specified, inspect wiring for sensor.
5. If voltage is as specified, replace HO2S.
6. Connect test box tool No. 1598/31, or equivalent, to ECM wiring harness.
7. Measure resistance as follows:
   a. Between connector terminal No. 3 and test box socket No. 25.
   b. Between terminal No. 4 and socket No. 26.
   c. If resistance is not less than 1.5 ohms, inspect wiring for open circuit.
   d. Inspect wiring connector terminals Nos. 3 and 4 for short circuit to terminals Nos. 1 and 2. Resistance should be infinite.
8. If no wiring malfunction is found, replace ECM.

After Three-Way Catalytic Converter

1. Disconnect HO2S 4-pin connector.
2. Measure voltage between connector terminals Nos. 3 and 4 with ignition On. There should be .4–.5 volts.
3. Turn ignition Off.
4. If voltage is not as specified, inspect wiring for sensor.
5. If voltage is as specified, replace HO2S.
6. Connect test box tool No. 1598/31, or equivalent, to ECM wiring harness.
7. Measure resistance as follows:
   a. Between connector terminal No. 3 and test box socket No. 51.
   b. Between terminal No. 4 and socket No. 52.
   c. If resistance is not less than 1.5 ohms, inspect wiring for open circuit.
   d. Inspect wiring connector terminals Nos. 3 and 4 for short circuit to terminals Nos. 1 and 2. Resistance should be infinite.
8. If no wiring malfunction is found, replace ECM.

PASSAT w/2.8L ENGINE

Before Three-Way Catalytic Converter

1. Disconnect HO2S 4-pin connector.
2. Measure voltage between connector terminals Nos. 3 and 4 with ignition On.

Diagnostic Trouble Codes (DTCs) SAE		Diagnostic Trouble Code (DTC) display	Corrective action
—		Throttle Pos.Actuator–V60	– Check cruise control system (CCS)
			– Check Mass Air Flow (MAF) sensor
—		Knock Sensor 1–G61	– Check knock sensor and knock control
—		Knock Sensor 2–G66	– Check knock sensor and knock control
—		RPM upper Limit exceeded	– Check engine for mechanical damage and erase DTC memory
			– Check engine speed (RPM) sensor

VW1029900138010X

Fig. 6 Motronic DTC interpretation chart (Part 1 of 24). 1999–2001 Golf & Jetta w/2.0L engine

Diagnostic Trouble Codes (DTCs) SAE		Diagnostic Trouble Code (DTC) display	Corrective action
—		Battery Positive Voltage (B+) Term. 30 Signal too high	– Check generator.
		Signal too low	– Check battery.
		Open circuit	– Check harness connectors and wiring using wiring diagram.
		Incorrect signal	– Check voltage supply of ECM -J220- ◆ Open circuit to voltage supply, correcting
—		Cruise Control Switch–E45 Incorrect signal	– Check cruise control system (CCS)
—		Brake Pedal Position Monitoring	– Check signal of brake light switch and brake pedal switch

VW1029900138030X

Fig. 6 Motronic DTC interpretation chart (Part 3 of 24). 1999–2001 Golf & Jetta w/2.0L engine

Diagnostic Trouble Codes (DTCs) SAE		Diagnostic Trouble Code (DTC) display	Corrective action
—		Knock Sensor Control Cyl.1 Limit exceeded	– Check knock sensor and knock control
—		Knock Sensor Control Cyl.2 Limit exceeded	– Eliminate unusual engine noises (accessories loose, brackets/bolts broken).
—		Knock Sensor Control Cyl.3 Limit exceeded	– Check harness connectors and wiring using wiring diagram.
—		Knock Sensor Control Cyl.4 Limit exceeded	– Loosen knock sensor and retighten to 20 Nm (15 ft lb). – Change type of fuel.

VW1029900138020X

Fig. 6 Motronic DTC interpretation chart (Part 2 of 24). 1999–2001 Golf & Jetta w/2.0L engine

Diagnostic Trouble Codes (DTCs) SAE		Diagnostic Trouble Code (DTC) display	Corrective action
—		Throttle Body Control Module–J338	– Adapt Motronic Engine Control Module (ECM) -J220- to throttle valve control module -J338-
			– Check throttle valve control module -J338-
—		Engine Control Module	– Replace Motronic Engine Control Module (ECM) -J220-
— [1]		Engine Control Module	– Replace Motronic Engine Control Module (ECM) -J220-

[1] Components or functions for cruise control system in Motronic Engine Control Module (ECM) -J220- malfunctioning.

VW1029900138040X

Fig. 6 Motronic DTC interpretation chart (Part 4 of 24). 1999–2001 Golf & Jetta w/2.0L engine

There should be .4–.5 volts.
3. Turn ignition Off.
4. If voltage is not as specified, inspect wiring for sensor.
5. If voltage is as specified, replace HO2S.
6. Connect test box tool No. 1598/31, or equivalent, to ECM wiring harness.
7. Measure resistance as follows:
   a. For Bank 1 Sensor 1, between connector terminal No. 3 and test box socket No. 25.
   b. Between terminal No. 4 and socket No. 26.
   c. For Bank 2 Sensor 1, between connector terminal No. 3 and test box socket No. 39.
   d. Between terminal No. 4 and socket No. 40.
   e. If resistance is not less than 1.5 ohms, inspect wiring for open circuit.
   f. Measure resistance for Bank 1 Sensor 1, between terminal No. 4 and socket No. 25.
   g. Measure resistance for Bank 2 Sensor 1, between terminal No. 4 and socket No. 39.
   h. If resistance is not infinite, inspect for short circuits.
   i. Measure resistance between terminal No. 4 and socket No. 14.
   j. Measure resistance between terminal No. 3 and socket No. 14.
   k. If resistance is not infinite, inspect for short circuits to wiring harness shielding.
8. If no wiring malfunction is found, replace ECM.

After Three-Way Catalytic Converter

1. Disconnect HO2S 4-pin connector.
2. Measure voltage between connector terminals Nos. 3 and 4 with ignition On. There should be .4–.5 volts.
3. Turn ignition Off.
4. If voltage is not as specified, inspect wiring for sensor.
5. If voltage is as specified, replace HO2S.
6. Connect test box tool No. 1598/31, or equivalent, to ECM wiring harness.
7. Measure resistance as follows:
   a. For Bank 1 Sensor 2, between connector terminal No. 3 and test box socket No. 51.
   b. Between terminal No. 4 and socket No. 52.
   c. For Bank 2 Sensor 2, between connector terminal No. 3 and test box socket No. 38.
   d. Between terminal No. 4 and socket No. 50.
   e. If resistance is not less than 1.5 ohms, inspect wiring for open circuit.
   f. Measure resistance for Bank 1 Sensor 1, between terminal No. 4 and socket No. 51.
   g. Measure resistance for Bank 2 Sensor 1, between terminal No. 4 and socket No. 38.
   h. If resistance is not infinite, inspect for short circuits.
   i. Measure resistance between terminal No. 4 and socket No. 14.
   j. Measure resistance between terminal No. 3 and socket No. 14.
   k. If resistance is not infinite, inspect for short circuits to wiring harness shielding.
8. If no wiring malfunction is found, replace ECM.

OXYGEN SENSOR (O2S) HEATING

1998 CABRIO, GOLF, GTI & JETTA

1. Disconnect HO2S 4-pin connector.
2. Measure resistance between connector terminals Nos. 1 and 2.
3. If resistance is not 0–24.2 ohms, replace HO2S.
4. If measurement is 0–24.2 ohms, measure voltage between connector terminals Nos. 1 and 2. There should be 11–14.5 volts.
5. If voltage is not present, measure voltage between connector terminal No. 1 and ground. There should be 11–14.5 volts.
6. If voltage is present, inspect wiring between terminal No. 1 and relay panel.
7. If voltage is within specifications, measure voltage between connector terminal No. 2 and battery positive terminal. There should be 11–14.5 volts.
8. If voltage is not present, connect test box tool No. 1598/18, or equivalent, to

Diagnostic Trouble Codes (DTCs) SAE		Diagnostic Trouble Code (DTC) display	Corrective action
P0102		Mass or Volume Air Flow Circ Low Input	– Check Mass Air Flow (MAF) sensor
P0103		Mass or Volume Air Flow Circ High Input	– Check intake air system for leaks (unmetered air) – Check fuse 43.
P0112		Intake Air Temp.Circ Low Input	– Check Intake Air Temperature (IAT) sensor
P0113		Intake Air Temp.Circ. High Input	
P0116		Engine Coolant Temp.Circ Range/Performance	– Check Engine Coolant Temperature (ECT) sensor – Check thermostat.
P0117		Engine Coolant Temp.Circ Low Input	
P0118		Engine Coolant Temp.Circ. High Input	

VW1029900138050X

Fig. 6 Motronic DTC interpretation chart (Part 5 of 24). 1999–2001 Golf & Jetta w/2.0L engine

Diagnostic Trouble Codes (DTCs) SAE		Diagnostic Trouble Code (DTC) display	Corrective action
P0120		Throttle/Pedal Pos.Sensor A Circ Malfunction	– Check throttle valve control module
P0121		Throttle/Pedal Pos.Sensor A Circ Range/Performance	
P0122		Throttle/Pedal Pos.Sensor A Circ. Low Input	
P0125		Insufficient Coolant Temp.for Closed Loop Fuel Control	– Check coolant temperature sensor – Check thermostat.
P0131		02 Sensor Circ., Bank1–Sensor1 Low Voltage	– Check oxygen sensor and control before Three Way Catalytic Converter (TWC) – Check oxygen sensor 1 aging
P0132		02 Sensor Circ., Bank1–Sensor1 High Voltage	
P0133		02 Sensor Circ., Bank1–Sensor1 Slow Response	– Check oxygen sensor and control after Three Way Catalytic Converter (TWC)
P0134		02 Sensor Circ., Bank1–Sensor1 No Activity Detected	– Check oxygen sensor and control before Three Way Catalytic Converter (TWC)

VW1029900138060X

Fig. 6 Motronic DTC interpretation chart (Part 6 of 24). 1999–2001 Golf & Jetta w/2.0L engine

Diagnostic Trouble Codes (DTCs) SAE		Diagnostic Trouble Code (DTC) display	Corrective action
P0135		02 Sensor Heater Circ., Bank1–Sensor1 Malfunction	– Check oxygen sensor heating before Three Way Catalytic Converter (TWC)
P0137		02 Sensor Circ., Bank1–Sensor2 Low Voltage	– Check oxygen sensor and control after Three Way Catalytic Converter (TWC)
P0138		02 Sensor Circ., Bank1–Sensor2 High Voltage	– Check oxygen sensor heating after Three Way Catalytic Converter (TWC)
P0140		02 Sensor Circ., Bank1–Sensor2 No Activity Detected	
P0141		02 Sensor Heater Circ., Bank1–Sensor2 Malfunction	– Check oxygen sensor heating after Three Way Catalytic Converter (TWC)

VW1029900138070X

Fig. 6 Motronic DTC interpretation chart (Part 7 of 24). 1999–2001 Golf & Jetta w/2.0L engine

Diagnostic Trouble Codes (DTCs) SAE		Diagnostic Trouble Code (DTC) display	Corrective action
P0171		Fuel Trim, Bank1 System too Lean	– Check fuel pressure regulator and holding pressure – Check quantity of fuel injected and check for leaks – Check fuel pump. – Check intake system for leaks – Check exhaust system for leaks. – Check Secondary Air Injection (AIR) system for leaks. – Check vacuum lines for leaks.

VW1029900138080X

Fig. 6 Motronic DTC interpretation chart (Part 8 of 24). 1999–2001 Golf & Jetta w/2.0L engine

ECM wiring harness.

9. Measure resistance between connector terminal No. 2 and test box socket No. 12.
10. If resistance is not less than 1.5 ohms, inspect wiring for open circuit.
11. If no wiring malfunction is found, replace ECM.

NEW BEETLE & 1999–2001 CABRIO, GOLF, GTI & JETTA w/2.0L ENGINE

1. Disconnect HO2S 4-pin connector.
2. Measure voltage between connector terminals Nos. 3 and 4 with ignition On. There should be .4–.5 volts.
3. Turn ignition Off.
4. If voltage is not as specified, connect test box tool No. 1598/31, or equivalent, to ECM wiring harness.
5. Measure resistance as follows:
   a. Between connector terminal No. 3 and test box socket No. 25.
   b. Between terminal No. 4 and socket No. 28.
   c. If resistance is not less than 1.5 ohms, inspect wiring for open circuit.
   d. Inspect terminals Nos. 3 and 4, then 1 and 2 for short circuits. Resistance should be infinite.
6. If no wiring malfunction is found, replace ECM.

1999–2001 GTI & JETTA w/2.8L ENGINE

1. Disconnect HO2S 6-pin connector.
2. Measure voltage between connector terminals Nos. 3 and 4 with ignition On. There should be .4–.5 volts.
3. Turn ignition Off.
4. If voltage is not as specified, connect test box tool No. 1598/31, or equivalent, to ECM wiring harness.
5. Measure resistance as follows:
   a. Between connector terminal No. 1 and test box socket No. 70.
   b. Between terminal No. 2 and socket No. 71.
   c. Between terminal No. 3 and socket No. 68.
   d. Between terminal No. 4 and socket No. 69.
   e. Between terminal No. 5 and socket No. 51.
   f. Between terminal No. 6 and socket No. 52.
   g. If resistance is not less than 1.5 ohms, inspect wiring for open circuit.
   h. Between connector terminal Nos. 3 and 4.
   i. Between terminal Nos. 1 and 2.
   j. If resistance is not infinite, inspect wiring for short circuit.
   k. Inspect all wires for short to one another. Resistance should be infinite.
6. If no wiring malfunction is found, replace HO2S.

PASSAT

1.8L Engine

1. Disconnect HO2S 4-pin connector.
2. Measure resistance between connector terminals Nos. 1 and 2.
3. If resistance is not 0–19.9 ohms, replace HO2S.
4. If measurement is 0–19.9 ohms, measure voltage between connector terminals Nos. 1 and 2 with engine idling. There should be 11–14.5 volts.
5. If voltage is not present, connect test box tool No. 1598/31, or equivalent, to ECM wiring harness.
6. Measure resistance between connector terminal No. 2 and test box socket No. 27.
7. If resistance is not less than 1.5 ohms, inspect wiring for open circuit.
8. If resistance is less than 1.5 ohms, inspect wiring between terminal No. 1 and fuel pump relay.
9. If no wiring malfunction is found, replace ECM.

2.8L Engine

1. Disconnect HO2S 4-pin connector.
2. Measure resistance between connector terminals Nos. 3 and 4.
3. If resistance is not 0–19.9 ohms, replace HO2S.

Diagnostic Trouble Codes (DTCs) SAE		Diagnostic Trouble Code (DTC) display	Corrective action
P0172		Fuel Trim, Bank1 System too rich	– Check fuel pressure regulator and holding pressure – Check quantity of fuel injected and check for leaks – Check Evaporative Emission (EVAP) canister purge regulator valve -N80-.
P0300		Random/Multiple Cylinder Misfire Detected	– Check fuel fuel injectors
P0301		Cyl.1 Misfire Detected	– Check ignition cables and spark plugs – Check ignition coils together with output stage – Check misfire detection
P0302		Cyl.2 Misfire Detected	
P0303		Cyl.3 Misfire Detected	
P0304		Cyl.4 Misfire Detected	

VW1029900138090X

Fig. 6 Motronic DTC interpretation chart (Part 9 of 24). 1999–2001 Golf & Jetta w/2.0L engine

Diagnostic Trouble Codes (DTCs) SAE		Diagnostic Trouble Code (DTC) display	Corrective action
P0321		Ign./Distributor Eng. Speed Inp.Circ Range/Performance	– Check engine speed (RPM) sensor
P0322		Ign./Distributor Eng.Speed Inp.Circ. No Signal	
P0327		Knock Sensor 1 Circ Low Input	– Check knock sensor and knock control – Loosen knock sensor and retighten to 20 Nm (15 ft lb).
P0328		Knock Sensor 1 Circ High Input	
P0332		Knock Sensor 2 Circ Low Input	
P0333		Knock Sensor 2 Circ. High Input	
P0341		Camshaft Pos.Sensor Circ Range/Performance	– Check camshaft position sensor

VW1029900138100X

Fig. 6 Motronic DTC interpretation chart (Part 10 of 24). 1999–2001 Golf & Jetta w/2.0L engine

Diagnostic Trouble Codes (DTCs) SAE		Diagnostic Trouble Code (DTC) display	Corrective action
P0411		Sec.Air Inj.Sys. Incorrect Flow Detected	– Check secondary air pump motor. – Check secondary air injection valve. – Check secondary air inlet valve. – Check hoses and lines to/between components:
P0422		Main Catalyst, Bank1 Efficiency Below Threshold	– Check Three Way Catalytic Converter (TWC).

VW1029900138110X

Fig. 6 Motronic DTC interpretation chart (Part 11 of 24). 1999–2001 Golf & Jetta w/2.0L engine

Diagnostic Trouble Codes (DTCs) SAE		Diagnostic Trouble Code (DTC) display	Corrective action
P0440		EVAP Emission Contr.Sys Malfunction	– Check Evaporative Emission (EVAP) canister purge regulator valve -N80- – Check Evaporative Emission (EVAP) canister purge regulator valve -N80-. – Check hoses and lines from fuel tank to throttle valve control module.
P0442		EVAP Emission Contr.Sys. (Small Leak) Leak Detected	– Check Evaporative Emission (EVAP) system.
P0455		EVAP Emission Contr.Sys. (Gross Leak) Leak Detected	
P0501		Vehicle Speed Sensor Range/Performance	– Check speed signal

VW1029900138120X

Fig. 6 Motronic DTC interpretation chart (Part 12 of 24). 1999–2001 Golf & Jetta w/2.0L engine

4. If measurement is 0–19.9 ohms, measure voltage between connector terminals Nos. 1 and 2 with engine idling. There should be 11–14.5 volts.
5. If voltage is not present, connect test box tool No. 1598/31, or equivalent, to ECM wiring harness.
6. Measure resistance between connector terminal No. 2 and test box socket No. 27.
7. If resistance is not less than 1.5 ohms, inspect wiring for open circuit.
8. If resistance is less than 1.5 ohms, inspect wiring between terminal No. 1 and fuel pump relay.
9. If no wiring malfunction is found, replace ECM.

MASS AIR FLOW (MAF) SENSOR

1998 CABRIO, GOLF, GTI & JETTA

1. Disconnect MAF sensor 4-pin connector.
2. Measure voltage between connector terminals Nos. 1 and 3 with ignition On, which should be 9–14.5 volts.
3. Turn ignition Off.
4. If measurement is not within specifications, connect test box tool No. 1598/18, or equivalent, to ECM wiring harness and measure resistance as follows:
   a. Between connector terminal No. 2 and test box socket No. 16.
   b. Between terminal No. 4 and socket 17.
   c. If resistance is not less than 1.5 ohms, inspect wiring for open circuit.
   d. Between terminal No. 4 and socket No. 16.
   e. If resistance is not infinite, inspect wiring for short circuits.
5. Measure voltage between connector terminal Nos. 2 then 4 and ground. If measurement is not zero volts, inspect wiring for short circuit to battery voltage.
6. If no wiring malfunction is found, replace MAF sensor.

NEW BEETLE & 1999–2001 CABRIO, GOLF, GTI & JETTA w/2.0L ENGINE

1. Disconnect MAF sensor 5-pin connector.
2. Measure voltage between connector terminals No. 2 and ground with engine idling, which should be 11–14.5 volts.
3. Turn ignition Off.
4. If voltage is not present, measure voltage between harness connector terminal No. 4 and ground with ignition On. There should be at least 4.5 volts.
5. If voltage is present, connect test box tool No. 1598/31, or equivalent, to ECM wiring harness and measure resistance as follows:
   a. Between connector terminal No. 5 and test box socket No. 13.
   b. Between terminal No. 4 and socket 11.
   c. Between terminal No. 3 and socket 12.
   d. If resistance is not less than 1.5 ohms, inspect wiring for open circuit.
   e. Inspect all wires for short to one another.
   f. Inspect wiring for short circuit to battery voltage.
6. If no wiring malfunction is found, replace MAF sensor.

1999–2001 GTI & JETTA w/2.8L ENGINE

1. Disconnect MAF sensor 5-pin connector.
2. Measure voltage between connector terminals No. 2 and ground with engine idling. There should be 11–15 volts.
3. Turn ignition Off.
4. If voltage is not present, measure resistance between harness connector

Diagnostic Trouble Codes (DTCs) SAE		Diagnostic Trouble Code (DTC) display	Corrective action
P0506		Idle Control System RPM Lower than Expected	- Check throttle valve control module
P0507		Idle Control System RPM Higher than Expected	
P0510		Closed Throttle Pos.Switch Malfunction	
P0605		Internal Contr.Module ROM Test Error	- Replace Motronic Engine Control Module (ECM) -J220-

VW1029900138130X

Fig. 6 Motronic DTC interpretation chart (Part 13 of 24). 1999–2001 Golf & Jetta w/2.0L engine

Diagnostic Trouble Codes (DTCs) SAE		Diagnostic Trouble Code (DTC) display	Corrective action
P1127		Long Term Fuel Trim mult.,Bank1 System too Rich	- Check fuel pressure regulator and holding pressure - Check quantity of fuel injected and check for leaks - Check Evaporative Emission (EVAP) canister purge regulator valve -N80-.

VW1029900138140X

Fig. 6 Motronic DTC interpretation chart (Part 14 of 24). 1999–2001 Golf & Jetta w/2.0L engine

Diagnostic Trouble Codes (DTCs) SAE		Diagnostic Trouble Code (DTC) display	Corrective action
P1128		Long Term Fuel Trim mult., Bank1 System too Lean	- Check fuel pressure regulator and holding pressure - Check fuel fuel injectors - Check fuel pump. - Check intake system for leaks - Check exhaust system for leaks. - Check Secondary Air Injection (AIR) system for leaks. - Check vacuum lines for leaks.
P1176		02 Correction Behind Catalyst,B1 Limit Attained	- Check oxygen sensor 1 aging - Check oxygen sensor and control after Three Way Catalytic Converter (TWC) - Check intake system for leaks

VW1029900138150X

Fig. 6 Motronic DTC interpretation chart (Part 15 of 24). 1999–2001 Golf & Jetta w/2.0L engine

Diagnostic Trouble Codes (DTCs) SAE		Diagnostic Trouble Code (DTC) display	Corrective action
P1213		Cyl.1–Fuel Inj.Circ Short to B+	- Check fuel fuel injectors
P1214		Cyl.2–Fuel Inj.Circ. Short to B+	
P1215		Cyl.3–Fuel Inj.Circ. Short to B+	
P1216		Cyl.4–Fuel Inj.Circ. Short to B+	
P1225		Cyl.1–Fuel Inj.Circ. Short to Ground	
P1226		Cyl.2–Fuel Inj.Circ. Short to Ground	
P1227		Cyl.3–Fuel Inj.Circ. Short to Ground	
P1228		Cyl.4–Fuel Inj.Circ. Short to Ground	

VW1029900138160X

Fig. 6 Motronic DTC interpretation chart (Part 16 of 24). 1999–2001 Golf & Jetta w/2.0L engine

terminal No. 2 and fuel pump relay. If resistance is not less than 1.5 ohms, inspect wiring for open circuit.

5. If voltage is present, measure voltage between connector terminal No. 4 and ground. There should be at least 4.5 volts.
6. If voltage is not present, connect test box tool No. 1598/31, or equivalent, to ECM wiring harness and measure resistance as follows:
   a. Between connector terminal No. 5 and test box socket No. 29.
   b. Between terminal No. 4 and socket 53.
   c. Between terminal No. 3 and socket 27.
   d. If resistance is not less than 1.5 ohms, inspect wiring for open circuit.
   e. Inspect all wires for short to one another. Resistance should be infinite.
   f. Inspect wiring for short circuit to battery voltage.
7. If no wiring malfunction is found, replace MAF sensor.

PASSAT w/1.8L ENGINE

1. Disconnect MAF sensor 3-pin connector.
2. Measure voltage between connector terminals Nos. 1 and 3 with engine idling. There should be at least 11–15 volts.
3. Turn ignition Off.
4. If voltage is not present, inspect wiring from terminal No. 3 to fuel pump relay.
5. If voltage is present, connect test box tool No. 1598/31, or equivalent, to ECM wiring harness and measure resistance as follows:
   a. Between connector terminal No. 4 and test box socket No. 13.
   b. Between terminal No. 2 and socket 12.
   c. Between connector terminal No 1 and ground.
   d. If resistance is not less than 1.5 ohms, inspect wiring for open circuit.
   e. Inspect all wires for shorting to one another. Resistance should be infinite.
6. If voltage supply and wiring are in good condition, replace MAF sensor.

PASSAT w/2.8L ENGINE

1. Disconnect MAF sensor 3-pin connector.
2. Measure voltage between connector terminals No. 3 and ground with engine idling. There should be at least 11.5 volts.
3. Turn ignition Off.
4. If voltage is not present, inspect wiring from terminal No. 3 to fuse panel.
5. If voltage is present, connect test box tool No. 1598/31, or equivalent, to ECM wiring harness and measure resistance as follows:
   a. Between connector terminal No. 1 and test box socket No. 13.
   b. Between terminal No. 2 and socket 12.
   c. If resistance is not less than 1.5 ohms, inspect wiring for open circuit.
6. If voltage supply and wiring are in good condition, replace MAF sensor.

ENGINE COOLANT TEMPERATURE (ECT) SENSOR

1998 CABRIO, GOLF, GTI & JETTA w/2.0L ENGINE

1. Disconnect ECT sensor 4-pin connector.
2. Connect test box tool No. 1598/18, or equivalent, to ECM wiring harness and measure resistance as follows:
   a. Between connector terminal No. 1 and test box socket No. 33.
   b. Between terminal No. 3 and socket 14.
   c. If resistance is not less than 1.5 ohms, inspect wiring for open circuit.
   d. Between terminal No. 3 and socket No. 33.
   e. If resistance is not infinite, inspect wiring for short circuits.
   f. Inspect both wires for short circuit to battery voltage. Resistance should be infinite.
3. Measure resistance between ECT sensor terminals Nos. 1 and 3, then compare to **Fig. 289.**

Diagnostic Trouble Codes (DTCs) SAE	Diagnostic Trouble Code (DTC) display	Corrective action
P1237	Cyl.1–Fuel Inj.Circ Open Circ	– Check fuel fuel injectors
P1238	Cyl.2–Fuel Inj.Circ. Open Circ.	
P1239	Cyl.3–Fuel Inj.Circ. Open Circ.	
P1240	Cyl.4–Fuel Inj.Circ. Open Circ.	
P1300	Misfire detected Reason: Fuel level too low	Fuel level lower than 2 gallons. – Fill with fuel. – Check fuel gauge sender signal. – Check wiring between Motronic Engine Control Module (ECM) -J220- and instrument cluster using wiring diagram.

VW1029900138170X

Fig. 6 Motronic DTC interpretation chart (Part 17 of 24). 1999–2001 Golf & Jetta w/2.0L engine

Diagnostic Trouble Codes (DTCs) SAE	Diagnostic Trouble Code (DTC) display	Corrective action
P1325	Cyl.1–Knock Contr Limit Attained	– Check knock sensor and knock control
P1326	Cyl.2–Knock Contr Limit Attained	– Rectify abnormal engine running noises (accessories loose, brackets/bolts broken).
P1327	Cyl.3–Knock Contr Limit Attained	– Check harness connectors and wiring using wiring diagrams.
P1328	Cyl.4–Knock Contr Limit Attained	– Loosen knock sensor and retighten to 15 ft lb – Change type of fuel.
P1410	Tank Ventilation Valve Circ Short to B+	– Check Evaporative Emission (EVAP) canister purge regulator valve -N80-

VW1029900138180X

Fig. 6 Motronic DTC interpretation chart (Part 18 of 24). 1999–2001 Golf & Jetta w/2.0L engine

Diagnostic Trouble Codes (DTCs) SAE	Diagnostic Trouble Code (DTC) display	Corrective action
P1420	Sec.Air Inj.Valve Circ Electrical Malfunction	– Check secondary air inlet valve
P1421	Sec.Air Inj.Valve Circ Short to Ground	
P1422	Sec.Air Inj.Sys.Contr. Valve Circ. Short to B+	
P1425	Tank Vent.Valve Short to Ground	– Check Evaporative Emission (EVAP) canister purge regulator valve -N80-
P1426	Tank Vent.Valve Open	
P1450	Sec.Air Inj.Sys.Circ Short to B+	– Check Secondary Air Injection (AIR) pump relay -J299-

VW1029900138190X

Fig. 6 Motronic DTC interpretation chart (Part 19 of 24). 1999–2001 Golf & Jetta w/2.0L engine

Diagnostic Trouble Codes (DTCs) SAE	Diagnostic Trouble Code (DTC) display	Corrective action
P1451	Sec.Air Inj.Sys. Circ Short to Ground	
P1452	Sec.Air Inj.Sys Open Circ	
P1471	EVAP Emission Contr.LDP Circ. Short to B+	– Check diagnostic pump.

VW1029900138200X

Fig. 6 Motronic DTC interpretation chart (Part 20 of 24). 1999–2001 Golf & Jetta w/2.0L engine

4. If resistance is not within specifications, replace ECT sensor.

1998 GTI & JETTA w/2.8L ENGINE

1. Disconnect ECT sensor 2-pin connector.
2. Connect test box tool No. 1598/18, or equivalent, to ECM wiring harness and measure resistance as follows:
   a. Between connector terminal No. 1 and test box socket No. 14.
   b. Between terminal No. 2 and socket 33.
   c. If resistance is not less than 1.5 ohms, inspect wiring for open circuit.
   d. Between terminal No. 2 and socket No. 14.
   e. If resistance is not infinite, inspect wiring for short circuits.
   f. Inspect both wires for short circuit to battery voltage. Resistance should be infinite.
3. Measure resistance between ECT sensor terminals Nos. 1 and 2, then compare to **Fig. 289.**
4. If resistance is not within specifications, replace ECT sensor.

NEW BEETLE & 1999–2001 CABRIO, GOLF, GTI & JETTA w/2.0L ENGINE

1. Disconnect ECT sensor 4-pin connector.
2. Connect test box tool No. 1598/31, or equivalent, to ECM wiring harness and measure resistance as follows:
   a. Between connector terminal No. 1 and test box socket No. 67.
   b. Between terminal No. 3 and socket 53.
   c. If resistance is not less than 1.5 ohms, inspect wiring for open circuit.
   d. Between terminal No. 3 and socket No. 67.
   e. Between terminal No. 3 and ground.
   f. If resistance is not infinite, inspect wiring for short circuits.
   g. Inspect both wires for short circuit to battery voltage. Resistance should be infinite.
3. Measure resistance between ECT sensor terminals No. 1 and 3, then compare to **Fig. 289.**
4. If resistance is not within specifications, replace ECT sensor.

1999–2001 GTI & JETTA w/2.8L ENGINE

1. Disconnect ECT sensor 4-pin connector.
2. Connect test box tool No. 1598/31, or equivalent, to ECM wiring harness and measure resistance as follows:
   a. Between connector terminal No. 1 and test box socket No. 108.
   b. Between terminal No. 3 and socket 93.
   c. If resistance is not less than 1.5 ohms, inspect wiring for open circuit.
   d. Between terminal No. 3 and socket No. 108.
   e. Between terminal No. 3 and ground.
   f. If resistance is not infinite, inspect wiring for short circuits.
   g. Inspect both wires for short circuit to battery voltage. Resistance should be infinite.
3. Measure resistance between ECT sensor terminals Nos. 1 and 3, then compare to **Fig. 289.**
4. If resistance is not within specifications, replace ECT sensor.

PASSAT w/1.8L ENGINE

1. Disconnect ECT sensor 4-pin connector.
2. Connect test box tool No. 1598/31, or equivalent, to ECM wiring harness and measure resistance as follows:
   a. Between connector terminal No. 3 and test box socket No. 67.
   b. Between terminal No. 1 and socket 53.
   c. If resistance is not less than 1.5

Diagnostic Trouble Codes (DTCs) SAE		Diagnostic Trouble Code (DTC) display	Corrective action
P1472		EVAP Emission Contr.LEDP Circ. Short to Ground	- Check Evaporative Emission (EVAP) system for leaks.
P1473		EVAP Emission Contr.LDP Circ. Open Circ.	
P1475		EVAP Emission Contr.LDP Circ Malfunction/Signal Circ.Open	
P1476		EVAP Emission Contr.LDP Circ. Malfunction/Insufficient Vacuum	
P1477		EVAP Emission Contr.LDP Circ. Malfunction	
P1500		Fuel Pump Relay Circ Electrical Malfunction	- Check fuel pump relay.
P1502		Fuel Pump Relay Circ. Short to B+	

VW1029900138210X

Fig. 6 Motronic DTC interpretation chart (Part 21 of 24). 1999–2001 Golf & Jetta w/2.0L engine

Diagnostic Trouble Codes (DTCs) SAE		Diagnostic Trouble Code (DTC) display	Corrective action
P1582		Idle Adaptation at Limit	- Check vacuum lines for leaks. - Check intake system for leaks - Check exhaust system for leaks. - Check Secondary Air Injection (AIR) system for leaks. - Check fuel pressure regulator and holding pressure - Check quantity of fuel injected and check for leaks - Check Evaporative Emission (EVAP) canister purge regulator valve -N80-.
P1612		Electronic Control Module Incorrect Coding	- Code Motronic Engine Control Module (ECM) -J220-
P1626		Data-Bus Powertrain Missing Message from Transm.Contr	- Check CAN-Bus

VW1029900138230X

Fig. 6 Motronic DTC interpretation chart (Part 23 of 24). 1999–2001 Golf & Jetta w/2.0L engine

Diagnostic Trouble Codes (DTCs) SAE		Diagnostic Trouble Code (DTC) display	Corrective action
P1543		Throttle Actuation Potentiometer Signal too Low	- Check throttle valve control module
P1544		Throttle Actuation Potentiometer Signal too High	
P1558		Throttle Actuator Electrical Malfunction	
P1565		Idle Speed Control Throttle Position Lower Limit not Attained	
P1580		Throttle Actuator B1 Malfunction	

VW1029900138220X

Fig. 6 Motronic DTC interpretation chart (Part 22 of 24). 1999–2001 Golf & Jetta w/2.0L engine

Diagnostic Trouble Codes (DTCs) SAE		Diagnostic Trouble Code (DTC) display	Corrective action
P1649		Data-Bus Powertrain Missing Message from Brake Contr	- Check CAN-Bus
P1681		Contr.Unit Programming Programming not Finished	- Replace Motronic Engine Control Module (ECM) -J220-
P1851		Data-Bus Powertrain Missing Message from Brake Contr	- Check CAN-Bus

VW1029900138240X

Fig. 6 Motronic DTC interpretation chart (Part 24 of 24). 1999–2001 Golf & Jetta w/2.0L engine

ohms, inspect wiring for open circuit.

d. Between terminal No. 1 and socket No. 67.
e. Between terminal No. 1 and ground.
f. If resistance is not infinite, inspect wiring for short circuits.
g. Inspect wiring between ECM and terminals Nos. 1 then 3 for short circuit to battery Voltage Resistance should be infinite.

3. Measure resistance between ECT sensor terminals Nos. 1 and 3, then compare to **Fig. 289.**
4. If resistance is not within specifications, replace ECT sensor.
5. If resistance is within specifications and wiring is good, replace ECM.

PASSAT w/2.8L ENGINE

1. Disconnect ECT sensor 4-pin connector.
2. Connect test box tool No. 1598/31, or equivalent, to ECM wiring harness and measure resistance as follows:
   a. Between connector terminal No. 4 and test box socket No. 67.
   b. Between terminal No. 4 and socket 53.
   c. If resistance is not less than 1.5 ohms, inspect wiring for open circuit.
   d. Between terminal No. 1 and socket No. 67.
   e. Between terminal No. 1 and ground.
   f. If resistance is not infinite, inspect wiring for short circuits.
   g. Inspect wiring between ECM and terminals Nos. 1 then 3 for short circuit to battery Voltage Resistance should be infinite.
3. Measure resistance between ECT sensor terminals Nos. 1 and 3, then compare to **Fig. 289.**
4. If resistance is not within specifications, replace ECT sensor.
5. If resistance is within specifications and wiring is good, replace ECM.

INTAKE AIR TEMPERATURE (IAT) SENSOR

1998 CABRIO, GOLF, GTI & JETTA

1. Disconnect IAT sensor 2-pin connector.
2. Connect test box tool No. 1598/18, or equivalent, to ECM wiring harness and measure resistance as follows:
   a. Between connector terminal No. 1 and test box socket No. 36.
   b. Between terminal No. 2 and socket 33.
   c. If resistance is not less than 1.5 ohms, inspect wiring for open circuit.
   d. Between terminal No. 2 and socket No. 36.
   e. Between terminal No. 2 and ground.
   f. If resistance is note infinite, Inspect wiring for short circuits.
   g. Inspect both wires for short circuit to battery voltage. Resistance should be infinite.
3. Measure resistance between IAT sensor terminals Nos. 1 and 2, then compare to **Fig. 289.**
4. If resistance is not within specifications, replace IAT sensor.

Diagnostic Trouble Code (DTC) SAE	VAG	Malfunction text	MIL switch-on conditions
P0102		Mass or Volume Air Flow Circuit Low Input	2 trips
P0103		Mass or Volume Air Flow Circuit High Input	2 trips
P0112		Intake Air Temperature Circuit Low Input	5 secs
P0113		Intake Air Temperature Circuit High input	5 secs.
P0117		Engine Coolant Temperature Circuit Low Input	5 secs.
P0118		Engine Coolant Temperature Circuit High Input	5 secs.
P0120		Throttle Position Sensor A Circuit Malfunction	5 secs.
P0121		Throttle Position Sensor A Circuit Range/Performance Problem	5 secs.
P0122		Throttle Position Sensor A Circuit Low Input	5 secs.
P0125		Insufficient Coolant Temperature for Closed Loop Fuel Control	2 trips

VW0159600020010A

Fig. 7 Motronic DTC interpretation chart (Part 1 of 8). 1998 GTI & Jetta w/2.8L engine

Diagnostic Trouble Code (DTC) SAE		Malfunction text	MIL switch-on conditions
P0131		O_2 Sensor Circuit Low Voltage (Bank 1 Sensor 1)	2 trips
P0132		O_2 Sensor Circuit High Voltage (Bank 1 Sensor 1)	2 trips
P0133		O_2 Sensor Circuit Slow Response (Bank 1 Sensor 1)	2 trips
P0134		O_2 Sensor Circuit No Activity Detected (Bank 1 Sensor 1)	2 trips
P0135		O_2 Sensor Heater Circuit Malfunction (Bank 1 Sensor 1)	2 trips
P0137		O_2 Sensor Circuit Low Voltage (Bank 1 Sensor 2)	2 trips
P0138		O_2 Sensor Circuit High Voltage (Bank 1 Sensor 2)	2 trips
P0140		O_2 Sensor Circuit No Activity Detected (Bank 1 Sensor 2)	2 trips
P0141		O_2 Sensor Heater Circuit Malfunction (Bank 1 Sensor 2)	2 trips
P0171		System too Lean (Bank 1)	2 trips
P0172		System too Rich (Bank 1)	2 trips

VW0159600020020A

Fig. 7 Motronic DTC interpretation chart (Part 2 of 8). 1998 GTI & Jetta w/2.8L engine

Diagnostic Trouble Code (DTC) SAE		Malfunction text	MIL switch-on conditions
P0300		Random Misfire Detected	2 trips / flashes [1)]
P0301		Cylinder 1 Misfire Detected	2 trips / flashes [1)]
P0302		Cylinder 2 Misfire Detected	2 trips / flashes [1)]
P0303		Cylinder 3 Misfire Detected	2 trips / flashes [1)]
P0304		Cylinder 4 Misfire Detected	2 trips / flashes [1)]
P0305		Cylinder 5 Misfire Detected	2 trips / flashes [1)]
P0306		Cylinder 6 Misfire Detected	2 trips / flashes [1)]
P0327		Knock Sensor 1 Circuit Low Input (Bank 1 or Single Sensor)	5 secs.
P0332		Knock Sensor 2 Circuit Low Input (Bank 2)	5 secs.
P0341		Camshaft Position Sensor Circuit Range/Performance	5 secs.

[1)] MIL may come on immediately or after 2 trips, may flash or be continuously illuminated depending on the type of misfire.

VW0159600020030A

Fig. 7 Motronic DTC interpretation chart (Part 3 of 8). 1998 GTI & Jetta w/2.8L engine

Diagnostic Trouble Code (DTC) SAE		Malfunction text	MIL switch-on conditions
P0411		Secondary Air Injection System Incorrect Flow Detected	2 trips
P0422		Main Catalyst Efficiency Below Threshold (Bank 1)	2 trips
P0440		Evaporative Emission Control System Malfunction	2 trips
P0501		Vehicle Speed Sensor Range/Performance	2 trips
P0510		Closed Throttle Position Switch Malfunction	2 trips
P0605		Internal Control Module Read Only Memory (ROM) Error (Module Identification Defined by SAE J1979)	2 trips
P0605		Internal Control Module Read Only Memory (ROM) Error (Module Identification Defined by SAE J1979)	2 trips

VW0159600020040A

Fig. 7 Motronic DTC interpretation chart (Part 4 of 8). 1998 GTI & Jetta w/2.8L engine

NEW BEETLE & 1999–2001 CABRIO, GOLF, GTI & JETTA w/2.0L ENGINE

1. Disconnect IAT sensor 5-pin connector.
2. Connect test box tool No. 1598/31, or equivalent, to ECM wiring harness and measure resistance as follows:
   a. Between connector terminal No. 1 and test box socket No. 40.
   b. Between terminal No. 3 and socket 12.
   c. If resistance is not less than 1.5 ohms, inspect wiring for open circuit.
   d. Inspect both wires for short circuit to battery voltage. Resistance should be infinite.
   e. Between terminal No. 2 and socket No. 36.
   f. Between terminal No. 2 and ground.
   g. If resistance is note infinite, Inspect wiring for short circuits.
3. Measure resistance between IAT sensor terminals Nos. 1 and 3, then compare to **Fig. 289.**
4. If resistance is not within specifications, replace IAT sensor.

1999–2001 GTI & JETTA w/2.8L ENGINE

1. Disconnect IAT sensor 5-pin connector.
2. Connect test box tool No. 1598/31, or equivalent, to ECM wiring harness and measure resistance as follows:
   a. Between connector terminal No. 1 and test box socket No. 26.
   b. Between terminal No. 3 and socket 27.
   c. If resistance is not less than 1.5 ohms, inspect wiring for open circuit.
   d. Inspect both wires for short circuit to battery voltage. Resistance should be infinite.
3. Measure resistance between IAT sensor terminals Nos. 1 and 3, then compare to **Fig. 289.**
4. If resistance is not within specifications, replace IAT sensor.

PASSAT

1. Disconnect IAT sensor 2-pin connector.
2. Connect test box tool No. 1598/31, or equivalent, to ECM wiring harness and measure resistance as follows:
   a. Between connector terminal No. 2 and test box socket No. 67.
   b. Between terminal No. 1 and socket 54.
   c. If resistance is not less than 1.5 ohms, inspect wiring for open circuit.
   d. Inspect both wires for short circuit to battery voltage. Resistance should be infinite.
3. Measure resistance between IAT sensor terminals Nos. 1 and 2, then compare to **Fig. 289.**
4. If resistance is not within specifications, replace IAT sensor.
5. If resistance is within specifications and wiring is good, replace ECM.

ENGINE SPEED (RPM) SENSOR

1998 CABRIO, GOLF, GTI & JETTA

1. Disconnect RPM sensor 3-pin connector.
2. Connect test box tool No. 1598/18, or equivalent, to ECM wiring harness and measure resistance as follows:
   a. Between connector terminal No. 1 and test box socket No. 67.
   b. Between terminal No. 2 and socket 68.
   c. Between terminal No. 3 and socket 56.

Diagnostic Trouble Code (DTC) SAE		Malfunction text	MIL switch-on conditions
P0715		Input/Turbine Speed Sensor Circuit Malfunction	2 trips
P0722		Output Speed Sensor Circuit No Signal	2 trips
P0725		Engine Speed Input Circuit Malfunction	2 trips
P0748		Pressure Control Solenoid Electrical	2 trips
P0753		Shift Solenoid A Electrical	2 trips
P0758		Shift Solenoid B Electrical	2 trips
P0763		Shift Solenoid C Electrical	2 trips
P0768		Shift Solenoid D Electrical	2 trips
P0773		Shift Solenoid E Electrical	2 trips

VW0159600020050A

Fig. 7 Motronic DTC interpretation chart (Part 5 of 8). 1998 GTI & Jetta w/2.8L engine

Diagnostic Trouble Code (DTC)		Malfunction text	MIL switch-on conditions
P1239		Injector Circ.Cyl.3 Open Circuit	5 secs.
P1240		Injector Circ.Cyl.4 Open Circuit	5 secs.
P1241		Cyl.5 Inj.Circ. Open Circuit	5 secs.
P1242		Cyl.6 Inj.Circ. Open Circuit	5 secs.
P1340		Camshaft/Crankshaft Pos.Sens.Signals Out of Sequence	5 secs.
P1410		Tank Ventilation Valve Short to B+	5 secs.
P1420		Sec.Air Inj.Control Module Short to B+	5 secs.
P1421		Sec.Air Inj.Valve Circ. Short to Ground	5 secs.
P1422		Sec.Air Inj.Sys.Control Valve Circ. Short to B+	5 secs.
P1425		Tank Vent. Valve Short to Ground	5 secs.
P1426		Tank Vent. Valve Open	5 secs.
P1450		Sec.Air Inj.Sys.Circ. Short to B+	5 secs.
P1451		Sec.Air Inj.Sys.Circ. Short to Ground	5 secs.
P1452		Sec.Air Inj.Sys. Open Circuit	5 secs.

VW0159600020070A

Fig. 7 Motronic DTC interpretation chart (Part 7 of 8). 1998 GTI & Jetta w/2.8L engine

Diagnostic Trouble Code (DTC) SAE		Malfunction text
P1127		Long Term Fuel Trim mul.(B1) System too Rich
P1128		Long Term Fuel Trim mul.(B1) System too Lean
P1213		Cyl.1 Fuel Injector Circ. Short to B+
P1214		Cyl.2 Fuel Injector Circ. Short to B+
P1215		Cyl.3 Fuel Injector Circ. Short to B+
P1216		Cyl.4 Fuel Injector Circ. Short to B+
P1217		Cyl.5 Fuel Inj.Circ. Short to B+
P1218		Cyl.6 Fuel Inj.Circ. Short to B+
P1225		Injector Circ.Cyl.1 Short to Ground
P1226		Injector Circ.Cyl.2 Short to Ground
P1227		Injector Circ.Cyl.3 Short to Ground
P1228		Injector Circ.Cyl.4 Short to Ground
P1229		Cyl.5 Inj.Circ. Short to Ground
P1230		Cyl.6 Inj.Circ. Short to Ground
P1237		Injector Circ.Cyl.1 Open Circuit
P1238		Injector Circ.Cyl.2 Open Circuit

VW0159600020060A

Fig. 7 Motronic DTC interpretation chart (Part 6 of 8). 1998 GTI & Jetta w/2.8L engine

Diagnostic Trouble Code (DTC) SAE		Malfunction text	MIL switch-on conditions
P1500		Fuel Pump Relay Circ. Electrical Malfunction	5 secs.
P1502		Fuel Pump Relay Circ. Short to B+	5 secs.
P1543		Throttle Actuation Potentiometer Signal too Low	5 secs.
P1544		Throttle Actuation Potentiometer Signal too High	5 secs.
P1580		Throttle Actuator (B1) Malfunction	5 secs.
P1582		Idle Adaptation at Limit	5 secs.
P1611		MIL Call-up Circ./Transm.Control Module Short to Ground	5 secs.
P1613		MIL Call-up Circ.Open Short to B+	5 secs.
P1778		Solenoid EV7 Electrical Malfunction	2 trips
P1780		Engine Intervention Readable	2 trips

VW0159600020080A

Fig. 7 Motronic DTC interpretation chart (Part 8 of 8). 1998 GTI & Jetta w/2.8L engine

d. If resistance is not less than 1.5 ohms, inspect wiring for open circuit.
e. Between terminal No. 2 and socket No. 56.
f. Between terminal No. 1 and socket 56.
g. Between terminal No. 1 and socket 68.
h. If resistance is not infinite, inspect wiring for short circuits

3. If no wiring malfunction is found, replace RPM sensor.

NEW BEETLE & 1999–2001 CABRIO, GOLF, GTI & JETTA w/2.0L ENGINE

1. Disconnect RPM sensor 3-pin connector.
2. Measure resistance between connector terminals Nos. 2 and 3, which should be 480–1000 ohms.
3. Measure resistance between sensor Nos. 1 and 2. Resistance should be infinite.
4. If resistance is not as specified, replace RPM sensor.
5. Connect test box tool No. 1598/31, or equivalent, to ECM wiring harness and measure resistance as follows:
   a. Between connector terminal No. 1 and test box socket No. 67.
   b. Between terminal No. 2 and socket 63.
   c. Between terminal No. 3 and socket 56.
   d. If resistance is not less than 1.5 ohms, inspect wiring for open circuit.
   e. Between terminal No. 1 and socket 63.
   f. Between terminal No. 1 and socket 56.
   g. Between terminal No. 2 and socket No. 67.
   h. If resistance is not infinite, inspect wiring for short circuits
6. If no wiring malfunction is found, remove sensor and inspect sensor wheel for fit, damage and runout.
7. If no sensor wheel malfunction is found, replace RPM sensor.

1999–2001 GTI & JETTA w/2.8L ENGINE

1. Disconnect RPM sensor 3-pin connector.
2. Measure resistance between connector terminals Nos. 2 and 3. Resistance should be 480–1000 ohms.
3. Measure resistance between sensor Nos. 1 and 2, then Nos. 1 and 3. Resistance should be infinite.
4. If resistance is not as specified, replace RPM sensor.
5. Connect test box tool No. 1598/31, or equivalent, to ECM wiring harness and measure resistance as follows:
   a. Between connector terminal No. 1 and test box socket No. 108.
   b. Between terminal No. 2 and socket 90.
   c. Between terminal No. 3 and socket 82.
   d. If resistance is not less than 1.5 ohms, inspect wiring for open circuit.
   e. Inspect wires for short to one another.
6. If no wiring malfunction is found, remove sensor and inspect sensor wheel for fit, damage and runout.
7. If no sensor wheel malfunction is found, replace RPM sensor.

DTC SAE	DTC VAG	DTC text	Corrective action
P0101	16485	Mass Air Flow (MAF) sensor -G70- implausible signal	- Check Mass Air Flow (MAF) sensor - Check intake system for leaks (false air)
P0102	16486	Mass Air Flow (MAF) sensor -G70- signal too small	
P0103	16487	Mass Air Flow (MAF) sensor -G70- signal too large	
P0106	16490	MAP sensor -G71-/BARO sensor -F96- 1) implausible signal	Check boost pressure system, charge air pressure sensor

1) Intake manifold pressure is determined by the charge air pressure sensor -G31- (instead of -G71- as indicated), air pressure is determined by the Barometric Pressure (BARO) sensor -F96- (in ECM).

VW1020000157010X

Fig. 8 Motronic DTC interpretation chart (Part 1 of 44). Golf, GTI & Jetta w/1.8L engine

DTC SAE	DTC VAG	DTC text	Corrective action
P0112	16496	Intake Air Temperature (IAT) sensor -G42- Signal too small	- Check Intake Air Temperature (IAT) sensor
P0113	16497	Intake Air Temperature (IAT) sensor -G42- Signal too large	
P0116	16500	Engine Coolant Temperature (ECT) sensor -G62- implausible signal	- Check Engine Coolant Temperature (ECT) sensor - Check coolant thermostat
P0117	16501	Engine Coolant Temperature (ECT) sensor -G62- Signal too small	
P0118	16502	Engine Coolant Temperature (ECT) sensor -G62- Signal too large	

VW1020000157020X

Fig. 8 Motronic DTC interpretation chart (Part 2 of 44). Golf, GTI & Jetta w/1.8L engine

DTC SAE	DTC VAG	DTC text	Corrective action
P0130	16514	Bank 1, sensor 1, electrical malfunction in circuit	- Check oxygen sensor heating before catalytic converter
P0131	16515	Bank 1, sensor 1, voltage too small	- Oxygen sensor and oxygen sensor control before catalytic converter, checking - Check oxygen sensor aging before catalytic converter
P0132	16516	Bank 1, sensor 1, voltage too large	
P0133	16517	Bank 1, sensor 1, signal too slow	
P0134	16518	Bank 1, sensor 1, no activity	

VW1020000157030X

Fig. 8 Motronic DTC interpretation chart (Part 3 of 44). Golf, GTI & Jetta w/1.8L engine

DTC SAE	DTC VAG	DTC text	Corrective action
P0136	16520	Bank 1, sensor 2, electrical malfunction in circuit	- Check oxygen sensor heating behind catalytic converter
P0137	16521	Bank 1, sensor 2, voltage too small	- Oxygen sensor and oxygen sensor control behind catalytic converter, checking - Check oxygen sensor heating behind catalytic converter - Check oxygen sensor aging behind catalytic converter - Checking operational readiness of Oxygen Sensor (O2S) behind Three Way Catalytic Converter (TWC)
P0138	16522	Bank 1, sensor 2, voltage too large	
P0139	16523	Bank 2, sensor 1, signal too slow	
P0140	16524	Bank 1, sensor 2, no activity	

VW1020000157040X

Fig. 8 Motronic DTC interpretation chart (Part 4 of 44). Golf, GTI & Jetta w/1.8L engine

PASSAT w/1.8L ENGINE

1. Disconnect RPM sensor 3-pin connector.
2. Measure resistance between connector terminals Nos. 1 and 2. Resistance should be 400–1000 ohms.
3. Measure resistance between sensor Nos. 1 and 2, then Nos. 1 and 3. Resistance should be infinite.
4. If resistance is not as specified, replace RPM sensor.
5. Connect test box tool No. 1598/31, or equivalent, to ECM wiring harness and measure resistance as follows:
   a. Between connector terminal No. 1 and test box socket No. 56.
   b. Between terminal No. 2 and socket 63.
   c. Between terminal No. 3 and socket 2.
   d. If resistance is not less than 1.5 ohms, inspect wiring for open circuit.
6. If no wiring malfunction is found, remove sensor and inspect sensor wheel for fit, damage and runout.
7. If no sensor wheel malfunction is found, replace RPM sensor.

PASSAT w/2.8L ENGINE

1. Disconnect RPM sensor 3-pin connector.
2. Measure resistance between connector terminals Nos. 1 and 2. Resistance should be 480–1000 ohms.
3. Measure resistance between sensor Nos. 1 and 2, then Nos. 1 and 3. Resistance should be infinite.
4. If resistance is not as specified, replace RPM sensor.
5. Connect test box tool No. 1598/31, or equivalent, to ECM wiring harness and measure resistance as follows:
   a. Between connector terminal No. 1 and test box socket No. 67.
   b. Between terminal No. 2 and socket 63.
   c. Between terminal No. 3 and socket 56.
   d. If resistance is not less than 1.5 ohms, inspect wiring for open circuit.
6. If no wiring malfunction is found, remove sensor and inspect sensor wheel for fit, damage and runout.
7. If no sensor wheel malfunction is found, replace RPM sensor.

BAROMETRIC SENSOR

PASSAT w/1.8L ENGINE

1. Disconnect sensor 3-pin connector.
2. Turn ignition On.
3. Measure voltage as follows:
   a. Between terminals Nos. 1 and 3.
   b. Between terminals Nos. 2 and 3.
   c. There should be 4.5–5.5 volts.
4. If measurement is not within specifications, connect test box tool No. 1598/31, or equivalent, to ECM harness and measure resistance as follows:
   a. Between connector terminal No. 1 and test box socket No. 61.
   b. Between terminal No. 2 and socket No. 62.
   c. Between terminal No. 3 and socket No. 67.
   d. If resistance is not less than 1.5 ohms, inspect wiring for open circuit.
   e. Inspect wiring for shorting to one another. Resistance should be infinite.
   f. Inspect wiring for short circuit to battery voltage. Resistance should be infinite.
5. If wiring is in satisfactory condition, replace barometric sensor.

INTAKE MANIFOLD TURNING (IMT) VALVE

1999–2001 GTI & JETTA w/2.8L ENGINE

1. Start and idle engine.
2. Fully depress accelerator pedal, then release before 4000 RPM.
3. Actuating element must rotate intake manifold barrel.
4. Measure resistance between IMT valve terminals.
5. If resistance is not 25–35 ohms, replace IMT valve.

PASSAT w/2.8L ENGINE

1. Start engine and idle.
2. Fully depress accelerator pedal, then release before 4500 RPM.
3. Actuating element must rotate intake manifold barrel.
4. Measure resistance between IMT valve terminals.
5. If resistance is not 25–35 ohms, replace IMT valve.

VEHICLE SPEED SENSOR (VSS)

1998 CABRIO, GOLF, GTI & JETTA

1. Disconnect VSS 3-pin connector.
2. Turn ignition On.

DTC		DTC text	Corrective action
SAE	VAG		
P0236	16620	Charge air pressure sensor -G31- implausible signal	- Charge air pressure sensor -G31-, check check boost pressure system, charge air pressure sensor
P0237	16621	Charge air pressure sensor -G31- signal too small	
P0238	16622	Charge air pressure sensor -G31- signal too large	

VW1020000157050X

Fig. 8 Motronic DTC interpretation chart (Part 5 of 44). Golf, GTI & Jetta w/1.8L engine

DTC		DTC text	Corrective action
SAE	VAG		
P0300	16684	Combustion misfire detected	- Check fuel injectors - Check ignition wires and spark plugs - Testing Ignition Coils with Power Output Stage - Check misfire recognition
P0301	16685	Cyl. 1 combustion misfire detected	
P0302	16686	Cyl. 2 combustion misfire detected	
P0303	16687	Cyl. 3 combustion misfire detected	
P0304	16688	Cyl. 4 combustion misfire detected	
P0321	16705	Engine Speed (RPM) sensor -G28- implausible signal	- Check engine speed (RPM) sensor
P0322	16706	Engine Speed (RPM) sensor -G28- no signal	

VW1020000157060X

Fig. 8 Motronic DTC interpretation chart (Part 6 of 44). Golf, GTI & Jetta w/1.8L engine

DTC		DTC text	Corrective action
SAE	VAG		
P0327	16711	Knock Sensor (KS) 1 -G61- signal too small	- Check knock sensors
P0328	16712	Knock Sensor (KS) 1 -G61- signal too large	
P0332	16716	Knock Sensor (KS) 2 -G66- signal too small	
P0333	16717	Knock Sensor (KS) 2 -G66- signal too large	

VW1020000157070X

Fig. 8 Motronic DTC interpretation chart (Part 7 of 44). Golf, GTI & Jetta w/1.8L engine

DTC		DTC text	Corrective action
SAE	VAG		
P0411	16795	Secondary Air Injection (AIR) system, throughput faulty	- Check Secondary Air Injection (AIR) pump motor - Check combination valve Secondary Air Injection (AIR) system - Check Secondary Air Injection (AIR) valve

VW1020000157080X

Fig. 8 Motronic DTC interpretation chart (Part 8 of 44). Golf, GTI & Jetta w/1.8L engine

3. Measure voltage between connector terminals Nos. 1 and 3. There should be 9–14.5 volts.
4. Turn ignition Off.
5. If no voltage was present, inspect wiring.
6. If voltage was within specifications, connect test box tool No. 1598/18, or equivalent, to ECM wiring harness and measure resistance between central electrical panel and test box socket No. 65. If resistance is not less than 1.5 ohms, inspect wiring for open circuit.
7. Measure voltage between test box sockets No. 56 and 65 while rotating lefthand front wheel with ignition On. Measurement should fluctuate between 0–4 volts.
8. If no wiring malfunction is found and there was voltage between terminals No. 1 and 3, replace VSS.

NEW BEETLE & 1999–2001 CABRIO, GOLF, GTI & JETTA w/2.0L ENGINE

1. Disconnect VSS 3-pin connector, then turn ignition On.
2. Connect test box tool No. 1598/31, or equivalent, to ECM wiring harness.
3. Measure resistance test box socket Nos. 2 and 20 while rotating lefthand front wheel with ignition On. Measurement should fluctuate between 0–4 volts.
4. If measurement is not fluctuating, inspect ECM harness connector terminal No. 20 to instrument cluster for open/short circuit.

1999–2001 GTI & JETTA w/2.8L ENGINE

1. Connect test box tool No. 1598/31, or equivalent, to ECM wiring harness.
2. Measure resistance test box socket Nos. 2 and 54 while rotating lefthand front wheel with ignition On. Measurement should fluctuate between 0–4 volts.
3. If measurement is not fluctuating, inspect wiring to speedometer/speedometer sensor.

PASSAT

1. Disconnect VSS 3-pin connector, then turn ignition On.
2. Connect test box tool No. 1598/31, or equivalent, to ECM wiring harness.
3. Measure resistance test box socket Nos. 2 and 20 while rotating lefthand front wheel with ignition On. Measurement should fluctuate between 0–4 volts.
4. If measurement is not fluctuating, inspect ECM harness connector terminal No. 20 to instrument cluster for open/short circuit.

ENGINE CONTROL MODULE (ECM)

1998 CABRIO, GOLF, GTI & JETTA

1. Turn ignition Off.
2. Connect test box tool No. 1598/18, or equivalent, to ECM wiring harness.
3. Measure voltage between test box sockets Nos. 1 and 54. If measurement is not 12–14.5 volts, inspect wiring for voltage supply terminal No. 30.
4. Measure voltage between test box sockets Nos. 1 and 23. If measurement is not 12–14.5 volts, inspect wiring for voltage supply terminal No. 15.

NEW BEETLE & 1999–2001 CABRIO, GOLF, GTI & JETTA w/2.0L ENGINE

1. Turn ignition Off.
2. Connect test box tool No. 1598/31, or equivalent, to ECM wiring harness.
3. Measure voltage between test box sockets Nos. 2 and 3. If measurement is not 11.5 volts, inspect wiring for voltage supply terminal No. 30.
4. Measure voltage between test box sockets Nos. 1 and 2. If measurement is not 11.5 volts, inspect wiring for voltage supply terminal No. 15.

1999–2001 GTI & JETTA w/2.8L ENGINE

1. Turn ignition Off.
2. Connect test box tool No. 1598/31, or equivalent, to ECM wiring harness.
3. Measure voltage between test box sockets Nos. 1 and 62. If measurement is not 11.5 volts, inspect wiring for voltage supply terminal No. 30.
4. Measure voltage between test box sockets Nos. 2 and 3. If measurement is not 11.5 volts, inspect wiring for voltage supply terminal No. 15.

PASSAT

1. Turn ignition Off.
2. Connect test box tool No. 1598/31, or equivalent, to ECM wiring harness.
3. Measure voltage between test box sockets Nos. 2 and 3. If measurement is not 11.5 volts, inspect wiring for voltage supply terminal No. 30.
4. Measure voltage between test box sockets Nos. 1 and 2. If measurement is not 11.5 volts, inspect wiring for voltage supply terminal No. 15.

DTC		DTC text	Corrective action
			- Check hoses and connecting pipes to and between components
P0422	16806	Bank 1 main catalytic converter, not effective enough	- Check catalytic converter

VW1020000157090X

Fig. 8 Motronic DTC interpretation chart (Part 9 of 44). Golf, GTI & Jetta w/1.8L engine

DTC		DTC text	Corrective action
SAE	VAG		
P0441	16825	Tank ventilation system throughput faulty	- Check Evaporative Emission (EVAP) Canister Purge Regulator Valve - Check Evaporative Emission (EVAP) canister purge regulator valve - Check hoses and connecting pipes from fuel tank to throttle valve control module
P0442	16826	Small leak detected in tank ventilation system	Check EVAP canister system
P0455	16839	Large leak detected in tank ventilation system	check EVAP system for leaks

VW1020000157100X

Fig. 8 Motronic DTC interpretation chart (Part 10 of 44). Golf, GTI & Jetta w/1.8L engine

DTC		DTC text	Corrective action
SAE	VAG		
P0501	16885	Vehicle speed signal unplausible signal	- Check vehicle speed signal
P0506	16890	Idle regulation RPM below specified value	- Checking throttle valve control module
P0507	16891	Idle regulation RPM above specified value	
P0560	16944	Voltage supply implausible signal	- Checking voltage supply
P0562	16946	Voltage supply voltage too low	
P0563	16947	Voltage supply voltage too large	
P0571	16955	Brake light switch -F1) implausible signal	- Check brake light switch and brake pedal switch

1) Brake pedal switch -F47- is monitored in addition to brake light switch -F-.

VW1020000157110X

Fig. 8 Motronic DTC interpretation chart (Part 11 of 44). Golf, GTI & Jetta w/1.8L engine

DTC		DTC text	Corrective action
SAE	VAG		
P0601	16985	Control module faulty	- Replace motronic Engine Control Module (ECM)
P0604	16988	Control module faulty	
P0605	16989	Control module faulty	
P0606	16990	Control module faulty	

VW1020000157120X

Fig. 8 Motronic DTC interpretation chart (Part 12 of 44). Golf, GTI & Jetta w/1.8L engine

INTAKE AIR PREHEATING

1998 CABRIO, GOLF, GTI & JETTA

1. Remove upper air cleaner housing and filter.
2. Connect hand vacuum pump tool No. 1390, or equivalent, to air temperature regulator vacuum unit.
3. Operate pump to ensure regulator flap movement freedom and vacuum unit functions.
4. Connect vacuum hose to temperature regulator, start and idle engine.
5. Inspect flap position after 20 seconds, as follows:
   a. Air temperature below 68°F, cold air inlet closed.
   b. Air temperature between 68–86°F, between cold and warm air inlet.
   c. Air temperature above 86°F, warm air inlet closed.

A/C COMPRESSOR SIGNAL

NEW BEETLE & 1999–2001 CABRIO, GOLF, GTI & JETTA w/2.0L ENGINE

1. Connect test box tool No. 1598/31, or equivalent, to ECM wiring harness.
2. Measure resistance between test box socket Nos. 8 and 10. If resistance is not less than 1.5 ohms, inspect wiring for open circuit.
3. If no wiring malfunction is found, inspect air conditioner control module.

1999–2001 GTI & JETTA w/2.8L ENGINE

1. Connect test box tool No. 1598/31, or equivalent, to ECM wiring harness.
2. Measure resistance between test box socket Nos. 10 and 41. If resistance is not less than 1.5 ohms, inspect wiring for open circuit.
3. If no wiring malfunction is found, inspect air conditioner control module.

PASSAT

1. Connect test box tool No. 1598/31, or equivalent, to ECM wiring harness.
2. Measure resistance between A/C control module and test box socket No. 8. If resistance is not less than 1.5 ohms, inspect wiring for open circuit.
3. If no wiring malfunction is found, inspect air conditioner control module.

CAN-BUS

1999–2001 CABRIO, GOLF, GTI & JETTA w/2.0L ENGINE

Automatic Transmission

1. Connect test box tool No. 1598/18, or equivalent, to transmission control module wiring harness.
2. Measure resistance between test box socket Nos. 3 and 25. Resistance should be 55–75 ohms.
3. If resistance is as specified, proceed as follows:
   a. Inspect wiring for short to battery voltage or ground.
   b. Connect transmission control module and clear DTC memory.
   c. If CAN-Bus malfunction is still displayed, replace transmission control module.
4. If resistance is 115–135 ohms, proceed as follows:
   a. Disconnect ECM connector.
   b. Measure resistance between test box socket Nos. 3 and 25.
   c. If resistance is not 115–135 ohms, proceed to next step.
5. If resistance is less than 5 ohms or more than 135 ohms, proceed as follows:
   a. Disconnect ECM.
   b. Measure resistance between test box socket Nos. 3 and 25.
   c. If resistance is not infinite, inspect wiring for short.
   d. If resistance is infinite, connect test box tool No. 1598/31, or equivalent, to ECM wiring harness.
   e. Measure resistance between test box tool No. VAG 1598/31 sockets Nos. 29 and 41, then test box tool No. VAG 1598/18 sockets Nos. 3 and 25.
   f. If resistance is not less than 1.5 ohms, inspect wiring for open circuit.
   g. Inspect wiring for short to battery voltage or ground.
   h. If no wiring malfunction is found, connect test box tool No. VAG 1598/21, or equivalent, to ABS control module.
   i. Measure resistance between test box tool No. VAG 1598/31 sockets Nos. 29 and 41, then test box tool No. VAG 1598/21 sockets Nos. 10 and 11.
   j. If resistance is not less than 1.5 ohms, inspect wiring for open circuit.

DTC		DTC text	Corrective action
SAE	VAG		
P1102	17510	Bank 1, sensor 1 heating circuit short circuit to B+	- Check oxygen sensor heating before catalytic converter
P1105	17513	Bank 1, sensor 2 heating circuit short circuit to B+	- Check oxygen sensor heating behind catalytic converter
P1111	17519	Oxygen sensor control bank 1, system too lean	- Oxygen sensor and oxygen sensor control before catalytic converter, check
P1112	17520	Oxygen sensor control bank 1, system too rich	
P1113	17521	Bank 1, sensor 1 inner resistance too large	- Check oxygen sensor heating before catalytic converter
P1114	17522	Bank 1, sensor 2 inner resistance too large	- Check oxygen sensor heating behind catalytic converter

VW1020000157130X

Fig. 8 Motronic DTC interpretation chart (Part 13 of 44). Golf, GTI & Jetta w/1.8L engine

DTC		DTC text	Corrective action
SAE	VAG		
P1115	17523	Bank 1, sensor 1 heating circuit short circuit to Ground (GND)	- Check oxygen sensor heating before catalytic converter
P1116	17524	Bank 1, sensor 1 heating circuit open circuit	
P1117	17525	Bank 1, sensor 2 heating circuit short circuit to Ground (GND)	- Check oxygen sensor heating behind catalytic converter
P1118	17526	Bank 1, sensor 2 heating circuit open circuit	
P1127	17535	Bank 1, mixture adaptation (mult.) System too rich	- Check fuel pressure regulator and residual pressure
			- Test fuel injectors fuel injection quantity and proper seal
			- Check Evaporative Emission (EVAP) canister purge regulator valve

VW1020000157140X

Fig. 8 Motronic DTC interpretation chart (Part 14 of 44). Golf, GTI & Jetta w/1.8L engine

DTC		DTC text	Corrective action
SAE	VAG		
P1128	17536	Bank 1, mixture adaption (mult.) system too lean	- Check fuel pressure regulator/residual pressure
			- Check air intake screen (if equipped) and filter for blockage
			- Check oxygen sensor and oxygen sensor control before and after catalyst
			- Check fuel injectors and EVAP canister purge regulator valve.
			- Check fuel pump
			- Check intake system and vacuum lines for leaks
			- Check Mass Air Flow (MAF) sensor
			- Check exhaust system and secondary air system for leaks

VW1020000157150X

Fig. 8 Motronic DTC interpretation chart (Part 15 of 44). Golf, GTI & Jetta w/1.8L engine

DTC		DTC text	Corrective action
SAE	VAG		
P1136	17544	Bank 1, mixture adaptation (add.) system too lean	- Check fuel pressure regulator and residual pressure
			- Test fuel injectors fuel injection quantity and proper seal
			- Check fuel pump
			- Check intake system for leaks
			- Check exhaust system for proper seal

Note:

add = additive, means that malfunction is only valid at closed throttle (idle).

VW1020000157160X

Fig. 8 Motronic DTC interpretation chart (Part 16 of 44). Golf, GTI & Jetta w/1.8L engine

Manual Transmission

1. Connect test box tool No. 1598/31, or equivalent, to ECM wiring harness.
2. Measure resistance between test box socket Nos. 29 and 41. If resistance is 115–135 ohms, proceed to next step. If resistance is not 115–135 ohms, proceed as follows:
   a. Remove air cleaner.
   b. Disconnect ABS control module harness connector.
   c. Measure resistance between test box sockets Nos. 29 and 41.
   d. If resistance is not infinite, inspect CAN-Bus wiring for short circuit.
3. Connect test box tool No. VAG 1598/21, or equivalent, to ABS control module.
4. Measure resistance between test box tool No. VAG 1598/31 sockets Nos. 29 and 41, then test box tool No. VAG 1598/21 sockets Nos. 10 and 11. If resistance is not less than 1.5 ohms, inspect wiring for open circuit and proceed to next step. If resistance is less than 1.5 ohms, proceed as follows:
   a. Remove air cleaner.
   b. Disconnect ABS control module harness connector.
   c. Inspect wiring between engine and ABS control module for short to ground and short to battery voltage.
   d. If no wiring malfunction is found, connect ECM harness connector.
   e. Connect test box tool No. VAG 1598/21 to ABS control module.
   f. Measure resistance between test box sockets Nos. 10 and 11.
   g. If resistance is not 115–135 ohms, replace ECM.
5. Inspect wiring for short to battery voltage or ground.
6. If no wiring malfunction is found, replace ABS control module.

1999–2001 GTI & JETTA w/2.8L ENGINE

Automatic Transmission

1. Connect test box tool No. 1598/31, or equivalent, to ECM wiring harness.
2. Measure resistance between test box socket Nos. 77 and 79. Resistance should be 60–72 ohms.
3. If resistance is not as specified, replace ECM.
4. If resistance is as specified, proceed as follows:
   a. Disconnect transmission control module.
   b. Measure resistance between test box socket Nos. 77 and 79.
   c. If resistance is not infinite, inspect wiring for short to one another.
   d. If resistance is infinite, inspect CAN-data bus components for short to battery voltage or ground or open circuit.

TRANSMISSION RANGE SELECTION

NEW BEETLE w/2.0L ENGINE & PASSAT W/2.8L ENGINE

1. Connect test box tool No. 1598/31, or equivalent, to ECM wiring harness.
2. Measure resistance between test box sockets Nos. 29 and 41.
3. If resistance is not less than 1.5 ohms, replace transmission control module.

DTC SAE	DTC VAG	DTC text	Corrective action
P1137	17545	Bank 1, mixture adaptation (add.) system too rich	- Check fuel pressure regulator and residual pressure
			- Test fuel injectors fuel injection quantity and proper seal
			- Check Evaporative Emission (EVAP) canister purge regulator valve
P1141	17549	Load detection unplausible value	- Check Mass Air Flow (MAF) sensor

Note:

add = additive, means that malfunction is only valid at closed throttle (idle).

VW1020000157170X

Fig. 8 Motronic DTC interpretation chart (Part 17 of 44). Golf, GTI & Jetta w/1.8L engine

DTC SAE	DTC VAG	DTC text	Corrective action
P1149	17557	Oxygen sensor control bank 1, unplausible control value	- Oxygen sensor and oxygen sensor control before catalytic converter, checking
P1171	17579	Angle sensor -2- for throttle drive (power accelerator actuation) -G188- unplausible signal 1)	- Checking throttle valve control module
P1172	17580	Angle sensor -2- for throttle drive (power accelerator actuation) -G188- signal too small 1)	
P1173	17581	Angle sensor -2- for throttle drive (power accelerator actuation) -G188- signal too large 1)	

1) For these malfunctions, ECM switches on the EPC warning lamp in instrument cluster.

VW1020000157180X

Fig. 8 Motronic DTC interpretation chart (Part 18 of 44). Golf, GTI & Jetta w/1.8L engine

DTC SAE	DTC VAG	DTC text	Corrective action
P1176	17584	Bank 1 oxygen sensor correction behind cat. control limit reached	- Test aging of Heated Oxygen Sensor (HO2S) 1
			- Oxygen sensor and oxygen sensor control behind catalytic converter, checking
P1198	17606	Bank 1, sensor 2 heating circuit, electrical malfunction	- Check oxygen sensor heating behind catalytic converter
P1201	17609	Cylinder 1 fuel injector -N30- electrical malfunction in circuit	- Check fuel injectors
P1202	17610	Cylinder 2 fuel injector -N31- electrical malfunction in circuit	
P1203	17611	Cylinder 3 fuel injector -N32- electrical malfunction in circuit	
P1204	17612	Cylinder 4 fuel injector -N33- electrical malfunction in circuit	

VW1020000157190X

Fig. 8 Motronic DTC interpretation chart (Part 19 of 44). Golf, GTI & Jetta w/1.8L engine

DTC SAE	DTC VAG	DTC text	Corrective action
P1213	17621	Cylinder 1 fuel injector -N30- short circuit to B+	- Check fuel injectors
P1214	17622	Cylinder 2 fuel injector -N31- short circuit to B+	
P1215	17623	Cylinder 3 fuel injector -N32- short circuit to B+	
P1216	17624	Cylinder 4 fuel injector -N33- short circuit to B+	
P1225	17633	Cylinder 1 fuel injector -N30- short circuit to Ground (GND)	
P1226	17634	Cylinder 2 fuel injector -N31- short circuit to Ground (GND)	
P1227	17635	Cylinder 3 fuel injector -N32- short circuit to Ground (GND)	
P1228	17636	Cylinder 4 fuel injector -N33- short circuit to Ground (GND)	

VW1020000157200X

Fig. 8 Motronic DTC interpretation chart (Part 20 of 44). Golf, GTI & Jetta w/1.8L engine

DTC SAE	DTC VAG	DTC text	Corrective action
P1237	17645	Cylinder 1 fuel injector -N30- open circuit	- Check fuel injectors
P1238	17646	Cylinder 2 fuel injector -N31- open circuit	
P1239	17647	Cylinder 3 fuel injector -N32- open circuit	
P1240	17648	Cylinder 4 fuel injector -N33- open circuit	
P1250	17658	Fuel level too low1)	- Fill fuel tank with fuel

1) The DTC "Fuel Level Too Low" is stored when there is/was too little fuel in fuel tank. The DTC is stored as a static malfunction and is not switched to sporadic even if fuel tank has been filled with fuel (e.g. by the customer) in the meantime. In this way, it can be determined that subsequent malfunctions were caused by lack of fuel, e.g. combustion misfires or oxygen control related malfunctions.

VW1020000157210X

Fig. 8 Motronic DTC interpretation chart (Part 21 of 44). Golf, GTI & Jetta w/1.8L engine

4. If DTC continues to display, replace ECM.

CLUTCH PEDAL SWITCH

NEW BEETLE & 1999–2001 CABRIO, GOLF, GTI & JETTA w/2.0L ENGINE

1. Measure resistance between switch terminals. With pedal depressed, resistance should be infinite. With pedal released, resistance should be less than 10 ohms.
2. If resistances are not within specifications, replace clutch vacuum vent valve switch.
3. If resistance is as specified, connect test box tool No. 1598/31, or equivalent, to ECM wiring harness.
4. Measure resistance between connector terminal No. 2 and text box socket No. 48.
5. If resistance is not less than 1.5 ohms, inspect wiring for open circuit.
6. If resistance is less than 1.5 ohms, measure resistance between harness connector terminal No. 2 and fuel pump relay.
7. If resistance is not less than 1.5 ohms, inspect wiring for open circuit.

1999–2001 GTI & JETTA w/2.8L ENGINE

1. Disconnect clutch vacuum vent valve switch 2-pin harness connector.
2. Measure resistance between switch terminals Nos. 1 and 2. With pedal depressed, resistance should be infinite. With pedal released, resistance should be less than 1.5 ohms.
3. If resistances are not within specifications, replace clutch vacuum vent valve switch.
4. If resistance is as specified, measure voltage between connector terminal No. 1 and ground. If measurement is as specified, inspect wiring between 2-pin harness connector terminal No. 1 and central electrics.
5. If resistance is as specified, connect test box tool No. 1598/31, or equivalent, to ECM wiring harness.
6. Measure resistance between connector terminal No. 2 and text box socket No. 39.
7. If resistance is not less than 1.5 ohms, inspect wiring for open circuit.
8. Inspect wiring for short to one another.
9. Inspect wiring for short to battery voltage or ground.

BRAKE LAMP SWITCH

NEW BEETLE & 1999–2001 CABRIO, GOLF, GTI & JETTA w/2.0L ENGINE

1. Measure resistance between switch terminals 1 and 4. With pedal depressed, resistance should be less than 1.5 ohms. With pedal released, resistance should be infinite.
2. Measure resistance between switch terminals 2 and 3. With pedal depressed, resistance should be infinite. With pedal released, resistance should be less than 1.5 ohms.
3. If resistances are not within specifications, replace brake lamp switch.
4. If resistance is as specified, connect test box tool No. 1598/31, or equivalent, to ECM wiring harness.
5. Measure resistance as follows:
   a. Between connector terminal No. 3

DTC SAE	DTC VAG	DTC text	Corrective action
P1287	17695	Recirculating valve for turbocharger -N249-, open circuit	- Check Recirculating valve for turbocharger -N249- boost pressure system, checking, recirculating valve for turbocharger
P1288	17696	Recirculating valve for turbocharger -N249-, short circuit to B+	
P1289	17697	Recirculating valve for turbocharger -N249-, short circuit to Ground (GND)	
P1295	17703	Bypass turbocharger, throughput faulty	- Check wastegate bypass regulator valve - Check hose setup between turbocharger and vacuum diaphragm for boost pressure regulator valve

VW1020000157220X

Fig. 8 Motronic DTC interpretation chart (Part 22 of 44). Golf, GTI & Jetta w/1.8L engine

DTC SAE	DTC VAG	DTC text	Corrective action
P1296	17704	Malfunction in cooling system 1)	- Check Engine Coolant Temperature (ECT) sensor - Check thermostat.
P1297	17705	Connection turbocharger - throttle valve pressure loss	- Check hoses between turbocharger and throttle valve

1) For these malfunctions, ECM does not switch on the Malfunction Indicator Lamp (MIL) unless malfunction is recognized again after another engine start.

VW1020000157230X

Fig. 8 Motronic DTC interpretation chart (Part 23 of 44). Golf, GTI & Jetta w/1.8L engine

DTC SAE	DTC VAG	DTC text	Corrective action
P1325	17733	Knock control cylinder 1 control limit reached	- Fill fuel tank with fuel of at least 91 RON
P1326	17734	Knock control cylinder 2 control limit reached	- Check harness connections:
P1327	17735	Knock control cylinder 3 control limit reached	- Repair cause of abnormal engine noise.
P1328	17736	Knock control cylinder 4 control limit reached	- Loosen knock sensors and tighten to 20 Nm again - Check knock sensors

VW1020000157240X

Fig. 8 Motronic DTC interpretation chart (Part 24 of 44). Golf, GTI & Jetta w/1.8L engine

DTC SAE	DTC VAG	DTC text	Corrective action
P1335	17743	Engine torque monitoring 2 control limit exceeded 1)	- Check hose setup - Check Intake Air Temperature (IAT) sensor
P1336	17744	Engine torque monitoring control limit exceeded	- Check Mass Air Flow (MAF) sensor - Check Engine Coolant Temperature (ECT) sensor

1) For these malfunctions, ECM switches on the EPC warning lamp in instrument cluster.

VW1020000157250X

Fig. 8 Motronic DTC interpretation chart (Part 25 of 44). Golf, GTI & Jetta w/1.8L engine

and text box socket No. 48.

b. Between terminal No. 4 and socket No. 47.
c. If resistance is not less than 1.5 ohms, inspect wiring for open circuit.
d. If resistance is less than 1.5 ohms, measure resistance between harness connector terminal No. 1 and fuel pump relay.

1999-2001 GTI & JETTA w/2.8L ENGINE

1. Disconnect brake lamp switch pedal connector.
2. Measure resistance between switch terminals 1 and 4. With pedal depress, resistance should be less than 1.5 ohms. With pedal released, resistance should be infinite.
3. Measure resistance between switch terminals 2 and 3. With pedal depress, resistance should be infinite. With pedal released, resistance should be less than 1.5 ohms.
4. If resistance is not within specifications, replace brake lamp switch.
5. If resistance is as specified, measure voltage between terminal No. 1 and ground, then terminal No. 2 and ground. There should be at least 11.5 volts.
6. If voltage is not as specified, inspect wiring between terminals Nos. 1 and 2 to central electrics.
7. If voltage is as specified, connect test box tool No. 1598/31, or equivalent, to ECM wiring harness.
8. Measure resistance as follows:
   a. Between connector terminal No. 3 and text box socket No. 55.
   b. Between terminal No. 4 and socket No. 56.
   c. If resistance is not less than 1.5 ohms, inspect wiring for open circuit.
   d. Inspect wires for short to one another.
   e. Inspect wires for short to battery voltage or ground.

DTC SAE	DTC VAG	DTC text	Corrective action
P1337	17745	Bank 1, Camshaft Position (CMP) sensor ⇒ -G40- Short circuit to Ground	- Check Camshaft Position (CMP) sensor
P1338	17746	Bank 1, Camshaft Position (CMP) sensor ⇒ -G40- Open circuit/short circuit to B+	
P1340	17748	Camshaft Position (CMP) / crankshaft position sensor incorrect allocation	- Check for proper seating of shutter wheel for Camshaft Position (CMP) sensor - Check valve timing
P1355	17763	Ignition timing, cyl. 1, open circuit	- Test Ignition Coils with Power Output Stages
P1356	17764	Ignition timing, cyl. 1 short circuit to B+	
P1357	17765	Ignition timing, cyl. 1 short circuit to Ground (GND)	
P1358	17766	Ignition timing, cyl. 2, open circuit	
P1359	17767	Ignition timing, cyl. 2 short circuit to B+	
P1360	17768	Ignition timing, cyl. 2 short circuit to Ground (GND)	

VW1020000157260X

Fig. 8 Motronic DTC interpretation chart (Part 26 of 44). Golf, GTI & Jetta w/1.8L engine

DTC SAE	DTC VAG	DTC text	Corrective action
P1409	17817	EVAP canister purge regulator valve -N80- electrical malfunction in circuit	- Check Evaporative Emission (EVAP) Canister Purge Regulator Valve
P1410	17818	EVAP canister purge regulator valve -N80- short circuit to B+	
P1420	17828	Secondary Air Injection (AIR) solenoid valve -N112- electrical malfunction in circuit	- Check Secondary Air Injection (AIR) valve
P1421	17829	Secondary Air Injection (AIR) solenoid valve -N112- short circuit to Ground (GND)	
P1422	17830	Secondary Air Injection (AIR) solenoid valve -N112- short circuit to B+	
P1424	17832	Bank 1, Secondary Air Injection (AIR) system, leak detected	- Check Secondary Air Injection (AIR) system for proper seal

VW1020000157280X

Fig. 8 Motronic DTC interpretation chart (Part 28 of 44). Golf, GTI & Jetta w/1.8L engine

DTC SAE	DTC VAG	DTC text	Corrective action
P1432	17840	Secondary Air Injection (AIR) solenoid valve -N112- open circuit	- Check Secondary Air Injection (AIR) valve
P1433	17841	Secondary Air Injection (AIR) pump relay -J299- open circuit	- Check Secondary Air Injection (AIR) pump relay
P1434	17842	Secondary Air Injection (AIR) pump relay -J299- short circuit to B+	
P1435	17843	Secondary Air Injection (AIR) pump relay -J299- short circuit to Ground (GND)	
P1436	17844	Secondary Air Injection (AIR) pump relay -J299-, electrical malfunction in circuit	

VW1020000157300X

Fig. 8 Motronic DTC interpretation chart (Part 30 of 44). Golf, GTI & Jetta w/1.8L engine

DTC SAE	DTC VAG	DTC text	Corrective action
P1477	17885	Leak Detection Pump (LDP) tank ventilation system malfunction	
P1478	17886	Leak Detection Pump (LDP), tank ventilation system, hose with no throughput detected	

VW1020000157320X

Fig. 8 Motronic DTC interpretation chart (Part 32 of 44). Golf, GTI & Jetta w/1.8L engine

DTC SAE	DTC VAG	DTC text	Corrective action
P1361	17769	Ignition timing, cyl. 3, open circuit	- Testing Ignition Coils with Power Output Stages
P1362	17770	Ignition timing, cyl. 3 short circuit to B+	
P1363	17771	Ignition timing, cyl. 3 short circuit to Ground (GND)	
P1364	17772	Ignition timing, cyl. 4, open circuit	
P1365	17773	Ignition timing, cyl. 4 short circuit to B+	
P1366	17774	Ignition timing, cyl. 4 short circuit to Ground (GND)	
P1386	17794	Control module faulty	- Replace motronic Engine Control Module (ECM)
P1387	17795	Control module faulty	
P1388	17796	Control module faulty[1]	

1) For these malfunctions, ECM switches on the EPC warning lamp in instrument cluster.

VW1020000157270X

Fig. 8 Motronic DTC interpretation chart (Part 27 of 44). Golf, GTI & Jetta w/1.8L engine

DTC SAE	DTC VAG	DTC text	Corrective action
P1425	17833	EVAP canister purge regulator valve -N80- short circuit to Ground (GND)	- Check Evaporative Emission (EVAP) Canister Purge Regulator Valve
P1426	17834	EVAP canister purge regulator valve -N80- open circuit	

VW1020000157290X

Fig. 8 Motronic DTC interpretation chart (Part 29 of 44). Golf, GTI & Jetta w/1.8L engine

DTC SAE	DTC VAG	DTC text	Corrective action
P1470	17878	Leak Detection Pump (LDP) tank ventilation system electrical malfunction in circuit	- Check Leak Detection Pump
P1471	17879	Leak Detection Pump (LDP) tank ventilation system Short circuit to B+	- Check EVAP canister system
P1472	17880	Leak Detection Pump (LDP) tank ventilation system Short circuit to Ground	
P1473	17881	Leak Detection Pump (LDP) tank ventilation system open circuit	
P1475	17883	Leak Detection Pump (LDP) tank ventilation system Malfunction / no signal	
P1476	17884	Leak Detection Pump (LDP) tank ventilation system Malfunction/vacuum pressure too low	

VW1020000157310X

Fig. 8 Motronic DTC interpretation chart (Part 31 of 44). Golf, GTI & Jetta w/1.8L engine

DTC SAE	DTC VAG	DTC text	Corrective action
P1500	17908	Fuel Pump (FP) relay -J17- electrical malfunction in circuit	- Check Fuel Pump (FP) relay
P1502	17910	Fuel Pump (FP) relay -J17- short circuit to B+	
P1517	17925	Motronic ECM power supply relay -J271-, Failure in electrical circuit	- Check motronic Engine Control Module (ECM) power supply relay
P1523	17931	Crash signal from airbag control module, implausible signal	- DTC memory of Engine Control Module (ECM), erasing and checking - Check airbag system

VW1020000157330X

Fig. 8 Motronic DTC interpretation chart (Part 33 of 44). Golf, GTI & Jetta w/1.8L engine

DTC SAE	DTC VAG	DTC text	Corrective action
P1539	17947	Clutch vacuum vent valve switch -F36- Implausible signal	- Check clutch vacuum vent valve switch
P1542	17950	Angle sensor -1- for throttle drive (power accelerator actuation) -G187- 1)	- Checking throttle valve control module
P1543	17951	Angle sensor -1- for throttle drive (power accelerator actuation) -G187- signal too small1)	
P1544	17952	Angle sensor -1- for throttle drive (power accelerator actuation) -G187- signal too large 1)	
P1545	17953	Throttle valve control, malfunction1)	

1) For these malfunctions, ECM switches on the EPC warning lamp in instrument cluster.

VW1020000157340X

Fig. 8 Motronic DTC interpretation chart (Part 34 of 44). Golf, GTI & Jetta w/1.8L engine

DTC SAE	DTC VAG	DTC text	Corrective action
P1559	17967	Throttle valve control module -J338- Malfunction in basic setting 1)	- Adapt Engine Control Module (ECM) to throttle valve control module
P1560	17968	Maximum engine speed exceeded	- DTC memory of Engine Control Module (ECM), erasing and checking - Repair mechanical damage
P1564	17972	Throttle valve control module -J338- voltage too low during basic setting 1)	- Check battery, charge if necessary - Adapt Engine Control Module (ECM) to throttle valve control module
P1565	17973	Throttle valve control module -J338- lower impact not being reached 1)	- Checking throttle valve control module
P1568	17976	Throttle valve control module -J338- mechanical malfunction1)	- Clean throttle valve control module

1) For these malfunctions, ECM switches on the EPC warning lamp in instrument cluster.

VW1020000157360X

Fig. 8 Motronic DTC interpretation chart (Part 36 of 44). Golf, GTI & Jetta w/1.8L engine

DTC SAE	DTC VAG	DTC text	Corrective action
P1602	18010	Voltage supply terminal 30 voltage too low	- Check voltage supply for control module
P1603	18011	Control module faulty	- Replace motronic Engine Control Module (ECM)
P1604	18012	Control module faulty1)	
P1606	18014	Rough terrain info/engine torque from ABS control module, electrical malfunction in circuit	- Check DTC memory of ABS control module - Check databus
P1609	18017	Crash shut-off was triggered	- DTC memory of Engine Control Module (ECM), erasing and checking - Check airbag system

1) For these malfunctions, ECM switches on the EPC warning lamp in instrument cluster.

VW1020000157380X

Fig. 8 Motronic DTC interpretation chart (Part 38 of 44). Golf, GTI & Jetta w/1.8L engine

DTC SAE	DTC VAG	DTC text	Corrective action
P1546	17954	Wastegate Bypass Regulator Valve -N75- Short circuit to B+	- Check wastegate bypass regulator valve
P1547	17955	Wastegate Bypass Regulator Valve -N75- Short circuit to Ground	
P1548	17956	Wastegate Bypass Regulator Valve -N75- Open circuit	
P1555	17963	Maximum boost pressure exceeded	
P1556	17964	Boost pressure regulation control limit not reached	
P1557	17965	Boost pressure regulation control limit exceeded	
P1558	17966	Throttle drive (power accelerator actuation) -G186- electrical malfunction in circuit1)	- Check throttle valve control module

1) For these malfunctions, ECM switches on the EPC warning lamp in instrument cluster.

VW1020000157350X

Fig. 8 Motronic DTC interpretation chart (Part 35 of 44). Golf, GTI & Jetta w/1.8L engine

DTC SAE	DTC VAG	DTC text	Corrective action
P1569	17977	Cruise control switch -E45- implausible signal	- Check cruise control system
P1570	17978	Engine control module locked	- Adapt motronic Engine Control Module (ECM) -J220- to electronic anti-theft immobilizer - Evaluate measuring value block 66
P1579	17987	Throttle valve control module -J338- Adaptation not started1)	- Adapt Engine Control Module (ECM) to throttle valve control module

1) For these malfunctions, ECM switches on the EPC warning lamp in instrument cluster.

VW1020000157370X

Fig. 8 Motronic DTC interpretation chart (Part 37 of 44). Golf, GTI & Jetta w/1.8L engine

DTC SAE	DTC VAG	DTC text	Corrective action
P1612	18020	Engine Control Module (ECM) incorrectly coded	- Code Engine Control Module
P1624	18032	Request for warning lamp on active	- Check DTC memory from automatic transmission:
P1626	18034	Powertrain databus missing massage from Transmission Control Module (TCM)	- Check databus

VW1020000157390X

Fig. 8 Motronic DTC interpretation chart (Part 39 of 44). Golf, GTI & Jetta w/1.8L engine

DTC SAE	DTC VAG	DTC text	Corrective action
P1630	18038	Throttle Position (TP) sensor -G79- signal too small1)	- Check accelerator pedal position sensor
P1631	18039	Throttle Position (TP) sensor -G79- signal too large1)	
P1633	18041	Sender -2- for accelerator pedal position -G185- signal too small1)	
P1634	18042	Sender -2- for accelerator pedal position -G185- signal too large1)	
P1636	18044	Powertrain databus missing massage from airbag control module	- Check databus - Check airbag system:

1) For these malfunctions, ECM switches on the EPC warning lamp in instrument cluster.

VW1020000157400X

Fig. 8 Motronic DTC interpretation chart (Part 40 of 44). Golf, GTI & Jetta w/1.8L engine

DTC SAE	DTC VAG	DTC text	Corrective action
P1639	18047	Throttle Position (TP) sensor -G79- + sender -2- for accelerator pedal position -G185-, implausible signal 1)	- Check accelerator pedal position sensor:
P1640	18048	Control module faulty	- Replace motronic Engine Control Module (ECM)

1) For these malfunctions, ECM switches on the EPC warning lamp in instrument cluster.

VW1020000157410X

Fig. 8 Motronic DTC interpretation chart (Part 41 of 44). Golf, GTI & Jetta w/1.8L engine

DTC SAE	DTC VAG	DTC text	Corrective action
P1648	18056	Powertrain databus faulty	- Check databus
P1649	18057	Powertrain databus missing massage from ABS control module	- Check databus - Check DTC memory of ABS control module
P1650	18058	Powertrain databus missing massage from instrument cluster	- Check databus - Check instrument cluster: perform On Board Diagnostic (OBD)

VW1020000157420X

Fig. 8 Motronic DTC interpretation chart (Part 42 of 44). Golf, GTI & Jetta w/1.8L engine

DTC SAE	DTC VAG	DTC text	Corrective action
P1676	18084	Fault light for power accelerator activation -K132- Electrical malfunction in circuit 1)	- Check warning lamp
P1677	18085	Fault light for power accelerator activation -K132- Short circuit to B+1)	
P1683	18091	Powertrain databus implausible massage from airbag control module	- Check databus - Check airbag system
P1690	18098	Malfunction Indicator Lamp (MIL) -K83- electrical malfunction in circuit	- Check warning lamp
P1693	18101	Malfunction Indicator Lamp (MIL) -K83- Short circuit to B+	

1) For these malfunctions, ECM switches on the EPC warning lamp in instrument cluster.

VW1020000157430X

Fig. 8 Motronic DTC interpretation chart (Part 43 of 44). Golf, GTI & Jetta w/1.8L engine

DTC SAE	DTC VAG	DTC text	Corrective action
P1853	18261	Powertrain databus implausible message from ABS control module	- Check databus - Check DTC memory of ABS control module:

VW1020000157440X

Fig. 8 Motronic DTC interpretation chart (Part 44 of 44). Golf, GTI & Jetta w/1.8L engine

DTC SAE	DTC V.A.G	DTC text	Corrective action
P0102	16486	Mass or Volume Air Flow Circ Low Input	- Check Mass Air Flow (MAF) meter
P0103	16487	Mass or Volume Air Flow Circ High Input	- Check intake system for leaks (unmetered air) - Check fuse 43
P0106	16490	Manifold Absolute Pressure or Barometric Pressure - G71-/-F96- 1) Range/Performance	- Check sensor for charge pressure

1) Manifold Absolute Pressure is communicated via charge air pressure sensor -G31- (instead of the implicated -G71-), Barometric pressure is communicated via Barometric pressure (BARO) sensor -F96- (in Engine Control Module -ECM-).

VW1020000156010X

Fig. 9 Motronic DTC interpretation chart (Part 1 of 38). New Beetle w/1.8L engine

DTC SAE	DTC V.A.G	DTC text	Corrective action
P0112	16496	Intake Air Temp.Circ Low Input	- Check intake air temperature sender
P0113	16497	Intake Air Temp.Circ. High Input	
P0116	16500	Engine Coolant Temp.Circ Range/Performance	- Check coolant temperature sender
P0117	16501	Engine Coolant Temp.Circ Low Input	- Check thermostat
P0118	16502	Engine Coolant Temp.Circ. High Input	

VW1020000156020X

Fig. 9 Motronic DTC interpretation chart (Part 2 of 38). New Beetle w/1.8L engine

DTC SAE	DTC V.A.G	DTC text	Corrective action
P0130	16514	O2 Sensor Circ., Bank1-Sensor1 Malfunction	- Check oxygen sensor heater before catalyst
P0131	16515	O2 Sensor Circ., Bank1-Sensor1 Low Voltage	- Check oxygen sensor and oxygen sensor control before catalytic converter
P0132	16516	O2 Sensor Circ., Bank1-Sensor1 High Voltage	- Check oxygen sensor aging Bank 1 oxygen sensor 1
P0133	16517	O2 Sensor Circ., Bank1-Sensor1 Slow Response	- Check oxygen sensor and oxygen sensor control after catalyst
P0134	16518	O2 Sensor Circ., Bank1-Sensor1 No Activity Detected	- Check oxygen sensor and oxygen sensor control before catalyst

VW1020000156030X

Fig. 9 Motronic DTC interpretation chart (Part 3 of 38). New Beetle w/1.8L engine

DTC SAE	DTC V.A.G	DTC text	Corrective action
P0136	16520	O2 Sensor Circ., Bank1-Sensor 2 Malfunction	- Check oxygen sensor and oxygen sensor control after catalyst
P0137	16521	O2 Sensor Circ., Bank1-Sensor 2 Low Voltage	- Check heated oxygen sensor after catalyst
P0138	16522	O2 Sensor Circ., Bank1-Sensor 2 High Voltage	
P0139	16523	O2 Sensor Circ., Bank1-Sensor 2 Slow Response	
P0140	16524	O2 Sensor Circ., Bank1-Sensor 2 No Activity Detected	

VW1020000156040X

Fig. 9 Motronic DTC interpretation chart (Part 4 of 38). New Beetle w/1.8L engine

DTC SAE	DTC V.A.G	DTC text	Corrective action
P0170	16554	Fuel Trim, Bank1 Malfunction	- Check fuel pressure regulator and holding pressure
			- Check injectors Checking quantity injected and for leaks
			- Check fuel pump
			- Check secondary air system for leaks
			- Check hoses and connecting pipes to/between components
			- Check vacuum pipes for leaks

VW1020000156050X

Fig. 9 Motronic DTC interpretation chart (Part 5 of 38). New Beetle w/1.8L engine

DTC SAE	DTC V.A.G	DTC text	Corrective action
P0172	16556	Fuel Trim, Bank1 System too Rich	- Check fuel pressure regulator and holding pressure
			- Check injectors Checking quantity injected and for leaks
			- Check activated charcoal filter solenoid valve 1
P0236	16620	Turbocharger Boost Sensor (A) Circ Range/Performance	- Check sensor for charge pressure
P0237	16621	Turbocharger Boost Sensor (A) Circ Low Input	
P0238	16622	Turbocharger Boost Sensor (A) Circ High Input	

VW1020000156070X

Fig. 9 Motronic DTC interpretation chart (Part 7 of 38). New Beetle w/1.8L engine

DTC SAE	DTC V.A.G	DTC text	Corrective action
P0321	16705	Ign./Distributor Eng. Speed Inp.Circ Range/Performance	- Check engine speed sender
P0322	16706	Ign./Distributor Eng.Speed Inp.Circ. No Signal	
P0327	16711	Knock Sensor 1 Circ Low Input	- Check knock sensor and knock control
P0328	16712	Knock Sensor 1 Circ High Input	- Loosen knock sensor and retighten to 15 ft lbs
P0332	16716	Knock Sensor 2 Circ Low Input	
P0333	16717	Knock Sensor 2 Circ High Input	

VW1020000156090X

Fig. 9 Motronic DTC interpretation chart (Part 9 of 38). New Beetle w/1.8L engine

DTC SAE	DTC V.A.G	DTC text	Corrective action
P0420	16804	Catalyst System, Bank1 Efficiency Below Threshold	- Check catalyst
P0440	16824	EVAP Emission Contr.Sys Malfunction	- Check activated charcoal filter solenoid valve 1
			- Check hoses and connecting pipes from fuel tank to throttle valve control module

VW1020000156110X

Fig. 9 Motronic DTC interpretation chart (Part 11 of 38). New Beetle w/1.8L engine

DTC SAE	DTC V.A.G	DTC text	Corrective action
P0171	16555	Fuel Trim, Bank1 System too Lean	- Check fuel pressure regulator and holding pressure
			- Check injectors Checking quantity injected and for leaks
			- Check fuel pump:
			- Check intake system for leaks
			- Check exhaust system for leaks
			- Check secondary air system for leaks
			- Check vacuum pipes for leaks

VW1020000156060X

Fig. 9 Motronic DTC interpretation chart (Part 6 of 38). New Beetle w/1.8L engine

DTC SAE	DTC V.A.G	DTC text	Corrective action
P0300	16684	Random/Multiple Cylinder Misfire Detected	- Check injectors
P0301	16685	Cyl.1 Misfire Detected	- Check ignition cables and spark plugs
P0302	16686	Cyl.2 Misfire Detected	- Check ignition with power output stages
P0303	16687	Cyl.3 Misfire Detected	- Check misfiring detection
P0304	16688	Cyl.4 Misfire Detected	

VW1020000156080X

Fig. 9 Motronic DTC interpretation chart (Part 8 of 38). New Beetle w/1.8L engine

DTC SAE	DTC V.A.G	DTC text	Corrective action
P0341	16725	Camshaft Pos.Sensor Circ Range/Performance	- Check Hall sender
P0342	16726	Camshaft Pos.Sensor Circ Low Input	
P0343	16727	Camshaft Pos.Sensor Circ High Input	
P0411	16795	Sec.Air Inj.Sys. Incorrect Flow Detected	- Check secondary air pump motor
			- Check combi-valve
			- Check secondary air inlet valve
			- Check hoses and connecting pipes to/between components

VW1020000156100X

Fig. 9 Motronic DTC interpretation chart (Part 10 of 38). New Beetle w/1.8L engine

DTC SAE	DTC V.A.G	DTC text	Corrective action
P0420	16804	Catalyst System, Bank1 Efficiency Below Threshold	- Check catalyst
P0440	16824	EVAP Emission Contr.Sys Malfunction	- Check activated charcoal filter solenoid valve 1
			- Check hoses and connecting pipes from fuel tank to throttle valve control module

VW1020000156120X

Fig. 9 Motronic DTC interpretation chart (Part 12 of 38). New Beetle w/1.8L engine

DTC SAE	DTC V.A.G	DTC text	Corrective action
P0441	16825	EVAP Emission Contr.Sys.Incorrect Purge Flow	- Check activated charcoal filter solenoid valve 1 - Check hoses and connecting pipes from fuel tank to throttle valve control module
P0442	16826	EVAP Emission Contr.Sys. (Small Leak) Leak Detected	- Check activated charcoal filter system
P0455	16839	EVAP Emission Contr.Sys. (Large Leak) Leak Detected	

VW1020000156130X

Fig. 9 Motronic DTC interpretation chart (Part 13 of 38). New Beetle w/1.8L engine

DTC SAE	DTC V.A.G	DTC text	Corrective action
P0501	16885	Vehicle Speed Sensor Range/Performance	- Checking speed signal
P0506	16890	Idle Control System RPM Lower than Expected	- Check throttle valve control module
P0507	16891	Idle Control System RPM Higher than Expected	
P0532	16916	A/C system Pressure Sensor Signal too Small	- Check pressure switch for A/C system: • A/C systems must only be serviced by properly trained technicians
P0533	16917	A/C system Pressure Sensor Signal too Large	

VW1020000156140X

Fig. 9 Motronic DTC interpretation chart (Part 14 of 38). New Beetle w/1.8L engine

DTC SAE	DTC V.A.G	DTC text	Corrective action
P0560	16944	System Voltage Malfunction	- Check voltage supply
P0562	16946	System Voltage Low Voltage	
P0563	16947	System Voltage High Voltage	
P0571	16955	Cruise/Brake Switch (A) Circ Malfunction1)	- Check brake light switch and brake pedal switch
P0601	16985	Internal Contr.Module Memory Check Sum Error	- Replace engine control module
P0604	16988	Internal Contr.Module Random Access Memory (RAM) Error	
P0605	16989	Internal Contr.Module ROM Test Error	

1) The system monitors both brake light switch -F and brake pedal switch -F47.

VW1020000156150X

Fig. 9 Motronic DTC interpretation chart (Part 15 of 38). New Beetle w/1.8L engine

DTC SAE	DTC V.A.G	DTC text	Corrective action
P1102	17510	O2 Sensor Heating Circ., Bank1-Sensor1 Short to B+	- Check heated oxygen sensor before catalyst
P1105	17513	O2 Sensor Heating Circ., Bank1-Sensor2 Short to B+	- Check heated oxygen sensor after catalyst
P1113	17521	Bank1-Sensor1, resistance too high	- Check heated oxygen sensor before catalyst
P1114	17522	O2 Sensor, Bank 1 Sensor 2, resistance too high	- Check heated oxygen sensor after catalyst
P1115	17523	O2 Sensor Heater Circ., Bank1-Sensor1 Short to Ground	- Check heated oxygen sensor before catalyst
P1116	17524	O2 Sensor Heater Circ., Bank1-Sensor1 Open	

VW1020000156160X

Fig. 9 Motronic DTC interpretation chart (Part 16 of 38). New Beetle w/1.8L engine

DTC SAE	DTC V.A.G	DTC text	Corrective action
P1117	17525	O2 Sensor Heater Circ., Bank1-Sensor2 Short to Ground	- Check heated oxygen sensor after catalyst
P1118	17526	O2 Sensor Heater Circ., Bank1-Sensor2 Open	
P1127	17535	Long Term Fuel Trim mult.,Bank1 System too Rich	- Check fuel pressure regulator and holding pressure - Check injectors Checking quantity injected and for leaks - Check tank ventilation valves

VW1020000156170X

Fig. 9 Motronic DTC interpretation chart (Part 17 of 38). New Beetle w/1.8L engine

DTC SAE	DTC V.A.G	DTC text	Corrective action
P1128	17536	Long Term Fuel Trim mult., Bank1 System too Lean	- Check fuel pressure regulator and holding pressure - Check injectors quantity injected and for leaks - Check fuel pump - Check intake system for leaks ⇒ Page 24-106 - Check exhaust system for leaks - Check secondary air system for leaks - Check vacuum pipes for leaks - Check Mass Air Flow (MAF) sensor - Check air filter and filter screen.

VW1020000156180X

Fig. 9 Motronic DTC interpretation chart (Part 18 of 38). New Beetle w/1.8L engine

DTC SAE	DTC V.A.G	DTC text	Corrective action
P1136	17544	Long Term Fuel Trim Add.Fuel, Bank1 System too Lean	- Check fuel pressure regulator and holding pressure - Check injectors for quantity injected, and leaks - Check fuel pump - Check intake system for leaks - Check exhaust system for leaks - Check secondary air system for leaks - Check vacuum pipes for leaks

Note:

add. = additive means, the malfunction only has an effect at idle speed.

VW1020000156190X

Fig. 9 Motronic DTC interpretation chart (Part 19 of 38). New Beetle w/1.8L engine

DTC SAE	DTC V.A.G	DTC text	Corrective action
P1137	17545	Long Term Fuel Trim Add.Fuel, Bank1 System too Rich	- Check fuel pressure regulator and holding pressure - Check injectors quantity injected and for leaks - Check tank ventilation valves

Note:

add. = additive means, the malfunction only has an effect at idle speed.

VW1020000156200X

Fig. 9 Motronic DTC interpretation chart (Part 20 of 38). New Beetle w/1.8L engine

DTC SAE	DTC V.A.G	DTC text	Corrective action
P1171	17579	Throttle Actuation Potentiometer Sign.2 Range/Performance [1]	- Check throttle valve control module
P1172	17580	Throttle Actuation Potentiometer Sign.2 Signal too Low [1]	
P1173	17581	Throttle Actuation Potentiometer Sign.2 Signal too High [1]	

1) Engine control module switches on the EPC warning lamp in instrument cluster with this malfunction.

VW1020000156210X

Fig. 9 Motronic DTC interpretation chart (Part 21 of 38). New Beetle w/1.8L engine

DTC SAE	DTC V.A.G	DTC text	Corrective action
P1213	17621	Cyl. 1-Fuel Inj.Circ. Short to B+	- Check injectors
P1214	17622	Cyl. 2-Fuel Inj.Circ. Short to B+	
P1215	17623	Cyl. 3-Fuel Inj.Circ. Short to B+	
P1216	17624	Cyl. 4-Fuel Inj.Circ. Short to B+	
P1225	17633	Cyl.1-Fuel Inj.Circ. Short to Ground	
P1226	17634	Cyl. 2-Fuel Inj.Circ. Short to Ground	
P1227	17635	Cyl. 3-Fuel Inj.Circ. Short to Ground	
P1228	17636	Cyl. 4-Fuel Inj.Circ. Short to Ground	

VW1020000156230X

Fig. 9 Motronic DTC interpretation chart (Part 23 of 38). New Beetle w/1.8L engine

DTC SAE	DTC V.A.G	DTC text	Corrective action
P1325	17733	Cyl.1-Knock Contr Limit Attained	- Check knock sensor and knock control
P1326	17734	Cyl.2-Knock Contr Limit Attained	- Rectify abnormal engine running noises (accessories loose, brackets/bolts broken)
P1327	17735	Cyl.3-Knock Contr Limit Attained	- Check connectors and wiring using wiring diagrams
P1328	17736	Cyl.4-Knock Contr Limit Attained	- Loosen knock sensor and re-tighten to 15 ft lbs - Change type of fuel

VW1020000156250X

Fig. 9 Motronic DTC interpretation chart (Part 25 of 38). New Beetle w/1.8L engine

DTC SAE	DTC V.A.G	DTC text	Corrective action
P1340	17748	Crankshaft-/Camshaft Pos.Sens.Signals Out of Sequence	- Check Hall sender - Check engine speed sender
P1355	17763	Ignition activation cyl. 1 open circuit	- Check ignition coils and power output stage
P1356	17764	Ignition activation cyl. 1 short circuit to B+	
P1357	17765	Ignition activation cyl. 1 short circuit to Ground (GND)	
P1358	17766	Ignition activation cyl. 2 open circuit	
P1359	17767	Ignition activation cyl. 2 short circuit to B+	
P1360	17768	Ignition activation cyl. 2 short circuit to Ground (GND)	

VW1020000156270X

Fig. 9 Motronic DTC interpretation chart (Part 27 of 38). New Beetle w/1.8L engine

DTC SAE	DTC V.A.G	DTC text	Corrective action
P1176	17584	O2 Correction Behind Catalyst,B1 Limit Attained	- Checking oxygen sensor aging Bank 1 oxygen sensor 1 - Checking oxygen sensor and oxygen sensor control after catalyst - Check intake system for leaks
P1196	17604	O2 Sensor Heater Circ., Bank1-Sensor1 Electrical Malfunction	- Check heated oxygen sensor before catalyst
P1198	17606	O2 Sensor Heater Circ., Bank1-Sensor2 Electrical Malfunction	- Check heated oxygen sensor after catalyst

VW1020000156220X

Fig. 9 Motronic DTC interpretation chart (Part 22 of 38). New Beetle w/1.8L engine

DTC SAE	DTC V.A.G	DTC text	Corrective action
P1237	17645	Cyl. 1-Fuel Inj.Circ. Open Circ.	- Check injectors
P1238	17646	Cyl. 2-Fuel Inj.Circ. Open Circ.	
P1239	17647	Cyl. 3-Fuel Inj.Circ. Open Circ.	
P1240	17648	Cyl. 4-Fuel Inj.Circ. Open Circ.	
P1287	17695	turbocharger bypass valve open	- Check bypass valve for turbocharger
P1288	17696	turbocharger bypass valve short to B+	
P1289	17697	turbocharger bypass valve short to ground	
P1296	17704	Malfunction in cooling system [1]	- Check Engine Coolant Temperature (ECT) sensor - Check thermostat.

VW1020000156240X

Fig. 9 Motronic DTC interpretation chart (Part 24 of 38). New Beetle w/1.8L engine

DTC SAE	DTC V.A.G	DTC text	Corrective action
P1335	17743	engine torque control 2 adaptation at limit [1]	- Check hose setup - Check intake air temperature sender
P1336	17744	engine torque control adaptation at limit	- Check Mass Air Flow (MAF) Sensor - Check coolant temperature sender

1) Engine control module switches on the EPC warning lamp in instrument cluster with this malfunction.

VW1020000156260X

Fig. 9 Motronic DTC interpretation chart (Part 26 of 38). New Beetle w/1.8L engine

DTC SAE	DTC V.A.G	DTC text	Corrective action
P1361	17769	Ignition activation cyl. 3 open circuit	- Check ignition coils and power output stage
P1362	17770	Ignition activation cyl. 3 short circuit to B+	
P1363	17771	Ignition activation cyl. 3 short circuit to Ground (GND)	
P1364	17772	Ignition activation cyl. 4 open circuit	
P1365	17773	Ignition activation cyl. 4 short circuit to B+	
P1366	17774	Ignition activation cyl. 4 short circuit to Ground (GND)	
P1386	17794	Control Module Malfunctioning [1]	- Replace engine control module
P1387	17795	Control Module Malfunctioning [1]	
P1388	17796	Control Module Malfunctioning [1]	

1) Engine control module switches on the EPC warning lamp in instrument cluster with this malfunction.

VW1020000156280X

Fig. 9 Motronic DTC interpretation chart (Part 28 of 38). New Beetle w/1.8L engine

DTC SAE	DTC V.A.G	DTC text	Corrective action
P1410	17818	Tank Ventilation Valve Circ Short to B+	- Check activated charcoal filter solenoid valve 1 output DTM
P1420	17828	Sec.Air Inj.Valve Circ Electrical Malfunction	- Check secondary air inlet valve
P1421	17829	Sec.Air Inj.Valve Circ Short to Ground	
P1422	17830	Sec.Air Inj.Sys.Contr.Valve Circ Short to B+	
P1424	17832	Sec.Air Inj.Sys.,Bank1 Leak Detected	- Check secondary air system for leaks
P1425	17833	Tank Vent.Valve Short to Ground	- Check activated charcoal filter solenoid valve 1
P1426	17834	Tank Vent.Valve Open	

VW1020000156290X

Fig. 9 Motronic DTC interpretation chart (Part 29 of 38). New Beetle w/1.8L engine

DTC SAE	DTC V.A.G	DTC text	Corrective action
P1471	17879	EVAP Emission Contr.LDP Circ. Short to B+	- Check diagnostic pump
P1472	17880	EVAP Emission Contr.LEDP Circ. Short to Ground	- Check activated charcoal filter system for leaks
P1473	17881	EVAP Emission Contr.LDP Circ. Open Circ.	
P1475	17883	EVAP Emission Contr.LDP Circ. Malfunction/Signal Circ.Open	
P1476	17884	EVAP Emission Contr.LDP Circ. Malfunction/Insufficient Vacuum	

VW1020000156310X

Fig. 9 Motronic DTC interpretation chart (Part 31 of 38). New Beetle w/1.8L engine

DTC SAE	DTC V.A.G	DTC text	Corrective action
P1546	17954	Boost Pressure Contr.Valve -N75 Short to B+	- Check boost pressure control valve
P1547	17955	Boost Pressure Contr.Valve -N75 Short to Ground	
P1548	17956	Boost Pressure Contr.Valve -N75 Open	
P1550	17958	Charge Pressure Deviation	
P1555	17963	Charge Pressure Upper Limit exceeded	
P1556	17964	Charge Pressure Contr Negative Deviation	
P1557	17965	Charge Pressure Contr Positive Deviation	

VW1020000156330X

Fig. 9 Motronic DTC interpretation chart (Part 33 of 38). New Beetle w/1.8L engine

DTC SAE	DTC V.A.G	DTC text	Corrective action
P1602	18010	Power supply (B+) Terminal 30 Low Voltage	- Check voltage supply for control module
P1603	18011	Internal Control Module, Self Check	- Replace engine control module (J220)
P1604	18012	Control module malfunctioning 1)	
P1626	18034	Data-Bus Powertrain Missing Message from Transm.Contr	- Check data bus

1) Engine control module switches on the EPC warning lamp in instrument cluster with this malfunction.

VW1020000156350X

Fig. 9 Motronic DTC interpretation chart (Part 35 of 38). New Beetle w/1.8L engine

DTC SAE	DTC V.A.G	DTC text	Corrective action
P1432	17840	Sec.Air Inj.Valve Open	- Check secondary air inlet valve
P1433	17841	Sec.Air Inj.Sys.Pump Relay Circ Open	- Check secondary air pump relay
P1434	17842	Sec.Air Inj.Sys.Pump Relay Circ. Short to B+	
P1435	17843	Sec.Air Inj.Sys.Pump Relay Circ. Short to Ground	

VW1020000156300X

Fig. 9 Motronic DTC interpretation chart (Part 30 of 38). New Beetle w/1.8L engine

DTC SAE	DTC V.A.G	DTC text	Corrective action
P1500	17908	Fuel Pump Relay -J17 Circ Electrical Malfunction	- Check Fuel Pump (FP) relay
P1501	17909	Fuel Pump Relay -J17 Circ Short to Ground	- Check fuel pump relay
P1502	17910	Fuel Pump Relay -J17 Circ. Short to B+	
P1539	17947	Clutch pedal switch -F36 Implausible signal	- Check clutch pedal switch
P1541	17949	Fuel Pump Relay -J17 Circ Open	- Check fuel pump relay
P1542	17950	Throttle Actuation Potentiometer -G187 Range/Performance 1)	- Check throttle valve control module
P1543	17951	Throttle Actuation Potentiometer -G187 Signal too Low 1)	
P1544	17952	Throttle Actuation Potentiometer -G187 Signal too High 1)	
P1545	17953	Throttle Pos.Contr Malfunction 1)	

1) Engine control module switches on the EPC warning lamp in instrument cluster with this malfunction.

VW1020000156320X

Fig. 9 Motronic DTC interpretation chart (Part 32 of 38). New Beetle w/1.8L engine

DTC SAE	DTC V.A.G	DTC text	Corrective action
P1558	17966	Throttle Actuator Electrical Malfunction1)	- Check throttle valve control module
P1559	17967	Idle Speed Contr.Throttle Pos Adaptation Malfunction 1)	- Adapt engine control module to throttle valve control module
P1565	17973	Idle Speed Control Throttle Position lower limit not attained	- Check throttle valve control module
P1568	17976	Idle Speed Contr.Throttle Pos., mechanical Malfunction 1)	
P1569	17977	Cruise control switch -E45- Unplausible signal	- Check cruise control switch

1) Engine control module switches on the EPC warning lamp in instrument cluster with this malfunction.

VW1020000156340X

Fig. 9 Motronic DTC interpretation chart (Part 34 of 38). New Beetle w/1.8L engine

DTC SAE	DTC V.A.G	DTC text	Corrective action
P1630	18038	Accelera.Pedal Pos.Sensor 1 Signal too Low1)	- Check accelerator pedal
P1631	18039	Accelera.Pedal Pos.Sensor 1 Signal too High 1)	
P1633	18041	Accelera.Pedal Pos.Sensor 2 Signal too Low 1)	
P1634	18042	Accelera.Pedal Pos.Sensor 2 Signal too High 1)	
P1639	18047	Accelera.Pedal Pos.Sensor 1 + 2 Range/Performance 1), 2)	

1) Engine control module switches on the EPC warning lamp in instrument cluster with this malfunction. Significance of EPC warning lamp ⇒ **Page 01-10**.

2) Incorrect DTC display. Correct display should be: Accelera. Pedal Pos. Sensor1 Range/Performance

VW1020000156360X

Fig. 9 Motronic DTC interpretation chart (Part 36 of 38). New Beetle w/1.8L engine

DTC SAE	DTC V.A.G	DTC text	Corrective action
P1640	18048	Internal Contr.Module (EEPROM) Error	- Replace engine control module (J220)
P1648	18056	Data Bus Powertrain defect	- Check data bus
P1649	18057	Data Bus Powertrain missing massage from ABS-CM	
P1650	18058	Data Bus Powertrain missing massage from instrument cluster	
P1676	18084	Drive by Wire-MIL Circ Electrical Malfunction 1)	- Check engine control module wiring to EPC warning lamp
P1677	18085	Drive by Wire-MIL Circ Short to B+	
P1678	18086	Drive by Wire-MIL Circ Short to Ground	
P1679	18087	Drive by Wire-MIL Circ Open	
P1681	18089	Contr.Unit Programming Programming not Finished	- Replace engine control module

VW1020000156370X

Fig. 9 Motronic DTC interpretation chart (Part 37 of 38). New Beetle w/1.8L engine

Diagnostic Trouble Codes (DTCs) SAE		Diagnostic Trouble Code display	Malfunction elimination
–		Cruise control switch E45, implausible Signal	Check cruise control
P0102		Mass or Volume Air Flow Circ. Low Input	Check Mass Air Flow sensor
P0103		Mass or Volume Air Flow Circ. High Input	
P0112		Intake Air Temp.Circ. Low Input	Check Intake Air Temperature sensor
P0113		Intake Air Temp.Circ. High Input	
P0116		Engine Coolant Temp.Circ. Range/Performance	Check Engine Coolant Temperature sensor
P0118		Engine Coolant Temp.Circ. Low Input	
P0118		Engine Coolant Temp.Circ. High Input	

VW1029900137010X

Fig. 10 Motronic DTC interpretation chart (Part 1 of 15). New Beetle w/2.0L engine

Diagnostic Trouble Codes (DTCs) SAE		Diagnostic Trouble Code display	Malfunction elimination
P0131		Bank 1 Sensor 1 Voltage too low	Check Oxygen sensor heating before catalyst
P0132		Bank 1 Sensor 1 High Voltage	Check Oxygen sensor aging and Oxygen sensor before catalyst
P0133		Bank 1 Sensor 1 Signal too slow	Check Oxygen sensor and Oxygen sensor control after catalyst
P0134		Bank 1 Sensor 1 no activity	Check Oxygen sensor and Oxygen sensor control before catalyst
P0135		Bank 1 Sensor 1 Heater circuit electrical malfunction	Check Oxygen sensor heating before catalyst

VW1029900137030X

Fig. 10 Motronic DTC interpretation chart (Part 3 of 15). New Beetle w/2.0L engine

Diagnostic Trouble Codes (DTCs) SAE		Diagnostic Trouble Code display	Malfunction elimination
P0300		Random / Multiple Cylinder Misfire Detected	Fuel shortage, fill fuel tank
P0301		Cyl. 1 Misfire Detected	Check injectors
P0302		Cyl. 2 Misfire Detected	Check ignition coils with power output stage
P0303		Cyl. 3 Misfire Detected	Check Engine Speed sensor (RPM)
P0304		Cyl. 4 Misfire Detected	Check misfiring detection

VW1029900137050X

Fig. 10 Motronic DTC interpretation chart (Part 5 of 15). New Beetle w/2.0L engine

DTC SAE	DTC V.A.G	DTC text	Corrective action
P1691	18099	Malfunction Indication Light Open	- Check wiring from engine control module to Malfunction Indicator Lamp (MIL)
P1692	18100	Malfunction Indication Light Short to Ground	
P1693	18101	Malfunction Indication Light Short to B+	
P1853	18261	CAN-Bus unplausible massage from ABS-SG	- Check data-bus

VW1020000156380X

Fig. 9 Motronic DTC interpretation chart (Part 38 of 38). New Beetle w/1.8L engine

Diagnostic Trouble Codes (DTCs) SAE		Diagnostic Trouble Code display	Malfunction elimination
P0120		Throttle Position sensor G69 electrical malfunction in circuit	Check Throttle Control Module
P0121		Throttle Position sensor A Circ. Malfunction	Check Throttle Control Module
P0122		Throttle Position Sensor A Circ. Low Input	
P0125		Engine Coolant Temperature target for Oxygen sensor control not obtained	Check Engine Coolant Temperature sensor Check thermostat

VW1029900137020X

Fig. 10 Motronic DTC interpretation chart (Part 2 of 15). New Beetle w/2.0L engine

Diagnostic Trouble Codes (DTCs) SAE		Diagnostic Trouble Code (DTC) display	Corrective action
P0137		Bank 1 Sensor 2 Voltage too low	Check Oxygen sensor and Oxygen sensor control after catalyst
P0138		02 Sensor Circ. (B1–S2) High Voltage	
P0140		02 Sensor Circ. (B1–S2) No Activity detected	
P0141		02 Sensor Heater Circ. (B1–S2) Malfunction	Check Oxygen sensor heating after catalyst

VW1029900137040X

Fig. 10 Motronic DTC interpretation chart (Part 4 of 15). New Beetle w/2.0L engine

Diagnostic Trouble Codes (DTCs) SAE		Diagnostic Trouble Code display	Malfunction elimination
P0321		Ign./Distributor Eng.Speed Inp.Circ. Range/Performance	Check Engine Speed sensor (RPM)
P0322		Ign./Distributor Eng.Speed Inp.Circ. No Signal	
P0327		Knock Sensor 1 Circ. Low Input	Loosen knock sensor and retighten to 15 ft lb
P0328		Knock sensor 1 -G61 Signal too high	
P0332		Knock Sensor 2 Circ. Low Input	Check knock sensors
P0333		Knock sensor 2 -G66 Signal too high	
P0341		Camshaft Position sensor G40 implausible signal	Check Camshaft Position sensor
P0411		Sec.Air Inj.Sys. Incorrect flow detected	Check Secondary Air Injection valve and secondary Air Injection pump relay
P0422		Bank 1 Main Catalyst Efficiency Below Threshold	Check catalyst

VW1029900137060X

Fig. 10 Motronic DTC interpretation chart (Part 6 of 15). New Beetle w/2.0L engine

Diagnostic Trouble Codes (DTCs) SAE		Diagnostic Trouble Code (DTC) display	Corrective action
P0440		Tank vent system, malfunction	EVAP canister purge regulator
P0442		EVAP Emission Contr.Sys. (Small Leak) leak detected	Check Evaporative emissions system
P0455		Tank vent system, (Large leak) leak detected	
P0501		Vehicle Speed Sensor Range/Performance	Check Vehicle Speed Signal
P0506		Idle Speed Control System, RPM Lower than Expected	Check Throttle Control Module
P0507		Idle speed control RPM over specified value	
P0510		Closed Throttle Position switch, F60 Malfunction	
P0605		Control Module malfunction	Replace Engine Control Module J220

VW1029900137070X

Fig. 10 Motronic DTC interpretation chart (Part 7 of 15). New Beetle w/2.0L engine

Diagnostic Trouble Codes (DTCs) SAE		Diagnostic Trouble Code display	Malfunction elimination
P1176		02 Correction Behind Catalyst B1, Limit Attained	Check intake system for leaks
			Check Oxygen sensor aging Bank 1 Oxygen sensor 1
			Check Oxygen sensor heating after catalyst
			Check Oxygen sensor and Oxygen sensor control after catalyst

VW1029900137080X

Fig. 10 Motronic DTC interpretation chart (Part 8 of 15). New Beetle w/2.0L engine

Diagnostic Trouble Codes (DTCs) SAE		Diagnostic Trouble Code display	Malfunction elimination
P1213		Cyl. 1 -N30 Fuel Inj. Circ. Short to B+	Check Fuel injectors
P1214		Cyl. 2 -N31 Fuel Inj. Circ. Short to B+	
P1215		Cyl. 3 -N32 Fuel Inj. Circ. Short to B+	
P1216		Cyl. 4 -N33 Fuel Inj. Circ. Short to B+	
P1225		Cyl. 1 -N30 Fuel Inj. Circ. Short to Ground	Check Fuel injectors
P1226		Cyl. 2 -N31 Fuel Inj. Circ. Short to Ground	
P1227		Cyl. 3 -N32 Fuel Inj. Circ. Short to Ground	
P1228		Cyl. 4 -N33 Fuel Inj. Circ. Short to Ground	

VW1029900137090X

Fig. 10 Motronic DTC interpretation chart (Part 9 of 15). New Beetle w/2.0L engine

Diagnostic Trouble Codes (DTCs) SAE		Diagnostic Trouble Code display	Malfunction elimination
P1237		Cyl. 1 -N30 Fuel Inj. Circ. Open Circ.	Check Fuel injectors
P1238		Cyl. 2 -N31 Fuel Inj. Circ. Open Circ.	
P1239		Cyl. 3 -N32 Fuel Inj. Circ. Open Circ.	
P1240		Cyl. 4 -N33 Fuel Inj. Circ. Open Circ.	
P1300		Combustion misfire recognized, Reason: fuel problem	Fuel level below 2 gallons, fill tank
			Check fuel gauge sensor signal
			Check wiring between ECM and instrument cluster using Wiring diagram

VW1029900137100X

Fig. 10 Motronic DTC interpretation chart (Part 10 of 15). New Beetle w/2.0L engine

Diagnostic Trouble Codes (DTCs) SAE		Diagnostic Trouble Code display	Malfunction elimination
P1325		Cyl.1–Knock Contr. Limit Attained	Loosen knock sensors and re-tighten to 15 ft lb
			Check knock sensors
P1326		Cyl.2–Knock Contr. Limit Attained	Fix cause of abnormal engine running noises
P1327		Cyl.3–Knock Contr. Limit Attained	Fill with fuel (91 RON minimum)
P1328		Cyl.4–Knock Contr. Limit Attained	

VW1029900137110X

Fig. 10 Motronic DTC interpretation chart (Part 11 of 15). New Beetle w/2.0L engine

Diagnostic Trouble Codes (DTCs) SAE		Diagnostic Trouble Code display	Malfunction elimination
P1410		Tank Vent Valve -N80 Short to B+	Check EVAP canister purge regulator
P1420		Secondary Air Injection valve -N112 electr. malfunctrion	Check Secondary Air Injection
P1421		Secondary Air Injection valve -N112 Short to ground	
P1422		Secondary Air Injection valve -N112 Circ. Short to B+	
P1425		Tank Vent valve -N80 Short to ground	Check EVAP canister purge regulator
P1426		Tank Vent Valve -N80 Open	
P1450		Secondary Air Injection system short to B+	Check Secondary Air Injection pump relay
P1451		Secondary Air Injection system short to ground	
P1452		Secondary Air Injection system Open	

VW1029900137120X

Fig. 10 Motronic DTC interpretation chart (Part 12 of 15). New Beetle w/2.0L engine

Diagnostic Trouble Codes (DTCs) SAE		Diagnostic Trouble Code display	Malfunction elimination
P1471		Leak Detection Pump Tank vent system Short to plus	Check Leak Detection Pump
P1472		Leak Detection Pump Tank vent system Short to ground	Check EVAP emissions system
P1473		Leak Detection Pump Tank vent system break (interruption)	
P1475		Leak Detection Pump Tank vent system malfunction / no signal	
P1476		Leak Detection Pump Tank vent system malfunction / pressure too low	
P1477		Leak Detection pump Tank ventilation system malfunction	

VW1029900137130X

Fig. 10 Motronic DTC interpretation chart (Part 13 of 15). New Beetle w/2.0L engine

Diagnostic Trouble Codes (DTCs) SAE		Diagnostic Trouble Code display	Malfunction elimination
P1500		Fuel Pump Relay J17 electrical malfunction	Check fuel pump relay ⇒ Wiring diagrams
P1502		Fuel Pump Relay -J17 Short to B+	
P1543		Angle sensor -1- for Throttle drive -G187 signal too small	Check Throttle Control Module
P1544		Angle sensor -1- for Throttle drive -G187 signal too high	Check intake air system for leaks
P1582		Idle Adaption at Limit	Check exhaust system for leaks
			Check fuel pressure regulator and residual pressure
			Check EVAP canister purge regulator

VW1029900137140X

Fig. 10 Motronic DTC interpretation chart (Part 14 of 15). New Beetle w/2.0L engine

Diagnostic Trouble Codes (DTCs) SAE		Diagnostic Trouble Code display	Malfunction elimination
P1612		Engine Control Module Incorrect Coding	Code Engine Control Module
P1626		Data bus Drive missing comand from man. trans. -SG	Drive range check signal
P1851		Data bus Drive missing command from ABS-SG	Activate DTC memory from ABS

VW1029900137150X

Fig. 10 Motronic DTC interpretation chart (Part 15 of 15). New Beetle w/2.0L engine

DTC code SAE		VAG 1551 DTC Display	Malfunction elimination
P0102		Mass or Volume Air Flow Circ. Low Input	Check Mass Air Flow sensor
P0103		Mass or Volume Air Flow Circ. High Input	
P0107		Manifold Abs.Pressure or Bar.Pressure Low Input	Check Barometric sensor
P0108		Manifold Abs.Pressure or Bar.Pressure High Input	
P0112		Intake Air Temp.Circ. Low Input	Check Intake Air Temperature sensor
P0113		Intake Air Temp.Circ. High Input	
P0116		Engine Coolant Temp.Circ. Range/Performance	Check Engine Coolant Temperature sensor
P0117		Engine Coolant Temp.Circ. Low Input	Check Engine Coolant Temperature sensor
P0118		Engine Coolant Temp.Circ. High Input	

VW1029900136010X

Fig. 11 Motronic DTC interpretation chart (Part 1 of 22). Passat w/1.8L AEB engine

DTC code SAE	VAG 1551 DTC Display	Malfunction elimination
P0121	Throttle/Pedal Pos.Sensor A Circ. malfunction	Check Throttle valve Control Module
P0122	Throttle/Pedal Pos.Sensor A Circ. Low Input	
P0123	Throttle/Pedal Pos.Sensor A Circ. High Input	
P0130	02 Sensor Circ., Bank1–Sensor1 malfunction	Check Oxygen sensor and Oxygen sensor control before catalyst
P0131	02 Sensor Circ. Bank1–Sensor1 Low Voltage	Check Oxygen sensor heating before catalyst
P0132	02 Sensor Circ. Bank1–Sensor1 High Voltage	Check Oxygen sensor aging and Oxygen sensor before catalyst
P0133	02 Sensor Circ. Bank1–Sensor1 Slow Response	Check Oxygen sensor and Oxygen sensor control after catalyst
P0134	02 Sensor Circ. Bank1–Sensor1 NO Activity Detected	Check Oxygen sensor and Oxygen sensor control before catalyst

VW1029900136020X

Fig. 11 Motronic DTC interpretation chart (Part 2 of 22). Passat w/1.8L AEB engine

DTC code SAE	VAG 1551 DTC Display	Malfunction elimination
P0300	Random/Multiple Cylinder Misfire Detected	Fuel shortage, fill fuel tank
P0301	Cyl. 1 Misfire Detected	Check injectors
P0302	Cyl. 2 Misfire Detected	Check ignition coils with output stage
P0303	Cyl. 3 Misfire Detected	Check engine speed sensor
P0304	Cyl. 4 Misfire Detected	Check misfiring detection

Note on misfiring:
For malfunctions caused by a shortage of fuel (e.g. misfiring) the DTC "P1250" will also be displayed when there is less than 2 gallons of fuel in tank.

VW1029900136040X

Fig. 11 Motronic DTC interpretation chart (Part 4 of 22). Passat w/1.8L AEB engine

DTC code SAE	VAG 1551 DTC Display	Malfunction elimination
P0422	Main Catalyst (B1) Efficiency Below Threshold	Check catalyst
P0441	EVAP Emission Contr.Sys.Incorrect Purge Flow	Check EVAP canister purge regulator
P0442	EVAP Emission Contr.Sys. (Small Leak) Leak Detected	Check EVAP system:
P0455	EVAP Emission Contr.Sys. (Gross Leak) Leak Detected	
P0501	Vehicle Speed Sensor Range/Performance	Check vehicle speed signal
P0506	Idle Control System RPM Lower than Expected	Check throttle valve Control Module
P0507	Idle Control System RPM Higher than Expected	

VW1029900136060X

Fig. 11 Motronic DTC interpretation chart (Part 6 of 22). Passat w/1.8L AEB engine

DTC code SAE	VAG 1551 DTC Display	Malfunction elimination
P1102	02 Sensor Heating Circ, Bank1–Sensor 1 Voltage too Low/Air Leak	Check Oxygen sensor heating before catalyst
P1105	02 Sensor Heating Circ., Bank1–Sensor 2 Short to B+	Check Oxygen sensor heating after catalyst

VW1029900136080X

Fig. 11 Motronic DTC interpretation chart (Part 8 of 22). Passat w/1.8L AEB engine

DTC code SAE	VAG 1551 DTC Display	Malfunction elimination
P1128	Long Term Fuel Trim mult., Bank1 System too Lean	Check Oxygen sensor and Oxygen sensor control before catalyst
		Check Oxygen sensor and Oxygen sensor control after catalyst
		Check fuel pump
		Check fuel pressure regulator and residual pressure
		Check fuel injectors

VW1029900136100X

Fig. 11 Motronic DTC interpretation chart (Part 10 of 22). Passat w/1.8L AEB engine

DTC code SAE	VAG 1551 DTC Display	Malfunction elimination
P0136	02 Sensor Circ., Bank1–Sensor 2 malfunction	Check Oxygen sensor and Oxygen sensor control after catalyst
P0137	02 Sensor Circ. Bank1–Sensor 2 Low Voltage	Check Oxygen sensor heating after catalyst
P0138	02 Sensor Circ. Bank1–Sensor 2 High Voltage	
P0140	02 Sensor Circ. Bank1–Sensor 2 NO Activity Detected	

VW1029900136030X

Fig. 11 Motronic DTC interpretation chart (Part 3 of 22). Passat w/1.8L AEB engine

DTC code SAE	VAG 1551 DTC Display	Malfunction elimination
P0321	Ign./Distributor Eng.Speed Inp.Circ. Range/Performance	Check engine speed sensor
P0322	Ign./Distributor Eng.Speed Inp.Circ. NO Signal	
P0327	Knock Sensor 1 Circ. Low Input	Loosen knock sensor and retighten to 20 Nm (15 ft lb)
P0332	Knock Sensor 2 Circ. Low Input	Check knock sensors

VW1029900136050X

Fig. 11 Motronic DTC interpretation chart (Part 5 of 22). Passat w/1.8L AEB engine

DTC code SAE	VAG 1551 DTC Display	Malfunction elimination
P0560	System Voltage malfunction	Check ECM voltage supply
P0562	System Voltage Low Voltage	Procedure after voltage supply open circuit
P0563	System Voltage High Voltage	
P0601	Internal Contr.Module Memory Check Sum Error	Replace ECM (J220)
P0604	Internal Contr.Module Random Access Memory (RAM) Error	
P0707	Transm. Range Sensor Circ. Low Input	Check Transmission range signal
P0708	Transm. Range Sensor Circ. High Input	

VW1029900136070X

Fig. 11 Motronic DTC interpretation chart (Part 7 of 22). Passat w/1.8L AEB engine

DTC code SAE	VAG 1551 DTC Display	Malfunction elimination
P1127	Long Term Fuel Trim mult., Bank1 System too Rich	Check Mass Air Flow sensor
		Check Oxygen sensor and Oxygen sensor control before catalyst
		Check Oxygen sensor and Oxygen sensor control after catalyst
		Check fuel pressure regulator and holding pressure
		Check fuel injectors
		Check EVAP canister purge regulator valve 1

VW1029900136090X

Fig. 11 Motronic DTC interpretation chart (Part 9 of 22). Passat w/1.8L AEB engine

DTC code SAE	VAG 1551 DTC Display	Malfunction elimination
P1136	Long Term Fuel Trim Add.Fuel, Bank 1 System too Lean	Check Oxygen sensor and Oxygen sensor control before catalyst
		Check fuel pump:
		Check fuel pressure regulator and residual pressure
		Check fuel injectors

VW1029900136110X

Fig. 11 Motronic DTC interpretation chart (Part 11 of 22). Passat w/1.8L AEB engine

DTC code SAE	VAG 1551 DTC Display	Malfunction elimination
P1137	Long Term Fuel Trim Add.Fuel, Bank1 System too Rich	Check Oxygen sensor and Oxygen sensor control before catalyst
		Check fuel pump
		Check fuel pressure regulator and residual pressure
		Check fuel injectors
		Check EVAP canister purge regulator valve 1

VW1029900136120X

Fig. 11 Motronic DTC interpretation chart (Part 12 of 22). Passat w/1.8L AEB engine

DTC code SAE	VAG 1551 DTC Display	Malfunction elimination
P1213	Cyl. 1–Fuel Inj. Circ. Short to B+	Check fuel injectors
P1214	Cyl. 2-Fuel Inj.Circ. Short to B+	
P1215	Cyl. 3–Fuel Inj.Circ. Short to B+	
P1216	Cyl. 4-Fuel Inj.Circ. Short to B+	
P1225	Cyl. 1–Fuel Inj.Circ. Short to Ground	
P1226	Cyl. 2–Fuel Inj.Circ. Short to Ground	
P1227	Cyl. 3–Fuel Inj.Circ. Short to Ground	
P1228	Cyl. 4–Fuel Inj.Circ. Short to Ground	

VW1029900136140X

Fig. 11 Motronic DTC interpretation chart (Part 14 of 22). Passat w/1.8L AEB engine

DTC code SAE	VAG 1551 DTC Display	Malfunction elimination
P1325	Cyl.1–Knock Contr. Limit Attained	Loosen knock sensors and re-torque to 15 ft lb Check knock sensors
P1326	Cyl.2–Knock Contr. Limit Attained	Correct cause of abnormal engine running noises
P1327	Cyl.3–Knock Contr. Limit Attained	Fill with fuel of 91 RON minimum
P1328	Cyl.4–Knock Contr. Limit Attained	
P1337	Camshaft Pos.Sensor, Bank 1 Short to Ground	Check Camshaft Position sensor
P1338	Camshaft Pos.Sensor, Bank1 Open Circ./Short to B+	

VW1029900136160X

Fig. 11 Motronic DTC interpretation chart (Part 16 of 22). Passat w/1.8L AEB engine

DTC code SAE	VAG 1551 DTC Display	Malfunction elimination
P1500	Fuel Pump Relay Circ. Electrical malfunction	Check fuel pump relay ⇒ Wiring Diagrams
P1501	Fuel pump Relay Circ. Short to Ground	Check fuel pump
P1502	Fuel Pump Relay Circ. Short to B+	
P1505	Closed Throttle Pos. Does Not Close/Open Circ.	Check Throttle valve Control Module
P1506	Closed Throttle Pos.Switch Does Not Open/Short to Ground	
P1543	Intake Camshaft Contr.Circ., Bank 2 Short to B+	
P1544	Throttle Actuation Potentiometer Signal too High	
P1545	Throttle Pos.Contr. malfunction	

VW1029900136180X

Fig. 11 Motronic DTC interpretation chart (Part 18 of 22). Passat w/1.8L AEB engine

DTC code SAE	VAG 1551 DTC Display	Malfunction elimination
P1176	02 Correction Behind Catalyst, B1 Limit Attained	Check intake system for leaks (unmeasured air)
		Check Oxygen sensor and Oxygen sensor control after catalyst
		Check Oxygen sensor for aging before catalyst
		Check Oxygen sensor heating after catalyst
P1196	02 Sensor Heater Circ., Bank1–Sensor 1 Electrical malfunction	Check Oxygen sensor heating before catalyst
P1198	02 Sensor Heater Circ., Bank1–Sensor 2 Electrical malfunction	Check Oxygen sensor heating after catalyst

VW1029900136130X

Fig. 11 Motronic DTC interpretation chart (Part 13 of 22). Passat w/1.8L AEB engine

DTC code SAE	VAG 1551 DTC Display	Malfunction elimination
P1237	Cyl.1–Fuel Inj.Circ. Open Circ.	Check fuel injectors
P1238	Cyl. 2–Fuel Inj.Circ. Open Circ.	
P1239	Cyl. 3–Fuel Inj.Circ. Open Circ.	
P1240	Cyl. 4–Fuel Inj.Circ. Open Circ.	
P1250	Fuel Level Too Low	Less than 2 gallons of fuel in tank, fill fuel tank Check fuel gauge sensor signal Check wiring between ECM and instrument cluster using Wiring Diagram

VW1029900136150X

Fig. 11 Motronic DTC interpretation chart (Part 15 of 22). Passat w/1.8L AEB engine

DTC code SAE	VAG 1551 DTC Display	Malfunction elimination
P1386	Internal Control Module Knock Control Circ.Error	Replace ECM (J220)
P1410	Tank Ventilation Valve Short to B+	Check EVAP canister purge regulator valve 1
P1425	Tank Vent.Valve Short to Ground	
P1426	Tank Vent.Valve Open	
P1471	EVAP Emission Contr.LDP Circ. Short to B+	Check Leak Detection Pump:
P1472	EVAP Emission Contr.LDP Circ. Short to Ground	Check Evaporative Emissions sys.
P1473	EVAP Emission Contr.LDP Circ. Open Circ.	
P1475	EVAP Emission Contr.LDP Circ. malfunction/Signal Circ.Open	
P1476	EVAP Emission Contr.LDP Circ. malfunction/Insufficient Vacuum	
P1477	EVAP Emission Contr.LDP Circ. malfunction	

VW1029900136170X

Fig. 11 Motronic DTC interpretation chart (Part 17 of 22). Passat w/1.8L AEB engine

DTC code SAE	VAG 1551 DTC Display	Malfunction elimination
P1546	Boost Pressure Contr.Valve Short to B+	Check Wastegate Bypass Regulator valve
P1547	Boost Pressure Contr.Valve Short to Ground	Check charge pressure control
P1548	Boost Pressure Contr. Valve Open	
P1555	Charge Pressure Upper Limit Exceeded	
P1556	Charge Pressure Contr. Negative Deviation	
P1557	Charge Pressure Contr. Positive Deviation	
P1558	Throttle Actuator Electrical malfunction	Check Throttle valve Control Module
P1559	Idle Speed Contr.Throttle Pos. Adaptation malfunction	
P1560	Maximum Engine Speed Exceeded	Repair mechanical damage
P1564	Idle Speed Contr.Throttle Pos. Low Voltage During Adaptation	Check Battery charge condition Check ECM voltage supply

VW1029900136190X

Fig. 11 Motronic DTC interpretation chart (Part 19 of 22). Passat w/1.8L AEB engine

DTC code SAE		VAG 1551 DTC Display	Malfunction elimination
P1602		Power Supply (B+) Terminal 30 Low Voltage	Check ECM voltage supply Procedure after voltage supply open circuit
P1606		Rough Road Spec. Engine Torque ABS–ECU Electrical malfunction	Check rough road recognition from ABS/EDL ECM

VW1029900136200X

Fig. 11 Motronic DTC interpretation chart (Part 20 of 22). Passat w/1.8L AEB engine

DTC code SAE		VAG 1551 DTC Display	Malfunction elimination
P1640		Internal Control Module (EEPROM) Error	Replace ECM (J220)
P1681		Control Module Programming not Finished	
P1693		Malfunction Indicator Lamp Short to B+	Check wiring between instrument cluster and ECM: ⇒ Wiring Diagrams

VW1029900136220X

Fig. 11 Motronic DTC interpretation chart (Part 22 of 22). Passat w/1.8L AEB engine

Fault code SAE	V.A.G	Fault text	Fault elimination
P0112	16496	Intake air temperature sender -G42 signal too low	- Check intake air temperature sender
P0113	16497	Intake air temperature sender -G42 signal too high	
P0116	16500	Coolant temperature sender -G62 implausible signal	- Check coolant temperature sender
P0117	16501	Coolant temperature sender -G62 signal too low	- Check thermostat
P0118	16502	Coolant temperature sender -G62 signal too high	

VW1020000154020X

Fig. 12 Motronic DTC interpretation chart (Part 2 of 39). Passat w/1.8L ATW engine

Fault code SAE	V.A.G	Fault text	Fault elimination
P0197	16581	Engine oil temperature sensor -G8- signal too small	Diagnose engine ailing system fault condition
P0198	16582	Engine oil temperature sensor -G8- signal too large	
P0236	16620	Charge pressure sender -G31 implausible signal	Check charge pressure system; Check charge pressure sender
P0237	16621	Charge pressure sender -G31 signal too low	
P0238	16622	Charge pressure sender -G31 signal too high	

VW1020000154040X

Fig. 12 Motronic DTC interpretation chart (Part 4 of 39). Passat w/1.8L ATW engine

Fault code SAE	V.A.G	Fault text	Fault elimination
P0300	16684	Misfire detected	- Check injectors
P0301	16685	Cyl.1 misfire detected	- Check ignition cables and spark plugs
P0302	16686	Cyl.2 misfire detected	- Check ignition coils with output stage
P0303	16687	Cyl.3 misfire detected	- Check misfiring detection
P0304	16688	Cyl. 4 misfire detected	
P0321	16705	Engine speed sender -G28 implausible signal	- Check engine speed sender
P0322	16706	Engine speed sender -G28 no signal	

VW1020000154050X

Fig. 12 Motronic DTC interpretation chart (Part 5 of 39). Passat w/1.8L ATW engine

DTC code SAE		VAG 1551 DTC Display	Malfunction elimination
P1611		MIL Call-up Circ./Transm.Control Module Short to Ground	Check wiring between TCM and ECM: ⇒ Wiring Diagrams
P1612		Electronic Control Module Incorrect Coding	Code ECM
P1613		MIL Call-up Open Circ. Open/Short to B+	Check wiring between TCM and ECM ⇒ Wiring Diagrams
P1624		MIL Request Sign.active	Check TCM DTC memory

VW1029900136210X

Fig. 11 Motronic DTC interpretation chart (Part 21 of 22). Passat w/1.8L AEB engine

Fault code SAE	V.A.G	Fault text	Fault elimination
P0101	16485	Mass air flow sensor -G70 implausible signal	- Check Mass air flow sensor
P0102	16486	Mass air flow sensor -G70 signal to low	- Check intake system for leaks (unmetered air)
P0103	16487	Mass air flow sensor -G70 signal to high	
P0106	16490	Intake manifold pressure/air pressure ⇒ -G71/-F96 1) implausible signal	Checking charge air system; Checking charge pressure sender
P0107	16491	Intake manifold pressure/air pressure ⇒ Low Input	
P0108	16492	Intake manifold pressure/air pressure ⇒ High Input	

1) The intake manifold pressure is established by the charge pressure sender -G31 (not -G71 as indicated), the air pressure is established by the altitude sender -F96 (in engine control unit).

VW1020000154010X

Fig. 12 Motronic DTC interpretation chart (Part 1 of 39). Passat w/1.8L ATW engine

Fault code SAE	V.A.G	Fault text	Fault elimination
P0130	16514	Bank 1 probe 1 electrical fault in current circuit	- Check Oxygen sensor heating before catalyst
P0131	16515	Bank 1 probe 1 voltage too low	- Check Oxygen sensor and Lambda control before catalyst
P0132	16516	Bank 1 probe 1 voltage too high	
P0133	16517	Bank 1 probe 1 signal to slow	
P0134	16518	Bank 1 probe 1 no activity	
P0136	16520	Bank 1 probe 2 electrical fault in circuit	- Check Oxygen sensor heating after catalyst
P0137	16521	Bank 1 probe 2 voltage too low	- Check Oxygen sensor and Lambda regulator after catalyst
P0138	16522	Bank 1 probe 2 voltage too high	- Check Oxygen sensor heating after catalyst
P0139	16523	Bank 1 probe 2 signal to slow	
P0140	16524	Bank 1 probe 2 no activity	

VW1020000154030X

Fig. 12 Motronic DTC interpretation chart (Part 3 of 39). Passat w/1.8L ATW engine

Fault code SAE	V.A.G	Fault text	Fault elimination
P0327	16711	Knock sensor 1 -G61 signal too low	- Check knock sensors
P0328	16712	Knock sensor 1 -G61 signal too high	
P0332	16716	Knock sensor 2 -G66 signal too low	
P0333	16717	Knock sensor 2 -G66 signal too high	
P0341	16725	Camshaft position sender -G40 implausible signal	- Check CMP sender

VW1020000154060X

Fig. 12 Motronic DTC interpretation chart (Part 6 of 39). Passat w/1.8L ATW engine

Fault code		Fault text	Fault elimination
SAE	V.A.G		
P0411	16795	Secondary air system incorrect flow detected	- Check secondary air pump motor
			- Check combi valve
			- Check secondary air inlet valve

VW1020000154070X

Fig. 12 Motronic DTC interpretation chart (Part 7 of 39). Passat w/1.8L ATW engine

Fault code		Fault text	Fault elimination
SAE	V.A.G		
P0441	16825	Tank breathing system flow rate faulty	- Check activated charcoal filter solenoid valve 1 Activated charcoal filter system
			- Check hoses and connecting pipes from fuel tank to throttle valve control module ⇒ Repair Group 20; Check fuel tank breather

VW1020000154090X

Fig. 12 Motronic DTC interpretation chart (Part 9 of 39). Passat w/1.8L ATW engine

Fault code		Fault text	Fault elimination
SAE	V.A.G		
P0501	16885	Vehicle speed signal implausible	- Check speed signal
P0506	16890	Idling speed regulation below specifications	- Check throttle valve control module
P0507	16891	Idling speed regulation above specifications	
P0560	16944	Voltage supply signal implausible	- Check voltage supply
P0562	16946	Voltage supply too low	- Procedure after interrupting voltage supply
P0563	16947	Voltage supply too high	
P0571	16955	Brake light switch -F 1) implausible signal	- Check brake light switch and brake pedal switch

1) The system monitors both brake light switch -F and brake pedal switch -F47.

VW1020000154110X

Fig. 12 Motronic DTC interpretation chart (Part 11 of 39). Passat w/1.8L ATW engine

Fault code		Fault text	Fault elimination
SAE	V.A.G		
P1102	17510	Bank 1, probe 1 heating current circuit short to positive	- Check Oxygen sensor heating before catalyst
P1105	17513	Bank 1, probe 2 heating current circuit short to positive	- Check Oxygen sensor heating after catalyst
P1111	17519	Lambda control Bank 1 system too lean	- Check Oxygen sensor and Lambda control before catalyst
P1112	17520	Lambda control Bank 1 system too rich	
P1113	17521	Bank1, probe 1 internal resistance too high	- Check Oxygen sensor heating before catalyst
P1114	17522	Bank1, probe 2 internal resistance too high	- Check Oxygen sensor heating after catalyst

VW1020000154130X

Fig. 12 Motronic DTC interpretation chart (Part 13 of 39). Passat w/1.8L ATW engine

Fault code		Fault text	Fault elimination
PO411	16795		- Check hoses and connecting pipes to/between components
P0422	16806	Bank 1 main catalyst efficiency too low	- Check catalyst

VW1020000154080X

Fig. 12 Motronic DTC interpretation chart (Part 8 of 39). Passat w/1.8L ATW engine

Fault code		Fault text	Fault elimination
P0442	16826	EVAP Emission Contr.Sys. (Small Leak) Leak Detected	Check activated charcoal filter system for leaks
P0455	16839	EVAP Emission Contr.Sys. (Gross Leak) Leak Detected	
P0455	16839	EVAP Emission Contr.Sys. (Gross Leak) Leak Detected	

VW1020000154100X

Fig. 12 Motronic DTC interpretation chart (Part 10 of 39). Passat w/1.8L ATW engine

Fault code		Fault text	Fault elimination
SAE	V.A.G		
P0601	16985	Control Module Malfunctioning	- Replace engine control module
P0604	16988	Control Module Malfunctioning	
P0605	16989	Control Module Malfunctioning	

VW1020000154120X

Fig. 12 Motronic DTC interpretation chart (Part 12 of 39). Passat w/1.8L ATW engine

Fault code		Fault text	Fault elimination
SAE	V.A.G		
P1115	17523	Bank 1, probe 1 heating current circuit short to Ground	- Check Oxygen sensor heating before catalyst
P1116	17524	Bank 1, probe 1 heating current circuit open circuit	
P1117	17525	Bank 1, probe 2 heating current circuit short to positive	- Check Oxygen sensor heating after catalyst
P1118	17526	Bank 1, probe 2 heating current circuit open circuit	
P1127	17535	Bank 1, mixture adaptation (mult.) system too rich	- Check fuel pressure regulator and holding pressure
			- Check injectors Check quantity injected and for leaks
			- Check activated charcoal filter solenoid valve 1 Activated charcoal filter system; Check activated charcoal filter solenoid valve 1

VW1020000154140X

Fig. 12 Motronic DTC interpretation chart (Part 14 of 39). Passat w/1.8L ATW engine

Fault code SAE	Fault code V.A.G	Fault text	Fault elimination
P1128	17536	Bank 1, mixture adaptation (mult.) system too lean	- Check fuel pressure regulator and holding pressure
			- Check injectors Check quantity injected and for leaks
			- Check fuel pump
			- Check intake system for leaks
			- Check exhaust system for leaks:
			- Check secondary air system for leaks

VW1020000154150X

Fig. 12 Motronic DTC interpretation chart (Part 15 of 39). Passat w/1.8L ATW engine

Fault code SAE	Fault code V.A.G	Fault text	Fault elimination
P1137	17545	Bank 1, mixture adaptation (add.) system too rich	- Check fuel pressure regulator and holding pressure
			- Check injectors Check quantity injected and for leaks
			- Check activated charcoal filter solenoid valve 1
			Activated charcoal filter system
P1141	17549	Load detection, implausible value	- Check Mass Air Flow (MAF) sensor

Notes:

add. = additive means, the fault only has an effect at idling speed.

VW1020000154170X

Fig. 12 Motronic DTC interpretation chart (Part 17 of 39). Passat w/1.8L ATW engine

Fault code SAE	Fault code V.A.G	Fault text	Fault elimination
P1213	17621	Injector Cyl. 1 -N30 short to positive	- Check injectors
P1214	17622	Injector Cyl. 2 -N31 short to positive	
P1215	17623	Injector Cyl. 3 -N32 short to positive	
P1216	17624	Injector Cyl. 4 -N33 short to positive	
P1225	17633	Injector Cyl. 1 -N30 short to Ground	
P1226	17634	Injector Cyl. 2 -N31 short to Ground	
P1227	17635	Injector Cyl. 3 -N32 short to Ground	
P1228	17636	Injector Cyl. 4 -N33 short to Ground	

VW1020000154190X

Fig. 12 Motronic DTC interpretation chart (Part 19 of 39). Passat w/1.8L ATW engine

Fault code SAE	Fault code V.A.G	Fault text	Fault elimination
P1136	17544	Bank 1, mixture adaptation (add.) system too lean	- Check fuel pressure regulator and holding pressure
			- Check injectors
			- Check fuel pump
			- Check intake system for leaks
			- Check exhaust system for leaks

VW1020000154160X

Fig. 12 Motronic DTC interpretation chart (Part 16 of 39). Passat w/1.8L ATW engine

Fault code SAE	Fault code V.A.G	Fault text	Fault elimination
P1149	17557	Lambda control Bank 1 implausible control value	- Check Oxygen sensor and Lambda control before catalyst
P1171	17579	Angle sender 2 for throttle valve drive -G188 implausible signal [1]	- Check throttle valve control module
P1172	17580	Angle sender 2 for throttle valve drive -G188 signal too low [1]	
P1173	17581	Angle sender 2 for throttle valve drive -G188 signal too high [1]	

[1] If this fault occurs the engine control unit switches on the EPC warning lamp in dash panel insert.

VW1020000154180X

Fig. 12 Motronic DTC interpretation chart (Part 18 of 39). Passat w/1.8L ATW engine

Fault code SAE	Fault code V.A.G	Fault text	Fault elimination
P1237	17645	Injector Cyl. 1 -N30 open circuit	- Check injectors
P1238	17646	Injector Cyl. 2 -N31 open circuit	
P1239	17647	Injector Cyl. 3 -N32 open circuit	
P1240	17648	Injector Cyl. 4 -N33 open circuit	
P1250	17658	Fuel level too low	- Fill fuel tank

VW1020000154200X

Fig. 12 Motronic DTC interpretation chart (Part 20 of 39). Passat w/1.8L ATW engine

Fault code SAE	Fault code V.A.G	Fault text	Fault elimination
P1287	17695	Recirculating valve for turbocharger -N249- open circuit	- Check Recirculating valve for turbocharger
P1288	17696	Turbocharger divert valve -N249 short to positive	
P1289	17697	Turbocharger divert valve -N249 short to Ground	
P1295	17703	Bypass Turbocharger throughput faulty	- Check solenoid valve for boost pressure limitation
			- Check hose setup between turbocharger and pressure unit for boost pressure regulator valve

VW1020000154210X

Fig. 12 Motronic DTC interpretation chart (Part 21 of 39). Passat w/1.8L ATW engine

Fault code		Fault text	Fault elimination
SAE	V.A.G		
P1325	17733	Cylinder 1 knock control, control limit reached	- Fill tank with minimum 91 RON
P1326	17734	Cylinder 2 knock control, control limit reached	- Check connectors
P1327	17735	Cylinder 3 knock control, control limit reached	- Eliminate cause for abnormal engine running noises
P1328	17736	Cylinder 4 knock control, control limit reached	- Loosen knock sensor and tighten again to 15ft lbs - Check knock sensors

VW1020000154220X

Fig. 12 Motronic DTC interpretation chart (Part 22 of 39). Passat w/1.8L ATW engine

Fault code		Fault text	Fault elimination
SAE	V.A.G		
P1337	17745	Bank 1, camshaft position sensor ⇒ -G163 short to Ground	- Check Hall sender
P1338	17746	Bank 1, camshaft position sensor ⇒ -G163 open circuit / short to positive	
P1340	17748	Camshaft position / crankshaft position sensor wrong allocation	
P1355	17763	Cyl. 1 ignition activation open circuit	- Check ignition coils with output stage
P1356	17764	Cyl. 1 ignition activation short to positive	
P1357	17765	Cyl. 1 ignition activation short to Ground	
P1358	17766	Cyl. 2 ignition activation open circuit	
P1359	17767	Cyl. 2 ignition activation short to positive	
P1360	17768	Cyl. 2 ignition activation short to Ground	

VW1020000154240X

Fig. 12 Motronic DTC interpretation chart (Part 24 of 39). Passat w/1.8L ATW engine

Fault code		Fault text	Fault elimination
SAE	V.A.G		
P1409	17817	Tank breathing valve -N80 electrical fault in current circuit	- Check activated charcoal filter solenoid valve 1
P1410	17818	Tank breathing valve -N80 short to positive	
P1420	17828	Secondary air inlet valve -N112 electrical fault in current circuit	- Check secondary air inlet valve
P1421	17829	Secondary air inlet valve -N112 short to Ground	
P1422	17830	Secondary air inlet valve -N112 short to positive	
P1424	17832	Bank 1 secondary air system leak recognized	- Check secondary air system for leaks
P1425	17833	Tank breathing valve -N80 short to Ground	- Check activated charcoal filter solenoid valve 1
P1426	17834	Tank breathing valve -N80 open circuit	

VW1020000154260X

Fig. 12 Motronic DTC interpretation chart (Part 26 of 39). Passat w/1.8L ATW engine

Fault code		Fault text	Fault elimination
SAE	V.A.G		
P1471	17879	EVAP Emission Contr.LDP Circ. Short to B+	Check diagnostic pump activated charcoal filter system

VW1020000154280X

Fig. 12 Motronic DTC interpretation chart (Part 28 of 39). Passat w/1.8L ATW engine

Fault code		Fault text	Fault elimination
P1472	17880	EVAP Emission Contr.LDP Circ. Short to Ground	Check activated charcoal filter system for leaks
P1473	17881	EVAP Emission Contr.LDP Circ. Open Circ.	
P1475	17883	EVAP Emission Contr.LDP Circ. Malfunction/Signal Circ.Open	
P1476	17884	EVAP Emission Contr.LDP Circ. Malfunction/Insufficient Vacuum	
P1477	17885	EVAP Emission Contr.LDP Circ. Malfunction	
P1477	17885	EVAP Emission Contr.LDP Circ. Malfunction	

VW1020000154290X

Fig. 12 Motronic DTC interpretation chart (Part 29 of 39). Passat w/1.8L ATW engine

Fault code		Fault text	Fault elimination
SAE	V.A.G		
P1335	17743	Engine torque monitoring 2 control limit exceeded 1)	- Check hoses Charge air system with turbocharger - Check intake air temperature sender
P1336	17744	Engine torque monitoring control limit exceeded	- Check Mass air flow sensor - Check coolant temperature sender

1) If this fault occurs the engine control unit switches on the EPC warning lamp in dash panel insert.

VW1020000154230X

Fig. 12 Motronic DTC interpretation chart (Part 23 of 39). Passat w/1.8L ATW engine

Fault code		Fault text	Fault elimination
SAE	V.A.G		
P1361	17769	Cyl. 3 ignition activation open circuit	- Check ignition coils with output stage
P1362	17770	Cyl. 3 ignition activation short to positive	
P1363	17771	Cyl. 3 ignition activation short to Ground	
P1364	17772	Cyl. 4 ignition activation open circuit	
P1365	17773	Cyl. 4 ignition activation short to positive	
P1366	17774	Cyl. 4 ignition activation short to Ground	
P1386	17794	Control Module Malfunctioning	- Replace engine control module
P1387	17795	Control Module Malfunctioning	
P1388	17796	Control Module Malfunctioning 1)	

1) If this fault occurs the engine control unit switches on the EPC warning lamp in dash panel insert.

VW1020000154250X

Fig. 12 Motronic DTC interpretation chart (Part 25 of 39). Passat w/1.8L ATW engine

Fault code		Fault text	Fault elimination
SAE	V.A.G		
P1432	17840	Secondary air inlet valve -N112 open circuit	- Check secondary air inlet valve
P1433	17841	Relay for secondary air inlet valve -J299 open circuit	- Check relay for secondary air inlet valve
P1434	17842	Relay for secondary air inlet valve -J299 short to positive	
P1435	17843	Relay for secondary air inlet valve -J299 short to Ground	
P1436	17844	Relay for secondary air inlet valve -J299 electrical fault in current circuit	

VW1020000154270X

Fig. 12 Motronic DTC interpretation chart (Part 27 of 39). Passat w/1.8L ATW engine

Fault code		Fault text	Fault elimination
SAE	V.A.G		
P1500	17908	Fuel pump relay -J17 electrical fault in circuit	- Check fuel pump relay:
P1502	17910	Fuel pump relay -J17 short to positive	
P1517	17925	Motronic Engine Control Module (ECM) power supply relay -J271- electrical malfunction in circuit	- Check motronic Engine Control Module (ECM) Power Supply Relay
P1523	17931	Crash-Signal vom Airbag-SG	- Check DTC memory of motronic control module and then erase

VW1020000154300X

Fig. 12 Motronic DTC interpretation chart (Part 30 of 39). Passat w/1.8L ATW engine

Fault code SAE	V.A.G	Fault text	Fault elimination
P1539	17947	Clutch pedal switch -F36 implausible signal	- Check clutch pedal switch
P1542	17950	Angle sender for throttle valve drive -G187 implausible signal 1)	- Check throttle valve control module
P1543	17951	Angle sender for throttle valve drive -G187 signal too low 1)	
P1544	17952	Angle sender for throttle valve drive -G187 signal too high 1)	
P1545	17953	Throttle valve control malfunction 1)	

1) If this fault occurs the engine control unit switches on the EPC warning lamp in dash panel insert.

VW1020000154310X

Fig. 12 Motronic DTC interpretation chart (Part 31 of 39). Passat w/1.8L ATW engine

Fault code SAE	V.A.G	Fault text	Fault elimination
P1546	17954	Solenoid valve for charge pressure control -N75 short to positive	- Check solenoid valve for charge pressure control
P1547	17955	Solenoid valve for charge pressure control -N75 short to Ground	Repair Group 21; Checking charge pressure system; Check charge pressure control
P1548	17956	Solenoid valve for charge pressure control -N75 open circuit	
P1555	17963	Maximum charge pressure exceeded	
P1556	17964	Charge pressure control, control limit not reached	
P1557	17965	Charge pressure control, control limit exceeded	
P1558	17966	Throttle Actuator Electrical Malfunction	Check throttle valve control module

1) If this fault occurs the engine control unit switches on the EPC warning lamp in dash panel insert.

VW1020000154320X

Fig. 12 Motronic DTC interpretation chart (Part 32 of 39). Passat w/1.8L ATW engine

Fault code SAE	V.A.G	Fault text	Fault elimination
P1559	17967	throttle valve control module -J338 fault in basic setting 1)	- Adapt engine control unit to the throttle valve control module
P1560	17968	Maximum engine revs surpassed	- Repair mechanical damage
P1564	17972	throttle valve control module -J338 low voltage at base setting 1)	- Check battery, charge if needed - Adapt engine control unit to throttle valve control module
P1565	17973	throttle valve control module -J338 lower limit not reached	- Check throttle valve control module
P1568	17976	throttle valve control module -J338 mechanical fault 1)	

1) If this fault occurs the engine control unit switches on the EPC warning lamp in dash panel insert.

VW1020000154330X

Fig. 12 Motronic DTC interpretation chart (Part 33 of 39). Passat w/1.8L ATW engine

Fault code SAE	V.A.G	Fault text	Fault elimination
P1569	17977	CCS switch -E45 implausible signal	- Check cruise control system - Evaluate measured value block 66
P1579	17987	Throttle valve control module -J338 Adaptation not started1)	- Adapt engine control unit to throttle valve control module

1) If this fault occurs the engine control unit switches on the EPC warning lamp in dash panel insert.

VW1020000154340X

Fig. 12 Motronic DTC interpretation chart (Part 34 of 39). Passat w/1.8L ATW engine

Fault code SAE	V.A.G	Fault text	Fault elimination
P1602	18010	Terminal 30 voltage supply too low	- Check voltage supply for control unit
P1603	18011	Control Module Malfunctioning	- Replace engine control unit
P1604	18012	Control Module Malfunctioning 1)	
P1606	18014	Rough road spec engine torque ABS-ECU electrical malfunction	- Check DTC memory of ABS control module: - Check data-bus
P1609	18017	Crash shut-off was triggered	- Check DTC memory of Engine Control Module (ECM) and then erase
P1612	18020	Engine control unit incorrectly coded	- Code engine control unit

1) If this fault occurs the engine control unit switches on the EPC warning lamp in dash panel insert.

VW1020000154350X

Fig. 12 Motronic DTC interpretation chart (Part 35 of 39). Passat w/1.8L ATW engine

Fault code SAE	V.A.G	Fault text	Fault elimination
P1615	18023	Engine oil temperature sensor -G8- implausible signal	check Engine oil temperature sensor
P1624	18032	Instruction warning lamp on active	- Check DTC memory of automatic transmission
P1626	18034	Drive train data bus no messages from transmission control unit	- Check data bus

VW1020000154360X

Fig. 12 Motronic DTC interpretation chart (Part 36 of 39). Passat w/1.8L ATW engine

Fault code SAE	V.A.G	Fault text	Fault elimination
P1630	18038	Accelerator pedal position sender -G79 signal too low 1)	- Check accelerator pedal position sender Accelerator mechanism
P1631	18039	Accelerator pedal position sender -G79 signal too high 1)	
P1633	18041	Accelerator pedal position sender 2 -G185 signal too low 1)	
P1634	18042	Accelerator pedal position sender 2 -G185 signal too high 1)	
P1636	18044	Data Bus Powertrain missing message from Airbag control	- Check data-bus
P1639	18047	Accelerator pedal position senders 1/2 -G79+G185 implausible signal 1)	
P1640	18048	Control Module Malfunctioning	- Replace engine control unit

1) If this fault occurs the engine control unit switches on the EPC warning lamp in dash panel insert.

VW1020000154370X

Fig. 12 Motronic DTC interpretation chart (Part 37 of 39). Passat w/1.8L ATW engine

Fault code SAE	V.A.G	Fault text	Fault elimination
P1648	18056	Drive train data bus malfunctioning	
P1649	18057	Drive train data bus no messages from ABS control unit	
P1649	18057	Drive train data bus no messages from ABS control unit	

VW1020000154380X

Fig. 12 Motronic DTC interpretation chart (Part 38 of 39). Passat w/1.8L ATW engine

Fault code SAE	Fault code V.A.G	Fault text	Fault elimination
P1676	18084	Fault lamp for electric accelerator operation -K132 electrical fault in current circuit[1]	- Check fault lamp Electronic power control (EPC) Checking fault lamp for electronic accelerator operation
P1677	18085	Fault lamp for electric accelerator operation -K132 short to positive [1]	
P1853	18261	Drive train data bus implausible info from ABS control unit	- Check data bus
P1690	18098	Malfunction Indicator Lamp (MIL) -K83- short circuit to B+	- Check indicator lamp
P1693	18101	Malfunction Indicator Lamp (MIL) -K83- electrical malfunction in circuit	
P1853	18261	Drive train data bus implausible info from ABS control unit	- Check data bus

[1] If this fault occurs the engine control unit switches on the EPC warning lamp in dash panel insert.

VW1020000154390X

Fig. 12 Motronic DTC interpretation chart (Part 39 of 39). Passat w/1.8L ATW engine

Diagnostic Trouble Code (DTC) SAE		Malfunction text	Corrective action
P0121		Throttle/Pedal Pos. Sensor A Circ. Range/Performance	- Check throttle valve control module -J338-
P0122		Throttle/Pedal Pos. Sensor A Circ. Low Input	
P0123		Throttle/Pedal Pos. Sensor A Circ. High Input	
P0130		O2 Sensor Circ., Bank1–Sensor1 Malfunction	- Check Heated Oxygen Sensor (HO2S) -G39- and O2S control before TWC (bank 1, sensor 1) - Check Oxygen Sensor (O2S) heater before TWC - Check HO2S -G39- aging (bank 1, sensor 1) - Check Oxygen Sensor (O2S) -G130- and Oxygen Sensor (O2S) control behind TWC (bank 1, sensor 2)
P0131		O2 Sensor Circ., Bank1–Sensor1 Low Voltage	
P0132		O2 Sensor Circ., Bank1–Sensor1 High Voltage	
P0133		O2 Sensor Circ., Bank1–Sensor1 Slow Response	
P0134		O2 Sensor Circ., Bank1–Sensor1 No Activity Detected	- Check Heated Oxygen Sensor (HO2S) -G39- and O2S control before TWC (bank 1, sensor 1)

VW1029900140020X

Fig. 13 Motronic DTC interpretation chart (Part 2 of 27). Passat w/2.8L AHA engine

Diagnostic Trouble Code (DTC) SAE		Malfunction text	Corrective action
P0150		O2 Sensor Circ., Bank2–Sensor1 Malfunction	- Check Heated Oxygen Sensor (HO2S) 2 -G108- and O2S control before TWC (bank 2, sensor 1) - Check Oxygen Sensor (O2S) heater before TWC - Check HO2S -G108- aging (bank 2, sensor 1) - Check Oxygen Sensor (O2S) 2 -G131- and Oxygen Sensor (O2S) control behind TWC (bank 2, sensor 2)
P0151		O2 Sensor Circ., Bank2–Sensor1 Low Voltage	
P0152		O2 Sensor Circ., Bank2–Sensor1 High Voltage	
P0153		O2 Sensor Circ., Bank2–Sensor1 Slow Response	
P0154		O2 Sensor Circ., Bank2–Sensor1 No Activity Detected	- Check Heated Oxygen Sensor (HO2S) 2 -G108- and O2S control before TWC (bank 2, sensor 1)
P0156		O2 Sensor Circ., Bank2–Sensor2 Malfunction	- Check Oxygen Sensor (O2S) 2 -G131- and Oxygen Sensor (O2S) control behind TWC (bank 2, sensor 2) - Check Oxygen Sensor (O2S) heater behind TWC
P0157		O2 Sensor Circ., Bank2–Sensor2 Low Voltage	
P0158		O2 Sensor Circ., Bank2–Sensor2 High Voltage	
P0160		O2 Sensor Circ., Bank2–Sensor2 No Activity Detected	

VW1029900140040X

Fig. 13 Motronic DTC interpretation chart (Part 4 of 27). Passat w/2.8L AHA engine

Diagnostic Trouble Code (DTC) SAE		Malfunction text	Corrective action
P0102		Mass or Volume Air Flow Circ. Low Input	- Check Mass Air Flow (MAF) sensor -G70-
P0103		Mass or Volume Air Flow Circ.. High Input	
P0112		Intake Air Temp. Circ. Low Input	- Check Intake Air Temperature (IAT) sensor -G42-
P0113		Intake Air Temp. Circ. High Input	
P0116		Engine Coolant Temp. Circ. Range/Performance	- Check Engine Coolant Temperature (ECT) sensor -G62- - Check thermostat
P0117		Engine Coolant Temp. Circ. Low Input	
P0118		Engine Coolant Temp. Circ. High Input	

VW1029900140010X

Fig. 13 Motronic DTC interpretation chart (Part 1 of 27). Passat w/2.8L AHA engine

Diagnostic Trouble Code (DTC) SAE		Malfunction text	Corrective action
P0136		O2 Sensor Circ., Bank1–Sensor2 Malfunction	- Check Oxygen Sensor (O2S) -G130- and Oxygen Sensor (O2S) control behind TWC (bank 1, sensor 2) - Check Oxygen Sensor (O2S) heater behind TWC
P0137		O2 Sensor Circ., Bank1–Sensor2 Low Voltage	
P0138		O2 Sensor Circ., Bank1–Sensor2 High Voltage	
P0140		O2 Sensor Circ., Bank1–Sensor2 No Activity Detected	

VW1029900140030X

Fig. 13 Motronic DTC interpretation chart (Part 3 of 27). Passat w/2.8L AHA engine

Diagnostic Trouble Code (DTC) SAE		Malfunction text	Corrective action
P0300		Random/Multiple Cylinder Misfire Detected	- Fuel level too low, check fuel level and add if necessary - Check misfire detection - Check fuel injectors - Check ignition coils and power output stage -N122- - Check Engine Speed (RPM) sensor -G28-
P0301		Cyl. 1 Misfire Detected	
P0302		Cyl. 2 Misfire Detected	
P0303		Cyl. 3 Misfire Detected	
P0304		Cyl. 4 Misfire Detected	
P0305		Cyl. 5 Misfire Detected	
P0306		Cyl. 6 Misfire Detected	
P0321		Ign./Distributor Eng. Speed Inp. Circ. Range/Performance	- Check Engine Speed (RPM) sensor -G28-
P0322		Ign./Distributor Eng. Speed Inp. Circ. No Signal	

Note on misfire malfunctions:

For malfunctions that may be caused by low fuel volume (i.e. combustion misfire) a low-fuel malfunction (DTC P1250) is also stored when there is less than 2 gallons of fuel remaining in the tank.

VW1029900140050X

Fig. 13 Motronic DTC interpretation chart (Part 5 of 27). Passat w/2.8L AHA engine

Diagnostic Trouble Code (DTC) SAE		Malfunction text	Corrective action
P0327		Knock Sensor1 Circ. Low Input	- Loosen knock sensor and re-tighten to 15 ft lb - Check knock sensors and knock sensor control
P0328		Knock Sensor1 Circ. High Input	
P0332		Knock Sensor2 Circ. Low Input	
P0333		Knock Sensor2 Circ. High Input	
P0411		Sec. Air Inj. Sys. Incorrect Flow Detected	- Check secondary Air Injection (AIR) solenoid valve -N112- and secondary Air Injection (AIR) pump relay -J299-
P0422		Main Catalyst, Bank1 Efficiency Below Threshold	- Check Three Way Catalytic Converter (TWC)
P0432		Main Catalyst, Bank2 Efficiency Below Threshold	
P0441		EVAP Emission Contr. Sys. Incorrect Purge Flow	- Check Evaporative Emission (EVAP) canister purge regulator valve -N80-

VW1029900140060X

Fig. 13 Motronic DTC interpretation chart (Part 6 of 27). Passat w/2.8L AHA engine

Diagnostic Trouble Code (DTC) SAE	Malfunction text	Corrective action
P0442	EVAP Emission Contr. Sys. (Small Leak) Leak Detected	– Check Evaporative Emission (EVAP) system
P0455	EVAP Emission Contr. Sys. (Gross Leak) Leak Detected	
P0501	Vehicle Speed Sensor Range/Performance	– Check vehicle speed signal
P0506	Idle Control System RPM Lower Than Expected	– Check throttle valve control module -J338-
P0507	Idle Control System RPM Higher Than Expected	
P0560	System Voltage Malfunction	– Check voltage supply for ECM
P0562	System Voltage Low Voltage	– Procedure after voltage supply open circuit
P0563	System Voltage High Voltage	
P0601	Internal Contr. Module Memory Check Sum Error	Replace Motronic ECM -J220-
P0604	Internal Contr. Module Random Access Memory (RAM) Error	
P0707	Transm. Range Sensor Circ. Low Input	– Check Transmission Range (TR) signal
P0708	Transm. Range Sensor Circ. High Input	

VW1029900140070X

Fig. 13 Motronic DTC interpretation chart (Part 7 of 27). Passat w/2.8L AHA engine

Diagnostic Trouble Code (DTC) SAE	Malfunction text	Corrective action
P1127	Long Term Fuel Trim mult., Bank1 System too Rich	– Check Mass Air Flow (MAF) sensor -G70-
		– Check Heated Oxygen Sensor (HO2S) -G39- and O2S control before TWC (bank 1, sensor 1)
		– Check Oxygen Sensor (O2S) -G130- and Oxygen Sensor (O2S) control behind TWC (bank 1, sensor 2)
		– Check fuel pressure, fuel pressure regulator and residual fuel pressure
		– Check fuel injectors ⇒ output
		– Check Evaporative Emission (EVAP) canister purge regulator valve -N80-

VW1029900140090X

Fig. 13 Motronic DTC interpretation chart (Part 9 of 27). Passat w/2.8L AHA engine

Diagnostic Trouble Code (DTC) SAE	Malfunction text	Corrective action
P1129	Long Term Fuel Trim mult., Bank2 System too Rich	– Check Mass Air Flow (MAF) sensor -G70-
		– Check Heated Oxygen Sensor (HO2S) 2 -G108- and O2S control before TWC (bank 2, sensor 1)
		– Check Oxygen Sensor (O2S) 2 -G131- and Oxygen Sensor (O2S) control behind TWC (bank 2, sensor 2)
		– Check fuel pressure, fuel pressure regulator and residual fuel pressure
		– Check fuel injectors

VW1029900140110X

Fig. 13 Motronic DTC interpretation chart (Part 11 of 27). Passat w/2.8L AHA engine

Diagnostic Trouble Code (DTC) SAE	Malfunction text	Corrective action
P1102	O2 Sensor Heating Circ., Bank1–Sensor1 Short to B+	– Check Oxygen Sensor (O2S) heater before TWC
P1105	O2 Sensor Heating Circ., Bank1–Sensor2 Short to B+	– Check Oxygen Sensor (O2S) heater behind TWC
P1107	O2 Sensor Heating Circ., Bank2–Sensor1 Short to B+	– Check Oxygen Sensor (O2S) heater before TWC
P1110	O2 Sensor Heating Circ., Bank2–Sensor2 Short to B+	– Check Oxygen Sensor (O2S) heater behind TWC

VW1029900140080X

Fig. 13 Motronic DTC interpretation chart (Part 8 of 27). Passat w/2.8L AHA engine

Diagnostic Trouble Code (DTC) SAE	Malfunction text	Corrective action
P1128	Long Term Fuel Trim mult., Bank1 System too Lean	– Check Heated Oxygen Sensor (HO2S) -G39- and O2S control before TWC (bank 1, sensor 1)
		– Check Oxygen Sensor (O2S) -G130- and Oxygen Sensor (O2S) control behind TWC (bank 1, sensor 2)
		– Check fuel pump
		– Check fuel pressure, fuel pressure regulator and residual fuel pressure
		– Check fuel injectors
		– Check Evaporative Emission (EVAP) canister purge regulator valve -N80-

VW1029900140100X

Fig. 13 Motronic DTC interpretation chart (Part 10 of 27). Passat w/2.8L AHA engine

Diagnostic Trouble Code (DTC) SAE	Malfunction text	Corrective action
P1130	Long Term Fuel Trim mult., Bank2 System too Lean	– Check Heated Oxygen Sensor (HO2S) 2 -G108- and O2S control before TWC (bank 2, sensor 1)
		– Check Oxygen Sensor (O2S) 2 -G131- and Oxygen Sensor (O2S) control behind TWC (bank 2, sensor 2)
		– Check fuel pump
		– Check fuel pressure, fuel pressure regulator and residual fuel pressure
		– Check fuel injectors
		– Check Evaporative Emission (EVAP) canister purge regulator valve -N80-

VW1029900140120X

Fig. 13 Motronic DTC interpretation chart (Part 12 of 27). Passat w/2.8L AHA engine

Diagnostic Trouble Code (DTC) SAE	Malfunction text	Corrective action
P1136	Long Term Fuel Trim Add. Fuel, Bank1 System too Lean	– Check Heated Oxygen Sensor (HO2S) -G39- and O2S control before TWC (bank 1, sensor 1)
		– Check fuel pump
		– Check intake air system for leaks (unmetered air)
		– Check Mass Air Flow (MAF) sensor -G70-
		– Check fuel pressure, fuel pressure regulator and residual fuel pressure
		– Check fuel injectors

VW1029900140130X

Fig. 13 Motronic DTC interpretation chart (Part 13 of 27). Passat w/2.8L AHA engine

Diagnostic Trouble Code (DTC) SAE	Malfunction text	Corrective action
P1137	Long Term Fuel Trim Add. Fuel, Bank1 System too Rich	– Check Heated Oxygen Sensor (HO2S) -G39- and O2S control before TWC (bank 1, sensor 1)
		– Check fuel pump
		– Check fuel pressure, fuel pressure regulator and residual pressure
		– Check fuel injectors
		– Check Evaporative Emission (EVAP) canister purge regulator valve -N80-

VW1029900140140X

Fig. 13 Motronic DTC interpretation chart (Part 14 of 27). Passat w/2.8L AHA engine

Diagnostic Trouble Code (DTC) SAE	Malfunction text	Corrective action
P1138	Long Term Fuel Trim Add. Fuel, Bank2 System too Lean	– Check Heated Oxygen Sensor (HO2S) 2 -G108- and O2S control before TWC (bank 2, sensor 1)
		– Check fuel pump
		– Check intake air system for leaks (unmetered air)
		– Check Mass Air Flow (MAF) sensor -G70-
		– Check fuel pressure, fuel pressure regulator and residual fuel pressure
		– Check fuel injectors

VW1029900140150X

Fig. 13 Motronic DTC interpretation chart (Part 15 of 27). Passat w/2.8L AHA engine

Diagnostic Trouble Code (DTC) SAE	Malfunction text	Corrective action
P1139	Long Term Fuel Trim Add. Fuel, Bank2 System too Rich	– Check Heated Oxygen Sensor (HO2S) 2 -G108- and O2S control before TWC (bank 2, sensor 1)
		– Check fuel pump
		– Check fuel pressure, fuel pressure regulator and residual pressure
		– Check fuel injectors
		– Check Evaporative Emission (EVAP) canister purge regulator valve -N80-
P1141	Load Calculation Cross Check Range/Performance	– Check Mass Air Flow (MAF) sensor -G70- – Check throttle valve control module -J338-

VW1029900140160X

Fig. 13 Motronic DTC interpretation chart (Part 16 of 27). Passat w/2.8L AHA engine

Diagnostic Trouble Code (DTC) SAE	Malfunction text	Corrective action
P1176	O2 Correction Behind Catalyst, B1 Limit Attained	– Check intake air system for leaks (unentered air)
		– Check Heated Oxygen Sensor (HO2S) aging (bank 1, sensor 1)
		– Check Oxygen Sensor (O2S) heater behind TWC
		– Check Oxygen Sensor (O2S) -G130- and Oxygen Sensor (O2S) control behind TWC (bank 1, sensor 2)
P1177	O2 Correction Behind Catalyst, B2 Limit Attained	– Check intake air system for leaks (unmetered air)
		– Check Heated Oxygen Sensor (HO2S) 2 aging (bank 2, sensor 1)
		– Check Oxygen Sensor (O2S) 2 heater behind TWC
		– Check Oxygen Sensor (O2S) 2 -G131- and Oxygen Sensor (O2S) control behind TWC (bank 2, sensor 2)

VW1029900140170X

Fig. 13 Motronic DTC interpretation chart (Part 17 of 27). Passat w/2.8L AHA engine

Diagnostic Trouble Code (DTC) SAE	Malfunction text	Corrective action
P1196	O2 Sensor Heater Circ., Bank1–Sensor1 Electrical Malfunction	– Check Oxygen Sensor (O2S) heater before TWC
P1197	O2 Sensor Heater Circ., Bank2–Sensor1 Electrical Malfunction	
P1198	O2 Sensor Heater Circ., Bank1–Sensor2 Electrical Malfunction	– Check Oxygen Sensor (O2S) heater behind TWC
P1199	O2 Sensor Heater Circ., Bank2–Sensor2 Electrical Malfunction	
P1213	Cyl.1–Fuel Inj. Circ. Short to B+	– Check fuel injectors
P1214	Cyl.2–Fuel Inj. Circ. Short to B+	
P1215	Cyl.3–Fuel Inj. Circ. Short to B+	
P1216	Cyl.4–Fuel Inj. Circ. Short to B+	
P1217	Cyl.5–Fuel Inj. Circ. Short to B+	

VW1029900140180X

Fig. 13 Motronic DTC interpretation chart (Part 18 of 27). Passat w/2.8L AHA engine

Diagnostic Trouble Code (DTC) SAE	Malfunction text	Corrective action
P1218	Cyl.6–Fuel Inj. Circ. Short to B+	– Check fuel injectors
P1225	Cyl.1–Fuel Inj. Circ. Short to Ground	
P1226	Cyl.2–Fuel Inj. Circ. Short to Ground	
P1227	Cyl.3–Fuel Inj. Circ. Short to Ground	
P1228	Cyl.4–Fuel Inj. Circ. Short to Ground	
P1229	Cyl.5–Fuel Inj. Circ. Short to Ground	
P1230	Cyl.6–Fuel Inj. Circ. Short to Ground	

VW1029900140190X

Fig. 13 Motronic DTC interpretation chart (Part 19 of 27). Passat w/2.8L AHA engine

Diagnostic Trouble Code (DTC) SAE	Malfunctioh text	Corrective action
P1325	Cyl.1–Knock Contr. Limit Attained	– Check knock sensors and knock sensor control – Loosen knock sensors and re-tighten to 15 ft lb – Repair cause of abnormal engine running noises – Fill with fuel of at least 91 RON
P1326	Cyl.2–Knock Contr. Limit Attained	
P1327	Cyl.3–Knock Contr. Limit Attained	
P1328	Cyl.4–Knock Contr. Limit Attained	
P1329	Cyl.5–Knock Contr. Limit Attained	
P1330	Cyl.6–Knock Contr. Limit Attained	
P1337	Camshaft Pos. Sensor, Bank1 Short to Ground	– Check Camshaft Position (CMP) sensor -G40-
P1338	Camshaft Pos. Sensor, Bank1 Open Circ./Short to B+	
P1386	Internal Control Module Knock Control Circ. Error	– Replace ECM

VW1029900140210X

Fig. 13 Motronic DTC interpretation chart (Part 21 of 27). Passat w/2.8L AHA engine

Diagnostic Trouble Code (DTC) SAE	Malfunction text	Corrective action
P1433	Sec. Air Inj. Sys. Pump Relay Circ. Open	– Check secondary Air Injection (AIR) pump relay -J299-
P1434	Sec. Air Inj. Sys. Pump Relay Circ. Short to B+	
P1435	Sec. Air Inj. Sys. Pump Relay Circ. Short to Ground	
P1436	Sec. Air Inj. Sys. Pump Relay Circ. Electrical Malfunction	
P1471	EVAP Emission Contr. LDP Circ. Short to B+	– Check Leak Detection Pump (LDP)
P1472	EVAP Emission Contr. LDP Circ. Short to Ground	– Check Evaporative Emission (EVAP) system
P1473	EVAP Emission Contr. LDP Circ. Open Circ.	
P1476	EVAP Emission Contr. LDP Circ. Malfunction/Insufficient Vacuum	
P1477	EVAP Emission Contr. LDP Circ. Malfunction	

VW1029900140230X

Fig. 13 Motronic DTC interpretation chart (Part 23 of 27). Passat w/2.8L AHA engine

Diagnostic Trouble Code (DTC) SAE	Malfunction text	Corrective action
P1237	Cyl.1–Fuel Inj. Circ. Open Circuit	– Check fuel injectors output
P1238	Cyl.2–Fuel Inj. Circ. Open Circuit	
P1239	Cyl.3–Fuel Inj. Circ. Open Circuit	
P1240	Cyl.4–Fuel Inj. Circ. Open Circuit	
P1241	Cyl.5–Fuel Inj. Circ. Open Circuit	
P1242	Cyl.6–Fuel Inj. Circ. Open Circuit	
P1250	Fuel Level Too Low	– Fuel volume less than 2 gallons; add fuel – Check fuel level sensor signal and fuel gauge

VW1029900140200X

Fig. 13 Motronic DTC interpretation chart (Part 20 of 27). Passat w/2.8L AHA engine

Diagnostic Trouble Code (DTC) SAE	Malfunction text	Corrective action
P1391	Camshaft Pos. Sensor, Bank2 Short to Ground	– Check Camshaft Position (CMP) sensor 2 -G163-
P1392	Camshaft Pos. Sensor, Bank2 Open Circ./Short to B+	
P1410	Tank Ventilation Valve Circ. Short to B+	– Check Evaporative Emission (EVAP) canister purge regulator valve -N80-
P1421	Sec. Air Inj. Valve Circ. Short to Ground	– Check secondary Air Injection (AIR) solenoid valve -N112-
P1422	Sec. Air Inj. Sys. Contr. Valve Circ. Short to B+	
P1425	Tank Vent Valve Short to Ground	– Check Evaporative Emission (EVAP) canister purge regulator valve -N80-
P1426	Tank Vent Valve Open	
P1432	Sec. Air Inj. Valve Open	– Check secondary Air Injection (AIR) solenoid valve -N112-

VW1029900140220X

Fig. 13 Motronic DTC interpretation chart (Part 22 of 27). Passat w/2.8L AHA engine

Diagnostic Trouble Code (DTC) SAE	Malfunction text	Corrective action
P1500	Fuel Pump Relay Circ. Electrical Malfunction	– Check fuel pump relay and relay actuation
P1501	Fuel Pump Relay Circ. Short to Ground	– Check fuel pump
P1502	Fuel Pump Relay Circ. Short to B+	
P1505	Closed Throttle Pos. Switch Does Not Close/Open Circ.	– Check throttle body and throttle valve control module -J338-
P1506	Closed Throttle Pos. Switch Does Not Open/Short to Ground	
P1512	Intake Manifold Changeover Valve Circ. Short to B+	– Check Intake Manifold Tuning (IMT) valve -N156- (change-over valve)
P1515	Intake Manifold Changeover Valve Circ. Short to Ground	
P1516	Intake Manifold Changeover Valve Circ. Open	

VW1029900140240X

Fig. 13 Motronic DTC interpretation chart (Part 24 of 27). Passat w/2.8L AHA engine

Diagnostic Trouble Code (DTC) SAE		Malfunction text	Corrective action
P1519		Intake Camshaft Contr., Bank1 Malfunction	– Check camshaft adjustment
P1522		Intake Camshaft Contr., Bank2 Malfunction	– Check valves -1- and -2- for camshaft adjustment -N205- and -N208-
P1543		Throttle Actuation Potentiometer Signal too Low	– Check throttle valve control module -J338-
P1544		Throttle Actuation Potentiometer Signal too High	
P1545		Throttle Pos. Contr. Malfunction	
P1558		Throttle Actuator Electrical Malfunction	
P1559		Idle Speed Contr. Throttle Pos. Adaptation Malfunction	
P1560		Maximum Engine Speed Exceeded	– Carry out engine mechanical repairs as necessary
P1564		Idle Speed Contr. Throttle Pos. Low Voltage During Adaptation	– Check voltage supply to ECM

VW1029900140250X

Fig. 13 Motronic DTC interpretation chart (Part 25 of 27). Passat w/2.8L AHA engine

Diagnostic Trouble Code (DTC) SAE		Malfunction text	Corrective action
P1640		Internal Contr. Module (EEPROM) Error	– Replace ECM
P1681		Contr. Unit Programming Programming not Finished	– Replace ECM
P1690		Malfunction Indicator Light Malfunction	– Check wire from ECM to Malfunction Indicator Lamp (MIL)
P1693		Malfunction Indicator Light Short to B+	– Check wire from ECM to Malfunction Indicator Lamp (MIL)

VW1029900140270X

Fig. 13 Motronic DTC interpretation chart (Part 27 of 27). Passat w/2.8L AHA engine

DTC SAE	DTC VAG	DTC text	Corrective action
P0130	16514	Bank 1, sensor 1, electrical malfunction in circuit	
P0131	16515	Bank 1, sensor 1, voltage too small	
P0132	16516	Bank 1, sensor 1, voltage too large	- Check oxygen sensor aging, bank 1, oxygen sensor 1
P0133	16517	Bank 1, sensor 1, signal too slow	- Oxygen sensor and oxygen sensor control behind catalytic converter.
P0134	16518	Bank 1, sensor 1, no activity	- Oxygen sensor and oxygen sensor control before catalytic converter.
P0136	16520	Bank 1, sensor 2, electrical malfunction in circuit	- Oxygen sensor and oxygen sensor control behind catalytic converter. - Check oxygen sensor heating behind catalytic converter

VW1020000155020X

Fig. 14 Motronic DTC interpretation chart (Part 2 of 36). Passat w/2.8L ATQ engine

Diagnostic Trouble Code (DTC) SAE		Malfunction text	Corrective action
P1565		Idle Speed Contr. Throttle Pos. Lower Impact Not Attained	– Check accelerator pedal cable adjustment
P1600		Power Supply (B+) Terminal 15 Low Voltage	– Check voltage supply to (ECM)
P1602		Power Supply (B+) Terminal 30 Low Voltage	– Check voltage supply to ECM – Procedure after voltage supply open circuit
P1606		Rough Road Spec Engine Torque ABS-ECU Electrical Malfunction	– Check rough road signal from ABS/EDL control module
P1612		Electronic Control Module Incorrect Coding	– Code ECM
P1624		MIL Request Sign. active	– Check DTC memory for Transmission Control Module (TCM) and correct malfunctions
P1626		CAN–Bus Missing Message from Transm. Contr.	– Check Transmission Range (TR) signal

VW1029900140260X

Fig. 13 Motronic DTC interpretation chart (Part 26 of 27). Passat w/2.8L AHA engine

DTC SAE	DTC VAG	DTC text	Corrective action
P0101	16486	Mass Air Flow (MAF) sensor -G70- implausible signal	
P0102	16486	Mass Air Flow (MAF) sensor -G70- signal too small	- Check Mass Air Flow (MAF) sensor
P0103	16487	Mass Air Flow (MAF) sensor -G70- signal too large	- Check intake system for leaks (false air) - Check fuse 43
P0106	16490	MAP sensor -G71-/BARO sensor -F96- implausible signal	
P0107	16491	MAP sensor -G71-/BARO sensor -F96- signal too small	
P0112	16496	Intake Air Temperature (IAT) sensor -G42- Signal too small	- Check Intake Air Temperature (IAT) sensor
P0113	16497	Intake Air Temperature (IAT) sensor -G42- Signal too large	
P0116	16500	Engine Coolant Temperature (ECT) sensor -G62- implausible signal	- Check Engine Coolant Temperature (ECT) sensor
P0117	16501	Engine Coolant Temperature (ECT) sensor -G62- Signal too small	- Check coolant regulator
P0118	16502	Engine Coolant Temperature (ECT) sensor -G62- Signal too large	

VW1020000155010X

Fig. 14 Motronic DTC interpretation chart (Part 1 of 36). Passat w/2.8L ATQ engine

DTC SAE	DTC VAG	DTC text	Corrective action
P0137	16521	Bank 1, sensor 2, voltage too small	- Oxygen sensor and oxygen sensor control behind catalytic converter, checking
P0138	16522	Bank 1, sensor 2, voltage too large	- Check oxygen sensor heating behind catalytic converter
P0139	16523	Bank 2, sensor 1, signal too slow	
P0140	16524	Bank 1, sensor 2, no activity	
P0150	16534	Bank 2, sensor 1, electrical malfunction in circuit	- Check oxygen sensor aging, bank 2, oxygen sensor 1
P0151	16535	Bank 2, sensor 1, voltage too small	- Oxygen sensor and oxygen sensor control before catalytic converter.
P0152	16536	Bank 2, sensor 1, voltage too large	
P0153	16537	Bank 2, sensor 1, signal too slow	- Oxygen sensor and oxygen sensor control before catalytic converter.
P0154	16538	Bank 2, sensor 1, no activity	

VW1020000155030X

Fig. 14 Motronic DTC interpretation chart (Part 3 of 36). Passat w/2.8L ATQ engine

DTC SAE	DTC VAG	DTC text	Corrective action
P0156	16540	Bank 2, sensor 2, electrical malfunction in circuit	- Check oxygen sensor heating behind catalytic converter
P0157	16541	Bank 2, sensor 2, voltage too small	- Oxygen sensor and oxygen sensor control behind catalytic converter.
P0158	16542	Bank 2, sensor 2, voltage too large	
P0159	16543	Bank 2, sensor 2, signal too slow	
P0160	16544	Bank 2, sensor 2, no activity	
P0197	16581	Engine oil temperature sensor -G8- signal too small	- Check oil level thermal sensor -G266-
P0198	16582	Engine oil temperature sensor -G8- signal too large	

VW1020000155040X

Fig. 14 Motronic DTC interpretation chart (Part 4 of 36). Passat w/2.8L ATQ engine

DTC SAE	DTC VAG	DTC text	Corrective action
P0327	16711	Knock Sensor (KS) 1 -G61- signal too small	- Check knock sensors
P0328	16712	Knock Sensor (KS) 1 -G61- signal too large	- Loosen knock sensors and tighten to 15 ft lbs again
P0332	16716	Knock Sensor (KS) 2 -G66- signal too small	
P0333	16717	Knock Sensor (KS) 2 -G66- signal too large	
P0341	16725	Camshaft Position (CMP) sensor -G40- unplausible signal	- Check Camshaft Position (CMP) sensor
P0346	16730	Camshaft Position (CMP) sensor -G163- unplausible signal	

VW1020000155060X

Fig. 14 Motronic DTC interpretation chart (Part 6 of 36). Passat w/2.8L ATQ engine

DTC SAE	DTC VAG	DTC text	Corrective action
P0506	16890	Idle regulation RPM below specified value	- Checking throttle valve control module
P0507	16891	Idle regulation RPM above specified value	
P0560	16944	Voltage supply implausible signal	- Checking voltage supply
P0562	16946	Voltage supply voltage too low	
P0563	16947	Voltage supply voltage too large	
P0571	16955	Brake light switch -F-[1] implausible signal	- Brake light switch and brake pedal switch, check
P0601	16985	Control module faulty	- Replace Motronic Engine Control Module (ECM) -J220-
P0604	16988	Control module faulty	
P0605	16989	Control module faulty	

[1] Brake pedal switch -F47- is monitored in addition to brake light switch -F-.

VW1020000155080X

Fig. 14 Motronic DTC interpretation chart (Part 8 of 36). Passat w/2.8L ATQ engine

DTC SAE	DTC VAG	DTC text	Corrective action
P1113	17521	Bank 1, sensor 1 inner resistance too large	- Check oxygen sensor heating before catalytic converter
P1114	17522	Bank 1, sensor 2 inner resistance too large	- Check oxygen sensor heating behind catalytic converter
P1115	17523	Bank 1, sensor 1 heating circuit short circuit to Ground (GND)	- Check oxygen sensor heating before catalytic converter
P1116	17524	Bank 1, sensor 1 heating circuit open circuit	
P1117	17525	Bank 1, sensor 2 heating circuit short circuit to Ground (GND)	- Check oxygen sensor heating behind catalytic converter
P1118	17526	Bank 1, sensor 2 heating circuit open circuit	

VW1020000155100X

Fig. 14 Motronic DTC interpretation chart (Part 10 of 36). Passat w/2.8L ATQ engine

DTC SAE	DTC VAG	DTC text	Corrective action
P0300	16684	Combustion misfire detected	- Check fuel injectors
P0301	16685	Cyl. 1 combustion misfire detected	- Check ignition wires and spark plugs
P0302	16686	Cyl. 2 combustion misfire detected	- Check ignition coil
P0303	16687	Cyl. 3 combustion misfire detected	- Check misfire recognition
P0304	16688	Cyl. 4 combustion misfire detected	
P0305	16689	Cyl. 5 combustion misfire detected	
P0306	16690	Cyl. 6 combustion misfire detected	
P0321	16705	Engine Speed (RPM) sensor -G28- implausible signal	- Check sender for fuel gauge
P0322	16706	Engine Speed (RPM) sensor -G28- no signal	

VW1020000155050X

Fig. 14 Motronic DTC interpretation chart (Part 5 of 36). Passat w/2.8L ATQ engine

DTC SAE	DTC VAG	DTC text	Corrective action
P0441	16825	Tank ventilation system throughput faulty	- Check Evaporative Emission (EVAP) canister purge regulator valve - Check hoses and connecting pipes from fuel tank to throttle valve control module
P0442	16826	Small leak detected in tank ventilation system	
P0455	16839	Large leak detected in tank ventilation system	
P0456	16840	Pinhole leak detected in tank ventilation system	
P0501	16885	Vehicle speed signal unplausible signal	- Check vehicle speed signal

VW1020000155070X

Fig. 14 Motronic DTC interpretation chart (Part 7 of 36). Passat w/2.8L ATQ engine

DTC SAE	DTC VAG	DTC text	Corrective action
P1102	17510	Bank 1, sensor 1 heating circuit short circuit to B+	- Check oxygen sensor heating before catalytic converter
P1105	17513	Bank 1, sensor 2 heating circuit short circuit to B+	- Check oxygen sensor heating behind catalytic converter
P1107	17515	Bank 2, sensor 1 heating circuit short circuit to B+	- Check oxygen sensor heating before catalytic converter
P1110	17518	Bank 2, sensor 2 heating circuit short circuit to B+	- Check oxygen sensor heating behind catalytic converter
P1111	17519	Oxygen sensor control (bank 1) system too lean	- Oxygen sensor and oxygen sensor control before catalytic converter, checking
P1112	17520	Oxygen sensor control (bank 1) system too rich	

VW1020000155090X

Fig. 14 Motronic DTC interpretation chart (Part 9 of 36). Passat w/2.8L ATQ engine

DTC SAE	DTC VAG	DTC text	Corrective action
P1119	17527	Bank 2, sensor 1 heating circuit short circuit to Ground (GND)	- Check oxygen sensor heating before catalytic converter
P1120	17528	Bank 2, sensor 1 heating circuit open circuit	
P1121	17529	Bank 2, sensor 2 heating circuit short circuit to Ground (GND)	- Check oxygen sensor heating behind catalytic converter
P1122	17530	Bank 2, sensor 2 heating circuit open circuit	
P1127	17535	Bank 1, mixture adaptation (mult.) System too rich	- Check fuel pressure regulator and residual pressure - Check fuel injectors fuel injection quantity and proper seal - Check Evaporative Emission (EVAP) canister purge regulator valve

VW1020000155110X

Fig. 14 Motronic DTC interpretation chart (Part 11 of 36). Passat w/2.8L ATQ engine

DTC SAE	DTC VAG	DTC text	Corrective action
P1128	17536	Bank 1, mixture adaptation (mult.) System too lean	- Check fuel pressure regulator and residual pressure
			- Check fuel injectors fuel injection quantity and proper seal
			- Check fuel pump
			- Check intake system for leaks
			- Check exhaust system for proper seal
			- Check secondary air system for proper seal
			- Check vacuum lines for proper seal

VW1020000155120X

Fig. 14 Motronic DTC interpretation chart (Part 12 of 36). Passat w/2.8L ATQ engine

DTC SAE	DTC VAG	DTC text	Corrective action
P1130	17538	Bank 2, mixture adaptation (mult.) System too lean	- Check fuel pressure regulator and residual pressure
			- Check fuel injectors fuel injection quantity and proper seal
			- Check fuel pump:
			- Check intake system for leaks
			- Check exhaust system for proper seal
			- Check secondary air system for proper seal
			- Check vacuum lines for proper seal
P1131	17539	Bank 2, sensor 1 inner resistance too large	- Check oxygen sensor heating before catalytic converter

VW1020000155140X

Fig. 14 Motronic DTC interpretation chart (Part 14 of 36). Passat w/2.8L ATQ engine

DTC SAE	DTC VAG	DTC text	Corrective action
P1137	17545	Bank 1, mixture adaptation (add.) system too rich	- Check fuel pressure regulator and residual pressure
			- Check fuel injectors fuel injection quantity and proper seal
			- Check Evaporative Emission (EVAP) canister purge regulator valve

Notes:

add = additive, means that malfunction is only valid at closed throttle (idle).

VW1020000155160X

Fig. 14 Motronic DTC interpretation chart (Part 16 of 36). Passat w/2.8L ATQ engine

DTC SAE	DTC VAG	DTC text	Corrective action
P1129	17537	Bank 2, mixture adaptation (mult.) System too rich	- Check fuel pressure regulator and residual pressure
			- Check fuel injectors fuel injection quantity and proper seal
			- Check Evaporative Emission (EVAP) canister purge regulator valve

VW1020000155130X

Fig. 14 Motronic DTC interpretation chart (Part 13 of 36). Passat w/2.8L ATQ engine

DTC SAE	DTC VAG	DTC text	Corrective action
P1136	17544	Bank 1, mixture adaptation (add.) system too lean	- Check fuel pressure regulator and residual pressure
			- Check fuel injectors fuel injection quantity and proper seal.
			- Check fuel pump
			- Check intake system for leaks
			- Check exhaust system for proper seal
			- Check secondary air system for proper seal
			- Check vacuum lines for proper seal

Notes:

add = additive, means that malfunction is only valid at closed throttle (idle).

VW1020000155150X

Fig. 14 Motronic DTC interpretation chart (Part 15 of 36). Passat w/2.8L ATQ engine

DTC SAE	DTC VAG	DTC text	Corrective action
P1138	17546	Bank 2, mixture adaptation (add.) system too lean	- Check fuel pressure regulator and residual pressure
			- Check fuel injectors fuel injection quantity and proper seal.
			- Check fuel pump
			- Check intake system for leaks
			- Check exhaust system for proper seal
			- Check secondary air system for proper seal:
			- Check vacuum lines for proper seal

Notes:

add = additive, means that malfunction is only valid at closed throttle (idle).

VW1020000155170X

Fig. 14 Motronic DTC interpretation chart (Part 17 of 36). Passat w/2.8L ATQ engine

DTC SAE	DTC VAG	DTC text	Corrective action
P1139	17547	Bank 2, mixture adaptation (add.) system too rich	- Check fuel pressure regulator and residual pressure - Check fuel injectors fuel injection quantity and proper seal - Check Evaporative Emission (EVAP) canister purge regulator valve
P1140	17548	Bank 2, sensor 2 inner resistance too large	- Check oxygen sensor heating behind catalytic converter
P1141	17549	Load detection unplausible value	- Checking throttle valve control module
P1143	17551	Load detection limit exceeded	- Check Mass Air Flow (MAF) sensor - Check Throttle Position (TP) sensor

Notes:

add = additive, means that malfunction is only valid at closed throttle (idle).

VW1020000155180X

Fig. 14 Motronic DTC interpretation chart (Part 18 of 36). Passat w/2.8L ATQ engine

DTC SAE	DTC VAG	DTC text	Corrective action
P1176	17584	Bank 1 oxygen sensor correction behind cat. control limit reached	- Check oxygen sensor aging, bank 1, oxygen sensor 1 - Oxygen sensor and oxygen sensor control behind catalytic converter, checking - Check intake system for leaks
P1177	17585	Bank 2 oxygen sensor correction behind cat. control limit reached	- Check oxygen sensor aging, bank 2, oxygen sensor 1 - Oxygen sensor and oxygen sensor control behind catalytic converter, check - Check intake system for leaks
P1198	17606	Bank 1, sensor 2 heating circuit electrical malfunction	- Check oxygen sensor heating behind catalytic converter
P1199	17607	Bank 2, sensor 2 heating circuit electrical malfunction	

VW1020000155200X

Fig. 14 Motronic DTC interpretation chart (Part 20 of 36). Passat w/2.8L ATQ engine

DTC SAE	DTC VAG	DTC text	Corrective action
P1213	17621	Cylinder 1 fuel injector -N30- short circuit to B+	- Check fuel injectors
P1214	17622	Cylinder 2 fuel injector -N31- short circuit to B+	
P1215	17623	Cylinder 3 fuel injector -N32- short circuit to B+	
P1216	17624	Cylinder 4 fuel injector -N33- short circuit to B+	
P1217	17625	Cylinder 5 fuel injector -N83- short circuit to B+	
P1218	17626	Cylinder 6 fuel injector -N84- short circuit to B+	
P1225	17633	Cylinder 1 fuel injector -N30- short circuit to Ground (GND)	
P1226	17634	Cylinder 2 fuel injector -N31- short circuit to Ground (GND)	
P1227	17635	Cylinder 3 fuel injector -N32- short circuit to Ground (GND)	
P1228	17636	Cylinder 4 fuel injector -N33- short circuit to Ground (GND)	
P1229	17637	Cylinder 5 fuel injector -N83- short circuit to Ground (GND)	
P1230	17638	Cylinder 6 fuel injector -N84- short circuit to Ground (GND)	

VW1020000155220X

Fig. 14 Motronic DTC interpretation chart (Part 22 of 36). Passat w/2.8L ATQ engine

DTC SAE	DTC VAG	DTC text	Corrective action
P1147	17555	Oxygen sensor control (bank 2) system too lean	- Oxygen sensor and oxygen sensor control before catalytic converter, checking
P1148	17556	Oxygen sensor control (bank 2) system too rich	
P1149	17557	Oxygen sensor control bank 1 unplausible control value	- Check oxygen sensor aging, bank 1, oxygen sensor 1
P1150	17558	Oxygen sensor control bank 2 unplausible control value	- Check oxygen sensor aging, bank 2, oxygen sensor 1
P1171	17579	Angle sensor -2- for throttle drive (power accelerator actuation) -G188- unplausible signal 1)	- Checking throttle valve control module
P1172	17580	Angle sensor -2- for throttle drive (power accelerator actuation) -G188- signal too small 1)	
P1173	17581	Angle sensor -2- for throttle drive (power accelerator actuation) -G188- signal too large 1)	

1) For these malfunctions, ECM switches on the EPC warning lamp in instrument cluster.

VW1020000155190X

Fig. 14 Motronic DTC interpretation chart (Part 19 of 36). Passat w/2.8L ATQ engine

DTC SAE	DTC VAG	DTC text	Corrective action
P1201	17609	Cylinder 1 fuel injector -N30- electrical malfunction in circuit	- Check fuel injectors
P1202	17610	Cylinder 2 fuel injector -N31- electrical malfunction in circuit	
P1203	17611	Cylinder 3 fuel injector -N32- electrical malfunction in circuit	
P1204	17612	Cylinder 4 fuel injector -N33- electrical malfunction in circuit	
P1205	17613	Cylinder 5 fuel injector -N83- electrical malfunction in circuit	
P1206	17614	Cylinder 6 fuel injector -N84- electrical malfunction in circuit	

VW1020000155210X

Fig. 14 Motronic DTC interpretation chart (Part 21 of 36). Passat w/2.8L ATQ engine

DTC SAE	DTC VAG	DTC text	Corrective action
P1237	17645	Cylinder 1 fuel injector -N30- open circuit	- Check fuel injectors
P1238	17646	Cylinder 2 fuel injector -N31- open circuit	
P1239	17647	Cylinder 3 fuel injector -N32- open circuit	
P1240	17648	Cylinder 4 fuel injector -N33- open circuit	
P1241	17649	Cylinder 5 fuel injector -N83- open circuit	
P1242	17650	Cylinder 6 fuel injector -N84- open circuit	
P1250	17658	Fuel level too low	Fuel level less than 2 gallons, add fuel to tank Signal from sender for fuel gauge -G-, check

VW1020000155230X

Fig. 14 Motronic DTC interpretation chart (Part 23 of 36). Passat w/2.8L ATQ engine

DTC SAE	DTC VAG	DTC text	Corrective action
P1325	17733	Knock control cylinder 1 control limit reached	- Check Knock Sensor (KS) and knock control - Repair abnormal engine noise (components loose, bracket/bolts broken) - Check harness connectors and wires - Loosen knock sensors and tighten to 15 ft lbs again - Change fuel types
P1326	17734	Knock control cylinder 2 control limit reached	
P1327	17735	Knock control cylinder 3 control limit reached	
P1328	17736	Knock control cylinder 4 control limit reached	
P1329	17737	Knock control cylinder 5 control limit reached	
P1330	17738	Knock control cylinder 6 control limit reached	

VW1020000155240X

Fig. 14 Motronic DTC interpretation chart (Part 24 of 36). Passat w/2.8L ATQ engine

DTC		DTC text	Corrective action
SAE	VAG		
P1335	17743	Engine torque monitoring 2 control limit exceeded	
P1336	17744	Engine torque monitoring control limit exceeded	- Check Mass Air Flow (MAF) sensor - Check Intake Air Temperature (IAT) sensor - Check Engine Coolant Temperature (ECT) sensor
P1337	17745	Bank 1 Camshaft Position (CMP) sensor -G40- short circuit to Ground (GND)	Check Camshaft Position (CMP) sensor
P1338	17746	Bank 1 Camshaft Position (CMP) sensor -G40- open circuit/short circuit to B+	
P1340	17748	CMP sensor/Crankshaft position sensor incorrect allocation	- Check Camshaft Position (CMP) sensor
P1347	17755	Bank 2, CMP sensor/Crankshaft position sensor incorrect allocation	- Check sender for fuel gauge

VW1020000155250X

Fig. 14 Motronic DTC interpretation chart (Part 25 of 36). Passat w/2.8L ATQ engine

DTC		DTC text	Corrective action
SAE	VAG		
P1386	17794	Control module faulty[1]	- Replace Motronic Engine Control Module (ECM) -J220-
P1387	17795	Control module faulty[1]	
P1388	17796	Control module faulty[1]	
P1391	17799	Bank 2 Camshaft Position (CMP) sensor 2 -G163- short circuit to Ground (GND)	Check Camshaft Position (CMP) sensor
P1392	17800	Bank 2 Camshaft Position (CMP) sensor 2 -G163- open circuit/short circuit to B+	
P1393	17801	Ignition output 1 electrical malfunction in circuit	- Check ignition wires and spark plugs
P1394	17802	Ignition output 2 electrical malfunction in circuit	- Check ignition coil
P1395	17803	Ignition output 3 electrical malfunction in circuit	- Check misfire recognition

[1] For these malfunctions, ECM switches on the EPC warning lamp in instrument cluster. Significance of EPC warning lamp

VW1020000155260X

Fig. 14 Motronic DTC interpretation chart (Part 26 of 36). Passat w/2.8L ATQ engine

DTC		DTC text	Corrective action
SAE	VAG		
P1409	17817	EVAP canister purge regulator valve -N80- electrical malfunction in circuit	
P1410	17818	EVAP canister purge regulator valve -N80- short circuit to B+	- Check Evaporative Emission (EVAP) Canister Purge Regulator Valve
P1411	17819	Bank 2 Secondary Air Injection (AIR) system throughput too small	- Check secondary air system for proper seal:
P1414	17822	Bank 2, Secondary Air Injection (AIR) system, leak detected	
P1420	17828	Secondary Air Injection (AIR) solenoid valve -N112- electrical malfunction in circuit	
P1421	17829	Secondary Air Injection (AIR) solenoid valve -N112- short circuit to Ground (GND)	- Check Secondary Air Injection (AIR) valve
P1422	17830	Secondary Air Injection (AIR) solenoid valve -N112- short circuit to B+	
P1423	17831	Bank 1 Secondary Air Injection (AIR) system throughput too small	
P1424	17832	Bank 1, Secondary Air Injection (AIR) system, leak detected	- Check secondary air system for proper seal

VW1020000155270X

Fig. 14 Motronic DTC interpretation chart (Part 27 of 36). Passat w/2.8L ATQ engine

DTC		DTC text	Corrective action
SAE	VAG		
P1425	17833	EVAP canister purge regulator valve -N80- short circuit to Ground (GND)	- Check Evaporative Emission (EVAP) Canister Purge Regulator Valve
P1426	17834	EVAP canister purge regulator valve -N80- open circuit	
P1432	17840	Secondary Air Injection (AIR) solenoid valve -N112- open circuit	- Check Secondary Air Injection (AIR) valve
P1433	17841	Secondary Air Injection (AIR) pump relay -J299- open circuit	- Check Secondary Air Injection (AIR) pump relay
P1434	17842	Secondary Air Injection (AIR) pump relay -J299- short circuit to B+	
P1435	17843	Secondary Air Injection (AIR) pump relay -J299- short circuit to Ground (GND)	
P1436	17844	Secondary Air Injection (AIR) pump relay -J299- electrical malfunction in circuit	

VW1020000155280X

Fig. 14 Motronic DTC interpretation chart (Part 28 of 36). Passat w/2.8L ATQ engine

DTC		DTC text	Corrective action
SAE	VAG		
P1471	17879	Leak Detection Pump (LDP), tank ventilation system, short circuit to B+	Check Leak Detection Pump (LDP):
P1472	17880	Leak Detection Pump (LDP), tank ventilation system, short circuit to Ground (GND)	Check EVAP canister system:
P1473	17881	Leak Detection Pump (LDP) tank ventilation system open circuit	
P1476	17884	Leak Detection Pump (LDP) tank ventilation system malfunction/vacuum pressure too low	
P1477	17885	Leak Detection Pump (LDP) tank ventilation system malfunction	

VW1020000155290X

Fig. 14 Motronic DTC interpretation chart (Part 29 of 36). Passat w/2.8L ATQ engine

DTC		DTC text	Corrective action
SAE	VAG		
P1500	17908	Fuel Pump (FP) relay -J17- electrical malfunction in circuit	
P1501	17909	Fuel Pump (FP) relay -J17- short circuit to Ground (GND)	- Check Fuel Pump (FP) relay
P1502	17910	Fuel Pump (FP) relay -J17- short circuit to B+	
P1511	17919	Intake manifold change-over valve -N156- electrical malfunction in circuit	
P1512	17920	Intake manifold change-over valve -N156- short circuit to B+	
P1515	17923	Intake manifold change-over valve -N156- short circuit to Ground (GND)	- Check intake manifold change-over valve
P1516	17924	Intake manifold change-over valve -N156- open circuit	

VW1020000155300X

Fig. 14 Motronic DTC interpretation chart (Part 30 of 36). Passat w/2.8L ATQ engine

DTC		DTC text	Corrective action
SAE	VAG		
P1519	17927	Bank 1, camshaft adjustment malfunction	Diagnose variable camshaft system MAL
P1522	17930	Bank 2, camshaft adjustment malfunction	
P1523	17931	Crash signal from airbag control module, implausible signal	- Check whether the control module is CAN bus capable, replace if necessary
P1529	17937	Camshaft adjustment short circuit to B+	- Check valves -1- and -2- for camshaft adjustment
P1530	17938	Camshaft adjustment short circuit to Ground	Diagnose variable camshaft system MAL
P1531	17939	Camshaft adjustment open circuit	

VW1020000155310X

Fig. 14 Motronic DTC interpretation chart (Part 31 of 36). Passat w/2.8L ATQ engine

DTC		DTC text	Corrective action
SAE	VAG		
P1539	17947	Clutch vacuum vent valve switch -F36- implausible signal	- Check clutch vacuum vent valve switch
P1541	17949	Fuel Pump (FP) relay -J17- open circuit	- Check Fuel Pump (FP) relay
P1542	17950	Angle sensor -1- for throttle drive (power accelerator actuation) -G187- 1)	- Checking throttle valve control module
P1543	17951	Angle sensor -1- for throttle drive (power accelerator actuation) -G187- signal too small[1]	
P1544	17952	Angle sensor -1- for throttle drive (power accelerator actuation) -G187- signal too large[1]	
P1545	17953	Throttle valve control, malfunction[1]	

[1] For these malfunctions, ECM switches on the EPC warning lamp in instrument cluster.

VW1020000155320X

Fig. 14 Motronic DTC interpretation chart (Part 32 of 36). Passat w/2.8L ATQ engine

DTC SAE	DTC VAG	DTC text	Corrective action
P1558	17966	Throttle drive (power accelerator actuation) -G186- electrical malfunction in circuit[1)]	- Checking throttle valve control module
P1559	17967	Throttle valve control module -J338- malfunction in basic setting[1)]	- Adapt Engine Control Module (ECM) to throttle valve control module
P1560	17968	Maximum engine speed exceeded	- Erase DTC Memory
P1564	17972	Throttle valve control module -J338- voltage too low during basic setting[1)]	- Check voltage supply for control module - Adapt Engine Control Module (ECM) to throttle valve control module
P1565	17973	Throttle valve control module -J338- lower impact not being reached[1)]	- Checking throttle valve control module
P1568	17976	Throttle valve control module -J338- mechanical malfunction[1)]	
P1569	17977	Cruise control switch -E45- implausible signal	- Check cruise control system: - Evaluate measuring value block 66

[1)] For these malfunctions, ECM switches on the EPC warning lamp in instrument cluster.

VW1020000155330X

Fig. 14 Motronic DTC interpretation chart (Part 33 of 36). Passat w/2.8L ATQ engine

DTC SAE	DTC VAG	DTC text	Corrective action
P1630	18038	Throttle Position (TP) sensor -G79- signal too small[1)]	- Check Throttle Position (TP) sensor:
P1631	18039	Throttle Position (TP) sensor -G79- signal too large[1)]	
P1633	18041	Sender -2- for accelerator pedal position -G185- signal too small[1)]	
P1634	18042	Sender -2- for accelerator pedal position -G185- signal too large[1)]	
P1636	18044	Powertrain databus missing message from airbag control module	- Check databus
P1639	18047	Throttle Position (TP) sensor -G79- and sender -2- for accelerator pedal position -G185- implausible signal[1)]	- Check Throttle Position (TP) sensor:
P1640	18048	Control module faulty	- Replace Motronic Engine Control Module (ECM)

[1)] For these malfunctions, ECM switches on the EPC warning lamp in instrument cluster.

VW1020000155350X

Fig. 14 Motronic DTC interpretation chart (Part 35 of 36). Passat w/2.8L ATQ engine

Diagnostic Trouble Codes (DTCs) SAE		Diagnostic Trouble Code (DTC) display	Corrective action
P0102		Mass or Volume Air Flow Circ Low Input	- Check Mass Air Flow (MAF) sensor
P0103		Mass or Volume Air Flow Circ High Input	- Check intake air system for leaks (unmetered air) - Check fuse 43.
P0112		Intake Air Temp.Circ Low Input	- Check Intake Air Temperature (IAT) sensor
P0113		Intake Air Temp.Circ. High Input	
P0116		Engine Coolant Temp.Circ Range/Performance	- Check Engine Coolant Temperature (ECT) sensor
P0117		Engine Coolant Temp.Circ Low Input	- Check thermostat.
P0118		Engine Coolant Temp.Circ. High Input	
P0130		02 Sensor Circ., Bank1-Sensor1 Malfunction	- Check oxygen sensor heating before Three Way Catalytic Converter (TWC)

VW1029900139010X

Fig. 15 Motronic DTC interpretation chart (Part 1 of 27). 1999–2001 GTI & Jetta w/2.8L engine

DTC SAE	DTC VAG	DTC text	Corrective action
P1579	17987	Throttle valve control module -J338- Adaptation not started	- Adapt Engine Control Module (ECM) to throttle valve control module
P1602	18010	Voltage supply terminal 30 voltage too low	- Check voltage supply for control module
P1603	18011	Control module faulty	- Replace Motronic Engine Control Module (ECM)
P1604	18012	Control module faulty	
P1612	18020	Engine Control Module (ECM) incorrectly coded	- Code Engine Control Module
P1624	18032	Request for warning lamp on active	- Check DTC memory and erase
P1626	18034	Powertrain databus missing message from Transmission Control Module (TCM)	- Check databus

VW1020000155340X

Fig. 14 Motronic DTC interpretation chart (Part 34 of 36). Passat w/2.8L ATQ engine

DTC SAE	DTC VAG	DTC text	Corrective action
P1648	18056	Powertrain databus faulty	- Check databus
P1649	18057	Powertrain databus missing message from ABS control module	
P1650	18058	Powertrain databus missing message from instrument cluster	
P1676	18084	Fault light for power accelerator activation -K132- electrical malfunction in circuit[1)]	
P1677	18085	Fault light for power accelerator activation -K132- Short circuit to B+[1)]	
P1678	18086	Fault light for power accelerator activation -K132- Short circuit to Ground (GND)[1)]	
P1679	18087	Fault light for power accelerator activation -K132- Open circuit[1)]	
P1683	18091	Powertrain databus implausible message from airbag control module	
P1853	18261	Powertrain databus implausible message from ABS control module	

[1)] For these malfunctions, ECM switches on the EPC warning lamp in instrument cluster.

VW1020000155360X

Fig. 14 Motronic DTC interpretation chart (Part 36 of 36). Passat w/2.8L ATQ engine

Diagnostic Trouble Codes (DTCs) SAE		Diagnostic Trouble Code (DTC) display	Corrective action
P0131		02 Sensor Circ., Bank1-Sensor1 Low Voltage	- Check oxygen sensor and control before Three Way Catalytic Converter (TWC)
P0132		02 Sensor Circ., Bank1-Sensor1 High Voltage	- Check oxygen sensor 1 aging
P0133		02 Sensor Circ., Bank1-Sensor1 Slow Response	- Check oxygen sensor and control after Three Way Catalytic Converter (TWC)
P0134		02 Sensor Circ., Bank1-Sensor1 No Activity Detected	- Check oxygen sensor and control before Three Way Catalytic Converter (TWC)
P0136		02 Sensor Circ., Bank1-Sensor2 Malfunction	- Check oxygen sensor and control after Three Way Catalytic Converter (TWC)
P0137		02 Sensor Circ., Bank1-Sensor2 Low Voltage	- Check oxygen sensor and control after Three Way Catalytic Converter (TWC)
P0138		02 Sensor Circ., Bank1-Sensor2 High Voltage	- Check oxygen sensor heating after Three Way Catalytic Converter (TWC)
P0139		02 Sensor Circ., Bank1-Sensor2 Slow Response	
P0140		02 Sensor Circ., Bank1-Sensor2 No Activity Detected	

VW1029900139020X

Fig. 15 Motronic DTC interpretation chart (Part 2 of 27). 1999–2001 GTI & Jetta w/2.8L engine

Diagnostic Trouble Codes (DTCs) SAE	Diagnostic Trouble Code (DTC) display	Corrective action
P0170	Fuel Trim, Bank1 Malfunction	- Check fuel pressure regulator and holding pressure - Check quantity of fuel injected and check for leaks - Check fuel pump. - Check intake system for leaks - Check Secondary Air Injection (AIR) system for leaks. - Check vacuum lines for leaks.

VW1029900139030X

Fig. 15 Motronic DTC interpretation chart (Part 3 of 27). 1999–2001 GTI & Jetta w/2.8L engine

Diagnostic Trouble Codes (DTCs) SAE	Diagnostic Trouble Code (DTC) display	Corrective action
P0172	Fuel Trim, Bank1 System too rich	- Check fuel pressure regulator and holding pressure - Check quantity of fuel injected and check for leaks - Check Evaporative Emission (EVAP) canister purge regulator valve -N80-.

VW1029900139050X

Fig. 15 Motronic DTC interpretation chart (Part 5 of 27). 1999–2001 GTI & Jetta w/2.8L engine

Diagnostic Trouble Codes (DTCs) SAE	Diagnostic Trouble Code (DTC) display	Corrective action
P0327	Knock Sensor 1 Circ Low Input	- Check knock sensor and knock control - Loosen knock sensor and retighten to 20 Nm (15 ft lb).
P0328	Knock Sensor 1 Circ High Input	
P0332	Knock Sensor 2 Circ Low Input	
P0333	Knock Sensor 2 Circ. High Input	
P0341	Camshaft Pos.Sensor Circ Range/Performance	- Check Camshaft Position (CMP) sensor -G40-
P0342	Camshaft Pos.Sensor Circ Low Input	
P0343	Camshaft Pos.Sensor Circ High Input	
P0411	Sec.Air Inj.Sys. Incorrect Flow Detected	- Check secondary air pump motor.
P0420	Catalyst System, Bank1 Efficiency Below Threshold	- Check Three Way Catalytic Converter (TWC).

VW1029900139070X

Fig. 15 Motronic DTC interpretation chart (Part 7 of 27). 1999–2001 GTI & Jetta w/2.8L engine

Diagnostic Trouble Codes (DTCs) SAE	Diagnostic Trouble Code (DTC) display	Corrective action
P0440	EVAP Emission Contr.Sys Malfunction	- Check Evaporative Emission (EVAP) canister purge regulator valve -N80- - Check Evaporative Emission (EVAP) canister purge regulator valve -N80-. - Check hoses and lines from fuel tank to throttle valve control module.

VW1029900139080X

Fig. 15 Motronic DTC interpretation chart (Part 8 of 27). 1999–2001 GTI & Jetta w/2.8L engine

Diagnostic Trouble Codes (DTCs) SAE	Diagnostic Trouble Code (DTC) display	Corrective action
P0171	Fuel Trim, Bank1 System too Lean	- Check fuel pressure regulator and holding pressure - Check quantity of fuel injected and check for leaks - Check fuel pump. - Check intake system for leaks - Check exhaust system for leaks. - Check Secondary Air Injection (AIR) system for leaks. - Check vacuum lines for leaks.

VW1029900139040X

Fig. 15 Motronic DTC interpretation chart (Part 4 of 27). 1999–2001 GTI & Jetta w/2.8L engine

Diagnostic Trouble Codes (DTCs) SAE	Diagnostic Trouble Code (DTC) display	Corrective action
P0300	Random/Multiple Cylinder Misfire Detected	- Check fuel injectors - Check ignition cables and spark plugs - Check ignition coils - Check misfire detection
P0301	Cyl.1 Misfire Detected	
P0302	Cyl.2 Misfire Detected	
P0303	Cyl.3 Misfire Detected	
P0304	Cyl.4 Misfire Detected	
P0305	Cyl.5 Misfire Detected	
P0306	Cyl.6 Misfire Detected	
P0321	Ign./Distributor Eng. Speed Inp.Circ Range/Performance	- Check engine speed (RPM) sensor
P0322	Ign./Distributor Eng.Speed Inp.Circ. No Signal	

VW1029900139060X

Fig. 15 Motronic DTC interpretation chart (Part 6 of 27). 1999–2001 GTI & Jetta w/2.8L engine

Diagnostic Trouble Codes (DTCs) SAE	Diagnostic Trouble Code (DTC) display	Corrective action
P0441	EVAP Emission Contr.Sys.Incorrect Purge Flow	- Check Evaporative Emission (EVAP) canister purge regulator valve -N80-. - Check hoses and lines from fuel tank to throttle valve control module.
P0442	EVAP Emission Contr.Sys. (Small Leak) Leak Detected	- Check Evaporative Emission (EVAP) system.
P0455	EVAP Emission Contr.Sys. (Gross Leak) Leak Detected	
P0501	Vehicle Speed Sensor Range/Performance	- Check speed signal
P0506	Idle Control System RPM Lower than Expected	- Check throttle valve control module
P0507	Idle Control System RPM Higher than Expected	

VW1029900139090X

Fig. 15 Motronic DTC interpretation chart (Part 9 of 27). 1999–2001 GTI & Jetta w/2.8L engine

Diagnostic Trouble Codes (DTCs) SAE		Diagnostic Trouble Code (DTC) display	Corrective action
P0560		System Voltage Malfunction	– Check voltage supply
P0562		System Voltage Low Voltage	– Procedure after interrupting voltage supply
P0563		System Voltage High Voltage	
P0571		Cruise/Brake Switch (A) Circ Malfunction[1]	– Check brake light switch and brake pedal switch
P0601		Internal Contr.Module Memory Check Slum Error	– Replace Motronic Engine Control Module (ECM) -J220-
P0603		Internal Contr.Module (KAM) Error	
P0604		Internal Contr.Module Random Access Memory (RAM) Error	
P0605		Internal Contr.Module ROM Test Error	– Replace Motronic Engine Control Module (ECM) -J220-

[1] The system monitors both brake light switch -F- and brake pedal switch -F47-.

VW1029900139100X

Fig. 15 Motronic DTC interpretation chart (Part 10 of 27). 1999–2001 GTI & Jetta w/2.8L engine

Diagnostic Trouble Codes (DTCs) SAE		Diagnostic Trouble Code (DTC) display	Corrective action
P1102		02 Sensor Heating Circ., Bank1–Sensor1 Short to B+	– Check oxygen sensor heating before Three Way Catalytic Converter (TWC)
P1105		02 Sensor Heating Circ., Bank1–Sensor2 Short to B+	– Check oxygen sensor heating after Three Way Catalytic Converter (TWC)
P1113		Bank1–Sensor1 Resistance too high	– Check oxygen sensor heating before Three Way Catalytic Converter (TWC)
P1115		02 Sensor Heater Circ., Bank1–Sensor1 Short to Ground	
P1116		02 Sensor Heater Circ., Bank1–Sensor1 Open	

VW1029900139110X

Fig. 15 Motronic DTC interpretation chart (Part 11 of 27). 1999–2001 GTI & Jetta w/2.8L engine

Diagnostic Trouble Codes (DTCs) SAE		Diagnostic Trouble Code (DTC) display	Corrective action
P1117		02 Sensor Heater Circ., Bank1–Sensor2 Short to Ground	– Check oxygen sensor heating after Three Way Catalytic Converter (TWC)
P1118		02 Sensor Heater Circ., Bank1–Sensor2 Open	
P1127		Long Term Fuel Trim mult.,Bank1 System too Rich	– Check fuel pressure regulator and holding pressure – Check quantity of fuel injected and check for leaks – Check Evaporative Emission (EVAP) canister purge regulator valve -N80-.

VW1029900139120X

Fig. 15 Motronic DTC interpretation chart (Part 12 of 27). 1999–2001 GTI & Jetta w/2.8L engine

Diagnostic Trouble Codes (DTCs) SAE		Diagnostic Trouble Code (DTC) display	Corrective action
P1128		Long Term Fuel Trim mult., Bank1 System too Lean	– Check fuel pressure regulator and holding pressure – Check quantity of fuel injected and check for leaks – Check fuel pump. – Check intake system for leaks – Check exhaust system for leaks. – Check Secondary Air Injection (AIR) system for leaks. – Check vacuum lines for leaks.

VW1029900139130X

Fig. 15 Motronic DTC interpretation chart (Part 13 of 27). 1999–2001 GTI & Jetta w/2.8L engine

Diagnostic Trouble Codes (DTCs) SAE		Diagnostic Trouble Code (DTC) display	Corrective action
P1136		Long Term Fuel Trim Add.Fuel, Bank1 System too Lean	– Check fuel pressure regulator and holding pressure – Check quantity of fuel injected and check for leaks – Check fuel pump. – Check intake system for leaks – Check exhaust system for leaks. – Check Secondary Air Injection (AIR) system for leaks. – Check vacuum lines for leaks.

Note:
Add. = additive (the malfunction only has an effect at idle).

VW1029900139140X

Fig. 15 Motronic DTC interpretation chart (Part 14 of 27). 1999–2001 GTI & Jetta w/2.8L engine

Diagnostic Trouble Codes (DTCs) SAE		Diagnostic Trouble Code (DTC) display	Corrective action
P1137		Long Term Fuel Trim Add.Fuel, Bank1 System too Rich	– Check fuel pressure regulator and holding pressure – Check quantity of fuel injected and check for leaks – Check Evaporative Emission (EVAP) canister purge regulator valve -N80-

Note:
Add. = additive (the malfunction only has an effect at idle).

VW1029900139150X

Fig. 15 Motronic DTC interpretation chart (Part 15 of 27). 1999–2001 GTI & Jetta w/2.8L engine

Diagnostic Trouble Codes (DTCs) SAE		Diagnostic Trouble Code (DTC) display	Corrective action
P1171		Throttle Actuation Potentiometer Sign.2 Range/Performance [1]	– Check throttle valve control module
P1172		Throttle Actuation Potentiometer Sign.2 Signal too Low [1]	
P1173		Throttle Actuation Potentiometer Sign.2 Signal too High [1]	
P1176		02 Correction Behind Catalyst,B1 Limit Attained	– Check oxygen sensor 1 aging – Check oxygen sensor and control after Three Way Catalytic Converter (TWC) – Check intake system for leaks
P1196		02 Sensor Heater Circ., Bank1–Sensor1 Electrical Malfunction	– Check oxygen sensor heating before Three Way Catalytic Converter (TWC)
P1198		02 Sensor Heater Circ., Bank1–Sensor2 Electrical Malfunction	– Check oxygen sensor heating after Three Way Catalytic Converter (TWC)

[1] The engine control module switches on the EPC warning lamp in the instrument cluster with this malfunction. Significance of the EPC warning lamp ⇒ 01-7.

VW1029900139160X

Fig. 15 Motronic DTC interpretation chart (Part 16 of 27). 1999–2001 GTI & Jetta w/2.8L engine

Diagnostic Trouble Codes (DTCs) SAE	Diagnostic Trouble Code (DTC) display	Corrective action
P1213	Cyl.1–Fuel Inj.Circ Short to B+	– Check quantity of fuel injected and check for leaks
P1214	Cyl.2–Fuel Inj.Circ. Short to B+	
P1215	Cyl.3–Fuel Inj.Circ. Short to B+	
P1216	Cyl.4–Fuel Inj.Circ. Short to B+	
P1217	Cyl. 5–Fuel Inj. Circ. Short to B+	
P1218	Cyl. 6–Fuel Inj. Circ. Short to B+	

VW1029900139170X

Fig. 15 Motronic DTC interpretation chart (Part 17 of 27). 1999–2001 GTI & Jetta w/2.8L engine

Diagnostic Trouble Codes (DTCs) SAE	Diagnostic Trouble Code (DTC) display	Corrective action
P1225	Cyl.1–Fuel Inj.Circ. Short to Ground	– Check quantity of fuel injected and check for leaks
P1226	Cyl.2–Fuel Inj.Circ. Short to Ground	
P1227	Cyl.3–Fuel Inj.Circ. Short to Ground	
P1228	Cyl.4–Fuel Inj.Circ. Short to Ground	
P1229	Cyl. 5–Fuel Inj.Circ. Short to Ground	
P1230	Cyl. 6–Fuel inj.Circ. Short to Ground	

VW1029900139180X

Fig. 15 Motronic DTC interpretation chart (Part 18 of 27). 1999–2001 GTI & Jetta w/2.8L engine

Diagnostic Trouble Codes (DTCs) SAE	Diagnostic Trouble Code (DTC) display	Corrective action
P1237	Cyl.1–Fuel Inj.Circ Open Circ	– Check quantity of fuel injected and check for leaks
P1238	Cyl.2–Fuel Inj.Circ. Open Circ.	
P1239	Cyl.3–Fuel Inj.Circ. Open Circ.	
P1240	Cyl.4–Fuel Inj.Circ. Open Circ.	
P1241	Cyl. 5–Fuel Inj.Circ. Open Circ.	
P1242	Cyl. 6–Fuel Inj.Circ. Open Circ.	
P1325	Cyl.1–Knock Contr Limit Attained	– Check knock sensor and knock control
P1326	Cyl.2–Knock Contr Limit Attained	– Rectify abnormal engine running noises (accessories loose, brackets/bolts broken).
P1327	Cyl.3–Knock Contr Limit Attained	– Check harness connectors and wiring using wiring diagrams.

VW1029900139190X

Fig. 15 Motronic DTC interpretation chart (Part 19 of 27). 1999–2001 GTI & Jetta w/2.8L engine

Diagnostic Trouble Codes (DTCs) SAE	Diagnostic Trouble Code (DTC) display	Corrective action
P1328	Cyl.4–Knock Contr Limit Attained	– Loosen knock sensor and retighten to 20 Nm (15 ft lb). – Change type of fuel.
P1329	Cyl.5–Knock Contr Limit Attained	
P1330	Cyl.6–Knock Contr Limit Attained	
P1336	Engine torque control adaptation at limit	– Check Mass Air Flow (MAF) sensor – Check intake air temperature sensor – Check engine coolant temperature sensor
P1340	Crankshaft-/Camshaft Pos.Sens.Signals Out of Sequence	– Check Camshaft Position (CMP) sensor -G40- – Check engine speed (RPM) sensor
P1341	Ignition Coil Power Output Stage 1 Short to Ground	– Check ignition cables and spark plugs – Check ignition coil – Check misfire recognition
P1343	Ignition Coil Power Output Stage 2 Short to Ground	
P1345	Ignition Coil Power Output Stage 3 Short to Ground	

VW1029900139200X

Fig. 15 Motronic DTC interpretation chart (Part 20 of 27). 1999–2001 GTI & Jetta w/2.8L engine

Diagnostic Trouble Codes (DTCs) SAE	Diagnostic Trouble Code (DTC) display	Corrective action
P1386	Internal Control Module Knock Control Circ.Error[1]	– Replace engine control module
P1387	Control unit internal altitude sensor[1]	
P1393	Ignition Coil Power Output Stage 1 Electrical Malfunction	– Check ignition cables and spark plugs
P1394	Ignition Coil Power Output Stage 2 Electrical Malfunction	– Check ignition coil
P1395	Ignition Coil Power Output Stage 3 Electrical Malfunction	– Check misfire recognition
P1410	Tank Ventilation Valve Circ Short to B+	– Check Evaporative Emission (EVAP) canister purge regulator valve -N80-
P1420	Sec.Air Inj.Valve Circ Electrical Malfunction	– Check secondary air injection valve
P1421	Sec.Air Inj.Valve Circ Short to Ground	
P1422	Sec.Air Inj.Sys.Contr. Valve Circ. Short to B+	

[1]The engine control module switches on the EPC warning lamp in the instrument cluster with this malfunction. Significance of the EPC warning lamp ⇒ 01-7.

VW1029900139210X

Fig. 15 Motronic DTC interpretation chart (Part 21 of 27). 1999–2001 GTI & Jetta w/2.8L engine

Diagnostic Trouble Codes (DTCs) SAE	Diagnostic Trouble Code (DTC) display	Corrective action
P1424	Sec.Air Inj.Sys.,Bank1 Leak Detected	– Check Secondary Air Injection (AIR) system for leaks.
P1425	Tank Vent.Valve Short to Ground	– Check Evaporative Emission (EVAP) canister purge regulator valve -N80-
P1426	Tank Vent.Valve Open	
P1432	Sec.Air Inj.Valve Open	– Check secondary air injection valve
P1433	Sec.Air Inj.Sys.Pump Relay Circ Open	– Check Secondary Air Injection (AIR) pump relay -J299-
P1434	Sec.Air Inj.Sys.Pump Relay Circ. Short to B+	
P1435	Sec.Air Inj.Sys.Pump Relay Circ. Short to Ground	

VW1029900139220X

Fig. 15 Motronic DTC interpretation chart (Part 22 of 27). 1999–2001 GTI & Jetta w/2.8L engine

Diagnostic Trouble Codes (DTCs) SAE	Diagnostic Trouble Code (DTC) display	Corrective action
P1471	EVAP Emission Contr.LDP Circ. Short to B+	– Check diagnostic pump.
P1472	EVAP Emission Contr.LEDP Circ. Short to Ground	– Check Evaporative Emission (EVAP) system for leaks.
P1473	EVAP Emission Contr.LDP Circ. Open Circ.	
P1475	EVAP Emission Contr.LDP Circ Malfunction/Signal Circ.Open	
P1476	EVAP Emission Contr.LDP Circ. Malfunction/Insufficient Vacuum	
P1501	Fuel Pump Relay Circ Short to Ground	– Check fuel pump relay.
P1502	Fuel Pump Relay Circ. Short to B+	
P1515	Intake Manifold Changeover Valve Circuit Short to Ground	– Check Intake Manifold Tuning (IMT) valve
P1516	Intake Manifold Changeover Valve Circuit Open	
P1539	Clutch pedal switch Implausible signal	– Check clutch pedal switch

VW1029900139230X

Fig. 15 Motronic DTC interpretation chart (Part 23 of 27). 1999–2001 GTI & Jetta w/2.8L engine

Diagnostic Trouble Codes (DTCs) SAE	Diagnostic Trouble Code (DTC) display	Corrective action
P1559	Idle Speed Contr.Throttle Pos Adaptation Malfunction [1]	– Adapt engine control module to throttle valve control module
P1565	Idle Speed Control Throttle Position Lower Limit not Attained	– Check throttle valve control module
P1568	Idle Speed Contr. Throttle Pos. Mechanical Malfunction [1]	
P1569	Switch for CCS -E45 Implausible signal[1]	
P1602	Power supply (B+) Terminal 30 Low Voltage	– Check voltage supply for control module
P1603	Internal Control Module Self Check	– Replace Motronic Engine Control Module (ECM) -J220-
P1612	Electronic Control Module Incorrect Coding	– Code engine control module
P1626	Data–Bus Powertrain Missing Message from Transm.Contr	– Check CAN-Bus

[1] The engine control module switches on the EPC warning lamp in the instrument cluster with this malfunction. Significance of the EPC warning lamp

VW1029900139250X

Fig. 15 Motronic DTC interpretation chart (Part 25 of 27). 1999–2001 GTI & Jetta w/2.8L engine

Diagnostic Trouble Codes (DTCs) SAE	Diagnostic Trouble Code (DTC) display	Corrective action
P1676	Drive by Wire–MIL Circ Electrical Malfunction [1]	– Check engine control module wiring to EPC warning lamp
P1677	Drive by Wire–MIL Circ Short to B+ [1]	
P1678	Drive by Wire–MIL Circ Short to Ground [1]	
P1679	Drive by Wire–MIL Circ Open [1]	
P1681	Contr.Unit Programming Programming not Finished	– Replace Motronic Engine Control Module (ECM) -J220-
P1691	Malfunction Indication Light Open	– Check wiring from engine control module to exhaust gas (EPC) warning lamp
P1692	Malfunction Indication Light Short to Ground	
P1693	Malfunction Indication Light Short to B+	

[1] The engine control module switches on the EPC warning lamp in the instrument cluster with this malfunction. Significance of the EPC warning lamp

VW1029900139270X

Fig. 15 Motronic DTC interpretation chart (Part 27 of 27). 1999–2001 GTI & Jetta w/2.8L engine

Diagnostic Trouble Codes (DTCs) SAE	Diagnostic Trouble Code (DTC) display	Corrective action
P1541	Fuel Pump Relay Circ Open	– Check fuel pump relay.
P1542	Throttle Actuation Potentiometer Range/Performance [1]	– Check throttle valve control module
P1543	Throttle Actuation Potentiometer Signal too Low	
P1544	Throttle Actuation Potentiometer Signal too High	
P1545	Throttle Pos.Contr Malfunction [1]	
P1558	Throttle Actuator Electrical Malfunction	

[1] The engine control module switches on the EPC warning lamp in the instrument cluster with this malfunction. Significance of the EPC warning lamp ⇒ page 01-7.

VW1029900139240X

Fig. 15 Motronic DTC interpretation chart (Part 24 of 27). 1999–2001 GTI & Jetta w/2.8L engine

Diagnostic Trouble Codes (DTCs) SAE	Diagnostic Trouble Code (DTC) display	Corrective action
P1630	Accelera.Pedal Pos.Sensor 1 Signal too Low[1]	– Check accelerator pedal.
P1631	Accelera.Pedal Pos.Sensor 1 Signal too High [1]	
P1633	Accelera.Pedal Pos.Sensor 2 Signal too Low [1]	
P1634	Accelera.Pedal Pos.Sensor 2 Signal too High [1]	
P1639	Accelera.Pedal Pos.Sensor 1+2 Range/Performance [1], [2]	
P1640	Internal Contr.Module (EEPROM) Error	– Replace Motronic Engine Control Module (ECM) -J220-
P1648	Data Bus Powertrain malfunctioning	– Check CAN-Bus

[1] The engine control module switches on the EPC warning lamp in the instrument cluster with this malfunction. Significance of the EPC warning lamp

[2] Incorrect malfunction display. Correct display should be: Accelera. Pedal Pos. Sensor1 Range/Performance

VW1029900139260X

Fig. 15 Motronic DTC interpretation chart (Part 26 of 27). 1999–2001 GTI & Jetta w/2.8L engine

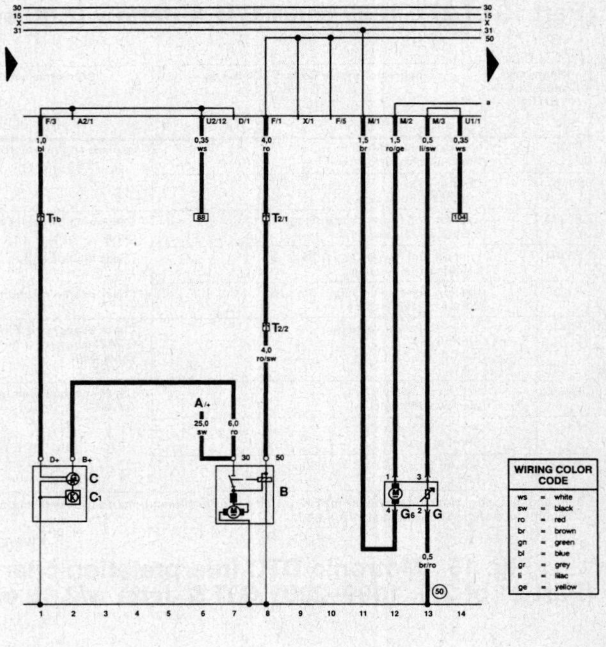

A – Battery
B – Starter
C – Generator (GEN)
C1 – Voltage Regulator (VR)
G – Fuel Level Sensor
G6 – Fuel Pump (FP)
T1 – Single Connector, near battery
T2 – Double Connector, behind fuse/relay panel
50 – Ground connection, in luggage compartment, left

VW1029900149010X

Fig. 16 Motronic wiring diagram (Part 1 of 8). 1998 Cabrio

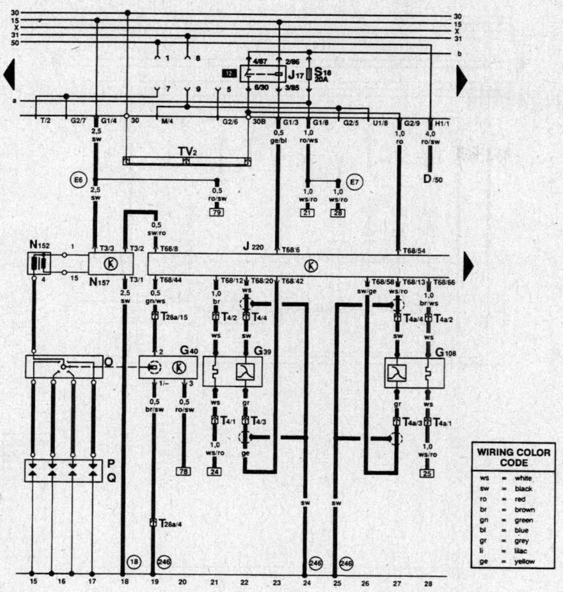

D – Ignition/Starter Switch
G39 – Heated Oxygen Sensor (HO2S)
G40 – Camshaft Position (CMP) Sensor
G108 – Heated Oxygen Sensor (HO2S) 2
J17 – Fuel Pump (FP) Relay
J220 – Motronic Engine Control Module (ECM)
N152 – Ignition Coil
N157 – Ignition Coil Power Output Stage
O – Ignition Distributor
P – Spark Plug Connectors
Q – Spark Plugs
T3 – 3-Pin Connector
T4 – 4-Pin Connector, near intake manifold
T4 – 4-Pin Connector
T28 – 28-Pin Connector, on engine
T68 – 68-Pin Connector
TV2 – Terminal 30 (B+) wire connector, above fuse/relay panel

(18) – Ground connection, on engine block
(246) – Ground connection (control module), in wiring harness engine
(E6) – Plus connection –1– (15), in motronic Multiport Fuel Injection (MFI) wiring harness
(E7) – Plus connection (87a), in Motronic Multiport Fuel Injection (MFI) wiring harness

VW1029900149020X

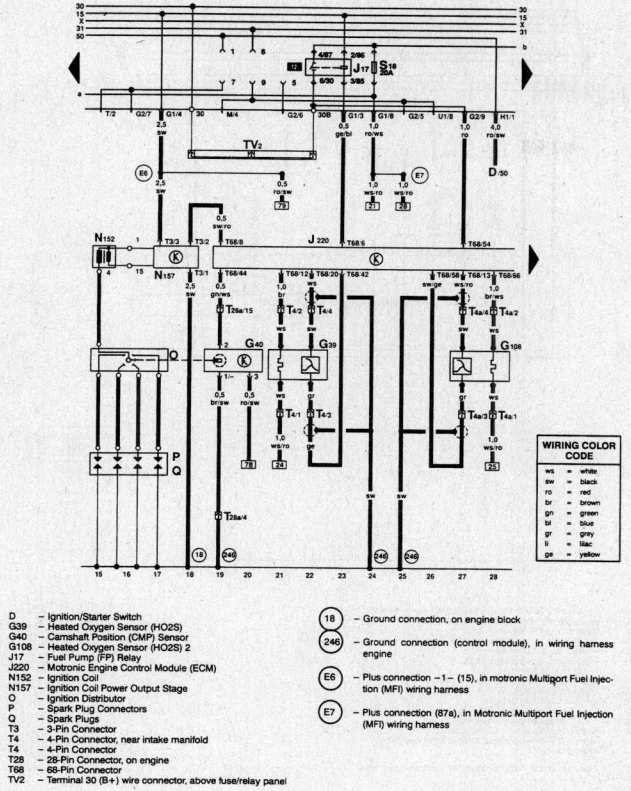

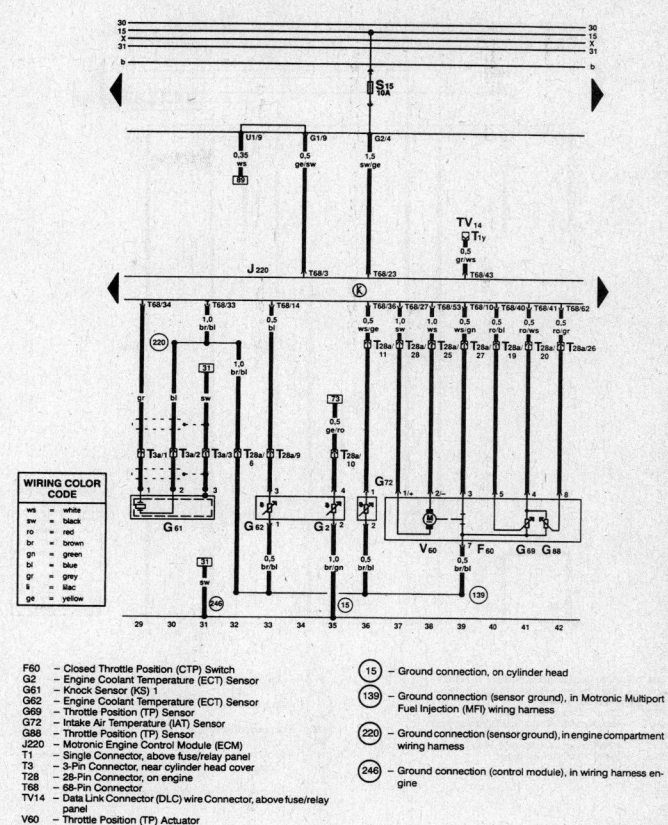

Fig. 16 Motronic wiring diagram (Part 2 of 8). 1998 Cabrio

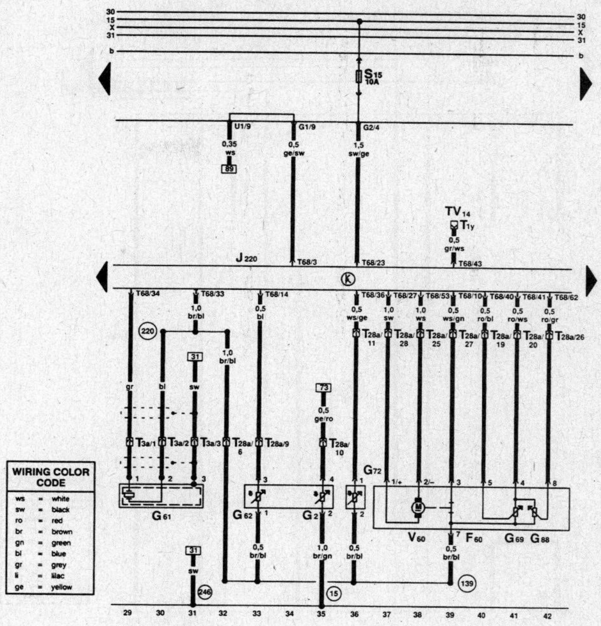

F60 – Closed Throttle Position (CTP) Switch
G2 – Engine Coolant Temperature (ECT) Sensor
G61 – Knock Sensor (KS) 1
G62 – Engine Coolant Temperature (ECT) Sensor
G69 – Throttle Position (TP) Sensor
G72 – Intake Air Temperature (IAT) Sensor
G88 – Throttle Position (TP) Sensor
J220 – Motronic Engine Control Module (ECM)
T1 – Single Connector, above fuse/relay panel
T3 – 3-Pin Connector, near cylinder head cover
T28 – 28-Pin Connector, on engine
T68 – 68-Pin Connector
TV14 – Data Link Connector (DLC) wire Connector, above fuse/relay panel
V60 – Throttle Position (TP) Actuator

(15) – Ground connection, on cylinder head
(139) – Ground connection (sensor ground), in Motronic Multiport Fuel Injection (MFI) wiring harness
(220) – Ground connection (sensor ground), in engine compartment wiring harness
(246) – Ground connection (control module), in wiring harness engine

VW1029900149030X

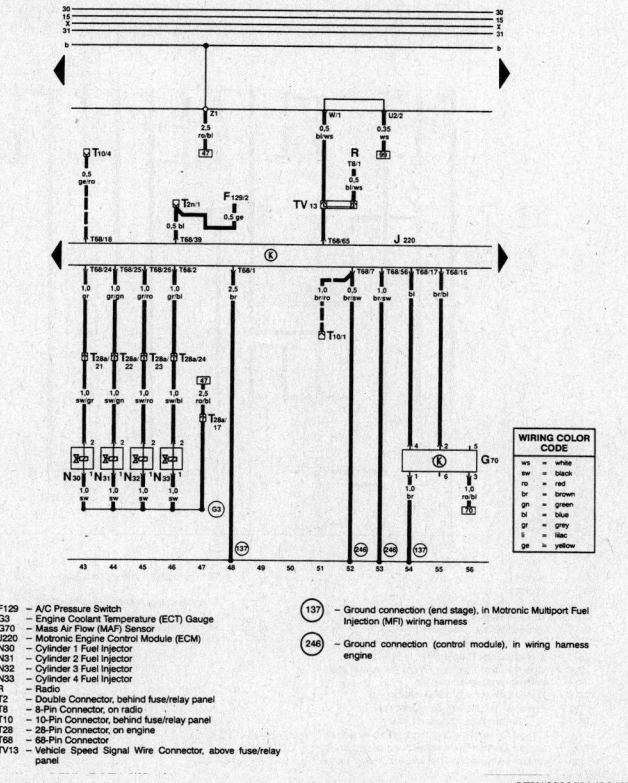

Fig. 16 Motronic wiring diagram (Part 3 of 8). 1998 Cabrio

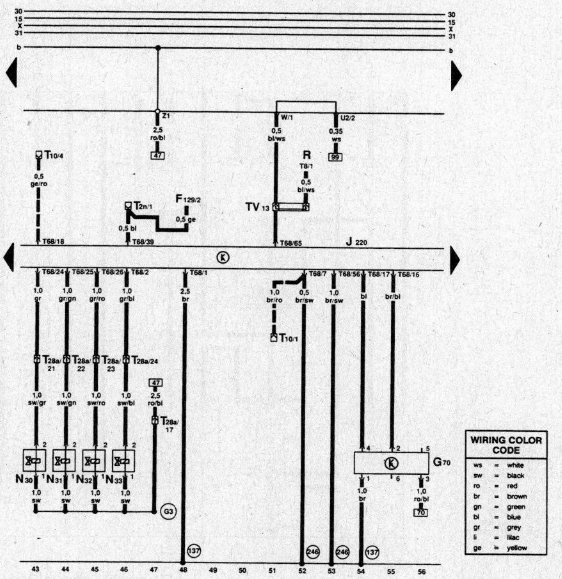

F129 – A/C Pressure Switch
G3 – Engine Coolant Temperature (ECT) Gauge
G70 – Mass Air Flow (MAF) Sensor
J220 – Motronic Engine Control Module (ECM)
N30 – Cylinder 1 Fuel Injector
N31 – Cylinder 2 Fuel Injector
N32 – Cylinder 3 Fuel Injector
N33 – Cylinder 4 Fuel Injector
R – Radio
T2 – Double Connector, behind fuse/relay panel
T8 – 8-Pin Connector, on radio
T10 – 10-Pin Connector, behind fuse/relay panel
T28 – 28-Pin Connector, on engine
T68 – 68-Pin Connector
TV13 – Vehicle Speed Signal Wire Connector, above fuse/relay panel

(137) – Ground connection (end stage), in Motronic Multiport Fuel Injection (MFI) wiring harness
(246) – Ground connection (control module), in wiring harness engine

VW1029900149040X

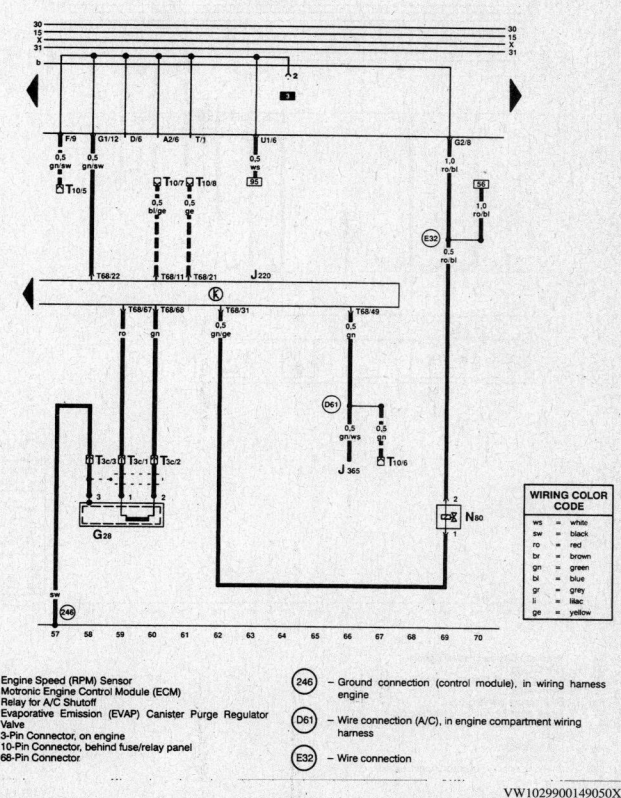

Fig. 16 Motronic wiring diagram (Part 4 of 8). 1998 Cabrio

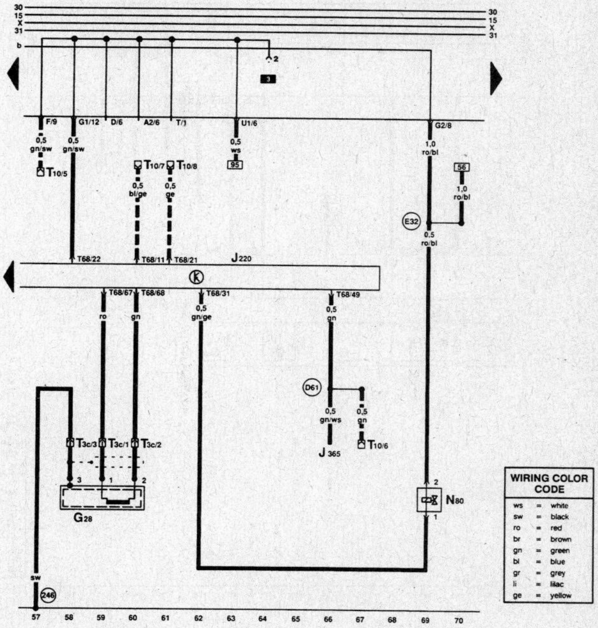

G28 – Engine Speed (RPM) Sensor
J220 – Motronic Engine Control Module (ECM)
J365 – Relay for A/C Shutoff
N80 – Evaporative Emission (EVAP) Canister Purge Regulator Valve
T3 – 3-Pin Connector, on engine
T10 – 10-Pin Connector, behind fuse/relay panel
T68 – 68-Pin Connector

(246) – Ground connection (control module), in wiring harness engine
(D61) – Wire connection (A/C), in engine compartment wiring harness
(E32) – Wire connection

VW1029900149050X

Fig. 16 Motronic wiring diagram (Part 5 of 8). 1998 Cabrio

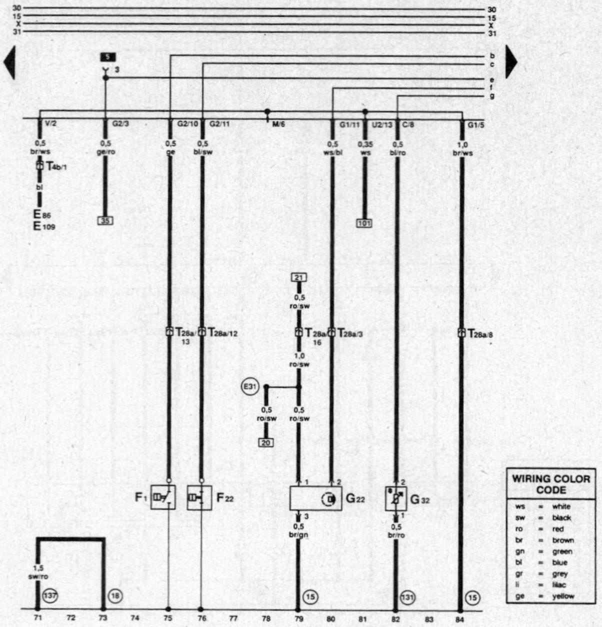

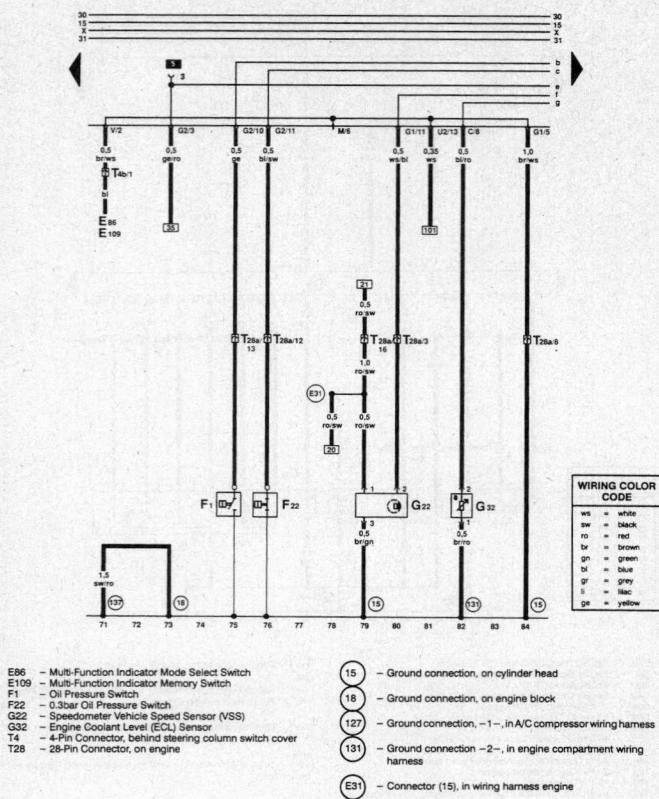

E86 – Multi-Function Indicator Mode Select Switch
E109 – Multi-Function Indicator Memory Switch
F1 – Oil Pressure Switch
F22 – 0.3bar Oil Pressure Switch
G22 – Speedometer Vehicle Speed Sensor (VSS)
G32 – Engine Coolant Level (ECL) Sensor
T4 – 4-Pin Connector, behind steering column switch cover
T28 – 28-Pin Connector, on engine

(15) – Ground connection, on cylinder head
(18) – Ground connection, on engine block
(127) – Ground connection, -1-, in A/C compressor wiring harness
(131) – Ground connection -2-, in engine compartment wiring harness
(E31) – Connector (15), in wiring harness engine

VW1029900149060X

Fig. 16 Motronic wiring diagram (Part 6 of 8). 1998 Cabrio

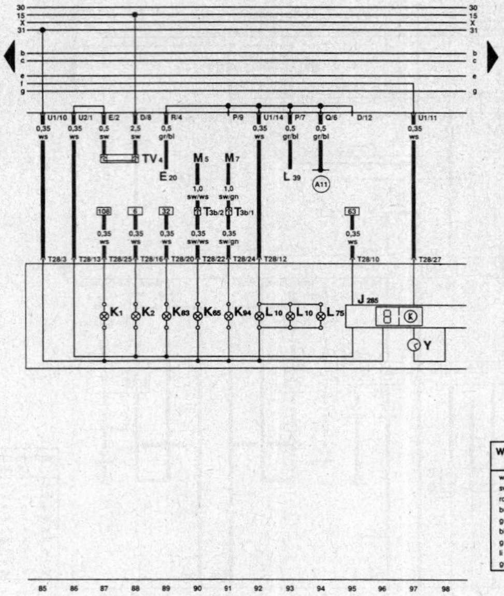

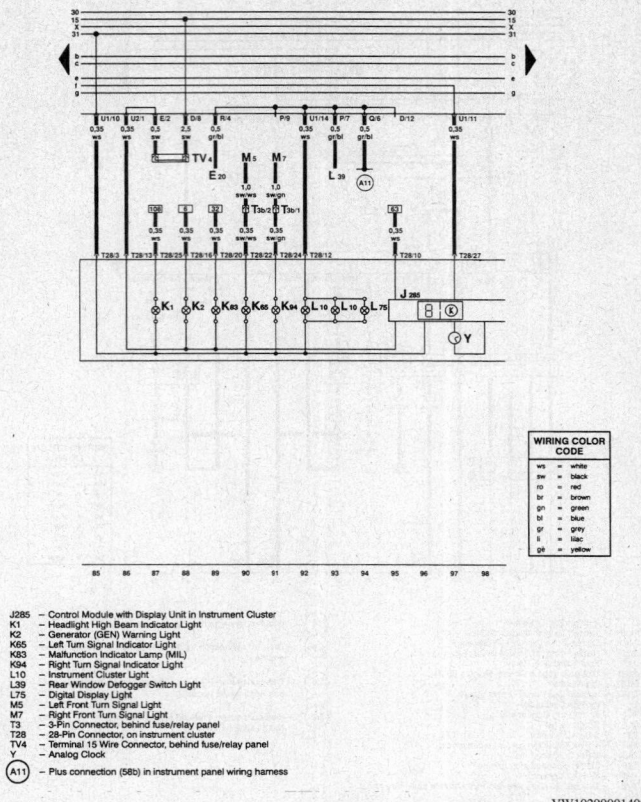

J285 – Control Module with Display Unit in Instrument Cluster
K1 – Headlight High Beam Indicator Light
K2 – Generator (GEN) Warning Light
K65 – Left Turn Signal Indicator Light
K83 – Malfunction Indicator Lamp (MIL)
K94 – Right Turn Signal Indicator Light
L10 – Instrument Cluster Light
L39 – Rear Window Defogger Switch Light
L75 – Digital Display Light
M5 – Left Front Turn Signal Light
M7 – Right Front Turn Signal Light
T3 – 3-Pin Connector, behind fuse/relay panel
T28 – 28-Pin Connector, on instrument cluster
TV4 – Terminal 15 Wire Connector, behind fuse/relay panel
Y – Analog Clock
(A11) – Plus connection (58b) in instrument panel wiring harness

VW1029900149070X

Fig. 16 Motronic wiring diagram (Part 7 of 8). 1998 Cabrio

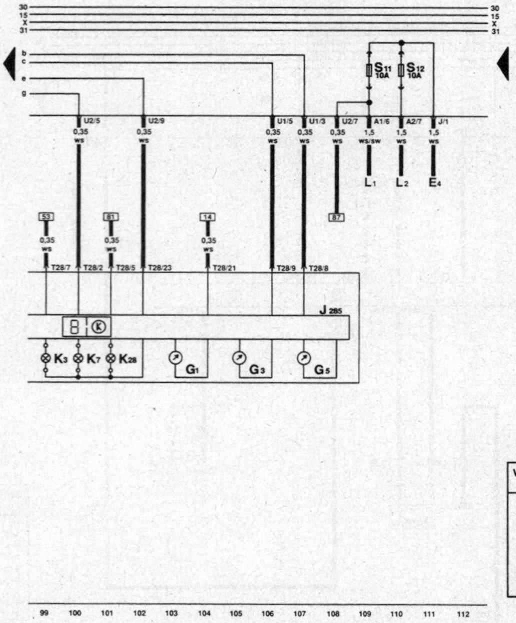

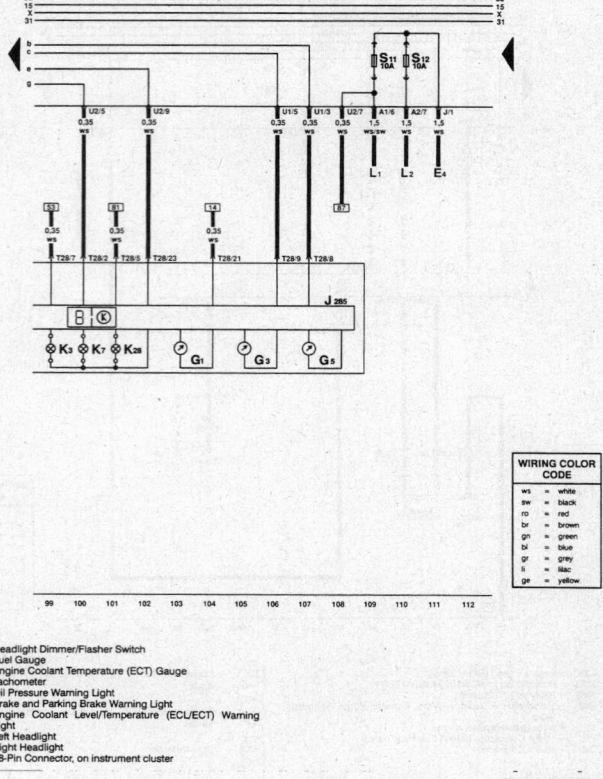

E4 – Headlight Dimmer/Flasher Switch
G1 – Fuel Gauge
G3 – Engine Coolant Temperature (ECT) Gauge
G5 – Tachometer
K3 – Oil Pressure Warning Light
K7 – Brake and Parking Brake Warning Light
K28 – Engine Coolant Level/Temperature (ECL/ECT) Warning Light
L1 – Left Headlight
L2 – Right Headlight
T28 – 28-Pin Connector, on instrument cluster

VW1029900149080X

Fig. 16 Motronic wiring diagram (Part 8 of 8). 1998 Cabrio

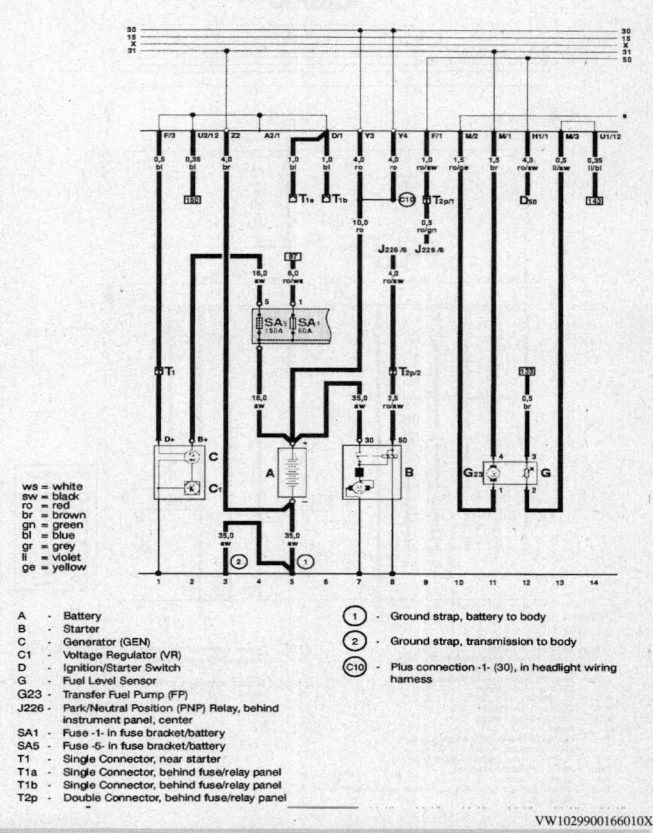

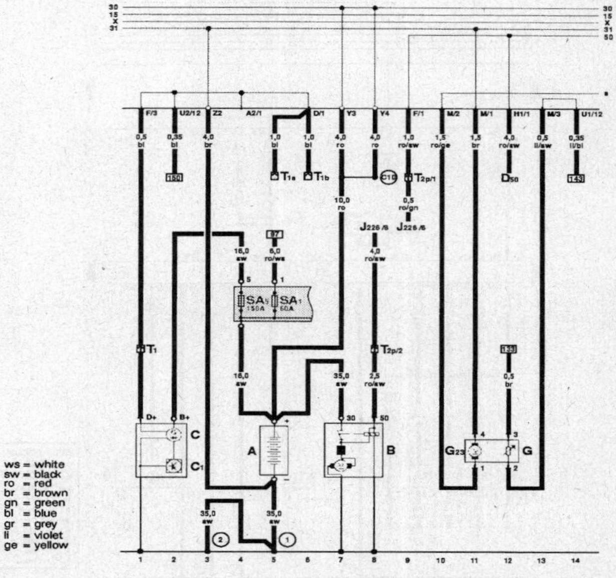

A - Battery
B - Starter
C - Generator (GEN)
C1 - Voltage Regulator (VR)
D - Ignition/Starter Switch
G - Fuel Level Sensor
G23 - Transfer Fuel Pump (FP)
J226 - Park/Neutral Position (PNP) Relay, behind instrument panel, center
SA1 - Fuse -1- in fuse bracket/battery
SA5 - Fuse -5- in fuse bracket/battery
T1 - Single Connector, near starter
T1a - Single Connector, behind fuse/relay panel
T1b - Single Connector, behind fuse/relay panel
T2p - Double Connector, behind fuse/relay panel

(1) - Ground strap, battery to body
(2) - Ground strap, transmission to body
(C10) - Plus connection -1- (30), in headlight wiring harness

VW1029900166010X

Fig. 17 Motronic wiring diagram (Part 1 of 11). 1999–2000 EuroVan

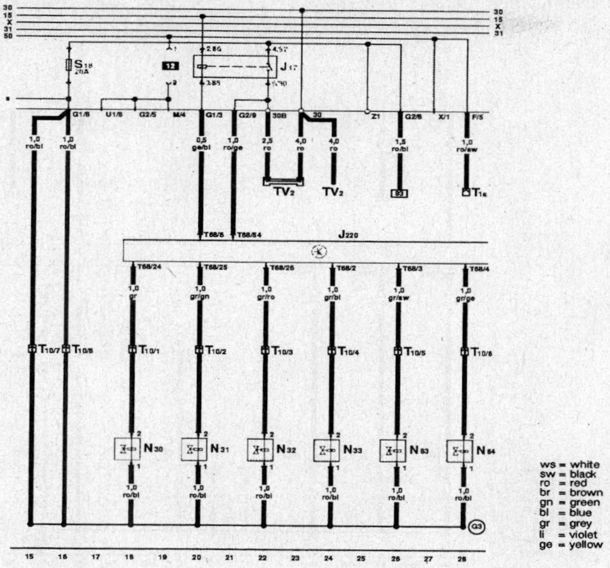

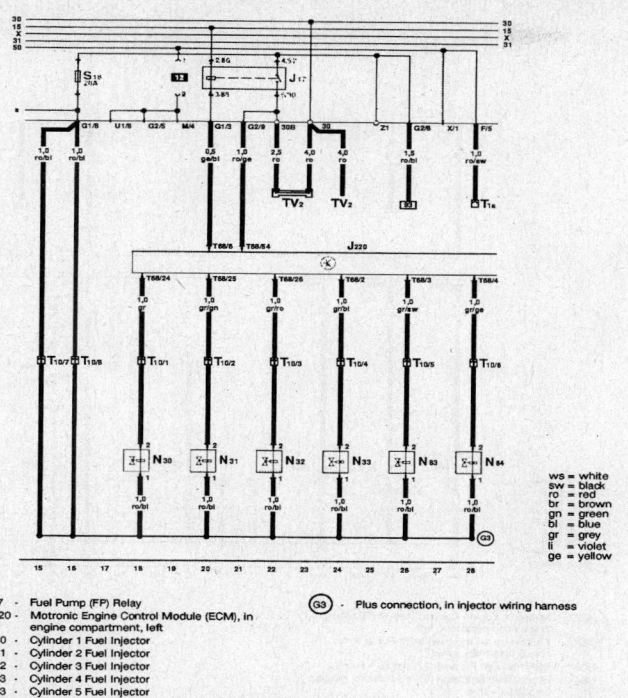

J17 - Fuel Pump (FP) Relay
J220 - Motronic Engine Control Module (ECM), in engine compartment, left
N30 - Cylinder 1 Fuel Injector
N31 - Cylinder 2 Fuel Injector
N32 - Cylinder 3 Fuel Injector
N33 - Cylinder 4 Fuel Injector
N83 - Cylinder 5 Fuel Injector
N84 - Cylinder 6 Fuel Injector
T1s - Single Connector, behind fuse/relay panel
T10 - 10-Pin Connector, near cylinder head cover
T68 - 68-Pin Connector
TV2 - Terminal 30 (B+) Wire Connector, red, each 6 points

(G3) - Plus connection, in injector wiring harness

VW1029900166020X

Fig. 17 Motronic wiring diagram (Part 2 of 11). 1999–2000 EuroVan

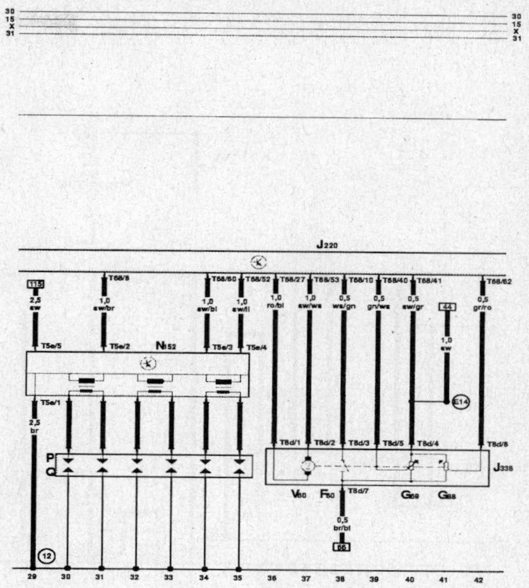

F60 - Closed Throttle Position (CTP) Switch
G69 - Throttle Position (TP) Sensor
G88 - Throttle Position (TP) Sensor
J220 - Motronic Engine Control Module (ECM), in engine compartment, left
J338 - Throttle Valve Control Module
N152 - Ignition Coil
P - Spark Plug Connectors
Q - Spark Plugs
T5e - 5-Pin Connector
T8d - 8-Pin Connector
T68 - 68-Pin Connector
V60 - Throttle Position (TP) Actuator

(12) - Ground connection, in engine compartment, left

(E14) - Wire connection -1-, in Motronic Multiport Fuel Injection (MFI) wiring harness

VW1029900166030X

Fig. 17 Motronic wiring diagram (Part 3 of 11). 1999–2000 EuroVan

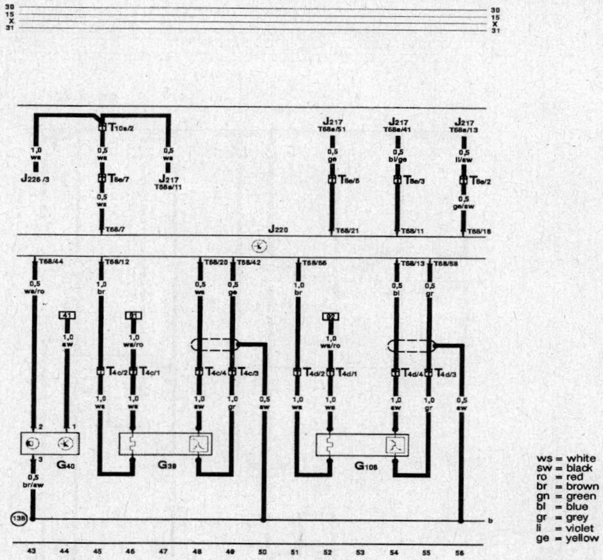

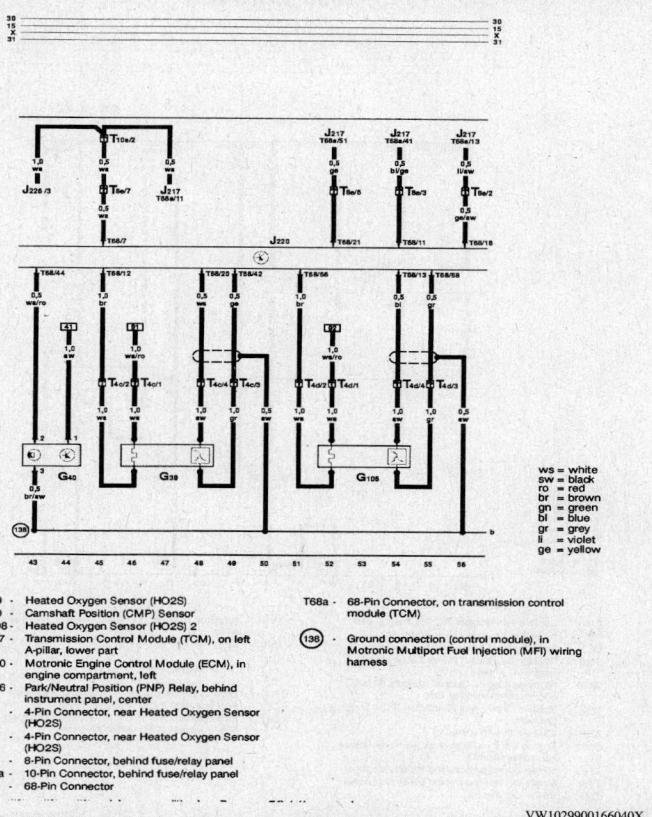

G39 - Heated Oxygen Sensor (HO2S)
G40 - Camshaft Position (CMP) Sensor
G108 - Heated Oxygen Sensor (HO2S) 2
J217 - Transmission Control Module (TCM), on left A-pillar, lower part
J220 - Motronic Engine Control Module (ECM), in engine compartment, left
J226 - Park/Neutral Position (PNP) Relay, behind instrument panel, center
T4c - 4-Pin Connector, near Heated Oxygen Sensor (HO2S)
T4d - 4-Pin Connector, near Heated Oxygen Sensor (HO2S)
T8e - 8-Pin Connector, behind fuse/relay panel
T10a - 10-Pin Connector, behind fuse/relay panel
T68 - 68-Pin Connector
T68a - 68-Pin Connector, on transmission control module (TCM)

(138) - Ground connection (control module), in Motronic Multiport Fuel Injection (MFI) wiring harness

VW1029900166040X

Fig. 17 Motronic wiring diagram (Part 4 of 11). 1999–2000 EuroVan

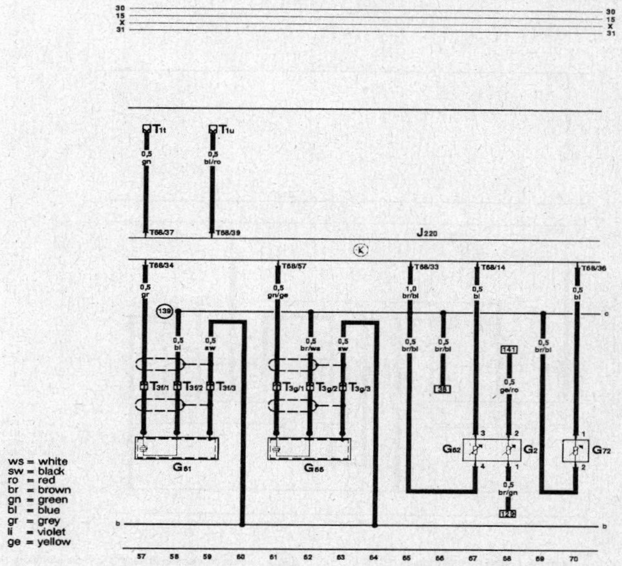

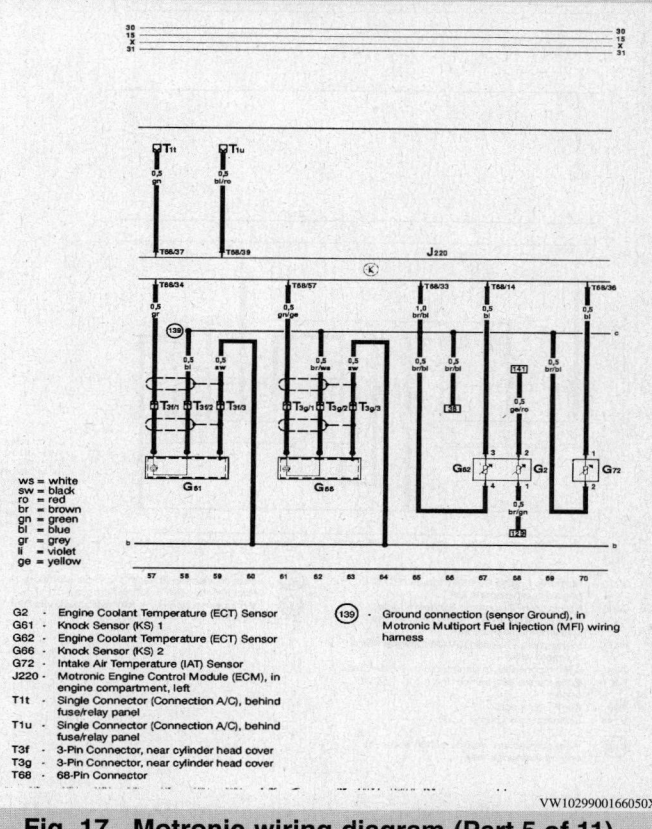

G2 - Engine Coolant Temperature (ECT) Sensor
G61 - Knock Sensor (KS) 1
G62 - Engine Coolant Temperature (ECT) Sensor
G66 - Knock Sensor (KS) 2
G72 - Intake Air Temperature (IAT) Sensor
J220 - Motronic Engine Control Module (ECM), in engine compartment, left
T1t - Single Connector (Connection A/C), behind fuse/relay panel
T1u - Single Connector (Connection A/C), behind fuse/relay panel
T3f - 3-Pin Connector, near cylinder head cover
T3g - 3-Pin Connector, near cylinder head cover
T68 - 68-Pin Connector

(139) - Ground connection (sensor Ground), in Motronic Multiport Fuel Injection (MFI) wiring harness

VW1029900166050X

Fig. 17 Motronic wiring diagram (Part 5 of 11). 1999–2000 EuroVan

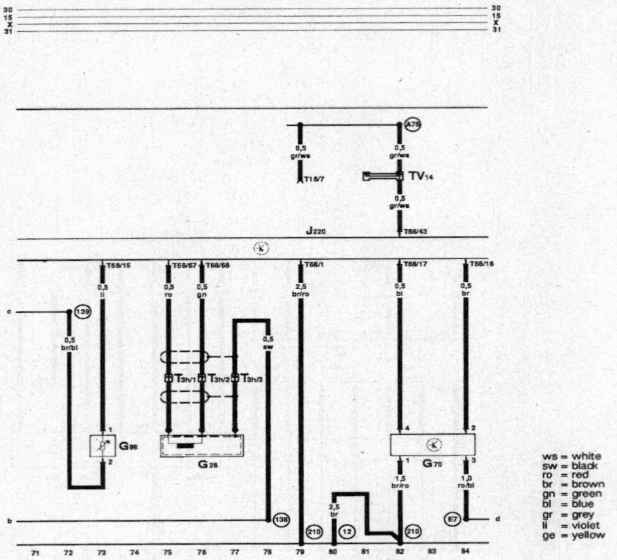

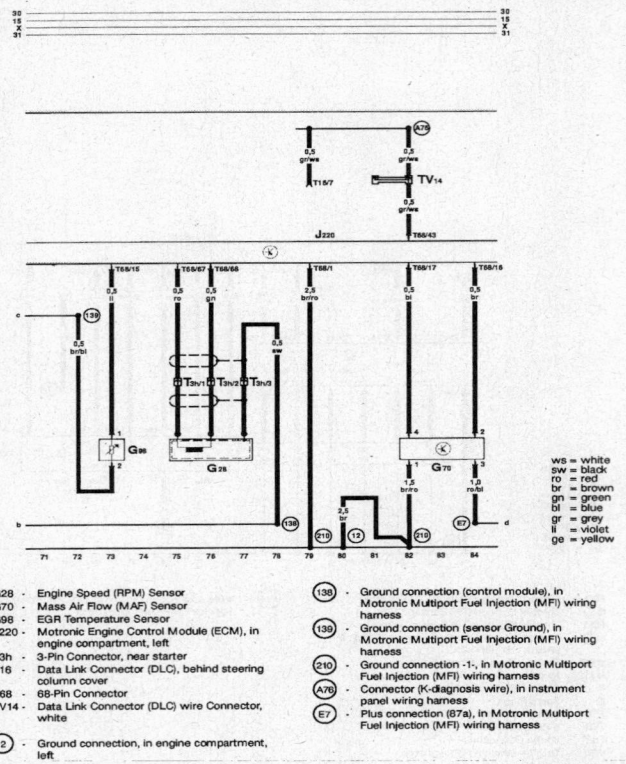

G28 - Engine Speed (RPM) Sensor
G70 - Mass Air Flow (MAF) Sensor
G98 - EGR Temperature Sensor
J220 - Motronic Engine Control Module (ECM), in engine compartment, left
T3h - 3-Pin Connector, near starter
T16 - Data Link Connector (DLC), behind steering column cover
T68 - 68-Pin Connector
TV14 - Data Link Connector (DLC) wire Connector, white

(12) - Ground connection, in engine compartment, left

(138) - Ground connection (control module), in Motronic Multiport Fuel Injection (MFI) wiring harness
(139) - Ground connection (sensor Ground), in Motronic Multiport Fuel Injection (MFI) wiring harness
(210) - Ground connection -1-, in Motronic Multiport Fuel Injection (MFI) wiring harness
(A76) - Connector (K-diagnosis wire), in instrument panel wiring harness
(E7) - Plus connection (87a), in Motronic Multiport Fuel Injection (MFI) wiring harness

VW1029900166060X

Fig. 17 Motronic wiring diagram (Part 6 of 11). 1999–2000 EuroVan

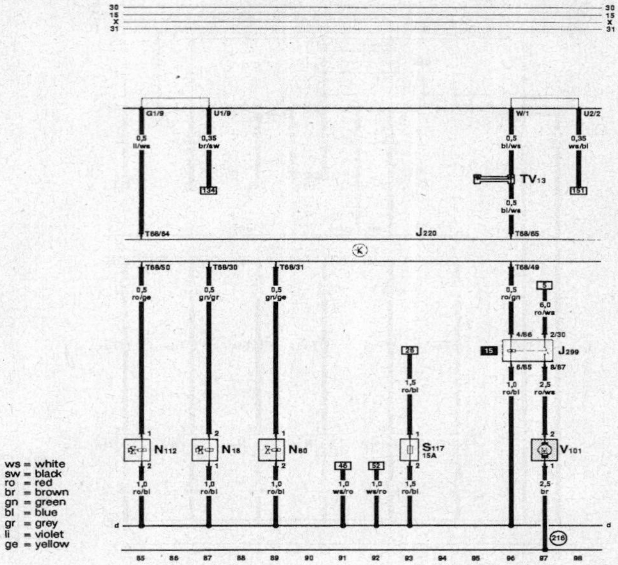

J220 - Motronic Engine Control Module (ECM), in engine compartment, left
J299 - Secondary Air Injection (AIR) Pump Relay, above fuse/relay panel
N18 - EGR Vacuum Regulator Solenoid Valve
N80 - Evaporative Emission (EVAP) Canister Purge Regulator Valve
N112 - Secondary Air Injection (AIR) Solenoid Valve
S117 - Fuse for control elements, above fuse/relay panel
T68 - 68-Pin Connector
TV13 - Vehicle Speed Signal Wire Connector, blue
V101 - Secondary Air Injection (AIR) Pump Motor

(216) - Ground connection -2-, in Motronic Multiport Fuel Injection (MFI) wiring harness

VW1029900166070X

Fig. 17 Motronic wiring diagram (Part 7 of 11). 1999–2000 EuroVan

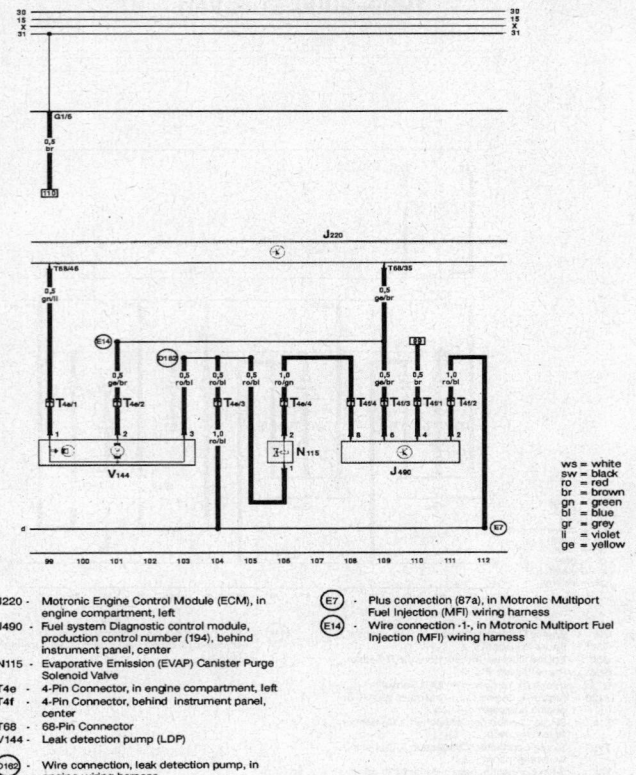

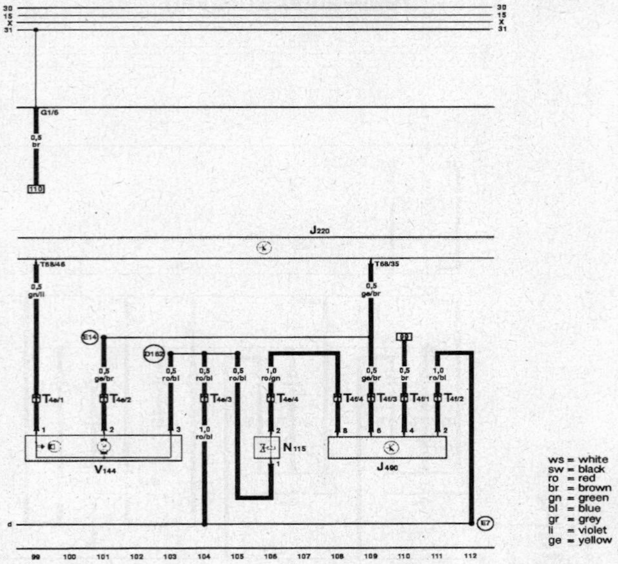

J220 - Motronic Engine Control Module (ECM), in engine compartment, left
J490 - Fuel system Diagnostic control module, production control number (194), behind instrument panel, center
N115 - Evaporative Emission (EVAP) Canister Purge Solenoid Valve
T4e - 4-Pin Connector, in engine compartment, left
T4f - 4-Pin Connector, behind instrument panel, center
T68 - 68-Pin Connector
V144 - Leak detection pump (LDP)

(D162) - Wire connection, leak detection pump, in engine wiring harness

(E7) - Plus connection (87a), in Motronic Multiport Fuel Injection (MFI) wiring harness
(E14) - Wire connection -1-, in Motronic Multiport Fuel Injection (MFI) wiring harness

VW1029900166080X

Fig. 17 Motronic wiring diagram (Part 8 of 11). 1999–2000 EuroVan

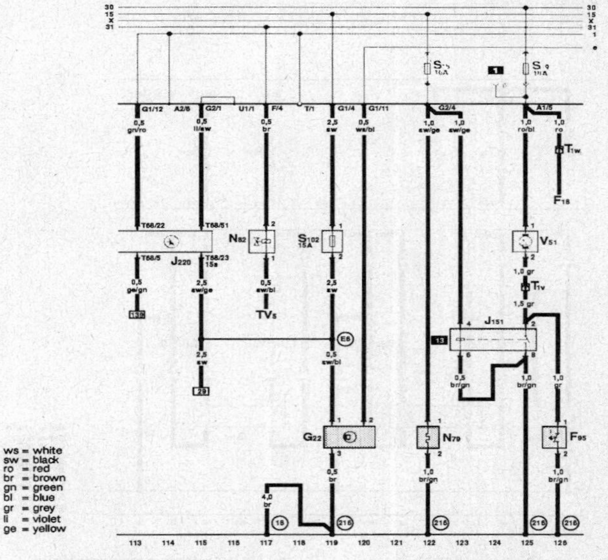

F18 - Coolant Fan Control (FC) Thermal Switch
F95 - After-Run Coolant Thermal Switch
G22 - Speedometer Vehicle Speed Sensor
J151 - Coolant Circulation Pump Relay, above fuse/relay panel
J220 - Motronic Engine Control Module (ECM), in engine compartment, left
N79 - Positive Crankcase Ventilation (PCV) Heating Element
N82 - Coolant Cut-off Valve
S102 - Engine Control Module (ECM) Fuse, above fuse/relay panel
T1v - Single Connector, behind fuse/relay panel
T1w - Single Connector, behind fuse/relay panel
T68 - 68-Pin Connector
TV5 - Terminal 15a Wire Connector, green, 4-Pin and 8-Pin
V51 - After-Run Coolant Pump

(18) - Ground connection, on engine block
(216) - Ground connection -2-, in Motronic Multiport Fuel Injection (MFI) wiring harness
(E6) - Plus connection -1- (15), in Motronic Multiport Fuel Injection (MFI) wiring harness

VW1029900166090X

Fig. 17 Motronic wiring diagram (Part 9 of 11). 1999–2000 EuroVan

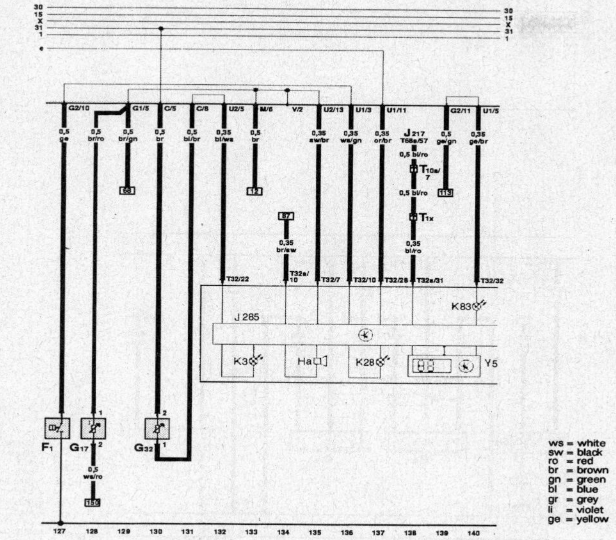

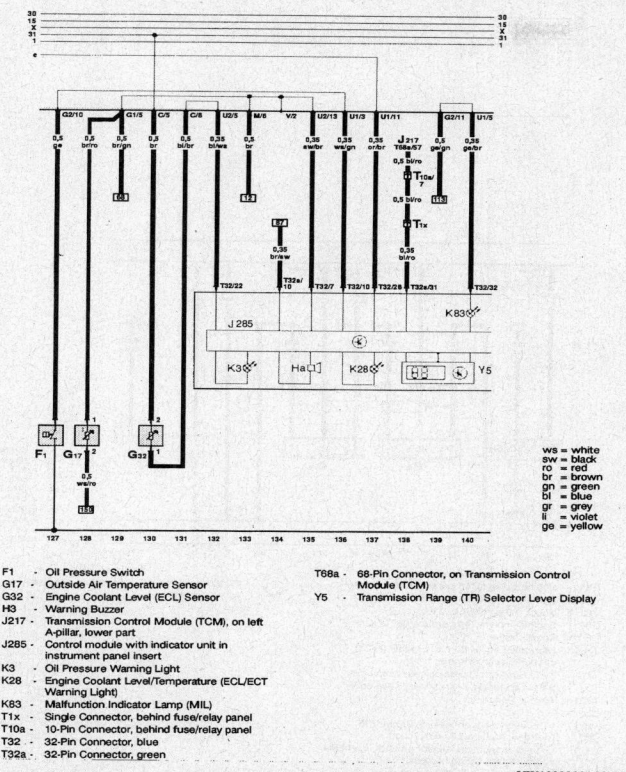

F1 - Oil Pressure Switch
G17 - Outside Air Temperature Sensor
G32 - Engine Coolant Level (ECL) Sensor
H3 - Warning Buzzer
J217 - Transmission Control Module (TCM), on left A-pillar, lower part
J285 - Control module with indicator unit in instrument panel insert
K3 - Oil Pressure Warning Light
K28 - Engine Coolant Level/Temperature (ECL/ECT Warning Light)
K83 - Malfunction Indicator Lamp (MIL)
T1x - Single Connector, behind fuse/relay panel
T10a - 10-Pin Connector, behind fuse/relay panel
T32 - 32-Pin Connector, blue
T32a - 32-Pin Connector, green
T68a - 68-Pin Connector, on Transmission Control Module (TCM)
Y5 - Transmission Range (TR) Selector Lever Display

VW1029900166100X

Fig. 17 Motronic wiring diagram (Part 10 of 11). 1999–2000 EuroVan

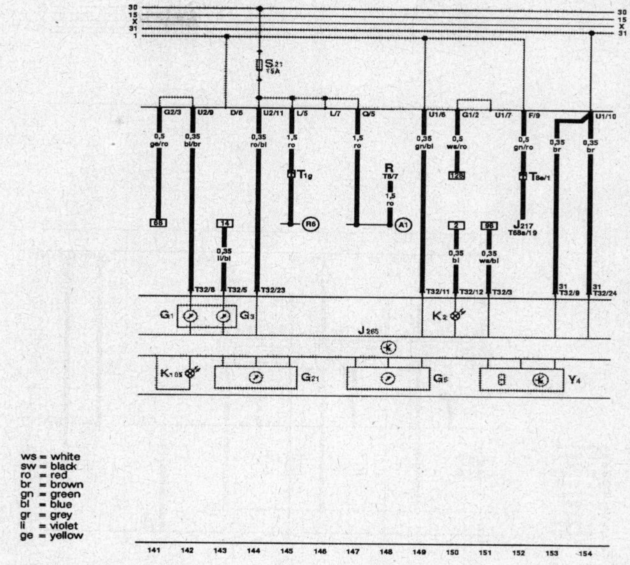

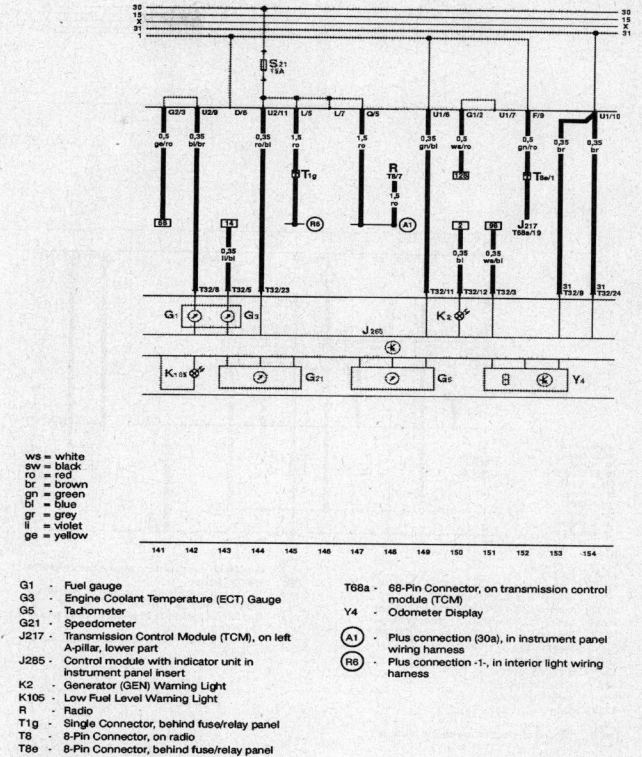

G1 - Fuel gauge
G3 - Engine Coolant Temperature (ECT) Gauge
G5 - Tachometer
G21 - Speedometer
J217 - Transmission Control Module (TCM), on left A-pillar, lower part
J285 - Control module with indicator unit in instrument panel insert
K2 - Generator (GEN) Warning Light
K105 - Low Fuel Level Warning Light
R - Radio
T1g - Single Connector, behind fuse/relay panel
T8 - 8-Pin Connector, on radio
T8e - 8-Pin Connector, behind fuse/relay panel
T32 - 32-Pin Connector, blue
T68a - 68-Pin Connector, on transmission control module (TCM)
Y4 - Odometer Display
(A1) - Plus connection (30a), in instrument panel wiring harness
(R6) - Plus connection -1-, in interior light wiring harness

VW1029900166110X

Fig. 17 Motronic wiring diagram (Part 11 of 11). 1999–2000 EuroVan

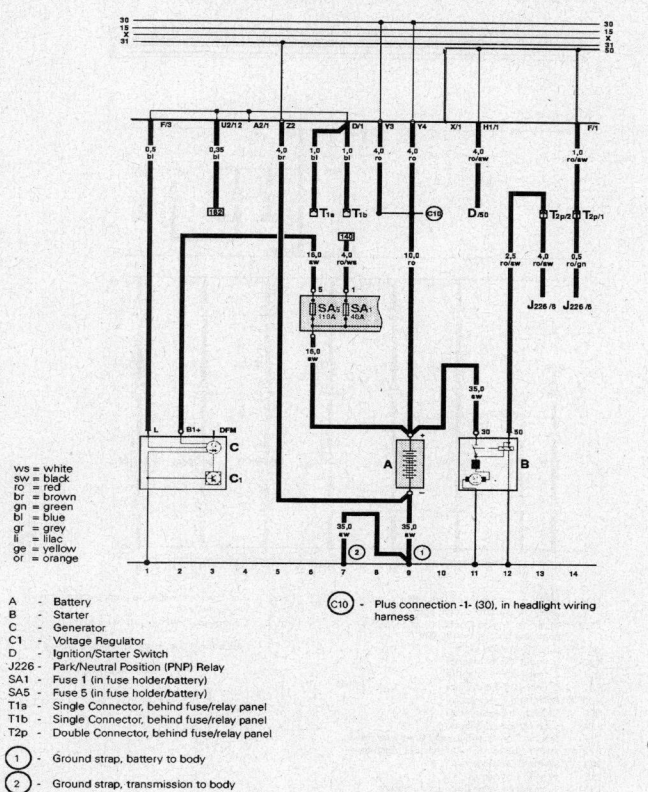

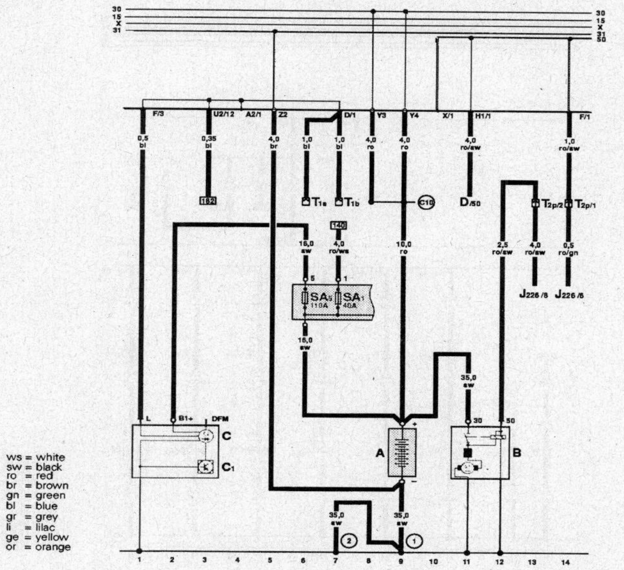

A - Battery
B - Starter
C - Generator
C1 - Voltage Regulator
D - Ignition/Starter Switch
J226 - Park/Neutral Position (PNP) Relay
SA1 - Fuse 1 (in fuse holder/battery)
SA5 - Fuse 5 (in fuse holder/battery)
T1a - Single Connector, behind fuse/relay panel
T1b - Single Connector, behind fuse/relay panel
T2p - Double Connector, behind fuse/relay panel
(1) - Ground strap, battery to body
(2) - Ground strap, transmission to body
(C10) - Plus connection -1- (30), in headlight wiring harness

VW1020100167010X

Fig. 18 Motronic wiring diagram (Part 1 of 14). 2001 EuroVan

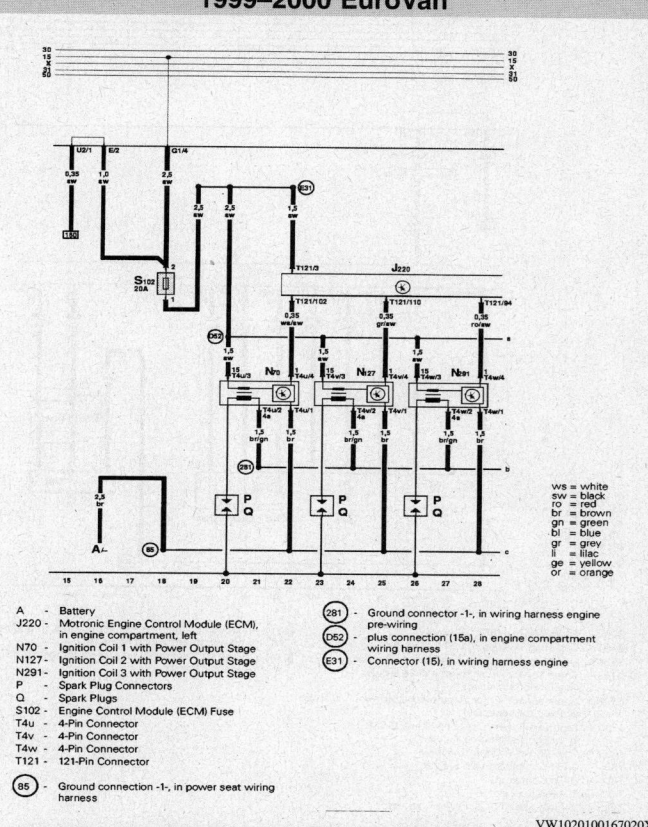

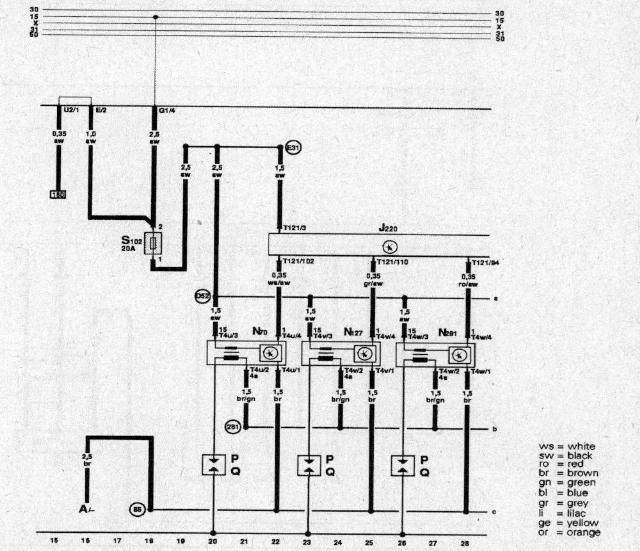

A - Battery
J220 - Motronic Engine Control Module (ECM), in engine compartment, left
N70 - Ignition Coil 1 with Power Output Stage
N127 - Ignition Coil 2 with Power Output Stage
N291 - Ignition Coil 3 with Power Output Stage
P - Spark Plug Connectors
Q - Spark Plugs
S102 - Engine Control Module (ECM) Fuse
T4u - 4-Pin Connector
T4v - 4-Pin Connector
T4w - 4-Pin Connector
T121 - 121-Pin Connector
(85) - Ground connection -1-, in power seat wiring harness
(281) - Ground connector -1-, in wiring harness engine pre-wiring
(D52) - plus connection (15a), in engine compartment wiring harness
(E31) - Connector (15), in wiring harness engine

VW1020100167020X

Fig. 18 Motronic wiring diagram (Part 2 of 14). 2001 EuroVan

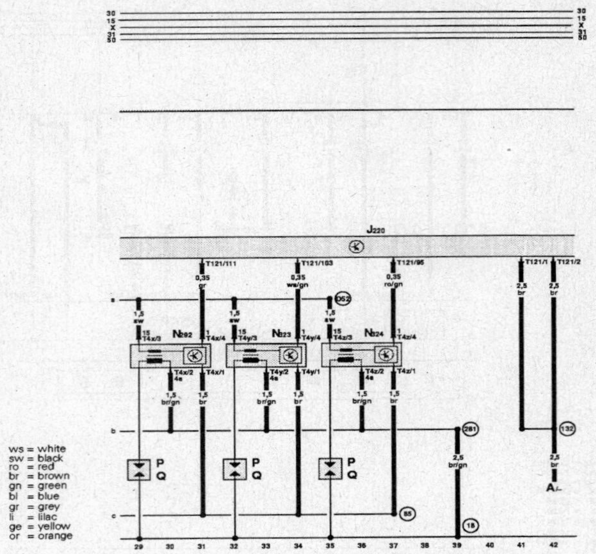

A - Battery
J220 - Motronic Engine Control Module (ECM), in engine compartment, left
N292 - Ignition Coil 4 with Power Output Stage
N323 - Ignition Coil 5 with Power Output Stage
N324 - Ignition Coil 6 with Power Output Stage
P - Spark Plug Connectors
Q - Spark Plugs
T4x - 4-Pin Connector
T4y - 4-Pin Connector
T4z - 4-Pin Connector
T121 - 121-Pin Connector

(18) - Ground connection, on engine block, left

(85) - Ground connection -1-, in engine compartment wiring harness
(132) - Ground connection -3-, in engine compartment wiring harness
(281) - Ground connector -1-, in wiring harness engine pre-wiring
(D52) - plus connection (15a), in engine compartment wiring harness

VW1020100167030X

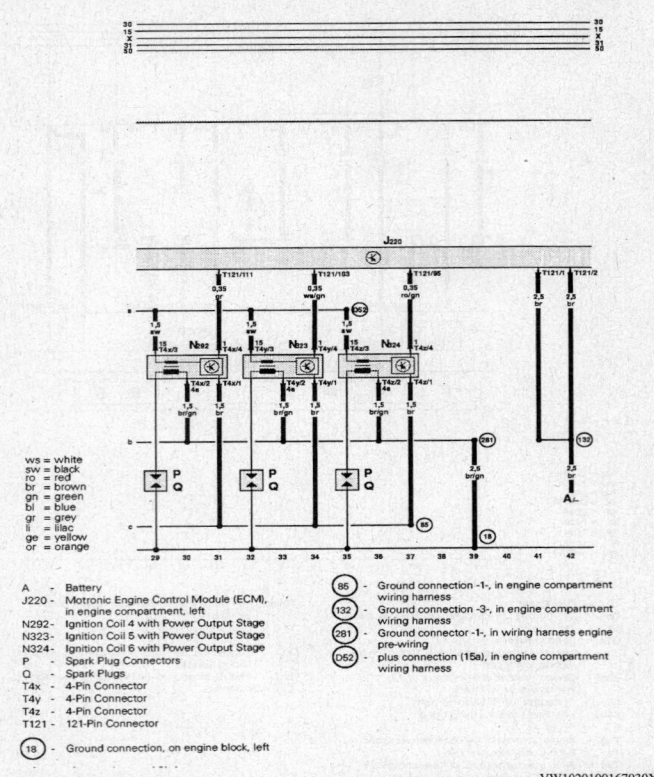

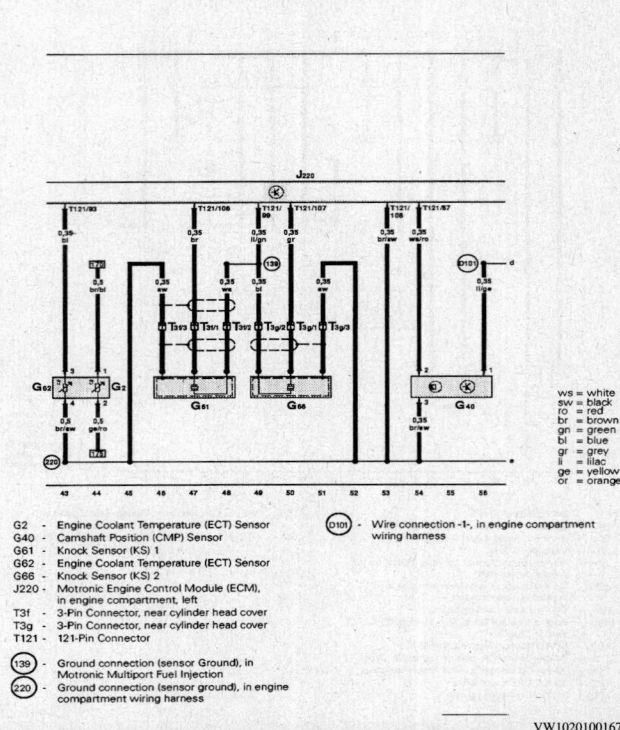

Fig. 18 Motronic wiring diagram (Part 3 of 14). 2001 EuroVan

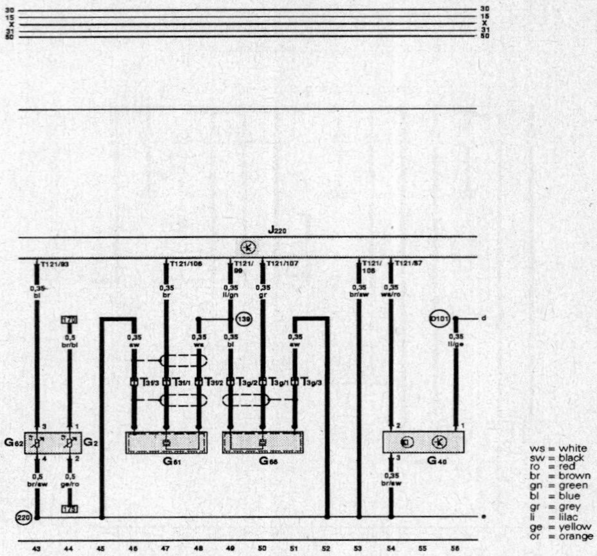

G2 - Engine Coolant Temperature (ECT) Sensor
G40 - Camshaft Position (CMP) Sensor
G61 - Knock Sensor (KS) 1
G62 - Engine Coolant Temperature (ECT) Sensor
G66 - Knock Sensor (KS) 2
J220 - Motronic Engine Control Module (ECM), in engine compartment, left
T3f - 3-Pin Connector, near cylinder head cover
T3g - 3-Pin Connector, near cylinder head cover
T121 - 121-Pin Connector

(139) - Ground connection (sensor Ground), in Motronic Multiport Fuel Injection
(220) - Ground connection (sensor ground), in engine compartment wiring harness

(D101) - Wire connection -1-, in engine compartment wiring harness

VW1020100167040X

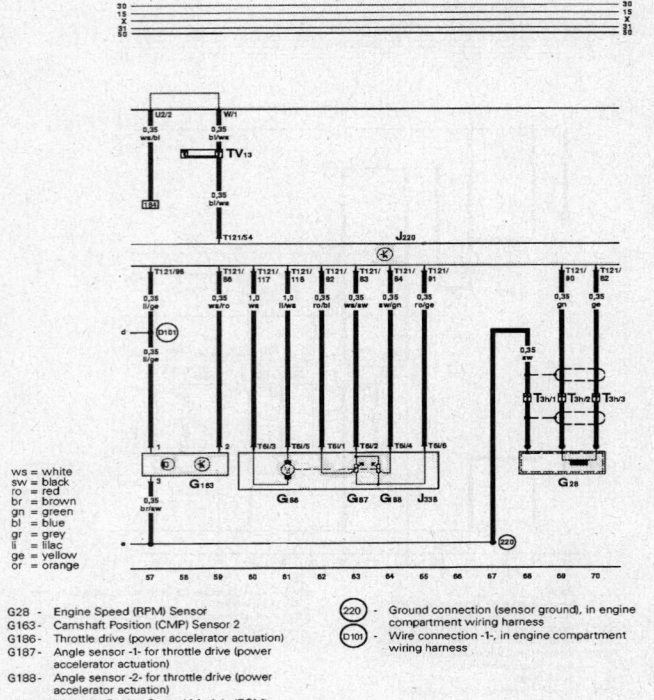

Fig. 18 Motronic wiring diagram (Part 4 of 14). 2001 EuroVan

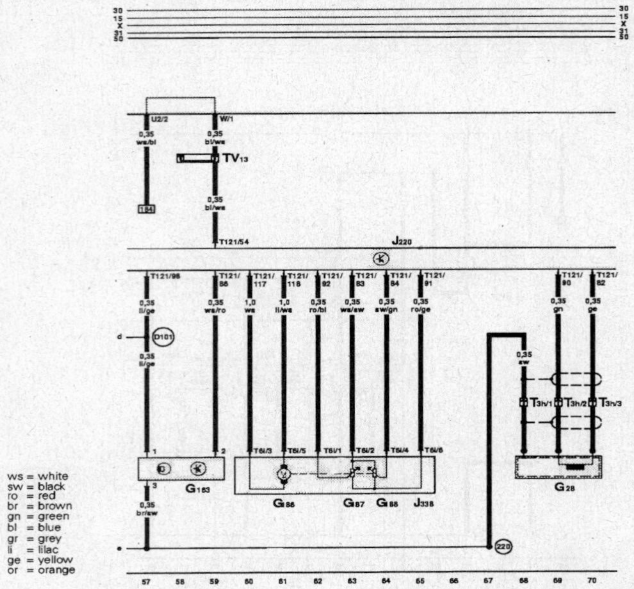

G28 - Engine Speed (RPM) Sensor
G163 - Camshaft Position (CMP) Sensor 2
G186 - Throttle drive (power accelerator actuation)
G187 - Angle sensor -1- for throttle drive (power accelerator actuation)
G188 - Angle sensor -2- for throttle drive (power accelerator actuation)
J220 - Motronic Engine Control Module (ECM), in engine compartment, left
J338 - Throttle Valve Control Module
T3h - 3-Pin Connector, near starter
T6i - 6-Pin Connector
T121 - 121-Pin Connector
TV13 - Vehicle Speed Signal Wire Connector

(220) - Ground connection (sensor ground), in engine compartment wiring harness
(D101) - Wire connection -1-, in engine compartment wiring harness

VW1020100167050X

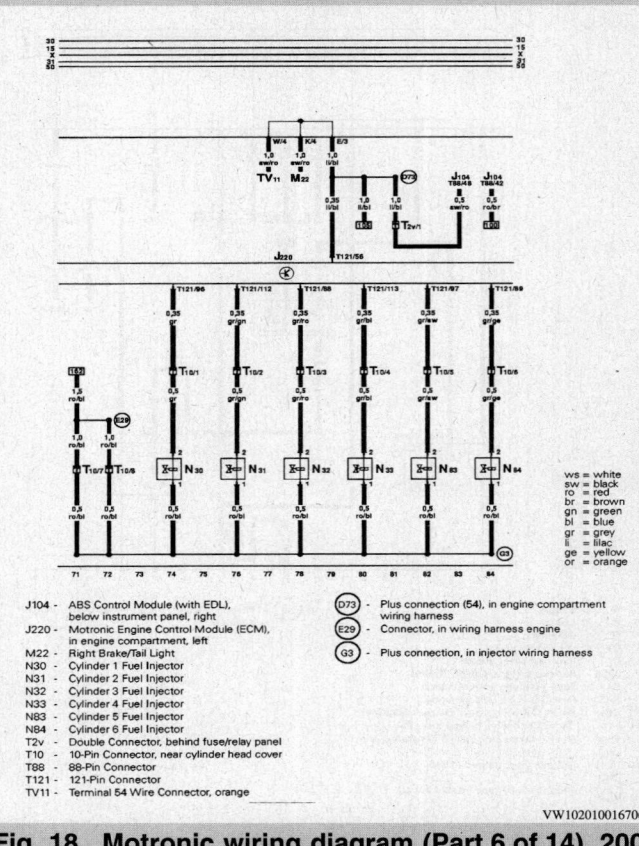

Fig. 18 Motronic wiring diagram (Part 5 of 14). 2001 EuroVan

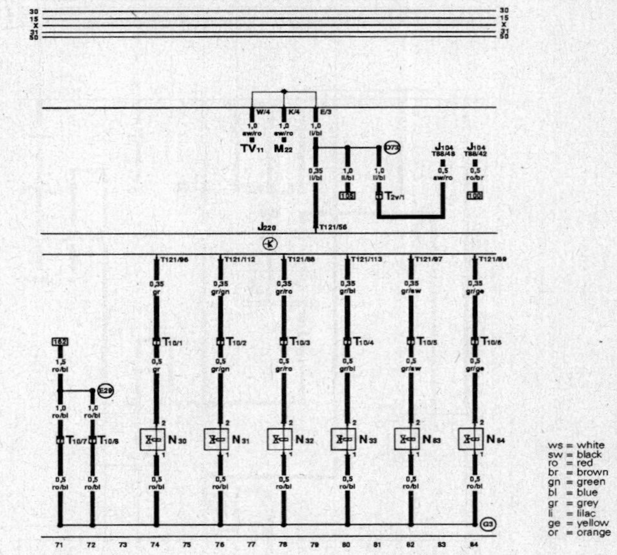

J104 - ABS Control Module (with EDL), below instrument panel, right
J220 - Motronic Engine Control Module (ECM), in engine compartment, left
M22 - Right Brake/Tail Light
N30 - Cylinder 1 Fuel Injector
N31 - Cylinder 2 Fuel Injector
N32 - Cylinder 3 Fuel Injector
N33 - Cylinder 4 Fuel Injector
N83 - Cylinder 5 Fuel Injector
N84 - Cylinder 6 Fuel Injector
T2v - Double Connector, behind fuse/relay panel
T10 - 10-Pin Connector, near cylinder head cover
T88 - 88-Pin Connector
T121 - 121-Pin Connector
TV11 - Terminal 54 Wire Connector, orange

(D73) - Plus connection (54), in engine compartment wiring harness
(E29) - Connector, in wiring harness engine
(G3) - Plus connection, in injector wiring harness

VW1020100167060X

Fig. 18 Motronic wiring diagram (Part 6 of 14). 2001 EuroVan

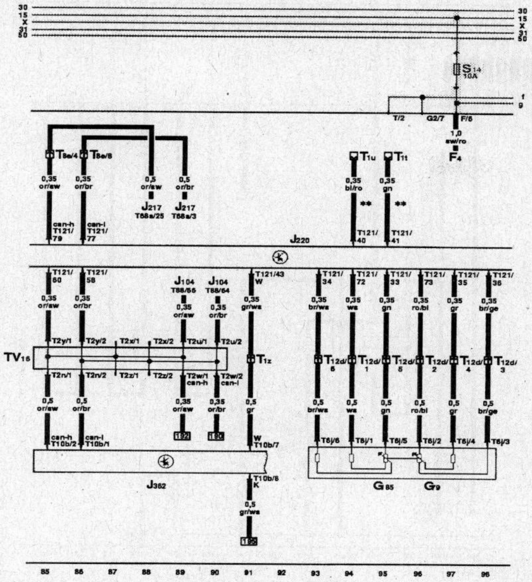

ws = white
sw = black
ro = red
br = brown
gn = green
bl = blue
gr = grey
li = lilac
ge = yellow
or = orange

F4 - Back-Up Light Switch
G79 - Throttle Position (TP) Sensor
G185 - Sender -2- for accelerator pedal position
J104 - ABS Control Module (with EDL), below instrument panel, right
J220 - Motronic Engine Control Module (ECM), in engine compartment, left
J217 - Transmission Control Module (TCM)
J362 - Control module for anti-theft immobilizer
T1t - Single Connector, behind fuse/relay panel
T1u - Single Connector, behind fuse/relay panel
T1z - Single Connector, behind fuse/relay panel
T2n - Double Connector
T2u - Double Connector
T2w - Double Connector
T2x - Double Connector
T2y - Double Connector
T2z - Double Connector
T6j - 6-Pin Connector
T8e - 8-Pin Connector, behind fuse/relay panel
T10b - 10-Pin Connector
T12d - 12-Pin Connector, behind fuse/relay panel
T68a - 68-Pin Connector
T88 - 88-Pin Connector
T121 - 121-Pin Connector
TV16 - Wire distributor for Data-Bus, on relay panel No. 5

** - A/C connection

VW1020100167070X

Fig. 18 Motronic wiring diagram (Part 7 of 14). 2001 EuroVan

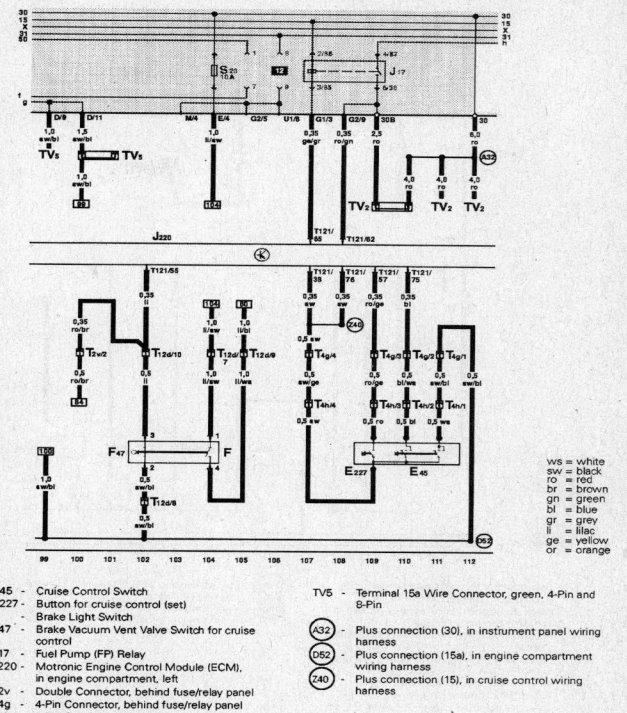

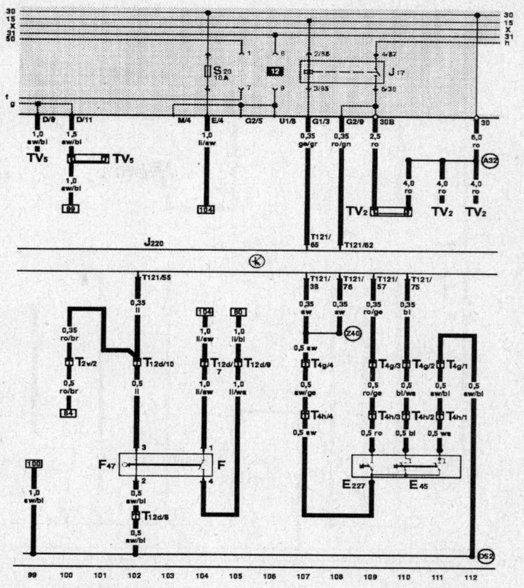

ws = white
sw = black
ro = red
br = brown
gn = green
bl = blue
gr = grey
li = lilac
ge = yellow
or = orange

E45 - Cruise Control Switch
E227 - Button for cruise control (set)
F - Brake Light Switch
F47 - Brake Vacuum Vent Valve Switch for cruise control
J17 - Fuel Pump (FP) Relay
J220 - Motronic Engine Control Module (ECM), in engine compartment, left
T2v - Double Connector, behind fuse/relay panel
T4g - 4-Pin Connector, behind fuse/relay panel
T4h - 4-Pin Connector, near steering column
T12d - 12-Pin Connector, behind fuse/relay panel
T121 - 121-Pin Connector
TV2 - Terminal 30 (B+) Wire Connector, red, each 6 points
TV5 - Terminal 15a Wire Connector, green, 4-Pin and 8-Pin

(A32) - Plus connection (30), in instrument panel wiring harness
(D52) - Plus connection (15a), in engine compartment wiring harness
(Z40) - Plus connection (15), in cruise control wiring harness

VW1020100167080X

Fig. 18 Motronic wiring diagram (Part 8 of 14). 2001 EuroVan

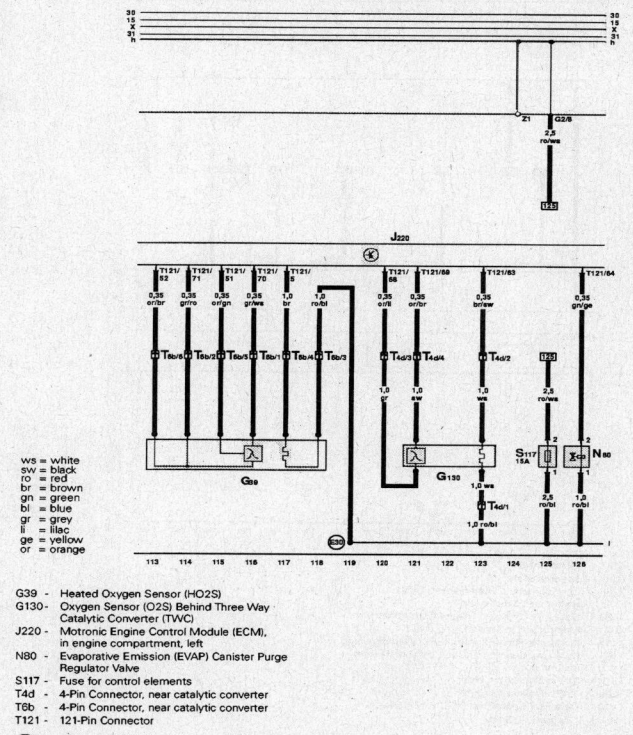

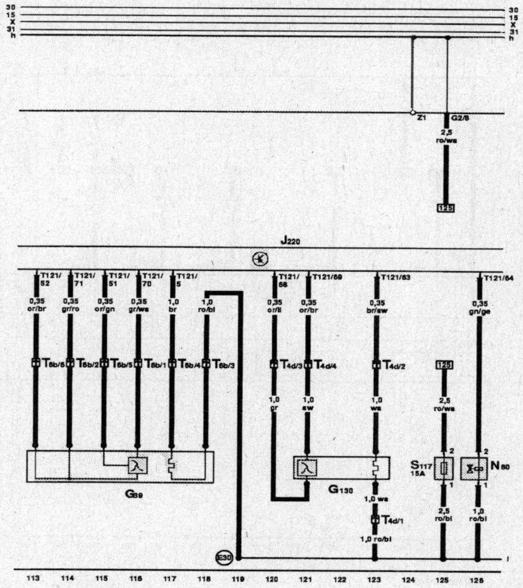

ws = white
sw = black
ro = red
br = brown
gn = green
bl = blue
gr = grey
li = lilac
ge = yellow
or = orange

G39 - Heated Oxygen Sensor (HO2S)
G130 - Oxygen Sensor (O2S) Behind Three Way Catalytic Converter (TWC)
J220 - Motronic Engine Control Module (ECM), in engine compartment, left
N80 - Evaporative Emission (EVAP) Canister Purge Regulator Valve
S117 - Fuse for control elements
T4d - 4-Pin Connector, near catalytic converter
T6b - 4-Pin Connector, near catalytic converter
T121 - 121-Pin Connector

(E30) - Connector (87a), in wiring harness engine

VW1020100167090X

Fig. 18 Motronic wiring diagram (Part 9 of 14). 2001 EuroVan

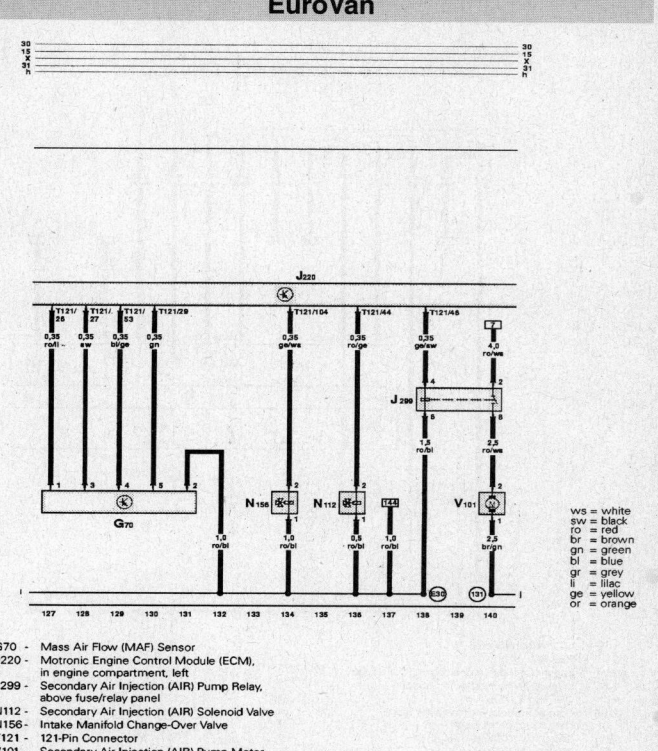

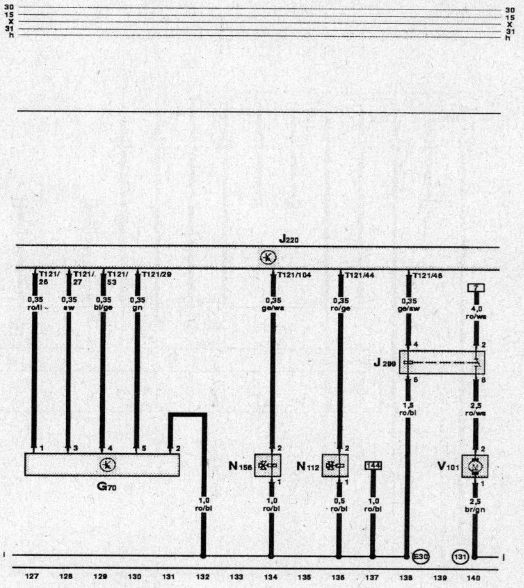

ws = white
sw = black
ro = red
br = brown
gn = green
bl = blue
gr = grey
li = lilac
ge = yellow
or = orange

G70 - Mass Air Flow (MAF) Sensor
J220 - Motronic Engine Control Module (ECM), in engine compartment, left
J299 - Secondary Air Injection (AIR) Pump Relay, above fuse/relay panel
N112 - Secondary Air Injection (AIR) Solenoid Valve
N156 - Intake Manifold Change-Over Valve
T121 - 121-Pin Connector
V101 - Secondary Air Injection (AIR) Pump Motor

(131) - Ground connection -2-, in engine compartment wiring harness
(E30) - Connector (87a), in wiring harness engine

VW1020100167100X

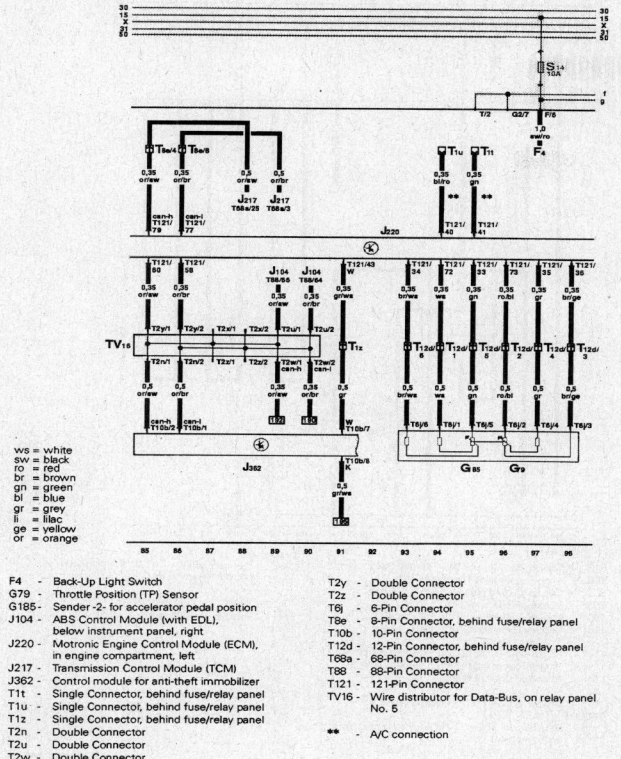

Fig. 18 Motronic wiring diagram (Part 10 of 14). 2001 EuroVan

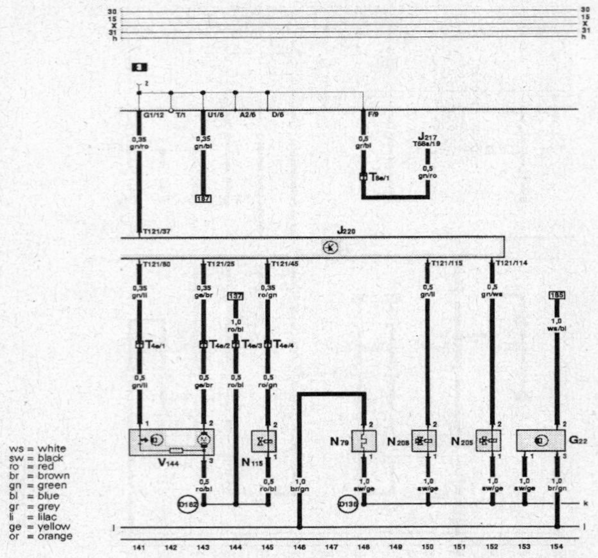

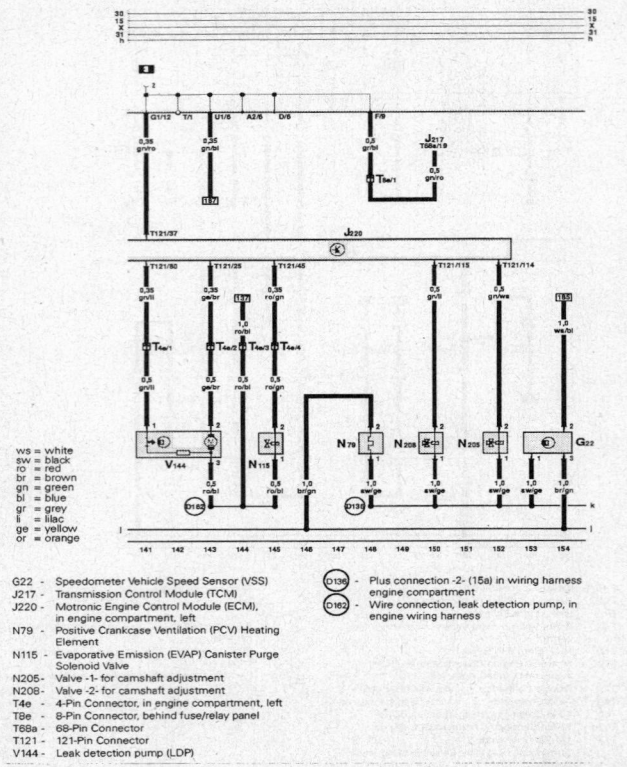

G22 - Speedometer Vehicle Speed Sensor (VSS)
J217 - Transmission Control Module (TCM)
J220 - Motronic Engine Control Module (ECM), in engine compartment, left
N79 - Positive Crankcase Ventilation (PCV) Heating Element
N115 - Evaporative Emission (EVAP) Canister Purge Solenoid Valve
N205 - Valve -1- for camshaft adjustment
N208 - Valve -2- for camshaft adjustment
T4e - 4-Pin Connector, in engine compartment, left
T8e - 8-Pin Connector, behind fuse/relay panel
T68a - 68-Pin Connector
T121 - 121-Pin Connector
V144 - Leak detection pump (LDP)

(D136) - Plus connection -2- (15a) in wiring harness engine compartment
(D162) - Wire connection, leak detection pump, in engine wiring harness

VW1020100167110X

Fig. 18 Motronic wiring diagram (Part 11 of 14). 2001 EuroVan

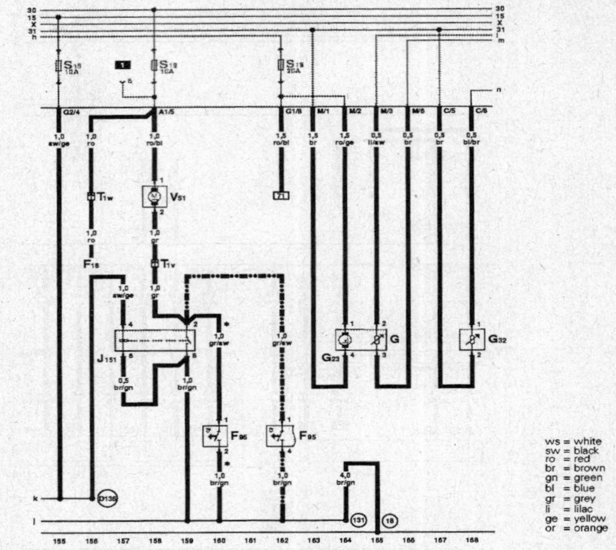

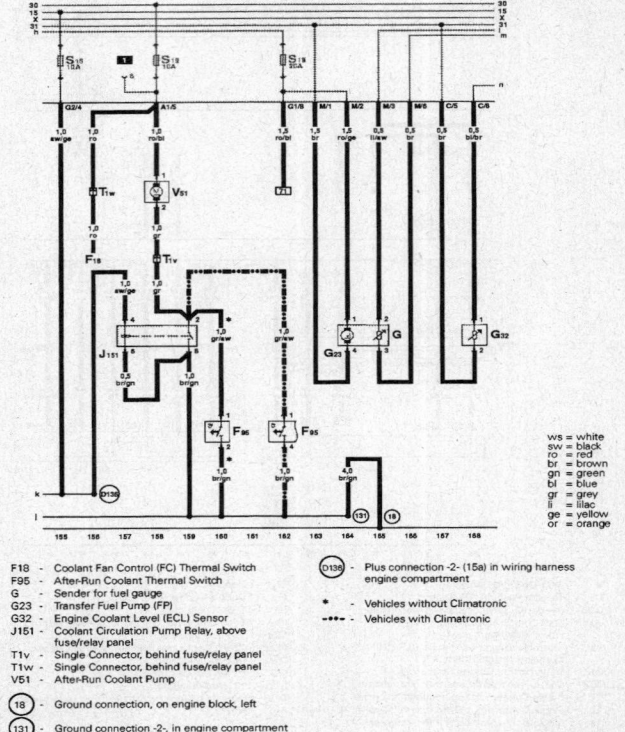

F18 - Coolant Fan Control (FC) Thermal Switch
F95 - After-Run Coolant Thermal Switch
G - Sender for fuel gauge
G23 - Transfer Fuel Pump (FP)
G32 - Engine Coolant Level (ECL) Sensor
J151 - Coolant Circulation Pump Relay, above fuse/relay panel
T1v - Single Connector, behind fuse/relay panel
T1w - Single Connector, behind fuse/relay panel
V51 - After-Run Coolant Pump

(18) - Ground connection, on engine block, left

(131) - Ground connection -2-, in engine compartment wiring harness

(D136) - Plus connection -2- (15a) in wiring harness engine compartment

* - Vehicles without Climatronic

-•••- - Vehicles with Climatronic

VW1020100167120X

Fig. 18 Motronic wiring diagram (Part 12 of 14). 2001 EuroVan

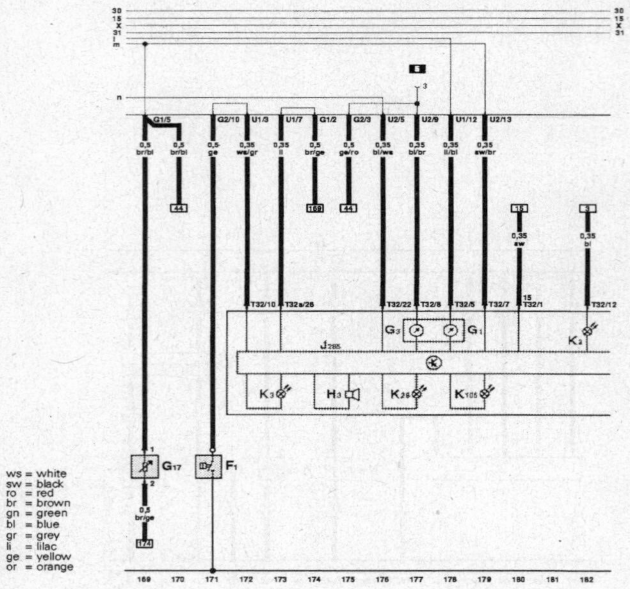

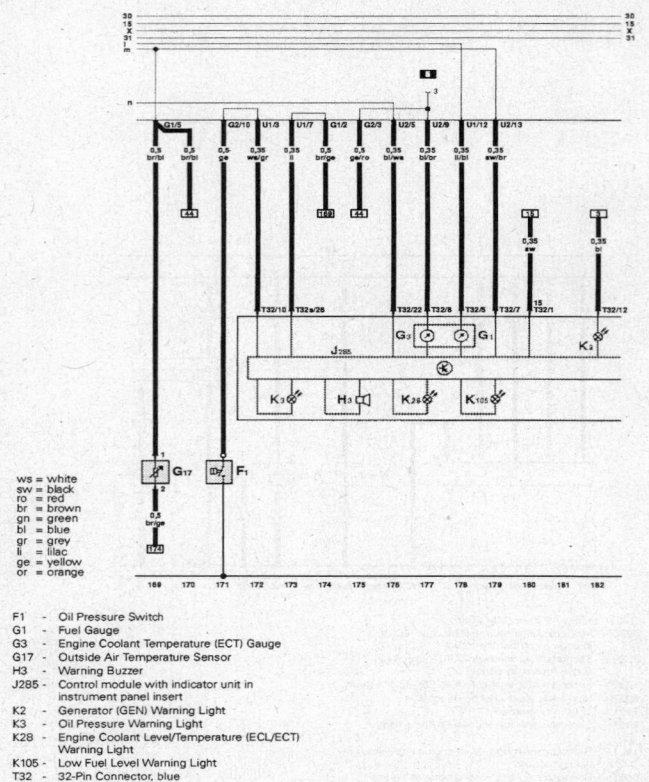

F1 - Oil Pressure Switch
G1 - Fuel Gauge
G3 - Engine Coolant Temperature (ECT) Gauge
G17 - Outside Air Temperature Sensor
H3 - Warning Buzzer
J285 - Control module with indicator unit in instrument panel insert
K2 - Generator (GEN) Warning Light
K3 - Oil Pressure Warning Light
K28 - Engine Coolant Level/Temperature (ECL/ECT) Warning Light
K105 - Low Fuel Level Warning Light
T32 - 32-Pin Connector, blue
T32a - 32-Pin Connector, green

VW1020100167130X

Fig. 18 Motronic wiring diagram (Part 13 of 14). 2001 EuroVan

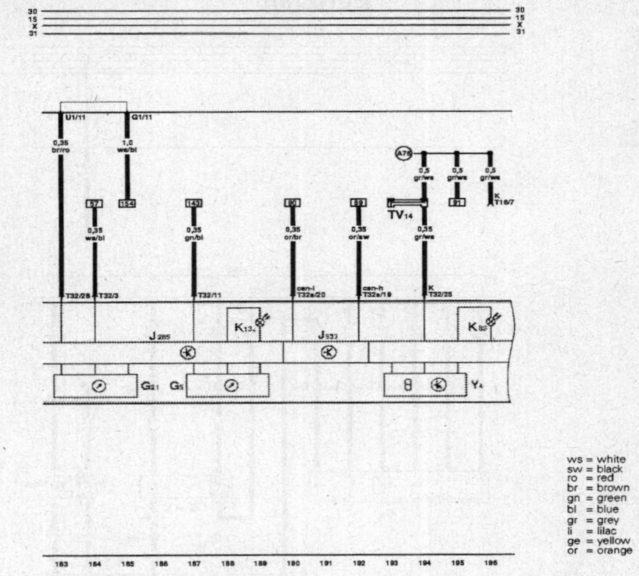

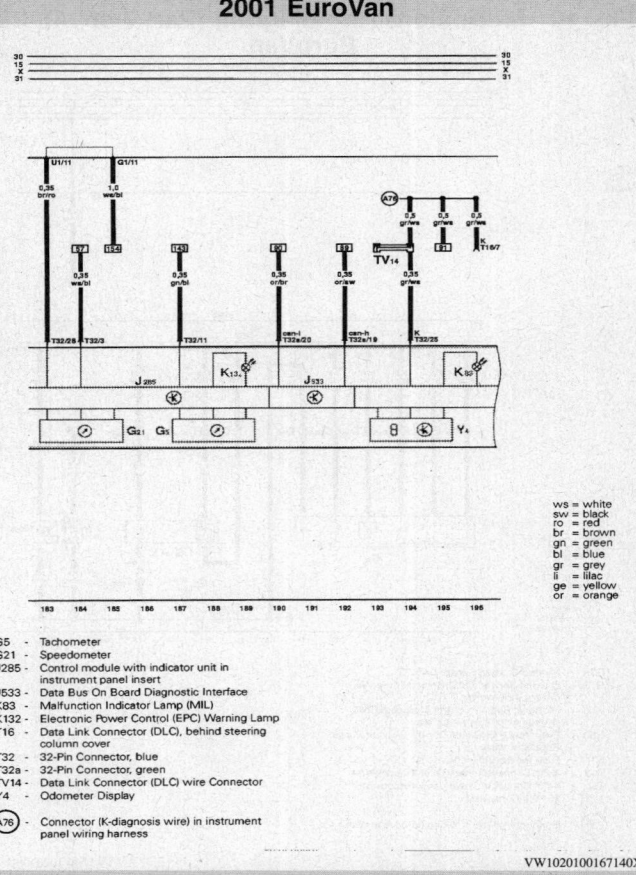

G5 - Tachometer
G21 - Speedometer
J285 - Control module with indicator unit in instrument panel insert
J533 - Data Bus On Board Diagnostic Interface
K83 - Malfunction Indicator Lamp (MIL)
K132 - Electronic Power Control (EPC) Warning Lamp
T16 - Data Link Connector (DLC), behind steering column cover
T32 - 32-Pin Connector, blue
T32a - 32-Pin Connector, green
TV14 - Data Link Connector (DLC) wire Connector
Y4 - Odometer Display

(A76) - Connector (K-diagnosis wire) in instrument panel wiring harness

VW1020100167140X

Fig. 18 Motronic wiring diagram (Part 14 of 14). 2001 EuroVan

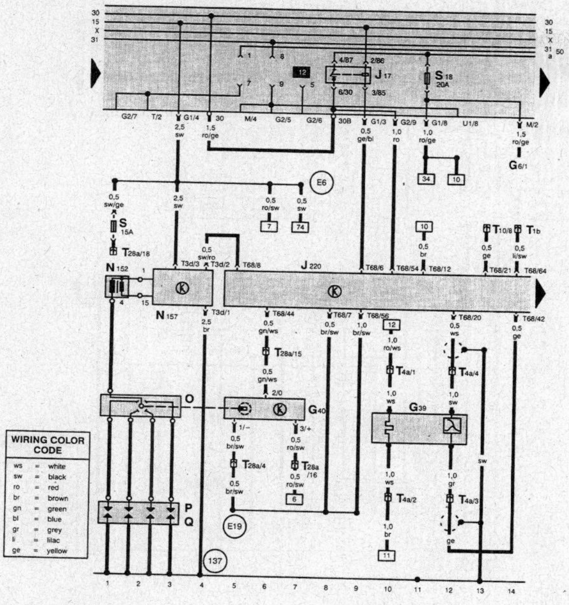

G6 – Fuel Pump (FP)
G39 – Heated Oxygen Sensor (HO2S) 1
G40 – Camshaft Position (CMP) Sensor
J17 – Fuel Pump (FP) Relay
J220 – Motronic Engine Control Module (ECM)
N152 – Ignition Coil
N157 – Ignition Coil Power Output Stage
O – Ignition Distributor
P – Spark Plug Connectors
Q – Spark Plugs
T1b – 1-Pin Connector
T3d – 3-Pin Connector, on Ignition Coil Power Output Stage
T4a – 4-Pin Connector
T10 – 10-Pin Connector
T28a – 28-Pin Connector, in engine compartment
T68 – 68-Pin Connector, on Motronic ECM

(137) – Ground connection (end stage), in Motronic MFI wiring harness
(E6) – Plus connection -1- (15), in Motronic MFI wiring harness
(E19) – Wire Connection– –, in Motronic Engine Control Module (EMC) wiring harness

VW1029900121010X

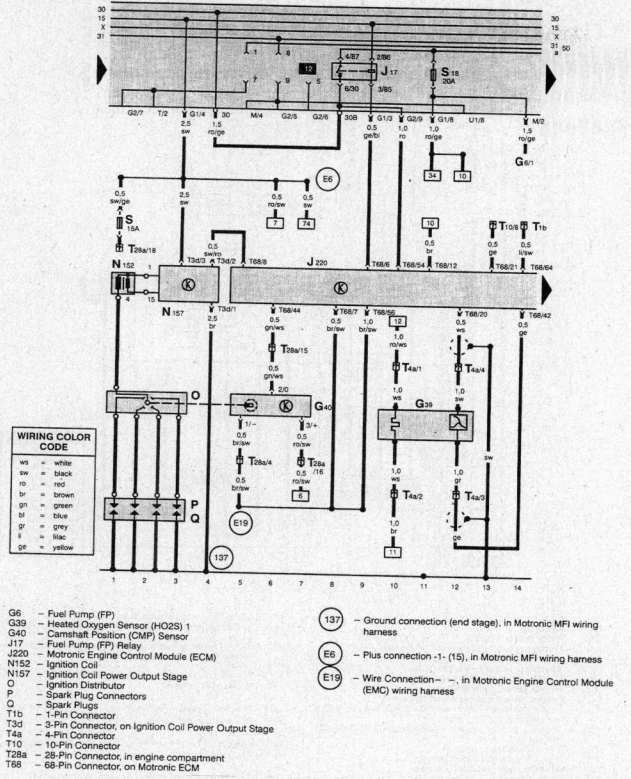

Fig. 19 Motronic wiring diagrams (Part 1 of 4). 1998 Golf, GTI & Jetta w/2.0L engine

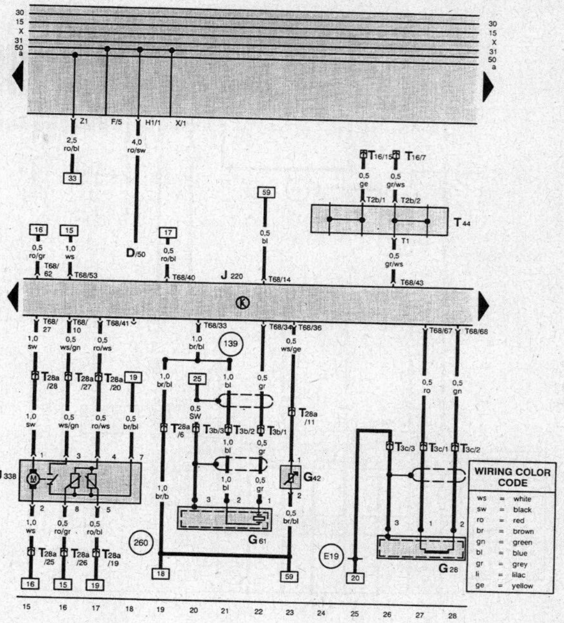

D – Ignition/Starter Switch
G28 – Engine Speed (RPM) Sensor
G42 – Intake Air Temperature (IAT)Sensor
G61 – Knock Sensor (KS) 1
J220 – Motronic Engine Control Module (ECM)
J338 – Throttle Valve Control Module
T2b – Double Connector, above fuse/relay panel
T3b – 3-Pin Connector
T3c – 3-Pin Connector
T16 – Data Link Connector (DLC), behind center of dash
T28a – 28-Pin Connector, in engine compartment
T42 – 42-Pin Connector
T44 – Junction Box for On-Board Diagnosis, above fuse/relay panel
T68 – 68-Pin Connector, on Motronic ECM

(138) – Ground connection (control module), in Motronic MFI wiring harness
(139) – Ground connection (sensor ground), in Motronic Multiport Fuel Injection (MFI) wiring harness
(260) – Ground connection (sensor ground), in injector wiring harness
(E19) – Wire Connection – –, in Motronic Engine Control Module (ECM) wiring harness

VW1029900121020X

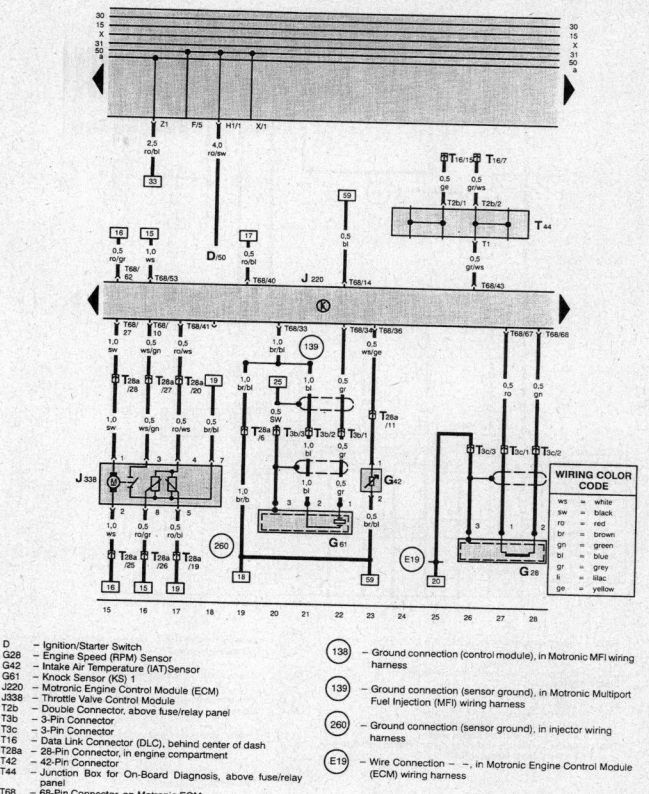

Fig. 19 Motronic wiring diagrams (Part 2 of 4). 1998 Golf, GTI & Jetta w/2.0L engine

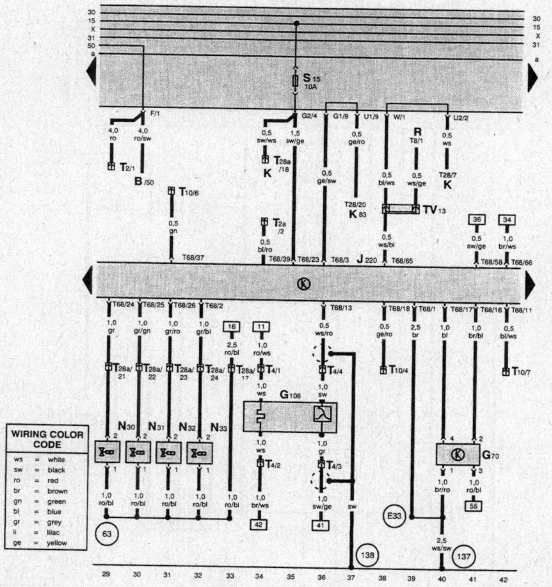

B – Starter
G70 – Mass Air Flow (MAF) Sensor
G108 – Heated Oxygen Sensor (HO2S)
J220 – Motronic Engine Control Module (ECM)
K – Instrument Cluster
K83 – Multi-Function Indicator Lamp (MIL)
N30 – Cylinder 1 Fuel Injector
N31 – Cylinder 2 Fuel Injector
N32 – Cylinder 3 Fuel Injector
N33 – Cylinder 4 Fuel Injector
R – Radio
T2 – Double Connector
T2a – Double Connector
T4 – 4-Pin Connector
T8 – 8-Pin Connector
T10 – 10-Pin Connector
T28 – 28-Pin Connector, instrument cluster
T28a – 28-Pin Connector, in engine compartment
T68 – 68-Pin Connector, on Motronic ECM

TV13 – Vehicle Speed Signal Wire Connector
(63) – Ground connection, on left taillight bulb holder
(137) – Ground connection (end stage), in Motronic MFI wiring harness
(138) – Ground connection (sensor ground), in Motronic MFI wiring harness
(E33) – Ground connection, in Motronic MFI wiring harness

VW1029900121030X

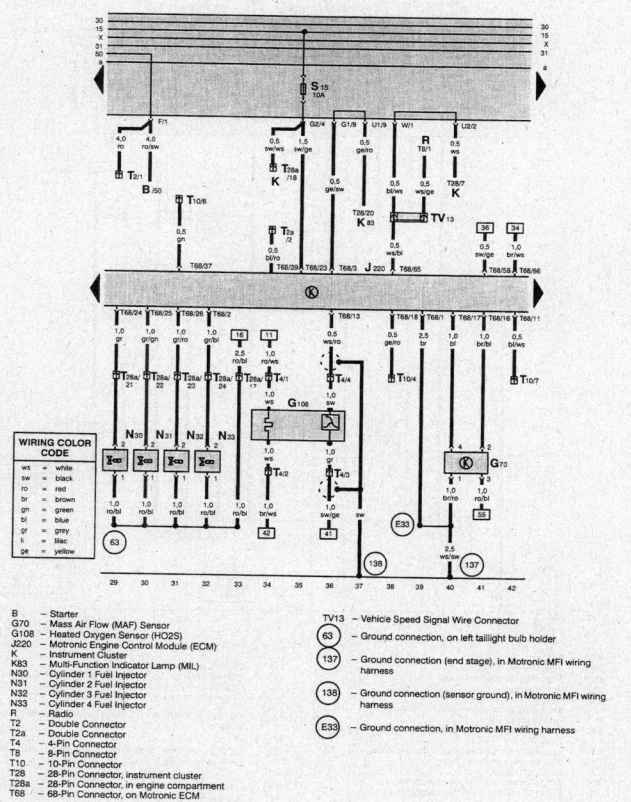

Fig. 19 Motronic wiring diagrams (Part 3 of 4). 1998 Golf, GTI & Jetta w/2.0L engine

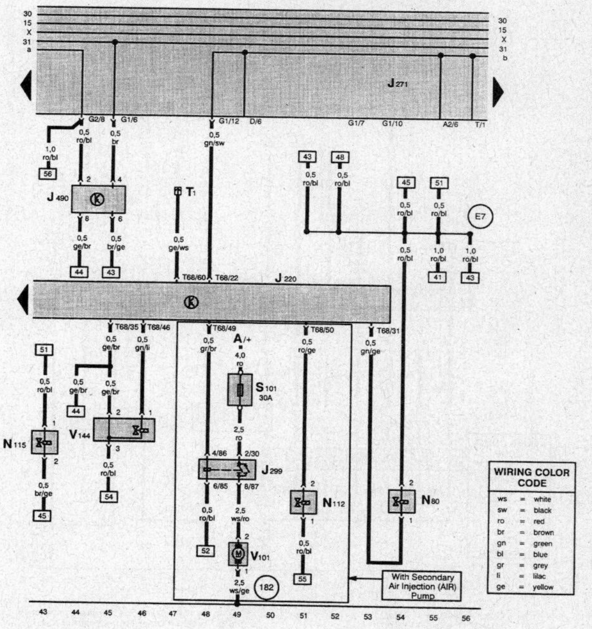

A – Battery
J220 – Motronic Engine Control Module (ECM)
J299 – Secondary Air Injection (AIR) Pump Relay
J490 – Fuel System Diagnostic Control Module
N80 – Evaporative Emission (EVAP) Canister Purge Regulator Valve
N112 – Secondary Air Injection (AIR) Solenoid Valve
N115 – Evaporative Emission (EVAP) Canister Purge Solenoid Valve

S101 – A/C-Climatronic Control Module Fuse
T68 – 68-Pin Connector, on Motronic ECM
V101 – Secondary Air Injection (AIR) Pump Motor
V144 – Leak Detection Pump (LDP)
T1 – 1-pin Connector, engine compartment wiring harness

(182) – Ground connection -1-, in engine compartment wiring harness
(E7) – Plus Connection (87a), in Motronic MFI wiring harness

VW1029900121040X

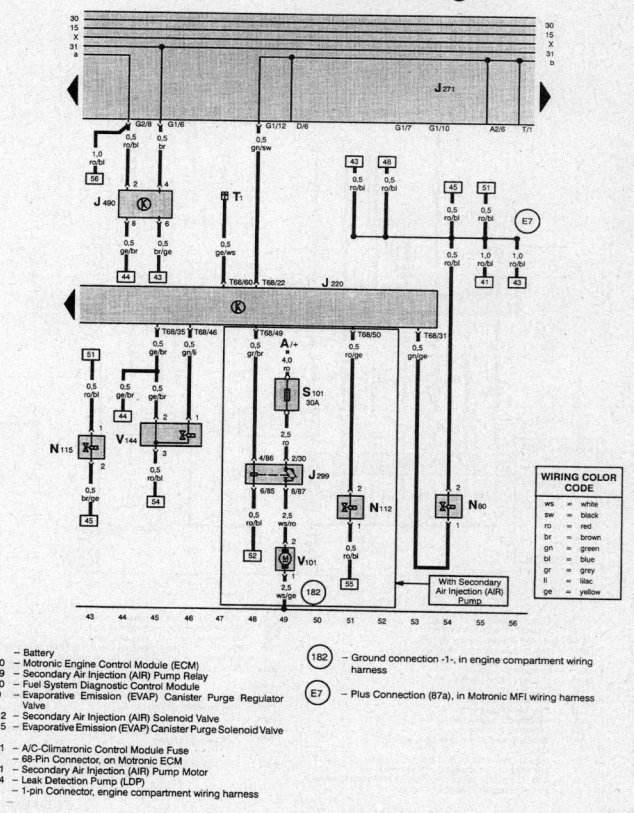

Fig. 19 Motronic wiring diagrams (Part 4 of 4). 1998 Golf, GTI & Jetta w/2.0L engine

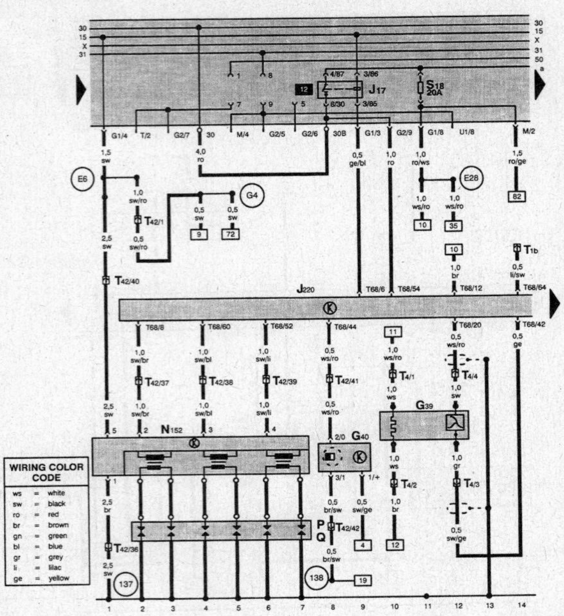

G39 – Heated Oxygen Sensor (HO2S) 1
G40 – Camshaft Position (CMP) Sensor
J17 – Fuel Pump (FP) Relay
J220 – Motronic Engine Control Module (ECM)
N152 – Ignition Coil
P – Spark Plug Connector
Q – Spark Plug
T1b – 1-Pin Connector
T4 – 4-Pin Connector, bottom right rear of engine compartment
T42 – 42-Pin Connector, left side of engine
T68 – 68-Pin Connector, under right side of hood, on Motronic Engine Control Module (ECM)

(E6) – Plus connection (15), in Motronic Multiport Fuel Injection (MFI) wiring harness
(G4) – Wire connection, in Injector wiring harness
(E28) – Wire connection (Lambda probe heater), in wiring harness Motronic
(137) – Ground connection (end stage), in Motronic Multiport Fuel Injection (MFI) wiring harness
(138) – Ground connection (control module), in Motronic Multiport Fuel Injection (MFI) wiring harness

VW1029900122010X

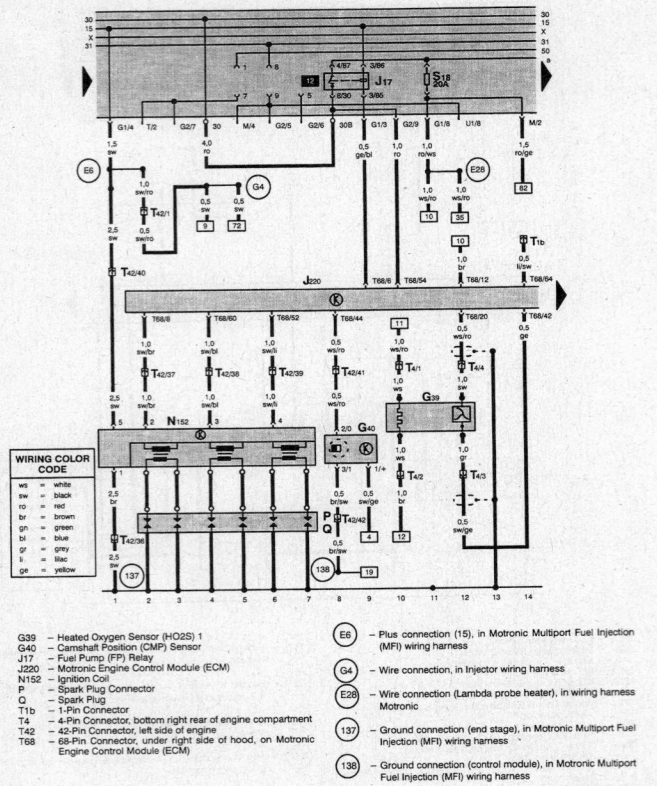

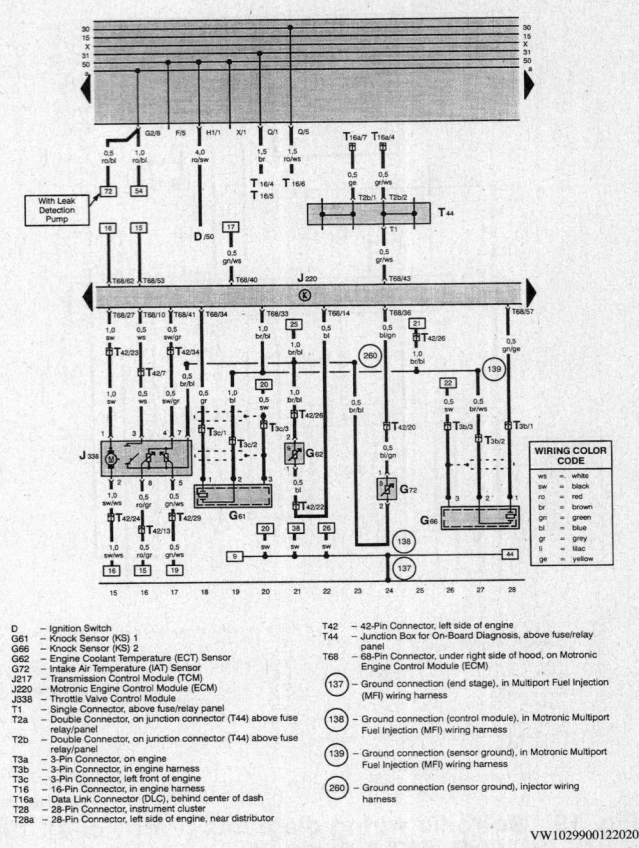

Fig. 20 Motronic wiring diagram (Part 1 of 5). 1998 GTI & Jetta w/2.8L engine

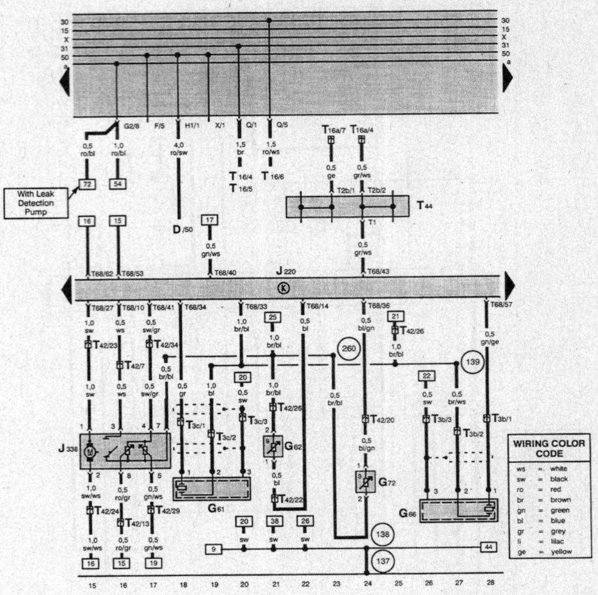

D – Ignition Switch
G61 – Knock Sensor (KS) 1
G66 – Knock Sensor (KS) 2
G62 – Engine Coolant Temperature (ECT) Sensor
G72 – Intake Air Temperature (IAT) Sensor
J217 – Transmission Control Module (TCM)
J220 – Motronic Engine Control Module (ECM)
J338 – Throttle Valve Control Module
T1 – Single Connector, above fuse/relay panel
T2a – Double Connector, on junction connector (T44) above fuse relay/panel
T2b – Double Connector, on junction connector (T44) above fuse relay/panel
T3a – 3-Pin Connector, on engine
T3b – 3-Pin Connector, in engine harness
T3c – 3-Pin Connector, left front of engine
T16 – 16-Pin Connector, in engine harness
T16a – Data Link Connector (DLC), behind center of dash
T28 – 28-Pin Connector, instrument cluster
T28a – 28-Pin Connector, left side of engine, near distributor
T42 – 42-Pin Connector, left side of engine
T44 – Junction Box for On-Board Diagnosis, above fuse/relay panel
T68 – 68-Pin Connector, under right side of hood, on Motronic Engine Control Module (ECM)

(137) – Ground connection (end stage), in Multiport Fuel Injection (MFI) wiring harness
(138) – Ground connection (control module), in Motronic Multiport Fuel Injection (MFI) wiring harness
(139) – Ground connection (sensor ground), in Motronic Multiport Fuel Injection (MFI) wiring harness
(260) – Ground connection (sensor ground), injector wiring harness

VW1029900122020X

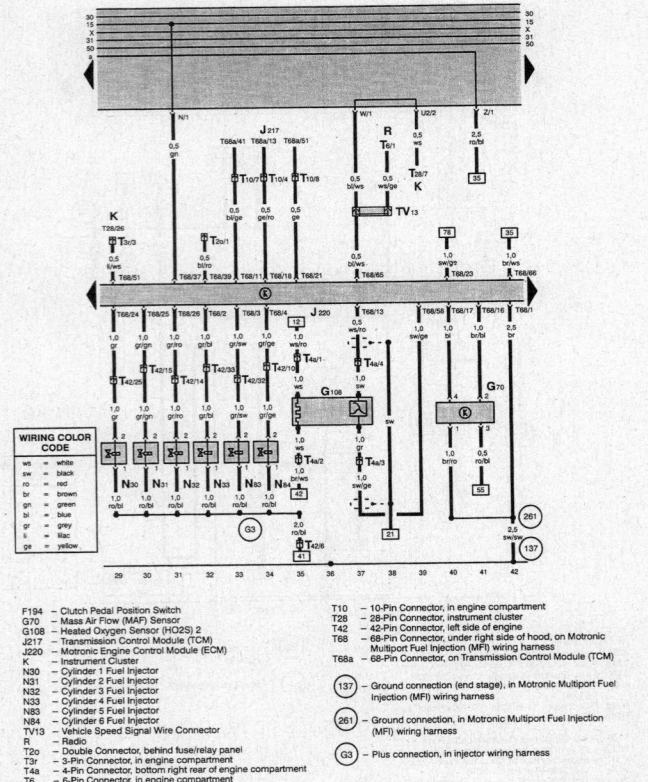

Fig. 20 Motronic wiring diagram (Part 2 of 5). 1998 GTI & Jetta w/2.8L engine

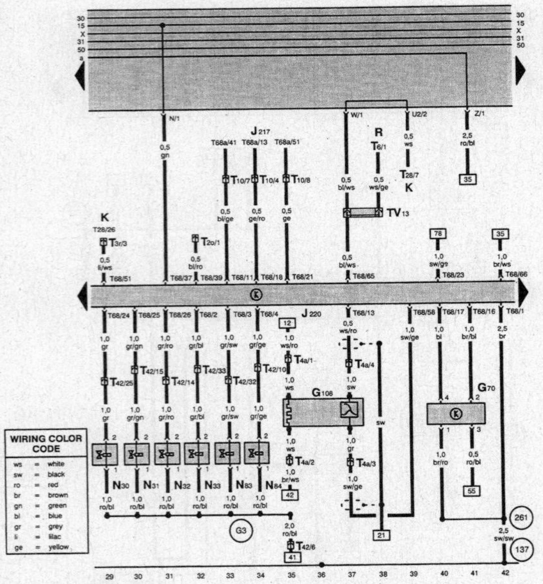

F194 – Clutch Pedal Position Switch
G70 – Mass Air Flow (MAF) Sensor
G108 – Heated Oxygen Sensor (HO2S) 2
J217 – Transmission Control Module (TCM)
J220 – Motronic Engine Control Module (ECM)
K – Instrument Cluster
N30 – Cylinder 1 Fuel Injector
N31 – Cylinder 2 Fuel Injector
N32 – Cylinder 3 Fuel Injector
N33 – Cylinder 4 Fuel Injector
N83 – Cylinder 5 Fuel Injector
N84 – Cylinder 6 Fuel Injector
TV13 – Vehicle Speed Signal Wire Connector
R – Radio
T2o – Double Connector, behind fuse/relay panel
T3r – 3-Pin Connector, in engine compartment
T4a – 4-Pin Connector, bottom right rear of engine compartment
T6 – 6-Pin Connector, in engine compartment
T10 – 10-Pin Connector, in engine compartment
T28 – 28-Pin Connector, instrument cluster
T42 – 42-Pin Connector, left side of engine
T68 – 68-Pin Connector, under right side of hood, on Motronic Multiport Fuel Injection (MFI) wiring harness
T68a – 68-Pin Connector, on Transmission Control Module (TCM)

(137) – Ground connection (end stage), in Motronic Multiport Fuel Injection (MFI) wiring harness
(261) – Ground connection, in Motronic Multiport Fuel Injection (MFI) wiring harness
(G3) – Plus connection, in injector wiring harness

VW1029900122030X

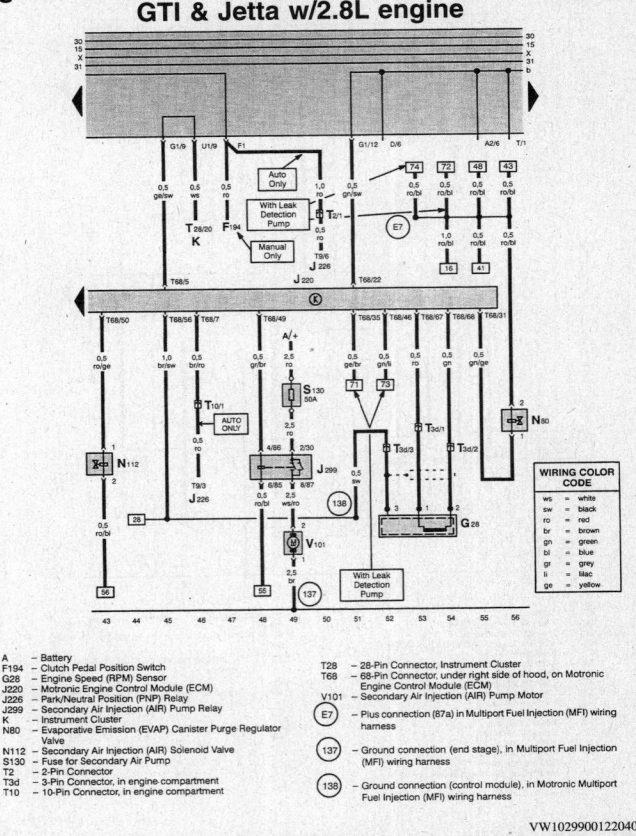

Fig. 20 Motronic wiring diagram (Part 3 of 5). 1998 GTI & Jetta w/2.8L engine

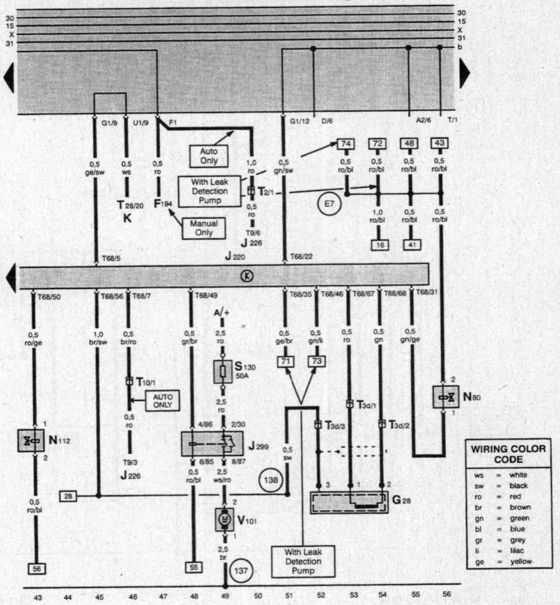

A – Battery
F194 – Clutch Pedal Position Switch
G28 – Engine Speed (RPM) Sensor
J220 – Motronic Engine Control Module (ECM)
J226 – Park/Neutral Position (PNP) Relay
J299 – Secondary Air Injection (AIR) Pump Relay
K – Instrument Cluster
N80 – Evaporative Emission (EVAP) Canister Purge Regulator Valve
N112 – Secondary Air Injection (AIR) Solenoid Valve
S130 – Fuse for Secondary Air Pump
T2 – 2-Pin Connector
T3d – 3-Pin Connector, in engine compartment
T10 – 10-Pin Connector, in engine compartment
T28 – 28-Pin Connector, Instrument Cluster
T68 – 68-Pin Connector, under right side of hood, on Motronic Engine Control Module (ECM)
V101 – Secondary Air Injection (AIR) Pump Motor

(E7) – Plus connection (87a) in Multiport Fuel Injection (MFI) wiring harness
(137) – Ground connection (end stage), in Multiport Fuel Injection (MFI) wiring harness
(138) – Ground connection (control module), in Motronic Multiport Fuel Injection (MFI) wiring harness

VW1029900122040X

Fig. 20 Motronic wiring diagram (Part 4 of 5). 1998 GTI & Jetta w/2.8L engine

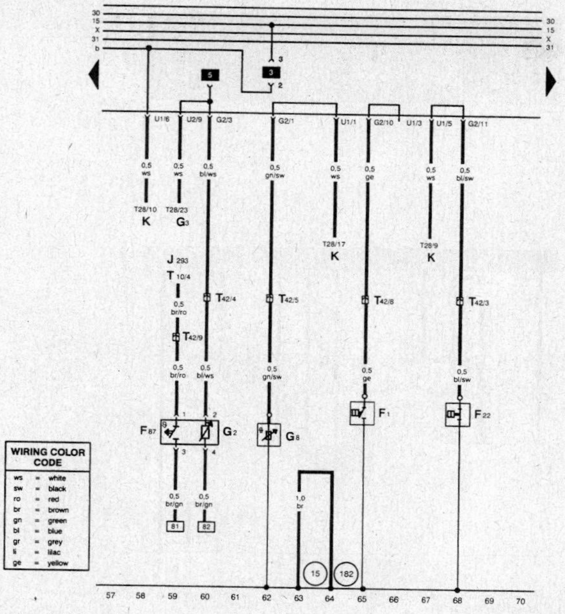

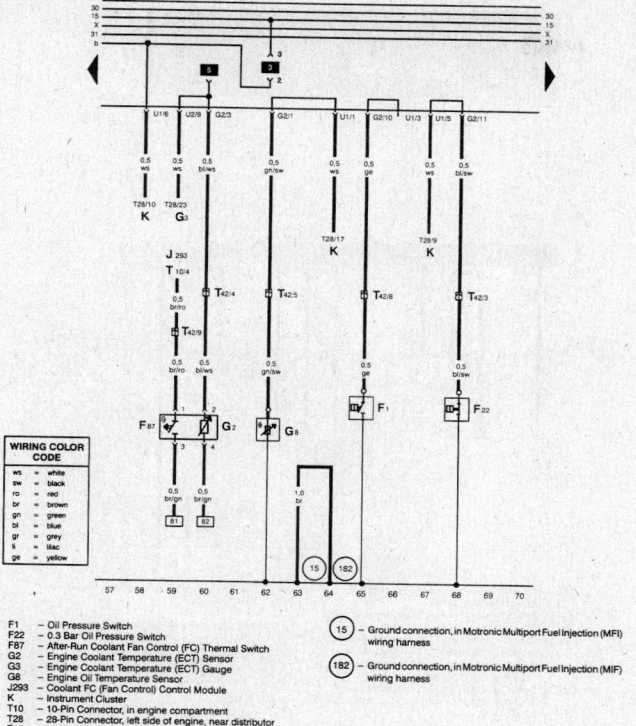

F1 – Oil Pressure Switch
F22 – 0.3 Bar Oil Pressure Switch
F87 – After-Run Coolant Fan Control (FC) Thermal Switch
G2 – Engine Coolant Temperature (ECT) Sensor
G3 – Engine Coolant Temperature (ECT) Gauge
G8 – Engine Oil Temperature Sensor
J293 – Coolant FC (Fan Control) Control Module
K – Instrument Cluster
T10 – 10-Pin Connector, in engine compartment
T28 – 28-Pin Connector, left side of engine, near distributor
T42 – 42-Pin Connector, left side of engine

(15) – Ground connection, in Motronic Multiport Fuel Injection (MFI) wiring harness
(182) – Ground connection, in Motronic Multiport Fuel Injection (MIF) wiring harness

VW1029900122050X

Fig. 20 Motronic wiring diagram (Part 5 of 5). 1998 GTI & Jetta w/2.8L engine

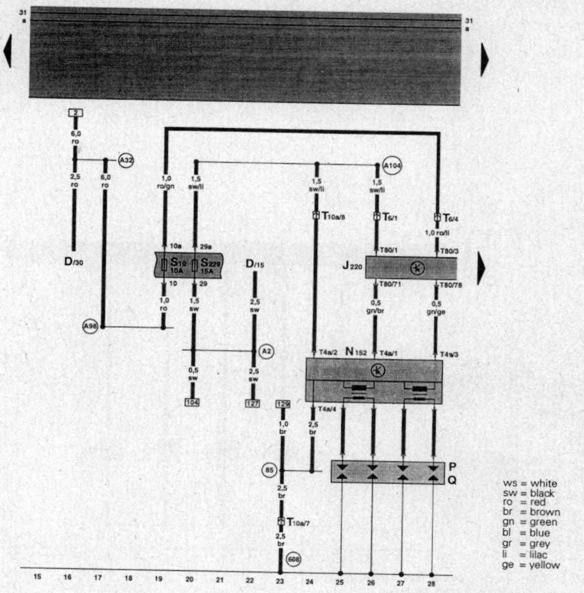

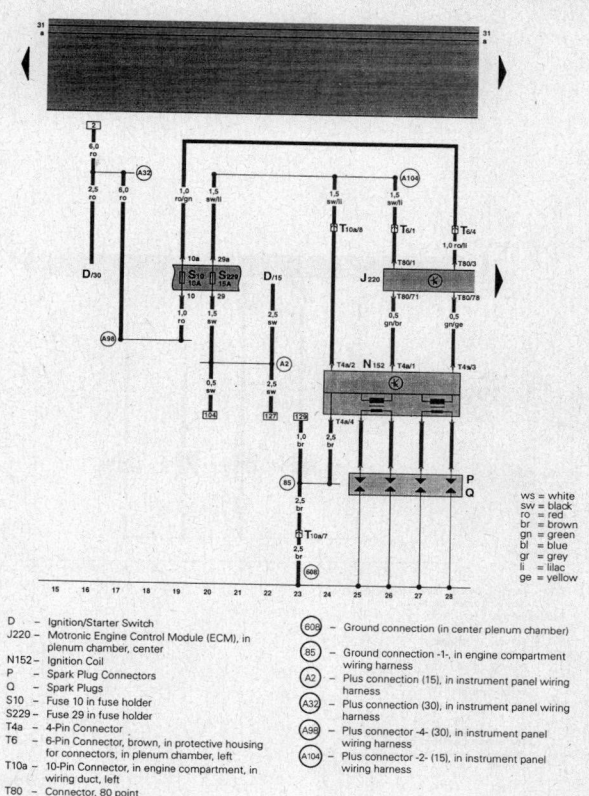

D – Ignition/Starter Switch
J220 – Motronic Engine Control Module (ECM), in plenum chamber, center
N152 – Ignition Coil
P – Spark Plug Connectors
Q – Spark Plugs
S10 – Fuse 10 in fuse holder
S229 – Fuse 29 in fuse holder
T4a – 4-Pin Connector
T6 – 6-Pin Connector, brown, in protective housing for connectors, in plenum chamber, left
T10a – 10-Pin Connector, in engine compartment, in wiring duct, left
T80 – Connector, 80 point

(606) – Ground connection (in center plenum chamber)
(85) – Ground connection -1-, in engine compartment wiring harness
(A2) – Plus connection (15), in instrument panel wiring harness
(A32) – Plus connection (30), in instrument panel wiring harness
(A98) – Plus connector -4- (30), in instrument panel wiring harness
(A104) – Plus connector -2- (15), in instrument panel wiring harness

VW1029900131010X

Fig. 21 Motronic wiring diagram (Ignition system). 1999–2001 Golf, GTI & Jetta w/2.0L engine

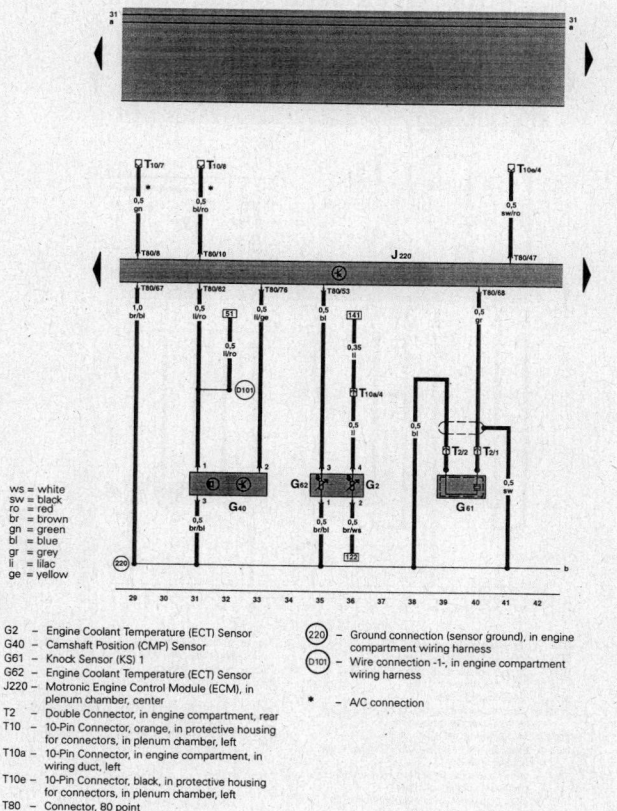

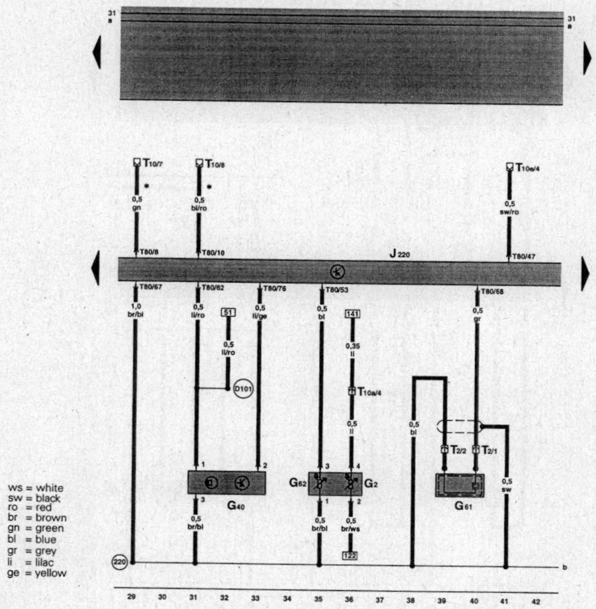

G2 – Engine Coolant Temperature (ECT) Sensor
G40 – Camshaft Position (CMP) Sensor
G61 – Knock Sensor (KS) 1
G62 – Engine Coolant Temperature (ECT) Sensor
J220 – Motronic Engine Control Module (ECM), in plenum chamber, center
T2 – Double Connector, in engine compartment, rear
T10 – 10-Pin Connector, orange, in protective housing for connectors, in plenum chamber, left
T10a – 10-Pin Connector, in engine compartment, in wiring duct, left
T10e – 10-Pin Connector, black, in protective housing for connectors, in plenum chamber, left
T80 – Connector, 80 point

(220) – Ground connection (sensor ground), in engine compartment wiring harness
(D101) – Wire connection -1-, in engine compartment wiring harness
* – A/C connection

VW1029900131020X

Fig. 22 Motronic wiring diagram (CMP & ECT sensor & KS 1). 1999–2001 Golf, GTI & Jetta w/2.0L engine

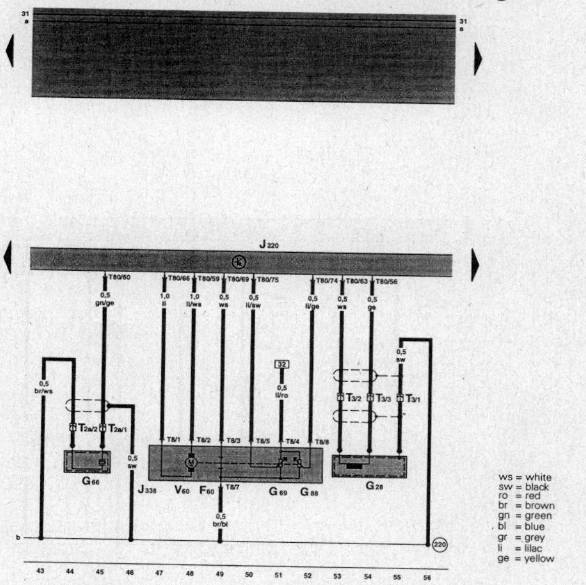

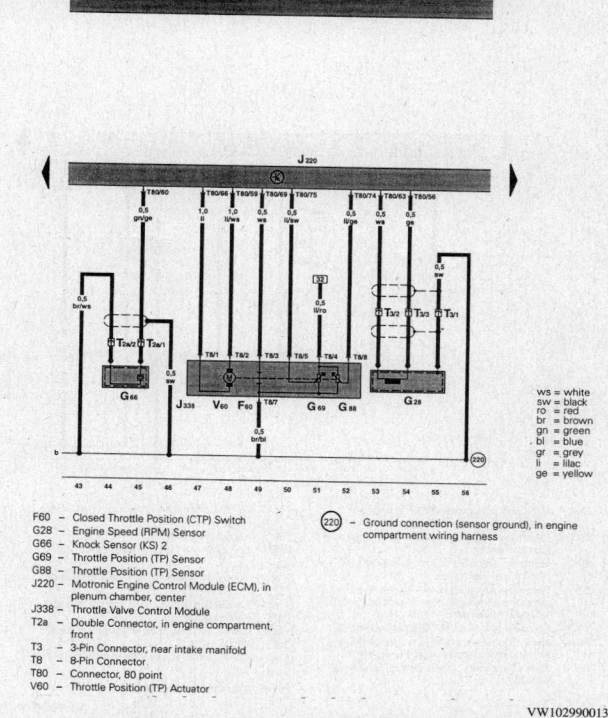

F60 – Closed Throttle Position (CTP) Switch
G28 – Engine Speed (RPM) Sensor
G66 – Knock Sensor (KS) 2
G69 – Throttle Position (TP) Sensor
G88 – Throttle Position (TP) Sensor
J220 – Motronic Engine Control Module (ECM), in plenum chamber, center
J338 – Throttle Valve Control Module
T2a – Double Connector, in engine compartment, front
T3 – 3-Pin Connector, near intake manifold
T8 – 8-Pin Connector
T80 – Connector, 80 point
V60 – Throttle Position (TP) Actuator

(220) – Ground connection (sensor ground), in engine compartment wiring harness

VW1029900131030X

Fig. 23 Motronic wiring diagram (Throttle valve control module, KS 2 & RPM sensor). 1999–2001 Golf, GTI & Jetta w/2.0L engine

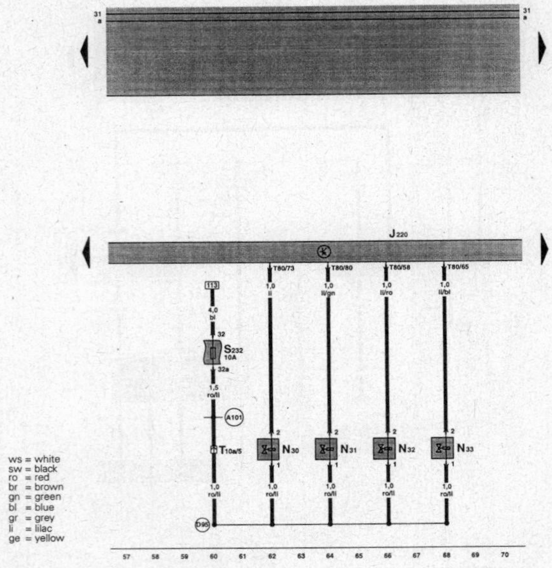

J220 – Motronic Engine Control Module (ECM), in plenum chamber, center
N30 – Cylinder 1 Fuel Injector
N31 – Cylinder 2 Fuel Injector
N32 – Cylinder 3 Fuel Injector
N33 – Cylinder 4 Fuel Injector
S232 – Fuse 32 in fuse holder
T10a – 10-Pin Connector, in engine compartment, in wiring duct, left
T80 – Connector, 80 point

D95 – Wire connection (injectors), in engine compartment wiring harness
A101 – Connector -3- (87a), in instrument panel wiring harness

VW1029900131040X

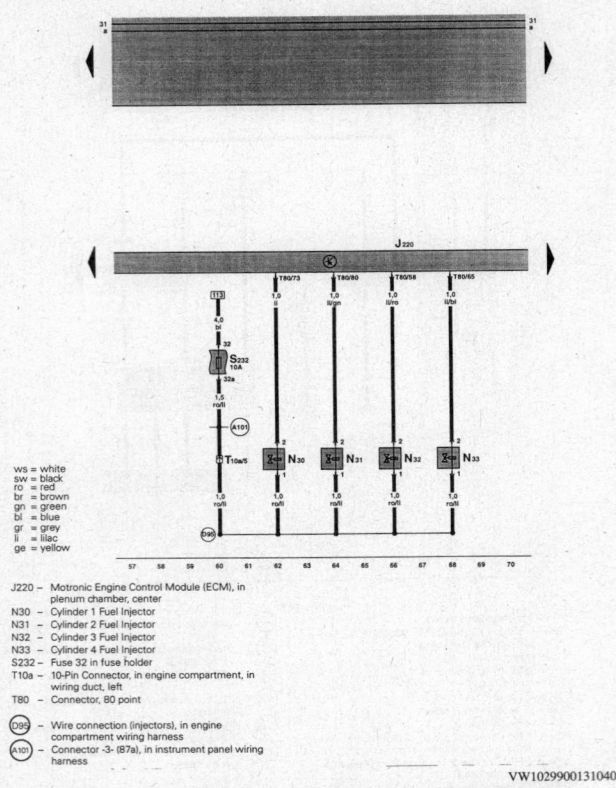

Fig. 24 Motronic wiring diagram (Injectors). 1999–2001 Golf, GTI & Jetta w/2.0L engine

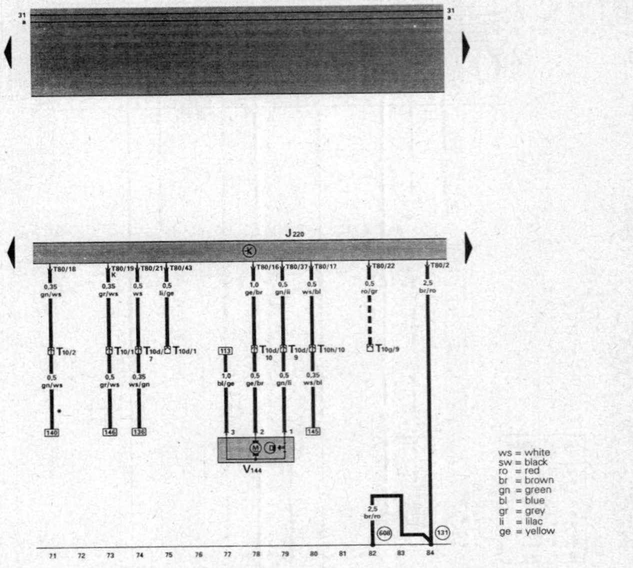

J220 – Motronic Engine Control Module (ECM), in plenum chamber, center
T10 – 10-Pin Connector, orange, in protective housing for connectors, in plenum chamber, left
T10d – 10-Pin Connector, green, in protective housing for connectors, in plenum chamber, left
T10h – 10-Pin Connector, blue, in protective housing for connectors, in plenum chamber, left
T10g – 10-Pin Connector, grey, in protective housing for connectors, in plenum chamber, left
T80 – Connector, 80 point
V144 – Leak detection pump (LDP)

608 – Ground Connection (in center plenum chamber)

131 – Ground connection -2-, in engine compartment wiring harness

* – Vehicles with Multi-Function Indicator (MFI) only

--- Automatic transmission only

VW1029900131050X

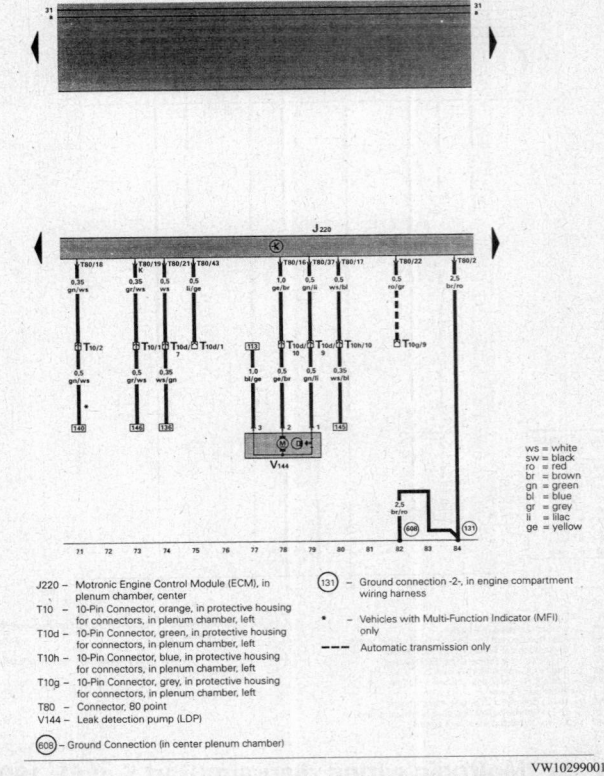

Fig. 25 Motronic wiring diagram (LDP). 1999–2001 Golf, GTI & Jetta w/2.0L engine

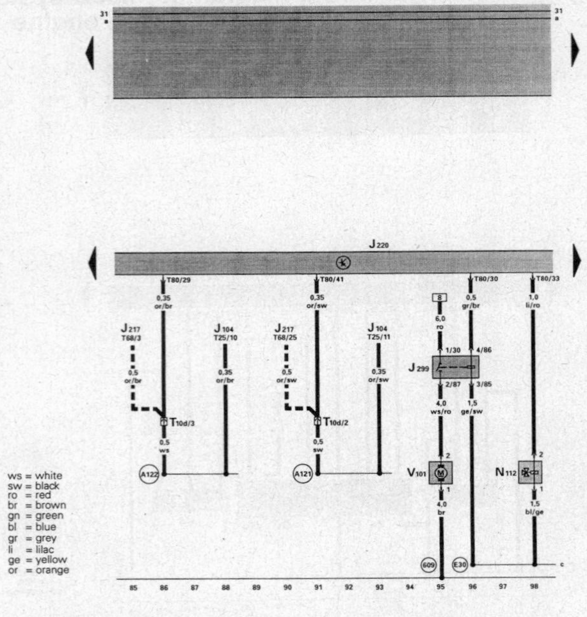

J104 – ABS Control Module (w/EDL), in engine compartment, left
J217 – Transmission Control Module (TCM), in plenum chamber, center
J220 – Motronic Engine Control Module (ECM), in plenum chamber, center
J299 – Secondary Air Injection (AIR) Pump Relay, in protective housing, in engine compartment, left, production control number (100)
N112 – Secondary Air Injection (AIR) Solenoid Valve
T10d – 10-Pin Connector, green, in protective housing for connectors, in plenum chamber, left
T25 – 25-Pin Connector, on ABS Control Module (w/EDL)
T68 – 68-Pin Connector, on Transmission Control Module (TCM)
T80 – Connector, 80 point
V101 – Secondary Air Injection (AIR) Pump Motor

609 – Ground Connection (in right plenum chamber)

A121 – Connection (high bus), in instrument panel wiring harness
A122 – Connection (low bus), in instrument panel wiring harness
E30 – Connector (87a), in wiring harness engine

--- Automatic transmission only

VW1029900131060X

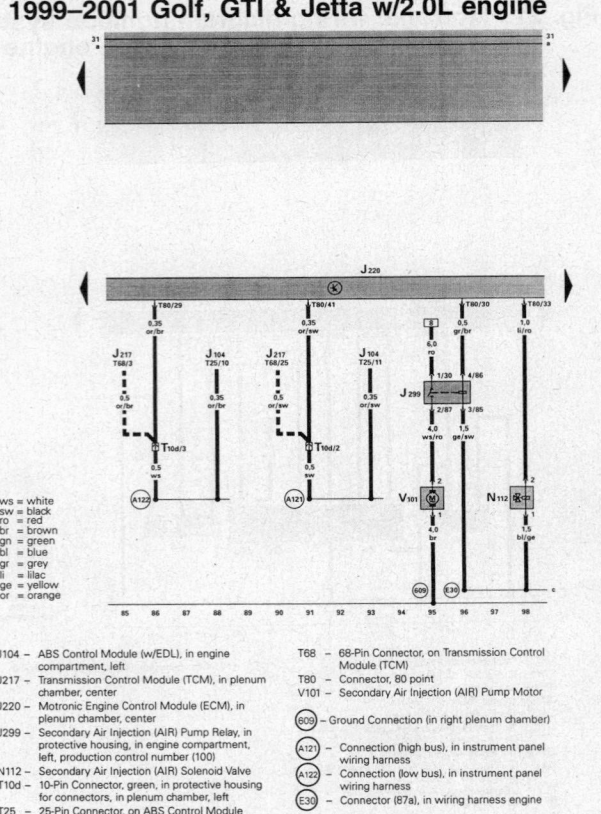

Fig. 26 Motronic wiring diagram (AIR pump motor & solenoid valve). 1999–2001 Golf, GTI & Jetta w/2.0L engine

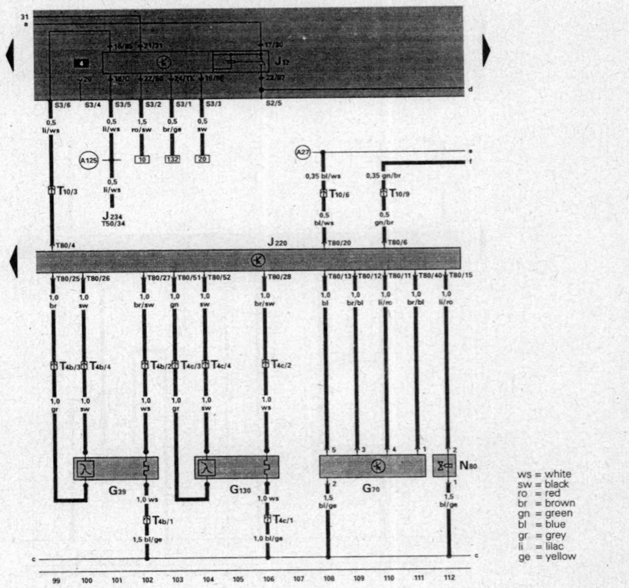

G39 – Heated Oxygen Sensor (HO2S)
G70 – Mass Air Flow (MAF) Sensor
G130 – Oxygen Sensor (O2S) behind Three Way Catalytic Converter (TWC)
J17 – Fuel Pump (FP) Relay
J220 – Motronic Engine Control Module (ECM), in plenum chamber, center
J234 – Airbag Control Module
N80 – Evaporative Emission (EVAP) Canister Purge Regulator Valve
T4b – 4-Pin Connector, in protective housing for connectors under right floor
T4c – 4-Pin Connector, in protective housing for connectors under right floor
T10 – 10-Pin Connector, orange, in protective housing for connectors, in plenum chamber, left
T50 – 50-Pin Connector
T80 – Connector, 80 point

A125 – Connection (crash signal) in instrument panel wiring harness
A27 – Wire Connection (vehicle speed signal), in instrument panel wiring harness

VW1029900131070X

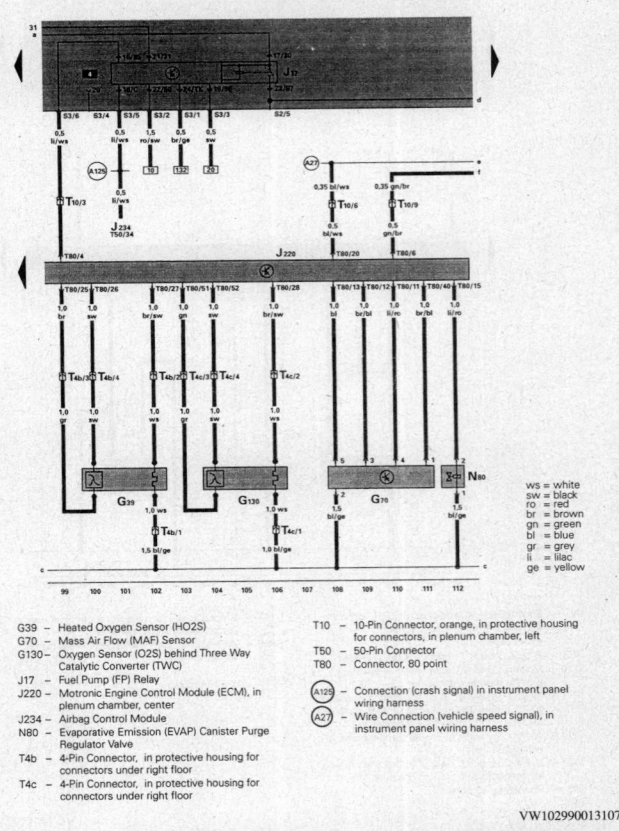

Fig. 27 Motronic wiring diagram (MAF sensor, HO2S & EVAP canister purge regulator valve). 1999–2001 Golf, GTI & Jetta w/2.0L engine

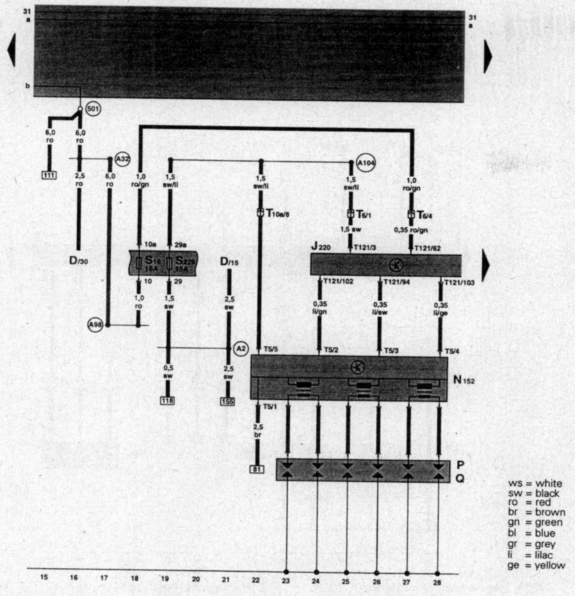

D – Ignition/Starter Switch
J220 – Motronic Engine Control Module (ECM), in plenum chamber, center
N152 – Ignition Coil
P – Spark Plug Connectors
Q – Spark Plugs
S10 – Fuse 10 in fuse holder
S229 – Fuse 29 in fuse holder
T5 – 5-Pin Connector
T6 – 6-Pin Connector, brown, in protective housing for connectors, in plenum chamber, left
T10a – 10-Pin Connector, in engine compartment, in wiring duct, left
T121 – Connector, 121 point

(501) – Threaded connection -2- (30) on the relay plate
(A2) – Plus connection (15), in instrument panel wiring harness
(A32) – Plus connection (30), in instrument panel wiring harness
(A98) – Plus connector -4- (30), in instrument panel wiring harness
(A104) – Plus connector -2- (15), in instrument panel wiring harness

VW1029900132010X

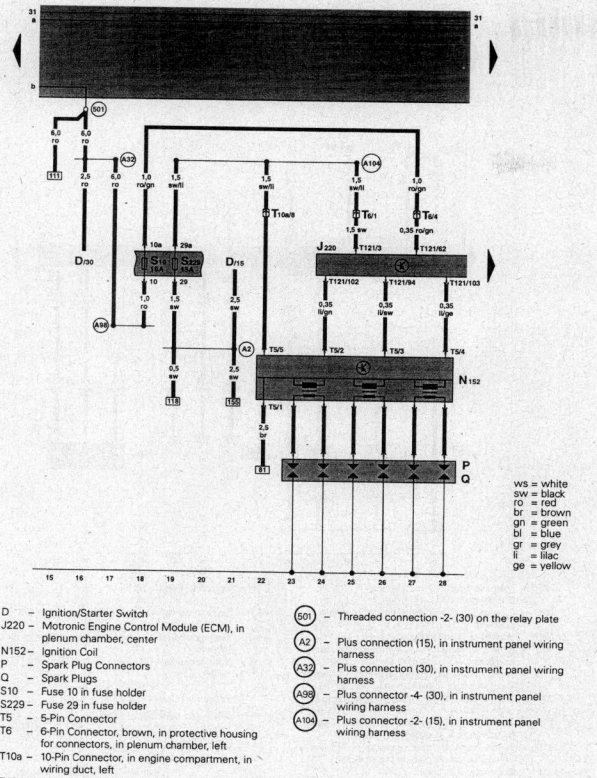

Fig. 28 Motronic wiring diagram (Ignition system). 1999–2001 GTI & Jetta w/2.8L engine

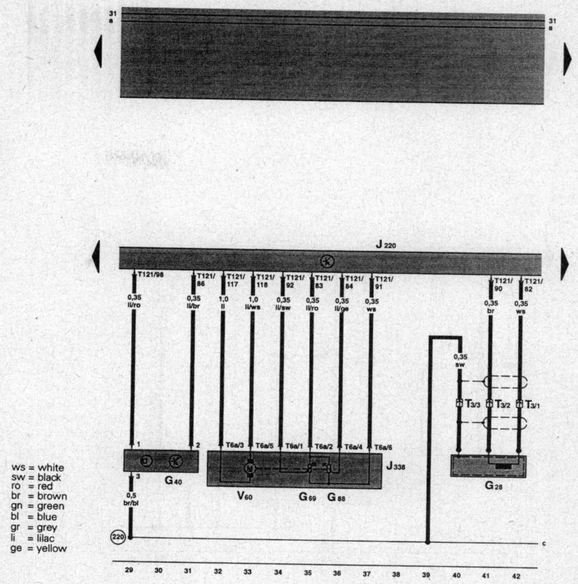

G28 – Engine Speed (RPM) Sensor
G40 – Camshaft Position (CMP) Sensor
G69 – Throttle Position (TP) Sensor
G88 – Throttle Position (TP) Sensor
J220 – Motronic Engine Control Module (ECM), in plenum chamber, center
J338 – Throttle Valve Control Module
T3 – 3-Pin Connector, near intake manifold
T6a – 6-Pin Connector
T121 – Connector, 121 point
V60 – Throttle Position (TP) Actuator

(220) – Ground connection (sensor ground), in engine compartment wiring harness

VW1029900132020X

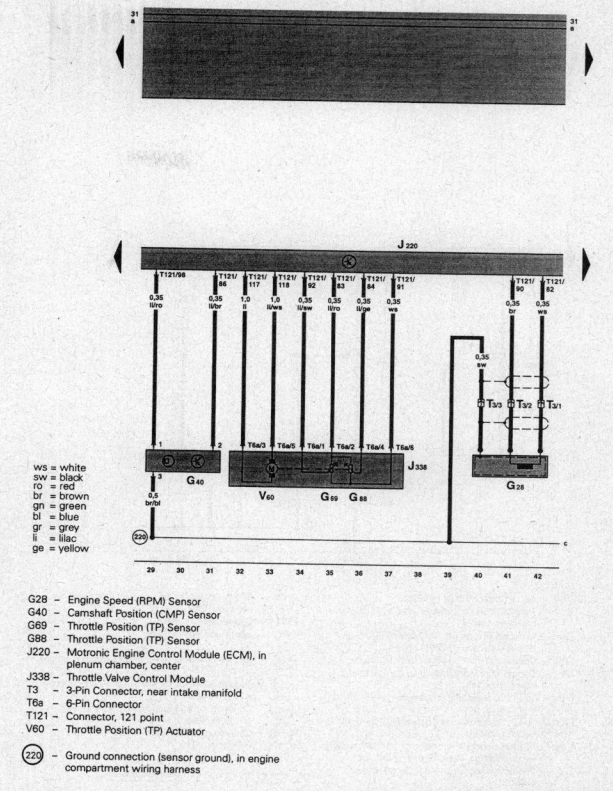

Fig. 29 Motronic wiring diagram (Throttle valve control module, RPM sensor & CMP sensor). 1999–2001 GTI & Jetta w/2.8L engine

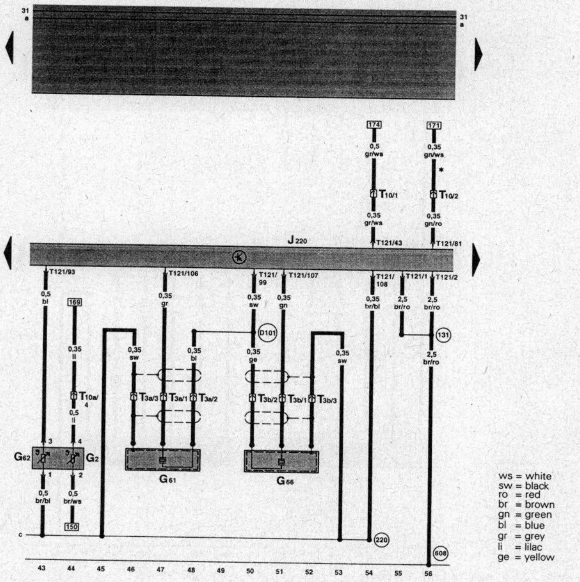

G2 – Engine Coolant Temperature (ECT) Sensor
G61 – Knock Sensor (KS) 1
G62 – Engine Coolant Temperature (ECT) Sensor
G66 – Knock Sensor (KS) 2
J220 – Motronic Engine Control Module (ECM), in plenum chamber, center
T3a – 3-Pin Connector, in engine compartment, rear
T3b – 3-Pin Connector, in engine compartment, front
T10 – 10-Pin Connector, orange, in protective housing for connectors, in plenum chamber, left
T10a – 10-Pin Connector, in engine compartment, in wiring duct, left
T121 – Connector, 121 point

(608) – Ground connection (in center plenum chamber)

(220) – Ground connection (sensor ground), in engine compartment wiring harness
(131) – Ground connection -2-, in engine compartment wiring harness
(D101) – Wire connection -1-, in engine compartment wiring harness

* – Vehicles with Multi-Function Indicator (MFI) only

VW1029900132030X

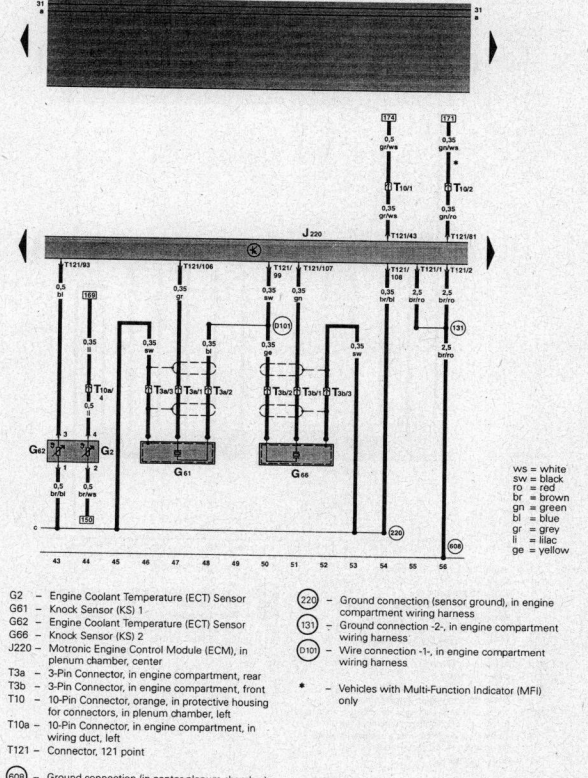

Fig. 30 Motronic wiring diagram (KS 1, KS 2 & ECT sensor). 1999–2001 GTI & Jetta w/2.8L engine

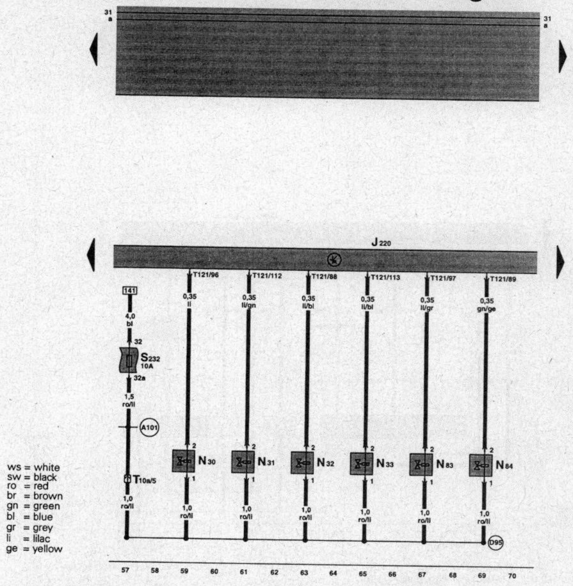

J220 – Motronic Engine Control Module (ECM), in plenum chamber, center
N30 – Cylinder 1 Fuel Injector
N31 – Cylinder 2 Fuel Injector
N32 – Cylinder 3 Fuel Injector
N33 – Cylinder 4 Fuel Injector
N83 – Cylinder 5 Fuel Injector
N84 – Cylinder 6 Fuel Injector
S232 – Fuse 32 in fuse holder
T10a – 10-Pin Connector, in engine compartment, in wiring duct, left
T121 – Connector, 121 point

(A101) – Connector -3- (87a), in instrument panel wiring harness

(D95) – Wire connection (injectors), in engine compartment wiring harness

VW1029900132040X

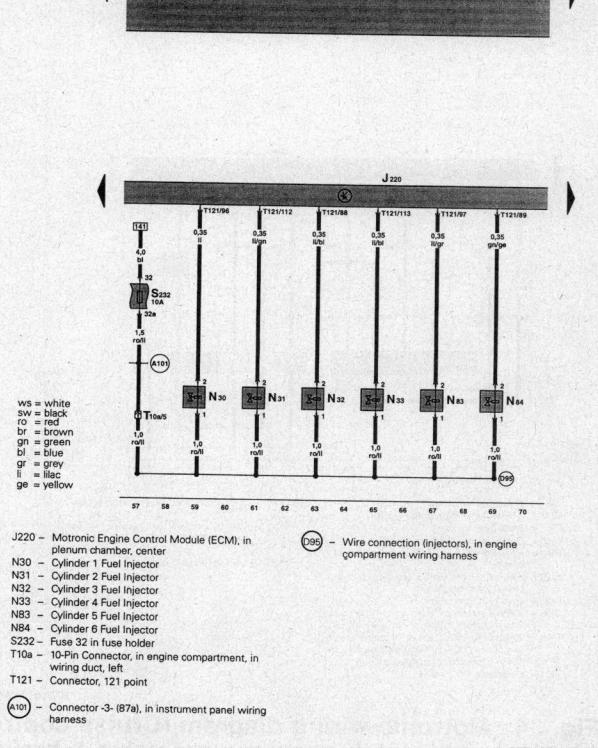

Fig. 31 Motronic wiring diagram (Injectors). 1999–2001 GTI & Jetta w/2.8L engine

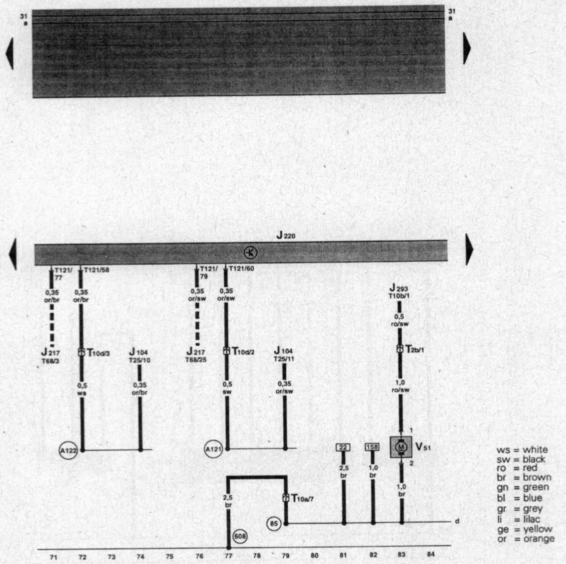

J104 – ABS Control Module (w/EDL)
J217 – Transmission Control Module (TCM), in plenum chamber, center
J220 – Motronic Engine Control Module (ECM), in plenum chamber, center
J293 – Coolant FC (Fan Control) Control Module
T2b – Double Connector, in engine compartment, in wiring duct, left
T10a – 10-Pin Connector, in engine compartment, in wiring duct, left
T10b – 10-Pin Connector, on Coolant FC (Fan Control) Control Module
T10d – 10-Pin Connector, green, in protective housing for connectors, in plenum chamber, left
T25 – 25-Pin Connector, on ABS Control Module (w/EDL)
T68 – 68-Pin Connector, on Transmission Control Module (TCM)
T121 – Connector, 121 point
V51 – After-Run Coolant Pump
(608) – Ground connection (in center plenum chamber)
(85) – Ground connection -1-, in engine compartment wiring harness
(A121) – Connection (high bus), in instrument panel wiring harness
(A122) – Connection (low bus), in instrument panel wiring harness
– – – Automatic transmission only

VW1029900132050X

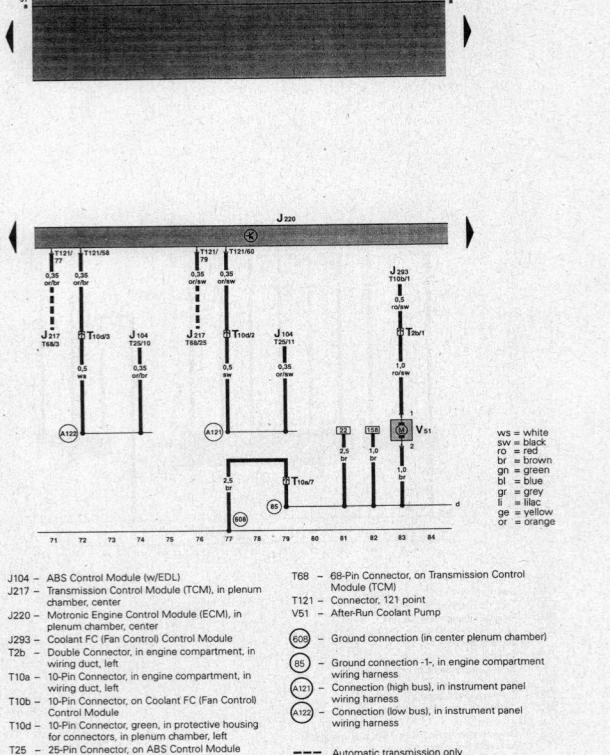

Fig. 32 Motronic wiring diagram (After-run coolant pump). 1999–2001 GTI & Jetta w/2.8L engine

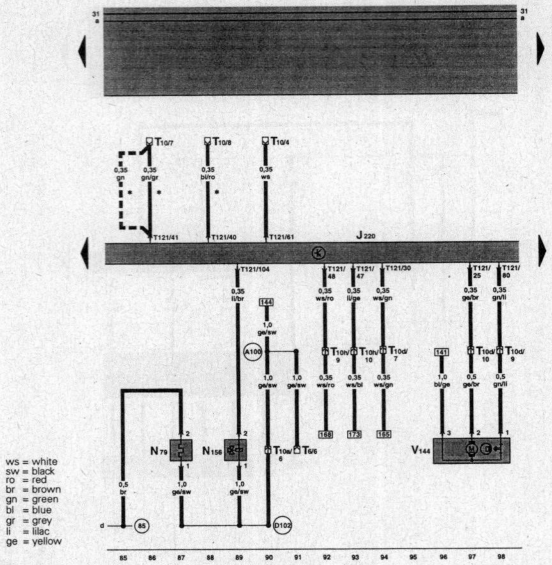

J220 – Motronic Engine Control Module (ECM), in plenum chamber, center
N79 – Positive Crankcase Ventilation (PCV) Heating Element
N156 – Intake Manifold Change-Over Valve
T6 – 6-Pin Connector, brown, in protective housing for connectors, in plenum chamber, left
T10 – 10-Pin Connector, orange, in protective housing for connectors, in plenum chamber, left
T10a – 10-Pin Connector, in engine compartment, in wiring duct, left
T10d – 10-Pin Connector, green, in protective housing for connectors, in plenum chamber, left
T10h – 10-Pin Connector, blue, in protective housing for connectors, in plenum chamber, left
T121 – Connector, 121 point
V144 – Leak detection pump (LDP)
(85) – Ground connection -1-, in engine compartment wiring harness
(A100) – Connector -2- (87), in instrument panel wiring harness
(D102) – Wire connection -2-, in engine compartment wiring harness
* – A/C connection
– – – Automatic transmission only

VW1029900132060X

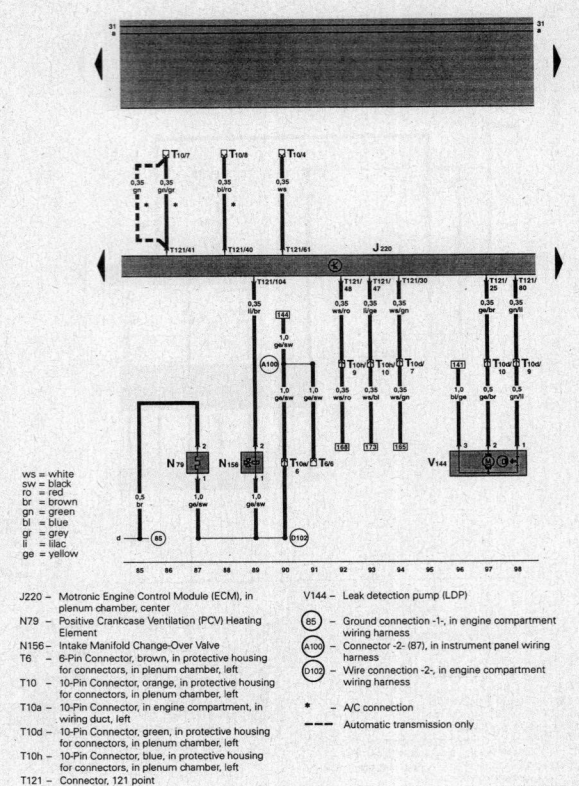

Fig. 33 Motronic wiring diagram (LDP, intake manifold change-over valve & PCV heating element). 1999–2001 GTI & Jetta w/2.8L engine

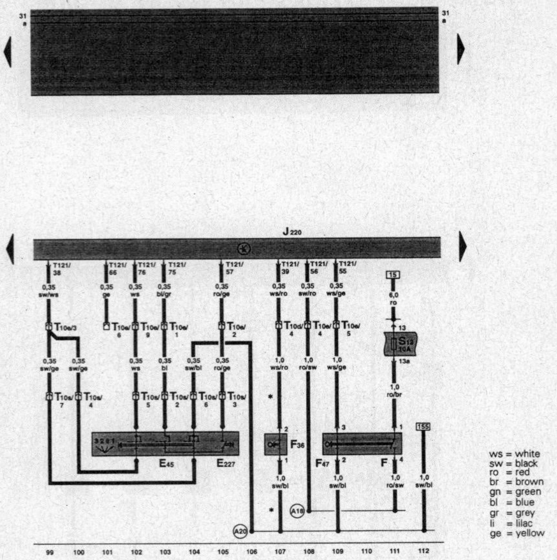

E45 – Cruise Control Switch
E227 – Cruise Control Push Button (SET)
F – Brake Light Switch
F36 – Clutch Vacuum Vent Valve Switch
F47 – Brake Vacuum Vent Valve Switch for cruise control
J220 – Motronic Engine Control Module (ECM), in plenum chamber, center
S13 – Fuse 13 in fuse holder
T10d – 10-Pin Connector, green, in protective housing for connectors, in plenum chamber, left
T10e – 10-Pin Connector, black, in protective housing for connectors, in plenum chamber, left
T10s – 10-Pin Connector, near steering column
T121 – Connector, 121 point
(A18) – Wire connection (54), in instrument panel
(A20) – Wire connection (15a), in instrument panel wiring harness
* – Manual transmission only

VW1029900132070X

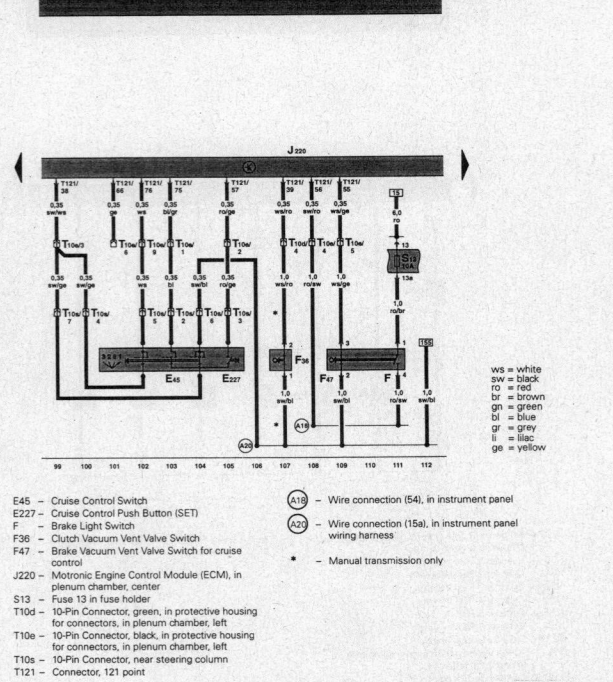

Fig. 34 Motronic wiring diagram (Cruise control, brake lamp, clutch vacuum vent valve & brake vacuum vent valve switches). 1999–2001 GTI & Jetta w/2.8L engine

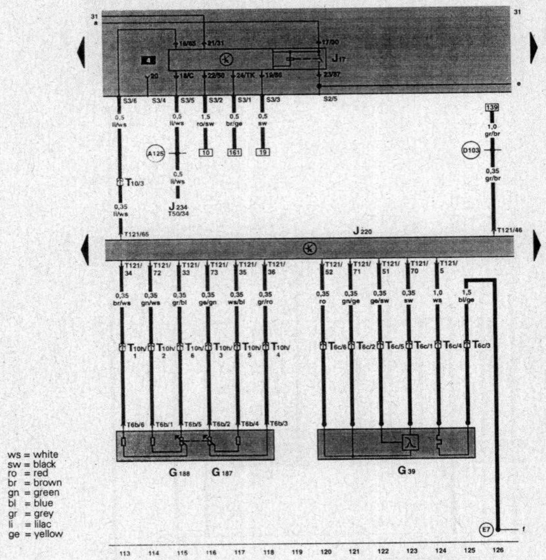

G39 – Heated Oxygen Sensor (HO2S)
G187 – Angle sensor -1- for throttle drive (power accelerator actuation)
G188 – Angle sensor -2- for throttle drive (power accelerator actuation)
J17 – Fuel Pump (FP) Relay
J220 – Motronic Engine Control Module (ECM), in plenum chamber, center
J234 – Airbag Control Module
T6b – 6-Pin Connector
T6c – 6-Pin Connector, in protective housing for connectors, in engine compartment, rear
T10 – 10-Pin Connector, orange, in protective housing for connectors, in plenum chamber, left
T10h – 10-Pin Connector, blue, in protective housing for connectors, in plenum chamber, left
T50 – 50-Pin Connector
T121 – Connector, 121 point
(A125) – Connection (crash signal) in instrument panel wiring harness
(D103) – Wire connection -3-, in engine compartment wiring harness
(E7) – Plus connection (87a), in Motronic Multiport Fuel Injection (MFI) wiring harness

VW1029900132080X

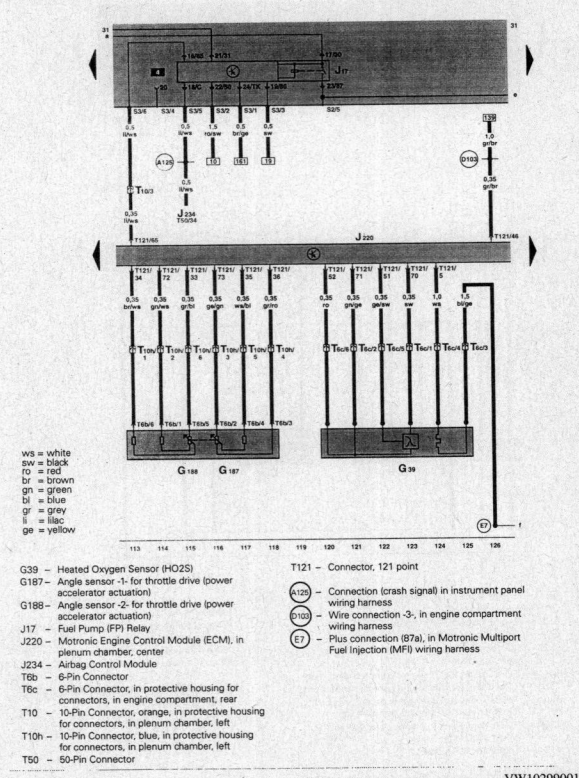

Fig. 35 Motronic wiring diagram (Throttle drive angle sensors & HO2S). 1999–2001 GTI & Jetta w/2.8L engine

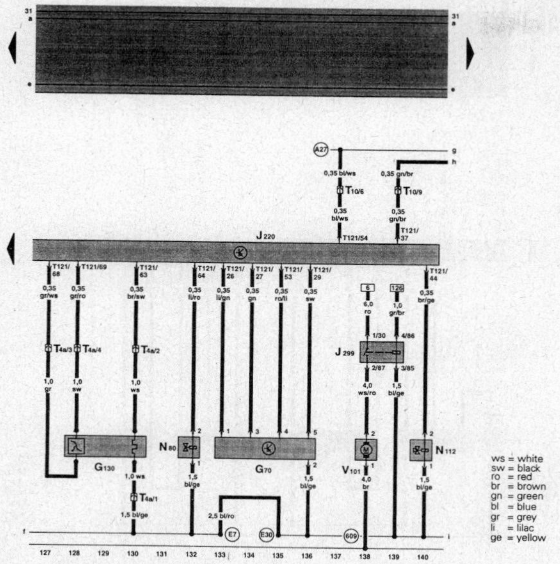

G70 – Mass Air Flow (MAF) Sensor
G130 – Oxygen Sensor (O2S) behind Three Way Catalytic Converter (TWC)
J220 – Motronic Engine Control Module (ECM), in plenum chamber, center
J299 – Secondary Air Injection (AIR) Pump Relay, in protective housing, in engine compartment, left, production control number (100)
N80 – Evaporative Emission (EVAP) Canister Purge Regulator Valve
N112 – Secondary Air Injection (AIR) Solenoid Valve
T4a – 4-Pin Connector, in protective housing for connectors, in engine compartment, rear
T10 – 10-Pin Connector, orange, in protective housing for connectors, in plenum chamber, left
T121 – Connector, 121 point
V101 – Secondary Air Injection (AIR) Pump Motor
(609) – Ground connection (in right plenum chamber)
(A27) – Wire Connection (vehicle speed signal), in instrument panel wiring harness
(E7) – Plus connection (87a), in Motronic Multiport Fuel Injection (MFI) wiring harness
(E30) – Connector (87a), in wiring harness engine

VW1029900132090X

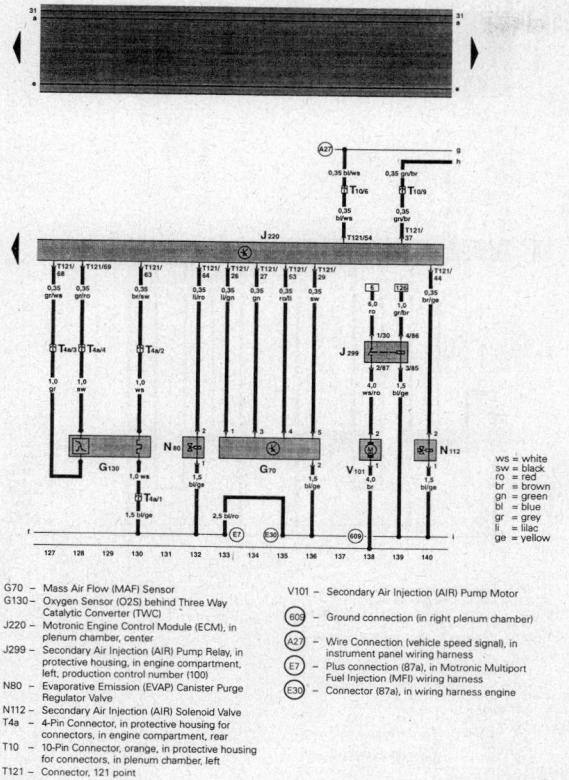

Fig. 36 Motronic wiring diagram (AIR pump system & O2S). 1999–2001 GTI & Jetta w/2.8L engine

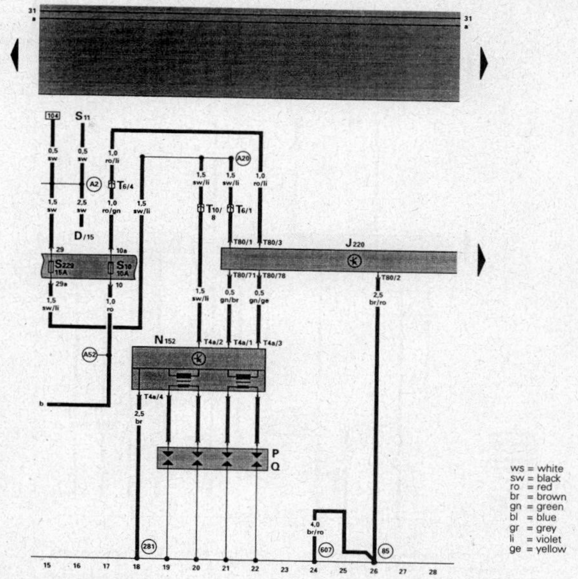

D – Ignition/Starter Switch
J220 – Motronic Engine Control Module (ECM), behind istrument panel, left
N152 – Ignition Coil
P – Spark Plug Connectors
Q – Spark Plugs
S10 – Fuse 10 in fuse holder
S11 – Fuse 11 in fuse holder
S229 – Fuse 29 in fuse holder
T4a – 4-Pin Connector, black
T6 – 6-Pin Connector, brown, behind instrument panel, left
T10 – 10-Pin Connector, in engine compartment, left
T80 – 80–Pin Connector, at Engine Control Module (ECM)
(85) – Ground connection -1-, in engine compartment wiring harness
(281) – Ground connector -1-, in wiring harness engine pre-wiring
(A2) – plus connection (15), in instrument panel wiring harness
(A20) – wite connection (15a), in instrument panel wiring harness
(A52) – plus connection (30), in instrument panel wiring harness
(607) – Ground Connection (in left plenum chamber)

VW1029800092020A

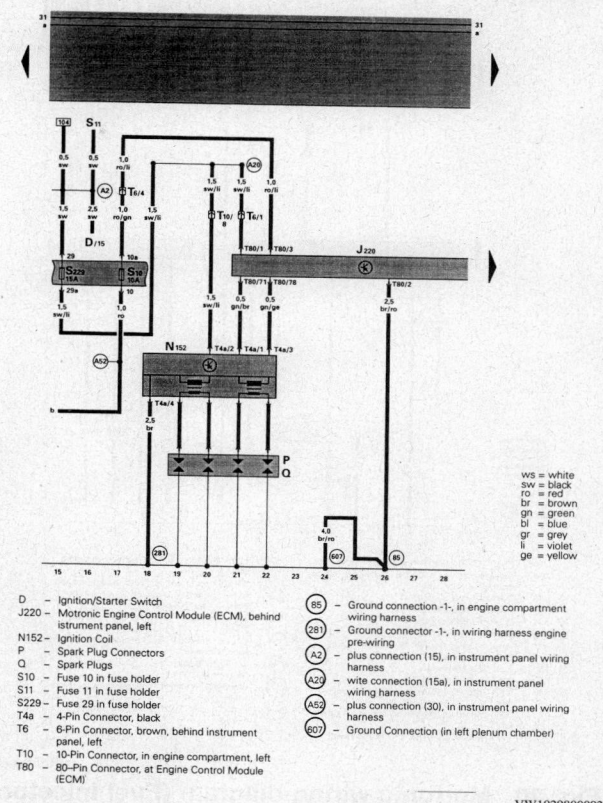

Fig. 37 Motronic wiring diagram (Ignition system) 1998 New Beetle w/2.0L engine

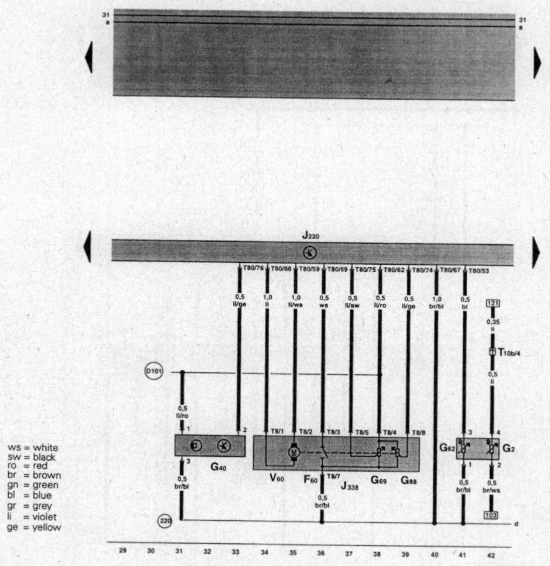

F60 – Closed Throttle Position (CTP) Switch
G2 – Engine Coolant Temperature (ECT) Sensor
G40 – Camshaft Position (CMP) Sensor
G62 – Engine Coolant Temperature (ECT) Sensor
G69 – Throttle Position (TP) Sensor
G88 – Throttle Position (TP) Sensor
J220 – Motronic Engine Control Module (ECM)
J338 – Throttle Valve Control Module
V60 – Throttle Position (TP) Actuator
T8 – 8-Pin Connector
T10b – 10-Pin Connector, behind instrument panel, left
T80 – Connector, 80-point, at Engine Control Module (ECM)
(220) – Ground connection (sensor ground), in engine compartment wiring harness
(D101) – Connection 1 (in engine compartment wiring harness)

VW1029800092030A

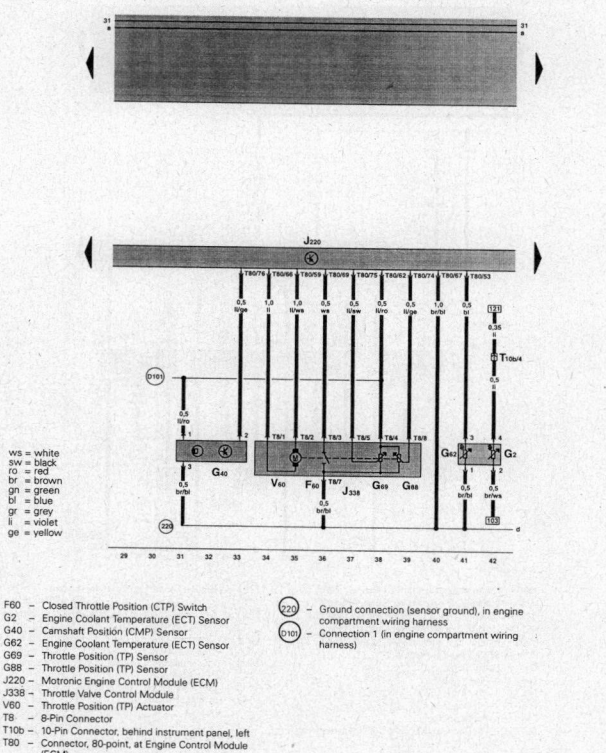

Fig. 38 Motronic wiring diagram (Throttle valve control module & CMP & ECT sensors) 1998 New Beetle w/2.0L engine

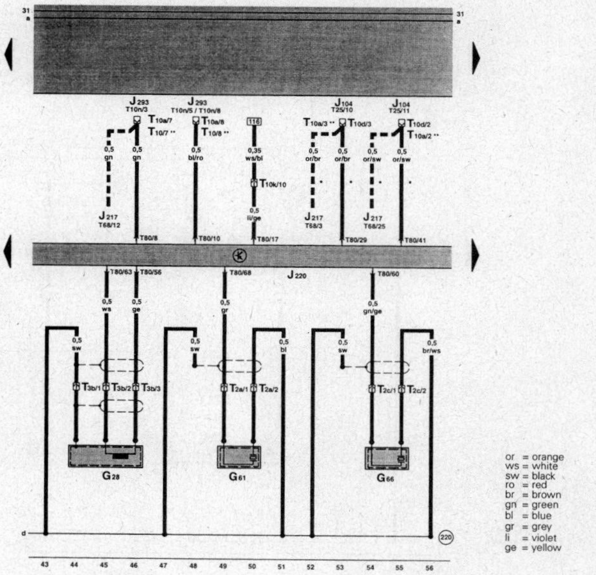

G28 – Engine Speed (RPM) Sensor
G61 – Knock Sensor (KS) 1
G66 – Knock Sensor (KS) 2
J104 – ABS Control Module (w/EDL)
J217 – Transmission Control Module (TCM), behind instrument panel
J220 – Motronic Engine Control Module (ECM), behind instrument panel, left
J255 – Climatronic Control Module
J293 – Coolant FC (Fan Control) Control Module
T2a – 3-Pin Connector
T3b – 3-Pin Connector
T2c – 3-Pin Connector
T6 – 6-Pin Connector, red, behind instrument panel
T10 – 10-Pin Connector, wihite, behind instrument panel, left
T10a – 10-Pin Connector, orange, behind instrument panel, left
T10d – 10-Pin Connector, green, behind instrument panel, left
T10k – 10-Pin Connector, blue, behind instrument panel, left
T25 – 25-Pin Connector, at J104
T68 – Connector, 68-point, on Transmisson Control Module (TCM)
T80 – Connector, 80-point, at Engine Control Module (ECM)
(220) – Ground connection (sensor ground), in engine compartment wiring harness
* – connection for DATA-bus
--- – automatic transmission only
** – early vehicles only

VW1029800092040A

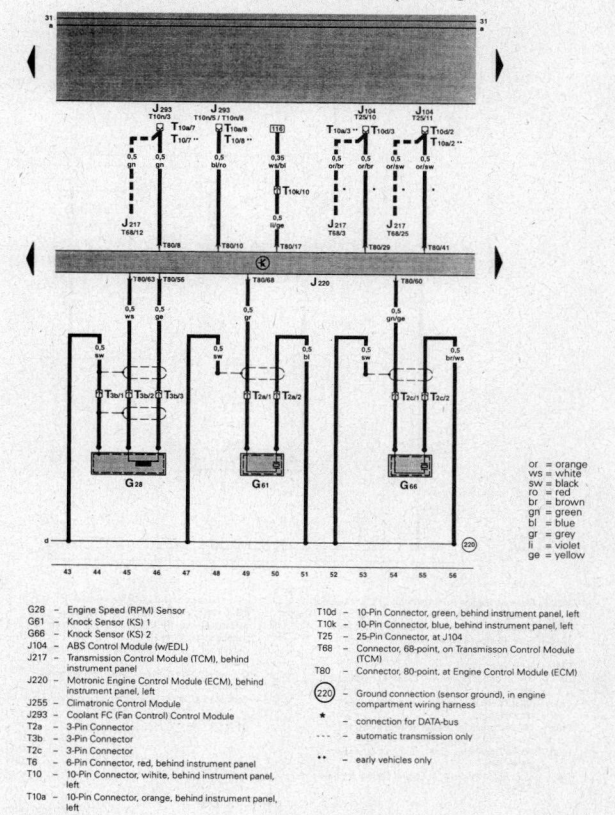

Fig. 39 Motronic wiring diagram (RPM sensor, KS 1 & KS 2) 1998 New Beetle w/2.0L engine

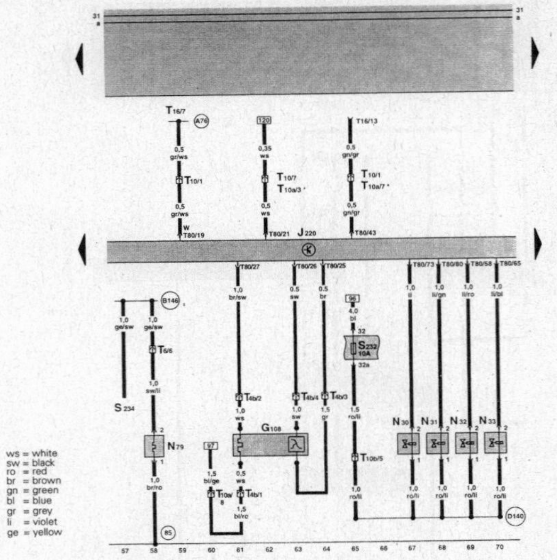

G108 – Heated Oxygen Sensor (HO2S) 2 brown
J220 – Motronic Engine Control Module (ECM), behind instrument panel, left
N30 – Cylinder 1 Fuel Injector
N31 – Cylinder 2 Fuel Injector
N32 – Cylinder 3 Fuel Injector
N33 – Cylinder 4 Fuel Injector
N79 – Positive Crankcase Ventilation (PCV) Heating Element
S232 – Fuse 32 in fuse holder
S234 – Fuse 34 in fuse holder
T4b – 4-Pin Connector, black, in engine compartment, left
T6 – 6-Pin Connector, red, behind instrument panel, left
T10 – 10-Pin Connector, white, behind instrument panel, left
T10a – 10-Pin Connector, orange, behind instrument panel, left
T10b – 10-Pin Connector, in engine compartment, left
T16 – 16-Pin Connector, Data Link Connector (DLC), below steering column
T80 – 80-Pin Connector, at Engine Control Module (ECM)
(85) – Ground connection -1-, in engine compartment wiring harness
(A76) – Connector (K-diagnosis wire), in instrument panel wiring harness
(D140) – Connector (injectors), in wiring harness, engine pre-wiring
(B146) – Plus connector -1- (87), in wiring harness interior
* – early vehicles only

VW1029800092050A

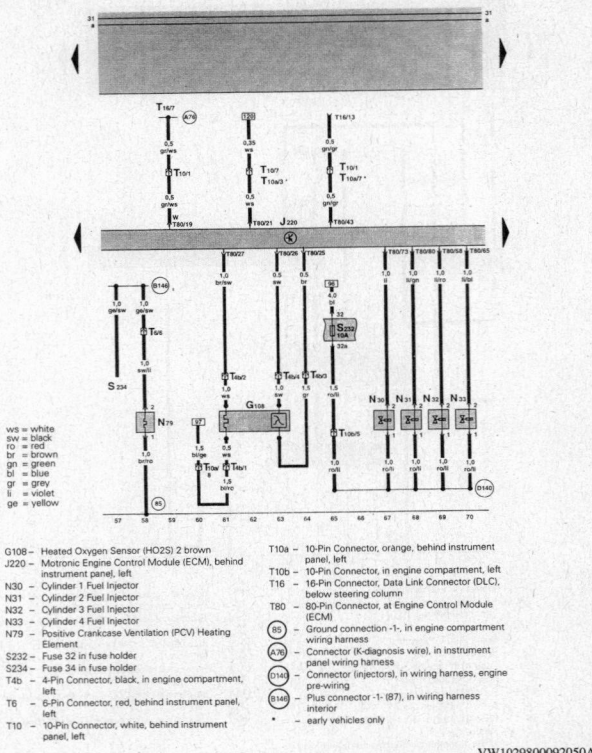

Fig. 40 Motronic wiring diagram (Fuel injectors HO2S & PCV heating element) 1998 New Beetle w/2.0L engine

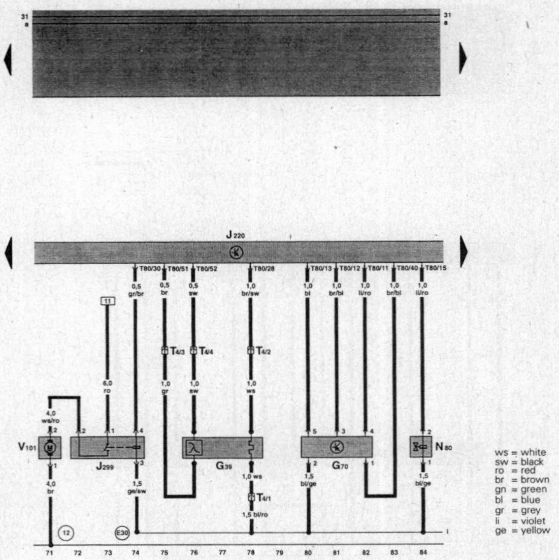

G39 – Heated Oxygen Sensor (HO2S), black
G70 – Mass Air Flow (MAF) Sensor
J220 – Motronic Engine Control Module (ECM), behind instrument panel, left
J299 – Secondary Air Injection (AIR) Pump Relay, in engine compartment, left
N80 – Evaporative Emission (EVAP) Canister Purge Regulator Valve
V101 – Secondary Air Injection (AIR) Pump Motor
T4 – 4-Pin Connector, brown
T80 – 80-Pin Connector
(12) – Ground connection, in engine compartment, left
(E30) – Connector (87a), in wiring harness engine

VW1029800092060A

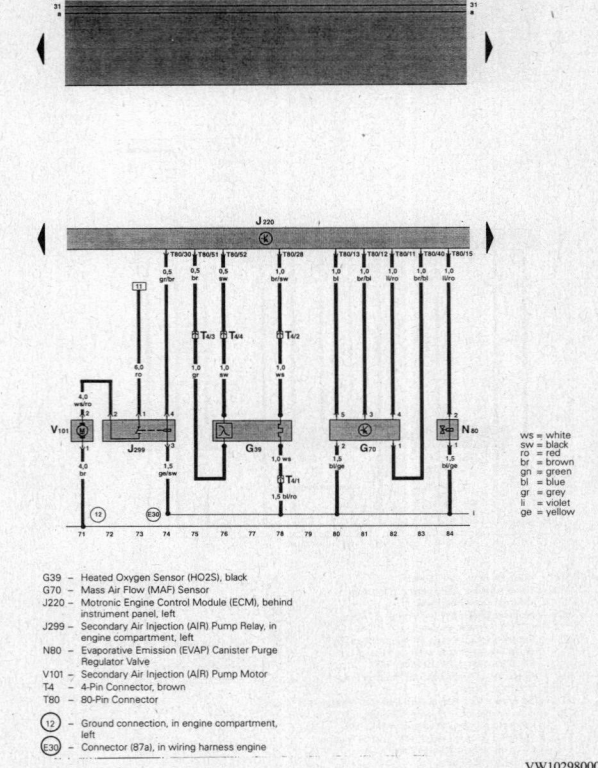

Fig. 41 Motronic wiring diagram (HO2S, MAF sensor, EVAP canister purge regulator valve & AIR system) 1998 New Beetle w/2.0L engine

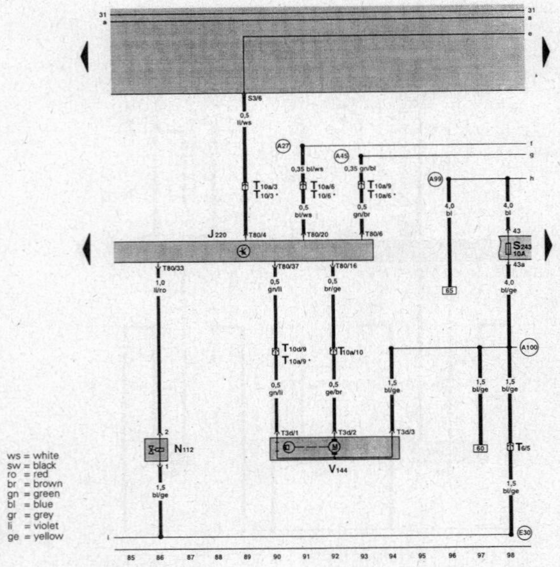

J220 – Motronic Engine Control Module (ECM), behind instrument panel, left
N112 – Secondary Air Injection (AIR) Solenoid Valve
S243 – Fuse 43 in fuse holder
V144 – Leak Detection Pump (LDP)
T3d – 3-Pin Connector
T6 – 6-Pin Connector, red, behind instrument panel, left
T10 – 10-Pin Connector, white, behind instrument panel, left
T10a – 10-Pin Connector, orange, behind instrument panel, left
T10d – 10-Pin Connector, green, behind instrument panel, left
T80 – Connector, 80-point, at Engine Control Module (ECM)
(A27) – wire Connection (vehicle speed signal), in instrument panel wiring harness
(A45) – wire connection (RPM-signal), in instrument panel wiring harness
(A99) – Connector -1- (87), in instrument panel wiring harness
(A100) – Connector -2- (87), in instrument panel wiring harness
(E30) – Connector (87a), in wiring harness engine
* – early vehicles only

VW1029800092070A

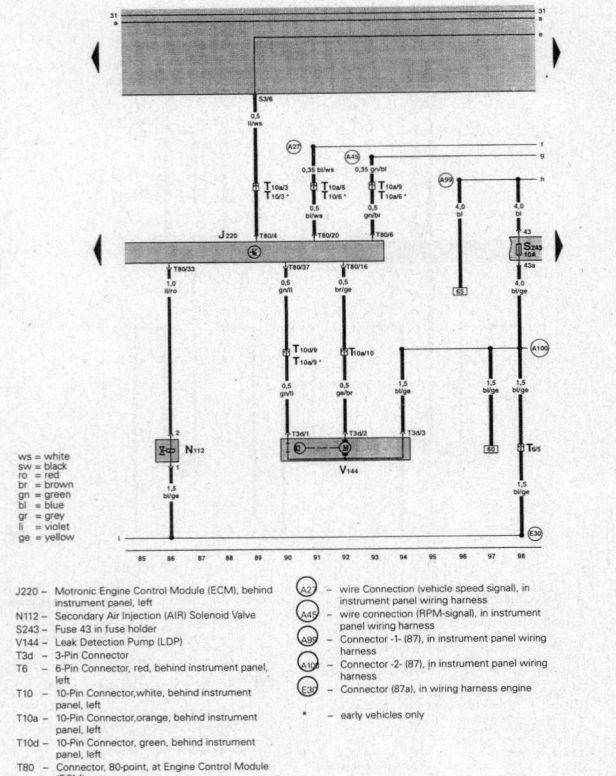

Fig. 42 Motronic wiring diagram (Diagnosis pump & AIR solenoid valve) 1998 New Beetle w/2.0L engine

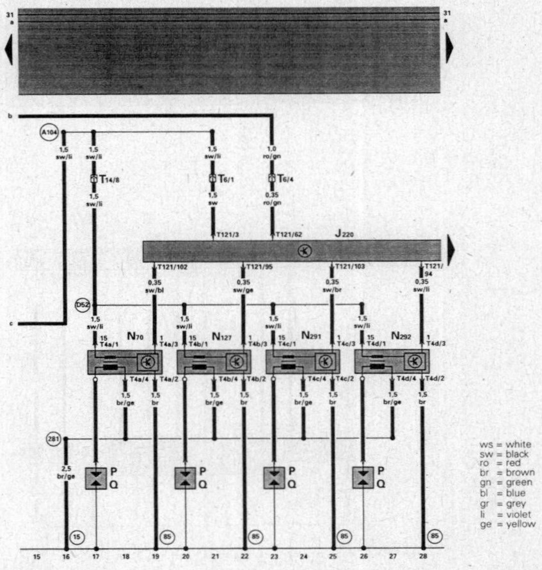

J220 – Motronic Engine Control Module (ECM)
N70 – Ignition Coil with Power Output Stage 1
N127 – Ignition Coil with Power Output Stage 2
N291 – Ignition Coil with Power Output Stage 3
N292 – Ignition Coil with Power Output Stage 4
P – Spark Plug Connectors
Q – Spark Plugs
T4a – 4-Pin Connector
T4b – 4-Pin Connector
T4c – 4-Pin Connector
T4d – 4-Pin Connector
T6 – 6-Pin Connector, brown, behind instrument panel, left
T14 – 14-Pin Connector, in engine compartment, left
T121 – 121-Pin Connector, at -J220-
(15) – Ground connection, on cylinder head
(85) – Ground connection –1–, in engine compartment wiring harness
(281) – Ground connector –1–, in wiring harness engine pre-wiring
(A104) – Plus connector –2– (15), in instrument panel wiring harness
(D52) – plus connection (15a), in engine compartment wiring harness

VW1029900129010X

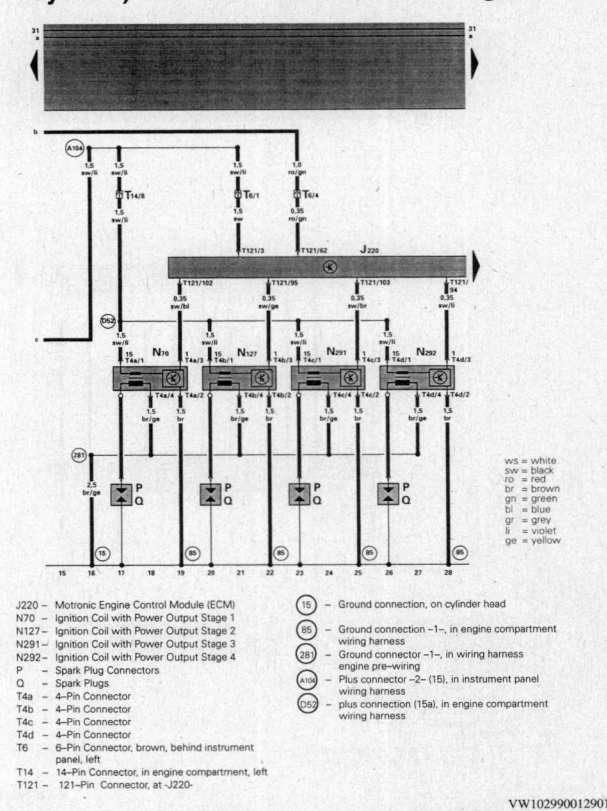

Fig. 43 Motronic wiring diagram (Ignition coil w/power stages & spark plugs). 1999–2001 New Beetle w/1.8L engine

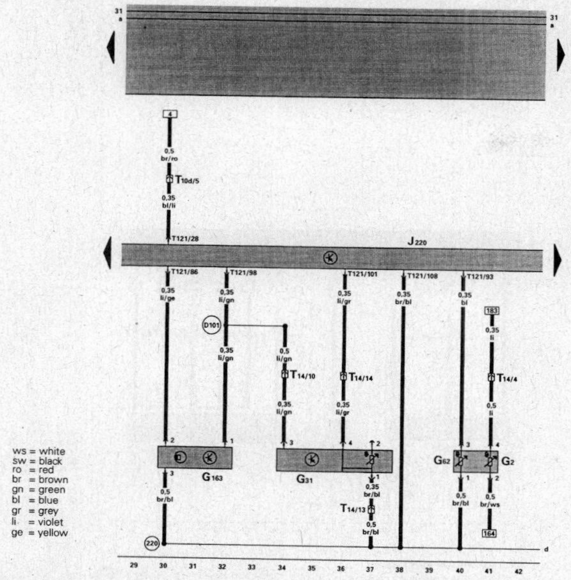

G2 – Engine Coolant Temperature (ECT) Sensor
G31 – Charge Air Pressure Sensor
G62 – Engine Coolant Temperature (ECT) Sensor
G163 – Camshaft Position (CMP) Sensor 2
J220 – Motronic Engine Control Module (ECM)
T14 – 14-Pin Connector, in engine compartment, left
T10d – 10-Pin Connector, green, behind instrument panel, left
T121 – 121-Pin Connector, at -J220-

(220) – Ground connection (sensor ground), in engine compartment wiring harness

(D101) – Wire connection -1-, in engine compartment wiring harness

VW1029900129020X

Fig. 44 Motronic wiring diagram (Charge air pressure sensor & CMP sensor 2). 1999–2001 New Beetle w/1.8L engine

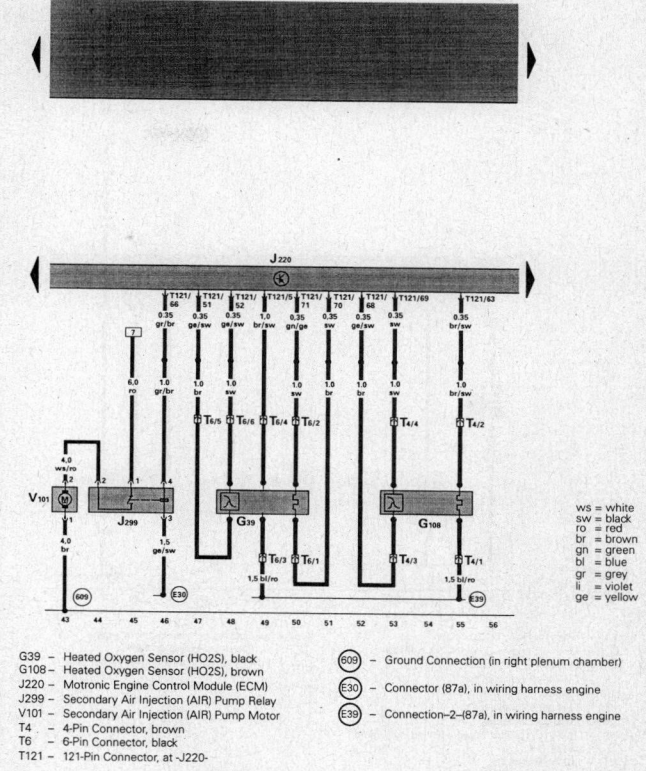

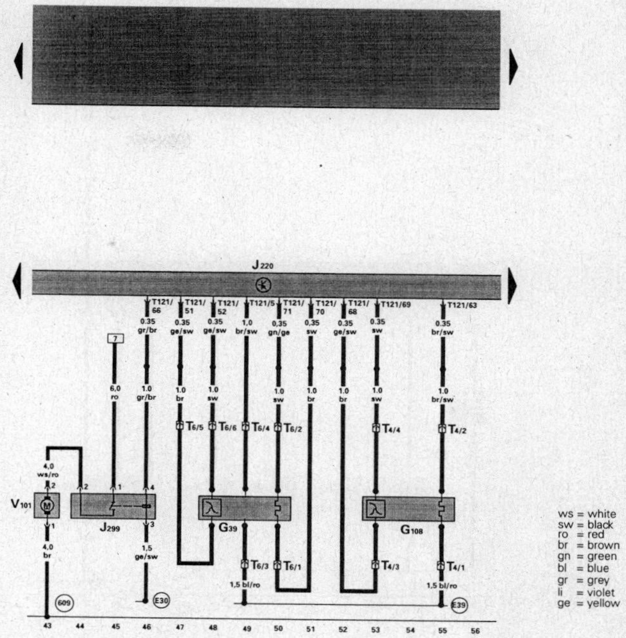

G39 – Heated Oxygen Sensor (HO2S), black
G108 – Heated Oxygen Sensor (HO2S), brown
J220 – Motronic Engine Control Module (ECM)
J299 – Secondary Air Injection (AIR) Pump Relay
V101 – Secondary Air Injection (AIR) Pump Motor
T4 – 4-Pin Connector, brown
T6 – 6-Pin Connector, black
T121 – 121-Pin Connector, at -J220-

(609) – Ground Connection (in right plenum chamber)

(E30) – Connector (87a), in wiring harness engine

(E39) – Connection-2-(87a), in wiring harness engine

VW1029900129030X

Fig. 45 Motronic wiring diagram (HO2S & AIR pump relay/motor). 1999–2001 New Beetle w/1.8L engine

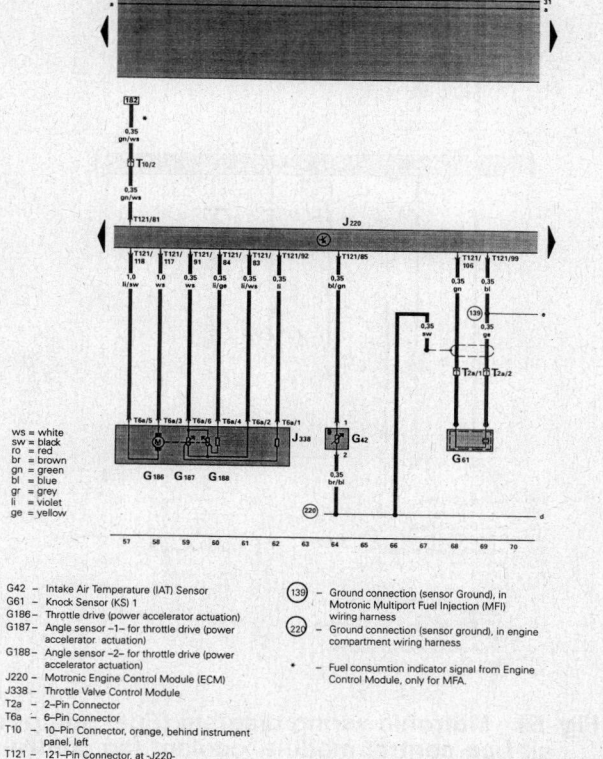

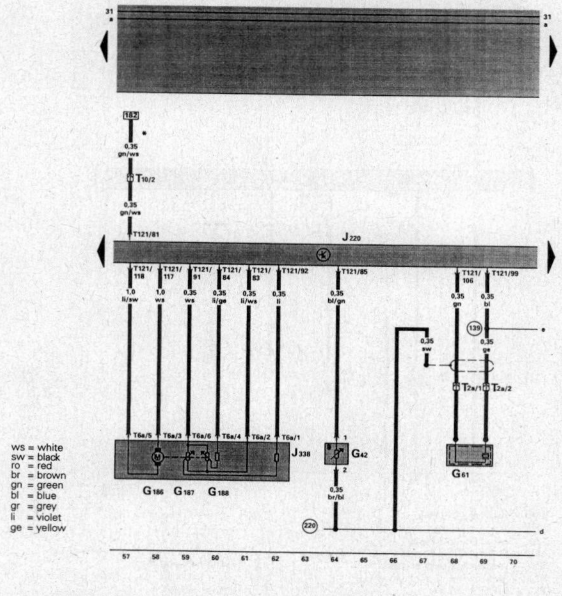

G42 – Intake Air Temperature (IAT) Sensor
G61 – Knock Sensor (KS) 1
G186 – Throttle drive (power accelerator actuation)
G187 – Angle sensor -1- for throttle drive (power accelerator actuation)
G188 – Angle sensor -2- for throttle drive (power accelerator actuation)
J220 – Motronic Engine Control Module (ECM)
J338 – Throttle Valve Control Module
T2a – 2-Pin Connector
T6a – 6-Pin Connector
T10 – 10-Pin Connector, orange, behind instrument panel, left
T121 – 121-Pin Connector, at -J220-

(139) – Ground connection (sensor Ground), in Motronic Multiport Fuel Injection (MFI) wiring harness

(220) – Ground connection (sensor ground), in engine compartment wiring harness

* – Fuel consumtion indicator signal from Engine Control Module, only for MFA.

VW1029900129040X

Fig. 46 Motronic wiring diagram (KS 1 & throttle drive). 1999–2001 New Beetle w/1.8L engine

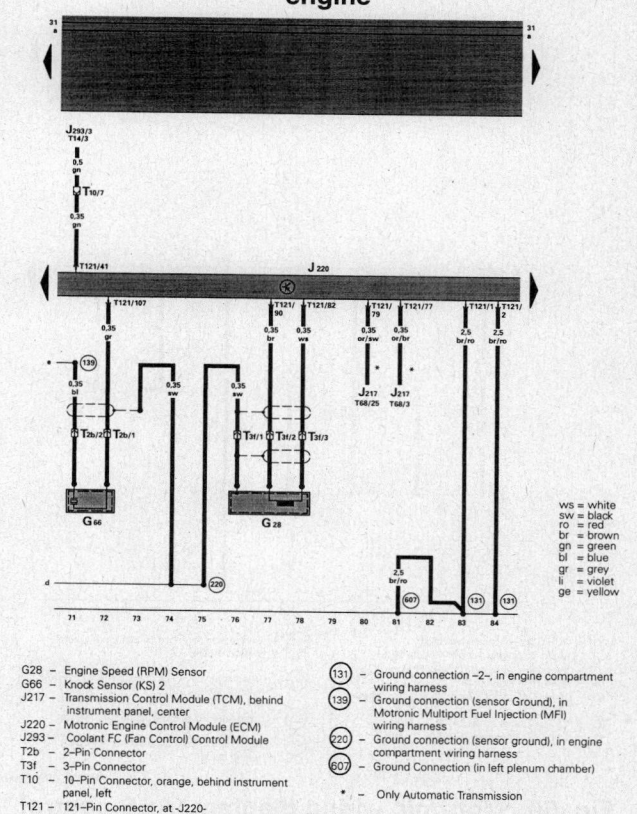

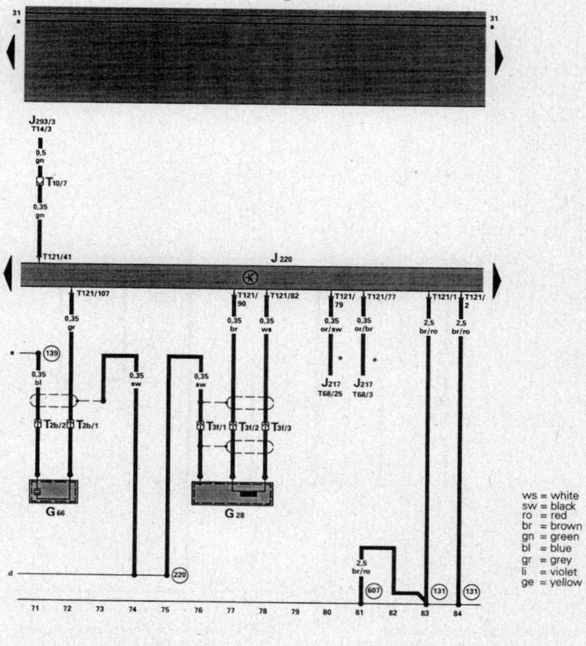

G28 – Engine Speed (RPM) Sensor
G66 – Knock Sensor (KS) 2
J217 – Transmission Control Module (TCM), behind instrument panel, center
J220 – Motronic Engine Control Module (ECM)
J293 – Coolant FC (Fan Control) Control Module
T2b – 2-Pin Connector
T3f – 3-Pin Connector
T10 – 10-Pin Connector, orange, behind instrument panel, left
T121 – 121-Pin Connector, at -J220-

(131) – Ground connection -2-, in engine compartment wiring harness

(139) – Ground connection (sensor Ground), in Motronic Multiport Fuel Injection (MFI) wiring harness

(220) – Ground connection (sensor ground), in engine compartment wiring harness

(607) – Ground Connection (in left plenum chamber)

* – Only Automatic Transmission

VW1029900129050X

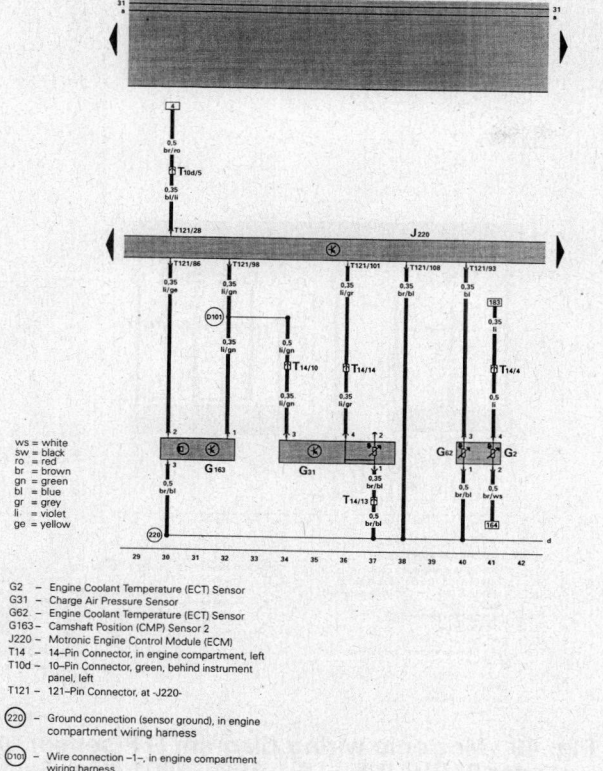

Fig. 47 Motronic wiring diagram (RPM sensor & KS 2). 1999–2001 New Beetle w/1.8L engine

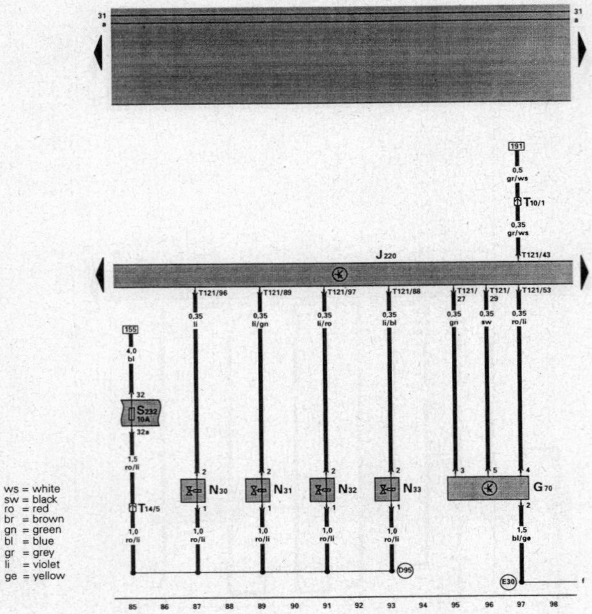

G70 – Mass Air Flow (MAF) Sensor
J220 – Motronic Engine Control Module (ECM)
N30 – Cylinder 1 Fuel Injector
N31 – Cylinder 2 Fuel Injector
N32 – Cylinder 3 Fuel Injector
N33 – Cylinder 4 Fuel Injector
S232 – Fuse in fuse holder
T10 – 10-Pin Connector, orange, behind instrument panel, left
T14 – 14-Pin Connector
T121 – 121-Pin Connector, on -J220-

D95 – wire connection (injectors), in engine compartment wiring harness
E30 – Connector (87a), in wiring harness engine

VW1029900129060X

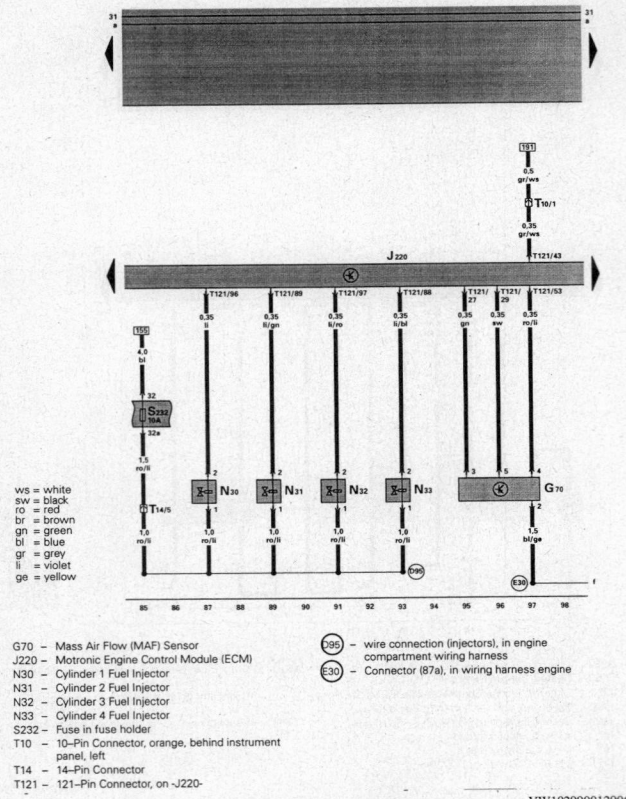

Fig. 48 Motronic wiring diagram (MAF sensor & fuel injectors). 1999–2001 New Beetle w/1.8L engine

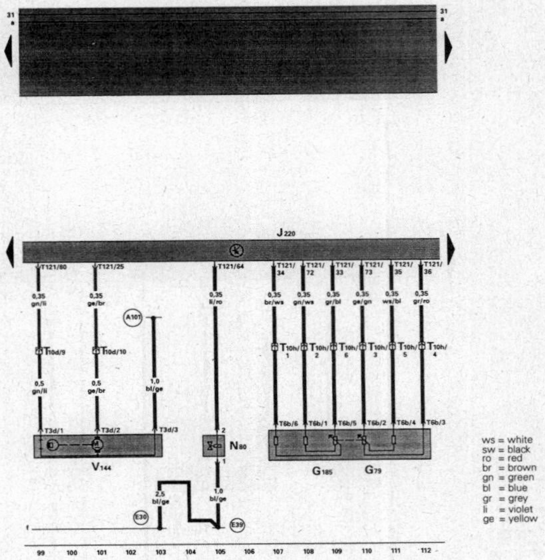

G79 – Throttle Position (TP) Sensor
G185 – Sender -2- for accelerator pedal position
J220 – Motronic Engine Control Module (ECM)
N80 – Evaporative Emission (EVAP) Canister Purge Regulator Valve
V144 – Leak Detection Pump (LDP)
T3d – 3-Pin Connector
T6b – 6-Pin Connector
T10d – 10-Pin Connector, green, behind instrument panel, left
T10h – 10-Pin Connector, blue, behind instrument panel, left
T121 – 121-Pin Connector, at -J220-

E30 – Connector (87a), in wiring harness engine
A101 – Connector -3- (87), in instrument panel wiring harness
E39 – Connection-2-(87a), in wiring harness engine

VW1029900129070X

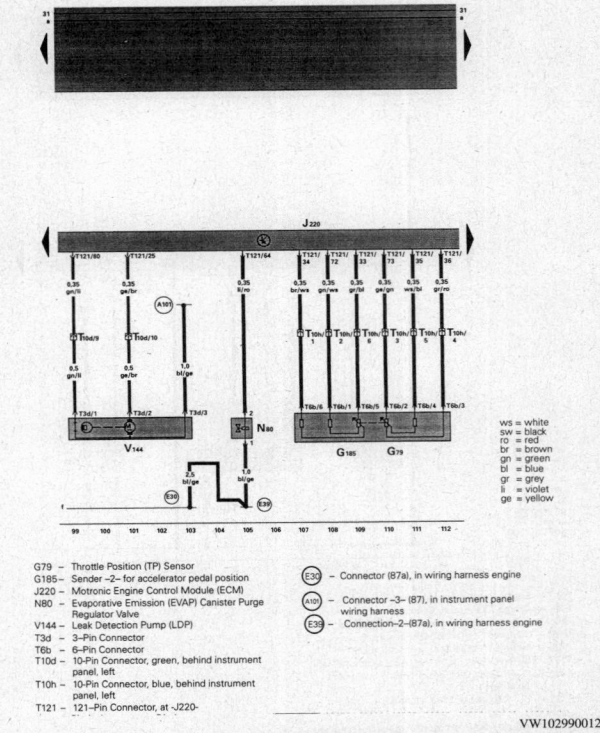

Fig. 49 Motronic wiring diagram (TP sensor, APP sender 2, EVAP & LDP). 1999–2001 New Beetle w/1.8L engine

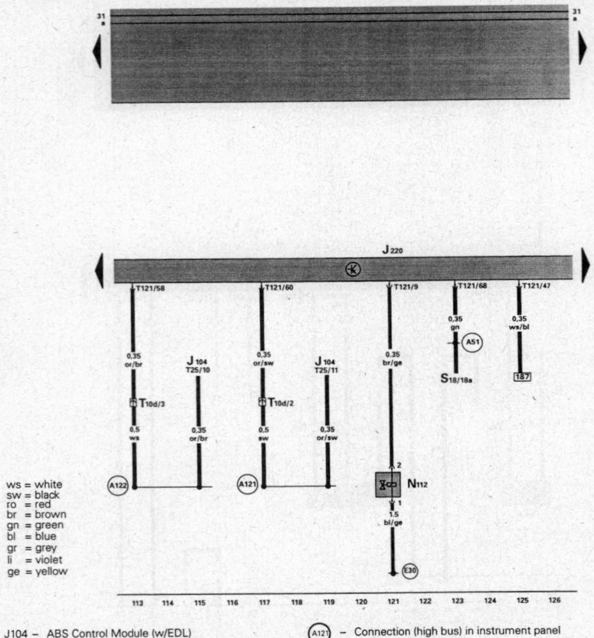

J104 – ABS Control Module (w/EDL)
J220 – Motronic Engine Control Module (ECM)
N112 – Secondary Air Injection (AIR) Solenoid Valve
S18 – Fuse 18 in fuse holder
T10d – 10-Pin Connector, green, behind instrument panel, left
T25 – 25-Pin Connector, at J104
T121 – 121-Pin Connector, at -J220-

A121 – Connection (high bus) in instrument panel wiring harness
A122 – Connection (low bus) in instrument panel wiring harness
E30 – Connector (87a), in wiring harness engine
A51 – wire connection (56), in instrument panel wiring harness

VW1029900129080X

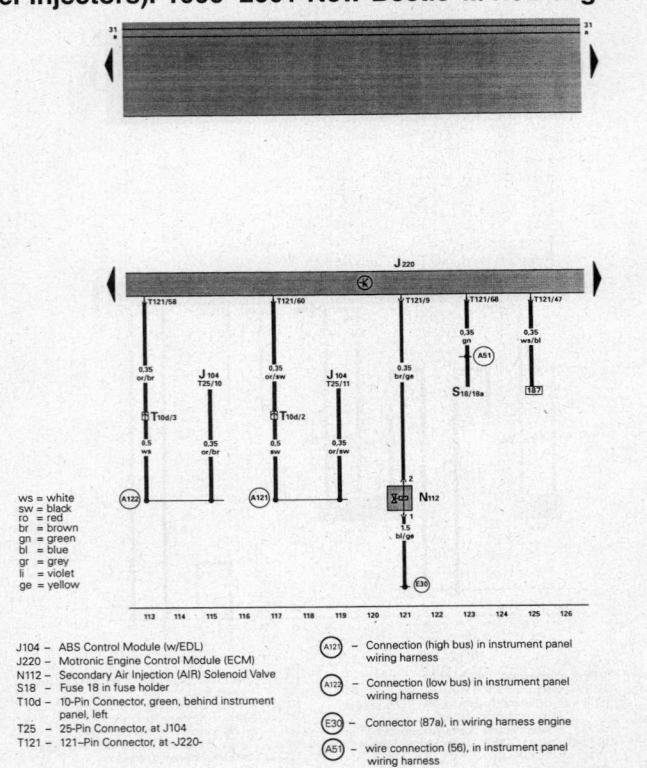

Fig. 50 Motronic wiring diagram (ABS control module, coolant fan control module, AIR solenoid valve & after run coolant pump). 1999–2001 New Beetle w/1.8L engine

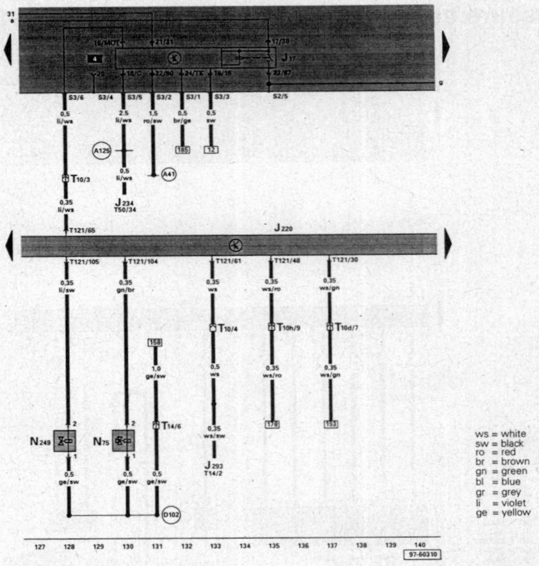

J17 – Fuel Pump (FP) Relay
J220 – Motronic Engine Control Module (ECM)
J234 – Airbag Control Module
J293 – Coolant FC (Fan Control) Control Module
N75 – Wastegate Bypass Regulator Valve
N249 – Recirculating valve for turbocharger
T3 – 3-Pin Connector
T14 – 14-Pin Connector
T10 – 10-Pin Connector, orange, behind instrument panel, left
T10d – 10-Pin Connector, green, behind instrument panel, left
T10h – 10-Pin Connector, blue, behind instrument panel, left
T50 – 50-Pin Connector
T121 – 121-Pin Connector, at -J220-

A125 – Connection (crash signal) in instrument panel wiring harness
D102 – Wire connection -2-, in engine compartment wiring harness
A41 – plus connection (50), in instrument panel wiring harness

VW1029900129090X

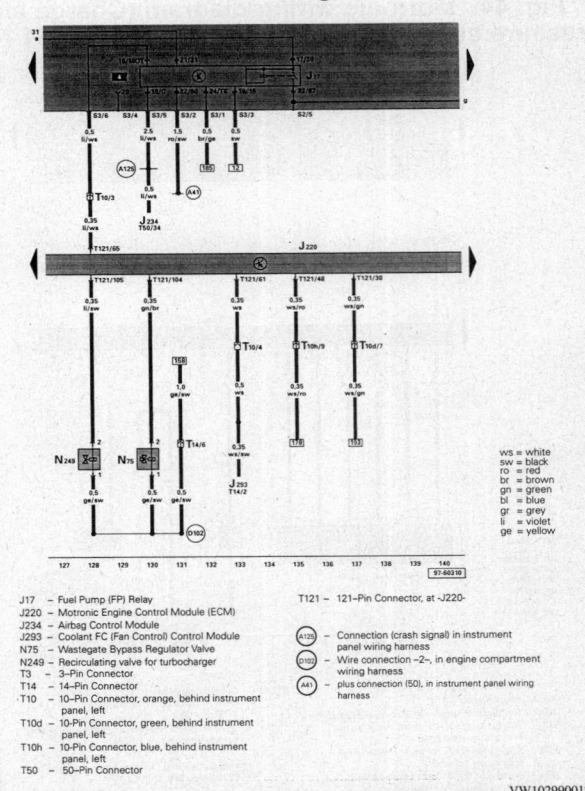

Fig. 51 Motronic wiring diagram (Fuel pump relay, air bag control module, coolant fan control, wastegate bypass regulator valve & turbocharger recirculating valve). 1999–2001 New Beetle w/1.8L engine

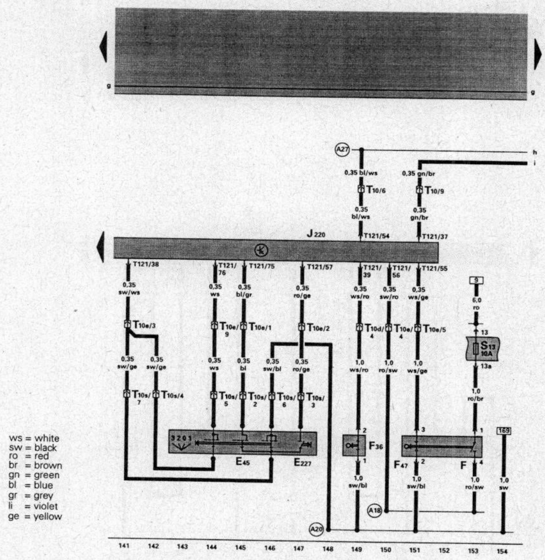

E45 – Cruise Control Switch
E227 – Button for cruise control (set)
F – Brake Light Switch
F36 – Clutch Vacuum Vent Valve Switch
F47 – Brake Vacuum Vent Valve Switch for cruise control
J220 – Motronic Engine Control Module (ECM)
S13 – Fuse 13 in fuse holder
T10 – 10-Pin Connector, orange, behind instrument panel, left
T10d – 10-Pin Connector, green, behind instrument panel, left
T10e – 10-Pin Connector, black, behind instrument panel, left
T10s – 10-Pin Connector, near steering column

T121 – 121-Pin Connector, at -J220-

(A18) – wire connection (54), in instrument panel wiring harness
(A20) – wire connection (15a), in instrument panel wiring harness
(A27) – Wire Connection (vehicle speed signal), in instrument panel wiring harness

VW1029900129100X

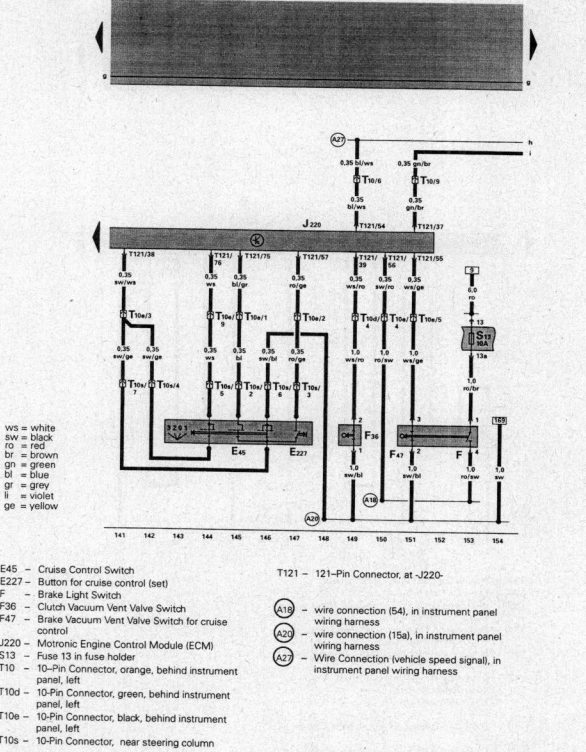

Fig. 52 Motronic wiring diagram (Cruise control switch, cruise control set button, brake lamp switch & clutch vacuum vent valve switch). 1999–2001 New Beetle w/1.8L engine

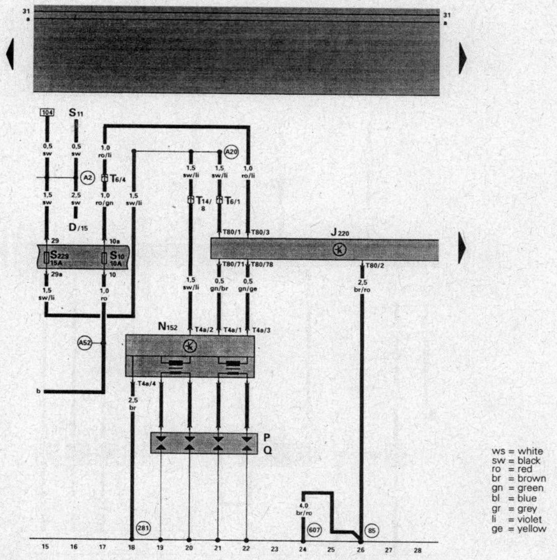

D – Ignition/Starter Switch
J220 – Motronic Engine Control Module (ECM), behind instrument panel, left
N152 – Ignition Coil
P – Spark Plug Connectors
Q – Spark Plugs
S10 – Fuse 10 in fuse holder
S11 – Fuse 11 in fuse holder
S229 – Fuse 29 in fuse holder
T4a – 4-Pin Connector, black
T6 – 6-Pin Connector, brown, behind instrument panel, left
T14 – 14-Pin Connector, in engine compartment, left
T80 – 80-Pin Connector, at Motronic Engine Control Module (ECM)
(85) – Ground connection -1-, in engine compartment wiring harness

(281) – Ground connector -1-, in wiring harness engine pre-wiring
(607) – Ground Connection (in left plenum chamber)
(A2) – plus connection (15), in instrument panel wiring harness
(A20) – wire connection (15a), in instrument panel wiring harness
(A52) – plus connection (30), in instrument panel wiring harness

VW1029900130010X

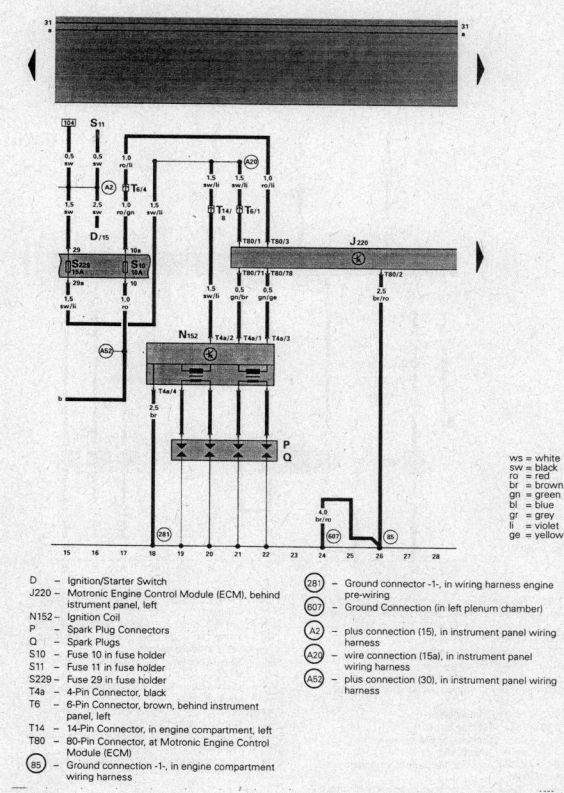

Fig. 53 Motronic wiring diagram (Ignition system). 1999–2001 New Beetle w/2.0L engine

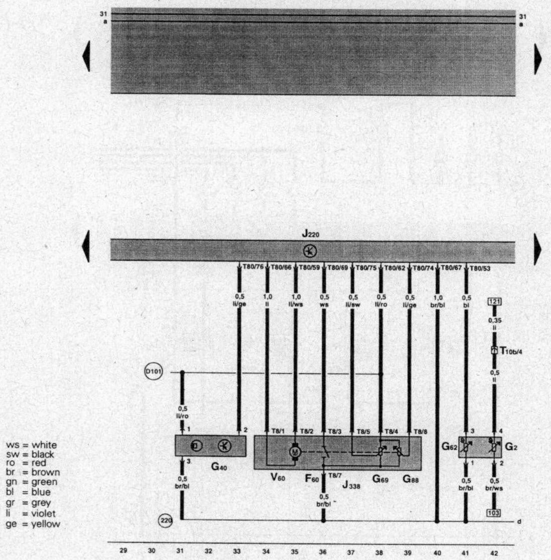

F60 – Closed Throttle Position (CTP) Switch
G2 – Engine Coolant Temperature (ECT) Sensor
G40 – Camshaft Position (CMP) Sensor
G62 – Engine Coolant Temperature (ECT) Sensor
G69 – Throttle Position (TP) Sensor
G88 – Throttle Position (TP) Sensor
J220 – Motronic Engine Control Module (ECM)
J338 – Throttle Valve Control Module
V60 – Throttle Position (TP) Actuator
T8 – 8-Pin Connector
T10b – 10-Pin Connector, behind instrument panel, left
T80 – Connector, 80-point, at Engine Control Module (ECM)

(220) – Ground connection (sensor ground), in engine compartment wiring harness
(D101) – Connection 1 (in engine compartment wiring harness)

VW1029900130020X

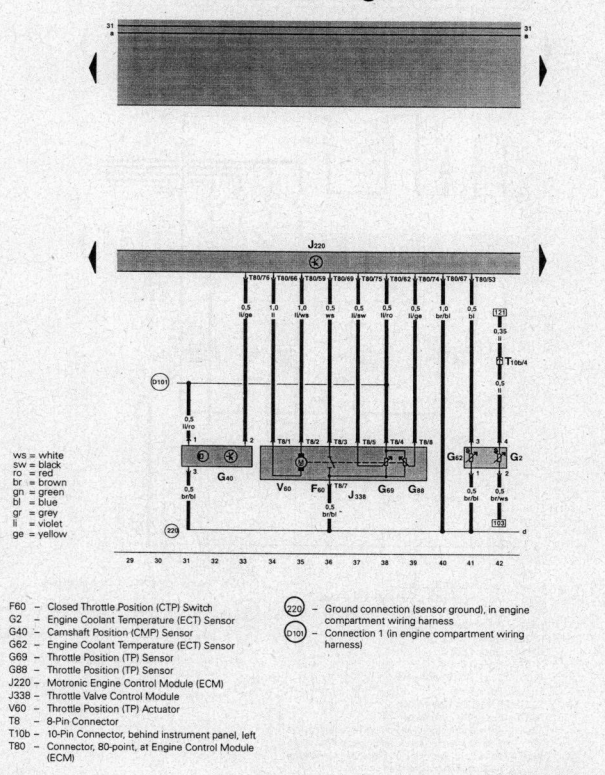

Fig. 54 Motronic wiring diagram (Throttle valve control module, CMP sensor & ECT sensor). 1999–2001 New Beetle w/2.0L engine

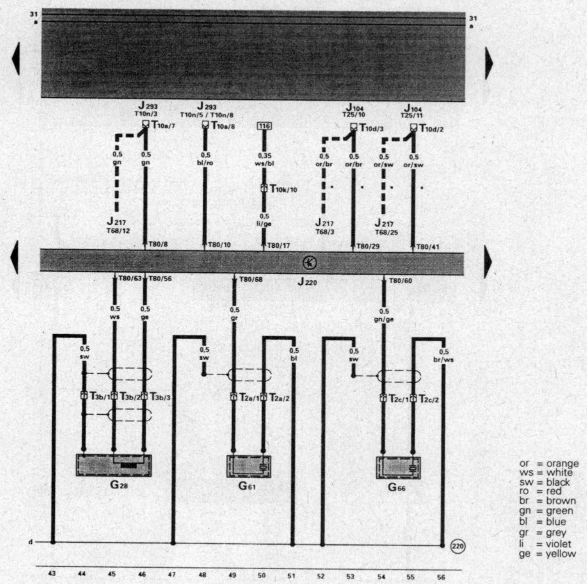

G28 – Engine Speed (RPM) Sensor
G61 – Knock Sensor (KS) 1
G66 – Knock Sensor (KS) 2
J104 – ABS Control Module (w/EDL)
J217 – Transmission Control Module (TCM), behind instrument panel
J220 – Motronic Engine Control Module (ECM), behind instrument panel, left
J293 – Coolant FC (Fan Control) Control Module
T2a – 2-Pin Connector
T3b – 3-Pin Connector
T2c – 2-Pin Connector
T6 – 6-Pin Connector, red, behind instrument panel
T10 – 10-Pin Connector, white, behind instrument panel, left
T10a – 10-Pin Connector, orange, behind instrument panel, left

T10d – 10-Pin Connector, green, behind instrument panel, left
T10k – 10-Pin Connector, blue, behind instrument panel, left
T25 – 25-Pin Connector, at J104
T68 – Connector, 68-point, on Transmission Control Module (TCM)
T80 – Connector, 80-point, at Engine Control Module (ECM)
(220) – Ground connection (sensor ground), in engine compartment wiring harness
* – Connection for DATA-bus
--- – Automatic transmission only

VW1029900130030X

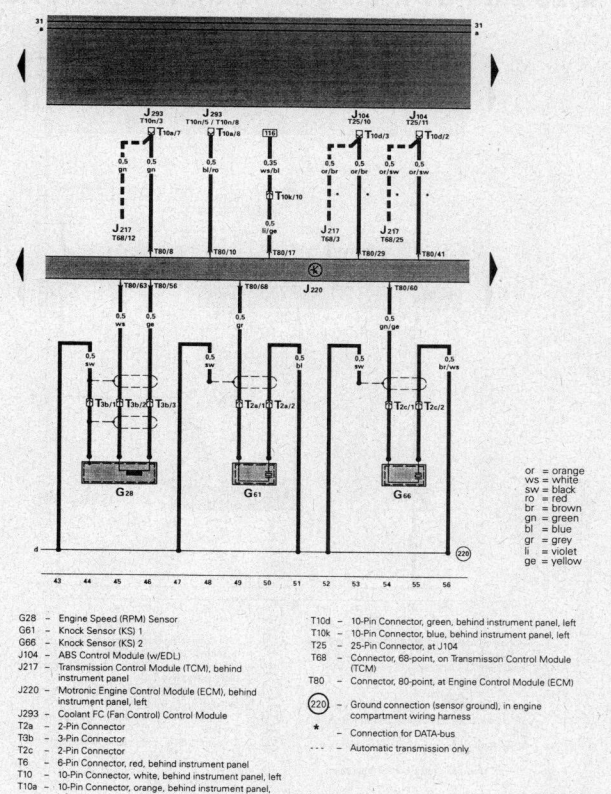

Fig. 55 Motronic wiring diagram (RPM sensor, KS 1 & KS 2). 1999–2001 New Beetle w/2.0L engine

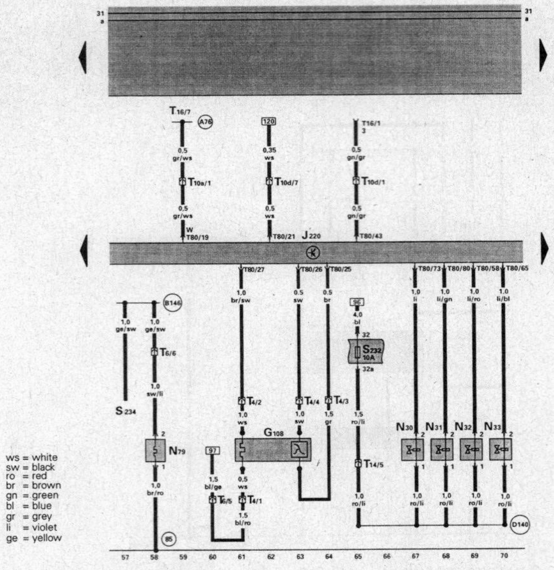

G108 – Heated Oxygen Sensor (HO2S) 2 brown
J220 – Motronic Engine Control Module (ECM), behind instrument panel, left
N30 – Cylinder 1 Fuel Injector
N31 – Cylinder 2 Fuel Injector
N32 – Cylinder 3 Fuel Injector
N33 – Cylinder 4 Fuel Injector
N79 – Positive Crankcase Ventilation (PCV) Heating Element
S232 – Fuse 32 in fuse holder
S234 – Fuse 34 in fuse holder
T4 – 4-Pin Connector, brown, in engine compartment, left
T6 – 6-Pin Connector, red, behind instrument panel, left
T10a – 10-Pin Connector, orange, behind instrument panel, left
T10d – 10-Pin Connector, green, behind instrument panel, left
T14 – 14-Pin Connector, in engine compartment, left
T16 – 16-Pin Connector, Data Link Connector (DLC), below steering column
T80 – 80-Pin Connector, at Engine Control Module (ECM)
(85) – Ground connection -1-, in engine compartment wiring harness
(A76) – Connector (K-diagnosis wire), in instrument panel wiring harness
(D140) – Connector (injectors), in wiring harness, engine pre-wiring
(B146) – Plus connector -1- (87), in wiring harness interior

VW1029900130040X

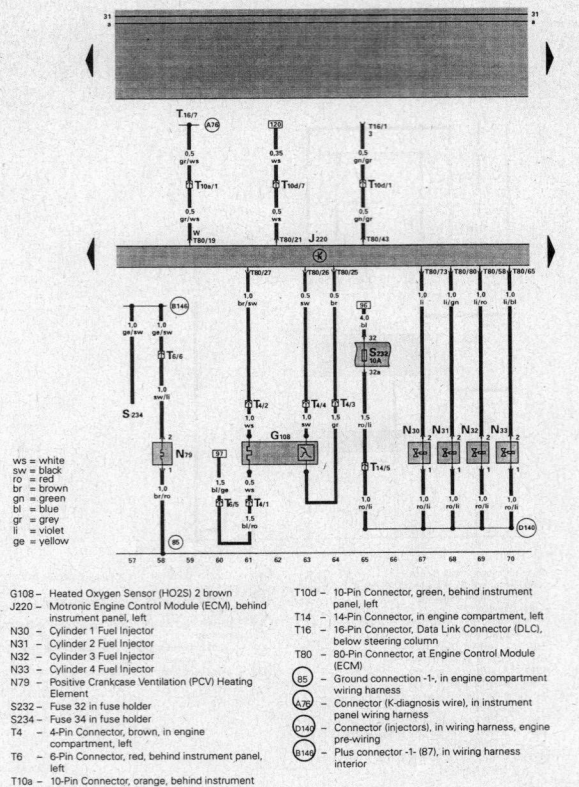

Fig. 56 Motronic wiring diagram (Fuel injectors, HO2S 2 & PCV heating element). 1999–2001 New Beetle w/2.0L engine

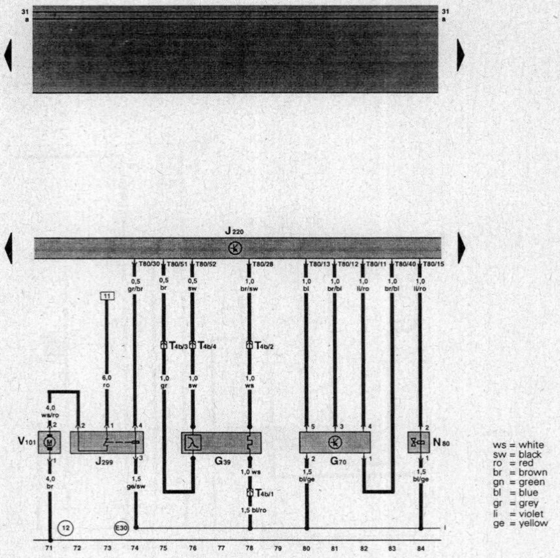

G39 – Heated Oxygen Sensor (HO2S), black
G70 – Mass Air Flow (MAF) Sensor
J220 – Motronic Engine Control Module (ECM), behind instrument panel, left
J299 – Secondary Air Injection (AIR) Pump Relay, in engine compartment, left
N80 – Evaporative Emission (EVAP) Canister Purge Regulator Valve
V101 – Secondary Air Injection (AIR) Pump Motor
T4b – 4-Pin Connector, black
T80 – 80-Pin Connector
(12) – Ground connection, in engine compartment, left
(E30) – Connector (87a), in wiring harness engine

VW1029900130050X

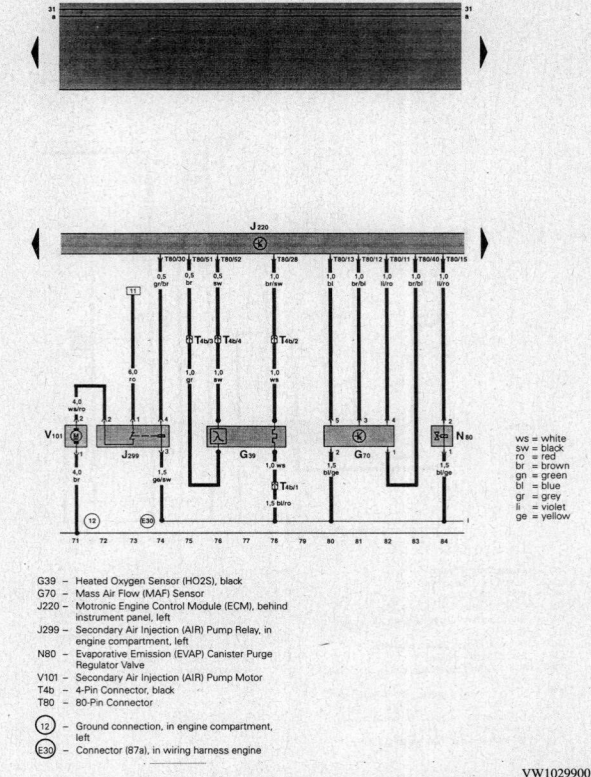

Fig. 57 Motronic wiring diagram (HO2S, MAF sensor, EVAP canister purge regulator valve & AIR system). 1999–2001 New Beetle w/2.0L engine

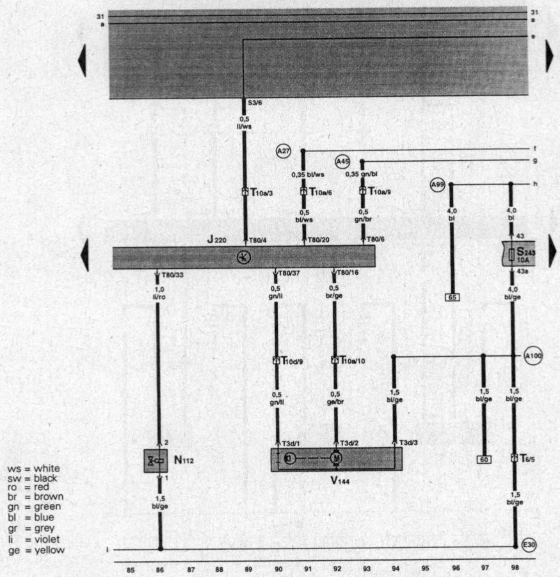

J220 – Motronic Engine Control Module (ECM), behind instrument panel, left
N112 – Secondary Air Injection (AIR) Solenoid Valve
S243 – Fuse 43 in fuse holder
V144 – Leak Detection Pump (LDP)
T3d – 3-Pin Connector
T6 – 6-Pin Connector, red, behind instrument panel, left
T10a – 10-Pin Connector,orange, behind instrument panel, left
T10d – 10-Pin Connector, green, behind instrument panel, left
T80 – Connector, 80-point, at Engine Control Module (ECM)
(A27) – wire Connection (vehicle speed signal), in instrument panel wiring harness
(A45) – wire connection (RPM-signal), in instrument panel wiring harness
(A99) – Connector -1- (87), in instrument panel wiring harness
(A100) – Connector -2- (87), in instrument panel wiring harness
(E30) – Connector (87a), in wiring harness engine

VW1029900130060X

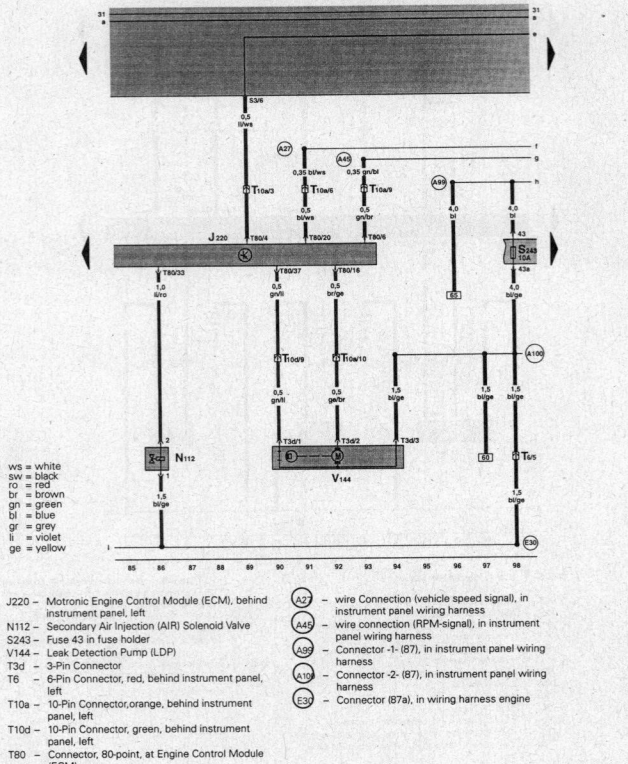

Fig. 58 Motronic wiring diagram (LDP & AIR solenoid valve). 1999 New Beetle w/2.0L engine

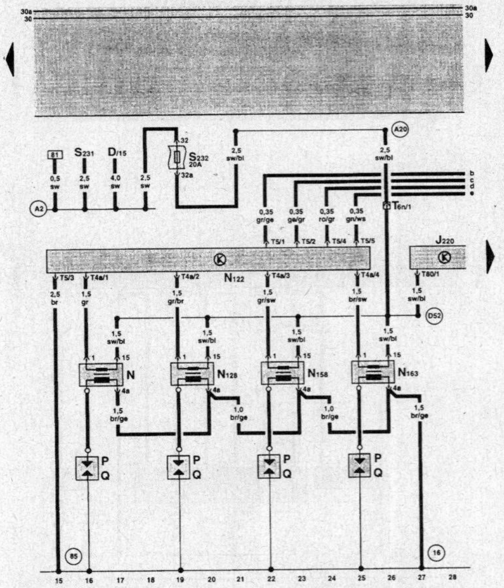

D – Ignition/Starter Switch
J220 – Motronic Engine Control Module (ECM)
N – Ignition Coil
N122 – Power Output Stage
N128 – Ignition Coil 2
N158 – Ignition Coil 3
N163 – Ignition Coil 4
P – Spark Plug Connectors
Q – Spark Plugs
S231 – Fuse 31 in fuse holder
S232 – Fuse 32 in fuse holder
T4a – 4-Pin Connector, black, on power output stage
T5 – 5-Pin Connector, black, on power output stage
T6n – 6-Pin Connector, red, on protective housing for control module, in engine compartment, left
T80 – Connector, 80 point, on Motronic Engine Control Module (ECM)
(16) – Ground connection -1-, on valve cover
(85) – Ground connection -1-, in engine compartment wiring harness
(A2) – plus connection (15), in instrument panel wiring harness
(A20) – wire connection (15a), in instrument panel wiring harness
(D52) – plus connection (15a), in engine compartment wiring harness

VW1029800093020X

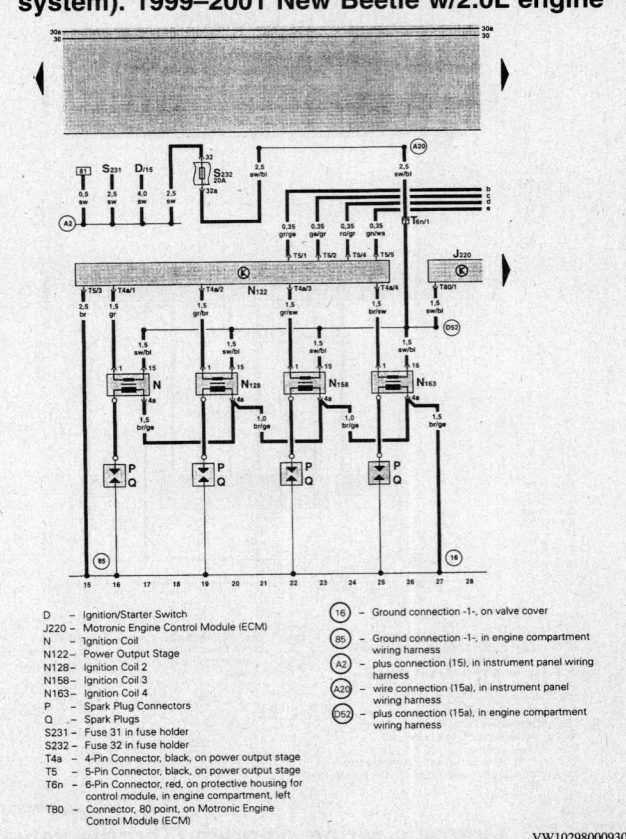

Fig. 59 Motronic wiring diagram (Ignition system). 1998 Passat w/1.8L engine

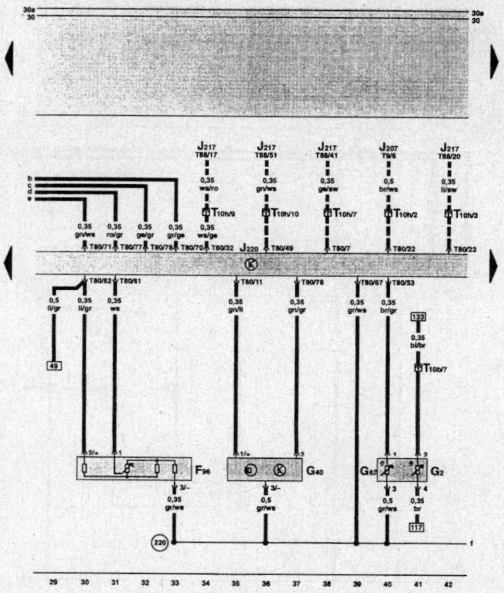

F96 – Barometric Pressure (BARO) Sensor
G2 – Engine Coolant Temperature (ECT) Sensor
G40 – Camshaft Position (CMP) Sensor
G62 – Engine Coolant Temperature (ECT) Sensor
J207 – Starting Interlock Relay
J217 – Transmission Control Module (TCM)
J220 – Motronic Engine Control Module (ECM)
T9 – 9-Pin Connector, on starting interlock relay
T10b – 10-Pin Connector, black, on protective housing for control module, in engine compartment, left
T10h – 10-Pin Connector, blue, on protective housing for control module, in engine compartment, left
T80 – Connector, 80 point, on Motronic Engine Control Module (ECM)
T88 – Connector, 88 point, on Transmission Control Module (TCM)

(220) – Ground connection (sensor ground), in engine compartment wiring harness

- - - automatic transmission only

VW1029800093030X

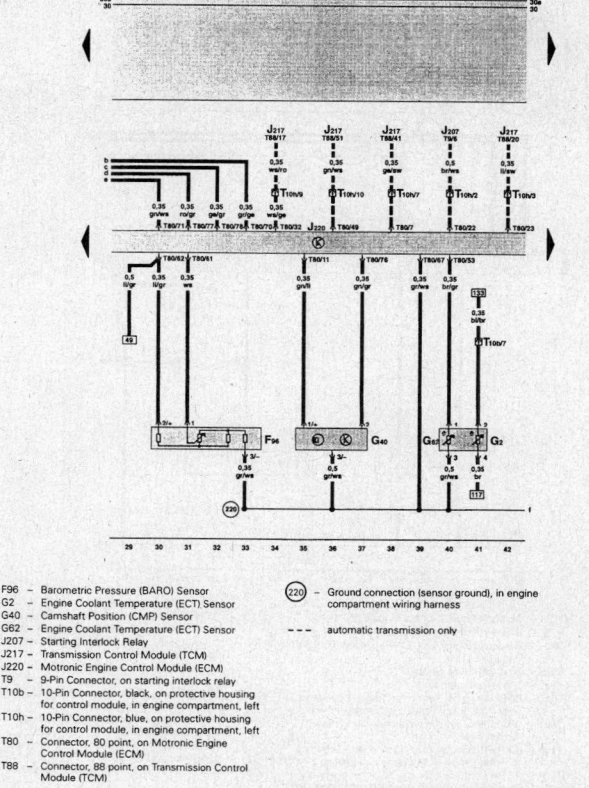

Fig. 60 Motronic wiring diagram (BARO, CMP & ECT sensors). 1998 Passat w/1.8L engine

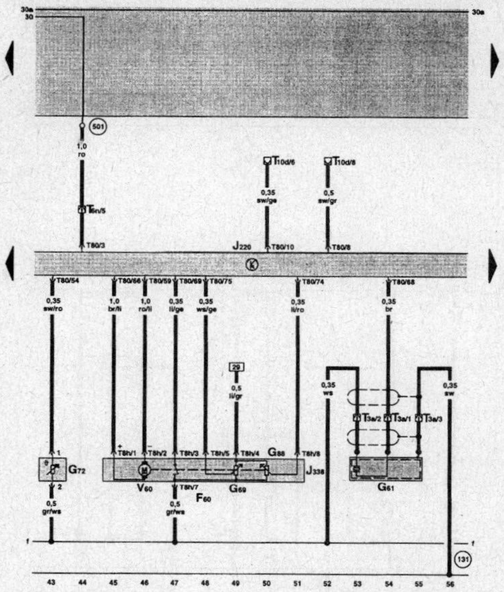

F60 – Closed Throttle Position (CTP) Switch
G61 – Knock Sensor (KS) 1
G69 – Throttle Position (TP) Sensor
G72 – Intake Air Temperature (IAT) Sensor
G88 – Throttle Position (TP) Sensor
J220 – Motronic Engine Control Module (ECM)
J338 – Throttle Valve Control Module
T3a – 3-Pin Connector, green, on firewall, left
T6n – 6-Pin Connector, red, on protective housing for control module, in engine compartment, left
T8h – 8-Pin Connector, black, on throttle valve control module
T10d – 10-Pin Connector, brown, on protective housing for control module, in engine compartment, left
T80 – Connector, 80 point, on Motronic Engine Control Module (ECM)
V60 – Throttle Position (TP) Actuator

(131) – Ground connection -2-, in engine compartment wiring harness
(501) – Screw connection -2- (30), on relay panel

VW1029800093040X

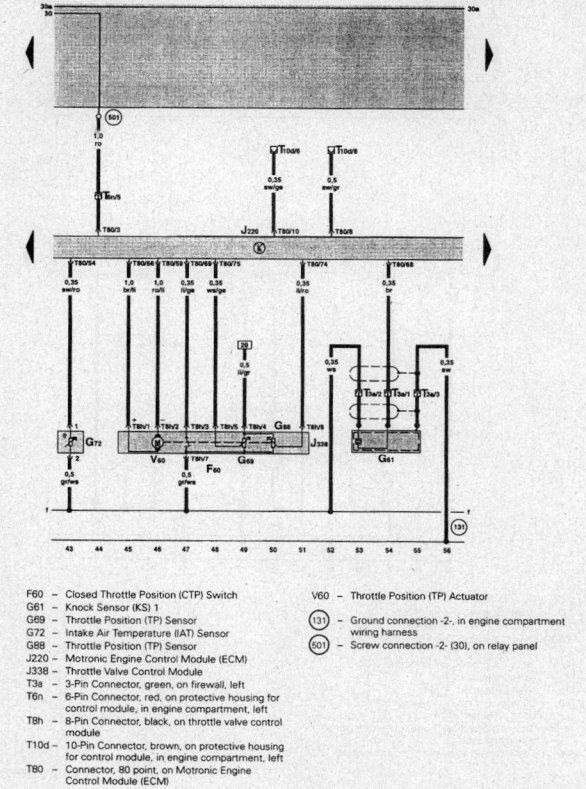

Fig. 61 Motronic wiring diagram (KS 1, throttle valve control module & IAT sensor). 1998 Passat w/1.8L engine

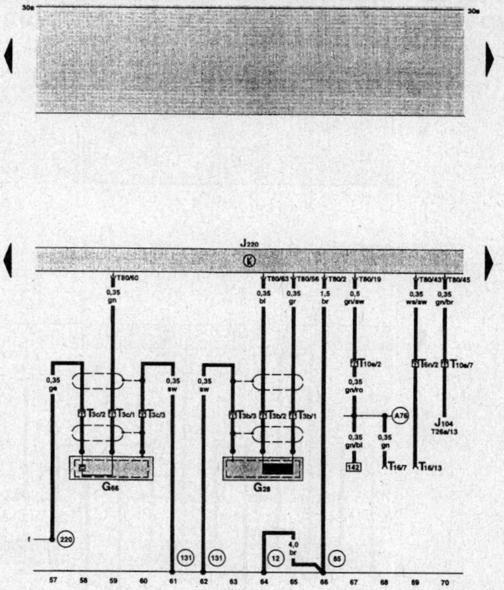

G28 – Engine Speed (RPM) Sensor
G66 – Knock Sensor (KS) 2
J104 – ABS Control Module (w/EDL)
J220 – Motronic Engine Control Module (ECM)
T3b – 3-Pin Connector, grey, on firewall, left
T3c – 3-Pin Connector, blue, on firewall, left
T6n – 6-Pin Connector, red, on protective housing for control module, in engine compartment, left
T10e – 10-Pin Connector, yellow, on protective housing for control module, in engine compartment, left
T16 – 16-Pin Connector, On Board Diagnostic (OBD), below instrument panel, left
T26a – 26-Pin Connector, on ABS control module (with EDL)
T80 – Connector, 80 point, on Motronic Engine Control Module (ECM)

(12) – Ground connection, in engine compartment, left
(85) – Ground connection -1-, in engine compartment wiring harness
(131) – Ground connection -2-, in engine compartment wiring harness
(220) – Ground connection (sensor ground), in engine compartment wiring harness
(A76) – Connector (K-diagnosis wire), in instrument panel wiring harness

VW1029800093050X

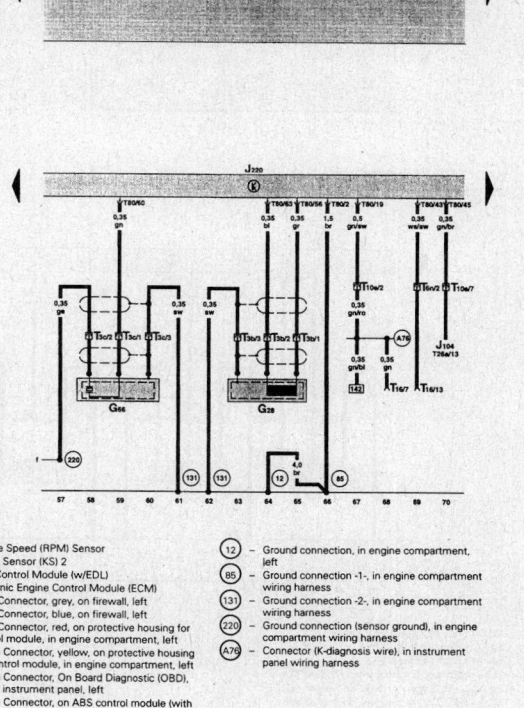

Fig. 62 Motronic wiring diagram (RPM sensor & KS 2). 1998 Passat w/1.8L engine

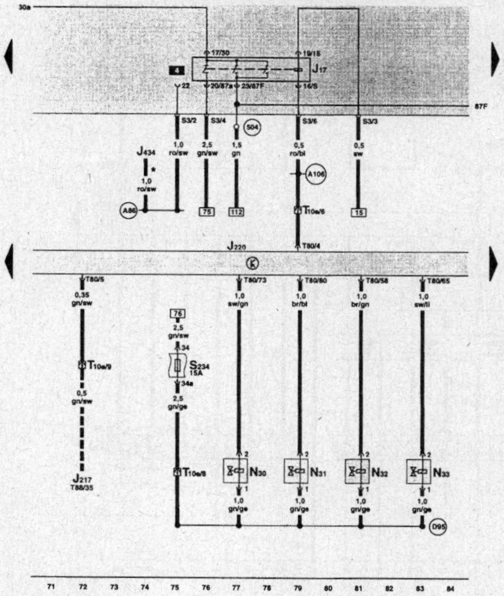

J17 – Fuel Pump (FP) Relay, production control number (208)
J217 – Transmission Control Module (TCM)
J220 – Motronic Engine Control Module (ECM)
J434 – Starting Interlock Realy (clutch position), manual transmission only
N30 – Cylinder 1 Fuel Injector
N31 – Cylinder 2 Fuel Injector
N32 – Cylinder 3 Fuel Injector
N33 – Cylinder 4 Fuel Injector
S234 – Fuse 34 in fuse holder
T10e – 10-Pin Connector, yellow, on protective housing for control module, in engine compartment, left
T80 – Connector, 80 point, on Motronic Engine Control Module (ECM)
T88 – Connector, 88 point, on Transmission Control Module (TCM)

(504) – Screw connection (87F), on relay panel
(A86) – Connection (50a), in instrument panel wiring harness
(A106) – Connector -2- (86s), in instrument panel wiring harness
(D95) – wire connection (injectors), in engine compartment wiring harness

* – manual transmission only
- - - automatic transmission only

VW1029800093060X

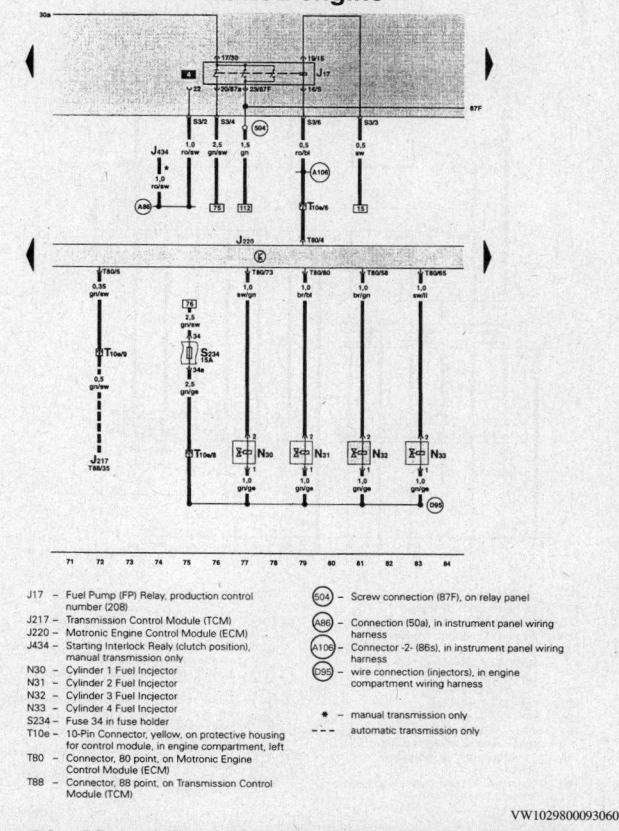

Fig. 63 Motronic wiring diagram (Fuel injectors & fuel pump relay). 1998 Passat w/1.8L engine

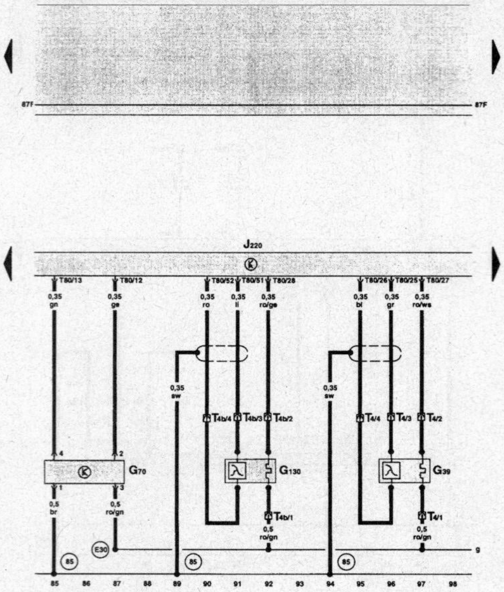

G39 – Heated Oxygen Sensor (HO2S)
G70 – Mass Air Flow (MAF) Sensor
G130 – Oxygen Sensor (O2S) Behind Three Way Catalytic Converter (TWC)
J220 – Motronic Engine Control Module (ECM)
T4 – 4-Pin Connector
T4b – 4-Pin Connector
T80 – Connector, 80 point, on Motronic Engine Control Module (ECM)
(85) – Ground connection -1-, in engine compartment wiring harness
(E30) – Connector (87a), in wiring harness engine

VW1029800093070X

Fig. 64 Motronic wiring diagram (MAF sensor, HO2S & O2S). 1998 Passat w/1.8L engine

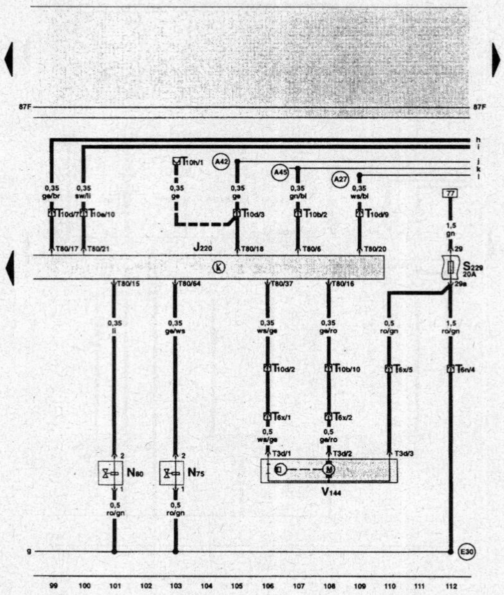

J220 – Motronic Engine Control Module (ECM)
N75 – Wastegate Bypass Regulator Valve
N80 – Evaporative Emission (EVAP) Canister Purge Regulator Valve
S229 – Fuse 29 in fuse holder
T3d – 3-Pin Connector, black
T6n – 6-Pin Connector, red, on protective housing for control module, in engine compartment, left
T6x – 6-Pin Connector, brown, connector station A-pillar, right
T10b – 10-Pin Connector, black, on protective housing for control module, in engine compartment, left
T10d – 10-Pin Connector, brown, on protective housing for control module, in engine compartment, left
T10e – 10-Pin Connector, yellow, on protective housing for control module, in engine compartment, left
T10h – 10-Pin Connector, blue, on protective housing for control module, in engine compartment, left
T80 – Connector, 80 point, on Motronic Engine Control Module (ECM)
V144 – Diagnosis pump for fuel system
(A27) – Wire Connection (vehicle speed signal), in instrument panel wiring harness
(A42) – plus connection (fuel gauge), in instrument panel wiring harness
(A45) – wire connection (RPM-signal), in instrument panel wiring harness
(E30) – Connector (87a), in wiring harness engine
--- automatic transmission only

VW1029800093080X

Fig. 65 Motronic wiring diagram (Wastegate bypass regulator valve & diagnosis pump). 1998 Passat w/1.8L engine

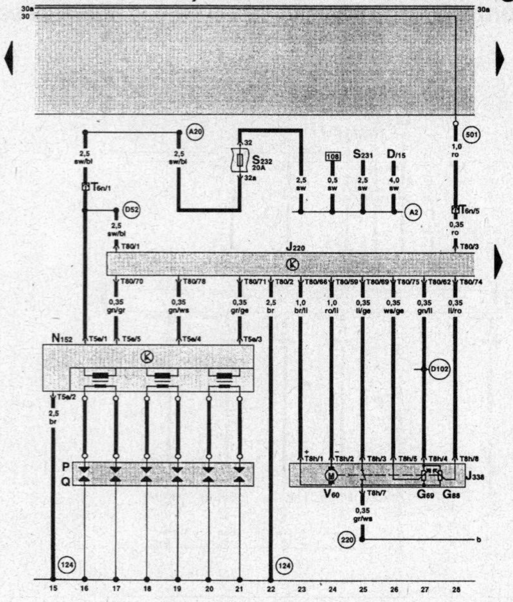

D – Ignition/Starter Switch
G88 – Throttle Position (TP) Sensor
J220 – Motronic Engine Control Module (ECM)
J338 – Throttle Valve Control Module
N152 – Ignition Coil
P – Spark Plug Connectors
Q – Spark Plugs
S231 – Fuse 31 in fuse holder
S232 – Fuse 32 in fuse holder
T5e – 5-Pin Connector
T6n – 6-Pin Connector, red, on protective housing for control module, in engine compartment, left
T8h – 8-Pin Connector, on throttle valve control module
T80 – Connector, 80 point, on Motronic Engine Control Module (ECM)
V60 – Throttle Position (TP) Actuator
(124) – ground connection, in engine compartment right wiring harness
(220) – Ground connection (sensor ground), in engine compartment wiring harness
(501) – Screw Connection -2- (30), on relay panel
(A2) – plus connection (15), in instrument panel wiring harness
(A20) – wire connection (15a), in instrument panel wiring harness
(D52) – plus connection (15a), in engine compartment wiring harness
(D102) – Wire connection -2-, in engine compartment wiring harness

VW1029800094020X

Fig. 66 Motronic wiring diagram (Throttle valve control module). 1998 Passat w/2.8L engine

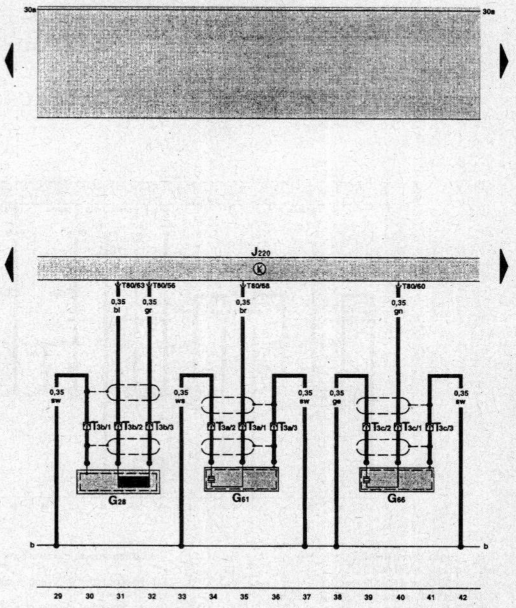

G28 – Engine Speed (RPM) Sensor
G61 – Knock Sensor (KS) 1
G66 – Knock Sensor (KS) 2
J220 – Motronic Engine Control Module (ECM)
T3a – 3-Pin Connector, blue, on firewall, left
T3b – 3-Pin Connector, grey, on firewall, left
T3c – 3-Pin Connector, blue, on firewall, left
T80 – Connector, 80 point, on Motronic Engine Control Module (ECM)

VW1029800094030X

Fig. 67 Motronic wiring diagram (RPM sensor & KS). 1998 Passat w/2.8L engine

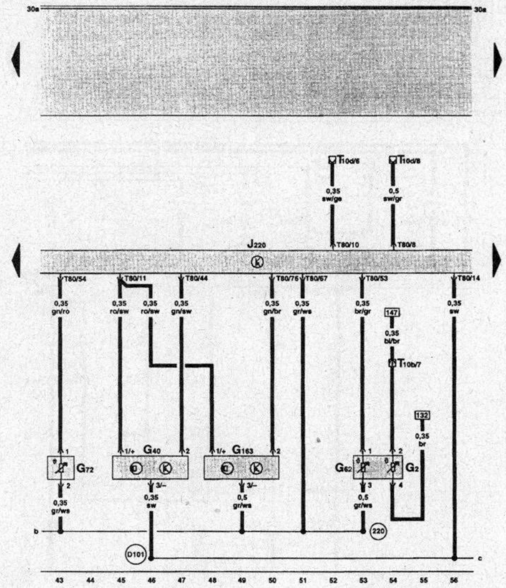

G2 – Engine Coolant Temperature (ECT) Sensor
G40 – Camshaft Position (CMP) Sensor
G62 – Engine Coolant Temperature (ECT) Sensor
G72 – Intake Air Temperature (IAT) Sensor
G163 – Camshaft Position (CMP) Sensor 2
J220 – Motronic Engine Control Module (ECM)
T10b – 10-Pin Connector, black, on protective housing for control module, in engine compartment, left
T10d – 10-Pin Connector, brown, on protective housing for control module, in engine compartment, left
T80 – Connector, 80 point, on Motronic Engine Control Module (ECM)

(220) – Ground connection (sensor ground), in engine compartment wiring harness
(D101) – Wire connection -1-, in engine compartment wiring harness

VW1029800094040X

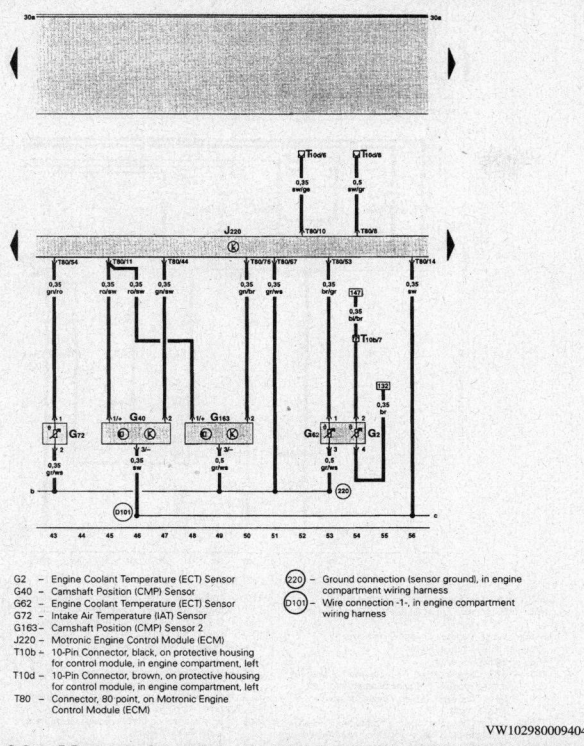

Fig. 68 Motronic wiring diagram (CMP, ECT & IAT sensors). 1998 Passat w/2.8L engine

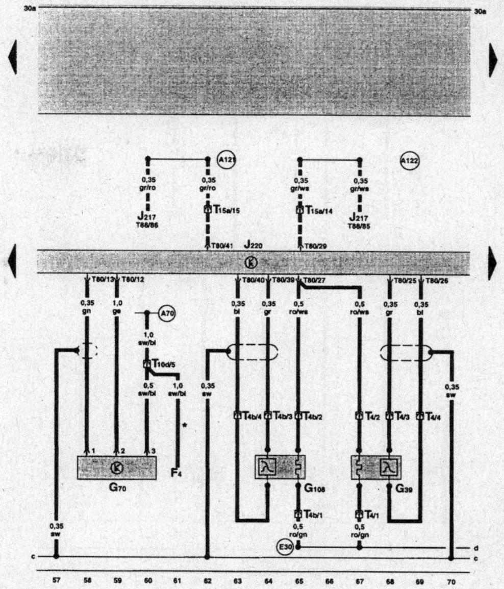

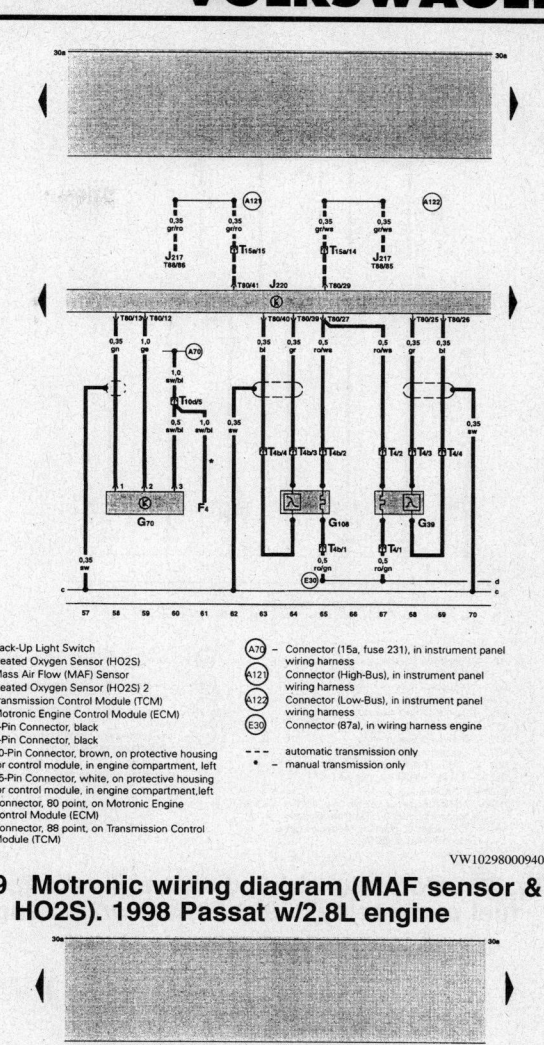

F4 – Back-Up Light Switch
G39 – Heated Oxygen Sensor (HO2S)
G70 – Mass Air Flow (MAF) Sensor
G108 – Heated Oxygen Sensor (HO2S) 2
J217 – Transmission Control Module (TCM)
J220 – Motronic Engine Control Module (ECM)
T4 – 4-Pin Connector, black
T4b – 4-Pin Connector, black
T10d – 10-Pin Connector, brown, on protective housing for control module, in engine compartment, left
T15a – 15-Pin Connector, white, on protective housing for control module, in engine compartment,left
T80 – Connector, 80 point, on Motronic Engine Control Module (ECM)
T88 – Connector, 88 point, on Transmission Control Module (TCM)

(A70) – Connector (15a, fuse 231), in instrument panel wiring harness
(A121) – Connector (High-Bus), in instrument panel wiring harness
(A122) – Connector (Low-Bus), in instrument panel wiring harness
(E30) – Connector (87a), in wiring harness engine
--- – automatic transmission only
• – manual transmission only

VW1029800094050X

Fig. 69 Motronic wiring diagram (MAF sensor & HO2S). 1998 Passat w/2.8L engine

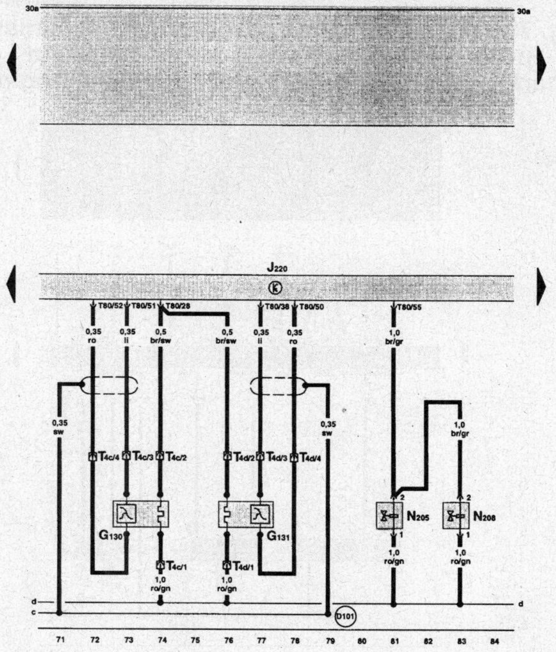

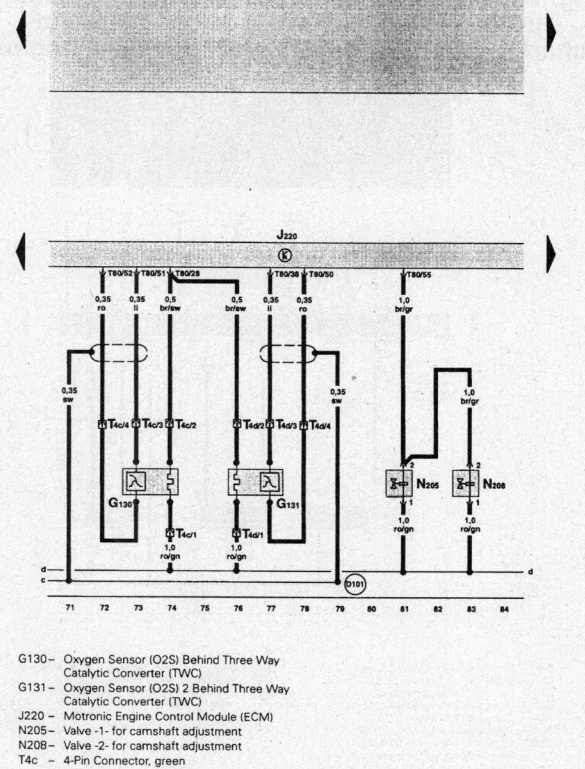

G130 – Oxygen Sensor (O2S) Behind Three Way Catalytic Converter (TWC)
G131 – Oxygen Sensor (O2S) 2 Behind Three Way Catalytic Converter (TWC)
J220 – Motronic Engine Control Module (ECM)
N205 – Valve -1- for camshaft adjustment
N208 – Valve -2- for camshaft adjustment
T4c – 4-Pin Connector, green
T4d – 4-Pin Connector, brown
T80 – Connector, 80 point, on Motronic Engine Control Module (ECM)

(D101) – Wire connection -1-, in engine compartment wiring harness

VW1029800094060X

Fig. 70 Motronic wiring diagram (O2S & valve for camshaft adjustment). 1998 Passat w/2.8L engine

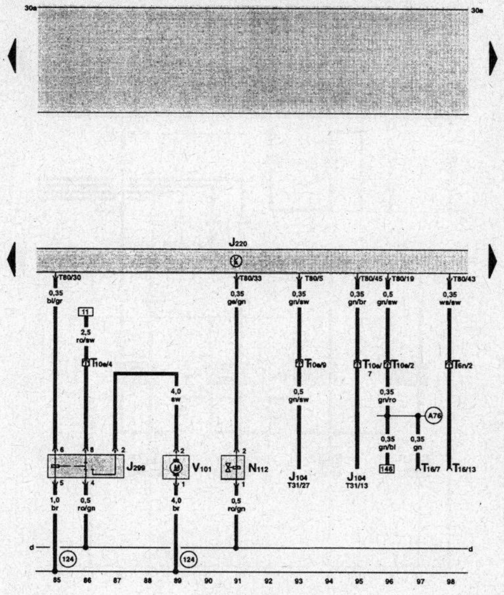

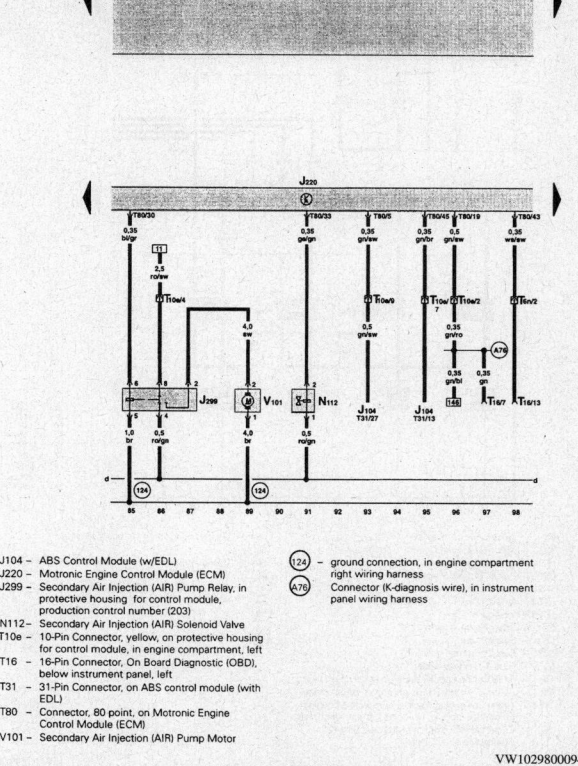

J104 – ABS Control Module (w/EDL)
J220 – Motronic Engine Control Module (ECM)
J299 – Secondary Air Injection (AIR) Pump Relay, in protective housing for control module, production control number (203)
N112 – Secondary Air Injection (AIR) Solenoid Valve
T10e – 10-Pin Connector, yellow, on protective housing for control module, in engine compartment, left
T16 – 16-Pin Connector, On Board Diagnostic (OBD), below instrument panel, left
T31 – 31-Pin Connector, on ABS control module (with EDL)
T80 – Connector, 80 point, on Motronic Engine Control Module (ECM)
V101 – Secondary Air Injection (AIR) Pump Motor

(124) – ground connection, in engine compartment right wiring harness
(A76) – Connector (K-diagnosis wire), in instrument panel wiring harness

VW1029800094070X

Fig. 71 Motronic wiring diagram (AIR system & OBD). 1998 Passat w/2.8L engine

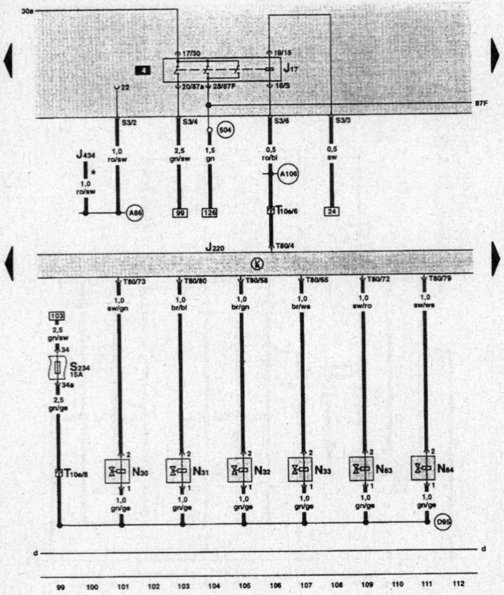

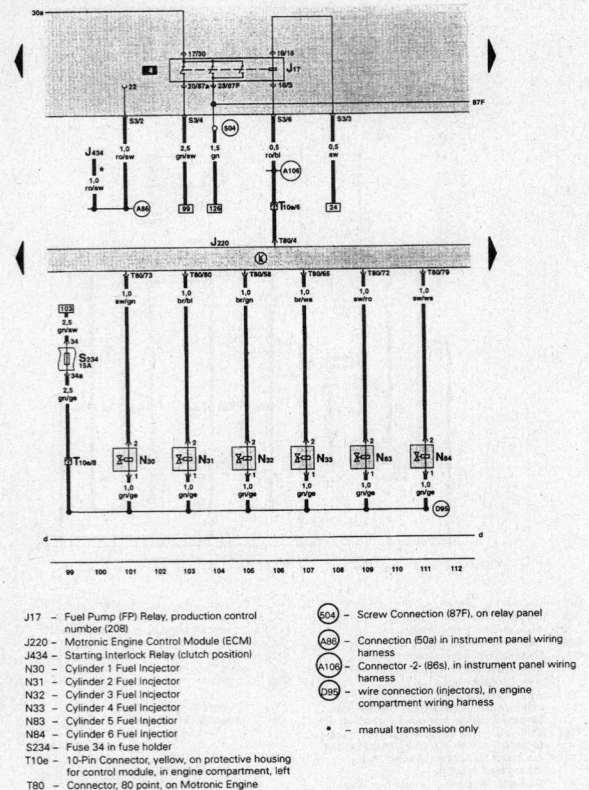

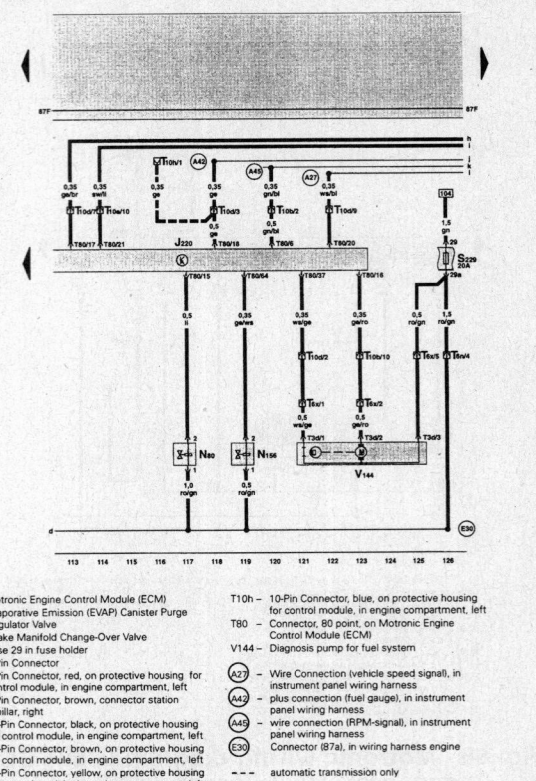

J17 – Fuel Pump (FP) Relay, production control number (208)
J220 – Motronic Engine Control Module (ECM)
J434 – Starting Interlock Relay (clutch position)
N30 – Cylinder 1 Fuel Injector
N31 – Cylinder 2 Fuel Injector
N32 – Cylinder 3 Fuel Injector
N33 – Cylinder 4 Fuel Injector
N83 – Cylinder 5 Fuel Injector
N84 – Cylinder 6 Fuel Injector
S234 – Fuse 34 in fuse holder
T10e – 10-Pin Connector, yellow, on protective housing for control module, in engine compartment, left
T80 – Connector, 80 point, on Motronic Engine Control Module (ECM)

(504) – Screw Connection (87F), on relay panel
(A86) – Connection (50a) in instrument panel wiring harness
(A106) – Connector -2- (86s), in instrument panel wiring harness
(D95) – wire connection (injectors), in engine compartment wiring harness
* – manual transmission only

VW1029800094080X

Fig. 72 Motronic wiring diagram (Fuel injectors & fuel pump relay). 1998 Passat w/2.8L engine

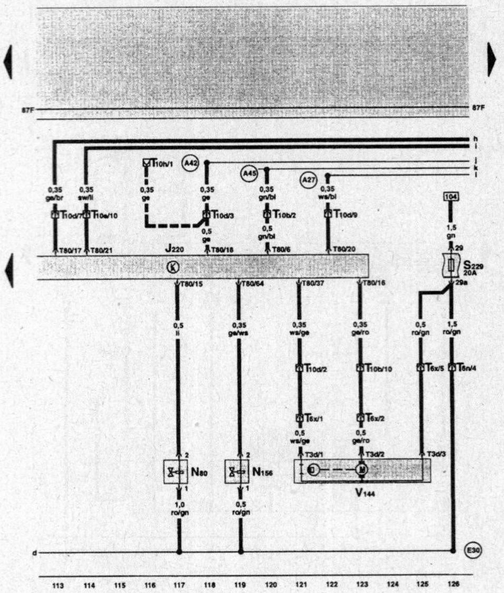

J220 – Motronic Engine Control Module (ECM)
N80 – Evaporative Emission (EVAP) Canister Purge Regulator Valve
N156 – Intake Manifold Change-Over Valve
S229 – Fuse 29 in fuse holder
T3d – 3-Pin Connector
T6n – 6-Pin Connector, red, on protective housing for control module, in engine compartment, left
T6x – 6-Pin Connector, brown, connector station A-pillar, right
T10b – 10-Pin Connector, black, on protective housing for control module, in engine compartment, left
T10d – 10-Pin Connector, brown, on protective housing for control module, in engine compartment, left
T10e – 10-Pin Connector, yellow, on protective housing for control module, in engine compartment, left
T10h – 10-Pin Connector, blue, on protective housing for control module, in engine compartment, left
T80 – Connector, 80 point, on Motronic Engine Control Module (ECM)
V144 – Diagnosis pump for fuel system

(A27) – Wire Connection (vehicle speed signal), in instrument panel wiring harness
(A42) – plus connection (fuel gauge), in instrument panel wiring harness
(A45) – wire connection (RPM-signal), in instrument panel wiring harness
(E30) Connector (87a), in wiring harness engine
- - - automatic transmission only

VW1029800094090X

Fig. 73 Motronic wiring diagram (EVAP canister purge regulator valve & intake manifold change-over valve). 1998 Passat w/2.8L engine

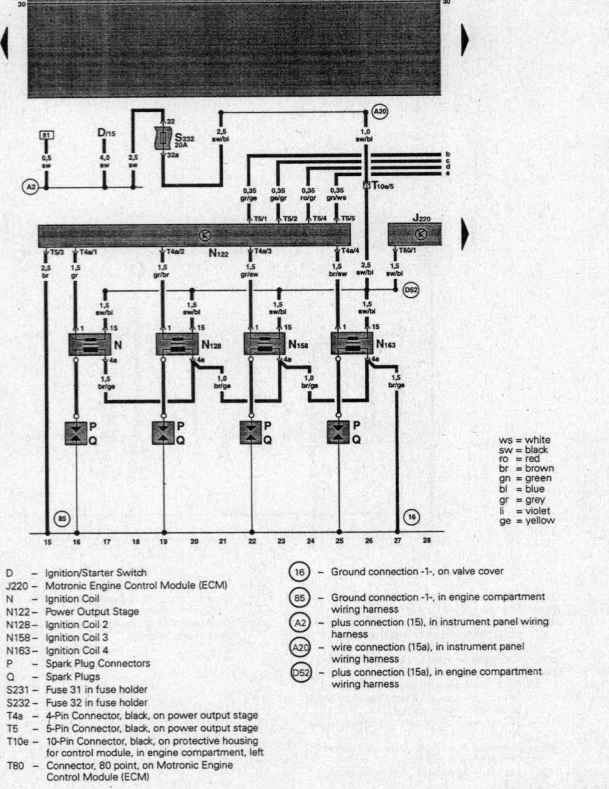

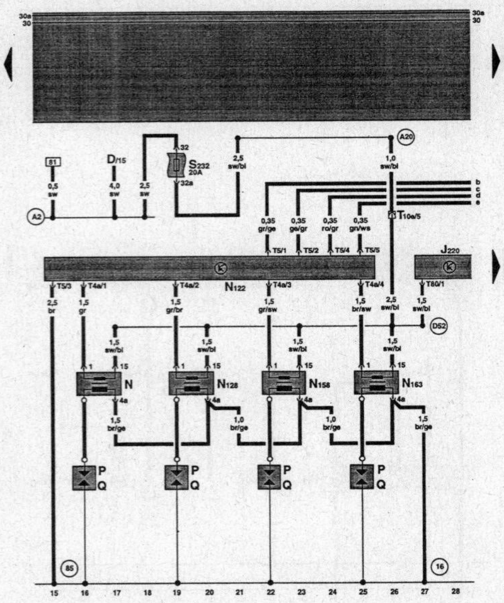

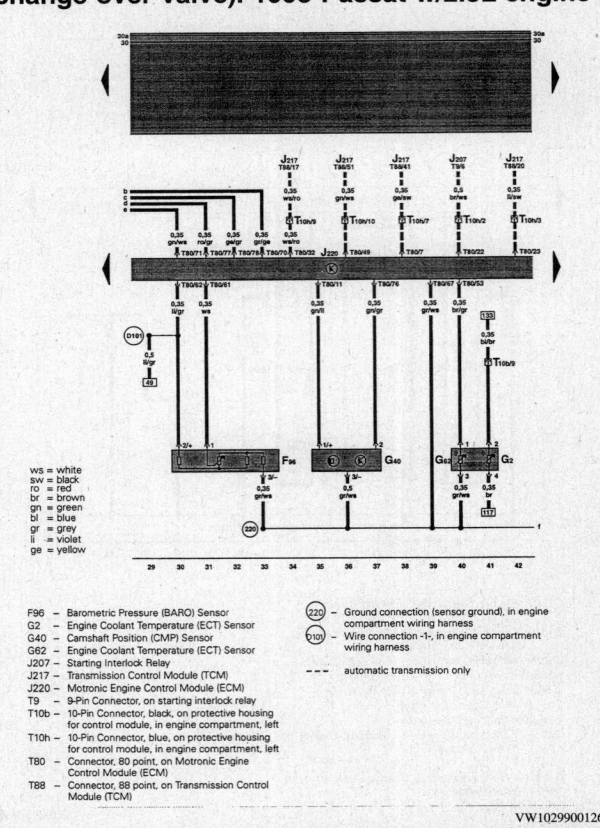

D – Ignition/Starter Switch
J220 – Motronic Engine Control Module (ECM)
N – Ignition Coil
N122 – Power Output Stage
N128 – Ignition Coil 2
N158 – Ignition Coil 3
N163 – Ignition Coil 4
P – Spark Plug Connectors
Q – Spark Plugs
S231 – Fuse 31 in fuse holder
S232 – Fuse 32 in fuse holder
T4a – 4-Pin Connector, black, on power output stage
T5 – 5-Pin Connector, black, on power output stage
T10e – 10-Pin Connector, black, on protective housing for control module, in engine compartment, left
T80 – Connector, 80 point, on Motronic Engine Control Module (ECM)

(16) – Ground connection -1-, on valve cover
(85) – Ground connection -1-, in engine compartment wiring harness
(A2) – plus connection (15), in instrument panel wiring harness
(A20) – wire connection (15a), in instrument panel wiring harness
(D52) – plus connection (15a), in engine compartment wiring harness

VW1029900126010X

Fig. 74 Motronic wiring diagram (Ignition system). 1999 Passat w/1.8L engine

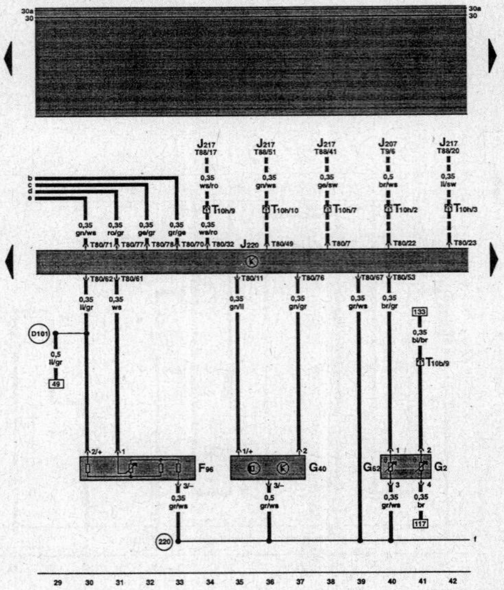

F96 – Barometric Pressure (BARO) Sensor
G2 – Engine Coolant Temperature (ECT) Sensor
G40 – Camshaft Position (CMP) Sensor
G62 – Engine Coolant Temperature (ECT) Sensor
J207 – Starting Interlock Relay
J217 – Transmission Control Module (TCM)
J220 – Motronic Engine Control Module (ECM)
T9 – 9-Pin Connector, on starting interlock relay
T10b – 10-Pin Connector, black, on protective housing for control module, in engine compartment, left
T10h – 10-Pin Connector, blue, on protective housing for control module, in engine compartment, left
T80 – Connector, 80 point, on Motronic Engine Control Module (ECM)
T88 – Connector, 88 point, on Transmission Control Module (TCM)

(220) – Ground connection (sensor ground), in engine compartment wiring harness
(D101) – Wire connection -1-, in engine compartment wiring harness
- - - automatic transmission only

VW1029900126020X

Fig. 75 Motronic wiring diagram (BARO, CMP & ECT sensors). 1999 Passat w/1.8L engine

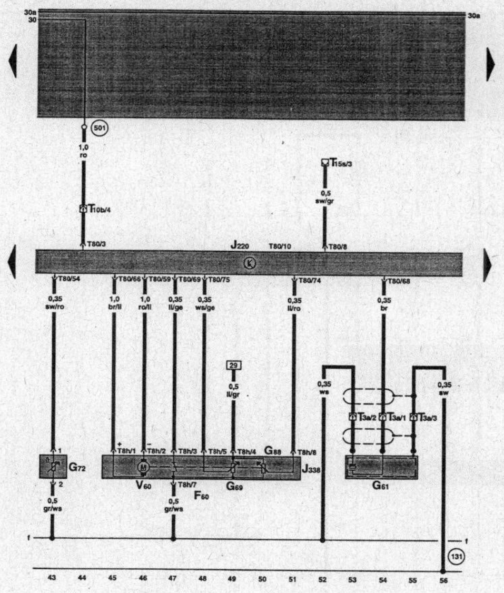

- F60 – Closed Throttle Position (CTP) Switch
- G61 – Knock Sensor (KS) 1
- G69 – Throttle Position (TP) Sensor
- G72 – Intake Air Temperature (IAT) Sensor
- G88 – Throttle Position (TP) Sensor
- J220 – Motronic Engine Control Module (ECM)
- J338 – Throttle Valve Control Module
- T3a – 3-Pin Connector, green, on firewall, left
- T8h – 8-Pin Connector, black, on throttle valve control module
- T10b – 10-Pin Connector, black, on protective housing for control module, in engine compartment, left
- T15s – 15-Pin Connector, red, on protective housing for control module, in engine compartment, left
- T80 – Connector, 80 point, on Motronic Engine Control Module (ECM)
- V60 – Throttle Position (TP) Actuator
- (131) – Ground connection -2-, in engine compartment wiring harness
- (501) – Screw connection -2- (30), on relay panel

VW1029900126030X

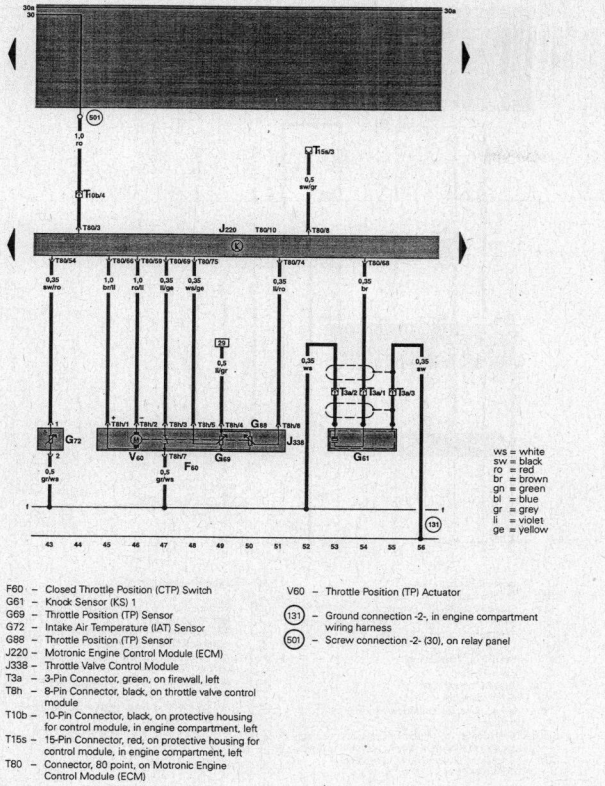

Fig. 76 Motronic wiring diagram (KS 1, throttle valve control module & IAT sensor). 1999 Passat w/1.8L engine

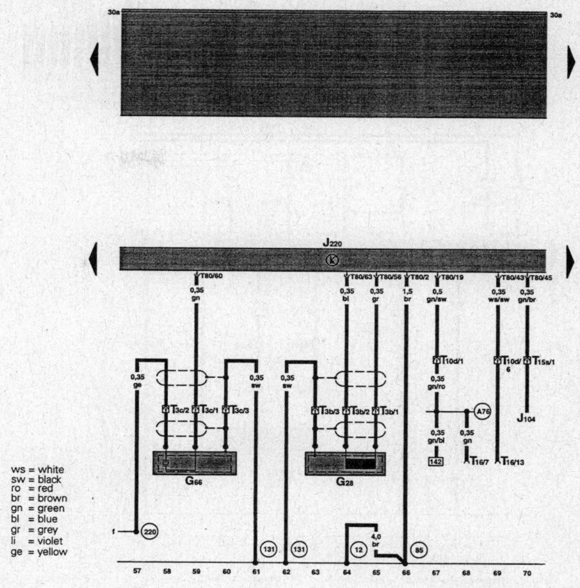

- G28 – Engine Speed (RPM) Sensor
- G66 – Knock Sensor (KS) 2
- J104 – ABS Control Module (w/EDL)
- J220 – Motronic Engine Control Module (ECM)
- T3b – 3-Pin Connector, grey, on firewall, left
- T3c – 3-Pin Connector, blue, on firewall, left
- T6n – 6-Pin Connector, red, on protective housing for control module, in engine compartment, left
- T10d – 10-Pin Connector, brown, on protective housing for control module, in engine compartment, left
- T10e – 10-Pin Connector, yellow, on protective housing for control module, in engine compartment, left
- T15s – 15-Pin Connector, red, on protective housing for control module, in engine compartment, left
- T16 – 16-Pin Connector, On Board Diagnostic (OBD), below instrument panel, left
- T80 – Connector, 80 point, on Motronic Engine Control Module (ECM)
- (12) – Ground connection, in engine compartment, left
- (85) – Ground connection -1-, in engine compartment wiring harness
- (131) – Ground connection -2-, in engine compartment wiring harness
- (220) – Ground connection (sensor ground), in engine compartment wiring harness
- (A76) – Connector (K-diagnosis wire), in instrument panel wiring harness

VW1029900126040X

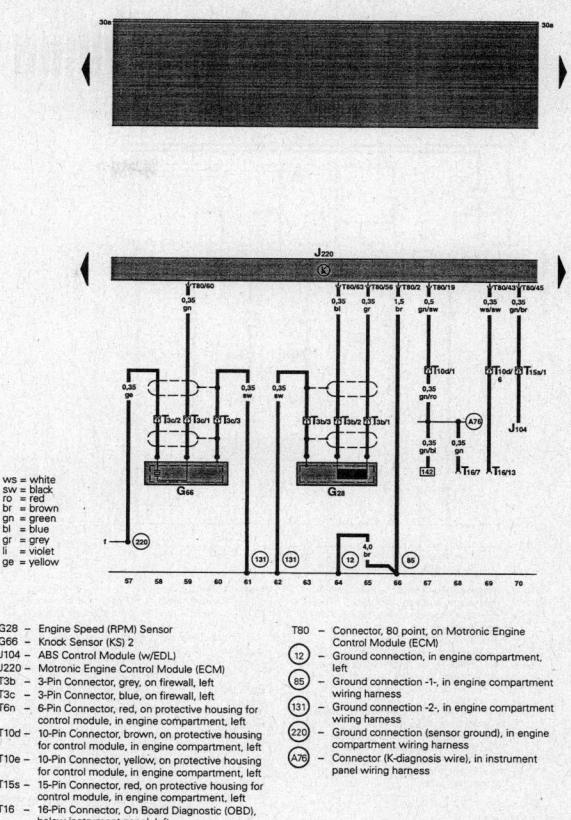

Fig. 77 Motronic wiring diagram (RPM sensor & KS 2). 1999 Passat w/1.8L engine

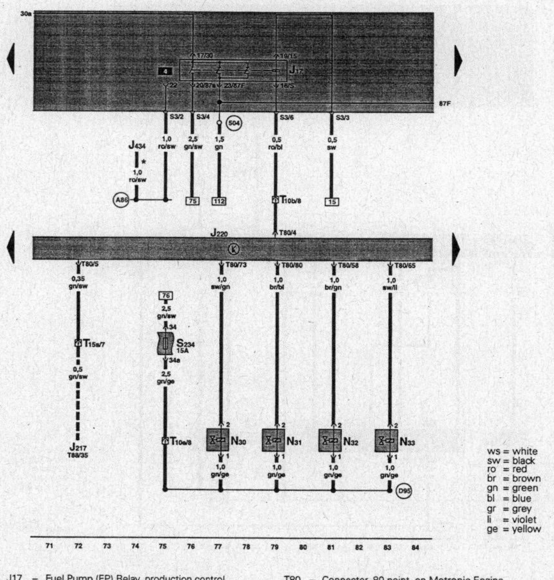

- J17 – Fuel Pump (FP) Relay, production control number (208)
- J217 – Transmission Control Module (TCM)
- J220 – Motronic Engine Control Module (ECM)
- J434 – Starting Interlock Realy (clutch position), manual transmission only
- N30 – Cylinder 1 Fuel Incjector
- N31 – Cylinder 2 Fuel Incjector
- N32 – Cylinder 3 Fuel Incjector
- N33 – Cylinder 4 Fuel Incjector
- S234 – Fuse 34 in fuse holder
- T10b – 10-Pin Connector, black, on protective housing for control module, in engine compartment, left
- T10e – 10-Pin Connector, yellow, on protective housing for control module, in engine compartment, left
- T15s – 10-Pin Connector, red, on protective housing for control module, in engine compartment, left
- T80 – Connector, 80 point, on Motronic Engine Control Module (ECM)
- T88 – Connector, 88 point, on Transmission Control Module (TCM)
- (504) – Screw connection (87F), on relay panel
- (A86) – Connection (50a), in instrument panel wiring harness
- (D95) – wire connection (injectors), in engine compartment wiring harness
- * – manual transmission only
- --- automatic transmission only

VW1029900126050X

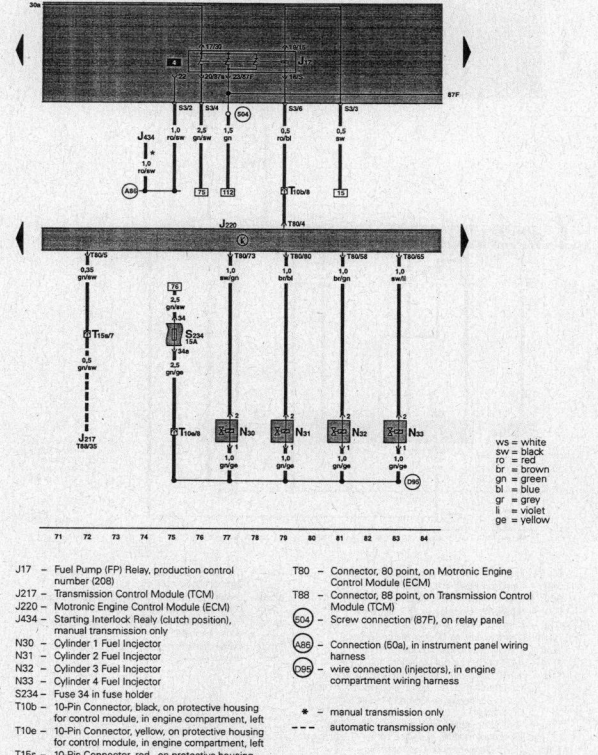

Fig. 78 Motronic wiring diagram (Fuel injectors & fuel pump relay). 1999 Passat w/1.8L engine

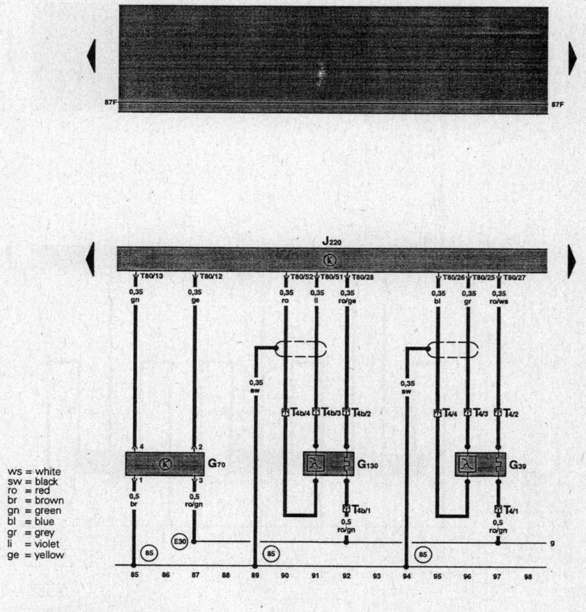

- G39 – Heated Oxygen Sensor (HO2S)
- G70 – Mass Air Flow (MAF) Sensor
- G130 – Oxygen Sensor (O2S) Behind Three Way Catalytic Converter (TWC)
- J220 – Motronic Engine Control Module (ECM)
- T4 – 4-Pin Connector
- T4b – 4-Pin Connector
- T80 – Connector, 80 point, on Motronic Engine Control Module (ECM)
- (85) – Ground connection -1-, in engine compartment wiring harness
- (E30) – Connector (87a), in wiring harness engine

VW1029900126060X

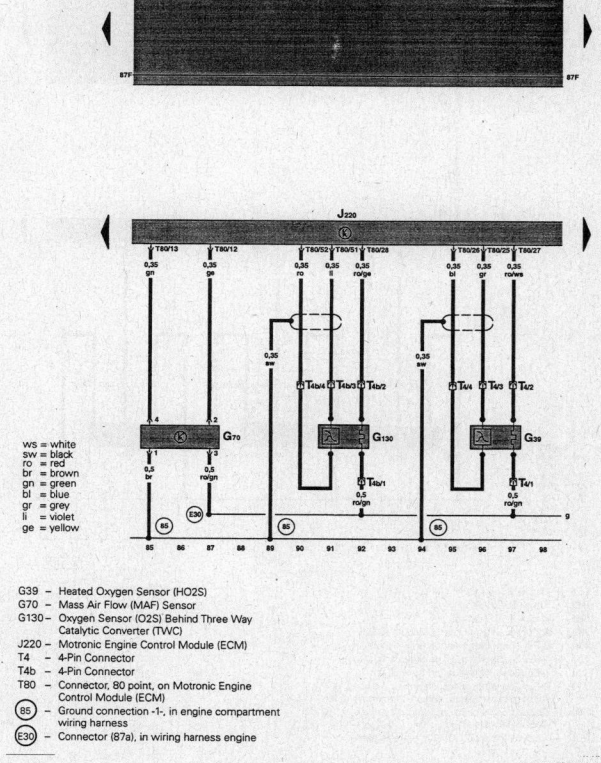

Fig. 79 Motronic wiring diagram (MAF sensor, HO2S & O2S). 1999 Passat w/1.8L engine

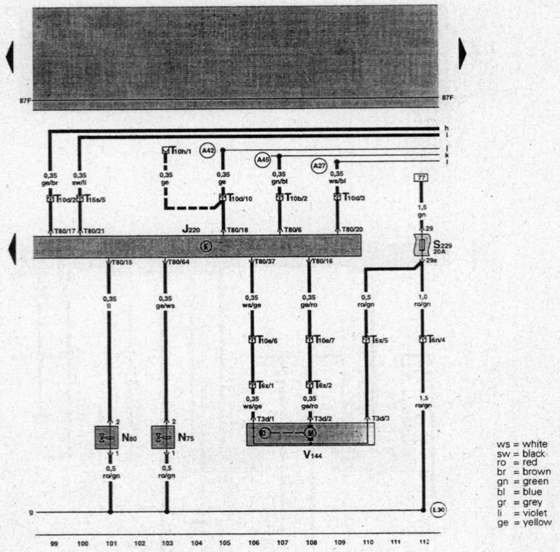

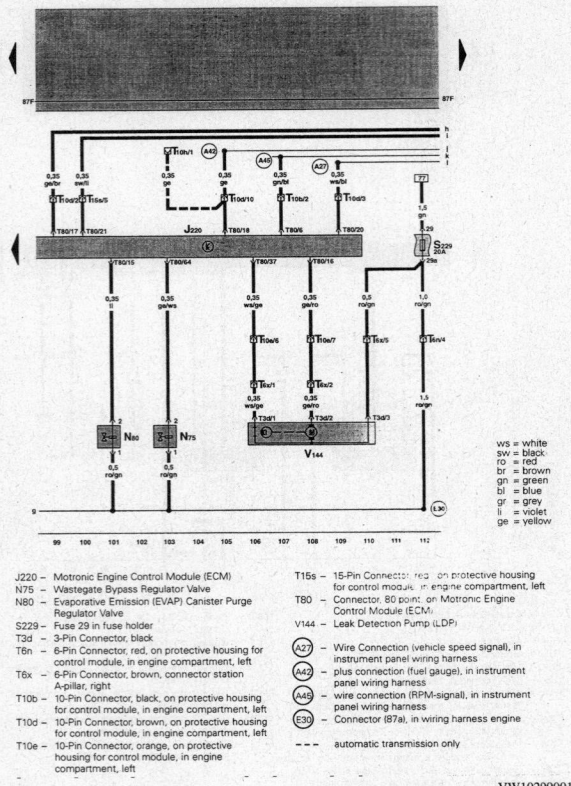

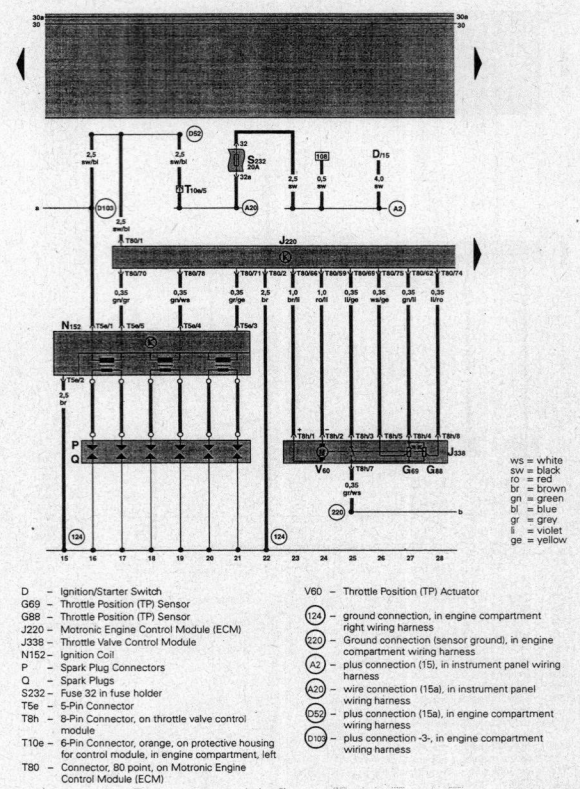

J220 – Motronic Engine Control Module (ECM)
N75 – Wastegate Bypass Regulator Valve
N80 – Evaporative Emission (EVAP) Canister Purge Regulator Valve
S229 – Fuse 29 in fuse holder
T3d – 3-Pin Connector, black
T6n – 6-Pin Connector, red, on protective housing for control module, in engine compartment, left
T6x – 6-Pin Connector, brown, connector station A-pillar, right
T10b – 10-Pin Connector, black, on protective housing for control module, in engine compartment, left
T10d – 10-Pin Connector, brown, on protective housing for control module, in engine compartment, left
T10e – 10-Pin Connector, orange, on protective housing for control module, in engine compartment, left
T15s – 15-Pin Connector, red, on protective housing for control module, in engine compartment, left
T80 – Connector, 80 point, on Motronic Engine Control Module (ECM)
V144 – Leak Detection Pump (LDP)

(A27) – Wire Connection (vehicle speed signal), in instrument panel wiring harness
(A42) – plus connection (fuel gauge), in instrument panel wiring harness
(A45) – wire connection (RPM-signal), in instrument panel wiring harness
(E30) – Connector (87a), in wiring harness engine

--- automatic transmission only

VW1029900126070X

Fig. 80 Motronic wiring diagram (Wastegate bypass regulator valve & LDP). 1999 Passat w/1.8L engine

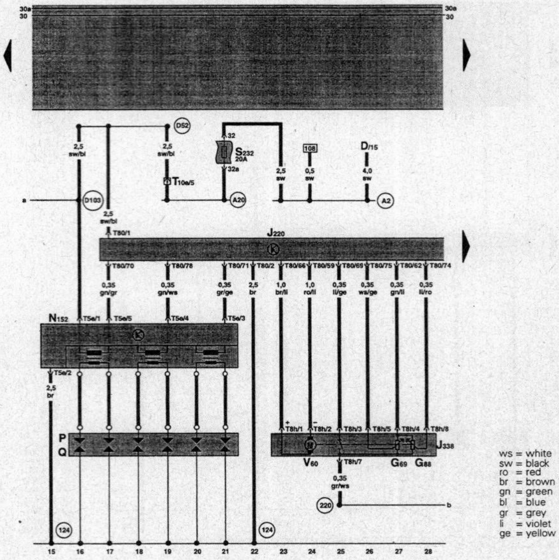

D – Ignition/Starter Switch
G69 – Throttle Position (TP) Sensor
G88 – Throttle Position (TP) Sensor
J220 – Motronic Engine Control Module (ECM)
J338 – Throttle Valve Control Module
N152 – Ignition Coil
P – Spark Plug Connectors
Q – Spark Plugs
S232 – Fuse 32 in fuse holder
T5e – 5-Pin Connector
T8h – 8-Pin Connector, on throttle valve control module
T10e – 6-Pin Connector, orange, on protective housing for control module, in engine compartment, left
T80 – Connector, 80 point, on Motronic Engine Control Module (ECM)
V60 – Throttle Position (TP) Actuator

(124) – ground connection, in engine compartment right wiring harness
(220) – Ground connection (sensor ground), in engine compartment wiring harness
(A2) – plus connection (15), in instrument panel wiring harness
(A20) – wire connection (15a), in instrument panel wiring harness
(D52) – plus connection (15a), in engine compartment wiring harness
(D103) – plus connection -3-, in engine compartment wiring harness

VW1029900127010X

Fig. 81 Motronic wiring diagram (Ignition system & throttle valve control module). 1999 Passat w/2.8L engine

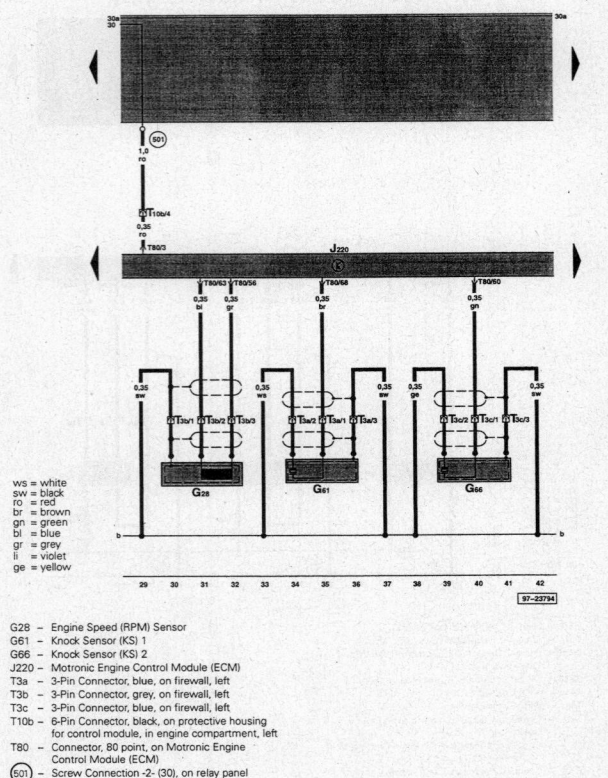

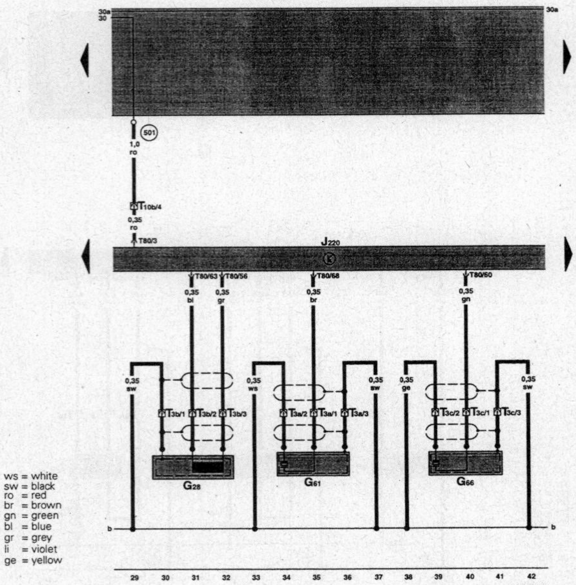

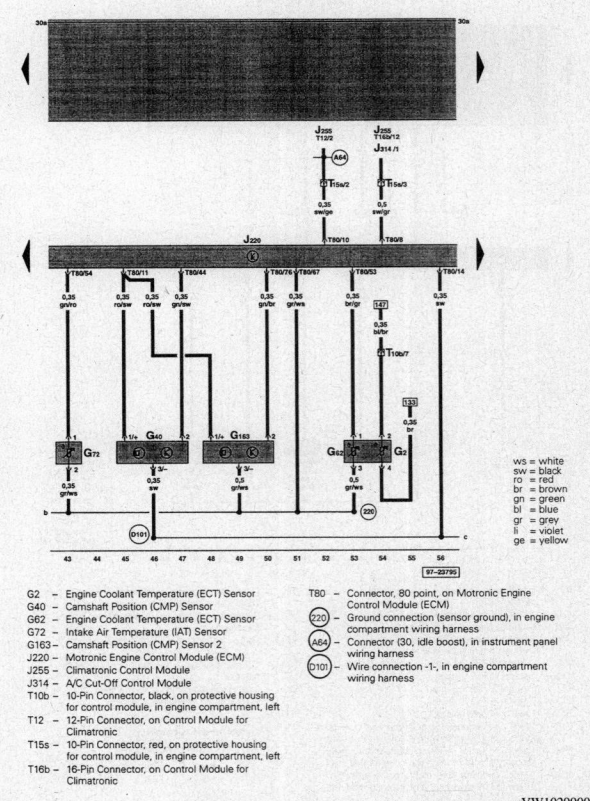

G28 – Engine Speed (RPM) Sensor
G61 – Knock Sensor (KS) 1
G66 – Knock Sensor (KS) 2
J220 – Motronic Engine Control Module (ECM)
T3a – 3-Pin Connector, blue, on firewall, left
T3b – 3-Pin Connector, grey, on firewall, left
T3c – 3-Pin Connector, blue, on firewall, left
T10b – 6-Pin Connector, black, on protective housing for control module, in engine compartment, left
T80 – Connector, 80 point, on Motronic Engine Control Module (ECM)
(501) – Screw Connection -2- (30), on relay panel

VW1029900127020X

Fig. 82 Motronic wiring diagram (RPM sensor & KS). 1999 Passat w/2.8L engine

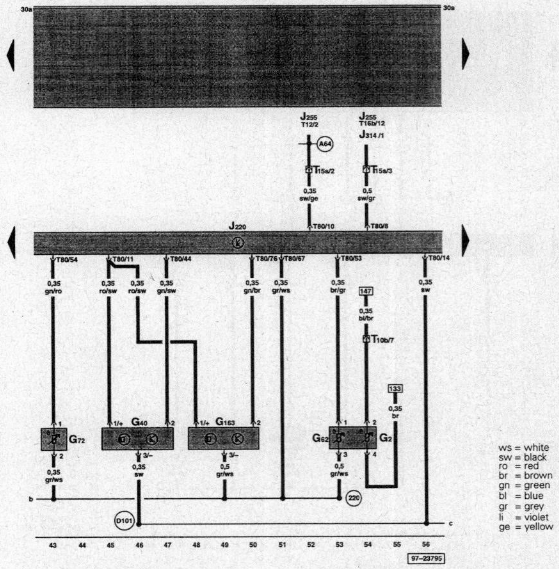

G2 – Engine Coolant Temperature (ECT) Sensor
G40 – Camshaft Position (CMP) Sensor
G62 – Engine Coolant Temperature (ECT) Sensor
G72 – Intake Air Temperature (IAT) Sensor
G163 – Camshaft Position (CMP) Sensor 2
J220 – Motronic Engine Control Module (ECM)
J255 – Climatronic Control Module
J314 – A/C Cut-Off Control Module
T10b – 10-Pin Connector, black, on protective housing for control module, in engine compartment, left
T12 – 12-Pin Connector, on Control Module for Climatronic
T15s – 10-Pin Connector, red, on protective housing for control module, in engine compartment, left
T16b – 16-Pin Connector, on Control Module for Climatronic
T80 – Connector, 80 point, on Motronic Engine Control Module (ECM)
(220) – Ground connection (sensor ground), in engine compartment wiring harness
(A64) – Connector (30, idle boost), in instrument panel wiring harness
(D101) – Wire connection -1-, in engine compartment wiring harness

VW1029900127030X

Fig. 83 Motronic wiring diagram (CMP, ECT & IAT sensors). 1999 Passat w/2.8L engine

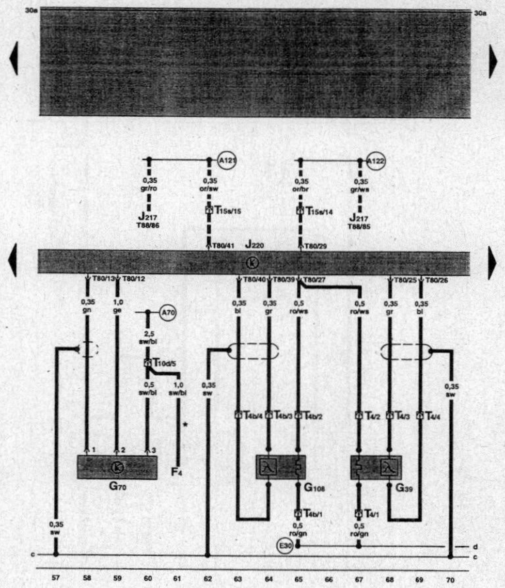

ws = white
sw = black
ro = red
br = brown
gn = green
bl = blue
gr = grey
li = violet
ge = yellow

F4 – Back-Up Light Switch
G39 – Heated Oxygen Sensor (HO2S)
G70 – Mass Air Flow (MAF) Sensor
G108 – Heated Oxygen Sensor (HO2S) 2
J217 – Transmission Control Module (TCM)
J220 – Motronic Engine Control Module (ECM)
T4 – 4-Pin Connector, black
T4b – 4-Pin Connector, black
T10d – 10-Pin Connector, brown, on protective housing for control module, in engine compartment, left
T15s – 15-Pin Connector, red, on protective housing for control module, in engine compartment,left
T80 – Connector, 80 point, on Motronic Engine Control Module (ECM)
T88 – Connector, 88 point, on Transmission Control Module (TCM)

A70 – Connector (15a, fuse 231), in instrument panel wiring harness
A121 Connector (High-Bus), in instrument panel wiring harness
A122 Connector (Low-Bus), in instrument panel wiring harness
E30 Connector (87a), in wiring harness engine
--- automatic transmission only
* – manual transmission only

VW1029900127040X

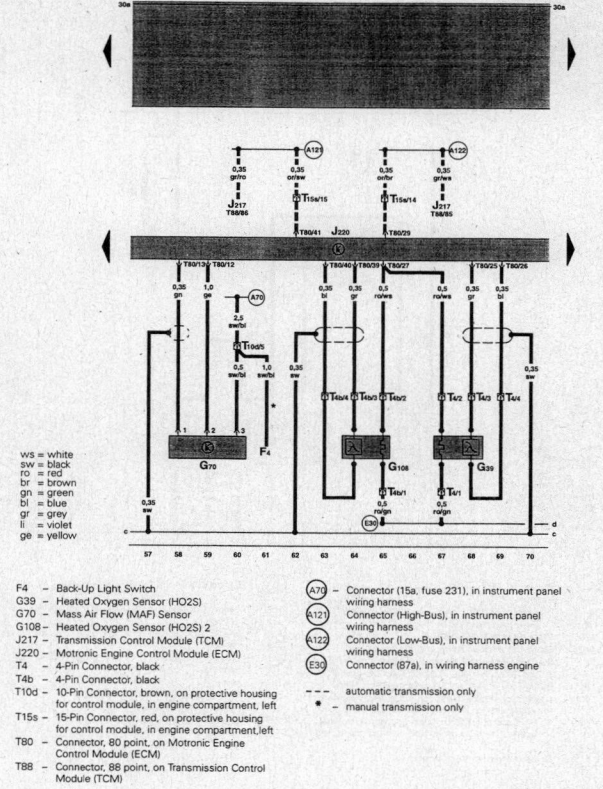

Fig. 84 Motronic wiring diagram (MAF sensor & HO2S). 1999 Passat w/2.8L engine

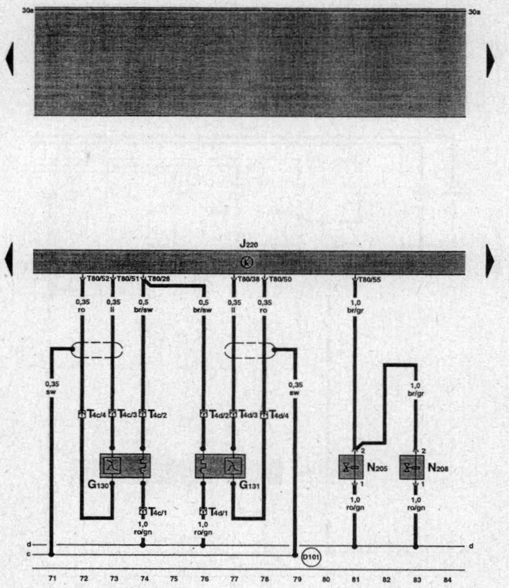

ws = white
sw = black
ro = red
br = brown
gn = green
bl = blue
gr = grey
li = violet
ge = yellow

G130 – Oxygen Sensor (O2S) Behind Three Way Catalytic Converter (TWC)
G131 – Oxygen Sensor (O2S) 2 Behind Three Way Catalytic Converter (TWC)
J220 – Motronic Engine Control Module (ECM)
N205 – Valve -1- for camshaft adjustment
N208 – Valve -2- for camshaft adjustment
T4c – 4-Pin Connector, green
T4d – 4-Pin Connector, brown
T80 – Connector, 80 point, on Motronic Engine Control Module (ECM)

D101 – Wire connection -1-, in engine compartment wiring harness

VW1029900127050X

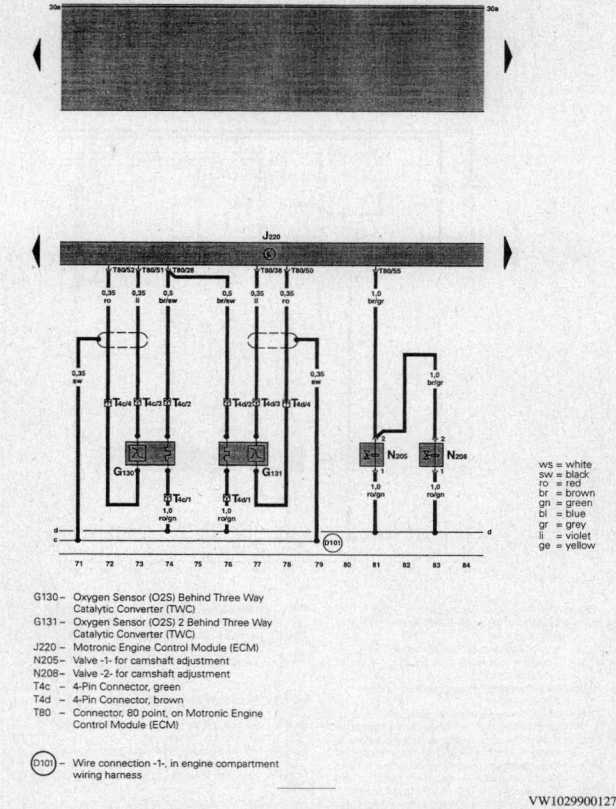

Fig. 85 Motronic wiring diagram (O2S & valve for camshaft adjustment). 1999 Passat w/2.8L engine

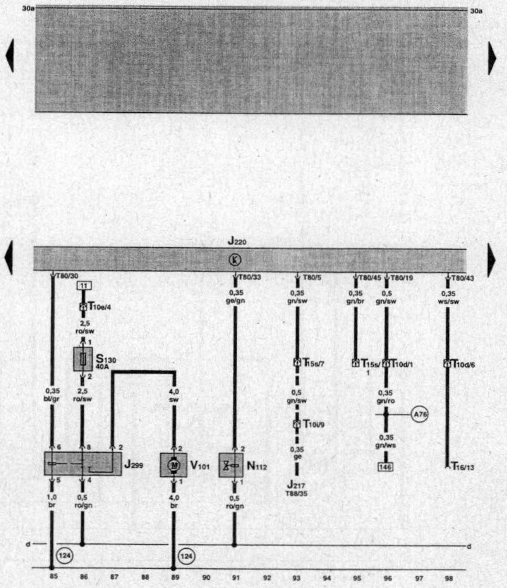

ws = white
sw = black
ro = red
br = brown
gn = green
bl = blue
gr = grey
li = violet
ge = yellow

J217 – Transmission Control Module (TCM)
J220 – Motronic Engine Control Module (ECM)
J299 – Secondary Air Injection (AIR) Pump Relay (203), in protective housing for control module
N112 – Secondary Air Injection (AIR) Solenoid Valve, green
S130 – Fuse for secondary air pump, in fuse adaptor above relay panel
T10d – 10-Pin Connector, brown, on protective housing for control module, in engine compartment, left
T10e – 10-Pin Connector, orange, on protective housing for control module, in engine compartment, left
T10i – 10-Pin Connector, blue, on coupling station A-pillar, right
T15s – 15-Pin Connector, red, on protective housing for control module, in engine compartment,left
T16 – Data Link Connector (DLC), below instrument panel, left
T80 – Connector, 80 point, on Motronic Engine Control Module (ECM)
T88 – Connector, 88 point, on Transmission Control Module (TCM)
V101 – Secondary Air Injection (AIR) Pump Motor

124 – ground connection, in engine compartment right wiring harness
A76 Connector (K-diagnosis wire), in instrument panel wiring harness
---- – automatic transmission only

VW1029900127060X

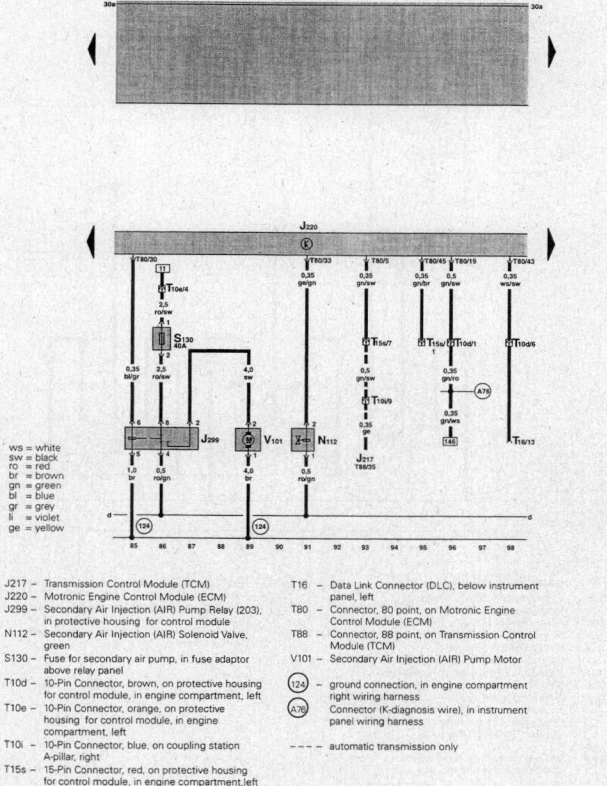

Fig. 86 Motronic wiring diagram (AIR system & OBD). 1999 Passat w/2.8L engine

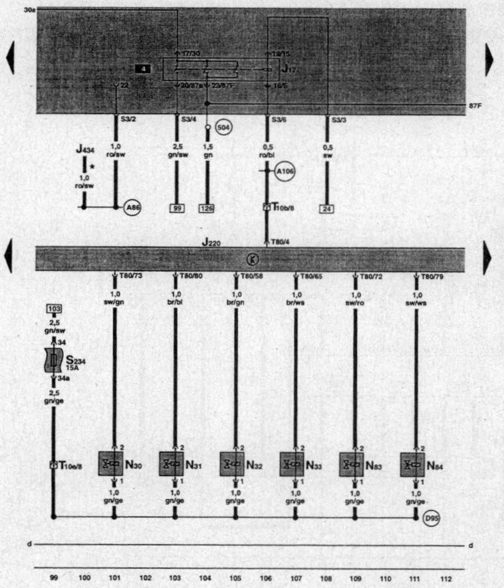

ws = white
sw = black
ro = red
br = brown
gn = green
bl = blue
gr = grey
li = violet
ge = yellow

J17 – Fuel Pump (FP) Relay, production control number (208)
J220 – Motronic Engine Control Module (ECM)
J434 – Starting Interlock Relay (clutch position)
N30 – Cylinder 1 Fuel Injector
N31 – Cylinder 2 Fuel Injector
N32 – Cylinder 3 Fuel Injector
N33 – Cylinder 4 Fuel Injector
N83 – Cylinder 5 Fuel Injector
N84 – Cylinder 6 Fuel Injector
S234 – Fuse 34 in fuse holder
T10b – 10-Pin Connector, black, on protective housing for control module, in engine compartment, left
T10e – 10-Pin Connector, yellow, on protective housing for control module, in engine compartment, left
T80 – Connector, 80 point, on Motronic Engine Control Module (ECM)

504 – Screw Connection (87F), on relay panel
A86 – Connection (50a) in instrument panel wiring harness
A106 – Connector -2- (86s), in instrument panel wiring harness
D95 – wire connection (injectors), in engine compartment wiring harness
* – manual transmission only

VW1029900127070X

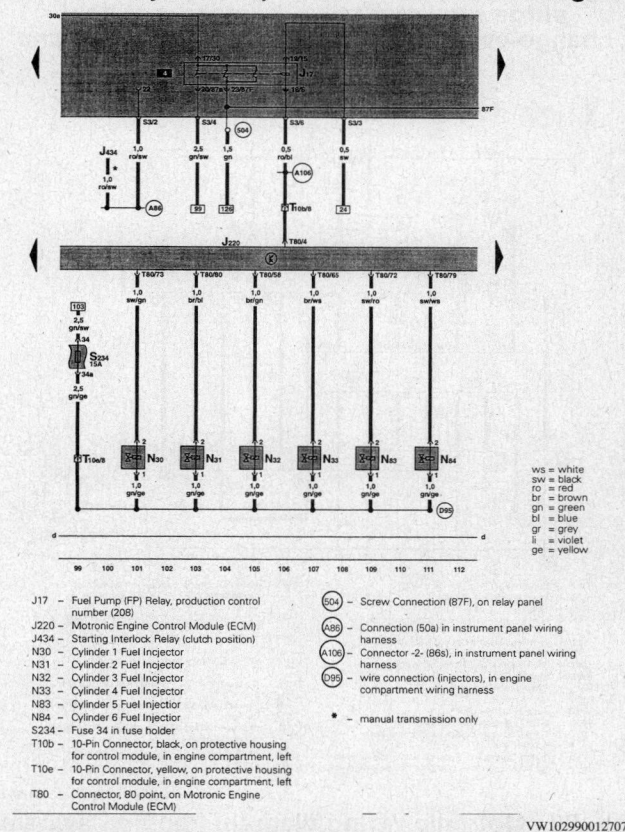

Fig. 87 Motronic wiring diagram (Fuel injectors & fuel pump relay). 1999 Passat w/2.8L engine

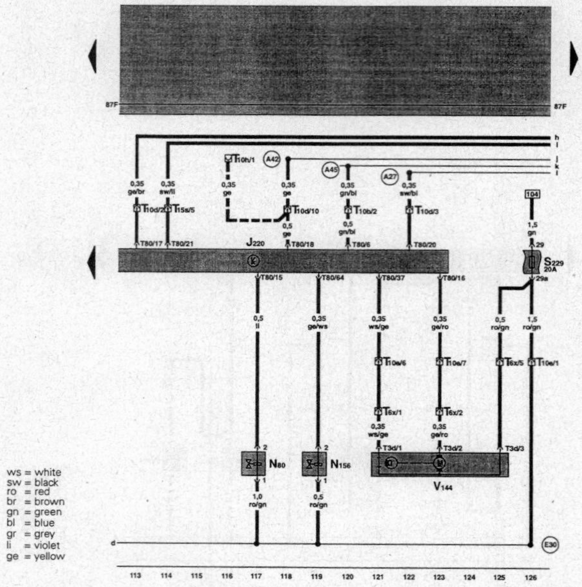

J220 – Motronic Engine Control Module (ECM)
N80 – Evaporative Emission (EVAP) Canister Purge Regulator Valve
N156 – Intake Manifold Change-Over Valve
S229 – Fuse 29 in fuse holder
T3d – 3-Pin Connector
T6x – 6-Pin Connector, brown, connector station A-pillar, right
T10b – 10-Pin Connector, black, on protective housing for control module, in engine compartment, left
T10d – 10-Pin Connector, brown, on protective housing for control module, in engine compartment, left
T10e – 10-Pin Connector, yellow, on protective housing for control module, in engine compartment, left
T10h – 10-Pin Connector, blue, on protective housing for control module, in engine compartment, left
T15s – 15-Pin Connector, red, on protective housing for control module, in engine compartment, left
T80 – Connector, 80 point, on Motronic Engine Control Module (ECM)
V144 – Diagnosis pump for fuel system
(A27) – Wire Connection (vehicle speed signal), in instrument panel wiring harness
(A42) – plus connection (fuel gauge), in instrument panel wiring harness
(A45) – wire connection (RPM-signal), in instrument panel wiring harness
(E30) Connector (87a), in wiring harness engine
- - - automatic transmission only

VW1029900127080X

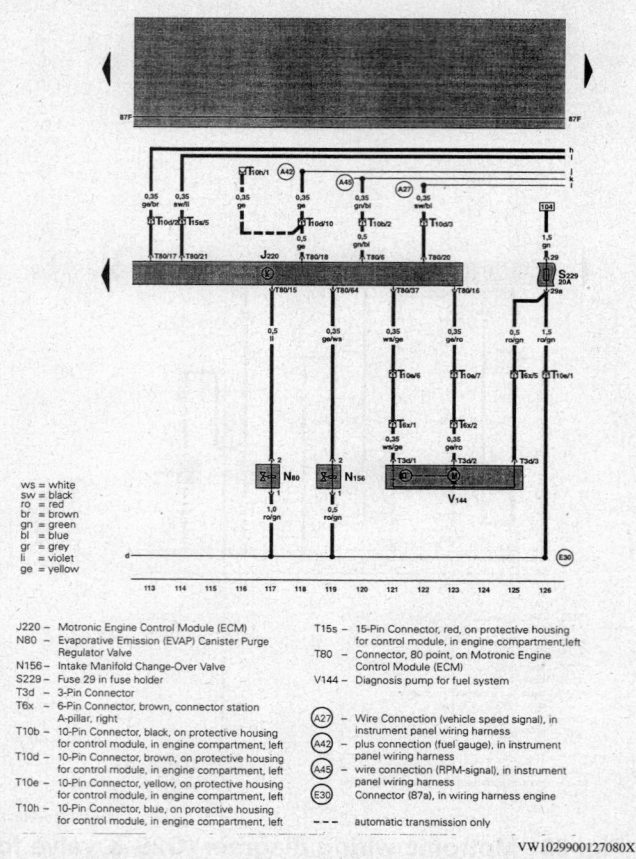

Fig. 88 Motronic wiring diagram (EVAP canister purge regulator valve & intake manifold change-over valve). 1999 Passat w/2.8L engine

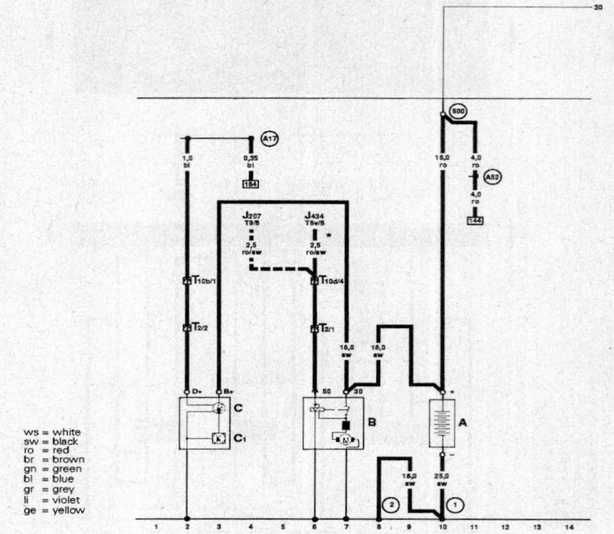

A - Battery
B - Starter
C - Generator (GEN)
C1 - Voltage Regulator (VR)
J207 - Starting Interlock Relay
J434 - Starting Interlock Relay (clutch position)
T2 - Double Connector, on engine right
T8v - 8-Pin Connector, on Starting Interlock Relay
T9 - 9-Pin Connector, on Starting Interlock Relay
T10b - 10-Pin Connector, black, on protective housing for control module, in engine compartment, left
T10d - 10-Pin Connector, brown, on protective housing for control module, in engine compartment, left
(1) - Ground strap, battery to body
(2) - Ground strap, transmission to body
(500) - Screw Connection -1- (30), on relay panel
(A17) - wire connection (61), in instrument panel wiring harness
(A52) - plus connection (30), in instrument panel wiring harness
- - - automatic transmission only
* - manual transmission only

VW1020000158010X

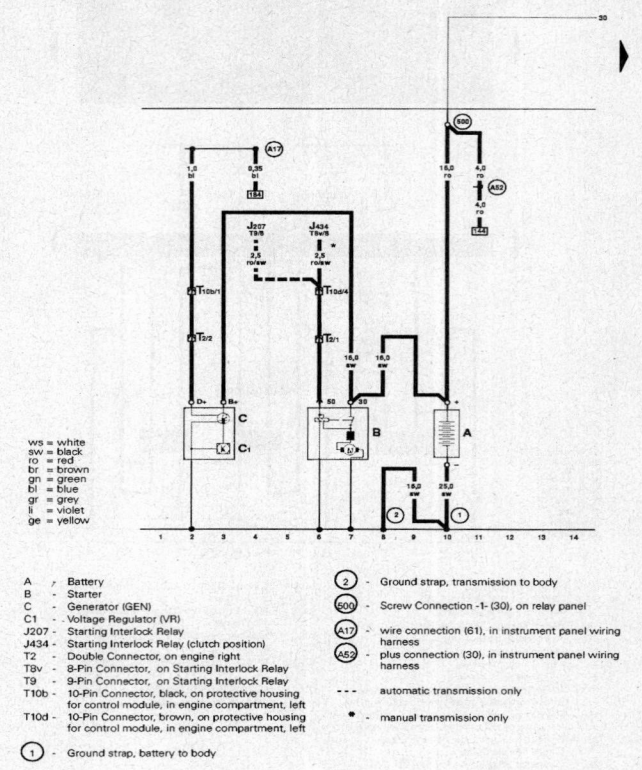

Fig. 89 Motronic wiring diagram (Battery, starter & alternator). 2000 Passat w/1.8L ATW engine

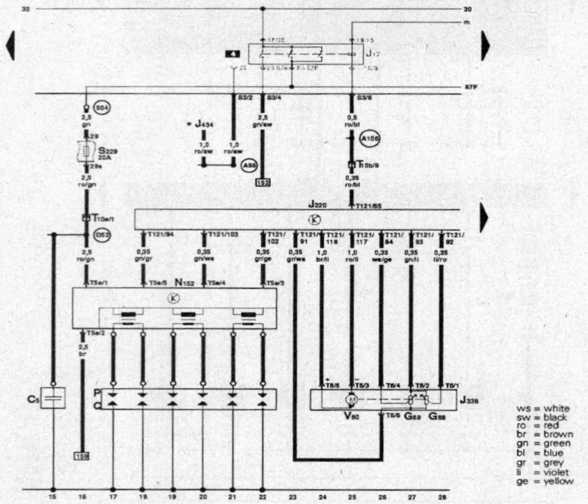

C5 - Suppressor (Terminal 15)
G69 - Throttle Position (TP) Sensor
G88 - Throttle Position (TP) Sensor
J17 - Fuel Pump (FP) Relay, production control number (208)
J220 - Motronic Engine Control Module (ECM)
J338 - Throttle Valve Control Module
J434 - Starting Interlock Relay (clutch position)
N152 - Ignition Coil
P - Spark Plug Connectors
Q - Spark Plugs
S229 - Fuse in fuse holder
T5e - 5-Pin Connector, black, on Ignition Coil
T6 - 6-Pin Connector, black, on Throttel Valve Control Module
T10b - 10-Pin Connector, black, on protective housing for control module, in engine compartment, left
T10e - 10-Pin Connector, orange, on protective housing for control module, in engine compartment, left
T121 - Connector, 121 point, on Motronic Engine Control Module (ECM)
V60 - Throttle Position (TP) Actuator
(504) - Screw Connection (87F), on relay panel
(A86) - Connection (50a) in instrument panel wiring harness
(A106) - Connector -2- (86s), in instrument panel wiring harness
(D52) - plus connection (15a), in engine compartment wiring harness
* - manual transmission only

VW1020000158020X

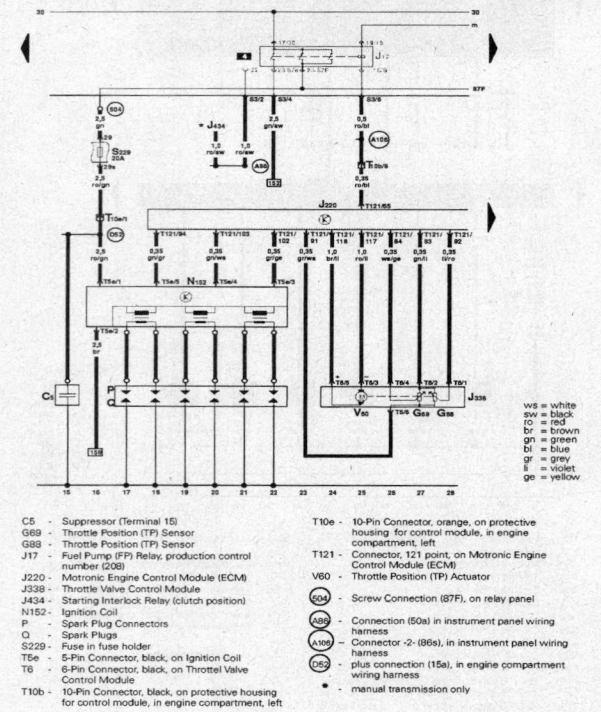

Fig. 90 Motronic wiring diagram (Ignition system, ECM & throttle valve control module. 2000 Passat w/1.8L ATW engine

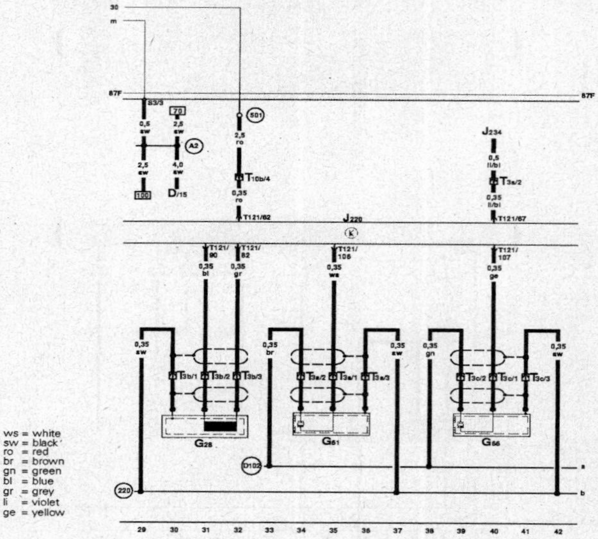

D - Ignition/Starter Switch
G28 - Engine Speed (RPM) Sensor
G61 - Knock Sensor (KS) 1
G66 - Knock Sensor (KS) 2
J220 - Motronic Engine Control Module (ECM)
J234 - Airbag Control Module
T3a - 3-Pin Connector, blue, on firewall, left
T3b - 3-Pin Connector, grey, on firewall, left
T3c - 3-Pin Connector, blue, on firewall, left
T3s - 3-Pin Connector, red, on protective housing for control module, in engine compartment, left
T121 - Connector, 121 point, on Motronic Engine Control Module (ECM)
(220) - Ground connection (sensor ground), in engine compartment wiring harness
(501) - Screw Connection -2- (30), on relay panel
(A2) - plus connection (15), in instrument panel wiring harness
(D102) - Wire connection -2-, in engine compartment wiring harness

VW1020000158030X

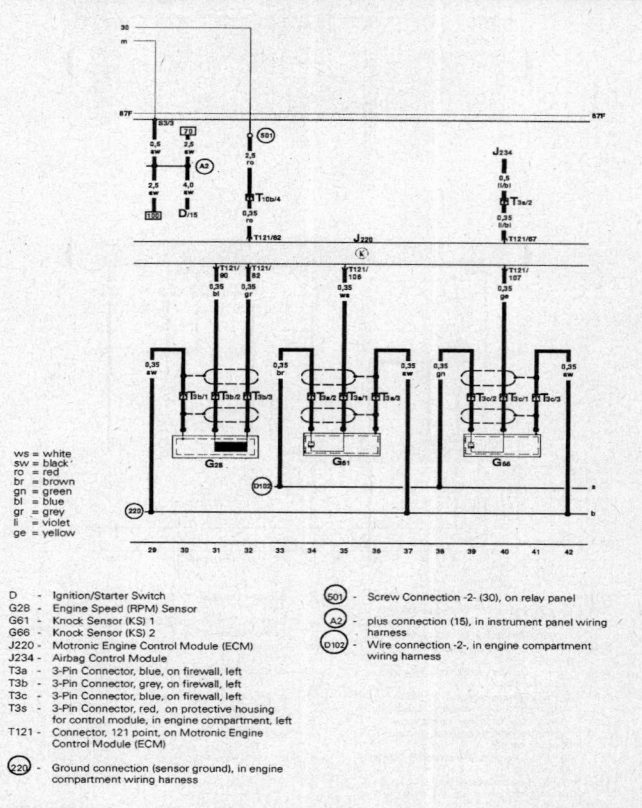

Fig. 91 Motronic wiring diagram (RPM & knock sensors). 2000 Passat w/1.8L ATW engine

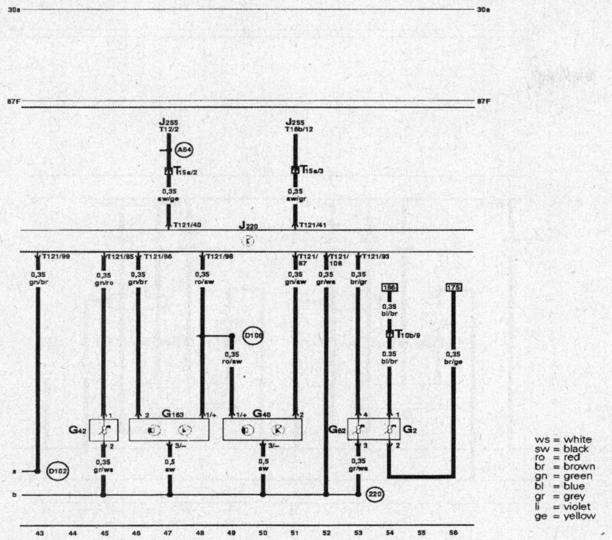

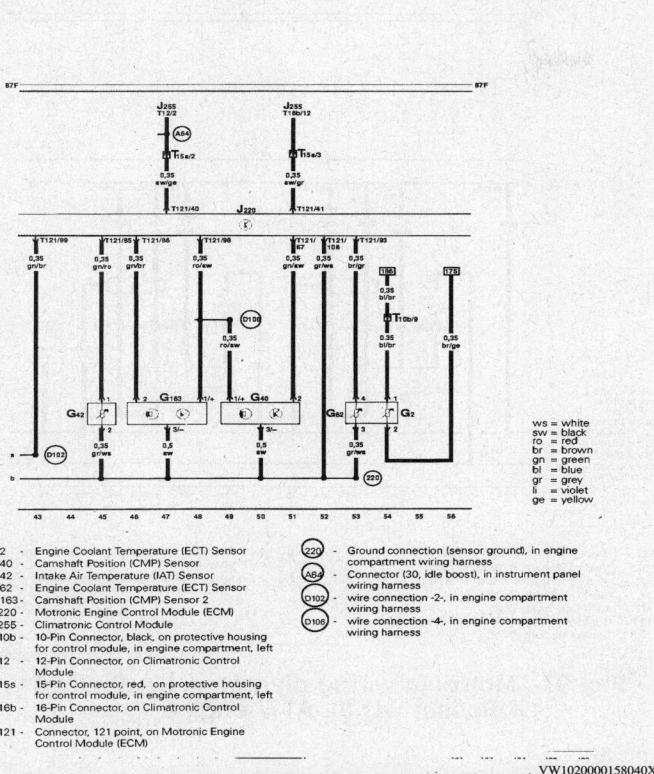

G2 - Engine Coolant Temperature (ECT) Sensor
G40 - Camshaft Position (CMP) Sensor
G42 - Intake Air Temperature (IAT) Sensor
G62 - Engine Coolant Temperature (ECT) Sensor
G163 - Camshaft Position (CMP) Sensor 2
J220 - Motronic Engine Control Module (ECM)
J255 - Climatronic Control Module
T10b - 10-Pin Connector, black, on protective housing for control module, in engine compartment, left
T12 - 12-Pin Connector, on Climatronic Control Module
T15s - 15-Pin Connector, red, on protective housing for control module, in engine compartment, left
T16b - 16-Pin Connector, on Climatronic Control Module
T121 - Connector, 121 point, on Motronic Engine Control Module (ECM)

(220) - Ground connection (sensor ground), in engine compartment wiring harness
(A64) - Connector (30, idle boost), in instrument panel wiring harness
(D102) - wire connection -2-, in engine compartment wiring harness
(D106) - wire connection -4-, in engine compartment wiring harness

VW1020000158040X

Fig. 92 Motronic wiring diagram (CMP, ECT & IAT sensors). 2000 Passat w/1.8L ATW engine

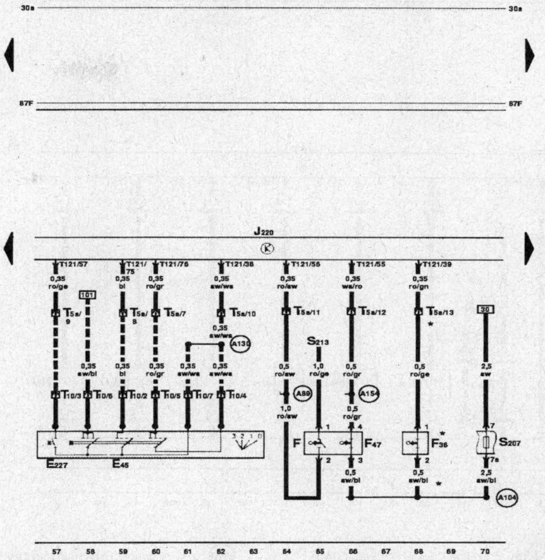

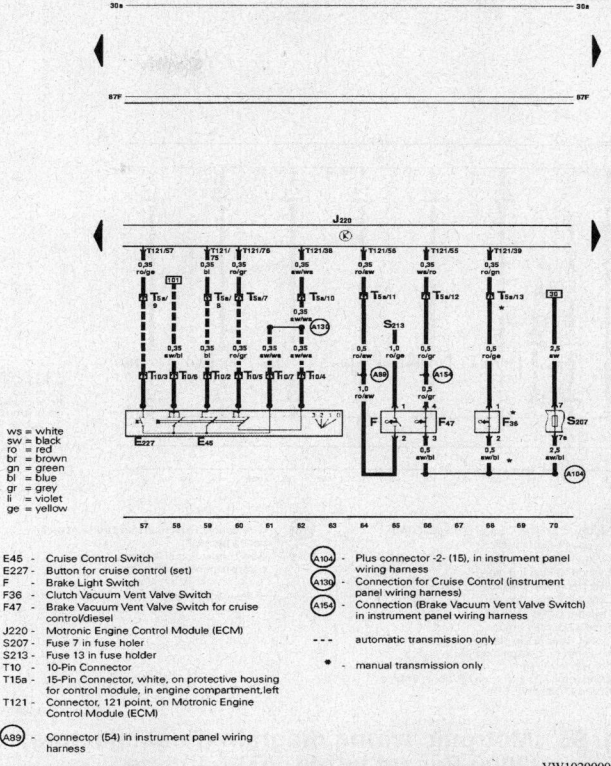

E45 - Cruise Control Switch
E227 - Button for cruise control (set)
F - Brake Light Switch
F36 - Clutch Vacuum Vent Valve Switch
F47 - Brake Vacuum Vent Valve Switch for cruise control/diesel
J220 - Motronic Engine Control Module (ECM)
S207 - Fuse 7 in fuse holer
S213 - Fuse 13 in fuse holder
T10 - 10-Pin Connector
T15a - 15-Pin Connector, white, on protective housing for control module, in engine compartment,left
T121 - Connector, 121 point, on Motronic Engine Control Module (ECM)

(A89) - Connector (54) in instrument panel wiring harness

(A104) - Plus connector -2- (15), in instrument panel wiring harness
(A130) - Connection for Cruise Control (instrument panel wiring harness)
(A154) - Connection (Brake Vacuum Vent Valve Switch) in instrument panel wiring harness

- - - automatic transmission only

* - manual transmission only

VW1020000158050X

Fig. 93 Motronic wiring diagram (Cruise control, brake lamp & clutch vacuum vent valve switches). 2000 Passat w/1.8L ATW engine

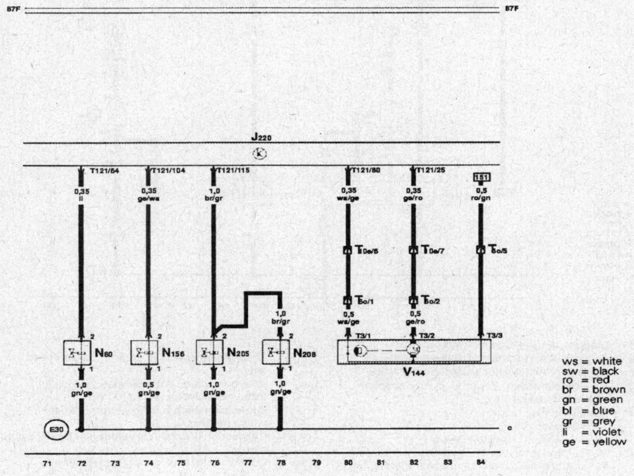

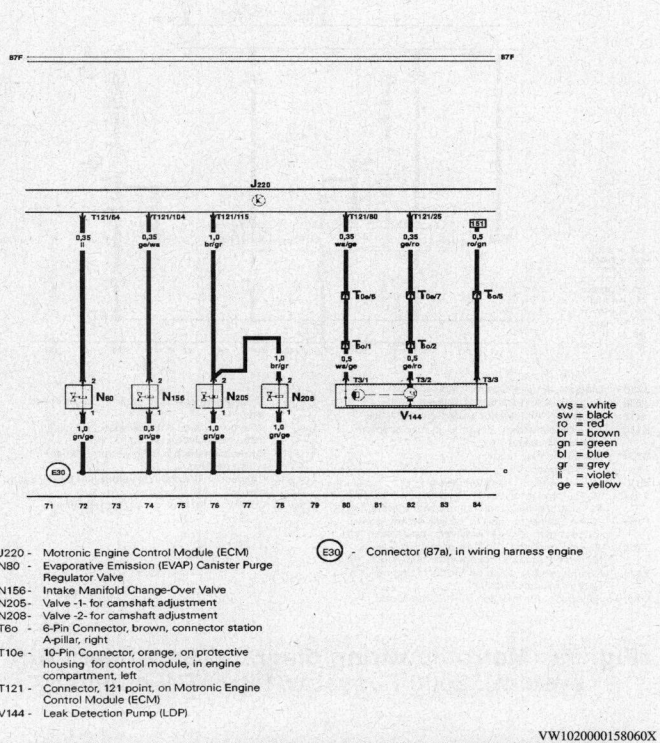

J220 - Motronic Engine Control Module (ECM)
N80 - Evaporative Emission (EVAP) Canister Purge Regulator Valve
N156 - Intake Manifold Change-Over Valve
N205 - Valve -1- for camshaft adjustment
N208 - Valve -2- for camshaft adjustment
T6o - 6-Pin Connector, brown, connector station A-pillar, right
T10e - 10-Pin Connector, orange, on protective housing for control module, in engine compartment, left
T121 - Connector, 121 point, on Motronic Engine Control Module (ECM)
V144 - Leak Detection Pump (LDP)

(E30) - Connector (87a), in wiring harness engine

VW1020000158060X

Fig. 94 Motronic wiring diagram (Camshaft adjuster valve & LDP). 2000 Passat w/1.8L ATW engine

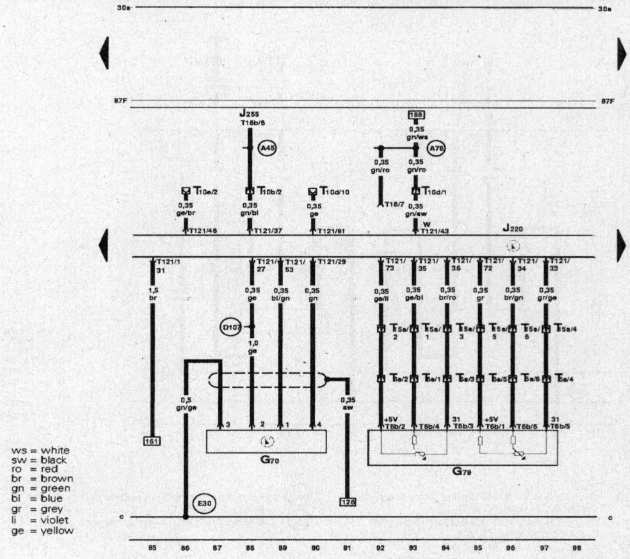

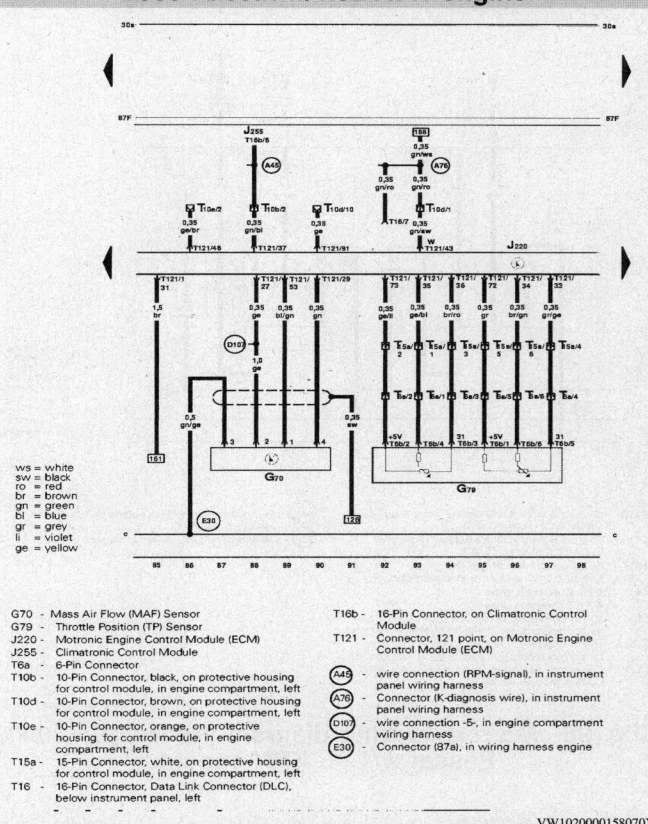

G70 - Mass Air Flow (MAF) Sensor
G79 - Throttle Position (TP) Sensor
J220 - Motronic Engine Control Module (ECM)
J255 - Climatronic Control Module
T6a - 6-Pin Connector
T10b - 10-Pin Connector, black, on protective housing for control module, in engine compartment, left
T10d - 10-Pin Connector, brown, on protective housing for control module, in engine compartment, left
T10e - 10-Pin Connector, orange, on protective housing for control module, in engine compartment, left
T15a - 15-Pin Connector, white, on protective housing for control module, in engine compartment, left
T16 - 16-Pin Connector, Data Link Connector (DLC), below instrument panel, left
T16b - 16-Pin Connector, on Climatronic Control Module
T121 - Connector, 121 point, on Motronic Engine Control Module (ECM)

(A45) - wire connection (RPM-signal), in instrument panel wiring harness
(A76) - Connector (K-diagnosis wire), in instrument panel wiring harness
(D107) - wire connection -5-, in engine compartment wiring harness
(E30) - Connector (87a), in wiring harness engine

VW1020000158070X

Fig. 95 Motronic wiring diagram (MAF, TPS & DLC). 2000 Passat w/1.8L ATW engine

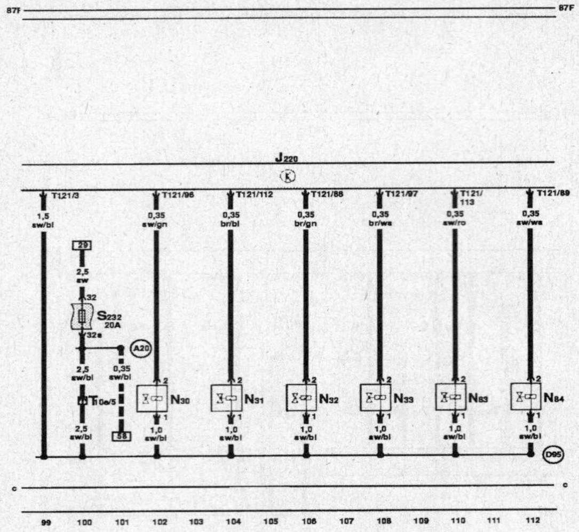

ws = white
sw = black
ro = red
br = brown
gn = green
bl = blue
gr = grey
li = violet
ge = yellow

J220 - Motronic Engine Control Module (ECM)
N30 - Cylinder 1 Fuel Injector
N31 - Cylinder 2 Fuel Injector
N32 - Cylinder 3 Fuel Injector
N33 - Cylinder 4 Fuel Injector
N83 - Cylinder 5 Fuel Injector
N84 - Cylinder 6 Fuel Injector
S232 - Fuse 32 in fuse holder
T10e - 10-Pin Connector, orange, on protective housing for control module, in engine compartment, left
T121 - Connector, 121 point, on Motronic Engine Control Module (ECM)

A20 - wire connection (15a), in instrument panel wiring harness
D95 - wire connection (injectors), in engine compartment wiring harness
--- cruise control only

VW1020000158080X

Fig. 96 Motronic wiring diagram (Fuel injectors). 2000 Passat w/1.8L ATW engine

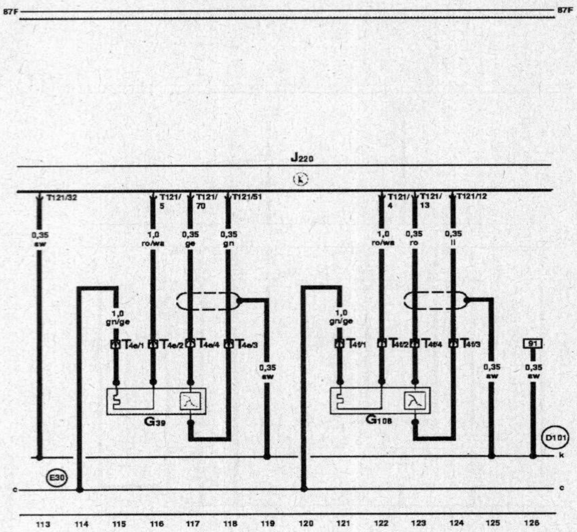

ws = white
sw = black
ro = red
br = brown
gn = green
bl = blue
gr = grey
li = violet
ge = yellow

G39 - Heated Oxygen Sensor (HO2S)
G108 - Heated Oxygen Sensor (HO2S) 2
J220 - Motronic Engine Control Module (ECM)
T4e - 4-Pin Connector, black
T4f - 4-Pin Connector, black
T121 - Connector, 121 point, on Motronic Engine Control Module (ECM)

D101 - wire connection -1-, in engine compartment wiring harness
E30 - Connector (87a), in wiring harness engine

VW1020000158090X

Fig. 97 Motronic wiring diagram (HO_2S). 2000 Passat w/1.8L ATW engine

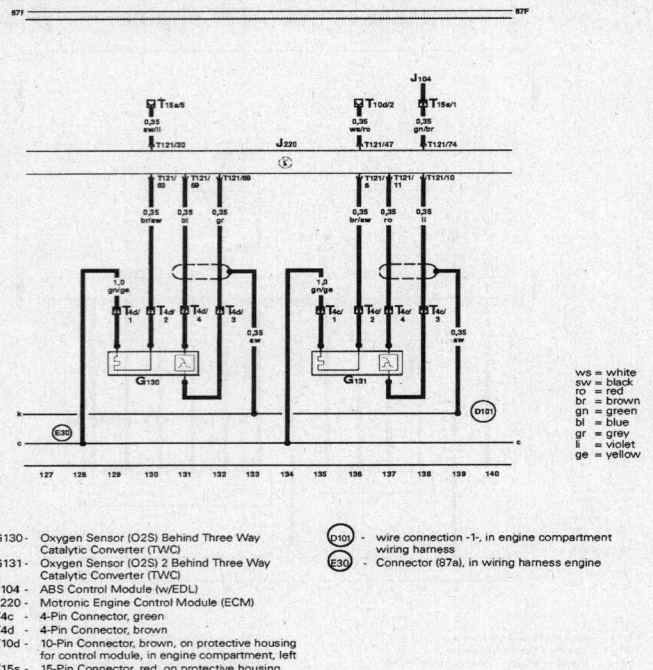

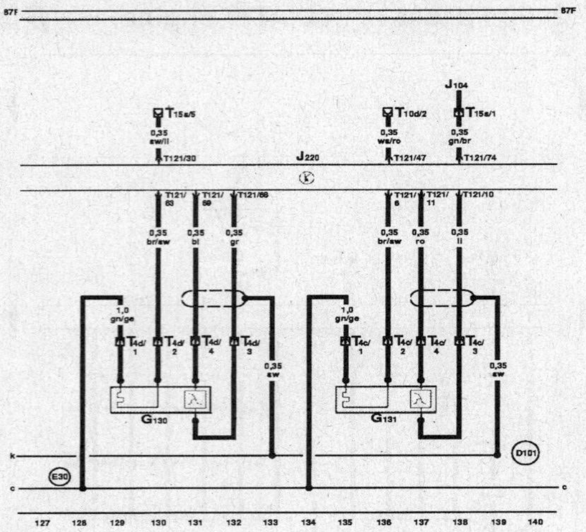

ws = white
sw = black
ro = red
br = brown
gn = green
bl = blue
gr = grey
li = violet
ge = yellow

G130 - Oxygen Sensor (O2S) Behind Three Way Catalytic Converter (TWC)
G131 - Oxygen Sensor (O2S) 2 Behind Three Way Catalytic Converter (TWC)
J104 - ABS Control Module (w/EDL)
J220 - Motronic Engine Control Module (ECM)
T4c - 4-Pin Connector, green
T4d - 4-Pin Connector, brown
T10d - 10-Pin Connector, brown, on protective housing for control module, in engine compartment, left
T15s - 15-Pin Connector, red, on protective housing for control module, in engine compartment, left
T121 - Connector, 121 point, on Motronic Engine Control Module (ECM)

D101 - wire connection -1-, in engine compartment wiring harness
E30 - Connector (87a), in wiring harness engine

VW1020000158100X

Fig. 98 Motronic wiring diagram (Rear O_2S). 2000 Passat w/1.8L ATW engine

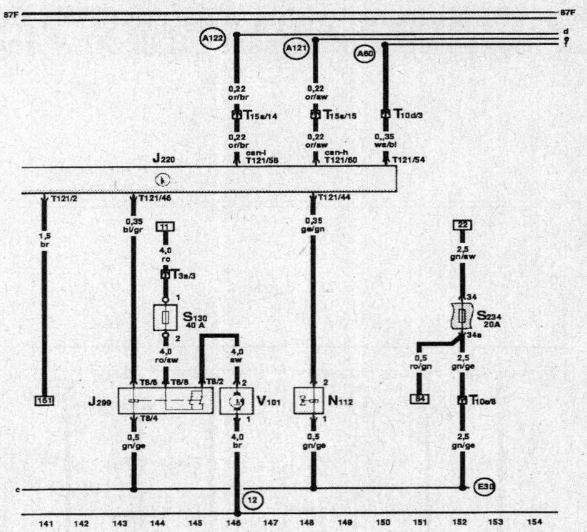

ws = white
sw = black
ro = red
br = brown
gn = green
bl = blue
gr = grey
li = violet
ge = yellow
or = orange

J220 - Motronic Engine Control Module (ECM)
J229 - Secondary Air Injection (AIR) Pump Relay
N112 - Secondary Air Injection (AIR) Solenoid Valve
S130 - Fuse for secondary air pump, in fuse adaptor above relay panel
S234 - Fuse 34 in fuse holder
T3a - 3-Pin Connector,
T8 - 8-Pin Connector, black on Radio
T10d - 10-Pin Connector, brown, on protective housing for control module, in engine compartment, left
T10e - 10-Pin Connector, yellow, on protective housing for control module, in engine compartment, left
T15s - 15-Pin Connector, red, , on protective housing for control module, in engine compartment, left
T121 - Connector, 121 point, on Motronic Engine Control Module (ECM)
V101 - Secondary Air Injection (AIR) Pump Motor

12 - Ground connection, in engine compartment, left
A60 - Wire connection (Vehicle speed signal), in instrument cluster wiring harness
A121 - Connection (high bus) in instrument panel wiring harness
A122 - Connection (low bus) in instrument panel wiring harness
E30 - Connector (87a), in wiring harness engine

VW1020000158110X

Fig. 99 Motronic wiring diagram (Secondary AIR system). 2000 Passat w/1.8L ATW engine

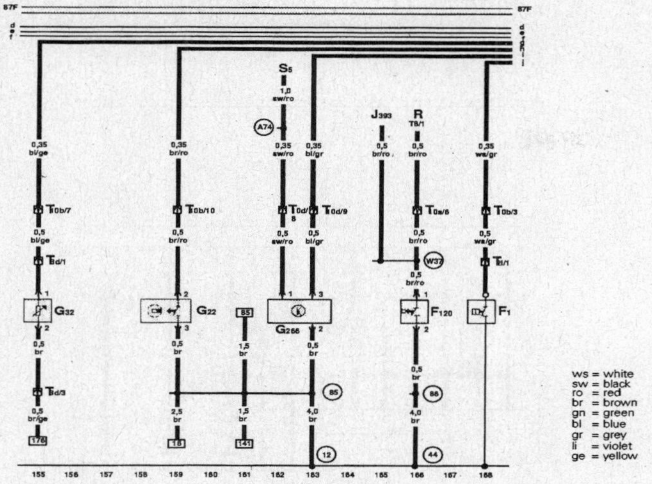

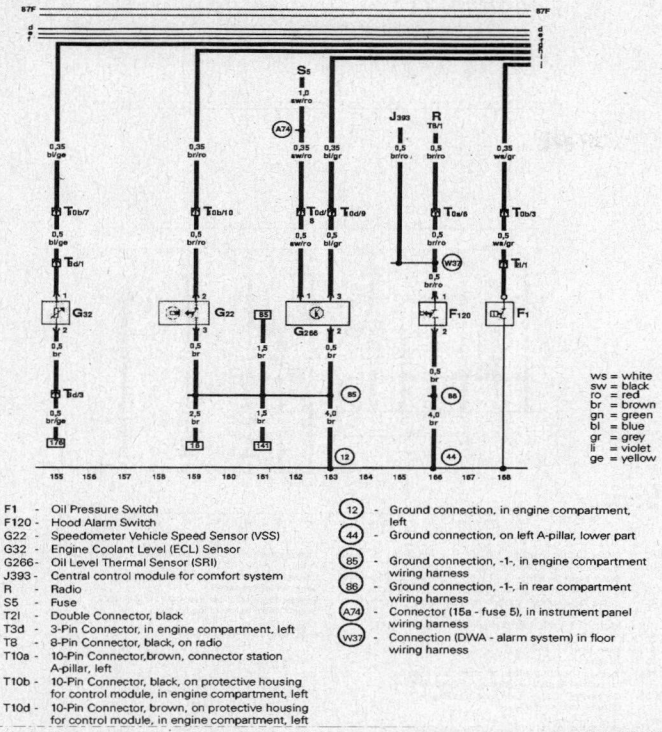

F1 - Oil Pressure Switch
F120 - Hood Alarm Switch
G22 - Speedometer Vehicle Speed Sensor (VSS)
G32 - Engine Coolant Level (ECL) Sensor
G266 - Oil Level Thermal Sensor (SRI)
J393 - Central control module for comfort system
R - Radio
S5 - Fuse
T2l - Double Connector, black
T3d - 3-Pin Connector, in engine compartment, left
T8 - 8-Pin Connector, black, on radio
T10a - 10-Pin Connector,brown, connector station A-pillar, left
T10b - 10-Pin Connector, black, on protective housing for control module, in engine compartment, left
T10d - 10-Pin Connector, brown, on protective housing for control module, in engine compartment, left

(12) - Ground connection, in engine compartment, left
(44) - Ground connection, on left A-pillar, lower part
(85) - Ground connection, -1-, in engine compartment wiring harness
(86) - Ground connection, -1-, in rear compartment wiring harness
(A74) - Connector (15a - fuse 5), in instrument panel wiring harness
(W37) - Connection (DWA - alarm system) in floor wiring harness

VW1020000158120X

Fig. 100 Motronic wiring diagram (VSS, coolant level & oil level sensors, hood alarm & oil pressure switches). 2000 Passat w/1.8L ATW engine

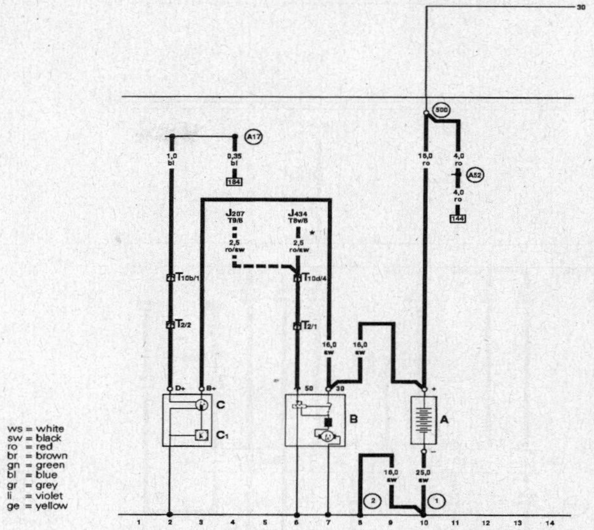

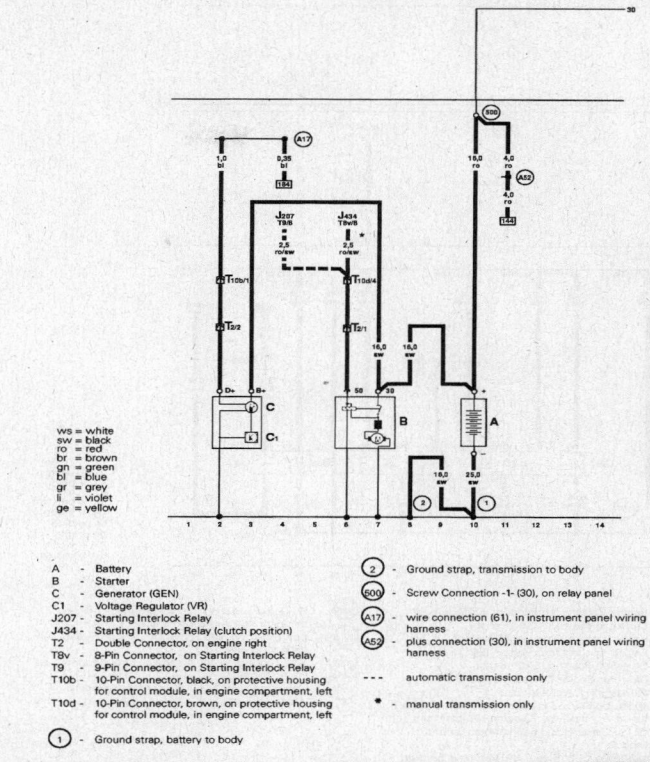

A - Battery
B - Starter
C - Generator (GEN)
C1 - Voltage Regulator (VR)
J207 - Starting Interlock Relay
J434 - Starting Interlock Relay (clutch position)
T2 - Double Connector, on engine right
T8v - 8-Pin Connector, on Starting Interlock Relay
T9 - 9-Pin Connector, on Starting Interlock Relay
T10b - 10-Pin Connector, black, on protective housing for control module, in engine compartment, left
T10d - 10-Pin Connector, brown, on protective housing for control module, in engine compartment, left

(1) - Ground strap, battery to body
(2) - Ground strap, transmission to body
(500) - Screw Connection -1- (30), on relay panel
(A17) - wire connection (61), in instrument panel wiring harness
(A52) - plus connection (30), in instrument panel wiring harness
--- - automatic transmission only
* - manual transmission only

VW1020000159010X

Fig. 101 Motronic wiring diagram (Battery, starter & alternator). 2000 Passat w/2.8L ATQ engine

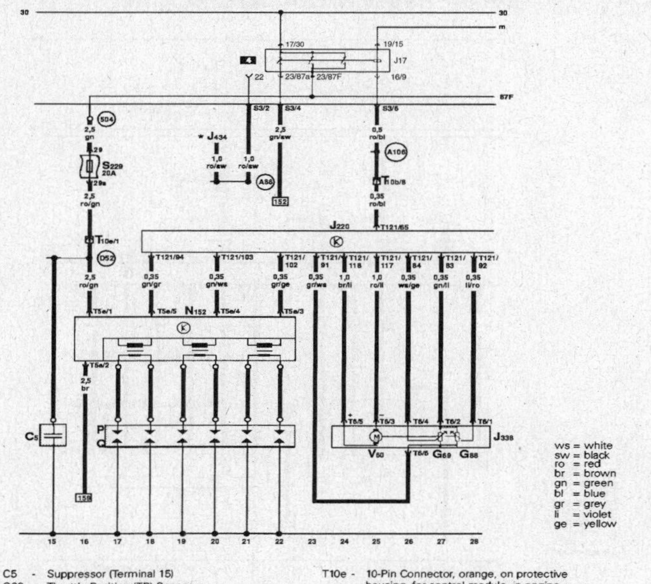

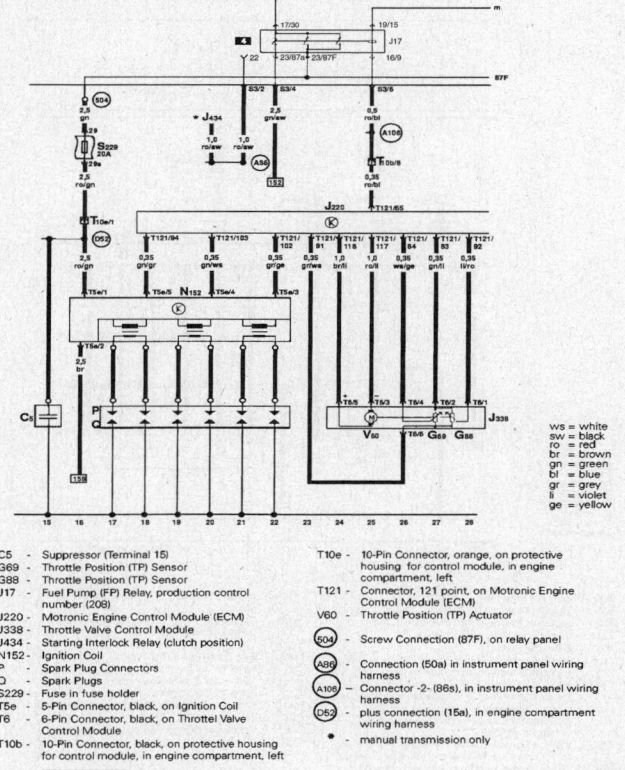

C5 - Suppressor (Terminal 15)
G69 - Throttle Position (TP) Sensor
G88 - Throttle Position (TP) Sensor
J17 - Fuel Pump (FP) Relay, production control number (208)
J220 - Motronic Engine Control Module (ECM)
J338 - Throttle Valve Control Module
J434 - Starting Interlock Relay (clutch position)
N152 - Ignition Coil
P - Spark Plug Connectors
Q - Spark Plugs
S229 - Fuse in fuse holder
T5e - 5-Pin Connector, black, on Ignition Coil
T6 - 6-Pin Connector, black, on Throttel Valve Control Module
T10b - 10-Pin Connector, black, on protective housing for control module, in engine compartment, left
T10e - 10-Pin Connector, orange, on protective housing for control module, in engine compartment, left
T121 - Connector, 121 point, on Motronic Engine Control Module (ECM)
V60 - Throttle Position (TP) Actuator

(504) - Screw Connection (87F), on relay panel
(A86) - Connection (50a) in instrument panel wiring harness
(A106) - Connector -2- (86s), in instrument panel wiring harness
(D52) - plus connection (15a), in engine compartment wiring harness
* - manual transmission only

VW1020000159020X

Fig. 102 Motronic wiring diagram (Ignition system, ECM, throttle valve control module). 2000 Passat w/2.8L ATQ engine

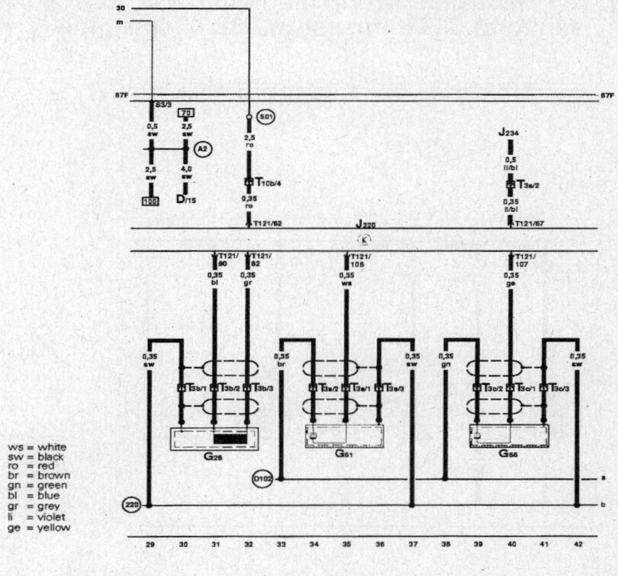

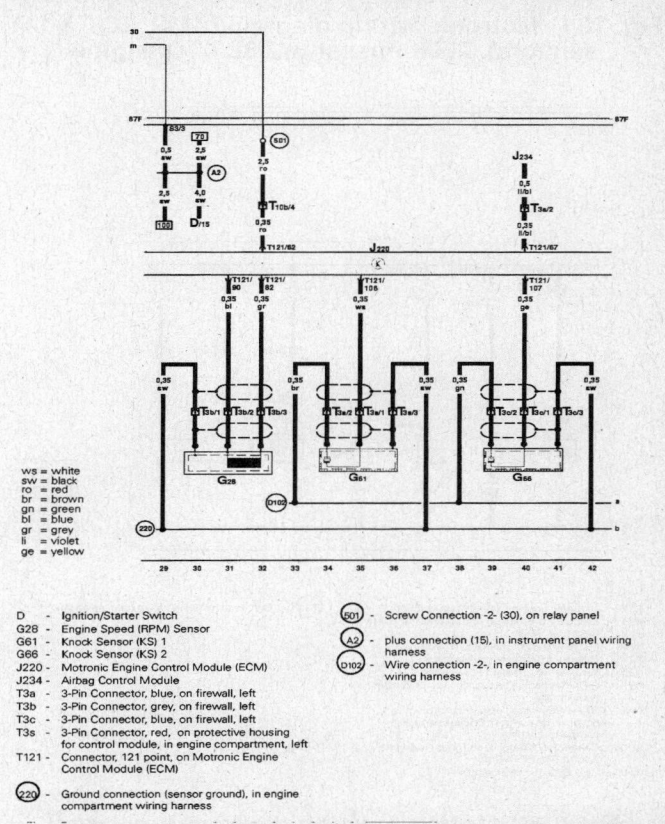

D - Ignition/Starter Switch
G28 - Engine Speed (RPM) Sensor
G61 - Knock Sensor (KS) 1
G66 - Knock Sensor (KS) 2
J220 - Motronic Engine Control Module (ECM)
J234 - Airbag Control Module
T3a - 3-Pin Connector, blue, on firewall, left
T3b - 3-Pin Connector, grey, on firewall, left
T3c - 3-Pin Connector, blue, on firewall, left
T3s - 3-Pin Connector, red, on protective housing for control module, in engine compartment, left
T121 - Connector, 121 point, on Motronic Engine Control Module (ECM)

(220) - Ground connection (sensor ground), in engine compartment wiring harness
(501) - Screw Connection -2- (30), on relay panel
(A2) - plus connection (15), in instrument panel wiring harness
(D102) - Wire connection -2-, in engine compartment wiring harness

VW1020000159030X

Fig. 103 Motronic wiring diagram (RPM & knock sensors). 2000 Passat w/2.8L ATQ engine

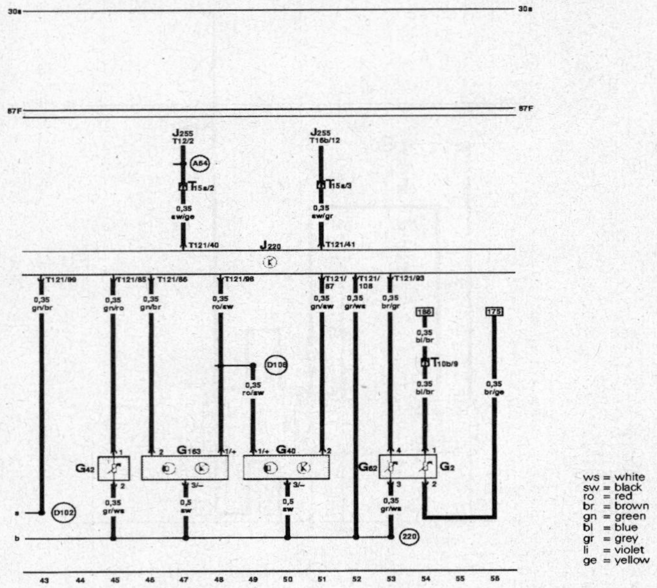

G2 - Engine Coolant Temperature (ECT) Sensor
G40 - Camshaft Position (CMP) Sensor
G42 - Intake Air Temperature (IAT) Sensor
G62 - Engine Coolant Temperature (ECT) Sensor
G163 - Camshaft Position (CMP) Sensor 2
J220 - Motronic Engine Control Module (ECM)
J255 - Climatronic Control Module
T10b - 10-Pin Connector, black, on protective housing for control module, in engine compartment, left
T12 - 12-Pin Connector, on Climatronic Control Module
T15s - 15-Pin Connector, red, on protective housing for control module, in engine compartment, left
T16b - 16-Pin Connector, on Climatronic Control Module
T121 - Connector, 121 point, on Motronic Engine Control Module (ECM)

(220) - Ground connection (sensor ground), in engine compartment wiring harness
(A64) - Connector (30, idle boost), in instrument panel wiring harness
(D102) - wire connection -2-, in engine compartment wiring harness
(D106) - wire connection -4-, in engine compartment wiring harness

VW1020000159040X

Fig. 104 Motronic wiring diagram (CMP, ECT & IAT sensors). 2000 Passat w/2.8L ATQ engine

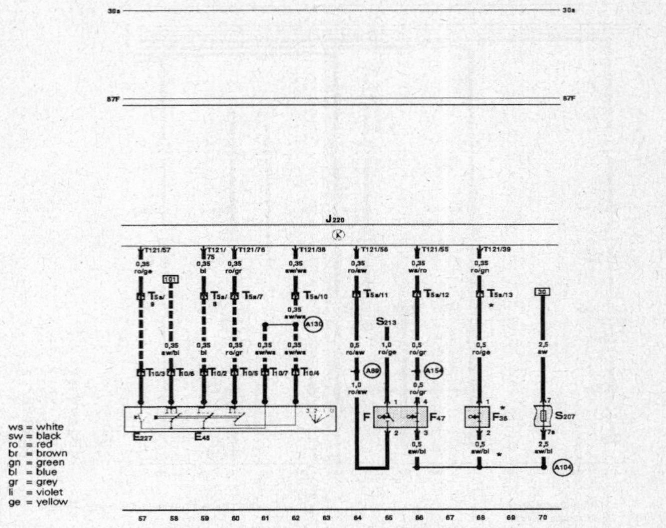

E45 - Cruise Control Switch
E227 - Button for cruise control (set)
F - Brake Light Switch
F36 - Clutch Vacuum Vent Valve Switch
F47 - Brake Vacuum Vent Valve Switch for cruise control/diesel
J220 - Motronic Engine Control Module (ECM)
S207 - Fuse 7 in fuse holer
S213 - Fuse 13 in fuse holder
T10 - 10-Pin Connector
T15a - 15-Pin Connector, white, on protective housing for control module, in engine compartment, left
T121 - Connector, 121 point, on Motronic Engine Control Module (ECM)

(A89) - Connector (54) in instrument panel wiring harness
(A104) - Plus connector -2- (15), in instrument panel wiring harness
(A130) - Connection for Cruise Control (instrument panel wiring harness)
(A154) - Connection (Brake Vacuum Vent Valve Switch) in instrument panel wiring harness

- - - automatic transmission only

* - manual transmission only

VW1020000159050X

Fig. 105 Motronic wiring diagram (Cruise control, brake lamp & clutch vacuum vent valve switches). 2000 Passat w/2.8L ATQ engine

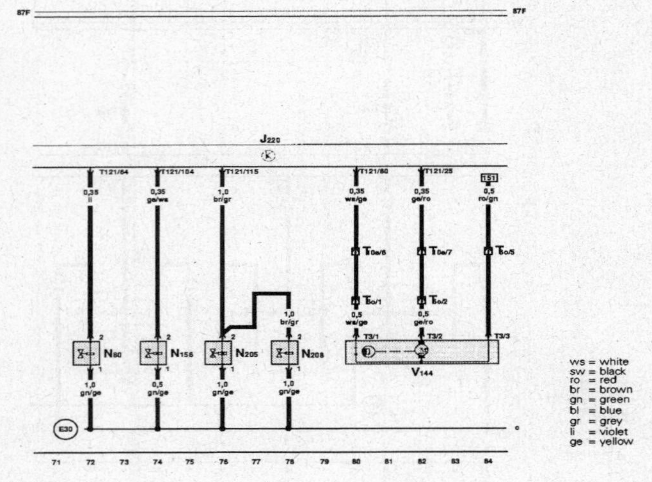

J220 - Motronic Engine Control Module (ECM)
N80 - Evaporative Emission (EVAP) Canister Purge Regulator Valve
N156 - Intake Manifold Change-Over Valve
N205 - Valve -1- for camshaft adjustment
N208 - Valve -2- for camshaft adjustment
T6o - 6-Pin Connector, brown, connector station A-pillar, right
T10e - 10-Pin Connector, orange, on protective housing for control module, in engine compartment, left
T121 - Connector, 121 point, on Motronic Engine Control Module (ECM)
V144 - Leak Detection Pump (LDP)

(E30) - Connector (87a), in wiring harness engine

VW1020000159060X

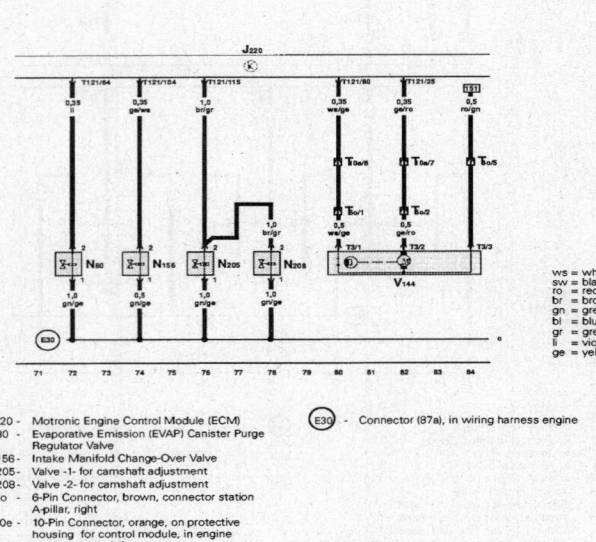

Fig. 106 Motronic wiring diagram (Camshaft adjuster valve & LDP). 2000 Passat w/2.8L ATQ engine

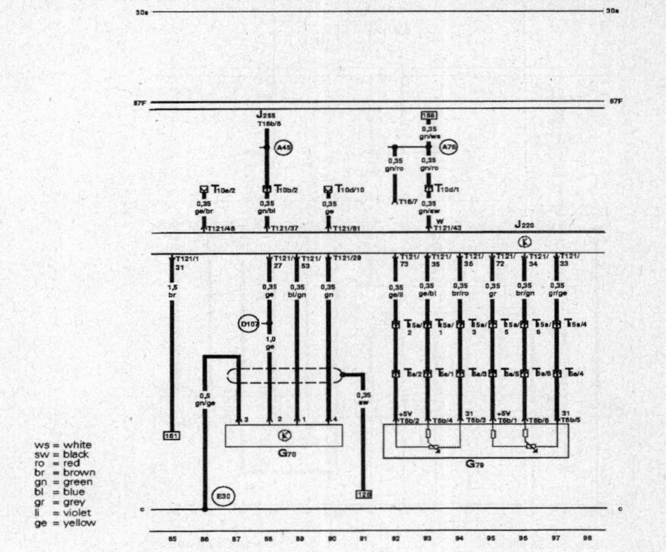

G70 - Mass Air Flow (MAF) Sensor
G79 - Throttle Position (TP) Sensor
J220 - Motronic Engine Control Module (ECM)
J255 - Climatronic Control Module
T6a - 6-Pin Connector
T10b - 10-Pin Connector, black, on protective housing for control module, in engine compartment, left
T10d - 10-Pin Connector, brown, on protective housing for control module, in engine compartment, left
T10e - 10-Pin Connector, orange, on protective housing for control module, in engine compartment, left
T15a - 15-Pin Connector, white, on protective housing for control module, in engine compartment, left
T16 - 16-Pin Connector, Data Link Connector (DLC), below instrument panel, left
T16b - 16-Pin Connector, on Climatronic Control Module
T121 - Connector, 121 point, on Motronic Engine Control Module (ECM)

(A45) - wire connection (RPM-signal), in instrument panel wiring harness
(A76) - Connector (K-diagnosis wire), in instrument panel wiring harness
(D107) - wire connection -5-, in engine compartment wiring harness
(E30) - Connector (87a), in wiring harness engine

VW1020000159070X

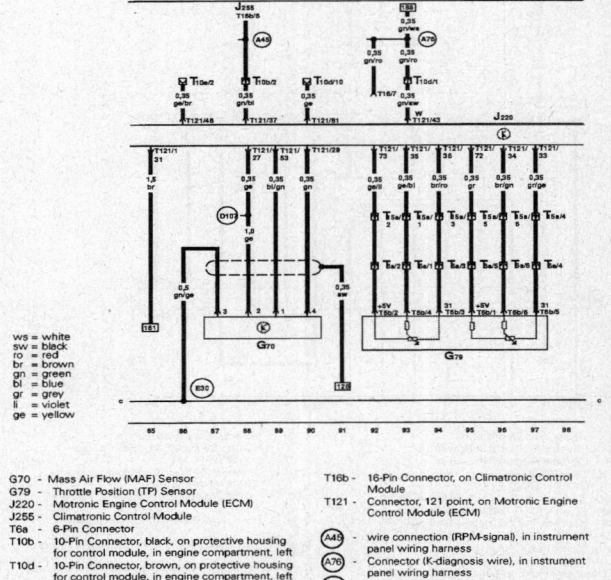

Fig. 107 Motronic wiring diagram (MAF, TPS & DLC). 2000 Passat w/2.8L ATQ engine

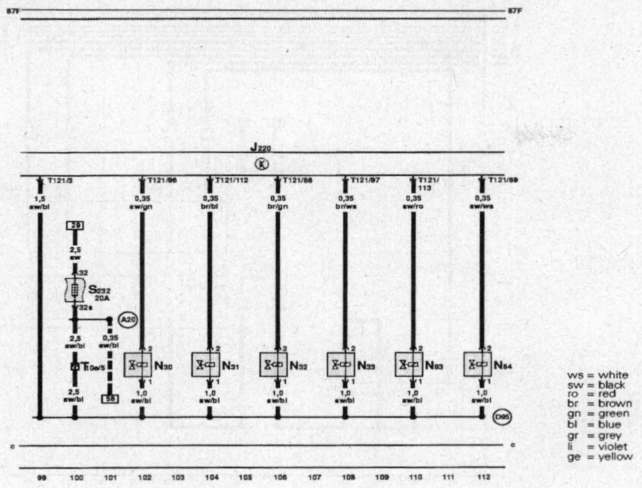

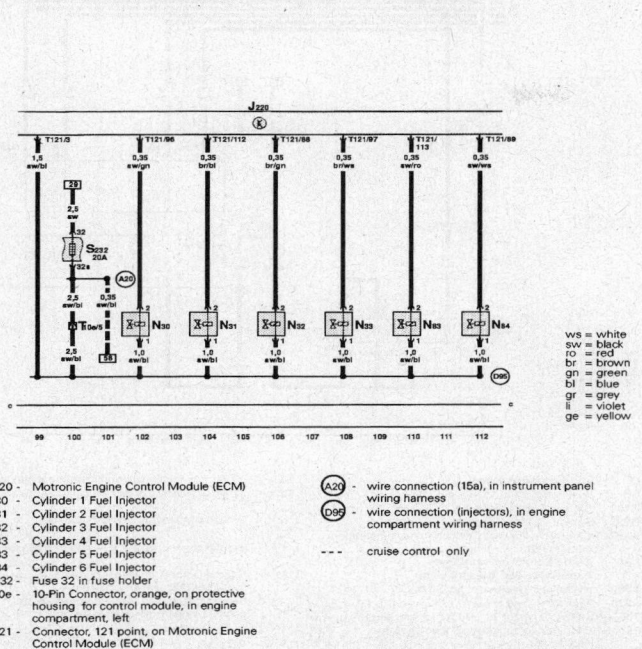

J220 - Motronic Engine Control Module (ECM)
N30 - Cylinder 1 Fuel Injector
N31 - Cylinder 2 Fuel Injector
N32 - Cylinder 3 Fuel Injector
N33 - Cylinder 4 Fuel Injector
N83 - Cylinder 5 Fuel Injector
N84 - Cylinder 6 Fuel Injector
S232 - Fuse 32 in fuse holder
T10e - 10-Pin Connector, orange, on protective housing for control module, in engine compartment, left
T121 - Connector, 121 point, on Motronic Engine Control Module (ECM)

A20 - wire connection (15a), in instrument panel wiring harness
D95 - wire connection (injectors), in engine compartment wiring harness
--- cruise control only

VW1020000159080X

Fig. 108 Motronic wiring diagram (Fuel injectors). 2000 Passat w/2.8L ATQ engine

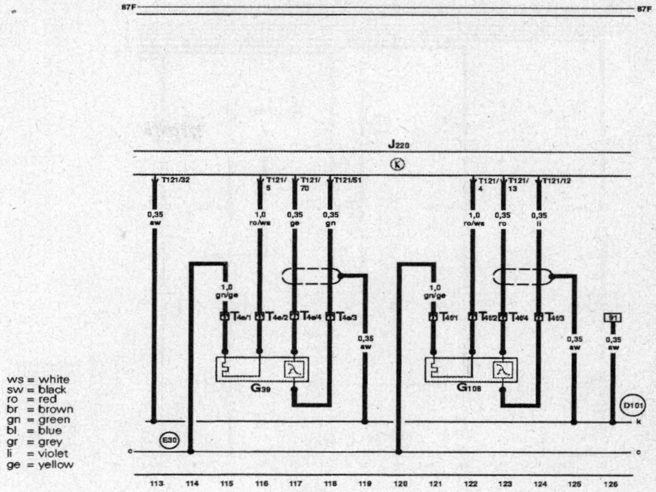

G39 - Heated Oxygen Sensor (HO2S)
G108 - Heated Oxygen Sensor (HO2S) 2
J220 - Motronic Engine Control Module (ECM)
T4e - 4-Pin Connector, black
T4f - 4-Pin Connector, black
T121 - Connector, 121 point, on Motronic Engine Control Module (ECM)

D101 - wire connection -1-, in engine compartment wiring harness
E30 - Connector (87a), in wiring harness engine

VW1020000159090X

Fig. 109 Motronic wiring diagram (HO_2S). 2000 Passat w/2.8L ATQ engine

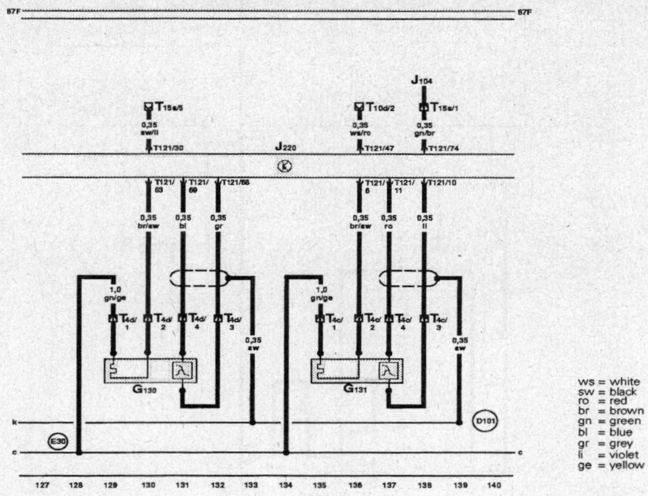

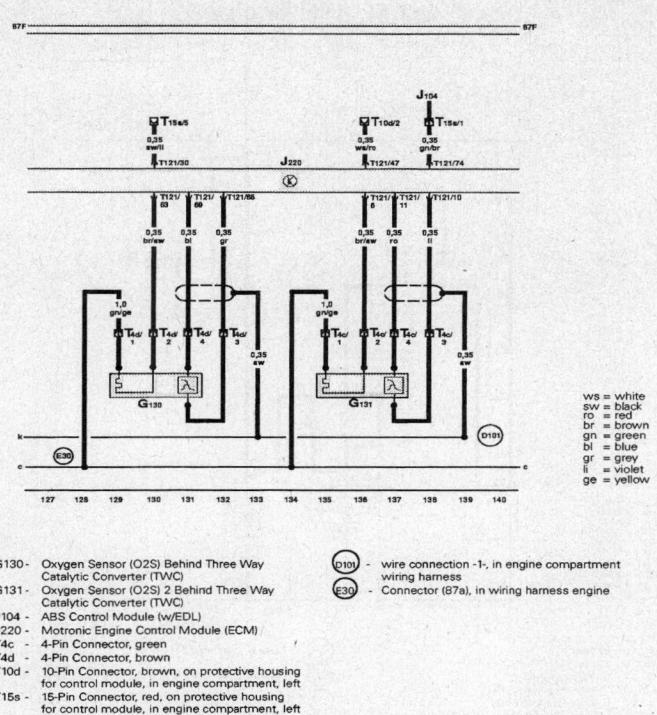

G130 - Oxygen Sensor (O2S) Behind Three Way Catalytic Converter (TWC)
G131 - Oxygen Sensor (O2S) 2 Behind Three Way Catalytic Converter (TWC)
J104 - ABS Control Module (w/EDL)
J220 - Motronic Engine Control Module (ECM)
T4c - 4-Pin Connector, green
T4d - 4-Pin Connector, brown
T10d - 10-Pin Connector, brown, on protective housing for control module, in engine compartment, left
T15s - 15-Pin Connector, red, on protective housing for control module, in engine compartment, left
T121 - Connector, 121 point, on Motronic Engine Control Module (ECM)

D101 - wire connection -1-, in engine compartment wiring harness
E30 - Connector (87a), in wiring harness engine

VW1020000159100X

Fig. 110 Motronic wiring diagram (Rear O_2S). 2000 Passat w/2.8L ATQ engine

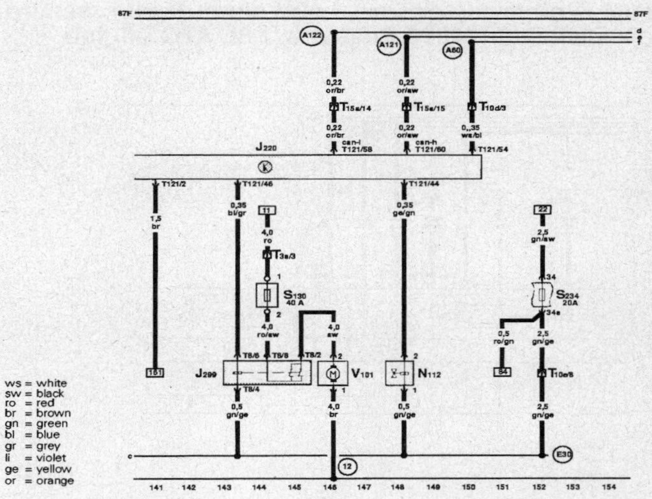

J220 - Motronic Engine Control Module (ECM)
J299 - Secondary Air Injection (AIR) Pump Relay
N112 - Secondary Air Injection (AIR) Solenoid Valve
S130 - Fuse for secondary air pump, in fuse adaptor above relay panel
S234 - Fuse 34 in fuse holder
T3a - 3-Pin Connector,
T8 - 8-Pin Connector, black on Radio
T10d - 10-Pin Connector, brown, on protective housing for control module, in engine compartment, left
T10e - 10-Pin Connector, yellow, on protective housing for control module, in engine compartment, left
T15s - 15-Pin Connector, red, , on protective housing for control module, in engine compartment, left
T121 - Connector, 121 point, on Motronic Engine Control Module (ECM)
V101 - Secondary Air Injection (AIR) Pump Motor

12 - Ground connection, in engine compartment, left
A60 - Wire connection (Vehicle speed signal), in instrument cluster wiring harness
A121 - Connection (high bus) in instrument panel wiring harness
A122 - Connection (low bus) in instrument panel wiring harness
E30 - Connector (87a), in wiring harness engine

VW1020000159110X

Fig. 111 Motronic wiring diagram (Secondary AIR system). 2000 Passat w/2.8L ATQ engine

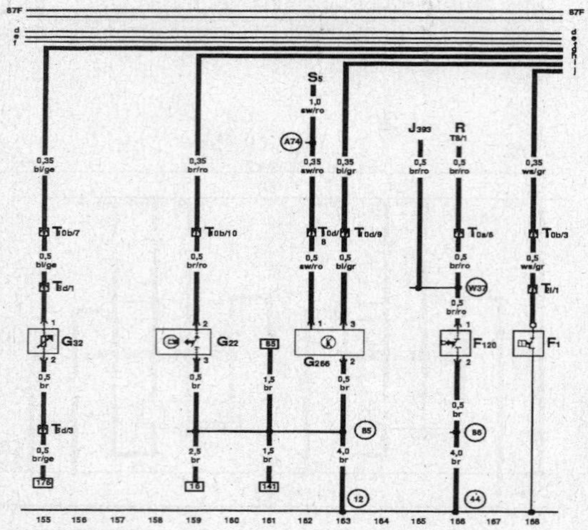

F1 - Oil Pressure Switch
F120 - Hood Alarm Switch
G22 - Speedometer Vehicle Speed Sensor (VSS)
G32 - Engine Coolant Level (ECL) Sensor
G266 - Oil Level Thermal Sensor (SRI)
J393 - Central control module for comfort system
R - Radio
S5 - Fuse
T2l - Double Connector, black
T3d - 3-Pin Connector, in engine compartment, left
T8 - 8-Pin Connector, black, on radio
T10a - 10-Pin Connector,brown, connector station A-pillar, left
T10b - 10-Pin Connector, black, on protective housing for control module, in engine compartment, left
T10d - 10-Pin Connector, brown, on protective housing for control module, in engine compartment, left

(12) - Ground connection, in engine compartment, left
(44) - Ground connection, on left A-pillar, lower part
(85) - Ground connection, -1-, in engine compartment wiring harness
(86) - Ground connection, -1-, in rear compartment wiring harness
(A74) - Connector (15a - fuse 5), in instrument panel wiring harness
(W37) - Connection (DWA - alarm system) in floor wiring harness

VW1020000159120X

Fig. 112 Motronic wiring diagram (VSS, coolant level & oil level sensors, hood alarm & oil pressure switches). 2000 Passat w/2.8L ATQ engine

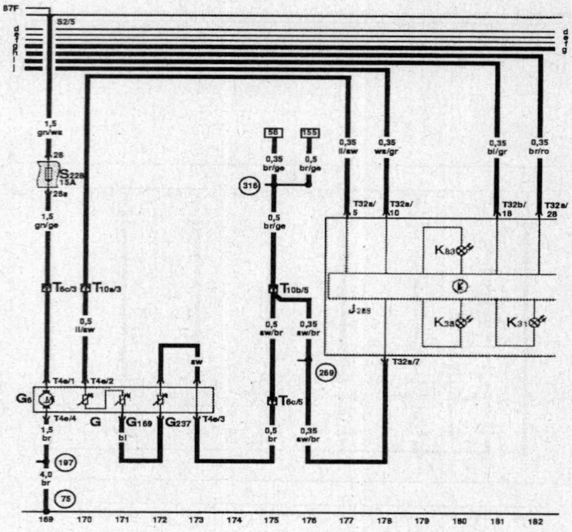

G - Sender for fuel gauge
G6 - Fuel Pump (FP)
G169 - Sender -2- for fuel supply
G237 - Sensor -3- for fuel supply
J285 - Control module with indicator unit in instrument panel insert
K31 - Cruise Control Indicator Light
K38 - Engine Oil Level Indicator Light
K83 - Malfunction Indicator Lamp (MIL)
S228 - Fuse 28 in fuse holder
T4e - 4-Pin Connector, on Sender for fuel gauge
T6c - 6-Pin Connector, blue, connector station A-pillar, left
T10a - 10-Pin Connector, brown, connector station A-pillar, left
T10b - 10-Pin Connector, black, on protective housing for control module, in engine compartment, left
T32a - 32-Pin Connector, blue, on instrument cluster
T32b - 32-Pin Connector, green, on instrument cluster

(75) - Ground connection, on right rear pillar
(197) - Ground connection -4-, in wiring harness rear
(269) - Ground connection (sensor ground) -1-, in instrument panel wiring harness
(316) - Ground connection (sensor ground -2-), in engine compartment wiring harness

VW1020000159130X

Fig. 113 Motronic wiring diagram (Fuel gauge sender & I/P unit w/control module). 2000 Passat w/2.8L ATQ engine

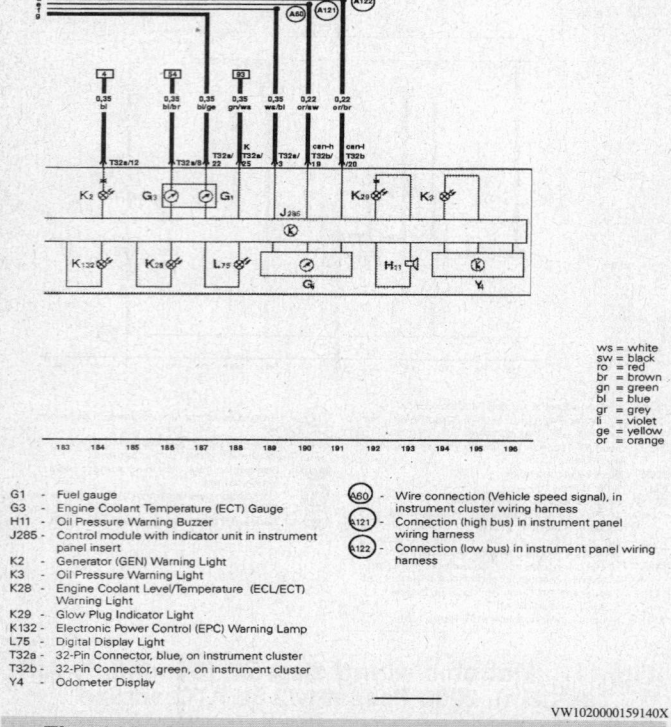

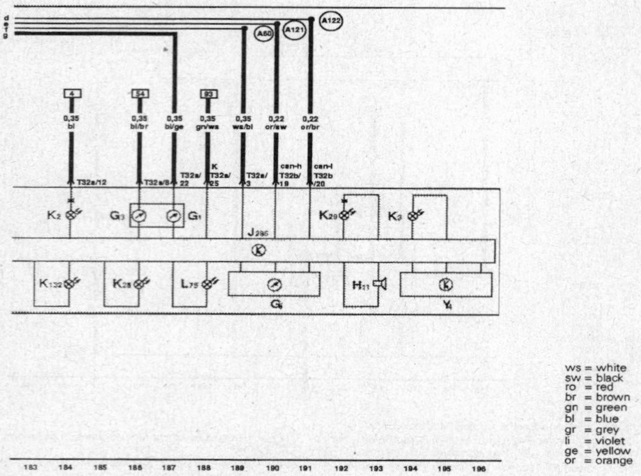

G1 - Fuel gauge
G3 - Engine Coolant Temperature (ECT) Gauge
H11 - Oil Pressure Warning Buzzer
J285 - Control module with indicator unit in instrument panel insert
K2 - Generator (GEN) Warning Light
K3 - Oil Pressure Warning Light
K28 - Engine Coolant Level/Temperature (ECL/ECT) Warning Light
K29 - Glow Plug Indicator Light
K132 - Electronic Power Control (EPC) Warning Lamp
L75 - Digital Display Light
T32a - 32-Pin Connector, blue, on instrument cluster
T32b - 32-Pin Connector, green, on instrument cluster
Y4 - Odometer Display

(A60) - Wire connection (Vehicle speed signal), in instrument cluster wiring harness
(A121) - Connection (high bus) in instrument panel wiring harness
(A122) - Connection (low bus) in instrument panel wiring harness

VW1020000159140X

Fig. 114 Motronic wiring diagram (I/P control module w/indicator unit). 2000 Passat w/2.8L ATQ engine

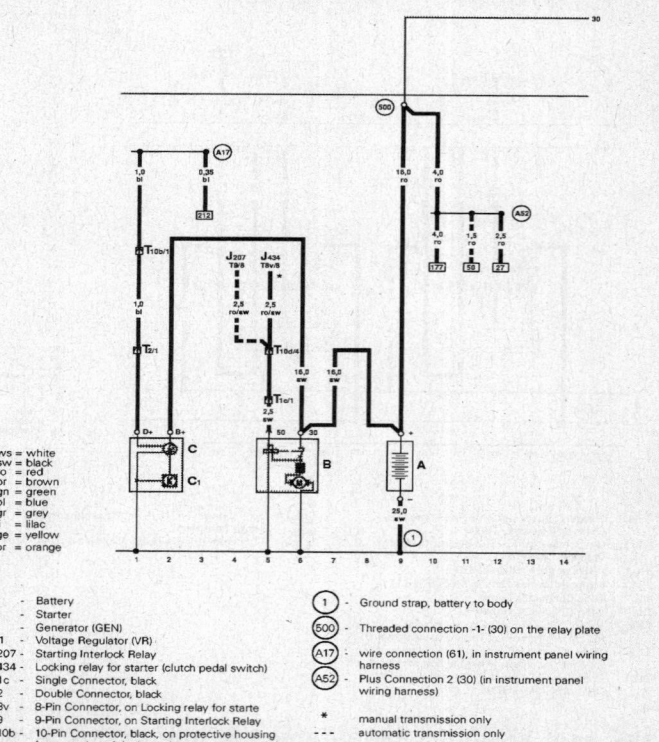

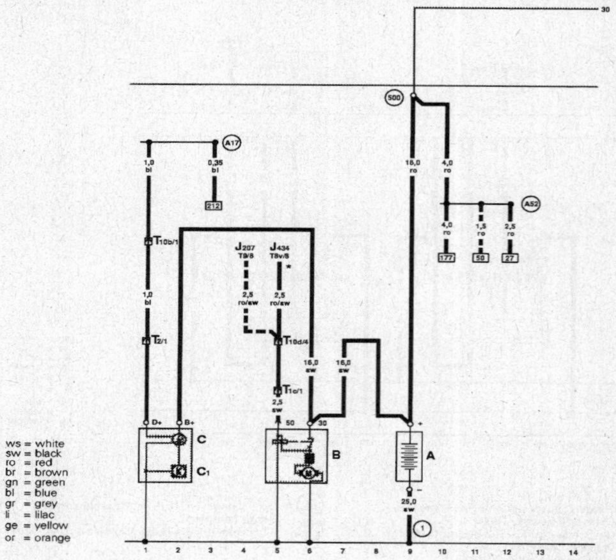

A - Battery
B - Starter
C - Generator (GEN)
C1 - Voltage Regulator (VR)
J207 - Starting Interlock Relay
J434 - Locking relay for starter (clutch pedal switch)
T1c - Single Connector, black
T2 - Double Connector, black
T8v - 8-Pin Connector, on Locking relay for starte
T9 - 9-Pin Connector, on Starting Interlock Relay
T10b - 10-Pin Connector, black, on protective housing for control module, in engine compartment, left
T10d - 10-Pin Connector, brown, on protective housing for control module, in engine compartment, left

(1) - Ground strap, battery to body
(500) - Threaded connection -1- (30) on the relay plate
(A17) - wire connection (61), in instrument panel wiring harness
(A52) - Plus Connection 2 (30) (in instrument panel wiring harness)
* manual transmission only
--- automatic transmission only

VW1020100160010X

Fig. 115 Motronic wiring diagram (Battery, starter & alternator). 2001 Passat w/1.8L ATW engine

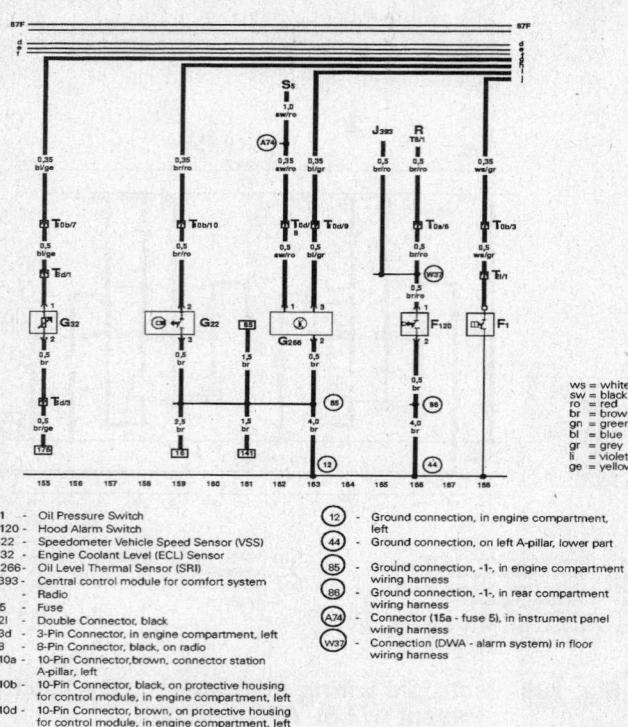

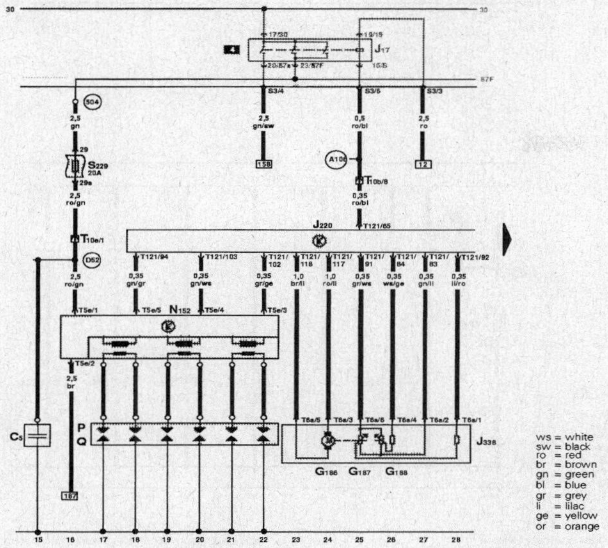

C5 - Suppressor (Terminal 15)
G186 - Throttle drive (power accelerator actuation)
G187 - Angle sensor -1- for throttle drive (power accelerator actuation)
G188 - Angle sensor -2- for throttle drive (power accelerator actuation)
J17 - Fuel Pump (FP) Relay
J220 - Motronic Engine Control Module (ECM)
J338 - Throttle Valve Control Module
N152 - Ignition Coil
P - Spark Plug Connectors
Q - Spark Plugs
S229 - Fuse in fuse holder
T5e - 5-Pin Connector, black, on Ignition Coil
T6a - 6-Pin Connector, black, on Throttle Valve Control Module
T10b - 10-Pin Connector, black, on protective housing for control module, in engine compartment, left
T10e - 10-Pin Connector, orange, on protective housing for control module, in engine compartment, left
T121 - Connector, 121 point, on Motronic Engine Control Module (ECM)
(504) - Threaded connection -1- (87) on the relay plate
(A106) - Connector -2- (86s), in instrument panel wiring harness
(D52) - plus connection (15a), in engine compartment wiring harness

VW1020100160020X

Fig. 116 Motronic wiring diagram (ECM, throttle drive & spark plug connectors). 2001 Passat w/1.8L ATW engine

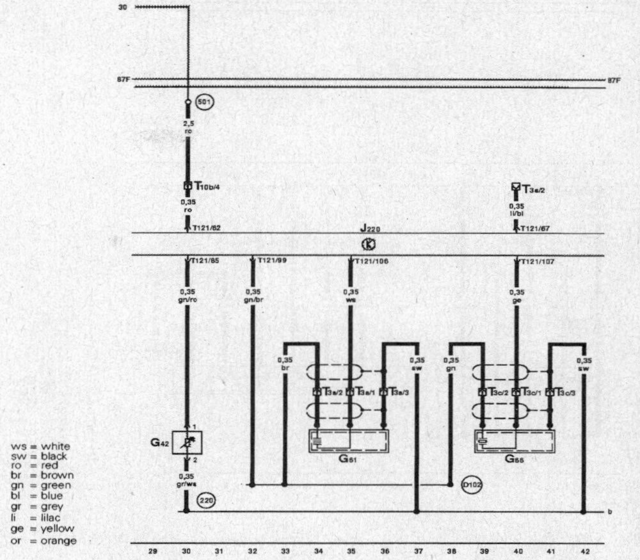

G42 - Intake Air Temperature (IAT) Sensor
G61 - Knock Sensor (KS) 1
G66 - Knock Sensor (KS) 2
J220 - Motronic Engine Control Module (ECM)
T3a - 3-Pin Connector, green, on firewall, left
T3c - 3-Pin Connector, blue, on firewall, left
T3s - 3-Pin Connector, red, on protective housing for control module, in engine compartment, left
T10b - 10-Pin Connector, black, on protective housing for control module, in engine compartment, left
T121 - Connector, 121 point, on Motronic Engine Control Module (ECM)
(220) - Ground connection (sensor ground), in engine compartment wiring harness
(501) - Threaded connection -2- (30) on the relay plate
(D102) - Wire connection -2-, in engine compartment wiring harness

VW1020100160030X

Fig. 117 Motronic wiring diagram (IAT & knock sensors). 2001 Passat w/1.8L ATW engine

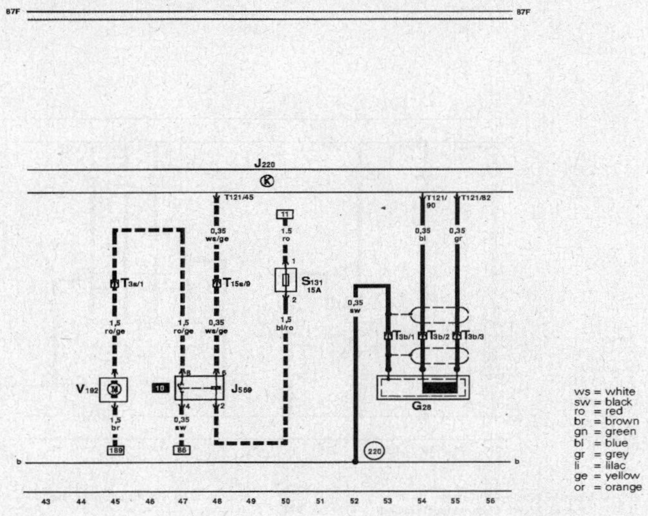

G28 - Engine Speed (RPM) Sensor
J220 - Motronic Engine Control Module (ECM)
J569 - Lamp Failure Control Module
S131 - Safety fuse 1
T3b - 3-Pin Connector, grey, on firewall, left
T3s - 3-Pin Connector, red, on protective housing for control module, in engine compartment, left
T15s - 15-Pin Connector, red, on protective housing for control module, in engine compartment, left
T121 - Connector, 121 point, on Motronic Engine Control Module (ECM)
V192 - Brake System Vacuum Pump
(220) - Ground connection (sensor ground), in engine compartment wiring harness
- - - automatic transmission only

VW1020100160040X

Fig. 118 Motronic wiring diagram (RPM sensor, lamp failure control module & brake system vacuum pump). 2001 Passat w/1.8L ATW engine

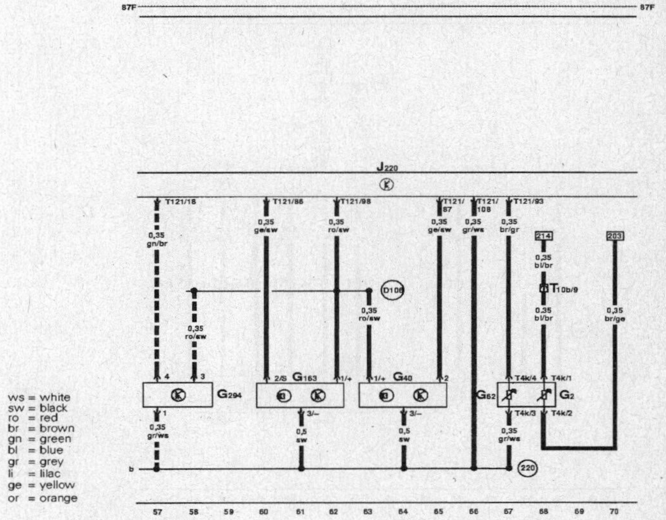

G2 - Engine Coolant Temperature (ECT) Sensor
G40 - Camshaft Position (CMP) Sensor
G62 - Engine Coolant Temperature (ECT) Sensor
G163 - Camshaft Position (CMP) Sensor 2
G294 - Brake Booster Pressure Sensor
J220 - Motronic Engine Control Module (ECM)
T4k - 4-Pin Connector, black, on Engine Coolant Temperature (ECT) Sensor
T10b - 10-Pin Connector, black, on protective housing for control module, in engine compartment, left
T121 - Connector, 121 point, on Motronic Engine Control Module (ECM)
(220) - Ground connection (sensor ground), in engine compartment wiring harness
(D106) - wire connection -4-, in engine compartment wiring harness
- - - automatic transmission only

VW1020100160050X

Fig. 119 Motronic wiring diagram (Brake booster pressure, CMP & ECT sensors). 2001 Passat w/1.8L ATW engine

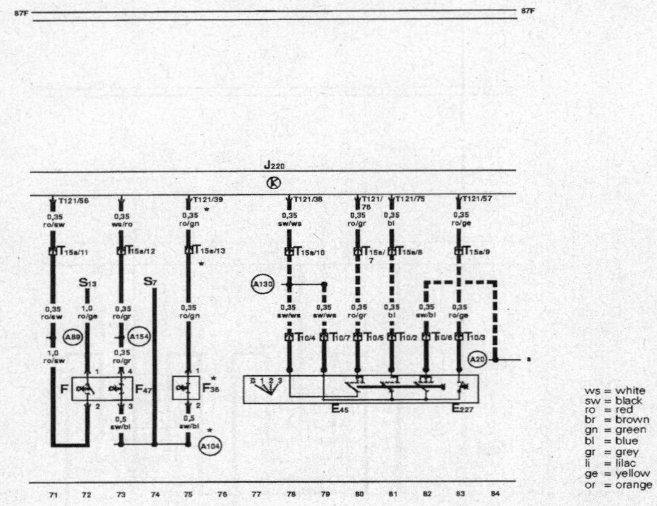

E45 - Cruise Control Switch
Position 0=OFF looked
Position 1=OFF pushed
Position 2=ON
Position 3=RES
E227 - Button for cruise control (set)
F - Brake Light Switch
F36 - Clutch Vacuum Vent Valve Switch
F47 - Brake Clutch Vacuum Vent Valve Switch for cruise control
J220 - Motronic Engine Control Module (ECM)
S7 - Fuse
S13 - Fuse
T10 - 10-Pin Connector, black
T15a - 15-Pin Connector, white, on protective housing for control module, in engine compartment, left
T121 - Connector, 121 point, on Motronic Engine Control Module (ECM)
(A20) - wire connection (15a), in instrument panel wiring harness
(A89) - Connection 2 (54) (in instrument panel wiring harness)
(A104) - Plus connector -2- (15), in instrument panel wiring harness
(A130) - Connection for Cruise Control (instrument panel wiring harness)
(A154) - Brake Pedal Switch Connection (in instrument panel wiring harness)
--- cruise control only
* manual transmission only

VW1020100160060X

Fig. 120 Motronic wiring diagram (Cruise control, brake lamp & clutch vacuum vent valve switch). 2001 Passat w/1.8L ATW engine

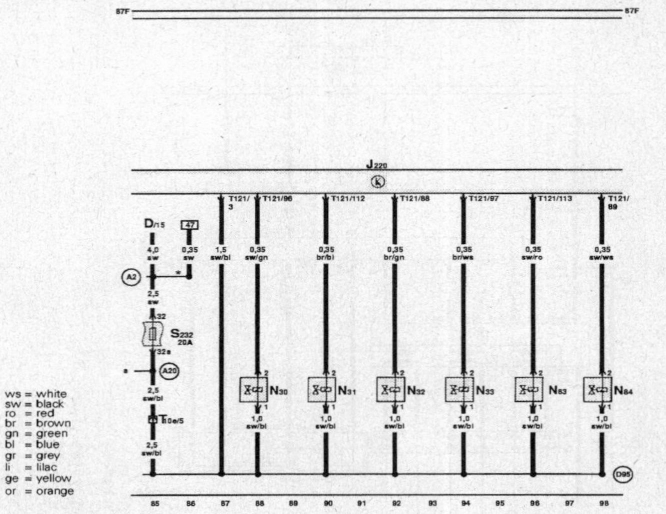

D - Ignition/Starter Switch
J220 - Motronic Engine Control Module (ECM)
N30 - Cylinder 1 Fuel Injector
N31 - Cylinder 2 Fuel Injector
N32 - Cylinder 3 Fuel Injector
N33 - Cylinder 4 Fuel Injector
N83 - Cylinder 5 Fuel Injector
N84 - Cylinder 6 Fuel Injector
S232 - Fuse in fuse holder
T10e - 10-Pin Connector, orange, on protective housing for control module, in engine compartment, left
T121 - Connector, 121 point, on Motronic Engine Control Module (ECM)
(A2) - plus connection (15), in instrument panel wiring harness
(A20) - wire connection (15a), in instrument panel wiring harness
(D95) - wire connection (injectors), in engine compartment wiring harness
* automatic transmission only

VW1020100160070X

Fig. 121 Motronic wiring diagram (Fuel injectors). 2001 Passat w/1.8L ATW engine

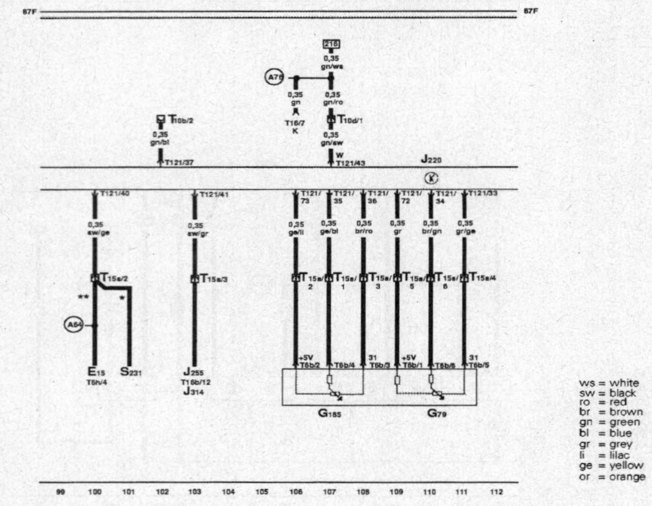

E15 - Rear window defogger switch
G79 - Throttle Position (TP) Sensor
G185 - Sender -2- for accelerator pedal position
J220 - Motronic Engine Control Module (ECM)
J255 - Climatronic Control Module
J314 - A/C Cut-Off Control Module
S231 - Fuse in fuse holder
T6b - 6-Pin Connector, on Throttle Position Sensor
T6h - 6-Pin Connector, black, on Rear window defogger switch
T10b - 10-Pin Connector, black, on protective housing for control module, in engine compartment, left
T10d - 10-Pin Connector, brown, on protective housing for control module, in engine compartment, left
T15a - 15-Pin Connector, while, on protective housing for control module, in engine compartment, left
T15s - 15-Pin Connector, red, on protective housing for control module, in engine compartment, left
T16 - 16-Pin Connector, Data Link Connector (DLC)
T16b - 16-Pin Connector, brown
T121 - Connector, 121 point, on Motronic Engine Control Module (ECM)
(A64) - Connector (30, idle boost), in instrument panel wiring harness
(A76) - Connector (K-diagnosis wire) in instrument panel wiring harness
* front wheel drive only
** 4-Motion only

VW1020100160080X

Fig. 122 Motronic wiring diagram (TP sensor & DLC). 2001 Passat w/1.8L ATW engine

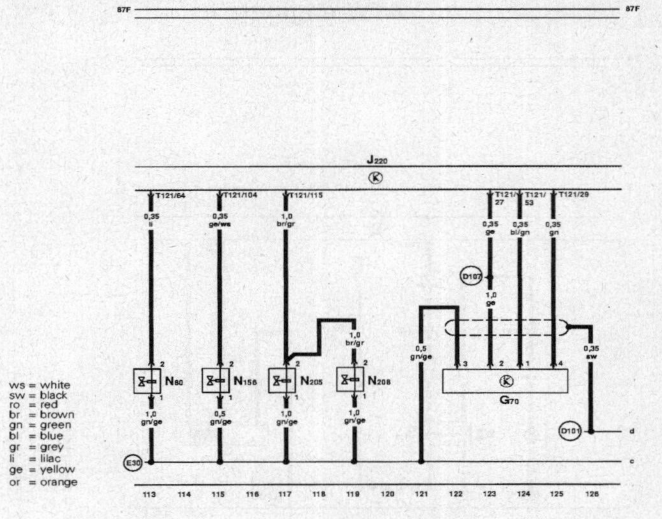

G70 - Mass Air Flow (MAF) Sensor
J220 - Motronic Engine Control Module (ECM)
N80 - Evaporative Emission (EVAP) Canister Purge Regulator Valve
N156 - Intake Manifold Change-Over Valve
N205 - Valve -1- for camshaft adjustment
N208 - Valve -2- for camshaft adjustment
T121 - Connector, 121 point, on Motronic Engine Control Module (ECM)
(E30) - Connector (87a), in wiring harness engine
(D101) - Wire connection -1-, in engine compartment wiring harness
(D107) - wire connection -5-, in engine compartment wiring harness

VW1020100160090X

Fig. 123 Motronic wiring diagram (Camshaft adjuster valve, EVAP canister purge regulator valve & MAF sensor). 2001 Passat w/1.8L ATW engine

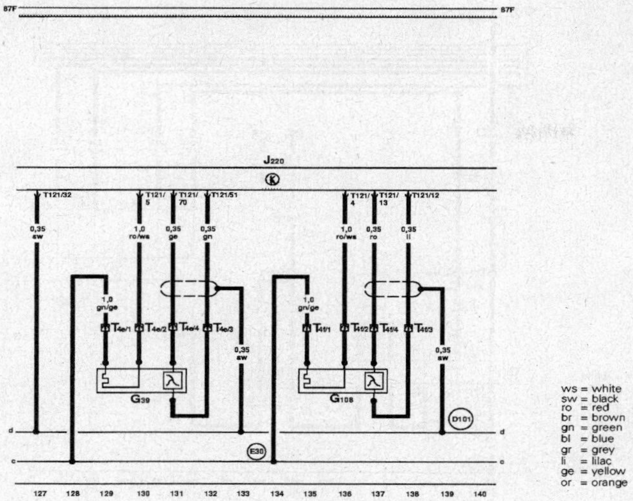

G39 - Heated Oxygen Sensor (HO2S)
G108 - Heated Oxygen Sensor (HO2S) 2
J220 - Motronic Engine Control Module (ECM)
T4e - 4-Pin Connector, black
T4f - 4-Pin Connector, black
T121 - Connector, 121 point, on Motronic Engine Control Module (ECM)

E30 - Connector (87a), in wiring harness engine
D101 - Wire connection -1-, in engine compartment wiring harness

VW1020100160100X

Fig. 124 Motronic wiring diagram (HO_2S). 2001 Passat w/1.8L ATW engine

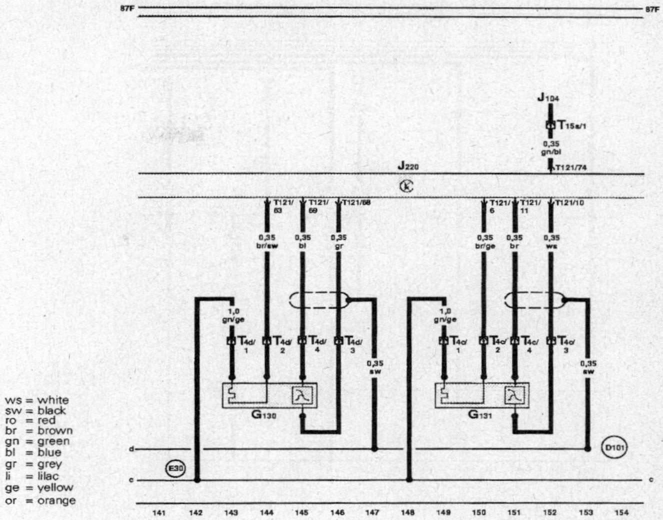

G130 - Oxygen Sensor (O2S) Behind Three Way Catalytic Converter (TWC)
G131 - Oxygen Sensor (O2S) 2 Behind Three Way Catalytic Converter (TWC)
J104 - ABS Control Module (w/EDL)
J220 - Motronic Engine Control Module (ECM)
T4c - 4-Pin Connector, brown
T4d - 4-Pin Connector, green
T15s - 15-Pin Connector, red, on protective housing for control module, in engine compartment, left
T121 - Connector, 121 point, on Motronic Engine Control Module (ECM)

E30 - Connector (87a), in wiring harness engine
D101 - Wire connection -1-, in engine compartment wiring harness

VW1020100160110X

Fig. 125 Motronic wiring diagram (Rear O_2S). 2001 Passat w/1.8L ATW engine

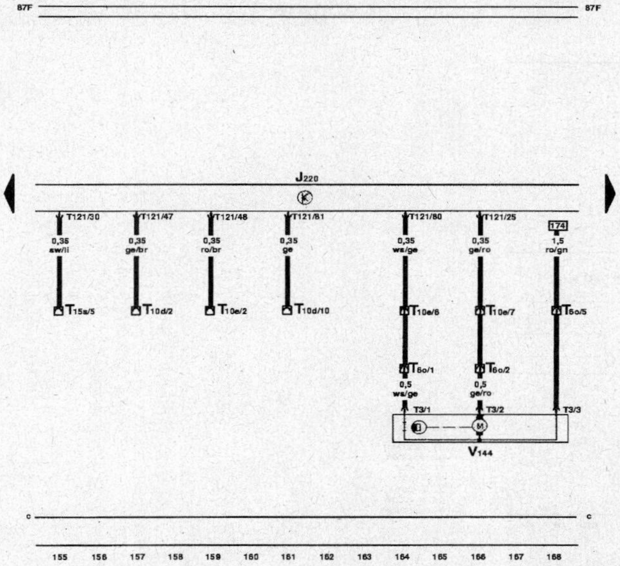

J220 - Motronic Engine Control Module (ECM)
T6o - 6-Pin Connector, brown, connector station A-pillar, right
T10d - 10-Pin Connector, brown, on protective housing for control module, in engine compartment, left
T10e - 10-Pin Connector, orange, on protective housing for control module, in engine compartment, left
T15s - 15-Pin Connector, red, on protective housing for control module, in engine compartment, left
T121 - Connector, 121 point, on Motronic Engine Control Module (ECM)
V144 - Leak Detection Pump (LDP)

VW1020100160120X

Fig. 126 Motronic wiring diagram (LDP). 2001 Passat w/1.8L ATW engine

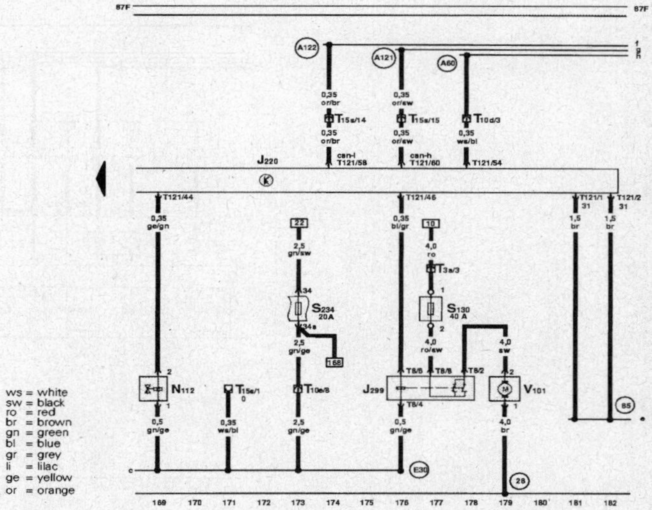

J220 - Motronic Engine Control Module (ECM)
J299 - Secondary Air Injection (AIR) Pump Relay
N112 - Secondary Air Injection (AIR) Solenoid Valve
S130 - Fuse for secondary air pump
S234 - Fuse in fuse holder
T3a - 3-Pin Connector, green
T8 - 8-Pin Connector, brown, on Secondary Air Injection (AIR) Pump Relay
T10d - 10-Pin Connector, brown, on protective housing for control module, in engine compartment, left
T10e - 10-Pin Connector, orange, on protective housing for control module, in engine compartment, left
T15s - 15-Pin Connector, red, on protective housing for control module, in engine compartment, left
T121 - Connector, 121 point, on Motronic Engine Control Module (ECM)
V101 - Secondary Air Injection (AIR) Pump Motor

28 - Ground connection, on firewall
85 - Ground connection -1-, in engine compartment wiring harness
A60 - Wire connection (Vehicle speed signal), in instrument cluster wiring harness
A121 - Connection (high bus) in instrument panel wiring harness
A122 - Connection (low bus) in instrument panel wiring harness
E30 - Connector (87a), in wiring harness engine

VW1020100160130X

Fig. 127 Motronic wiring diagram (Secondary AIR pump, relay, motor & solenoid valve). 2001 Passat w/1.8L ATW engine

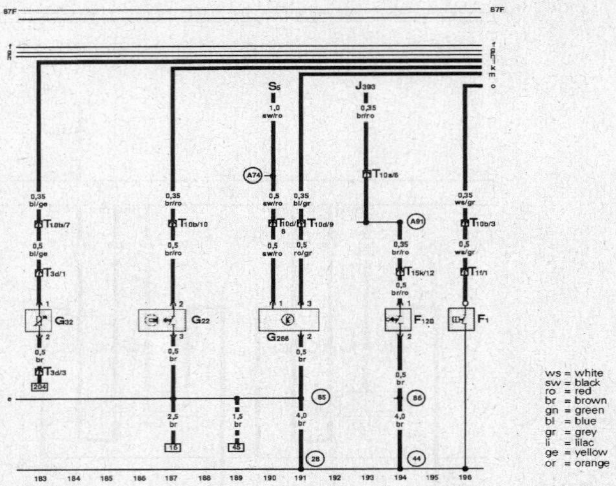

- F1 - Oil Pressure Switch
- F120 - Hood Alarm Switch
- G22 - Speedometer Vehicle Speed Sensor (VSS)
- G32 - Engine Coolant Level (ECL) Sensor
- G266 - Oil Level Thermal Sensor
- J393 - Central control module for comfort system
- S5 - Fuse
- T1f - Single Connector, black
- T3d - 3-Pin Connector,
- T10a - 10-Pin Connector, brown
- T10b - 10-Pin Connector, black, on protective housing for control module, in engine compartment, left
- T10d - 10-Pin Connector, brown, on protective housing for control module, in engine compartment, left
- T15k - 15-Pin Connector, grey
- (28) - Ground connection, on firewall
- (44) - Ground connection, on left A-pillar, lower part
- (85) - Ground connection -1-, in engine compartment wiring harness
- (86) - Ground connection -1-, in rear wiring harness
- (A74) - Connector (15a - fuse 5) in instrument panel wiring harness
- (A91) - Connector (signal for instrument panel insert), in instrument panel wiring harness
- - - - automatic transmission only

VW1020100160140X

Fig. 128 Motronic wiring diagram (Oil pressure & hood alarm switches, VSS, engine coolant level & oil level thermal sensors). 2001 Passat w/1.8L ATW engine

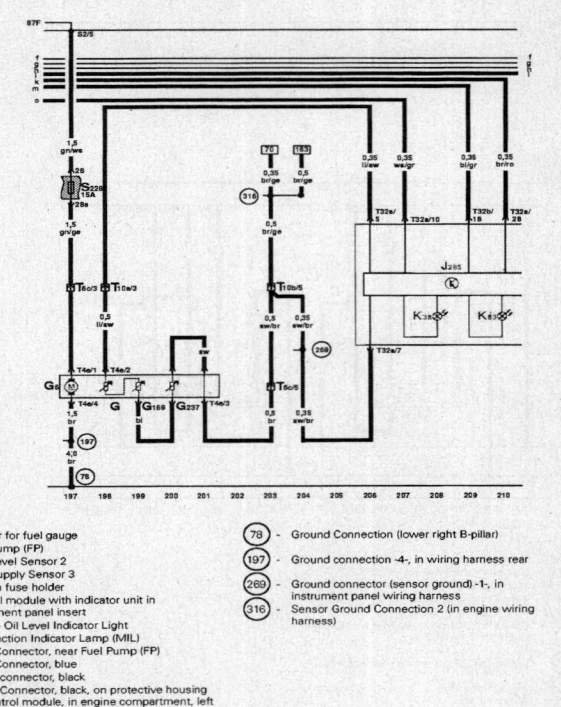

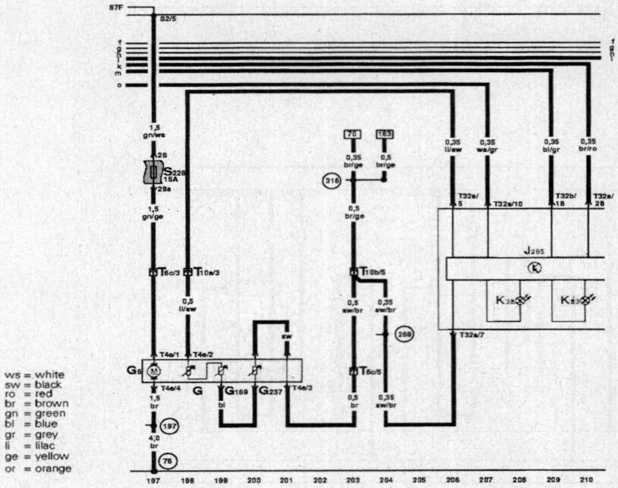

- G - Sender for fuel gauge
- G6 - Fuel Pump (FP)
- G169 - Fuel Level Sensor 2
- G237 - Fuel Supply Sensor 3
- S228 - Fuse in fuse holder
- J285 - Control module with indicator unit in instrument panel insert
- K38 - Engine Oil Level Indicator Light
- K83 - Malfunction Indicator Lamp (MIL)
- T4e - 4-Pin Connector, near Fuel Pump (FP)
- T6c - 6-Pin Connector, blue
- T10a - 10-Pin connector, black
- T10b - 10-Pin Connector, black, on protective housing for control module, in engine compartment, left
- T32a - 32-Pin Connector, bue, on instrument cluster
- T32b - 32-Pin Connector, green, on instrument cluster
- (78) - Ground Connection (lower right B-pillar)
- (197) - Ground connection -4-, in wiring harness rear
- (269) - Ground connector (sensor ground) -1-, in instrument panel wiring harness
- (316) - Sensor Ground Connection 2 (in engine wiring harness)

VW1020100160150X

Fig. 129 Motronic wiring diagram (Control module w/indicator unit, fuel pump, fuel level & supply sensors & tank sender). 2001 Passat w/1.8L ATW engine

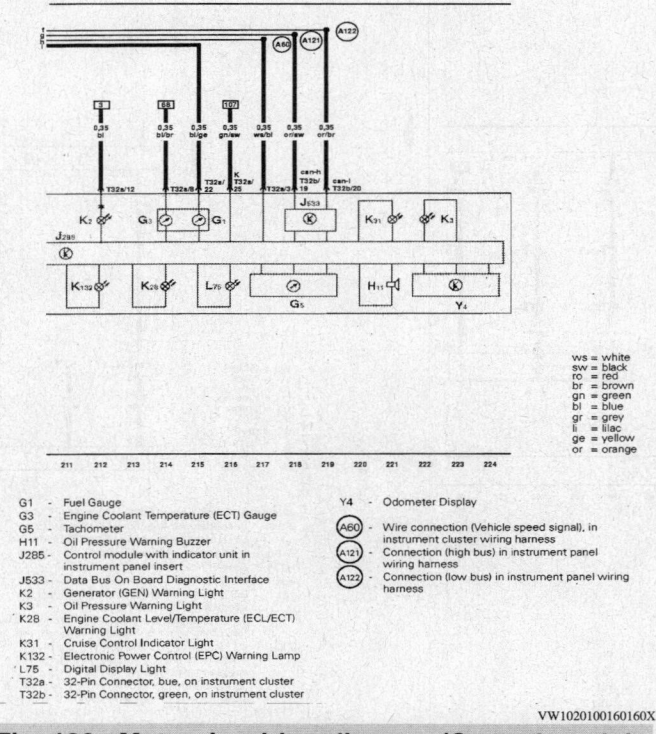

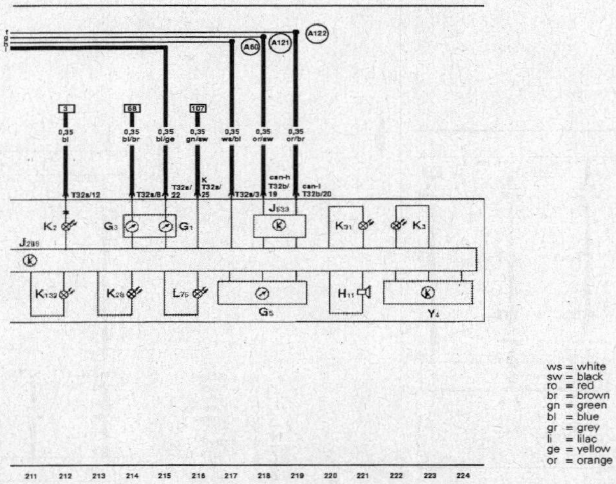

- G1 - Fuel Gauge
- G3 - Engine Coolant Temperature (ECT) Gauge
- G5 - Tachometer
- H11 - Oil Pressure Warning Buzzer
- J285 - Control module with indicator unit in instrument panel insert
- J533 - Data Bus On Board Diagnostic Interface
- K2 - Generator (GEN) Warning Light
- K3 - Oil Pressure Warning Light
- K28 - Engine Coolant Level/Temperature (ECL/ECT) Warning Light
- K31 - Cruise Control Indicator Light
- K132 - Electronic Power Control (EPC) Warning Lamp
- L75 - Digital Display Light
- T32a - 32-Pin Connector, bue, on instrument cluster
- T32b - 32-Pin Connector, green, on instrument cluster
- Y4 - Odometer Display
- (A60) - Wire connection (Vehicle speed signal), in instrument cluster wiring harness
- (A121) - Connection (high bus) in instrument panel wiring harness
- (A122) - Connection (low bus) in instrument panel wiring harness

VW1020100160160X

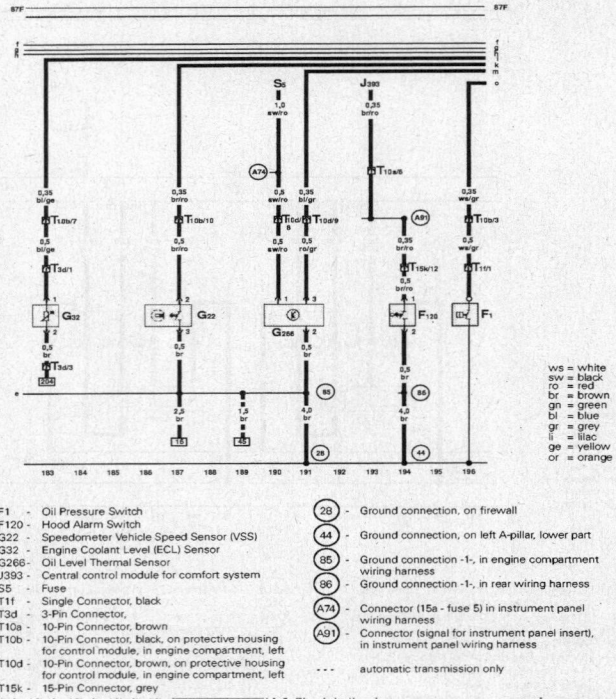

Fig. 130 Motronic wiring diagram (Control module w/indicator unit & data bus OBD interface). 2001 Passat w/1.8L ATW engine

DIAGNOSTIC CHART INDEX

Code	Description	Page No.	Fig. No.
1998 CABRIO, GOLF, GTI & JETTA w/2.0L ENGINE			
P0102	MAF Circuit Low Input	17-124	131
P0112	IAT Circuit Low Input	17-124	132
P0113	IAT Circuit High Input	17-124	133
P0117	ECT Circuit Low Input	17-125	134
P0118	ECT Circuit High Input	17-125	135
P0120	TP Sensor A Circuit Malfunction	17-125	136
P0121	TP Sensor A Circuit Range/Performance Problem	17-126	137
P0122	TP Sensor A Circuit Low Input	17-127	138
P0125	Insufficient Coolant Temperature For Closed Loop Fuel Control	17-128	139
P0131	O2S Circuit Low Voltage Bank 1 Sensor 1	17-128	140
P0133	O2S Circuit Slow Response Bank 1 Sensor 1	17-129	141
P0134	O2S Circuit No Activity Detected Bank 1 Sensor 1	17-129	142
P0135	O2S Heater Circuit Malfunction Bank 1 Sensor 1	17-130	143
P0137	O2S Circuit Low Voltage Bank 1 Sensor	17-130	144
P0138	O2S Circuit High Voltage Bank 1 Sensor 2	17-130	145
P0140	O2S Circuit No Activity Detected Bank 1 Sensor 2	17-131	146
P0141	O2S heater Circuit Malfunction Bank 1 Sensor 2	17-131	147
P0171	System Too Lean Bank 1	17-131	148
P0172	System Too Rich Bank 1	17-132	149
P0300	Random Misfire Detected	17-133	150
P0301	Cylinder 1 Misfire Detected	17-133	151
P0302	Cylinder 2 Misfire Detected	17-134	152
P0303	Cylinder 3 Misfire Detected	17-134	153
P0304	Cylinder 4 Misfire Detected	17-135	154
P0327	KS 1 Circuit Low Input Bank 1	17-135	155
P0341	CMP Sensor Circuit Range/Performance	17-136	156
P0411	Secondary Air Injection System Improper Flow Detected	17-136	157
P0422	Main Catalyst Efficiency Below Threshold Bank 1	17-136	158
P0440	EVAP Emission Control System Malfunction	17-136	159
P0501	VSS Range Performance	17-137	160
P0605	Internal Control Module ROM Error	17-137	161
P0715	Input/TSS Circuit Malfunction	17-137	162
P0722	Output Speed Sensor Circuit No Signal	17-138	163
P0725	Engine Speed Input Circuit Malfunction	17-138	164
P0748	Pressure Control Solenoid Electrical	17-138	165
P0753	Shift Solenoid A Electrical	17-138	166
P0758	Shift Solenoid B Electrical	17-138	167
P0763	Shift Solenoid C Electrical	17-138	168
P0768	Shift Solenoid D Electrical	17-138	169
P0773	Shift Solenoid E Electrical	17-138	170
P1127	Long Term Fuel Trim Mul System Too Rich	17-139	171
P1128	Long Term Fuel Trim Mul System Too Lean	17-139	172
P1213	Cylinder 1 Fuel Injector Circuit Short To Voltage	17-139	173
P1214	Cylinder 2 Fuel Injector Circuit Short To Voltage	17-139	174
P1215	Cylinder 3 Fuel Injector Circuit Short To Voltage	17-140	175
P1216	Cylinder 4 Fuel Injector Circuit Short To Voltage	17-140	176
P1225	Injector Circuit Cylinder 1 Short To Ground	17-140	177
P1226	Injector Circuit Cylinder 2 Short To Ground	17-140	178
P1227	Injector Circuit Cylinder 3 Short To Ground	17-140	179
P1228	Injector Circuit Cylinder 4 Short To Ground	17-141	180
P1237	Injector Circuit Cylinder 1 Open Circuit	17-141	181
P1238	Injector Circuit Cylinder 2 Open Circuit	17-141	182
P1239	Injector Circuit Cylinder 3 Open Circuit	17-141	183
P1240	Injector Circuit Cylinder 4 Open Circuit	17-142	184
P1340	CMP/CKP Sensors Signals Out Of Sequence	17-142	185
P1410	Tank Ventilation Valve Short To Voltage	17-142	186

Continued

DIAGNOSTIC CHART INDEX—Continued

Code	Description	Page No.	Fig. No.
1998 CABRIO, GOLF, GTI & JETTA w/2.0L ENGINE			
P1420	Secondary Air Injection Control Module Short To Voltage	17-142	187
P1421	Secondary Air Injection Circuit Short To Ground	17-143	188
P1422	Secondary Air Injection System Control Valve Circuit Short To Voltage	17-143	189
P1425	Tank Ventilation Valve Short To Ground	17-143	190
P1426	Tank Ventilation Valve Open Circuit	17-143	191
P1450	Secondary Air Injection System Circuit Short To Voltage	17-143	192
P1451	Secondary Air Injection System Short To Ground	17-144	193
P1452	Secondary Air Injection System Open Circuit	17-144	194
P1500	Fuel Pump Relay Circuit Electrical Malfunction	17-144	195
P1502	Fuel Pump Relay Circuit Short To Voltage	17-145	196
P1544	Throttle Actuation Potentiometer Signal Too Low/Too High	17-145	197
P1580	Throttle Actuator Malfunction	17-145	198
P1582	Idle Adaptation At Limit	17-146	199
P1611	MIL Call-Up Circuit/Transmission Control Module Short To Ground	17-146	200
P1613	MIL Call-Up Circuit Open Short To Voltage	17-146	201
P1778	Solenoid EV7 Electrical Malfunction	17-146	202
P1780	Engine Intervention Readable	17-146	203
1998 GTI & JETTA			
P0102	Mass Or Volume Air Flow Circuit Low Input	17-146	204
P0103	Mass Or Volume Air Flow Circuit High Input	17-146	205
P0112	Intake Air Temperature Circuit Low Input	17-147	206
P0113	Intake Air Temperature Circuit High Input	17-147	207
P0117	Engine Coolant Temperature Circuit Low Input	17-147	208
P0118	Engine Coolant Temperature Circuit High Input	17-147	209
P0120	Throttle Position Sensor A Circuit Malfunction	17-148	210
P0121	Throttle Position Sensor A Circuit Range/Performance Problem	17-148	211
P0122	Throttle Position A Circuit Low Input	17-149	212
P0125	Insufficient Coolant Temperature For Closed Loop Fuel Control	17-150	213
P0131	Oxygen Sensor Circuit Low Voltage Bank 1 Sensor 1	17-150	214
P0132	Oxygen Sensor Circuit High Voltage Bank 1 Sensor 1	17-150	215
P0133	Oxygen Sensor Circuit Slow Response Bank 1 Sensor 1	17-150	216
P0134	Oxygen Sensor Circuit No Activity Detected Bank 1 Sensor 1	17-151	217
P0135	Oxygen Sensor Heater Circuit Malfunction Bank 1 Sensor 1	17-151	218
P0137	Oxygen Sensor Circuit Low Voltage Bank 1 Sensor 2	17-151	219
P0138	Oxygen Sensor Circuit High Voltage Bank 1 Sensor 2	17-151	220
P0140	Oxygen Sensor Circuit No Activity Detected Bank 1 Sensor 2	17-152	221
P0141	Oxygen Sensor Heater Circuit Malfunction Bank 1 Sensor 2	17-152	222
P0171	System Too Lean Bank 1	17-152	223
P0172	System Too Rich Bank 1	17-153	224
P0300	Random Misfire Detected	17-153	225
P0301	Cylinder 1 Misfire Detected	17-154	226
P0302	Cylinder 2 Misfire Detected	17-154	227
P0303	Cylinder 3 Misfire Detected	17-154	228
P0304	Cylinder 4 Misfire Detected	17-155	229
P0305	Cylinder 5 Misfire Detected	17-155	230
P0306	Cylinder 6 Misfire Detected	17-156	231
P0327	Knock Sensor 1 Circuit Low Input Bank 1 Or Single Sensor	17-156	232
P0332	Knock Sensor 2 Circuit Low Input Bank 2	17-156	233
P0341	Camshaft Position Sensor Circuit Range/Performance	17-156	234
P0411	Secondary Air Injection System Improper Flow Detected	17-157	235
P0422	Main Catalyst Efficiency Below Threshold Bank 1	17-157	236
P0440	Evaporative Emission Control System Malfunction	17-157	237
P0501	Vehicle Speed Sensor Range Performance	17-157	238
P0510	Closed Throttle Position Switch Malfunction	17-158	239
P0605	Internal Control Module Read Only Memory Error	17-158	240
P0715	Input/Turbine Speed Sensor Circuit Malfunction	17-158	241

Continued

DIAGNOSTIC CHART INDEX—Continued

Code	Description	Page No.	Fig. No.
1998 GTI & JETTA			
P0722	Output Speed Sensor No Signal	17-158	242
P0725	Engine Speed Input Circuit Malfunction	17-158	243
P0748	Pressure Control Solenoid Electrical Malfunction	17-159	244
P0753	Shift Solenoid A Electrical Malfunction	17-159	245
P0758	Shift Solenoid B Electrical Malfunction	17-159	246
P0763	Shift Solenoid C Electrical Malfunction	17-159	247
P0768	Shift Solenoid D Electrical Malfunction	17-159	248
P0773	Shift Solenoid E Electrical Malfunction	17-159	249
P1127	Long Term Fuel Trim, B1 System Too Rich	17-159	250
P1128	Long Term Fuel Trim, B1 System Too Lean	17-160	251
P1213	Cylinder 1 Injector Circuit Shorted To Voltage	17-160	252
P1214	Cylinder 2 Injector Circuit Shorted To Voltage	17-160	253
P1215	Cylinder 3 Injector Circuit Shorted To Voltage	17-160	254
P1216	Cylinder 4 Injector Circuit Shorted To Voltage	17-160	255
P1217	Cylinder 5 Injector Circuit Shorted To Voltage	17-161	256
P1218	Cylinder 6 Injector Circuit Shorted To Voltage	17-161	257
P1225	Cylinder 1 Injector Circuit Shorted To Ground	17-161	258
P1226	Cylinder 2 Injector Circuit Shorted To Ground	17-161	259
P1227	Cylinder 3 Injector Circuit Shorted To Ground	17-161	260
P1228	Cylinder 4 Injector Circuit Shorted To Ground	17-161	261
P1229	Cylinder 5 Injector Circuit Shorted To Ground	17-162	262
P1230	Cylinder 6 Injector Circuit Shorted To Ground	17-162	263
P1237	Cylinder 1 Injector Circuit Open	17-162	264
P1238	Cylinder 2 Injector Circuit Open	17-162	265
P1239	Cylinder 3 Injector Circuit Open	17-162	266
P1240	Cylinder 4 Injector Circuit Open	17-163	267
P1241	Cylinder 5 Injector Circuit Open	17-163	268
P1242	Cylinder 6 Injector Circuit Open	17-163	269
P1340	Camshaft/Crankshaft Position Sensor Signals Out Of Sequence	17-163	270
P1410	Tank Ventilation Valve Circuit Shorted To Voltage	17-163	271
P1420	Secondary Air Injection Control Module Shorted To Voltage	17-164	272
P1421	Secondary Air Injection Valve Circuit Shorted To Ground	17-164	273
P1422	Secondary Air Injection Valve Circuit Shorted To Voltage	17-164	274
P1425	Tank Ventilation Valve Shorted To Ground	17-164	275
P1426	Tank Ventilation Valve Open Circuit	17-164	276
P1450	Secondary Air Injection System Circuit Shorted To Voltage	17-164	277
P1451	Secondary Air Injection Circuit Shorted To Ground	17-165	278
P1452	Secondary Air Injection System Circuit Open	17-165	279
P1500	Fuel Pump Relay Electrical Circuit Malfunction	17-165	280
P1502	Fuel Pump Relay Shorted To Positive	17-165	281
P1543	Throttle Actuation Potentiometer Signal Too Low/Too High	17-165	282
P1544	Throttle Actuation Potentiometer Signal Too Low/Too High	17-165	282
P1580	Throttle Actuator B1 Malfunction	17-166	283
P1582	Idle Adaptation At Limit	17-166	284
P1611	MIL Call-Up Circuit/Transaxle Control Module Short To Ground	17-166	285
P1613	MIL Call-Up Circuit Open/Short To Voltage	17-166	286
P1778	Solenoid EV7 Electrical Malfunction	17-167	287
P1780	Engine Intervention Readable	17-167	288

Malfunction text: **Mass or Volume Air Flow Circuit Low Input**	
Cause:	Remedy:
Signal from Mass Air Flow (MAF) sensor -G70- to Engine Control Module (ECM) too low	– Eliminate unmetered (outside) air between MAF sensor -G70- and throttle valve control module -J338- Check voltage supply to MAF sensor: – Connect VAG 1598/18 test box – Disconnect 4-pin harness connector from MAF sensor – Switch ignition on – Bridge test box sockets 1 and 6, measure voltage between connector terminals 1 and 3 on 4-pin harness connector. Specification: min. 11.5 volts If no voltage is measured: – Switch ignition off – Check Ground (GND) cable resistance between connector terminal 1 and Ground (GND). Specification: max. 1.5 Ω – Measure resistance between connector terminal 1 and test box socket 1. Specification: max. 1.5 Ω If resistance is OK: – Use wiring diagram to locate and repair wiring open circuit from Fuel Pump (FP) relay -J17- to MAF sensor -G70-
	Continued ▼

VW0159900110010X

Fig. 131 Code P0102: MAF Circuit Low Input (Part 1 of 3). 1998 Cabrio, Golf, GTI & Jetta w/2.0L Engine

Malfunction text: **Mass or Volume Air Flow Circuit Low Input**		
		If the voltage supply to MAF sensor is at least 11.5 volts, check other wiring between MAF sensor and ECM -J220- as follows: – Bridge connector terminals 1 and 2, measure resistance between test box sockets 1 and 16. Specification: max. 1.5 Ω – Bridge connector terminals 1 and 4, measure resistance between test box sockets 1 and 17. Specification: max. 1.5 Ω – Do not bridge connector terminals, measure resistance between test box sockets 16 and 17. Specification: ∞ Ω If the specifications are not attained: – Use wiring diagram to locate and repair wiring open or short circuits to one another.
Malfunction cause for P0102 found: No ▼	Yes ▶	– After repairing malfunction, disconnect connector from ECM -J220- for 10 seconds, then clear DTC memory and create readiness code
Malfunction cause for P0102	▶	If resistance specifications are attained: – MAF sensor faulty, replace. Disconnect connector from ECM -J220- for 10 seconds, then clear DTC memory and create readiness code

VW0159900110020X

Fig. 131 Code P0102: MAF Circuit Low Input (Part 2 of 3). 1998 Cabrio, Golf, GTI & Jetta w/2.0L Engine

Malfunction text: **Mass or Volume Air Flow Circuit High Input**		
Cause:		Remedy:
Signal from Mass Air Flow (MAF) sensor -G70- to Engine Control Module (ECM) too high		– Switch ignition off. – Connect VAG 1598/18 test box. – Disconnect 4-pin connector from MAF sensor – Measure resistance between connector terminal 1 and test box socket 1. Specification: max. 1.5 Ω – Bridge connector terminals 1 and 2, measure resistance between test box sockets 1 and 16. Specification: max. 1.5 Ω – Bridge connector terminals 1 and 4, measure resistance between test box sockets 1 and 17. Specification: max. 1.5 Ω – Do not bridge connector terminals, measure resistance between test box sockets 16 and 17. Specification: ∞ Ω If the specifications are not attained: – Use wiring diagram to locate and repair wiring open or short circuits to one another.
Malfunction cause for P0103 found: No ▼	Yes ▶	– After repairing malfunction, disconnect connector from ECM -J220- for 10 seconds, then clear DTC memory and create readiness code
Malfunction cause for P0103	▶	If resistance specifications are attained: – MAF sensor faulty, replace. Disconnect connector from ECM -J220- for 10 seconds, then clear DTC memory and create readiness code

VW0159900110030X

Fig. 131 Code P0102: MAF Circuit Low Input (Part 3 of 3). 1998 Cabrio, Golf, GTI & Jetta w/2.0L Engine

Malfunction text: **Intake Air Temperature Circuit Low Input**	
Cause:	Remedy:
Engine Control Module (ECM) detects short circuit in wiring or in Intake Air Temperature (IAT) sensor -G72-	– Switch ignition off – Connect VAG 1598/18 test box – Measure sensor resistance value corresponding to ambient temperature between sockets 33 and 36, value must be within specified range If the resistance value is not attained: – Disconnect connector from intake air temperature sensor -G72- – Measure resistance between connector terminal 1 and test box socket 36. Specification: max.1.5 Ω If measured value is: ∞ Ω wiring has open circuit: – Locate and repair using wiring diagram – Measure resistance between connector terminal 1 and test box socket 33. Specification: ∞ Ω If measured value is not ∞ Ω: wiring has short circuit to Ground (GND): – Locate and repair using wiring diagram
	Continued ▼

VW0159900111010X

Fig. 132 Code P0112: IAT Circuit Low Input (Part 1 of 2). 1998 Cabrio, Golf, GTI & Jetta w/2.0L Engine

Malfunction text: **Intake Air Temperature Circuit Low Input**		
		If the specifications are attained, check intake air temperature sensor as follows: – Remove intake air temperature sensor and connect multimeter (Fluke 83 or equivalent) to terminals 1 and 2 of sensor connector – Spray sensor with a commercial chilling spray • Measure sensor resistance between terminals 1 and 2, value must increase without interruption. When sensor is heated (e.g. with hot air blower VAG 1416) resistance must drop back again. If the sensor does not react correctly to temperature changes: – Replace sensor
Malfunction cause for P0112 found: No ▼	Yes ▶	– After repairing malfunction, disconnect connector from ECM -J220- for 10 seconds, then clear DTC memory and create readiness code
Malfunction cause for P0112	▶	If the temperature changes were correctly recognized by intake air temperature sensor -G72-: – ECM -J220- faulty, replace. Then clear DTC memory and create readiness code.

VW0159900111020X

Fig. 132 Code P0112: IAT Circuit Low Input (Part 2 of 2). 1998 Cabrio, Golf, GTI & Jetta w/2.0L Engine

Malfunction text: **Intake Air Temperature Circuit High Input**	
Cause:	Remedy:
Engine Control Module (ECM) detects too high resistance and/or wiring open circuit to Intake Air Temperature (IAT) sensor -G72-	– Switch ignition off – Connect VAG 1598/18 test box – Measure sensor resistance value corresponding to ambient temperature between sockets 33 and 36, value must be within specified range If the resistance value is not attained: – Disconnect connector from intake air temperature sensor -G72- – Measure resistance between connector terminal 1 and test box socket 36. Specification: max.1.5 Ω If the measured value is ∞ Ω: wiring has open circuit – Locate and repair this malfunction using wiring diagram – Measure resistance between connector terminal 1 and test box socket 33. Specification: ∞ Ω If the measured value is not ∞ Ω: wiring has short circuit to Ground (GND) – Locate and repair this malfunction using wiring diagram.
	Continued ▼

VW0159900112010X

Fig. 133 Code P0113: IAT Circuit High Input (Part 1 of 2). 1998 Cabrio, Golf, GTI & Jetta w/2.0L Engine

Malfunction text: Intake Air Temperature Circuit High Input		
		If the specifications are not attained, check intake air temperature sensor -G72- as follows: – Remove intake air temperature sensor and connect multimeter (Fluke 83 or equivalent) to terminals 1 and 2 of sensor – Spray sensor with commercial chilling spray • Measure sensor resistance between terminals 1 and 2, value must increase without interruption. When sensor is heated (e.g. with hot air blower VAG 1416) value must drop back again. If the sensor does not react to the temperature changes: – Replace sensor
Malfunction cause for P0113 found: No ▼	Yes ▶	– After repairing malfunction disconnect connector from ECM -J220- for 10 seconds, then clear DTC memory and create readiness code
Malfunction cause for P0113	▶	If the temperature changes were correctly recognized by intake air temperature sensor -G72-: – ECM -J220- faulty, replace. Then clear DTC memory and create readiness code

VW0159900112020X

Fig. 133 Code P0113: IAT Circuit High Input (Part 2 of 2). 1998 Cabrio, Golf, GTI & Jetta w/2.0L Engine

Malfunction text: Engine Coolant Temperature Circuit Low Input		
		If the specifications are attained, check engine coolant temperature sensor -G62- as follows: – Release pressure from cooling system, remove engine coolant temperature sensor and seal opening – Connect multimeter (Fluke 83 or equivalent) to terminals 1 and 3 of sensor – Spray sensor with commercial chilling spray • Measure sensor resistance between terminals 1 and 3, value must increase without interruption. When sensor is heated (e.g. with hot air blower VAG 1416) value must drop back again. If the sensor does not react to the temperature changes: – Replace sensor
Malfunction cause for P0117 found: No ▼	Yes ▶	– After repairing malfunction, clear DTC memory and create readiness code
Malfunction cause for P0117	▶	If the temperature changes are correctly recognized by Engine Coolant Temperature (ECT) sensor -G62-: – ECM -J220- faulty, replace. Clear DTC memory and create readiness code.

VW0159900113020X

Fig. 134 Code P0117: ECT Circuit Low Input (Part 2 of 2). 1998 Cabrio, Golf, GTI & Jetta w/2.0L Engine

Malfunction text: Engine Coolant Temperature Circuit High Input		
		If the specifications are attained, check engine coolant temperature sensor -G62- as follows: – Release pressure from cooling system, remove engine coolant temperature sensor -G62- and seal. – Connect multimeter (Fluke 83 or equivalent) to terminals 1 and 3 of sensor – Spray sensor with commercial chilling spray • Measure sensor resistance between terminals 1 and 3, resistance must distinctly increase without interruption. When sensor is heated (e.g. with hot air blower VAG 1416) resistance value must drop back again. If the sensor does not react to the temperature changes: – Replace sensor
Malfunction cause for P0118 found: No ▼	Yes ▶	– After repairing malfunction, clear DTC memory and create readiness code
Malfunction cause for P0118	▶	If the temperature changes are correctly recognized by Engine Coolant Temperature (ECT) sensor -G62-: – ECM -J220- faulty, replace. Clear DTC memory and create readiness code

VW0159900114020X

Fig. 135 Code P0118: ECT Circuit High Input (Part 2 of 2). 1998 Cabrio, Golf, GTI & Jetta w/2.0L Engine

Malfunction text: Engine Coolant Temperature Circuit Low Input	
Cause: Engine Control Module (ECM) detects short circuit in wiring or in Engine Coolant Temperature (ECT) sensor -G62-	Remedy: – Switch ignition off – Connect VAG 1598/18 test box – Measure engine coolant temperature sensor -G62- resistance corresponding to actual coolant temperature between sockets 14 and 33 If the specification is not attained: – Disconnect connector from sensor -G62-, terminal assignment – Measure resistance between connector terminal 3 and test box socket 14. Specification: max.1.5 Ω If the measured value is ∞ Ω: wiring has open circuit – Locate and repair this malfunction using wiring diagram – Measure resistance between connector terminal 3 and test box socket 33. Specification: ∞ Ω If the measured value is not ∞ Ω: wiring has short circuit to Ground (GND) – Locate and repair this malfunction using wiring diagram.
	Continued ▼

VW0159900113010X

Fig. 134 Code P0117: ECT Circuit Low Input (Part 1 of 2). 1998 Cabrio, Golf, GTI & Jetta w/2.0L Engine

Malfunction text: Engine Coolant Temperature Circuit High Input	
Cause: Engine Control Module (ECM) detects too high resistance and/or wiring open circuit to Engine Coolant Temperature (ECT) sensor -G62-	Remedy: – Switch ignition off – Check connector on engine coolant temperature sensor -G62- for loose connection – Connect VAG 1598/18 test box – Measure engine coolant temperature sensor -G62- resistance value corresponding to actual coolant temperature between sockets 14 and 33 If the resistance value is not attained: – Disconnect connector from sensor -G62-, terminal assignment – Check whether coolant has caused resistance in connector to sensor – Measure resistance between connector terminal 3 and test box socket 14. Specification: max.1.5 Ω If the measured value is not ∞ Ω: the wire has open circuit – Locate and repair this malfunction using wiring diagram – Measure resistance between connector terminal 3 and test box socket 33. Specification: ∞ Ω If the measured value is not ∞ Ω: the wire has short circuit to Ground (GND) – Locate and repair this malfunction using wiring diagram
	Continued ▼

VW0159900114010X

Fig. 135 Code P0118: ECT Circuit High Input (Part 1 of 2). 1998 Cabrio, Golf, GTI & Jetta w/2.0L Engine

Malfunction text: Throttle Position Sensor A Circuit Malfunction	
Cause: Throttle Position (TP) sensor supplies implausible signal to Engine Control Module (ECM)	Remedy: – Switch ignition off – Check throttle valve control module -J338- voltage supply at 8-pin connector: (terminal assignment) – Disconnect 8-pin connector from throttle valve control module – Switch ignition on – Check voltage between connector terminals 4 and 7. Specification: approx. 5 volts – Check voltage between connector terminals 3 and 7. Specification: approx. 10 volts If the specifications are not attained: – Switch ignition off – Connect VAG 1598/18 test box Check resistance as follows: – Connector terminal 3 and test box socket 10 – Connector terminal 4 and test box socket 41 – Connector terminal 7 and test box socket 33 Specifications: max.1.5 Ω If the specifications are not attained: – Use wiring diagram to locate and repair open circuit If no open circuit is detected: – Replace ECM -J220-
	Continued ▼

VW0159900115010X

Fig. 136 Code P0120: TP Sensor A Circuit Malfunction (Part 1 of 6). 1998 Cabrio, Golf, GTI & Jetta w/2.0L Engine

Malfunction text: Throttle Position Sensor A Circuit Malfunction		
		If the voltage supply specifications are attained: – Switch ignition off – Re-connect 8-pin connector to throttle valve control module – Connect VAG 1598/18 test box Check resistance as follows: – At wide open throttle position between test box sockets 10 and 33. Specification: ∞ Ω – At closed throttle position between test box sockets 10 and 33. Specification: max.10 Ω – At closed throttle position between test box sockets 27 and 53. Specification: 3 – 200 Ω If the specifications are not attained: – Disconnect 8-pin connector from throttle valve control module Check resistance as follows: – Connector terminal 1 and test box socket 27 – Connector terminal 2 and test box socket 53 – Connector terminal 5 and test box socket 40 – Connector terminal 8 and test box socket 62, Specifications: max.1.5 Ω If the resistances do not correspond to specifications: – Use wiring diagram to locate and repair open circuit
Continued ▼		

VW0159900115020X

Fig. 136 Code P0120: TP Sensor A Circuit Malfunction (Part 2 of 6). 1998 Cabrio, Golf, GTI & Jetta w/2.0L Engine

Malfunction text: Throttle Position Sensor A Circuit Malfunction		
Cause:		Remedy:
Mass Air Flow (MAF) sensor signal does not agree with Throttle Position (TP) sensor signal		– Switch ignition off – Connect VAG 1598/18 test box – Disconnect 4-pin connector from MAF sensor – Measure resistance between connector terminal 1 and test box socket 1. Specification: max. 1.5 Ω – Bridge connector terminals 1 and 2, measure resistance between test box sockets 1 and 16. Specification: max. 1.5 Ω – Bridge connector terminals 1 and 4, measure resistance between test box sockets 1 and 17. Specification: max. 1.5 Ω – Do not bridge connector terminals. Measure resistance between test box sockets 16 and 17. Specification: ∞ Ω If the specifications are not attained: – Use wiring diagram to locate and repair short circuit between wiring or open circuit
Malfunction cause for P0120 found: No ▼	Yes ▶	– After repairing malfunction, clear DTC memory and create readiness code
Continued ▼		

VW0159900115040X

Fig. 136 Code P0120: TP Sensor A Circuit Malfunction (Part 4 of 6). 1998 Cabrio, Golf, GTI & Jetta w/2.0L Engine

Malfunction text: Throttle Position Sensor A Circuit Malfunction		
		If the specifications are attained, check engine coolant temperature sensor -G62- as follows: – Release pressure from cooling system, remove engine coolant temperature sensor -G62- and seal. – Connect multimeter (Fluke 83 or equivalent) to terminals 1 and 3 of sensor – Spray sensor with commercial chilling spray • Measure sensor resistance between terminals 1 and 3, resistance must distinctly increase without interruption. When sensor is heated (e.g. with hot air blower VAG 1416) resistance value must drop back again. If the sensor does not react to the temperature changes: – Replace sensor
Malfunction cause for P0120 found: No ▼	Yes ▶	– After repairing malfunction, clear DTC memory and create readiness code
		If the temperature changes are correctly recognized by Engine Coolant Temperature (ECT) sensor -G62-:
Malfunction cause for P0120	▶	– ECM -J220- faulty, replace. Clear DTC memory and create readiness code

VW0159900115060X

Fig. 136 Code P0120: TP Sensor A Circuit Malfunction (Part 6 of 6). 1998 Cabrio, Golf, GTI & Jetta w/2.0L Engine

Malfunction text: Throttle Position Sensor A Circuit Malfunction		
		If the specifications are attained: – Also measure resistance (with 8-pin connector disconnected) between test box sockets 10, 27, 33, 40, 41, 53 and 62. Specification: ∞ Ω If the specifications are not ∞ Ω: – Use wiring diagram to locate and repair short circuit between wires If the specifications with wide open/closed throttle are not attained, but the wiring is OK: – Replace throttle valve control module -J338-
Malfunction cause for P0120 found: No ▼	Yes ▶	– After repairing malfunction, disconnect connector from ECM -J220- for 10 seconds, then clear DTC memory and create readiness code
		If no malfunction can be found in the throttle valve control module:
Continued ▼		

VW0159900115030X

Fig. 136 Code P0120: TP Sensor A Circuit Malfunction (Part 3 of 6). 1998 Cabrio, Golf, GTI & Jetta w/2.0L Engine

Malfunction text: Throttle Position Sensor A Circuit Malfunction	
Cause:	Remedy:
Engine Control Module (ECM) cannot use engine coolant temperature signal	– Switch ignition off – Check connector on Engine Coolant Temperature (ECT) sensor -G62- for loose connection – Connect VAG 1598/18 test box – Correct sensor resistance corresponding to actual coolant temperature must be measured between sockets 14 and 33 If the resistance value is not attained: – Disconnect connector from sensor -G62-, terminal assignment – Check whether coolant has caused resistance in connector to sensor – Measure resistance between connector terminal 3 and test box socket 14. Specification: max.1.5 Ω If the measured value is ∞ Ω: the wiring has an open circuit – Use wiring diagram to locate and repair malfunction – Measure resistance between connector terminal 3 and test box 33. Specification: ∞ Ω If the measured value is not ∞ Ω: – Use wiring diagram to locate and repair a short circuit to Ground (GND) in wiring
Continued ▼	

VW0159900115050X

Fig. 136 Code P0120: TP Sensor A Circuit Malfunction (Part 5 of 6). 1998 Cabrio, Golf, GTI & Jetta w/2.0L Engine

Malfunction text: Throttle Position Sensor A Circuit Range/Performance Problem		
Cause:		Remedy:
Throttle Position (TP) sensor supplies implausible signal to Engine Control Module (ECM)		– Switch ignition off – Check throttle valve control module -J338- voltage supply at 8-pin connector: (terminal assignment – Disconnect 8-pin connector from throttle valve control module – Switch ignition on Check voltage as follows: – Between connector terminals 4 and 7. Specification: approx. 5 volts – Between connector terminals 3 and 7. Specification: approx. 10 volts If the specifications are not attained: – Switch ignition off – Connect VAG 1598/18 test box Check resistance as follows: – Connector terminal 3 and test box socket 10 – Connector terminal 4 and test box socket 41 – Connector terminal 7 and test box socket 33 Specifications: max.1.5 Ω If the specifications are not attained: – Use wiring diagram to locate and repair open circuit If no open circuit is detected: – Replace ECM -J220-
Malfunction cause for P0121 found: No ▼	Yes ▶	– After repairing malfunction, disconnect connector from ECM -J220- for 10 seconds, then clear DTC memory and create readiness code
Continued ▼		

VW0159900116010X

Fig. 137 Code P0121: TP Sensor A Circuit Range/ Performance Problem (Part 1 of 4). 1998 Cabrio, Golf, GTI & Jetta w/2.0L Engine

Malfunction text: **Throttle Position Sensor A Circuit Range/Performance Problem**	
	If the voltage supply specifications are attained: – Switch ignition off – Connect 8-pin connector to throttle valve control module – Connect VAG 1598/18 test box – At wide open throttle position, check resistance between test box sockets 10 and 33. Specification ∞ Ω – At closed throttle position, check resistance between test box sockets 10 and 33. Specification max.10 Ω – At closed throttle position, check resistance between test box sockets 27 and 53. Specification 3 – 200 Ω If the specifications are not attained: – Disconnect 8-pin connector and check resistances as follows: – Connector terminal 1 and test box socket 27 – Connector terminal 2 and test box socket 53 – Connector terminal 5 and test box socket 40 – Connector terminal 8 and test box socket 62 Specifications: max.1.5 Ω If the resistance does not correspond to specifications: – Use wiring diagram to locate and repair open circuit
Continued ▼	

VW0159900116020X

Fig. 137 Code P0121: TP Sensor A Circuit Range/ Performance Problem (Part 2 of 4). 1998 Cabrio, Golf, GTI & Jetta w/2.0L Engine

Malfunction text: **Throttle Position Sensor A Circuit Range/Performance Problem**		
Cause: Mass Air Flow (MAF) sensor signal does not agree with Throttle Position (TP) sensor signal		Remedy: – Switch ignition off – Connect test box 1598/18 – Disconnect 4-pin connector from MAF sensor – Measure resistance between connector terminal 1 and test box socket 1. Specification: max. 1.5 Ω – Bridge connector terminals 1 and 2, measure resistance between test box sockets 1 and 16. Specification: max. 1.5 Ω – Bridge connector terminals 1 and 4, measure resistance between test box sockets 1 and 17. Specification: max. 1.5 Ω – Do not bridge connector terminals. Measure resistance between test box sockets 16 and 17. Specification: ∞ Ω If the specifications are not attained: – Use wiring diagram to locate and repair short circuit between wires
Malfunction cause for P0121 found: No ▼	Yes ▶	– After repairing malfunction, disconnect connector from ECM -J220- for 10 seconds, then clear DTC memory and create readiness code
Malfunction cause for P0121	▶	– ECM -J220- faulty, replace. Clear DTC memory and create readiness code

VW0159900116040X

Fig. 137 Code P0121: TP Sensor A Circuit Range/ Performance Problem (Part 4 of 4). 1998 Cabrio, Golf, GTI & Jetta w/2.0L Engine

Malfunction text: **Throttle Position Sensor A Circuit Low Input**	
	If the voltage supply specifications are attained: – Switch ignition off – Attach 8-pin connector to throttle valve control module – Connect VAG 1598/18 test box – At wide open throttle position, check resistance between test box sockets 10 and 33. Specification: ∞ Ω – At closed throttle position, check resistance between test box sockets 10 and 33. Specification: max.10 Ω – At closed throttle position, check resistance between test box sockets 27 and 53. Specification: 3 – 200 Ω If the specifications are not attained: – Disconnect 8-pin connector Check resistances as follows: – Connector terminal 1 and test box socket 27 – Connector terminal 2 and test box socket 53 – Connector terminal 5 and test box socket 40 – Connector terminal 8 and test box socket 62 Specifications: max.1.5 Ω If the resistance does not correspond to specifications: – Use wiring diagram to locate and repair open circuit If the specifications are attained with 8-pin connector disconnected: – Measure resistance between test box sockets 10, 27, 33, 40, 41, 53 and 62. Specification: ∞ Ω
Continued ▼	

VW0159900117020X

Fig. 138 Code P0122: TP Sensor A Circuit Low Input (Part 2 of 6). 1998 Cabrio, Golf, GTI & Jetta w/2.0L Engine

Malfunction text: **Throttle Position Sensor A Circuit Range/Performance Problem**		
		If the specifications are attained: – Also measure resistance (with 8-pin connector disconnected) between test box sockets 10, 27, 33, 40, 41, 53 and 62. Specification: ∞ Ω If the specifications are not attained: – Use wiring diagram to locate and repair short circuit between wires If the specifications with open/closed throttle are not attained, but the wiring is OK: – Replace throttle valve control module -J338-
Malfunction cause for P0121 found: No ▼	Yes ▶	– After repairing malfunction, disconnect connector from ECM -J220- for 10 seconds, then clear DTC memory and create readiness code
		If no malfunction can be found in the throttle valve control module:
Continued ▼		

VW0159900116030X

Fig. 137 Code P0121: TP Sensor A Circuit Range/ Performance Problem (Part 3 of 4). 1998 Cabrio, Golf, GTI & Jetta w/2.0L Engine

Malfunction text: **Throttle Position Sensor A Circuit Low Input**		
Cause: Throttle Position (TP) sensor supplies implausible signal to Engine Control Module (ECM)		Remedy: – Check throttle valve control module -J338- voltage supply at 8-pin connector: (terminal assignment – Disconnect 8-pin connector from throttle valve control module – Switch ignition on Check voltage as follows: – Between connector terminals 4 and 7. Specification: approx. 5 volts – Between connector terminals 3 and 7. Specification: approx. 10 volts If the specifications are not attained: – Switch ignition off – Connect VAG 1598/18 test box Check resistance as follows: – Connector terminal 3 and test box socket 10 – Connector terminal 4 and test box socket 41 – Connector terminal 7 and test box socket 33 Specifications: max.1.5 Ω If the specifications are not attained: – Use wiring diagram to locate and repair open circuit If no open circuit is found: – Replace ECM -J220-
Malfunction cause for P0122 found: No ▼	Yes ▶	– After repairing malfunction, disconnect connector from ECM -J220- for 10 seconds, then clear DTC memory and create readiness code
Continued ▼		

VW0159900117010X

Fig. 138 Code P0122: TP Sensor A Circuit Low Input (Part 1 of 6). 1998 Cabrio, Golf, GTI & Jetta w/2.0L Engine

Malfunction text: **Throttle Position Sensor A Circuit Low Input**		
		If the specifications are not ∞ Ω: – Use wiring diagram to locate and repair short circuit between wires If the specifications with throttle open/closed are not attained, but the wiring is OK: – Replace throttle valve control module -J338-
Malfunction cause for P0122 found: No ▼	Yes ▶	– After repairing malfunction, disconnect connector from ECM -J220- for 10 seconds, then clear DTC memory and create readiness code
		If no malfunction can be found in the throttle valve control module:
Continued ▼		

VW0159900117030X

Fig. 138 Code P0122: TP Sensor A Circuit Low Input (Part 3 of 6). 1998 Cabrio, Golf, GTI & Jetta w/2.0L Engine

Malfunction text: **Throttle Position Sensor A Circuit Low Input**	
Cause:	Remedy:
Mass Air Flow (MAF) sensor signal does not agree with Throttle Position (TP) sensor signal	– Switch ignition off – Connect VAG 1598/18 test box – Disconnect 4-pin connector from MAF sensor – Measure resistance between connector terminal 1 and test box socket 1. Specification: max. 1.5 Ω – Bridge connector terminals 1 and 2, measure resistance between test box sockets 1 and 16. Specification: max. 1.5 Ω – Bridge connector terminals 1 and 4, measure resistance between test box sockets 1 and 17. Specification: max. 1.5 Ω – Do not bridge connector terminals, measure resistance between test box sockets 16 and 17. Specification: ∞ Ω If the specifications are not attained: – Use wiring diagram to locate and repair short circuit between wiring or open circuit
Malfunction cause for P0122 found: No ▼ Yes ▶	– After repairing malfunction, clear DTC memory and create readiness code
Continued ▼	

VW0159900117040X

Fig. 138 Code P0122: TP Sensor A Circuit Low Input (Part 4 of 6). 1998 Cabrio, Golf, GTI & Jetta w/2.0L Engine

Malfunction text: **Throttle Position Sensor A Circuit Low Input**	
	If the specifications are attained, check engine coolant temperature sensor -G62- as follows: – Release pressure from cooling system, remove engine coolant temperature sensor -G62- and seal – Connect multimeter (Fluke 83 or equivalent) to terminals 1 and 3 of sensor – Spray sensor with commercial chilling spray • Measure sensor resistance between terminals 1 and 3, resistance must distinctly increase without interruption. When sensor is heated (e.g. with hot air blower VAG 1416) resistance value must drop back again. If the sensor does not react to the temperature changes: – Replace sensor
Malfunction cause for P0122 found: No ▼ Yes ▶	– After repairing malfunction, clear DTC memory and create readiness code
Malfunction cause for P0122 ▶	If the temperature changes are correctly recognized by engine coolant temperature sensor -G62-: – ECM -J220- faulty, replace. Clear DTC memory and create readiness code

VW0159900117060X

Fig. 138 Code P0122: TP Sensor A Circuit Low Input (Part 6 of 6). 1998 Cabrio, Golf, GTI & Jetta w/2.0L Engine

Malfunction text: **Insufficient Coolant Temperature for Closed Loop Fuel Control**	
	If the specifications are attained, check engine coolant temperature sensor -G62- as follows: – Release pressure from cooling system, remove engine coolant temperature sensor -G62- and seal – Connect multimeter (Fluke 83 or equivalent) to terminals 1 and 3 of sensor – Spray sensor with commercial chilling spray • Measure sensor resistance between terminals 1 and 3, resistance must distinctly increase without interruption. When sensor is heated (e.g. with hot air blower VAG 1416) resistance value must drop back again. If the sensor does not react to the temperature changes: – Replace sensor
Malfunction cause for P0125 found: No ▼ Yes ▶	– After repairing malfunction, clear DTC memory and create readiness code
Malfunction cause for P0125 ▶	If the temperature changes are correctly recognized by engine coolant temperature sensor -G62-: – Thermostat faulty, replace. Clear DTC memory and create readiness code

VW0159900118020X

Fig. 139 Code P0125: Insufficient Coolant Temperature For Closed Loop Fuel Control (Part 2 of 2). 1998 Cabrio, Golf, GTI & Jetta w/2.0L Engine

Malfunction text: **Throttle Position Sensor A Circuit Low Input**	
Cause:	Remedy:
Engine Control Module (ECM) cannot use engine coolant temperature signal	– Switch ignition off – Connect VAG 1598/18 test box – Measure sensor resistance value corresponding to the actual coolant temperature between sockets14 and 33 If the resistance value is not attained: – Check connector on Engine Coolant Temperature (ECT) sensor -G62- for loose connection – Disconnect connector from sensor -G62-, terminal assignment – Check whether coolant has caused resistance in sensor connector – Measure resistance between connector terminal 3 and test box socket 14. Specification: max.1.5 Ω If the measured resistance value is ∞ Ω: wire has open circuit – Use wiring diagram to locate and repair malfunction – Measure resistance between connector terminal 3 and test box socket 33. Specification: ∞ Ω If the measured resistance value is not ∞ Ω: – Use wiring diagram to locate and repair short circuit to Ground (GND)
	Continued ▼

VW0159900117050X

Fig. 138 Code P0122: TP Sensor A Circuit Low Input (Part 5 of 6). 1998 Cabrio, Golf, GTI & Jetta w/2.0L Engine

Malfunction text: **Insufficient Coolant Temperature for Closed Loop Fuel Control**	
Cause:	Remedy:
Engine Control Module (ECM) cannot use engine coolant temperature signal for Oxygen Sensor (O2S) control, or the time taken for engine to reach normal operating temperature is too long	– Switch ignition off – Check connector on Engine Coolant Temperature (ECT) sensor -G62- for loose connection – Connect VAG 1598/18 test box – Measure sensor resistance value corresponding to the actual coolant temperature between sockets 14 and 33 If the specification is not attained: – Disconnect connector from sensor -G62-, terminal assignment – Check whether coolant has caused resistance in connector to sensor – Measure resistance between connector terminal 3 and test box socket 14. Specification: max.1.5 Ω If the measured value is ∞ Ω: the wire has open circuit – Use wiring diagram to locate and repair malfunction – Measure resistance between connector terminal 3 and test box socket 33. Specification: ∞ Ω If the measured value is not ∞ Ω: the wire has short circuit to Ground (GND) – Use wiring diagram to locate and repair malfunction
	Continued ▼

VW0159900118010X

Fig. 139 Code P0125: Insufficient Coolant Temperature For Closed Loop Fuel Control (Part 1 of 2). 1998 Cabrio, Golf, GTI & Jetta w/2.0L Engine

Malfunction text: **0_2 Sensor Circuit Low Voltage (Bank 1 Sensor 1)**	
Cause:	Remedy:
Heated Oxygen Sensor (HO2S) -G39- (before three way catalytic converter) has short circuit to Ground (GND) for longer than 200 secs	– Disconnect HO2S connector (black connector), terminal assignment – Connect multimeter (Fluke 83 or equivalent) between terminals 3 and 4 of HO2S connector – With engine at normal working temperature run at idle. • The multimeter must indicate a voltage between 0.2 – 0.8 volts – Increase engine speed by revving up several times • The multimeter must indicate voltage jumps from 0.2 volts (lean mixture) to 0.9 volts (rich mixture) If no voltage jumps are indicated: – Replace HO2S -G39- (before three way catalytic converter)
Malfunction cause for P0131 found: No ▼ Yes ▶	– After repairing malfunction, disconnect connector from Engine Control Module (ECM) -J220- for 10 seconds, then clear DTC memory and create readiness code
	Continued ▼

VW0159900119010X

Fig. 140 Code P0131: O2S Circuit Low Voltage Bank 1 Sensor 1 (Part 1 of 5). 1998 Cabrio, Golf, GTI & Jetta w/2.0L Engine

Malfunction text: 0_2 Sensor Circuit Low Voltage (Bank 1 Sensor 1)		
		If the HO2S produces voltage jumps: – Switch ignition off – Connect VAG 1598/18 test box – Measure resistance between connector terminal 3 and test box socket 42. Specification: max. 1.5 Ω – Measure resistance between connector terminal 4 and test box socket 20. Specification: max. 1.5 Ω – Measure resistance between connector terminal 3 and test box socket 56. Specification: ∞ Ω – Measure resistance between connector terminal 4 and test box socket 56. Specification: ∞ Ω If these specifications are not attained: the wiring has an open circuit or a short circuit to Ground (GND) – Use wiring diagram to locate and repair malfunction.
Malfunction cause for P0131 found: No ▼	Yes ▶	– After repairing malfunction, clear DTC memory and create readiness code
		Continued ▼

VW0159900119020X

Fig. 140 Code P0131: O2S Circuit Low Voltage Bank 1 Sensor 1 (Part 2 of 5). 1998 Cabrio, Golf, GTI & Jetta w/2.0L Engine

Malfunction text: 0_2 Sensor Circuit High Voltage (Bank 1 Sensor 1)		
Cause:		Remedy:
Heated Oxygen Sensor (HO2S) -G39- (before three way catalytic converter) or wiring to HO2S has short circuit to positive		– Disconnect connector to HO2S (black connector), terminal assignment – Switch ignition on – Measure basic voltage from Engine Control Module (ECM) to HO2S connector between terminals 3 and 4. Specification: 0.45 volts If the specification is exceeded: – Switch ignition off – Connect VAG 1598/18 test box – Remove fuse 18 – Measure resistance between upper terminal for fuse 18 and test box socket 20. Specification: ∞ Ω – Measure resistance between upper terminal for use 18 and test box socket 42. Specification: ∞ Ω If the specification is not attained, the wiring has a short circuit to positive: – Use wiring diagram to locate and repair malfunction
Malfunction cause for P0132 found: No ▼	Yes ▶	– After repairing malfunction, clear DTC memory and create readiness code
		Continued ▼

VW0159900119040X

Fig. 140 Code P0131: O2S Circuit Low Voltage Bank 1 Sensor 1 (Part 4 of 5). 1998 Cabrio, Golf, GTI & Jetta w/2.0L Engine

Malfunction text: 0_2 Sensor Circuit Slow Response (Bank 1 Sensor 1)	
Cause:	Remedy:
Heated Oxygen Sensor (HO2S) -G39- (before three way catalytic converter) is dirty, aged or contaminated	• Before performing any test or starting this malfunction repair, heat up HO2S to operating temperature (self-cleaning effect). To do this run engine at approx. 3500 RPM for at least 3 minutes, with vehicle stationary – Connect generic Scan Tool (ST), set to scan tool function with address word 33 and clear DTC memory – Road test vehicle ♦ If the MIL is not switched on after the test drive, and no malfunction is stored in DTC memory, the HO2S was dirty. ♦ If the MIL is switched on after the test drive: – Switch ignition off – Connect VAG 1598/18 test box – Disconnect HO2S connector (black connector) terminal assignment – Switch ignition on – Bridge test box sockets 1 and 6 – Measure voltage between connector terminal 1 and Ground (GND). Specification: min.11.5 volts
	Continued ▼

VW0159900120010X

Fig. 141 Code P0133: O2S Circuit Slow Response Bank 1 Sensor 1 (Part 1 of 3). 1998 Cabrio, Golf, GTI & Jetta w/2.0L Engine

Malfunction text: 0_2 Sensor Circuit Slow Response (Bank 1 Sensor 1)	
	If the O2S heating is malfunction free: – Connect generic Scan Tool (ST), and set to scan tool function with address word 33 – Check HO2S signal output via mode 5 – Select test ID 9 and check minimum voltage If the HO2S actual value exceeds or falls short of the min./max. value: – Replace HO2S (before three way catalytic converter)
Malfunction cause for P0133 ▶	– HO2S (before three way catalytic converter) faulty, replace. After repairing malfunction, disconnect connector from ECM -J220- for 10 seconds, then clear DTC memory and create readiness code

VW0159900120030X

Fig. 141 Code P0133: O2S Circuit Slow Response Bank 1 Sensor 1 (Part 3 of 3). 1998 Cabrio, Golf, GTI & Jetta w/2.0L Engine

Malfunction text: 0_2 Sensor Circuit Low Voltage (Bank 1 Sensor 1)	
	If the specifications are attained and no malfunction can be found in the wiring: – Disconnect HO2S connector (black connector), terminal assignment – Switch ignition on – Measure basic voltage from ECM to HO2S connector between terminals 3 and 4. Specification: 0.45 volts If the specification 0.45 volts is not attained: – Switch ignition off
Malfunction cause for P0131 ▶	– ECM -J220- faulty, replace. Clear DTC memory and create readiness code

VW0159900119030X

Fig. 140 Code P0131: O2S Circuit Low Voltage Bank 1 Sensor 1 (Part 3 of 5). 1998 Cabrio, Golf, GTI & Jetta w/2.0L Engine

Malfunction text: 0_2 Sensor Circuit High Voltage (Bank 1 Sensor 1)		
		When all wiring to HO2S is free of malfunction: – Measure resistance at disconnected HO2S connector between terminals 1 and 3 and 1 and 4. Specification: ∞ Ω If the specifications are not attained, the HO2S has a short circuit to positive – Replace HO2S (before three way catalytic converter)
Malfunction cause for P0132 found: No ▼	Yes ▶	– After repairing malfunction disconnect connector from Engine Control Module (ECM) -J220- for 10 seconds, then clear DTC memory and create readiness code.
Malfunction cause for P0132 ▶		If the specifications are attained: – ECM -J220- faulty, replace. Clear DTC memory and create readiness code

VW0159900119050X

Fig. 140 Code P0131: O2S Circuit Low Voltage Bank 1 Sensor 1 (Part 5 of 5). 1998 Cabrio, Golf, GTI & Jetta w/2.0L Engine

Malfunction text: 0_2 Sensor Circuit Slow Response (Bank 1 Sensor 1)		
		If the specification of min. 11.5 volts is not attained: – Switch ignition off – Remove fuse 18 – Measure resistance between upper terminal for fuse 18 and connector terminal 1. Specification: max. 1.5 Ω – Measure resistance between connector terminal 2 and test box socket 12. Specification: max. 1.5 Ω If the specification is not attained: – Use wiring diagram to locate and repair open circuit If the specification of min. 11.5 volts is attained: – Check heating element resistance in HO2S at connector terminals 1 and 2. Specification at approx. 20°C (68°F) ambient temperature: max. 20 Ω If the specification of 20 Ω is not attained: – Oxygen Sensor (O2S) heating open circuit, replace HO2S (before three way catalytic converter)
Malfunction cause for P0133 found: No ▼	Yes ▶	– After repairing malfunction, disconnect connector from Engine Control Module (ECM) -J220- for 10 seconds, then clear DTC memory and create readiness code.
		Continued ▼

VW0159900120020X

Fig. 141 Code P0133: O2S Circuit Slow Response Bank 1 Sensor 1 (Part 2 of 3). 1998 Cabrio, Golf, GTI & Jetta w/2.0L Engine

Malfunction text: 0_2 Sensor Circuit No Activity Detected (Bank 1 Sensor 1)		
Cause:		Remedy:
Heated Oxygen Sensor (HO2S) (before three way catalytic converter) signal is not recognized by Engine Control Module (ECM)		– Switch ignition off – Disconnect HO2S connector (black connector), terminal assignment – Connect multimeter (Fluke 83 or equivalent) between terminals 3 and 4 of HO2S connector – With engine at normal operating temperature run at idle • The multimeter must indicate a voltage between 0.2 – 0.8 volts – Increase engine speed by revving up several times • The multimeter must indicate voltage jumps from 0.2 volts (lean mixture) to 0.9 volts (rich mixture) If no voltage jumps are indicated: – Replace HO2S (before three way catalytic converter)
Malfunction cause for P0134 found: No ▼	Yes ▶	– After repairing malfunction, disconnect connector from ECM -J220- for 10 seconds, then clear DTC memory and create readiness code.
		Continued ▼

VW0159900121010X

Fig. 142 Code P0134: O2S Circuit No Activity Detected Bank 1 Sensor 1 (Part 1 of 2). 1998 Cabrio, Golf, GTI & Jetta w/2.0L Engine

Malfunction text: O_2 Sensor Circuit No Activity Detected (Bank 1 Sensor 1)		
		If the HO2S produces voltage jumps: – Switch ignition off. – Disconnect HO2S connector (black connector) terminal assignment – Connect VAG 1598/18 test box – Measure resistance between connector terminal 3 and test box socket 42. Specification max. 1.5 Ω – Measure resistance between connector terminal 4 and test box socket 20. Specification max. 1.5 Ω – Measure resistance between connector terminal 3 and test box socket 56. Specification: ∞ Ω – Measure resistance between connector terminal 4 and test box socket 56. Specification: ∞ Ω If these specifications are not attained: the wiring has an open circuit or a short circuit to Ground (GND) – Use wiring diagram to locate and repair malfunction
Malfunction cause for P0134 found: No ▼	Yes ▶	– After repairing malfunction, clear DTC memory and create readiness code
Malfunction cause for P0134	▶	If all wiring to HO2S is malfunction free: – HO2S (before three way catalytic converter) faulty, replace. After repairing malfunction, disconnect connector from ECM -J220- for 10 seconds, then clear DTC memory and create readiness code

VW0159900121020X

Fig. 142 Code P0134: O2S Circuit No Activity Detected Bank 1 Sensor 1 (Part 2 of 2). 1998 Cabrio, Golf, GTI & Jetta w/2.0L Engine

Malfunction text: O_2 Sensor Heater Circuit Malfunction (Bank 1 Sensor 1)		
		If the specifications are attained: – Measure resistance between connector terminal 2 and test box socket 12. Specification: max. 1.5 Ω If the specification is not attained: – Use wiring diagram to locate and repair open circuit in wiring to ECM If the specification is attained: – Check heating element resistance in HO2S on connector terminals 1 and 2. Specification at approx., 20°C (68°F) ambient temperature: max. 20 Ω If the specification is not attained: – Replace HO2S
Malfunction cause for P0135 found: No ▼	Yes ▶	– After repairing malfunction, disconnect connector from ECM -J220- for 10 seconds, then clear DTC memory and create readiness code
Malfunction cause for P0135	▶	– ECM -J220- faulty, replace. Clear DTC memory and create readiness code.

VW0159900122020X

Fig. 143 Code P0135: O2S Heater Circuit Malfunction Bank 1 Sensor 1 (Part 2 of 2). 1998 Cabrio, Golf, GTI & Jetta w/2.0L Engine

Malfunction text: O_2 Sensor Circuit Low Voltage (Bank 1 Sensor 2)		
		If these specifications are not attained: the wiring has an open circuit or a short circuit to Ground (GND) – Use wiring diagram to locate and repair malfunction
Malfunction cause for P0137 found: No ▼	Yes ▶	– After repairing malfunction, clear DTC memory and create readiness code
Malfunction cause for P0137	▶	If the specifications are attained, the wiring is malfunction free, but 0.45 volts was not measured: – ECM -J220- faulty, replace. Clear DTC memory and create readiness code.

VW0159900123020X

Fig. 144 Code P0137: O2S Circuit Low Voltage Bank 1 Sensor 2 (Part 2 of 2). 1998 Cabrio, Golf, GTI & Jetta w/2.0L Engine

Malfunction text: O_2 Sensor Heater Circuit Malfunction (Bank 1 Sensor 1)	
Cause:	Remedy:
Heating for Oxygen Sensors (O2S) not functioning	– Switch ignition off – Check Heated Oxygen Sensor (HO2S) connector (black connector) for damage or contamination – Connect VAG 1598/18 test box – Disconnect HO2S connector, terminal assignment ⇒ page ST-188, Fig. 2 – Switch ignition on – Bridge test box sockets 1 and 6 – Measure voltage between connector terminal 1 and Ground (GND). Specification: min.11.5 volts If the specification is not attained: – Switch ignition off – Remove fuse 18 – Check resistance between fuse 18 upper terminal and connector terminal 1. Specification max. 1.5 Ω If the specification is not attained: – Use wiring diagram to locate and repair open circuit
	Continued ▼

VW0159900122010X

Fig. 143 Code P0135: O2S Heater Circuit Malfunction Bank 1 Sensor 1 (Part 1 of 2). 1998 Cabrio, Golf, GTI & Jetta w/2.0L Engine

Malfunction text: O_2 Sensor Circuit Low Voltage (Bank 1 Sensor 2)	
Cause:	Remedy:
Heated Oxygen Sensor (HO2S) 2 -G108- (after three way catalytic converter) has short circuit to Ground (GND) exceeding 200 seconds	– Check connectors to HO2S (before three way catalytic converter) and HO2S 2 (after three way catalytic converter) for damage or contamination, and repair if necessary – Disconnect HO2S 2 connector (brown connector), terminal assignment – Switch ignition on – Measure basic voltage from Engine Control Module (ECM) to HO2S 2 connector between terminals 3 and 4. Specification: 0.45 volts If the specification 0.45 volts is not attained: – Switch ignition off – Connect VAG 1598/18 test box – Measure resistance between connector terminal 3 and test box socket 58. Specification max. 1.5 Ω – Measure resistance between connector terminal 4 and test box socket 13. Specification max. 1.5 Ω – Measure resistance between connector terminal 3 and test box socket 56. Specification: ∞ Ω – Measure resistance between connector terminal 4 and test box socket 56. Specification: ∞ Ω
	Continued ▼

VW0159900123010X

Fig. 144 Code P0137: O2S Circuit Low Voltage Bank 1 Sensor 2 (Part 1 of 2). 1998 Cabrio, Golf, GTI & Jetta w/2.0L Engine

Malfunction text: O_2 Sensor Circuit High Voltage (Bank 1 Sensor 2)		
Cause:		Remedy:
Heated Oxygen Sensor (HO2S) 2 (after three way catalytic converter) or wiring to HO2S 2 has short circuit to positive		– Disconnect connector to HO2S 2 (brown connector), terminal assignment – Switch ignition on – Measure basic voltage from Engine Control Module (ECM) to HO2S 2 connector between terminals 3 and 4. Specification: 0.45 volts. If the specification is exceeded: – Switch ignition off – Connect VAG 1598/18 test box – Remove fuse 18 – Measure resistance between upper terminal for fuse 18 and test box socket 13. Specification ∞ Ω – Measure resistance between upper terminal for fuse 18 and test box socket 58. Specification ∞ Ω If the measured value is not ∞ Ω, the wiring has a short circuit to positive – Use wiring diagram to locate and repair malfunction
Malfunction cause for P0138 found: No ▼	Yes ▶	– After repairing malfunction, clear DTC memory and create readiness code
		Continued ▼

VW0159900124010X

Fig. 145 Code P0138: O2S Circuit High Voltage Bank 1 Sensor 2 (Part 1 of 2). 1998 Cabrio, Golf, GTI & Jetta w/2.0L Engine

Malfunction text: O_2 Sensor Circuit High Voltage (Bank 1 Sensor 2)		
		When all wiring to HO2S 2 is malfunction free: – Measure resistance at disconnected HO2S 2 connector between terminals 1 and 3, and1 and 4. Specification: ∞ Ω If the measured values are not ∞ Ω, HO2S 2 has a short circuit to positive – Replace HO2S 2 (after three way catalytic converter)
Malfunction cause for P0138 found: No ▼	Yes ▶	– After repairing malfunction disconnect connector from ECM -J220- for 10 seconds, then clear DTC memory and create readiness code
Malfunction cause for P0138	▶	If the measured values are: ∞ Ω – ECM -J220- faulty, replace. Clear DTC memory and create readiness code

VW0159900124020X

Fig. 145 Code P0138: O2S Circuit High Voltage Bank 1 Sensor 2 (Part 2 of 2). 1998 Cabrio, Golf, GTI & Jetta w/2.0L Engine

Malfunction text: O_2 Sensor Circuit No Activity Detected (Bank 1 Sensor 2)		
Malfunction cause for P0140 found: No ▼	Yes ▶	– After repairing malfunction, clear DTC memory and create readiness code
Cause: Heating for Oxygen Sensors (O2S) not functioning		Remedy: – Switch ignition off – Connect VAG 1598/18 test box – Switch ignition on – Bridge test box sockets 1 and 6 – Measure voltage between connector terminal 1 and Ground (GND). Specification: min.11.5 volts If the specification is not attained: – Switch ignition off – Remove fuse 18 – Check resistance between fuse 18 upper terminal and connector terminal 1. Specification max.1.5 Ω If the specification is not attained: – Use wiring diagram to locate and repair open circuit If the specification is attained: – Check heating element resistance in HO2S on connector terminals 1 and 2. Specification at approx. 20°C (68°F) ambient temperature: max. 20 Ω If the specification is not attained: – Replace HO2S
		Continued ▼

VW0159900125020X

Fig. 146 Code P0140: O2S Circuit No Activity Detected Bank 1 Sensor 2 (Part 2 of 3). 1998 Cabrio, Golf, GTI & Jetta w/2.0L Engine

Malfunction text: O_2 Sensor Heater Circuit Malfunction (Bank 1 Sensor 2)	
Cause: Heating for Oxygen Sensors (O2S) not functioning	Remedy: – Switch ignition off – Check HO2S 2 connector (after three way catalytic converter) for damage or contamination – Connect VAG 1598/18 test box – Disconnect HO2S 2 connector, terminal assignment ⇒ page ST-189 – Switch ignition on – Bridge test box sockets 1 and 6 – Measure voltage between connector terminal 1 and Ground (GND). Specification: min.11.5 volts If the specification is not attained: – Switch ignition off – Remove fuse 18 – Check resistance between fuse 18 upper terminal and connector terminal 1. Specification max.1.5 Ω If the specification is not attained: – Use wiring diagram to locate and repair open circuit If the specifications are attained: – Measure resistance between connector terminal 2 and test box socket 66. Specification: max. 1.5 Ω
	Continued ▼

VW0159900126010X

Fig. 147 Code P0141: O2S heater Circuit Malfunction Bank 1 Sensor 2 (Part 1 of 2). 1998 Cabrio, Golf, GTI & Jetta w/2.0L Engine

Malfunction text: O_2 Sensor Circuit No Activity Detected (Bank 1 Sensor 2)	
Cause: Heated Oxygen Sensor (HO2S) 2 (after three way catalytic converter) is dirty, aged or contaminated	Remedy: • Before performing any test or starting this malfunction repair, heat up oxygen sensors to operating temperature (self-cleaning effect). To do this run engine at approx. 3500 RPM for at least 3 minutes with vehicle stationary – Connect generic Scan Tool (ST), set to scan tool function with address word 33 and clear DTC memory – Road test vehicle ♦ If the MIL is not switched on after the test drive, and no malfunction is stored in DTC memory: HO2S was dirty ♦ If the MIL is switched on again after the test drive, there is a malfunction in the Oxygen Sensor (O2S) control: – Switch ignition off – Connect VAG 1598/18 test box – Disconnect HO2S 2 connector (brown connector), terminal assignment – Measure resistance between connector terminal 3 and test box socket 58. Specification max. 1.5 Ω – Measure resistance between connector terminal 4 and test box socket 13. Specification max. 1.5 Ω If these specifications are not attained: the wiring has an open circuit or a short circuit to Ground (GND) – Use wiring diagram to locate and repair malfunction
	Continued ▼

VW0159900125010X

Fig. 146 Code P0140: O2S Circuit No Activity Detected Bank 1 Sensor 2 (Part 1 of 3). 1998 Cabrio, Golf, GTI & Jetta w/2.0L Engine

Malfunction text: O_2 Sensor Circuit No Activity Detected (Bank 1 Sensor 2)		
Malfunction cause for P0140 found: No ▼	Yes ▶	– After repairing malfunction disconnect connector from Engine Control Module (ECM) -J220- for 10 second, then clear DTC memory and create readiness code
Malfunction cause for P0140	▶	If the specification is attained: – End stage in ECM faulty, replace ECM. Clear DTC memory and create readiness code

VW0159900125030X

Fig. 146 Code P0140: O2S Circuit No Activity Detected Bank 1 Sensor 2 (Part 3 of 3). 1998 Cabrio, Golf, GTI & Jetta w/2.0L Engine

Malfunction text: O_2 Sensor Heater Circuit Malfunction (Bank 1 Sensor 2)		
		If the specification is not attained: – Use wiring diagram to locate and repair open circuit in wiring to Engine Control Module (ECM) If the specification is attained: – Check heating element resistance in HO2S on connector terminals 1 and 2. Specification at approx. 20°C (68°F) ambient temperature: max. 20 Ω If the specification is not attained: – Replace HO2S
Malfunction cause for P0141 found: No ▼	Yes ▶	– After repairing malfunction disconnect connector from ECM -J220- for 10 second, then clear DTC memory and create readiness code
Malfunction cause for P0141	▶	– End stage in ECM faulty, replace ECM. – Clear DTC memory and create readiness code.

VW0159900126020X

Fig. 147 Code P0141: O2S heater Circuit Malfunction Bank 1 Sensor 2 (Part 2 of 2). 1998 Cabrio, Golf, GTI & Jetta w/2.0L Engine

Displayed text: (B1) System too Lean		
Cause: The mixture is so weak that the Oxygen sensor control cannot enrich further.		Remedy: – Start engine and run at idle speed. – Check whether the engine is drawing in unmeasured air between Mass Air Flow sensor G70 and cylinder head. – To do this spray all vacuum hoses, hose connections and gaskets between Mass Air Flow sensor G70 and cylinder head with leak detector spray. If no leaks can be found: for this malfunction advice always check the Secondary Air Injection system combi-valve as described in Diagnostic Trouble Code P0411
Malfunction cause for P0171 found: No ▼	Yes ▶	After repairing malfunction, erase DTC memory and create Readiness Code.
		Continued

VW0159900127010X

Fig. 148 Code P0171: System Too Lean Bank 1 (Part 1 of 4). 1998 Cabrio, Golf, GTI & Jetta w/2.0L Engine

Displayed text: (B1) System too Lean		
Cause: Signal from Mass Air Flow sensor G70 too low.		– Switch OFF ignition. – Connect Test Box VAG 1598/18. – Pull 4 pin connector off Mass Air Flow sensor. – Measure resistance between connector terminal 1 and Test Box socket 1. specification: max. 1.5 Ω – Bridge connector terminals 1+2, measure resistance between Test Box sockets 1+16. specification: max. 1.5 Ω – Bridge connector terminals 1+4, measure resistance between Test Box sockets 1+17. specification: max. 1.5 Ω – Do not bridge connector terminals. Measure resistance between Test Box sockets 16+17. specification: ∞ Ω If specifications are not obtained: – Locate and eliminate short between wires or open circuit using wiring diagram;
Malfunction cause for P0171 found: No ▼	Yes ▶	After repairing malfunction, erase DTC memory and create Readiness Code.
		If wiring to Mass Air Flow sensor OK: – Disconnect Test Box VAG 1598/18.
		Continued

VW0159900127020X

Fig. 148 Code P0171: System Too Lean Bank 1 (Part 2 of 4). 1998 Cabrio, Golf, GTI & Jetta w/2.0L Engine

Displayed text: (B1) System too Lean		
Cause: Injectors coked-up, and not opening fully.		Remedy: – Check whether air is flowing around injectors via connecting hose – Remove intake manifold upper part with injectors. – Check whether all injectors are clean. If one or more injectors are coked-up: – Replace injectors.
Malfunction cause for P0171 found: No ▼	Yes ▶	After repairing malfunction, erase DTC memory and create Readiness Code.
		If the injectors are malfunction free:
Malfunction cause for P0171	▶	Oxygen sensor 1 (before catalyst) faulty, replace. After repairing malfunction: Erase DTC memory and create Readiness Code.

VW0159900127040X

Fig. 148 Code P0171: System Too Lean Bank 1 (Part 4 of 4). 1998 Cabrio, Golf, GTI & Jetta w/2.0L Engine

Malfunction text: System too Rich (Bank 1)	
	– Measure resistance between connector terminal 3 and test box socket 42. Specification max. 1.5 Ω If the specification is not attained: wiring has open circuit – Use wiring diagram to locate and repair malfunction – Measure resistance between connector terminal 4 and test box socket 20. Specification max. 1.5 Ω If the specification is not attained: wiring has open circuit – Use wiring diagram to locate and repair malfunction If the measured values are OK:
Cause: Fuel pressure too high	Remedy: – Switch ignition off – Cover test port on fuel rail with a rag and open – Connect VAG 1318 fuel injection pressure gauge with VAG 1318/1 pressure gauge adapter and VAG 1318/10 adapter – Check vacuum hose to fuel pressure regulator for tight fit/damage If no malfunction is found: – Start engine and run at idle – Measure fuel pressure. Specification: approx. 3.5 bar (51 psi) – While engine is running, remove hose from pressure regulator. • Fuel pressure must increase to 4.0 bar (58 psi) If the specification of 4.0 bar (58 psi) is not attained: – Switch ignition off – Replace fuel pressure regulator If the pressure was too high before disconnecting hose: fuel return line is restricted or blocked.
	Continued ▼

VW0159900128020X

Fig. 149 Code P0172: System Too Rich Bank 1 (Part 2 of 3). 1998 Cabrio, Golf, GTI & Jetta w/2.0L Engine

Displayed text: (B1) System too Lean		
Cause: Fuel pressure too low, or quantity of fuel supplied insufficient.		Remedy: Check whether vehicle has performance problems: When vehicle has performance problems which only occur at full acceleration: – Replace fuel filter. If the engine output is impaired at small throttle openings, or the vehicle jerks at small throttle openings: – Switch off engine. – Cover test connection on fuel rail with a cloth and open. – Connect pressure gauge VAG 1318 with hose VAG 1318/1 and adapter VAG 1318/10. – Start engine and run at idle speed. – Measure fuel pressure. specification: approx. 2.5 bar. If specification is not obtained: – Check whether fuel supply line is pinched If the fuel supply line is not faulty: – Replace fuel pump (G23).
Malfunction cause for P0171 found: No ▼	Yes ▶	After repairing malfunction, erase DTC memory and create Readiness Code.
		If the fuel supply line and the fuel pump are defect free:
		Continued

VW0159900127030X

Fig. 148 Code P0171: System Too Lean Bank 1 (Part 3 of 4). 1998 Cabrio, Golf, GTI & Jetta w/2.0L Engine

Malfunction text: System too Rich (Bank 1)		
Cause: The mixture is so rich that Oxygen Sensor (O2S) control cannot weaken it further		Remedy: – Check whether crankcase dilution has caused engine to run rich, if necessary, change engine oil – Check whether the exhaust system is leaking between cylinder head and Three Way Catalytic Converter (TWC) If no leaks can be found: – Switch ignition off – Connect VAG 1598/18 test box – Measure resistance between test box sockets 20 and 42. Specification: ∞ Ω – Disconnect HO2S connector, terminal assignment ⇒ page ST-188, Fig. 2 – Check resistance between connector terminal 3 and test box socket 56. Specification: ∞ Ω – Check resistance between connector terminal 4 and test box socket 56. Specification: ∞ Ω If the measured values are not ∞ Ω, the wiring has a short circuit to cable shielding – Use wiring diagram to locate and repair malfunction If the measured values are: ∞ Ω
Malfunction cause for P0172 found: No ▼	Yes ▶	– After repairing malfunction, clear DTC memory and create readiness code
		Continued ▼

VW0159900128010X

Fig. 149 Code P0172: System Too Rich Bank 1 (Part 1 of 3). 1998 Cabrio, Golf, GTI & Jetta w/2.0L Engine

Malfunction text: System too Rich (Bank 1)		
Malfunction cause for P0172 found: No ▼	Yes ▶	– After repairing malfunction, clear DTC memory and create readiness code
Cause: Fuel injector is dirty and not closing (dripping)		Remedy: – Remove intake manifold upper section, and remove fuel injectors complete with fuel rail – Wipe off fuel injectors with a clean cloth – Use the fuel pressure still present in system for fuel injector leakage check When droplets form on fuel injector: – Replace leaking fuel injector.
		If the fuel injectors are not leaking:
Malfunction cause for P0172	▶	– Heated Oxygen Sensor (HO2S) (before three way catalytic converter) faulty, replace. After repairing malfunction disconnect connector from Engine Control Module (ECM) -J220- for 10 seconds, then clear DTC memory and create readiness code

VW0159900128030X

Fig. 149 Code P0172: System Too Rich Bank 1 (Part 3 of 3). 1998 Cabrio, Golf, GTI & Jetta w/2.0L Engine

Malfunction text: Random Misfire Detected		
Cause: Engine Control Module (ECM) detects uneven engine running (misfiring)		Remedy: • Before starting tests or removing components, make sure that fuel tank contains correct fuel (check for Diesel fuel or contamination by water or similar) If the fuel quality is OK: – Run engine at idle or slightly above idle, and check spark plug connectors/ignition wires for arcing to Ground (GND) If arcing is detected: – Switch ignition off – Replace appropriate spark plug connector with wire – Remove spark plugs and check condition. When doing this, also check that plugs installed have correct heat range
Malfunction cause for P0300 found: No ▼	Yes ▶	– After repairing malfunction, clear DTC memory and create readiness code
		Continued ▼

VW0159900129010X

Fig. 150 Code P0300: Random Misfire Detected (Part 1 of 4). 1998 Cabrio, Golf, GTI & Jetta w/2.0L Engine

Malfunction text: Random Misfire Detected	
Cause: Harness connector on ignition coil has electrical malfunction or loose connection	Remedy: – Switch ignition off – Disconnect connector from ignition coil, terminal assignment ⇒ – Switch ignition on – Measure voltage supply between connector terminals 1 and 3. Specification: min. 11.5 volts If the specification of min.11.5 volts is not attained: – Switch ignition off – Connect VAG 1598/18 test box – Measure resistance between connector terminal 1 and test box socket 1. Specification: max.1.5 Ω If the specification is not attained: – Use wiring diagram to locate and repair open circuit in Ground (GND) wire to ignition coil If the specification is attained: – Use wiring diagram to locate and repair open circuit in positive wire to ignition coil connector terminal 3 If min. 11.5 volts is attained, check remaining wiring: – Switch ignition off – Measure resistance between connector terminal 2 and test box socket 8. Specification: max.1.5 Ω
	Continued ▼

VW0159900129030X

Fig. 150 Code P0300: Random Misfire Detected (Part 3 of 4). 1998 Cabrio, Golf, GTI & Jetta w/2.0L Engine

Malfunction text: Cylinder 1 Misfire Detected	
Cause: Uneven engine running causes Engine Control Module (ECM) to detect misfiring	Remedy: – Run engine slightly above idle, and check spark plug connectors/ignition wires for arcing to Ground (GND) If arcing is detected: – Stop engine: switch ignition off – Replace spark plug connector with ignition wire – Remove spark plugs and check condition. Check that spark plugs with correct heat range have been installed. If no arcing can be detected: – Connect VAG 1598/18 test box – Check ignition coil -N152- connector for loose connection or contamination – Disconnect connector from ignition coil, terminal assignment ⇒ page ST-190, Fig. 5 – Switch ignition on – Measure voltage supply between connector terminals 1 and 3 Specification: min. 11.5 volts If the specification of min. 11.5 volts is not attained: – Switch ignition off – Measure resistance between connector terminal 1 and test box socket 1. Specification: max.1.5 Ω If the specification is not attained: – Use wiring diagram to locate and repair open circuit in Ground (GND) wire to ignition coil
	Continued ▼

VW0159900130010X

Fig. 151 Code P0301: Cylinder 1 Misfire Detected (Part 1 of 3). 1998 Cabrio, Golf, GTI & Jetta w/2.0L Engine

Malfunction text: Random Misfire Detected		
Cause: Engine speed (RPM) sensor -G28- supplies implausible signal.		Remedy: – Check engine speed (RPM) sensor -G28- for tightening torque (sensor loose or gap to sensor wheel too large causing malfunction) – Remove sensor and check for contamination by metal particles – Check sensor wheel on crankshaft for damage or contamination, to do this remove sensor and check through sensor mounting hole in engine block – Check connector for resistance due to contamination (loose connection on connector causes misfiring)
Malfunction cause for P0300 found: No ▼	Yes ▶	– After repairing malfunction, clear DTC memory and create readiness code
		Continued ▼

VW0159900129020X

Fig. 150 Code P0300: Random Misfire Detected (Part 2 of 4). 1998 Cabrio, Golf, GTI & Jetta w/2.0L Engine

Malfunction text: Random Misfire Detected		
		If the specifications are not attained: the wires have open circuit. – Use wiring diagram to locate and repair open circuit If the specifications are attained, additionally: – Check connector terminals 1 and 2 for short circuit to one another. Specification: ∞ Ω – Check connector terminals 2 and 3 for short circuit to one another. Specification: ∞ Ω • If the specifications are not attained: the wires have a short circuit to one another and must be replaced If the specifications are attained: – Check ignition coil primary resistance between terminals 1 and 15. Specification: 0.5 – 1.2 Ω – Check ignition coil secondary resistance between terminals 4 and 15. Specification: 3 – 4 kΩ If the specifications are not attained: – Replace ignition coil -N152-
Malfunction cause for P0300 found: No ▼	Yes ▶	– After repairing malfunction, clear DTC memory and create readiness code
Malfunction cause for P0300	▶	If malfunction also occurs with a new ignition coil: – Engine Control Module (ECM) -J220- faulty, replace Clear DTC memory and create readiness code.

VW0159900129040X

Fig. 150 Code P0300: Random Misfire Detected (Part 4 of 4). 1998 Cabrio, Golf, GTI & Jetta w/2.0L Engine

Malfunction text: Cylinder 1 Misfire Detected		
		If the specification is attained: – Use wiring diagram to locate and repair open circuit in the positive wire to ignition coil connector terminal 3 If min. 11.5 volts is attained, check remaining wiring: – Measure resistance between connector terminal 2 and test box socket 8. Specification: max.1.5 Ω – Check connector terminals 1 and 2 for short circuit to one another. – Check connector terminals 3 and 4 for short circuit to one another. Specifications: ∞ Ω If the specifications are not attained: the wiring has a short or open circuit – Use wiring diagram to locate and repair malfunction
Malfunction cause for P0301 found: No ▼	Yes ▶	– After repairing malfunction, clear DTC memory and create readiness code
		If no open circuit or short circuit is detected:
		Continued ▼

VW0159900130020X

Fig. 151 Code P0301: Cylinder 1 Misfire Detected (Part 2 of 3). 1998 Cabrio, Golf, GTI & Jetta w/2.0L Engine

Malfunction text: Cylinder 1 Misfire Detected	
Cause: Wiring or cylinder 1 fuel injector -N30- has open circuit or short circuit to Ground (GND)	Remedy: – Remove fuse 18 – Measure resistance between lower terminal for fuse 18 and test box socket 24. Specification 15 – 23 Ω If the specification is not attained: – Disconnect connector from fuel injector – Disconnect 4-pin connector from Mass Air Flow (MAF) sensor – Measure resistance between connector terminal 1 and test box socket 1. Specification: ∞ Ω – Measure resistance between connector terminal 2 and test box socket 1. Specification: ∞ Ω If the measured values are not ∞ Ω – Use wiring diagram to locate and repair short circuit to Ground (GND) – Measure resistance between connector terminal 1 and lower terminal for fuse 18. Specification: 1.5 Ω – Measure resistance between connector terminal 2 and test box socket 24. Specification: max. 1.5 Ω If the specifications are not attained: – Use wiring diagram to locate and repair open circuit
Malfunction cause for P0301 ▶	If no open circuit is detected: – Cylinder 1 fuel injector mechanically faulty, replace. Clear DTC memory and create readiness code

VW0159900130030X

Fig. 151 Code P0301: Cylinder 1 Misfire Detected (Part 3 of 3). 1998 Cabrio, Golf, GTI & Jetta w/2.0L Engine

Malfunction text: Cylinder 2 Misfire Detected		
		If the specification is not attained: – Use wiring diagram to locate and repair open circuit in Ground (GND) wire to ignition coil If the specification is attained: – Use wiring diagram to locate and repair open circuit in the positive wire to ignition coil connector terminal 3 If min. 11.5 volts is attained, check remaining wiring: – Measure resistance between connector terminal 2 and test box socket 8. Specification: max.1.5 Ω – Check connector terminals 1 and 2 for short circuit to one another. – Check connector terminals 3 and 4 for short circuit to one another. Specification: ∞ Ω If the specifications are not attained: the wiring has a short or open circuit – Use wiring diagram to locate and repair malfunction
Malfunction cause for P0302 found: No ▼	Yes ▶	– After repairing malfunction, clear DTC memory and create readiness code
		If no open or short circuit is detected:
		Continued ▼

VW0159900131020X

Fig. 152 Code P0302: Cylinder 2 Misfire Detected (Part 2 of 3). 1998 Cabrio,

Malfunction text: Cylinder 3 Misfire Detected	
Cause: Uneven engine running causes Engine Control Module (ECM) to detect misfiring	Remedy: – Run engine slightly above idle, and check spark plug connectors/ignition wires for arcing to Ground (GND) If arcing is detected: – Stop engine: switch ignition off – Replace spark plug connector with ignition wire – Remove spark plugs and check condition. Check that spark plugs with correct heat range have been installed If no arcing can be detected: – Connect VAG 1598/18 test box – Check ignition coil -N152- connector for loose connection or contamination – Disconnect connector from ignition coil – Switch ignition on – Measure voltage supply between connector terminals 1 and 3 Specification: min. 11.5 volts If the specification of min. 11.5 volts is not attained: – Switch ignition off – Measure resistance between connector terminal 1 and test box socket 1. Specification: max.1.5 Ω
	Continued ▼

VW0159900132010X

Fig. 153 Code P0303: Cylinder 3 Misfire Detected (Part 1 of 3). 1998 Cabrio, Golf, GTI & Jetta w/2.0L Engine

Malfunction text: Cylinder 2 Misfire Detected	
Cause: Uneven engine running causes Engine Control Module (ECM) to detect misfiring	Remedy: – Run engine slightly above idle, and check spark plug connectors/ignition wires for arcing to Ground (GND) If arcing is detected: – Stop engine: switch ignition off – Replace spark plug connector with ignition wire – Remove spark plugs and check condition. Check that spark plugs with correct heat range have been installed. If no arcing can be detected: – Connect VAG 1598/18 test box – Check ignition coil -N152- connector for loose connection or contamination – Disconnect connector from ignition coil, terminal assignment – Switch ignition on – Measure voltage between connector terminals 1 and 3. Specification: min. 11.5 volts If the specification of min. 11.5 volts is not attained: – Switch ignition off – Measure resistance between connector terminal 1 and test box socket 1. Specification: max.1.5 Ω
	Continued ▼

VW0159900131010X

Fig. 152 Code P0302: Cylinder 2 Misfire Detected (Part 1 of 3). 1998 Cabrio, Golf, GTI & Jetta w/2.0L Engine

Malfunction text: Cylinder 2 Misfire Detected	
Cause: Wiring or cylinder 2 fuel injector -N31- has open or short circuit to Ground (GND)	Remedy: – Remove fuse 18 – Measure resistance between lower terminal for fuse 18 and test box socket 25. Specification 15 – 23 Ω If the specification is not attained: – Disconnect connector from fuel injector – Disconnect 4-pin connector from Mass Air Flow (MAF) sensor – Measure resistance between connector terminal 1 and test box socket 1. Specification: ∞ Ω – Measure resistance between connector terminal 2 and test box socket 1. Specification: ∞ Ω If the measured value is not ∞ Ω: – Use wiring diagram to locate and repair short circuit to Ground (GND) – Measure resistance between connector terminal 1 and lower terminal for fuse 18. Specification max. 1.5 Ω – Measure resistance between connector terminal 2 and test box socket 25. Specification max. 1.5 Ω If the specifications are not attained: – Use wiring diagram to locate and repair open circuit
Malfunction cause for P0302 ▶	If no open circuit is detected: – Cylinder 2 fuel injector mechanically faulty, replace. Clear DTC memory and create readiness code

VW0159900131030X

Fig. 152 Code P0302: Cylinder 2 Misfire Detected (Part 3 of 3). 1998 Cabrio

Malfunction text: Cylinder 3 Misfire Detected		
		If the specification is not attained: – Use wiring diagram to locate and repair open circuit in Ground (GND) wire to ignition coil If the specification is attained: – Use wiring diagram to locate and repair open circuit in the positive wire to ignition coil connector terminal 3 If min. 11.5 volts is attained, check remaining wiring: – Measure resistance between connector terminal 2 and test box socket 8. Specification: max.1.5 Ω – Check connector terminals 1 and 2 for short circuit to one another. Specification: ∞ Ω – Check connector terminals 3 and 4 for short circuit to one another. Specification: ∞ Ω If the specifications are not attained: the wiring has a short or open circuit – Use wiring diagram to locate and repair malfunction
Malfunction cause for P0303 found: No ▼	Yes ▶	– After repairing malfunction, clear DTC memory and create readiness code
		If no open circuit or short circuit is detected:
		Continued ▼

VW0159900132020X

Fig. 153 Code P0303: Cylinder 3 Misfire Detected (Part 2 of 3). 1998 Cabrio, Golf, GTI & Jetta w/2.0L Engine

Malfunction text: Cylinder 3 Misfire Detected	
Cause: Wiring or cylinder 3 fuel injector -N32- has open circuit or short circuit to Ground (GND)	Remedy: – Remove fuse 18 – Measure resistance between lower terminal for fuse 18 and test box socket 26. Specification 15 – 23 Ω If the specification is not attained: – Disconnect connector from fuel injector – Disconnect 4-pin connector from Mass Air Flow (MAF) sensor – Measure resistance between connector terminal 1 and test box socket 1. Specification: ∞ Ω – Measure resistance between connector terminal 2 and test box socket 1. Specification: ∞ Ω If the measured values are not ∞ Ω: – Use wiring diagram to locate and repair short circuit to Ground (GND) – Measure resistance between connector terminal 1 and lower terminal for fuse 18. Specification max. 1.5 Ω – Measure resistance between connector terminal 2 and test box socket 26. Specification max. 1.5 Ω If the specifications are not attained: – Use wiring diagram to locate and repair open circuit
	If not open circuit is detected:
Malfunction cause for P0303 ▶	– Cylinder 3 fuel injector mechanically faulty, replace. Clear DTC memory and create readiness code

VW0159900132030X

Fig. 153 Code P0303: Cylinder 3 Misfire Detected (Part 3 of 3). 1998 Cabrio, Golf, GTI & Jetta w/2.0L Engine

Malfunction text: Cylinder 4 Misfire Detected	
	If the specification is not attained: – Use wiring diagram to locate and repair open circuit in Ground (GND) wire to ignition coil If the specification is attained: – Use wiring diagram to locate and repair open circuit in the positive wire to ignition coil connector terminal 3 If min. 11.5 volts is attained, check remaining wiring: – Measure resistance between connector terminal 2 and test box socket 8. Specification: max.1.5 Ω – Check connector terminals 1 and 2 for short circuit to one another. – Check connector terminals 3 and 4 for short circuit to one another. Specification: ∞ Ω If the specifications are not attained: the wiring has a short or open circuit – Use wiring diagram to locate and repair malfunction
Malfunction cause for P0304 found: No ▼ Yes ▶	– After repairing malfunction, clear DTC memory and create readiness code
	If no open circuit or short circuit is detected:
	Continued ▼

VW0159900133020X

Fig. 154 Code P0304: Cylinder 4 Misfire Detected (Part 2 of 3). 1998 Cabrio, Golf, GTI & Jetta w/2.0L Engine

Malfunction text: Knock Sensor 1 Circuit Low Input (Bank 1 or Single Sensor)	
Cause: Signal from Knock Sensor (KS) 1 too low or not recognized by Engine Control Module (ECM)	Remedy: – Switch ignition off – Check tightening torque of knock sensor If the knock sensor is loose: – Unscrew knock sensor, clean contact surfaces and tighten to correct torque. Make sure bolt is of correct length!
Malfunction cause for P0327 found: No ▼ Yes ▶	– After repairing malfunction, clear DTC memory and create readiness code
	If the knock sensor was not loose: – Connect VAG 1598/18 test box – Disconnect connector to knock sensor – Measure resistance between connector terminal 1 and test box socket 56. Specification: ∞ Ω – Measure resistance between connector terminal 2 and test box socket 56. Specification: ∞ Ω If the measured values not ∞ Ω, the wiring has short circuit to cable shielding: – Use wiring diagram to locate and repair malfunction
	Continued ▼

VW0159900134010X

Fig. 155 Code P0327: KS 1 Circuit Low Input Bank 1 (Part 1 of 2). 1998 Cabrio, Golf, GTI & Jetta w/2.0L Engine

Malfunction text: Cylinder 4 Misfire Detected	
Cause: Uneven engine running causes Engine Control Module (ECM) to detect misfiring	Remedy: – Run engine slightly above idle, and check spark plug connectors/ignition wires for arcing to Ground (GND) If arcing is detected: – Stop engine: switch ignition off – Replace spark plug connector with ignition wire – Remove spark plugs and check condition. Check that spark plugs with correct heat range have been installed. If no arcing can be detected: – Connect VAG 1598/18 test box – Check ignition coil -N152- connector for loose connection or contamination. – Disconnect connector from ignition coil, terminal assignment – Switch ignition on – Measure voltage supply between connector terminals 1 and 3 Specification: min. 11.5 volts If the specification of min. 11.5 volts is not attained: – Switch ignition off – Measure resistance between connector terminal 1 and test box socket 1. Specification: max.1.5 Ω
	Continued ▼

VW0159900133010X

Fig. 154 Code P0304: Cylinder 4 Misfire Detected (Part 1 of 3). 1998 Cabrio, Golf, GTI & Jetta w/2.0L Engine

Malfunction text: Cylinder 4 Misfire Detected	
Cause: Wiring or cylinder 4 fuel injector -N33- has open circuit or short circuit to Ground (GND)	Remedy: – Remove fuse 18 – Measure resistance between lower terminal for fuse 18 and test box socket 2. Specification 15 – 23 Ω If the specification is not attained: – Disconnect connector from fuel injector – Disconnect 4-pin connector from Mass Air Flow (MAF) sensor – Measure resistance between connector terminal 1 and test box socket 1. Specification: ∞ Ω. – Measure resistance between connector terminal 2 and test box socket 1. Specification: ∞ Ω. If the measured values are not ∞ Ω: – Use wiring diagram to locate and repair short circuit to Ground (GND) – Measure resistance between connector terminal 1 and lower terminal for fuse 18. Specification max. 1.5 Ω – Measure resistance between connector terminal 2 and test box socket 2. Specification max. 1.5 Ω If the specifications are not attained: – Use wiring diagram to locate and repair open circuit
	If no open circuit is detected:
Malfunction cause for P0304 ▶	– Cylinder 4 fuel injector mechanically faulty, replace. Clear DTC memory and create readiness code

VW0159900133030X

Fig. 154 Code P0304: Cylinder 4 Misfire Detected (Part 3 of 3). 1998 Cabrio, Golf, GTI & Jetta w/2.0L Engine

Malfunction text: Knock Sensor 1 Circuit Low Input (Bank 1 or Single Sensor)	
	If the measured values are ∞ Ω: – Measure resistance between connector terminal 1 and test box socket 34. Specification: max. 1.5 Ω – Measure resistance between connector terminal 2 and test box socket 33. Specification: max.1.5 Ω – Measure resistance between connector terminal 3 and test box socket 56. Specification: max.1.5 Ω If the specifications are not attained: the wiring has open circuit – Use wiring diagram to locate and repair open circuit
Malfunction cause for P0327 found: No ▼ Yes ▶	– After repairing malfunction, clear DTC memory and create readiness code
	If all specifications are attained: – Replace knock sensor 1
Malfunction cause for P0327 found: No ▼ Yes ▶	– After repairing malfunction, clear DTC memory and create readiness code
	– Road test vehicle If after the test drive the malfunction is still stored in DTC memory:
Malfunction cause for P0327 ▶	– ECM -J220- faulty, replace. Clear DTC memory and create readiness code

VW0159900134020X

Fig. 155 Code P0327: KS 1 Circuit Low Input Bank 1 (Part 2 of 2). 1998 Cabrio, Golf, GTI & Jetta w/2.0L Engine

Malfunction text: Camshaft Position Sensor Circuit Range/Performance		
Cause: Camshaft Position (CMP) sensor -G40- supplies implausible signal to Engine Control Module (ECM)		Remedy: – Disconnect connector from camshaft position sensor -G40- – Check whether there is a loose terminal in connector to sensor. – Switch ignition on – Measure voltage supply between connector terminals 1 and 3. Terminal assignment Specification: min. 11.5 volts If the specification of min. 11.5 volts is not attained: – Switch ignition off – Connect VAG 1598/18 test box – Measure resistance between connector terminal 1 and test box socket 56. Specification: max.1.5 Ω If the specification is not attained: – Use wiring diagram to locate and repair open circuit in Ground (GND) wire to camshaft position sensor If the specification is attained: – Use wiring diagram to locate and repair open circuit in the positive wire to camshaft position sensor (connector terminal 3)
Malfunction cause for P0341 found: No ▼	Yes ▶	– After repairing malfunction, clear DTC memory and create readiness code
		Continued ▼

VW0159900135010X

Fig. 156 Code P0341: CMP Sensor Circuit Range/ Performance (Part 1 of 2). 1998 Cabrio, Golf, GTI & Jetta w/2.0L Engine

Displayed text: Sec.Air Inj.Sys. Incorrect Flow Detected	
Cause: Secondary Air Injection pump is functioning, however air quantity is insufficient as measured by the Oxygen sensor.	Remedy: – Switch OFF ignition. – Connect Test Box VAG 1598/18. – Pull connector off Secondary Air Injection valve (N112). – Measure resistance between connector terminal 1 and Test Box socket 50, specification: 1.5 Ω If specification not obtained, locate and eliminate open circuit using wiring diagram. If specification obtained: – Re-attach connector – Pull vacuum hose off Secondary Air Injection valve (N112) and connect a piece of scrap hose. – Switch ON ignition. – Bridge Test Box sockets 1 and 6.
	Continued

VW0159900172010X

Fig. 157 Code P0411: Secondary Air Injection System Improper Flow Detected (Part 1 of 3). 1998 Cabrio, Golf, GTI & Jetta w/2.0L Engine

Displayed text: Sec.Air Inj.Sys. Incorrect Flow Detected		
		– Check at pressure connection whether secondary air is being created. If no, but the pump motor runs: – Replace Secondary Air Injection pump motor (fan wheel faulty). If secondary air is being produced: – Check whether the vacuum hose from Secondary Air Injection valve (N112) leading to combi-valve is damaged or disconnected. If no malfunction can be found: – Connect hand vacuum pump to vacuum hose to combi-valve. – Start engine and run at idle speed. – Operate hand vacuum pump several times, the combi-valve must open and the change in noise must be distinctly audible. When the idle noise change is not distinct:
Malfunction cause for P0411	▶	Combi-valve faulty, replace. Erase DTC memory and create Readiness Code.

VW0159900172030X

Fig. 157 Code P0411: Secondary Air Injection System Improper Flow Detected (Part 3 of 3). 1998 Cabrio, Golf, GTI & Jetta w/2.0L Engine

Displayed text: Main Catalyst (B1) Efficiency Below Threshold		
Cause: Engine Control Module J220 recognises a malfunction via Oxygen sensor 2 (after catalyst).		– Check Oxygen sensor 2 (after catalyst) according to information described in Diagnostic Trouble Code P0137 to P014. – After repairing carry out test drive.
Malfunction cause for P0422 found: No ▼	Yes ▶	After repairing malfunction: Erase DTC memory and create Readiness Code.
		If the malfunction has not been eliminated after the test drive:
Cause: If the malfunction P0422 is stored on its own, the Control Module has recognized catalyst efficiency too low, via the Oxygen sensor 2 (after catalyst).		Remedy: – Start engine and let idle – When engine reaches operating temperature, increase engine speed to approx. 3000 rpm for at least 3 minutes. – Run engine again at idle. – Using a CO tester check catalyst efficiency at idle. If, when the engine and catalyst are at normal working temperature the CO content is greater than 0.2 Vol.%:
Malfunction cause for P0422		Catalyst faulty, replace. Erase DTC memory and create Readiness Code.

VW0159900136020X

Fig. 158 Code P0422: Main Catalyst Efficiency Below Threshold Bank 1 (Part 2 of 2). 1998 Cabrio, Golf, GTI & Jetta w/2.0L Engine

Malfunction text: Camshaft Position Sensor Circuit Range/Performance		
		If the specification of min. 11.5 volts is attained: – Measure resistance between connector terminal 2 and test box socket 44. Specification max.1.5 Ω If the specification is not attained: – Use wiring diagram to locate and repair open circuit If the specification is attained: – Replace Camshaft Position (CMP) sensor -G40-
Malfunction cause for P0341 found: No ▼	Yes ▶	– After repairing malfunction, clear DTC memory and create readiness code
Malfunction cause for P0341	▶	– ECM -J220- faulty, replace. Clear DTC memory and create readiness code

VW0159900135020X

Fig. 156 Code P0341: CMP Sensor Circuit Range/ Performance (Part 2 of 2). 1998 Cabrio, Golf, GTI & Jetta w/2.0L Engine

Displayed text: Sec.Air Inj.Sys. Incorrect Flow Detected		
		– Briefly connect Test Box socket 50 to vehicle Ground and at same time blow into aux. hose. – Secondary Air Injection valve must open during activation, and close again after activation. If the Secondary Air Injection valve does not open and close: – Switch OFF ignition. – Replace Secondary Air Injection valve.
Malfunction cause for P0411 found: No ▼	Yes ▶	After repairing malfunction, erase DTC memory and create Readiness Code.
		If the Secondary Air Injection valve opens and closes: – Remove Secondary Air Injection pump pressure hose at engine. To do this squeeze together securing ring on pressure hose and pull pressure hose off. – Check pressure hose for damage, replace if faulty. – Switch ON ignition. – Bridge Test Box sockets 1 and 6. – Briefly connect Test Box socket 49 to vehicle Ground. While the Secondary Air Injection pump motor (V101) is activated:
		Continued

VW0159900172020X

Fig. 157 Code P0411: Secondary Air Injection System Improper Flow Detected (Part 2 of 3). 1998 Cabrio, Golf, GTI & Jetta w/2.0L Engine

Displayed text: Main Catalyst (B1) Efficiency Below Threshold		
Cause: If the Engine Control Module recognises malfunction P0422 in conjunction with an additional malfunction, the additional malfunction stored must be repaired first.		Remedy: – Select Mode 2 with the Generic Scan Tool, and check current data – Repair any additional malfunctions. If any additionally stored Diagnostic Trouble Codes do not affect Oxygen sensor 1: – Check Oxygen sensor 1 according to information described in Diagnostic Trouble Code P0131 to P0135. If Oxygen sensor 1 and or the wiring to Oxygen sensor 1 is not faulty: – Check exhaust system for leaks using a concentrated soap solution, applied with a brush to all flanges/bolted joints
Malfunction cause for P0422 found: No ▼	Yes ▶	After repairing malfunction: Erase DTC memory and create Readiness Code.
		If no leaks can be found:
		Continued

VW0159900136010X

Fig. 158 Code P0422: Main Catalyst Efficiency Below Threshold Bank 1 (Part 1 of 2). 1998 Cabrio, Golf, GTI & Jetta w/2.0L Engine

Malfunction text: Evaporative Emission Control System Malfunction		
Cause: Evaporative Emission (EVAP) canister purge regulator valve -N80- in tank venting system malfunction		Remedy: – Engine at normal working temperature and run at idle • When EVAP canister purge regulator valve -N80- is activated (pulsed), squeeze hose to intake manifold together with fingers, the pulsing must be perceptible If pulsing is not perceptible and EVAP canister purge regulator valve does not click: – Check that connector is not loose or damaged If no connector malfunction is detected: – Switch ignition off – Connect VAG 1598/18 test box – Disconnect connector from EVAP canister purge regulator valve – Check resistance between connector terminal 1 and test box socket 31. Specification: max. 1.5 Ω – Measure resistance between connector terminal 2 and fuse 18 upper terminal. Specification max. 1.5 Ω If the specifications are not attained: – Use wiring diagram to locate and repair open circuit
Malfunction cause for P0440 found: No ▼	Yes ▶	– After repairing malfunction, clear DTC memory and create readiness code
Malfunction cause for P0440	▶	If no wiring malfunction is detected: – EVAP canister purge regulator valve -N80- faulty, replace. Clear DTC memory and create readiness code

VW0159900137010X

Fig. 159 Code P0440: EVAP Emission Control System Malfunction. 1998 Cabrio, Golf, GTI & Jetta w/2.0L Engine

Malfunction text: **Vehicle Speed Sensor Range Performance**		
Cause:		Remedy:
Engine Control Module (ECM) not receiving a usable speed signal		– Check speedometer Vehicle Speed Sensor (VSS) -G22- connector and sensor for tightening torque If OK: – Disconnect connector from sensor – Switch ignition on – Measure voltage supply between connector terminals 1 and 3. Specification: min. 11.5 volts If the voltage supply specification is not attained: – Switch ignition off – Connect VAG 1598/18 test box – Measure resistance between connector terminal 3 and test box socket 1. Specification: max.1.5 Ω If the specification is not attained: – Use wiring diagram to locate and repair open circuit in Ground (GND) wire If the specification is attained: – Use wiring diagram to locate and repair open circuit in the positive wire to sensor
		Continued ▼

VW0159900137020X

Fig. 160 Code P0501: VSS Range Performance (Part 1 of 5). 1998 Cabrio, Golf, GTI & Jetta w/2.0L Engine

Malfunction text: **Closed Throttle Position Switch Malfunction**		
Cause:		Remedy:
Engine Control Module (ECM) not receiving a usable signal from Closed Throttle Position (CTP) switch		– Check throttle valve control module -J338- voltage supply at 8-pin connector, terminal assignment – Disconnect 8-pin connector to throttle valve control module – Switch ignition on Check voltage as follows: – Between connector terminals 4 and 7. Specification: approx. 5 volts – Between connector terminals 3 and 7. Specification: approx. 10 volts If the specifications are not attained: – Switch ignition off – Connect VAG 1598/18 test box Check resistance as follows: – Connector terminal 3 and test box socket 10. – Connector terminal 4 and test box socket 41. – Connector terminal 7 and test box socket 33. Specifications: max.1.5 Ω If the specifications are not attained: – Use wiring diagram to locate and repair open circuit If no open circuit is detected: – Replace ECM -J220-
Malfunction cause for P0510 found: No ▼	Yes ▶	– After repairing malfunction, clear DTC memory and create readiness code
		Continued ▼

VW0159900137040X

Fig. 160 Code P0501: VSS Range Performance (Part 3 of 5). 1998 Cabrio, Golf, GTI & Jetta w/2.0L Engine

Malfunction text: **Closed Throttle Position Switch Malfunction**		
		If the specifications are not attained: – Use wiring diagram to locate and repair wiring short circuits to one another. If the specifications with throttle open/closed are not attained, but the wiring is OK: – Replace throttle valve control module -J338-
Malfunction cause for P0510 found: No ▼	Yes ▶	– After repairing malfunction disconnect connector from Engine Control Module (ECM) -J220- for 10 seconds, then clear DTC memory and create readiness code
Malfunction cause	▶	– ECM -J220- faulty, replace. Clear DTC memory and create readiness code

VW0159900137060X

Fig. 160 Code P0501: VSS Range Performance (Part 5 of 5). 1998 Cabrio, Golf, GTI & Jetta w/2.0L Engine

Malfunction text: **Internal Control Module Read Only Memory (ROM) Error (Module Identification Defined by SAE J1979)**		
Cause:		Remedy:
Control module recognizes itself, components in Engine Control Module (ECM) as faulty		– Switch ignition off – Disconnect connector from control module – Reconnect control module, making sure that the connector is properly located – Start engine and run for approx. 3 minutes at idle – Switch ignition off – Switch ignition on – Clear DTC memory and check again If the malfunction is still present:
Malfunction cause for P0605	▶	– Engine Control Module (ECM) -J220- faulty, replace. Clear DTC memory and create readiness code

VW0159900138000X

Fig. 161 Code P0605: Internal Control Module ROM Error. 1998 Cabrio, Golf, GTI & Jetta w/2.0L Engine

Malfunction text: **Vehicle Speed Sensor Range Performance**		
		If the sensor voltage supply is OK: – Switch ignition on – Raise front of vehicle, and rotate left front wheel – Measure voltage between test box sockets 56 and 65: • Voltage must fluctuate between 0 – 10 volts If no voltage is measured: – Switch ignition off – Disconnect connector from speedometer vehicle speed sensor -G22- – Measure resistance between connector terminal 3 and Ground (GND). Specification max. 1.5 Ω – Measure resistance between connector terminal 1 and fuse 15. Specification max. 1.5 Ω – Measure resistance between connector terminal 2 and instrument cluster connection. Specification max. 1.5 Ω If the specifications are not attained: – Use wiring diagram to locate and repair wiring open or short circuits to one another.
Malfunction cause for P0501 found: No ▼	Yes ▶	– After repairing malfunction, clear DTC memory and create readiness code
Malfunction cause for P0501	▶	– Vehicle speed sensor faulty, replace. Clear DTC memory and create readiness code

VW0159900137030X

Fig. 160 Code P0501: VSS Range Performance (Part 2 of 5). 1998 Cabrio, Golf, GTI & Jetta w/2.0L Engine

Malfunction text: **Closed Throttle Position Switch Malfunction**	
	If the voltage supply specifications are attained: – Switch ignition off – Connect 8-pin connector – Connect VAG 1598/18 test box Check resistance as follows: – At wide open throttle, between test box sockets 10 and 33: Specification: ∞ Ω – At closed throttle position, between test box sockets 10 and 33. Specification: max.10 Ω – At closed throttle position, between test box sockets 27 and 53. Specification: 3 – 200 Ω If the specifications are not attained: – Disconnect 8-pin connector to throttle valve control module Check resistances as follows: – Connector terminal 1 and test box socket 27 – Connector terminal 2 and test box socket 53 – Connector terminal 5 and test box socket 40 – Connector terminal 8 and test box socket 62: Specification: max.1.5 Ω If the resistances do not correspond to specifications: – Use wiring diagram to locate and repair open circuit Also when the specifications are not attained (with disconnected 8-pin connector): – Measure resistance between test box sockets 10, 27, 33, 40, 41, 53 and 62. Specification: ∞ Ω
	Continued ▼

VW0159900137050X

Fig. 160 Code P0501: VSS Range Performance (Part 4 of 5). 1998 Cabrio, Golf, GTI & Jetta w/2.0L Engine

Malfunction text: **Input/Turbine Speed Sensor Circuit Malfunction**		
Cause:		Remedy:
Transmission Control Module (TCM) not receiving signal from Transmission Vehicle Speed Sensor (VSS) -G38-		– Switch ignition off – Connect VAG 1598/18 test box – Measure resistance between text box sockets 21 and 66. Specification: min. 0.8 kΩ; max. 0.9 kΩ If the specification is not attained: – Use wiring diagram to locate and repair short circuit to Ground (GND) – Replace transmission vehicle speed sensor.
Malfunction cause for P0715 found: No ▼	Yes ▶	– After repairing malfunction, clear DTC memory
Malfunction cause	▶	– Transmission Control Module (TCM) -J217- faulty. Replace TCM -J217- and clear DTC memory.

VW0159900140000X

Fig. 162 Code P0715: Input/TSS Circuit Malfunction. 1998 Cabrio, Golf, GTI & Jetta w/2.0L Engine

Malfunction text: Output Speed Sensor Circuit No Signal		
Cause:		Remedy:
Transmission Control Module (TCM) not receiving signal from Vehicle Speed Sensor (VSS) -G68-		- Switch ignition off - Connect VAG 1598/18 test box. - Measure resistance between test box sockets 20 and 65. Specification: min. 0.8 kΩ; max. 0.9 kΩ If the specification is not attained: - Use wiring diagram to locate and repair short circuit to Ground (GND) - Replace vehicle speed sensor
Malfunction cause for P0722 found: No ▼	Yes ▶	- After repairing malfunction, clear DTC memory
Malfunction cause	▶	- Transmission Control Module (TCM) -J217- faulty. Replace TCM -J217- and clear DTC memory

VW0159900141000X

Fig. 163 Code P0722: Output Speed Sensor Circuit No Signal. 1998 Cabrio, Golf, GTI & Jetta w/2.0L Engine

Malfunction text: Pressure Control Solenoid Electrical		
Cause:		Remedy:
Valve body solenoid valve not receiving a signal		- Switch ignition off - Connect VAG 1598/18 test box - Measure resistance between test box sockets 58 and 22. Specification: min. 4.5 Ω; max. 6.5 Ω - Measure resistance between test box sockets 58 and 1. Specification: ∞ Ω - Measure resistance between test box sockets 22 and 1. Specification: ∞ Ω If the specification is not attained: - Use wiring diagram to locate and repair open circuit or short circuit to Ground (GND) - Replace valve body
Malfunction cause for P0748 found: No ▼	Yes ▶	- After repairing malfunction, clear DTC memory
Malfunction cause	▶	- Transmission Control Module (TCM) -J217- faulty. Replace TCM -J217- and clear DTC memory.

VW0159900143000X

Fig. 165 Code P0748: Pressure Control Solenoid Electrical. 1998 Cabrio, Golf, GTI & Jetta w/2.0L Engine

Malfunction text: Shift Solenoid B Electrical		
Cause:		Remedy:
Solenoid valve 2 not receiving a signal		- Switch ignition off - Connect VAG 1598/18 test box. - Measure resistance between test box sockets 54 and 67. Specification: min. 55 Ω; max. 70.5 Ω - Measure resistance between test box sockets 54 and 1. Specification: ∞ Ω If the specification is not attained: - Use wiring diagram to locate and repair open circuit or short circuit to Ground (GND) - Replace valve body
Malfunction cause for P0758 found: No ▼	Yes ▶	- After repairing malfunction, clear DTC memory
Malfunction cause	▶	- Transmission Control Module (TCM) -J217- faulty. Replace TCM -J217- and clear DTC memory

VW0159900145000X

Fig. 167 Code P0758: Shift Solenoid B Electrical. 1998 Cabrio, Golf, GTI & Jetta w/2.0L Engine

Malfunction text: Shift Solenoid D Electrical		
Cause:		Remedy:
Solenoid valve 3 not receiving a signal		- Switch ignition off - Connect VAG 1598/18 test box - Measure resistance between test box sockets 47 and 67. Specification: min. 4.5 Ω; max. 6.5 Ω - Measure resistance between test box sockets 47 and 1. Specification: ∞ Ω If the specification is not attained: - Use wiring diagram to locate and repair open circuit or short circuit to Ground (GND) - Replace valve body
Malfunction cause for P0768 found: No ▼	Yes ▶	- After repairing malfunction, clear DTC memory
Malfunction cause	▶	- Transmission Control Module (TCM) -J217- faulty. Replace TCM -J217- and clear DTC memory

VW0159900147000X

Fig. 169 Code P0768: Shift Solenoid D Electrical. 1998 Cabrio, Golf, GTI & Jetta w/2.0L Engine

Malfunction text: Engine Speed Input Circuit Malfunction		
Cause:		Remedy:
Transmission Control Module (TCM) does not receive signal from Engine Control Module (ECM)		- Switch ignition off - Connect VAG 1598/18 test box - Use wiring diagram to locate and repair wiring short circuits - Interrogate ECM Diagnostic Trouble Code (DTC) memory
Malfunction cause for P0725 found: No ▼	Yes ▶	- After repairing malfunction, clear DTC memory
Malfunction cause	▶	- TCM -J217- faulty, replace TCM and clear DTC memory

VW0159900142000X

Fig. 164 Code P0725: Engine Speed Input Circuit Malfunction. 1998 Cabrio, Golf, GTI & Jetta w/2.0L Engine

Malfunction text: Shift Solenoid A Electrical		
Cause:		Remedy:
Solenoid valve 1 not receiving a signal		- Switch ignition off - Connect VAG 1598/18 test box. - Measure resistance between test box sockets 55 and 67. Specification: min. 55 Ω; max. 70.5 Ω - Measure resistance between test box sockets 55 and 1. Specification: ∞ Ω If the specification is not attained: - Use wiring diagram to locate and repair wiring open or short circuit to Ground (GND) - Replace valve body
Malfunction cause for P0753 found: No ▼	Yes ▶	- After repairing malfunction, clear DTC memory
Malfunction cause	▶	- Transmission Control Module (TCM) -J217- faulty. Replace TCM -J217- and clear DTC memory

VW0159900144000X

Fig. 166 Code P0753: Shift Solenoid A Electrical. 1998 Cabrio, Golf, GTI & Jetta w/2.0L Engine

Malfunction text: Shift Solenoid C Electrical		
Cause:		Remedy:
Solenoid valve 3 not receiving a signal		- Switch ignition off - Connect VAG 1598/18 test box - Measure resistance between test box sockets 9 and 67. Specification: min. 55 Ω; max. 70.5 Ω - Measure resistance between test box sockets 9 and 1. Specification: ∞ Ω If the specification is not attained: - Use wiring diagram to locate and repair open circuit or short circuit to Ground (GND) - Replace valve body
Malfunction cause for P0763 found: No ▼	Yes ▶	- After repairing malfunction, clear DTC memory
Malfunction cause	▶	- Transmission Control Module (TCM) -J217- faulty. Replace TCM -J217- and clear DTC memory.

VW0159900146000X

Fig. 168 Code P0763: Shift Solenoid C Electrical. 1998 Cabrio, Golf, GTI & Jetta w/2.0L Engine

Malfunction text: Shift Solenoid E Electrical		
Cause:		Remedy:
Solenoid valve 4 not receiving a signal		- Switch ignition off - Connect VAG 1598/18 test box - Measure resistance between test box sockets 56 and 67. Specification: min. 55 Ω; max. 70.5 Ω - Measure resistance between test box sockets 56 and 1. Specification: ∞ Ω If the specification is not attained: - Use wiring diagram to locate and repair open circuit or short circuit to Ground (GND) - Replace valve body
Malfunction cause for P0773 found: No ▼	Yes ▶	- After repairing malfunction, clear DTC memory
Malfunction cause	▶	- Transmission Control Module (TCM) -J217- faulty. Replace TCM -J217- and clear DTC memory

VW0159900148000X

Fig. 170 Code P0773: Shift Solenoid E Electrical. 1998 Cabrio, Golf, GTI & Jetta w/2.0L Engine

Malfunction text: Long Term Fuel Trim mul. (B1) System too Rich		
Cause: Mixture so rich that the Oxygen Sensor (O2S) control is on lean limit		***Note:*** *When a O2S malfunction (P0131 to P0141) is also stored with this malfunction, O2S malfunction should be repaired first.*
Cause: Mass Air Flow (MAF) sensor -G70- signal to Engine Control Module (ECM) too high		Remedy: – Switch ignition off – Connect VAG 1598/18 test box – Disconnect 4-pin connector from MAF sensor – Measure resistance between connector terminal 1 and test box socket 1. Specification: max. 1.5 Ω – Bridge connector terminals 1 and 2, measure resistance between test box sockets 1 and 16. Specification: max. 1.5 Ω – Bridge connector terminals 1 and 4, measure resistance between test box sockets 1 and 17. Specification: max. 1.5 Ω – Do not bridge connector terminals, measure resistance between test box sockets 16 and 17. Specification: ∞ Ω If the specifications are not attained: – Use wiring diagram to locate and repair wiring short or open circuits to one another.
Malfunction cause for P1127 found: No ▼	Yes ▶	– After repairing malfunction, clear DTC memory create readiness code
		If the resistance specifications are attained:
		Continued ▼

VW0159900149010X

Fig. 171 Code P1127: Long Term Fuel Trim Mul System Too Rich (Part 1 of 3). 1998 Cabrio, Golf, GTI & Jetta w/2.0L Engine

Malfunction text: Long Term Fuel Trim mul. (B1) System too Rich		
Cause: Fuel injector is dirty and does not close (dripping)		Remedy: – Remove intake manifold upper section and remove fuel injectors complete with fuel rail – Wipe fuel injectors dry with a clean cloth – Use fuel pressure still available to check fuel injectors for leaks. If droplets form on fuel injector(s):
Malfunction cause for P1127	▶	– Fuel injector faulty, replace. Clear DTC memory and create readiness code

VW0159900149030X

Fig. 171 Code P1127: Long Term Fuel Trim Mul System Too Rich (Part 3 of 3). 1998 Cabrio, Golf, GTI & Jetta w/2.0L Engine

Malfunction text: Long Term Fuel Trim mul. (B1) System too Lean		
		If the specification of approx. 3.5 bar (51 psi) is attained:
Cause: Fuel injector sticking, not opening		Remedy: – Remove intake manifold upper section and remove fuel injectors complete with fuel rail – Place a fuel resistant container under the fuel injectors, and turn engine at starter speed – Check whether all fuel injectors open proportionately – Check whether all fuel injectors produce uniform spray pattern If one or more valves are not functioning properly:
Malfunction cause for P1128	▶	– Replace faulty fuel injector. Clear DTC memory and create readiness code.

VW0159900150020X

Fig. 172 Code P1128: Long Term Fuel Trim Mul System Too Lean (Part 2 of 2). 1998 Cabrio, Golf, GTI & Jetta w/2.0L Engine

Malfunction text: Cyl.1 Fuel Injector Circ. Short to B+		
Cause: Wiring or fuel injector has short circuit to positive.		Remedy: – Switch ignition off – Connect VAG 1598/18 test box – Remove fuse 18 – Disconnect connector from fuel injector – Measure resistance between connector terminal 2 and fuse 18 lower terminal. Specification: ∞ Ω. If the specification is not attained: – Use wiring diagram to locate and repair short circuit to positive in the wiring from Engine Control Module (ECM) to fuel injector
Malfunction cause for P1213 found: No ▼	Yes ▶	– After repairing malfunction, clear DTC memory and create readiness code
		If the specification is attained: – Measure resistance between fuel injector terminals 1 and 2. Specification: approx. 15 – 23 Ω If the specification is not attained – Replace cyl. 1 fuel injector
If no wiring or fuel injector malfunction is found:		
Malfunction cause	▶	– Engine Control Module (ECM) -J220- faulty, replace. Clear DTC memory and create readiness code

VW0159900151000X

Fig. 173 Code P1213: Cylinder 1 Fuel Injector Circuit Short To Voltage. 1998 Cabrio, Golf, GTI & Jetta w/2.0L Engine

Malfunction text: Long Term Fuel Trim mul. (B1) System too Rich		
Cause: Excessive fuel pressure		Remedy: – Check vacuum hose to fuel pressure regulator If no leaks can be found: – Check fuel return line from fuel tank to fuel rail on engine A restricted return line causes excessive fuel pressure build-up – Switch engine off – Cover test port on fuel rail with a rag and open – Connect VAG 1318 fuel injection pressure gauge with VAG 1318/1 and VAG 1318/10 pressure gauge adapter – Start engine and run at idle – Measure fuel pressure. Specification: approx. 3.5 bar (51 psi) – While engine is running, disconnect hose from pressure regulator • Fuel pressure must increase to 4.0 bar (58 psi) If the specification of 4.0 bar (58 psi) is not attained: – Replace fuel pressure regulator If the specification is exceeded before disconnecting hose, the return line is restricted or blocked
Malfunction cause for P1127 found: No ▼	Yes ▶	– After repairing malfunction, clear DTC memory and create readiness code
		If the specification is not exceeded:
		Continued ▼

VW0159900149020X

Fig. 171 Code P1127: Long Term Fuel Trim Mul System Too Rich (Part 2 of 3). 1998 Cabrio, Golf, GTI & Jetta w/2.0L Engine

Malfunction text: Long Term Fuel Trim mul. (B1) System too Lean		
Cause: Mixture so lean that the Oxygen Sensor (O2S) control is on rich limit		***Note:*** *When a HO2S malfunction (P0131 to P0141) is also stored with this malfunction, HO2S malfunction should be repaired first.*
Cause: Fuel pressure too low/fuel quantity supplied too low		Remedy: Check whether vehicle has performance problems: Check whether performance problems only occur at full acceleration: – Replace fuel filter If the engine output is impaired at lower throttle openings, or the vehicle jerks at lower throttle openings: – Switch engine off – Cover test port on fuel rail with a rag and open – Connect VAG 1318 fuel injection pressure gauge with VAG 1318/1 and VAG 1318/10 pressure gauge adapter – Start engine and run at idle – Measure fuel pressure. Specification: approx. 3.5 bar (51 psi) If the specification is not attained: – Check whether the fuel supply line is restricted If the fuel supply line is not faulty: – Replace transfer Fuel Pump (FP) -G23-
Malfunction cause for P1128 found: No ▼	Yes ▶	– After repairing malfunction, clear DTC memory and create readiness code
		Continued ▼

VW0159900150010X

Fig. 172 Code P1128: Long Term Fuel Trim Mul System Too Lean (Part 1 of 2). 1998 Cabrio, Golf, GTI & Jetta w/2.0L Engine

Malfunction text: Cyl.2 Fuel Injector Circ. Short to B+		
Cause: Wiring or fuel injector has short circuit to positive		Remedy: – Switch ignition off – Connect VAG 1598/18 test box – Remove fuse 18 – Disconnect connector from fuel injector – Measure resistance between connector terminal 2 and fuse 18 lower terminal. Specification: ∞ Ω If the specification is not attained: – Use wiring diagram to locate and repair short circuit to positive in the wiring from engine control module to fuel injector
Malfunction cause for P1214 found: No ▼	Yes ▶	– After repairing malfunction, clear DTC memory and create readiness code
		If the specification is attained: – Measure resistance between fuel injector terminals 1 and 2. Specification: approx. 15 – 23 Ω If the specification is not attained: – Replace cyl. 2 fuel injector
If no wiring or fuel injector malfunction is found:		
Malfunction cause	▶	– Engine Control Module (ECM) -J220- faulty, replace. Clear DTC memory and create readiness code

VW0159900152000X

Fig. 174 Code P1214: Cylinder 2 Fuel Injector Circuit Short To Voltage. 1998 Cabrio, Golf, GTI & Jetta w/2.0L Engine

Malfunction text: **Cyl.3 Fuel Injector Circ. Short to B+**		
Cause: Wiring or fuel injector has short circuit to positive		Remedy: – Switch ignition off – Connect VAG 1598/18 test box – Remove fuse 18 – Disconnect connector from fuel injector – Measure resistance between connector terminal 2 and fuse 18 lower terminal. Specification: ∞ Ω If the specification is not attained: – Use wiring diagram to locate and repair short circuit to positive in the wiring from engine control module to fuel injector
Malfunction cause for P1215 found: No ▼	Yes ▶	– After repairing malfunction, clear DTC memory and create readiness code
		If the specification is attained: – Measure resistance between fuel injector terminals 1 and 2. Specification: approx. 15 – 23 Ω If the specification is not attained: – Replace cyl. 3 fuel injector
If no wiring or fuel injector malfunction is found:		
Malfunction cause	▶	– Engine Control Module (ECM) -J220- faulty, replace. Clear DTC memory and create readiness code

VW0159900153000X

Fig. 175 Code P1215: Cylinder 3 Fuel Injector Circuit Short To Voltage. 1998 Cabrio, Golf, GTI & Jetta w/2.0L Engine

Malfunction text: **Injector Circ.Cyl.1 Short to Ground**		
Cause: Wiring or fuel injector has open circuit or short circuit to Ground (GND)		Remedy: – Switch ignition off – Connect VAG 1598/18 test box – Remove fuse 18 – Measure resistance between lower terminal for fuse 18 and test box socket 24. Specification 15 – 23 Ω If the specification is not attained: – Disconnect connector from fuel injector – Disconnect 4-pin connector from Mass Air Flow (MAF) sensor – Measure resistance between connector terminal 1 and test box socket 1. Specification: ∞ Ω – Measure resistance between connector terminal 2 and test box socket 1. Specification: ∞ Ω If the specification is not attained: – Use wiring diagram to locate and repair short circuit to Ground (GND)
Malfunction cause for P1225 found: No ▼	Yes ▶	– After repairing malfunction, clear DTC memory and create readiness code
Continued ▼		

VW0159900155010X

Fig. 177 Code P1225: Injector Circuit Cylinder 1 Short To Ground (Part 1 of 2). 1998 Cabrio, Golf, GTI & Jetta w/2.0L Engine

Malfunction text: **Injector Circ.Cyl.2 Short to Ground**		
Cause: Wiring or fuel injector has open circuit or short circuit to Ground (GND)		Remedy: – Switch ignition off – Connect VAG 1598/18 test box – Remove fuse 18 – Measure resistance between lower terminal for fuse 18 and test box socket 25. Specification 15 – 23 Ω If the specification is not attained: – Disconnect connector from fuel injector – Disconnect 4-pin connector from Mass Air Flow (MAF) sensor – Measure resistance between connector terminal 1 and test box socket 1. Specification: ∞ Ω – Measure resistance between connector terminal 2 and test box socket 1. Specification: ∞ Ω If the specification is not attained: – Use wiring diagram to locate and repair short circuit to Ground (GND)
Malfunction cause for P1226 found: No ▼	Yes ▶	– After repairing malfunction, clear DTC memory and create readiness code
Continued ▼		

VW0159900156010X

Fig. 178 Code P1226: Injector Circuit Cylinder 2 Short To Ground (Part 1 of 2). 1998 Cabrio, Golf, GTI & Jetta w/2.0L Engine

Malfunction text: **Cyl.4 Fuel Injector Circ. Short to B+**		
Cause: Wiring or fuel injector has short circuit to positive		Remedy: – Switch ignition off. – Connect VAG 1598/18 test box – Remove fuse 18 – Disconnect connector from fuel injector – Measure resistance between connector terminal 2 and fuse 18 lower terminal. Specification: ∞ Ω If the specification is not attained: – Use wiring diagram to locate and repair short circuit to positive in the wiring from engine control module to fuel injector
Malfunction cause for P1216 found: No ▼	Yes ▶	– After repairing malfunction, clear DTC memory and create readiness code
		If the specification is attained: – Measure resistance between fuel injector terminals 1 and 2. Specification: approx. 15 – 23 Ω If the specification is not attained: – Replace cyl. 4 fuel injector
If no wiring or fuel injector malfunction is found:		
Malfunction cause	▶	– Engine Control Module (ECM) -J220- faulty, replace. Clear DTC memory and create readiness code

VW0159900154000X

Fig. 176 Code P1216: Cylinder 4 Fuel Injector Circuit Short To Voltage. 1998 Cabrio, Golf, GTI & Jetta w/2.0L Engine

Malfunction text: **Injector Circ.Cyl.1 Short to Ground**		
		If all specifications are attained: – Disconnect connector from fuel injector – Measure resistance between fuel injector terminals 1 and 2. Specification: 15 – 23 Ω If the specification is not attained: – Cyl. 1 fuel injector faulty, replace
Malfunction cause for P1225 found: No ▼	Yes ▶	– After repairing malfunction, clear DTC memory and create readiness code
If no malfunction in the wiring or fuel injector can be found:		
Malfunction cause	▶	– Engine Control Module (ECM) -J220- faulty, replace. Clear DTC memory and create readiness code

VW0159900155020X

Fig. 177 Code P1225: Injector Circuit Cylinder 1 Short To Ground (Part 2 of 2). 1998 Cabrio, Golf, GTI & Jetta w/2.0L Engine

Malfunction text: **Injector Circ.Cyl.2 Short to Ground**		
		If all specifications are attained: – Disconnect connector from fuel injector – Measure resistance between fuel injector terminals 1 and 2. Specification: 15 – 23 Ω If the specification is not attained: – Cyl. 2 fuel injector faulty, replace
Malfunction cause for P1226 found: No ▼	Yes ▶	– After repairing malfunction, clear DTC memory and create readiness code
If no malfunction in the wiring or fuel injector can be found:		
Malfunction cause	▶	– Engine Control Module (ECM) -J220- faulty, replace. Clear DTC memory and create readiness code

VW0159900156020X

Fig. 178 Code P1226: Injector Circuit Cylinder 2 Short To Ground (Part 2 of 2). 1998 Cabrio, Golf, GTI & Jetta w/2.0L Engine

Malfunction text: **Injector Circ.Cyl.3 Short to Ground**		
Cause: Wiring or fuel injector has open circuit or short circuit to Ground (GND)		Remedy: – Switch ignition off – Connect VAG 1598/18 test box – Remove fuse 18 – Measure resistance between lower terminal for fuse 18 and test box socket 26. Specification 15 – 23 Ω If the specification is not attained: – Disconnect connector from fuel injector – Disconnect 4-pin connector from Mass Air Flow (MAF) sensor – Measure resistance between connector terminal 1 and test box socket 1. Specification: ∞ Ω – Measure resistance between connector terminal 2 and test box socket 1. Specification: ∞ Ω If the specification is not attained: – Use wiring diagram to locate and repair short circuit to Ground (GND)
Malfunction cause for P1227 found: No ▼	Yes ▶	– After repairing malfunction, clear DTC memory and create readiness code
Continued ▼		

VW0159900157010X

Fig. 179 Code P1227: Injector Circuit Cylinder 3 Short To Ground (Part 1 of 2). 1998 Cabrio, Golf, GTI & Jetta w/2.0L Engine

Malfunction text: Injector Circ.Cyl.3 Short to Ground		
		If all specifications are attained: - Disconnect connector from fuel injector - Measure resistance between fuel injector terminals 1 and 2. Specification: 15 – 23 Ω If the specification is not attained: - Cyl. 3 fuel injector faulty, replace
Malfunction cause for P1227 found: No ▼	Yes ▶	- After repairing malfunction, clear DTC memory and create readiness code
If no malfunction in the wiring or fuel injector can be found:		
Malfunction cause	▶	- Engine Control Module (ECM) -J220- faulty, replace. Clear DTC memory and create readiness code

VW0159900157020X

Fig. 179 Code P1227: Injector Circuit Cylinder 3 Short To Ground (Part 2 of 2). 1998 Cabrio, Golf, GTI & Jetta w/2.0L Engine

Malfunction text: Injector Circ.Cyl.4 Short to Ground		
		If all specifications are attained: - Disconnect connector from fuel injector - Measure resistance between fuel injector terminals 1 and 2 Specification: 15 – 23 Ω If the specification is not attained: - Cyl. 4 fuel injector faulty, replace
Malfunction cause for P1228 found: No ▼	Yes ▶	- After repairing malfunction, clear DTC memory and create readiness code
If no malfunction in the wiring or fuel injector can be found:		
Malfunction cause	▶	- Engine Control Module (ECM) -J220- faulty, replace. Clear DTC memory and create readiness code

VW0159900158020X

Fig. 180 Code P1228: Injector Circuit Cylinder 4 Short To Ground (Part 2 of 2). 1998 Cabrio, Golf, GTI & Jetta w/2.0L Engine

Malfunction text: Injector Circ.Cyl.1 Open Circuit		
		- Check resistance between connector terminal 2 and test box socket 24. Specification max. 1.5 Ω If the specification is not attained: - Use wiring diagram to locate and repair open circuit in the activation wire from Engine Control Module (ECM) to cyl. 1 fuel injector If all specifications are attained: - Disconnect connector from fuel injector - Measure resistance between terminals 1 and 2 of fuel injector Specification: 15 – 23 Ω If the specification is not attained: - Cyl. 1 fuel injector faulty, replace
Malfunction cause for P1237 found: No ▼	Yes ▶	- After repairing malfunction, clear DTC memory and create readiness code
If no malfunction in the wiring or fuel injector can be found:		
Malfunction cause	▶	- ECM -J220- faulty, replace. Clear DTC memory and create readiness code

VW0159900159020X

Fig. 181 Code P1237: Injector Circuit Cylinder 1 Open Circuit (Part 2 of 2). 1998 Cabrio, Golf, GTI & Jetta w/2.0L Engine

Malfunction text: Injector Circ.Cyl.2 Open Circuit		
		- Measure resistance between connector terminal 2 and test box socket 25. Specification max. 1.5 Ω If the specification is not attained: - Use wiring diagram to locate and repair open circuit in the activation wire from Engine Control Module (ECM) to cyl. 2 fuel injector If all specifications are attained: - Disconnect connector from fuel injector - Measure resistance between terminals 1 and 2 of fuel injector Specification: 15 – 23 Ω If the specification is not attained: - Cyl. 2 fuel injector faulty, replace
Malfunction cause for P1238 found: No ▼	Yes ▶	- After repairing malfunction, clear DTC memory and create readiness code
If no malfunction in the wiring or fuel injector can be found:		
Malfunction cause	▶	- ECM -J220- faulty, replace. Clear DTC memory and create readiness code

VW0159900160020X

Fig. 182 Code P1238: Injector Circuit Cylinder 2 Open Circuit (Part 2 of 2). 1998 Cabrio, Golf, GTI & Jetta w/2.0L Engine

Malfunction text: Injector Circ.Cyl.4 Short to Ground		
Cause: Wiring or fuel injector has open circuit or short circuit to Ground (GND)		Remedy: - Switch ignition off - Connect VAG 1598/18 test box - Remove fuse 18 - Measure resistance between lower terminal for fuse 18 and test box socket 2. Specification 15 – 23 Ω If the specification is not attained: - Disconnect connector from fuel injector - Disconnect 4-pin connector from Mass Air Flow (MAF) sensor - Measure resistance between connector terminal 1 and test box socket 1. Specification: ∞ Ω - Measure resistance between connector terminal 2 and test box socket 1. Specification: ∞ Ω If the specification is not attained: - Use wiring diagram to locate and repair short circuit to Ground (GND)
Malfunction cause for P1228 found: No ▼	Yes ▶	- After repairing malfunction, clear DTC memory and create readiness code
Continued ▼		

VW0159900158010X

Fig. 180 Code P1228: Injector Circuit Cylinder 4 Short To Ground (Part 1 of 2). 1998 Cabrio, Golf, GTI & Jetta w/2.0L Engine

Malfunction text: Injector Circ.Cyl.1 Open Circuit		
Cause: Wiring or fuel injector has open circuit		Remedy: - Switch ignition off - Connect VAG 1598/18 test box - Remove fuse 18 - Measure resistance between lower terminal for fuse 18 and test box socket 24. Specification 15 – 23 Ω If the specification is not attained: - Measure resistance between connector terminal 1 and fuse 18 lower terminal. Specification max. 1.5 Ω If the specification is not attained, there is an open circuit between the fuel injector connector and positive connector (G3) in wiring harness - Use wiring diagram to locate and repair open circuit
Malfunction cause for P1237 found: No ▼	Yes ▶	- After repairing malfunction, clear DTC memory and create readiness code
Continued ▼		

VW0159900159010X

Fig. 181 Code P1237: Injector Circuit Cylinder 1 Open Circuit (Part 1 of 2). 1998 Cabrio, Golf, GTI & Jetta w/2.0L Engine

Malfunction text: Injector Circ.Cyl.2 Open Circuit		
Cause: Wiring or fuel injector has open circuit.		Remedy: - Switch ignition off - Connect VAG 1598/18 test box - Remove fuse 18 - Measure resistance between lower terminal for fuse 18 and test box socket 25. Specification 15 – 23 Ω If the specification is not attained: - Measure resistance between connector terminal 1 and fuse 18 lower terminal. Specification max. 1.5 Ω If the specification is not attained, there is an open circuit between the fuel injector connector and positive connector (G3) in wiring harness - Use wiring diagram to locate and repair open circuit
Malfunction cause for P1238 found: No ▼	Yes ▶	- After repairing malfunction, clear DTC memory and create readiness code
Continued ▼		

VW0159900160010X

Fig. 182 Code P1238: Injector Circuit Cylinder 2 Open Circuit (Part 1 of 2). 1998 Cabrio, Golf, GTI & Jetta w/2.0L Engine

Malfunction text: Injector Circ.Cyl.3 Open Circuit		
Cause: Wiring or fuel injector has open circuit		Remedy: - Switch ignition off - Connect VAG 1598/18 test box - Remove fuse 18 - Measure resistance between lower terminal for fuse 18 and test box socket 26. Specification 15 – 23 Ω If the specification is not attained: - Measure resistance between connector terminal 1 and fuse 18 lower terminal. Specification max. 1.5 Ω If the specification is not attained, there is an open circuit between the fuel injector connector and positive connector (G3) in wiring harness - Use wiring diagram to locate and repair open circuit
Malfunction cause for P1239 found: No ▼	Yes ▶	- After repairing malfunction, clear DTC memory and create readiness code
Continued ▼		

VW0159900161010X

Fig. 183 Code P1239: Injector Circuit Cylinder 3 Open Circuit (Part 1 of 2). 1998 Cabrio, Golf, GTI & Jetta w/2.0L Engine

Malfunction text: Injector Circ.Cyl.3 Open Circuit		
		– Measure resistance between connector terminal 2 and test box socket 26. Specification max. 1.5 Ω If the specification is not attained: – Use wiring diagram to locate and repair open circuit in the activation wire from Engine Control Module (ECM) to cyl. 3 fuel injector If all specifications are attained: – Disconnect connector from fuel injector – Measure resistance between terminals 1 and 2 of fuel injector. Specification: 15 – 23 Ω If the specification is not attained: – Cyl. 3 fuel injector faulty, replace
Malfunction cause for P1239 found: No ▼	Yes ▶	– After repairing malfunction, clear DTC memory and create readiness code
If no malfunction in the wiring or fuel injector can be found:		
Malfunction cause	▶	– ECM -J220- faulty, replace. Clear DTC memory and create readiness code

VW0159900161020X

Fig. 183 Code P1239: Injector Circuit Cylinder 3 Open Circuit (Part 2 of 2). 1998 Cabrio, Golf, GTI & Jetta w/2.0L Engine

Malfunction text: Injector Circ.Cyl.4 Open Circuit		
		– Measure resistance between connector terminal 2 and test box socket 2. Specification max. 1.5 Ω If the specification is not attained: – Use wiring diagram to locate and repair open circuit in the activation wire from Engine Control Module (ECM) to cyl. 4 fuel injector If all specifications are attained: – Disconnect connector from fuel injector – Measure resistance between terminals 1 and 2 of fuel injector. Specification: 15 – 23 Ω If the specification is not attained: – Cyl. 4 fuel injector faulty, replace
Malfunction cause for P1240 found: No ▼	Yes ▶	– After repairing malfunction, clear DTC memory and create readiness code
If no malfunction in the wiring or fuel injector can be found:		
Malfunction cause	▶	– ECM -J220- faulty, replace. Clear DTC memory and create readiness code

VW0159900162020X

Fig. 184 Code P1240: Injector Circuit Cylinder 4 Open Circuit (Part 2 of 2). 1998 Cabrio, Golf, GTI & Jetta w/2.0L Engine

Malfunction text: Camshaft/Crankshaft Pos.Sens.Signals Out of Sequence		
		If the specifications are not ∞ Ω, the wiring has a short circuit to cable shielding – Use wiring diagram to locate and repair short circuit If the specifications are ∞ Ω: – Measure resistance between connector terminal 1 and test box socket 67. Specification: max. 1.5 Ω – Measure resistance between connector terminal 2 and test box socket 68. Specification: max.1.5 Ω If the specifications are not attained: the wiring has open circuit – Use wiring diagram to locate and repair open circuit If the specifications are attained: – Remove sensor and check for contamination by metal particles – Check sensor wheel on crankshaft for damage or contamination via sensor mounting hole in engine block. If no malfunction can be found:
Malfunction cause for P1340	▶	– ECM -J220- faulty, replace. Clear DTC memory and create readiness code

VW0159900163020X

Fig. 185 Code P1340: CMP/CKP Sensors Signals Out Of Sequence (Part 2 of 2). 1998 Cabrio, Golf, GTI & Jetta w/2.0L Engine

Displayed text: Sec.Air Inj.Control Module Short to B+	
Cause: Engine Control Module activates the Secondary Air Injection valve (N112), however Oxygen sensor 1 does not detect Secondary Air Injection	Remedy: – Switch OFF ignition – Check whether the connector is connected to Secondary Air Injection valve (N112) (near pump motor). When the connector is firmly attached: – Connect Test Box VAG 1598/18. – Pull connector off valve. – Measure resistance between connector terminal 1 and Test Box socket 50: specification: max.1.5 Ω If specification not obtained: – Locate and eliminate open circuit in wiring using wiring diagram.
If specification is obtained:	
Continued	

VW0159900173010X

Fig. 187 Code P1420: Secondary Air Injection Control Module Short To Voltage (Part 1 of 2). 1998 Cabrio, Golf, GTI & Jetta w/2.0L Engine

Malfunction text: Injector Circ.Cyl.4 Open Circuit		
Cause: Wiring or fuel injector has open circuit		Remedy: – Switch ignition off – Connect VAG 1598/18 test box – Remove fuse 18 – Measure resistance between lower terminal for fuse 18 and test box socket 2. Specification 15 – 23 Ω If the specification is not attained: – Measure resistance between connector terminal 1 and fuse 18 lower terminal. Specification max. 1.5 Ω If the specification is not attained, there is an open circuit between the fuel injector connector and positive connector (G3) in wiring harness – Use wiring diagram to locate and repair open circuit
Malfunction cause for P1240 found: No ▼	Yes ▶	– After repairing malfunction, clear DTC memory and create readiness code
		Continued ▼

VW0159900162010X

Fig. 184 Code P1240: Injector Circuit Cylinder 4 Open Circuit (Part 1 of 2). 1998 Cabrio, Golf, GTI & Jetta w/2.0L Engine

Malfunction text: Camshaft/Crankshaft Pos.Sens.Signals Out of Sequence		
Cause: Engine speed (RPM) sensor -G28- supplies implausible signals to the Engine Control Module (ECM)		Remedy: – Switch ignition off – Check engine speed (RPM) sensor -G28- for tightening torque (connector or sensor loose, or too large a gap to sensor wheel will cause a malfunction) – Connect VAG 1598/18 test box – Check resistance between test box sockets 67 and 68. Specification: 500 – 700 Ω If the specification is not attained: – Replace engine speed (RPM) sensor -G28-
Malfunction cause for P1340 found: No ▼	Yes ▶	– After repairing malfunction disconnect connector from ECM -J220- for 10 seconds, then clear DTC memory and create readiness code
		If the specification is attained: – Disconnect connector from RPM sensor – Measure resistance between connector terminal 1 and test box socket 56. Specification: ∞ Ω – Measure resistance between connector terminal 2 and test box socket 56. Specification: ∞ Ω
		Continued ▼

VW0159900163010X

Fig. 185 Code P1340: CMP/CKP Sensors Signals Out Of Sequence (Part 1 of 2). 1998 Cabrio, Golf, GTI & Jetta w/2.0L Engine

Malfunction text: Tank Ventilation Valve Short to B+		
Cause: Tank venting system Evaporative Emission (EVAP) canister purge regulator valve -N80- malfunction		Remedy: – Switch ignition off – Disconnect connector from Engine Control Module (ECM) – Disconnect connector from EVAP canister purge regulator valve – Measure resistance at valve between connector terminal 1 and 2. Specification: ∞ Ω If the specification is not ∞ Ω: short circuit to positive in the activation wire – Use wiring diagram to locate and repair short circuit
Malfunction cause for P1410 found: No ▼	Yes ▶	– After repairing malfunction, clear DTC memory and create readiness code
If no wiring malfunction can be found:		
Malfunction cause for P1410	▶	– EVAP canister purge regulator valve -N80- faulty, replace. Clear DTC memory and create readiness code

VW0159900164010X

Fig. 186 Code P1410: Tank Ventilation Valve Short To Voltage. 1998 Cabrio, Golf, GTI & Jetta w/2.0L Engine

Displayed text: Sec.Air Inj.Control Module Short to B+		
		– Switch ON ignition. – Bridge Test Box sockets 1+6. – Connect Test Box socket 50 to vehicle Ground. – Measure voltage supply at valve connector between connector terminal 1 and 2: specification: min. 11.5 Volt. If specification is not obtained: – Locate and eliminate wiring open circuit between connector terminal 2 and fuse 18 lower terminal using wiring diagram.
Malfunction cause for P1420 found: No ▼	Yes ▶	After repairing malfunction, erase DTC memory and create Readiness Code.
If specification of min. 11.5 Volt is obtained:		
		– Measure resistance between Secondary Air Injection valve terminals 1+2, specification: 40 to 80 Ω If specification exceeded or not obtained: – Replace Secondary Air Injection valve.
If specification is obtained:		
Malfunction cause for P1420	▶	ECM J220 faulty, replace. Erase DTC memory and create Readiness Code.

VW0159900173020X

Fig. 187 Code P1420: Secondary Air Injection Control Module Short To Voltage (Part 2 of 2). 1998 Cabrio, Golf, GTI & Jetta w/2.0L Engine

Displayed text: **Sec.Air Inj.Valve Circ. Short to Ground**	
Cause: Engine Control Module detects short to Ground when activating the Secondary Air Injection valve (N112).	Remedy: – Switch OFF ignition. – Connect Test Box VAG 1598/18. – Pull connector off Secondary Air Injection valve. – Measure resistance between connector terminal 1 and Test Box socket 50: specification: max.1.5 Ω – Measure resistance between connector terminal 1 and Test Box socket 1: specification: ∞ Ω If specifications are not obtained: – Locate and eliminate wiring open/short to Ground using wiring diagram.
	If no wiring malfunction is found:
	– Measure resistance between Secondary Air Injection valve terminals 1+2, specification: 20 to 50 Ω If this specification is exceeded or not obtained: – Replace Secondary Air Injection valve.
	If specification is obtained:
Malfunction cause for P1421 ▶	ECM J220 faulty, replace. Erase DTC memory and create Readiness Code.

VW0159900174000X

Fig. 188 Code P1421: Secondary Air Injection Circuit Short To Ground. 1998 Cabrio, Golf, GTI & Jetta w/2.0L Engine

Malfunction text: **Tank Ventilation Valve Short to Ground**		
Cause: Evaporative Emission (EVAP) canister purge regulator valve -N80- in tank venting system or activation wire has short circuit to Ground (GND)		Remedy: – Switch ignition off – Measure resistance between connector terminal 1 and test box socket 1. Specification: max. ∞ Ω – Measure resistance between connector terminal 2 and fuse 18 upper terminal. Specification max. 1.5 Ω If the specifications are not attained: – Use wiring diagram to locate and repair open circuit/short circuit to Ground (GND) – Measure resistance between connector terminal 1 and test box socket 1. Specification: ∞ Ω If the specification is not ∞ Ω: short circuit to Ground (GND) in activation wire – Use wiring diagram to locate and repair short circuit
Malfunction cause for P1425 found: No ▼	Yes ▶	– After repairing malfunction, clear DTC memory and create readiness code
		Continued ▼

VW0159900164020X

Fig. 190 Code P1425: Tank Ventilation Valve Short To Ground (Part 1 of 2). 1998 Cabrio, Golf, GTI & Jetta w/2.0L Engine

Malfunction text: **Tank Ventilation Valve Open Circuit**	
Cause: Evaporative Emission (EVAP) canister purge regulator valve -N80- in tank venting system or activation wire has short circuit to Ground (GND)	Remedy: – Switch ignition off – Connect VAG 1598/18 test box – Disconnect connector from EVAP canister purge regulator valve – Switch ignition on – Bridge test box sockets 1 and 6 – Measure voltage supply at valve connector between connector terminal 2 and Ground (GND). Specification: min. 11.5 volts If the specification is not attained: – Switch ignition off – Measure resistance between connector terminal 1 and test box socket 31. Specification: max.1.5 Ω – Measure resistance between connector terminal 2 and fuse 18 upper terminal. Specification max. 1.5 Ω If the specifications are not attained: – Use wiring diagram to locate and repair open circuit – Measure resistance between connector terminal 1 and test box socket 1. Specification: ∞ Ω
	Continued ▼

VW0159900164040X

Fig. 191 Code P1426: Tank Ventilation Valve Open Circuit (Part 1 of 2). 1998 Cabrio, Golf, GTI & Jetta w/2.0L Engine

Displayed text: **Sec.Air Inj.Sys.Control Valve Circ. Short to B+**	
Cause: Engine Control Module detects short to positive when activating the Secondary Air Injection valve (N112).	Remedy: – Switch OFF ignition. – Connect Test Box VAG 1598/18. – Pull connector off Secondary Air Injection valve. – Measure resistance between connector terminal 1 and Test Box socket 50: specification: max.1.5 Ω – Pull out fuse 18. – Measure resistance between fuse 18 lower terminal and Test Box socket 50: specification: ∞ Ω If specifications are not obtained: – Locate and eliminate short to positive using wiring diagram.
	If no wiring malfunction is found:
	– Measure resistance between Secondary Air Injection valve terminals 1+2, specification: 20 to 50 Ω If this specification is exceeded or not obtained: – Replace Secondary Air Injection valve.
	If specification is obtained:
Malfunction cause for P1422 ▶	ECM J220 faulty, replace. Erase DTC memory and create Readiness Code.

VW0159900175000X

Fig. 189 Code P1422: Secondary Air Injection System Control Valve Circuit Short To Voltage. 1998 Cabrio, Golf, GTI & Jetta w/2.0L Engine

Malfunction text: **Tank Ventilation Valve Short to Ground**	
	If no wiring malfunction is found:
	– Measure resistance between solenoid valve terminals 1 and 2. Specification: 20 – 50 Ω If this specification is exceeded or not attained: – Replace Evaporative Emission (EVAP) canister purge regulator valve -N80-
	If the specification is attained:
Malfunction cause for P1425 ▶	– Engine Control Module (ECM) -J220- faulty, replace. Clear DTC memory and create readiness code

VW0159900164030X

Fig. 190 Code P1425: Tank Ventilation Valve Short To Ground (Part 2 of 2). 1998 Cabrio, Golf, GTI & Jetta w/2.0L Engine

Malfunction text: **Tank Ventilation Valve Open Circuit**		
		If the specification is not ∞ Ω: short circuit to Ground (GND) in activation wire – Use wiring diagram to locate and repair short circuit
Malfunction cause for P1426 found: No ▼	Yes ▶	– After repairing malfunction, clear DTC memory and create readiness code
		If no wiring malfunction is found:
		– Measure resistance between EVAP canister purge regulator valve terminals 1 and 2. Specification: 20 – 50 Ω If this specification is exceeded or not attained: – Replace Evaporative Emission (EVAP) canister purge regulator valve -N80-
		If the specification is attained:
Malfunction cause for P1426 ▶		– Engine Control Module (ECM) -J220- faulty, replace. Clear DTC memory and create readiness code

VW0159900164050X

Fig. 191 Code P1426: Tank Ventilation Valve Open Circuit (Part 2 of 2). 1998 Cabrio, Golf, GTI & Jetta w/2.0L Engine

Displayed text: **Sec.Air Inj.Sys.Circ. Short to B+**		
Cause: Engine Control Module detects short to positive when activating the Secondary Air Injection pump relay.		Remedy: – Switch OFF ignition. – Connect Test Box VAG 1598/18. – Remove Secondary Air Injection pump relay (J299) from socket – Measure resistance between Test Box socket 49 and base plate socket 6. specification: ∞ Ω – Measure resistance between Test Box socket 49 and Battery positive terminal. specification: ∞ Ω If specifications are not obtained: – Locate and eliminate short to positive using wiring diagram.
		If no wiring malfunction is found:
		– Replace Secondary Air Injection pump relay (J299).
Malfunction cause for P1450 found: No ▼	Yes ▶	After repairing malfunction, erase DTC memory and create Readiness Code.
		If the malfunction is still present after replacing Secondary Air Injection pump relay and erasing DTC memory:
Malfunction cause for P1450 ▶		ECM J220 faulty, replace. Erase DTC memory and create Readiness Code.

VW0159900176000X

Fig. 192 Code P1450: Secondary Air Injection System Circuit Short To Voltage. 1998 Cabrio, Golf, GTI & Jetta w/2.0L Engine

Displayed text: Sec.Air Inj.Sys. Short to Ground	
Cause: Engine Control Module detects short to Ground when activating the Secondary Air Injection pump relay.	Remedy: – Switch OFF ignition. – Connect Test Box VAG 1598/18. – Pull Secondary Air Injection pump relay (J299) off base plate – Measure resistance between Test Box sockets 1 and 49. specification: ∞ Ω If specification not obtained: – Locate and eliminate short to Ground using wiring diagram.
	If no wiring malfunction is found:
	– Replace Secondary Air Injection pump relay (J299).
Malfunction cause for P1451 found: No ▼ — Yes ▶	After repairing malfunction, erase DTC memory and create Readiness Code.
	If the malfunction is still present after replacing Secondary Air Injection pump relay and erasing DTC memory:
Malfunction cause for P1451 ▶	ECM J220 faulty, replace. Erase DTC memory and create Readiness Code.

VW0159900177000X

Fig. 193 Code P1451: Secondary Air Injection System Short To Ground. 1998 Cabrio, Golf, GTI & Jetta w/2.0L Engine

Displayed text: Sec.Air Inj.Sys. Open Circuit	
	– Check thermo fuse (30 amp.) in fuse holder above the Secondary Air Injection pump relay (J299) when it is in a cold condition, replace if necessary.
	When the fuse is not damaged: – Locate and eliminate wiring open circuit using wiring diagram.
	If no wiring malfunction is found:
	– Pull connector off Secondary Air Injection pump (V101). – Measure resistance between base plate chamber 8 and connector terminal 2, specification: max. 1.5 Ω. – Measure resistance between terminal 1 and Test Box socket 1 specification: max. 1.5 Ω. If specifications are not obtained: – Replace Secondary Air Injection pump relay.
Malfunction cause for P1452 found: No ▼ — Yes ▶	After repairing malfunction, erase DTC memory and create Readiness Code.
	If the malfunction is still present after replacing Secondary Air Injection pump relay and erasing DTC memory:
Malfunction cause for P1452 ▶	Secondary Air Injection pump motor (V101) faulty, replace. Erase DTC memory and create Readiness Code.

VW0159900178020X

Fig. 194 Code P1452: Secondary Air Injection System Open Circuit (Part 2 of 2). 1998 Cabrio, Golf, GTI & Jetta w/2.0L Engine

Malfunction text: Fuel Pump Relay Circ. Electrical Malfunction	
	If the specification is not attained: – Use wiring diagram to locate and repair open circuit – Measure resistance between test box sockets 1 and 6. Specification: ∞ Ω If the specification is not attained, the wiring has short circuit to Ground (GND) – Use wiring diagram to locate and repair short circuit to Ground (GND)
Malfunction cause for P1500 found: No ▼ — Yes ▶	– After repairing malfunction, clear DTC memory and create readiness code
	If the fuel pump runs: – Disconnect center connector – Remove secondary air injection pump relay – Disconnect connectors from Mass Air Flow (MAF) sensor, EVAP canister purge regulator valve -N80- and secondary air injection solenoid valve – Remove fuse 18 – Measure resistance between fuse 18 lower terminal and Ground (GND). Specification: ∞ Ω
	Continued ▼

VW0159900164070X

Fig. 195 Code P1500: Fuel Pump Relay Circuit Electrical Malfunction (Part 2 of 3). 1998 Cabrio, Golf, GTI & Jetta w/2.0L Engine

Displayed text: Sec.Air Inj.Sys. Open Circuit	
Cause: Secondary Air Injection pump relay (J299) is activated by Engine Control Module, but Secondary Air Injection pump motor (V101) does not run.	Remedy: – Switch OFF ignition. – Connect Test Box VAG 1598/18. – Pull Secondary Air Injection pump relay (J299) out of base plate – Measure resistance between Test Box socket 49 and socket 4. specification: max. 1.5 Ω – Remove fuse 18. – Measure resistance between base plate chamber 6 and fuse 18 lower terminal. specification: max. 1.5 Ω If specifications are not obtained: – Locate and eliminate wiring open circuit using wiring diagram. – Measure resistance between base plate chamber 2 and Battery positive terminal. specification: max. 1.5 Ω If specification is not obtained:
	Continued

VW0159900178010X

Fig. 194 Code P1452: Secondary Air Injection System Open Circuit (Part 1 of 2). 1998 Cabrio, Golf, GTI & Jetta w/2.0L Engine

Malfunction text: Fuel Pump Relay Circ. Electrical Malfunction	
Cause:	Remedy:
Electrical malfunction in Fuel Pump (FP) relay -J17-	– Switch ignition off – Check that fuel delivery unit connector is firmly attached – Remove fuse 18 If the fuse is faulty: – Use wiring diagram to locate and repair short circuit to transfer fuel pump -G23- or to Oxygen Sensor (O2S) heating before and after three way catalytic converter
Malfunction cause for P1500 found: No ▼ — Yes ▶	– After repairing malfunction, clear DTC memory and create readiness code
	If the fuse is OK: – Connect VAG 1598/18 test box – Switch ignition on – Bridge test box sockets 1 and 6 • The transfer fuel pump -G23- must run audibly If the fuel pump does not run: – Disconnect fuel pump relay from relay panel – Check resistance between test box socket 6 and relay socket 3. Specification: max.1.5 Ω
	Continued ▼

VW0159900164060X

Fig. 195 Code P1500: Fuel Pump Relay Circuit Electrical Malfunction (Part 1 of 3). 1998 Cabrio, Golf, GTI & Jetta w/2.0L Engine

Malfunction text: Fuel Pump Relay Circ. Electrical Malfunction	
	If the specification is not attained: The positive wire to MAF sensor, EVAP canister purge regulator valve -N80- and secondary air injection solenoid valve has short circuit to Ground (GND) – Use wiring diagram to locate and repair short circuit to Ground (GND) If the specification is attained: – Reconnect center connector – Measure resistance between fuse 18 lower terminal and Ground (GND). Specification: ∞ Ω If the specification is not attained: the positive wire to fuel injectors has short circuit to Ground (GND) – Use wiring diagram to locate and repair short circuit to Ground (GND) If the specification is attained: – Fuel pump relay -J17- faulty, replace
Malfunction cause for P1500 found: No ▼ — Yes ▶	– After repairing malfunction, clear DTC memory and create readiness code
	If the malfunction is still present even with new fuel pump relay:
Malfunction cause ▶	– Engine Control Module (ECM) -J220- faulty, replace. Clear DTC memory and create readiness code

VW0159900164080X

Fig. 195 Code P1500: Fuel Pump Relay Circuit Electrical Malfunction (Part 3 of 3). 1998 Cabrio, Golf, GTI & Jetta w/2.0L Engine

Malfunction text: **Fuel Pump Relay Circ. Short to B+**	
Cause: Engine Control Module (ECM) -J220- detects short circuit to positive via the activation wire to Fuel Pump (FP) relay -J17-	Remedy: – Switch ignition off – Connect VAG 1598/18 test box – Disconnect fuel pump relay from relay panel – Measure resistance between test box socket 6 and relay socket 3. Specification: max.1.5 Ω If the specification is not attained: – Use wiring diagram to locate and repair open circuit – Measure resistance between test box sockets 1 and 6. Specification: ∞ Ω If the specification is not attained: the wire has short circuit to Ground (GND) – Use wiring diagram to locate and repair short circuit to Ground (GND)
Malfunction cause for P1502 found: No ▼ — Yes ▶	– After repairing malfunction, clear DTC memory and create readiness code
	If no short circuit to Ground (GND) is detected in the activation wire: – Fuel pump relay -J17- faulty, replace
Malfunction cause ▶	If the malfunction is still present even with new fuel pump relay: – ECM -J220- faulty, replace. Clear DTC memory and create readiness code

VW0159900165000X

Fig. 196 Code P1502: Fuel Pump Relay Circuit Short To Voltage. 1998 Cabrio, Golf, GTI & Jetta w/2.0L Engine

Malfunction text: **Throttle Actuation Potentiometer Signal Too Low / Signal too High**	
	If the voltage supply specifications are attained: – Switch ignition off – Re-attach 8-pin connector to throttle valve control module – Connect VAG 1598/18 test box – At wide open throttle position, check resistance between test box sockets 10 and 33: ∞ Ω – At closed throttle position, check resistance between test box sockets 10 and 33: max.10 Ω – At closed throttle position, check resistance between test box sockets 27 and 53: 3 – 200 Ω If the specifications are not attained: – Disconnect 8-pin connector from throttle valve control module Check resistances as follows: – Connector terminal 1 and test box socket 27. – Connector terminal 2 and test box socket 53. – Connector terminal 5 and test box socket 40. – Connector terminal 8 and test box socket 62. Specifications: max.1.5 Ω If the resistance does not correspond to specifications: – Use wiring diagram to locate and repair open circuit Even if the specifications are attained, also measure resistance with 8-pin connector disconnected: – Measure resistance to one another between test box sockets 10, 27, 33, 40, 41, 53 and 62. Specification: ∞ Ω
Continued ▼	

VW0159900166020X

Fig. 197 Code P1544: Throttle Actuation Potentiometer Signal Too Low/Too High (Part 2 of 3). 1998 Cabrio, Golf, GTI & Jetta w/2.0L Engine

Malfunction text: **Throttle Actuator (B1) Malfunction**	
Cause: Engine Control Module (ECM) -J220- detects a faulty Throttle Position (TP) actuator -V60- in the throttle valve control module -J338-	Remedy: – Check throttle valve control module -J338- at 8-pin connector: (terminal assignment – Disconnect 8-pin connector from throttle valve control module – Switch ignition on Check voltage as follows: – Between connector terminals 4 and 7. Specification: approx. 5 volts – Between connector terminals 3 and 7. Specification: approx. 10 volts If the specifications are not attained: – Switch ignition off – Connect VAG 1598/18 test box Check resistances as follows: – Connector terminal 3 and test box socket 10. – Connector terminal 4 and test box socket 41. – Connector terminal 7 and test box socket 33. Specifications: max.1.5 Ω If the specifications are not attained: – Use wiring diagram to locate and repair open circuit If no open circuit is found: – Replace ECM -J220-
Continued ▼	

VW0159900167010X

Fig. 198 Code P1580: Throttle Actuator Malfunction (Part 1 of 3). 1998 Cabrio, Golf, GTI & Jetta w/2.0L Engine

Malfunction text: **Throttle Actuation Potentiometer Signal Too Low / Signal too High**	
Cause: Throttle Position (TP) sensor -G88- in throttle valve control module supplies too low/too high signal to Engine Control Module (ECM)	Remedy: – Check throttle valve control module -J338- at 8-pin connector: terminal assignment – Disconnect 8-pin connector from throttle valve control module – Switch ignition on Check voltage as follows: – Between connector terminals 4 and 7. Specification: approx. 5 volts – Between connector terminals 3 and 7. Specification: approx. 10 volts If the specifications are not attained: – Switch ignition off – Connect VAG 1598/18 test box Check resistances as follows: – Connector terminal 3 and test box socket 10. – Connector terminal 4 and test box socket 41. – Connector terminal 7 and test box socket 33. Specifications: max.1.5 Ω If the specifications are not attained: – Use wiring diagram to locate and repair open circuit If no wiring open circuit is found: – Replace ECM -J220-
Continued ▼	

VW0159900166010X

Fig. 197 Code P1544: Throttle Actuation Potentiometer Signal Too Low/Too High (Part 1 of 3). 1998 Cabrio, Golf, GTI & Jetta w/2.0L Engine

Malfunction text: **Throttle Actuation Potentiometer Signal Too Low / Signal too High**	
	If the specifications are not ∞ Ω: – Use wiring diagram to locate and repair short circuit between wires If the specifications with open/closed throttle are not attained, but the wiring is OK: – Replace throttle valve control module -J338-
Malfunction cause for P1543/P1544 ▶	– Throttle position sensor faulty, replace throttle valve control module -J338-. After repairing malfunction disconnect connector from ECM -J220- for 10 seconds, then clear DTC memory and create readiness code

VW0159900166030X

Fig. 197 Code P1544: Throttle Actuation Potentiometer Signal Too Low/Too High (Part 3 of 3). 1998 Cabrio, Golf, GTI & Jetta w/2.0L Engine

Malfunction text: **Throttle Actuator (B1) Malfunction**	
	If the voltage supply specifications are attained: – Switch ignition off – Re-attach 8-pin connector to throttle valve control module – Connect VAG 1598/18 test box – At wide open throttle position, check resistance between test box sockets 10 and 33. Specification: ∞ Ω – At closed throttle position, check resistance between test box sockets 10 and 33. Specification: max.10 Ω – At closed throttle position, check resistance between test box sockets 27 and 53. Specification: 3 – 200 Ω If the specifications are not attained: – Disconnect 8-pin connector Check resistances as follows: – Connector terminal 1 and test box socket 27. – Connector terminal 2 and test box socket 53. – Connector terminal 5 and test box socket 40. – Connector terminal 8 and test box socket 62. Specifications: max.1.5 Ω If the resistance does not correspond to specifications: – Use wiring diagram to locate and repair open circuit Even if the specifications are attained, also measure resistance with 8-pin connector disconnected: – Measure resistance to one another between test box sockets 10, 27, 33, 40, 41, 53 and 62. Specification: ∞ Ω
Continued ▼	

VW0159900167020X

Fig. 198 Code P1580: Throttle Actuator Malfunction (Part 2 of 3). 1998 Cabrio, Golf, GTI & Jetta w/2.0L Engine

Malfunction text: **Throttle Actuator (B1) Malfunction**	
	If the specifications are not ∞ Ω: – Use wiring diagram to locate and repair short circuit between wires If the specifications with open/close throttle are not attained, but the wiring is OK: – Replace throttle valve control module -J338-
Malfunction cause for P1580 ▶	– Throttle position actuator -V60- faulty, replace throttle valve control module -J338-. After repairing malfunction disconnect connector from ECM -J220- for 10 seconds, then clear DTC memory and create readiness code

VW0159900167030X

Fig. 198 Code P1580: Throttle Actuator Malfunction (Part 3 of 3). 1998 Cabrio, Golf, GTI & Jetta w/2.0L Engine

Malfunction text: Idle Adaptation at Limit		
Cause: Crankcase dilution		Remedy: – Fast drive on open roads, however an engine oil change is better
Malfunction cause for P1582 found: No ▼	Yes ▶	– After repairing malfunction disconnect connector from Engine Control Module (ECM) -J220- for 10 seconds, then clear DTC memory and create readiness code
		If the idle adaptation is exceeded even though engine oil has been changed, fuel injectors worn:
Cause: Opening time for fuel injectors too long, and do not allow idle adaptation		Remedy: – Replace worn fuel injectors
Cause: Motor runs outside idle adaptation due to high blow by		Remedy: – Check compression pressures. Specification: 9 – 13 bar (130 – 189 psi), max. permissible difference between cylinders: 3 bar (44 psi) If compression pressure is below 7.5 bar (109 psi): – Repair engine
		If the compression pressure is within specification:
Malfunction cause	▶	– Malfunction in throttle valve control module -J338-, replace – After repairing malfunction disconnect connector from ECM -J220- for 10 seconds, then clear DTC memory and create readiness code

VW0159900167040X

Fig. 199 Code P1582: Idle Adaptation At Limit. 1998 Cabrio, Golf, GTI & Jetta w/2.0L Engine

Malfunction text: MIL Call-up Circ.Open Short to B+		
Cause: MIL does not light up due to short circuit to positive, and causes malfunction to be stored.		Remedy: – Switch ignition off – Connect VAG 1598/18 test box – Bridge test box sockets 1 and 3 – Switch ignition on • MIL must light-up If the MIL does not light-up: – Switch ignition off – Check bulb in MIL If bulb is OK: – Use wiring diagram to locate and repair short/open circuit from Engine Control Module (ECM) to MIL
Malfunction cause for P1613 found: No ▼	Yes ▶	– After repairing malfunction disconnect connector from ECM -J220- for 10 seconds, then clear DTC memory and create readiness code
		If in the MIL wire no malfunction is found:
Malfunction cause	▶	– ECM -J220- faulty, replace. Clear DTC memory and create readiness code

VW0159900169000X

Fig. 201 Code P1613: MIL Call-Up Circuit Open Short To Voltage. 1998 Cabrio, Golf, GTI & Jetta w/2.0L Engine

Malfunction text: Engine Intervention Readable		
Cause: Engine Control Module (ECM) does not receive a signal from Transmission Control Module (TCM)		Remedy: – Connect VAG 1598/18 test box – Check wiring between socket 13 and ECM connector terminal 18 for open circuit – Use wiring diagram to locate and repair open circuit/short circuit to Ground (GND)
Malfunction cause for P1780 found: No ▼	Yes ▶	– After repairing malfunction, clear DTC memory
Malfunction cause	▶	– TCM -J217- faulty. Replace TCM -J217- and clear DTC memory

VW0159900171000X

Fig. 203 Code P1780: Engine Intervention Readable. 1998 Cabrio, Golf, GTI & Jetta w/2.0L Engine

		If the voltage supply to MAF sensor is at least 11.5 volts, check other wiring between MAF sensor and ECM -J220- as follows: – Bridge connector terminals 1 and 2, measure resistance between test box sockets 1 and 16. Specification: max. 1.5 Ω – Bridge connector terminals 1 and 4, measure resistance between test box sockets 1 and 17. Specification: max. 1.5 Ω – Do not bridge connector terminals, measure resistance between test box sockets 16 and 17. Specification: ∞ Ω If the specifications are not attained: – Use wiring diagram to locate and repair wiring open or short circuits to one another.
Malfunction cause for P0102 found: No ▼	Yes ▶	– After repairing malfunction, disconnect connector from ECM -J220- for 10 seconds, then clear DTC memory and create readiness code
		If resistance specifications are attained:
Malfunction cause for P0102	▶	– MAF sensor faulty, replace. Disconnect connector from ECM -J220- for 10 seconds, then clear DTC memory and create readiness code

VW0159600021020X

Fig. 204 Code P0102: Mass Or Volume Air Flow Circuit Low Input (Part 2 of 2). 1998 GTI & Jetta w/2.8L Engine

Malfunction text: MIL Call-up Circ./Transm.Control Module Short to Ground		
Cause: MIL permanently lit, and malfunction P1611 is stored in DTC memory		Remedy: – Switch ignition off – Connect VAG 1598/18 test box – Measure resistance between test box socket 21 and connector terminal 51 of 10-pin connector for automatic transmission. Specification: max. 1.5 Ω If the specification is not attained: – Open/short circuit to Ground (GND) in the communication wire from automatic transmission to Engine Control Module (ECM) -J220- – Use wiring diagram to locate and repair open circuit/short circuit to Ground (GND)
Malfunction cause for P1611 found: No ▼	Yes ▶	– After repairing malfunction disconnect connector from ECM -J220- for 10 seconds, then clear DTC memory and create readiness code
		If the specification is attained and no short circuit to Ground (GND) is found:
Malfunction cause	▶	– ECM -J220- faulty, replace. Clear DTC memory and create readiness code

VW0159900168000X

Fig. 200 Code P1611: MIL Call-Up Circuit/ Transmission Control Module Short To Ground. 1998 Cabrio, Golf, GTI & Jetta w/2.0L Engine

Malfunction text: Solenoid EV7 Electrical Malfunction		
Cause: Valve body solenoid valve does not receive a signal		Remedy: – Connect VAG 1598/18 test box – Measure resistance between test box sockets 10 and 67: Specification: min. 55 Ω; max. 70.5 Ω – Measure resistance between test box sockets 10 and 1: Specification: ∞ Ω If the specification is not attained: – Use wiring diagram to locate and repair open/short circuit to Ground (GND) – Replace valve body
Malfunction cause for P1778 found: No ▼	Yes ▶	– After repairing malfunction, clear DTC memory
Malfunction cause	▶	– Transmission Control Module (TCM) -J217- faulty. Replace TCM -J217- and clear DTC memory

VW0159900170000X

Fig. 202 Code P1778: Solenoid EV7 Electrical Malfunction. 1998 Cabrio, Golf, GTI & Jetta w/2.0L Engine

Cause:	Remedy:
Signal from Mass Air Flow (MAF) sensor -G70- to Engine Control Module (ECM) too low	– Eliminate unmetered (outside) air between MAF sensor -G70- and throttle valve control module -J338- Check voltage supply to MAF sensor: – Connect VAG 1598/18 test box – Disconnect 4-pin harness connector from MAF sensor – Switch ignition on – Bridge test box sockets 1 and 6, measure voltage between connector terminals 1 and 3 on 4-pin harness connector. Specification: min. 11.5 volts If no voltage is measured: – Switch ignition off – Check Ground (GND) cable resistance between connector terminal 1 and Ground (GND). Specification: max. 1.5 Ω – Measure resistance between connector terminal 1 and test box socket 1. Specification: max. 1.5 Ω If resistance is OK: – Use wiring diagram to locate and repair wiring open circuit from Fuel Pump (FP) relay -J17- to MAF sensor -G70-

VW0159600021010X

Fig. 204 Code P0102: Mass Or Volume Air Flow Circuit Low Input (Part 1 of 2). 1998 GTI & Jetta w/2.8L Engine

Cause:		Remedy:
Signal from Mass Air Flow (MAF) sensor -G70- to Engine Control Module (ECM) too high		– Switch ignition off. – Connect VAG 1598/18 test box. – Disconnect 4-pin connector from MAF sensor – Measure resistance between connector terminal 1 and test box socket 1. Specification: max. 1.5 Ω – Bridge connector terminals 1 and 2, measure resistance between test box sockets 1 and 16. Specification: max. 1.5 Ω – Bridge connector terminals 1 and 4, measure resistance between test box sockets 1 and 17. Specification: max. 1.5 Ω – Do not bridge connector terminals, measure resistance between test box sockets 16 and 17. Specification: ∞ Ω If the specifications are not attained: – Use wiring diagram to locate and repair wiring open or short circuits to one another.
Malfunction cause for P0103 found: No ▼	Yes ▶	– After repairing malfunction, disconnect connector from ECM -J220- for 10 seconds, then clear DTC memory and create readiness code
		If resistance specifications are attained:
Malfunction cause for P0103	▶	– MAF sensor faulty, replace. Disconnect connector from ECM -J220- for 10 seconds, then clear DTC memory and create readiness code

VW0159600022000X

Fig. 205 Code P0103: Mass Or Volume Air Flow Circuit High Input. 1998 GTI & Jetta w/2.8L Engine

Cause:	Remedy:
Engine Control Module (ECM) detects short circuit in wiring or in Intake Air Temperature (IAT) sensor -G72-	– Switch ignition off – Connect VAG 1598/18 test box – Measure sensor resistance value corresponding to ambient temperature between sockets 33 and 36, value must be within specified range If the resistance value is not attained: – Disconnect connector from intake air temperature sensor -G72- – Measure resistance between connector terminal 1 and test box socket 36. Specification: max.1.5 Ω If measured value is: ∞ Ω wiring has open circuit: – Locate and repair using wiring diagram – Measure resistance between connector terminal 1 and test box socket 33. Specification: ∞ Ω If measured value is not ∞ Ω: wiring has short circuit to Ground (GND): – Locate and repair using wiring diagram

VW0159600023010X

Fig. 206 Code P0112: Intake Air Temperature Circuit Low Input (Part 1 of 2). 1998 GTI & Jetta w/2.8L Engine

Cause:	Remedy:
Engine Control Module (ECM) detects too high resistance and/or wiring open circuit to Intake Air Temperature (IAT) sensor -G72-	– Switch ignition off – Connect VAG 1598/18 test box – Measure sensor resistance value corresponding to ambient temperature between sockets 33 and 36, value must be within specified range If the resistance value is not attained: – Disconnect connector from intake air temperature sensor -G72- – Measure resistance between connector terminal 1 and test box socket 36. Specification: max.1.5 Ω If the measured value is ∞ Ω: wiring has open circuit – Locate and repair this malfunction using wiring diagram – Measure resistance between connector terminal 1 and test box socket 33. Specification: ∞ Ω If the measured value is not ∞ Ω: wiring has short circuit to Ground (GND) – Locate and repair this malfunction using wiring diagram.

VW0159600024010X

Fig. 207 Code P0113: Intake Air Temperature Circuit High Input (Part 1 of 2). 1998 GTI & Jetta w/2.8L Engine

Cause:	Remedy:
Engine Control Module (ECM) detects short circuit in wiring or in Engine Coolant Temperature (ECT) sensor -G62-	– Switch ignition off – Connect VAG 1598/18 test box – Measure engine coolant temperature sensor -G62- resistance corresponding to actual coolant temperature between sockets 14 and 33 If the specification is not attained: – Measure resistance between connector terminal 1 and test box socket 14. Specification: max.1.5 Ω If the measured value is ∞ Ω: wiring has open circuit – Locate and repair this malfunction using wiring diagram – Measure resistance between connector terminal 1 and test box socket 33. Specification: ∞ Ω If the measured value is not ∞ Ω: wiring has short circuit to Ground (GND) – Locate and repair this malfunction using wiring diagram.

VW0159600025010X

Fig. 208 Code P0117: Engine Coolant Temperature Circuit Low Input (Part 1 of 2). 1998 GTI & Jetta w/2.8L Engine

Cause:	Remedy:
Engine Control Module (ECM) detects too high resistance and/or wiring open circuit to Engine Coolant Temperature (ECT) sensor -G62-	– Switch ignition off – Check connector on engine coolant temperature sensor -G62- for loose connection – Connect VAG 1598/18 test box – Measure engine coolant temperature sensor -G62- resistance value corresponding to actual coolant temperature between sockets 14 and 33 If the resistance value is not attained: – Check whether coolant has caused resistance in connector to sensor – Measure resistance between connector terminal 1 and test box socket 14. Specification: max.1.5 Ω If the measured value is not ∞ Ω: the wire has open circuit – Locate and repair this malfunction using wiring diagram – Measure resistance between connector terminal 1 and test box socket 33. Specification: ∞ Ω If the measured value is not ∞ Ω: the wire has short circuit to Ground (GND) – Locate and repair this malfunction using wiring diagram

VW0159600026010X

Fig. 209 Code P0118: Engine Coolant Temperature Circuit High Input (Part 1 of 2). GTI & Jetta w/2.8L Engine

		If the specifications are attained, check intake air temperature sensor as follows: – Remove intake air temperature sensor and connect multimeter (Fluke 83 or equivalent) to terminals 1 and 2 of sensor connector – Spray sensor with a commercial chilling spray • Measure sensor resistance between terminals 1 and 2, value must increase without interruption. When sensor is heated (e.g. with hot air blower VAG 1416) resistance must drop back again. If the sensor does not react correctly to temperature changes, it must be replaced.
Malfunction cause for P0112 found: No ▼	Yes ▶	– After repairing malfunction, disconnect connector from ECM -J220- for 10 seconds, then clear DTC memory and create readiness code
		If the temperature changes were correctly recognized by intake air temperature sensor -G72-:
Malfunction cause for P0112	▶	– ECM -J220- faulty, replace. Then clear DTC memory and create readiness code.

VW0159600023020X

Fig. 206 Code P0112: Intake Air Temperature Circuit Low Input (Part 2 of 2). 1998 GTI & Jetta w/2.8L Engine

		If the specifications are not attained, check intake air temperature sensor -G72- as follows: – Remove intake air temperature sensor and connect multimeter (Fluke 83 or equivalent) to terminals 1 and 2 of sensor – Spray sensor with commercial chilling spray • Measure sensor resistance between terminals 1 and 2, value must increase without interruption. When sensor is heated (e.g. with hot air blower VAG 1416) value must drop back again. If the sensor does not react to the temperature changes, it should be replaced.
Malfunction cause for P0113 found: No ▼	Yes ▶	– After repairing malfunction disconnect connector from ECM -J220- for 10 seconds, then clear DTC memory and create readiness code
		If the temperature changes were correctly recognized by intake air temperature sensor -G72-:
Malfunction cause for P0113	▶	– ECM -J220- faulty, replace. Then clear DTC memory and create readiness code

VW0159600024020X

Fig. 207 Code P0113: Intake Air Temperature Circuit High Input (Part 2 of 2). 1998 GTI & Jetta w/2.8L Engine

		If the specifications are attained, check engine coolant temperature sensor -G62- as follows: – Release pressure from cooling system, remove engine coolant temperature sensor -G62- and seal opening – Connect multimeter (Fluke 83 or equivalent) to terminals 1 and 2 of sensor – Spray sensor with commercial chilling spray • Measure sensor resistance between terminals 1 and 2, value must increase without interruption. When sensor is heated (e.g. with hot air blower VAG 1416) value must drop back again. If the sensor does not react to the temperature changes, it must be replaced
Malfunction cause for P0117 found: No ▼	Yes ▶	– After repairing malfunction, clear DTC memory and create readiness code
		If the temperature changes are correctly recognized by engine coolant temperature sensor -G62-:
Malfunction cause for P0117	▶	– ECM -J220- faulty, replace. Clear DTC memory and create readiness code.

VW0159600025020X

Fig. 208 Code P0117: Engine Coolant Temperature Circuit Low Input (Part 2 of 2). 1998 GTI & Jetta w/2.8L Engine

		If the specifications are attained, check engine coolant temperature sensor -G62- as follows: – Release pressure from cooling system, remove engine coolant temperature sensor -G62- and seal. – Connect multimeter (Fluke 83 or equivalent) to terminals 1 and 2 of sensor – Spray sensor with commercial chilling spray • Measure sensor resistance between terminals 1 and 2, resistance must distinctly increase without interruption. When sensor is heated (e.g. with hot air blower VAG 1416) resistance value must drop back again. If the sensor does not react to the temperature changes, it should be replaced.
Malfunction cause for P0118 found: No ▼	Yes ▶	– After repairing malfunction, clear DTC memory and create readiness code
		If the temperature changes are correctly recognized by Engine Coolant Temperature (ECT) sensor -G62-:
Malfunction cause for P0118	▶	– ECM -J220- faulty, replace. Clear DTC memory and create readiness code

VW0159600026020X

Fig. 209 Code P0118: Engine Coolant Temperature Circuit High Input (Part 2 of 2). 1998 GTI & Jetta w/2.8L Engine

Cause:	Remedy:
Throttle Position (TP) sensor supplies implausible signal to Engine Control Module (ECM)	- Switch ignition off - Check throttle valve control module -J338- voltage supply at 8-pin connector: (terminal assignment) - Disconnect 8-pin connector from throttle valve control module - Switch ignition on - Check voltage between connector terminals 4 and 7. Specification: approx. 5 volts - Check voltage between connector terminals 3 and 7. Specification: approx. 10 volts If the specifications are not attained: - Switch ignition off - Connect VAG 1598/18 test box and check resistance as follows: - Connector terminal 3 and test box socket 10 - Connector terminal 4 and test box socket 41 - Connector terminal 7 and test box socket 33 Specifications: max.1.5 Ω If the specifications are not attained: - Use wiring diagram to locate and repair open circuit If no open circuit is detected: - Replace ECM -J220-

VW0159600027010X

Fig. 210 Code P0120: Throttle Position Sensor A Circuit Malfunction (Part 1 of 6). 1998 GTI & Jetta w/2.8L Engine

		If the specifications are attained: - Also measure resistance (with 8-pin connector disconnected) between test box sockets 10, 27, 33, 40, 41, 53 and 62. Specification: ∞ Ω If the specifications are not ∞ Ω: - Use wiring diagram to locate and repair short circuit between wires If the specifications with wide open/closed throttle are not attained, but the wiring is OK: - Replace throttle valve control module -J338-
Malfunction cause for P0120 found: No ▼	Yes ▶	- After repairing malfunction, disconnect connector from ECM -J220- for 10 seconds, then clear DTC memory and create readiness code
		If no malfunction can be found in the throttle valve control module:

VW0159600027030X

Fig. 210 Code P0120: Throttle Position Sensor A Circuit Malfunction (Part 3 of 6). 1998 GTI & Jetta w/2.8L Engine

Cause:	Remedy:
Engine Control Module (ECM) cannot use engine coolant temperature signal	- Switch ignition off - Check connector on Engine Coolant Temperature (ECT) sensor -G62- for loose connection - Connect VAG 1598/18 test box - Correct sensor resistance corresponding to actual coolant temperature must be measured between sockets 14 and 33 If the resistance value is not attained: - Check whether coolant has caused resistance in connector to sensor - Measure resistance between connector terminal 1 and test box socket 14. Specification: max.1.5 Ω If the measured value is ∞ Ω: the wiring has an open circuit - This should be located and repaired using wiring diagram - Measure resistance between connector terminal 1 and test box 33. Specification: ∞ Ω If the measured value is not ∞ Ω: - Use wiring diagram to locate and repair a short circuit to Ground (GND) in wiring

VW0159600027050X

Fig. 210 Code P0120: Throttle Position Sensor A Circuit Malfunction (Part 5 of 6). 1998 GTI & Jetta w/2.8L Engine

Cause:		Remedy:
Throttle Position (TP) sensor supplies implausible signal to Engine Control Module (ECM)		- Switch ignition off - Check throttle valve control module -J338- voltage supply at 8-pin connector: (terminal assignment) - Disconnect 8-pin connector from throttle valve control module - Switch ignition on Check voltage as follows: - Between connector terminals 4 and 7. Specification: approx. 5 volts - Between connector terminals 3 and 7. Specification: approx. 10 volts If the specifications are not attained: - Switch ignition off - Connect VAG 1598/18 test box Check resistance as follows: - Connector terminal 3 and test box socket 10 - Connector terminal 4 and test box socket 41 - Connector terminal 7 and test box socket 33 Specifications: max.1.5 Ω
		If the specifications are not attained: - Use wiring diagram to locate and repair open circuit If no open circuit is detected: - Replace ECM -J220-
Malfunction cause for P0121 found: No ▼	Yes ▶	- After repairing malfunction, disconnect connector from ECM -J220- for 10 seconds, then clear DTC memory and create readiness code

VW0159600028010X

Fig. 211 Code P0121: Throttle Position Sensor A Circuit Range/Performance Problem (Part 1 of 4). 1998 GTI & Jetta w/2.8L Engine

	If the voltage supply specifications are attained: - Switch ignition off - Re-connect 8-pin connector to throttle valve control module - Connect VAG 1598/18 test box Check resistance as follows: - At wide open throttle position between test box sockets 10 and 33. Specification: ∞ Ω - At closed throttle position between test box sockets 10 and 33. Specification: max.10 Ω - At closed throttle position between test box sockets 27 and 53. Specification: 3 – 200 Ω If the specifications are not attained: - Disconnect 8-pin connector from throttle valve control module Check resistance as follows: - Connector terminal 1 and test box socket 27 - Connector terminal 2 and test box socket 53 - Connector terminal 5 and test box socket 40 - Connector terminal 8 and test box socket 62, Specifications: max.1.5 Ω If the resistances do not correspond to specifications: - Use wiring diagram to locate and repair open circuit

VW0159600027020X

Fig. 210 Code P0120: Throttle Position Sensor A Circuit Malfunction (Part 2 of 6). 1998 GTI & Jetta w/2.8L Engine

Cause:		Remedy:
Mass Air Flow (MAF) sensor signal does not agree with Throttle Position (TP) sensor signal		- Switch ignition off - Connect VAG 1598/18 test box - Disconnect 4-pin connector from MAF sensor - Measure resistance between connector terminal 1 and test box socket 1. Specification: max. 1.5 Ω - Bridge connector terminals 1 and 2, measure resistance between test box sockets 1 and 16. Specification: max. 1.5 Ω - Bridge connector terminals 1 and 4, measure resistance between test box sockets 1 and 17. Specification: max. 1.5 Ω - Do not bridge connector terminals. Measure resistance between test box sockets 16 and 17. Specification: ∞ Ω If the specifications are not attained: - Use wiring diagram to locate and repair short circuit between wiring or open circuit
Malfunction cause for P0120 found: No ▼	Yes ▶	- After repairing malfunction, clear DTC memory and create readiness code

VW0159600027040X

Fig. 210 Code P0120: Throttle Position Sensor A Circuit Malfunction (Part 4 of 6). 1998 GTI & Jetta w/2.8L Engine

		If the specifications are attained, check engine coolant temperature sensor -G62- as follows: - Release pressure from cooling system, remove engine coolant temperature sensor -G62- and seal. - Connect multimeter (Fluke 83 or equivalent) to terminals 1 and 2 of sensor - Spray sensor with commercial chilling spray • Measure sensor resistance between terminals 1 and 2, resistance must distinctly increase without interruption. When sensor is heated (e.g. with hot air blower VAG 1416) resistance value must drop back again. If the sensor does not react to the temperature changes, it should be replaced.
Malfunction cause for P0120 found: No ▼	Yes ▶	- After repairing malfunction, clear DTC memory and create readiness code
Malfunction cause for P0120	▶	If the temperature changes are correctly recognized by engine coolant temperature sensor -G62-: - ECM -J220- faulty, replace. Clear DTC memory and create readiness code

VW0159600027060X

Fig. 210 Code P0120: Throttle Position Sensor A Circuit Malfunction (Part 6 of 6). 1998 GTI & Jetta w/2.8L Engine

	If the voltage supply specifications are attained: - Switch ignition off - Connect 8-pin connector to throttle valve control module - Connect VAG 1598/18 test box - At wide open throttle position, check resistance between test box sockets 10 and 33. Specification ∞ Ω - At closed throttle position, check resistance between test box sockets 10 and 33. Specification max.10 Ω - At closed throttle position, check resistance between test box sockets 27 and 53. Specification 3 – 200 Ω If the specifications are not attained: - Disconnect 8-pin connector and check resistances as follows: - Connector terminal 1 and test box socket 27 - Connector terminal 2 and test box socket 53 - Connector terminal 5 and test box socket 40 - Connector terminal 8 and test box socket 62 Specifications: max.1.5 Ω If the resistance does not correspond to specifications: - Use wiring diagram to locate and repair open circuit

VW0159600028020X

Fig. 211 Code P0121: Throttle Position Sensor A Circuit Range/Performance Problem (Part 2 of 4). 1998 GTI & Jetta w/2.8L Engine

		If the specifications are attained: – Also measure resistance (with 8-pin connector disconnected) between test box sockets 10, 27, 33, 40, 41, 53 and 62. Specification: ∞ Ω If the specifications are not attained: – Use wiring diagram to locate and repair short circuit between wires If the specifications with open/closed throttle are not attained, but the wiring is OK: – Replace throttle valve control module -J338-
Malfunction cause for P0121 found: No ▼	Yes ▶	– After repairing malfunction, disconnect connector from ECM -J220- for 10 seconds, then clear DTC memory and create readiness code
		If no malfunction can be found in the throttle valve control module:

VW0159600028030X

Fig. 211 Code P0121: Throttle Position Sensor A Circuit Range/Performance Problem (Part 3 of 4). 1998 GTI & Jetta w/2.8L Engine

Cause:		Remedy:
Throttle Position (TP) sensor supplies implausible signal to Engine Control Module (ECM)		– Check throttle valve control module -J338- voltage supply at 8-pin connector: (terminal assignment) – Disconnect 8-pin connector from throttle valve control module – Switch ignition on Check voltage as follows: – Between connector terminals 4 and 7. Specification: approx. 5 volts – Between connector terminals 3 and 7. Specification: approx. 10 volts If the specifications are not attained: – Switch ignition off – Connect VAG 1598/18 test box Check resistance as follows: – Connector terminal 3 and test box socket 10 – Connector terminal 4 and test box socket 41 – Connector terminal 7 and test box socket 33 Specifications: max.1.5 Ω If the specifications are not attained: – Use wiring diagram to locate and repair open circuit If no open circuit is found: – Replace ECM -J220-
Malfunction cause for P0122 found: No ▼	Yes ▶	– After repairing malfunction, disconnect connector from ECM -J220- for 10 seconds, then clear DTC memory and create readiness code

VW0159600029010X

Fig. 212 Code P0122: Throttle Position A Circuit Low Input (Part 1 of 6). 1998 GTI & Jetta w/2.8L Engine

		If the specifications are not ∞ Ω: – Use wiring diagram to locate and repair short circuit between wires If the specifications with throttle open/closed are not attained, but the wiring is OK: – Replace throttle valve control module -J338-
Malfunction cause for P0122 found: No ▼	Yes ▶	– After repairing malfunction, disconnect connector from ECM -J220- for 10 seconds, then clear DTC memory and create readiness code
		If no malfunction can be found in the throttle valve control module:

VW0159600029030X

Fig. 212 Code P0122: Throttle Position A Circuit Low Input (Part 3 of 6). 1998 GTI & Jetta w/2.8L Engine

Cause:	Remedy:
Engine Control Module (ECM) cannot use engine coolant temperature signal	– Switch ignition off – Connect VAG 1598/18 test box – Measure sensor resistance value corresponding to the actual coolant temperature between sockets14 and 33 If the resistance value is not attained:. – Check connector on Engine Coolant Temperature (ECT) sensor -G62- for loose connection – Check whether coolant has caused resistance in sensor connector – Measure resistance between connector terminal 1 and test box socket 14. Specification: max.1.5 Ω If the measured resistance value is ∞ Ω: the wire has open circuit – This should be located and repaired using wiring diagram – Measure resistance between connector terminal 1 and test box socket 33. Specification: ∞ Ω If the measured resistance value is not ∞ Ω: – Use wiring diagram to locate and repair a short circuit to Ground (GND)

VW0159600029050X

Fig. 212 Code P0122: Throttle Position A Circuit Low Input (Part 5 of 6). 1998 GTI & Jetta w/2.8L Engine

Cause:		Remedy:
Mass Air Flow (MAF) sensor signal does not agree with Throttle Position (TP) sensor signal		– Switch ignition off – Connect test box 1598/18 – Disconnect 4-pin connector from MAF sensor – Measure resistance between connector terminal 1 and test box socket 1. Specification: max. 1.5 Ω – Bridge connector terminals 1 and 2, measure resistance between test box sockets 1 and 16. Specification: max. 1.5 Ω – Bridge connector terminals 1 and 4, measure resistance between test box sockets 1 and 17. Specification: max. 1.5 Ω – Do not bridge connector terminals. Measure resistance between test box sockets 16 and 17. Specification: ∞ Ω If the specifications are not attained: – Use wiring diagram to locate and repair short circuit between wires
Malfunction cause for P0121 found: No ▼	Yes ▶	– After repairing malfunction, disconnect connector from ECM -J220- for 10 seconds, then clear DTC memory and create readiness code
Malfunction cause for P0121	▶	– ECM -J220- faulty, replace. Clear DTC memory and create readiness code

VW0159600028040X

Fig. 211 Code P0121: Throttle Position Sensor A Circuit Range/Performance Problem (Part 4 of 4). 1998 GTI & Jetta w/2.8L Engine

	If the voltage supply specifications are attained: – Switch ignition off – Attach 8-pin connector – Connect VAG 1598/18 test box – At wide open throttle position, check resistance between test box sockets 10 and 33. Specification: ∞ Ω – At closed throttle position, check resistance between test box sockets 10 and 33. Specification: max.10 Ω – At closed throttle position, check resistance between test box sockets 27 and 53. Specification: 3 – 200 Ω
	If the specifications are not attained: – Disconnect 8-pin connector. Check resistances as follows: – Connector terminal 1 and test box socket 27 – Connector terminal 2 and test box socket 53 – Connector terminal 5 and test box socket 40 – Connector terminal 8 and test box socket 62 Specifications: max.1.5 Ω If the resistance does not correspond to specifications: – Use wiring diagram to locate and repair open circuit If the specifications are attained with 8-pin connector disconnected: – Measure resistance between test box sockets 10, 27, 33, 40, 41, 53 and 62. Specification: ∞ Ω

VW0159600029020X

Fig. 212 Code P0122: Throttle Position A Circuit Low Input (Part 2 of 6). 1998 GTI & Jetta w/2.8L Engine

Cause:		Remedy:
Mass Air Flow (MAF) sensor signal does not agree with Throttle Position (TP) sensor signal		– Switch ignition off – Connect VAG 1598/18 test box – Disconnect 4-pin connector from MAF sensor – Measure resistance between connector terminal 1 and test box socket 1. Specification: max. 1.5 Ω – Bridge connector terminals 1 and 2, measure resistance between test box sockets 1 and 16. Specification: max. 1.5 Ω – Bridge connector terminals 1 and 4, measure resistance between test box sockets 1 and 17. Specification: max. 1.5 Ω – Do not bridge connector terminals, measure resistance between test box sockets 16 and 17. Specification: ∞ Ω If the specifications are not attained: – Use wiring diagram to locate and repair short circuit between wiring or open circuit
Malfunction cause for P0122 found: No ▼	Yes ▶	– After repairing malfunction, clear DTC memory and create readiness code

VW0159600029040X

Fig. 212 Code P0122: Throttle Position A Circuit Low Input (Part 4 of 6). 1998 GTI & Jetta w/2.8L Engine

		If the specifications are attained, check engine coolant temperature sensor -G62- as follows: – Release pressure from cooling system, remove engine coolant temperature sensor -G62- and seal – Connect multimeter (Fluke 83 or equivalent) to terminals 1 and 2 of sensor – Spray sensor with commercial chilling spray • Measure sensor resistance between terminals 1 and 2, resistance must distinctly increase without interruption. When sensor is heated (e.g. with hot air blower VAG 1416) resistance value must drop back again. If the sensor does not react to the temperature changes, it should be replaced
Malfunction cause for P0122 found: No ▼	Yes ▶	– After repairing malfunction, clear DTC memory and create readiness code
		If the temperature changes are correctly recognized by engine coolant temperature sensor -G62-:
Malfunction cause for P0122	▶	– ECM -J220- faulty, replace. Clear DTC memory and create readiness code

VW0159600029060X

Fig. 212 Code P0122: Throttle Position A Circuit Low Input (Part 6 of 6). 1998 GTI & Jetta w/2.8L Engine

Cause:	Remedy:
Engine Control Module (ECM) cannot use engine coolant temperature signal for Oxygen Sensor (O2S) control, or the time taken for engine to reach normal operating temperature is too long	– Switch ignition off – Check connector on Engine Coolant Temperature (ECT) sensor -G62- for loose connection – Connect VAG 1598/18 test box – Measure sensor resistance value corresponding to the actual coolant temperature between sockets 14 and 33 If the specification is not attained: – Check whether coolant has caused resistance in connector to sensor – Measure resistance between connector terminal 1 and test box socket 14. Specification: max.1.5 Ω If the measured value is ∞ Ω: the wire has open circuit – This should be located and repaired using wiring diagram – Measure resistance between connector terminal 1 and test box socket 33. Specification: ∞ Ω If the measured value is not ∞ Ω: the wire has short circuit to Ground (GND) – This should be located and repaired using wiring diagram

VW0159600030010X

Fig. 213 Code P0125: Insufficient Coolant Temperature For Closed Loop Fuel Control (Part 1 of 2). 1998 GTI & Jetta w/2.8L Engine

Cause:		Remedy:
Heated Oxygen Sensor (HO2S) -G39- (before three way catalytic converter) has short circuit to Ground (GND) for longer than 200 secs		– Disconnect HO2S connector (black connector), terminal assignment – Connect multimeter (Fluke 83 or equivalent) between terminals 3 and 4 of HO2S connector – With engine at normal working temperature run at idle. • The multimeter must indicate a voltage between 0.2 – 0.8 volts – Increase engine speed by revving-up several times • The multimeter must indicate voltage jumps from 0.2 volts (lean mixture) to 0.9 volts (rich mixture) If no voltage jumps are indicated: – Replace HO2S -G39- (before three way catalytic converter)
Malfunction cause for P0131 found: No ▼	Yes ▶	– After repairing malfunction, disconnect connector from Engine Control Module (ECM) -J220- for 10 seconds, then clear DTC memory and create readiness code

VW0159600031010X

Fig. 214 Code P0131: Oxygen Sensor Circuit Low Voltage Bank 1 Sensor 1 (Part 1 of 3). 1998 GTI & Jetta w/2.8L Engine

		If the specifications are attained and no malfunction can be found in the wiring: – Disconnect HO2S connector (black connector), terminal assignment – Switch ignition on – Measure basic voltage from ECM to HO2S connector between terminals 3 and 4. Specification: 0.45 volts If the specification 0.45 volts is not attained: – Switch ignition off
Malfunction cause for P0131	▶	– ECM -J220- faulty, replace. Clear DTC memory and create readiness code

VW0159600031030X

Fig. 214 Code P0131: Oxygen Sensor Circuit Low Voltage Bank 1 Sensor 1 (Part 3 of 3). 1998 GTI & Jetta w/2.8L Engine

		If all wiring to HO2S is free of malfunction: – Measure resistance at disconnected HO2S connector between terminals 1 and 3 and 1 and 4. Specification: ∞ Ω If the specifications are not attained, the HO2S has a short circuit to positive – Replace HO2S (before three way catalytic converter)
Malfunction cause for P0132 found: No ▼	Yes ▶	– After repairing malfunction disconnect connector from Engine Control Module (ECM) -J220- for 10 seconds, then clear DTC memory and create readiness code.
Malfunction cause for P0132	▶	If the specifications are attained: – ECM -J220- faulty, replace. Clear DTC memory and create readiness code

VW0159600032020X

Fig. 215 Code P0132: Oxygen Sensor Circuit High Voltage Bank 1 Sensor 1 (Part 2 of 2). 1998 GTI & Jetta w/2.8L Engine

Cause:	Remedy:
Heated Oxygen Sensor (HO2S) -G39- (before three way catalytic converter) is dirty, aged or contaminated	• Before performing any test or starting this malfunction repair, heat up HO2S to operating temperature (self-cleaning effect). To do this run engine at approx. 3500 RPM for at least 3 minutes, with vehicle stationary – Connect generic Scan Tool (ST), set to scan tool function address word 33 and clear DTC memory – Road test vehicle ♦ If the MIL is not switched on after the test drive, and no malfunction is stored in DTC memory, the HO2S was dirty. ♦ If the MIL is switched on after the test drive: – Switch ignition off – Connect VAG 1598/18 test box – Disconnect HO2S connector (black connector) terminal assignment – Switch ignition on – Bridge test box sockets 1 and 6 – Measure voltage between connector terminal 1 and Ground (GND). Specification: min.11.5 volts

VW0159600033010X

Fig. 216 Code P0133: Oxygen Sensor Circuit Slow Response Bank 1 Sensor 1 (Part 1 of 3). 1998 GTI & Jetta w/2.8L Engine

		If the specifications are attained, check engine coolant temperature sensor -G62- as follows: – Release pressure from cooling system, remove engine coolant temperature sensor -G62- and seal – Connect multimeter (Fluke 83 or equivalent) to terminals 1 and 2 of sensor – Spray sensor with commercial chilling spray • Measure sensor resistance between terminals 1 and 2, resistance must distinctly increase without interruption. When sensor is heated (e.g. with hot air blower VAG 1416) resistance value must drop back again. If the sensor does not react to the temperature changes, it should be replaced.
Malfunction cause for P0125 found: No ▼	Yes ▶	– After repairing malfunction, clear DTC memory and create readiness code
Malfunction cause for P0125	▶	If the temperature changes are correctly recognized by engine coolant temperature sensor -G62-: – Thermostat faulty, replace. Clear DTC memory and create readiness code

VW0159600030020X

Fig. 213 Code P0125: Insufficient Coolant Temperature For Closed Loop Fuel Control (Part 2 of 2). 1998 GTI & Jetta w/2.8L Engine

		If the HO2S produces voltage jumps: – Switch ignition off – Connect VAG 1598/18 test box – Measure resistance between connector terminal 3 and test box socket 42. Specification: max. 1.5 Ω – Measure resistance between connector terminal 4 and test box socket 20. Specification: max. 1.5 Ω – Measure resistance between connector terminal 3 and test box socket 56. Specification: ∞ Ω – Measure resistance between connector terminal 4 and test box socket 56. Specification: ∞ Ω If these specifications are not attained: the wiring has an open circuit or a short circuit to Ground (GND) – This should be located and repaired using wiring diagram.
Malfunction cause for P0131 found: No ▼	Yes ▶	– After repairing malfunction, clear DTC memory and create readiness code

VW0159600031020X

Fig. 214 Code P0131: Oxygen Sensor Circuit Low Voltage Bank 1 Sensor 1 (Part 2 of 3). 1998 GTI & Jetta w/2.8L Engine

Cause:		Remedy:
Heated Oxygen Sensor (HO2S) -G39- (before three way catalytic converter) or wiring to HO2S has short circuit to positive		– Disconnect connector to HO2S (black connector), terminal assignment – Switch ignition on – Measure basic voltage from Engine Control Module (ECM) to HO2S connector between terminals 3 and 4. Specification: 0.45 volts If the specification is exceeded: – Switch ignition off – Connect VAG 1598/18 test box – Remove fuse 18 – Measure resistance between upper terminal for fuse 18 and test box socket 20. Specification ∞ Ω – Measure resistance between upper terminal for fuse 18 and test box socket 42. Specification: ∞ Ω If the specification is not attained, the wiring has a short circuit to positive: – This should be located and repaired using wiring diagram
Malfunction cause for P0132 found: No ▼	Yes ▶	– After repairing malfunction, clear DTC memory and create readiness code

VW0159600032010X

Fig. 215 Code P0132: Oxygen Sensor Circuit High Voltage Bank 1 Sensor 1 (Part 1 of 2). 1998 GTI & Jetta w/2.8L Engine

		If the specification of min. 11.5 volts is not attained: – Switch ignition off – Remove fuse 18 – Measure resistance between upper terminal for fuse 18 and connector terminal 1. Specification: max. 1.5 Ω – Measure resistance between connector terminal 2 and test box socket 12. Specification: max. 1.5 Ω If the specification is not attained: – Use wiring diagram to locate and repair open circuit If the specification of min. 11.5 volts is attained: – Check heating element resistance in HO2S at connector terminals 1 and 2. Specification at approx. 20°C (68°F) ambient temperature: max. 20 Ω If the specification of 20 Ω is not attained: – Oxygen Sensor (O2S) heating open circuit, replace HO2S (before three way catalytic converter)
Malfunction cause for P0133 found: No ▼	Yes ▶	– After repairing malfunction, disconnect connector from Engine Control Module (ECM) -J220- for 10 seconds, then clear DTC memory and create readiness code.

VW0159600033020X

Fig. 216 Code P0133: Oxygen Sensor Circuit Slow Response Bank 1 Sensor 1 (Part 2 of 3). 1998 GTI & Jetta w/2.8L Engine

		If the O2S heating is malfunction free: – Connect generic Scan Tool (ST), and set to scan tool function address word 33 – Check HO2S signal output via mode 5 – Select test ID 9 and check minimum voltage If the HO2S actual value exceeds or falls short of the min./max. value: – Replace HO2S (before three way catalytic converter)
Malfunction cause for P0133	▶	– HO2S (before three way catalytic converter) faulty, replace. After repairing malfunction, disconnect connector from ECM -J220- for 10 seconds, then clear DTC memory and create readiness code

VW0159600033030X

Fig. 216 Code P0133: Oxygen Sensor Circuit Slow Response Bank 1 Sensor 1 (Part 3 of 3). 1998 GTI & Jetta w/2.8L Engine

		If the HO2S produces voltage jumps: – Switch ignition off. – Disconnect HO2S connector (black connector) terminal assignment – Connect VAG 1598/18 test box – Measure resistance between connector terminal 3 and test box socket 42. Specification max. 1.5 Ω – Measure resistance between connector terminal 4 and test box socket 20. Specification max. 1.5 Ω – Measure resistance between connector terminal 3 and test box socket 56. Specification: ∞ Ω – Measure resistance between connector terminal 4 and test box socket 56. Specification: ∞ Ω If these specifications are not attained: the wiring has an open circuit or a short circuit to Ground (GND) – This should be located and repaired using wiring diagram
Malfunction cause for P0134 found: No ▼	Yes ▶	– After repairing malfunction, clear DTC memory and create readiness code
Malfunction cause for P0134	▶	If all wiring to HO2S is malfunction free: – HO2S (before three way catalytic converter) faulty, replace. After repairing malfunction, disconnect connector from ECM -J220- for 10 seconds, then clear DTC memory and create readiness code

VW0159600034020X

Fig. 217 Code P0134: Oxygen Sensor Circuit No Activity Detected Bank 1 Sensor 1 (Part 2 of 2). 1998 GTI & Jetta w/2.8L Engine

		If the specifications are attained: – Measure resistance between connector terminal 2 and test box socket 12. Specification: max. 1.5 Ω If the specification is not attained: – Use wiring diagram to locate and repair open circuit in wiring to ECM If the specification is attained: – Check heating element resistance in HO2S on connector terminals 1 and 2. Specification at approx., 20°C (68°F) ambient temperature: max. 20 Ω If the specification is not attained: – Replace HO2S
Malfunction cause for P0135 found: No ▼	Yes ▶	– After repairing malfunction, disconnect connector from ECM -J220- for 10 seconds, then clear DTC memory and create readiness code
Malfunction cause for P0135	▶	– ECM -J220- faulty, replace. Clear DTC memory and create readiness code.

VW0159600035020X

Fig. 218 Code P0135: Oxygen Sensor Heater Circuit Malfunction Bank 1 Sensor 1 (Part 2 of 2). 1998 GTI & Jetta w/2.8L Engine

		If these specifications are not attained: the wiring has an open circuit or a short circuit to Ground (GND) – This should be located and repaired using wiring diagram
Malfunction cause for P0137 found: No ▼	Yes ▶	– After repairing malfunction, clear DTC memory and create readiness code
Malfunction cause for P0137	▶	If the specifications are attained, the wiring is malfunction free, but 0.45 volts was not measured: – ECM -J220- faulty, replace. Clear DTC memory and create readiness code.

VW0159600036020X

Fig. 219 Code P0137: Oxygen Sensor Circuit Low Voltage Bank 1 Sensor 2 (Part 2 of 2). 1998 GTI & Jetta w/2.8L Engine

Cause:		Remedy:
Heated Oxygen Sensor (HO2S) (before three way catalytic converter) signal is not recognized by Engine Control Module (ECM)		– Switch ignition off – Disconnect HO2S connector (black connector), terminal assignment – Connect multimeter (Fluke 83 or equivalent) between terminals 3 and 4 of HO2S connector – With engine at normal operating temperature run at idle • The multimeter must indicate a voltage between 0.2 – 0.8 volts – Increase engine speed by revving up several times • The multimeter must indicate voltage jumps from 0.2 volts (lean mixture) to 0.9 volts (rich mixture) If no voltage jumps are indicated: – Replace HO2S (before three way catalytic converter)
Malfunction cause for P0134 found: No ▼	Yes ▶	– After repairing malfunction, disconnect connector from ECM -J220- for 10 seconds, then clear DTC memory and create readiness code.

VW0159600034010X

Fig. 217 Code P0134: Oxygen Sensor Circuit No Activity Detected Bank 1 Sensor 1 (Part 1 of 2). 1998 GTI & Jetta w/2.8L Engine

Cause:	Remedy:
Heating for Oxygen Sensors (O2S) not functioning	– Switch ignition off – Check Heated Oxygen Sensor (HO2S) connector (black connector) for damage or contamination – Connect VAG 1598/18 test box – Disconnect HO2S connector, terminal assignment – Switch ignition on – Bridge test box sockets 1 and 6 – Measure voltage between connector terminal 1 and Ground (GND). Specification: min.11.5 volts If the specification is not attained: – Switch ignition off – Remove fuse 18 – Check resistance between fuse 18 upper terminal and connector terminal 1. Specification max. 1.5 Ω If the specification is not attained: – Use wiring diagram to locate and repair open circuit

VW0159600035010X

Fig. 218 Code P0135: Oxygen Sensor Heater Circuit Malfunction Bank 1 Sensor 1 (Part 1 of 2). 1998 GTI & Jetta w/2.8L Engine

Cause:	Remedy:
Heated Oxygen Sensor (HO2S) 2 -G108- (after three way catalytic converter) has short circuit to Ground (GND) exceeding 200 seconds	– Check connectors to HO2S (before three way catalytic converter) and HO2S 2 (after three way catalytic converter) for damage or contamination, and repair if necessary – Disconnect HO2S 2 connector (brown connector), terminal assignment – Switch ignition on – Measure basic voltage from Engine Control Module (ECM) to HO2S 2 connector between terminals 3 and 4. Specification: 0.45 volts If the specification 0.45 volts is not attained: – Switch ignition off – Connect VAG 1598/18 test box – Measure resistance between connector terminal 3 and test box socket 58. Specification max. 1.5 Ω – Measure resistance between connector terminal 4 and test box socket 13. Specification max. 1.5 Ω – Measure resistance between connector terminal 3 and test box socket 56. Specification: ∞ Ω – Measure resistance between connector terminal 4 and test box socket 56. Specification: ∞ Ω

VW0159600036010X

Fig. 219 Code P0137: Oxygen Sensor Circuit Low Voltage Bank 1 Sensor 2 (Part 1 of 2). 1998 GTI & Jetta w/2.8L Engine

Cause:		Remedy:
Heated Oxygen Sensor (HO2S) 2 (after three way catalytic converter) or wiring to HO2S 2 has short circuit to positive		– Disconnect connector to HO2S 2 (brown connector), terminal assignment – Switch ignition on – Measure basic voltage from Engine Control Module (ECM) to HO2S 2 connector between terminals 3 and 4. Specification: 0.45 volts. If the specification is exceeded: – Switch ignition off – Connect VAG 1598/18 test box – Remove fuse 18 – Measure resistance between upper terminal for fuse 18 and test box socket 13. Specification ∞ Ω – Measure resistance between upper terminal for fuse 18 and test box socket 58. Specification ∞ Ω If the measured value is not ∞ Ω, the wiring has a short circuit to positive – This should be located and repaired using wiring diagram
Malfunction cause for P0138 found: No ▼	Yes ▶	– After repairing malfunction, clear DTC memory and create readiness code

VW0159600037010X

Fig. 220 Code P0138: Oxygen Sensor Circuit High Voltage Bank 1 Sensor 2 (Part 1 of 2). 1998 GTI & Jetta w/2.8L Engine

		If all wiring to HO2S 2 is malfunction free: – Measure resistance at disconnected HO2S 2 connector between terminals 1 and 3, and1 and 4. Specification: ∞ Ω If the measured values are not ∞ Ω, HO2S 2 has a short circuit to positive – Replace HO2S 2 (after three way catalytic converter)
Malfunction cause for P0138 found: No ▼	Yes ▶	– After repairing malfunction disconnect connector from ECM -J220- for 10 seconds, then clear DTC memory and create readiness code
Malfunction cause for P0138	▶	If the measured values are: ∞ Ω – ECM -J220- faulty, replace. Clear DTC memory and create readiness code

VW0159600037020X

Fig. 220 Code P0138: Oxygen Sensor Circuit High Voltage Bank 1 Sensor 2 (Part 2 of 2). 1998 GTI & Jetta w/2.8L Engine

		If these specifications are not attained: the wiring has an open circuit or a short circuit to Ground (GND) – This should be located and repaired using wiring diagram
Malfunction cause for P0140 found: No ▼	Yes ▶	– After repairing malfunction, clear DTC memory and create readiness code
Cause: Heating for Oxygen Sensors (O2S) not functioning		Remedy: – Switch ignition off – Connect VAG 1598/18 test box – Switch ignition on – Bridge test box sockets 1 and 6 – Measure voltage between connector terminal 1 and Ground (GND). Specification: min.11.5 volts If the specification is not attained: – Switch ignition off – Remove fuse 18 – Check resistance between fuse 18 upper terminal and connector terminal 1. Specification max.1.5 Ω If the specification is not attained: – Use wiring diagram to locate and repair open circuit If the specification is attained: – Check heating element resistance in HO2S on connector terminals 1 and 2. Specification at approx. 20°C (68°F) ambient temperature: max. 20 Ω If the specification is not attained: – Replace HO2S

VW0159600038020X

Fig. 221 Code P0140: Oxygen Sensor Circuit No Activity Detected Bank 1 Sensor 2 (Part 2 of 3). 1998 GTI & Jetta w/2.8L Engine

Cause:	Remedy:
Heating for Oxygen Sensors (O2S) not functioning	– Switch ignition off – Check HO2S 2 connector (after three way catalytic converter) for damage or contamination – Connect VAG 1598/18 test box – Disconnect HO2S 2 connector, terminal assignment – Switch ignition on – Bridge test box sockets 1 and 6 – Measure voltage between connector terminal 1 and Ground (GND). Specification: min.11.5 volts If the specification is not attained: – Switch ignition off – Remove fuse 18 – Check resistance between fuse 18 upper terminal and connector terminal 1. Specification max.1.5 Ω If the specification is not attained: – Use wiring diagram to locate and repair open circuit If the specifications are attained: – Measure resistance between connector terminal 2 and test box socket 66. Specification: max. 1.5 Ω

VW0159600039010X

Fig. 222 Code P0141: Oxygen Sensor Heater Circuit Malfunction Bank 1 Sensor 2 (Part 1 of 2). 1998 GTI & Jetta w/2.8L Engine

Cause:		Remedy:
The mixture is so weak that the Oxygen Sensor (O2S) control cannot enrich further		– Start engine and run at idle – Check whether the engine is pulling in unmetered (outside) air between Mass Air Flow (MAF) sensor -G70- and cylinder head – Spray all vacuum hoses, hose connections and gaskets between MAF sensor -G70- and cylinder head with leak detector spray If no leaks can be found: – For this malfunction repair always check the secondary air injection system combination valve as described in Diagnostic Trouble Code (DTC) P0411
Malfunction cause for P0171 found: No ▼	Yes ▶	– After repairing malfunction, clear DTC memory and create readiness code.

VW0159600040010X

Fig. 223 Code P0171: System Too Lean Bank 1 (Part 1 of 4). 1998 GTI & Jetta w/2.8L Engine

Cause:	Remedy:
Heated Oxygen Sensor (HO2S) 2 (after three way catalytic converter) is dirty, aged or contaminated	• Before performing any test or starting this malfunction repair, heat up oxygen sensors to operating temperature (self-cleaning effect). To do this run engine at approx. 3500 RPM for at least 3 minutes with vehicle stationary – Connect generic Scan Tool (ST), set to scan tool function address word 33 and clear DTC memory – Road test vehicle • If the MIL is not switched on after the test drive, and no malfunction is stored in DTC memory: HO2S was dirty • If the MIL is switched on again after the test drive, there is a malfunction in the Oxygen Sensor (O2S) control: – Switch ignition off – Connect VAG 1598/18 test box – Disconnect HO2S 2 connector (brown connector), terminal assignment – Measure resistance between connector terminal 3 and test box socket 58. Specification max. 1.5 Ω – Measure resistance between connector terminal 4 and test box socket 13. Specification max. 1.5 Ω

VW0159600038010X

Fig. 221 Code P0140: Oxygen Sensor Circuit No Activity Detected Bank 1 Sensor 2 (Part 1 of 3). 1998 GTI & Jetta w/2.8L Engine

Malfunction cause for P0140 found: No ▼	Yes ▶	– After repairing malfunction disconnect connector from Engine Control Module (ECM) -J220- for 10 second, then clear DTC memory and create readiness code
Malfunction cause for P0140	▶	If the specification is attained: – End stage in ECM faulty, replace ECM. Clear DTC memory and create readiness code

VW0159600038030X

Fig. 221 Code P0140: Oxygen Sensor Circuit No Activity Detected Bank 1 Sensor 2 (Part 3 of 3). 1998 GTI & Jetta w/2.8L Engine

		If the specification is not attained: – Use wiring diagram to locate and repair open circuit in wiring to Engine Control Module (ECM) If the specification is attained: – Check heating element resistance in HO2S on connector terminals 1 and 2. Specification at approx. 20°C (68°F) ambient temperature: max. 20 Ω If the specification is not attained: – Replace HO2S
Malfunction cause for P0141 found: No ▼	Yes ▶	– After repairing malfunction disconnect connector from ECM -J220- for 10 second, then clear DTC memory and create readiness code
Malfunction cause for P0141	▶	– End stage in ECM faulty, replace ECM. – Clear DTC memory and create readiness code.

VW0159600039020X

Fig. 222 Code P0141: Oxygen Sensor Heater Circuit Malfunction Bank 1 Sensor 2 (Part 2 of 2). 1998 GTI & Jetta w/2.8L Engine

Cause:		Remedy:
Signal from Mass Air Flow (MAF) sensor -G70- too low		– Switch ignition off – Connect VAG 1598/18 test box – Disconnect 4-pin connector from MAF sensor – Measure resistance between connector terminal 1 and test box socket 1. Specification: max. 1.5 Ω – Bridge connector terminals 1 and 2, measure resistance between test box sockets 1 and 16. Specification: max. 1.5 Ω – Bridge connector terminals 1 and 4, measure resistance between test box sockets 1 and 17. Specification: max. 1.5 Ω – Do not bridge connector terminals. Measure resistance between test box sockets 16 and 17. Specification: ∞ Ω If the specifications are not attained: – Use wiring diagram to locate and repair short circuit between wires or open circuit
Malfunction cause for P0171 found: No ▼	Yes ▶	– After repairing malfunction, clear DTC memory and create readiness code
		If the wiring to MAF sensor is free of malfunctions: – Disconnect VAG 1598/18 test box

VW0159600040020X

Fig. 223 Code P0171: System Too Lean Bank 1 (Part 2 of 4). 1998 GTI & Jetta w/2.8L Engine

Cause:		Remedy:
Fuel pressure too low, or quantity of fuel supplied insufficient		Check whether vehicle has performance problems. If performance problems only occur at full acceleration: – Replace fuel filter If engine output is impaired at lower throttle openings, or vehicle jerks at lower throttle openings: – Switch engine off – Cover test port on fuel rail with a rag and open – Connect VAG 1318 fuel injection pressure gauge with VAG 1318/1 pressure gauge adapter and VAG 1318/10 adapter – Start engine and run at idle – Measure fuel pressure. Specification: approx. 3.5 bar (51 psi) If the specification is not attained: – Check whether fuel supply line is restricted If the fuel supply line is not faulty: – Replace transfer Fuel Pump (FP) -G23-
Malfunction cause for P0171 found: No ▼	Yes ▶	– After repairing malfunction, clear DTC memory and create readiness code
		If the fuel supply line and the fuel pump are malfunction free:

VW0159600040030X

Fig. 223 Code P0171: System Too Lean Bank 1 (Part 3 of 4). 1998 GTI & Jetta w/2.8L Engine

Cause:		Remedy:
Fuel injector clogged by carbon build up and not opening fully.		– Remove intake manifold upper section and fuel injectors complete with fuel rail – Place a fuel resistant container under the fuel injectors, and turn engine at starter speed – Check whether all fuel injectors open proportionately – Check whether all fuel injectors produce uniform spray pattern If one or more fuel injectors are not functioning properly: – Replace fuel injector
Malfunction cause for P0171 found: No ▼	Yes ▶	– After repairing malfunction, clear DTC memory and create readiness code
		If the fuel injectors function correctly:
Malfunction cause for P0171	▶	– HO2S (before three way catalytic converter) faulty, replace. After repairing malfunction, disconnect connector from Engine Control Module (ECM) -J220- for 10 seconds, then clear DTC memory and create readiness code.

VW0159600040040X

Fig. 223 Code P0171: System Too Lean Bank 1 (Part 4 of 4). 1998 GTI & Jetta w/2.8L Engine

	– Measure resistance between connector terminal 3 and test box socket 42. Specification max. 1.5 Ω If the specification is not attained: wiring has open circuit – This should be located and repaired using wiring diagram – Measure resistance between connector terminal 4 and test box socket 20. Specification max. 1.5 Ω If the specification is not attained: wiring has open circuit – This should be located and repaired using wiring diagram
	If the measured values are OK:
Cause: Fuel pressure too high	Remedy: – Switch ignition off – Cover test port on fuel rail with a rag and open – Connect VAG 1318 fuel injection pressure gauge with VAG 1318/1 pressure gauge adapter and VAG 1318/10 adapter – Check vacuum hose to fuel pressure regulator for tight fit/damage If no malfunction is found: – Start engine and run at idle – Measure fuel pressure. Specification: approx. 3.5 bar (51 psi) – While engine is running, remove hose from pressure regulator. • Fuel pressure must increase to 4.0 bar (58 psi) If the specification of 4.0 bar (58 psi) is not attained: – Switch ignition off – Replace fuel pressure regulator
	If the pressure was too high before disconnecting hose: fuel return line is restricted or blocked.

VW0159600107020X

Fig. 224 Code P0172: System Too Rich Bank 1 (Part 2 of 3). 1998 GTI & Jetta w/2.8L Engine

Cause:		Remedy:
Engine Control Module (ECM) detects uneven engine running (misfiring)		• Before starting tests or removing components, make sure that fuel tank contains correct fuel (possibly Diesel fuel or contaminated by water or similar) If the fuel quality is OK: – Run engine at idle or slightly above idle, and check spark plug connectors/ignition wires for arcing to Ground (GND) If arcing is detected: – Switch ignition off – Replace appropriate spark plug connector with wire – Remove spark plugs and check condition. Also, check that plugs installed have correct heat range
Malfunction cause for P0300 found: No ▼	Yes ▶	– After repairing malfunction, clear DTC memory and create readiness code

VW0159600041010X

Fig. 225 Code P0300: Random Misfire Detected (Part 1 of 4). 1998 GTI & Jetta w/2.8L Engine

Cause:	Remedy:
Harness connector on ignition coil has electrical malfunction or loose connection	– Switch ignition off – Disconnect connector from ignition coil, terminal assignment – Switch ignition on – Measure voltage supply between connector terminals 1 and 5. Specification: min. 11.5 volts If the specification of min.11.5 volts is not attained: – Switch ignition off – Connect VAG 1598/18 test box – Measure resistance between connector terminal 1 and test box socket 1. Specification: max.1.5 Ω If the specification is not attained: – Use wiring diagram to locate and repair open circuit in Ground (GND) wire to ignition coil If the specification is attained: – Use wiring diagram to locate and repair open circuit in positive wire to ignition coil connector terminal 5 If min. 11.5 volts is attained, check remaining wiring: – Switch ignition off – Measure resistance between connector terminal 2 and test box socket 8. Specification: max.1.5 Ω – Measure resistance between connector terminal 3 and test box socket 60. Specification: max.1.5 Ω – Measure resistance between connector terminal 4 and test box socket 52. Specification: max.1.5 Ω

VW0159600041030X

Fig. 225 Code P0300: Random Misfire Detected (Part 3 of 4). 1998 GTI & Jetta w/2.8L Engine

Cause:		Remedy:
The mixture is so rich that Oxygen Sensor (O2S) control cannot weaken it further		– Check whether crankcase dilution has caused engine to run rich, if necessary change engine oil – Check whether the exhaust system is leaking between cylinder head and Three Way Catalytic Converter (TWC) If no leaks can be found: – Switch ignition off – Connect VAG 1598/18 test box – Measure resistance between test box sockets 20 and 42. Specification: ∞ Ω – Disconnect HO2S connector, terminal assignment – Check resistance between connector terminal 3 and test box socket 56. Specification: ∞ Ω – Check resistance between connector terminal 4 and test box socket 56. Specification: ∞ Ω If the measured values are not ∞ Ω, the wiring has a short circuit to cable shielding – This should be located and repaired using wiring diagram If the measured values are: ∞ Ω
Malfunction cause for P0172 found: No ▼	Yes ▶	– After repairing malfunction, clear DTC memory and create readiness code

VW0159600107010X

Fig. 224 Code P0172: System Too Rich Bank 1 (Part 1 of 3). 1998 GTI & Jetta w/2.8L Engine

Malfunction cause for P0172 found: No ▼	Yes ▶	– After repairing malfunction, clear DTC memory and create readiness code
Cause: Fuel injector is dirty and not closing (dripping)		Remedy: – Remove intake manifold upper section, and remove fuel injectors complete with fuel rail – Wipe off fuel injectors with a clean cloth – Use the fuel pressure still present in system for fuel injector leakage check If droplets form on fuel injector: – Replace leaking fuel injector.
		If the fuel injectors are not leaking:
Malfunction cause for P0172	▶	– Heated Oxygen Sensor (HO2S) (before three way catalytic converter) faulty, replace. After repairing malfunction disconnect connector from Engine Control Module (ECM) -J220- for 10 seconds, then clear DTC memory and create readiness code

VW0159600107030X

Fig. 224 Code P0172: System Too Rich Bank 1 (Part 3 of 3). 1998 GTI & Jetta w/2.8L Engine

Cause:		Remedy:
Engine speed (RPM) sensor -G28- supplies implausible signal.		– Check engine speed sensor -G28- for tightening torque (sensor loose or gap to sensor wheel too large causing malfunction) – Remove sensor and check for contamination by metal particles – Check sensor wheel on crankshaft for damage or contamination, to do this remove sensor and check through sensor mounting hole in engine block – Check connector for resistance due to contamination (loose connection on connector causes misfiring)
Malfunction cause for P0300 found: No ▼	Yes ▶	– After repairing malfunction, clear DTC memory and create readiness code

VW0159600041020X

Fig. 225 Code P0300: Random Misfire Detected (Part 2 of 4). 1998 GTI & Jetta w/2.8L Engine

		If the specifications are not attained: the wires have open circuit. – Use wiring diagram to locate and repair open circuit If the specifications are attained: – Check connector terminals 2 and 3 for short circuit to one another. Specification: ∞ Ω – Check connector terminals 3 and 4 for short circuit to one another. Specification: ∞ Ω • If the specifications are not attained: the wires have a short circuit to one another and must be replaced If the specifications are attained: – Replace ignition coil -N152-
Malfunction cause for P0300 found: No ▼	Yes ▶	– After repairing malfunction, clear DTC memory and create readiness code
		Malfunction also occurs with a new ignition coil:
Malfunction cause for P0300	▶	– Engine Control Module (ECM) -J220- faulty, replace Clear DTC memory and create readiness code.

VW0159600041040X

Fig. 225 Code P0300: Random Misfire Detected (Part 4 of 4). 1998 GTI & Jetta w/2.8L Engine

Cause:	Remedy:
Uneven engine running causes Engine Control Module (ECM) to detect misfiring	– Run engine slightly above idle, and check spark plug connectors/ignition wires for arcing to Ground (GND) If arcing is detected: – Stop engine: switch ignition off – Replace spark plug connector with ignition wire – Remove spark plugs and check condition. Check that spark plugs with correct heat range have been installed. If no arcing can be detected: – Connect VAG 1598/18 test box – Check ignition coil -N152- connector for loose connection or contamination – Disconnect connector from ignition coil, terminal assignment – Switch ignition on – Measure voltage supply between connector terminals 1 and 5 Specification: min. 11.5 volts

VW0159600042010X

Fig. 226 Code P0301: Cylinder 1 Misfire Detected (Part 1 of 4). 1998 GTI & Jetta w/2.8L Engine

		If the specifications are not attained: the wiring has a short or open circuit – This should be located and repaired using wiring diagram
Malfunction cause for P0301 found: No ▼	Yes ▶	– After repairing malfunction, clear DTC memory and create readiness code
Cause: Wiring or cylinder 1 fuel injector -N30- has open circuit or short circuit to Ground (GND)		If no open circuit or short circuit is detected: Remedy: – Remove fuse 18 – Measure resistance between lower terminal for fuse 18 and test box socket 24. Specification 15 – 23 Ω If the specification is not attained: – Disconnect connector from fuel injector – Disconnect 4-pin connector from Mass Air Flow (MAF) sensor – Measure resistance between connector terminal 1 and test box socket 1. Specification: ∞ Ω – Measure resistance between connector terminal 2 and test box socket 1. Specification: ∞ Ω

VW0159600042030X

Fig. 226 Code P0301: Cylinder 1 Misfire Detected (Part 3 of 4). 1998 GTI & Jetta w/2.8L Engine

Cause:	Remedy:
Uneven engine running causes Engine Control Module (ECM) to detect misfiring	– Run engine slightly above idle, and check spark plug connectors/ignition wires for arcing to Ground (GND) If arcing is detected: – Stop engine: switch ignition off – Replace spark plug connector with ignition wire – Remove spark plugs and check condition. Check that spark plugs with correct heat range have been installed. If no arcing can be detected: – Connect VAG 1598/18 test box – Check ignition coil -N152- connector for loose connection or contamination – Disconnect connector from ignition coil, terminal assignment – Switch ignition on – Measure voltage between connector terminals 1 and 5. Specification: min. 11.5 volts If the specification of min. 11.5 volts is not attained: – Switch ignition off – Connect VAG 1598/18 test box – Measure resistance between connector terminal 1 and test box socket 1. Specification: max.1.5 Ω

VW0159600043010X

Fig. 227 Code P0302: Cylinder 2 Misfire Detected (Part 1 of 3). 1998 GTI & Jetta w/2.8L Engine

Cause: Wiring or cylinder 2 fuel injector -N31- has open or short circuit to Ground (GND)	If no open or short circuit is detected: Remedy: – Remove fuse 18 – Measure resistance between lower terminal for fuse 18 and test box socket 25. Specification 15 – 23 Ω If the specification is not attained: – Disconnect connector from fuel injector – Disconnect 4-pin connector from Mass Air Flow (MAF) sensor – Measure resistance between connector terminal 1 and test box socket 1. Specification: ∞ Ω – Measure resistance between connector terminal 2 and test box socket 1. Specification: ∞ Ω If the measured value is not ∞ Ω: – Use wiring diagram to locate and repair short circuit to Ground (GND) – Measure resistance between connector terminal 1 and lower terminal for fuse 18. Specification max. 1.5 Ω – Measure resistance between connector terminal 2 and test box socket 25. Specification max. 1.5 Ω If the specifications are not attained: – Use wiring diagram to locate and repair open circuit
	If no open circuit is detected:
Malfunction cause for P0302 ▶	– Cylinder 2 fuel injector mechanically faulty, replace. Clear DTC memory and create readiness code

VW0159600043030X

Fig. 227 Code P0302: Cylinder 2 Misfire Detected (Part 3 of 3). 1998 GTI & Jetta w/2.8L Engine

	If the specification of min. 11.5 volts is not attained: – Switch ignition off – Connect VAG 1598/18 test box – Measure resistance between connector terminal 1 and test box socket 1. Specification: max.1.5 Ω If the specification is not attained: – Use wiring diagram to locate and repair open circuit in Ground (GND) cable to ignition coil If the specification is attained: – Use wiring diagram to locate and repair open circuit in the positive wire to ignition coil connector terminal 5 If min. 11.5 volts is attained, check remaining wiring: – Measure resistance between connector terminal 2 and test box socket 8. Specification: max.1.5 Ω – Measure resistance between connector terminal 3 and test box socket 60. Specification: max.1.5 Ω – Measure resistance between connector terminal 4 and test box socket 52. Specification: max.1.5 Ω – Check connector terminals 2 and 3 for short circuit to one another. Specification: ∞ Ω – Check connector terminals 3 and 4 for short circuit to one another. Specification: ∞ Ω

VW0159600042020X

Fig. 226 Code P0301: Cylinder 1 Misfire Detected (Part 2 of 4). 1998 GTI & Jetta w/2.8L Engine

Malfunction text: Cylinder 1 Misfire Detected	Observe notes on wiring and component check with VAG 1598/18 test box
	If the measured values are not ∞ Ω – Use wiring diagram to locate and repair short circuit to Ground (GND) – Measure resistance between connector terminal 1 and lower terminal for fuse 18. Specification: 1.5 Ω – Measure resistance between connector terminal 2 and test box socket 24. Specification: max. 1.5 Ω If the specifications are not attained: – Use wiring diagram to locate and repair open circuit
Malfunction cause for P0301 ▶	If no open circuit is detected: – Cylinder 1 fuel injector mechanically faulty, replace. Clear DTC memory and create readiness code

VW0159600042040X

Fig. 226 Code P0301: Cylinder 1 Misfire Detected (Part 4 of 4). 1998 GTI & Jetta w/2.8L Engine

		If the specification is not attained: – Use wiring diagram to locate and repair open circuit in Ground (GND) wire to ignition coil If the specification is attained: – Use wiring diagram to locate and repair open circuit in the positive wire to ignition coil connector terminal 5 If min. 11.5 volts is attained, check remaining wiring: – Measure resistance between connector terminal 2 and test box socket 8. Specification: max.1.5 Ω – Measure resistance between connector terminal 3 and test box socket 60. Specification: max.1.5 Ω – Check resistance between connector terminal 4 and test box socket 52. Specification: max.1.5 Ω – Check connector terminals 2 and 3 for short circuit to one another. Specification: ∞ Ω – Check connector terminals 3 and 4 for short circuit to one another. Specification: ∞ Ω
		If the specifications are not attained: the wiring has a short or open circuit – This should be located and repaired using wiring diagram
Malfunction cause for P0302 found: No ▼	Yes ▶	– After repairing malfunction, clear DTC memory and create readiness code

VW0159600043020X

Fig. 227 Code P0302: Cylinder 2 Misfire Detected (Part 2 of 3). 1998 GTI & Jetta w/2.8L Engine

Cause:	Remedy:
Uneven engine running causes Engine Control Module (ECM) to detect misfiring	– Run engine slightly above idle, and check spark plug connectors/ignition wires for arcing to Ground (GND) If arcing is detected: – Stop engine: switch ignition off – Replace spark plug connector with ignition wire – Remove spark plugs and check condition. Check that spark plugs with correct heat range have been installed. If no arcing can be detected: – Connect VAG 1598/18 test box – Check ignition coil -N152- connector for loose connection or contamination – Disconnect connector from ignition coil (terminal assignment – Switch ignition on – Measure voltage supply between connector terminals 1 and 5 Specification: min. 11.5 volts If the specification of min. 11.5 volts is not attained: – Switch ignition off – Connect VAG 1598/18 test box – Measure resistance between connector terminal 1 and test box socket 1. Specification: max.1.5 Ω

VW0159600044010X

Fig. 228 Code P0303: Cylinder 3 Misfire Detected (Part 1 of 3). 1998 GTI & Jetta w/2.8L Engine

		If the specification is not attained: – Use wiring diagram to locate and repair open circuit in Ground (GND) wire to ignition coil If the specification is attained: – Use wiring diagram to locate and repair open circuit in the positive wire to ignition coil connector terminal 5 If min. 11.5 volts is attained, check remaining wiring: – Measure resistance between connector terminal 2 and test box socket 8. Specification: max.1.5 Ω – Measure resistance between connector terminal 3 and test box 60. Specification: max.1.5 Ω – Measure resistance between connector terminal 4 and test box socket 52. Specification: max.1.5 Ω – Check connector terminals 2 and 3 for short circuit to one another. Specification: ∞ Ω – Check connector terminals 3 and 4 for short circuit to one another. Specification: ∞ Ω If the specifications are not attained: the wiring has a short or open circuit – This should be located and repaired using wiring diagram
Malfunction cause for P0303 found: No ▼	Yes ►	– After repairing malfunction, clear DTC memory and create readiness code
		If no open circuit or short circuit is detected:

VW0159600044020X

Fig. 228 Code P0303: Cylinder 3 Misfire Detected (Part 2 of 3). 1998 GTI & Jetta w/2.8L Engine

Cause:	Remedy:
Uneven engine running causes Engine Control Module (ECM) to detect misfiring	– Run engine slightly above idle, and check spark plug connectors/ignition wires for arcing to Ground (GND) If arcing is detected: – Stop engine: switch ignition off – Replace spark plug connector with ignition wire – Remove spark plugs and check condition. Check that spark plugs with correct heat range have been installed. If no arcing can be detected: – Connect VAG 1598/18 test box – Check ignition coil -N152- connector for loose connection or contamination. – Disconnect connector from ignition coil, terminal assignment – Switch ignition on – Measure voltage supply between connector terminals 1 and 5 Specification: min. 11.5 volts If the specification of min. 11.5 volts is not attained: – Switch ignition off – Connect VAG 1598/18 test box – Measure resistance between connector terminal 1 and test box socket 1. Specification: max.1.5 Ω

VW0159600045010X

Fig. 229 Code P0304: Cylinder 4 Misfire Detected (Part 1 of 3). 1998 GTI & Jetta w/2.8L Engine

	If no open circuit or short circuit is detected:
Cause: Wiring or cylinder 4 fuel injector -N33- has open circuit or short circuit to Ground (GND)	Remedy: – Remove fuse 18 – Measure resistance between lower terminal for fuse 18 and test box socket 2. Specification 15 – 23 Ω If the specification is not attained: – Disconnect connector from fuel injector – Disconnect 4-pin connector from Mass Air Flow (MAF) sensor – Measure resistance between connector terminal 1 and test box socket 1. Specification: ∞ Ω. – Measure resistance between connector terminal 2 and test box socket 1. Specification: ∞ Ω. If the measured values are not ∞ Ω: – Use wiring diagram to locate and repair short circuit to Ground (GND) – Measure resistance between connector terminal 1 and lower terminal for fuse 18. Specification max. 1.5 Ω – Measure resistance between connector terminal 2 and test box socket 2. Specification max. 1.5 Ω If the specifications are not attained: – Use wiring diagram to locate and repair open circuit
	If no open circuit is detected:
Malfunction cause for P0304 ►	– Cylinder 4 fuel injector mechanically faulty, replace. Clear DTC memory and create readiness code

VW0159600045030X

Fig. 229 Code P0304: Cylinder 4 Misfire Detected (Part 3 of 3). 1998 GTI & Jetta w/2.8L Engine

		If the specification is not attained: – Use wiring diagram to locate and repair open circuit in Ground (GND) wire to ignition coil If the specification is attained: – Use wiring diagram to locate and repair open circuit in the positive wire to ignition coil connector terminal 5 If min. 11.5 volts is attained, check remaining wiring: – Measure resistance between connector terminal 2 and test box socket 8. Specification: max.1.5 Ω – Measure resistance between connector terminal 3 and test box socket 60 – Measure resistance between connector terminal 4 and test box socket 52. Specification: max.1.5 Ω – Check connector terminals 2 and 3 for short circuit to one another. Specification: ∞ Ω – Check connector terminals 3 and 4 for short circuit to one another. Specification: ∞ Ω If the specifications are not attained: the wiring has a short or open circuit – This should be located and repaired using wiring diagram
Malfunction cause for P0305 found: No ▼	Yes ►	– After repairing malfunction, clear DTC memory and create readiness code
		If no open circuit or short circuits detected:

VW0159600046020X

Fig. 230 Code P0305: Cylinder 5 Misfire Detected (Part 2 of 3). 1998 GTI & Jetta w/2.8L Engine

	If no open circuit or short circuit is detected:
Cause: Wiring or cylinder 3 fuel injector -N32- has open circuit or short circuit to Ground (GND)	Remedy: – Remove fuse 18 – Measure resistance between lower terminal for fuse 18 and test box socket 26. Specification 15 – 23 Ω If the specification is not attained: – Disconnect connector from fuel injector – Disconnect 4-pin connector from Mass Air Flow (MAF) sensor – Measure resistance between connector terminal 1 and test box socket 1. Specification: ∞ Ω – Measure resistance between connector terminal 2 and test box socket 1. Specification: ∞ Ω If the measured values are not ∞ Ω: – Use wiring diagram to locate and repair short circuit to Ground (GND) – Measure resistance between connector terminal 1 and lower terminal for fuse 18. Specification max. 1.5 Ω – Measure resistance between connector terminal 2 and test box socket 26. Specification max. 1.5 Ω If the specifications are not attained: – Use wiring diagram to locate and repair open circuit
	If not open circuit is detected:
Malfunction cause for P0303 ►	– Cylinder 3 fuel injector mechanically faulty, replace. Clear DTC memory and create readiness code

VW0159600044030X

Fig. 228 Code P0303: Cylinder 3 Misfire Detected (Part 3 of 3). 1998 GTI & Jetta w/2.8L Engine

		If the specification is not attained: – Use wiring diagram to locate and repair open circuit in Ground (GND) wire to ignition coil If the specification is attained: – Use wiring diagram to locate and repair open circuit in the positive wire to ignition coil connector terminal 5 If min. 11.5 volts is attained, check remaining wiring: – Measure resistance between connector terminal 2 and test box socket 8. Specification: max.1.5 Ω – Measure resistance between connector terminal 3 and test box socket 60. Specification: max.1.5 Ω – Measure resistance between connector terminal 4 and test box socket 52. Specification: max.1.5 Ω – Check connector terminals 2 and 3 for short circuit to one another. Specification: ∞ Ω – Check connector terminals 3 and 4 for short circuit to one another. Specification: ∞ Ω If the specifications are not attained: the wiring has a short or open circuit – This should be located and repaired using wiring diagram
Malfunction cause for P0304 found: No ▼	Yes ►	– After repairing malfunction, clear DTC memory and create readiness code

VW0159600045020X

Fig. 229 Code P0304: Cylinder 4 Misfire Detected (Part 2 of 3). 1998 GTI & Jetta w/2.8L Engine

Cause:	Remedy:
Uneven engine running causes Engine Control Module (ECM) to detect misfiring	– Run engine slightly above idle, and check spark plug connectors/ignition wires for arcing to Ground (GND) If arcing is detected: – Stop engine: switch ignition off – Replace spark plug connector with ignition wire – Remove spark plugs and check condition. Check that spark plugs with correct heat range have been installed. If no arcing can be detected: – Connect VAG 1598/18 test box – Check ignition coil -N152- connector for loose connection or contamination – Disconnect connector from ignition coil, terminal assignment – Switch ignition on – Measure voltage supply between connector terminals 1 and 5 Specification: min. 11.5 volts If the specification of min. 11.5 volts is not attained: – Switch ignition off – Connect VAG 1598/18 test box – Measure resistance between connector terminal 1 and test box socket 1. Specification: max.1.5 Ω

VW0159600046010X

Fig. 230 Code P0305: Cylinder 5 Misfire Detected (Part 1 of 3). 1998 GTI & Jetta w/2.8L Engine

Cause: Wiring or cylinder 5 fuel injector -N83- has open/short circuit to Ground (GND)	Remedy: – Remove fuse 18 – Measure resistance between lower terminal for fuse 18 and test box socket 3. Specification 15 – 23 Ω If the specification is not attained: – Disconnect connector from fuel injector – Disconnect 4-pin connector from Mass Air Flow (MAF) sensor – Measure resistance between connector terminal 1 and test box socket 1. Specification: ∞ Ω – Measure resistance between connector terminal 2 and test box socket 1. Specification: ∞ Ω If the measured values are not ∞ Ω: – Use wiring diagram to locate and repair short circuit to Ground (GND) – Measure resistance between connector terminal 1 and lower terminal for fuse 18. Specification max. 1.5 Ω – Measure resistance between connector terminal 2 and test box socket 3. Specification max. 1.5 Ω If the specifications are not attained: – Use wiring diagram to locate and repair open circuit
	If no open circuit is detected:
Malfunction cause for P0305 ►	– Cylinder 5 fuel injector mechanically faulty, replace. Clear DTC memory and create readiness code

VW0159600046030X

Fig. 230 Code P0305: Cylinder 5 Misfire Detected (Part 3 of 3). 1998 GTI & Jetta w/2.8L Engine

Cause:		Remedy:
Uneven engine running causes Engine Control Module (ECM) to detect misfiring		– Run engine slightly above idle, and check spark plug connectors/ignition wires for arcing to Ground (GND) If arcing is detected: – Stop engine: switch ignition off – Replace spark plug connector with ignition wire – Remove spark plugs and check condition. Check that spark plugs with correct heat range have been installed. If no arcing can be detected: – Connect VAG 1598/18 test box – Check ignition coil -N152- connector for loose connection or contamination – Disconnect connector from ignition coil, terminal assignment – Switch ignition on – Measure voltage supply between connector terminals 1 and 5 Specification: min. 11.5 volts If the specification of min. 11.5 volts is not attained: – Switch ignition off – Connect VAG 1598/18 test box – Measure resistance between connector terminal 1 and test box socket 1. Specification: max.1.5 Ω

VW0159600047010X

Fig. 231 Code P0306: Cylinder 6 Misfire Detected (Part 1 of 3). 1998 GTI & Jetta w/2.8L Engine

Cause:		Remedy:
Wiring or cylinder 6 fuel injector -N84- has open circuit or short circuit to Ground (GND)		– Remove fuse 18 – Measure resistance between lower terminal for fuse 18 and test box socket 4. Specification 15 – 23 Ω If the specification is not attained: – Disconnect connector from fuel injector – Disconnect 4-pin connector from Mass Air Flow (MAF) sensor – Measure resistance between connector terminal 1 and test box socket 1. Specification: ∞ Ω – Measure resistance between connector terminal 2 and test box socket 1. Specification: ∞ Ω If the measured values are not ∞ Ω: – Use wiring diagram to locate and repair short circuit to Ground (GND) – Measure resistance between connector terminal 1 and lower terminal for fuse 18. Specification max. 1.5 Ω – Measure resistance between connector terminal 2 and test box socket 4. Specification max. 1.5 Ω If the specifications are not attained: – Use wiring diagram to locate and repair open circuit
		If no open circuit is detected:
Malfunction cause for P0306	▶	– Cylinder 6 fuel injector mechanically faulty, replace. Clear DTC memory and create readiness code

VW0159600047030X

Fig. 231 Code P0306: Cylinder 6 Misfire Detected (Part 3 of 3). 1998 GTI & Jetta w/2.8L Engine

		If the measured values are ∞ Ω: – Measure resistance between connector terminal 1 and test box socket 34. Specification: max. 1.5 Ω – Measure resistance between connector terminal 2 and test box socket 33. Specification: max.1.5 Ω – Measure resistance between connector terminal 3 and test box socket 56. Specification: max.1.5 Ω If the specifications are not attained: the wiring has open circuit – Use wiring diagram to locate and repair open circuit
Malfunction cause for P0327 found: No ▼	Yes ▶	– After repairing malfunction, clear DTC memory and create readiness code
		If all specifications are attained: – Replace knock sensor 1
Malfunction cause for P0327 found: No ▼	Yes ▶	– After repairing malfunction, clear DTC memory and create readiness code
		– Road test vehicle If after the test drive the malfunction is still stored in DTC memory:
Malfunction cause for P0327	▶	– ECM -J220- faulty, replace. Clear DTC memory and create readiness code

VW0159600048020X

Fig. 232 Code P0327: Knock Sensor 1 Circuit Low Input Bank 1 Or Single Sensor (Part 2 of 2). 1998 GTI & Jetta w/2.8L Engine

Cause:		Remedy:
Signal from Knock Sensor (KS) 2 too low or not recognized by Engine Control Module (ECM)		– Switch ignition off – Check tightening torque of knock sensor If the knock sensor is loose: – Unscrew knock sensor, clean contact surfaces and tighten to correct torque. Make sure bolt is of correct length!
Malfunction cause for P0332 found: No ▼	Yes ▶	– After repairing malfunction, clear DTC memory and create readiness code
		If the knock sensor was not loose: – Connect VAG 1598/18 test box – Disconnect connector to knock sensor – Measure resistance between connector terminal 1 and test box socket 56. Specification: ∞ Ω – Measure resistance between connector terminal 2 and test box socket 56. Specification: ∞ Ω If the measured values not ∞ Ω, the wiring has short circuit to cable shielding – This should be located and repaired using wiring diagram

VW0159600049020X

Fig. 233 Code P0332: Knock Sensor 2 Circuit Low Input Bank 2 (Part 2 of 2). 1998 GTI & Jetta w/2.8L Engine

		If the specification is not attained: – Use wiring diagram to locate and repair open circuit in Ground (GND) wire to ignition coil If the specification is attained: – Use wiring diagram to locate and repair open circuit in the positive wire to ignition coil connector terminal 5 If min. 11.5 volts is attained, check remaining wiring: – Measure resistance between connector terminal 2 and test box socket 8. Specification: max.1.5 Ω – Measure resistance between connector terminal 3 and test box socket 60. Specification: max.1.5 Ω – Measure resistance between connector terminal 4 and test box socket 52. Specification: max.1.5 Ω – Check connector terminals 2 and 3 for short circuit to one another. Specification: ∞ Ω – Check connector terminals 3 and 4 for short circuit to one another. Specification: ∞ Ω If the specifications are not attained: the wiring has a short or open circuit – This should be located and repaired using wiring diagram
Malfunction cause for P0306 found: No ▼	Yes ▶	– After repairing malfunction, clear DTC memory and create readiness code
		If no open circuit or short circuit is detected:

VW0159600047020X

Fig. 231 Code P0306: Cylinder 6 Misfire Detected (Part 2 of 3). 1998 GTI & Jetta w/2.8L Engine

Cause:		Remedy:
Signal from Knock Sensor (KS) 1 too low or not recognized by Engine Control Module (ECM)		– Switch ignition off – Check tightening torque of knock sensor If the knock sensor is loose: – Unscrew knock sensor, clean contact surfaces and tighten to correct torque. Make sure bolt is of correct length!
Malfunction cause for P0327 found: No ▼	Yes ▶	– After repairing malfunction, clear DTC memory and create readiness code
		If the knock sensor was not loose: – Connect VAG 1598/18 test box – Disconnect connector to knock sensor – Measure resistance between connector terminal 1 and test box socket 56. Specification: ∞ Ω – Measure resistance between connector terminal 2 and test box socket 56. Specification: ∞ Ω If the measured values not ∞ Ω, the wiring has short circuit to cable shielding: – This should be located and repaired using wiring diagram

VW0159600048010X

Fig. 232 Code P0327: Knock Sensor 1 Circuit Low Input Bank 1 Or Single Sensor (Part 1 of 2). 1998 GTI & Jetta w/2.8L Engine

Cause:		Remedy:
Signal from Knock Sensor (KS) 2 too low or not recognized by Engine Control Module (ECM)		– Switch ignition off – Check tightening torque of knock sensor If the knock sensor is loose: – Unscrew knock sensor, clean contact surfaces and tighten to correct torque. Make sure bolt is of correct length!
Malfunction cause for P0332 found: No ▼	Yes ▶	– After repairing malfunction, clear DTC memory and create readiness code
		If the knock sensor was not loose: – Connect VAG 1598/18 test box – Disconnect connector to knock sensor – Measure resistance between connector terminal 1 and test box socket 56. Specification: ∞ Ω – Measure resistance between connector terminal 2 and test box socket 56. Specification: ∞ Ω If the measured values not ∞ Ω, the wiring has short circuit to cable shielding – This should be located and repaired using wiring diagram

VW0159600049010X

Fig. 233 Code P0332: Knock Sensor 2 Circuit Low Input Bank 2 (Part 1 of 2). 1998 GTI & Jetta w/2.8L Engine

Cause:		Remedy:
Camshaft Position (CMP) sensor -G40- supplies implausible signal to Engine Control Module (ECM)		– Disconnect connector from camshaft position sensor -G40- – Check whether there is a loose terminal in connector to sensor. – Switch ignition on – Measure voltage supply between connector terminals 1 and 3. (Terminal assignment.) Specification: min. 11.5 volts If the specification of min. 11.5 volts is not attained: – Switch ignition off – Connect VAG 1598/18 test box – Measure resistance between connector terminal 3 and test box socket 56. Specification: max.1.5 Ω If the specification is not attained: – Use wiring diagram to locate and repair open circuit in Ground (GND) wire to camshaft position sensor If the specification is attained: – Use wiring diagram to locate and repair open circuit in the positive wire to camshaft position sensor
Malfunction cause for P0341 found: No ▼	Yes ▶	– After repairing malfunction, clear DTC memory and create readiness code

VW0159600050010X

Fig. 234 Code P0341: Camshaft Position Sensor Circuit Range/Performance (Part 1 of 2). 1998 GTI & Jetta w/2.8L Engine

		If the specification of min. 11.5 volts is attained: – Measure resistance between connector terminal 2 and test box socket 44. Specification max.1.5 Ω If the specification is not attained: – Use wiring diagram to locate and repair open circuit If the specification is attained: – Replace Camshaft Position (CMP) sensor -G40-
Malfunction cause for P0341 found: No ▼	Yes ▶	– After repairing malfunction, clear DTC memory and create readiness code
Cause: Diagnostic Trouble Code (DTC) P0341 is stored after clearing DTC memory.		Remedy: – Check sensor wheel is secure on camshaft chain sprocket; note assembly instructions – Check ignition timing
Malfunction cause for P0341 found: No ▼	Yes ▶	– After repairing malfunction, clear DTC memory and create readiness code
Malfunction cause for P0341	▶	– ECM -J220- faulty, replace. Clear DTC memory and create readiness code

VW0159600050020X

Fig. 234 Code P0341: Camshaft Position Sensor Circuit Range/Performance (Part 2 of 2). 1998 GTI & Jetta w/2.8L Engine

		If the secondary air injection solenoid valve does not open and close: – Switch ignition off – Replace secondary air injection solenoid valve
Malfunction cause for P0411 found: No ▼	Yes ▶	– After repairing malfunction, clear DTC memory and create readiness code
		If the secondary air injection solenoid valve opens and closes: – Remove secondary air injection pump pressure hose at engine. Squeeze mounting clamp on pressure hose together and remove pressure hose – Check pressure hose for damage, replace if necessary – Switch ignition on – Bridge test box sockets 1 and 6 – Briefly connect test box socket 49 to Ground (GND) While the secondary air injection pump motor -V101- is activated: – Check for secondary air pressure at connection to pump If no secondary air injection is being created, but pump motor runs: – Replace secondary air injection pump motor (pump fan faulty) If secondary air is being produced: – Check whether the vacuum hose from secondary air injection solenoid valve -N112- leading to combination valve is damaged or disconnected

VW0159600051020X

Fig. 235 Code P0411: Secondary Air Injection System Improper Flow Detected (Part 2 of 3). 1998 GTI & Jetta w/2.8L Engine

Cause: If the Engine Control Module (ECM) recognizes malfunction P0422 in conjunction with an additional malfunction, the additional malfunction stored must be repaired first		Remedy: – Select mode 2 with the generic Scan Tool (ST), and check operating conditions – Repair additional malfunction If the additionally stored DTC does not affect Heated Oxygen Sensor (HO2S) before three way catalytic converter: – Check HO2S according to information described in DTC P0131 to P0135 If the HO2S and the wiring to HO2S are not faulty: – Check exhaust system for leaks. Use a concentrated soap solution, apply solution with a brush to all flanges/bolted joints.
Malfunction cause for P0422 found: No ▼	Yes ▶	– After repairing malfunction disconnect connector from ECM -J220- for 10 seconds, then clear DTC memory and create readiness code
		If no leaks can be found:

VW0159600052010X

Fig. 236 Code P0422: Main Catalyst Efficiency Below Threshold Bank 1 (Part 1 of 2). 1998 GTI & Jetta w/2.8L Engine

Cause: Evaporative Emission (EVAP) canister purge regulator valve -N80- in tank venting system malfunction		Remedy: – Engine at normal working temperature and run at idle • When EVAP canister purge regulator valve -N80- is activated (pulsed), squeeze hose to intake manifold together with fingers, the pulsing must be perceptible If pulsing is not perceptible and EVAP canister purge regulator valve does not click: – Check that connector is not loose or damaged If no connector malfunction is detected: – Switch ignition off – Connect VAG 1598/18 test box – Disconnect connector from EVAP canister purge regulator valve – Check resistance between connector terminal 1 and test box socket 31. Specification: max. 1.5 Ω – Measure resistance between connector terminal 2 and fuse 18 upper terminal. Specification max. 1.5 Ω If the specifications are not attained: – Use wiring diagram to locate and repair open circuit
Malfunction cause for P0440 found: No ▼	Yes ▶	– After repairing malfunction, clear DTC memory and create readiness code
Malfunction cause for P0440	▶	If no wiring malfunction is detected: – EVAP canister purge regulator valve -N80- faulty, replace. Clear DTC memory and create readiness code

VW0159600053000X

Fig. 237 Code P0440: Evaporative Emission Control System Malfunction. 1998 GTI & Jetta w/2.8L Engine

Cause: Secondary air injection pump is functioning, however quantity of air is recognized as insufficient by Heated Oxygen Sensor (HO2S)	Remedy: – Switch ignition off – Connect VAG 1598/18 test box – Disconnect connector from secondary air injection solenoid valve -N112- – Measure resistance between connector terminal 1 and test box socket 50, Specification: 1.5 Ω. If the specification is not attained – Use wiring diagram to locate and repair open circuit If the specification is attained: – Attach connector again – Disconnect a vacuum hose from secondary air injection solenoid valve -N112- and connect an aux. hose – Switch ignition on – Bridge test box sockets 1 and 6 – Briefly connect test box socket 50 to Ground (GND) and at same time blow into aux. hose • The secondary air injection solenoid valve must open during activation, and close again after activation

VW0159600051010X

Fig. 235 Code P0411: Secondary Air Injection System Improper Flow Detected (Part 1 of 3). 1998 GTI & Jetta w/2.8L Engine

		If no malfunction can be found: – Connect hand vacuum pump to vacuum hose to combination valve – Start engine and run at idle • Operate hand vacuum pump several times, the combination valve must open and noise change must be distinctly audible If the idle noise change is not distinct;
Malfunction cause for P0411	▶	– Combination valve faulty, replace. Clear DTC memory and create readiness code

VW0159600051030X

Fig. 235 Code P0411: Secondary Air Injection System Improper Flow Detected (Part 3 of 3). 1998 GTI & Jetta w/2.8L Engine

Cause: ECM -J220- recognizes a malfunction via HO2S 2 (after three way catalytic converter)		Remedy: – Check HO2S 2 (after three way catalytic converter) according to information described in DTC P0137 to P0141 – After repairing, test drive vehicle
Malfunction cause for P0422 found: No ▼	Yes ▶	– After repairing malfunction disconnect connector from ECM -J220- for 10 seconds, then clear DTC memory and create readiness code
Cause: If the malfunction P0422 is stored on its own, the control module has recognized Three Way Catalytic Converter (TWC) efficiency too low, via the HO2S 2 (after three way catalytic converter)		If the malfunction has not been eliminated after the test drive: Remedy: – Start engine and run at idle – If the engine is at normal working temperature, increase engine speed to 3000 RPM for at least 3 minutes – Run engine again at idle – Using a CO tester check three way catalytic converter efficiency and idle If with engine and three way catalytic converter at normal working temperature the CO content is greater than 0.2 Vol.%:
Malfunction cause for P0422	▶	– Three Way Catalytic Converter (TWC) faulty, replace. Clear DTC memory and create readiness code.

VW0159600052020X

Fig. 236 Code P0422: Main Catalyst Efficiency Below Threshold Bank 1 (Part 2 of 2). 1998 GTI & Jetta w/2.8L Engine

Cause: Engine Control Module (ECM) not receiving a usable speed signal	Remedy: – Check speedometer Vehicle Speed Sensor (VSS) -G22- connector and sensor for tightening torque If OK: – Disconnect connector from sensor – Switch ignition on – Measure voltage supply between connector terminals 1 and 3. Specification: min. 11.5 volts If the voltage supply specification is not attained: – Switch ignition off – Connect VAG 1598/18 test box – Measure resistance between connector terminal 3 and test box socket 1. Specification: max.1.5 Ω If the specification is not attained: – Use wiring diagram to locate and repair open circuit in Ground (GND) wire If the specification is attained: – Use wiring diagram to locate and repair open circuit in the positive wire to sensor

VW0159600054010X

Fig. 238 Code P0501: Vehicle Speed Sensor Range Performance (Part 1 of 2). 1998 GTI & Jetta w/2.8L Engine

		If the sensor voltage supply is OK: – Switch ignition on – Raise front of vehicle, and rotate left front wheel – Measure voltage between test box sockets 56 and 65: • Voltage must fluctuate between 0 – 10 volts If no voltage is measured: – Switch ignition off – Disconnect connector from speedometer vehicle speed sensor -G22- – Measure resistance between connector terminal 3 and Ground (GND). Specification max. 1.5 Ω – Measure resistance between connector terminal 1 and fuse 15. Specification max. 1.5 Ω – Measure resistance between connector terminal 2 and instrument cluster connection. Specification max. 1.5 Ω If the specifications are not attained: – Use wiring diagram to locate and repair wiring open or short circuits to one another.
Malfunction cause for P0501 found: No ▼	Yes ▶	– After repairing malfunction, clear DTC memory and create readiness code
Malfunction cause for P0501	▶	– Vehicle speed sensor faulty, replace. Clear DTC memory and create readiness code

VW0159600054020X

Fig. 238 Code P0501: Vehicle Speed Sensor Range Performance (Part 2 of 2). 1998 GTI & Jetta w/2.8L Engine

	If the voltage supply specifications are attained: – Switch ignition off – Connect 8-pin connector – Connect VAG 1598/18 test box Check resistance as follows: – At wide open throttle, between test box sockets 10 and 33: Specification: ∞ Ω – At closed throttle position, between test box sockets 10 and 33. Specification: max.10 Ω – At closed throttle position, between test box sockets 27 and 53. Specification: 3 – 200 Ω If the specifications are not attained: – Disconnect 8-pin connector to throttle valve control module Check resistances as follows: – Connector terminal 1 and test box socket 27 – Connector terminal 2 and test box socket 53 – Connector terminal 5 and test box socket 40 – Connector terminal 8 and test box socket 62: Specification: max.1.5 Ω If the resistances do not correspond to specifications: – Use wiring diagram to locate and repair open circuit Also, if the specifications are not attained (with disconnected 8-pin connector): – Measure resistance between test box sockets 10, 27, 33, 40, 41, 53 and 62. Specification: ∞ Ω

VW0159600055020X

Fig. 239 Code P0510: Closed Throttle Position Switch Malfunction (Part 2 of 3). 1998 GTI & Jetta w/2.8L Engine

Cause:		Remedy:
Control module recognizes itself, components in Engine Control Module (ECM) as faulty		– Switch ignition off – Disconnect connector from ECM – Reconnect ECM, making sure that the connector is properly located – Start engine and run for approx. 3 minutes at idle – Switch ignition off – Switch ignition on – Clear DTC memory and check again If the malfunction is still present:
Malfunction cause for P0605	▶	– ECM -J220- faulty, replace. Clear DTC memory and create readiness code

VW0159600056010X

Fig. 240 Code P0605: Internal Control Module Read Only Memory Error (Part 1 of 2). 1998 GTI & Jetta w/2.8L Engine

Cause:		Remedy:
Transmission Control Module (TCM) not receiving signal from Transmission Vehicle Speed Sensor (VSS) -G38-		– Switch ignition off – Connect VAG 1598/18 test box – Measure resistance between text box sockets 21 and 66. Specification: min. 0.8 KΩ; max. 0.9 KΩ If the specification is not attained: – Use wiring diagram to locate and repair short circuit to Ground (GND) – Replace transmission vehicle speed sensor.
Malfunction cause for P0715 found: No ▼	Yes ▶	– After repairing malfunction, clear DTC memory
Malfunction cause	▶	– TCM -J217- faulty. Replace TCM -J217- and clear DTC memory.

VW0159600058000X

Fig. 241 Code P0715: Input/Turbine Speed Sensor Circuit Malfunction. 1998 GTI & Jetta w/2.8L Engine

Cause:		Remedy:
Engine Control Module (ECM) not receiving a usable signal from Closed Throttle Position (CTP) switch		– Check throttle valve control module -J338- voltage supply at 8-pin connector, terminal assignment – Disconnect 8-pin connector to throttle valve control module – Switch ignition on Check voltage as follows: – Between connector terminals 4 and 7. Specification: approx. 5 volts – Between connector terminals 3 and 7. Specification: approx. 10 volts If the specifications are not attained: – Switch ignition off – Connect VAG 1598/18 test box Check resistance as follows: – Connector terminal 3 and test box socket 10. – Connector terminal 4 and test box socket 41. – Connector terminal 7 and test box socket 33. Specifications: max.1.5 Ω If the specifications are not attained: – Use wiring diagram to locate and repair open circuit If no open circuit is detected: – Replace ECM -J220-
Malfunction cause for P0510 found: No ▼	Yes ▶	– After repairing malfunction, clear DTC memory and create readiness code

VW0159600055010X

Fig. 239 Code P0510: Closed Throttle Position Switch Malfunction (Part 1 of 3). 1998 GTI & Jetta w/2.8L Engine

		If the specifications are not attained: – Use wiring diagram to locate and repair wiring short circuits to one another. If the specifications with throttle open/closed are not attained, but the wiring is OK: – Replace throttle valve control module -J338-
Malfunction cause for P0510 found: No ▼	Yes ▶	– After repairing malfunction disconnect connector from Engine Control Module (ECM) -J220- for 10 seconds, then clear DTC memory and create readiness code
Malfunction cause	▶	– ECM -J220- faulty, replace. Clear DTC memory and create readiness code

VW0159600055030X

Fig. 239 Code P0510: Closed Throttle Position Switch Malfunction (Part 3 of 3). 1998 GTI & Jetta w/2.8L Engine

Cause:		Remedy:
Control module recognizes itself, components in Transmission Control Module (TCM) as faulty		– Switch ignition off – Disconnect connector from control module – Reconnect control module, making sure that the connector is properly located – Switch ignition on – Clear DTC memory and check again If the malfunction is still present:
Malfunction cause for P0605	▶	– TCM -J217- faulty. Replace TCM and clear DTC memory

VW0159600056020X

Fig. 240 Code P0605: Internal Control Module Read Only Memory Error (Part 2 of 2). 1998 GTI & Jetta w/2.8L Engine

Cause:		Remedy:
Transmission Control Module (TCM) not receiving signal from Vehicle Speed Sensor (VSS) -G68-		– Switch ignition off – Connect VAG 1598/18 test box. – Measure resistance between test box sockets 20 and 65. Specification: min. 0.8 KΩ; max. 0.9 KΩ If the specification is not attained: – Use wiring diagram to locate and repair short circuit to Ground (GND) – Replace vehicle speed sensor
Malfunction cause for P0722 found: No ▼	Yes ▶	– After repairing malfunction, clear DTC memory
Malfunction cause	▶	– TCM -J217- faulty. Replace TCM -J217- and clear DTC memory

VW0159600059000X

Fig. 242 Code P0722: Output Speed Sensor No Signal. 1998 GTI & Jetta w/2.8L Engine

Cause:		Remedy:
Transmission Control Module (TCM) does not receive signal from Engine Control Module (ECM)		– Switch ignition off – Connect VAG 1598/18 test box – Use wiring diagram to locate and repair wiring short circuits to one another. – ECM -J220- faulty, replace
Malfunction cause for P0725 found: No ▼	Yes ▶	– After repairing malfunction, clear DTC memory
Malfunction cause	▶	– TCM -J217- faulty, replace TCM and clear DTC memory

VW0159600060000X

Fig. 243 Code P0725: Engine Speed Input Circuit Malfunction. 1998 GTI & Jetta w/2.8L Engine

Cause:		Remedy:
Valve body solenoid valve not receiving a signal		– Switch ignition off – Connect VAG 1598/18 test box – Measure resistance between test box sockets 58 and 22. Specification: min. 4.5 Ω; max. 6.5 Ω – Measure resistance between test box sockets 58 and 1. Specification: ∞ Ω – Measure resistance between test box sockets 22 and 1. Specification: ∞ Ω If the specification is not attained: – Use wiring diagram to locate and repair open circuit or short circuit to Ground (GND) – Replace valve body
Malfunction cause for P0748 found: No ▼	Yes ▶	– After repairing malfunction, clear DTC memory
Malfunction cause	▶	– Transmission Control Module (TCM) -J217- faulty. Replace TCM -J217- and clear DTC memory.

VW0159600061000X

Fig. 244 Code P0748: Pressure Control Solenoid Electrical Malfunction. 1998 GTI & Jetta w/2.8L Engine

Cause:		Remedy:
Valve body solenoid valve not receiving a signal		– Switch ignition off – Connect VAG 1598/18 test box. – Measure resistance between test box sockets 54 and 67. Specification: min. 55 Ω; max. 70.5 Ω – Measure resistance between test box sockets 54 and 1. Specification: ∞ Ω If the specification is not attained: – Use wiring diagram to locate and repair open circuit or short circuit to Ground (GND) – Replace valve body
Malfunction cause for P0758 found: No ▼	Yes ▶	– After repairing malfunction, clear DTC memory
Malfunction cause	▶	– Transmission Control Module (TCM) -J217- faulty. Replace TCM -J217- and clear DTC memory

VW0159600063000X

Fig. 246 Code P0758: Shift Solenoid B Electrical Malfunction. 1998 GTI & Jetta w/2.8L Engine

Cause:		Remedy:
Valve body solenoid valve not receiving a signal		– Switch ignition off – Connect VAG 1598/18 test box – Measure resistance between test box sockets 47 and 67. Specification: min. 4.5 Ω; max. 6.5 Ω – Measure resistance between test box sockets 47 and 1. Specification: ∞ Ω If the specification is not attained: – Use wiring diagram to locate and repair open circuit or short circuit to Ground (GND) – Replace valve body
Malfunction cause for P0768 found: No ▼	Yes ▶	– After repairing malfunction, clear DTC memory
Malfunction cause	▶	– Transmission Control Module (TCM) -J217- faulty. Replace TCM -J217- and clear DTC memory

VW0159600065000X

Fig. 248 Code P0768: Shift Solenoid D Electrical Malfunction. 1998 GTI & Jetta w/2.8L Engine

Cause:		*Note:*
Mixture so rich that the Oxygen Sensor (O2S) control is on lean limit		*If an O2S malfunction (P0131 to P0141) is also stored along with this malfunction, the O2S malfunction should be repaired first.*
Cause: Mass Air Flow (MAF) sensor -G70- signal to Engine Control Module (ECM) too high		Remedy: – Switch ignition off – Connect VAG 1598/18 test box – Disconnect 4-pin connector from MAF sensor – Measure resistance between connector terminal 1 and test box socket 1. Specification: max. 1.5 Ω – Bridge connector terminals 1 and 2, measure resistance between test box sockets 1 and 16. Specification: max. 1.5 Ω – Bridge connector terminals 1 and 4, measure resistance between test box sockets 1 and 17. Specification: max. 1.5 Ω – Do not bridge connector terminals, measure resistance between test box sockets 16 and 17. Specification: ∞ Ω If the specifications are not attained: – Use wiring diagram to locate and repair wiring short or open circuits to one another.
Malfunction cause for P1127 found: No ▼	Yes ▶	– After repairing malfunction, clear DTC memory create readiness code
		If the resistance specifications are attained:

VW0159600067010X

Fig. 250 Code P1127: Long Term Fuel Trim, B1 System Too Rich (Part 1 of 4). 1998 GTI & Jetta w/2.8L Engine

Cause:		Remedy:
Valve body solenoid valve not receiving a signal		– Switch ignition off – Connect VAG 1598/18 test box. – Measure resistance between test box sockets 55 and 67. Specification: min. 55 Ω; max. 70.5 Ω – Measure resistance between test box sockets 55 and 1. Specification: ∞ Ω If the specification is not attained: – Use wiring diagram to locate and repair wiring open or short circuit to Ground (GND) – Replace valve body
Malfunction cause for P0753 found: No ▼	Yes ▶	– After repairing malfunction, clear DTC memory
Malfunction cause	▶	– Transmission Control Module (TCM) -J217- faulty. Replace TCM -J217- and clear DTC memory

VW0159600062000X

Fig. 245 Code P0753: Shift Solenoid A Electrical Malfunction. 1998 GTI & Jetta w/2.8L Engine

Cause:		Remedy:
Valve body solenoid valve not receiving a signal		– Switch ignition off – Connect VAG 1598/18 test box – Measure resistance between test box sockets 9 and 67. Specification: min. 55 Ω; max. 70.5 Ω – Measure resistance between test box sockets 9 and 1. Specification: ∞ Ω If the specification is not attained: – Use wiring diagram to locate and repair open circuit or short circuit to Ground (GND) – Replace valve body
Malfunction cause for P0763 found: No ▼	Yes ▶	– After repairing malfunction, clear DTC memory
Malfunction cause	▶	– Transmission Control Module (TCM) -J217- faulty. Replace TCM -J217- and clear DTC memory.

VW0159600064000X

Fig. 247 Code P0763: Shift Solenoid C Electrical Malfunction. 1998 GTI & Jetta w/2.8L Engine

Cause:		Remedy:
Valve body solenoid valve not receiving a signal		– Switch ignition off – Connect VAG 1598/18 test box – Measure resistance between test box sockets 56 and 67. Specification: min. 55 Ω; max. 70.5 Ω – Measure resistance between test box sockets 56 and 1. Specification: ∞ Ω If the specification is not attained: – Use wiring diagram to locate and repair open circuit or short circuit to Ground (GND) – Replace valve body
Malfunction cause for P0773 found: No ▼	Yes ▶	– After repairing malfunction, clear DTC memory
Malfunction cause	▶	– Transmission Control Module (TCM) -J217- faulty. Replace TCM -J217- and clear DTC memory

VW0159600066000X

Fig. 249 Code P0773: Shift Solenoid E Electrical Malfunction. 1998 GTI & Jetta w/2.8L Engine

Cause:		Remedy:
Unmetered (outside) air between cylinder head and HO2S caused by secondary air injection system combination valve permanently open		Check combination valve in secondary air injection system: – Disconnect connector for secondary air injection pump and secondary air injection solenoid valve from engine – Disconnect pressure hose from combination valve – Run engine at idle • Air must not pulsate at open connection on combination valve If pulsing is perceptible: – Replace combination valve An electrical malfunction on secondary air injection pump relay or in the wiring can also activate the system and therefore lead to unmetered (outside) air – Check secondary air injection system wiring as described for DTC P0411
Malfunction cause for P1127 found: No ▼	Yes ▶	– After repairing malfunction, clear DTC memory and create readiness code

VW0159600067020X

Fig. 250 Code P1127: Long Term Fuel Trim, B1 System Too Rich (Part 2 of 4). 1998 GTI & Jetta w/2.8L Engine

Cause:		Remedy:
Excessive fuel pressure		– Check vacuum hose to fuel pressure regulator If no leaks can be found: – Check fuel return line from fuel tank to fuel rail on engine A restricted return line causes excessive fuel pressure build-up! – Switch engine off – Cover test port on fuel rail with a rag and open – Connect VAG 1318 fuel injection pressure gauge with VAG 1318/1 pressure gauge adapter and VAG 1318/10 adapter – Start engine and run at idle – Measure fuel pressure. Specification: approx. 3.5 bar (51 psi) – While engine is running, disconnect hose from pressure regulator • Fuel pressure must increase to 4.0 bar (58 psi) If the specification of 4.0 bar (58 psi) is not attained: – Replace fuel pressure regulator If the specification is exceeded before disconnecting hose, the return line is restricted or blocked
Malfunction cause for P1127 found: No ▼	Yes ▶	– After repairing malfunction, clear DTC memory and create readiness code
		If the specification is not exceeded:

VW0159600067030X

Fig. 250 Code P1127: Long Term Fuel Trim, B1 System Too Rich (Part 3 of 4). 1998 GTI & Jetta w/2.8L Engine

Cause:		*Note:*
Mixture so lean that the Oxygen Sensor (O2S) control is on rich limit		*If an O2S malfunction (P0131 to P0141) is also stored along with this malfunction, the O2S malfunction should be repaired first.*
Cause: Fuel pressure too low/fuel quantity supplied too low		Remedy: Check whether vehicle has performance problems: Check whether performance problems only occur at full acceleration: – Replace fuel filter If the engine output is impaired at lower throttle openings, or the vehicle jerks at lower throttle openings: – Switch engine off – Cover test port on fuel rail with a rag and open – Connect VAG 1318 fuel injection pressure gauge with VAG 1318/1 pressure gauge adapter and VAG 1318/10 adapter – Start engine and run at idle – Measure fuel pressure. Specification: approx. 3.5 bar (51 psi) If the specification is not attained: – Check whether the fuel supply line is restricted If the fuel supply line is not faulty: – Replace transfer Fuel Pump (FP) -G23-
Malfunction cause for P1128 found: No ▼	Yes ▶	– After repairing malfunction, clear DTC memory and create readiness code

VW0159600068010X

Fig. 251 Code P1128: Long Term Fuel Trim, B1 System Too Lean (Part 1 of 2). 1998 GTI & Jetta w/2.8L Engine

Cause:		Remedy:
Wiring or fuel injector has short circuit to positive.		– Switch ignition off – Connect VAG 1598/18 test box – Remove fuse 18 – Disconnect connector from fuel injector – Measure resistance between connector terminal 2 and fuse 18 lower terminal. Specification: ∞ Ω. If the specification is not attained: – Use wiring diagram to locate and repair short circuit to positive in the wiring from Engine Control Module (ECM) to fuel injector
Malfunction cause for P1213 found: No ▼	Yes ▶	– After repairing malfunction, clear DTC memory and create readiness code
		If the specification is attained: – Measure resistance between fuel injector terminals 1 and 2. Specification: approx. 15 – 23 Ω If the specification is not attained – Replace Cyl. 1 fuel injector
If no wiring or fuel injector malfunction is found:		
Malfunction cause	▶	– ECM -J220- faulty, replace. Clear DTC memory and create readiness code

VW0159600069000X

Fig. 252 Code P1213: Cylinder 1 Injector Circuit Shorted To Voltage. 1998 GTI & Jetta w/2.8L Engine

Cause:		Remedy:
Wiring or fuel injector has short circuit to positive		– Switch ignition off – Connect VAG 1598/18 test box – Remove fuse 18 – Disconnect connector from fuel injector – Measure resistance between connector terminal 2 and fuse 18 lower terminal. Specification: ∞ Ω If the specification is not attained: – Use wiring diagram to locate and repair short circuit to positive in the wiring from control module to fuel injector
Malfunction cause for P1215 found: No ▼	Yes ▶	– After repairing malfunction, clear DTC memory and create readiness code
		If the specification is attained: – Measure resistance between fuel injector terminals 1 and 2. Specification: approx. 15 – 23 Ω If the specification is not attained: – Replace Cyl. 3 fuel injector
If no wiring or fuel injector malfunction is found:		
Malfunction cause	▶	– Engine Control Module (ECM) -J220- faulty, replace. Clear DTC memory and create readiness code

VW0159600071000X

Fig. 254 Code P1215: Cylinder 3 Injector Circuit Shorted To Voltage. 1998 GTI & Jetta w/2.8L Engine

Cause:		Remedy:
Fuel injector is dirty and does not close (dripping)		– Remove intake manifold upper section and remove fuel injectors complete with fuel rail – Wipe fuel injectors dry with a clean cloth – Use fuel pressure still available to check fuel injectors for leaks. If droplets form on fuel injector(s):
Malfunction cause for P1127	▶	– Fuel injector faulty, replace. Clear DTC memory and create readiness code

VW0159600067040X

Fig. 250 Code P1127: Long Term Fuel Trim, B1 System Too Rich (Part 4 of 4). 1998 GTI & Jetta w/2.8L Engine

Cause: Fuel injector sticking, not opening		If the specification of approx. 3.5 bar (51 psi) is attained: Remedy: – Remove intake manifold upper section and remove fuel injectors complete with fuel rail – Place a fuel resistant container under the fuel injectors, and turn engine at starter speed – Check whether all fuel injectors open proportionately – Check whether all fuel injectors produce uniform spray pattern If one or more valves are not functioning properly:
Malfunction cause for P1128	▶	– Replace faulty fuel injector. Clear DTC memory and create readiness code.

VW0159600068020X

Fig. 251 Code P1128: Long Term Fuel Trim, B1 System Too Lean (Part 2 of 2). 1998 GTI & Jetta w/2.8L Engine

Cause:		Remedy:
Wiring or fuel injector has short circuit to positive		– Switch ignition off – Connect VAG 1598/18 test box – Remove fuse 18 – Disconnect connector from fuel injector – Measure resistance between connector terminal 2 and fuse 18 lower terminal. Specification: ∞ Ω If the specification is not attained: – Use wiring diagram to locate and repair short circuit to positive in the wiring from control module to fuel injector
Malfunction cause for P1214 found: No ▼	Yes ▶	– After repairing malfunction, clear DTC memory and create readiness code
		If the specification is attained: – Measure resistance between fuel injector terminals 1 and 2. Specification: approx. 15 – 23 Ω If the specification is not attained: – Replace Cyl. 2 fuel injector
If no wiring or fuel injector malfunction is found:		
Malfunction cause	▶	– Engine Control Module (ECM) -J220- faulty, replace. Clear DTC memory and create readiness code

VW0159600070000X

Fig. 253 Code P1214: Cylinder 2 Injector Circuit Shorted To Voltage. 1998 GTI & Jetta w/2.8L Engine

Cause:		Remedy:
Wiring or fuel injector has short circuit to positive		– Switch ignition off. – Connect VAG 1598/18 test box – Remove fuse 18 – Disconnect connector from fuel injector – Measure resistance between connector terminal 2 and fuse 18 lower terminal. Specification: ∞ Ω If the specification is not attained: – Use wiring diagram to locate and repair short circuit to positive in the wiring from control module to fuel injector
Malfunction cause for P1216 found: No ▼	Yes ▶	– After repairing malfunction, clear DTC memory and create readiness code
		If the specification is attained: – Measure resistance between fuel injector terminals 1 and 2. Specification: approx. 15 – 23 Ω If the specification is not attained: – Replace Cyl. 4 fuel injector
If no wiring or fuel injector malfunction is found:		
Malfunction cause	▶	– Engine Control Module (ECM) -J220- faulty, replace. Clear DTC memory and create readiness code

VW0159600072000X

Fig. 255 Code P1216: Cylinder 4 Injector Circuit Shorted To Voltage. 1998 GTI & Jetta w/2.8L Engine

Cause:		Remedy:
Wiring or fuel injector has short circuit to positive		– Switch ignition off – Connect VAG 1598/18 test box – Remove fuse 18 – Disconnect connector from fuel injector – Measure resistance between connector terminal 2 and fuse 18 lower terminal. Specification: ∞ Ω If the specification is not attained: – Use wiring diagram to locate and repair short circuit to positive in the wiring from control module to fuel injector
Malfunction cause for P1217 found: No ▼	Yes ▶	– After repairing malfunction, clear DTC memory and create readiness code
		If the specification is attained: – Measure resistance between fuel injector terminals 1 and 2. Specification: approx. 15 – 23 Ω If the specification is not attained: – Replace Cyl. 5 fuel injector
If no wiring or fuel injector malfunction is found:		
Malfunction cause	▶	– Engine Control Module (ECM) -J220- faulty, replace. Clear DTC memory and create readiness code

VW0159600073000X

Fig. 256 Code P1217: Cylinder 5 Injector Circuit Shorted To Voltage. 1998 GTI & Jetta w/2.8L Engine

Cause:		Remedy:
Wiring or fuel injector has open circuit or short circuit to Ground (GND)		– Switch ignition off – Connect VAG 1598/18 test box – Remove fuse 18 – Measure resistance between lower terminal for fuse 18 and test box socket 24. Specification 15 – 23 Ω If the specification is not attained: – Disconnect connector from fuel injector – Disconnect 4-pin connector from Mass Air Flow (MAF) sensor – Measure resistance between connector terminal 1 and test box socket 1. Specification: ∞ Ω – Measure resistance between connector terminal 2 and test box socket 1. Specification: ∞ Ω If the specification is not attained: – Use wiring diagram to locate and repair short circuit to Ground (GND)
Malfunction cause for P1225 found: No ▼	Yes ▶	– After repairing malfunction, clear DTC memory and create readiness code

VW0159600075010X

Fig. 258 Code P1225: Cylinder 1 Injector Circuit Shorted To Ground (Part 1 of 2). 1998 GTI & Jetta w/2.8L Engine

Cause:		Remedy:
Wiring or fuel injector has open circuit or short circuit to Ground (GND)		– Switch ignition off – Connect VAG 1598/18 test box – Remove fuse 18 – Measure resistance between lower terminal for fuse 18 and test box socket 25. Specification 15 – 23 Ω If the specification is not attained: – Disconnect connector from fuel injector – Disconnect 4-pin connector from Mass Air Flow (MAF) sensor – Measure resistance between connector terminal 1 and test box socket 1. Specification: ∞ Ω – Measure resistance between connector terminal 2 and test box socket 1. Specification: ∞ Ω If the specification is not attained: – Use wiring diagram to locate and repair short circuit to Ground (GND)
Malfunction cause for P1226 found: No ▼	Yes ▶	– After repairing malfunction, clear DTC memory and create readiness code

VW0159600076010X

Fig. 259 Code P1226: Cylinder 2 Injector Circuit Shorted To Ground (Part 1 of 2). 1998 GTI & Jetta w/2.8L Engine

Cause:		Remedy:
Wiring or fuel injector has open circuit or short circuit to Ground (GND)		– Switch ignition off – Connect VAG 1598/18 test box – Remove fuse 18 – Measure resistance between lower terminal for fuse 18 and test box socket 26. Specification 15 – 23 Ω If the specification is not attained: – Disconnect connector from fuel injector – Disconnect 4-pin connector from Mass Air Flow (MAF) sensor – Measure resistance between connector terminal 1 and test box socket 1. Specification: ∞ Ω – Measure resistance between connector terminal 2 and test box socket 1. Specification: ∞ Ω If the specification is not attained: – Use wiring diagram to locate and repair short circuit to Ground (GND)
Malfunction cause for P1227 found: No ▼	Yes ▶	– After repairing malfunction, clear DTC memory and create readiness code

VW0159600077010X

Fig. 260 Code P1227: Cylinder 3 Injector Circuit Shorted To Ground (Part 1 of 2). 1998 GTI & Jetta w/2.8L Engine

Cause:		Remedy:
Wiring or fuel injector has short circuit to positive		– Switch ignition off – Connect VAG 1598/18 test box – Remove fuse 18 – Disconnect connector from fuel injector – Measure resistance between connector terminal 2 and fuse 18 lower terminal. Specification: ∞ Ω If the specification is not attained: – Use wiring diagram to locate and repair short circuit to positive in the wiring from control module to fuel injector
Malfunction cause for P1218 found: No ▼	Yes ▶	– After repairing malfunction, clear DTC memory and create readiness code
		If the specification is attained: – Measure resistance between fuel injector terminals 1 and 2. Specification approx. 15 – 23 Ω If the specification is not attained: – Replace Cyl. 6 fuel injector
If no wiring or fuel injector malfunction is found:		
Malfunction cause	▶	– Engine Control Module (ECM) -J220- faulty, replace. Clear DTC memory and create readiness code

VW0159600074000X

Fig. 257 Code P1218: Cylinder 6 Injector Circuit Shorted To Voltage. 1998 GTI & Jetta w/2.8L Engine

		If all specifications are attained: – Disconnect connector from fuel injector – Measure resistance between fuel injector terminals 1 and 2. Specification: 15 – 23 Ω If the specification is not attained: – Cyl. 1 fuel injector faulty, replace
Malfunction cause for P1225 found: No ▼	Yes ▶	– After repairing malfunction, clear DTC memory and create readiness code
If no malfunction in the wiring or fuel injector can be found:		
Malfunction cause	▶	– Engine Control Module (ECM) -J220- faulty, replace. Clear DTC memory and create readiness code

VW0159600075020X

Fig. 258 Code P1225: Cylinder 1 Injector Circuit Shorted To Ground (Part 2 of 2). 1998 GTI & Jetta w/2.8L Engine

		If all specifications are attained: – Disconnect connector from fuel injector – Measure resistance between fuel injector terminals 1 and 2. Specification: 15 – 23 Ω If the specification is not attained: – Cyl. 2 fuel injector faulty, replace
Malfunction cause for P1226 found: No ▼	Yes ▶	– After repairing malfunction, clear DTC memory and create readiness code
If no malfunction in the wiring or fuel injector can be found:		
Malfunction cause	▶	– Engine Control Module (ECM) -J220- faulty, replace. Clear DTC memory and create readiness code

VW0159600076020X

Fig. 259 Code P1226: Cylinder 2 Injector Circuit Shorted To Ground (Part 2 of 2). 1998 GTI & Jetta w/2.8L Engine

		If all specifications are attained: – Disconnect connector from fuel injector – Measure resistance between fuel injector terminals 1 and 2. Specification: 15 – 23 Ω If the specification is not attained: – Cyl. 3 fuel injector faulty, replace
Malfunction cause for P1227 found: No ▼	Yes ▶	– After repairing malfunction, clear DTC memory and create readiness code
If no malfunction in the wiring or fuel injector can be found:		
Malfunction cause	▶	– Engine Control Module (ECM) -J220- faulty, replace. Clear DTC memory and create readiness code

VW0159600077020X

Fig. 260 Code P1227: Cylinder 3 Injector Circuit Shorted To Ground (Part 2 of 2). 1998 GTI & Jetta w/2.8L Engine

Cause:		Remedy:
Wiring or fuel injector has open circuit or short circuit to Ground (GND)		– Switch ignition off – Connect VAG 1598/18 test box – Remove fuse 18 – Measure resistance between lower terminal for fuse 18 and test box socket 2. Specification 15 – 23 Ω If the specification is not attained: – Disconnect connector from fuel injector – Disconnect 4-pin connector from Mass Air Flow (MAF) sensor – Measure resistance between connector terminal 1 and test box socket 1. Specification: ∞ Ω – Measure resistance between connector terminal 2 and test box socket 1. Specification: ∞ Ω If the specification is not attained: – Use wiring diagram to locate and repair short circuit to Ground (GND)
Malfunction cause for P1228 found: No ▼	Yes ▶	– After repairing malfunction, clear DTC memory and create readiness code

VW0159600078010X

Fig. 261 Code P1228: Cylinder 4 Injector Circuit Shorted To Ground (Part 1 of 2). 1998 GTI & Jetta w/2.8L Engine

		If all specifications are attained: – Disconnect connector from fuel injector – Measure resistance between fuel injector terminals 1 and 2 Specification: 15 – 23 Ω If the specification is not attained: – Cyl. 4 fuel injector faulty, replace
Malfunction cause for P1228 found: No ▼	Yes ▶	– After repairing malfunction, clear DTC memory and create readiness code
If no malfunction in the wiring or fuel injector can be found:		
Malfunction cause	▶	– Engine Control Module (ECM) -J220- faulty, replace. Clear DTC memory and create readiness code

VW0159600078020X

Fig. 261 Code P1228: Cylinder 4 Injector Circuit Shorted To Ground (Part 2 of 2). 1998 GTI & Jetta w/2.8L Engine

		If all specifications are attained: – Disconnect connector from fuel injector – Measure resistance between fuel injector terminals 1 and 2 Specification: 15 – 23 Ω If the specification is not attained: – Cylinder 5 fuel injector faulty, replace
Malfunction cause for P1229 found: No ▼	Yes ▶	– After repairing malfunction, clear DTC memory and create readiness code
If no malfunction in the wiring or fuel injector can be found:		
Malfunction cause	▶	– Engine Control Module (ECM) -J220- faulty, replace. Clear DTC memory and create readiness code

VW0159600079020X

Fig. 262 Code P1229: Cylinder 5 Injector Circuit Shorted To Ground (Part 2 of 2). 1998 GTI & Jetta w/2.8L Engine

		If all specifications are attained: – Disconnect connector from fuel injector – Measure resistance between fuel injector terminals 1 and 2 Specification: 15 – 23 Ω If the specification is not attained: – Cylinder 6 fuel injector faulty, replace
Malfunction cause for P1230 found: No ▼	Yes ▶	– After repairing malfunction, clear DTC memory and create readiness code
If no malfunction in the wiring or fuel injector can be found:		
Malfunction cause	▶	– Engine Control Module (ECM) -J220- faulty, replace. Clear DTC memory and create readiness code

VW0159600080020X

Fig. 263 Code P1230: Cylinder 6 Injector Circuit Shorted To Ground (Part 2 of 2). 1998 GTI & Jetta w/2.8L Engine

		– Check resistance between connector terminal 2 and test box socket 24. Specification max. 1.5 Ω If the specification is not attained: – Use wiring diagram to locate and repair open circuit in the activation wire from Engine Control Module (ECM) to cyl. 1 fuel injector If all specifications are attained: – Disconnect connector from fuel injector – Measure resistance between terminals 1 and 2 of fuel injector Specification: 15 – 23 Ω If the specification is not attained: – Cyl. 1 fuel injector faulty, replace
Malfunction cause for P1237 found: No ▼	Yes ▶	– After repairing malfunction, clear DTC memory and create readiness code
If no malfunction in the wiring or fuel injector can be found:		
Malfunction cause	▶	– ECM -J220- faulty, replace. Clear DTC memory and create readiness code

VW0159600081020X

Fig. 264 Code P1237: Cylinder 1 Injector Circuit Open (Part 2 of 2). 1998 GTI & Jetta w/2.8L Engine

		– Measure resistance between connector terminal 2 and test box socket 25. Specification max. 1.5 Ω If the specification is not attained: – Use wiring diagram to locate and repair open circuit in the activation wire from Engine Control Module (ECM) to cyl. 2 fuel injector If all specifications are attained: – Disconnect connector from fuel injector – Measure resistance between terminals 1 and 2 of fuel injector Specification: 15 – 23 Ω If the specification is not attained: – Cyl. 2 fuel injector faulty, replace
Malfunction cause for P1238 found: No ▼	Yes ▶	– After repairing malfunction, clear DTC memory and create readiness code
If no malfunction in the wiring or fuel injector can be found:		
Malfunction cause	▶	– ECM -J220- faulty, replace. Clear DTC memory and create readiness code

VW0159600082020X

Fig. 265 Code P1238: Cylinder 2 Injector Circuit Open (Part 2 of 2). 1998 GTI & Jetta w/2.8L Engine

Cause:		Remedy:
Wiring or fuel injector has open circuit or short circuit to Ground (GND)		– Switch ignition off – Connect VAG 1598/18 test box – Remove fuse 18 – Measure resistance between lower terminal for fuse 18 and test box socket 3. Specification 15 – 23 Ω If the specification is not attained: – Disconnect connector from fuel injector – Disconnect 4-pin connector from Mass Air Flow (MAF) sensor – Measure resistance between connector terminal 1 and test box socket 1. Specification: ∞ Ω – Measure resistance between connector terminal 2 and test box socket 1. Specification: ∞ Ω If the specification is not attained: – Use wiring diagram to locate and repair open circuit
Malfunction cause for P1229 found: No ▼	Yes ▶	– After repairing malfunction, clear DTC memory and create readiness code

VW0159600079010X

Fig. 262 Code P1229: Cylinder 5 Injector Circuit Shorted To Ground (Part 1 of 2). 1998 GTI & Jetta w/2.8L Engine

Cause:		Remedy:
Wiring or fuel injector has open circuit or short circuit to Ground (GND)		– Switch ignition off – Connect VAG 1598/18 test box – Remove fuse 18 – Measure resistance between lower terminal for fuse 18 and test box socket 4. Specification 15 – 23 Ω If the specification is not attained: – Disconnect connector from fuel injector – Disconnect 4-pin connector from Mass Air Flow (MAF) sensor – Measure resistance between connector terminal 1 and test box socket 1. Specification: ∞ Ω – Measure resistance between connector terminal 2 and test box socket 1. Specification: ∞ Ω If the specification is not attained: – Use wiring diagram to locate and repair open circuit
Malfunction cause for P1230 found: No ▼	Yes ▶	– After repairing malfunction, clear DTC memory and create readiness code

VW0159600080010X

Fig. 263 Code P1230: Cylinder 6 Injector Circuit Shorted To Ground (Part 1 of 2). 1998 GTI & Jetta w/2.8L Engine

Cause:		Remedy:
Wiring or fuel injector has open circuit		– Switch ignition off – Connect VAG 1598/18 test box – Remove fuse 18 – Measure resistance between lower terminal for fuse 18 and test box socket 24. Specification 15 – 23 Ω If the specification is not attained: – Measure resistance between connector terminal 1 and fuse 18 lower terminal. Specification max. 1.5 Ω If the specification is not attained, there is an open circuit between the fuel injector connector and the positive connection (G3) in wiring harness – Use wiring diagram to locate and repair open circuit
Malfunction cause for P1237 found: No ▼	Yes ▶	– After repairing malfunction, clear DTC memory and create readiness code

VW0159600081010X

Fig. 264 Code P1237: Cylinder 1 Injector Circuit Open (Part 1 of 2). 1998 GTI & Jetta w/2.8L Engine

Cause:		Remedy:
Wiring or fuel injector has open circuit.		– Switch ignition off – Connect VAG 1598/18 test box – Remove fuse 18 – Measure resistance between lower terminal for fuse 18 and test box socket 25. Specification 15 – 23 Ω If the specification is not attained: – Measure resistance between connector terminal 1 and fuse 18 lower terminal. Specification max. 1.5 Ω If the specification is not attained, there is an open circuit between the fuel injector connector and the positive connection (G3) in wiring harness – Use wiring diagram to locate and repair open circuit
Malfunction cause for P1238 found: No ▼	Yes ▶	– After repairing malfunction, clear DTC memory and create readiness code

VW0159600082010X

Fig. 265 Code P1238: Cylinder 2 Injector Circuit Open (Part 1 of 2). 1998 GTI & Jetta w/2.8L Engine

Cause:		Remedy:
Wiring or fuel injector has open circuit		– Switch ignition off – Connect VAG 1598/18 test box – Remove fuse 18 – Measure resistance between lower terminal for fuse 18 and test box socket 26. Specification 15 – 23 Ω If the specification is not attained: – Measure resistance between connector terminal 1 and fuse 18 lower terminal. Specification max. 1.5 Ω If the specification is not attained, there is an open circuit between the fuel injector connector and the positive connection (G3) in wiring harness – Use wiring diagram to locate and repair open circuit
Malfunction cause for P1239 found: No ▼	Yes ▶	– After repairing malfunction, clear DTC memory and create readiness code

VW0159600083010X

Fig. 266 Code P1239: Cylinder 3 Injector Circuit Open (Part 1 of 2). 1998 GTI & Jetta w/2.8L Engine

		– Measure resistance between connector terminal 2 and test box socket 26. Specification max. 1.5 Ω If the specification is not attained: – Use wiring diagram to locate and repair open circuit in the activation wire from Engine Control Module (ECM) to cyl. 3 fuel injector If all specifications are attained: – Disconnect connector from fuel injector – Measure resistance between terminals 1 and 2 of fuel injector. Specification: 15 – 23 Ω If the specification is not attained: – Cyl. 3 fuel injector faulty, replace
Malfunction cause for P1239 found: No ▼	Yes ▶	– After repairing malfunction, clear DTC memory and create readiness code
If no malfunction in the wiring or fuel injector can be found:		
Malfunction cause	▶	– ECM -J220- faulty, replace. Clear DTC memory and create readiness code

VW0159600083020X

Fig. 266 Code P1239: Cylinder 3 Injector Circuit Open (Part 2 of 2). 1998 GTI & Jetta w/2.8L Engine

		– Measure resistance between connector terminal 2 and test box socket 2. Specification max. 1.5 Ω If the specification is not attained: – Use wiring diagram to locate and repair open circuit in the activation wire from Engine Control Module (ECM) to cyl. 4 fuel injector If all specifications are attained: – Disconnect connector from fuel injector – Measure resistance between terminals 1 and 2 of fuel injector. Specification: 15 – 23 Ω If the specification is not attained: – Cyl. 4 fuel injector faulty, replace
Malfunction cause for P1240 found: No ▼	Yes ▶	– After repairing malfunction, clear DTC memory and create readiness code
If no malfunction in the wiring or fuel injector can be found:		
Malfunction cause	▶	– ECM -J220- faulty, replace. Clear DTC memory and create readiness code

VW0159600084020X

Fig. 267 Code P1240: Cylinder 4 Injector Circuit Open (Part 2 of 2). 1998 GTI & Jetta w/2.8L Engine

		– Measure resistance between connector terminal 2 and test box socket 3. Specification max. 1.5 Ω If the specification is not attained: – Use wiring diagram to locate and repair open circuit in the activation wire from Engine Control Module (ECM) to cyl. 5 fuel injector If all specifications are attained: – Disconnect connector from fuel injector – Measure resistance between terminals 1 and 2 of fuel injector Specification: 15 – 23 Ω If the specification is not attained: – Cyl. No. 5 fuel injector faulty, replace
Malfunction cause for P1241 found: No ▼	Yes ▶	– After repairing malfunction, clear DTC memory and create readiness code
		If no malfunction in the wiring or fuel injector can be found:
Malfunction cause	▶	– ECM -J220- faulty, replace. Clear DTC memory and create readiness code

VW0159600085020X

Fig. 268 Code P1241: Cylinder 5 Injector Circuit Open (Part 2 of 2). 1998 GTI & Jetta w/2.8L Engine

		– Measure resistance between connector terminal 2 and test box socket 4. Specification max. 1.5 Ω If the specification is not attained: – Use wiring diagram to locate and repair open circuit in the activation wire from Engine Control Module (ECM) to cyl. 6 fuel injector If all specifications are attained: – Disconnect connector from fuel injector – Measure resistance between terminals 1 and 2 of fuel injector. Specification: 15 – 23 Ω If the specification is not attained: – Cyl. 6 fuel injector faulty, replace
Malfunction cause for P1242 found: No ▼	Yes ▶	– After repairing malfunction, clear DTC memory and create readiness code
If no malfunction in the wiring or fuel injector can be found:		
Malfunction cause	▶	– ECM -J220- faulty, replace. Clear DTC memory and create readiness code

VW0159600086020X

Fig. 269 Code P1242: Cylinder 6 Injector Circuit Open (Part 2 of 2). 1998 GTI & Jetta w/2.8L Engine

		If the specifications are not ∞ Ω, the wiring has a short circuit to cable shielding – Use wiring diagram to locate and repair short circuit If the specifications are ∞ Ω: – Measure resistance between connector terminal 1 and test box socket 67. Specification: max. 1.5 Ω – Measure resistance between connector terminal 2 and test box socket 68. Specification: max.1.5 Ω If the specifications are not attained: the wiring has open circuit – Use wiring diagram to locate and repair open circuit If the specifications are attained: – Remove sensor and check for contamination by metal particles – Check sensor wheel on crankshaft for damage or contamination via sensor mounting hole in engine block. If no malfunction can be found:
Malfunction cause for P1340	▶	– ECM -J220- faulty, replace. Clear DTC memory and create readiness code

VW0159600087020X

Fig. 270 Code P1340: Camshaft/Crankshaft Position Sensor Signals Out Of Sequence (Part 2 of 2). 1998 GTI & Jetta w/2.8L Engine

Cause:		Remedy:
Wiring or fuel injector has open circuit		– Switch ignition off – Connect VAG 1598/18 test box – Remove fuse 18 – Measure resistance between lower terminal for fuse 18 and test box socket 2. Specification 15 – 23 Ω If the specification is not attained: – Measure resistance between connector terminal 1 and fuse 18 lower terminal. Specification max. 1.5 Ω If the specification is not attained, there is an open circuit between the fuel injector connector and the positive connection (G3) in wiring harness – Use wiring diagram to locate and repair open circuit
Malfunction cause for P1240 found: No ▼	Yes ▶	– After repairing malfunction, clear DTC memory and create readiness code

VW0159600084010X

Fig. 267 Code P1240: Cylinder 4 Injector Circuit Open (Part 1 of 2). 1998 GTI & Jetta w/2.8L Engine

Cause:		Remedy:
Wiring or fuel injector has open circuit		– Switch ignition off – Connect VAG 1598/18 test box – Remove fuse 18 – Measure resistance between lower terminal for fuse 18 and test box socket 3. Specification 15 – 23 Ω If the specification is not attained: – Measure resistance between connector terminal 1 and fuse 18 lower terminal. Specification max. 1.5 Ω If the specification is not attained, there is an open circuit between the fuel injector connector and the positive connection (G3) in wiring harness – Use wiring diagram to locate and repair open circuit
Malfunction cause for P1241 found: No ▼	Yes ▶	– After repairing malfunction, clear DTC memory and create readiness code

VW0159600085010X

Fig. 268 Code P1241: Cylinder 5 Injector Circuit Open (Part 1 of 2). 1998 GTI & Jetta w/2.8L Engine

Cause:		Remedy:
Wiring or fuel injector has open circuit		– Switch ignition off – Connect VAG 1598/18 test box – Remove fuse 18 – Measure resistance between lower terminal for fuse 18 and test box socket 4. Specification 15 – 23 Ω If the specification is not attained: – Measure resistance between connector terminal 1 and fuse 18 lower terminal. Specification max. 1.5 Ω If the specification is not attained, there is an open circuit between the fuel injector connector and the positive connection (G3) in wiring harness – Use wiring diagram to locate and repair open circuit
Malfunction cause for P1242 found: No ▼	Yes ▶	– After repairing malfunction, clear DTC memory and create readiness code

VW0159600086010X

Fig. 269 Code P1242: Cylinder 6 Injector Circuit Open (Part 1 of 2). 1998 GTI & Jetta w/2.8L Engine

Cause:		Remedy:
Engine speed (RPM) sensor -G28- supplies implausible signals to the Engine Control Module (ECM)		– Switch ignition off – Check engine speed (RPM) sensor -G28- for tightening torque (connector or sensor loose, or too large a gap to sensor wheel will cause a malfunction) – Connect VAG 1598/18 test box – Check resistance between test box sockets 67 and 68. Specification: 500 – 700 Ω If the specification is not attained: – Replace engine speed (RPM) sensor -G28-
Malfunction cause for P1340 found: No ▼	Yes ▶	– After repairing malfunction disconnect connector from ECM -J220- for 10 seconds, then clear DTC memory and create readiness code
		If the specification is attained: – Disconnect connector from sensor – Measure resistance between connector terminal 1 and test box socket 56. Specification: ∞ Ω – Measure resistance between connector terminal 2 and test box socket 56. Specification: ∞ Ω

VW0159600087010X

Fig. 270 Code P1340: Camshaft/Crankshaft Position Sensor Signals Out Of Sequence (Part 1 of 2). 1998 GTI & Jetta w/2.8L Engine

Cause:		Remedy:
Tank venting system Evaporative Emission (EVAP) canister purge regulator valve -N80- malfunction		– Switch ignition off – Disconnect connector from Engine Control Module (ECM) – Disconnect connector from EVAP canister purge regulator valve – Measure resistance at valve between connector terminal 1 and 2. Specification: ∞ Ω If the specification is not ∞ Ω: short circuit to positive in the activation wire – Use wiring diagram to locate and repair short circuit
Malfunction cause for P1410 found: No ▼	Yes ▶	– After repairing malfunction, clear DTC memory and create readiness code
If no wiring malfunction can be found:		
Malfunction cause for P1410	▶	– EVAP canister purge regulator valve -N80- faulty, replace. Clear DTC memory and create readiness code

VW0159600088000X

Fig. 271 Code P1410: Tank Ventilation Valve Circuit Shorted To Voltage. 1998 GTI & Jetta w/2.8L Engine

Cause:	Remedy:
Engine Control Module (ECM) activates the secondary air injection solenoid valve -N112-, however the HO2S does not detect secondary air injection	– Switch ignition off – Check whether the connector is connected to secondary air injection solenoid valve -N112- (near pump motor) If the connector is firmly attached: – Connect VAG 1598/18 test box – Disconnect connector from valve – Measure resistance between connector terminal 1 and test box socket 50. Specification: max.1.5 Ω If the specification is not attained: – Use wiring diagram to locate and repair open circuit
If the specification is attained:	
	– Switch ignition on – Bridge test box sockets 1 and 6 – Connect test box socket 50 to Ground (GND) – Measure voltage supply at valve connector between connector terminal 1 and 2. Specification: min. 11.5 volts If the specification is not attained: – Use wiring diagram to locate and repair open circuit between connector terminal 2 and fuse 18 lower terminal

VW0159600089010X

Fig. 272 Code P1420: Secondary Air Injection Control Module Shorted To Voltage (Part 1 of 2). 1998 GTI & Jetta w/2.8L Engine

Cause:	Remedy:
Engine Control Module (ECM) detects short circuit to Ground (GND) when activating the secondary air injection solenoid valve -N112-	– Switch ignition off – Connect VAG 1598/18 test box – Disconnect connector from secondary air injection solenoid valve – Measure resistance between connector terminal 1 and test box socket 50. Specification: max.1.5 Ω – Measure resistance between connector terminal 1 and test box socket 1. Specification: ∞ Ω If the specifications are not attained: – Use wiring diagram to locate and repair wiring open/short circuit to Ground (GND)
If no wiring malfunction is found:	
	– Measure resistance between secondary air injection solenoid valve terminals 1 and 2. Specification: 20 – 50 Ω If this specification is exceeded or not attained: – Replace secondary air injection solenoid valve
If the specification is attained:	
Malfunction cause for P1421 ▶	– ECM -J220- faulty, replace. Clear DTC memory and create readiness code

VW0159600090000X

Fig. 273 Code P1421: Secondary Air Injection Valve Circuit Shorted To Ground. 1998 GTI & Jetta w/2.8L Engine

Cause:		Remedy:
Evaporative Emission (EVAP) canister purge regulator valve -N80- in tank venting system or activation wire has short circuit to Ground (GND)		– Switch ignition off – Measure resistance between connector terminal 1 and test box socket 1. Specification: max.∞ Ω – Measure resistance between connector terminal 2 and fuse 18 upper terminal. Specification max. 1.5 Ω If the specifications are not attained: – Use wiring diagram to locate and repair open circuit/short circuit to Ground (GND) – Measure resistance between connector terminal 1 and test box socket 1. Specification: ∞ Ω If the specification is not ∞ Ω: short circuit to Ground (GND) in activation wire – Use wiring diagram to locate and repair short circuit
Malfunction cause for P1425 found: No ▼	Yes ▶	– After repairing malfunction, clear DTC memory and create readiness code
If no wiring malfunction is found:		

VW0159600092010X

Fig. 275 Code P1425: Tank Ventilation Valve Shorted To Ground (Part 1 of 2). 1998 GTI & Jetta w/2.8L Engine

Cause:	Remedy:
Evaporative Emission (EVAP) canister purge regulator valve -N80- in tank venting system or activation wire has short circuit to Ground (GND)	– Switch ignition off – Connect VAG 1598/18 test box – Disconnect connector from EVAP canister purge regulator valve – Switch ignition on – Bridge test box sockets 1 and 6 – Measure voltage supply at valve connector between connector terminal 2 and Ground (GND). Specification: min. 11.5 volts If the specification is not attained: – Switch ignition off – Measure resistance between connector terminal 1 and test box socket 31. Specification: max.1.5 Ω – Measure resistance between connector terminal 2 and fuse 18 upper terminal. Specification max. 1.5 Ω If the specifications are not attained: – Use wiring diagram to locate and repair open circuit – Measure resistance between connector terminal 1 and test box socket 1. Specification: ∞ Ω

VW0159600093010X

Fig. 276 Code P1426: Tank Ventilation Valve Open Circuit (Part 1 of 2). 1998 GTI & Jetta w/2.8L Engine

Malfunction cause for P1420 found: No ▼	Yes ▶	– After repairing malfunction, clear DTC memory and create readiness code
If the specification of min. 11.5 volts is attained:		
		– Measure resistance between secondary air injection solenoid valve terminals 1 and 2. Specification: 40 – 80 Ω If this specification is exceeded or not attained: – Replace secondary air injection solenoid valve
If the specification is attained:		
Malfunction cause for P1420	▶	– ECM -J220- faulty, replace. Clear DTC memory and create readiness code

VW0159600089020X

Fig. 272 Code P1420: Secondary Air Injection Control Module Shorted To Voltage (Part 2 of 2). 1998 GTI & Jetta w/2.8L Engine

Cause:	Remedy:
Engine Control Module (ECM) detects short circuit to positive when activating the secondary air injection solenoid valve -N112-	– Switch ignition off – Connect VAG 1598/18 test box – Disconnect connector from secondary air injection solenoid valve – Measure resistance between connector terminal 1 and test box socket 50. Specification: max.1.5 Ω – Remove fuse 18 – Measure resistance between fuse 18 lower terminal and test box socket 50. Specification: ∞ Ω If the specifications are not attained: – Use wiring diagram to locate and repair short circuit to positive
If no wiring malfunction is found:	
	– Measure resistance between secondary air injection solenoid valve terminals 1 and 2. Specification: 20 – 50 Ω If this specification is exceeded or not attained: – Replace secondary air injection solenoid valve
If the specification is attained:	
Malfunction cause for P1422 ▶	– ECM -J220- faulty, replace. Clear DTC memory and create readiness code

VW0159600091000X

Fig. 274 Code P1422: Secondary Air Injection Valve Circuit Shorted To Voltage. 1998 GTI & Jetta w/2.8L Engine

	– Measure resistance between solenoid valve terminals 1 and 2. Specification: 20 – 50 Ω If this specification is exceeded or not attained: – Replace Evaporative Emission (EVAP) canister purge regulator valve -N80-
If the specification is attained:	
Malfunction cause for P1425 ▶	– Engine Control Module (ECM) -J220- faulty, replace. Clear DTC memory and create readiness code

VW0159600092020X

Fig. 275 Code P1425: Tank Ventilation Valve Shorted To Ground (Part 2 of 2). 1998 GTI & Jetta w/2.8L Engine

		If the specification is not ∞ Ω: short circuit to Ground (GND) in activation wire – Use wiring diagram to locate and repair short circuit
Malfunction cause for P1426 found: No ▼	Yes ▶	– After repairing malfunction, clear DTC memory and create readiness code
If no wiring malfunction is found:		
		– Measure resistance between EVAP canister purge regulator valve terminals 1 and 2. Specification: 20 – 50 Ω If this specification is exceeded or not attained: – Replace EVAP canister purge regulator valve -N80-
If the specification is attained:		
Malfunction cause for P1426	▶	– Engine Control Module (ECM) -J220- faulty, replace. Clear DTC memory and create readiness code

VW0159600093020X

Fig. 276 Code P1426: Tank Ventilation Valve Open Circuit (Part 2 of 2). 1998 GTI & Jetta w/2.8L Engine

Cause:		Remedy:
Engine Control Module (ECM) detects short circuit to positive when activating the secondary air injection pump relay		– Switch ignition off – Connect VAG 1598/18 test box – Disconnect secondary air injection pump relay -J299- from relay panel, location – Measure resistance between test box socket 49 and relay socket 6. Specification: ∞ Ω – Measure resistance between test box socket 49 and battery positive terminal (B+). Specification: ∞ Ω If the specifications are not attained: – Use wiring diagram to locate and repair short circuit to positive
If no wiring malfunction is found:		
		– Replace secondary air injection pump relay -J299-
Malfunction cause for P1450 found: No ▼	Yes ▶	– After repairing malfunction, clear DTC memory and create readiness code
		If the malfunction is still present after replacing secondary air injection pump relay and clearing DTC memory:
Malfunction cause for P1450	▶	– ECM -J220- faulty, replace. Clear DTC memory and create readiness code

VW0159600094000X

Fig. 277 Code P1450: Secondary Air Injection System Circuit Shorted To Voltage. 1998 GTI & Jetta w/2.8L Engine

Cause:	Remedy:
Engine Control Module (ECM) detects short circuit to Ground (GND) when activating the secondary air injection pump relay	– Switch ignition off – Connect VAG 1598/18 test box – Disconnect secondary air injection pump relay -J299- from relay panel, location – Measure resistance between test box sockets 1 and 49. Specification: ∞ Ω If the specification is not attained: – Use wiring diagram to locate and repair short circuit to Ground (GND)
	If no wiring malfunction is found: – Replace secondary air injection pump relay -J299-
Malfunction cause for P1451 found: No ▼ Yes ▶	– After repairing malfunction, clear DTC memory and create readiness code
	If the malfunction is still present after replacing secondary air injection pump relay and clearing DTC memory:
Malfunction cause for P1451 ▶	– ECM -J220- faulty, replace. Clear DTC memory and create readiness code

VW0159600095000X

Fig. 278 Code P1451: Secondary Air Injection Circuit Shorted To Ground. 1998 GTI & Jetta w/2.8L Engine

	If no wiring malfunction is found: – Disconnect connector from secondary air injection pump motor -V101- – Measure resistance between relay socket 8 and connector terminal 2. Specification: max. 1.5 Ω – Measure resistance between connector terminal 1 and test box socket 1. Specification: max. 1.5 Ω If the specifications are not attained: – Replace secondary air injection pump relay
Malfunction cause for P1452 found: No ▼ Yes ▶	– After repairing malfunction, clear DTC memory and create readiness code
	If the malfunction is still present after replacing secondary air injection pump relay and clearing DTC memory:
Malfunction cause for P1452 ▶	– Secondary air injection pump motor -V101- faulty, replace – Clear DTC memory and create readiness code

VW0159600096020X

Fig. 279 Code P1452: Secondary Air Injection System Circuit Open (Part 2 of 2). 1998 GTI & Jetta w/2.8L Engine

	If the specification is not attained: – Use wiring diagram to locate and repair open circuit – Measure resistance between test box sockets 1 and 6. Specification: ∞ Ω If the specification is not attained, the wiring has short circuit to Ground (GND) – Use wiring diagram to locate and repair short circuit to Ground (GND)
Malfunction cause for P1500 found: No ▼ Yes ▶	– After repairing malfunction, clear DTC memory and create readiness code
	If the fuel pump runs: – Disconnect center connector – Remove secondary air injection pump relay – Disconnect connectors from Mass Air Flow (MAF) sensor, Evaporative Emission (EVAP) canister purge regulator valve -N80- and secondary air injection solenoid valve – Remove fuse 18 – Measure resistance between fuse 18 lower terminal and Ground (GND). Specification: ∞ Ω

VW0159600097020X

Fig. 280 Code P1500: Fuel Pump Relay Electrical Circuit Malfunction (Part 2 of 3). 1998 GTI & Jetta w/2.8L Engine

Cause:	Remedy:
Engine Control Module (ECM) -J220- detects short circuit to positive via the activation wire to Fuel Pump (FP) relay -J17-	– Switch ignition off – Connect VAG 1598/18 test box – Disconnect fuel pump relay from relay panel – Measure resistance between test box socket 6 and relay socket 3. Specification: max.1.5 Ω If the specification is not attained: – Use wiring diagram to locate and repair open circuit – Measure resistance between test box sockets 1 and 6. Specification: ∞ Ω If the specification is not attained: the wire has short circuit to Ground (GND) – Use wiring diagram to locate and repair short circuit to Ground (GND)
Malfunction cause for P1502 found: No ▼ Yes ▶	– After repairing malfunction, clear DTC memory and create readiness code
	If no short circuit to Ground (GND) is detected in the activation wire: – Fuel pump relay -J17- faulty, replace
	If the malfunction is still present even with new fuel pump relay:
Malfunction cause ▶	– ECM -J220- faulty, replace. Clear DTC memory and create readiness code

VW0159600098000X

Fig. 281 Code P1502: Fuel Pump Relay Shorted To Voltage. 1998 GTI & Jetta w/2.8L Engine

Cause:	Remedy:
Secondary air injection pump relay -J299- is activated by Engine Control Module (ECM), secondary air injection pump motor -V101- does not run	– Switch ignition off – Connect VAG 1598/18 test box – Disconnect secondary air injection pump relay -J299- from relay panel, location – Measure resistance between test box socket 49 and relay socket 4. Specification: max. 1.5 Ω – Remove fuse 18 – Measure resistance between relay socket 6 and fuse 18 lower terminal. Specification: max. 1.5 Ω If the specifications are not attained: – Use wiring diagram to locate and repair open circuit – Measure resistance between relay socket 2 and battery positive terminal (B+). Specification: max. 1.5 Ω If the specification is not attained: – Check fuse (30 amp) in fuse box next to secondary air injection pump relay -J299- and replace if necessary
	If the fuse is not damaged: – Use wiring diagram to locate and repair open circuit

VW0159600096010X

Fig. 279 Code P1452: Secondary Air Injection System Circuit Open (Part 1 of 2). 1998 GTI & Jetta w/2.8L Engine

Cause:	Remedy:
Electrical malfunction in Fuel Pump (FP) relay -J17-	– Switch ignition off – Check that fuel delivery unit connector is firmly attached – Remove fuse 18 If the fuse is faulty: – Use wiring diagram to locate and repair short circuit to transfer Fuel Pump (FP) -G23- or to Oxygen Sensor (O2S) heating before and after three way catalytic converter
Malfunction cause for P1500 found: No ▼ Yes ▶	– After repairing malfunction, clear DTC memory and create readiness code
	If the fuse is OK: – Connect VAG 1598/18 test box – Switch ignition on – Bridge test box sockets 1 and 6 • The transfer fuel pump -G23- must run audibly If the fuel pump does not run: – Disconnect fuel pump relay from relay panel – Check resistance between test box socket 6 and relay socket 3. Specification: max.1.5 Ω

VW0159600097010X

Fig. 280 Code P1500: Fuel Pump Relay Electrical Circuit Malfunction (Part 1 of 3). 1998 GTI & Jetta w/2.8L Engine

	If the specification is not attained: The positive wire to MAF sensor, EVAP canister purge regulator valve -N80- and secondary air injection solenoid valve has short circuit to Ground (GND) – Use wiring diagram to locate and repair short circuit to Ground (GND) If the specification is attained: – Reconnect center connector – Measure resistance between fuse 18 lower terminal and Ground (GND). Specification: ∞ Ω If the specification is not attained: the positive wire to fuel injectors has short circuit to Ground (GND) – Use wiring diagram to locate and repair short circuit to Ground (GND) If the specification is attained: – Fuel pump relay -J17- faulty, replace
Malfunction cause for P1500 found: No ▼ Yes ▶	– After repairing malfunction, clear DTC memory and create readiness code
	If the malfunction is still present even with new fuel pump relay:
Malfunction cause ▶	– Engine Control Module (ECM) -J220- faulty, replace. Clear DTC memory and create readiness code

VW0159600097030X

Fig. 280 Code P1500: Fuel Pump Relay Electrical Circuit Malfunction (Part 3 of 3). 1998 GTI & Jetta w/2.8L Engine

Cause:	Remedy:
Throttle Position (TP) sensor -G88- in the throttle valve control module supplies a too low/too high signal to Engine Control Module (ECM)	– Check throttle valve control module -J338- at 8-pin connector: (terminal assignment) – Disconnect 8-pin connector from throttle valve control module – Switch ignition on Check voltage as follows: – Between connector terminals 4 and 7. Specification: approx. 5 volts – Between connector terminals 3 and 7. Specification: approx. 10 volts If the specifications are not attained: – Switch ignition off – Connect VAG 1598/18 test box Check resistances as follows: – Connector terminal 3 and test box socket 10. – Connector terminal 4 and test box socket 41. – Connector terminal 7 and test box socket 33. Specifications: max.1.5 Ω If the specifications are not attained: – Use wiring diagram to locate and repair open circuit If no open circuit is found: – Replace ECM -J220-

VW0159600099010X

Fig. 282 Codes P1543 & P1544: Throttle Actuation Potentiometer Signal Too Low/Too High (Part 1 of 3). 1998 GTI & Jetta w/2.8L Engine

	If the voltage supply specifications are attained: – Switch ignition off – Re-attach 8-pin connector to throttle valve control module – Connect VAG 1598/18 test box – At wide open throttle position, check resistance between test box sockets 10 and 33: ∞ Ω – At closed throttle position, check resistance between test box sockets 10 and 33: max.10 Ω – At closed throttle position, check resistance between test box sockets 27 and 53: 3 – 200 Ω If the specifications are not attained: – Disconnect 8-pin connector from throttle valve control module Check resistances as follows: – Connector terminal 1 and test box socket 27. Specification: max.1.5 Ω – Connector terminal 2 and test box socket 53. Specification: max.1.5 Ω – Connector terminal 5 and test box socket 40. Specification: max.1.5 Ω – Connector terminal 8 and test box socket 62. Specification: max.1.5 Ω If the resistance does not correspond to specifications: – Use wiring diagram to locate and repair open circuit Even if the specifications are attained, also measure resistance with 8-pin connector disconnected: – Measure resistance to one another between test box sockets 10, 27, 33, 40, 41, 53 and 62. Specification: ∞ Ω

VW0159600099020X

Fig. 282 Codes P1543 & P1544: Throttle Actuation Potentiometer Signal Too Low/Too High (Part 2 of 3). 1998 GTI & Jetta w/2.8L Engine

Cause:	Remedy:
Engine Control Module (ECM) -J220- detects a faulty Throttle Position (TP) -V60- in the throttle valve control module -J338-	– Check throttle valve control module -J338- at 8-pin connector: (terminal assignment) – Disconnect 8-pin connector from throttle valve control module – Switch ignition on Check voltage as follows: – Between connector terminals 4 and 7. Specification: approx. 5 volts – Between connector terminals 3 and 7. Specification: approx. 10 volts If the specifications are not attained: – Switch ignition off – Connect VAG 1598/18 test box Check resistances as follows: – Connector terminal 3 and test box socket 10. – Connector terminal 4 and test box socket 41. – Connector terminal 7 and test box socket 33. Specifications: max.1.5 Ω If the specifications are not attained: – Use wiring diagram to locate and repair open circuit If no open circuit is found: – Replace ECM -J220-

VW0159600100010X

Fig. 283 Code P1580: Throttle Actuator B1 Malfunction (Part 1 of 3). 1998 GTI & Jetta w/2.8L Engine

		If the specifications are not ∞ Ω: – Use wiring diagram to locate and repair short circuit between wires If the specifications with open/close throttle are not attained, but the wiring is OK: – Replace throttle valve control module -J338-
Malfunction cause for P1580	▶	– Throttle position actuator -V60- faulty, replace throttle valve control module -J338- – After repairing malfunction disconnect connector from ECM -J220- for 10 seconds, then clear DTC memory and create readiness code

VW0159600100030X

Fig. 283 Code P1580: Throttle Actuator B1 Malfunction (Part 3 of 3). 1998 GTI & Jetta w/2.8L Engine

Cause:		Remedy:
MIL permanently lit, and malfunction P1611 is stored in DTC memory		– Switch ignition off – Connect VAG 1598/18 test box – Measure resistance between test box socket 21 and connector terminal 8 of 10-pin connector for automatic transmission. Specification: max. 1.5 Ω If the specification is not attained: – Open/short circuit to Ground (GND) in the communication wire from automatic transmission to Engine Control Module (ECM) -J220- – Use wiring diagram to locate and repair open circuit/short circuit to Ground (GND)
Malfunction cause for P1611 found: No ▼	Yes ▶	– After repairing malfunction disconnect connector from ECM -J220- for 10 seconds, then clear DTC memory and create readiness code
		If the specification is attained and no short circuit to Ground (GND) is found:
Malfunction cause	▶	– ECM -J220- faulty, replace. Clear DTC memory and create readiness code

VW0159600102000X

Fig. 285 Code P1611: MIL Call-Up Circuit/Transaxle Control Module Short To Ground. 1998 GTI & Jetta w/2.8L Engine

		If the specifications are not ∞ Ω: – Use wiring diagram to locate and repair short circuit between wires If the specifications with open/closed throttle are not attained, but the wiring is OK: – Replace throttle valve control module -J338-
Malfunction cause for P1543/P1544	▶	– Throttle Position (TP) sensor faulty, replace throttle valve control module -J338-. – After repairing malfunction disconnect connector from ECM -J220- for 10 seconds, then clear DTC memory and create readiness code

VW0159600099030X

Fig. 282 Codes P1543 & P1544: Throttle Actuation Potentiometer Signal Too Low/Too High (Part 3 of 3). 1998 GTI & Jetta w/2.8L Engine

	If the voltage supply specifications are attained: – Switch ignition off – Attach 8-pin connector to throttle valve control module – Connect VAG 1598/18 test box – At wide open throttle position, check resistance between test box sockets 10 and 33. Specification: ∞ Ω – At closed throttle position, check resistance between test box sockets 10 and 33. Specification: max.10 Ω – At closed throttle position, check resistance between test box sockets 27 and 53. Specification: 3 – 200 Ω If the specifications are not attained: – Disconnect 8-pin connector Check resistances as follows: – Connector terminal 1 and test box socket 27. – Connector terminal 2 and test box socket 53. – Connector terminal 5 and test box socket 40. – Connector terminal 8 and test box socket 62. Specifications: max.1.5 Ω If the resistance does not correspond to specifications: – Use wiring diagram to locate and repair open circuit Even if the specifications are attained, also measure resistance with 8-pin connector disconnected: – Measure resistance to one another between test box sockets 10, 27, 33, 40, 41, 53 and 62. Specification: ∞ Ω

VW0159600100020X

Fig. 283 Code P1580: Throttle Actuator B1 Malfunction (Part 2 of 3). 1998 GTI & Jetta w/2.8L Engine

Cause:		Remedy:
Crankcase dilution		– Fast drive on open roads, however an engine oil change is better
Malfunction cause for P1582 found: No ▼	Yes ▶	– After repairing malfunction disconnect connector from Engine Control Module (ECM) -J220- for 10 seconds, then clear DTC memory and create readiness code
Cause: Opening time for fuel injectors too long, and do not allow idle adaptation		If idle adaptation is exceeded even though engine oil has been changed, fuel injectors worn: Remedy: – Replace worn fuel injectors
Cause: Motor runs outside idle adaptation due to high blow by		Remedy: – Check compression pressures. Specification: 10 – 13 bar (145 – 189 psi), max. permissible difference between cylinders: 3 bar (44 psi) If compression pressure is below 7.5 bar (109 psi): – Repair engine
		If the compression pressure is within specification:
Malfunction cause	▶	– Malfunction in throttle valve control module -J338-, replace – After repairing malfunction disconnect connector from ECM -J220- for 10 seconds, then clear DTC memory and create readiness code

VW0159600101000X

Fig. 284 Code P1582: Idle Adaptation At Limit. 1998 GTI & Jetta w/2.8L Engine

Cause:		Remedy:
MIL does not light up due to short circuit to positive, and causes malfunction to be stored.		– Switch ignition off – Connect VAG 1598/18 test box – Bridge test box sockets 1 and 5 – Switch ignition on • MIL must light-up If the MIL does not light-up: – Switch ignition off – Check bulb in MIL If bulb is OK: – Use wiring diagram to locate and repair short/open circuit from Engine Control Module (ECM) to MIL
Malfunction cause for P1613 found: No ▼	Yes ▶	– After repairing malfunction disconnect connector from ECM -J220- for 10 seconds, then clear DTC memory and create readiness code
		If in the MIL wire no malfunction is found:
Malfunction cause	▶	– ECM -J220- faulty, replace. Clear DTC memory and create readiness code

VW0159600103000X

Fig. 286 Code P1613: MIL Call-Up Circuit Open/ Short To Positive. 1998 GTI & Jetta w/2.8L Engine

Cause:		Remedy:
Valve body solenoid valve does not receive a signal		– Connect VAG 1598/18 test box – Measure resistance between test box sockets 10 and 67: Specification: min. 55 Ω; max. 70.5 Ω – Measure resistance between test box sockets 10 and 1: Specification: ∞ Ω If the specification is not attained: – Use wiring diagram to locate and repair open/short circuit to Ground (GND) – Replace valve body
Malfunction cause for P1778 found: No ▼	Yes ▶	– After repairing malfunction, clear DTC memory
Malfunction cause	▶	– Transmission Control Module (TCM) -J217- faulty. Replace TCM -J217- and clear DTC memory

VW0159600104000X

Fig. 287 Code P1778: Solenoid EV7 Electrical Malfunction. 1998 GTI & Jetta w/2.8L Engine

Cause:		Remedy:
Engine Control Module (ECM) does not receive a signal from Transmission Control Module (TCM)		– Connect VAG 1598/18 test box – Check wiring between socket 13 and ECM connector terminal 18 for open circuit – Use wiring diagram to locate and repair open circuit/short circuit to Ground (GND)
Malfunction cause for P1780 found: No ▼	Yes ▶	– After repairing malfunction, clear DTC memory
Malfunction cause	▶	TCM -J217- faulty: – Replace TCM -J217- and clear DTC memory

VW0159600105000X

Fig. 288 Code P1780: Engine Intervention Readable. 1998 GTI & Jetta w/2.8L Engine

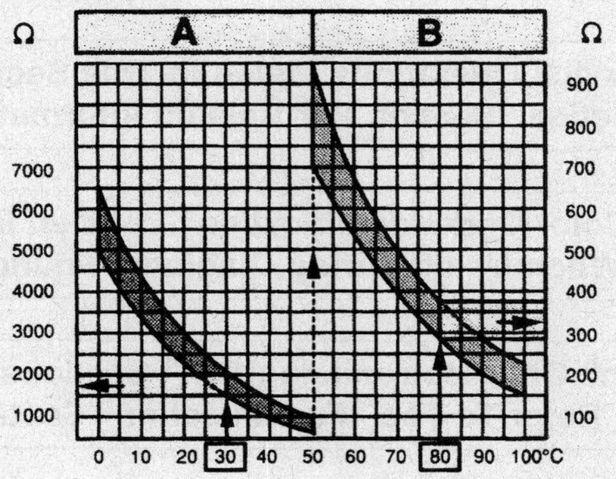

VW1029900144000X

Fig. 289 ECT & IAT sensor resistance chart

Diesel Turbo Direct Injection (TDI)

NOTE: If Unsure Of The System Used On The Vehicle Being Serviced, Refer To The "Engine Systems Identification Chart." Further Assistance For The Proper Use Of Information Contained In This Section Can Also Be Found In The Front Of This Tabbed Section Under "How To Use This Manual."

NOTE: On Air Bag Equipped Models, Refer To "Air Bag System Precautions" Located In The Front Of This Manual For System Disarming & Arming Procedures.

NOTE: Prior To Performing Any Service Operations Listed In This Section, Consult The "Technical Service Bulletins" Section For Related Information.

NOTE: "Electrical Symbol & Wire Color Code Identification" Located In The Front Of This Manual May Be Used As An Aid When Using Wiring Diagrams Found In This Section.

NOTE: Refer To The "Fuel Injection" Or "Electronic Ignition" Sections For Related Diagnostic Information Not Found In This Section. Also, Refer To The "Fuel Injection" Section For System Wiring Diagrams.

NOTE: Refer To "Computer Relearn Procedures" Located In The Front Of This Manual When Battery Power To The Computer Has Been Interrupted.

INDEX

Page No.

Description 17-169
Diagnosis & Testing 17-169
Accessing Diagnostic Trouble Codes 17-169
Clearing Diagnostic Trouble Codes 17-169
Component Locations 17-169
Component Testing 17-169
A/C Compressor Signal 17-174
Brake Lamp Switch 17-170
CAN-Bus 17-174
Clutch Vacuum Vent Valve Switch 17-171
Engine Control Module (ECM) 17-173
Engine Coolant Temperature (ECT) Sensors 17-170
Engine Speed (RPM) Sensor . 17-169
Intake Air Temperature (IAT) Sensors 17-172
Intake Manifold Change-Over Valve 17-173
Manifold Absolute Pressure (MAP) & Barometric Pressure (BARO) Sensors ... 17-170
Mass Air Flow (MAF) Sensor .. 17-172
Vehicle Speed Sensor (VSS) . 17-173
Wastegate Bypass Regulator Valve 17-172
Diagnostic Tests 17-169
1998 Jetta 17-169
New Beetle & 1999–2001 Jetta 17-169
Diagnostic Trouble Code Interpretation 17-169
Wiring Diagrams 17-169
Diagnostic Chart Index 17-191
Precautions 17-169
Air Bag Systems 17-169
Audio Coded Anti-Theft System . 17-169
Battery Ground Cable 17-169
Sensor & Fuel Injector Specifications 17-169

SENSOR & FUEL INJECTOR SPECIFICATIONS

Sensor	Temperature, Degrees F.	Resistance, Ohms
ECT	86	1500–2000
	176	275–375
Engine Speed (RPM)	—	1000–1500
Fuel Temperature	86	1500–2000
IAT	86	1500–2000
	176	275–375
Modulating Position Displacement	—	5–7
Needle Lift	—	80–120
Throttle Position①	—	1000–1500

① — At Closed Throttle Position (CTP).

PRECAUTIONS

Air Bag Systems

Refer to "Air Bag System Precautions" in the front of this manual for system disarming and arming procedures.

Audio Coded Anti-Theft System

Do not use computer memory saver tool. Using the tool will keep the air bag system charged and may cause accidental air bag unit activation.

Obtain the security code from the vehicle operator prior to disconnecting the battery or removing the radio. Refer to the owner's manual for security code disarming and arming procedures.

Battery Ground Cable

Prior to service, disconnect battery ground cable and isolate as required.

DIAGNOSIS & TESTING

Accessing Diagnostic Trouble Codes

Connect suitably programmed scan tool to Data Link Connector (DLC), **Figs. 1 through 3.** Follow scan tool manufacturer's instructions to access Diagnostic Trouble Codes (DTCs).

Diagnostic Trouble Code Interpretation

Refer to **Figs. 4 through 6** for Diagnostic Trouble Code (DTC) interpretation.

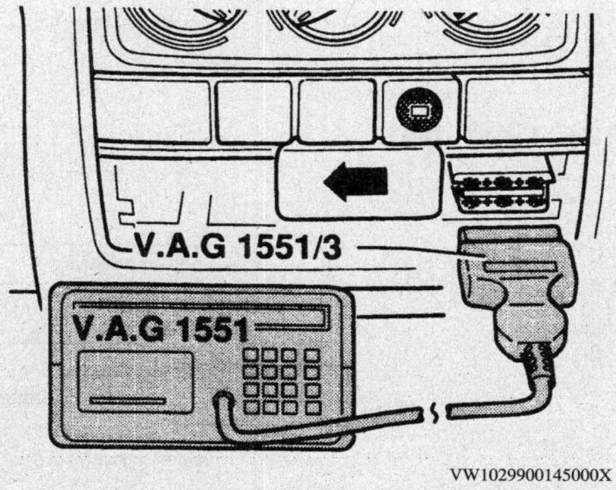

Fig. 1 DLC connection. 1998 Jetta

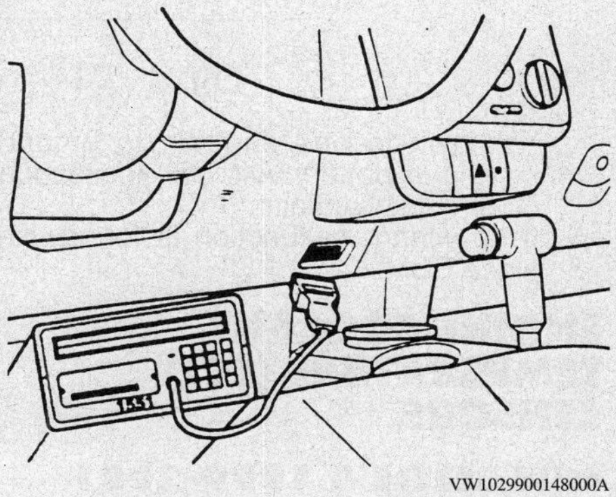

Fig. 3 DLC connection. New Beetle

Component Locations

Refer to **Figs. 7 through 9** for component locations.

Wiring Diagrams

Refer to **Figs. 10 through 42** for wiring diagrams.

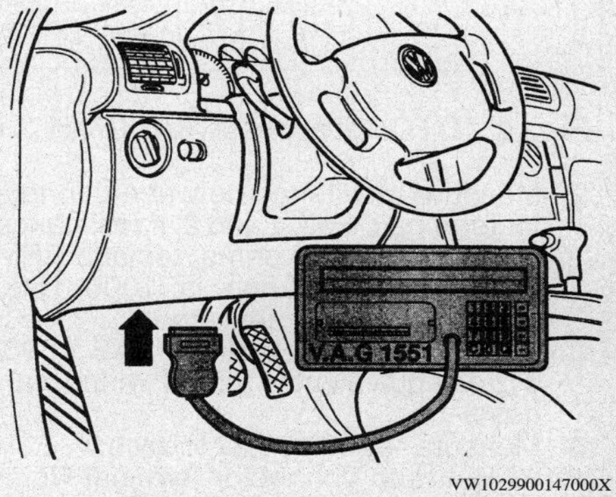

Fig. 2 DLC connection. 1999–2001 Jetta

Diagnostic Tests

1998 JETTA

Refer to **Figs. 43 through 65** for diagnostic tests.

NEW BEETLE & 1999-2001 JETTA

Refer to "Component Testing."

Clearing Diagnostic Trouble Codes

Follow scan tool manufacturer's instructions to clear DTCs.

Component Testing

ENGINE SPEED (RPM) SENSOR

NEW BEETLE & 1999-2001 JETTA

1. Disconnect RPM sensor 3-pin connector.

Scan Tool display	Blink code	MIL	Possible causes	Possible effects
00310 Temperature sensor 1 for Catalyst -G20	1414	On		
Open circuit or short to positive			♦ G20 malfunctioning ♦ Open wire or short circuit	♦ Increased emission values
Short to ground	1414	On	♦ G20 malfunctioning ♦ Wire short to ground	

VW0159600106010X

Fig. 4 DTC interpretation (Part 1 of 12). 1998 Jetta

Scan Tool display	Blink code	MIL	Possible causes	Possible effects
00312 Temperature sensor 2 for Catalyst -G132.	1422	On		
Open circuit or short to positive			♦ G132 malfunctioning ♦ Open wire or short circuit	♦ Increased emission values
Short to ground	1422	On	♦ G132 malfunctioning ♦ Wire short to ground	
00313 Catalyst	1423	On		
Questionable signal			♦ Catalyst malfunctioning ♦ Metering Pump V54 malfunctioning	♦ Increased emission values

VW0159600106020X

Fig. 4 DTC interpretation (Part 2 of 12). 1998 Jetta

Scan Tool display	Blink code	MIL	Possible causes	Possible effects
00513 Engine Speed (rpm) Sensor -G28	2111	On		
Questionable signal			♦ G28 malfunctioning ♦ Engine Speed (rpm) Sensor or sensor wheel too large ♦ Metal particles on G28 or mounting looses	♦ Glow Plug Indicator Light (K29) flashes ♦ Increased idling speed ♦ Poor starting ♦ Engine running rough ♦ Reduced output ♦ No indication on tachometer
No signal	2111	On	♦ G28 malfunctioning ♦ Open wire or short circuit	

VW0159600106030X

Fig. 4 DTC interpretation (Part 3 of 12). 1998 Jetta

Scan Tool display	Blink code	MIL	Possible causes	Possible effects
00519 Manifold Absolute Pressure (MAP) Sensor -G71	2222	On		
Questionable signal			♦ Wastegate Bypass Regulator Valve (N75) malfunctioning ♦ Direct Fuel Injection (DFI) Engine Control Module (ECM) J248 malfunctioning ♦ Hose connection interchanged, not connected	♦ Reduced output ♦ Increased emission values
Short to positive Open circuit or short to ground	2222	On	♦ G71 in ECM J248 malfunctioning	♦ Reduced output ♦ Increased emission values
00522 Engine Coolant Temperature (ECT) Sensor -G62	2312	On		
Short to ground			♦ G62 malfunctioning ♦ Wiring short circuit to ground	♦ Black exhaust when starting ♦ Engine pre-warming not functioning ♦ Pre-glow is always approx. 20 seconds
Open circuit or short to positive	2312	On	♦ G62 malfunctioning ♦ Open wire circuit or short to positive	

VW0159600106040X

Fig. 4 DTC interpretation (Part 4 of 12). 1998 Jetta

2. Measure resistance between connector terminals Nos. 1 and 2. If resistance is not 1000–1500 ohms, replace RPM sensor. If resistance is 1000–1500 ohms, proceed to next step.
3. Connect test box tool No. VAG 1598/31, or equivalent, to ECM wiring harness.
4. Measure resistance as follows:
   a. Between connector terminal No. 1 and test box socket No. 69.
   b. Between terminal No. 2 and socket No. 67.
   c. Between terminal No. 3 and socket No. 71.
   d. If resistance is not less than 1.5 ohms, inspect wiring for open circuit.
   e. Inspect connector wires for short circuit to one another, to ground and to battery voltage. Resistance should be infinite.
5. If no wiring malfunction is found, replace ECM.

MANIFOLD ABSOLUTE PRESSURE (MAP) & BAROMETRIC PRESSURE (BARO) SENSORS

NEW BEETLE & 1999–2001 JETTA

1. Turn ignition Off.
2. Connect test box tool No. VAG 1598/31, or equivalent, to ECM wiring harness.
3. Disconnect MAP sensor 4-pin connector.
4. Measure resistance as follows:
   a. Between connector terminal No. 3 and test box socket No. 39.
   b. Between terminal No. 4 and socket No. 40.
   c. If resistance is not less than 1.5 ohms, inspect wiring for open circuit.
   d. Inspect connector wires for short circuit to one another, to ground and to battery voltage. Resistance should be infinite.
5. If no wiring malfunction is found, replace ECM.

ENGINE COOLANT TEMPERATURE (ECT) SENSORS

NEW BEETLE & 1999–2001 JETTA

1. Disconnect ECT sensor 4-pin connector.
2. Measure resistance as follows:
   a. Between connector terminals Nos. 1 and 3.
   b. Compare resistance to **Fig. 66.**
   c. 86°F (30°C) corresponds to 1500–2000 ohms.
   d. 176°F (80°C) corresponds to 275–375 ohms.
   e. If resistance is not as specified, replace ECT sensor.
   f. If resistance is as specified, proceed to next step.
3. Connect test box tool No. VAG 1598/31, or equivalent, to ECM wiring harness.
4. Measure resistance as follows:
   a. Between connector terminal No. 1 and test box socket No. 70.
   b. Between terminal No. 3 and socket No. 64.
   c. If resistance is not less than 1.5 ohms, inspect wiring for open circuit.
   d. Inspect connector wires for short circuit to one another, to ground and to battery voltage.
   e. Resistance should be infinite.
5. If no wiring malfunction is found, replace ECM.

BRAKE LAMP SWITCH

NEW BEETLE & 1999–2001 JETTA

1. Measure resistance between switch terminals 1 and 4. With pedal depress, resistance should be less than 1.5 ohms. With pedal released, resistance should be infinite.
2. Measure resistance between switch terminals 2 and 3. With pedal depress, resistance should be infinite. With pedal released, resistance should be less than 1.5 ohms.
3. If resistance is not within specifications, replace brake lamp switch.
4. If resistance is as specified, connect

Scan Tool display	Blink code	MIL	Possible causes	Possible effects
00527	2412	On		
Intake Air Temperature (IAT) Sensor -G72				
Short to ground			♦ G72 malfunctioning ♦ Wiring short to ground	♦ Engine pre-warming not functioning
Open circuit or short to positive	2412	On	♦ G72 malfunctioning ♦ Open wire circuit or short to positive	
00532	2234	On		
Supply voltage				
Questionable signal			♦ Power Supply (Terminal 30, B+) Relay (J317) malfunctioning	♦ Various running problems including engine stalls
00539	2311	On		
Fuel Temperature Sensor -G81				
Short to ground			♦ G81 malfunctioning ♦ Wiring short to ground	♦ Increased emission values
Open circuit or short to positive	2311	On	♦ G81 malfunctioning ♦ Open wire circuit or short to positive	

VW0159600106050X

Fig. 4 DTC interpretation (Part 5 of 12). 1998 Jetta

Scan Tool display	Blink code	MIL	Possible causes	Possible effects
00542	2211	On		
Needle Lift Sensor -G80				
Input open			♦ G80 malfunctioning ♦ Open wire or short circuit	♦ Glow Plug Indicator Light (K29) flashes ♦ Engine running rough ♦ Reduced output ♦ Increased emission values
Questionable signal	2211	On	♦ G80 malfunctioning ♦ Injection system wiring to third cylinder not OK ♦ Fuel shortage ♦ Vapor lock	
00550	2244	On		
Injection start control				
Control difference			♦ Cold Start Injector (N108) malfunctioning ♦ Needle Lift Sensor (G80) malfunctioning ♦ Fuel tank empty ♦ Fuel supply not OK, fuel shortage ♦ Vapor lock ♦ Start of delivery not OK	♦ Engine running rough ♦ Reduced output ♦ Increased emission values ♦ Poor cold start characteristics

VW0159600106060X

Fig. 4 DTC interpretation (Part 6 of 12). 1998 Jetta

Scan Tool display	Blink code	MIL	Possible causes	Possible effects
00553	2324	On		
Mass Air Flow (MAF) Sensor -G70				
Questionable signal			♦ G70 malfunctioning	♦ Reduced output ♦ Black exhaust
Open circuit or short to ground	2324	On	♦ G70 malfunctioning ♦ Open wire circuit or short to ground	
Short to positive	2324	On	♦ G70 malfunctioning ♦ Open wire circuit or short to positive	
00575	2221	On		
Manifold Absolute Pressure (Map)				
Control difference			♦ Wastegate Bypass Regulator Valve (N75) malfunctioning ♦ Hose connections interchanged, not connected	♦ Reduced output

VW0159600106070X

Fig. 4 DTC interpretation (Part 7 of 12). 1998 Jetta

Scan Tool display	Blink code	MIL	Possible causes	Possible effects
00625	—	Off		
Vehicle speed signal				
Questionable signal			♦ With electrical Speedometer: no signal from Speedometer (G21) or Speedometer Vehicle Speed Sensor (G22) ♦ With mechanical speedometer: no signal from Vehicle Speed Sensor (G54)	♦ Speedometer indicator not OK
00668	—	Off		
Battery Positive Voltage (B+), Terminal 30				
Signal too low			♦ Power Supply (Terminal 30, B+) Relay (J317) malfunctioning	♦ Engine does not start ♦ Various running problems including engine stalls

VW0159600106080X

Fig. 4 DTC interpretation (Part 8 of 12). 1998 Jetta

test box tool No. 1598/31, or equivalent, to ECM wiring harness.

5. Measure resistance as follows:
   a. Between connector terminal No. 2 and text box socket No. 2.
   b. Between terminal No. 2 and socket No. 28.
   c. Between terminal No. 3 and socket No. 9.
   d. Between terminal No. 4 and socket No. 20.
   e. If resistance is not less than 1.5 ohms, inspect wiring for open circuit.
   f. Inspect connector wires for short circuit to one another, to ground and to battery voltage. Resistance should be infinite.
6. If no wiring malfunction is found, replace ECM.

CLUTCH VACUUM VENT VALVE SWITCH

1998 JETTA

1. Remove instrument panel trim and disconnect clutch vacuum vent valve switch connector.
2. Measure resistance at switch terminals.
3. With pedal released, resistance should be infinite. With pedal depressed, resistance should be less than 10 ohms.
4. If resistance is not within specification, replace switch.
5. If resistance is within specifications, connect test box adapter tool No. 1598/10, or equivalent, to ECM wiring harness.
6. Measure resistance between connector terminal No. 1 and test box socket No. 33, then terminal No. 2 and socket No. 17.
7. Resistance should not be more than 1.5 ohms. If resistance is not within specifications, inspect for open circuit.
8. Inspect for shorts between wires. Resistance should be infinite.
9. If no malfunctions are found, replace Direct Fuel Injection (DFI) Engine Control Module (ECM).

NEW BEETLE & 1999-2001 JETTA

1. Measure resistance at switch terminals.
2. With pedal released, resistance should be infinite. With pedal depressed, resistance should be not more than 10 ohms.
3. If resistance is not within specification, replace switch.
4. If resistance is within specifications, connect test box adapter tool No. 1598/31, or equivalent, to ECM wiring harness.
5. Measure resistance as follows:
   a. Between connector terminal No. 1 and test box socket No. 2.
   b. Between terminal No. 1 and socket No. 28.
   c. Between terminal No. 2 and socket 46.
   d. If resistance is not than 1.5 ohms, inspect for open circuit.
   e. Inspect wires for short to one another, to ground and to battery voltage. Resistance should be infinite.

Scan Tool display	Blink code	MIL	Possible causes	Possible effects
00671 Cruise Control Switch (CCS) -E45	—	Off		
Undefined switch position			♦ E45 malfunctioning ♦ Open wire or short circuit	♦ Cruise control system turned OFF
00741 Brake pedal position monitoring	—	Off		
Questionable signal			♦ Brake Light Switch (F) malfunctioning ♦ Brake Pedal Switch (F47) malfunctioning ♦ F and F47 switch positions not synchronized	♦ Brake light malfunctioning
00765 Modulating Piston Displacement Sensor -G149	1412	On	♦ Injection pump malfunctioning ♦ Open wire or short circuit	♦ Glow Plug Indicator Light (K29) flashes ♦ Various engine running problems ♦ Engine stalls

VW0159600106090X

Fig. 4 DTC interpretation (Part 9 of 12). 1998 Jetta

Scan Tool display	Blink code	MIL	Possible causes	Possible effects
01237 Fuel Cut-off Valve -N109	4321	On		
Mechanical malfunction			♦ N109 malfunctioning, leaking or stuck	♦ Reduced output ♦ Engine stalls
Open circuit or short to ground	4321	On	♦ N109 malfunctioning ♦ Open wire circuit or short to ground	
01242 Final stage in Control Module	4332	On		
Questionable signal			♦ Additional Metering Pump (V54) malfunctioning ♦ EGR Valve (N18) malfunctioning	♦ Various engine running problems ♦ Engine stalls
Open circuit or short to positive	—	Off	♦ All components activated by output Diagnostic Test Mode	♦ Various engine running problems ♦ Engine stalls

VW0159600106110X

Fig. 4 DTC interpretation (Part 11 of 12). 1998 Jetta

Scan Tool display	Blink code	MIL	Possible causes	Possible effects
00777 Throttle Position (TP) Sensor -G79	3131	On		
Questionable signal			♦ G79 malfunctioning ♦ G79 incorrectly set	♦ Glow Plug Indicator Light (K29) flashes ♦ Increased idling speed
Short to positive	3131	On	♦ G79 malfunctioning ♦ Wire short to positive	
01117 Generator load signal for terminal DF	—	Off		
Questionable signal			♦ Generator malfunctioning ♦ Voltage Regulator malfunctioning	♦ Engine pre-heating not operating
01208 Data record	—	Off		
Changed			♦ Error in data record ♦ Data record altered	♦ Vehicle registration withdrawn

VW0159600106100X

Fig. 4 DTC interpretation (Part 10 of 12). 1998 Jetta

Scan Tool display	Blink code	MIL	Possible causes of fault	Possible effects
01268 Quantity Adjuster -N146	4113	On		
Control difference			♦ Injection pump malfunctioning ♦ Open wire or short circuit	♦ Glow Plug Indicator Light (K29) flashes ♦ Various engine running problems ♦ Engine stalls
65535 Direct Fuel Injection (DFI) Engine Control Module (ECM) -J248 malfunctioning	1111	On	♦ Control module internally malfunctioning	♦ Various engine running problems ♦ Engine stalls

VW0159600106120X

Fig. 4 DTC interpretation (Part 12 of 12). 1998 Jetta

6. If no wiring malfunctions are found, replace ECM.

INTAKE AIR TEMPERATURE (IAT) SENSORS

NEW BEETLE & 1999–2001 JETTA

1. Disconnect MAP sensor 4-pin connector.
2. Measure resistance as follows:
   a. Between connector terminals Nos. 1 and 2.
   b. Compare resistance to **Fig. 66.**
   c. 86°F (30°C) corresponds to 1500–2000 ohms.
   d. 176°F (80°C) corresponds to 275–375 ohms.
   e. If resistance is not as specified, replace MAP sensor.
   f. If resistance is as specified, proceed to next step.
3. Connect test box tool No. VAG 1598/31, or equivalent, to ECM wiring harness.
4. Measure resistance as follows:
   a. Between connector terminal No. 1 and test box socket No. 25.
   b. Between terminal No. 2 and socket No. 13.
   c. If resistance is not less than 1.5 ohms, inspect wiring for open circuit.
   d. Inspect connector wires for short circuit to one another, to ground and to battery voltage. Resistance should be infinite.
5. If no wiring malfunction is found, replace ECM.

WASTEGATE BYPASS REGULATOR VALVE

NEW BEETLE

1. Turn ignition Off.
2. Disconnect wastegate bypass regulator valve connector.
3. Measure resistance between connector terminals. If resistance is not 25–45 ohms, replace wastegate bypass regulator valve. If resistance is 25–45 ohms, proceed to next step.
4. Measure voltage between connector terminals with ignition On. If measurement is not approximately battery voltage, proceed to next step.
5. Turn ignition Off.
6. Connect test box tool No. VAG 1598/31, or equivalent, to ECM wiring harness.
7. Measure resistance as follows:
   a. Between connector terminal No. 1 and test box socket No. 28.
   b. Between terminal No. 2 and socket No. 15.
   c. If resistance is not less than 1.5 ohms, inspect wiring for open circuit.
   d. Inspect connector wires for short circuit to one another, to ground and to battery voltage. Resistance should be infinite.
8. If no wiring malfunction is found, replace ECM.

MASS AIR FLOW (MAF) SENSOR

NEW BEETLE & 1999–2001 JETTA

1. Disconnect MAF sensor 5-pin connector.

VAG 1551/1552 Scan Tool Display	SAE Code	Possible Malfunction Cause	Possible Effects	Malfunction Elimination
00513 Engine Speed sensor G28				
Implausible signal	P0321	♦ G28 faulty ♦ RPM sensor or sensor wheel distance too great ♦ Metal chips in G28 and/or socket loose	♦ Engine runs irregular ♦ Engine stalls ♦ Glow plug indicator light blinks	– Check G28
No signal	P0322	♦ G28 faulty ♦ Break in wiring or short circuit		

VW0159900202010X

Fig. 5 DTC interpretation (Part 1 of 33). New Beetle

VAG 1551/1552 Scan Tool Display	SAE Code	Possible Malfunction Cause	Possible Effects	Malfunction Elimination
00519 Intake Air Temperature Sensor G71				
Short to positive	P1155	♦ G71 in ECM faulty ♦ Boost pressure too high ♦ Wastegate bypass regulator valve N75 faulty ♦ Wiring open circuit or short to positive	♦ Reduced power output ♦ Increased emission values	– Check Manifold Absolute Pressure sensor and BARO sensor – Check N75 – Renew ECM
Break in wiring/short to ground	P1156	♦ G71 faulty ♦ Break in wiring or wiring has short to ground		
Voltage supply	P1157	♦ Break in wiring or short circuit		

VW0159900202020X

Fig. 5 DTC interpretation (Part 2 of 33). New Beetle

VAG 1551/1552 Scan Tool Display	SAE Code	Possible Malfunction Cause	Possible Effects	Malfunction Elimination
00522 Engine Coolant Temperature Sensor -G62				
Implausible signal	P0116	♦ G62 faulty ♦ ECM faulty	♦ Black smoke during start ♦ Engine pre-heating not functioning ♦ Pre-glow always takes approx. 15 – 20 seconds	– G62 checking
Short to ground	P1255	♦ G62 faulty ♦ Wiring has short to ground		
Break in wiring/short to positive	P1256	♦ G62 faulty ♦ Break in wiring or wiring short to positive		

VW0159900202030X

Fig. 5 DTC interpretation (Part 3 of 33). New Beetle

VAG 1551/1552 Scan Tool Display	SAE Code	Possible Malfunction Cause	Possible Effects	Malfunction Elimination
00527 Intake Air Temperature (IAT) Sensor -G72				
Short to ground	P1160	♦ G72 faulty ♦ Wiring has short to ground	♦ Engine pre–heating not functioning	– Check G72
Break in wiring/short to positive	P1161	♦ G72 faulty ♦ Break in wiring and/or short to positive		

VW0159900202040X

Fig. 5 DTC interpretation (Part 4 of 33). New Beetle

2. Turn ignition On.
3. Measure voltage between connector terminals as follows:
   a. Between terminal No. 2 and ground.
   b. Between terminal Nos. 2 and 3.
   c. There should be approximately battery voltage.
   d. Between terminal No. 4 and ground.
   e. Between terminal Nos. 3 and 4.
   f. There should be approximately 5 volts.
   g. Turn ignition Off.
   h. If no voltage is present, proceed to next step.
4. Connect test box tool No. VAG 1598/31, or equivalent, to ECM wiring harness.
5. Measure resistance as follows:
   a. Between connector terminal No. 2 and test box socket No. 2.
   b. Between terminal No. 2 and socket No. 28.
   c. Between terminal No. 3 and socket No. 4.
   d. Between terminal No. 4 and socket No. 50.
   e. Between terminal No. 5 and socket No. 52.
   f. If resistance is not less than 1.5 ohms, inspect wiring for open circuit.
   g. Inspect connector wires for short circuit to one another, to ground and to battery voltage. Resistance should be infinite.
6. If no wiring malfunction is found, replace ECM.

INTAKE MANIFOLD CHANGE-OVER VALVE

NEW BEETLE & 1999-2001 JETTA

1. Start and idle engine.
2. Turn ignition Off and observe intake manifold change-over valve flap.
3. Disconnect vacuum unit hose and connect hand vacuum pump tool No. VAG 1390, or equivalent.
4. Operate pump and observe intake manifold flap change-over mechanism for movement ease and operation. If no mechanical component malfunction is found, proceed to next step.
5. Disconnect intake manifold flap change-over valve connector.
6. Measure resistance between change-over valve terminals. If resistance is not 25–45 ohms, replace change-over valve. If resistance is 25–45 ohms, proceed to next step.
7. Measure voltage between connector terminals with engine idling. There should be 5–6 volts.
8. Turn ignition Off. If voltage does not increase to 11–15 volts, then after approximately three seconds, drop to zero volts, proceed to next step.
9. Connect test box tool No. VAG 1598/31, or equivalent, to ECM wiring harness.
10. Measure resistance as follows:
    a. Between connector terminal No. 1 and test box socket No. 3.
    b. Between terminal No. 2 and socket No. 2.
    c. Between terminal No. 2 and socket No. 28.
    d. If resistance is not less than 1.5 ohms, inspect wiring for open circuit.
    e. Inspect connector wires for short circuit to one another, to ground and to battery voltage. Resistance should be infinite.
11. If no wiring malfunction is found, replace ECM.

ENGINE CONTROL MODULE (ECM)

1999-2001 JETTA

1. Connect test box tool No. VAG 1598/31, or equivalent, to ECM wiring harness.
2. Bridge text box sockets 33 and 1 with suitable jumper wires.
3. Measure voltage as follows:
   a. Between test box socket Nos. 2 and 1.
   b. Between socket Nos. 1 and 28.
   c. Between socket Nos. 2 and 27.
   d. Between socket Nos. 27 and 28.
   e. If measurement is not approximately battery voltage, inspect voltage supply relay terminal No. 30.
   f. Inspect connector wires for open circuit, short circuit and transfer resistance.
4. If no wiring malfunction is found, replace ECM.

VEHICLE SPEED SENSOR (VSS)

NEW BEETLE & 1999-2001 JETTA

1. Connect test box tool No. 1598/31, or equivalent, to ECM wiring harness.
2. Connect suitable LED tester between test box socket Nos. 1 and 51.
3. Rotate lefthand front wheel with ignition On.
4. LED must flash approximately four times per wheel rotation.
5. If LED does perform as described, inspect ECM harness connector terminal No. 52 to instrument cluster for open/short circuit.

VAG 1551/1552 Scan Tool Display	SAE Code	Possible Malfunction Cause	Possible Effects	Malfunction Elimination
00532 Voltage supply				
Implausible signal	P0560	♦ Voltage supply relay terminal 30 J317 faulty	♦ Various engine running problems including engine will not start	– Check voltage supply for Diesel direct injection system ECM
00539 Fuel Temperature Sensor -G81				
Short to ground	P1162	♦ G81 faulty ♦ Wiring has short to ground	♦ Increased exhaust emission values	– Check G81
Break in wiring/short to positive	P1163	♦ G81 faulty ♦ Break in wiring and/or short to positive		

VW0159900202050X

Fig. 5 DTC interpretation (Part 5 of 33). New Beetle

VAG 1551/1552 Scan Tool Display	SAE Code	Possible Malfunction Cause	Possible Effects	Malfunction Elimination
Implausible signal	P1246	♦ Injection pump faulty	♦ DTC 01268 – Quantity adjuster control difference – stored ♦ Engine runs unevenly, misfires ♦ No throttle response after deceleration	Replace injection pump, do not replace G80
		♦ (Sporadic) wiring open circuit to fuel shut-off valve	♦ Glow plug indicator light blinks ♦ Engine will not start ♦ Misfiring	– Check wiring and connector on injection pump
		♦ Engine Speed sensor disk bent or loose	♦ Glow plug indicator light blinks ♦ Misfiring at exactly 3000 rpm	– Check sensor disk

VW0159900202070X

Fig. 5 DTC interpretation (Part 7 of 33). New Beetle

VAG 1551/1552 Scan Tool Display	SAE Code	Possible Malfunction Cause	Possible Effects	Malfunction Elimination
00542 Needle Lift Sensor -G80				
Short to ground	P1245	♦ G80 faulty ♦ Wiring has short to ground	♦ Glow plug indicator light blinks ♦ Engine runs rough ♦ Reduced power ♦ Increased exhaust emission values	– Check G80
Implausible signal	P1246	♦ Fuel supply has been interrupted ♦ Lack of fuel ♦ Injection line to cylinder 3 not OK ♦ Filter plugged ♦ Air in fuel system	♦ Glow plug indicator light blinks ♦ Possible DTC 00550 start of injection control difference stored ♦ Misfiring, bucking	– Check fuel system

VW0159900202060X

Fig. 5 DTC interpretation (Part 6 of 33). New Beetle

VAG 1551/1552 Scan Tool Display	SAE Code	Possible Malfunction Cause	Possible Effects	Malfunction Elimination
Implausible signal	P1246	♦ G80 faulty	♦ Glow plug indicator light blinks ♦ Engine runs rough ♦ Reduced power output ♦ Increased exhaust emission values	– Check G80
Break in wiring/short to positive	P1247	♦ G80 faulty ♦ Break in wiring and/or short to positive		
00545 Engine/transmission electrical connection				
Implausible signal	–	♦ Break in wiring or short circuit	♦ Hard to shift	– Check signals from/to automatic transmission

VW0159900202080X

Fig. 5 DTC interpretation (Part 8 of 33). New Beetle

A/C COMPRESSOR SIGNAL

NEW BEETLE & 1999–2001 JETTA

1. Connect test box tool No. 1598/31, or equivalent, to ECM wiring harness.
2. Measure resistance between test box socket Nos. 48 and A/C system. If resistance is not less than 1.5 ohms, inspect wiring for open circuit.
3. If no wiring malfunction is found, inspect A/C control module.

CAN-BUS

1999–2001 JETTA

Automatic Transaxle

1. Connect test box tool No. 1598/18, or equivalent, to transmission control module wiring harness.
2. Measure resistance between test box socket Nos. 3 and 25. Resistance should be 55–75 ohms.
3. If resistance is as specified, proceed as follows:
   a. Inspect wiring for short to battery voltage or ground.
   b. Connect transmission control module and clear DTC memory.
   c. If CAN-Bus malfunction is still displayed, replace transmission control module.
4. If resistance is 115–135 ohms, proceed as follows:
   a. Disconnect ECM connector.
   b. Measure resistance between test box socket Nos. 3 and 25.
   c. If resistance is not 115–135 ohms, proceed to next step.
5. If resistance is less than 5 ohms or more than 135 ohms, proceed as follows:
   a. Disconnect ECM.
   b. Measure resistance between test box socket Nos. 3 and 25.
   c. If resistance is not infinite, inspect wiring for short.
   d. If resistance is infinite, connect test box tool No. 1598/31, or equivalent, to ECM wiring harness.
   e. Measure resistance between test box tool No. VAG 1598/31 sockets Nos. 29 and 41, then test box tool No. VAG 1598/18 sockets Nos. 3 and 25.
   f. If resistance is not less than 1.5 ohms, inspect wiring for open circuit.
   g. Inspect wiring for short to battery voltage or ground.
   h. If no wiring malfunction is found, connect test box tool No. VAG 1598/21, or equivalent, to ABS control module.
   i. Measure resistance between test box tool No. VAG 1598/31 sockets Nos. 29 and 41, then test box tool No. VAG 1598/21 sockets Nos. 10 and 11.
   j. If resistance is not less than 1.5 ohms, inspect wiring for open circuit.

Manual Transaxle

1. Connect test box tool No. 1598/31, or equivalent, to ECM wiring harness.
2. Measure resistance between test box socket Nos. 68 and 75. If resistance is 115–135 ohms, proceed to next step. If resistance is not 115–135 ohms, proceed as follows:
   a. Remove air cleaner.
   b. Disconnect ABS control module harness connector.
   c. Measure resistance between test box sockets Nos. 68 and 75.
   d. If resistance is not infinite, inspect CAN-Bus wiring for short circuit.
3. Connect test box tool No. VAG 1598/21, or equivalent, to ABS control module.
4. Measure resistance between test box tool No. VAG 1598/31 sockets Nos. 68 and 75, then test box tool No. VAG 1598/21 sockets Nos. 75 and 11. If resistance is not less than 1.5 ohms, inspect wiring for open circuit and proceed to next step. If resistance is less than 1.5 ohms, proceed as follows:
   a. Remove air cleaner.
   b. Disconnect ABS control module harness connector.
   c. Inspect wiring between engine and ABS control module for short to ground and short to battery voltage.
   d. If no wiring malfunction is found, connect ECM harness connector.
   e. Connect test box tool No. VAG 1598/21 to ABS control module.
   f. Measure resistance between test box sockets Nos. 10 and 11.
   g. If resistance is not 115–135 ohms, replace ECM.
5. Inspect wiring for short to battery voltage or ground.
6. If no wiring malfunction is found, replace ABS control module.

VAG 1551/1552 Scan Tool Display	SAE Code	Possible Malfunction Cause	Possible Effects	Malfunction Elimination
00550 Injection start control				
Control difference	P1248	♦ Cold Start Injector N108 faulty ♦ Needle Lift Sensor G80 faulty ♦ Fuel tank run dry ♦ Fuel supply not OK, lack of fuel ♦ Air in fuel system ♦ Start of supply not OK	♦ Engine runs rough ♦ Reduced power output ♦ Increased exhaust emission values ♦ Poor cold starting performance	– Check N108 – Check G80 – Fuel filter and/or fuel hoses plugged – Check start of injection

VW0159900202090X

Fig. 5 DTC interpretation (Part 9 of 33). New Beetle

VAG 1551/1552 Scan Tool Display	SAE Code	Possible Malfunction Cause	Possible Effects	Malfunction Elimination
00560 Exhaust gas recirculation system				
Control difference	P1403	♦ Unmeasured air ♦ EGR valve faulty (valve sticking, diaphragm rod does not move)	♦ Reduced power output, black exhaust ♦ Too little or too much EGR	– Check EGR and Mass Air Flow sensor function
00575 Intake manifold pressure				
Control difference	P1550	♦ Wastegate Bypass Regulator valve N75 faulty ♦ Hose connections transposed, not connected	♦ Reduced power output	– Check N75 – Check Boost pressure control

VW0159900202110X

Fig. 5 DTC interpretation (Part 11 of 33). New Beetle

VAG 1551/1552 Scan Tool Display	SAE Code	Possible Malfunction Cause	Possible Effects	Malfunction Elimination
00626 Glow Plug Indicator Light -K29				
Short to positive	P1616	♦ Short to positive	♦ Glow plug indicator light not working	– Check K29
Break in wiring/short to ground	P1617	♦ Break in wiring ♦ Glow plug indicator light faulty	♦ Glow plug indicator light not working	
		♦ Short to ground	♦ Glow plug indicator light continuously ON	
00668 On-board Voltage terminal 30				
Implausible signal	–	♦ Power Supply relay J317 (Terminal 30, B+) faulty ♦ Relay hangs up sporadically	♦ Engine does not start ♦ Driving performance problems until engine stops	– Check Voltage supply

VW0159900202130X

Fig. 5 DTC interpretation (Part 13 of 33). New Beetle

VAG 1551/1552 Scan Tool Display	SAE Code	Possible Malfunction Cause	Possible Effects	Malfunction Elimination
00750 Exhaust Warning Light -K83				
Short to positive	P1693	♦ Short to positive	♦ Glow period warning light not functioning	– Check K83
Break in wiring/short to ground	P1694	♦ Break in wiring ♦ Glow plug indicator faulty	♦ MIL lamp not working	
		♦ Short to ground	♦ MIL lamp lit up continuously	
00765 Modulating Piston Displacement Sensor -G149				
(no display)	P1354	♦ Injection pump faulty ♦ Break in wiring or short circuit	♦ Glow plug indicator light blinks ♦ Poor driving performance ♦ Engine stalled	– Check G149

VW0159900202150X

Fig. 5 DTC interpretation (Part 15 of 33). New Beetle

VAG 1551/1552 Scan Tool Display	SAE Code	Possible Malfunction Cause	Possible Effects	Malfunction Elimination
00553 Mass Air Flow sensor -G70				
Implausible signal	P0101	♦ G70 faulty	♦ Reduced power output ♦ Black exhaust	– Check EGR and Mass Air Flow sensor function
Break in wiring/short to ground	P1144	♦ G70 faulty ♦ Break in wiring and/or short to ground		
Short to positive	P1145	♦ G70 faulty ♦ Break in wiring and/or short to positive		
Voltage supply	P1146	♦ Break in wiring or short circuit		

VW0159900202100X

Fig. 5 DTC interpretation (Part 10 of 33). New Beetle

VAG 1551/1552 Scan Tool Display	SAE Code	Possible Malfunction Cause	Possible Effects	Malfunction Elimination
00625 Speed signal				
Implausible signal	P0501	♦ With electric speedo: no signal from G21 speedometer and/or Speedometer Vehicle Speed sensor G22	♦ Speed display not OK ♦ Cruise Control system shut off ♦ Vehicle bucks during shifting ♦ A/C system shut off	– Check speed signal
Signal too high	P1540			

VW0159900202120X

Fig. 5 DTC interpretation (Part 12 of 33). New Beetle

VAG 1551/1552 Scan Tool Display	SAE Code	Possible Malfunction Cause	Possible Effects	Malfunction Elimination
00671 Cruise Control Switch -E45				
Undefined switch status	–	♦ E45 faulty ♦ Break in wiring or short circuit	♦ Cruise Control System switched OFF	– Check Cruise Control System
00741 Brake pedal monitor				
Implausible signal	–	♦ Brake Light Switch F faulty ♦ Brake Pedal Switch F47 faulty ♦ Switch points for the two switches not synchronized ♦ Faulty fuse ♦ Both brake lights faulty	♦ Glow plug indicator light blinks ♦ Sometimes no throttle response, or loss of power	– Check switches F and F47

VW0159900202140X

Fig. 5 DTC interpretation (Part 14 of 33). New Beetle

VAG 1551/1552 Scan Tool Display	SAE Code	Possible Malfunction Cause	Possible Effects	Malfunction Elimination
00777 Throttle Position sensor G79				
Implausible signal	P0121	♦ G79 faulty ♦ G79 incorrectly adjusted	♦ Glow plug indicator light blinks ♦ Increased idle speed	– Check/adjust G79
Short to positive	P0123	♦ G79 faulty ♦ Wiring has short to positive	♦ Glow period warning light blinks ♦ Engine governed at 1100 rpm	– Check G79
Voltage supply	P1632	♦ Break in wiring or short circuit	♦ Increased idle speed	

VW0159900202160X

Fig. 5 DTC interpretation (Part 16 of 33). New Beetle

VAG 1551/1552 Scan Tool Display	SAE Code	Possible Malfunction Cause	Possible Effects	Malfunction Elimination
01044 Control module incorrectly coded				
(No display)	P1612	♦ Invalid ECM coding	♦ Glow period warning light blinks	– Code ECM
01050 Glow plug monitoring				
(No display)	P0380	♦ Glow plug faulty ♦ Different glow plugs installed	♦ No glow period ♦ Engine runs rough	– Check glow plugs – Check glow plug relay

VW0159900202170X

Fig. 5 DTC interpretation (Part 17 of 33). New Beetle

VAG 1551/1552 Scan Tool Display	SAE Code	Possible Malfunction Cause	Possible Effects	Malfunction Elimination
01117 Load signal for Generator terminal DF				
Implausible signal	–	♦ Generator faulty ♦ Voltage regulator faulty	♦ Engine preheating not functioning	– Check Generator ⇒ Wiring diagrams, Electrical Trouble-shooting and Component Location binder

VW0159900202180X

Fig. 5 DTC interpretation (Part 18 of 33). New Beetle

VAG 1551/1552 Scan Tool Display	SAE Code	Possible Malfunction Cause	Possible Effects	Malfunction Elimination
01162 Combustion misfiring recognized				
(no display)	P0300	♦ Misfiring recognized in several cylinders	♦ Reduced power and then engine stalls	– Check fuel system
Cyl. 1 combustion misfiring recognized	P0301	♦ Lack of fuel ♦ Air in fuel system ♦ Filter plugged ♦ Injection pump faulty ♦ Malfunction in electrical system ♦ Engine speed sensor disk bent or loose ♦ Insufficient compression	♦ Engine runs rough ♦ Misfiring, bucking ♦ Increased exhaust emissions	– Check wiring and plug connection on the injection pump – Check sensor disc – Check compression pressure

VW0159900202200X

Fig. 5 DTC interpretation (Part 20 of 33). New Beetle

VAG 1551/1552 Scan Tool Display	SAE Code	Possible Malfunction Cause	Possible Effects	Malfunction Elimination
01193 Relay for Preheating Coolant, Low Heat Output -J359				
Short to positive	–	♦ Short to positive	♦ Engine preheating not functioning	– Check J359 or J360 – Check wiring

VW0159900202220X

Fig. 5 DTC interpretation (Part 22 of 33). New Beetle

VAG 1551/1552 Scan Tool Display	SAE Code	Possible Malfunction Cause	Possible Effects	Malfunction Elimination
01237 Fuel Cut–off Valve -N109				
mechanical malfunction	P1537	♦ N109 faulty, leaks or sticks	♦ Reduced power output ♦ Engine stalled	– Check N109
Break in wiring/short to ground	P1538	♦ N109 faulty ♦ Break in wiring and/or short to ground	♦ Engine stalled	
01262 Wastegate Bypass Regulator Valve -N75				
Short to positive	P1546	♦ Short to positive	♦ Reduced power output ♦ Boost pressure too low	– Check N75

VW0159900202240X

Fig. 5 DTC interpretation (Part 24 of 33). New Beetle

VAG 1551/1552 Scan Tool Display	SAE Code	Possible Malfunction Cause	Possible Effects	Malfunction Elimination
01265 EGR Vacuum regulator solenoid valve -N18				
Short to positive	P1402	♦ Short to positive	♦ NO EGR	– Check N18
Break in wiring/short to ground	P1441	♦ Break in wiring ♦ EGR Vacuum regulator solenoid valve faulty	♦ NO EGR	
		♦ Short to ground	♦ Too much EGR ♦ Reduced power output, black smoke	

VW0159900202260X

Fig. 5 DTC interpretation (Part 26 of 33). New Beetle

VAG 1551/1552 Scan Tool Display	SAE Code	Possible Malfunction Cause	Possible Effects	Malfunction Elimination
01180 Engine accessories electrical connections				
Short to positive	–	♦ Short circuit in wiring	♦ Vehicle acceleration impaired when A/C switched ON	– Check A/C compressor

VW0159900202190X

Fig. 5 DTC interpretation (Part 19 of 33). New Beetle

VAG 1551/1552 Scan Tool Display	SAE Code	Possible Malfunction Cause	Possible Effects	Malfunction Elimination
Cyl. 2 combustion misfiring recognized	P0302			
Cyl. 4 combustion misfiring recognized	P0304			
Cyl. 3 combustion misfiring recognized	P0303	as for cyl. 1, and additionally: ♦ Needle Lift Sensor -G80 or faulty injector line to cyl. 3		– Check G80

VW0159900202210X

Fig. 5 DTC interpretation (Part 21 of 33). New Beetle

VAG 1551/1552 Scan Tool Display	SAE Code	Possible Malfunction Cause	Possible Effects	Malfunction Elimination
01194 Relay for Preheating Coolant, High Heat Output -J360				
Short to positive	–	♦ Short to positive	♦ Engine preheating not functioning	– Check J359 or J360 – Check wiring

VW0159900202230X

Fig. 5 DTC interpretation (Part 23 of 33). New Beetle

VAG 1551/1552 Scan Tool Display	SAE Code	Possible Malfunction Cause	Possible Effects	Malfunction Elimination
01262 Wastegate Bypass Regulator Valve -N75				
Break in wiring/short to ground	P1549	♦ Break in wiring ♦ Solenoid valve faulty	♦ Reduced power output ♦ Boost pressure too low	– Check N75
		♦ Short to ground	♦ Reduced power output ♦ Boost pressure too high	

VW0159900202250X

Fig. 5 DTC interpretation (Part 25 of 33). New Beetle

VAG 1551/1552 Scan Tool Display	SAE Code	Possible Malfunction Cause	Possible Effects	Malfunction Elimination
01266 Glow Plug Relay -J52				
Short to positive	P1618	♦ Short to positive	♦ Glow plug system not functioning	– Check J52
Break in wiring/short to ground	P1619	♦ Break in wiring ♦ Glow Plug Relay faulty	♦ Glow plug system not functioning	
		♦ Short to ground	♦ Glow plug system on continuously	

VW0159900202270X

Fig. 5 DTC interpretation (Part 27 of 33). New Beetle

VAG 1551/1552 Scan Tool Display	SAE Code	Possible Malfunction Cause	Possible Effects	Malfunction Elimination
01268 Quantity Adjuster -N146				
Control difference	P1561	♦ Injection pump faulty ♦ Break in wiring or short circuit	♦ Glow plug indicator light blinks ♦ Poor driving performance ♦ Engine stopped	– Check N146
Upper limit value	P1562	♦ Quantity adjuster incorrectly adjusted	♦ Glow plug indicator light blinks ♦ Jerking, poor performance	
Lower limit value	P1563	♦ Quantity adjuster incorrectly adjusted or blocked (dirt, chips)	♦ Glow plug indicator light blinks ♦ Black smoke ♦ Rough idle	

VW0159900202280X

Fig. 5 DTC interpretation (Part 28 of 33). New Beetle

VAG 1551/1552 Scan Tool Display	SAE Code	Possible Malfunction Cause	Possible Effects	Malfunction Elimination
65535 Control module faulty				
Faulty	P0605	♦ ECM has internal malfunction	♦ Poor driving performance ♦ Engine stalled	– Replace J248
		♦ Communication problem between Scan Tool and ECM	♦ No effect	– Erase DTC memory, continue monitoring vehicle

VW0159900202300X

Fig. 5 DTC interpretation (Part 30 of 33). New Beetle

VAG 1551/1552 Scan Tool Display	SAE Code	Possible Malfunction Cause	Possible Effects	Malfunction Elimination
18259 Drive data bus				
No message from ABS Control Module	P1851	♦ Malfunction in data lines to ABS Control Module	♦ No driving dynamics control	– Check ECM data wires, pins 68 + 75 using wiring diagram for break in wiring or short circuit:
		♦ Malfunction in ABS system		– Check ABS Control Module

VW0159900202320X

Fig. 5 DTC interpretation (Part 32 of 33). New Beetle

VAG 1551 display	Possible causes	Possible effects	Corrective action
16485 P0101 Mass Air Flow (MAF) Sensor -G70-			
Open circuit/short to ground	♦ -G70- inoperative ♦ Open circuit/short to ground	♦ Reduced power ♦ Black smoke	– Check -G70-
16550 P0116 Engine Coolant Temperature Sensor -G62-			
Implausible signal	♦ -G62- inoperative	♦ Black smoke when starting ♦ Engine glow period inoperative ♦ Glow period is always approx. 20 seconds	– Check -G62-

VW0159900203010X

Fig. 6 DTC interpretation (Part 1 of 28). 1999–2001 Jetta

VAG 1551/1552 Scan Tool Display	SAE Code	Possible Malfunction Cause	Possible Effects	Malfunction Elimination
01269 Cold Start Injector -N108				
Short to positive	P1251	♦ Short to positive	♦ Engine hunts iduring idle, since start of injection is continuously "advanced"	– Check N108
Break in wiring/short to ground	P1252	♦ Break in wiring ♦ Cold Start Injector faulty	♦ Engine hunts during idle, since start of injection is continuously "advanced"	
		♦ Short to ground	♦ Loss of power, since start of injection is continuously "retarded"	

VW0159900202290X

Fig. 5 DTC interpretation (Part 29 of 33). New Beetle

VAG 1551/1552 Scan Tool Display	SAE Code	Possible Malfunction Cause	Possible Effects	Malfunction Elimination
18034 Drive data bus				
No message from Transmission Control Module	P1626	♦ Malfunction in the data lines to the Transmission Control Module	♦ Driving performance problems (jerky shifting, bumpy load changes)	– Check ECM data wires, pins 68 + 75 using wiring diagram for break in wiring or short circuit:
		♦ Automatic transmission malfunction		– Check TCM

VW0159900202310X

Fig. 5 DTC interpretation (Part 31 of 33). New Beetle

VAG 1551/1552 Scan Tool Display	SAE Code	Possible Malfunction Cause	Possible Effects	Malfunction Elimination
18262 Drive data bus				
Hardware malfunction	P1854	♦ Malfunction in data lines to TCM and/or ABS Control Module ♦ Automatic transmission and/or ABS malfunction	♦ Driving performance problems (jerky shifting, bumpy load changes)	– Check ECM data wires, pins 68 + 75 using wiring diagram for break in wiring or short circuit:
		♦ Automatic transmission system malfunction		– Check TCM

VW0159900202330X

Fig. 5 DTC interpretation (Part 33 of 33). New Beetle

VAG 1551 display	Possible causes	Possible effects	Corrective action
16705 P0321 RPM Sensor -G28-			
Implausible signal	♦ -G28- inoperative ♦ RPM sensor/sensor wheel gap too wide ♦ Metal chips on -G28- or retaining base loose	♦ Engine will not start ♦ Engine stalls ♦ Glow Plug Indicator Lamp -K29- flashes ♦ Speedometer inoperative	– Check -G28-
16706 P0322 Engine RPM Sensor -G28-			
No signal	♦ -G28- inoperative ♦ Open/short circuit	♦ Engine will not start ♦ Engine stalls ♦ Glow Plug Indicator Lamp -K29- flashes ♦ Speedometer inoperative	– Check -G28-

VW0159900203020X

Fig. 6 DTC interpretation (Part 2 of 28). 1999–2001 Jetta

VAG 1551 display	Possible causes	Possible effects	Corrective action
16885 P0501 Vehicle Speed Signal (VSS) Implausible signal	♦ No signal from Speedometer Vehicle Speed (VSS) Sensor -G22-	♦ Speedometer display inoperative ♦ Cruise control off ♦ Vehicle jerks when changing gear ♦ Air conditioner off	– Check Speedometer Vehicle Speed (VSS) sensor
16989 P0605 Engine Control Module (ECM) -J248- inoperative	♦ ECM inoperative	♦ Various running problems ♦ Engine will not start	– Replace Engine Control Module (ECM) -J248-

VW0159900203030X

Fig. 6 DTC interpretation (Part 3 of 28). 1999–2001 Jetta

VAG 1551 display	Possible causes	Possible effects	Corrective action
17552 P1144 Mass Air Flow (MAF) Sensor -G70- Open circuit/short to ground	♦ -G70- inoperative ♦ Open circuit/short to ground	♦ Reduced power ♦ Black smoke	– Check -G70-
17553 P1145 Mass Air Flow (MAF) Sensor -G70- Short to positive (B+)	♦ -G70- inoperative ♦ Open circuit/short to positive (B+)	♦ Reduced power ♦ Black smoke	– Check -G70-

VW0159900203040X

Fig. 6 DTC interpretation (Part 4 of 28). 1999–2001 Jetta

VAG 1551 display	Possible causes	Possible effects	Corrective action
17554 P1146 Mass Air Flow (MAF) Sensor -G70- Supply voltage	♦ Operating voltage too high or too low ♦ Open circuit	♦ Reduced power ♦ Black smoke	– Check -G70-
17563 P1155 Manifold Absolute Pressure (MAP) Sensor -G71- Short to positive (B+)	♦ -G71- inoperative ♦ Short to positive (B+)	♦ Reduced power	– Check -G71–

VW0159900203050X

Fig. 6 DTC interpretation (Part 5 of 28). 1999–2001 Jetta

VAG 1551 display	Possible causes	Possible effects	Corrective action
17564 P1156 Manifold Absolute Pressure (MAP) Sensor -G71- Open circuit/short to ground	♦ -G71- inoperative ♦ Open circuit/short to ground	♦ Reduced power ♦ Increased emission values	– Check -G71-
17565 P1157 Manifold Absolute Pressure (MAP) Sensor -G71- Supply voltage	♦ G71 inoperative ♦ Open circuit/short circuit	♦ Reduced power ♦ Increased emission values	– Check -G71-

VW0159900203060X

Fig. 6 DTC interpretation (Part 6 of 28). 1999–2001 Jetta

VAG 1551 display	Possible causes	Possible effects	Corrective action
17566 P1157 Manifold Absolute Pressure (MAP) Sensor -G71- Implausible signal	♦ -G71- inoperative	♦ Reduced power ♦ Increased emission values	– Check -G71-
17568 P1160 Intake Air Temperature (IAT) Sensor -G72- Short to ground	♦ -G72- inoperative ♦ Short to ground	♦ Constant temperature of 136.8° C (275° F)	– Check -G72-

VW0159900203070X

Fig. 6 DTC interpretation (Part 7 of 28). 1999–2001 Jetta

VAG 1551 display	Possible causes	Possible effects	Corrective action
17569 P1161 Intake Air Temperature (IAT) Sensor -G72- Open circuit/short to positive (B+)	♦ -G72- inoperative ♦ Open circuit or short to positive (B+)	♦ Goes to constant temperature of 136.8 °C (275° F) ♦ Engine glow period inoperative	– Check -G72-
17570 P1162 Fuel Temperature Sensor -G81- Short to ground	♦ -G81- inoperative ♦ Short to ground	♦ Increased emission values	– Check -G81-

VW0159900203080X

Fig. 6 DTC interpretation (Part 8 of 28). 1999–2001 Jetta

VAG 1551 display	Possible causes	Possible effects	Corrective action
17571 P1163 Fuel Temperature Sensor -G81- Open circuit/short to positive (B+)	♦ -G81- inoperative ♦ Open circuit/short to positive (B+)	♦ Increased emission values	– Check -G81-
17572 P1164 Fuel Temperature Sensor -G81- Implausible signal	♦ -G81- inoperative	♦ Increased emission values	– Check -G81

VW0159900203090X

Fig. 6 DTC interpretation (Part 9 of 28). 1999–2001 Jetta

VAG 1551 display	Possible causes	Possible effects	Corrective action
17653 P1245 Needle Lift Sensor -G80- Short to ground	♦ -G80- inoperative ♦ Short to ground	♦ Glow Plug Indicator Lamp -K29- flashes ♦ Engine runs rough ♦ Reduced power ♦ Increased emission values	– Check -G80-
17654 P1246 Needle Lift Sensor -G80- Implausible signal	♦ -G80- inoperative ♦ No. 3 Cyl. injector line damaged ♦ Fuel shortage ♦ Air in fuel system	♦ Glow Plug Indicator Lamp -K29- flashes ♦ Engine runs rough ♦ Reduced power ♦ Increased emission values	– Check -G80-

VW0159900203100X

Fig. 6 DTC interpretation (Part 10 of 28). 1999–2001 Jetta

VAG 1551 display	Possible causes	Possible effects	Corrective action
17655 P1247 Needle Lift Sensor -G80- Open circuit/short to positive (B+)	♦ -G80- inoperative ♦ Open circuit/short circuit	♦ Glow Plug Indicator Lamp -K29- flashes ♦ Engine runs rough ♦ Reduced power ♦ Increased emission values	– Check -G80-
17656 P1248 Start of cold start injector -N108- Control difference	♦ Cold Start Injector -N108- inoperative ♦ Needle Lift Sensor -G80- inoperative ♦ Fuel tank empty ♦ Fuel supply low ♦ Start of delivery not OK.	♦ Engine runs rough ♦ Reduced power ♦ Increased emission values ♦ Poor cold start	– Check N108 – Check -G80- – Check and adjust injection start control dynamically – Fuel filter or fuel line blocked

VW0159900203110X

Fig. 6 DTC interpretation (Part 11 of 28). 1999–2001 Jetta

VAG 1551 display	Possible causes	Possible effects	Corrective action
17659 P1251 Start of Cold Start Injector -N108- Short to positive (B+)	♦ Short to positive (B+)	♦ Engine knocks at idle, start of injection is "advanced" continuously	– Check -N108-
17660 P1252 Start of Cold Start Injector -N108- Open circuit/short to ground	♦ -N108- inoperative ♦ Open circuit	♦ Engine knocks at idle, cold start is "advanced" continuously	– Check -N108-
	♦ Short to ground	♦ Poor performance, start of injection is "advanced" continually	

VW0159900203120X

Fig. 6 DTC interpretation (Part 12 of 28). 1999–2001 Jetta

VAG 1551 display	Possible causes	Possible effects	Corrective action
17663 P1255 Engine Coolant Temperature (ECT) Sensor -G62- Short to ground	♦ -G62- inoperative ♦ Short to ground	♦ Black smoke when starting ♦ Glow period is always approx. 20 seconds	– Check -G62-
17664 P1256 Engine Coolant Temperature (ECT) Sensor -G62- Open circuit/short to positive (B+)	♦ -G62- inoperative ♦ Open circuit or short to positive (B+)	♦ Black smoke when starting ♦ Glow period is always approx. 20 seconds	– Check -G62-

VW0159900203130X

Fig. 6 DTC interpretation (Part 13 of 28). 1999–2001 Jetta

VAG 1551 display	Possible causes	Possible effects	Corrective action
17811 P1403 Exhaust Gas Recirculation (EGR) system Control difference	♦ Unmetered air ♦ Hose connections interchanged, disconnected ♦ EGR Valve inoperative (valve sticking, diaphragm rod does not move)	♦ Reduced power ♦ Black smoke ♦ Too little or too much EGR	– Check EGR:
17849 P1441 EGR Vacuum Regulator Solenoid Valve -N18- Open circuit/short to ground	♦ Open circuit ♦ -N18- inoperative	♦ No EGR	– Check -N18-
	♦ Short to ground	♦ Too much EGR ♦ Reduced power ♦ Black smoke	

VW0159900203150X

Fig. 6 DTC interpretation (Part 15 of 28). 1999–2001 Jetta

VAG 1551 display	Possible causes	Possible effects	Corrective action
17948 P1540 Vehicle speed signal Signal too high	♦ Vehicle speed more than 260 km/h (162 mph) ♦ Instrument cluster inoperative ♦ No signal from Speedometer Vehicle Speed Sensor (VSS) -G22-	♦ Speedometer display inoperative ♦ Cruise control off ♦ Vehicle jerks when changing gear ♦ A/C off	– Check vehicle speed signal
17955 P1546 Wastegate Bypass Regulator valve -N75- Short to positive (B+)	♦ Short to positive (B+)	♦ Reduced power ♦ Charge pressure too low	– Check -N75-

VW0159900203170X

Fig. 6 DTC interpretation (Part 17 of 28). 1999–2001 Jetta

VAG 1551 display	Possible causes	Possible effects	Corrective action
17969 P1561 Quantity adjuster -N146- Control difference	♦ Injection pump inoperative ♦ Open/short circuit	♦ Glow Plug Indicator Lamp -K29- flashes ♦ Various running problems ♦ Engine will not start	– Check N146-
17970 P1562 Quantity adjuster -N146- Upper stop value	– Quantity adjuster -N146- inoperative/blocked – Upper stop value obtained	– Reduced power – Jerking	– Check -N146-

VW0159900203190X

Fig. 6 DTC interpretation (Part 19 of 28). 1999–2001 Jetta

VAG 1551 display	Possible causes	Possible effects	Corrective action
17762 P1354 Modulating Piston Displacement Sensor -G149- Electrical malfunction in circuit	♦ Injection pump inoperative ♦ Open/short circuit	♦ Glow Plug Indicator Lamp -K29- flashes ♦ Various running problems ♦ Engine will not start	– Check -G149-
17795 P1387 Engine Control Module (ECM) -J248- inoperative	♦ ECM inoperative	♦ Various running problems ♦ Engine will not start	– Replace ECM -
17810 P1402 EGR Vacuum Regulator Solenoid Valve -N18- Short to positive (B+)	♦ Short to positive (B+)	♦ No EGR	– Check EGR Vacuum Regulator Solenoid Valve -N18-

VW0159900203140X

Fig. 6 DTC interpretation (Part 14 of 28). 1999–2001 Jetta

VAG 1551 display	Possible causes	Possible effects	Corrective action
17945 P1537 Fuel Cut-off Valve -N109- Incorrect function	♦ -N109- inoperative, leaking or sticking	♦ Reduced power ♦ Engine will not start	– Check -N109-
17946 P1538 Fuel Cut-off Valve -N109- Open circuit/short to ground	♦ -N109- inoperative ♦ Open circuit/short to ground	♦ Reduced power ♦ Engine will not start	– Check -N109-

VW0159900203160X

Fig. 6 DTC interpretation (Part 16 of 28). 1999–2001 Jetta

VAG 1551 display	Possible causes	Possible effects	Corrective action
17957 P1549 Wastegate By-pass Regulator valve -N75- Open circuit/short to ground	♦ -N75- inoperative ♦ Open circuit	♦ Reduced power ♦ Charge pressure too low	– Check -N75-
	♦ Short to ground	♦ Reduced power ♦ Charge pressure too high	
17958 P1550 Charge pressure Control difference	♦ Wastegate Bypass Regulator valve -N75- inoperative ♦ Hose connections interchanged, disconnected	♦ Reduced power	– Check -N75- – Check charge pressure control

VW0159900203180X

Fig. 6 DTC interpretation (Part 18 of 28). 1999–2001 Jetta

VAG 1551 display	Possible causes	Possible effects	Corrective action
17971 P1563 Quantity adjuster -N146- Lower stop value	– -N146- inoperative/blocked – Lower stop value obtained	– Black smoke – Rough idle	– Check -N146-
18008 P1600 Supply voltage terminal 15 Voltage too low	♦ No voltage supply when ignition is on (terminal 15)	♦ Various running problems ♦ Engine will not start	– Check voltage supply for Engine Control Module (ECM) -J248-

VW0159900203200X

Fig. 6 DTC interpretation (Part 20 of 28). 1999–2001 Jetta

VAG 1551 display	Possible causes	Possible effects	Corrective action
18020 P1612 Engine Control Module (ECM) -J248- incorrectly coded	◆ Invalid ECM code	◆ Glow Plug Indicator Lamp -K29- flashes	– Code ECM -J248-
18024 P1616 Glow Plug Indicator Lamp -K29- Short to positive (B+)	◆ Short to positive (B+)	◆ Glow Plug Indicator Lamp -K29- inoperative	– Check K29

VW0159900203210X

Fig. 6 DTC interpretation (Part 21 of 28). 1999–2001 Jetta

VAG 1551 display	Possible causes	Possible effects	Corrective action
18027 P1619 Glow Plug Relay -J52- Open circuit/short to ground	◆ -J52- inoperative ◆ Open circuit/short to ground	◆ No glow period ◆ Poor cold starting ◆ Glow Plug Indicator Lamp -K29- flashes	– Check -J52-

VW0159900203230X

Fig. 6 DTC interpretation (Part 23 of 28). 1999–2001 Jetta

VAG 1551 display	Possible causes	Possible effects	Corrective action
18040 P1632 Throttle Position (TP) Sensor -G79- Supply voltage	◆ Voltage too high or too low ◆ Open circuit	◆ Glow Plug Indicator Lamp -K29- flashes ◆ Increased idle speed	– Check -G79-

VW0159900203250X

Fig. 6 DTC interpretation (Part 25 of 28). 1999–2001 Jetta

VAG 1551 display	Possible causes	Possible effects	Corrective action
18056 P1648 Drive train CAN-Bus System component inoperative	◆ Malfunction in CAN-Bus circuit to transmission or ABS Control Module -J104-	◆ Various running problems (gear change jolts, load change jolts) ◆ No electronic control	– Check CAN-Bus
18057 P1649 Drive train CAN-Bus Implausible signal from ABS Control Module -J104-	◆ Malfunction in CAN-Bus circuit to ABS Control Module -J104-	◆ No electronic control	– Check CAN-Bus
	◆ Malfunction in system (disconnected Control Module for ABS, ABS incorrectly coded)		

VW0159900203270X

Fig. 6 DTC interpretation (Part 27 of 28). 1999–2001 Jetta

VAG 1551 display	Possible causes	Possible effects	Corrective action
18025 P1617 Glow Plug Indicator Lamp -K29- Open circuit/short to ground	◆ Open circuit ◆ Bulb inoperative	◆ Glow Plug Indicator Lamp -K29- inoperative	– Check -K29-
	◆ Short to ground	◆ Glow Plug Indicator Lamp -K29- on continuously	
18026 P1618 Glow Plug Relay -J52- Short to positive (B+)	◆ -J52- inoperative ◆ Short to positive (B+)	◆ No glow period ◆ Poor cold starting ◆ Glow Plug Indicator Lamp -K29- flashes	– Check -J52-

VW0159900203220X

Fig. 6 DTC interpretation (Part 22 of 28). 1999–2001 Jetta

VAG 1551 display	Possible causes	Possible effects	Corrective action
18034 P1626 Drive train CAN-Bus Implausible signal from Transmission Control Module (TCM) -J217-	◆ Malfunction in Transmission Control Module -J217-	◆ Various running problems (gear change jolts, load change jolts)	– Check CAN-Bus
	◆ Malfunction in Transmission Control Module -J217-	◆ TCM in emergency run mode	
18039 P1631 Throttle Position (TP) Sensor -G79- Signal too high	◆ -G79- malfunction	◆ Glow Plug Indicator Lamp -K29- flashes ◆ Increased idle speed	– Check -G79-

VW0159900203240X

Fig. 6 DTC interpretation (Part 24 of 28). 1999–2001 Jetta

VAG 1551 display	Possible causes	Possible effects	Corrective action
18047 P1639 Throttle Position (TP) Sensor 1/2 -G79- + Sender 2 -G185-[1)] Implausible signal	◆ -G79- inoperative	◆ Increased idle speed	– Check -G79-
18048 P1640 Engine Control Module (ECM) -J248- inoperative	◆ ECM -J248- malfunction	◆ Various running problems ◆ Engine will not start	– Replace ECM -J248-

1) Incorrect DTC text display. Display must indicate: Throttle Position (TP) Sensor -G79- implausible signal

VW0159900203260X

Fig. 6 DTC interpretation (Part 26 of 28). 1999–2001 Jetta

VAG 1551 display	Possible causes	Possible effects	Corrective action
18259 P1851 Drive train CAN-Bus Implausible signal from ABS Control Module -J104-	◆ Malfunction in CAN-Bus wiring to transmission or ABS Control Module -J104-	◆ No electronic control	– Check CAN-Bus
	◆ Malfunction in ABS system		
18262 P1854 Drive train CAN-Bus Inoperative	◆ Malfunction in CAN-Bus wiring to transmission or ABS Control Module -J104- ◆ Malfunction in system: Automatic transmission or ABS	◆ Various running problems (gear change jolts, load change jolts) ◆ No electronic control	– Check CAN-Bus

VW0159900203280X

Fig. 6 DTC interpretation (Part 28 of 28). 1999–2001 Jetta

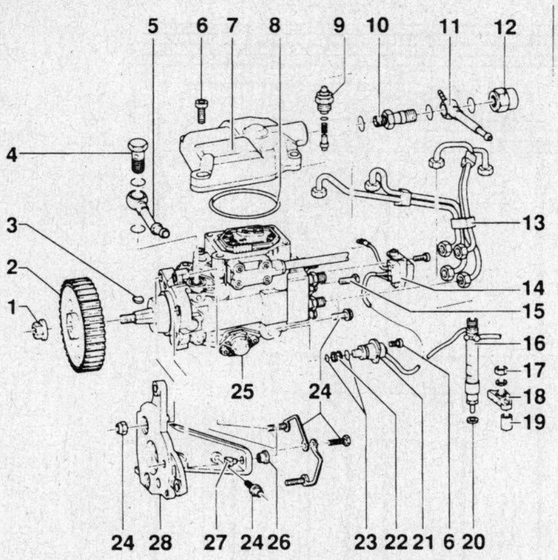

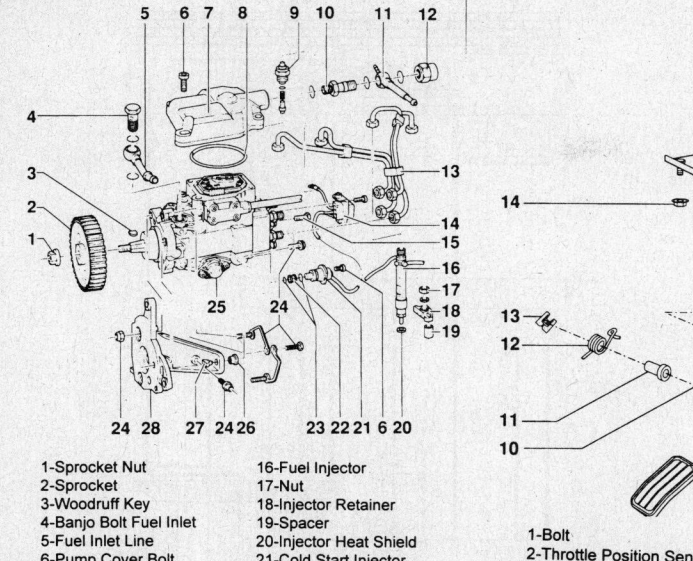

1-Sprocket Nut
2-Sprocket
3-Woodruff Key
4-Banjo Bolt Fuel Inlet
5-Fuel Inlet Line
6-Pump Cover Bolt
7-Pump Cover
8-Gasket
9-Fuel Shut Off Valve
10-Union/Reducer
11-Fuel Return Line
12-Cap Nut Fuel Return
13-Fuel Injector Pipe Set
14-Connector
15-Bolt
16-Fuel Injector
17-Nut
18-Injector Retainer
19-Spacer
20-Injector Heat Shield
21-Cold Start Injector
22-Strainer
23-O-ring
24-Bolt
25-Timing Control Cover
26-Tapered Sleeve
27-Tapered Nut
28-Pump Mount

VW1029600069000X

Fig. 7 Injection pump components

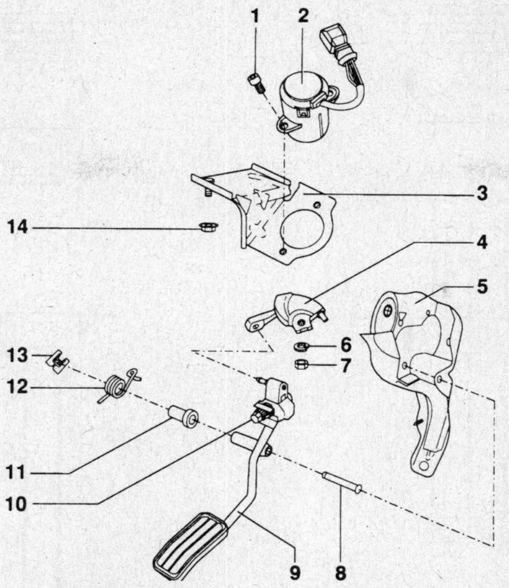

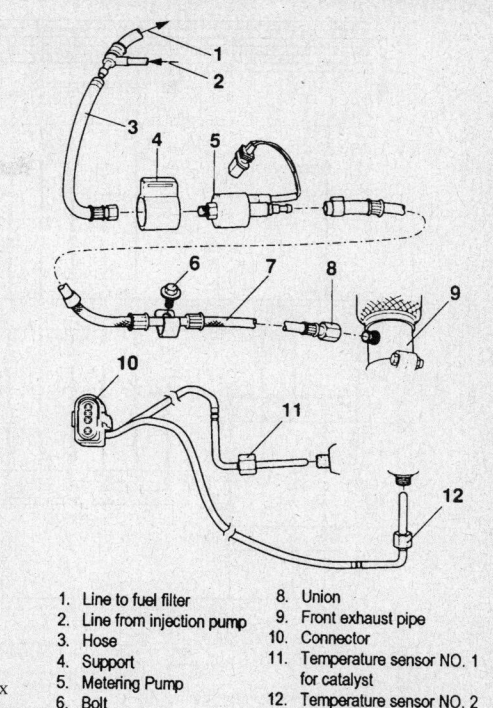

1-Bolt
2-Throttle Position Sensor
3-Mounting Bracket
4-Cam
5-Mounting Pedestal
6-Lockwasher
7-Nut
8-Dowel Pin
9-Pedal
10-Adjustment Bolt
11-Bushing
12-Spring
13-Circlip
14-Nut

VW1029600073000X

Fig. 8 Throttle position sensor components

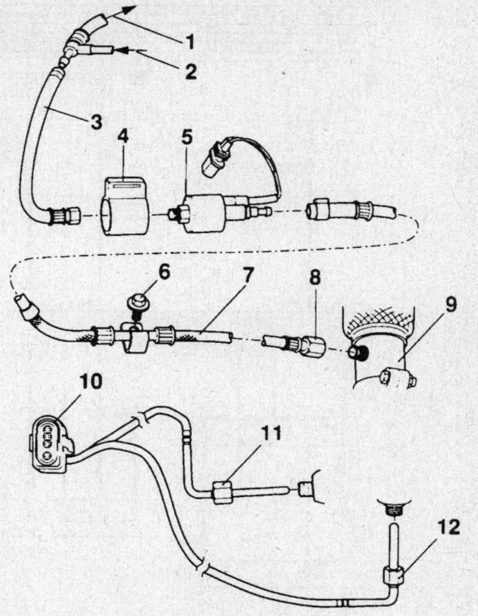

1. Line to fuel filter
2. Line from injection pump
3. Hose
4. Support
5. Metering Pump
6. Bolt
7. Hose
8. Union
9. Front exhaust pipe
10. Connector
11. Temperature sensor NO. 1 for catalyst
12. Temperature sensor NO. 2 for catalyst

VW1029600091000X

Fig. 9 Additional fuel metering device component locations. Automatic transaxle

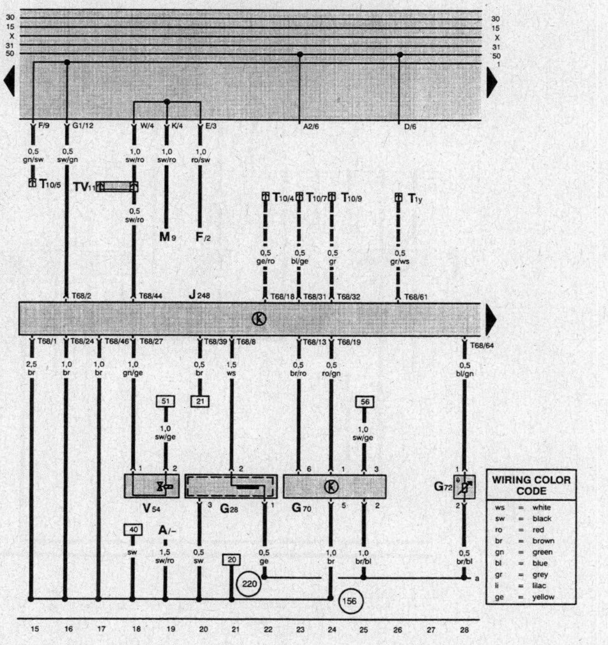

A – Battery
F – Brake Light Switch
G28 – Engine Speed (RPM) Sensor
G70 – Mass Air Flow (MAF) Sensor
G72 – Intake Air Temperature (IAT) Sensor
J248 – Diesel Direct Fuel Injection (DFI) Engine Control Module (ECM)
M9 – Left Brake Light
T1y – Single Connector
T10 – 10-Pin Connector
T68 – 68-Pin Connector
TV11 – Terminal 54 Wire Connector
V54 – Metering Pump

(156) – Ground connection, in Diesel Direct Fuel Injection (DFI) wiring harness

(220) – Ground connection (sensor ground), in engine compartment wiring harness

VW1029900123010X

Fig. 10 TDI wiring diagram (Part 1 of 4). 1998 Jetta

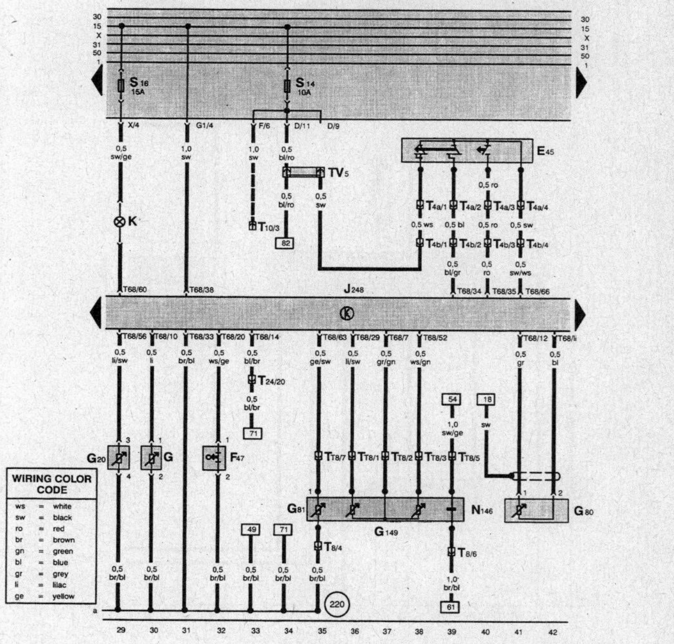

E45 – Cruise Control Switch
F47 – Brake Switch
G – Sender for Fuel Gauge
G20 – Temperature Sensor I for Catalyst
G80 – Needle Lift Sensor
G81 – Fuel Temperature Sensor
G149 – Modulating Piston Displacement Sensor
J248 – Diesel Direct Fuel Injection (DFI) Engine Control Module (ECM)
K – Instrument Cluster
N146 – Quantity Adjuster
T4a – 4-Pin Connector
T4b – 4-Pin Connector
T8 – 8-Pin Connector
T10 – 10-Pin Connector
T24 – 24-Pin Connector, in engine compartment
T68 – 68-Pin Connector, on Diesel DFI ECM
TV5 – Terminal 15a Wire Connector

(220) – Ground connection (sensor ground), in engine compartment wiring harness

VW1029900123020X

Fig. 10 TDI wiring diagram (Part 2 of 4). 1998 Jetta

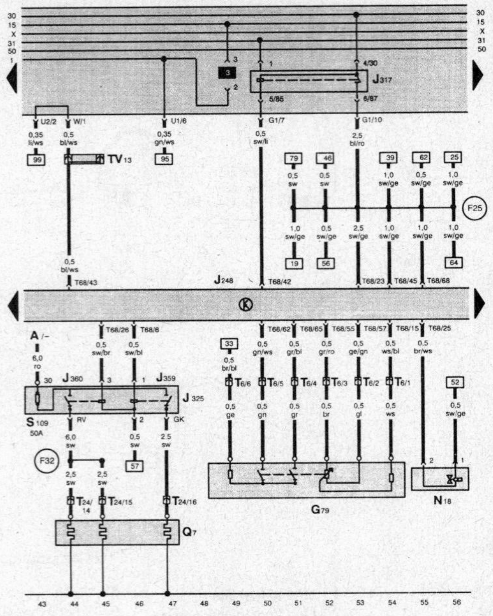

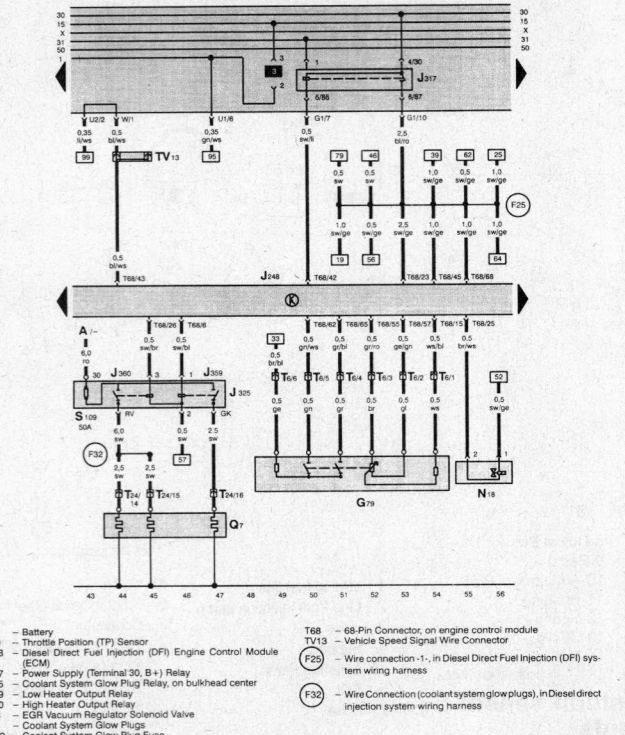

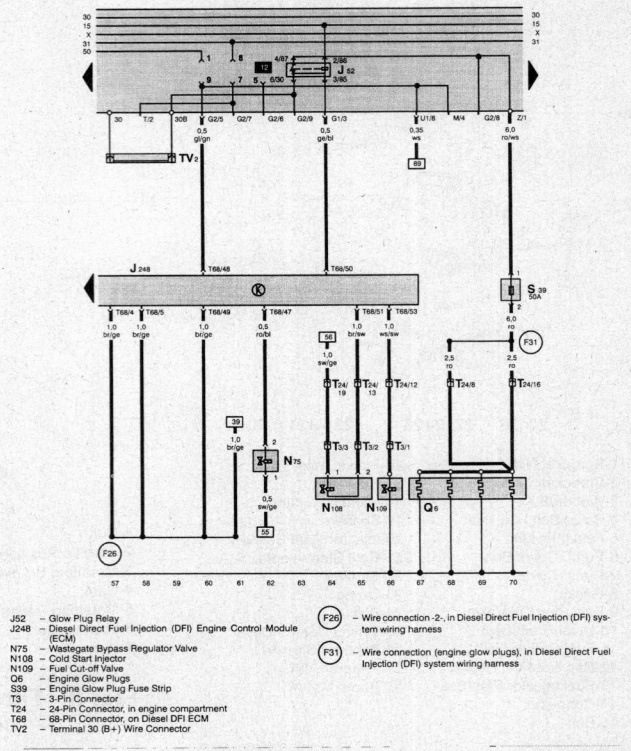

A – Battery
G79 – Throttle Position (TP) Sensor
J248 – Diesel Direct Fuel Injection (DFI) Engine Control Module (ECM)
J317 – Power Supply (Terminal 30, B+) Relay
J325 – Coolant System Glow Plug Relay, on bulkhead center
J359 – Low Heater Output Relay
J360 – High Heater Output Relay
N18 – EGR Vacuum Regulator Solenoid Valve
Q7 – Coolant System Glow Plugs
S109 – Coolant System Glow Plug Fuse
T6 – 6-Pin Connector, in footwell, front right
T24 – 24-Pin Connector, on engine
T68 – 68-Pin Connector, on engine control module
TV13 – Vehicle Speed Signal Wire Connector
(F25) – Wire connection -1-, in Diesel Direct Fuel Injection (DFI) system wiring harness
(F32) – Wire Connection (coolant system glow plugs), in Diesel direct injection system wiring harness

VW1029900123030X

Fig. 10 TDI wiring diagram (Part 3 of 4). 1998 Jetta

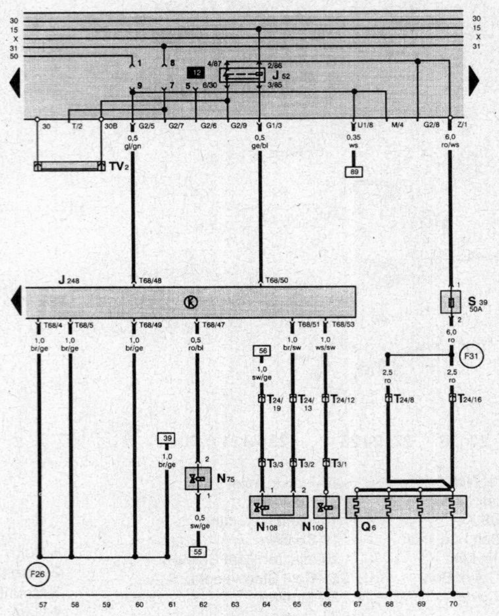

J52 – Glow Plug Relay
J248 – Diesel Direct Fuel Injection (DFI) Engine Control Module (ECM)
N75 – Wastegate Bypass Regulator Valve
N108 – Cold Start Injector
N109 – Fuel Cut-off Valve
Q6 – Engine Glow Plugs
S39 – Engine Glow Plug Fuse Strip
T3 – 3-Pin Connector
T24 – 24-Pin Connector, in engine compartment
T68 – 68-Pin Connector, on Diesel DFI ECM
TV2 – Terminal 30 (B+) Wire Connector
(F26) – Wire connection -2-, in Diesel Direct Fuel Injection (DFI) system wiring harness
(F31) – Wire connection (engine glow plugs), in Diesel Direct Fuel Injection (DFI) system wiring harness

VW1029900123040X

Fig. 10 TDI wiring diagram (Part 4 of 4). 1998 Jetta

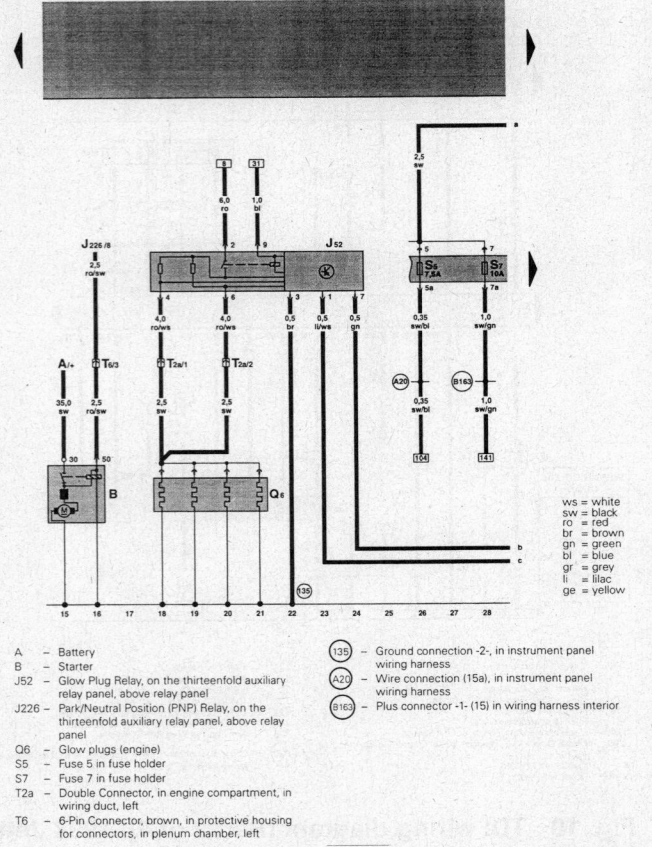

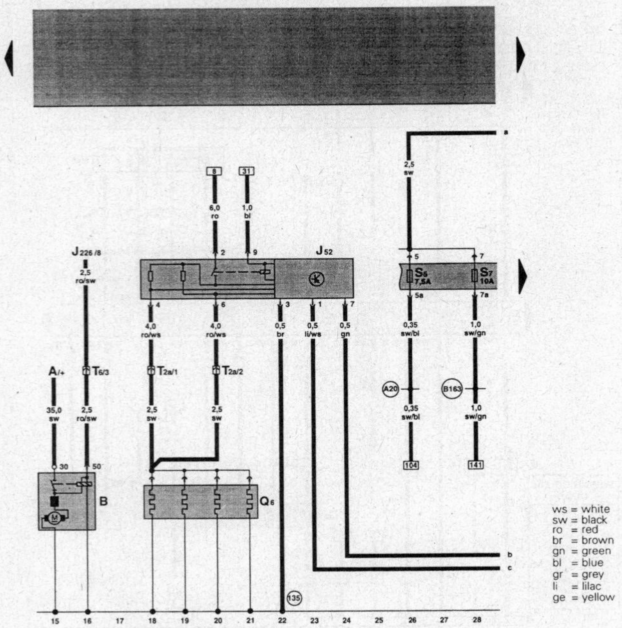

A – Battery
B – Starter
J52 – Glow Plug Relay, on the thirteenfold auxiliary relay panel, above relay panel
J226 – Park/Neutral Position (PNP) Relay, on the thirteenfold auxiliary relay panel, above relay panel
Q6 – Glow plugs (engine)
S5 – Fuse 5 in fuse holder
S7 – Fuse 7 in fuse holder
T2a – Double Connector, in engine compartment, in wiring duct, left
T6 – 6-Pin Connector, brown, in protective housing for connectors, in plenum chamber, left
(135) – Ground connection -2-, in instrument panel wiring harness
(A20) – Wire connection (15a), in instrument panel wiring harness
(B163) – Plus connector -1- (15) in wiring harness interior

VW1029900134010X

Fig. 11 TDI wiring diagram (Engine glow plugs & glow plug relay). 1999 Jetta w/A/T

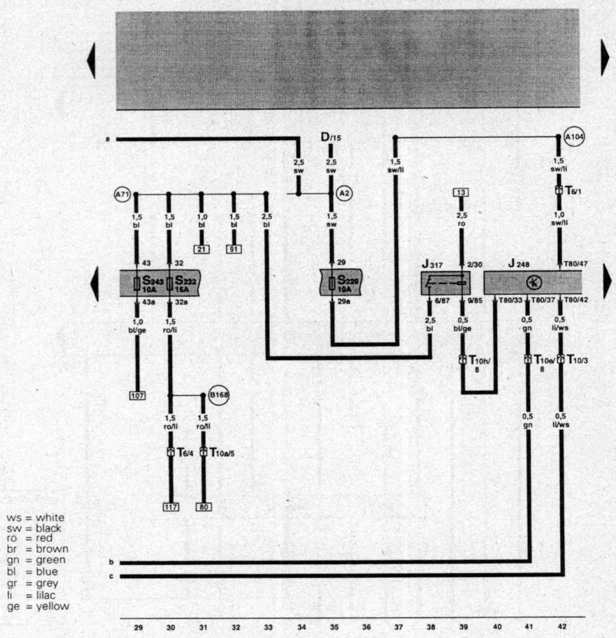

D – Ignition/Starter Switch
J248 – Diesel Direct Fuel Injection (DFI) Engine Control Module (ECM), in plenum chamber, center
J317 – Power Supply (Terminal 30, B+) Relay, on the thirteenfold auxiliary relay panel, above relay panel
S229 – Fuse 29 in fuse holder
S232 – Fuse 32 in fuse holder
S243 – Fuse 43 in fuse holder
T6 – 6-Pin Connector, brown, in protective housing for connectors, in plenum chamber, left
T10 – 10-Pin Connector, orange, in protective housing for connectors, in plenum chamber, left
T10a – 10-Pin Connector, in engine compartment, in wiring duct, left
T10e – 10-Pin Connector, black, in protective housing for connectors, in plenum chamber, left
T10h – 10-Pin Connector, blue, in protective housing for connectors, in plenum chamber, left
T80 – Connector, 80 point
(A2) – Plus connection (15), in instrument panel wiring harness
(A71) – Connector (86), in instrument panel wiring harness
(A104) – Plus connector -2- (15), in instrument panel wiring harness
(B168) – Connection (86) in passenger compartment wiring harness

VW1029900134020X

Fig. 12 TDI wiring diagram (Power supply relay). 1999 Jetta w/A/T

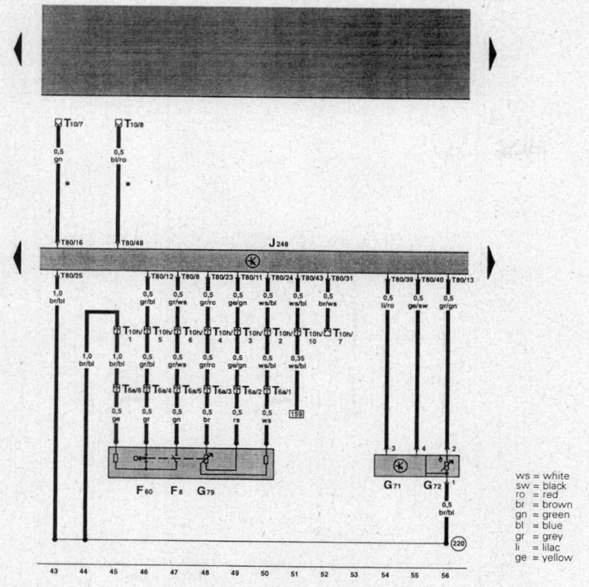

F8 – Kick Down Switch
F60 – Closed Throttle Position (CTP) Switch
G71 – Manifold Absolute Pressure (MAP) Sensor
G72 – Intake Air Temperature (IAT) Sensor
G79 – Throttle Position (TP) Sensor
J248 – Diesel Direct Fuel Injection (DFI) Engine Control Module (ECM), in plenum chamber, center
T6a – 6-Pin Connector, behind instrument panel, left
T10 – 10-Pin Connector, orange, in protective housing for connectors, in plenum chamber, left
T10h – 10-Pin Connector, blue, in protective housing for connectors, in plenum chamber, left
T80 – Connector, 80 point

(220) – Ground connection (sensor ground), in engine compartment wiring harness

* – A/C connection

VW1029900134030X

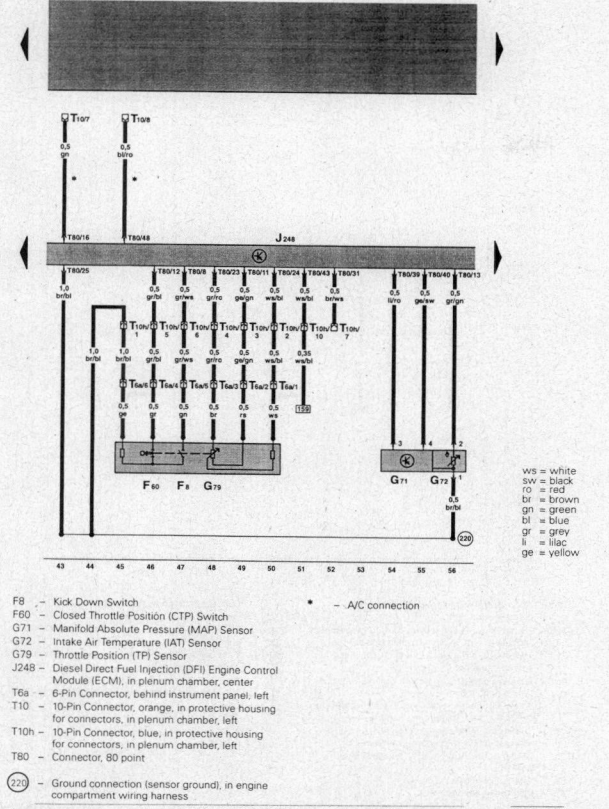

Fig. 13 TDI wiring diagram (CTP switch, IAT sensor & MAP sensor). 1999 Jetta w/A/T

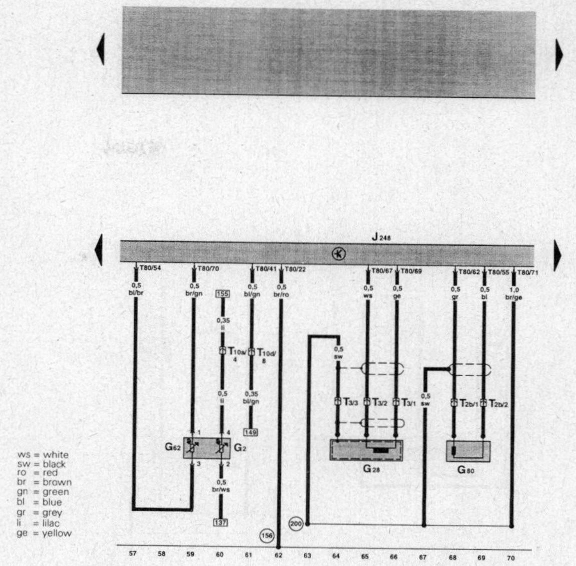

G2 – Engine Coolant Temperature (ECT) Sensor
G28 – Engine Speed (RPM) Sensor
G62 – Engine Coolant Temperature (ECT) Sensor
G80 – Needle Lift Sensor
J248 – Diesel Direct Fuel Injection (DFI) Engine Control Module (ECM), in plenum chamber, center
T2b – Double Connector, in engine compartment, front
T3 – 3-Pin Connector, in engine compartment, front
T10a – 10-Pin Connector, in engine compartment, in wiring duct, left
T10d – 10-Pin Connector, green, in protective housing for connectors, in plenum chamber, left
T80 – Connector, 80 point

(156) – Ground connection, in Diesel Direct Fuel Injection (DFI) wiring harness
(200) – Ground connection (shielding), in engine compartment wiring harness

VW1029900134040X

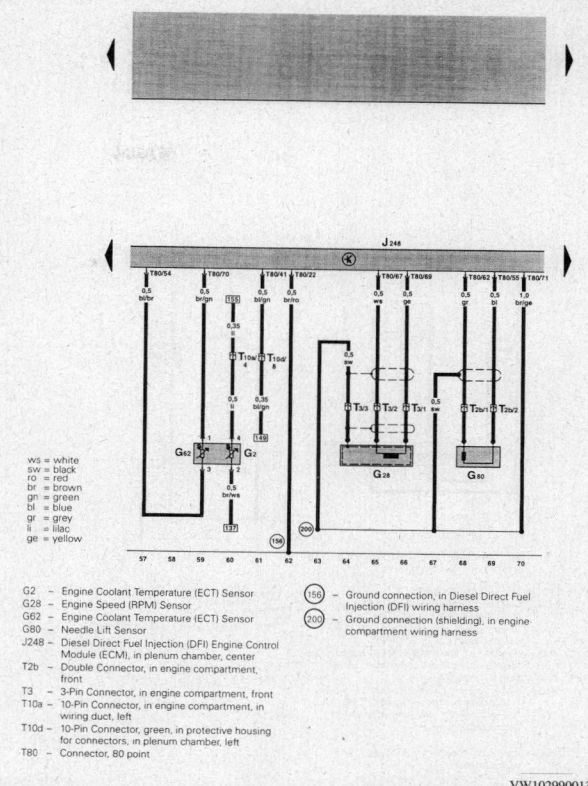

Fig. 14 TDI wiring diagram (RPM, ECT & needle lift sensors). 1999 Jetta w/A/T

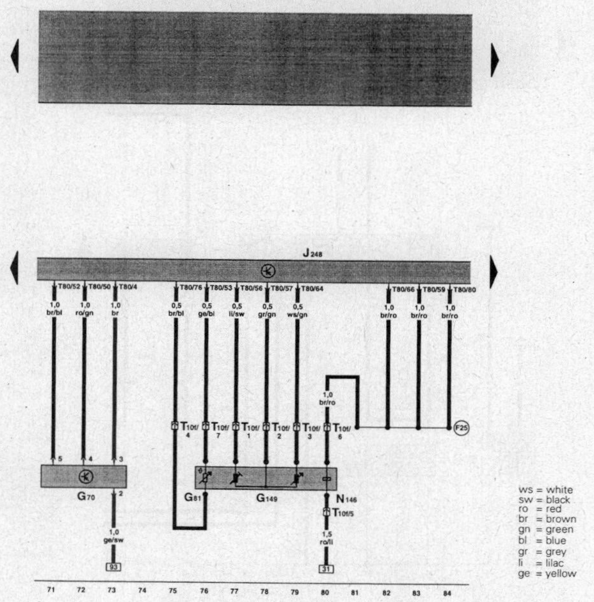

G70 – Mass Air Flow (MAF) Sensor
G81 – Fuel Temperature Sensor
G149 – Modulating Piston Displacement Sensor
J248 – Diesel Direct Fuel Injection (DFI) Engine Control Module (ECM), in plenum chamber, center
N146 – Quantity Adjuster
T10f – 10-Pin Connector, in engine compartment, front
T80 – Connector, 80 point

(F25) – Wire connection -1-, in Diesel Direct Fuel Injection (DFI) system wiring harness

VW1029900134050X

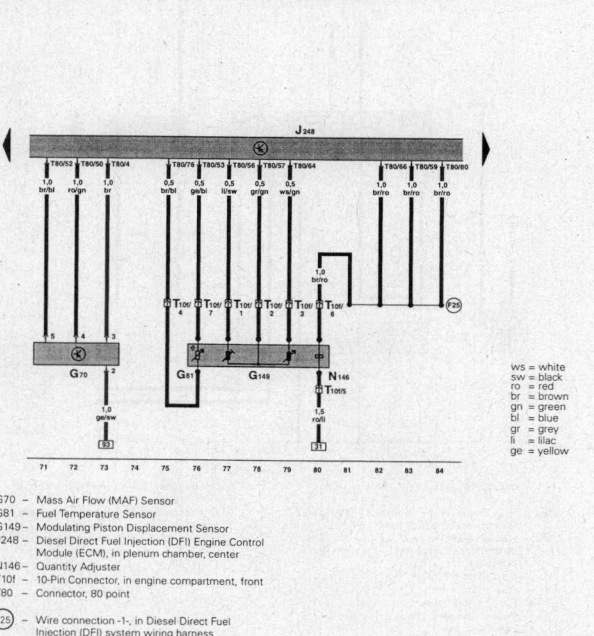

Fig. 15 TDI wiring diagram (Quantity adjuster & MAF, fuel temperature and modulating piston displacement sensors). 1999 Jetta w/A/T

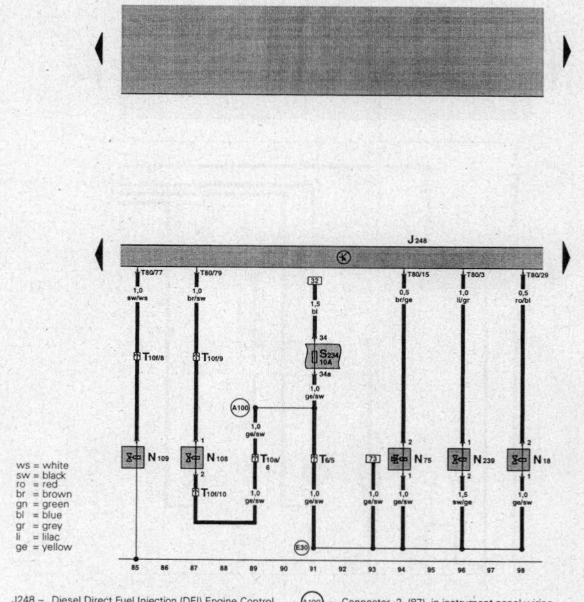

J248 – Diesel Direct Fuel Injection (DFI) Engine Control Module (ECM), in plenum chamber, center
N18 – EGR Vacuum Regulator Solenoid Valve
N75 – Wastegate Bypass Regulator Valve
N108 – Cold Start Injector
N109 – Fuel Cut-off Valve
N239 – Change-over valve for intake manifold flap
S234 – Fuse 34 in fuse holder
T6 – 6-Pin Connector, brown, in protective housing for connectors, in plenum chamber, left
T10a – 10-Pin Connector, in engine compartment, in wiring duct, left
T10f – 10-Pin Connector, in engine compartment, front
T80 – Connector, 80 point

(A100) – Connector -2- (87), in instrument panel wiring harness
(E30) – Connector (87a), in wiring harness engine

VW1029900134060X

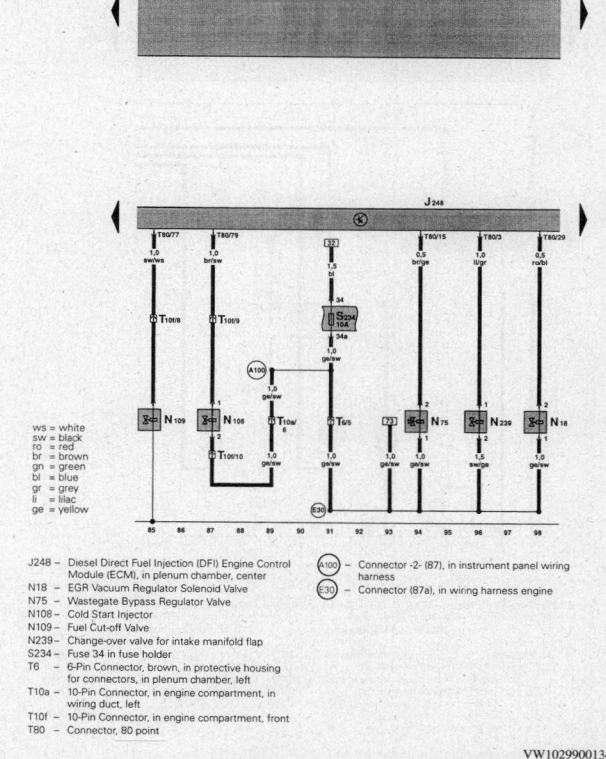

Fig. 16 TDI wiring diagram (Cold start injector, fuel cutoff valve, wastegate bypass regulator valve & EGR vacuum regulator solenoid valve). 1999 Jetta w/A/T

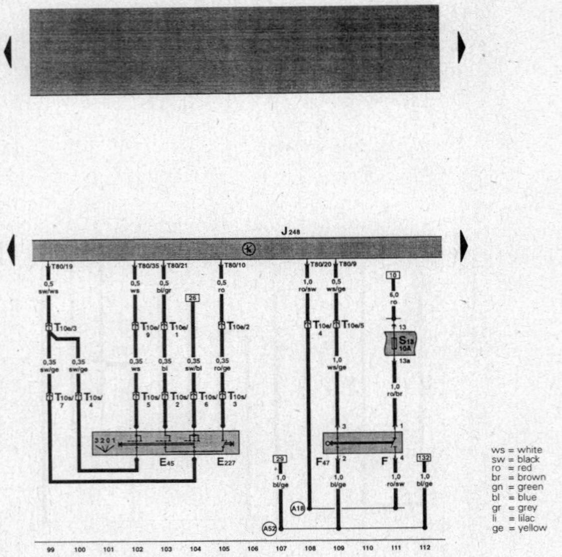

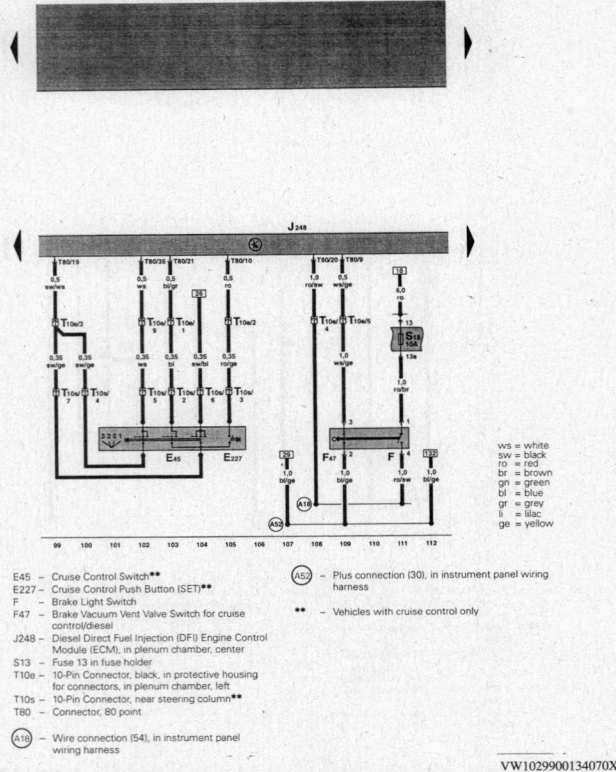

E45 – Cruise Control Switch**
E227 – Cruise Control Push Button (SET)**
F – Brake Light Switch
F47 – Brake Vacuum Vent Valve Switch for cruise control/diesel
J248 – Diesel Direct Fuel Injection (DFI) Engine Control Module (ECM), in plenum chamber, center
S13 – Fuse 13 in fuse holder
T10e – 10-Pin Connector, black, in protective housing for connectors, in plenum chamber, left
T10s – 10-Pin Connector, near steering column**
T80 – Connector, 80 point

(A18) – Wire connection (54), in instrument panel wiring harness

(A52) – Plus connection (30), in instrument panel wiring harness

** – Vehicles with cruise control only

VW1029900134070X

Fig. 17 TDI wiring diagram (Cruise control, brake vacuum vent valve & brake lamp switches). 1999 Jetta w/A/T

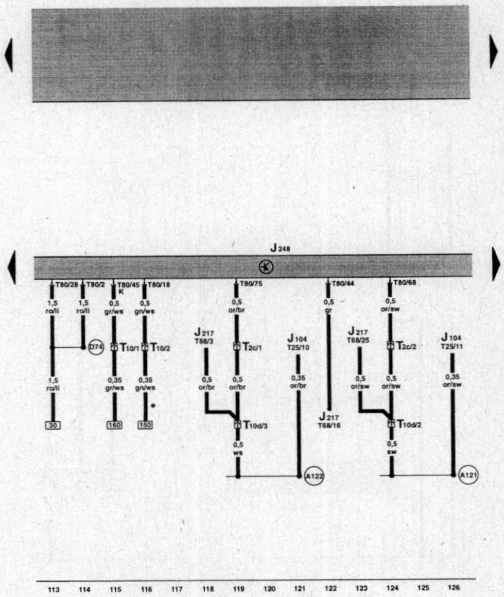

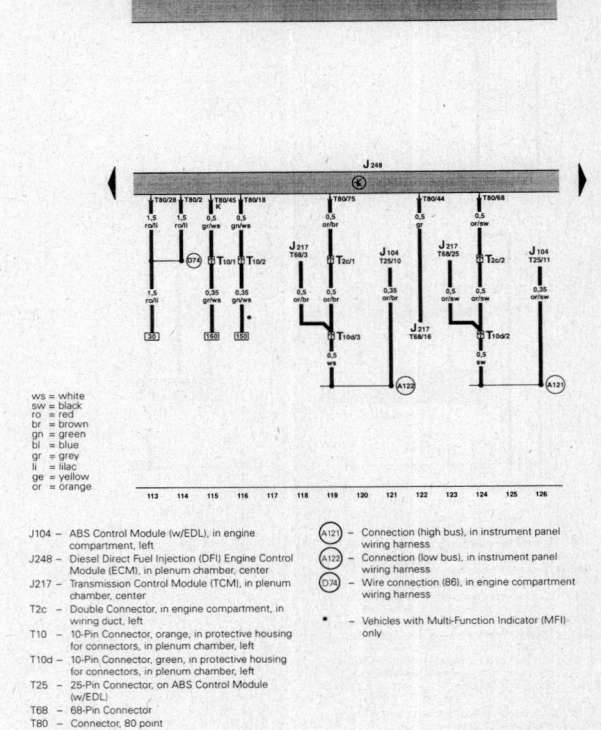

J104 – ABS Control Module (w/EDL), in engine compartment, left
J248 – Diesel Direct Fuel Injection (DFI) Engine Control Module (ECM), in plenum chamber, center
J217 – Transmission Control Module (TCM), in plenum chamber, center
T2c – Double Connector, in engine compartment, in wiring duct, left
T10 – 10-Pin Connector, orange, in protective housing for connectors, in plenum chamber, left
T10d – 10-Pin Connector, green, in protective housing for connectors, in plenum chamber, left
T25 – 25-Pin Connector, on ABS Control Module (w/EDL)
T68 – 68-Pin Connector
T80 – Connector, 80 point

(A121) – Connection (high bus), in instrument panel wiring harness
(A122) – Connection (low bus), in instrument panel wiring harness
(D74) – Wire connection (86), in engine compartment wiring harness

* – Vehicles with Multi-Function Indicator (MFI) only

VW1029900134080X

Fig. 18 TDI wiring diagram (ECM). 1999 Jetta w/A/T

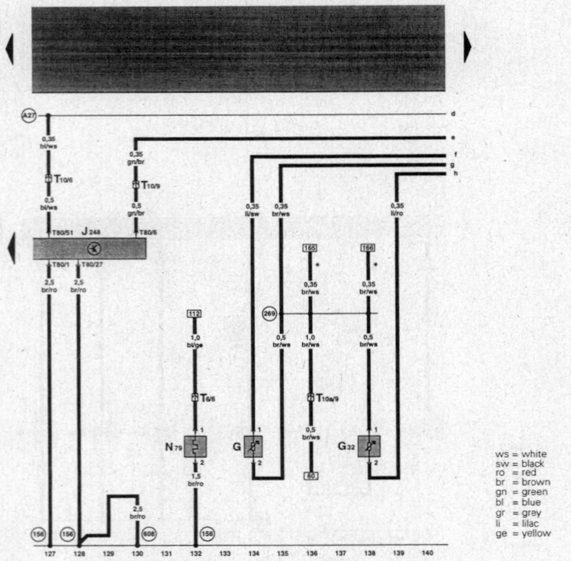

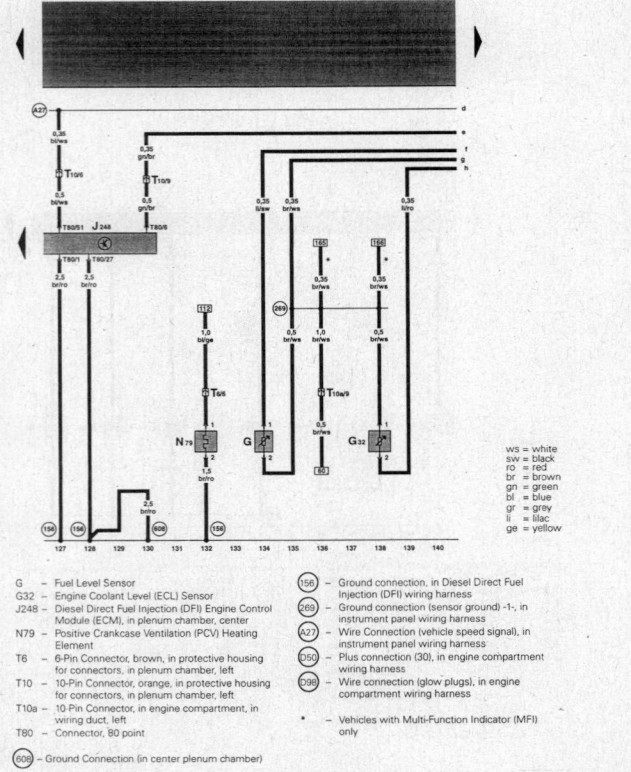

G – Fuel Level Sensor
G32 – Engine Coolant Level (ECL) Sensor
J248 – Diesel Direct Fuel Injection (DFI) Engine Control Module (ECM), in plenum chamber, center
N79 – Positive Crankcase Ventilation (PCV) Heating Element
T6 – 6-Pin Connector, brown, in protective housing for connectors, in plenum chamber, left
T10 – 10-Pin Connector, orange, in protective housing for connectors, in plenum chamber, left
T10a – 10-Pin Connector, in engine compartment, in wiring duct, left
T80 – Connector, 80 point

(608) – Ground Connection (in center plenum chamber)

(156) – Ground connection, in Diesel Direct Fuel Injection (DFI) wiring harness
(269) – Ground connection (sensor ground) -1-, in instrument panel wiring harness
(A27) – Wire Connection (vehicle speed signal), in instrument panel wiring harness
(D50) – Plus connection (30), in engine compartment wiring harness
(D98) – Wire connection (glow plugs), in engine compartment wiring harness

* – Vehicles with Multi-Function Indicator (MFI) only

VW1029900134090X

Fig. 19 TDI wiring diagram (Fuel level sensor, engine coolant level sensor & PCV heating element). 1999 Jetta w/A/T

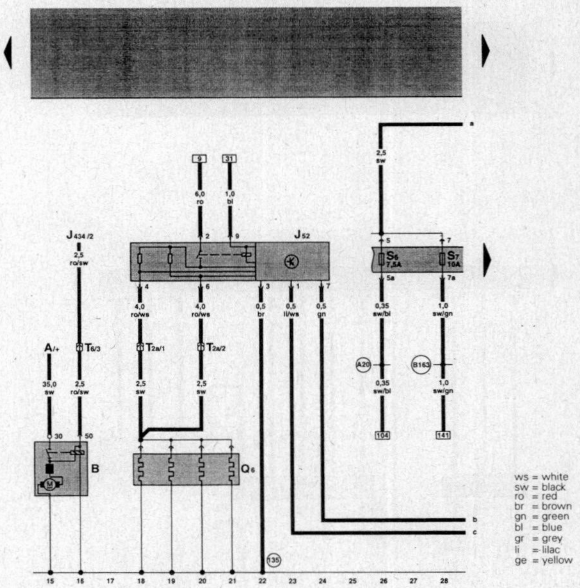

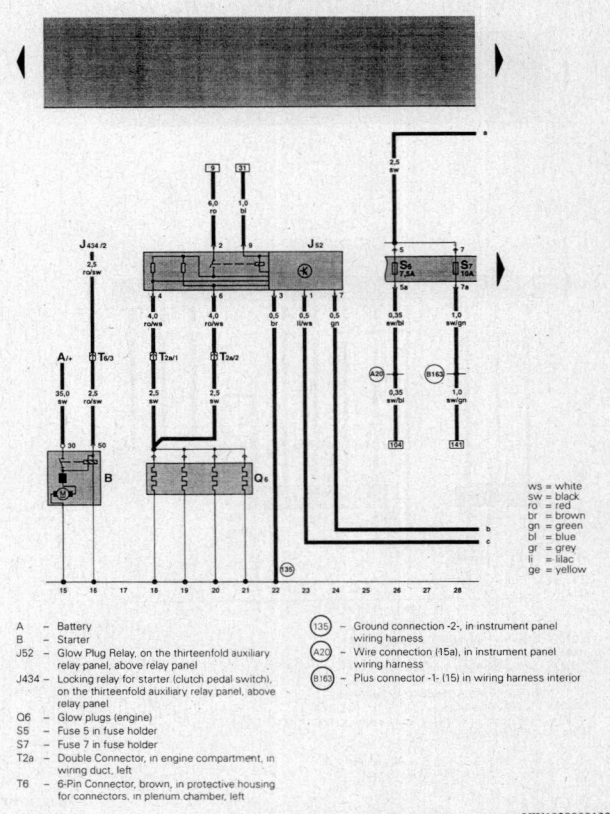

A – Battery
B – Starter
J52 – Glow Plug Relay, on the thirteenfold auxiliary relay panel, above relay panel
J434 – Locking relay for starter (clutch pedal switch), on the thirteenfold auxiliary relay panel, above relay panel
Q6 – Glow plugs (engine)
S5 – Fuse 5 in fuse holder
S7 – Fuse 7 in fuse holder
T2a – Double Connector, in engine compartment, in wiring duct, left
T6 – 6-Pin Connector, brown, in protective housing for connectors, in plenum chamber, left

(135) – Ground connection -2-, in instrument panel wiring harness
(A20) – Wire connection (15a), in instrument panel wiring harness
(B163) – Plus connector -1- (15) in wiring harness interior

VW1029900133010X

Fig. 20 TDI wiring diagram (Engine glow plugs & glow plug relay). 1999 Jetta w/M/T

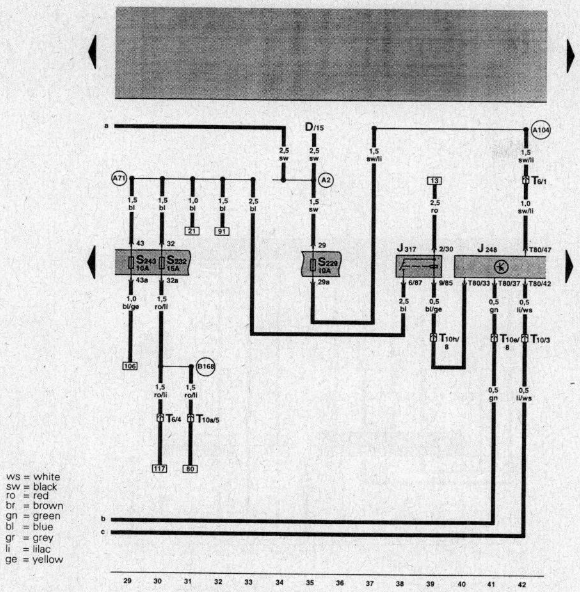

D – Ignition/Starter Switch
J248 – Diesel Direct Fuel Injection (DFI) Engine Control Module (ECM), in plenum chamber, center
J317 – Power Supply (Terminal 30, B+) Relay, on the thirteenfold auxiliary relay panel, above relay panel
S229 – Fuse 29 in fuse holder
S232 – Fuse 32 in fuse holder
S243 – Fuse 43 in fuse holder
T6 – 6-Pin Connector, brown, in protective housing for connectors, in plenum chamber, left
T10 – 10-Pin Connector, orange, in protective housing for connectors, in plenum chamber, left
T10a – 10-Pin Connector, in engine compartment, in wiring duct, left
T10e – 10-Pin Connector, black, in protective housing for connectors, in plenum chamber, left
T10h – 10-Pin Connector, blue, in protective housing for connectors, in plenum chamber, left
T80 – Connector, 80 point

(A2) – Plus connection (15), in instrument panel wiring harness
(A71) – Connector (86), in instrument panel wiring harness
(A104) – Plus connector -2- (15), in instrument panel wiring harness
(B168) – Connection (86) in passenger compartment wiring harness

VW1029900133020X

Fig. 21 TDI wiring diagram (Power supply relay). 1999 Jetta w/M/T

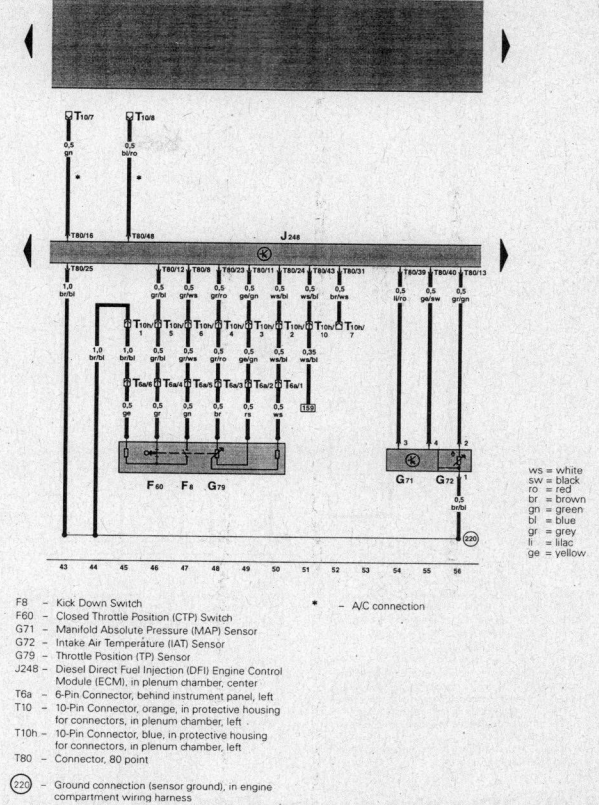

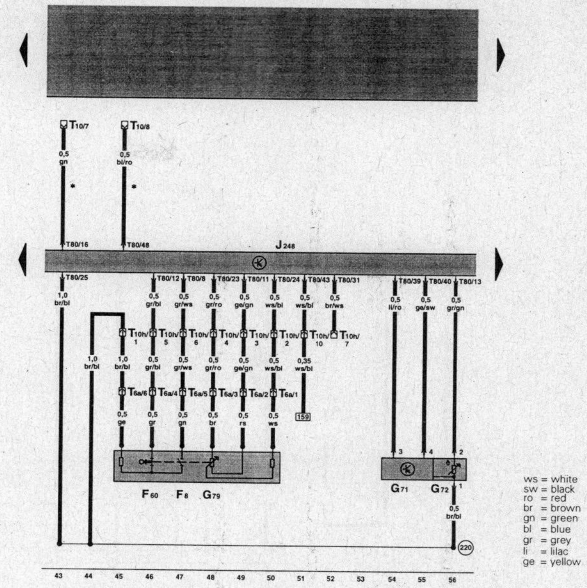

F8 – Kick Down Switch
F60 – Closed Throttle Position (CTP) Switch
G71 – Manifold Absolute Pressure (MAP) Sensor
G72 – Intake Air Temperature (IAT) Sensor
G79 – Throttle Position (TP) Sensor
J248 – Diesel Direct Fuel Injection (DFI) Engine Control Module (ECM), in plenum chamber, center
T6a – 6-Pin Connector, behind instrument panel, left
T10 – 10-Pin Connector, orange, in protective housing for connectors, in plenum chamber, left
T10h – 10-Pin Connector, blue, in protective housing for connectors, in plenum chamber, left
T80 – Connector, 80 point

(220) – Ground connection (sensor ground), in engine compartment wiring harness

* – A/C connection

VW1029900133030X

Fig. 22 TDI wiring diagram (CTP switch, IAT sensor & MAP sensor). 1999 Jetta w/M/T

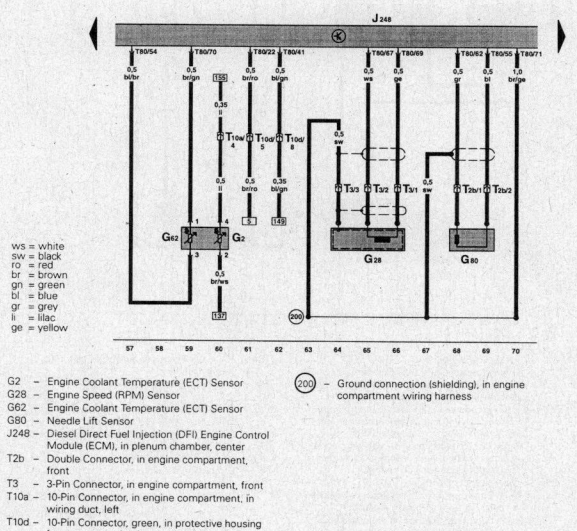

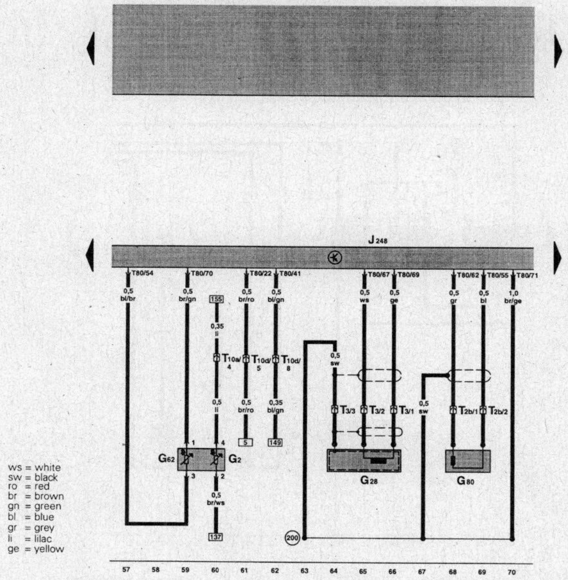

G2 – Engine Coolant Temperature (ECT) Sensor
G28 – Engine Speed (RPM) Sensor
G62 – Engine Coolant Temperature (ECT) Sensor
G80 – Needle Lift Sensor
J248 – Diesel Direct Fuel Injection (DFI) Engine Control Module (ECM), in plenum chamber, center
T2b – Double Connector, in engine compartment, front
T3 – 3-Pin Connector, in engine compartment, front
T10a – 10-Pin Connector, in engine compartment, in wiring duct, left
T10d – 10-Pin Connector, green, in protective housing for connectors, in plenum chamber, left
T80 – Connector, 80 point

(200) – Ground connection (shielding), in engine compartment wiring harness

VW1029900133040X

Fig. 23 TDI wiring diagram (RPM, ECT & needle lift sensors). 1999 Jetta w/M/T

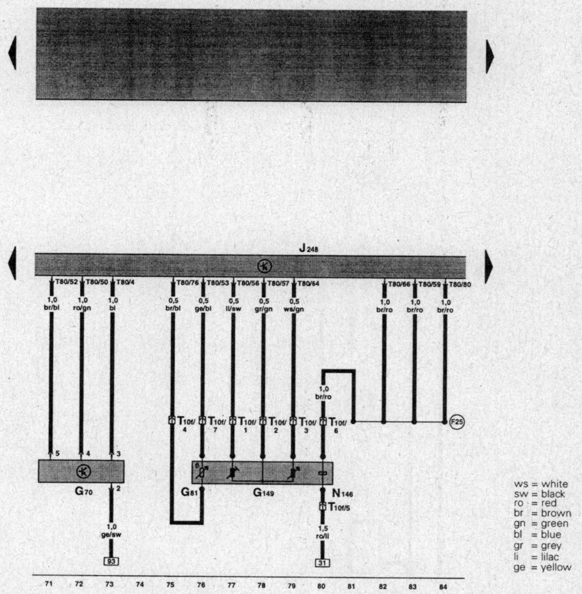

G70 – Mass Air Flow (MAF) Sensor
G81 – Fuel Temperature Sensor
G149 – Modulating Piston Displacement Sensor
J248 – Diesel Direct Fuel Injection (DFI) Engine Control Module (ECM), in plenum chamber, center
N146 – Quantity Adjuster
T10f – 10-Pin Connector, in engine compartment, front
T80 – Connector, 80 point

(F25) – Wire connection -1-, in Diesel Direct Fuel Injection (DFI) system wiring harness

VW1029900133050X

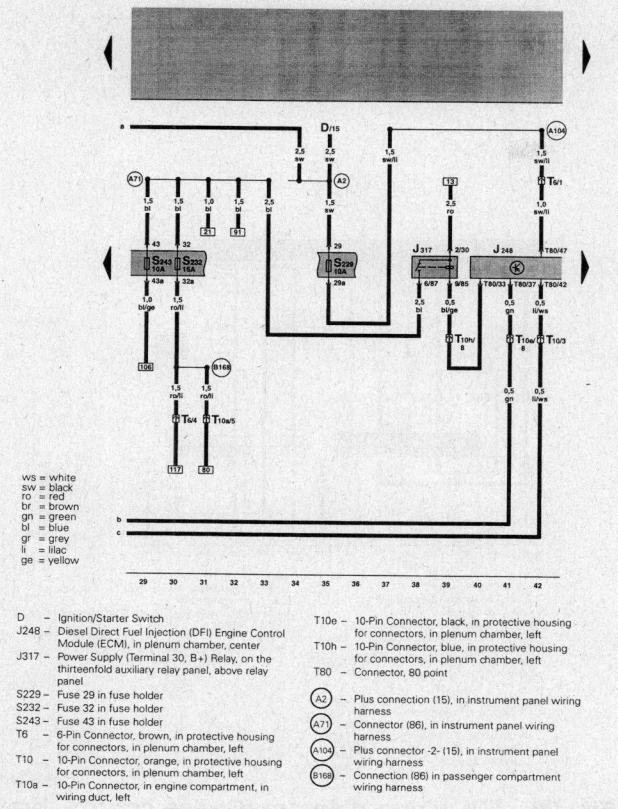

Fig. 24 TDI wiring diagram (Quantity adjuster & MAF, fuel temperature & modulating piston displacement sensors). 1999 Jetta w/M/T

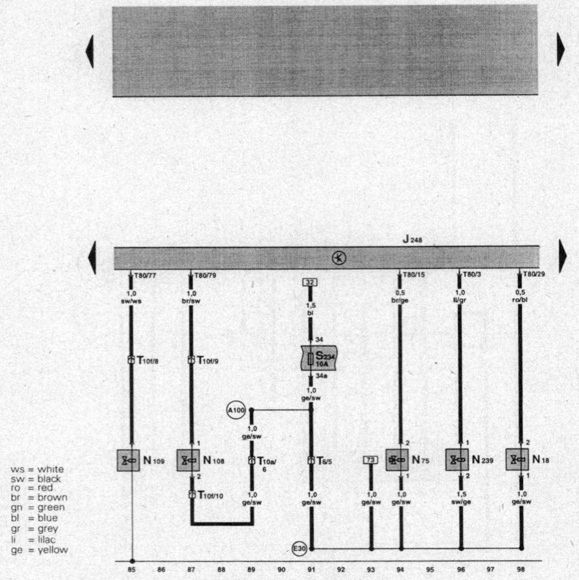

J248 – Diesel Direct Fuel Injection (DFI) Engine Control Module (ECM), in plenum chamber, center
N18 – EGR Vacuum Regulator Solenoid Valve
N75 – Wastegate Bypass Regulator Valve
N108 – Cold Start Injector
N109 – Fuel Cut-off Valve
N239 – Change-over valve for intake manifold flap
S234 – Fuse 34 in fuse holder
T6 – 6-Pin Connector, brown, in protective housing for connectors, in plenum chamber, left
T10a – 10-Pin Connector, in engine compartment, in wiring duct, left
T10f – 10-Pin Connector, in engine compartment, front
T80 – Connector, 80 point

(A100) – Connector -2- (87), in instrument panel wiring harness
(E30) – Connector (87a), in wiring harness engine

VW1029900133060X

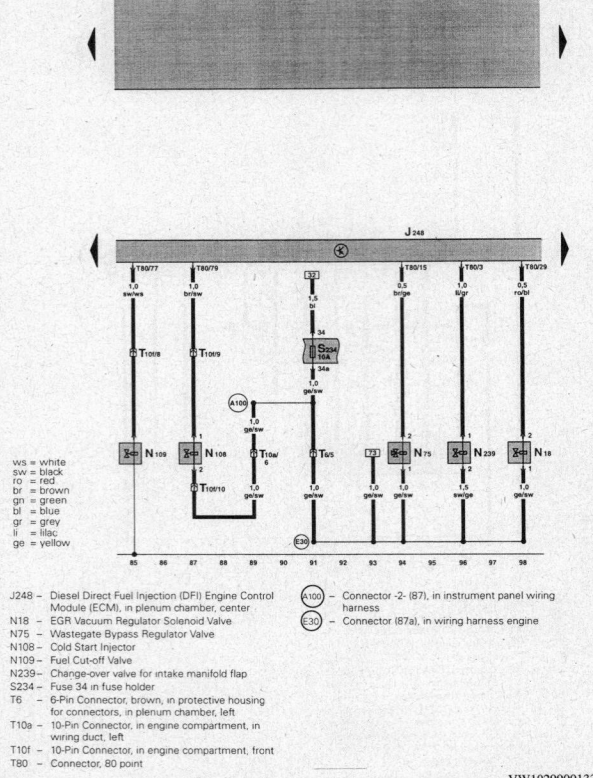

Fig. 25 TDI wiring diagram (Cold start injector, fuel cutoff valve, wastegate bypass regulator valve & EGR vacuum regulator solenoid valve). 1999 Jetta w/M/T

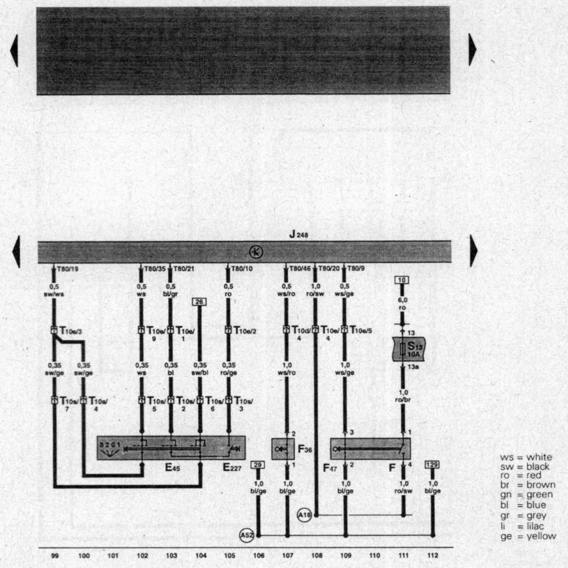

E45 – Cruise Control Switch**
E227 – Cruise Control Push Button (SET)**
F – Brake Light Switch
F36 – Clutch Vacuum Vent Valve Switch
F47 – Brake Vacuum Vent Valve Switch for cruise control/diesel
J248 – Diesel Direct Fuel Injection (DFI) Engine Control Module (ECM), in plenum chamber, center
S13 – Fuse 13 in fuse holder
T10d – 10-Pin Connector, green, in protective housing for connectors, in plenum chamber, left
T10e – 10-Pin Connector, black, in protective housing for connectors, in plenum chamber, left
T10s – 10-Pin Connector, near steering column**
T80 – Connector, 80 point

(A18) – Wire connection (54), in instrument panel wiring harness
(A52) – Plus connection (30), in instrument panel wiring harness

** – Vehicles with cruise control only

VW1029900133070X

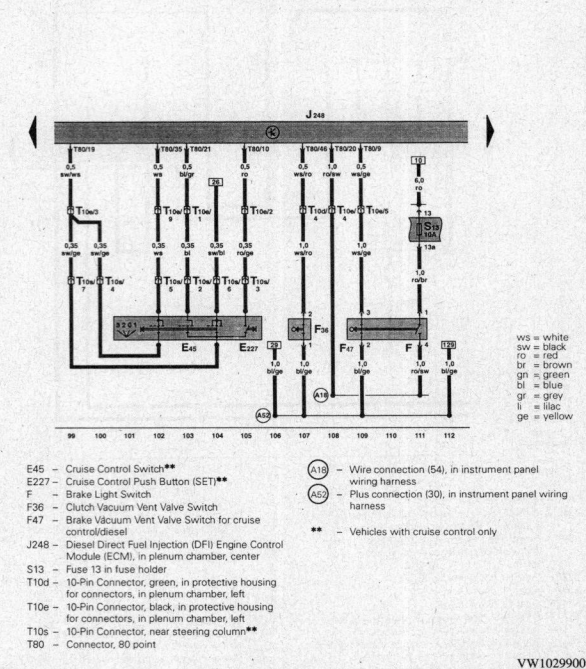

Fig. 26 TDI wiring diagram (Cruise control, brake vacuum vent valve, brake lamp & clutch vacuum vent valve switches). 1999 Jetta w/M/T

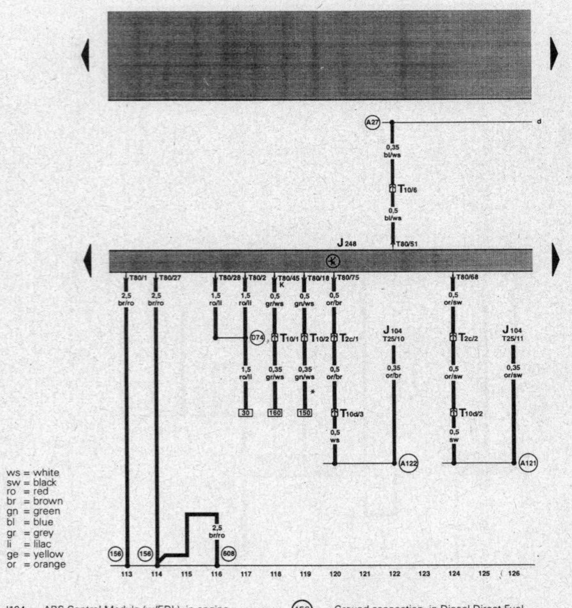

J104 – ABS Control Module (w/EDL), in engine compartment, left
J248 – Diesel Direct Fuel Injection (DFI) Engine Control Module (ECM), in plenum chamber, center
T2c – Double Connector, in engine compartment, in wiring duct, left
T10 – 10-Pin Connector, orange, in protective housing for connectors, in plenum chamber, left
T10d – 10-Pin Connector, green, in protective housing for connectors, in plenum chamber, left
T25 – 25-Pin Connector, on ABS Control Module (w/EDL)
T80 – Connector, 80 point

(608) – Ground Connection (in center plenum chamber)

(156) – Ground connection, in Diesel Direct Fuel Injection (DFI) wiring harness
(A27) – Wire Connection (vehicle speed signal), in instrument panel wiring harness
(A121) – Connection (high bus), in instrument panel wiring harness
(A122) – Connection (low bus), in instrument panel wiring harness
(D74) – Wire connection (86), in engine compartment wiring harness
* – Vehicles with Multi-Function Indicator (MFI) only

VW1029900133080X

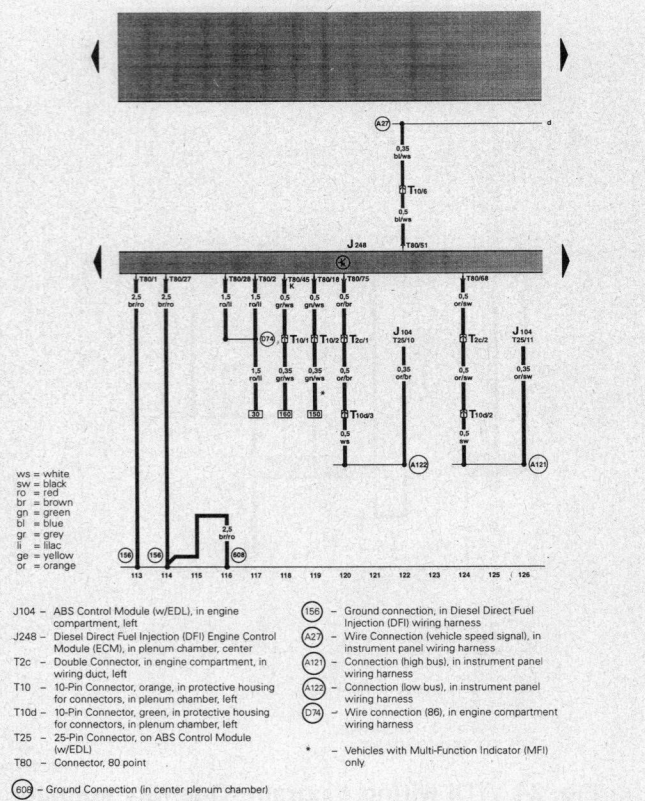

Fig. 27 TDI wiring diagram (ECM). 1999 Jetta w/M/T

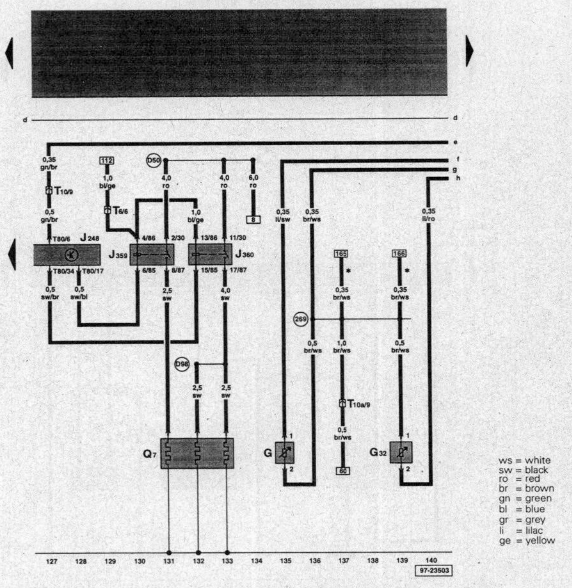

G – Fuel Level Sensor
G32 – Engine Coolant Level (ECL) Sensor
J248 – Diesel Direct Fuel Injection (DFI) Engine Control Module (ECM), in plenum chamber, center
J359 – Relay for preheating coolant, low heat output, in protective housing, in engine compartment, left, production control number (53)
J360 – Relay for preheating coolant, high heat output, in protective housing, in engine compartment, left, production control number (53)
Q7 – Glow plugs (coolant)
T6 – 6-Pin Connector, brown, in protective housing for connectors, in plenum chamber, left
T10 – 10-Pin Connector, orange, in protective housing for connectors, in plenum chamber, left
T10a – 10-Pin Connector, in engine compartment, in wiring duct, left
T80 – Connector, 80 point

(269) – Ground connection (sensor ground) -1-, in instrument panel wiring harness
(D50) – Plus connection (30), in engine compartment wiring harness
(D98) – Wire connection (glow plugs), in engine compartment wiring harness

* – Vehicles with Multi-Function Indicator (MFI) only

VW1029900133090X

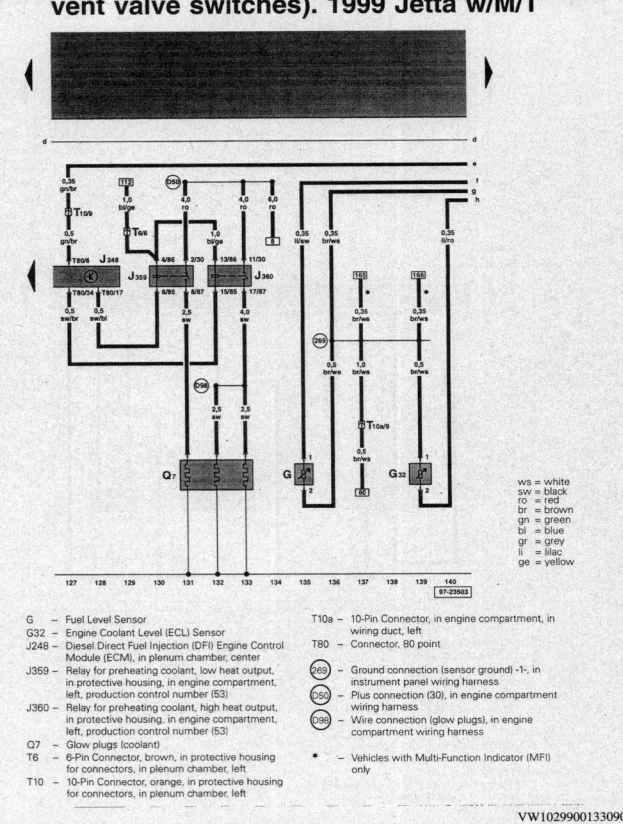

Fig. 28 TDI wiring diagram (Fuel level sensor, coolant glow plugs & engine coolant level sensor). 1999 Jetta w/M/T

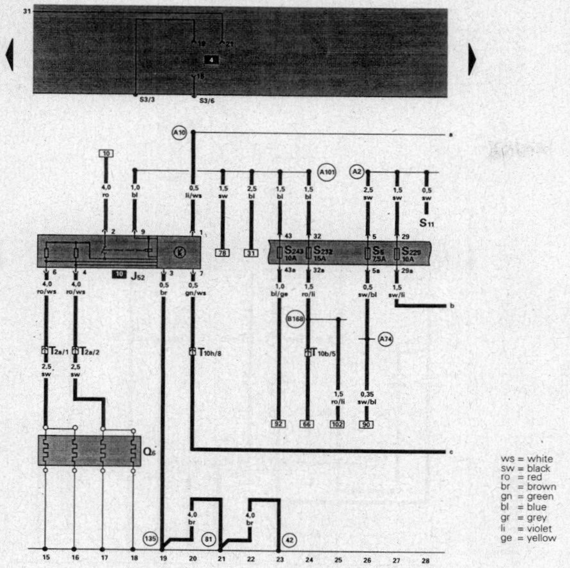

J52 – Glow Plug Relay (180), on the thirteen position auxiliary relay panel, above relay panel
Q6 – Glow plugs (engine)
S5 – Fuse 5 in fuse holder
S11 – Fuse 11 in fuse holder
S229 – Fuse 29 in fuse holder
S232 – Fuse 32 in fuse holder
S243 – Fuse 43 in fuse holder
T2a – Double Connector, in engine compartment, left
T10b – 10-Pin Connector, in engine compartment, left
T10h – 10-Pin Connector, black, behind instrument panel, left
(42) – Ground connection, beside steering column
(81) – Ground connection -1-, in instrument panel wiring harness
(135) – Ground connection -2-, in instrument panel wiring harness
(A2) – plus connection (15), in instrument panel wiring harness
(A10) – wire connection (glow plug control) in instrument panel wiring harness
(A74) – Connector (15a - fuse 5), in instrument panel wiring harness
(A101) – Connector -3- (87), in instrument panel wiring harness
(B168) – Connection (86) in passenger compartment wiring harness

VW1029800095020A

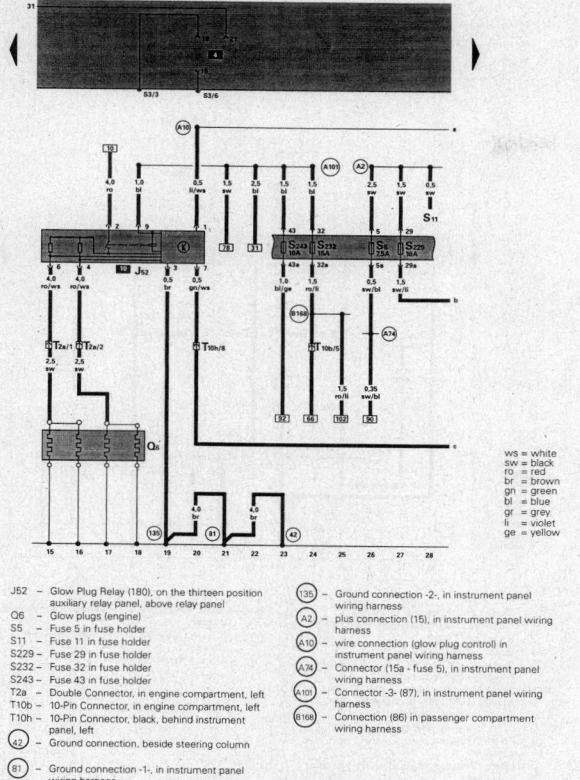

Fig. 29 TDI fuel injection wiring diagram (Engine glow plugs & glow plug relay). 1998 New Beetle

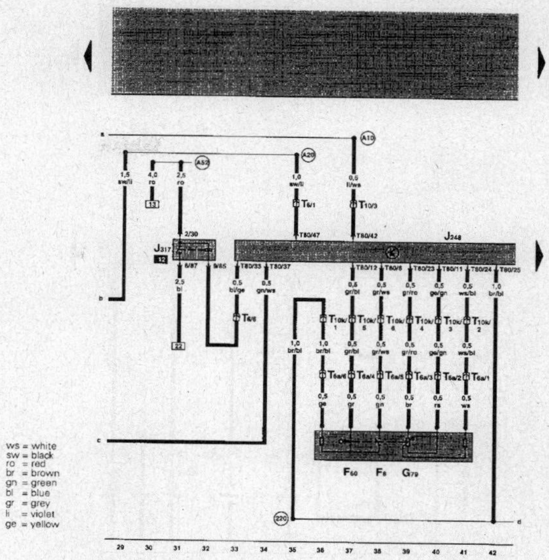

F8 – Kick Down Switch
F60 – Closed Throttle Position (CTP) Switch
G79 – Throttle Position (TP) Sensor
J248 – Diesel Direct Fuel Injection (DFI) Engine Control Module (ECM), behind instrument panel, left
J317 – Power Supply (Terminal 30, B+) Relay
T6 – 6-Pin Connector, red, behind instrument panel, left
T6a – 6-Pin Connector, behind instrument panel, left
T10 – 10-Pin Connector, white, behind instrument panel, left
T10k – 10-Pin Connector, blue, behind instrument panel, left
T80 – Connector, 80 point, at Diesel Direct Fuel Injection (DFI) Engine Control Module (ECM)
(220) – Ground connection (sensor ground), in engine compartment wiring harness
(A10) – wire connection (glow plug control) in instrument panel wiring harness
(A20) – wire connection (15a), in instrument panel wiring harness
(A52) – plus connection (30), in instrument panel wiring harness

VW1029800095030X

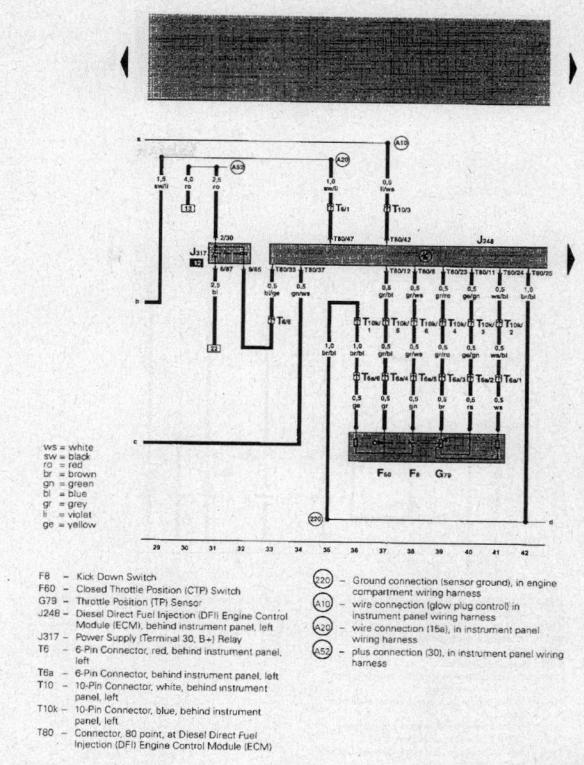

Fig. 30 TDI fuel injection wiring diagram (Power supply relay, kick down switch & TP sensor). 1998 New Beetle

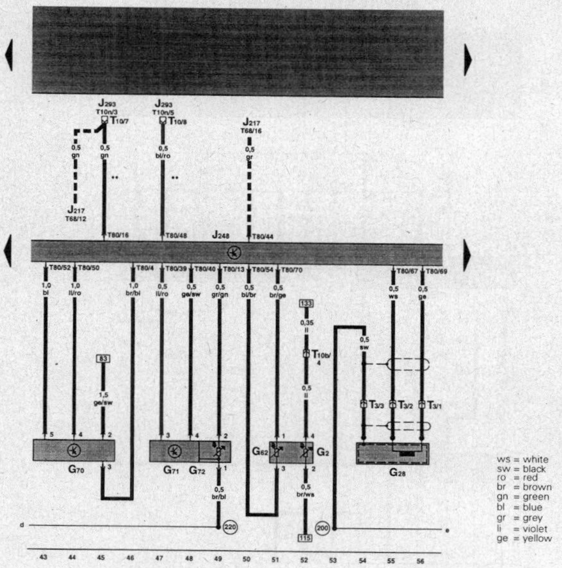

G2 – Engine Coolant Temperature (ECT) Sensor
G28 – Engine Speed (RPM) Sensor
G62 – Engine Coolant Temperature (ECT) Sensor
G70 – Mass Air Flow (MAF) Sensor
G71 – Manifold Absolute Pressure (MAP) Sensor
G72 – Intake Air Temperature (IAT) Sensor
J217 – Transmission Control Module (TCM), behind instrument panel, center
J248 – Diesel Direct Fuel Injection (DFI) Engine Control Module (ECM), behind instrument panel, left
J293 – Coolant FC (Fan Control) Control Module
T3 – 3-Pin Connector, on engine, front
T10 – 10-Pin Connector, white, behind instrument panel, left
T10b – 10-Pin Connector, in engine compartment, left
T10n – 10-Pin Connector, on J293
T68 – 68-Pin Connector, on Transmission Control Module (TCM)
T80 – Connector, 80 point
(200) – Ground connection (shielding), in engine compartment wiring harness
(220) – Ground connection (sensor ground), in engine compartment wiring harness
** – A/C Connection
- - - Automatic transmission only

VW1029800095040A

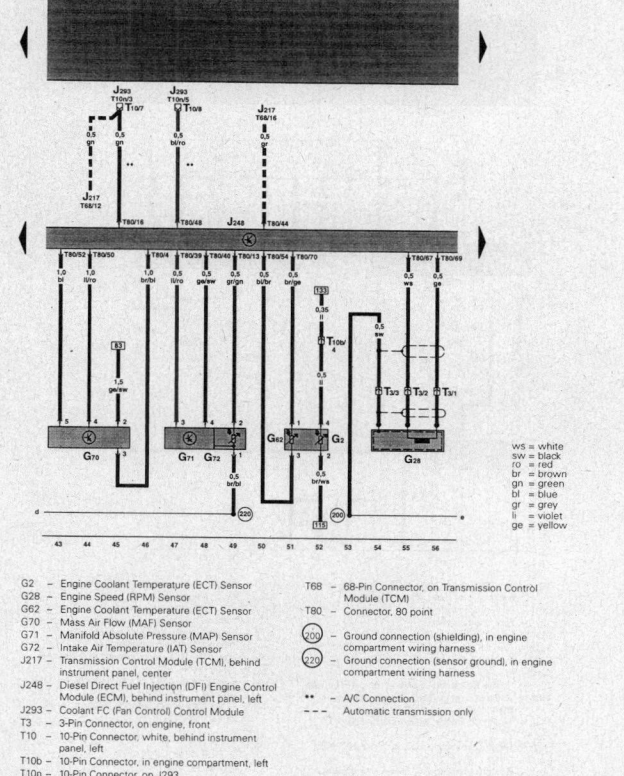

Fig. 31 TDI fuel injection wiring diagram (MAF & RPM sensors). New Beetle

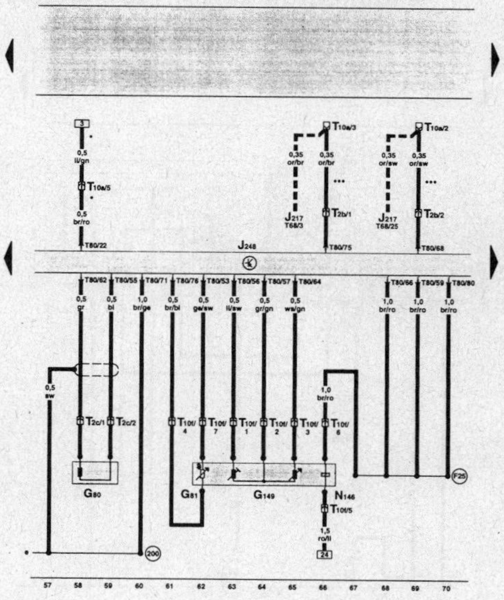

G80 – Needle Lift Sensor
G81 – Fuel Temperature Sensor
G149 – Modulating Piston Displacement Sensor
J217 – Transmission Control Module (TCM), behind instrument panel, center
J248 – Diesel Direct Fuel Injection (DFI) Engine Control Module (ECM), behind instrument panel, left
N146 – Quantity Adjuster
T2b – Double Connector, behind instrument panel, left
T2c – Double Connector, on engine, front
T10a – 10-Pin Connector, orange, behind instrument panel, left
T10f – 10-Pin Connector, on engine, front
T68 – 68-Pin Connector, on Transmission Control Module (TCM)
T80 – Connector, 80 point
(200) – Ground connection (shielding), in engine compartment wiring harness
(F25) – Wire connection -1-, in Diesel Direct Fuel Injection (DFI) system wiring harness
* – manual transmission only
*** – connection DATA-Bus
- - - automatic transmission only

VW1029800095050X

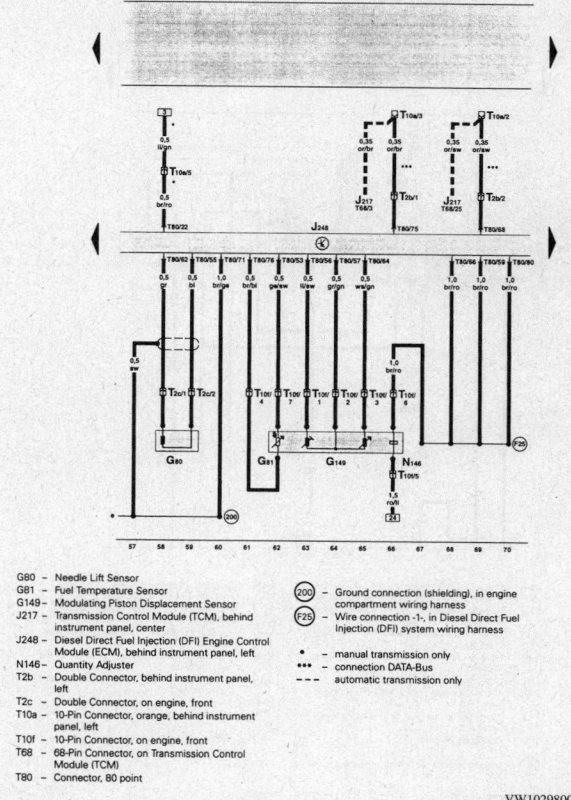

Fig. 32 TDI fuel injection wiring diagram (Needle lift, fuel temperature & modulating piston displacement sensors). New Beetle

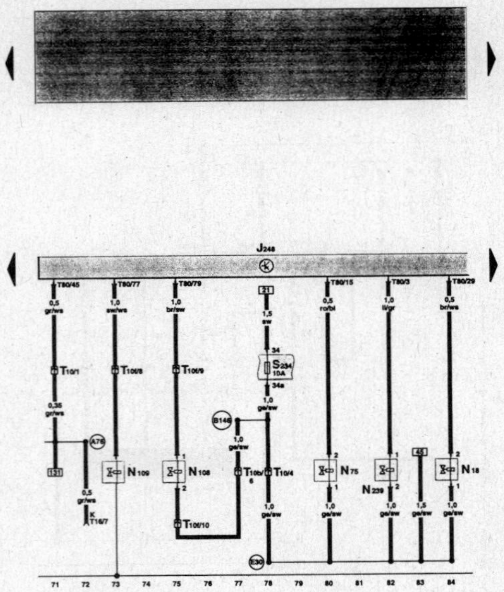

J248 – Diesel Direct Fuel Injection (DFI) Engine Control Module (ECM), in plenum chamber, left
N18 – EGR Vacuum Regulator Solenoid Valve
N75 – Wastegate Bypass Regulator Valve
N108 – Cold Start Injector
N109 – Fuel Cut-off Valve
N239 – Change-over valve for intake manifold flap
S234 – Fuse 34 in fuse holder
T10 – 10-Pin Connector, white, behind instrument panel, left
T10b – 10-Pin Connector, in engine compartment, left
T10f – 10-Pin Connector, on engine, front
T16 – 16-Pin Connector, Data Link Connector (DLC), below steering column
T80 – Connector, 80 point

(A76) – Connector (K-diagnosis wire), in instrument panel wiring harness
(B146) – Plus connector -1- (87), in wiring harness interior
(E30) – Connector (87a), in wiring harness engine

VW1029800095060X

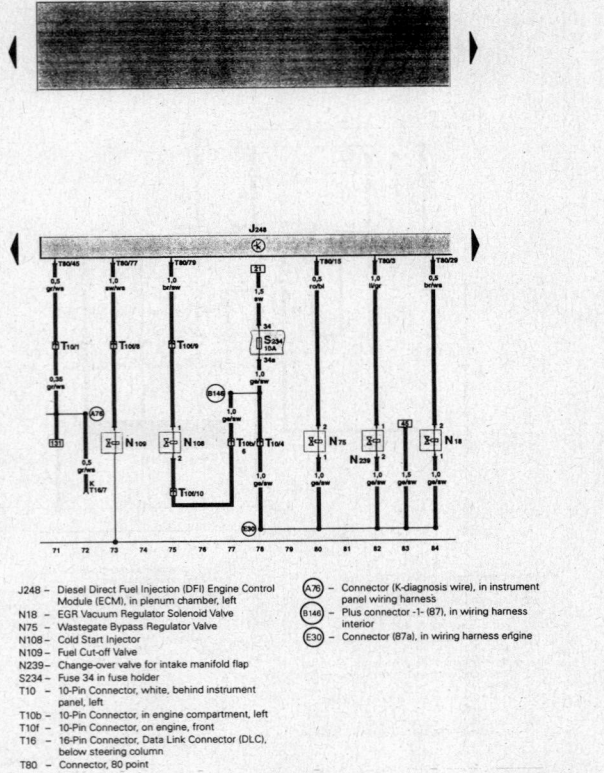

Fig. 33 TDI fuel injection wiring diagram (EGR vacuum regulator solenoid valve, cold start injector & fuel cutoff valve). New Beetle

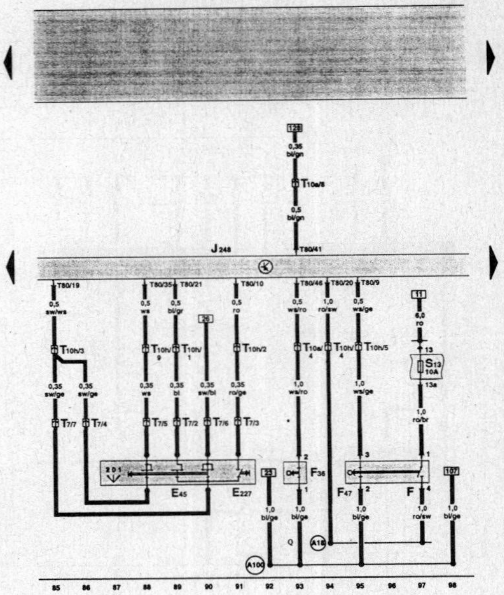

ws = white
sw = black
ro = red
br = brown
gn = green
bl = blue
gr = grey
li = violet
ge = yellow

E45 – Cruise Control Switch (if equipped)
E227 – Button for cruise control (set), (if equipped)
F – Brake Light Switch
F36 – Clutch Vacuum vent Valve Switch
F47 – Brake Vacuum Vent Valve Switch for cruise control/diesel fuel injection (DFI)
J248 – Diesel Direct Fuel Injection (DFI) Engine Control Module (ECM), behind instrument panel, left
S13 – Fuse 13 in fuse holder
T7 – 7-Pin Connector, near steering column
T10a – 10-Pin Connector, orange, behind instrument panel, left
T10h – 10-Pin Connector, black, behind instrument panel, left
T80 – Connector, 80 point

(A18) – wire connection (54), in instrument panel wiring harness
(A100) – Connector -2- (87), in instrument panel wiring harness
• – manual transmission only

VW1029800095070X

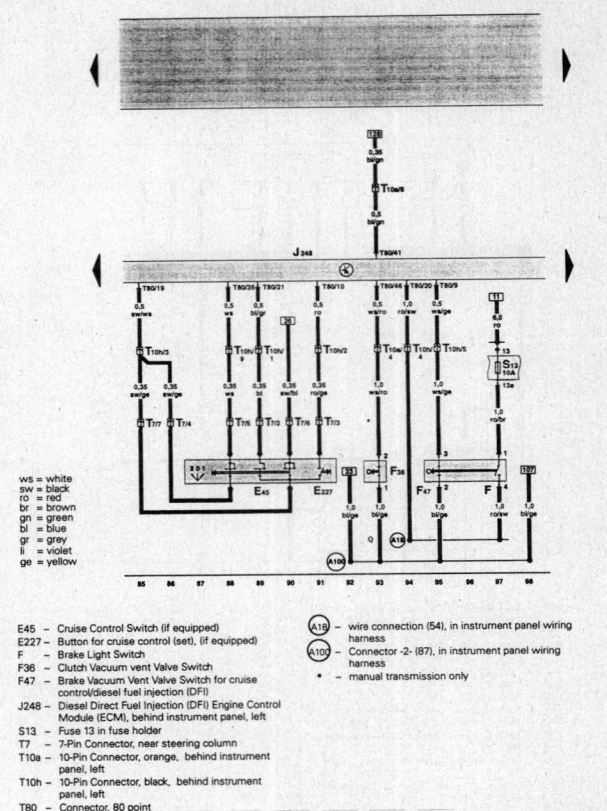

Fig. 34 TDI fuel injection wiring diagram (Cruise control, brake lamp and clutch vacuum vent valve switches). New Beetle

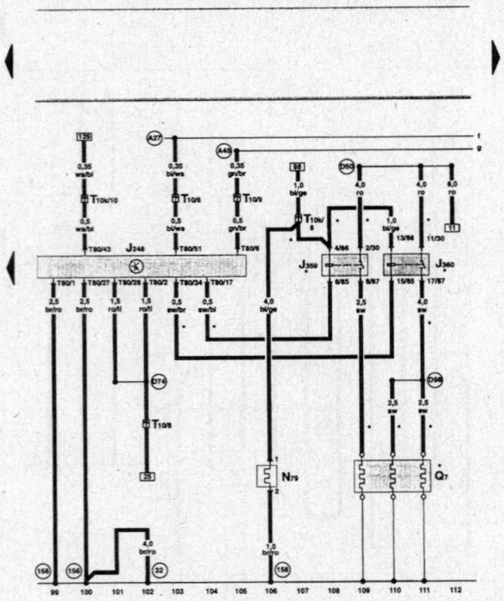

J248 – Diesel Direct Fuel Injection (DFI) Engine Control Module (ECM), behind instrument panel, left
J359 – Relay for preheating coolant, low heat output, in engine compartment
J360 – Relay for preheating coolant, high heat output, in engine compartment
N79 – Positive Crankcase Ventilation (PCV) Heating Element
Q7 – glow plugs (coolant)
T10 – 10-Pin Connector, white, behind instrument panel, left
T10k – 10-Pin Connector, blue, behind instrument panel, left
T80 – Connector, 80 point

(32) – Ground connection, behind instrument panel, left

(156) – Ground connection, in Diesel Direct Fuel Injection (DFI) wiring harness
(A27) – wire Connection (vehicle speed signal), in instrument panel wiring harness
(A45) – wire connection (RPM-signal), in instrument panel wiring harness
(D50) – plus connection (30), in engine compartment wiring harness
(D74) – wire connection (86), in engine compartment wiring harness
(D98) – Wire connection (glow plugs), in engine compartment wiring harness
• – manual transmission only

VW1029800095080X

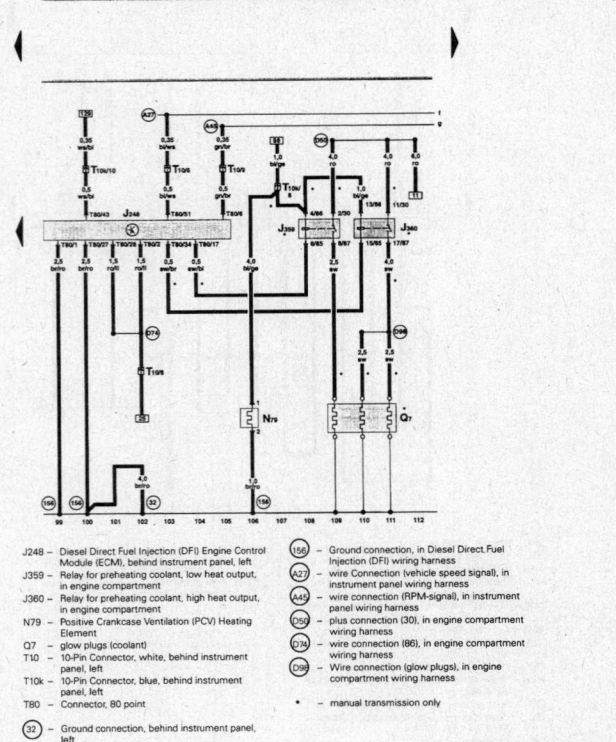

Fig. 35 TDI fuel injection wiring diagram (Preheating coolant replay & coolant glow plugs). New Beetle

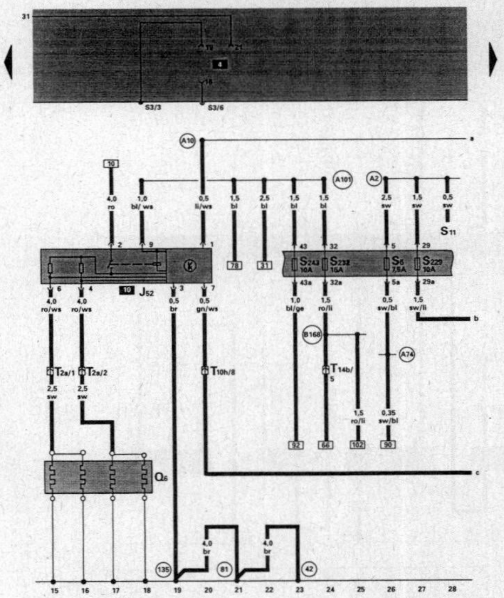

ws = white
sw = black
ro = red
br = brown
gn = green
bl = blue
gr = grey
li = violet
ge = yellow

J52 – Glow Plug Relay (180), on the thirteen position auxiliary relay panel, above relay panel
Q6 – Glow plugs (engine)
S5 – Fuse 5 in fuse holder
S11 – Fuse 11 in fuse holder
S229 – Fuse 29 in fuse holder
S232 – Fuse 32 in fuse holder
S243 – Fuse 43 in fuse holder
T2a – Double Connector, in engine compartment, left
T10h – 10-Pin Connector, black, behind instrument panel, left
T14b – 14-Pin Connector, in plenum chamber

(42) – Ground connection, beside steering column

(81) – Ground connection -1-, in instrument panel wiring harness

(135) – Ground connection -2-, in instrument panel wiring harness
(A2) – plus connection (15), in instrument panel wiring harness
(A10) – wire connection (glow plug control) in instrument panel wiring harness
(A74) – Connector (15a - fuse 5), in instrument panel wiring harness
(A101) – Connector -3- (87), in instrument panel wiring harness
(B168) – Connection (86) in passenger compartment wiring harness

VW1029900128010X

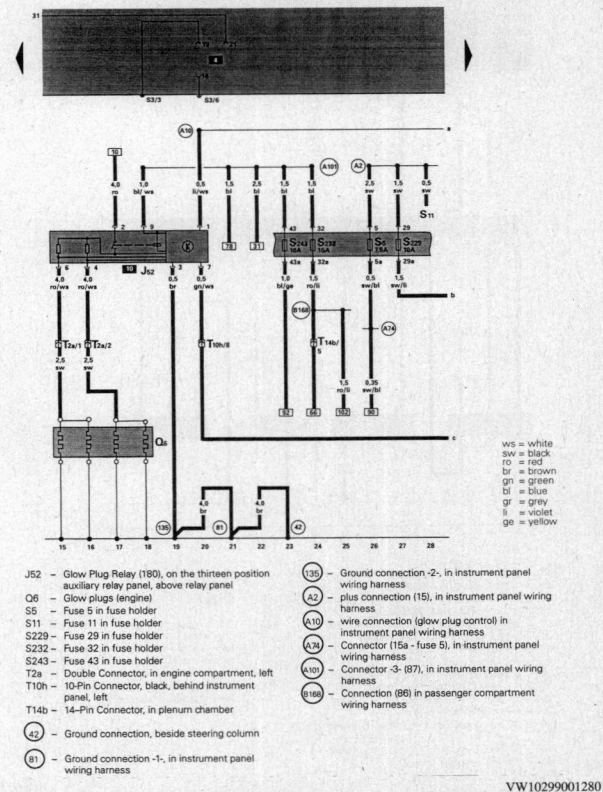

Fig. 36 TDI wiring diagram (Engine glow plugs & glow plug relay). 1999 New Beetle

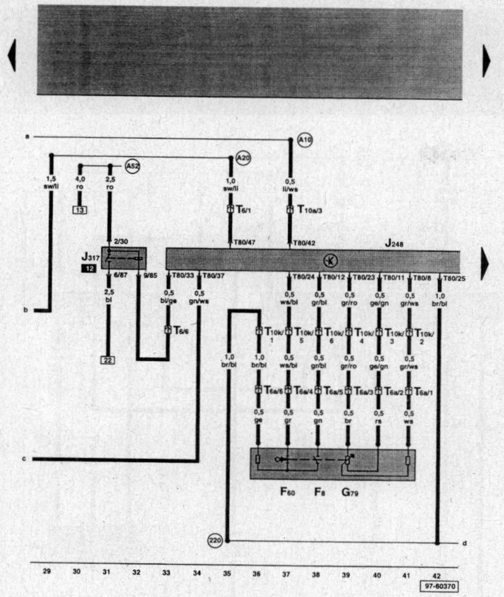

ws = white
sw = black
ro = red
br = brown
gn = green
bl = blue
gr = grey
li = violet
ge = yellow

F8 – Kick Down Switch
F60 – Closed Throttle Position (CTP) Switch
G79 – Throttle Position (TP) Sensor
J248 – Diesel Direct Fuel Injection (DFI) Engine Control Module (ECM), behind instrument panel, left
J317 – Power Supply (Terminal 30, B+) Relay
T6 – 6-Pin Connector, red, behind instrument panel, left
T6a – 6-Pin Connector, behind instrument panel, left
T10a – 10-Pin Connector, orange, behind instrument panel, left
T10k – 10-Pin Connector, blue, behind instrument panel, left
T80 – 80-Pin Connector, at -J248-

(220) – Ground connection (sensor ground), in engine compartment wiring harness
(A10) – wire connection (glow plug control) in instrument panel wiring harness
(A20) – wire connection (15a), in instrument panel wiring harness
(A52) – plus connection (30), in instrument panel wiring harness

VW1029900128020X

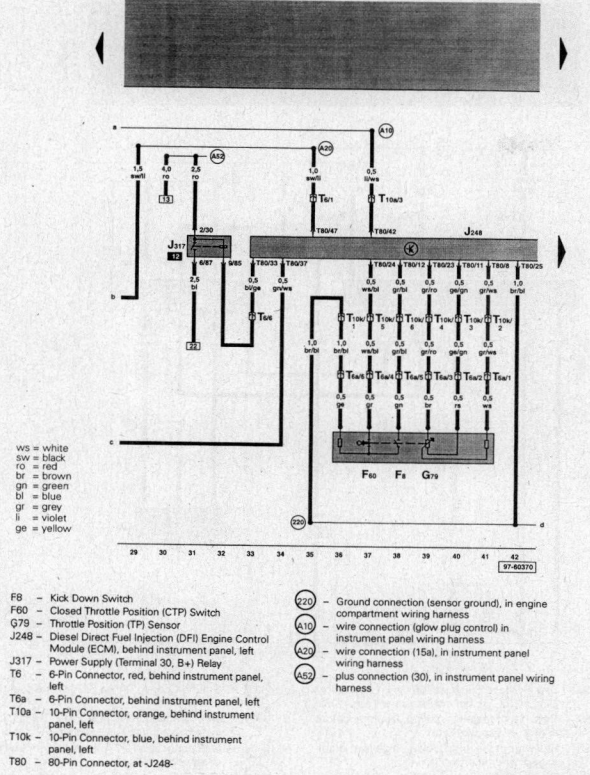

Fig. 37 TDI wiring diagram (Power supply relay, kick down switch & TP sensor). 1999 New Beetle

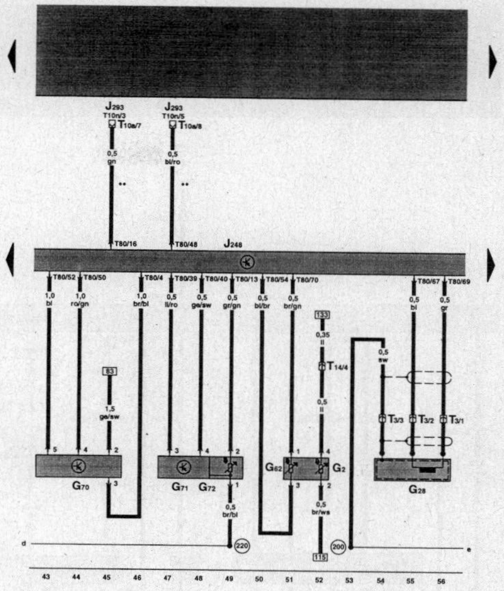

ws = white
sw = black
ro = red
br = brown
gn = green
bl = blue
gr = grey
li = violet
ge = yellow

G2 – Engine Coolant Temperature (ECT) Sensor
G28 – Engine Speed (RPM) Sensor
G62 – Engine Coolant Temperature (ECT) Sensor
G70 – Mass Air Flow (MAF) Sensor
G71 – Manifold Absolute Pressure (MAP) Sensor
G72 – Intake Air Temperature (IAT) Sensor
J248 – Diesel Direct Fuel Injection (DFI) Engine Control Module (ECM), behind instrument panel, left
J293 – Coolant FC (Fan Control) Control Module
T3 – 3-Pin Connector, on engine, front
T10a – 10-Pin Connector, orange, behind instrument panel, left
T10n – 10-Pin Connector, on J293
T14 – 14-Pin Connector (in center plenum chamber)
T80 – 80-Pin Connector, at -J248-

(200) – Ground connection (shielding), in engine compartment wiring harness
(220) – Ground connection (sensor ground), in engine compartment wiring harness
** – A/C Connection
- - - Automatic transmission only

VW1029900128030X

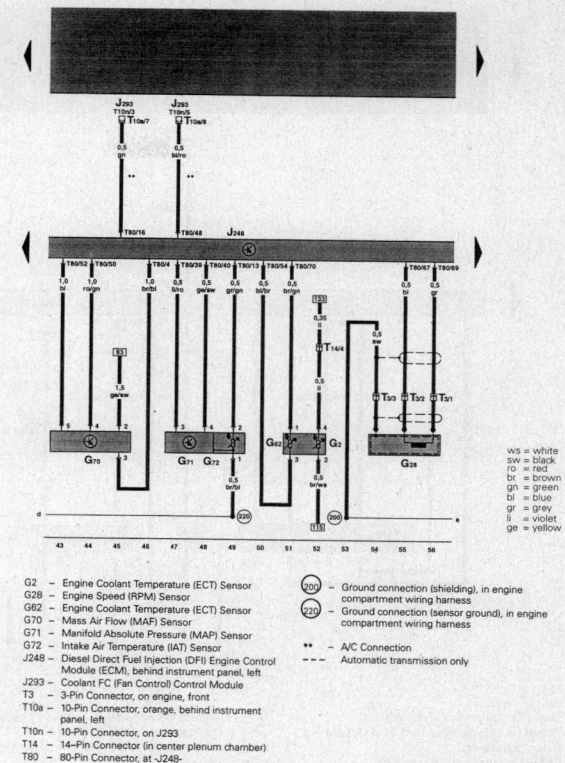

Fig. 38 TDI wiring diagram (MAF & RPM sensors). 1999 New Beetle

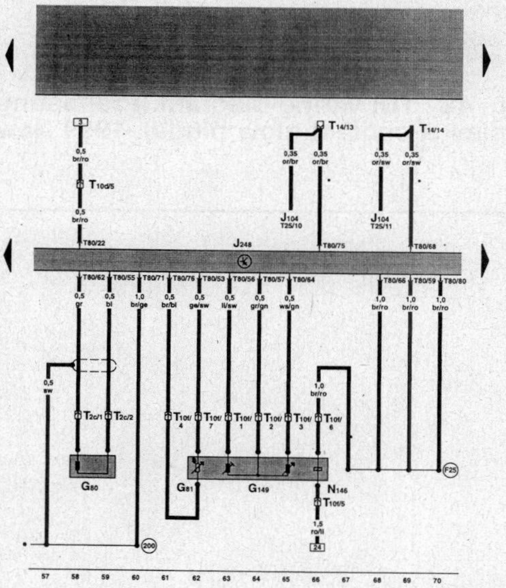

ws = white
sw = black
ro = red
br = brown
gn = green
bl = blue
gr = grey
li = violet
ge = yellow

G80 – Needle Lift Sensor
G81 – Fuel Temperature Sensor
G149 – Modulating Piston Displacement Sensor
J104 – ABS Control Module (w/EDL), center
J248 – Diesel Direct Fuel Injection (DFI) Engine Control Module (ECM), behind instrument panel, left
N146 – Quantity Adjuster
T2c – Double Connector, on engine, front
T10d – 10-Pin Connector, green, behind instrument panel, left
T10f – 10-Pin Connector, on engine, front
T14 – 14-Pin Connector (in center plenum chamber)
T25 – 25-Pin Connector
T80 – 80-Pin Connector, at -J248-
(200) – Ground connection (shielding), in engine compartment wiring harness

(F25) – Wire connection -1-, in Diesel Direct Fuel Injection (DFI) system wiring harness
* – DATA-Bus connection

VW1029900128040X

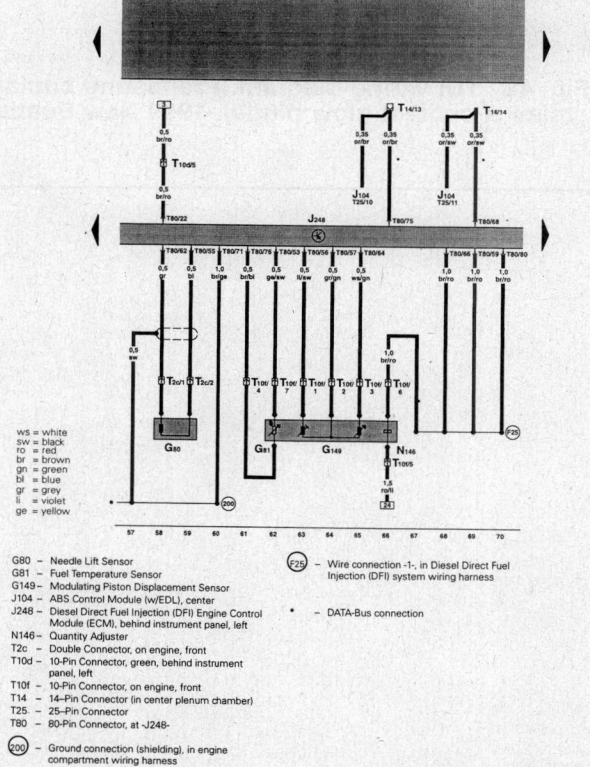

Fig. 39 TDI wiring diagram (Needle lift, fuel temperature & modulating piston displacement sensors). 1999 New Beetle

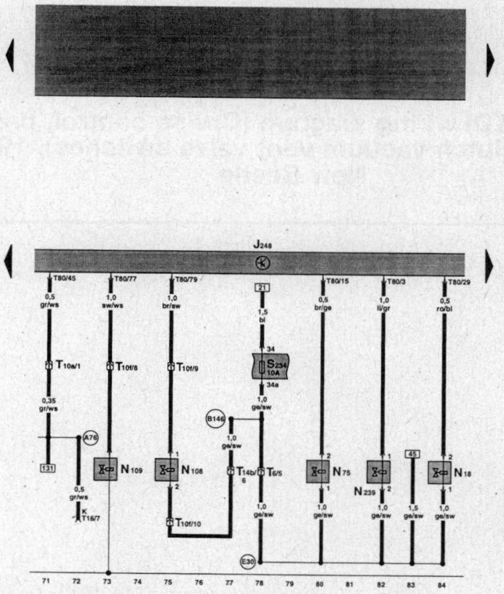

ws = white
sw = black
ro = red
br = brown
gn = green
bl = blue
gr = grey
li = violet
ge = yellow

J248 – Diesel Direct Fuel Injection (DFI) Engine Control Module (ECM), in plenum chamber, left
N18 – EGR Vacuum Regulator Solenoid Valve
N75 – Wastegate Bypass Regulator Valve
N108 – Cold Start Injector
N109 – Fuel Cut-off Valve
N239 – Change-over valve for intake manifold flap
S234 – Fuse 34 in fuse holder
T6 – 6-Pin Connector, brown, behind instrument panel, left
T10a – 10-Pin Connector, orange, behind instrument panel, left
T10f – 10-Pin Connector, black, on engine, front
T14 – 14-Pin Connector, in plenum chamber, center
T16 – 16-Pin Connector, Data Link Connector (DLC), below steering column

T80 – 80-Pin Connector, at -J248-
(A76) – Connector (K-diagnosis wire), in instrument panel wiring harness
(B146) – Plus connector -1- (B7), in wiring harness interior
(E30) – Connector (87a), in wiring harness engine

VW1029900128050X

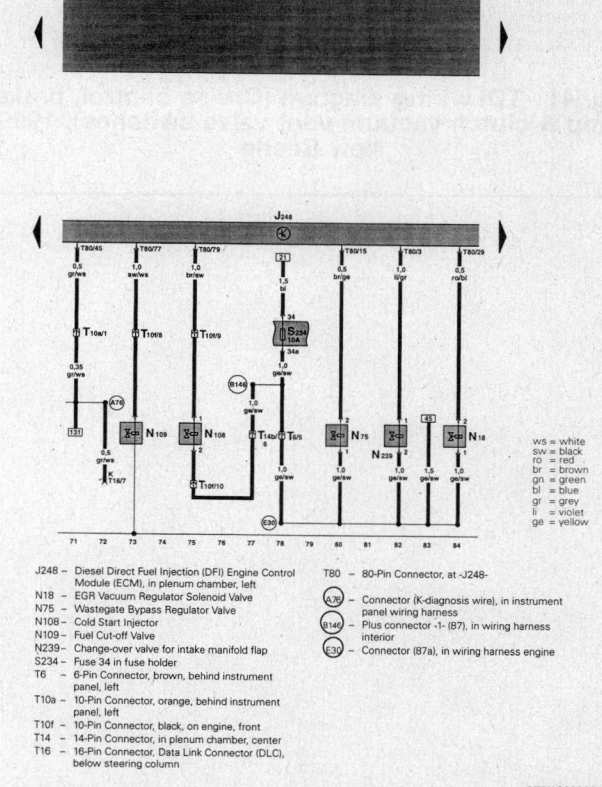

Fig. 40 TDI wiring diagram (EGR vacuum regulator solenoid valve, cold start injector & fuel cutoff valve). 1999 New Beetle

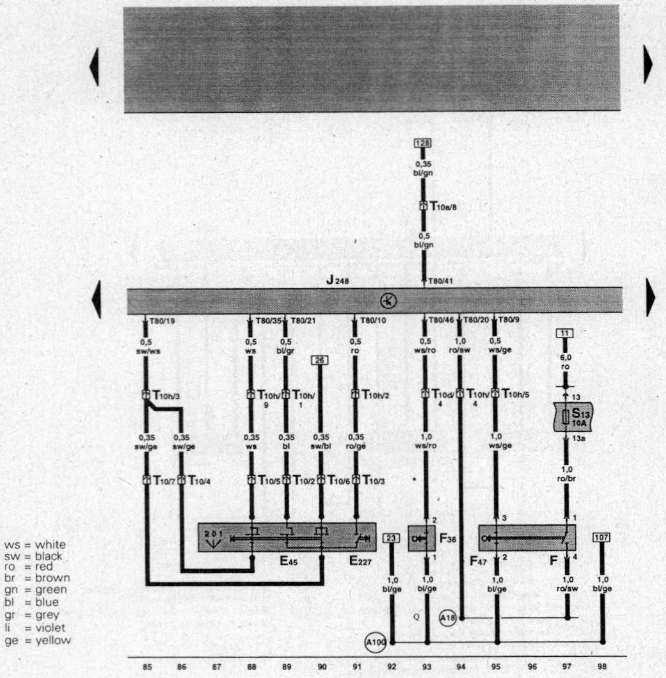

E45 – Cruise Control Switch (if equipped)
E227 – Button for cruise control (set), (if equipped)
F – Brake Light Switch
F36 – Clutch Vacuum vent Valve Switch
F47 – Brake Vacuum Vent Valve Switch for cruise control/diesel fuel injection (DFI)
J248 – Diesel Direct Fuel Injection (DFI) Engine Control Module (ECM), behind instrument panel, left
S13 – Fuse 13 in fuse holder
T10 – 10-Pin Connector, black, near steering column
T10d – 10-Pin Connector, green, behind instrument panel, left
T10h – 10-Pin Connector, black, behind instrument panel, left
T80 – 80-Pin Connector, at -J248-

(A18) – wire connection (54), in instrument panel wiring harness
(A100) – Connector -2- (87), in instrument panel wiring harness
• – Manual transmission only

VW1029900128060X

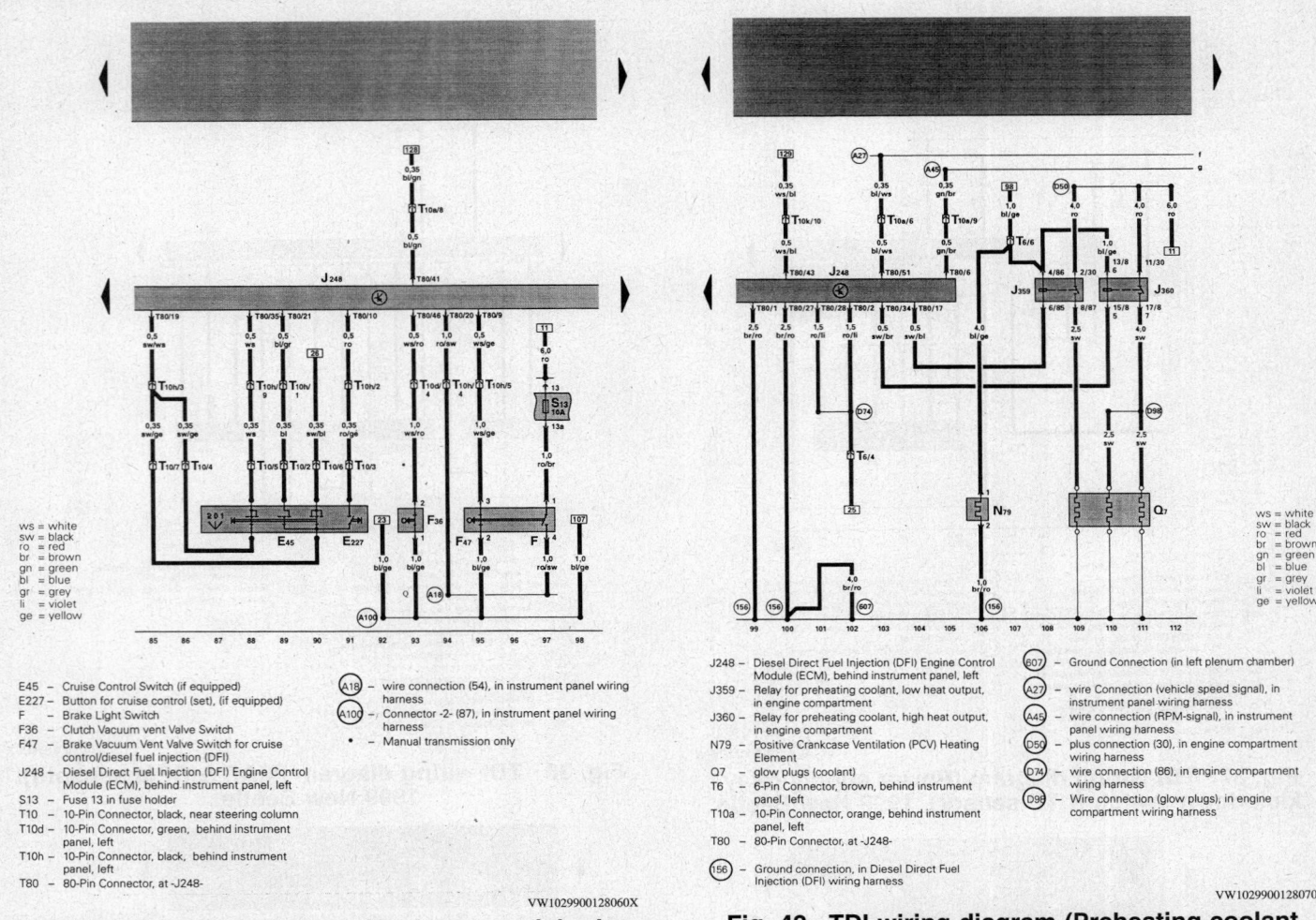

Fig. 41 TDI wiring diagram (Cruise control, brake lamp & clutch vacuum vent valve switches). 1999 New Beetle

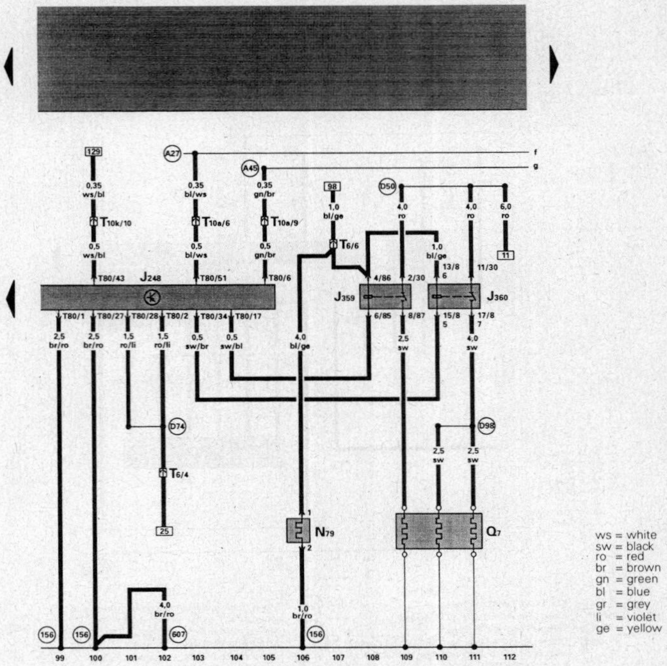

J248 – Diesel Direct Fuel Injection (DFI) Engine Control Module (ECM), behind instrument panel, left
J359 – Relay for preheating coolant, low heat output, in engine compartment
J360 – Relay for preheating coolant, high heat output, in engine compartment
N79 – Positive Crankcase Ventilation (PCV) Heating Element
Q7 – glow plugs (coolant)
T6 – 6-Pin Connector, brown, behind instrument panel, left
T10a – 10-Pin Connector, orange, behind instrument panel, left
T80 – 80-Pin Connector, at -J248-

(156) – Ground connection, in Diesel Direct Fuel Injection (DFI) wiring harness

(607) – Ground Connection (in left plenum chamber)
(A27) – wire Connection (vehicle speed signal), in instrument panel wiring harness
(A45) – wire connection (RPM-signal), in instrument panel wiring harness
(D50) – plus connection (30), in engine compartment wiring harness
(D74) – wire connection (86), in engine compartment wiring harness
(D98) – Wire connection (glow plugs), in engine compartment wiring harness

VW1029900128070X

Fig. 42 TDI wiring diagram (Preheating coolant relay & coolant glow plugs). 1999 New Beetle

DIAGNOSTIC CHART INDEX

Code	Description	Page No.	Fig. No.
1998 JETTA			
00310	Temperature Sensor I For Catalyst Open Circuit, Short To Positive Or Short To Ground	17-192	43
00312	Temperature Sensor II For Catalyst Open Circuit, Short To Positive Or Short To Ground	17-192	44
00313	Catalyst Questionable Signal	17-192	45
00513	RPM Sensor Questionable Signal	17-193	46
	RPM Sensor No Signal	17-193	47
00522	ECT Sensor Short To Ground Or Open Circuit, Short To Positive	17-193	48
	ECT Sensor Short To Ground Or Open Circuit, Short To Positive	17-194	49
00527	IAT Sensor Short To Ground Or Open Circuit, Short To Positive	17-194	50
00532	Supply Voltage Questionable Signal	17-195	51
00539	Fuel Temperature Sensor Short To Ground Or Open Circuit, Short To Positive	17-195	52
00542	Needle Lift Sensor Input Open	17-195	53
	Needle Lift Sensor Questionable Signal	17-195	54
00553	MAF Sensor Questionable Signal	17-196	55
	MAF Sensor Open Circuit, Short To Ground Or Short To Positive	17-196	56
00575	MAP Control Difference	17-196	57
00625	VSS Questionable Signal	17-197	58
00668	Battery Positive Voltage Terminal 30 Signal Too Low	17-195	51
00741	Brake Pedal Position Monitoring Questionable Signal	17-197	59
00765	Modulating Piston Displacement Sensor	17-197	60
00777	TP Sensor Questionable Signal	17-198	61
	TP Sensor Short To Voltage	17-198	62
01237	Fuel Cutoff Valve Open Circuit Or Short To Ground	17-198	63
01242	Final Stage In Control Module Questionable Signal	17-198	64
01268	Quantity Adjuster Control Difference	17-199	65

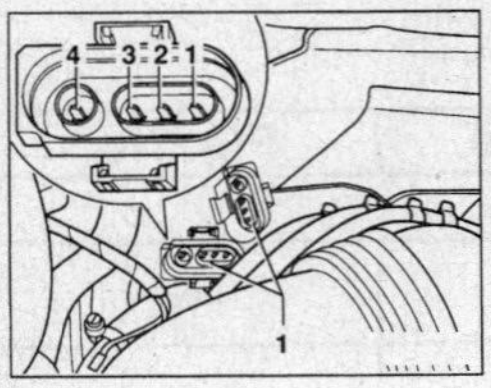

- Turn OFF ignition.
- Unplug connector for temperature sensor for catalyst -1-.
- Connect multimeter using aux. cable from VW 1594 to sensor connector terminals 1 + 2.

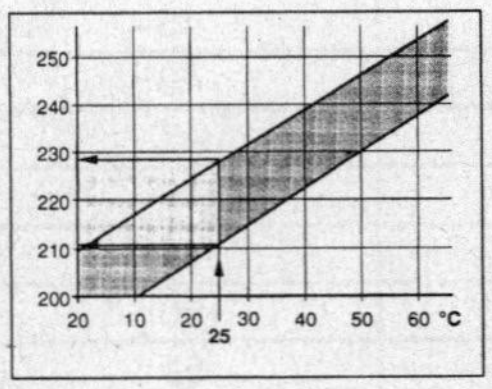

- Measure sensor resistance.
  Specification: see graph

Example:

25°C (77°F) equates to a resistance of 212...228 Ω

If resistance specified is not attained:

- Replace temperature sensors 1 and 2

VW0159900179010X

Fig. 43 Code 00310: Temperature Sensor I For Catalyst Open Circuit, Short To Positive Or Ground (Part 1 of 2). 1998 Jetta

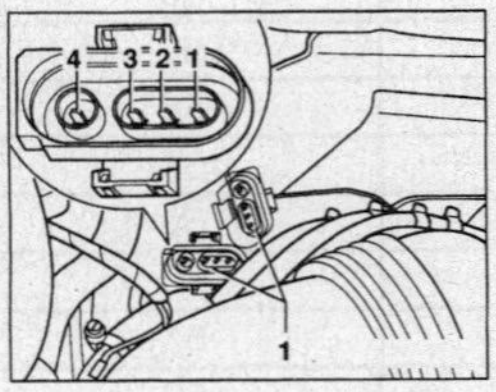

- Unplug connector for temperature sensor for catalyst -1-.
- Connect multimeter using auxiliary cables from VW 1594 to sensor connector terminals 3 + 4.

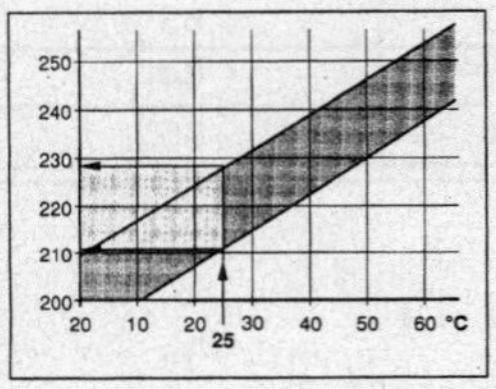

- Resistance graph for
  - ♦ Temperature sensor II for Catalyst (G132)
  - ♦ Temperature sensor I for Catalyst (G20)

Example:

25°C (77°F) equates to a resistance of 212...228 Ω

If resistance specified is not attained:

- Replace temperature sensors 1 and 2.

If resistance specified is attained:

VW0159900180010X

Fig. 44 Code 00312: Temperature Sensor II For Catalyst Open Circuit, Short To Positive Or Ground (Part 1 of 2). 1998 Jetta

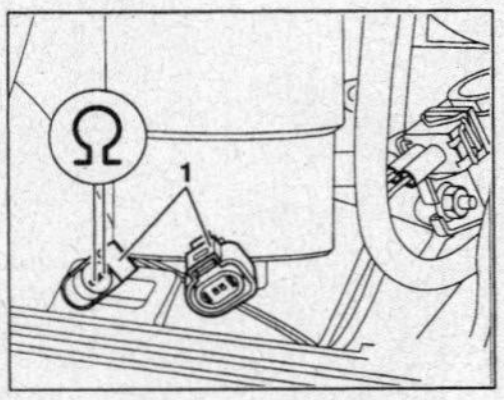

- Turn OFF ignition.
- Inspect additional fuel metering device wiring for proper connection and damage.
- Unplug connector -1- to Metering Pump (V54).

VW0159900181010X

Fig. 45 Code 00313: Catalyst Questionable Signal (Part 1 of 2). 1998 Jetta

If resistance specified is attained:

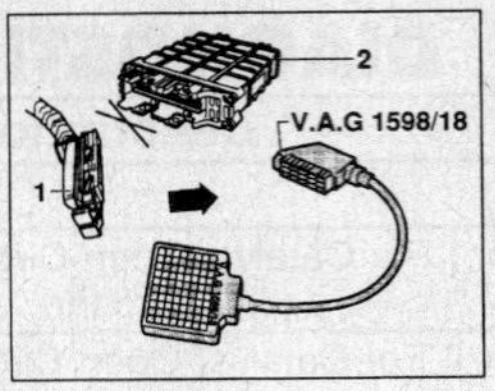

- Connect Adapter VAG 1598/18 to ECM wiring harness.

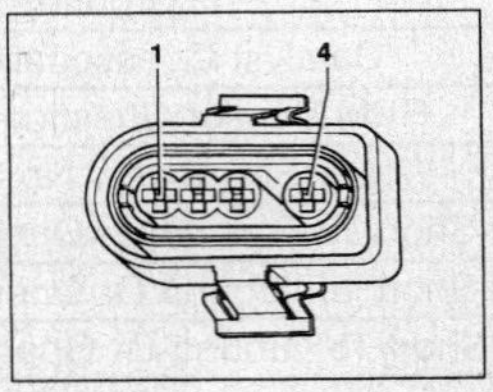

- Inspect wiring between adapter and connector for open circuit per electrical wiring diagram.
  Terminal 1 + socket 10
  Terminal 2 + socket 33
  Wire resistance: max. 1.5 Ω
- Check for shorts between wires.
  Specification: ∞Ω

If no malfunction is detected:

- Replace Direct Fuel Injection (DFI) Engine Control Module.

VW0159900179020X

Fig. 43 Code 00310: Temperature Sensor 1 For Catalyst Open Circuit, Short To Positive Or Ground (Part 2 of 2). 1998 Jetta

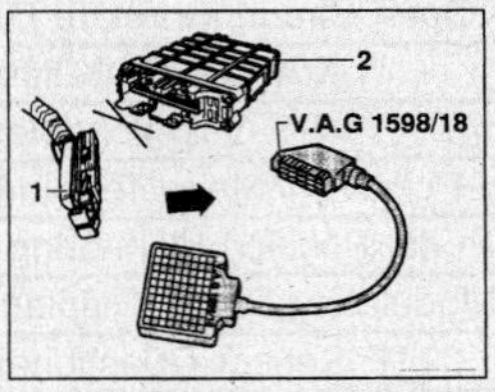

- Connect Adapter VAG 1598/18 to ECM wiring harness.

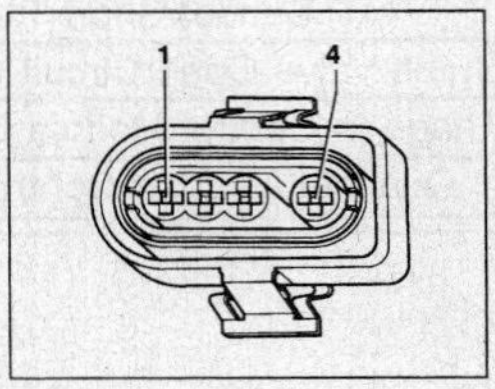

- Inspect wiring between adapter and connector for open circuit per electrical wiring diagram.
  Terminal 3 + socket 56
  Terminal 4 + socket 33
  Wire resistance: max. 1.5 Ω
- Check for shorts between wires.
  Specification: ∞Ω

If no malfunction is detected:

- Replace Direct Fuel Injection (DFI) Engine Control Module (ECM) (J248).

VW0159900180020X

Fig. 44 Code 00312: Temperature Sensor II For Catalyst Open Circuit, Short To Positive Or Ground (Part 2 of 2). 1998 Jetta

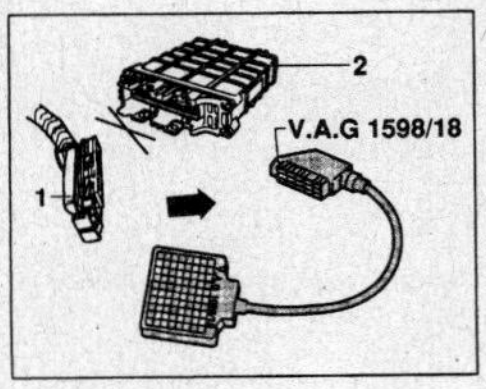

- Measure resistance between pump terminals.
  Specification: 8...12 Ω

If resistance specified is not attained:

- Replace Metering Pump (V54).

If resistance specified is attained:

- Connect Adapter VAG 1598/18 to ECM wiring harness.

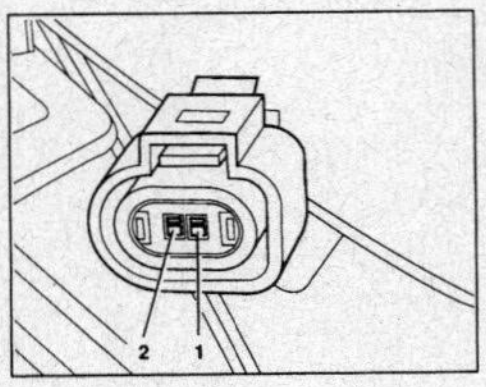

- Inspect wiring between adapter and connector for open circuit per electrical wiring diagram.
  Terminal 1 + socket 27
  Terminal 2 + socket 45
  Wire resistance: max. 1.5 Ω
- Check for shorts between wires.
  Specification: ∞Ω

If no malfunction in additional fuel metering device is found:

- Allow catalyst to cool for at least 1 hour.
- Connect Scan Tool VAG 1551 and select "engine electronics" with address word 01.

VW0159900181020X

Fig. 45 Code 00313: Catalyst Questionable Signal (Part 2 of 2). 1998 Jetta

– Turn OFF ignition.

– Check whether engine speed sensor is secure and wiring to sensor is not damaged.

– Remove and check sensor for metal particles or other damage.

– Check whether sensor wheel is cracked, loose or damaged.

If no malfunction is found:

– Check sensor and wiring as described under DTC code: 00513.

VW0159900182000X

Fig. 46 Code 00513: RPM Sensor Questionable Signal. 1998 Jetta

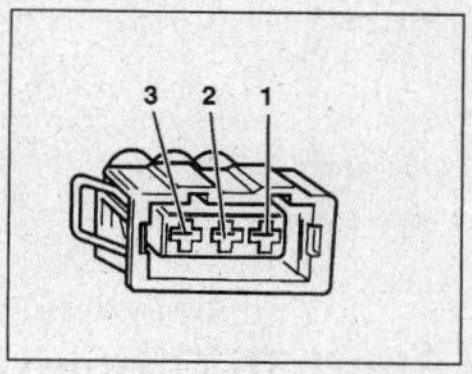

– Check wiring between Adapter VAG 1598/18 and 3 pin connector for open circuit per electrical wiring diagram.
Terminal 1 + socket 33
Terminal 2 + socket 8
Terminal 3 + socket 1
Wire resistance: max. 1.5 Ω

– Check wiring at 3 pin connector for short between terminals per electrical wiring diagram.
Specification: ∞ Ω

If no malfunction is detected:

– Replace Direct Fuel Injection (DFI) Engine Control Module (ECM) (J248).

VW0159900183020X

Fig. 47 Code 00513: RPM Sensor No Signal (Part 2 of 2). 1998 Jetta

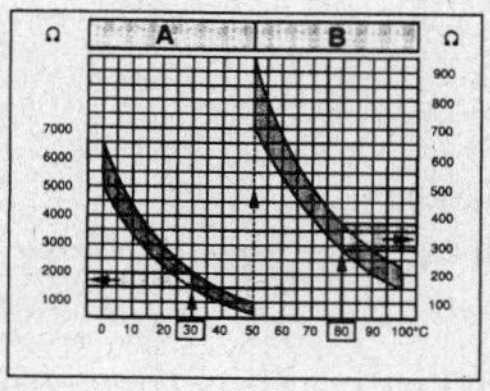

Resistance graph for

- Engine Coolant Temperature (ECT) Sensor (G62)

Scale A shows resistance values for temperature range 0...50°C (32...122°F) and scale B values for temperature range 50...100°C (122...212°F).

Examples:

- 30°C (86°F) corresponds to a resistance from 1500...2000 Ω
- 80°C (176°F) corresponds to a resistance from 275...375 Ω

If resistance specified is not attained:

– Replace ECT Sensor (G62).

If resistance specified is attained:

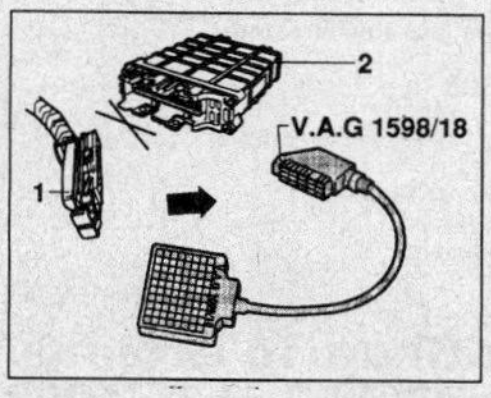

– Connect Adapter VAG 1598/18 to ECM wiring harness.

VW0159900184020X

Fig. 48 Code 00522: ECT Sensor Short To Ground Or Open Circuit, Short To Positive (Part 2 of 3). 1998 Jetta

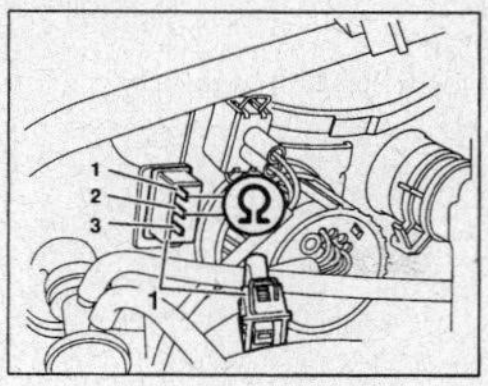

– Turn OFF ignition.
– Check whether engine speed sensor is secure and wiring to sensor is not damaged.

– Unplug connector -1- for engine speed sensor.

– Measure resistance between connector terminals 1 + 2.
Specification: 1.0 ... 1.5 kΩ

If resistance specified is not attained:

– Replace Engine Speed (rpm) Sensor (G28).

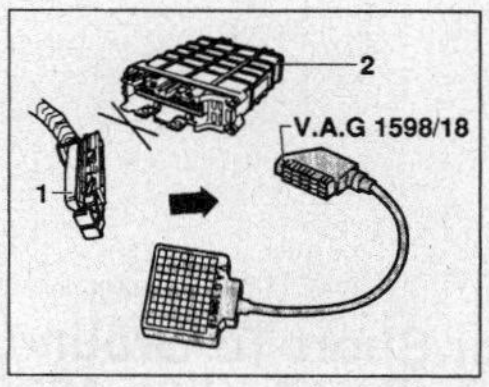

If resistance specified is attained:

– Connect Adapter VAG 1598/18 to ECM wiring harness.

VW0159900183010X

Fig. 47 Code 00513: RPM Sensor No Signal (Part 1 of 2). 1998 Jetta

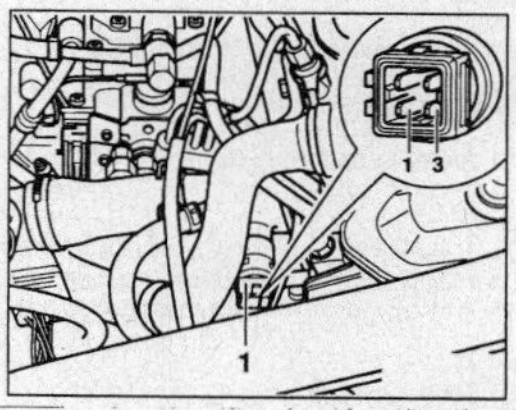

– Turn OFF ignition.

– Unplug ECT Sensor -1- connector.

– Measure resistance between sensor terminals 1 + 3.

VW0159900184010X

Fig. 48 Code 00522: ECT Sensor Short To Ground Or Open Circuit, Short To Positive (Part 1 of 3). 1998 Jetta

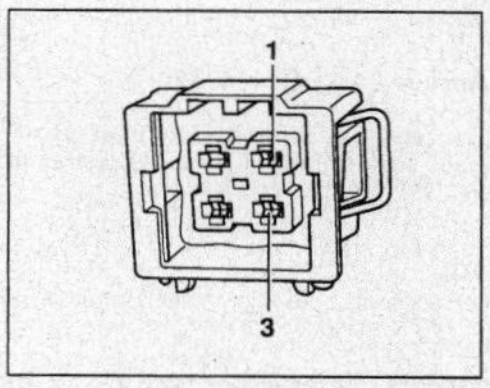

– Check wiring between Adapter VAG 1598/18 and 4 pin connector for open circuit per electrical wiring diagram.
Terminal 1 + socket 33
Terminal 3 + socket 14
Wire resistance: max. 1.5 Ω

– Check for shorts between wires.
Specification: ∞Ω

If no malfunction is detected:

– Replace Direct Fuel Injection (DFI) Engine Control Module (ECM) (J248).

DTC code: 00522
Engine Coolant Temperature (ECT) Sensor (G62)
Short to ground, or SP
or
Open circuit, short to positive, or SP

Special tools, testers and auxiliary items

- Adapter VAG 1598/18
- Digital Multimeter Fluke 83 or equivalent
- Connector Test Kit VW 1594
- Electrical wiring diagram

VW0159900184030X

Fig. 48 Code 00522: ECT Sensor Short To Ground Or Open Circuit, Short To Positive (Part 3 of 3). 1998 Jetta

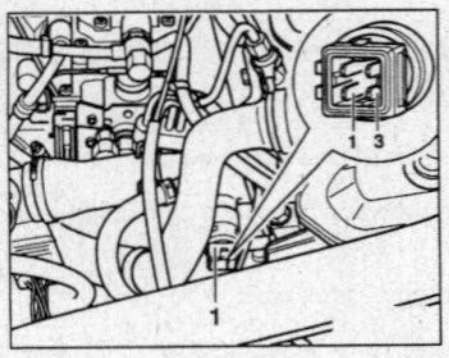

- Turn OFF ignition.
- Unplug Engine Coolant Temperature (ECT) Sensor -1- connector.

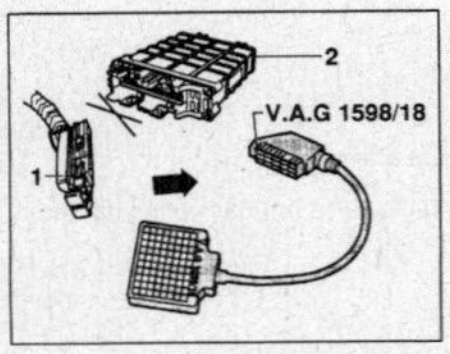

- Connect Adapter VAG 1598/18 to ECM wiring harness.

VW0159900185010X

Fig. 49 Code 00522: ECT Sensor Short To Ground Or Open Circuit, Short To Positive (Part 1 of 3). 1998 Jetta

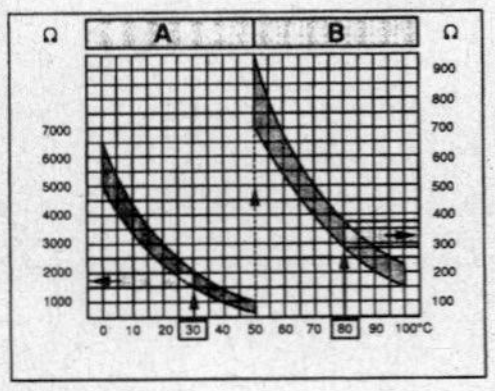

Resistance graph for

- Engine Coolant Temperature (ECT) Sensor (G62)
- Start engine and run at Closed Throttle Position.
- Resistance must decrease uniformly as engine warms up.

Note:

If problems occur at certain temperature ranges and resistance value does not fall without stopping, then temperature signal is periodically interrupted and sensor must be replaced.

- Erase DTC memory.
(Unplugging ECT Sensor is registered as a malfunction).

VW0159900185030X

Fig. 49 Code 00522: ECT Sensor Short To Ground Or Open Circuit, Short To Positive (Part 3 of 3). 1998 Jetta

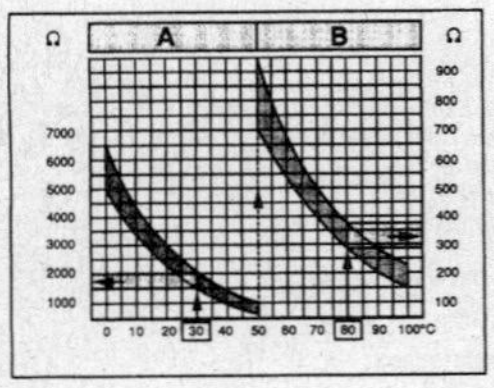

Resistance graph for

- Intake Air Temperature (IAT) Sensor (G72)

Scale A shows resistance values for temperature range 0...50°C (32...122°F) and scale B the values for temperature range 50...100°C (122...212°F).

Examples:

- 30°C (86°F) corresponds to a resistance from 1500...2000 Ω
- 80°C (176°F) corresponds to a resistance from 275...375 Ω

If resistance specified is not attained:

- Replace IAT Sensor (G72).

If resistance specified is attained:

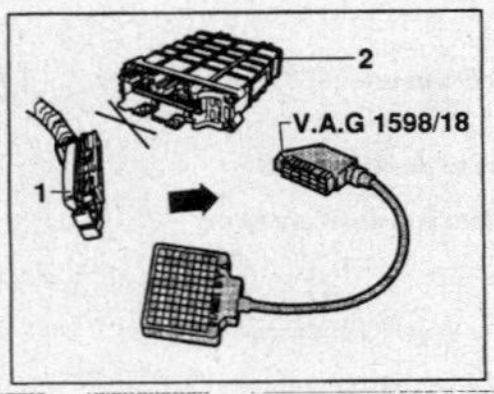

- Connect Adapter VAG 1598/18 to ECM wiring harness.

VW0159900186020X

Fig. 50 Code 00527: IAT Sensor Short To Ground Or Open Circuit, Short To Positive (Part 2 of 3). 1998 Jetta

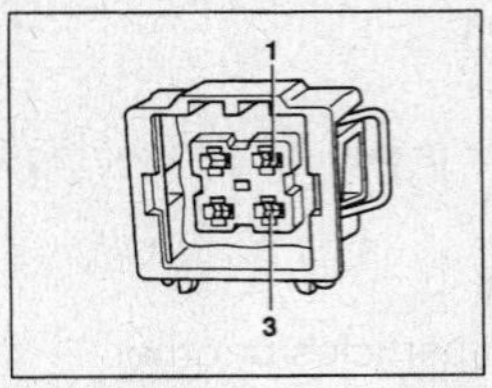

- Check wiring between adapter and 4 pin connector for open circuit per electrical wiring diagram.
  Terminal1 + socket 33
  Terminal 3 + socket 14
  Wire resistance: max. 1.5 Ω

If no malfunction is detected:

- Allow engine to cool.

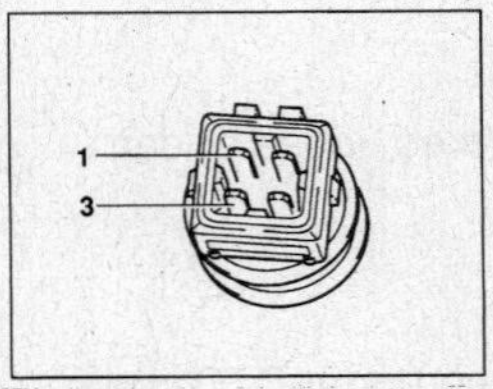

- Measure sensor resistance by connecting terminals 1 + 3 to multimeter with cables from VW 1594.

VW0159900185020X

Fig. 49 Code 00522: ECT Sensor Short To Ground Or Open Circuit, Short To Positive (Part 2 of 3). 1998 Jetta

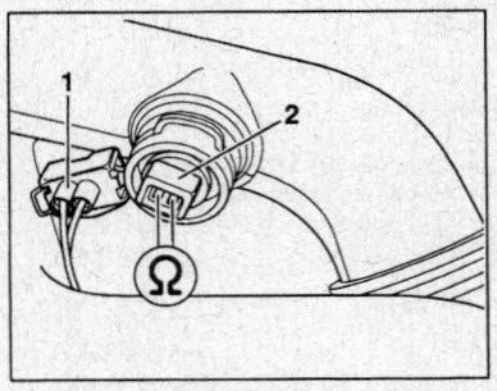

- Turn OFF ignition.
- Unplug IAT Sensor -2- connector -1-.
- Measure resistance between sensor terminals.

VW0159900186010X

Fig. 50 Code 00527: IAT Sensor Short To Ground Or Open Circuit, Short To Positive (Part 1 of 3). 1998 Jetta

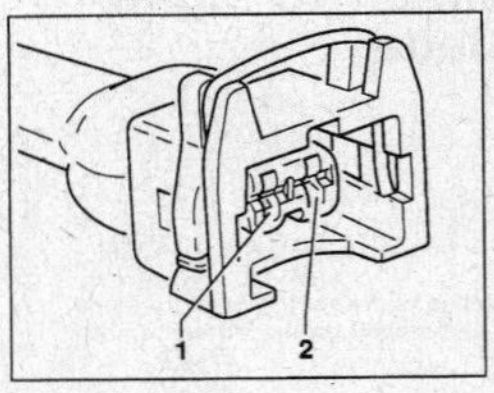

- Check wiring between Adapter VAG 1598/18 and connector for open circuit per electrical wiring diagram.
  Terminal1 + socket 64
  Terminal 2 + socket 33
  Wire resistance: max. 1.5 Ω
- Check for shorts between wires.
  Specification: ∞Ω

If no malfunction is detected:

- Replace Direct Fuel Injection (DFI) Engine Control Module (ECM) (J248).

DTC code: 00532
Supply voltage
Questionable signal
or
DTC code: 00668
Battery positive voltage (B+), terminal 30
Signal too low

Special tools, testers and auxiliary items

- Adapter VAG 1598/18
- Digital Multimeter Fluke 83 or equivalent
- Connector Test Kit VW 1594
- Electrical wiring diagram

VW0159900186030X

Fig. 50 Code 00527: IAT Sensor Short To Ground Or Open Circuit, Short To Positive (Part 3 of 3). 1998 Jetta

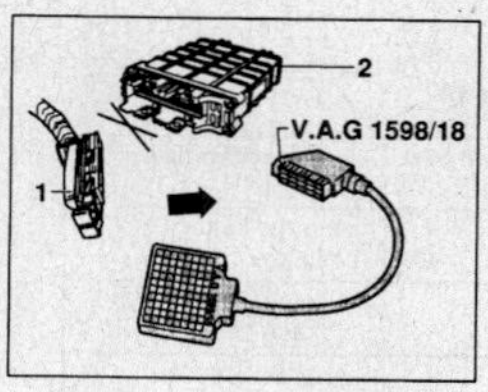

- Turn OFF ignition.
- Connect Adapter VAG 1598/18 to ECM wiring harness.
- Bridge sockets 42 + 46 with auxiliary cables from VW 1594.
- Measure voltage between following sockets:
  45 + 1, 68 + 1, 23 + 1 and 23 + 24
  Specification: approx. battery voltage

If voltage specified is not attained:

- Check Power Supply (Terminal 30, B+) Relay (J317).
- Check connections for open circuit, short circuit and transfer resistance at terminals per electrical wiring diagram.

If no malfunction is found in wiring and relay:

- Replace Direct Fuel Injection (DFI) Engine Control Module (ECM) (J248).

VW0159900187000X

Fig. 51 Codes 00532 & 00668: Supply Voltage Questionable Signal & Battery Positive Voltage Terminal 30 Signal Too Low. 1998 Jetta

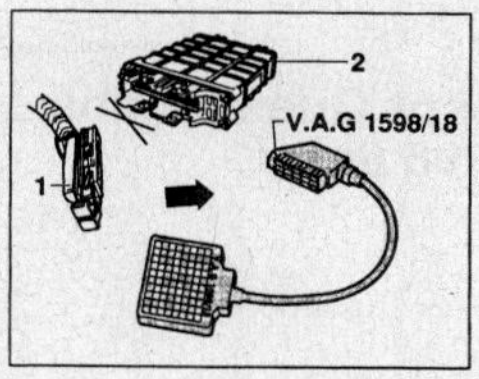

If resistance specified is not attained:

- Replace Fuel Temperature Sensor (G81)

If resistance specified is attained:

- Connect Adapter VAG 1598/18 to ECM wiring harness.

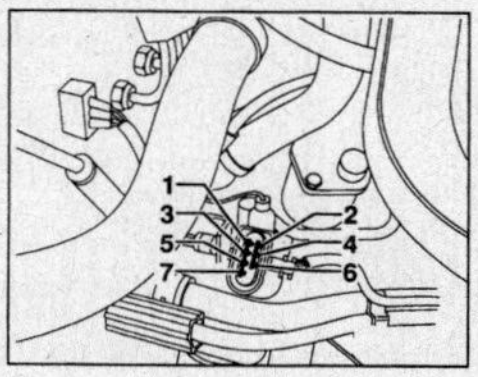

- Check wiring between Adapter VAG 1598/18 and connector for open circuit per electrical wiring diagram.
  Terminal 7 + socket 63
  Terminal 4 + socket 33
  Wire resistance: max. 1.5 Ω
- Check for shorts between wires.
  Specification: ∞Ω

If no malfunction is detected:

- Replace Direct Fuel Injection (DFI) Engine Control Module (ECM) (J248).

VW0159900188020X

Fig. 52 Code 00539: Fuel Temperature Sensor Short To Ground Or Open Circuit, Short To Positive (Part 2 of 2). 1998 Jetta

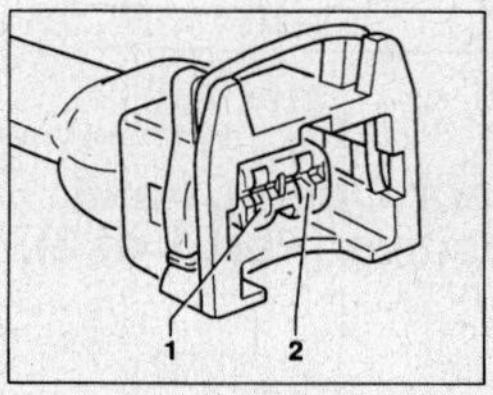

- Check wiring between Adapter VAG 1598/18 and connector for open circuit per electrical wiring diagram.
  Terminal1 + socket 12
  Terminal 2 + socket 11
  Wire resistance: max. 1.5 Ω
- Check for shorts between wires.
  Specification: ∞Ω

If no malfunction is detected:

- Replace Direct Fuel Injection (DFI) Engine Control Module (ECM) (J248).

VW0159900189020X

Fig. 53 Code 00542: Needle Lift Sensor Input Open (Part 2 of 2). 1998 Jetta

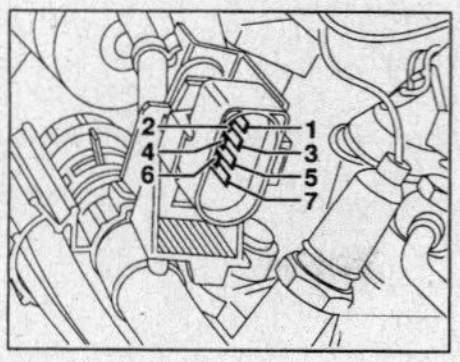

- Press → key.
- Press keys 0 and 6 to select Function 06 "End data transfer" and confirm with Q key.
- Turn OFF ignition.
- Unplug connector for Fuel Temperature Sensor (G81)(connection to injection pump metering control).
- Measure sensor resistance at terminals 4 + 7.

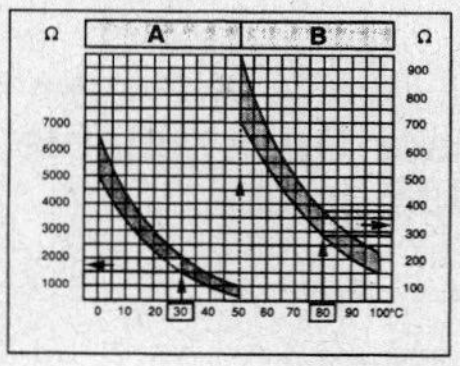

Resistance graph for

- Engine Coolant Temperature (ECT) Sensor (G62)

Scale A shows resistance values for temperature range 0...50°C (32...122°F) and scale B the values for temperature range 50...100°C (122...212°F).

Examples:

- 30°C (86°F) corresponds to a resistance from 1500...2000 Ω
- 80°C (176°F) corresponds to a resistance from 275...375 Ω

VW0159900188010X

Fig. 52 Code 00539: Fuel Temperature Sensor Short To Ground Or Open Circuit, Short To Positive (Part 1 of 2).1998 Jetta

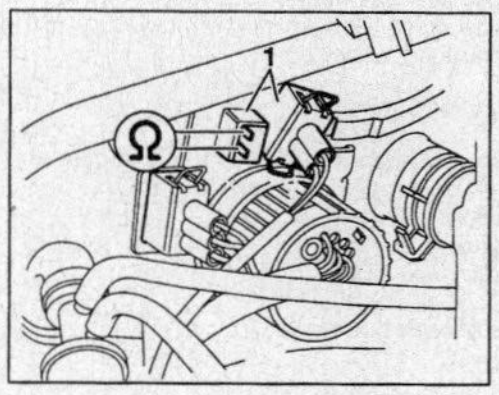

- Unplug connector -1- for Needle Lift Sensor (G80).
- Measure resistance between connector terminals.
  Specification: 80...120 Ω

If resistance specified is not attained:

- Replace No. 3 cylinder injector with Needle Lift Sensor (G80).

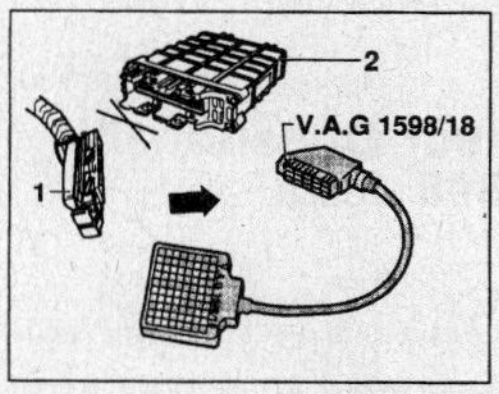

If resistance specified is attained:

- Connect Adapter VAG 1598/18 to ECM wiring harness.

VW0159900189010X

Fig. 53 Code 00542: Needle Lift Sensor Input Open (Part 1 of 2). 1998 Jetta

- Turn OFF ignition.
- Check No. 3 cylinder injector lines for damage and kinks.
- Check fuel supply.
- Check fuel system for vapor lock.

If no malfunction is found:

- Replace No. 3 cylinder injector with Needle Lift Sensor (G80).

DTC code: 00550
Injection start control
Control difference

If in addition to DTC code 00550, DTC code 00542, Needle Lift Sensor (G80) is displayed:

- *Check Needle Lift Sensor (G80).*
  Malfunction: input open
  Malfunction: questionable signal

Rapid data transfer	HELP
Select function XX	

Indicated on display:

- Check Cold Start Injector (N108) in Output Diagnostic Test Mode (DTM)

If no malfunction is found:

- Injection timing, dynamically checking and adjusting

VW0159900190000X

Fig. 54 Code 00542: Needle Lift Sensor Questionable Signal. 1998 Jetta

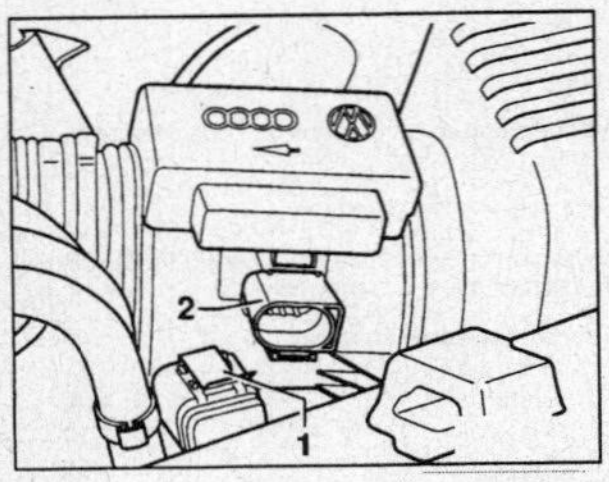

- Turn OFF ignition.
- Unplug MAF Sensor -2- connector -1-.
- Turn ON ignition.

VW0159900191010X

Fig. 55 Code 00553: MAF Sensor Questionable Signal (Part 1 of 3). 1998 Jetta

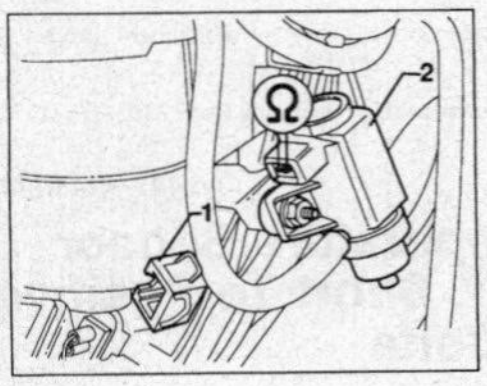

If resistances specified are attained:

- Check EGR Valve (N18) as follows:
- Unplug EGR Valve -2- connector -1-.
- Measure resistance at valve.
  Specification: 14 ... 18 Ω

If the resistance specified is not attained:

- Replace EGR Valve (N18).

Note:

At room temperature (warmer than +15°C (59°F)) resistance lies in lower tolerance range. At operating temperature (80°C (176°F)) in upper tolerance range.

If resistance specified is attained:

- Check wiring between adapter VAG 1598/18 and connector for open circuit per electrical wiring diagram.
  Terminal 1 + socket 68
  Terminal 2 + socket 25
  Wire resistance: max. 1.5 Ω
- Check for shorts between wires.
  Specification: ∞Ω

If no malfunction is detected:

- Replace Direct Fuel Injection (DFI) Engine Control Module (ECM) (J248).

VW0159900191030X

Fig. 55 Code 00553: MAF Sensor Questionable Signal (Part 3 of 3). 1998 Jetta

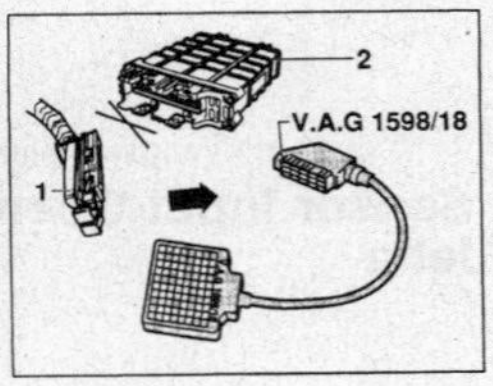

- Connect Adapter VAG 1598/18 to ECM wiring harness.
- Check wiring between Adapter VAG 1598/18 and connections for open circuit per electrical wiring diagram.
  Terminal 1 + socket 19
  Terminal 2 + socket 33
  Terminal 3 + socket 23
  Terminal 5 + socket 1
  Terminal 6 + socket 13
  Wire resistance: max. 1.5 Ω
- Check for shorts between wires.
  Specification: ∞Ω

If voltage values are attained and no malfunction in wiring can be found:

- Replace MAF Sensor (G70).

If voltages specified are attained:

- Replace Direct Fuel Injection (DFI) Engine Control Module (ECM) (J248).

DTC code: 00575
Manifold Absolute Pressure (MAP) Control difference

Special tools, testers and auxiliary items

- Adapter VAG 1598/18
- Digital Multimeter Fluke 83 or equivalent

VW0159900192020X

Fig. 56 Code 00553: MAF Sensor Open Circuit, Short To Ground Or Short To Positive (Part 2 of 2). 1998 Jetta

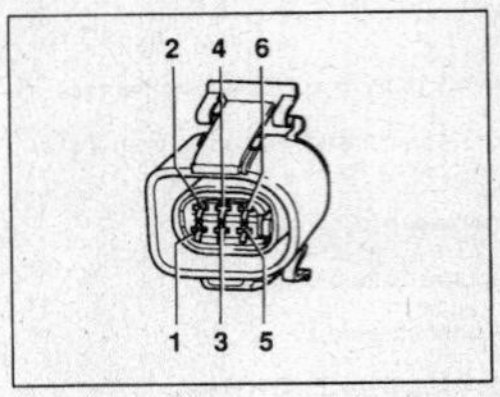

- Measure MAF sensor voltage supply between following connector terminals:

Connector on terminal -G70	Specification
3 + ground	Approx. battery voltage
3 + 5	Approx. battery voltage
1 + ground	Approx. 5 V
1 + 5	Approx. 5 V

If voltages specified are not attained:

- Turn OFF ignition.

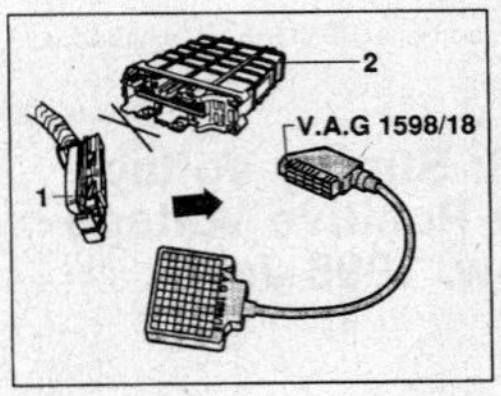

- Connect Adapter VAG 1598/18 to ECM wiring harness.
- Check wiring between adapter and connections for open circuit per electrical wiring diagram.
  Terminal 1 + socket 19
  Terminal 2 + socket 33
  Terminal 3 + socket 23
  Terminal 5 + socket 1
  Terminal 6 + socket 13
  Wire resistance: max. 1.5 Ω
- Check for shorts between wires.
  Specification: ∞Ω

VW0159900191020X

Fig. 55 Code 00553: MAF Sensor Questionable Signal (Part 2 of 3). 1998 Jetta

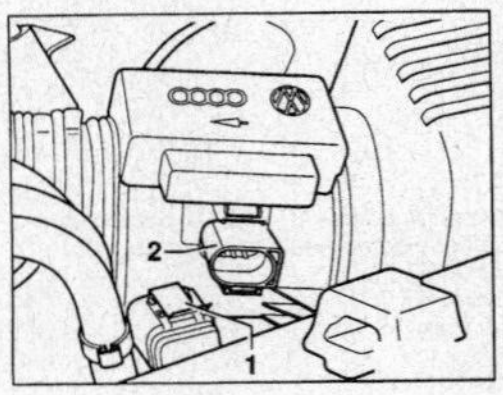

- Unplug MAF Sensor -2- connector -1-.
- Turn ON ignition.

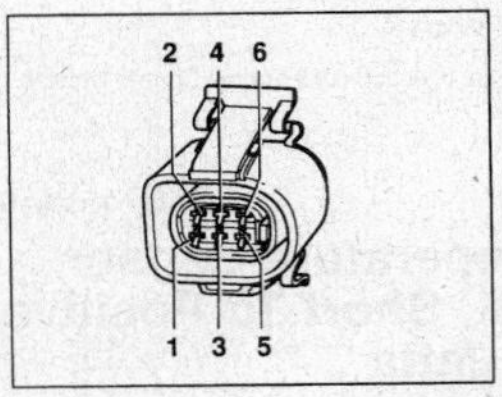

- Measure MAF Sensor voltage supply between following connector terminals:

Connector on terminal -G70	Specification
3 + ground	Approx. battery voltage
3 + 5	Approx. battery voltage
1 + ground	Approx. 5 V
1 + 5	Approx. 5 V

- Turn OFF ignition.

VW0159900192010X

Fig. 56 Code 00553: MAF Sensor Open Circuit, Short To Ground Or Short To Positive (Part 1 of 2). 1998 Jetta

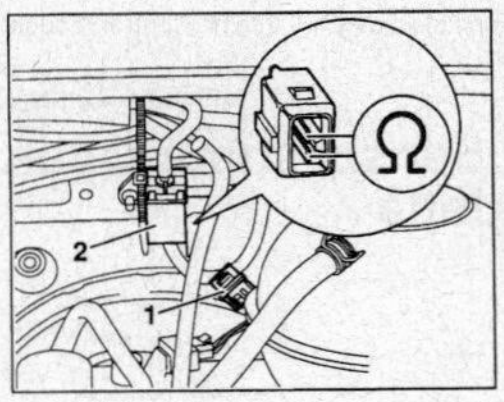

- Turn OFF ignition after completing test drive.
- Unplug Wastegate Bypass Regulator Valve (N75) -2- connector -1-.
- Measure resistance between valve contacts.
  Specification: 25...45 Ω

If specified resistance is not attained:

- Replace Wastegate Bypass Regulator Valve (N75).

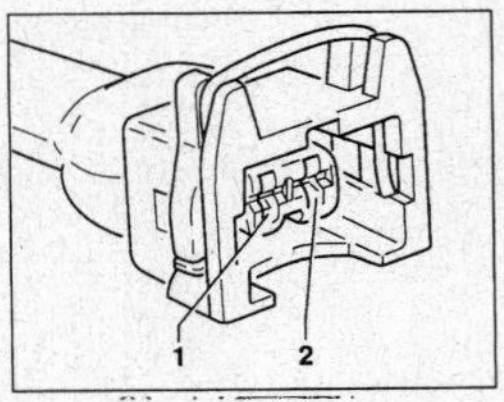

If specified resistance attained:

- Turn ON ignition.
- Measure voltage at valve connector terminal -1- and engine ground.
  Specification: approx. battery voltage

If voltage specified is not attained:

- Turn OFF ignition.

VW0159900193010X

Fig. 57 Code 00575: MAP Control Difference (Part 1 of 2). 1998 Jetta

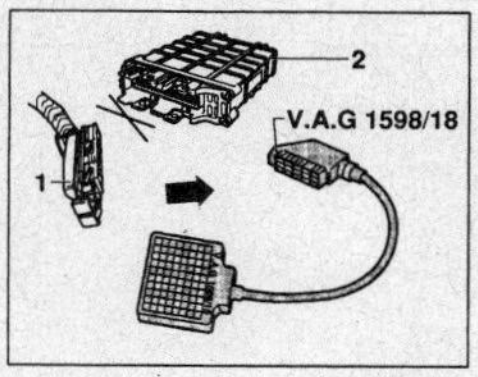

- Connect Adapter VAG 1598/18 to ECM wiring harness.
- Check wiring between Adapter VAG 1598/18 and connector for open circuit per electrical wiring diagram.
  Terminal 1 + socket 68
  Terminal 2 + socket 47
  Wire resistance: max. 1.5 Ω
- Check for shorts between wires.
  Specification: ∞Ω

If no malfunction is detected:

- Replace Direct Fuel Injection (DFI) Engine Control Module (ECM) (J248).

DTC code: 00625
Vehicle Speed signal
Questionable signal

Special tools, testers and auxiliary items

- Adapter VAG 1598/18
- Digital Multimeter Fluke 83 or equivalent
- Connector Test Kit VW 1594
- Electrical wiring diagram

VW0159900193020X

Fig. 57 Code 00575: MAP Control Difference (Part 2 of 2). 1998 Jetta

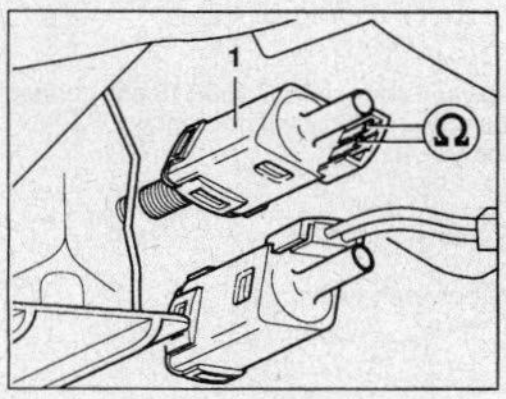

- Turn OFF ignition.
- Unplug Brake Pedal Switch (F47) -1- connector.
- Measure resistance between switch terminals.
  Specification:
  Brake pedal not depressed: less than 10 Ω
  Brake pedal depressed: ∞Ω

If resistance specified is not attained:

- Replace Brake Pedal Switch (F47).

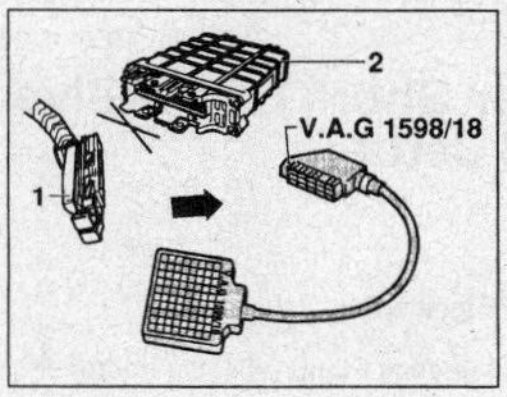

If resistance specified is attained:

- Connect Adapter VAG 1598/18 to ECM wiring harness.

VW0159900195010X

Fig. 59 Code 00741: Brake Pedal Position Monitoring Questionable Signal (Part 1 of 2). 1998 Jetta

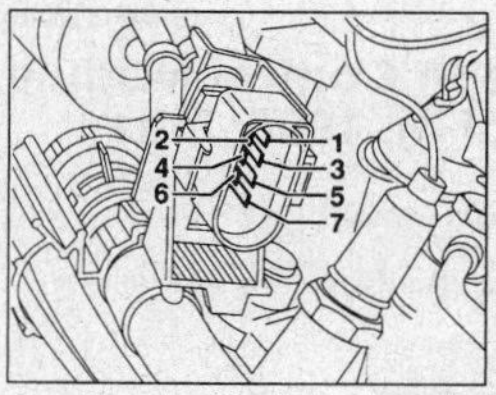

- Turn OFF ignition.
- Disconnect connection for Fuel Temperature Sensor (G81) (connection to Quantity Adjuster (N146)).
- Measure resistance between connector terminals 1 + 2 and 2 + 3.
  Specification: 5 ... 7 Ω

If resistance specified is not attained:

- Replace injection pump.

VW0159900196010X

Fig. 60 Code 00765: Modulating Piston Displacement Sensor (Part 1 of 2). 1998 Jetta

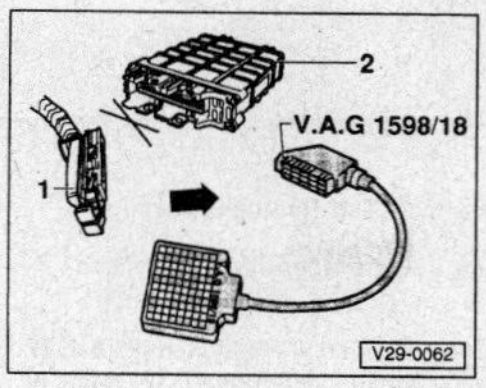

- Turn OFF ignition.
- Connect Adapter VAG 1598/18 to ECM wiring harness.
- Turn ON ignition.
- Bridge sockets 1 + 42 with auxiliary cables from VW 1594.
- Set multimeter scale to measure voltage and connect between adapter sockets 43 + 33.
- Raise front left-hand wheel.
- Rotate front wheel and observe voltage indicated.
  Specification: between 0 and min. 5 volt fluctuating

If voltage does not fluctuate:

- Check wiring to speedometer or to Vehicle Speed Sensor (VSS).

VW0159900194000X

Fig. 58 Code 00625: VSS Questionable Signal. 1998 Jetta

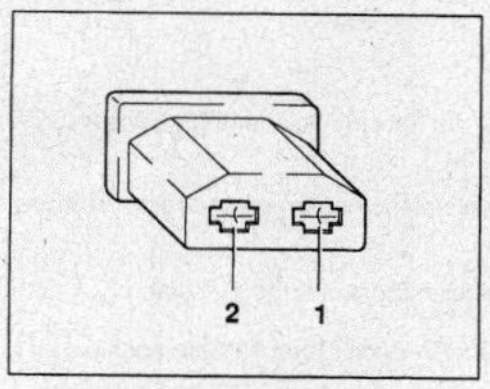

- Check wiring between Adapter VAG 1598/18 and connector for open circuit per electrical wiring diagram.
  Terminal 1 + socket 20
  Terminal 2 + socket 33
  Wire resistance: max. 1.5 Ω
- Check for shorts between wires.
  Specification: ∞Ω

Right-hand display does not change:

- Press → key.
- Press keys 0 and 6 to select Function 06 "End data transfer" and confirm with Q key.
- Turn OFF ignition.
- Set multimeter to measure voltage and connect between Adapter VAG 1598/18 sockets 44 + 1.
- Observe voltage indicated.
  Specification:
  Brake pedal not depressed: 0 Volt
  Brake pedal depressed: approx. battery voltage

No voltage is displayed:

- Check whether brake light functions.

Brake light OK:

- Check wiring to Brake Light Switch (F) for open or short circuit per electrical wiring diagram.

Brake light not OK:

- Replace Brake Light Switch (F).

VW0159900195020X

Fig. 59 Code 00741: Brake Pedal Position Monitoring Questionable Signal (Part 2 of 2). 1998 Jetta

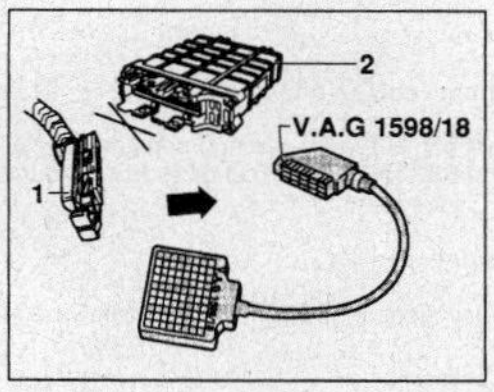

If resistance specified is attained:

- Connect Adapter VAG 1598/18 to ECM wiring harness.

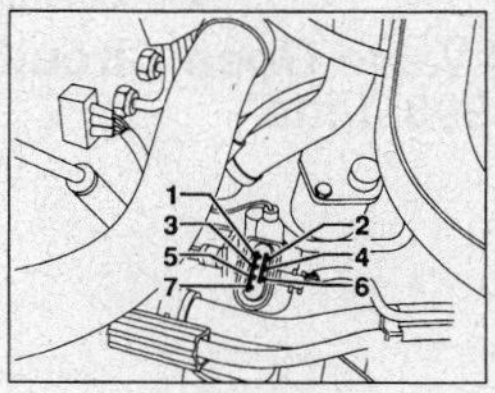

- Check wiring between Adapter VAG 1598/18 and connector for open circuit per electrical wiring diagram.
  Terminal 1 + socket 29
  Terminal 2 + socket 7
  Terminal 3 + socket 52
  Wire resistance: max. 1.5 Ω
- Check for shorts between wires.
  Specification: ∞Ω

If no malfunction is detected:

- Replace Direct Fuel Injection (DFI) Engine Control Module (ECM) (J248).

VW0159900196020X

Fig. 60 Code 00765: Modulating Piston Displacement Sensor (Part 2 of 2). 1998 Jetta

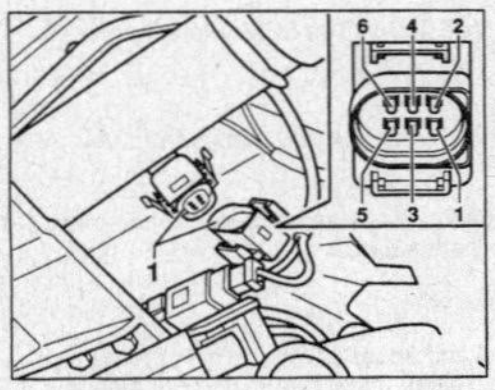

– Turn OFF ignition.

– Unplug TP Sensor -1-.

– Measure sensor resistance between connector terminals 1 + 3.
  Specification:
  Accelerator Pedal in Closed Throttle Position:
  1.0...1.5 kΩ
  Accelerator Pedal in Wide Open Throttle position:
  1.5...2.5 kΩ

– Check Closed Throttle Position (CTP) Switch (F60) in TP Sensor by measuring resistance between connector terminals 4 + 6.
  Specification:
  Accelerator Pedal in Closed Throttle Position: max.1.5 kΩ
  Accelerator Pedal depressed: ∞ Ω

If resistance specified is not attained:

– Replace Throttle Position (TP) Sensor (G79).

VW0159900197010X

Fig. 61 Code 00777: TP Sensor Questionable Signal (Part 1 of 2). 1998 Jetta

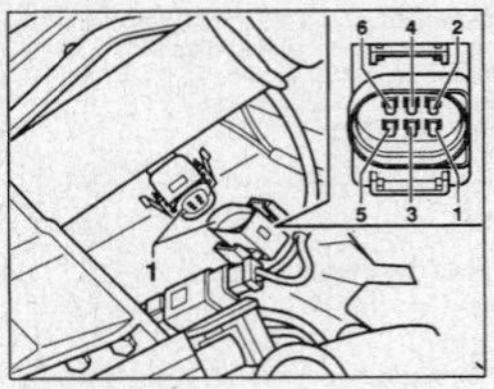

– Turn OFF ignition.

– Unplug connector for Throttle Position (TP) Sensor (G79) -1-.

– Measure sensor resistance between connector terminals 1 + 3.
  Specification:
  Accelerator Pedal in Closed Throttle Position:
  1.0...1.5 kΩ
  Accelerator Pedal in Wide Open Throttle position:
  1.5...2.5 kΩ

If resistance specified is not attained:

– Replace Throttle Position (TP) Sensor (G79).

If resistance specified is attained:

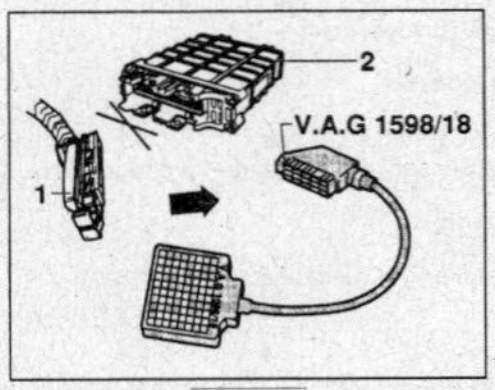

– Connect Adapter VAG 1598/18 to ECM wiring harness.

VW0159900198010X

Fig. 62 Code 00777: TP Sensor Short To Positive (Part 1 of 2). 1998 Jetta

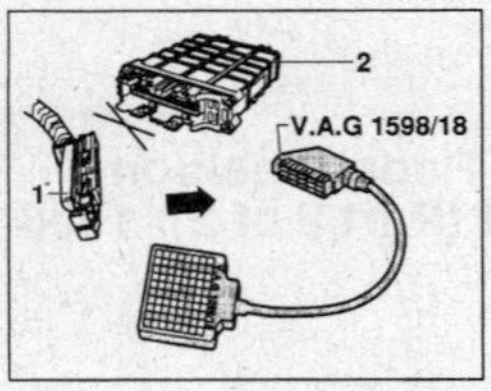

– Turn OFF ignition.

– Connect Adapter VAG 1598/18 to ECM wiring harness.

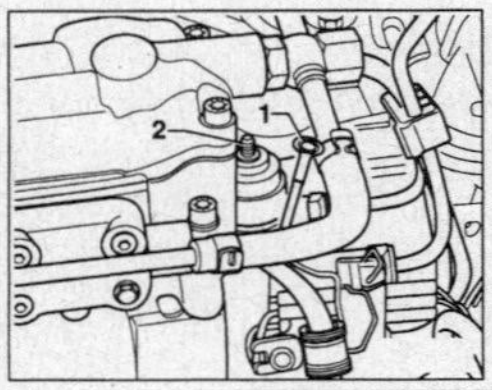

– Remove line -1- from Fuel Cut-off Valve (N109) -2-.

– Check wire connection between eye ring and adapter VAG 1598/18 socket 53 for open circuit or short to ground per electrical wiring diagram.

If no malfunction is detected:

– Replace Direct Fuel Injection (DFI) Engine Control Module. (ECM) (J248)

VW0159900199000X

Fig. 63 Code 01237: Fuel Cutoff Valve Open Circuit Or Short To Ground. 1998 Jetta

If resistance specified is attained:

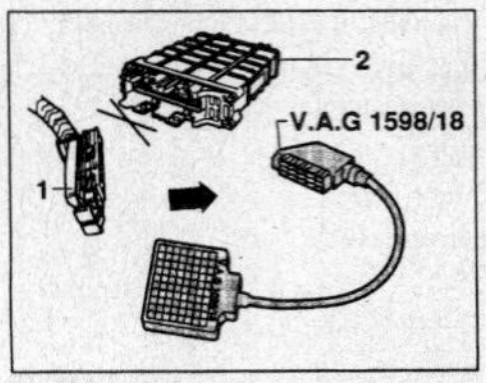

– Connect Adapter VAG 1598/18 to ECM wiring harness.

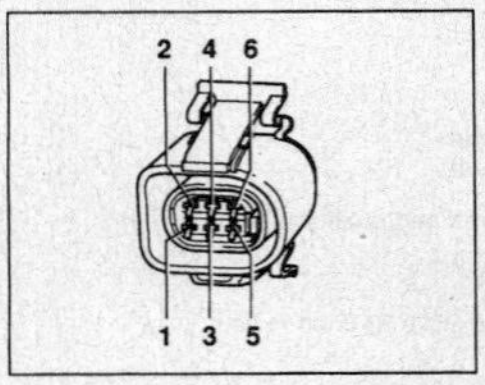

– Check wiring between Adapter VAG 1598/18 and connector for open circuit per electrical wiring diagram.
  Terminal 1 + socket 15
  Terminal 2 + socket 57
  Terminal 3 + socket 55
  Terminal 4 + socket 65
  Terminal 5 + socket 62
  Terminal 6 + socket 33
  Wire resistance: max. 1.5 Ω

– Check for shorts between wires.
  Specification: ∞Ω

If no malfunction is detected:

– Replace Direct Fuel Injection (DFI) Engine Control Module (ECM) (J248) .

VW0159900197020X

Fig. 61 Code 00777: TP Sensor Questionable Signal (Part 2 of 2). 1998 Jetta

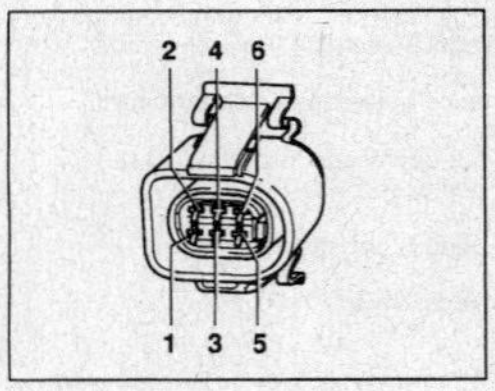

– Check wiring between Adapter VAG 1598/18 and connector for open circuit per electrical wiring diagram.
  Terminal 1 + socket 15
  Terminal 2 + socket 57
  Terminal 3 + socket 55
  Wire resistance: max. 1.5 Ω

– Check for shorts between wires.
  Specification: ∞Ω

If no malfunction is detected:

– Replace Direct Fuel Injection (DFI) Engine Control Module.

VW0159900198020X

Fig. 62 Code 00777: TP Sensor Short To Positive (Part 2 of 2). 1998 Jetta

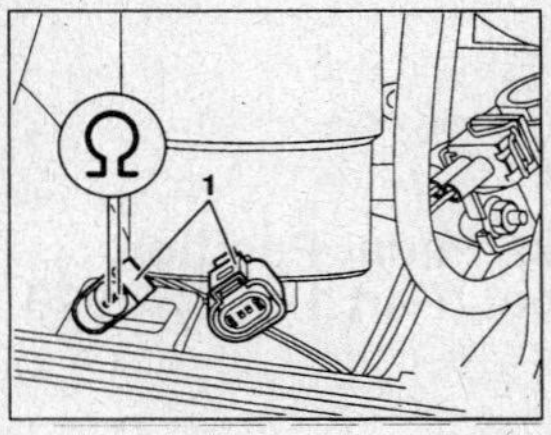

– Turn OFF ignition.

– Unplug Metering Pump (V54) connector -1-.

– Measure resistance between pump terminals.
  Specification: 8...12 Ω

If resistance specified is not attained:

– Replace Metering Pump (V54).

VW0159900200010X

Fig. 64 Code 01242: Final Stage In Control Module Questionable Signal (Part 1 of 3). 1998 Jetta

If resistance specified is attained:

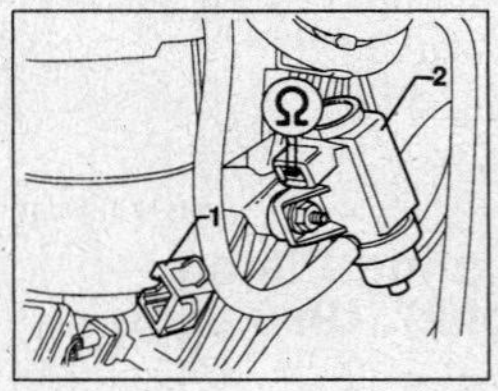

– Unplug Exhaust Gas Recirculation Valve (EGR Valve) (N18) -2- connector -1-.

– Measure resistance at valve.
  Specification: 14 ... 18 Ω

If resistance specified is not attained:

– Replace EGR Valve (N18).

Note:

At room temperature (warmer than +15°C (59°F)) resistance lies in lower tolerance range. At operating temperature (80°C (176°F))in upper tolerance range.

If resistance specified is attained:

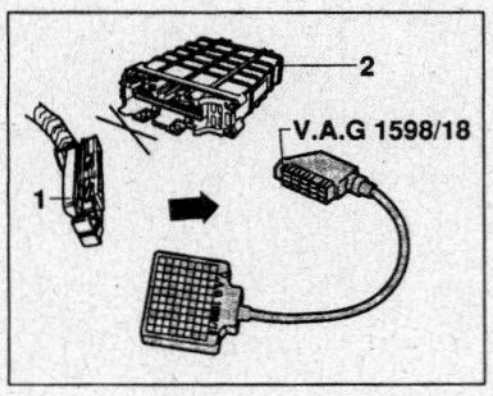

– Connect Adapter VAG 1598/18 to ECM wiring harness.

VW0159900200020X

Fig. 64 Code 01242: Final Stage In Control Module Questionable Signal (Part 2 of 3). 1998 Jetta

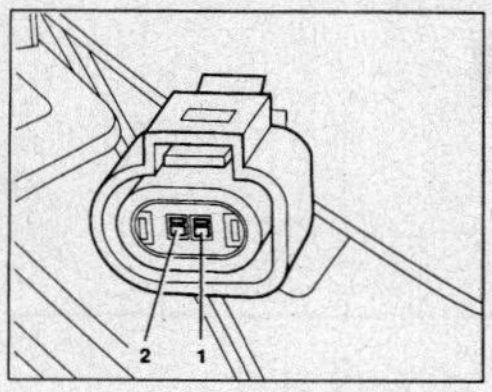

- Check wiring between Adapter VAG 1598/18 and connector to Metering Pump (V54) for open circuit per electrical wiring diagram.
  Terminal 1 + socket 27
  Terminal 2 + socket 45
  Wire resistance: max. 1.5 Ω

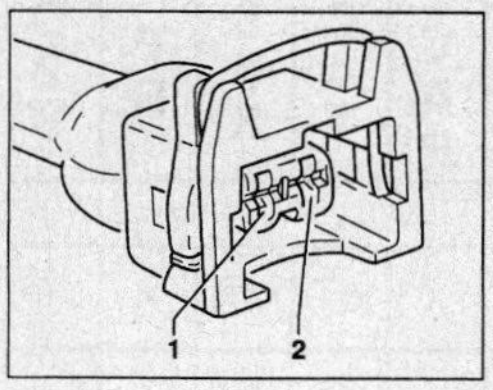

- Check wiring between Adapter VAG 1598/18 and connector to EGR Valve (N18) for open circuit per electrical wiring diagram.
  Terminal 1 + socket 68
  Terminal 2 + socket 25
  Wire resistance: max. 1.5 Ω
- Check for shorts between wires.
  Specification: ∞Ω

If no malfunction is detected:

- Replace Diesel Fuel Injection (DFI) Engine Control Module (ECM) (J248).

VW0159900200030X

Fig. 64 Code 01242: Final Stage In Control Module Questionable Signal (Part 3 of 3). 1998 Jetta

If resistance specified is attained:

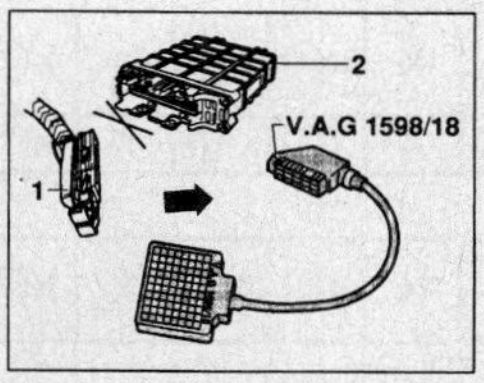

- Connect Adapter VAG 1598/18 to ECM wiring harness.

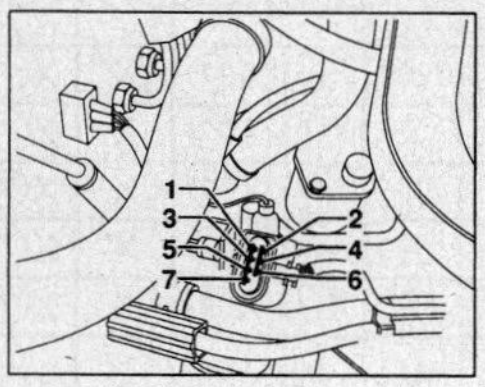

- Check wiring between Adapter VAG 1598/18 and connector for open circuit per electrical wiring diagram.
  Terminal 5 + sockets 23, 45 and 68
  Terminal 6 + sockets 4, 5 and 49
  Wire resistance: max. 1.5 Ω
- Check for shorts between wires.
  Specification: ∞Ω

If no malfunction is detected:

- Replace Direct Fuel Injection (DFI) Engine Control Module (ECM) (J248).

VW0159900201020X

Fig. 65 Code 01268: Quantity Adjuster Control Difference (Part 2 of 2). 1998 Jetta

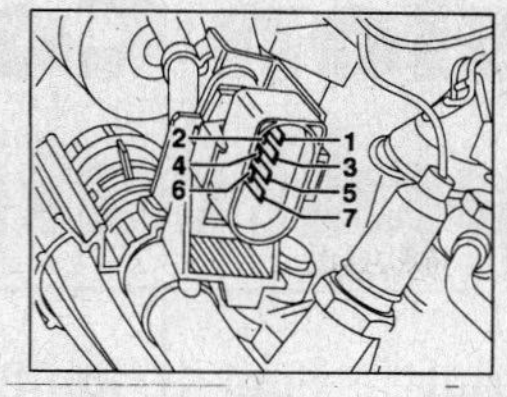

- Turn OFF ignition.
- Unplug Quantity Adjuster (N146) connector (connector to injection pump quantity adjuster).
- Measure resistance between connector terminals 5 + 6.
  Specification: 0.5...2.5 Ω

If resistance specified is not attained:

- Replace injection pump .

VW0159900201010X

Fig. 65 Code 01268: Quantity Adjuster Control Difference (Part 1 of 2). 1998 Jetta

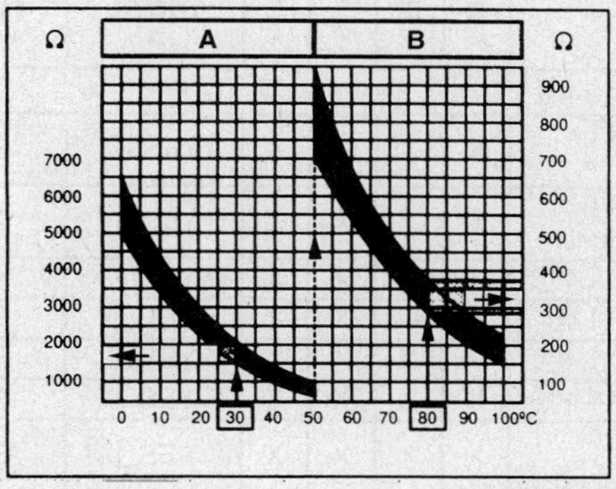

VW1019900148000X

Fig. 66 ECT & IAT sensors temperature/resistance chart

Emission Control System Application Charts

Engine Liters/CID/Type	Certification Type		Trans. Type		Computerized Engine Management	Fuel Induction System Type	Ignition Timing, Deg. BTDC @ RPM	TSB	EPA & CARB Emission Recall	Emission Control System SRI	Emission Control Systems								
	CA	FED	A/T	M/T							PCV	ACL	AIS	EGR	EVAP	CAT	SPK	FR	O2S
1998																			
1.8L/109/L4 Turbo	X	X	X	X	YES⑭	SFI	②	—	—	X	—	—	—	—	X	X①	X⑱	X	X⑦
1.9L/116/L4 Turbo Diesel	X	X	X	X	YES⑪	⑪	—	—	—	—	X	—	—	X⑨	—	X⑫	—	—	—
2.0L/121/L4⑮	X	X	X	X	YES④	SFI	②	—	—	—	X	—	—	—	X	X①	X⑰	X	X⑦
2.0L/121/L4⑧	X	—	X	X	YES④	SFI	②	—	—	X	X	—	X③	—	X	X①	X⑰	X	X⑦
2.0L/121/L4⑧	—	X	X	X	YES④	SFI	②	—	—	X	X	—	—	—	X	X①	X⑰	X	X⑦
2.0L/121/L4⑲	X	X	X	X	YES④	SFI	②	—	—	—	X	—	X③	—	X	X①	X⑰	X	X⑦
2.8L/170/ V6⑧⑬	X	X	X	X	YES④	SFI	②	—	—	X	X	—	X③	—	X	X①	X⑰	X	X⑦
2.8L/170/V6⑯	X	X	X	X	YES④	SFI	②	—	—	—	X	—	X③	X⑨	X	X①	X⑰	X	X⑦
1999																			
1.8L/109/L4 Turbo	X	X	X	X	YES⑭	SFI	②	—	—	X	—	—	—	—	X	X①	X⑱	X	X⑦
1.9L/116/L4 Turbo Diesel	X	X	X	X	YES⑪	⑪	—	—	—	—	X	—	—	X⑨	—	X⑫	—	—	—
2.0L/121/L4⑮	X	X	X	X	YES④	SFI	②	—	—	—	X	—	—	—	X	X①	X⑰	X	X⑦
2.0L/121/L4⑧	X	—	X	X	YES④	SFI	②	—	—	X	X	—	X③	—	X	X①	X⑰	X	X⑦
2.0L/121/L4⑧	—	X	X	X	YES④	SFI	②	—	—	X	X	—	—	—	X	X①	X⑰	X	X⑦
2.0L/121/L4⑲	X	—	X	X	YES④	SFI	②	—	—	—	X	—	X③	—	X	X①	X⑰	X	X⑦
2.0L/121/L4⑲	—	X	X	X	YES④	SFI	②	—	—	—	X	—	—	—	X	X①	X⑰	X	X⑦
2.8L/170/ V6⑥⑧	X	X	X	X	YES④	SFI	②	—	—	X	X	—	—	—	X	X⑳	X⑰	X	X⑦
2.8L/170/V6⑤	X	X	X	X	YES④	SFI	②	—	—	X	X	—	—	—	X	X⑳	X⑰	X	X⑩
2.8L/170/V6⑯	X	—	X	X	YES④	SFI	②	—	—	—	X	—	X③	—	X	X①	X⑰	X	X⑦
2.8L/170/V6⑯	—	X	X	X	YES④	SFI	②	—	—	—	X	—	—	—	X	X①	X⑰	X	X⑦
2000																			
1.8L/109/L4 Turbo	X	X	X	X	YES⑭	SFI	②	—	—	X	—	—	—	—	X	X①	X⑱	X	X⑦
1.9L/116/L4 Turbo Diesel	X	X	X	X	YES⑪	⑪	②	—	—	—	X	—	—	X⑨	—	X⑫	—	—	—
2.0L/121/L4⑮	X	X	X	X	YES④	SFI	②	—	—	—	X	—	—	—	X	X①	X⑰	X	X⑦
2.0L/121/ L4⑧⑲	X	—	X	X	YES④	SFI	②	—	—	X	X	—		—	X	X①	X⑰	X	X⑦
2.0L/121/ L4⑧⑲	—	X	X	X	YES④	SFI	②	—	—	X	X	—	—	—	X	X①	X⑰	X	X⑦
2.8L/170/V6⑧	X	X	X	X	YES④	SFI	②	—	—	X	X	—	X③	—	X	X⑳	X⑰	X	X⑦
2.8L/170/V6⑬	X	X	X	X	YES④	SFI	②	—	—	X	X	—	—	—	X	X⑳	X⑰	X	X⑩
2.8L/170/V6⑯	X	—	X	X	YES④	SFI	②	—	—	—	X	—	X③	—	X	X①	X⑰	X	X⑦
2001																			
1.8L/109/L4 Turbo	X	X	X	X	YES⑭	SFI	②	—	—	X	—	—	—	—	X	X①	X⑱	X	X⑦
1.9L/116/L4 Turbo Diesel	X	X	X	X	YES⑪	⑪	②	—	—	—	X	—	—	X⑨	—	X⑫	—	—	—
2.0L/121/L4⑮	X	X	X	X	YES④	SFI	②	—	—	—	X	—	—	—	X	X①	X⑰	X	X⑦
2.0L/121/ L4⑧⑲	X	—	X	X	YES④	SFI	②	—	—	X	X	—		—	X	X①	X⑰	X	X⑦
2.0L/121/ L4⑧⑲	—	X	X	X	YES④	SFI	②	—	—	X	X	—	—	—	X	X①	X⑰	X	X⑦

Continued

Engine Liters/CID/ Type	Certification Type		Trans. Type		Computerized Engine Management	Fuel Induction System Type	Ignition Timing, Deg. BTDC @ RPM	TSB	EPA & CARB Emission Recall	Emission Control System SRI	Emission Control Systems								
	CA	FED	A/T	M/T							PCV	ACL	AIS	EGR	EVAP	CAT	SPK	FR	O2S
2.8L/170/V6⑧	X	X	X	X	YES④	SFI	②	—	—	X	X	—	X③	—	X	X⑳	X⑰	X	X⑦
2.8L/170/V6⑬	X	X	X	X	YES④	SFI	②	—	—	X	X	—	—	—	X	X⑳	X⑰	X	X⑩
2.8L/170/V6⑯	X	—	X	X	YES④	SFI	②	—	—	—	X	—	X③	—	X	X①	X⑰	X	X⑦
2.8L/170/V6⑯		X	X	X	YES④	SFI	②	—	—	—	X	—	X	—	X	X①	X⑰	X	X⑦

X — Equipped
— Not Equipped
① — Type TWC. Number of catalytic converters, 1.
② — Refer to emission control information label.
③ — Pump type.
④ — Motronic System. Equipped w/MIL.
⑤ — Passat Wagon.
⑥ — Passat Sedan.
⑦ — Two HO2S.
⑧ — Golf & Jetta.
⑨ — Electronically controlled EGR.
⑩ — Four HO2S.
⑪ — Electronically Controlled Direct Injection.
⑫ — Catalytic converter with 2 temperature sensors.
⑬ — Passat.
⑭ — Motronic 5.9/OBD II.
⑮ — Cabrio.
⑯ — Eurovan.
⑰ — EI/Solid State Ignition System.
⑱ — Coil Over Plug Ignition System.
⑲ — New Beetle.
⑳ — Type TWC. Number of catalytic converters, 2.
ACL — Air Cleaner (Thermostatic Air Cleaner)
AIS — Air Injection System
A/T — Automatic Transmission
BTDC — Before Top Dead Center
CA — California
CAT — Catalytic Converter
CIS — Continuous Injection System
CIS-E — Continuous Injection System-Electronic
DI — Distributor Ignition
EDI — Electronically Controlled Direct Injection
EGR — Exhaust Gas Recirculation
EVAP — Evaporative Emission Control System
EI — Electronic Ignition
FED — Federal
FI — Fuel Injection
FR — Fillpipe Restrictor
MFI — Multi-Point Fuel Injection
MIL — Malfunction Indicator Lamp
M/T — Manual Transmission
OC — Oxidation Catalytic Converter
O2S — Oxygen Sensor
PCV — Positive Crankcase Ventilation
RPM — Revolutions Per Minute
SFI — Sequential Fuel Injection
SPK — Spark Control
SRI — Service Reminder Indicator
TSB — Technical Service Bulletin
TWC — Three Way Catalytic Converter

Vacuum Hose Routings

NOTE: Refer To The Vehicle's Underhood Emissions Control Label For Vacuum Hose Routings.

Engine Compartment Reference Diagrams

INDEX

	PAGE NO.	FIG. NO.
CABRIO:		
2.0L Engine:		
1998	17-203	2
1999–2001	17-204	3
GOLF, GTI & JETTA:		
1.8L Engine w/AWD	17-203	1
1.9L TDI Diesel Engine:		
1998	17-204	4
1999–2001	17-205	5
2.0L Engine:		
1998	17-203	2
1999–2001	17-204	3
2.8L Engine:		
1998	17-205	6
1999–2001	17-206	7
NEW BEETLE:		
1.8L Engine	17-206	8
1.9L TDI Diesel Engine	17-206	9
2.0L Engine	17-207	10
PASSAT:		
1.8L Engine:		
AEB Engine	17-207	11
ATW Engine	17-208	12
1.9L TDI Diesel Engine	17-208	13
2.8L Engine:		
AHA Engine	17-209	14
ATQ Engine	17-210	15

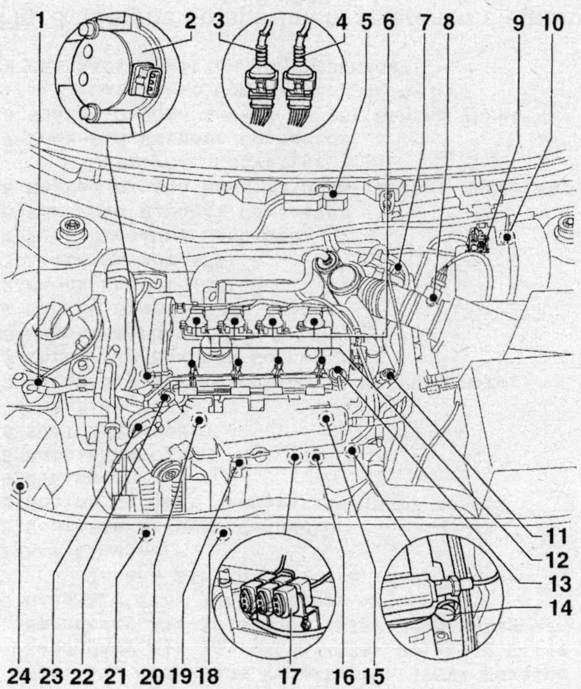

1. EVAP canister solenoid valve
2. CMP sensor Hall sender
3. Front HO2S connector
4. Rear HO2S connector
5. ECM
6. Ignition coils
7. Charge pressure limitation solenoid valve
8. MAF sensor
9. Secondary AIR pump relay
10. Clutch pedal, brake lamp & brake pedal switches
11. ECT sensor
12. Fuel injectors
13. Fuel pressure regulator
14. RPM sensor
15. KS 2
16. Turbocharger diverter valve
17. KS & RPM sensor connectors
18. Secondary AIR pump motor
19. Secondary air inlet valve
20. KS 1
21. PSP switch
22. IAT sensor
23. Throttle valve control module
24. Charge pressure sender

VW10200000161000X

Fig. 1 Engine compartment reference diagram. Golf, GTI & Jetta w/1.8L AWD engine

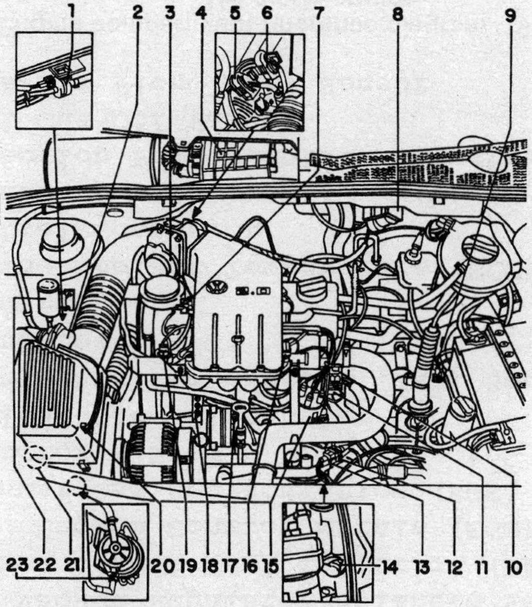

1 Evaporative Emmission (EVAP) Canister Purge Regulator Valve
2 Mass Air Flow (MAF) Sensor
3 Throttle Valve Control Module
4 Engine Control Module (ECM)
5 Connector
6 Connector
7 Intake Air Temperature (IAT) Sensor
8 Ignition Coil
9 Speedometer Vehicle Speed Sensor (VSS)
10 Engine Coolant Temperature (ECT) Sensor
11 Central Connector
12 Connector
13 Connector
14 Engine Speed (RPM) Sensor
15 Distributor w/Camshaft Position (CMP) Sensor
16 Fuel Injectors
17 Knock Sensor (KS) 1
18 Fuel Pressure Regulator
19 Temperature Regulator Thermal Vacuum Valve (TVV)
20 EVAP Canister
22 Leak Diagnosis Pump (LDP) Filter
23 Leak Diagnosis Pump (LDP)

VW10293000850000A

Fig. 2 Engine compartment reference diagram. 1998 Cabrio, Golf, GTI & Jetta w/2.0L engine

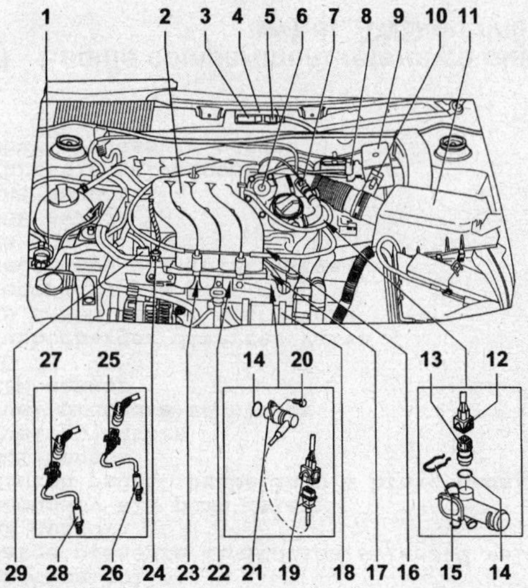

1 EVAP Canister Purge Regulator Valve
2 Intake Manifold
3 Harness Connector
4 Motronic Engine Control Module (ECM)
5 28-Pin Connector
6 Throttle Valve Control Module
7 Positive Crankcase Ventilation (PCV) Heating Element
8 Secondary Air Injection (AIR) Solenoid Valve
9 Seconbdry Air Injection (AIR) Pump Relay
10 Mass Air Flow (MAF) Sensor w/ Intake Air Temperature (IAT) Sensor
11 Air Cleaner
12 Four-Pin Harness Connector
13 Engine Coolant Temperature (ECT) Sensor
14 O-Ring
15 Retaining Clip
16 Fuel Injectors
17 Ignition Coils
18 Seconbdry Air Injection (AIR) Pump Motor
19 Three-Pin Harness Connector
20 Mounting Bolt
21 Engine Speed (RPM) Sensor
22 Knock Sensor (KS) 2
23 Knock Sensor (KS) 1
24 Fuel Pressure Regulator
25 Four-Pin Harness Connector
26 Heated Oxygen Sensor (HO2S) Before Three-Way Catalytic Converter
27 Four-Pin Harness Connector
28 Heated Oxygen Sensor (HO2S) Behind Three-Way Catalytic Converter
29 Camshaft Position (CMP) Sensor

VW1029900118000X

Fig. 3 Engine compartment reference diagram. 1999–2001 Cabrio, Golf, GTI & Jetta w/2.0L engine

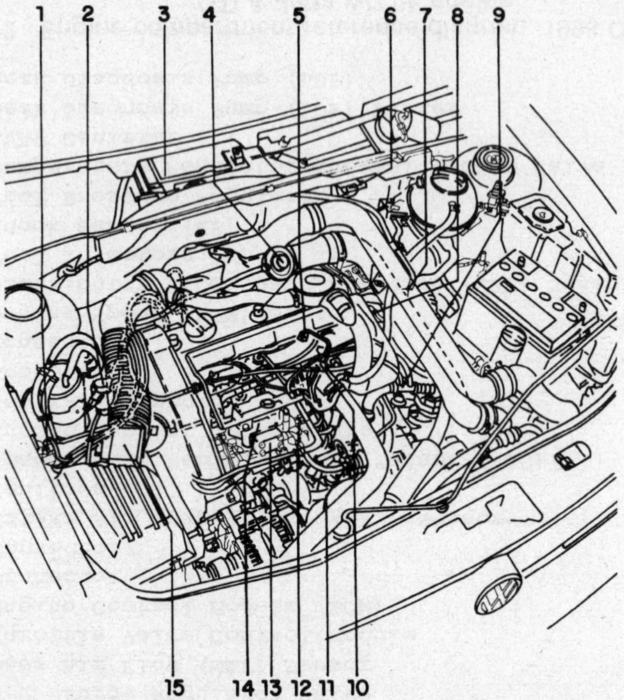

1 Wastegate Bypass Regulator
2 EGR Vacuum Regulator Solenoid Valve
3 Diesel Direct Fuel Injection (DFI) Engine Control Module (ECM)
4 Exhaust Gas Recirculation (EGR) Valve
5 Injector w/Needle Lift Sensor
6 Coolant Glow Plug Relay
7 Intake Air Temperature (IAT) Sensor
8 Connector
9 Connector
10 Engine Coolant Temperature (ECT) Sensor
11 Central Connector
12 Connector
13 Injection Pump Quantity Adjuster
14 Fuel Cut-Off Valve
15 Mass Air Flow (MAF) Sensor

VW1029900116000X

Fig. 4 Engine compartment reference diagram. 1998 Jetta w/1.9L TDI diesel engine

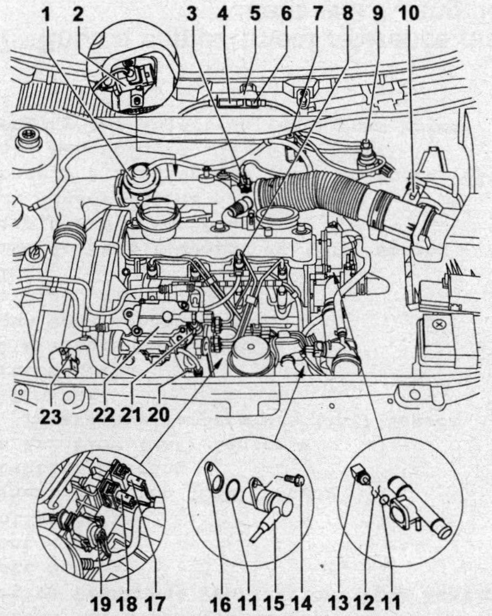

1 Exhaust Gas Recirculation (EGR) Valve
2 Intake Manifold Change-Over Valve
3 Positive Crankcase Ventilation (PCV) Heating Element
4 52-Pin Connector
5 Diesel Direct Injection (DFI) System Engine Control Module (ECM)
6 28-Pin Connector
7 EGR Vacuum Regulator Solenoid
8 Injector w/Needle Lift Sensor
9 Wastegate Bypass Regulator Valve
10 Mass Air Flow (MAF) Sensor
11 O-Ring
12 Retaining Clip
13 Engine Coolant Temperature (ECT) Sensor
14 Bolt
15 Engine Speed (RPM) Sensor
16 Spacer
17 Two-Pin Connector
18 Two-Pin Connector
19 10-Pin Connector
20 Cold Start Injector
21 Fuel Cut-Off Valve
22 Injection Pump Quantity Adjuster
23 Manifold Absolute Pressure (MAP) Sensor & Intake Air Temperature (IAT) Sensor

VW1029900117000X

Fig. 5 Engine compartment reference diagram. 1999–2001 Golf, GTI & Jetta w/1.9L TDI diesel engine

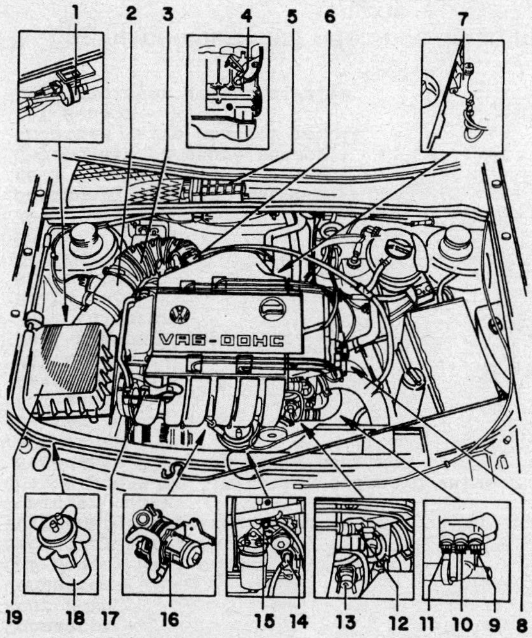

1 Evaporative Emmission (EVAP) Canister Purge Regulator Valve
2 Mass Air Flow (MAF) Sensor
3 Intake Air Duct
4 Knock Sensor (KS) 1
5 Engine Control Module (ECM)
6 Throttle Valve Control Module
7 Ground Connection
8 Ignition Coil
9 A/C Cut-Out Thermal Switch & Third Speed Coolant Fan Control Thermal Switch
10 Engine Coolant Temperature (ECT) Sensor
11 After-Run Coolant Fan Control Thermal Switch & Engine Coolant Termperature (ECT) Sensor
12 Intake Air Temperature (IAT) Sensor
13 Fuel Pressure Regulator
14 Engine Speed (RPM) Sensor
15 Knock Sensor (KS) 2
16 Secondary Air Injection (AIR) Pump Motor
17 Fuel Injectors
18 EVAP Canister
19 Air Cleaner

VW1029300087000A

Fig. 6 Engine compartment reference diagram. 1998 GTI & Jetta w/2.8L engine

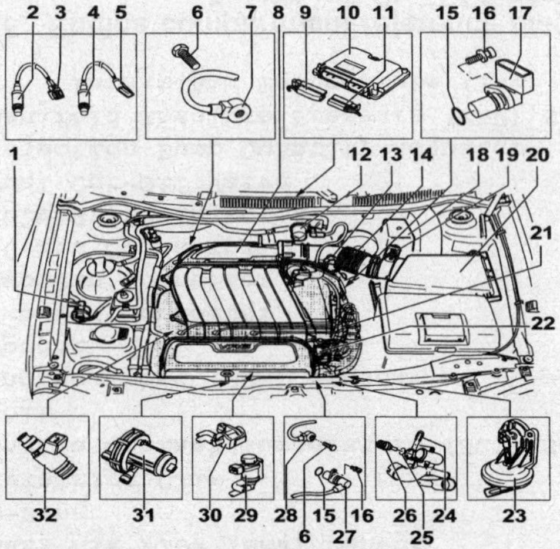

1 EVAP Canister Purge Regulator Valve
2 Heated Oxygen Sensor (HO2S) Before Three-Way Catalytic Converter
3 Six-Pin Harness Connector
4 Heated Oxygen Sensor (HO2S) Behind Three-Way Catalytic Converter
5 Four-Pin Connector
6 Mounting Bolt
7 Knock Sensor (KS) 1
8 Intake Manifold Upper Section
9 81-Pin Harness Connector
10 Motronic Engine Control Module (ECM)
11 40-Pin Harness Connector
12 Throttle Valve Control Module
13 Positive Crankcase Ventilation (PCV) Heating Element
14 Intake Hose
15 O-Ring
16 Mounting Bolt
17 Camshaft Position (CMP) Sensor
18 Protective Housing
19 Mass Air Flow (MAF) Sensor w/ Intake Air Temperature (IAT) Sensor
20 Air Cleaner
21 Ignition Coils
22 Fuel Pressure Regulator
23 Vacuum Positioning Element
24 Retaining Clip
25 O-Ring
26 Engine Coolant Temperature (ECT) Sensor
27 Engine Speed (RPM) Sensor
28 Knock Sensor (KS) 2
29 Secondary Air Injection (AIR) Solenoid Valve
30 Intake Manifold Tuning (IMT) valve
31 Seconbdry Air Injection (AIR) Pump Motor
32 Fuel Injectors

VW1029900119000X

Fig. 7 Engine compartment reference diagram. 1999–2001 GTI & Jetta w/2.8L engine

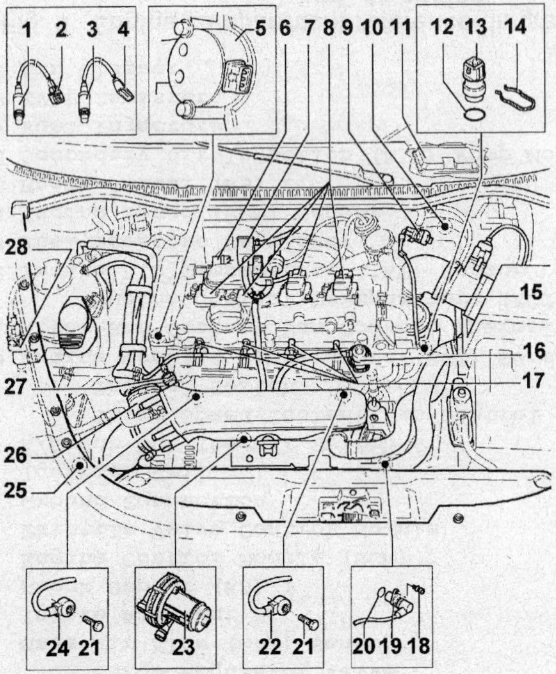

1. Front HO2S
2. Connector
3. Rear HO2S
4. Connector
5. CMP sensor Hall sender
6. Secondary air inlet valve
7. Turbocharger recirculation valve
8. Ignition coils
9. Charge pressure limitation solenoid valve
10. Secondary AIR pump relay housing
11. ECM
12. O-ring
13. ECT sensor
14. Retainer clip
15. MAF sensor
16. Fuel pressure regulator
17. Fuel injectors
18. Bolt
19. RPM sensor
20. O-ring
21. Bolt
22. KS 2
23. Secondary AIR pump motor
24. KS 1
25. Charge air pressure sensor
26. Throttle valve control module
27. IAT sensor
28. EVAP canister solenoid valve

VW1020000162000X

Fig. 8 Engine compartment reference diagram. New Beetle w/1.8L engine

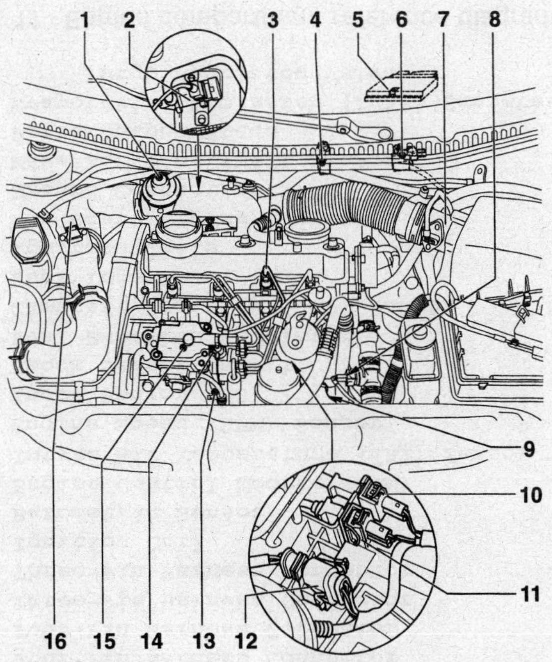

1 EGR Valve
2 Intake Manifold Change-Over Valve
3 Injector w/Needle Lift Sensor
4 EGR Vacuum Regulaotr Solenoid Valve
5 Diesel Direct Injection System Engine Control Module (ECM)
6 Wastegate Bypass Regulator Valve
7 Mass Air Flow (MAF) Sensor
8 Engine Coolant Temperature (ECT) Sensor
9 Engine Speed (RPM) Sensor
10 Harness Connector
11 Harness Connector
12 Harness Connector
13 Cold Start Injector
14 Fuel Shut-Off Valve
15 Injection Pump Quantity Adjuster
16 Manifold Absolute Pressure (MAP) Sensor & Intake Air Temperature (IAT) Sensor

VW1029800098000A

Fig. 9 Engine compartment reference diagram. New Beetle w/1.9L TDI diesel engine

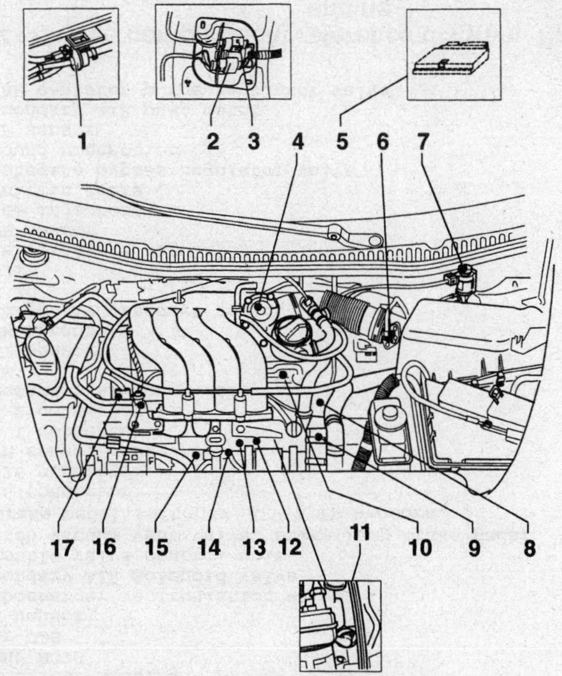

1 EVAP Canister Purge Regulator Valve
2 Four-Pin Harness Connector
3 Four-Pin Harness Connector
4 Throttle Control Module
5 Engine Control Module (ECM)
6 Mass Air Flow (MAF) Sensor w/ Intake Air Temperature (IAT) Sensor
7 Seconbdry Air Injection (AIR) Solenoid Valve
8 Engine Coolant Temperature (ECT) Sensor
9 Seconbdry Air Injection (AIR) Pump Motor
10 Injector
11 Engine Speed (RPM) Sensor
12 Ignition Coils
13 Three-Pin Harness Connector
14 Knock Sensor (KS) 2
15 Knock Sensor (KS) 1
16 Fuel Pressure Regulator
17 Camshaft Position (CMP) Sensor

VW1029800099000A

Fig. 10 Engine compartment reference diagram. New Beetle w/2.0L engine

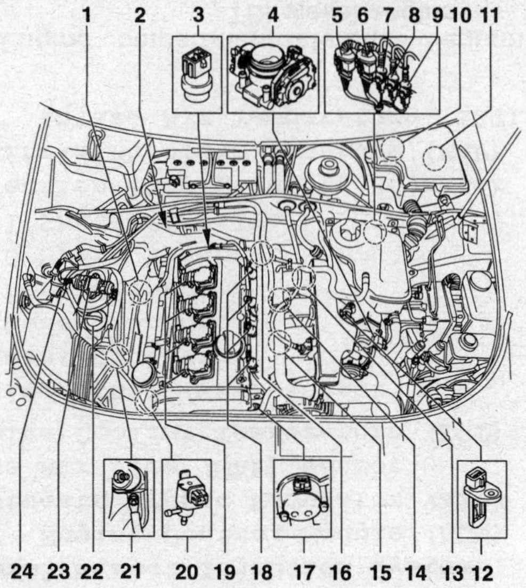

1 Oxygen Sensor 1 Before Three-Way Catalyst
2 Oxygen Sensor 2 After Three-Way Catalyst
3 Engine Coolant Temperature (ECT) Sensor
4 Throttle Body Control Module
5 Four-Pin Harness Connector
6 Four-Pin Harness Connector
7 Three-Pin Harness Connector
8 Three-Pin Harness Connector
9 Ignition Coil
10 Barometric Sensor
11 Engine Control Module (ECM)
12 Intake Air Temperature (IAT) Sensor
13 Engine Speed (RPM) Sensor
14 Knock Sensor (KS) 2
15 Knock Sensor (KS) 1
16 Fuel Pressure Regulator
17 Camshaft Position (CMP) Sensor
18 Fuel Injectors
19 Ignition Coils
20 Wastegate Bypass Regulator
21 Ground Connection
22 Mass Air Flow (MAF) Sensor
23 Power Output Stage
24 Evaporative Emmission (EVAP) Canister Purge Regulator Valve

VW1029800100000A

Fig. 11 Engine compartment reference diagram. Passat w/1.8L AEB engine

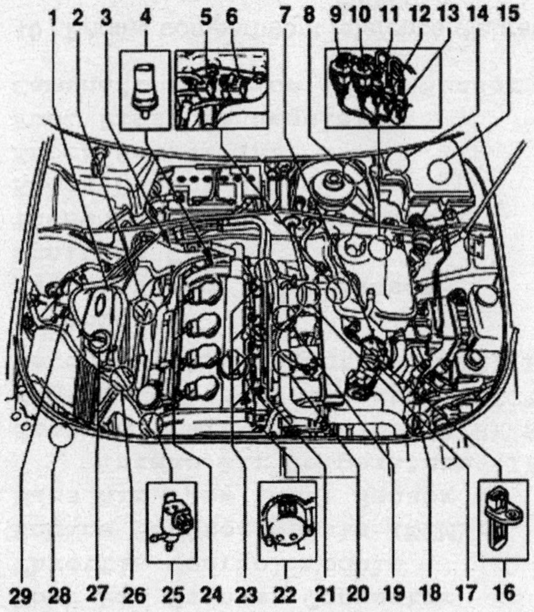

1. Air filter housing
2. Front HO2S
3. Rear O2S
4. ECT sensor
5. Turbocharger recirculation valve
6. Secondary AIR solenoid valve
7. Throttle valve control unit
8. Clutch vacuum vent valve, brake lamp brake pedal & brake pedal switches, APP & TP sensors
9. HO2S connector
10. HO2S connector
11. RPM sensor connector
12. KS 1 connector
13. KS 2 connector
14. Secondary AIR pump relay
15. ECM
16. IAT sensor
17. RPM sensor
18. Charge air pressure sensor
19. KS 2
20. KS 1
21. Fuel pressure regulator
22. CMP sensor
23. Fuel injectors
24. Ignition coils
25. Wastegate bypass regulator valve
26. Ground connection
27. MAF sensor
28. Secondary AIR pump motor
29. EVAP canister purge regulator valve

VW1020000163000X

Fig. 12 Engine compartment reference diagram. Passat w/1.8L ATW engine

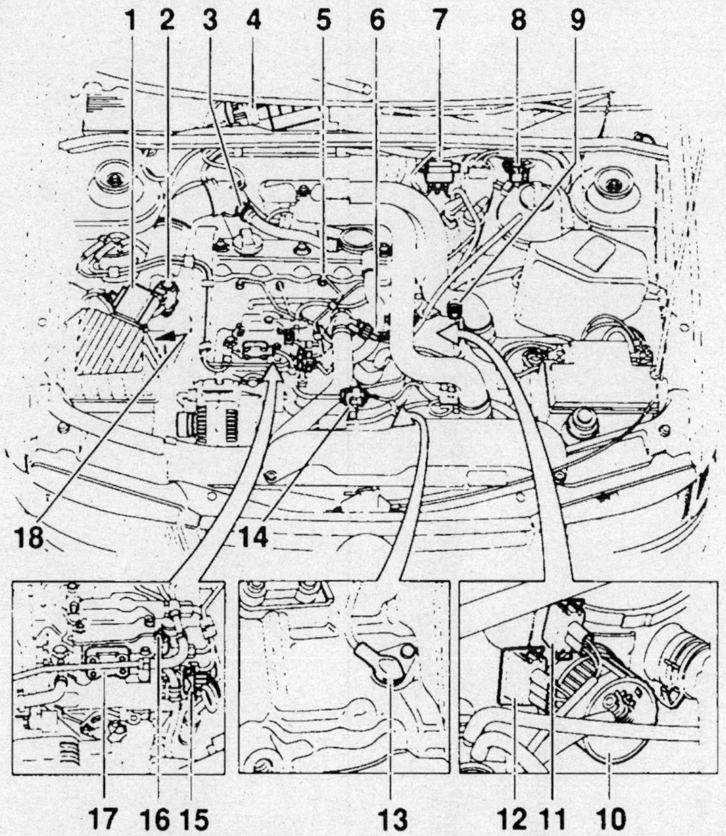

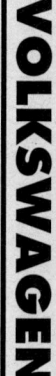

1. Mass Air Flow (MAF) sensor
2. Exhaust Gas Recirculation (EGR) valve
3. Heater Line
4. Turbo Direct Fuel Injection (TDI) Engine Control Module (ECM)
5. Injector with needle lift sensor
6. Engine Coolant Temperature (ECT) sensor
7. Supplementary coolant glow plug relay
8. Wastegate bypass regulator valve
9. Intake Air Temperature (IAT) sensor
10. Central connnector
11. Two pin connector
12. Three pin connector
13. Engine Speed (RPM) sensor
14. Seven pin connector
15. Three pin connector
16. Fuel cut off valve
17. Injection pump quanity adjuster
18. Metering pump

VW1029600090000X

Fig. 13 Engine compartment reference diagram. Passat w/1.9L TDI diesel engine

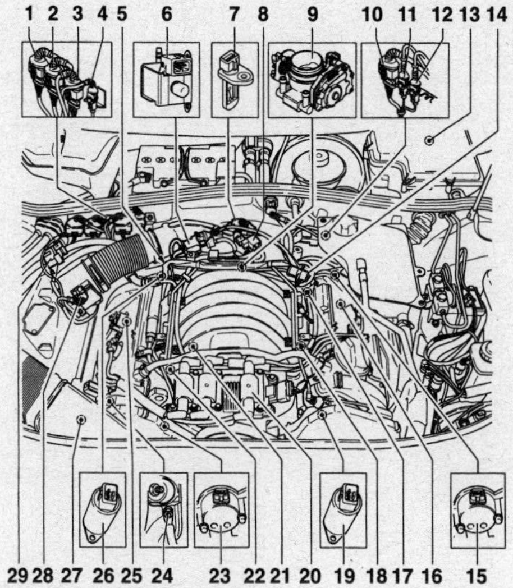

1 Harness Connector
2 Harness Connector
3 Harness Connector
4 Harness Connector
5 Engine Coolant Temperature (ECT) Sensor
6 Secondary Air Injection (AIR) Solenoid Valve
7 Intake Air Temperature (IAT) Sensor
8 Intake Manifold Tuning (IMT) Valve
9 Throttle Valve Control Module
10 Harness Connector
11 Harness Connector
12 Harness Conenctor
13 Motronic Engine Control Module (ECM)
14 Fuel Pressure Regulator
15 Camshaft Position (CMP) Sensor
16 Heated Oxygen Sensor (HO2S)2
17 Engine Speed (RPM) Sensor
18 Knock Sensor (KS) 2
19 Valve For Camshaft Adjustment
20 Ignition Coils
21 Knock Sensor (KS) 1
22 Fuel Injectors
23 Camshaft Position (CMP) Sensor
24 Ground Connection
25 Heated Oxygen Sensor (HO2S)
26 Valve For Camshaft Adjustment
27 Seconbdry Air Injection (AIR) Pump Motor
28 Mass Air Flow (MAF) Sensor
29 EVAP Canister Purge Regulator Valve

VW1029900120000X

Fig. 14 Engine compartment reference diagram. Passat w/2.8L AHA engine

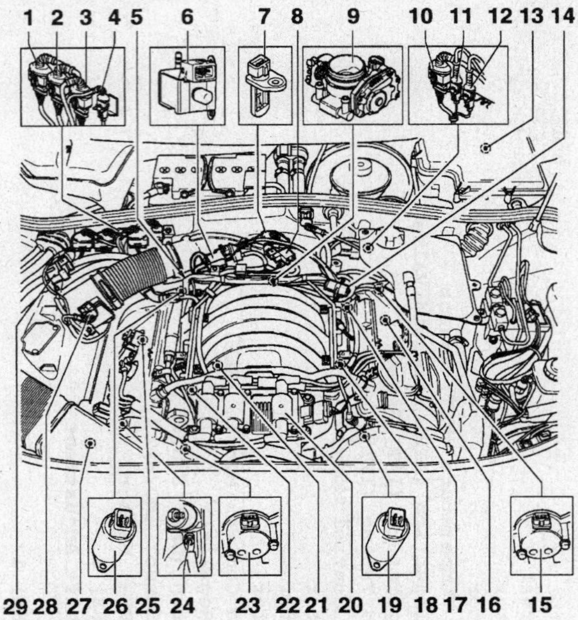

1. Rear HO2S Bank 1 connector
2. Rear HO2S Bank 2 connector
3. Front HO2S Bank 1 connector
4. KS Bank 1 connector
5. ECT sensor
6. Secondary AIR solenoid valve
7. IAT sensor
8. Intake manifold change-over valve
9. Throttle valve control module
10. Front HO2S Bank 2 connector
11. KS Bank 2 connector
12. RPM sensor connector
13. ECM
14. Fuel pressure regulator
15. CMP sensor Bank 2
16. Front HO2S Bank 2
17. RPM sensor
18. KS Bank 2
19. Camshaft adjuster valve Bank 2
20. Ignition coils
21. KS bank 2
22. Fuel injectors
23. CMP sensor Bank 1
24. Ground connection
25. Front HO2S Bank 1
26. Camshaft adjuster valve Bank 1
27. Secondary AIR pump motor
28. MAF sensor
29. EVAP canister purge regulator valve

VW1020000164000X

Fig. 15 Engine compartment reference diagram. Passat w/2.8L ATQ engine

Emission Controls

INDEX

	Page No.
Evaporative Emission Control System	17-211
Description	17-211
Diagnosis & Testing	17-211
EVAP Canister Purge Regulator Valve	17-211
Leak Detection Pump (LDP)	17-211
Exhaust Gas Recirculation (EGR)	17-211
Description	17-211
Diagnosis & Testing	17-211
EGR Vacuum Regulator Solenoid Vale	17-212
EGR Valve	17-211
Secondary Air Injection (AIR) System	17-212
Description	17-212
Diagnosis & Testing	17-212
Air Pump Motor	17-212
Combination Valve	17-213
Solenoid Valve	17-212

EVAPORATIVE EMISSION CONTROL SYSTEM

Description

This system limits emission of fuel vapors into the atmosphere and prevents raw fuel from escaping the fuel tank. An expansion chamber for the fuel tank and vent lines are part of the fuel tank vent system. These components prevent raw fuel from escaping at extremely high outside temperatures and when the vehicle is driven or parked on an incline or non-level position. Vapors from the fuel tank are trapped in a container filled with activated charcoal. This filter is connected to the fuel tank vent system and allows fuel vapors to pass through it and deposit hydrocarbons on its surface. When the engine is running, fresh air entering the charcoal filter through an opening cleans the filter and routes these hydrocarbons, via the air cleaner, back to the engine where they are burned during combustion.

Diagnosis & Testing

EVAP CANISTER PURGE REGULATOR VALVE

New Beetle & 1999–2001 Cabrio, Golf, GTI & Jetta

1. Ensure fuel tank cap is secure and seal is not damaged. Repair or replace as required.
2. Fold rear seat bottom forward and remove cover under seat bench.
3. Ensure fuel pump nut is tightened and seal is undamaged. Repair or replace as required.
4. Remove lefthand rear wheel housing liner.
5. Inspect Leak Detection Pump (LDP) as described under "Leak Detection Pump (LDP)."
6. Inspect lines and hoses between EVAP canister and regulator valve. Repair or replace as required.
7. Remove EVAP canister from wheel housing, then inspect for cracks and leaks. Repair or replace as required.

Passat w/1.8L Engine

1. Ensure fuel tank cap is secure and seal is not damaged. Repair or replace as required.
2. Fold rear seat bottom forward and remove cover under seat bench.
3. Ensure fuel pump nut is tightened and seal is undamaged. Repair or replace as required.
4. Remove EVAP canister from spare wheel well, then inspect for cracks and leaks. Repair or replace as required.

Passat w/2.8L Engine

1. Ensure fuel tank cap is secure and seal is not damaged. Repair or replace as required.
2. Fold rear seat bottom forward and remove cover under seat bench.
3. Ensure fuel pump nut is tightened and seal is undamaged. Repair or replace as required.
4. Remove lefthand rear wheel housing liner.
5. Remove EVAP canister from wheel housing, then inspect for cracks and leaks. Repair or replace as required.

LEAK DETECTION PUMP (LDP)

New Beetle, Passat & 1999–2001 Cabrio, Golf, GTI & Jetta

1. Remove lefthand rear wheel housing liner.
2. Disconnect Leak Detection Pump (LDP) 3-pin connector.
3. Connect LED voltage tester tool No. 1527B, or equivalent, between connector terminal No. 3 and ground.
4. Start and idle engine. If LED does light, proceed to next step. If LED does not light, proceed as follows:
   a. Measure resistance between connector terminal No. 3 and relay panel.
   b. If resistance is not less than 1.5 ohms, inspect wiring for open circuit.
5. Connect test box tool No. VAG 1598/31 to ECM wiring harness.
6. Measure resistance as follows:
   a. Resistance should be 640–720 ohms.
   b. Between LDP terminals Nos. 2 and 3.
   c. Resistance should be 12.5–19.5 ohms.
   d. If resistance is not as specified, replace LDP.
   e. Between connector terminal No. 1 and test box socket No. 37.
   f. Between terminal No. 2 and socket No. 16.
   g. If resistance is not less than 1.5 ohms, inspect wiring for open circuit.
   h. Inspect wiring for short to one another or ground. Resistance should be infinite.
   i. Between LDP terminals Nos. 1 and 3.
7. If no wiring malfunction is found and there is voltage between terminal No. 3 and ground, replace LDP.

EXHAUST GAS RECIRCULATION (EGR)

Description

Exhaust gas recirculation is used to control part throttle exhaust emissions. During recirculation, a small amount of exhaust gas enters the intake manifold. This allows a reduction in the useful volume of the fuel/air mixture. This smaller volume means lower combustion temperatures, which reduces the formation of oxides of nitrogen.

On 1.9L TDI engines, EGR functions are controlled by the Engine Control Module (ECM) through the EGR vacuum solenoid regulator valve. Using input from various engine sensors the ECM sends signals to the vacuum solenoid regulator to open and close the EGR valve to provide the best engine performance with optimum reduction of emissions.

Diagnosis & Testing

EGR VALVE

1998 Cabrio, Golf, GTI & Jetta

1. Start and idle engine. Ensure engine oil temperature is at least 122°F.
2. Disconnect EGR vacuum regulator solenoid valve.
3. Connect hand vacuum pump tool No. 1390, or equivalent, to disconnected hose.
4. Operate vacuum pump. If idle quality

does not worsen, inspect lines and connections of obstructions. If required, replace EGR valve.

5. If all systems pass functional tests and performance fault condition still exists, replace EGR temperature sensor.

EGR VACUUM REGULATOR SOLENOID VALE

New Beetle w/1.9L TDI Engine

1. Disconnect EGR vacuum regulator solenoid valve.
2. Measure resistance between terminals. If resistance is not 14–20 ohms, replace EGR vacuum regulator solenoid valve. If resistance is 14–20 ohms, proceed to next step.
3. Measure voltage between connector terminal No. 1 and ground. If measurement is not approximately battery voltage, connect test box tool No. 1598/31, or equivalent, to ECM wiring harness and measure resistance as follows:
   a. Between test box sockets Nos. 1 and 2.
   b. Between sockets Nos. 1 and 28.
   c. Between sockets Nos. 2 and 29.
   d. If resistance is not less than 1.5 ohms, inspect wiring for open circuit.
   e. Inspect wires for short circuit to one another, to ground and to battery voltage. Resistance should be infinite.
4. If no wiring malfunction is found, replace ECM.

1999–2001 Golf & Jetta w/1.9L TDI Engine

1. Disconnect EGR vacuum regulator solenoid valve.
2. Measure resistance between terminals. If resistance is not 12–20 ohms, replace EGR vacuum regulator solenoid valve. If resistance is 12–20 ohms, proceed to next step.
3. Measure voltage between terminal No. 1 and ground. If measurement is not at least 11.5 volts, connect test box tool No. 1598/31, or equivalent, to ECM wiring harness and measure resistance as follows:
   a. Between test box sockets Nos. 1 and 2.
   b. Between sockets Nos. 1 and 28.
   c. Between sockets Nos. 2 and 29.
   d. If resistance is not less than 1.5 ohms, inspect wiring for open circuit.
   e. Inspect wires for short circuit to one another, to ground and to battery voltage. Resistance should be infinite.
4. If no wiring malfunction is found, replace ECM.

SECONDARY AIR INJECTION (AIR) SYSTEM

Description

AIR is used to shorten cold start catalyst light-off time by injection of air behind the exhaust valve into the fuel rich exhaust stream for a predetermined time.

The AIR system is controlled by the ECU through the pump relay, combination valve and solenoid valve.

This system will operate for 30 seconds after the initial cold start with engine temperatures of 40–105°F.

Diagnosis & Testing

AIR PUMP MOTOR

1998 GTI & Jetta w/2.8L Engine

1. Ensure engine oil temperature is 58–185°F.
2. Disconnect AIR inlet valve pressure hose and route upward.
3. Start and idle engine.
4. After approximately 20 seconds, AIR pump should run for five seconds and air should be felt at pressure hose.
5. If pump motor does not run, turn ignition Off.
6. Disconnect AIR pump 2-pin connector.
7. Connect LED tester tool No. 1527B, or equivalent, to connector terminals.
8. Start and idle engine.
9. After approximately 20 seconds, LED should light for approximately five seconds.
10. If LED lights, replace AIR pump motor.
11. If LED does not light, connect AIR pump 2-pin connector and inspect wiring.

1998 Cabrio, Golf, GTI & Jetta w/2.0L Engine

This procedure has been revised by a Technical Service Bulletin.

1. Turn ignition Off.
2. Connect test box tool No. VAG 1598/18, or equivalent, to ECM wiring harness.
3. Disconnect pneumatic valve pressure line.
4. Turn ignition On.
5. Bridge test box sockets Nos. 1 and 6 using suitable jumper wires.
6. Bridge test box sockets No. 49 to ground using suitable jumper wires. If pump runs but no air exits hose, inspect pressure line, then repair or replace as required. If pump does not run, proceed to next step.
7. Disconnect AIR pump motor connector.
8. Connect LED tester tool No. 1527B, or equivalent, to connector terminals.
9. If LED lights, replace AIR pump motor.
10. If LED does not light, connect AIR pump 2-pin connector and inspect wiring.

New Beetle & 1999–2001 Cabrio, Golf, GTI & Jetta w/2.0L Engine

1. Remove upper engine cover.
2. Disconnect AIR pump motor pressure hose.
3. Connect test box tool No. VAG 1598/31, or equivalent, to ECM wiring harness.
4. Turn ignition On.
5. Bridge test box sockets Nos. 1 and 30 using suitable jumper wires.
6. If pump runs but no air exits hose, inspect pressure line, then repair or replace as required. If pump does not run, proceed to next step.
7. Disconnect AIR pump motor connector.
8. Connect LED tester tool No. 1527B, or equivalent, to connector terminals.
9. If LED lights, replace AIR pump motor.
10. If LED does not light, connect AIR pump 2-pin connector and inspect wiring.

1999–2001 GTI & Jetta w/2.8L Engine

1. Remove upper engine cover.
2. Disconnect AIR pump motor pressure hose.
3. Connect test box tool No. VAG 1598/31, or equivalent, to ECM wiring harness.
4. Turn ignition On.
5. Bridge test box sockets Nos. 3 and 46 using suitable jumper wires. If pump runs but no air exits hose, turn ignition Off and replace AIR pump motor. If pump does not run, proceed to next step.
6. Disconnect AIR pump motor connector.
7. Connect LED tester tool No. 1527B, or equivalent, to connector terminals.
8. If LED lights, turn ignition Off and replace AIR pump motor.
9. If LED does not light, connect AIR pump 2-pin connector and inspect wiring.

SOLENOID VALVE

1998 GTI & Jetta w/2.8L Engine

1. Ensure engine oil temperature is 58–185°F.
2. Disconnect AIR inlet valve vacuum hose and route upward.
3. Start and idle engine.
4. After approximately 20 seconds, AIR pump motor should run for five seconds and there should be intake manifold vacuum at hose. If there is no vacuum, proceed to next step.
5. Turn ignition Off.
6. Disconnect AIR solenoid valve connector.

7. Connect LED tester tool No. 1527B, or equivalent, to connector terminals.
8. Start and idle engine.
9. After approximately 20 seconds, LED should light for approximately five seconds.
10. If LED lights, replace AIR solenoid valve.
11. If LED does not light, connect AIR pump 2-pin connector and inspect wiring.

1998 Cabrio, Golf, GTI & Jetta w/2.0L Engine

This procedure has been revised by a Technical Service Bulletin.

1. Disconnect solenoid valve vacuum hose at brake servo.
2. Connect hand vacuum pump tool No. VAG 1390, or equivalent, to hose.
3. Disconnect pneumatic valve vacuum hose.
4. Turn ignition Off.
5. Connect test box tool No. VAG 1598/18 to ECM wiring harness.
6. Bridge test box sockets Nos. 1 and 6 using suitable jumper wires.
7. Operate hand pump. If vacuum does not build up, replace solenoid valve. If vacuum builds up, proceed to next step.
8. Bridge test box sockets No. 50 to ground using suitable jumper wires. Valve must open.
9. Operate hand pump. Vacuum must not build up. If vacuum builds up, proceed to next step.
10. Disconnect solenoid valve 2-pin connector.
11. Connect LED tester tool No. 1527B, or equivalent, to connector terminals. If LED lights, replace solenoid valve. If LED does not light, proceed to next step.
12. Measure resistance between test box socket No. 50 and terminal No. 2. If resistance is not less than 1.5 ohms, inspect wiring between connector terminal 1 and central electric for open circuit.

New Beetle & 1999-2001 Cabrio, Golf, GTI & Jetta

1. Ensure engine oil temperature is 41–91°F.
2. Disconnect AIR solenoid valve vacuum hose.
3. Start and idle engine.
4. AIR pump motor should run and there should be intake manifold vacuum at hose. If there is no vacuum, proceed to next step.
5. Turn ignition Off.
6. Disconnect AIR solenoid valve connector.
7. Connect LED tester tool No. 1527B, or equivalent, to connector terminals.
8. Start and idle engine.
9. If LED lights, replace AIR solenoid valve.
10. If LED does not light, connect AIR pump 2-pin connector and inspect wiring.

COMBINATION VALVE

1998 Cabrio, Golf, GTI & Jetta w/2.0L Engine

This procedure has been revised by a Technical Service Bulletin.

Do not use compressed air.

1. Remove upper engine cover.
2. Disconnect AIR solenoid valve vacuum hose.
3. Connect hand vacuum pump tool No. VAG 1390, or equivalent, to hose.
4. Remove pressure hose between AIR pump motor and connecting line.
5. Blow slight pressure into pressure hose. Combination valve must remain closed.
6. Operate pump. If valve does not open, replace as required.

New Beetle w/2.0L Engine, Passat & 1999-2001 GTI & Jetta w/2.8L Engine

Do not use compressed air.

1. Disconnect AIR solenoid valve vacuum hose.
2. Connect hand vacuum pump tool No. VAG 1390, or equivalent, to hose.
3. Remove pressure hose between AIR pump motor and connecting line. Both valves must remain closed.
4. Operate pump. Combination valve must open. If valve does not open, replace as required.

1999-2001 Cabrio, Golf, GTI & Jetta w/2.0L Engine

Do not use compressed air.

1. Remove upper engine cover.
2. Disconnect AIR solenoid valve vacuum hose.
3. Connect hand vacuum pump tool No. VAG 1390, or equivalent, to hose.
4. Remove pressure hose between AIR pump motor and connecting line.
5. Blow slight pressure into pressure hose. Combination valve must remain closed.
6. Operate pump. If valve does not open, replace as required.
7. Connect test box tool No. 1598/31, or equivalent, to ECM wiring harness.
8. Turn ignition On.
9. Bridge test box sockets Nos. 1 and 30 with suitable jumper wires.
10. If AIR pump motor runs, but no exists hose, turn ignition Off and replace AIR pump motor. If AIR pump motor does not run, proceed to next step.
11. Connect LED voltage test tool No. 1527B, or equivalent, to wiring connector terminals.
12. If LED lights, replace AIR pump motors.
13. If LED does not light, connect harness connector and inspect wiring.

Technical Service Bulletins

INDEX

	Page No.
Codes 01050 & 01266	17-214
Passat w/1.9L Diesel Engine	17-214
Codes P1545 & P1558	17-214
2000 Passat w/2.8L ATQ Engine & A/T	17-214
Engine Cranks, Does Not Start	17-214
1998–99 Models w/2.8L 5-Valve Engine	17-214
MIL Lighting, Code P0411 Stored In Memory	17-214
1999–2000 Golf & Jetta w/1.8L Turbo Engine	17-214
Poor Driveability	17-214
Vehicle Hesitates Or Will Not Move After Stopping	17-214
Models w/Electronic Throttle Control & A/T	17-214

POOR DRIVEABILITY

On some models there may be poor driveability under all driving conditions.

This condition may be cause be a deteriorated wire shield, allowing magnetic interference of the oxygen sensor signal. To correct this condition, proceed as follows:

1. Inspect O2S wire shield for condition and proper ground.
2. Replace harness and/or repair ground as required.
3. If O2S wire shield and ground appear in good condition, proceed as follows:
   a. Disconnect harness connector from ECM.
   b. Remove O2S pin from ECM connector using suitable tool, then connect to ECM.
   c. Test drive vehicle. If driveability fault condition has been corrected, replace O2S harness.

CODES 01050 & 01266

Passat w/1.9L Diesel Engine

On some of these models, Codes 01050 (Glow Plug Monitoring) and 01266 (Glow Plug Heater Circuit) may be stored in DTC memory.

This condition may could be caused by improper components. To correct this condition, proceed as follows:

1. Ensure relay bridge position 12 part number is 3A0 941 817.
2. Ensure glow plug relay part number, located above fuse relay panel, is 028 911 253.
3. Replace as required.
4. If glow plug relay is replaced, ensure 80 amp fuse located next to glow plug relay is satisfactory.
5. Clear DTCs and ensure MIL does not light.

VEHICLE HESITATES OR WILL NOT MOVE AFTER STOPPING

Models w/Electronic Throttle Control & A/T

On these models, the owner may notice these conditions after activating the accelerator pedal.

This may be caused by applying the brake pedal and accelerator pedal at the same time. Owners who drive with their left foot resting on the brake pedal are more likely to experience this condition. The brake pedal has the "upper hand" over the accelerator pedal and will override any throttle application. If the brakes are applied while the accelerator is depressed the engine will automatically return to idle speed, but will not set a DTC. Full engine RPM control will return as soon as the brake pedal is released and the accelerator is rapidly applied, or if the accelerator is released and then depressed again.

To correct this condition, first inspect for and correct any stored DTCs. If no DTCs are discovered, inform owner of the likely brake pedal-accelerator interference and caution against resting the left foot on the brake.

MIL LIGHTING, CODE P0411 STORED IN MEMORY

1999–2000 Golf & Jetta w/1.8L Turbo Engine

On these models, this condition may be caused by a faulty charge pressure bypass valve. If the valve does not hold vacuum, there will not be sufficient vacuum during secondary air diagnosis to open the combi-valve which shares a common vacuum source with the bypass valve.

To correct this condition, proceed as follows:

1. Remove engine upper cover.
2. Disconnect vacuum hose at bypass valve, **Fig. 1.**
3. Connect hand vacuum pump tool No. VAG 1390, or equivalent, to bypass valve.
4. Operate pump to produce 15 inches of vacuum.
5. If system holds at least 15 inches of vacuum, continue with diagnosis for DTC P0411.
6. If system cannot hold specified vacuum, replace charge pressure bypass valve.

CODES P1545 & P1558

2000 Passat w/2.8L ATQ Engine & A/T

On these models, these codes and others may be stored in the DTC memory. The vehicle may be in Limp Mode.

To correct this condition, instal a new Engine Control Module (ECM) part No. 3B0 907 551 AN. **Do not replace Throttle Body Injection (TBI) unit for this condition.**

ENGINE CRANKS, DOES NOT START

1998–99 Models w/2.8L 5-Valve Engine

On these models this condition may occur after the vehicle has sat several hours. An overnight situation is a typical example.

Ensure the battery is fully charged and fuel tank has a sufficient quantity of fuel, then proceed as follows:

1. Connect scan tool No. VAG 1551, or equivalent, to DLC.
2. Select vehicle system "01-Engine Electronics."
3. Select diagnosis function "08-Read Measuring Value Block."
4. Read and print Measuring Value Blocks 4, 6, 32, 55 and 60.
5. Print any stored DTCs.
6. Diagnose and correct any DTCs. In most cases none will have been discovered.
7. Allow vehicle to cool down completely, preferably overnight.
8. Turn ignition On.
9. Ensure values in Measuring Value Block 4 approximately equal ambient temperature.
10. Ensure throttle linkage operates properly and travels smoothly from CTP through WOT.
11. Crank engine while observing throttle angle specifications in data block 60. Throttle angle must be greater than 6°.
12. Inspect and record fuel pressure as outlined under "Fuel Pressure" in "Diagnosis & Testing" in "2.8L Engine" section.
13. If coolant temperature sensor, fuel pressure and throttle linkage are satisfactory, proceed as follows:
    a. Perform compression inspection as outlined in appropriate engine section.
    b. Perform a cylinder leak-down inspection.
    c. Low compression may be an indication of carbon particle buildup on intake and exhaust valves and in combustion chambers, causing valves to seat improperly.
14. If compression and leak-down results are satisfactory, contact Volkswagen for further assistance.
15. If compression and leak-down results are not satisfactory, proceed as follows:
    a. Install old spark plugs.
    b. Remove thermostat as outlined under "Thermostat, Replace" in "2.8L Engine" in Chassis chapter.
    c. Install revised thermostat part No. 078 121 113 G with O-ring part No. N901 368 02. **Ensure jiggle pin port is at 12 o'clock position. Temperature gauge will read slightly higher because new thermostat opens at 198°F compared to 189°F for old one.**
16. Depress accelerator to floor and crank engine until it starts.
17. Turn ignition Off.
18. Remove carbon deposits using decarb tool kit No. US 9025 and Wynn's X-Tend V.I.C. Combustion Chamber Cleaner part No. 61510.
19. Change engine oil.
20. Remove spark plugs.
21. Disconnect fuel injector wiring and crank engine for a minimum of 30 seconds.
22. Connect injector wiring.
23. Install new NGK spark plugs part No. BKR6EQUPA (Volkswagen part No. 101 000 067 AA).
24. Ensure battery is fully charged.
25. Start engine. It may be required to fully depress accelerator to floor while cranking.
26. Bring engine to operating temperature.
27. Road test vehicle for 10 miles with engine RPM between 4000–6000 RPM under load. Use appropriate lower gear to keep within posted speed limits.
28. Advise owner to switch to high detergent fuel to prevent recurrence of carbon buildup.

VWA009900001000X

Fig. 1 Bypass valve vacuum hose

Abbreviations & Acronyms

A/C: Air Conditioning
CKS: Crankshaft Sensor
CMP: Camshaft Position
CO: Carbon Monoxide
CTP: Closed Throttle Position
CV: Crankcase Ventilation
DI: Distributor Ignition
DLC: Data Link Connector
DTC: Diagnostic Trouble Code
ECL: Engine Coolant Level
ECM: Engine Control Module
ECT: Engine Coolant Temperature
ECTS: Engine Coolant Temperature Sensor
ECU: Electronic Control Unit
EEPROM: Electronically Erasable Programmable Read Only Memory
EGR: Exhaust Gas Recirculation System
EVAP: Evaporative Emission Control System
FI: Fuel Injection
FP: Fuel Pump
FPM: Fuel Pump Module
FPR: Fuel Pump Relay
GEN: Generator
HO2S: Heated Oxygen Sensor
IAC: Idle Air Control
IATS: Intake Air Temperature Sensor
IATSF: Intake Air Temperature Sensor Injection
IATSI: Intake Air Temperature Sensor Ignition
IAVC: Idle Air Control Valve
IC: Ignition Control System
ICM: Ignition Control Module
IFSS: Inertia Fuel Shutoff Switch
ISC: Idle Speed Control
KS: Knock Sensor
MAF: Mass Air Flow
MAFS: Mass Air Flow Sensor
MAP: Manifold Absolute Pressure
MAPS: Manifold Absolute Pressure Sensor
MFI: Multi-Port Fuel Injection
MIL: Malfunction Indicator Lamp
OBD: On Board Diagnostic System
OXS: Oxygen Sensor
PCV: Positive Crankcase Ventilation
RAM: Random Access Memory
ROM: Read Only Memory
RPM: Revolutions Per Minute
ST: Scan Tool
TDI: Turbo Direct Injection
TPS: Throttle Position Sensor
TWC: Three Way Catalytic Converter
VR: Voltage Regulator
VSS: Vehicle Speed Sensor

VOLVO

TABLE OF CONTENTS

Page No.

EMISSIONS:
Abbreviations & Acronyms 18-66
Application Charts 18-58
Emission Controls 18-62
Emission Control System Application Chart . . . 18-58
Engine Compartment Reference Diagrams 18-60

ENGINE SYSTEMS IDENTIFICATION 18-2

FUEL SYSTEMS:
Abbreviations & Acronyms 18-66
Electric Fuel Pumps 18-55
Engine Compartment Reference Diagrams 18-60
Fuel Injection 18-16
Technical Service Bulletins 18-65

ENGINE TUNE UP & PERFORMANCE:
Abbreviations & Acronyms 18-66
Inline 4 Cylinder Gasoline Engine 18-5
Inline 5 & 6 Cylinder Gasoline Engine 18-6
Specifications 18-3

Page No.
Technical Service Bulletins 18-65

GENERAL INFORMATION:
Abbreviations & Acronyms 18-66
Air Bag System Precautions 0-12
Air Quality Standards 0-23
Computer Relearn Procedures 0-10
Electrical Symbol & Wire Color Code Identification 0-33
Engine Systems Identification 18-2
How To Use This Manual 0-1
Quick Reference 18-1
Service Reminder & Warning Lamp Reset Procedure 0-14
Vehicle Identification 0-3
Vehicle Maintenance Schedules 0-45

IGNITION SYSTEMS:
Abbreviations & Acronyms 18-66
Engine Compartment Reference Diagrams 18-60
Ignition Systems 18-7
Technical Service Bulletins 18-65

Induction System:
Turbochargers 18-56

Quick Reference

Application	Page No.
ACCESSING DIAGNOSTIC TROUBLE CODES	
Engine Control, Motronic 4.3 & 4.4	18-16
CLEARING DIAGNOSTIC TROUBLE CODES	
Engine Control, Motronic 4.3 & 4.4	18-16
COMPRESSION PRESSURE SPECIFICATIONS	
Four Cylinder Gasoline Engine	18-5
Inline Five & Six Cylinder Gasoline Engine	18-6
IGNITION COIL SPECIFICATIONS	
EZK-116-K	18-9
EZ-129-K	18-11
SENSOR SPECIFICATIONS	
Engine Control, Motronic 4.3 & 4.4	18-18

Engine Systems Identification

Note: The engine number is stamped on the righthand side of the engine block, or on a plate on the timing belt cover.

Model	Engine Code	Displacement, Liters	Fuel System	Page No.	Ignition System	Page No.	Computer System	Page No.
1998								
C70	B5234 T3	2.3L	Motronic 4.4 Drivetrain Control System	18-17	Motronic 4.4 Drivetrain Control System	18-17	Motronic 4.4 Drivetrain Control System	18-17
S70, S70 GLT, V70 & V70 GLT	B5254 S①	2.4L	Motronic 4.4 Drivetrain Control System	18-17	Motronic 4.4 Drivetrain Control System	18-17	Motronic 4.4 Drivetrain Control System	18-17
S70 T5 & V70 T5	B5234 T3	2.3L	Motronic 4.4 Drivetrain Control System	18-17	Motronic 4.4 Drivetrain Control System	18-17	Motronic 4.4 Drivetrain Control System	18-17
S90 & V90	B6304 S	2.9L	Motronic 4.4 Drivetrain Control System	18-17	Motronic 4.4 Drivetrain Control System	18-17	Motronic 4.4 Drivetrain Control System	18-17
1999–2001								
S40/V40	B4204T2/3	1.9L	Motronic 7.0 Drivetrain Control System	—	Motronic 7.0 Drivetrain Control System	—	Motronic 7.0 Drivetrain Control System	—
C70	B5234 T3	2.3L	Motronic 7.0 Drivetrain Control System	—	Motronic 7.0 Drivetrain Control System	—	Motronic 7.0 Drivetrain Control System	—
S70 & V70	B5254 S①	2.4L	Nippon-Denso Drivetrain Control System	—	Nippon-Denso Drivetrain Control System	—	Nippon-Denso Drivetrain Control System	—
S70 GLT & V70 GLT	B5254 T①	2.4L	Motronic 7.0 Drivetrain Control System	—	Motronic 7.0 Drivetrain Control System	—	Motronic 7.0 Drivetrain Control System	—
S70 T5 & V70 T5	B5234 T3	2.3L	Motronic 7.0 Drivetrain Control System	—	Motronic 7.0 Drivetrain Control System	—	Motronic 7.0 Drivetrain Control System	—
S80	B6284 T①	2.8L	Motronic 7.0 Drivetrain Control System	—	Motronic 7.0 Drivetrain Control System	—	Motronic 7.0 Drivetrain Control System	—
	B6304 S①	2.9L	Motronic 7.0 Drivetrain Control System	—	Motronic 7.0 Drivetrain Control System	—	Motronic 7.0 Drivetrain Control System	—

① — Transitional Low Emission Vehicle (TLEV).

Tune Up Specifications

Year	Engine	Spark Plug Gap Inch	Ignition Timing			Curb Idle Speed②		Fuel Pressure, PSI	Valve Lash, Inch
			Firing Order	Timing BTDC	Timing Mark Fig	Man. Trans.	Auto. Trans.		
1998	2.3L/4	.030	1-3-4-2	12	A	775③	775③	36	①
	2.3L/V6 Turbo	.030	1-2-4-5-3	6	—	—	850③	58	①
	2.4L	.030	1-2-4-5-3	5	—	850③	850③	44	①
	2.9L	.030	1-5-3-6-2-4	9	—	—	750③	44	①
1999	2.3L	—	—	—	—	—	—	—	—
	2.4L	—	—	—	—	—	—	—	—
	2.8L	—	—	—	—	—	—	—	—
	2.9L	—	—	—	—	—	—	—	—
2000–01	1.9L	—	—	—	—	—	—	—	—
	2.3L	—	—	—	—	—	—	—	—
	2.4L	—	—	—	—	—	—	—	—
	2.8L	—	—	—	—	—	—	—	—
	2.9L	—	—	—	—	—	—	—	—

BTDC — Before Top Dead Center
C — Cold
H — Hot
① — Equipped w/hydraulic valve lash adjusters.

② — When adjusting idle speed, set parking brake & chock drive wheels.

③ — Controlled by Constant Idle Speed (CIS) system.

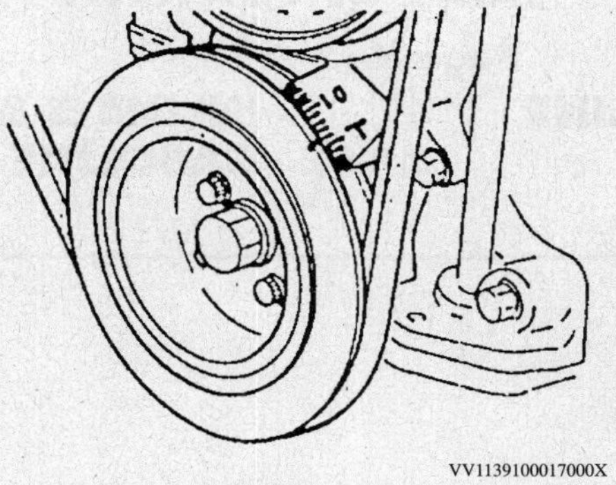

Fig. A

Engine Tune Up & Performance

NOTE: If Unsure Of The System Used On The Vehicle Being Serviced, Refer To "The Engine Systems Identification Chart." Further Assistance For The Proper Use Of Information Contained In This Section Can Also Be Found In The Front Of This Tabbed Section Under "How To Use This Manual."

NOTE: On Air Bag Equipped Models, Refer To "Air Bag System Precautions" Located In The Front Of This Manual For System Disarming & Arming Procedures.

NOTE: Refer To "Computer Relearn Procedures" Located In The Front Of This Manual When Battery Power To The Computer Has Been Interrupted.

NOTE: Prior To Performing Any Service Operations Listed In This Section, Consult The "Technical Service Bulletins" Section For Related Information.

NOTE: "Electrical Symbol & Wire Color Code Identification" Located In The Front Of This Manual May Be Used As An Aid When Using Wiring Circuits Found In This Section.

TABLE OF CONTENTS

	Page No.
INLINE 4 CYLINDER GASOLINE ENGINE	18-5
INLINE 5 & 6 CYLINDER GASOLINE ENGINES	18-6

Inline 4 Cylinder Gasoline Engine

INDEX

	Page No.		Page No.		Page No.
Compression Pressures.........	18-5	Ignition Timing	18-5	Valve Adjustment	18-5
Idle Speed & Mixture Adjustments	18-5	Spark Plugs.......................	18-5	Valve Arrangement..............	18-5
		Valves............................	18-5		

SPARK PLUGS

Spark plugs should be replaced at 30,000 mile intervals. **Torque** spark plugs to 15–21 ft. lbs. Refer to "Tune Up Specifications" chart for correct spark plug gap.

COMPRESSION PRESSURES

Prior to checking compression, disconnect ignition coil negative primary lead. Otherwise, ignition system damage may result.

When checking compression, pressures should be 128–156 psi with the lowest cylinder reading being within 80 percent of the highest. Perform compression test with engine at normal operating temperature, spark plugs removed and throttle in the wide open position.

IGNITION TIMING

Refer to Tune Up Specifications chart for correct ignition timing and firing order.

1. Connect timing light and tachometer to engine.
2. Start engine and allow to warm up.
3. Ensure idle speed is at specifications. Idle is controlled by the ECU and is not adjustable.
4. Check ignition timing. Ignition timing is controlled by the ECU and is not adjustable.

IDLE SPEED & MIXTURE ADJUSTMENTS

The Constant Idle Speed (CIS) system controls engine idle speed by regulation of air. The ECU reads engine idle from the crankshaft position sensor, the ECU controls idle by allowing air to bypass the throttle plate through the Idle Air Control (IAC) valve as needed to maintain a fixed idle speed.

Fuel mixture is controlled by the ECU and is not adjustable.

VALVES

Valve Arrangement

Front to Rear ....E-I-E-I-E-I-E-I

Valve Adjustment

1. Remove valve cover.
2. Rotate crankshaft until cam lobes of cylinder No. one point upward and timing mark of cylinder No. one is at zero.
3. Insert a feeler gauge between cam lobe and valve shim to measure valve clearance. When checking, on B230F engines, clearance should be .014–.018 inch cold or .012–.106 inch hot on both exhaust and intake valves, on all except B230F engines, clearance should be .010–.018 inch cold or .012–.020 inch hot on both intake and exhaust valves.
4. If valve clearance is incorrect, align valve depressors so notches are at right angles to engine centerline.
5. Attach tool No. 5022, or equivalent, then depress valve depressors until depressor groove is just above edge and accessible with pliers.
6. Remove valve adjustment disc using tool No. 5026, or equivalent, then measure disc thickness. Calculate shim thickness necessary to obtain specified clearance. Shims are available from .13–.18 inch in .001 inch increments, install shims with marks downward. Valve clearance should be adjusted to .014–.016 inch cold or .016–.018 inch hot.
7. Coat new shim with lubricant, then install into valve depressor.
8. Repeat adjustment procedure for cylinders three, four then two.

Inline 5 & 6 Cylinder Gasoline Engines

INDEX

	Page No.
Compression Pressures	18-6
Idle Speed & Mixture Adjustments	18-6
Ignition Timing	18-6
Spark Plugs	18-6
Valves	18-6
Valve Adjustment	18-6

SPARK PLUGS

Torque spark plugs to 18 ft. lbs. Refer to "Tune Up Specifications" chart for correct spark plug gap.

COMPRESSION PRESSURES

1. Disconnect timing pick-up connector and remove ignition wiring cover.
2. **On models equipped with six-cylinder engine,** remove throttle pulley cover, then the ignition coils.
3. **On all models,** lock throttle in fully-open position and remove spark plugs.
4. Connect remote starter switch tool No. 115 8263, or equivalent, between alternator positive and service socket.
5. Using compression gauge tool No. 9689 and extension sleeve tool No. 115 8540, or equivalents, measure compression in all cylinders. Compression should be 188–218 psi on normally aspirated engines and 160–188 psi on turbocharged engines.
6. Reinstall spark plugs, ignition coils, ignition wiring cover and throttle pulley cover and connect timing pickup connector.

IGNITION TIMING

Refer to "Tune Up Specifications" chart for correct ignition timing and firing order.

Ignition timing cannot be adjusted.

IDLE SPEED & MIXTURE ADJUSTMENTS

Idle speed and mixture cannot be adjusted. Refer to Tune Up Specifications chart for correct idle speeds.

VALVES

Valve Adjustment

Models are equipped with hydraulic valve lash adjusters and cannot be adjusted.

Ignition Systems

TABLE OF CONTENTS

	Page No.		Page No.
EZ-116-K DISTRIBUTOR........	18-7	EZ-129-K DISTRIBUTOR........	18-11

EZ-116-K Distributor Ignition

NOTE: If Unsure Of The System Used On The Vehicle Being Serviced, Refer To "The Engine Systems Identification Chart." Further Assistance For The Proper Use Of Information Contained In This Section Can Also Be Found In The Front Of This Tabbed Section Under "How To Use This Manual."

NOTE: On Air Bag Equipped Models, Refer To "Air Bag System Precautions" Located In The Front Of This Manual For System Disarming & Arming Procedures.

NOTE: Refer To "Computer Relearn Procedures" Located In The Front Of This Manual When Battery Power To The Computer Has Been Interrupted.

NOTE: Prior To Performing Any Service Operations Listed In This Section, Consult The "Technical Service Bulletins" Section For Related Information.

NOTE: "Electrical Symbol & Wire Color Code Identification" Located In The Front Of This Manual May Be Used As An Aid When Using Wiring Circuits Found In This Section.

INDEX

	Page No.
Description	18-7
Diagnosis & Testing	18-7
Accessing Diagnostic Trouble Codes	18-7
Control Function No. 1........	18-7
Control Function No. 2........	18-8
Clearing Diagnostic Trouble Codes	18-8
Component Testing	18-8
Control Unit..................	18-8
Engine Coolant Temperature Sensor	18-9
Ignition System	18-8
Knock Sensors	18-9
Load From Fuel System Control Unit	18-9
Power Stage & Ignition Coil...	18-9
Pulse Generator	18-9
Throttle Switch...............	18-9
Diagnostic Trouble Code Interpretation	18-8
Precautions	18-7
Air Bag Systems...............	18-7
ECU Power.....................	18-7

PRECAUTIONS

Air Bag Systems

Refer to "Air Bag System Precautions" in the front of this manual for system disarming and arming procedures.

ECU Power

The control module power supply must be disconnected when connecting or disconnecting the connector or measuring unit or damage will result. Disconnect battery ground cable whenever connecting or disconnecting.

DESCRIPTION

The EZ-116-K power stage, **Figs. 1 and 2**, is supplied with ignition pulses from the control unit, which receives its signal from the inductive speed pickup and other sources. It sends a constant current to the ignition coil, distributor and spark plugs.

DIAGNOSIS & TESTING

Refer to **Figs. 3 and 4**, for wiring schematics and component locations.

Accessing Diagnostic Trouble Codes

CONTROL FUNCTION NO. 1

1. Check throttle switch operation.
2. Ensure pulse generator leads are properly connected at bulkhead.

1. Open diagnostic socket cover, then connect lead to socket six, **Fig. 5.**
2. Turn ignition on.
3. Select control function No. 1, depress diagnostic socket for more than one second, then count and record the number of flashes, depress socket button again to display up to three diagnostic trouble codes.
4. Refer to "Diagnostic Trouble Code Interpretation" for diagnostic trouble code interpretation.

CONTROL FUNCTION NO. 2

1. Open diagnostic socket cover, then connect lead to socket six, **Fig. 5.**
2. Turn ignition switch on.
3. Depress diagnostic unit button twice, each for more than one second, lamp should flash rapidly, if not proceed to "Component Testing."
4. Operate throttle control, lamp should go out, then display diagnostic trouble code 3-3-4, indicating throttle switch is operating properly in idle position, if diagnostic trouble code is not displayed but light continues to flash, proceed to "Diagnostic Trouble Code Interpretation."
5. Operate starter motor, lamp should go out, then display diagnostic trouble code 1-4-1, indicating pulse generator signal is correct, if diagnostic trouble code is not displayed but light continues to flash, proceed to "Diagnostic Trouble Code Interpretation."
6. Turn ignition switch off.

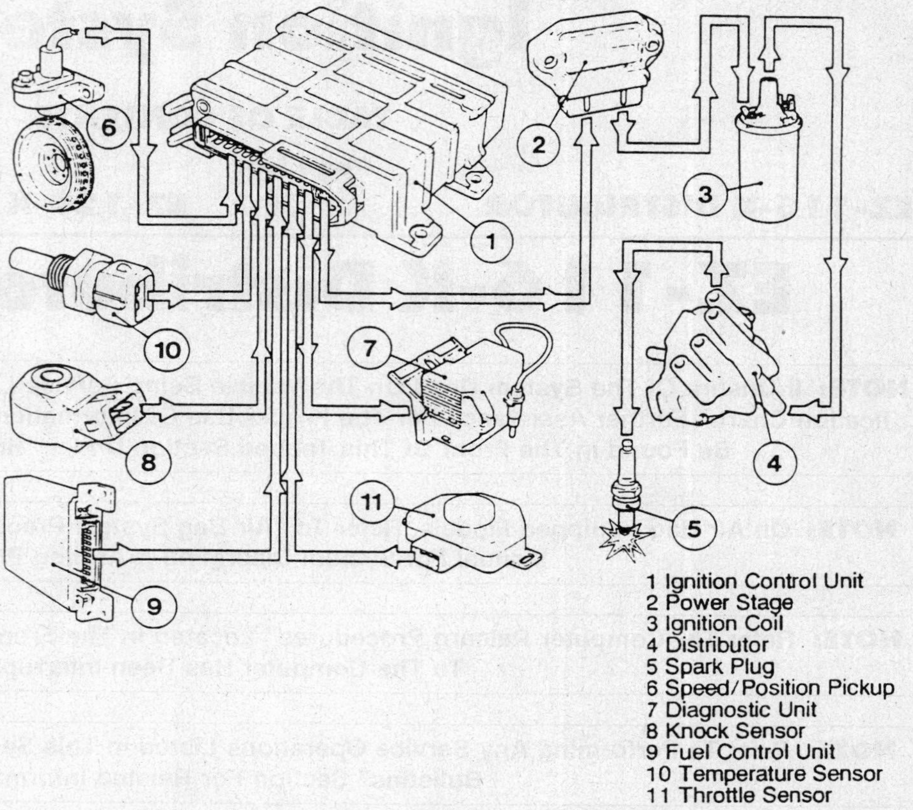

Fig. 1 EZ-116-K ignition system components

Diagnostic Trouble Code Interpretation

After consulting the following list, refer to "Component Testing" for component tests and **Figs. 3 and 4,** for wiring schematics and component locations.

Code 111: No fault.
Code 142: Control unit faulty, replace control unit.
Code 143: Knock sensor signal absent.
Code 144: Fuel system load signal absent.
Code 214: Pulse generator intermittently absent.
Code 224: Engine temperature sensor faulty.
Code 234: Throttle switch improperly adjusted or open/short to ground.

Clearing Diagnostic Trouble Codes

1. Turn ignition switch on.
2. Read diagnostic trouble codes again as outlined under "Accessing Diagnostic Trouble Codes," "Control Function No. 1."
3. Depress diagnostic socket button for more than five seconds.
4. After three seconds diode should illuminate.
5. With diode illuminated, depress diagnostic socket button for five seconds, then release button, diode should not be illuminated.
6. Ensure memory is erased, then depress socket button for more than one second but less than three seconds. Diagnostic trouble code 1-1-1 (no fault) should be indicated.

Component Testing

IGNITION SYSTEM

1. Ensure control unit and power stage grounds (brown and black) are properly connected to intake manifold.
2. Disconnect one spark plug lead wire at a time and connect it to a separate spark plug. Ground spark plug to engine and crank starter motor.
3. If spark is present at plug, there is an engine or fuel system malfunction. If spark is not present at plug, proceed to next step.
4. Check spark at ignition coil as follows:
   a. Connect high tension lead and spark plug to ignition coil.
   b. Ground spark plug to engine and crank starter motor.
   c. If spark is present, check distributor rotor, cap and wires. If spark is not present, proceed to next step.
5. With ignition switch off, remove left-hand lower instrument panel, then disconnect control unit electrical connector. **Do not insert instrument probes in front of connector terminals, as connector damage may occur. Terminal numbers are marked on side of connector.**
6. Using suitable voltmeter, measure voltage between control unit terminal five (brown) and ground, 12 volts should be indicated, if not, check lead between control unit and busbar 30 supply at fuse panel.

CONTROL UNIT

1. Turn ignition switch on.
2. Connect test lead to diagnostic socket No. 6.
3. Measure voltage between control unit terminal one (yellow/red) and ground.
4. Voltage should be 12 volts. Depress diagnostic socket button, 0 volts should be indicated.
5. If voltage is not as indicated, measure voltage at diagnostic connector between blue lead and ground, 12 volts should be indicated.
6. Measure resistance between connector black lead and ground, 0 ohms should be indicated, turn ignition switch off.
7. Measure resistance between diagnostic test lead and pin No. 8 below function selector, **Fig. 6.**
8. Infinite ohm should be indicated. Depress function selector button, 0 ohms should be indicated.
9. Connect red diode test probe to pin

under LED, then connect black probe to test lead. If diode tester gives indication, LED is operating properly. If no indication is observed, replace diagnostic unit.

10. Inspect control unit voltage as follows:
    a. Turn ignition switch on.
    b. Measure voltage between control unit terminal six (blue) and ground, 12 volts should be indicated.
    c. Turn ignition switch off.
    d. Measure resistance between terminals 20 (brown) and ground and terminal 14 (black) and ground, 0 ohms should be indicated.

ENGINE COOLANT TEMPERATURE SENSOR

1. Measure resistance between sensor terminal two and ground, **Fig. 7.**
2. Refer to "Sensor Specifications" in appropriate fuel injection section, for temperature sensor.
3. If value is not as indicated, measure resistance directly between sensor terminals to determine if sensor or lead is faulty, repair or replace as required.

THROTTLE SWITCH

1. Measure resistance between control unit terminal 7 (orange) and ground. 0 ohms should be indicated.
2. Depress accelerator until throttle switch opens slightly. Resistance should increase to infinite.
3. Measure throttle switch resistance to determine if fault is in wiring or switch itself. Replace or adjust as required.
4. Adjust throttle switch as follows:
    a. Open throttle slightly. Listen to switch. Click should be heard as idle contact opens (throttle opens).
    b. Loosen mounting screws, turn switch clockwise, then turn counterclockwise until click is heard from contacts.
    c. Tighten attaching screws, then recheck operation.

LOAD FROM FUEL SYSTEM CONTROL UNIT

1. Measure voltage between connector terminal eight (yellow) and ground.
2. Turn ignition on, voltage should be 0.1 volts.
3. If voltage is not indicated, open between control units lead of fault in fuel system control unit.
4. Turn ignition off.

PULSE GENERATOR

1. Measure resistance between connector terminals ten (red) and 23 (blue). 215–265 ohms should be indicated.
2. Ensure screen is connected to terminal 11.

KNOCK SENSORS

1. Disconnect knock sensor connector bridge terminals one and two, measure resistance between connector terminals 12 (black) and 13 (green), 0 ohms should be indicated, then check

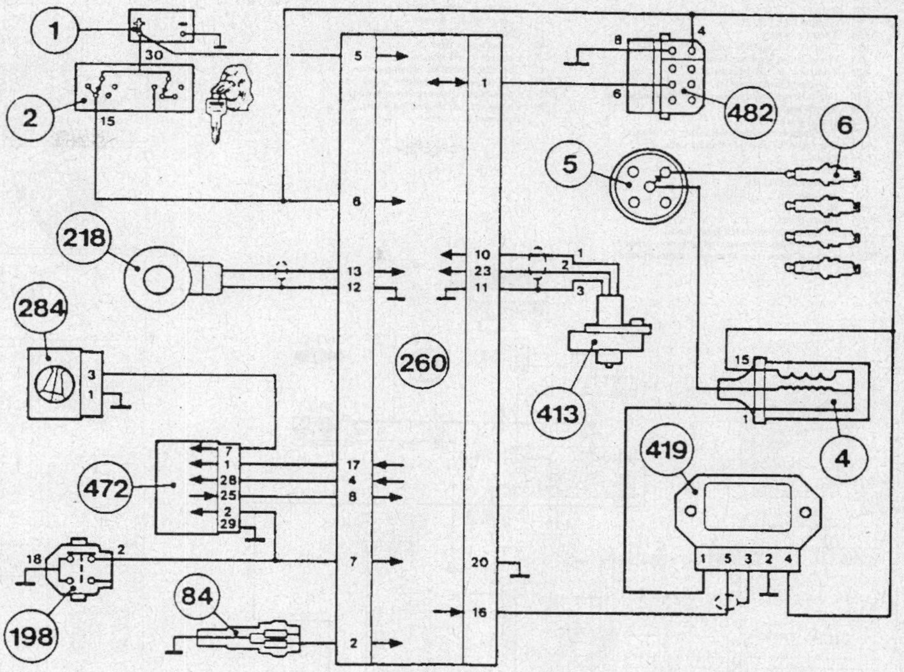

1 Battery
2 Ignition Switch
4 Ignition Coil
5 Distributor
6 Spark Plug
84 Temperature Sensor
198 Throttle Switch
218 Knock Sensor
260 Ignition Control Unit
284 Air Mass Meter
413 Speed/Position Pickup
419 Power Stage
472 Fuel Control Unit
482 Diagnostic Unit

VV1119100002000X

Fig. 2 EZ-116-K ignition system schematic

resistance to ground, infinite ohms should be indicated.

2. If resistance is too high, open or short is indicated one or both knock sensor circuits.
3. Remove jumper, measure each lead resistance, repair or replace as required.
4. If leads or good, replace knock sensor, then reconnect knock sensor and control unit electrical connectors.

POWER STAGE & IGNITION COIL

1. Ensure ignition switch is off, then remove air cleaner and filter.
2. Pull connector rubber sleeve rearward to expose terminals. **Do not insert probes to front of terminals as damage may result.**
3. Measure resistance between connector terminals one (red/white) and four (blue), .6–1.0 ohms should be indicated.
4. If resistance is too low, replace ignition coil.
5. If resistance is too high, measure resistance between ignition coil terminals 1 and 15, **Fig. 8.**
6. If resistance is still too high, replace ignition coil.
7. If resistance is as indicated, check ignition coil leads between terminals one and four, replace leads as required.
8. Measure resistance between ignition coil terminals HT and one, 6.5–9.0 ohms should be indicated, if resistance is not as indicated, replace ignition coil.
9. Measure resistance between power stage terminal one (black) and ground, zero ohms should be indicate.
10. Ensure power stage terminal three (gray) to control unit is properly screened.
11. Inspect voltage at ignition coil and power stage as follows:
    a. Turn ignition switch on.
    b. Measure voltage between power stage terminal four and ground, 12 volts should be indicated.
    c. Operate starter motor, less than 10.5 volts should be indicated.
    d. If voltage is too low, check battery and charging system.
    e. If no voltage is present, check and/or replace blue lead between fuse panel and ignition coil/power stage.
12. Inspect control signal from control unit to power stage as follows:
    a. Measure voltage between power stage connector terminal five and ground.
    b. Operate starter, voltage should oscillate between 0–2 volts.
    c. If voltage is as indicated, repeat test with new power stage.
13. Turn ignition switch off, then reconnect power stage electrical connector, install air cleaner, reconnect air mass meter and hoses.
14. Clear all diagnostic trouble codes as outlined under "Clearing Diagnostic Trouble Codes."

1/1	Battery
3/1	Ignition lock
3/50	Throttle switch
4/10	Control unit, ignition lock EZ-K
4/15	Power stage, ignition system EZ-K
4/23	Control unit, LH-jetronic 2.4
5/1	Combined instrument
7/16	Engine temperature sensor, fuel/ignition system
7/24	Knock sensor
7/25	Impulse sensor
7/37	Temperature sensor EGR (Only California)
8/17	Converter EGR (Only California)
11/1-26	Fuses
15/1	Positive terminal
17/11	Diagnostic socket
20/1	Ignition coil
20/2	Distributor
20/3-6	Spark plugs
31/2	Ground connection left front fender
31/32	Ground connection on engine (power ground)
31/33	Ground connection on engine (signal ground)

A	Connector, right A-post
B	Connector, left A-post
C	Connector, left suspension tower
E	Connector, at firewall
F	Connector, left suspension tower
G	Connector, right suspension tower
M	Connector, left suspension tower
N	Connector, right suspension tower
H	Connector, left suspension tower, 2-pin moisture-proof

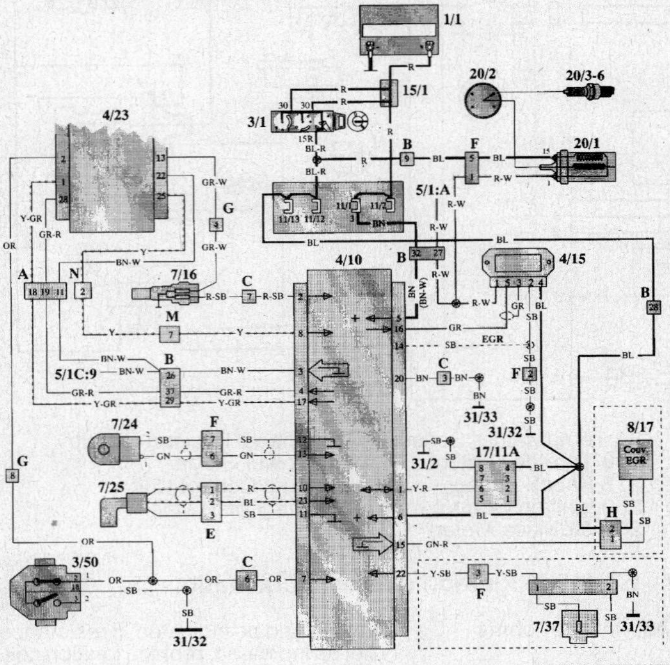

Fig. 3 EZ-116-K ignition wiring diagram

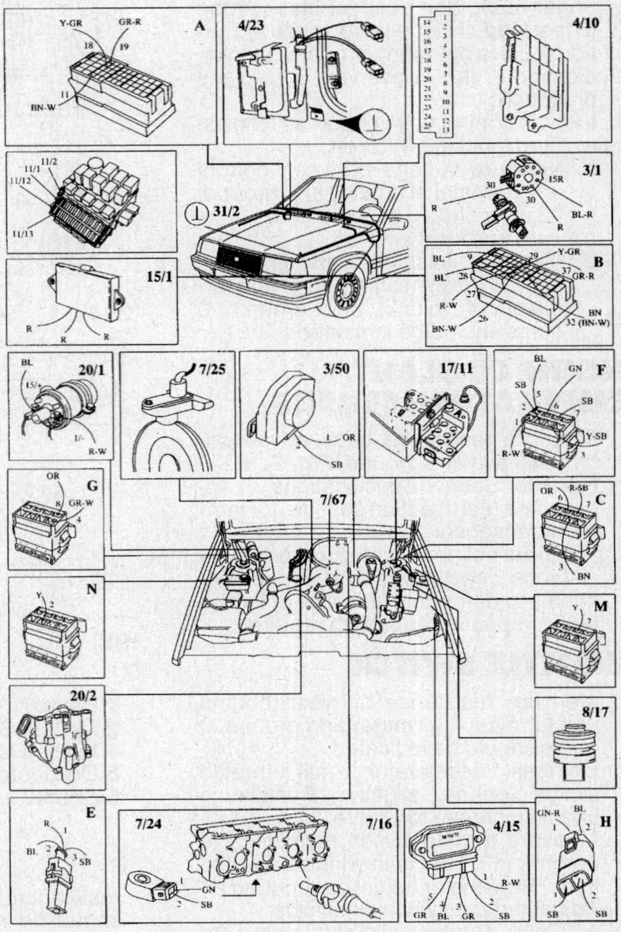

Fig. 4 EZ-116-K component locations

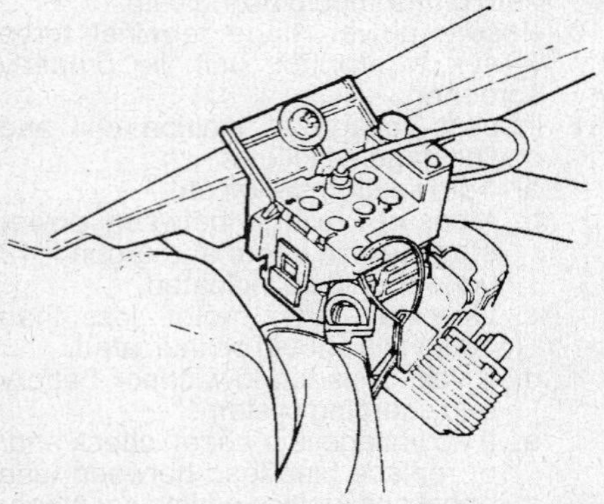

Fig. 5 Diagnostic socket

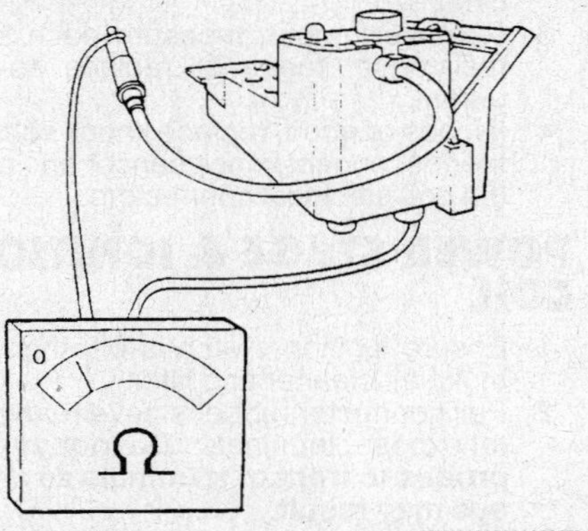

Fig. 6 Control unit inspection

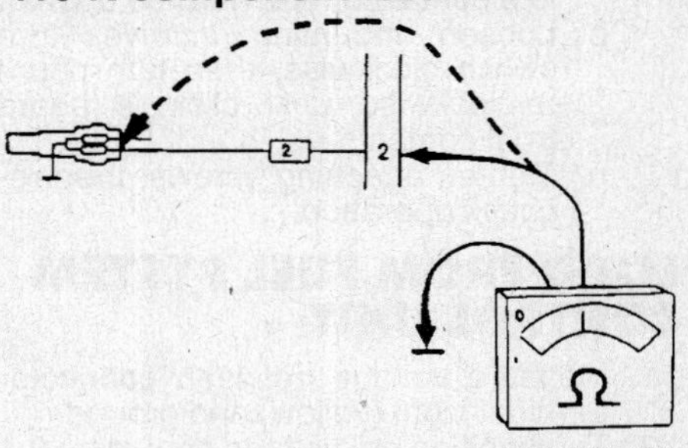

Fig. 7 Engine coolant temperature sensor inspection

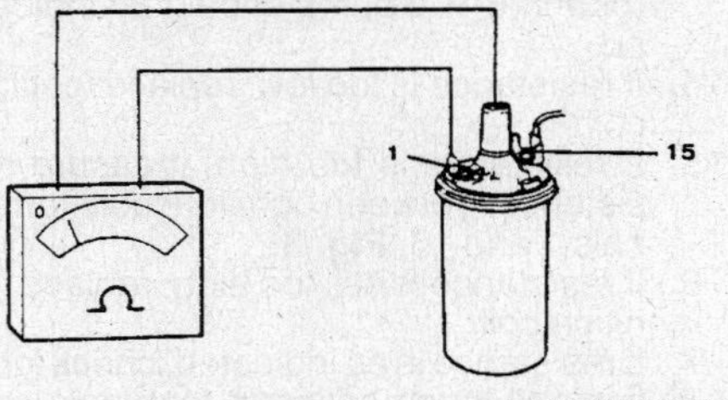

Fig. 8 Ignition coil test

EZ-129-K Distributor Ignition

NOTE: If Unsure Of The System Used On The Vehicle Being Serviced, Refer To "The Engine Systems Identification Chart." Further Assistance For The Proper Use Of Information Contained In This Section Can Also Be Found In The Front Of This Tabbed Section Under "How To Use This Manual."

NOTE: On Air Bag Equipped Models, Refer To "Air Bag System Precautions" Located In The Front Of This Manual For System Disarming & Arming Procedures.

NOTE: Refer To "Computer Relearn Procedures" Located In The Front Of This Manual When Battery Power To The Computer Has Been Interrupted.

NOTE: Prior To Performing Any Service Operations Listed In This Section, Consult The "Technical Service Bulletins" Section For Related Information.

NOTE: "Electrical Symbol & Wire Color Code Identification" Located In The Front Of This Manual May Be Used As An Aid When Using Wiring Circuits Found In This Section.

INDEX

	Page No.
Description	18-11
Accessing Diagnostic Trouble Codes	18-11
Diagnostic Test Mode 1	18-11
Clearing Diagnostic Trouble Codes	18-15
Cleared Diagnostic Trouble Code Verification	18-15
System Memory	18-15
Diagnostic Tests	18-11
Code 1-1-2: Control Module Check	18-11
Code 1-2-3: Temperature Sensor Check	18-12
Code 1-4-4: Load Signal Check	18-13
Code 3-1-1: Speed Signal Check	18-14
Code 4-1-1: Throttle Switch Check	18-15
Codes 1-3-1 & 2-1-4: Vehicle Speed Sensor (VSS) Check	18-12
Codes 1-4-3 & 4-3-3: Knock Sensor Check	18-13
Codes 3-1-4 & 3-2-4: Camshaft Position Sensor (CMP) Check	18-14
Codes 4-3-2 & 5-1-3: Checking Temperature In Control Module Box	18-15
Diagnostic Trouble Code Interpretation	18-11
Diagnosis & Testing	18-11
Precautions	18-11
Air Bag Systems	18-11
ECU Power	18-11

PRECAUTIONS

Air Bag Systems

Refer to "Air Bag System Precautions" in the front of this manual for system disarming and arming procedures.

ECU Power

The control module power supply must be disconnected when connecting or disconnecting the connector or measuring unit or damage will result. Disconnect battery ground cable whenever connecting or disconnecting.

DESCRIPTION

This distributor type ignition system consists of an Electronic Control Unit (ECU), distributor, Camshaft Position (CMP) sensor, crankshaft position sensor, ignition coil with power stage and dual knock sensors. The ECU uses information from engine sensors to produce the optimum spark timing for current engine conditions and load.

DIAGNOSIS & TESTING

Refer to **Fig. 1,** for system wiring circuits and component locations.

Accessing Diagnostic Trouble Codes

The diagnostic module is located in front of the control modules in the righthand front of engine compartment.

DIAGNOSTIC TEST MODE 1

1. Turn ignition switch to On position, then connect test lead to socket A6 of diagnostic module, **Fig. 2.**
2. Press test button and keep depressed for more than one second, but not more than three seconds.
3. Observe LED and count number of flashes which comprise a code.
4. If LED does not light when button is depressed, check diagnostic module.
5. If LED lights when button is depressed but control module does not respond, check diagnostic module.
6. If control module displays a diagnostic trouble code (DTC) , record DTC.
7. Operate test button again and record DTC, if any. Repeat procedure until first DTC is repeated. Memory is full when 13 DTCs are displayed. No further DTCs can be recorded until first DTCs have been corrected and cleared from memory.

Diagnostic Trouble Code Interpretation

Refer to **Fig. 3,** for DTC identification.

Diagnostic Tests

CODE 1-1-2: CONTROL MODULE CHECK

The control module runs a program

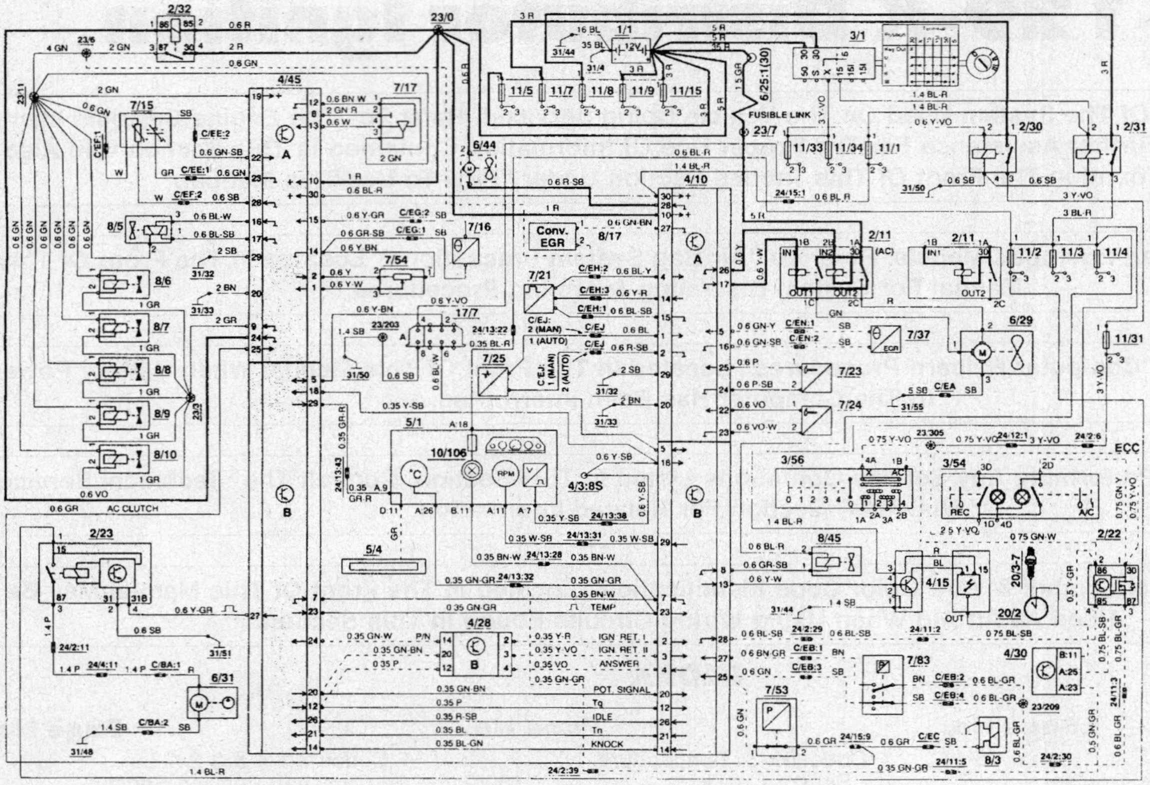

VV1119100013010X

Fig. 1 EZ-129-K ignition wiring diagram & component locations (Part 1 of 3)

check when the engine is started, and monitors the knock control circuit and temperature sensor when the car is driven. If program check reveals errors, or if the knock control or temperature sensor conditions are not correct, DTC 1-1-2 will be recorded. Timing will be adjusted to “fail safe” value of 6° in the event of a knock control circuit fault.

1. Clear DTC, turn ignition switch to On position and wait a few seconds, then start engine. Repeat several times and observe if DTC recurs.
2. If DTC recurs, replace DI control module.
3. Drive vehicle at high load and at speed above 3000 RPM to check knock control circuit.
4. If DTC recurs, replace DI control module.

CODE 1-2-3: TEMPERATURE SENSOR CHECK

The control module is dependent on the temperature sensor signal to compute timing at different temperatures. The signal is supplied in digital form by the MFI control module. The DI control module will interpret a signal higher than 302°F (150°C) or lower than −105°F (−40°C) as a fault, and will record a DTC. The control module then assumes a substitute value equivalent to 203°F (95°C) and will then operate the cooling fan at half speed.

1. Check for DTCs in other systems as follows:
   a. Check if DTCs have been recorded by fuel system and combined instrument.
   b. Activate diagnostic test mode one for fuel system (socket A2) and combined instrument (socket A7).
   c. If MFI DTC 1-2-3 and combined instrument DTCs 1-2-1 and 1-2-2 are displayed, check MFI DTC 1-2-3.
   d. If DTC is recorded in DI system and combined instrument system but not in MFI system, check DTC in DI system and combined instrument.
   e. If DTC is not recorded in MFI system or combined instrument, check DTC in DI system but not in combined instrument.
2. Check DTC in DI system and combined instrument as follows:
   a. Check lead between MFI system terminal 53 (B23) and DI system terminal 53 (B23) for open circuit or short circuit.
   b. If lead is satisfactory, repeat test with new MFI control module.
3. Check DTC in DI system but not in combined instrument as follows:
   a. If DTC is recorded in DI system but not in MFI system or combined instrument, check lead between MFI system terminal 53 (B23) and DI system terminal 53 (B23) for open circuit.
   b. If lead is satisfactory, repeat test with new DI control module.

CODES 1-3-1 & 2-1-4: VEHICLE SPEED SENSOR (VSS) CHECK

If VSS signal is absent for six engine revolutions as counted by camshaft position, DTC 1-3-1 is recorded and engine will not start. If signal is restored, engine will start.

If DI control module counts a tooth less or a tooth more on toothed wheel during one revolution, DTC 2-1-4 will be recorded. DTC will be recorded only if engine runs.

1. Connect measuring unit 981 3190 and adapter 981 3195 as follows:
   a. Disconnect battery ground cable, then remove control module cover.
   b. Remove DI control module, then press adapter onto DI control module and pull lead upwards through slot alongside module.
   c. Press DI control module, with adapter connected, into connector in bottom of control module box, then connect measuring unit to adapter 60-pole connector.
2. Check VSS signal as follows:
   a. Connect ac millivoltmeter (mV) across terminals one (A1) and two (A2), then operate starter motor. Millivoltmeter should indicate 300–400 mV ac with ignition in starting position and approximately one Volt when engine starts.
   b. If signal is absent or faulty, check sensor resistance.
3. Check sensor resistance as follows:

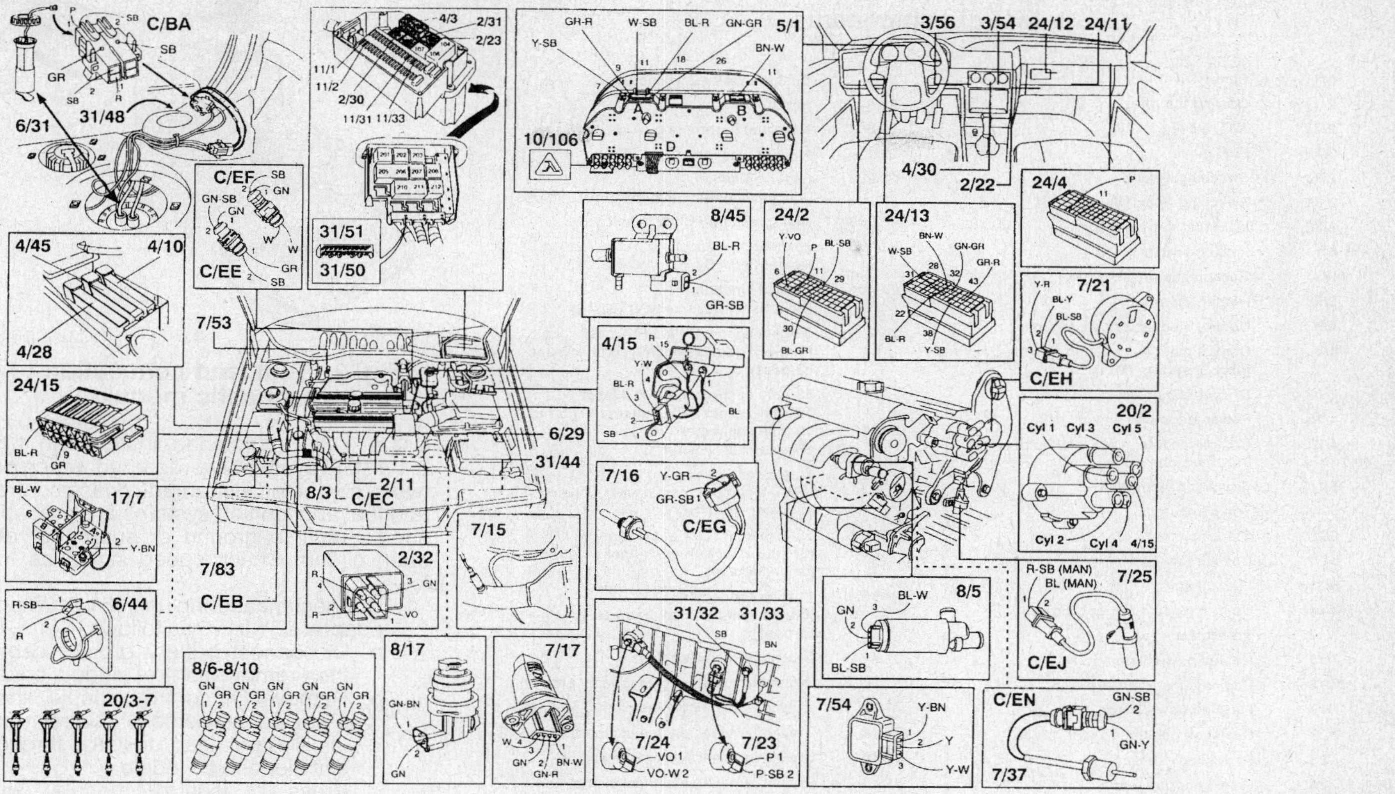

VV1119100013020X

Fig. 1 EZ-129-K ignition component locations & component locations (Part 2 of 3)

a. Connect ohmmeter across terminals one (A1) and two (A2). Resistance should be 200–400 ohms depending on sensor temperature.

4. Check sensor ground connection as follows:
   a. Connect ohmmeter across terminals two (A2) and 20 (A20). Ohmmeter should read approximately 0 ohms.
5. Check sensor signal in diagnostic test mode two as follows:
   a. Disconnect CMP connector to prevent it from delivering trouble code in diagnostic test mode 2.
   b. Activate diagnostic test mode two, then operate starter motor. VSS response DTC 1-4-1 should be displayed.
   c. If DTC is not displayed, repeat diagnostic test with new DI control module.
   d. If fault tracing reveals no electrical fault, check that carrier plate is not damaged or distorted. **This may prevent engine from starting, cause running problems and initiate a DTC. This applies particularly to automatic transmissions.**

CODES 1-4-3 & 4-3-3: KNOCK SENSOR CHECK

DTCs will be recorded if engine speed is at least 2970 RPM and a certain engine load has been exceeded, or if the signal from either knock sensor to control module is less than 255 mV during 96 successive ignitions. Control module will then safety-retard timing.

1. Connect measuring unit 981 3190 and adapter 981 3195 as follows:
   a. Disconnect battery ground cable, then remove control module cover.
   b. Remove DI control module, then press adapter onto DI control module and pull lead upwards through slot alongside module.
   c. Press DI control module, with adapter connected, into connector in bottom of control module box, then connect measuring unit to adapter 60-pole connector.
2. Check wiring as follows:
   a. Disconnect sensor connector, check connector for faults, then bridge connector terminals.
   b. Connect ohmmeter between terminals 22 (A22) and 23 (A23) or 24 (A24) and 25 (A25) as appropriate. Ohmmeter should indicate approximately 0 ohms.
   c. If reading is correct, replace knock sensor.
   d. If reading is incorrect, check DI control module wiring.

CODE 1-4-4: LOAD SIGNAL CHECK

The timing varies with the load signal supplied by the MFI control module. The DTC will be recorded if the signal is constantly high or low during 20 ignitions. In this case, the full-load value will be assumed and the cooling fan will continue to run for six minutes after the engine has been switched Off.

1. Check for DTCs in other systems as follows:
   a. Check for DTCs in MFI system. Activate diagnostic test mode 1.
   b. Display DTCs, if any, and correct faults, then clear DTCs in DI and MFI systems and test drive vehicle.
   c. If DI system DTC 1-4-4 recurs, check signal to DI control module.
2. Connect measuring unit 981 3190 and adapter 981 3195 as follows:
   a. Disconnect battery ground cable, then remove control module cover.
   b. Remove DI control module, then press adapter onto DI control module and pull lead upwards through slot alongside module.
   c. Press DI control module, with adapter connected, into connector in bottom of control module box, then connect measuring unit to adapter 60-pole connector.
3. Check signal to DI control module as follows:
   a. Start engine, then connect voltmeter across terminals 42 (B12) and 20 (A20). Voltmeter should indicate approximately 50 mV when idling with engine hot. Rev engine. Reading should increase with speed.
   b. If signal is present, repeat test with different DI control module.
   c. If signal is absent or faulty, check lead between control modules.

List of components

1/1	Battery
2/11	Cooling fan relay
2/22	A/C relay
2/23	Fuel pump
2/30	Switching relay X+
2/31	Switching relay 15+
2/32	Main fuel system relay
3/1	Ignition switch
3/54	Recirculation/A/C switch
3/56	Heater fan switch
4/3	Control module, cruise control
4/8	Control module, multiport fuel injection (LH3.2) system (MFI)
4/10	DI control module, (EZ-129K)
4/15	Power stage and ignition coil
4/28	Control module, AW 50-42 automatic transmission
5/1	Combined instrument
5/4	Trip computer
6/25	Starter motor
6/29	Cooling fan
6/31	Fuel pump
6/44	Control module box cooling fan
7/13	Pressostat
7/15	Heated oxygen sensor (HO2S)
7/16	Engine temperature sensor
7/17	Mass air flow sensor
7/21	Camshaft position sensor (CMP)
7/23	Rear knock sensor
7/24	Front knock sensor
7/25	Vehicle speed sensor
7/53	High-pressure switch
7/54	Throttle switch
8/3	A/C electromagnetic clutch
8/5	Idle air control valve (IAC valve)
8/6 - 10	Injectors
8/14	Variable-flow intake manifold, solenoid valve
10/79	Gear-change indicating lamp (manual transmissioon), winter program and gear selector indicator (automatics)
10/106	Emission warning lamp
11/1 - 40	Fuses
17/7	Diagnostic module A
20/2	Distributor
20/3 - 7	Spark plugs

23/0	Busbar 30+ supply junction
23/3	Injector + junction
23/6	Main fuel system relay junction
23/11	Injector junction
23/203	Ground junction, electrical distribution unit ground (31/50)
23/209	High-pressure switch junction
23/305	Junction, X+ supply Heater fan/A/C
23/404	Ground junction, Right-hand crossmember (31/48)
24/2	53-pole connector at LH A-post (Firewall harness/engine compartment harness)
24/4	53-pole connector at RH A-post Firewall harness/RH bottom rail harness)
24/11	10-pole connector (Firewall harness/A/C)
24/12	4-pole connector (Engine compartment harness/engine harness)
24/13	53-pole connector at LH A-post (Engine compartment harness/instrument panel harness)
24/15	14-pole connector (Engine compartment harness/engine harness)
31/4	Ground terminal, engine
31/32	Ground terminal, engine (supply ground)
31/33	Ground terminal, engine (signal ground)
31/44	Ground terminal, engine compartment
31/48	Ground terminal, RH crossmember
31/50	Ground terminal, electrical distribution unit (supply ground)
31/51	Ground terminal, electrical distribution unit (signal ground)
31/55	Ground terminal, cooling fan
C/BA	2-pole connector, fuel pump
C/EA	Single-pole connector, cooling fan
C/EB	4-pole connector, high-pressure switch
C/EC	Single-pole connector, A/C electromagnetic clutch
C/EE	2-pole connector, HO2S sensor
C/EF	2-pole connector, HO2S sensor
C/EG	2-pole connector, engine temperature sensor
C/EH	3-pole connector, CMP
C/EJ	2-pole connector, VSS sensor

VV1119100013030X

Fig. 1 EZ-129-K ignition component locations & component locations (Part 3 of 3)

4. Check lead between MFI and DI control modules as follows:
   a. Connect ohmmeter between terminals 42 (B12) and 20 (A20). Ohmmeter should read infinite. Reading of 0 ohms indicates that lead is short circuit to ground.
   b. Connect voltmeter across terminals 42 (B12) and 20 (A20), then turn ignition switch to On position. If voltmeter indicates battery voltage, lead is short circuit to supply.
   c. If readings are correct but signal is still absent, measure resistance of lead between DI control module terminal 42 (B12) and MFI control module terminal 42 (B12).
   d. If lead is satisfactory but signal is still absent, repeat test with new MFI control module.
5. Clear DTCs, if any, in other systems, then activate diagnostic test mode 1 for automatic transmission if temperature sensor signal DTC is displayed.

CODE 3-1-1: SPEED SIGNAL CHECK

If speed exceeds 3000 RPM, the load signal is equivalent to part load and the signal is absent for five seconds, a DTC will be recorded.

If speedometer does not operate, fault is not in ignition system. If speedometer operates, combined instrument is receiving input signal. Check if DTC for speedometer signal (12-púlse output signal) is recorded by combined instrument (ignition system).

Activate diagnostic test mode 1 for combined instrument (socket A7) and MFI system (socket A2) in that order. Display DTCs, if any.

If speedometer signal is absent, and

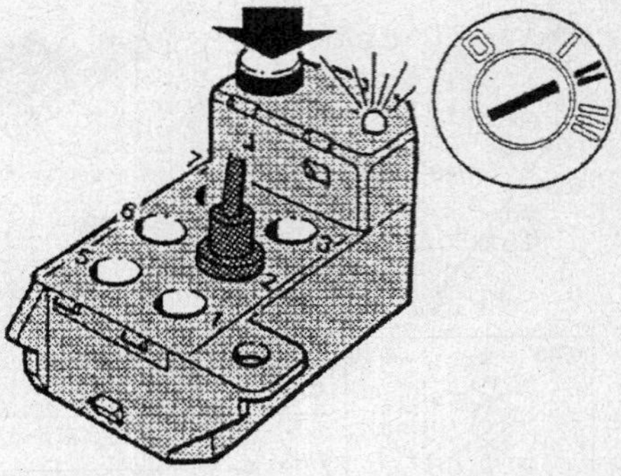

VV1119100014000X

Fig. 2 Test lead connection to diagnostic module.

DTCs 1-3-1 (combined instrument) and 3-1-1 (MFI system) are recorded, wiring between combined instrument, cruise control, and fuel and ignition systems are probably short circuit to ground or supply, or are open circuit. Check speed signal as follows:

1. Connect measuring unit 981 3190 and adapter 981 3195 as follows:
   a. Disconnect battery ground cable, then remove control module cover.
   b. Remove DI control module, then press adapter onto DI control module and pull lead upwards through slot alongside module.
   c. Press DI control module, with adapter connected, into connector in bottom of control module box, then connect measuring unit to adapter 60-pole connector.
2. Check speed signal as follows:
   a. Raise vehicle until wheels are free of ground and support, then turn ignition switch to On position.
   b. Connect voltmeter across terminals 20 (A20) and 48 (B18), then spin front wheels. Voltmeter should oscillate between 0 V and 12 V.
   c. If reading is consistently high (battery voltage) or low (0 V), check lead for short circuit or open circuit.
   d. If no fault is detected, replace MFI control module.

CODES 3-1-4 & 3-2-4: CAMSHAFT POSITION SENSOR (CMP) CHECK

The function of the sensor is to enable the control module to determine which cylinder requires fuel and ignition. Since the camshaft performs two revolutions per crankshaft revolution, the signal is high during one revolution and low during the next. DTC 3-1-4 will be recorded if the signal (which is compared with the VSS signal) remains continuously high or low during six crankshaft revolutions. If this occurs, the engine will neither start nor stop.

DTC 3-2-4 will be recorded if the DI control module does not detect a CMP signal reversal within a short period. However, the engine will continue to run without problems if the signal is again detected.

1. Connect measuring unit 981 3190 and adapter 981 3195 as follows:
   a. Disconnect battery ground cable,

then remove control module cover.

b. Remove DI control module, then press adapter onto DI control module and pull lead upwards through slot alongside module.

c. Press DI control module, with adapter connected, into connector in bottom of control module box, then connect measuring unit to adapter 60-pole connector.

2. Measure CMP signal as follows:
   a. Connect voltmeter across terminals four (A4) and 20 (A20), then run starter motor. Voltmeter should oscillate between 0.1 and five V.
   b. If reading is incorrect, measure at CMP connector.
   c. If signal is still absent or faulty, check CMP ground and supply.
3. Check CMP ground connection as follows:
   a. Connect ohmmeter between terminals 15(A15) and 20 (A20). Ohmmeter should read approximately 0 ohms.
   b. If reading is incorrect, repeat test with new DI control module.
4. Check CMP supply as follows:
   a. Connect voltmeter across terminals 14 (A14) and 20 (A20), then turn ignition switch to On position. Reading should be approximately 10 V.
   b. If supply and ground connections are satisfactory, but signal is still absent, measure at CMP connector.
   c. If sensor supply and ground connections are satisfactory, but signal is still absent, replace CMP.
5. Check CMP signal in diagnostic test mode two as follows:
   a. Disconnect VSS connector to prevent it from displaying trouble code in diagnostic test mode two, then activate diagnostic test mode 2.
   b. Start engine, code 3-4-2 should be displayed.
   c. If code is not displayed, repeat test with new DI control module.

* = Emission warning lamp
1-1-1 No fault detected by diagnostic system
*1-1-2 Control module fault
1-2-3 Engine temperature signal from fuel system absent or faulty
1-3-1 Vehicle speed sensor (VSS) signal absent
*1-4-3 Front knock sensor signal absent or faulty
*1-4-4 Load signal from MFI absent or faulty
2-1-4 Vehicle speed sensor (VSS) signal intermittent
3-1-1 Speedometer signal absent or faulty
3-1-4 Camshaft position sensor (CMP) signal absent or faulty
3-2-4 Camshaft signal intermittent
*4-1-1 Throttle switch signal from MFI absent or faulty
4-3-2 High temperature warning (T> 85°C) in control module box
*4-3-3 Rear knock sensor signal absent or faulty
*5-1-3 High temperature warning (T> 95°C) in control module box

VV1119100015000X

Fig. 3 Diagnostic trouble code (DTC) identification

CODE 4-1-1: THROTTLE SWITCH CHECK

The purpose of the throttle switch is to indicate the throttle opening from fully closed to wide open. The signal is also used to switch out the A/C system at full load for a maximum of 15 seconds. The DI control module will interpret a low (less than 0.25 V) or a high (over 4.75 V) throttle switch signal during 50 successive ignitions as a fault, and will record the DTC. The control module will assume a substitute value equivalent to a throttle opening of approximately 68.°

1. Check for DTCs in other systems as follows:
   a. Activate MFI system diagnostic test mode one (socket A2) and check whether the throttle switch DTC is recorded.
   b. If code is displayed, correct this fault first.
   c. If fault is not in MFI system, check lead between DI and MFI control modules.
2. Connect measuring unit tool No. 981 3190 and adapter tool No. 981 3195, or equivalents, as follows:
   a. Disconnect battery ground cable, then remove control module cover.
   b. Remove DI control module, then press adapter onto DI control module and pull lead upwards through slot alongside module.
   c. Press DI control module, with adapter connected, into connector in bottom of control module box, then connect measuring unit to adapter 60-pole connector.
3. Check lead between DI and MFI control modules as follows:
   a. Connect ohmmeter between terminals 50 (B20) and 20 (A20). Ohmmeter should indicate extremely high or infinite resistance. Reading of 0 ohm indicates that lead is short circuited to ground.
   b. Connect voltmeter across terminals 50 (B20) and 20 (A20), then turn ignition switch to On position. If voltmeter indicates battery voltage, lead is short circuited to supply.
   c. If values are satisfactory, but signal is still absent measure resistance between DI control module terminal 50 (B20) and MFI control module terminal 50 (B20). If lead is satisfactory but signal is still absent, repeat test with new MFI control module.
4. Activate diagnostic test mode two and recheck signal from MFI system. If DTC 3-4-4 is not displayed, repeat test with new DI control module.
5. Clear DTCs, if any, in other systems, then check diagnostic test mode one for automatic transmission to determine if throttle switch DTC is displayed.

CODES 4-3-2 & 5-1-3: CHECKING TEMPERATURE IN CONTROL MODULE BOX

To prevent damage to the control modules in the control module box, the DI control module is equipped with a high-temperature warning sensor. DTC 4-3-2 is recorded if the temperature in the box exceeds 185°F (85°C) for more than 18 seconds. DTC 5-1-3 is recorded if the temperature continues to rise and exceeds 203°F (95°C) for more than 18 seconds.

The DI control module continuously monitors the temperature sensor. The occurrence of DTC 1-1-2 (internal DI control module fault) may be due to a temperature sensor fault. If this DTC is not displayed, check the control module box air supply and filter, and check that the cooling fan operates in diagnostic test mode 3.

If no fault is identified when DTC 5-1-3 is recorded, a cooling fan should be installed in the control module box.

Clearing Diagnostic Trouble Codes

SYSTEM MEMORY

The diagnostic system memory should be cleared when all ignition system diagnostic trouble codes have been displayed at least once and faults have been corrected.

1. Turn ignition switch to On position, then press test button for more than 5 seconds.
2. Release button. LED should light after 3 seconds.
3. Press button again for more than 5 seconds.
4. Release button. LED should go out.

CLEARED DIAGNOSTIC TROUBLE CODE VERIFICATION

1. Press button once for more than 1 second but not more than 3 seconds.
2. If code 1-1-1 is displayed, diagnostic trouble codes have been cleared.

Fuel Injection

Motronic 4.3 & 4.4 Drivetrain Control System

NOTE: If Unsure Of The System Used On The Vehicle Being Serviced, Refer To "The Engine Systems Identification Chart." Further Assistance For The Proper Use Of Information Contained In This Section Can Also Be Found In The Front Of This Tabbed Section Under "How To Use This Manual."

NOTE: On Air Bag Equipped Models, Refer To "Air Bag System Precautions" Located In The Front Of This Manual For System Disarming & Arming Procedures.

NOTE: Refer To "Computer Relearn Procedures" Located In The Front Of This Manual When Battery Power To The Computer Has Been Interrupted.

NOTE: Prior To Performing Any Service Operations Listed In This Section, Consult The "Technical Service Bulletins" Section For Related Information.

NOTE: "Electrical Symbol & Wire Color Code Identification" Located In The Front Of This Manual May Be Used As An Aid When Using Wiring Circuits Found In This Section.

INDEX

	Page No.
Description	18-19
Diagnosis & Testing	18-22
Accessing Diagnostic Trouble Codes	18-22
Clearing Diagnostic Trouble Codes	18-53
Component Tests	18-53
Fuel Pressure	18-53
Diagnostic Tests	18-23
Code P0101: Mass Air Flow Sensor Faulty Signal	18-23
Code P0102: Mass Air Flow Sensor Low Input	18-24
Code P0103: Mass Air Flow Sensor High Input	18-25
Code P0106: Atmospheric Pressure Sensor Signal Sporadic	18-25
Code P0107: Atmospheric Pressure Sensor Signal Low	18-25
Code P0108: Atmospheric Pressure Sensor Signal High	18-34
Code P0111: Outside Temperature Sensor Signal Sporadic	18-34
Code P0112: Outside Temperature Sensor Signal Low	18-34
Code P0113: Outside Temperature Sensor Signal High	18-34
Code P0117: Engine Coolant Temperature Sensor Low Input	18-35
Code P0118: Engine Coolant Temperature Sensor High Input	18-35
Code P0122: Throttle Position Sensor Low Input	18-35
Code P0123: Throttle Position Sensor High Input	18-35
Code P0130: Front Heated Oxygen Sensor Signal	18-36
Code P0131: Front Heated Oxygen Sensor Low Input	18-36
Code P0132: Front Heated Oxygen Sensor High Input	18-36
Code P0133: Front Heated Oxygen Sensor Slow Input	18-37
Code P0135: Front Heated Oxygen Sensor Preheating	18-37
Code P0136: Rear Heated Oxygen Sensor Signal	18-37
Code P0137: Rear Heated Oxygen Sensor Low Input	18-38
Code P0138: Rear Heated Oxygen Sensor High Input	18-38
Code P0140: Rear Heated Oxygen Sensor Control	18-38
Code P0141: Rear Heated Oxygen Sensor Preheating	18-39
Code P0171: Long Term Fuel Trim Low Input	18-39
Code P0172: Long Term Fuel Trim High Input	18-40
Code P0244: Boost Pressure Control	18-40
Code P0244: Turbocharger Control Valve Signal Missing	18-41
Code P0245: Turbocharger Control Valve Signal Low	18-41
Code P0246: Turbocharger	

Page No.

Control Valve Signal High ... 18-41
Code P0335: Engine Speed Sensor Signal ... 18-43
Code P0340: Camshaft Position Sensor Signal ... 18-43
Code P0410: Pulsed Secondary Air Injection System ... 18-43
Code P0412: Pulsed Secondary Air Injection Missing Signal ... 18-43
Code P0422: Three Way Catalytic Converter Low Input ... 18-44
Code P0440: EVAP Canister Purge Valve Leakage ... 18-44
Code P0442: Fuel Tank System Leak ... 18-45
Code P0443: EVAP Canister Purge Valve Signal ... 18-46
Code P0446: EVAP Canister Shutoff Valve Missing Signal ... 18-46
Code P0451: Fuel Tank Pressure Sensor Signal Sporadic ... 18-46
Code P0452: Fuel Tank Pressure Sensor Signal Low ... 18-47
Code P0453: Fuel Tank Pressure Sensor Signal High ... 18-48
Code P0455: Fuel Tank System Large Leak ... 18-48
Code P0500: Speedometer Signal ... 18-50
Code P0505: Adaptive Idle Air Trim Upper/Lower Limit ... 18-50
Code P0531: Air Conditioning Pressure Sensor Signal Faulty ... 18-51
Code P0532: Air Conditioning Pressure Sensor Signal Low ... 18-51
Code P0533: Air Conditioning Pressure Sensor Signal High ... 18-51

Page No.

Code P0560: Battery Voltage . 18-51
Code P0605: ECM Permanent Fault ... 18-51
Code P1307: Accelerometer Low Input ... 18-51
Code P1308: Accelerometer High Input ... 18-52
Code P1505: Idle Air Control Valve Opening Low Input ... 18-52
Code P1506: Idle Air Control Valve Opening High Input ... 18-52
Code P1507: Idle Air Control Valve Closing Low Input ... 18-52
Code P1508: Idle Air Control Valve Closing High Input ... 18-52
Code P1603: Ignition Discharge Module Group C. . 18-52
Code P1604: Ignition Discharge Module Group D. . 18-52
Code P1605: Ignition Discharge Module Group E. . 18-53
Code P1617: AW 50-42 Transmission Control Module Low Input ... 18-53
Code P1618: AW 50-42 Transmission Control Module High Input ... 18-53
Code P1619: Engine Cooling Fan Missing Signal ... 18-53
Code P1620: Engine Cooling Fan High Input ... 18-53
Codes P0115 & P0116: Engine Coolant Temperature Sensor Signal ... 18-35
Codes P0201, P0202, P0203, P0204 & P0205: Injector Low/High Input ... 18-40
Codes P0300, P0301, P0302, P0303, P0304 & P0305: Misfiring Cylinder ... 18-41
Codes P0325 & P0330: Knock Sensor Signal ... 18-42
Codes P0413 & P0414: Pulsed Secondary Air Injection High/Low Input ... 18-44
Codes P0444 & P0445: EVAP Canister Purge Valve

Page No.

High/Low Input ... 18-46
Codes P0447: EVAP Canister Shutoff Signal Low ... 18-46
Codes P0448: EVAP Canister Shutoff Signal High ... 18-46
Codes P1405 & P1406: Temperature Warning ... 18-52
Diagnostic Trouble Code Interpretation ... 18-23
Wiring Diagrams & ECM Pin Identification ... 18-23

Precautions ... 18-19
Air Bag Systems ... 18-19
Battery Ground Cable ... 18-19
ECM Power ... 18-19
Power Supply Interruption ... 18-19

Sensor & Fuel Injector Specifications ... 18-18

System Service ... 18-53
Adjustments ... 18-54
Throttle Pulley & Harness ... 18-54
Component Replacement ... 18-53
Engine Control Module (ECM) Replacement ... 18-54
Fuel Pressure Regulator ... 18-54
Injectors ... 18-53
Knock Sensor ... 18-54
Throttle Body ... 18-53

Troubleshooting ... 18-19
Engine Cooling Fan Not Operating Correctly ... 18-22
Engine Fails To Start ... 18-20
Engine Is Difficult To Start ... 18-20
Engine Speed Dips When A/C Is Turned On ... 18-21
Engine Speed Dips When Gear Is Selected (Automatic Transaxle) ... 18-21
High Idle Speed ... 18-21
Low Idle Speed ... 18-21
Poor Acceleration, Lack Of Power ... 18-21
Severe Engine Shudder After Engine Braking ... 18-22
Severe Engine Shudder During Acceleration ... 18-22
Uneven Idling ... 18-20

SENSOR & FUEL INJECTOR SPECIFICATIONS

Sensor	Temperature, °F	Resistance, Ohms
C70, S70 & V70		
Coolant Temperature Sensor	32	7300
	68	2800
	104	1200
	176	300
	212	150
EGR Controller	68	75–95
Engine Speed	68	260–340
EVAP Valve	68	26
Fuel Pump	—	.9
Heated Oxygen Sensor (H02S)	68	3
	662 & Above	13
IAC Valve	68	10–14
IAT Sensor	68	2500
Injectors	68	⑥
Main Relay	68	80–130
Mass Air Flow Sensor	—	110②
Outside Temperature Sensor	14	2190–2270
	32	1390–1420
	50	890–930
	68	590–630
	86	400–430
	104	270–300
Oxygen Sensor	68	1.5–2.5
	660	6–10
Rotor	—	900–1300

Continued

SENSOR & FUEL INJECTOR SPECIFICATIONS—Continued

Sensor	Temperature, °F	Resistance, Ohms
C70, S70 & V70		
Throttle Position Sensor	—	⑦
Turbocharger Control Valve	68	22.4–25.4
S90 & V90		
Canister Purge Valve	—	26
Coolant Temperature Sensor	32	7300
	68	2800
	104	1200
	176	300
	212	150
Engine Speed & Position Sensor	—	240–400
Fuel Pump	—	1
Fuel Pump Relay	—	100
Heated Oxygen Sensor (H02S)	68	3
	662 & Above	13
IAC Valve	68	10–14①
Ignition Coil	—	④
Ignition Coil Relay	—	85
Injectors	68	15.6–16.4
Main Relay	68	80③
Mass Air Flow Sensor	—	2.5–4.0⑤
Oxygen Sensor	68	1.5–2.5
	660	6–10
Pulsed Secondary Air Injection System	—	30–33
Pulsed Secondary Air Injection System Relay	—	85
Throttle Position Sensor	—	2600

① — Between terminals No. 1 & 2 or 2 & 3.
② — Between terminals No. 1 & 4.
③ — Measured between terminals 85 & 86.
④ — Primary winding between terminal No. 15 & 1, .5–1.5 ohms; secondary coil between connector No. 15 and HT, 8000–9000 ohms.
⑤ — Between connectors No. 2 & 3.
⑥ — 700, 900, S90 & V90 models, 15–17 ohms; 850, C70, S70 & V70 models w/5234 engine, 15.55–16.25 ohms, w/5252 engine, 14–18 ohms.
⑦ — Between terminals 1 & 3, idling speed, 900–1100 ohms; at wide open throttle, 2300–2900 ohms.

PRECAUTIONS

Air Bag Systems

Refer to "Air Bag System Precautions" in the front of this manual for system disarming and arming procedures.

Battery Ground Cable

Prior to service, disconnect battery ground cable and isolate as required.

ECM Power

The Engine Control Module (ECM) power supply must be disconnected when connecting or disconnecting the connector or measuring unit or damage will result. Disconnect battery ground cable whenever connecting or disconnecting the ECM.

Power Supply Interruption

Do not work on the vehicle until the main relay has interrupted the power supply. After turning the ignition switch to Off position this may take up to 2½ minutes after the ignition has been switched off, or more than four minutes if the car is equipped with immobilizer.

DESCRIPTION

The Motronic 4.3 and 4.4 drivetrain control system integrates the fuel injection, ignition, turbocharger, air conditioning, engine cooling fan and transaxle systems. The system control unit is equipped with adaptive Lambda control, idle control functions and a timing retardation function to eliminate knock.

TROUBLESHOOTING

Before performing the following troubleshooting procedures, inspect for the following:

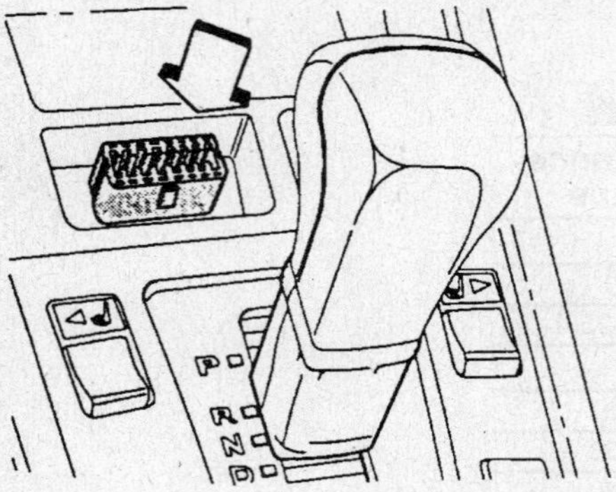

VV1029500089000X

Fig. 1 OBD II Diagnostic Link Connector (DLC) location

1. Ensure there are no DTCs stored which would give a direct diagnostic step.
2. Ensure problem is not intermittent.

Engine Fails To Start

1. Ensure the starter motor functions correctly.
2. Ensure the camshaft belt is in good condition.
3. Check fuel pump as follows:
   a. Check for open circuit in fuel pump relay ground, signal and/or power supply wiring.
   b. Check for short circuit in fuel pump relay signal and/or power supply wiring.
   c. Check for open or short in wiring to fuel pump from fuel pump relay.
   d. Check for high resistance in connectors for fuel pump circuit.
   e. Check for defective fuel pump or relay.
4. Check RPM sensor as follows:
   a. Check for open circuit in RPM sensor ground and/or signal wiring.
   b. Check for short circuit in RPM sensor signal wiring.
   c. Check for high resistance in connectors for RPM sensor circuit.
   d. Check for defective RPM sensor.
5. Check Camshaft Position (CMP) Sensor as follows:
   a. Check for open circuit in CMP sensor ground, voltage and/or signal wiring.
   b. Check for short circuit in CMP sensor voltage and/or signal wiring.
   c. Check for high resistance in connectors for CMP sensor circuit.
   d. Check for defective CMP sensor.
6. Check ignition coil power stage as follows:
   a. Check for open circuit in power stage ground, voltage and/or signal wiring.
   b. Check for short circuit in power stage voltage and/or signal wiring.
   c. Check for high resistance in connectors for Mass Air Flow (MAF) circuit.
   d. Check for defective MAF sensor.
7. Check MAF sensor as follows:
   a. Check for open circuit in MAF sensor ground, voltage and/or signal wiring.
   b. Check for short circuit in MAF voltage and/or signal wiring.
   c. Check for high resistance in connectors for power stage circuit.
   d. Check for defective power stage.
   e. Check for voltage flash over in power stage, coil, spark plugs, ignition leads, rotor and/or distributor cap.
8. Check Engine Coolant Temperature (ECT) sensor as follows:
   a. Check for open or short circuit in ECT sensor wiring.
   b. Check for high resistance in connectors for power stage circuit.
   c. Check for defective ECT sensor.

OBD II code	Fault text	Signal
P0100	Mass air flow (MAF) sensor, signal	
P0102	Mass air flow (MAF) sensor, signal	Low
P0103	Mass air flow (MAF) sensor, signal	High
P0115	Engine coolant temperature (ECT) sensor, signal	Missing
P0116	Engine coolant temperature (ECT) sensor, signal	
P0117	Engine coolant temperature (ECT) sensor, signal	Low
P0118	Engine coolant temperature (ECT) sensor, signal	High
P0120	Throttle position (TP) sensor, signal	
P0122	Throttle position (TP) sensor, signal	Low
P0123	Throttle position (TP) sensor, signal	High
P0130	Front heated oxygen sensor (HO2S), signal	Missing/faulty
P0131	Front heated oxygen sensor (HO2S), signal	Low
P0132	Front heated oxygen sensor (HO2S), signal	High
P0133	Front heated oxygen sensor (HO2S), too slow Rear heated oxygen sensor (HO2S), compensation	Low high Low/high
P0135	Front heated oxygen sensor (HO2S), heating	Low/high
P0136	Rear heated oxygen sensor (HO2S), signal	Missing/faulty
P0137	Rear heated oxygen sensor (HO2S), signal	Low
P0138	Rear heated oxygen sensor (HO2S), signal	High
P0140	Rear heated oxygen sensor (HO2S), control	Low/high
P0141	Rear heated oxygen sensor (HO2S), heating	Low/high
P0170	Long-term fuel trim, part load Long-term fuel trim, idling	
P0171	Long-term fuel trim, part load Long-term fuel trim, idling	Lower limit Lower limit
P0172	Long-term fuel trim, part load Long-term fuel trim, idling	Upper limit Upper limit
P0201	Injector 1	Low/high
P0202	Injector 2	Low/high
P0203	Injector 3	Low/high
P0204	Injector 4	Low/high
P0205	Injector 5	Low/high

VV1029600094010X

Fig. 2 Fuel injection DTC description & identification (Part 1 of 3). Motronic 4.4 drivetrain control system

Engine Is Difficult To Start

1. Check for high resistance in RPM sensor connections.
2. Check for defective RPM sensor.
3. Check for high resistance in Camshaft Position (CMP) sensor connections.
4. Check for defective CMP sensor.
5. Check for high resistance in Engine Coolant Temperature (ECT) sensor connections.
6. Check for defective ECT sensor.
7. Check for defective spark plugs and/or wires.
8. Check for defective distributor cap and/or rotor.
9. Check fuel system, pressure and residual pressure.
10. Check for high resistance in power stage connections.

Uneven Idling

1. Ensure the engine is at normal operating temperature.
2. Check for defective spark plugs and/or wires.
3. Check for blocked/leaking injectors.
4. Check for uneven compression.
5. Check for defective distributor cap and/or rotor.
6. Check for defective EGR valve.
7. Check for faulty sensor signals.
8. Check for moisture in spark plug wells.

OBD II code	Fault text	Signal
P0300	Misfire emission level from at least 1 cylinder. Misfire with three-way catalytic converter (TWC) damage from at least 1 cylinder	High High
P0301	Misfire emission level cylinder 1 Misfire with three-way catalytic converter (TWC) damage cylinder 1	High High
P0302	Misfire emission level cylinder 2 Misfire with three-way catalytic converter (TWC) damage cylinder 2	High High
P0303	Misfire emission level cylinder 3 Misfire with three-way catalytic converter (TWC) damage cylinder 3	High High
P0304	Misfire emission level cylinder 4 Misfire with three-way catalytic converter (TWC) damage cylinder 4	High High
P0305	Misfire emission level cylinder 5 Misfire with three-way catalytic converter (TWC) damage cylinder 5	High High
P0325	Front knock sensor (KS), signal	Faulty
P0330	Rear knock sensor (KS), signal	Faulty
P0335	Engine speed (RPM) sensor, Engine speed (RPM) sensor signal, signal sporadic	Missing Faulty
P0340	Camshaft position (CMP) sensor, signal	Faulty
P0410	Pulsed secondary air injection system (PAIR), flow fault Pulsed secondary air injection system (PAIR) pump, flow fault Pulsed secondary air injection system (PAIR) valve, leakage Pulsed secondary air injection system (PAIR) pump, signal	Low/high Low/high Low/high Low/high
P0412	Pulsed secondary air injection system (PAIR) solenoid valve, signal	Missing
P0413	Pulsed secondary air injection system (PAIR) solenoid valve, signal	High
P0414	Pulsed secondary air injection system (PAIR) solenoid valve, signal	Low
P0422	Three-way catalytic converter (TWC) efficiency	Low
P0440	Canister purge (CP) valve, leakage EVAP canister shut-off valve, flow fault	High Low
P0442	Fuel tank system, small leak	Low
P0443	Canister purge (CP) valve, signal	Missing
P0444	Canister purge (CP) valve, signal	High
P0445	Canister purge (CP) valve, signal	Low
P0446	EVAP canister shut-off valve, signal	Missing
P0447	EVAP canister shut-off valve, signal	High
P0448	EVAP canister shut-off valve, signal	Low
P0451	Fuel tank pressure sensor, signal	
P0452	Fuel tank pressure sensor, signal	Low
P0453	Fuel tank pressure sensor, signal	High
P0455	Fuel tank system, large leak	Low/high
P0500	Speedometer, signal	Faulty
P0505	Adaptive idle air trim	Upper/lower

VV1029600094020X

Fig. 2 Fuel injection DTC description & identification (Part 2 of 3). Motronic 4.4 drivetrain control system

OBD II code	Fault text	Signal
P0530	A/C pressure sensor, signal	
P0560	Battery voltage	Low/high
P0605	Fault in engine control module (ECM), memory fault	Faulty
P1307	Accelerometer, signal	Low
HO2S1=	Accelerometer, signal	High
P1326	Fault in engine control module (ECM), knock control circuit.	Short-term fuel trim test
P1327	Fault in engine control module (ECM), knock control circuit.	–
P1328	Fault in engine control module (ECM), knock control circuit.	–
P1329	Fault in engine control module (ECM), knock control circuit.	Zero test
P1401	Fault in engine coolant temperature (ECT), engine coolant temperature (ECT) sensor circuit NTC switch	Faulty
P1403	Fault in engine control module (ECM), control module box temperature sensor	Low
P1404	Fault in engine control module (ECM), control module box temperature sensor	High
P1405	Temperature warning >110°C	Missing
P1406	Temperature warning >100°C	Missing
P1505	Idle air control (IAC) valve opening, signal	Low
P1506	Idle air control (IAC) valve opening, signal	High
P1507	Idle air control (IAC) valve closing, signal	Low
P1508	Idle air control (IAC) valve closing, signal	High
P1602	Ignition discharge module (IDM) group B	High
P1604	Ignition discharge module (IDM) group D	High
P1605	Ignition discharge module (IDM) group E	High
P1617		Low
P1618	Cable fault between AW 50–42 transmission control module (TCM) and Motronic 4.4 engine control module (ECM) (MIL lights)	High
P1619	Engine cooling fan (FC) low-speed, signal	Low/missing
P1620	Engine cooling fan (FC) low-speed, signal	High
P1621	Diagnostic trouble code (DTC) in automatic transmission control module (TCM)	

VV1029600094030X

Fig. 2 Fuel injection DTC description & identification (Part 3 of 3). Motronic 4.4 drivetrain control system

9. Check for wrongly adjusted camshafts.

High Idle Speed

1. Check for throttle harness sticking.
2. Check for throttle body incorrectly adjusted.
3. Check for air leakage.
4. Check for defective Idle Air Control (IAC) valve.

Low Idle Speed

1. Ensure the engine is at normal operating temperature.
2. Check for throttle body incorrectly adjusted.
3. Check for defective Idle Air Control (IAC) valve.

Engine Speed Dips When A/C Is Turned On

1. Check for open in A/C compressor signal wire.
2. Check for defective IAC valve.
3. Check for open in A/C relay signal wire.

Engine Speed Dips When Gear Is Selected (Automatic Transaxle)

1. Ensure the engine is at normal operating temperature.
2. Check for short or open in AW-50 Transaxle Control Module (TCM) signal wire.
3. Check for defective IAC valve.
4. Check for high resistance in signal circuit connectors.
5. Check for defective gear selector mechanism.

Poor Acceleration, Lack Of Power

1. Ensure the engine is at normal operating temperature.
2. Check for timing retarded due to engine knock.
3. Check for defective distributor rotor and/or cap.
4. Check for damaged ignition wires.
5. Check for blocked air cleaner and/or air intake.
6. Check for uneven compression.
7. Check for low fuel pressure.
8. Check for blocked exhaust system.
9. Check for faulty sensor signals.
10. **On models equipped with turbocharged engine,** check for defective turbocharger and/or wastegate valve stuck open.

OBD II code	Fault message	Signal
P0101	Mass air flow (MAF) sensor, signal	Faulty
P0102	Mass air flow (MAF) sensor, signal	Low
P0103	Mass air flow (MAF) sensor, signal	High
P0106	Atmospheric pressure sensor, signal	Sporadic
P0107	Atmospheric pressure sensor, signal	Low
P0108	Atmospheric pressure sensor, signal	High
P0111	Outside temperature sensor, signal	Sporadic
P0112	Outside temperature sensor, signal	Low
P0113	Outside temperature sensor, signal	High
P0115	Engine coolant temperature (ECT) sensor, signal	Missing
P0117	Engine coolant temperature (ECT) sensor, signal	Low
P0118	Engine coolant temperature (ECT) sensor, signal	High
P0122	Throttle position (TP) sensor, signal	Low
P0123	Throttle position (TP) sensor, signal	High
P0130	Front heated oxygen sensor (HO2S), signal	Missing/Faulty
P0131	Front heated oxygen sensor (HO2S), signal	Low
P0132	Front heated oxygen sensor (HO2S), signal	High
P0133	Front heated oxygen sensor (HO2S) slow response Rear heated oxygen sensor (HO2S), compensation	Low/High Low/High
P0135	Front heated oxygen sensor (HO2S), preheating	Low/High/Missing/Faulty
P0136	Rear heated oxygen sensor (HO2S), signal	Missing/Faulty
P0137	Rear heated oxygen sensor (HO2S), signal	Low
P0138	Rear heated oxygen sensor (HO2S), signal	High
P0140	Rear heated oxygen sensor (HO2S), control	Low/High/
P0141	Rear heated oxygen sensor (HO2S), preheating	Low/High/Missing/Faulty
P0171	Long-term fuel trim, part load Long-term fuel trim, idling	Lower limit

VV1029700101010X

Fig. 3 Fuel injection DTC description & identification (Part 1 of 4). C70, S70 & V70 w/Motronic 4.4 drivetrain control system

OBD II code	Fault message	Signal
P0172	Long-term fuel trim, part load Long-term fuel trim, idling	Upper limit
P0201	Injector 1	Missing
P0202	Injector 2	Missing
P0203	Injector 3	Missing
P0204	Injector 4	Missing
P0205	Injector 5	Missing
P0243	Turbocharger (TC) control valve, signal	Missing
P0243	Boost pressure control	
P0245	Turbocharger (TC) control valve, signal	Low
P0246	Turbocharger (TC) control valve, signal	High
P0261	Injector 1	Low
P0262	Injector 1	High
P0264	Injector 2	Low
P0265	Injector 2	High
P0267	Injector 3	Low
P0268	Injector 3	High
P0270	Injector 4	Low
P0271	Injector 4	High
P0273	Injector 5	Low
P0274	Injector 5	High
P0300	Misfire emission level from at least 1 cylinder Misfire with three-way catalytic converter (TWC) damage from at least 1 cylinder	High
P0301	Misfire emission level cylinder 1 Misfire with three-way catalytic converter damage cylinder 1	High
P0302	Misfire emission level cylinder 2 Misfire with three-way catalytic converter damage cylinder 2	High
P0303	Misfire emission level cylinder 3 Misfire with three-way catalytic converter damage cylinder 3	High
P0304	Misfire emission level cylinder 4 Misfire with three-way catalytic converter damage cylinder 4	High
P0305	Misfire emission level cylinder 5 Misfire with three-way catalytic converter damage cylinder 5	High
P0325	Front knock sensor (KS), signal	Faulty
P0330	Rear knock sensor (KS), signal	Faulty
P0340	Camshaft position (CMP) sensor, signal	Faulty

VV1029700101020X

Fig. 3 Fuel injection DTC description & identification (Part 2 of 4). C70, S70 & V70 w/Motronic 4.4 drivetrain control system

Severe Engine Shudder After Engine Braking

1. **On models less turbocharged engine,** check the fuel pump and relay two stage system.
2. **On all models,** check throttle body and/or throttle switch adjustment.

Severe Engine Shudder During Acceleration

1. **On models less turbocharged engine,** check the fuel pump and relay two stage system.
2. **On all models,** check condition of high tension spark system.
3. Check for moisture in spark plug wells.
4. Check for high resistance in the Mass Air Flow (MAF) sensor system.

Engine Cooling Fan Not Operating Correctly

1. Ensure the engine is at normal operating temperature.
2. Fan runs at constant low speed:
   a. Check for low speed signal wire from relay to ECU shorted to ground.
   b. Check for defective fan control relay.
3. Fan runs at constant high speed:
   a. Check for high speed signal wire from relay to ECU shorted to ground.
   b. Check for defective fan control relay.
4. Fan will not run at low speed:
   a. Check for low speed signal wire from relay to ECU open.
   b. Check for defective fan control relay and/or fan motor.
5. Fan will not run at high speed:
   a. Check for high speed signal wire from relay to ECU open.
   b. Check for defective fan control relay and/or fan motor.
6. Fan will not run at high or low speed:
   a. Check for open power supply and ground wires to fan motor.
   b. Check for defective fan control relay and/or fan motor.

DIAGNOSIS & TESTING

Accessing Diagnostic Trouble Codes

Connect a suitable scan tool to OBD II connector in center console and follow

OBD II code	Fault message	Signal
P0410	Pulsed secondary air injection system (PAIR), flow fault Pulsed secondary air injection system (PAIR) pump, flow fault Pulsed secondary air injection system (PAIR) valve, leakage Pulsed secondary air injection system (PAIR) pump, signal	Low/High
P0413	Pulsed secondary air injection system (PAIR) solenoid valve, signal	Missing
P0414	Pulsed secondary air injection system (PAIR) solenoid valve, signal	Low/High
P0422	Three-way catalytic converter (TWC) efficiency	Low
P0440	Canister purge (CP) valve leakage EVAP canister shut-off valve flow fault.	
P0442	Fuel tank system, small leak	Low
P0443	Canister purge (CP) valve, signal	Missing
P0444	Canister purge (CP) valve, signal	High
P0445	Canister purge (CP) valve, signal	Low
P0446	EVAP canister shut-off valve, signal	Missing
P0447	EVAP canister shut-off valve, signal	Missing
P0448	EVAP canister shut-off valve, signal	Low/High
P0453	Fuel tank pressure sensor	High
P0455	Fuel tank system, large leak	
P0500	Speedometer, signal	Faulty
P0505	Adaptive idle air trim	Upper/lower
P0531	Air conditioning (A/C) pressure sensor, signal	Faulty
P0532	Air conditioning (A/C) pressure sensor, signal	Low
P0533	Air conditioning (A/C) pressure sensor, signal	High
P0535	Engine speed (RPM) sensor, signal	Missing Sporadic
P0562	Battery voltage	Low
P0563	Battery voltage	High
P0605	Fault in engine control module (ECM), memory fault	Faulty
P1307	Accelerometer, signal	Low
P1308	Accelerometer, signal	High
P1326	Fault in engine control module (ECM), knock control circuit.	Short-term fuel trim test
P1329	Fault in engine control module (ECM), knock control circuit.	Zero test
P1401	Fault in engine control module (ECM), engine coolant temperature (ECT) sensor circuit NTC switching	Faulty
P1403	Fault in engine control module (ECM), control module box temperature sensor	Low
P1404	Fault in engine control module (ECM), control module box temperature sensor	High
P1405	Temperature warning >110°C (230°F)	Missing

VV1029700101030X

Fig. 3 Fuel injection DTC description & identification (Part 3 of 4). C70, S70 & V70 w/Motronic 4.4 drivetrain control system

OBD II code	Fault message	Signal
P1406	Temperature warning >100°C (212°F)	Missing
P1505	Idle air control (IAC) valve opening, signal	Low/missing
P1506	Idle air control (IAC) valve opening, signal	High
P1507	Idle air control (IAC) valve closing, signal	Low/missing
P1508	Idle air control (IAC) valve closing, signal	High
P1604	Ignition discharge module (IDM) group D	High
P1605	Ignition discharge module (IDM) group E	High
P1617	Cable fault between AW 50–42 transmission control module (TCM) and Motronic 4.4 engine control module (ECM) (lamp lights)	Low/Missing/ Faulty
P1618	Cable fault between AW 50–42 transmission control module (TCM) and Motronic 4.4 engine control module (ECM) (lamp lights)	High
P1619	Engine cooling fan (FC) low-speed, signal	Low/Missing
P1620	Engine cooling fan (FC) low-speed, signal	High
P1621	Diagnostic trouble code (DTC) in automatic transmission control module (TCM)	

VV1029700101040X

Fig. 3 Fuel injection DTC description & identification (Part 4 of 4). C70, S70 & V70 w/Motronic 4.4 drivetrain control system

scan tool manufacturer's instructions to access Diagnostic Trouble Codes (DTCs), **Fig. 1.**

Diagnostic Trouble Code Interpretation

Refer to **Figs. 2 through 4,** for Diagnostic Trouble Code (DTC) description and identification.

Wiring Diagrams & ECM Pin Identification

Refer to **Figs. 5 through 8,** for wiring diagrams and component locations.

Refer to **Figs. 9 and 10,** for pin identification and to **Figs. 11 through 14,** for signal specifications.

Diagnostic Tests

Refer to "Precautions" before performing any tests.

CODE P0101: MASS AIR FLOW SENSOR FAULTY SIGNAL

1. Turn ignition switch to On position and connect suitable scan tool. Read throttle position sensor values. At closed throttle, reading should be .2–.6 volts. At wide open throttle, reading should be 3.8–4.6 volts. If readings are as indicated, proceed to next step. If readings are not as indicated, proceed to step 3.
2. With ignition switch in On position, read throttle position sensor values while throttle slowly opens from closed to wide open. If signal does not follow throttle position or has interference, replace throttle position sensor. If signal follows throttle position without interference, proceed to step 7.
3. With ignition switch in Off position, inspect throttle position sensor and Engine Control Module (ECM) connectors for contact resistance and oxidation. Connect throttle position sensor and ECM connectors and turn ignition switch to On position. Read throttle position sensor values. At closed throttle, read should be .2–.6 volts. At wide open throttle, reading should be 3.8–4.6 volts. If readings are as indicated, condition was caused by loose throttle position sensor and/or ECM connections. If readings are not as indicated, proceed to next step.
4. With ignition switch in Off position, disconnect throttle position sensor. Connect ohmmeter between throttle position sensor connector terminal No. 1 and ground. If reading is zero ohms, proceed to next step. If reading is not zero ohms, inspect harness between throttle position sensor terminal No. 1 and ECM No. A18 for contact resistance and oxidation, and repair as necessary.
5. With ignition switch in On position and throttle position sensor disconnected, connect voltmeter between throttle position sensor connector terminal No. 3 and ground. If reading is 5–6 volts, proceed to next step. If reading is not 5–6 volts, inspect harness between throttle position sensor terminal No. 3 and ECM No. A16 for contact resistance and oxidation and repair as necessary.
6. With ignition switch in Off position, disconnect throttle position sensor. Connect ohmmeter between throttle position sensor terminal No. 2 and ground. If reading is .4–.8 ohms, replace throttle position sensor. If reading is not .4–.8 ohms, inspect harness between throttle position sensor terminal No. 3 and ECM No. A15 for contact resistance and oxidation, and repair as necessary.

OBD II code	Fault text	Signal
P0100	Mass air flow (MAF) sensor, signal	
P0102	Mass air flow (MAF) sensor, signal	Low
P0103	Mass air flow (MAF) sensor, signal	High
P0115	Engine coolant temperature (ECT) sensor, signal	Missing
P0116	Engine coolant temperature (ECT) sensor, signal	
P0117	Engine coolant temperature (ECT) sensor, signal	Low
P0118	Engine coolant temperature (ECT) sensor, signal	High
P0120	Throttle position (TP) sensor, signal	
P0122	Throttle position (TP) sensor, signal	Low
P0123	Throttle position (TP) sensor, signal	High
P0130	Front heated oxygen sensor (HO2S), signal	Missing Faulty
P0131	Front heated oxygen sensor (HO2S), signal	Low
P0132	Front heated oxygen sensor (HO2S), signal	High
P0133	Front heated oxygen sensor (HO2S) slow response Rear heated oxygen sensor (HO2S), compensation	Low/high Low/high
P0135	Front heated oxygen sensor (HO2S), preheating	Low/high
P0136	Rear heated oxygen sensor (HO2S), signal	Missing/ Faulty
P0137	Rear heated oxygen sensor (HO2S), signal	Low
P0138	Rear heated oxygen sensor (HO2S), signal	High
P0140	Rear heated oxygen sensor (HO2S), control	Low/high
P0141	Rear heated oxygen sensor (HO2S), preheating	Low/high
P0170	Long term fuel trim, part load	
P0171	Long term fuel trim, part load Long term fuel trim, idling	Lower limit Lower limit
P0172	Long term fuel trim, part load Long term fuel trim, idling	Upper limit Upper limit
P0201	Injector 1	Low/high
P0202	Injector 2	Low/high
P0203	Injector 3	Low/high
P0204	Injector 4	Low/high
P0205	Injector 5	Low/high
P0206	Injector 6	Low/high
P0300	Misfire emission level from at least 1 cylinder. Misfire with catalytic converter damage from at 1 cylinder	High High
P0301	Misfire emission level cylinder 1 Misfire with catalytic converter damage cylinder 1	High High
P0302	Misfire emission level cylinder 2 Misfire with catalytic converter damage cylinder 2	High High
P0303	Misfire emission level cylinder 3 Misfire with catalytic converter damage cylinder 3	High High
P0304	Misfire emission level cylinder 4 Misfire with catalytic converter damage cylinder 4	High High
P0305	Misfire emission level cylinder 5 Misfire with catalytic converter damage cylinder 5	High High

VV1029600095010X

Fig. 4 Fuel injection DTC description & identification (Part 1 of 2). 960, S90 & V90

OBD II code	Fault text	Signal
P0306	Misfire emission level cylinder 6 Misfire with catalytic converter damage cylinder 6	High High
P0325	Front knock sensor (KS), signal	Faulty
P0330	Rear knock sensor (KS), signal	Faulty
P0340	Camshaft position (CMP) sensor, signal	Faulty
P0410	Pulsed secondary air injection system (PAIR), flow fault Pulsed secondary air injection system (PAIR) pump, flow fault Pulsed secondary air injection system (PAIR) valve, leakage Pulsed secondary air injection system (PAIR) pump, signal	Low/high Low/high Low/high Low/high
P0412	Solenoid pulsed secondary air injection system (PAIR), signal	Missing
P0413	Solenoid pulsed secondary air injection system (PAIR), signal	High
P0414	Solenoid pulsed secondary air injection system (PAIR), signal	Low
P0422	Catalytic converter efficiency	Low
P0440	EVAP valve, leakage	High
P0443	EVAP valve, signal	Missing
P0444	EVAP valve, signal	Low
P0445	EVAP valve, signal	High
P0500	Speedometer signal	Faulty
P0505	Idle air trim	Upper/lower
P0530	A/C pressure sensor, signal	
P0535	Speed sensor, signal	Missing Faulty
P0560	Battery voltage	Low/high
P0605	Engine control module (ECM) fault, memory fault	Faulty
P1307	Acceleration sensor, signal	Low
P1308	Acceleration sensor, signal	High
P1326	Engine control module (ECM) fault, knock control circuit	Integrator test
P1327	Engine control module (ECM) fault, knock control circuit	-
P1328	Engine control module (ECM) fault, knock control circuit	-
P1329	Engine control module (ECM) fault, knock control circuit	Zero test
P1401	Engine control module (ECM) fault, engine coolant temperature sensor circuit NTC switching	Faulty
P1505	Idle air valve opening	Low
P1506	Idle air valve opening	High
P1507	Idle air valve closing	Low
P1508	Idle air valve closing	High
P1604	Ignition discharge module (IDM) group D	High
P1605	Ignition discharge module (IDM) group E	High
P1617	Cable fault between AW 30-40/43 and Motronic 4.4 (MIL lights)	Low
P1618	Cable fault between AW 30-40/43 and Motronic 4.4 (MIL lights)	High
P1619	Engine coolant fan (FC), low-speed	Low/missing
P1620	Engine coolant fan (FC), Low-speed	High
P1621	MIL request from another ECU	

VV1029600095020X

Fig. 4 Fuel injection DTC description & identification (Part 2 of 2). 960, S90 & V90

7. Inspect for intake system air leaks. If there is a leak, repair as necessary. If there is no leak, proceed to next step.
8. Turn ignition switch to Off position and disconnect MAF sensor. Connect ohmmeter between MAF sensor connector terminal No. 1 and ground. If reading is zero ohms, proceed to step 10. If reading is not zero ohms, proceed to next step.
9. With ignition switch in Off position, disconnect MAF sensor. Inspect connector for contact resistance and oxidation, and repair as necessary. Inspect harness and connections. With control module connected, connect ohmmeter between MAF sensor connector terminal No. 1 and ground. If reading is zero ohms, proceed to next step. If reading is not zero ohms, inspect harness between MAF sensor terminal No. 1 and ECM No. A3 for contact resistance and oxidation, repair as necessary.
10. With ignition switch in Off position and MAF sensor disconnected, connect ohmmeter between MAF sensor terminal No. 2 and ground. If reading is zero ohms, proceed to step 12. If reading is not zero ohms, proceed to next step.
11. With ignition switch in Off position and MAF sensor disconnected, inspect control module connector for contact resistance and oxidation, and repair as necessary. Connect ECM. Connect ohmmeter between MAF sensor connector terminal No. 2 and ground. If reading is zero ohms, proceed to next step. If reading is not zero ohms, inspect harness between MAF sensor terminal No. 2 and ECM No. A5 for contact resistance and oxidation, and repair as necessary.
12. With ignition switch in Off position. Disconnect MAF sensor and turn ignition switch to On position. Connect voltmeter between MAF sensor connector terminal No. 3 and ground. If reading is battery voltage, proceed to next step. If reading is not battery voltage, inspect harness between MAF sensor terminal No. 3 and main relay (2/32) terminal No. 3 for contact resistance and oxidation, and repair as necessary.
13. With ignition switch in On position and MAF sensor disconnected, connect voltmeter between MAF sensor connector terminal No. 4 and ground. If reading is 0–1 volts, proceed to next step. If reading is not 0–1 volts, inspect harness between MAF sensor terminal No. 4 and ECM No. A4 for contact resistance and oxidation, and repair as necessary.
14. With ignition switch in Off position, connect MAF sensor, breakout box and control module. Connect voltmeter between terminals No. A5 and A4, turn ignition switch to On position. If reading is .1–.2 volt, inspect connectors for contact resistance and oxidation. Repair as necessary. If reading is not .1–.2 volts, replace MAF sensor.

CODE P0102: MASS AIR FLOW SENSOR LOW INPUT

1. Turn ignition switch to Off position.
2. Ensure fresh air intake is intact and properly connected. If air intake is satisfactory, proceed to next step. If air intake is not satisfactory, repair as necessary.
3. Turn ignition switch to Off position and disconnect MAF sensor electrical connector.
4. Turn ignition switch to On position and connect suitable voltmeter between MAF connector terminal No. 3 and

ground. If reading is equal to battery voltage, proceed to next step. If reading is not equal to battery voltage, repair wiring harness between terminal No. 3 and control module.

5. Turn ignition switch to Off position and wait approximately three minutes.
6. Disconnect MAF sensor, connect ohmmeter between MAF connector terminal No. 4 and ground. If resistance is 9–11 ohms, proceed to next step. If resistance is not 9–11 ohms, repair wiring harness between terminal No. 4 and control module.
7. Turn ignition switch to Off position and connect MAF sensor electrical connector.
8. Turn ignition switch to On position, connect voltmeter between MAF connector terminals No. 2 and 4. If reading is .1–.2 volts, repair fault in MAF sensor connector. If reading is not .1–.2 volts, replace MAF sensor.

CODE P0103: MASS AIR FLOW SENSOR HIGH INPUT

1. Turn ignition switch to Off position and disconnect MAF sensor, then connect a suitable ohmmeter between MAF connector terminal No. 1 and ground. If resistance is zero ohms, proceed to next step. If resistance is not zero ohms, repair or replace wiring harness as necessary.
2. Connect ohmmeter between MAF connector terminal No. 2 and ground. If resistance is zero ohms, proceed to next step. If resistance is not zero ohms, repair or replace wiring harness as necessary.
3. Connect MAF sensor connector and connect ohmmeter between MAF connector terminal No. 1 and ground. If resistance is zero ohms, proceed to next step. If resistance is not zero, repair or replace wiring harness as necessary.
4. Turn ignition switch to On position, connect voltmeter between MAF connector terminals No. 2 and No. 4. If reading is .1–.2 volts, repair fault in MAF sensor connector. If reading is not .1–.2, replace MAF sensor.

CODE P0106: ATMOSPHERIC PRESSURE SENSOR SIGNAL SPORADIC

1. Turn ignition switch to Off position. Inspect atmospheric pressure sensor lilac connector for contact resistance and oxidation, and repair as necessary.
2. Inspect Engine Control Module (ECM) connector for contact resistance and oxidation, and repair as necessary.
3. Connect sensor and ECM connectors, start engine and idle for five minutes. Access codes. If Code P0106 is stored as an intermittent, condition was caused by loose sensor and/or ECM connections. If code is stored as permanent, proceed to next step.
4. Inspect sensor and ECM connectors for loose connections, and repair as necessary.
5. Inspect harness between sensor terminal No. 1 and ECM No. B29 for intermittent open and/or short circuit, and repair as necessary.
6. Inspect harness between sensor terminal No. 3 and ECM No. B2 for intermittent open and/or short circuit, and repair as necessary.
7. Inspect harness between sensor terminal No. 2 and ECM No. B28 for intermittent open circuit, and repair as necessary.
8. Inspect harness between air conditioning pressure sensor terminal No. 3 and ECM No. B29 for short circuit, and replace as necessary.
9. Inspect harness between tank pressure sensor terminal No. 1 and ECM No. B15 for short circuit, and repair as necessary.
10. Inspect harness between accelerometer terminal No. 1 and ECM No. B1 for short circuit, and repair as necessary.
11. Install all components, start engine and idle for five minutes. Access codes. If Code P0106 is stored as an intermittent, condition has been corrected. If code is stored as permanent, proceed to next step.
12. Turn ignition switch to Off position and connect atmospheric pressure sensor. Disconnect air conditioning pressure sensor, start engine and idle for five minutes. Access codes. If Code P0106 is stored as an intermittent, replace air conditioning pressure sensor. If code is stored as permanent, proceed to next step.
13. Turn ignition switch to Off position, and connect atmospheric pressure sensor and air conditioning pressure sensor. Disconnect accelerometer, start engine and idle for five minutes. Access codes. If Code P0106 is stored as an intermittent, replace accelerometer. If code is stored as permanent, proceed to next step.
14. Turn ignition switch to Off position, and connect atmospheric pressure sensor, air conditioning pressure sensor and accelerometer. Disconnect fuel tank pressure sensor, start engine and idle for five minutes. Access codes. If Code P0106 is stored as an intermittent, replace fuel tank pressure sensor. If code is stored as permanent, replace atmospheric pressure sensor.

CODE P0107: ATMOSPHERIC PRESSURE SENSOR SIGNAL LOW

1. Turn ignition switch to Off position and disconnect atmospheric pressure sensor. Turn ignition to On position and connect voltmeter between sensor connector terminal No. 1 and ground. If reading is five volts, proceed to next step. If reading is not five volts, proceed to step 4.
2. Turn ignition switch to Off position. With atmospheric pressure sensor disconnected, connect ohmmeter between sensor connect No. 3 and ground. If reading is more than .2 Mohms, proceed to next step. If reading is .2 Mohms or less, inspect harness between sensor terminal No. 3 and Engine Control Module (ECM) No. B22 for short circuit, and repair as necessary.
3. With ignition switch in Off position, connect atmospheric pressure sensor. Start engine and idle. Access scrolling values. If atmospheric pressure sensor signal value is approximately 4.5 volts at sea level, condition was caused by loose sensor connections. Inspect connector for contact resistance and oxidation, and repair as necessary. If value is not approximately 4.5 volts, replace atmospheric pressure sensor.
4. Turn ignition switch to Off position. With atmospheric pressure sensor disconnected, connect ohmmeter between sensor connect No. 1 and ground. If reading is 200–1500 ohms, proceed to next step. If reading is not 200–1500 ohms, proceed to step 9.
5. With ignition switch in Off position and atmospheric pressure sensor disconnected, disconnect accelerometer. Connect ohmmeter between sensor connect No. 1 and ground. If reading is 200–1500 ohms, replace accelerometer. If reading is not 200–1500 ohms, proceed to next step.
6. With ignition switch in Off position, and atmospheric pressure sensor and accelerometer disconnected, disconnect fuel tank pressure sensor. Connect ohmmeter between sensor connect No. 1 and ground. If reading is 200–1500 ohms, replace fuel tank pressure sensor. If reading is not 200–1500 ohms, proceed to next step.
7. With ignition switch in Off position, and atmospheric pressure sensor, accelerometer and fuel tank pressure sensor disconnected, disconnect air conditioning pressure sensor. Connect ohmmeter between sensor connect No. 1 and ground. If reading is 200–1500 ohms, replace air conditioning pressure sensor. If reading is not 200–1500 ohms, proceed to next step.
8. Inspect harness between air conditioning pressure sensor terminal No. 3 and ECM No. B29 for short circuit, and replace as necessary. Inspect harness between tank pressure sensor terminal No. 1 and ECM No. B15 for short circuit, and replace as necessary. Inspect harness between accelerometer terminal No. 1 and ECM No. B1 for short circuit, and replace as necessary. Inspect harness between atmospheric pressure sensor terminal No. 1 and ECM No. B29 for short circuit, and replace as necessary.
9. With ignition switch in Off position and atmospheric pressure sensor disconnected, inspect ECM connector for contact resistance and oxidation. Repair as necessary. Connect ECM connector, and ohmmeter between sensor connector No. 1 and ground. If reading is 200–1500 ohms, condition was caused by loose ECM connector. If reading is not 200–1500 ohms, inspect harness between sensor terminal No. 31 and ECM No. B29 for open circuit.

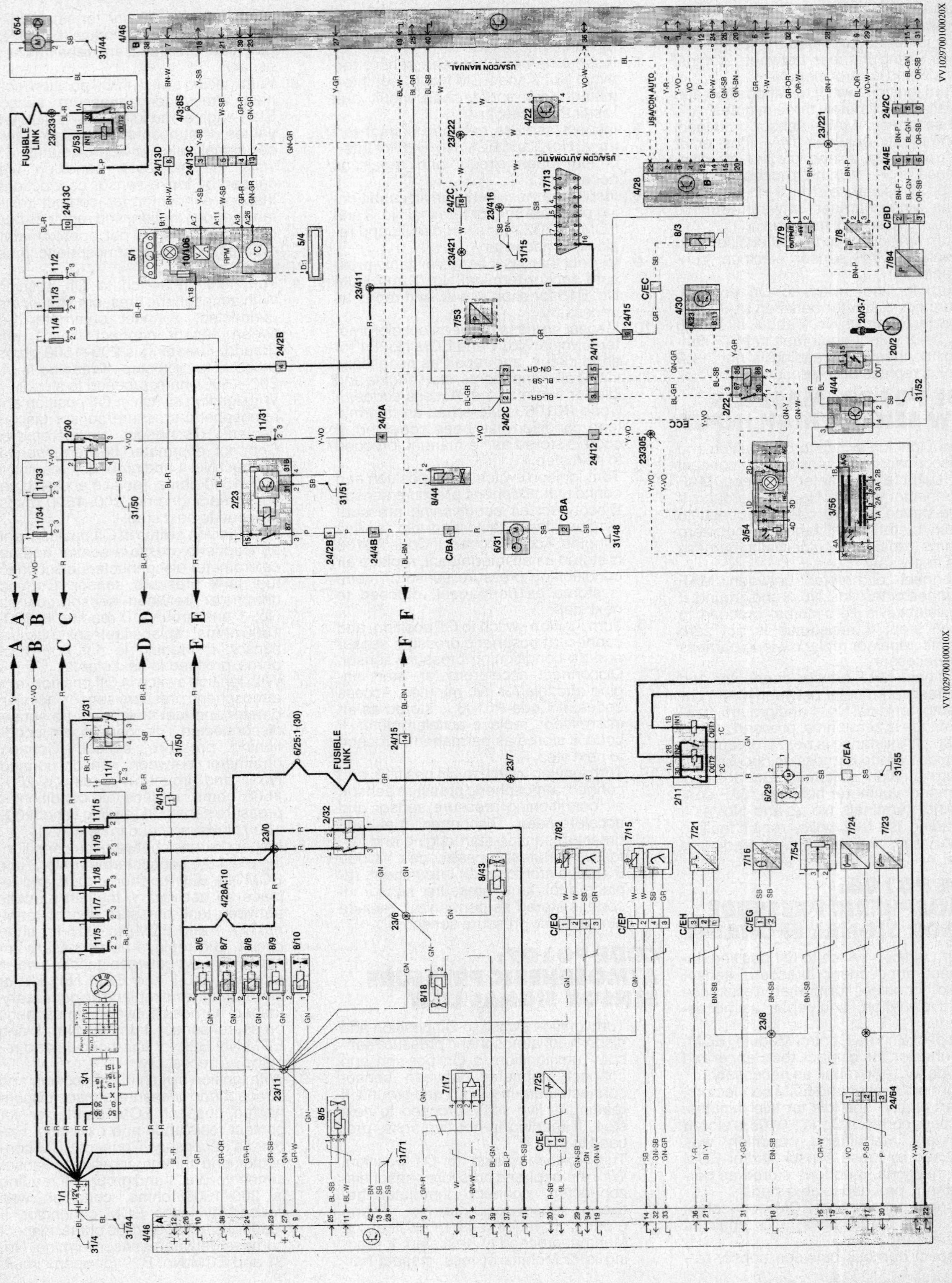

Fig. 5 Wiring diagram & component locations (Part 1 of 4). Motronic 4.4 drivetrain control

Fig. 5 Wiring diagram & component locations (Part 2 of 4). Motronic 4.4 drivetrain control

1/1	Battery
2/1	Main headlight relay with bulb failure warning sensor
2/5	Seat belt reminder/key warning relay
2/7	Central locking/delayed inner lighting relay
2/11	Engine cooling fan relay
2/14	Glow automatics relay
2/15	Relay, exhaust temperature sensor
2/22	A/C relay
2/23	Fuel pump relay
2/28	Alarm relay
2/30	Overload relay X+
2/31	Overload relay 15+
2/32	Main relay, fuel system
2/47	Relay, deadlock setting
2/53	Relay, secondary air pump
2/60	Overload relay X+
2/74	Extra heater relay
2/105	Driver door, 2-stage central locking relay
2/110	Remote control central locking/indication LED electronic immobilizer relay
3/1	Ignition switch
3/2	Light switch
3/3	Switch, turn signal/high and low beam
3/4	Controls, cruise control
3/6	Switch, hazard lights with flasher relay
3/9	Stop (brake) light switch
3/38	Contact, brake pedal
3/39	Contact, clutch pedal
3/47	Handbrake contact
3/54	REC / A/C switch
3/55	A/C panel lights
3/56	Blower fan switch
3/57	Climate control
3/58	Switch, rear fog light
3/61	Controls, trip computer
3/62	Alarm switch, bonnet
3/63	Program selector, automatic transmission
3/71	Transmission range sensor
3/72	Kick-down switch, throttle control
3/74	Lock module, front left
3/75	Lock module, front right
3/76	Lock module, rear left
3/77	Lock module, rear right
3/78	Lock module, trunk/tailgate
3/93	Seat belt lock, left front seat
3/94	Seat belt lock, right front seat
3/95	Switch, TRACS
3/98	Switch, central locking
4/3	Control module, cruise control
4/4	Rheostat
4/5	Safety circuit SRS
4/9	SRS sensor unit
4/10	Control module, EZK (DI) ignition system
4/15	DI power stage and ignition coil
4/16	ABS control module
4/22	Electronic immobilizer
4/28	Control module, AW 50-42 automatic transmission
4/29	Control module, left front seat
4/30	Control module, ECC
4/34	Voltage regulator, 8 volts
4/35	Voltage regulator, 5 volts
4/36	Combined instrument panel microprocessor
4/37	Control module, right front seat
4/44	DI power stage and ignition coil
4/45	Control module, LH-Jetronic 3.2 MFI
4/46	Engine control module
5/1	Combined instrument panel
5/2	Clock module
5/3	Outside temperature/clock module
5/4	Trip computer
6/25	Starter motor
6/26	Generator
6/29	Engine cooling fan
6/31	Fuel pump/fuel injection pump
6/33	Fuel level sensor
6/33L	Left fuel level sensor
6/33R	Right fuel level sensor
6/34	Power antenna
6/37	Central locking motor, tank cap
6/54	Secondary air pump
7/1	Bulb failure warning sensor, rear
7/4	Brake fluid level sensor
7/5	Washer fluid level sensor
7/6	Oil pressure sensor
7/8	A/C pressure sensor
7/12	ECC solar sensor and indication LED alarm/electronic immobilizer
7/15	Heated oxygen sensor (HO2S), front
7/16	Engine coolant temperature sensor ECT+
7/17	Mass air flow (MAF) sensor/mass air flow sensor
7/21	Camshaft position sensor (CMP)
7/22	Tachometer
7/23	Knock sensor (KS), rear
7/24	Knock sensor (KS), front
7/25	Pulse sensor
7/31	ABS sensor, front left
7/32	ABS sensor, front right
7/33	Speedometer
7/39	Antenna ring
7/47	PTC resistor, pre-heater
7/51	Accelerator pedal sensor
7/53	Pressostat A/C
7/54	Throttle position (TP) sensor
7/56	ABS sensor, rear left
7/57	ABS sensor, rear right
7/69	Outside temperature sensor, trip computer
7/71	Boost pressure sensor
7/73	Coolant level sensor
7/74	Oil temperature sensor, automatic transmission
7/77	Temperature sensor, intake air
7/79	Accelerometer
7/81	Pressure sensor, intake manifold
7/82	Heated oxygen sensor (HO2S), rear
7/83	High-pressure sensor A/C
7/84	Tank pressure sensor
7/85	EBD pressure sensor
7/94	Needle lift sensor
7/95	High Altitude sensor
7/100	Tilt sensor
7/101	Breaking glass sensor
7/105	Outer temperatur sensor engine control module
8/3	Solenoid switch A/C
8/5	IAC idling valve
8/6-10	Injectors
8/17	EGR converter
8/18	EVAP valve
8/28	Turbo control valve
8/37	Solenoids, automatic transmission
8/43	Solenoid, aux. air intake
8/44	Canister valve
8/45	Solenoid, variable intake manifold
8/49	Stop solenoid
8/50	Pre-setting valve
9/26-28	Extra heater
10/1	Left front light
10/2	Right front light
10/13	Left turn signal, front
10/14	Right turn signal, front
10/15	Left side flasher light
10/16	Right side flasher light
10/20	License plate lighting
10/22	Courtesy light
10/24	Trunk lighting
10/26	Reading light, rear left
10/27	Reading light, rear right
10/29	Glove compartment lighting
10/30	Open-door warning lamp, front left
10/31	Open-door warning lamp, front right
10/32	Open-door warning lamp, rear left
10/33	Open-door warning lamp, rear right
10/47	Lamp, right turn signal, rear
10/48	Right back-up (reversing) light
10/54	Lamp, left turn signal, rear
10/55	Left back-up (reversing) light
10/64	Right high beam
10/66	Right low beam
10/68	Left high beam

VV1029700100030X

Fig. 5 Wiring diagram & component locations (Part 3 of 4). Motronic 4.4 drivetrain control

10/70	Left low beam
10/74	Warning lamp, exhaust temperature
10/76	Diesel pre-heating indicator lamp
10/77	Warning lamp, SRS
10/79	Warning lamp, winter program low gear selection (automatic transmission)
10/82	Warning lamp, ABS
10/83	Warning lamp, handbrake
10/84	Brake warning lamp
10/85	Warning lamp, high beam
10/86	Warning lamp, oil pressure
10/87	Warning lamp, charging
10/88	Warning lamp, bulb failure warning sensor
10/89	Warning light, rear fog lights
10/90	Warning light, washer fluid level
10/91	Service warning
10/94	Indicator lamp, right turn signal
10/95	Indicator lamp, left turn signal
10/96	Instrument lighting
10/97	Entry lighting, driver side
10/102	Entry lighting, passenger side
10/105	Warning lamp, fuel level
10/106	Warning lamp, Check engine
10/107	Warning lamp, TRACS
10/109	Warning lamp, trailer
10/110	Warning lamp, coolant level
10/113	Indication LED alarm/electronic immobilizer
10/114	Vanity mirror lighting, left side
10/115	Vanity mirror lighting, right side
11/1-40	Fuses, in central electrical unit
11A/1-9	Fuses in relay/fuse box in engine compartment
11B/1-5	Fuses in relay/fuse box in engine compartment
15/2	30-rail in central electrical unit
15/4	15I-rail in central electrical unit
15/8	X-rail in central electrical unit
16/1	Radio
16/2	Amplifier
16/3	Loudspeaker, right front door
16/4	Loudspeaker, left front door
16/5	Loudspeaker, right rear door
16/6	Loudspeaker, left rear door
16/7	Loudspeaker, instrument panel, right side
16/8	Loudspeaker, instrument panel, left side
16/9	Antenna
16/15	CD changer
16/16	Antenna amplifier
16/17	Loudspeaker, rear shelf/D-pillar left side
16/18	Loudspeaker, rear shelf/D-pillar right side
16/19	Alarm horn
16/35	Alarm siren
17/1	Service socket for starter motor
17/13	On-board diagnostics socket
19/1	Engine temperature sensor
19/2	Tachometer
19/3	Speedometer
19/5	Fuel gauge
19/6	Exciter, tachometer
19/7	Exciter, speedometer, engine coolant temperature gauge, fuel gauge
20/2	Distributor
20/3-7	Spark plugs
20/11	Ballast resistor
20/22-26	Glow plugs
23/0-601	Branching points
24/1	Connector Instrument panel harness - firewall harness
24/2	Connector Engine compartment harness - firewall harness
24/3	Connector Firewall harness - left door sill harness
24/4	Connector Firewall harness - right door sill harness
24/5	Connector, 24-pin Firewall harness - left front door harness
24/6	Connector, 24-pin Firewall harness - right front door harness
24/7	Connector, 14-pin Firewall harness - tunnel harness
24/9	Connector, 4-pin Firewall harness - roof harness
24/11	Connector, 10-pin Firewall harness - climate unit harness
24/12	Connector, 4-pin Firewall harness - blower fan harness/climate unit
24/13	Connector Engine compartment harness - instrument panel harness
24/14	Connector Engine compartment harness - left door sill harness
24/15	Connector, 14-pin Engine compartment harness - engine harness
24/17	Connector, 11-pin Left door sill harness - left rear door harness
24/18	Connector, 11-pin Right door sill harness - right rear door harness
24/19	Connector, 4-pin Right door sill harness - rear wheel sensor harness
24/21	Connector, 6-pin Left door sill harness - left front seat
24/22	Connector, 6-pin Right door sill harness - right front seat
24/25	Connector, 14-pin Left door sill harness - tailgate harness
24/43	Connector, 8-pin Engine compartment harness - engine harness
24/44	Connector, 2-pin Engine compartment harness - engine harness
24/53	Connector, engine harness - automatic transmission
24/54	Connector, 3-pin stop solenoid and lovad valve
24/64	Knock sensor (KS) connector 3-pin
24/65	Connector, 2-pin at left A-pillar
24/66	Connector, 2-pin at right A-pillar
31/4	Ground point, engine (ground point, battery - engine)
31/7	Ground point, A-pillar driver side
31/11	Ground point, trunk, left side
31/12	Ground point, trunk, right side
31/15	Ground point, A-pillar passenger side
31/32	Ground point, on engine (power ground)/ground point at engine
31/33	Ground point, on engine (signal ground)
31/44	Ground point, engine compartment (ground point, battery - body)
31/47	Ground point, left cross member
31/48	Ground point, right cross member
31/50	Ground point, central electrical unit, power ground
31/51	Ground point, central electrical unit, signal ground
31/52	Ground point, DI power stage and ignition coil
31/55	Ground point, engine cooling fan
31/71	Ground point right side member in engine compartment
C/BA	Connector, 2-pin, fuel pump
C/BB	Connector, 2-pin, fuel level sensor
C/BC	Connector, 4-pin, power antenna/antenna amplifier
C/BD	Connector, 3-pin, tank pressure sensor
C/CJ	Connector, 6-pin, cruise control
C/CR	Connector, 14-pin, audio
C/CS	Connector, 10-pin, audio
C/EA	Connector, 1-pin, engine cooling fan
C/EB	Connector, 4-pin, high pressure sensor, A/C
C/EC	Connector, 1-pin, solenoid switch A/C
C/EG	Connector, 2-pin, engine coolant temperature sensor
C/EH	Connector, 3-pin, chamshaft position sensor (CMP)
C/EJ	Connector, 2-pin, pulse sensor
C/EP	Connector, 4-pin, heated oxygen sensor (HO2S), front
C/EQ	Connector, 4-pin, heated oxygen sensor (HO2S), rear

VV1029700100040X

Fig. 5 Wiring diagram & component locations (Part 4 of 4). Motronic 4.4 drivetrain control

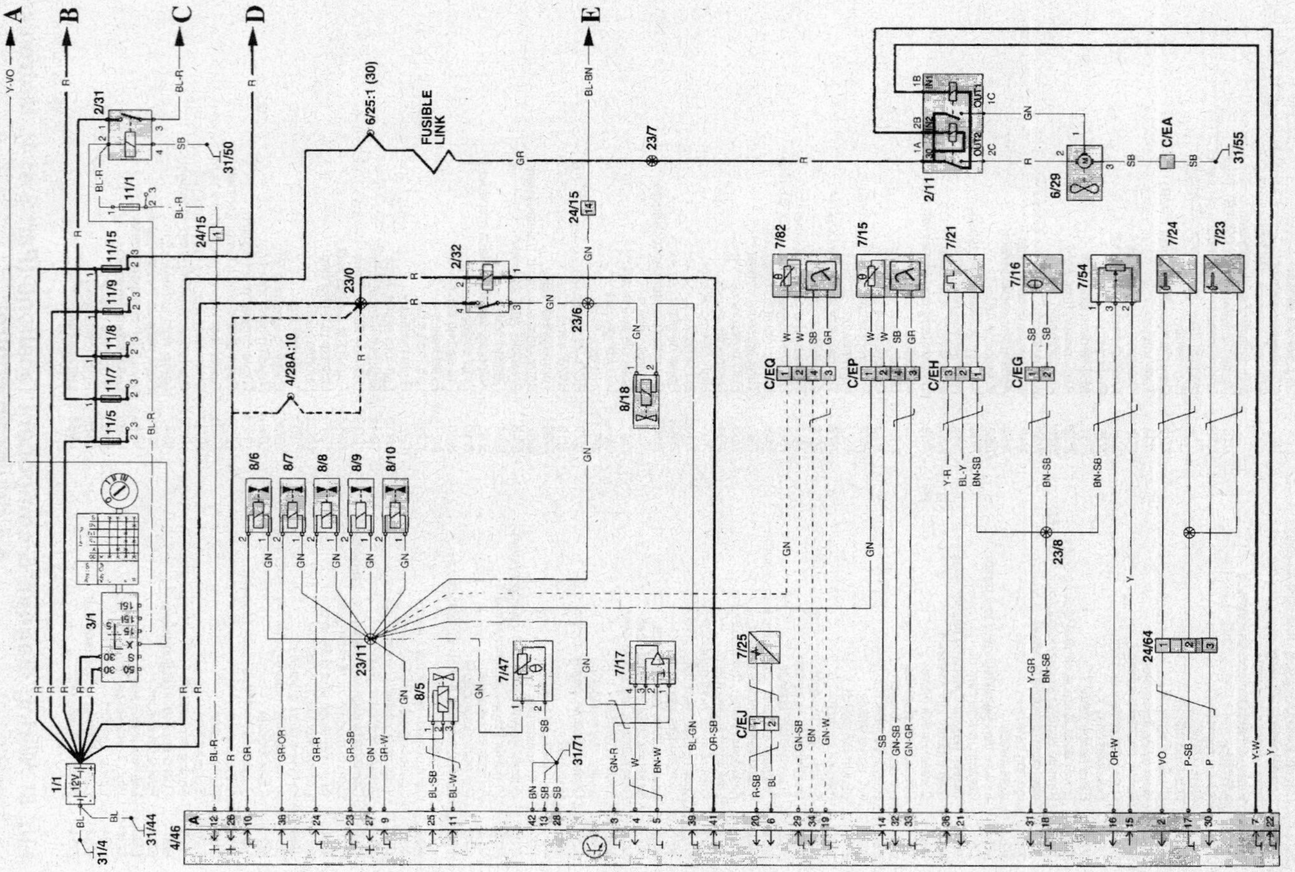

VV10297000098010X

Fig. 6 Wiring diagram (Part 1 of 4). Turbocharged

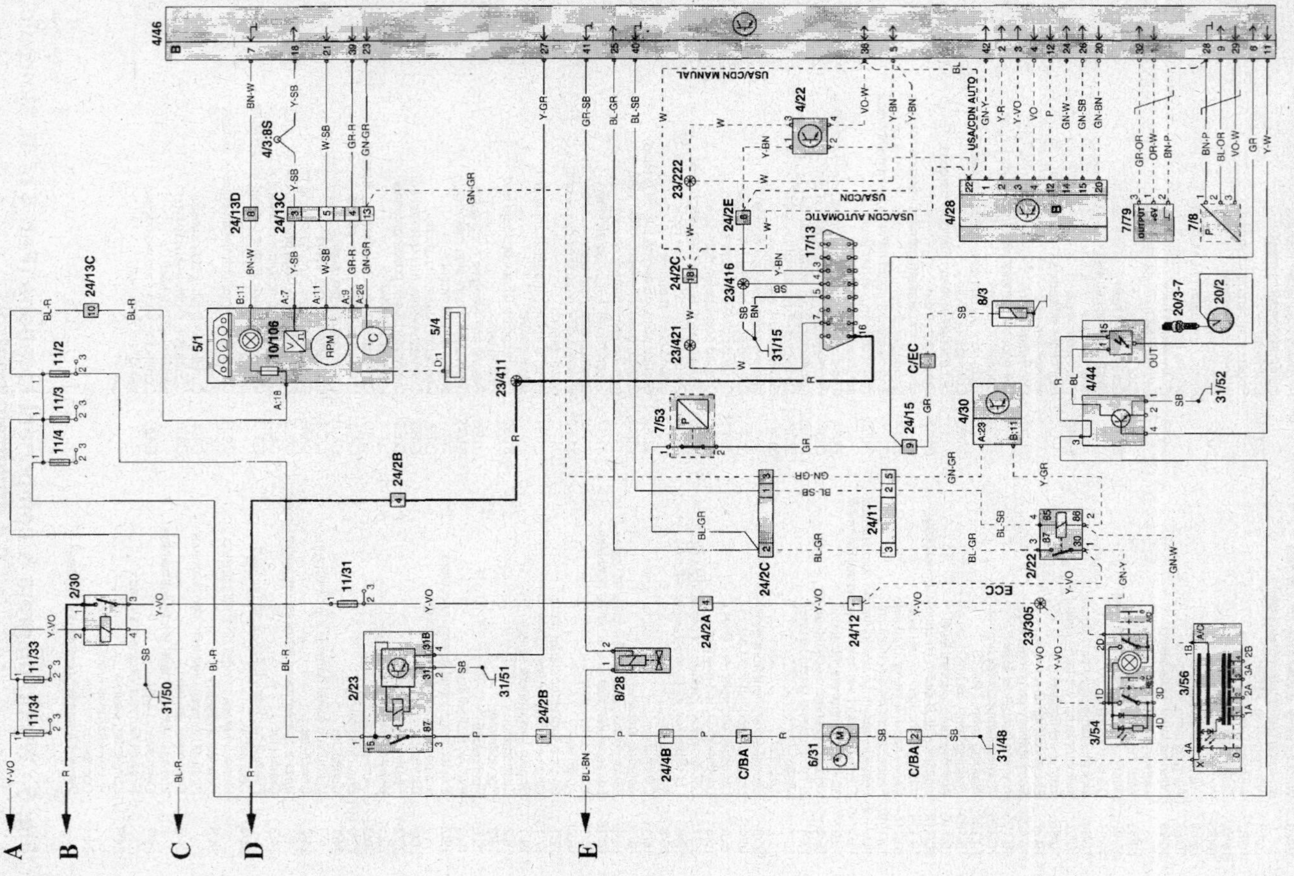

VV10297000098020X

Fig. 6 Wiring diagram (Part 2 of 4). Turbocharged

1/1	Battery
2/1	Main headlight relay with bulb failure warning sensor
2/5	Seat belt reminder/key warning relay
2/7	Central locking/delayed inner lighting relay
2/11	Engine cooling fan relay
2/14	Glow automatics relay
2/15	Relay, exhaust temperature sensor
2/22	A/C relay
2/23	Fuel pump relay
2/28	Alarm relay
2/30	Overload relay X+
2/31	Overload relay 15+
2/32	Main relay, fuel system
2/47	Relay, deadlock setting
2/53	Relay, secondary air pump
2/60	Overload relay X+
2/74	Extra heater relay
2/105	Driver door, 2-stage central locking relay
2/110	Remote control central locking/indication LED electronic immobilizer relay
3/1	Ignition switch
3/2	Light switch
3/3	Switch, turn signal/high and low beam
3/4	Controls, cruise control
3/6	Switch, hazard lights with flasher relay
3/9	Stop (brake) light switch
3/38	Contact, brake pedal
3/39	Contact, clutch pedal
3/47	Handbrake contact
3/54	REC / A/C switch
3/55	A/C panel lights
3/56	Blower fan switch
3/57	Climate control
3/58	Switch, rear fog light
3/61	Controls, trip computer
3/62	Alarm switch, bonnet
3/63	Program selector, automatic transmission
3/71	Transmission range sensor
3/72	Kick-down switch, throttle control
3/74	Lock module, front left
3/75	Lock module, front right
3/76	Lock module, rear left
3/77	Lock module, rear right
3/78	Lock module, trunk/tailgate
3/93	Seat belt lock, left front seat
3/94	Seat belt lock, right front seat
3/95	Switch, TRACS
3/98	Switch, central locking
4/3	Control module, cruise control
4/4	Rheostat
4/5	Safety circuit SRS
4/9	SRS sensor unit
4/10	Control module, EZK (DI) ignition system
4/15	DI power stage and ignition coil
4/16	ABS control module
4/22	Electronic immobilizer
4/28	Control module, AW 50-42 automatic transmission
4/29	Control module, left front seat
4/30	Control module, ECC
4/34	Voltage regulator, 8 volts
4/35	Voltage regulator, 5 volts
4/36	Combined instrument panel microprocessor
4/37	Control module, right front seat
4/44	DI power stage and ignition coil
4/45	Control module, LH-Jetronic 3.2 MFI
4/46	Engine control module
5/1	Combined instrument panel
5/2	Clock module
5/3	Outside temperature/clock module
5/4	Trip computer
6/25	Starter motor
6/26	Generator
6/29	Engine cooling fan
6/31	Fuel pump/fuel injection pump
6/33	Fuel level sensor
6/33L	Left fuel level sensor
6/33R	Right fuel level sensor
6/34	Power antenna
6/37	Central locking motor, tank cap
6/54	Secondary air pump
7/1	Bulb failure warning sensor, rear
7/4	Brake fluid level sensor
7/5	Washer fluid level sensor
7/6	Oil pressure sensor
7/8	A/C pressure sensor
7/12	ECC solar sensor and indication LED alarm/electronic immobilizer
7/15	Heated oxygen sensor (HO2S), front
7/16	Engine coolant temperature sensor ECT+
7/17	Mass air flow (MAF) sensor/mass air flow sensor
7/21	Camshaft position sensor (CMP)
7/22	Tachometer
7/23	Knock sensor (KS), rear
7/24	Knock sensor (KS), front
7/25	Pulse sensor
7/31	ABS sensor, front left
7/32	ABS sensor, front right
7/33	Speedometer
7/39	Antenna ring
7/47	PTC resistor, pre-heater
7/51	Accelerator pedal sensor
7/53	Pressostat A/C
7/54	Throttle position (TP) sensor
7/56	ABS sensor, rear left
7/57	ABS sensor, rear right
7/69	Outside temperature sensor, trip computer
7/71	Boost pressure sensor
7/73	Coolant level sensor
7/74	Oil temperature sensor, automatic transmission
7/77	Temperature sensor, intake air
7/79	Accelerometer
7/81	Pressure sensor, intake manifold
7/82	Heated oxygen sensor (HO2S), rear
7/83	High-pressure sensor A/C
7/84	Tank pressure sensor
7/85	EBD pressure sensor
7/94	Needle lift sensor
7/95	High Altitude sensor
7/100	Tilt sensor
7/101	Breaking glass sensor
7/105	Outer temperatur sensor engine control module
8/3	Solenoid switch A/C
8/5	IAC idling valve
8/6-10	Injectors
8/17	EGR converter
8/18	EVAP valve
8/28	Turbo control valve
8/37	Solenoids, automatic transmission
8/43	Solenoid, aux. air intake
8/44	Canister valve
8/45	Solenoid, variable intake manifold
8/49	Stop solenoid
8/50	Pre-setting valve
9/26-28	Extra heater
10/1	Left front light
10/2	Right front light
10/13	Left turn signal, front
10/14	Right turn signal, front
10/15	Left side flasher light
10/16	Right side flasher light
10/20	License plate lighting
10/22	Courtesy light
10/24	Trunk lighting
10/26	Reading light, rear left
10/27	Reading light, rear right
10/29	Glove compartment lighting
10/30	Open-door warning lamp, front left
10/31	Open-door warning lamp, front right
10/32	Open-door warning lamp, rear left
10/33	Open-door warning lamp, rear right
10/47	Lamp, right turn signal, rear
10/48	Right back-up (reversing) light
10/54	Lamp, left turn signal, rear
10/55	Left back-up (reversing) light
10/64	Right high beam
10/66	Right low beam
10/68	Left high beam

VV1029700098030X

Fig. 6 Wiring diagram (Part 3 of 4). Turbocharged

10/70	Left low beam
10/74	Warning lamp, exhaust temperature
10/76	Diesel pre-heating indicator lamp
10/77	Warning lamp, SRS
10/79	Warning lamp, winter program low gear selection (automatic transmission)
10/82	Warning lamp, ABS
10/83	Warning lamp, handbrake
10/84	Brake warning lamp
10/85	Warning lamp, high beam
10/86	Warning lamp, oil pressure
10/87	Warning lamp, charging
10/88	Warning lamp, bulb failure warning sensor
10/89	Warning light, rear fog lights
10/90	Warning light, washer fluid level
10/91	Service warning
10/94	Indicator lamp, right turn signal
10/95	Indicator lamp, left turn signal
10/96	Instrument lighting
10/97	Entry lighting, driver side
10/102	Entry lighting, passenger side
10/105	Warning lamp, fuel level
10/106	Warning lamp, Check engine
10/107	Warning lamp, TRACS
10/109	Warning lamp, trailer
10/110	Warning lamp, coolant level
10/113	Indication LED alarm/electronic immobilizer
10/114	Vanity mirror lighting, left side
10/115	Vanity mirror lighting, right side
11/1-40	Fuses, in central electrical unit
11A/1-9	Fuses in relay/fuse box in engine compartment
11B/1-5	Fuses in relay/fuse box in engine compartment
15/2	30-rail in central electrical unit
15/4	15l-rail in central electrical unit
15/8	X-rail in central electrical unit
16/1	Radio
16/2	Amplifier
16/3	Loudspeaker, right front door
16/4	Loudspeaker, left front door
16/5	Loudspeaker, right rear door
16/6	Loudspeaker, left rear door
16/7	Loudspeaker, instrument panel, right side
16/8	Loudspeaker, instrument panel, left side
16/9	Antenna
16/15	CD changer
16/16	Antenna amplifier
16/17	Loudspeaker, rear shelf/D-pillar left side
16/18	Loudspeaker, rear shelf/D-pillar right side
16/19	Alarm horn
16/35	Alarm siren
17/1	Service socket for starter motor
17/13	On-board diagnostics socket
19/1	Engine temperature sensor
19/2	Tachometer
19/3	Speedometer
19/5	Fuel gauge
19/6	Exciter, tachometer
19/7	Exciter, speedometer, engine coolant temperature gauge, fuel gauge
20/2	Distributor
20/3-7	Spark plugs
20/11	Ballast resistor
20/22-26	Glow plugs
23/0-601	Branching points
24/1	Connector Instrument panel harness - firewall harness
24/2	Connector Engine compartment harness - firewall harness
24/3	Connector Firewall harness - left door sill harness
24/4	Connector Firewall harness - right door sill harness
24/5	Connector, 24-pin Firewall harness - left front door harness
24/6	Connector, 24-pin Firewall harness - right front door harness
24/7	Connector, 14-pin Firewall harness - tunnel harness
24/9	Connector, 4-pin Firewall harness - roof harness
24/11	Connector, 10-pin Firewall harness - climate unit harness
24/12	Connector, 4-pin Firewall harness - blower fan harness/climate unit
24/13	Connector Engine compartment harness - instrument panel harness
24/14	Connector Engine compartment harness - left door sill harness
24/15	Connector, 14-pin Engine compartment harness - engine harness
24/17	Connector, 11-pin Left door sill harness - left rear door harness
24/18	Connector, 11-pin Right door sill harness - right rear door harness
24/19	Connector, 4-pin Right door sill harness - rear wheel sensor harness
24/21	Connector, 6-pin Left door sill harness - left front seat
24/22	Connector, 6-pin Right door sill harness - right front seat
24/25	Connector, 14-pin Left door sill harness - tailgate harness
24/43	Connector, 8-pin Engine compartment harness - engine harness
24/44	Connector, 2-pin Engine compartment harness - engine harness
24/53	Connector, engine harness - automatic transmission
24/54	Connector, 3-pin stop solenoid and lovad valve
24/64	Knock sensor (KS) connector 3-pin
24/65	Connector, 2-pin at left A-pillar
24/66	Connector, 2-pin at right A-pillar
31/4	Ground point, engine (ground point, battery - engine)
31/7	Ground point, A-pillar driver side
31/11	Ground point, trunk, left side
31/12	Ground point, trunk, right side
31/15	Ground point, A-pillar passenger side
31/32	Ground point, on engine (power ground)/ ground point at engine
31/33	Ground point, on engine (signal ground)
31/44	Ground point, engine compartment (ground point, battery - body)
31/47	Ground point, left cross member
31/48	Ground point, right cross member
31/50	Ground point, central electrical unit, power ground
31/51	Ground point, central electrical unit, signal ground
31/52	Ground point, DI power stage and ignition coil
31/55	Ground point, engine cooling fan
31/71	Ground point right side member in engine compartment
C/BA	Connector, 2-pin, fuel pump
C/BB	Connector, 2-pin, fuel level sensor
C/BC	Connector, 4-pin, power antenna/ antenna amplifier
C/BD	Connector, 3-pin, tank pressure sensor
C/CJ	Connector, 6-pin, cruise control
C/CR	Connector, 14-pin, audio
C/CS	Connector, 10-pin, audio
C/EA	Connector, 1-pin, engine cooling fan
C/EB	Connector, 4-pin, high pressure sensor, A/C
C/EC	Connector, 1-pin, solenoid switch A/C
C/EG	Connector, 2-pin, engine coolant temperature sensor
C/EH	Connector, 3-pin, chamshaft position sensor (CMP)
C/EJ	Connector, 2-pin, pulse sensor
C/EP	Connector, 4-pin, heated oxygen sensor (HO2S), front
C/EQ	Connector, 4-pin, heated oxygen sensor (HO2S), rear

VV1029700098040X

Fig. 6 Wiring diagram (Part 4 of 4). Turbocharged

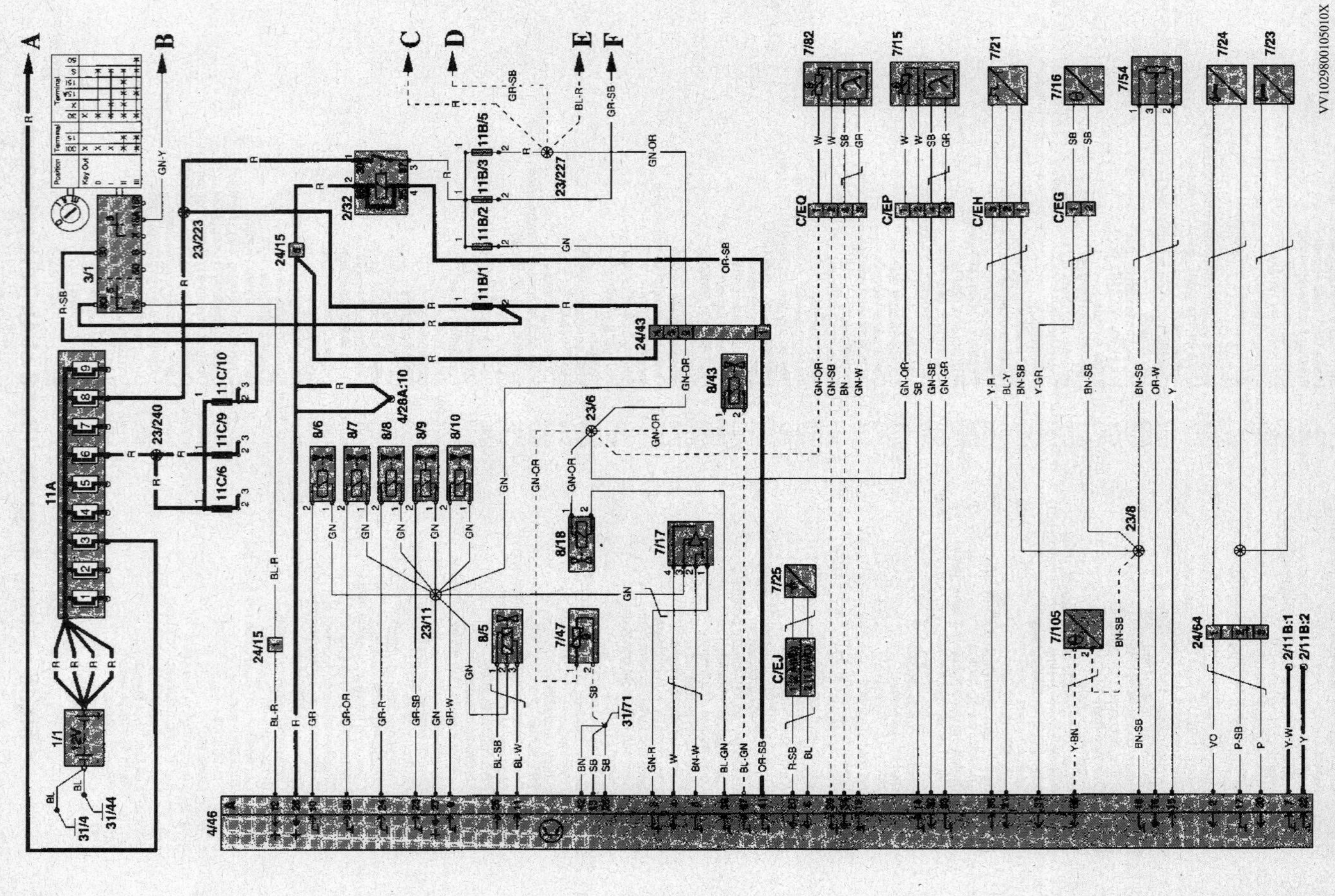

Fig. 7 Wiring diagram & component locations (Part 1 of 5). C70, S70 & V70

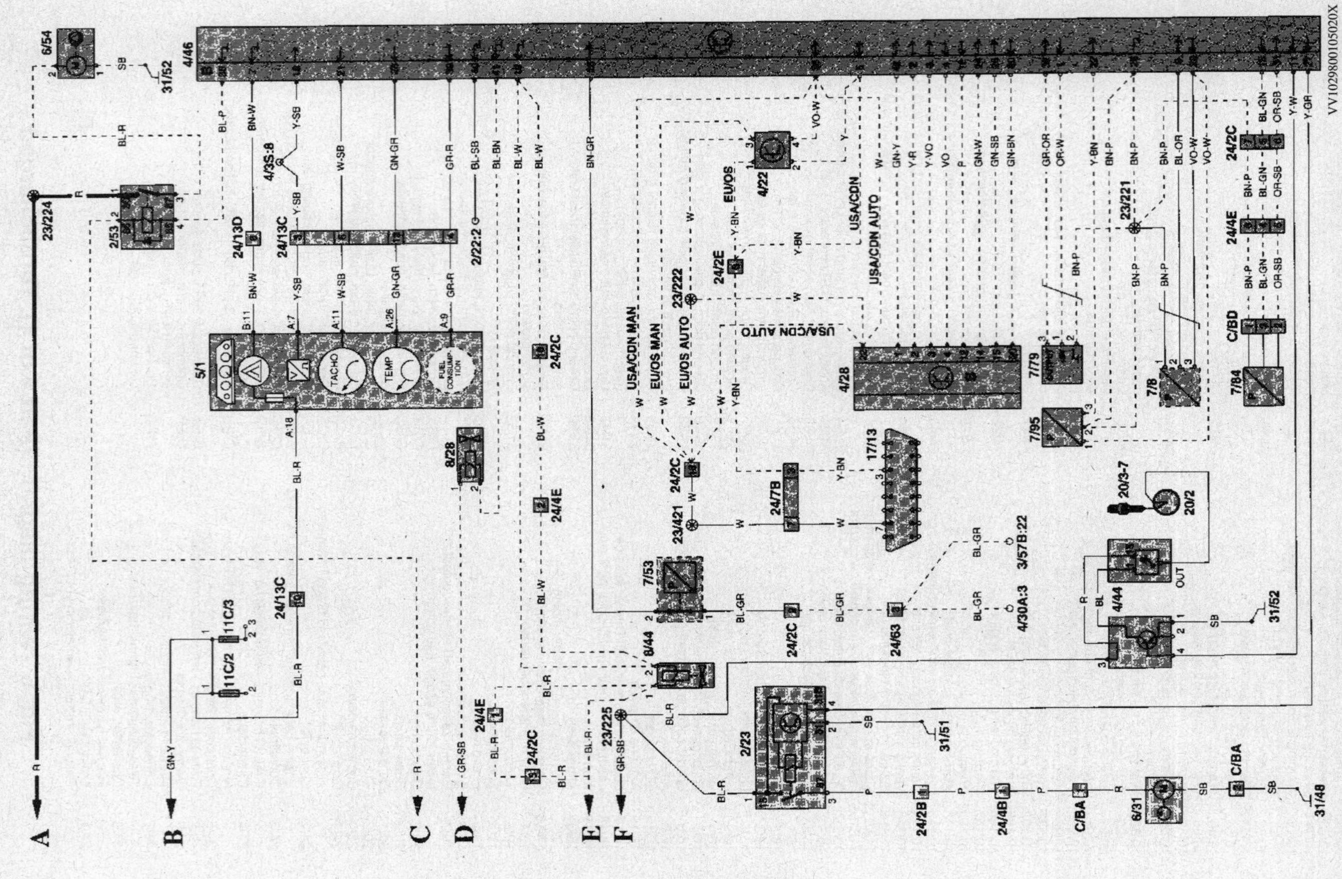

Fig. 7 Wiring diagram & component locations (Part 2 of 5). C70, S70 & V70

1/1	Battery
2/1	Main headlamp relay with bulb failure warning sensor
2/5	Relay, seat belt reminder/key warning
2/6	Overload relay 15I-supply
2/11	Relay engine coolant fan (FC)
2/14	Glow plug relay
2/22	A/C relay
2/23	Fuel pump relay
2/30	Overload relay X-supply
2/32	Fuel system main relay
2/35	Starter motor relay
2/44	Relay, heated rear window/door mirrors
2/53	Relay, pulsed secondary air injection system (PAIR) pump
2/54	Relay 30-supply cargo compartment
2/74	Relay heating plugs coolant
2/76	Control module central locking/alarm
3/1	Ignition switch
3/2	Light switch
3/3	Turn indicator/ DIM-DIP switch
3/4	Control cruise control
3/8	Switch, heated rear window/ door mirrors
3/9	Stop (brake) lamp switch
3/10	Back-up (reversing) lamps switch
3/20	Power window switch front passenger door
3/35	Tailgate switch
3/38	Brake switch
3/39	Clutch pedal switch
3/41	Power door mirrors switch
3/57	Climate control system
3/58	Switch rear foglamp
3/71	Gear position sensor
3/76	Lock unit left rear
3/77	Lock unit right rear
3/78	Lock unit tailgate
3/84	Cargo compartment fans switch
3/85	Power window switch left rear door
3/86	Power window switch right rear door
3/93	Seat belt lock, left front seat
3/94	Seat belt lock, right front seat
3/97	Power window switch driver's door
3/100	Lock unit driver's door
3/109	Trunk lid/fuel tank filler cover switch
3/110	Lock unit passenger door
4/3	Control module, cruise control
4/4	Rheostat
4/9	SRS Supplemental Restraint System Crash Sensor
4/16	ABS control module
4/19	Remote control unit central locking/alarm
4/22	Electronic start inhibitor (Immobilizer)
4/28	Control module AW 50-42
4/30	ECC climate control module
4/31	Power unit blower fan
4/44	Ignition discharge module (IDM) and ignition coil
4/46	Engine control module (ECM)
5/1	Combined instrument panel
6/9	Power window motor driver's door
6/11	Power window motor passenger door front
6/13	Driver's side power door mirror
6/14	Passenger side power door mirror
6/25	Starter motor
6/26	Generator
6/28	Blower fan
6/31	Fuel pump (FP)/Fuel injection pump
6/34	Power antenna
6/37	Central locking motor, fuel tank filler cover
6/48	Servo motor recirculation shutter
6/54	Pulsed secondary air injection system (PAIR) pump
6/59	Power window motor left rear door
6/61	Power window motor right rear door
6/69	Servo motor, floor, defroster and ventilation shutter
6/95	Servo motor temperature shutter left-hand side
6/96	Servo motor temperature shutter right-hand side
6/97	Left cargo compartment fan
6/98	Right cargo compartment fan
7/1	Bulb failure warning sensor rear
7/8	A/C pressure sensor
7/11	Outside temperature sensor (ECC)
7/12	ECC sun sensor and LED indicator alarm immobilizer
7/15	Front oxygen sensor (HO2S)
7/16	Engine coolant temperature (ECT) sensor
7/17	Mass air flow (MAF) sensor/air volume sensor
7/21	Camshaft position (CMP) sensor
7/23	Knock sensor (KS) rear
7/24	Knock sensor (KS) front
7/25	Engine speed (RPM) sensor
7/39	Antenna ring/key lighting
7/47	PTC resistor preheating of air
7/51	Accelerator pedal (AP) position sensor
7/53	A/C pressure switch (Pressostat)
7/54	Throttle position (TP) sensor
7/64	Cabin temperature sensor
7/71	Boost pressure sensor
7/79	Accelerometer
7/82	Rear oxygen sensor (HO2S)
7/84	Tank pressure sensor
7/94	Needle lift sensor
7/95	Altitude sensor
7/105	Outside temperature sensor
8/3	A/C solenoid switch
8/5	Idle air control (IAC) valve
8/6-10	Injectors
8/17	EGR converter
8/18	EVAP valve
8/28	Turbo control valve
8/43	Solenoid valve PAIR system
8/44	EVAP Canister valve
8/49	Stop solenoid
8/50	Injection timing valve

VV1029800105030X

Fig. 7 Wiring diagram & component locations (Part 3 of 5). C70, S70 & V70

9/2	Heated rear window
9/26-28	Heating plugs coolant
9/31	Additional heater
10/3	License plate lighting
10/13	Left front turn signal lamp
10/14	Right front turn signal lamp
10/15	Left side turn signal flasher
10/16	Right side turn signal flasher
10/17	Right tail lamp unit
10/18	Left tail lamp unit
10/22	Passenger compartment courtesy lamp
10/43	Right stop (brake) lamp
10/44	Right position-/tail lamps
10/45	Right position-/tail lamps
10/46	Right side rear fog lamp
10/47	Rear right turn signal lamp
10/48	Right back-up (reversing) lamp
10/50	Left stop (brake) lamp
10/51	Left rear position lamps
10/52	Left rear position lamps
10/53	Left side rear fog lamp
10/54	Rear left turn signal lamp
10/55	Left back-up (reversing) lamp
10/113	Indicator LED alarm/electronic immobilizer
11A/1-9	Main fuses
11B/1-5	Fuses
11C/1-40	Fuses
15/4	15I-rail
16/1	Radio
16/2	Amplifier
16/3	Loudspeaker right front door
16/4	Loudspeaker left front door
16/5	Loudspeaker right rear door
16/6	Loudspeaker left rear door
16/7	Loudspeaker dashboard right side
16/8	Loudspeaker dashboard left side
16/9	Antenna
16/15	CD-changer
16/16	Antenna booster
16/17	Loudspeaker parcel shelf left side
16/18	Loudspeaker parcel shelf right side
16/26	Dashboard center loudspeaker
16/45	RTI control module
16/53	Antenna booster
16/57	Loudspeaker left-hand side D-pillar
16/58	Loudspeaker right-hand side D-pillar
16/72	Dolby module
17/1	Service socket for turning over starter motor
17/13	Data link connector DLC
20/2	Distributor
20/3-7	Spark plugs
20/18	Blower fan resistor
20/22-26	Glow plugs
23/0-702	Branching points
24/1	Connector Dashboard harness - firewall harness
24/2	Connector Engine compartment harness - firewall harness
24/3	Connector Firewall harness - left door sill harness
24/4	Connector Firewall harness - right door sill harness
24/7B	10-pin connector Firewall harness - tunnel harness
24/9	Connector Firewall harness - roof harness
24/13	Connector Engine compartment harness - firewall harness
24/14	Connector Engine compartment harness - left door sill harness
24/15	14-pin connector Engine compartment harness - engine harness
24/17	11-pin connector Left door sill harness - harness left back door
24/18	11-pin connector Right door sill harness - right back door harness
24/21	6-pin connector Left door sill harness - left seat
24/22	6-pin connector Right door sill harness - right seat
24/25	14-pin connector Left door sill harness - tailgate harness
24/35	Connector 8 point, accessories
24/43	8-pin connector Engine compartment harness - engine harness
24/44	2-pin connector Engine compartment harness - engine harness
24/50	24-pin connector Firewall harness - driver's door harness
24/53	Connector Engine harness - automatic transmission
24/54	3-pin connector stop solenoid and injection timing valve

VV1029800105040X

Fig. 7 Wiring diagram & component locations (Part 4 of 5). C70, S70 & V70

24/60	24-pin connector Firewall harness - passenger door harness
24/61	15-pin connector Firewall harness - RTI harness
24/63	14-pin connector Firewall harness - climate control harness
24/64	3-pin connector knock sensor
24/74	Connector Engine compartment harness - glow plugs
24/81	6-pin connector tow hook
24/86	2-pin connector Left sill harness - cargo compartment fan switch harness
24/87	2-pin cool box connector
31/4	Engine ground point (battery ground terminal - engine)
31/5	Heated rear windshield ground
31/7	Ground terminal driver's side A post
31/11	Ground terminal cargo compartment left-hand side
31/12	Ground terminal cargo compartment right-hand side
31/15	Ground terminal passenger side A post
31/44	Engine compartment ground point (battery ground terminal - body)
31/47	Ground terminal left cross member
31/48	Ground terminal right cross member
31/50	Ground rail (power ground)
31/51	Ground rail (signal ground)
31/52	Ground terminal left spring strut turret
31/71	Ground terminal right front side member

C/BA	2-pin connector fuel pump (FP)
C/BC	4-pin connector power antenna/antenna booster
C/BD	3-pin connector fuel tank pressure sensor
C/BE	14-pin connector rear bulb failure warning sensor
C/CR	14-pin connector audio
C/CS	10-pin connector audio
C/EC	1-pin connector solenoid switch A/C
C/EG	2-pin connector engine coolant temperature (ECT) sensor
C/EH	3-pin connector camshaft position (CMP) sensor
C/EJ	2-pin connector engine speed (RPM) sensor
C/EP	4-pin connector heated oxygen sensor (HO2S) front
C/EQ	4-pin connector heated oxygen sensor (HO2S) rear

VV1029800105050X

Fig. 7 Wiring diagram & component locations (Part 5 of 5). C70, S70 & V70

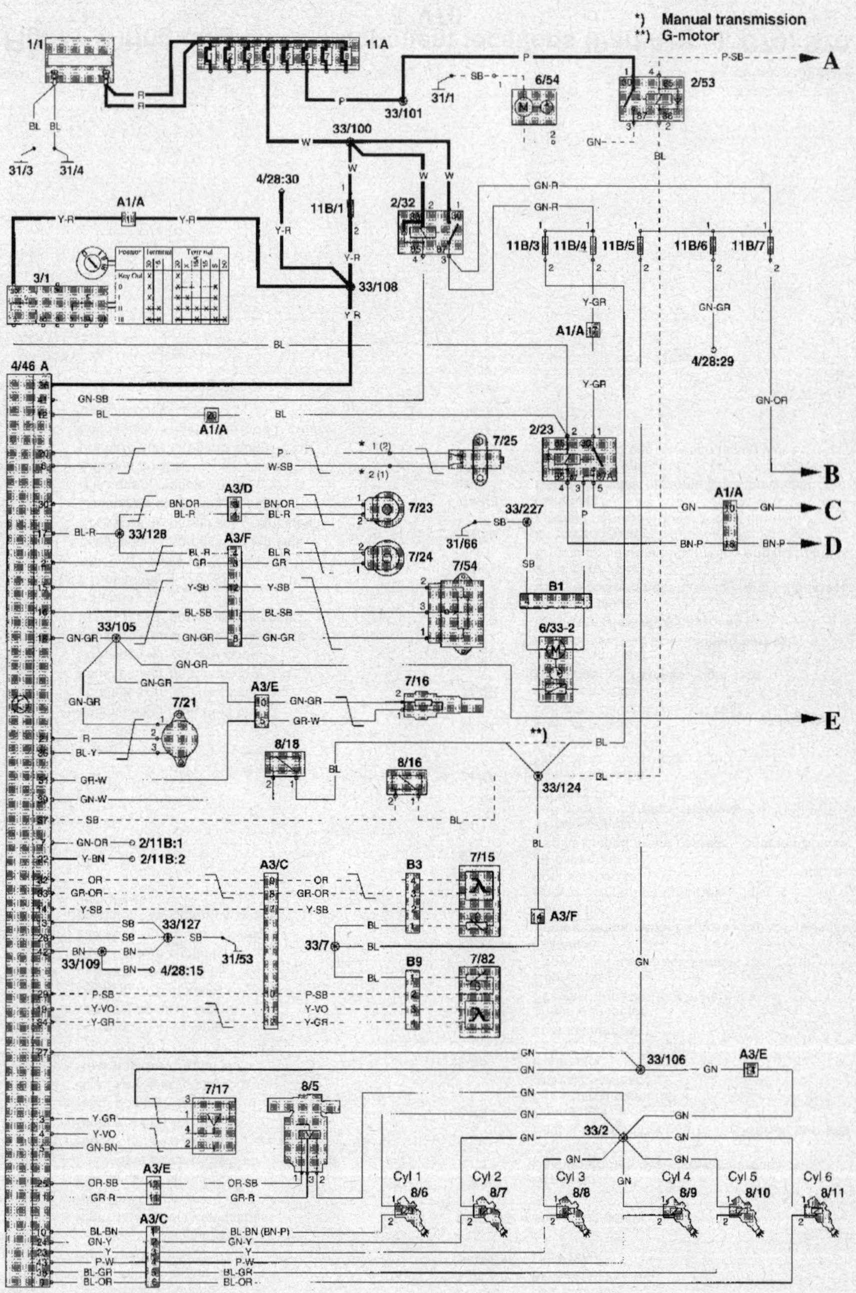

VV1029600093010X

Fig. 8 Wiring diagram & component locations (Part 1 of 3). S90 & V90

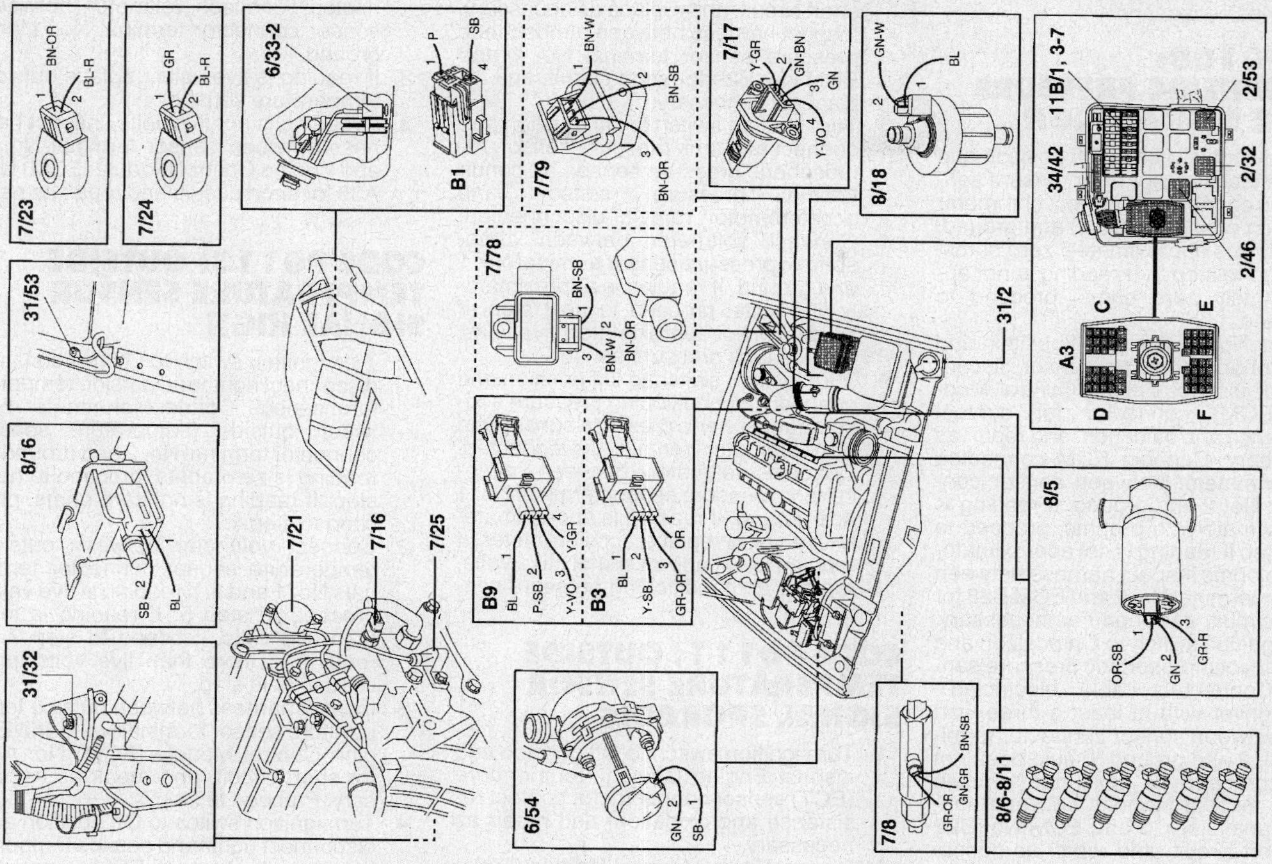

Fig. 8 Wiring diagram & component locations (Part 3 of 3). S90 & V90

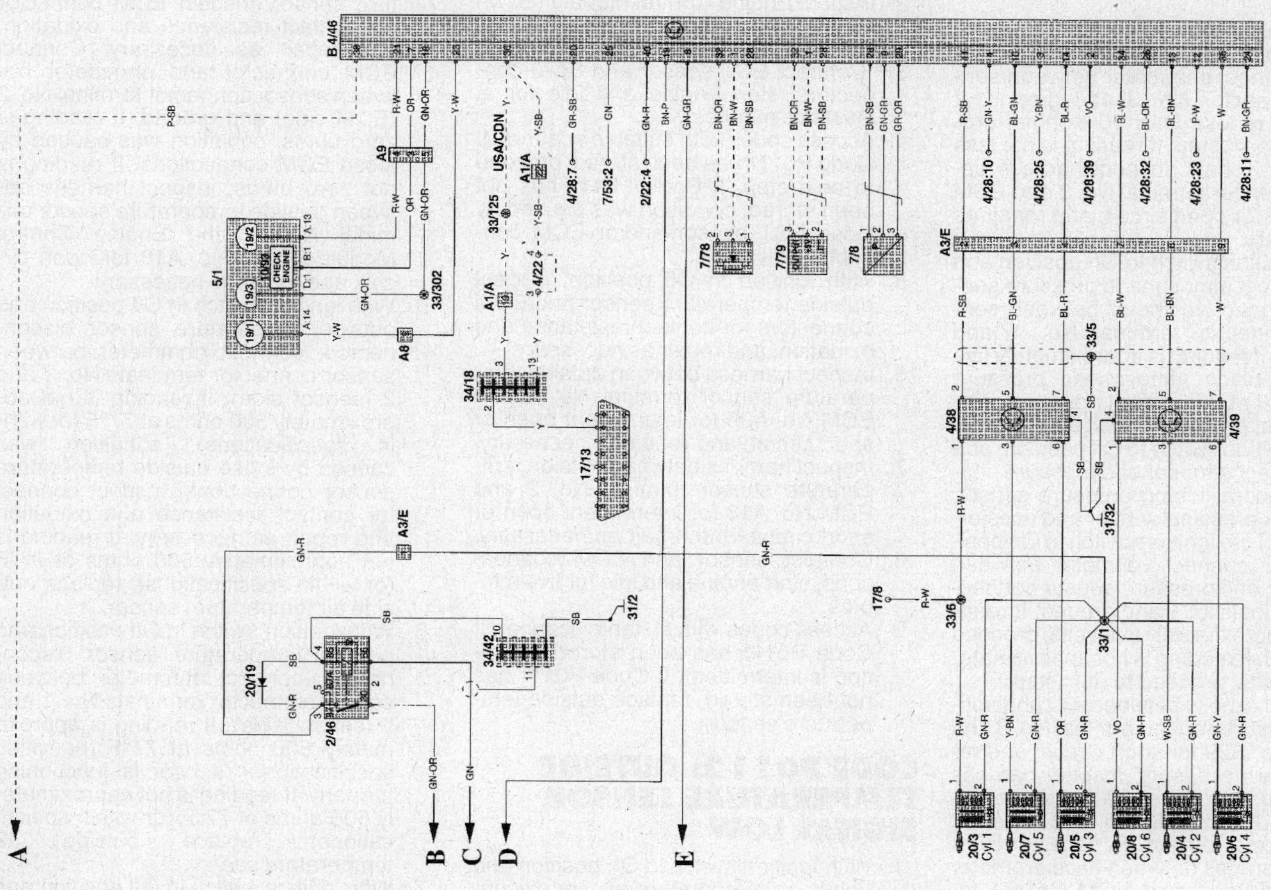

Fig. 8 Wiring diagram & component locations (Part 2 of 3). S90 & V90

Repair as necessary.

CODE P0108: ATMOSPHERIC PRESSURE SENSOR SIGNAL HIGH

1. Turn ignition switch to Off position and disconnect atmospheric pressure sensor lilac connector. Connect ohmmeter between connector No. 2 and ground. If reading is approximately zero ohms, proceed to step 3. If reading is not approximately zero ohms, proceed to next step.
2. With ignition switch in Off position and atmospheric pressure sensor disconnected, inspect Engine Control Module (ECM) connector for contact resistance and oxidation, and repair as necessary. Connect ECM connector, and ohmmeter between sensor connector No. 2 and ground. If reading is approximately zero ohms, proceed to next step If reading is not approximately zero ohms inspect harness between sensor terminal No. 2 and ECM B28 for open circuit, and repair as necessary.
3. Turn ignition switch to On position and disconnect atmospheric pressure sensor. Connect suitable electrician's screwdriver with at least a three watt bulb between sensor connector terminal No. 2 and ground. If bulb does not light, proceed to next step. If bulb lights, inspect harness between sensor terminal No. 3 and ECM No. B22 for short circuit, and repair as necessary.
4. Turn ignition switch to Off position and disconnect atmospheric pressure sensor. Connect ohmmeter between sensor connector No. 3 and ground. If reading is less than 10 Kohms, proceed to next step. If reading is not less than 10 Kohms, inspect harness between sensor terminal No. 3 and ECM No. B22 for open circuit, and repair as necessary.
5. Turn ignition switch to On position and disconnect atmospheric pressure sensor. Connect voltmeter between sensor connector terminal No. 1 and ground. If reading is approximately five volts, replace atmospheric pressure sensor. If reading is not approximately five volts, proceed to next step.
6. Turn ignition switch to Off position, and disconnect atmospheric pressure sensor, air conditioning pressure sensor, fuel tank pressure sensor and accelerometer. Turn ignition switch to On position and connect voltmeter between atmospheric pressure sensor connector terminal No. 1 and ground. If reading is approximately five volts, proceed to step 8. If reading is not approximately five volts, proceed to next step.
7. Inspect harness between air conditioning pressure sensor terminal No. 3 and ECM No. B29 for short circuit, and replace as necessary. Inspect harness between tank pressure sensor terminal No. 1 and ECM No. B15 for short circuit, and replace as necessary. Inspect harness between accelerometer terminal No. 1 and ECM No. B1 for short circuit, and replace as necessary. Inspect harness between atmospheric pressure sensor terminal No. 1 and ECM No. B29 for short circuit, and replace as necessary.
8. Turn ignition switch to Off position and connect fuel tank pressure sensor. Atmospheric pressure sensor, air conditioning pressure sensor and accelerometer remain disconnected. Connect voltmeter between atmospheric pressure sensor terminal No. 1 and ground. If reading is approximately five volts, proceed to next step. If reading is not approximately five volts, replace tank pressure sensor.
9. Turn ignition switch to Off position and connect air conditioning pressure sensor. Atmospheric pressure sensor and accelerometer remain disconnected. Connect voltmeter between atmospheric pressure sensor terminal No. 1 and ground. If reading is approximately five volts, replace accelerometer. If reading is not approximately five volts, replace air conditioning pressure sensor.

CODE P0111: OUTSIDE TEMPERATURE SENSOR SIGNAL SPORADIC

1. Turn ignition switch to Off position and inspect Engine Coolant Temperature (ECT) sensor connector for contact resistance and oxidation, and repair as necessary.
2. Inspect Engine Control Module (ECM) connector for contact resistance and oxidation, and repair as necessary.
3. Connect ECT sensor and ECM connectors, start engine and idle for at least five minutes.
4. Access codes with suitable scanner. If Code P0111 has been stored, proceed to next step. If Code P0111 has not been stored, condition was caused by loose ECT sensor and/or ECM connections.
5. With ignition in Off position, inspect outside temperature sensor and ECM connectors for contact resistance and oxidation, and repair as necessary.
6. Inspect harness between outside temperature sensor terminal No. 1 and ECM No. A35 for intermittent open or short circuit, and repair as necessary.
7. Inspect harness between outside temperature sensor terminal No. 2 and ECM No. A18 for intermittent open or short circuit, and repair as necessary.
8. Connect sensor and ECM connections, start engine and idle for five minutes.
9. Access codes with suitable scanner. If Code P0111 has been stored, condition is intermittent. If Code P0111 has not been stored, replace outside temperature sensor.

CODE P0112: OUTSIDE TEMPERATURE SENSOR SIGNAL LOW

1. With ignition switch in On position and righthand temperature sensor disconnected, connect voltmeter between sensor connector terminal No. 1 and ground.
2. If reading is five volts, replace outside temperature sensor.
3. If reading is not five volts, inspect harness between sensor terminal No. 1 and Engine Control Module (ECM) No. A35 for short circuit, and repair as necessary.

CODE P0113: OUTSIDE TEMPERATURE SENSOR SIGNAL HIGH

1. Turn ignition switch to Off position and disconnect righthand outside temperature sensor. Connect ohmmeter between outside temperature sensor connector terminal No. 2 and ground. If reading is zero ohms, proceed to next step. If reading is not zero ohms, proceed to step 4.
2. Connect voltmeter between outside temperature sensor connector terminals No. 1 and 2. If reading is five volts, proceed to step 5. If reading is less than five volts, proceed to step 7. If reading is more than five volts, proceed to next step.
3. Inspect harness between outside temperature sensor terminal No. 1 and Engine Control Module (ECM) No. A35 for short circuit, and repair as necessary. Proceed to step 6.
4. Turn ignition switch to Off position and disconnect righthand outside temperature sensor. Inspect ECM connector for contact resistance and oxidation, and repair as necessary. Connect ECM connector and ohmmeter between sensor connector terminal No. 2 (ECM side) and ground. If reading is zero ohms, condition was caused by loose ECM connections. If reading is not zero ohms, inspect harness between outside temperature sensor terminal No. 2 and Engine Control Module (ECM) No. A18 for open circuit, and repair as necessary.
5. With ignition switch in Off position and outside temperature sensor disconnected, connect ohmmeter between sensor connector terminals No. 1 and 2 (sensor side). If reading is not approximately 500 ohms at 77°F (or within specifications), condition was caused by loose outside temperature sensor connections. Inspect connect for contact resistance and oxidation and repair as necessary. If reading is not approximately 500 ohms at 77°F (or within specifications), replace outside air temperature sensor.
6. With ignition switch in Off position and outside temperature sensor disconnected, connect ohmmeter between sensor connector terminals No. 1 and 2 (sensor side). If reading is approximately 500 ohms at 77°F (or within specifications), sensor is functioning properly. If reading is not approximately 500 ohms at 77°F (or within specifications), replace outside air temperature sensor.
7. With ignition switch in Off position and

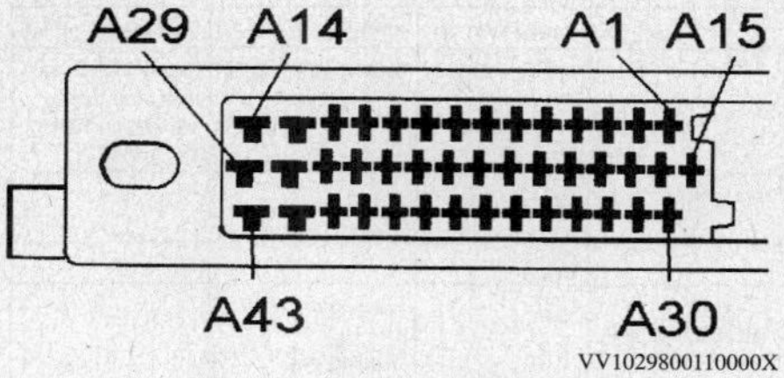

Fig. 9 Connector A pin identification

temperature sensor disconnected, inspect ECM connector for contact resistance and oxidation, and repair as necessary. Connect ECM connector and turn ignition switch to On position. Connect voltmeter between sensor connector terminals No. 1 and 2 (ECM side). If reading is five volts, condition was caused by loose ECM connections. If reading is not five volts, inspect harness between outside temperature sensor terminal No. 1 and Engine Control Module (ECM) No. A35 for short circuit, and repair as necessary.

CODES P0115 & P0116: ENGINE COOLANT TEMPERATURE SENSOR SIGNAL

Before diagnosing codes, disconnect engine cooling fan relay connector A so cooling fan will not run. Codes P1619 and P1620 may be stored while fan is disconnected. Reconnect connector when work is complete.

1. Connect suitable voltmeter with temperature box tool No. 999 5281 and temperature sensor tool No. 999 5282, or equivalents, and carefully remove expansion tank cap. Clamp hose between radiator and thermostat housing, and disconnect hose from thermostat housing. Inset sensor in thermostat housing and connect hose. Remove clamp and access suitable scan tool scrolling values. Start engine and run to operating temperature when thermostat opens. Ensure engine coolant temperature is within specifications. If temperature is not within specifications, proceed to next step. If temperature is within specifications, inspect frozen values. If frozen values at time code was stored were not within specifications, replace ECT sensor. Ensure thermostat opens at correct temperature. Replace both ECT sensor and thermostat if no faults are found.
2. With ignition switch in On position, access scrolling values and disconnect temperature ECT sensor. If reading is approximately .5 volt, proceed to step 4. If reading is not approximately .5 volt, proceed to next step.
3. With ignition in Off position and ECT sensor disconnected, inspect ECM connector for contact resistance and oxidation, and repair as necessary. Connect ECM connector, turn ignition switch to On position and access scrolling values. If reading is approximately five volts, condition was caused by loose ECM connections. If reading is not approximately five volts, inspect harness between ECT sensor terminal No. 1 and ECM No. A31 for short circuit, and repair as necessary.
4. With ignition switch in Off position, disconnect ECT sensor and connect ohmmeter between ECT connector terminal No. 2 (ECM side) and ground. If reading is approximately zero ohms, replace ECT sensor. If reading is not approximately zero ohms, proceed to next step.
5. With ignition switch in Off position and ECT disconnected, inspect ECM connector for contact resistance and oxidation, and repair as necessary. Connect ECM connector and connect ohmmeter between ECT connector terminal No. 2 (ECM side) and ground. If reading is approximately zero ohms, condition was caused by loose ECM connections. If reading is not approximately zero ohms, Inspect harness between ECT terminal No. 2 and ECM No. A18 for open circuit, and repair as necessary.

CODE P0117: ENGINE COOLANT TEMPERATURE SENSOR LOW INPUT

Before diagnosing codes, disconnect engine cooling fan relay connector A so cooling fan will not run. Codes P1619 and P1620 may be stored while fan is disconnected. Reconnect connector when work is complete.

1. Turn ignition switch to On position, connect a suitable scan tool, access scrolling values and then disconnect ECT sensor.
2. Connect voltmeter and measure voltage across ECT sensor.
3. If reading is five volts, replace ECT sensor.
4. If reading is not five volts, repair or replace wiring harness as necessary.

CODE P0118: ENGINE COOLANT TEMPERATURE SENSOR HIGH INPUT

Before diagnosing codes, disconnect engine cooling fan relay connector A so cooling fan will not run. Codes P1619 and P1620 may be stored while fan is disconnected. Reconnect connector when work is complete.

1. Turn ignition switch to Off position and wait approximately 2½ minutes.
2. Disconnect ECT sensor and connect a suitable ohmmeter between ECT connector terminal (ECM side) No. 2 and ground. If resistance is zero ohms, proceed to next step. If resistance is not zero ohms, proceed as follows:
   a. Turn ignition switch to Off position
   b. Measure resistance between ECT connector terminal (ECM side) No. 2 and ground.
   c. If resistance is zero ohms, repair ECM connector contact.
   d. If resistance is not zero ohms, repair or replace wiring harness as necessary.

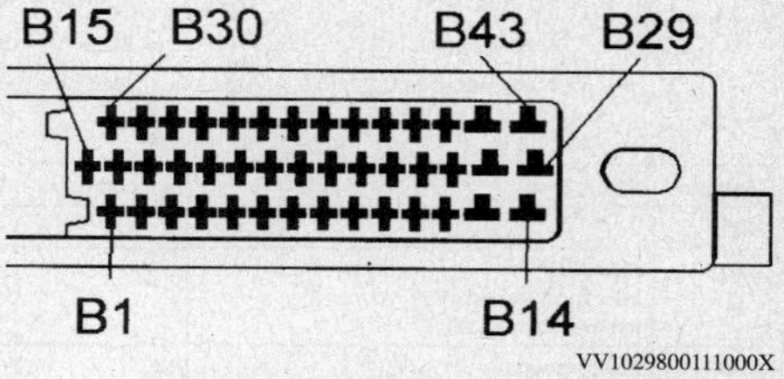

Fig. 10 Connector B pin identification

3. Turn ignition switch to On position and measure voltage between ECT connector terminals (ECM side) No. 1 and No. 2. If reading is less than five volts, proceed to next step. If reading is five volts or more, proceed as follows:
   a. Turn ignition switch to Off position
   b. Measure resistance between ECT connector terminal (ECM side) No. 2 and ground.
   c. If resistance is zero ohms, repair ECM connector contact.
   d. If resistance is not zero ohms, repair or replace wiring harness as necessary.
4. Connect ohmmeter between ECT connector terminals (ECM side) No. 1 and No. 2. If resistance is 2,200 ohms at 77°F, repair fault in ECT connector. If resistance is not 2200 ohms at 77°F, replace ECT sensor.

CODE P0122: THROTTLE POSITION SENSOR LOW INPUT

1. Turn ignition switch to Off position and disconnect TP sensor, then connect a suitable ohmmeter between TP connector terminal No. 2 and ground. If resistance is 400–800 ohms, proceed to next step. If resistance is more than 800 ohms, check ECM connector and repair or replace as necessary. If resistance is less than 400 ohms, repair or replace harness.
2. Connect voltmeter between TP connector terminal No. 3 and ground. If reading is five volts, proceed to next step. If reading is not five volts, repair or replace wiring harness as necessary.
3. Connect TP sensor connector and scan tool and start engine, access parameter list and read throttle angle. If angle is 0° at idle and increases as accelerator pedal is depressed, repair TP connector. If throttle angle is not as specified, replace TP sensor.

CODE P0123: THROTTLE POSITION SENSOR HIGH INPUT

1. Turn ignition switch to Off position and disconnect TP sensor, then connect ohmmeter between TP connector terminal No. 1 and ground. If resistance is more than zero ohms, proceed to next step. If resistance is zero ohms, check ECM connector for proper contact and

$U =$	AC in volts (V)	$U_{AC} =$	alternating current in volts (V)
$U_{bat} =$	battery voltage	$f =$	frequency in Hertz (Hz
$U_{ibg} =$	voltage close to 0 V or 0 V	%duty =	duty cycle (pulse quotient) in percent (%)
$t =$	time in milliseconds (ms)		

Terminal	Signal type	Ignition on	Idling	Remarks
#A1	–	–	–	–
#A2	Signal (+) front knock sensor (KS) (measured to #A17)	U_{low}		
#A3	Power ground mass air flow (MAF) sensor	U_{low}		
#A4	Signal mass air flow (MAF) sensor (Measured to #A5)	U = 0,1 – 0,2 V	U ≈ 0.9 V	U increases with increasing air mass
#A5	Signal ground mass air flow (MAF) sensor	U_{low}		
#A6	Signal ground engine speed (RPM) sensor	U_{low}		
#A7	Control signal engine cooling fan (FC) low-speed	Engine cooling fan (FC) off: U_{bat} Engine cooling fan (FC) on: U ≈ 0.1 V		
#A8	–	–	–	–
#A9	Control signal injector 5	U_{bat}	t = 2.2 – 3.6 ms	t increases with engine speed (RPM) and load (Measured with EVAP not active)
#A10	Control signal injector 1	U_{bat}	t = 2.2 – 3.6 ms	t increases with engine speed (RPM) and load (Measured with EVAP not active)

VV1029700103010X

Fig. 11 Motronic 4.4 signal specifications (Part 1 of 7)

Terminal	Signal type	Ignition on	Idling	Remarks
#A11	Opening signal idle air control (IAC) valve	%duty ≈ 25%	%duty = 21 – 32%	%duty increases with load (Measured with EVAP not active)
#A12	15–supply (Supply voltage from ignition switch)	U_{bat}		
#A13	Power ground	U_{low}		
#A14	Control signal front heated oxygen sensor (HO2S), heating	U_{bat}	Heating off: $U \approx U_{bat}$ Heating on: U ≈ 0.4 V	
#A15	Supply voltage throttle position (TP) sensor	U ≈ 4.8 V		
#A16	Signal throttle position (TP) sensor	U ≈ 0.5 V at closed throttle position (CTP) (idling) U ≈ 4.3 V at wide open throttle (WOT)		
#A17	Signal (–) front and rear knock sensor (KS)	U_{low}		
#A18	Signal ground sensor (measured to battery negative terminal)	U_{low}		
#A19	Signal (–) rear heated oxygen sensor (HO2S)	U ≈ 0.7 V	Only measured with ignition on	
#A20	Signal engine speed (RPM) sensor (Measured to #A6)	U_{low}	$U_{AC} \approx 1.6$ V f = 825 Hz	
#A21	Signal camshaft position (CMP) sensor	$U = U_{low}$ or 5.0 V $U = U_{low}$ or U_{bat}	f ≈ 7Hz	f increases with engine speed (RPM)
#A22	Control signal engine cooling fan (FC) high-speed	Engine cooling fan (FC) off: U_{bat} Engine cooling fan (FC) on: U < 0.3 V		
#A23	Control signal injector 4	U_{bat}	t = 2.2 – 3.6 ms	t increases with engine speed (RPM) and load (Measured with EVAP not active)
#A24	Control signal injector 3	U_{bat}	t = 2.2 – 3.6 ms	t increases with engine speed (RPM) and load (Measured with EVAP not active)

VV1029700103020X

Fig. 11 Motronic 4.4 signal specifications (Part 2 of 7)

repair as necessary.

2. Turn ignition switch to On position, connect voltmeter between TP connector terminal No. 2 and ground. If reading is five volts, proceed to next step. If reading is not five volts, repair or replace harness as necessary.
3. Connect voltmeter between TP connector terminal No. 3 and ground. If reading is five volts or more, proceed to next step. If reading is less than five volts, check ECM connector and repair as necessary.
4. Turn ignition switch to Off position, then connect TP sensor connector.
5. Connect scan tool, start engine and allow to idle. Access scrolling values and read throttle angle.
6. If angle is 0° at idle and increases as accelerator pedal is depressed, repair fault in TP connector. If throttle angle is not as specified, replace TP sensor.

CODE P0130: FRONT HEATED OXYGEN SENSOR SIGNAL

1. Turn ignition switch to Off position and wait approximately 2½ minutes.
2. Disconnect front heated oxygen sensor (black connector), connect ohmmeter between heated oxygen sensor connector terminal No. 4 (ECM side) and ground. If resistance is 50 Kohms, proceed to next step. If resistance is not 50 Kohms, check ECM connector and repair as necessary.
3. Connect ohmmeter between front heated oxygen sensor connector terminal (ECM side) No. 3 and ground. If resistance is 200 ohms, proceed to next step. If resistance is not 200 ohms, check ECM connector and repair as necessary.
4. Connect suitable scan tool, then start and idle engine.
5. Access scrolling values and read front heated oxygen sensor value. If within 10 minutes the oxygen sensor value is .1–.9 volts, repair fault in front heated oxygen sensor connector. If oxygen sensor value is not as specified, replace front heated oxygen sensor.

CODE P0131: FRONT HEATED OXYGEN SENSOR LOW INPUT

1. Connect test box tool No. 981 3190, or equivalent, and check ground terminals and connect ECM.
2. Turn ignition switch to On position and connect a suitable voltmeter between test box terminals No. 33 and No. 42. If reading is not one volt, proceed to next step. If reading is one volt, proceed as follows:
   a. Disconnect rear oxygen sensor (gray connector).
   b. Turn ignition switch to On position and measure voltage between test box terminals No. 33 and No. 42.
   c. If reading is one volt, replace rear heated oxygen sensor.
   d. If reading is not one volt, proceed to next step.
3. Turn ignition switch to Off position and disconnect front heated oxygen sensor. Turn ignition switch to On position and measure voltage between test box terminals No. 33 and No. 42. If reading is one volt, replace front heated oxygen sensor. If reading is not one volt, repair wiring harness as necessary.

CODE P0132: FRONT HEATED OXYGEN SENSOR HIGH INPUT

1. Connect test box tool No. 981 3190, or equivalent, and test ground terminals.
2. Turn ignition switch to On position and connect a suitable multimeter between test box terminals No. 33 and No. 42. If reading is one volt, proceed to next step. If reading is not one volt, repair wiring harness between control unit and oxygen sensor.
3. Turn ignition switch to Off position and disconnect front heated oxygen sensor (black connector). Turn ignition switch to On position and measure voltage between test box terminals No. 33 and No. 42. If reading is one volt,

Terminal	Signal type	Ignition on	Idling	Remarks
#A25	Closing signal idle air control (IAC) valve	%duty = 75%	%duty = 68 – 78%	% duty decreases with load (Measured with EVAP not active)
#A26	30–supply (Power supply from battery)	U_{bat}		
#A27	Power supply (From main relay)	U_{bat}		
#A28	Power ground control module	U_{low}		
#A29	Control signal rear heated oxygen sensor (HO2S), heating	U_{bat}	Heating off: U ≈ U_{bat} Heating on: U ≈ 0.4 V	
#A30	Signal (+) rear knock sensor (KS) (Measured to #A17)	U_{low}		
#A31	Signal	engine coolant temperature (ECT) sensor	(+20 °C) U ≈ 1.81 V (+30 °C) U ≈ 1.34 V (+45 °C) U ≈ 0.83 V (+46 °C) U ≈ 4.0 V (+80 °C) U ≈ 2.73 V (+100 °C) U ≈ 1.96 V	
		(At engine coolant temperature (ECT) +46°C the engine control module (ECM) changes voltage range)		
#A32	Signal (+) front heated oxygen sensor (HO2S)	U = 1.1 – 1.2 V (Measured to #A42)	U oscillates between 0.0 – 0.9V when the heated oxygen sensor (HO2S) is warm. Low voltage = engine lean High voltage = engine rich (Measured to #A33)	
#A33	Signal (–) front heated oxygen sensor (HO2S)	U ≈ 0.7 V	Only measured with ignition on	

VV1029700103030X

Fig. 11 Motronic 4.4 signal specifications (Part 3 of 7)

Terminal	Signal type	Ignition on	Idling	Remarks
#A34	Signal (+) rear heated oxygen sensor (HO2S)	U_{low} (measured to #A42)	U on even load approx. 0.6 V can vary between 0.0 – 0.9 V depending on drop in load. (measured to #A19)	
#A35	–	–	–	–
#A36	Power supply camshaft position (CMP) sensor	U ≈ U_{bat}		
#A37	Pulsed secondary air injection system (PAIR) pump valve control signal	U_{bat}	pulsed secondary air injection system (PAIR) pump valve not active ≈ U_{bat}	active ≈ U_{low}
#A38	Control signal injector 2	U_{bat}	t ≈ 2.2 – 3.6 ms	t increases with engine speed (RPM) and load (Measured with EVAP not active)
#A39	Control signal Canister purge (CP) valve	U_{bat}	Canister purge (CP) valve: %duty = 0 – 33%	
#A40	–	–	–	–
#A41	Control signal Main relay	U ≈ 1 V		
#A42	Signal ground control module (Measured to battery negative terminal)	U_{low}		
#A43	–	–	–	–

VV1029700103040X

Fig. 11 Motronic 4.4 signal specifications (Part 4 of 7)

replace front heated oxygen sensor. If reading is not one volt, proceed to next step.

4. Disconnect rear heated oxygen sensor (gray connector) and turn ignition switch to On position and measure voltage between test box terminals No. 33 and No. 42. If reading is one volt, replace rear heated oxygen sensor. If reading is not one volt, repair or replace harness as necessary.

CODE P0133: FRONT HEATED OXYGEN SENSOR SLOW INPUT

1. Check compression on all cylinders. If compression check is within specification, proceed to next step. If compression is not within specification, repair as necessary.
2. Inspect intake system connectors and hoses for air leakage. If leakage is not present, proceed to next step. If leakage is present, repair as necessary.
3. Inspect exhaust system for leaks. If there is no leakage present, proceed to next step. If exhaust leakage is present, repair or replace as necessary.
4. Check fuel pressure. If fuel pressure is within specifications, replace front heated oxygen sensor.

CODE P0135: FRONT HEATED OXYGEN SENSOR PREHEATING

1. Turn ignition switch to Off position, disconnect front heated oxygen sensor (black connector).
2. Turn ignition switch to On position and connect a suitable multimeter between front heated oxygen sensor connector terminal No. 1 and ground. If reading is equal to battery voltage, proceed to next step. If reading is not equal to battery voltage, repair or replace wiring harness as necessary.
3. Connect multimeter between front heated oxygen sensor connector terminal No. 2 (ECM side) and ground. If reading is zero, proceed to next step. If reading is not zero, repair or replace wiring harness as necessary.
4. Turn ignition switch to Off position and disconnect ECM connector, then connect multimeter between front heated oxygen sensor connector terminal No. 2 (ECM side) and ground. If resistance is infinite, proceed to next step. If resistance is not infinite, repair or replace wiring harness as necessary.
5. Connect test box tool No. 981 3190, or equivalent, to ECM connector and test ground terminals.
6. Connect multimeter between front heated oxygen sensor connector terminal No. 2 (ECM side) and test box terminal No. 14. If resistance is zero ohms, proceed to next step. If resistance is not zero ohms, repair or replace wiring harness as necessary.
7. Connect front heated oxygen sensor and disconnect ECM connector.
8. Connect multimeter between test box tool No. 981 3190, or equivalent, terminals No. 27 and 14. If resistance is 1.5–13 ohms, repair faulty front heated sensor connector. If resistance is not 1.5–13 ohms, replace front heated oxygen sensor.

CODE P0136: REAR HEATED OXYGEN SENSOR SIGNAL

1. Turn ignition switch to Off position and disconnect rear heated oxygen sensor (gray connector). Connect a suitable multimeter between rear heated oxygen sensor connector terminal (ECM side) No. 4 and ground. If resistance is 50 Kohms, proceed to next step. If resistance is not 50 Kohms, repair wiring harness and/or connector.
2. Connect multimeter between rear heated oxygen sensor connector terminal (ECM side) No. 3 and ground. If resistance is 200 ohms, proceed to next step. If resistance is not 200 ohms, repair wiring harness and/or connector.
3. Connect suitable scan tool, then start and idle engine. Access scrolling values. If rear heated oxygen sensor value is .1–.9 V within 10 minutes, repair harness and/or connector. If rear heated oxygen sensor value is not .1–.9 V within 10 minutes and replace rear heated oxygen sensor.

Terminal	Signal type	Ignition on	Idling	Remarks
#B1	Power supply Accelerometer	$U \approx 5.0$ V		
B2*	Signal torque limiting (From automatic transmission)	$U \approx 1–2$ V below U_{bat}		U_{low} on ignition retardation request (retardation level 2 and 3)
#B3	Signal torque limiting (From automatic transmission)	$U \approx 1–2$ V below U_{bat}		U_{low} on ignition retardation request (retardation level 1 and 3)
#B4	Signal torque limiting acknowledgement (To automatic transmission)	$U \approx 2.0$ V below U_{bat}		U_{low} when request has been received
#B5	–	–	–	–
#B6	Signal A/C compressor status	U_{low}	A/C compressor off: $U < 0.1$ V A/C–compressor on: $U \approx U_{bat}$	–
#B7	Control signal malfunction indicator lamp (MIL) (To combined instrument panel)	Lamp lit: $U \approx 0.8$ V Lamp out: U_{bat}		
#B8	–	–	–	–
#B9	Signal A/C pressure sensor	$U \approx 0.9$ V	$U \approx 0.9$ V (When the A/C system has not been connected) U increases with A/C pressure	–
#B10	–	–	–	–
#B11	Control signal ignition driver stage	$U \approx 0.1$ V	$f \approx 35$ Hz *	U and f increase with engine speed.
#B12	Signal load Tq, (To automatic transmission)	$U \approx 0.8$ V	$f \approx 35$ Hz	f increases with engine speed (RPM)
#B13	–	–	–	–
#B14	–	–	–	–
#B15	Power supply fuel tank pressure sensor	$U \approx 5$ V		–
#B16	–	–	–	–
#B17	–	–	–	–
#B18	Signal speed (From combined instrument panel)	$U \approx U_{low}$ or U_{bat} (Voltage depending on position of front wheels)		f increases with speed $f = 40$ Hz at 20 km/h.

VV1029700103050X

Fig. 11 Motronic 4.4 signal specifications (Part 5 of 7)

Terminal	Signal type	Ignition on	Idling	Remarks
#B19	Control signal EVAP canister shut-off valve	$U \approx U_{bat}$	Closed $U \approx U_{bat}$	Active $U \approx U_{low}$
#B20	Signal throttle position (TP) sensor (To automatic transmission)	$U \approx 0.5$ V at closed throttle position (CTP) (idling) $U \approx 4.3$ V at wide open throttle (WOT)		
#B21	Signal tachometer (To combined instrument panel)	$U \approx U_{bat}$	$f \approx 28$ Hz	f increases with engine speed (RPM)
#B22		–	–	–
#B23	Signal engine coolant temperature (ECT) (To ECC and combined instrument panel)	Cold engine (+20°C): $f \approx 40$ Hz Warm engine (+100°C): $f \approx 21$ Hz		
#B24	Signal constant idle speed compensation P/N position, (From the automatic transmission).	P/N position: $U \approx U_{bat}$ Other positions: $U \approx U_{low}$ Manual $U \approx 9.0$ V		
#B25	Signal A/C relay, status	U_{low}	A/C relay not activated: $U < 0.1$ V A/C–relay activated: $U \approx U_{bat}$	
#B26	Signal malfunction indicator lamp (MIL) request (From automatic transmission)	$U \approx 0 – 1$ V	$U \approx U_{bat}$ NOTE! Other values apply if there are diagnostic trouble codes (DTCs) stored in the transmission control module (TCM)	
#B27	Control signal fuel pump (FP)	$U \approx 7.5$ V	$f = 42$ Hz (multimeter set to U_{AC})	
#B28	Signal ground sensor (Measured to battery negative terminal)	$U < 0.1$ V		
#B29	Power supply A/C pressure sensor	$U \approx 5.0$ V		
#B30	–	–	–	–

VV1029700103060X

Fig. 11 Motronic 4.4 signal specifications (Part 6 of 7)

CODE P0137: REAR HEATED OXYGEN SENSOR LOW INPUT

1. Connect test box tool No. 981 3190, or equivalent, and test ground terminals.
2. Turn ignition switch to On position and connect a suitable multimeter between test box terminals No. 33 and No. 42. If reading is one volt, proceed to next step. If reading is not one volt, repair wiring harness and/or connector.
3. Connect multimeter between test box terminals No. 32 and No. 42. If reading is 1.5 volts, proceed to next step. If reading is not 1.5 volts, repair wiring harness and or connector.
4. Turn ignition switch to Off position and disconnect rear heated oxygen sensor (gray connector). Turn ignition switch to On position and connect multimeter between test box terminals No. 34 and No. 42. If reading is 1.5 volts, replace front heated oxygen sensor. If reading is not 1.5 volts, repair wiring harness and/or connector.

CODE P0138: REAR HEATED OXYGEN SENSOR HIGH INPUT

1. Connect test box tool No. 981 3190, or equivalent, and test ground terminals.
2. Connect ECM and turn ignition switch to On position. Connect voltmeter between test box terminals No. 33 and No. 42. If reading is one volt, proceed to next step. If reading is not one volt, further diagnosis is required to determine fault.
3. Turn ignition switch to Off position and disconnect front heated oxygen sensor (black connector).
4. Connect ECM and voltmeter between test box terminals No. 33 and No. 42. If reading is one volt, replace front heated oxygen sensor. If reading is not one volt, proceed to next step.
5. Disconnect front heated oxygen sensor and rear heated oxygen sensor (gray connector).
6. Turn ignition switch to On position and connect voltmeter between test box terminals No. 33 and No. 42. If reading is one volt and replace rear heated oxygen sensor. If reading is not one volt, repair wiring harness and/or connector.

CODE P0140: REAR HEATED OXYGEN SENSOR CONTROL

1. Complete a compression check on all cylinders. If compression check is within specifications, proceed to next step. If compression is not within specifications, repair fault as necessary.
2. Inspect intake system connectors and hoses for air leakage. If leakage is not present, proceed to next step. If leakage is present, repair fault on intake system.
3. Inspect exhaust system for leaks. If there is no leakage present, proceed to next step. If exhaust leakage is present, repair or replace as necessary.
4. Turn ignition switch to Off position and install pressure gauge kit tool No. 999 5011, 998 9725, 999 5479, or equivalents.

Terminal	Signal type	Ignition on	Idling	Remarks
#B31	Fuel tank pressure sensor (Only certain markets)	U_{max} ≈ 4.7 V U_{nom} ≈ 2.5 V U_{min} = 0.6 V		
#B32	Signal accelerometer	U ≈ 2.5 V		
#B33	–	–	–	–
#B34	–	–	–	–
#B35	–	–	–	–
#B36	Diagnostic lead K–link	U ≈ 1– 2 V below U_{bat}	Other values apply if a generic fault-tracing instrument is connected to the data link connector (DLC)	
#B37	–	–	–	–
#B38	Control signal pulsed secondary air injection system (PAIR) pump relay	U ≈ U_{bat}	pulsed secondary air injection system (PAIR) pump valve off U ≈ U_{bat}	pulsed secondary air injection system (PAIR) pump valve active U ≈ U_{low}
#B39	Signal fuel consumption (To trip computer)	U ≈ 2 V below U_{bat} Trip computer absent: U ≈ U_{bat}	f ≈ 14 – 25 Hz	f increases with engine speed (RPM) and load (Measured with EVAP not active)
#B40	Control signal A/C relay (Allows A/C start)	U ≈ 9 V	A/C not permitted: U_{low} A/C not permitted: U ≈ 11 V	
#B41	–	–	–	–
#B42	–	–	–	–
#B43	–	–	–	–

VV1029700103070X

Fig. 11 Motronic 4.4 signal specifications (Part 7 of 7)

U =	DC in volts (V)	U_{AC} =	AC in volts (V)
U_{bat} =	battery voltage	f =	frequency in Hertz (Hz)
U_{low} =	voltage approx. 0 V or O V	%duty =	duty cycle (pulse ratio) as a percentage (%)
t=	time in milliseconds (ms)		

Terminal	Signal type	Ignition on	Idling	Remarks
#A1	–	–	–	–
#A2	Signal (+) front knock sensor (KS) (measured to #A17)	U_{low}		
#A3	Power ground mass air flow (MAF) sensor	U_{low}		
#A4	Signal mass air flow (MAF) sensor (measured to #A5)	U = 0.1 – 0.2 V	U ≈ 0.9 V	U increases with increasing air mass
#A5	Signal ground mass air flow (MAF) sensor	U_{low}		
#A6	Signal ground engine speed (RPM) sensor	U_{low}		
#A7	Control signal engine cooling fan (FC) low-speed	Engine cooling fan (FC) off: U_{bat} Engine cooling fan (FC) on: U ≈ 0.1 V		
#A8	–	–	–	–
#A9	Control signal injector 5	U_{bat}	t = 2.2 – 3.6 ms	t increases with engine speed (RPM) and load (measured with EVAP not active)

VV1029800106010X

Fig. 12 Motronic 4.4 signal specifications (Part 1 of 8). C70, S70 & V70

5. Remove fuel pump relay and start fuel pump using a jumper harness across fuel pump relay base terminals No. 1 and No. 3. If system pressure is as specified in "Gasoline Engine Tune Up Specifications," proceed to next step. If system pressure is not as specified in "Gasoline Engine Tune Up Specifications," replace pressure regulator.
6. Disconnect jumper harness between fuel pump relay terminals No. 1 and No. 3 and install fuel pump relay.
7. If residual pressure does not fall below 29 psi in less than 20 minutes, proceed to next step. If pressure does fall below 29 psi, repair fault as necessary.
8. Ensure ignition switch is in Off position and remove pressure gauge kit.
9. If both pressure readings were within specifications, replace rear heated oxygen sensor. If both pressure readings were not within specifications, repair fault as necessary.

CODE P0141: REAR HEATED OXYGEN SENSOR PREHEATING

1. Ensure ignition switch is in Off position and disconnect rear heated oxygen sensor (gray connector).
2. Turn ignition switch to On position and connect voltmeter between rear heated oxygen sensor connector terminal (main relay 2/32 side) No. 1 and ground. If reading is battery voltage, proceed to next step. If reading is not battery voltage, repair harness and/or connector.
3. Connect voltmeter between rear heated oxygen sensor connector terminal (ECM side) No. 2 and ground. If reading is zero volts, proceed to next step. If reading is not zero volts, repair wiring harness and/or connector.
4. Turn ignition switch to Off position, and disconnect rear heated oxygen sensor and ECM. Connect ohmmeter between rear heated oxygen sensor connector terminal (ECM side) No. 2 and ground. If resistance is infinite, proceed to next step. If resistance is not infinite, repair wiring harness and/or connector.
5. Connect test box tool No. 981 3190, or equivalent, and test ground terminals. Connect ohmmeter between rear heated oxygen sensor connector terminal (ECM side) No. 2 and test box terminal No. 14. If resistance is zero ohms, proceed to next step. If resistance is not zero ohms, repair wiring harness and/or connector.
6. Connect a ohmmeter between test box tool connector terminals No. 27 and No. 14. If resistance is 1.5–13 ohms, repair fault in rear heated sensor connector contact. If resistance is not 1.5–13 ohms, replace front heated oxygen sensor.

CODE P0171: LONG TERM FUEL TRIM LOW INPUT

1. Disconnect MAF sensor and turn ignition switch to On position. Connect a voltmeter between MAF connector terminals No. 2 and No. 4. If reading is .1–.2 volts, proceed to next step. If reading is not .1–.2 volts, replace MAF sensor.
2. Inspect exhaust system for leaks. If there is no leakage present, proceed to next step. If exhaust leakage is present, repair or replace as necessary.
3. Turn ignition switch to Off position and install pressure gauge kit tool No. 999 5011, 998 9725, 999 5479, or equivalents.
4. Remove fuel pump relay and start fuel pump using a jumper harness across fuel pump relay base terminals No. 1 and No. 3. If system pressure is as specified in "Gasoline Engine Tune Up Specifications,"proceed to next step. If system pressure is not as specified in "Gasoline Engine Tune Up Specifications," replace pressure regulator.
5. Disconnect jumper harness between fuel pump relay terminals No. 1 and No. 3 and install fuel pump relay.
6. If residual pressure does not fall below 29 psi in less than 20 minutes, proceed. If pressure does fall below 29 psi, repair fault as necessary.
7. Ensure ignition switch is in Off position and remove pressure gauge kit.
8. If both pressure readings were within specifications, replace rear heated oxygen sensor. If both pressure readings were not within specifications, repair fault as necessary.
9. Remove hose to intake manifold from canister purge valve, connect a vacuum pump tool No. 999 5843, or equivalent, to canister purge valve connector, then pump up a vacuum. If vacuum readings remain steady, proceed to next step. If vacuum readings do not remain steady, replace canister purge valve.
10. Remove oil dipstick and inspect engine oil level. If oil level is between marks MIN and MAX, proceed to next step. If oil level is not between marks, add oil until level is within specifications.
11. Connect suitable scan tool, and start and idle engine for three minutes. Access scrolling values, read and record short term fuel trim value. Disconnect

Terminal	Signal type	Ignition on	Idling	Remarks
#A10	Control signal injector 1	U_{bat}	t = 2.2 – 3.6 ms	t increases with engine speed (RPM) and load (measured with EVAP not active)
#A11	Opening signal idle air control (IAC) valve	%duty ≈ 25%	%duty = 21 – 32%	%duty increases with load (measured with EVAP not active)
#A12	15–supply (power supply from ignition switch)	U_{bat}		
#A13	Power ground	U_{low}		
#A14	Control signal front heated oxygen sensor (HO2S), preheating	U_{bat}	Preheating off: $U \approx U_{bat}$ Preheating on: U ≈ 0.4 V	
#A15	Power supply throttle position (TP) sensor	U ≈ 4.8 V		
#A16	Signal throttle position (TP) sensor	U ≈ 0.5 V at closed throttle position (CTP) (idling) U ≈ 4.3 V at wide open throttle (WOT)		
#A17	Signal (–) front and rear knock sensors (KS)	U_{low}		
#A18	Signal ground sensor (measured to battery negative terminal)	U_{low}		
#A19	Signal (–) rear heated oxygen sensor (HO2S)	U ≈ 0.7 V	Only measured with ignition on	
#A20	Signal engine speed (RPM) sensor (measured to #A6)	U_{low}	$U_{AC} \approx$ 1.6 V f = 825 Hz	
#A21	Signal camshaft position (CMP) sensor	$U = U_{low}$ or 5.0 V $U = U_{low}$ or U_{bat}	f ≈ 7 Hz	f increases with engine speed (RPM)
#A22	Control signal engine cooling fan (FC) high-speed	Engine cooling fan (FC) off: U_{bat} Engine cooling fan (FC) on: U < 0.3 V		
#A23	Control signal injector 4	U_{bat}	t = 2.2 – 3.6 ms	t increases with engine speed (RPM) and load (measured with EVAP not active)

VV1029800106020X

Fig. 12 Motronic 4.4 signal specifications (Part 2 of 8). C70, S70 & V70

Terminal	Signal type	Ignition on	Idling	Remarks
#A24	Control signal injector 3	U_{bat}	t = 2.2 – 3.6 ms	t increases with engine speed (RPM) and load (measured with EVAP not active)
#A25	Closing signal idle air control (IAC) valve	%duty = 75%	%duty = 68 – 78%	% duty decreases with load (measured with EVAP not active)
#A26	30–supply (power supply from battery)	U_{bat}		
#A27	Power supply (from main relay)	U_{bat}		
#A28	Power ground engine control module (ECM)	U_{low}		
#A29	Control signal rear heated oxygen sensor (HO2S), preheating	U_{bat}	Preheating off: $U \approx U_{bat}$ Preheating on: U ≈ 0.4 V	
#A30	Signal (+) rear knock sensor (KS) (Measured to #A17)	U_{low}		
#A31	Signal	Engine coolant temperature (ECT) sensor (At engine coolant temperature (ECT) +46°C (114.8°F) the engine control module (ECM) changes voltage range)	(+20 °C (68°F)) U ≈ 1.81 V (+30 °C (86°F)) U ≈ 1.34 V (+45 °C (113°F)) U ≈ 0.83 V (+46 °C (114.8°F)) U ≈ 4.0 V (+80 °C (176°F)) U ≈ 2.73 V (+100 °C (212°F)) U ≈ 1.96 V	
#A32	Signal (+) front heated oxygen sensor (HO2S)	U = 1.1 – 1.2 V (measured to #A42)	U oscillates between 0.0 – 0.9 V when the heated oxygen sensor (HO2S) is warm. Low voltage = lean engine High voltage = rich engine (measured to #A33)	
#A33	Signal (–) front heated oxygen sensor (HO2S)	U ≈ 0.7 V	Only measured with ignition on	
#A34	Signal (+) rear heated oxygen sensor (HO2S)	U_{low} (measured to #A42)	U at even load approx. 0.6 V can vary between 0.0 – 0.9 V depending on drop in load (measured to #A19)	
#A35	Outside temperature sensor	U ≈ 4.9 V	–	–

VV1029800106030X

Fig. 12 Motronic 4.4 signal specifications (Part 3 of 8). C70, S70 & V70

and plug crankcase ventilation and read short term fuel trim value again. If values read same for both, proceed to next step. If values do not read same, replace oil and oil filter.

12. Connect test box tool No. 981 3190, or equivalent, and test ground terminals, then reconnect ECM. Refer to **Figs. 11 through 14,** for signal specifications.
13. If all signals are within specifications and fault was corrected. If all signals are not within specifications, repair fault in circuit.

CODE P0172: LONG TERM FUEL TRIM HIGH INPUT

1. Disconnect MAF sensor and turn ignition switch to On position. Connect a voltmeter between MAF connector terminals No. 2 and No. 4. If reading is .1–.2 volts, proceed to next step. If reading is not .1–.2 volts, replace MAF sensor.
2. Inspect intake system connectors and hoses for air leakage. If leakage is not present, proceed to next step. If leakage is present, repair fault on intake system.
3. Inspect exhaust system for leaks. If there is no leakage present, proceed to next step. If exhaust leakage is present, repair or replace as necessary.
4. Turn ignition switch to Off position and install pressure gauge kit tool No. 999 5011, 998 9725, 999 5479, or equivalents.
5. Remove fuel pump relay and start fuel pump using a jumper harness across fuel pump relay base terminals No. 1 and No. 3. If system pressure is as specified in "Gasoline Engine Tune Up Specifications," proceed to next step. If system pressure is not as specified in "Gasoline Engine Tune Up Specifications," replace pressure regulator.
6. Disconnect jumper harness between fuel pump relay terminals No. 1 and No. 3 and install fuel pump relay.
7. If residual pressure does not fall below 29 psi in less than 20 minutes, proceed. If pressure does fall below 29 psi, repair fault as necessary.
8. Ensure ignition switch is in Off position and remove pressure gauge kit.
9. If both pressure readings were within specifications, replace rear heated oxygen sensor. If both pressure readings were not within specifications, repair fault as necessary.
10. Connect test box tool No. 981 3190, or equivalent, and test ground terminals, then reconnect ECM. Refer to **Figs. 11 through 14,** for signal specifications. If all signals are within specifications and fault was corrected. If all signals are not within specifications, repair fault in circuit.

CODES P0201, P0202, P0203, P0204 & P0205: INJECTOR LOw/HIGH INPUT

1. Turn ignition switch to Off position and disconnect injector. Connect ohmmeter between: injector connector terminal No. 2 and ECM connector terminals No. A10, A38, A24, A23 and A9. If resistance is infinite, proceed to next step. If resistance is not infinite, repair wiring harness and/or connector.
2. Connect ohmmeter between injector connector terminals No. 1 and No. 2. If resistance is 16 ohms at 68°F, repair or replace harness. If resistance is not 16 ohms, replace injector.

CODE P0244: BOOST PRESSURE CONTROL

1. Turn ignition switch to On position and

Terminal	Signal type	Ignition on	Idling	Remarks
#A36	Power supply camshaft position (CMP) sensor	$U \approx U_{bat}$		
#A37	Pulsed secondary air injection system (PAIR) pump valve control signal	U_{bat}	pulsed secondary air injection system (PAIR) pump valve not active ≈ U_{bat}	active ≈ U_{low}
#A38	Control signal injector 2	U_{bat}	t ≈ 2.2 – 3.6 ms	t increases with engine speed (RPM) and load (measured with EVAP not active)
#A39	Control signal canister purge (CP) valve	U_{bat}	canister purge (CP) valve: %duty = 0 – 33%	
#A40	–	–	–	–
#A41	Control signal main relay	U ≈ 1 V		
#A42	Signal ground engine control module (ECM) (measured to battery negative terminal)	U_{low}		
#A43	–	–	–	–

VV1029800106040X

Fig. 12 Motronic 4.4 signal specifications (Part 4 of 8). C70, S70 & V70

Terminal	Signal type	Ignition on	Idling	Remarks
#B1	Power supply accelerometer	U ≈ 5.0 V		
#B2	Signal (+) torque limiting (from automatic transmission)	U ≈ 1– 2 V under U_{bat}		U_{low} on ignition retardation request (retardation level 2 and 3)
#B3	Signal torque limiting (from automatic transmission)	U ≈ 1– 2 V under U_{bat}		U_{low} on ignition retardation request (retardation level 1 and 3)
#B4	Signal torque limiting acknowledgement (to automatic transmission)	U ≈ 2.0 V under U_{bat}		U_{low} when request has been received
#B5	–	–	–	–
#B6	Signal air conditioning (A/C) compressor status	U_{low}	air conditioning (A/C) compressor off: U < 0.1 V air conditioning (A/C) compressor on: $U \approx U_{bat}$	–
#B7	Control signal malfunction indicator lamp (MIL) (to combined instrument panel)	Lamp lit: U ≈ 0.8 V Lamp unlit: U_{bat}		
#B8	–	–	–	–

VV1029800106050X

Fig. 12 Motronic 4.4 signal specifications (Part 5 of 8). C70, S70 & V70

ensure the Mass Air Flow (MAF) sensor is connected. Connect ohmmeter between MAF sensor connector terminals No. 2 and 4. If reading is .1–.2 volts, proceed to step 3. If reading is not .1–.2 volts, proceed to next step.

2. Turn ignition switch to Off position and inspect MAF sensor and Engine Control Module (ECM) connectors for contact resistance and oxidation, and repair as necessary. Connect MAF sensor and ECM, and turn ignition switch to On position. Connect voltmeter between MAF sensor connector terminals No. 2 and 4. If reading is .1–.2 volts, condition was caused by loose connection. If reading is not .1–.2 volts, replace MAF sensor.
3. Turn ignition switch to Off position, connect breakout box and inspect ground terminal. Disconnect ECM and turn ignition switch to On position. Connect voltmeter between breakout box connector No. B42 and ground. If reading is battery voltage, proceed to next step. If reading is not battery voltage, return to previous step.
4. Turn ignition switch to Off position and inspect turbocharger control valve and ECM connectors for contact resistance and oxidation, and repair as necessary. Connect control valve and ECM connectors, turn ignition switch to On position and activate turbocharger control valve. If control valve works, proceed to next step. If valve does not work, replace turbocharger control valve.
5. Turn ignition switch to Off position and ensure hoses between turbocharger and control valve, and control valve and pressure servo to boost pressure control valve are not blocked or pinched. Ensure when control valve is not active that valve is open between red and yellow connectors. If there is a blockage, repair as necessary. If there is no blockage, proceed to next step.
6. Turn ignition switch to Off position and disconnect hose from pressure servo. Connect manometer tool No. 999 5230 and pressure tester tool No. 999 5496, or equivalents, to pressure servo. Pump pressure to approximately 16.7 psi. If pressure servo opens fully, inspect pressure servo setting. If it does not open fully, replace pressure servo.

CODE P0244: TURBOCHARGER CONTROL VALVE SIGNAL MISSING

1. Turn ignition switch to Off position and disconnect turbocharger control valve. Turn ignition switch to On position and connect voltmeter between valve connector No. 1 and ground. If reading is battery voltage, proceed to next step. If reading is not battery voltage, inspect harness between valve terminal No. 1 and main relay (2/32) terminal No. 3 for open circuit. Repair as necessary and proceed to next step.
2. With ignition switch in On position and control valve disconnected, connect voltmeter between valve connector No. 2 and ground. If reading is approximately six volts, proceed to next step. If reading is not approximately six volts, proceed to step 4.
3. With ignition switch in Off position and control valve disconnected, connect ohmmeter between valve connector terminals No. 1 and 2. If reading is 24 ohms at 60°F, condition was caused by loose control valve or ECM connections. Inspect for loose connectors, and contact resistance or oxidation, and repair as necessary. If reading is not 24 ohms at 60°F, replace control valve.
4. With ignition switch in Off position and control valve disconnected, inspect ECM connector for contact resistance or oxidation, and repair as necessary.
5. Connect ECM and turn ignition switch to On position. Connect voltmeter between control valve connector No. 2 and ground. If reading is approximately six volts, condition was caused by loose ECM connections. If reading is not approximately six volts, inspect harness between control valve terminal No. 2 and ECM No. B41 for open circuit, repair as necessary.

CODE P0245: TURBOCHARGER CONTROL VALVE SIGNAL LOW

1. Inspect harness between turbocharger control valve terminal No. 2 and ECM No. B41 for short circuit. Repair as necessary.
2. Turn ignition switch to On position and activate turbocharger control valve. If valve clicks when activated, condition has been corrected. If valve does not click, start test over.

CODE P0246: TURBOCHARGER CONTROL VALVE SIGNAL HIGH

1. Turn ignition switch to Off position and disconnect turbocharger control valve.
2. Connect ohmmeter between valve connector terminals No. 1 and 2.
3. If reading is approximately 24 ohms at 60°F, inspect harness between control valve terminal No. 2 and ECM No. B41 for short circuit. Repair as necessary and proceed to next step. If reading is not approximately 24 ohms at 60°F, install new control valve and proceed to next step.
4. Turn ignition switch to On position and activate turbocharger control valve. If valve clicks when activated, condition has been corrected. If valve does not click, start test over.

CODES P0300, P0301, P0302, P0303, P0304 & P0305: MISFIRING CYLINDER

1. Remove all spark plugs and inspect them individually. If a spark plug is a

Terminal	Signal type	Ignition on	Idling	Remarks
#B9	Signal air conditioning (A/C) pressure sensor	U ≈ 0.9 V	U ≈ 0.9 V (when the air conditioning (A/C) has not been connected) U increases with air conditioning (A/C) pressure	–
#B10	–	–	–	–
#B11	Control signal ignition driver stage	U ≈ 0.1 V	f ≈ 35 Hz *	U and f increase with engine speed
#B12	Signal load Tq (to automatic transmission)	U ≈ 0.8 V	f ≈ 35 Hz	f increases with engine speed (RPM)
#B13	–	–	–	–
#B14	–	–	–	–
#B15	Power supply fuel tank pressure sensor	U ≈ 5 V		–
#B16	–	–	–	–
#B17	–	–	–	–
#B18	Signal speed (from combined instrument panel)	U ≈ U_{low} or U_{bat} (voltage depending on position of front wheels)		f increases with speed f = 40 Hz at 20 km/h.
#B19	Control signal EVAP canister shut-off valve	U ≈ U_{bat}	Closed U ≈ U_{bat}	Active U ≈ U_{low}
#B20	Signal throttle position (TP) sensor (to automatic transmission)	U ≈ 0.5 V at closed throttle position (CTP) (idling) U ≈ 4.3 V at wide open throttle (WOT)		
#B21	Signal tachometer (to combined instrument panel)	U ≈ U_{bat}	f ≈ 28 Hz	f increases with engine speed (RPM)
#B22	Atmospheric pressure sensor	U ≈ 4.6 V	–	–
#B23	Signal engine coolant temperature (ECT) (to ECC and combined instrument panel)	Cold engine (+20°C (68°F)): f ≈ 40 Hz Hot engine (+100°C (212°F)): f ≈ 21 Hz		
#B24	Signal constant idle speed compensation P/N-position (from automatic transmission)	P/N–position: U ≈ U_{bat} Other positions: U ≈ U_{low} Manual: U ≈ 9.0 V		

VV1029800106060X

Fig. 12 Motronic 4.4 signal specifications (Part 6 of 8). C70, S70 & V70

Terminal	Signal type	Ignition on	Idling	Remarks
#B25	Signal air conditioning (A/C) relay status	U_{low}	air conditioning (A/C) relay not activated: U < 0.1 V air conditioning (A/C) relay activated: U ≈ U_{bat}	
#B26	Signal malfunction indicator lamp (MIL) request (from automatic transmission)	U ≈ 0 – 1 V	U ≈ U_{bat} **NOTE!** Other values apply if there are diagnostic trouble codes (DTCs) stored in the transmission control module (TCM)	
#B27	Control signal fuel pump (FP)	U ≈ 7.5 V	f ≈ 42 Hz (multimeter set to U_{AC})	
#B28	Signal ground sensor (measured to battery negative terminal)	U < 0.1 V		
#B29	Power supply air conditioning (A/C) pressure sensor	U ≈ 5.0 V		
#B30	–	–	–	–
#B31	Fuel tank pressure sensor (certain markets only)	U_{max} ≈ 4.7 V U_{nom} ≈ 2.5 V U_{min} ≈ 0.6 V		
#B32	Signal accelerometer	U ≈ 2.5 V		
#B33	–	–	–	–
#B34	–	–	–	–
#B35	–	–	–	–
#B36	Diagnostic lead K–link	U ≈ 1 – 2 V under U_{bat}	Other values apply if a generic fault-tracing instrument is connected to the data link connector (DLC)	
#B37	–	–	–	–
#B38	Control signal pulsed secondary air injection system (PAIR) pump relay	U ≈ U_{bat}	pulsed secondary air injection system (PAIR) pump valve of U ≈ U_{bat}	pulsed secondary air injection system (PAIR) pump valve active U ≈ U_{low}

VV1029800106070X

Fig. 12 Motronic 4.4 signal specifications (Part 7 of 8). C70, S70 & V70

lighter color than one from another cylinder, replace injector for cylinder in question. If a spark plug is a similar color, proceed to next step.

2. Complete a compression check on all cylinders. If compression check is within specifications, proceed to next step. If compression is not within specifications, repair fault as necessary.
3. Connect pressure tester tool No. 998 5496, or equivalent, to expansion tank and pump up pressure up to 14.5 psi. Shine a flashlight into each cylinder to ensure there is no leakage between cooling system and cylinder. If leakage is present, repair fault as necessary. If no leakage is present, proceed to next step.
4. Remove all spark plug wires and inspect them individually for damage, cracking and flashover. Using an ohmmeter, measure the resistance of each wire. If resistance is 1.5–4.5 Kohms at 68°F, proceed to next step. If resistance is not 1.5–4.5 Kohms, replace spark plug wire.
5. Remove distributor cap and inspect both the cap and rotor for damage, cracking and flashover. If fault is suspected, repair or replace as necessary. If fault is not suspected, proceed to next step.
6. Connect suitable scan tool, and start and idle engine. Access parameter list. If values B, C, D and E reads -.391 to +.387, proceed to next step. If values B, C, D and E do not read -.391 to +.387, repair probable fault with RPM sensor probe and/or flywheel/pulse wheel.
7. Further diagnosis is required to determine condition of injector harness and terminals. If both harness and terminals are determined to be in satisfactory condition, proceed to next step. If both harness and terminals are determined not to be in satisfactory condition, repair fault as necessary.
8. Inspect intake system connectors and hoses for air leakage. If leakage is not present, proceed to next step. If leakage is present, repair fault on intake system.
9. Turn ignition switch to Off position and install pressure gauge kit tool No. 999 5011, 998 9725, 999 5479, or equivalents.
10. Remove fuel pump relay and start fuel pump using a jumper harness across fuel pump relay base terminals No. 1 and No. 3. If system pressure is as specified in "Gasoline Engine Tune Up Specifications," proceed to next step. If system pressure is not as specified in "Gasoline Engine Tune Up Specifications," replace pressure regulator.
11. Disconnect jumper harness between fuel pump relay terminals No. 1 and No. 3 and install fuel pump relay.
12. If residual pressure does not fall below 29 psi in less than 20 minutes, proceed. If pressure does fall below 29 psi, repair fault as necessary.
13. Ensure ignition switch is in Off position and remove pressure gauge kit.
14. If both pressure readings were within specifications, replace rear heated oxygen sensor. If both pressure readings were not within specifications, repair fault as necessary.

CODES P0325 & P0330: KNOCK SENSOR SIGNAL

1. Turn ignition switch to Off position and wait approximately 2½ minutes (cars with immobilizer, 4 minutes).
2. Disconnect knock sensor and connect a suitable ohmmeter between knock sensor connector terminal No. 2 and ground. If resistance is zero ohms, proceed to next step. If resistance is not zero ohms, repair wiring harness and/or connector.
3. Connect ohmmeter between knock sensor connector terminal No. 1 and ground. If resistance is 1,000 ohms, proceed to next step. If resistance is

Terminal	Signal type	Ignition on	Idling	Remarks
#B39	Signal fuel consumption (to trip computer)	$U \approx 2$ V under U_{bat} Trip computer absent: $U \approx U_{bat}$	$f \approx 14 - 25$ Hz	f increases with engine speed (RPM) and load (measured with EVAP not active)
#B40	Control signal air conditioning (A/C) relay (allows A/C start)	$U \approx 9$ V	air conditioning (A/C) not permitted: U_{low} air conditioning (A/C) not permitted: $U \approx 11$ V	
#B41	Turbocharger (TC) control valve control signal	U_{bat}	–	Voltage decreases with increased valve synchronization.
#B42	Turbocharger (TC) boost pressure limiting signal (from automatic transmission)	–	–	–
#B43	–	–	–	–

VV1029800106080X

Fig. 12 Motronic 4.4 signal specifications (Part 8 of 8). C70, S70 & V70

not 1,000 ohms, repair wiring harness and/or connector.

4. Connect suitable scan tool, and start engine and warm-up to working temperature. Access scrolling values and rev engine to 3500 RPM. If knock sensor signal value is 2–6 at engine speeds above 3500 RPM, repair fault in knock sensor connector contact. If knock sensor signal value is not 2–6 at engine speeds above 3500 RPM, replace knock sensor.

CODE P0335: ENGINE SPEED SENSOR SIGNAL

1. Turn ignition switch to Off position and disconnect RPM sensor. Connect a suitable ohmmeter between RPM sensor connector terminals (ECM side) No. 1 and No. 2. If resistance is 200–500 ohms, proceed to next step. If resistance is not 200–500 ohms, replace RPM sensor.
2. Connect ohmmeter between RPM sensor connector terminal (ECM side) No. 2 and ground. If resistance is zero ohms, proceed to next step. If resistance is not zero ohms, repair wiring harness and/or connector.
3. Connect ohmmeter between RPM connector terminal (ECM side) No. 1 and ground. If resistance is 15–25 Kohms, proceed to next step. If resistance is not 15–25 Kohms, repair wiring harness and/or connector.
4. Turn ignition switch to On position and disconnect RPM sensor. Connect voltmeter between RPM connector terminals (ECM side) No. 1 and No. 2. If reading is 1–2 volts, repair fault in ECM connector contact. If reading is 1–2 volts, repair wiring harness.

CODE P0340: CAMSHAFT POSITION SENSOR SIGNAL

1. Ensure ignition switch is in Off position and disconnect CMP sensor, then connect a suitable ohmmeter between CMP connector (ECM side) No. 1 and ground. If resistance is zero ohms, proceed to next step. If resistance is not zero ohms, repair wiring harness.
2. Turn ignition switch to On position and disconnect CMP sensor. Connect voltmeter between CMP connector (ECM side) No. 3 and ground. If reading is battery voltage, proceed to next step. If reading is not battery voltage, repair wiring harness.
3. Connect voltmeter between CMP connector (ECM side) No. 2 and chassis ground. If reading is battery voltage, proceed to next step. If voltage is not battery voltage, repair wiring harness and/or connector.
4. Connect a test lamp between CMP connector (ECM side) No. 2 and chassis ground. If test lamp lights, repair wiring harness. If test lamp did not light, proceed to next step.
5. Connect CMP sensor and try to start engine. If engine starts, repair CMP connector contact. If engine does not start, replace CMP sensor.

Terminal	Signal type	Ignition on.	Idling	Miscellaneous
#A1	–	–	–	–
#A2	Signal (+), front knock sensor (KS) (measured to #A17)	U_{low}		
#A3	Power ground, mass air flow (MAF) sensor	U_{low}		
#A4	Signal, mass air flow (MAF) sensor (measured to #A5)	$U = 0.1 - 0.2$ V	$U \approx 1.0$ V	U increases with increasing air mass
#A5	Signal ground, mass air flow (MAF) sensor	U_{low}		
#A6	Signal ground, engine speed (RPM) sensor	U_{low}		
#A7	Control signal, engine cooling fan (FC) low-speed	Engine cooling fan (FC) off: U_{bat} Engine cooling fan (FC) on: $U < 0.3$ V ≈ 0.1 V		
#A8	–	–	–	–
#A9	Control signal, injector 6	U_{bat}	$t = 2.2 - 3.6$ ms	t increases with engine speed (RPM) and load (Measured with EVAP not active)
#A10	Control signal, injector 1	U_{bat}	$t = 2.2 - 3.6$ ms	t increases with engine speed (RPM) and load (Measured with EVAP not active)
#A11	Opening signal, idle air control (IAC) valve	%duty ≈ 25%	%duty = 21 – 32%	%duty increases with load (Measured with EVAP not active)

VV1029800108010X

Fig. 13 Motronic 4.4 signal specifications (Part 1 of 6)

CODE P0410: PULSED SECONDARY AIR INJECTION SYSTEM

1. Ensure ignition switch is in Off position and remove power harness from pump relay. Connect voltmeter to measure voltage between relay connector A and ground. If reading is battery voltage, proceed to next step. If voltage is not battery voltage, repair wiring harness and/or connector
2. Disconnect harness from relay connector B and connect ohmmeter between relay connector B and ground. If resistance is infinite, proceed to next step. If resistance is not infinite, repair wiring harness.
3. Connect test box tool No. 981 3190, or equivalent, and test ground terminals. Disconnect PAIR pump relay harness and connect ohmmeter between relay connector B terminal No. 1 and ground. If resistance is zero ohms, proceed to next step. If resistance is not zero ohms, repair wiring harness.
4. Connect all harnesses to PAIR (pump relay). Connect suitable scan tool, then turn ignition switch to On position. Select "Components/Functions," to activate PAIR pump. If pump is activated, repair fault in PAIR pump relay connector contact. If pump is not activated, replace PAIR pump relay.
5. Carefully disconnect lilac hose from solenoid valve. Connect a vacuum gauge to solenoid valve. Connect suitable scan tool, and start and idle engine.
6. When engine coolant temperature is above 140°F, select "Components/Functions" to activate PAIR pump. If vacuum gauge gives a reading, proceed to next step. If vacuum gauge does not give a reading, repair wiring harness.
7. Disconnect PAIR valve from pipe, leave hoses in place. Connect a scan tool and turn ignition switch to On position. Select "Components/Functions" to activate pump. If air leaked through valve outlet, replace PAIR solenoid valve. If air does not leak through valve outlet, then further diagnosis is required to determine fault.
8. Disconnect solenoid valve connector and connect a vacuum gauge to solenoid valve. Connect suitable scan tool, and start and idle engine. When engine coolant temperature is above 140°F, select "Components/Functions" to activate PAIR pump. If vacuum gauge gives a reading, replace solenoid valve. If vacuum gauge does not give a reading, repair wiring harness.

CODE P0412: PULSED SECONDARY AIR INJECTION MISSING SIGNAL

1. Ensure ignition switch is in Off position

Terminal	Signal type	Ignition on.	Idling	Miscellaneous
#A1	–	–	–	–
#A12	15–supply (power supply from ignition switch)	U_{bat}		
#A13	Power ground	U_{low}		
#A14	Control signal, preheating front heated oxygen sensor (HO2S)	U_{bat}	Preheating off: $U \approx U_{bat}$ Preheating on: $U \approx 0.4$ V	
#A15	Power supply, throttle position (TP) sensor	$U \approx 4.8$ V		
#A16	Signal, throttle position (TP) sensor	$U \approx 0.5$ V at closed throttle position (CTP) (idling) $U \approx 4.5$ V at wide open throttle (WOT)		
#A17	Signal (–), front and rear knock sensors (KS)	U_{low}		
#A18	Signal ground, sensor (measured to battery negative terminal)	U_{low}		
#A19	Signal (–), rear heated oxygen sensor (HO2S) Only certain markets.	$U \approx 0.7$ V	Only measured with ignition on	
#A20	Signal, engine speed (RPM) sensor (measured to #A6)	U_{low}	$U_{AC} \approx 1.8$ V f = 740 Hz	
#A21	Signal, camshaft position (CMP) sensor	$U = U_{low}$ or 5.0	f = 6 Hz	f increases with engine speed (RPM)
#A22	Control signal, engine cooling fan (FC) high-speed	Engine cooling fan (FC) off: U_{bat} Engine cooling fan (FC) on: $U < 0.3$ V		
#A23	Control signal, injector 3	U_{bat}	t = 2.2 – 3.6 ms	t increases with engine speed (RPM) and load (Measured with EVAP not active)
#A24	Control signal, injector 2	U_{bat}	t = 2.2 – 3.6 ms	t increases with engine speed (RPM) and load (Measured with EVAP not active)
#A25	Closing signal, idle air control (IAC) valve	%duty = 75%	%duty = 68 – 89%	% duty decreases with load (Measured with EVAP not active)
#A26	30–supply (supply voltage from battery)	U_{bat}		
#A27	Power supply (from main relay)	U_{bat}		
#A28	Power ground, control module	U_{low}		
#A29	Control signal, preheating rear heated oxygen sensor (HO2S) Only certain markets.	U_{bat}	Preheating off: $U \approx U_{bat}$ Preheating on: $U \approx 0.4$ V	
#A30	Signal (+), rear knock sensor (KS) (measured to #A17)	U_{low}		

VV1029800108020X

Fig. 13 Motronic 4.4 signal specifications (Part 2 of 6)

Terminal	Signal type	Ignition on.	Idling	Miscellaneous
#A1	–	–	–	–
#A31	Signal, engine coolant temperature (ECT) sensor	((+20°C (68°F)) ((+30°C (+86°F)) $U \approx 1.34$ V (+30°C (+86°F)) $U \approx 1.34$ V ((+45°C (+113°F)) $U \approx 0.83$ V (+45°C (+113°F)) $U \approx 0.83$ V (+46°C (+114.8°F)) $U \approx 4.0$ V (+80°C (+176°F)) $U \approx 2.73$ V (+100°C (+212°F)) $U \approx 1.96$ V (At engine coolant temperature (ECT) +46°C (+114.8°F) the engine control module (ECM) switches voltage range)		
#A32	Signal (+), front heated oxygen sensor (HO2S)	U = 1.1 – 1.2 V (measured to #A42)	U oscillates rapidly between 0.0 – 0.9 V when the heated oxygen sensor (HO2S) is hot. Low voltage = lean engine High voltage = rich engine (Measured to #A33)	
#A33	Signal (–), front heated oxygen sensor (HO2S)	$U \approx 0.7$ V	Only measured with ignition on	
#A34	Signal (+), rear heated oxygen sensor (HO2S) Only certain markets.	U = 1.18 V (measured to #A42)	U at even load approx. 0.7 V, can vary between 0.0 – 0.9 V depending on operating conditions. (Measured to #A19)	
#A35	–	–	–	–
#A36	Power supply, camshaft position (CMP) sensor	$U \approx U_{bat}$		
#A37	Control signal, pulsed secondary air injection system (PAIR) pump valve	–	–	
#A38	Control signal, injector 5	U_{bat}	t ≈ 2.2 – 3.6 ms	t increases with engine speed (RPM) and load (Measured with EVAP not active)
#A39	Control signal, canister purge (CP) valve	U_{bat}	Canister purge (CP) valve: %duty = 0 – 33%	
#A40	–	–	–	–
#A41	Control signal, main relay	$U \approx 1$ V		
#A42	Signal ground, control module (measured to battery negative terminal)	U_{low}		
#A43	Control signal, injector 4	U_{bat}	t ≈ 2.2 – 3.6 ms	t increases with engine speed (RPM) and load (Measured with EVAP not active)

VV1029800108030X

Fig. 13 Motronic 4.4 signal specifications (Part 3 of 6)

and disconnect solenoid valve connector. Turn ignition switch to On position and connect a suitable voltmeter between solenoid valve connector terminal No. 1 and ground. If reading is battery voltage, proceed to next step. If reading is not battery voltage, repair wiring harness.

2. Connect ohmmeter between solenoid valve connector terminals No. 1 and No. 2. If resistance is 30–33 ohms, proceed to next step. If resistance is not 30–33 ohms, replace solenoid valve.
3. Connect test box tool No. 981 3190, or equivalent, and test ground terminals. Connect ohmmeter between test box terminal No. 37 and solenoid valve connector terminal No. 2. If resistance is zero ohms, repair ECM and/or solenoid valve connector contacts. If resistance is not zero ohms, repair wiring harness.

CODES P0413 & P0414: PULSED SECONDARY AIR INJECTION HIGH/LOW INPUT

1. Ensure ignition switch is in Off position and disconnect solenoid valve connector.
2. Turn ignition switch to On position and connect a test lamp between solenoid valve connector terminal No. 2 and ground.
3. If test lamp lights, repair wiring harness. If test lamp did not light, replace solenoid valve.

CODE P0422: THREE WAY CATALYTIC CONVERTER LOW INPUT

1. Complete a compression check on all cylinders. If compression check is within specifications, proceed to next step. If compression is not within specifications, repair fault as necessary.
2. Inspect intake system connectors and hoses for air leakage. If leakage is not present, proceed to next step. If leakage is present, repair fault on intake system.
3. Inspect exhaust system for leaks. If there is no leakage present, proceed to next step. If exhaust leakage is present, repair or replace as necessary.
4. Turn ignition switch to Off position and install pressure gauge kit tool No. 999 5011, 998 9725, 999 5479, or equivalents.
5. Remove fuel pump relay and start fuel pump using a jumper harness across fuel pump relay base terminals No. 1 and No. 3. If system pressure is as specified in "Gasoline Engine Tune Up Specifications,"proceed to next step. If system pressure is not as specified in "Gasoline Engine Tune Up Specifications," replace pressure regulator.
6. Disconnect jumper harness between fuel pump relay terminals No. 1 and No. 3 and install fuel pump relay.
7. If residual pressure does not fall below 29 psi in less than 20 minutes, proceed. If pressure does fall below 29 psi, repair fault as necessary.
8. Ensure ignition switch is in Off position and remove pressure gauge kit.
9. If both pressure readings were within specifications, replace rear heated oxygen sensor. If both pressure readings were not within specifications, repair fault as necessary.

CODE P0440: EVAP CANISTER PURGE VALVE LEAKAGE

C70, S70 & V70

1. Start and idle engine. Open fuel tank filler cap and access scrolling values. If tank pressure is higher than -.14 psi, proceed to next step. If pressure is not more than -.14 psi, replace fuel tank pressure sensor.
2. Disconnect hose between canister purge valve and EVAP canister from valve. With engine idling, access scrolling values. If there is vacuum with

Terminal	Signal type	Ignition on.	Idling	Miscellaneous
#B1	Power supply Accelerometer Only certain markets.	U ≈ 5.0 V		
#B2	Signal, Torque limiting (from automatic transmission)	U ≈ 1 – 2 V below U_{bat}		U_{low} on ignition retardation request (retardation level 2 and 3)
#B3	Signal, Torque limiting (from automatic transmission)	U ≈ 1 – 2 V below U_{bat}		U_{low} on ignition retardation request (retardation level 1 and 3)
#B4	Signal, torque limiting acknowledged (to automatic transmission)	U ≈ 2.0 V under U_{bat}		U_{low} when request has been received
#B5	–	–	–	–
#B6	Signal, status air conditioning (A/C) compressor	U_{low}	air conditioning (A/C) compressor off: U < 0.1 V air conditioning (A/C) compressor on: U ≈ U_{bat}	–
#B7	Control signal,malfunction indicator lamp (MIL) (to combined instrument panel)	Lamp lit: U ≈ 0.8 V Lamp unlit: U_{bat}		
#B8	–	–	–	–
#B9	Signal, Air conditioning (A/C) pressure sensor	U ≈ 0.9 V	U ≈ 0.9 V (when the air conditioning has not been connected) U increases with air conditioning (A/C) pressure –	
#B10	Signal ignition coil cylinder 5	U ≈ 0.1 V	f ≈ 6.5 Hz U ≈ 0.2 V	U increases with engine speed (RPM)

VV1029800108040X

Fig. 13 Motronic 4.4 signal specifications (Part 4 of 6)

Terminal	Signal type	Ignition on.	Idling	Miscellaneous
#B11	Signal ignition coil cylinder 1 ignition discharge module (IDM)	U ≈ 0.1 V	f ≈ 6.5 Hz U ≈ 0.2 V	U increases with engine speed (RPM)
#B12	Signal,load tq (to automatic transmission)	U ≈ 0.8 V	f ≈ 37 Hz	f increases with engine speed (RPM)
#B13	Signal ignition coil cylinder 2	U ≈ 0.1 V	f ≈ 6.5 Hz U ≈ 0.2 V	U increases with engine speed (RPM)
#B14	Signal ignition coil cylinder 3	U ≈ 0.1 V	f ≈ 6.5 Hz U ≈ 0.2 V	U increases with engine speed (RPM)
#B15	– Fuel tank pressure sensor	–	–	–
#B16	–	–	–	–
#B17	–	–	–	–
#B18	Signal, Speed (from combined instrument panel)	U ≈ U_{low} or U_{bat} (Voltage depending on position of front wheels)		f increases with speed f ≈ 40 Hz at 20 km/h.
#B19	Control signal, fuel pump (FP)	U ≈ U_{bat}	U ≈ 0.1 V	–
#B20	Signal,Throttle position (TP) sensor (to automatic transmission)	U ≈ 0.5 V at closed throttle position (CTP) (idling) U ≈ 4.5 V at wide open throttle (WOT)		
#B21	Signal, Tachometer (to combined instrument panel)	U ≈ U_{bat}	f ≈ 25 Hz	f increases with engine speed (RPM)
#B22	–	–	–	–
#B23	Signal,engine coolant temperature (ECT) (to combined instrument panel)	Cold engine (+20°C (+68°F)): f ≈ 40 Hz Hot engine (+100°C (+212°F)): f ≈ 21 Hz		
#B24	Signal constant idle speed compensation P/N–position (from automatic transmission)	P/N–position: U ≈ U_{bat} Other positions: U ≈ U_{low} Manual U ≈ 9.0 V		
#B25	Air conditioning (A/C) request from climate control	U_{bat}	Air conditioning (A/C) request active: U ≈ 0.6 V Air conditioning (A/C) request not active: U ≈ U_{bat}	
#B26	Signal,request malfunction indicator lamp (MIL) (from automatic transmission)	U ≈ 0 – 1 V	U ≈ U_{bat} NOTE! Other values apply if there are diagnostic trouble codes (DTCs) stored in the transmission control module (TCM)	
#B27	– fuel pump (FP)	–	–	
#B28	Signal ground,sensor (measured to battery negative terminal)	U < 0.1 V		
#B29	Power supply,Air conditioning (A/C) pressure sensor	U ≈ 5.0 V		
#B30	–	–	–	–

VV1029800108050X

Fig. 13 Motronic 4.4 signal specifications (Part 5 of 6)

canister purge valve not activate, replace valve. If there is no vacuum when valve is not active, proceed to next step.

3. With ignition switch in Off position, inspect hose between EVAP canister and EVAP canister shutoff valve for pinches and folds. If hose is not pinched or folded, carefully disconnect it and ensure it is not blocked. If it is blocked, repair as necessary and proceed to next step. If it is not blocked, proceed to step 5.
4. With ignition switch in Off position, carefully disconnect EVAP canister shutoff valve hose from EVAP canister. Inspect EVAP canister shutoff valve connector on EVAP canister. If connector is damaged, replace canister. If it is not damaged, replace canister shutoff valve.

S90 & V90

1. Start and idle engine. Open fuel tank filler cap and access scrolling values. If tank pressure is higher than -.15 psi, proceed to next step. If pressure is not more than -.15 psi, replace fuel tank pressure sensor.
2. Disconnect hose between canister purge valve and EVAP canister from valve. With engine idling, access scrolling values. If there is vacuum with canister purge valve not activated, replace valve. If there is no vacuum when valve is not activated, proceed to next step.
3. With ignition switch in Off position, inspect hose between EVAP canister shutoff valve and filter for pinches and folds. If hose is not pinched or folder, carefully disconnect it and filter, and ensure they not blocked. If they are blocked, repair as necessary. If they are not blocked, proceed to next step.
4. With ignition switch in Off position, carefully disconnect EVAP canister shutoff valve hose from EVAP canister. Inspect EVAP canister shutoff valve connector on EVAP canister. If connector is damaged, replace canister. If it is not damaged, return to step 3.

CODE P0442: FUEL TANK SYSTEM LEAK

1. Ensure fuel filler cap is on securely and that its seal is intact. Inspect EVAP canister, rollover valve, fuel pressure regulator, fuel tank hoses and hose connectors. If any faults were detected, repair or replace fault. If no faults were detected, proceed to next step.
2. Connect suitable scan tool, and start and idle engine. Access scrolling values, and read fuel tank pressure and canister purge valve value. If fuel tank pressure drops when canister purge valve opens, proceed to next step. If fuel tank pressure does not drop when canister purge valve opens, proceed to next step.
3. **On C70, S70 and V70 models,** ensure there is no more than 7.92 gallons in fuel tank.
4. **On S90 and V90 models,** ensure there is no more than 13.2 gallons in fuel tank.
5. **On all models,** ensure ignition switch is in Off position. Clamp hose between canister purge valve and intake manifold with a hose clip to seal it off.
6. Remove lefthand fender liner and remove EVAP canister. Carefully disconnect EVAP canister shutoff valve hose from EVAP canister.
7. Connect pressure gauge tool No. 999 5646, or equivalent, to EVAP canister, setting pressure at one psi. **Maximum pressure is 1.45 psi.** Allow pressure to build for five minutes and shut off tap, read pressure and wait 10 minutes. **Never leave car unattended with its system pressurized.**
8. If fuel tank pressure is stable, proceed to next step. If fuel tank pressure is not stable, further diagnosis is required to determine if leaks are present.
9. Inspect seal and connectors of EVAP canister shutoff valve hose. If hose is determined to be in working condition, replace EVAP canister shutoff valve. If hose is determined not to be in working

Terminal	Signal type	Ignition on.	Idling	Miscellaneous
#B31	–	–	–	–
#B32	Signal,accelerometer CO potentiometer	$U \approx 2.5$ V		
#B33	–	–	–	–
#B34	Signal ignition coil cylinder 6	$U \approx 0.1$ V	$f \approx 6.5$ Hz $U \approx 0.2$ V	U increases with engine speed (RPM)
#B35	Signal ignition coil cylinder 4	$U \approx 0.1$ V	$f \approx 6.5$ Hz $U \approx 0.2$ V	U increases with engine speed (RPM)
#B36	Diagnostic lead OBD II K–Link	$U \approx 1 - 2$ V below U_{bat}	Other values apply if a generic fault–tracing instrument is connected to the data link connector (DLC)	
#B37	–	–	–	–
#B38	Control signal, pulsed secondary air injection system (PAIR) pump relay	$U \approx U_{bat}$	–	–
#B39	–	–	–	–
#B40	Control signal, air conditioning (A/C) relay (permits air conditioning (A/C) start)	$U \approx U_{bat}$	Air conditioning (A/C) permitted: U_{low} Air conditioning (A/C) not permitted: $U \approx 11 V = U_{bat}$	
#B41	–	–	–	–
#B42	–	–	–	–
#B43	–	–	–	–

VV1029800108060X

Fig. 13 Motronic 4.4 signal specifications (Part 6 of 6)

$U =$	DC voltage in volts (V)	$U_{AC} =$	AC voltage in volts (V)
$U_{bat} =$	battery voltage	$f =$	frequency in Hertz (Hz)
$U_{Low} =$	voltage approximately 0 V or O V	%duty =	duty cycle (pulse ratio) as a percentage (%)
t=	time in milliseconds (ms)		

Terminal	Signal type	Ignition on.	Idling	Remarks
#A1	-	-	-	-
#A2	Signal (+) front knock sensor (KS) (measured to #A17)	U_{low}		
#A3	Power ground mass air flow (MAF) sensor	U_{low}		
#A4	Signal mass air flow (MAF) sensor (Measured to #A5)	$U = 0.1 - 0.2$ V	$U \approx 1$ V	U increases with increasing air mass
#A5	Signal ground mass air flow (MAF) sensor	U_{low}		
#A6	Signal ground engine speed (RPM) sensor	U_{low}		
#A7	Control signal engine cooling fan (FC) low-speed	Engine cooling fan (FC) off: U_{bat} Engine cooling fan (FC) on: $U \approx 0.1$ V		
#A8	-	-	-	-

VV1029800109010X

Fig. 14 Motronic 4.4 signal specifications (Part 1 of 8). S90 & V90

condition, replace EVAP canister hose.

10. Remove fuel tank pressure sensor and remove hose with Y-nipple, ensuring that hose and nipple are not blocked. If nipple and hose are blocked, replace nipple and/or hose. If nipple and hose are not blocked, replace fuel tank pressure sensor.

CODE P0443: EVAP CANISTER PURGE VALVE SIGNAL

1. Turn ignition switch to Off position and disconnect canister purge valve. Turn ignition switch to On position and connect a suitable voltmeter between EVAP connector 1 and ground. If reading is battery voltage, proceed to next step. If voltage is not battery voltage, repair wiring harness.
2. Connect ohmmeter between canister purge valve terminals No. 1 and No. 2. If resistance is 22–30 ohms, proceed to next step. If resistance is not 22–30 ohms, replace canister purge valve.
3. Connect test box tool No. 981 3190, or equivalent, and test ground terminals. Connect ohmmeter between test box terminal No. 39 and canister purge valve connector terminal No. 2. If resistance is zero ohms, repair ECM and/or canister purge valve canister connector contacts. If resistance is not zero ohms, repair wiring harness.

CODES P0444 & P0445: EVAP CANISTER PURGE VALVE HIGH/LOW INPUT

1. Ensure ignition switch is in Off position and disconnect canister purge valve connector.
2. Turn ignition switch to On position and connect a test lamp between canister purge valve connector terminal No. 2 and ground.
3. If test lamp lights, repair wiring harness. If test lamp did not light, replace canister purge valve.

CODE P0446: EVAP CANISTER SHUTOFF VALVE MISSING SIGNAL

1. Ensure ignition switch is in Off position.
2. Remove lefthand fender liner.
3. Disconnect EVAP canister shutoff valve connector and turn ignition switch to On position. Connect suitable voltmeter between EVAP canister shutoff valve connector terminal No. 1 and ground. If reading is battery voltage, proceed to next step. If reading is not battery voltage, inspect power harness between EVAP canister shutoff valve terminal No. 1 and main relay (2/32) for open circuit.
4. Ensure ignition switch is in Off position and connect ohmmeter between EVAP canister shutoff valve connector terminals No. 1 and No. 2. If resistance is 14–20 ohms, proceed to next step. If resistance is not 14–20 ohms, replace EVAP canister shutoff valve.
5. Ensure ignition switch is in Off position and connect test box tool No. 981 3190, or equivalent, and test ground terminals. Connect ohmmeter between test box terminal No. 19 and EVAP canister shutoff valve connector terminal No. 2. If resistance is zero ohms, condition was caused by ECM and/or EVAP canister shutoff value connectors. Inspect connectors for contact resistance and oxidation, and repair as necessary. If resistance is not zero ohms, inspect harness between EVAP canister shutoff valve terminal No. 2 and ECM No. B19 for open circuit.

CODES P0447: EVAP CANISTER SHUTOFF SIGNAL LOW

Inspect harness between solenoid valve terminal No. 2 and Engine Control Module (ECM) No. B19 for short circuit.

CODES P0448: EVAP CANISTER SHUTOFF SIGNAL HIGH

1. Ensure ignition switch is in Off position.
2. Remove lefthand fender liner.
3. Disconnect EVAP canister shutoff valve connector and turn ignition switch to On position.
4. Connect suitable (at least three watt bulb) electricians screwdriver between solenoid valve connector terminal No. 2 and ground.
5. If test lamp does not light, replace EVAP canister shutoff valve.
6. If test lamp lights, inspect signal harness between EVAP canister shutoff valve connector terminal No. 2 and Engine Control Module (ECM) No. B19 for short circuit.

CODE P0451: FUEL TANK PRESSURE SENSOR SIGNAL SPORADIC

1. Inspect fuel tank pressure sensor and Engine Control Module (ECM) connector for loose connections.
2. Inspect harness between fuel tank pressure sensor terminal No. 3 and ECM No. B15, fuel tank pressure sensor terminal No. 2 and ECM No. B31, and fuel tank pressure sensor terminal No. 1 and ECM No. B28 for intermittent open circuits.
3. Inspect harness between air conditioning pressure sensor terminal No. 3 and

Terminal	Signal type	Ignition on.	Idling	Remarks
#A9	Control signal injector 6	U_{bat}	t = 2.2 - 3.6 ms	t increases with engine speed (RPM) and load (measured with EVAP not active)
#A10	Control signal injector 1	U_{bat}	t = 2.2 - 3.6 ms	t increases with engine speed (RPM) and load (measured with EVAP not active)
#A11	Opening signal idle air control (IAC) valve	%duty ≈ 25 %	%duty = 21 -32%	%duty increases with load (measured with EVAP not active)
#A12	15-supply (power supply from ignition switch)	U_{bat}		
#A13	Power ground	U_{low}		
#A14	Control signal front heated oxygen sensor (HO2S), preheating	U_{bat}	Preheating off: U ≈ U_{bat} Preheating on: U ≈ 0.4 V	
#A15	Power supply throttle position (TP) sensor position	U ≈ 4.8 V		
#A16	Signal throttle position (TP) sensor	U ≈ 0.5 V at closed throttle position (CTP) (idling) U ≈ 4.5 V at wide open throttle (WOT)		
#A17	Signal (-) front and rear knock sensors (KS)	U_{low}		
#A18	Signal ground sensor (measured to battery negative terminal)	U_{low}		
#A19	Signal (-) rear heated oxygen sensor (HO2S)	U ≈ 0.7 V	Only measured with ignition on	
#A20	Signal engine speed (RPM) sensor (measured to #A6)	U_{low}	U_{AC} ≈ 1.8 V. f = 740 Hz	
#A21	Signal camshaft position (CMP) sensor	U = U_{low} or U_{bat}	f ≈ 6 Hz	f increases with engine speed (RPM)
#A22	Control signal engine cooling fan (FC) high-speed	Engine cooling fan (FC) off: U_{bat} Engine cooling fan (FC) on: U ≈ 0.1 V		

VV1029800109020X

Fig. 14 Motronic 4.4 signal specifications (Part 2 of 8). S90 & V90

Terminal	Signal type	Ignition on.	Idling	Remarks
#A23	Control signal injector 3	U_{bat}	t = 2.2 - 3.6 ms	t increases with engine speed (RPM) and load (measured with EVAP not active)
#A24	Control signal injector 2	U_{bat}	t = 2.2 - 3.6 ms	t increases with engine speed (RPM) and load (measured with EVAP not active)
#A25	Closing signal idle air control (IAC) valve	%duty = 75%	%duty = 68 - 89%	% duty decreases with load (measured with EVAP not active)
#A26	30-supply (power supply from battery)	U_{bat}		
#A27	Power supply (from main relay)	U_{bat}		
#A28	Power ground control module	U_{low}		
#A29	Control signal rear heated oxygen sensor (HO2S), preheating	U_{bat}	Preheating off: U ≈ U_{bat} Preheating on: U ≈ 0.4 V	
#A30	Signal (+) rear knock sensor (KS) (measured to #A17)	U_{low}		
#A31	Signal engine coolant temperature (ECT) sensor	(at engine coolant temperature (ECT) +46 °C (115 °F) the engine control module (ECM) switches voltage range)	(+20 °C (68 °F) U ≈ 1.81 V (+30 °C (86 °F)) U ≈ 1.34 V (+45 °C (113 °F)) U ≈ 0.83 V (+46 °C (115 °F)) U ≈ 4.0 V (+80 °C (176 °F)) U ≈ 2.73 V (+100 °C (212 °F)) U ≈ 1.96 V	
#A32	Signal (+) front heated oxygen sensor (HO2S)	U = 1.1 - 1.2 V (measured to #A42)	U oscillates rapidly between 0.0 - 0.9 V when the heated oxygen sensor (HO2S) is hot. Low voltage = lean engine High voltage = rich engine (measured to #A33)	
#A33	Signal (-) front heated oxygen sensor (HO2S)	U ≈ 0.7 V	Only measured with ignition on	

VV1029800109030X

Fig. 14 Motronic 4.4 signal specifications (Part 3 of 8). S90 & V90

ECM No. B29, and atmospheric pressure sensor terminal No. 1 and ECM No. B15 for intermittent short circuits.

4. Install all components, start engine and idle for five minutes. Connect suitable scan tool and access Diagnostic Trouble Codes (DTCs). If DTC P0451 is not stored, condition was caused by loose connections. If DTC P0451 was stored, proceed to next step.
5. With ignition switch in Off position and fuel tank pressure sensor disconnected, disconnect A/C pressure sensor. Start engine and idle for five minutes. Connect suitable scan tool and access DTCs. If DTC P0451 is not stored, replace A/C pressure sensor. If DTC P0451 was stored, proceed to next step.
6. With ignition switch in Off position, and fuel tank pressure sensor and A/C pressure sensor disconnected, disconnect accelerometer. Start engine and idle for five minutes. Connect suitable scan tool and access DTCs. If DTC P0451 is not stored, replace accelerometer. If DTC P0451 was stored, proceed to next step.
7. With ignition switch in Off position, and fuel tank pressure sensor, A/C pressure sensor and accelerometer disconnected, disconnect atmospheric pressure sensor. Start engine and idle for five minutes. Connect suitable scan tool and access DTCs. If DTC P0451 is not stored, replace atmospheric pressure sensor. If DTC P0451 was stored, replace fuel tank pressure sensor.

CODE P0452: FUEL TANK PRESSURE SENSOR SIGNAL LOW

1. Turn ignition switch to Off position, disconnect tank pressure sensor and connect ohmmeter between fuel tank pressure sensor connector terminal No. 3 (ECM Side) and ground. If resistance is 200–1500 ohms, proceed to step 7. If resistance less than 200–1500 ohms, proceed to next step. If resistance is more than 200–1500 ohms, proceed to step 6.
2. With ignition switch in Off position and tank pressure sensor disconnected, disconnect accelerometer. Connect ohmmeter between fuel tank pressure sensor connector terminal No. 3 (ECM side) and ground. If resistance is 200–1500 ohms, replace accelerometer. If resistance is not 200–1500 ohms, proceed next step.
3. With ignition switch in Off position, and tank pressure sensor and accelerometer disconnected, disconnect air conditioning pressure sensor. Connect ohmmeter between fuel tank pressure sensor connector terminal No. 3 (ECM side) and ground. If resistance is 200–1500 ohms, replace A/C pressure sensor. If resistance is not 200–1500 ohms, proceed next step.
4. With ignition switch in Off position, and tank pressure sensor, accelerometer and air conditioning pressure sensor disconnected disconnect atmospheric pressure sensor. Connect ohmmeter between fuel tank pressure sensor connector terminal No. 3 (ECM side) and ground. If resistance is 200–1500 ohms, replace atmospheric pressure sensor. If resistance is not 200–1500 ohms, proceed next step.
5. Inspect harness between tank pressure sensor terminal No. 3 and ECM No. B15, accelerometer terminal No. 1 and ECM No. B1, and A/C pressure sensor terminal No. 3 and ECM No. B29 for short circuit, and repair as necessary.
6. With ignition switch in Off position and tank pressure sensor disconnect, inspect ECM connector, and connector 24/2 and 24/4 for contact resistance and oxidation, and repair as necessary. Connect ECM connector, and

Terminal	Signal type	Ignition on.	Idling	Remarks
#A34	Signal (+) rear heated oxygen sensor (HO2S)	U=1.18 V (Measured to #A42)	U on even load approximately 0.7 V can vary between 0.0 - 0.9 V depending on drop in load (measured to #A19)	
#A35	Outside temperature sensor.	$U \approx 4.9$ V	-	-
#A36	Power supply camshaft position (CMP) sensor	$U \approx U_{bat}$		
#A37	Pulsed secondary air injection system (PAIR) pump valve control signal	U_{bat}	pulsed secondary air injection system (PAIR) pump valve not active ≈ U_{bat}	active ≈ U_{low}
#A38	Control signal injector 5	U_{bat}	$t \approx 2.2 - 3.6$ ms	t increases with engine speed (RPM) and load (measured with EVAP not active)
#A39	Control signal Canister purge (CP) valve	U_{bat}	Canister purge (CP) valve: %duty = 0 - 33%	
#A40	Fuel pump control signal	$U \approx U_{bat}$	U_{low}	-
#A41	Control signal main relay	$U \approx 1$ V		
#A42	Signal ground engine control module (ECM) (measured to battery negative terminal)	U_{low}		
#A43	Control signal, injector 4	U_{bat}	$t \approx 2.2 - 3.6$ ms	t increases with engine speed (RPM) and load (measured with EVAP not active)

VV1029800109040X

Fig. 14 Motronic 4.4 signal specifications (Part 4 of 8). S90 & V90

Terminal	Signal type	Ignition on.	Idling	Remarks
#B1	Power supply accelerometer	$U \approx 5.0$ V		
#B2	Signal torque limiting (from automatic transmission)	$U \approx 1 - 2$ V below U_{bat}		U_{low} on ignition retardation request (retardation level 2 and 3)
#B3	Signal torque limiting (from automatic transmission)	$U \approx 1 - 2$ V below U_{bat}		U_{low} on ignition retardation request (retardation level 1 and 3)
#B4	Signal torque limiting acknowledgement (To automatic transmission)	$U \approx 2.0$ V below U_{bat}		U_{low} when request has been received
#B5	-	-	-	-
#B6	Signal air conditioning (A/C) compressor status	U_{low}	air conditioning (A/C) compressor off: $U < 0.1$ V Air conditioning (A/C) compressor on: $U \approx U_{bat}$	-
#B7	Control signal malfunction indicator lamp (MIL) (to combined instrument panel)	Lamp lit: $U \approx 0.8$ V Lamp unlit: U_{bat}		
#B8	-	-	-	-

VV1029800109050X

Fig. 14 Motronic 4.4 signal specifications (Part 5 of 8). S90 & V90

connector 24/2 and 24/4. Connect ohmmeter between fuel tank pressure sensor connector terminal No. 3 (ECM side) and ground. If resistance is 200–1500 ohms, condition was caused by loose connections. If resistance is not 200–1500 ohms, proceed next step.

7. Inspect harness between fuel tank pressure sensor terminal No. 3 and ECM No. B15 for open circuit.
8. With tank pressure sensor disconnected, turn ignition switch to On position. Connect voltmeter between fuel tank pressure sensor connector terminal No. 2 (ECM side) and ground. If reading is 5–6 volts, replace fuel tank pressure sensor. If reading is not 5–6 volts, inspect cable between fuel tank pressure sensor terminal No. 2 and ECM No. B31 for open circuit.

CODE P0453: FUEL TANK PRESSURE SENSOR SIGNAL HIGH

1. Turn ignition switch to Off position and disconnect tank pressure sensor. Connect ohmmeter between fuel tank pressure sensor connector terminal (ECM Side) No. 1 and ground. If resistance is zero ohms, proceed to step 3. If resistance is not zero ohms, proceed to next step.
2. With ignition switch in Off position and tank pressure sensor disconnected, inspect connector 24/4 for contact resistance and oxidation, and repair as necessary. Connect ECM connector and connector 24/4. Connect ohmmeter between connector 24/4 terminal No. 1 (ECM side) and ground. If resistance is zero ohms, condition was caused by loose connector 24/4 connections. If resistance is not zero ohms, inspect ground cable between fuel tank pressure sensor terminal No. 2 and ECM No. B28 for open circuit.
3. With ignition switch in On position and tank pressure sensor disconnected, connect voltmeter between fuel tank pressure sensor connector terminal No. 2 (ECM side) and ground. If reading is 5–6 volts, condition has been corrected. If reading is less than 5–6 volts, proceed to next step. If reading is more than 5–6 volts, inspect harness between fuel tank pressure sensor terminal No. 2 and ECM No. B31 for short circuit.
4. With ignition switch in Off position and tank pressure sensor disconnected, inspect ECM connector, and connectors 24/2 and 24/4 for contact resistance and oxidation, and repair as necessary. Connect ECM connector connectors 24/2 and 24/4, and turn ignition switch to On position. Connect voltmeter between tank pressure sensor connector terminal No. 2 (ECM side) and ground. If reading is approximately five volts, condition was caused by loose connections. If reading is not approximately five volts, inspect harness between fuel tank pressure sensor terminal No. 2 and ECM No. B31 for open circuit.

CODE P0455: FUEL TANK SYSTEM LARGE LEAK

C70, S70 & V70

1. Ensure fuel tank filler cap is on properly and seal is intact. Inspect hoses and connectors at EVAP canister, EVAP canister shutoff valve and fuel tank. Repair as necessary. Proceed to next step.
2. Start engine and idle. Disconnect hose between canister purge (CP) valve and EVAP canister from canister purge valve. Access scrolling values. If canister purge valve is active, proceed to next step. If valve is not active, proceed to step 4.
3. Turn ignition switch to Off position, install canister purge valve hose and remove canister purge hose from EVAP canister. Start engine and idle. Access scrolling values. If canister purge valve is active, proceed to step 5. If valve is not active, inspect hose between canister purge valve and EVAP canister, and repair blockages and traps.
4. Connect hose between canister purge valve and EVAP canister, start engine and idle. Disconnect hose between canister purge valve and intake manifold at canister purge valve. If there is vacuum in hose, replace canister purge valve. If there is no vacuum, ensure hose between canister purge valve and intake manifold is not blocked, and inspect connection at intake manifold. Repair as necessary.
5. Inspect EVAP canister inlets and outlets. If they are airtight, replace EVAP canister. If they are not airtight, proceed to next step.
6. Inspect hose between fuel tank and EVAP canister. If it is airtight and not trapped, proceed to next step. If not airtight, replace hose.
7. With no more than 7 gallons in fuel tank and ignition switch in Off position, connect fuel tank hose to EVAP canister. Clamp hose between EVAP canister shutoff valve and EVAP canister and carefully disconnect EVAP canister hose from canister purge valve. Connect manometer tool No. 999 5646, or equivalent, to hose and pressure regulator tool No. 999 5544, or equivalent, to manometer.
8. Set manometer to one psi and cock at

Terminal	Signal type	Ignition on.	Idling	Remarks
#B9	Signal Air conditioning (A/C) pressure sensor	U=1.0 V ≈ 590 kPa (85.6 psi) (air conditioning (A/C) system off for a long period) U=2.2 V ≈ 1,400 kPa (203 psi) U=2.8 V ≈ 1,800 kPa (261 psi) (engine cooling fan (FC) starts at low-speed) U=3.7 V ≈ 2,400 kPa (348 psi) (engine cooling fan (FC) starts at low-speed)		
#B10	Signal, ignition coil cylinder 5	U ≈ 0.1 V	f ≈ 6.5 Hz U ≈ 0.2 V	U increases with engine speed (RPM)
#B11	Signal, ignition coil cylinder 1	U ≈ 0.1 V	f ≈ 6.5 Hz U ≈ 0.2 V	U increases with engine speed (RPM)
#B12	Signal load Tq (to automatic transmission)	U ≈ 0.8 V	f ≈ 37 Hz	f increases with engine speed (RPM)
#B13	Signal, ignition coil cylinder 2	U ≈ 0.1 V	f ≈ 6.5 Hz U ≈ 0.2 V	U increases with engine speed (RPM)
#B14	Signal, ignition coil cylinder 3	U ≈ 0.1 V	f ≈ 6.5 Hz U ≈ 0.2 V	U increases with engine speed (RPM)
#B15	Power supply fuel tank pressure sensor	U ≈ 5 V		-
#B16	-	-	-	-
#B17	-	-	-	-
#B18	Signal speed (from combined instrument panel)	$U \approx U_{low}$ or U_{bat} (voltage depends on rear wheel position)		f increases with speed f = 40 Hz at 20 km/h (12 mph).
#B19	Control signal EVAP canister shut-off valve	$U \approx U_{bat}$	Closed $U \approx U_{bat}$	Active $U \approx U_{low}$
#B20	Signal throttle position (TP) sensor (to automatic transmission)	U ≈ 0.5 V at closed throttle position (CTP) (idling) U ≈ 4.5 V at wide open throttle (WOT)	-	-
#B21	Signal tachometer (to combined instrument panel)	$U \approx U_{bat}$	f ≈ 25 Hz	f increases with engine speed (RPM)
#B22	-	-	-	-
#B23	Signal engine coolant temperature (ECT) (to combined instrument panel)	Cold engine (+20 °C (68 °F)): f ≈ 40 Hz Hot engine (+100 °C (212 °F)): f ≈ 21 Hz	-	-

VV1029800109060X

Fig. 14 Motronic 4.4 signal specifications (Part 6 of 8). S90 & V90

Terminal	Signal type	Ignition on.	Idling	Remarks
#B24	Signal constant idle speed compensation, P/N position (from automatic transmission)	P/N position: $U \approx U_{bat}$ Other positions: $U \approx U_{low}$ Manual: U ≈ 9.0 V	-	-
#B25	Air conditioning (A/C) request from climate control	U_{bat}	Air conditioning (A/C) request active: U ≈ 0.6 V Air conditioning (A/C) not active: $U \approx U_{bat}$	-
#B26	Signal malfunction indicator lamp (MIL) request (from automatic transmission)	U ≈ 0 - 1 V	$U \approx U_{bat}$ **NOTE!** Other values apply if there are diagnostic trouble codes (DTCs) stored in the transmission control module (TCM).	-
#B27	-	-	-	-
#B28	Signal ground sensor (measured to battery negative terminal)	U < 0.1 V	-	-
#B29	Power supply Air conditioning (A/C) pressure sensor	U ≈ 5.0 V	-	-
#B30	-	-	-	-
#B31	Signal fuel tank pressure sensor	U_{max} ≈ 4.7 V. U_{nom} ≈ 2.5 V U_{min} ≈ 0.6 V	-	-
#B32	Signal accelerometer	U ≈ 2.5 V	-	-
#B33	-	-	-	-
#B34	Signal, ignition coil cylinder 6	U ≈ 0.1 V	f ≈ 6.5 Hz U ≈ 0.2 V	U increases with engine speed (RPM)
#B35	Signal, ignition coil cylinder 4	U ≈ 0.1 V	f ≈ 6.5 Hz U ≈ 0.2 V	U increases with engine speed (RPM)
#B36	Diagnostic lead, K-link	U ≈ 1 - 2 V below U_{bat}	Other values apply if a generic fault-tracing instrument is connected to the data link connector (DLC)	-
#B37	-	-	-	-

VV1029800109070X

Fig. 14 Motronic 4.4 signal specifications (Part 7 of 8). S90 & V90

right angles to hoses. Let pressure build for five minutes. **Maximum pressure of 1.4 psi.** Shut cock off (pressure may drop to .14–.18 psi before stabilizing) and record pressure. Remove EVAP canister hose cock and wait 10 minutes. **Do not leave car unattended with pressurized fuel tank.**

9. If pressure is stable (there may be a slight rise because of fuel evaporation), proceed to next step. If pressure is not stable, proceed to step 14.
10. Disconnect pressure regulator tool and connect EVAP canister hose. Remove clamp between canister purge valve and intake manifold. Start engine and idle. Access scrolling values and read fuel tank pressure and canister purge valve values.
11. When canister purge valve opens, if fuel tank pressure drops, proceed to next step. If fuel tank pressure does not drop, proceed to step 13.
12. If EVAP canister shutoff valve hose is airtight and connected properly, replace EVAP canister shutoff valve. If it is not, repair as necessary.
13. With ignition switch in Off position, remove fuel tank pressure sensor and hose Y-nipple. If nipple or hose are blocked, replace as necessary. If they are not blocked, replace fuel tank pressure sensor.
14. With ignition switch in Off position, carefully pressurize fuel tank system to one psi (not more than 1.4 psi) and cock hoses at right angles.
15. Inspect fuel tank system for leaks by spraying soapy water from EVAP canister to canister purge valve, between fuel tank and EVAP canister shutoff valve, filler pipe and fuel tank filler cap.

S90 & V90

1. Ensure fuel tank filler cap is on properly and seal is intact. Inspect hoses and connectors at EVAP canister, roll-over valve, EVAP canister shutoff valve and fuel tank. Repair as necessary. Proceed to next step.
2. Start engine and idle. Disconnect hose between canister purge valve and EVAP canister from canister purge valve. Access scrolling values. If canister purge valve is active, proceed to next step. If valve is not active, proceed to step 4.
3. Turn ignition switch to Off position, install canister purge valve hose and remove canister purge hose from EVAP canister. Start engine and idle. Access scrolling values. If canister purge valve is active, proceed to step 5. If valve is not active, inspect hose between canister purge valve and EVAP canister, and repair blockages and traps.
4. Connect hose between canister purge valve and EVAP canister, start engine and idle. Disconnect hose between canister purge valve and intake manifold at canister purge valve. If there is vacuum in hose, replace canister purge valve. If there is no vacuum, ensure hose between canister purge valve and intake manifold is not blocked, and inspect connection at intake manifold. Repair as necessary.
5. Inspect EVAP canister inlets and outlets. If they are airtight, proceed to next step. If they are not airtight, replace EVAP canister.
6. Carefully disconnect hose to fuel tank from EVAP canister, connect vacuum pump to fuel tank hose and attempt to pump up vacuum. If vacuum cannot be pumped up, proceed to next step. If vacuum can be pumped up, proceed as follows:
   a. Ensure roll-over valve is airtight.
   b. Ensure hose between fuel tank and EVAP canister is airtight and not trapped.
   c. Repair as necessary.

Terminal	Signal type	Ignition on.	Idling	Remarks
#B38	Control signal pulsed secondary air injection system (PAIR) pump relay	$U \approx U_{bat}$	pulsed secondary air injection system (PAIR) pump valve off $U \approx U_{bal}$	pulsed secondary air injection system (PAIR) pump valve active $U \approx U_{low}$
#B39	-	-	-	-
#B40	Control signal air conditioning (A/C) relay (allows A/C start)	$U \approx 9$ V	air conditioning (A/C) permitted: U_{low} air conditioning (A/C) not permitted: $U \approx 11$ V	-
#B41	-	-	-	-
#B42	-	-	-	-
#B43	-	-	-	-

VV1029800109080X

Fig. 14 Motronic 4.4 signal specifications (Part 8 of 8). S90 & V90

7. Inspect hose between fuel tank and EVAP canister. If it is airtight and not trapped, proceed to next step. If not airtight, replace hose.
8. With no more than 7 gallons in fuel tank and ignition switch in Off position, connect fuel tank hose to EVAP canister. Remove EVAP canister shutoff valve from bracket. Clamp hose between EVAP canister shutoff valve and EVAP canister and carefully disconnect EVAP canister hose from canister purge valve. Connect manometer tool No. 999 5646, or equivalent, to hose and pressure regulator tool No. 999 5544, or equivalent, to manometer.
9. Set manometer to one psi and cock at right angles to hoses. Let pressure built for five minutes. **Maximum pressure of 1.4 psi.** Shut cock off (pressure may drop to .15–.30 psi before stabilizing) and record pressure. Remove EVAP canister hose cock and wait 10 minutes. **Do not leave car unattended with pressurized fuel tank.**
10. If pressure is stable (there may be a slight rise because of fuel evaporation), proceed to next step. If pressure is not stable, proceed to step 14.
11. Disconnect pressure regulator tool and connect EVAP canister hose. Remove clamp between canister purge valve and intake manifold. Start engine and idle. Access scrolling values and read fuel tank pressure and canister purge valve values.
12. When canister purge valve opens, if fuel tank pressure drops, proceed to next step. If fuel tank pressure does not drop, proceed to step 13.
13. If EVAP canister shutoff valve hose is airtight and connected properly, replace EVAP canister shutoff valve. If it is not, repair as necessary.
14. With ignition switch in Off position, remove fuel tank pressure sensor and hose Y-nipple. If nipple or hose are blocked, replace as necessary. If they are not blocked, replace fuel tank pressure sensor.
15. With ignition switch in Off position, carefully pressurize fuel tank system to one psi (not more than 1.4 psi) and cock hoses at right angles.
16. Inspect fuel tank system for leaks by spraying soapy water from EVAP canister to canister purge valve, between fuel tank and EVAP canister shutoff valve, filler pipe and fuel tank filler cap.

CODE P0500: SPEEDOMETER SIGNAL

Yazaki Instrument Panel

1. Connect suitable scan tool and search for any DTCs stored in ABS system.
2. If there were DTCs stored, repair fault as necessary. If there where no DTCs stored, repair fault in instrument panel and/or vehicle speed sensor.
3. Connect test box tool No. 981 3190, or equivalent, and test ground terminals. Connect ECM and move gear lever into Neutral position.
4. Raise and support vehicle so that front wheels hang free and turn ignition switch to On position.
5. Connect voltmeter between test box terminals No. 18 and No. 28. Rotate front wheels. **ABS system DTCs must be cleared after procedure is complete.**
6. If reading is .5 volt or more than battery voltage, repair or replace harness. If reading is not .5 volt or more than battery voltage, proceed to next step.
7. Connect a voltmeter between test box terminals No. 18 and No. 28. Rotate front wheels.
8. If reading is .5 volt or more than battery voltage, repair or replace harness. If reading is not .5 volt or more than battery voltage proceed to next step.
9. Connect a test lamp between test box terminals No. 18 and No. 28.
10. If test lamp lights, repair short circuit in harness. If test lamp does not light repair open in circuit.

VDO Instrument Panel

1. Connect suitable scan tool and turn ignition switch to On position. Search for active DTCs.
2. If any DTCs are stored, repair fault as necessary. If no DTCs are stored proceed to next step.
3. Connect test box tool No. 981 3190, or equivalent, and test ground terminals, then connect ECM.
4. Move gear lever into N position, and raise and support vehicle so that front wheels hang free. Turn ignition switch to On position and connect voltmeter to measure voltage between test box terminals No. 18 and No. 28. Rotate front wheels. **ABS system DTCs must be cleared after procedure is complete.**
5. If reading is .5 volt or more than battery voltage, repair or replace harness. If voltage is not .5 volt or more than battery voltage proceed to next step.
6. Turn ignition switch to Off position. Connect a ohmmeter between combined instrument panel connector A terminal No. 7 and test box terminal No. 18.
7. If resistance is zero ohms, repair fault as necessary. If resistance is not zero ohms, repair or replace harness.

CODE P0505: ADAPTIVE IDLE AIR TRIM UPPER/ LOWER LIMIT

1. Ensure ignition switch is in Off position and inspect throttle body adjusting screw seal.
2. If seal is intact, replace throttle body. If seal is not intact, proceed to next step.
3. Inspect air cleaner, air intake hoses and pipes between air cleaner and throttle body, and connectors for idle air control valve.
4. If all are in operating condition, proceed to next step. If all are not in operating condition repair as necessary.
5. Disconnect idle air control valve. Connect ohmmeter between idle air control valve terminals No. 1 and No. 3.
6. If resistance is 18–28 ohms at 68°F proceed to next step. If resistance is not 18–28 ohms and replace idle air control valve
7. Remove idle air control valve. Grasp idle air control valve control slide, twist valve rapidly back and forth.
8. If idle air control valve control slide switched back and forth, repair fault in harness. If idle air control valve control slide does not move, then replace idle air control valve.
9. Inspect throttle body adjusting screw seal.
10. If seal is intact, replace throttle body. If seal is not intact, proceed to next step.
11. Ensure throttle spindle is in contact with adjustment screw and that throttle pulley is in contact with idling stop.
12. If throttle mechanism is in operating condition, proceed to next step. If throttle mechanism is not in operating condition repair as necessary.
13. Inspect throttle body hoses and connectors for air leakage.
14. If there is air leakage present, repair fault as necessary. If there is no air leakage present, then proceed to next step.
15. Connect suitable scan tool and turn ignition switch to On position. Select "Components/Functions" and activate idle air control valve.
16. Inspect connectors and ECM connectors and retest.
17. If valve makes a clicking sound, proceed to step No. 10 . If valve makes no noise replace valve.

18. Disconnect idle air control valve. Connect ohmmeter between idle air control valve terminals No. 1 and No. 3.
19. If resistance is 18–28 ohms at 68°F, proceed to next step. If not, replace idle air control valve.
20. remove fresh air intake between air cleaner and throttle body. **Ensure throttle is undamaged, that it moves properly and that its secured on throttle spindle.**
21. If throttle is in operating condition and replace idle air control valve. If not and replace throttle body.

CODE P0531: AIR CONDITIONING PRESSURE SENSOR SIGNAL FAULTY

If air condition system is not working properly, repair as necessary. If A/C system functioning properly, replace A/C pressure sensor.

CODE P0532: AIR CONDITIONING PRESSURE SENSOR SIGNAL LOW

1. Turn ignition switch to Off position and disconnect air conditioning pressure sensor. Turn ignition switch to On position and connect voltmeter between sensor connector terminal No. 3 and ground. If reading is five volts, proceed to step 3. If reading is less than five volts, proceed to step 5. If reading is more than five volts, proceed to next step.
2. Inspect harness between accelerometer terminal No. 1 and ECM No. B1 for short circuit, and repair as necessary. Inspect harness between air conditioning pressure sensor terminal No. 3 and ECM No. B29 for short circuit, and repair as necessary. Inspect harness between atmosphere pressure sensor terminal No. 1 and ECM No. B29 for short circuit, and repair as necessary. Inspect harness between tank pressure sensor terminal No. 1 and ECM No. B29 for short circuit, and repair as necessary.
3. With ignition switch in Off position and A/C pressure sensor disconnected, connect ohmmeter between sensor connector No. 2 and ground. If reading is approximately 10 Kohms, proceed to next step. If reading is not approximately 10 Kohms, inspect harness between sensor terminal No. 2 and ECM No. B9 for short circuit, and repair as necessary.
4. With ignition switch in Off position, connect A/C pressure sensor. Start engine and idle. Turn A/C and fan blower to On positions, and access scrolling values. If voltage increased when A/C compressor starts, condition was caused by loose connection. Inspect connector for contact resistance and oxidation, and repair as necessary. If voltage does not increase when A/C compressor starts, replace A/C pressure sensor.
5. With ignition switch in Off position and A/C pressure sensor disconnected, connect ohmmeter between sensor connector No. 3 and ground. If reading is approximately 200–1500 ohms, proceed to next step. If reading is not approximately 200–1500 ohms, proceed to step 10.
6. With ignition switch in Off position and A/C pressure sensor disconnected, disconnect accelerometer. Connect ohmmeter between sensor connector No. 3 and ground. If reading is approximately 200–1500 ohms, replace accelerometer. If reading is not approximately 200–1500 ohms, proceed to next step.
7. With ignition switch in Off position, and A/C pressure sensor and accelerometer disconnected, disconnect atmosphere pressure sensor. Connect ohmmeter between A/C pressure sensor connector No. 3 and ground. If reading is approximately 200–1500 ohms, replace atmosphere pressure sensor. If reading is not approximately 200–1500 ohms and car has been leak diagnosed, proceed to next step. If the car has not been leak diagnosed, Proceed to step 9.
8. With ignition switch in Off position and A/C pressure sensor, accelerometer and atmosphere pressure sensor disconnected, disconnect fuel tank pressure sensor. Connect ohmmeter between A/C pressure sensor connector No. 3 and ground. If reading is approximately 200–1500 ohms, replace fuel tank pressure sensor. If reading is not approximately 200–1500 ohms, proceed to next step.
9. Inspect harness between accelerometer terminal No. 1 and ECM No. B1 for short circuit, and replace as necessary. Inspect harness between A/C pressure sensor terminal No. 1 and ECM No. B29 for short circuit, and replace as necessary. Inspect harness between atmospheric pressure sensor terminal No. 1 and ECM No. B29 for short circuit, and replace as necessary. Inspect harness between tank pressure sensor terminal No. 1 and ECM No. B15 for short circuit, and replace as necessary.
10. With ignition switch in Off position and A/C pressure sensor disconnected, inspect ECM connector for contact resistance and oxidation, and repair as necessary. Connect ECM connector, and ohmmeter between sensor connector No. 3 and ground. If reading is approximately 200–1500 ohms, condition was caused by loose ECM connections. If reading is not approximately 200–1500 ohms, inspect harness between sensor terminal No. 3 and ECM No. B29 for open circuit, and repair as necessary.

CODE P0533: AIR CONDITIONING PRESSURE SENSOR SIGNAL HIGH

1. Turn ignition switch to Off position and disconnect air conditioning pressure sensor. Connect ohmmeter between sensor connector No. 1 and ground. If reading is approximately zero ohms, proceed to step 3. If reading is not approximately zero ohms, proceed to next step.
2. With ignition switch in Off position and pressure sensor disconnected, inspect Engine Control Module (ECM) connector for contact resistance and oxidation, and repair as necessary. Connect ECM connector and connect ohmmeter between pressure sensor connector No. 1 and ground. If reading is approximately zero ohms, proceed to next step. If reading is not approximately zero ohms, inspect harness between sensor terminal No. 1 and ECM No. B28 for open circuit, and repair as necessary.
3. Turn ignition switch to On position and disconnect air conditioning pressure sensor. Connect voltmeter between sensor connector terminal No. 2 and ground. If reading is zero volts, proceed to next step. If reading is not zero volts, inspect harness between sensor terminal No. 2 and ECM No. B9 for short circuit, and repair as necessary.
4. With ignition in Off position and pressure sensor disconnected, connect ohmmeter between sensor terminal No. 2 and ground. If reading is approximately 10 ohms , proceed to next step. If reading is not approximately 10 ohms, inspect harness between sensor terminal No. 2 and ECM No. B9 for open circuit, and repair as necessary.
5. With ignition in Off position, connect pressure sensor, start engine and idle. Set A/C button and fan blower to On positions. Access scrolling values. If voltage increases when A/C compressor starts, condition was caused by loose pressure sensor connections. Check connector for contact resistance and oxidation, and repair as necessary. If voltages does not increase when A/C compressor starts, replace A/C pressure sensor

CODE P0560: BATTERY VOLTAGE

1. Inspect charging system.
2. If reading is 12–15 volts, repair fault in harness between ECM and battery.
3. If reading is not within specifications repair fault in charging system.

CODE P0605: ECM PERMANENT FAULT

ECM is faulty and must be replaced.

CODE P1307: ACCELEROMETER LOW INPUT

1. Ensure ignition switch is in Off position and disconnect accelerometer.
2. Turn ignition switch to On position and connect voltmeter between accelerometer connector terminal No. 3 and ground.
3. If reading is five volts, replace accelerometer. If voltage does not read five volts repair fault in harness.

CODE P1308: ACCELEROMETER HIGH INPUT

1. Ensure ignition switch is in Off position and disconnect accelerometer.
2. Turn ignition switch to On position and connect voltmeter between accelerometer connector terminal No. 1 and ground.
3. If reading is five volts, proceed to next step. If reading is lower, proceed to step 16. If reading is higher, repair fault in harness.
4. Turn ignition switch to Off position and connect ohmmeter between accelerometer connector terminal No. 2 and ground.
5. If resistance is zero ohms, proceed to step 9. If not, proceed to next step.
6. Further diagnosis is required to determine condition of ECM connector contact and reconnect ECM connector.
7. Connect ohmmeter between accelerometer connector terminal No. 2 and ground.
8. If resistance is zero ohms, repair fault in ECM connector contact. If not, repair or replace harness.
9. Turn ignition switch to On position and connect voltmeter to measure voltage between accelerometer connector terminal No. 3 and ground.
10. If reading is five volts, proceed to step 14. If reading is lower, proceed to next step. If reading is higher, repair or replace harness.
11. Further diagnosis is required to determine condition of ECM connector contact, reconnect ECM connector.
12. Connect ohmmeter to measure resistance between accelerometer connector terminal No. 3 and ground.
13. If resistance is zero ohms, repair fault in ECM connector contact. If not, repair or replace harness.
14. Connect suitable scan tool and turn ignition switch to On position. Connect accelerometer and erase DTC P1308. Start and idle engine and search for active DTC P1308.
15. If DTC recurred, replace accelerometer. If not, repair fault in accelerometer connector contact.
16. Turn ignition switch to Off position and disconnect accelerometer.
17. Connect ohmmeter between accelerometer connector terminal No. 1 and ground.
18. If resistance is zero ohms, proceed to next step. If resistance is not zero ohms proceed to step 20.
19. If vehicle has A/C, proceed to step 22. If not, proceed to step 27.
20. Connect ohmmeter to measure resistance between accelerometer connector terminal No. 1 and ground.
21. If resistance is .2–1.5 Kohms, repair fault in ECM connector contact. If not, repair or replace harness.
22. Disconnect A/C pressure sensor and connect an ohmmeter between accelerometer connector terminal No. 1 and ground.
23. If resistance is .2–1.5 Kohms, replace A/C pressure sensor. If not, proceed to next step.
24. If vehicle requires leak diagnosis, proceed to next step. If not, proceed to step 27.
25. Disconnect tank pressure sensor. Connect ohmmeter between accelerometer connector terminal No. 1 and ground.
26. If resistance is .2–1.5 Kohms, replace tank pressure sensor. If not, proceed to next step.
27. Further diagnosis is required to determine if there is a short circuit in accelerometer, A/C pressure sensor or tank pressure sensor to the ECM.
28. If a short circuit is present, repair fault as necessary. If not, then procedure is complete.

CODES P1405 & P1406: TEMPERATURE WARNING

1. Connect suitable scan tool and turn ignition switch to On position. Select "Components /Functions" to activate engine cooling fan.
2. If engine cooling fan operates properly, proceed to next step. If not, repair fault as necessary.
3. Set blower fan switch to highest speed and close all dashboard vents.
4. If a gentle stream of air is blown out of the control module box air hose and engine cooling fan is operating properly, erase DTC.
5. If a gentle stream of air does not blow out of the control module box air hose, repair fault as necessary.

CODE P1505: IDLE AIR CONTROL VALVE OPENING LOW INPUT

1. Ensure ignition switch is in Off position and disconnect IAC valve. Turn ignition switch to On position and connect a suitable voltmeter between IAC valve connector terminal No. 2 and ground. If reading is battery voltage, proceed to next step. If reading is not battery voltage, repair wiring harness.
2. Connect ohmmeter between IAC valve connector terminals No. 1 and No. 2. If resistance is 20–40 Kohms, proceed to next step. If resistance is not 20–40 Kohms, repair IAC harness connector.
3. Connect ohmmeter between IAC valve connector terminals No. 1 and No. 2 and between IAC valve connector terminals No. 2 and No. 3. If resistance for both tests is 9–14 ohms at 68°F, repair IAC valve connector contacts. If resistance for both tests is not 9–14 ohms at 68°F, replace IAC valve.

CODE P1506: IDLE AIR CONTROL VALVE OPENING HIGH INPUT

1. Ensure ignition switch is in Off position and disconnect IAC valve.
2. Turn ignition switch to On position and connect voltmeter between IAC valve connector terminal No. 3 and ground.
3. If reading is less than one volt, replace IAC valve.
4. If reading is not less than one volt, repair wiring harness.

CODE P1507: IDLE AIR CONTROL VALVE CLOSING LOW INPUT

1. Ensure ignition switch is in Off position and disconnect IAC valve. Turn ignition switch to On position and connect a suitable voltmeter between IAC valve connector terminal No. 2 and ground. If reading is battery voltage, proceed to next step. If reading is not battery voltage, repair wiring harness.
2. Connect ohmmeter between IAC valve connector terminals No. 1 and No. 3. If resistance is 20–40 Kohms, proceed to next step. If resistance is not 20–40 Kohms, repair harness and/or connector.
3. Connect ohmmeter between IAC valve connector terminals No. 1 and No. 2 and between IAC valve connector terminals No. 2 and No. 3. If resistance for both tests is 9–14 ohms at 68°F, repair IAC valve connector contacts. If resistance for both tests is not 9–14 ohms at 68°F, replace IAC valve.

CODE P1508: IDLE AIR CONTROL VALVE CLOSING HIGH INPUT

1. Ensure ignition switch is in Off position and disconnect IAC valve.
2. Turn ignition switch to On position and connect voltmeter between IAC valve connector terminal No. 1 and ground.
3. If reading is less than one volt, replace IAC valve.
4. If reading is not less than one volt, repair wiring harness.

CODE P1603: IGNITION DISCHARGE MODULE GROUP C

Ensure Engine Control Module (ECM) terminal No. B19 (car side) is empty, and No. B19 and adjacent pins are undamaged.

CODE P1604: IGNITION DISCHARGE MODULE GROUP D

1. Try to start engine. If engine starts, proceed to next step. If engine does not start, repair or replace fuel pump relay.
2. Connect suitable scan tool and turn ignition switch to On position. Select "Components/Functions" to activate engine cooling fan. If engine cooling fan is running, proceed to next step. If engine cooling fan is not running, repair fault as necessary.
3. Connect test box tool No. 981 3190, or equivalent, and test ground terminals. Connect ECM and turn ignition switch to On position. Connect a test lamp between test box terminals No. B28 and No. B12. If test lamp lights, repair wiring harness. If test lamp did not light, proceed to next step.
4. Connect voltmeter between test box terminals No. B7 and No. B28. If reading is 0–2 volts, repair MIL connector

contact. If voltage is not 0–2 volts, repair wiring harness.

CODE P1605: IGNITION DISCHARGE MODULE GROUP E

1. Ensure ignition switch is in Off position and connect suitable scan tool. Turn ignition switch to On position and search for active DTCs. If P0410 DTC is active, refer to "P0410: Pulsed Secondary Air Injection System" for diagnostic procedure. If P0410 DTC is not active, proceed to next step.
2. Turn ignition switch to Off position and connect a test box tool No. 981 3190, or equivalent, and test ground terminals. Turn A/C button ON, then set blower fan at low speed.
3. Start and idle engine and connect a suitable voltmeter between test box terminals No. B40 and No. B28. If reading is 0–2 volts, repair wiring harness. If reading is not 0–2 volts, proceed to next step.
4. Turn ignition switch to Off position and disconnect A/C relay. Turn A/C switch ON and set blower fan at low speed. Start and idle engine, then connect voltmeter between test box connectors No. B40 and No. B28. If reading is between 0–2 volts, replace A/C relay. If reading is not 0–2 volts, repair wiring harness.

CODE P1617: AW 50-42 TRANSMISSION CONTROL MODULE LOW INPUT

1. Ensure ignition switch is in Off position and connect test box tool No. 981 3190, or equivalent, and test ground terminals.
2. Connect ohmmeter between test box terminals No. B26 and ground.
3. If resistance is infinite, replace harness and/or terminals.
4. If resistance is not infinite, repair wiring harness.

CODE P1618: AW 50-42 TRANSMISSION CONTROL MODULE HIGH INPUT

1. Ensure ignition switch is in Off position and connect test box tool No. 981 3190, or equivalent, and test ground terminals.
2. Connect ohmmeter between test box terminals No. B26 and ground.
3. If resistance is 0–3000 ohms, replace harness and/or terminals.
4. If resistance is not 0–3000 ohms, repair wiring harness.

CODE P1619: ENGINE COOLING FAN MISSING SIGNAL

1. Ensure ignition switch is in Off position and disconnect connector A from fan control relay. Connect a suitable voltmeter between fan control relay connector A (ECM side) and ground. If reading is battery voltage, proceed to next step. If reading is not battery voltage, repair wiring harness between starter motor and engine control fan relay.
2. Disconnect engine cooling fan relay connector B and turn ignition switch to On position. Connect voltmeter between relay connector B terminal (ECM side) No. 1 and ground. If reading is approximately six volts, proceed to next step. If reading is not approximately six volts, repair wiring harness.
3. Connect voltmeter between fan control relay connector B (ECM side) No. 2 and ground. If reading is three volts, proceed to next step. If reading is not three volts, repair wiring harness.
4. Turn ignition switch to Off position and connect fan control relay connectors A and B. Connect suitable scan tool, and start and idle engine. Read off DTC status message. If DTC is still permanent, replace engine cooling fan relay. If DTC is not still permanent, repair engine cooling fan relay connector contact.

CODE P1620: ENGINE COOLING FAN HIGH INPUT

1. Ensure ignition switch is in Off position and disconnect engine cooling fan relay connector B.
2. Turn ignition switch to On position and connect a suitable voltmeter between engine cooling fan relay connector B (ECM side) terminal No. 1 and ground
3. If reading is approximately six volts, replace engine cooling fan relay.
4. If reading is not approximately six volts, repair wiring harness.

Component Tests

FUEL PRESSURE

1. Disconnect pressure regulator vacuum hose and ensure hose is not blocked.
2. Remove fuel rail valve safety cap and connect pressure gauge tool No. 999 5011, or equivalent, with adapter and nipple.
3. Remove fuel pump relay and connect suitable jumper harness across relay base terminals No. 1 and 3.
4. Switch ignition switch to On position and ensure fuel pump starts.
5. Read pressure gauge. Refer to "Gasoline Engine Tune Up Specifications" for specifications.

Clearing Diagnostic Trouble Codes

Follow scan tool manufacturer's instructions to clear DTCs.

SYSTEM SERVICE

Component Replacement

THROTTLE BODY

REMOVAL

1. Remove throttle pulley cover.
2. **On C70, S70 and V70 models,** remove air cleaner inlet hose.
3. **On all models,** remove fresh air intake between air cleaner and throttle body, and link between throttle pulley and throttle body.
4. Remove throttle position sensor connector and throttle body.

INSTALLATION

1. Install new gasket and throttle body.
2. Connect throttle position sensor.
3. Loosen link locknut, pull link as far back as possible, release one end and ensure link springs back easily to innermost position.
4. Ensure throttle spindle contacts adjustment screw and pulley contacts idling stop.
5. Tighten link locknut.
6. Open and close throttle to ensure spindle contacts adjustment screw when throttle is closed.
7. Adjust throttle pulley and harness as outlined under "Adjustment."
8. Install fresh air intake between air cleaner and throttle body.
9. **On C70, S70 and V70 models,** install air cleaner inlet hose.
10. **On all models,** install throttle pulley cover.

INJECTORS

C70, S70 & V70

1. Turn ignition switch to Off position and relieve fuel pressure as outlined under "Electric Fuel Pumps."
2. Remove fuel rail cover, injector connectors and fuel line clips.
3. Remove mounting screws and lift fuel rail with injectors.
4. Place suitable shop rag under connector to soak up spilling fuel, twist fuel rail approximately 90° and pull it away from fuel line.
5. Remove injector holders, mounting screws and mounting rail and the injectors.
6. Reverse procedure to install with O-ring lubricated with suitable petroleum jelly. **Torque** mounting screws to 84 inch lbs.

S90 & V90

1. Turn ignition switch to Off position and relieve fuel pressure as outlined under "Electric Fuel Pumps."
2. Remove cruise control vacuum reservoir, injector covers and connectors,

then the fuel pressure regulator bracket mounting screws.
3. Remove mounting screws and lift fuel rail with injectors.
4. Remove screws holding mounting rail to fuel rail, then the injectors.
5. Reverse procedure to install with O-ring lubricated with suitable petroleum jelly. **Torque** mounting screws to 84 inch lbs.

FUEL PRESSURE REGULATOR

C70, S70 & V70

1. Turn ignition switch to Off position and relieve fuel pressure as outlined under "Electric Fuel Pumps."
2. Remove large clamp.
3. Remove fuel pressure regulator.
4. Remove small clamp.
5. Disconnect hose.
6. Reverse procedure to install.

S90 & V90

1. Turn ignition switch to Off position and relieve fuel pressure as outlined under "Electric Fuel Pumps."
2. Place suitable shop rag under regulator to absorb spilled fuel.
3. Remove fuel lines and vacuum hose from regulator.
4. Reverse procedure to install.

KNOCK SENSOR

C70, S70 & V70

1. Remove throttle pulley cover, throttle harness, spark plug cover and cylinder head crankcase ventilation.
2. Remove fuel rail as previous outlined.
3. Remove air cleaner air intake and intake hose, then the canister purge valve hose at intake manifold.
4. Remove canister purge valve mounting screws from cooling fan shroud, then the canister purge valve connector.
5. Remove cooling fan shroud mounting screws and air duct to Engine Control Module (ECM).
6. Fold back shroud, pull relay mounting up and disconnect cooling fan connectors.
7. Disconnect pulsed secondary air injection system pump valve hoses.
8. Remove spacers, cooling fan and shroud, then the radiator protective panel.
9. Remove Idle Air Control (IAC) valve and throttle position sensor connectors.
10. Remove brake system servo hose, fresh air hose and injector harness clip.
11. Remove intake manifold upper mounting bolts, dipstick and lower mounting bolts.
12. Remove support bracket bolt and intake manifold.
13. Remove connectors and knock sensors
14. Reverse procedure to install. **Torque** knock sensors and intake manifold mounting bolts to 15 ft. lbs.

S90 & V90

Front

1. Remove Mass Air Flow (MAS) sensor connector and harness mounting, then the MAF fresh air hose.
2. Remove air cleaner cover.
3. Remove connector and knock sensor.
4. Reverse procedure to install. **Torque** knock sensor to 15 ft. lbs.

Rear

1. Remove bracket mounting screw and turn dip stick.
2. Remove connector and knock sensor.
3. Reverse procedure to install. **Torque** knock sensor to 15 ft. lbs.

ENGINE CONTROL MODULE (ECM) REPLACEMENT

1. Drill locking strip security screw head, insert screw puller, and remove security screw and locking strip.
2. Remove ECM from bracket and pull straight down.
3. Disconnect ECM harness connector.
4. Reverse procedure to install.

Adjustments

THROTTLE PULLEY & HARNESS

1. Ensure pulley moves easily without sticking.
2. Ensure harness is taut in idling position without affecting throttle pulley position.
3. Ensure pulley seats against idling stop and adjust harness as required.
4. Press accelerator pedal to floor and ensure pulley seats against full-load stop.
5. Ensure Engine Control Module (ECM) is receiving information that throttle is wide open.

Electric Fuel Pumps

NOTE: Fuel Pump & Fuel Pressure Testing Is Interrelated With The Fuel Injection Systems. For Systems & Components Not Covered In This Section, Refer To "Fuel Injection."

NOTE: On Air Bag Equipped Models, Refer To "Air Bag System Precautions" Located In The Front Of This Manual For System Disarming & Arming Procedures.

NOTE: Refer To "Computer Relearn Procedures" Located In The Front Of This Manual When Battery Power To The Computer Has Been Interrupted.

NOTE: Prior To Performing Any Service Operations Listed In This Section, Consult The Technical Service Bulletin Section For Related Information.

INDEX

	Page No.
Fuel Pressure Relief	18-55
Fuel Pump Relay Location	18-55
C70, S70 & V70	18-55
S90 & V90	18-55
Fuel Pump Replacement	18-55
C70, S70 & V70	18-55
S90 & V90	18-55
Precautions	18-55
Air Bag Systems	18-55
Battery Ground Cable	18-55

PRECAUTIONS

Air Bag Systems

Refer to "Air Bag System Precautions" in the front of this manual for system disarming and arming procedures.

Battery Ground Cable

Prior to service, disconnect battery ground cable and isolate as required.

FUEL PUMP RELAY LOCATION

C70, S70 & V70

The fuel pump relay is located in the fuse/relay box, at the rear lefthand side of the engine compartment.

S90 & V90

The fuel pump relay is located in the fuse/relay box, behind the lefthand side of the instrument panel.

FUEL PRESSURE RELIEF

1. Connect fuel pressure gauge tool No. 999 5011, or equivalent, to fuel pressure test fitting on fuel distribution manifold.
2. Place fuel return line of pressure gauge into suitable fuel container.
3. Open valve on fuel pressure gauge and allow fuel under residual pressure to drain.

FUEL PUMP REPLACEMENT

S90 & V90

1. Turn ignition switch to Off position and relieve fuel pressure.
2. **On four-door models,** remove spare wheel cover and luggage compartment carpet.
3. **On five-door models,** remove lefthand wheel well cover, and floor panel behind rear seat.
4. **On all models,** remove fuel tank cover and clean area around unit and hose connectors.
5. Remove fuel tank hoses.
6. Remove hose clamp, then fuel pump collar with fuel pump wrench tool No. 999 5448, or equivalent.
7. Remove gasket.
8. Unhook lower and upper pump mounting, and disconnect harness.
9. Loose hose clamp and carefully pull pump from hose.
10. Reverse procedure to install, noting following:
    a. Use new, dry gasket.
    b. Lubricate mating surface with thin layer of suitable petroleum jelly.
    c. Seat fuel tank unit stamped markings in tank's plastic joints.

C70, S70 & V70

1. Turn ignition switch to Off position and relieve fuel pressure, "Electric Fuel Pumps."
2. **On four-door models,** proceed as follows:
    a. Fold righthand rear seat forward.
    b. Remove luggage compartment mat.
    c. Fold wheel arch panel corner back by shock absorber mount.
    d. Remove fuel pump cover.
3. **On five-door models,** proceed as follows:
    a. Remove floor hatches and fold back carpet.
    b. Remove fuel pump cover.
4. **On all models,** disconnect fuel pump connector and note hoses and pump color markings for assembly.
5. Disconnect delivery and return hoses quick-release connectors.
6. Remove fuel pump mounting nut with fuel pump wrench tool No. 999 5485, or equivalent.
7. Lift pump out and remove rubber seal. **Do not grip connectors with pliers or other sharp tools.**
8. Reverse procedure to install, noting following:
    a. Use new, dry seal.
    b. Lubricate mating surface with thin layer of suitable petroleum jelly.
    c. Install fuel pump with heater connection facing righthand side of car.
    d. **Torque** mounting nut to 30 ft. lbs.

Turbochargers

NOTE: If Unsure Of The System Used On The Vehicle Being Serviced, Refer To "The Engine Systems Identification Chart." Further Assistance For The Proper Use Of Information Contained In This Section Can Also Be Found In The Front Of This Tabbed Section Under "How To Use This Manual."

NOTE: On Air Bag Equipped Models, Refer To "Air Bag System Precautions" Located In The Front Of This Manual For System Disarming & Arming Procedures.

NOTE: Refer To "Computer Relearn Procedures" Located In The Front Of This Manual When Battery Power To The Computer Has Been Interrupted.

NOTE: Prior To Performing Any Service Operations Listed In This Section, Consult The "Technical Service Bulletins" Section For Related Information.

INDEX

	Page No.
Description	18-56
Diagnosis & Testing	18-57
Boost Pressure Inspection	18-57
Bypass Valve	18-57
Charge Air Overpressure Switch	18-57
Precautions	18-56
Battery Ground Cable	18-56
Lubrication	18-56
System Service	18-57
Adjustments	18-58
Boost Pressure	18-58
Component Replacement	18-57
Control Valve	18-57
Pressure Actuator	18-57
Turbocharger	18-57
Wastegate Valve Servo	18-57
Wastegate Valve	18-57
Troubleshooting	18-56
Boost Pressure Too High	18-56
Boost Pressure Too Low	18-56
Engine Knocks	18-56
Engine Surges During Engine Braking	18-57
Metallic Noise From Wastegate	18-56
Noise Or Vibration From Turbocharger	18-57
Oil Leakage At Turbocharger Shaft Seals	18-57

PRECAUTIONS

Battery Ground Cable

Prior to service, disconnect battery ground cable and isolate as required.

Lubrication

Proper lubrication is essential for proper turbocharger operation. Since it is lubricated by engine oil pressure, three important practices should be observed:

1. Do not race engine immediately after starting. Let engine idle to provide initial lubrication.
2. Do not switch engine off while running at high RPM as turbocharger will continue to spin at high RPM without oil pressure. Letting engine idle before shutdown will also lower turbine temperatures.
3. The oil and filter must be changed every 3750 miles or every six months. Oil must meet API Service SE-CC or SF-CC. Do not use SE-CD oils.

DESCRIPTION

A turbocharger is used on the B5234T and B5254T engines. The turbocharger is an exhaust driven device which compresses the intake air to increase engine power on a demand basis. This allows for performance equal to that of a larger displacement naturally aspirated engine without the added weight and fuel consumption. Other benefits of a turbocharged engine are lower noise and emission levels.

Several devices are used to allow the engine to use relatively high boost pressures at mid-range RPMs without being overboosted at higher RPMs. A wastegate that begins to open at 6 psi to prevent excessive boost pressure is used. If the wastegate fails, an overload protection switch that senses boost pressure in the intake manifold opens the fuel pump relay ground circuit at 12.1 psi boost. This momentarily stops the fuel and engine to reduce boost pressure.

TROUBLESHOOTING

Boost Pressure Too Low

1. Air cleaner clogged.
2. Throttle control incorrectly adjusted.
3. Engine fault such as low compression, incorrect valve clearance, or poor fuel supply.
4. Leakage between compressor housing and cylinder head or between cylinder head and exhaust turbine housing.
5. Wastegate stuck open.
6. Exhaust system restricted.
7. Boost pressure improperly adjusted.
8. Faulty turbocharger.
9. Bypass valve leaking or seized in open position.
10. Bypass valve does not close.

Boost Pressure Too High

1. Leakage from hose between compressor housing and pressure actuator.
2. Pressure actuator diaphragm damaged.
3. Wastegate stuck closed.
4. Boost pressure improperly adjusted.

Engine Knocks

1. Fuel octane rating too low.
2. Ignition setting or retardation incorrect.
3. Boost pressure too high.
4. Air filter blocked.
5. Defective fuel supply.
6. Blocked PCV system.

Metallic Noise From Wastegate

1. Preheating plates loose or cracked.
2. Wastegate housing or exhaust pipe loose.
3. Wastegate loose in guide.

Engine Surges During Engine Braking

1. Bypass valve does not open.
2. Throttle switch incorrectly adjusted.

Noise Or Vibration From Turbocharger

1. Preheating plates loose or cracked.
2. Intake or exhaust system leakage.
3. Poor turbocharger lubrication.
4. Imbalance on turbo shaft, turbine wheel, or compressor wheel due to damage.

Oil Leakage At Turbocharger Shaft Seals

1. Air cleaner clogged (oil leakage on inlet side causes white smoke).
2. Exhaust system loose or leaks.
3. Excessive crankcase pressure.
4. Turbocharger oil return pipe clogged.
5. Turbocharger shaft seals damaged.

DIAGNOSIS & TESTING

Boost Pressure Inspection

1. Connect a pressure gauge between line to boost pressure gauge and tapping on intake manifold. Place gauge so it can be read from inside vehicle.
2. Start engine and allow to reach normal operating temperatures.
3. Operate vehicle in 2nd gear at about 1500 RPM.
4. Press accelerator to floor, but not as far as kickdown. When RPM reaches 3000 RPM, apply brake while keeping accelerator pedal floored.
5. Maintain RPM while reading boost pressure on pressure gauge. Maximum boost pressure should be 7–8 psi. **Low boost pressure is not necessarily caused by a turbocharger fault. Refer to "Troubleshooting."**

Charge Air Overpressure Switch

1. Using a vacuum tee, connect pressure gauge 5230 or equivalent and a pressure tester to overpressure switch hose at intake manifold.
2. Start engine and increase pressure until engine stalls. Engine should stall at 12.1–13.5 psi and pointer should be in red sector of dashboard pressure gauge. **Do not exceed 17 psi or dashboard pressure gauge may be damaged.**
3. Replace charge air over pressure switch if defective. The switch is located under the dash above the pedal assembly.

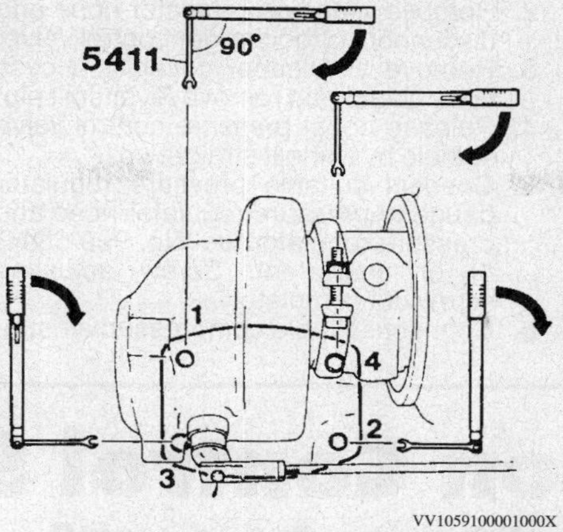

Fig. 1 Turbocharger bolt tightening sequence

Bypass Valve

Bypass valve should open during engine braking to prevent surging.

1. Disconnect the large upper hose from bypass valve and ensure valve is closed.
2. Connect a vacuum pump to vacuum hose on the intake manifold.
3. Operate vacuum pump and ensure valve opens at approximately 3.1 psi.
4. Replace bypass hose if defective and reconnect hoses.

SYSTEM SERVICE

Component Replacement

TURBOCHARGER

1. Disconnect charge air hose from compressor housing.
2. Disconnect wastegate operating air line and compressor air inlet hose.
3. Disconnect lines from shaft housing.
4. Clamp coolant lines using suitable clamps and disconnect coolant lines from shaft housing.
5. Disconnect front exhaust pipe and remove bracket at flywheel/torque converter housing.
6. Disconnect pressure oil line from shaft housing and plug inlet passage.
7. **On Garrett models,** remove bracket at front of compressor housing.
8. **On all models,** remove turbocharger from manifold with oil return line.
9. Disconnect oil return line and plug passage in turbocharger.
10. Remove oil supply pipe and cover openings on turbo.
11. Check radial and axial clearance by inspecting turbine and compressor for contact with housing.
12. Install oil return line using new gasket and rubber seal.
13. Install turbocharger and lubricate studs with suitable thread locking compound and install nuts.
14. Using suitable wrench and tool No. 5411, or equivalent, **torque** nuts to 22 ft. lbs. in sequence shown in **Fig. 1.**
15. Remove plug from oil inlet and fill hole with oil.
16. Install oil pressure line.
17. **On Garrett models,** install front mounting bracket to compressor.
18. **On all models,** install coolant lines, then release clamps.
19. Connect exhaust pipe and install nuts and **torque** to 22 ft. lbs.
20. **Torque** catalytic converter joint bolts to 18 ft. lbs.
21. Connect wastegate air line, compressor charge air hose and batter ground harness.
22. Check boost pressure.

CONTROL VALVE

1. Remove intake hose and control valve connector.
2. Remove MAF sensor clip and fresh air hose.
3. Remove blue marked fresh air hose.
4. Press valve out of rubber mounting and remove hoses.
5. Reverse procedure to install with new rubber mounting.

WASTEGATE VALVE SERVO

1. Remove turbocharger heat shield.
2. Disconnect valve arm lock pin and remove valve hose.
3. Remove fresh air hose from turbocharger and MAF sensor.
4. Remove mounting bolts and valve.
5. Reverse procedure to install. **Torque** mounting bolts to 15 ft. lbs.

PRESSURE ACTUATOR

1. Remove pressure actuator nuts and disconnect hose.
2. Disconnect rod end from wastegate lever and remove pressure actuator.
3. Install new actuator without connecting hose.
4. Connect pressure pump and gauge to actuator.
5. Apply 7–7.8 psi of pressure to actuator.
6. Push wastegate lever forward to hold wastegate in closed position. Adjust rod end to fit precisely on lever pin.
7. Install new circlip and tighten locknut.
8. Remove pressure pump and gauge.
9. Connect pressure actuator hose.
10. Check boost pressure.

WASTEGATE VALVE

Garrett

1. Disconnect hose from valve.
2. Disconnect vacuum hose from valve and compressor inlet hose.
3. Remove valve mounting bolts by loosening evenly. **Valve housing is spring loaded.**
4. Clean and inspect valve components, replace as necessary.
5. Install valve with new gasket, tightening bolts evenly.
6. Connect hoses.

Mitsubishi

1. Disconnect vacuum hose from valve and remove valve mounting bolts.

2. Remove valve.
3. Install new valve, ensuring O-ring is intact.
4. Tighten mounting bolts evenly and connect vacuum hose.

Adjustments

BOOST PRESSURE

1. Remove heat deflector plate above exhaust manifold.
2. Remove pressure regulator hose and disconnect turbocharger control valve.
3. Remove air cleaner cover to access hose clamp and remove lever split pin.
4. Release boost pressure control valve spindle by lifting it straight up.
5. Connect suitable pressure regulator gauge to pressure regulator hose and pressure regulator tool No. 999 5544-4, or equivalent. Screw adjusting screw out completely.
6. Connect suitable compressed air supply to pressure regulator.
7. **On models equipped with B5234T engine,** adjust pressure to 1.8 psi.
8. **On models equipped with B5254T engine,** adjust pressure to 2.6 psi.
9. **On all models,** push boost pressure control valve lever toward housing and valve should be closed.
10. Ensure boost pressure control valve spindle locates on lever lug. If necessary, adjust.
11. Reverse procedure to install.

Emission Control System Application Charts

Engine Liter	Certification Type		Trans. Type		Computerized Engine Management	Fuel Induction System Type	Ignition Timing, Deg. BTDC @ RPM	Emission Control System SRI	Emission Control Systems								
	CA	FED	A/T	M/T					PCV	ACL	AIS	EGR	EVAP	CAT	SPK	FR	O2S
1998																	
2.3L Turbo	X	X	X	X	YES⑩	SFI	6@ 850④	—	X	—	—	—	X	X①	X③	X	X⑨
2.4L Non-Turbo	X	X	X	X	YES⑩	MFI	3-7@ 850④⑧	—	X	—	—	—	X	X①	X③	X	X⑨
2.4L Turbo	X	X	X	X	YES⑩	MFI	④	—	X	—	—	—	X	X①	X③	X	X⑨
2.9L	X	X	X	—	YES⑩	MFI	7–11@ 750④	—	X	—	X⑥	—	X	X①	X⑤	X	X⑨
1999																	
2.3L/140/L5 Turbo	X	X	X	X	YES⑩	SFI	④	—	X	—	—	—	X	X①	X③	X	X⑨
2.4L/146/L5	X	X	X	X	YES⑩	MFI	④	—	X	—	—	—	X	X①	X③	X	X⑨
2.4L/146/L5 Turbo	X	X	X	X	YES⑩	MFI	④	—	X	—	—	—	X	X①	X⑩	X	X⑨
2.8L/178/L6 Turbo CVVT	X	X	X	—	YES⑩	MFI	④	—	X	—	X⑥	—	X	X⑯	X③	X	X⑰
2.9L/178/L6 CVVT	X	X	X	—	YES⑩	MFI	④	—	X	—	X⑥	—	X	X⑯	X③	X	X⑰
2000																	
1.9L//L4 Turbo CVVT	X	X	X	X	YES⑱	SFI	0–15@750㉑	—	X	—	—	—	X	X①	X⑤	X	X⑨
2.3L/140/L5 Turbo	X	X	X	X	YES⑲	SFI	5@850㉑	—	X	—	—	—	X	X①	X⑤	X	X⑨
2.4L/146/L5	X	X	X	—	YES⑳	MFI	12@850㉑	—	X	—	—	—	X	X①	X⑤	X	X⑨
2.4L/146/L5	X	X	—	X	YES⑳	MFI	5@850㉑	—	X	—	—	—	X	X①	X⑤	X	X⑨
2.4L/146/L5 Turbo	X	X	X	X	YES⑲	MFI	8@850㉑	—	X	—	—	—	X	X①	X⑤	X	X⑨
2.8L/178/L6 Turbo CVVT	X	X	X	—	YES⑲	MFI	10@650㉑	—	X	—	X⑥	—	X	X⑯	X⑤	X	X⑰
2.9L/178/L6 CVVT	X	X	X	—	YES⑲	MFI	10@650㉑	—	X	—	X⑥	—	X	X⑯	X⑤	X	X⑰
2001																	
1.9L//L4 Turbo CVVT	X	X	X	X	YES⑱	SFI	0–15@750㉑	—	X	—	—	—	X	X①	X⑤	X	X⑨
2.3L/140/L5 Turbo	X	X	X	X	YES⑲	SFI	6@670㉑	—	X	—	—	—	X	X①	X⑤	X	X⑨
2.4L/146/L5	X	X	X	X	YES⑳	MFI	6@750㉑	—	X	—	—	—	X	X①	X⑤	X	X⑨
2.4L/146/L5 Turbo	X	X	X	X	YES⑲	MFI	6@670㉑	—	X	—	—	—	X	X①	X⑤	X	X⑨

Continued

Engine Liter	Certification Type		Trans. Type		Computerized Engine Management	Fuel Induction System Type	Ignition Timing, Deg. BTDC @ RPM	Emission Control System SRI	Emission Control Systems								
	CA	FED	A/T	M/T					PCV	ACL	AIS	EGR	EVAP	CAT	SPK	FR	O2S
2001																	
2.8L/178/L6 Turbo CVVT	X	X	X	—	YES⑲	MFI	10@650㉑	—	X	—	X⑥	—	X	X⑯	X⑤	X	X⑰
2.9L/178/L6 CVVT	X	X	X	—	YES⑲	MFI	10@650㉑	—	X	—	X⑥	—	X	X⑯	X⑤	X	X⑰

X — Equipped
— Not Equipped
① — Type TWC, number of catalytic converters, 1.
② — EGR & O2S.
③ — DI/Spark Timing Control.
④ — Refer to the emission control information label.
⑤ — EI/DIS.
⑥ — Pump type.
⑦ — CIS with Constant Idle Speed System.
⑧ — Timing can be inspected, but not adjusted.
⑨ — Two HO2S.
⑩ — Bosch Motronic 4.4.
⑪ — Bosch Motronic.
⑫ — Exc. 940, Bosch LH-Jetronic Fuel Injection System; 940, Regina Fuel Injection System.
⑬ — Bosch LH-Jetronic Fuel Injection System.
⑭ — Electronically controlled EGR.
⑮ — One O2S.
⑯ — Type TWC, number of catalytic converters, 2.
⑰ — Four HO2S.
⑱ — Siemens BMS 2000.
⑲ — Bosch ME 7.0. Equipped w/MIL.
⑳ — Nippondenso Engine Management System.
㉑ — PCM controlled, not adjustable.

ACL — Air Cleaner (Thermostatic Air Cleaner)
AIS — Air Injection System
A/T — Automatic Transmission
BTDC — Before Top Dead Center
CA — California
CAT — Catalytic Converter
CID — Cubic Inch Displacement
CIS — Continuous Injection System
DI — Distributor Ignition
EGR — Exhaust Gas Recirculation
EI — Electronic Ignition
EVAP — Evaporative Emission Control System
FED — Federal
FI — Fuel Injection
FR — Fillpipe Restrictor
MFI — Multi-Point Fuel Injection
M/T — Manual Transmission
OBD II — On Board Diagnostics II
OC — Oxidation Catalytic Converter
O2S — Oxygen Sensor
PCV — Positive Crankcase Ventilation
RPM — Revolutions Per Minute
SFI — Sequential Fuel Injection
SPK — Spark Control
SRI — Service Reminder Indicator
TSB — Technical Service Bulletin
TWC — Three Way Catalytic Converter

Engine Compartment Reference Diagrams

INDEX

	PAGE NO.	FIG. NO.
C70, S70 & V70:		
Motronic 4.4 Drivetrain Control System	18-61	1
S90 & V90:		
Motronic 4.4 Drivetrain Control System	18-61	2

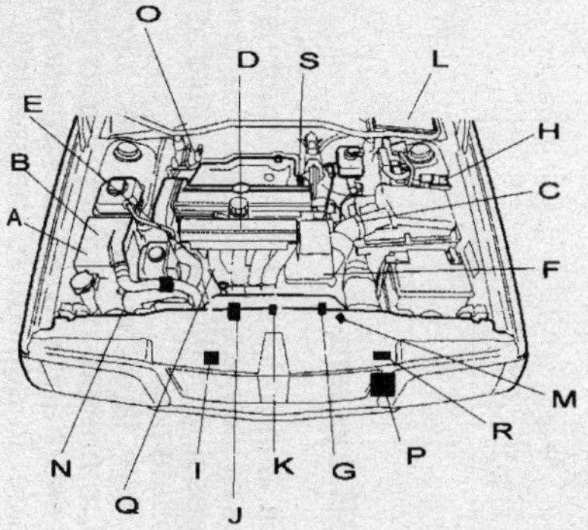

Engine compartment

A	AW50–42 transmission control module (TCM)
B	Motronic 4.4 Engine Control Module (ECM)
C	Mass air flow (MAF) sensor
D	Injectors
E	Engine coolant temperature (ECT) sensor
F	Idle air control (IAC) valve
G	Main relay
H	Ignition coil Ignition driver stage
I	Accelerometer
J	Engine cooling fan (FC) relay
K	Solenoid valve pulsed secondary air injection system (PAIR)
L	Central electrical unit
M	Canister purge (CP) valve
N	A/C pressure sensor
O	Pressure switch (Pressostat)
P	Pulsed secondary air injection system (PAIR) pump
Q_1	Front knock sensor (KS)
Q_2	Rear knock sensor (KS)
R	Pulsed secondary air injection system (PAIR) pump relay
S	Pulsed secondary air injection system (PAIR) valve

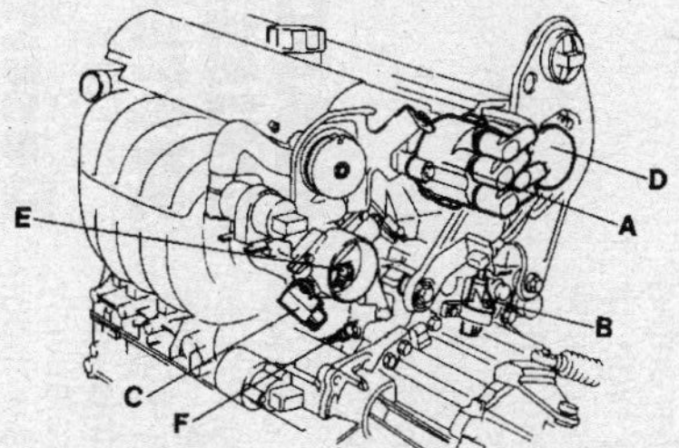

Rear of engine

A	Distributor
B	Engine speed (RPM) sensor
C	Throttle position sensor (TP sensor)
D	Camshaft position (CMP) sensor
E	Power ground
F	Signal ground

VV1019600001000X

Fig. 1 Engine compartment reference diagram. C70, S70 & V70 w/Motronic 4.4 drivetrain control system

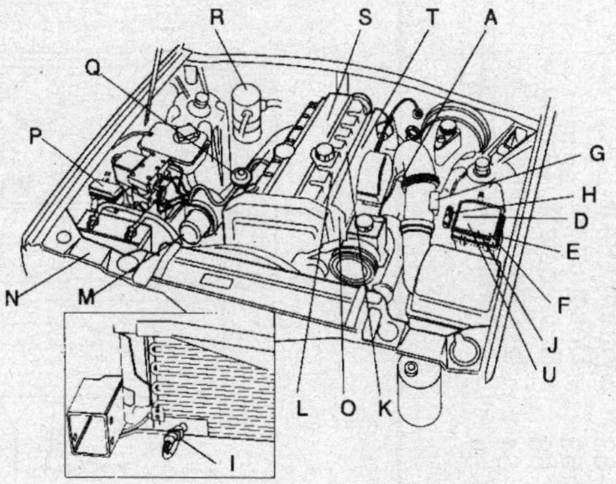

Engine compartment

A	Idle air control (IAC) valve
B	EVAP valve
C	Acceleration sensor
D	Connector, 55-pin
E	Central electrical unit (relays and fuses)
F	Pulsed secondary air injection system (PAIR) pump relay
G	Mass air flow (MAF) sensor
H	Solenoid, pulsed secondary air injection system (PAIR)
I	A/C pressure sensor
J	Main relay
K	Signal ground
L	Power ground
M	Pulsed secondary air injection system (PAIR) pump
N	Fan control relay
O	Engine coolant temperature (ECT) sensor
P	Main fuse box
Q	Pulsed secondary air injection system (PAIR) valve
R	Pressure switch (Pressostat)
S	Ignition coils
T	Injectors
U	Relay, ignition coils

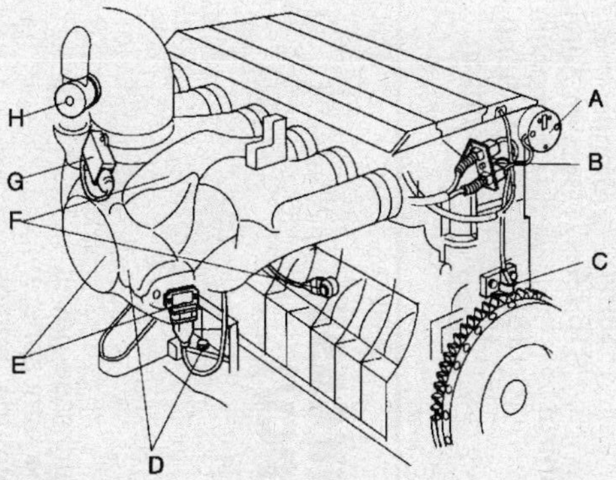

Rear of engine

A	Camshaft position (CMP) sensor
B	Test output, ignition coil 1
C	Engine speed (RPM) sensor
D	Ignition discharge module (IDM) ground
E	Ignition discharge module (IDM)
F	Knock sensor (KS)
G	Throttle position (TP) sensor
H	Idle air control (IAC) valve

VV1019600002000X

Fig. 2 Engine compartment reference diagram. S90 & V90 w/Motronic 4.4 drivetrain control system

Emission Controls

NOTE: Prior To Performing Any Service Operations Listed In This Section, Consult The "Technical Service Bulletins" Section For Related Information.

INDEX

Page No.

Altitude Compensating Control Pressure Regulator 18-64
Description 18-64
Catalytic Converter 18-64
Description 18-64
Diagnosis & Testing 18-64
Evaporative Emission Control System 18-62
Description 18-62
System Service 18-63
Component Replacement 18-63
Exhaust Gas Recirculation (EGR) System 18-63
Description 18-63
Diagnosis & Testing 18-63
System Service 18-63
Component Replacement 18-63
Lambda-Sond System 18-64
Description 18-64
Positive Crankcase Ventilation (PCV) System 18-62
Description 18-62
Pulsed Secondary Air Injection System (PAIR) 18-64
Description 18-64
Diagnosis & Testing 18-64
System Service 18-64
Component Replacement 18-64

POSITIVE CRANKCASE VENTILATION (PCV) SYSTEM

Description

This system prevents crankcase gases from being released into the atmosphere. The gases are drawn into the engine through the intake manifold and routed to the combustion chamber.

Between the oil trap and intake manifold there is a hose which is connected to the intake manifold by means of a calibrated nipple. Between the rocker arm casing and air cleaner there is a hose connected for fresh air supply. At the connection to the rocker arm casing there is a flame arrester, which consists of metal filter. The partial vacuum which exists in the intake manifold during engine operation, creates a vacuum in the crankcase through the hose. Fresh air supplied to the rocker arm casing is routed through the air cleaner and hose. A plate in the rocker arm casing ensures that fresh air circulates sufficiently in order to mix with the crankcase gases.

As fresh air passes through the carburetor air cleaner, impurities are prevented from entering the engine. During high or medium amounts of vacuum in the crankcase, which occurs during idling and when operating under light loads, the system operates as outlined above. When vacuum in the crankcase is less than that in the air cleaner, which occurs at full load and/or with large flow quantities, no fresh air is supplied. Instead, the flow in the connection between the rocker arm casing and air cleaner reverses and crankcase gases pass both ways, partially through the air cleaner to the intake manifold. In this way, the PCV system can deal with relatively large quantities of crankcase gases without any entering the atmosphere. The PCV valve should be replaced every 25,000 miles.

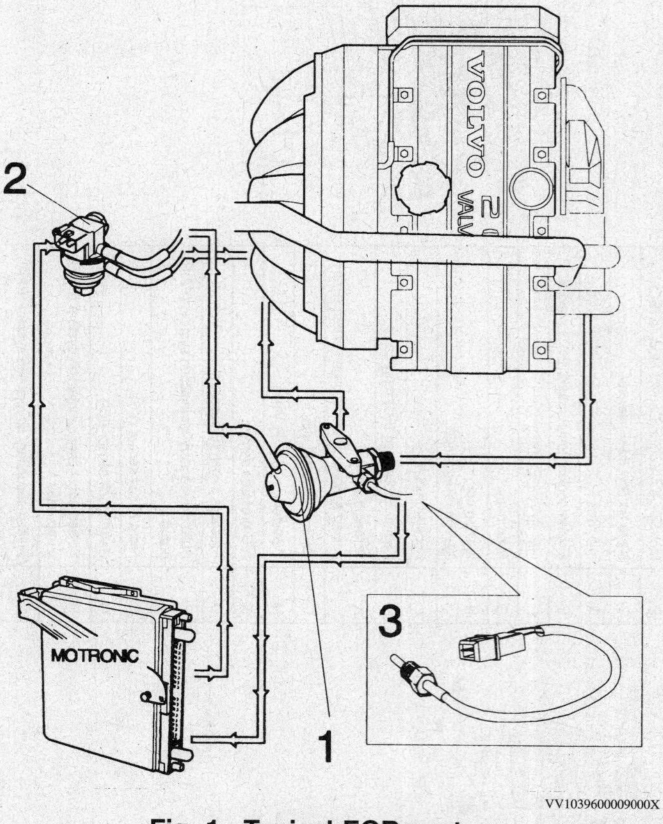

Fig. 1 Typical EGR system

EVAPORATIVE EMISSION CONTROL SYSTEM

Description

Vapor which evaporates in the fuel tank is routed and stored in a charcoal canister where it is introduced into the combustion process by way of the EVAP valve and negative pressure in the intake manifold at the appropriate time.

The fuel tank has been specially designed to prevent deforming due to negative pressure and has a plate screwed to it's underside. In addition to the specially designed fuel tank, the system utilizes a rollover valve which prevents fuel leakage in the event of a vehicle roll-over, a charcoal

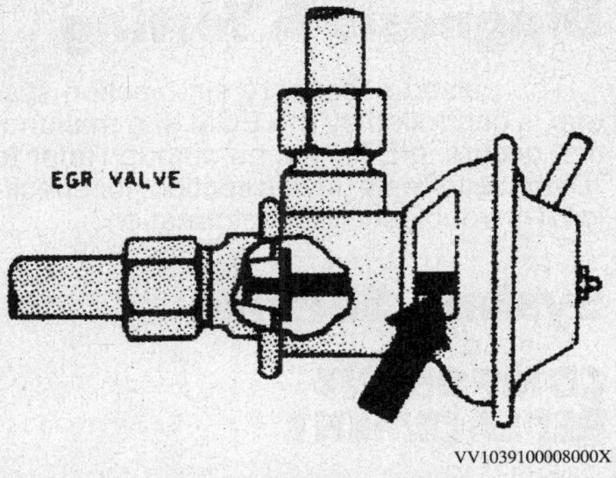

Fig. 2 EGR valve rod movement inspection

canister that stores the fuel vapors, a canister purge valve to control the flow of fuel vapor from the EVAP canister and an EVAP canister shut-off valve to aid in the detection of leaks in the EVAP system.

Normally the canister purge valve is closed and only opens when the engine control module (ECM) is emptying the canister. The EVAP canister is emptied by pulsing the valve to bring the mixture from the canister up to the canister purge control valve. Because of the negative pressure in the intake manifold, fresh air is sucked into the engine through the EVAP canister opening or through the EVAP canister shut-off valve. As the air passes through the EVAP canister, fuel stored in the activated charcoal is drawn into the engine and burned

System Service

COMPONENT REPLACEMENT

EVAP CANISTER

C70, S70 & V70

1. Disconnect outlet and inlet connectors, and remove hose from canister bracket.
2. Squeeze clamp with suitable wrench, hold in place and pry apart with suitable small screwdriver.
3. Remove air hose from valve.
4. Disconnect hoses and remove rubber mounting with valve from bracket.
5. Remove canister mounting screws and fuel filter bracket mounting nut.
6. Remove canister with bracket and loosen mounting screws.
7. Remove canister from bracket.
8. Reverse procedure to install. **Torque** mounting screws to 18 ft. lbs. and nut to 15 ft. lbs.

S90 & V90

1. Raise and support vehicle.
2. Loose lefthand mounting nut.
3. Loose righthand front mounting nut and remove righthand rear screw.
4. Angle bracket rear edge down and remove hoses.
5. Remove mounting screw from underside of bracket, then the lefthand mounting nut.
6. Remove canister.
7. Reverse procedure to install. **Torque** mounting screws and nuts to 18 ft. lbs.

EVAP CANISTER SHUTOFF VALVE

C70, S70 & V70

1. Disconnect connector.
2. Squeeze clamp with suitable wrench, hold in place and pry apart with suitable small screwdriver.
3. Disconnect hoses and remove rubber mounting with valve from bracket.
4. Reverse procedure to install.

S90 & V90

1. Remove valve.
2. Remove connectors.
3. Remove hoses.
4. Reverse procedure to install. Apply suitable low-temperature grease to connectors.

EXHAUST GAS RECIRCULATION (EGR) SYSTEM

Description

The EGR (exhaust gas recirculation) system reduces the content of nitrogen oxides (NOx) in the exhaust gases. Nitrogen oxides are formed at the high temperatures that are present in the engine combustion chambers under high load conditions.

The combustion temperature is lowered by returning a portion of the exhaust gases to the engine thereby reducing nitrogen oxide levels. The EGR system is not activated when the engine is cold or idling, or when turbo boost pressure is present. During these conditions nitrogen oxide levels are relatively low.

The system consists of an EGR valve (1), an EGR vacuum controller (2) and an EGR temperature sensor (3), **Fig. 1.**

Diagnosis & Testing

The EGR valve operates on a vacuum signal from the throttle plate. With the engine idling, the valve must be closed (check by observing the rod movement through the observation window in the valve housing, **Fig. 2.** If the valve is open at idle, rough idle will result. Adjust the throttle stop screw to position the throttle butterfly so that the valve will be closed at idle. This can be checked by connecting a vacuum gauge to the vacuum line from the intake manifold to the EGR valve. With the throttle plate properly adjusted, there should be no vacuum gauge reading at idle.

Some systems incorporate a thermostatic valve. This valve cuts off the vacuum signal to the EGR valve when the engine is cold.

System Service

The EGR valve should be checked and cleaned every 15,000 miles and replaced at 30,000 miles.

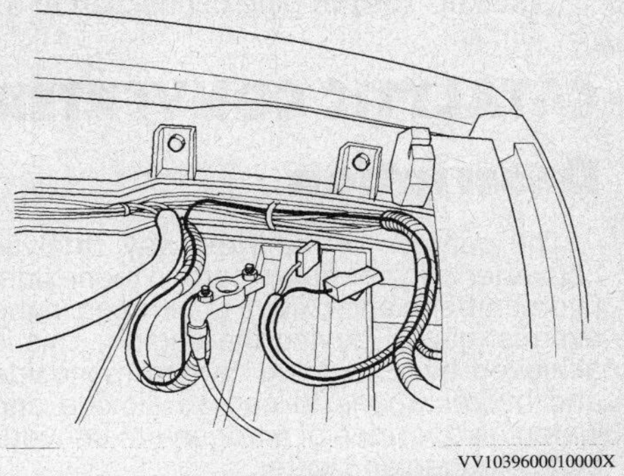

Fig. 3 Pulsed secondary air injection pump fusible link replacement

After servicing the EGR valve, the EGR indicator light switch must be reset. To do this, remove the rear cover on the special odometer and depress the white button. The special odometer is located under the dashboard at the rear of the instrument panel.

COMPONENT REPLACEMENT

C70, S70 & V70

EGR Vacuum Controller

1. Remove EGR controller hoses and outer mounting screw.
2. Disconnect controller connector and remove mounting bracket.
3. Reverse procedure to install with electrical connection facing upward toward relay shelf top.

EGR Valve

1. **On models equipped with turbocharged engine,** remove upper charge-air pipe.
2. **On models less turbocharged engine,** remove air cleaner air intake and intake hose.
3. Remove EVAP valve mounting screws from cooling fan shroud.
4. Remove cooling fan shroud mounting screws and air duct to Engine Control Module (ECM).
5. Fold back shroud, pull relay mounting up and disconnect cooling fan connectors. Place relay holder across intake manifold.
6. Remove spacers, cooling fan and shroud, then the radiator protective panel.
7. **On models equipped with turbocharged engine,** remove lower pipe.
8. **On models less turbocharged engine,** remove fresh-air pipe.
9. **On all models,** disconnect EGR temperature sensor and remove connector from holder.
10. Remove EGR valve vacuum hose and disconnect gas recirculation pipe from valve.
11. Remove mounting screws, valve and gasket.
12. Remove temperature sensor and clean carefully.
13. Reverse procedure to install with new

gasket. **Torque** pipe connection to 37 ft. lbs.

CATALYTIC CONVERTER

Description

The purpose of the three-way catalytic converter is to neutralize carbon monoxide, hydrocarbons and oxides of nitrogen in the exhaust gases leaving the engine. This is achieved by converting carbon monoxide and hydrocarbons to carbon dioxide and water. Also, oxides of nitrogen are converted to nitrogen and water.

Diagnosis & Testing

Upstream of the catalytic converter is a plug for connecting a CO meter. The efficiency of the converter can be measured by comparing readings obtained upstream (plug connection) and downstream (inserting a probe in the tailpipe).

ALTITUDE COMPENSATING CONTROL PRESSURE REGULATOR

Description

This regulator automatically adjusts fuel injection pressure at different altitudes. The regulator decreases the injection pressure at higher altitudes to automatically adjust for lower air density. This maintains satisfactory air/fuel mixture and helps to reduce emissions.

LAMBDA-SOND SYSTEM

Description

This is a self adjusting engine control system designed to reduce emissions and improve fuel economy. The Lambda-Sond sensor or oxygen sensor monitors oxygen content of exhaust gases leaving the engine. Sensor output is fed to the control unit to help adjust air fuel ratio to provide optimum conditions for combustion.

PULSED SECONDARY AIR INJECTION SYSTEM (PAIR)

Description

The pulsed secondary air injection system reduces emission of hydrocarbons (HC) and carbon dioxide (CO), and heats the catalytic converter more rapidly after cold starting. On initial cold start the pulsed secondary air injection system introduces fresh air into the exhaust manifold in order to promote afterburning of hydrocarbons and carbon monoxide. This makes it possible to increase the injection period and to retard the ignition, increasing exhaust temperature and activating the catalytic converter more quickly.

The system consists of a pulsed secondary air injection pump which is activated through the pump relay, the pulsed secondary air injection valve with a built in check valve to prevent exhaust gases from being forced into the air injection system and a check valve to maintain negative pressure.

Diagnosis & Testing

The pulsed secondary air injection system is controlled by the ECM. If a malfunction occurs, a DTC will be output. Refer to "Diagnostic Tests" in this section, for specific DTC troubleshooting information.

System Service

COMPONENT REPLACEMENT

Pulsed Secondary Air Injection System Power Cable (Fusible Link), Replace

1. Remove mass air flow sensor connector, intake air hose, fresh air hose from mass air flow sensor and preheating hose from air cleaner housing.
2. Remove air cleaner housing and move to one side.
3. Remove battery cables and hold down clamps, then the battery.
4. Disconnect voltage supply and signal cable connectors from pulsed secondary air injection pump relay.
5. Cut tie straps holding cable, then move onto battery shelf.
6. Remove cable duct cover and fold it to one side. Open remaining cable sleeve and take out voltage supply cable, **Fig. 3.**
7. Cut voltage supply cable as close to positive cable terminal as possible.
8. Connect new voltage supply cable to positive cable terminal, replace in cable sleeve and cable dust and route in original position.
9. Reinstall all cable sleeves with insulation tape, reinstall cable dust cover and secure with new tie straps.
10. Route cabling to pulsed secondary air injection system pump relay, then connect connectors to relay and clamp cabling in position.
11. Install remaining components in reverse order of removal.

Technical Service Bulletins

INDEX

	Page No.
Control Module Box Cooling Fan Installation	18-65
Difficult To Start Or Ignition Problems	18-65
C70, S70 & V70	18-65
DTC P0442 or P0455	18-65
Motronic 4.4, C70, S70 & V70	18-65
Poor Driveability	18-65

DIFFICULT TO START OR IGNITION PROBLEMS

C70, S70 & V70

On these models, the engine may be difficult to start or have ignition problems.

This condition may be caused by ground terminal or excessive voltage drop across ignition coil contacts and ignition drive stage because of oxidation. To correct this condition, proceed as follows:

1. Clean ground bolt with emery cloth.
2. Ensure harness terminal is intact and correctly crimped.
3. Install new ground bolt (part No. 946544-4) and apply suitable rust-proofing agent to bolt and terminal.
4. Remove ground connect from terminal.
5. Remove contact surface oxidation by disconnecting and connecting halves at least 10 times. Blow clean with compressed air.
6. Ensure pins are intact and correctly located.
7. Apply suitable low-temperature grease to connections.
8. If ignition or starting difficulties continue, check distributor and HT leads.
9. Replace spark plugs.
10. Replace battery negative harness.

DTC P0442 OR P0455

Motronic 4.4, C70, S70 & V70

On these models, Diagnostic Trouble Codes (DTC) P0442 or P0455 may be set.

This condition may be caused by fueling car while engine is running or not tighten gas cap. To correct this condition, proceed as follows:

1. Ensure gas cap is tightened.
2. Turn ignition switch to On position and clear DTCs.

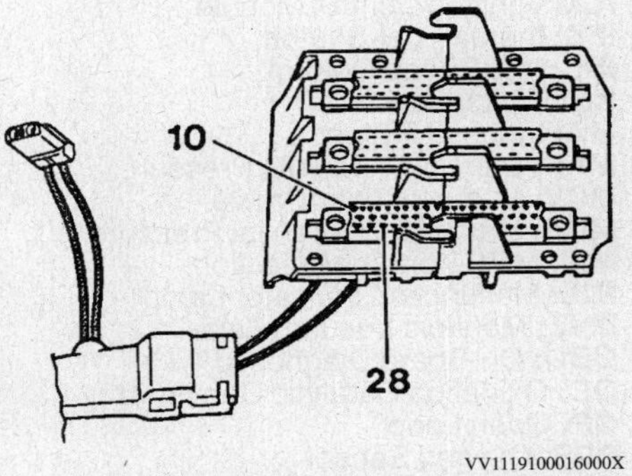

Fig. 1 DI control module terminal identification

3. Position gear selector in P or N position and warm engine to at least 158°F. Let engine idle.
4. Turn A/C off and use scan tool to run diagnosis.
5. If diagnosis does not go through, switch engine off and restart.
6. Inspect for DTCs. If DTC P0442 or P0455 do not reoccur, condition was caused by fueling car while engine is running or not tighten gas cap. If codes do occur, condition to follow DTC diagnosis.

CONTROL MODULE BOX COOLING FAN INSTALLATION

1. Disconnect battery ground cable and remove washer reservoir tube.
2. Disconnect air supply hose to control module box and remove control module cover.
3. Remove control modules, then the upper half of control module box.
4. Disconnect control module box air connection and remove baseplate rubber protector.
5. Lift baseplate to provide access to underside and cut leads with moisture-proof harness terminals to approximately 15¾ inches.
6. Connect suitable female mini timer type harness terminal to one lead, suitable moisture-proof terminal of this lead to terminal one of a two-pole sleeve insulator, then the second lead to terminal No. 2.
7. Run leads through harness duct to underside of control module baseplate, open catch on control module base by pushing sideways and connect lead with harness terminal to terminal 28 (A28) on DI control module, **Fig. 1.**
8. Disconnect lead connected to DI control module terminal No. A10, connect both leads to female mini timer type harness terminal and reconnect to terminal No. A10 and press catch on control module base back into position.
9. Install baseplate rubber protector, then the fan in place of control module box air connection.
10. Install upper half of control module box, then the control modules.
11. Install control module cover and connect air supply hose to control module box.
12. Connect washer reservoir tube, connector to fan and battery ground cable.
13. Test operation in diagnostic test mode three with air hose disconnected to observe fan operation. When main cooling fan starts in diagnostic test mode three, control module box fan should also start an supply air to box.

POOR DRIVEABILITY

Many driveability problems can be corrected or prevented by proper cleaning and protection of ignition and injection system connectors.

Using care not to damage the connector water seals, separate connector and plug and spray rust remover part No. 1161425-1 or 1161034-2, or equivalent, into cavities to clean. Using a low temperature grease No. part No. 1161417-9 or 1161236-3, or equivalent, to coat connector cavities and install connector.

Abbreviations & Acronyms

A/C: Air Conditioning
ACL: Air Cleaner
BVSV: Bimetal Vacuum Switching Valve
CAC: Charge Air Cooler
CFI: Continuous Fuel Injection
CKP: Crankshaft Position Sensor
CL: Closed Loop
CMP: Camshaft Position Sensor
CPP: Clutch Pedal Position
CTP: Closed Throttle Position
DI: Direct Ignition
DLC1: Data Link Connector 1
DLC2: Data Link Connector 2
DLC3: Data Link Connector 3
DTC: Diagnostic Trouble Code
DTM: Diagnostic Test Mode
ECL: Engine Control Level
ECM: Engine Control Module
ECU: Electronic Control Unit
ECT: Engine Coolant Temperature
EEPROM: Electrically Erasable Programmable Read Only Memory
EFI: Electronic Fuel Injection
EGR: Exhaust Gas Recirculation
EI: Electronic Ignition
EPROM: Erasable Programmable Read Only Memory
EVAP: Evaporative Emission
FC: Fan Control
FEEPROM: Flash Electrically Erasable Programmable Read Only Memory
GEN: Generator
GND: Ground
HCV: Heat Control Valve
HO2S: Heated Oxygen Sensor
IAC: Idle Air Control
IAT: Intake Air Temperature
ICM: Ignition Control Module
IFS: Inertia Fuel-Shutoff
ISC: Idle Speed Control
KS: Knock Sensor
MAF: Mass Air Flow
MAP: Manifold Absolute Pressure
MCV: Mixture Control Valve
MDP: Manifold Differential Pressure
MFI: Multi-Port Fuel Injection
MIL: Malfunction Indicator Lamp
MVZ: Manifold Vacuum Zone
OBD: On-Board Diagnostic
OC: Oxidation Catalytic Converter
OP: Open Loop
O2S: Oxygen Sensor
PCM: Powertrain Control Module
PNP: Park/Neutral Position
PROM: Programmable Read Only Memory
PSP: Power Steering Pressure
RAM: Random Access Memory
RM: Relay Module
ROM: Read Only Memory
RPM: Engine Speed
SFI: Sequential Multi-Port Fuel Injection
SRI: Service Reminder Indicator
SRT: System Readiness Test
ST: Scan Tool
TB: Throttle Body
TC: Turbocharger
TCC: Torque Converter Clutch
TCM: Transmission Control Module
TP: Throttle Position
TR: Transmission Range
TVSV: Thermostatic Vacuum Switching Valve
TVV: Thermal Vacuum Valve
TWC: Three-Way Catalytic Converter
TWC+OC: Three-Way+Oxidation Catalytic Converter
VR: Voltage Regulator
VSS: Vehicle Speed Sensor
VSV: Vacuum Switching Valve
WOT: Wide Open Throttle

DECIMAL & MILLIMETER EQUIVALENTS

Inch	Inch	mm
1/64	.015625	.397
1/32	.03125	.794
3/64	.046875	1.191
1/16	.0625	1.587
5/64	.078125	1.984
3/32	.09375	2.381
7/64	.109375	2.778
1/8	.125	3.175
9/64	.140625	3.572
5/32	.15625	3.969
11/64	.17185	4.366
3/16	.1875	4.762
13/64	.203125	5.159
7/32	.21875	5.556
15/64	.234375	5.953
1/4	.25	6.350
17/64	.265626	6.747
9/32	.28125	7.144
19/64	.296875	7.541
5/16	.3125	7.937
21/64	.328125	8.334
11/32	.34375	8.731

Inch	Inch	mm
23/64	.359375	9.128
3/8	.375	9.525
25/64	.390625	9.922
13/32	.40625	10.319
27/64	.421875	10.716
7/16	.4375	11.113
29/64	.453125	11.509
15/32	.46875	11.906
31/64	.484375	12.303
1/2	.5	12.700
33/64	.515625	13.097
17/32	.53125	13.494
35/64	.546875	13.890
9/16	.5625	14.287
37/64	.578125	14.684
19/32	.59375	15.081
39/64	.609375	15.478
5/8	.625	15.875
41/64	.640625	16.272
21/32	.65625	16.669
43/64	.671875	17.065

Inch	Inch	mm
11/16	.6875	17.462
45/64	.703125	17.859
23/32	.71875	18.265
47/64	.734375	18.653
3/4	.75	19.505
49/64	.765625	19.447
25/32	.78125	19.884
51/64	.796875	20.240
13/16	.8125	20.637
53/64	.828125	21.034
27/32	.84375	21.431
55/64	.859375	21.828
7/8	.875	22.225
57/64	.890625	22.622
29/32	.90625	23.019
59/64	.921875	23.415
15/16	.9375	23.812
61/64	.953125	24.209
31/32	.96875	24.606
63/64	.984375	25.003
1	1	25.400

Manual Information Locator

All Wheel Drive Models

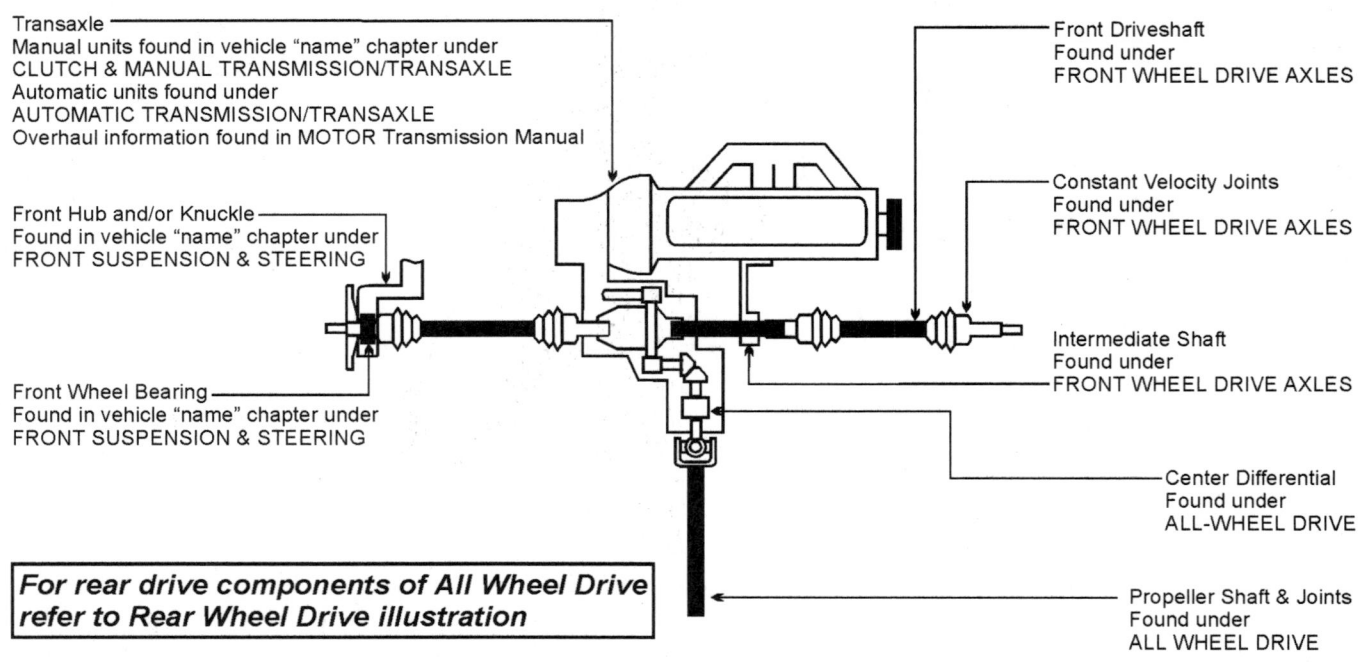

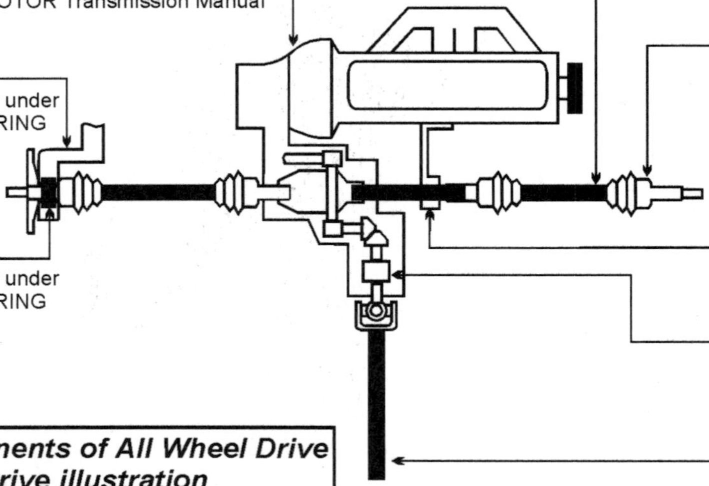

Rear Wheel Drive Models

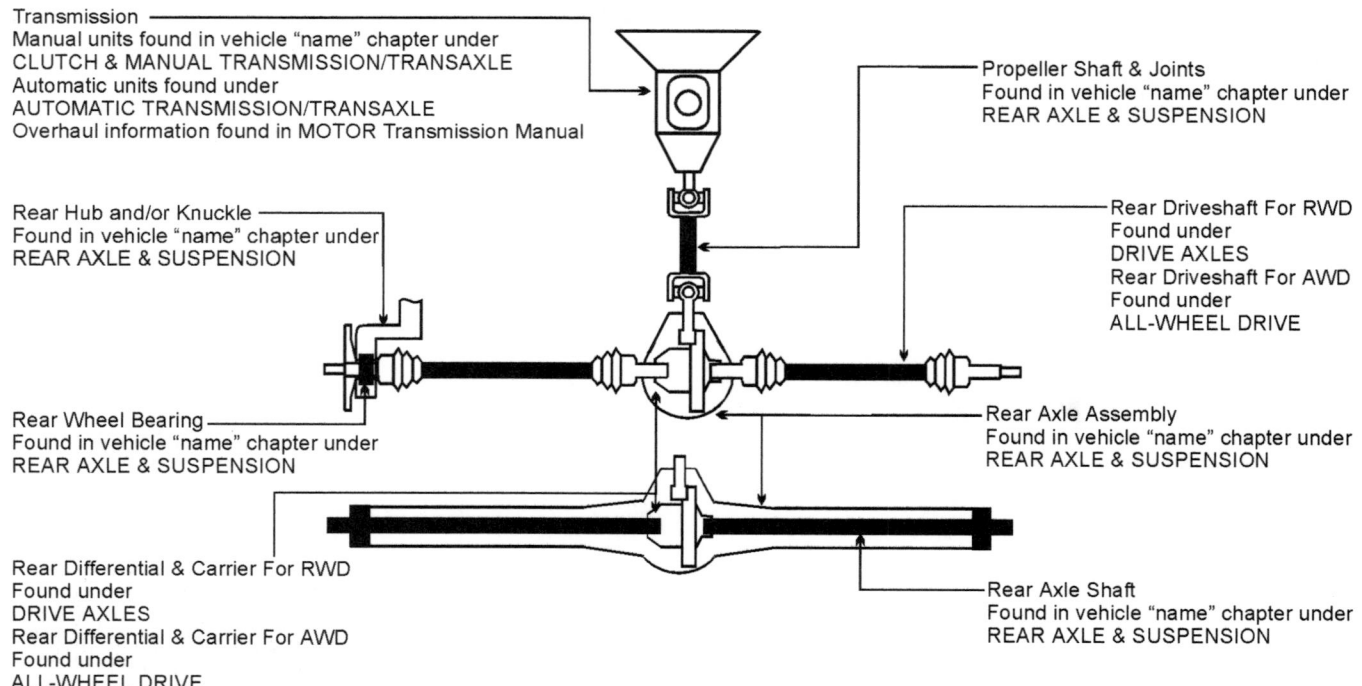

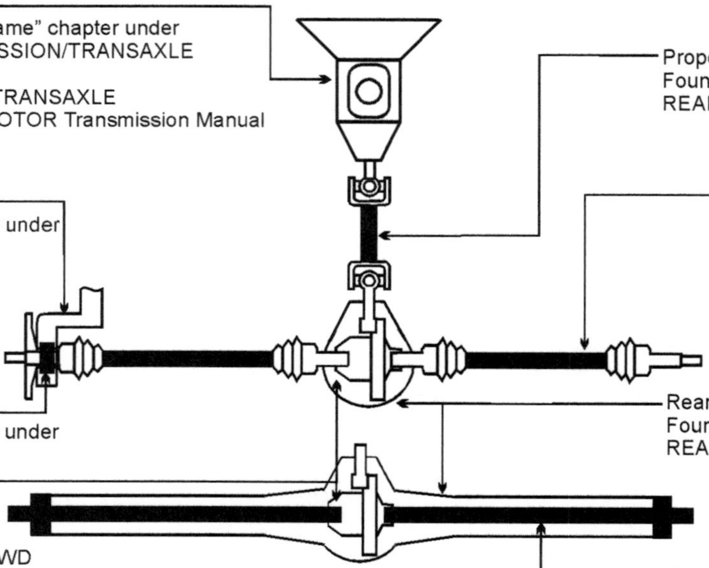